2019
Harris
California
Manufacturers Register

MERGENT

Exclusive Provider of
Dun & Bradstreet Library Solutions

dun & bradstreet

Published January 2019 next update January 2020

Publisher

Mergent Inc.
444 Madison Ave
New York, NY 10022

©Mergent Inc All Rights Reserved
2019 Mergent Business Press
ISSN 1080-2614
ISBN 978-1-64141-175-2

TABLE OF CONTENTS

SUMMARY OF CONTENTS

Number of Companies 26,408

Number of Decision Makers 78,260

Minimum Number of Employees 10

EXPLANATORY NOTES

How to Cross-Reference in This Directory

This directory includes manufacturing establishments and corporate offices of manufacturing establishments. All of these firms are listed under Standard Industrial Classifications (SIC codes) 1011-1499 and 2011 through 3999. In addition, Prepackaged Software (SIC 7372), Tire Retreading & Repair Shops (SIC 7534), Welding Repair (SIC 7692), and Armature Rewinding Shops (SIC 7694) are also included in this directory because they frequently provide value-added services that can be considered a manufacturing process.

Source Suggestions Welcome

Although all known sources were used to compile this directory, it is possible that companies were inadvertently omitted. Your assistance in calling attention to such omissions would be greatly appreciated. A special form on the facing page will help you in the reporting process.

Analysis

Every effort has been made to contact all firms to verify their information. The one exception to this rule is the annual sales figure, which is considered by many companies to be confidential information. Therefore, estimated sales have been calculated by multiplying the nationwide average sales per employee for the firm's major SIC code by the firm's number of employees. Nationwide averages for sales per employee by 4-digit SIC code are provided by the U.S. Department of Commerce and are updated annually. All sales—sales (est)—have been estimated by this method. The exceptions are parent companies (PA), division headquarters (DH) and headquarter locations (HQ) which may include an actual corporate sales figure—sales (corporate-wide) if available.

Types of Companies

Descriptive and statistical data are included for companies in the entire state. These comprise manufacturers, machine shops, fabricators, assemblers, and printers. Also identified are corporate offices in the state.

Employment Data

This directory contains companies with 10 or more employees. The employment figure shown in the Products & Services Section includes male and female employees and embraces all levels of the company: administrative, clerical, sales and maintenance. This figure is for the facility listed and does not include other plants or offices. It should be recognized that these figures represent an approximate year-round average. These employment figures are broken into codes A through F and used in the Alphabetic and Geographic Sections to further help you in qualifying a company. Be sure to check the footnotes on the bottom right hand pages for the code breakdowns.

Standard Industrial Classification (SIC)

The Standard Industrial Classification (SIC) system used in this directory was developed by the federal government for use in classifying establishments by the type of activity they are engaged in. The SIC classifications used in this directory are from the 1987 edition published by the U.S. Government's Office of Management and Budget. The SIC system separates all activities into broad industrial divisions (e.g., manufacturing, mining, retail trade). It further subdivides each division. The range of manufacturing industry classes extends from two-digit codes (major industry group) to four-digit codes (product).

For example:

Industry Breakdown	Code	Industry, Product, etc.
*Major industry group	20	Food and kindred products
Industry group	203	Canned and frozen foods
*Industry	2033	Fruits and vegetables, etc.

*Classifications used in this directory

Only two-digit and four-digit codes are used in this directory.

Arrangement

1. The **Product & Services Section** contains complete in-depth corporate data. This section lists companies under their primary SIC. SIC codes are in numerical order with companies listed alphabetically under each code. A numerical and alphabetical index precedes this section.

IMPORTANT NOTICE: It is a violation of both federal and state law to transmit an unsolicited advertisement to a facsimile machine. Any user of this product that violates such laws may be subject to civil and criminal penalties, which may exceed $500 for each transmission of an unsolicited facsimile. Mergent Inc. provides fax numbers for lawful purposes only and expressly forbids the use of these numbers in any unlawful manner.

3. The **Alphabetic Section** lists all companies with their full physical or mailing addresses and telephone number.

4. The **Geographic Section** is sorted by cities listed in alphabetic order and companies listed alphabetically within each city.

Selectory® Online Business Database

Get unlimited online access to the most accurate, up-to-date company profiles for ALL companies in the U.S., Mexico and Canada, as well as 200 countries worldwide. Build targeted lists and find new opportunities for sales in minutes! Register for your free trial at **mergentprivateonline.com**.

USER'S GUIDE TO LISTINGS

PRODUCT & SERVICES SECTION

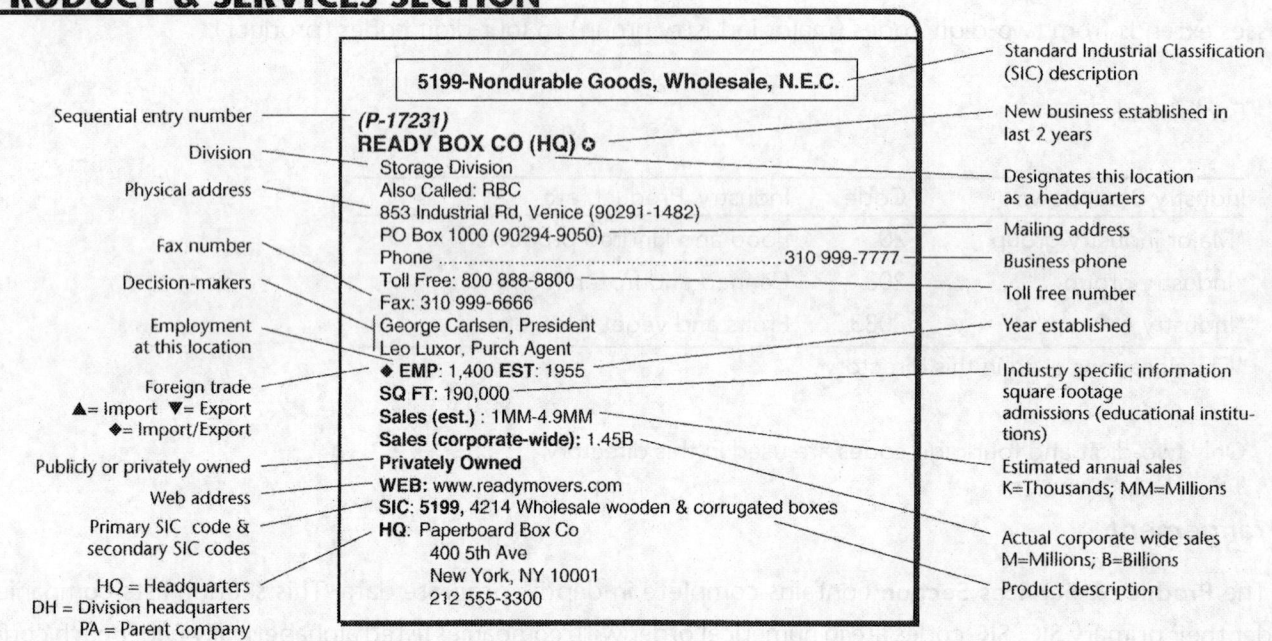

Standard Industrial Classification (SIC) description

New business established in last 2 years

Designates this location as a headquarters

Mailing address

Business phone

Toll free number

Year established

Industry specific information square footage admissions (educational institutions)

Estimated annual sales K=Thousands; MM=Millions

Actual corporate wide sales M=Millions; B=Billions

Product description

Sequential entry number

Division

Physical address

Fax number

Decision-makers

Employment at this location

Foreign trade
▲= Import ▼= Export
◆= Import/Export

Publicly or privately owned

Web address

Primary SIC code & secondary SIC codes

HQ = Headquarters
DH = Division headquarters
PA = Parent company

ALPHABETIC SECTION

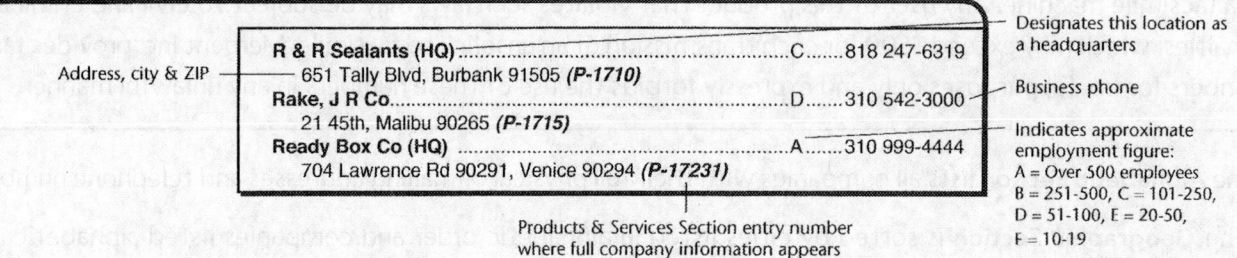

Address, city & ZIP

Designates this location as a headquarters

Business phone

Indicates approximate employment figure:
A = Over 500 employees
B = 251-500, C = 101-250,
D = 51-100, E = 20-50,
F = 10-19

Products & Services Section entry number where full company information appears

GEOGRAPHIC SECTION

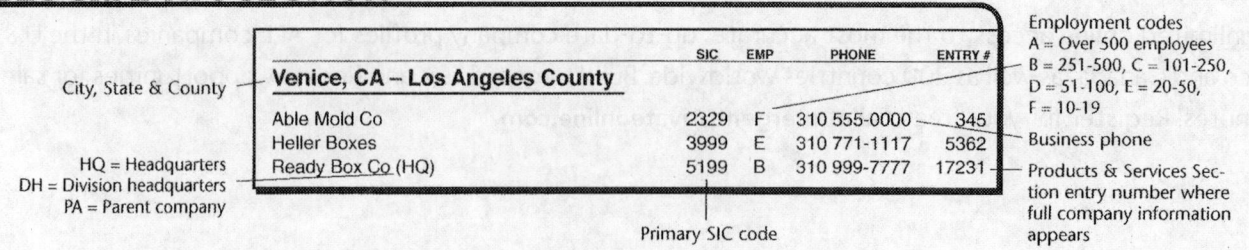

City, State & County

HQ = Headquarters
DH = Division headquarters
PA = Parent company

Primary SIC code

Employment codes
A = Over 500 employees
B = 251-500, C = 101-250,
D = 51-100, E = 20-50,
F = 10-19

Business phone

Products & Services Section entry number where full company information appears

NUMERICAL INDEX of SIC DESCRIPTIONS
ALPHABETICAL INDEX of SIC DESCRIPTIONS

PRODUCTS & SERVICES SECTION
Companies listed alphabetically under thier primary SIC
In-depth company data listed

ALPHABETIC SECTION
Company listings in alphabetical order

GEOGRAPHIC INDEX
Companies sorted by city in alphabetical order

SIC INDEX

PRDTS & SVCS

ALPHABETIC

GEOGRAPHIC

California
County Map

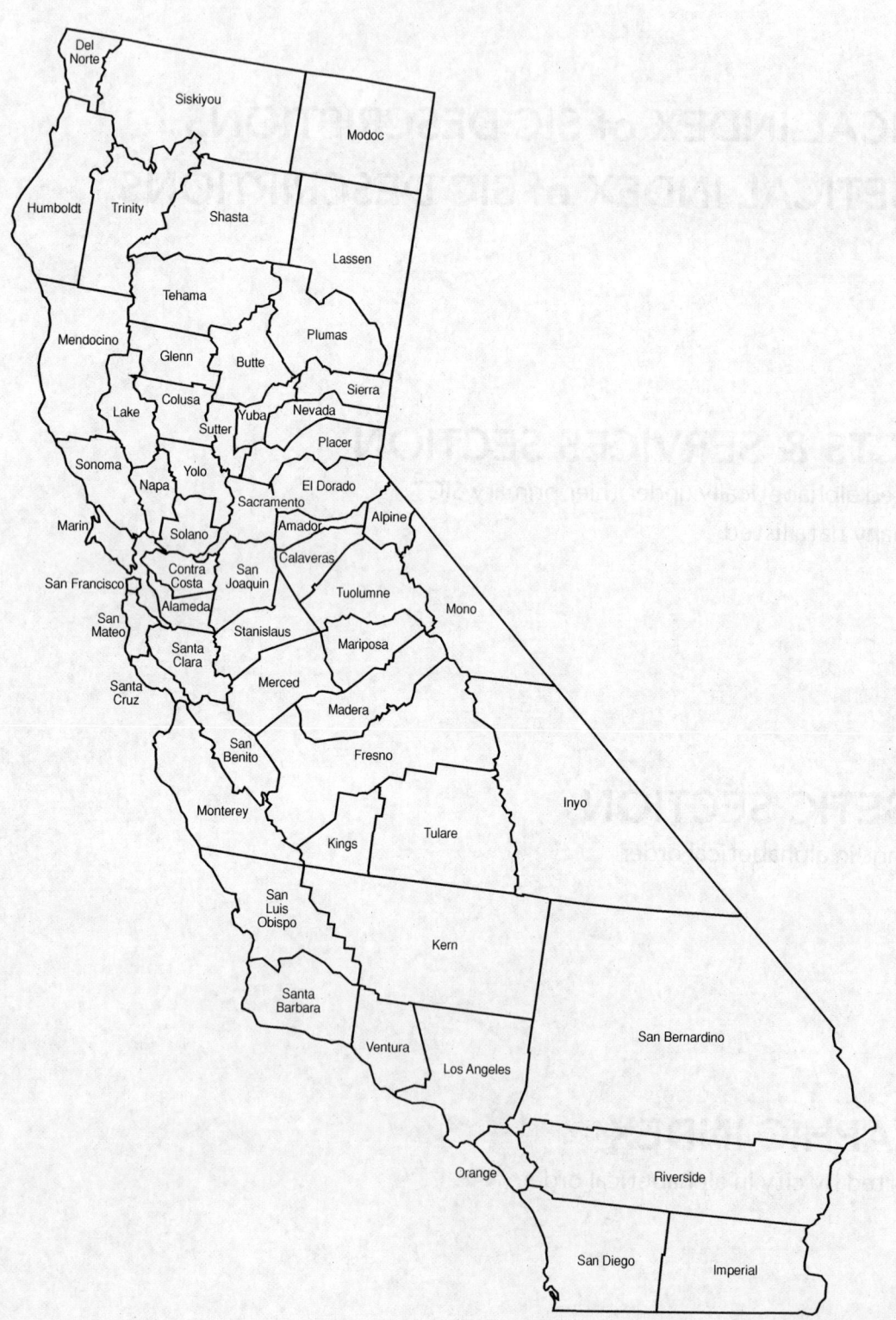

SIC INDEX

Standard Industrial Classification Numerical Index

SIC NO	PRODUCT

10 METAL MINING

1041 Gold Ores
1044 Silver Ores
1081 Metal Mining Svcs

12 COAL MINING

1221 Bituminous Coal & Lignite: Surface Mining
1241 Coal Mining Svcs

13 OIL AND GAS EXTRACTION

1311 Crude Petroleum & Natural Gas
1321 Natural Gas Liquids
1381 Drilling Oil & Gas Wells
1382 Oil & Gas Field Exploration Svcs
1389 Oil & Gas Field Svcs, NEC

14 MINING AND QUARRYING OF NONMETALLIC MINERALS, EXCEPT FUELS

1411 Dimension Stone
1422 Crushed & Broken Limestone
1423 Crushed & Broken Granite
1429 Crushed & Broken Stone, NEC
1442 Construction Sand & Gravel
1446 Industrial Sand
1455 Kaolin & Ball Clay
1459 Clay, Ceramic & Refractory Minerals, NEC
1479 Chemical & Fertilizer Mining
1481 Nonmetallic Minerals Svcs, Except Fuels
1499 Miscellaneous Nonmetallic Mining

20 FOOD AND KINDRED PRODUCTS

2011 Meat Packing Plants
2013 Sausages & Meat Prdts
2015 Poultry Slaughtering, Dressing & Processing
2021 Butter
2022 Cheese
2023 Milk, Condensed & Evaporated
2024 Ice Cream
2026 Milk
2032 Canned Specialties
2033 Canned Fruits, Vegetables & Preserves
2034 Dried Fruits, Vegetables & Soup
2035 Pickled Fruits, Vegetables, Sauces & Dressings
2037 Frozen Fruits, Juices & Vegetables
2038 Frozen Specialties
2041 Flour, Grain Milling
2043 Cereal Breakfast Foods
2044 Rice Milling
2045 Flour, Blended & Prepared
2046 Wet Corn Milling
2047 Dog & Cat Food
2048 Prepared Feeds For Animals & Fowls
2051 Bread, Bakery Prdts Exc Cookies & Crackers
2052 Cookies & Crackers
2053 Frozen Bakery Prdts
2062 Sugar, Cane Refining
2063 Sugar, Beet
2064 Candy & Confectionery Prdts
2066 Chocolate & Cocoa Prdts
2068 Salted & Roasted Nuts & Seeds
2075 Soybean Oil Mills
2076 Vegetable Oil Mills
2077 Animal, Marine Fats & Oils
2079 Shortening, Oils & Margarine
2082 Malt Beverages
2084 Wine & Brandy
2085 Liquors, Distilled, Rectified & Blended
2086 Soft Drinks
2087 Flavoring Extracts & Syrups
2091 Fish & Seafoods, Canned & Cured
2092 Fish & Seafoods, Fresh & Frozen
2095 Coffee
2096 Potato Chips & Similar Prdts
2097 Ice
2098 Macaroni, Spaghetti & Noodles
2099 Food Preparations, NEC

21 TOBACCO PRODUCTS

2111 Cigarettes
2121 Cigars
2131 Tobacco, Chewing & Snuff

22 TEXTILE MILL PRODUCTS

2211 Cotton, Woven Fabric
2221 Silk & Man-Made Fiber
2231 Wool, Woven Fabric
2241 Fabric Mills, Cotton, Wool, Silk & Man-Made
2251 Hosiery, Women's Full & Knee Length
2252 Hosiery, Except Women's
2253 Knit Outerwear Mills
2254 Knit Underwear Mills
2257 Circular Knit Fabric Mills
2258 Lace & Warp Knit Fabric Mills
2259 Knitting Mills, NEC
2261 Cotton Fabric Finishers
2262 Silk & Man-Made Fabric Finishers
2269 Textile Finishers, NEC
2273 Carpets & Rugs
2281 Yarn Spinning Mills
2282 Yarn Texturizing, Throwing, Twisting & Winding Mills
2284 Thread Mills
2295 Fabrics Coated Not Rubberized
2297 Fabrics, Nonwoven
2298 Cordage & Twine
2299 Textile Goods, NEC

23 APPAREL AND OTHER FINISHED PRODUCTS MADE FROM FABRICS AND SIMILAR MATERIAL

2311 Men's & Boys' Suits, Coats & Overcoats
2321 Men's & Boys' Shirts
2322 Men's & Boys' Underwear & Nightwear
2323 Men's & Boys' Neckwear
2325 Men's & Boys' Separate Trousers & Casual Slacks
2326 Men's & Boys' Work Clothing
2329 Men's & Boys' Clothing, NEC
2331 Women's & Misses' Blouses
2335 Women's & Misses' Dresses
2337 Women's & Misses' Suits, Coats & Skirts
2339 Women's & Misses' Outerwear, NEC
2341 Women's, Misses' & Children's Underwear & Nightwear
2342 Brassieres, Girdles & Garments
2353 Hats, Caps & Millinery
2361 Children's & Infants' Dresses & Blouses
2369 Girls' & Infants' Outerwear, NEC
2371 Fur Goods
2381 Dress & Work Gloves
2384 Robes & Dressing Gowns
2386 Leather & Sheep Lined Clothing
2387 Apparel Belts
2389 Apparel & Accessories, NEC
2391 Curtains & Draperies
2392 House furnishings: Textile
2393 Textile Bags
2394 Canvas Prdts
2395 Pleating & Stitching For The Trade
2396 Automotive Trimmings, Apparel Findings, Related Prdts
2399 Fabricated Textile Prdts, NEC

24 LUMBER AND WOOD PRODUCTS, EXCEPT FURNITURE

2411 Logging
2421 Saw & Planing Mills
2426 Hardwood Dimension & Flooring Mills
2429 Special Prdt Sawmills, NEC
2431 Millwork
2434 Wood Kitchen Cabinets
2435 Hardwood Veneer & Plywood
2439 Structural Wood Members, NEC
2441 Wood Boxes
2448 Wood Pallets & Skids
2449 Wood Containers, NEC
2451 Mobile Homes
2452 Prefabricated Wood Buildings & Cmpnts
2491 Wood Preserving
2493 Reconstituted Wood Prdts
2499 Wood Prdts, NEC

25 FURNITURE AND FIXTURES

2511 Wood Household Furniture
2512 Wood Household Furniture, Upholstered
2514 Metal Household Furniture
2515 Mattresses & Bedsprings
2517 Wood TV, Radio, Phono & Sewing Cabinets
2519 Household Furniture, NEC
2521 Wood Office Furniture
2522 Office Furniture, Except Wood
2531 Public Building & Related Furniture
2541 Wood, Office & Store Fixtures
2542 Partitions & Fixtures, Except Wood
2591 Drapery Hardware, Window Blinds & Shades
2599 Furniture & Fixtures, NEC

26 PAPER AND ALLIED PRODUCTS

2611 Pulp Mills
2621 Paper Mills
2631 Paperboard Mills
2652 Set-Up Paperboard Boxes
2653 Corrugated & Solid Fiber Boxes
2655 Fiber Cans, Tubes & Drums
2656 Sanitary Food Containers
2657 Folding Paperboard Boxes
2671 Paper Coating & Laminating for Packaging
2672 Paper Coating & Laminating, Exc for Packaging
2673 Bags: Plastics, Laminated & Coated
2674 Bags: Uncoated Paper & Multiwall
2675 Die-Cut Paper & Board
2676 Sanitary Paper Prdts
2677 Envelopes
2678 Stationery Prdts
2679 Converted Paper Prdts, NEC

27 PRINTING, PUBLISHING, AND ALLIED INDUSTRIES

2711 Newspapers: Publishing & Printing
2721 Periodicals: Publishing & Printing
2731 Books: Publishing & Printing
2732 Book Printing, Not Publishing
2741 Misc Publishing
2752 Commercial Printing: Lithographic
2754 Commercial Printing: Gravure
2759 Commercial Printing
2761 Manifold Business Forms
2771 Greeting Card Publishing
2782 Blankbooks & Looseleaf Binders
2789 Bookbinding
2791 Typesetting
2796 Platemaking & Related Svcs

28 CHEMICALS AND ALLIED PRODUCTS

2812 Alkalies & Chlorine
2813 Industrial Gases
2816 Inorganic Pigments
2819 Indl Inorganic Chemicals, NEC
2821 Plastics, Mtrls & Nonvulcanizable Elastomers
2822 Synthetic Rubber (Vulcanizable Elastomers)
2824 Synthetic Organic Fibers, Exc Cellulosic
2833 Medicinal Chemicals & Botanical Prdts
2834 Pharmaceuticals
2835 Diagnostic Substances
2836 Biological Prdts, Exc Diagnostic Substances
2841 Soap & Detergents
2842 Spec Cleaning, Polishing & Sanitation Preparations
2843 Surface Active & Finishing Agents, Sulfonated Oils
2844 Perfumes, Cosmetics & Toilet Preparations
2851 Paints, Varnishes, Lacquers, Enamels
2861 Gum & Wood Chemicals
2865 Cyclic-Crudes, Intermediates, Dyes & Org Pigments
2869 Industrial Organic Chemicals, NEC
2873 Nitrogenous Fertilizers
2874 Phosphatic Fertilizers
2875 Fertilizers, Mixing Only
2879 Pesticides & Agricultural Chemicals, NEC
2891 Adhesives & Sealants
2892 Explosives
2893 Printing Ink
2895 Carbon Black
2899 Chemical Preparations, NEC

29 PETROLEUM REFINING AND RELATED INDUSTRIES

2911 Petroleum Refining
2951 Paving Mixtures & Blocks
2952 Asphalt Felts & Coatings
2992 Lubricating Oils & Greases
2999 Products Of Petroleum & Coal, NEC

30 RUBBER AND MISCELLANEOUS PLASTICS PRODUCTS

3011 Tires & Inner Tubes
3021 Rubber & Plastic Footwear
3052 Rubber & Plastic Hose & Belting
3053 Gaskets, Packing & Sealing Devices
3061 Molded, Extruded & Lathe-Cut Rubber Mechanical

SIC NO	PRODUCT
	Goods
3069	Fabricated Rubber Prdts, NEC
3081	Plastic Unsupported Sheet & Film
3082	Plastic Unsupported Profile Shapes
3083	Plastic Laminated Plate & Sheet
3084	Plastic Pipe
3085	Plastic Bottles
3086	Plastic Foam Prdts
3087	Custom Compounding Of Purchased Plastic Resins
3088	Plastic Plumbing Fixtures
3089	Plastic Prdts

31 LEATHER AND LEATHER PRODUCTS

3111	Leather Tanning & Finishing
3131	Boot & Shoe Cut Stock & Findings
3142	House Slippers
3143	Men's Footwear, Exc Athletic
3144	Women's Footwear, Exc Athletic
3149	Footwear, NEC
3161	Luggage
3171	Handbags & Purses
3172	Personal Leather Goods
3199	Leather Goods, NEC

32 STONE, CLAY, GLASS, AND CONCRETE PRODUCTS

3211	Flat Glass
3221	Glass Containers
3229	Pressed & Blown Glassware, NEC
3231	Glass Prdts Made Of Purchased Glass
3241	Cement, Hydraulic
3251	Brick & Structural Clay Tile
3253	Ceramic Tile
3255	Clay Refractories
3259	Structural Clay Prdts, NEC
3261	China Plumbing Fixtures & Fittings
3262	China, Table & Kitchen Articles
3263	Earthenware, Whiteware, Table & Kitchen Articles
3264	Porcelain Electrical Splys
3269	Pottery Prdts, NEC
3271	Concrete Block & Brick
3272	Concrete Prdts
3273	Ready-Mixed Concrete
3274	Lime
3275	Gypsum Prdts
3281	Cut Stone Prdts
3291	Abrasive Prdts
3292	Asbestos products
3295	Minerals & Earths: Ground Or Treated
3296	Mineral Wool
3297	Nonclay Refractories
3299	Nonmetallic Mineral Prdts, NEC

33 PRIMARY METAL INDUSTRIES

3312	Blast Furnaces, Coke Ovens, Steel & Rolling Mills
3313	Electrometallurgical Prdts
3315	Steel Wire Drawing & Nails & Spikes
3316	Cold Rolled Steel Sheet, Strip & Bars
3317	Steel Pipe & Tubes
3321	Gray Iron Foundries
3322	Malleable Iron Foundries
3324	Steel Investment Foundries
3325	Steel Foundries, NEC
3331	Primary Smelting & Refining Of Copper
3334	Primary Production Of Aluminum
3339	Primary Nonferrous Metals, NEC
3341	Secondary Smelting & Refining Of Nonferrous Metals
3351	Rolling, Drawing & Extruding Of Copper
3353	Aluminum Sheet, Plate & Foil
3354	Aluminum Extruded Prdts
3355	Aluminum Rolling & Drawing, NEC
3356	Rolling, Drawing-Extruding Of Nonferrous Metals
3357	Nonferrous Wire Drawing
3363	Aluminum Die Castings
3364	Nonferrous Die Castings, Exc Aluminum
3365	Aluminum Foundries
3366	Copper Foundries
3369	Nonferrous Foundries: Castings, NEC
3398	Metal Heat Treating
3399	Primary Metal Prdts, NEC

34 FABRICATED METAL PRODUCTS, EXCEPT MACHINERY AND TRANSPORTATION EQUIPMENT

3411	Metal Cans
3412	Metal Barrels, Drums, Kegs & Pails
3421	Cutlery
3423	Hand & Edge Tools
3425	Hand Saws & Saw Blades
3429	Hardware, NEC
3431	Enameled Iron & Metal Sanitary Ware
3432	Plumbing Fixture Fittings & Trim, Brass

SIC NO	PRODUCT
3433	Heating Eqpt
3441	Fabricated Structural Steel
3442	Metal Doors, Sash, Frames, Molding & Trim
3443	Fabricated Plate Work
3444	Sheet Metal Work
3446	Architectural & Ornamental Metal Work
3448	Prefabricated Metal Buildings & Cmpnts
3449	Misc Structural Metal Work
3451	Screw Machine Prdts
3452	Bolts, Nuts, Screws, Rivets & Washers
3462	Iron & Steel Forgings
3463	Nonferrous Forgings
3465	Automotive Stampings
3466	Crowns & Closures
3469	Metal Stampings, NEC
3471	Electroplating, Plating, Polishing, Anodizing & Coloring
3479	Coating & Engraving, NEC
3482	Small Arms Ammunition
3483	Ammunition, Large
3484	Small Arms
3489	Ordnance & Access, NEC
3491	Industrial Valves
3492	Fluid Power Valves & Hose Fittings
3493	Steel Springs, Except Wire
3494	Valves & Pipe Fittings, NEC
3495	Wire Springs
3496	Misc Fabricated Wire Prdts
3497	Metal Foil & Leaf
3498	Fabricated Pipe & Pipe Fittings
3499	Fabricated Metal Prdts, NEC

35 INDUSTRIAL AND COMMERCIAL MACHINERY AND COMPUTER EQUIPMENT

3511	Steam, Gas & Hydraulic Turbines & Engines
3519	Internal Combustion Engines, NEC
3523	Farm Machinery & Eqpt
3524	Garden, Lawn Tractors & Eqpt
3531	Construction Machinery & Eqpt
3532	Mining Machinery & Eqpt
3533	Oil Field Machinery & Eqpt
3534	Elevators & Moving Stairways
3535	Conveyors & Eqpt
3536	Hoists, Cranes & Monorails
3537	Indl Trucks, Tractors, Trailers & Stackers
3541	Machine Tools: Cutting
3542	Machine Tools: Forming
3543	Industrial Patterns
3544	Dies, Tools, Jigs, Fixtures & Indl Molds
3545	Machine Tool Access
3546	Power Hand Tools
3547	Rolling Mill Machinery & Eqpt
3548	Welding Apparatus
3549	Metalworking Machinery, NEC
3552	Textile Machinery
3553	Woodworking Machinery
3554	Paper Inds Machinery
3555	Printing Trades Machinery & Eqpt
3556	Food Prdts Machinery
3559	Special Ind Machinery, NEC
3561	Pumps & Pumping Eqpt
3562	Ball & Roller Bearings
3563	Air & Gas Compressors
3564	Blowers & Fans
3565	Packaging Machinery
3566	Speed Changers, Drives & Gears
3567	Indl Process Furnaces & Ovens
3568	Mechanical Power Transmission Eqpt, NEC
3569	Indl Machinery & Eqpt, NEC
3571	Electronic Computers
3572	Computer Storage Devices
3575	Computer Terminals
3577	Computer Peripheral Eqpt, NEC
3578	Calculating & Accounting Eqpt
3579	Office Machines, NEC
3581	Automatic Vending Machines
3582	Commercial Laundry, Dry Clean & Pressing Mchs
3585	Air Conditioning & Heating Eqpt
3589	Service Ind Machines, NEC
3592	Carburetors, Pistons, Rings & Valves
3593	Fluid Power Cylinders & Actuators
3594	Fluid Power Pumps & Motors
3596	Scales & Balances, Exc Laboratory
3599	Machinery & Eqpt, Indl & Commercial, NEC

36 ELECTRONIC AND OTHER ELECTRICAL EQUIPMENT AND COMPONENTS, EXCEPT COMPUTER

3612	Power, Distribution & Specialty Transformers
3613	Switchgear & Switchboard Apparatus
3621	Motors & Generators
3624	Carbon & Graphite Prdts

SIC NO	PRODUCT
3625	Relays & Indl Controls
3629	Electrical Indl Apparatus, NEC
3631	Household Cooking Eqpt
3632	Household Refrigerators & Freezers
3634	Electric Household Appliances
3635	Household Vacuum Cleaners
3639	Household Appliances, NEC
3641	Electric Lamps
3643	Current-Carrying Wiring Devices
3644	Noncurrent-Carrying Wiring Devices
3645	Residential Lighting Fixtures
3646	Commercial, Indl & Institutional Lighting Fixtures
3647	Vehicular Lighting Eqpt
3648	Lighting Eqpt, NEC
3651	Household Audio & Video Eqpt
3652	Phonograph Records & Magnetic Tape
3661	Telephone & Telegraph Apparatus
3663	Radio & T V Communications, Systs & Eqpt, Broadcast/Studio
3669	Communications Eqpt, NEC
3671	Radio & T V Receiving Electron Tubes
3672	Printed Circuit Boards
3674	Semiconductors
3675	Electronic Capacitors
3676	Electronic Resistors
3677	Electronic Coils & Transformers
3678	Electronic Connectors
3679	Electronic Components, NEC
3691	Storage Batteries
3692	Primary Batteries: Dry & Wet
3694	Electrical Eqpt For Internal Combustion Engines
3695	Recording Media
3699	Electrical Machinery, Eqpt & Splys, NEC

37 TRANSPORTATION EQUIPMENT

3711	Motor Vehicles & Car Bodies
3713	Truck & Bus Bodies
3714	Motor Vehicle Parts & Access
3715	Truck Trailers
3716	Motor Homes
3721	Aircraft
3724	Aircraft Engines & Engine Parts
3728	Aircraft Parts & Eqpt, NEC
3731	Shipbuilding & Repairing
3732	Boat Building & Repairing
3743	Railroad Eqpt
3751	Motorcycles, Bicycles & Parts
3761	Guided Missiles & Space Vehicles
3764	Guided Missile/Space Vehicle Propulsion Units & parts
3769	Guided Missile/Space Vehicle Parts & Eqpt, NEC
3792	Travel Trailers & Campers
3795	Tanks & Tank Components
3799	Transportation Eqpt, NEC

38 MEASURING, ANALYZING AND CONTROLLING INSTRUMENTS; PHOTOGRAPHIC, MEDICAL AN

3812	Search, Detection, Navigation & Guidance Systs & Instrs
3821	Laboratory Apparatus & Furniture
3822	Automatic Temperature Controls
3823	Indl Instruments For Meas, Display & Control
3824	Fluid Meters & Counters
3825	Instrs For Measuring & Testing Electricity
3826	Analytical Instruments
3827	Optical Instruments
3829	Measuring & Controlling Devices, NEC
3841	Surgical & Medical Instrs & Apparatus
3842	Orthopedic, Prosthetic & Surgical Appliances/Splys
3843	Dental Eqpt & Splys
3844	X-ray Apparatus & Tubes
3845	Electromedical & Electrotherapeutic Apparatus
3851	Ophthalmic Goods
3861	Photographic Eqpt & Splys
3873	Watch & Clock Devices & Parts

39 MISCELLANEOUS MANUFACTURING INDUSTRIES

3911	Jewelry: Precious Metal
3914	Silverware, Plated & Stainless Steel Ware
3915	Jewelers Findings & Lapidary Work
3931	Musical Instruments
3942	Dolls & Stuffed Toys
3944	Games, Toys & Children's Vehicles
3949	Sporting & Athletic Goods, NEC
3951	Pens & Mechanical Pencils
3952	Lead Pencils, Crayons & Artist's Mtrls
3953	Marking Devices
3955	Carbon Paper & Inked Ribbons
3961	Costume Jewelry & Novelties
3965	Fasteners, Buttons, Needles & Pins
3991	Brooms & Brushes
3993	Signs & Advertising Displays

SIC NO	PRODUCT
3995	Burial Caskets
3996	Linoleum & Hard Surface Floor Coverings, NEC
3999	Manufacturing Industries, NEC

73 BUSINESS SERVICES

SIC NO	PRODUCT
7372	Prepackaged Software

76 MISCELLANEOUS REPAIR SERVICES

SIC NO	PRODUCT
7692	Welding Repair
7694	Armature Rewinding Shops

SIC

SIC INDEX

Standard Industrial Classification Alphabetical Index

SIC NO	PRODUCT

A

3291 Abrasive Prdts
2891 Adhesives & Sealants
3563 Air & Gas Compressors
3585 Air Conditioning & Heating Eqpt
3721 Aircraft
3724 Aircraft Engines & Engine Parts
3728 Aircraft Parts & Eqpt, NEC
2812 Alkalies & Chlorine
3363 Aluminum Die Castings
3354 Aluminum Extruded Prdts
3365 Aluminum Foundries
3355 Aluminum Rolling & Drawing, NEC
3353 Aluminum Sheet, Plate & Foil
3483 Ammunition, Large
3826 Analytical Instruments
2077 Animal, Marine Fats & Oils
2389 Apparel & Accessories, NEC
2387 Apparel Belts
3446 Architectural & Ornamental Metal Work
7694 Armature Rewinding Shops
3292 Asbestos products
2952 Asphalt Felts & Coatings
3822 Automatic Temperature Controls
3581 Automatic Vending Machines
3465 Automotive Stampings
2396 Automotive Trimmings, Apparel Findings, Related Prdts

B

2673 Bags: Plastics, Laminated & Coated
2674 Bags: Uncoated Paper & Multiwall
3562 Ball & Roller Bearings
2836 Biological Prdts, Exc Diagnostic Substances
1221 Bituminous Coal & Lignite: Surface Mining
2782 Blankbooks & Looseleaf Binders
3312 Blast Furnaces, Coke Ovens, Steel & Rolling Mills
3564 Blowers & Fans
3732 Boat Building & Repairing
3452 Bolts, Nuts, Screws, Rivets & Washers
2732 Book Printing, Not Publishing
2789 Bookbinding
2731 Books: Publishing & Printing
3131 Boot & Shoe Cut Stock & Findings
2342 Brassieres, Girdles & Garments
2051 Bread, Bakery Prdts Exc Cookies & Crackers
3251 Brick & Structural Clay Tile
3991 Brooms & Brushes
3995 Burial Caskets
2021 Butter

C

3578 Calculating & Accounting Eqpt
2064 Candy & Confectionery Prdts
2033 Canned Fruits, Vegetables & Preserves
2032 Canned Specialties
2394 Canvas Prdts
3624 Carbon & Graphite Prdts
2895 Carbon Black
3955 Carbon Paper & Inked Ribbons
3592 Carburetors, Pistons, Rings & Valves
2273 Carpets & Rugs
3241 Cement, Hydraulic
3253 Ceramic Tile
2043 Cereal Breakfast Foods
2022 Cheese
1479 Chemical & Fertilizer Mining
2899 Chemical Preparations, NEC
2361 Children's & Infants' Dresses & Blouses
3261 China Plumbing Fixtures & Fittings
3262 China, Table & Kitchen Articles
2066 Chocolate & Cocoa Prdts
2111 Cigarettes
2121 Cigars
2257 Circular Knit Fabric Mills
3255 Clay Refractories
1459 Clay, Ceramic & Refractory Minerals, NEC
1241 Coal Mining Svcs
3479 Coating & Engraving, NEC
2095 Coffee
3316 Cold Rolled Steel Sheet, Strip & Bars
3582 Commercial Laundry, Dry Clean & Pressing Mchs
2759 Commercial Printing
2754 Commercial Printing: Gravure
2752 Commercial Printing: Lithographic
3646 Commercial, Indl & Institutional Lighting Fixtures
3669 Communications Eqpt, NEC

3577 Computer Peripheral Eqpt, NEC
3572 Computer Storage Devices
3575 Computer Terminals
3271 Concrete Block & Brick
3272 Concrete Prdts
3531 Construction Machinery & Eqpt
1442 Construction Sand & Gravel
2679 Converted Paper Prdts, NEC
3535 Conveyors & Eqpt
2052 Cookies & Crackers
3366 Copper Foundries
2298 Cordage & Twine
2653 Corrugated & Solid Fiber Boxes
3961 Costume Jewelry & Novelties
2261 Cotton Fabric Finishers
2211 Cotton, Woven Fabric
3466 Crowns & Closures
1311 Crude Petroleum & Natural Gas
1423 Crushed & Broken Granite
1422 Crushed & Broken Limestone
1429 Crushed & Broken Stone, NEC
3643 Current-Carrying Wiring Devices
2391 Curtains & Draperies
3087 Custom Compounding Of Purchased Plastic Resins
3281 Cut Stone Prdts
3421 Cutlery
2865 Cyclic-Crudes, Intermediates, Dyes & Org Pigments

D

3843 Dental Eqpt & Splys
2835 Diagnostic Substances
2675 Die-Cut Paper & Board
3544 Dies, Tools, Jigs, Fixtures & Indl Molds
1411 Dimension Stone
2047 Dog & Cat Food
3942 Dolls & Stuffed Toys
2591 Drapery Hardware, Window Blinds & Shades
2381 Dress & Work Gloves
2034 Dried Fruits, Vegetables & Soup
1381 Drilling Oil & Gas Wells

E

3263 Earthenware, Whiteware, Table & Kitchen Articles
3634 Electric Household Appliances
3641 Electric Lamps
3694 Electrical Eqpt For Internal Combustion Engines
3629 Electrical Indl Apparatus, NEC
3699 Electrical Machinery, Eqpt & Splys, NEC
3845 Electromedical & Electrotherapeutic Apparatus
3313 Electrometallurgical Prdts
3675 Electronic Capacitors
3677 Electronic Coils & Transformers
3679 Electronic Components, NEC
3571 Electronic Computers
3678 Electronic Connectors
3676 Electronic Resistors
3471 Electroplating, Plating, Polishing, Anodizing & Coloring
3534 Elevators & Moving Stairways
3431 Enameled Iron & Metal Sanitary Ware
2677 Envelopes
2892 Explosives

F

2241 Fabric Mills, Cotton, Wool, Silk & Man-Made
3499 Fabricated Metal Prdts, NEC
3498 Fabricated Pipe & Pipe Fittings
3443 Fabricated Plate Work
3069 Fabricated Rubber Prdts, NEC
3441 Fabricated Structural Steel
2399 Fabricated Textile Prdts, NEC
2295 Fabrics Coated Not Rubberized
2297 Fabrics, Nonwoven
3523 Farm Machinery & Eqpt
3965 Fasteners, Buttons, Needles & Pins
2875 Fertilizers, Mixing Only
2655 Fiber Cans, Tubes & Drums
2091 Fish & Seafoods, Canned & Cured
2092 Fish & Seafoods, Fresh & Frozen
3211 Flat Glass
2087 Flavoring Extracts & Syrups
2045 Flour, Blended & Prepared
2041 Flour, Grain Milling
3824 Fluid Meters & Counters
3593 Fluid Power Cylinders & Actuators
3594 Fluid Power Pumps & Motors
3492 Fluid Power Valves & Hose Fittings

2657 Folding Paperboard Boxes
3556 Food Prdts Machinery
2099 Food Preparations, NEC
3149 Footwear, NEC
2053 Frozen Bakery Prdts
2037 Frozen Fruits, Juices & Vegetables
2038 Frozen Specialties
2371 Fur Goods
2599 Furniture & Fixtures, NEC

G

3944 Games, Toys & Children's Vehicles
3524 Garden, Lawn Tractors & Eqpt
3053 Gaskets, Packing & Sealing Devices
2369 Girls' & Infants' Outerwear, NEC
3221 Glass Containers
3231 Glass Prdts Made Of Purchased Glass
1041 Gold Ores
3321 Gray Iron Foundries
2771 Greeting Card Publishing
3769 Guided Missile/Space Vehicle Parts & Eqpt, NEC
3764 Guided Missile/Space Vehicle Propulsion Units & parts
3761 Guided Missiles & Space Vehicles
2861 Gum & Wood Chemicals
3275 Gypsum Prdts

H

3423 Hand & Edge Tools
3425 Hand Saws & Saw Blades
3171 Handbags & Purses
3429 Hardware, NEC
2426 Hardwood Dimension & Flooring Mills
2435 Hardwood Veneer & Plywood
2353 Hats, Caps & Millinery
3433 Heating Eqpt
3536 Hoists, Cranes & Monorails
2252 Hosiery, Except Women's
2251 Hosiery, Women's Full & Knee Length
2392 House furnishings: Textile
3142 House Slippers
3639 Household Appliances, NEC
3651 Household Audio & Video Eqpt
3631 Household Cooking Eqpt
2519 Household Furniture, NEC
3632 Household Refrigerators & Freezers
3635 Household Vacuum Cleaners

I

2097 Ice
2024 Ice Cream
2819 Indl Inorganic Chemicals, NEC
3823 Indl Instruments For Meas, Display & Control
3569 Indl Machinery & Eqpt, NEC
3567 Indl Process Furnaces & Ovens
3537 Indl Trucks, Tractors, Trailers & Stackers
2813 Industrial Gases
2869 Industrial Organic Chemicals, NEC
3543 Industrial Patterns
1446 Industrial Sand
3491 Industrial Valves
2816 Inorganic Pigments
3825 Instrs For Measuring & Testing Electricity
3519 Internal Combustion Engines, NEC
3462 Iron & Steel Forgings

J

3915 Jewelers Findings & Lapidary Work
3911 Jewelry: Precious Metal

K

1455 Kaolin & Ball Clay
2253 Knit Outerwear Mills
2254 Knit Underwear Mills
2259 Knitting Mills, NEC

L

3821 Laboratory Apparatus & Furniture
2258 Lace & Warp Knit Fabric Mills
3952 Lead Pencils, Crayons & Artist's Mtrls
2386 Leather & Sheep Lined Clothing
3199 Leather Goods, NEC
3111 Leather Tanning & Finishing
3648 Lighting Eqpt, NEC
3274 Lime
3996 Linoleum & Hard Surface Floor Coverings, NEC
2085 Liquors, Distilled, Rectified & Blended
2411 Logging

S I C

SIC NO	PRODUCT
2992	Lubricating Oils & Greases
3161	Luggage

M

SIC NO	PRODUCT
2098	Macaroni, Spaghetti & Noodles
3545	Machine Tool Access
3541	Machine Tools: Cutting
3542	Machine Tools: Forming
3599	Machinery & Eqpt, Indl & Commercial, NEC
3322	Malleable Iron Foundries
2082	Malt Beverages
2761	Manifold Business Forms
3999	Manufacturing Industries, NEC
3953	Marking Devices
2515	Mattresses & Bedsprings
3829	Measuring & Controlling Devices, NEC
2011	Meat Packing Plants
3568	Mechanical Power Transmission Eqpt, NEC
2833	Medicinal Chemicals & Botanical Prdts
2329	Men's & Boys' Clothing, NEC
2323	Men's & Boys' Neckwear
2325	Men's & Boys' Separate Trousers & Casual Slacks
2321	Men's & Boys' Shirts
2311	Men's & Boys' Suits, Coats & Overcoats
2322	Men's & Boys' Underwear & Nightwear
2326	Men's & Boys' Work Clothing
3143	Men's Footwear, Exc Athletic
3412	Metal Barrels, Drums, Kegs & Pails
3411	Metal Cans
3442	Metal Doors, Sash, Frames, Molding & Trim
3497	Metal Foil & Leaf
3398	Metal Heat Treating
2514	Metal Household Furniture
1081	Metal Mining Svcs
3469	Metal Stampings, NEC
3549	Metalworking Machinery, NEC
2026	Milk
2023	Milk, Condensed & Evaporated
2431	Millwork
3296	Mineral Wool
3295	Minerals & Earths: Ground Or Treated
3532	Mining Machinery & Eqpt
3496	Misc Fabricated Wire Prdts
2741	Misc Publishing
3449	Misc Structural Metal Work
1499	Miscellaneous Nonmetallic Mining
2451	Mobile Homes
3061	Molded, Extruded & Lathe-Cut Rubber Mechanical Goods
3716	Motor Homes
3714	Motor Vehicle Parts & Access
3711	Motor Vehicles & Car Bodies
3751	Motorcycles, Bicycles & Parts
3621	Motors & Generators
3931	Musical Instruments

N

SIC NO	PRODUCT
1321	Natural Gas Liquids
2711	Newspapers: Publishing & Printing
2873	Nitrogenous Fertilizers
3297	Nonclay Refractories
3644	Noncurrent-Carrying Wiring Devices
3364	Nonferrous Die Castings, Exc Aluminum
3463	Nonferrous Forgings
3369	Nonferrous Foundries: Castings, NEC
3357	Nonferrous Wire Drawing
3299	Nonmetallic Mineral Prdts, NEC
1481	Nonmetallic Minerals Svcs, Except Fuels

O

SIC NO	PRODUCT
2522	Office Furniture, Except Wood
3579	Office Machines, NEC
1382	Oil & Gas Field Exploration Svcs
1389	Oil & Gas Field Svcs, NEC
3533	Oil Field Machinery & Eqpt
3851	Ophthalmic Goods
3827	Optical Instruments
3489	Ordnance & Access, NEC
3842	Orthopedic, Prosthetic & Surgical Appliances/Splys

P

SIC NO	PRODUCT
3565	Packaging Machinery
2851	Paints, Varnishes, Lacquers, Enamels
2671	Paper Coating & Laminating for Packaging
2672	Paper Coating & Laminating, Exc for Packaging
3554	Paper Inds Machinery

SIC NO	PRODUCT
2621	Paper Mills
2631	Paperboard Mills
2542	Partitions & Fixtures, Except Wood
2951	Paving Mixtures & Blocks
3951	Pens & Mechanical Pencils
2844	Perfumes, Cosmetics & Toilet Preparations
2721	Periodicals: Publishing & Printing
3172	Personal Leather Goods
2879	Pesticides & Agricultural Chemicals, NEC
2911	Petroleum Refining
2834	Pharmaceuticals
3652	Phonograph Records & Magnetic Tape
2874	Phosphatic Fertilizers
3861	Photographic Eqpt & Splys
2035	Pickled Fruits, Vegetables, Sauces & Dressings
3085	Plastic Bottles
3086	Plastic Foam Prdts
3083	Plastic Laminated Plate & Sheet
3084	Plastic Pipe
3088	Plastic Plumbing Fixtures
3089	Plastic Prdts
3082	Plastic Unsupported Profile Shapes
3081	Plastic Unsupported Sheet & Film
2821	Plastics, Mtrls & Nonvulcanizable Elastomers
2796	Platemaking & Related Svcs
2395	Pleating & Stitching For The Trade
3432	Plumbing Fixture Fittings & Trim, Brass
3264	Porcelain Electrical Splys
2096	Potato Chips & Similar Prdts
3269	Pottery Prdts, NEC
2015	Poultry Slaughtering, Dressing & Processing
3546	Power Hand Tools
3612	Power, Distribution & Specialty Transformers
3448	Prefabricated Metal Buildings & Cmpnts
2452	Prefabricated Wood Buildings & Cmpnts
7372	Prepackaged Software
2048	Prepared Feeds For Animals & Fowls
3229	Pressed & Blown Glassware, NEC
3692	Primary Batteries: Dry & Wet
3399	Primary Metal Prdts, NEC
3339	Primary Nonferrous Metals, NEC
3334	Primary Production Of Aluminum
3331	Primary Smelting & Refining Of Copper
3672	Printed Circuit Boards
2893	Printing Ink
3555	Printing Trades Machinery & Eqpt
2999	Products Of Petroleum & Coal, NEC
2531	Public Building & Related Furniture
2611	Pulp Mills
3561	Pumps & Pumping Eqpt

R

SIC NO	PRODUCT
3663	Radio & T V Communications, Systs & Eqpt, Broadcast/Studio
3671	Radio & T V Receiving Electron Tubes
3743	Railroad Eqpt
3273	Ready-Mixed Concrete
2493	Reconstituted Wood Prdts
3695	Recording Media
3625	Relays & Indl Controls
3645	Residential Lighting Fixtures
2044	Rice Milling
2384	Robes & Dressing Gowns
3547	Rolling Mill Machinery & Eqpt
3351	Rolling, Drawing & Extruding Of Copper
3356	Rolling, Drawing-Extruding Of Nonferrous Metals
3021	Rubber & Plastic Footwear
3052	Rubber & Plastic Hose & Belting

S

SIC NO	PRODUCT
2068	Salted & Roasted Nuts & Seeds
2656	Sanitary Food Containers
2676	Sanitary Paper Prdts
2013	Sausages & Meat Prdts
2421	Saw & Planing Mills
3596	Scales & Balances, Exc Laboratory
3451	Screw Machine Prdts
3812	Search, Detection, Navigation & Guidance Systs & Instrs
3341	Secondary Smelting & Refining Of Nonferrous Metals
3674	Semiconductors
3589	Service Ind Machines, NEC
2652	Set-Up Paperboard Boxes
3444	Sheet Metal Work
3731	Shipbuilding & Repairing
2079	Shortening, Oils & Margarine
3993	Signs & Advertising Displays

SIC NO	PRODUCT
2262	Silk & Man-Made Fabric Finishers
2221	Silk & Man-Made Fiber
1044	Silver Ores
3914	Silverware, Plated & Stainless Steel Ware
3484	Small Arms
3482	Small Arms Ammunition
2841	Soap & Detergents
2086	Soft Drinks
2075	Soybean Oil Mills
2842	Spec Cleaning, Polishing & Sanitation Preparations
3559	Special Ind Machinery, NEC
2429	Special Prdt Sawmills, NEC
3566	Speed Changers, Drives & Gears
3949	Sporting & Athletic Goods, NEC
2678	Stationery Prdts
3511	Steam, Gas & Hydraulic Turbines & Engines
3325	Steel Foundries, NEC
3324	Steel Investment Foundries
3317	Steel Pipe & Tubes
3493	Steel Springs, Except Wire
3315	Steel Wire Drawing & Nails & Spikes
3691	Storage Batteries
3259	Structural Clay Prdts, NEC
2439	Structural Wood Members, NEC
2063	Sugar, Beet
2062	Sugar, Cane Refining
2843	Surface Active & Finishing Agents, Sulfonated Oils
3841	Surgical & Medical Instrs & Apparatus
3613	Switchgear & Switchboard Apparatus
2824	Synthetic Organic Fibers, Exc Cellulosic
2822	Synthetic Rubber (Vulcanizable Elastomers)

T

SIC NO	PRODUCT
3795	Tanks & Tank Components
3661	Telephone & Telegraph Apparatus
2393	Textile Bags
2269	Textile Finishers, NEC
2299	Textile Goods, NEC
3552	Textile Machinery
2284	Thread Mills
3011	Tires & Inner Tubes
2131	Tobacco, Chewing & Snuff
3799	Transportation Eqpt, NEC
3792	Travel Trailers & Campers
3713	Truck & Bus Bodies
3715	Truck Trailers
2791	Typesetting

V

SIC NO	PRODUCT
3494	Valves & Pipe Fittings, NEC
2076	Vegetable Oil Mills
3647	Vehicular Lighting Eqpt

W

SIC NO	PRODUCT
3873	Watch & Clock Devices & Parts
3548	Welding Apparatus
7692	Welding Repair
2046	Wet Corn Milling
2084	Wine & Brandy
3495	Wire Springs
2331	Women's & Misses' Blouses
2335	Women's & Misses' Dresses
2339	Women's & Misses' Outerwear, NEC
2337	Women's & Misses' Suits, Coats & Skirts
3144	Women's Footwear, Exc Athletic
2341	Women's, Misses' & Children's Underwear & Nightwear
2441	Wood Boxes
2449	Wood Containers, NEC
2511	Wood Household Furniture
2512	Wood Household Furniture, Upholstered
2434	Wood Kitchen Cabinets
2521	Wood Office Furniture
2448	Wood Pallets & Skids
2499	Wood Prdts, NEC
2491	Wood Preserving
2517	Wood T V, Radio, Phono & Sewing Cabinets
2541	Wood, Office & Store Fixtures
3553	Woodworking Machinery
2231	Wool, Woven Fabric

X

SIC NO	PRODUCT
3844	X-ray Apparatus & Tubes

Y

SIC NO	PRODUCT
2281	Yarn Spinning Mills
2282	Yarn Texturizing, Throwing, Twisting & Winding Mills

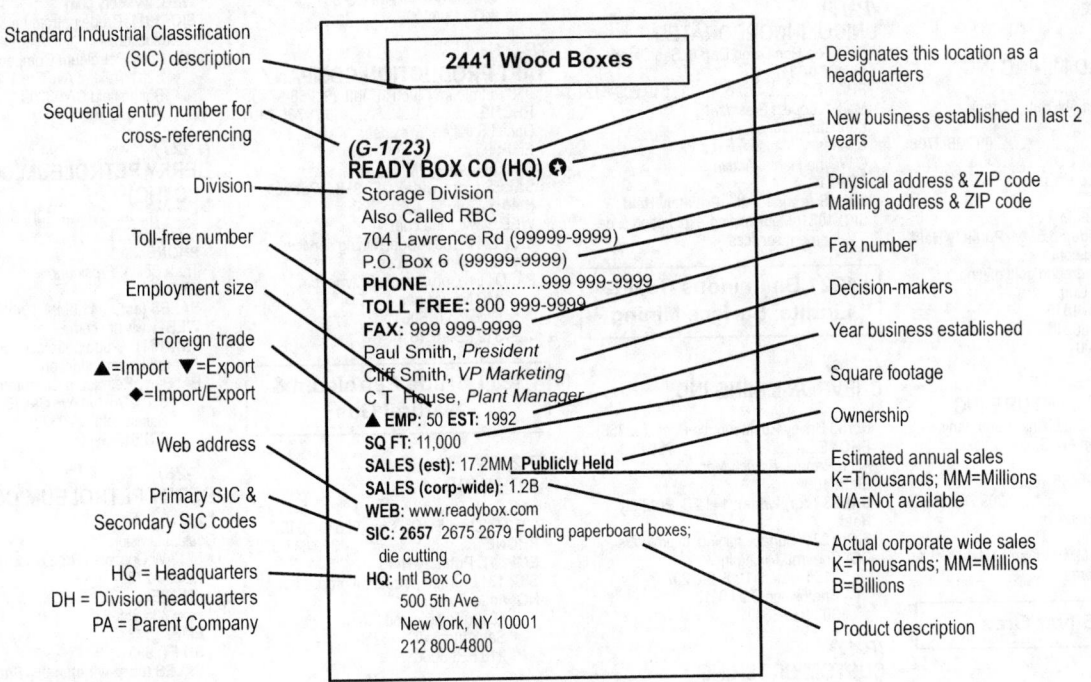

Standard Industrial Classification (SIC) description

2441 Wood Boxes

Designates this location as a headquarters

Sequential entry number for cross-referencing

New business established in last 2 years

Division

Physical address & ZIP code
Mailing address & ZIP code

Toll-free number

Fax number

Employment size

Decision-makers

Foreign trade
▲=Import ▼=Export
◆=Import/Export

Year business established

Square footage

Web address

Ownership

Primary SIC & Secondary SIC codes

Estimated annual sales
K=Thousands; MM=Millions
N/A=Not available

HQ = Headquarters
DH = Division headquarters
PA = Parent Company

Actual corporate wide sales
K=Thousands; MM=Millions
B=Billions

Product description

(G-1723)
READY BOX CO (HQ) ✪
Storage Division
Also Called RBC
704 Lawrence Rd (99999-9999)
P.O. Box 6 (99999-9999)
PHONE......................999 999-9999
TOLL FREE: 800 999-9999
FAX: 999 999-9999
Paul Smith, *President*
Cliff Smith, *VP Marketing*
C T House, *Plant Manager*
▲ **EMP:** 50 **EST:** 1992
SQ FT: 11,000
SALES (est): 17.2MM **Publicly Held**
SALES (corp-wide): 1.2B
WEB: www.readybox.com
SIC: 2657 2675 2679 Folding paperboard boxes; die cutting
HQ: Intl Box Co
500 5th Ave
New York, NY 10001
212 800-4800

- Companies in this section are listed numerically under their primary SIC Companies are in alphabetical order under each code.

- A numerical and alphabetcal index precedes this section.

- **Sequential Entry Numbers.** Each establishment in this section is numbered sequentially. The number assigned to each establishment's Entry Number. To make cross-referencing easier, each listing in the Product's & Services, Alphabetic and Geographical Section includes the establishment's entry number. To facilitate locating an entry in this section, the entry numbers for the first listing on the left page and the last listing on the right page are printed at the top of the page next to the Standard Industrial Classification (SIC) description.

- Further information can be found in the Explanatory Notes starting on page 5.

- See the footnotes for symbols and abbreviations.

IMPORTANT NOTICE: It is a violation of both federal and state law to transmit an unsolicited advertisement to a facsimile machine. Any user of this product that violates such laws may be subject to civil and criminal penalties which may exceed $500 for each transmission of an unsolicited facsimile. Harris InfoSource provides fax numbers for lawful purposes only and expressly forbids the use of these numbers in any unlawful manner.

PRODUCTS & SVCS

1041 Gold Ores

(P-1)
BARRICK GOLD CORPORATION
Also Called: Mc Laughlin Mine
26775 Morgan Valley Rd, Lower Lake (95457-9411)
PHONE.................................707 995-6070
Pat Purtell, *Branch Mgr*
EMP: 100
SALES (est): 11.8MM
SALES (corp-wide): 8.3B **Privately Held**
WEB: www.barrick.com
SIC: 1041 Gold ores
PA: Barrick Gold Corporation
161 Bay St Suite 3700
Toronto ON M5J 2
416 861-9911

(P-2)
CRYSTAL MINING CORPORATION
20380 Stevens Creek Blvd, Cupertino (95014-2299)
PHONE.................................386 479-5823
Sylvestre Ygay IV, *CEO*
EMP: 15
SALES (est): 760.7K **Privately Held**
SIC: 1041 Gold ores processing

(P-3)
FIRST GOLD CORP
3108 Ponte Morino Dr # 210, Cameron Park (95682-7453)
PHONE.................................530 677-5974
Stephen Akerfeldt, *CEO*
James W Kluber, *CFO*
EMP: 10
SALES (est): 577.1K **Privately Held**
SIC: 1041 Gold ores mining

(P-4)
GOLDEN QUEEN MINING CO LLC
2818 Silver Queen Rd, Mojave (93501-7021)
P.O. Box 1030 (93502-1030)
PHONE.................................661 824-4300
Thomas Clay, *Ch of Bd*
Robert Walish, *President*
Andree St-Germain, *CFO*
Brenda Dayton, *Admin Sec*
Ken Mann, *Administration*
EMP: 180
SQ FT: 2,500
SALES (est): 70MM **Privately Held**
SIC: 1041 Gold ores mining

(P-5)
LITTLE DIGGER MINING & SUP LLC
3524 Maine Ave, Baldwin Park (91706-5153)
PHONE.................................626 856-3366
Curtis Timmons,
EMP: 40
SALES (est): 3.1MM **Privately Held**
SIC: 1041 Open pit gold mining

(P-6)
LOST DUTCHMANS MININGS ASSN (DH)
43445 Bus Pk Dr Ste 113, Temecula (92590-3671)
P.O. Box 891509 (92589-1509)
PHONE.................................951 699-4749
Perry Massie, *President*
Tom Massie, *Admin Sec*
▲ **EMP:** 30
SQ FT: 3,200
SALES (est): 2.3MM
SALES (corp-wide): 122.8MM **Privately Held**
SIC: 1041 Gold ores
HQ: Outdoor Channel Holdings, Inc.
1000 Chopper Cir
Denver CO 80204
951 699-6991

(P-7)
MERIDIAN GOLD INC
Also Called: Royal Mountain King
4461 Rock Creek Rd, Copperopolis (95228)
PHONE.................................209 785-3222
Edgar Smith, *Branch Mgr*
EMP: 160
SALES (corp-wide): 1.8B **Privately Held**
SIC: 1041 Gold ores
HQ: Meridian Gold Inc.
4635 Longley Ln Ste 110
Reno NV 89502
-

(P-8)
STAVATTI INDUSTRIES LTD
1443 S Gage St, San Bernardino (92408-2835)
P.O. Box 211258, Eagan MN (55121-2658)
PHONE.................................651 238-5369
Christopher R Beskar, *Branch Mgr*
Christopher Beskar, *CEO*
EMP: 60
SALES (corp-wide): 2MM **Privately Held**
SIC: 1041 1081 3511 3533 Gold ores mining; metal mining exploration & development services; turbines & turbine generator set units, complete; oil & gas field machinery; truck trailers

---

PA: Stavatti Industries Ltd
1061 Tiffany Dr
Eagan MN 55123
651 238-5369

(P-9)
SUTTER GOLD MINING INC
Also Called: Sgm
11500 Stringbean Aly, Sutter Creek
(95685)
PHONE...........................209 736-2708
Clayr Alexander, *CEO*
Keith Larson, *Vice Pres*
EMP: 14
SALES (est): 1.3MM
SALES (corp-wide): 6.5MM **Publicly Held**
WEB: www.usnrg.com
SIC: 1041 Underground gold mining
PA: U.S. Energy Corp.
950 S St Ste 1515
Denver CO 80246
303 993-3200

(P-10)
USECB JOINT VENTURE INC
Also Called: Sutter Gold Mining Company
11500 String Bean Aly, Sutter Creek
(95685)
P.O. Box 1689 (95685-1689)
PHONE...........................209 267-5594
Stacy Rhodes, *President*
EMP: 14
SALES (est): 1.1MM **Privately Held**
SIC: 1041 Gold ores

1044 Silver Ores

(P-11)
MAGELLAN GOLD CORPORATION
2010a Harbison Dr 312, Vacaville
(95687-3900)
PHONE...........................707 884-3766
W Pierce Carson, *President*
Michael P Martinez, *CFO*
John C Power, *Bd of Directors*
EMP: 38
SALES (est): 89.4K **Privately Held**
SIC: 1044 1031 Silver ores; lead & zinc
ores

1081 Metal Mining Svcs

(P-12)
NATIONAL EWP INC
1961 Meeker Ave, Richmond (94804-6405)
PHONE...........................510 236-6282
Chris Tatum, *Branch Mgr*
EMP: 13
SALES (corp-wide): 107.3MM **Privately Held**
SIC: 1081 Metal mining exploration & development services
PA: National Ewp, Inc.
1200 W San Pedro St
Gilbert AZ 85233
530 419-2117

(P-13)
NATIONAL EWP INC
Also Called: National Explrtion Wells Pumps
5566 Arrow Hwy, Montclair (91763-1606)
PHONE...........................909 931-4014
Tom Moreland, *Branch Mgr*
EMP: 22
SALES (corp-wide): 107.3MM **Privately Held**
SIC: 1081 Metal mining exploration & development services
PA: National Ewp, Inc.
1200 W San Pedro St
Gilbert AZ 85233
530 419-2117

(P-14)
OK MINE COMPANY INCORPORATED
520 Chestnut Ave, Long Beach
(90802-2213)
PHONE...........................323 440-4333
Malachi Tobin, *Principal*
EMP: 12

SALES (est): 303.7K **Privately Held**
SIC: 1081 Metal mining services

(P-15)
UNICO INCORPORATED
8880 Rio San Diego Dr # 8, San Diego
(92108-1634)
PHONE...........................619 209-6124
Mark A Lopez, *President*
Kenneth Wiedrich, *CFO*
Charles M Madsen, *Exec VP*
C Wayne Hartle, *Admin Sec*
EMP: 16
SALES (est): 1.1MM **Privately Held**
SIC: 1081 Metal mining exploration & development services

1221 Bituminous Coal & Lignite: Surface Mining

(P-16)
CHEVRON MINING INC
Moly
67750 Bailey Rd, Mountain Pass (92366)
PHONE...........................760 856-7625
Allen Randle, *Branch Mgr*
EMP: 400
SALES (corp-wide): 141.7B **Publicly Held**
SIC: 1221 Surface mining, bituminous
HQ: Chevron Mining Inc.
116 Invrneco Dr E Ste 207
Englewood CO 80112
303 930-3600

(P-17)
CUSTOM CRUSHING INDUSTRIES
2409 E Oberlin Rd, Yreka (96097-9577)
P.O. Box 357, Grenada (96038-0357)
PHONE...........................530 842-5544
Clara Goodwin, *Treasurer*
Paul Goodwin, *President*
EMP: 11
SALES (est): 5.5MM **Privately Held**
SIC: 1221 3295 3281 1499 Strip mining, bituminous; minerals, ground or treated; stone, quarrying & processing of own stone products; peat mining & processing; excavation & grading, building construction; highway & street construction

(P-18)
KENNEDY HILLS ENTERPRISES LLC
Also Called: Kennedy Hills Materials
19486 Woodlands Dr, Huntington Beach
(92648-5570)
PHONE...........................714 596-7444
EMP: 10
SALES: 3MM **Privately Held**
SIC: 1221

1241 Coal Mining Svcs

(P-19)
GREKA INC
1791 Sinton Rd, Santa Maria (93458-9708)
P.O. Box 5489 (93456-5489)
PHONE...........................805 347-8700
Andy Devegvar, *President*
Randeep Grewal, *CEO*
EMP: 150
SQ FT: 3,000
SALES: 40MM **Privately Held**
SIC: 1241 1081 Coal mining services; metal mining services

(P-20)
RIO TINTO MINERALS INC
Also Called: Reno Tenco
14486 Borax Rd, Boron (93516-2017)
PHONE...........................760 762-7121
Xiaoling Liu, *CEO*
Preston Chiaro, *President*
Hugo Bague, *Principal*
Brett Horton, *Engineer*
Trevor Plote, *Engineer*
▼ **EMP:** 150
SALES (est): 17.1MM
SALES (corp-wide): 40B **Privately Held**
SIC: 1241 Coal mining services

HQ: U.S. Borax Inc.
8051 E Maplewood Ave # 100
Greenwood Village CO 80111
303 713-5000

(P-21)
TAFT PRODUCTION COMPANY
950 Petroleum Club Rd, Taft (93268-9748)
PHONE...........................661 765-7194
Daniel S Jaffee, *President*
EMP: 95
SALES (est): 6.9MM
SALES (corp-wide): 262.3MM **Publicly Held**
WEB: www.oildri.com
SIC: 1241 1081 Coal mining services; metal mining services
PA: Oil-Dri Corporation Of America
410 N Michigan Ave Fl 4
Chicago IL 60611
312 321-1515

1311 Crude Petroleum & Natural Gas

(P-22)
ANDEAVOR
Also Called: Tesoro
2350 E 223rd St, Carson (90810-1615)
PHONE...........................310 847-5705
EMP: 11 **Publicly Held**
SIC: 1311 Crude petroleum production
HQ: Andeavor Llc
19100 Ridgewood Pkwy
San Antonio TX 78259
210 626-6000

(P-23)
ARMSTRONG PETROLEUM CORP (PA)
1080 W 17th St, Costa Mesa (92627-4503)
P.O. Box 1547, Newport Beach (92659-0547)
PHONE...........................949 650-4000
William Armstrong, *President*
Margaret Armstrong, *Admin Sec*
▲ **EMP:** 31
SQ FT: 2,000
SALES (est): 2.3MM **Privately Held**
SIC: 1311 1389 Crude petroleum production; servicing oil & gas wells

(P-24)
BENTLEY-SIMONSON INC
1746 S Victoria Ave Ste F, Ventura
(93003-6190)
PHONE...........................805 650-2794
James Bentley, *Ch of Bd*
Theodore Bentley, *Ch of Bd*
Clifton O Simonson, *President*
Petter Romming, *Vice Pres*
EMP: 100
SQ FT: 1,000
SALES (est): 4.1MM **Privately Held**
SIC: 1311 Crude petroleum & natural gas production

(P-25)
BERRY PETROLEUM COMPANY LLC
25121 Sierra Hwy, Newhall (91321-2007)
PHONE...........................661 255-6066
Eddie Azevedo, *Manager*
EMP: 13
SALES (corp-wide): 641.6MM **Publicly Held**
WEB: www.bry.com
SIC: 1311 Crude petroleum production; natural gas production
HQ: Berry Petroleum Company, Llc
5201 Truxtun Ave Ste 100
Bakersfield CA 93309
661 616-3900

(P-26)
BERRY PETROLEUM COMPANY LLC
28700 Hovey Hills Rd, Taft (93268)
PHONE...........................661 769-8820
Tom Cruise, *Manager*
EMP: 37

SALES (corp-wide): 641.6MM **Publicly Held**
WEB: www.bry.com
SIC: 1311 Crude petroleum & natural gas production
HQ: Berry Petroleum Company, Llc
5201 Truxtun Ave Ste 100
Bakersfield CA 93309
661 616-3900

(P-27)
BERRY PETROLEUM COMPANY LLC (HQ)
5201 Truxtun Ave Ste 100, Bakersfield
(93309-0422)
PHONE...........................661 616-3900
Trem Smith, *President*
EMP: 65
SALES (est): 641.6MM **Publicly Held**
WEB: www.bry.com
SIC: 1311 Crude petroleum production; natural gas production
PA: Berry Petroleum Corporation
5201 Truxtun Ave Ste 100
Bakersfield CA 93309
661 616-3900

(P-28)
BERRY PETROLEUM COMPANY LLC
Coastal Division
5713 W Gonzales Rd, Oxnard
(93036-2739)
PHONE...........................805 984-0053
Fax: 805 985-8362
EMP: 12
SQ FT: 685
SALES (corp-wide): 4.9B **Publicly Held**
SIC: 1311
HQ: Berry Petroleum Company, Llc
600 Travis St Ste 4900
Houston TX 93309
281 840-4000

(P-29)
BERRY PETROLEUM CORPORATION (PA)
5201 Truxtun Ave Ste 100, Bakersfield
(93309-0422)
PHONE...........................661 616-3900
Arthur T Smith, *President*
Brent S Buckley, *Ch of Bd*
Gary A Grove, *COO*
Cary Baetz, *CFO*
Kurt Neher, *Exec VP*
EMP: 11
SALES (est): 641.6MM **Publicly Held**
SIC: 1311 Crude petroleum production

(P-30)
BEVERLY HILLCREST OIL CORP
27241 Burbank, El Toro (92610-2500)
PHONE...........................949 598-7300
Morris Hodges, *President*
Katherine Hodges, *Vice Pres*
EMP: 15
SALES (est): 1.2MM **Privately Held**
SIC: 1311 1321 Crude petroleum production; natural gas liquids production

(P-31)
BP WEST COAST PRODUCTS LLC
22600 Wilmington Ave, Carson
(90745-4307)
PHONE...........................310 816-8787
EMP: 310
SALES (corp-wide): 240.2B **Privately Held**
SIC: 1311 Crude petroleum & natural gas
HQ: Bp West Coast Products Llc
4519 Grandview Way
Blaine WA 98230
310 549-6204

(P-32)
BP WEST COAST PRODUCTS LLC
1306 Canal Blvd, Richmond (94804-3556)
PHONE...........................510 231-4724
Fred Glueck, *Vice Pres*
EMP: 310
SQ FT: 4,550

▲ = Import ▼=Export
◆ =Import/Export

SALES (corp-wide): 240.2B **Privately Held**
SIC: 1311 Crude petroleum production
HQ: Bp West Coast Products Llc
4519 Grandview Rd
Blaine WA 98230
310 549-6204

(P-33)
BREA CANON OIL CO INC
23903 Normandie Ave, Harbor City (90710-1400)
PHONE..................310 326-4002
Andrew Barkler, *President*
Ray Javier, *Vice Pres*
Rod Benny, *Manager*
EMP: 17
SALES (est): 745.6K **Privately Held**
SIC: 1311 Crude petroleum production

(P-34)
BREITBURN GP LLC
707 Wilshire Blvd # 4600, Los Angeles (90017-3501)
PHONE..................213 225-5900
Halbert S Washburn, *CEO*
EMP: 833
SALES (est): 16.6MM **Privately Held**
SIC: 1311 Crude petroleum & natural gas
PA: Breitburn Energy Partners Lp
707 Wilshire Blvd # 4600
Los Angeles CA 90017

(P-35)
BREITBURN OPERATING LP (HQ)
707 Wilshire Blvrd 4600, Los Angeles (90017)
PHONE..................213 225-5900
James G Jackson, *Partner*
EMP: 14
SALES (est): 1.4MM **Privately Held**
SIC: 1311 1389 Crude petroleum & natural gas production; construction, repair & dismantling services

(P-36)
CALIFORNIA HEAVY OIL INC
10889 Wilshire Blvd, Los Angeles (90024-4201)
PHONE..................888 848-4754
Todd A Stevens, *CEO*
EMP: 35
SALES (est): 853.6K
SALES (corp-wide): 2B **Publicly Held**
SIC: 1311 Crude petroleum production
PA: California Resources Corporation
9200 Oakdale Ave Ste 900
Chatsworth CA 91311
888 848-4754

(P-37)
CALIFORNIA RESOURCES CORP
1320 4th St, Los Osos (93402-1206)
PHONE..................661 763-6107
EMP: 46
SALES (corp-wide): 2B **Publicly Held**
SIC: 1311 Crude petroleum production
PA: California Resources Corporation
9200 Oakdale Ave Ste 900
Chatsworth CA 91311
888 848-4754

(P-38)
CALIFORNIA RESOURCES CORP
5000 Stockdale Hwy, Bakersfield (93309-2650)
PHONE..................661 395-8000
EMP: 23
SALES (corp-wide): 2B **Publicly Held**
SIC: 1311 Crude petroleum production
PA: California Resources Corporation
9200 Oakdale Ave Ste 900
Chatsworth CA 91311
888 848-4754

(P-39)
CALIFORNIA RESOURCES CORP
111 W Ocean Blvd Ste 800, Long Beach (90802-7930)
PHONE..................562 624-3400

EMP: 103
SALES (corp-wide): 2B **Publicly Held**
SIC: 1311 Crude petroleum production
PA: California Resources Corporation
9200 Oakdale Ave Ste 900
Chatsworth CA 91311
888 848-4754

(P-40)
CALIFORNIA RESOURCES CORP
2692 Amerada Rd, Rio Vista (94571-1121)
PHONE..................707 374-4109
EMP: 23
SALES (corp-wide): 2B **Publicly Held**
SIC: 1311 Crude petroleum & natural gas
PA: California Resources Corporation
9200 Oakdale Ave Ste 900
Chatsworth CA 91311
888 848-4754

(P-41)
CALIFORNIA RESOURCES CORP
3055 Pacific Coast Hwy, Ventura (93001-9742)
PHONE..................805 641-5566
Paul Roden, *Manager*
EMP: 13
SALES (corp-wide): 2B **Publicly Held**
WEB: www.vintagetul.com
SIC: 1311 Crude petroleum production
PA: California Resources Corporation
9200 Oakdale Ave Ste 900
Chatsworth CA 91311
888 848-4754

(P-42)
CALIFORNIA RESOURCES CORP
270 Quail Ct Ste 100, Santa Paula (93060-9205)
PHONE..................310 208-8800
Steven Prow, *Manager*
EMP: 46
SALES (corp-wide): 2B **Publicly Held**
SIC: 1311 Crude petroleum production; natural gas production
PA: California Resources Corporation
9200 Oakdale Ave Ste 900
Chatsworth CA 91311
888 848-4754

(P-43)
CALIFORNIA RESOURCES PROD CORP
3450 E 5th St, Oxnard (93033-2100)
PHONE..................805 483-8017
EMP: 83
SALES (corp-wide): 2.4B **Publicly Held**
SIC: 1311 1382
HQ: California Resources Production Corporation
11109 River Run Blvd
Bakersfield CA 93311
661 869-8000

(P-44)
CALIFORNIA RESOURCES PROD CORP
855 Harter Pkwy Ste 200, Yuba City (95993-9462)
PHONE..................530 671-8201
EMP: 40
SALES (corp-wide): 2B **Publicly Held**
SIC: 1311 1382 Crude petroleum production; oil & gas exploration services
HQ: California Resources Production Corporation
11109 River Run Blvd
Bakersfield CA 93311
661 869-8000

(P-45)
CALIFORNIA RESOURCES PROD CORP (HQ)
Also Called: Vintage Production California
11109 River Run Blvd, Bakersfield (93311-8957)
PHONE..................661 869-8000
Todd A Stevens, *Principal*
Richard Oringderff, *President*
Todd Stevens, *CEO*
EMP: 125

SALES (est): 92.1MM
SALES (corp-wide): 2B **Publicly Held**
WEB: www.oxy.com
SIC: 1311 1382 Crude petroleum production; oil & gas exploration services
PA: California Resources Corporation
9200 Oakdale Ave Ste 900
Chatsworth CA 91311
888 848-4754

(P-46)
CARBON CALIFORNIA COMPANY LLC
270 Quail Ct Ste B, Santa Paula (93060-9204)
PHONE..................805 933-1901
Patrick R McDonald, *CEO*
Mark D Pierce, *President*
Kevin D Struzeski, *CFO*
EMP: 72 EST: 2016
SALES (est): 841.9K
SALES (corp-wide): 22.4MM **Publicly Held**
SIC: 1311 Crude petroleum & natural gas
PA: Carbon Energy Corporation
1700 Broadway Ste 1170
Denver CO 80290
720 407-7043

(P-47)
CHEVRON CORPORATION
Also Called: Unocal
3602 Harris Grade Rd, Lompoc (93436-2206)
P.O. Box 625 (93438-0625)
PHONE..................805 733-5174
Phil Hosch, *Branch Mgr*
EMP: 16
SALES (corp-wide): 141.7B **Publicly Held**
WEB: www.chevrontexaco.com
SIC: 1311 Crude petroleum & natural gas
PA: Chevron Corporation
6001 Bollinger Canyon Rd
San Ramon CA 94583
925 842-1000

(P-48)
CHEVRON USA INC
6001 Bollinger Canyon Rd, San Ramon (94583-5737)
P.O. Box 6017 (94583-0717)
PHONE..................925 842-0855
Kim Smith, *Branch Mgr*
Bruce Lincoln, *Supervisor*
EMP: 100
SALES (corp-wide): 141.7B **Publicly Held**
SIC: 1311 2911 Crude petroleum & natural gas; petroleum refining
HQ: Chevron U.S.A. Inc.
6001 Bollinger Canyon Rd D1248
San Ramon CA 94583
925 842-1000

(P-49)
COALINGA CORPORATION (PA)
12575 Beatrice St, Los Angeles (90066-7001)
P.O. Box 66902 (90066-0902)
PHONE..................310 578-5900
William M Keck II, *President*
Hasting Carl D, *Vice Pres*
EMP: 11 EST: 1957
SQ FT: 22,000
SALES: 5MM **Privately Held**
SIC: 1311 Crude petroleum production; natural gas production

(P-50)
COMMERCIAL ENERGY MONTANA INC
Also Called: Commercial Energy California
7677 Oakport St Ste 525, Oakland (94621-1944)
PHONE..................510 567-2700
John Curry Stypula, *Branch Mgr*
Fred Jackson, *CFO*
Arielle Bosch, *Accounts Exec*
EMP: 20
SALES (corp-wide): 4.7MM **Privately Held**
SIC: 1311 Crude petroleum production

PA: Commercial Energy Of Montana Inc.
118 E Main St
Cut Bank MT 59427
406 873-3300

(P-51)
COOPER & BRAIN INC
655 E D St, Wilmington (90744-6003)
P.O. Box 1177 (90748-1177)
PHONE..................310 834-4411
Robert E Brain, *President*
Joel A Cooper, *Corp Secy*
EMP: 11
SQ FT: 4,000
SALES (est): 1.6MM **Privately Held**
SIC: 1311 Crude petroleum production

(P-52)
CRC MARKETING INC
Also Called: Crcm
111 W Ocean Blvd Ste 800, Long Beach (90802-7930)
P.O. Box 2900 (90801-2900)
PHONE..................562 624-3400
Parks Wesson, *CEO*
Bill Aldright, *President*
Mohammed Mahyoub, *Manager*
EMP: 12
SALES (est): 4.4MM
SALES (corp-wide): 2B **Publicly Held**
SIC: 1311 Crude petroleum & natural gas
PA: California Resources Corporation
9200 Oakdale Ave Ste 900
Chatsworth CA 91311
888 848-4754

(P-53)
CRC SERVICES LLC
9200 Oakdale Ave Fl 9, Chatsworth (91311-6506)
PHONE..................888 848-4754
James Kahrhoff Jr,
EMP: 18
SALES (est): 3.8MM
SALES (corp-wide): 2B **Publicly Held**
SIC: 1311 Crude petroleum & natural gas
PA: California Resources Corporation
9200 Oakdale Ave Ste 900
Chatsworth CA 91311
888 848-4754

(P-54)
CRIMSON RESOURCE MGT CORP
5001 California Ave # 206, Bakersfield (93309-1692)
PHONE..................303 892-8878
Greg Juengst, *Manager*
EMP: 21
SALES (est): 2.3MM
SALES (corp-wide): 3.9MM **Privately Held**
SIC: 1311 Crude petroleum production; crude petroleum & natural gas production
PA: Crimson Resource Management Corp.
410 17th St Ste 1010
Denver CO 80202
303 892-9333

(P-55)
E & B NTRAL RESOURCES MGT CORP (PA)
1600 Norris Rd, Bakersfield (93308-2234)
PHONE..................661 679-1714
Steve Layton, *President*
Ronkese Frank, *CFO*
Frank J Ronkese, *CFO*
Jeff Blesener, *Senior VP*
Joyce Holtzclaw, *Senior VP*
EMP: 65
SALES: 326.3MM **Privately Held**
WEB: www.ebresources.com
SIC: 1311 Crude petroleum & natural gas

(P-56)
ENERGY OPERATIONS MANAGEMENT
2981 Gold Canal Dr, Rancho Cordova (95670-6126)
PHONE..................916 859-4700
Derek C Jones, *CEO*
Vern Jones, *Ch of Bd*
Gloria Jones, *Admin Sec*
EMP: 10
SQ FT: 18,000

P R O D U C T S & S V C S

SALES (est): 1.6MM **Privately Held**
SIC: 1311 Natural gas production

(P-57)
FREEPORT-MCMORAN OIL & GAS LLC
760 W Hueneme Rd, Oxnard (93033-9013)
PHONE...............................805 567-1601
Eric Vang, *Branch Mgr*
EMP: 27
SALES (corp-wide): 16.4B **Publicly Held**
SIC: 1311 Crude petroleum production
HQ: Freeport-Mcmoran Oil & Gas Llc
700 Milam St Ste 3100
Houston TX 77002
713 579-6000

(P-58)
FREEPORT-MCMORAN OIL & GAS LLC
3252 W Crocker Springs Rd, Fellows (93224)
PHONE...............................661 768-4831
Tom Kaldenberg, *Branch Mgr*
EMP: 34
SALES (corp-wide): 16.4B **Publicly Held**
SIC: 1311 Crude petroleum & natural gas
HQ: Freeport-Mcmoran Oil & Gas Llc
700 Milam St Ste 3100
Houston TX 77002
713 579-6000

(P-59)
FREEPORT-MCMORAN OIL & GAS LLC
1200 Discovery Dr Ste 500, Bakersfield (93309-7038)
PHONE...............................661 322-7600
Kiran Leal, *Manager*
EMP: 60
SALES (corp-wide): 16.4B **Publicly Held**
SIC: 1311 Crude petroleum & natural gas
HQ: Freeport-Mcmoran Oil & Gas Llc
700 Milam St Ste 3100
Houston TX 77002
713 579-6000

(P-60)
FREEPORT-MCMORAN OIL & GAS LLC
5640 S Fairfax Ave, Los Angeles (90056-1266)
PHONE...............................323 298-2200
Charlotte Hargett, *Director*
Scott McGurk, *Engineer*
Jeff Sande, *Engineer*
EMP: 34
SALES (corp-wide): 16.4B **Publicly Held**
SIC: 1311 Crude petroleum production
HQ: Freeport-Mcmoran Oil & Gas Llc
700 Milam St Ste 3100
Houston TX 77002
713 579-6000

(P-61)
GREGG HAMMORK ENTERPRIZES INC
Also Called: Gregg's Mission Viejo Mobile
23002 Alicia Pkwy, Mission Viejo (92692-1636)
PHONE...............................949 586-7902
Gregg Hammork, *President*
EMP: 12
SQ FT: 3,000
SALES (est): 9.9MM **Privately Held**
WEB: www.mobileoil.com
SIC: 1311 Crude petroleum & natural gas production

(P-62)
HATHAWAY LLC
4205 Atlas Ct, Bakersfield (93308-4510)
P.O. Box 81385 (93380-1385)
PHONE...............................661 393-2004
Chad Hathaway,
Ryan Yarger, *Engineer*
Charles Hathaway,
Curtis Huge, *Manager*
Mark Yarlot, *Manager*
EMP: 38
SQ FT: 4,500
SALES: 11MM **Privately Held**
SIC: 1311 Crude petroleum production

(P-63)
HELLMAN PROPERTIES LLC
711 First St, Seal Beach (90740)
PHONE...............................562 431-6022
Jerry Tone,
EMP: 11
SQ FT: 200
SALES (est): 2.3MM **Privately Held**
SIC: 1311 Crude petroleum production

(P-64)
LINNCO LLC
5201 Truxtun Ave, Bakersfield (93309-0421)
PHONE...............................661 616-3900
Gordon Beagley, *Technician*
Greg Williams, *Technology*
Jared Gilarducci, *Engineer*
Dom Sylvester, *VP Opers*
EMP: 1432
SALES (corp-wide): 40.7MM **Publicly Held**
SIC: 1311 Crude petroleum & natural gas
PA: Linnco, Llc
600 Travis St Ste 5100
Houston TX 77002
281 840-4000

(P-65)
NAFTEX WESTSIDE PARTNERS LIMIT
1900 Avenue Of The Stars, Los Angeles (90067-4301)
PHONE...............................310 277-9004
Hormoz Ameri, *General Ptnr*
EMP: 22
SQ FT: 1,200
SALES (est): 3.5MM **Privately Held**
SIC: 1311 Crude petroleum & natural gas

(P-66)
NUSTAR LOGISTICS LP
1100 Willow Pass Rd, Pittsburg (94565-1800)
P.O. Box 781609, San Antonio TX (78278-1609)
PHONE...............................925 427-6880
Dan Thomas, *Branch Mgr*
Al Gray, *Manager*
EMP: 10 **Publicly Held**
SIC: 1311 Crude petroleum & natural gas production
HQ: Nustar Logistics, L.P.
19003 W Interstate 10
San Antonio TX 78257
210 918-2000

(P-67)
OXY USA INC
9600 Ming Ave Ste 300, Bakersfield (93311-1365)
PHONE...............................661 869-8000
Gary O Lee Jr, *Credit Mgr*
EMP: 125
SALES (corp-wide): 13.2B **Publicly Held**
SIC: 1311 Crude petroleum & natural gas
HQ: Oxy Usa Inc.
1001 S County Rd W
Odessa TX 79763
432 335-0995

(P-68)
PACIFIC ENERGY RESOURCES LTD (PA)
111 W Ocean Blvd Ste 1240, Long Beach (90802-4645)
PHONE...............................562 628-1526
Richard Young, *Partner*
Gina Gillette, *Partner*
David Hoy, *Partner*
Elizabeth Young Weinstein, *Partner*
EMP: 17 **EST:** 1977
SQ FT: 4,000
SALES (est): 3.6MM **Privately Held**
SIC: 1311 Crude petroleum & natural gas

(P-69)
PETROLEUM SALES INC
2066 Redwood Hwy, Greenbrae (94904-2467)
PHONE...............................415 256-1600
Stephanie Shimk, *Branch Mgr*
EMP: 70

SALES (corp-wide): 31.7MM **Privately Held**
SIC: 1311 Crude petroleum & natural gas
PA: Petroleum Sales Inc
1475 2nd St
San Rafael CA 94901
415 256-1600

(P-70)
QUANTUM TECHNOLOGIES INC
25242 Arctic Ocean Dr, Lake Forest (92630-8821)
PHONE...............................949 399-4500
Dean K Aoki, *CEO*
Alan Niedzwiecki, *President*
Bradley J Timon, *CFO*
Mark Arold, *Vice Pres*
Neel Sirosh, *Principal*
EMP: 140
SALES (est): 38.2MM **Privately Held**
SIC: 1311 Crude petroleum & natural gas

(P-71)
REINHART OIL & GAS INC
Also Called: RMS Monty Crystal
1953 San Elijo Ave # 200, Cardiff By The Sea (92007-2348)
P.O. Box 6749, Snowmass Village CO (81615-6749)
PHONE...............................760 753-3330
Reiner Klawiter, *President*
EMP: 10
SQ FT: 2,500
SALES: 1.2MM **Privately Held**
SIC: 1311 8711 Crude petroleum & natural gas production; petroleum engineering

(P-72)
ROYALE ENERGY FUNDS INC
1870 Cordell Ct Ste 210, El Cajon (92020-0916)
PHONE...............................619 383-6600
Donald H Hosmer, *President*
Stephen M Hosmer, *President*
Ronald Lipnick, *Finance*
EMP: 11
SALES: 1MM
SALES (corp-wide): 4.7MM **Publicly Held**
WEB: www.royl.com
SIC: 1311 Crude petroleum & natural gas production
PA: Royale Energy, Inc.
1870 Cordell Ct Ste 210
El Cajon CA 92020
619 383-6600

(P-73)
SAMEDAN OIL CORPORATION
Also Called: Noble Energy
1360 Landing Ave, Seal Beach (90740-6525)
PHONE...............................661 319-5038
EMP: 336
SALES (corp-wide): 34.8MM **Privately Held**
SIC: 1311 Crude petroleum production
PA: Samedan Oil Corporation
1001 Noble Energy Way
Houston TX 77070
580 223-4110

(P-74)
SAN JOAQUIN FACILITIES MGT INC (PA)
4520 California Ave # 300, Bakersfield (93309-1190)
PHONE...............................661 631-8713
Mike Kranyak, *President*
Kenneth E Fait, *Vice Pres*
Michael Gooding, *General Mgr*
Matt Jennings, *Engineer*
EMP: 13
SALES (est): 1.7MM **Privately Held**
SIC: 1311 1389 Crude petroleum & natural gas production; servicing oil & gas wells

(P-75)
SILURIA TECHNOLOGIES INC
409 Illinois St, San Francisco (94158-2509)
PHONE...............................415 978-2170
Robert Trout, *CEO*
Alex Tkachenko, *President*
Erik Scher, *COO*
Karl Kurz, *Chairman*
Gary Koehler, *Vice Pres*

EMP: 30
SALES (est): 21MM **Privately Held**
SIC: 1311 Natural gas production

(P-76)
STRAND ENERGY COMPANY
Also Called: Breitburn Energy Co
10350 Heritage Park Dr, Santa Fe Springs (90670-3787)
PHONE...............................562 944-9580
EMP: 227
SALES (corp-wide): 394.4MM **Privately Held**
SIC: 1311 Crude petroleum & natural gas
PA: The Strand Energy Company
515 S Flower St Ste 4800
Los Angeles CA 90071
213 225-5900

(P-77)
TERMO COMPANY
3275 Cherry Ave, Long Beach (90807-5213)
P.O. Box 2767 (90801-2767)
PHONE...............................562 595-7401
David E Combs, *President*
Norbert Buss, *Vice Pres*
Francis Roth, *Vice Pres*
Donna Sheaffer, *Admin Sec*
Calvin Ito, *Foreman/Supr*
EMP: 21
SQ FT: 18,034
SALES (est): 26.1MM **Privately Held**
WEB: www.termoco.com
SIC: 1311 Crude petroleum production

(P-78)
TIDELANDS OIL PRODUCTION INC (DH)
Also Called: Partnership Of Paramount Petro
301 E Ocean Blvd Ste 300, Long Beach (90802-4830)
PHONE...............................562 436-9918
Michael Domanski, *President*
Todd Stevens, *President*
OXY Wilmington, *President*
Mark S Kapelke, *Vice Pres*
EMP: 25
SQ FT: 22,000
SALES (est): 9MM **Privately Held**
SIC: 1311 8748 4925 Crude petroleum production; business consulting; gas production and/or distribution
HQ: Neste Oil Services, Inc.
1800 West Loop S Ste 1700
Houston TX 77027
713 407-4411

(P-79)
TIDELANDS OIL PRODUCTION INC
705 Pico Ave, Long Beach (90813)
P.O. Box 1330 (90801-1330)
PHONE...............................562 436-2836
Tom Straton, *Branch Mgr*
EMP: 27 **Privately Held**
SIC: 1311 Crude petroleum production
HQ: Tidelands Oil Production, Inc.
301 E Ocean Blvd Ste 300
Long Beach CA 90802
562 436-9918

(P-80)
TPG PARTNERS III LP (HQ)
Also Called: Tpg Growth
345 California St # 3300, San Francisco (94104-2606)
PHONE...............................415 743-1500
William E McGlashan, *Managing Prtnr*
David Bonderman, *Partner*
Fred Cohen, *Partner*
James G Coulter, *Partner*
William S Price, *Partner*
EMP: 40
SALES (est): 1.3B **Privately Held**
SIC: 1311 1389 4922 5082 Crude petroleum production; natural gas production; oil field services; natural gas transmission; oil field equipment

(P-81)
TRC OPERATING COMPANY INC
805 Blackgold Ct, Taft (93268-9736)
P.O. Box 227 (93268-0227)
PHONE...............................661 763-0081
Tracy Rogers, *CEO*

Charles Comfort, *Corp Secy*
Ronnie Rogers, *Vice Pres*
EMP: 14
SALES (est): 2.5MM **Privately Held**
SIC: 1311 Crude petroleum production

(P-82)
TRUSTED ENERGY LLC
5478 Wilshire Blvd # 303, Los Angeles
(90036-4230)
PHONE..................................818 646-3137
Nathan Cartwright,
EMP: 10 **EST:** 2010
SALES (est): 565.3K **Privately Held**
SIC: 1311 4911 Natural gas production;

(P-83)
UNOCAL CORPORATION (HQ)
6001 Bollinger Canyon Rd, San Ramon
(94583-2324)
PHONE..................................310 726-7600
Charles R Williamson, *Ch of Bd*
Terry G Dallas, *CFO*
John W Creighton Jr, *Vice Ch Bd*
Samuel H Gillespie III,
Douglas M Miller, *Vice Pres*
EMP: 350
SALES (est): 486.7MM
SALES (corp-wide): 141.7B **Publicly Held**
WEB: www.unocal.com
SIC: 1311 2873 2911 4612 Crude petroleum production; natural gas production; nitrogenous fertilizers; coke, petroleum; crude petroleum pipelines; refined petroleum pipelines; geothermal drilling
PA: Chevron Corporation
6001 Bollinger Canyon Rd
San Ramon CA 94583
925 842-1000

(P-84)
VAQUERO ENERGY INCORPORATED
15545 Hermosa Rd, Bakersfield
(93307-9477)
PHONE..................................661 363-7240
Ken Hunter, *President*
EMP: 50
SALES (est): 953.9K **Privately Held**
SIC: 1311 Crude petroleum production

(P-85)
VENOCO INC
4483 Mcgrath St Ste 101, Ventura
(93003-7737)
PHONE..................................805 644-1400
Fax: 805 644-1401
EMP: 24
SALES (corp-wide): 224.2MM **Privately Held**
SIC: 1311
HQ: Venoco, Inc.
370 17th St Ste 3900
Denver CO 80202
303 626-8300

(P-86)
VICTORY OIL COMPANY
461 W 6th St Ste 300, San Pedro
(90731-2678)
PHONE..................................310 519-9500
Eric Johnson, *President*
S L Hutchison, *Vice Pres*
Byung Kim, *Human Resources*
EMP: 35
SQ FT: 8,500
SALES (est): 7.7MM **Privately Held**
WEB: www.victory-group.com
SIC: 1311 Crude petroleum production

(P-87)
WEST NEWPORT OIL COMPANY
1080 W 17th St, Costa Mesa (92627-4503)
P.O. Box 1487, Newport Beach (92659-0487)
PHONE..................................949 631-1100
Robert A Armstrong, *President*
Jay Stair, *Vice Pres*
Margaret Armstrong, *Admin Sec*
EMP: 13
SQ FT: 3,000
SALES: 3.2MM
SALES (corp-wide): 2.3MM **Privately Held**
SIC: 1311 Crude petroleum production

PA: Armstrong Petroleum Corporation
1080 W 17th St
Costa Mesa CA 92627
949 650-4000

(P-88)
WORLD OIL CORP
9302 Garfield Ave, South Gate
(90280-3896)
P.O. Box 1 (90280-0001)
PHONE..................................562 928-0100
Robert S Roth, *CEO*
EMP: 30
SALES (est): 10.3MM **Privately Held**
SIC: 1311 Crude petroleum & natural gas

1321 Natural Gas Liquids

(P-89)
BLYTHE ENERGY INC
385 N Buck Blvd, Blythe (92225-3301)
P.O. Box 1210 (92226-1210)
PHONE..................................561 304-5126
David M Harris, *CEO*
Paul Thessen, *President*
Mark Brennan, *Treasurer*
Scott Carver, *Admin Sec*
EMP: 15
SALES (est): 3.6MM **Privately Held**
SIC: 1321 4939 Natural gas liquids production; combination utilities
HQ: Altagas Power Holdings (U.S.) Inc.
1411 3rd St Ste A
Port Huron MI 48060
810 887-4105

(P-90)
S & J PROF PROPERTY SVCS
Also Called: S & J Pro Clean Services
9615 Aqueduct Ave, North Hills
(91343-2003)
P.O. Box 7148, Van Nuys (91409-7148)
PHONE..................................818 892-0181
Rafael A Gayle, *CEO*
Francisco Sotelo, *President*
EMP: 10
SALES (est): 818K **Privately Held**
SIC: 1321 Propane (natural) production

1381 Drilling Oil & Gas Wells

(P-91)
AA PRODUCTION SERVICES INC
8032 County Road 61, Princeton
(95970-9501)
PHONE..................................530 982-0123
Elden Hinkle, *Vice Pres*
EMP: 31
SALES (corp-wide): 4.5MM **Privately Held**
WEB: www.aaproduction.com
SIC: 1381 Drilling oil & gas wells
PA: Aa Production Services, Inc.
433 2nd St Ste 103
Woodland CA 95695
530 668-7525

(P-92)
AERA ENERGY LLC (HQ)
10000 Ming Ave, Bakersfield (93311-1301)
P.O. Box 11164 (93389-1164)
PHONE..................................661 665-5000
Christina S Sistrunk, *President*
Bill Hanson, *Exec VP*
Robert C Alberstadt, *Senior VP*
Brent D Carnahan, *Senior VP*
Lynne J Carrithers, *Senior VP*
EMP: 800
SALES (est): 2.1B
SALES (corp-wide): 305.1B **Privately Held**
WEB: www.aeraenergy.com
SIC: 1381 Directional drilling oil & gas wells
PA: Royal Dutch Shell Plc
Shell Centre
London SE1 7
207 934-1234

(P-93)
AERA ENERGY LLC
Also Called: Security Front Desk
59231 Main Camp Rd, Mc Kittrick
(93251-9740)
PHONE..................................661 665-4400
Mike Brown, *Principal*
Todd Bivens, *Supervisor*
Lisa Danforth, *Supervisor*
EMP: 47
SALES (corp-wide): 305.1B **Privately Held**
WEB: www.aeraenergy.com
SIC: 1381 Directional drilling oil & gas wells
HQ: Aera Energy Llc
10000 Ming Ave
Bakersfield CA 93311
661 665-5000

(P-94)
AERA ENERGY LLC
Also Called: Aera Energy South Midway
29235 Highway 33, Maricopa
(93252-9793)
PHONE..................................661 665-3200
Andy Anderson, *Manager*
Bob Alberstadt, *Vice Pres*
Joshua Boling, *Purch Agent*
Jay Licata, *Production*
Richard Stringer, *Manager*
EMP: 60
SALES (corp-wide): 305.1B **Privately Held**
WEB: www.aeraenergy.com
SIC: 1381 Directional drilling oil & gas wells
HQ: Aera Energy Llc
10000 Ming Ave
Bakersfield CA 93311
661 665-5000

(P-95)
ALUMATEC INC
18411 Sherman Way, Reseda
(91335-4319)
PHONE..................................818 609-7460
Francesco Chinaglia, *President*
Yazmin Ibarlucea, *Treasurer*
Laura Chinaglia, *Admin Sec*
EMP: 80
SALES (est): 7.1MM **Privately Held**
WEB: www.alumatec.com
SIC: 1381 Drilling oil & gas wells

(P-96)
AMS DRILLING
120 Tustin Ave Ste C, Newport Beach
(92663-4729)
PHONE..................................949 232-1149
Adrienne Marie Salyer, *President*
John Clark, *Partner*
EMP: 10
SALES (est): 457.7K **Privately Held**
SIC: 1381 Drilling oil & gas wells

(P-97)
ASTA CONSTRUCTION CO INC (PA)
1090 Saint Francis Way, Rio Vista
(94571-1200)
P.O. Box 758 (94571-0758)
PHONE..................................707 374-6472
Walt Koenig, *CEO*
Christien Koenig, *President*
Joan Brown, *Corp Secy*
Schmitt V Scott, *Vice Pres*
Lisa Ramsey, *Office Mgr*
▲ **EMP:** 32
SQ FT: 1,200
SALES (est): 13.8MM **Privately Held**
WEB: www.astaconstruction.com
SIC: 1381 1611 5032 Drilling oil & gas wells; general contractor, highway & street construction; sand, construction; gravel

(P-98)
BAKERSFIELD WELL CASING LLC
17876 Zerker Rd, Bakersfield
(93308-9221)
P.O. Box 82575 (93380-2575)
PHONE..................................661 399-2976
James S Camp, *Mng Member*

Richard C Camp,
Jane Camp-Micks,
Candi Glen,
Don M Hart,
EMP: 10
SQ FT: 10,000
SALES: 1MM **Privately Held**
SIC: 1381 Drilling water intake wells

(P-99)
BISON COMPANY
9013 Cavendish Ct, Stockton
(95209-1742)
PHONE..................................209 474-8700
F L Tuitama, *President*
Joseph Onell, *Corp Secy*
EMP: 12
SALES (est): 970K **Privately Held**
SIC: 1381 Reworking oil & gas wells

(P-100)
BLE INC
Also Called: Beryl Lockhart Enterprises
11360 Goss St, Sun Valley (91352-3205)
PHONE..................................818 504-9577
Beryl P Lockhart, *CEO*
EMP: 15
SQ FT: 2,200
SALES (est): 2.7MM **Privately Held**
SIC: 1381 Drilling oil & gas wells

(P-101)
DICK BROWN TECHNICAL SERVICES
Also Called: Aera Energy
553 Airport Rd Ste B, Rio Vista
(94571-1293)
P.O. Box 1035 (94571-3035)
PHONE..................................707 374-2133
Richard Brown, *President*
EMP: 18
SALES (est): 2.1MM **Privately Held**
SIC: 1381 Drilling oil & gas wells

(P-102)
DIRECT DRILLING INC
1255 Treat Blvd, Walnut Creek
(94597-7968)
PHONE..................................925 472-6850
Todd R Carr, *President*
Nikki Carr, *Admin Sec*
EMP: 35
SALES: 2.5MM **Privately Held**
SIC: 1381 1799 Service well drilling; core drilling & cutting

(P-103)
ELYSIUM JENNINGS LLC
1600 Norris Rd, Bakersfield (93308-2234)
PHONE..................................661 679-1700
Steve Layton,
EMP: 200
SALES (est): 8.7MM **Privately Held**
SIC: 1381 Drilling oil & gas wells
PA: E & B Natural Resources Management Corporation
1600 Norris Rd
Bakersfield CA 93308

(P-104)
EXCALIBUR WELL SERVICES CORP (PA)
22034 Rosedale Hwy, Bakersfield
(93314-9704)
PHONE..................................661 589-5338
Stephen Layton, *President*
Frachsco Galesi, *President*
Gordon Isbel, *Vice Pres*
Mary Telupessy, *Business Mgr*
EMP: 78
SALES (est): 40.3MM **Privately Held**
SIC: 1381 1389 Drilling oil & gas wells; fishing for tools, oil & gas field

(P-105)
GOLDEN STATE DRILLING INC
3500 Fruitvale Ave, Bakersfield
(93308-5106)
PHONE..................................661 589-0730
Philip F Phelps, *President*
James Phelps, *Treasurer*
Velma Phelps, *Vice Pres*
Russ Lueck, *Manager*
Mike McCutcheon, *Manager*
EMP: 75

SALES (est): 14.1MM **Privately Held**
WEB: www.gsdrilling.com
SIC: 1381 Directional drilling oil & gas
wells

(P-106)
HOWELL DICK HOLE DRILLING SVC
Also Called: Howell Drilling
2579 E 67th St, Long Beach (90805-1701)
PHONE...................................562 633-9898
Richard Howell Jr, *President*
Patty Howell, *Treasurer*
Paul Howell, *Vice Pres*
EMP: 12 **EST:** 1971
SALES (est): 1.6MM **Privately Held**
SIC: 1381 1629 1741 Drilling oil & gas
wells; blasting contractor, except building
demolition; foundation building

(P-107)
J & H DRILLING CO INC
7431 Walnut Ave, Buena Park
(90620-1761)
PHONE...................................714 994-0402
Brian Hoien, *President*
Stephen Jones, *Corp Secy*
William Jones, *Vice Pres*
Carlos Pedroza, *Assistant*
EMP: 13
SQ FT: 5,000
SALES (est): 4MM **Privately Held**
SIC: 1381 8748 Directional drilling oil &
gas wells; environmental consultant

(P-108)
JA WOUTERS INC
2305 Iron Stone Loop, Templeton
(93465-8396)
PHONE...................................805 221-5333
Justin Wouters, *CEO*
Julie Anderson, *President*
EMP: 10
SALES: 2.9MM **Privately Held**
SIC: 1381 Directional drilling oil & gas
wells

(P-109)
KENAI DRILLING LIMITED (HQ)
6430 Cat Canyon Rd, Santa Maria
(93454-9712)
P.O. Box 2248, Orcutt (93457-2248)
PHONE...................................805 937-7871
Hank Crist, *Vice Pres*
▲ **EMP:** 23
SQ FT: 3,000
SALES (est): 11.8MM
SALES (corp-wide): 249.4MM **Privately
Held**
WEB: www.kenaidrilling.com
SIC: 1381 Drilling oil & gas wells
PA: Kenai Drilling Limited
6430 Cat Canyon Rd
Santa Maria CA 93454
805 937-7871

(P-110)
KUSTER CO OIL WELL SERVICES
Also Called: Kuster Company
2900 E 29th St, Long Beach (90806-2398)
PHONE...................................562 595-0661
John Davidson, *CEO*
▲ **EMP:** 23
SALES: 8MM **Privately Held**
WEB: www.kusterco.com
SIC: 1381 Drilling oil & gas wells
PA: Probe Holdings, Inc.
1132 Everman Pkwy Ste 100
Fort Worth TX 76140

(P-111)
LEGEND PUMP & WELL SERVICE INC
1324 W Rialto Ave, San Bernardino
(92410-1611)
PHONE...................................909 384-1000
Keith Collier, *President*
EMP: 20 **EST:** 2010
SALES (est): 4.6MM **Privately Held**
SIC: 1381 1781 Service well drilling; water
well servicing

(P-112)
LEON KROUS DRILLING INC
9300 Borden Ave, Sun Valley (91352-2006)
PHONE...................................818 833-4654
Leon Krus, *President*
EMP: 25
SQ FT: 1,000
SALES (est): 12.1MM **Privately Held**
SIC: 1381 Directional drilling oil & gas
wells

(P-113)
NABORS WELL SERVICES CO
1025 Earthmover Ct, Bakersfield
(93314-9529)
PHONE...................................661 588-6140
Tom Jaquez, *Manager*
EMP: 160 **Privately Held**
SIC: 1381 Drilling oil & gas wells
HQ: Nabors Well Services Co.
515 W Greens Rd Ste 1000
Houston TX 77067
281 874-0035

(P-114)
NATIONAL OILWELL VARCO LP
743 N Eckhoff St, Orange (92868-1005)
PHONE...................................714 456-1244
Greg Renfro, *Branch Mgr*
EMP: 13
SALES (corp-wide): 7.3B **Publicly Held**
SIC: 1381 Drilling oil & gas wells
HQ: National Oilwell Varco, L.P.
7909 Parkwood Circle Dr
Houston TX 77036
713 960-5100

(P-115)
PACIFIC OPERATORS INC
205 E Carrillo St Ste 200, Santa Barbara
(93101-7181)
PHONE...................................805 899-3144
Richard L Carone, *President*
Robert P Carone, *Vice Pres*
EMP: 30
SQ FT: 3,100
SALES (est): 3.2MM **Privately Held**
SIC: 1381 Drilling oil & gas wells

(P-116)
PAUL GRAHAM DRILLING & SVC CO
2500 Airport Rd, Rio Vista (94571-1034)
P.O. Box 669 (94571-0669)
PHONE...................................707 374-5123
Kevin P Graham, *President*
Jill Graham, *CFO*
Clarence Santos, *Vice Pres*
Eddie Woodruff, *General Mgr*
Alyssa Graham, *Graphic Designe*
EMP: 170
SQ FT: 30,000
SALES (est): 30MM **Privately Held**
SIC: 1381 7389 7359 Drilling oil & gas
wells; crane & aerial lift service; industrial
truck rental

(P-117)
PETRO-LUD INC
12625 Jomani Dr Ste 104, Bakersfield
(93312-3445)
PHONE...................................661 747-4779
Clayton Ludington, *Principal*
EMP: 12
SALES (est): 3.2MM **Privately Held**
SIC: 1381 Drilling oil & gas wells

(P-118)
PRIMEBORE DIRECTIONAL BORING
10822 Vernon Ave, Ontario (91762-4041)
P.O. Box 3115, Pomona (91769-3115)
PHONE...................................909 821-4643
Jess B Basave, *CEO*
EMP: 13 **EST:** 2003
SALES (est): 770K **Privately Held**
SIC: 1381 Directional drilling oil & gas
wells

(P-119)
SCIENTIFIC DRILLING INTL INC
31101 Coberly Rd, Shafter (93263-9702)
PHONE...................................661 831-0636
Joe Williams, *Manager*
EMP: 20

SALES (corp-wide): 20.8MM **Privately
Held**
SIC: 1381 Directional drilling oil & gas
wells
PA: Scientific Drilling International, Inc.
16071 Greenspoint Park
Houston TX 77060
281 443-3300

(P-120)
T & D SERVICES INC
Also Called: T&D Trenchless
42363 Guava St, Murrieta (92562-7271)
P.O. Box 609 (92564-0609)
PHONE...................................951 304-1190
Donald Van Dyke, *President*
Dawn Van Dyke, *Treasurer*
EMP: 13
SQ FT: 1,200
SALES (est): 6.2MM **Privately Held**
SIC: 1381 Directional drilling oil & gas
wells

(P-121)
TERVITA (US OPERATIONS) LLC
12459 Arrow Rte, Rancho Cucamonga
(91739-9807)
PHONE...................................909 899-7504
Corison Swartz, *Branch Mgr*
EMP: 12
SALES (corp-wide): 1.8B **Privately Held**
SIC: 1381 Drilling oil & gas wells
PA: Tervita Corporation
140 10 Ave Se Suite 1600
Calgary AB T2G 0
855 837-8482

(P-122)
WEST AMERICAN ENERGY CORP
4949 Buckley Way Ste 207, Bakersfield
(93309-4882)
P.O. Box 22016 (93390-2016)
PHONE...................................661 747-7732
Howard Caywood, *President*
EMP: 12
SQ FT: 640
SALES (est): 1.2MM **Privately Held**
SIC: 1381 Drilling oil & gas wells

(P-123)
WESTERN STRATA EXPLORATION INC
52360 Willow Point Rd, Clarksburg (95612)
P.O. Box 657 (95612-0657)
PHONE...................................916 744-1440
Sylvie Jensen, *President*
Gordon Jensen, *Vice Pres*
Diane Lewis, *Financial Exec*
Tom Scott, *Opers Mgr*
EMP: 17
SQ FT: 1,000
SALES (est): 4.9MM **Privately Held**
WEB: www.westernstrata.com
SIC: 1381 Drilling oil & gas wells

(P-124)
WOODWARD DRILLING COMPANY
550 River Rd, Rio Vista (94571-1216)
P.O. Box 336 (94571-0336)
PHONE...................................707 374-4300
Concing Woodward, *President*
Wayne G Woodward, *Ch of Bd*
Ryan Woodward, *Manager*
EMP: 28
SQ FT: 40,000
SALES (est): 9.8MM **Privately Held**
WEB: www.woodwarddrilling.com
SIC: 1381 1781 Service well drilling; water
well drilling

┌─────────────────────────────┐
│ **1382 Oil & Gas Field**   │
│ **Exploration Svcs**   │
└─────────────────────────────┘

(P-125)
ARGUELLO INC
17100 Clle Mariposa Reina, Goleta
(93117-9737)
PHONE...................................805 567-1632
James C Flores, *President*
Winston Taldert, *CFO*
Doss Dourgeois, *Exec VP*

John F Wombwell, *Exec VP*
EMP: 25
SALES (est): 1.7MM
SALES (corp-wide): 16.4B **Publicly Held**
WEB: www.arguello.com
SIC: 1382 Oil & gas exploration services
HQ: Freeport-Mcmoran Oil & Gas Llc
700 Milam St Ste 3100
Houston TX 77002
713 579-6000

(P-126)
BNK PETROLEUM (US) INC
760 Paseo Camarillo # 350, Camarillo
(93010-6000)
PHONE...................................805 484-3613
Wolf E Regener, *President*
Gary W Johnson, *CFO*
Ray W Payne, *Vice Pres*
Steven M Warshauer, *Executive*
Jason Byl, *Exploration*
EMP: 25
SQ FT: 3,000
SALES (est): 10.4MM **Privately Held**
SIC: 1382 Oil & gas exploration services

(P-127)
CALIFORNIA RESOURCES CORP
11109 River Run Blvd, Bakersfield
(93311-8957)
PHONE...................................661 412-5222
Karen Plotts, *Branch Mgr*
Jose Sandoval, *Engineer*
EMP: 12
SALES (corp-wide): 2B **Publicly Held**
SIC: 1382 Oil & gas exploration services
PA: California Resources Corporation
9200 Oakdale Ave Ste 900
Chatsworth CA 91311
888 848-4754

(P-128)
CALIFORNIA RESOURCES CORP (PA)
9200 Oakdale Ave Ste 900, Chatsworth
(91311-6559)
PHONE...................................888 848-4754
Todd A Stevens, *President*
William E Albrecht, *Ch of Bd*
Marshall D Smith, *CFO*
Justin Gannon, *Bd of Directors*
Ronald Havner, *Bd of Directors*
EMP: 77
SALES: 2B **Publicly Held**
SIC: 1382 Oil & gas exploration services

(P-129)
CONSOLIDATED GEOSCIENCE INC
Also Called: R M A Geoscience
14738 Central Ave, Chino (91710-9502)
PHONE...................................909 393-9700
EMP: 11 **EST:** 2004
SALES (est): 950K **Privately Held**
SIC: 1382 8999

(P-130)
DCOR LLC (PA)
290 Maple Ct Ste 290 # 290, Ventura
(93003-9144)
P.O. Box 3401 (93006-3401)
PHONE...................................805 535-2000
Bill Templeton,
Andrew Prestridge, *President*
Alan C Templeton, *CFO*
Greg Cavette, *Vice Pres*
Dennis Conley, *Vice Pres*
EMP: 76
SALES (est): 154.1MM **Privately Held**
WEB: www.dcor.com
SIC: 1382 Oil & gas exploration services

(P-131)
DCOR LLC
290 Maple Ct Ste 290, Ventura
(93003-9144)
PHONE...................................805 576-1200
Stephanie Rice, *Branch Mgr*
EMP: 56
SALES (corp-wide): 154.1MM **Privately
Held**
SIC: 1382 Oil & gas exploration services

PA: Dcor, L.L.C.
290 Maple Ct Ste 290 # 290
Ventura CA 93003
805 535-2000

(P-132)
DELCO OPERATING CO LP
Also Called: Delco Oheb Energy
1999 Avenue Of The Stars, Los Angeles
(90067-6022)
PHONE..................310 525-3535
Aziz Delrahim, *Partner*
Bianca Delrahim, *Partner*
Shahram Delrahim, *Partner*
Shawn Delrahim, *Partner*
EMP: 16
SALES (est): 1MM **Privately Held**
WEB: www.delcopetroleum.com
SIC: 1382 Oil & gas exploration services

(P-133)
DEMENNO KERDOON
2000 N Alameda St, Compton
(90222-2799)
PHONE..................310 537-7100
Shane Bamelin, *Principal*
Jim Tice, *Principal*
Jim Ennis, *Director*
EMP: 125
SQ FT: 11,614
SALES (est): 25.6MM **Privately Held**
WEB: www.demennokerdoon.com
SIC: 1382 Oil & gas exploration services

(P-134)
E & B NTRAL RESOURCES MGT CORP
1848 Perkins Rd, New Cuyama (93254)
P.O. Box 179 (93254-0179)
PHONE..................661 766-2501
Edward Fetterman, *Branch Mgr*
EMP: 30 **Privately Held**
SIC: 1382 Oil & gas exploration services
PA: E & B Natural Resources Management
Corporation
1600 Norris Rd
Bakersfield CA 93308

(P-135)
E AND B NATURAL RESOURCES
1600 Norris Rd, Bakersfield (93308-2234)
PHONE..................661 679-1700
Francesco Galesi, *CEO*
EMP: 51
SALES (est): 8.5MM **Privately Held**
SIC: 1382 Oil & gas exploration services

(P-136)
EAGLE DOMINION ENERGY CORP
Also Called: Eagle Dominion Trust
200 N Hayes Ave, Oxnard (93030-5420)
PHONE..................202 380-9649
Roger H Shears, *President*
Nancy Davis, *Vice Pres*
EMP: 36
SQ FT: 1,500
SALES (est): 1.4MM **Privately Held**
SIC: 1382 Oil & gas exploration services

(P-137)
GREKA INTEGRATED INC (PA)
1700 Sinton Rd, Santa Maria (93458-9708)
P.O. Box 5489 (93456-5489)
PHONE..................805 347-8700
Randeep S Grewal, *CEO*
Ken Miller, *CFO*
Susan Whalen, *Vice Pres*
▲ EMP: 28
SALES (est): 107MM **Privately Held**
WEB: www.grekaenergy.com
SIC: 1382 Oil & gas exploration services

(P-138)
GRENFIELD CONSULTING
1801 Century Park E Fl 23, Los Angeles
(90067-2325)
PHONE..................310 286-0200
Bobby Greenfield, *President*
EMP: 26
SALES (est): 1MM **Privately Held**
SIC: 1382 8742

(P-139)
LUCA INTERNATIONAL GROUP LLC (PA)
39650 Liberty St Ste 490, Fremont
(94538-2261)
PHONE..................510 498-8829
Bing Yang, *President*
James Diaz, *CFO*
Lily Lei, *Vice Pres*
Angie Yip,
▲ EMP: 17
SALES (est): 3.4MM **Privately Held**
SIC: 1382 Oil & gas exploration services

(P-140)
MAGNETRON POWER INVENTIONS INC
2226 W 232nd St, Torrance (90501-5720)
PHONE..................310 462-6970
Ninan N Johnson, *CEO*
EMP: 22
SQ FT: 2,500
SALES (est): 3.4MM **Privately Held**
SIC: 1382 Oil & gas exploration services

(P-141)
NATIONS PETROLEUM CAL LLC
9600 Ming Ave Ste 300, Bakersfield
(93311-1365)
PHONE..................661 387-6402
Phil Sorvet,
EMP: 60
SALES (est): 4MM **Privately Held**
SIC: 1382 Oil & gas exploration services
PA: Nations Petroleum Company Ltd
255 5 Ave Sw Suite 750
Calgary AB T2P 3
403 206-1420

(P-142)
NEWPORT ENERGY LLC
19200 Von Karman Ave # 400, Irvine
(92612-8553)
PHONE..................408 230-7545
Nyle Khan, *CEO*
Gordon Burk, *COO*
EMP: 25 EST: 2012
SQ FT: 5,000
SALES (est): 953.6K **Privately Held**
SIC: 1382 Oil & gas exploration services

(P-143)
OPTASENSE INC
3060 Saturn St Ste 101, Brea
(92821-1732)
PHONE..................714 482-1922
Edward Zisk, *General Mgr*
EMP: 11
SQ FT: 6,500
SALES (est): 557.5K **Privately Held**
SIC: 1382 Geophysical exploration, oil & gas field

(P-144)
PAULSSON INC
16543 Arminta St, Van Nuys (91406-1745)
PHONE..................310 780-2219
Bjorn Paulsson, *President*
Phillip Oseas, *CFO*
EMP: 11
SALES (est): 3.8MM **Privately Held**
SIC: 1382 7382 Oil & gas exploration services; security systems services

(P-145)
QRE OPERATING LLC
707 Wilshire Blvd # 4600, Los Angeles
(90017-3501)
PHONE..................213 225-5900
Alan L Smith, *Mng Member*
EMP: 208
SALES (est): 708K **Privately Held**
SIC: 1382 Oil & gas exploration services
HQ: Qr Energy, Lp
707 Wilshire Blvd # 4600
Los Angeles CA 90017

(P-146)
QUANTUM ENERGY LLC
Also Called: Quaneco
22801 Ventura Blvd # 200, Woodland Hills
(91364-1222)
PHONE..................800 950-3519
Harrison Schumacher, *Branch Mgr*

EMP: 20
SALES (corp-wide): 3.6MM **Privately Held**
SIC: 1382 Oil & gas exploration services
PA: Quantum Energy Llc
10405 Locust Grove Dr
Chardon OH 44024
440 285-7381

(P-147)
R W LYALL & COMPANY INC (DH)
2665 Research Dr, Corona (92882-6918)
P.O. Box 2259 (92878-2259)
PHONE..................951 270-1500
Jeffrey W Lyall, *President*
Jennifer Fritchle, *COO*
Bruce Lange, *COO*
Tony Mauer, *CFO*
▲ EMP: 168
SQ FT: 70,000
SALES (est): 152.4MM
SALES (corp-wide): 3.6B **Publicly Held**
WEB: www.rwlyall.com
SIC: 1382 Oil & gas exploration services

(P-148)
RTS OIL HOLDINGS INC
1306 E Edinger Ave Ste C, Santa Ana
(92705-4426)
PHONE..................714 665-8777
Gafur Kassymov, *Branch Mgr*
EMP: 20 **Publicly Held**
SIC: 1382 Oil & gas exploration services
PA: Rts Oil Holdings, Inc.
2319 S Foothill Dr # 160
Salt Lake City UT 84109

(P-149)
SANTA MARIA ENRGY HOLDINGS LLC
2811 Airpark Dr, Santa Maria (93455-1417)
P.O. Box 7202 (93456-7202)
PHONE..................805 938-3320
David Pratt, *CEO*
EMP: 20
SALES (est): 2.9MM **Privately Held**
SIC: 1382 Oil & gas exploration services

(P-150)
SEISMIC RESERVOIR 2020 INC
3 Pointe Dr Ste 212, Brea (92821-7624)
PHONE..................562 697-9711
Robert Heming, *CEO*
Deanna Monzon, *CFO*
EMP: 21
SALES (est): 4MM **Privately Held**
SIC: 1382

(P-151)
SHARPE ENERGY SERVICES INC
5094 Northlawn Dr, San Jose
(95130-1835)
PHONE..................408 489-3581
Kelly Sharpe, *President*
David Koshiyama, *Vice Pres*
Terry Sharpe, *Vice Pres*
Steven Sharpe, *General Mgr*
EMP: 15
SALES (est): 907.7K **Privately Held**
SIC: 1382 Oil & gas exploration services

(P-152)
SIGNAL HILL PETROLEUM INC
2633 Cherry Ave, Signal Hill (90755-2008)
PHONE..................562 595-6440
Jerrel Barto, *Ch of Bd*
Craig C Barto, *President*
Susan George, *Office Mgr*
Bill Summerfield, *Project Engr*
Floyd Leeson, *Engineer*
EMP: 49
SALES (est): 19.4MM **Privately Held**
WEB: www.shpi.net
SIC: 1382 Geological exploration, oil & gas field

(P-153)
SOLIMAR ENERGY LLC
121 N Fir St Ste H, Ventura (93001-2094)
PHONE..................805 643-4100
Frank Petruzzeli, *Mng Member*
EMP: 10

SALES (est): 802.2K **Privately Held**
SIC: 1382 Oil & gas exploration services

(P-154)
SR2020 INC
3 Pointe Dr Ste 212, Brea (92821-7624)
PHONE..................714 482-1922
William Bartling, *CEO*
Deanna L Monzon, *CFO*
Martin Karrenbach, *Senior VP*
EMP: 24
SALES (est): 5MM **Privately Held**
SIC: 1382 Oil & gas exploration services

(P-155)
U S WEATHERFORD L P
19608 Broken Ct, Shafter (93263-9583)
PHONE..................661 746-3415
EMP: 27 **Privately Held**
SIC: 1382
HQ: U S Weatherford L P
2000 Saint James Pl
Houston TX 70395
713 693-4000

(P-156)
UNDERGROUND ENERGY INC
7 W Figueroa St Fl 3, Santa Barbara
(93101-5109)
P.O. Box 761, Pismo Beach (93448-0761)
PHONE..................805 455-6042
Michael H Kobler, *President*
Bruce Berwager, *COO*
Peter Ballachey, *CFO*
EMP: 20
SALES (est): 245.6K **Privately Held**
SIC: 1382 Oil & gas exploration services
PA: Underground Energy Corporation
340 Harbour Ave
North Vancouver BC V7J 2
604 904-0085

(P-157)
UNIVERSAL DYNAMICS INC
5313 3rd St, Irwindale (91706-2085)
PHONE..................626 480-0035
Issa Alasker, *President*
Sahak Sahakian, *Accounting Mgr*
EMP: 12
SQ FT: 15,000
SALES (est): 1.2MM **Privately Held**
SIC: 1382 7382 Oil & gas exploration services; security systems services

(P-158)
VACA ENERGY LLC
4407 Sturgis Rd, Oxnard (93030)
PHONE..................310 385-3684
Clint Walker, *Mng Member*
EMP: 14
SALES (est): 1.2MM **Privately Held**
SIC: 1382 Oil & gas exploration services

(P-159)
WEP TRANSPORT HOLDINGS LLC
16909 Via De Santa Fe, Rancho Santa Fe
(92067-9519)
P.O. Box 7068 (92067-7068)
PHONE..................858 756-1010
Steven Marshall, *President*
EMP: 14
SALES (est): 675.3K **Privately Held**
SIC: 1382 Oil & gas exploration services

(P-160)
WESTERN ENERGY PRODUCTION LLC
16909 Via De Santa Fe, Rancho Santa Fe
(92067-9519)
P.O. Box 7068 (92067-7068)
PHONE..................858 756-1010
Steven Marshall, *President*
EMP: 10
SALES (est): 940K **Privately Held**
SIC: 1382 Geological exploration, oil & gas field

(P-161)
WPX ENERGY INC
1122 B St Ste 220, Hayward (94541-4241)
PHONE..................510 727-9708
Ralph A Hill, *President*
EMP: 10 **Publicly Held**
SIC: 1382 Oil & gas exploration services

P R O D U C T S & S V C S

PA: Wpx Energy, Inc.
3500 One Williams Ctr
Tulsa OK 74172
-

1389 Oil & Gas Field Svcs, NEC

(P-162)
260 RESOURCE MANAGEMENT LLC
100 Bayview Cir Ste 505, Newport Beach (92660-2984)
P.O. Box 112, Lawndale (90260-0112)
PHONE...................................866 700-1031
Kevin Williams, *Mng Member*
EMP: 12
SQ FT: 4,000
SALES (est): 378.6K **Privately Held**
SIC: 1389 Gas field services

(P-163)
AA PRODUCTION SERVICES INC (PA)
433 2nd St Ste 103, Woodland (95695-4065)
PHONE...................................530 668-7525
John Adams, *President*
Elden D Hinkle, *Vice Pres*
Daniel Miantre, *Vice Pres*
EMP: 35
SQ FT: 3,500
SALES (est): 4.5MM **Privately Held**
WEB: www.aaproduction.com
SIC: 1389 Oil & gas wells: building, repairing & dismantling

(P-164)
AC PUMPING UNIT REPAIR INC
2625 Dawson Ave, Signal Hill (90755-2019)
PHONE...................................562 492-1300
Michael Quike, *CEO*
Micheal Quirke, *President*
Alfonso Campas, *CEO*
EMP: 25
SALES (est): 3MM **Privately Held**
SIC: 1389 Oil & gas wells: building, repairing & dismantling

(P-165)
ALLY ENTERPRISES
5001 E Commercecenter Dr, Bakersfield (93309-1659)
P.O. Box 20580 (93390-0580)
PHONE...................................661 412-9933
Rick Noland, *President*
EMP: 20
SALES (est): 462.7K **Privately Held**
SIC: 1389 Oil field services

(P-166)
AMERICAN TRUCK DISMANTLING
15303 Arrow Blvd, Fontana (92335-1206)
PHONE...................................909 429-2166
Vrej Mairman, *Owner*
EMP: 18 **EST:** 1998
SQ FT: 4,000
SALES (est): 1.5MM **Privately Held**
WEB: www.amtrkdism.com
SIC: 1389 3714 Construction, repair & dismantling services; motor vehicle parts & accessories

(P-167)
ANATESCO INC
128 Bedford Way, Bakersfield (93308-1702)
P.O. Box 5694 (93388-5694)
PHONE...................................661 399-6990
Douglas Paul Denesha, *President*
Jean Denesha, *Vice Pres*
Jeremy Denesha, *Technology*
EMP: 15
SQ FT: 3,000
SALES (est): 1.2MM **Privately Held**
WEB: www.anatesco.com
SIC: 1389 Testing, measuring, surveying & analysis services

(P-168)
ARCHROCK INC
3333 Gibson St, Bakersfield (93308-5255)
PHONE...................................661 321-0271
Gerald Quinn, *Manager*
EMP: 16 **Publicly Held**
WEB: www.exterran.com
SIC: 1389 5084 Gas compressing (natural gas) at the fields; compressors, except air conditioning
PA: Archrock Inc.
9807 Katy Fwy Ste 100
Houston TX 77024

(P-169)
B & L CASING SERVICE LLC
Also Called: United Wealth Control
21054 Kratzmeyer Rd, Bakersfield (93314-9482)
P.O. Box 22260 (93390-2260)
PHONE...................................661 589-9080
Larry Jenkins, *Mng Member*
Brian Jenkins, *Vice Pres*
Rod Ledesma, *Vice Pres*
Stacy Lopez, *Admin Asst*
Austin Brown, *Purch Mgr*
EMP: 13
SALES (est): 3.3MM **Privately Held**
SIC: 1389 Oil field services

(P-170)
BAKER HGHES OLFLD OPRTIONS LLC
Also Called: Baker Oil Tools
5551 Aldrin Ct, Bakersfield (93313-2108)
PHONE...................................661 834-2844
Jim Summerlin, *Manager*
David Escobar, *Opers Staff*
EMP: 20
SALES (corp-wide): 122B **Publicly Held**
WEB: www.bot.bhi-net.com
SIC: 1389 Oil field services
HQ: Baker Hughes Oilfield Operations Llc
17021 Aldine Westfield Rd
Houston TX 77073
713 879-1000

(P-171)
BAKER HGHES OLFLD OPRTIONS LLC
Also Called: Baker Atlas
4730 Armstrong Rd, Bakersfield (93313-2115)
P.O. Box 956, Taft (93268-0956)
PHONE...................................661 831-5200
Steve Tipton, *Manager*
EMP: 10
SALES (corp-wide): 122B **Publicly Held**
WEB: www.bakeratlas.com
SIC: 1389 Cementing oil & gas well casings
HQ: Baker Hughes Oilfield Operations Llc
17021 Aldine Westfield Rd
Houston TX 77073
713 879-1000

(P-172)
BAKER HGHES OLFLD OPRTIONS LLC
Also Called: Baker Oil Tools
15421 Assembly Ln, Huntington Beach (92649-1329)
PHONE...................................714 891-8544
Steve Cook, *Manager*
EMP: 17
SQ FT: 10,000
SALES (corp-wide): 122B **Publicly Held**
WEB: www.bot.bhi-net.com
SIC: 1389 Oil field services
HQ: Baker Hughes Oilfield Operations Llc
17021 Aldine Westfield Rd
Houston TX 77073
713 879-1000

(P-173)
BAKER HGHES OLFLD OPRTIONS LLC
Also Called: Baker Oil Tools
4230 Foster Ave, Bakersfield (93308-4559)
PHONE...................................661 324-9488
Craig Whitler, *Branch Mgr*
EMP: 35

(P-174)
BAKER HGHES OLFLD OPRTIONS LLC
5700 Doolittle Ave, Shafter (93263-4035)
PHONE...................................661 834-9654
Bob Ledet, *Manager*
EMP: 50
SALES (corp-wide): 122B **Publicly Held**
WEB: www.bot.bhi-net.com
SIC: 1389 7353 5084 Oil field services; oil field equipment, rental or leasing; drilling bits
HQ: Baker Hughes Oilfield Operations Llc
17021 Aldine Westfield Rd
Houston TX 77073
713 879-1000

(P-175)
BAKER HUGHES A GE COMPANY LLC
3901 Fanucchi Way, Shafter (93263-9539)
PHONE...................................661 834-9654
Rebecca Garnett, *Manager*
EMP: 41
SALES (corp-wide): 122B **Publicly Held**
SIC: 1389 Oil field services
HQ: Baker Hughes, A Ge Company, Llc
17021 Aldine Westfield Rd
Houston TX 77073
713 439-8600

(P-176)
BAKER HUGHES A GE COMPANY LLC
1127 Carrier Parkway Ave, Bakersfield (93308-9666)
PHONE...................................661 387-1010
Charles Laymance, *Branch Mgr*
EMP: 87
SALES (corp-wide): 122B **Publicly Held**
SIC: 1389 Oil field services
HQ: Baker Hughes, A Ge Company, Llc
17021 Aldine Westfield Rd
Houston TX 77073
713 439-8600

(P-177)
BAKER HUGHES A GE COMPANY LLC
3901 Fanucchi Way, Shafter (93263-9539)
PHONE...................................661 831-7686
Richard Mounts, *Manager*
EMP: 70
SALES (corp-wide): 122B **Publicly Held**
WEB: www.bjservices.com
SIC: 1389 Oil field services
HQ: Baker Hughes, A Ge Company, Llc
17021 Aldine Westfield Rd
Houston TX 77073
713 439-8600

(P-178)
BAKER HUGHES A GE COMPANY LLC
5145 Boylan St, Bakersfield (93308-4511)
PHONE...................................800 229-7447
Lori Robinson, *Manager*
Doug Thomas, *General Mgr*
Sebastian Jung,
EMP: 87
SALES (corp-wide): 122B **Publicly Held**
WEB: www.bakerhughes.com
SIC: 1389 Oil field services
HQ: Baker Hughes, A Ge Company, Llc
17021 Aldine Westfield Rd
Houston TX 77073
713 439-8600

(P-179)
BAKER HUGHES A GE COMPANY LLC
Also Called: Unichem
19433 Colombo St, Bakersfield (93308-9517)
PHONE...................................661 391-0794
Rusty Davis, *Branch Mgr*
EMP: 12

SALES (corp-wide): 122B **Publicly Held**
WEB: www.bot.bhi-net.com
SIC: 1389 Oil field services
HQ: Baker Hughes Oilfield Operations Llc
17021 Aldine Westfield Rd
Houston TX 77073
713 879-1000

(P-180)
BAKER PETROLITE LLC
2280 Bates Ave Ste A, Concord (94520-1235)
PHONE...................................925 682-3313
Joe Rund, *Manager*
EMP: 11
SALES (corp-wide): 122B **Publicly Held**
WEB: www.bakerpetrolite.com
SIC: 1389 Oil field services
HQ: Baker Petrolite Llc
12645 W Airport Blvd
Sugar Land TX 77478
281 276-5400

(P-181)
BAKER PETROLITE LLC
5125 Boylan St, Bakersfield (93308-4511)
PHONE...................................661 325-4138
Doug Thomas, *Manager*
EMP: 60
SALES (corp-wide): 122B **Publicly Held**
WEB: www.bakerpetrolite.com
SIC: 1389 Oil field services
HQ: Baker Petrolite Llc
12645 W Airport Blvd
Sugar Land TX 77478
281 276-5400

(P-182)
BAKER PETROLITE LLC
11808 Bloomfield Ave, Santa Fe Springs (90670-4610)
PHONE...................................562 406-7090
Bob Whitton, *Manager*
EMP: 12
SALES (corp-wide): 122B **Publicly Held**
WEB: www.bakerpetrolite.com
SIC: 1389 Oil field services
HQ: Baker Petrolite Llc
12645 W Airport Blvd
Sugar Land TX 77478
281 276-5400

(P-183)
BAKER PETROLITE LLC
Also Called: Baker Hughes
265 Quail Ct, Santa Paula (93060-9653)
PHONE...................................805 525-4404
Brad Porchuk, *Manager*
EMP: 20
SALES (corp-wide): 122B **Publicly Held**
SIC: 1389 Oil field services
HQ: Baker Petrolite Llc
12645 W Airport Blvd
Sugar Land TX 77478
281 276-5400

(P-184)
BASIC ENERGY SERVICES INC
12891 Nelson St, Garden Grove (92840-5018)
PHONE...................................714 530-0855
Roe T M Patterson, *Manager*
EMP: 34
SALES (corp-wide): 864MM **Publicly Held**
SIC: 1389 Construction, repair & dismantling services; oil field services
PA: Basic Energy Services, Inc.
801 Cherry St Unit 2
Fort Worth TX 76102
817 334-4100

(P-185)
BASIC ENERGY SERVICES INC
6710 Stewart Way, Bakersfield (93308)
PHONE...................................661 588-3800
EMP: 34
SALES (corp-wide): 547.5MM **Publicly Held**
SIC: 1389
PA: Basic Energy Services, Inc.
801 Cherry St Unit 2
Fort Worth TX 76102
817 334-4100

(P-186)
BLOWOUT TOOLS INC
19484 Broken Ct, Shafter (93263-3146)
PHONE..............................661 746-1700
EMP: 14 Publicly Held
SIC: 1389 Oil field services
HQ: Blowout Tools, Inc.
2202 Oil Center Ct
Houston TX 77073
405 671-3800

(P-187)
BURKE JE CONSTRUCTION
120 E Center St, Taft (93268-3601)
P.O. Box 365 (93268-0365)
PHONE..............................661 745-4890
Joseph Burke, *President*
Deanna Long, *Office Mgr*
EMP: 14
SALES (est): 1.9MM Privately Held
SIC: 1389 Oil field services

(P-188)
C & H TESTING SERVICE INC
(PA)
6224 Price Way, Bakersfield (93308-5117)
P.O. Box 9907 (93389-1907)
PHONE..............................661 589-4030
Donald T Hoover, *President*
Karen K Hoover, *Corp Secy*
EMP: 31
SQ FT: 1,500
SALES (est): 7.7MM Privately Held
SIC: 1389 Oil field services

(P-189)
C CASE COMPANY INC
Also Called: Case's Oil
7010 W Cerini Ave, Riverdale (93656-9622)
PHONE..............................559 867-3912
Coofas Wayne Case Jr, *President*
Rodney Craig Case, *Vice Pres*
Sarah Dewey, *Admin Sec*
EMP: 33
SALES (est): 5MM Privately Held
SIC: 1389 1311 Oil & gas wells: building, repairing & dismantling; crude petroleum production

(P-190)
CAL COAST ACIDIZING CO
Also Called: Cal Coast Acidizing Service
6226 Dominion Rd, Santa Maria (93454-9177)
P.O. Box 2050, Orcutt (93457-2050)
PHONE..............................805 934-2411
Bruce Edward Conway, *CEO*
EMP: 18
SQ FT: 2,000
SALES (est): 2.6MM Privately Held
SIC: 1389 Acidizing wells

(P-191)
CAL QUAKE CONSTRUCTION INC
636 N Formosa Ave, Los Angeles (90036-1943)
PHONE..............................323 931-2969
Sheldon Perluss, *President*
John Taferner, *Vice Pres*
Isael Duarte, *Director*
Joseph Goldberger, *Director*
EMP: 20
SALES (est): 1.2MM Privately Held
WEB: www.cal-quake.com
SIC: 1389 Construction, repair & dismantling services

(P-192)
CALIFRNIA RSURCES LONG BCH INC
111 W Ocean Blvd Ste 800, Long Beach (90802-7930)
PHONE..............................562 624-3204
Frank Komin, *CEO*
EMP: 137
SALES (est): 1.6MM
SALES (corp-wide): 2B Publicly Held
SIC: 1389 Oil field services
PA: California Resources Corporation
9200 Oakdale Ave Ste 900
Chatsworth CA 91311
888 848-4754

(P-193)
CALPI INC
7141 Downing Ave, Bakersfield (93308-5815)
P.O. Box 81795 (93380-1795)
PHONE..............................661 589-5648
Robert Larkie Barnett, *President*
Jeff Barnett, *Vice Pres*
EMP: 11 EST: 1981
SQ FT: 5,032
SALES (est): 1MM Privately Held
WEB: www.calpi.net
SIC: 1389 4959 Cleaning wells; servicing oil & gas wells; toxic or hazardous waste cleanup

(P-194)
CARRERA CONSTRUCTION INC
Also Called: S&J Carrera Constructions
1961 Main St Ste 261, Watsonville (95076-3027)
PHONE..............................831 728-3299
Steven Carrera, *President*
EMP: 10
SALES (est): 1.8MM Privately Held
SIC: 1389 Construction, repair & dismantling services

(P-195)
CENTRAL CALIFORNIA CNSTR INC
7221 Downing Ave, Bakersfield (93308-5817)
PHONE..............................661 978-8230
Dereke Gerecke, *Principal*
Tammie K Rankin-Gerecke, *Principal*
Urssula Sizemore, *Bookkeeper*
EMP: 11
SALES (est): 1.3MM Privately Held
SIC: 1389 Construction, repair & dismantling services

(P-196)
CHEM-O-LENE CO
2745 Sherwin Ave Ste 3, Ventura (93003-8533)
PHONE..............................805 648-6247
Ray Martin, *President*
EMP: 10
SQ FT: 3,200
SALES (est): 730K Privately Held
SIC: 1389 Oil field services

(P-197)
CJD CONSTRUCTION SERVICES INC
416 S Vermont Ave, Glendora (91741-6256)
PHONE..............................626 335-1116
Diego A Debenedetto, *President*
Diego Dibenedetto, *President*
EMP: 40
SALES (est): 3.9MM Privately Held
SIC: 1389 Construction, repair & dismantling services

(P-198)
CL KNOX INC
Also Called: Advanced Industrial Services
34933 Imperial St, Bakersfield (93308)
PHONE..............................661 837-0477
Leslie Knox, *President*
Chris Knox, *Corp Secy*
EMP: 80
SALES (est): 10.6MM Privately Held
SIC: 1389 8742 Oil field services; industrial consultant

(P-199)
COLT SERVICES LP
Also Called: Colt Group
1399 E Burnett St, Signal Hill (90755-3511)
PHONE..............................562 988-2658
David Balster, *Branch Mgr*
EMP: 12
SALES (corp-wide): 10.5MM Privately Held
SIC: 1389 7699 Construction, repair & dismantling services; boiler & heating repair services
PA: Colt Services, L.P.
626 N 16th St
La Porte TX 77571
281 471-9099

(P-200)
CORE LABORATORIES LP
3437 Landco Dr, Bakersfield (93308-6187)
PHONE..............................661 325-5657
Bryon Bell, *Partner*
EMP: 20
SALES (corp-wide): 659.8MM Privately Held
SIC: 1389 Oil field services
HQ: Core Laboratories Lp
6316 Windfern Rd
Houston TX 77040
-

(P-201)
CRAIG R WILLIAMS CNSTR INC
100 N Crescent Dr Ste 100, Beverly Hills (90210-5447)
PHONE..............................310 550-9250
Craig R Williams, *President*
EMP: 10
SALES (est): 1.1MM Privately Held
SIC: 1389 Construction, repair & dismantling services

(P-202)
CUMMINGS VACUUM SERVICE INC
Also Called: Cummings Transportation
19605 Broken Ct, Shafter (93263-9583)
PHONE..............................661 746-1786
Pam Cummings, *President*
Ted Cummings, *Vice Pres*
Shiloh Smith, *Engineer*
Dave Stitt, *Maint Spvr*
EMP: 60
SQ FT: 3,000
SALES (est): 7.6MM Privately Held
SIC: 1389 Oil field services

(P-203)
DAWSON ENTERPRISES
Also Called: Cavins Oil Well Tools
815 Main St, Taft (93268-3118)
P.O. Box 695 (93268-0695)
PHONE..............................661 765-2181
Charles Palmer, *Manager*
Jerry Craig, *Manager*
EMP: 11
SALES (corp-wide): 10.5MM Privately Held
WEB: www.cavins.com
SIC: 1389 Well logging
PA: Dawson Enterprises
2853 Cherry Ave
Signal Hill CA 90755
562 424-8564

(P-204)
DE VRIES INTERNATIONAL INC
(PA)
17671 Armstrong Ave, Irvine (92614-5727)
PHONE..............................949 252-1212
Don Devries, *President*
▲ **EMP: 44**
SALES (est): 22.8MM Privately Held
WEB: www.devriesintl.com
SIC: 1389 Lease tanks, oil field: erecting, cleaning & repairing

(P-205)
DTE STOCKTON LLC
2526 W Washington St, Stockton (95203-2952)
PHONE..............................209 467-3838
Nelson Nail, *Mng Member*
EMP: 34
SALES (est): 4.2MM Publicly Held
SIC: 1389 Construction, repair & dismantling services
HQ: Dte Energy Services, Inc.
414 S Main St Ste 600
Ann Arbor MI 48104
-

(P-206)
DWAYNES ENGINEERING & CNSTR
3655 Addie Ave, Mc Kittrick (93251)
P.O. Box 116 (93251-0116)
PHONE..............................661 762-7261
Dwayne Emfinger, *President*
EMP: 78

SALES (est): 7.8MM Privately Held
WEB: www.dwayneseng.com
SIC: 1389 Construction, repair & dismantling services

(P-207)
ENGEL & GRAY INC
745 W Betteravia Rd Ste A, Santa Maria (93455-1298)
P.O. Box 5020 (93456-5020)
PHONE..............................805 925-2771
Carl W Engel Jr, *President*
Robert Engel, *Vice Pres*
EMP: 35
SQ FT: 3,000
SALES (est): 7.1MM Privately Held
WEB: www.recycleaward.com
SIC: 1389 1623 7389 2875 Construction, repair & dismantling services; haulage, oil field; pipeline construction; crane & aerial lift service; compost

(P-208)
ENGINEERED WELL SVC INTL INC
3120 Standard St, Bakersfield (93308-6241)
PHONE..............................866 913-6283
Paul Sturgeon, *CEO*
John E Powell Jr, *Principal*
EMP: 125 EST: 2009
SALES (est): 44MM Privately Held
SIC: 1389 Oil field services

(P-209)
ETHOSENERGY FIELD SERVICES LLC
2485 Courage Dr Ste 100, Fairfield (94533-6740)
PHONE..............................707 399-0420
Ed Moore, *Branch Mgr*
EMP: 14
SALES (corp-wide): 5.3B Privately Held
SIC: 1389 Oil consultants
HQ: Field Ethosenergy Services Llc
10455 Slusher Dr Bldg 12
Santa Fe Springs CA 90670

(P-210)
ETHOSENERGY FIELD SERVICES LLC (DH)
Also Called: Wg
10455 Slusher Dr Bldg 12, Santa Fe Springs (90670-3750)
PHONE..............................310 639-3523
Rob Duby, *President*
Patricia Lelito, *CFO*
Mike Fieldhouse, *Vice Pres*
Mary Ros, *General Mgr*
Gary Goddard, *Sales Staff*
EMP: 75
SALES (est): 29.9MM
SALES (corp-wide): 5.3B Privately Held
WEB: www.woodgroupgts.com
SIC: 1389 8711 3462 Oil consultants; industrial engineers; pump, compressor & turbine forgings

(P-211)
ETHOSENERGY PWR PLANT SVCS LLC
3215 47th Ave, Sacramento (95824-2400)
PHONE..............................916 391-2993
EMP: 29
SALES (corp-wide): 5.3B Privately Held
WEB: www.wgpo.com
SIC: 1389 Cementing oil & gas well casings
HQ: Ethosenergy Power Plant Services, Llc
12600 Drfeld Pkwy Ste 315
Alpharetta GA 30004
678 393-7800

(P-212)
FIELD FOUNDATION
15306 Carmenita Rd, Santa Fe Springs (90670-5606)
P.O. Box 4236, Cerritos (90703-4236)
PHONE..............................562 921-3567
Irwin Field, *Owner*
EMP: 50
SALES: 24.3K Privately Held
SIC: 1389 Oil sampling service for oil companies

PRODUCTS & SVCS

(P-213)
FIRST ENERGY SERVICES INC
1031 Carrier Parkway Ave, Bakersfield
(93308-9670)
P.O. Box 80844 (93380-0844)
PHONE.....................................661 387-1972
Richard Chase, *President*
Charlotte Maddon, *Treasurer*
Jack Chase, *Vice Pres*
EMP: 20
SQ FT: 7,000
SALES (est): 4MM **Privately Held**
SIC: 1389 Servicing oil & gas wells; oil field
services

(P-214)
GAINES WELL SERVICE INC (PA)
10063 Colony Rd, Wilton (95693-9506)
P.O. Box 369 (95693-0369)
PHONE.....................................916 687-6751
Joseph Gaines, *President*
Reba Gaines, *Treasurer*
Michael Gaines, *Vice Pres*
Gregory Gaines, *Admin Sec*
EMP: 20
SALES (est): 1.6MM **Privately Held**
SIC: 1389 Servicing oil & gas wells

(P-215)
GAS RECOVERY SYSTEMS LLC
20662 Newport Coast Dr, Irvine (92612)
PHONE.....................................949 718-1430
Tom Holter, *Manager*
EMP: 16
SALES (corp-wide): 198.7MM **Privately
Held**
SIC: 1389 Removal of condensate gaso-
line from field (gathering) lines
HQ: Gas Recovery Systems, Llc
   1 N Lexington Ave Ste 620
   White Plains NY 10601
   914 421-4903

(P-216)
**GENE WATSON CONSTRUCTION
A CA**
801 Kern St, Taft (93268-2734)
PHONE.....................................661 763-5254
Gene Watson, *Ltd Ptnr*
Patricia Watson, *Ltd Ptnr*
EMP: 530
SALES (est): 11.2MM **Privately Held**
WEB: www.gwc-ltd.com
SIC: 1389 1382 Oil field services; oil &
gas exploration services

(P-217)
GRAYSON SERVICE INC
1845 Greeley Rd, Bakersfield
(93314-9547)
PHONE.....................................661 589-5444
Carol A Grayson, *President*
Cheryl Grayson, *Vice Pres*
EMP: 150
SALES (est): 5.7MM **Privately Held**
SIC: 1389 Servicing oil & gas wells

(P-218)
GROUNDMETRICS INC
Also Called: GMI
3954 Murphy Canyon Rd D207, San Diego
(92123-4420)
PHONE.....................................619 786-8023
George A Eiskamp, *CEO*
Jeffrey Symington, *CFO*
Jessie Kaffai, *Vice Pres*
Carlos Heredia, *Admin Sec*
Jason Liu, *Information Mgr*
EMP: 15
SALES (est): 2.7MM **Privately Held**
SIC: 1389 3829 Oil field services; survey-
ing instruments & accessories

(P-219)
HALLIBURTON COMPANY
34722 7th Standard Rd, Bakersfield
(93314-9435)
PHONE.....................................661 393-8111
Dennis Lovett, *Branch Mgr*
Mark Hansen, *Technical Staff*
Patty Drew, *Human Res Mgr*
Rocky Lawrence, *Manager*
EMP: 87 **Publicly Held**
SIC: 1389 Oil field services

PA: Halliburton Company
   3000 N Sam Houston Pkwy E
   Houston TX 77032

(P-220)
HARBISON-FISCHER INC
116 E Main St, Taft (93268-9727)
P.O. Box 1015 (93268-1015)
PHONE.....................................661 765-7792
Robin Carter, *Principal*
EMP: 31
SALES (corp-wide): 1.4B **Publicly Held**
SIC: 1389 Oil field services
HQ: Harbison-Fischer, Inc.
   901 N Crowley Rd
   Crowley TX 76036
   817 297-2211

(P-221)
HAZE BERT AND ASSOSSIATES
3188 Airway Ave Ste K1, Costa Mesa
(92626-4652)
PHONE.....................................714 557-1567
Bert Haze, *Owner*
Gail Fischer, *Office Mgr*
EMP: 14
SQ FT: 2,000
SALES (est): 300K **Privately Held**
WEB: www.berthaze.com
SIC: 1389 Testing, measuring, surveying &
analysis services

(P-222)
**HILLS WLDG & ENGRG CONTR
INC**
Also Called: Hwe Mechanical
22038 Stockdale Hwy, Bakersfield
(93314-8889)
PHONE.....................................661 746-5400
Debora M Hill, *Vice Pres*
Robert Hill, *Shareholder*
EMP: 92
SALES (est): 7.1MM **Privately Held**
SIC: 1389 Testing, measuring, surveying &
analysis services

(P-223)
HIRSH INC
Also Called: Better Mens Clothes
860 S Los Angeles St # 900, Los Angeles
(90014-3311)
PHONE.....................................213 622-9441
Mistie Banks, *General Mgr*
Stanley Hirsh, *President*
EMP: 50
SALES (est): 1MM **Privately Held**
SIC: 1389 Lease tanks, oil field: erecting,
cleaning & repairing

(P-224)
HORIZON WELL LOGGING INC
711 Saint Andrews Way, Lompoc
(93436-1326)
PHONE.....................................805 733-0972
Doug Milham, *President*
Jim Eastes, *Opers Mgr*
James Eastes, *Director*
William Gilmore, *Director*
▲ **EMP:** 16
SALES (est): 1.5MM **Privately Held**
WEB: www.horizon-well-logging.com
SIC: 1389 Well logging

(P-225)
**HUNTING ENERGY SERVICES
INC**
Also Called: Hunting-Vinson
4900 California Ave 100a, Bakersfield
(93309-7024)
PHONE.....................................661 633-4272
Bobby Ford, *Branch Mgr*
EMP: 76
SALES (corp-wide): 722.9MM **Privately
Held**
WEB: www.hunting-inc.com
SIC: 1389 Oil field services
HQ: Hunting Energy Services, Inc.
   16825 Northchase Dr # 600
   Houston TX 77060

(P-226)
HVI CAT CANYON INC
2617 E Clark Ave, Santa Maria
(93455-5815)
PHONE.....................................805 621-5800
Randeep S Grewal, *President*
Ken Miller, *CFO*
Susan Whalen, *Vice Pres*
EMP: 125
SALES (est): 9.6MM **Privately Held**
SIC: 1389 Oil field services

(P-227)
**INNOVATIVE RV
TECHNOLOGIES**
Also Called: Hydralift
205 Via Morada, San Clemente
(92673-3504)
PHONE.....................................949 559-5372
Brad Christian, *President*
▲ **EMP:** 40
SALES (est): 1.1MM **Privately Held**
SIC: 1389 Hydraulic fracturing wells

(P-228)
JERRY MELTON & SONS CNSTR
Also Called: Jerry Melton & Sons Cnstr
100 Jamison Ln, Taft (93268-4329)
PHONE.....................................661 765-5546
Jerry W Melton, *President*
Karen Melton, *Treasurer*
Judy Melton, *Vice Pres*
Steven Melton, *Admin Sec*
EMP: 85
SALES (est): 11.6MM **Privately Held**
WEB: www.jerrymelton.com
SIC: 1389 Oil & gas wells: building, repair-
ing & dismantling; grading oil & gas well
foundations

(P-229)
JIM GRAHAM INC
4 Hill Ct, Rio Vista (94571-1400)
PHONE.....................................707 374-5114
Jim Graham, *President*
Dorothy Graham, *Treasurer*
Robert Graham, *Vice Pres*
Edwina Messina, *Controller*
EMP: 28
SALES: 750K **Privately Held**
WEB: www.adamgraham.com
SIC: 1389 7359 Servicing oil & gas wells;
tool rental

(P-230)
JOHN M PHILLIPS LLC
Also Called: John M Phillips Oil Field Eqp
2800 Gibson St, Bakersfield (93308-6106)
PHONE.....................................661 327-3118
Melody Shamaker, *Office Mgr*
EMP: 11
SALES (est): 380.7K
SALES (corp-wide): 8.1MM **Privately
Held**
SIC: 1389 Oil field services
PA: John M. Phillips, Llc
   2755 Dawson Ave
   Signal Hill CA 90755
   562 595-7363

(P-231)
KATERRA INC (PA)
2494 Sand Hill Rd Ste 100, Menlo Park
(94025-6981)
PHONE.....................................650 422-3572
Brad Knight, *CEO*
Ben Janofsky, *Vice Pres*
Ravi Naik, *Vice Pres*
Robert Wagner, *Vice Pres*
Steve Weilbach, *Vice Pres*
EMP: 100 **EST:** 2015
SALES: 125MM **Privately Held**
SIC: 1389 8741 8711 Construction, repair
& dismantling services; construction man-
agement; construction & civil engineering

(P-232)
KBA LTD OF KERN COUNTY LLP
2152 Mohawk St, Bakersfield (93308)
PHONE.....................................661 323-0487
Brad Orear, *Partner*
Brad O'Rear, *Partner*
EMP: 15
SQ FT: 3,000

SALES (est): 630.2K **Privately Held**
SIC: 1389 Construction, repair & dismantling services

(P-233)
KEY ENERGY SERVICES INC
5080 California Ave # 150, Bakersfield
(93309-1697)
PHONE.....................................661 334-8100
Lori Hatfield, *Manager*
EMP: 46
SALES (corp-wide): 436.1MM **Publicly
Held**
WEB: www.keyenergy.com
SIC: 1389 Oil field services
PA: Key Energy Services, Inc.
   1301 Mckinney St Ste 1800
   Houston TX 77010
   713 651-4300

(P-234)
KEY ENERGY SERVICES INC
3587 N Ventura Ave, Ventura (93001-1230)
PHONE.....................................805 653-1300
Bob Wentz, *Branch Mgr*
EMP: 46
SALES (corp-wide): 436.1MM **Publicly
Held**
SIC: 1389 Servicing oil & gas wells
PA: Key Energy Services, Inc.
   1301 Mckinney St Ste 1800
   Houston TX 77010
   713 651-4300

(P-235)
M-I LLC
4400 Fanucchi Way, Shafter (93263-9552)
PHONE.....................................661 321-5400
Forest Purpiance, *Branch Mgr*
EMP: 31 **Publicly Held**
SIC: 1389 Mud service, oil field drilling; oil
field services
HQ: M-I L.L.C.
   5950 N Course Dr
   Houston TX 77072
   281 561-1300

(P-236)
**MARK SHEFFIELD
CONSTRUCTION**
9105 Langley Rd, Bakersfield
(93312-2156)
PHONE.....................................661 589-8520
Mark Sheffield, *President*
Linda Sheffield, *Treasurer*
Steven Sheffield, *Vice Pres*
EMP: 20
SALES: 2MM **Privately Held**
SIC: 1389 7389 Oil field services; crane &
aerial lift service

(P-237)
MIC LABS
7643 Corrinne Pl, San Ramon
(94583-4010)
PHONE.....................................925 822-2847
Michael J Knudtson, *Owner*
EMP: 10
SQ FT: 1,690
SALES: 70K **Privately Held**
SIC: 1389 Gas field services

(P-238)
MID OHIO FIELD SERVICES LLC
4686 Ontario Mills Pkwy, Ontario
(91764-5104)
PHONE.....................................614 755-5067
EMP: 10
SALES (est): 610K **Privately Held**
SIC: 1389

(P-239)
MMI SERVICES INC
4042 Patton Way, Bakersfield
(93308-5030)
PHONE.....................................661 589-9366
Steve McGowan, *President*
Mel McGowan, *CEO*
Eric Olson, *Vice Pres*
Roxanne Campbell, *Info Tech Dir*
Erick Olson, *Human Res Dir*
EMP: 250
SQ FT: 4,500
SALES (est): 51.3MM **Privately Held**
WEB: www.mmi-services.com
SIC: 1389 Oil field services

▲ = Import ▼=Export
◆ =Import/Export

(P-240)
MR T TRANSPORT
15535 Garfield Ave, Paramount
(90723-4033)
PHONE...................................562 602-5536
Telesoro Torres, *CEO*
Erica Torres, *CFO*
Oscar Torres, *Director*
EMP: 17
SQ FT: 9,426
SALES (est): 1.7MM **Privately Held**
SIC: 1389 4212 7629 Servicing oil & gas wells; local trucking, without storage; telecommunication equipment repair (except telephones)

(P-241)
MTS STIMULATION SERVICES INC (PA)
Also Called: M T S
7131 Charity Ave, Bakersfield
(93308-5870)
PHONE...................................661 589-5804
Tommy T Reed, *President*
Polly Clark, *Shareholder*
Gary Starling, *Shareholder*
Craig Barto, *Ch of Bd*
Lorena Quintero, *Office Mgr*
EMP: 40
SQ FT: 1,400
SALES (est): 8.4MM **Privately Held**
WEB: www.mts-stim.com
SIC: 1389 Oil field services

(P-242)
NABORS WELL SERVICES CO
7515 Rosedale Hwy, Bakersfield
(93308-5727)
PHONE...................................661 589-3970
Alan Pounds, *Sales Executive*
Melanie Mendoza, *Maintence Staff*
EMP: 270 **Privately Held**
SIC: 1389 1382 Servicing oil & gas wells; oil & gas exploration services
HQ: Nabors Well Services Co.
515 W Greens Rd Ste 1000
Houston TX 77067
281 874-0035

(P-243)
NABORS WELL SERVICES CO
19431 S Santa Fe Ave, Compton
(90221-5912)
PHONE...................................310 639-7074
Bernie Fish, *Manager*
Juan Landron, *Technology*
Gary Kaufman, *Human Res Mgr*
EMP: 230 **Privately Held**
SIC: 1389 Gas field services; oil field services
HQ: Nabors Well Services Co.
515 W Greens Rd Ste 1000
Houston TX 77067
281 874-0035

(P-244)
NABORS WELL SERVICES CO
1954 James Rd, Bakersfield (93308-9749)
PHONE...................................661 392-7668
Dave Warner, *District Mgr*
EMP: 76 **Privately Held**
SIC: 1389 Oil field services
HQ: Nabors Well Services Co.
515 W Greens Rd Ste 1000
Houston TX 77067
281 874-0035

(P-245)
NASCO PETROLEUM LLC
20532 El Toro Rd Ste 102, Mission Viejo
(92692-5309)
PHONE...................................949 461-5212
EMP: 10 **EST:** 2013
SQ FT: 800
SALES (est): 530K **Privately Held**
SIC: 1389 5172

(P-246)
NATIONAL CNSTR RENTALS INC
1045 S Greenwood Ave, Montebello
(90640-6001)
PHONE...................................323 838-1800
Glen Green, *Manager*
EMP: 13

SALES (corp-wide): 123.3MM **Privately Held**
WEB: www.rentnational.com
SIC: 1389 Construction, repair & dismantling services
HQ: National Construction Rentals, Inc.
15319 Chatsworth St
Mission Hills CA 91345
818 221-6000

(P-247)
NATIONAL OILWELL VARCO INC
Also Called: Pacific Inspection
1438b Ohm Rd, Arbuckle (95912)
PHONE...................................530 682-0571
EMP: 10
SALES (corp-wide): 20B **Publicly Held**
SIC: 1389
PA: National Oilwell Varco, Inc.
7909 Parkwood Circle Dr
Houston TX 77036
713 346-7500

(P-248)
NATIONAL OILWELL VARCO LP
Also Called: R & M Energy System
19417 Colombo St, Bakersfield
(93308-9517)
PHONE...................................661 387-9316
Darryll May, *Branch Mgr*
Jan Wollitz, *Sales Staff*
EMP: 15
SALES (corp-wide): 7.3B **Publicly Held**
WEB: www.rmenergy.com
SIC: 1389 Oil field services
HQ: National Oilwell Varco, L.P.
7909 Parkwood Circle Dr
Houston TX 77036
713 960-5100

(P-249)
NOBLE METHANE INC
104 Matmor Rd, Woodland (95776-6006)
PHONE...................................530 668-7961
Brent Noble, *President*
Tiana Noble, *Admin Sec*
EMP: 10
SALES (est): 150K **Privately Held**
SIC: 1389 Servicing oil & gas wells

(P-250)
NORMAN WIRELINE SERVICE INC
1301 James Rd, Bakersfield (93308-9844)
PHONE...................................661 399-5697
James Norman, *President*
EMP: 13
SALES: 600K **Privately Held**
SIC: 1389 Construction, repair & dismantling services; oil field services

(P-251)
OIL WELL SERVICE COMPANY (PA)
10840 Norwalk Blvd, Santa Fe Springs
(90670-3826)
PHONE...................................562 612-0600
Jack Frost, *President*
Connie Laws, *Treasurer*
Richard Laws, *Vice Pres*
Matt Hensley, *Admin Sec*
EMP: 225
SQ FT: 9,000
SALES (est): 35.5MM **Privately Held**
WEB: www.ows1.com
SIC: 1389 Oil field services

(P-252)
OIL WELL SERVICE COMPANY
10255 Enos Ln, Shafter (93263-9572)
PHONE...................................661 589-2333
Rick Hobbs, *Office Mgr*
EMP: 45
SALES (corp-wide): 35.5MM **Privately Held**
WEB: www.ows1.com
SIC: 1389 Swabbing wells
PA: Oil Well Service Company
10840 Norwalk Blvd
Santa Fe Springs CA 90670
562 612-0600

(P-253)
OIL WELL SERVICE COMPANY
1015 Mission Rock Rd, Santa Paula
(93060-9730)
PHONE...................................805 525-2103
Harvey Himinell, *Manager*
EMP: 21
SALES (est): 562K
SALES (corp-wide): 35.5MM **Privately Held**
WEB: www.ows1.com
SIC: 1389 Oil field services
PA: Oil Well Service Company
10840 Norwalk Blvd
Santa Fe Springs CA 90670
562 612-0600

(P-254)
PACHUNGA GAS STATION
45000 Pechanga Pkwy, Temecula
(92592-5810)
PHONE...................................951 506-4575
Butch Murphy, *CEO*
EMP: 10
SALES (est): 453.4K **Privately Held**
SIC: 1389 Gas field services

(P-255)
PACIFIC PERFORATING INC
25090 Highway 33, Fellows (93224-9777)
PHONE...................................661 768-9224
Troy Ducharme, *President*
Perry Parker, *Vice Pres*
▼ **EMP:** 35
SQ FT: 4,000
SALES (est): 4.5MM **Privately Held**
WEB: www.pacificperforating.com
SIC: 1389 Oil field services

(P-256)
PACIFIC PROCESS SYSTEMS INC (PA)
7401 Rosedale Hwy, Bakersfield
(93308-5736)
PHONE...................................661 321-9681
Jerry Wise, *CEO*
Robert Peterson, *CFO*
Alan George, *Corp Secy*
Terry Alberts, *Purchasing*
Curt Avis, *Opers Mgr*
▼ **EMP:** 90
SQ FT: 7,000
SALES (est): 262.1MM **Privately Held**
WEB: www.pps-equipment.com
SIC: 1389 7353 5082 Testing, measuring, surveying & analysis services; oil field equipment, rental or leasing; oil field equipment

(P-257)
PALMER TANK & CONSTRUCTION INC
2464 S Union Ave, Bakersfield
(93307-5007)
PHONE...................................661 834-1110
Jerry Palmer, *President*
EMP: 20
SQ FT: 1,200
SALES (est): 2.2MM **Privately Held**
SIC: 1389 5731 Oil & gas wells: building, repairing & dismantling; antennas

(P-258)
PC MECHANICAL INC
2803 Industrial Pkwy, Santa Maria
(93455-1811)
PHONE...................................805 925-2888
Lew Parker, *President*
Brandon Burginger, *COO*
Mary Parker, *Exec VP*
Mitch Caron, *Vice Pres*
Diane Caron, *Admin Asst*
EMP: 50
SQ FT: 67,000
SALES (est): 11.3MM **Privately Held**
WEB: www.pcmechanical.com
SIC: 1389 Oil field services

(P-259)
PIXLEY CONSTRUCTION INC
27607 Industrial Blvd, Hayward
(94545-4044)
P.O. Box 185 (94557-0185)
PHONE...................................510 783-3020
Chuck Pixley, *President*

EMP: 13 **EST:** 2013
SALES (est): 1.1MM **Privately Held**
SIC: 1389 Construction, repair & dismantling services

(P-260)
PRO VAC
26857 Henry Rd, Fellows (93224-9794)
P.O. Box 153, Taft (93268-8153)
PHONE...................................661 765-7298
Dennis Hill, *Owner*
EMP: 15
SALES (est): 1.6MM **Privately Held**
SIC: 1389 Oil field services

(P-261)
PRODUCTION DATA INC
1210 33rd St, Bakersfield (93301-2124)
P.O. Box 3266 (93385-3266)
PHONE...................................661 327-4776
Gerald Tonnelli, *President*
EMP: 19
SQ FT: 1,800
SALES (est): 2.2MM **Privately Held**
WEB: www.productiondatainc.com
SIC: 1389 Oil field services

(P-262)
PROS INCORPORATED
3400 Patton Way, Bakersfield
(93308-5722)
P.O. Box 20996 (93390-0996)
PHONE...................................661 589-5400
Robert Lewis, *President*
Lori Buller, *Human Resources*
Randy Dubois, *Manager*
EMP: 58
SALES (est): 19.7MM **Privately Held**
SIC: 1389 Oil field services

(P-263)
PSC INDUSTRIAL OUTSOURCING LP
Also Called: Hydrochempsc
200 Old Yard Dr, Bakersfield (93307-4268)
PHONE...................................661 833-9991
Peter Burger, *Principal*
EMP: 18
SALES (corp-wide): 750MM **Privately Held**
WEB: www.tscnow.com
SIC: 1389 Oil field services
PA: Psc Industrial Outsourcing, Lp
900 Georgia Ave
Deer Park TX 77536
713 393-5600

(P-264)
RESOURCE CEMENTING LLC
2500 Airport Rd, Rio Vista (94571-1034)
P.O. Box 1027 (94571-3027)
PHONE...................................707 374-3350
Kevin P Graham, *Mng Member*
EMP: 15 **EST:** 2014
SALES (est): 183.3K **Privately Held**
SIC: 1389 1781 Cementing oil & gas well casings; geothermal drilling

(P-265)
RICHARD YARBROUGH
Also Called: R & R Pumping Unit Repr & Svc
2493 N Ventura Ave, Ventura (93001-1314)
PHONE...................................805 643-1021
Richard Yarbrough, *Owner*
EMP: 33
SALES (est): 1.8MM **Privately Held**
SIC: 1389 Oil & gas wells: building, repairing & dismantling; pumping of oil & gas wells

(P-266)
RIDGE CEMENTING LLC
7085 Eddy Rd G, Arbuckle (95912-9789)
PHONE...................................530 476-3333
Richard Chow, *President*
EMP: 10
SQ FT: 137,000
SALES (est): 487.5K **Privately Held**
SIC: 1389 Cementing oil & gas well casings

(P-267)
RPC INC
9457 Adlai Ter, Lakeside (92040-4830)
PHONE...................................619 647-9911
Roger Ramos, *Principal*

EMP: 10
SALES (est): 947.5K Privately Held
SIC: 1389 Oil field services

(P-268)
S D DRILLING
24660 E Old Julian Hwy, Ramona
(92065-6760)
P.O. Box 1818 (92065-0915)
PHONE..................................760 789-5658
Ruth Torres, *Partner*
Ruben Levezma, *Partner*
Maria Ledezma, *Office Mgr*
EMP: 10
SALES (est): 1.1MM Privately Held
WEB: www.sddrilling.com
SIC: 1389 1381 Building oil & gas well
foundations on site; grading oil & gas well
foundations; drilling oil & gas wells

(P-269)
SAYBOLT LP
21730 S Wilmington Ave # 203, Carson
(90810-1640)
PHONE..................................310 518-4400
Ken Nabi, *Manager*
EMP: 17
SALES (corp-wide): 659.8MM Privately
Held
WEB: www.corelab.com
SIC: 1389 Testing, measuring, surveying &
analysis services
HQ: Saybolt Lp
6316 Windfern Rd
Houston TX 77040
713 328-2673

(P-270)
SCHLUMBERGER
TECHNOLOGY CORP
Also Called: Schlumberger Oilfield Services
1710 Callens Rd, Ventura (93003-5611)
PHONE..................................805 642-8230
Ken Gade, *Manager*
EMP: 25 Publicly Held
SIC: 1389 Oil field services
HQ: Schlumberger Technology Corp
100 Gillingham Ln
Sugar Land TX 77478
281 285-8500

(P-271)
SCHLUMBERGER
TECHNOLOGY CORP
Also Called: Schlumberger Well Services
2841 Pegasus Dr, Bakersfield
(93308-6896)
PHONE..................................661 864-4750
Fax: 661 642-2065
EMP: 70 Privately Held
SIC: 1389 1382
HQ: Schlumberger Technology Corp
100 Gillingham Ln
Sugar Land TX 77478
281 285-8500

(P-272)
SCHLUMBERGER
TECHNOLOGY CORP
Schlumberger, Well Completions
12131 Industry St, Garden Grove
(92841-2813)
PHONE..................................714 379-7332
Gene Barnett, *Systems Mgr*
EMP: 51 Publicly Held
SIC: 1389 3561 Oil & gas wells: building,
repairing & dismantling; pumps & pump-
ing equipment
HQ: Schlumberger Technology Corp
100 Gillingham Ln
Sugar Land TX 77478
281 285-8500

(P-273)
SCHLUMBERGER
TECHNOLOGY CORP
Also Called: Schlumberger Well Services
3530 Arundell Cir, Ventura (93003-4922)
PHONE..................................805 644-8325
Steve Emerick, *Manager*
EMP: 10 Publicly Held
SIC: 1389 Oil field services

HQ: Schlumberger Technology Corp
100 Gillingham Ln
Sugar Land TX 77478
281 285-8500

(P-274)
SIERRA ASSET SERVICING LLC
10232 Donner Pass Rd # 4, Truckee
(96161-2337)
PHONE..................................530 582-7300
Kevin Crosby, *Principal*
EMP: 10
SALES (est): 977.4K Privately Held
SIC: 1389 Roustabout service

(P-275)
SMITH INTERNATIONAL INC
Also Called: Omni Seals, Inc.
11031 Jersey Blvd Ste A, Rancho Cuca-
monga (91730-5150)
PHONE..................................909 906-7900
Monte Russell, *Managing Dir*
EMP: 130 Publicly Held
SIC: 1389 Oil field services
HQ: Smith International, Inc.
1310 Rankin Rd
Houston TX 77073
281 443-3370

(P-276)
SMITH INTERNATIONAL INC
Smith Services
3101 Steam Ct, Bakersfield (93308-5725)
PHONE..................................661 589-8304
EMP: 10
SALES (corp-wide): 190.3K Privately
Held
SIC: 1389
HQ: Smith International, Inc.
1310 Rankin Rd
Houston TX 77073
281 443-3370

(P-277)
SOLI-BOND INC
4230 Foster Ave, Bakersfield (93308-4559)
PHONE..................................661 631-1633
Dwight Hartley, *President*
EMP: 50
SALES (corp-wide): 34.8MM Privately
Held
SIC: 1389 Oil field services
PA: Soli-Bond, Inc.
2377 2 Mile Rd
Bay City MI 48706
989 684-9611

(P-278)
SOUTH COAST SCREEN AND
CASING
19112 S Santa Fe Ave, Compton
(90221-5910)
PHONE..................................310 632-3200
Tyson Skimo, *Owner*
EMP: 12
SALES (est): 1.3MM Privately Held
SIC: 1389 Cementing oil & gas well cas-
ings

(P-279)
SOUTH VALLEY OIL FIELD
ELECTRI
309 Windsor Park Dr, Bakersfield
(93311-4916)
PHONE..................................661 665-9809
Darren P Scott, *President*
EMP: 14
SALES (est): 1MM Privately Held
SIC: 1389 Oil field services

(P-280)
STEELCLAD INC
2664 Saturn St Ste A, Brea (92821-6789)
PHONE..................................714 529-0277
Caren Hallam, *President*
EMP: 25
SQ FT: 4,000
SALES: 2.3MM Privately Held
WEB: www.steelcladinc.com
SIC: 1389 0782 Oil field services; land-
scape contractors

(P-281)
TEAM CASING
5073 Arboga Rd, Marysville (95901)
P.O. Box 1723 (95901-0050)
PHONE..................................530 743-5424
William W Cates, *President*
William Scheiber, *Treasurer*
Sandra Cates, *Admin Sec*
EMP: 16
SQ FT: 700
SALES (est): 1.4MM Privately Held
SIC: 1389 Running, cutting & pulling cas-
ings, tubes & rods

(P-282)
TITAN OILFIELD SERVICES INC
21535 Kratzmeyer Rd, Bakersfield
(93314-9482)
PHONE..................................661 861-1630
Terry Hibbitts, *President*
Tim Barman, *Vice Pres*
Tony Palacpac, *Admin Sec*
EMP: 13
SALES (est): 1.8MM Privately Held
SIC: 1389 Oil field services

(P-283)
TOMS SIERRA COMPANY INC
Also Called: Sierra Energy
4710 Marshall Rd, Garden Valley
(95633-9472)
PHONE..................................530 333-4620
Don Saldey, *Manager*
EMP: 10
SQ FT: 3,080
SALES (corp-wide): 95.8MM Privately
Held
WEB: www.sierraenergy.net
SIC: 1389 Gas field services
PA: Toms Sierra Company, Inc.
1020 Winding Creek Rd
Roseville CA 95678
916 218-1600

(P-284)
TOTAL-WESTERN INC (HQ)
8049 Somerset Blvd, Paramount
(90723-4396)
PHONE..................................562 220-1450
Paul F Conrad, *CEO*
Kris Schramm, *President*
Mary A Pool, *CFO*
Leonard Crespo, *Vice Pres*
Earl Grebing, *Vice Pres*
EMP: 50
SQ FT: 13,000
SALES (est): 123.6MM
SALES (corp-wide): 337.2MM Privately
Held
WEB: www.total-western.com
SIC: 1389 Oil field services; construction,
repair & dismantling services; excavating
slush pits & cellars; grading oil & gas well
foundations
PA: Bragg Investment Company, Inc.
6251 N Paramount Blvd
Long Beach CA 90805
562 984-2400

(P-285)
TRINGEN CORPORATION
Also Called: Allied Engrg & Consulting
238 E Norris Rd, Bakersfield (93308-3572)
PHONE..................................661 393-3039
Fax: 661 393-0799
EMP: 10
SQ FT: 1,000
SALES (est): 1.1MM Privately Held
WEB: www.tringen.com
SIC: 1389

(P-286)
TRUITT OILFIELD MAINT CORP
1051 James Rd, Bakersfield (93308-9753)
P.O. Box 5066 (93388-5066)
PHONE..................................661 871-4099
Kimberly Sue New, *President*
Steve New, *Vice Pres*
EMP: 300
SQ FT: 3,000
SALES (est): 51.3MM Privately Held
SIC: 1389 Oil field services

(P-287)
TRYAD SERVICE CORPORATION
5900 E Lerdo Hwy, Shafter (93263-4023)
PHONE..................................661 391-1524
James Varner, *President*
Estate of Burl G Varner, *Shareholder*
Danny Seely, *Vice Pres*
▲ EMP: 90
SALES (est): 9.7MM Privately Held
SIC: 1389 Oil & gas wells: building, repair-
ing & dismantling

(P-288)
TUBOSCOPE PIPELINE SVCS
INC
Also Called: Tuboscope Nat Oilwell Varco
4621 Burr St, Bakersfield (93308-6143)
PHONE..................................661 321-3400
Bill Grahm, *Manager*
EMP: 35
SALES (corp-wide): 7.3B Publicly Held
SIC: 1389 Pipe testing, oil field service
HQ: Tuboscope Pipeline Services Inc.
2835 Holmes Rd
Houston TX 77051

(P-289)
U S WEATHERFORD L P
2815 Fruitvale Ave, Bakersfield
(93308-5907)
PHONE..................................661 589-9483
Rick Benton, *Branch Mgr*
EMP: 100 Privately Held
WEB: www.gaslift.com
SIC: 1389 Oil field services
HQ: U S Weatherford L P
179 Weatherford Dr
Schriever LA 70395
985 493-6100

(P-290)
ULTRAMAR INC
Also Called: Valero
961 S La Paloma Ave, Wilmington
(90744-6420)
PHONE..................................310 834-7254
Mark Phair, *Manager*
EMP: 40
SALES (corp-wide): 93.9B Publicly Held
WEB: www.divi.com
SIC: 1389 Gas field services
HQ: Ultramar Inc.
1 Valero Way
San Antonio TX 78249
210 345-2000

(P-291)
VALLEY WATER MANAGEMENT
CO
7500 Meany Ave, Bakersfield (93308-5178)
PHONE..................................661 410-7500
John Gatlin, *President*
EMP: 12
SQ FT: 23,522
SALES: 7.5MM Privately Held
SIC: 1389 Oil field services

(P-292)
VAQUERO ENERGY INC
5060 California Ave, Bakersfield
(93309-0728)
P.O. Box 13550 (93389-3550)
PHONE..................................661 616-0600
Kenneth H Hunter, *CEO*
Seth Hunter, *Vice Pres*
Cary Nikkel, *Admin Sec*
Wendy Hall, *Accountant*
Nikki Tramel, *Controller*
EMP: 21
SALES (est): 3.8MM Privately Held
WEB: www.vaqueroenergy.com
SIC: 1389 Testing, measuring, surveying &
analysis services

(P-293)
WATSON ME INC (PA)
801 Kern St, Taft (93268-2734)
PHONE..................................661 763-5254
Gene Watson, *CEO*
Pat Watson, *Vice Pres*
Joe Weninger, *Manager*
EMP: 12
SQ FT: 6,000

SALES (est): 51.7MM **Privately Held**
SIC: **1389** Oil field services

(P-294)
WEATHERFORD COMPLETION SYSTEMS
Also Called: Peric Oil Tool
19468 Creek Rd, Bakersfield (93314-8451)
PHONE............................661 746-1391
Dennis Church, *District Mgr*
▲ EMP: 29
SALES (est): 1.7MM **Privately Held**
SIC: **1389** Oil field services

(P-295)
WEATHERFORD INTERNATIONAL LLC
201 Hallock Dr, Santa Paula (93060-9647)
P.O. Box 31 (93061-0031)
PHONE............................805 933-0242
Larry Brixey, *Manager*
EMP: 32 **Privately Held**
WEB: www.weatherford.com
SIC: **1389** Oil field services
HQ: Weatherford International, Llc
2000 Saint James Pl
Houston TX 77056
713 693-4000

(P-296)
WEATHERFORD INTERNATIONAL LLC
1880 Santa Barbara Ave # 220, San Luis Obispo (93401-4481)
PHONE............................805 781-3580
Chris Smith, *Principal*
EMP: 73 **Privately Held**
SIC: **1389** Oil field services
HQ: Weatherford International, Llc
2000 Saint James Pl
Houston TX 77056
713 693-4000

(P-297)
WEATHERFORD INTERNATIONAL LLC
Also Called: Coroc
21728 Rosedale Hwy, Bakersfield (93314-9787)
PHONE............................661 587-9753
Mark Sarcen, *Branch Mgr*
EMP: 60 **Privately Held**
WEB: www.weatherford.com
SIC: **1389** Oil field services
HQ: Weatherford International, Llc
2000 Saint James Pl
Houston TX 77056
713 693-4000

(P-298)
WEATHERFORD INTERNATIONAL LLC
400 Rocklite Rd, Ventura (93001-1523)
P.O. Box 1668 (93002-1668)
PHONE............................805 643-1279
Scott Antosen, *Branch Mgr*
EMP: 14 **Privately Held**
WEB: www.weatherford.com
SIC: **1389** Oil field services
HQ: Weatherford International, Llc
2000 Saint James Pl
Houston TX 77056
713 693-4000

1411 Dimension Stone

(P-299)
ARCHWOOD MFG GROUP INC
15058 Delano St, Van Nuys (91411-2016)
PHONE............................818 781-7673
Carlos E Subero, *Principal*
EMP: 11
SALES (est): 918.6K **Privately Held**
SIC: **1411** Marble, dimension-quarrying

(P-300)
BO DEAN CO INC (PA)
1060 N Dutton Ave, Santa Rosa (95401-5011)
PHONE............................707 576-8205
Dean N Soiland, *CEO*
Belinda Soiland, *Vice Pres*
Charlie Young, *Project Mgr*

William Reid, *Opers Staff*
Heather Hammerich, *Manager*
EMP: 30
SQ FT: 5,000
SALES (est): 18.1MM **Privately Held**
WEB: www.bodeancompany.com
SIC: **1411** 2951 Greenstone, dimension-quarrying; concrete, asphaltic (not from refineries)

(P-301)
CHANDLER AGGREGATES INC (PA)
24867 Maitri Rd, Corona (92883-5136)
P.O. Box 78450 (92877-0148)
PHONE............................951 277-1341
Larry Werner, *President*
Skip Begg, *Sales Executive*
EMP: 20
SALES (est): 6.7MM **Privately Held**
SIC: **1422** Dimension stone; crushed & broken limestone

(P-302)
COSA MARBLE CO
13040 San Fernando Rd A, Sylmar (91342-3692)
PHONE............................818 364-8800
Halie Cieollo, *Office Mgr*
◆ EMP: 13
SALES (est): 655.5K **Privately Held**
SIC: **1411** Marble, dimension-quarrying

(P-303)
ESTATE GRANITE & MARBLE
4950 Mtn Lakes Blvd Ste C, Redding (96003-1473)
PHONE............................530 241-7866
Hal Davis, *Manager*
Mike Huber, *Treasurer*
EMP: 15
SALES (est): 1MM **Privately Held**
WEB: www.estategranite.com
SIC: **1411** Dimension stone

(P-304)
MINESTONE
17739 Valley Vista Blvd, Encino (91316-3746)
PHONE............................818 775-5999
Richard McDonald, *Principal*
▲ EMP: 10
SALES (est): 854.3K **Privately Held**
SIC: **1411** Limestone & marble dimension stone

(P-305)
REGIONAL MTLS RECOVERY INC
Also Called: Wyroc Materials
2142 Industrial Ct Ste D, Vista (92081-7960)
P.O. Box 1239 (92085-1239)
PHONE............................760 727-0878
Jeffrey C Halloran, *President*
EMP: 20 EST: 1995
SALES: 950K **Privately Held**
SIC: **1411**

(P-306)
SPARK STONE LLC
2300 E Winston Rd, Anaheim (92806-5529)
PHONE............................714 772-7575
Jacek G Chyczewski,
EMP: 15
SALES (est): 1.6MM **Privately Held**
SIC: **1411** Granite dimension stone

(P-307)
TAKE IT FOR GRANITE INC
345 Phelan Ave, San Jose (95112-4104)
PHONE............................408 790-2812
Jason Krulee, *President*
▲ EMP: 20 EST: 1997
SQ FT: 32,000
SALES (est): 6.1MM **Privately Held**
WEB: www.tifgranite.com
SIC: **1411** Dimension stone

(P-308)
WYROC INC (PA)
2142 Industrial Ct Ste D, Vista (92081-7960)
P.O. Box 1239 (92085-1239)
PHONE............................760 727-0878
William Halloran, *President*
Dorothy Leckband, *Asst Treas*
EMP: 12 EST: 1960
SQ FT: 2,500
SALES (est): 1.4MM **Privately Held**
WEB: www.wyroc.com
SIC: **1411** 1423 Sandstone, dimension-quarrying; crushed & broken granite

---
1422 Crushed & Broken Limestone

(P-309)
AZUSA ROCK LLC (DH)
3901 Fish Canyon Rd, Azusa (91702)
PHONE............................858 530-9444
Ron McAbee, *President*
Ed Kelly, *Senior VP*
Jeff McOrmick, *Vice Pres*
Ronnie Walker, *Vice Pres*
Paul Stanford, *Admin Sec*
EMP: 10
SQ FT: 40,000
SALES (est): 17.8MM **Publicly Held**
SIC: **1422** 3273 2951 1442 Cement rock, crushed & broken-quarrying; ready-mixed concrete; asphalt paving mixtures & blocks; construction sand & gravel
HQ: Legacy Vulcan, Llc
1200 Urban Center Dr
Vestavia AL 35242
205 298-3000

(P-310)
AZUSA ROCK INC
3605 Dehesa Rd, El Cajon (92019-2903)
PHONE............................619 440-2363
Tom Nelson, *Manager*
EMP: 13 **Publicly Held**
SIC: **1422** Crushed & broken limestone
HQ: Azusa Rock, Llc
3901 Fish Canyon Rd
Azusa CA 91702
858 530-9444

(P-311)
CALMAT CO
16101 Hwy 156, Maricopa (93252)
P.O. Box 22800, Bakersfield (93390-2800)
PHONE............................661 858-2673
Angela Bailey, *Manager*
EMP: 35 **Publicly Held**
SIC: **1422** Crushed & broken limestone
HQ: Calmat Co.
500 N Brand Blvd Ste 500 # 500
Glendale CA 91203
818 553-8821

(P-312)
CEMEX CNSTR MTLS PCF LLC
Also Called: Cem - Long Bch Terminal
601 Pier D Ave, Long Beach (90802-6240)
PHONE............................562 435-0195
Steve Dillion, *Branch Mgr*
EMP: 10 **Privately Held**
SIC: **1422** Crushed & broken limestone
HQ: Cemex Construction Materials Pacific, Llc
1501 Belvedere Rd
West Palm Beach FL 33406
561 833-5555

(P-313)
LEGACY VULCAN LLC
Parkridge & Quarry Sts, Corona (92877)
P.O. Box 1058 (92878-1058)
PHONE............................714 737-2922
Donald Purcell, *Branch Mgr*
George Hanny, *President*
EMP: 45 **Publicly Held**
WEB: www.vulcanmaterials.com
SIC: **1422** Crushed & broken limestone
HQ: Legacy Vulcan, Llc
1200 Urban Center Dr
Vestavia AL 35242
205 298-3000

(P-314)
LEGACY VULCAN LLC
365 N Canyon Pkwy, Livermore (94551)
PHONE............................925 373-1802
Don Kahler, *Branch Mgr*
EMP: 26 **Publicly Held**
WEB: www.vulcanmaterials.com
SIC: **1422** Crushed & broken limestone
HQ: Legacy Vulcan, Llc
1200 Urban Center Dr
Vestavia AL 35242
205 298-3000

(P-315)
MARTIN MARIETTA MATERIALS INC
Also Called: Table Mountain Quarry
2216 Table Mountain Blvd, Oroville (95965-9109)
PHONE............................530 534-4517
Jim Cusick, *Manager*
EMP: 14 **Publicly Held**
WEB: www.martinmarietta.com
SIC: **1422** Crushed & broken limestone
PA: Martin Marietta Materials Inc
2710 Wycliff Rd
Raleigh NC 27607

(P-316)
SPECIALTY MINERALS INC
Minerals Technology
6565 Meridian Rd, Lucerne Valley (92356-8602)
P.O. Box 558 (92356-0558)
PHONE............................760 248-5300
Doug Mayger, *Branch Mgr*
EMP: 150 **Publicly Held**
WEB: www.specialtyminerals.com
SIC: **1422** Crushed & broken limestone
HQ: Specialty Minerals Inc.
622 3rd Ave Fl 38
New York NY 10017
212 878-1800

(P-317)
SYAR INDUSTRIES INC
885 Lake Herman Rd, Vallejo (94591-8324)
P.O. Box 2540, NAPA (94558-0524)
PHONE............................707 643-3261
Mike Burneson, *Manager*
EMP: 100
SALES (corp-wide): 100.2MM **Privately Held**
WEB: www.syar.com
SIC: **1422** 5211 Crushed & broken limestone; cement
PA: Syar Industries, Inc.
2301 Napa Vallejo Hwy
Napa CA 94558
707 252-8711

(P-318)
UNITED ROCK PRODUCTS CORP
Also Called: Sully Miller Contracting
135 S State College Blvd # 400, Brea (92821-5819)
PHONE............................626 358-4558
Vic Serri, *President*
Tom Snider, *Foreman/Supr*
EMP: 45
SQ FT: 2,000
SALES (est): 4MM
SALES (corp-wide): 95.5MM **Privately Held**
SIC: **1422** 1442 Cement rock, crushed & broken-quarrying; construction sand & gravel
HQ: Sully-Miller Contracting Company Inc
135 S State College Blvd # 400
Brea CA 92821
714 578-9600

(P-319)
VULCAN MATERIALS COMPANY
3605 Dehesa Rd, El Cajon (92019-2903)
PHONE............................619 440-2363
Tom Nelson, *Branch Mgr*
EMP: 17 **Publicly Held**
SIC: **1422** Crushed & broken limestone

PA: Vulcan Materials Company
1200 Urban Center Dr
Vestavia AL 35242

(P-320)
VULCAN MATERIALS COMPANY
500 N Brand Blvd Ste 500, Glendale
(91203-3319)
PHONE..............................818 241-7356
Alan Wessel, *Branch Mgr*
EMP: 16 **Publicly Held**
SIC: 1422 Limestones, ground
PA: Vulcan Materials Company
1200 Urban Center Dr
Vestavia AL 35242

1423 Crushed & Broken Granite

(P-321)
JUNIPER ROCK CORPORATION
Also Called: ARB
26000 Commercentre Dr, Lake Forest
(92630-8816)
PHONE..............................949 500-1797
Eric Amlee, *General Mgr*
EMP: 409
SALES (est): 54.3MM
SALES (corp-wide): 2.3B **Publicly Held**
SIC: 1423 Crushed & broken granite
PA: Primoris Services Corporation
2100 Mckinney Ave # 1500
Dallas TX 75201
214 740-5600

(P-322)
KIEWIT CORPORATION
Also Called: Aggregate - Red Hill Quarry
Hwy 395 And Cinder Rd, Little Lake
(93542)
P.O. Box 18 (93542-0018)
PHONE..............................760 377-3117
Benton Boyd, *Branch Mgr*
EMP: 20
SALES (corp-wide): 16.6B **Privately Held**
SIC: 1423 Crushed & broken granite
HQ: Kiewit Corporation
3555 Farnam St Ste 1000
Omaha NE 68131
402 342-2052

(P-323)
MARTIN MARIETTA MATERIALS INC
1500 Rubidoux Blvd, Riverside
(92509-1840)
PHONE..............................951 682-0918
Marietta Martin, *CEO*
EMP: 21 **Publicly Held**
SIC: 1423 Crushed & broken granite
PA: Martin Marietta Materials Inc
2710 Wycliff Rd
Raleigh NC 27607

1429 Crushed & Broken Stone, NEC

(P-324)
AGGREGATE PRODUCTS INC (PA)
100 Brawley Ave, Thermal (92274-8420)
PHONE..............................760 395-5312
John Corcoran, *President*
James Atherton-Ham, *Vice Pres*
Maria E Corcoran, *Vice Pres*
EMP: 12
SQ FT: 1,000
SALES (est): 8.1MM **Privately Held**
SIC: 1429 Igneous rock, crushed & broken-quarrying

(P-325)
BOHAN & CANELIS - AUSTIN CRK
Also Called: Austn Creek Materials
1528 Copperhill Pkwy F, Santa Rosa
(95403-8200)
PHONE..............................707 632-5296

Timothy Canelis, *President*
Homer Canelis, *Treasurer*
EMP: 15 **EST:** 1946
SQ FT: 800
SALES: 2MM **Privately Held**
WEB: www.bohancanelis.com
SIC: 1429 Basalt, crushed & broken-quarrying

(P-326)
CHILI BAR LLC
Also Called: Chili Bar Slate
11380 State Highway 193, Placerville
(95667-9601)
P.O. Box 1046 (95667-1046)
PHONE..............................530 622-3325
Jacob Montazeri, *Principal*
EMP: 18 **EST:** 2012
SALES (est): 2.4MM **Privately Held**
SIC: 1429 Slate, crushed & broken-quarrying

(P-327)
GM MARBLE & GRANITE INC
Also Called: Granite Kitchen Countertops
1375 Franquette Ave Ste F, Concord
(94520-7932)
PHONE..............................925 676-8385
Gregory Markiel, *CEO*
EMP: 11
SQ FT: 3,000
SALES: 900K **Privately Held**
SIC: 1429 Marble, crushed & broken-quarrying

(P-328)
LANGLEY HILL QUARRY
12 Langley Hill Rd, Woodside
(94062-4829)
P.O. Box 620626 (94062-0626)
PHONE..............................650 851-0179
Michael Dempsey, *Partner*
Patrick Dempsey, *Partner*
EMP: 15
SALES: 1.9MM **Privately Held**
SIC: 1429 Igneous rock, crushed & broken-quarrying

(P-329)
NORBERG CRUSHING INC
592 Tyrone St, El Cajon (92020-2233)
PHONE..............................619 390-4200
Stephen Norberg, *President*
Heidi Spicer, *CFO*
Dana Farrell, *Vice Pres*
EMP: 15
SQ FT: 3,500
SALES (est): 2.7MM **Privately Held**
SIC: 1429 Igneous rock, crushed & broken-quarrying

(P-330)
OLIVER DE SILVA INC (PA)
Also Called: Gallagher & Burk
11555 Dublin Blvd, Dublin (94568-2854)
P.O. Box 2922 (94568-0922)
PHONE..............................925 829-9220
Edwin O De Silva, *Chairman*
Richard B Gates, *President*
David De Silva, *Exec VP*
J Scott Archibald, *Vice Pres*
Ernest Lampkin, *Vice Pres*
EMP: 20
SQ FT: 60,000
SALES (est): 83.8MM **Privately Held**
SIC: 1429 Igneous rock, crushed & broken-quarrying

(P-331)
PAUL HUBBS CONSTRUCTION INC (PA)
542 W C St, Colton (92324-2140)
PHONE..............................951 360-3990
Jay P Hubbs, *President*
Lucile M Hubbs, *Treasurer*
John L Hubbs, *Vice Pres*
Pat Hubbs, *Admin Sec*
EMP: 18
SQ FT: 4,000
SALES (est): 2.6MM **Privately Held**
SIC: 1429 Riprap quarrying

(P-332)
REED GROUP
686 E Lockeford St, Lodi (95240-0712)
P.O. Box 1630 (95241-1630)
PHONE..............................209 334-0790
Edward Berlier, *Manager*
EMP: 15
SALES (corp-wide): 197.8MM **Privately Held**
WEB: www.reed.net
SIC: 1429 Boulder, crushed & broken-quarrying
HQ: The Reed Group
928 12th St Ste 700
Modesto CA 95354
209 521-7423

(P-333)
SAN RAFAEL ROCK QUARRY INC (HQ)
Also Called: Dutra Materials
1000 Point San Pedro Rd, San Rafael
(94901-8312)
PHONE..............................415 459-7740
Bill Toney Dutra, *CEO*
EMP: 70
SALES (est): 70MM
SALES (corp-wide): 145.1MM **Privately Held**
SIC: 1429 1629 Basalt, crushed & broken-quarrying; marine construction
PA: The Dutra Group
2350 Kerner Blvd Ste 200
San Rafael CA 94901
415 258-6876

(P-334)
TRIANGLE ROCK PRODUCTS LLC
500 N Brand Blvd Ste 500 # 500, Glendale
(91203-3319)
PHONE..............................818 553-8820
Stanley G Bass, *President*
Annie Hovanessian,
EMP: 30
SQ FT: 20,000
SALES (est): 1.5MM **Publicly Held**
SIC: 1429 1442 2951 3273 Igneous rock, crushed & broken-quarrying; construction sand & gravel; asphalt paving mixtures & blocks; ready-mixed concrete; nonresidential building operators
HQ: Calmat Co.
500 N Brand Blvd Ste 500 # 500
Glendale CA 91203
818 553-8821

1442 Construction Sand & Gravel

(P-335)
A TEICHERT & SON INC
Also Called: Teichert Aggregates
13879 Butterfield Dr, Truckee
(96161-3331)
P.O. Box 447 (96160-0447)
PHONE..............................530 587-3811
Ed Herrnberger, *Plant Mgr*
EMP: 40
SALES (corp-wide): 784MM **Privately Held**
SIC: 1442 Construction sand & gravel
HQ: A. Teichert & Son, Inc.
3500 American River Dr
Sacramento CA 95864

(P-336)
A TEICHERT & SON INC
Also Called: Teichert Aggregates
36314 S Bird Rd, Tracy (95304-8678)
PHONE..............................209 832-4150
Jerry Hansen, *Plant Mgr*
EMP: 40
SALES (corp-wide): 784MM **Privately Held**
SIC: 1442 Construction sand & gravel
HQ: A. Teichert & Son, Inc.
3500 American River Dr
Sacramento CA 95864

(P-337)
A TEICHERT & SON INC
Also Called: Teichert Aggregates
35030 County Road 20, Woodland
(95695-9251)
PHONE..............................530 661-4290
Brandon Stauffer, *Plant Mgr*
EMP: 30
SALES (corp-wide): 784MM **Privately Held**
SIC: 1442 Construction sand & gravel
HQ: A. Teichert & Son, Inc.
3500 American River Dr
Sacramento CA 95864
-

(P-338)
A TEICHERT & SON INC
Also Called: Teichert Aggregates
36314 S Bird Rd, Tracy (95304-8678)
PHONE..............................209 834-8300
Jerry Hansen, *Plant Mgr*
EMP: 40
SALES (corp-wide): 784MM **Privately Held**
SIC: 1442 Construction sand & gravel
HQ: A. Teichert & Son, Inc.
3500 American River Dr
Sacramento CA 95864

(P-339)
A TEICHERT & SON INC
Also Called: Teichert Aggregates
2601 State Highway 49, Cool
(95614-9528)
P.O. Box 280 (95614-0280)
PHONE..............................530 885-4244
Ed Herrnberger, *Plant Mgr*
EMP: 15
SALES (corp-wide): 784MM **Privately Held**
SIC: 1442 Construction sand & gravel
HQ: A. Teichert & Son, Inc.
3500 American River Dr
Sacramento CA 95864

(P-340)
A TEICHERT & SON INC
Also Called: Teichert Aggregates
3331 Walnut Ave, Marysville (95901-9421)
PHONE..............................530 749-1230
Brandon Stauffer, *Plant Mgr*
EMP: 40
SALES (corp-wide): 784MM **Privately Held**
SIC: 1442 Construction sand & gravel
HQ: A. Teichert & Son, Inc.
3500 American River Dr
Sacramento CA 95864

(P-341)
A TEICHERT & SON INC
Also Called: Teichert Aggregates
4249 Hmmnton Smrtvlle Rd, Marysville
(95901)
PHONE..............................530 743-6111
Brandon Stauffer, *Plant Mgr*
EMP: 40
SALES (corp-wide): 784MM **Privately Held**
SIC: 1442 Construction sand & gravel
HQ: A. Teichert & Son, Inc.
3500 American River Dr
Sacramento CA 95864

(P-342)
A TEICHERT & SON INC
Also Called: Teichert Aggregates
3417 Grant Line Rd, Rancho Cordova
(95742-7000)
P.O. Box 981, Folsom (95763-0981)
PHONE..............................916 351-0123
Mike Cunnigham, *Plant Mgr*
EMP: 40
SALES (corp-wide): 784MM **Privately Held**
SIC: 1442 Construction sand & gravel
HQ: A. Teichert & Son, Inc.
3500 American River Dr
Sacramento CA 95864

(P-343)
A TEICHERT & SON INC
Also Called: Teichert Aggregates
8760 Kiefer Blvd, Sacramento
(95826-3917)
P.O. Box 15002 (95851-0002)
PHONE..................................916 386-6900
Mike Cunnigham, *Plant Mgr*
EMP: 40
SALES (corp-wide): 784MM **Privately Held**
SIC: 1442 Construction sand & gravel
HQ: A. Teichert & Son, Inc.
   3500 American River Dr
   Sacramento CA 95864

(P-344)
AGGTECH INC
34428 Yucaipa Blvd E344, Yucaipa
(92399-2474)
PHONE..................................909 795-4774
Stanley Robert Houck, *President*
EMP: 20 **EST:** 2014
SALES (est): 1.5MM **Privately Held**
SIC: 1442 3531 Construction sand &
   gravel; grinders, stone: portable

(P-345)
**ALAMEDA CONSTRUCTION
SVCS INC**
2528 E 125th St, Compton (90222-1502)
PHONE..................................310 635-3277
Kevin Ramsey, *CEO*
Tracey Watson, *Vice Pres*
Traci Watson, *Vice Pres*
Ray Coronado, *Superintendent*
EMP: 20
SQ FT: 8,000
SALES (est): 6MM **Privately Held**
SIC: 1442 Construction sand & gravel

(P-346)
BAY AREA DRILLING INC
1860 Loveridge Rd, Pittsburg (94565-4111)
PHONE..................................925 427-7574
Mark Lucido, *CEO*
EMP: 15
SALES (est): 2.7MM **Privately Held**
SIC: 1442 Construction sand & gravel

(P-347)
BROWN SAND INC
800 Mossdale Rd, Lathrop (95330-8650)
P.O. Box 1429 (95330-1429)
PHONE..................................209 234-1500
Robert H Brown Jr, *President*
Mike Brown, *Corp Secy*
Jeff Brown, *Vice Pres*
Reggie Pomicpic, *Sales Dir*
Tim Clement, *Maint Spvr*
EMP: 35
SALES (est): 9.7MM **Privately Held**
SIC: 1442 Construction sand & gravel

(P-348)
BUTTE SAND AND GRAVEL
10373 S Butte Rd, Sutter (95982-9316)
P.O. Box 749 (95982-0749)
PHONE..................................530 755-0225
Darren Morehead, *President*
Martin Morehead, *CFO*
Joseph Morehead II, *Vice Pres*
EMP: 20
SQ FT: 1,000
SALES (est): 4.3MM **Privately Held**
WEB: www.buttesand.com
SIC: 1442 5211 Gravel mining; sand &
   gravel

(P-349)
CALPORTLAND
2025 E Financial Way, Glendora
(91741-4692)
P.O. Box 567, Thousand Palms (92276-
0567)
PHONE..................................760 343-3403
Terri Stelter, *President*
Debra Rubenzer, *Corp Secy*
Diane Sarauer, *Vice Pres*
EMP: 15
SQ FT: 480
SALES (est): 1.8MM **Privately Held**
WEB: www.a-1aggregates.com
SIC: 1442 Gravel mining; construction
   sand mining

(P-350)
CALPORTLAND
72200 Vista Chino, Thousand Palms
(92276-2605)
P.O. Box 567 (92276-0567)
PHONE..................................760 343-3126
Terri Stelter, *President*
EMP: 15
SALES (corp-wide): 8.1B **Privately Held**
SIC: 1442 Construction sand & gravel
HQ: Calportland
   20601 Ne Marine Dr
   Fairview OR 97024

(P-351)
CANYON ROCK CO INC
Also Called: River Ready Mix
7525 Hwy 116, Forestville (95436-9227)
P.O. Box 639 (95436-0639)
PHONE..................................707 887-2207
Wendell Trappe, *President*
Gwen Trappe, *Vice Pres*
Phillip Driver, *Controller*
EMP: 20
SQ FT: 3,000
SALES (est): 11.8MM **Privately Held**
SIC: 1442 3273 Construction sand &
   gravel; ready-mixed concrete

(P-352)
**CHANDLERS PALOS VERDES
SAND A**
26311 Palos Verdes Dr E, Rllng HLS Est
(90274-4254)
P.O. Box 15450, Irvine (92623-5450)
PHONE..................................310 784-2900
John Roberston Sr, *President*
Linda Wood, *Treasurer*
▲ **EMP:** 13 **EST:** 1937
SQ FT: 4,000
SALES (est): 3.1MM **Privately Held**
SIC: 1442 Construction sand mining;
   gravel mining
PA: Chandler's Sand And Gravel, Llc
   17392 Daimler St
   Irvine CA 92614
   310 784-2900

(P-353)
**COLOR MARBLE PROJECT
GROUP INC**
20521 Earlgate St, Walnut (91789-2909)
PHONE..................................909 595-8858
TSE Min Jemmy You, *President*
▲ **EMP:** 10
SALES (est): 1.2MM **Privately Held**
SIC: 1442 Construction sand & gravel

(P-354)
CONSTRUCTION ON TIME INC
5657 Meridian Ave, San Jose (95118-3436)
PHONE..................................408 209-1799
Peter Luckiewicz, *President*
EMP: 10
SALES: 200K **Privately Held**
SIC: 1442 Construction sand & gravel

(P-355)
DAN COPP CRUSHING CORP
22895 Savi Ranch Pkwy C, Yorba Linda
(92887-4630)
PHONE..................................714 777-6400
Karen Ayres, *Admin Sec*
Jason Ayres, *President*
Robert Virgil, *Vice Pres*
EMP: 38 **EST:** 1978
SQ FT: 4,000
SALES (est): 8.3MM **Privately Held**
SIC: 1442 Construction sand & gravel

(P-356)
ENNISS INC
12535 Vigilante Rd, Lakeside (92040-1167)
P.O. Box 1769 (92040-0917)
PHONE..................................619 561-1101
David Von Bhren, *President*
D Lois Miller, *Admin Sec*
Eric Enniss, *Manager*
EMP: 40
SQ FT: 4,700

SALES (est): 7.9MM **Privately Held**
SIC: 1442 4212 3271 4953 Sand mining;
   local trucking, without storage; architectural concrete: block, split, fluted, screen,
   etc.; recycling, waste materials; iron work,
   structural

(P-357)
FISHER SAND & GRAVEL CO
24560 Cooperstown Rd, Oakdale (95361)
PHONE..................................602 619-0325
Derek Schoonover, *Branch Mgr*
EMP: 10
SALES (corp-wide): 314MM **Privately
Held**
SIC: 1442 Construction sand mining
PA: Fisher Sand & Gravel Co.
   3020 Energy Dr
   Dickinson ND 58601
   701 456-9184

(P-358)
GAIL MATERIALS INC
10060 Dawson Canyon Rd, Corona
(92883-2112)
PHONE..................................951 667-6106
Nick Leinen, *CEO*
Mitch Leinen, *President*
Dave Dzwilewski, *Sales Mgr*
Adrian Ruvalcaba,
June Hand, *Manager*
EMP: 30
SQ FT: 5,000
SALES (est): 4.7MM **Privately Held**
SIC: 1442 Construction sand & gravel

(P-359)
GRANITE ROCK CO (PA)
350 Technology Dr, Watsonville
(95076-2488)
P.O. Box 50001 (95077-5001)
PHONE..................................831 768-2000
Thomas H Squeri, *CEO*
Bruce G Woolpert, *Vice Chairman*
Mary E Woolpert, *Chairman*
Todd Barreras, *Officer*
Greg Diehl, *Vice Pres*
EMP: 100
SQ FT: 10,000
SALES (est): 1.1B **Privately Held**
WEB: www.graniterock.com
SIC: 1442 3273 5032 2951 Gravel min-
   ing; construction sand mining; ready-
   mixed concrete; sand, construction;
   stone, crushed or broken; asphalt & as-
   phaltic paving mixtures (not from refiner-
   ies); highway & street paving contractor;
   concrete block & brick

(P-360)
GRANITE ROCK CO
Also Called: AR Wilson Quarry
Quarry Rd, Aromas (95004)
P.O. Box 699 (95004-0699)
PHONE..................................831 768-2300
Bruce Wollepert, *President*
EMP: 100
SALES (corp-wide): 1.1B **Privately Held**
WEB: www.graniterock.com
SIC: 1442 2951 Gravel mining; asphalt
   paving mixtures & blocks
PA: Granite Rock Co.
   350 Technology Dr
   Watsonville CA 95076
   831 768-2000

(P-361)
**HANSEN BROS ENTERPRISES
(PA)**
Also Called: Hbe Rental
11727 La Barr Meadows Rd, Grass Valley
(95949-7722)
P.O. Box 1599 (95945-1599)
PHONE..................................530 273-3100
Orson Hansen, *President*
Frank Bennallack, *Treasurer*
Helen Hansen, *Vice Pres*
Sue Peterson, *Vice Pres*
Brandon Hall, *Project Mgr*
EMP: 90
SQ FT: 20,000
SALES (est): 36.2MM **Privately Held**
WEB: www.gohbe.com
SIC: 1442 3273 1794 7359 Gravel min-
   ing; ready-mixed concrete; excavation
   work; equipment rental & leasing

(P-362)
HANSON AGGREGATES LLC
24001 Stevens Creek Blvd, Cupertino
(95014-5659)
PHONE..................................408 996-4000
Steve Tarantino, *Branch Mgr*
Pattie Lovell, *Warehouse Mgr*
EMP: 28
SALES (corp-wide): 20.3B **Privately Held**
WEB: www.hansonind.com
SIC: 1442 Construction sand & gravel
HQ: Hanson Aggregates Llc
   8505 Freport Pkwy Ste 500
   Irving TX 75063
   469 417-1200

(P-363)
HANSON AGGREGATES LLC
13550 Live Oak Ln, Baldwin Park
(91706-1318)
PHONE..................................626 856-6700
Michael Rogers, *Manager*
EMP: 40
SALES (corp-wide): 20.3B **Privately Held**
WEB: www.hansonind.com
SIC: 1442 Construction sand & gravel
HQ: Hanson Aggregates Llc
   8505 Freport Pkwy Ste 500
   Irving TX 75063
   469 417-1200

(P-364)
HANSON AGGREGATES LLC
5325 Foxen Canyon Rd, Santa Maria
(93454-9550)
PHONE..................................805 934-4931
Rick Sanford, *Manager*
EMP: 12
SALES (corp-wide): 20.3B **Privately Held**
WEB: www.hansonind.com
SIC: 1442 Common sand mining
HQ: Hanson Aggregates Llc
   8505 Freport Pkwy Ste 500
   Irving TX 75063
   469 417-1200

(P-365)
HANSON AGGREGATES LLC
131 Suburban Rd, San Luis Obispo
(93401-7506)
P.O. Box 71 (93406-0071)
PHONE..................................805 543-8100
Dave Grummitt, *Branch Mgr*
EMP: 22
SALES (corp-wide): 20.3B **Privately Held**
WEB: www.hansonind.com
SIC: 1442 Common sand mining
HQ: Hanson Aggregates Llc
   8505 Freport Pkwy Ste 500
   Irving TX 75063
   469 417-1200

(P-366)
LEGACY VULCAN LLC
Also Called: Durbin Rock Plant
13000 Los Angeles St, Irwindale
(91706-2240)
PHONE..................................626 856-6150
Danny Robinson, *Manager*
EMP: 20 **Publicly Held**
WEB: www.vulcanmaterials.com
SIC: 1442 Construction sand & gravel
HQ: Legacy Vulcan, Llc
   1200 Urban Center Dr
   Vestavia AL 35242
   205 298-3000

(P-367)
LEGACY VULCAN LLC
San Bernardino Division
2400 W Highland Ave, San Bernardino
(92407-6408)
PHONE..................................909 875-1150
Darryl Charleson, *Sales/Mktg Dir*
Allyson Noah, *Manager*
Floyd Sibole, *Manager*
EMP: 50 **Publicly Held**
WEB: www.vulcanmaterials.com
SIC: 1442 3273 Sand mining; ready-mixed
   concrete
HQ: Legacy Vulcan, Llc
   1200 Urban Center Dr
   Vestavia AL 35242
   205 298-3000

P R O D U C T S & S V C S

(P-368)
LEGACY VULCAN LLC
6232 Santos Diaz St, Irwindale
(91702-3267)
PHONE..................................626 856-6153
Jack Perkins, *Branch Mgr*
EMP: 12 **Publicly Held**
WEB: www.vulcanmaterials.com
SIC: 1442 Construction sand & gravel
HQ: Legacy Vulcan, Llc
1200 Urban Center Dr
Vestavia AL 35242
205 298-3000

(P-369)
LEGACY VULCAN LLC
11447 Tuxford St, Sun Valley (91352-2639)
PHONE..................................818 983-1323
Joe Ellison, *Manager*
EMP: 22 **Publicly Held**
WEB: www.vulcan.materials.com
SIC: 1442 Construction sand & gravel
HQ: Legacy Vulcan, Llc
1200 Urban Center Dr
Vestavia AL 35242
205 298-3000

(P-370)
LEGACY VULCAN LLC
Also Called: Palmdale Rock and Asphalt
6851 E Avenue T, Littlerock (93543-1705)
PHONE..................................661 533-2127
EMP: 22 **Publicly Held**
WEB: www.vulcanmaterials.com
SIC: 1442 Construction sand & gravel
HQ: Legacy Vulcan, Llc
1200 Urban Center Dr
Vestavia AL 35242
205 298-3000

(P-371)
LEGACY VULCAN LLC
Also Called: Western Division
20350 Highland Ave, Rialto (92377)
PHONE..................................909 875-5180
Darol Charlson, *Manager*
EMP: 30 **Publicly Held**
WEB: www.vulcanmaterials.com
SIC: 1442 Construction sand & gravel
HQ: Legacy Vulcan, Llc
1200 Urban Center Dr
Vestavia AL 35242
205 298-3000

(P-372)
LEGACY VULCAN LLC
13900 Lang Station Rd, Canyon Country
(91387-2213)
PHONE..................................661 252-1010
Frank Parra, *Manager*
EMP: 25 **Publicly Held**
WEB: www.vulcanmaterials.com
SIC: 1442 Construction sand & gravel
HQ: Legacy Vulcan, Llc
1200 Urban Center Dr
Vestavia AL 35242
205 298-3000

(P-373)
LEGACY VULCAN LLC
Also Called: Reliance Rock
16001 E Foothill Blvd, Irwindale
(91702-2813)
PHONE..................................626 856-6143
Donnie McDuffie, *Manager*
EMP: 30 **Publicly Held**
WEB: www.vulcanmaterials.com
SIC: 1442 Construction sand & gravel
HQ: Legacy Vulcan, Llc
1200 Urban Center Dr
Vestavia AL 35242
205 298-3000

(P-374)
MAGORIAN MINE SERVICES (PA)
10310 Sierra Hills Ln, Auburn
(95602-9402)
P.O. Box 8015 (95604-8015)
PHONE..................................530 269-1960
Don Magorian, *Owner*
EMP: 12
SALES (est): 2.8MM **Privately Held**
WEB: www.magmineserv.com
SIC: 1442 Gravel & pebble mining

(P-375)
NEVOCAL ENTERPRISES INC
Also Called: Kh Construction
5320 N Barcus Ave, Fresno (93722-5050)
PHONE..................................559 277-0700
Frank Cornell, *President*
EMP: 75
SQ FT: 4,575
SALES (est): 4.2MM **Privately Held**
SIC: 1442 Construction sand & gravel

(P-376)
NORTH COUNTY SAND AND GRAV INC
26227 Sherman Rd, Sun City
(92585-9223)
PHONE..................................951 928-2881
M J La Paglia III, *President*
Michael J La Paglia III, *President*
Tracy Paglia, *CFO*
EMP: 18
SALES (est): 5.5MM **Privately Held**
SIC: 1442 5032 Construction sand & gravel; sand, construction; gravel

(P-377)
NORTHERN AGGREGATES INC
500 Cropley Ln, Willits (95490-4140)
P.O. Box 1566 (95490-1566)
PHONE..................................707 459-3929
Frank Dutra, *President*
Randy Lucchetti, *Vice Pres*
EMP: 25
SQ FT: 10,000
SALES (est): 5MM **Privately Held**
SIC: 1442 Construction sand & gravel

(P-378)
PECK ROAD GRAVEL PIT
128 Live Oak Ave, Monrovia (91016-5050)
P.O. Box 1286 (91017-1286)
PHONE..................................626 574-7570
Steve Bubalo, *President*
Louise Bubalo, *Treasurer*
Stephanie Bubalo Becerra, *Vice Pres*
EMP: 30
SALES (est): 3.7MM **Privately Held**
SIC: 1442 Construction sand & gravel

(P-379)
PERRAULT CORPORATION
30640 N River Rd, Bonsall (92003-7123)
P.O. Box 578 (92003-0578)
PHONE..................................760 466-1024
Charles Perrault, *CEO*
EMP: 10
SALES (est): 2.4MM **Privately Held**
SIC: 1442 Construction sand & gravel

(P-380)
SANTA FE AGGREGATES INC (HQ)
11650 Shaffer Rd, Winton (95388-9604)
PHONE..................................209 358-3303
Ron C Turcotte, *President*
EMP: 18 EST: 1938
SALES (est): 3.4MM
SALES (corp-wide): 784MM **Privately Held**
SIC: 1442 Construction sand & gravel
PA: Teichert, Inc.
3500 American River Dr
Sacramento CA 95864
916 484-3011

(P-381)
SIERRA CASCADE AGGREGATE & ASP
6600 Old Ski Rd, Chester (96020)
P.O. Box 1193 (96020-1193)
PHONE..................................530 258-4555
Kacie Holland, *President*
Caleb Holland, *Treasurer*
EMP: 15
SALES (est): 3.2MM **Privately Held**
SIC: 1442 Construction sand & gravel

(P-382)
SPECIALTY ROCK INC
5405 Alton Pkwy Irvine, Irvine (92604)
PHONE..................................909 334-2265
Michael Holcomb, *CEO*
Richard Newman, *Treasurer*
▼ EMP: 13
SQ FT: 4,100

SALES: 4.5MM **Privately Held**
SIC: 1442 Construction sand & gravel

(P-383)
STONE VALLEY MATERIALS LLC
3500b Pyrite St, Riverside (92509-1123)
PHONE..................................951 681-7830
Brady Kooiman,
Chris Van Veldhuizen,
Stephen Vanderhart,
EMP: 10 EST: 2010
SALES (est): 637.7K **Privately Held**
WEB: www.stonevalleymaterials.com
SIC: 1442 Construction sand & gravel

(P-384)
STONY POINT ROCK QUARRY INC (PA)
7171 Stony Point Rd, Cotati (94931-9724)
PHONE..................................707 795-1775
Marvin Soiland, *President*
Marlene Berney, *Vice Pres*
EMP: 18
SQ FT: 1,600
SALES (est): 3.3MM **Privately Held**
WEB: www.sprqinc.com
SIC: 1442 Gravel mining

(P-385)
SWA MOUNTAIN GATE
20285 Radcliffe, Redding (96003)
P.O. Box 492335 (96049-2335)
PHONE..................................530 221-3406
Corkey Harmon, *Manager*
EMP: 15
SQ FT: 800
SALES (est): 1.1MM **Privately Held**
SIC: 1442 Construction sand & gravel

(P-386)
THOMES CREEK ROCK CO INC
6069 99w, Corning (96021-9130)
PHONE..................................530 824-0191
Mary Belle Coulter, *President*
EMP: 12
SQ FT: 1,000
SALES (est): 1.6MM **Privately Held**
SIC: 1442 Gravel & pebble mining

(P-387)
VULCAN AGGREGATES COMPANY LLC
Also Called: Lexington Quarry
18500 Limekiln Canyon Rd, Los Gatos
(95033-8629)
PHONE..................................408 354-7904
EMP: 14 **Publicly Held**
SIC: 1442 Construction sand & gravel
HQ: Vulcan Aggregates Company, Llc
2215 Olan Mills Dr Ste A
Chattanooga TN 37421
423 510-2605

(P-388)
VULCAN CONSTRUCTION MTLS LLC
346 Mathew St, Santa Clara (95050-3114)
PHONE..................................408 213-4270
EMP: 16 **Publicly Held**
SIC: 1442 Construction sand mining
HQ: Vulcan Construction Materials, Llc
1200 Urban Center Dr
Vestavia AL 35242
205 298-3000

(P-389)
VULCAN MATERIALS COMPANY
16005 E Foothill Blvd, Irwindale
(91702-2813)
PHONE..................................626 334-4913
Mitchell Clark, *Manager*
Luis A Guzman, *Plant Supt*
Rosemary Luna, *Sales Staff*
EMP: 13 **Publicly Held**
SIC: 1442 Construction sand & gravel
PA: Vulcan Materials Company
1200 Urban Center Dr
Vestavia AL 35242

(P-390)
WAYNE J SAND & GRAVEL INC
9455 Buena Vista St, Moorpark (93021)
PHONE..................................805 529-1323
Brett Jones, *President*

EMP: 14
SALES (est): 1.7MM **Privately Held**
SIC: 1442 Construction sand mining; gravel mining

(P-391)
WEST COAST AGGREGATE SUPPLY
Also Called: Aggregate West Coast
92500 Airport Blvd, Thermal (92274)
P.O. Box 790 (92274-0790)
PHONE..................................760 342-7598
Marvin Struiksma, *President*
EMP: 50
SALES (est): 5.4MM **Privately Held**
SIC: 1442 Common sand mining

(P-392)
WEST COAST SAND GRAVEL
7715 Avenue 296, Visalia (93291-9540)
PHONE..................................559 625-9426
Dan Reynebeld, *CEO*
EMP: 20
SALES (est): 1.8MM **Privately Held**
SIC: 1442 Construction sand & gravel

(P-393)
WM J CLARK TRUCKING SVC INC
Also Called: Arroyo Seco Rock
319 Division St, King City (93930-3005)
P.O. Box 682 (93930-0682)
PHONE..................................831 385-4000
Sonama Clark, *President*
Sonoma Clark, *President*
William Clark, *Treasurer*
Emmy Clark, *Admin Sec*
EMP: 13
SQ FT: 800
SALES (est): 1.3MM **Privately Held**
SIC: 1442 4212 Construction sand & gravel; local trucking, without storage

---

1446 Industrial Sand

(P-394)
BCJ SAND AND ROCK INC
3388 Regional Pkwy Ste A, Santa Rosa
(95403-8219)
P.O. Box 440, Fulton (95439-0440)
PHONE..................................707 544-0303
J Brad Slender, *President*
EMP: 16
SALES (est): 2.8MM **Privately Held**
SIC: 1446 Industrial sand

(P-395)
COVIA HOLDINGS CORPORATION
1300 Camino Diablo Rd, Byron (94514)
P.O. Box 216 (94514-0216)
PHONE..................................925 634-3575
Massoud Keshari, *Manager*
EMP: 30
SALES (corp-wide): 136.2MM **Publicly Held**
WEB: www.unimin.com
SIC: 1446 Silica mining
HQ: Covia Holdings Corporation
3 Summit Park Dr Ste 700
Independence OH 44131
800 255-7263

(P-396)
PIONEER SANDS LLC
9952 Enos Ln, Bakersfield (93314)
PHONE..................................661 746-5789
Donna Bartlett, *Branch Mgr*
EMP: 22
SALES (corp-wide): 5.4B **Publicly Held**
SIC: 1446 Silica mining
HQ: Pioneer Sands Llc
5205 N O Connor Blvd # 200
Irving TX 75039
972 444-9001

(P-397)
PIONEER SANDS LLC
31302 Ortega Hwy, San Juan Capistrano
(92675)
PHONE..................................949 728-0171
Mike Miclette, *Branch Mgr*
EMP: 53

▲ = Import ▼ =Export
◆ =Import/Export

SALES (corp-wide): 5.4B **Publicly Held**
SIC: **1446** Silica sand mining
HQ: Pioneer Sands Llc
5205 N O Connor Blvd # 200
Irving TX 75039
972 444-9001

(P-398)
PW GILLIBRAND CO INC
4537 Ish Dr, Simi Valley (93063-7667)
P.O. Box 1019 (93062-1019)
PHONE.....................................805 526-2195
Celine Gillibrand, *CEO*
Richard Valencia, *President*
Jim Costello, *Corp Secy*
EMP: 75
SQ FT: 11,000
SALES (est): 30MM **Privately Held**
WEB: www.pwgcoinc.com
SIC: **1446** Grinding sand mining; foundry
sand mining

1455 Kaolin & Ball Clay

(P-399)
IMERYS CLAYS INC
2500 Miguelito Rd, Lompoc (93436-9743)
PHONE.....................................805 737-2445
Chris Leu, *Manager*
Rose Wood, *Manager*
EMP: 10
SALES (corp-wide): 2.6MM **Privately
Held**
SIC: **1455** Kaolin mining
HQ: Imerys Clays, Inc.
100 Mansell Ct E Ste 300
Roswell GA 30076
770 594-0660

1459 Clay, Ceramic & Refractory Minerals, NEC

(P-400)
BLUE SKY HOME & ACC INC
1360 E Locust St, Ontario (91761-4567)
PHONE.....................................909 930-6200
Henry Wang, *Controller*
▲ EMP: 25
SALES (est): 1.6MM **Privately Held**
SIC: **1459** Clay & related minerals

(P-401)
ELEMENTIS SPECIALTIES INC
31763 Mountain View Rd, Newberry
Springs (92365-9763)
PHONE.....................................760 257-9112
Mike McGath, *Manager*
Angela Harrell, *Manager*
EMP: 39
SALES (corp-wide): 782.7MM **Privately
Held**
WEB: www.elementis-specialties.com
SIC: **1459** Clays, except kaolin & ball
HQ: Elementis Specialties, Inc.
469 Old Trenton Rd
East Windsor NJ 08512
609 443-2000

1479 Chemical & Fertilizer Mining

(P-402)
MORTON SALT INC
1050 Pier F Ave, Long Beach
(90802-6215)
P.O. Box 2289 (90801-2289)
PHONE.....................................562 437-0071
Ken Dobson, *Branch Mgr*
EMP: 14
SALES (corp-wide): 4.2B **Privately Held**
SIC: **1479** Salt & sulfur mining
HQ: Morton Salt, Inc.
444 W Lake St Ste 3000
Chicago IL 60606

(P-403)
**SEARLES VALLEY MINERALS
INC**
80201 Trona Rd, Trona (93562)
PHONE.....................................760 372-2259
Burnell Blanchard, *Vice Pres*
EMP: 600
SALES (corp-wide): 703.3MM **Privately
Held**
SIC: **1479** Salt & sulfur mining
HQ: Searles Valley Minerals Inc.
9401 Indn Crk Pkwy # 1000
Overland Park KS 66210
913 344-9500

1481 Nonmetallic Minerals Svcs, Except Fuels

(P-404)
DEMETRIUS POHL
2179 W 20th St, Los Angeles (90018-1407)
PHONE.....................................323 735-1027
Demetrius Pohl, *Owner*
Cris Carlson, *Director*
EMP: 12
SALES (est): 398.1K **Privately Held**
SIC: **1481** Nonmetallic mineral services

(P-405)
**IMERYS MINERALS CALIFORNIA
INC**
Also Called: Imerys Filtration Minerals
2500 Miguelito Canyon Rd, Lompoc
(93436)
PHONE.....................................805 736-1221
Kenneth Schweibert, *Manager*
EMP: 346
SALES (corp-wide): 2.6MM **Privately
Held**
SIC: **1481** **3295** Nonmetallic mineral serv-
ices; minerals, ground or treated
HQ: Imerys Minerals California, Inc.
2500 San Miguelito Rd
Lompoc CA 93436

(P-406)
**LIMITED ACCESS UNLIMITED
INC**
Also Called: Pacific Drilling
5220 Anna Ave Ste A, San Diego
(92110-4019)
PHONE.....................................619 294-3682
Todd Clark, *President*
Craig Roberts, *Vice Pres*
EMP: 10
SALES (est): 790K **Privately Held**
WEB: www.pacdrill.com
SIC: **1481** Mine development, nonmetallic
minerals

(P-407)
MP MINE OPERATIONS LLC
67750 Bailey Rd, Mountain Pass (92366)
PHONE.....................................702 277-0848
Michael Rosethal, *Mng Member*
James H Litinsky,
EMP: 108
SALES (est): 220.2K **Privately Held**
SIC: **1481** Mine exploration, nonmetallic
minerals

1499 Miscellaneous Nonmetallic Mining

(P-408)
CELITE CORPORATION
2500 San Miguelito Rd, Lompoc
(93436-9743)
PHONE.....................................805 736-1221
EMP: 10
SALES (est): 845K **Privately Held**
SIC: **1499** Miscellaneous nonmetallic min-
erals

(P-409)
**DAKOTAHOUSE INDUSTRIES
INC**
5262 Cartwright Ave Apt 4, North Hollywood
(91601-5437)
PHONE.....................................310 596-1100

Joshua Gbelawoe, *Principal*
EMP: 12
SALES (est): 514.7K **Privately Held**
SIC: **1499** **6082** **1041** Diamond mining,
industrial; foreign trade & international
banking institutions; open pit gold mining

(P-410)
DICAPERL CORPORATION (DH)
Also Called: Grefco Dicaperl
23705 Crenshaw Blvd, Torrance
(90505-5236)
PHONE.....................................610 667-6640
Ray Perelman, *CEO*
Glenn Jones, *President*
Mike Cull, *Treasurer*
Barry Katz, *Senior VP*
▼ EMP: 90
SQ FT: 5,000
SALES (est): 9.5MM **Privately Held**
SIC: **1499** **3677** Perlite mining; filtration
devices, electronic
HQ: Grefco Minerals Inc.
1 Bala Ave Ste 310
Bala Cynwyd PA 19004
610 660-8820

(P-411)
FEATHEROCK INC (PA)
20219 Bahama St, Chatsworth
(91311-6204)
PHONE.....................................818 882-3888
Eric Anderson, *President*
Bob Campagna, *Controller*
Olivia Nicholson, *Sales Staff*
EMP: 15
SQ FT: 20,000
SALES (est): 1.7MM **Privately Held**
SIC: **1499** Pumice mining

(P-412)
GLOBAL PUMICE LLC
19968 Bear Valley Rd C, Apple Valley
(92308-5105)
P.O. Box 174 (92307-0003)
PHONE.....................................760 240-3544
Thomas Hrubik,
EMP: 11
SALES: 1.5MM **Privately Held**
SIC: **1499** Pumice mining

(P-413)
H LIMA COMPANY INC
704 E Yosemite Ave, Manteca
(95336-5827)
PHONE.....................................209 239-6787
Michael Lima, *President*
Frank Lima, *Owner*
Debbie Enos, *Corp Secy*
Henry Frank Lima Jr, *Vice Pres*
Mark Lima, *Vice Pres*
EMP: 26
SQ FT: 1,300
SALES (est): 5.6MM **Privately Held**
SIC: **1499** Gypsum mining

(P-414)
IMERYS FILTRATION MINERALS
71 Daggett Dr, San Jose (95134-2109)
PHONE.....................................408 643-0092
EMP: 10
SALES (est): 722.1K **Privately Held**
SIC: **1499** Miscellaneous nonmetallic min-
erals

(P-415)
**IMERYS FILTRATION MINERALS
INC (DH)**
1732 N 1st St Ste 450, San Jose
(95112-4579)
PHONE.....................................805 562-0200
Douglas A Smith, *CEO*
John Oskan, *President*
Fred Weber, *Treasurer*
Paul Woodberry, *Vice Ch Bd*
Bob Wood, *Administration*
◆ EMP: 50
SQ FT: 11,600
SALES (est): 1.2B
SALES (corp-wide): 2.6MM **Privately
Held**
SIC: **1499** Diatomaceous earth mining
HQ: Imerys Usa, Inc.
100 Mansell Ct E Ste 300
Roswell GA 30076
770 645-3300

(P-416)
**IMERYS MINERALS CALIFORNIA
INC (DH)**
2500 San Miguelito Rd, Lompoc
(93436-9743)
P.O. Box 519 (93438-0519)
PHONE.....................................805 736-1221
Douglas A Smith, *President*
John Oskam, *CEO*
John Leichty, *CFO*
Bruno Van Herpen, *Vice Pres*
Bill Kinman, *Administration*
▼ EMP: 70
SQ FT: 11,600
SALES (est): 1B
SALES (corp-wide): 2.6MM **Privately
Held**
SIC: **1499** **3295** Diatomaceous earth min-
ing; minerals, ground or treated

(P-417)
MONARCHY DIAMOND INC
550 S Hill St Ste 1088, Los Angeles
(90013-2417)
PHONE.....................................213 924-1161
Rajnikumar Patel, *President*
EMP: 425
SALES (est): 12.3MM **Privately Held**
SIC: **1499** Gem stones (natural) mining

(P-418)
ORGANICSORB LLC
Also Called: Save-Sorb
630 S Los Angeles St, Los Angeles
(90014-2178)
PHONE.....................................310 795-4011
Chase Ahders,
Elma Salari, *CFO*
Ronnie Ebanks,
Brie Gennusa,
Fatina Johnston,
EMP: 15
SALES (est): 1.2MM **Privately Held**
SIC: **1499** Miscellaneous nonmetallic min-
erals

(P-419)
**UNITED STATES PUMICE
COMPANY (PA)**
Also Called: Featherrock
20219 Bahama St, Chatsworth
(91311-6287)
PHONE.....................................818 882-0300
Eric L Anderson, *President*
Robert Campagna, *CFO*
▲ EMP: 12 EST: 1942
SQ FT: 2,000
SALES (est): 4.1MM **Privately Held**
WEB: www.uspumice.com
SIC: **1499** **3291** Pumice mining; abrasive
buffs, bricks, cloth, paper, stones, etc.

2011 Meat Packing Plants

(P-420)
ASIA FOOD INC
566 Monterey Pass Rd, Monterey Park
(91754-2417)
PHONE.....................................626 284-1328
Bingham Lee, *CEO*
Chui Lee, *President*
Lee Bingham, *Manager*
EMP: 15
SQ FT: 15,000
SALES (est): 2.5MM **Privately Held**
SIC: **2011** **2032** **2092** **2037** Meat packing
plants; Chinese foods: packaged in cans,
jars, etc.; fresh or frozen packaged fish;
frozen fruits & vegetables; frozen special-
ties; fruit (fresh) packing services; veg-
etable packing services

(P-421)
BURNETT & SON MEAT CO INC
1420 S Myrtle Ave, Monrovia (91016-4153)
PHONE.....................................626 357-2165
Donald L Burnett, *President*
Lauren Garcia, *Manager*
▲ EMP: 80 EST: 1978
SQ FT: 20,000

SALES (est): 17.6MM **Privately Held**
WEB: www.burnettandson.com
SIC: **2011** Meat by-products from meat slaughtered on site; beef products from beef slaughtered on site

(P-422)
CALPERF INC
1810 Richard Ave, Santa Clara (95050-2818)
PHONE..............................408 829-7779
Saswata Bhattacharya, *President*
Lali Dasgupta, *Director*
EMP: 10
SALES: 3.8MM **Privately Held**
SIC: **2011** 5147 5144 Lamb products from lamb slaughtered on site; meats & meat products; poultry products

(P-423)
CARGILL MEAT SOLUTIONS CORP
2350 Academy Ave, Sanger (93657-9559)
PHONE..............................559 875-2232
Robert Case, *Branch Mgr*
EMP: 198
SALES (corp-wide): 51.2B **Privately Held**
SIC: **2011** Meat packing plants
HQ: Cargill Meat Solutions Corp
    151 N Main St Ste 900
    Wichita KS 67202
    316 291-2500

(P-424)
CARGILL MEAT SOLUTIONS CORP
Cargill Food Distribution
10602 N Trademark Pkwy # 500, Rancho Cucamonga (91730-5937)
PHONE..............................909 476-3120
Guy Milam, *General Mgr*
EMP: 42
SALES (corp-wide): 51.2B **Privately Held**
SIC: **2011** Meat by-products from meat slaughtered on site
HQ: Cargill Meat Solutions Corp
    151 N Main St Ste 900
    Wichita KS 67202
    316 291-2500

(P-425)
CARGILL MEAT SOLUTIONS CORP
3115 S Fig Ave, Fresno (93706-5647)
PHONE..............................559 268-5586
Tod Ventura, *Manager*
EMP: 200
SALES (corp-wide): 51.2B **Privately Held**
SIC: **2011** Beef products from beef slaughtered on site
HQ: Cargill Meat Solutions Corp
    151 N Main St Ste 900
    Wichita KS 67202
    316 291-2500

(P-426)
CENTRAL VALLEY MEAT CO INC
10431 8 3/4 Ave, Hanford (93230-9248)
PHONE..............................559 583-9624
Brian Coelho, *CEO*
Lawrence Coelho, *President*
Bruce Hunt, *CFO*
Steve Coelho, *Vice Pres*
Brain Cohen, *Vice Pres*
▲ EMP: 200
SQ FT: 30,000
SALES (est): 56MM **Privately Held**
WEB: www.centralvalleymeat.com
SIC: **2011** Meat packing plants

(P-427)
CERTIFIED MEAT PRODUCTS INC
4586 E Commerce Ave, Fresno (93725-2203)
P.O. Box 12051 (93776-2051)
PHONE..............................559 256-1433
Cassi Maxery, *CEO*
Matthew Lloyd, *Prdtn Mgr*
Rob Maxey, *Manager*
EMP: 45
SALES: 81.7MM **Privately Held**
WEB: www.certifiedmeatproducts.com
SIC: **2011** Meat packing plants

(P-428)
CLAUSEN MEAT COMPANY INC
19455 W Clausen Rd, Turlock (95380)
P.O. Box 1826 (95381-1826)
PHONE..............................209 667-8690
Ping Lau, *CEO*
Ying Hung Vinh, *CFO*
▲ EMP: 40
SQ FT: 15,000
SALES (est): 6.2MM **Privately Held**
SIC: **2011** Meat packing plants

(P-429)
CLOUGHERTY PACKING LLC (DH)
Also Called: Smithfield Foods
3049 E Vernon Ave, Vernon (90058-1800)
P.O. Box 58870, Los Angeles (90058-0870)
PHONE..............................323 583-4621
Kenneth J Baptist, *President*
Martin Chen, *Vice Pres*
Gary Jamison, *Vice Pres*
Lidwina Van Kooten, *Vice Pres*
Bob Vandygrift, *Executive*
EMP: 300
SQ FT: 1,000,000
SALES (est): 269MM **Privately Held**
WEB: www.farmerjohn.com
SIC: **2011** 2013 Meat packing plants; sausages & other prepared meats
HQ: Smithfield Foods, Inc.
    200 Commerce St
    Smithfield VA 23430
    757 365-3000

(P-430)
COLUMBUS FOODS LLC
30977 San Antonio St, Hayward (94544-7109)
PHONE..............................510 921-3400
Ralph Denisco, *CEO*
John Piccetti, *Ch of Bd*
Adam Ferrif, *CFO*
Thomas Dacquisto, *Analyst*
▲ EMP: 345
SALES (est): 63.5MM **Privately Held**
SIC: **2011** 5143 5147 Luncheon meat from meat slaughtered on site; cheese; meats & meat products

(P-431)
DON PEDROS MEAT
725 E Edna Pl, Covina (91723-1409)
PHONE..............................626 339-3963
Andres Jaramillo, *CEO*
EMP: 11
SALES (est): 1.3MM **Privately Held**
SIC: **2011** 5421 Meat packing plants; meat & fish markets

(P-432)
ELLENSBURG LAMB COMPANY INC
Also Called: Superior Packing Co
7390 Rio Dixon Rd, Dixon (95620-9665)
P.O. Box 940 (95620-0940)
PHONE..............................707 678-3091
Martin Ducken, *Manager*
EMP: 150 **Privately Held**
SIC: **2011** Meat packing plants
HQ: Ellensburg Lamb Company, Inc.
    2530 River Plaza Dr # 200
    Sacramento CA 95833

(P-433)
ELLENSBURG LAMB COMPANY INC (HQ)
Also Called: Superior Farms
2530 River Plaza Dr # 200, Sacramento (95833-3675)
PHONE..............................530 758-3091
Les Oestereich, *President*
Jeff Evanson, *CFO*
Gary Pfeiffer, *Exec VP*
Eric Tiller, *Vice Pres*
Rebecca Adkins, *Executive*
▼ EMP: 18
SQ FT: 7,500
SALES (est): 31.5MM **Privately Held**
SIC: **2011** Lamb products from lamb slaughtered on site

(P-434)
FIRSTCLASS FOODS - TROJAN INC
Also Called: First Class Foods
12500 Inglewood Ave, Hawthorne (90250-4217)
P.O. Box 2397 (90251-2397)
PHONE..............................310 676-2500
Salomon Benzimra, *President*
Lucy Benzimra, *CFO*
Albert Benzimra, *Corp Secy*
Felix Benzimra, *VP Sales*
EMP: 135
SQ FT: 45,000
SALES (est): 23.6MM **Publicly Held**
WEB: www.firstclassfoods.com
SIC: **2011** 5147 Meat packing plants; meats & meat products
HQ: Us Foods, Inc.
    9399 W Higgins Rd Ste 500
    Rosemont IL 60018

(P-435)
FLANAGAN-GORHAM INC (PA)
Also Called: Real Meat Company, The
2029 Verdugo Blvd Ste 311, Montrose (91020-1626)
PHONE..............................818 279-2473
EMP: 12
SALES (est): 2.9MM **Privately Held**
SIC: **2011** Canned meats (except baby food), meat slaughtered on site

(P-436)
GAYLORDS H R I MEATS INC
Also Called: Gaylord's Meat Co
1100 E Ash Ave Ste C, Fullerton (92831-5004)
PHONE..............................714 526-2278
Michael Smith, *Ch of Bd*
Vance Dixon, *President*
EMP: 18 EST: 1975
SQ FT: 10,000
SALES (est): 1.5MM **Privately Held**
SIC: **2011** 5147 5144 Meat packing plants; meats & meat products; poultry & poultry products

(P-437)
GOLDEN VALLEY INDUSTRIES INC
960 Lone Palm Ave, Modesto (95351-1533)
PHONE..............................209 939-3370
Mike Sullivan, *President*
EMP: 40
SQ FT: 40,000
SALES (est): 10.8MM **Privately Held**
WEB: www.goldenvalleyindustries.com
SIC: **2011** Meat packing plants

(P-438)
GOLDEN WEST FOOD GROUP INC (PA)
4401 S Downey Rd, Vernon (90058-2518)
PHONE..............................888 807-3663
Erik Litmanovich, *CEO*
EMP: 36 EST: 2011
SALES (est): 18.8MM **Privately Held**
SIC: **2011** 2013 2015 Meat packing plants; sausages & other prepared meats; poultry, slaughtered & dressed

(P-439)
HARRIS RANCH BEEF COMPANY
16277 S Mccall Ave, Selma (93662-9458)
P.O. Box 220 (93662-0220)
PHONE..............................559 896-3081
John Harris, *Ch of Bd*
Robert Kettle, *CFO*
Randy Dehart, *Info Tech Mgr*
Lindsey Rinard, *Sales Staff*
William Shafer, *Manager*
▼ EMP: 700
SALES (est): 146.1MM
SALES (corp-wide): 4.5B **Privately Held**
WEB: www.harrisranchbeef.com
SIC: **2011** 2013 Meat packing plants; sausages & other prepared meats
PA: Harris Farms, Inc.
    29475 Fresno Coalinga Rd
    Coalinga CA 93210
    559 884-2435

(P-440)
JOBBERS MEAT PACKING CO INC
3336 Fruitland Ave, Vernon (90058-3714)
P.O. Box 58368, Los Angeles (90058-0368)
PHONE..............................323 585-6328
Martin Evanson, *CEO*
Steig Osberg, *Vice Pres*
EMP: 12 EST: 1978
SQ FT: 19,000
SALES (est): 4MM **Privately Held**
WEB: www.jobbersmeat.com
SIC: **2011** Beef products from beef slaughtered on site

(P-441)
K & M PACKING CO INC
Also Called: K & M Meat Co
2443 E 27th St, Vernon (90058-1219)
PHONE..............................323 585-5318
Felix Goldberg, *President*
Roz White, *Executive*
EMP: 150
SQ FT: 30,000
SALES (est): 18.1MM **Privately Held**
SIC: **2011** Meat packing plants

(P-442)
LOS BANOS ABATTOIR CO INC
1312 W Pacheco Blvd, Los Banos (93635-7807)
P.O. Box 949 (93635-0949)
PHONE..............................209 826-2212
Steven La Salvia, *President*
Laura La Salvia, *Vice Pres*
EMP: 35
SQ FT: 7,500
SALES (est): 5.9MM **Privately Held**
SIC: **2011** 5147 Beef products from beef slaughtered on site; veal from meat slaughtered on site; meats & meat products

(P-443)
MANNINGS BEEF LLC
9531 Beverly Rd, Pico Rivera (90660-2134)
P.O. Box 1156 (90660-1156)
PHONE..............................562 908-1089
Anthony Di Maria, *Mng Member*
Andrew D Broberg,
Lloyd Manning,
EMP: 79
SQ FT: 75,000
SALES (est): 16.1MM **Privately Held**
SIC: **2011** Meat packing plants

(P-444)
MOHAWK LAND & CATTLE CO INC
1660 Old Bayshore Hwy, San Jose (95112-4304)
P.O. Box 601 (95106-0601)
PHONE..............................408 436-1800
Steve Tognoli, *President*
▼ EMP: 64 EST: 1957
SQ FT: 50,000
SALES (est): 6.3MM **Privately Held**
SIC: **2011** Meat packing plants
HQ: Smithfield Packaged Meats Corp.
    805 E Kemper Rd
    Cincinnati OH 45246
    513 782-3800

(P-445)
NAGLES VEAL INC
1411 E Base Line St, San Bernardino (92410-4113)
PHONE..............................909 383-7075
Michael Lemler, *President*
Timothy Haggard, *General Mgr*
Cathy Martin,
▲ EMP: 50
SQ FT: 12,500
SALES (est): 8.1MM **Privately Held**
SIC: **2011** Veal from meat slaughtered on site; beef products from beef slaughtered on site; lamb products from lamb slaughtered on site

(P-446)
OLLI SALUMERIA AMERICANA LLC
1301 Rocky Point Dr, Oceanside
(92056-5864)
PHONE..........................804 427-7866
Oliviero Colmignoli,
Marco Terenghi, *Officer*
EMP: 15
SALES (corp-wide): 3.9MM **Privately Held**
SIC: 2011 Meat packing plants
PA: Olli Salumeria Americana, Llc
8505 Bell Creek Rd Ste H
Mechanicsville VA 23116
804 427-7866

(P-447)
R B R MEAT COMPANY INC
Also Called: Rightway
5151 Alcoa Ave, Vernon (90058-3715)
P.O. Box 58225, Los Angeles (90058-0225)
PHONE..........................323 973-4868
Irwin Miller, *President*
Larry Vanden Bos, *Vice Pres*
James Craig, *Vice Pres*
EMP: 75 EST: 1951
SQ FT: 65,000
SALES (est): 12MM **Privately Held**
SIC: 2011 Meat packing plants

(P-448)
RALPHS RANCHES
Also Called: Prather Ranch
1833 W Ball Mountain Rd, Macdoel
(96058)
PHONE..........................530 398-4182
Chris Lawson, *Branch Mgr*
EMP: 10
SALES (corp-wide): 4MM **Privately Held**
WEB: www.pratherranch.com
SIC: 2011 Beef products from beef slaughtered on site
PA: Ralphs Ranches
2338 Ball Mountain Rd
Macdoel CA 96058
530 336-6667

(P-449)
RAMAR INTERNATIONAL CORP
Also Called: Orientex
539 Garcia Ave Ste E, Pittsburg
(94565-7403)
PHONE..........................925 432-4267
Tito Sanchez, *Manager*
Rainee Bautest, *Manager*
EMP: 30
SALES (corp-wide): 28.2MM **Privately Held**
SIC: 2011 Sausages from meat slaughtered on site
PA: Ramar International Corp
1101 Railroad Ave
Pittsburg CA 94565
925 439-9009

(P-450)
RICHWOOD MEAT COMPANY INC
2751 N Santa Fe Ave, Merced
(95348-4109)
P.O. Box 2599 (95344-0599)
PHONE..........................209 722-8171
Michael J Wood, *President*
Carol J Wood, *Shareholder*
Diane Fragie, *CFO*
Hellen Diane Inks-Fragie, *CFO*
Steve Wood, *Vice Pres*
EMP: 100
SQ FT: 43,000
SALES: 61.8MM **Privately Held**
WEB: www.richwoodmeat.com
SIC: 2011 5147 5421 Meat packing plants; meats, fresh; meats, cured or smoked; meat & fish markets

(P-451)
SMITHFIELD PACKAGED MEATS CORP
Mohawk Packing
1660 Old Bayshore Hwy, San Jose
(95112-4304)
PHONE..........................408 392-0442
Kevin Connor, *Manager*
Cameron McKinney, *Engineer*
Pablo Pineda, *Human Res Mgr*
Larry Scicluna, *Safety Mgr*
Chuck Carlson, *Manager*
EMP: 130
SQ FT: 32,942 **Privately Held**
WEB: www.johnmorrell.com
SIC: 2011 Meat packing plants
HQ: Smithfield Packaged Meats Corp.
805 E Kemper Rd
Cincinnati OH 45246
513 782-3800

(P-452)
TRANSHUMANCE HOLDING CO INC
Also Called: Superior Farms
7390 Rio Dixon Rd, Dixon (95620-9665)
P.O. Box 940 (95620-0940)
PHONE..........................707 693-2303
Julie Angel, *Manager*
Dave Lipsitt, *Technical Staff*
Greg Ahart, *Plant Mgr*
Sebastian Postel, *Sales Staff*
Ray Bodine, *Director*
EMP: 200 **Privately Held**
WEB: www.superiorfarms.com
SIC: 2011 Lamb products from lamb slaughtered on site
PA: Transhumance Holding Company, Inc.
2530 River Plaza Dr # 200
Sacramento CA 95833

(P-453)
TYSON FRESH MEATS INC
Also Called: I B P Inc
500 S Kraemer Blvd # 380, Brea
(92821-6728)
PHONE..........................714 528-5543
Brian Holeman, *Manager*
EMP: 15
SALES (corp-wide): 40B **Publicly Held**
SIC: 2011 Meat packing plants
HQ: Tyson Fresh Meats, Inc.
800 Stevens Port Dr
Dakota Dunes SD 57049
605 235-2061

(P-454)
V J PROVISION INC
Also Called: Jacobellis
410 S Varney St, Burbank (91502-2124)
PHONE..........................818 843-3945
Sam Jacobellis, *President*
George Jacobellis, *Treasurer*
Vito Jacobellis, *Vice Pres*
Tony Jacobellis, *Admin Sec*
EMP: 18
SQ FT: 11,300
SALES: 5MM **Privately Held**
WEB: www.jacobellis.com
SIC: 2011 Meat packing plants

(P-455)
VENUS FOODS INC
770 S Stimson Ave, City of Industry
(91745-1638)
PHONE..........................626 369-5188
Gin Shen Wu, *Ch of Bd*
Robert Y Tsai, *President*
Shih-Ai Meng, *Treasurer*
Stanley Chow, *Vice Pres*
T K Chow, *Vice Pres*
▲ EMP: 20 EST: 1980
SQ FT: 20,000
SALES (est): 3.7MM **Privately Held**
WEB: www.venusfoods.com
SIC: 2011 2099 Meat packing plants; food preparations

(P-456)
VIZ CATTLE CORPORATION
Also Called: Sukarne
17890 Castleton St # 350, City of Industry
(91748-5793)
PHONE..........................310 884-5260
Edwin Botero, *President*
Aofonso Marco, *CFO*
Arturo Villarrel, *Vice Pres*
Anna Vizcarra, *Vice Pres*
▲ EMP: 24
SALES: 700MM **Privately Held**
SIC: 2011 5154 Meat packing plants; cattle

PA: Grupo Viz, S.A. De C.V.
Av. Diana Tang No. 59-A
Culiacan SIN. 80300

(P-457)
WEST LAKE FOOD CORPORATION
Also Called: Tay Ho
2430 Cape Cod Way, Santa Ana
(92703-3540)
PHONE..........................714 973-2286
Chieu Nguyen, *CEO*
Chuong Nguyen, *Vice Pres*
Jayce Yenson, *Admin Sec*
◆ EMP: 75
SQ FT: 11,238
SALES: 12MM **Privately Held**
SIC: 2011 Meat packing plants

(P-458)
WHOLESOME HARVEST BAKING INC
Also Called: Maple Consumer Foods
7840 Madison Ave Ste 135, Fair Oaks
(95628-3591)
PHONE..........................916 967-1633
EMP: 10
SALES (corp-wide): 4.2B **Privately Held**
SIC: 2011
HQ: Wholesome Harvest Baking, Inc.
1011 E Touhy Ave Ste 500
Des Plaines IL 60631
847 655-8100

(P-459)
YOSEMITE VLY BEEF PKG CO INC
970 E Sandy Mush Rd, Merced
(95341-7903)
P.O. Box 1828, Duarte (91009-4828)
PHONE..........................626 435-0170
Michael Ban, *President*
E K Ban, *Controller*
Wesley Jones, *QC Mgr*
Ek Ban, *Manager*
EMP: 28
SQ FT: 5,000
SALES (est): 4.8MM **Privately Held**
SIC: 2011 Meat packing plants

2013 Sausages & Meat Prdts

(P-460)
AI FOODS CORPORATION
1700 N Soto St, Los Angeles (90033-1127)
PHONE..........................323 222-0827
Clarissa Takakawa, *CEO*
▲ EMP: 25
SALES (est): 4.2MM **Privately Held**
SIC: 2013 Sausages & other prepared meats

(P-461)
AIDELLS SAUSAGE COMPANY INC
2411 Baumann Ave, San Lorenzo
(94580-1801)
PHONE..........................510 614-5450
Ernie Gabiati, *President*
EMP: 900
SQ FT: 15,000
SALES (est): 186.3MM
SALES (corp-wide): 40B **Publicly Held**
WEB: www.aidells.com
SIC: 2013 5147 Sausages from purchased meat; meats & meat products
HQ: The Hillshire Brands Company
400 S Jefferson St Fl 1
Chicago IL 60607
312 614-6000

(P-462)
ALPENA SAUSAGE INC
5329 Craner Ave, North Hollywood
(91601-3313)
PHONE..........................818 505-9482
Frederick Thaller, *President*
EMP: 15
SQ FT: 6,000
SALES: 2.5MM **Privately Held**
SIC: 2013 Sausages from purchased meat

(P-463)
ALPINE MEATS INC
9850 Lower Sacramento Rd, Stockton
(95210-3915)
PHONE..........................209 477-2691
Rick Martin, *CEO*
William Kraljev, *Controller*
Robby Jaynes, *Manager*
EMP: 50
SALES (est): 8.1MM **Privately Held**
SIC: 2013 Smoked meats from purchased meat

(P-464)
AMERICAN CUSTOM MEATS LLC
4276 N Tracy Blvd, Tracy (95304-1501)
PHONE..........................209 839-8800
Neil Kinney, *President*
EMP: 88
SQ FT: 75,000
SALES: 39.3MM **Privately Held**
SIC: 2013 2015 2032 Prepared beef products from purchased beef; roast beef from purchased meat; prepared pork products from purchased pork; poultry slaughtering & processing; puddings, except meat: packaged in cans, jars, etc.

(P-465)
ARMONA FROZEN FOOD LOCKERS
Also Called: Raven's Deli
10870 14th Ave, Armona (93202)
P.O. Box 367 (93202-0367)
PHONE..........................559 584-3948
William M Raven, *Owner*
Marlene Raven, *Co-Owner*
EMP: 10
SQ FT: 13,000
SALES (est): 884.8K **Privately Held**
SIC: 2013 5411 5421 Beef, dried: from purchased meat; delicatessens; meat markets, including freezer provisioners

(P-466)
BAR-S FOODS CO
392 Railroad Ct, Milpitas (95035-4339)
PHONE..........................408 941-9958
Olga Vasquez, *Manager*
EMP: 346 **Privately Held**
SIC: 2013 Sausages & other prepared meats
HQ: Bar-S Foods Co.
5090 N 40th St Ste 300
Phoenix AZ 85018
602 264-7272

(P-467)
BAR-S FOODS CO
Also Called: Bar-S Foods Co. Los Angeles
4919 Alcoa Ave, Vernon (90058-3022)
PHONE..........................323 589-3600
EMP: 290 **Privately Held**
SIC: 2013 Sausages & other prepared meats
HQ: Bar-S Foods Co.
5090 N 40th St Ste 300
Phoenix AZ 85018
602 264-7272

(P-468)
BOYD SPECIALTIES LLC
1016 E Cooley Dr Ste N, Colton
(92324-3962)
PHONE..........................909 219-5120
Jae Boyd, *President*
Sue Boyd, *Manager*
▲ EMP: 52
SQ FT: 10,000
SALES: 6MM **Privately Held**
WEB: www.carnivorecandy.com
SIC: 2013 Snack sticks, including jerky: from purchased meat

(P-469)
BUMBLE BEE HOLDINGS INC (HQ)
280 10th Ave, San Diego (92101-7406)
P.O. Box 85362 (92186-5362)
PHONE..........................858 715-4000
Robert P Kirby, *Ch of Bd*
Richard J Sosnoski, *CFO*
David J Carmany, *Treasurer*
Peter D Lemahieu, *Senior VP*

Scott Cameron, *Vice Pres*
◆ **EMP:** 420 **EST:** 1926
SQ FT: 275,000
SALES (est): 177.1MM **Privately Held**
WEB: www.castleberrys.com
SIC: 2013 2032 2033 Beef stew from purchased meat; canned meats (except baby food) from purchased meat; frozen meats from purchased meat; chili with or without meat: packaged in cans, jars, etc.; vegetables & vegetable products in cans, jars, etc.

(P-470)
BUSSETO FOODS INC
1090 W Church Ave, Fresno (93706-3917)
PHONE 559 237-9591
G Grazier, *President*
EMP: 69
SALES (corp-wide): 39.2MM **Privately Held**
SIC: 2013 Sausages from purchased meat
PA: Busseto Foods, Inc.
  1351 N Crystal Ave
  Fresno CA 93728
  559 485-9882

(P-471)
BUSSETO FOODS INC (PA)
1351 N Crystal Ave, Fresno (93728-1142)
P.O. Box 12403 (93777-2403)
PHONE 559 485-9882
G Michael Grazier, *President*
Randy Hergenroeder, *CFO*
Ed Fanucchi, *Admin Sec*
▲ **EMP:** 155
SQ FT: 40,000
SALES (est): 39.2MM **Privately Held**
WEB: www.busseto.com
SIC: 2013 Sausages from purchased meat

(P-472)
C R W DISTRIBUTORS INC
1223 Wilshire Blvd, Santa Monica (90403-5406)
PHONE 310 463-4577
Brian Wrye, *President*
EMP: 21
SQ FT: 7,000
SALES: 2.7MM **Privately Held**
SIC: 2013 Prepared beef products from purchased beef

(P-473)
CATTANEO BROS INC
769 Caudill St, San Luis Obispo (93401-5729)
PHONE 805 543-7188
Mike Kaney, *President*
Jayne Kaney, *Corp Secy*
William Cattaneo Sr, *Founder*
Ken Castro, *Opers Staff*
Katelyn Kaney, *Marketing Staff*
EMP: 20
SQ FT: 5,500
SALES: 1.2MM **Privately Held**
WEB: www.cattaneobros.com
SIC: 2013 5961 Beef, dried: from purchased meat; sausages from purchased meat; food, mail order

(P-474)
CHOICE FOOD PRODUCTS INC
Also Called: Saladino Sausage Company
1822 W Hedges Ave, Fresno (93728-1140)
PHONE 559 266-1674
Ty Kenny, *President*
Ty Kinney, *President*
Marlese Kinney, *Treasurer*
EMP: 15
SQ FT: 3,048
SALES (est): 2.2MM **Privately Held**
WEB: www.saladinosausage.com
SIC: 2013 Sausages & other prepared meats

(P-475)
CLOUGHERTY PACKING LLC
3922 Avenue 120, Corcoran (93212-9532)
P.O. Box 247 (93212-0247)
PHONE 559 992-8421
Don Davidson, *Manager*
EMP: 10 **Privately Held**
WEB: www.farmerjohn.com
SIC: 2013 Sausages & other prepared meats

HQ: Clougherty Packing, Llc
  3049 E Vernon Ave
  Vernon CA 90058
  323 583-4621

(P-476)
COLUMBUS MANUFACTURING INC (HQ)
30977 San Antonio St, Hayward (94544-7109)
PHONE 510 921-3423
Joe Ennen, *CEO*
Randy Sieve, *CFO*
▲ **EMP:** 100
SQ FT: 121,000
SALES (est): 79.8MM
SALES (corp-wide): 9.1B **Publicly Held**
SIC: 2013 Sausages & related products, from purchased meat; roast beef from purchased meat
PA: Hormel Foods Corporation
  1 Hormel Pl
  Austin MN 55912
  507 437-5611

(P-477)
CORRALITOS MARKET & SAUSAGE CO
569 Corralitos Rd, Watsonville (95076-0596)
PHONE 831 722-2633
Dave Peterson, *President*
Ken Wong, *Vice Pres*
Jo Ellen Tartala, *Admin Sec*
EMP: 19
SQ FT: 5,000
SALES (est): 2.8MM **Privately Held**
SIC: 2013 5411 Sausages & other prepared meats; grocery stores

(P-478)
COURAGE PRODUCTION LLC
2475 Courage Dr, Fairfield (94533-6723)
PHONE 707 422-6300
Philip Gatto, *Mng Member*
Randy Rohrback, *QC Mgr*
EMP: 100
SALES (est): 23.1MM **Privately Held**
SIC: 2013 Sausages from purchased meat

(P-479)
DEMES GOURMET CORPORATION
Also Called: Master Link Sausage
327 N State College Blvd, Fullerton (92831-4205)
PHONE 714 870-6040
Randy Martin, *President*
Mary Martin, *Vice Pres*
EMP: 22
SQ FT: 17,600
SALES (est): 3.6MM **Privately Held**
SIC: 2013 Sausages & other prepared meats

(P-480)
DEREK AND CONSTANCE LEE CORP (PA)
Also Called: Great River Food
19355 San Jose Ave, City of Industry (91748-1420)
PHONE 909 595-8831
Derek E Lee, *President*
▲ **EMP:** 95
SQ FT: 50,000
SALES (est): 20.5MM **Privately Held**
SIC: 2013 1541 Sausages & other prepared meats; food products manufacturing or packing plant construction

(P-481)
E G MEAT AND PROVISION INC (PA)
4350 Alcoa Ave, Vernon (90058-2410)
PHONE 323 588-5333
Encarnacion Gutierrez, *CEO*
EMP: 14 **EST:** 2007
SALES (est): 2.5MM **Privately Held**
SIC: 2013 5146 Roast beef from purchased meat; pork, smoked: from purchased meat; fish & seafoods

(P-482)
ENJOY FOODS INTERNATIONAL
Also Called: Saab Enterprises
10601 Beech Ave, Fontana (92337-7204)
PHONE 909 823-2228
Waleed Saab, *Ch of Bd*
EMP: 40
SALES (est): 6.7MM **Privately Held**
WEB: www.enjoyfoods.com
SIC: 2013 Beef, dried: from purchased meat

(P-483)
EVERGOOD SAUSAGE CO
Also Called: Evergood Fine Foods
1932 Van Dyke Ave, San Francisco (94124)
PHONE 415 822-4660
Harlan Miller Sr, *President*
Donald Miller, *Vice Pres*
Harlan J Miller Jr, *Vice Pres*
Kathy Barnes, *Office Mgr*
Ron Delucchi, *Sales Mgr*
EMP: 98
SQ FT: 30,000
SALES (est): 17.7MM **Privately Held**
WEB: www.evergoodfoods.com
SIC: 2013 Sausages from purchased meat

(P-484)
FORMOSA MEAT COMPANY INC
Also Called: Universal Meat Company
10646 Fulton Ct, Rancho Cucamonga (91730-4848)
PHONE 909 987-0470
Cheng-Ting Shih, *Vice Pres*
Hsiu-O Kan, *Treasurer*
▲ **EMP:** 40
SQ FT: 23,000
SALES (est): 6.6MM **Privately Held**
SIC: 2013 Snack sticks, including jerky: from purchased meat

(P-485)
FRA MANI LLC
Also Called: Fra' Mani Handcrafted Salumi
1311 8th St, Berkeley (94710-1453)
PHONE 510 526-7000
Paul Bertolli, *General Ptnr*
Linda Bertolli, *Vice Pres*
Jasmine Smith, *Production*
Howard Nep, *Regl Sales Mgr*
Paula Smith, *Sales Mgr*
EMP: 12
SQ FT: 10,000
SALES (est): 2.7MM **Privately Held**
SIC: 2013 Sausages & related products, from purchased meat

(P-486)
FULLFILLMENT SYSTEMS INC
Also Called: D'Ambrosio Bros
1228 Reamwood Ave, Sunnyvale (94089-2225)
PHONE 408 745-7675
Pasquale Vitonti, *Manager*
Pasquale Bitonti, *Opers Mgr*
EMP: 75
SALES (corp-wide): 77.8MM **Privately Held**
WEB: www.nicolinosgardencafe.com
SIC: 2013 2011 Sausages from purchased meat; sausages from meat slaughtered on site
PA: Fullfillment Systems, Inc.
  1228 Reamwood Ave
  Sunnyvale CA 94089
  408 745-7675

(P-487)
GLENOAKS FOOD INC
11030 Randall St, Sun Valley (91352-2621)
PHONE 818 768-9091
John J Fallon III, *President*
Marvin Caeser, *Shareholder*
Katty Majailovic, *Shareholder*
Amy Hackett, *Manager*
EMP: 25
SQ FT: 30,000
SALES (est): 3.2MM **Privately Held**
WEB: www.glenoaksfood.com
SIC: 2013 2015 Beef, dried: from purchased meat; poultry slaughtering & processing

(P-488)
GOLDEN ISLAND JERKY CO INC (DH)
10646 Fulton Ct, Rancho Cucamonga (91730-4848)
PHONE 844 362-3222
Cheng Shih, *President*
▲ **EMP:** 31 **EST:** 2012
SALES (est): 10MM
SALES (corp-wide): 40B **Publicly Held**
SIC: 2013 Snack sticks, including jerky: from purchased meat
HQ: The Hillshire Brands Company
  400 S Jefferson St Fl 1
  Chicago IL 60607
  312 614-6000

(P-489)
GOLDEN ISLAND JERKY CO INC
9955 6th St, Rancho Cucamonga (91730-5752)
PHONE 844 362-3222
EMP: 11
SALES (corp-wide): 40B **Publicly Held**
SIC: 2013 Snack sticks, including jerky: from purchased meat
HQ: Golden Island Jerky Company, Inc.
  10646 Fulton Ct
  Rancho Cucamonga CA 91730
  844 362-3222

(P-490)
HAWA CORPORATION
Also Called: Beef Jerky Factory
125 E Laurel St, Colton (92324-2462)
PHONE 909 825-8882
Waleed Saab, *Vice Pres*
EMP: 20
SALES (est): 1.6MM **Privately Held**
SIC: 2013 Beef, dried: from purchased meat

(P-491)
HILLSHIRE BRANDS COMPANY
9357 Richmond Pl Ste 101, Rancho Cucamonga (91730-6032)
PHONE 909 481-0760
Jerry Newham, *Branch Mgr*
EMP: 322
SALES (corp-wide): 40B **Publicly Held**
SIC: 2013 2053 2051 Sausages & other prepared meats; frozen bakery products, except bread; bread, cake & related products
HQ: The Hillshire Brands Company
  400 S Jefferson St Fl 1
  Chicago IL 60607
  312 614-6000

(P-492)
HILLSHIRE BRANDS COMPANY
Also Called: Sara Lee
2411 Baumann Ave, San Lorenzo (94580-1801)
PHONE 510 276-1300
Alfred Yu, *Branch Mgr*
Linda Saxton, *MIS Mgr*
Peter Ni, *Engineer*
Patricia Jeffery, *Controller*
William Sereni, *Manager*
EMP: 400
SQ FT: 20,000
SALES (corp-wide): 40B **Publicly Held**
SIC: 2013 Sausages & other prepared meats
HQ: The Hillshire Brands Company
  400 S Jefferson St Fl 1
  Chicago IL 60607
  312 614-6000

(P-493)
HILLSHIRE BRANDS COMPANY
Also Called: Superior Coffee & Foods
10715 Springdale Ave # 5, Santa Fe Springs (90670-3858)
PHONE 562 903-9260
Kevin Mc Klavende, *Branch Mgr*
EMP: 50
SALES (corp-wide): 40B **Publicly Held**
SIC: 2013 Sausages & other prepared meats
HQ: The Hillshire Brands Company
  400 S Jefferson St Fl 1
  Chicago IL 60607
  312 614-6000

(P-494)
HORMEL FOODS CORP SVCS LLC
2 Venture Ste 250, Irvine (92618-7408)
PHONE..............................949 753-5350
Randy Kemmipz, *Manager*
Bill Landrigan, *Sales Staff*
Randal S Kemnitz, *Director*
Judy Alcala, *Manager*
Regan Schultz, *Manager*
EMP: 40
SALES (corp-wide): 9.1B **Publicly Held**
SIC: 2013 Canned meats (except baby food) from purchased meat; beef stew from purchased meat; corned beef from purchased meat; spreads, sandwich: meat from purchased meat
HQ: Hormel Foods Corporate Services, Llc
1 Hormel Pl
Austin MN 55912
507 437-5611

(P-495)
HSIN TUNG YANG FOODS COMPANY
Also Called: New Horizon
405 S Airport Blvd, South San Francisco (94080-6909)
PHONE..............................650 589-7689
Kaiyen MAI, *CEO*
Su Wuan MAI, *Ch of Bd*
▲ EMP: 11
SQ FT: 86,000
SALES (est): 2.2MM **Privately Held**
WEB: www.htyusa.com
SIC: 2013 5149 2051 Sausages & other prepared meats; canned goods: fruit, vegetables, seafood, meats, etc.; bread, cake & related products

(P-496)
JENSEN MEAT COMPANY INC
2550 Britannia Blvd # 101, San Diego (92154-7404)
PHONE..............................619 754-6400
Abel Olivera, *CEO*
Jeff Hamann, *Co-Owner*
Sam Acuna, *CFO*
EMP: 95
SQ FT: 25,000
SALES (est): 42.3MM **Privately Held**
SIC: 2013 Sausages & other prepared meats

(P-497)
JODY MARONIS ITALIAN
2011 Ocean Front Walk, Venice (90291-4118)
PHONE..............................310 822-5639
Jordan A Monkarsh, *President*
Richard Leivenberg, *Vice Pres*
EMP: 20
SQ FT: 2,200
SALES (est): 1.6MM **Privately Held**
SIC: 2013 5812 Sausages & other prepared meats; eating places

(P-498)
KADI ENTERPRISES INC
802 N Victory Blvd, Burbank (91502-1630)
P.O. Box 3148 (91508-3148)
PHONE..............................818 556-3400
Sami El Kadi, *President*
EMP: 11
SQ FT: 2,000
SALES (est): 2.4MM **Privately Held**
WEB: www.kadienterprise.com
SIC: 2013 Snack sticks, including jerky: from purchased meat

(P-499)
KITCHEN CUTS LLC
6045 District Blvd, Maywood (90270)
PHONE..............................323 560-7415
Raul Tapia Sr, *CEO*
EMP: 49
SALES (est): 3.2MM
SALES (corp-wide): 266.4MM **Privately Held**
SIC: 2013 Beef stew from purchased meat
PA: Tapia Enterprises Inc.
6067 District Blvd
Maywood CA 90270
323 560-7415

(P-500)
KMB FOODS INC (PA)
1010 S Sierra Way, San Bernardino (92408-2124)
PHONE..............................626 447-0545
Scott Biedermann, *President*
Sam Mangiaterra, *COO*
Becky Benham, *Administration*
▲ EMP: 20 EST: 1998
SQ FT: 6,000
SALES (est): 9MM **Privately Held**
SIC: 2013 2099 Prepared beef products from purchased beef; food preparations

(P-501)
KRAVE PURE FOODS INC
Also Called: Krave Jerky
117 W Napa St Ste A, Sonoma (95476-6691)
PHONE..............................707 939-9176
Jonathan A Sebastiani, *CEO*
Johanna Creighton, *Business Dir*
Brian Link, *Regional Mgr*
Robert Daniels, *Finance Mgr*
Chris Davis, *Marketing Mgr*
EMP: 58
SALES (est): 23.9MM
SALES (corp-wide): 7.5B **Publicly Held**
SIC: 2013 5147 Snack sticks, including jerky: from purchased meat; meats & meat products
PA: Hershey Company
100 Crystal A Dr
Hershey PA 17033
717 534-4200

(P-502)
KRUSE AND SON INC
235 Kruse Ave, Monrovia (91016-4899)
P.O. Box 945 (91017-0945)
PHONE..............................626 358-4536
David R Kruse, *CEO*
EMP: 25
SQ FT: 20,000
SALES (est): 5.3MM **Privately Held**
SIC: 2013 Ham, smoked: from purchased meat; bacon, side & sliced: from purchased meat

(P-503)
LA ESPANOLA MEATS INC
25020 Doble Ave, Harbor City (90710-3155)
PHONE..............................310 539-0455
Alex Motamedi, *CEO*
Juana Faraone, *President*
Frank Faraone, *Treasurer*
◆ EMP: 25
SQ FT: 8,800
SALES (est): 5MM **Privately Held**
WEB: www.laespanolameats.com
SIC: 2013 5421 Sausages & related products, from purchased meat; meat markets, including freezer provisioners

(P-504)
MARISA FOODS LLC
1401 Santa Fe Ave, Long Beach (90813-1236)
PHONE..............................562 437-7775
Vincent Passanisi,
Liana Passanisi,
EMP: 11
SALES (est): 1.7MM **Privately Held**
SIC: 2013 Sausages & other prepared meats

(P-505)
MARTIN PUREFOODS CORPORATION
1713 W 2nd St, Pomona (91766-1253)
PHONE..............................909 865-4440
Rick Martin, *President*
▲ EMP: 10
SQ FT: 7,700
SALES (est): 1.2MM **Privately Held**
WEB: www.martinpurefoods.com
SIC: 2013 2011 Sausages & other prepared meats; sausages from meat slaughtered on site

(P-506)
MEADOW FARMS SAUSAGE CO INC
6215 S Western Ave, Los Angeles (90047-1441)
PHONE..............................323 752-2300
Joe Toia, *President*
EMP: 10
SQ FT: 8,000
SALES (est): 1MM **Privately Held**
SIC: 2013 Sausages from purchased meat

(P-507)
MIKAILIAN MEAT PRODUCT INC
25310 Avenue Stanford, Santa Clarita (91355-1214)
PHONE..............................661 257-1055
Gebril Mikailian, *President*
Swedlanan Mikailian, *Vice Pres*
EMP: 10
SQ FT: 14,000
SALES (est): 3MM **Privately Held**
SIC: 2013 Ham, roasted: from purchased meat; bologna from purchased meat; sausages from purchased meat

(P-508)
MILLER PACKING COMPANY
Also Called: Miller Hot Dogs
1122 Industrial Way, Lodi (95240-3119)
P.O. Box 1390 (95241-1390)
PHONE..............................209 339-2310
Michael A De Benedetti, *President*
Staige P Debenedetti, *CEO*
Dianne Blankenship, *VP Admin*
EMP: 50
SQ FT: 40,000
SALES (est): 6.8MM **Privately Held**
WEB: www.millerhotdogs.com
SIC: 2013 Sausages & other prepared meats
PA: Victor Meat Co
201 2nd St
Oakland CA
510 451-7200

(P-509)
MONDELEZ GLOBAL LLC
Also Called: Kraft Foods
6201 Knott Ave, Buena Park (90620-1010)
PHONE..............................714 690-7428
Jeferey Orchard, *Branch Mgr*
EMP: 562 **Publicly Held**
WEB: www.kraftfoods.com
SIC: 2013 Sausages & other prepared meats
HQ: Mondelez Global Llc
3 N Pkwy Ste 300
Deerfield IL 60015
847 943-4000

(P-510)
OHANYANS INC (PA)
Also Called: Ohanyan's Deli
3296 W Sussex Way, Fresno (93722-4929)
PHONE..............................559 225-4290
Jerry Hancer, *President*
Robert Hancer, *Treasurer*
Markos Garabetyan, *Vice Pres*
Hayik Garabetyan, *Admin Sec*
EMP: 10
SQ FT: 9,000
SALES (est): 3MM **Privately Held**
SIC: 2013 5411 Beef, dried: from purchased meat; sausages from purchased meat; delicatessens

(P-511)
P G MOLINARI & SONS INC
Also Called: Molinari Salami Co
1401 Yosemite Ave, San Francisco (94124-3321)
PHONE..............................415 822-5555
Frank P Giorgi, *President*
Gloria Giorgi, *Vice Pres*
Frank Gorgi, *Info Tech Dir*
▲ EMP: 23
SQ FT: 48,000
SALES (est): 5.5MM **Privately Held**
WEB: www.molinarisalame.com
SIC: 2013 Sausages from purchased meat; spiced meats from purchased meat

(P-512)
PAMPANGA FOODS COMPANY INC
1835 N Orngthrp Park A, Anaheim (92801-1143)
PHONE..............................714 773-0537
Ray Reyes, *President*
Coni Reyes, *Vice Pres*
EMP: 15
SQ FT: 11,000
SALES (est): 2.7MM **Privately Held**
WEB: www.pampangafoods.com
SIC: 2013 5812 8742 2011 Sausages & other prepared meats; eating places; food & beverage consultant; sausages from meat slaughtered on site

(P-513)
PAPA CANTELLAS INCORPORATED
Also Called: Papa Cantella's Sausage Plant
3341 E 50th St, Vernon (90058-3003)
PHONE..............................323 584-7272
Thomas P Cantella, *CEO*
Chris Stafford, *Vice Pres*
Christian Stafford, *Vice Pres*
Emily Lewis, *Research*
EMP: 60
SQ FT: 13,000
SALES (est): 15.4MM **Privately Held**
WEB: www.papacantella.com
SIC: 2013 Sausages from purchased meat

(P-514)
PEOPLES SAUSAGE COMPANY
1132 E Pico Blvd, Los Angeles (90021-2224)
PHONE..............................213 627-8633
Mark Bianchetti, *President*
Brian Bianchetti, *Managing Dir*
EMP: 16
SQ FT: 5,500
SALES (est): 2.4MM **Privately Held**
WEB: www.peopleschoicebeefjerky.com
SIC: 2013 5147 Beef, dried: from purchased meat; meats, fresh

(P-515)
POCINO FOODS COMPANY
14250 Lomitas Ave, City of Industry (91746-3014)
P.O. Box 2219, La Puente (91746-0219)
PHONE..............................626 968-8000
Frank J Pocino, *President*
Ravi Sheshadri, *CFO*
Dennis Pocino, *Vice Pres*
Frank G Pocino, *Vice Pres*
Hilda Basulto, *Executive*
▲ EMP: 100
SQ FT: 70,000
SALES (est): 28.7MM **Privately Held**
WEB: www.pocinofoods.com
SIC: 2013 Sausages from purchased meat; roast beef from purchased meat

(P-516)
PROVENA FOODS INC (HQ)
5010 Eucalyptus Ave, Chino (91710-9216)
PHONE..............................909 627-1082
Theodore L Arena, *President*
Thomas J Mulroney, *CFO*
Santo Zito, *Vice Pres*
Ronald A Provera, *Admin Sec*
▲ EMP: 60 EST: 1960
SALES (est): 29.3MM
SALES (corp-wide): 9.1B **Publicly Held**
SIC: 2013 2032 2098 Sausages & other prepared meats; canned specialties; Italian foods: packaged in cans, jars, etc.; macaroni: packaged in cans, jars, etc.; macaroni & spaghetti
PA: Hormel Foods Corporation
1 Hormel Pl
Austin MN 55912
507 437-5611

(P-517)
PROVENA FOODS INC
Swiss-American Sausage
251 Darcy Pkwy, Lathrop (95330-8756)
PHONE..............................209 858-5555
Theodore Arena, *Branch Mgr*
EMP: 45
SQ FT: 49,000

P
R
O
D
U
C
T
S

&

S
V
C
S

SALES (corp-wide): 9.1B **Publicly Held**
SIC: 2013 Sausages & other prepared meats
HQ: Provena Foods Inc.
5010 Eucalyptus Ave
Chino CA 91710
909 627-1082

(P-518)
RAEMICA INC
Also Called: Far West Meats
7759 Victoria Ave, Highland (92346-5637)
P.O. Box 248 (92346-0248)
PHONE..................909 864-1990
Thomas R Serrato, CEO
Michael Serrato, Corp Secy
Wade Snyder, Vice Pres
EMP: 41 EST: 1978
SQ FT: 35,000
SALES (est): 8.8MM **Privately Held**
SIC: 2013 Bacon, side & sliced: from purchased meat

(P-519)
RICE FIELD CORPORATION
14500 Valley Blvd, City of Industry (91746-2918)
PHONE..................626 968-6917
Derek Lee, Principal
Robert Jarne, QC Mgr
▲ EMP: 120
SQ FT: 100,000
SALES (est): 18.8MM **Privately Held**
SIC: 2013 Sausages & other prepared meats

(P-520)
S & S FOODS LLC
1120 W Foothill Blvd, Azusa (91702-2818)
PHONE..................626 633-1609
Kirk Smith,
Randy Shuman, President
Robert Horowitz, CEO
Horst Sieben, CFO
Pam Cardinale, Finance Dir
▲ EMP: 220
SQ FT: 115,000
SALES (est): 41.4MM **Privately Held**
SIC: 2013 Cooked meats from purchased meat; frozen meats from purchased meat; sausages & related products, from purchased meat
PA: Cti Foods Holding Co., Llc
22303 Highway 95
Wilder ID 83676
-

(P-521)
SAAB ENTERPRISES INC
Also Called: Enjoy Food
1433 Miller Dr, Colton (92324-2456)
PHONE..................909 823-2228
Waleed Saab, President
Walleb Saab, President
Saadi Kabab, Vice Pres
EMP: 70
SQ FT: 38,000
SALES (est): 10.4MM **Privately Held**
WEB: www.enjoybeefjerky.com
SIC: 2013 Beef, dried: from purchased meat

(P-522)
SAAGS PRODUCTS LLC
1799 Factor Ave, San Leandro (94577-5617)
P.O. Box 2078 (94577-0207)
PHONE..................510 678-3412
Jim Mosle, CEO
Timothy Dam, President
Maureen O'Callaghan, Administration
Peter Turcotte, Technology
Julien Hamon, Engineer
▲ EMP: 85
SQ FT: 40,000
SALES (est): 18MM
SALES (corp-wide): 9.1B **Publicly Held**
WEB: www.saags.com
SIC: 2013 Sausages from purchased meat; spiced meats from purchased meat
PA: Hormel Foods Corporation
1 Hormel Pl
Austin MN 55912
507 437-5611

(P-523)
SAPAR USA INC (PA)
Also Called: Fabrique Delices
1610 Delta Ct Ste 1, Hayward (94544-7043)
PHONE..................510 441-9500
Marc Poinsignon, President
Antonio Pinheiro, Vice Pres
Vanessa Sanchez, Office Mgr
Julie Pinheiro, QC Mgr
Sebastiene Espinasse, VP Sls/Mktg
EMP: 25
SQ FT: 20,000
SALES (est): 2.8MM **Privately Held**
WEB: www.fabriquedelices.com
SIC: 2013 Spreads, sandwich: meat from purchased meat

(P-524)
SAVORY CREATIONS INTERNATIONAL
32611 Central Ave, Union City (94587-2008)
PHONE..................510 477-0395
Douglas Eakiewa, Owner
EMP: 20 EST: 2011
SALES (est): 2.6MM **Privately Held**
SIC: 2013 Sausages & other prepared meats

(P-525)
SERV-RITE MEAT COMPANY INC
Also Called: Packers Bar M
2515 N San Fernando Rd, Los Angeles (90065-1325)
P.O. Box 65026 (90065-0026)
PHONE..................323 227-1911
Gary Marks, CEO
Norman Marks, Vice Pres
Phil Tanico, Regional Mgr
Norma Marks, Admin Sec
Nora Hizon, Human Res Dir
EMP: 55
SQ FT: 55,000
SALES (est): 14.7MM **Privately Held**
SIC: 2013 Sausages & other prepared meats

(P-526)
SETTLERS JERKY INCORPORATED
307 Paseo Sonrisa, Walnut (91789-2721)
PHONE..................909 444-3999
Aaron J Anderson, CEO
EMP: 27
SQ FT: 20,000
SALES: 5MM **Privately Held**
SIC: 2013 Snack sticks, including jerky: from purchased meat

(P-527)
SPAR SAUSAGE CO
Also Called: Caspers
688 Williams St, San Leandro (94571-2624)
PHONE..................510 614-8100
Jack Dorian, Manager
EMP: 13
SQ FT: 9,750
SALES (est): 2MM
SALES (corp-wide): 1.9MM **Privately Held**
SIC: 2013 Sausages from purchased meat
PA: Spar Sausage Co
3508 Mt Diablo Blvd Ste J
Lafayette CA 94549
925 283-6877

(P-528)
SQUARE H BRANDS INC
Also Called: Hoffy
2731 S Soto St, Vernon (90058-8026)
PHONE..................323 267-4600
Henry Haskell, CEO
William Hannigan, CFO
◆ EMP: 150
SQ FT: 100,000
SALES (est): 41.9MM **Privately Held**
WEB: www.squarehbrands.com
SIC: 2013 Sausages from purchased meat

(P-529)
SUNNYVALLEY SMOKED MEATS INC
2475 W Yosemite Ave, Manteca (95337-9641)
P.O. Box 2158 (95336-1159)
PHONE..................209 825-0288
William Andreetta, President
Treva Andreetta, Vice Pres
Laura Tomlinson, Executive
Randy Long, Opers Mgr
Debi Hawkes, QC Mgr
▲ EMP: 110
SQ FT: 41,000
SALES (est): 39.8MM **Privately Held**
WEB: www.sunnyvalleysmokedmeats.com
SIC: 2013 Ham, smoked: from purchased meat; corned beef from purchased meat

(P-530)
SWIFT BEEF COMPANY
Also Called: Jbs Case Ready
15555 Meridian Pkwy, Riverside (92518-3046)
PHONE..................951 571-2237
Andre Nogueira, CEO
EMP: 200
SALES (est): 306.8K **Publicly Held**
SIC: 2013 Beef, dried: from purchased meat
HQ: Jbs Usa Food Company
1770 Promontory Cir
Greeley CO 80634
970 506-8000

(P-531)
T&J SAUSAGE KITCHEN INC
Also Called: T & J Sausage Kitchen
2831 E Miraloma Ave, Anaheim (92806-1804)
PHONE..................714 632-8350
Tom Drozdowski, CEO
Walter Wolpert, CFO
David Armendariz, Vice Pres
Julie Granger, Director
EMP: 45
SQ FT: 20,000
SALES (est): 7.8MM **Privately Held**
WEB: www.tandjsausage.com
SIC: 2013 Sausages & other prepared meats

(P-532)
TRANSHUMANCE HOLDING CO INC
Also Called: Superior Farms
2851 E 44th St, Vernon (90058-2401)
P.O. Box 58106, Los Angeles (90058-0106)
PHONE..................323 583-5503
Joey Garraird, Manager
EMP: 10 **Privately Held**
WEB: www.superiorfarms.com
SIC: 2013 5147 2011 Sausages & other prepared meats; meats & meat products; lamb products from lamb slaughtered on site
PA: Transhumance Holding Company, Inc.
2530 River Plaza Dr # 200
Sacramento CA 95833
-

(P-533)
VALLEY PROTEIN LLC
1828 E Hedges Ave, Fresno (93703-3633)
PHONE..................559 498-7115
Robert Coyle, Mng Member
Angela Sanchez, Controller
Nate Coyle, Purchasing
EMP: 95 EST: 2010
SALES (est): 22.4MM **Privately Held**
SIC: 2013 Prepared beef products from purchased beef

(P-534)
VIET HUNG PARIS INC
Also Called: V H Paris Co
1975 Chota Rd, La Habra Heights (90631-8403)
PHONE..................562 944-4919
Vinh P Pham, President
EMP: 15
SQ FT: 6,000
SALES (est): 1.8MM **Privately Held**
SIC: 2013 Sausages from purchased meat

(P-535)
WYCEN FOODS INC (PA)
560 Estabrook St, San Leandro (94577-3512)
PHONE..................510 351-1987
Arthur Leong, President
Nancy Leong, Treasurer
▲ EMP: 17
SQ FT: 25,000
SALES (est): 2.1MM **Privately Held**
SIC: 2013 2038 Sausages from purchased meat; ethnic foods, frozen

(P-536)
YONEKYU USA INC
3615 E Vernon Ave, Vernon (90058-1815)
PHONE..................323 581-4194
Osamu Saito, President
Kenji Ikeda, CEO
Arihito Tanaka, CFO
Don Ferris, Exec VP
Hiroyuki Tashiro, Prdtn Mgr
▼ EMP: 52
SQ FT: 31,000
SALES (est): 18.5MM
SALES (corp-wide): 7.8B **Privately Held**
SIC: 2013 Sausages from purchased meat
HQ: Yonekyu Corporation
1259, Terabayashi, Okanomiya
Numazu SZO 410-0
559 225-321

2015 Poultry Slaughtering, Dressing & Processing

(P-537)
EGGS WEST LLC
14460 Palm Ave, Wasco (93280-9551)
PHONE..................661 758-9700
Scott Simpkins, Mng Member
David Demler, Mng Member
▲ EMP: 26
SALES (est): 2.1MM **Privately Held**
SIC: 2015 Egg processing

(P-538)
FIELD TO FAMILY NATURAL FOODS
224 Weller St Ste C, Petaluma (94952-3136)
P.O. Box 2917 (94953-2917)
PHONE..................707 765-6756
Wayne Dufond, President
Amy Dufond, Vice Pres
EMP: 10
SALES (est): 843.7K **Privately Held**
SIC: 2015 Chicken, processed: fresh

(P-539)
FOSTER POULTRY FARMS (PA)
Also Called: Foster Farms
1000 Davis St, Livingston (95334-1526)
P.O. Box 457 (95334-0457)
PHONE..................209 394-6914
Ron M Foster, President
Donald Jackson, President
Leslie Cardoso, COO
Caryn Doyle, CFO
Jose Fagoaga, Treasurer
◆ EMP: 250
SQ FT: 40,000
SALES (est): 3B **Privately Held**
WEB: www.fosterfarms.com
SIC: 2015 Poultry slaughtering & processing

(P-540)
FOSTER POULTRY FARMS
Also Called: Foster Farms
1307 Ellenwood Rd, Waterford (95386-8702)
PHONE..................209 394-7901
Jay Husman, Manager
Janice Cardoza, Supervisor
EMP: 50
SQ FT: 68,316
SALES (corp-wide): 3B **Privately Held**
WEB: www.fosterfarms.com
SIC: 2015 Poultry slaughtering & processing

PA: Foster Poultry Farms
1000 Davis St
Livingston CA 95334
209 394-6914

(P-541)
FOSTER POULTRY FARMS
Also Called: Foster Farms
1333 Swan St, Livingston (95334-1559)
P.O. Box 457 (95334-0457)
PHONE...................................209 394-7901
Brent Allen, *Branch Mgr*
Dan Huber, *Senior VP*
Jonathan Foster, *Vice Pres*
Kathleen Romley, *Regional Mgr*
Adam Little, *Engineer*
EMP: 125
SALES (corp-wide): 3B **Privately Held**
WEB: www.fosterfarms.com
SIC: 2015 Poultry slaughtering & processing
PA: Foster Poultry Farms
1000 Davis St
Livingston CA 95334
209 394-6914

(P-542)
FOSTER POULTRY FARMS
770 N Plano St, Porterville (93257-6329)
PHONE...................................559 793-5501
Paul Bravinder, *Manager*
EMP: 400
SALES (corp-wide): 3B **Privately Held**
WEB: www.fosterfarms.com
SIC: 2015 5421 Chicken, processed:
fresh; meat & fish markets
PA: Foster Poultry Farms
1000 Davis St
Livingston CA 95334
209 394-6914

(P-543)
FOSTER POULTRY FARMS
1805 N Santa Fe Ave, Compton
(90221-1009)
PHONE...................................310 223-1499
Ronald Altman, *Branch Mgr*
Norma Bustamante, *Director*
EMP: 257
SALES (corp-wide): 3B **Privately Held**
WEB: www.conagra.com
SIC: 2015 Poultry slaughtering & processing
PA: Foster Poultry Farms
1000 Davis St
Livingston CA 95334
209 394-6914

(P-544)
INGENUE INC
Also Called: Q C Poultry
6114 Scott Way, Commerce (90040-3518)
P.O. Box 17238, Anaheim (92817-7238)
PHONE...................................323 726-8084
Nick Macis, *President*
Michelle Macis, *Admin Sec*
Angelique Macis, *Assistant*
EMP: 100
SQ FT: 10,000
SALES (est): 26MM **Privately Held**
SIC: 2015 Poultry slaughtering & processing

(P-545)
KIFUKI USA CO INC (HQ)
15547 1st St, Irwindale (91706-6201)
PHONE...................................626 334-8090
Kuniaki Ishikawa, *President*
▲ EMP: 90
SQ FT: 52,000
SALES (est): 76.9MM
SALES (corp-wide): 4.9B **Privately Held**
SIC: 2015 2013 2035 Eggs, processed:
dehydrated; poultry, processed: beef,
dried: from purchased meat; seasonings
& sauces, except tomato & dry; dress-
ings, salad: raw & cooked (except dry
mixes); mayonnaise
PA: Kewpie Corporation
1-4-13, Shibuya
Shibuya-Ku TKY 150-0
334 863-331

(P-546)
LOS ANGELES POULTRY CO INC
4816 Long Beach Ave, Los Angeles
(90058-1915)
P.O. Box 58328 (90058-0328)
PHONE...................................323 232-3475
David Dahan, *President*
Dror Dahan, *Vice Pres*
Mario Perez, *General Mgr*
Jamie Kidder, *Info Tech Mgr*
EMP: 88
SQ FT: 32,000
SALES (est): 14.2MM **Privately Held**
WEB: www.lapoultry.com
SIC: 2015 Poultry slaughtering & process-
ing

(P-547)
LUUS FAMILY CORP
302 S San Joaquin St, Stockton
(95203-3536)
PHONE...................................209 466-1952
Doc Luu, *President*
Ming Lou, *Manager*
EMP: 40
SALES: 6MM **Privately Held**
WEB: www.luufamily.net
SIC: 2015 Chicken slaughtering & process-
ing

(P-548)
OLIVERA EGG RANCH LLC
Also Called: Olivera Foods
3315 Sierra Rd, San Jose (95132-3099)
P.O. Box 32126 (95152-2126)
PHONE...................................408 258-8074
Edward F Olivera,
▲ EMP: 60
SQ FT: 35,000
SALES (est): 17.6MM **Privately Held**
SIC: 2015 5143 5142 5144 Egg process-
ing; cheese; butter; packaged frozen
goods; eggs

(P-549)
PHU HUONG FOODS CO INC
9008 Garvey Ave Ste I, Rosemead
(91770-3361)
PHONE...................................626 280-8607
Long Nguyen, *President*
EMP: 14
SQ FT: 4,000
SALES (est): 1.3MM **Privately Held**
SIC: 2015 Poultry slaughtering & processing

(P-550)
RICH CHICKS LLC
13771 Gramercy Pl, Gardena
(90249-2470)
PHONE...................................209 879-4104
Charlie Brust, *Vice Pres*
EMP: 20 **Privately Held**
SIC: 2015 Chicken, processed: frozen
PA: Rich Chicks, Llc
4276 N Tracy Blvd
Tracy CA 95304
-

(P-551)
RICH CHICKS LLC (PA)
Also Called: Rich Chicks, Rich In Nutrition
4276 N Tracy Blvd, Tracy (95304-1501)
PHONE...................................209 879-4104
Neil Kinney, *Managing Prtnr*
Paul Byrd, *General Mgr*
EMP: 34
SALES: 5MM **Privately Held**
SIC: 2015 Chicken, processed: frozen

(P-552)
TWENTY-NINERS PROVISIONS INC
Also Called: Twenty Niners Club
1784 E Vernon Ave, Vernon (90058-1526)
PHONE...................................323 233-7864
Seiichi Shibata, *President*
EMP: 35
SALES (est): 2.8MM **Privately Held**
WEB: www.macsei.com
SIC: 2015 2013 Poultry slaughtering &
processing; sausages & other prepared
meats

(P-553)
VALLEY FRESH INC (HQ)
1404 S Fresno Ave, Stockton (95206-1174)
PHONE...................................209 943-5411
Ronald W Fielding, *CEO*
Eugene Carney, *Vice Pres*
EMP: 50
SQ FT: 120,000
SALES (est): 47.2MM
SALES (corp-wide): 9.1B **Publicly Held**
WEB: www.valleyfresh.com
SIC: 2015 Poultry, processed: canned;
poultry, processed: frozen
PA: Hormel Foods Corporation
1 Hormel Pl
Austin MN 55912
507 437-5611

(P-554)
VUE-TEMP INC (PA)
618 S Kilroy Rd, Turlock (95380-9531)
PHONE...................................209 634-2914
Anthony Volks, *President*
▲ EMP: 60
SQ FT: 66,981
SALES (est): 7.6MM **Privately Held**
WEB: www.volkenterprises.com
SIC: 2015 5084 3089 Chicken slaughter-
ing & processing; machine tools & metal-
working machinery; plastic processing

(P-555)
WESTERN SUPREME INC
Also Called: California Poultry
865 Produce Ct, Los Angeles
(90021-1831)
PHONE...................................213 627-3861
Frank Fogarty, *President*
Marlene Fogarty, *Corp Secy*
EMP: 125
SQ FT: 10,000
SALES (est): 12.7MM **Privately Held**
SIC: 2015 Chicken slaughtering & process-
ing

(P-556)
WIN FAT FOOD LLC
700 Monterey Pass Rd A, Monterey Park
(91754-3618)
PHONE...................................323 261-1869
MEI Lan Liang,
Jun Yuan Liang,
EMP: 50
SALES (est): 3.2MM **Privately Held**
SIC: 2015 Poultry slaughtering & process-
ing

(P-557)
ZACKY & SONS POULTRY LLC
Also Called: Zacky Farms
13200 Crossroads P, City of Industry
(91746)
P.O. Box 12556, Fresno (93778-2556)
PHONE...................................559 443-2700
Lillian Zacky, *CEO*
Kirk Vandergeest, *CFO*
EMP: 155 EST: 2013
SQ FT: 14,000
SALES (est): 204.8MM **Privately Held**
SIC: 2015 Poultry slaughtering & process-
ing

2021 Butter

(P-558)
BONELLI FINE FOOD INC
3525 Del Mar Heights Rd, San Diego
(92130-2199)
PHONE...................................650 906-9896
Ali Tabatabaei, *President*
▼ EMP: 10
SALES (est): 837.3K **Privately Held**
SIC: 2021 2035 Creamery butter; spreads,
garlic

(P-559)
CALIFORNIA DAIRIES INC
1175 E Pacheco Blvd, Los Banos
(93635-4331)
P.O. Box 2198 (93635-2198)
PHONE...................................209 826-4901
Janelle Cone, *Branch Mgr*
EMP: 56

SALES (corp-wide): 265.8MM **Privately Held**
WEB: www.californiadairies.com
SIC: 2021 2026 2023 2022 Creamery
butter; milk processing (pasteurizing, homogenizing, bottling); powdered skim
milk; cheese, natural & processed
PA: California Dairies, Inc.
2000 N Plaza Dr
Visalia CA 93291
559 625-2200

(P-560)
CALIFORNIA DAIRIES INC
Also Called: San Joaquin Valley Dairymen
475 S Tegner Rd, Turlock (95380-9406)
PHONE...................................209 656-1942
Tamara Staggs, *Branch Mgr*
EMP: 80
SALES (corp-wide): 265.8MM **Privately Held**
WEB: www.californiadairies.com
SIC: 2021 2023 2026 Creamery butter;
dry, condensed, evaporated dairy prod-
ucts; fluid milk
PA: California Dairies, Inc.
2000 N Plaza Dr
Visalia CA 93291
559 625-2200

(P-561)
MIYOKOS KITCHEN
2086 Marina Ave, Petaluma (94954-6714)
PHONE...................................415 448-5807
Miyoko Schinner, *CEO*
John Breen, *Officer*
Maria Chan, *Admin Mgr*
Lauren Heminez, *Production*
Cathleen Mandigo, *Mktg Dir*
◆ EMP: 40
SALES (est): 9.5MM **Privately Held**
SIC: 2021 2022 Creamery butter; cheese,
natural & processed; cheese spreads,
dips, pastes & other cheese products

(P-562)
STRAUS FAMILY CREAMERY INC
1105 Industrial Ave # 200, Petaluma
(94952-1141)
PHONE...................................707 776-2887
Albert Straus, *CEO*
Deborah Parrish, *CFO*
EMP: 64
SQ FT: 40,000
SALES (est): 14.9MM **Privately Held**
SIC: 2021 2023 2026 Creamery butter;
ice cream mix, unfrozen: liquid or dry; yo-
gurt

(P-563)
VENTURA FOODS LLC
Also Called: Saffola Quality Foods
2900 Jurupa St, Ontario (91761-2915)
PHONE...................................323 262-9157
Tom Bospic, *Manager*
EMP: 148 **Privately Held**
WEB: www.venturafoods.com
SIC: 2021 2035 5199 2079 Creamery
butter; dressings, salad: raw & cooked
(except dry mixes); oils, animal or veg-
etable; edible fats & oils
PA: Ventura Foods, Llc
40 Pointe Dr
Brea CA 92821

2022 Cheese

(P-564)
ARIZA CHEESE CO INC
7602 Jackson St, Paramount (90723-4912)
PHONE...................................562 630-4144
Fatima Cristina Ariza, *CEO*
Ausencio Ariza, *President*
EMP: 40
SQ FT: 8,000
SALES (est): 6.8MM **Privately Held**
SIC: 2022 Cheese, natural & processed

(P-565)
CACIQUE INC (PA)
Also Called: Cacique Cheese
800 Royal Oaks Dr Ste 200, Monrovia
(91016-6364)
PHONE....................................626 961-3399
Ana De Cardenas-Raptis, *CEO*
Francoise Mattice, *CFO*
Wendy Morgan, *CFO*
Jennie De Cardenas, *Exec VP*
Gilbert B De Cardenas, *Vice Pres*
EMP: 230 **EST:** 1976
SQ FT: 82,000
SALES (est): 88.6MM **Privately Held**
WEB: www.caciqueusa.com
SIC: 2022 Natural cheese

(P-566)
CASTLE IMPORTING INC
14550 Miller Ave, Fontana (92336-1696)
PHONE....................................909 428-9200
Vito Borruso, *President*
Giancomo Borruso, *CFO*
Josephine Borruso, *Admin Sec*
▲ **EMP:** 17
SQ FT: 68,000
SALES (est): 4.1MM **Privately Held**
WEB: www.castleimporting.com
SIC: 2022 5812 Processed cheese; eating
places

(P-567)
CHEESE ADMINISTRATIVE
CORP INC
429 H St, Los Banos (93635-4113)
PHONE....................................209 826-3744
Frank Peluso, *CEO*
EMP: 35
SQ FT: 3,000
SALES (est): 5.7MM **Privately Held**
SIC: 2022 Natural cheese

(P-568)
CYPRESS GROVE CHEVRE INC
1330 Q St, Arcata (95521-5740)
PHONE....................................707 825-1100
Pamela Dressler, *President*
▲ **EMP:** 52
SQ FT: 12,500
SALES (est): 9.5MM
SALES (corp-wide): 251.6MM **Privately**
Held
WEB: www.cypressgrovechevre.com
SIC: 2022 Natural cheese
HQ: Emmi Ag
Landenbergstrasse 1
Luzern LU
582 272-727

(P-569)
DAIRY FARMERS AMERICA INC
600 Trade Way, Turlock (95380-9433)
PHONE....................................209 667-9627
Thomas Baker, *Manager*
EMP: 93
SQ FT: 63,976
SALES (corp-wide): 14.6B **Privately Held**
WEB: www.dfamilk.com
SIC: 2022 2026 Cheese, natural &
processed; fluid milk
PA: Dairy Farmers Of America, Inc.
1405 N 98th St
Kansas City KS 66111
816 801-6455

(P-570)
EINSTEIN NOAH REST GROUP
INC
Also Called: Noah's New York Bagels
16304 Beach Blvd, Westminster
(92683-7857)
PHONE....................................714 847-4609
Fransico Valdez, *Manager*
EMP: 15
SALES (corp-wide): 2.2B **Privately Held**
WEB: www.noahs.com
SIC: 2022 5812 Spreads, cheese; cafe
HQ: Einstein Noah Restaurant Group, Inc.
555 Zang St Ste 300
Lakewood CO 80228

(P-571)
EINSTEIN NOAH REST GROUP
INC
Also Called: Noah's
15996 Los Gatos Blvd, Los Gatos
(95032-3424)
PHONE....................................408 358-5895
Susan Asef, *Manager*
EMP: 13
SALES (corp-wide): 2.2B **Privately Held**
WEB: www.noahs.com
SIC: 2022 5812 Spreads, cheese; cafe
HQ: Einstein Noah Restaurant Group, Inc.
555 Zang St Ste 300
Lakewood CO 80228

(P-572)
ESTATE CHEESE GROUP LLC
(PA)
670 W Napa St Ste G, Sonoma
(95476-6437)
PHONE....................................707 996-1000
John Crean,
Lou Biaggi,
David Viviani,
▼ **EMP:** 20
SALES (est): 1.9MM **Privately Held**
SIC: 2022 Natural cheese

(P-573)
EXCELPRO INC (PA)
1630 Amapola Ave, Torrance (90501-3101)
PHONE....................................323 415-8544
Peter Ernster, *President*
Gregg Rowland, *CFO*
John H Ernster Jr, *Admin Sec*
EMP: 16 **EST:** 1973
SQ FT: 36,000
SALES (est): 1.7MM **Privately Held**
SIC: 2022 2023 Processed cheese; di-
etary supplements, dairy & non-dairy
based

(P-574)
GALLO GLOBAL NUTRITION
LLC
Also Called: Joseph Farms
10561 Highway 140, Atwater (95301-9309)
P.O. Box 775 (95301-0775)
PHONE....................................209 394-7984
Michael Gallo, *CEO*
Kenneth Jelacich, *Manager*
EMP: 105
SQ FT: 5,000
SALES (est): 15.7MM **Privately Held**
SIC: 2022 8099 0241 Cheese spreads,
dips, pastes & other cheese products; nu-
trition services; dairy farms

(P-575)
GOLDEN VALLEY DAIRY
PRODUCTS
1025 E Bardsley Ave, Tulare (93274-5752)
PHONE....................................559 687-1188
John Prince, *CEO*
EMP: 125
SALES (est): 11.5MM
SALES (corp-wide): 12.8B **Privately Held**
WEB: www.realcheese.com
SIC: 2022 Cheese, natural & processed
PA: Land O'lakes, Inc.
4001 Lexington Ave N
Arden Hills MN 55126
651 375-2222

(P-576)
GREEN VALLEY FOODS
PRODUCT
25684 Community Blvd, Barstow
(92311-9671)
PHONE....................................760 964-1105
Hector Huerta, *President*
EMP: 15
SQ FT: 10,000
SALES (est): 2.5MM **Privately Held**
SIC: 2022 Cheese, natural & processed

(P-577)
HILMAR CHEESE COMPANY INC
3600 W Canal Dr, Turlock (95380-8507)
P.O. Box 910, Hilmar (95324-0910)
PHONE....................................209 667-6076
David Ahlem, *CEO*

EMP: 54
SALES (corp-wide): 299MM **Privately**
Held
SIC: 2022 Natural cheese
PA: Hilmar Cheese Company, Inc.
8901 Lander Ave
Hilmar CA 95324
209 667-6076

(P-578)
HILMAR CHEESE COMPANY INC
(PA)
Also Called: Hilmar Ingredients
8901 Lander Ave, Hilmar (95324-9327)
P.O. Box 910 (95324-0910)
PHONE....................................209 667-6076
John J Jeter, *President*
Donald Jay Hicks, *CFO*
Rich Yvarra, *Controller*
Amy Houghtialing, *Human Resources*
James Shriver, *Sales Mgr*
◆ **EMP:** 277
SALES (est): 299MM **Privately Held**
WEB: www.hilmarcheese.com
SIC: 2022 Natural cheese

(P-579)
IDB HOLDINGS INC (DH)
601 S Rockefeller Ave, Ontario
(91761-7871)
PHONE....................................909 390-5624
Jim Dekeyser, *CEO*
Peter Dolan, *Corp Secy*
Daniel O'Connell, *Asst Sec*
◆ **EMP:** 15
SQ FT: 4,000
SALES (est): 116MM
SALES (corp-wide): 1.8B **Privately Held**
SIC: 2022 5143 Processed cheese;
cheese
HQ: Ornua Foods Uk Limited
Sunnyhills Road Barnfields Industrial
Estate
Leek STAFFS ST13
153 839-9111

(P-580)
KAROUN DAIRIES INC
5117 Santa Monica Blvd, Los Angeles
(90029-2413)
PHONE....................................323 666-6222
EMP: 10
SALES (corp-wide): 13.2MM **Privately**
Held
SIC: 2022 5143
PA: Karoun Dairies, Inc.
13023 Arroyo St
San Fernando CA 91340
818 365-3333

(P-581)
KAROUN DAIRIES INC (PA)
13023 Arroyo St, San Fernando
(91340-1540)
PHONE....................................818 767-7000
Anto Baghdassarian, *President*
Rostom Baghdassarian, *COO*
Tsolak Khatcherian, *CFO*
Ohan Baghdassarian, *Vice Pres*
Seta Baghdassarian, *Admin Sec*
▲ **EMP:** 70
SQ FT: 70,000
SALES (est): 13.5MM **Privately Held**
WEB: www.karoundairies.com
SIC: 2022 5143 Natural cheese; cheese

(P-582)
KRAFT HEINZ FOODS COMPANY
3735 Imperial Way, Stockton (95215-9691)
PHONE....................................209 942-0102
EMP: 213
SALES (corp-wide): 26.2B **Publicly Held**
SIC: 2022 Processed cheese
HQ: Kraft Heinz Foods Company
1 Ppg Pl Ste 3200
Pittsburgh PA 15222
412 456-5700

(P-583)
LAND OLAKES INC
400 S M St, Tulare (93274-5431)
PHONE....................................559 687-8287
Jack Gherty, *CEO*
EMP: 96

SALES (corp-wide): 12.8B **Privately Held**
WEB: www.landolakes.com
SIC: 2022 Cheese, natural & processed
PA: Land O'lakes, Inc.
4001 Lexington Ave N
Arden Hills MN 55126
651 375-2222

(P-584)
LAND OLAKES INC
3601 County Road C, Orland (95963-9117)
PHONE....................................530 865-7626
Carolyn Macon, *CEO*
EMP: 29
SALES (corp-wide): 12.8B **Privately Held**
WEB: www.landolakes.com
SIC: 2022 Cheese, natural & processed
PA: Land O'lakes, Inc.
4001 Lexington Ave N
Arden Hills MN 55126
651 375-2222

(P-585)
LAURA CHENELS CHEVRE INC
Also Called: Parent Is Sas Ltries H Trbllat
22085 Carneros Vinyrd Way, Sonoma
(95476-2826)
PHONE....................................707 996-4477
Hugues Triballat, *CEO*
Pierre Girier, *COO*
Sylvie Forero, *CFO*
▲ **EMP:** 68
SALES (est): 15.6MM
SALES (corp-wide): 4.4MM **Privately**
Held
WEB: www.laurachenel.com
SIC: 2022 Cheese spreads, dips, pastes &
other cheese products
HQ: Laiteries H. Triballat

Les Aix D Angillon 18220
248 662-200

(P-586)
LEPRINO FOODS COMPANY
2401 N Macarthur Dr, Tracy (95376-2095)
PHONE....................................209 835-8340
Joel Crane, *General Mgr*
Andy Gregorich, *Plant Mgr*
Ed Ellingen, *Mfg Spvr*
Lisa Melo, *Plant Engr*
Charles Withers, *Maint Spvr*
EMP: 300
SALES (corp-wide): 1.8B **Privately Held**
WEB: www.leprinofoods.com
SIC: 2022 Processed cheese
PA: Leprino Foods Company
1830 W 38th Ave
Denver CO 80211
303 480-2600

(P-587)
LEPRINO FOODS COMPANY
490 F St, Lemoore (93245-2661)
PHONE....................................559 924-7722
Dave Direking, *Branch Mgr*
Cullen Cooper, *Project Engr*
Anna Nicks, *Human Res Mgr*
Ben Hutchison, *Buyer*
EMP: 275
SALES (corp-wide): 1.8B **Privately Held**
WEB: www.leprinofoods.com
SIC: 2022 Natural cheese; whey, raw or
liquid
PA: Leprino Foods Company
1830 W 38th Ave
Denver CO 80211
303 480-2600

(P-588)
LEPRINO FOODS COMPANY
351 Belle Haven Dr, Lemoore
(93245-9247)
PHONE....................................559 924-7939
James Leprino, *President*
Ben Schlegelmilch, *Maintence Staff*
Joe Enriquez, *Supervisor*
EMP: 200
SALES (corp-wide): 1.8B **Privately Held**
WEB: www.leprinofoods.com
SIC: 2022 Natural cheese
PA: Leprino Foods Company
1830 W 38th Ave
Denver CO 80211
303 480-2600

(P-589)
LIFELINE FOOD CO INC
118 Cypress Lakes Ct, Marina
(93933-2521)
PHONE..................................831 899-5040
Jone Chappell, *President*
EMP: 10
SQ FT: 2,750
SALES (est): 1MM **Privately Held**
WEB: www.lifetimefatfree.com
SIC: 2022 5143 Natural cheese; cheese

(P-590)
LOLETA CHEESE COMPANY INC
252 Loleta Dr, Loleta (95551)
PHONE..................................707 733-5470
Robert E Laffranchi, *President*
EMP: 11
SALES (est): 1.1MM **Privately Held**
SIC: 2022 Cheese, natural & processed

(P-591)
LYRICAL FOODS INC
Also Called: Kite Hill
3180 Corporate Pl, Hayward (94545-3916)
PHONE..................................510 784-0955
John Haugen, *CEO*
Jean Prebot, *COO*
David Bauer, *Vice Pres*
John Murphy, *Vice Pres*
Jean Prevot, *Vice Pres*
▲ EMP: 108 EST: 2012
SQ FT: 20,000
SALES (est): 18MM **Privately Held**
SIC: 2022 Natural cheese

(P-592)
MARIN FRENCH CHEESE COMPANY
Also Called: Rouge & Noir
7500 Red Hill Rd, Petaluma (94952-9438)
PHONE..................................707 762-6001
Hugues Triballat, *CEO*
Amelie Curis, *Site Mgr*
Alex Borgo, *Manager*
EMP: 12 EST: 1865
SQ FT: 10,000
SALES (est): 1.9MM
SALES (corp-wide): 4.4MM **Privately Held**
WEB: www.marinfrenchcheese.com
SIC: 2022 Natural cheese
HQ: Laiteries H. Triballat

    Les Aix D Angillon 18220
    248 662-200

(P-593)
MARQUEZ BROTHERS INTL INC
4393 N Golden State Blvd, Fresno
(93722-3828)
PHONE..................................559 276-7800
Jaime Marquez, *President*
Jerry Santamaria, *Vice Pres*
EMP: 26
SALES (corp-wide): 329.4MM **Privately Held**
SIC: 2022 Natural cheese
PA: Marquez Brothers International, Inc.
    5801 Rue Ferrari
    San Jose CA 95138
    408 960-2700

(P-594)
OAKDALE CHEESE & SPECIALTIES
10040 State Highway 120, Oakdale
(95361-8718)
PHONE..................................209 848-3139
Walter Bulk, *Owner*
John Bulk, *Co-Owner*
Leneka Bulk, *Co-Owner*
EMP: 10
SALES (est): 946.1K **Privately Held**
WEB: www.oakdalecheese.com
SIC: 2022 5143 Natural cheese; cheese

(P-595)
RIZO-LOPEZ FOODS INC
Also Called: Don Francisco Cheese
201 S Mcclure Rd, Modesto (95357-0519)
P.O. Box 1689, Empire (95319-1689)
PHONE..................................800 626-5587
Edwin Rizo, *President*
Ivan Rizo, *CEO*

Sergio Vaca, *Controller*
Juan Luis De La Torre, *Plant Mgr*
▲ EMP: 178
SQ FT: 3,800
SALES (est): 40.1MM **Privately Held**
SIC: 2022 5143 2023 5141 Natural cheese; whey, raw or liquid; processed cheese; dairy products, except dried or canned; dry, condensed, evaporated dairy products; yogurt mix; groceries, general line

(P-596)
RUMIANO CHEESE CO (PA)
1629 County Road E, Willows
(95988-9642)
P.O. Box 863 (95988-0863)
PHONE..................................530 934-5438
Baird Rumiano, *President*
John F Rumiano, *Vice Pres*
▲ EMP: 106
SQ FT: 30,000
SALES (est): 35.5MM **Privately Held**
SIC: 2022 Natural cheese

(P-597)
RUMIANO CHEESE CO
511 9th St, Crescent City (95531-3408)
P.O. Box 305 (95531-0305)
PHONE..................................707 465-1535
Baird Rumiano, *Manager*
EMP: 30
SALES (corp-wide): 35.5MM **Privately Held**
SIC: 2022 Cheese, natural & processed
PA: Rumiano Cheese Co.
    1629 County Road E
    Willows CA 95988
    530 934-5438

(P-598)
SAPUTO CHEESE USA INC
800 E Paige Ave, Tulare (93274-6863)
PHONE..................................559 687-8411
EMP: 300 **Privately Held**
SIC: 2022 Cheese spreads, dips, pastes & other cheese products
HQ: Saputo Cheese Usa Inc.
    1 Overlook Pt Ste 300
    Lincolnshire IL 60069
    -

(P-599)
SAPUTO CHEESE USA INC
Also Called: Stella Cheese
901 E Levin Ave, Tulare (93274-6525)
PHONE..................................559 687-9999
Bob Timmons, *Manager*
EMP: 150 **Privately Held**
SIC: 2022 Natural cheese
HQ: Saputo Cheese Usa Inc.
    1 Overlook Pt Ste 300
    Lincolnshire IL 60069

(P-600)
SAPUTO CHEESE USA INC
Stell Foods
5611 Imperial Hwy, South Gate
(90280-7419)
PHONE..................................562 862-7686
Rick McKenney, *Manager*
EMP: 200 **Privately Held**
SIC: 2022 5143 Natural cheese; cheese
HQ: Saputo Cheese Usa Inc.
    1 Overlook Pt Ste 300
    Lincolnshire IL 60069

(P-601)
SCHREIBER FOODS INC
1901 Via Burton, Fullerton (92831-5341)
PHONE..................................714 490-7360
EMP: 181
SALES (corp-wide): 2.4B **Privately Held**
SIC: 2022 Processed cheese; natural cheese
PA: Schreiber Foods, Inc.
    400 N Washington St
    Green Bay WI 54301
    920 437-7601

(P-602)
SIERRA NEVADA CHEESE CO INC
6505 County Road 39, Willows
(95988-9709)
PHONE..................................530 934-8660
Ben Gregersen, *President*
John Dundon, *Vice Pres*
Racheloriana Schraeder, *Director*
EMP: 58
SQ FT: 27,000
SALES (est): 14.3MM **Privately Held**
WEB: www.sierranevadacheese.com
SIC: 2022 Natural cheese

(P-603)
TALAMO FOOD SERVICE INC
Also Called: Talamo Foods
18675 Madrone Pkwy 100, Morgan Hill
(95037-2868)
PHONE..................................408 612-8751
Mario Talamo, *President*
Joseph Talamo, *COO*
Fred Gotto, *Purchasing*
Rebecca Cabrera, *Sales Staff*
EMP: 49
SQ FT: 10,000
SALES (est): 13.3MM **Privately Held**
WEB: www.talamofoods.com
SIC: 2022 Cheese spreads, dips, pastes & other cheese products

(P-604)
TOP BRANDS DISTRIBUTION INC
9675 Distribution Ave, San Diego
(92121-2307)
PHONE..................................858 578-0319
Steve Kwon, *CEO*
EMP: 15
SALES (est): 3.7MM **Privately Held**
SIC: 2022 Cheese spreads, dips, pastes & other cheese products

---

2023 Milk, Condensed & Evaporated

(P-605)
BETTER NUTRITIONALS LLC
17120 S Figueroa St B, Gardena
(90248-3021)
PHONE..................................310 502-2277
Sharon Hoffman, *Mng Member*
EMP: 25
SQ FT: 18,000
SALES: 5MM **Privately Held**
SIC: 2023 Dietary supplements, dairy & non-dairy based

(P-606)
BF SUMA PHARMACEUTICALS INC
5077 Walnut Grove Ave, San Gabriel
(91776-2023)
PHONE..................................626 285-8366
Chak Yeung Chan, *President*
Yanbing Chen, *QA Dir*
Annie Cheng, *Controller*
▲ EMP: 13
SQ FT: 10,000
SALES (est): 1.1MM **Privately Held**
SIC: 2023 Dietary supplements, dairy & non-dairy based

(P-607)
BIO-NUTRITIONAL RES GROUP INC (PA)
Also Called: Bnrg
6 Morgan Ste 100, Irvine (92618-1920)
P.O. Box 3669, Torrance (90510-3669)
PHONE..................................714 427-6990
Kevin Lawrence, *CEO*
Curtis Steinhaus, *CFO*
Karen L Stensby, *Corp Secy*
Jack Thomas, *Vice Pres*
Jason Siebert, *Sales Mgr*
EMP: 67 EST: 1991
SQ FT: 3,000
SALES (est): 63.9MM **Privately Held**
WEB: www.bnrg.com
SIC: 2023 Dietary supplements, dairy & non-dairy based

(P-608)
CAPS & TABS INC
3111 Camino Del Rio N # 400, San Diego
(92108-5720)
PHONE..................................619 285-5400
Jeffery S Grossman, *President*
EMP: 42
SALES (est): 4.3MM **Privately Held**
WEB: www.capsandtabs.com
SIC: 2023 Dietary supplements, dairy & non-dairy based

(P-609)
CYTOSPORT INC
1340 Treat Blvd Ste 350, Walnut Creek
(94597-7581)
PHONE..................................707 751-3942
Lisa Selk, *CEO*
Greg Pickett, *Ch of Bd*
Mike Pickett, *President*
David Weber, *COO*
Mike Dittman, *CFO*
▲ EMP: 190
SALES (corp-wide): 9.1B **Publicly Held**
SIC: 2086 Dry, condensed, evaporated dairy products; soft drinks: packaged in cans, bottles, etc.
PA: Hormel Foods Corporation
    1 Hormel Pl
    Austin MN 55912
    507 437-5611

(P-610)
CYVEX NUTRITION INC
1851 Kaiser Ave, Irvine (92614-5707)
PHONE..................................949 622-9030
Joe Vidal, *President*
Bret Scholtes, *CEO*
▲ EMP: 10
SALES (est): 1.4MM **Privately Held**
WEB: www.cyvex.com
SIC: 2023 8742 Dietary supplements, dairy & non-dairy based; marketing consulting services
HQ: Omega Protein Corporation
    2105 City W Blvd Ste 500
    Houston TX 77042
    713 623-0060

(P-611)
DEAN FOODS COMPANY CAL INC
6408 Regio Ave, Buena Park (90620-1017)
PHONE..................................714 684-2160
Joe Scalo, *President*
Mike Mullin, *Opers Mgr*
EMP: 40
SQ FT: 44,000
SALES (est): 6.3MM **Publicly Held**
SIC: 2023 Dry, condensed, evaporated dairy products
HQ: Dean Holding Company
    2711 N Haskell Ave
    Dallas TX 75204
    214 303-3400

(P-612)
DO WELL LABORATORIES INC
14791 Myford Rd, Tustin (92780-7228)
PHONE..................................949 252-0001
Houn Simon Hsia, *President*
▲ EMP: 15
SALES (est): 1.8MM **Privately Held**
SIC: 2023 Dietary supplements, dairy & non-dairy based

(P-613)
ESPERER WEBSTORES LLC
Also Called: Diatomaceous Earth.com
3820 State St Ste B, Santa Barbara
(93105-3182)
PHONE..................................805 880-1900
David Stephen Sorensen, *Mng Member*
EMP: 19
SALES (est): 643.7K **Privately Held**
SIC: 2023 5499 Dietary supplements, dairy & non-dairy based; vitamin food stores

(P-614)
EXCELSIOR NUTRITION INC
Also Called: 4excelsior
1206 N Miller St Unit D, Anaheim
(92806-1960)
PHONE..................................657 999-5188

Yisheng Lin, *CEO*
EMP: 48
SQ FT: 78,000
SALES (est): 1.9MM **Privately Held**
SIC: 2023 Dietary supplements, dairy & non-dairy based

(P-615)
FEIHE INTERNATIONAL INC (PA)
2275 Huntington Dr # 278, San Marino (91108-2640)
PHONE..............................626 757-8885
You B Leng, *President*
Hua Liu, *Vice Pres*
EMP: 1932
SALES (est): 340.5MM **Privately Held**
SIC: 2023 Dry, condensed, evaporated dairy products

(P-616)
FIVE FLAVORS HERBS
344 40th St, Oakland (94609-2609)
PHONE..............................510 923-0178
Benjamin Zappin, *Partner*
EMP: 10
SALES (est): 737K **Privately Held**
SIC: 2023 Dietary supplements, dairy & non-dairy based

(P-617)
FOSTER DAIRY FARMS
572 State Highway 1, Fortuna (95540-9705)
PHONE..............................707 725-6182
Rich Gilladuci, *Manager*
EMP: 115
SALES (corp-wide): 320.5MM **Privately Held**
SIC: 2023 Powdered milk
PA: Foster Dairy Farms
      529 Kansas Ave
      Modesto CA 95351
      209 576-3400

(P-618)
FREAL FOODS LLC
6121 Hollis St Ste 500, Emeryville (94608-2078)
PHONE..............................800 483-3218
Dinsh Guzdar, *President*
Bruce Robinson, *Business Dir*
◆ **EMP:** 100
SALES (est): 21.3MM
SALES (corp-wide): 4B **Privately Held**
WEB: www.frealfoods.com
SIC: 2023 Milkshake mix
PA: Rich Products Corporation
      1 Robert Rich Way
      Buffalo NY 14213
      716 878-8000

(P-619)
FUSION DIET SYSTEMS INC (PA)
620 Nwport Ctr Dr Ste 350, Newport Beach (92660)
PHONE..............................801 783-1194
Yin Yan, *President*
EMP: 10
SALES (est): 300K **Privately Held**
SIC: 2023 Dietary supplements, dairy & non-dairy based; powdered whey

(P-620)
GSL TECH INC
3134 Maxson Rd, El Monte (91732-3102)
PHONE..............................626 572-9617
Weihua Zhang, *President*
Shu Zhang, *Vice Pres*
▲ **EMP:** 16
SALES (est): 1.8MM **Privately Held**
SIC: 2023 5499 2834

(P-621)
HERBS YEH MANUFACTURING CO
Also Called: Natural Medicine Intl
195 N 2nd Ave, Upland (91786-6019)
PHONE..............................909 946-0794
Pearl Weh, *President*
Timothy Yeh, *Vice Pres*
EMP: 10
SALES (est): 760.8K **Privately Held**
SIC: 2023 Dietary supplements, dairy & non-dairy based

(P-622)
HERITAGE DISTRIBUTING COMPANY
Also Called: Ninth Avenue Foods
425 S 9th Ave, City of Industry (91746-3314)
PHONE..............................626 333-9526
Ted De Groot, *President*
EMP: 22 **Privately Held**
SIC: 2023 2026 Dry, condensed, evaporated dairy products; fluid milk
PA: Heritage Distributing Company
      5743 Smithway St Ste 105
      Commerce CA 90040

(P-623)
HILMAR WHEY PROTEIN INC (PA)
9001 Lander Ave, Hilmar (95324-8320)
P.O. Box 910 (95324-0910)
PHONE..............................209 667-6076
John J Jeter, *President*
EMP: 324 **EST:** 1991
SALES (est): 36.4MM **Privately Held**
SIC: 2023 Concentrated whey

(P-624)
HILMAR WHEY PROTEIN INC
8901 Lander Ave, Hilmar (95324-9327)
P.O. Box 910 (95324-0910)
PHONE..............................209 667-6076
EMP: 76
SALES (corp-wide): 36.4MM **Privately Held**
SIC: 2023 Concentrated whey
PA: Hilmar Whey Protein Inc
      9001 Lander Ave
      Hilmar CA 95324
      209 667-6076

(P-625)
K-MAX HEALTH PRODUCTS INTERNAT
1468 E Mission Blvd, Pomona (91766-2229)
PHONE..............................909 455-0158
Angela Ye, *CEO*
▲ **EMP:** 14
SALES (est): 2MM **Privately Held**
SIC: 2023 Dietary supplements, dairy & non-dairy based

(P-626)
KAGED MUSCLE LLC
101 Main St Ste 360, Huntington Beach (92648-8107)
PHONE..............................208 850-0174
Justin White, *President*
◆ **EMP:** 20 **EST:** 2016
SQ FT: 2,000
SALES (est): 1.5MM **Privately Held**
SIC: 2023 Dietary supplements, dairy & non-dairy based

(P-627)
KERRY INC
64405 Lincoln St, Mecca (92254-6501)
PHONE..............................760 396-2116
Darren Worden, *President*
EMP: 65 **Privately Held**
SIC: 2023 Dry, condensed, evaporated dairy products
HQ: Kerry Inc.
      3330 Millington Rd
      Beloit WI 53511
      608 363-1200

(P-628)
LEANER CREAMER LLC
9107 Wilshire Blvd # 450, Beverly Hills (90210-5531)
PHONE..............................818 621-5274
Jonathan Kashani,
EMP: 10
SALES (est): 987.1K **Privately Held**
SIC: 2023 Powdered cream

(P-629)
LONIX PHARMACEUTICAL INC
5001 Earle Ave, Rosemead (91770-1169)
PHONE..............................626 287-4700
Chak Yeung Chan, *President*
Wendy Cheung, *Office Mgr*
EMP: 18

SQ FT: 5,000
SALES: 500K **Privately Held**
SIC: 2023 Dietary supplements, dairy & non-dairy based

(P-630)
MATTHIAS RATH INC (HQ)
1260 Memorex Dr, Santa Clara (95050-2812)
PHONE..............................408 567-5000
Matthias Rath, *President*
Aleksandra Niedzwiecki, *Vice Pres*
EMP: 10
SQ FT: 4,000
SALES (est): 2.8MM **Privately Held**
WEB: www.matthiasrath.com
SIC: 2023 Dietary supplements, dairy & non-dairy based
PA: Matthias Rath Holding B.V.
      Sourethweg 9
      Heerlen 6422
      457 111-100

(P-631)
MIRACLE GREENS INC
8477 Steller Dr, Culver City (90232-2424)
PHONE..............................800 521-5867
Michael G Dave, *President*
EMP: 120
SALES (est): 9.7MM **Privately Held**
SIC: 2023 Dietary supplements, dairy & non-dairy based

(P-632)
MISSION AG RESOURCES LLC
Also Called: Sierra Feeds
6801 Avenue 430 Unit A, Reedley (93654-9002)
PHONE..............................559 591-3333
Al Cumin, *Mng Member*
Therald Benevedo, *Mng Member*
Michelle Bonce, *Assistant*
EMP: 20
SALES (est): 3.8MM **Privately Held**
SIC: 2023 Dietary supplements, dairy & non-dairy based

(P-633)
MUSCLEPHARM CORPORATION (PA)
4400 W Vanowen St, Burbank (91505-1134)
PHONE..............................303 396-6100
Ryan Drexler, *Ch of Bd*
Brian Casutto, *Exec VP*
Lynn Wilsey, *Info Tech Dir*
Sarah Gwinn, *Human Res Mgr*
Adam Ullrich, *Sales Associate*
EMP: 74
SQ FT: 30,302
SALES (est): 102.1MM **Publicly Held**
SIC: 2023 Dietary supplements, dairy & non-dairy based

(P-634)
MYOSCI TECHNOLOGIES INC
Also Called: True Protein
1211 Liberty Way Ste B, Vista (92081-8307)
PHONE..............................760 433-5376
Douglas A Smith, *CEO*
Brian Trudel, *Vice Pres*
Tom Finney, *General Mgr*
Carl Manes, *General Mgr*
EMP: 13
SQ FT: 5,000
SALES (est): 1.5MM **Privately Held**
WEB: www.trueprotein.com
SIC: 2023 Dietary supplements, dairy & non-dairy based

(P-635)
NATURALIFE ECO VITE LABS
Also Called: Paragon Laboratories
20433 Earl St, Torrance (90503-2414)
PHONE..............................310 370-1563
Jay Kaufman, *CEO*
Steven Billis, *CFO*
Richard Kaufman, *Exec VP*
Claire Kaufman, *Admin Sec*
Vicky Hembree, *Purchasing*
▲ **EMP:** 100
SQ FT: 25,000

SALES (est): 25.3MM **Privately Held**
WEB: www.paragonlabsusa.com
SIC: 2023 2844 2834 5122 Dietary supplements, dairy & non-dairy based; toilet preparations; suppositories; vitamins & minerals

(P-636)
NATURES PWR NTRACEUTICALS CORP
Also Called: NP Nutra
15161 15171 S Figueroa St, Gardena (90248)
PHONE..............................310 694-3031
Thomas Walton, *Principal*
Axel Wippich, *President*
Sarah Dunlap, *Accounts Mgr*
Kris Fitzgerald, *Accounts Mgr*
Denise Guggenheim, *Accounts Mgr*
▲ **EMP:** 40
SALES: 12MM **Privately Held**
SIC: 2023 Dietary supplements, dairy & non-dairy based

(P-637)
NESTLE HOLDINGS INC (HQ)
800 N Brand Blvd, Glendale (91203-1245)
PHONE..............................818 549-6000
Brad Alford, *Ch of Bd*
Don Gosline, *Treasurer*
John Gatlin, *Senior VP*
Yun Au, *Admin Sec*
William Holden, *Technology*
◆ **EMP:** 14
SQ FT: 500,000
SALES (est): 12.8B
SALES (corp-wide): 90.8B **Privately Held**
SIC: 2023 2032 2038 2033 Dry, condensed, evaporated dairy products; canned specialties; soups & broths: canned, jarred, etc.; beans & bean sprouts, canned, jarred, etc.; Italian foods: packaged in cans, jars, etc.; frozen specialties; fruits & fruit products in cans, jars, etc.; vegetables & vegetable products in cans, jars, etc.; jams, jellies & preserves: packaged in cans, jars, etc.; tomato products: packaged in cans, jars, etc.; candy & other confectionery products; fluid milk
PA: Nestle S.A.
      Avenue Nestle 55
      Vevey VD 1800
      219 242-111

(P-638)
NESTLE USA INC
Also Called: Nestle Dsd
4065 E Therese Ave, Fresno (93725-8920)
PHONE..............................559 834-2554
Miguel Alvarez, *Branch Mgr*
EMP: 18
SALES (corp-wide): 90.8B **Privately Held**
SIC: 2023 Evaporated milk
HQ: Nestle Usa, Inc.
      1812 N Moore St
      Rosslyn VA 22209
      818 549-6000

(P-639)
NESTLE USA INC
Also Called: Nestle Confections Factory
736 Garner Rd, Modesto (95357-0515)
PHONE..............................209 574-2000
Stephanie Hart, *Branch Mgr*
EMP: 85
SALES (corp-wide): 90.8B **Privately Held**
WEB: www.nestleusa.com
SIC: 2023 2033 2064 2099 Evaporated milk; canned milk, whole; cream substitutes; fruits: packaged in cans, jars, etc.; tomato paste: packaged in cans, jars, etc.; tomato sauce: packaged in cans, jars, etc.; candy & other confectionery products; breakfast bars; pasta, uncooked: packaged with other ingredients
HQ: Nestle Usa, Inc.
      1812 N Moore St
      Rosslyn VA 22209
      818 549-6000

▲ = Import ▼=Export
◆ =Import/Export

(P-640)
NEUROHACKER COLLECTIVE LLC
179 Calle Magdalena # 100, Encinitas (92024-3779)
PHONE..................................855 281-2328
James Schmachtenberge,
Shawn Ramer, *Senior VP*
Robert Greenhall,
Daniel Schmachtenberger,
EMP: 18
SQ FT: 4,500
SALES (est): 979.2K **Privately Held**
SIC: 2023 Dietary supplements, dairy & non-dairy based

(P-641)
NUTRI GRANULATIONS INC
16024 Phoebe Ave, La Mirada (90638-5606)
PHONE..................................714 994-7855
Gene E Alley, *CEO*
Patrick Marantette, *President*
▲ EMP: 70
SQ FT: 45,000
SALES (est): 8.5MM
SALES (corp-wide): 319MM **Privately Held**
WEB: www.nutrigran.com
SIC: 2023 Dietary supplements, dairy & non-dairy based
PA: E. T. Horn Company
16050 Canary Ave
La Mirada CA 90638
714 523-8050

(P-642)
OMANA GROUP LLC
11562 Knott St Ste 5, Garden Grove (92841-1823)
PHONE..................................714 891-9488
Than Nguyen, *Principal*
Harrison Phan, *Managing Dir*
EMP: 10
SQ FT: 2,000
SALES (est): 943.7K **Privately Held**
WEB: www.eomana.com
SIC: 2023 5122 Dietary supplements, dairy & non-dairy based; drugs, proprietaries & sundries

(P-643)
PEAK FRANCHISING INC
Also Called: Max Muscle
1500 S Sunkist St Ste D, Anaheim (92806-5815)
PHONE..................................714 456-0700
Joe Wells, *Principal*
EMP: 25
SALES (est): 2MM **Privately Held**
SIC: 2023 Dietary supplements, dairy & non-dairy based

(P-644)
PHARMACHEM LABORATORIES LLC
2929 E White Star Ave, Anaheim (92806-2628)
PHONE..................................714 630-6000
George Joseph, *Vice Pres*
EMP: 16
SALES (corp-wide): 3.2B **Publicly Held**
SIC: 2023 Dietary supplements, dairy & non-dairy based
HQ: Pharmachem Laboratories, Llc
265 Harrison Tpke
Kearny NJ 07032
201 246-1000

(P-645)
PHYTO ANIMAL HEALTH LLC
550 W C St Ste 2040, San Diego (92101-3565)
PHONE..................................888 871-4505
Stuart Titus, *CEO*
Ian Quinn, *CEO*
EMP: 20
SQ FT: 15,000
SALES (est): 671.8K **Privately Held**
SIC: 2023 Dietary supplements, dairy & non-dairy based

(P-646)
PREMIUM HERBAL USA LLC
Also Called: Dr. J'S Natural
15121 Graham St Ste 108, Huntington Beach (92649-1133)
PHONE..................................800 567-7878
Jacqueline Nguyen, *CEO*
EMP: 10
SALES (est): 311.7K **Privately Held**
SIC: 2023 Dietary supplements, dairy & non-dairy based

(P-647)
PROLACTA BIOSCIENCE INC
1800 Highland Ave, Duarte (91010-2837)
PHONE..................................626 599-9260
Scott A Elster, *CEO*
EMP: 29
SALES (corp-wide): 41.2MM **Privately Held**
SIC: 2023 Dried & powdered milk & milk products
PA: Prolacta Bioscience, Inc.
757 Baldwin Park Blvd
City Of Industry CA 91746
626 599-9260

(P-648)
SANTINI FOODS INC
Also Called: Santini Fine Wines
16505 Worthley Dr, San Lorenzo (94580-1811)
PHONE..................................510 317-8888
Bruce Liu, *President*
Alyssia Smith, *Admin Asst*
Punit Dave, *Research*
Emily Wong, *Graphic Designe*
Phil Mosca, *Safety Mgr*
◆ EMP: 133
SQ FT: 105,000
SALES (est): 39.4MM **Privately Held**
WEB: www.santinifoods.com
SIC: 2023 2026 2032 2087 Condensed, concentrated & evaporated milk products; milk processing (pasteurizing, homogenizing, bottling); ethnic foods: canned, jarred, etc.; beverage bases, concentrates, syrups, powders & mixes

(P-649)
SELECT SUPPLEMENTS INC
2390 Oak Ridge Way, Vista (92081-8345)
PHONE..................................760 431-7509
Hector A Gudino, *Exec VP*
Hector Gudino, *Exec VP*
Julie Chavez, *Technology*
Joel Imaizumi, *Controller*
James Morales, *Prdtn Mgr*
▲ EMP: 10
SALES (est): 1.3MM
SALES (corp-wide): 16.6B **Privately Held**
WEB: www.select-ssi.com
SIC: 2023 2087 Dry, condensed, evaporated dairy products; powders, drink
HQ: Kyowa Hakko U. S. A., Inc.
600 3rd Ave Fl 19
New York NY 10016
212 319-5353

(P-650)
SOURCE OF HEALTH INC
1055 Bay Blvd Ste A, Chula Vista (91911-1628)
PHONE..................................619 409-9500
Oskar Thorvaldsson, *President*
Helene Lindblom, *Buyer*
▲ EMP: 21 EST: 2000
SALES (est): 2.7MM **Privately Held**
SIC: 2023 Dietary supplements, dairy & non-dairy based

(P-651)
TROPICAL FUNCTIONAL LABS LLC
Also Called: Tahiti Trading Company
7111 Arlington Ave Ste F, Riverside (92503-1522)
PHONE..................................951 688-2619
Lawrence Logsdon, *President*
▲ EMP: 11
SALES (est): 1.8MM **Privately Held**
SIC: 2023 Dietary supplements, dairy & non-dairy based

(P-652)
VITAMIN FRIENDS LLC
5300 Beethoven St, Los Angeles (90066-7069)
PHONE..................................310 502-2277
Sharon Hoffman, *Principal*
▲ EMP: 50
SQ FT: 5,000
SALES (est): 5.4MM **Privately Held**
SIC: 2023 Dietary supplements, dairy & non-dairy based

(P-653)
XHALE DISTRIBUTORS
464 E 4th St, Los Angeles (90013-1604)
PHONE..................................888 942-5355
Zara Hbaiu, *Co-Owner*
Alex Hbaiu, *Owner*
EMP: 11 EST: 2008
SQ FT: 6,000
SALES: 3.8MM **Privately Held**
SIC: 2023 Dietary supplements, dairy & non-dairy based

(P-654)
YBCC INC
17800 Castleton St # 386, City of Industry (91748-1791)
PHONE..................................626 213-3945
Xiuhua Song, *President*
EMP: 38
SALES (est): 2.1MM **Privately Held**
SIC: 2023 Dietary supplements, dairy & non-dairy based

2024 Ice Cream

(P-655)
AMPERSAND ICE CREAM LLC
1940 N Echo Ave, Fresno (93704-6004)
PHONE..................................559 264-8000
Amelia Bennett,
Jeffrey Bennett,
EMP: 12
SQ FT: 1,640
SALES: 500K **Privately Held**
SIC: 2024 Ice cream & frozen desserts

(P-656)
ARCTIC ZERO INC
4241 Jutland Dr Ste 305, San Diego (92117-3654)
PHONE..................................619 342-1423
Amit Pandhi, *CEO*
Jason Paine, *President*
Greg Holtman, *COO*
Deanna Spooner, *CFO*
Carlos Cat, *Project Mgr*
EMP: 31
SQ FT: 4,000
SALES: 22.7MM **Privately Held**
SIC: 2024 5143 5142 Dairy based frozen desserts; non-dairy based frozen desserts; frozen dairy desserts; packaged frozen goods

(P-657)
BERENICE 2 AM CORP
Also Called: BOBBOI
8008 Girard Ave Ste 150, La Jolla (92037-4159)
PHONE..................................858 255-8693
Andrea Racca, *Officer*
EMP: 10
SQ FT: 900
SALES: 1.1MM **Privately Held**
SIC: 2024 Ice cream & frozen desserts

(P-658)
BERT & ROCKYS CREAM CO INC
242 Yale Ave, Claremont (91711-4724)
PHONE..................................909 625-1852
Sherry Hunter, *Manager*
EMP: 10
SALES (est): 547.8K
SALES (corp-wide): 1.4MM **Privately Held**
WEB: www.bertandrockys.com
SIC: 2024 5143 5812 Ice cream & frozen desserts; ice cream & ices; ice cream, soft drink & soda fountain stands
PA: Bert & Rockys Cream Co Inc
555 N Benson Ave Ste K
Upland CA 91786
909 946-6805

(P-659)
BLITZERS PREMIUM FROZEN YOGURT
29101 Newport Rd, Menifee (92584-5110)
PHONE..................................951 679-7709
Roger Copp, *Principal*
EMP: 10
SALES (est): 456K **Privately Held**
SIC: 2024 Yogurt desserts, frozen

(P-660)
BROTHERS INTL DESSERTS
2727 S Susan St, Santa Ana (92704-5817)
PHONE..................................949 655-0080
Gary M Winkler, *CEO*
▲ EMP: 120
SQ FT: 30,000
SALES (est): 33.3MM **Privately Held**
WEB: www.brothersdesserts.com
SIC: 2024 Ice cream, bulk; ices, flavored (frozen dessert)

(P-661)
CHANTILLY
Also Called: Chantilly Ice Cream
202 Park Ave, Laguna Beach (92651-2142)
PHONE..................................949 494-7702
Robert Sarhaddar, *Owner*
A Sauveur Ghozland, *Treasurer*
EMP: 30
SQ FT: 1,300
SALES (est): 2.6MM **Privately Held**
WEB: www.chantilly.com
SIC: 2024 5461 Ice cream & frozen desserts; bread

(P-662)
CHILL SPOT INC
11706 Moorpark St, Studio City (91604-2111)
PHONE..................................818 762-0041
Yevgeniy Shneyder, *Principal*
EMP: 10
SALES (est): 775.9K **Privately Held**
SIC: 2024 Yogurt desserts, frozen

(P-663)
COLDSTONE CREAMERY 256
25395 Madison Ave 106d, Murrieta (92562-9093)
PHONE..................................951 304-9777
Maureen Kaczarski, *Owner*
John Kaczarski, *Co-Owner*
EMP: 17
SALES (est): 1.6MM **Privately Held**
SIC: 2024 Ice cream, bulk

(P-664)
COLDSTONE MIRA MESA 114
10716 Westview Pkwy, San Diego (92126-2962)
PHONE..................................858 695-9771
Doug Ducey, *President*
EMP: 14
SALES (est): 1.6MM **Privately Held**
SIC: 2024 2999 Ice cream, bulk; coke

(P-665)
DANONE US LLC
3500 Barranca Pkwy # 240, Irvine (92606-8226)
PHONE..................................949 474-9670
John Mastrotaolo, *Director*
EMP: 390
SALES (corp-wide): 718.1MM **Privately Held**
SIC: 2024 Ice cream & frozen desserts
HQ: Danone Us, Llc
1 Maple Ave
White Plains NY 10605
914 872-8400

(P-666)
DOLCE DOLCI LLC
Also Called: Villa Dolce Gelato
16745 Saticoy St Ste 112, Van Nuys (91406-2710)
PHONE..................................818 343-8400
Wes Schertz,
EMP: 25

SALES (corp-wide): 16MM **Privately Held**
SIC: **2024** Ice cream & ice milk
PA: Dolce Dolci, Llc
6900 Canby Ave Ste 106
Reseda CA 91335
818 343-8400

(P-667)
EDEN CREAMERY LLC (PA)
Also Called: Halo Top
4470 W Sunset Blvd # 90182, Los Angeles
(90027-6302)
PHONE............................855 425-6867
Doug Bouton, COO
Rich Franzosa, Financial Analy
Bailey Bazzar, Analyst
Lily Dang, Marketing Staff
Justin Woolverton,
EMP: 10
SALES (est): 5.3MM **Privately Held**
SIC: **2024** Ice cream, bulk

(P-668)
EL PARAISO NO 2
1760 E Florence Ave, Los Angeles
(90001-2550)
PHONE............................323 587-2073
Ramon Romero, Owner
EMP: 29
SQ FT: 2,760
SALES (est): 1.6MM **Privately Held**
SIC: **2024** Ice cream & ice milk

(P-669)
FARCHITECTURE BB LLC
Also Called: Coolhaus
8588 Washington Blvd, Culver City
(90232-7463)
PHONE............................917 701-2777
Natasha Case, Mng Member
Daniel Fishman, President
James Curtright, General Mgr
Jake Vita, Store Mgr
Nastassia Johnson, Opers Staff
EMP: 30
SALES (est): 584.8K **Privately Held**
SIC: **2024** Ice cream, packaged: molded,
on sticks, etc.

(P-670)
FIORELLOS ITALIAN ICE CREAM
3100 Kerner Blvd Ste Hh, San Rafael
(94901-5445)
PHONE............................415 459-8004
Anthony Bonviso, Owner
EMP: 11
SQ FT: 716
SALES (est): 1.1MM **Privately Held**
SIC: **2024** 5143 Ice cream, bulk; ice
cream & ices

(P-671)
FLOR DE CALIFORNIA
1930 S Bon View Ave # 18, Ontario
(91761-5532)
PHONE............................909 673-1968
Jose Vertiz, Owner
EMP: 20
SQ FT: 1,381
SALES (est): 1.1MM **Privately Held**
SIC: **2024** Ice cream & frozen desserts

(P-672)
FONO UNLIMITED INC (PA)
Also Called: Bravo Fono
99 Stanford Shopping Ctr, Palo Alto
(94304-1424)
PHONE............................650 322-4664
Paulette Fono, President
Laslo Fono, Vice Pres
EMP: 30
SALES: 3MM **Privately Held**
SIC: **2024** 5812 5813 Ice cream, bulk;
Italian restaurant; drinking places

(P-673)
FROST BITE NOVELTIES INC
931 S Cypress St, La Habra (90631-6833)
PHONE............................714 680-0030
Keith Carey, CEO
EMP: 20
SALES: 1.5MM **Privately Held**
SIC: **2024** Ice cream, packaged: molded,
on sticks, etc.

(P-674)
FRUITI POPS INC
15418 Cornet St, Santa Fe Springs
(90670-5534)
PHONE............................562 404-2568
Rodolpho Aguado, Partner
Jaqueline Aguado, Partner
EMP: 12
SQ FT: 13,000
SALES (est): 1.8MM **Privately Held**
WEB: www.fruitipops.net
SIC: **2024** Fruit pops, frozen

(P-675)
GOLDEN SPOON FROZEN YOGURT
Also Called: Golden Spoon of R S M
31431 Santa Margarita, Rcho STA Marg
(92688-1833)
PHONE............................949 888-8810
John Baker, Principal
EMP: 20
SALES (est): 1.9MM **Privately Held**
SIC: **2024** Yogurt desserts, frozen

(P-676)
GUNTHERS QUALITY ICE CREAM
2801 Franklin Blvd, Sacramento
(95818-2719)
PHONE............................916 457-3339
Richard D Klopp, Partner
Marlena Klopp, Partner
EMP: 13
SQ FT: 4,800
SALES: 830K **Privately Held**
SIC: **2024** 5143 5812 Ice cream, bulk; ice
cream & ices; ice cream stands or dairy
bars

(P-677)
HALO TOP INTERNATIONAL LLC
Also Called: Halo Top Creamery
1348 N Sierra Bonita Ave # 107, West Hol-
lywood (90046-8528)
PHONE............................434 409-2057
Doug Bouton, Mng Member
Justin Woolverton,
EMP: 50
SALES (est): 323.5K **Privately Held**
SIC: **2024** Ice cream & frozen desserts

(P-678)
HARRISON BEVERAGE INC
Also Called: Harrison Group
726 Arabian Ln, Walnut (91789-1297)
PHONE............................626 961-1959
Diana Tsai, President
▲ EMP: 15
SQ FT: 72,000
SALES: 3MM **Privately Held**
SIC: **2024**

(P-679)
HELADOS VALLARTA INC
1418 G St, Fresno (93706)
PHONE............................559 709-1177
Emilio Sandoval, President
David Valdivia, Vice Pres
EMP: 10
SQ FT: 5,000
SALES: 482K **Privately Held**
WEB: www.icesations.com
SIC: **2024** 5143 Ice cream & frozen
desserts; ice cream & ices

(P-680)
LOCO VENTURES INC
Also Called: Loard's Ice Cream and Candies
2000 Wayne Ave, San Leandro
(94577-3333)
PHONE............................510 351-0405
Steven Cohen, President
Scott Cohen, Vice Pres
EMP: 25
SQ FT: 16,000
SALES (est): 3.5MM **Privately Held**
SIC: **2024** 2064 5812 5441 Ice cream,
bulk; candy & other confectionery prod-
ucts; ice cream stands or dairy bars;
candy

(P-681)
LONG BEACH CREAMERY LLC
4141 Long Beach Blvd, Long Beach
(90807-2651)
PHONE............................562 252-2730
Dina Amadril, Mng Member
EMP: 13 EST: 2014
SALES: 273K **Privately Held**
SIC: **2024** Ice cream & frozen
desserts; ice cream & ices; ice cream
(packaged)

(P-682)
MACKIE INTERNATIONAL INC (PA)
Also Called: Sun Ice USA
7344 Magnolia Ave Ste 205, Riverside
(92504-3819)
PHONE............................951 346-0530
Ernesto U Dacay Jr, President
▲ EMP: 40
SQ FT: 70,000
SALES: 3MM **Privately Held**
WEB: www.mackieinternational.net
SIC: **2024** 2086 5199 Ices, flavored
(frozen dessert); fruit pops, frozen; gelatin
pops, frozen; fruit drinks (less than 100%
juice): packaged in cans, etc.; baskets

(P-683)
MARIANNES ICE CREAM LLC
218 State Park Dr, Aptos (95003-4324)
PHONE............................831 713-4746
Charles Wilcox, Mng Member
EMP: 40 **Privately Held**
SIC: **2024** Custard, frozen
PA: Marianne's Ice Cream, Llc
2100 Delaware Ave Ste B
Santa Cruz CA 95060

(P-684)
MARIANNES ICE CREAM LLC (PA)
2100 Delaware Ave Ste B, Santa Cruz
(95060-6362)
PHONE............................831 457-1447
Charles Wilcox, Mng Member
Kelly Dillon,
▲ EMP: 10
SALES (est): 4.3MM **Privately Held**
SIC: **2024** 5812 Ice cream & frozen
desserts; ice cream stands or dairy bars

(P-685)
MATTERHORN ICE CREAM INC
1221 66th St, Sacramento (95819-4323)
PHONE............................208 287-8916
Thomas Nist, President
Todd Wilson, CFO
EMP: 85
SQ FT: 24,000
SALES (est): 9.4MM **Privately Held**
SIC: **2024** Ice cream & ice milk

(P-686)
MAVENS CREAMERY LLC
1701 S 7th St Ste 7, San Jose
(95112-6000)
PHONE............................408 216-9270
Kim Lam, Mng Member
Tony Lam, Mng Member
EMP: 30
SQ FT: 5,000
SALES (est): 2.9MM **Privately Held**
SIC: **2024** Ice cream & frozen desserts

(P-687)
NADOLIFE INC
Also Called: Moo Time
2709 Newton Ave, San Diego
(92113-3713)
P.O. Box 182225, Coronado (92178-2225)
PHONE............................619 522-6890
David Spatafore, CEO
Leroy Mossell, Vice Pres
Jennifer Spatafore, Principal
EMP: 60
SALES (est): 10.1MM **Privately Held**
WEB: www.mootime.com
SIC: **2024** Ice cream, bulk

(P-688)
NAIA INC
Also Called: Gelateria Naia
736 Alfred Nobel Dr, Hercules
(94547-1805)
PHONE............................510 724-2479
Christopher C Tan, Principal
Jesse Porter, Opers Mgr
EMP: 34
SALES (est): 6.2MM **Privately Held**
SIC: **2024** Ice cream, bulk

(P-689)
NESTLE DREYERS ICE CREAM CO
Also Called: Dreyer's Grand Ice Cream
7301 District Blvd, Bakersfield
(93313-2042)
PHONE............................661 398-5448
Mark McLenithan, Manager
EMP: 10
SALES (corp-wide): 90.8B **Privately Held**
WEB: www.dreyersinc.com
SIC: **2024** Ice cream, packaged: molded,
on sticks, etc.
HQ: Nestle Dreyer's Ice Cream Company
5929 College Ave
Oakland CA 94618
510 594-9466

(P-690)
RAMAR INTERNATIONAL CORP (PA)
Also Called: Orientex Foods
1101 Railroad Ave, Pittsburg (94565-2641)
P.O. Box 111 (94565-0011)
PHONE............................925 439-9009
Primo Quesada, President
Susan Quesada, Administration
Warren Ngo, Controller
George Levy, Sales Mgr
Eric Cendejas, Marketing Staff
◆ EMP: 40 EST: 1968
SALES (est): 28.2MM **Privately Held**
SIC: **2024** 2013 5141 Ice cream & frozen
desserts; sausages & other prepared
meats; groceries, general line

(P-691)
RICHARD PAOLA
Also Called: Gaia Gelato
300 Carlsbad Village Dr # 104, Carlsbad
(92008-2900)
PHONE............................442 500-8231
Paola Richard, Owner
EMP: 10
SALES (est): 342.9K **Privately Held**
SIC: **2024** Ice cream & frozen desserts

(P-692)
RITAS FELICITA
1875 S Centre City Pkwy, Escondido
(92025-6585)
PHONE............................760 975-3302
Chris Uhles, Owner
EMP: 18
SALES (est): 1MM **Privately Held**
SIC: **2024** 5812 Ice cream & frozen
desserts; caterers

(P-693)
ROSA BROTHERS MILK CO INC (PA)
10090 2nd Ave, Hanford (93230-9370)
PHONE............................559 582-8825
Noel M Rosa, President
Rolland Rosa, Vice Pres
EMP: 35
SALES (est): 2.9MM **Privately Held**
SIC: **2024** 2026 Ice cream & frozen
desserts; half & half

(P-694)
SCREAMIN MIMIS INC
6902 Sebastopol Ave, Sebastopol
(95472-3411)
PHONE............................707 823-5902
Maraline Olson, President
EMP: 18
SALES (est): 1.8MM **Privately Held**
WEB: www.screaminmimisicecream.com
SIC: **2024** 5812 Ice cream, bulk; ice
cream, soft drink & soda fountain stands

(P-695)
STREMICKS HERITAGE FOODS LLC
11503 Pierce St, Riverside (92505-3350)
PHONE..................................951 352-1344
Andy Holm, *Branch Mgr*
EMP: 70
SALES (corp-wide): 429.7MM **Privately Held**
WEB: www.stremicksheritagefoods.com
SIC: 2024 Ice cream & frozen desserts
PA: Stremicks Heritage Foods, Llc
4002 Westminster Ave
Santa Ana CA 92703
714 775-5000

(P-696)
SUPER STORE INDUSTRIES
Also Called: Mid Valley Dairy
2600 Spengler Way, Turlock (95380-8591)
PHONE..................................209 668-2100
Joe Mc Gill, *Manager*
Jeff Woodsmall, *Executive*
Karen Ferreira, *QC Mgr*
Mark Hujdic, *Manager*
EMP: 100
SALES (corp-wide): 279.6MM **Privately Held**
SIC: 2024 5143 Ice cream & frozen desserts; ice cream & ices
PA: Super Store Industries
2800 W March Ln Ste 210
Stockton CA 95219
209 473-8100

(P-697)
SUPERIOR DAIRY PRODUCTS CO
325 N Douty St, Hanford (93230-3993)
PHONE..................................559 582-0481
Susan Wing, *President*
Tim Jones, *Vice Pres*
EMP: 34
SQ FT: 7,500
SALES: 825K **Privately Held**
WEB: www.superiordairy.com
SIC: 2024 Ice cream & ice milk

(P-698)
SWEETY NOVELTY INC
Also Called: Frupaletta
633 Monterey Pass Rd, Monterey Park (91754-2418)
PHONE..................................626 282-4482
Traci Lee, *President*
Stephen Lee, *Vice Pres*
Patty Lee, *Manager*
▲ **EMP:** 13
SQ FT: 11,680
SALES (est): 1.7MM **Privately Held**
SIC: 2024 Ice cream & frozen desserts

(P-699)
THREE TWINS ORGANIC INC (PA)
Also Called: Three Twins Organic Ice Cream
419 1st St, Petaluma (94952-4226)
PHONE..................................707 763-8946
Neal H Gottlieb, *CEO*
Matt Grebil, *Opers Staff*
Darryl Davis, *VP Sales*
Nathan Reynolds, *Manager*
Edith Jimenez, *Assistant*
EMP: 21
SALES (est): 3.7MM **Privately Held**
SIC: 2024 5199 5812 Ice cream, bulk; ice, manufactured or natural; ice cream stands or dairy bars

(P-700)
TROPICALE FOODS INC
1237 W State St, Ontario (91762-4015)
P.O. Box 2224, Chino (91708-2224)
PHONE..................................909 635-0390
Ruben Gutierrez, *President*
Yemeni Mesa, *Office Mgr*
Lupe Gutierrez, *Admin Sec*
Erika Ruiz, *Human Res Mgr*
Elizabeth Sanchez, *Human Res Mgr*
▲ **EMP:** 49
SALES (est): 22.5MM **Privately Held**
WEB: www.tropicalefoods.com
SIC: 2024 Ice milk, packaged: molded, on sticks, etc.

(P-701)
VAMPIRE PENGUIN LLC (PA)
907 K St, Sacramento (95814-3511)
PHONE..................................916 553-4197
Leo Alejandro San Luis, *Mng Member*
EMP: 11
SALES (est): 1.7MM **Privately Held**
SIC: 2024 Ice cream, bulk

(P-702)
VENTURE CAPITAL ENTPS LLC
Also Called: Twist Frozen Yogurt
10669 Wellworth Ave, Los Angeles (90024-5011)
PHONE..................................914 275-7305
Abdelmajid Sabour, *Mng Member*
EMP: 10 **EST:** 2012
SALES: 1.5MM **Privately Held**
SIC: 2024 Yogurt desserts, frozen

(P-703)
VON HOPPEN ICE CREAM (HQ)
Also Called: Frutstix Company
1525 State St Ste 203, Santa Barbara (93101-6512)
PHONE..................................805 965-2009
William McKinley, *President*
Mariam Schroeder, *Admin Sec*
▲ **EMP:** 10
SALES: 3.6MM
SALES (corp-wide): 14.8MM **Privately Held**
WEB: www.frutstix.com
SIC: 2024 Juice pops, frozen
PA: The Lafayette Corporation
1525 State St Ste 203
Santa Barbara CA 93101
805 965-2009

(P-704)
VON HOPPEN ICE CREAM
Also Called: Frutstix Company
8221 Arjons Dr Ste A, San Diego (92126-6319)
PHONE..................................858 695-9111
Jim Elwel, *Manager*
Thomas Triffo, *Opers Dir*
EMP: 15
SALES (corp-wide): 14.8MM **Privately Held**
WEB: www.frutstix.com
SIC: 2024 Ice cream, bulk
HQ: Von Hoppen Ice Cream
1525 State St Ste 203
Santa Barbara CA 93101
805 965-2009

(P-705)
WE THE PIE PEOPLE LLC
Also Called: Jc's Pie Pops
9909 Topanga Canyon Blvd # 159, Chatsworth (91311-3602)
PHONE..................................818 349-1880
Jennifer Constantine, *Mng Member*
Thomas Spler,
Charles Crane, *Assistant*
▲ **EMP:** 50
SALES (est): 5.4MM **Privately Held**
SIC: 2024 Non-dairy based frozen desserts

(P-706)
WHOLESOME YO CURD
19755 Colima Rd, Rowland Heights (91748-3206)
PHONE..................................909 859-8758
Charanjit Jaujhar, *Owner*
EMP: 10
SALES (est): 405.9K **Privately Held**
SIC: 2024 Yogurt desserts, frozen

(P-707)
ZIEGENFELDER COMPANY
12290 Colony Ave, Chino (91710-2095)
PHONE..................................909 590-0493
Allan Hawthorne, *Branch Mgr*
EMP: 40
SALES (corp-wide): 21MM **Privately Held**
SIC: 2024 Ice cream, packaged: molded, on sticks, etc.
PA: The Ziegenfelder Company
87 18th St
Wheeling WV 26003
304 232-6360

2026 Milk

(P-708)
ALBERT GOYENETCHE DAIRY
6041 Brandt Rd, Buttonwillow (93206-9547)
PHONE..................................661 764-6176
Albert Goyenetche, *Owner*
EMP: 12
SALES (est): 1.2MM **Privately Held**
SIC: 2026 Milk processing (pasteurizing, homogenizing, bottling); gasoline service stations

(P-709)
ALTA-DENA CERTIFIED DAIRY LLC
123 Aero Camino, Goleta (93117-3177)
PHONE..................................805 685-8328
EMP: 134 **Publicly Held**
SIC: 2026
HQ: Alta-Dena Certified Dairy, Llc
17637 E Valley Blvd
City Of Industry CA 91744
626 964-6401

(P-710)
ALTA-DENA CERTIFIED DAIRY LLC
17851 Railroad St, City of Industry (91748-1118)
PHONE..................................800 395-7004
Michael Greenwald, *Accounts Mgr*
EMP: 134 **Publicly Held**
SIC: 2026 Cottage cheese
HQ: Alta-Dena Certified Dairy, Llc
17637 E Valley Blvd
City Of Industry CA 91744
626 964-6401

(P-711)
ALTA-DENA CERTIFIED DAIRY LLC (DH)
17637 E Valley Blvd, City of Industry (91744-5731)
PHONE..................................626 964-6401
John Keith,
Jack Tewers, *CFO*
Bob Pettigrew, *Vice Pres*
Steve Schaffer, *General Mgr*
Manuel Castanon, *Admin Asst*
EMP: 370 **EST:** 1945
SQ FT: 100,000
SALES (est): 183.3MM **Publicly Held**
WEB: www.altadenadairy.com
SIC: 2026 Milk & cream, except fermented, cultured & flavored

(P-712)
BERKELEY FARMS LLC
7444 Reese Rd, Sacramento (95828-3706)
PHONE..................................916 689-7613
Richard Hunter, *General Mgr*
EMP: 30 **Publicly Held**
WEB: www.berkeleyfarms.com
SIC: 2026 Fluid milk
HQ: Berkeley Farms, Llc
25500 Clawiter Rd
Hayward CA 94545
510 265-8600

(P-713)
CALIFORNIA DAIRIES INC (PA)
2000 N Plaza Dr, Visalia (93291-9358)
PHONE..................................559 625-2200
Andrei Mikhalevsky, *CEO*
John Azevedo, *Ch of Bd*
Dave Bush, *COO*
David Camp, *CFO*
Joe L Heffington, *Senior VP*
◆ **EMP:** 80 **EST:** 1938
SALES (est): 265.8MM **Privately Held**
WEB: www.californiadairies.com
SIC: 2026 2021 2023 Fluid milk; creamery butter; dry, condensed, evaporated dairy products

(P-714)
CALIFORNIA DAIRIES INC
755 F St, Fresno (93706-3416)
P.O. Box 11865 (93775-1865)
PHONE..................................559 233-5154
Bill Twist, *Branch Mgr*

EMP: 100
SALES (corp-wide): 265.8MM **Privately Held**
WEB: www.californiadairies.com
SIC: 2026 2021 2023
PA: California Dairies, Inc.
2000 N Plaza Dr
Visalia CA 93291
559 625-2200

(P-715)
CALIFORNIA DAIRIES INC
11709 Artesia Blvd, Artesia (90701-3803)
PHONE..................................562 809-2595
Joe Heffington, *Branch Mgr*
John C Rocha, *Bd of Directors*
Pete Cassinerio, *Vice Pres*
EMP: 65
SALES (corp-wide): 265.8MM **Privately Held**
WEB: www.californiadairies.com
SIC: 2026 Milk processing (pasteurizing, homogenizing, bottling)
PA: California Dairies, Inc.
2000 N Plaza Dr
Visalia CA 93291
559 625-2200

(P-716)
CALVA PRODUCTS CO INC
4351 E Winery Rd, Acampo (95220-9506)
P.O. Box 126 (95220-0126)
PHONE..................................209 339-1516
Jim Cook Sr, *CEO*
Bill Cook, *Vice Pres*
◆ **EMP:** 39 **EST:** 1975
SQ FT: 62,000
SALES (est): 13.5MM
SALES (corp-wide): 12.8B **Privately Held**
WEB: www.calvaproducts.com
SIC: 2026 Fluid milk
HQ: Purina Animal Nutrition Llc
1080 County Road F W
Shoreview MN 55126

(P-717)
CREST BEVERAGE LLC
8870 Liquid Ct, San Diego (92121-2234)
PHONE..................................858 452-2300
Steven S Sourapas, *Mng Member*
Rich Pagan, *Division Mgr*
Tricia Barclay, *Admin Sec*
Rene Salazar, *Merchandising*
David Scrivner, *Sales Staff*
▲ **EMP:** 400
SQ FT: 200,000
SALES (est): 48.4MM **Privately Held**
SIC: 2026 2082 Beer & other fermented malt liquors

(P-718)
CRYSTAL CREAM & BUTTER CO (HQ)
8340 Belvedere Ave, Sacramento (95826-5902)
PHONE..................................916 444-7200
Donald K Hansen, *Chairman*
Michael J Newell, *President*
Dan Kosewski, *Vice Pres*
EMP: 100
SQ FT: 100,000
SALES (est): 51.2MM
SALES (corp-wide): 2.1B **Privately Held**
WEB: www.crystal-milk.com
SIC: 2026 2021 2024 Milk processing (pasteurizing, homogenizing, bottling); cottage cheese; yogurt; creamery butter; ice cream & ice milk
PA: Hp Hood Llc
6 Kimball Ln Ste 400
Lynnfield MA 01940
617 887-8441

(P-719)
DAIRY FARMERS AMERICA INC
170 N Maple St Ste 106, Corona (92880-1781)
PHONE..................................951 493-4900
Glenn Wallace, *Manager*
Linda Wdowicki, *Controller*
EMP: 15
SALES (corp-wide): 14.6B **Privately Held**
WEB: www.dfamilk.com
SIC: 2026 Fluid milk

PA: Dairy Farmers Of America, Inc.
1405 N 98th St
Kansas City KS 66111
816 801-6455

(P-720)
DAIRY FARMERS AMERICA INC
170 N Maple St Ste 106, Corona
(92880-1781)
P.O. Box 849, Hughson (95326-0849)
PHONE............................209 883-4461
John Crockett, *Manager*
Kristin Naranjo, *Controller*
Eric Janitz, *Purch Agent*
Sagar Sidhu, *Safety Mgr*
Don Faust, *Plant Engr*
EMP: 40
SALES (corp-wide): 14.6B **Privately Held**
WEB: www.dfamilk.com
SIC: 2026 2021 2022 2023 Milk process-
ing (pasteurizing, homogenizing, bottling);
creamery butter; cheese, natural &
processed; dried nonfat milk; milk depot;
milk & cream, fluid; butter; ice cream &
frozen desserts
PA: Dairy Farmers Of America, Inc.
1405 N 98th St
Kansas City KS 66111
816 801-6455

(P-721)
DAIRY FARMERS AMERICA INC
4375 N Ventura Ave, Ventura (93001-1124)
PHONE............................805 653-0042
Kevin Clark, *Manager*
EMP: 90
SALES (corp-wide): 14.6B **Privately Held**
WEB: www.dfamilk.com
SIC: 2026 2022 2021 2023 Milk process-
ing (pasteurizing, homogenizing, bottling);
natural cheese; creamery butter; con-
densed milk; ice cream & ice milk;
roasted coffee
PA: Dairy Farmers Of America, Inc.
1405 N 98th St
Kansas City KS 66111
816 801-6455

(P-722)
DEAN FOODS COMPANY
605 N J St, Tulare (93274-2845)
PHONE............................559 687-1927
Buck Buchanan, *Branch Mgr*
EMP: 19 **Publicly Held**
SIC: 2026 Fluid milk
PA: Dean Foods Company
2711 N Haskell Ave
Dallas TX 75204
-

(P-723)
DRIFTWOOD DAIRY INC
10724 Lower Azusa Rd, El Monte
(91731-1390)
P.O. Box 5508 (91734-1508)
PHONE............................626 444-9591
P Kelly Olds, *CEO*
Monty Zwieg, *Vice Pres*
Jeff Carter, *VP Finance*
Marco Sandoval, *Human Res Mgr*
Steve Nuckolls, *Opers Staff*
EMP: 215
SALES (est): 86.4MM **Privately Held**
WEB: www.driftwooddairy.com
SIC: 2026 Milk processing (pasteurizing,
homogenizing, bottling)

(P-724)
FARMDALE CREAMERY INC
1049 W Base Line St, San Bernardino
(92411-2310)
PHONE............................909 888-4938
Norman R Shotts II, *CEO*
Michael Shotts, *President*
Scott Hofferber, *CFO*
Nicholas J Sibilio, *Vice Pres*
Nicholas Sibilio, *Vice Pres*
▲ **EMP:** 100
SQ FT: 110,000
SALES (est): 23.7MM **Privately Held**
WEB: www.farmdale.net
SIC: 2026 2022 Buttermilk, cultured; natu-
ral cheese

(P-725)
FROGLANDERS LA JOLLA
915 Pearl St Ste A, La Jolla (92037-5073)
PHONE............................858 459-3764
Esther Thompson, *Owner*
EMP: 12
SALES (est): 635.7K **Privately Held**
SIC: 2026 5812 5451 Fluid milk; eating
places; dairy products stores

(P-726)
GENERAL MILLS INC
1055 Sandhill Ave, Carson (90746-1312)
P.O. Box 4589 (90749-4589)
PHONE............................310 605-6108
Jeff Crandle, *Manager*
EMP: 20
SQ FT: 62,497
SALES (corp-wide): 15.7B **Publicly Held**
WEB: www.generalmills.com
SIC: 2026 2041 Yogurt; flour mixes
PA: General Mills, Inc.
1 General Mills Blvd
Minneapolis MN 55426
763 764-7600

(P-727)
GOLDEN STATE MIXING INC
415 D St, Turlock (95380-5452)
P.O. Box 3046 (95381-3046)
PHONE............................209 632-3656
Tim D Brewster, *President*
Brant Enoch, *Vice Pres*
EMP: 25 EST: 2009
SALES (est): 5MM **Privately Held**
SIC: 2026 Fluid milk

(P-728)
**HERITAGE DISTRIBUTING
COMPANY (PA)**
Also Called: Rex Creamery
5743 Smithway St Ste 105, Commerce
(90040-1548)
P.O. Box 668, Downey (90241-0668)
PHONE............................323 838-1225
Ted S Degroot, *President*
Gary Ericks, *Accounts Mgr*
EMP: 43
SALES (est): 11MM **Privately Held**
SIC: 2026 Milk processing (pasteurizing,
homogenizing, bottling)

(P-729)
HP HOOD LLC
8340 Belvedere Ave, Sacramento
(95826-5902)
PHONE............................916 379-9266
Gary Saavedra, *Branch Mgr*
Karen Tobin, *Manager*
EMP: 296
SALES (corp-wide): 2.1B **Privately Held**
SIC: 2026 Fluid milk
PA: Hp Hood Llc
6 Kimball Ln Ste 400
Lynnfield MA 01940
617 887-8441

(P-730)
JACKSON-MITCHELL INC (PA)
Also Called: Meyenburg Goat Milk Products
1240 South Ave, Turlock (95380-5113)
P.O. Box 934 (95381-0934)
PHONE............................209 667-0786
Robert Jackson, *Ch of Bd*
Doug Buehrle, *CFO*
Carol Jackson, *Treasurer*
Jonathan Mitchell, *Admin Sec*
Charlotte Cordova, *Admin Asst*
EMP: 22
SQ FT: 11,200
SALES (est): 5.9MM **Privately Held**
WEB: www.jackson-mitchell.com
SIC: 2026 2023 Milk, ultra-high tempera-
ture (longlife); evaporated milk; powdered
milk

(P-731)
MID VALLEY MILK CO
10786 Avenue 144, Tipton (93272-9526)
PHONE............................661 721-8419
Myron Schotanus, *Owner*
EMP: 13
SALES (est): 1.3MM **Privately Held**
SIC: 2026 Fluid milk

(P-732)
PAC FILL INC
Also Called: Sun Dairy
5471 W San Fernando Rd, Los Angeles
(90039-1014)
PHONE............................818 409-0117
Vahik Sarkissian, *CEO*
Edward Sarkissian, *Vice Pres*
Jerry Nicoghosian, *Admin Sec*
Ed Sarkissian, *Director*
EMP: 25
SQ FT: 22,000
SALES (est): 5.6MM **Privately Held**
SIC: 2026 2086 Yogurt; carbonated soft
drinks, bottled & canned

(P-733)
PARAMOUNT DAIRY INC (PA)
17801 Cartwright Rd, Irvine (92614-6216)
PHONE............................949 265-8077
Adiel Gorel Mana, *CEO*
▲ **EMP:** 28
SALES (est): 9.3MM **Privately Held**
SIC: 2026 Yogurt

(P-734)
PARAMOUNT DAIRY INC
15255 Texaco Ave, Paramount
(90723-3917)
PHONE............................949 265-8000
Phillip C Chang, *Branch Mgr*
EMP: 30
SALES (corp-wide): 9.3MM **Privately
Held**
SIC: 2026 Yogurt
PA: Paramount Dairy, Inc.
17801 Cartwright Rd
Irvine CA 92614
949 265-8077

(P-735)
**SAPUTO DAIRY FOODS USA
LLC**
Also Called: Morningstar Foods
299 5th Ave, Gustine (95322-1202)
PHONE............................209 854-6461
Richard Rosemire, *Manager*
Micki Ponder, *Human Res Dir*
Lisa Crist, *Human Res Mgr*
EMP: 175
SQ FT: 5,000 **Privately Held**
WEB: www.morningstarfoods.com
SIC: 2026 Cream, whipped
HQ: Saputo Dairy Foods Usa, Llc
2711 N Haske Ave Ste 3700
Dallas TX 75204
214 863-2300

(P-736)
**SAPUTO DAIRY FOODS USA
LLC**
1901 Via Burton, Fullerton (92831-5341)
PHONE............................714 772-8861
Klein Ron, *Branch Mgr*
Craig Murphy, *Manager*
EMP: 125 **Privately Held**
SIC: 2026 Cream, whipped
HQ: Saputo Dairy Foods Usa, Llc
2711 N Haske Ave Ste 3700
Dallas TX 75204
214 863-2300

(P-737)
**STREMICKS HERITAGE FOODS
LLC (PA)**
4002 Westminster Ave, Santa Ana
(92703-1310)
PHONE............................714 775-5000
Louis J Stremick, *Mng Member*
Rob Ball, *Vice Pres*
Jin Jo, *Vice Pres*
Jason Jones, *Vice Pres*
Jerry Moran, *Vice Pres*
▼ **EMP:** 300
SALES (est): 429.7MM **Privately Held**
WEB: www.stremicksheritagefoods.com
SIC: 2026 Cream, sour

(P-738)
SWEET XO LP
5825 Kanan Rd, Agoura Hills (91301-1651)
PHONE............................818 889-9696
EMP: 10

SALES (corp-wide): 2.7MM **Privately
Held**
SIC: 2026 Yogurt
PA: Sweet Xo, Lp
6265 Variel Ave
Woodland Hills CA 91367
818 789-5550

(P-739)
VITAFOODS AMERICA LLC
Also Called: Dr. Shica's Healthy Surprises
680 E Colo Blvd Ste 180, Pasadena
(91101)
PHONE............................800 695-4750
Washica Little,
Ladale Jackson,
EMP: 10 EST: 2014
SQ FT: 900
SALES: 10MM **Privately Held**
SIC: 2026 Whipped topping, except frozen
or dry mix

(P-740)
WIN SOON INC
Also Called: Epoca Yocool
4569 Firestone Blvd, South Gate
(90280-3343)
PHONE............................323 564-5070
Jun Sang Lee, *Principal*
Byung K Yoo, *Vice Pres*
Brian Ju, *General Mgr*
Justin Lee, *Accountant*
Jay Song, *Purchasing*
▲ **EMP:** 25
SQ FT: 7,000
SALES (est): 5.5MM **Privately Held**
WEB: www.winsoon.com
SIC: 2026 5149 Yogurt; soft drinks

(P-741)
WWF OPERATING COMPANY
Also Called: White Wave Foods
18275 Arenth Ave Bldg 1, City of Industry
(91748-1225)
PHONE............................626 810-1775
Bob King, *Manager*
EMP: 235
SALES (corp-wide): 718.1MM **Privately
Held**
WEB: www.morningstarfoods.com
SIC: 2026 Milk processing (pasteurizing,
homogenizing, bottling)
HQ: Wwf Operating Company
12002 Airport Way
Broomfield CO 80021
214 303-3400

(P-742)
YOPLAIT U S A INC
1055 Sandhill Ave, Carson (90746-1332)
PHONE............................310 632-9502
Terry Lennon, *Principal*
EMP: 20
SALES (est): 3.5MM **Privately Held**
SIC: 2026 Yogurt

2032 Canned Specialties

(P-743)
ADESA INTERNATIONAL LLC
1440 S Vineyard Ave, Ontario
(91761-8042)
PHONE............................909 321-8240
Alberto Santiago,
Francisco Gonzalez, *QC Mgr*
EMP: 24
SQ FT: 1,500
SALES (est): 2.4MM **Privately Held**
SIC: 2032 Mexican foods: packaged in
cans, jars, etc.

(P-744)
**AFP ADVANCED FOOD
PRODUCTS LLC**
1211 E Noble Ave, Visalia (93292-3040)
PHONE............................559 627-2070
Barry Ritchard, *Branch Mgr*
Bill Orban, *CFO*
EMP: 130

SALES (corp-wide): 6.3B **Privately Held**
WEB: www.afpllc.com
SIC: 2032 2022 2026 Puddings, except meat: packaged in cans, jars, etc.; soups, except seafood: packaged in cans, jars, etc.; cheese spreads, dips, pastes & other cheese products; spreads, cheese; pastes, cheese; fluid milk
HQ: Afp Advanced Food Products Llc
402 S Custer Ave
New Holland PA 17557
717 355-8667

(P-745)
BABYS WORLD
14222 Brookhurst St, Garden Grove (92843-4662)
PHONE.................................714 539-2229
Anthony Nugent, *Owner*
EMP: 10 EST: 2000
SALES (est): 823.6K **Privately Held**
SIC: 2032 Baby foods, including meats: packaged in cans, jars, etc.

(P-746)
BASTAN CORPORATION
2260 Main St Ste 17, Chula Vista (91911-3956)
PHONE.................................619 424-3416
Teresa Delenne, *President*
Alonso Anciza, *Vice Pres*
EMP: 16
SALES (est): 2MM **Privately Held**
SIC: 2032 5812 Mexican foods: packaged in cans, jars, etc.; Mexican restaurant

(P-747)
BIEN PADRE FOODS INC
1459 Railroad St, Eureka (95501-2147)
P.O. Box 3748 (95502-3748)
PHONE.................................707 442-4585
Benito Lim, *President*
Rosita Lim, *Treasurer*
Bob McCall, *Vice Pres*
Domingo Bernardo Jr, *Admin Sec*
▲ EMP: 28
SQ FT: 14,000
SALES (est): 5.4MM **Privately Held**
WEB: www.bienpadre.com
SIC: 2032 5149 2099 2096 Ethnic foods: canned, jarred, etc.; canned goods: fruit, vegetables, seafood, meats, etc.; spices & seasonings; tortillas, fresh or refrigerated; potato chips & similar snacks

(P-748)
BOBBY SLZARS MXCAN FD PDTS INC (PA)
Also Called: Bobby Salazar Corporate
2810 San Antonio Dr, Fowler (93625-9799)
PHONE.................................559 834-4787
Robert Salazar, *CEO*
Bobby Salazar, *President*
Charles Gamoian, *Vice Pres*
Sheila Martinez, *Sales Staff*
Laura Navarro, *Manager*
EMP: 25
SQ FT: 16,375
SALES: 5MM **Privately Held**
SIC: 2032 5812 Mexican foods: packaged in cans, jars, etc.; Mexican restaurant

(P-749)
CAER INC
Also Called: Yumi
129 N Laurel Ave, Los Angeles (90048-3511)
PHONE.................................415 879-9864
Angela Sutherland, *CEO*
Evelyn Rusli, *President*
EMP: 27 EST: 2015
SALES (est): 2.3MM **Privately Held**
SIC: 2032 7389 Baby foods, including meats: packaged in cans, jars, etc.;

(P-750)
CAMPBELL SOUP COMPANY
8380 Pedrick Rd, Dixon (95620-9606)
P.O. Box 340 (95620-0340)
PHONE.................................707 678-4406
Fred Tyler, *Branch Mgr*
Renee Branda, *Technology*
EMP: 225

SALES (corp-wide): 8.6B **Publicly Held**
WEB: www.campbellsoups.com
SIC: 2032 2038 2033 2052 Spaghetti: packaged in cans, jars, etc.; frozen specialties; canned fruits & specialties; cookies & crackers; bread, cake & related products; potato chips & similar snacks
PA: Campbell Soup Company
1 Campbell Pl
Camden NJ 08103
856 342-4800

(P-751)
CAMPBELL SOUP COMPANY
2300 River Plaza Dr # 175, Sacramento (95833-4256)
PHONE.................................916 922-2836
Ray Oldach, *Vice Pres*
EMP: 100
SALES (corp-wide): 8.6B **Publicly Held**
WEB: www.campbellsoups.com
SIC: 2032 2038 2033 2052 Canned specialties; frozen specialties; canned fruits & specialties; cookies & crackers; bread, cake & related products; potato chips & similar snacks
PA: Campbell Soup Company
1 Campbell Pl
Camden NJ 08103
856 342-4800

(P-752)
CAMPBELL SOUP COMPANY
28605 County Road 104, Davis (95618-9615)
PHONE.................................530 753-2116
Hasan Bolkan, *Enginr/R&D Mgr*
EMP: 45
SALES (corp-wide): 8.6B **Publicly Held**
WEB: www.campbellsoups.com
SIC: 2032 2038 2033 2052 Spaghetti: packaged in cans, jars, etc.; frozen specialties; canned fruits & specialties; cookies & crackers; bread, cake & related products; potato chips & similar snacks
PA: Campbell Soup Company
1 Campbell Pl
Camden NJ 08103
856 342-4800

(P-753)
CG FINANCIAL LLC
Also Called: SD Fresh Products
7020 Alamitos Ave Ste B, San Diego (92154-4710)
P.O. Box 212996, Chula Vista (91921-2996)
PHONE.................................619 656-2919
Gustavo Gonzalez Jr, *Mng Member*
Catherine Gonzalez, *President*
EMP: 15
SALES: 3.4MM **Privately Held**
SIC: 2032 Mexican foods: packaged in cans, jars, etc.

(P-754)
CORN MAIDEN FOODS INC
24201 Frampton Ave, Harbor City (90710-2105)
PHONE.................................310 784-0400
Pascal Dropsy, *President*
EMP: 65
SQ FT: 40,000
SALES (est): 11.1MM **Privately Held**
WEB: www.cornmaidenfoods.com
SIC: 2032 Canned specialties

(P-755)
DEMAIZ INC
77 S 28th St, San Jose (95116-2315)
PHONE.................................650 518-6268
Alejandro Arreola, *CEO*
Celia Madrid, *Vice Pres*
EMP: 13
SQ FT: 7,200
SALES (est): 469.1K **Privately Held**
SIC: 2032 Tamales: packaged in cans, jars, etc.

(P-756)
EDS WRAP AND ROLL FOODS LLC
2545 Barrington Ct, Hayward (94545-1167)
PHONE.................................510 266-0888
Chan Fan Ho, *Owner*
Ide Ng, *Co-Owner*

EMP: 20
SALES: 1.2MM **Privately Held**
SIC: 2032 Chinese foods: packaged in cans, jars, etc.

(P-757)
FRESH PACKING CORPORATION
4333 S Maywood Ave, Vernon (90058-2521)
P.O. Box 3009, Alhambra (91803-0009)
PHONE.................................213 612-0136
Monica Zambada Lopez, *CEO*
EMP: 20
SALES (est): 4.2MM **Privately Held**
SIC: 2032 Chili with or without meat: packaged in cans, jars, etc.

(P-758)
HOMESTEAD RAVIOLI COMPANY INC
Also Called: Homestead Fine Foods
315 S Maple Ave Ste 106, South San Francisco (94080-6335)
PHONE.................................650 615-0750
Terry Hall, *President*
Charles Osborne, *Treasurer*
Christopher Osborne, *Admin Sec*
EMP: 20 EST: 1904
SQ FT: 19,000
SALES (est): 2.1MM **Privately Held**
WEB: www.homesteadpasta.com
SIC: 2032 2038 5149 2098 Ravioli: packaged in cans, jars, etc.; frozen specialties; sauces; macaroni & spaghetti; pickles, sauces & salad dressings

(P-759)
IF COPACK LLC
Also Called: Initiative Foods
1912 Industrial Way, Sanger (93657-9508)
PHONE.................................559 875-3354
John Ypma, *President*
Jeff Jankovic, *CFO*
EMP: 42
SQ FT: 51,348
SALES (est): 1.2MM **Privately Held**
SIC: 2032 Baby foods, including meats: packaged in cans, jars, etc.

(P-760)
INITIATIVE FOODS LLC
1912 Industrial Way, Sanger (93657-9508)
PHONE.................................559 875-3354
John Ypma,
Richard Turner,
EMP: 130
SALES (est): 21.9MM
SALES (corp-wide): 38.5MM **Privately Held**
SIC: 2032 Baby foods, including meats: packaged in cans, jars, etc.
PA: If Holding, Inc.
1912 Industrial Way
Sanger CA 93657
559 875-3354

(P-761)
JIMENEZ MEXICAN FOODS INC
11010 Wells Ave, Riverside (92505-2751)
PHONE.................................951 351-0102
Roberto Jimenez, *CEO*
Veronica Jimenez, *CFO*
EMP: 20
SALES (est): 83K **Privately Held**
SIC: 2032 Mexican foods: packaged in cans, jars, etc.

(P-762)
JUANITAS FOODS
Also Called: Pico Pica Foods
645 Eubank Ave, Wilmington (90744-6055)
P.O. Box 847 (90748-0847)
PHONE.................................310 834-5339
Aaron De La Torre, *CEO*
James Steveson, *President*
Mark De La Torre, *Chairman*
Richard Werblin, *Finance Mgr*
Regina Chen, *Manager*
EMP: 125
SQ FT: 85,000
SALES (est): 36.4MM **Privately Held**
WEB: www.juanitasfoods.com
SIC: 2032 Mexican foods: packaged in cans, jars, etc.

(P-763)
KINGS ASIAN GOURMET INC
683 Brannan St Unit 304, San Francisco (94107-1592)
PHONE.................................415 222-6100
Inja Wang, *President*
Jane Park, *Financial Exec*
Victor Wang, *Sales Executive*
Walter Wang, *Manager*
▲ EMP: 37
SQ FT: 25,000
SALES (est): 2.9MM **Privately Held**
WEB: www.kingsasian.com
SIC: 2032 Ethnic foods: canned, jarred, etc.

(P-764)
KRAFT HEINZ FOODS COMPANY
57 Stonebridge Ct, Tracy (95376)
PHONE.................................209 832-4269
James Brimgham, *Manager*
EMP: 50
SALES (corp-wide): 26.2B **Publicly Held**
SIC: 2032 Canned specialties
HQ: Kraft Heinz Foods Company
1 Ppg Pl Ste 3200
Pittsburgh PA 15222
412 456-5700

(P-765)
KRAFT HEINZ FOODS COMPANY
2450 White Rd, Irvine (92614-6250)
PHONE.................................949 250-4080
Dan Foss, *Manager*
EMP: 220
SALES (corp-wide): 26.2B **Publicly Held**
SIC: 2032 2035 Soups, except seafood: packaged in cans, jars, etc.; seasonings & sauces, except tomato & dry; dressings, salad: raw & cooked (except dry mixes)
HQ: Kraft Heinz Foods Company
1 Ppg Pl Ste 3200
Pittsburgh PA 15222
412 456-5700

(P-766)
LA INDIANA TAMALES INC
15268 Proctor Ave, City of Industry (91745-1036)
PHONE.................................323 262-4682
Raul Ramos, *President*
EMP: 32 EST: 1999
SQ FT: 8,000
SALES (est): 4.3MM **Privately Held**
WEB: www.laindianatamales.com
SIC: 2032 Tamales: packaged in cans, jars, etc.

(P-767)
MARIN FOOD SPECIALTIES INC
14800 Byron Hwy, Byron (94514)
P.O. Box 609 (94514-0609)
PHONE.................................925 634-6126
Fred J Vuylsteke, *President*
Larry Brucia, *Corp Secy*
▲ EMP: 35
SQ FT: 27,000
SALES (est): 6.4MM **Privately Held**
SIC: 2032 Canned specialties

(P-768)
MICHAEL BS LLC
22625 S Western Ave, Torrance (90501-4950)
PHONE.................................310 320-0141
Michael Boden,
EMP: 30
SALES (est): 2.4MM **Privately Held**
SIC: 2032 Canned specialties

(P-769)
NATURAS FOODS CALIFORNIA INC
334 Paseo Sonrisa, Walnut (91789-2720)
PHONE.................................909 594-7838
Ariel Espinoza, *President*
EMP: 15
SQ FT: 4,500
SALES (est): 1.3MM **Privately Held**
SIC: 2032 Mexican foods: packaged in cans, jars, etc.

PRODUCTS & SVCS

(P-770)
PANORAMA INTL CL CO INC
200 Toland St, San Francisco
(94124-1120)
PHONE..................................415 891-8478
EMP: 11
SALES (corp-wide): 8MM **Privately Held**
SIC: 2032 Italian foods: packaged in cans,
jars, etc.
  PA: Panorama International Clothing Com-
pany, Inc.
0 Meadowood Dr
Larkspur CA 94939
415 891-8478

(P-771)
RAMONAS FOOD GROUP LLC
13633 S Western Ave, Gardena
(90249-2597)
PHONE..................................310 323-1950
Robert Banuelos-Medina, *Mng Member*
Edward Medina,
EMP: 160
SQ FT: 55,000
SALES: 8MM **Privately Held**
SIC: 2032 Mexican foods: packaged in
cans, jars, etc.

(P-772)
**REYNALDOS MEXICAN FOOD
CO LLC (PA)**
3301 E Vernon Ave, Vernon (90058-1809)
PHONE..................................562 803-3188
Douglas Reed, *CFO*
Gilbert D Cardenas, *Principal*
Lonnie Cope, *Sales Dir*
Marisol Scrugham,
Al Soto, *Mng Member*
EMP: 160
SALES (est): 30.2MM **Privately Held**
WEB: www.rmfood.com
SIC: 2032 Mexican foods: packaged in
cans, jars, etc.

(P-773)
SHINE FOOD INC (PA)
19216 Normandie Ave, Torrance
(90502-1011)
PHONE..................................310 329-3829
Stephen Y S Lee, *CEO*
Tracy Lee, *Vice Pres*
▲ **EMP:** 50 **EST:** 1986
SQ FT: 30,000
SALES (est): 14.6MM **Privately Held**
WEB: www.shinefood.com
SIC: 2032 Canned specialties

(P-774)
SILGAN CAN COMPANY
6200 Franklin Blvd # 100, Sacramento
(95824-3400)
PHONE..................................916 422-8030
Jim Moses, *Opers-Prdtn-Mfg*
EMP: 14
SALES (corp-wide): 4B **Publicly Held**
SIC: 2032 Canned specialties
  HQ: Silgan Can Company
21600 Oxnard St Ste 1600
Woodland Hills CA 91367
818 348-3700

(P-775)
SONOMA VALLEY FOODS INC
3645 Standish Ave, Santa Rosa
(95407-8142)
PHONE..................................707 585-2200
Rene Valencia, *CEO*
Lilly Ramos, *Marketing Mgr*
Adrian Rodriguez, *Sales Mgr*
EMP: 22
SALES (est): 4MM **Privately Held**
SIC: 2032 5411 Tortillas: packaged in
cans, jars, etc.; supermarkets

(P-776)
T & T FOODS INC
Also Called: Colonel Lee's Enterprises
3080 E 50th St, Vernon (90058-2918)
PHONE..................................323 588-2158
Michelle MA, *CEO*
David MA, *Vice Pres*
Andrew Lam, *Manager*
EMP: 50
SQ FT: 19,000

SALES (est): 9.2MM **Privately Held**
SIC: 2032 2099 Ethnic foods: canned,
jarred, etc.; food preparations

(P-777)
TAY HO FOOD CORPORATION
2430 Cape Cod Way, Santa Ana
(92703-3540)
PHONE..................................714 973-2286
Jayce Yenson, *CEO*
Chuong Nguyen, *Vice Pres*
MAI Nguyen, *Admin Sec*
EMP: 35
SQ FT: 27,000
SALES (est): 3.7MM **Privately Held**
WEB: www.tayho.com
SIC: 2032 Ethnic foods: canned, jarred,
etc.

(P-778)
TEASDALE FOODS INC (PA)
Also Called: Teasdale Latin Foods
901 Packers St, Atwater (95301-4614)
P.O. Box 814 (95301-0814)
PHONE..................................209 358-5616
Chris Kiser, *CEO*
Russell Kenerly, *CFO*
Paula Demuria, *Ch Credit Ofcr*
Cale Nelson, *Chief Mktg Ofcr*
Marco Casillas, *Vice Pres*
▼ **EMP:** 277
SQ FT: 250,000
SALES (est): 285.9MM **Privately Held**
SIC: 2032 2034 Beans, baked without
meat: packaged in cans, jars, etc.; chili
with or without meat: packaged in cans,
jars, etc.; Mexican foods: packaged in
cans, jars, etc.; dehydrated fruits, vegeta-
bles, soups

(P-779)
WALEEDS FOOD INC
42170 Sarah Way, Temecula (92590-3401)
PHONE..................................951 694-8800
Waleed Soro, *CEO*
Dylan Soro, *Treasurer*
Sheri Soro, *Admin Sec*
EMP: 11
SQ FT: 8,000
SALES: 1.2MM **Privately Held**
SIC: 2032 Italian foods: packaged in cans,
jars, etc.

(P-780)
WEI LABORATORIES INC
2880 Zanker Rd Ste 205, San Jose
(95134-2122)
PHONE..................................408 970-8700
Jeffery WEI, *CEO*
Jeffrey Horan, *President*
Sarah LI, *Vice Pres*
Katie Pierce, *Manager*
Devon Davidson, *Accounts Mgr*
EMP: 25
SALES (est): 3.2MM **Privately Held**
WEB: www.weilab.com
SIC: 2032 Chinese foods: packaged in
cans, jars, etc.

(P-781)
WELLINGTON FOODS INC
1930 California Ave, Corona (92881-6491)
PHONE..................................562 989-0111
Anthony E Harnack Sr, *Chairman*
Jim Melvani, *CFO*
Naomi Abe, *Research*
Carole Moody, *Research*
Linda Childs, *Purch Mgr*
▲ **EMP:** 50 **EST:** 1974
SQ FT: 50,000
SALES (est): 13.3MM **Privately Held**
SIC: 2032 Canned specialties

(P-782)
YUCATAN FOODS LP
5901 W Century Blvd # 1578, Los Angeles
(90045-5437)
PHONE..................................310 342-5363
Ardeshir Haerizadeh, *CEO*
Dan Walton, *CFO*
Michael Modjeski, *VP Sales*
Jessica Brown, *Sales Staff*
▲ **EMP:** 15

SALES (est): 7.3MM **Privately Held**
WEB: www.avocado.com
SIC: 2032 5149 Mexican foods: packaged
in cans, jars, etc.; specialty food items

**2033 Canned Fruits,
Vegetables & Preserves**

(P-783)
ABSINTHE GROUP INC
2043 Airpark Ct Ste 30, Auburn
(95602-9009)
PHONE..................................530 823-8527
Kim Sullivan, *Director*
EMP: 20
SALES (corp-wide): 6.4MM **Privately
Held**
WEB: www.absinthe.com
SIC: 2033 2099 8742 2035 Barbecue
sauce: packaged in cans, jars, etc.; food
preparations; food & beverage consultant;
pickles, sauces & salad dressings
  PA: The Absinthe Group Inc
368 Hayes St
San Francisco CA 94102
415 864-2693

(P-784)
**AMAZON PRSRVATION
PARTNERS INC**
Also Called: Zola Acai
1501a Vermont St, San Francisco
(94107-3250)
PHONE..................................415 775-6355
Chris Cuvelier, *CEO*
Robin Ynes, *CFO*
Dorothy Huynh, *Opers Staff*
Faryn Schatz, *Marketing Mgr*
Devin Cardoza, *Sales Staff*
▲ **EMP:** 24
SQ FT: 1,500
SALES (est): 6.9MM **Privately Held**
WEB: www.zolaacai.com
SIC: 2033 Fruit juices: fresh

(P-785)
BEAUMONT JUICE INC
Also Called: Perricone Juices
550 B St, Beaumont (92223-2672)
PHONE..................................951 769-7171
Robert Paul Rovzar, *CEO*
Joe Perricone, *CFO*
Paul Golub, *Treasurer*
Thomas M Carmody, *Principal*
▲ **EMP:** 98
SQ FT: 30,000
SALES (est): 27.4MM
SALES (corp-wide): 5.3MM **Privately
Held**
SIC: 2033 Fruit juices: fresh
  PA: G B & P Citrus Co Inc
1601 E Olympic Blvd # 111
Los Angeles CA 90021
213 312-1380

(P-786)
BELL-CARTER FOODS INC (PA)
Also Called: Bell-Carter Olive Company
590 Ygnacio Valley Rd # 300, Walnut Creek
(94596-3807)
PHONE..................................925 284-5933
Timothy T Carter, *CEO*
John Toth, *CFO*
Paul Adcock, *Exec VP*
Doug Reifsteck, *Exec VP*
Pat Campbell, *Vice Pres*
◆ **EMP:** 277 **EST:** 1912
SQ FT: 9,000
SALES (est): 177.6MM **Privately Held**
WEB: www.bellcarter.com
SIC: 2033 Olives: packaged in cans, jars,
etc.

(P-787)
BELL-CARTER FOODS INC
Also Called: Bell-Carter Packaging
4207 Finch Rd, Modesto (95357-4101)
PHONE..................................209 549-5939
Bill Floyd, *Manager*
Patrick McGovern, *Director*
EMP: 20

SALES (corp-wide): 177.6MM **Privately
Held**
WEB: www.bellcarter.com
SIC: 2033 Olives: packaged in cans, jars,
etc.
  PA: Bell-Carter Foods, Inc.
590 Ygnacio Valley Rd # 300
Walnut Creek CA 94596
925 284-5933

(P-788)
BIG HEART PET BRANDS
Also Called: Del Monte Foods 48
2 Nestle Way, Lathrop (95330-9707)
PHONE..................................209 547-7200
Glenn Lewis, *Manager*
EMP: 15
SALES (corp-wide): 7.3B **Publicly Held**
SIC: 2033 5149 Fruits & fruit products in
cans, jars, etc.; canned goods: fruit, veg-
etables, seafood, meats, etc.
  HQ: Big Heart Pet Brands
1 Maritime Plz Fl 2
San Francisco CA 94111
415 247-3000

(P-789)
BIG HEART PET BRANDS
Also Called: Star-Kist
24700 Main St, Carson (90745-6321)
PHONE..................................310 519-3791
EMP: 190
SALES (corp-wide): 5.6B **Publicly Held**
SIC: 2033
  HQ: Big Heart Pet Brands
1 Maritime Plz Fl 2
San Francisco CA 94111
415 247-3000

(P-790)
CALIFORNIA TREATS INC
Also Called: Betty Clark's Confections
2131 Tyler Ave, El Monte (91733-2754)
PHONE..................................626 454-4099
Steve Nelson, *President*
EMP: 60
SQ FT: 25,818
SALES (est): 4.7MM **Privately Held**
WEB: www.caltreats.com
SIC: 2033 2034 2035 2099 Jellies, edi-
ble, including imitation: in cans, jars, etc.;
soup mixes; seasonings; meat sauces
(except tomato & dry); food preparations;
potato chips & similar snacks; popcorn
balls or other treated popcorn products

(P-791)
CONAGRA BRANDS INC
554 S Yosemite Ave, Oakdale
(95361-4037)
PHONE..................................209 847-0321
Earl Ehret, *Branch Mgr*
EMP: 1145
SQ FT: 40,000
SALES (corp-wide): 7.9B **Publicly Held**
WEB: www.conagra.com
SIC: 2033 Tomato products: packaged in
cans, jars, etc.
  PA: Conagra Brands, Inc.
222 Merchandise Mart Plz
Chicago IL 60654
312 549-5000

(P-792)
**DEL MAR FOOD PRODUCTS
CORP**
1720 Beach Rd, Watsonville (95076-9536)
P.O. Box 891 (95077-0891)
PHONE..................................831 722-3516
P J Mecozzi, *CEO*
Wayne Jordan, *CFO*
Paul Wendt, *CFO*
Carolyn Mecozzi, *Treasurer*
Roger Wyant, *Vice Pres*
◆ **EMP:** 500
SQ FT: 53,408
SALES (est): 113.6MM **Privately Held**
WEB: www.delmarfoods.com
SIC: 2033 2099 Canned fruits & special-
ties; food preparations

(P-793)
DEL MONTE FOODS INC
1509 Draper St Ste A, Kingsburg
(93631-1950)
PHONE..................................559 419-9214

▲ = Import ▼ =Export
◆ =Import/Export

Brian Okland, *Manager*
EMP: 85
SQ FT: 111,920
SALES (corp-wide): 2.2B **Privately Held**
SIC: 2033 Fruits: packaged in cans, jars, etc.; vegetables: packaged in cans, jars, etc.; preserves, including imitation: in cans, jars, etc.; jams, including imitation: packaged in cans, jars, etc.
HQ: Del Monte Foods, Inc.
3003 Oak Rd Ste 600
Walnut Creek CA 94597
925 949-2772

(P-794)
DEL MONTE FOODS INC
10652 Jackson Ave, Hanford (93230-9552)
PHONE..........................559 639-6160
Ted Leaman, *Manager*
Rick Koch, *Engineer*
Alan Schroeder, *Controller*
Phil McNabb, *Warehouse Mgr*
Tony Silva, *Maintence Staff*
EMP: 104
SALES (corp-wide): 2.2B **Privately Held**
SIC: 2033 2035 Tomato paste: packaged in cans, jars, etc.; tomato purees: packaged in cans, jars, etc.; tomato sauce: packaged in cans, jars, etc.; pickles, sauces & salad dressings
HQ: Del Monte Foods, Inc.
3003 Oak Rd Ste 600
Walnut Creek CA 94597
925 949-2772

(P-795)
DEL MONTE FOODS INC
4000 Yosemite Blvd, Modesto (95357-1580)
P.O. Box 576008 (95357-6008)
PHONE..........................209 548-5509
Jim Fullmer, *Manager*
Eduardo Barron, *Engineer*
Ron Collins, *Engineer*
Justin Mullins, *Human Res Dir*
Jolynn Bush, *Purch Agent*
EMP: 280
SQ FT: 5,000
SALES (corp-wide): 2.2B **Privately Held**
SIC: 2033 Tomato purees: packaged in cans, jars, etc.
HQ: Del Monte Foods, Inc.
3003 Oak Rd Ste 600
Walnut Creek CA 94597
925 949-2772

(P-796)
DEL MONTE FOODS INC (HQ)
3003 Oak Rd Ste 600, Walnut Creek (94597-4501)
PHONE..........................925 949-2772
Nils Lommerin, *CEO*
Paul Miller, *CFO*
Bibie Wu, *Chief Mktg Ofcr*
Tim Bernard, *Vice Pres*
Robert Long, *Vice Pres*
◆ **EMP:** 125 **EST:** 2013
SALES (est): 1.1B
SALES (corp-wide): 2.2B **Privately Held**
SIC: 2033 5149 Canned fruits & specialties; groceries & related products
PA: Del Monte Pacific Limited
17 Bukit Pasoh Road
Singapore 08983
632 468-22

(P-797)
DEL MONTE FOODS INC
205 N Wiget Ln, Walnut Creek (94598-2458)
PHONE..........................925 944-7300
Victor Morelli, *Principal*
Xander Shapiro, *General Mgr*
Wendy Zebert, *Project Mgr*
Loren Druz, *Research*
Steven Bautista, *Director*
EMP: 107
SQ FT: 31,208
SALES (corp-wide): 2.2B **Privately Held**
SIC: 2033 8731 Vegetables & vegetable products in cans, jars, etc.; food research
HQ: Del Monte Foods, Inc.
3003 Oak Rd Ste 600
Walnut Creek CA 94597
925 949-2772

(P-798)
EARTH & VINE PROVISIONS INC
160 Flocchini Cir, Lincoln (95648-1700)
P.O. Box 1637, Loomis (95650-1637)
PHONE..........................916 434-8399
Tressa Cooper, *President*
Ron Cooper, *CFO*
Debbie Soto, *Office Mgr*
EMP: 10 **EST:** 1997
SQ FT: 5,000
SALES (est): 1MM **Privately Held**
SIC: 2033 2099 5149 Jams, jellies & preserves: packaged in cans, jars, etc.; sauces: gravy, dressing & dip mixes; sauces

(P-799)
EL BURRITO MXICAN FD PDTS CORP
14944 Don Julian Rd, City of Industry (91746-3111)
PHONE..........................626 369-7828
Shigeru Natake, *President*
Shige Harukoga, *CFO*
Maria Cardenas, *Marketing Staff*
Catalina Castillo, *Manager*
EMP: 18
SALES (est): 2.9MM
SALES (corp-wide): 2.1MM **Privately Held**
SIC: 2033 2099 Canned fruits & specialties; food preparations
PA: House Foods Holding Usa Inc
14944 Don Julian Rd
City Of Industry CA 91746
626 369-7828

(P-800)
FRUIT FILLINGS INC
2531 E Edgar Ave, Fresno (93706-5410)
PHONE..........................559 237-4715
Sg Norcross, *CEO*
Stephen Norcross, *President*
Keith Siemens, *Treasurer*
Everett Norcross III, *Admin Sec*
▼ **EMP:** 25
SQ FT: 3,600
SALES (est): 9.1MM **Privately Held**
WEB: www.fruitfillings.com
SIC: 2033 Fruit pie mixes & fillings: packaged in cans, jars, etc.

(P-801)
G L MEZZETTA INC
105 Mezzetta Ct, American Canyon (94503-9604)
PHONE..........................707 648-1050
Jeffery Mezzetta, *CEO*
Ronald J Mezzetta, *President*
◆ **EMP:** 80 **EST:** 1957
SQ FT: 35,000
SALES (est): 32.1MM **Privately Held**
SIC: 2033 Pizza sauce: packaged in cans, jars, etc.; spaghetti & other pasta sauce: packaged in cans, jars, etc.

(P-802)
GEORGE DELALLO COMPANY INC
Also Called: Delallo Italian Foods
1800 Idora St, Oroville (95966-6767)
PHONE..........................530 533-3303
George Hoag, *Manager*
EMP: 20
SQ FT: 48,750
SALES (corp-wide): 184.2MM **Privately Held**
SIC: 2033 Olives: packaged in cans, jars, etc.
PA: George Delallo Company, Inc.
1 Delallo Way
Mount Pleasant PA 15666
724 925-2222

(P-803)
HAPPY GIRL KITCHEN CO
173 Central Ave, Pacific Grove (93950-3015)
PHONE..........................831 373-4475
Todd Champagne, *Owner*
Jessica J Champagne, *Co-Owner*
EMP: 10
SQ FT: 2,700
SALES: 300K **Privately Held**
SIC: 2033 Preserves, including imitation: in cans, jars, etc.

(P-804)
HEIDENS INC
Also Called: Heiden's Foods
2900 E Blue Star St, Anaheim (92806-2509)
PHONE..........................714 525-3414
Robert E Heiden, *President*
Dawne Walker, *Corp Secy*
Derek Walker, *Vice Pres*
Valerie Uribe, *Manager*
EMP: 12
SQ FT: 10,000
SALES (est): 1.9MM **Privately Held**
WEB: www.heidensfoods.com
SIC: 2033 2032 Barbecue sauce: packaged in cans, jars, etc.; soups, except seafood: packaged in cans, jars, etc.

(P-805)
HIGHLAND WHOLESALE FOODS INC
1604 Tillie Lewis Dr, Stockton (95206-1170)
PHONE..........................209 933-0580
T Gregory Stagnitto, *President*
Bill Burch, *COO*
Tommy Sodaro, *Senior VP*
Melissa Hobbie, *Director*
▼ **EMP:** 49
SQ FT: 140,000
SALES (est): 20.2MM **Privately Held**
SIC: 2033 Canned fruits & specialties

(P-806)
HK CANNING INC (PA)
130 N Garden St, Ventura (93001-2529)
PHONE..........................805 652-1392
Henry Knaust, *President*
Carol Knaust, *Vice Pres*
EMP: 21
SQ FT: 91,552
SALES: 4MM **Privately Held**
SIC: 2033 Vegetables: packaged in cans, jars, etc.

(P-807)
HUY FONG FOODS INC
4800 Azusa Canyon Rd, Irwindale (91706-1938)
PHONE..........................626 286-8328
David Tran, *President*
Ada Tran, *CFO*
Donna Lam, *Admin Sec*
◆ **EMP:** 20
SQ FT: 68,000
SALES (est): 6.1MM **Privately Held**
SIC: 2033 Chili sauce, tomato: packaged in cans, jars, etc.

(P-808)
INGOMAR PACKING COMPANY LLC (PA)
9950 S Ingomar Grade, Los Banos (93635)
P.O. Box 1448 (93635-1448)
PHONE..........................209 826-9494
Gregory Pruett, *President*
William B Cahill Jr, *Vice Pres*
John F Bennett,
◆ **EMP:** 100
SQ FT: 10,000
SALES (est): 70.7MM **Privately Held**
WEB: www.ingomarpacking.com
SIC: 2033 Tomato paste: packaged in cans, jars, etc.

(P-809)
J M SMUCKER COMPANY
800 Commercial Ave, Oxnard (93030-7234)
P.O. Box 5161 (93031-5161)
PHONE..........................805 487-5483
Al Yamamoto, *Manager*
June Macnab, *Analyst*
Phillip Lopez, *Manager*
Linda Vaccani, *Manager*
EMP: 25
SQ FT: 20,000
SALES (corp-wide): 7.3B **Publicly Held**
WEB: www.smuckers.com
SIC: 2033 Canned fruits & specialties

PA: The J M Smucker Company
1 Strawberry Ln
Orrville OH 44667
330 682-3000

(P-810)
JG BOSWELL TOMATO - KERN LLC
36889 Hwy 58, Buttonwillow (93206)
PHONE..........................661 764-9000
Sherm Railsback,
James W Boswell, *Principal*
Joel Molina, *Accounting Mgr*
◆ **EMP:** 33
SQ FT: 1,080
SALES (est): 11.6MM **Privately Held**
WEB: www.riobravotomato.com
SIC: 2033 Tomato products: packaged in cans, jars, etc.

(P-811)
JUICE HEADS INC
Also Called: Lorton's Fresh Squeezed Juices
735 E Base Line St, San Bernardino (92410-3912)
PHONE..........................909 386-7933
Fax: 909 884-6297
EMP: 10
SQ FT: 10,000
SALES (est): 561.8K
SALES (corp-wide): 1.3B **Privately Held**
SIC: 2033 4212
HQ: Sunopta Global Organic Ingredients Inc.
100 Enterprise Way Ste B1
Scotts Valley CA 95066

(P-812)
KADBANOU LLC
1951 Gardena Ave, Glendale (91204-2910)
PHONE..........................818 409-0118
Vahik Sarkissian, *Mng Member*
EMP: 10
SALES (est): 821.6K **Privately Held**
SIC: 2033 Fruits & fruit products in cans, jars, etc.; vegetables & vegetable products in cans, jars, etc.

(P-813)
KAGOME INC (HQ)
333 Johnson Rd, Los Banos (93635-9768)
PHONE..........................209 826-8850
Luis De Oliviera, *President*
Pete Watanabe, *CFO*
Luis De Oliveira, *Officer*
Ann Hall, *Vice Pres*
Molly Miller, *Vice Pres*
◆ **EMP:** 176
SQ FT: 175,000
SALES (est): 75.5MM
SALES (corp-wide): 1.9B **Privately Held**
WEB: www.kagomeusa.com
SIC: 2033 Tomato products: packaged in cans, jars, etc.
PA: Kagome Co.,Ltd.
3-21-1, Nihombashihamacho
Chuo-Ku TKY 103-0
356 238-501

(P-814)
KOZLOWSKI FARMS A CORPORATION
5566 Hwy 116, Forestville (95436-9697)
PHONE..........................707 887-1587
Cindy Kozlowski Hayworth, *CEO*
Carol Kozlowski Every, *Vice Pres*
EMP: 20 **EST:** 1949
SQ FT: 8,000
SALES (est): 3.6MM **Privately Held**
WEB: www.kozlowskifarms.com
SIC: 2033 5149 2035 2099 Jams, jellies & preserves: packaged in cans, jars, etc.; fruit butters: packaged in cans, jars, etc.; condiments; sauces; pickles, sauces & salad dressings; vinegar

(P-815)
KRAFT HEINZ FOODS COMPANY
2494 S Orange Ave, Fresno (93725-1328)
PHONE..........................559 441-8515
Mark Librizzi, *Branch Mgr*
EMP: 400
SQ FT: 167,590

PRODUCTS & SVCS

SALES (corp-wide): 26.2B **Publicly Held**
WEB: www.kraftfoods.com
SIC: 2033 Fruit juices: packaged in cans, jars, etc.
HQ: Kraft Heinz Foods Company
1 Ppg Pl Ste 3200
Pittsburgh PA 15222
412 456-5700

(P-816)
KRAFT HEINZ FOODS COMPANY
2603 Camino Ramon Ste 180, San Ramon (94583-9127)
PHONE................................925 242-4504
EMP: 15
SALES (corp-wide): 18.3B **Publicly Held**
SIC: 2033
HQ: Heinz Kraft Foods Company
1 Ppg Pl Ste 3200
Pittsburgh PA 15222
412 456-5700

(P-817)
KRAFT HEINZ FOODS COMPANY
1905 Mchenry Ave, Escalon (95320-9601)
PHONE................................209 552-6021
Scott Adrian, *Branch Mgr*
EMP: 300
SALES (corp-wide): 26.2B **Publicly Held**
SIC: 2033 Canned fruits & specialties
HQ: Kraft Heinz Foods Company
1 Ppg Pl Ste 3200
Pittsburgh PA 15222
412 456-5700

(P-818)
LANDEC CORPORATION (PA)
5201 Great America Pkwy, Santa Clara (95054-1122)
PHONE................................650 306-1650
Molly A Hemmeter, *President*
Steven Goldby, *Ch of Bd*
Ronald L Midyett, *COO*
Gregory S Skinner, *CFO*
Albert Bolles, *Bd of Directors*
EMP: 103
SQ FT: 14,600
SALES: 524.2MM **Publicly Held**
WEB: www.landec.com
SIC: 2033 5148 5999 Fruits: packaged in cans, jars, etc.; vegetables: packaged in cans, jars, etc.; fresh fruits & vegetables; medical apparatus & supplies

(P-819)
LIBERTY FOODS TRADING CO LLC
Also Called: Pacific Coast Producers
631 N Cluff Ave, Lodi (95240-0756)
P.O. Box 1600 (95241-1600)
PHONE................................209 367-8800
Mona O Shulman,
◆ EMP: 20 EST: 2013
SALES (est): 2.7MM
SALES (corp-wide): 668MM **Privately Held**
SIC: 2033 Barbecue sauce: packaged in cans, jars, etc.
PA: Pacific Coast Producers
631 N Cluff Ave
Lodi CA 95240
209 367-8800

(P-820)
LIDESTRI FOODS INC
Also Called: International Co-Packing Co
568 S Temperance Ave, Fresno (93727-6601)
PHONE................................559 251-1000
Willie Bynum, *Branch Mgr*
Jose Bonilla, *Prdtn Mgr*
EMP: 100
SALES (corp-wide): 247.9MM **Privately Held**
WEB: www.francescorinaldi.com
SIC: 2033 Spaghetti & other pasta sauce: packaged in cans, jars, etc.; tomato products: packaged in cans, jars, etc.
PA: Lidestri Foods, Inc.
815 Whitney Rd W
Fairport NY 14450
585 377-7700

(P-821)
LOS GATOS TOMATO PRODUCTS LLC (PA)
7041 N Van Ness Blvd, Fresno (93711-7169)
P.O. Box 429, Huron (93234-0429)
PHONE................................559 945-2700
Reuben Peterson, *Mng Member*
◆ EMP: 20
SQ FT: 35,000
SALES (est): 5.6MM **Privately Held**
WEB: www.losgatostomato.com
SIC: 2033 Tomato paste: packaged in cans, jars, etc.

(P-822)
LOS OLIVOS PACKAGING INC (PA)
929 Ridgecrest St, Monterey Park (91754-4622)
PHONE................................323 261-2218
Fax: 323 261-1026
▲ EMP: 105 EST: 1925
SQ FT: 22,000
SALES (est): 9.3MM **Privately Held**
SIC: 2033

(P-823)
LYONS MAGNUS INC (PA)
3158 E Hamilton Ave, Fresno (93702-4163)
PHONE................................559 268-5966
Robert E Smittcamp, *President*
Muriel Smittcamp, *Corp Secy*
Jim Davis, *Vice Pres*
Rod Wright, *Vice Pres*
Osvaldo Velazquez, *Human Resources*
◆ EMP: 285
SQ FT: 63,000
SALES (est): 233.5MM **Privately Held**
WEB: www.lyonsmagnus.com
SIC: 2033 2026 2087 Jams, including imitation: packaged in cans, jars, etc.; jellies, edible, including imitation: in cans, jars, etc.; preserves, including imitation: in cans, jars, etc.; fruit pie mixes & fillings: packaged in cans, jars, etc.; yogurt; syrups, flavoring (except drink); extracts, flavoring

(P-824)
LYONS MAGNUS INC
1636 S 2nd St, Fresno (93702-4143)
PHONE................................559 268-5966
Robert E Smittcamp, *Branch Mgr*
Rich Connor, *President*
Michelle Heckel, *Opers Staff*
Ken Atkins, *Maintenance Dir*
EMP: 30
SALES (corp-wide): 233.5MM **Privately Held**
SIC: 2033 2026 2087 Jams, including imitation: packaged in cans, jars, etc.; jellies, edible, including imitation: in cans, jars, etc.; preserves, including imitation: in cans, jars, etc.; fruit pie mixes & fillings: packaged in cans, jars, etc.; yogurt; syrups, flavoring (except drink); extracts, flavoring
PA: Lyons Magnus, Inc.
3158 E Hamilton Ave
Fresno CA 93702
559 268-5966

(P-825)
MANGIA INC
1 Marconi Ste F, Irvine (92618-2560)
PHONE................................949 581-1274
Matt A Maslowski, *President*
Joe Wirth, *Accountant*
Lisa Malilay, *Director*
Rachel Zimmerman, *Director*
Morgan Patterson, *Manager*
▲ EMP: 12
SALES (est): 2.6MM **Privately Held**
WEB: www.mangiainc.com
SIC: 2033 Canned fruits & specialties

(P-826)
MANZANA PRODUCTS CO INC
9141 Green Valley Rd, Sebastopol (95472-2245)
P.O. Box 209 (95473-0209)
PHONE................................707 823-5313
Jean-Jacques Ducom, *CEO*

Suzanne C Kaido, *President*
Richard H Norton, *Treasurer*
Ralph E Sandborn, *Vice Pres*
Edith Norton, *Admin Sec*
◆ EMP: 40 EST: 1920
SQ FT: 91,000
SALES (est): 12MM **Privately Held**
SIC: 2033 2099 Apple sauce: packaged in cans, jars, etc.; fruit juices: packaged in cans, jars, etc.; vinegar

(P-827)
MONTEREY BAY BEVERAGE CO INC
14535 Benefit St Unit 4, Sherman Oaks (91403-3741)
PHONE................................818 784-4885
Mark Fields, *CEO*
EMP: 25
SQ FT: 5,500
SALES (est): 2.1MM **Privately Held**
SIC: 2033 5921

(P-828)
MORNING STAR COMPANY
Also Called: Morning Star Packing
13448 Volta Rd, Los Banos (93635-9785)
PHONE................................209 827-2724
Chris Rufer, *President*
EMP: 60
SALES (corp-wide): 53.7MM **Privately Held**
SIC: 2033 Tomato paste: packaged in cans, jars, etc.
PA: The Morning Star Company
724 Main St Ste 202
Woodland CA 95695
530 666-6600

(P-829)
MORNING STAR PACKING CO LP
2211 Old Highway 99, Williams (95987)
PHONE................................530 473-3642
Rich Rostomily, *Branch Mgr*
EMP: 30
SALES (corp-wide): 48.3MM **Privately Held**
SIC: 2033 Tomato paste: packaged in cans, jars, etc.
PA: The Morning Star Packing Company L P
13448 Volta Rd
Los Banos CA 93635
209 826-8000

(P-830)
MOTU GLOBAL LLC
924 W 9th St, Upland (91786-4576)
PHONE................................801 471-7800
EMP: 10
SQ FT: 8,200
SALES: 10K **Privately Held**
SIC: 2033

(P-831)
NASCO GOURMET FOODS INC
Also Called: Platinum Distribution
22720 Savi Ranch Pkwy, Yorba Linda (92887-4608)
PHONE................................714 279-2100
Burhan Nasser, *President*
Mary Beth Nasser, *Corp Secy*
Jerry Pascoe, *Vice Pres*
EMP: 65
SQ FT: 42,000
SALES (est): 17.6MM
SALES (corp-wide): 133.7MM **Privately Held**
WEB: www.platinum-distribution.com
SIC: 2033 Seasonings, tomato: packaged in cans, jars, etc.
PA: Nasser Company, Inc.
22720 Savi Ranch Pkwy
Yorba Linda CA 92887
714 279-2100

(P-832)
NEIL JONES FOOD COMPANY
San Benito Foods
711 Sally St, Hollister (95023-3934)
P.O. Box 100 (95024-0100)
PHONE................................831 637-0573
Steven Arnoldy, *Manager*
EMP: 80

SALES (corp-wide): 66.7MM **Privately Held**
SIC: 2033 Canned fruits & specialties
PA: The Neil Jones Food Company
1701 W 16th St
Vancouver WA 98660
360 696-4356

(P-833)
NEIL JONES FOOD COMPANY
Also Called: Toma Tek
2502 N St, Firebaugh (93622-2456)
PHONE................................559 659-5100
Steve Arnoldy, *Vice Pres*
EMP: 25
SALES (corp-wide): 66.7MM **Privately Held**
WEB: www.neiljonesfoodcompany.com
SIC: 2033 Tomato products: packaged in cans, jars, etc.
PA: The Neil Jones Food Company
1701 W 16th St
Vancouver WA 98660
360 696-4356

(P-834)
NU-HEALTH CALIFORNIA LLC
16910 Cherie Pl, Carson (90746-1305)
P.O. Box 12376, Marina Del Rey (90295-3376)
PHONE................................800 806-0519
Dmitriy Sharin,
EMP: 15
SALES: 800K **Privately Held**
SIC: 2033 Canned fruits & specialties

(P-835)
OASIS FOODS INC
10881 Toews Ave, Le Grand (95333-9754)
PHONE................................209 382-0263
Eric Stephen Bocks, *President*
Lorraine Bocks, *Corp Secy*
EMP: 50 EST: 1975
SQ FT: 3,367
SALES (est): 5.5MM **Privately Held**
WEB: www.oasisfoodsinc.com
SIC: 2033 Fruits & fruit products in cans, jars, etc.

(P-836)
ODWALLA INC
700 Isis Ave, Inglewood (90301-2913)
PHONE................................310 342-3920
Doug Kinsey, *Manager*
EMP: 30
SALES (corp-wide): 35.4B **Publicly Held**
WEB: www.odwalla.com
SIC: 2033 Fruit juices: packaged in cans, jars, etc.; vegetable juices: packaged in cans, jars, etc.
HQ: Odwalla, Inc.
1 Coca Cola Plz Nw
Atlanta GA 30313
479 721-6260

(P-837)
ODWALLA INC
1805 Las Plumas Ave, San Jose (95133-1706)
PHONE................................408 254-5800
Ron Kennedy, *Principal*
EMP: 20
SALES (corp-wide): 35.4B **Publicly Held**
WEB: www.odwalla.com
SIC: 2033 Fruit juices: packaged in cans, jars, etc.; vegetable juices: packaged in cans, jars, etc.
HQ: Odwalla, Inc.
1 Coca Cola Plz Nw
Atlanta GA 30313
479 721-6260

(P-838)
OH JUICE INC
5631 Palmer Way Ste A, Carlsbad (92010-7243)
PHONE................................619 318-0207
Hanna Gregor, *CEO*
Michael Mendoza, *Shareholder*
EMP: 15 EST: 2013
SALES (est): 581.4K **Privately Held**
SIC: 2033 Fruit juices: packaged in cans, jars, etc.; vegetable juices: packaged in cans, jars, etc.

(P-839)
OLAM TOMATO PROCESSORS INC
205 E River Park Cir # 310, Fresno
(93720-1571)
P.O. Box 160, Lemoore (93245-0160)
PHONE......................................559 447-1390
Sunny Verghese, *CEO*
Greg Estep, *President*
John Gibbons, *Principal*
◆ EMP: 62
SALES (est) 65K
SALES (corp-wide): 19.3B **Privately Held**
SIC: 2033 0723 Tomato sauce: packaged
in cans, jars, etc.; crop preparation serv-
ices for market
HQ: Olam Americas Inc
25 Union Pl Ste 3
Fresno CA 93720
559 447-1390

(P-840)
OLAM WEST COAST INC
Also Called: Olam Spices and Vegetables
1400 Churchill Downs Ave, Woodland
(95776-6113)
PHONE......................................530 473-4290
Rich Freidas, *Branch Mgr*
EMP: 800
SALES (corp-wide): 19.3B **Privately Held**
SIC: 2033 Tomato products: packaged in
cans, jars, etc.
HQ: Olam West Coast, Inc.
205 E Rver Pk Cir Ste 310
Fresno CA 93720
559 447-1390

(P-841)
OLIVE MUSCO PRODUCTS INC (PA)
Also Called: Musco Family Olive Co
17950 Via Nicolo, Tracy (95377-9767)
PHONE......................................209 836-4600
Nicholas Musco, *CEO*
Felix Musco, *CEO*
Scott Hamilton, *CFO*
John Hamliton, *CFO*
Bill McFarland, *Vice Pres*
▲ EMP: 300
SQ FT: 350,000
SALES (est): 96.7MM **Privately Held**
SIC: 2033 2035 Canned fruits & special-
ties; olives, brined: bulk

(P-842)
PACIFIC COAST PRODUCERS
741 S Stockton St, Lodi (95240-4809)
P.O. Box 880 (95241-0880)
PHONE......................................209 334-3352
Mike Van Gundy, *Branch Mgr*
Mike Vangundy, *Manager*
EMP: 60
SALES (corp-wide): 668MM **Privately Held**
SIC: 2033 Vegetables: packaged in cans,
jars, etc.; fruits: packaged in cans, jars,
etc.
PA: Pacific Coast Producers
631 N Cluff Ave
Lodi CA 95240
209 367-8800

(P-843)
PACIFIC COAST PRODUCERS (PA)
631 N Cluff Ave, Lodi (95240-0756)
P.O. Box 1600 (95241-1600)
PHONE......................................209 367-8800
Daniel L Vincent, *CEO*
Matthew Strong, *CFO*
Stewart Easton, *Treasurer*
Zeb Rocha, *Treasurer*
Andrew K Russick, *Vice Pres*
◆ EMP: 300
SQ FT: 20,000
SALES: 668MM **Privately Held**
WEB: www.pcoastp.com
SIC: 2033 Fruits: packaged in cans, jars,
etc.; vegetables: packaged in cans, jars,
etc.

(P-844)
PACIFIC COAST PRODUCERS
1601 Mitchell Ave, Oroville (95965-5863)
P.O. Box 311 (95965-0311)
PHONE......................................530 533-4311
Niraj Raj, *Principal*
Kim Bryson, *Purch Agent*
EMP: 140
SQ FT: 60,000
SALES (corp-wide): 668MM **Privately Held**
SIC: 2033 Fruits: packaged in cans, jars,
etc.; vegetables: packaged in cans, jars,
etc.
PA: Pacific Coast Producers
631 N Cluff Ave
Lodi CA 95240
209 367-8800

(P-845)
PACIFIC COAST PRODUCERS
Also Called: Contadina Foods
1376 Lemen Ave, Woodland (95776-3369)
PHONE......................................530 662-8661
Craig Powell, *Branch Mgr*
Maryann Newman, *Persnl Mgr*
EMP: 400
SALES (corp-wide): 668MM **Privately Held**
SIC: 2033 Canned fruits & specialties
PA: Pacific Coast Producers
631 N Cluff Ave
Lodi CA 95240
209 367-8800

(P-846)
PACIFIC COAST PRODUCERS
1376 Lemen Ave, Woodland (95776-3369)
PHONE......................................530 534-1344
Niraj Raj, *Branch Mgr*
EMP: 124
SALES (corp-wide): 668MM **Privately Held**
SIC: 2033 Fruits: packaged in cans, jars,
etc.; vegetables: packaged in cans, jars,
etc.
PA: Pacific Coast Producers
631 N Cluff Ave
Lodi CA 95240
209 367-8800

(P-847)
PACIFICA FOODS LLC
13415 Estelle St, Corona (92879-1877)
PHONE......................................951 371-3123
Mark Sorenson,
EMP: 21 **Privately Held**
WEB: www.pacificafoods.net
SIC: 2033 2035 Tomato products: pack-
aged in cans, jars, etc.; seasonings &
sauces, except tomato & dry
PA: Pacifica Foods, Llc
13415 Estelle St
Corona CA 92879
-

(P-848)
PAGES PRODUCE COMPANY
Also Called: Crower's Marketing
4601 Pacific Blvd, Vernon (90058-2209)
PHONE......................................323 277-3660
EMP: 55
SQ FT: 31,000
SALES (est): 11.2MM
SALES (corp-wide): 433.3MM **Privately Held**
WEB: www.lamexfoods.com
SIC: 2033 Chili sauce, tomato: packaged
in cans, jars, etc.; spaghetti & other pasta
sauce: packaged in cans, jars, etc.;
tomato sauce: packaged in cans, jars,
etc.; apple sauce: packaged in cans, jars,
etc.
HQ: Italian Rose Garlic Products Llc
1380 W 15th St
Riviera Beach FL 33404
561 863-5556

(P-849)
PRESS BROTHERS JUICERY LLC
2551 Beverly Blvd Ste A, Los Angeles
(90057-1020)
P.O. Box 27699 (90027-0699)
PHONE......................................213 389-3645
Jack David Jones,

EMP: 20
SALES: 800K **Privately Held**
SIC: 2033 5499 Fruit juices: fresh; juices,
fruit or vegetable

(P-850)
PURITY ORGANICS INC
14900 W Belmont Ave, Kerman
(93630-9602)
PHONE......................................559 842-5600
Nick Koretoff, *CEO*
Greg Holzman, *President*
Liza Bennett, *Controller*
Demian Flores, *Controller*
Bernadette C Aguirre, *Marketing Staff*
EMP: 25
SQ FT: 10,000
SALES (est): 7.5MM **Privately Held**
WEB: www.purityorganic.com
SIC: 2033 Fruit juices: fresh

(P-851)
PURVEYORS KITCHEN
2043 Airpark Ct Ste 30, Auburn
(95602-9009)
PHONE......................................530 823-8527
Karen Foley, *CEO*
John Foley, *Principal*
EMP: 20
SALES (est): 5MM
SALES (corp-wide): 6.4MM **Privately Held**
SIC: 2033 2099 8742 2035 Barbecue
sauce: packaged in cans, jars, etc.; food
preparations; food & beverage consultant;
pickles, sauces & salad dressings
PA: The Absinthe Group Inc
368 Hayes St
San Francisco CA 94102
415 864-2693

(P-852)
RIO PLUMA COMPANY LLC (HQ)
1900 Highway 99, Gridley (95948-9401)
P.O. Box 948 (95948-0948)
PHONE......................................530 846-5200
Brad Stapleton, *President*
Eric Heitman,
Gavin Heitman,
◆ EMP: 32
SQ FT: 100,000
SALES (est): 5.2MM
SALES (corp-wide): 40.6MM **Privately Held**
SIC: 2033 2034 2068 0723 Fruits & fruit
products in cans, jars, etc.; dried & dehy-
drated fruits; nuts: dried, dehydrated,
salted or roasted; fruit crops market
preparation services
PA: Stapleton - Spence Packing Co.
1900 State Highway 99
Gridley CA 95948
408 297-8815

(P-853)
ROBEKS CORPORATION
Also Called: Robeks Juice
3891 Overland Ave, Culver City
(90232-3306)
PHONE......................................310 838-2332
Cesar Torres, *Manager*
EMP: 11 **Privately Held**
SIC: 2033 5149 Fruit juices: fresh; juices
PA: Robeks Corporation
5220 Pacific Concourse Dr
Los Angeles CA 90045
-

(P-854)
SAN JOAQUIN TOMATO GROWERS INC
22001 E St, Crows Landing (95313)
P.O. Box 578 (95313-0578)
PHONE......................................209 837-4721
Thomas Perez, *President*
Earl Perez, *Vice Pres*
EMP: 10
SALES (est): 9MM **Privately Held**
SIC: 2033 Tomato products: packaged in
cans, jars, etc.

(P-855)
SENECA FOODS CORPORATION
2801 Finch Rd, Modesto (95354-4120)
PHONE......................................209 572-5201
Anet Reclusado, *Manager*

Lawrence Siu, *IT/INT Sup*
Tim Bracco, *Prdtn Mgr*
Albert Flores, *Supervisor*
Ida Weaver, *Supervisor*
EMP: 127
SALES (corp-wide): 1.3B **Publicly Held**
SIC: 2033 Fruits & fruit products in cans,
jars, etc.
PA: Seneca Foods Corporation
3736 S Main St
Marion NY 14505
315 926-8100

(P-856)
SENECA FOODS CORPORATION
2801 Finch Rd, Modesto (95354-4120)
PHONE......................................209 572-5694
Tom Bart, *Branch Mgr*
EMP: 500
SALES (corp-wide): 1.3B **Publicly Held**
SIC: 2033 2099 Fruits: packaged in cans,
jars, etc.; food preparations
PA: Seneca Foods Corporation
3736 S Main St
Marion NY 14505
315 926-8100

(P-857)
SFFI COMPANY INC (PA)
Also Called: Simply Fresh Fruit
4383 Exchange Ave, Vernon (90058-2619)
PHONE......................................323 586-0000
William T Sander, *President*
Bruce Spiro, *Vice Pres*
Jaxon Potter, *General Mgr*
Able Aleman, *Human Resources*
Dominic Marlia, *Purchasing*
▲ EMP: 175
SQ FT: 65,000
SALES (est): 28MM **Privately Held**
SIC: 2033 Canned fruits & specialties

(P-858)
SIMPLY FRESH FRUIT INC
4383 Exchange Ave, Vernon (90058-2619)
PHONE......................................323 586-0000
Gustavo Fernandez, *CEO*
William Sander, *President*
Jaxon Potter, *Vice Pres*
Bruce Spiro, *Vice Pres*
◆ EMP: 99
SQ FT: 60,000
SALES (est): 21.2MM
SALES (corp-wide): 28MM **Privately Held**
WEB: www.simplyfreshfruit.com
SIC: 2033 Fruits: packaged in cans, jars,
etc.
PA: Sffi Company, Inc.
4383 Exchange Ave
Vernon CA 90058
323 586-0000

(P-859)
STANISLAUS FOOD PRODUCTS CO (PA)
1202 D St, Modesto (95354-2407)
P.O. Box 3951 (95352-3951)
PHONE......................................209 548-3537
Thomas A Cortopassi, *CEO*
William D Butler, *Exec VP*
Mark Kimmel, *Senior VP*
Rick Serpa, *Senior VP*
▼ EMP: 105
SQ FT: 50,000
SALES (est): 25.6MM **Privately Held**
SIC: 2033 Tomato paste: packaged in
cans, jars, etc.; tomato purees: packaged
in cans, jars, etc.; tomato sauce: pack-
aged in cans, jars, etc.; tomato juice:
packaged in cans, jars, etc.

(P-860)
SUNDOWN FOODS USA INC
10891 Business Dr, Fontana (92337-8235)
PHONE......................................909 606-6797
Jeff Wartell, *President*
Kathye Guccione, *Office Mgr*
Mary Salcido, *Opers Staff*
▲ EMP: 30
SALES (est): 5.7MM **Privately Held**
WEB: www.sundownfoods.com
SIC: 2033 Vegetables & vegetable prod-
ucts in cans, jars, etc.

PRODUCTS & SVCS

(P-861)
SUNNY DELIGHT BEVERAGES CO
1230 N Tustin Ave, Anaheim (92807-1617)
PHONE..................714 630-6251
J C Oswalt, *Branch Mgr*
Elaine Sanchez, *Human Resources*
EMP: 120
SALES (corp-wide): 1.3B **Privately Held**
SIC: 2033 3085 Fruit juices: packaged in cans, jars, etc.; plastics bottles
HQ: Sunny Delight Beverage Co
    10300 Alliance Rd Ste 500
    Blue Ash OH 45242
    513 483-3300

(P-862)
SUNNYGEM LLC
500 N F St, Wasco (93280-1435)
PHONE..................661 758-0491
Charles R Bye,
Lisa Lamborn, *Executive*
Johnny Gambino, *Administration*
Susan Huseman, *Controller*
Buck Moore, *Plant Mgr*
◆ **EMP:** 300
SQ FT: 270,000
SALES (est): 83.4MM **Privately Held**
SIC: 2033 3556 Fruit juices: fresh; juice extractors, fruit & vegetable: commercial type

(P-863)
TREE TOP INC
1250 E 3rd St, Oxnard (93030-6107)
P.O. Box 248, Selah WA (98942-0248)
PHONE..................509 697-7251
Keith Gomes, *Branch Mgr*
Tom Stokes, *CEO*
Dan Hagerty, *Senior VP*
EMP: 236
SALES (corp-wide): 399.9MM **Privately Held**
SIC: 2033 Fruit juices: packaged in cans, jars, etc.
PA: Tree Top, Inc.
    220 E 2nd Ave
    Selah WA 98942
    509 697-7251

(P-864)
TROPICAL PRESERVING CO INC
1711 E 15th St, Los Angeles (90021-2715)
PHONE..................213 748-5108
Ronald Randall, *President*
EMP: 23 **EST:** 1928
SQ FT: 25,000
SALES (est): 4.2MM **Privately Held**
WEB: www.tropicalpreserving.com
SIC: 2033 Jams, jellies & preserves: packaged in cans, jars, etc.

(P-865)
TROPICANA PRODUCTS INC
240 N Orange Ave, City of Industry (91744-3433)
PHONE..................626 968-1299
Kevin Frebert, *Plant Mgr*
Philippe Leys, *Engineer*
Julie Goodenough, *Accounting Mgr*
Dave Perry, *Finance Mgr*
Rodrigo Martinez, *Manager*
EMP: 150
SQ FT: 1,512
SALES (corp-wide): 63.5B **Publicly Held**
WEB: www.tropicana.com/biz
SIC: 2033 Fruit juices: fresh
HQ: Tropicana Products, Inc.
    1001 13th Ave E
    Bradenton FL 34208
    941 747-4461

(P-866)
VALLEY VIEW FOODS INC
7547 Sawtelle Ave, Yuba City (95991-9514)
PHONE..................530 673-7356
Jaswant Bains, *President*
Satwant Bains, *Admin Sec*
Anneke Amiga, *Administration*
EMP: 70
SQ FT: 80,000
SALES: 10MM **Privately Held**
SIC: 2033 Fruit juices: fresh

(P-867)
VANNELLI BRANDS LLC
4031 Alvis Ct, Rocklin (95677-4011)
PHONE..................916 824-1717
Chuck Eaton, *President*
Jerry Moore, *Director*
EMP: 12
SQ FT: 25,000
SALES: 5.5MM **Privately Held**
SIC: 2033 Spaghetti & other pasta sauce: packaged in cans, jars, etc.

(P-868)
VIE-DEL COMPANY (PA)
11903 S Chestnut Ave, Fresno (93725-9618)
P.O. Box 2908 (93745-2908)
PHONE..................559 834-2525
Dianne S Nury, *President*
Richard D Watson, *Treasurer*
Janice Terry, *Executive Asst*
Massud S Nury, *Admin Sec*
Richard Watson, *Controller*
▲ **EMP:** 75
SQ FT: 500,000
SALES (est): 12.8MM **Privately Held**
SIC: 2033 2084 Fruit juices: concentrated, hot pack; brandy

(P-869)
VITA-PAKT CITRUS PRODUCTS CO (PA)
203 E Badillo St, Covina (91723-2116)
P.O. Box 309 (91723-0309)
PHONE..................626 332-1101
James R Boyles, *CEO*
Lloyd Shimizu, *CFO*
◆ **EMP:** 50
SQ FT: 70,000
SALES (est): 26.5MM **Privately Held**
WEB: www.vita-pakt.com
SIC: 2033 2037 Apple sauce: packaged in cans, jars, etc.; fruit juices: fresh; fruit juices, frozen

(P-870)
WARD E WALDO & SON INC
Also Called: Ward E Waldo & Son Marmalades
273 E Highland Ave, Sierra Madre (91024-2014)
P.O. Box 266 (91025-0266)
PHONE..................626 355-1218
Richard H Ward, *President*
Jeffrey Ward, *Vice Pres*
EMP: 12
SQ FT: 10,000
SALES (est): 1.8MM **Privately Held**
WEB: www.waldoward.com
SIC: 2033 Preserves, including imitation: in cans, jars, etc.; jellies, edible, including imitation: in cans, jars, etc.; fruits: packaged in cans, jars, etc.

(P-871)
WILDBRINE LLC
322 Bellevue Ave, Santa Rosa (95407-7711)
PHONE..................707 657-7607
Chris Glab, *Mng Member*
Richard Goldberg,
EMP: 40 **EST:** 2012
SQ FT: 9,000
SALES: 3.3MM **Privately Held**
SIC: 2033 5149 Sauerkraut: packaged in cans, jars, etc.; beverages, except coffee & tea

---

2034 Dried Fruits, Vegetables & Soup

(P-872)
AGUSA
1055 S 19th Ave, Lemoore (93245-9747)
PHONE..................559 924-4785
Joel Delira, *CEO*
Inigo Martinez, *COO*
Javier Souchard, *CFO*
Joel De Lira, *General Mgr*
Danny Serrano, *Finance Mgr*
◆ **EMP:** 36
SQ FT: 28,000

SALES (est): 8.2MM **Privately Held**
WEB: www.agusa.net
SIC: 2034 Dried & dehydrated fruits

(P-873)
AMERICAN FOOD INGREDIENTS INC
4021 Avenida Plata 501, Oceanside (92056)
PHONE..................760 967-6287
Karen Koppenhaver, *CEO*
▲ **EMP:** 30
SQ FT: 2,000
SALES (est): 7.5MM **Privately Held**
SIC: 2034 Dried & dehydrated vegetables

(P-874)
BARLETTA DEHYDRATOR INC
4101 County Road S, Orland (95963-9818)
PHONE..................530 865-9318
Richard Conte, *Principal*
Sharon Ellis, *Principal*
EMP: 10
SALES (est): 1.1MM **Privately Held**
SIC: 2034 Dehydrated fruits, vegetables, soups

(P-875)
BASIC AMERICAN INC (PA)
Also Called: Basic American Foods
2999 Oak Rd Ste 800, Walnut Creek (94597-2054)
PHONE..................925 472-4438
Bryan Reese, *President*
James Collins, *CFO*
John Barnecut, *Admin Sec*
Amanda Neel, *Controller*
Sharon Posteele, *Human Resources*
◆ **EMP:** 60
SALES (est): 443.9MM **Privately Held**
WEB: www.baf.com
SIC: 2034 2099 Potato products, dried & dehydrated; vegetables, dried or dehydrated (except freeze-dried); potatoes, peeled for the trade

(P-876)
BATTH DEHYDRATOR LLC
4624 W Nebraska Ave, Caruthers (93609-9566)
P.O. Box 309 (93609-0309)
PHONE..................559 864-3501
Charanjit S Batth,
Kanwarjit S Batth,
▲ **EMP:** 40
SQ FT: 217,800
SALES (est): 5.5MM **Privately Held**
SIC: 2034 Raisins

(P-877)
CALIFORNIA DRIED FRUIT INC
Also Called: Midway Farms
9145 W Herndon Ave, Fresno (93723-9302)
P.O. Box 11187 (93772-1187)
PHONE..................559 233-0970
Christopher Cubre, *Principal*
Jennifer Dart, *Office Mgr*
EMP: 22
SQ FT: 1,200
SALES (est): 3.4MM **Privately Held**
SIC: 2034 Dried & dehydrated fruits

(P-878)
CARO NUT COMPANY
2904 S Angus Ave, Fresno (93725-1939)
PHONE..................559 439-2365
David Mahaffy, *CEO*
Todd Crosswell, *General Mgr*
▲ **EMP:** 50 **EST:** 2008
SALES (est): 32.9MM
SALES (corp-wide): 57.4MM **Privately Held**
SIC: 2034 Dried & dehydrated fruits
PA: Candor-Ags, Inc.
    9491 N Fort Washington Rd # 102
    Fresno CA 93730
    559 439-2365

(P-879)
CARUTHERS RAISIN PKG CO INC (PA)
12797 S Elm Ave, Caruthers (93609-9711)
PHONE..................559 864-9448
Donald Kizirian, *President*
Don Kizirian, *President*

Gina Elsea, *CFO*
Dennis Housepian, *Exec VP*
Gregg Weaver, *Regional Mgr*
◆ **EMP:** 70
SQ FT: 4,000
SALES (est): 17.9MM **Privately Held**
WEB: www.caruthersraisin.com
SIC: 2034 Dehydrated fruits, vegetables, soups

(P-880)
CAULIPOWER LLC
16200 Ventura Blvd # 400, Encino (91436-4918)
PHONE..................310 606-1648
Gail Becker, *Mng Member*
EMP: 15
SQ FT: 500
SALES: 5.5MM **Privately Held**
SIC: 2034 Vegetable flour, meal & powder

(P-881)
CULINARY FARMS INC
1244 E Beamer St, Woodland (95776-6002)
PHONE..................916 375-3000
Kirk Bewley, *President*
Andy Chih, *Research*
▲ **EMP:** 50
SALES (est): 14.9MM **Privately Held**
WEB: www.culinaryfarms.com
SIC: 2034 Dried & dehydrated vegetables

(P-882)
DEL REY ENTERPRISES INC
8898 E Central Ave, Del Rey (93616)
PHONE..................559 233-4452
Robert E Naugle, *President*
Michael Graves, *Treasurer*
Aaron Avedian, *Vice Pres*
Mark Avedian, *Vice Pres*
EMP: 12
SQ FT: 20,000
SALES (est): 1.5MM **Privately Held**
SIC: 2034 Dried & dehydrated fruits; raisins

(P-883)
INLAND EMPIRE FOODS INC (PA)
5425 Wilson St, Riverside (92509-2434)
PHONE..................951 682-8222
Mark H Sterner, *President*
Paul Stiritz, *Vice Pres*
Dave Macias, *Sales Mgr*
▼ **EMP:** 35
SQ FT: 85,000
SALES (est): 13.6MM **Privately Held**
WEB: www.inlandempirefoods.com
SIC: 2034 Vegetables, dried or dehydrated (except freeze-dried)

(P-884)
LA VIENA RANCH
9408 Road 23, Madera (93637-9358)
P.O. Box 457 (93639-0457)
PHONE..................559 674-6725
Carrie Besuner, *President*
EMP: 50
SALES (est): 4MM **Privately Held**
SIC: 2034 Dried & dehydrated fruits

(P-885)
LION RAISINS INC (PA)
Also Called: Lion Packing Co
9500 S De Wolf Ave, Selma (93662-9534)
P.O. Box 1350 (93662-1350)
PHONE..................559 834-6677
Alfred Lion Jr, *President*
Allan Lion, *Vice Pres*
Bruce Lion, *Vice Pres*
Isabel Lion, *Principal*
Larry Lion, *Principal*
◆ **EMP:** 400
SQ FT: 130,000
SALES (est): 105.8MM **Privately Held**
WEB: www.lionraisins.com
SIC: 2034 Raisins

(P-886)
MARIANI PACKING CO INC
Also Called: Mariani Bros
9281 Highway 70, Marysville (95901-3064)
PHONE..................530 749-6565
Mark Kettmann, *Manager*
EMP: 20

▲ = Import ▼=Export
◆ =Import/Export

SALES (corp-wide): 109.2MM **Privately Held**
WEB: www.marianifruit.com
SIC: 2034 Prunes, dried
PA: Mariani Packing Co., Inc.
500 Crocker Dr
Vacaville CA 95688
707 452-2800

(P-887)
MELKONIAN ENTERPRISES INC
Also Called: California Fruit Basket
2730 S De Wolf Ave, Sanger (93657-9770)
PHONE..................................559 485-6191
Mark Melkonian, *CEO*
Dennis Melkonian, *Vice Pres*
Douglas Melkonian, *Vice Pres*
EMP: 20
SQ FT: 160,000
SALES (est): 3.7MM **Privately Held**
WEB: www.californiafruitbasket.com
SIC: 2034 0172 5431 Raisins; fruits, dried
or dehydrated, except freeze-dried;
grapes; fruit stands or markets

(P-888)
MERCER FOODS LLC
1836 Lapham Dr, Modesto (95354-3900)
PHONE..................................209 529-0150
David A Noland, *CEO*
Pamela Denney, *Owner*
Clark Driftmier, *Exec VP*
Mike Alaga, *Vice Pres*
Jeff Hulme, *Vice Pres*
▲ **EMP:** 16
SQ FT: 160,000
SALES (est): 19.6MM
SALES (corp-wide): 251.3MM **Privately
Held**
WEB: www.mercerfoods.com
SIC: 2034 Dehydrated fruits, vegetables,
soups
PA: Graham Partners, Inc.
3811 West Chester Pike # 200
Newtown Square PA 19073
610 408-0500

(P-889)
MOLES FARM
9503 S Hughes Ave, Fresno (93706-9731)
PHONE..................................559 444-0324
Ray Moles, *President*
EMP: 65
SALES (est): 2.9MM **Privately Held**
SIC: 2034 Raisins

(P-890)
NSI GROUP LLC (PA)
Also Called: Natural Sourcing International
17031 Ventura Blvd, Encino (91316-4128)
PHONE..................................818 639-8335
Vincent Grignon, *Mng Member*
Jean-Victor Mariolle, *Vice Pres*
Chris Mon, *Accountant*
EMP: 22
SQ FT: 7,000
SALES: 20MM **Privately Held**
SIC: 2034 Dried & dehydrated fruits

(P-891)
SALWASSER INC
4087 N Howard Ave, Kerman (93630-9674)
P.O. Box 296, Biola (93606-0296)
PHONE..................................559 843-2882
George J Salwasser, *President*
George Salwasser, *President*
Charlotte Salwasser, *Vice Pres*
EMP: 56 EST: 1977
SQ FT: 50,000
SALES: 4MM **Privately Held**
SIC: 2034 Raisins

(P-892)
**SENSIENT NTRAL INGREDIENTS
LLC**
7474 Cressey Way, Livingston (95334)
PHONE..................................209 394-7979
Kris Van Elsywk, *Principal*
EMP: 13
SALES (corp-wide): 1.3B **Publicly Held**
SIC: 2034 Dehydrated fruits, vegetables,
soups
HQ: Sensient Natural Ingredients Llc
151 S Walnut Rd
Turlock CA 95380
209 667-2777

(P-893)
**SENSIENT NTRAL INGREDIENTS
LLC (HQ)**
Also Called: Sensient Dehydrated Flavors
151 S Walnut Rd, Turlock (95380-5127)
P.O. Box 1524 (95381-1524)
PHONE..................................209 667-2777
Paul Manning, *President*
Mike Hagood, *Plant Mgr*
Michael Swenson, *Marketing Mgr*
Jim Shank, *Maintence Staff*
Felipe Aguilar, *Director*
EMP: 69
SALES (est): 53.7MM
SALES (corp-wide): 1.3B **Publicly Held**
SIC: 2034 Vegetables, dried or dehydrated
(except freeze-dried)
PA: Sensient Technologies Corporation
777 E Wisconsin Ave # 1100
Milwaukee WI 53202
414 271-6755

(P-894)
SOUP BASES LOADED INC
2355 E Francis St, Ontario (91761-7727)
PHONE..................................909 230-6890
Alan Portney, *President*
EMP: 45
SQ FT: 27,000
SALES (est): 10MM **Privately Held**
WEB: www.soupbasesloaded.com
SIC: 2034 2099 Dried & dehydrated soup
mixes; seasonings: dry mixes

(P-895)
STUTZ PACKING COMPANY
82689 Avenue 45, Indio (92201-2386)
PHONE..................................760 342-1666
Jack Stutz, *President*
Patty Stutz, *Admin Sec*
EMP: 13
SALES (est): 5.7MM **Privately Held**
SIC: 2034 Dehydrated fruits, vegetables,
soups

(P-896)
**SUN VLLEY RSINS INC A CAL
CORP**
9595 S Hughes Ave, Fresno (93706-9731)
PHONE..................................559 233-8070
Ermel Ray Moles, *President*
Debra Moles, *Vice Pres*
▼ **EMP:** 15
SQ FT: 18,000
SALES (est): 4.6MM **Privately Held**
SIC: 2034 Raisins

(P-897)
SUNRISE FRESH LP
2716 E Miner Ave, Stockton (95205-4705)
P.O. Box 128, Linden (95236-0128)
PHONE..................................209 932-0192
James Samuel, *Partner*
EMP: 25 EST: 2014
SALES (est): 3.8MM **Privately Held**
SIC: 2034 Dehydrated fruits, vegetables,
soups

(P-898)
SUNSWEET DRYERS
23760 Loleta Ave, Corning (96021-9699)
P.O. Box 201 (96021-0201)
PHONE..................................530 824-5854
Dan Lima, *Manager*
EMP: 12
SALES (corp-wide): 244.8MM **Privately
Held**
SIC: 2034 Prunes, dried
HQ: Sunsweet Dryers
901 N Walton Ave
Yuba City CA 95993
530 846-5578

(P-899)
SUNSWEET DRYERS
26 E Evans Reimer Rd, Gridley
(95948-9544)
PHONE..................................530 846-5578
Jeff Wilson, *Manager*
EMP: 60
SALES (corp-wide): 244.8MM **Privately
Held**
SIC: 2034 Prunes, dried

HQ: Sunsweet Dryers
901 N Walton Ave
Yuba City CA 95993
530 846-5578

(P-900)
SUNSWEET DRYERS INC
28390 Avenue 12, Madera (93637-9102)
P.O. Box 607 (93639-0607)
PHONE..................................559 673-4140
Javier Celerda, *Office Mgr*
Javier Delacerda, *Manager*
Mike Russell, *Superintendent*
EMP: 17
SALES (est): 1.8MM **Privately Held**
SIC: 2034 Dried & dehydrated fruits

(P-901)
SUNSWEET GROWERS INC (PA)
901 N Walton Ave, Yuba City (95993-9370)
PHONE..................................800 417-2253
Dane Lance, *President*
Brendon S Flynn, *Ch of Bd*
Ana Klein, *CEO*
Sharon Braun, *Vice Pres*
Deb Macias, *Vice Pres*
◆ **EMP:** 600 EST: 1917
SQ FT: 1,200,000
SALES (est): 244.8MM **Privately Held**
WEB: www.sunsweet.com
SIC: 2034 2037 2086 Dried & dehydrated
fruits; fruit juices; fruit drinks (less than
100% juice): packaged in cans, etc.

(P-902)
TRUE LEAF FARMS LLC
1275 San Justo Rd, San Juan Bautista
(95045-9733)
P.O. Box 509, Salinas (93902-0509)
PHONE..................................831 623-4667
Rio Farms, *Mng Member*
Kori T Tuggle, *Marketing Staff*
EMP: 500
SALES (est): 126.1MM **Privately Held**
WEB: www.trueleaffarms.com
SIC: 2034 Vegetables, dried or dehydrated
(except freeze-dried)

(P-903)
VACAVILLE FRUIT CO INC
2055 Cessna Dr, Vacaville (95688-8838)
P.O. Box 1537 (95696-1537)
PHONE..................................707 448-5292
Nicole Ciarabellini, *Principal*
Sonia Nunez, *Accountant*
Mary Quinonez, *Sales Dir*
◆ **EMP:** 40
SQ FT: 15,000
SALES (est): 9MM **Privately Held**
WEB: www.vacavillefruit.com
SIC: 2034 Prunes, dried; fruits, dried or de-
hydrated, except freeze-dried

(P-904)
VALLEY VIEW PACKING CO INC
1764 The Alameda, San Jose
(95126-1729)
P.O. Box 5699 (95150-5699)
PHONE..................................408 289-8300
Salvadore Rubino, *CEO*
Patricia Rubino, *Corp Secy*
◆ **EMP:** 50
SQ FT: 9,000
SALES (est): 5.5MM **Privately Held**
WEB: www.valleyviewpacking.com
SIC: 2034 2033 Fruits, dried or dehy-
drated, except freeze-dried; prunes, dried;
fruit juices: packaged in cans, jars, etc.;
fruit juices: concentrated, hot pack

(P-905)
VICTOR PACKING INC
11687 Road 27 1/2, Madera (93637-9440)
PHONE..................................559 673-5908
Victor Sahatdjian, *President*
Margaret Sahatdjian, *Vice Pres*
Justin Surabian, *Technology*
Stephanie Kerber, *Accountant*
Jennifer Williams, *Accountant*
▼ **EMP:** 50
SQ FT: 150,000
SALES (est): 11.7MM **Privately Held**
WEB: www.victorpacking.com
SIC: 2034 Raisins

(P-906)
VSP PRODUCTS INC
3324 Orestimba Rd, Newman
(95360-9628)
PHONE..................................209 862-1200
Chris J Rufer, *President*
Robert Benech, *President*
▲ **EMP:** 53
SQ FT: 27,000
SALES (est): 7MM
SALES (corp-wide): 53.7MM **Privately
Held**
SIC: 2034 Dehydrated fruits, vegetables,
soups
PA: The Morning Star Company
724 Main St Ste 202
Woodland CA 95695
530 666-6600

(P-907)
WEST COAST GROWERS INC
1849 N Helm Ave Ste 110, Fresno
(93727-1624)
PHONE..................................559 843-2294
Charlotte E Salwasser, *President*
George Sousa, *President*
Mark Mariani, *CEO*
Janice Husnagl, *CFO*
Charlotte Salwasser, *Principal*
▼ **EMP:** 40
SQ FT: 50,000
SALES (est): 8.9MM
SALES (corp-wide): 109.2MM **Privately
Held**
WEB: www.marianifruit.com
SIC: 2034 5149 Raisins; fruits, dried
PA: Mariani Packing Co., Inc.
500 Crocker Dr
Vacaville CA 95688
707 452-2800

(P-908)
WILL PAK FOODS INC
Also Called: Taste Adventure
4471 Santa Ana St Ste C, Ontario
(91761-8110)
PHONE..................................800 874-0883
Gary L Morris, *President*
EMP: 10
SQ FT: 10,000
SALES (est): 1MM **Privately Held**
WEB: www.tasteadventure.com
SIC: 2034 Dehydrated fruits, vegetables,
soups

**2035 Pickled Fruits,
Vegetables, Sauces &
Dressings**

(P-909)
**A-1 ESTRN-HOME-MADE PICKLE
INC**
1832 Johnston St, Los Angeles
(90031-3447)
PHONE..................................323 223-1141
Martin Morhar, *President*
Murray Berger, *Vice Pres*
EMP: 29
SQ FT: 40,000
SALES (est): 5.4MM **Privately Held**
SIC: 2035 Pickled fruits & vegetables

(P-910)
BELL-CARTER FOODS INC
Also Called: Bell-Carterolive Company
1012 2nd St, Corning (96021-3248)
PHONE..................................530 528-4820
Steve Henderson, *Branch Mgr*
Patty Beth, *Accounting Mgr*
Lori Rindahl, *Buyer*
Bob Asmus, *Plant Engr*
America Garman, *Marketing Staff*
EMP: 300
SALES (corp-wide): 177.6MM **Privately
Held**
WEB: www.bellcarter.com
SIC: 2035 2033 Olives, brined: bulk;
canned fruits & specialties
PA: Bell-Carter Foods, Inc.
590 Ygnacio Valley Rd # 300
Walnut Creek CA 94596
925 284-5933

P
R
O
D
U
C
T
S
&
S
V
C
S

(PA)=Parent Co (HQ)=Headquarters (DH)=Div Headquarters
✪ = New Business established in last 2 years
2019 California
Manufacturers Register
51

(P-911)
CALCHEF FOODS LLC
4335 N Star Way Ste D, Modesto
(95356-8628)
PHONE..................................888 638-7083
Dan Costa,
EMP: 81
SALES (est): 213.2K
SALES (corp-wide): 35.6MM **Privately Held**
SIC: 2035 2032 5142 Pickles, sauces & salad dressings; ethnic foods: canned, jarred, etc.; dinners, frozen
PA: Noble Rider, Llc
4335 N Star Way Ste D
Modesto CA 95356
209 566-7800

(P-912)
GARLIC VALLEY FARMS INC
624 Ruberta Ave, Glendale (91201-2335)
PHONE..................................818 247-9600
William Anderson, *President*
Sonja Anderson, *Corp Secy*
Bill Brock, *Research*
Jared Valenzuela, *Natl Sales Mgr*
EMP: 11
SQ FT: 11,250
SALES (est): 1.3MM **Privately Held**
WEB: www.garlicvalleyfarms.com
SIC: 2035 5812 Seasonings & sauces, except tomato & dry; eating places

(P-913)
GFF INC
Also Called: Girard Food Service
145 Willow Ave, City of Industry
(91746-2047)
PHONE..................................323 232-6255
Jack Tucey, *Chairman*
Bill Perry, *President*
William Perry, *President*
Farrell Hirsch, *CEO*
▲ **EMP:** 89
SQ FT: 92,000
SALES (est): 33.7MM **Privately Held**
WEB: www.girardsdressings.com
SIC: 2035 Pickles, sauces & salad dressings

(P-914)
GINGER GOLDEN PRODUCTS INC
5860 Bandini Blvd, Commerce
(90040-2925)
PHONE..................................323 838-1070
Koichi Takeuchi, *President*
Yoshiji Kono, *Vice Pres*
▲ **EMP:** 27
SQ FT: 15,000
SALES (est): 3.8MM **Privately Held**
SIC: 2035 2099 Pickled fruits & vegetables; food preparations

(P-915)
H V FOOD PRODUCTS COMPANY
1221 Broadway, Oakland (94612-1837)
PHONE..................................510 271-7612
George C Roeth, *President*
Pamela Fletcher, *Vice Pres*
EMP: 200
SQ FT: 218,000
SALES (est): 16.7MM
SALES (corp-wide): 6.1B **Publicly Held**
WEB: www.kingsford.com
SIC: 2035 Pickles, sauces & salad dressings
HQ: The Kingsford Products Company Llc
1221 Broadway Ste 1300
Oakland CA 94612
510 271-7000

(P-916)
JUST INC
2000 Folsom St, San Francisco
(94110-1318)
PHONE..................................844 423-6637
Joshua Tetrick, *CEO*
Beth Lawrence, *Partner*
Alexandra Dallago, *President*
Lee Chae, *Vice Pres*
Sean Lynch, *Vice Pres*
EMP: 249
SQ FT: 2,300

SALES (est): 89.9MM **Privately Held**
SIC: 2035 2052 Mayonnaise; cookies

(P-917)
KIKKOMAN FOODS INC
1000 Glenn Dr, Folsom (95630-3164)
PHONE..................................916 355-8078
Masashi Kasuga, *President*
Wynnie Ng, *Opers Mgr*
Aj Moyer, *Maintence Staff*
Deanna Eastman, *Manager*
EMP: 30
SALES (corp-wide): 4B **Privately Held**
SIC: 2035 Soy sauce
HQ: Kikkoman Foods, Inc.
N1365 Six Corners Rd
Walworth WI 53184
262 275-6181

(P-918)
KRINOS FOODS LLC
Also Called: Santa Barbara Olives Co
1105 E Foster Rd Ste E, Santa Maria
(93455-6438)
PHONE..................................805 922-6700
Lourdez Clayton, *Manager*
EMP: 17
SALES (corp-wide): 57.7MM **Privately Held**
SIC: 2035 Olives, brined: bulk
PA: Krinos Foods Llc
1750 Bathgate Ave
Bronx NY 10457
718 729-9000

(P-919)
KRUGER FOODS INC
18362 E Highway 4, Stockton
(95215-9433)
P.O. Box 220, Farmington (95230-0220)
PHONE..................................209 941-8518
Kara Kruger, *CEO*
Leslie Kruger, *COO*
Eric Kruger, *VP Opers*
▼ **EMP:** 100
SQ FT: 80,000
SALES (est): 47.4MM **Privately Held**
WEB: www.krugerfoods.com
SIC: 2035 Pickles, vinegar; vegetables, pickled

(P-920)
LEE BROTHERS INC
1011 Timothy Dr, San Jose (95133-1043)
PHONE..................................650 964-9650
Gene Lee, *President*
Jay Lee, *Corp Secy*
Jim Lee, *Vice Pres*
EMP: 72
SQ FT: 46,000
SALES (est): 16.3MM **Privately Held**
SIC: 2035 Dressings, salad: raw & cooked (except dry mixes); soy sauce

(P-921)
MAJESTIC GARLIC INC
2222 Foothill Blvd Ste E, La Canada
(91011-1485)
PHONE..................................951 677-0555
Lucie Sabounjian, *Owner*
EMP: 15
SALES (est): 500K **Privately Held**
SIC: 2035 Spreads, garlic

(P-922)
MOREHOUSE FOODS INC
760 Epperson Dr, City of Industry
(91748-1336)
PHONE..................................626 854-1655
David L Latter Sr, *Chairman*
David L Latter Jr, *President*
Sean Simpson, *General Mgr*
Juan Trujillo, *Maintence Staff*
Paul Latter, *Manager*
▲ **EMP:** 50
SQ FT: 65,000
SALES (est): 11MM **Privately Held**
WEB: www.morehousefoods.com
SIC: 2035 5149 Mustard, prepared (wet); horseradish, prepared; seasonings, sauces & extracts

(P-923)
NOR CAL FOOD SOLUTIONS LLC
Also Called: Mad Wills Food Company
2043 Airpark Ct, Auburn (95602-9009)
PHONE..................................530 823-8527
Scott Bartosh, *Mng Member*
Tonya Gregerson, *Bookkeeper*
▼ **EMP:** 14
SALES (est): 3MM **Privately Held**
SIC: 2035 2099 Pickles, sauces & salad dressings; sauces: gravy, dressing & dip mixes

(P-924)
OLIVE MUSCO PRODUCTS INC
Swift & 5th St # 5, Orland (95963)
P.O. Box 368 (95963-0368)
PHONE..................................530 865-4111
Dennis Burreson, *Plant Mgr*
EMP: 30
SALES (corp-wide): 96.7MM **Privately Held**
SIC: 2035 2033 Pickles, sauces & salad dressings; olives: packaged in cans, jars, etc.
PA: Olive Musco Products Inc
17950 Via Nicolo
Tracy CA 95377
209 836-4600

(P-925)
ORGANIC HORSERADISH CO
7890 County Road 120, Tulelake
(96134-8228)
PHONE..................................530 664-3862
David Krizo, *Partner*
Jacqueline Krizo, *Partner*
EMP: 30
SALES (est): 2.2MM **Privately Held**
SIC: 2035 Horseradish, prepared

(P-926)
PACIFIC CHOICE BRANDS INC (PA)
4667 E Date Ave, Fresno (93725-2101)
PHONE..................................559 892-5365
Allan R Andrews, *CEO*
◆ **EMP:** 275 **EST:** 1930
SQ FT: 225,000
SALES (est): 69.3MM **Privately Held**
WEB: www.pacificchoicebrands.com
SIC: 2035 Pickled fruits & vegetables

(P-927)
PACIFIC PICKLE WORKS INC
718 Union Ave Snta Brbara Santa Barbara,
Santa Barbara (93103)
PHONE..................................805 765-1779
Bradley Bennett, *CEO*
EMP: 13 **EST:** 2010
SALES (est): 1.6MM **Privately Held**
SIC: 2035 2087 Pickled fruits & vegetables; cocktail mixes, nonalcoholic

(P-928)
PACIFICA FOODS LLC (PA)
13415 Estelle St, Corona (92879-1877)
PHONE..................................951 371-3123
Milt Liu, *CEO*
EMP: 23
SALES (est): 7.6MM **Privately Held**
WEB: www.pacificafoods.net
SIC: 2035 5149 2033 Seasonings & sauces, except tomato & dry; dressings, salad: raw & cooked (except dry mixes); sauces; tomato products: packaged in cans, jars, etc.; barbecue sauce: packaged in cans, jars, etc.

(P-929)
Q & B FOODS INC (DH)
15547 1st St, Irwindale (91706-6201)
PHONE..................................626 334-8090
Kuniaki Ishikaiwa, *President*
Akio Okumura, *CEO*
Jerry Shepherd, *Exec VP*
Norman Ives, *Vice Pres*
Paul Yun, *Sales Mgr*
◆ **EMP:** 69
SQ FT: 52,000

SALES (est): 16.9MM
SALES (corp-wide): 4.9B **Privately Held**
WEB: www.qbfoods.com
SIC: 2035 Dressings, salad: raw & cooked (except dry mixes); mayonnaise
HQ: Kifuki U.S.A. Co., Inc.
15547 1st St
Irwindale CA 91706
626 334-8090

(P-930)
RED SHELL FOODS INC
825 Baldwin Park Blvd, City of Industry
(91746-1205)
P.O. Box 91744 (91715-1744)
PHONE..................................626 937-6501
Hiro Watanabe, *President*
EMP: 10
SQ FT: 2,400
SALES (est): 125.6K **Privately Held**
WEB: www.redshell.com
SIC: 2035 Dressings, salad: raw & cooked (except dry mixes)

(P-931)
S M S BRINERS INC
17750 E Highway 4, Stockton
(95215-9721)
PHONE..................................209 941-8515
Kara Kruger, *CEO*
Frances Sousa, *President*
Laurie Flatter, *Corp Secy*
Arnold Sousa, *Vice Pres*
EMP: 15
SQ FT: 5,000
SALES (est): 3.3MM **Privately Held**
SIC: 2035 Vegetables, brined

(P-932)
SCOTTS FOOD PRODUCTS INC
7331 Alondra Blvd, Paramount
(90723-4013)
P.O. Box 17 (90723-0017)
PHONE..................................562 630-8448
Tony Lobue, *Owner*
Carrianne Lobue, *Sales Mgr*
▼ **EMP:** 10
SALES (est): 1MM **Privately Held**
WEB: www.scottsfoodproducts.com
SIC: 2035 Pickles, sauces & salad dressings

(P-933)
SONOMA GOURMET INC
Also Called: Pometta's
21684 8th St E Ste 100, Sonoma
(95476-2816)
PHONE..................................707 939-3700
William K Weber, *President*
Rodger C Declercq, *Vice Pres*
EMP: 25
SQ FT: 50,000
SALES (est): 4.3MM **Privately Held**
WEB: www.sonomagourmet.com
SIC: 2035 Pickles, sauces & salad dressings

(P-934)
SUNOPTA GLBAL ORGNIC ING INC (DH)
Also Called: Sunopta Food Solutions
100 Enterprise Way Ste B1, Scotts Valley
(95066-3248)
PHONE..................................831 685-6506
Joseph Stern, *President*
Loren Morr, *Vice Pres*
▲ **EMP:** 20
SQ FT: 2,800
SALES (est): 8MM
SALES (corp-wide): 1.2B **Privately Held**
WEB: www.organic-ingredients.com
SIC: 2035 2033 Relishes, vinegar; fruit nectars: packaged in cans, jars, etc.; fruit purees: packaged in cans, jars, etc.; fruit juices: concentrated, hot pack; vegetable purees: packaged in cans, jars, etc.

(P-935)
TAPATIO FOODS LLC
Also Called: Tapatio Hot Sauce
4685 District Blvd, Vernon (90058-2731)
PHONE..................................323 587-8933
Jose L Saavedra, *Mng Member*
Dolores McCoy,
EMP: 16
SQ FT: 30,000

SALES (est): 4.1MM **Privately Held**
WEB: www.tapatiohotsauce.com
SIC: **2035** Pickles, sauces & salad dressings

(P-936)
TMARZETTI COMPANY
Also Called: Marzetti West
876 Yosemite Dr, Milpitas (95035-5437)
PHONE..............................408 263-7540
John Herlihy, *Manager*
Maria Parada, *Safety Mgr*
EMP: 140
SQ FT: 50,000
SALES (corp-wide): 1.2B **Publicly Held**
SIC: **2035** Dressings, salad: raw & cooked (except dry mixes)
HQ: T.Marzetti Company
380 Polaris Pkwy Ste 400
Westerville OH 43082
614 846-2232

(P-937)
TULKOFF FOOD PRODUCTS WEST INC
705 Bliss Ave, Pittsburg (94565-5005)
PHONE..............................925 427-5157
Philip J Tulkoff, *CEO*
Paul Rostkowski, *CFO*
Alec Tulkoff, *Vice Pres*
EMP: 27
SQ FT: 40,000
SALES (est): 4.6MM
SALES (corp-wide): 26MM **Privately Held**
WEB: www.tulkoff.com
SIC: **2035** Horseradish, prepared
PA: Tulkoff Food Products, Inc.
2229 Van Deman St
Baltimore MD 21224
410 864-0526

(P-938)
U S ENTERPRISE CORPORATION
Also Called: Wing Nien Company
30560 San Antonio St, Hayward (94544-7102)
PHONE..............................510 487-8877
David H Hall, *President*
Ken Jue MD, *Vice Pres*
Gregory Hall, *Admin Sec*
▲ EMP: 30
SQ FT: 40,000
SALES (est): 5.1MM **Privately Held**
WEB: www.wnfoods.com
SIC: **2035 5141** Seasonings & sauces, except tomato & dry; groceries, general line

(P-939)
VALLEY GARLIC INC
500 Enterprise Pkwy, Coalinga (93210-9513)
PHONE..............................559 934-1763
Gary Caneza, *President*
EMP: 20
SALES (est): 3.6MM **Privately Held**
SIC: **2035** Spreads, garlic

2037 Frozen Fruits, Juices & Vegetables

(P-940)
CAL PCIFIC SPECIALTY FOODS LLC
1320 S Main St 302, Salinas (93901-2109)
PHONE..............................831 722-3615
William R Leblanc, *Mng Member*
Julie Munger, *CFO*
Scott Taylor, *VP Mfg*
Jesse Dornan, *Maintence Staff*
Luis De Alcuaz,
◆ EMP: 10
SALES (est): 1.9MM **Privately Held**
WEB: www.calpacificsf.com
SIC: **2037** Frozen fruits & vegetables

(P-941)
CALIFORNIA CONCENTRATE COMPANY
Also Called: Kimberley Wine Vinegars
18678 N Highway 99, Acampo (95220-9557)
PHONE..............................209 334-9112
Dennis Alexander, *President*
Andy Alexander, *Vice Pres*
Thomas P Alexander, *Vice Pres*
◆ EMP: 20 EST: 1969
SQ FT: 17,000
SALES (est): 4.2MM **Privately Held**
WEB: www.californiaconcentrate.com
SIC: **2037 2082** Fruit juice concentrates, frozen; malt extract

(P-942)
CANADAS FINEST FOODS INC
Also Called: Reliant Foodservice
26090 Ynez Rd, Temecula (92591-6000)
PHONE..............................951 296-1040
David Canada, *President*
Rick Joslen, *Sales Staff*
▲ EMP: 70
SQ FT: 102,000
SALES (est): 520MM **Privately Held**
SIC: **2037 2024** Fruit juices; dairy based frozen desserts

(P-943)
CHIQUITA BRANDS INTL INC
3586 Arden Rd, Hayward (94545-3921)
PHONE..............................510 732-9500
Dan Clay, *Branch Mgr*
EMP: 18
SALES (corp-wide): 3B **Privately Held**
WEB: www.chiquita.com
SIC: **2037** Fruit juices
HQ: Chiquita Brands International, Inc.
1855 Griffin Rd Ste C436
Dania FL 33004
954 453-1201

(P-944)
CLEUGHS FROZEN FOODS INC
6571 Altura Blvd Ste 200, Buena Park (90620-1020)
PHONE..............................714 521-1002
Michael W Cleugh, *President*
Jeremy Kendall, *Ch of Bd*
John Dietrich, *CFO*
David Michael Cleugh, *Exec VP*
Steve Bromley, *Vice Pres*
EMP: 20 EST: 1933
SQ FT: 3,000
SALES (est): 3.6MM
SALES (corp-wide): 1.2B **Privately Held**
SIC: **2037** Frozen fruits & vegetables
PA: Sunopta Inc
2233 Argentia Rd Suite 401
Mississauga ON L5N 2
905 821-9669

(P-945)
CROWN CITRUS COMPANY INC
551 W Main St, Brawley (92227-2262)
PHONE..............................760 344-1930
Mark McBroom, *President*
EMP: 10
SALES (est): 1.5MM **Privately Held**
SIC: **2037** Citrus pulp, dried

(P-946)
DEL REY JUICE CO
Also Called: Paramount Food Processing
5286 S Del Rey Ave, Del Rey (93616)
PHONE..............................559 888-8533
EMP: 99
SALES (est): 8.1MM **Privately Held**
SIC: **2037**

(P-947)
DOLE PACKAGED FOODS LLC (HQ)
Also Called: Glacier Foods Division
3059 Townsgate Rd Ste 400, Westlake Village (91361-3190)
P.O. Box 5132 (91359-5132)
PHONE..............................805 601-5500
David A Delorenzo, *Mng Member*
Jon Rodacy, *Vice Pres*
Jim Johnston,
Tim Nelson,
Takamasa Tsuzuki,

▲ EMP: 550
SALES (est): 234.8MM
SALES (corp-wide): 51.7B **Privately Held**
WEB: www.jrwood.com
SIC: **2037** Fruits, quick frozen & cold pack (frozen); vegetables, quick frozen & cold pack, excl. potato products
PA: Itochu Corporation
2-5-1, Kitaaoyama
Minato-Ku TKY 107-0
334 972-121

(P-948)
DOLE PACKAGED FOODS LLC
Also Called: Glacier Foods Division
1117 K St, Sanger (93657-3200)
PHONE..............................559 875-3354
Alvin Mc Avoy, *Manager*
Teri Thomas, *Executive Asst*
Sandra Stratton, *Admin Asst*
Maureen Brennan, *Human Res Mgr*
Nicholas Barker, *Opers Staff*
EMP: 180
SALES (corp-wide): 51.7B **Privately Held**
WEB: www.jrwood.com
SIC: **2037 2033 2095 2032** Fruits, quick frozen & cold pack (frozen); canned fruits & specialties; roasted coffee; canned specialties; frozen specialties
HQ: Dole Packaged Foods, Llc
3059 Townsgate Rd Ste 400
Westlake Village CA 91361
805 601-5500

(P-949)
FORAGER PROJECT LLC
235 Montgomery St Ste 730, San Francisco (94104-2917)
PHONE..............................855 729-5253
Stephen Williamson, *Mng Member*
Erica Kirmayer, *Marketing Staff*
Will Bomberry, *Manager*
EMP: 55
SALES (est): 6MM **Privately Held**
SIC: **2037** Fruit juices

(P-950)
HAYWARD ENTERPRISES INC
2700 Napa Valley Corp Dr, NAPA (94558)
PHONE..............................707 261-5100
Tracy Collier Hayward, *President*
Jose Osuch, *CFO*
▼ EMP: 15
SQ FT: 8,166
SALES (est): 1.9MM **Privately Held**
WEB: www.perfectpuree.com
SIC: **2037** Frozen fruits & vegetables

(P-951)
HUSKS UNLIMITED
1616 Silvas St, Chula Vista (91911-4622)
PHONE..............................619 476-8301
Luis Duenas, *CEO*
Eric Brenk, *President*
EMP: 62
SQ FT: 15,000
SALES: 5MM **Privately Held**
SIC: **2037** Frozen fruits & vegetables

(P-952)
IMPERIAL VALLEY FOODS INC
1961 Buchanan Ave, Calexico (92231-4306)
P.O. Box 233 Paulin Ave (92231)
PHONE..............................760 203-1896
Gustavo Cabellero Jr, *President*
Edna Cabellero, *Treasurer*
Fernando Cabellero, *Vice Pres*
▲ EMP: 300
SALES (est): 37.3MM **Privately Held**
SIC: **2037** Frozen fruits & vegetables

(P-953)
J HELLMAN FROZEN FOODS INC (PA)
1601 E Olympic Blvd # 200, Los Angeles (90021-1941)
P.O. Box 86267 (90086-0267)
PHONE..............................213 243-9105
Tracy Hellman, *CEO*
Bryce Hellman, *President*
EMP: 50
SQ FT: 21,000
SALES (est): 9MM **Privately Held**
SIC: **2037** Frozen fruits & vegetables

(P-954)
JR SIMPLOT COMPANY
12688 S Colorado Ave, Fresno (93729)
P.O. Box 28955 (93729-8955)
PHONE..............................559 439-3900
EMP: 54
SALES (corp-wide): 5.1B **Privately Held**
SIC: **2037** Potato products, quick frozen & cold pack
PA: J.R. Simplot Company
1099 W Front St
Boise ID 83702
208 780-3287

(P-955)
JUMP START JUICE BAR
Also Called: Jumpstart Juice
8001 Irvine Center Dr # 40, Irvine (92618-2938)
PHONE..............................949 754-3120
EMP: 15
SALES (est): 630K **Privately Held**
SIC: **2037**

(P-956)
L & H INDUSTRIES
925 E Arlee Pl, Anaheim (92805-5645)
PHONE..............................714 635-1555
Kevin Heenan, *Partner*
Randy Ricketts, *Partner*
EMP: 11 EST: 1961
SQ FT: 5,000
SALES: 1MM **Privately Held**
SIC: **2037** Fruits, quick frozen & cold pack (frozen)

(P-957)
LA ALOE LLC
2301 E 7th St Ste A152, Los Angeles (90023-1044)
PHONE..............................888 968-2563
Dino Sarti,
Manuel Campos,
Daniel Stepper,
▲ EMP: 21
SQ FT: 47,000
SALES: 4MM **Privately Held**
SIC: **2037** Fruit juices

(P-958)
LANGER JUICE COMPANY INC
Also Called: Langers Juice
16195 Stephens St, City of Industry (91745-1718)
PHONE..............................626 336-3100
Nathan Langer, *President*
Bruce Langer, *Treasurer*
David Langer, *Vice Pres*
Massimo Freda, *General Mgr*
Davinder Singh, *Research*
◆ EMP: 250 EST: 1957
SQ FT: 140,000
SALES (est): 116.7MM **Privately Held**
WEB: www.langers.com
SIC: **2037** Fruit juices

(P-959)
LIVE FRESH CORPORATION
1055 E Cooley Ave, San Bernardino (92408-2819)
PHONE..............................909 478-0895
James Rosenberg, *CEO*
Shawn Sugarman, *President*
EMP: 180
SQ FT: 70,000
SALES (est): 10.5MM **Privately Held**
WEB: www.evolutionfresh.com
SIC: **2037** Fruit juices

(P-960)
OXNARD LEMON COMPANY
2001 Sunkist Cir, Oxnard (93033-3902)
P.O. Box 2240 (93034-2240)
PHONE..............................805 483-1173
Sam Mayhew, *General Mgr*
Nancy Low, *Office Mgr*
Karina Acevedo, *Admin Asst*
Kevin Carlson, *Accountant*
Laura Miller, *Manager*
EMP: 15
SALES (est): 3.5MM **Privately Held**
WEB: www.oxnardlemon.com
SIC: **2037 0723 5148** Frozen fruits & vegetables; crop preparation services for market; fresh fruits & vegetables

P R O D U C T S & S V C S

(P-961)
PACKERS FOOD PRODUCTS INC
Also Called: Gems of Fruit Co
701 W Kimberly Ave # 210, Placentia (92870-6342)
PHONE.............................913 262-6200
Ed Haft, *President*
Ivan Veselic, *Vice Pres*
▲ EMP: 47
SQ FT: 2,500
SALES (est): 6MM **Privately Held**
WEB: www.gemsoffruit.com
SIC: 2037 Fruits, quick frozen & cold pack (frozen); fruit juice concentrates, frozen

(P-962)
PATTERSON FROZEN FOODS INC
10 S 3rd St, Patterson (95363-2509)
P.O. Box 487 (95363-0487)
PHONE.............................209 892-5060
Angelo Ielmini, *President*
Susan Scheuber, *CFO*
◆ EMP: 11
SQ FT: 600,000
SALES (est): 1.8MM **Privately Held**
WEB: www.pattersonfrozenfoods.com
SIC: 2037 Fruits, quick frozen & cold pack (frozen); vegetables, quick frozen & cold pack, excl. potato products

(P-963)
PERFECT PUREE OF NAPA VLY LLC
2700 Napa Valley Corp Dr, NAPA (94558)
PHONE.............................707 261-5100
Kevin Zeigler, *President*
Medhane Kidane, *Finance*
Becky Walker, *Human Res Dir*
Mark Smith, *Opers Staff*
Maddie Clark, *Sales Staff*
▲ EMP: 19
SALES (est): 6.2MM **Privately Held**
SIC: 2037 Frozen fruits & vegetables

(P-964)
PURITY ORGANIC LLC
405 14th St Ste 1000, Oakland (94612-2706)
PHONE.............................415 440-7777
Greg Holzman, *Mng Member*
EMP: 25
SALES (est): 121.5K **Privately Held**
SIC: 2037 Fruit juices

(P-965)
QUALITY PRODUCED LLC
Also Called: Pulp Story
987 N Enterprise St, Orange (92867-5448)
PHONE.............................310 592-8834
EMP: 15
SALES (corp-wide): 1MM **Privately Held**
SIC: 2037 Fruit juices
PA: Quality Produced Llc
  11693 San Vicente Blvd
  Los Angeles CA 90049
  310 592-8834

(P-966)
SMOOTHIE OPERATOR INC
8690 Sierra College Blvd, Roseville (95661-5961)
PHONE.............................916 773-9541
Ritchie Labate, *Principal*
Leslie Sue Broadland, *Principal*
EMP: 16
SALES (est): 215.3K **Privately Held**
SIC: 2037 Frozen fruits & vegetables

(P-967)
SONOMA BEVERAGE COMPANY LLC (PA)
2710 Giffen Ave, Santa Rosa (95407-7331)
PHONE.............................707 431-1099
David Langer, *Mng Member*
Tim Snowden, *General Mgr*
Bruce Langer,
▲ EMP: 20
SALES (est): 3.9MM **Privately Held**
SIC: 2037 Fruit juices

(P-968)
SUN TROPICS INC
2430 Camino Ramon Ste 111, San Ramon (94583-4214)
P.O. Box 407 (94583-0407)
PHONE.............................925 202-2221
Ashley Lao, *CEO*
Sharon Sy, *Vice Pres*
◆ EMP: 16
SQ FT: 1,500
SALES (est): 3.7MM **Privately Held**
WEB: www.suntropics.com
SIC: 2037 Fruit juices

(P-969)
SUNSATION INC
100 S Cambridge Ave, Claremont (91711-4842)
PHONE.............................909 542-0280
Perry Eichor, *President*
David Bryant, *CFO*
EMP: 25
SQ FT: 30,000
SALES (est): 6.1MM **Privately Held**
SIC: 2037 Fruit juices

(P-970)
TITAN FROZEN FRUIT LLC (PA)
585 Auto Center Dr Ste A, Watsonville (95076-3764)
PHONE.............................831 540-4110
Jonathan V Larsen,
EMP: 22
SALES (est): 6.9MM **Privately Held**
SIC: 2037 Frozen fruits & vegetables

(P-971)
VENTURA COASTAL LLC (PA)
2325 Vista Del Mar Dr, Ventura (93001-3751)
P.O. Box 69 (93002-0069)
PHONE.............................805 653-7000
William M Borgers,
Bill Borgers, *CEO*
Donald Dames,
Rolph Scherer,
Dean Uhlrich,
◆ EMP: 80
SQ FT: 25,000
SALES (est): 18.6MM **Privately Held**
WEB: www.vcoastal.com
SIC: 2037 Fruit juice concentrates, frozen

(P-972)
VENTURA COASTAL LLC
12310 Avenue 368, Visalia (93291-9500)
PHONE.............................559 737-9836
Gene Keck, *Branch Mgr*
EMP: 14
SALES (est): 1.9MM
SALES (corp-wide): 18.6MM **Privately Held**
WEB: www.vcoastal.com
SIC: 2037 2087 2033 Fruit juices; flavoring extracts & syrups; canned fruits & specialties
PA: Ventura Coastal, Llc
  2325 Vista Del Mar Dr
  Ventura CA 93001
  805 653-7000

(P-973)
WAWONA FROZEN FOODS (PA)
100 W Alluvial Ave, Clovis (93611-9176)
PHONE.............................559 299-2901
William Smittcamp, *President*
Earl Smittcamp, *Ch of Bd*
Julie Olsen, *CFO*
Muriel Smittcamp, *Corp Secy*
Kristi Losson, *Executive Asst*
▲ EMP: 2200
SQ FT: 125,000
SALES (est): 228.8MM **Privately Held**
SIC: 2037 Fruits, quick frozen & cold pack (frozen)

2038 Frozen Specialties

(P-974)
AJINOMOTO FOODS NORTH AMER INC
Also Called: Windsor Foods
2395 American Ave, Hayward (94545-1807)
PHONE.............................510 293-1838
Janet Zhou, *Accountant*
Lynda Pacho, *Buyer*
James Herger, *Safety Dir*
EMP: 15
SALES (corp-wide): 10.8B **Privately Held**
SIC: 2038 2037 Frozen specialties; frozen fruits & vegetables
HQ: Ajinomoto Foods North America, Inc.
  4200 Concours Ste 100
  Ontario CA 91764

(P-975)
AJINOMOTO FOODS NORTH AMER INC
Also Called: Windsor Foods
4200 Concours Ste 100, Ontario (91764-4982)
PHONE.............................909 477-4700
Steve Charles, *Manager*
EMP: 244
SALES (corp-wide): 10.8B **Privately Held**
SIC: 2038 5142 Frozen specialties; packaged frozen goods
HQ: Ajinomoto Foods North America, Inc.
  4200 Concours Ste 100
  Ontario CA 91764

(P-976)
AJINOMOTO FOODS NORTH AMER INC (DH)
Also Called: Ajinomoto Windsor, Inc.
4200 Concours Ste 100, Ontario (91764-4982)
PHONE.............................909 477-4700
Bernard Kreilmann, *President*
Fon Wong, *CFO*
Haruo Kurata, *Chairman*
John Gordon, *Treasurer*
George Jurkovich, *Exec VP*
▲ EMP: 100
SQ FT: 100,000
SALES (est): 206.8MM
SALES (corp-wide): 10.8B **Privately Held**
WEB: www.ajichem.com
SIC: 2038 2037 Frozen specialties; frozen fruits & vegetables
HQ: Ajinomoto North America Holdings, Inc.
  7124 N Marine Dr
  Portland OR 97203
  503 505-5783

(P-977)
AJINOMOTO WINDSOR INC
Also Called: Golden Tiger
6711 S Alameda St, Los Angeles (90001-2123)
PHONE.............................323 277-7000
Jean Lee, *Branch Mgr*
EMP: 250
SALES (corp-wide): 10.8B **Privately Held**
SIC: 2038 Ethnic foods, frozen
HQ: Ajinomoto Foods North America, Inc.
  4200 Concours Ste 100
  Ontario CA 91764

(P-978)
AMYS KITCHEN INC
1650 Corp Cir Ste 200, Petaluma (94954)
P.O. Box 449 (94953-0449)
PHONE.............................707 568-4500
Shayne Young, *Branch Mgr*
Mark Rudolph, *CFO*
Andy Kopral, *Treasurer*
Kim Barrier, *Officer*
Peter Wong, *Vice Pres*
EMP: 27

SALES (corp-wide): 278.7MM **Privately Held**
WEB: www.amyskitchen.com
SIC: 2038 2053 Dinners, frozen & packaged; frozen bakery products, except bread
PA: Amy's Kitchen, Inc.
  2330 Northpoint Pkwy
  Santa Rosa CA 95407
  707 578-7188

(P-979)
AMYS KITCHEN INC (PA)
2330 Northpoint Pkwy, Santa Rosa (95407-5004)
P.O. Box 4759, Petaluma (94955-4759)
PHONE.............................707 578-7188
Andy Berliner, *CEO*
Xavier Unkovic, *President*
Andrew Koprel, *CFO*
Michael Resch, *Exec VP*
Rachel Berliner, *Vice Pres*
◆ EMP: 800
SQ FT: 100,000
SALES (est): 278.7MM **Privately Held**
WEB: www.amyskitchen.com
SIC: 2038 2053 Dinners, frozen & packaged; frozen bakery products, except bread

(P-980)
ARISTA FOODS CORPORATION
1240 N Barsten Way, Anaheim (92806-1822)
PHONE.............................714 666-1001
Fax: 714 666-8488
EMP: 11
SQ FT: 11,989
SALES (est): 680K **Privately Held**
SIC: 2038

(P-981)
ARMANINO FOODS DISTINCTION INC
30588 San Antonio St, Hayward (94544-7102)
PHONE.............................510 441-9300
Edmond J Pera, *CEO*
Edgar Estonina, *CFO*
Jeff Goshorn, *Vice Pres*
Georgianne Stephen, *Opers Mgr*
Deborah Armanino, *Sales Staff*
▼ EMP: 41
SQ FT: 31,783
SALES (est): 8.8MM **Privately Held**
WEB: www.armanino.biz
SIC: 2038 2099 Frozen specialties; sauces: gravy, dressing & dip mixes

(P-982)
BABA FOODS SLO LLC
Also Called: Baba Small Batch
3889 Long St Ste 100, San Luis Obispo (93401-7581)
P.O. Box 507, Avila Beach (93424-0507)
PHONE.............................805 439-2250
Moez Bensalem,
Cecilia Boettcher, *General Mgr*
Cecilia Voettcher, *General Mgr*
EMP: 16
SQ FT: 4,000
SALES: 900K **Privately Held**
SIC: 2038 Ethnic foods, frozen

(P-983)
BENS ALTERNATIVE FOODS
2712 Marina Blvd Ste 36, San Leandro (94577-4056)
PHONE.............................510 614-6745
Benjamin Meshack, *Owner*
▼ EMP: 15
SALES (est): 673.2K **Privately Held**
SIC: 2038 Ethnic foods, frozen

(P-984)
CAMINO REAL FOODS INC
2638 E Vernon Ave, Vernon (90058-1825)
PHONE.............................323 585-6599
Rueh Taylor, *Branch Mgr*
EMP: 260
SALES (corp-wide): 132.8MM **Privately Held**
WEB: www.crfoods.com
SIC: 2038 Ethnic foods, frozen

PA: Camino Real Foods, Inc.
2638 E Vernon Ave
Vernon CA 90058
323 585-6599

(P-985)
CEDARLANE NATURAL FOODS INC (PA)
1135 E Artesia Blvd, Carson (90746-1602)
PHONE...................................310 886-7720
Robert Atallah, *CEO*
Neil Holmes, *CFO*
Ash Husain, *Exec VP*
Celia Gonzalez, *Executive*
Ellen Nicholas, *Research*
▲ EMP: 100
SQ FT: 270,000
SALES: 87.6MM **Privately Held**
WEB: www.cedarlanefoods.com
SIC: 2038 Dinners, frozen & packaged

(P-986)
CHANG FOOD COMPANY
2214 W Knox Ave, Santa Ana
(92704-5543)
PHONE...................................714 265-9990
Van Nguyen, *President*
Nhuan Nguyen, *Vice Pres*
▲ EMP: 21 EST: 1981
SQ FT: 4,000
SALES (est): 3.4MM **Privately Held**
SIC: 2038 Ethnic foods, frozen

(P-987)
CRAVE FOODS INC
2043 Imperial St, Los Angeles
(90021-3203)
PHONE...................................562 900-7272
Shaheda Sayed, *President*
Riaz A Surti, *Senior VP*
▲ EMP: 40 EST: 1992
SQ FT: 20,000
SALES (est): 3MM **Privately Held**
SIC: 2038 Frozen specialties

(P-988)
CULINARY BRANDS INC
3280 E 44th St, Vernon (90058-2426)
PHONE...................................626 289-3000
Frank Calma, *President*
Mohsen Ganeian, *Principal*
EMP: 150 EST: 2011
SQ FT: 2,000
SALES (est): 34.9MM **Privately Held**
SIC: 2038 Frozen specialties

(P-989)
DEL REAL LLC
Also Called: Del Real Foods
11041 Inland Ave, Mira Loma (91752-1155)
PHONE...................................951 681-0395
Jesus Cardenas, *Mng Member*
Jose Cardenas,
EMP: 120
SQ FT: 175,000
SALES (est): 46MM **Privately Held**
WEB: www.delrealfoods.com
SIC: 2038 Ethnic foods, frozen

(P-990)
DON MIGUEL MEXICAN FOODS INC (HQ)
Also Called: Don Miguel Foods
333 S Anita Dr Ste 1000, Orange
(92868-3318)
PHONE...................................714 385-4500
Jeff Frank, *CEO*
Robert Cuevas, *Treasurer*
Saralyn Brown, *Vice Pres*
Cindy Williams, *Administration*
Terry Girch, *CTO*
▲ EMP: 45 EST: 1908
SQ FT: 80,000
SALES (est): 177MM **Privately Held**
WEB: www.donmiguel.com
SIC: 2038 Frozen specialties

(P-991)
DUBON & SONS INC
2852 E 11th St, Los Angeles (90023-3406)
P.O. Box 15282 (90015-0282)
PHONE...................................213 923-1182
David Dubon Jr, *CEO*
▲ EMP: 16
SQ FT: 140,000

SALES: 53.5MM **Privately Held**
SIC: 2038 2086 5145 5149 Snacks, including onion rings, cheese sticks, etc.; carbonated beverages, nonalcoholic: bottled & canned; snack foods; beverages, except coffee & tea

(P-992)
EXCELLINE FOOD PRODUCTS LLC
833 N Hollywood Way, Burbank
(91505-2814)
PHONE...................................818 701-7710
Carlos Angulo, *CEO*
EMP: 116
SQ FT: 23,000
SALES: 30MM **Privately Held**
WEB: www.excellinefoods.com
SIC: 2038 Ethnic foods, frozen

(P-993)
EXCELLINE FOODS INC
833 N Hollywood Way, Burbank
(91505-2814)
PHONE...................................818 701-7710
EMP: 15 EST: 2012
SALES (est): 3.2MM **Privately Held**
SIC: 2038 Ethnic foods, frozen

(P-994)
FIVE STAR GOURMET FOODS INC
3880 Ebony St, Ontario (91761-1500)
PHONE...................................909 390-0032
Tal Shoshan, *CEO*
Bryan Leonard, *COO*
Michelle Eoff, *Exec VP*
Steve Fleckenstein, *Vice Pres*
Richard Ontiveros, *Plant Mgr*
EMP: 750
SQ FT: 130,000
SALES (est): 84.7MM **Privately Held**
SIC: 2038 2099 Frozen specialties; ready-to-eat meals, salads & sandwiches; salads, fresh or refrigerated

(P-995)
GOLDEN STATE FOODS CORP
Quality Customer Dist Svcs
640 S 6th Ave, City of Industry
(91746-3086)
PHONE...................................626 968-6431
Micky Hammer, *Branch Mgr*
Frank Listi, *President*
Larry Jacobsen, *Vice Pres*
Joe Soran, *Technology*
Danny V Constantino, *Opers Mgr*
EMP: 250
SALES (corp-wide): 1.3B **Privately Held**
WEB: www.goldenstatefoods.com
SIC: 2038 2087 2026 2051 Frozen specialties; flavoring extracts & syrups; fluid milk; bread, cake & related products
PA: Golden State Foods Corp.
18301 Von Karman Ave # 1100
Irvine CA 92612
949 247-8000

(P-996)
HARVEST FARMS INC
45000 Yucca Ave, Lancaster (93534-2526)
PHONE...................................661 945-3636
Craig Shugert, *CEO*
Eric Shiring, *CFO*
Joe Hughes, *General Mgr*
▲ EMP: 100
SQ FT: 18,000
SALES (est): 26.3MM
SALES (corp-wide): 61.9MM **Privately Held**
SIC: 2038 5144 Lunches, frozen & packaged; poultry & poultry products
HQ: Good Source Solutions, Inc.
3115 Melrose Dr Ste 160
Carlsbad CA 92010
858 455-4800

(P-997)
ICEE COMPANY (HQ)
1205 S Dupont Ave, Ontario (91761-1536)
PHONE...................................800 426-4233
Gerald B Shreiber, *President*
Dan Fachner, *President*
Kent Galloway, *CFO*
Rodney N Sexton, *Vice Pres*
Durre Hasan, *Admin Asst*

▲ EMP: 80
SQ FT: 30,000
SALES (est): 325.4MM
SALES (corp-wide): 1B **Publicly Held**
WEB: www.theiceecompany.com
SIC: 2038 5145 3559 2087 Frozen specialties; popcorn & supplies; plastics working machinery; flavoring extracts & syrups
PA: J & J Snack Foods Corp.
6000 Central Hwy
Pennsauken NJ 08109
856 665-9533

(P-998)
ICEE COMPANY
4250 E Lowell St, Ontario (91761-1529)
PHONE...................................909 974-3518
Dan Fachner, *Branch Mgr*
EMP: 33
SALES (corp-wide): 1B **Publicly Held**
SIC: 2038 Frozen specialties
HQ: The Icee Company
1205 S Dupont Ave
Ontario CA 91761
800 426-4233

(P-999)
LA MOUSSE
11150 La Grange Ave, Los Angeles
(90025-5632)
PHONE...................................310 478-6051
Nadine Korman, *President*
EMP: 60
SQ FT: 11,000
SALES (est): 9MM **Privately Held**
WEB: www.lamoussedesserts.com
SIC: 2038 Frozen specialties

(P-1000)
NATES FINE FOODS LLC
8880 Industrial Ave # 100, Roseville
(95678-5946)
PHONE...................................310 897-2690
Nathan Barker, *COO*
EMP: 39
SQ FT: 50,000
SALES (est): 638.7K **Privately Held**
SIC: 2038 Ethnic foods, frozen; lunches, frozen & packaged

(P-1001)
NESTLE PIZZA COMPANY INC
Also Called: Kraft Foods
2530 E 11th St, Oakland (94601-1425)
PHONE...................................510 261-8001
John McCormick, *Branch Mgr*
EMP: 19
SALES (corp-wide): 90.8B **Privately Held**
SIC: 2038 Pizza, frozen
HQ: Nestle Pizza Company, Inc.
1 Kraft Ct
Glenview IL 60025
847 646-2000

(P-1002)
NESTLE USA INC
Also Called: Nestle Dist Ctr & Logistics
3450 Dulles Dr, Mira Loma (91752-3242)
PHONE...................................951 360-7200
Dean Ingram, *Branch Mgr*
EMP: 18
SALES (corp-wide): 90.8B **Privately Held**
WEB: www.nestleusa.com
SIC: 2038 Frozen specialties
HQ: Nestle Usa, Inc.
1812 N Moore St
Rosslyn VA 22209
818 549-6000

(P-1003)
NIPPON INDUSTRIES INC
2430 S Watney Way, Fairfield
(94533-6730)
PHONE...................................707 427-3127
Eric D Wong, *President*
◆ EMP: 31 EST: 1999
SQ FT: 30,000
SALES (est): 9.9MM **Privately Held**
SIC: 2038 Dinners, frozen & packaged

(P-1004)
OTTOS PIZZA STIX INC
9040 Sunland Blvd, Sun Valley
(91352-2049)
P.O. Box 337 (91353-0337)
PHONE...................................562 519-5304
Otto Rafael Penarredonda, *CEO*
EMP: 10
SALES (est): 395.8K **Privately Held**
SIC: 2038 Pizza, frozen

(P-1005)
OVERHILL FARMS INC
431 Isis Ave, Inglewood (90301-2009)
P.O. Box 58806, Los Angeles (90058-0806)
PHONE...................................323 587-5985
James Rudis, *President*
EMP: 250
SALES (corp-wide): 13B **Privately Held**
WEB: www.overhillfarms.com
SIC: 2038 2015 8734 2099 Frozen specialties; poultry slaughtering & processing; testing laboratories; food preparations
HQ: Overhill Farms, Inc.
2727 E Vernon Ave
Vernon CA 90058
323 582-9977

(P-1006)
OVERHILL FARMS INC (DH)
Also Called: Chicago Brothers
2727 E Vernon Ave, Vernon (90058-1822)
P.O. Box 58806 (90058-0806)
PHONE...................................323 582-9977
James Rudis, *President*
Rick Alvarez, *President*
Denise Ouellette, *President*
Robert C Bruning, *CFO*
Robert A Olivarez, *Vice Pres*
EMP: 39
SQ FT: 170,000
SALES (est): 159.7MM
SALES (corp-wide): 13B **Privately Held**
WEB: www.overhillfarms.com
SIC: 2038 Frozen specialties
HQ: Bellisio Foods, Inc
1201 Harmon Pl Ste 302
Minneapolis MN 55403
218 723-5555

(P-1007)
OVERHILL FARMS INC
3055 E 44th St, Vernon (90058-2439)
P.O. Box 806, Los Angeles (90078-0806)
PHONE...................................323 584-4375
Cruz Quirod, *Superintendent*
Robert Ramos, *Vice Pres*
John Martinez, *Prdtn Mgr*
EMP: 214
SQ FT: 3,000
SALES (corp-wide): 13B **Privately Held**
WEB: www.overhillfarms.com
SIC: 2038 2013 2015 Frozen specialties; sausages & other prepared meats; poultry, processed: frozen
HQ: Overhill Farms, Inc.
2727 E Vernon Ave
Vernon CA 90058
323 582-9977

(P-1008)
PAMPANGA FOODS INCORPORATED
1835 N Orngthrp Park A, Anaheim
(92801-1143)
PHONE...................................714 331-7206
Rey Reyes, *President*
Coni Reyes, *Admin Sec*
Janet Ferinejal, *Controller*
▲ EMP: 40
SQ FT: 10,000
SALES (est): 8.2MM **Privately Held**
SIC: 2038 2099 2098 8742 Ethnic foods, frozen; food preparations; noodles (e.g. egg, plain & water), dry; food & beverage consultant; meat packing plants

(P-1009)
PASCO CORPORATION OF AMERICA
19191 S Vt Ave Ste 420, Torrance
(90502-1051)
PHONE...................................503 289-6500
Hiroyuki Horie, *CEO*

▼ **EMP:** 50
SALES (est): 10.4MM
SALES (corp-wide): 1.4B **Privately Held**
WEB: www.pascoamerica.com
SIC: 2038 Ethnic foods, frozen
PA: Pasco Shikishima Corporation
　5-3, Shirakabe, Higashi-Ku
　Nagoya AIC 461-0
　529 332-111

(P-1010)
PICTSWEET COMPANY
732 Hanson Way, Santa Maria
(93458-9710)
P.O. Box 5878 (93456-5878)
PHONE..................................805 928-4414
Thomas Kerulas, *Branch Mgr*
EMP: 300
SALES (corp-wide): 380.1MM **Privately
Held**
WEB: www.pictsweet.com
SIC: 2038 2099 Frozen specialties; food
　preparations
PA: The Pictsweet Company
　10 Pictsweet Dr
　Bells TN 38006
　731 663-7600

(P-1011)
RICHANDRE INC
Also Called: Ardella's
1170 Sandhill Ave, Carson (90746-1315)
PHONE..................................310 762-1560
Andre Oviedo, *President*
Hap Frank, *CFO*
Janet Wade, *CFO*
Richard Shanz, *Admin Sec*
Frank Oviedo, *VP Opers*
EMP: 12
SQ FT: 25,000
SALES: 10MM **Privately Held**
SIC: 2038 Frozen specialties

(P-1012)
**RUIZ FOOD PRODUCTS INC
(PA)**
501 S Alta Ave, Dinuba (93618-2100)
P.O. Box 37 (93618-0037)
PHONE..................................559 591-5510
Rachel Cullen, *President*
Kim R Beck, *Ch of Bd*
David Auchterlonie, *CFO*
Forrest Chandler, *CFO*
Olga Balderama, *Vice Pres*
EMP: 2500 **EST:** 1965
SQ FT: 200,000
SALES (est): 228.8MM **Privately Held**
WEB: www.elmonterey.com
SIC: 2038 2099 Ethnic foods, frozen; food
　preparations

(P-1013)
SAN FRANCISCO FOODS INC
14054 Catalina St, San Leandro
(94577-5508)
PHONE..................................510 357-7343
Hamad M Malak, *CEO*
Robert F Steel, *President*
Charley Luckhardt, *General Mgr*
John Sims, *Engineer*
Richard Earle, *Mfg Staff*
▲ **EMP:** 55
SQ FT: 12,000
SALES (est): 11.8MM **Privately Held**
SIC: 2038 Pizza, frozen

(P-1014)
SAVAGE RIVER INC (PA)
Also Called: Beyond Meat
111 Main St, El Segundo (90245-3802)
PHONE..................................805 669-8673
Ethan Walden Brown, *CEO*
Kim Fernandez, *Vice Pres*
Fred Storck, *Vice Pres*
Allison Aronoff, *Comms Mgr*
Lisa Yamaguchi, *Engineer*
▲ **EMP:** 20
SQ FT: 4,200
SALES (est): 33.2MM **Privately Held**
SIC: 2038 Frozen specialties

(P-1015)
SAVAGE RIVER INC
Also Called: Beyond Meat
1325 E El Segundo Blvd, El Segundo
(90245-4303)
PHONE..................................310 567-3323
Aaron Hicks, *Branch Mgr*
EMP: 26
SALES (corp-wide): 33.2MM **Privately
Held**
SIC: 2038 Frozen specialties
PA: Savage River, Inc.
　111 Main St
　El Segundo CA 90245
　805 669-8673

(P-1016)
SHINE FOOD INC
Jesse Lord
21100 S Western Ave, Torrance
(90501-1700)
PHONE..................................310 533-6010
John Freschi, *Manager*
EMP: 20
SALES (corp-wide): 14.6MM **Privately
Held**
WEB: www.shinefood.com
SIC: 2038 2053 2052 2051 Frozen spe-
　cialties; frozen bakery products, except
　bread; cookies & crackers; bread, cake &
　related products
PA: Shine Food, Inc.
　19216 Normandie Ave
　Torrance CA 90502
　310 329-3829

(P-1017)
STIR FOODS LLC
1820 E Walnut Ave, Fullerton (92831-4844)
PHONE..................................714 871-9231
Phil Decarion, *CEO*
Celia Ayala, *Human Res Mgr*
EMP: 25
SALES (corp-wide): 34.4MM **Privately
Held**
SIC: 2038 2099 Frozen specialties; food
　preparations
PA: Stir Foods, Llc
　1581 N Main St
　Orange CA 92867
　714 637-6050

(P-1018)
STIR FOODS LLC (PA)
1581 N Main St, Orange (92867-3439)
PHONE..................................714 637-6050
Milton Liu, *CEO*
Pablo Gallo Llorente, *CFO*
Zef Delgadillo, *Vice Pres*
Bill Happy, *Vice Pres*
Glenn Weber, *Vice Pres*
EMP: 110
SQ FT: 40,000
SALES (est): 34.4MM **Privately Held**
WEB: www.stirfoods.com
SIC: 2038 2099 Frozen specialties; food
　preparations

(P-1019)
**VALLEY FINE FOODS COMPANY
INC**
300 Epley Dr, Yuba City (95991-7221)
PHONE..................................530 671-7200
Ryan Tu, *President*
EMP: 13
SALES (est): 2.5MM **Privately Held**
SIC: 2038 Frozen specialties
PA: Valley Fine Foods Company, Inc.
　3909 Park Rd Ste H
　Benicia CA 94510

(P-1020)
**WESTECH INV ADVISORS LLC
(PA)**
104 La Mesa Dr 102, Portola Valley
(94028-7510)
PHONE..................................650 234-4300
Jay Cohan,
Ronald W Swenson, *Ch of Bd*
Martin Eng, *CFO*
EMP: 34
SQ FT: 1,500

SALES (est): 4.7MM **Privately Held**
SIC: 2038 7359 6141 Frozen specialties;
　equipment rental & leasing; personal
　credit institutions

(P-1021)
WHITTIER ENTERPRISE LLC
Also Called: Popkoff's
18901 Railroad St, City of Industry
(91748-1322)
PHONE..................................844 767-5633
Igor Cherdak, *Mng Member*
▲ **EMP:** 20 **EST:** 2010
SQ FT: 50,000
SALES: 5.2MM **Privately Held**
SIC: 2038 Frozen specialties

(P-1022)
ZEN MONKEY LLC
655 N Central Ave Fl 1700, Glendale
(91203-1439)
PHONE..................................310 504-2899
Eric Glandian, *Mng Member*
EMP: 10 **EST:** 2013
SALES (est): 1.1MM **Privately Held**
SIC: 2038 Breakfasts, frozen & packaged

2041 Flour, Grain Milling

(P-1023)
ADM MILLING CO
1603 Old Hwy 99 W, Arbuckle (95912)
PHONE..................................530 476-2662
Johnny Barnette, *Branch Mgr*
EMP: 76
SALES (corp-wide): 60.8B **Publicly Held**
WEB: www.admmilling.com
SIC: 2041 Grain mills (except rice)
HQ: Adm Milling Co.
　8000 W 110th St Ste 300
　Overland Park KS 66210
　913 491-9400

(P-1024)
ANDREW LLC
Also Called: Sanluisina
1710 S Grove Ave Ste A&B, Ontario
(91761-4545)
PHONE..................................909 270-9356
Miriam Navarro, *Mng Member*
EMP: 18
SALES: 1.5MM **Privately Held**
SIC: 2041 Corn meal

(P-1025)
**ARCHER-DANIELS-MIDLAND
COMPANY**
Also Called: ADM
455 N 6th St, Colton (92324-2988)
PHONE..................................909 783-7574
Stephen Brooks, *General Mgr*
EMP: 12
SALES (corp-wide): 60.8B **Publicly Held**
WEB: www.admworld.com
SIC: 2041 Flour & other grain mill products
PA: Archer-Daniels-Midland Company
　77 W Wacker Dr Ste 4600
　Chicago IL 60601
　312 634-8100

(P-1026)
**ARCHER-DANIELS-MIDLAND
COMPANY**
Also Called: ADM
1543 Calada St, Los Angeles (90023-3210)
PHONE..................................323 266-2750
John Vanpleabe, *Manager*
EMP: 50
SALES (corp-wide): 60.8B **Publicly Held**
WEB: www.admworld.com
SIC: 2041 Flour & other grain mill products
PA: Archer-Daniels-Midland Company
　77 W Wacker Dr Ste 4600
　Chicago IL 60601
　312 634-8100

(P-1027)
**ARCHER-DANIELS-MIDLAND
COMPANY**
ADM
2282 Davis Ct, Hayward (94545-1114)
PHONE..................................510 346-3309
Mike Alo, *Branch Mgr*
EMP: 112

SALES (corp-wide): 60.8B **Publicly Held**
WEB: www.admworld.com
SIC: 2041 Flour & other grain mill products
PA: Archer-Daniels-Midland Company
　77 W Wacker Dr Ste 4600
　Chicago IL 60601
　312 634-8100

(P-1028)
**ARCHER-DANIELS-MIDLAND
COMPANY**
Also Called: ADM
3691 Noakes St, Los Angeles
(90023-3244)
PHONE..................................323 269-8175
Dan Munoz, *Manager*
EMP: 15
SQ FT: 20,264
SALES (corp-wide): 60.8B **Publicly Held**
WEB: www.admworld.com
SIC: 2041 Flour & other grain mill products
PA: Archer-Daniels-Midland Company
　77 W Wacker Dr Ste 4600
　Chicago IL 60601
　312 634-8100

(P-1029)
**ARCHER-DANIELS-MIDLAND
COMPANY**
Also Called: ADM
350 N Guild Ave, Lodi (95240-0803)
P.O. Box 2675 (95241-2675)
PHONE..................................209 339-1252
EMP: 135
SALES (corp-wide): 60.8B **Publicly Held**
SIC: 2041 Flour & other grain mill products
PA: Archer-Daniels-Midland Company
　77 W Wacker Dr Ste 4600
　Chicago IL 60601
　312 634-8100

(P-1030)
ARDENT MILLS LLC
2020 E Steel Rd, Colton (92324-4008)
PHONE..................................951 201-1170
Brad Beckwith, *Branch Mgr*
EMP: 33
SALES (corp-wide): 631.7MM **Privately
Held**
WEB: www.conagra.com
SIC: 2041 Flour & other grain mill products
PA: Ardent Mills, Llc
　1875 Lawrence St Ste 1400
　Denver CO 80202
　800 851-9618

(P-1031)
ARDENT MILLS LLC
5471 Ferguson Dr, Commerce
(90022-5118)
PHONE..................................323 725-0771
Dagoberto Castillo, *Branch Mgr*
EMP: 10
SALES (corp-wide): 631.7MM **Privately
Held**
WEB: www.horizonmilling.com
SIC: 2041 Flour & other grain mill products
PA: Ardent Mills, Llc
　1875 Lawrence St Ste 1400
　Denver CO 80202
　800 851-9618

(P-1032)
ARDENT MILLS LLC
Also Called: Cargill Flour Milling Division
19684 Cajon Blvd, San Bernardino
(92407-1813)
PHONE..................................909 887-3407
Nelson Selmer, *Branch Mgr*
EMP: 27
SQ FT: 26,180
SALES (corp-wide): 631.7MM **Privately
Held**
WEB: www.horizonmilling.com
SIC: 2041 Flour mills, cereal (except rice)
PA: Ardent Mills, Llc
　1875 Lawrence St Ste 1400
　Denver CO 80202
　800 851-9618

(P-1033)
BAKAKERS SPECIALTY FOODS INC
Also Called: Martha's All Natural
2619 Lycoming St Ste 200, Stockton (95206-4902)
PHONE.....................209 234-5935
Roylene F Brown, *President*
▼ EMP: 15
SQ FT: 9,000
SALES (est): 3.2MM Privately Held
SIC: 2041 2066 2099 Flour & other grain mill products; chocolate & cocoa products; food preparations

(P-1034)
BUNGE MILLING INC
845 Kentucky Ave, Woodland (95695-2744)
PHONE....................530 666-1691
Eduardo Mastrantonio, *Planning*
Carrie Wade, *Human Res Mgr*
John Pappenheim, *Maintence Staff*
Troy Smith, *Manager*
EMP: 139 Privately Held
SIC: 2041 Flour & other grain mill products
HQ: Bunge Milling, Inc.
  11720 Borman Dr
  Saint Louis MO 63146
  314 292-2000

(P-1035)
CENTRAL VALLEY AG GRINDING INC (PA)
Also Called: Cvag
5509 Langworth Rd, Oakdale (95361-7909)
PHONE....................209 869-1721
Michael Barry, *President*
Ryan Hogan, *CFO*
EMP: 29
SQ FT: 80,000
SALES (est): 24.5MM Privately Held
SIC: 2041 0723 Flour & other grain mill products; grain milling, custom services

(P-1036)
CONAGRA BRANDS INC
2201 E 7th St, Oakland (94606-5301)
PHONE....................510 536-9555
Bart Hahlweg, *Manager*
EMP: 44
SQ FT: 87,628
SALES (corp-wide): 7.9B Publicly Held
WEB: www.conagra.com
SIC: 2041 Flour
PA: Conagra Brands, Inc.
  222 Merchandise Mart Plz
  Chicago IL 60654
  312 549-5000

(P-1037)
CONAGRA FLOUR MILLING COMPANY
2201 E 7th St, Oakland (94606-5301)
PHONE....................510 536-9555
Bart Hahlweg, *Plant Mgr*
EMP: 40
SALES (est): 6.8MM Privately Held
SIC: 2041 Flour & other grain mill products

(P-1038)
D & D GOLD PRODUCT CORP
11608 Quartz Ave Fl 2, Fountain Valley (92708-2532)
PHONE....................714 550-0372
Trong Nguyen, *President*
Lang Nguyen, *Treasurer*
Hung Nguyen, *Admin Sec*
▲ EMP: 19
SQ FT: 12,000
SALES (est): 2.5MM Privately Held
SIC: 2041 2099 Flour & other grain mill products; spices, including grinding

(P-1039)
GENERAL MILLS INC
4309 Fruitland Ave, Vernon (90058-3176)
PHONE....................323 584-3433
Jeff Shapiro, *Branch Mgr*
EMP: 40
SQ FT: 81,186
SALES (corp-wide): 15.7B Publicly Held
WEB: www.generalmills.com
SIC: 2041 Flour mills, cereal (except rice)

PA: General Mills, Inc.
  1 General Mills Blvd
  Minneapolis MN 55426
  763 764-7600

(P-1040)
GIUSTOS SPECIALTY FOODS LLC (PA)
344 Littlefield Ave, South San Francisco (94080-6103)
PHONE....................650 873-6566
Craig A Moore, *Mng Member*
Jarjeet Bahia, *COO*
Ann Moore, *CFO*
Daniel Weggenman, *Vice Pres*
Shelby Chih, *QC Mgr*
▲ EMP: 43
SQ FT: 5,000
SALES: 24MM Privately Held
SIC: 2041 Flour mills, cereal (except rice); grain mills (except rice)

(P-1041)
GIUSTOS SPECIALTY FOODS LLC
241 E Harris Ave, South San Francisco (94080-6807)
PHONE....................650 873-6566
Craig A Moore, *Branch Mgr*
EMP: 37
SALES (est): 3MM
SALES (corp-wide): 24MM Privately Held
SIC: 2041 Flour & other grain mill products
PA: Giusto's Specialty Foods, Llc
  344 Littlefield Ave
  South San Francisco CA 94080
  650 873-6566

(P-1042)
GK FOODS INC
Also Called: San Marcos Trading Company
133 Mata Way Ste 101, San Marcos (92069-2937)
PHONE....................760 752-5230
Laurence James Hickerson, *CEO*
John Bartelt, *Admin Sec*
Armando Ramos, *Prdtn Mgr*
EMP: 20
SQ FT: 15,000
SALES (est): 7.1MM Privately Held
WEB: www.globalkaizen.com
SIC: 2041 7389 5149 Flour & other grain mill products; packaging & labeling services; organic & diet foods

(P-1043)
GRAIN CRAFT INC
Also Called: California Milling Co
1861 E 55th St, Los Angeles (90058-3836)
PHONE....................323 585-0131
Kurt Gallehugh, *Branch Mgr*
Kelly Nguyen, *Manager*
EMP: 45
SALES (corp-wide): 320.5MM Privately Held
WEB: www.cerealfood.com
SIC: 2041 Flour mills, cereal (except rice)
PA: Grain Craft, Inc.
  201 W Main St Ste 203
  Chattanooga TN 37408
  423 265-2313

(P-1044)
KASHI COMPANY
140 Marine View Ave # 101, Solana Beach (92075-2122)
P.O. Box 649 (92075-0649)
PHONE....................858 274-8870
Gary H Pilnick, *CEO*
Abigail Borck, *Analyst*
Rachel Motycka, *Marketing Staff*
Martin Dschaak, *Senior Mgr*
Daniel Barba, *Director*
EMP: 38
SALES (est): 931.4K
SALES (corp-wide): 12.9B Publicly Held
WEB: www.kashi.com
SIC: 2041 Flour & other grain mill products
PA: Kellogg Company
  1 Kellogg Sq
  Battle Creek MI 49017
  269 961-2000

(P-1045)
LACEY MILLING COMPANY INC
217 W 5th St Ste 231, Hanford (93230-5034)
P.O. Box 1193 (93232-1193)
PHONE....................559 584-6634
Charles Lendrum, *President*
Karen Lacey, *Shareholder*
Tim Lacey, *Shareholder*
Scott Lendrum, *Treasurer*
Holly Caldera, *Admin Sec*
EMP: 15 EST: 1887
SQ FT: 40,000
SALES (est): 2.3MM Privately Held
SIC: 2041 Flour

(P-1046)
MILLER MILLING COMPANY LLC
2908 S Maple Ave, Fresno (93725-2220)
PHONE....................559 441-8133
Damon Sidles, *Manager*
Bonnie Kiehl, *Technology*
Alisha Ruiz, *Buyer*
John Renteria, *Facilities Mgr*
Trinidad Ramos, *Manager*
EMP: 25
SALES (corp-wide): 5B Privately Held
WEB: www.millermillingca.com
SIC: 2041 2045 Flour; prepared flour mixes & doughs
HQ: Miller Milling Company, Llc
  7808 Creekridge Cir # 100
  Minneapolis MN 55439
  952 826-6331

(P-1047)
PILLSBURY COMPANY LLC
220 S Kenwood St Ste 202, Glendale (91205-1671)
PHONE....................818 522-3952
Linda Goodman, *Branch Mgr*
EMP: 55
SALES (corp-wide): 15.7B Publicly Held
SIC: 2041 Doughs & batters
HQ: The Pillsbury Company Llc
  1 General Mills Blvd
  Minneapolis MN 55426

(P-1048)
ROAN MILLS LLC
11069 Penrose St, Sun Valley (91352-2722)
PHONE....................818 249-4686
Robert P Dedlow, *Principal*
EMP: 10
SALES (est): 1MM Privately Held
SIC: 2041 Flour & other grain mill products

(P-1049)
TURLOCK SHEET METAL & WLDG INC
Also Called: P & F Metals
301 S Broadway, Turlock (95380-5414)
PHONE....................209 667-4716
Jim Vieira, *CEO*
Sarah Snyder, *Office Mgr*
Gary Pinheiro, *Admin Sec*
EMP: 45 EST: 1956
SQ FT: 12,000
SALES (est): 9.7MM Privately Held
SIC: 2041 1761 Grain mills (except rice); sheet metalwork

(P-1050)
VALLEY FINE FOODS COMPANY INC (PA)
Also Called: Pasta Prima
3909 Park Rd Ste H, Benicia (94510-1167)
PHONE....................707 746-6888
Chia-CHI Tu, *CEO*
Ryan Tu, *President*
Wayne Tu, *COO*
David Weber, *CFO*
MEI Tu, *Vice Pres*
▲ EMP: 375
SQ FT: 83,598
SALES (est): 109MM Privately Held
WEB: www.valleyfinefoods.com
SIC: 2041 2038 Doughs, frozen or refrigerated; frozen specialties; snacks, including onion rings, cheese sticks, etc.

(P-1051)
VICOLO WHOLESALE (PA)
Also Called: Vicolo Pizza
31112 San Clemente St, Hayward (94544-7802)
PHONE....................510 475-6019
Eric Mount, *Partner*
Richard Sander, *Partner*
EMP: 29
SQ FT: 1,400
SALES (est): £.2MM Privately Held
WEB: www.vicolopizza.com
SIC: 2041 Flour & other grain mill products

(P-1052)
WESTERN FOODS LLC (PA)
420 N Pioneer Ave, Woodland (95776-6122)
P.O. Box 115 (95776-0115)
PHONE....................530 601-5991
Miguel Reyna, *Mng Member*
Matthew Labriola,
▲ EMP: 50 EST: 2010
SALES (est): 15.4MM Privately Held
WEB: www.westernfoodsco.com
SIC: 2041 Flour

2043 Cereal Breakfast Foods

(P-1053)
AGRA-FARM FOODS INC
Also Called: Sincere Food Co
2223 Seaman Ave, El Monte (91733-2630)
PHONE....................626 443-2335
Wen Yian Ling, *President*
EMP: 19
SQ FT: 11,000
SALES (est): 2.2MM Privately Held
SIC: 2043 Soy: prepared as cereal breakfast food

(P-1054)
ANNONA COMPANY LLC
Also Called: Earnest Eats
444 S Cedros Ave Ste 175, Solana Beach (92075-1974)
PHONE....................858 299-4238
Andrew Aussie, *Mng Member*
Mark Oliver, *Mng Member*
Andrew Brayton, *Manager*
EMP: 10 EST: 2006
SQ FT: 5,000
SALES: 4MM Privately Held
SIC: 2043 2064 Cereal breakfast foods; breakfast bars; granola & muesli, bars & clusters

(P-1055)
CARIBBEAN COFFEE COMPANY INC
495 Pine Ave Ste A, Goleta (93117-3709)
PHONE....................805 692-2200
John O Goerke, *CEO*
EMP: 16
SALES (est): 3.5MM Privately Held
SIC: 2043 2095 Coffee substitutes, made from grain; roasted coffee; freeze-dried coffee

(P-1056)
CHEERPAK
7778 Varna Ave, North Hollywood (91605-1739)
PHONE....................818 922-5451
Sargis Danielyan, *Principal*
EMP: 12
SALES (est): 438.8K Privately Held
SIC: 2043 Cereal breakfast foods

(P-1057)
EAST WEST TEA COMPANY LLC
Also Called: Golden Temple
1616 Preuss Rd, Los Angeles (90035-4212)
PHONE....................310 275-9891
Gurudhan S Khalsa, *Manager*
K Khalsa, *Vice Pres*
EMP: 16

SALES (est): 1.5MM
SALES (corp-wide): 59MM **Privately Held**
WEB: www.peacecereal.com
SIC: 2043 2099 2064 8721 Cereal breakfast foods; tea blending; candy & other confectionery products; billing & bookkeeping service
PA: East West Tea Company, Llc
1325 Westec Dr
Eugene OR 97402
541 461-2160

(P-1058)
ELLEN LARK FARM
Also Called: Grainless Goodness
410 Bryant Cir Ste A, Ojai (93023-4200)
PHONE..................................805 272-8448
Kelley D'Angelo, *President*
EMP: 11 EST: 2015
SQ FT: 3,000
SALES: 500K **Privately Held**
SIC: 2043 Cereal breakfast foods

(P-1059)
GENERAL MILLS INC
2000 W Turner Rd, Lodi (95242-2239)
P.O. Box 3002 (95241-1906)
PHONE..................................209 334-7061
Fax: 209 333-2949
EMP: 50
SALES (corp-wide): 17.6B **Publicly Held**
SIC: 2043 2045
PA: General Mills, Inc.
1 General Mills Blvd
Minneapolis MN 55426
763 764-7600

(P-1060)
GENERAL MILLS INC
620 N Kenwood St, Glendale (91206-2323)
PHONE..................................818 553-6777
EMP: 58
SALES (corp-wide): 15.7B **Publicly Held**
SIC: 2043 Wheat flakes: prepared as cereal breakfast food
PA: General Mills, Inc.
1 General Mills Blvd
Minneapolis MN 55426
763 764-7600

(P-1061)
GENERAL MILLS INC
11618 Mulberry Ave, Fontana (92337-7618)
PHONE..................................951 685-7030
Gary M Roth, *Manager*
EMP: 100
SALES (corp-wide): 15.7B **Publicly Held**
WEB: www.generalmills.com
SIC: 2043 2041 2045 2099 Wheat flakes: prepared as cereal breakfast food; oats, rolled: prepared as cereal breakfast food; corn flakes: prepared as cereal breakfast food; rice: prepared as cereal breakfast food; flour; flour mixes; prepared flour mixes & doughs; cake mixes, prepared: from purchased flour; biscuit mixes, prepared: from purchased flour; dessert mixes & fillings; frosting mixes, dry: for cakes, cookies, etc.; potatoes, dried: packaged with other ingredients; pasta, uncooked: packaged with other ingredients; fruit & fruit peel confections; granola & muesli, bars & clusters; corn chips & other corn-based snacks
PA: General Mills, Inc.
1 General Mills Blvd
Minneapolis MN 55426
763 764-7600

(P-1062)
INTELLIGENT BLENDS LP
5330 Eastgate Mall, San Diego (92121-2804)
PHONE..................................858 888-7937
Michael Ishayik, *President*
▲ EMP: 38
SALES (est): 7.1MM **Privately Held**
SIC: 2043 Cereal breakfast foods

(P-1063)
KELLOGG COMPANY
2001 N Main St Ste 450, Walnut Creek (94596-7268)
PHONE..................................925 952-8423

EMP: 385
SALES (corp-wide): 12.9B **Publicly Held**
SIC: 2043 Cereal breakfast foods
PA: Kellogg Company
1 Kellogg Sq
Battle Creek MI 49017
269 961-2000

(P-1064)
KELLOGG COMPANY
475 Eggo Way, San Jose (95116-1016)
PHONE..................................408 295-8656
Virgil Thomas, *Branch Mgr*
EMP: 207
SALES (corp-wide): 12.9B **Publicly Held**
WEB: www.kelloggs.com
SIC: 2043 Cereal breakfast foods
PA: Kellogg Company
1 Kellogg Sq
Battle Creek MI 49017
269 961-2000

(P-1065)
KELLOGG SALES COMPANY
300 Harding Blvd Ste 215, Roseville (95678-2474)
PHONE..................................916 787-0414
Shawn Snyder, *Principal*
EMP: 50
SALES (corp-wide): 12.9B **Publicly Held**
WEB: www.kellogg.com
SIC: 2043 Cereal breakfast foods
HQ: Kellogg Sales Company
1 Kellogg Sq
Battle Creek MI 49017
269 961-2000

(P-1066)
LADERA FOODS INC
1061 Lucky Ave, Menlo Park (94025-6231)
PHONE..................................650 823-7186
Brian Tetrud, *CEO*
Daniel Imperiale-Hagerman, *VP Mktg*
EMP: 14 EST: 2013
SQ FT: 3,000
SALES (est): 1MM **Privately Held**
SIC: 2043 Granola & muesli, except bars & clusters

(P-1067)
LE BARBOCCE INC
Also Called: Cafe Fanny
1328 6th St Frnt Frnt, Berkeley (94710-1460)
PHONE..................................510 526-7664
James Maser, *President*
Alice Waters, *Vice Pres*
EMP: 20
SQ FT: 3,400
SALES (est): 2.6MM **Privately Held**
WEB: www.cafefanny.com
SIC: 2043 5812 Cereal breakfast foods; cafe

(P-1068)
NORTHERN QUINOA PROD CORP
Also Called: Tiny Hero
200 Kansas St Ste 215, San Francisco (94103-5146)
PHONE..................................806 535-8118
Nick Kelley, *CEO*
William Hauser, *CFO*
EMP: 40
SQ FT: 10,000
SALES: 10MM **Privately Held**
SIC: 2043 Oats, rolled: prepared as cereal breakfast food

(P-1069)
ORGANIC MILLING INC
505 W Allen Ave, San Dimas (91773-1487)
PHONE..................................800 638-8686
Wolfgang Buehler, *Principal*
Lupe Martinez, *Vice Pres*
Josie Chea, *Accounts Mgr*
EMP: 89
SALES (est): 18.1MM **Privately Held**
SIC: 2043 Cereal breakfast foods

(P-1070)
ORGANIC MILLING CORPORATION (PA)
505 W Allen Ave, San Dimas (91773-1487)
PHONE..................................909 599-0161
Bruce Olsen, *President*

Norm Bowers, *Vice Pres*
John Duenas, *Principal*
Chris Wadden, *General Mgr*
Jaziby Alvarado, *Project Mgr*
▲ EMP: 108
SQ FT: 43,000
SALES (est): 30.7MM **Privately Held**
WEB: www.organicmilling.com
SIC: 2043 Granola & muesli, except bars & clusters

(P-1071)
ORGANIC MILLING CORPORATION
305 S Acacia St Unit A, San Dimas (91773-2925)
PHONE..................................909 305-0185
Lupe Martinez, *Branch Mgr*
EMP: 17
SALES (corp-wide): 30.7MM **Privately Held**
WEB: www.organicmilling.com
SIC: 2043 Granola & muesli, except bars & clusters
PA: Organic Milling Corporation
505 W Allen Ave
San Dimas CA 91773
909 599-0961

(P-1072)
PLUM INC
Also Called: Plum Organics
1485 Park Ave Ste 101, Emeryville (94608-3560)
PHONE..................................510 225-4018
Neil Grimmer, *CEO*
Sheryl O'Loughlin, *President*
Mike Meyer, *COO*
Sangita Forth, *Vice Pres*
Bentley Hall, *Vice Pres*
▲ EMP: 11
SQ FT: 2,000
SALES (est): 4.5MM
SALES (corp-wide): 8.6B **Publicly Held**
SIC: 2043 Cereal breakfast foods
PA: Campbell Soup Company
1 Campbell Pl
Camden NJ 08103
856 342-4800

2044 Rice Milling

(P-1073)
AMERICAN RICE INC
Comet Rice Division
1 Comet Ln, Maxwell (95955)
PHONE..................................530 438-2265
Jonn Burrnet, *Manager*
EMP: 60 **Privately Held**
WEB: www.amrice.com
SIC: 2044 Rice milling
HQ: American Rice Inc.
10700 North Fwy Ste 800
Houston TX 77037
281 272-8800

(P-1074)
BUNGE NORTH AMERICA INC
Also Called: Pacific Intl Rice Mills
845 Kentucky Ave, Woodland (95695-2744)
P.O. Box 652 (95776-0652)
PHONE..................................530 666-1691
Melveryn Anderson, *President*
EMP: 100 **Privately Held**
SIC: 2044 Rice milling
HQ: Bunge North America, Inc.
1391 Tmberlake Manor Pkwy
Chesterfield MO 63017
314 292-2000

(P-1075)
CALIFORNIA FAMILY FOODS LLC
6550 Struckmeyer Rd, Arbuckle (95912)
PHONE..................................530 476-3326
David Myers, *President*
Holly Sweet, *Sales Staff*
Perry Charter,
Tom Charter, *Mng Member*
Bruce Meyers, *Mng Member*
▼ EMP: 75
SQ FT: 75,000

SALES (est): 18.2MM **Privately Held**
SIC: 2044 0723 Rice milling; rice drying services

(P-1076)
CALIFORNIA HERITAGE MILLS INC
1 Comet Ln, Maxwell (95955)
P.O. Box 152 (95955-0152)
PHONE..................................530 438-2100
Paul Richter, *President*
Steven Sutter, *CEO*
Stuart Bruhn, *Plant Mgr*
Patrick Brandon, *Mktg Dir*
◆ EMP: 30 EST: 2011
SALES: 6.8MM **Privately Held**
SIC: 2044 Rice milling

(P-1077)
CALIFRNIA PCF RICE MIL A CA LP
194 W Main St, Woodland (95695-2999)
P.O. Box 8729 (95776-8729)
PHONE..................................530 661-1923
Grant F Chappell, *Partner*
Joe Westover, *Partner*
EMP: 102
SQ FT: 10,000
SALES (est): 7.1MM **Privately Held**
SIC: 2044 Rice milling

(P-1078)
FAR WEST RICE INC
3455 Nelson Rd, Nelson (95958)
P.O. Box 370, Durham (95938-0370)
PHONE..................................530 891-1339
C W Johnson, *CEO*
Gregory Johnson, *President*
Charles Schwab, *Treasurer*
◆ EMP: 35
SQ FT: 3,000
SALES (est): 12.2MM **Privately Held**
WEB: www.farwestrice.com
SIC: 2044 5141 2099 Rice milling; groceries, general line; food preparations

(P-1079)
FARMERS RICE COOPERATIVE (PA)
Also Called: Frc
2566 River Plaza Dr, Sacramento (95833-3673)
P.O. Box 15223 (95851-0223)
PHONE..................................916 923-5100
Frank Bragg, *CEO*
Bill Tanimoto, *CFO*
H Kirk Messick, *Senior VP*
Keith Hargrove, *Vice Pres*
Rob Paschoal, *Vice Pres*
◆ EMP: 35
SQ FT: 12,000
SALES (est): 109.5MM **Privately Held**
WEB: www.farmersrice.com
SIC: 2044 Rice milling

(P-1080)
FARMERS RICE COOPERATIVE
1800 Terminal Rd, Sacramento (95820)
PHONE..................................916 373-5549
Karen Martinelli, *Branch Mgr*
EMP: 50
SALES (corp-wide): 109.5MM **Privately Held**
WEB: www.farmersrice.com
SIC: 2044 Rice milling
PA: Farmers Rice Cooperative
2566 River Plaza Dr
Sacramento CA 95833
916 923-5100

(P-1081)
FARMERS RICE COOPERATIVE
2224 Industrial Blvd, West Sacramento (95691-3429)
P.O. Box 15223, Sacramento (95851-0223)
PHONE..................................916 373-5500
Keith Hargrove, *Manager*
EMP: 125
SALES (corp-wide): 109.5MM **Privately Held**
WEB: www.farmersrice.com
SIC: 2044 Rice milling

PA: Farmers Rice Cooperative
2566 River Plaza Dr
Sacramento CA 95833
916 923-5100

(P-1082)
FARMERS RICE COOPERATIVE
2224 Industrial Blvd, West Sacramento
(95691-3429)
PHONE.....................................916 373-5500
EMP: 150
SALES (corp-wide): 109.5MM **Privately
Held**
WEB: www.farmersrice.com
SIC: 2044 Rice milling
PA: Farmers Rice Cooperative
2566 River Plaza Dr
Sacramento CA 95833
916 923-5100

(P-1083)
GOLD RIVER MILLS LLC (PA)
1620 E Kentucky Ave, Woodland
(95776-6110)
P.O. Box 8729 (95776-8729)
PHONE.....................................530 661-1923
Thomas S Atkinson II,
Timothy R Magil,
John Perry,
▲ EMP: 51
SALES (est): 7.6MM **Privately Held**
WEB: www.goldrivermills.com
SIC: 2044 Rice milling

(P-1084)
I AMIRA GRAND FOODS INC (PA)
1 Park Plz Ste 600, Irvine (92614-5987)
PHONE.....................................949 852-4468
Karan A Chanana, Chairman
Bruce C Wacha, CFO
◆ EMP: 15
SALES (est): 4.6MM **Privately Held**
SIC: 2044 Brown rice

(P-1085)
KODA FARMS INC
22540 Russell Ave, South Dos Palos
(93665)
P.O. Box 10 (93665-0010)
PHONE.....................................209 392-2191
Edward K Koda, President
Laura Koda, Vice Pres
Robin Koda, Vice Pres
Ross Koda, Vice Pres
Tama T Koda, Vice Pres
▲ EMP: 50 EST: 1946
SQ FT: 20,000
SALES (est): 8.3MM **Privately Held**
WEB: www.kodafarms.com
SIC: 2044 0112 Rice milling; rice

(P-1086)
KODA FARMS MILLING INC
22540 Russell Ave, South Dos Palos
(93665)
P.O. Box 10 (93665-0010)
PHONE.....................................209 392-2191
Ross K Koda, CEO
Karen Crutcher, Admin Sec
EMP: 25
SALES (est): 7.8MM **Privately Held**
SIC: 2044 2099 Rice milling; rice, un-
cooked: packaged with other ingredients

(P-1087)
MARS FOOD US LLC (HQ)
2001 E Cashdan St Ste 201, Rancho
Dominguez (90220-6438)
PHONE.....................................310 933-0670
Vincent Howell, Mng Member
Stephanie Oliver, Manager
◆ EMP: 500
SALES (est): 140.6MM
SALES (corp-wide): 34.2B **Privately Held**
WEB: www.kalkan.com
SIC: 2044 Rice milling
PA: Mars, Incorporated
6885 Elm St
Mc Lean VA 22101
703 821-4900

(P-1088)
MARS FOOD US LLC
Also Called: Uncle Ben's
6875 Pacific View Dr, Los Angeles
(90068-1831)
PHONE.....................................562 616-7347
EMP: 350
SALES (corp-wide): 34.2B **Privately Held**
SIC: 2044 Rice milling
HQ: Mars Food Us, Llc
2001 E Cashdan St Ste 201
Rancho Dominguez CA 90220
310 933-0670

(P-1089)
POLIT FARMS INC
4334 Old Hwy 99w 99 W, Maxwell (95955)
PHONE.....................................530 438-2759
Mike Polit, President
Sherry Polit, Vice Pres
▼ EMP: 10
SQ FT: 6,000
SALES (est): 1.7MM **Privately Held**
SIC: 2044 Milled rice

(P-1090)
RIVERBEND RICE MILL INC
234 Main St, Colusa (95932)
P.O. Box 830 (95932-0830)
PHONE.....................................530 458-8561
Fax: 530 458-8569
EMP: 17
SALES (est): 2.2MM **Privately Held**
SIC: 2044

(P-1091)
**SUN VALLEY RICE COMPANY
LLC**
7050 Eddy Rd, Arbuckle (95912-9789)
P.O. Box 8, Dunnigan (95937-0008)
PHONE.....................................530 476-3000
Kenneth M Lagrande, Mng Member
Chris Fantl, Administration
Brett Lagrande, Accountant
Joan Quinlan, Controller
Marta Stegall, Human Res Dir
◆ EMP: 98
SQ FT: 20,000
SALES (est): 19.2MM **Privately Held**
WEB: www.sunvalleyrice.com
SIC: 2044 Rice milling

(P-1092)
SUNFOODS LLC
194 W Main St Ste 200, Woodland
(95695-2999)
P.O. Box 8729 (95776-8729)
PHONE.....................................530 661-1923
Matt Alonso, CEO
EMP: 10 **Privately Held**
SIC: 2044 Rice milling
HQ: Sunfoods, Llc
1620 E Kentucky Ave
Woodland CA 95776

(P-1093)
TAMAKI RICE CORPORATION
1701 Abel Rd, Williams (95987-5156)
PHONE.....................................530 473-2862
Masami Kitagawa, President
Kurt Barrett, General Mgr
▲ EMP: 20
SQ FT: 14,000
SALES (est): 2.8MM
SALES (corp-wide): 201.6MM **Privately
Held**
WEB: www.tamakimai.com
SIC: 2044 Rice milling
PA: Hombo Shoten Co.,Ltd.
8-56, Kinkocho
Kagoshima KGM 892-0
992 236-223

(P-1094)
WEHAH FARM INC
Also Called: Lundberg Family Farms
5311 Midway, Richvale (95974)
P.O. Box 369 (95974-0369)
PHONE.....................................530 538-3500
Grant Lundberg, CEO
Mike Denny, Vice Pres
Carol Hubbard, Office Admin
Bradley Thomson, Engineer
Dirk Burgon, Sales Staff
EMP: 255

SALES (est): 63.1MM **Privately Held**
SIC: 2044 Rice milling

**2045 Flour, Blended &
Prepared**

(P-1095)
BAKEMARK USA LLC (PA)
7351 Crider Ave, Pico Rivera (90660-3705)
PHONE.....................................562 949-1054
Gary Schmidt, President
Jim Parker, President
Gene Russo, General Mgr
Jesus Sotelo, Marketing Staff
◆ EMP: 300
SQ FT: 275,000
SALES (est): 615.9MM **Privately Held**
WEB: www.yourbakemark.com
SIC: 2045 5149 3556 2099 Flours & flour
mixes, from purchased flour; bakery prod-
ucts; food products machinery; food
preparations

(P-1096)
**BRIDGFORD FOODS
CORPORATION (HQ)**
1308 N Patt St, Anaheim (92801-2551)
P.O. Box 3773 (92803-3773)
PHONE.....................................714 526-5533
John V Simmons, President
William L Bridgford, Ch of Bd
Raymond F Lancy, CFO
Allan L Bridgford, Vice Pres
Hugh Wm Bridgford, Vice Pres
EMP: 277
SQ FT: 100,000
SALES: 167.2MM **Publicly Held**
WEB: www.bridgford.com
SIC: 2045 2099 2015 2013 Biscuit
dough, prepared: from purchased flour;
doughs, frozen or refrigerated: from pur-
chased flour; sandwiches, assembled &
packaged: for wholesale market; salads,
fresh or refrigerated; poultry sausage,
luncheon meats & other poultry products;
snack sticks, including jerky: from purchased meat; cheese, natural &
processed; dips, cheese-based; frozen
specialties
PA: Bridgford Industries Incorporated
1601 S Good Latimer Expy
Dallas TX 75226
214 428-1535

(P-1097)
LANGLOIS COMPANY
Also Called: Langlois Flour Company
10810 San Sevaine Way, Mira Loma
(91752-1116)
PHONE.....................................951 360-3900
Richard W Langlois, President
Lynn Langlois Nye, Treasurer
Jeff Langlois, Vice Pres
Sally Langlois, Vice Pres
Annette Salce, Credit Mgr
▼ EMP: 50
SQ FT: 48,000
SALES (est): 17.9MM **Privately Held**
WEB: www.langloiscompany.com
SIC: 2045 2035 2079 2099 Blended
flour: from purchased flour; mayonnaise;
dressings, salad: raw & cooked (except
dry mixes); vegetable refined oils (except
corn oil); gelatin dessert preparations; fla-
voring extracts & syrups

(P-1098)
POPLA INTERNATIONAL INC
1740 S Sacramento Ave, Ontario
(91761-7744)
PHONE.....................................909 923-6899
Mike Shinozaki, President
Ashley Shinozaki, Admin Sec
▲ EMP: 20
SQ FT: 8,000
SALES (est): 3.7MM **Privately Held**
WEB: www.popla.com
SIC: 2045 Prepared flour mixes & doughs

2046 Wet Corn Milling

(P-1099)
**CORN PRODUCTS
DEVELOPMENT INC (HQ)**
1021 Industrial Dr, Stockton (95206-3928)
P.O. Box 6129 (95206-0129)
PHONE.....................................209 982-1920
Samuel Scott, Principal
EMP: 10
SALES (est): 7.4MM
SALES (corp-wide): 5.8B **Publicly Held**
SIC: 2046 Wet corn milling
PA: Ingredion Incorporated
5 Westbrook Corporate Ctr # 500
Westchester IL 60154
708 551-2600

(P-1100)
INGREDION INCORPORATED
Also Called: Corn Products-Stockton Plant
1021 Industrial Dr, Stockton (95206-3928)
P.O. Box 6129 (95206-0129)
PHONE.....................................209 982-1920
Mark Madsen, Manager
Enrique Casillas, Engineer
Michael Levy,
Roger Hoffdahl, Manager
EMP: 76
SALES (corp-wide): 5.8B **Publicly Held**
WEB: www.cornproducts.com
SIC: 2046 Corn sugars & syrups
PA: Ingredion Incorporated
5 Westbrook Corporate Ctr # 500
Westchester IL 60154
708 551-2600

(P-1101)
SIN MA IMPORTS COMPANY
Also Called: Lucky Foods
1425 Minnesota St, San Francisco
(94107-3519)
PHONE.....................................415 285-9369
Fred S Pang, Owner
▲ EMP: 10 EST: 1973
SQ FT: 7,500
SALES (est): 927.4K **Privately Held**
SIC: 2046 2075 2074 Corn oil, refined;
soybean oil mills; cottonseed oil mills

(P-1102)
TAPIOCA EXPRESS
81 Curtner Ave, San Jose (95125-1064)
PHONE.....................................408 999-0128
Vivian Nguyen, Owner
EMP: 15 EST: 2011
SALES (est): 1.2MM **Privately Held**
SIC: 2046 Tapioca

(P-1103)
TAPIOCA EXPRESS
6145 El Cajon Blvd Ste G, San Diego
(92115-3923)
PHONE.....................................619 286-0484
Nip Lee, Owner
EMP: 11
SALES (est): 92.7K **Privately Held**
SIC: 2046 Tapioca

(P-1104)
**WOLF CANYON OF AMERICA
INC**
Also Called: Wolf Canyon Asia Pacific
3013 Lighthouse Ln, Marina (93933-6026)
PHONE.....................................831 626-1320
Claudoi Goldschmidt, President
EMP: 18
SALES (est): 1.4MM **Privately Held**
SIC: 2046 Potato starch; wheat gluten

2047 Dog & Cat Food

(P-1105)
ARCHEYY & FRIENDS LLC
3630 Andrews Dr Apt 114, Pleasanton
(94588-3015)
PHONE.....................................703 579-7649
Sean Marler,
EMP: 20

PRODUCTS & SVCS

SALES (est): 671.8K **Privately Held**
SIC: 2047 0752 Dog food; animal boarding services; showing services, pet & animal specialties; grooming services, pet &
animal specialties

(P-1106)
ARIES PREPARED BEEF COMPANY
11850 Sheldon St, Sun Valley
(91352-1507)
PHONE..................................818 771-0181
Zelco Majstorich, *Branch Mgr*
EMP: 45
SALES (corp-wide): 13.7MM **Privately Held**
SIC: 2047 Dog food
PA: Aries Prepared Beef Company
17 W Magnolia Blvd
Burbank CA 91502
818 526-4855

(P-1107)
ARTHUR DOGSWELL LLC (PA)
11301 W Olympic Blvd, Los Angeles
(90064-1653)
PHONE..................................888 559-8833
Brad Casper, *Mng Member*
Michael Green, *Vice Pres*
Stephen Koven, *Vice Pres*
Scott Link, *Vice Pres*
Berenice Officer, *Vice Pres*
▲ EMP: 33
SQ FT: 2,000
SALES (est): 24.5MM **Privately Held**
SIC: 2047 5149 Dog food; pet foods

(P-1108)
BARKSTRONG LLC
Also Called: Pioneer Natural Foods
4325 Glencoe Ave # 10846, Marina Del Rey
(90292-6444)
PHONE..................................855 381-5888
EMP: 38
SALES (corp-wide): 5.2MM **Privately Held**
SIC: 2047 Dog food
PA: Barkstrong Llc
22647 Ventura Blvd 308
Woodland Hills CA 91364
818 835-6216

(P-1109)
BIG HEART PET BRANDS (DH)
1 Maritime Plz Fl 2, San Francisco
(94111-3407)
P.O. Box 193575 (94119-3575)
PHONE..................................415 247-3000
Richard K Smucker, *CEO*
David J West, *President*
Mark R Belgya, *CFO*
Barry C Dunaway, *Senior VP*
Jill Penrose, *Vice Pres*
◆ EMP: 300
SALES (est): 2.1B
SALES (corp-wide): 7.3B **Publicly Held**
WEB: www.delmontefoods.com
SIC: 2047 Dog & cat food

(P-1110)
CANIDAE CORPORATION
Also Called: Canidae Pet Foods
1975 Tandem, Norco (92860-3608)
P.O. Box 3610, San Luis Obispo (93403-3610)
PHONE..................................909 599-5190
John Gordon, *President*
Scott Whipple, *CFO*
Brittney Robinson, *Admin Asst*
Ryan Hon, *Administration*
Frank Hon, *Opers Staff*
EMP: 10 EST: 1963
SALES (est): 2.1MM **Privately Held**
WEB: www.canidae.com
SIC: 2047 Dog & cat food

(P-1111)
DEXTERS DELI
2508 El Cmino Real Ste B2, Carlsbad
(92008)
PHONE..................................760 720-7507
Rosay Tori, *Owner*
EMP: 30
SALES (corp-wide): 1.8MM **Privately Held**
SIC: 2047 Dog & cat food

PA: Dexters Deli
1229 Camino Del Mar
Del Mar CA 92014
858 792-3707

(P-1112)
DIAMOND PET FOOD PROCESSORS O
250 Roth Rd, Lathrop (95330-9724)
PHONE..................................209 983-4900
Michael Kampeter, *Mng Member*
Richard Kampeter,
Gary Schell,
Mark Schell,
◆ EMP: 45 EST: 1998
SALES (est): 5.8MM **Privately Held**
SIC: 2047 Dog & cat food

(P-1113)
GENTLE GIANTS PRODUCTS INC
4867 Pedley Ave, Norco (92860-1646)
PHONE..................................951 818-2512
Tracy Posner Ward, *CEO*
Burt Ward, *President*
EMP: 10 EST: 2005
SQ FT: 15,000
SALES (est): 2.1MM **Privately Held**
SIC: 2047 Dog & cat food

(P-1114)
INABA FOODS (USA) INC
19301 Pcf Gtwy Dr Ste 120, Torrance
(90502)
PHONE..................................310 818-2270
Atsuhiro Inaba, *CEO*
▲ EMP: 10
SALES (est): 1MM **Privately Held**
SIC: 2047 Dog & cat food

(P-1115)
J & R TAYLOR BROS ASSOC INC
Also Called: Premium Pet Foods
16321 Arrow Hwy, Irwindale (91706-2018)
PHONE..................................626 334-9301
Rick Taylor, *President*
◆ EMP: 58
SALES (est): 6.8MM
SALES (corp-wide): 2B **Publicly Held**
WEB: www.breeders-choice.com
SIC: 2047 2048 Dog food; prepared feeds
PA: Central Garden & Pet Company
1340 Treat Blvd Ste 600
Walnut Creek CA 94597
925 948-4000

(P-1116)
MARS PETCARE US INC
2765 Lexington Way, San Bernardino
(92407-1842)
PHONE..................................909 887-8131
Ed Skokan, *Manager*
EMP: 50
SQ FT: 76,000
SALES (corp-wide): 32.1B **Privately Held**
SIC: 2047 2048 Dog food; prepared feeds
HQ: Mars Petcare Us, Inc.
315 Cool Springs Blvd
Franklin TN 37067
615 807-4626

(P-1117)
MARS PETCARE US INC
13243 Nutro Way, Victorville (92395-7789)
PHONE..................................760 261-7900
EMP: 50
SALES (corp-wide): 32.1B **Privately Held**
SIC: 2047 Cat food; dog food
HQ: Mars Petcare Us, Inc.
315 Cool Springs Blvd
Franklin TN 37067
615 807-4626

(P-1118)
NESTLE PURINA PETCARE COMPANY
800 N Brand Blvd Fl 5, Glendale
(91203-4281)
PHONE..................................314 982-1000
EMP: 125
SALES (corp-wide): 90.8B **Privately Held**
WEB: www.purina.com
SIC: 2047 Dog & cat food

HQ: Nestle Purina Petcare Company
901 Chouteau Ave
Saint Louis MO 63102
314 982-1000

(P-1119)
PET CAROUSEL INC
2350 Academy Ave, Sanger (93657-9559)
PHONE..................................316 291-2500
Gary D Becker, *CEO*
Siegfried W Habild, *President*
EMP: 28
SQ FT: 36,000
SALES (est): 4.4MM **Privately Held**
SIC: 2047 Dog & cat food

(P-1120)
PRIMAL PET FOODS INC
535 Watt Dr Ste B, Fairfield (94534-1790)
PHONE..................................415 642-7400
Matthew Koss, *CEO*
Sarah Quinn, *Accounting Mgr*
Matt Pirz, *VP Sales*
Diane Hurst, *Regl Sales Mgr*
Megan Pearson, *Regl Sales Mgr*
▲ EMP: 12
SQ FT: 5,000
SALES (est): 1.8MM **Privately Held**
WEB: www.primalpetfoods.com
SIC: 2047 Dog & cat food

(P-1121)
SCHELL & KAMPETER INC
250 Roth Rd, Lathrop (95330-9724)
PHONE..................................209 983-4900
Gary Schell, *Branch Mgr*
EMP: 45
SALES (corp-wide): 68.2K **Privately Held**
SIC: 2047 Dog food
PA: Schell & Kampeter, Inc.
103 N Olive St
Meta MO 65058
573 229-4203

2048 Prepared Feeds For Animals & Fowls

(P-1122)
ARTEMIS PET FOOD COMPANY INC
18010 S Figueroa St, Gardena
(90248-4213)
PHONE..................................818 771-0700
Ken Park, *President*
Alex J Kim, *Vice Pres*
▲ EMP: 10
SQ FT: 10,000
SALES (est): 1.5MM **Privately Held**
SIC: 2048 Canned pet food (except dog &
cat); dry pet food (except dog & cat);
frozen pet food (except dog & cat)

(P-1123)
BORIS BS FRMS VTRNARY SVCS INC
9245 Laguna Springs Dr, Elk Grove
(95758-7987)
PHONE..................................916 730-4225
Boris Baidoo, *CEO*
Nana OSI Akumia, *CFO*
Edwin Korankye, *Admin Sec*
EMP: 64
SALES: 6MM **Privately Held**
SIC: 2048 Poultry feeds
PA: Bori's B's Farms & Veterinary Supplies
Ghana Ltd
Plot 9, Block 5 North Suntreso Main
Road
Kumasi
322 033-80

(P-1124)
BROOKHURST MILL
3315 Van Buren Blvd, Riverside
(92503-5697)
PHONE..................................951 688-3511
Bradley C Pope, *CEO*
Bradley Pope, *President*
Gail Morrison, *Corp Secy*
Kevin Pope, *Office Mgr*
▼ EMP: 14
SQ FT: 10,800
SALES (est): 2.6MM **Privately Held**
SIC: 2048 Poultry feeds; livestock feeds

(P-1125)
CANINE CAVIAR PET FOODS INC
4131 Tigris Way, Riverside (92503-4844)
P.O. Box 5872, Norco (92860-8029)
PHONE..................................714 223-1800
Jeff Baker, *President*
Gary Ward, *Vice Pres*
Dawn Barraco, *Relations*
▲ EMP: 30
SQ FT: 6,000
SALES (est): 6.5MM **Privately Held**
WEB: www.caninecaviar.com
SIC: 2048 Canned pet food (except dog &
cat)

(P-1126)
DAIRYMENS FEED & SUP COOP ASSN
323 E Washington St, Petaluma
(94952-3120)
PHONE..................................707 763-1585
Jerry Renner, *President*
Arnold Riebli, *CEO*
Bob McClure, *Vice Pres*
EMP: 14
SQ FT: 50,000
SALES (est): 5.5MM **Privately Held**
WEB: www.dairymensfeed.com
SIC: 2048 Livestock feeds

(P-1127)
DEXT COMPANY OF MARYLAND (DH)
Also Called: Reconserve of Maryland
2811 Wilshire Blvd # 410, Santa Monica
(90403-4803)
P.O. Box 2211 (90407-2211)
PHONE..................................310 458-1574
Meyer Luskin, *Ch of Bd*
Robert McMullen, *President*
Rida Hamed, *Vice Pres*
Gerald Truelove, *Vice Pres*
EMP: 20
SQ FT: 4,000
SALES: 70MM
SALES (corp-wide): 203.7MM **Privately Held**
SIC: 2048 Prepared feeds
HQ: Reconserve, Inc.
2811 Wilshire Blvd # 410
Santa Monica CA 90403
310 458-1574

(P-1128)
ECONOMY STOCK FEED COMPANY
10508 E Central Ave, Del Rey
(93616-9711)
PHONE..................................559 888-2187
Rod Kramer, *President*
Judy Kramer, *Vice Pres*
EMP: 15
SQ FT: 1,200
SALES (est): 1.9MM **Privately Held**
SIC: 2048 Prepared feeds

(P-1129)
ELK GROVE MILLING INC
8320 Eschinger Rd, Elk Grove
(95757-9739)
PHONE..................................916 684-2056
Robert Lent, *President*
Jerry Mayberry, *COO*
Lisa Lent, *Vice Pres*
Mark Groom, *Controller*
Steven Ruiz, *Opers Mgr*
▲ EMP: 25
SQ FT: 400,000
SALES (est): 5.5MM **Privately Held**
WEB: www.elkgrovemilling.com
SIC: 2048 3541 5191 Livestock feeds;
shell crushing, for feed; machine tools,
metal cutting type; animal feeds

(P-1130)
FEEDSTUFFS PROCESSING CO
112 Lark Ct, Alamo (94507-1800)
PHONE..................................925 820-5454
Craig Zellmer, *President*
Vernon Johnson, *Shareholder*
Barbara Corneille, *Treasurer*
Pat Conklin, *Admin Sec*
▼ EMP: 15 EST: 1943
SQ FT: 50,000

SALES: 5.5MM **Privately Held**
SIC: 2048 Feed supplements

(P-1131)
FOSTER COMMODITIES
Also Called: Foster Farms
1900 Kern St, Kingsburg (93631-9687)
P.O. Box 457, Livingston (95334-0457)
PHONE..................559 897-1081
Todd Elrod, *Manager*
Monica Sandoval, *Purch Agent*
Joel Sparks, *Plant Mgr*
EMP: 25
SALES (est): 3.1MM **Privately Held**
SIC: 2048 Prepared feeds

(P-1132)
FOSTER FARMS LLC
1900 Kern St, Kingsburg (93631-9687)
PHONE..................559 897-1081
Donald Jones, *Branch Mgr*
EMP: 28
SALES (corp-wide): 1.4B **Privately Held**
WEB: www.fosterfarms.com
SIC: 2048 Poultry feeds
PA: Foster Farms, Llc
1000 Davis St
Livingston CA 95334
209 394-7901

(P-1133)
FOSTER POULTRY FARMS
221 Stefani Ave, Livingston (95334-1543)
PHONE..................209 394-7950
Jeremiah Nord, *Manager*
Anna Hasenjaeger, *HR Admin*
Janet Dewey, *Purch Mgr*
Vivian Lim, *Purch Agent*
Kyle Beth, *Regl Sales Mgr*
EMP: 25
SALES (corp-wide): 3B **Privately Held**
WEB: www.fosterfarms.com
SIC: 2048 Poultry feeds
PA: Foster Poultry Farms
1000 Davis St
Livingston CA 95334
209 394-6914

(P-1134)
FRONTIER AG CO INC (PA)
46735 County Road 32b, Davis (95618-9501)
PHONE..................530 297-1020
John Pereira, *President*
Mathew Labriola, *Admin Sec*
EMP: 50
SALES (est): 13MM **Privately Held**
WEB: www.frontieragco.com
SIC: 2048 0723 Livestock feeds; rice drying services

(P-1135)
GEORGE VERHOEVEN GRAIN INC (PA)
5355 E Airport Dr, Ontario (91761-8604)
PHONE..................909 605-1531
Randall Verhoeven, *President*
Robert Verhoeven, *Vice Pres*
EMP: 15
SQ FT: 2,100
SALES (est): 3.9MM **Privately Held**
SIC: 2048 5153 Livestock feeds; grain elevators

(P-1136)
HARBOR GREEN GRAIN LP
19100 S Susana Rd, Compton (90221-5708)
PHONE..................310 609-1094
Zach Xu, *CEO*
Kevin Yoon, *COO*
Greg Brent, *Vice Pres*
◆ EMP: 45
SQ FT: 179,000
SALES (est): 16.2MM **Privately Held**
SIC: 2048 Alfalfa, cubed

(P-1137)
HRK PET FOOD PRODUCTS INC
12924 Pierce St, Pacoima (91331-2526)
PHONE..................818 897-2521
Joey Herrick, *President*
Lynnda Herrick, *Vice Pres*
▲ EMP: 19
SQ FT: 30,000

SALES (est): 1.9MM **Privately Held**
SIC: 2048 Canned pet food (except dog & cat)

(P-1138)
INTERNATIONAL PROCESSING CORP (DH)
233 Wilshire Blvd Ste 310, Santa Monica (90401-1206)
P.O. Box 2211 (90407-2211)
PHONE..................310 458-1574
Bob McMullen, *President*
EMP: 25 EST: 1953
SALES (est): 27.7MM
SALES (corp-wide): 203.7MM **Privately Held**
SIC: 2048 Prepared feeds
HQ: Reconserve, Inc.
2811 Wilshire Blvd # 410
Santa Monica CA 90403
310 458-1574

(P-1139)
J D HEISKELL HOLDINGS LLC
11518 Road 120, Pixley (93256-9727)
P.O. Box 1379, Tulare (93275-1379)
PHONE..................559 757-3135
Robert Hodgen, *Manager*
EMP: 80
SALES (corp-wide): 682.5MM **Privately Held**
SIC: 2048 5191 Prepared feeds; animal feeds
PA: J. D. Heiskell Holdings, Llc
1939 Hillman St
Tulare CA 93274
559 685-6100

(P-1140)
J S WEST MILLING CO INC
501 9th St, Modesto (95354-3420)
P.O. Box 1041 (95353-1041)
PHONE..................209 529-4232
D Gary West, *President*
Robert J Benson, *Ch of Bd*
Bob Metz, *CFO*
Eric Benson, *Vice Pres*
Jill Benson, *Vice Pres*
EMP: 26
SQ FT: 1,692
SALES (est): 4.7MM **Privately Held**
SIC: 2048 0252 5999 5191

(P-1141)
KOCH FEEDS INC
10916 Amsterdam Rd, Winton (95388-9749)
PHONE..................209 725-8253
Rochelle Koch, *President*
EMP: 20 EST: 2000
SALES (est): 1.7MM **Privately Held**
SIC: 2048 Feed supplements

(P-1142)
KOIS & PONDS INC
4460 Brooks St Ste B, Montclair (91763-4135)
PHONE..................800 936-3638
Michael Hernandez, *CEO*
Michelle Swanson, *Principal*
EMP: 10
SQ FT: 1,300
SALES (est): 128.4K **Privately Held**
SIC: 2048 Fish food

(P-1143)
LAWLEYS INC
4554 Qantas Ln, Stockton (95206-4919)
P.O. Box 31447 (95213-1447)
PHONE..................209 572-1700
Kenneth Lawley, *President*
Donna Enoch, *Corp Secy*
Ron Lawley, *Vice Pres*
Casey Lawley, *General Mgr*
EMP: 19
SQ FT: 4,200
SALES (est): 4.3MM **Privately Held**
WEB: www.lawleys.com
SIC: 2048 Feed premixes

(P-1144)
LIND MARINE INC (PA)
100 E D St, Petaluma (94952-3109)
PHONE..................707 762-7251
Mike Lind, *President*
Bill Butler, *Vice Pres*

Christian Lind, *Vice Pres*
Chris Lind, *General Mgr*
EMP: 40
SQ FT: 18,500
SALES (est): 8.3MM **Privately Held**
WEB: www.jericoproducts.com
SIC: 2048 1629 Oyster shells, ground; prepared as animal feed; dredging contractor

(P-1145)
MANCHESTER FEEDS INC (PA)
Also Called: Manchester Feeds San Marcos
1520 E Barham Dr, San Marcos (92078-4505)
P.O. Box 1987, Perris (92572-1987)
PHONE..................714 637-7062
William Richard Cramer, *President*
Bertrum Bonner, *Treasurer*
EMP: 19 EST: 1962
SQ FT: 7,542
SALES (est): 1.7MM **Privately Held**
SIC: 2048 Chicken feeds, prepared

(P-1146)
MANNA PRO PRODUCTS LLC
Also Called: Manna Pro Feeds
2962 S Cedar Ave, Fresno (93725-2301)
P.O. Box 1027, Goshen (93227-1027)
PHONE..................559 486-1810
Richard Beral, *Manager*
EMP: 20
SALES (corp-wide): 89.5MM **Privately Held**
SIC: 2048 5191 Prepared feeds; animal feeds
PA: Manna Pro Products, Llc
707 Spirit 40 Park Dr # 150
Chesterfield MO 63005
636 681-1700

(P-1147)
MARYBELLE FARMS INC
Also Called: Ross Hay
3761 Nicolaus Rd, Lincoln (95648-9531)
PHONE..................916 645-8568
Gary Ross, *President*
EMP: 20
SALES (est): 2.4MM **Privately Held**
WEB: www.marybellefarms.com
SIC: 2048 0139 Cereal-, grain-, & seed-based feeds; hay farm; alfalfa farm

(P-1148)
MENEZES HAY CO
5030 Dwight Way, Livingston (95334-9604)
PHONE..................209 394-3111
Jeremy Menezes, *President*
EMP: 12
SALES (est): 1.6MM **Privately Held**
SIC: 2048 Hay, cubed

(P-1149)
NATURAL BALANCE PET FOODS INC (DH)
100 N First St Ste 200, Burbank (91502-1845)
PHONE..................800 829-4493
Joseph Herrick, *President*
David J West, *CEO*
Lynnda Herrick, *Corp Secy*
Lee Kunkler, *District Mgr*
James Matthews, *District Mgr*
▲ EMP: 21
SQ FT: 55,000
SALES (est): 24.3MM
SALES (corp-wide): 7.3B **Publicly Held**
WEB: www.naturalbalanceinc.com
SIC: 2048 5199 Prepared feeds; pet supplies
HQ: Big Heart Pet Brands
1 Maritime Plz Fl 2
San Francisco CA 94111
415 247-3000

(P-1150)
NEXSTEPPE INC
400 E Jamie Ct Ste 202, South San Francisco (94080-6230)
P.O. Box 1561, Hereford TX (79045-1561)
PHONE..................650 887-5700
Anna Rath, *CEO*
Jerry O'Rear, *Vice Pres*
Rodrigo Ritter, *Technology*
Mauricio Barbosa, *Director*
Jacob Becker, *Manager*

EMP: 40
SALES (est): 157.2K **Privately Held**
SIC: 2048 Livestock feeds

(P-1151)
NUTRA BLEND LLC
Also Called: Thomas Products
2140 W Industrial Ave, Madera (93637-5210)
PHONE..................559 661-6161
Mike Osborne, *Branch Mgr*
EMP: 70
SALES (corp-wide): 12.8B **Privately Held**
SIC: 2048 5191 Pulverized oats, prepared as animal feed; animal feeds
HQ: Nutra-Blend, L.L.C.
3200 2nd St
Neosho MO 64850
417 451-6111

(P-1152)
NUTRIUS LLC
39494 Clarkson Dr, Kingsburg (93631-9100)
PHONE..................559 897-5862
Jim Hansen,
▲ EMP: 45
SALES (est): 12.5MM **Privately Held**
SIC: 2048 Prepared feeds

(P-1153)
NUWEST MILLING LLC
4636 Geer Rd, Hughson (95326-9403)
P.O. Box 1031 (95326-1031)
PHONE..................209 883-1163
Gary West, *Mng Member*
Eric H Benson,
Barbara Abeloe, *Manager*
◆ EMP: 16
SQ FT: 1,250
SALES (est): 4.6MM **Privately Held**
SIC: 2048 Prepared feeds

(P-1154)
PACIFIC CATCH INC
770 Tamalpais Dr Ste 400, Corte Madera (94925-1739)
PHONE..................415 504-6905
Keith M Cox, *President*
Mary Christensen, *Marketing Mgr*
Jack Basilotta, *Manager*
EMP: 17
SALES (est): 3.3MM **Privately Held**
SIC: 2048 Prepared feeds

(P-1155)
PITMAN FAMILY FARMS
10365 Iona Ave, Hanford (93230-9553)
PHONE..................559 585-3330
Al Ward, *Plant Mgr*
EMP: 55
SALES (est): 10.3MM
SALES (corp-wide): 57.6MM **Privately Held**
WEB: www.cargill.com
SIC: 2048 Livestock feeds
PA: Pitman Family Farms
1075 North Ave
Sanger CA 93657
559 875-9300

(P-1156)
PURINA ANIMAL NUTRITION LLC
1125 Paulson Rd, Turlock (95380-5542)
PHONE..................209 634-9101
Dan McNutt, *Manager*
EMP: 35
SALES (corp-wide): 12.8B **Privately Held**
SIC: 2048 Prepared feeds
HQ: Purina Animal Nutrition Llc
1080 County Road F W
Shoreview MN 55126

(P-1157)
RECONSERVE INC (HQ)
Also Called: Dexl Company
2811 Wilshire Blvd # 410, Santa Monica (90403-4803)
P.O. Box 2211 (90407-2211)
PHONE..................310 458-1574
Meyer Luskin, *CEO*
David Luskin, *COO*
John Hawrylko, *Vice Pres*
Aaron Cummins, *General Mgr*
Todd Hoerig, *General Mgr*

EMP: 25 **EST:** 1966
SQ FT: 5,000
SALES: 264.6MM
SALES (corp-wide): 203.7MM **Privately Held**
SIC: 2048 Livestock feeds
PA: Scope Industries
2811 Wilshire Blvd # 410
Santa Monica CA 90403
310 458-1574

(P-1158)
REED MARICULTURE INC
Also Called: Instant Algae
900 E Hamilton Ave # 100, Campbell
(95008-0664)
P.O. Box 1049, Freedom (95019-1049)
PHONE...................................408 377-1065
Timothy Allen Reed, *CEO*
Lyn Reed, *COO*
Shawn Neverve, *Vice Pres*
Edwin Reed, *Admin Sec*
▲ **EMP:** 18
SQ FT: 217,800
SALES (est): 3.4MM **Privately Held**
WEB: www.reedmariculture.com
SIC: 2048 Fish food

(P-1159)
RIPON MILLING LLC (PA)
30636 E Carter Rd, Farmington
(95230-9633)
PHONE...................................209 599-4269
George E Jenkins,
Arie E Den Dulk III, *Vice Pres*
Walter Den Dulk, *Vice Pres*
Ronald Den Dulk,
EMP: 25
SQ FT: 8,000
SALES (est): 5MM **Privately Held**
SIC: 2048 Poultry feeds

(P-1160)
ROBINSON FARMS FEED COMPANY
7000 S Inland Dr, Stockton (95206-9688)
PHONE...................................209 466-7915
Michael S Robinson, *President*
Dale L Drury, *Corp Secy*
Jerry N Robinson, *Vice Pres*
EMP: 17
SQ FT: 10,000
SALES (est): 2.4MM **Privately Held**
WEB: www.championhorses.com
SIC: 2048 0139 0119 0115 Feed pre-mixes; stock feeds, dry; alfalfa or alfalfa meal, prepared as animal feed; alfalfa farm; safflower farm; corn; wheat

(P-1161)
ROUDYBUSH INC (PA)
340 Hanson Way, Woodland (95776-6212)
PHONE...................................530 668-6196
Thomas Roudybush, *President*
▼ **EMP:** 13
SQ FT: 32,000
SALES (est): 2.1MM **Privately Held**
WEB: www.roudybush.com
SIC: 2048 Cereal-, grain-, & seed-based feeds

(P-1162)
SAN FRANCISCO BAY BRAND INC (PA)
8239 Enterprise Dr, Newark (94560-3305)
PHONE...................................510 792-7200
Andreas Schmidt, *President*
Anthony Schmidt, *Exec VP*
Dave Fedde, *Vice Pres*
Yana Dutt-Singkh, *Research*
Kearny Wong, *Controller*
◆ **EMP:** 35
SQ FT: 30,000
SALES (est): 6.7MM **Privately Held**
WEB: www.sfbb.com
SIC: 2048 Fish food

(P-1163)
SAVORY CREATIONS INTERNATIONAL
1900 Ofarrell St Ste 180, San Mateo
(94403-1332)
PHONE...................................650 638-1024
Doug Takizawa, *President*
Hidemasa Takizawa, *Principal*

Olivia Anderson, *Info Tech Mgr*
Taki Savory, *Marketing Mgr*
Kaz Yoshihara,
▲ **EMP:** 15
SALES (est): 2MM **Privately Held**
WEB: www.savory-creations.com
SIC: 2048 Feed concentrates

(P-1164)
SEED FACTORY NORTHWEST INC (PA)
4319 Jessup Rd, Ceres (95307-9604)
P.O. Box 245 (95307-0245)
PHONE...................................209 634-8522
Randall Steele, *President*
Lynda Blakemore, *Admin Sec*
Dennis Drake, *Director*
▲ **EMP:** 20
SQ FT: 30,000
SALES (est): 2.9MM **Privately Held**
WEB: www.seedfactory.com
SIC: 2048 Bird food, prepared

(P-1165)
SMOOTH RUN EQUINE INC
11590 W Bernardo Ct # 110, San Diego
(92127-1624)
PHONE...................................760 751-8988
Mark Kane-Berman, *President*
EMP: 12
SALES (est): 1.5MM **Privately Held**
SIC: 2048

(P-1166)
SOUTHWEST PROCESSORS INC
Also Called: Southwest Treatment Systems
4120 Bandini Blvd, Vernon (90058-4294)
PHONE...................................323 269-9876
Richard T Jerome, *President*
Donna Jerome, *Treasurer*
Susan Alfonso, *Admin Sec*
Jeffery Jerome, *Manager*
EMP: 12
SQ FT: 2,000
SALES (est): 2MM **Privately Held**
SIC: 2048 Feeds, specialty: mice, guinea pig, etc.

(P-1167)
STAR MILLING CO
24067 Water Ave, Perris (92570-7395)
P.O. Box 1987 (92572-1987)
PHONE...................................951 657-3143
William R Cramer Jr, *President*
Jane Anderson, *Admin Sec*
◆ **EMP:** 131 **EST:** 1970
SQ FT: 25,000
SALES (est): 45.6MM **Privately Held**
WEB: www.starmilling.com
SIC: 2048 Poultry feeds

(P-1168)
SUN-GRO COMMODITIES INC (PA)
34575 Famoso Rd, Bakersfield
(93308-9769)
PHONE...................................661 393-2612
Donald G Smith, *CEO*
Lori Melendez, *Treasurer*
Scott Smith, *Vice Pres*
Wendy Smith, *Admin Sec*
EMP: 25
SQ FT: 1,400
SALES: 4.7MM **Privately Held**
SIC: 2048 4212 Livestock feeds; local trucking, without storage

(P-1169)
VIRTUS NUTRITION LLC
520 Industrial Ave, Corcoran (93212-9629)
PHONE...................................559 992-5033
Jim Hyer, *Mng Member*
Matt Swanson,
EMP: 10
SALES (est): 2MM
SALES (corp-wide): 120.6MM **Privately Held**
SIC: 2048 Prepared feeds
PA: Associated Feed & Supply Co.
5213 W Main St
Turlock CA 95380
209 667-2708

(P-1170)
WESTWAY FEED PRODUCTS LLC
Also Called: Cargill Molasses
2130 W Washington St, Stockton
(95203-2932)
PHONE...................................209 466-4391
Joe Marchado, *Branch Mgr*
EMP: 13
SALES (corp-wide): 10.6B **Privately Held**
WEB: www.westway.com
SIC: 2048 Feed supplements
HQ: Westway Feed Products Llc
365 Canal St Ste 2929
New Orleans LA 70130
504 934-1850

2051 Bread, Bakery Prdts Exc Cookies & Crackers

(P-1171)
A TASTE OF DENMARK
3401 Telegraph Ave, Oakland
(94609-3002)
PHONE...................................510 420-8889
Mark Davis, *President*
Carmen Luna, *Treasurer*
Michael Kang, *Vice Pres*
Cathy Caulkett, *General Mgr*
Edward Yoo, *Admin Sec*
EMP: 27
SQ FT: 10,000
SALES (est): 2.8MM **Privately Held**
SIC: 2051 Cakes, bakery: except frozen

(P-1172)
ACME BREAD CO
362 E Grand Ave, South San Francisco
(94080-6210)
PHONE...................................650 938-2978
Drew Wescott, *Principal*
EMP: 85
SALES (est): 8.8MM **Privately Held**
WEB: www.acmebread.com
SIC: 2051 Bakery: wholesale or whole-sale/retail combined

(P-1173)
ANDRE-BOUDIN BAKERIES INC
67 Broadwalk Ln, Walnut Creek (94596)
PHONE...................................925 935-4375
Andrew Friedman, *Manager*
EMP: 15 **Privately Held**
WEB: www.boudinbakery.com
SIC: 2051 5812 Bread, cake & related products; cafe
HQ: Andre-Boudin Bakeries, Inc.
50 Francisco St Ste 200
San Francisco CA 94133
415 882-1849

(P-1174)
ANDRE-BOUDIN BAKERIES INC
Also Called: Boudin Souerdough BAKery& Cafe
2855 Stevens Crk 2451, San Jose (95128)
PHONE...................................408 249-4101
Doug Wheelar, *Manager*
EMP: 15 **Privately Held**
WEB: www.boudinbakery.com
SIC: 2051 Bread, cake & related products
HQ: Andre-Boudin Bakeries, Inc.
50 Francisco St Ste 200
San Francisco CA 94133
415 882-1849

(P-1175)
ANNIES BAKING LLC (DH)
1610 5th St, Berkeley (94710-1715)
PHONE...................................510 558-7500
John Foraker, *Mng Member*
EMP: 32 **EST:** 2014
SALES (est): 18.4MM
SALES (corp-wide): 15.7B **Publicly Held**
SIC: 2051 2052 5149 Bakery: wholesale or wholesale/retail combined; bakery products, dry; bakery products

(P-1176)
ANTONINAS ARTISAN BAKERY LLC
1316 Dupont Ct, Manteca (95336-6004)
PHONE...................................209 665-4176

EMP: 38
SALES (corp-wide): 2.7MM **Privately Held**
SIC: 2051 Bakery: wholesale or whole-sale/retail combined
PA: Antonina's Artisan Bakery Llc
2535 152nd Ave Ne
Redmond WA 98052
425 637-3357

(P-1177)
ARTISAN CRUST
754 E Florence Ave, Los Angeles
(90001-2322)
PHONE...................................323 759-7000
Maziar Mansori, *Mng Member*
EMP: 25
SALES: 1.8MM **Privately Held**
SIC: 2051 Bakery: wholesale or whole-sale/retail combined

(P-1178)
BAGELRY INC (PA)
320 Cedar St Ste A, Santa Cruz
(95060-4362)
PHONE...................................831 429-8049
John Hamstra, *President*
Laurie Rivin, *Vice Pres*
EMP: 35
SQ FT: 3,000
SALES: 1.9MM **Privately Held**
SIC: 2051 5812 2052 Bakery: wholesale or wholesale/retail combined; eating places; cookies & crackers

(P-1179)
BAKE R US INC
Also Called: Dave's Donuts & Baking Co
13400 S Western Ave, Gardena
(90249-1928)
PHONE...................................310 630-5873
Fairy Aframian, *CEO*
Mike Aframian, *President*
EMP: 14
SALES (est): 163.7K **Privately Held**
WEB: www.bakerus.com
SIC: 2051 Doughnuts, except frozen

(P-1180)
BAKED IN SUN
Also Called: S & S Bakery
2560 Progress St, Vista (92081-8465)
PHONE...................................760 591-9045
Rachel Shein, *CEO*
Steve Pilarski, *President*
EMP: 250
SQ FT: 60,000
SALES: 18MM **Privately Held**
WEB: www.bakedinthesun.com
SIC: 2051 Bagels, fresh or frozen

(P-1181)
BAKERY DEPOT INC
4489 Bandini Blvd, Vernon (90058-4309)
PHONE...................................323 261-8388
Wilton Thinh Thai, *CEO*
◆ **EMP:** 15
SALES (est): 5.2MM **Privately Held**
SIC: 2051 Bakery: wholesale or whole-sale/retail combined

(P-1182)
BALBOA ACQUISITION LLC
Also Called: Spot On Treats
1760 E Wilshire Ave, Santa Ana
(92705-4615)
PHONE...................................714 972-4972
Maryknoll Benner, *Mng Member*
Rudy Pollak,
EMP: 50
SALES (est): 7.9MM **Privately Held**
WEB: www.balboadessert.com
SIC: 2051 Cakes, pies & pastries

(P-1183)
BANH MI & CHE CALI
13838 Brookhurst St, Garden Grove
(92843-3121)
PHONE...................................714 534-6987
Boyce Nguyen Jr, *Owner*
EMP: 28
SALES (est): 2MM **Privately Held**
SIC: 2051 Bread, cake & related products

▲ = Import ▼=Export
◆ =Import/Export

(P-1184)
BAY CITIES ITALIAN BAKERY INC
1120 W Mahalo Pl, Compton (90220-5443)
PHONE...............................310 608-1881
Linda Ferrera, *President*
Mario Ferrera, *CEO*
EMP: 13
SQ FT: 7,200
SALES (est): 650K Privately Held
SIC: 2051 5461 Bakery: wholesale or wholesale/retail combined; bakeries

(P-1185)
BECKMANNS OLD WORLD BAKERY LTD
104 Bronson St Ste 6, Santa Cruz (95062-3487)
PHONE...............................831 423-9242
Beth Holland, *CEO*
Peter Beckmann, *President*
Sharon May, *Vice Pres*
Jeremy Siemon, *Sales Mgr*
▲ EMP: 150
SQ FT: 17,000
SALES (est): 24.4MM Privately Held
WEB: www.beckmannsbakery.com
SIC: 2051 5461 Bakery: wholesale or wholesale/retail combined; bakeries

(P-1186)
BEST EXPRESS FOODS INC
1742 Sabre St, Hayward (94545-1016)
PHONE...............................510 782-5338
Jesus Mendoza, *President*
Daniel Mendoza, *Vice Pres*
EMP: 270
SQ FT: 35,000
SALES: 45MM Privately Held
SIC: 2051 Breads, rolls & buns

(P-1187)
BIMBO BAKERIES USA INC
1749 Reliance St, Modesto (95358-5708)
PHONE...............................209 538-6170
Gary Harris, *Manager*
EMP: 15 Privately Held
SIC: 2051 Bread, cake & related products
HQ: Bimbo Bakeries Usa, Inc
255 Business Center Dr # 200
Horsham PA 19044
215 347-5500

(P-1188)
BIMBO BAKERIES USA INC
3580 Sueldo St, San Luis Obispo (93401-7338)
PHONE...............................805 544-7687
Carol Rounsaville, *Principal*
EMP: 80 Privately Held
SIC: 2051 Bread, all types (white, wheat, rye, etc): fresh or frozen
HQ: Bimbo Bakeries Usa, Inc
255 Business Center Dr # 200
Horsham PA 19044
215 347-5500

(P-1189)
BIMBO BAKERIES USA INC
385 N Sherman Ave, Corona (92882-1890)
PHONE...............................951 280-9044
EMP: 18 Privately Held
SIC: 2051 Cakes, bakery: except frozen
HQ: Bimbo Bakeries Usa, Inc
255 Business Center Dr # 200
Horsham PA 19044
215 347-5500

(P-1190)
BIMBO BAKERIES USA INC
Also Called: Bimbo Bakeries U.S.A.
480 S Vale Ave, Montebello (90640)
PHONE...............................323 720-6099
Edgar Jaramillo, *Director*
Jose Acosta, *Accounting Mgr*
Wally Caro, *Safety Mgr*
Robert Tong, *Plant Mgr*
Margie Gonzalez, *Manager*
EMP: 18 Privately Held
SIC: 2051 Bread, all types (white, wheat, rye, etc): fresh or frozen
HQ: Bimbo Bakeries Usa, Inc
255 Business Center Dr # 200
Horsham PA 19044
215 347-5500

(P-1191)
BIMBO BAKERIES USA INC
Also Called: Sara Lee Bakery Group
3495 Swetzer Rd, Loomis (95650-9581)
P.O. Box 5387, Sacramento (95817-0387)
PHONE...............................916 456-3863
Fred Grinder, *Branch Mgr*
EMP: 15
SQ FT: 1,159 Privately Held
SIC: 2051 Bakery: wholesale or wholesale/retail combined
HQ: Bimbo Bakeries Usa, Inc
255 Business Center Dr # 200
Horsham PA 19044
215 347-5500

(P-1192)
BIMBO BAKERIES USA INC
7601 Wilbur Way, Sacramento (95828-4927)
PHONE...............................916 681-8069
EMP: 24 Privately Held
SIC: 2051 Bakery: wholesale or wholesale/retail combined
HQ: Bimbo Bakeries Usa, Inc
255 Business Center Dr # 200
Horsham PA 19044
215 347-5500

(P-1193)
BIMBO BAKERIES USA INC
3231 6th Ave, Sacramento (95817-3276)
P.O. Box 5387 (95817-0387)
PHONE...............................916 732-4733
Belsrida Plunk, *Branch Mgr*
Carla Makiney, *Purch Mgr*
Thomas Meuser, *Director*
Sherry Novotny, *Manager*
EMP: 700 Privately Held
SIC: 2051 Bread, all types (white, wheat, rye, etc): fresh or frozen; rolls, bread type: fresh or frozen
HQ: Bimbo Bakeries Usa, Inc
255 Business Center Dr # 200
Horsham PA 19044
215 347-5500

(P-1194)
BIMBO BAKERIES USA INC
2069 Aldergrove Ave, Escondido (92029-1902)
PHONE...............................760 737-7700
Eduardo Aiza, *Principal*
EMP: 18 Privately Held
SIC: 2051 Bread, cake & related products
HQ: Bimbo Bakeries Usa, Inc
255 Business Center Dr # 200
Horsham PA 19044
215 347-5500

(P-1195)
BIMBO BAKERIES USA INC
Also Called: Oroweat Foods
4000 Ruffin Rd Ste B, San Diego (92123-1866)
PHONE...............................858 677-0573
Mark Edwards, *Principal*
WEB: www.englishmuffin.com
SIC: 2051 Bakery: wholesale or wholesale/retail combined
HQ: Bimbo Bakeries Usa, Inc
255 Business Center Dr # 200
Horsham PA 19044
215 347-5500

(P-1196)
BIMBO BAKERIES USA INC
1836 G St, Fresno (93706-1617)
PHONE...............................559 498-3632
EMP: 18
SALES (corp-wide): 13.7B Privately Held
SIC: 2051
HQ: Bimbo Bakeries Usa, Inc
255 Business Center Dr # 200
Horsham PA 19044
215 347-5500

(P-1197)
BIMBO BAKERIES USA INC
14388 Washington Ave, San Leandro (94578-3419)
PHONE...............................510 614-4500
Juan Muldoon, *Principal*
EMP: 18
SQ FT: 9,320 Privately Held

(P-1198)
BIMBO BAKERIES USA INC
264 S Spruce Ave, South San Francisco (94080-4550)
PHONE...............................650 583-5828
Laura Thompson, *Branch Mgr*
EMP: 20 Privately Held
SIC: 2051 Bread, cake & related products
HQ: Bimbo Bakeries Usa, Inc
255 Business Center Dr # 200
Horsham PA 19044
215 347-5500

(P-1199)
BIMBO BAKERIES USA INC
366 S Acacia Ave, Fullerton (92831-4724)
PHONE...............................714 441-2555
Bruce White, *Manager*
EMP: 33 Privately Held
WEB: www.bimbobakeriesusa.com
SIC: 2051 Bread, cake & related products
HQ: Bimbo Bakeries Usa, Inc
255 Business Center Dr # 200
Horsham PA 19044
215 347-5500

(P-1200)
BIMBO BAKERIES USA INC
Also Called: Oroweat Foods
1220 Howell St, Anaheim (92805)
PHONE...............................714 634-8068
Mike Prichard, *General Mgr*
EMP: 60 Privately Held
WEB: www.englishmuffin.com
SIC: 2051 Bread, cake & related products
HQ: Bimbo Bakeries Usa, Inc
255 Business Center Dr # 200
Horsham PA 19044
215 347-5500

(P-1201)
BIMBO BAKERIES USA INC
11400 Commercial Pkwy, Castroville (95012-3202)
PHONE...............................831 633-7100
Jessica Higgle, *Manager*
EMP: 22 Privately Held
SIC: 2051 Bakery: wholesale or wholesale/retail combined
HQ: Bimbo Bakeries Usa, Inc
255 Business Center Dr # 200
Horsham PA 19044
215 347-5500

(P-1202)
BIMBO BAKERIES USA INC
116 Ponderosa Dr, Sonora (95370-4818)
PHONE...............................209 532-5185
Sandy Wynne, *Branch Mgr*
EMP: 76 Privately Held
SIC: 2051 Bakery: wholesale or wholesale/retail combined
HQ: Bimbo Bakeries Usa, Inc
255 Business Center Dr # 200
Horsham PA 19044
215 347-5500

(P-1203)
BIMBO BAKERIES USA INC
Also Called: Mrs Baird's Bakeries
1771 Blake Ave, Los Angeles (90031-1006)
PHONE...............................323 913-7214
Joe Dangelmaier, *Vice Pres*
EMP: 50 Privately Held
WEB: www.mrsbairds.com
SIC: 2051 Bakery: wholesale or wholesale/retail combined
HQ: Bimbo Bakeries Usa, Inc
255 Business Center Dr # 200
Horsham PA 19044
215 347-5500

(P-1204)
BIMBO BAKERIES USA INC
Also Called: Old Country Bakery
475 S Canal St, South San Francisco (94080-4607)
PHONE...............................650 583-3259
Dan Hobson, *Manager*
EMP: 40 Privately Held

WEB: www.englishmuffin.com
SIC: 2051 Bread, cake & related products
HQ: Bimbo Bakeries Usa, Inc
255 Business Center Dr # 200
Horsham PA 19044
215 347-5500

(P-1205)
BIMBO BAKERIES USA INC
333 Dawson Dr Ste A, Camarillo (93012-8093)
PHONE...............................805 384-1059
Robert Hernandez, *Manager*
EMP: 15 Privately Held
SIC: 2051 Bakery: wholesale or wholesale/retail combined
HQ: Bimbo Bakeries Usa, Inc
255 Business Center Dr # 200
Horsham PA 19044
215 347-5500

(P-1206)
BIMBO BAKERIES USA INC
2740 Soquel Ave, Santa Cruz (95062-1409)
PHONE...............................831 465-1214
Rick Roberts, *Manager*
EMP: 12 Privately Held
SIC: 2051 Bakery: wholesale or wholesale/retail combined
HQ: Bimbo Bakeries Usa, Inc
255 Business Center Dr # 200
Horsham PA 19044
215 347-5500

(P-1207)
BIMBO BAKERIES USA INC
Also Called: Oroweat
1201 El Camino Ave, Sacramento (95815-2615)
PHONE...............................916 922-1307
Michael Smith, *Manager*
EMP: 20 Privately Held
WEB: www.englishmuffin.com
SIC: 2051 Bread, cake & related products
HQ: Bimbo Bakeries Usa, Inc
255 Business Center Dr # 200
Horsham PA 19044
215 347-5500

(P-1208)
BIMBO BAKERIES USA INC
3525 Arden Rd Ste 300, Hayward (94545-3909)
PHONE...............................510 436-5350
Bob Thompson, *Branch Mgr*
EMP: 250 Privately Held
SIC: 2051 Bread, all types (white, wheat, rye, etc): fresh or frozen; buns, bread type: fresh or frozen; rolls, bread type: fresh or frozen
HQ: Bimbo Bakeries Usa, Inc
255 Business Center Dr # 200
Horsham PA 19044
215 347-5500

(P-1209)
BIMBO BAKERIES USA INC
2380 N Clovis Ave, Fresno (93727-1213)
PHONE...............................650 291-3213
Allen Petersen, *Manager*
EMP: 30 Privately Held
SIC: 2051 Bakery: wholesale or wholesale/retail combined
HQ: Bimbo Bakeries Usa, Inc
255 Business Center Dr # 200
Horsham PA 19044
215 347-5500

(P-1210)
BIMBO BAKERIES USA INC
Rainbo Bread
3292 S Willow Ave Ste 101, Fresno (93725-9906)
P.O. Box 132 (93707-0132)
PHONE...............................559 489-0980
Chuck Linthicum, *Branch Mgr*
EMP: 175
SQ FT: 110,000 Privately Held
SIC: 2051 Bakery: wholesale or wholesale/retail combined
HQ: Bimbo Bakeries Usa, Inc
255 Business Center Dr # 200
Horsham PA 19044
215 347-5500

PRODUCTS & SVCS

(P-1211)
BLUE RIBBON BAKING INC
823 W 8th St, Azusa (91702-2247)
PHONE..................................626 815-8809
Linda J Baisley, *President*
EMP: 105
SALES (est): 10.4MM **Privately Held**
SIC: 2051 Bread, cake & related products

(P-1212)
BON APPETIT DANISH INC
Also Called: Bon Appetit Bakery
4525 District Blvd, Vernon (90058-2711)
PHONE..................................323 584-9500
Mahasti Mashhoon, *President*
Mahasti Mashon, *Vice Pres*
Bob Matwiczak, *Vice Pres*
Rhonda Freeman, *Executive*
Michael Pittman, *Executive*
EMP: 100
SQ FT: 19,727
SALES (est): 37.9MM **Privately Held**
WEB: www.bonappetitbakery.com
SIC: 2051 Bread, cake & related products

(P-1213)
BORDENAVES MARIN BAKING
Also Called: Bordenaves
1512 4th St, San Rafael (94901-2713)
P.O. Box 150505 (94915-0505)
PHONE..................................415 453-2957
Fred Radwan,
EMP: 53
SQ FT: 24,000
SALES (est): 11MM **Privately Held**
SIC: 2051 Bread, all types (white, wheat,
   rye, etc): fresh or frozen

(P-1214)
BROOKS STREET COMPANIES
Also Called: Brooks Street Baking Company
5560 Brooks St, Montclair (91763-4522)
P.O. Box 1667, Ontario (91762-0667)
PHONE..................................909 983-6090
Fred Scalzo, *President*
Fred Sealzo, *President*
EMP: 125
SQ FT: 22,000
SALES (est): 14MM **Privately Held**
WEB: www.brooksstreetbakery.com
SIC: 2051 Bakery: wholesale or whole-
   sale/retail combined

(P-1215)
**CALIFORNIA CHURROS
CORPORATION**
751 Via Lata, Colton (92324-3930)
PHONE..................................909 370-4777
Jorge D Martinez, *CEO*
Jorge D Martinez Sr, *President*
Frank Ruvalcaba, *Vice Pres*
Eva A Martinez, *Admin Sec*
EMP: 130
SQ FT: 54,800
SALES (est): 22.8MM
SALES (corp-wide): 1B **Publicly Held**
WEB: www.churros.com
SIC: 2051 Pastries, e.g. danish: except
   frozen
HQ: J & J Snack Foods Corp. Of California
   5353 S Downey Rd
   Vernon CA 90058
   323 581-0171

(P-1216)
CALIFORNIA SMART FOODS
2565 3rd St Ste 342, San Francisco
(94107-3159)
PHONE..................................415 826-0449
Rudy Melnitzer, *Owner*
Helaine Melnitzer, *Co-Owner*
EMP: 22
SALES: 5.3MM **Privately Held**
SIC: 2051 Bread, cake & related products

(P-1217)
CARAVAN BAKERY INC
33300 Western Ave, Union City
(94587-2211)
PHONE..................................510 487-2600
Joseph Maroun Sr, *President*
EMP: 26
SALES (est): 7.3MM **Privately Held**
SIC: 2051 Bakery: wholesale or whole-
   sale/retail combined

(P-1218)
CARAVAN TRADING COMPANY
Also Called: Sterling Foods
33300 Western Ave, Union City
(94587-2211)
PHONE..................................510 487-8090
John Likovich, *President*
Steve Reesing, *CFO*
Ira Hermann, *Vice Pres*
Carmen Maroun, *Vice Pres*
EMP: 85
SQ FT: 100,000
SALES (est): 20.9MM **Privately Held**
WEB: www.caravantrd.com
SIC: 2051 Bagels, fresh or frozen
HQ: Sterling Foods, Llc
   1075 Arion Pkwy
   San Antonio TX 78216
   210 490-0607

(P-1219)
CHANTILLY BAKERY INC
12714 Chandon Ct, San Diego
(92130-2794)
PHONE..................................858 693-3300
Christina L Manly, *CEO*
Christina Manly, *Owner*
EMP: 18
SALES: 1MM **Privately Held**
SIC: 2051 Bread, cake & related products

(P-1220)
CHEESE CAKE CITY INC
1225 4th St, Berkeley (94710-1302)
PHONE..................................510 524-9404
Steve Zwetsch, *President*
Lori Hughes, *Admin Sec*
EMP: 10
SQ FT: 3,700
SALES (est): 900.3K **Privately Held**
WEB: www.cheesecakecity.com
SIC: 2051 5961 2053 2024 Cakes, bak-
   ery: except frozen; food, mail order;
   frozen bakery products, except bread; ice
   cream & frozen desserts

(P-1221)
**CHEESECAKE FACTORY
BAKERY INC (HQ)**
26950 Agoura Rd, Agoura Hills
(91301-5335)
PHONE..................................818 880-9323
David Overton, *Ch of Bd*
Keith T Carango, *President*
Max Byfuglin, *Exec VP*
▼ **EMP:** 350
SQ FT: 60,000
SALES (est): 90.2MM **Publicly Held**
SIC: 2051 5812 Cakes, bakery: except
   frozen; eating places

(P-1222)
CHEF BRAND FOODS
Also Called: Chef Brands
8637 W Doe Ave, Visalia (93291-8938)
PHONE..................................559 651-1696
J L Logan, *Owner*
EMP: 20
SALES (est): 1.7MM **Privately Held**
SIC: 2051 Pastries, e.g. danish: except
   frozen

(P-1223)
CITY BAKING COMPANY
1373 Lowrie Ave, South San Francisco
(94080-6403)
PHONE..................................650 589-8128
Alex Bulazo, *President*
Judie Gee, *Cust Mgr*
EMP: 55 **EST:** 1991
SALES (est): 9.9MM **Privately Held**
WEB: www.citybaking.com
SIC: 2051 Bread, cake & related products

(P-1224)
CLAUDIOS SPECIALTY BREADS
11185 Commercial Pkwy, Castroville
(95012-3215)
PHONE..................................831 633-5051
Claudio Cantore, *President*
EMP: 12
SQ FT: 3,000
SALES (est): 1.5MM **Privately Held**
WEB: www.claudiosbreads.com
SIC: 2051 Bread, cake & related products

(P-1225)
CORBIN-HILL INC
Also Called: Corbin Foods
2961 W Macarthur Blvd, Santa Ana
(92704-6913)
PHONE..................................714 966-6695
Jl Corbin, *Ch of Bd*
A Moreno, *President*
R W Carlyle, *CFO*
Karen Kelley, *Admin Sec*
EMP: 100
SQ FT: 20,000
SALES (est): 9.3MM **Privately Held**
WEB: www.edibowls.com
SIC: 2051 Bread, cake & related products

(P-1226)
CREATIVE INTL PASTRIES
950 Illinois St, San Francisco (94107-3136)
PHONE..................................415 255-1128
Gerhard Michler, *President*
Mary Michler, *Vice Pres*
Alex Leong, *Human Res Mgr*
EMP: 25
SQ FT: 3,000
SALES: 400K **Privately Held**
WEB: www.gerhardmichler.com
SIC: 2051 2052 Cakes, pies & pastries;
   cookies

(P-1227)
CUCINA HOLDINGS INC
4 Embarcadero Ctr Lbby 4 # 4, San Fran-
cisco (94111-4112)
PHONE..................................415 986-8688
Patrick Dougherty, *Manager*
EMP: 10 **Privately Held**
WEB: www.javacity.com
SIC: 2051 5812 Bread, all types (white,
   wheat, rye, etc): fresh or frozen; cafe
HQ: Cucina Holdings, Inc.
   1300 Del Paso Rd
   Sacramento CA 95834
   916 565-5500

(P-1228)
D GOLDENWEST INC
2700 Pacific Coast Hwy # 2, Torrance
(90505-7061)
PHONE..................................310 564-2641
Dan Almquist, *President*
Robert Jonas, *Vice Pres*
EMP: 50
SQ FT: 5,000
SALES (est): 3.2MM **Privately Held**
SIC: 2051 Sponge goods, bakery: except
   frozen

(P-1229)
DAWN FOOD PRODUCTS INC
Also Called: Dawn Bakery Service Center
2845 Faber St, Union City (94587-1203)
PHONE..................................510 487-9007
Paul Lawrence, *Branch Mgr*
EMP: 30
SALES (corp-wide): 1.6B **Privately Held**
WEB: www.dawnfoods.com
SIC: 2051 2045 5046 Bread, cake & re-
   lated products; prepared flour mixes &
   doughs; bakery equipment & supplies
HQ: Dawn Food Products, Inc.
   3333 Sargent Rd
   Jackson MI 49201

(P-1230)
DESSERTS ON US INC
57 Belle Falor Ct, Arcata (95521-9234)
PHONE..................................707 822-0160
Emran Essa, *CEO*
Kathleen Essa, *Admin Sec*
▲ **EMP:** 15
SQ FT: 20,000
SALES (est): 3.7MM **Privately Held**
WEB: www.dessertsonus.com
SIC: 2051 2099 2052 Pastries, e.g. dan-
   ish: except frozen; dessert mixes & fill-
   ings; cookies

(P-1231)
DISTINCT INDULGENCE INC
Also Called: Mrs Appletree's Bakery
5018 Lante St, Baldwin Park (91706-1839)
PHONE..................................818 546-1700
Robert W Gray, *President*
Suzanne Gray, *Corp Secy*

▲ **EMP:** 38
SQ FT: 10,000
SALES (est): 6.6MM **Privately Held**
SIC: 2051 5499 Bakery: wholesale or
   wholesale/retail combined; health & di-
   etetic food stores

(P-1232)
DO-NUT WHEEL INC
10250 N De Anza Blvd, Cupertino
(95014-2219)
PHONE..................................408 252-8193
Daniel Taing, *President*
EMP: 10
SALES (est): 550K **Privately Held**
SIC: 2051 Doughnuts, except frozen

(P-1233)
DOBAKE BAKERIES INC
Also Called: Happy Doughnuts
810 81st Ave, Oakland (94621-2569)
P.O. Box 1447, Sonoma (95476-1447)
PHONE..................................510 834-3134
Daniel W Giraudo, *CEO*
Ron Tallia, *Vice Pres*
EMP: 100
SQ FT: 36,000
SALES (est): 21.6MM
SALES (corp-wide): 47.4MM **Privately
Held**
WEB: www.dobake.com
SIC: 2051 Bakery: except frozen
PA: Gold Coast Baking Company, Inc.
   1590 E Saint Gertrude Pl
   Santa Ana CA 92705
   714 545-2253

(P-1234)
DOUCE DE FRANCE
686 Brdwy St, Redwood City (94063)
PHONE..................................650 369-9644
Mauro Ferreira, *Manager*
EMP: 14
SALES (est): 1.4MM
SALES (corp-wide): 586.9K **Privately
Held**
WEB: www.doucefrancebakery.com
SIC: 2051 Bread, cake & related products
PA: Douce De France
   104 Town And Country Vlg
   Palo Alto CA 94301
   650 322-3601

(P-1235)
DOUGHTRONICS INC (PA)
Also Called: Acme Bread Company
1601 San Pablo Ave, Berkeley
(94702-1317)
PHONE..................................510 524-1327
Steven Sullivan, *President*
Susan Sullivan, *Vice Pres*
Doug Volkmer, *Vice Pres*
EMP: 30
SALES (est): 15.7MM **Privately Held**
SIC: 2051 5461 Bakery: wholesale or
   wholesale/retail combined; bread

(P-1236)
DOUGHTRONICS INC
Also Called: Acme Bread Co Div II
2730 9th St, Berkeley (94710-2633)
PHONE..................................510 843-2978
Rick Kirkby, *Manager*
EMP: 50
SQ FT: 4,372
SALES (corp-wide): 15.7MM **Privately
Held**
SIC: 2051 Bakery: wholesale or whole-
   sale/retail combined
PA: Doughtronics, Inc.
   1601 San Pablo Ave
   Berkeley CA 94702
   510 524-1327

(P-1237)
DOUGHTRONICS INC
1 Ferry Building Ste 15, San Francisco
(94111-4228)
PHONE..................................415 288-2978
Drew Westcott, *Branch Mgr*
Monica Contois, *Manager*
EMP: 30
SALES (corp-wide): 15.7MM **Privately
Held**
SIC: 2051 Bread, cake & related products

PA: Doughtronics, Inc.
1601 San Pablo Ave
Berkeley CA 94702
510 524-1327

(P-1238)
DTBM INC
Also Called: Fortune Bakery
1825 Durfee Ave Ste C, South El Monte
(91733-3742)
PHONE.............................626 579-7033
Terry C Peng, *President*
▲ EMP: 13
SQ FT: 5,000
SALES: 600K **Privately Held**
WEB: www.dtbm.com
SIC: 2051 5461 Pastries, e.g. danish: ex-
cept frozen; bakeries

(P-1239)
E D D INVESTMENT CO
Also Called: Polly's Tasty Foods & Pies
2025 N Tustin St, Orange (92865-3901)
PHONE.............................714 637-3040
Arlene Larochelle, *Manager*
EMP: 50
SQ FT: 5,000
SALES (corp-wide): 29.2MM **Privately
Held**
SIC: 2051 Cakes, pies & pastries
PA: E D D Investment Co
14325 Iseli Rd
Santa Fe Springs CA 90670
562 921-5410

(P-1240)
EDNAS INC
390 Buckley Rd Ste F, San Luis Obispo
(93401-8164)
P.O. Box 4610 (93403-4610)
PHONE.............................805 541-3563
Edna Ryzebol, *President*
EMP: 15
SQ FT: 10,000
SALES (est): 1.6MM **Privately Held**
SIC: 2051 Cakes, pies & pastries

(P-1241)
EDNER CORPORATION
Also Called: Wayfarers
528 Oakshire Pl, Alamo (94507-2325)
PHONE.............................925 831-1248
Ehud L Kirshner, *President*
EMP: 30
SQ FT: 21,408
SALES (est): 3.6MM **Privately Held**
SIC: 2051 5149 Bread, cake & related
products; groceries & related products

(P-1242)
EL METATE FOODS INC
Also Called: El Metate Mercado
125n Rancho Santiago Blvd, Orange
(92869-3501)
PHONE.............................714 542-3913
Mike Mercado, *Branch Mgr*
EMP: 10
SALES (corp-wide): 36.8MM **Privately
Held**
WEB: www.elmetate.com
SIC: 2051 2052 2099 5812 Breads, rolls
& buns; cakes, pies & pastries; cookies;
tortillas, fresh or refrigerated; Mexican
restaurant
PA: El Metate Foods Inc.
838 E 1st St
Santa Ana CA 92701
714 542-3913

(P-1243)
EL METATE FOODS INC
Also Called: El Metate Market
817 W 19th St, Costa Mesa (92627-3518)
PHONE.............................949 646-9362
Brian Murrieta, *Branch Mgr*
EMP: 50
SALES (corp-wide): 36.8MM **Privately
Held**
WEB: www.elmetate.com
SIC: 2051 2052 2099 5812 Breads, rolls
& buns; cakes, pies & pastries; cookies;
tortillas, fresh or refrigerated; Mexican
restaurant

PA: El Metate Foods Inc.
838 E 1st St
Santa Ana CA 92701
714 542-3913

(P-1244)
EL SEGUNDO BREAD BAR LLC
701 E El Segundo Blvd, El Segundo
(90245-4108)
PHONE.............................310 615-9898
Myrna Al-Midani, *CEO*
Ali Chalabi, *President*
▲ EMP: 32
SQ FT: 8,000
SALES (est): 2.7MM **Privately Held**
SIC: 2051 5149 Bread, all types (white,
wheat, rye, etc): fresh or frozen; bakery
products

(P-1245)
ELIZABETHS FOOD CO INC (PA)
19301 S Santa Fe Ave # 104, Compton
(90221-5918)
PHONE.............................310 638-2168
Francis Peter Bastasch, *CEO*
EMP: 45
SQ FT: 12,500
SALES (est): 13.4MM **Privately Held**
WEB: www.croutons.com
SIC: 2051 Bread, cake & related products

(P-1246)
FARGO CHOICE FOODS LLC
2885 Adeline St, Oakland (94608-4409)
P.O. Box 220, San Ramon (94583-0220)
PHONE.............................510 774-0064
Daniel Mendoza, *President*
Jesus Mendoza, *Vice Pres*
EMP: 48
SQ FT: 24,000
SALES: 3.7MM **Privately Held**
SIC: 2051 Breads, rolls & buns

(P-1247)
FEEMSTER CO INC
Also Called: Some Crust Bakery
119 Yale Ave, Claremont (91711-4723)
PHONE.............................909 621-9772
Larry Feemster, *President*
Sandra Feemster, *Officer*
Tasha Cockrell, *Business Mgr*
Scott Feemster, *Manager*
EMP: 30 EST: 1997
SQ FT: 3,000
SALES (est): 3.6MM **Privately Held**
WEB: www.somecrust.com
SIC: 2051 5461 Bread, cake & related
products; bakeries

(P-1248)
FIESTA MEXICAN FOODS INC
979 G St, Brawley (92227-2615)
PHONE.............................760 344-3580
Raymond Armenta, *President*
EMP: 30 EST: 1956
SQ FT: 4,000
SALES (est): 3.2MM **Privately Held**
SIC: 2051 2099 Pastries, e.g. danish: ex-
cept frozen; tortillas, fresh or refrigerated

(P-1249)
FLOUR FUSION
133 N Main St, Lake Elsinore
(92530-4105)
PHONE.............................951 245-1166
EMP: 12
SALES (est): 774.2K **Privately Held**
SIC: 2051 5812 Bakery: wholesale or
wholesale/retail combined; coffee shop

(P-1250)
**FLOWERS BAKING CO
MODESTO LLC**
736 Mariposa Rd, Modesto (95354-4133)
PHONE.............................209 857-4600
Paul Holshouser,
EMP: 99
SQ FT: 250,000
SALES (est): 14.7MM
SALES (corp-wide): 3.9B **Publicly Held**
SIC: 2051 Breads, rolls & buns
PA: Flowers Foods, Inc.
1919 Flowers Cir
Thomasville GA 31757
229 226-9110

(P-1251)
**FOOD FOR LIFE BAKING CO
INC (PA)**
Also Called: Natural Food Mill
2991 Doherty St, Corona (92879-5811)
P.O. Box 1434 (92878-1434)
PHONE.............................951 273-3031
R James Torres, *President*
Scott Kraus, *CFO*
Charles Torres, *Vice Pres*
Sundeep Panchal, *QA Dir*
Sandy Coleman, *Controller*
▲ EMP: 100
SQ FT: 170,000
SALES (est): 25.5MM **Privately Held**
WEB: www.davitafoods.com
SIC: 2051 Bread, all types (white, wheat,
rye, etc): fresh or frozen

(P-1252)
FREEPORT BAKERY INC
2966 Freeport Blvd, Sacramento
(95818-3855)
PHONE.............................916 442-4256
Marlene Goetzeler, *President*
Walter Goetzeler, *Principal*
EMP: 45
SALES (est): 6.3MM **Privately Held**
WEB: www.freeportbakery.com
SIC: 2051 5461 5812 Bread, cake & re-
lated products; bakeries; eating places

(P-1253)
**FRESNO FRENCH BREAD
BAKERY INC**
Also Called: Basque French Bakery
2625 Inyo St, Fresno (93721-2732)
P.O. Box 432 (93708-0432)
PHONE.............................559 268-7088
Al Lewis, *President*
Rita Ingmire, *Vice Pres*
EMP: 34 EST: 1963
SQ FT: 32,000
SALES (est): 5.4MM **Privately Held**
SIC: 2051 Bread, all types (white, wheat,
rye, etc): fresh or frozen

(P-1254)
FRISCO BAKING COMPANY INC
621 W Avenue 26, Los Angeles
(90065-1095)
PHONE.............................323 225-6111
Aldo Pricco Jr, *CEO*
James Pricco, *President*
Ronald Perata, *Treasurer*
Mary Anne Fetter, *Vice Pres*
John Pricco, *Vice Pres*
EMP: 115
SQ FT: 18,000
SALES (est): 29.1MM **Privately Held**
WEB: www.buonaforchetta.com
SIC: 2051 Bread, all types (white, wheat,
rye, etc): fresh or frozen

(P-1255)
**FULLBLOOM BAKING COMPANY
INC**
6500 Overlake Pl, Newark (94560-1083)
PHONE.............................510 456-3638
Karen Trilevsky, *CEO*
Mike Larue, *Engineer*
Leslie Hill, *VP Finance*
Leo Carpio, *Manager*
Javier Urenda, *Manager*
▲ EMP: 286
SQ FT: 95,000
SALES (est): 55.5MM
SALES (corp-wide): 4.4B **Privately Held**
SIC: 2051 Bread, cake & related products
HQ: Aryzta Llc
6080 Center Dr Ste 900
Los Angeles CA 90045
310 417-4700

(P-1256)
FUN O CAKE
2324 4th Ave Apt 201, Los Angeles
(90018-4901)
PHONE.............................323 213-8684
Rashaad Lassiter, *Principal*
EMP: 10
SALES (est): 342.9K **Privately Held**
SIC: 2051 Bakery: wholesale or whole-
sale/retail combined

(P-1257)
FUSION FOOD FACTORY
Also Called: La Jolla Baking Co
9350 Trade Pl Ste A, San Diego
(92126-6334)
PHONE.............................858 578-8001
Steve Kwon, *President*
Bianca Juarez, *Managing Prtnr*
Jose Ramirez, *General Mgr*
Mayra Noriega, *Accounts Mgr*
EMP: 45
SQ FT: 8,000
SALES (est): 7.3MM **Privately Held**
SIC: 2051 Bread, cake & related products

(P-1258)
FUTURE FINE FOODS
2615 De La Vina St Ste 1, Santa Barbara
(93105-4144)
PHONE.............................805 682-9421
Peter Zadeh, *Owner*
EMP: 12 EST: 1998
SALES (est): 1.1MM **Privately Held**
WEB: www.futurefinefoods.com
SIC: 2051 Bread, cake & related products

(P-1259)
GALDAZA FOOD CORPORATION
Also Called: D'Lido Bakery
1147 W Washington Blvd, Los Angeles
(90015-3315)
PHONE.............................213 747-4025
Luis Galdamez, *President*
Anna Galdamez, *Vice Pres*
EMP: 25
SQ FT: 11,500
SALES (est): 2.2MM **Privately Held**
SIC: 2051 Bakery: wholesale or whole-
sale/retail combined

(P-1260)
GANPAC DISTRIBUTION LLC
7727 Formula Pl, San Diego (92121-2419)
PHONE.............................858 586-1868
Stanley Smiedt,
Julian Josephson,
Rick Ronald,
EMP: 24
SALES (est): 1.9MM **Privately Held**
SIC: 2051 Bagels, fresh or frozen

(P-1261)
GFORCE CORPORATION
1144 N Grove St, Anaheim (92806-2109)
PHONE.............................714 630-0909
Farren Mataele, *President*
▲ EMP: 16
SALES (est): 2MM **Privately Held**
SIC: 2051 Bakery: wholesale or whole-
sale/retail combined

(P-1262)
GHS CHAMPION INC
550 Waverley St, Palo Alto (94301-1720)
PHONE.............................650 326-8485
Henry Chan, *President*
Sophia Chan, *Treasurer*
Garland Chan, *Vice Pres*
EMP: 24
SALES (est): 2.5MM **Privately Held**
SIC: 2051 Bakery: wholesale or whole-
sale/retail combined

(P-1263)
**GIULIANO-PAGANO
CORPORATION**
Also Called: Giuliano's Bakery
1264 E Walnut St, Carson (90746-1319)
PHONE.............................310 537-7700
Nancy Ritmire Giuliano, *Ch of Bd*
Gregory Ritmire, *President*
EMP: 100
SQ FT: 40,000
SALES (est): 24.2MM **Privately Held**
SIC: 2051 Bakery: wholesale or whole-
sale/retail combined

(P-1264)
**GOLD COAST BAKING
COMPANY INC (PA)**
Also Called: Gold Coast Bakeries
1590 E Saint Gertrude Pl, Santa Ana
(92705-5310)
PHONE.............................714 545-2253
Rick Anderson, *CEO*

Mark Press, *President*
Terrilynn Vu, *Controller*
Daniel Stromberg, *Director*
Albina Macias, *Supervisor*
EMP: 97
SQ FT: 60,000
SALES (est): 65.7MM **Privately Held**
SIC: 2051 Bakery: wholesale or whole-
sale/retail combined

(P-1265)
GOLDEN OCTAGON INC
Also Called: San Francisco Fine Bakery
2537 Middlefield Rd, Redwood City
(94063-2825)
P.O. Box 610145 (94061-0145)
PHONE.............................650 369-8573
Greg Endom, *Business Mgr*
Daniel Huang, *CEO*
EMP: 75
SALES (est): 7.3MM **Privately Held**
SIC: 2051 Bakery: wholesale or whole-
sale/retail combined

(P-1266)
GOLDEN SHEAF BREAD CO INC
125 Hangar Way Ste 230, Watsonville
(95076-2493)
PHONE.............................831 722-0179
Joe Platin, *CEO*
EMP: 30
SQ FT: 7,500
SALES (est): 4.2MM **Privately Held**
SIC: 2051 Bakery: wholesale or whole-
sale/retail combined

(P-1267)
GOLDILOCKS CORP CALIFORNIA (PA)
Also Called: Goldilocks Bakeshop and Rest
10329 Painter Ave, Santa Fe Springs
(90670-3427)
PHONE.............................562 946-9995
Mendrei Leelin, *President*
Menard Leelin, *President*
Cecilia Leelin, *Treasurer*
EMP: 50
SQ FT: 12,000
SALES (est): 9.4MM **Privately Held**
SIC: 2051 Bread, cake & related products

(P-1268)
GRAND CASINO ON MAIN INC
3826 Main St, Culver City (90232-2620)
PHONE.............................310 253-9066
Linda Boyle, *President*
Frank Lamanna, *Vice Pres*
▲ **EMP:** 25
SALES (est): 1.5MM **Privately Held**
SIC: 2051 Bread, cake & related products

(P-1269)
GRUMA CORPORATION
Also Called: Arga's Mexican Food Products
2825 Pellissier Pl, City of Industry
(90601-1512)
PHONE.............................562 692-9502
Tom Brunner, *Branch Mgr*
EMP: 156 **Privately Held**
WEB: www.missionfoods.com
SIC: 2051 2099 Bread, all types (white,
wheat, rye, etc): fresh or frozen; food
preparations
HQ: Gruma Corporation
5601 Executive Dr Ste 800
Irving TX 75038
972 232-5000

(P-1270)
HANNAHMAX BAKING INC
14601 S Main St, Gardena (90248-1916)
PHONE.............................310 380-6778
Joanne Adirim, *CEO*
Stuart Scwartz, *President*
Ericka Gettman Karner, *Vice Pres*
EMP: 145
SQ FT: 15,000
SALES (est): 14.5MM **Privately Held**
WEB: www.hannahmax.com
SIC: 2051 Bakery: wholesale or whole-
sale/retail combined

(P-1271)
HEALTH BREADS INC
Also Called: Oasis Breads
155 Mata Way Ste 112, San Marcos
(92069-2983)
PHONE.............................760 747-7390
Jim Pickell, *President*
Dennis Walsh, *President*
Mike Valadez, *CFO*
Raul Davila, *Maintence Staff*
EMP: 25
SQ FT: 9,500
SALES (est): 4.8MM **Privately Held**
WEB: www.oasisbreads.com
SIC: 2051 Bakery: wholesale or whole-
sale/retail combined

(P-1272)
HOLSUM BAKERY INC
21540 Blythe St, Canoga Park
(91304-4910)
PHONE.............................818 884-6562
EMP: 45
SALES (corp-wide): 3.9B **Publicly Held**
SIC: 2051 Bakery: wholesale or whole-
sale/retail combined
HQ: Holsum Bakery, Inc.
2322 W Lincoln St
Phoenix AZ 85009
602 252-2351

(P-1273)
HOUSE OF BAGELS INC (PA)
1007 Washington St, San Carlos
(94070-5318)
PHONE.............................650 595-4700
Larry Chassy, *President*
EMP: 15
SALES (est): 7.4MM **Privately Held**
SIC: 2051 5461 Bread, cake & related
products; bakeries

(P-1274)
IBAKEUM INC
Also Called: Original Jack's Baking Co
8252 Whittier Blvd, Pico Rivera
(90660-2522)
P.O. Box 6411 (90661-6411)
PHONE.............................562 699-2296
Jack Avedissian, *President*
Peter Avedissian, *COO*
▼ **EMP:** 30
SQ FT: 48,000
SALES (est): 5.6MM **Privately Held**
WEB: www.lahvash.com
SIC: 2051 Bread, cake & related products

(P-1275)
JEANNINES BKG CO SANTA BARBARA (PA)
Also Called: Jeannine's Bakery
15 E Figueroa St, Santa Barbara
(93101-2781)
PHONE.............................805 966-1717
Gordon W Hardey, *CEO*
Eleanor Hardey, *President*
EMP: 34
SQ FT: 1,800
SALES (est): 1.5MM **Privately Held**
SIC: 2051 5812 Bread, cake & related
products; American restaurant

(P-1276)
LA BREA BAKERY HOLDINGS INC
14490 Catalina St, San Leandro
(94577-5516)
PHONE.............................818 742-4242
John Yamin, *CEO*
Brendan Maguire, *General Mgr*
Gary McArthur, *Engineer*
Mark Loera, *Finance*
Alex Aparicio, *Opers Staff*
▼ **EMP:** 500
SQ FT: 65,000
SALES (est): 170.9MM
SALES (corp-wide): 4.4B **Privately Held**
SIC: 2051 Bread, all types (white, wheat,
rye, etc): fresh or frozen
PA: Aryzta Ag
Talacker 41
ZUrich ZH 8001
445 834-200

(P-1277)
LARRYRON ENTERPRISES INC
Also Called: Randy's Donuts
805 W Manchester Blvd, Inglewood
(90301-1524)
PHONE.............................310 645-4707
Larry Weintraub, *President*
Ron Weintraub, *Vice Pres*
EMP: 13
SQ FT: 1,000
SALES (est): 2MM **Privately Held**
SIC: 2051 Doughnuts, except frozen

(P-1278)
LARTISAN VALLEY BAKING CO
31130 Plantation Dr, Thousand Palms
(92276-6606)
PHONE.............................760 343-2888
Fred R Estrada, *President*
Severine Estrada, *Admin Sec*
EMP: 15
SQ FT: 7,000
SALES: 1.5MM **Privately Held**
WEB: www.lartisanvbc.com
SIC: 2051 Bakery: wholesale or whole-
sale/retail combined

(P-1279)
LAS CUATROS MILPAS
856 N Mount Vernon Ave, San Bernardino
(92411-2753)
P.O. Box 7555 (92411-0555)
PHONE.............................909 885-3344
Henry Mata, *Owner*
EMP: 12
SALES (est): 635.3K **Privately Held**
WEB: www.korkyt.net
SIC: 2051 2099 Bread, cake & related
products; tortillas, fresh or refrigerated

(P-1280)
LAURAS FRENCH BAKING CO INC
722 S Oxford Ave Apt 107, Los Angeles
(90005-2996)
PHONE.............................323 585-5144
Laura Kim, *President*
Mike Ji, *Vice Pres*
Sterling Kim, *Vice Pres*
EMP: 23
SQ FT: 18,600
SALES (est): 3.9MM **Privately Held**
WEB: www.labakery.com
SIC: 2051 Bakery: wholesale or whole-
sale/retail combined

(P-1281)
LAVASH CORPORATION
Also Called: Old Fashion Lavash
2835 Newell St, Los Angeles (90039-3817)
PHONE.............................323 663-5249
Edmond Hartounin, *President*
EMP: 25
SQ FT: 10,000
SALES (est): 4.6MM **Privately Held**
SIC: 2051 Bread, cake & related products

(P-1282)
LEY GRAND FOODS CORPORATION
287 S 6th Ave, La Puente (91746-2916)
PHONE.............................626 336-2244
Frank Chen, *President*
Chien Chen, *Vice Pres*
J J Chen, *Admin Sec*
▲ **EMP:** 23
SQ FT: 4,000
SALES (est): 3.8MM **Privately Held**
SIC: 2051 Bread, cake & related products

(P-1283)
LEYVAS MEXICAN FOOD
4032 Tyler Ave, El Monte (91731-2040)
PHONE.............................626 350-6328
Octaviano Leyva, *Partner*
EMP: 20
SALES (est): 1.7MM **Privately Held**
SIC: 2051 Bakery: wholesale or whole-
sale/retail combined

(P-1284)
LIBERTY CAFE
410 Cortland Ave, San Francisco
(94110-5538)
PHONE.............................415 695-8777

Vega Freeman, *Owner*
EMP: 28
SALES (est): 2.2MM **Privately Held**
SIC: 2051 5812 Bakery: wholesale or
wholesale/retail combined; American
restaurant

(P-1285)
LITTLE BROTHERS BAKERY LLC
320 W Alondra Blvd, Gardena
(90248-2423)
PHONE.............................310 225-3790
Paul C Giuliano, *Mng Member*
Anthony S Giuliano,
Joann Giuliano,
Paul G Giuliano Jr,
Arve Johansson, *Manager*
▲ **EMP:** 65
SQ FT: 15,000
SALES (est): 13.2MM **Privately Held**
WEB: www.littlebrothersbakery.com
SIC: 2051 5149 Bakery: wholesale or
wholesale/retail combined; bakery prod-
ucts

(P-1286)
LUPITAS BAKERY INC (PA)
1848 W Florence Ave, Los Angeles
(90047-2123)
PHONE.............................323 752-2391
Able Diaz, *President*
Martha Diaz, *Admin Sec*
EMP: 18
SQ FT: 8,000
SALES (est): 1.7MM **Privately Held**
SIC: 2051 5461 Bread, all types (white,
wheat, rye, etc): fresh or frozen; bread

(P-1287)
LY BROTHERS CORPORATION (PA)
Also Called: Sugar Bowl Bakery
1963 Sabre St, Hayward (94545-1021)
PHONE.............................510 782-2118
Andrew A Ly, *President*
Tom Ly, *Chairman*
Paul Ly, *Treasurer*
Sam Ly, *Exec VP*
Binh Ly, *Vice Pres*
▲ **EMP:** 37
SQ FT: 100,000
SALES (est): 78MM **Privately Held**
WEB: www.sugarbowlbakery.com
SIC: 2051 Bakery: wholesale or whole-
sale/retail combined

(P-1288)
LY BROTHERS CORPORATION
Also Called: Sugar Bowl Bakery
20389 Corsair Blvd, Hayward
(94545-1026)
PHONE.............................510 782-2118
Andrew A Ly, *President*
EMP: 223
SALES (corp-wide): 78MM **Privately
Held**
SIC: 2051 Bakery: wholesale or whole-
sale/retail combined
PA: Ly Brothers Corporation
1963 Sabre St
Hayward CA 94545
510 782-2118

(P-1289)
MARY ANNS BAKING CO INC
8371 Carbide Ct, Sacramento
(95828-5636)
PHONE.............................916 681-7444
George A Demas, *President*
Robert Burzinski, *CFO*
John Demas, *Admin Sec*
Lori Hoffelt, *Opers Staff*
Scott Wilhite, *Maintence Staff*
EMP: 200
SQ FT: 75,000
SALES: 33MM **Privately Held**
WEB: www.maryannsbaking.com
SIC: 2051 Doughnuts, except frozen; rolls,
sweet: except frozen; rolls, bread type:
fresh or frozen

▲ = Import ▼=Export
◆ =Import/Export

(P-1290)
MIDDLE EAST BAKING CO
1380 Marsten Rd, Burlingame
(94010-2406)
PHONE..................................650 348-7200
Isaac Cohen, *Owner*
▲ EMP: 20
SALES (est): 2.6MM **Privately Held**
SIC: 2051 Bakery: wholesale or whole-
sale/retail combined

(P-1291)
MIKAWAYA (PA)
5563 Alcoa Ave, Vernon (90058-3730)
PHONE..................................323 587-5504
Jerry Bucan, *CEO*
Michael Cheng, *Info Tech Dir*
Hernan Pazmino, *Research*
Joel L Friedman, *Site Mgr*
Joel Freeman, *Manager*
▲ EMP: 30
SQ FT: 10,000
SALES (est): 14.7MM **Privately Held**
WEB: www.mikawayausa.com
SIC: 2051 2024 Cakes, pies & pastries;
ice cream & frozen desserts

(P-1292)
MONDELEZ GLOBAL LLC
Also Called: Kraft Foods
1220 Howell St, Anaheim (92805)
PHONE..................................714 634-2773
Harry Irwin, *Branch Mgr*
EMP: 22 **Publicly Held**
SIC: 2051 Bakery: wholesale or whole-
sale/retail combined
HQ: Mondelez Global Llc
3 N Pkwy Ste 300
Deerfield IL 60015
847 943-4000

(P-1293)
MRS REDDS PIE CO INC
150 S La Cadena Dr, Colton (92324-3416)
P.O. Box 555 (92324-0555)
PHONE..................................909 825-4800
Tom P Telliard, *President*
Nick Telliard, *Vice Pres*
EMP: 20
SQ FT: 76,030
SALES (est): 3.6MM **Privately Held**
SIC: 2051 Cakes, bakery: except frozen;
pies, bakery: except frozen; yeast goods,
sweet: except frozen

(P-1294)
NAPOLEON BAKERY INC
Also Called: Melrose Bakery
7356 Melrose Ave, Los Angeles
(90046-7527)
PHONE..................................323 651-3822
Kevin Chapchin, *President*
EMP: 80
SQ FT: 10,000
SALES (est): 18.9MM **Privately Held**
WEB: www.viennacafe.com
SIC: 2051 Bakery: wholesale or whole-
sale/retail combined

(P-1295)
**NEW YORK FROZEN FOODS
INC**
Mamma Bella Foods
5100 Rivergrade Rd, Baldwin Park
(91706-1406)
PHONE..................................626 338-3000
Bob Willist, *Branch Mgr*
EMP: 50
SALES (corp-wide): 1.2B **Publicly Held**
WEB: www.lancaster.com
SIC: 2051 Buns, bread type: fresh or
frozen
HQ: New York Frozen Foods, Inc.
25900 Fargo Ave
Bedford OH 44146
216 292-5655

(P-1296)
**NORMANDIE COUNTRY BAKERY
INC (PA)**
3022 S Cochran Ave, Los Angeles
(90016-3706)
PHONE..................................323 939-5528
Josette Leblond, *President*
▲ EMP: 21

SQ FT: 12,000
SALES (est): 3.3MM **Privately Held**
SIC: 2051 2011 Bakery: wholesale or
wholesale/retail combined; sausages from
meat slaughtered on site

(P-1297)
**NORTHS BAKERY CALIFORNIA
INC**
5430 Satsuma Ave, North Hollywood
(91601-2837)
PHONE..................................818 761-2892
Graham North, *CEO*
Karl North, *Treasurer*
Sally Walheim, *Manager*
EMP: 35
SQ FT: 35,000
SALES (est): 6.2MM **Privately Held**
SIC: 2051 Bakery: wholesale or whole-
sale/retail combined

(P-1298)
NOUSHIG INC
Also Called: Amoretti
451 Lombard St, Oxnard (93030-5143)
PHONE..................................805 983-2903
Jack Barsoumian, *CEO*
Hayop L Barsoumian, *President*
Maral Barsoumian, *Corp Secy*
▲ EMP: 50
SQ FT: 10,000
SALES (est): 10.4MM **Privately Held**
WEB: www.capriccio.com
SIC: 2051 5149 Bread, cake & related
products; soft drinks

(P-1299)
**OAKHURST INDUSTRIES INC
(PA)**
Also Called: Freund Baking
2050 S Tubeway Ave, Commerce
(90040-1624)
P.O. Box 911457, Los Angeles (90091-
1238)
PHONE..................................323 724-3000
James Freund, *President*
Jonathan Freund, *Vice Pres*
Ronald Martin, *Vice Pres*
Linda F Freund, *Admin Sec*
Will Gallardo, *Safety Mgr*
EMP: 140
SQ FT: 81,000
SALES (est): 98.3MM **Privately Held**
WEB: www.oakhurstproperties.com
SIC: 2051 5149 Buns, bread type: fresh or
frozen; rolls, bread type: fresh or frozen;
groceries & related products

(P-1300)
OC BAKING COMPANY
1960 N Glassell St, Orange (92865-4314)
PHONE..................................714 998-2253
Dean Kim, *President*
EMP: 80
SALES (est): 13MM **Privately Held**
SIC: 2051 Bakery: wholesale or whole-
sale/retail combined

(P-1301)
**OLD NEW YORK BAGEL & DELI
CO (PA)**
Also Called: Old New York Deli & Bagel Co
4972 Verdugo Way, Camarillo
(93012-8632)
PHONE..................................805 484-3354
Michael J Raimondo, *President*
Julie Raimondo, *Vice Pres*
Omar Najera, *General Mgr*
William Salinas, *Accounts Mgr*
EMP: 16
SQ FT: 2,400
SALES (est): 2.7MM **Privately Held**
WEB: www.oldnewyork.com
SIC: 2051 5812 Bakery: wholesale or
wholesale/retail combined; coffee shop

(P-1302)
**OVEN FRESH BAKERY
INCORPORATED**
23188 Foley St, Hayward (94545-1602)
PHONE..................................650 366-9201
Juanita Casillas, *President*
Jorge A Alfonso, *Treasurer*
EMP: 15
SQ FT: 18,000

SALES (est): 2MM **Privately Held**
SIC: 2051 2053 Bakery: wholesale or
wholesale/retail combined; frozen bakery
products, except bread

(P-1303)
**PAMELAS PRODUCTS
INCORPORATED**
1 Carousel Ln Ste D, Ukiah (95482-9509)
PHONE..................................707 462-6605
Pamela L Giusto, *CEO*
EMP: 85
SALES (est): 20.2MM **Privately Held**
WEB: www.pamelasproducts.com
SIC: 2051 2052 Bakery products, partially
cooked (except frozen); cookies & crack-
ers

(P-1304)
PAN-O-RAMA BAKING INC
500 Florida St, San Francisco
(94110-1415)
PHONE..................................415 522-5500
Bill Upson, *President*
Bob Mannion, *Sales Executive*
Pierre Bellevue, *Marketing Staff*
EMP: 40
SALES (est): 4.7MM **Privately Held**
WEB: www.panoramabaking.com
SIC: 2051 Bakery: wholesale or whole-
sale/retail combined

(P-1305)
PANCHOS BAKERY
1759 E Florence Ave, Los Angeles
(90001-2523)
PHONE..................................323 582-9109
Francisco Cedillo, *Owner*
EMP: 20
SQ FT: 5,000
SALES (est): 1.3MM **Privately Held**
SIC: 2051 5461 Bakery: wholesale or
wholesale/retail combined; bakeries

(P-1306)
PARIS CROISSANT LLC (PA)
Also Called: Donut King
6890 Cherry Ave, Long Beach
(90805-1719)
PHONE..................................562 630-8711
Chhean Uk,
Scott Ngov, *CFO*
▲ EMP: 20
SQ FT: 1,150
SALES (est): 3.7MM **Privately Held**
SIC: 2051 Bakery: wholesale or whole-
sale/retail combined

(P-1307)
PASTRIES BY EDIE INC
7226 Topanga Canyon Blvd, Canoga Park
(91303-1239)
PHONE..................................818 340-0203
Edie Gour, *President*
Michele Gour, *Vice Pres*
Jason Gour, *Admin Sec*
EMP: 35
SALES (est): 4.8MM **Privately Held**
WEB: www.pastriesbyedie.com
SIC: 2051 Bread, cake & related products

(P-1308)
PEDRO PALLAN
Also Called: San Antonio Bakery
344 W Rosecrans Ave, Compton
(90222-4055)
PHONE..................................310 638-1763
Salvador Martinez, *President*
EMP: 18
SQ FT: 2,400
SALES (est): 1.4MM **Privately Held**
SIC: 2051 2052 5149 5461 Sponge
goods, bakery: except frozen; cookies;
cookies; bakery products; cookies; bread

(P-1309)
PETITS PAINS & CO LP
1730 Gilbreth Rd, Burlingame
(94010-1305)
PHONE..................................650 692-6000
Alain Bourgade, *Principal*
EMP: 18
SALES (est): 3.4MM **Privately Held**
SIC: 2051 Bakery: wholesale or whole-
sale/retail combined

(P-1310)
PORTOS FOOD PRODUCT INC
2085 Garfield Ave, Commerce
(90040-1803)
PHONE..................................323 480-8400
Raul Porto, *Owner*
▲ EMP: 92
SALES (est): 8.4MM **Privately Held**
SIC: 2051 Bakery: wholesale or whole-
sale/retail combined

(P-1311)
PRINCESS BRANDY CORP (PA)
Also Called: Incredible Cheesecake
3161 Adams Ave, San Diego (92116-1638)
PHONE..................................619 563-9722
Michelle Satren, *President*
Scott Satren, *Vice Pres*
EMP: 10
SQ FT: 3,300
SALES (est): 957.8K **Privately Held**
WEB: www.incrediblecheesecake.net
SIC: 2051 5461 Cakes, bakery: except
frozen; cakes

(P-1312)
PURITAN BAKERY INC
1624 E Carson St, Carson (90745-2599)
PHONE..................................310 830-5451
Matthew R Grimes, *President*
John G Markulis, *Corp Secy*
John John Markulis, *Vice Pres*
EMP: 200
SQ FT: 60,000
SALES (est): 65.1MM **Privately Held**
SIC: 2051 Bakery products, partially
cooked (except frozen)

(P-1313)
**PYRENEES FRENCH BAKERY
INC**
717 E 21st St, Bakersfield (93305-5240)
P.O. Box 3626 (93385-3626)
PHONE..................................661 322-7159
Marianne Laxague, *President*
Juanita Laxague, *Corp Secy*
EMP: 26
SQ FT: 33,750
SALES (est): 2.6MM **Privately Held**
WEB: www.pyreneesbakery.com
SIC: 2051 5461 Bakery: wholesale or
wholesale/retail combined; bread, all
types (white, wheat, rye, etc): fresh or
frozen; bakeries

(P-1314)
QUEENS BAKERY INC (PA)
2311 Pasadena Ave, Los Angeles
(90031-2592)
PHONE..................................323 222-6447
Jack Yen, *President*
EMP: 10
SQ FT: 9,000
SALES (est): 1.6MM **Privately Held**
WEB: www.queensbakery.com
SIC: 2051 2052 Bread, all types (white,
wheat, rye, etc): fresh or frozen; cookies

(P-1315)
ROMA BAKERY INC
655 S Almaden Ave, San Jose
(95110-2999)
P.O. Box 348 (95103-0348)
PHONE..................................408 294-0123
Robert Pera, *President*
Mario Pera II, *Vice Pres*
Steven Pera, *Admin Sec*
EMP: 60
SQ FT: 15,000
SALES (est): 9.2MM **Privately Held**
SIC: 2051 Bread, all types (white, wheat,
rye, etc): fresh or frozen; rolls, bread type:
fresh or frozen

(P-1316)
ROSSMOOR PASTRIES MGT INC
2325 Redondo Ave, Signal Hill
(90755-4019)
PHONE..................................562 498-2253
Charles Feder, *CEO*
Janice Ahlgren, *Partner*
EMP: 80 EST: 2000
SALES (est): 11.3MM **Privately Held**
WEB: www.rossmoorpastries.com
SIC: 2051 Bakery: wholesale or whole-
sale/retail combined

(P-1317)
SACRAMENTO BAKING CO INC
9221 Beatty Dr, Sacramento (95826-9702)
PHONE.................................916 361-2000
Samir Elajou, *CEO*
Juma Al Ajon, *President*
Juma Elajou, *President*
Samira Al Ajon, *CEO*
EMP: 30
SQ FT: 10,000
SALES (est): 5.3MM **Privately Held**
SIC: 2051 5812 Bread, all types (white, wheat, rye, etc): fresh or frozen; pastries, e.g. danish: except frozen; cafe

(P-1318)
SARA LEE FRESH INC
5200 S Alameda St, Vernon (90058-3420)
PHONE.................................215 347-5500
Alfred Penny, *President*
Ed Penny, *President*
Barry Horner, *Info Tech Dir*
Jesus Castaneda, *Plant Mgr*
Carmen Gonzalez, *Manager*
▲ EMP: 607
SQ FT: 120,000
SALES (est): 48.8K **Privately Held**
SIC: 2051 Bread, all types (white, wheat, rye, etc): fresh or frozen; rolls, bread type: fresh or frozen; bagels, fresh or frozen
HQ: Bimbo Bakeries Usa, Inc
    255 Business Center Dr # 200
    Horsham PA 19044
    215 347-5500

(P-1319)
SCIAMBR-PASSINI FRENCH BKY INC
Also Called: Sciambra French Bakery
685 S Freeway Dr, NAPA (94558-6057)
PHONE.................................707 252-3072
Micheal Sciambra, *President*
Patricia Spears, *Treasurer*
EMP: 30
SQ FT: 8,000
SALES (est): 4.5MM **Privately Held**
SIC: 2051 Breads, rolls & buns

(P-1320)
SCONE HENGE INC
2787 Shattuck Ave, Berkeley (94705-1036)
PHONE.................................510 845-5168
June Lee, *President*
Yong Lee, *Vice Pres*
EMP: 15 EST: 1998
SALES (est): 1.4MM **Privately Held**
SIC: 2051 Bread, cake & related products

(P-1321)
SHENG-KEE BAKERY
201 S Hill Dr, Brisbane (94005-1204)
PHONE.................................415 468-3800
Mark KAO, *Owner*
▲ EMP: 61
SALES (est): 1.3MM **Privately Held**
SIC: 2051 Bakery: wholesale or wholesale/retail combined

(P-1322)
SLJ WHOLESALE LLC
Also Called: Sweet Lady Jane
13850 Del Sur St, San Fernando (91340-3440)
PHONE.................................323 662-8900
Sabrina Sin, *Principal*
Oscar Gomez, *Opers Staff*
EMP: 20
SQ FT: 7,000
SALES (est): 2.1MM **Privately Held**
SIC: 2051 2053 Cakes, bakery: except frozen; pies, bakery: except frozen; cakes, bakery: frozen; pies, bakery: frozen

(P-1323)
STANS MICHEGAAS (PA)
Also Called: Stan's San Frncsco Cheesecakes
1022 Revere Ave, San Francisco (94124-3443)
PHONE.................................415 839-8442
Stan Goldberg, *CEO*
Claudette Goldberg, *President*
EMP: 22
SQ FT: 3,600

SALES (est): 1.2MM **Privately Held**
SIC: 2051 Cakes, bakery: except frozen

(P-1324)
SUGAR FOODS CORPORATION
6190 E Slauson Ave, Commerce (90040-3010)
PHONE.................................323 727-8290
Harland Gray, *Manager*
Sherry De Keyser, *Human Resources*
EMP: 100
SALES (corp-wide): 286.3MM **Privately Held**
WEB: www.sugarfoods.com
SIC: 2051 2052 2099 Bread, cake & related products; cookies & crackers; food preparations
PA: Sugar Foods Corporation
    950 3rd Ave Fl 21
    New York NY 10022
    212 753-6900

(P-1325)
SUNRISE BAKERY
Also Called: Sunrise Bakery and Cafe
1561 Geer Rd, Turlock (95380-3200)
PHONE.................................209 632-9400
Filameh Givargis, *Owner*
Shargon Eddy, *Opers Mgr*
EMP: 12
SQ FT: 2,400
SALES (est): 986.3K **Privately Held**
SIC: 2051 Bakery: wholesale or wholesale/retail combined

(P-1326)
SWEET PRODUCTION INC
915 Terminal Way Ste B, San Carlos (94070-3224)
P.O. Box 1161 (94070-1161)
PHONE.................................650 631-7777
Doreen Chin, *President*
▲ EMP: 64 EST: 2008
SALES (est): 8.9MM **Privately Held**
SIC: 2051 Bakery: wholesale or wholesale/retail combined

(P-1327)
SWEETIE PIES LLC
520 Main St, NAPA (94559-3353)
PHONE.................................707 257-7280
Toni M Chiappetta,
EMP: 19
SQ FT: 600
SALES (est): 3.3MM **Privately Held**
WEB: www.sweetiepies.com
SIC: 2051 5812 Bakery: wholesale or wholesale/retail combined; eating places

(P-1328)
SWEETS 4JC LLC
Also Called: Little Bliss Cakery
5741 Oak Creek Pl, Granite Bay (95746-9621)
PHONE.................................916 791-6453
James Calton,
Wendi Calton,
EMP: 10
SQ FT: 925
SALES (est): 722.9K **Privately Held**
SIC: 2051 Cakes, bakery: except frozen

(P-1329)
TABLE DE FRANCE INC
2020 S Haven Ave, Ontario (91761-0735)
PHONE.................................909 923-5205
Herve Le Bayon, *President*
Philip Le Bayon, *CFO*
Teresa Aguirre, *General Mgr*
Erwan Lebayon, *Marketing Staff*
EMP: 12
SQ FT: 30,000
SALES (est): 1.9MM **Privately Held**
SIC: 2051 Bakery: wholesale or wholesale/retail combined

(P-1330)
TAHOE HOUSE INC
625 W Lake Blvd, Tahoe City (96145)
P.O. Box 1899 (96145-1899)
PHONE.................................530 583-1377
Barbara Vogt, *President*
Caroline Vogt, *Treasurer*
Helen Vogt, *Vice Pres*
▲ EMP: 12
SQ FT: 6,800

SALES: 1MM **Privately Held**
WEB: www.tahoe-house.com
SIC: 2051 Bakery: wholesale or wholesale/retail combined

(P-1331)
TANBIL BAKERY INC
Also Called: Tanbit Bakery
8150 Garvey Ave Ste 104, Rosemead (91770-2473)
PHONE.................................626 280-2638
Chia Fu Fang, *President*
Wang A Hsueh Fang, *Admin Sec*
▲ EMP: 11
SALES (est): 780.5K **Privately Held**
SIC: 2051 Bakery: wholesale or wholesale/retail combined

(P-1332)
TARTINE LP
Also Called: Tartine Bakery & Cafe
600 Guerrero St, San Francisco (94110-1528)
PHONE.................................415 487-2600
Frederic Soulies, *CEO*
Elisabeth Prueitt, *Principal*
Chad Robertson, *Principal*
Josh Drew, *Director*
EMP: 45
SALES (est): 4.8MM **Privately Held**
SIC: 2051 5812 5921 Breads, rolls & buns; cakes, pies & pastries; cafe; wine & beer

(P-1333)
THE FRENCH PATISSERIE INC
Also Called: Looka Patisserie
1080 Palmetto Ave, Pacifica (94044-2216)
PHONE.................................650 738-4990
Marta Spasic, *President*
Frank Spasic, *Vice Pres*
Joann Leong, *Technology*
◆ EMP: 90
SQ FT: 34,000
SALES (est): 18.2MM **Privately Held**
WEB: www.frenchpatisserie.com
SIC: 2051 Bread, cake & related products

(P-1334)
TOUFIC INC
Also Called: La Boulangerie
2324 Grand Canal Blvd # 1, Stockton (95207-8214)
PHONE.................................209 478-4780
Raymond Bitar, *President*
John Bitar, *Corp Secy*
Allen Bitar, *Officer*
EMP: 14
SQ FT: 3,000
SALES (est): 840K **Privately Held**
WEB: www.toufic.com
SIC: 2051 5812 Bread, cake & related products; eating places

(P-1335)
UNITED BAKERY INC
727 S Flower St, Burbank (91502-2014)
PHONE.................................818 843-1892
Daniel Sanchez, *President*
Mark Sanchez, *Treasurer*
EMP: 35
SQ FT: 20,000
SALES: 2.3MM **Privately Held**
WEB: www.unitedbakery.com
SIC: 2051 Bakery: wholesale or wholesale/retail combined

(P-1336)
VALLEY LAHVOSH BAKING CO INC
502 M St, Fresno (93721-3013)
PHONE.................................559 485-2700
Janet F Saghatelian, *President*
Agnes Wilson, *Vice Pres*
Lori Miller, *Admin Asst*
Rebecca Cline, *Administration*
Danny Giosa, *Safety Mgr*
▲ EMP: 30
SQ FT: 27,000
SALES (est): 7.6MM **Privately Held**
WEB: www.valleylahvosh.com
SIC: 2051 5461 Bread, all types (white, wheat, rye, etc): fresh or frozen; breads, rolls & buns; bread

(P-1337)
VENICE BAKING CO
134 Main St, El Segundo (90245-3801)
PHONE.................................310 322-7357
James N Desisto, *CEO*
Larry De Sisto, *President*
Craig Gebhart, *Project Mgr*
Harrison Billig, *Research*
Phil Alva, *Purch Mgr*
EMP: 40 EST: 1959
SQ FT: 35,000
SALES (est): 8.7MM **Privately Held**
SIC: 2051 5149 Bread, all types (white, wheat, rye, etc): fresh or frozen; baking supplies; pizza supplies

(P-1338)
VITAL VITTLES BAKERY INC
Also Called: Schwin and Tran Mill & Bakery
2810 San Pablo Ave, Berkeley (94702-2204)
PHONE.................................510 644-2022
Binh Tran, *President*
EMP: 18
SQ FT: 2,424
SALES (est): 1.2MM **Privately Held**
SIC: 2051 2052 5461 Bakery: wholesale or wholesale/retail combined; cookies & crackers; bakeries

(P-1339)
WESTERN BAGEL BAKING CORP (PA)
7814 Sepulveda Blvd, Van Nuys (91405-1062)
PHONE.................................818 786-5847
Steven Ustin, *President*
Debbie Simonowitz, *Office Mgr*
Mark Weisner, *Info Tech Mgr*
Elias Carvajal, *Technology*
David Beltran, *Controller*
▼ EMP: 225
SQ FT: 23,500
SALES: 56.6MM **Privately Held**
WEB: www.westernbagel.com
SIC: 2051 5461 Bagels, fresh or frozen; bagels

(P-1340)
WESTERN BAGEL BAKING CORP
21749 Ventura Blvd, Woodland Hills (91364-1835)
PHONE.................................818 887-5451
Tim Brennen, *Principal*
EMP: 35
SALES (corp-wide): 56.6MM **Privately Held**
WEB: www.westernbagel.com
SIC: 2051 5461 Bagels, fresh or frozen; bagels
PA: Western Bagel Baking Corp
    7814 Sepulveda Blvd
    Van Nuys CA 91405
    818 786-5847

(P-1341)
WESTERN BAGEL BAKING CORP
Also Called: Western Bagel Too
11628 Santa Monica Blvd # 12, Los Angeles (90025-2950)
PHONE.................................310 479-4823
Fax: 310 826-2383
EMP: 20
SALES (corp-wide): 39.6MM **Privately Held**
SIC: 2051
PA: Western Bagel Baking Corp
    7814 Sepulveda Blvd
    Van Nuys CA 91405
    818 786-5847

(P-1342)
WESTLAKE BAKERY INC
Also Called: Bread Basket
7099 Mission St, Daly City (94014-2253)
PHONE.................................650 994-7741
Jaime Cavan, *President*
Nelly Cavan, *Vice Pres*
EMP: 15
SQ FT: 5,000
SALES (est): 1.8MM **Privately Held**
SIC: 2051 5461 Bakery: wholesale or wholesale/retail combined; bakeries

(P-1343)
WHOLESOME HARVEST BAKING LLC
Also Called: Maple Leaf Bakery
3200 Regatta Blvd Ste G, Richmond (94804-6401)
PHONE..................510 231-7200
Kevin Kamkar, *Branch Mgr*
EMP: 200 **Privately Held**
SIC: 2051 Bakery: wholesale or wholesale/retail combined
HQ: Wholesome Harvest Baking, Llc
8550 W Bryn Mawr Ave # 10
Chicago IL 60631
800 550-6810

(P-1344)
WHOLESOME HARVEST BAKING LLC
Also Called: Pioneer French Bakery
2701 Statham Blvd, Oxnard (93033-3920)
PHONE..................805 487-5191
Donald Hall, *Plant Mgr*
EMP: 150 **Privately Held**
WEB: www.mapleleaffoodsusa.com
SIC: 2051 Breads, rolls & buns; bread, all types (white, wheat, rye, etc): fresh or frozen
HQ: Wholesome Harvest Baking, Llc
8550 W Bryn Mawr Ave # 10
Chicago IL 60631
800 550-6810

(P-1345)
WINDMILL CORPORATION
Also Called: Wedemeyer Bakery
314 Harbor Way, South San Francisco (94080-6900)
PHONE..................650 873-1000
Larry Strain, *President*
EMP: 25 **EST**: 2004
SALES (est): 4.3MM **Privately Held**
SIC: 2051 5461 5149 Bread, all types (white, wheat, rye, etc): fresh or frozen; rolls, bread type: fresh or frozen; bakeries; groceries & related products

(P-1346)
XANADU FRENCH BAKERY
Also Called: Xanadu Bakery
1028 Coast Village Rd A, Santa Barbara (93108-0718)
PHONE..................805 845-7232
Amiran Amiri, *Partner*
Ghobad Amiri, *Partner*
Hengameh Amiri, *Partner*
EMP: 29
SALES (est): 2.4MM **Privately Held**
SIC: 2051 2099 Bakery: wholesale or wholesale/retail combined; food preparations

---

2052 Cookies & Crackers

(P-1347)
AMAYS BAKERY & NOODLE CO INC (PA)
837 E Commercial St, Los Angeles (90012-3413)
PHONE..................213 626-2713
Kee Hom, *CEO*
▲ EMP: 63
SQ FT: 20,000
SALES (est): 12.1MM **Privately Held**
WEB: www.amaysbakery.com
SIC: 2052 2098 Cookies; noodles (e.g. egg, plain & water), dry

(P-1348)
ARBO INC
Also Called: Joy of Cookies
1205 Stanford Ave, Oakland (94608-2621)
P.O. Box 8688 (94662-0688)
PHONE..................510 658-3700
Adele Connor, *President*
Joe Connor, *Vice Pres*
EMP: 21
SQ FT: 5,400
SALES (est): 2.5MM **Privately Held**
WEB: www.suncakes.net
SIC: 2052 Cookies

(P-1349)
ARYZTA HOLDINGS IV LLC (HQ)
6080 Center Dr Ste 900, Los Angeles (90045-9226)
PHONE..................310 417-4700
John Yamin, *CEO*
Ronan Minahan, *COO*
Robin Jones, *CFO*
▼ EMP: 235
SALES: 1.7B
SALES (corp-wide): 4.4B **Privately Held**
SIC: 2052 2053 2045 2051 Cookies & crackers; cookies; frozen bakery products, except bread; bread & bread type roll mixes: from purchased flour; breads, rolls & buns
PA: Aryzta Ag
Talacker 41
ZUrich ZH 8001
445 834-200

(P-1350)
ARYZTA LLC
Also Called: Fresh Start Bakeries
1220 S Baker Ave, Ontario (91761-7739)
P.O. Box 1283, Alhambra (91802-1283)
PHONE..................909 472-3500
Rob Crawford, *General Mgr*
EMP: 197
SALES (corp-wide): 4.4B **Privately Held**
WEB: www.fsbglobal.net
SIC: 2052 Cookies
HQ: Aryzta Llc
6080 Center Dr Ste 900
Los Angeles CA 90045
310 417-4700

(P-1351)
ARYZTA LLC
2350 Pullman St, Santa Ana (92705-5507)
PHONE..................949 261-7400
Zac Morris, *Branch Mgr*
Nancy Kirksey, *Vice Pres*
Robert Mina, *General Mgr*
EMP: 115
SALES (corp-wide): 4.4B **Privately Held**
SIC: 2052 Cookies
HQ: Aryzta Llc
6080 Center Dr Ste 900
Los Angeles CA 90045
310 417-4700

(P-1352)
ARYZTA LLC (DH)
6080 Center Dr Ste 900, Los Angeles (90045-9226)
PHONE..................310 417-4700
Dave Johnson, *Officer*
Debra Gray, *President*
Eric Robinson, *President*
Suzanne Wooley, *President*
Andrew Brimacombe, *Officer*
◆ EMP: 235 **EST**: 1977
SQ FT: 90,000
SALES: 1.6B
SALES (corp-wide): 4.4B **Privately Held**
WEB: www.spunkmeyer.com
SIC: 2052 2053 2051 Cookies; frozen bakery products, except bread; cakes, pies & pastries; breads, rolls & buns

(P-1353)
ARYZTA US HOLDINGS I CORP
14490 Catalina St, San Leandro (94577-5516)
PHONE..................800 938-1900
John Yamin, *CEO*
Brian Younglove, *President*
Ronan Minahan, *COO*
Robin Jones, *CFO*
Dan Bailey, *Senior VP*
EMP: 9500
SALES (est): 228.8MM
SALES (corp-wide): 4.4B **Privately Held**
SIC: 2052 2053 2051 Cookies; frozen bakery products, except bread; cakes, pies & pastries
PA: Aryzta Ag
Talacker 41
ZUrich ZH 8001
445 834-200

(P-1354)
BISCOMERICA CORP
565 W Slover Ave, Rialto (92377)
P.O. Box 1070 (92377-1070)
PHONE..................909 877-5997
Nadi Soltan, *Ch of Bd*
Ayad Fargo, *President*
Joanne Tomlinson, *Admin Asst*
Brian Hotchkiss, *Engineer*
Angelica Lopez, *Traffic Mgr*
▲ EMP: 250
SQ FT: 250,000
SALES (est): 65.7MM **Privately Held**
WEB: www.biscomerica.com
SIC: 2052 2064 Cookies & crackers; candy & other confectionery products

(P-1355)
BLOOMFIELD BAKERS
10711 Bloomfield St, Los Alamitos (90720-2503)
PHONE..................626 610-2253
William R Ross, *General Ptnr*
Maggie Acquisition Corp, *General Ptnr*
Aiko Acquisition Corp, *Partner*
Gary Marx, *Branch Mgr*
▼ EMP: 600
SQ FT: 75,000
SALES (est): 123.3MM
SALES (corp-wide): 6.3B **Publicly Held**
SIC: 2052 2064 Cookies; candy & other confectionery products
HQ: Treehouse Private Brands, Inc.
800 Market St Ste 2600
Saint Louis MO 63101

(P-1356)
BREAD LOS ANGELES
1527 Beach St, Montebello (90640-5431)
PHONE..................323 201-3953
Vachik M Elchibegian,
Melecio Espain, *Opers Mgr*
Beatrice M Elchibegian,
▲ EMP: 40
SALES (est): 8.2MM **Privately Held**
SIC: 2052 2051 Cookies & crackers; bread, cake & related products

(P-1357)
BRICKSTONE GROUP INC
4722 San Fernando Rd, Glendale (91204-1841)
PHONE..................818 242-8569
Isaac Kaplan, *CEO*
EMP: 11
SQ FT: 2,571
SALES (est): 432.2K **Privately Held**
SIC: 2052 Cookies

(P-1358)
BROWNIE BAKER INC
4870 W Jacquelyn Ave, Fresno (93722-5027)
PHONE..................559 277-7070
Dennis Perkins, *CEO*
Tom Quisenberry, *COO*
Glenn Jones, *Vice Pres*
Bob Ross, *CTO*
Ryan Perkins, *Research*
▲ EMP: 70 **EST**: 1979
SQ FT: 30,000
SALES (est): 14.3MM **Privately Held**
WEB: www.brownbaker.com
SIC: 2052 2051 Cookies; bread, cake & related products

(P-1359)
D F STAUFFER BISCUIT CO INC
Laguna Cookie Company
4041 W Garry Ave, Santa Ana (92704-6315)
PHONE..................714 546-6855
Albert Ovalle, *Plant Mgr*
Eddie Wallace, *Manager*
EMP: 50
SALES (corp-wide): 11.6B **Privately Held**
WEB: www.stauffers.net
SIC: 2052 Cookies
HQ: D F Stauffer Biscuit Co Inc
360 S Belmont St
York PA 17403
717 815-4600

(P-1360)
DAWN FOOD PRODUCTS INC
2455 Tenaya Dr, Modesto (95354-3918)
PHONE..................517 789-4400
Ty Hackman, *Manager*
M Ewald, *Sales Mgr*
EMP: 15
SALES (corp-wide): 1.6B **Privately Held**
WEB: www.dawnfoods.com
SIC: 2052 Bakery products, dry
HQ: Dawn Food Products, Inc.
3333 Sargent Rd
Jackson MI 49201

(P-1361)
DEEP FOODS INC
4000 Whipple Rd, Union City (94587-1506)
PHONE..................510 475-1900
Archit Amin, *Branch Mgr*
EMP: 11
SALES (corp-wide): 45.3MM **Privately Held**
WEB: www.deepfoods.com
SIC: 2052 Bakery products, dry; crackers, dry
PA: Deep Foods Inc
1090 Springfield Rd Ste 1
Union NJ 07083
908 810-7500

(P-1362)
DIBELLA BAKING COMPANY INC
3524 Seagate Way Ste 110, Oceanside (92056-2673)
PHONE..................951 797-4144
Edward Ragone, *Ch of Bd*
Dennis M Dice, *President*
Stefan Fischer, *Senior VP*
Joyce Ragone, *Vice Pres*
Angie Pilato, *Administration*
EMP: 65
SQ FT: 25,000
SALES: 2.5MM **Privately Held**
SIC: 2052 Cookies

(P-1363)
ELEMENTS FOOD GROUP INC
5560 Brooks St, Montclair (91763-4522)
PHONE..................909 983-2011
Wayne Sorensen, *President*
EMP: 60
SQ FT: 23,000
SALES (est): 12MM **Privately Held**
SIC: 2052 2038 Bakery products, dry; breakfasts, frozen & packaged; dinners, frozen & packaged; lunches, frozen & packaged

(P-1364)
FOWLIE ENTERPRISES INC
Also Called: Pretzelmaker
1143 Fern Oaks Dr, Santa Paula (93060-1203)
PHONE..................805 583-2800
William Fowlie, *CEO*
Donna Fowlie, *President*
EMP: 25
SALES (est): 1.6MM **Privately Held**
SIC: 2052 2096

(P-1365)
INTERNTNAL DESSERTS DELICACIES
Also Called: Cookie Lovers
743 Milford St, Glendale (91203-1570)
PHONE..................818 549-0056
Robbie Jacobs, *President*
Bonnie Jacobs, *Vice Pres*
Jeffrey Jacobs, *Admin Sec*
EMP: 16
SQ FT: 4,000
SALES (est): 2.4MM **Privately Held**
SIC: 2052 Cookies

(P-1366)
J & J SNACK FOODS CORP CAL (HQ)
5353 S Downey Rd, Vernon (90058-3725)
PHONE..................323 581-0171
Gerald B Shreiber, *CEO*
Dennis Moore, *Vice Pres*
Leong Tan, *Controller*
Margaret Sewell, *Human Res Mgr*

Megan O'Neil, *Supervisor*
◆ **EMP:** 203
SQ FT: 132,000
SALES (est): 117.5MM
SALES (corp-wide): 1B **Publicly Held**
WEB: www.jjsnack.com
SIC: 2052 5149 Pretzels; cookies
PA: J & J Snack Foods Corp.
6000 Central Hwy
Pennsauken NJ 08109
856 665-9533

(P-1367)
JUST OFF MELROSE INC
1196 Montalvo Way, Palm Springs
(92262-5441)
PHONE....................714 533-4566
Brandon Tesmer, *President*
Mary Tesmer, *Agent*
EMP: 40
SQ FT: 12,000
SALES (est): 6.2MM **Privately Held**
WEB: www.justoffmelrose.com
SIC: 2052 2051 Crackers, dry; cookies;
bakery products, dry; bread, cake & re-
lated products

(P-1368)
KEEBLER COMPANY
14000 183rd St, La Palma (90623-1010)
PHONE....................714 228-1555
Bob Cox, *Manager*
Alex Menjivar, *Manager*
EMP: 60
SALES (corp-wide): 12.9B **Publicly Held**
WEB: www.keebler.com
SIC: 2052 2051
HQ: Keebler Company
1 Kellogg Sq
Battle Creek MI 49017
269 961-2000

(P-1369)
LAGUNA COOKIE COMPANY INC
4041 W Garry Ave, Santa Ana
(92704-6315)
PHONE....................714 546-6855
Takeshi Izumi, *CEO*
Rod Sanchez, *Manager*
EMP: 100
SQ FT: 55,000
SALES (est): 17.9MM
SALES (corp-wide): 11.6B **Privately Held**
WEB: www.stauffers.net
SIC: 2052 Cookies & crackers
HQ: D F Stauffer Biscuit Co Inc
360 S Belmont St
York PA 17403
717 815-4600

(P-1370)
MARTHA OLSONS GREAT FOODS INC
Also Called: Martha's All Natural
4407 Giannecchini Ln, Stockton
(95206-3954)
PHONE....................209 234-5935
Michael Brown, *CEO*
Roylene Brown, *CFO*
EMP: 10
SQ FT: 7,250
SALES (est): 1.4MM **Privately Held**
WEB: www.marthasallnatural.com
SIC: 2052 2034 2035 Bakery products,
dry; soup mixes; pickles, sauces & salad
dressings

(P-1371)
MICROBIOTIC HEALTH FOODS INC
Also Called: Nana's Cookie Company
4901 Morena Blvd Ste 403, San Diego
(92117-7305)
PHONE....................858 273-5775
Miriam Diamond, *President*
Janet Nager, *VP Sales*
EMP: 14
SQ FT: 3,000
SALES (est): 1.9MM **Privately Held**
SIC: 2052 Cookies

(P-1372)
MURRAY BISCUIT COMPANY LLC
Also Called: Famous Amos Chclat Chip
Cookie
5250 Claremont Ave, Stockton
(95207-5700)
PHONE....................209 472-3718
Chris Lopes, *Branch Mgr*
EMP: 23
SALES (corp-wide): 12.9B **Publicly Held**
WEB: www.littlebrownie.com
SIC: 2052 Cookies
HQ: Murray Biscuit Company, L.L.C.
1550 Marvin Griffin Rd
Augusta GA 30906
706 798-8600

(P-1373)
PADERIA LLC
18279 Brookhurst St Ste 1, Fountain Valley
(92708-6750)
PHONE....................949 478-5273
Nathan Vuong,
EMP: 14
SALES (est): 993.8K **Privately Held**
SIC: 2052 Cookies & crackers

(P-1374)
PAK GROUP LLC
Also Called: Dellarise
236 N Chester Ave Ste 200, Pasadena
(91106-5166)
PHONE....................626 316-6555
Walter Postelwait, *President*
Khosrow Pakravan,
▲ **EMP:** 21
SQ FT: 6,200
SALES (est): 3.2MM
SALES (corp-wide): 538.2K **Privately Held**
SIC: 2052 2099 5149 Bakery products,
dry; food preparations; yeast
PA: Tech Us Corp
236 N Chester Ave Ste 200
Pasadena CA 91106
626 316-6555

(P-1375)
PHENIX GOURMET LLC
Also Called: Monaco Baking Company
4225 N Palm St, Fullerton (92835-1045)
PHONE....................562 404-5028
Philip Moreau, *Mng Member*
Stephanie Cigana, *President*
Timothy Dean,
Daniel Maguire,
John O'Brien,
▲ **EMP:** 135
SALES (est): 20.5MM **Privately Held**
SIC: 2052 Cookies

(P-1376)
PRESIDENT GLOBAL CORPORATION (HQ)
6965 Aragon Cir, Buena Park (90620-1118)
PHONE....................714 994-2990
Ping Chih Wu, *President*
▲ **EMP:** 10
SQ FT: 37,000
SALES (est): 34.2MM
SALES (corp-wide): 13.2B **Privately Held**
SIC: 2052 5149 2099 Cookies & crack-
ers; groceries & related products; food
preparations
PA: Uni-President Enterprises Corp.
301, Jhongjheng Rd.,
Tainan City 71001
625 321-21

(P-1377)
RENAISSANCE FOOD INC
Also Called: Renaissance Pastry
14540 Friar St, Van Nuys (91411-2308)
PHONE....................818 778-6230
Eric Khayam, *President*
EMP: 11
SALES (est): 1.1MM **Privately Held**
WEB: www.renaissancefood.com
SIC: 2052 Cookies

(P-1378)
SANTA BRBARA ESSNTIAL FODS LLC
233 E Gutierrez St, Santa Barbara
(93101-1704)
PHONE....................805 965-1948
Peter Kayfetz-Gaum, *CEO*
Janet Kayfetz-Gaum,
EMP: 35
SQ FT: 2,000
SALES (est): 6.4MM **Privately Held**
SIC: 2052 Pretzels

(P-1379)
SHENG-KEE OF CALIFORNIA INC
Also Called: Wawa
10961 N Wolfe Rd, Cupertino
(95014-0617)
PHONE....................408 865-6000
Hsaio Y KAO, *Manager*
EMP: 20
SALES (corp-wide): 27.8MM **Privately Held**
WEB: www.shengkee.com
SIC: 2052 Bakery products, dry; cones, ice
cream; biscuits, dry
PA: Sheng-Kee Of California, Inc.
1941 Irving St
San Francisco CA 94122
415 564-4800

(P-1380)
SONORA MILLS FOODS INC (PA)
Also Called: Pop Chips
3064 E Maria St, E Rncho Dmngz
(90221-5804)
PHONE....................310 639-5333
Patrick Turpin, *CEO*
Martin Basch, *Vice Pres*
▲ **EMP:** 200
SQ FT: 80,000
SALES (est): 60.5MM **Privately Held**
WEB: www.sonoramills.com
SIC: 2052 Rice cakes

(P-1381)
SOOJIANS INC
Also Called: AK Mak Bakeries Division
89 Academy Ave, Sanger (93657-2104)
PHONE....................559 875-5511
Manoog Soojian, *President*
Hagop Soojian, *Vice Pres*
Terstzan Soojian, *Prdtn Mgr*
EMP: 30
SQ FT: 8,000
SALES (est): 4.8MM **Privately Held**
SIC: 2052 5046 Crackers, dry; bakery
equipment & supplies

(P-1382)
SOUTH COAST BAKING LLC (HQ)
Also Called: South Coast Baking Co.
1722 Kettering, Irvine (92614-5616)
PHONE....................949 851-9654
Kent Hayden, *CEO*
Rick Ptak, *COO*
James Bergeson, *CFO*
Carole Ann Sushkoff, *Controller*
◆ **EMP:** 55
SQ FT: 22,500
SALES: 110.3MM
SALES (corp-wide): 172.8MM **Privately Held**
SIC: 2052 5149 Cookies; cookies
PA: Le Petit Pain Holdings, Llc
676 N Michigan Ave
Chicago IL 60611
312 981-3770

(P-1383)
TIMKEV INTERNATIONAL INC
9050 Rosecrans Ave, Bellflower
(90706-2038)
PHONE....................562 232-1691
Jeong Hwan RHO, *CEO*
▲ **EMP:** 10
SALES (est): 1.1MM **Privately Held**
SIC: 2052 Cookies & crackers

(P-1384)
TRADITIONAL BAKING INC
2575 S Willow Ave, Bloomington
(92316-3256)
PHONE....................909 877-8471
Kathleen V Cunningham, *President*
▲ **EMP:** 75
SQ FT: 60,000
SALES (est): 19.2MM **Privately Held**
WEB: www.traditionalbaking.com
SIC: 2052 Cookies

(P-1385)
TRIPLE C FOODS INC
Also Called: Golden Phoenix Bakery
1465 Factor Ave, San Leandro
(94577-5615)
PHONE....................510 357-8880
Tom Chua, *President*
Kim Chua, *Vice Pres*
Aaron Chua, *Office Mgr*
EMP: 80
SQ FT: 65,000
SALES (est): 9.7MM **Privately Held**
SIC: 2052 Cookies

(P-1386)
UMEYA INC
Also Called: Umeya Rice Cake Co
414 Crocker St, Los Angeles (90013-2115)
P.O. Box 1071, Glendale (91209-1071)
PHONE....................213 626-8341
Tak Hamano, *President*
Bunji Hayata, *Corp Secy*
▲ **EMP:** 30 **EST:** 1938
SQ FT: 16,000
SALES (est): 3.9MM **Privately Held**
WEB: www.umeyaricecake.com
SIC: 2052 Cookies; crackers, dry

(P-1387)
UTBBB INC
10711 Bloomfield St, Los Alamitos
(90720-2503)
PHONE....................562 594-4411
Gary Marks, *CEO*
William R Ross, *President*
Gene Kester, *Principal*
◆ **EMP:** 200
SQ FT: 1,000
SALES (est): 15.9MM
SALES (corp-wide): 6.3B **Publicly Held**
WEB: www.bloomfieldbakers.com
SIC: 2052 5141 Cookies & crackers; food
brokers
HQ: Treehouse Private Brands, Inc.
800 Market St Ste 2600
Saint Louis MO 63101

(P-1388)
WETZELS PRETZELS LLC (HQ)
35 Hugus Aly Ste 300, Pasadena
(91103-3648)
PHONE....................626 432-6900
Bill Phelps, *CEO*
Doug Flaig, *Vice Pres*
Vincent Montanelli, *Vice Pres*
Don Braxton, *Regional Mgr*
Anthony Guzman, *Accountant*
▼ **EMP:** 10
SQ FT: 4,000
SALES (est): 18MM
SALES (corp-wide): 24.4MM **Privately Held**
SIC: 2052 5461 6794 Pretzels; pretzels;
franchises, selling or licensing
PA: Centeroak Partners Llc
100 Crescent Ct Ste 1700
Dallas TX 75201
214 301-4201

2053 Frozen Bakery Prdts

(P-1389)
ASTROCHEF INC
Also Called: Pegasus Foods
1111 Mateo St, Los Angeles (90021-1717)
P.O. Box 86404 (90086-0404)
PHONE....................213 627-9860
Jim Zaferis, *CEO*
Evangelos Ambatielos, *President*
Stephen Castanedo, *General Mgr*
Steve Koufoudakis, *Manager*

EMP: 55
SQ FT: 60,000
SALES (est): 20.7MM **Privately Held**
SIC: 2053 Frozen bakery products, except bread

(P-1390)
BENNETTS BAKING COMPANY
Also Called: Bennett's Bakery
2530 Tesla Way, Sacramento (95825-1912)
PHONE......................916 481-3349
Michael Bennett, *President*
EMP: 15
SQ FT: 3,000
SALES: 2MM **Privately Held**
SIC: 2053 Frozen bakery products, except bread

(P-1391)
CHRISTINE MILNE
Also Called: Upper Crust
1133 Francisco Blvd E H, San Rafael (94901-5426)
PHONE......................415 485-5658
Christine Milne, *Owner*
EMP: 10
SQ FT: 3,800
SALES (est): 860.6K **Privately Held**
WEB: www.christinespies.com
SIC: 2053 2051 Pies, frozen; bread, cake & related products

(P-1392)
COPENHAGEN ACQUISITION LLC (PA)
11400 Olypc Blvd Ste 1400, Los Angeles (90064)
PHONE......................310 899-9200
John O'Hare, *Managing Prtnr*
EMP: 76 EST: 2008
SALES (est): 2.8MM **Privately Held**
SIC: 2053 Frozen bakery products, except bread

(P-1393)
DEBBIES DELIGHTS INC
233 E Gutierrez St, Santa Barbara (93101-1704)
PHONE......................805 966-3504
Peter Gaum, *CEO*
EMP: 20
SALES: 1.2MM **Privately Held**
SIC: 2053 Buns, sweet: frozen

(P-1394)
GALAXY DESSERTS
1100 Marina Way S Ste D, Richmond (94804-3727)
PHONE......................510 439-3160
Paul Levitan, *CEO*
Jean-Yves Charon, *Vice Pres*
Rohana Stone Rice, *Controller*
▲ **EMP:** 160
SQ FT: 56,000
SALES (est): 37.7MM
SALES (corp-wide): 5.9MM **Privately Held**
WEB: www.galaxydesserts.com
SIC: 2053 Frozen bakery products, except bread
HQ: Brioche Pasquier Cerqueux

　　Les Cerqueux 49360
　　241 295-400

(P-1395)
HC BRILL
Also Called: Telco Food
2111 W Valley Blvd, Colton (92324-1814)
PHONE......................909 825-7343
Michelle Stirling, *Principal*
EMP: 500
SALES (corp-wide): 962.9K **Privately Held**
WEB: www.bestbrandscorp.com
SIC: 2053 2051 Pies, bakery: frozen; bread, cake & related products
PA: H.C. Brill
　　2003 S Bibb Dr
　　Tucker GA
　　770 723-3449

(P-1396)
HORIZON SNACK FOODS INC
Also Called: Cutie Pie Snack Pies
197 Darcy Pkwy, Lathrop (95330-9222)
PHONE......................925 373-7700
William D Reynolds, *President*
Andrew Kunkler, *CFO*
Lee Rucker, *CFO*
Betty Blakely, *Manager*
EMP: 62
SQ FT: 9,000
SALES (est): 14.9MM
SALES (corp-wide): 84.4MM **Privately Held**
WEB: www.cutiepie.com
SIC: 2053 Pies, bakery: frozen
PA: Horizon Holdings Llc
　　1 Bush St Ste 650
　　San Francisco CA 94104
　　415 788-2000

(P-1397)
INTERNATIONALLY DELICIOUS INC (PA)
Also Called: Masterpiece Cookies
174 Lawrence Dr Ste J, Livermore (94551-5150)
PHONE......................925 426-6155
Steven Wechler, *President*
Alan Brooks, *Treasurer*
Renee Stocks, *Admin Sec*
EMP: 20 EST: 1996
SALES (est): 4.7MM **Privately Held**
SIC: 2053 Frozen bakery products, except bread

(P-1398)
MARYS COUNTRY KITCHEN
Also Called: Malibu Kitchen
3900 Cross Creek Rd Ste 3, Malibu (90265-4962)
PHONE......................310 456-7845
William Miller, *Owner*
EMP: 15
SALES (est): 1.6MM **Privately Held**
SIC: 2053 Pies, bakery: frozen

(P-1399)
NATURAL DECADENCE LLC
3750 Harris St, Eureka (95503-4854)
PHONE......................707 444-2629
Milia Lando, *Principal*
Rosa Dixon, *Vice Pres*
EMP: 12
SALES (est): 1.1MM **Privately Held**
SIC: 2053 2052 Pies, bakery: frozen; cookies

(P-1400)
OPERA PATISSERIE FINES INC (PA)
8480 Redwood Creek Ln, San Diego (92126-1067)
PHONE......................858 536-5800
Diane Cahez, *CEO*
Thierry Cahez, *President*
Rosemary Hollingsworth, *Vice Pres*
Vincent Garcia, *Admin Sec*
Lauren Gehrke, *Technology*
EMP: 45
SQ FT: 9,000
SALES: 3.5MM **Privately Held**
WEB: www.operapatisserie.com
SIC: 2053 5812 Pastries (danish): frozen; cafe

2062 Sugar, Cane Refining

(P-1401)
C&H SUGAR COMPANY INC
Also Called: C&H Sugar
830 Loring Ave, Crockett (94525-1104)
PHONE......................510 787-2121
Antonio L Contreras, *CEO*
Luis J Fernandez, *President*
Gregory H Smith, *CFO*
Gregory A Maitner, *Treasurer*
Antonio Contreras, *Co-President*
▲ **EMP:** 550
SQ FT: 385,000

SALES (est): 107.4MM
SALES (corp-wide): 1.8B **Privately Held**
WEB: www.chsugar.com
SIC: 2062 Refined cane sugar from purchased raw sugar or syrup
HQ: American Sugar Refining, Inc.
　　1 N Clematis St Ste 200
　　West Palm Beach FL 33401
　　561 366-5100

(P-1402)
C&H SUGAR COMPANY INC
Also Called: C&H Sugar Company
830 Loring Ave, Crockett (94525-1104)
PHONE......................510 787-6763
Charles Nelson, *Branch Mgr*
EMP: 400
SALES (corp-wide): 1.8B **Privately Held**
WEB: www.dominospecialtyingredients.com
SIC: 2062 Granulated cane sugar from purchased raw sugar or syrup
HQ: American Sugar Refining, Inc.
　　1 N Clematis St Ste 200
　　West Palm Beach FL 33401
　　561 366-5100

2063 Sugar, Beet

(P-1403)
IMPERIAL SUGAR COMPANY
Also Called: Spreckels Sugar
395 W Keystone Rd, Brawley (92227-9739)
P.O. Box 581 (92227-0581)
PHONE......................760 344-3110
Bill Stewart, *Opers-Prdtn-Mfg*
EMP: 130
SALES (corp-wide): 44B **Privately Held**
SIC: 2063 2062 Beet sugar from beet sugar refinery; cane sugar refining
HQ: Imperial Sugar Company
　　3 Sugar Creek Center Blvd # 500
　　Sugar Land TX 77478
　　281 491-9181

(P-1404)
SPRECKELS SUGAR COMPANY INC
395 W Keystone Rd, Brawley (92227-9739)
P.O. Box 581 (92227-0581)
PHONE......................760 344-3110
John A Richmond, *President*
Neil Rudeen, *Ch of Bd*
Jeff Plathe, *CEO*
Karen Mercer, *Treasurer*
Sergio Bastidas, *Accountant*
▲ **EMP:** 260 EST: 1905
SALES (est): 58MM
SALES (corp-wide): 418.1MM **Privately Held**
WEB: www.smbsc.com
SIC: 2063 Beet sugar from beet sugar refinery
PA: Southern Minnesota Beet Sugar Cooperative
　　83550 County Road 21
　　Renville MN 56284
　　320 329-8305

2064 Candy & Confectionery Prdts

(P-1405)
18 RABBITS INC (PA)
995 Market St Fl 2, San Francisco (94103-1732)
P.O. Box 411142 (94141-1142)
PHONE......................415 922-6006
Alison Vercruysse, *CEO*
Kelly Lecoy, *Marketing Mgr*
Greg Reimer, *Marketing Mgr*
Craig Vercruysse, *Director*
EMP: 19
SALES (est): 3.3MM **Privately Held**
SIC: 2064 Granola & muesli, bars & clusters

(P-1406)
ADAMS AND BROOKS INC
4345 Hallmark Pkwy, San Bernardino (92407-1829)
PHONE......................213 392-8700
EMP: 90
SALES (corp-wide): 23MM **Privately Held**
SIC: 2064
PA: Adams And Brooks, Inc.
　　4345 Hallmark Pkwy
　　San Bernardino CA 92407
　　909 880-2305

(P-1407)
AMERICAN LICORICE COMPANY
2477 Liston Way, Union City (94587-1979)
P.O. Box 826 (94587-0826)
PHONE......................510 487-5500
John Sullivan, *Principal*
James Kretchmer, *President*
Ed Silva, *Manager*
EMP: 350
SALES (corp-wide): 114.3MM **Privately Held**
WEB: www.redvines.com
SIC: 2064 Licorice candy
PA: American Licorice Company
　　1900 Whirlpool Dr S
　　La Porte IN 46350
　　510 487-5500

(P-1408)
ANNABELLE CANDY INC
27211 Industrial Blvd, Hayward (94545-3392)
P.O. Box 3665 (94540-3665)
PHONE......................510 783-2900
Susan Gamson Karl, *CEO*
Annabelle Altschuler Block, *Ch of Bd*
Shelley Craft, *Vice Pres*
Jim Macintire, *Vice Pres*
Victor Moreno, *Safety Mgr*
EMP: 75
SQ FT: 60,000
SALES (est): 15.4MM **Privately Held**
WEB: www.annabelle-candy.com
SIC: 2064 Candy bars, including chocolate covered bars; chocolate candy, except solid chocolate

(P-1409)
CALIFORNIA SNACK FOODS INC
Also Called: California Candy
2131 Tyler Ave, El Monte (91733-2754)
PHONE......................626 444-4508
Murl W Nelson, *CEO*
Steve Nelson, *President*
Paul Mullen, *Vice Pres*
Mary Nelson, *Admin Sec*
EMP: 45
SQ FT: 30,000
SALES (est): 6.9MM **Privately Held**
WEB: www.cal-snacks.com
SIC: 2064 2024 2099 2051 Fruits: candied, crystallized, or glazed; juice pops, frozen; popcorn, packaged: except already popped; cakes, pies & pastries; dried & dehydrated soup mixes; novelties & specialties, metal

(P-1410)
CANDIES TOLTECA
2139 N Pleasant Ave, Fresno (93705-4730)
P.O. Box 4729 (93744-4729)
PHONE......................559 266-9193
Aaron Ordaz, *CEO*
EMP: 35
SQ FT: 5,000
SALES (est): 6MM **Privately Held**
SIC: 2064 Candy & other confectionery products

(P-1411)
CARBERRY LLC (HQ)
17130 Muskrat Ave Ste B, Adelanto (92301-2473)
PHONE......................800 564-0842
Roy McFarland, *Director*
EMP: 24 EST: 2017
SQ FT: 12,000

P
R
O
D
U
C
T
S
&
S
V
C
S

SALES (est): 1.2MM
SALES (corp-wide): 1.1MM **Privately Held**
SIC: **2064** Chewing candy, not chewing gum
PA: Plus Products Holdings Inc.
2174 Waverley St
Palo Alto CA 94301
800 564-0842

(P-1412)
CENTURY SNACKS LLC
5560 E Slauson Ave, Commerce (90040-2921)
PHONE................................323 278-9578
Valerie Oswalt, *CEO*
Stephen Famolaro, *CFO*
David Lowe, *Chairman*
Tiffany Obenchain, *Vice Pres*
EMP: 330 EST: 1999
SQ FT: 280,000
SALES: 120MM
SALES (corp-wide): 177.6MM **Privately Held**
SIC: **2064** 5145 Nuts, candy covered; nuts, glace; nuts, salted or roasted
HQ: Scncs, Llc
5560 E Slauson Ave
Commerce CA 90040
323 278-9578

(P-1413)
CHIODO CANDY CO
2923 Adeline St, Oakland (94608-4422)
P.O. Box 8155 (94662-0155)
PHONE................................510 464-2977
Louis J Chiodo, *President*
EMP: 65
SALES (est): 6MM **Privately Held**
SIC: **2064** Candy & other confectionery products

(P-1414)
CHUAO CHOCOLATIER INC (HQ)
2345 Camino Vida Roble, Carlsbad (92011-1505)
PHONE................................760 476-1668
Chef Michael Antonorsi, *Chairman*
Richard Antonorsi, *Exec VP*
Cheryl Hunt, *Admin Asst*
Adam Werner, *Natl Sales Mgr*
Dominic Jones, *Sales Staff*
▲ EMP: 12
SQ FT: 1,000
SALES (est): 7MM **Privately Held**
WEB: www.chuaochocolatier.com
SIC: **2064** Candy & other confectionery products
PA: The Kairos Group Inc
2350 Camino Vida Roble A
Carlsbad CA 92011
760 476-1668

(P-1415)
CJS TOFFEE & TOPPINGS LLC
Also Called: Toffee Tops
2269 Chestnut St 298, San Francisco (94123-2600)
PHONE................................415 929-7852
Catherine J Hughes, *Mng Member*
EMP: 10
SALES: 200K **Privately Held**
SIC: **2064** Candy & other confectionery products

(P-1416)
CONFECTIONS MICHAEL RECCHIUTI (PA)
Also Called: Recchiuti Confections
2565 3rd St Ste 225, San Francisco (94107-3160)
PHONE................................415 826-2868
Michael Recchiuti, *Mng Member*
Courtnie Gallego, *Finance Asst*
Cara Loffredo, *Marketing Staff*
Alexandra Bitker, *Sales Staff*
Deena Yahiro, *Sales Staff*
▲ EMP: 19 EST: 2000
SALES (est): 1.8MM **Privately Held**
WEB: www.recchiuticonfections.com
SIC: **2064** Candy bars, including chocolate covered bars

(P-1417)
COUNTRY HOUSE
Also Called: Seloah Gourmet Food
2852 Walnut Ave Ste C1, Tustin (92780-7033)
PHONE................................714 505-8988
Monica Ching, *Owner*
Monica Diggan, *Manager*
◆ EMP: 18 EST: 1994
SQ FT: 9,400
SALES (est): 573.2K **Privately Held**
WEB: www.countryhouse.com
SIC: **2064** Candy & other confectionery products

(P-1418)
DEBRITOS CHOCOLATE FACTORY
160b Briggs Rd, Hollister (95023-9001)
PHONE................................831 637-0164
Alene Debrito, *Owner*
▲ EMP: 12
SALES (est): 1.1MM **Privately Held**
SIC: **2064** Candy & other confectionery products

(P-1419)
EL CHAVITO INC
6020 Progressive Ave # 600, San Diego (92154-6638)
PHONE................................844 424-2848
Bashar Ballo, *CEO*
Hugo Farias, *Opers Staff*
EMP: 14 EST: 2017
SQ FT: 13,000
SALES (est): 876.5K **Privately Held**
SIC: **2064** Candy & other confectionery products

(P-1420)
EL SUPER LEON PNCHIN SNCKS INC
315 Quintard St, Chula Vista (91911-4106)
PHONE................................619 271-0846
Ildefonso Guerrero, *President*
Ada Guerrero, *Vice Pres*
▲ EMP: 35
SQ FT: 22,000
SALES: 5MM **Privately Held**
SIC: **2064** 2096 5145 Candy & other confectionery products; corn chips & other corn-based snacks; candy

(P-1421)
EL SUPER LEON PNCHIN SNCKS INC
8650 Avenida Costa Blanca, San Diego (92154-6232)
PHONE................................619 426-2968
Alfonso Guerrero, *President*
EMP: 21 **Privately Held**
SIC: **2064** Candy & other confectionery products
PA: El Super Leon Ponchin Snacks, Inc.
315 Quintard St
Chula Vista CA 91911

(P-1422)
EZAKI GLICO USA CORP
17780 Fitch Ste 140, Irvine (92614-6084)
PHONE................................949 251-0144
Akitoshi Oku, *President*
George Iwashita, *Marketing Staff*
Marie Pumilia, *Marketing Staff*
Delron Dozier, *Sales Staff*
Lisa Merren, *Sales Staff*
▲ EMP: 19
SALES: 3.4MM
SALES (corp-wide): 3.3B **Privately Held**
WEB: www.glico.co.jp
SIC: **2064** 8111 Candy & other confectionery products; general practice attorney, lawyer
PA: Ezaki Glico Co.,Ltd.
4-6-5, Utajima, Nishiyodogawa-Ku
Osaka OSK 555-0
664 778-352

(P-1423)
FOOD TECHNOLOGY AND DESIGN LLC
Also Called: Food Pharma
10012 Painter Ave, Santa Fe Springs (90670-3016)
PHONE................................562 944-7821
Glen Marinelli, *Mng Member*
Jerry Jacobs, *CFO*
Regina Medina, *Safety Mgr*
Vicki Cortese, *Sales Mgr*
Remmell Gopez, *Mng Member*
EMP: 40
SQ FT: 20,000
SALES (est): 9MM **Privately Held**
WEB: www.foodpharma.com
SIC: **2064** Candy & other confectionery products

(P-1424)
GENESIS FOODS CORPORATION (DH)
Also Called: Garvey Nut & Candy
8825 Mercury Ln, Pico Rivera (90660-6707)
PHONE................................323 890-5890
Steven R Corri, *President*
▲ EMP: 60
SQ FT: 35,000
SALES (est): 11.8MM
SALES (corp-wide): 1.4MM **Privately Held**
SIC: **2064** 5149 Candy & other confectionery products; cookies

(P-1425)
GOLD RUSH KETTLE KORN LLC
Also Called: Kettle Pop
4690 E 2nd St Ste 9, Benicia (94510-1008)
PHONE................................707 747-6773
Jeff Schletewitz, *Mng Member*
Jason Holdaway, *Opers Mgr*
William Baker Jr,
Aaron Reimer, *Manager*
▲ EMP: 20
SQ FT: 1,596
SALES (est): 3.4MM **Privately Held**
SIC: **2064** Popcorn balls or other treated popcorn products

(P-1426)
HAWAIIAN HOST CANDIES LA INC
15601 S Avalon Blvd, Gardena (90248-2371)
PHONE................................310 532-0543
Keith Sakamoto, *President*
◆ EMP: 60
SQ FT: 100,000
SALES (est): 12.4MM
SALES (corp-wide): 88.1MM **Privately Held**
WEB: www.hawaiianhost.com
SIC: **2064** Candy & other confectionery products
PA: Hawaiian Host, Inc.
500 Alakawa St Rm 111
Honolulu HI 96817
808 848-0500

(P-1427)
HGC HOLDINGS INC
3303 Mrtn Lthr King Jr Bl, Lynwood (90262-1905)
PHONE................................323 567-2226
Robert I Hadgraft, *CEO*
David Worth, *CEO*
Robert Worth, *Admin Sec*
EMP: 120
SQ FT: 90,000
SALES (est): 16.6MM **Privately Held**
SIC: **2064** 5441 Chocolate candy, except solid chocolate; candy

(P-1428)
HOTLIX (PA)
Also Called: Hotlix Candy
966 Griffin St, Grover Beach (93433-3019)
P.O. Box 447 (93483-0447)
PHONE................................805 473-0596
Larry Peterman, *President*
Richard Lara, *Data Proc Staff*
Kathy Mitchell, *Accounts Mgr*
▼ EMP: 50

SQ FT: 1,500
SALES (est): 5.8MM **Privately Held**
WEB: www.hotlix.com
SIC: **2064** Lollipops & other hard candy

(P-1429)
INSIGNIA SC HOLDINGS LLC (HQ)
1333 N Calif Blvd Ste 520, Walnut Creek (94596-4534)
PHONE................................925 399-8900
Dave Lowe, *Ch of Bd*
EMP: 814
SALES (est): 177.6MM **Privately Held**
SIC: **2064** 5145 Nuts, candy covered; nuts, salted or roasted
PA: Insignia Capital Partners, L.P.
1333 N Calif Blvd Ste 520
Walnut Creek CA 94596
925 399-8900

(P-1430)
ISLAND SNACKS INC
Also Called: Island Products
7650 Stage Rd, Buena Park (90621-1226)
PHONE................................714 994-1228
Alin Barak, *President*
Koby Kalfus, *Regl Sales Mgr*
◆ EMP: 20
SQ FT: 6,600
SALES: 14MM **Privately Held**
WEB: www.islandsnacks.com
SIC: **2064** Candy & other confectionery products

(P-1431)
JELLY BELLY CANDY COMPANY (PA)
1 Jelly Belly Ln, Fairfield (94533-6741)
PHONE................................707 428-2800
Robert M Simpson Jr, *CEO*
Herman G Rowland Sr, *Ch of Bd*
Robert Simpson, *President*
Lisa Brasher, *Corp Secy*
William Kelley, *Vice Ch Bd*
◆ EMP: 400 EST: 1900
SQ FT: 350,000
SALES (est): 215.4MM **Privately Held**
WEB: www.jellybelly.com
SIC: **2064** Candy & other confectionery products

(P-1432)
JELLY BELLY CANDY COMPANY
2400 N Watney Way, Fairfield (94533-6734)
PHONE................................707 428-2800
Albert Larson, *Vice Pres*
Jeff Brown, *Director*
EMP: 40
SALES (corp-wide): 215.4MM **Privately Held**
WEB: www.jellybelly.com
SIC: **2064** Candy & other confectionery products
PA: Jelly Belly Candy Company
1 Jelly Belly Ln
Fairfield CA 94533
707 428-2800

(P-1433)
JEWEL DATE COMPANY INC
84675 60th Ave, Thermal (92274-8780)
PHONE................................760 399-4474
Gregory Raumin, *President*
◆ EMP: 20
SALES (est): 4.4MM **Privately Held**
SIC: **2064** Sugared dates

(P-1434)
JOSE MARTINEZ
Also Called: Jose Martinez Candy
1281 S Hicks Ave, Los Angeles (90023-3238)
PHONE................................323 263-6230
Jose Martinez, *Owner*
▼ EMP: 10
SQ FT: 3,000
SALES (est): 1.3MM **Privately Held**
SIC: **2064** 5145 Candy & other confectionery products; candy

(P-1435)
KONA BAR LLC
2601 Ocean Park Blvd # 310, Santa Monica
(90405-5270)
PHONE..............................808 927-1934
Christian Zenger, CEO
EMP: 15
SQ FT: 10,000
SALES (est): 1MM **Privately Held**
SIC: 2064 Candy bars, including chocolate
covered bars

(P-1436)
LA ZAMORANA CANDY
7100 Wilson Ave, Los Angeles
(90001-2249)
PHONE..............................323 583-7100
Vicente Mendez, President
Carmen Artiaga, Co-Owner
EMP: 12
SALES (est): 737.9K **Privately Held**
SIC: 2064 5145 Candy & other confec-
tionery products; candy

(P-1437)
LDVC INC
Also Called: Lasdos Victorias Candy Com-
pany
9606 Valley Blvd, Rosemead (91770-1510)
PHONE..............................626 448-4611
Jenny Lee, President
David Lee, CFO
EMP: 20
SQ FT: 8,000
SALES (est): 2.3MM **Privately Held**
SIC: 2064 Candy & other confectionery
products

(P-1438)
LE BELGE CHOCOLATIER INC
761 Skyway Ct, NAPA (94558-7510)
PHONE..............................707 258-9200
David Grunhut, CEO
Debby Kelly, Vice Pres
◆ EMP: 25
SQ FT: 15,000
SALES (est): 5.4MM
SALES (corp-wide): 85MM **Privately
Held**
WEB: www.lebelgechocolatier.com
SIC: 2064 2066 Chocolate candy, except
solid chocolate; chocolate candy, solid
PA: Astor Chocolate Corp.
651 New Hampshire Ave
Lakewood NJ 08701
732 901-1000

(P-1439)
**LOCHIRCO FRUIT AND
PRODUCE INC**
Also Called: Happy Apple
41899 Road 120, Orosi (93647-9452)
PHONE..............................559 528-4194
John Myer, Manager
EMP: 25
SALES (corp-wide): 7.7MM **Privately
Held**
WEB: www.happyapples.com
SIC: 2064 Fruits: candied, crystallized, or
glazed
PA: Lochirco Fruit And Produce, Inc.
527 Commercial Dr
Union MO 63084
636 583-5000

(P-1440)
**MAGIC GUMBALL
INTERNATIONAL**
9310 Mason Ave, Chatsworth
(91311-5201)
PHONE..............................818 716-1888
Don Hart, President
Guy Hart, Vice Pres
▼ EMP: 30
SALES (est): 5.8MM **Privately Held**
WEB: www.magicgumball.com
SIC: 2064 3581 2067 Candy & other con-
fectionery products; automatic vending
machines; chewing gum

(P-1441)
**MARICH CONFECTIONERY CO
INC**
2101 Bert Dr, Hollister (95023-2562)
PHONE..............................831 634-4700

Bradley M Van Dam, President
Von Packard, Shareholder
Ronald B Packard, Chairman
Jose Her, Info Tech Mgr
Kim Clayton, Purch Mgr
▲ EMP: 150
SQ FT: 60,000
SALES (est): 33.3MM **Privately Held**
WEB: www.marich.com
SIC: 2064 2099 2068 Candy & other con-
fectionery products; food preparations;
salted & roasted nuts & seeds

(P-1442)
MARIMIX COMPANY INC
987 N Enterprise St, Orange (92867-5448)
PHONE..............................714 633-7300
Mari Fassett, President
EMP: 10
SQ FT: 11,000
SALES (est): 1.2MM **Privately Held**
WEB: www.marimix.com
SIC: 2064 Candy & other confectionery
products

(P-1443)
MAVE ENTERPRISES INC
Also Called: It's Delish
11555 Cantara St Ste B-E, North Hollywood
(91605-1652)
P.O. Box 480620, Los Angeles (90048-
1620)
PHONE..............................818 767-4533
Amy Grawitzky, CEO
Moshe Grawitzky, Vice Pres
Roberto Munoz, Office Mgr
Rochell Legarreta, Admin Sec
▲ EMP: 35
SQ FT: 35,000
SALES (est): 6MM **Privately Held**
WEB: www.itsdelish.com
SIC: 2064 2099 2033 2068 Candy &
other confectionery products; seasonings
& spices; canned fruits & specialties;
salted & roasted nuts & seeds

(P-1444)
**MCKEEVER DANLEE
CONFECTIONARY**
760 N Mckeever Ave, Azusa (91702-2349)
PHONE..............................626 334-8964
Gerald Morris, President
David A Pistole, CFO
Brian Halpert, Corp Secy
EMP: 20
SQ FT: 10,000
SALES (est): 1.7MM **Privately Held**
WEB: www.specialtimesgifts.com
SIC: 2064 Candy & other confectionery
products
HQ: Morris National, Inc.
760 N Mckeever Ave
Azusa CA 91702
626 385-2000

(P-1445)
**NELLSON NUTRACEUTICAL
INC (PA)**
5801 Ayala Ave, Irwindale (91706-6216)
PHONE..............................626 812-6522
Scott Greenwood, CEO
Ben Muhlenkamp, President
Jeff Moran, CEO
Paul Hanson, Senior VP
Bart Child, Vice Pres
▲ EMP: 297
SQ FT: 100,000
SALES (est): 38.7MM **Privately Held**
SIC: 2064 Candy bars, including chocolate
covered bars

(P-1446)
**NELLSON NUTRACEUTICAL
LLC (PA)**
5115 E La Palma Ave, Anaheim
(92807-2018)
PHONE..............................714 765-7000
James Better, CEO
Jean Filion, COO
Manuel Martinez, CFO
Bart Child, Vice Pres
Raymond Collins, Vice Pres
EMP: 277
SALES (est): 316.3MM **Privately Held**
SIC: 2064 Candy bars, including chocolate
covered bars

(P-1447)
**POCO DOLCE CONFECTIONS
INC**
1020 Illinois St, San Francisco
(94107-3120)
PHONE..............................415 817-1551
Kathy Wiley, President
EMP: 15
SALES (est): 581.4K **Privately Held**
SIC: 2064 Breakfast bars

(P-1448)
POPCORNOPOLIS LLC (PA)
3200 E Slauson Ave, Vernon (90058-3919)
PHONE..............................310 414-6700
Wallis Arnold, CEO
Ben Menezes, CFO
Kathleen Arnold, Vice Pres
Jyotsna Bhatt, Vice Pres
Taylor Davis, Executive
▲ EMP: 200
SQ FT: 20,000
SALES (est): 135.5MM **Privately Held**
SIC: 2064 Candy & other confectionery
products

(P-1449)
**ROBERTS FERRY NUT
COMPANY INC**
20493 Yosemite Blvd, Waterford
(95386-9506)
PHONE..............................209 874-3247
Nic West, President
Kim West, Treasurer
Brad Humble, Vice Pres
Stacey Humble, Admin Sec
EMP: 12
SQ FT: 10,000
SALES (est): 2.2MM **Privately Held**
WEB: www.robertsferrynuts.com
SIC: 2064 5145 Nuts, candy covered;
nuts, salted or roasted

(P-1450)
S & C FOODS INC
Also Called: Garvey Nut and Candy
6094 Malburg Way, Vernon (90058)
PHONE..............................323 205-6887
Steve Corri, President
EMP: 20
SALES (corp-wide): 1.4MM **Privately
Held**
SIC: 2064 Candy & other confectionery
products
HQ: Genesis Foods Corporation
8825 Mercury Ln
Pico Rivera CA 90660
323 890-5890

(P-1451)
**SANDERS CANDY FACTORY
INC**
5051 Calmview Ave, Baldwin Park
(91706-1802)
PHONE..............................626 814-2038
Timothy Sanders, CEO
Steven L Peralez, Treasurer
Mark Sanders, Vice Pres
Charlie Profilet, General Mgr
EMP: 20
SQ FT: 40,000
SALES (est): 5.3MM **Privately Held**
SIC: 2064 Candy & other confectionery
products

(P-1452)
SCONZA CANDY COMPANY
1 Sconza Candy Ln, Oakdale
(95361-7899)
PHONE..............................209 845-3700
James R Sconza, President
Ronald J Sconza, Vice Pres
▲ EMP: 100 EST: 1939
SQ FT: 40,000
SALES (est): 34.8MM **Privately Held**
WEB: www.sconzacandy.com
SIC: 2064 Lollipops & other hard candy

(P-1453)
SEES CANDIES INC (DH)
210 El Camino Real, South San Francisco
(94080-5998)
PHONE..............................650 761-2490
Warren E Buffett, Ch of Bd
Bradley D Kinstler, President

Ken Scott, CFO
Bernie Bishop, Vice Pres
Eileen Duag, Vice Pres
▲ EMP: 500
SQ FT: 250,000
SALES (est): 673.6MM
SALES (corp-wide): 242.1B **Publicly
Held**
WEB: www.seescandies.com
SIC: 2064 5441 Candy & other confec-
tionery products; candy
HQ: See's Candy Shops, Incorporated
210 El Camino Real
South San Francisco CA 94080
650 761-2490

(P-1454)
**SEES CANDY SHOPS
INCORPORATED (HQ)**
Also Called: See's Candies
210 El Camino Real, South San Francisco
(94080-5968)
PHONE..............................650 761-2490
Brad Kinstler, President
Warren E Buffet, Ch of Bd
Daryl Wollenburg, Treasurer
Roger Simon, Controller
Sherilyn Freeman, Sales Staff
▲ EMP: 40
SQ FT: 250,000
SALES (est): 673.6MM
SALES (corp-wide): 242.1B **Publicly
Held**
WEB: www.sees.com
SIC: 2064 5441 Candy & other confec-
tionery products; candy; confectionery
PA: Berkshire Hathaway Inc.
3555 Farnam St Ste 1140
Omaha NE 68131
402 346-1400

(P-1455)
**SEES CANDY SHOPS
INCORPORATED**
9839 Paramount Blvd, Downey
(90240-3803)
PHONE..............................562 928-2912
Gayle Hill, Manager
EMP: 10
SQ FT: 1,317
SALES (corp-wide): 242.1B **Publicly
Held**
WEB: www.sees.com
SIC: 2064 5441 Candy & other confec-
tionery products; candy; confectionery
HQ: See's Candy Shops, Incorporated
210 El Camino Real
South San Francisco CA 94080
650 761-2490

(P-1456)
**SEES CANDY SHOPS
INCORPORATED**
Also Called: See's Candies
3423 S La Cienega Blvd, Los Angeles
(90016-4401)
PHONE..............................310 559-4919
Greg Ward, Director
Iris Eshoo, Vice Pres
Debbie Tapia, Opers Mgr
Ava Foreman, Maintenance Dir
EMP: 200
SQ FT: 170,396
SALES (corp-wide): 242.1B **Publicly
Held**
WEB: www.sees.com
SIC: 2064 2066 Candy & other confec-
tionery products; chocolate & cocoa prod-
ucts
HQ: See's Candy Shops, Incorporated
210 El Camino Real
South San Francisco CA 94080
650 761-2490

(P-1457)
SENCHA NATURALS INC
104 N Union Ave, Los Angeles
(90026-5408)
PHONE..............................213 353-9908
David Kerdoon, President
Gary Ehasoo, Sales Staff
▲ EMP: 15
SALES (est): 680K **Privately Held**
SIC: 2064 Candy & other confectionery
products

(P-1458)
SENOR SNACKS MANUFACTURING LTD
2325 Raymer Ave, Fullerton (92833-2514)
PHONE.................714 739-1073
Jose V Mazon, *Partner*
EMP: 60
SALES (est): 5MM **Privately Held**
SIC: 2064 Candy & other confectionery products

(P-1459)
SIERRA FOOTHILLS FUDGE FACTORY
Also Called: Fudge Factory Farm
2860 High Hill Rd, Placerville (95667-5102)
PHONE.................530 644-3492
Jean Reinders, *Owner*
EMP: 15
SQ FT: 600
SALES: 200K **Privately Held**
SIC: 2064 5441 0175 Chocolate candy, except solid chocolate; candy, nut & confectionery stores; apple orchard

(P-1460)
SUNSHINE RAISIN CORPORATION (PA)
Also Called: National Raisin Company
626 S 5th St, Fowler (93625-9745)
P.O. Box 219 (93625-0219)
PHONE.................559 834-5981
Lindakay Abdulian, *President*
Krikor Bedrosian, *Treasurer*
Joe Leon, *Purch Mgr*
Vincent Fernandez, *Director*
◆ EMP: 249 EST: 1968
SQ FT: 400,000
SALES (est): 146.6MM **Privately Held**
SIC: 2064 0723 Candy & other confectionery products; crop preparation services for market

(P-1461)
THATS IT NUTRITION LLC
834 S Broadway Ste 800, Los Angeles (90014-3525)
PHONE.................818 782-1701
Miriam Lewensztain, *Mng Member*
Lior Lewensztein,
EMP: 11 EST: 2012
SQ FT: 8,000
SALES: 20MM **Privately Held**
SIC: 2064 Granola & muesli, bars & clusters

(P-1462)
TOFFEE BOUTIQUE INC
11353 Pyrites Way, Rancho Cordova (95670-4454)
PHONE.................916 638-8462
Lisa Ferrato, *CEO*
William Ferrato, *Vice Pres*
EMP: 10
SQ FT: 2,000
SALES: 80K **Privately Held**
SIC: 2064 Candy & other confectionery products

(P-1463)
TOM CLARK CONFECTIONS
Also Called: Popcorn Tree
1193 Nicole Ct, Glendora (91740-5387)
PHONE.................909 599-4700
Timothy D Clark, *CEO*
Beverly Clark, *Corp Secy*
Tim Clark, *Vice Pres*
EMP: 32
SQ FT: 18,500
SALES (est): 10.9MM **Privately Held**
SIC: 2064 Popcorn balls or other treated popcorn products

(P-1464)
TORN RANCH INC (PA)
2198 S Mcdowell Blvd Ext, Petaluma (94954-6902)
PHONE.................415 506-3000
Su Morrow, *CEO*
Dean Morrow, *President*
Mark Ebling, *Vice Pres*
Kimberly Delasantos, *Controller*
Michelle Chodor, *Natl Sales Mgr*
◆ EMP: 80

SALES (est): 14.9MM **Privately Held**
WEB: www.tornranch.com
SIC: 2064 Candy & other confectionery products

2066 Chocolate & Cocoa Prdts

(P-1465)
BARRY CALLEBAUT USA LLC
1175 Commerce Blvd Ste D, American Canyon (94503-9626)
PHONE.................707 642-8200
Peter Dell,
Barry Humphries, *Site Mgr*
EMP: 18
SALES (corp-wide): 45.9MM **Privately Held**
SIC: 2066 Chocolate
HQ: Barry Callebaut U.S.A. Llc
600 W Chicago Ave Ste 860
Chicago IL 60654

(P-1466)
BLOMMER CHOCOLATE CO CAL INC
1515 Pacific St, Union City (94587-2041)
PHONE.................510 471-4300
Henry J Blommer Jr, *CEO*
Joseph W Blommer, *President*
Peter W Blommer, *Vice Pres*
Martin Krueger, *Vice Pres*
Jack S Larsen, *Vice Pres*
▲ EMP: 200
SQ FT: 142,000
SALES (est): 34.6MM **Privately Held**
WEB: www.blommer.com
SIC: 2066 Chocolate coatings & syrup; powdered cocoa; cocoa butter
PA: The Blommer Chocolate Company
1101 Blommer Dr
East Greenville PA 18041
800 825-8181

(P-1467)
CALIFORNIA GOLD BARS INC (PA)
1041 Folger Ave, Berkeley (94710-2819)
PHONE.................510 848-9292
Daniel Hood, *CEO*
Jonathan Schwartz, *Director*
EMP: 10 EST: 2014
SALES: 500K **Privately Held**
SIC: 2066 5149 Chocolate & cocoa products; chocolate

(P-1468)
COCO DELICE
1555 Park Ave Ste A, Emeryville (94608-3586)
PHONE.................510 601-1394
Dennis Michael Kearney, *CEO*
EMP: 10
SALES (est): 1.3MM **Privately Held**
SIC: 2066

(P-1469)
ECLIPSE CHOCOLATE BAR & BISTRO
2145 Fern St, San Diego (92104-5517)
PHONE.................619 578-2984
William Gustwiller, *Owner*
EMP: 11
SALES (est): 1MM **Privately Held**
SIC: 2066 Chocolate

(P-1470)
GODIVA CHOCOLATIER INC
3251 20th Ave Ste 154, San Francisco (94132-1934)
PHONE.................415 566-5058
Yohannes Hagos, *Branch Mgr*
EMP: 24 **Privately Held**
WEB: www.godiva.com
SIC: 2066 Chocolate
HQ: Godiva Chocclatier, Inc.
333 W 34th St Fl 6
New York NY 10001
212 984-5900

(P-1471)
GUITTARD CHOCOLATE CO
10 Guittard Rd, Burlingame (94010-2203)
P.O. Box 4308 (94011-4308)
PHONE.................650 697-4427
Gary W Guittard, *President*
Gerrit Dirkmaat, *CFO*
Brad Newcom, *Executive*
Brad Newcombe, *Executive*
Michael Simon, *Administration*
◆ EMP: 240 EST: 1868
SALES (est): 80.5MM **Privately Held**
WEB: www.guittard.com
SIC: 2066 2064 Chocolate; cocoa & cocoa products; candy & other confectionery products

(P-1472)
NAYLOR CORP
Spc 112 Pier 39, San Francisco (94133)
PHONE.................415 421-1789
Robert Lee, *Office Mgr*
John Naylor, *President*
EMP: 28
SALES (est): 2.7MM **Privately Held**
SIC: 2066 Chocolate

(P-1473)
SHELTON INC
Also Called: Judy's Candy Company
1225 8th St, Berkeley (94710-1413)
PHONE.................510 524-2430
Mary Shelton, *CEO*
Judy Shelton, *President*
EMP: 25
SQ FT: 7,400
SALES (est): 3MM **Privately Held**
WEB: www.judyscandy.com
SIC: 2066 2064 Chocolate candy, solid; candy & other confectionery products; fudge (candy)

(P-1474)
SSI G DEBBAS CHOCOLATIER LLC
2794 N Larkin Ave, Fresno (93727-1315)
PHONE.................559 294-2071
Bret Lorenc, *President*
EMP: 37
SALES (est): 4.1MM **Privately Held**
SIC: 2066 Chocolate & cocoa products

(P-1475)
TCHO VENTURES INC
1900 Powell St Ste 600, Emeryville (94608-1885)
PHONE.................415 981-0189
Marcel Bens, *CEO*
EMP: 13
SALES (est): 2.2MM **Privately Held**
SIC: 2066 Chocolate
PA: Tcho Ventures, Inc.
3100 San Pablo Ave
Berkeley CA 94702

(P-1476)
TCHO VENTURES INC (PA)
3100 San Pablo Ave, Berkeley (94702-2498)
PHONE.................844 877-8246
Marcel Bens, *CEO*
Ben Fineberg, *CFO*
Mauro Rojas, *Opers Staff*
ARI Morimoto, *Manager*
EMP: 46
SQ FT: 29,734
SALES (est): 7.5MM **Privately Held**
SIC: 2066 Chocolate & cocoa products

(P-1477)
TRC COCOA LLC
3721 Douglas Blvd Ste 375, Roseville (95661-4255)
PHONE.................916 847-2390
Jay Kaeila, *President*
Xavier Verspieren, *CFO*
EMP: 12 EST: 2017
SQ FT: 6,000
SALES (est): 25MM **Privately Held**
SIC: 2066 Cocoa & cocoa products
HQ: Trc Trading Corporation
3721 Douglas Blvd Ste 375
Roseville CA 95661
-

(P-1478)
VERY SPECIAL CHOCOLATS INC
760 N Mckeever Ave, Azusa (91702-2349)
PHONE.................626 334-7838
Gerry Morris Zubatoff, *CEO*
Gerald Morris, *President*
David Pistole, *CFO*
Bram Morris, *Admin Sec*
▲ EMP: 150
SQ FT: 40,000
SALES: 8.5MM **Privately Held**
WEB: www.morrisnational.com
SIC: 2066 Chocolate & cocoa products
HQ: Morris National, Inc.
760 N Mckeever Ave
Azusa CA 91702
626 385-2000

2068 Salted & Roasted Nuts & Seeds

(P-1479)
180 SNACKS (PA)
Also Called: Mareblu Naturals
1173 N Armando St, Anaheim (92806-2609)
PHONE.................714 238-1192
Michael Kim, *President*
Katherine Kim, *Vice Pres*
Eugene Kim, *QA Dir*
Mike Runion, *Opers Staff*
Michael Runion, *VP Sales*
◆ EMP: 47
SQ FT: 10,000
SALES: 16MM **Privately Held**
SIC: 2068 2034 Salted & roasted nuts & seeds; dried & dehydrated fruits

(P-1480)
ALMOND COMPANY
22782 Road 9, Chowchilla (93610-8967)
PHONE.................559 665-4405
Russell Harris, *President*
▼ EMP: 80
SALES (est): 12.6MM **Privately Held**
SIC: 2068 Nuts: dried, dehydrated, salted or roasted

(P-1481)
ALMOND VALLEY NUT CO
11255 E Whitmore Ave, Denair (95316-9741)
P.O. Box 68, Hickman (95323-0068)
PHONE.................209 480-7300
Brent Zehrung, *Partner*
EMP: 22
SALES (est): 1.4MM **Privately Held**
SIC: 2068 Nuts: dried, dehydrated, salted or roasted

(P-1482)
ASSALI HULLING & SHELLING
8618 E Whitmore Ave, Hughson (95326-9446)
P.O. Box 69 (95326-0069)
PHONE.................209 883-4263
Frank Assali, *President*
EMP: 10 EST: 1970
SALES (est): 1.1MM **Privately Held**
WEB: www.assalihullingandshelling.com
SIC: 2068 Nuts: dried, dehydrated, salted or roasted

(P-1483)
BLUE DIAMOND GROWERS
10840 E Mckinley Ave, Sanger (93657-9480)
PHONE.................559 251-4044
EMP: 143
SALES (corp-wide): 1.6B **Privately Held**
SIC: 2068 Nuts: dried, dehydrated, salted or roasted
PA: Diamond Blue Growers
1802 C St
Sacramento CA 95811
916 442-0771

(P-1484)
CAL TRADERS
Also Called: Farmers International
1260 Muir Ave, Chico (95973-8644)
PHONE.................530 566-1405
Monish Seth, *Administration*

▲ = Import ▼=Export
◆ =Import/Export

Versha Seth, *Admin Sec*
EMP: 10
SALES (est): 743.1K **Privately Held**
SIC: 2068 Nuts: dried, dehydrated, salted or roasted

(P-1485)
CAL TREEHOUSE ALMONDS LLC
2115 Road 144, Delano (93215-9524)
P.O. Box 286 (93216-0286)
PHONE..................................661 725-6334
Robert Houston, *President*
EMP: 120
SQ FT: 68,803
SALES (corp-wide): 10.8MM **Privately Held**
SIC: 2068 Nuts: dried, dehydrated, salted or roasted
PA: Treehouse California Almonds Llc
6914 Road 160
Earlimart CA 93219
559 757-5020

(P-1486)
CONAGRA BRANDS INC
Conagra Specialty Snacks
5626 E Shields Ave, Fresno (93727-7818)
P.O. Box 7907 (93747-7907)
PHONE..................................559 291-0231
Larry Adams, *Branch Mgr*
EMP: 96
SALES (corp-wide): 7.9B **Publicly Held**
WEB: www.conagra.com
SIC: 2068 Nuts: dried, dehydrated, salted or roasted; seeds: dried, dehydrated, salted or roasted
PA: Conagra Brands, Inc.
222 Merchandise Mart Plz
Chicago IL 60654
312 549-5000

(P-1487)
DIAMOND FOODS LLC (PA)
Also Called: Diamond of California
1050 Diamond St, Stockton (95205-7020)
PHONE..................................209 467-6000
Brian J Driscoll, *President*
Lloyd J Johnson, *President*
David Colo, *COO*
Ray Silcock, *CFO*
Isobel Jones, *Exec VP*
◆ **EMP:** 575 **EST:** 2015
SALES (est): 569.2MM **Privately Held**
WEB: www.diamondfoods.com
SIC: 2068 2096 Salted & roasted nuts & seeds; potato chips & similar snacks

(P-1488)
DIAMOND FOODS LLC
600 Montgomery St Fl 17, San Francisco (94111-2719)
PHONE..................................209 467-6000
Carter Dunlap, *Manager*
Gary Santos, *Administration*
Christina Rotondo, *Credit Staff*
EMP: 11
SALES (corp-wide): 569.2MM **Privately Held**
SIC: 2068 Salted & roasted nuts & seeds
PA: Diamond Foods, Llc
1050 Diamond St
Stockton CA 95205
209 467-6000

(P-1489)
G & P GROUP INC
Also Called: Mr. Nature
1105 Kearny St, Los Angeles (90033-2159)
PHONE..................................323 268-2686
George Barraza, *Managing Dir*
Philip Borup, *Managing Dir*
▼ **EMP:** 13 **EST:** 2011
SQ FT: 11,000
SALES (est): 1.9MM **Privately Held**
SIC: 2068 0723 Salted & roasted nuts & seeds; fruit (farm-dried) packing services

(P-1490)
HUGHSON NUT INC (PA)
1825 Verduga Rd, Hughson (95326-9675)
P.O. Box 1150 (95326-1150)
PHONE..................................209 883-0403
Martin Pohl, *President*
Sonia Romero, *Human Resources*

◆ **EMP:** 375
SQ FT: 40,000
SALES (est): 87.6MM **Privately Held**
SIC: 2068 Salted & roasted nuts & seeds

(P-1491)
JOHN B SANFILIPPO & SON INC
29241 Cottonwood Rd, Gustine (95322-9574)
PHONE..................................209 854-2455
Isidro Cortez, *Manager*
EMP: 400
SQ FT: 1,286
SALES (corp-wide): 888.6MM **Publicly Held**
WEB: www.jbssinc.com
SIC: 2068 Nuts: dried, dehydrated, salted or roasted
PA: John B. Sanfilippo & Son, Inc.
1703 N Randall Rd
Elgin IL 60123
847 289-1800

(P-1492)
KLEIN BROS HOLDINGS LTD
Also Called: Klein Bros Snacks
1515 S Fresno Ave, Stockton (95206-1179)
PHONE..................................209 465-5033
Thomas B Klein, *Ch of Bd*
Robert J Corkern, *CEO*
EMP: 35 **EST:** 1977
SQ FT: 130,000
SALES (est): 6.2MM **Privately Held**
WEB: www.jumbosnacks.net
SIC: 2068 4783 5141 Seeds: dried, dehydrated, salted or roasted; nuts: dried, dehydrated, salted or roasted; packing & crating; groceries, general line

(P-1493)
KRAFT HEINZ FOODS COMPANY
Also Called: Heinz Seeds
6755 C E Dixon St, Stockton (95206-4947)
PHONE..................................209 932-5700
Ross Siragusa, *Director*
EMP: 35
SALES (corp-wide): 26.2B **Publicly Held**
SIC: 2068 3999 Seeds: dried, dehydrated, salted or roasted; seeds, coated or treated, from purchased seeds
HQ: Kraft Heinz Foods Company
1 Ppg Pl Ste 3200
Pittsburgh PA 15222
412 456-5700

(P-1494)
KRAFT HEINZ FOODS COMPANY
Also Called: Cornnuts Division of Planters
4343 E Florence Ave, Fresno (93725-1151)
PHONE..................................559 237-9206
F Chavez, *Opers-Prdtn-Mfg*
EMP: 70
SQ FT: 55,200
SALES (corp-wide): 26.2B **Publicly Held**
WEB: www.kraftfoods.com
SIC: 2068 2096 Nuts: dried, dehydrated, salted or roasted; potato chips & similar snacks
HQ: Kraft Heinz Foods Company
1 Ppg Pl Ste 3200
Pittsburgh PA 15222
412 456-5700

(P-1495)
LAKE COUNTY WALNUT INC
4545 Loasa Dr, Kelseyville (95451)
P.O. Box 308 (95451-0308)
PHONE..................................707 279-1200
Ray Snyder, *President*
Mark Snyder, *Vice Pres*
EMP: 18
SALES (est): 2.1MM **Privately Held**
WEB: www.lcwalnut.com
SIC: 2068 Nuts: dried, dehydrated, salted or roasted

(P-1496)
MELLACE FAMILY BRANDS INC
6195 El Camino Real, Carlsbad (92009-1602)
P.O. Box 22831, San Diego (92192-2831)
PHONE..................................760 448-1940
Michael Mellace, *President*
▲ **EMP:** 125
SQ FT: 45,000

SALES (est): 16.1MM **Privately Held**
SIC: 2068 Nuts: dried, dehydrated, salted or roasted

(P-1497)
MELLACE FAMILY BRANDS CAL INC
6195 El Camino Real, Carlsbad (92009-1602)
P.O. Box 22831, San Diego (92192-2831)
PHONE..................................760 448-1940
V Pulla, *President*
Vincent Cosentino, *CFO*
J Pulla, *Vice Pres*
EMP: 50
SQ FT: 50,000
SALES (est): 4.2MM
SALES (corp-wide): 143.1MM **Privately Held**
SIC: 2068 Salted & roasted nuts & seeds
PA: Johnvince Foods
555 Steeprock Dr
North York ON M3J 2
416 636-6146

(P-1498)
MIXED NUTS INC
3366 Fruitland Ave, Vernon (90058-3714)
PHONE..................................323 587-6887
Vanik Hartounian, *President*
▲ **EMP:** 25
SQ FT: 25,000
SALES (est): 6.4MM **Privately Held**
WEB: www.mixednutsinc.com
SIC: 2068 5145 Nuts: dried, dehydrated, salted or roasted; nuts, salted or roasted

(P-1499)
NATIONAL PECAN SHELLING (HQ)
Also Called: National Pecan-Youn
1050 Diamond St, Stockton (95205-7020)
PHONE..................................800 952-7771
Gary Ford, *CEO*
Steve Zaffarano, *President*
Todd Ojo, *CFO*
Karen Birmingham, *Hum Res Coord*
◆ **EMP:** 15
SQ FT: 85,000
SALES (est): 18.4MM **Privately Held**
SIC: 2068 Nuts: dried, dehydrated, salted or roasted
PA: Diamond Foods Llc
6300 West Loop S
Bellaire TX 77401
713 791-9167

(P-1500)
NICHOLS PISTACHIO
Also Called: Nichols Farms
13762 1st Ave, Hanford (93230-9316)
PHONE..................................559 584-6811
Susan Nichols, *Treasurer*
Kari Arnett, *Sales Staff*
Nicholas Rush, *Manager*
◆ **EMP:** 200
SQ FT: 110,000
SALES (est): 54.1MM **Privately Held**
SIC: 2068 Salted & roasted nuts & seeds

(P-1501)
PADDACK ENTERPRISES
Also Called: Paddack Almond Hlling Shelling
27052 State Highway 120, Escalon (95320-9502)
PHONE..................................209 838-1536
Vernon Paddack, *President*
Pauline Paddack, *Treasurer*
EMP: 25
SQ FT: 3,000
SALES (est): 1.3MM **Privately Held**
WEB: www.pad-enterprises.com
SIC: 2068 Nuts: dried, dehydrated, salted or roasted

(P-1502)
PRIMEX FARMS LLC (PA)
16070 Wildwood Rd, Wasco (93280-9210)
PHONE..................................661 758-7790
Ali Amin, *President*
Andrik Sarkasian, *Human Res Dir*
Luis Fabian, *Plant Mgr*
Mark Sherrell, *Plant Mgr*
EMP: 30
SQ FT: 136,837

SALES: 116.5MM **Privately Held**
WEB: www.primexfarms.com
SIC: 2068 Nuts: dried, dehydrated, salted or roasted

(P-1503)
SNAK CLUB LLC
Also Called: New Century Snacks
5560 E Slauson Ave, Commerce (90040-2921)
PHONE..................................323 278-9578
Farhad Morshed, *President*
EMP: 25
SALES (corp-wide): 177.6MM **Privately Held**
SIC: 2068 2099 Salted & roasted nuts & seeds; food preparations
HQ: Snak Club, Llc
607 N Nash St
El Segundo CA 90245
310 322-4400

(P-1504)
STEWART & JASPER MARKETING INC (PA)
Also Called: Stewart & Jasper Orchards
3500 Shiells Rd, Newman (95360-9798)
PHONE..................................209 862-9600
Jim Jasper, *President*
Susan S Dompe, *Corp Secy*
Ray Henriques, *Vice Pres*
Jason Jasper, *Vice Pres*
Jeff Meyer, *Controller*
▼ **EMP:** 175
SQ FT: 225,000
SALES (est): 54.5MM **Privately Held**
WEB: www.stewartandjasper.com
SIC: 2068 0723 0173 5148 Nuts: dried, dehydrated, salted or roasted; crop preparation services for market; almond hulling & shelling services; tree nuts; fresh fruits & vegetables; food preparations

(P-1505)
SUNDIAL ORCHRDS HULLING DRYING
1500 Kirk Rd, Gridley (95948-9417)
PHONE..................................530 846-6155
Brad Barrow, *Principal*
EMP: 20
SALES (est): 1.9MM **Privately Held**
SIC: 2068 Nuts: dried, dehydrated, salted or roasted

(P-1506)
WIZARD MANUFACTURING INC
2244 Ivy St, Chico (95928-7172)
PHONE..................................530 342-1861
Alan Reiff, *CEO*
Justin McCurdy, *Engineer*
Bruce Clements, *Purchasing*
Dave Mulqueeney, *Buyer*
EMP: 19
SALES (est): 3.5MM **Privately Held**
SIC: 2068 Nuts: dried, dehydrated, salted or roasted

(P-1507)
WONDERFUL PSTCHIOS ALMONDS LLC (HQ)
Also Called: Paramount Farms
11444 W Olympic Blvd, Los Angeles (90064-1549)
P.O. Box 200937, Dallas TX (75320-0937)
PHONE..................................310 966-4650
Stewart Resnick, *President*
Gary Dunn, *CFO*
Bill Phillimore, *Exec VP*
Craig B Cooper, *Senior VP*
Mike Celani, *Vice Pres*
◆ **EMP:** 25
SQ FT: 15,000
SALES (est): 402.5MM
SALES (corp-wide): 1.5B **Privately Held**
WEB: www.almondaccents.com
SIC: 2068 Salted & roasted nuts & seeds
PA: The Wonderful Company Llc
11444 W Olympic Blvd # 210
Los Angeles CA 90064
310 966-5700

PRODUCTS & SVCS

2075 Soybean Oil Mills

(P-1508)
GOLDEN GATE TOFU INCORPORATED
1265 Griffith St, San Francisco (94124-3408)
PHONE....................415 822-5613
Robert Chen, *President*
▲ EMP: 14
SALES (est): 1.7MM **Privately Held**
SIC: 2075 Soybean protein concentrates & isolates

(P-1509)
HOUSE FOODS AMERICA CORP (HQ)
Also Called: Hinoichi Tofu
7351 Orangewood Ave, Garden Grove (92841-1411)
PHONE....................714 901-4350
Tatsumi Yamaguchi, *President*
▲ EMP: 180
SQ FT: 30,000
SALES (est): 26.6MM
SALES (corp-wide): 2.5B **Privately Held**
WEB: www.house-foods.com
SIC: 2075 Soybean oil, cake or meal
PA: House Foods Group Inc.
1-5-7, Sakaemachi, Mikuriya
Higashi-Osaka OSK 577-0
667 881-231

(P-1510)
MIYAKO ORIENTAL FOODS INC
4287 Puente Ave, Baldwin Park (91706-3420)
PHONE....................626 962-9633
Noritoshi Kanai, *President*
Teruo Shimizu, *Vice Pres*
▲ EMP: 14
SQ FT: 18,000
SALES (est): 2.9MM
SALES (corp-wide): 2.5B **Privately Held**
WEB: www.coldmountainmiso.com
SIC: 2075 Soybean oil, cake or meal
HQ: Mutual Trading Co., Inc.
431 Crocker St
Los Angeles CA 90013
213 626-9458

(P-1511)
MLINE TRANSPORTATION COMPANY
6621 Clear Creek Ct, Citrus Heights (95610-4609)
P.O. Box 643 (95611-0643)
PHONE....................916 729-1053
Mary Jo Rablin, *President*
EMP: 29
SALES (est): 3MM **Privately Held**
SIC: 2075 4731 Soybean oil mills; truck transportation brokers

(P-1512)
SOYFOODS OF AMERICA
1091 Hamilton Rd, Duarte (91010-2743)
PHONE....................626 358-3836
Ka Nin Lee, *President*
EMP: 27
SQ FT: 15,000
SALES (est): 4.9MM **Privately Held**
WEB: www.soyfoods.org
SIC: 2075 Soybean oil mills

(P-1513)
VISOY FOOD PRODUCTS & MFG INC
111 W Elmyra St, Los Angeles (90012-1818)
PHONE....................323 221-4079
Wayne Wong, *President*
Lap T Kwan, *Vice Pres*
EMP: 10
SQ FT: 2,500
SALES (est): 848.1K
SALES (corp-wide): 975.1K **Privately Held**
SIC: 2075 Soybean oil mills

PA: Zhuhai Bocom Pharmacy Co., Ltd.
Xiaolin Hongdengwei,Hongqi
Town,Jinwang District
Zhuhai 51909
756 399-2888

2076 Vegetable Oil Mills

(P-1514)
AMERICAN VEGETABLE OILS INC
Also Called: Avo
7244 Condor Ave, Commerce (90040-2702)
PHONE....................800 728-8089
Jiayang Tsai, *CEO*
◆ EMP: 10
SQ FT: 25,500
SALES (est): 2.9MM **Privately Held**
SIC: 2076 Vegetable oil mills

(P-1515)
BUNGE OILS INC
Also Called: Bunge North America
436 S Mcclure Rd, Modesto (95357-0519)
PHONE....................209 574-9981
Dale Casky, *Manager*
Simon Stoakes, *Comptroller*
EMP: 72
SQ FT: 76,824 **Privately Held**
WEB: www.bungeoils.com
SIC: 2076 Vegetable oil mills
HQ: Bunge Oils, Inc.
11720 Borman Dr
Saint Louis MO 63146
314 292-2000

(P-1516)
PEARL CROP INC
Also Called: Turkhan Nuts
17641 French Camp Rd, Ripon (95366-9799)
PHONE....................209 982-9933
EMP: 25
SALES (corp-wide): 140MM **Privately Held**
SIC: 2076 Walnut oil; tung oil
PA: Pearl Crop, Inc.
1550 Industrial Dr
Stockton CA 95206
209 808-7575

(P-1517)
WILMAR OILS FATS STOCKTON LLC
2008 Port Road B, Stockton (95203-2923)
PHONE....................925 627-1600
Thomas Lim, *Mng Member*
SNG Miow Ching,
Mike Fargas,
▲ EMP: 25
SALES: 136MM **Privately Held**
SIC: 2076 Palm kernel oil

2077 Animal, Marine Fats & Oils

(P-1518)
ARTISAN MOSS LLC
3450 Palmer Dr Ste 4, Cameron Park (95682-8274)
PHONE....................833 667-7278
Erin Kinsey,
EMP: 15 EST: 2016
SALES (est): 1.3MM **Privately Held**
SIC: 2077 Animal & marine fats & oils

(P-1519)
BAKER COMMODITIES INC (PA)
4020 Bandini Blvd, Vernon (90058-4274)
PHONE....................323 268-2801
James M Andreoli, *President*
Denis Luckey, *Exec VP*
Mitchell Ebright, *Vice Pres*
▼ EMP: 150
SQ FT: 12,000
SALES: 161.3MM **Privately Held**
WEB: www.bakercommodities.com
SIC: 2077 2048 Tallow rendering, inedible; poultry feeds

(P-1520)
BAKER COMMODITIES INC
16801 W Jensen Ave, Kerman (93630-9194)
P.O. Box 416 (93630-0416)
PHONE....................559 237-4320
Manuel Ponte, *Director*
EMP: 30
SQ FT: 28,690
SALES (corp-wide): 161.3MM **Privately Held**
WEB: www.bakercommodities.com
SIC: 2077 Tallow rendering, inedible
PA: Baker Commodities, Inc.
4020 Bandini Blvd
Vernon CA 90058
323 268-2801

(P-1521)
BAKER COMMODITIES INC
7480 Hanford Armona Rd, Hanford (93230-9343)
P.O. Box 1286 (93232-1286)
PHONE....................559 686-4797
Doug Fletcher, *Manager*
EMP: 26
SALES (corp-wide): 161.3MM **Privately Held**
WEB: www.bakercommodities.com
SIC: 2077 2048 Tallow rendering, inedible; prepared feeds
PA: Baker Commodities, Inc.
4020 Bandini Blvd
Vernon CA 90058
323 268-2801

(P-1522)
BAKER COMMODITIES INC
3001 Sierra Pine Ave, Vernon (90058-4120)
PHONE....................323 318-8260
EMP: 38
SALES (corp-wide): 161.3MM **Privately Held**
SIC: 2077 Animal & marine fats & oils
PA: Baker Commodities, Inc.
4020 Bandini Blvd
Vernon CA 90058
323 268-2801

(P-1523)
CAPTEK SOFTGEL INTL INC (PA)
16218 Arthur St, Cerritos (90703-2131)
PHONE....................562 921-9511
David Wood, *CEO*
Tim Chiprich, *President*
Lisa Clark, *President*
Bart Smith, *COO*
Joseph Sklencar, *CFO*
▲ EMP: 147
SQ FT: 90,000
SALES (est): 140.5MM **Privately Held**
WEB: www.capteksoftgel.com
SIC: 2077 2834 Fish oil; vitamin, nutrient & hematinic preparations for human use

(P-1524)
DARLING INGREDIENTS INC
429 Amador St Pier 92, San Francisco (94124-1232)
P.O. Box 880006 (94188-0006)
PHONE....................415 647-4890
Gene Hanson, *General Mgr*
Don Desmet, *General Mgr*
Steve Pieroni, *General Mgr*
EMP: 55
SALES (corp-wide): 3.6B **Publicly Held**
WEB: www.darlingii.com
SIC: 2077 2048 5172 Grease rendering, inedible; tallow rendering, inedible; bone meal, except as animal feed; meat meal & tankage, except as animal feed; prepared feeds; lubricating oils & greases
PA: Darling Ingredients Inc.
251 Oconnor Ridge Blvd
Irving TX 75038
972 717-0300

(P-1525)
DARLING INGREDIENTS INC
795 W Belgravia Ave, Fresno (93706)
P.O. Box 11445 (93773-1445)
PHONE....................559 268-5325
Edward H Jenkins, *Manager*
EMP: 30
SQ FT: 10,500

SALES (corp-wide): 3.6B **Publicly Held**
WEB: www.darlingii.com
SIC: 2077 2048 Animal & marine fats & oils; prepared feeds
PA: Darling Ingredients Inc.
251 Oconnor Ridge Blvd
Irving TX 75038
972 717-0300

(P-1526)
DARLING INGREDIENTS INC
2626 E 25th St, Los Angeles (90058-1212)
P.O. Box 58725 (90058-0725)
PHONE....................323 583-6311
Thomas Nunley, *General Mgr*
Adam Roth, *Manager*
EMP: 77
SALES (corp-wide): 3.6B **Publicly Held**
WEB: www.darlingii.com
SIC: 2077 2048 Animal & marine fats & oils; prepared feeds
PA: Darling Ingredients Inc.
251 Oconnor Ridge Blvd
Irving TX 75038
972 717-0300

(P-1527)
DARLING INTERNATIONAL INC
11946 Carpenter Rd, Crows Landing (95313-9749)
P.O. Box 1608, Turlock (95381-1608)
PHONE....................209 667-9153
Dick Labuga, *General Mgr*
Richard Searcy, *Plant Mgr*
EMP: 35
SQ FT: 43,498
SALES (corp-wide): 3.6B **Publicly Held**
WEB: www.darlingii.com
SIC: 2077 2048 Grease rendering, inedible; tallow rendering, inedible; bone meal, except as animal feed; meat meal & tankage, except as animal feed; prepared feeds
PA: Darling Ingredients Inc.
251 Oconnor Ridge Blvd
Irving TX 75038
972 717-0300

(P-1528)
JR GREASE SERVICES
5900 S Eastrn Ave Ste 104, Commerce (90040)
P.O. Box 226894, Los Angeles (90022-0594)
PHONE....................323 318-2096
Jesse Rodriguez, *Principal*
EMP: 20
SALES (est): 2MM **Privately Held**
SIC: 2077 Grease rendering, inedible

(P-1529)
NORDIC NATURALS INC (PA)
Also Called: Westport Scandinavia
111 Jennings Way, Watsonville (95076-2054)
PHONE....................800 662-2544
Joar A Opheim, *CEO*
Michele Opheim, *Vice Pres*
Cecile Lariviere, *Comms Dir*
Mark Timares, *Info Tech Mgr*
Oscar Alaniz, *Tech/Comp Coord*
▲ EMP: 115
SALES (est): 29.3MM **Privately Held**
WEB: www.nordicnaturals.com
SIC: 2077 Fish oil

(P-1530)
NORTH STATE RENDERING CO INC
15 Shippee Rd, Oroville (95965-9297)
P.O. Box 1478, Chico (95927-1478)
PHONE....................530 343-6076
Chris Ottone, *President*
Patrick Ottone, *Vice Pres*
William Ottone, *Admin Sec*
EMP: 23
SQ FT: 15,000
SALES (est): 3.7MM **Privately Held**
SIC: 2077 Tallow rendering, inedible

(P-1531)
PARK WEST ENTERPRISES
Also Called: Co-West Commodities
2586 Shenandoah Way, San Bernardino (92407-1845)
PHONE....................909 383-8341

Sergio Perez, *CEO*
Freddie Peterson, *CFO*
EMP: 30
SALES (est): 7MM **Privately Held**
SIC: 2077 Animal & marine fats & oils

(P-1532)
SALINAS TALLOW CO INC
1 Work Cir, Salinas (93901-4349)
PHONE...................................831 422-6436
William Ottone, *President*
Philip Ottone, *Vice Pres*
EMP: 20
SALES (est): 3.4MM **Privately Held**
SIC: 2077 2079 Tallow rendering, inedible; cooking oils, except corn: vegetable refined

(P-1533)
SRC MILLING CO LLC
Also Called: Sacramento Rendering Co
11350 Kiefer Blvd, Sacramento (95830-9405)
PHONE...................................916 363-4821
Jim Walsh, *Mng Member*
A Michael Koewler,
Michael Patrick Koewler,
Timothy D Koewler,
Richard Wilbur,
▲ **EMP:** 20 **EST:** 1996
SALES (est): 2.9MM **Privately Held**
WEB: www.srccompanies.com
SIC: 2077 Rendering

2079 Shortening, Oils & Margarine

(P-1534)
ALHAMBRA VALLEY OLIVE OIL CO (PA)
5371 Stonehurst Dr, Martinez (94553-9642)
PHONE...................................925 370-8500
Tom Powers, *Principal*
EMP: 10 **EST:** 2008
SALES (est): 18.2MM **Privately Held**
SIC: 2079 Olive oil

(P-1535)
CALIFORNIA OLIVE AND VINE LLC
Also Called: Sutter Buttes Olive Oil
1670 Poole Blvd, Yuba City (95993-2610)
PHONE...................................530 763-7921
Alka Kumar, *President*
EMP: 15
SQ FT: 10,000
SALES (est): 3MM **Privately Held**
SIC: 2079 5921 Olive oil; liquor stores

(P-1536)
CALIFORNIA OLIVE RANCH INC (PA)
1367 E Lassen Ave Ste A1, Chico (95973-7881)
PHONE...................................530 846-8000
Gregory B Kelly, *CEO*
Pedro Olabrria, *Ch of Bd*
Mike Forbes, *Vice Pres*
Jim Lipman, *Vice Pres*
Antonio Valla, *Vice Pres*
◆ **EMP:** 43
SALES (est): 14.4MM **Privately Held**
WEB: www.californiaoliveranch.com
SIC: 2079 Olive oil

(P-1537)
CARGILL INCORPORATED
566 N Gilbert St, Fullerton (92833-2549)
PHONE...................................323 588-2274
EMP: 50
SQ FT: 28,410
SALES (corp-wide): 134.8B **Privately Held**
SIC: 2079 2046 2013 2011
PA: Cargill, Incorporated
15407 Mcginty Rd W
Wayzata MN 55391
952 742-7575

(P-1538)
CIUTI INTERNATIONAL INC
Also Called: Cuiti International
8790 Rochester Ave Ste A, Rancho Cucamonga (91730-4925)
PHONE...................................909 484-1414
Marcello Trincale, *CEO*
Eric Trincale, *President*
▲ **EMP:** 15
SQ FT: 20,000
SALES: 18MM **Privately Held**
SIC: 2079 5149 Olive oil; groceries & related products

(P-1539)
DECAMILLA BROTHERS LLC
Also Called: West Coast Products
717 Tehama St, Orland (95963-1248)
PHONE...................................530 865-3379
Mark J De Camilla, *Mng Member*
▲ **EMP:** 12
SALES (est): 1.4MM **Privately Held**
SIC: 2079 Olive oil

(P-1540)
GEMSA ENTERPRISES LLC
Also Called: Gemsa Oils
14370 Gannet St, La Mirada (90638-5221)
PHONE...................................714 521-1736
Emilio Viscomi, *Principal*
Angela Verrico Viscomi,
▲ **EMP:** 20
SQ FT: 60,000
SALES (est): 7.3MM **Privately Held**
SIC: 2079 Edible fats & oils

(P-1541)
IL FIORELLO OLIVE OIL CO
2625 Mankas Corner Rd, Fairfield (94534-3137)
PHONE...................................707 864-1529
Mark Sievers, *Owner*
Ann Sievers, *Co-Owner*
Stephanie Oriarte, *Manager*
▲ **EMP:** 50
SQ FT: 5,000
SALES (est): 3.8MM **Privately Held**
SIC: 2079 2084 Olive oil; wines

(P-1542)
LIBERTY VEGETABLE OIL COMPANY
15306 Carmenita Rd, Santa Fe Springs (90670-5606)
P.O. Box 4207, Cerritos (90703-4207)
PHONE...................................562 921-3567
Irwin Field, *President*
Ronald Field, *Admin Sec*
Edward Field, *VP Finance*
Jim Tomchak, *Consultant*
▼ **EMP:** 20 **EST:** 1948
SQ FT: 30,000
SALES (est): 11.2MM **Privately Held**
SIC: 2079 Olive oil

(P-1543)
LUCERO OLIVE OIL MNFACTURE LLC (PA)
2120 Loleta Ave, Corning (96021-9696)
PHONE...................................530 824-2190
Robert Crane, *Mng Member*
Liz Tagami, *General Mgr*
Joe Antonucci, *Controller*
▲ **EMP:** 20 **EST:** 2008
SQ FT: 50,000
SALES: 4MM **Privately Held**
SIC: 2079 Olive oil

(P-1544)
MCEVOY OF MARIN LLC
Also Called: McEvoy Ranch
5935 Red Hill Rd, Petaluma (94952-9437)
P.O. Box 341 (94953-0341)
PHONE...................................707 778-2307
Nion McEvoy,
Nan Tucker McEvoy,
▲ **EMP:** 100
SALES (est): 17.3MM **Privately Held**
SIC: 2079 Olive oil

(P-1545)
MY FRUITY FACES LLC
2400 Lincoln Ave, Altadena (91001-5436)
PHONE...................................877 358-9210
Bob D Ntoya, *Mng Member*

Kevin Cammarata,
Adam Gerber,
Jason Gerber,
Brian Jones,
EMP: 10
SALES: 1MM **Privately Held**
SIC: 2079 Edible fats & oils; gelatin: edible, technical, photographic or pharmaceutical
PA: 3becom, Inc.
2400 Lincoln Ave Ste 216
Altadena CA 91001
-

(P-1546)
NICK SCIABICA & SONS A CORP
Also Called: Sciabica's
2150 Yosemite Blvd, Modesto (95354-3931)
PHONE...................................209 577-5067
Gemma Sciabica, *CEO*
Joseph N Sciabica, *President*
Daniel R Sciabica, *Corp Secy*
Craig Hilliker, *Project Mgr*
Guadalupe Hernandez, *Warehouse Mgr*
▲ **EMP:** 20 **EST:** 1925
SQ FT: 68,728
SALES (est): 4.7MM **Privately Held**
WEB: www.sciabica.com
SIC: 2079 5149 Olive oil; cooking oils

(P-1547)
OLIVE BARI OIL COMPANY
40063 Road 56, Dinuba (93618-9708)
PHONE...................................559 595-9260
Kyle Sawatzky, *CEO*
Ryan Sawatzky, *COO*
Breann Janes, *Sales Mgr*
Breann Borges, *Accounts Mgr*
EMP: 12
SQ FT: 20,000
SALES: 500K **Privately Held**
SIC: 2079 Olive oil

(P-1548)
OLIVE BARIANI OIL LLC
1330 Waller St, San Francisco (94117-2921)
PHONE...................................415 864-1917
Emmanuel Bariani, *Principal*
EMP: 19
SALES (corp-wide): 569.7K **Privately Held**
SIC: 2079 Olive oil
PA: Olive Bariani Oil Llc
9460 Bar Du Ln
Sacramento CA 95829
530 666-1563

(P-1549)
OLIVE CORTO L P
10201 Live Oak Rd, Stockton (95212-9319)
P.O. Box 1706, Lodi (95241-1706)
PHONE...................................209 888-8100
Brady Whitlow, *President*
▲ **EMP:** 15
SALES: 4MM **Privately Held**
WEB: www.corto-olive.com
SIC: 2079 Olive oil

(P-1550)
OLIVE PRESS LLC (PA)
24724 Arnold Dr, Sonoma (95476-2814)
PHONE...................................707 939-8900
Ed Stolman,
Eve Priestly, *Controller*
Chris Gilmore, *Prdtn Mgr*
Debra Rogers,
▲ **EMP:** 12
SALES (est): 28.5MM **Privately Held**
WEB: www.theolivepress.com
SIC: 2079 5199 Olive oil; oils, animal or vegetable

(P-1551)
SPECTRUM ORGANIC PRODUCTS LLC
Also Called: Spectrum Naturals
2201 S Mcdowell Blvd Ext, Petaluma (94954-7624)
PHONE...................................888 343-6637
Neil G Blomquist, *President*
Jethren P Phillips, *Ch of Bd*
Randall H Sias, *Vice Pres*
Nils Michael Langenborg, *VP Mktg*

▲ **EMP:** 66 **EST:** 1980
SQ FT: 18,600
SALES (est): 13.4MM **Publicly Held**
WEB: www.spectrumorganics.com
SIC: 2079 2035 2099 2834 Edible fats & oils; dressings, salad: raw & cooked (except dry mixes); mayonnaise; vinegar; vitamin, nutrient & hematinic preparations for human use
PA: The Hain Celestial Group Inc
1111 Marcus Ave Ste 100
New Hyde Park NY 11042

(P-1552)
VENTURA FOODS LLC
2900 Jurupa St, Ontario (91761-2915)
PHONE...................................714 257-3700
Wayne Kess, *Manager*
EMP: 164 **Privately Held**
WEB: www.venturafoods.com
SIC: 2079 2035 Vegetable shortenings (except corn oil); cooking oils, except corn: vegetable refined; pickles, sauces & salad dressings
PA: Ventura Foods, Llc
40 Pointe Dr
Brea CA 92821

(P-1553)
VENTURA FOODS LLC (PA)
Also Called: Lou Ana Foods
40 Pointe Dr, Brea (92821-3652)
PHONE...................................714 257-3700
Christopher Furman, *President*
Scott Anthony, *CFO*
Andy Euser, *Officer*
Alan Blake, *Exec VP*
John Buckles, *Exec VP*
◆ **EMP:** 200
SALES (est): 218.3MM **Privately Held**
WEB: www.venturafoods.com
SIC: 2079 2035 Vegetable shortenings (except corn oil); cooking oils, except corn: vegetable refined; pickles, sauces & salad dressings

(P-1554)
VERONICA FOODS COMPANY
1991 Dennison St, Oakland (94606-5225)
P.O. Box 2225 (94621-0125)
PHONE...................................510 535-6833
Michael Bradley, *President*
Veronica Bradley, *Vice Pres*
◆ **EMP:** 50 **EST:** 1940
SALES (est): 11.1MM **Privately Held**
WEB: www.evoliveoil.com
SIC: 2079 5149 Cooking oils, except corn: vegetable refined; olive oil; salad oils, except corn: vegetable refined; cooking oils & shortenings; dried or canned foods

(P-1555)
WILSEY FOODS INC
40 Pointe Dr, Brea (92821-3652)
PHONE...................................714 257-3700
Takashi Fukunaga, *CEO*
Steve Takagi, *President*
Hiro Matsumura, *Vice Pres*
◆ **EMP:** 2100
SQ FT: 103,378
SALES (est): 210MM
SALES (corp-wide): 45.9B **Privately Held**
SIC: 2079 5149 Cooking oils, except corn: vegetable refined; vegetable shortenings (except corn oil); shortening, vegetable
PA: Mitsui & Co., Ltd.
1-1-3, Marunouchi
Chiyoda-Ku TKY 100-0
332 851-111

2082 Malt Beverages

(P-1556)
23 BOTTLES OF BEER LLC
Also Called: Russian River Brewing Co
725 4th St, Santa Rosa (95404-4407)
PHONE...................................707 545-2337
Vinnie Cilurzo, *Mng Member*
Natalie Cilurzo,
▲ **EMP:** 40
SALES (est): 7.7MM **Privately Held**
WEB: www.russianriverbrewing.com
SIC: 2082 Beer (alcoholic beverage)

(P-1557)
ABSOLUTION BREWING
COMPANY (PA)
2878 Columbia St, Torrance (90503-3808)
PHONE...................................310 787-9563
Nigel Heath, *CEO*
Steve Farguson, *Admin Sec*
▲ EMP: 10 EST: 2013
SQ FT: 7,000
SALES (est): 1.5MM Privately Held
SIC: 2082 Malt liquors

(P-1558)
ANDERSON VALLEY BREWING
INC
Also Called: Anderson Valley Brewing Co
17700 Hwy 253, Boonville (95415)
P.O. Box 505 (95415-0505)
PHONE...................................707 895-2337
Kenneth D Allen, *President*
Tara Abrams, *Area Mgr*
Steve Miller, *Marketing Mgr*
Mike Halligan, *Sales Staff*
Jason Raimondi, *Maintenance Dir*
◆ EMP: 45
SQ FT: 5,000
SALES (est): 8.6MM Privately Held
SIC: 2082 5812 Ale (alcoholic beverage);
porter (alcoholic beverage); stout (alcoholic beverage); cafe

(P-1559)
ANHEUSER-BUSCH LLC
15800 Roscoe Blvd, Van Nuys
(91406-1379)
PHONE...................................818 989-5300
Gary P Lee, *Manager*
Aida Miller, *Treasurer*
Kathy Casso, *Vice Pres*
Bruce Borst, *General Mgr*
Luis Cayo, *General Mgr*
EMP: 162
SALES (corp-wide): 1.9B Privately Held
WEB: www.hispanicbud.com
SIC: 2082 Beer (alcoholic beverage)
HQ: Anheuser-Busch, Llc
1 Busch Pl
Saint Louis MO 63118
314 632-6777

(P-1560)
ANHEUSER-BUSCH LLC
5959 Santa Fe St, San Diego
(92109-1623)
P.O. Box 80758 (92138-0758)
PHONE...................................858 581-7000
Denise Cooper, *General Mgr*
Daniel Dahistrom, *Opers Mgr*
Randy Burch, *Plant Mgr*
Vince Gonzalez, *Mktg Dir*
Marie Foley, *Accounts Mgr*
EMP: 200
SALES (corp-wide): 1.9B Privately Held
WEB: www.hispanicbud.com
SIC: 2082 Beer (alcoholic beverage)
HQ: Anheuser-Busch, Llc
1 Busch Pl
Saint Louis MO 63118
314 632-6777

(P-1561)
ARTISAN BREWERS LLC
Also Called: Drake's Brewing Company
1933 Davis St Ste 177, San Leandro
(94577-1256)
PHONE...................................510 567-4926
John Martin,
Roy Kirkorian,
◆ EMP: 44
SALES (est): 5.9MM Privately Held
SIC: 2082 Beer (alcoholic beverage)

(P-1562)
ASSOCIATED
MICROBREWERIES INC
9675 Scranton Rd, San Diego
(92121-1761)
PHONE...................................858 587-2739
Bryan King, *Branch Mgr*
EMP: 93
SALES (corp-wide): 72.1MM Privately
Held
SIC: 2082 Beer (alcoholic beverage)

PA: Associated Microbreweries, Inc.
5985 Santa Fe St
San Diego CA 92109
858 273-2739

(P-1563)
ASSOCIATED
MICROBREWERIES INC
901 S Coast Dr Ste A, Costa Mesa
(92626-7790)
PHONE...................................714 546-2739
David Sadeler, *Manager*
EMP: 70
SALES (corp-wide): 72.1MM Privately
Held
SIC: 2082 Beer (alcoholic beverage)
PA: Associated Microbreweries, Inc.
5985 Santa Fe St
San Diego CA 92109
858 273-2739

(P-1564)
ASSOCIATED
MICROBREWERIES INC (PA)
Also Called: Karl Strauss Brewery Garden
5985 Santa Fe St, San Diego
(92109-1623)
PHONE...................................858 273-2739
Christopher W Cramer, *President*
Matthew H Rattner, *CFO*
EMP: 50
SQ FT: 2,000
SALES (est): 72.1MM Privately Held
WEB: www.karlstrauss.com
SIC: 2082 5812 Beer (alcoholic beverage); ale (alcoholic beverage); eating
places

(P-1565)
ASSOCIATED
MICROBREWERIES INC
Also Called: Karl Strauss Brewery & Rest
1157 Columbia St, San Diego
(92101-3511)
PHONE...................................619 234-2739
Shawn Phaby, *Manager*
EMP: 105
SALES (corp-wide): 72.1MM Privately
Held
WEB: www.karlstrauss.com
SIC: 2082 5812 Beer (alcoholic beverage); eating places
PA: Associated Microbreweries, Inc.
5985 Santa Fe St
San Diego CA 92109
858 273-2739

(P-1566)
BALLAST POINT SPIRITS LLC
Also Called: Ballast Point Brewing
9045 Carroll Way, San Diego (92121-2405)
PHONE...................................858 695-2739
Jack R White, *Principal*
Jeremy Kirby, *Vice Pres*
Lacey Henderson, *General Mgr*
Julia Cain, *Research*
Steve Burchill, *Engineer*
◆ EMP: 148
SALES: 26.6MM
SALES (corp-wide): 7.5B Publicly Held
SIC: 2082 Malt beverages
HQ: Home Brew Mart, Inc.
9045 Carroll Way
San Diego CA 92121

(P-1567)
BAREBOTTLE BREWING
COMPANY INC
1525 Cortland Ave # 6, San Francisco
(94110-5714)
PHONE...................................415 926-8617
Michael Seitz, *CEO*
Ben Sterling, *Principal*
Lester Koga, *Admin Sec*
EMP: 19 EST: 2011
SQ FT: 17,000
SALES: 550K Privately Held
SIC: 2082 Ale (alcoholic beverage)

(P-1568)
BEAR REPUBLIC BREWING CO
INC (PA)
110 Sandholm Ln Ste 10, Cloverdale
(95425-4439)
PHONE...................................707 894-2722
Richard R Norgrove, *President*
Tammy Hucke-Norgrove, *CFO*
Tami Norgrove, *CFO*
Sandra D Norgrove, *Admin Sec*
Kyle Ellis, *Manager*
EMP: 10
SQ FT: 6,500
SALES (est): 18.5MM Privately Held
WEB: www.bearrepublic.com
SIC: 2082 5812 5813 Beer (alcoholic beverage); eating places; drinking places

(P-1569)
BEAR REPUBLIC BREWING CO
INC
345 Healdsburg Ave, Healdsburg
(95448-4105)
PHONE...................................707 433-2337
Richard Norgrove, *Branch Mgr*
EMP: 10
SALES (est): 926.8K Privately Held
SIC: 2082 Beer (alcoholic beverage)
PA: Bear Republic Brewing Co Inc
110 Sandholm Ln Ste 10
Cloverdale CA 95425

(P-1570)
BELCHING BEAVER BREWERY
1334 Rocky Point Dr, Oceanside
(92056-5864)
PHONE...................................760 599-5832
Tom Vogel, *Owner*
EMP: 145
SALES: 17MM Privately Held
SIC: 2082 Malt beverages

(P-1571)
BLANCO BASURA BEVERAGE
INC
Also Called: Bruvado Imports
5776 Stoneridge Mall Rd # 338, Pleasanton
(94588-2832)
PHONE...................................888 705-7225
Scott D Gold, *CEO*
Chad Blair, *President*
Pete Noto, *President*
Karen Watts, *CFO*
EMP: 150
SALES (est): 5.9MM Privately Held
SIC: 2082 Beer (alcoholic beverage)

(P-1572)
BLINKING OWL DISTILLERY
210 N Bush St, Santa Ana (92701-5361)
PHONE...................................949 370-4688
Thomas A Zeigler, *Principal*
▲ EMP: 10
SALES (est): 619.9K Privately Held
SIC: 2082 Beer (alcoholic beverage)

(P-1573)
BREW4U LLC
935 Washington St, San Carlos
(94070-5316)
PHONE...................................415 516-8211
Christopher Garrett, *Mng Member*
EMP: 15
SALES (est): 1.3MM Privately Held
SIC: 2082 2812 Beer (alcoholic beverage); soda ash, sodium carbonate (anhydrous)

(P-1574)
BREWMASTER INC
Also Called: Speakeasy Ales & Lagers
1195 Evans Ave, San Francisco
(94124-1704)
P.O. Box 882724 (94188-2724)
PHONE...................................415 642-3371
Thomas E Baird, *CEO*
Forest Gray, *President*
Kushal Hall, *Sales Dir*
Dan Ghiglieri, *Manager*
Andrew Swatzell, *Manager*
▲ EMP: 33
SQ FT: 11,000

SALES (est): 7.7MM Privately Held
WEB: www.goodbeer.com
SIC: 2082 Beer (alcoholic beverage)
PA: Hunters Point Brewery, Llc
8380 Pardee Dr
Oakland CA
-

(P-1575)
BU LLC
9073 Pulsar Ct Ste A, Corona
(92883-7357)
PHONE...................................951 277-7470
Ryan Mason, *Mng Member*
Andres Kummen, *Officer*
EMP: 15
SQ FT: 1,500
SALES: 2MM Privately Held
SIC: 2082 Malt beverages

(P-1576)
BUZZWORKS INC
365 11th St, San Francisco (94103-4313)
PHONE...................................415 863-5964
Vladimir Cood, *CEO*
EMP: 15
SALES (est): 1.2MM Privately Held
SIC: 2082 5813 Beer (alcoholic beverage); tavern (drinking places)

(P-1577)
CASA AGRIA
701 Del Norte Blvd, Oxnard (93030-7909)
PHONE...................................805 485-1454
Ryan Exline, *Principal*
EMP: 10
SALES (est): 1MM Privately Held
SIC: 2082 Malt beverages

(P-1578)
CHARLIES BEER COMPANY USA
LLC
9581 Bus Ctr Dr Ste G, Rancho Cucamonga (91730)
PHONE...................................909 980-0436
Lamont Jefferies,
▲ EMP: 13
SQ FT: 1,800
SALES (est): 1.5MM Privately Held
SIC: 2082 Beer (alcoholic beverage)

(P-1579)
CLEOPHUS QUEALY BEER
COMPANY
448 Hester St, San Leandro (94577-1024)
PHONE...................................510 463-4534
Peter Henderson Baker, *CEO*
Kate Albee, *Marketing Staff*
EMP: 10
SALES (est): 811.5K Privately Held
SIC: 2082 Beer (alcoholic beverage)

(P-1580)
COMEBACK BREWING II INC
Also Called: Trumer Brauerei
1404 4th St, Berkeley (94710-1323)
PHONE...................................510 526-1160
Carlos Alverez, *President*
Lars Larson, *Master*
EMP: 15
SALES (est): 2.2MM
SALES (corp-wide): 8.6MM Privately
Held
WEB: www.gambrinus.com
SIC: 2082 Beer (alcoholic beverage)
PA: Comeback Brewing Ii, Inc.
14800 San Pedro Ave Fl 3
San Antonio TX 78232
210 490-9128

(P-1581)
COORS BREWING COMPANY
3001 Douglas Blvd Ste 200, Roseville
(95661-3809)
PHONE...................................916 786-2666
Fax: 916 786-9396
EMP: 20
SALES (corp-wide): 3.5B Publicly Held
SIC: 2082 5181
HQ: Coors Brewing Company
17735 W 32nd Ave
Golden CO 80401
303 279-6565

▲ = Import ▼=Export
◆ =Import/Export

(P-1582)
CRISPINIAN INC
Also Called: Crispin Cider Works, The
1213 S Auburn St Ste A, Colfax
(95713-9800)
PHONE..................................530 346-8411
Scott Whitley, *CEO*
Trevor John Heron, *CEO*
Lesley Anne Heron, *Admin Sec*
▲ EMP: 22
SALES (est): 5.1MM **Privately Held**
SIC: 2082 5999 Ale (alcoholic beverage);
  alcoholic beverage making equipment &
  supplies

(P-1583)
CWS BEVERAGE
2732 Danley Ct Ste 101, Paso Robles
(93446-7020)
P.O. Box 457 (93447-0457)
PHONE..................................805 286-2735
EMP: 12
SALES (est): 1.3MM **Privately Held**
SIC: 2082

(P-1584)
CYDEA INC
Also Called: Beveragefactory.com
8510 Miralani Dr, San Diego (92126-4351)
PHONE..................................800 710-9939
Craig Costanzo, *President*
Michael Costanzo, *CFO*
Barbara Costanzo, *Admin Sec*
Schuyler Madsen, *Administration*
Rayna Jordan, *Opers Mgr*
◆ EMP: 20
SQ FT: 12,000
SALES (est): 6.1MM **Privately Held**
SIC: 2082 2084 5046 Beer (alcoholic bev-
  erage); wines, brandy & brandy spirits;
  coffee brewing equipment & supplies

(P-1585)
D&S BREWING SOLUTIONS INC
6148 E Oakbrook St, Long Beach
(90815-2228)
PHONE..................................650 207-4524
Dylan Mobley, *President*
EMP: 49 EST: 2014
SALES (est): 1.9MM **Privately Held**
SIC: 2082 Malt beverages

(P-1586)
DELTA COAST BEER LLC
2034 E Lincoln Ave, Anaheim
(92806-4101)
PHONE..................................213 604-2428
Daniel Wheeler, *CEO*
Wing Lam, *COO*
EMP: 10
SALES (est): 342.9K **Privately Held**
SIC: 2082 5182 7389 Beer (alcoholic bev-
  erage); liquor;

(P-1587)
DESERT BROTHERS CRAFT
Also Called: Angry Horse Brewing
603 W Whittier Blvd, Montebello
(90640-5235)
PHONE..................................323 530-0015
Nathan McCusker, *President*
EMP: 10 EST: 2014
SALES (est): 336.4K **Privately Held**
SIC: 2082 Malt beverages

(P-1588)
DUDES BREWING COMPANY
1840 W 208th St, Somis (93066)
P.O. Box 276 (93066-0276)
PHONE..................................424 271-2915
Toby Humes, *Owner*
EMP: 20
SALES (est): 2.4MM **Privately Held**
SIC: 2082 5921 Beer (alcoholic bever-
  age); beer (packaged)

(P-1589)
ENCINITAS OGGIS INC
305 Encinitas Blvd, Encinitas (92024-3724)
PHONE..................................760 579-3211
Charidy Mann Alcoser, *Principal*
EMP: 10
SALES (est): 924.4K **Privately Held**
SIC: 2082 Malt beverages

(P-1590)
ENGLISH ALES BREWERS INC
223 Reindollar Ave Ste A, Marina
(93933-3851)
PHONE..................................831 883-3000
Peter Blackwell, *President*
EMP: 11
SALES (est): 1.4MM **Privately Held**
WEB: www.englishalesbrewery.com
SIC: 2082 Beer (alcoholic beverage)

(P-1591)
FIRESTONE WALKER INC (PA)
Also Called: Firestone Walker Brewing Co
1400 Ramada Dr, Paso Robles
(93446-3993)
PHONE..................................805 225-5911
David Walker, *CEO*
Adam Firestone, *Principal*
▲ EMP: 225
SALES (est): 151.3MM **Privately Held**
WEB: www.firestonewalker.com
SIC: 2082 Beer (alcoholic beverage)

(P-1592)
FIRESTONE WALKER LLC
Also Called: Firestone Walker Brewing Co
10130 Commercial Ave, Penn Valley
(95946-9466)
PHONE..................................805 225-5911
David Walker, *CEO*
EMP: 64
SALES (corp-wide): 151.3MM **Privately Held**
SIC: 2082 Beer (alcoholic beverage)
PA: Firestone Walker, Inc.
  1400 Ramada Dr
  Paso Robles CA 93446
  805 225-5911

(P-1593)
FISH ON RICE LLC
Also Called: Kamikaze 7 Sushi Joint
3250 Grey Hawk Ct, Carlsbad
(92010-6651)
PHONE..................................619 696-6262
Kevin Telles Roberts, *Mng Member*
EMP: 10 EST: 2012
SALES (est): 972.7K **Privately Held**
SIC: 2082 Beer (alcoholic beverage)

(P-1594)
GFBC INC
Also Called: Green Flash Brewing
6550 Mira Mesa Blvd, San Diego
(92121-4100)
PHONE..................................858 622-0085
Michael Hinkley, *CEO*
Chris Ross, *COO*
Aaron Grossman, *Creative Dir*
Elena Bolino, *District Mgr*
Alex Padilla, *District Mgr*
EMP: 15
SALES (est): 3.6MM **Privately Held**
SIC: 2082 Beer (alcoholic beverage)

(P-1595)
GLACIER DESIGN SYSTEMS INC (PA)
5405 Production Dr, Huntington Beach
(92649-1524)
PHONE..................................714 897-2337
Robert Asahi, *VP Opers*
▲ EMP: 15
SQ FT: 8,500
SALES (est): 3.2MM **Privately Held**
WEB: www.glacier-design.com
SIC: 2082 5078 Beer (alcoholic bever-
  age); refrigerated beverage dispensers

(P-1596)
GORDON BIERSCH BREWING COMPANY
357 E Taylor St, San Jose (95112-3105)
PHONE..................................408 792-1546
William Bullard, *Manager*
EMP: 93
SALES (corp-wide): 108.9MM **Privately Held**
SIC: 2082 Malt beverages
PA: Gordon Biersch Brewing Company
  10801 W Charleston Blvd # 600
  Las Vegas NV 89135
  702 221-4475

(P-1597)
GRAMIC ENTERPRISES INC
21770 Deveron Cv, Yorba Linda
(92887-2662)
PHONE..................................714 329-8627
Michael Sy, *President*
▲ EMP: 15
SALES (est): 1.4MM **Privately Held**
SIC: 2082 Malt beverages

(P-1598)
HOLLISTER BREWING COMPANY LLC
6980 Market Place Dr, Goleta
(93117-2997)
PHONE..................................805 968-2810
Marshall A Rose,
Larry Kreider,
Eric Rose,
Jennifer Rose, *Manager*
EMP: 45
SALES (est): 5.8MM **Privately Held**
WEB: www.hollisterbrewco.com
SIC: 2082 Malt beverages

(P-1599)
HOME BREW MART INC
9045 Carroll Way, San Diego (92121-2405)
PHONE..................................858 695-2739
Aaron Justin, *Branch Mgr*
EMP: 20
SALES (corp-wide): 7.5B **Publicly Held**
WEB: www.homebrewmart.com
SIC: 2082 5999 Ale (alcoholic beverage);
  alcoholic beverage making equipment &
  supplies
HQ: Home Brew Mart, Inc.
  9045 Carroll Way
  San Diego CA 92121

(P-1600)
HOME BREW MART INC (HQ)
Also Called: Ballast Pt Brewing & Spirits
9045 Carroll Way, San Diego (92121-2405)
PHONE..................................858 790-6900
Jim Buechler, *CEO*
Jack White, *CEO*
Yuseff Cherney, *COO*
Rick Morgan, *CFO*
Julie Buechler, *Admin Sec*
▲ EMP: 200
SQ FT: 107,000
SALES (est): 200.3MM
SALES (corp-wide): 7.5B **Publicly Held**
WEB: www.homebrewmart.com
SIC: 2082 5999 Ale (alcoholic beverage);
  alcoholic beverage making equipment &
  supplies
PA: Constellation Brands, Inc.
  207 High Point Dr # 100
  Victor NY 14564
  585 678-7100

(P-1601)
INDIAN WELLS COMPANIES
Also Called: Indian Wells Brewery
2565 State Highway 14, Inyokern
(93527-2700)
PHONE..................................760 377-4290
Greg Antonaros, *Partner*
Rick Lovett, *Partner*
▲ EMP: 20
SALES: 960K **Privately Held**
SIC: 2082 2086 Beer (alcoholic bever-
  age); pasteurized & mineral waters, bot-
  tled & canned

(P-1602)
ISLAND BREWING CO
5049 6th St, Carpinteria (93013-2001)
PHONE..................................805 745-8272
Paul Wright, *President*
EMP: 16
SALES (est): 2MM **Privately Held**
WEB: www.islandbrewingcompany.com
SIC: 2082 Malt beverages

(P-1603)
KARL STRAUSS BREWING COMPANY (PA)
5985 Santa Fe St, San Diego
(92109-1623)
P.O. Box 5965 (92165-5965)
PHONE..................................858 273-2739
Chris Cramer, *CEO*
Karl Strauss, *Executive*
Matt Rattner, *Principal*
Bill McAvoy, *Engineer*
Jeff Schroeder, *VP Opers*
EMP: 80
SALES (est): 18.1MM **Privately Held**
SIC: 2082 Beer (alcoholic beverage)

(P-1604)
LEFT COAST BREWING COMPANY
1245 Puerta Del Sol, San Clemente
(92673-6310)
PHONE..................................949 218-3961
George Hadjis, *President*
Dora Hadjis, *CFO*
Martin Medina, *Sales Mgr*
Kim Faris, *Marketing Staff*
Stephanie Glass, *Sales Staff*
EMP: 15 EST: 2004
SQ FT: 7,500
SALES: 1.4MM **Privately Held**
SIC: 2082 Beer (alcoholic beverage)

(P-1605)
LENGTHWISE BREWING COMPANY
7700 District Blvd, Bakersfield
(93313-4861)
PHONE..................................661 836-2537
Jeffery James Williams, *CEO*
Darin Schwicker, *Vice Pres*
EMP: 48
SQ FT: 6,000
SALES (est): 6.1MM **Privately Held**
WEB: www.lengthwise.com
SIC: 2082 Beer (alcoholic beverage)

(P-1606)
LORD LEVIASON ENTERPRISES LLC
Also Called: Sweeneys Ale House
17337 Ventura Blvd Ste 10, Encino
(91316-3903)
PHONE..................................818 453-8245
Jackson Fox, *General Mgr*
EMP: 30 EST: 2015
SALES (est): 1.4MM **Privately Held**
SIC: 2082 Ale (alcoholic beverage)

(P-1607)
LOS ANGELES ALE WORKS LLC
12918 Cerise Ave, Hawthorne
(90250-5521)
PHONE..................................213 422-6569
Kristofor Barnes, *Mng Member*
Kandice TSE, *Controller*
Andrew Fowler,
Jeff Szafarski,
EMP: 12
SALES (est): 1.4MM **Privately Held**
SIC: 2082 Beer (alcoholic beverage)

(P-1608)
LUCKY LUKE BREWING COMPANY
610 W Avenue O Ste 104, Palmdale
(93551-3661)
PHONE..................................661 270-5588
Samantha Schmitz, *Mng Member*
EMP: 13
SALES: 750K **Privately Held**
SIC: 2082 Beer (alcoholic beverage)

(P-1609)
MCLEAN BREWERY INC
Also Called: Magnolia Pub & Brewery
1398 Haight St, San Francisco
(94117-2909)
PHONE..................................415 864-7468
David McLean, *President*
▲ EMP: 24
SQ FT: 4,000
SALES (est): 3.3MM **Privately Held**
WEB: www.magnoliapub.com
SIC: 2082 Malt beverages

(P-1610)
MENDOCINO BREWING COMPANY INC
Also Called: Hopland Brewery
13351 S Highway 101, Hopland (95449)
PHONE................................707 744-1015
Leeq Q Whitman, *Manager*
EMP: 50
SALES (corp-wide): 33MM **Publicly Held**
SIC: 2082 Malt beverages
HQ: Mendocino Brewing Company Inc
   1601 Airport Rd
   Ukiah CA 95482
   707 463-2627

(P-1611)
MENDOCINO BREWING COMPANY INC (HQ)
1601 Airport Rd, Ukiah (95482-6456)
PHONE................................707 463-2627
Yashpal Singh, *President*
Vijay Mallya, *Ch of Bd*
Mahadevan Narayanan, *CFO*
Carlos Swinney, *Safety Mgr*
Keith Tabayoyon, *Sales Staff*
▲ EMP: 57
SALES: 31.1MM
SALES (corp-wide): 33MM **Publicly Held**
SIC: 2082 Beer (alcoholic beverage); brewers' grain
PA: United Breweries (Holdings) Limited
   Level 12-16, Ub Tower, Ub City 24,
   Bengaluru KA 56000
   802 224-5066

(P-1612)
MILLERCOORS LLC
15801 1st St, Irwindale (91706-6202)
PHONE................................626 969-6811
Edward Beers, *Branch Mgr*
EMP: 75
SQ FT: 800,000
SALES (corp-wide): 11B **Publicly Held**
SIC: 2082 Beer (alcoholic beverage)
HQ: Millercoors Llc
   250 S Wacker Dr Ste 800
   Chicago IL 60606
   312 496-2700

(P-1613)
NORTH COAST BREWING CO INC (PA)
Also Called: Brew Building
455 N Main St, Fort Bragg (95437-3215)
PHONE................................707 964-2739
Mark E Ruedrich, *CEO*
Tom Allen, *Vice Pres*
▲ EMP: 50
SQ FT: 3,000
SALES (est): 13.2MM **Privately Held**
WEB: www.northcoastbrewing.com
SIC: 2082 5812 5813 Beer (alcoholic beverage); eating places; bars & lounges

(P-1614)
NUTRACEUTICAL BREWS FOR LF INC
Also Called: Dr. Jekyll's
825 Cambridge Ct, Pasadena (91107-1977)
PHONE................................310 273-8339
Thomas Costa, *CEO*
Gene Lim, *COO*
EMP: 10
SALES: 300K **Privately Held**
SIC: 2082 7389 Beer (alcoholic beverage);

(P-1615)
OCEAN AVENUE BREWING CO
Also Called: Ocean Brewing Company
237 Ocean Ave, Laguna Beach (92651-2106)
PHONE................................949 497-3381
Jonathan Thomas, *President*
EMP: 25
SQ FT: 3,500
SALES (est): 3MM **Privately Held**
WEB: www.oceanbrewing.com
SIC: 2082 5812 Beer (alcoholic beverage); eating places

(P-1616)
OGGIS PIZZA & BREWING CO
Also Called: HEI
12840 Carmel Country Rd, San Diego (92130-2155)
PHONE................................858 481-7883
George Hadjis, *President*
Dora Hadjis, *Vice Pres*
John Hadjis, *Vice Pres*
EMP: 45
SQ FT: 3,200
SALES (est): 5.6MM **Privately Held**
SIC: 2082 5813 5812 Beer (alcoholic beverage); bar (drinking places); pizza restaurants

(P-1617)
OTTANO INC
11555 Los Osos Valley Rd # 201, San Luis Obispo (93405-6472)
PHONE................................805 547-2088
Nipool Patel, *President*
EMP: 12
SALES (est): 1.6MM **Privately Held**
SIC: 2082 Beer (alcoholic beverage)

(P-1618)
OUTLAW BEVERAGE INC
405 14th St Ste 1000, Oakland (94612-2706)
P.O. Box 3478, La Habra (90632-3478)
PHONE................................310 424-5077
Douglas Weekes, *CEO*
Lance Collins, *Founder*
Julia Weekes, *Director*
EMP: 18
SALES (est): 2.1MM **Privately Held**
SIC: 2082 Malt beverages

(P-1619)
PABST BREWING COMPANY LLC (PA)
10635 Santa Monica Blvd, Los Angeles (90025-8300)
PHONE................................310 470-0962
Simon Thorpe, *CEO*
Eugene Kashper, *Ch of Bd*
Cordell Sweeney, *CFO*
Matt Bruhn, *Chief Mktg Ofcr*
Dan McHugh, *Chief Mktg Ofcr*
▼ EMP: 280
SQ FT: 12,500
SALES (est): 205.9MM **Privately Held**
SIC: 2082 Beer (alcoholic beverage)

(P-1620)
PLEASANTON MAIN ST BREWRY INC
830 Main St Ste Frnt, Pleasanton (94566-6076)
PHONE................................925 462-8218
Matt Billings, *Partner*
Sharon Billings, *Partner*
EMP: 10
SALES (est): 1MM **Privately Held**
SIC: 2082 5812 Malt beverages; eating places

(P-1621)
PORT BREWING LLC
155 Mata Way Ste 104, San Marcos (92069-2983)
PHONE................................800 918-6816
Vince Marsaglia, *Mng Member*
Jim Comstock, *CFO*
Matthew Webster, *Production*
Tomme Arthur, *Mng Member*
▲ EMP: 37
SALES (est): 7.6MM **Privately Held**
SIC: 2082 Beer (alcoholic beverage)

(P-1622)
PYRAMID BREWERIES INC
Also Called: Pyramid Alhuse At Wllnut Creek
1410 Locust St, Walnut Creek (94596-4514)
PHONE................................925 946-1520
Cade Crockett, *Manager*
EMP: 98 **Privately Held**
SIC: 2082 Ale (alcoholic beverage); beer (alcoholic beverage)
HQ: Pyramid Breweries Inc.
   91 S Royal Brougham Way
   Seattle WA 98134
   206 682-8322

(P-1623)
SIERRA NEVADA BREWING CO (PA)
1075 E 20th St, Chico (95928-6722)
PHONE................................530 893-3520
Kenneth Grossman, *President*
Paul Janicki, *CFO*
Megan Andrews, *Social Dir*
Jeremy Austin, *Social Dir*
Chad McRae, *Social Dir*
◆ EMP: 475
SALES: 300MM **Privately Held**
WEB: www.sierranevada.com
SIC: 2082 5812 Beer (alcoholic beverage); eating places

(P-1624)
SILVERADO BREWING CO L L C
4104 Saint Helena Hwy, Calistoga (94515-9629)
PHONE................................707 341-3089
Michael Fradelizio,
Debbie Fradelizio,
Ken Mee,
EMP: 20
SALES (est): 2.1MM **Privately Held**
WEB: www.silveradobrewery.com
SIC: 2082 5812 Malt beverages; American restaurant

(P-1625)
SINGHA NORTH AMERICA INC
303 Twin Dolphin Dr # 600, Redwood City (94065-1422)
PHONE................................714 206-5097
Palit Bbhakdi, *CEO*
Soravij B Bhakdi, *President*
Mario Ylanan, *Treasurer*
▲ EMP: 15
SALES: 1.9MM
SALES (corp-wide): 248.4MM **Privately Held**
SIC: 2082 Beer (alcoholic beverage)
PA: Boonrawd Brewery Company Limited
   999 Samsen Road
   Dusit 10300
   224 240-00

(P-1626)
STEINBECK BREWING COMPANY
Also Called: Buffalo Bills Brewery
1082 B St, Hayward (94541-4108)
PHONE................................510 888-0695
Geoffrey A Harries, *President*
EMP: 84
SQ FT: 4,000
SALES (est): 13.7MM **Privately Held**
WEB: www.buffalobillsbrewery.com
SIC: 2082 5812 Beer (alcoholic beverage); eating places

(P-1627)
STRAUSS KARL BREWERY AND REST
1044 Wall St Ste C, La Jolla (92037-4437)
PHONE................................858 551-2739
Chris Cramer, *President*
EMP: 40
SALES (est): 3.8MM **Privately Held**
SIC: 2082 Beer (alcoholic beverage)

(P-1628)
TABLE BLUFF BREWING INC (PA)
Also Called: Lost Coast Brewery & Cafe
617 4th St, Eureka (95501-1013)
PHONE................................707 445-4480
Barbara Groom, *CEO*
Wendy Pound, *Corp Secy*
Kurt Kovacs, *Vice Pres*
◆ EMP: 30
SALES (est): 8.6MM **Privately Held**
WEB: www.lostcoast.com
SIC: 2082 5812 5813 Beer (alcoholic beverage); eating places; bar (drinking places)

(P-1629)
TABLE BLUFF BREWING INC
Also Called: Lostcoast
1600 Sunset Dr, Eureka (95503-2401)
PHONE................................707 445-4484
Barbara Groom, *President*
EMP: 15

SALES (corp-wide): 8.6MM **Privately Held**
WEB: www.lostcoast.com
SIC: 2082 Beer (alcoholic beverage)
PA: Table Bluff Brewing Inc
   617 4th St
   Eureka CA 95501
   707 445-4480

(P-1630)
TELEGRAPH BREWING CO INC
418 N Salsipuedes St, Santa Barbara (93103-3127)
PHONE................................805 963-5018
Brian Thompson, *Principal*
EMP: 10
SALES (est): 1.1MM
SALES (corp-wide): 8.8MM **Privately Held**
SIC: 2082 Malt beverages
PA: Epic Brewing Company, L.L.C.
   825 S State St
   Salt Lake City UT 84111
   801 906-0123

(P-1631)
THIRSTY BEAR BREWING CO LLC
661 Howard St, San Francisco (94105-3915)
PHONE................................415 974-0905
Ronald Silberstein,
Robert McCarthy, *Executive*
Daniel Silberstein, *Marketing Staff*
Ragnhild Lorentzen,
Lissa Arnold, *Manager*
EMP: 100
SQ FT: 18,000
SALES (est): 14.3MM **Privately Held**
WEB: www.thirstybear.com
SIC: 2082 5812 7299 Beer (alcoholic beverage); eating places; banquet hall facilities

(P-1632)
TOWNE PARK BREW INC
1566 W Lincoln Ave, Anaheim (92801-5850)
PHONE................................714 844-2492
Brett Lawrence, *President*
EMP: 25
SQ FT: 20,000
SALES: 250K **Privately Held**
SIC: 2082 5149 Beer (alcoholic beverage); beverages, except coffee & tea

(P-1633)
UKIAH BREWING CO LLC
551 Cypress Ave, Ukiah (95482-3923)
PHONE................................707 468-5898
Bret Cooperrider,
Sid Cooperrider,
Bret Coopperrider,
EMP: 30
SQ FT: 5,000
SALES (est): 600K **Privately Held**
WEB: www.ukiahbrewingco.com
SIC: 2082 5812 Beer (alcoholic beverage); cafe

2084 Wine & Brandy

(P-1634)
3 BADGE BEVERAGE CORPORATION
32 Patten St, Sonoma (95476-6727)
PHONE................................707 343-1167
Richard Zeller, *President*
August David Sebastiani, *CEO*
Keith Casale, *COO*
Holly Milner, *Administration*
Alice Castorena, *Controller*
EMP: 15
SALES (est): 3MM **Privately Held**
SIC: 2084 5182 Wine cellars, bonded: engaged in blending wines; bottling wines & liquors

(P-1635)
55 DEGREE WINE
3111 Glendale Blvd Ste 2, Los Angeles (90039-1841)
PHONE................................323 662-5556
Andy Hasroun, *President*

▲ = Import ▼=Export
◆ =Import/Export

EMP: 10 EST: 2008
SALES (est): 685.9K **Privately Held**
SIC: 2084 2082 Wines, brandy & brandy
spirits; beer (alcoholic beverage)

(P-1636)
6630 ANDIS WINES C O PERF
11000 Shenandoah Rd, Plymouth
(95669-9570)
P.O. Box 190 (95669-0190)
PHONE..............................209 245-6177
Andrew D Friedlander, *Owner*
Janis Akuna, *Executive*
EMP: 10
SALES (est): 942.7K **Privately Held**
SIC: 2084 Wines

(P-1637)
7 & 8 LLC
Also Called: Vineyard 7 & 8
4028 Spring Mountain Rd, Saint Helena
(94574-9773)
PHONE..............................707 963-9425
John L Steffens,
Wesley Steffens, *General Mgr*
James Imbach, *Sales Dir*
Julia Sanchez, *Director*
EMP: 11 EST: 2002
SALES (est): 1.4MM **Privately Held**
SIC: 2084 Wines

(P-1638)
A W DIRECT LLC
Also Called: Home of Wine Trees Portfolio
980 Airway Ct Ste A, Santa Rosa
(95403-2000)
PHONE..............................707 200-2859
Bruce Cunningham, *Vice Pres*
Kim Cunningham, *VP Opers*
Anna Frizzell, *Marketing Mgr*
▲ EMP: 10
SALES (est): 2.3MM **Privately Held**
SIC: 2084 Wines

(P-1639)
ADVANCED VITICULTURE INC
930 Shiloh Rd Bldg 44-E, Windsor
(95492-9664)
P.O. Box 2236 (95492-2236)
PHONE..............................707 838-3805
Mark Greenspan, *President*
Linda Greenspan, *Vice Pres*
EMP: 12
SALES (est): 542.9K **Privately Held**
SIC: 2084 0762 0172 0721 Wines; vine-
yard management & maintenance serv-
ices; grapes; orchard tree & vine serv-
ices; scientific consulting

(P-1640)
AGUA DULCE VINEYARDS LLC
9640 Sierra Hwy, Agua Dulce
(91390-4622)
PHONE..............................661 268-7402
Raymond A Watt,
Steve Wizan, *General Mgr*
EMP: 20
SALES (est): 3.4MM **Privately Held**
WEB: www.aguadulcevineyards.com
SIC: 2084 5921 Wines; wine

(P-1641)
ALFRED DOMAINE
7525 Orcutt Rd, San Luis Obispo
(93401-8341)
PHONE..............................805 541-9463
Terry Speizer, *President*
▲ EMP: 12 EST: 1997
SQ FT: 3,000
SALES (est): 1MM **Privately Held**
WEB: www.domainealfred.com
SIC: 2084 Wines

(P-1642)
**ALMA ROSA WINERY
VINEYARDS LLC (PA)**
181 Industrial Way Ste C, Buellton
(93427-9680)
PHONE..............................805 688-9090
J R Sanford,
Gaston Leyack, *General Mgr*
Richard Sanford, *Prdtn Mgr*
Amanda McBride, *Rector*
Alison Jackson,
EMP: 12

SALES (est): 1.6MM **Privately Held**
SIC: 2084 Wines

(P-1643)
ALPHA OMEGA WINERY LLC
Also Called: Ao Winery
1155 Mee Ln, Rutherford (94573)
P.O. Box 822 (94573-0822)
PHONE..............................707 963-9999
Kenneth Robin Baggett, *Mng Member*
▲ EMP: 10
SALES (est): 2MM **Privately Held**
WEB: www.alphaomegawinery.com
SIC: 2084 Wines

(P-1644)
ANCHOR DISTILLING COMPANY
1705 Mariposa St, San Francisco
(94107-2334)
PHONE..............................415 863-8350
Charles Keith Greggor, *President*
Lynn Lackey, *VP Mktg*
Carolyn Stewart, *Director*
▲ EMP: 26 EST: 1988
SALES (est): 4MM **Privately Held**
SIC: 2084 Wine cellars, bonded: engaged
in blending wines

(P-1645)
ANTINORI CALIFORNIA
Also Called: Antica NAPA Valley
3149 Soda Canyon Rd, NAPA
(94558-9448)
PHONE..............................707 265-8866
Marchase P Antinori, *President*
▲ EMP: 22
SALES (est): 3.5MM **Privately Held**
SIC: 2084 5921 Wines; wine

(P-1646)
**ARCHANGEL INVESTMENTS
LLC**
Also Called: Baldacci Family Vineyard
6236 Silverado Trl, NAPA (94558-9414)
PHONE..............................707 944-9261
Michael Baldacci, *President*
Kellie Duckhorn, *General Mgr*
Elizabeth Burchard, *Director*
EMP: 10
SALES (est): 606.7K **Privately Held**
SIC: 2084 Wines

(P-1647)
ASV WINES INC (PA)
1998 Road 152, Delano (93215-9437)
PHONE..............................661 792-3159
Marko B Zaninovich, *President*
Kent Stephens, *CFO*
▲ EMP: 25 EST: 1981
SQ FT: 4,000
SALES (est): 4.9MM **Privately Held**
SIC: 2084 Wines

(P-1648)
AVV WINERY CO LLC
Also Called: Alexander Valley Vineyards
8644 Highway 128, Healdsburg
(95448-9021)
P.O. Box 175 (95448-0175)
PHONE..............................707 433-7209
Harry H Wetzel III, *Mng Member*
Katie Wetzel, *Managing Prtnr*
Linda Wetzel, *COO*
Kevin Hall, *Lab Dir*
Hank Wetzel, *Software Engr*
▲ EMP: 25
SQ FT: 32,000
SALES (est): 5MM **Privately Held**
WEB: www.avvwine.com
SIC: 2084 Wines

(P-1649)
AWG LTD INC
Also Called: Andretti Winery
4162 Big Ranch Rd, NAPA (94558-1405)
PHONE..............................707 259-6777
Mike O' Connell, *President*
Joseph Antonini, *President*
Jennifer Miguel, *Admin Asst*
Ruth Fevre, *Opers Staff*
Roger De Lorimier, *Marketing Staff*
▲ EMP: 12
SALES (est): 2MM **Privately Held**
WEB: www.andrettiwinery.com
SIC: 2084 Wines

(P-1650)
B & R VINYARDS INC
4350 Monterey Rd, Gilroy (95020-8029)
P.O. Box 247 (95021-0247)
PHONE..............................408 842-5649
John Rapazzini, *President*
Zondra Rapazzini, *Vice Pres*
EMP: 15
SQ FT: 12,000
SALES (est): 1.1MM **Privately Held**
SIC: 2084 5182 5411 2035 Wines; wine;
delicatessens; pickles, sauces & salad
dressings

(P-1651)
BAILEY ESSEL WILLIAM JR
Also Called: Knights Bridge Winery
1373 Lincoln Ave, Calistoga (94515-1701)
PHONE..............................707 341-3391
Essel William Bailey Jr, *Owner*
EMP: 10 EST: 2015
SALES (est): 301.1K **Privately Held**
SIC: 2084 Wines

(P-1652)
BARBOUR VINEYARDS LLC
104 Camino Dorado, NAPA (94558-6212)
PHONE..............................707 257-1829
Jim Barbour, *Mng Member*
EMP: 90
SALES (est): 13.9MM **Privately Held**
SIC: 2084 Wines

(P-1653)
**BARREL TEN QARTER CIR
LAND INC (HQ)**
6342 Bystrum Rd, Ceres (95307-6652)
P.O. Box 3400, NAPA (94558-0551)
PHONE..............................707 258-0550
Fred T Franzia, *President*
▲ EMP: 22
SALES (est): 3.1MM
SALES (corp-wide): 182.4MM **Privately
Held**
SIC: 2084 Wines
PA: Bronco Wine Company
6342 Bystrum Rd
Ceres CA 95307
209 538-3131

(P-1654)
BAYWOOD CELLARS INC
Also Called: Hook or Crook Cellars
5573 W Woodbridge Rd, Lodi
(95242-9497)
PHONE..............................415 606-4640
William Stokes, *CEO*
John Healy, *Partner*
Allen Lambardi, *Partner*
EMP: 30
SALES (est): 30MM **Privately Held**
SIC: 2084 Wines

(P-1655)
BEDFORD WINERY
448 Bell St, Los Alamos (93440)
PHONE..............................805 344-2107
Stephan Bedford, *Owner*
EMP: 10
SALES (est): 719.3K **Privately Held**
WEB: www.bedfordthompsonwinery.com
SIC: 2084 Wines

(P-1656)
BERNARDO WINERY INC
13330 Pseo Del Vrano Nrte, San Diego
(92128)
PHONE..............................858 487-1866
Ross Rizzo, *President*
EMP: 20 EST: 1932
SALES (est): 3.4MM **Privately Held**
WEB: www.bernardowinery.com
SIC: 2084 5921 7941 Wines; wine; sports
field or stadium operator, promoting
sports events

(P-1657)
BERNARDUS LLC (PA)
Also Called: Bernardus Winery
5 W Carmel Valley Rd, Carmel Valley
(93924)
P.O. Box 1800 (93924-1800)
PHONE..............................831 659-1900
Bernardus Pon, *Mng Member*
Mark Chesebro,

▲ EMP: 26
SQ FT: 5,000
SALES (est): 5.3MM **Privately Held**
WEB: www.bernardus.com
SIC: 2084 0172 Wines; grapes

(P-1658)
BERTAGNA ORCHARDS INC
3329 Hegan Ln, Chico (95928-9589)
PHONE..............................530 343-8014
Ben N Bertagna, *President*
Mary Jane Bertagna, *Vice Pres*
EMP: 12
SALES (est): 3MM **Privately Held**
SIC: 2084 Wines

(P-1659)
BFW ASSOCIATES LLC (HQ)
Also Called: Benzinger Family Winery
1883 London Ranch Rd, Glen Ellen
(95442-9728)
PHONE..............................707 935-3000
David Mackesey, *President*
Gerard N Benziger,
▲ EMP: 30
SQ FT: 6,000
SALES (est): 6.5MM
SALES (corp-wide): 151.9MM **Privately
Held**
WEB: www.benziger.com
SIC: 2084 0172 Wines; grapes
PA: The Wine Group Llc
4596 S Tracy Blvd
Tracy CA 95377
415 986-8700

(P-1660)
BIALE ESTATE
Also Called: Robert Biale Vineyards
4038 Big Ranch Rd, NAPA (94558-1405)
PHONE..............................707 257-7555
Robert A Biale, *Owner*
Chris Dearden, *COO*
Jeannie Coleman, *Administration*
Maggie Pramuk, *Manager*
Wendy Biale, *Consultant*
▲ EMP: 10
SALES (est): 1.2MM **Privately Held**
SIC: 2084 Wines

(P-1661)
BLACK STALLION WINERY LLC
4089 Silverado Trl, NAPA (94558-1113)
PHONE..............................707 253-1400
Terrance J Maglich,
Michael G Maglich,
▲ EMP: 11
SALES (est): 1MM **Privately Held**
SIC: 2084 Wines

(P-1662)
BOEGER WINERY INC
1709 Carson Rd, Placerville (95667-5195)
PHONE..............................530 622-8094
Greg Boeger, *President*
Susan Boeger, *Treasurer*
EMP: 50
SQ FT: 8,000
SALES (est): 6.9MM **Privately Held**
WEB: www.boegerwinery.com
SIC: 2084 0172 Wines; grapes

(P-1663)
BONNEAU WINES LLC
Also Called: Egret
75 Bonneau Rd, Sonoma (95476-9229)
PHONE..............................707 996-0420
John Bambury, *Mng Member*
Barbara Church, *Administration*
Salman Rehman, *Director*
EMP: 15
SALES (est): 600.1K **Privately Held**
SIC: 2084 Wines

(P-1664)
BONNY DOON VINEYARD (PA)
328 Ingalls St, Santa Cruz (95060-5882)
PHONE..............................831 425-3625
Lisa Kohrf, *Owner*
Bonny Vineyard, *Area Mgr*
Lee Codding, *General Mgr*
Sara Rossini, *Executive Asst*
Ed Moya, *Opers Mgr*
EMP: 12
SALES (est): 1.2MM **Privately Held**
SIC: 2084 Wines

PRODUCTS & SVCS

(P-1665)
BONNY DOON WINERY INC
328 Ingalls St, Santa Cruz (95060-5882)
PHONE..................................831 425-3625
Randall Grahm, *President*
Lisa Kohrs, *CFO*
▲ EMP: 60
SQ FT: 20,000
SALES (est): 6.6MM **Privately Held**
WEB: www.bonnydoonwinery.com
SIC: 2084 Wines

(P-1666)
BOUCHAINE VINEYARDS INC
Also Called: Bouchaine Wineary
1075 Buchli Station Rd, NAPA
(94559-9716)
PHONE..................................707 252-9065
Tatiana Copeland, *President*
Gerret Copeland, *Chairman*
Carla Bosco, *Comms Dir*
Chris Kajani, *Manager*
Thalia Balderas, *Assistant*
EMP: 18
SQ FT: 35,000
SALES: 3MM **Privately Held**
WEB: www.bouchaine.com
SIC: 2084 5812 Wines; eating places

(P-1667)
BRIDLEWOOD WINERY
Also Called: E and J Gallo
3555 Roblar Ave, Santa Ynez
(93460-9724)
PHONE..................................805 688-9000
Ej Gallo, *President*
EMP: 22
SQ FT: 28,000
SALES (est): 2.5MM **Privately Held**
WEB: www.bridlewoodwinery.com
SIC: 2084 5182 Wines; wine

(P-1668)
BROKEN EARTH WINERY
5625 E Highway 46, Paso Robles
(93446-6301)
P.O. Box 1498 (93447-1498)
PHONE..................................805 239-2562
Chris Cameron, *Vice Pres*
EMP: 11
SALES (est): 1.3MM **Privately Held**
SIC: 2084 Wines

(P-1669)
BROWN ESTATE VINEYARD LLC
3233 Sage Canyon Rd, Saint Helena
(94574-9642)
PHONE..................................707 963-2435
David Brown,
Stefanie Kelly, *Opers Staff*
Dave Brown, *Marketing Mgr*
Eric Molinatti, *Sales Mgr*
Susan Terracciano, *Sales Mgr*
EMP: 12
SALES (est): 1.6MM **Privately Held**
WEB: www.brownestate.com
SIC: 2084 Wines

(P-1670)
BRUTOCAO CELLARS (PA)
1400 Highway 175, Hopland (95449-9754)
P.O. Box 780 (95449-0780)
PHONE..................................707 744-1066
Steve Brutocao, *Partner*
Leonard Brutocao, *Partner*
◆ EMP: 12
SALES (est): 2.2MM **Privately Held**
WEB: www.brutocaocellars.com
SIC: 2084 Wine cellars, bonded: engaged
in blending wines; wines

(P-1671)
BURGESS CELLARS INC
1108 Deer Park Rd, Saint Helena
(94574-9728)
P.O. Box 282 (94574-0282)
PHONE..................................707 963-4766
Thomas E Burgess, *President*
Diane Abreu, *Human Res Mgr*
Charlotte Ryan, *Marketing Staff*
EMP: 14
SQ FT: 20,000
SALES (est): 2.4MM **Privately Held**
WEB: www.burgesscellars.com
SIC: 2084 0172 Wines; grapes

(P-1672)
BUTTONWOOD FARM WINERY INC
1500 Alamo Pintado Rd, Solvang
(93463-9756)
P.O. Box 1007 (93464-1007)
PHONE..................................805 688-3032
Bret C Davenport, *President*
Elizabeth Williams, *Corp Secy*
Seyburn Zorthian, *Vice Pres*
EMP: 12
SALES (est): 1.9MM **Privately Held**
SIC: 2084 Wines

(P-1673)
C MONDAVI & FAMILY (PA)
Also Called: Charles Krug Winery
2800 Main St, Saint Helena (94574-9502)
P.O. Box 191 (94574-0191)
PHONE..................................707 967-2200
John Lennon, *President*
Peter Mondavi Jr, *Treasurer*
Mark Mondavi, *Admin Sec*
▲ EMP: 85 EST: 1866
SQ FT: 175,000
SALES (est): 20.7MM **Privately Held**
WEB: www.charleskrug.com
SIC: 2084 0172 Wine cellars, bonded: en-
gaged in blending wines; grapes

(P-1674)
CACCIATORE FINE WNS & OLV OIL (PA)
1875 S Elm St, Pixley (93256-9524)
P.O. Box 923 (93256-0923)
PHONE..................................559 757-9463
Vincent Cacciatore, *President*
EMP: 10
SALES (est): 2.6MM **Privately Held**
WEB: www.cwocorp.com
SIC: 2084 0172 Wines; grapes

(P-1675)
CAIN CELLARS INC
Also Called: Cain Vineyard & Winery
3800 Langtry Rd, Saint Helena
(94574-9772)
PHONE..................................707 963-1616
Nancy Medlock, *President*
James Medlock, *Vice Pres*
William Medlock, *Vice Pres*
Jj McCarthy, *Executive*
Chris Howell, *General Mgr*
▲ EMP: 20
SQ FT: 30,000
SALES (est): 3.9MM **Privately Held**
WEB: www.cainfive.com
SIC: 2084 5921 Wines; wine

(P-1676)
CAKEBREAD CELLARS
Also Called: Cakebread Cellar Vineyards
8300 Saint Helena Hwy, Rutherford
(94573)
P.O. Box 216 (94573-0216)
PHONE..................................707 963-5221
Jack E Cakebread, *CEO*
Bruce Cakebread, *President*
Josef Wally, *CFO*
Dennis Cakebread, *Exec VP*
Dolores Cakebread, *Senior VP*
▲ EMP: 60
SQ FT: 100,000
SALES (est): 11.3MM **Privately Held**
WEB: www.cakebread.com
SIC: 2084 Wines

(P-1677)
CALF CANYON WINERY LLC
679 Calf Canyon Hwy, Creston
(93432-9700)
PHONE..................................805 226-8600
Liz Holtzclaw, *Principal*
EMP: 10
SALES (est): 919.7K **Privately Held**
SIC: 2084 Wines

(P-1678)
CALLAWAY VINEYARD & WINERY
32720 Rancho Cal Rd, Temecula
(92591-4925)
PHONE..................................951 676-4001
Mike Jellison, *President*
▲ EMP: 70 EST: 1969

SALES (est): 9MM **Privately Held**
SIC: 2084 Wine cellars, bonded: engaged
in blending wines; wines

(P-1679)
CANANDAIGUA WINE COMPANY INC
12667 Road 24, Madera (93637-9020)
PHONE..................................559 673-7071
Marvin Sands, *Ch of Bd*
Richard Sands, *President*
Thomas Howe, *Treasurer*
Lynn K Fetterman, *Vice Pres*
James P Finkle, *Vice Pres*
▲ EMP: 700
SALES (est): 70.4MM
SALES (corp-wide): 7.5B **Publicly Held**
WEB: www.cbrands.com
SIC: 2084 Wines, brandy & brandy spirits
PA: Constellation Brands, Inc.
207 High Point Dr # 100
Victor NY 14564
585 678-7100

(P-1680)
CARVALHO FAMILY WINERY LLC
35265 Willow Ave, Clarksburg (95612)
P.O. Box 278 (95612-0278)
PHONE..................................916 744-1615
John Carvalho Jr, *Principal*
EMP: 11
SALES (est): 1.4MM **Privately Held**
SIC: 2084 Wines

(P-1681)
CASTORO CELLARS
6465 Von Dollen Rd, San Miguel
(93451-9567)
PHONE..................................805 467-2002
Niels Udsen, *President*
Luke Udsen, *Sales Staff*
Sherrie Holzer, *Assistant*
EMP: 19
SALES (est): 2.8MM
SALES (corp-wide): 4.1MM **Privately Held**
SIC: 2084 Wines
PA: Castoro Cellars
1315 N Bethel Rd
Templeton CA 93465
805 467-2002

(P-1682)
CASTORO CELLARS (PA)
1315 N Bethel Rd, Templeton
(93465-9403)
P.O. Box 954 (93465-0954)
PHONE..................................805 467-2002
Neils Udsen, *President*
Berit Udsen, *Vice Pres*
▼ EMP: 25
SALES (est): 4.1MM **Privately Held**
WEB: www.castorobottling.com
SIC: 2084 Wines

(P-1683)
CEDAR MOUNTAIN WINERY INC
Also Called: Brushy Peak Winery
10843 Reuss Rd, Livermore (94550-9734)
PHONE..................................925 373-6636
Linda Ault, *CEO*
Earl Ault, *Principal*
EMP: 12
SQ FT: 2,500
SALES (est): 1.4MM **Privately Held**
SIC: 2084 Wines

(P-1684)
CELEBRATION CELLARS LLC
Also Called: Miramonte Winery
33410 Rancho Cal Rd, Temecula
(92591-4928)
PHONE..................................951 506-5500
Cane Vanederhoof,
Tiffany Halverson, *Social Dir*
Dawn Zuniga, *Asst Controller*
Alex Saenz, *Sales Dir*
Paul Irby, *General Counsel*
EMP: 10
SQ FT: 63,000
SALES (est): 2MM **Privately Held**
WEB: www.miramontewinery.com
SIC: 2084 Wines

(P-1685)
CENTRAL COAST WINE WAREHOUSE (PA)
Also Called: Central Coast Wine Services
2717 Aviation Way Ste 101, Santa Maria
(93455-1506)
PHONE..................................805 928-9210
Jim Lunt, *Ltd Ptnr*
Jeff Maiken, *Ltd Ptnr*
▲ EMP: 30
SQ FT: 35,000
SALES (est): 5.1MM **Privately Held**
WEB: www.centralcoastwineservices.com
SIC: 2084 5182 7389 Wines; bottling
wines & liquors; field warehousing

(P-1686)
CHAMISAL VINEYARDS LLC
7525 Orcutt Rd, San Luis Obispo
(93401-8341)
PHONE..................................866 808-9463
Andrea De Palo, *Principal*
Norman L Goss, *Principal*
Andrea Palo, *Sales Staff*
▲ EMP: 15
SALES (est): 43.3K
SALES (corp-wide): 63.2MM **Publicly Held**
SIC: 2084 0172 Wines; grapes
PA: Crimson Wine Group, Ltd.
2700 Napa Vly Corp Dr B
Napa CA 94558
800 486-0503

(P-1687)
CHAPPELLET WINERY INC (PA)
1581 Sage Canyon Rd, Saint Helena
(94574-9628)
PHONE..................................707 286-4268
Cyril Donn Chappellet, *CEO*
Mary Alice Chappellet, *Admin Sec*
▲ EMP: 35
SQ FT: 22,472
SALES (est): 4.3MM **Privately Held**
WEB: www.chappellet.com
SIC: 2084 Wines

(P-1688)
CHATEAU DIANA LLC (PA)
6195 Dry Creek Rd, Healdsburg
(95448-8100)
P.O. Box 1013 (95448-1013)
PHONE..................................707 433-6992
Corey Manning, *Mng Member*
Danna Gibson, *CFO*
Ed Hajeian,
Krystle Lindberg,
Donna Manning,
▲ EMP: 15 EST: 1978
SQ FT: 8,000
SALES (est): 3.4MM **Privately Held**
WEB: www.chateaud.com
SIC: 2084 Wines

(P-1689)
CHATEAU MASSON LLC
Also Called: Mountain Winery
14831 Pierce Rd, Saratoga (95070-9724)
PHONE..................................408 741-7002
William Hirschman,
Jaclyn Skull, *Finance Mgr*
Gina Harper, *Sales Dir*
Stuart Ferguson,
Jay Campbell, *Director*
EMP: 25
SQ FT: 1,500
SALES (est): 6.2MM **Privately Held**
WEB: www.mountainwinery.com
SIC: 2084 Wines

(P-1690)
CHATEAU MONTELENA WINERY
1429 Tubbs Ln, Calistoga (94515-9726)
PHONE..................................707 942-5105
James L Barrett, *General Ptnr*
Bo Barrett,
Matt Crafton,
Cameron Parry,
Dave Vella,
◆ EMP: 30
SQ FT: 22,000
SALES (est): 6.5MM **Privately Held**
WEB: www.chateaumontelena.net
SIC: 2084 0172 Wines; grapes

(P-1691)
CHATEAU POTELLE INC
528 Coombs St, NAPA (94559-3340)
PHONE..............................707 255-9440
Jean Fourmeaux, *President*
Marketta Fourmeaux, *Admin Sec*
▲ EMP: 20
SQ FT: 5,000
SALES (est): 2.4MM **Privately Held**
WEB: www.chateaupotelle.com
SIC: 2084 0172 Wines; grapes

(P-1692)
CHATEAU POTELLE HOLDINGS LLC
1200 Dowdell Ln, Saint Helena (94574-1407)
PHONE..............................707 255-9440
Jean-Noel Fourmeaux, *Principal*
EMP: 13
SALES (est): 1.8MM **Privately Held**
SIC: 2084 Wines

(P-1693)
CLENDENEN LINDQUIST VINTNERS
4665 Santa Maria Mesa Rd, Santa Maria (93454-9638)
P.O. Box 998 (93456-0998)
PHONE..............................805 937-9801
Jim Clendenen, *President*
Michael Meluskey, *CFO*
EMP: 10
SALES (est): 910.1K **Privately Held**
SIC: 2084 Wines

(P-1694)
CLIFF VINE WINERY INC
7400 Silverado Trl, NAPA (94558-9425)
PHONE..............................707 944-2388
Nell Sweeney, *President*
EMP: 12
SQ FT: 5,000
SALES (est): 910K **Privately Held**
WEB: www.vinecliff.com
SIC: 2084 5812 Wines; eating places

(P-1695)
CLOS DE LA TECH LLC
575 Eastview Way, Woodside (94062-4009)
PHONE..............................650 722-3038
Thurman J Rodgers, *Mng Member*
Valeta Massey, *Mng Member*
EMP: 14
SALES (est): 2.7MM **Privately Held**
WEB: www.closdelatech.com
SIC: 2084 Wines

(P-1696)
CLOS DU BOIS WINES INC
Also Called: Constlltion Brnds US Oprations
19410 Geyserville Ave, Geyserville (95441-9603)
PHONE..............................707 857-1651
Eric Olsen, *President*
Jon Moramarco, *President*
Tom Hobart, *Vice Pres*
Mike Jellison, *Vice Pres*
▲ EMP: 35
SALES (est): 5MM
SALES (corp-wide): 76.5MM **Privately Held**
WEB: www.closdubois.com
SIC: 2084 Wines
HQ: Beam Suntory Inc.
222 Merchandise Mart Plz # 1600
Chicago IL 60654
312 964-6999

(P-1697)
CLOS DU VAL WINE COMPANY LTD
Also Called: Golet Wine Estates
5330 Silverado Trl, NAPA (94558-9410)
PHONE..............................707 259-2200
Bernard Portet, *Chairman*
Adam Torpy, *CEO*
▲ EMP: 50
SQ FT: 32,000
SALES (est): 12.3MM **Privately Held**
WEB: www.closduval.com
SIC: 2084 Wines

(P-1698)
CLOS LA CHANCE WINES INC
1 Hummingbird Ln, San Martin (95046-9473)
PHONE..............................408 686-1050
Bill Murphy, *Ch of Bd*
Brenda Murphy, *President*
Bob Dunnett, *Corp Secy*
▲ EMP: 45
SQ FT: 25,000
SALES (est): 7.1MM **Privately Held**
WEB: www.closlachance.com
SIC: 2084 Wine cellars, bonded: engaged in blending wines; wines

(P-1699)
COASTAL VINEYARD SERVICES LLC
120 Callie Ct, Arroyo Grande (93420-2939)
PHONE..............................805 441-4465
Kevin Wilkinson, *Principal*
EMP: 11
SALES (est): 1.6MM **Privately Held**
SIC: 2084 Wines

(P-1700)
CODORNIU NAPA INC
Also Called: Artesa Winery
1345 Henry Rd, NAPA (94559-9705)
PHONE..............................707 254-2148
Xavier Pages, *CEO*
Arthur O'Connor, *President*
Michael Kenton, *Principal*
Susan Sueiro, *General Mgr*
David Gilbreath, *Admin Sec*
▲ EMP: 89
SQ FT: 120,000
SALES (est): 14.4MM
SALES (corp-wide): 567.9K **Privately Held**
WEB: www.artesawinery.com
SIC: 2084 Wines
HQ: Codorniu Sa
Avenida Jaume De Codorniu, S/N
Sant Sadurni D Anoia 08770
933 441-515

(P-1701)
CONETECH CUSTOM SERVICES LLC
Also Called: Martini Prati Winery
2191 Laguna Rd, Santa Rosa (95401-3705)
PHONE..............................707 823-2404
Wayne Salk, *Principal*
EMP: 15
SQ FT: 1,280
SALES (est): 1.5MM **Privately Held**
SIC: 2084 Wines

(P-1702)
CONSTELLATION BRANDS INC
1255 Battery St, San Francisco (94111-1166)
PHONE..............................415 912-3880
Anushil Kumar, *Vice Pres*
Militza Manzano, *Vice Pres*
Thalia Postel, *Vice Pres*
Dale Stratton, *Vice Pres*
Ben Duemler, *VP Finance*
EMP: 38
SALES (corp-wide): 7.5B **Publicly Held**
SIC: 2084 Wines
PA: Constellation Brands, Inc.
207 High Point Dr # 100
Victor NY 14564
585 678-7100

(P-1703)
CONSTELLATION BRANDS INC
Also Called: Dunnewood Vineyards
2399 N State St, Ukiah (95482-3129)
PHONE..............................707 467-4840
George Phelan, *Opers-Prdtn-Mfg*
EMP: 20
SALES (corp-wide): 7.5B **Publicly Held**
WEB: www.cbrands.com
SIC: 2084 0172 Wines; grapes
PA: Constellation Brands, Inc.
207 High Point Dr # 100
Victor NY 14564
585 678-7100

(P-1704)
CONSTELLATION BRANDS US OPRS
1255 Battery St Ste 300, San Francisco (94111-1164)
PHONE..............................415 912-3700
Jeff Muller, *Principal*
Teresa Tamayo, *Info Tech Mgr*
Miguel Sanchez, *Opers Mgr*
Randy Addington, *Foreman/Supr*
Aaron Boyd, *Foreman/Supr*
EMP: 30
SALES (corp-wide): 7.5B **Publicly Held**
SIC: 2084 Wines
HQ: Constellation Brands U.S. Operations, Inc.
235 N Bloomfield Rd
Canandaigua NY 14424
585 396-7600

(P-1705)
CONSTELLATION BRANDS US OPRS
Also Called: Mission Bell Winery
12667 Road 24, Madera (93637-9020)
PHONE..............................559 485-0141
Michael Othites, *Branch Mgr*
Bryan Sturmer, *Senior Mgr*
Healy Adams, *Director*
Kent Lindgren, *Director*
Nick Stock, *Manager*
EMP: 773
SALES (corp-wide): 7.5B **Publicly Held**
SIC: 2084 Wines
HQ: Constellation Brands U.S. Operations, Inc.
235 N Bloomfield Rd
Canandaigua NY 14424
585 396-7600

(P-1706)
CONSTELLATION BRANDS US OPRS
Also Called: Beam Wine Estates
349 Healdsburg Ave, Healdsburg (95448-4137)
PHONE..............................707 433-8268
EMP: 773
SALES (corp-wide): 7.5B **Publicly Held**
SIC: 2084 0172 Wines; grapes
HQ: Constellation Brands U.S. Operations, Inc.
235 N Bloomfield Rd
Canandaigua NY 14424
585 396-7600

(P-1707)
COPAIN WINE CELLARS LLC
Also Called: Copain Wine Sellers
7800 Eastside Rd, Healdsburg (95448-9375)
PHONE..............................707 836-8822
Clifford J Thomson, *Mng Member*
Wells Guthrie,
EMP: 12
SALES (est): 1.9MM **Privately Held**
SIC: 2084 Wines

(P-1708)
COSENTINO SIGNATURE WINERIES (PA)
Also Called: Cosentino Winery
7415 St Helena Hwy, Yountville (94599)
P.O. Box 2818 (94599-2818)
PHONE..............................707 921-2809
Mitch Cosentino, *President*
Larry J Soldinger, *Ch of Bd*
EMP: 22
SQ FT: 7,000
SALES (est): 1.8MM **Privately Held**
WEB: www.cosentinowinery.com
SIC: 2084 Wines

(P-1709)
COURTSIDE CELLARS LLC
2425 Mission St, San Miguel (93451-9556)
PHONE..............................805 467-2882
David McHenry, *General Mgr*
EMP: 30
SALES (corp-wide): 5.5MM **Privately Held**
WEB: www.tolosawinery.com
SIC: 2084 Wine cellars, bonded: engaged in blending wines; wines

PA: Courtside Cellars, Llc
4910 Edna Rd
San Luis Obispo CA 93401
805 782-0500

(P-1710)
COURTSIDE CELLARS LLC (PA)
Also Called: Tolosa Winery
4910 Edna Rd, San Luis Obispo (93401-7938)
PHONE..............................805 782-0500
Bob Schiebelhut,
Carla Wiley, *CFO*
Tish Loosley, *Creative Dir*
Cathe Lincoln, *Admin Asst*
Cathy Agler, *Controller*
▲ EMP: 30
SQ FT: 70,000
SALES (est): 5.5MM **Privately Held**
WEB: www.tolosawinery.com
SIC: 2084 Wines

(P-1711)
CREW WINE COMPANY LLC
12300 County Rd 92b, Zamora (95698)
P.O. Box 493 (95698-0493)
PHONE..............................530 662-1032
Lane Giguiere,
Blake Wolfe, *Regional Mgr*
Jennifer Figueroa, *Accountant*
Rocio Rodriguez, *Accountant*
Rob Vacha, *Sales Mgr*
▲ EMP: 10
SALES (est): 1.7MM
SALES (corp-wide): 7.5B **Publicly Held**
SIC: 2084 Wines
PA: Constellation Brands, Inc.
207 High Point Dr # 100
Victor NY 14564
585 678-7100

(P-1712)
CRIMSON WINE GROUP LTD (PA)
2700 Napa Vly Corp Dr B, NAPA (94558)
PHONE..............................800 486-0503
Patrick M Delorg, *President*
John D Cumming, *Ch of Bd*
Karen L Diepholz, *CFO*
Mike S Cekay, *Senior VP*
Heath Larson, *Office Admin*
EMP: 178
SQ FT: 13,200
SALES: 63.2MM **Publicly Held**
SIC: 2084 Wines

(P-1713)
CRYSTAL BASIN CELLARS
3550 Carson Rd, Camino (95709-9330)
PHONE..............................530 303-3749
Mike Owen, *Owner*
Jack Wohler, *Technology*
Todd Smith, *Engineer*
Lesli Bohm, *Relations*
EMP: 16
SALES (est): 2MM **Privately Held**
SIC: 2084 Wines

(P-1714)
DANZA DEL SOL WINERY INC
39050 De Portola Rd, Temecula (92592-8833)
P.O. Box 892889 (92589-2889)
PHONE..............................951 302-6363
Robert Olson, *President*
Georgiana Wong, *Vice Pres*
Mary Knight, *Admin Asst*
Kelly Hefley, *Merchandise Mgr*
Sean Miller, *Director*
EMP: 11 EST: 2015
SALES (est): 147K **Privately Held**
SIC: 2084 Wines

(P-1715)
DARCIE KENT VINEYARDS
4590 Tesla Rd, Livermore (94550-9002)
PHONE..............................925 243-9040
Darcie Kent, *Principal*
▲ EMP: 18
SALES (est): 2.4MM **Privately Held**
SIC: 2084 Wines

PRODUCTS & SVCS

(P-1716)
DARIOUSH KHALEDI WINERY
LLC
4240 Silverado Trl, NAPA (94558-1117)
PHONE...........................707 257-2345
Darioush Khaledi, *Mng Member*
Steve Devitt, *Vice Pres*
Jessica Hague, *Vice Pres*
Ted Ball, *Accounting Dir*
Viktoriya Kobzar, *Accounting Mgr*
▲ EMP: 21
SALES (est): 4.3MM **Privately Held**
SIC: 2084 Wines

(P-1717)
DAVID BRUCE WINERY INC
21439 Bear Creek Rd, Los Gatos
(95033-9429)
PHONE...........................408 354-4214
David Bruce, *Ch of Bd*
Robert Serna, *Executive Asst*
Alex Lewis, *Director*
EMP: 15
SQ FT: 12,000
SALES (est): 3MM **Privately Held**
WEB: www.davidbrucewinery.com
SIC: 2084 0172 Wines; grapes

(P-1718)
DEERFIELD RANCH WINERY
LLC
1310 Warm Springs Rd, Glen Ellen
(95442-9709)
PHONE...........................707 833-5215
Robert W Rex,
Paulette Rex, *Managing Prtnr*
Robert Rex,
Fred Parker, *Art Dir*
Sandra Rex, *Manager*
▲ EMP: 10
SQ FT: 4,000
SALES (est): 1.7MM **Privately Held**
WEB: www.deerfieldranch.com
SIC: 2084 Wines

(P-1719)
DELICATO VINEYARDS (PA)
Also Called: Costal Brands
12001 S Highway 99, Manteca
(95336-8499)
PHONE...........................209 824-3600
Christopher Indelicato, *CEO*
Vince Indelicato, *Chairman*
Jon Guggino, *Exec VP*
Dorothy Indelicato, *Principal*
Marie Indelicato Mathews, *Admin Sec*
◆ EMP: 150
SQ FT: 12,000
SALES: 46.5MM **Privately Held**
WEB: www.winequest.com
SIC: 2084 Wines

(P-1720)
DELICATO VINEYARDS
12001 S Highway 99, Manteca
(95336-8499)
PHONE...........................209 824-3501
Christopher Indelicato, *Principal*
EMP: 14
SALES (corp-wide): 46.5MM **Privately**
Held
SIC: 2084 Wines
PA: Delicato Vineyards
12001 S Highway 99
Manteca CA 95336
209 824-3600

(P-1721)
DELICATO VINEYARDS
455 Devlin Rd Ste 201, NAPA
(94558-7562)
PHONE...........................707 265-1700
Chris Indelicato, *Manager*
David De Boer, *Vice Pres*
EMP: 42
SALES (corp-wide): 46.5MM **Privately**
Held
WEB: www.winequest.com
SIC: 2084 Wines
PA: Delicato Vineyards
12001 S Highway 99
Manteca CA 95336
209 824-3600

(P-1722)
DELICATO VINEYARDS
4089 Silverado Trl, NAPA (94558-1113)
PHONE...........................707 253-1400
Ana Simoes, *Manager*
EMP: 20
SALES (corp-wide): 46.5MM **Privately**
Held
SIC: 2084 Wines
PA: Delicato Vineyards
12001 S Highway 99
Manteca CA 95336
209 824-3600

(P-1723)
DELICATO VINEYARDS
Also Called: Cypress Ridge Winery
51955 Oasis Rd, King City (93930-9778)
PHONE...........................831 385-7587
Jim Thompson, *Manager*
EMP: 13
SALES (corp-wide): 46.5MM **Privately**
Held
WEB: www.winequest.com
SIC: 2084 Wines
PA: Delicato Vineyards
12001 S Highway 99
Manteca CA 95336
209 824-3600

(P-1724)
DIAGEO NORTH AMERICA INC
Also Called: Glen Ellen Carneros Winery
21468 8th St E Ste 1, Sonoma
(95476-9782)
P.O. Box 1636 (95476-1636)
PHONE...........................707 939-6200
Fax: 707 938-2592
EMP: 75
SALES (corp-wide): 16.6B **Privately Held**
SIC: 2084 0172
HQ: Diageo North America Inc.
801 Main Ave
Norwalk CT 06851
203 229-2100

(P-1725)
DIAGEO NORTH AMERICA INC
Also Called: United Distlrs Vintners N Amer
1160 Battery St Ste 30, San Francisco
(94111-1215)
PHONE...........................415 835-7300
Karen Cass, *Branch Mgr*
Dowell Heppe, *Manager*
EMP: 96
SALES (corp-wide): 16.3B **Privately Held**
SIC: 2084 2082 Wines, brandy & brandy
spirits; malt beverages
HQ: Diageo North America Inc.
801 Main Ave
Norwalk CT 06851
203 229-2100

(P-1726)
DIAGEO NORTH AMERICA INC
Also Called: Diageno Chateau & Estate
Wines
555 Gateway Dr, NAPA (94558-6291)
PHONE...........................707 299-2600
Ray Chadwick, *General Mgr*
Robyn Eldridge, *Marketing Mgr*
Brandon Groves, *Manager*
EMP: 80
SALES (corp-wide): 16.3B **Privately Held**
SIC: 2084 Wines, brandy & brandy spirits
HQ: Diageo North America Inc.
801 Main Ave
Norwalk CT 06851
203 229-2100

(P-1727)
DIAMOND CREEK VINEYARD
1500 Diamond Mountain Rd, Calistoga
(94515-9669)
PHONE...........................707 942-6926
Adelle Brounstein, *Owner*
▲ EMP: 12
SQ FT: 1,799
SALES (est): 1.8MM **Privately Held**
WEB: www.diamondcreekvineyards.com
SIC: 2084 0172 Wines; grapes

(P-1728)
DOGPATCH WINEWORKS
170 Henry St, San Francisco (94114-1217)
PHONE...........................415 525-4440

Lynne Carmichael, *Principal*
EMP: 14 EST: 2011
SALES (est): 1.6MM **Privately Held**
SIC: 2084 Wines

(P-1729)
DOMAINE CHANDON INC (DH)
1 California Dr, Yountville (94599-1426)
PHONE...........................707 944-8844
Matthew Wood, *CEO*
Greg Godchaux, *Vice Pres*
Lisa Meyer, *Executive*
Denise Gracier, *Admin Asst*
Thomas Duhameau, *Controller*
▲ EMP: 100 EST: 1973
SQ FT: 240,000
SALES (est): 38MM
SALES (corp-wide): 315.2MM **Privately**
Held
WEB: www.chandon.com
SIC: 2084 5812 0762 5813 Wines; eating
places; vineyard management & mainte-
nance services; drinking places
HQ: Moet Hennessy Usa, Inc.
85 10th Ave Fl 2
New York NY 10011
212 888-7575

(P-1730)
DOMAINE DE LA TERRE ROUGE
Also Called: Terre Rouge Winery
10801 Dickson Rd, Plymouth (95669)
P.O. Box 41, Fiddletown (95629-0041)
PHONE...........................209 245-4277
Bill Easton, *President*
EMP: 10
SALES (est): 1.1MM **Privately Held**
SIC: 2084 5182 Wines; brandy & brandy
spirits

(P-1731)
DOMINUS ESTATE
CORPORATION
2570 Napa Nook Rd, Yountville
(94599-1455)
PHONE...........................707 944-8954
Christian Moueix, *President*
Carmel Greenberg, *Lab Dir*
Kassidy Harris, *Marketing Mgr*
Julia Levitan, *Manager*
▲ EMP: 18
SQ FT: 4,000
SALES (est): 2.4MM **Privately Held**
WEB: www.dominusestate.com
SIC: 2084 Wines

(P-1732)
DON SEBASTIANI & SONS
INTERNAT
520 Airpark Rd, NAPA (94558-7535)
PHONE...........................707 224-0410
John Nicolette, *Manager*
EMP: 32
SALES (corp-wide): 54.6MM **Privately**
Held
SIC: 2084 Wines
PA: Don Sebastiani & Sons International
Wine Negociants
19150 Sonoma Hwy 12
Sonoma CA 95476
707 933-1704

(P-1733)
DRY CREEK VINEYARD INC
3770 Lambert Bridge Rd, Healdsburg
(95448-9713)
P.O. Box T (95448-0107)
PHONE...........................707 433-1000
Don Wallace,
Kim Wallace, *Vice Pres*
Joe Czesnakowicz, *General Mgr*
Jerry Smith, *General Mgr*
Salina Littleton, *Administration*
▲ EMP: 35
SQ FT: 11,000
SALES (est): 7.6MM **Privately Held**
WEB: www.drycreekvineyard.com
SIC: 2084 0172 Wines; grapes

(P-1734)
DUCKHORN WINE COMPANY
14100 Mountain House Rd, Hopland
(95449-9782)
PHONE...........................707 744-2800
Daniel J Duckhorn, *President*
EMP: 27

SALES (corp-wide): 27.3MM **Privately**
Held
SIC: 2084 0172 Wines; grapes
HQ: Duckhorn Wine Company
1000 Lodi Ln
Saint Helena CA 94574
707 963-7108

(P-1735)
DUCKHORN WINE COMPANY
(HQ)
Also Called: Goldeneye
1000 Lodi Ln, Saint Helena (94574-9410)
PHONE...........................707 963-7108
Alex Ryan, *CEO*
Lori Beaudoin, *CFO*
Noi Singhavara, *Administration*
Bret Fenton, *Sales Staff*
Erin Kinney, *Sales Staff*
▲ EMP: 40
SALES (est): 11.8MM
SALES (corp-wide): 27.3MM **Privately**
Held
WEB: www.goldeneyewinery.com
SIC: 2084 0172 Wines; grapes
PA: Tsg Consumer Partners, Llc
600 Montgomery St # 2900
San Francisco CA 94111
415 217-2300

(P-1736)
DUCKHORN WINE COMPANY
Also Called: Goldeneye Winery
9200 Highway 128, Philo (95466-9516)
P.O. Box 137 (95466-0137)
PHONE...........................707 895-3202
Bob Nye, *Manager*
EMP: 13
SALES (corp-wide): 27.3MM **Privately**
Held
WEB: www.goldeneyewinery.com
SIC: 2084 Wines
HQ: Duckhorn Wine Company
1000 Lodi Ln
Saint Helena CA 94574
707 963-7108

(P-1737)
DUFF BEVILL VINEYARD
MANAGMENT
4724 Dry Creek Rd, Healdsburg
(95448-9714)
PHONE...........................707 433-6691
Duffern P Bevill, *Owner*
EMP: 35
SALES (est): 2MM **Privately Held**
SIC: 2084 Wines

(P-1738)
DURNEY WINERY
CORPORATION
Also Called: Heller State
18820 Cachagua Rd, Carmel Valley
(93924-9393)
P.O. Box 999 (93924-0999)
PHONE...........................831 659-2690
Rich Tanguay, *Manager*
EMP: 10
SALES (corp-wide): 853.3K **Privately**
Held
WEB: www.durneywines.com
SIC: 2084 Wines
PA: Durney Winery Corporation
69 W Carmel Valley Rd
Carmel Valley CA 93924
831 659-6220

(P-1739)
E & J GALLO WINERY (PA)
Also Called: San Joaquin Vly Concentrates
600 Yosemite Blvd, Modesto (95354-2760)
P.O. Box 1130 (95353-1130)
PHONE...........................209 341-3111
Joseph E Gallo, *CEO*
Chris Kalabokes, *Vice Pres*
Jehangir Jasavala, *Associate Dir*
Steve Wallace, *Managing Dir*
Janet Ackerson, *Executive Asst*
◆ EMP: 2500
SALES (est): 2.6B **Privately Held**
WEB: www.gallo.com
SIC: 2084 0172 Wines; grapes

(P-1740)
E & J GALLO WINERY
5610 E Olive Ave, Fresno (93727-2707)
P.O. Box 1081 (93714-1081)
PHONE..............................559 458-0807
Joe Rossi, *Branch Mgr*
Craig Trzepkowski, *Software Engr*
Brock Baker, *Project Mgr*
Phillip Moore, *Engineer*
Kent Johnson, *Buyer*
EMP: 140
SALES (corp-wide): 2.6B **Privately Held**
WEB: www.gallo.com
SIC: 2084 0172 Wines; grapes
PA: E. & J. Gallo Winery
600 Yosemite Blvd
Modesto CA 95354
209 341-3111

(P-1741)
E & J GALLO WINERY
Also Called: San Joaquin Vly Concentrates
5631 E Olive Ave, Fresno (93727-2708)
PHONE..............................559 458-2500
Gary Schmidt, *Principal*
Phillip Prull, *Business Anlyst*
Kai Loo, *QC Mgr*
Edmundo Marinez, *Opers Staff*
EMP: 57
SALES (corp-wide): 2.6B **Privately Held**
WEB: www.gallo.com
SIC: 2084 Wines
PA: E. & J. Gallo Winery
600 Yosemite Blvd
Modesto CA 95354
209 341-3111

(P-1742)
E & J GALLO WINERY
Also Called: Gallo Os Sonoma
3387 Dry Creek Rd, Healdsburg
(95448-9740)
PHONE..............................707 431-1946
Wayne Van Wagner, *Director*
Marcello Monticelli, *Vice Pres*
Mary McDaniel, *Executive Asst*
Christine Hansen, *Engineer*
Gary Vanderwerff, *Engineer*
EMP: 20
SQ FT: 2,700
SALES (corp-wide): 2.6B **Privately Held**
WEB: www.gallo.com
SIC: 2084 0172 Wines; grapes
PA: E. & J. Gallo Winery
600 Yosemite Blvd
Modesto CA 95354
209 341-3111

(P-1743)
E & J GALLO WINERY
2101 Yosemite Blvd, Modesto
(95354-3024)
PHONE..............................209 341-3111
Joseph E Gallo, *CEO*
Robert Barrios, *Vice Pres*
William McMorran, *Vice Pres*
Mark Barry, *Managing Dir*
Brant Scott, *Regional Mgr*
EMP: 19
SALES (corp-wide): 2.6B **Privately Held**
SIC: 2084 Wines
PA: E. & J. Gallo Winery
600 Yosemite Blvd
Modesto CA 95354
209 341-3111

(P-1744)
E & J GALLO WINERY
Also Called: Lerexa Winery
18000 River Rd, Livingston (95334-9514)
PHONE..............................209 394-6215
Kent Mann, *Manager*
James Mulhearn, *Project Mgr*
Ann Padilla, *Project Engr*
Jose Castillo, *Engineer*
Carl Porterejgallo, *Engineer*
EMP: 250
SALES (corp-wide): 2.6B **Privately Held**
WEB: www.gallo.com
SIC: 2084 0172 Wines; grapes
PA: E. & J. Gallo Winery
600 Yosemite Blvd
Modesto CA 95354
209 341-3111

(P-1745)
E & J GALLO WINERY
Also Called: Edna Valley Vineyard
2585 Biddle Ranch Rd, San Luis Obispo
(93401-8319)
PHONE..............................805 544-5855
Josh Baker, *Branch Mgr*
EMP: 209
SALES (corp-wide): 2.6B **Privately Held**
SIC: 2084 Wines
PA: E. & J. Gallo Winery
600 Yosemite Blvd
Modesto CA 95354
209 341-3111

(P-1746)
E & J GALLO WINERY
2650 Commerce Way, Commerce
(90040-1413)
PHONE..............................323 720-6400
Bob Gillespie, *Opers Mgr*
Scott Triou, *Executive*
John Sanchez, *General Mgr*
Barbara Hale, *Accountant*
Cale Minear, *Manager*
EMP: 300
SALES (corp-wide): 2.6B **Privately Held**
WEB: www.gallo.com
SIC: 2084 Wines
PA: E. & J. Gallo Winery
600 Yosemite Blvd
Modesto CA 95354
209 341-3111

(P-1747)
E & J GALLO WINERY
Also Called: Louis M. Martini Winery
254 Saint Helena Hwy S, Saint Helena
(94574-2203)
PHONE..............................707 963-2736
Ernest Gallo, *Ch of Bd*
Carolyn Martini, *Director*
EMP: 50
SALES (corp-wide): 2.6B **Privately Held**
WEB: www.gallo.com
SIC: 2084 0172 Wines; grapes
PA: E. & J. Gallo Winery
600 Yosemite Blvd
Modesto CA 95354
209 341-3111

(P-1748)
E & J GALLO WINERY
Also Called: Gallo Advertising
200 E Sandy Blvd, Modesto (95354)
P.O. Box 1348 (95353-1348)
PHONE..............................209 341-7862
Pat Broughton, *Principal*
Ross Partridge, *Project Mgr*
Dante Stovall, *Engineer*
EMP: 13
SALES (corp-wide): 2.6B **Privately Held**
WEB: www.gallo.com
SIC: 2084 Wines
PA: E. & J. Gallo Winery
600 Yosemite Blvd
Modesto CA 95354
209 341-3111

(P-1749)
ELLISTON VINEYARDS INC
463 Kilkare Rd, Sunol (94586-9415)
PHONE..............................925 862-2377
Donna Flavetta, *President*
Mark Piche, *Vice Pres*
Katie Montgomery, *Sales Mgr*
EMP: 55
SQ FT: 1,000
SALES (est): 5.9MM **Privately Held**
WEB: www.elliston.com
SIC: 2084 Wines; wine cellars, bonded:
engaged in blending wines

(P-1750)
ENVY WINES LLC
1170 Tubbs Ln, Calistoga (94515-1054)
PHONE..............................707 942-4670
Mark J Carter, *Mng Member*
Nils Venge,
▲ **EMP:** 10
SALES (est): 1MM **Privately Held**
SIC: 2084 Wines

(P-1751)
EOS ESTATE WINERY
2300 Airport Rd, Paso Robles
(93446-8549)
PHONE..............................805 239-2562
Frank Arciero, *Partner*
Phil Arciero, *Partner*
Fern Underwood, *Partner*
▲ **EMP:** 47
SALES (est): 5.9MM **Privately Held**
WEB: www.eosvintage.com
SIC: 2084 0172 3172 Wines; grapes; personal leather goods

(P-1752)
ESCALERA-BOULET LLC
Also Called: Consilience Converge
2923 Grand Ave, Los Olivos (93441)
P.O. Box 529 (93441-0529)
PHONE..............................805 691-1020
William Sanger, *Mng Member*
Jodie Boulet Daughters, *Administration*
EMP: 10
SALES (est): 690.4K **Privately Held**
SIC: 2084 Wines

(P-1753)
ESTANCIA ESTATES
980 Bryant Cyn, Soledad (93960-2830)
PHONE..............................707 431-1975
Richard Sands, *President*
▲ **EMP:** 72
SALES (est): 5.2MM **Privately Held**
WEB: www.estanciaestates.com
SIC: 2084 Wines

(P-1754)
ETUDE WINES INC
1250 Cuttings Wharf Rd, NAPA
(94559-9738)
P.O. Box 3382 (94558-0338)
PHONE..............................707 257-5300
Jon Priest, *Manager*
David Cone, *Sales Staff*
Melanie Edwards, *Manager*
EMP: 16
SQ FT: 6,000
SALES (est): 2MM **Privately Held**
WEB: www.etudewines.com
SIC: 2084 Wines

(P-1755)
F KORBEL & BROS (PA)
Also Called: Korbel Champagne Cellers
13250 River Rd, Guerneville (95446-9593)
PHONE..............................707 824-7000
Gary B Heck, *President*
David Faris, *Treasurer*
Dan Baker, *Exec VP*
Danny Baker, *Exec VP*
Harold Duncan, *Senior VP*
▲ **EMP:** 300
SQ FT: 66,000
SALES (est): 93.2MM **Privately Held**
WEB: www.korbel.com
SIC: 2084 0172 Wines; grapes

(P-1756)
F KORBEL & BROS
Also Called: Heck Cellars
15401 Bear Mtn Winery Rd, Di Giorgio
(93203-9743)
PHONE..............................661 854-6120
Guy Ruhland, *Opers-Prdtn-Mfg*
EMP: 36
SQ FT: 250,000
SALES (corp-wide): 93.2MM **Privately Held**
WEB: www.korbel.com
SIC: 2084 0172 Wines; grapes
PA: F. Korbel & Bros.
13250 River Rd
Guerneville CA 95446
707 824-7000

(P-1757)
FALKNER WINERY INC
40620 Calle Contento, Temecula
(92591-5041)
PHONE..............................951 676-6741
Ray Falkner, *CEO*
Loretta Falkner, *Principal*
Nora Addam, *Manager*
Holly Estrema, *Manager*
EMP: 65
SALES (est): 10.1MM **Privately Held**
WEB: www.falknerwinery.com
SIC: 2084 7299 Wines; banquet hall facilities

(P-1758)
FAR NIENTE WINERY INC
Also Called: Far Niente Wine Estates
1350 Acacia Dr, Oakville (94562)
P.O. Box 327 (94562-0327)
PHONE..............................707 944-2861
Larry Maguire, *CEO*
Erik Nickel, *Partner*
Jeremy Nickel, *Partner*
Laura Harwood, *CFO*
Mary Grace, *Vice Pres*
▲ **EMP:** 100 **EST:** 1979
SQ FT: 30,000
SALES (est): 24.1MM **Privately Held**
WEB: www.farniente.com
SIC: 2084 Wines

(P-1759)
FERRAR-CRANO VNYRDS
WINERY LLC (PA)
Also Called: Prevail Wines
8761 Dry Creek Rd, Healdsburg
(95448-9133)
P.O. Box 1549 (95448-1549)
PHONE..............................707 433-6700
Donald L Carano, *Mng Member*
Jim Boswell, *Manager*
▲ **EMP:** 110
SQ FT: 46,000
SALES (est): 22.5MM **Privately Held**
WEB: www.fcwinery.com
SIC: 2084 0172 Wines; grapes

(P-1760)
FETZER VINEYARDS (HQ)
12901 Old River Rd, Hopland
(95449-9813)
P.O. Box 611 (95449-0611)
PHONE..............................707 744-1250
Eduardo Guilisasti Gana, *CEO*
Wade Grote, *President*
Blake Krynicky, *President*
Sid Goldstein, *Vice Pres*
Dennis Martin, *Vice Pres*
◆ **EMP:** 242
SALES (est): 66.8MM **Privately Held**
WEB: www.earlytimes.com
SIC: 2084 Wines

(P-1761)
FETZER VINEYARDS
Also Called: Fetzer Production Facility
8998 N River Rd, Paso Robles
(93446-6334)
PHONE..............................805 467-0192
Will Roddick, *Branch Mgr*
EMP: 19 **Privately Held**
WEB: www.earlytimes.com
SIC: 2084 Wines
HQ: Fetzer Vineyards
12901 Old River Rd
Hopland CA 95449
707 744-1250

(P-1762)
FIELD STONE WINERY &
VINEYARD
10075 Highway 128, Healdsburg
(95448-9025)
PHONE..............................707 433-7266
John C Staten, *President*
Ben Staten, *Corp Secy*
Staten Katrina J, *Vice Pres*
Katrina J Staten, *Vice Pres*
EMP: 12
SQ FT: 4,000
SALES (est): 1.7MM **Privately Held**
WEB: www.fieldstonewinery.com
SIC: 2084 5921 Wines; wine

(P-1763)
FIRESTONE VINEYARD LP
Also Called: Curtis Winery
5000 Zaca Station Rd, Los Olivos (93441)
P.O. Box 244 (93441-0244)
PHONE..............................805 688-3940
Michael L Gravelle, *Partner*
Adam Firestone, *Partner*
▲ **EMP:** 85
SQ FT: 45,000

SALES (est): 9.4MM
SALES (corp-wide): 61.5MM **Privately Held**
WEB: www.firestonewine.com
SIC: **2084** 0172 Wines; grapes
HQ: Foley Family Wines, Inc.
2300 Airport Rd
Paso Robles CA 93446

(P-1764)
FLOOD RANCH COMPANY
Also Called: Rancho Sisquoc Winery
6600 Foxen Canyon Rd, Santa Maria
(93454-9656)
PHONE.....................................805 937-3616
Ed A Holt, *Manager*
Becki Rodriguez, *Manager*
EMP: 15
SALES (est): 2.7MM
SALES (corp-wide): 2.6MM **Privately Held**
SIC: **2084** Wines
PA: Flood Ranch Company
870 Market St Ste 1100
San Francisco CA 94102
415 982-5645

(P-1765)
FLORA SPRINGS WINE COMPANY
1978 Zinfandel Ln, Saint Helena
(94574-1611)
PHONE.....................................707 963-5711
John Komes, *President*
Martha Komes, *Treasurer*
Patrick Garvey, *Vice Pres*
Julie Garvey, *Admin Sec*
Dale Hickman, *Info Tech Mgr*
▲ EMP: 19
SQ FT: 16,000
SALES (est): 3.5MM **Privately Held**
SIC: **2084** Wines

(P-1766)
FLOWERS VINEYARD & WINERY LLC
28500 Seaview Rd, Cazadero
(95421-9767)
PHONE.....................................707 847-3661
Jason Jardine, *President*
▲ EMP: 15
SALES (est): 2.3MM **Privately Held**
WEB: www.flowerswinery.com
SIC: **2084** Wines

(P-1767)
FOLEY FAMILY WINES INC (HQ)
Also Called: Foley Wine Group
2300 Airport Rd, Paso Robles
(93446-8549)
P.O. Box 244, Los Olivos (93441-0244)
PHONE.....................................805 688-3940
William Patrick Foley II, *CEO*
◆ EMP: 40
SALES (est): 61.5MM **Privately Held**
SIC: **2084** 0172 Wines; grapes
PA: Foley Family Wines Holdings, Inc.
200 Concourse Blvd
Santa Rosa CA 95403
805 688-3940

(P-1768)
FOX BARREL CIDER COMPANY INC
1213 S Auburn St Ste A, Colfax
(95713-9800)
P.O. Box 753 (95713-0753)
PHONE.....................................530 346-9699
Bruce Nissen, *President*
Sean Deorsey, *CFO*
EMP: 50
SALES (est): 5.7MM
SALES (corp-wide): 11B **Publicly Held**
WEB: www.foxbarrel.com
SIC: **2084** Wines
HQ: Crispin Cider Company
1213 S Auburn St Ste A
Colfax CA 95713
530 346-9699

(P-1769)
FRANCIS FORD CPPOLA PRSNTS LLC
Also Called: Francis Ford Coppola Winery
300 Via Archimedes, Geyserville
(95441-9325)
PHONE.....................................707 251-3200
Francis Coppola, *Mng Member*
Eleanor Coppola,
Wendy Putman,
◆ EMP: 20
SALES: 6.4MM **Privately Held**
SIC: **2084** Wines

(P-1770)
FRANCISCAN VINEYARDS INC
Also Called: Ravenswood Winery
18701 Gehricke Rd, Sonoma (95476-4710)
PHONE.....................................707 938-1960
Fax: 707 933-2383
EMP: 188
SALES (corp-wide): 7.5B **Publicly Held**
SIC: **2084** 5921
HQ: Franciscan Vineyards Inc.
1178 Galleron Rd
Saint Helena CA 94574
707 963-7111

(P-1771)
FRANCISCAN VINEYARDS INC
Also Called: Woodbridge Winery
5950 E Woodbridge Rd, Acampo
(95220-9429)
P.O. Box 1260, Woodbridge (95258-1260)
PHONE.....................................209 369-5861
Mark Garbrielli, *Manager*
EMP: 300
SQ FT: 2,450
SALES (corp-wide): 7.5B **Publicly Held**
WEB: www.robertmondaviwinery.com
SIC: **2084** Wines
HQ: Franciscan Vineyards Inc.
1178 Galleron Rd
Saint Helena CA 94574
707 963-7111

(P-1772)
FRANCISCAN VINEYARDS INC (HQ)
1178 Galleron Rd, Saint Helena
(94574-9790)
PHONE.....................................707 963-7111
Agustin Francisco Huneeus, *President*
Bill Skowronski, *CFO*
▲ EMP: 75
SQ FT: 110,000
SALES (est): 46.5MM
SALES (corp-wide): 7.5B **Publicly Held**
WEB: www.ravenswood-wine.com
SIC: **2084** Wines
PA: Constellation Brands, Inc.
207 High Point Dr # 100
Victor NY 14564
585 678-7100

(P-1773)
FRANCISCAN VINYARDS INC
Also Called: Simi Winery
16275 Healdsburg Ave, Healdsburg
(95448-9075)
P.O. Box 698 (95448-0698)
PHONE.....................................707 433-6981
Hustin Huneeus, *President*
Susan Lueker, *Technician*
▲ EMP: 75
SALES (est): 6.8MM
SALES (corp-wide): 7.5B **Publicly Held**
WEB: www.simiwinery.com
SIC: **2084** 0172 5812 Wines; grapes; eating places
PA: Constellation Brands, Inc.
207 High Point Dr # 100
Victor NY 14564
585 678-7100

(P-1774)
FRANZIA/SANGER WINERY
Also Called: Franzia Winery
17000 E State Highway 120, Ripon
(95366-9412)
PHONE.....................................209 599-4111
Arthur Ciocca, *Partner*
F Lynn Bates, *Partner*
▲ EMP: 200 EST: 1933
SQ FT: 160,000

SALES (est): 38.2MM **Privately Held**
SIC: **2084** Wines

(P-1775)
FREEMARK ABBEY WNERY LTD PRTNR
3022 Saint Helena Hwy N, Saint Helena
(94574-9652)
P.O. Box 410 (94574-0410)
PHONE.....................................707 963-9694
John Bryan,
EMP: 20
SQ FT: 4,500
SALES (est): 1.9MM **Privately Held**
SIC: **2084** 0172 Wines; grapes

(P-1776)
FREIXENET SONOMA CAVES INC
Also Called: Gloria Ferrer Winery
23555 Arnold Dr, Sonoma (95476-9285)
P.O. Box 1949 (95476-1949)
PHONE.....................................707 996-4981
Jose M Ferrer, *CEO*
Diego Jimenez, *President*
▲ EMP: 40
SQ FT: 4,000
SALES (est): 8.5MM
SALES (corp-wide): 760.2MM **Privately Held**
SIC: **2084** 5812 Wines; eating places
HQ: Freixenet Sa
Plaza Joan Sala 2
Sant Sadurni D Anoia 08770
938 917-000

(P-1777)
FROGS LEAP WINERY
8815 Conn Creek Rd, Rutherford (94573)
P.O. Box 189 (94573-0189)
PHONE.....................................707 963-4704
John T Williams, *President*
Michelle Migliacacca, *Office Mgr*
Leah S White, *Executive Asst*
Kristy Byrd, *Sales Mgr*
Michelle Watkins, *Sales Mgr*
◆ EMP: 36
SQ FT: 8,000
SALES (est): 6.1MM **Privately Held**
WEB: www.frogsleap.com
SIC: **2084** Wines

(P-1778)
GANDONA INC A CALIFORNIA CORP
1535 Sage Canyon Rd, Saint Helena
(94574-9628)
PHONE.....................................707 967-5550
Manuel Pires, *President*
EMP: 10
SALES (est): 876.9K **Privately Held**
SIC: **2084** Wines

(P-1779)
GEKKEIKAN SAKE USAINC
1136 Sibley St, Folsom (95630-3223)
PHONE.....................................916 985-3111
Masahiro Namise, *CEO*
Yu Hyodo, *Admin Sec*
◆ EMP: 25
SQ FT: 390,000
SALES (est): 7.9MM
SALES (corp-wide): 240.9MM **Privately Held**
WEB: www.gekkeikan-sake.com
SIC: **2084** Wines
PA: Gekkeikan Sake Company,Ltd.
247, Minamihamacho, Fushimi-Ku
Kyoto KYO 612-8
756 232-001

(P-1780)
GEORIS WINERY
4 Pilot Rd, Carmel Valley (93924-9515)
PHONE.....................................831 659-1050
Walter Georgis, *Owner*
▲ EMP: 10
SALES (est): 1.3MM **Privately Held**
WEB: www.georiswine.com
SIC: **2084** Wines

(P-1781)
GEYSER PEAK WINERY
Also Called: Canyon Road Winery
2306 Magnolia Dr, Healdsburg
(95448-9406)
PHONE.....................................707 857-9463
Stephen Brower, *President*
Tim Matz, *Director*
Ashley Balistreri, *Manager*
▲ EMP: 45
SALES (est): 6.9MM **Privately Held**
SIC: **2084** Wines

(P-1782)
GIBSON WINE COMPANY
1720 Academy Ave, Sanger (93657-3704)
PHONE.....................................559 875-2505
Wayne Albrecht, *CEO*
Donald Weber, *Treasurer*
Kim Spruance, *Admin Sec*
EMP: 25 EST: 1939
SQ FT: 2,000
SALES (est): 6.1MM
SALES (corp-wide): 182.4MM **Privately Held**
SIC: **2084** Wines
PA: Bronco Wine Company
6342 Bystrum Rd
Ceres CA 95307
209 538-3131

(P-1783)
GIMELLI VINEYARDS
403 Grass Valley Rd, Hollister
(95023-9621)
PHONE.....................................831 637-5445
Ken Gimelli, *Owner*
EMP: 12
SQ FT: 500
SALES (est): 1.1MM **Privately Held**
SIC: **2084** Wines

(P-1784)
GIVENS AND HALPERN INC
1099 Essex Ave, Richmond (94801-2112)
PHONE.....................................415 884-9999
Lisa Consani, *Principal*
Christian Maalihan, *VP Opers*
EMP: 22
SALES (est): 3.5MM **Privately Held**
SIC: **2084** Wines

(P-1785)
GNEKOW FAMILY WINERY LLC
17347 E Gawne Rd, Stockton
(95215-9646)
PHONE.....................................209 463-0697
Sean Gnekow,
Rudy Gnekow,
EMP: 14
SQ FT: 18,000
SALES (est): 2.3MM **Privately Held**
SIC: **2084** Wines

(P-1786)
GOLDEN STATE VINTNERS (PA)
4596 S Tracy Blvd, Tracy (95377-8106)
PHONE.....................................707 254-4900
Brian Jay Vos, *CEO*
John Oliver Sutton, *CFO*
▼ EMP: 15
SQ FT: 8,000
SALES (est): 49.7MM **Privately Held**
SIC: **2084** Wines; brandy

(P-1787)
GOLDEN STATE VINTNERS
1075 Golden Gate Dr, NAPA (94558-6187)
PHONE.....................................707 254-1985
Mike Blom,
EMP: 49
SALES (corp-wide): 49.7MM **Privately Held**
SIC: **2084** Wine cellars, bonded: engaged in blending wines
PA: Golden State Vintners
4596 S Tracy Blvd
Tracy CA 95377
707 254-4900

(P-1788)
GOLDEN STATE VINTNERS
1777 Metz Rd, Soledad (93960-2805)
PHONE.....................................831 678-3991
Jay Clark, *Manager*
EMP: 34

▲ = Import ▼ =Export
◆ =Import/Export

SALES (corp-wide): 49.7MM **Privately Held**
SIC: 2084 0172 Wines; grapes
PA: Golden State Vintners
4596 S Tracy Blvd
Tracy CA 95377
707 254-4900

(P-1789)
GOLDEN STATE VINTNERS
1175 Commmerce Blvd, Vallejo (94503)
PHONE....................707 553-6480
Jeff Neil, *Branch Mgr*
EMP: 27
SALES (corp-wide): 49.7MM **Privately Held**
SIC: 2084 Wines; brandy & brandy spirits
PA: Golden State Vintners
4596 S Tracy Blvd
Tracy CA 95377
707 254-4900

(P-1790)
GOLDEN VLY GRAPE JICE WINE LLC (PA)
11770 Road 27 1/2, Madera (93637-9108)
PHONE....................559 661-4657
Gerard Pantaleo, *Mng Member*
Rodger Williams, *Sales Staff*
Frank Pantaleo,
Jerry Pantaleo,
Nicholas Pantaleo,
▲ **EMP:** 40
SALES: 19.9MM **Privately Held**
SIC: 2084 Wines

(P-1791)
GOLDSTONE LAND COMPANY LLC
Also Called: Bear Creek Winery
11900 Furry Rd, Lodi (95240-7201)
PHONE....................209 368-3113
Joan M Kautz, *Mng Member*
Craig Rous, *Opers Staff*
Stan Hall, *Maintence Staff*
Stephen J Kautz, *Mng Member*
◆ **EMP:** 30
SALES (est): 6.6MM **Privately Held**
SIC: 2084 Wines

(P-1792)
GOOSECROSS CELLARS A CAL CORP
1119 State Ln, Yountville (94599-9407)
PHONE....................707 944-1986
David Topper, *CEO*
Geoffrey Gorsuch, *Vice Pres*
Neil Bason, *Director*
EMP: 14
SALES (est): 1.8MM **Privately Held**
SIC: 2084 Wine cellars, bonded: engaged in blending wines; wines

(P-1793)
GOOSECROSS CELLARS COORSTEK
1119 State Ln, Yountville (94599-9407)
PHONE....................707 944-1986
Christi Coors Ficeli, *CEO*
Phil Borgmeye, *CFO*
Alora Horne, *Bookkeeper*
Daniel Prince, *Bookkeeper*
Theresa Engelstad, *Sales Staff*
EMP: 14
SALES (est): 25.3K **Privately Held**
WEB: www.goosecross.com
SIC: 2084 5921 Wines; wine

(P-1794)
GRAPE LINKS INC
Also Called: Barefoot Cellars
420 Aviation Blvd Ste 106, Santa Rosa (95403-1039)
P.O. Box 1130, Modesto (95353-1130)
PHONE....................707 524-8000
Michael C Houlihan, *President*
Martin A Jones, *Exec VP*
Bonnie Harvey, *Vice Pres*
Jennifer Wall, *Admin Sec*
Aaron J Fein, *Sales Staff*
EMP: 17
SQ FT: 4,200

SALES (est): 2MM
SALES (corp-wide): 2.6B **Privately Held**
WEB: www.barefootcellars.com
SIC: 2084 Wines
PA: E. & J. Gallo Winery
600 Yosemite Blvd
Modesto CA 95354
209 341-3111

(P-1795)
GREAT AMERICAN WINERIES INC
2511 Garden Rd Ste B100, Monterey (93940-5344)
P.O. Box 444, New York NY (10272-0444)
PHONE....................831 920-4736
Robert S Brower Sr, *President*
Robert S Brower, *President*
Patricia Brower, *Vice Pres*
EMP: 20 EST: 1982
SQ FT: 14,000
SALES (est): 3.4MM **Privately Held**
SIC: 2084 5182 Wines, brandy & brandy spirits; wines; wine

(P-1796)
GREGORY GRAZIANO
Also Called: Domaine Saint Gregory
1170 Bel Arbres Dr, Redwood Valley (95470-9695)
PHONE....................707 485-9463
Gregory Graziano, *Owner*
EMP: 10
SQ FT: 35,000
SALES (est): 852.8K **Privately Held**
SIC: 2084 Wines

(P-1797)
GRGICH HILLS CELLAR
Also Called: G and H Vineyards
1829 St Helena Hwy, Rutherford (94573)
P.O. Box 450 (94573-0450)
PHONE....................707 963-2784
Miljenko Mike Grgich, *President*
Austin E Hills, *Shareholder*
Violet Grgich, *Corp Secy*
Kim Bors, *Vice Pres*
Ivo Jeramaz, *Vice Pres*
▲ **EMP:** 35
SQ FT: 43,000
SALES (est): 7.4MM **Privately Held**
WEB: www.grgich.com
SIC: 2084 5812 0172 Wines; eating places; grapes

(P-1798)
GROSKOPF WAREHOUSE & LOGISTICS
20580 8th St E, Sonoma (95476-9590)
P.O. Box 128, Vineburg (95487-0128)
PHONE....................707 939-3100
Alec Merriam, *Owner*
▲ **EMP:** 41 EST: 2001
SALES (est): 14.2MM **Privately Held**
WEB: www.groskopf.com
SIC: 2084 Wines

(P-1799)
GROWEST INC (PA)
Also Called: Growest Development
10490 Dawson Canyon Rd, Corona (92883-4139)
PHONE....................951 638-1000
John Bremer, *President*
EMP: 15
SQ FT: 10,000
SALES (est): 11.4MM **Privately Held**
SIC: 2084 5193 Wines; nursery stock

(P-1800)
GUENOC WINERY INC
Also Called: Langtry Estates and Vineyards
200 Concourse Blvd, Santa Rosa (95403-8210)
PHONE....................707 987-2385
Easton Manson, *President*
Michael Schochet, *CFO*
EMP: 32
SALES (est): 5MM **Privately Held**
WEB: www.guenoc.com
SIC: 2084 Wine cellars, bonded: engaged in blending wines; wines

(P-1801)
HAGAFEN CELLARS INC
4160 Silverado Trl, NAPA (94558-1118)
PHONE....................707 252-0781
Ernie Weir, *President*
Irit Weir, *Vice Pres*
Michael Gelven, *Marketing Staff*
▲ **EMP:** 12
SQ FT: 6,000
SALES (est): 1.8MM **Privately Held**
WEB: www.hagafen.com
SIC: 2084 Wines

(P-1802)
HAHN ESTATE
Also Called: Smith & Hook Winery Inc
37700 Foothill Rd, Soledad (93960-9620)
P.O. Box C (93960-0167)
PHONE....................831 678-2132
Philip Hahn, *CEO*
Nicolaus Hahn, *Ch of Bd*
Gabrielle Hahn, *Admin Sec*
▲ **EMP:** 55
SQ FT: 25,000
SALES (est): 9.4MM
SALES (corp-wide): 19.7MM **Privately Held**
SIC: 2084 0172 Wines; grapes
PA: Kvl Holdings, Inc.
37700 Foothill Rd
Soledad CA 93960
831 678-2132

(P-1803)
HALTER WINERY LLC
8910 Adelaida Rd, Paso Robles (93446-8798)
PHONE....................805 226-9455
Mitchell S Wyss,
Hansjorg Wyss,
EMP: 25
SALES (est): 1.5MM **Privately Held**
SIC: 2084 Wines

(P-1804)
HANDLEY CELLARS LTD
Also Called: Handley Cellars Winery
3151 Highway 128, Philo (95466-9468)
P.O. Box 66 (95466-0066)
PHONE....................707 895-3876
Milla Handley, *General Ptnr*
Raymond Handley, *Partner*
EMP: 18
SQ FT: 10,000
SALES: 1.2MM **Privately Held**
WEB: www.handleycellars.com
SIC: 2084 Wines

(P-1805)
HANNA WINERY INC (PA)
9280 Highway 128, Healdsburg (95448-8028)
PHONE....................707 431-4310
Christine Hanna, *President*
Elias S Hanna, *CEO*
Shelley Witten, *Office Mgr*
Carol Machi, *Manager*
▲ **EMP:** 15
SQ FT: 3,000
SALES (est): 3MM **Privately Held**
WEB: www.hannawinery.com
SIC: 2084 Wines

(P-1806)
HANZELL VINEYARDS
18596 Lomita Ave, Sonoma (95476-4619)
PHONE....................707 996-3860
Jean L Arnold, *President*
Alexander De Brye, *Treasurer*
Lauren Wood, *Asst Controller*
Dawn Angelosante, *Marketing Staff*
Amelia Behm, *Marketing Staff*
EMP: 15
SALES (est): 2.6MM **Privately Held**
WEB: www.hanzell.com
SIC: 2084 Wines

(P-1807)
HARMONY CELLARS
3255 Harmony Valley Rd, Harmony (93435-5000)
PHONE....................805 927-1625
Kimberly Mulligan, *Partner*
Charles Mulligan, *Partner*
EMP: 13

SALES (est): 1.8MM **Privately Held**
WEB: www.harmonycellars.com
SIC: 2084 5813 5921 Wine cellars, bonded: engaged in blending wines; wine bar; wine

(P-1808)
HARTFORD JACKSON LLC
Also Called: Hartford Family Winery
8075 Martinelli Rd, Forestville (95436-9255)
P.O. Box 1459 (95436-1459)
PHONE....................707 887-1756
Don Hartford,
EMP: 15
SQ FT: 40,000
SALES (est): 1.9MM **Privately Held**
WEB: www.hartfordwines.com
SIC: 2084 Wines

(P-1809)
HDD LLC
Also Called: Vml Winery
4035 Westside Rd, Healdsburg (95448-9456)
P.O. Box 1532 (95448-1532)
PHONE....................707 433-9545
EMP: 15
SALES (corp-wide): 6.4MM **Publicly Held**
SIC: 2084 Wines
HQ: H.D.D. Llc
125 Foss Creek Cir
Healdsburg CA 95448
707 395-0289

(P-1810)
HEDGESIDE VINTNERS
Also Called: Del Dotto
1055 Atlas Peak Rd, NAPA (94558-1501)
PHONE....................707 963-2134
Dave Del Dotto, *Owner*
Bradley Saunders, *CFO*
▲ **EMP:** 20
SALES (est): 3.1MM **Privately Held**
SIC: 2084 Wines

(P-1811)
HESS COLLECTION WINERY (DH)
Also Called: Hess Collection Import Co
4411 Redwood Rd, NAPA (94558-9708)
P.O. Box 4140 (94558-0565)
PHONE....................707 255-1144
Timothy Persson, *CEO*
Clement J Firko, *President*
Tom Selfridge, *President*
John Grant, *COO*
Brian Dunn, *CFO*
◆ **EMP:** 25
SQ FT: 100,000
SALES (est): 25MM **Privately Held**
WEB: www.hesscollection.com
SIC: 2084 Wines
HQ: Colome Holding Ag
Hohle Gasse 4
Liebefeld BE
319 703-131

(P-1812)
HOMEWOOD WINERY
23120 Burndale Rd, Sonoma (95476-9722)
PHONE....................707 996-6353
Dave Homewood, *Owner*
▲ **EMP:** 10
SALES (est): 620K **Privately Held**
WEB: www.homewoodwinery.com
SIC: 2084 Wines

(P-1813)
HOPE FAMILY WINES (PA)
1585 Live Oak Rd, Paso Robles (93446-9637)
P.O. Box 3260 (93447-3260)
PHONE....................805 238-4112
Austin Hope, *President*
EMP: 22
SALES (est): 3.3MM **Privately Held**
SIC: 2084 Wines

(P-1814)
HTR LLC
Also Called: Hill Top Winery
30803 Hilltop View Ct, Valley Center (92082-6793)
P.O. Box 2570 (92082-2570)
PHONE....................760 297-4402

Michael Schimpf, *Mng Member*
EMP: 12
SALES (est): 995.1K **Privately Held**
SIC: 2084 7389 Wines; packaging & label-ing services

(P-1815)
HUNEEUS VINTNERS LLC (PA)
Also Called: Quintessa Vinyards
1040 Main St Ste 204, NAPA (94559-2605)
P.O. Box 505, Rutherford (94573-0505)
PHONE..............................707 286-2724
Aguistin Huneeus, *Mng Member*
Valeria Huneeus,
▲ **EMP:** 25
SQ FT: 40,000
SALES (est): 3.9MM **Privately Held**
SIC: 2084 Wines, brandy & brandy spirits

(P-1816)
HUSCH VINEYARDS INC (PA)
4400 Highway 128, Philo (95466-9476)
P.O. Box 189, Talmage (95481-0189)
PHONE..............................707 895-3216
Zac Robinson, *President*
Richard Robinson, *President*
Amanda Robinson, *CFO*
Al White, *Finance Mgr*
Brad Holstine, *Mfg Dir*
EMP: 30
SALES (est): 3.6MM **Privately Held**
WEB: www.huschvineyards.com
SIC: 2084 0172 Wines; grapes

(P-1817)
INGLENOOK
1991 St Helena Hwy, Rutherford (94573)
PHONE..............................707 968-1100
Francis Ford Coppola, *Principal*
▲ **EMP:** 11
SALES (est): 1.1MM **Privately Held**
SIC: 2084 Wines

(P-1818)
J LOHR WINERY CORPORATION (PA)
Also Called: J Lohr Viney
1000 Lenzen Ave, San Jose (95126-2739)
PHONE..............................408 288-5057
Steven W Lohr, *CEO*
Jerome J Lohr, *President*
Bruce Arkley, *Vice Pres*
James Schuett, *Vice Pres*
▲ **EMP:** 50
SQ FT: 47,000
SALES (est): 21.1MM **Privately Held**
WEB: www.jlohr.com
SIC: 2084 Wines

(P-1819)
J PEDRONCELLI WINERY
1220 Canyon Rd, Geyserville (95441-9639)
PHONE..............................707 857-3531
John A Pedroncelli, *President*
James A Pedroncelli, *Treasurer*
EMP: 20
SQ FT: 25,000
SALES (est): 4MM **Privately Held**
WEB: www.pedroncelli.com
SIC: 2084 0172 Wine cellars, bonded: en-gaged in blending wines; grapes

(P-1820)
JACKSON FAMILY FARMS LLC (PA)
425 Aviation Blvd, Santa Rosa (95403-1069)
PHONE..............................707 837-1000
Don Hartford,
Kathy Reddick, *Training Dir*
EMP: 34 EST: 1999
SALES (est): 12.9MM **Privately Held**
SIC: 2084 Wines

(P-1821)
JACKSON FAMILY FARMS LLC
5660 Skylane Blvd, Santa Rosa (95403-1086)
PHONE..............................707 836-2047
Jeff Jackson, *Manager*
EMP: 34
SALES (corp-wide): 12.9MM **Privately Held**
SIC: 2084 Wines

PA: Jackson Family Farms Llc
425 Aviation Blvd
Santa Rosa CA 95403
707 837-1000

(P-1822)
JACKSON FAMILY WINES INC
Also Called: Card Nale Tasting Room,
7600 Saint Helena Hwy, Oakville (94562)
P.O. Box 328 (94562-0328)
PHONE..............................707 948-2643
Ed Farver, *Manager*
EMP: 40
SALES (corp-wide): 350MM **Privately Held**
WEB: www.cambriawines.com
SIC: 2084 Wines
PA: Jackson Family Wines, Inc.
421 And 425 Aviation Blvd
Santa Rosa CA 95403
707 544-4000

(P-1823)
JACKSON FAMILY WINES INC
Also Called: La Crema Winery
3690 Laughlin Rd, Windsor (95492-8241)
PHONE..............................707 528-6278
Richard Bonatati, *General Mgr*
EMP: 30
SQ FT: 400,000
SALES (corp-wide): 350MM **Privately Held**
WEB: www.cambriawines.com
SIC: 2084 Wines
PA: Jackson Family Wines, Inc.
421 And 425 Aviation Blvd
Santa Rosa CA 95403
707 544-4000

(P-1824)
JACKSON FAMILY WINES INC (PA)
Also Called: Vineyards of Monterey
421 And 425 Aviation Blvd, Santa Rosa (95403)
PHONE..............................707 544-4000
Barbara Banke, *Director*
Matt Conneely, *President*
Hugh Reimers, *COO*
Gayle Bartscherer, *Senior VP*
David K Bowman, *Senior VP*
▲ **EMP:** 100
SQ FT: 25,000
SALES (est): 350MM **Privately Held**
WEB: www.cambriawines.com
SIC: 2084 0172 5813 Wines; grapes; wine bar

(P-1825)
JACKSON FAMILY WINES INC
Also Called: Cambria Winery
5475 Chardonnay Ln, Santa Maria (93454-9600)
PHONE..............................805 938-7300
Bill Hammond, *Branch Mgr*
EMP: 30
SALES (corp-wide): 350MM **Privately Held**
WEB: www.cambriawines.com
SIC: 2084 Wines
PA: Jackson Family Wines, Inc.
421 And 425 Aviation Blvd
Santa Rosa CA 95403
707 544-4000

(P-1826)
JACKSON FAMILY WINES INC
Stonestreet Winery
7111 Highway 128, Healdsburg (95448-8090)
PHONE..............................707 433-9463
Robert Carroll, *General Mgr*
EMP: 20
SALES (corp-wide): 350MM **Privately Held**
WEB: www.cambriawines.com
SIC: 2084 0172 Wines; grapes
PA: Jackson Family Wines, Inc.
421 And 425 Aviation Blvd
Santa Rosa CA 95403
707 544-4000

(P-1827)
JAMES FRASINETTI & SONS
Also Called: Frasinettis Winery & Rest
7395 Frasinetti Rd, Sacramento (95828-3718)
P.O. Box 292368 (95829-2368)
PHONE..............................916 383-2447
Howard Frasinetti, *Partner*
Gary Frasinetti, *Partner*
EMP: 36
SQ FT: 15,000
SALES (est): 2MM **Privately Held**
WEB: www.frasinetti.com
SIC: 2084 5812 5921 Wines; American restaurant; wine

(P-1828)
JAMES TOBIN CELLARS INC
8950 Union Rd, Paso Robles (93446-9356)
PHONE..............................805 239-2204
Tobin J Shumrick, *President*
Claire Silver, *Shareholder*
Monica Martin, *General Mgr*
Ben Lunt, *Manager*
Lance Silver, *Manager*
EMP: 30
SQ FT: 10,000
SALES (est): 5.6MM **Privately Held**
WEB: www.tobinjames.com
SIC: 2084 Wine cellars, bonded: engaged in blending wines

(P-1829)
JARVIS
Also Called: Jarvis Winery
2970 Monticello Rd, NAPA (94558-9615)
PHONE..............................707 255-5280
William R Jarvis, *President*
William E Jarvis, *Ch of Bd*
Deanna Martinez, *CFO*
Leticia Jarvis, *Vice Pres*
Dan Heim, *Natl Sales Mgr*
EMP: 30
SQ FT: 45,000
SALES (est): 6.7MM **Privately Held**
WEB: www.jarvisnapa.com
SIC: 2084 Wines

(P-1830)
JESSIES GROVE WINERY
1973 W Turner Rd, Lodi (95242-9677)
P.O. Box 1406, Woodbridge (95258-1406)
PHONE..............................209 368-0880
Greg Burns, *President*
Wanda Bechthold, *Vice Pres*
EMP: 15
SALES (est): 2.4MM **Privately Held**
WEB: www.jgwinery.com
SIC: 2084 Wines

(P-1831)
JESSUP CELLARS INC
6740 Washington St, Yountville (94599-1304)
PHONE..............................707 944-8523
Dan Blue, *Mng Member*
Vance Thompson,
Elise Kuhar-Pitters, *Manager*
EMP: 20
SALES (est): 2MM **Privately Held**
SIC: 2084 Wines

(P-1832)
JIM BEAUREGARD
1661 Pine Flat Rd, Santa Cruz (95060-9713)
PHONE..............................831 423-9453
Jim Beauregard, *Owner*
EMP: 100
SALES (est): 4.4MM **Privately Held**
SIC: 2084 Wines

(P-1833)
JOHN PINA JR & SONS
Also Called: Pina Cellars
7960 Silverado Trl, NAPA (94558-9433)
P.O. Box 373, Oakville (94562-0373)
PHONE..............................707 944-2229
David Pina, *Partner*
John C Pina, *Partner*
John White, *Partner*
▲ **EMP:** 50
SALES (est): 4.1MM **Privately Held**
SIC: 2084 Wines

(P-1834)
JORDAN VINEYARD & WINERY LP
1474 Alexander Valley Rd, Healdsburg (95448-9003)
PHONE..............................707 431-5250
Jordan John, *President*
Terri Murphy, *CTO*
▲ **EMP:** 28
SALES (est): 4.7MM **Privately Held**
SIC: 2084 Wines

(P-1835)
JUSTIN VINEYARDS & WINERY LLC (DH)
11680 Chimney Rock Rd, Paso Robles (93446-9792)
PHONE..............................805 238-6932
David Ricanati, *President*
Deborah Baldwin, *Vice Pres*
Will Torres, *Executive*
Craig B Cooper,
Babbette Miller, *Manager*
◆ **EMP:** 50
SQ FT: 60,000
SALES (est): 10.8MM
SALES (corp-wide): 1.5B **Privately Held**
WEB: www.justinwine.com
SIC: 2084 Wines
HQ: Fiji Water Company, Llc
11444 W Olympic Blvd # 250
Los Angeles CA 90064
310 966-5700

(P-1836)
JVW CORPORATION
Also Called: Jordan Vineyard & Winery
1474 Alexander Valley Rd, Healdsburg (95448-9003)
P.O. Box 878 (95448-0878)
PHONE..............................707 431-5250
John Jordan, *CEO*
Thomas N Jordan Jr, *President*
◆ **EMP:** 75
SQ FT: 50,000
SALES (est): 18.5MM **Privately Held**
WEB: www.jordanwinery.com
SIC: 2084 0172 Wines; grapes

(P-1837)
KB WINES LLC
Also Called: Kosta Browne
220 Morris St, Sebastopol (95472-3801)
P.O. Box 1959 (95473-1959)
PHONE..............................707 823-7430
Chris Costello,
Michael Brown,
Casey Castello,
Daniel Kosta,
▼ **EMP:** 28
SALES (est): 2.5MM **Privately Held**
SIC: 2084 Wines

(P-1838)
KEITH NICHOLS
Also Called: Nichols Winery & Cellars
8180 Manitoba St Apt 356, Playa Del Rey (90293-8653)
PHONE..............................310 305-0397
Keith Nichols, *Owner*
▲ **EMP:** 25
SQ FT: 1,700
SALES: 1MM **Privately Held**
WEB: www.nicholswinery.com
SIC: 2084 0172 Wines; grapes

(P-1839)
KELSEY SEE CANYON VINEYARDS
1945 See Canyon Rd, San Luis Obispo (93405-8023)
PHONE..............................805 595-9700
Delores Kelsey, *Owner*
Dick Kelsey, *Co-Owner*
Kelsey Canyon, *Director*
EMP: 10
SALES (est): 1.2MM **Privately Held**
WEB: www.kelseywine.com
SIC: 2084 Wines

▲ = Import ▼=Export
◆ =Import/Export

(P-1840)
KENDALL-JACKSON WINE ESTATES (HQ)
425 Aviation Blvd, Santa Rosa (95403-1069)
PHONE.................707 544-4000
Edward Pitlik, *CEO*
Jonathan Hollister, *President*
Jess Jackson, *President*
Jill Bartley, *CEO*
Tyler Comstock, *Treasurer*
EMP: 275
SQ FT: 10,000
SALES (est): 89.9MM
SALES (corp-wide): 350MM **Privately Held**
SIC: 2084 Wines
PA: Jackson Family Wines, Inc.
421 And 425 Aviation Blvd
Santa Rosa CA 95403
707 544-4000

(P-1841)
KOSTA BROWNE WINES LLC
Also Called: Kosta Browne Winery
220 Morris St, Sebastopol (95472-3801)
P.O. Box 1959 (95473-1959)
PHONE.................707 823-7430
Kosta Browne,
▲ **EMP:** 29
SALES (est): 2.5MM **Privately Held**
SIC: 2084 Wines

(P-1842)
KRUPP BROTHERS LLC
1345 Hestia Way, NAPA (94558-2105)
PHONE.................707 226-2215
Jan Krurpp,
Sandy Huffine, *Vice Pres*
Cathy Stern, *Opers Mgr*
Nikki Lincoln, *Regl Sales Mgr*
Bart Krurpp,
▲ **EMP:** 10
SALES (est): 1.1MM **Privately Held**
WEB: www.veraison.net
SIC: 2084 0172 Wines; grapes

(P-1843)
KULETO VILLA LLC
Also Called: Kuleto Estate
200 Concourse Blvd, Santa Rosa (95403-8210)
PHONE.................707 967-8577
Pat Kuleto, *Mng Member*
Ken Hearnsberger, *CFO*
▲ **EMP:** 20
SALES (est): 2.5MM **Privately Held**
WEB: www.kuletoestate.com
SIC: 2084 Wines

(P-1844)
KUNDE ENTERPRISES INC
Also Called: Kunde Estate Winery
9825 Sonoma Hwy, Kenwood (95452)
P.O. Box 639 (95452-0639)
PHONE.................707 833-5501
Don Chase, *President*
▲ **EMP:** 60
SQ FT: 15,000
SALES (est): 9.2MM **Privately Held**
SIC: 2084 Wine cellars, bonded: engaged in blending wines; wines

(P-1845)
KUNIN WINES LLC
28 Anacapa St Ste A, Santa Barbara (93101-1882)
PHONE.................805 963-9633
Seth H Kunin,
EMP: 11 EST: 1998
SALES (est): 1.4MM **Privately Held**
SIC: 2084 Wines

(P-1846)
L FOPPIANO WINE CO
Also Called: Foppiano Vineyards
12707 Old Redwood Hwy, Healdsburg (95448-9241)
P.O. Box 606 (95448-0606)
PHONE.................707 433-2736
Louis J Foppiano, *President*
Christine Wells, *Office Mgr*
Paul Foppiano, *CTO*
EMP: 20
SQ FT: 140,000

SALES (est): 4.2MM **Privately Held**
WEB: www.foppiano.com
SIC: 2084 Wines

(P-1847)
LADERA VINEYARDS LLC
150 White Cottage Rd S, Angwin (94508-9615)
P.O. Box 313, Saint Helena (94574-0313)
PHONE.................707 965-2445
Patrick L Stotesbery,
Kit Rye, *CFO*
Pat Stotesbery, *Info Tech Dir*
Daniel Saavedra, *Sales Staff*
Christopher Rye,
▲ **EMP:** 11
SALES (est): 2MM **Privately Held**
WEB: www.laderavineyards.com
SIC: 2084 Wines

(P-1848)
LADERA WINERY LLC
Also Called: Chateau Woltner
150 White Cottage Rd S, Angwin (94508-9615)
PHONE.................707 965-2445
Patrick L Stotesbery, *Mng Member*
Christopher Rye,
▲ **EMP:** 30
SALES (est): 4.3MM **Privately Held**
WEB: www.laderawinery.com
SIC: 2084 Wines

(P-1849)
LAETITIA VINEYARD & WINERY INC
Also Called: Laetitia Winery
453 Laetitia Vineyard Dr, Arroyo Grande (93420-9701)
PHONE.................805 481-1772
Selim K Zilkha, *President*
Nadia Wellisz, *Vice Pres*
Wendell Cottle, *Controller*
Jan Wilkinson, *Human Res Mgr*
Jackie Ross, *Sales Staff*
▲ **EMP:** 65
SALES (est): 10.9MM **Privately Held**
WEB: www.laetitiawine.com
SIC: 2084 Wines

(P-1850)
LAGUNA OAKS VNYARDS WINERY INC
Also Called: Balletto Vineyards
5700 Occidental Rd, Santa Rosa (95401-5533)
P.O. Box 2579, Sebastopol (95473-2579)
PHONE.................707 568-2455
John G Balletto, *President*
Teresa M Balleto, *Vice Pres*
▲ **EMP:** 12
SQ FT: 9,600
SALES (est): 1.9MM **Privately Held**
SIC: 2084 Wines

(P-1851)
LAIRD FAMILY ESTATE LLC (PA)
5055 Solano Ave, NAPA (94558-1326)
PHONE.................707 257-0360
Rebecca A Laird, *Mng Member*
Gail Laird,
Ken Laird, *Mng Member*
Kathy Holston, *Manager*
▲ **EMP:** 42
SQ FT: 64,000
SALES (est): 7.8MM **Privately Held**
WEB: www.lairdfamilyestate.com
SIC: 2084 Wines

(P-1852)
LAMBERT BRIDGE WINERY INC
4085 W Dry Creek Rd, Healdsburg (95448-9117)
PHONE.................707 431-9600
Patricia A Chambers, *President*
EMP: 14
SQ FT: 13,000
SALES (est): 2MM **Privately Held**
WEB: www.lambertbridge.com
SIC: 2084 Wines

(P-1853)
LANCASTER VINEYARDS INC
Also Called: Lancaster Estate
200 Concourse Blvd, Santa Rosa (95403-8210)
PHONE.................707 433-8178
Theodore Simpkins, *President*
EMP: 10 EST: 1953
SALES (est): 1.2MM **Privately Held**
WEB: www.lancasterestate.com
SIC: 2084 Wines

(P-1854)
LANE BENNETT WINERY
3340 State Highway 128, Calistoga (94515-9727)
PHONE.................707 942-6684
Randy Lynch, *Owner*
Stefanie Longton, *General Mgr*
Miguel Alcaraz, *Controller*
Travis Elder, *Manager*
▲ **EMP:** 10
SALES (est): 1.4MM **Privately Held**
SIC: 2084 Wines

(P-1855)
LANGETWINS WINE COMPANY INC
Also Called: Langetwins Winery & Vineyards
1525 E Jahant Rd, Acampo (95220-9187)
PHONE.................209 334-9780
Marissa Lange, *President*
Aaron Lange, *CFO*
Kendra Altnow, *Vice Pres*
Philip Lange, *Admin Sec*
Joseph Lange, *Asst Sec*
EMP: 22
SALES: 20MM **Privately Held**
SIC: 2084 Wines

(P-1856)
LARSON FAMILY WINERY INC
Also Called: Sonoma Creek Winery
23355 Millerick Rd, Sonoma (95476-9282)
PHONE.................707 938-3031
Tom Larson, *President*
Thomas C Larson, *Vice Pres*
▲ **EMP:** 10
SQ FT: 5,500
SALES (est): 1.2MM **Privately Held**
WEB: www.larsonfamilywinery.com
SIC: 2084 Wines

(P-1857)
LASSETER FAMILY WINERY LLC
1 Vintage Ln, Glen Ellen (95442-9415)
P.O. Box 1299 (95442-1299)
PHONE.................707 933-2800
John Lasseter,
Nancy Lasseter,
▲ **EMP:** 19
SALES (est): 2.9MM **Privately Held**
SIC: 2084 Wines

(P-1858)
LATCHAM GRANITE INC
Also Called: Latcham Vineyards
2860 Omo Ranch Rd, Somerset (95684-9204)
P.O. Box 80, Mount Aukum (95656-0080)
PHONE.................530 620-6642
Franklin C Latcham, *President*
Patricia Latcham, *Corp Secy*
Jonathon Latcham, *Senior VP*
Margaret Latcham, *Senior VP*
EMP: 14
SQ FT: 6,000
SALES (est): 1.3MM **Privately Held**
WEB: www.latcham.com
SIC: 2084 0172 5921 5182 Wines; grapes; wine; wine & distilled beverages

(P-1859)
LAVA SPRINGS INC
Also Called: Lava Cap Winery
2221 Fruitridge Rd, Placerville (95667-3700)
PHONE.................530 621-0175
Thomas D Jones, *President*
Jeanne H Jones, *Chairman*
Kevin Jones, *Marketing Staff*
Danny Mantle, *Sales Staff*
▲ **EMP:** 30
SQ FT: 18,000

SALES (est): 4.4MM **Privately Held**
WEB: www.lavacap.com
SIC: 2084 Wines

(P-1860)
LEONESSE CELLARS LLC
38311 De Portola Rd, Temecula (92592-8923)
P.O. Box 1371 (92593-1371)
PHONE.................951 302-7601
Gary Winder, *Mng Member*
Kelly Newcomb, *Buyer*
Michael Rennie,
Krystal Aponte, *Manager*
Gabriel Gonzales, *Manager*
▲ **EMP:** 25
SQ FT: 6,000
SALES (est): 5.7MM **Privately Held**
WEB: www.leonessecellars.com
SIC: 2084 Wines

(P-1861)
LEVECKE LLC
10810 Inland Ave, Mira Loma (91752-3235)
PHONE.................951 681-8600
Tim Levecke, *General Mgr*
Andrew Simone, *CFO*
Felix Camacho, *Production*
Steve Vento, *VP Sls/Mktg*
Jim Barnicle, *Regl Sales Mgr*
EMP: 70
SQ FT: 150,000
SALES (est): 5.5MM **Privately Held**
SIC: 2084 Wines, brandy & brandy spirits

(P-1862)
LINDQUIST ROBERT N & ASSOC (PA)
4665 Santa Maria Mesa Rd, Santa Maria (93454-9638)
PHONE.................805 937-9801
Robert Lindquist, *President*
EMP: 11
SALES (est): 1.2MM **Privately Held**
SIC: 2084 Wines

(P-1863)
LOCKWOOD VINEYARD (PA)
9777 Blue Larkspur Ln # 101, Monterey (93940-6554)
PHONE.................831 642-9566
R Paul Toeppen, *Partner*
Philip Johnson, *Partner*
W B Lindley, *Partner*
◆ **EMP:** 10
SALES (est): 1.9MM **Privately Held**
WEB: www.lockwoodwine.com
SIC: 2084 8741 0172 Wines; management services; grapes

(P-1864)
LOTUS BEVERAGES
Also Called: Mendias Imports
2542 San Gabriel Blvd, Rosemead (91770-3252)
PHONE.................213 216-1434
Scott Mendias, *Owner*
EMP: 10
SALES: 900K **Privately Held**
SIC: 2084 Wines, brandy & brandy spirits

(P-1865)
LOUIDAR LLC
Also Called: Mount Palomar Winery
33820 Rancho Cal Rd, Temecula (92591-4930)
P.O. Box 891510 (92589-1510)
PHONE.................951 676-5047
Peter Poole, *Principal*
Carol Darwish, *General Mgr*
Louis Darwish, *Mng Member*
Shar Martin, *Manager*
EMP: 30
SQ FT: 4,000
SALES (est): 3.6MM **Privately Held**
SIC: 2084 Wines

(P-1866)
LUNA VINEYARDS INC
2921 Silverado Trl, NAPA (94558-2016)
PHONE.................707 255-2474
Andre Crisp, *President*
Mary Ann Tsai, *President*
E Michael Moone, *Co-COB*
George A Vare, *Co-COB*

PRODUCTS & SVCS

Janel Sizelove, *Corp Secy*
▲ EMP: 20
SALES (est): 4.5MM **Privately Held**
WEB: www.lunawine.com
SIC: 2084 5182 5921 Wines; wine; wine

(P-1867)
MADRIGAL VINEYARD MANAGEMENT
Also Called: Madrigal Vineyards
3718 Saint Helena Hwy, Calistoga
(94515-9651)
P.O. Box 937 (94515-0937)
PHONE..................................707 942-8691
Jesus Madrigal, *Owner*
Chris Madrigal, *CEO*
Justin Ovard, *CFO*
EMP: 50
SALES (est): 4.7MM **Privately Held**
WEB: www.madrigalvineyards.com
SIC: 2084 Wines

(P-1868)
MAGITO & COMPANY LLC
1446 Industrial Ave, Sebastopol
(95472-4848)
PHONE..................................707 567-1521
Tom Meadowcroft,
▼ EMP: 10
SALES (est): 1MM **Privately Held**
SIC: 2084 Wines

(P-1869)
MARIETTA CELLARS INCORPORATED
Also Called: Marietta Marketing
22295 Chianti Rd, Geyserville (95441)
P.O. Box 800 (95441-0800)
PHONE..................................707 433-2747
Chris Bilbro, *President*
Barry Ackerman, *Controller*
Will Hunter, *Sales Staff*
Tais Tillman, *Manager*
▲ EMP: 15
SALES (est): 2.5MM **Privately Held**
WEB: www.mariettacellars.com
SIC: 2084 Wines

(P-1870)
MARIMAR TORRES ESTATE CORP
Also Called: Caliame
11400 Graton Rd, Sebastopol
(95472-8901)
PHONE..................................707 823-4365
Marimar Torres, *President*
▲ EMP: 10
SQ FT: 1,040
SALES (est): 1.3MM **Privately Held**
WEB: www.marimarestate.com
SIC: 2084 5812 Wine cellars, bonded: engaged in blending wines; eating places

(P-1871)
MARTELLOTTO INC
Also Called: One Vine Wines
12934 Francine Ter, Poway (92064-4114)
PHONE..................................619 567-9244
Greg Martellotto, *President*
▲ EMP: 10
SQ FT: 2,500
SALES (est): 828.8K **Privately Held**
SIC: 2084 Wines

(P-1872)
MARTIN WEYRICH WINERY LLC
4230 Buena Vista Dr, Paso Robles
(93446-9533)
PHONE..................................805 226-9296
Joni Nilsby, *Branch Mgr*
EMP: 10
SALES (corp-wide): 5.1MM **Privately Held**
WEB: www.martinweyrich.com
SIC: 2084 Wines, brandy & brandy spirits
PA: Martin Weyrich Winery, Llc
4990 Wing Way Fl 2
Paso Robles CA

(P-1873)
MATANZAS CREEK WINERY
6097 Bennett Valley Rd, Santa Rosa
(95404-8570)
PHONE..................................707 528-6464

Jeff Jackson, *President*
▲ EMP: 35
SQ FT: 20,000
SALES (est): 3.8MM **Privately Held**
WEB: www.matanzascreek.com
SIC: 2084 0172 Wine cellars, bonded: engaged in blending wines; grapes

(P-1874)
MAURICE CARRIE WINERY
34225 Rancho Cal Rd, Temecula
(92591-5054)
PHONE..................................951 676-1711
Buddy Linn, *President*
Cheri Linn, *Vice Pres*
EMP: 30
SQ FT: 14,000
SALES: 1MM **Privately Held**
WEB: www.mauricecarriewinery.com
SIC: 2084 5921 0172 Wines; wine; grapes

(P-1875)
MCNAB RIDGE WINERY LLC
2350 Mcnab Ranch Rd, Ukiah
(95482-9350)
PHONE..................................707 462-2423
John A Parducci, *Mng Member*
Willard A Carle,
Richard M Lawson,
EMP: 11
SALES (est): 920K **Privately Held**
SIC: 2084 Wines

(P-1876)
MELVILLE WINERY LLC
5185 E Highway 246, Lompoc
(93436-9613)
PHONE..................................805 735-7030
Ronald Melville, *President*
Kurt Ammann, *General Mgr*
Marina Brennan, *Admin Asst*
Brent Melville,
Chad Melville,
EMP: 12
SALES (est): 1.6MM **Privately Held**
SIC: 2084 Wines, brandy & brandy spirits

(P-1877)
MERRYVALE VINEYARDS LLC
Also Called: Starmont Winery
1000 Main St, Saint Helena (94574-2011)
PHONE..................................707 963-2225
Rene Schlatter, *President*
Mark Evans, *COO*
Kevin Bersofsky, *CFO*
Tom Purcell, *Vice Pres*
Guillermo Llamas, *Technician*
▲ EMP: 40
SQ FT: 30,850
SALES (est): 13.2MM **Privately Held**
WEB: www.merryvale.com
SIC: 2084 0172 Wines; grapes

(P-1878)
MICHEL-SCHLMBERGER PARTNERS LP
Also Called: Michel-Schlumberger Fine Wine
4155 Wine Creek Rd, Healdsburg
(95448-9112)
PHONE..................................707 433-7427
Jacques Schlumberger, *General Ptnr*
Simone Popov, *Business Dir*
▲ EMP: 20
SQ FT: 20,000
SALES (est): 2MM **Privately Held**
WEB: www.michelschlumberger.com
SIC: 2084 Wines

(P-1879)
MILDARA BLASS INC
Also Called: Windsor Vineyards
205 Concourse Blvd, Santa Rosa
(95403-8258)
P.O. Box 368, Windsor (95492-0368)
PHONE..................................707 836-5000
Kate Langford, *President*
▲ EMP: 160
SALES (est): 21.5MM **Privately Held**
SIC: 2084 5182 Wines; brandy & brandy spirits
PA: Vintage Wine Estates, Inc.
205 Concourse Blvd
Santa Rosa CA 95403

(P-1880)
MILL CREEK VNEYARDS WINERY INC
1401 Westside Rd, Healdsburg
(95448-9462)
P.O. Box 925 (95448-0925)
PHONE..................................707 433-4788
William C Kreck, *President*
Yvonne Kreck, *Admin Sec*
EMP: 15
SQ FT: 1,500
SALES (est): 1.8MM **Privately Held**
SIC: 2084 5921 Wines; wine

(P-1881)
MJA VINEYARDS LLC
24900 Highland Way, Los Gatos
(95033-8002)
PHONE..................................408 353-6000
Marin Artukovich, *Owner*
EMP: 12 EST: 2011
SALES (est): 790.2K **Privately Held**
SIC: 2084 Wines

(P-1882)
MODERN DEV CO A LTD PARTNR
3380 Branch Rd, Paso Robles
(93446-8314)
PHONE..................................805 239-1167
Glenn Allen Bianchi, *Manager*
EMP: 14
SALES (corp-wide): 17.7MM **Privately Held**
SIC: 2084 Wines
PA: Modern Development Co, A Limited Partnership
3146 Red Hill Ave Ste 220
Costa Mesa CA 92626
949 646-6400

(P-1883)
MONT ST JOHN CELLARS INC
5400 Old Sonoma Rd, NAPA (94559-9708)
PHONE..................................707 255-8864
Andrea Bartolucci, *President*
EMP: 10 EST: 1977
SQ FT: 14,000
SALES: 1.2MM **Privately Held**
WEB: www.madonnaestate.com
SIC: 2084 Wines

(P-1884)
MONTE DE ORO WINERY
35820 Rancho Cal Rd, Temecula
(92591-5126)
PHONE..................................951 491-6551
Kenneth Zignorski, *Principal*
Kelley O'Neill, *Admin Asst*
David Allbright, *Assistant*
Ashley Gorman, *Supervisor*
EMP: 12
SALES (est): 1.7MM **Privately Held**
SIC: 2084 Wines

(P-1885)
MONTERY WINE COMPANY LLC
1010 Industrial Way, King City
(93930-2506)
PHONE..................................831 386-1100
Steven McIntyre,
Jose Espinosa, *Maintence Staff*
Alan Yanagimachi, *Director*
EMP: 19
SALES (est): 5.9MM **Privately Held**
WEB: www.montereywinecompany.com
SIC: 2084 Wines

(P-1886)
MONTICELLO CELLARS INC
4242 Big Ranch Rd, NAPA (94558-1396)
P.O. Box 2486 (94558-0248)
PHONE..................................707 253-2802
John Kevin Corley, *President*
EMP: 15
SQ FT: 25,000
SALES: 2.1MM
SALES (corp-wide): 3MM **Privately Held**
WEB: www.monticellovineyards.com
SIC: 2084 Wines
PA: Monticello Vineyards
4242 Big Ranch Rd
Napa CA
707 253-2802

(P-1887)
MORGAN WINERY INC (PA)
590 Brunken Ave Ste C, Salinas
(93901-4355)
PHONE..................................831 751-7777
Daniel Lee, *President*
Donna Lee, *Vice Pres*
Jason Auxier, *Marketing Mgr*
Marc Cutino, *Manager*
◆ EMP: 10
SALES (est): 1.4MM **Privately Held**
WEB: www.morganwinery.com
SIC: 2084 Wines

(P-1888)
MOSAIC VINEYARDS & WINERY INC
2001 Highway 128, Geyserville
(95441-9489)
PHONE..................................707 857-2000
Tom Fuchs, *President*
Bill Mc Cardell, *Corp Secy*
EMP: 15
SQ FT: 2,113
SALES (est): 1MM **Privately Held**
SIC: 2084 Wine cellars, bonded: engaged in blending wines

(P-1889)
MUNSELLE VINEYARDS LLC
3660 Highway 128, Geyserville
(95441-9432)
P.O. Box 617 (95441-0617)
PHONE..................................707 857-9988
Reta Munselle, *Mng Member*
EMP: 15
SALES (est): 805.2K **Privately Held**
SIC: 2084 Wines

(P-1890)
MUSCARDINI CELLARS LLC
9380 Sonoma Hwy, Kenwood
(95452-9032)
PHONE..................................707 933-9305
Michael Muscardini, *Principal*
Alice Schimm, *Office Mgr*
Todd Harbron, *Accountant*
Natalie Owdom, *Sales Staff*
Jennifer Kosko, *Manager*
EMP: 11
SALES (est): 1.5MM **Privately Held**
SIC: 2084 Wines

(P-1891)
N C W G INC
Also Called: Nevada City Winery
321 Spring St, Nevada City (95959-2420)
PHONE..................................530 265-9463
John Chase, *General Mgr*
Wyn Spiller, *CEO*
EMP: 10
SQ FT: 7,500
SALES: 858.1K **Privately Held**
WEB: www.ncwinery.com
SIC: 2084 Wines

(P-1892)
NAPA BEAUCANON ESTATE
1006 Monticello Rd, NAPA (94558-2032)
PHONE..................................707 254-1460
Louis De Coninck, *President*
Chantal De Coninck, *Vice Pres*
▲ EMP: 11
SQ FT: 18,000
SALES (est): 1.1MM **Privately Held**
WEB: www.beaucanon.com
SIC: 2084 Wines

(P-1893)
NAPA WINE COMPANY LLC
7830 St Helena Hwy 40, Oakville
(94562-9200)
P.O. Box 434 (94562-0434)
PHONE..................................707 944-8669
Rob Lawson,
Andy Hoxsey,
▲ EMP: 35
SQ FT: 100,000
SALES (est): 5.7MM **Privately Held**
WEB: www.napawineco.com
SIC: 2084 Wines; wine cellars, bonded: engaged in blending wines

▲ = Import ▼=Export
◆ =Import/Export

(P-1894)
NAVARRO WINERY
Also Called: Navarro Vineyard
5601 Highway 128, Philo (95466-9513)
P.O. Box 47 (95466-0047)
PHONE..................707 895-3686
Edward T Bennett, *Partner*
Deborah S Cahn, *Partner*
Ted Bennett, *CFO*
▲ EMP: 75 EST: 1974
SQ FT: 10,000
SALES (est): 10.4MM **Privately Held**
WEB: www.navarrowine.com
SIC: 2084 0172 5921 Wine cellars, bonded: engaged in blending wines; grapes; wine

(P-1895)
NEAL FAMILY VINEYARDS LLC
716 Liparita Ave, Angwin (94508-9693)
PHONE..................707 965-2800
Mark Neal,
▲ EMP: 10 EST: 2000
SQ FT: 3,096
SALES (est): 1.1MM **Privately Held**
WEB: www.nealvineyards.com
SIC: 2084 Wines

(P-1896)
NELSON & SONS INC
Also Called: Nelson Family Vineyard
550 Nelson Ranch Rd, Ukiah (95482-9316)
PHONE..................707 462-3755
Gregory Nelson, *President*
Christopher Nelson, *Vice Pres*
Tyler Nelson, *Vice Pres*
EMP: 20
SALES (est): 3.3MM **Privately Held**
WEB: www.nelsonfamilyvineyard.com
SIC: 2084 0172 Wines; grapes

(P-1897)
NEW VAVIN INC
Also Called: Ehlers Estate
3222 Ehlers Ln, Saint Helena (94574-9657)
PHONE..................707 963-5972
Kelly McElearney, *General Mgr*
Kevin Morrisey, *General Mgr*
Stacy Spring, *Office Mgr*
Brad Akkerman, *Sales Executive*
Andy Bartee, *Sales Dir*
▲ EMP: 20
SALES (est): 3.1MM **Privately Held**
WEB: www.ehlersestate.com
SIC: 2084 Wines

(P-1898)
NEWTON VINEYARD LLC (DH)
2555 Madrona Ave, Saint Helena (94574-2300)
PHONE..................707 963-9000
Peter L Newton,
Peter Newton, *General Mgr*
Russell J Bollman,
Dr Su Hua Newton,
Robert Mann, *Director*
◆ EMP: 40
SQ FT: 2,500
SALES (est): 21.4MM
SALES (corp-wide): 315.2MM **Privately Held**
WEB: www.newtonvineyard.com
SIC: 2084 0172 Wines; grapes
HQ: Moet Hennessy
Moet Hennessy Estates & Wines 24 A 32
Paris 75008
144 132-222

(P-1899)
NICHOLSON RANCH LLC
4200 Napa Rd, Sonoma (95476-2800)
PHONE..................707 938-8822
Ramona Nicholson,
Deepak Gulrajani,
EMP: 20
SALES (est): 3MM **Privately Held**
WEB: www.nicholsonranch.com
SIC: 2084 Wines

(P-1900)
NIEBAM-CPPOLA ESTATE WINERY LP
Also Called: Cafe Niebaum Coppola
916 Kearny St, San Francisco (94133-5107)
PHONE..................415 291-1700
Krista Voisin, *Manager*
EMP: 20 **Privately Held**
SIC: 2084 Wines
PA: Niebaum-Coppola Estate Winery, L.P.
1991 St Helena Hwy
Rutherford CA 94573

(P-1901)
NIEBAM-CPPOLA ESTATE WINERY LP (PA)
1991 St Helena Hwy, Rutherford (94573)
P.O. Box 208 (94573-0208)
PHONE..................707 968-1100
Gordon Wang, *CFO*
Niebaum-Coppola Estate Winery, *General Ptnr*
The Coppola Family Trust, *Ltd Ptnr*
American Zoetrope, *Ltd Ptnr*
Earl Martin, *President*
▲ EMP: 150
SALES (est): 23.8MM **Privately Held**
SIC: 2084 Wines

(P-1902)
NINER WINE ESTATES LLC
2400 W Highway 46, Paso Robles (93446-8602)
PHONE..................805 239-2233
Richard T Niner,
Tucker Spear, *Sales Dir*
Joann Murrell,
Keith Patterson, *Director*
Alicia Wooten, *Director*
▲ EMP: 12
SALES (est): 1.9MM **Privately Held**
SIC: 2084 Wines

(P-1903)
OAK RIDGE WINERY LLC
6100 E Hwy 12 Victor Rd, Lodi (95240)
PHONE..................209 369-4768
Rudy Maggio,
Keith Auerbach, *Division Mgr*
Scott Parker, *Controller*
Chue Her, *Prdtn Mgr*
Stephen BEI, *Sales Mgr*
▲ EMP: 50
SALES (est): 10.6MM **Privately Held**
WEB: www.oakridgewinery.com
SIC: 2084 Wines

(P-1904)
OLD CREEK RANCH WINERY INC
10024 Creek Rd, Oak View (93022-9728)
P.O. Box 173 (93022-0173)
PHONE..................805 649-4132
Andrew Holguin, *President*
EMP: 12
SQ FT: 600
SALES (est): 113.1K **Privately Held**
WEB: www.oldcreekranch.com
SIC: 2084 Wines

(P-1905)
OPAL MOON WINERY LLC
21660 8th St E Ste A, Sonoma (95476-2828)
PHONE..................707 996-0420
John Bambury,
Kenny Anderson, *Admin Asst*
EMP: 15 EST: 2011
SQ FT: 30,000
SALES (est): 1MM **Privately Held**
SIC: 2084 Wines

(P-1906)
OPOLO VINEYARDS INC (PA)
7110 Vineyard Dr, Paso Robles (93446-7684)
PHONE..................805 238-9593
Richard Lawrence Quinn, *CEO*
EMP: 27
SALES (est): 5.4MM **Privately Held**
SIC: 2084 Wines

(P-1907)
OPUS ONE WINERY LLC (PA)
7900 St Helena Hwy, Oakville (94562)
P.O. Box 6 (94562-0006)
PHONE..................707 944-9442
David Pearson, *CEO*
Robert Fowles, *CFO*
Roger Asleson, *Vice Pres*
Robert Ruex, *Vice Pres*
Michael Silacci, *Vice Pres*
▲ EMP: 75
SQ FT: 85,000
SALES (est): 19.6MM **Privately Held**
WEB: www.opusonewinery.com
SIC: 2084 Wines

(P-1908)
ORFILA VINEYARDS INC (PA)
Also Called: Orfila Vineyards & Winery
13455 San Pasqual Rd, Escondido (92025-7833)
PHONE..................760 738-6500
Alejandro Orfila, *President*
Danica Gvozden, *Officer*
Justin Mund, *Vice Pres*
Helga Orfila, *Vice Pres*
▲ EMP: 31
SQ FT: 12,000
SALES (est): 2.7MM **Privately Held**
WEB: www.orfila.com
SIC: 2084 0172 7299 Wines; grapes; wedding chapel, privately operated

(P-1909)
OVERLOOK VINEYARDS LLC (DH)
Also Called: Landmark Vineyards
101 Adobe Canyon Rd, Kenwood (95452-9045)
P.O. Box 340 (95452-0340)
PHONE..................707 833-0053
Mike Colhoun,
Margaret Benelli,
Mary Colhoun,
Kim Pasquali, *Senior Mgr*
Donna Carroll, *Manager*
▲ EMP: 27
SQ FT: 10,000
SALES (est): 2.2MM
SALES (corp-wide): 1.5B **Privately Held**
WEB: www.landmarkwine.com
SIC: 2084 0172 Wines; grapes
HQ: Fiji Water Company, Llc
11444 W Olympic Blvd # 250
Los Angeles CA 90064
310 966-5700

(P-1910)
OVERLOOK VINEYARDS LLC
Also Called: Hop Kiln Winery, The
58 W North St Ste 101, Healdsburg (95448-4843)
PHONE..................707 433-6491
EMP: 10
SALES (corp-wide): 1.5B **Privately Held**
SIC: 2084 Wines
HQ: Overlook Vineyards Llc
101 Adobe Canyon Rd
Kenwood CA 95452
707 833-0053

(P-1911)
OZEKI SAKE U S A INC (HQ)
249 Hillcrest Rd, Hollister (95023-4921)
PHONE..................831 637-9217
Bunjiro Osabe, *Ch of Bd*
Norio Sumomogi, *Treasurer*
Kozo Yamamoto, *Treasurer*
Masaru Ogihara, *Vice Pres*
Ruth Reid, *Office Mgr*
▲ EMP: 25
SQ FT: 22,000
SALES (est): 4.3MM
SALES (corp-wide): 64.2MM **Privately Held**
WEB: www.ozekisake.com
SIC: 2084 Wines
PA: Ozeki Co., Ltd.
1-2-9, Minato
Chuo-Ku TKY 104-0
332 973-241

(P-1912)
PAN MAGNA GROUP
Also Called: Domaine St George Winery
1141 Grant Ave, Healdsburg (95448-9570)
P.O. Box 548 (95448-0548)
PHONE..................707 433-5508
Somchai Likitprakong, *Principal*
EMP: 22
SQ FT: 1,237
SALES (est): 3.1MM
SALES (corp-wide): 9.5MM **Privately Held**
WEB: www.domainesaintgeorge.com
SIC: 2084 0172 Wines; grapes
PA: Pan Magna Group
350 Sansome St Ste 1010
San Francisco CA
415 394-7244

(P-1913)
PARADIGM WINERY
683 Dwyer Rd, Oakville (94562)
P.O. Box 323 (94562-0323)
PHONE..................707 944-1683
Marilyn Harris, *Partner*
Ren Harris, *Partner*
▲ EMP: 15
SALES (est): 700K **Privately Held**
WEB: www.paradigmwinery.com
SIC: 2084 5182 5921 Wines; wine; wine

(P-1914)
PARADISE RIDGE WINERY
4545 Thomas Lk Harris Dr, Santa Rosa (95403-0108)
PHONE..................707 528-9463
Walter Byck, *Owner*
▲ EMP: 10
SALES (est): 1.1MM **Privately Held**
WEB: www.prwinery.com
SIC: 2084 Wines

(P-1915)
PARDUCCI WINE ESTATES LLC
Also Called: Mendicino Wine Company
501 Parducci Rd, Ukiah (95482-3015)
PHONE..................707 463-5350
Carl Thoma,
Mike Huizenga, *Comp Spec*
Michele Pearson, *Accounting Mgr*
Dale Gatcuum, *Sales Mgr*
Kevin Baldwin, *Maintence Staff*
▲ EMP: 35
SALES (est): 5.4MM **Privately Held**
WEB: www.parducci.com
SIC: 2084 Wines

(P-1916)
PATZ AND HALL WINE COMPANY (DH)
21200 8th St E, Sonoma (95476-2819)
PHONE..................707 265-7700
Russell Joy, *President*
James Hall, *Principal*
Anne Moses, *Principal*
Heather Patz, *Principal*
Donald Patz, *Sales Staff*
◆ EMP: 11
SALES (est): 1.3MM
SALES (corp-wide): 25.5B **Publicly Held**
WEB: www.patzhall.com
SIC: 2084 Wines
HQ: Michelle Ste Wine Estates Ltd
14111 Ne 145th St
Woodinville WA 98072
425 488-1133

(P-1917)
PAUL HOBBS WINERY LP
3355 Gravenstein Hwy N, Sebastopol (95472-2327)
PHONE..................707 824-9879
Paul Hobbs, *Partner*
Joan Maxwell, *CFO*
Jenifer Freebairn, *Vice Pres*
Matt Hobbs, *General Mgr*
Megan Baccitich, *Director*
▲ EMP: 10
SQ FT: 1,995
SALES (est): 1.8MM **Privately Held**
WEB: www.paulhobbs.com
SIC: 2084 Wines

PRODUCTS & SVCS

(P-1918)
PEAR VALLEY VINEYARD INC
4900 Union Rd, Paso Robles (93446-9345)
PHONE..................................805 237-2861
Kathleen Maas, *Co-Owner*
Melissa Jones, *Office Mgr*
EMP: 13
SALES (est): 1.9MM Privately Held
SIC: 2084 Wines

(P-1919)
PEAY VINEYARDS LLC
207a N Cloverdale Blvd, Cloverdale
(95425-3318)
PHONE..................................707 894-8720
Nicholas Peay, *Mng Member*
Gordon A Peay,
EMP: 12
SALES (est): 1.8MM Privately Held
SIC: 2084 Wines

(P-1920)
PELLEGRINI RANCHES
Also Called: Pellegrine Wine Company
4055 W Olivet Rd, Santa Rosa
(95401-3839)
PHONE..................................707 545-8680
Robert V Pellegrini, *CEO*
Fred Reno, *President*
Alexia Pellegrini, *Opers Staff*
EMP: 10
SQ FT: 4,000
SALES (est): 924.2K Privately Held
SIC: 2084 Wines

(P-1921)
PERNOD RICARD USA LLC
Also Called: Kenwood Vineyards
9592 Sonoma Hwy, Kenwood
(95452-8028)
P.O. Box 669 (95452-0669)
PHONE..................................707 833-5891
EMP: 75
SQ FT: 1,414
SALES (corp-wide): 182.4MM Privately
Held
WEB: www.korbel.com
SIC: 2084 0172 Wines; grapes
HQ: Pernod Ricard Usa, Llc
250 Park Ave Ste 17a
New York NY 10177
212 372-5400

(P-1922)
PERNOD RICARD USA LLC
Also Called: Mumm NAPA Valley
8445 Silverado Trl, Rutherford (94573)
PHONE..................................707 967-7770
Samuel Bronfman II, *Branch Mgr*
EMP: 65
SALES (corp-wide): 182.4MM Privately
Held
WEB: www.adw-academy.com
SIC: 2084 Wines
HQ: Pernod Ricard Usa, Llc
250 Park Ave Ste 17a
New York NY 10177
212 372-5400

(P-1923)
PERRY CREEK WINERY
7400 Perry Creek Rd, Somerset
(95684-9207)
PHONE..................................530 620-5175
Peter Juergens, *Owner*
▲ EMP: 11
SALES (est): 1.2MM Privately Held
SIC: 2084 Wines

(P-1924)
PETALUMAIDENCE OPCO LLC
Also Called: Vineyard Post Acute
101 Monroe St, Petaluma (94954-2328)
PHONE..................................707 763-4109
Barbara Matson, *Principal*
Mark Hancock, *Principal*
Jason Murray, *Principal*
EMP: 99
SALES (est): 9.8MM Privately Held
SIC: 2084 Wines

(P-1925)
PINE RIDGE WINERY LLC
Also Called: Pine Ridge Vineyards
5901 Silverado Trl, NAPA (94558-9417)
P.O. Box 2508, Yountville (94599-2508)
PHONE..................................707 253-7500
Michael Beaulac,
Winnie St John, *Controller*
Ian M Cumming,
Joseph A Orlando,
Joseph S Stienbert,
▲ EMP: 100
SQ FT: 17,000
SALES (est): 18.6MM
SALES (corp-wide): 63.2MM Publicly
Held
SIC: 2084 5812 0172 Wines; eating
places; grapes
PA: Crimson Wine Group, Ltd.
2700 Napa Vly Corp Dr B
Napa CA 94558
800 486-0503

(P-1926)
PJK WINERY LLC
Also Called: Quivira Vineyards
4900 W Dry Creek Rd, Healdsburg
(95448-9721)
PHONE..................................707 431-8333
Pete Kight, *Mng Member*
Patty Tiso,
EMP: 25
SQ FT: 5,400
SALES (est): 1.8MM Privately Held
WEB: www.quivirawine.com
SIC: 2084 Wines

(P-1927)
PLC LLC
Also Called: McNab Ridge Winery
2350 Mcnab Ranch Rd, Ukiah
(95482-9350)
PHONE..................................707 462-2423
John Parducci, *Mng Member*
Bill Carle,
EMP: 11
SQ FT: 30,000
SALES (est): 1.7MM Privately Held
WEB: www.mcnabridge.com
SIC: 2084 Wines

(P-1928)
**POMAR JUNCTION CELLARS
LLC**
5036 S El Pomar Rd, Templeton
(93465-8673)
P.O. Box 789 (93465-0789)
PHONE..................................805 238-9940
Dana Merrill, *Info Tech Mgr*
Marcia Merrill,
Matthew Merrill,
Nicole Merrill,
EMP: 20
SQ FT: 1,600
SALES (est): 1.2MM Privately Held
SIC: 2084 5182 Wines; wine

(P-1929)
PRESQUILE WINERY
5391 Presquile Dr, Santa Maria
(93455-5811)
PHONE..................................805 937-8110
Robert Madison Murphy II, *President*
Annie Braunschweig, *CFO*
Anna Murphy, *Vice Pres*
Jonathan Murphy, *Admin Sec*
Janeen Garcia, *Accountant*
EMP: 10
SALES (est): 1.2MM Privately Held
SIC: 2084 Wines

(P-1930)
PRESTON VINEYARDS INC
Also Called: Preston Vineyards & Winery
9282 W Dry Creek Rd, Healdsburg
(95448-9134)
PHONE..................................707 433-3372
Louis Preston, *President*
Susan Preston, *Vice Pres*
Ken Blair, *Sales Dir*
Sara Parnow, *Sales Staff*
Jacque Garrison, *Manager*
EMP: 15 EST: 1973

(P-1931)
PROVENANCE VINEYARDS
1695 Saint Helena Hwy S, Saint Helena
(94574-9777)
P.O. Box 688, Rutherford (94573-0688)
PHONE..................................707 968-3633
Tom Rinaldi, *Owner*
▲ EMP: 14
SALES (est): 1.3MM Privately Held
WEB: www.provenancevineyards.com
SIC: 2084 Wines
HQ: Treasury Wine Estates Americas Com-
pany
555 Gateway Dr
Napa CA 94558
707 259-4500

(P-1932)
PURPLE WINE COMPANY LLC
9119 Graton Rd, Graton (95444-9373)
P.O. Box 390 (95444-0390)
PHONE..................................707 829-6100
Derek Benham, *Mng Member*
Ron Janowczyk, *Senior VP*
Lisa Ehrlich, *Vice Pres*
Michael Mestas, *Vice Pres*
Chris Braman, *Sales Staff*
▲ EMP: 28
SALES (est): 2MM Privately Held
SIC: 2084 Wines

(P-1933)
PYRAMIDS WINERY INC
5875 Lakeville Hwy, Petaluma
(94954-9263)
PHONE..................................707 765-2768
Arturo Keller, *President*
▲ EMP: 40
SALES (est): 3MM Privately Held
WEB: www.kellerestate.com
SIC: 2084 Wines

(P-1934)
QUADY LLC (PA)
13181 Road 24, Madera (93637-9087)
P.O. Box 728 (93639-0728)
PHONE..................................559 673-8068
Andrew Quady, *CEO*
Laurel Quady, *CFO*
Cheryl Russell, *General Mgr*
EMP: 46
SQ FT: 16,000
SALES (est): 2.9MM Privately Held
SIC: 2084 Wines

(P-1935)
QUADY WINERY INC
13181 Road 24, Madera (93637-9087)
P.O. Box 728 (93639-0728)
PHONE..................................559 673-8068
Andrew K Quady, *President*
Laurel Quady, *Vice Pres*
Allie Quady, *Comms Mgr*
Shelley George, *Technology*
David Glover, *Technology*
EMP: 16 EST: 1979
SQ FT: 16,000
SALES (est): 3.5MM Privately Held
WEB: www.quadywinery.com
SIC: 2084 Wines

(P-1936)
RAMADOR INC (PA)
Also Called: Renwood Winery
12225 Steiner Rd, Plymouth (95669-9502)
P.O. Box 399 (95669-0399)
PHONE..................................209 245-6979
Robert Smerling, *Ch of Bd*
Robert I Smerling, *Ch of Bd*
Mike Dinapoli, *CFO*
Laura Bratsch, *Lab Dir*
Luis Paniagua, *Technology*
▲ EMP: 10
SQ FT: 7,000
SALES (est): 8.4MM Privately Held
SIC: 2084 Wines

(P-1937)
RAMS GATE WINERY LLC
28700 Arnold Dr, Sonoma (95476-9700)
PHONE..................................707 721-8700

Jeffrey O'Neill, *Mng Member*
Emily Rasmussen, *Comms Mgr*
Michael J John,
Peter Mullin,
Paul Violich,
▲ EMP: 38
SALES (est): 8MM Privately Held
SIC: 2084 Wines

(P-1938)
RAMSPUR WINERY LLC
3100 Old Sonoma Rd, NAPA (94558-5405)
PHONE..................................707 251-3948
Nancy Otton, *Principal*
EMP: 11
SALES (est): 1.3MM Privately Held
SIC: 2084 Wines

(P-1939)
RANCHO DE SOLIS WINERY INC
3920 Hecker Pass Rd, Gilroy (95020-8805)
PHONE..................................408 847-6306
David Vanni, *President*
EMP: 10
SALES (est): 945.6K Privately Held
WEB: www.soliswinery.com
SIC: 2084 Wines

(P-1940)
**RANG DONG JOINT STOCK
COMPANY**
Also Called: Rang Dong Winery
3 Executive Way, NAPA (94558-6271)
PHONE..................................707 259-9446
Mailynh Phan, *General Mgr*
EMP: 14
SQ FT: 47,900
SALES (est): 845.9K
SALES (corp-wide): 45.4MM Privately
Held
SIC: 2084 Wines
PA: Rang Dong Joint Stock Company
J45 Ton Duc Thang Street,
Phan Thiet
252 382-2301

(P-1941)
RB WINE ASSOCIATES LLC
Also Called: Rack & Riddle
499 Moore Ln, Healdsburg (95448)
P.O. Box 2400 (95448-2400)
PHONE..................................707 433-8400
Bruce Lundquist,
Kathy Dogali, *Admin Asst*
Tracy McCall, *Administration*
Stacey Lafave, *Accountant*
Rebecca Faust,
EMP: 80
SQ FT: 100,000
SALES: 11MM Privately Held
SIC: 2084 Wines

(P-1942)
RBZ VINEYARDS LLC
Also Called: Sextant Wines
2324 W Highway 46, Paso Robles
(93446-8602)
P.O. Box 391 (93447-0391)
PHONE..................................805 542-0133
Craig Stoller, *Principal*
Ashlie Leslie, *Portfolio Mgr*
EMP: 30
SALES (est): 5.3MM Privately Held
SIC: 2084 Wines

(P-1943)
REGAL III LLC
Also Called: Regal Wine Co
1190 Kittyhawk Blvd, Windsor (95492)
PHONE..................................707 836-2100
Donald M Hartford Jr, *Mng Member*
Brent Bolding, *Vice Pres*
Melinda Arnold, *Executive*
Cindy Ahlgrim, *Sales Staff*
Anne Hunter, *Sales Staff*
▲ EMP: 63
SQ FT: 8,000
SALES: 100K Privately Held
SIC: 2084 Wines

(P-1944)
REGUSCI VINEYARD MGT INC
Also Called: Regusi Winery
5584 Silverado Trl, NAPA (94558-9411)
PHONE..................................707 254-0403
James Regusci, *President*

▲ = Import ▼=Export
◆ =Import/Export

Diana Regusci, *Vice Pres*
Dawn Lemasters, *Human Res Dir*
Skip Karabian, *Natl Sales Mgr*
Jason Lauritsen, *Director*
EMP: 30
SALES (est): 6.6MM **Privately Held**
WEB: www.regusciwinery.com
SIC: 2084 0762 Wines; vineyard management & maintenance services

(P-1945)
REN ACQUISITION INC
12225 Steiner Rd, Plymouth (95669-9502)
PHONE..............................209 245-6979
Robert I Smerling, *Chairman*
▲ **EMP:** 11
SALES (est): 1.3MM **Privately Held**
SIC: 2084 Wines

(P-1946)
REVERIE ON DIAMOND MTN LLC
Also Called: Reverie Winery
4410 Lake County Hwy, Calistoga (94515-9706)
PHONE..............................707 942-6800
Norman Kiken,
Evelyn Kiken,
▲ **EMP:** 10
SALES (est): 780K **Privately Held**
WEB: www.reveriewine.com
SIC: 2084 Wines

(P-1947)
RHYS VINEYARDS LLC
11715 Skyline Blvd, Los Gatos (95033-9588)
PHONE..............................650 419-2050
Kevin Harvey,
Javier Meza,
▲ **EMP:** 17
SALES (est): 3.1MM **Privately Held**
SIC: 2084 Wines

(P-1948)
RIDEAU VINEYARD LLC
1562 Alamo Pintado Rd, Solvang (93463-9756)
PHONE..............................805 688-0717
Iris Rideau,
Jennifer Iverson,
Caren Rideau,
Seth Hudson, *Manager*
Adrienne St John, *Associate*
▲ **EMP:** 10
SALES (est): 1.5MM **Privately Held**
WEB: www.rideauvineyard.com
SIC: 2084 Wines

(P-1949)
RIOS-LOVELL ESTATE WINERY
Also Called: Rios-Lovell Winery
6500 Tesla Rd, Livermore (94550-9123)
PHONE..............................925 443-0434
Max Rios, *Partner*
Katie Lovell, *Partner*
Dan Baldwin, *Consultant*
EMP: 20
SALES (est): 2.2MM **Privately Held**
WEB: www.rioslovellwinery.com
SIC: 2084 Wines

(P-1950)
ROBERT MONDAVI CORPORATION (HQ)
166 Gateway Rd E, NAPA (94558-7576)
P.O. Box 106, Oakville (94562-0106)
PHONE..............................707 967-2100
Gregory Evans, *President*
Gregory M Evans, *President*
Henry J Salvo Jr, *CFO*
Timothy J Mondavi, *Vice Ch Bd*
▲ **EMP:** 75 **EST:** 1966
SQ FT: 5,000
SALES (est): 65.7MM
SALES (corp-wide): 7.5B **Publicly Held**
WEB: www.rmcoastalwines.com
SIC: 2084 Wines
PA: Constellation Brands, Inc.
207 High Point Dr # 100
Victor NY 14564
585 678-7100

(P-1951)
ROBERT MONDAVI CORPORATION
770 N Guild Ave, Lodi (95240-0861)
PHONE..............................209 365-2995
Rick Anderson, *Manager*
EMP: 30
SALES (corp-wide): 7.5B **Publicly Held**
WEB: www.rmcoastalwines.com
SIC: 2084 Wines
HQ: The Robert Mondavi Corporation
166 Gateway Rd E
Napa CA 94558
707 967-2100

(P-1952)
ROBINSON FAMILY WINERY
5880 Silverado Trl, NAPA (94558-9418)
PHONE..............................707 287-8428
Thomas Butler, *President*
EMP: 10
SALES (est): 432.8K **Privately Held**
SIC: 2084 Wines

(P-1953)
ROBLEDO FAMILY WINERY INC (PA)
21901 21903 Bonness Rd, Sonoma (95476)
PHONE..............................707 939-6903
Reynaldo Robledo, *CEO*
EMP: 10
SALES (est): 1.2MM **Privately Held**
SIC: 2084 Wines

(P-1954)
ROCK WALL WINE COMPANY INC
2301 Monarch St, Alameda (94501-7554)
PHONE..............................510 522-5700
Kent Rosenblum, *CEO*
EMP: 10
SQ FT: 200
SALES (est): 3.4MM **Privately Held**
SIC: 2084 Wines

(P-1955)
ROMBAUER VINEYARDS INC
3522 Silverado Trl N, Saint Helena (94574-9663)
PHONE..............................707 963-5170
Koerner Rombauer, *President*
Bob Knebel, *COO*
Kendall Tompioner, *Executive Asst*
Brandye Alexander, *CTO*
Sheana Rombauer, *Info Tech Dir*
▲ **EMP:** 52
SQ FT: 25,000
SALES (est): 32.8MM **Privately Held**
WEB: www.rombauer.com
SIC: 2084 Wines

(P-1956)
ROTARY CLUB OF AJAI WEST
1129 Maricopa Hwy, Ojai (93023-3126)
PHONE..............................805 646-3794
Michael Caldwell, *President*
Laurie Johnson, *Admin Sec*
EMP: 50
SALES (est): 2.9MM **Privately Held**
SIC: 2084 7991 Wines; athletic club & gymnasiums; membership

(P-1957)
ROTTA WINERY INC
250 Winery Rd, Templeton (93465-9597)
PHONE..............................805 237-0510
Michael D Giubbini, *President*
Mike Giubbini, *President*
Steve Pasetti, *Vice Pres*
Elaine Taunt, *Manager*
EMP: 10
SALES (est): 665.7K **Privately Held**
WEB: www.rottawinery.com
SIC: 2084 Wines

(P-1958)
ROUND HILL CELLARS
Also Called: Rutherford Wine Company
1680 Silverado Trl S, Saint Helena (94574-9542)
P.O. Box 387, Rutherford (94573-0387)
PHONE..............................707 968-3200
Marko B Zaninovich, *President*
Theo Zaninovich, *Principal*

Marc Anderson, *Controller*
▼ **EMP:** 55
SQ FT: 31,000
SALES (est): 10.5MM **Privately Held**
WEB: www.rutherfordranch.com
SIC: 2084 Wines

(P-1959)
ROYAL WINE CORPORATION
Also Called: Herzog Wine Cellars
3201 Camino Del Sol, Oxnard (93030-8915)
PHONE..............................805 983-1560
Joseph Herzog, *General Mgr*
Amie Hastings, *Asst Controller*
Jacy Basile, *Controller*
Catheryn Cranford, *Human Res Dir*
Jenny Guy, *Marketing Staff*
EMP: 25
SALES (corp-wide): 44MM **Privately Held**
SIC: 2084 5182 Wines; wine; liquor
PA: Royal Wine Corporation
63 Lefante Dr
Bayonne NJ 07002
718 384-2400

(P-1960)
RUDD WINES INC (PA)
Also Called: Rudd Winery
500 Oakville Xrd, Oakville (94562)
P.O. Box 105 (94562-0105)
PHONE..............................707 944-8577
Leslei Rudd, *President*
▲ **EMP:** 20
SALES (est): 1.2MM **Privately Held**
WEB: www.ruddwines.com
SIC: 2084 Wines

(P-1961)
RUSSIAN RIVER WINERY INC
2191 Laguna Rd, Santa Rosa (95401-3705)
PHONE..............................707 824-2005
Courtney M Benham, *CEO*
EMP: 39
SQ FT: 76,000
SALES: 5.1MM **Privately Held**
SIC: 2084 Wines

(P-1962)
S L CELLARS
9380 Sonoma Hwy, Kenwood (95452-9032)
PHONE..............................707 833-5070
J Bruce Jacobs, *President*
EMP: 12
SQ FT: 4,000
SALES (est): 631.5K
SALES (corp-wide): 1.9MM **Privately Held**
WEB: www.slcellars.com
SIC: 2084 Wines
PA: Simon Levi Company, Ltd.
9380 Sonoma Hwy
Kenwood CA
707 833-4455

(P-1963)
SAINTSBURY LLC
1500 Los Carneros Ave, NAPA (94559-9742)
PHONE..............................707 252-0592
Richard Ward, *General Mgr*
Virginia Rogstad, *Administration*
Heather Vance, *Accountant*
Lisa Van Stuijvenberg, *Controller*
David Graves,
EMP: 18
SQ FT: 32,500
SALES (est): 3MM **Privately Held**
WEB: www.saintsbury.com
SIC: 2084 Wines

(P-1964)
SAN ANTONIO WINERY INC (PA)
Also Called: San Antonio Gift Shop
737 Lamar St, Los Angeles (90031-2591)
PHONE..............................323 223-1401
Santo Riboli, *CEO*
Maddelena Riboli, *Corp Secy*
Cathey Riboli, *Asst Treas*
◆ **EMP:** 101 **EST:** 1917
SQ FT: 310,000

SALES (est): 24.6MM **Privately Held**
WEB: www.sanantoniowinery.com
SIC: 2084 5182 5812 Wines; wine; eating places

(P-1965)
SAN JOAQUIN WINE COMPANY INC
Also Called: Sjwc
21081 Avenue 16, Madera (93637)
PHONE..............................559 673-0066
Stephen L Schafer, *CEO*
Cindy Schafer, *General Mgr*
Gil Soto, *Sales Staff*
EMP: 14
SALES (est): 1.7MM **Privately Held**
SIC: 2084 Wines

(P-1966)
SANTA BARBARA WINERY
202 Anacapa St, Santa Barbara (93101-1887)
PHONE..............................805 963-3646
Pierre Lafond, *Owner*
EMP: 30
SALES (corp-wide): 5MM **Privately Held**
WEB: www.sbwinery.com
SIC: 2084 Wine cellars, bonded: engaged in blending wines
HQ: Santa Barbara Winery
202 Anacapa St
Santa Barbara CA 93101
805 962-9303

(P-1967)
SAVANNAH CHANELLE VINEYARDS
Also Called: Mariani Winery
23600 Big Basin Way, Saratoga (95070-9755)
PHONE..............................408 741-2934
Michael Ballard, *President*
Kellie Ballard, *CFO*
EMP: 22
SALES (est): 2.5MM **Privately Held**
WEB: www.savannahchanelle.com
SIC: 2084 5812 0172 Wines; eating places; grapes

(P-1968)
SBRAGIA FAMILY VINEYARDS LLC
9990 Dry Creek Rd, Geyserville (95441-9686)
PHONE..............................707 473-2992
Edward Sbargia, *Mng Member*
Ed Sbragia, *Consultant*
EMP: 23
SALES (est): 4.3MM **Privately Held**
SIC: 2084 Wines

(P-1969)
SEAVEY VINEYARD LTD PARTNR
1310 Conn Valley Rd, Saint Helena (94574-9610)
PHONE..............................707 963-8339
Dorothy Seavey, *CFO*
Arthur Seavey, *General Mgr*
EMP: 10
SALES (est): 376.2K **Privately Held**
SIC: 2084 Wines

(P-1970)
SEBASTIANI VINEYARDS INC
Also Called: Sebastiani Vineyards & Winery
389 4th St E, Sonoma (95476-5790)
PHONE..............................707 938-5532
Mary Ann Sebastiani Cuneo, *CEO*
Richard Cuneo, *Ch of Bd*
Emma Swain, *COO*
Paul Bergena, *Exec VP*
◆ **EMP:** 100
SQ FT: 2,000
SALES (est): 15.1MM
SALES (corp-wide): 61.5MM **Privately Held**
WEB: www.sebastiani.com
SIC: 2084 Wines
HQ: Foley Family Wines, Inc.
2300 Airport Rd
Paso Robles CA 93446

P R O D U C T S & S V C S

(P-1971)
SEGHESIO WINERIES INC
Also Called: Seghesio Winery
700 Grove St, Healdsburg (95448-4753)
PHONE................................707 433-3579
Eugene Peter Seghesio, *CEO*
Amy Seghesio, *Treasurer*
Raymond Seghesio, *Vice Pres*
Edward H Seghesio Jr, *Admin Sec*
Stephanie Friedman, *Director*
▼ **EMP:** 20
SQ FT: 6,000
SALES (est): 3.4MM **Privately Held**
WEB: www.seghesio.com
SIC: 2084 0172 Wines; grapes

(P-1972)
SELBY INC
Also Called: Selby Winery
498 Moore Ln Ste A, Healdsburg
(95448-4840)
PHONE................................707 431-1703
Susie Selby, *President*
EMP: 10
SALES (est): 990K **Privately Held**
WEB: www.selbywinery.com
SIC: 2084 Wines

(P-1973)
SHAFER VINEYARDS
6154 Silverado Trl, NAPA (94558-9748)
PHONE................................707 944-2877
John Shafer, *Chairman*
Elizabeth S Cafaro, *Shareholder*
Bradford J Shafer, *Shareholder*
Bradford Shafer, *Shareholder*
Douglas S Shafer, *President*
▲ **EMP:** 17
SQ FT: 2,000
SALES (est): 2.6MM **Privately Held**
WEB: www.shafervineyards.com
SIC: 2084 Wines

(P-1974)
SHANNON RIDGE INC
13888 Point Lakeview Rd, Lower Lake
(95457-9617)
P.O. Box 676 (95457-0676)
PHONE................................707 994-9656
Clay Shannon, *President*
Mark Altrecht, *CFO*
Sheila Lapoint, *Controller*
Angie Bigham, *Natl Sales Mgr*
Sal Spena, *Sales Staff*
EMP: 20 **EST:** 2003
SALES: 14MM **Privately Held**
SIC: 2084 5921 Wines; wine

(P-1975)
SIERRA SUNRISE VINEYARD INC
Also Called: Montevina Winery
20680 Shenandoah Schl Rd, Plymouth
(95669-9511)
P.O. Box 248, Saint Helena (94574-0248)
PHONE................................209 245-6942
Louis Trinchero, *Ch of Bd*
Robery Tortelson, *President*
Roger Trinchero, *CEO*
Jeff Meyers, *Vice Pres*
Vera Trinchero Torres, *Admin Sec*
EMP: 26
SQ FT: 52,000
SALES (est): 3.3MM
SALES (corp-wide): 196.8MM **Privately Held**
WEB: www.frewines.com
SIC: 2084 0172 Wines; grapes
PA: Sutter Home Winery, Inc.
100 Saint Helena Hwy S
Saint Helena CA 94574
707 963-3104

(P-1976)
SILENUS VINTNERS
5225 Solano Ave, NAPA (94558-1019)
PHONE................................707 299-3930
Bob Williamson, *Owner*
▲ **EMP:** 11
SALES (est): 1.5MM **Privately Held**
SIC: 2084 Wines
HQ: Henan Meijing Group Co., Ltd.
Room 1601, Torch Building B, Hi-Tech
Industrial Development Area
Zhengzhou
371 569-9516

(P-1977)
SILVER HORSE VINEYARDS INC
Also Called: Silver Ranch and Winery
1205 Beaver Creek Ln, Paso Robles
(93446-4942)
P.O. Box 2010 (93447-2010)
PHONE................................805 467-9463
Jim Kroener, *President*
EMP: 18
SALES (est): 1.6MM **Privately Held**
WEB: www.silverhorsevineyards.com
SIC: 2084 Wines

(P-1978)
SILVER OAK WINE CELLARS LP (PA)
915 Oakville Cross Rd, Oakville (94562)
P.O. Box 414 (94562-0414)
PHONE................................707 942-7022
David R Duncan, *Partner*
Raymond Duncan, *Partner*
Bruce Gatschet, *CTO*
EMP: 15
SALES (est): 12.8MM **Privately Held**
SIC: 2084 Wines

(P-1979)
SOCIETE BREWING COMPANY LLC
8262 Clairemont Mesa Blvd, Del Mar
(92014)
PHONE................................858 598-5415
EMP: 15
SALES: 1MM **Privately Held**
SIC: 2084

(P-1980)
SONOMA WINE COMPANY LLC
9119 Graton Rd, Graton (95444-9373)
P.O. Box 390 (95444-0390)
PHONE................................707 829-6100
Derek Benham, *Mng Member*
Robin Nehasil, *Controller*
Jim Neely, *Facilities Mgr*
Joann Borja, *Warehouse Mgr*
Lynne Ryno, *Manager*
▲ **EMP:** 160
SALES (est): 27.6MM **Privately Held**
SIC: 2084 Wine cellars, bonded: engaged
in blending wines; wines

(P-1981)
SONOMA WINE HARDWARE INC
360 Swift Ave Ste 34, South San Francisco
(94080-6220)
PHONE................................650 866-3020
James Mackey, *President*
EMP: 20
SALES (est): 118.4K **Privately Held**
SIC: 2084 Wines, brandy & brandy spirits

(P-1982)
SOUTH COAST WINERY INC
Also Called: South Coast Winery Resort Spa
34843 Rancho Cal Rd, Temecula
(92591-4006)
PHONE................................951 587-9463
James A Carter, *President*
Julie Cort, *Executive*
Patty Ramirez, *Lab Dir*
Stephanie Espinoza, *Director*
Kimberly Polk, *Director*
▲ **EMP:** 32
SALES (est): 8.3MM
SALES (corp-wide): 9MM **Privately Held**
SIC: 2084 7011 7991 Wines; resort hotel;
spas
PA: Grove Spruce Inc
3719 S Plaza Dr
Santa Ana CA 92704
714 546-4255

(P-1983)
SOUTHWEST WINE & SPIRITS LLC (PA)
144 S Beverly Dr Fl 600, Beverly Hills
(90212-3024)
PHONE................................213 765-3213
Maurice Marciano,
Paul Marciano,
Christian Navarro,
EMP: 17
SALES (est): 6.9MM **Privately Held**
SIC: 2084 Wines, brandy & brandy spirits

(P-1984)
SPANISH CASTLE INC
Also Called: Union Wine Company
22201 Camay Ct, Calabasas (91302-6116)
PHONE................................818 222-4496
Steve Ventrello, *President*
Steve Stump, *Vice Pres*
Steven H Stumpf, *Vice Pres*
EMP: 14
SALES (est): 1.2MM **Privately Held**
WEB: www.spanishcastle.com
SIC: 2084 Wines

(P-1985)
SPRING MOUNTAIN VINEYARDS INC
2805 Spring Mountain Rd, Saint Helena
(94574-1775)
P.O. Box 991 (94574-0491)
PHONE................................707 967-4188
Don Yannias, *President*
Jean-Pierre Boustany, *Vice Pres*
George Peterson, *General Mgr*
Valli Ferrell, *Director*
Sara Livermore, *Director*
EMP: 42
SQ FT: 16,000
SALES (est): 8MM **Privately Held**
WEB: www.springmtn.com
SIC: 2084 0762 Wines; vineyard management & maintenance services

(P-1986)
ST GEORGE SPIRITS INC
2601 Monarch St, Alameda (94501-7541)
PHONE................................510 769-1601
Jorg Rupf, *Principal*
Lance Winters, *President*
Paul Skiera, *Vice Pres*
Meysa Budzinski, *Admin Asst*
James Lee, *Production*
◆ **EMP:** 25
SQ FT: 65,000
SALES (est): 4.8MM **Privately Held**
WEB: www.stgeorgespirits.com
SIC: 2084 2085 Brandy spirits; distilled &
blended liquors

(P-1987)
ST SUPERY INC (DH)
Also Called: Skalli Vineyards
8440 St Helena Hwy, Rutherford (94573)
P.O. Box 38 (94573-0038)
PHONE................................707 963-4507
Emma Swain, *CEO*
▲ **EMP:** 50
SQ FT: 20,000
SALES (est): 8.8MM **Privately Held**
SIC: 2084 Wines
HQ: Chanel, Inc.
9 W 57th St Bsmt 2b
New York NY 10019
212 688-5055

(P-1988)
STAGS LEAP WINE CELLARS
Also Called: Hawk Crest
5766 Silverado Trl, NAPA (94558-9413)
PHONE................................707 944-2020
Warren Winiarski, *Principal*
Bertha Rodriguez, *Executive*
Dan McPherson, *Mktg Dir*
Karla Jensen, *Sales Staff*
Jack Carr, *Maintence Staff*
▲ **EMP:** 110
SQ FT: 40,000
SALES (est): 17.3MM **Privately Held**
WEB: www.cask23.com
SIC: 2084 Wines

(P-1989)
STAMA WINERY LLC
17521 N Davis Rd, Lodi (95242)
PHONE................................209 727-3314
Frank Kapiniaris, *CEO*
Madeleine Cook, *Vice Pres*
EMP: 10
SALES (est): 227.1K **Privately Held**
SIC: 2084 Wines, brandy & brandy spirits

(P-1990)
STEELE WINES INC
4350 Thomas Dr, Kelseyville (95451)
P.O. Box 190 (95451-0190)
PHONE................................707 279-9475
Jedediah T Steele, *President*

Steve Tylicki, *General Mgr*
Pamela Duncan, *Executive Asst*
Naomi Key, *Admin Sec*
Pam Prisco, *Manager*
EMP: 25
SALES (est): 2.6MM **Privately Held**
WEB: www.steelewines.com
SIC: 2084 Wines

(P-1991)
STERLING VINEYARDS INC (PA)
1111 Dunaweal Ln, Calistoga (94515-9799)
P.O. Box 365 (94515-0365)
PHONE................................707 942-3300
Samuel Bronfman II, *Ch of Bd*
Ron Lilly, *Vice Pres*
Mike Westrick, *Vice Pres*
Jannie Abler, *Controller*
Michael Maul, *Opers Mgr*
▲ **EMP:** 50
SQ FT: 80,000
SALES (est): 25MM **Privately Held**
WEB: www.sterlingvineyards.com
SIC: 2084 0172 Wine cellars, bonded: engaged in blending wines; grapes

(P-1992)
STERLING VINEYARDS INC
1105 Oak Knoll Ave, NAPA (94558-1304)
P.O. Box 365, Calistoga (94515-0365)
PHONE................................707 252-7410
Vincent Vinnodo, *Manager*
EMP: 30
SALES (est): 2MM
SALES (corp-wide): 25MM **Privately Held**
WEB: www.sterlingvineyards.com
SIC: 2084 0172 Wines, brandy & brandy
spirits; grapes
PA: Sterling Vineyards, Inc.
1111 Dunaweal Ln
Calistoga CA 94515
707 942-3300

(P-1993)
STERLING VINEYARDS INC
3690 Santa Lina Hwy, Calistoga (94515)
PHONE................................707 942-9602
Jim Munk, *Principal*
EMP: 10
SALES (corp-wide): 25MM **Privately Held**
WEB: www.sterlingvineyards.com
SIC: 2084 Wine cellars, bonded: engaged
in blending wines
PA: Sterling Vineyards, Inc.
1111 Dunaweal Ln
Calistoga CA 94515
707 942-3300

(P-1994)
STEVEN KENT LLC
Also Called: La- Rochelle
5443 Tesla Rd, Livermore (94550-9621)
PHONE................................925 243-6442
Steven Mirassou, *Vice Pres*
Michael Ghielnitti, *Admin Sec*
▲ **EMP:** 29 **EST:** 2001
SALES (est): 2.2MM **Privately Held**
WEB: www.stevenkent.com
SIC: 2084 Wines

(P-1995)
STOLPMAN VINEYARDS LLC (PA)
2434 Alamo Pintado Rd, Los Olivos
(93441)
PHONE................................805 736-5000
Thomas Stolpman,
Marilyn Stolpman, *Mng Member*
EMP: 15
SALES (est): 8.7MM **Privately Held**
SIC: 2084 Wines

(P-1996)
STOLPMAN VINEYARDS LLC
1700 Industrial Way B, Lompoc
(93436-4947)
P.O. Box B, Los Olivos (93441)
PHONE................................805 736-5000
Tom Stolpman, *Branch Mgr*
EMP: 47
SALES (corp-wide): 8.7MM **Privately Held**
SIC: 2084 Wines

▲ = Import ▼=Export
◆ =Import/Export

PA: Stolpman Vineyards Llc
2434 Alamo Pintado Rd
Los Olivos CA 93441
805 736-5000

(P-1997)
STONE BRIDGE CELLARS INC (PA)
Also Called: Joseph Phelps Vineyards
200 Taplin Rd, Saint Helena (94574-9544)
P.O. Box 1031 (94574-0531)
PHONE....................707 963-2745
Joseph Phelps, *Ch of Bd*
Robert Boyd, *President*
Clarice Turner, *President*
William H Phelps, *CEO*
AMI Iadarola, *CFO*
▲ EMP: 100
SQ FT: 50,000
SALES (est): 16.1MM **Privately Held**
WEB: www.jpvwines.com
SIC: 2084 Wines

(P-1998)
STONE EDGE WINERY LLC
Also Called: Stone Edge Farm
19330 Carriger Rd, Sonoma (95476-6229)
P.O. Box 487 (95476-0487)
PHONE....................707 935-6520
John A McQuown,
Dorothy Cicchetti, *Sales Staff*
EMP: 12
SQ FT: 1,500
SALES (est): 1.3MM **Privately Held**
SIC: 2084 Wines

(P-1999)
STONECUSHION INC (PA)
Also Called: Wilson Artisan Wineries
1400 Lytton Springs Rd, Healdsburg
(95448-9695)
P.O. Box 487, Geyserville (95441-0487)
PHONE....................707 433-1911
Kenneth C Wilson, *President*
Jon Pelleriti, *CFO*
EMP: 25
SALES (est): 4.2MM **Privately Held**
SIC: 2084 Wines

(P-2000)
STUART CELLARS LLC
41006 Simi Ct, Temecula (92591-4988)
PHONE....................951 676-6414
Marshall Stuart,
▲ EMP: 17 EST: 1996
SQ FT: 2,240
SALES (est): 1.6MM **Privately Held**
SIC: 2084 Wines

(P-2001)
SUGARLOAF FARMING CORPORATION
Also Called: Peter Michael Winery
12400 Ida Clayton Rd, Calistoga
(94515-9507)
PHONE....................707 942-4459
Scott Rodde, *President*
Bill Vyenielo, *Vice Pres*
▼ EMP: 25
SQ FT: 1,000
SALES (est): 5.3MM
SALES (corp-wide): 49.7MM **Privately Held**
WEB: www.petermichaelwinery.com
SIC: 2084 Wines
PA: Stockford Limited
Sheet Street
Windsor BERKS SL4 1
-

(P-2002)
SUTTER HOME WINERY INC (PA)
Also Called: Trinchero Family Estates
100 Saint Helena Hwy S, Saint Helena
(94574-2204)
P.O. Box 248 (94574-0248)
PHONE....................707 963-3104
Roger J Trinchero, *CEO*
Louis Trinchero, *CEO*
Glenn Andrade, *Vice Pres*
Anthony R Torres, *Vice Pres*
◆ EMP: 200
SQ FT: 17,000

SALES (est): 196.8MM **Privately Held**
WEB: www.frewines.com
SIC: 2084 0172 Wines; grapes

(P-2003)
SUTTER HOME WINERY INC
560 Gateway Dr, NAPA (94558-7517)
PHONE....................707 963-3104
EMP: 42
SALES (corp-wide): 196.8MM **Privately Held**
SIC: 2084 Wines
PA: Sutter Home Winery, Inc.
100 Saint Helena Hwy S
Saint Helena CA 94574
707 963-3104

(P-2004)
SVP WINERY LLC
Also Called: Tarrica Wine Cellars
111 Clark Rd, Shandon (93461)
P.O. Box 195 (93461-0195)
PHONE....................805 237-8693
Sam Balakian, *Mng Member*
EMP: 15 EST: 1999
SQ FT: 1,624
SALES (est): 1.9MM **Privately Held**
WEB: www.tarricawinecellars.com
SIC: 2084 Wines

(P-2005)
SYLVESTER WINERY INC
5115 Buena Vista Dr, Paso Robles
(93446-8558)
PHONE....................805 227-4000
Syliva Phillini, *President*
Scott Keller, *CFO*
Sharon Curran, *Administration*
Lori Pywtorak, *Comptroller*
Zina Miakinkova, *Marketing Mgr*
EMP: 38
SALES (est): 2.4MM **Privately Held**
WEB: www.sylvesterwinery.com
SIC: 2084 Wines

(P-2006)
TABLAS CREEK VINEYARD LLC
9339 Adelaida Rd, Paso Robles
(93446-9785)
PHONE....................805 237-1231
Bob Haas, *Partner*
Neil Collins, *Technology*
Heather Hildenbrand, *Asst Controller*
Denise Chouinard, *Controller*
Jason Haas, *Mktg Dir*
▲ EMP: 18
SQ FT: 40,000
SALES (est): 3.6MM **Privately Held**
WEB: www.tablascreek.com
SIC: 2084 Wines

(P-2007)
TAFT STREET INC
Also Called: Taft Street Winery
2030 Barlow Ln, Sebastopol (95472-2555)
PHONE....................707 823-2049
Michael Tierney, *President*
Mike Martini, *CFO*
Martin Tierney Jr, *Vice Pres*
David Gast, *Sales Mgr*
Laurie Keith, *Sales Mgr*
EMP: 20
SQ FT: 30,000
SALES (est): 3.5MM **Privately Held**
WEB: www.taftstreetwinery.com
SIC: 2084 Wines

(P-2008)
TANDEM WINES LLC
Also Called: La Follette Wines
4900 W Dry Creek Rd, Healdsburg
(95448-9721)
PHONE....................707 395-3902
Peter J Kight, *Mng Member*
Dave Lese,
Carolyne Abrams, *Manager*
EMP: 12
SALES (est): 1.1MM **Privately Held**
SIC: 2084 Wine cellars, bonded: engaged
in blending wines

(P-2009)
TEMECULA VALLEY WINERY MGT LLC
Also Called: Leonesse Cellars
27495 Diaz Rd, Temecula (92590-3414)
PHONE....................951 699-8896
Willem Rebaux Steyn,
Tim Kramer, *COO*
Keith Kramer, *CFO*
Rebaux Steyn, *General Mgr*
Catherine Pruhsmeier, *Accounting Mgr*
EMP: 56
SQ FT: 40,000
SALES (est): 10.4MM **Privately Held**
SIC: 2084 Wines

(P-2010)
TERRAVANT WINE COMPANY LLC
35 Industrial Way, Buellton (93427-9565)
PHONE....................805 686-9400
Lew Eisaguirre, *President*
Robert Boller, *COO*
Dave Moser, *Vice Pres*
Joe Padilla, *Lab Dir*
Chantel Green, *Administration*
EMP: 34 EST: 2015
SALES (est): 6.8MM **Privately Held**
SIC: 2084 Wines

(P-2011)
TERRAVANT WINE COMPANY LLC
70 Industrial Way, Buellton (93427-9567)
PHONE....................805 688-4245
Lew Eisaguirre, *President*
Eric J Guerra, *Senior VP*
Tom Hoke, *Vice Pres*
Rodger Mannka, *Vice Pres*
Joyce Soares, *Vice Pres*
▲ EMP: 110
SQ FT: 25,000
SALES (est): 23.4MM **Privately Held**
WEB: www.terravant.com
SIC: 2084 Wines

(P-2012)
TESLA VINEYARDS LP
Also Called: Concannon Vineyard
4590 Tesla Rd, Livermore (94550-9002)
PHONE....................925 456-2500
Eric Wente, *Partner*
Edward Lanphier, *Partner*
Henry Wilder, *Partner*
Dennis Wood, *Partner*
Michael Wood, *Partner*
▲ EMP: 15
SALES (est): 2.5MM **Privately Held**
WEB: www.concannonvineyard.com
SIC: 2084 0721 Wines; vines, cultivation
of

(P-2013)
TESTAROSSA VINEYARDS LLC
300 College Ave Apt A, Los Gatos
(95030-7066)
P.O. Box 969 (95031-0969)
PHONE....................408 354-6150
Diana Jensen,
Matt Classen, *Natl Sales Mgr*
Julie Scopazzi, *Marketing Mgr*
Robert Jensen,
Clay Burke, *Manager*
▲ EMP: 25
SQ FT: 10,000
SALES (est): 5.4MM **Privately Held**
WEB: www.testarossa.com
SIC: 2084 Wines

(P-2014)
THOMAS DEHLINGER
Also Called: Dehlinger Winery
4101 Ginehill Rd, Sebastopol (95472)
PHONE....................707 823-2378
Thomas Dehlinger, *Owner*
EMP: 12
SQ FT: 18,000
SALES (est): 1.2MM **Privately Held**
SIC: 2084 0172 Wines; grapes

(P-2015)
THOMAS LEONARDINI
Also Called: Whitehall Lane Winery
1563 Saint Helena Hwy S, Saint Helena
(94574-9775)
PHONE....................707 963-9454
Thomas Leonardini, *Owner*
▲ EMP: 15
SQ FT: 24,000
SALES (est): 2MM **Privately Held**
WEB: www.bennettlane.com
SIC: 2084 0172 Wines; grapes

(P-2016)
THORNTON WINERY
Also Called: Cafe Champagne
32575 Rancho Cal Rd, Temecula
(92591-4935)
P.O. Box 9008 (92589-9008)
PHONE....................951 699-0099
John M Thornton, *Ch of Bd*
Steve Thornton, *President*
EMP: 98
SQ FT: 41,000
SALES (est): 15.5MM **Privately Held**
WEB: www.thorntonwine.com
SIC: 2084 5812 5947 Wine cellars,
bonded: engaged in blending wines; eat-
ing places; gift shop

(P-2017)
THREE STICKS WINES LLC
21692 8th St E Ste 280, Sonoma
(95476-2804)
P.O. Box 1869 (95476-1869)
PHONE....................707 996-3328
Bill Price, *Owner*
EMP: 21
SALES (est): 1.7MM **Privately Held**
SIC: 2084 Wines

(P-2018)
TOAD HOLLOW VINEYARDS INC
4024 Westside Rd, Healdsburg
(95448-9356)
P.O. Box 876 (95448-0876)
PHONE....................707 431-1441
Robert Todd Williams, *President*
Erik Thorson, *Info Tech Mgr*
Bill Zuur, *Technician*
Cherie Zouzounis, *Mfg Mgr*
▲ EMP: 14
SQ FT: 3,000
SALES (est): 2.8MM **Privately Held**
WEB: www.toadhollow.com
SIC: 2084 Wines

(P-2019)
TREANA WINERY LLC
Also Called: Liberty School
4280 Second Wind Way, Paso Robles
(93446-6309)
P.O. Box 3260 (93447-3260)
PHONE....................805 237-2932
Charles Hope,
Charles Wagner,
▲ EMP: 30
SALES (est): 5.9MM **Privately Held**
WEB: www.treana.com
SIC: 2084 Wines

(P-2020)
TREASURY CHATEAU & ESTATES
Also Called: Carmenet Vineyards
1700 Moon Mountain Rd, Sonoma
(95476-3022)
PHONE....................707 996-5870
EMP: 13
SQ FT: 1,232
SALES (corp-wide): 16.6B **Privately Held**
SIC: 2084
HQ: Treasury Chateau & Estates
10300 Chalk Hill Rd
Healdsburg CA 95448
707 299-2600

(P-2021)
TREASURY WINE ESTATES AMERICAS (HQ)
555 Gateway Dr, NAPA (94558-6291)
P.O. Box 4500 (94558-0005)
PHONE....................707 259-4500
Michael Clarke, *CEO*
Robert Foye, *President*

Don McCall, *President*
Bob Spooner, *President*
Noel Meehan, *CFO*
◆ **EMP:** 400 **EST:** 1973
SQ FT: 26,000
SALES (est): 426.7MM **Privately Held**
WEB: www.stclement.com
SIC: 2084 Wines

(P-2022)
TREASURY WINE ESTATES AMERICAS
Also Called: Beringer Vineyards
2000 Main St, Saint Helena (94574-9500)
P.O. Box 111 (94574-0111)
PHONE..............................707 963-7115
Brenda Wand, *Manager*
Yesenia Plascencia, *Human Res Mgr*
Ed Broshears, *Manager*
EMP: 81 **Privately Held**
WEB: www.stclement.com
SIC: 2084 Wines
HQ: Treasury Wine Estates Americas Company
555 Gateway Dr
Napa CA 94558
707 259-4500

(P-2023)
TREASURY WINE ESTATES AMERICAS
Also Called: Beringer Vinyards
1000 Pratt Ave, Saint Helena (94574-1020)
P.O. Box 111 (94574-0111)
PHONE..............................707 963-4812
Walter Klenz, *Manager*
Ronald Dover, *Maintence Staff*
Kevin Gorgen, *Manager*
EMP: 300 **Privately Held**
WEB: www.stclement.com
SIC: 2084 5182 5921 Wines; wine; liquor stores
HQ: Treasury Wine Estates Americas Company
555 Gateway Dr
Napa CA 94558
707 259-4500

(P-2024)
TREASURY WINE ESTATES AMERICAS
Also Called: Chateau St Jean
8555 Sonoma Hwy, Kenwood (95452-9026)
P.O. Box 293 (95452-0293)
PHONE..............................707 833-4134
Lisa Saroni, *Principal*
EMP: 20 **Privately Held**
WEB: www.stclement.com
SIC: 2084 0172 Wines; grapes
HQ: Treasury Wine Estates Americas Company
555 Gateway Dr
Napa CA 94558
707 259-4500

(P-2025)
TREASURY WINE ESTATES AMERICAS
Also Called: Asti Winery
26150 Asti Rd, Cloverdale (95425-7003)
PHONE..............................707 894-2541
Lou Toninato, *Director*
EMP: 35 **Privately Held**
WEB: www.stclement.com
SIC: 2084 Wines
HQ: Treasury Wine Estates Americas Company
555 Gateway Dr
Napa CA 94558
707 259-4500

(P-2026)
TREASURY WINE ESTATES AMERICAS
2000 Saint Helena Hwy N, Saint Helena (94574)
PHONE..............................707 963-7115
Sally Buchanan, *General Mgr*
EMP: 81 **Privately Held**
WEB: www.stclement.com
SIC: 2084 Wines

HQ: Treasury Wine Estates Americas Company
555 Gateway Dr
Napa CA 94558
707 259-4500

(P-2027)
TREFETHEN VINEYARDS WINERY INC
Also Called: Trefethen Family Vineyards
1160 Oak Knoll Ave, NAPA (94558-1398)
P.O. Box 2460 (94558-0291)
PHONE..............................707 255-7700
Jon Ruel, *President*
Carla Trefethen, *Shareholder*
Loren Trefethen, *Exec VP*
David Whitehouse, *Vice Pres*
Betty Calvin, *Executive*
▲ **EMP:** 50
SQ FT: 4,000
SALES (est): 10.2MM **Privately Held**
WEB: www.trefethen.com
SIC: 2084 5921 Wines; wine

(P-2028)
TRINCHERO FAMILY ESTATES INC
Also Called: Folie A Deux Winery
3070 Saint Helena Hwy N, Saint Helena (94574-9656)
PHONE..............................707 963-1160
Richard Peterson, *Branch Mgr*
EMP: 10
SALES (corp-wide): 196.8MM **Privately Held**
WEB: www.frewines.com
SIC: 2084 0172 Wines; grapes
PA: Sutter Home Winery, Inc.
100 Saint Helena Hwy S
Saint Helena CA 94574
707 963-3104

(P-2029)
TRUETT-HURST INC (PA)
125 Foss Creek Cir, Healdsburg (95448-4288)
P.O. Box 1532 (95448-1532)
PHONE..............................707 431-4423
Philip L Hurst, *Ch of Bd*
Karen Weaver, *CFO*
Jason Strobbe, *Exec VP*
▲ **EMP:** 31 **EST:** 2007
SQ FT: 2,500
SALES: 6.4MM **Publicly Held**
SIC: 2084 Wine cellars, bonded: engaged in blending wines

(P-2030)
TULOCAY WINERY
1426 Coombsville Rd, NAPA (94558-3907)
PHONE..............................707 255-4064
William C Cadman, *Owner*
EMP: 10
SALES: 148K **Privately Held**
WEB: www.tulocay.com
SIC: 2084 Wines

(P-2031)
TURLEY WINE CELLARS
2900 Vineyard Dr, Templeton (93465-9417)
PHONE..............................805 434-1030
Larry Turley, *President*
Rich Ardson, *General Mgr*
Tegan Passalacqua, *Director*
Malani Anderson, *Manager*
Nick Finarelli, *Assistant*
EMP: 12 **EST:** 1928
SQ FT: 3,500
SALES (est): 1.2MM **Privately Held**
WEB: www.turleywinecellars.com
SIC: 2084 Wine cellars, bonded: engaged in blending wines

(P-2032)
TURLEY WINE CELLARS INC
Also Called: Pesenti Winery
3358 Saint Helena Hwy N, Saint Helena (94574-9660)
PHONE..............................707 968-2700
Larry Turley, *President*
Ellen Ushioka, *Office Mgr*
Christina Turley, *Sales Staff*
EMP: 11
SALES (est): 2MM **Privately Held**
SIC: 2084 Wines

(P-2033)
TURNBULL WINE CELLARS
8210 St Helena Hwy, Oakville (94562)
P.O. Box 29 (94562-0029)
PHONE..............................707 963-5839
Patrick O'Dell, *President*
Peter Heitz, *Opers Mgr*
▲ **EMP:** 10 **EST:** 1977
SQ FT: 1,600
SALES (est): 1.4MM
SALES (corp-wide): 9.4MM **Privately Held**
SIC: 2084 Wines
PA: Humboldt Group
180 S Fortuna Blvd
Fortuna CA
707 725-6661

(P-2034)
TWIN PEAKS WINERY INC
1473 Yountville Cross Rd, Yountville (94599-9471)
PHONE..............................707 945-0855
Cliff Lede, *Principal*
EMP: 13
SALES (est): 1.9MM **Privately Held**
SIC: 2084 Wines

(P-2035)
TWISTED OAK WINERY LLC (PA)
4280 Red Hill Rd, Vallecito (95251)
PHONE..............................209 728-3000
Jeffrey Stai,
EMP: 20
SQ FT: 1,000
SALES (est): 2.7MM **Privately Held**
SIC: 2084 Wine cellars, bonded: engaged in blending wines; wines

(P-2036)
TWO BLIND MICE LLC
Also Called: Maestro Cellers
5016 E Crescent Dr, Anaheim (92807-3631)
PHONE..............................714 279-0600
Kevin Crampton, *Mng Member*
Kevin P Crampton, *Mng Member*
EMP: 11
SALES: 1.3MM **Privately Held**
SIC: 2084 Wines

(P-2037)
VALLEY OF MOON WINERY
777 Madrone Rd, Glen Ellen (95442-9522)
P.O. Box 1951 (95442-1951)
PHONE..............................707 939-4500
Gary Heck, *President*
Andrea Raymond, *Marketing Staff*
▲ **EMP:** 25
SQ FT: 10,000
SALES (est): 3.2MM
SALES (corp-wide): 93.2MM **Privately Held**
WEB: www.vomwinery.com
SIC: 2084 0172 Wines; grapes
PA: F. Korbel & Bros.
13250 River Rd
Guerneville CA 95446
707 824-7000

(P-2038)
VIADER VINEYARDS
Also Called: Viader Vineyard & Winery
1120 Deer Park Rd, Deer Park (94576-9715)
P.O. Box 280 (94576-0280)
PHONE..............................707 963-3816
Delia Viader, *CEO*
Ian Dooley, *Manager*
▲ **EMP:** 10
SQ FT: 5,000
SALES (est): 1.3MM **Privately Held**
WEB: www.viader.com
SIC: 2084 Wines

(P-2039)
VIE-DEL COMPANY
13363 S Indianola Ave, Kingsburg (93631-9268)
PHONE..............................559 896-3065
Richard Watson, *Principal*
EMP: 20
SALES (corp-wide): 12.8MM **Privately Held**
SIC: 2084 2037 Brandy; wines; frozen fruits & vegetables

PA: Vie-Del Company
11903 S Chestnut Ave
Fresno CA 93725
559 834-2525

(P-2040)
VIGNETTE WINERY LLC
Also Called: Wine Foundry
45 Enterprise Ct Ste 3, NAPA (94558-7586)
PHONE..............................707 637-8821
Aaron Hayos, *Principal*
EMP: 11
SALES (corp-wide): 2.6MM **Privately Held**
SIC: 2084 Wines
PA: Vignette Winery, Llc
45 Enterprise Ct
Napa CA 94558
707 637-8821

(P-2041)
VILLA AMOROSA
Also Called: Castello Diamorosa
4045 Saint Helena Hwy, Calistoga (94515-9609)
PHONE..............................707 942-8200
Georg Falzner, *President*
Kevin Kennedy, *Marketing Staff*
Carol Sass, *Director*
▲ **EMP:** 100
SALES (est): 15MM **Privately Held**
SIC: 2084 Wines

(P-2042)
VILLA ENCINAL PARTNERS LP
Also Called: Plumjack Winery
620 Oakville Cross Rd, NAPA (94558-9740)
PHONE..............................707 945-1220
Gavin Newsom, *General Ptnr*
▲ **EMP:** 10
SALES (est): 682.6K **Privately Held**
SIC: 2084 5812 Wine cellars, bonded: engaged in blending wines; eating places

(P-2043)
VILLA TOSCANO WINERY
10600 Shenandoah Rd, Plymouth (95669-9513)
P.O. Box 1029 (95669-1029)
PHONE..............................209 245-3800
Jerry Wright, *Owner*
▲ **EMP:** 27
SQ FT: 18,000
SALES (est): 2.3MM **Privately Held**
WEB: www.villatoscano.com
SIC: 2084 Wines

(P-2044)
VINEBURG WINE COMPANY INC (PA)
Also Called: Bartholomew Park Winery
2000 Denmark St, Sonoma (95476-9615)
P.O. Box 1, Vineburg (95487-0001)
PHONE..............................707 938-5277
Jim Bundschu, *CEO*
Nancy Bundschu, *President*
Lisa Dencklau, *Executive*
▲ **EMP:** 25
SQ FT: 4,000
SALES (est): 5.8MM **Privately Held**
WEB: www.gunbun.com
SIC: 2084 0172 Wines; grapes

(P-2045)
VINEYARD 29 LLC
2929 Saint Helena Hwy N, Saint Helena (94574-9701)
P.O. Box 93 (94574-0093)
PHONE..............................707 963-9292
Chuck McMinn, *Owner*
▲ **EMP:** 10
SQ FT: 1,464
SALES (est): 1.3MM **Privately Held**
SIC: 2084 Wines

(P-2046)
VINTAGE POINT LLC
564 Broadway, Sonoma (95476-6602)
PHONE..............................707 939-6766
David H Biggar,
Tom Peterson, *Opers Staff*
Teresa M Sullivan,
▲ **EMP:** 25
SQ FT: 2,400

SALES (est): 3.1MM **Privately Held**
SIC: 2084 Wines

(P-2047)
VINTAGE WINE ESTATES INC
1060 Dunaweal Ln, Calistoga
(94515-9798)
PHONE..................................707 942-4981
Patrick Roney, *President*
EMP: 12 **Privately Held**
SIC: 2084 Wines
PA: Vintage Wine Estates, Inc.
    205 Concourse Blvd
    Santa Rosa CA 95403
    -

(P-2048)
VINTAGE WINE ESTATES INC
Also Called: B.R. Cohn
15000 Hwy 12, Glen Ellen (95442-9454)
PHONE..................................707 933-9675
EMP: 35 **Privately Held**
SIC: 2084 0172 5921 Wines; grapes;
wine
PA: Vintage Wine Estates, Inc.
    205 Concourse Blvd
    Santa Rosa CA 95403
    -

(P-2049)
WEIBEL INCORPORATED
Also Called: Weibel Champagne Vineyards
1 Winemaster Way Ste D, Lodi
(95240-0860)
PHONE..................................209 365-9463
Fred E Weibel Jr, *President*
Suzanne Cruz-Y-Corro, *Treasurer*
Gary Habluetzel, *Vice Pres*
Doug Richards, *Vice Pres*
▲ EMP: 35
SALES (est): 7.2MM **Privately Held**
WEB: www.weibel.com
SIC: 2084 Wines

(P-2050)
WENTE BROS (PA)
Also Called: Wente Vineyards
5565 Tesla Rd, Livermore (94550-9149)
PHONE..................................925 456-2300
Eric P Wente, *CEO*
Carolyn Wente, *President*
Jean Wente, *Chairman*
Tyson Overton, *Exec VP*
Dan Carroll, *Vice Pres*
▼ EMP: 100 EST: 1883
SQ FT: 168,000
SALES (est): 130.8MM **Privately Held**
WEB: www.wentevineyards.com
SIC: 2084 8742 Wines; restaurant & food
services consultants

(P-2051)
WENTE BROS
Also Called: Wente Brothers Winery
37995 Elm Ave, Greenfield (93927-9710)
PHONE..................................831 674-5642
Keith Roberts, *Manager*
Marta Marquez, *Human Resources*
EMP: 25
SALES (corp-wide): 130.8MM **Privately
Held**
WEB: www.wentevineyards.com
SIC: 2084 Wines
PA: Wente Bros.
    5565 Tesla Rd
    Livermore CA 94550
    925 456-2300

(P-2052)
WG BEST WEINKELLEREI INC
Also Called: Montesquieu Winery
8221 Arjons Dr Ste F, San Diego
(92126-6319)
PHONE..................................858 627-1747
Fonda Hopkins, *President*
Frank Kryger, *Admin Sec*
▲ EMP: 18
SQ FT: 29,000
SALES (est): 3.4MM **Privately Held**
SIC: 2084 5182 5921 Wine cellars,
bonded: engaged in blending wines; wine;
wine

(P-2053)
WHEELER WINERY INC
849 Zinfandel Ln, Saint Helena
(94574-1645)
PHONE..................................415 979-0630
Jean Boisset, *President*
Alain Leonnet, *Vice Pres*
EMP: 35
SQ FT: 50,000
SALES (est): 5.1MM
SALES (corp-wide): 2.7MM **Privately
Held**
WEB: www.boissetamerica.com
SIC: 2084 Wines
HQ: Jean-Claude Boisset Wines U.S.A.,
    Inc.
    849 Zinfandel Ln
    Saint Helena CA 94574
    707 967-7667

(P-2054)
WHISPERKOOL CORPORATION
Also Called: Whisperkoll
1738 E Alpine Ave, Stockton (95205-2505)
PHONE..................................800 343-9463
Thomas R Schneider, *CEO*
Doug Smith, *Sales Dir*
EMP: 14
SQ FT: 32,000
SALES (est): 12MM **Privately Held**
SIC: 2084 Wine coolers (beverages)

(P-2055)
WIENS CELLARS LLC
35055 Via Del Ponte, Temecula
(92592-8022)
PHONE..................................951 694-9892
George M Wiens, *General Mgr*
Jeff Wiens, *General Mgr*
Dave Wiens, *Marketing Mgr*
David Owthwaite, *Sales Associate*
Eric Strong, *Manager*
EMP: 24 EST: 2001
SALES (est): 3.7MM **Privately Held**
SIC: 2084 Wines

(P-2056)
WILLIAM HILL WINERY
1761 Atlas Peak Rd, NAPA (94558-1251)
PHONE..................................707 224-5424
Bill Newlands, *President*
▲ EMP: 20
SQ FT: 10,000
SALES (est): 2.1MM **Privately Held**
WEB: www.williamhillwinery.com
SIC: 2084 5148 Wines; fruits

(P-2057)
WILLIAMS & SELYEM WINERY
Also Called: Williams Selyem
7227 Westside Rd, Healdsburg
(95448-8357)
PHONE..................................707 433-6425
John Dyson,
Jana Churich, *Social Dir*
Jessica Gilmore, *Opers Mgr*
Mark Malpiede, *Marketing Staff*
Nick Miller, *Sales Staff*
▼ EMP: 12
SQ FT: 18,000
SALES (est): 2.7MM **Privately Held**
SIC: 2084 Wines

(P-2058)
WILSON CREEK WNERY VNYARDS INC
35960 Rancho Cal Rd, Temecula
(92591-5088)
PHONE..................................951 699-9463
Gerald R Wilson, *CEO*
William J Wilson, *CEO*
Rosemary Wilson, *Vice Pres*
Barbara Hilde, *Executive Asst*
Natalie Hutchins, *Executive Asst*
EMP: 110
SQ FT: 6,000
SALES (est): 21.8MM **Privately Held**
WEB: www.wilsoncreekwinery.com
SIC: 2084 8999 Wines; personal services

(P-2059)
WINDSOR OAKS VINEYARDS LLP
10810 Hillview Rd, Windsor (95492-7519)
P.O. Box 883 (95492-0883)
PHONE..................................707 433-4050
Windsor Oaks, *Partner*
Doug Lumgair, *Manager*
◆ EMP: 20
SALES (est): 3MM **Privately Held**
WEB: www.windsoroaks.com
SIC: 2084 Wines

(P-2060)
WINE CELLAR IMPRESSIONS INC
2013 Stone Ave, San Jose (95125-1447)
PHONE..................................408 277-0100
Thang Hoang Nguyen, *President*
▲ EMP: 15
SALES (est): 1.4MM **Privately Held**
WEB: www.wcimpression.com
SIC: 2084 Wine cellars, bonded: engaged
in blending wines

(P-2061)
WINE COMPANY OF SAN FRANCISCO
Also Called: Gomberg Fredrikson & Assoc
231 Ware Rd Ste 823, Woodside
(94062-4538)
PHONE..................................650 851-0965
John Fredrikson, *President*
EMP: 10
SALES (est): 30.5K **Privately Held**
SIC: 2084 Wines

(P-2062)
WINE GROUP INC (HQ)
Also Called: Mogan David Wine
17000 E State Highway 120, Ripon
(95366-9412)
PHONE..................................209 599-4111
Brian Jay Vos, *CEO*
Arthur Ciocca, *Ch of Bd*
Morris Ball, *Vice Pres*
Stephen Hughes, *Vice Pres*
Louis Quaccia, *Vice Pres*
◆ EMP: 200
SQ FT: 3,000
SALES (est): 145.4MM
SALES (corp-wide): 151.9MM **Privately
Held**
SIC: 2084 Wines
PA: The Wine Group Llc
    4596 S Tracy Blvd
    Tracy CA 95377
    415 986-8700

(P-2063)
WINE MAKERS INC
Also Called: Wine Tailor, The
8916 Foothill Blvd Ste K3, Rancho Cuca-
monga (91730-3470)
PHONE..................................909 481-5050
Mark Mitzenmacher, *Principal*
EMP: 10
SALES (est): 859.5K **Privately Held**
SIC: 2084 Brandy

(P-2064)
WISE VILLA WINERY LLC
4226 Wise Rd, Lincoln (95648-8528)
PHONE..................................916 543-0323
Grover Cleveland Lee, *Mng Member*
EMP: 16
SALES (est): 2.3MM **Privately Held**
SIC: 2084 Wines

(P-2065)
ZARIF COMPANIES
4187 Carpinteria Ave, Carpinteria
(93013-3300)
PHONE..................................805 318-1800
EMP: 11
SALES (est): 1.3MM **Privately Held**
SIC: 2084 Wines

2085 Liquors, Distilled, Rectified & Blended

(P-2066)
BAR NONE INC
1302 Santa Fe Dr, Tustin (92780-6495)
PHONE..................................714 259-8450
John Underwood, *President*
Elizabeth Underwood, *Corp Secy*
EMP: 18
SQ FT: 20,000
SALES (est): 3.4MM
SALES (corp-wide): 569.5MM **Privately
Held**
WEB: www.barnone.net
SIC: 2085 2087 3565 Cocktails, alcoholic;
cordials & premixed alcoholic cocktails;
beverage bases, concentrates, syrups,
powders & mixes; bottling machinery: fill-
ing, capping, labeling
HQ: First Advantage Corporation
    1 Concrse Pkwy Ne Ste 200
    Atlanta GA 30328
    800 888-5773

(P-2067)
BOOCHERY INC
Also Called: Boochcraft
684 Anita St Ste F, Chula Vista
(91911-7170)
PHONE..................................619 738-1008
Adam Hiner, *President*
Michael Kent, *Corp Secy*
Andrew Clark, *Vice Pres*
EMP: 17
SQ FT: 5,000
SALES (est): 1.4MM **Privately Held**
SIC: 2085 Distilled & blended liquors

(P-2068)
BOUDOIR SPIRITS INC
Also Called: Boudoir Vodka
7197 Boulder Ave Ste 12, Highland
(92346-3498)
PHONE..................................909 714-6644
Adam Ames, *CEO*
EMP: 10
SQ FT: 1,500
SALES: 90K **Privately Held**
SIC: 2085 Distilled & blended liquors

(P-2069)
BRANDED SPIRITS USA LTD
500 Sansome St Ste 600, San Francisco
(94111-3222)
PHONE..................................415 813-5045
George Chen, *CEO*
Britt Bachner, *COO*
Joan Bowie, *Manager*
EMP: 10
SALES (est): 799.8K **Privately Held**
SIC: 2085 5921 Distilled & blended
liquors; hard liquor

(P-2070)
DIAGEO NORTH AMERICA INC
Also Called: Beaulieu Vineyard
1960 Saint Helena Hwy, Rutherford
(94573)
PHONE..................................707 967-5200
Armond Rist, *Dir Ops-Prd-Mfg*
EMP: 100
SALES (corp-wide): 16.3B **Privately Held**
SIC: 2085 2084 0172 Distilled & blended
liquors; wines, brandy & brandy spirits;
grapes
HQ: Diageo North America Inc.
    801 Main Ave
    Norwalk CT 06851
    203 229-2100

(P-2071)
FRANK-LIN DISTILLERS PDTS LTD
2455 Huntington Dr, Fairfield (94533-9734)
PHONE..................................408 259-8900
Vince Maestri, *Vice Pres*
Lindley Maestri, *Project Mgr*
EMP: 100
SQ FT: 150,000
SALES (corp-wide): 109.9MM **Privately
Held**
SIC: 2085 Distilled & blended liquors

PRODUCTS & SVCS

PA: Frank-Lin Distillers Products, Ltd.
2455 Huntington Dr
Fairfield CA 94533
408 259-8900

(P-2072)
JIM BEAM BRANDS CO
Also Called: Beam Suntory
17901 Von Karman Ave, Irvine
(92614-6297)
PHONE..................................949 200-7200
Susan Morris, *Manager*
EMP: 10
SALES (corp-wide): 76.5MM **Privately Held**
WEB: www.jbbworldwide.com
SIC: 2085 Distillers' dried grains & solubles & alcohol
HQ: Jim Beam Brands Co.
510 Lake Cook Rd Ste 200
Deerfield IL 60015
847 948-8903

(P-2073)
LIN FRANK DISTILLERS
2455 Huntington Dr, Fairfield (94533-9734)
PHONE..................................707 437-1092
Frank Lin, *Principal*
EMP: 16
SALES (est): 3.5MM **Privately Held**
SIC: 2085 Distilled & blended liquors

(P-2074)
POINT BLANKS INC
43 S Olive St, Ventura (93001-2501)
PHONE..................................805 643-8616
Yvon Chouinard, *President*
▲ **EMP:** 15
SQ FT: 1,200
SALES (est): 1.3MM **Privately Held**
WEB: www.pointblanks.com
SIC: 2085 Scotch whiskey

(P-2075)
RARE BREED DISTILLING LLC (DH)
Also Called: Wild Turkey Distillery
55 Francisco St Ste 100, San Francisco (94133-2136)
PHONE..................................415 315-8060
Francesca Mazzoleni, *Principal*
▼ **EMP:** 29
SALES (est): 9.4MM **Privately Held**
SIC: 2085 Distilled & blended liquors
HQ: Davide Campari Milano Spa
Via Franco Sacchetti 20
Sesto San Giovanni MI 20099
022 247-2558

(P-2076)
SAZERAC COMPANY INC
2202 E Del Amo Blvd, Carson (90749)
P.O. Box 6263 (90749-6263)
PHONE..................................310 604-8717
Michael Dominick, *Manager*
EMP: 45
SALES (corp-wide): 306.3MM **Privately Held**
WEB: www.bartoninc.com
SIC: 2085 Distilled & blended liquors
PA: Sazerac Company, Inc.
3850 N Causeway Blvd # 1695
Metairie LA 70002
504 831-9450

(P-2077)
STILLHOUSE LLC
8201 Beverly Blvd Ste 300, Los Angeles (90048-4542)
PHONE..................................323 498-1111
Brad Beckerman, *CEO*
Paul Sheppard, *COO*
Alex Blough, *Executive*
Jared Poe, *Opers Staff*
Amy Dobbins, *Marketing Mgr*
EMP: 32
SALES: 6MM **Privately Held**
SIC: 2085 Corn whiskey

(P-2078)
SUPERNOVA SPIRITS INC
10288 Richwood Dr, Cupertino (95014-3361)
PHONE..................................415 819-3154
Vijay Caveripakkam, *President*
Ward Karson, *COO*

▲ **EMP:** 25
SALES: 3MM **Privately Held**
SIC: 2085 Vodka (alcoholic beverage)

(P-2079)
TAKARA SAKE USA INC (DH)
Also Called: Numano Sake Company
708 Addison St, Berkeley (94710-1925)
PHONE..................................510 540-8250
Yoshihiro Naka, *CEO*
Yoichiro Miyakuni, *President*
Atsushi Himeno, *General Mgr*
Shigeyuki Yoshioka, *Administration*
Michiyo Ihara, *Purchasing*
◆ **EMP:** 32
SQ FT: 15,000
SALES (est): 7.3MM
SALES (corp-wide): 2.5B **Privately Held**
WEB: www.takarasake.com
SIC: 2085 5182 Grain alcohol for beverage purposes; wine

2086 Soft Drinks

(P-2080)
ADVANCED REFRESHMENT LLC (HQ)
Also Called: Advanced H2o
2560 E Philadelphia St, Ontario (91761-7768)
PHONE..................................425 746-8100
Robert Abramowitz,
EMP: 15
SQ FT: 270,000
SALES (est): 14.3MM
SALES (corp-wide): 362.8MM **Privately Held**
WEB: www.advanced-h2o.com
SIC: 2086 Mineral water, carbonated: packaged in cans, bottles, etc.
PA: Niagara Bottling, Llc
2560 E Philadelphia St
Ontario CA 91761
909 230-5000

(P-2081)
AMCAN BEVERAGES INC
Also Called: Pokka Beverages
1201 Commerce Blvd, American Canyon (94503-9611)
PHONE..................................707 557-0500
Don Soetaert, *President*
EMP: 125
SQ FT: 250,000
SALES (est): 14MM
SALES (corp-wide): 35.4B **Publicly Held**
SIC: 2086 Iced tea & fruit drinks, bottled & canned; fruit drinks (less than 100% juice): packaged in cans, etc.
PA: The Coca-Cola Company
1 Coca Cola Plz Nw
Atlanta GA 30313
404 676-2121

(P-2082)
AMERICAN BOTTLING COMPANY
Also Called: Seven-Up Bottling
2210 S Mcdowell Blvd Ext, Petaluma (94954-5659)
PHONE..................................707 766-9750
Ray Gutendorf, *Manager*
EMP: 30
SQ FT: 1,600 **Publicly Held**
WEB: www.7upcal.com
SIC: 2086 Bottled & canned soft drinks
HQ: The American Bottling Company
5301 Legacy Dr
Plano TX 75024

(P-2083)
AMERICAN BOTTLING COMPANY
Also Called: Seven-Up Bottling
100 Wabash Ave, Ukiah (95482-6313)
PHONE..................................707 462-8871
Allen Brown, *Manager*
EMP: 16 **Publicly Held**
WEB: www.7upcal.com
SIC: 2086 Bottled & canned soft drinks

HQ: The American Bottling Company
5301 Legacy Dr
Plano TX 75024

(P-2084)
AMERICAN BOTTLING COMPANY
230 E 18th St, Bakersfield (93305-5609)
PHONE..................................661 323-7921
Brian Sutton, *Manager*
EMP: 37 **Publicly Held**
WEB: www.cs-americas.com
SIC: 2086 5149 Bottled & canned soft drinks; soft drinks
HQ: The American Bottling Company
5301 Legacy Dr
Plano TX 75024

(P-2085)
AMERICAN BOTTLING COMPANY
2012 S Pearl St, Fresno (93721-3312)
PHONE..................................559 442-1553
Mariel Guardado, *Manager*
EMP: 60
SQ FT: 25,000 **Publicly Held**
WEB: www.cs-americas.com
SIC: 2086 Soft drinks: packaged in cans, bottles, etc.
HQ: The American Bottling Company
5301 Legacy Dr
Plano TX 75024

(P-2086)
AMERICAN BOTTLING COMPANY
1981 N Broadway Ste 215, Walnut Creek (94596-3872)
PHONE..................................925 938-8777
Linda Orcy, *Branch Mgr*
Clay Brady, *Manager*
Rob Love, *Manager*
EMP: 70 **Publicly Held**
WEB: www.7upcal.com
SIC: 2086 Soft drinks: packaged in cans, bottles, etc.
HQ: The American Bottling Company
5301 Legacy Dr
Plano TX 75024

(P-2087)
AMERICAN BOTTLING COMPANY
1166 Arroyo St, San Fernando (91340-1824)
PHONE..................................818 898-1471
Ed Nemecek, *Branch Mgr*
EMP: 200 **Publicly Held**
WEB: www.cs-americas.com
SIC: 2086 5149 Bottled & canned soft drinks; soft drinks
HQ: The American Bottling Company
5301 Legacy Dr
Plano TX 75024

(P-2088)
AMERICAN BOTTLING COMPANY
618 Hanson Way, Santa Maria (93458-9734)
PHONE..................................805 928-1001
Richard Roese, *Branch Mgr*
EMP: 31 **Publicly Held**
WEB: www.cs-americas.com
SIC: 2086 Soft drinks: packaged in cans, bottles, etc.
HQ: The American Bottling Company
5301 Legacy Dr
Plano TX 75024

(P-2089)
AMERICAN BOTTLING COMPANY
Also Called: 7 Up / R C Bottling Co
3220 E 26th St, Vernon (90058-8008)
PHONE..................................323 268-7779
Russ Wolfe, *Controller*
EMP: 500 **Publicly Held**
WEB: www.cs-americas.com

HQ: The American Bottling Company
5301 Legacy Dr
Plano TX 75024

SIC: 2086 5149 Soft drinks: packaged in cans, bottles, etc.; groceries & related products
HQ: The American Bottling Company
5301 Legacy Dr
Plano TX 75024

(P-2090)
AMERICAN BOTTLING COMPANY
Also Called: Seven-Up Btlg Co Marysville
2720 Land Ave, Sacramento (95815-1834)
PHONE..................................916 929-3575
Jim Hough, *Manager*
EMP: 13 **Publicly Held**
WEB: www.7upcal.com
SIC: 2086 Bottled & canned soft drinks
HQ: The American Bottling Company
5301 Legacy Dr
Plano TX 75024

(P-2091)
AMERICAN BOTTLING COMPANY
2670 Land Ave, Sacramento (95815-2380)
PHONE..................................916 929-7777
EMP: 70 **Publicly Held**
SIC: 2086 Soft drinks: packaged in cans, bottles, etc.
HQ: The American Bottling Company
5301 Legacy Dr
Plano TX 75024

(P-2092)
AMERICAN BOTTLING COMPANY
11205 Commercial Pkwy, Castroville (95012-3205)
PHONE..................................831 632-0777
EMP: 70 **Publicly Held**
SIC: 2086 Soft drinks: packaged in cans, bottles, etc.
HQ: The American Bottling Company
5301 Legacy Dr
Plano TX 75024

(P-2093)
AMERICAN BOTTLING COMPANY
6160 Stoneridge Mall Rd # 280, Pleasanton (94588-3285)
PHONE..................................925 251-3001
EMP: 70 **Publicly Held**
SIC: 2086 Soft drinks: packaged in cans, bottles, etc.
HQ: The American Bottling Company
5301 Legacy Dr
Plano TX 75024

(P-2094)
AMERIPEC INC
6965 Aragon Cir, Buena Park (90620-1118)
PHONE..................................714 690-9191
Ping C Wu, *CEO*
Ed Muratori, *General Mgr*
Chuck Caplinger, *Human Res Mgr*
Mathew Bamberger, *Purchasing*
Hue Ngo, *QC Mgr*
EMP: 150
SQ FT: 215,000
SALES (est): 34.2MM
SALES (corp-wide): 13.2B **Privately Held**
WEB: www.ameripecinc.com
SIC: 2086 Carbonated soft drinks, bottled & canned
HQ: President Global Corporation
6965 Aragon Cir
Buena Park CA 90620
714 994-2990

(P-2095)
AQUAHYDRATE INC
5870 W Jefferson Blvd A, Los Angeles (90016-3159)
PHONE..................................310 559-5058
John Cochran, *CEO*
Joe Gleason, *President*
Al Hermsen, *President*
Mark E Loeffler, *Corp Secy*
Ericka Pittman, *Chief Mktg Ofcr*

▲ = Import ▼=Export
◆ =Import/Export

◆ **EMP:** 66
SALES (est): 24.6MM **Privately Held**
SIC: 2086 Mineral water, carbonated: packaged in cans, bottles, etc.

(P-2096)
ASEPTIC SLTONS USA VNTURES LLC
Also Called: Aseptic Solutions USA-Corona
484 Alcoa Cir, Corona (92880-9323)
PHONE..............................951 736-9230
Alan Morris,
Bob Danko, *Vice Pres*
Aaron Harris, *Vice Pres*
Jim Parr, *Engineer*
Sariah Salazar, *Human Res Mgr*
▲ **EMP:** 117
SQ FT: 67,000
SALES (est): 26.5MM **Privately Held**
WEB: www.asepticusa.com
SIC: 2086 Carbonated beverages, nonal-coholic: bottled & canned
PA: Glanbia Public Limited Company
Glanbia House
Kilkenny R95 E

(P-2097)
AT MOBILE BOTTLING LINE LLC
413 Saint Andrews Dr, NAPA (94558-1534)
PHONE..............................707 257-3757
John W Davis, *Principal*
EMP: 14 **EST:** 2007
SALES (est): 2MM **Privately Held**
SIC: 2086 Bottled & canned soft drinks

(P-2098)
AVITA BEVERAGE COMPANY INC (PA)
18401 Burbank Blvd # 121, Tarzana (91356-2822)
PHONE..............................213 477-1979
Clinton Stokes III, *CEO*
Kenneth Mayeaux, *COO*
Jamie Mayeaux, *CFO*
EMP: 10
SQ FT: 3,000
SALES: 879K **Privately Held**
SIC: 2086 Water, pasteurized: packaged in cans, bottles, etc.

(P-2099)
BLUE CAN WATER (PA)
8309 Laurel Cny Blvd 219, Sun Valley (91352)
PHONE..............................818 450-3290
Rick Eye, *CEO*
James Skylar, *CFO*
Danna Gillespie, *General Mgr*
EMP: 11
SALES: 1MM **Privately Held**
SIC: 2086 Mineral water, carbonated: packaged in cans, bottles, etc.

(P-2100)
BOTTLERS UNLIMITED INC
753 Jefferson St, NAPA (94559-2424)
PHONE..............................707 255-0595
Carole R Kelly, *President*
Sharon Puffer, *Vice Pres*
EMP: 45
SALES: 800K **Privately Held**
SIC: 2086 Bottled & canned soft drinks

(P-2101)
BOTTLING GROUP LLC
1150 E North Ave, Fresno (93725-1929)
PHONE..............................559 485-5050
EMP: 14
SALES (corp-wide): 63.5B **Publicly Held**
SIC: 2086 Bottled & canned soft drinks
HQ: Bottling Group, Llc
1111 Westchester Ave
White Plains NY 10604
914 767-6000

(P-2102)
BOTTLING GROUP LLC
Also Called: Pepsico
6659 Sycamore Canyon Blvd, Riverside (92507-0733)
PHONE..............................951 697-3200
Jon Hess, *Principal*
Greg Sawyer, *Purch Mgr*
Dave Alhadeff, *Safety Mgr*

Becky Banda, *QC Mgr*
Jesse Arias, *Manager*
EMP: 31
SALES (est): 8MM **Privately Held**
SIC: 2086 Carbonated soft drinks, bottled & canned

(P-2103)
BULLETPROOF BRANDS CO INC
1704 Halifax Way, El Dorado Hills (95762-5834)
PHONE..............................916 635-3718
EMP: 11
SQ FT: 3,200
SALES (est): 1.2MM **Privately Held**
SIC: 2086

(P-2104)
CALIFIA FARMS LLC (PA)
1321 Palmetto St, Los Angeles (90013-2228)
PHONE..............................213 694-4667
Greg Stelpenpoho, *CEO*
Demir Vangelov, *CFO*
Derek Brown, *Engineer*
Jesse Arroyo, *Buyer*
Natasha Cuda, *Sales Dir*
▼ **EMP:** 50 **EST:** 2010
SALES (est): 100MM **Privately Held**
SIC: 2086 Fruit drinks (less than 100% juice): packaged in cans, etc.

(P-2105)
CALIFIA FARMS LLC
33374 Lerdo Hwy, Bakersfield (93308-9782)
PHONE..............................661 679-1000
Evans Berne, *Owner*
Demir Vangelov, *CFO*
Vilma Livas, *Vice Pres*
JC McConnell, *Vice Pres*
Andrew Fendelman, *Sales Mgr*
EMP: 14
SALES (est): 562.3K **Privately Held**
SIC: 2086 Fruit drinks (less than 100% juice): packaged in cans, etc.

(P-2106)
CALIFORNIA BOTTLING COMPANY
Also Called: High Country Water
8250 Industrial Ave, Roseville (95678-5900)
PHONE..............................916 772-1000
Robert Wikse, *President*
Christopher Crain, *Vice Pres*
L Douglas McKenzie, *Vice Pres*
EMP: 50
SQ FT: 50,000
SALES (est): 10.2MM **Privately Held**
WEB: www.cbcwater.com
SIC: 2086 Water, pasteurized: packaged in cans, bottles, etc.

(P-2107)
CALIFORNIA HOT SPRINGS WATER
42231 Hot Springs Dr, Calif Hot Spg (93207-9715)
P.O. Box 146 (93207-0146)
PHONE..............................661 548-6582
Ronald Gilbert, *Owner*
EMP: 10
SQ FT: 25,000
SALES (est): 900K **Privately Held**
WEB: www.cahsrealty.com
SIC: 2086 Water, pasteurized: packaged in cans, bottles, etc.

(P-2108)
CAPITOL BEVERAGE PACKERS
Also Called: Seven Up Bottling
2670 Land Ave, Sacramento (95815-2380)
PHONE..............................916 929-7777
Millard C Tonkin, *President*
Millard Tonkin, *Shareholder*
▲ **EMP:** 96
SQ FT: 110,360
SALES (est): 11.7MM **Privately Held**
SIC: 2086 5078 Carbonated beverages, nonalcoholic: bottled & canned; refrigerated beverage dispensers

(P-2109)
CCBCC OPERATIONS LLC
Also Called: Coca-Cola
1123 W Avenue L14, Lancaster (93534-7061)
PHONE..............................661 723-0714
Robert Macias, *Branch Mgr*
EMP: 112
SQ FT: 15,895
SALES (corp-wide): 4.3B **Publicly Held**
SIC: 2086 Soft drinks: packaged in cans, bottles, etc.
HQ: Ccbcc Operations, Llc
4100 Coca Cola Plz
Charlotte NC 28211
704 364-8728

(P-2110)
CG ROXANE LLC
Also Called: Cg Roxane Shasta
1400 Marys Dr, Weed (96094-9643)
P.O. Box 560 (96094-0560)
PHONE..............................530 225-1260
Rick Moore, *Manager*
EMP: 80
SALES (corp-wide): 168.2MM **Privately Held**
WEB: www.cgroxane.com
SIC: 2086 Water, pasteurized: packaged in cans, bottles, etc.
PA: Cg Roxane Llc
1210 State Hwy 395
Olancha CA 93549
760 764-2885

(P-2111)
CG ROXANE LLC (PA)
Also Called: Crystal Geyser Alpine Spring W
1210 State Hwy 395, Olancha (93549)
P.O. Box A (93549-0903)
PHONE..............................760 764-2885
Ronan Papillaud, *President*
Page Beykpour, *COO*
Patrice Marquet, *Senior VP*
Veronique Belgum, *Vice Pres*
▲ **EMP:** 100
SQ FT: 75,000
SALES (est): 168.2MM **Privately Held**
WEB: www.cgroxane.com
SIC: 2086 Water, pasteurized: packaged in cans, bottles, etc.

(P-2112)
CHAMELEON BEVERAGE COMPANY INC (PA)
6444 E 26th St, Commerce (90040-3214)
PHONE..............................323 724-8223
Derek Reineman, *President*
Erin Zheo, *CFO*
Morgan Reed, *General Mgr*
Lok Man Chiu, *Technology*
Araceli Ramirez, *QC Mgr*
▲ **EMP:** 70
SQ FT: 100,000
SALES (est): 14.6MM **Privately Held**
WEB: www.chameleonbeverage.com
SIC: 2086 5149 Water, pasteurized: packaged in cans, bottles, etc.; soft drinks

(P-2113)
CL-ONE CORPORATION
29582 Spotted Bull Ln, San Juan Capistrano (92675-1034)
P.O. Box 458, Placentia (92871-0458)
PHONE..............................949 364-2895
Les Gilmer, *CEO*
Marcus Franco, *Vice Pres*
EMP: 100
SQ FT: 18,000
SALES (est): 5.4MM **Privately Held**
SIC: 2086 Carbonated beverages, nonalcoholic: bottled & canned

(P-2114)
COASTAL COCKTAILS INC (PA)
Also Called: Modern Gourmet Foods
18011 Mitchell S Ste B, Irvine (92614-6863)
PHONE..............................949 250-3129
Nadeem Mumal, *CEO*
Mark Greenhall, *President*
Riley Coughlin, *Merchandising*
Jian Qiu,
Jee Kim, *Director*
▲ **EMP:** 40

SALES: 48MM **Privately Held**
SIC: 2086 Bottled & canned soft drinks

(P-2115)
COCA COLA BTLG OF EUREKA CAL
Also Called: Coca-Cola
1335 Albee St, Eureka (95501-2224)
PHONE..............................707 443-2796
Dave Hallagan, *Manager*
Jim Slade, *Manager*
EMP: 15 **EST:** 1962
SALES (est): 1.6MM **Privately Held**
SIC: 2086 Bottled & canned soft drinks

(P-2116)
COCA-COLA COMPANY
1650 S Vintage Ave, Ontario (91761-3656)
PHONE..............................909 975-5200
Melvin Robinson, *Manager*
EMP: 103
SALES (corp-wide): 35.4B **Publicly Held**
SIC: 2086 Bottled & canned soft drinks
PA: The Coca-Cola Company
1 Coca Cola Plz Nw
Atlanta GA 30313
404 676-2121

(P-2117)
COCA-COLA COMPANY
13255 Amar Rd, City of Industry (91746-1203)
PHONE..............................626 855-4440
Kimberly Curtis, *Branch Mgr*
EMP: 50
SALES (corp-wide): 35.4B **Publicly Held**
WEB: www.cocacola.com
SIC: 2086 Bottled & canned soft drinks
PA: The Coca-Cola Company
1 Coca Cola Plz Nw
Atlanta GA 30313
404 676-2121

(P-2118)
COCA-COLA COMPANY
3 Park Plz Ste 600, Irvine (92614-2575)
PHONE..............................949 250-5961
Dan Manning, *Manager*
Nancy Kung, *Executive*
EMP: 125
SALES (corp-wide): 35.4B **Publicly Held**
WEB: www.cocacola.com
SIC: 2086 Soft drinks: packaged in cans, bottles, etc.
PA: The Coca-Cola Company
1 Coca Cola Plz Nw
Atlanta GA 30313
404 676-2121

(P-2119)
COCA-COLA COMPANY
2121 E Winston Rd, Anaheim (92806-5535)
PHONE..............................714 991-7031
Linda Martin, *Branch Mgr*
EMP: 28
SALES (corp-wide): 35.4B **Publicly Held**
WEB: www.cocacola.com
SIC: 2086 Bottled & canned soft drinks
PA: The Coca-Cola Company
1 Coca Cola Plz Nw
Atlanta GA 30313
404 676-2121

(P-2120)
COCA-COLA COMPANY
2025 Pike Ave, San Leandro (94577-6708)
PHONE..............................510 476-7048
EMP: 116
SALES (corp-wide): 35.4B **Publicly Held**
SIC: 2086 Bottled & canned soft drinks
PA: The Coca-Cola Company
1 Coca Cola Plz Nw
Atlanta GA 30313
404 676-2121

(P-2121)
COCA-COLA REFRESHMENTS USA INC
5335 Walker St, Ventura (93003-7499)
PHONE..............................805 644-2211
EMP: 116
SALES (corp-wide): 35.4B **Publicly Held**
SIC: 2086 Bottled & canned soft drinks

P
R
O
D
U
C
T
S

&

S
V
C
S

HQ: Coca-Cola Refreshments Usa, Inc.
2500 Windy Ridge Pkwy Se
Atlanta GA 30339
770 989-3000

(P-2122)
COCA-COLA REFRESHMENTS USA INC
3900 Ocean Ranch Blvd, Oceanside (92056-2692)
PHONE..................760 435-7111
Coca Refreshments, *Branch Mgr*
EMP: 57
SALES (corp-wide): 35.4B **Publicly Held**
WEB: www.cokecce.com
SIC: 2086 Bottled & canned soft drinks
HQ: Coca-Cola Refreshments Usa, Inc.
2500 Windy Ridge Pkwy Se
Atlanta GA 30339
770 989-3000

(P-2123)
CRYSTAL BOTTLING COMPANY INC
Also Called: Crystal Mountain Springwater
8631 Younger Creek Dr, Sacramento (95828-1028)
PHONE..................916 568-3300
Hayes Johnson, *CEO*
EMP: 80
SQ FT: 12,000
SALES (est): 7.7MM **Privately Held**
WEB: www.crystalwater.com
SIC: 2086 5963 Pasteurized & mineral waters, bottled & canned; bottled water delivery

(P-2124)
CRYSTAL GEYSER WATER COMPANY
5001 Fermi Dr, Fairfield (94534-6894)
PHONE..................707 647-4410
Ernesto Olivarez, *Branch Mgr*
EMP: 30
SALES (corp-wide): 11B **Privately Held**
WEB: www.crystalgeyserasw.com
SIC: 2086 Water, pasteurized: packaged in cans, bottles, etc.
HQ: Crystal Geyser Water Company
501 Washington St
Calistoga CA 94515
707 942-0500

(P-2125)
CRYSTAL GEYSER WATER COMPANY
1233 E California Ave, Bakersfield (93307-1205)
PHONE..................661 323-6296
Gerhard Gaugel, *Branch Mgr*
Jon Ellis, *Vice Pres*
Carmen Maib, *Plant Mgr*
EMP: 30
SALES (corp-wide): 11B **Privately Held**
WEB: www.crystalgeyserasw.com
SIC: 2086 5141 2099 2033 Mineral water, carbonated: packaged in cans, bottles, etc.; carbonated beverages, nonalcoholic: bottled & canned; groceries, general line; food preparations; canned fruits & specialties; bottled water delivery
HQ: Crystal Geyser Water Company
501 Washington St
Calistoga CA 94515
707 942-0500

(P-2126)
CRYSTAL GEYSER WATER COMPANY
2351 E Brundage Ln Ste A, Bakersfield (93307-3063)
PHONE..................661 321-0896
Robert Hofferd, *Manager*
Kevin Moloughney, *Vice Pres*
EMP: 15
SALES (corp-wide): 11B **Privately Held**
WEB: www.crystalgeyserasw.com
SIC: 2086 Mineral water, carbonated: packaged in cans, bottles, etc.
HQ: Crystal Geyser Water Company
501 Washington St
Calistoga CA 94515
707 942-0500

(P-2127)
CUSTOM LABELING & BTLG CORP
15005 Concord Cir, Morgan Hill (95037-5417)
PHONE..................408 371-6171
Tillie Pacheco, *President*
Tom Wilkenson, *Vice Pres*
EMP: 15
SQ FT: 120,000
SALES (est): 2.5MM **Privately Held**
SIC: 2086 Bottled & canned soft drinks

(P-2128)
DANSIG (CHAPTER S CORPORATION)
Also Called: Freshers
25011 Avenue Stanford G, Valencia (91355-1235)
PHONE..................661 295-0899
Darin Elias, *Manager*
EMP: 10
SALES (corp-wide): 2.9MM **Privately Held**
SIC: 2086 5963 5149 Lemonade: packaged in cans, bottles, etc.; beverage services, direct sales; juices
PA: Dansig Inc (Chapter S Corporation)
17452 Irvine Blvd Ste 101
Tustin CA
714 838-0505

(P-2129)
DESIGNER DRINKS
Also Called: New Generation Sourcing
5050 Avenida Encinas, Carlsbad (92008-4381)
PHONE..................760 444-2355
David Jenkins, *Owner*
EMP: 25
SALES (est): 1.5MM **Privately Held**
SIC: 2086 Water, pasteurized: packaged in cans, bottles, etc.

(P-2130)
DR PEPPER/SEVEN UP INC
1901 Russell Ave, Santa Rosa (95403-2646)
PHONE..................707 545-7797
Ray Gutendorf, *Principal*
EMP: 68 **Publicly Held**
SIC: 2086 Soft drinks: packaged in cans, bottles, etc.
HQ: Dr Pepper/Seven Up, Inc.
5301 Legacy Dr Fl 1
Plano TX 75024
972 673-7000

(P-2131)
DS SERVICES OF AMERICA INC
Also Called: Sparkletts Water
1449 N Avenue 46, Los Angeles (90041-3410)
PHONE..................323 551-5724
Reggie Doster, *Manager*
EMP: 55
SALES (corp-wide): 2.2B **Privately Held**
SIC: 2086 5499 Bottled & canned soft drinks; beverage stores
HQ: Ds Services Of America, Inc.
2300 Windy Ridge Pkwy Se 500n
Atlanta GA 30339
770 933-1400

(P-2132)
ESSENCE WATER INC
12802 Knott St, Garden Grove (92841-3906)
PHONE..................855 738-7426
Joel Gabriel, *CEO*
Jaci Conrad, *CFO*
EMP: 12
SQ FT: 20,000
SALES (est): 2.4MM **Privately Held**
SIC: 2086 Water, pasteurized: packaged in cans, bottles, etc.

(P-2133)
FAST TRACK ENERGY DRINK LLC
8447 Wilshire Blvd # 401, Beverly Hills (90211-3226)
PHONE..................310 281-2045
Kenneth White Sr, *Chairman*
Brian Slover Sr, *President*

EMP: 25 EST: 2010
SALES (est): 1.4MM **Privately Held**
SIC: 2086 Carbonated beverages, nonalcoholic: bottled & canned

(P-2134)
FIRE MOUNTAIN BEVERAGE
27240 Turnberry Ln # 200, Valencia (91355-1029)
PHONE..................661 362-0716
Anthony Miller, *CEO*
EMP: 50
SALES (est): 2.8MM **Privately Held**
SIC: 2086 Water, pasteurized: packaged in cans, bottles, etc.

(P-2135)
FORTUNE DRINK INC
19925 Stevens Creek Blvd # 100, Cupertino (95014-2300)
PHONE..................408 805-9526
Robert Chen, *President*
EMP: 10
SALES (est): 283.4K **Privately Held**
SIC: 2086 2087 Bottled & canned soft drinks; flavoring extracts & syrups

(P-2136)
GREEN SPOT PACKAGING INC
100 S Cambridge Ave, Claremont (91711-4842)
PHONE..................909 625-8771
John Tsu, *CEO*
Dana Staal, *COO*
Luis Sanchez, *Administration*
Stephanie Rodriguez, *Manager*
EMP: 20
SQ FT: 100,000
SALES (est): 4.6MM **Privately Held**
WEB: www.greenspotusa.com
SIC: 2086 Fruit drinks (less than 100% juice): packaged in cans, etc.
PA: Green Spot International
C/O Grand Pavilion Main Entrance
West Bay GR CAYMAN

(P-2137)
GTS LIVING FOODS LLC
Also Called: Synergy Beverages
4646 Hampton St, Vernon (90058-2116)
P.O. Box 2352, Beverly Hills (90213-2352)
PHONE..................323 581-7787
George Thomas Dave,
EMP: 700
SALES (est): 44.1MM **Privately Held**
SIC: 2086 Bottled & canned soft drinks

(P-2138)
H A RIDER & SONS
2482 Freedom Blvd, Watsonville (95076-1099)
PHONE..................831 722-3882
George C Rider, *Partner*
Thomas Rider, *Partner*
Kenneth Czaja, *Vice Pres*
Dassie Hernandez, *Technology*
Tina Lewis, *Persnl Mgr*
▲ EMP: 45
SQ FT: 168,000
SALES (est): 9.7MM **Privately Held**
WEB: www.hariderandsons.com
SIC: 2086 Soft drinks: packaged in cans, bottles, etc.

(P-2139)
HINT INC
2124 Union St Ste D, San Francisco (94123-4044)
P.O. Box 29078 (94129-0078)
PHONE..................415 513-4051
Kara Goldin, *CEO*
Theodore Goldin, *COO*
Kae Lim, *Executive Asst*
Tuyen Le, *Technology*
Beth Gray, *VP Finance*
EMP: 44
SALES (est): 17.2MM **Privately Held**
WEB: www.drinkhint.com
SIC: 2086 Mineral water, carbonated: packaged in cans, bottles, etc.; fruit drinks (less than 100% juice): packaged in cans, etc.; carbonated beverages, nonalcoholic: bottled & canned

(P-2140)
HORIZON BOTTLED WATER
1371 S Santa Fe Ave, San Jacinto (92583-4637)
PHONE..................951 654-0954
William Roberts, *Owner*
EMP: 11
SALES (est): 590K **Privately Held**
SIC: 2086 Water, pasteurized: packaged in cans, bottles, etc.

(P-2141)
JOHN FITZPATRICK & SONS
Also Called: Pepsico
1480 Beltline Rd, Redding (96003-1410)
PHONE..................530 241-3216
John Fitzpatrick Jr, *CEO*
Jerome Fitzpatrick, *Vice Pres*
EMP: 17 EST: 1958
SQ FT: 2,000
SALES (est): 2.7MM **Privately Held**
SIC: 2086 Carbonated soft drinks, bottled & canned

(P-2142)
KEURIG DR PEPPER INC
1188 Mt Vernon Ave, Riverside (92507-1829)
PHONE..................951 341-7500
EMP: 94 **Publicly Held**
SIC: 2086 Soft drinks: packaged in cans, bottles, etc.
PA: Keurig Dr Pepper Inc.
53 South Ave
Burlington MA 01803

(P-2143)
KEURIG DR PEPPER INC
306 Otterson Dr, Chico (95928-8250)
PHONE..................530 893-4501
Barry Thompson, *Principal*
EMP: 34 **Publicly Held**
WEB: www.7upbottling.com
SIC: 2086 Soft drinks: packaged in cans, bottles, etc.
PA: Keurig Dr Pepper Inc.
53 South Ave
Burlington MA 01803

(P-2144)
KEURIG DR PEPPER INC
1981 N Broadway, Walnut Creek (94596-3852)
PHONE..................925 938-8777
James Fox, *Branch Mgr*
Debby Steele, *Accounts Exec*
EMP: 99 **Publicly Held**
SIC: 2086 Soft drinks: packaged in cans, bottles, etc.
PA: Keurig Dr Pepper Inc.
53 South Ave
Burlington MA 01803

(P-2145)
KEVITA INC (HQ)
2220 Celsius Ave Ste A, Oxnard (93030-5181)
PHONE..................805 200-2250
Andrea Theodore, *CEO*
Nate Patena, *COO*
Ada Cheng, *CFO*
James Linesch, *CFO*
Russell Barnett, *Chief Mktg Ofcr*
EMP: 60
SQ FT: 17,000
SALES: 60MM
SALES (corp-wide): 63.5B **Publicly Held**
SIC: 2086 Bottled & canned soft drinks
PA: Pepsico, Inc.
700 Anderson Hill Rd
Purchase NY 10577
914 253-2000

(P-2146)
KUANTUM BRANDS LLC
1747 Hancock St Ste A, San Diego (92101-1130)
PHONE..................760 412-2432
Will Righeimer, *President*
Lorena Aguirre, *CFO*
EMP: 200 EST: 2015

SALES: 50MM **Privately Held**
SIC: **2086** Carbonated beverages, nonalcoholic: bottled & canned

(P-2147)
LA BOTTLEWORKS INC
1605 Beach St, Montebello (90640-5432)
PHONE..................................323 724-4076
Ryan Marsh, *CEO*
Matthew Marsh, *Vice Pres*
Linda Valenzuela, *General Mgr*
EMP: 20
SALES (est): 4.6MM **Privately Held**
SIC: **2086** Bottled & canned soft drinks

(P-2148)
LIFEAID BEVERAGE CO
Also Called: PARTYAID
2833 Mission St, Santa Cruz (95060-5755)
P.O. Box 761 (95061-0761)
PHONE..................................800 855-1113
Orion Melehan, *CEO*
Andy Halliday, *COO*
Aaron Hinde, *COO*
Erik Gundersen, *Creative Dir*
Darrick Gitomer, *Area Mgr*
◆ EMP: 55
SQ FT: 9,105
SALES: 19.8MM **Privately Held**
WEB: www.lifeaidbevco.com
SIC: **2086** Bottled & canned soft drinks

(P-2149)
MC CLELLAN BOTTLING GROUP
4712 Mountain Lakes Blvd, Redding
(96003-1475)
PHONE..................................530 241-2600
Christina Holden, *Principal*
EMP: 13
SALES (est): 1.9MM **Privately Held**
SIC: **2086** Bottled & canned soft drinks

(P-2150)
MONSTER BEVERAGE 1990 CORP (HQ)
1 Monster Way, Corona (92879-7101)
PHONE..................................951 739-6200
Rodney C Sacks, *Ch of Bd*
Hilton H Schlosberg, *President*
Nick R Gagliardi, *COO*
Mark J Hall, *Chief Mktg Ofcr*
Thomas J Kelly, *Senior VP*
◆ EMP: 53
SQ FT: 141,000
SALES: 3.3B **Publicly Held**
WEB: www.hansens.com
SIC: **2086** Soft drinks: packaged in cans,
bottles, etc.; carbonated beverages, non-
alcoholic: bottled & canned; iced tea &
fruit drinks, bottled & canned
PA: Monster Beverage Corporation
1 Monster Way
Corona CA 92879
951 739-6200

(P-2151)
MONSTER BEVERAGE COMPANY
1990 Pomona Rd, Corona (92880-6955)
PHONE..................................866 322-4466
Mark Hall, *Principal*
Mitch Covington, *Vice Pres*
Darin Kimball, *Software Engr*
James Garrard, *Production*
Brent Hamilton, *Marketing Staff*
EMP: 776
SALES (est): 41.6MM
SALES (corp-wide): 3.3B **Publicly Held**
SIC: **2086** Soft drinks: packaged in cans,
bottles, etc.
HQ: Monster Beverage 1990 Corporation
1 Monster Way
Corona CA 92879
951 739-6200

(P-2152)
MONSTER BEVERAGE CORPORATION (PA)
1 Monster Way, Corona (92879-7101)
PHONE..................................951 739-6200
Rodney C Sacks, *Ch of Bd*
Guy Carling, *President*
Hilton H Schlosberg, *President*
Emelie Tirre, *President*
Gary Fayard, *Bd of Directors*

EMP: 75
SQ FT: 141,000
SALES: 3.3B **Publicly Held**
SIC: **2086** Carbonated beverages, nonalcoholic: bottled & canned

(P-2153)
NEO SUPERWATER CORP
535 Mission St Ste 1820, San Francisco
(94105-2997)
PHONE..................................800 604-7051
Behnam Behrouzi, *CEO*
EMP: 12
SQ FT: 4,000
SALES (est): 2.6MM **Privately Held**
SIC: **2086** Water, pasteurized: packaged in
cans, bottles, etc.

(P-2154)
NIAGARA BOTTLING LLC
1401 Alder Ave, Rialto (92376-3005)
PHONE..................................909 230-5000
EMP: 11
SALES (corp-wide): 362.8MM **Privately
Held**
SIC: **2086** Bottled & canned soft drinks
PA: Niagara Bottling, Llc
2560 E Philadelphia St
Ontario CA 91761
909 230-5000

(P-2155)
NOAHS BOTTLED WATER
416 Hosmer Ave, Modesto (95351-3920)
PHONE..................................209 526-2945
John Varty, *President*
EMP: 50
SALES (est): 4.1MM **Privately Held**
SIC: **2086** Water, pasteurized: packaged in
cans, bottles, etc.

(P-2156)
NOR-CAL BEVERAGE CO INC
1375 Terminal St, West Sacramento
(95691-3514)
PHONE..................................916 372-1700
Larry Buban, *Manager*
EMP: 30
SALES (corp-wide): 248.5MM **Privately
Held**
SIC: **2086** **5181** Carbonated beverages,
nonalcoholic: bottled & canned; soft
drinks: packaged in cans, bottles, etc.;
beer & ale
PA: Nor-Cal Beverage Co., Inc.
2150 Stone Blvd
West Sacramento CA 95691
916 372-0600

(P-2157)
ONE WORLD ENTERPRISES LLC
Also Called: One Natural Experience
1333 S Mayflower Ave # 100, Monrovia
(91016-5265)
PHONE..................................310 802-4220
Rodrigo Veloso, *CEO*
▲ EMP: 30
SALES (est): 3.9MM **Privately Held**
SIC: **2086** Water, pasteurized: packaged in
cans, bottles, etc.

(P-2158)
ORANGE BANG INC
13115 Telfair Ave, Sylmar (91342-3574)
PHONE..................................818 833-1000
David Fox, *President*
EMP: 40
SQ FT: 33,000
SALES (est): 6.5MM **Privately Held**
SIC: **2086** Soft drinks: packaged in cans,
bottles, etc.

(P-2159)
ORGAIN INC
16631 Millikan Ave, Irvine (92606-5028)
P.O. Box 4918 (92616-4918)
PHONE..................................949 930-0039
Andrew Abraham, *CEO*
Carter Elenz, *President*
Stephen Hennessy, *Vice Pres*
Karla Malone, *Buyer*
Rima Jauregui, *QC Mgr*
EMP: 10

SALES (est): 2.7MM **Privately Held**
SIC: **2086** Fruit drinks (less than 100%
juice): packaged in cans, etc.

(P-2160)
P-AMERICAS LLC
Also Called: Pepsico
3586 Arden Rd, Hayward (94545-3921)
PHONE..................................510 732-9500
EMP: 25
SALES (corp-wide): 63.5B **Publicly Held**
SIC: **2086** Carbonated soft drinks, bottled
& canned
HQ: P-Americas Llc
1 Pepsi Way
Somers NY 10589
336 896-5740

(P-2161)
P-AMERICAS LLC
Also Called: Pepsi
4375 N Ventura Ave, Ventura (93001-1124)
P.O. Box 25070 (93002-5070)
PHONE..................................805 641-4200
Daniel Sassen, *Branch Mgr*
EMP: 107
SALES (corp-wide): 63.5B **Publicly Held**
SIC: **2086** Carbonated soft drinks, bottled
& canned
HQ: P-Americas Llc
1 Pepsi Way
Somers NY 10589
336 896-5740

(P-2162)
PACIFIC AUTOMATED LLC
Also Called: Brix Beverage
1951 Monarch St 200, Alameda
(94501-7574)
PHONE..................................800 372-5098
Sky Pace, *President*
Alberto Silva, *Vice Pres*
EMP: 12
SQ FT: 32,000
SALES: 1.9MM **Privately Held**
WEB: www.pacificautomated.com
SIC: **2086** **3585** Carbonated beverages,
nonalcoholic: bottled & canned; soda
fountain & beverage dispensing equip-
ment & parts

(P-2163)
PEPSI COLA BTLG OF BKERSFIELD
215 E 21st St, Bakersfield (93305-5186)
PHONE..................................661 327-9992
James B Lindsey Jr, *President*
Fay W Penney, *Corp Secy*
Marjorie Lindsey, *Vice Pres*
EMP: 200
SQ FT: 30,000
SALES (est): 12.3MM **Privately Held**
SIC: **2086** Soft drinks: packaged in cans,
bottles, etc.

(P-2164)
PEPSI-COLA BOTTLING GROUP
Also Called: Pepsico
215 E 21st St, Bakersfield (93305-5186)
PHONE..................................661 635-1100
Steve Longfield, *Branch Mgr*
EMP: 150
SALES (corp-wide): 63.5B **Publicly Held**
SIC: **2086** Carbonated soft drinks, bottled
& canned
HQ: Pepsi-Cola Bottling Group
1111 Westchester Ave
White Plains NY 10604
914 767-6000

(P-2165)
PEPSI-COLA METRO BTLG CO INC
Also Called: Pepsico
2345 Thompson Way, Santa Maria
(93455-1050)
PHONE..................................805 739-2160
Joe Pearson, *Branch Mgr*
EMP: 60
SALES (corp-wide): 63.5B **Publicly Held**
WEB: www.pbg.com
SIC: **2086** Carbonated soft drinks, bottled
& canned

HQ: Pepsi-Cola Metropolitan Bottling Company, Inc.
1111 Westchester Ave
White Plains NY 10604
914 767-6000

(P-2166)
PEPSI-COLA METRO BTLG CO INC
6261 Caballero Blvd, Buena Park
(90620-1191)
PHONE..................................714 522-9635
Margaret Gramann, *Manager*
Jim E Williams, *Business Mgr*
Migel Huertas, *Purch Agent*
Randy Williams, *Maintence Staff*
Belen Otero, *Manager*
EMP: 500
SALES (corp-wide): 63.5B **Publicly Held**
WEB: www.joy-of-cola.com
SIC: **2086** **5149** Soft drinks: packaged in
cans, bottles, etc.; soft drinks
HQ: Pepsi-Cola Metropolitan Bottling Com-
pany, Inc.
1111 Westchester Ave
White Plains NY 10604
914 767-6000

(P-2167)
PEPSI-COLA METRO BTLG CO INC
4699 Old Ironsides Dr # 150, Santa Clara
(95054-1824)
PHONE..................................408 617-2200
Jerry Titwell, *Branch Mgr*
EMP: 200
SALES (corp-wide): 63.5B **Publicly Held**
WEB: www.joy-of-cola.com
SIC: **2086** Soft drinks: packaged in cans,
bottles, etc.
HQ: Pepsi-Cola Metropolitan Bottling Com-
pany, Inc.
1111 Westchester Ave
White Plains NY 10604
914 767-6000

(P-2168)
PEPSI-COLA METRO BTLG CO INC
19700 Figueroa St, Carson (90745-1098)
PHONE..................................310 327-4222
Stefan Freeman, *Manager*
Oscar Dela-Cruz, *Technology*
Carol Clodius, *Production*
EMP: 700
SALES (corp-wide): 63.5B **Publicly Held**
WEB: www.joy-of-cola.com
SIC: **2086** **5149** Carbonated soft drinks,
bottled & canned; soft drinks
HQ: Pepsi-Cola Metropolitan Bottling Com-
pany, Inc.
1111 Westchester Ave
White Plains NY 10604
914 767-6000

(P-2169)
PEPSI-COLA METRO BTLG CO INC
7550 Reese Rd, Sacramento (95828-3707)
PHONE..................................916 423-1000
Randy Kieser, *Manager*
Ken Dibartolo, *Admin Sec*
Michael Hassel, *Technical Staff*
Stephen Camara, *Sales Staff*
Laura Thayer, *Maintence Staff*
EMP: 400
SALES (corp-wide): 63.5B **Publicly Held**
WEB: www.joy-of-cola.com
SIC: **2086** **5962** Soft drinks: packaged in
cans, bottles, etc.; merchandising ma-
chine operators
HQ: Pepsi-Cola Metropolitan Bottling Com-
pany, Inc.
1111 Westchester Ave
White Plains NY 10604
914 767-6000

(P-2170)
PEPSI-COLA METRO BTLG CO INC
Also Called: Pepsico
4225 Pepsi Pl, Stockton (95215-2316)
PHONE..................................209 367-7140
Sydney Van Vusan, *Principal*
EMP: 50

P R O D U C T S & S V C S

SALES (corp-wide): 63.5B **Publicly Held**
WEB: www.pbg.com
SIC: **2086** Carbonated soft drinks, bottled & canned
HQ: Pepsi-Cola Metropolitan Bottling Company, Inc.
1111 Westchester Ave
White Plains NY 10604
914 767-6000

(P-2171)
PEPSI-COLA METRO BTLG CO INC
6659 Sycamore Canyon Blvd, Riverside (92507-0733)
PHONE..............................909 885-0741
Eli Bernard, *Manager*
EMP: 300
SALES (corp-wide): 63.5B **Publicly Held**
SIC: **2086** Soft drinks: packaged in cans, bottles, etc.
HQ: Pepsi-Cola Metropolitan Bottling Company, Inc.
1111 Westchester Ave
White Plains NY 10604
914 767-6000

(P-2172)
PEPSI-COLA METRO BTLG CO INC
Also Called: Pepsico
7995 Armour St, San Diego (92111-3780)
PHONE..............................858 560-6735
Art Brennan, *Branch Mgr*
Rick Mailloux, *General Mgr*
Steven Cuellar, *Admin Sec*
Edward Serna, *Admin Sec*
Joshua Bowman, *Sales Staff*
EMP: 400
SALES (corp-wide): 63.5B **Publicly Held**
WEB: www.pbg.com
SIC: **2086** Carbonated soft drinks, bottled & canned
HQ: Pepsi-Cola Metropolitan Bottling Company, Inc.
1111 Westchester Ave
White Plains NY 10604
914 767-6000

(P-2173)
PEPSI-COLA METRO BTLG CO INC
135 Martella St, Salinas (93901-2894)
PHONE..............................831 796-2000
Oscar Broyer, *Manager*
Gilbert Romo, *Sales Dir*
EMP: 120
SALES (corp-wide): 63.5B **Publicly Held**
WEB: www.joy-of-cola.com
SIC: **2086 5149** Bottled & canned soft drinks; groceries & related products
HQ: Pepsi-Cola Metropolitan Bottling Company, Inc.
1111 Westchester Ave
White Plains NY 10604
914 767-6000

(P-2174)
PEPSI-COLA METRO BTLG CO INC
2471 Nadeau St, Mojave (93501-1507)
PHONE..............................661 824-2051
Blaine Sherritt, *Manager*
Kyra W Gilbert, *Senior Mgr*
EMP: 75
SALES (corp-wide): 63.5B **Publicly Held**
WEB: www.joy-of-cola.com
SIC: **2086 5149** Bottled & canned soft drinks; soft drinks
HQ: Pepsi-Cola Metropolitan Bottling Company, Inc.
1111 Westchester Ave
White Plains NY 10604
914 767-6000

(P-2175)
PEPSI-COLA METRO BTLG CO INC
83801 Citrus Ave, Indio (92201-3458)
PHONE..............................760 775-2660
Rick Valenti, *Manager*
EMP: 10

SALES (corp-wide): 63.5B **Publicly Held**
WEB: www.joy-of-cola.com
SIC: **2086** Soft drinks: packaged in cans, bottles, etc.
HQ: Pepsi-Cola Metropolitan Bottling Company, Inc.
1111 Westchester Ave
White Plains NY 10604
914 767-6000

(P-2176)
PEPSI-COLA METRO BTLG CO INC
29000 Hesperian Blvd, Hayward (94545-5014)
PHONE..............................510 781-3600
Toll Free:..............................877
Greg Knabe, *Manager*
Valerie Lomas, *Human Resources*
Mark Sabato, *Opers Mgr*
Pranav Desai, *QC Mgr*
EMP: 350
SALES (corp-wide): 63.5B **Publicly Held**
WEB: www.joy-of-cola.com
SIC: **2086** Soft drinks: packaged in cans, bottles, etc.
HQ: Pepsi-Cola Metropolitan Bottling Company, Inc.
1111 Westchester Ave
White Plains NY 10604
914 767-6000

(P-2177)
PEPSI-COLA METRO BTLG CO INC
Also Called: Pepsico
27717 Aliso Creek Rd, Aliso Viejo (92656-3804)
PHONE..............................949 643-5700
Natolie Daniel, *Manager*
Naqeeb Hasan, *Finance*
Brian J Ler, *Sales Staff*
Francisco Lozano, *Sales Staff*
Tracy Nord, *Manager*
EMP: 200
SALES (corp-wide): 63.5B **Publicly Held**
WEB: www.pbg.com
SIC: **2086** Carbonated soft drinks, bottled & canned
HQ: Pepsi-Cola Metropolitan Bottling Company, Inc.
1111 Westchester Ave
White Plains NY 10604
914 767-6000

(P-2178)
PEREGRINE MOBILE BOTTLING LLC
20590 Pueblo Ave, Sonoma (95476-7956)
PHONE..............................707 637-7584
Thomas Jordan, *Principal*
Justin Cude, *Opers Mgr*
EMP: 14
SALES (est): 2.1MM **Privately Held**
SIC: **2086** Bottled & canned soft drinks

(P-2179)
POSITIVE ENERGY BEVERAGES LLC
101 Academy Ste 100, Irvine (92617-3081)
PHONE..............................949 735-6080
Michael Cancelleri, *Mng Member*
Bryan Spivey, *VP Sales*
EMP: 10
SALES: 5MM **Privately Held**
SIC: **2086 2087** Bottled & canned soft drinks; beverage bases, concentrates, syrups, powders & mixes; fruit juices: concentrated for fountain use

(P-2180)
PURE-FLO WATER CO (PA)
Also Called: Pure Flo Water
7737 Mission Gorge Rd, Santee (92071-3306)
P.O. Box 660579, Dallas TX (75266-0579)
PHONE..............................619 596-4130
Braian Grant, *CEO*
Marian Grant, *Treasurer*
Leslie Alstad, *General Mgr*
Bernadette Meyer, *General Mgr*
Heather Schoeneman, *Admin Asst*
EMP: 75
SQ FT: 9,000

SALES (est): 11.4MM **Privately Held**
SIC: **2086** Water, pasteurized: packaged in cans, bottles, etc.; pasteurized & mineral waters, bottled & canned

(P-2181)
RAINBOW ORCHARDS
2569 Larsen Dr, Camino (95709-9704)
PHONE..............................530 644-1594
Tom Heflin, *Partner*
Christa Campbell, *Partner*
EMP: 11
SALES (est): 1.5MM **Privately Held**
SIC: **2086 0175** Fruit drinks (less than 100% juice): packaged in cans, etc.; apple orchard

(P-2182)
RED BULL NORTH AMERICA INC
1630 Stewart St Ste A, Santa Monica (90404-4020)
PHONE..............................310 393-4647
Jennifer Barney, *Branch Mgr*
EMP: 54
SALES (corp-wide): 3.9B **Privately Held**
SIC: **2086** Carbonated beverages, nonalcoholic: bottled & canned
HQ: Red Bull North America, Inc.
1740 Stewart St
Santa Monica CA 90404
-

(P-2183)
REEDS INC
13000 S Spring St, Los Angeles (90061-1634)
PHONE..............................310 217-9400
Val Stalowir, *CEO*
John Bello, *Ch of Bd*
Mark B Beaton, *COO*
Daniel V Miles, *CFO*
Charles Cargile, *Bd of Directors*
◆ EMP: 22
SQ FT: 76,000
SALES: 37.7MM **Privately Held**
WEB: www.reedsgingerbrew.com
SIC: **2086 2064 2024** Soft drinks: packaged in cans, bottles, etc.; candy & other confectionery products; ice cream & ice milk

(P-2184)
REFRESCO BEVERAGES US INC
631 S Waterman Ave, San Bernardino (92408-2329)
PHONE..............................909 915-1400
Armando Martinez, *Branch Mgr*
EMP: 92
SALES (corp-wide): 58.5K **Privately Held**
SIC: **2086** Carbonated beverages, nonalcoholic: bottled & canned
HQ: Refresco Beverages Us Inc.
8112 Woodland Center Blvd
Tampa FL 33614
813 313-1800

(P-2185)
REFRESCO BEVERAGES US INC
26205 Cottonwood St, Murrieta (92563-4055)
PHONE..............................951 461-3328
Frank Weiss, *Branch Mgr*
EMP: 92
SALES (corp-wide): 58.5K **Privately Held**
SIC: **2086** Carbonated beverages, nonalcoholic: bottled & canned
HQ: Refresco Beverages Us Inc.
8112 Woodland Center Blvd
Tampa FL 33614
813 313-1800

(P-2186)
REYES COCA-COLA BOTTLING LLC (PA)
3 Park Plz Ste 600, Irvine (92614-2575)
PHONE..............................213 744-8616
James Quincy, *CEO*
Nehal Desai, *CFO*
◆ EMP: 300
SQ FT: 80,000
SALES (est): 648.9MM **Privately Held**
SIC: **2086** Bottled & canned soft drinks

(P-2187)
REYES COCA-COLA BOTTLING LLC
4320 Ride St, Bakersfield (93313-4831)
PHONE..............................661 324-6531
Ed Shell, *Manager*
EMP: 100
SALES (corp-wide): 648.9MM **Privately Held**
SIC: **2086** Bottled & canned soft drinks
PA: Reyes Coca-Cola Bottling, L.L.C.
3 Park Plz Ste 600
Irvine CA 92614
213 744-8616

(P-2188)
REYES COCA-COLA BOTTLING LLC
1555 Old Bayshore Hwy, San Jose (95112-4303)
PHONE..............................408 436-3700
Larry Loeffer, *Manager*
EMP: 100
SALES (corp-wide): 648.9MM **Privately Held**
SIC: **2086** Bottled & canned soft drinks
PA: Reyes Coca-Cola Bottling, L.L.C.
3 Park Plz Ste 600
Irvine CA 92614
213 744-8616

(P-2189)
REYES COCA-COLA BOTTLING LLC
8729 Cleta St, Downey (90241-5202)
PHONE..............................562 803-8100
Kim Curtis, *Manager*
EMP: 90
SQ FT: 76,395
SALES (corp-wide): 648.9MM **Privately Held**
SIC: **2086 5149** Soft drinks: packaged in cans, bottles, etc.; groceries & related products
PA: Reyes Coca-Cola Bottling, L.L.C.
3 Park Plz Ste 600
Irvine CA 92614
213 744-8616

(P-2190)
REYES COCA-COLA BOTTLING LLC
1551 Atlantic St, Union City (94587-2005)
PHONE..............................510 476-7000
Andy Darren, *Branch Mgr*
EMP: 80
SALES (corp-wide): 648.9MM **Privately Held**
SIC: **2086 5149** Soft drinks: packaged in cans, bottles, etc.; groceries & related products
PA: Reyes Coca-Cola Bottling, L.L.C.
3 Park Plz Ste 600
Irvine CA 92614
213 744-8616

(P-2191)
REYES COCA-COLA BOTTLING LLC
14655 Wicks Blvd, San Leandro (94577-6715)
PHONE..............................510 667-6300
Ron King, *Branch Mgr*
EMP: 110
SALES (corp-wide): 648.9MM **Privately Held**
SIC: **2086 2087 2037 2095** Soft drinks: packaged in cans, bottles, etc.; syrups, drink; fruit juice concentrates, frozen; roasted coffee; tea blending; wines
PA: Reyes Coca-Cola Bottling, L.L.C.
3 Park Plz Ste 600
Irvine CA 92614
213 744-8616

(P-2192)
REYES COCA-COLA BOTTLING LLC
3220 E Malaga Ave, Fresno (93725-9353)
PHONE..............................559 264-4631
Mike Lozier, *Branch Mgr*
EMP: 95
SQ FT: 62,365

SALES (corp-wide): 648.9MM **Privately Held**
SIC: 2086 Bottled & canned soft drinks
PA: Reyes Coca-Cola Bottling, L.L.C.
3 Park Plz Ste 600
Irvine CA 92614
213 744-8616

(P-2193)
REYES COCA-COLA BOTTLING LLC
5335 Walker St, Ventura (93003-7406)
PHONE................................805 644-2211
Jim Donelson, *Manager*
EMP: 100
SALES (corp-wide): 648.9MM **Privately Held**
SIC: 2086 5149 Soft drinks: packaged in cans, bottles, etc.; groceries & related products
PA: Reyes Coca-Cola Bottling, L.L.C.
3 Park Plz Ste 600
Irvine CA 92614
213 744-8616

(P-2194)
REYES COCA-COLA BOTTLING LLC
1467 El Pinal Dr, Stockton (95205-2672)
PHONE................................209 466-9501
Clay Frenzel, *Manager*
EMP: 45
SALES (corp-wide): 648.9MM **Privately Held**
SIC: 2086 Bottled & canned soft drinks
PA: Reyes Coca-Cola Bottling, L.L.C.
3 Park Plz Ste 600
Irvine CA 92614
213 744-8616

(P-2195)
REYES COCA-COLA BOTTLING LLC
86375 Industrial Way, Coachella (92236-2729)
PHONE................................760 396-4500
Andrell Gritley, *General Mgr*
EMP: 67
SALES (corp-wide): 648.9MM **Privately Held**
SIC: 2086 Bottled & canned soft drinks
PA: Reyes Coca-Cola Bottling, L.L.C.
3 Park Plz Ste 600
Irvine CA 92614
213 744-8616

(P-2196)
REYES COCA-COLA BOTTLING LLC
715 Vandenberg St, Salinas (93905-3355)
PHONE................................831 755-8300
Bill Neighbors, *Branch Mgr*
EMP: 55
SALES (corp-wide): 648.9MM **Privately Held**
SIC: 2086 Bottled & canned soft drinks
PA: Reyes Coca-Cola Bottling, L.L.C.
3 Park Plz Ste 600
Irvine CA 92614
213 744-8616

(P-2197)
REYES COCA-COLA BOTTLING LLC
10670 6th St, Rancho Cucamonga (91730-5912)
PHONE................................909 980-3121
Sid Campa, *Manager*
EMP: 115
SALES (corp-wide): 648.9MM **Privately Held**
SIC: 2086 5149 Soft drinks: packaged in cans, bottles, etc.; groceries & related products
PA: Reyes Coca-Cola Bottling, L.L.C.
3 Park Plz Ste 600
Irvine CA 92614
213 744-8616

(P-2198)
REYES COCA-COLA BOTTLING LLC
1000 Fairway Dr, Santa Maria (93455-1512)
PHONE................................805 614-3702

Dan Suchecki, *Manager*
EMP: 75
SALES (corp-wide): 648.9MM **Privately Held**
SIC: 2086 Bottled & canned soft drinks
PA: Reyes Coca-Cola Bottling, L.L.C.
3 Park Plz Ste 600
Irvine CA 92614
213 744-8616

(P-2199)
REYES COCA-COLA BOTTLING LLC
1580 Beltline Rd, Redding (96003-1408)
PHONE................................530 241-4315
David Hallagan, *Manager*
EMP: 25
SQ FT: 75,000
SALES (corp-wide): 648.9MM **Privately Held**
SIC: 2086 Bottled & canned soft drinks
PA: Reyes Coca-Cola Bottling, L.L.C.
3 Park Plz Ste 600
Irvine CA 92614
213 744-8616

(P-2200)
REYES COCA-COLA BOTTLING LLC
8729 Cleta St, Downey (90241-5202)
PHONE................................562 803-8165
Kim Curtis, *Branch Mgr*
Dave Glancy, *Opers Staff*
Archie Amerson, *Manager*
Melissa Blalock, *Manager*
Steve Richards, *Manager*
EMP: 120
SALES (corp-wide): 648.9MM **Privately Held**
SIC: 2086 Bottled & canned soft drinks
PA: Reyes Coca-Cola Bottling, L.L.C.
3 Park Plz Ste 600
Irvine CA 92614
213 744-8616

(P-2201)
REYES COCA-COLA BOTTLING LLC
1348 47th St, San Diego (92102-2510)
PHONE................................619 266-6300
Randy Cleveland, *Manager*
Rollin Pearson, *Executive*
Donna Desousa, *Analyst*
Jason Whitney, *Supervisor*
EMP: 35
SQ FT: 20,000
SALES (corp-wide): 648.9MM **Privately Held**
SIC: 2086 5149 Soft drinks: packaged in cans, bottles, etc.; groceries & related products
PA: Reyes Coca-Cola Bottling, L.L.C.
3 Park Plz Ste 600
Irvine CA 92614
213 744-8616

(P-2202)
REYES COCA-COLA BOTTLING LLC
666 Union St, Montebello (90640-6624)
PHONE................................323 278-2600
Gary Drees, *Manager*
EMP: 100
SQ FT: 127,556
SALES (corp-wide): 648.9MM **Privately Held**
SIC: 2086 Bottled & canned soft drinks
PA: Reyes Coca-Cola Bottling, L.L.C.
3 Park Plz Ste 600
Irvine CA 92614
213 744-8616

(P-2203)
REYES COCA-COLA BOTTLING LLC
1430 Melody Rd, Marysville (95901)
PHONE................................530 743-6533
Tom Quilty, *Manager*
EMP: 20
SALES (corp-wide): 648.9MM **Privately Held**
SIC: 2086 Bottled & canned soft drinks

PA: Reyes Coca-Cola Bottling, L.L.C.
3 Park Plz Ste 600
Irvine CA 92614
213 744-8616

(P-2204)
REYES COCA-COLA BOTTLING LLC
700 W Grove Ave, Orange (92865-3214)
PHONE................................714 974-1901
Thomas Murphy, *Branch Mgr*
EMP: 118
SQ FT: 7,043
SALES (corp-wide): 648.9MM **Privately Held**
SIC: 2086 Bottled & canned soft drinks
PA: Reyes Coca-Cola Bottling, L.L.C.
3 Park Plz Ste 600
Irvine CA 92614
213 744-8616

(P-2205)
REYES COCA-COLA BOTTLING LLC
530 Getty Ct, Benicia (94510-1139)
PHONE................................707 747-2000
Gerold Henderickson, *Manager*
EMP: 120
SALES (corp-wide): 648.9MM **Privately Held**
SIC: 2086 Bottled & canned soft drinks
PA: Reyes Coca-Cola Bottling, L.L.C.
3 Park Plz Ste 600
Irvine CA 92614
213 744-8616

(P-2206)
REYES COCA-COLA BOTTLING LLC
1338 E 14th St, Los Angeles (90021-2344)
PHONE................................213 744-8659
Perry Fitch, *General Mgr*
EMP: 50
SALES (corp-wide): 648.9MM **Privately Held**
SIC: 2086 Bottled & canned soft drinks
PA: Reyes Coca-Cola Bottling, L.L.C.
3 Park Plz Ste 600
Irvine CA 92614
213 744-8616

(P-2207)
REYES COCA-COLA BOTTLING LLC
2603 Camino Ramon Ste 550, San Ramon (94583-9131)
PHONE................................925 830-6500
Jim Hegenbart, *Manager*
EMP: 90
SALES (corp-wide): 648.9MM **Privately Held**
SIC: 2086 Bottled & canned soft drinks
PA: Reyes Coca-Cola Bottling, L.L.C.
3 Park Plz Ste 600
Irvine CA 92614
213 744-8616

(P-2208)
REYES COCA-COLA BOTTLING LLC
19875 Pacific Gateway Dr, Torrance (90502-1118)
PHONE................................310 965-2653
David Carey, *Manager*
EMP: 175
SQ FT: 65,998
SALES (corp-wide): 648.9MM **Privately Held**
SIC: 2086 Bottled & canned soft drinks
PA: Reyes Coca-Cola Bottling, L.L.C.
3 Park Plz Ste 600
Irvine CA 92614
213 744-8616

(P-2209)
REYES COCA-COLA BOTTLING LLC
15346 Anacapa Rd, Victorville (92392-2448)
PHONE................................760 241-2653
Rose Wols, *Manager*
EMP: 50
SALES (corp-wide): 648.9MM **Privately Held**
SIC: 2086 Bottled & canned soft drinks

PA: Reyes Coca-Cola Bottling, L.L.C.
3 Park Plz Ste 600
Irvine CA 92614
213 744-8616

(P-2210)
REYES COCA-COLA BOTTLING LLC
126 S 3rd St, El Centro (92243-2542)
PHONE................................760 352-1561
Jose Chaira, *Manager*
EMP: 27
SALES (corp-wide): 648.9MM **Privately Held**
SIC: 2086 Bottled & canned soft drinks
PA: Reyes Coca-Cola Bottling, L.L.C.
3 Park Plz Ste 600
Irvine CA 92614
213 744-8616

(P-2211)
RISING BEVERAGE COMPANY LLC
10351 Santa Monica Blvd # 210, Los Angeles (90025-6908)
PHONE................................310 556-4500
Anders D Eisner, *Chairman*
Reza Mirza, *President*
Craig Berger, *CFO*
Burke H Eiteljorg, *Co-Founder*
EMP: 55
SALES (est): 8MM **Privately Held**
SIC: 2086 Fruit drinks (less than 100% juice): packaged in cans, etc.; lemonade: packaged in cans, bottles, etc.; mineral water, carbonated: packaged in cans, bottles, etc.

(P-2212)
RIVIERA BEVERAGES LLC
12782 Monarch St, Garden Grove (92841-3928)
PHONE................................714 895-5169
Ken Klentz,
Chris Solberg, *Engineer*
Wilfredo Orozco, *Mfg Staff*
Kevin Clark,
Francisco Antillon, *Manager*
EMP: 40 EST: 2009
SALES (est): 5.5MM **Privately Held**
SIC: 2086 Water, pasteurized: packaged in cans, bottles, etc.

(P-2213)
ROCKSTAR INC
Also Called: Rockstar Energy Drink
8530 Wilshire Blvd Fl 3, Beverly Hills (90211-3114)
PHONE................................323 785-2820
Taylor Liptak, *Marketing Mgr*
EMP: 149
SALES (corp-wide): 96.3MM **Privately Held**
SIC: 2086 Carbonated beverages, nonalcoholic: bottled & canned
PA: Rockstar, Inc.
101 Convention Center Dr # 777
Las Vegas NV 89109
702 939-5535

(P-2214)
ROGER ENRICO
Also Called: Pepsi-Cola
1150 E North Ave, Fresno (93725-1929)
PHONE................................559 485-5050
Eric Foss, *CEO*
Craig Weatherup, *Ch of Bd*
Robert King, *President*
Terri Scherer, *Analyst*
Corinne Rogers, *Human Res Dir*
EMP: 500 EST: 1900
SQ FT: 250,000
SALES (est): 29.8K **Privately Held**
SIC: 2086 Soft drinks: packaged in cans, bottles, etc.; carbonated beverages, nonalcoholic: bottled & canned

(P-2215)
SACRAMENTO COCA-COLA BTLG INC (HQ)
4101 Gateway Park Blvd, Sacramento (95834-1951)
P.O. Box 160608 (95816-0608)
PHONE................................916 928-2300
Steven A Cahillane, *CEO*

David Etheridge, *President*
EMP: 365
SQ FT: 260,000
SALES (est): 44.2MM
SALES (corp-wide): 648.9MM **Privately Held**
WEB: www.saccoke.com
SIC: 2086 Bottled & canned soft drinks
PA: Reyes Coca-Cola Bottling, L.L.C.
3 Park Plz Ste 600
Irvine CA 92614
213 744-8616

(P-2216)
SACRAMENTO COCA-COLA BTLG INC
1733 Morgan Rd Ste 200, Modesto (95358-5841)
PHONE...................................209 541-3200
Rex McGowen, *Principal*
EMP: 50
SALES (corp-wide): 648.9MM **Privately Held**
SIC: 2086 Soft drinks: packaged in cans, bottles, etc.
HQ: Sacramento Coca-Cola Bottling Co., Inc.
4101 Gateway Park Blvd
Sacramento CA 95834
916 928-2300

(P-2217)
SBM DAIRIES INC (HQ)
Also Called: Heartland Farms
17851 Railroad St, City of Industry (91748-1118)
PHONE...................................626 923-3000
Jack H Brown, *CEO*
Paul Bikowitz, *President*
Mirna Diaz, *Regional*
▼ EMP: 66
SQ FT: 250,000
SALES (est): 55.2MM **Publicly Held**
SIC: 2086 2026 2033 Fruit drinks (less than 100% juice): packaged in cans, etc.; fluid milk; milk processing (pasteurizing, homogenizing, bottling); buttermilk, cultured; canned fruits & specialties

(P-2218)
SEQUOIA PURE WATER INC
1640 W 134th St, Compton (90222-1624)
PHONE...................................310 637-8500
Dae Young Lee, *President*
EMP: 20
SQ FT: 80,000
SALES (est): 1.5MM **Privately Held**
SIC: 2086 Pasteurized & mineral waters, bottled & canned

(P-2219)
SEVEN UP BTLG CO SAN FRANCISCO (HQ)
Also Called: Seven-Up Bottling
2875 Prune Ave, Fremont (94539-6731)
PHONE...................................925 938-8777
Roger Easley, *Ch of Bd*
Linda Orsi, *Vice Pres*
EMP: 175
SALES (est): 75.9MM **Publicly Held**
WEB: www.7upcal.com
SIC: 2086 5149 4225 Soft drinks: packaged in cans, bottles, etc.; groceries & related products; general warehousing & storage

(P-2220)
SEVEN UP BTLG CO SAN FRANCISCO
Also Called: Seven-Up Bottling
11205 Commercial Pkwy, Castroville (95012-3205)
PHONE...................................831 632-0777
Frank Reyes, *General Mgr*
EMP: 45 **Publicly Held**
WEB: www.7upcal.com
SIC: 2086 Bottled & canned soft drinks
HQ: Seven Up Bottling Company Of San Francisco
2875 Prune Ave
Fremont CA 94539
925 938-8777

(P-2221)
SEVEN UP BTLG CO SAN FRANCISCO
Also Called: Seven-Up Bottling
2670 Land Ave, Sacramento (95815-2380)
P.O. Box 15820 (95852-0820)
PHONE...................................916 929-7777
Tom Tontes, *Manager*
Wayne Buffington, *Production*
Jo Duarte, *Cust Mgr*
Kelly Dixon, *Manager*
EMP: 96 **Publicly Held**
WEB: www.7upcal.com
SIC: 2086 5078 Soft drinks: packaged in cans, bottles, etc.; refrigerated beverage dispensers
HQ: Seven Up Bottling Company Of San Francisco
2875 Prune Ave
Fremont CA 94539
925 938-8777

(P-2222)
SEVEN-UP RC OF CHICO
306 Otterson Dr Ste 10, Chico (95928-8250)
P.O. Box 3610 (95927-3610)
PHONE...................................530 893-4501
Edward Frazer, *President*
EMP: 22 EST: 1930
SQ FT: 23,000
SALES (est): 3.2MM **Privately Held**
WEB: www.7uprcofchico.com
SIC: 2086 Bottled & canned soft drinks

(P-2223)
SHASTA BEVERAGES INC (DH)
Also Called: National Bevpak
26901 Indl Blvd, Hayward (94545)
PHONE...................................954 581-0922
Joseph G Caporella, *CEO*
John Minton, *President*
Dean McCoy, *Vice Pres*
Nick Caporella, *Principal*
Jerry House, *Plant Supt*
◆ EMP: 80
SQ FT: 156,000
SALES (est): 141.7MM
SALES (corp-wide): 975.7MM **Publicly Held**
SIC: 2086 Soft drinks: packaged in cans, bottles, etc.; carbonated beverages, nonalcoholic: bottled & canned

(P-2224)
SHASTA BEVERAGES INC
14405 Artesia Blvd, La Mirada (90638-5886)
PHONE...................................714 523-2280
Bruce McDowell, *Opers-Prdtn-Mfg*
Bruce W McDowell, *Plant Mgr*
Randy Terry, *Plant Mgr*
Mike Haskell, *Manager*
Arthur Semerdjian, *Manager*
EMP: 100
SALES (corp-wide): 975.7MM **Publicly Held**
SIC: 2086 5149 Soft drinks: packaged in cans, bottles, etc.; soft drinks
HQ: Shasta Beverages, Inc.
26901 Indl Blvd
Hayward CA 94545
954 581-0922

(P-2225)
SMUCKER NATURAL FOODS INC (HQ)
37 Speedway Ave, Chico (95928-9554)
P.O. Box 369 (95927-0369)
PHONE...................................530 899-5000
Richard K Smucker, *CEO*
Timothy P Smucker, *President*
Julia Sabin, *Vice Pres*
Darlene Weber, *Administration*
Kim Dietz, *Human Res Dir*
◆ EMP: 130
SQ FT: 85,000
SALES (est): 341.6MM
SALES (corp-wide): 7.3B **Publicly Held**
WEB: www.knudsenjuices.com
SIC: 2086 2033 2087 Iced tea & fruit drinks, bottled & canned; carbonated beverages, nonalcoholic: bottled & canned; canned fruits & specialties; syrups, drink

PA: The J M Smucker Company
1 Strawberry Ln
Orrville OH 44667
330 682-3000

(P-2226)
SOLANO COUNTY WATER AGENCY
810 Vaca Valley Pkwy # 203, Vacaville (95688-8835)
P.O. Box 349, Elmira (95625-0349)
PHONE...................................707 455-1105
David Okita, *Manager*
Thomas Tate, *Principal*
Marcie Fehrenkamp, *Admin Asst*
Sandra McLean, *Admin Asst*
Katherine Phillips, *Admin Asst*
EMP: 10
SALES (est): 980K **Privately Held**
WEB: www.scwa2.com
SIC: 2086 Pasteurized & mineral waters, bottled & canned

(P-2227)
SVC MFG INC A CORP
Also Called: Pepsi Co
5625 International Blvd, Oakland (94621-4403)
PHONE...................................510 261-5800
David Chu, *Principal*
▲ EMP: 11
SALES (est): 2.4MM **Privately Held**
SIC: 2086 Carbonated soft drinks, bottled & canned

(P-2228)
TOGNAZZINI BEVERAGE SERVICE
Also Called: Coca-Cola
241 Roemer Way, Santa Maria (93454-1129)
PHONE...................................805 928-1144
Jim Tognazzini, *Owner*
Meck Tognazzini, *Co-Owner*
EMP: 12
SQ FT: 18,000
SALES (est): 3.9MM **Privately Held**
WEB: www.togbev.com
SIC: 2086 7699 Soft drinks: packaged in cans, bottles, etc.; fountain repair

(P-2229)
TRENT BEVERAGE COMPANY LLC
Also Called: Trent Beverages
47230 Golden Bush Ct, Palm Desert (92260-6079)
PHONE...................................310 384-6776
Bruce Trent, *Mng Member*
EMP: 12
SALES (est): 800K **Privately Held**
SIC: 2086 Carbonated beverages, nonalcoholic: bottled & canned

(P-2230)
UNIX PACKAGING INC
Also Called: Mammoth Water
9 Minson Way, Montebello (90640-6744)
PHONE...................................213 627-5050
Bobby Melamed, *CEO*
Kourosh Melamed, *CFO*
Shawn Arianpour, *Vice Pres*
▲ EMP: 120
SQ FT: 125,000
SALES (est): 40MM **Privately Held**
SIC: 2086 Pasteurized & mineral waters, bottled & canned

(P-2231)
VARNI BROTHERS CORPORATION (PA)
Also Called: Stanislaus Distributing Co
400 Hosmer Ave, Modesto (95351-3920)
PHONE...................................209 521-1777
John Varni, *President*
Fred Varni, *Corp Secy*
John Salzman, *Maintence Staff*
▲ EMP: 80
SQ FT: 80,000
SALES (est): 77.9MM **Privately Held**
WEB: www.noahs7up.com
SIC: 2086 5182 5181 Carbonated beverages, nonalcoholic: bottled & canned; wine; beer & other fermented malt liquors

(P-2232)
VARNI BROTHERS CORPORATION
Also Called: 7 Up
1109 W Anderson St, Stockton (95206-1158)
PHONE...................................209 464-7778
Larry Varni, *Manager*
EMP: 20
SALES (corp-wide): 77.9MM **Privately Held**
WEB: www.noahs7up.com
SIC: 2086 Carbonated beverages, nonalcoholic: bottled & canned
PA: Varni Brothers Corporation
400 Hosmer Ave
Modesto CA 95351
209 521-1777

(P-2233)
WAIAKEA INC
Also Called: Wiakea Springs
5800 Hannum Ave Ste A135, Culver City (90230-6685)
P.O. Box 12468, Marina Del Rey (90295-3468)
PHONE...................................855 924-2532
Ryan Emmons, *CEO*
Matthew Meyer, *COO*
Robert Emmons, *Treasurer*
Sophia Lotter, *Mktg Dir*
Alexandra Alegria, *Manager*
EMP: 10 EST: 2012
SQ FT: 2,000
SALES (est): 1MM
SALES (corp-wide): 867.6K **Privately Held**
SIC: 2086 Water, pasteurized: packaged in cans, bottles, etc.
PA: Waiakea Investments Llc
736 Cima Linda Ln
Santa Barbara CA 93108
805 450-0981

(P-2234)
WAIAKEA INVESTMENTS LLC (PA)
736 Cima Linda Ln, Santa Barbara (93108-1813)
PHONE...................................805 450-0981
Robert Emmons, *Mng Member*
Ryan Emmons,
Matthew Meyer,
EMP: 10
SALES (est): 867.6K **Privately Held**
SIC: 2086 Water, pasteurized: packaged in cans, bottles, etc.

(P-2235)
WIT GROUP
1822 Buenaventura Blvd # 101, Redding (96001-6313)
PHONE...................................530 243-4447
Paul A Kassis, *President*
James Akers, *Vice Pres*
Jim Akers, *Marketing Staff*
▼ EMP: 35
SQ FT: 1,100
SALES (est): 6.1MM **Privately Held**
SIC: 2086 Water, pasteurized: packaged in cans, bottles, etc.

(P-2236)
ZEVIA LLC
15821 Ventura Blvd # 145, Encino (91436-5201)
PHONE...................................310 202-7000
Padraic Spence, *Mng Member*
Natalie Gershon, *Vice Pres*
Kenneth Panitz, *Vice Pres*
Jonathan Prince, *Vice Pres*
Stephanie Yuen, *Asst Controller*
EMP: 36
SQ FT: 5,000
SALES (est): 36.4MM **Privately Held**
WEB: www.zevia.com
SIC: 2086 Carbonated soft drinks, bottled & canned

(P-2237)
ZICO BEVERAGES LLC (HQ)
2101 E El Segundo Blvd # 403, El Segundo (90245-4519)
PHONE...................................866 729-9426
Ronald J Lewis, *Mng Member*

Marie D Quintero-Johnson, *Mng Member*
▲ **EMP:** 38
SQ FT: 10,000
SALES (est): 7.4MM
SALES (corp-wide): 35.4B **Publicly Held**
SIC: 2086 Bottled & canned soft drinks
PA: The Coca-Cola Company
1 Coca Cola Plz Nw
Atlanta GA 30313
404 676-2121

2087 Flavoring Extracts & Syrups

(P-2238)
AA LABORATORY EGGS INC (PA)
Also Called: Balut Pateros
15075 Weststate St, Westminster
(92683-6526)
PHONE..................................714 893-5675
Thomas Dam, *President*
EMP: 15
SQ FT: 2,000
SALES (est): 2.5MM **Privately Held**
WEB: www.egglab.com
SIC: 2087 0252 5499 Concentrates, drink; chicken eggs; eggs & poultry

(P-2239)
ADINA FOR LIFE INC
660 York St Ste 205, San Francisco
(94110-2102)
PHONE..................................415 285-9300
Norman E Snyder, *President*
Sherbrook Capital, *Shareholder*
Bradmer Foods, *Shareholder*
Social Enterprise Expansion Fu, *Shareholder*
Seraph LLC, *Shareholder*
EMP: 26
SALES (est): 3.2MM **Privately Held**
WEB: www.adinaworld.com
SIC: 2087 5149 Beverage bases, concentrates, syrups, powders & mixes; beverages, except coffee & tea

(P-2240)
AMERICAN FRUITS & FLAVORS LLC (HQ)
Also Called: Juice Division
10725 Sutter Ave, Pacoima (91331-2553)
P.O. Box 331060 (91333-1060)
PHONE..................................818 899-9574
William Haddad, *President*
Sara Tapia, *CFO*
Bill Haddad, *Vice Pres*
Jack Haddad, *Vice Pres*
Laurie Katalbas, *Executive Asst*
◆ **EMP:** 125
SQ FT: 10,000
SALES (est): 131.2MM
SALES (corp-wide): 3.3B **Publicly Held**
WEB: www.americanfruit.com
SIC: 2087 Concentrates, drink; powders, drink; syrups, drink
PA: Monster Beverage Corporation
1 Monster Way
Corona CA 92879
951 739-6200

(P-2241)
AMERICAN FRUITS & FLAVORS LLC
Also Called: Flavors Division
1547 Knowles Ave, Los Angeles
(90063-1606)
PHONE..................................323 264-7791
Stacy West, *Branch Mgr*
EMP: 20
SALES (corp-wide): 3.3B **Publicly Held**
WEB: www.americanfruit.com
SIC: 2087 Extracts, flavoring
HQ: American Fruits And Flavors, Llc
10725 Sutter Ave
Pacoima CA 91331
818 899-9574

(P-2242)
BARFRESH FOOD GROUP INC
8383 Wilshire Blvd # 750, Beverly Hills
(90211-2443)
PHONE..................................310 598-7113
Riccardo Delle Coste, *Ch of Bd*

Joseph S Tesoriero, *CFO*
Christine Conroy, *Vice Pres*
Arnold Tinter, *Admin Sec*
Tim Trant, *Cust Mgr*
EMP: 34 **EST:** 2010
SALES: 2MM **Privately Held**
SIC: 2087 Flavoring extracts & syrups

(P-2243)
BERRI PRO INC
929 Colorado Ave, Santa Monica
(90401-2716)
PHONE..................................909 964-1201
Jerome Joseph TSE, *CEO*
EMP: 19
SALES: 1MM **Privately Held**
SIC: 2087 Concentrates, drink

(P-2244)
BETTER BEVERAGES INC (PA)
Also Called: Chem-Mark of Orange County
10624 Midway Ave, Cerritos (90703-1581)
P.O. Box 1399, Bellflower (90707-1399)
PHONE..................................562 924-8321
H Ronald Harris, *CEO*
Tricia Harris, *Corp Secy*
Patrick Dickson, *Vice Pres*
William Kendig, *Vice Pres*
▲ **EMP:** 40
SQ FT: 15,000
SALES (est): 11.6MM **Privately Held**
WEB: www.betbev.com
SIC: 2087 7359 5169 Beverage bases; syrups, drink; equipment rental & leasing; industrial gases

(P-2245)
BI NUTRACEUTICALS INC (HQ)
2384 E Pacifica Pl, Rancho Dominguez
(90220-6214)
PHONE..................................310 669-2100
George Pontiakos, *CEO*
Christoph Kirchner, *CFO*
Farzad Forough, *Accountant*
Rose Bocade, *Accounts Mgr*
▲ **EMP:** 30
SQ FT: 7,600
SALES (est): 27.3MM **Privately Held**
WEB: www.botanicals.com
SIC: 2087 2833 5122 5149 Flavoring extracts & syrups; medicinals & botanicals; vitamins & minerals; pharmaceuticals; medicinals & botanicals; seasonings, sauces & extracts; spices & seasonings; flavourings & fragrances

(P-2246)
BLOSSOM VALLEY FOODS INC
Also Called: Pepper Plant, The
20 Casey Ln, Gilroy (95020-4539)
PHONE..................................408 848-5520
Robert M Wagner, *President*
Michael Wagner, *Controller*
EMP: 25
SQ FT: 27,000
SALES (est): 5.1MM **Privately Held**
WEB: www.blossomvalleyfoods.com
SIC: 2087 2099 Cocktail mixes, nonalcoholic; food preparations; vinegar

(P-2247)
BLUE PCF FLVORS FRAGRANCES INC
1354 Marion Ct, City of Industry
(91745-2418)
PHONE..................................626 934-0099
Donald F Wilkes, *President*
▲ **EMP:** 20
SQ FT: 40,000
SALES (est): 4.9MM **Privately Held**
SIC: 2087 2869 Extracts, flavoring; perfumes, flavorings & food additives

(P-2248)
BYRNES & KIEFER CO
501 Airpark Dr, Fullerton (92833-2501)
PHONE..................................714 554-4000
EMP: 55 **EST:** 2012
SALES (est): 5MM **Privately Held**
SIC: 2087 Colorings, confectioners'

(P-2249)
CALIFORNIA COCKTAILS INC
Also Called: Lataz Product
345 Oak Pl, Brea (92821-4122)
P.O. Box 459 (92822-0459)
PHONE..................................714 990-0982
Larry Casey, *President*
▲ **EMP:** 13
SQ FT: 18,000
SALES (est): 963.3K **Privately Held**
SIC: 2087 2099 Cocktail mixes, nonalcoholic; food preparations

(P-2250)
CALIFORNIA CUSTOM FRUITS (PA)
Also Called: California Cstm Frt & Flavors
15800 Tapia St, Irwindale (91706-2178)
PHONE..................................626 736-4130
Mike Mulhausen, *President*
Nicole Banuelos, *President*
James Fragnoli, *CFO*
Teresa Montejano, *Administration*
Daniel Birshan, *Research*
◆ **EMP:** 76
SALES (est): 21MM **Privately Held**
SIC: 2087 2033 2099 5083 Extracts, flavoring; fruits: packaged in cans, jars, etc.; food preparations; dairy machinery & equipment

(P-2251)
CARMI FLVR & FRAGRANCE CO INC (PA)
Also Called: Carmi Flavors
6030 Scott Way, Commerce (90040-3516)
PHONE..................................323 888-9240
Eliot Carmi, *President*
Janine Bell, *Office Mgr*
Sarah Foster, *Office Mgr*
Lauren Contreras, *Marketing Staff*
Brynn Kramer, *Sales Staff*
▲ **EMP:** 40
SQ FT: 35,000
SALES: 16MM **Privately Held**
SIC: 2087 2844 Extracts, flavoring; toilet preparations

(P-2252)
COCA-COLA COMPANY
1650 S Vintage Ave, Ontario (91761-3656)
PHONE..................................909 975-5200
EMP: 100
SALES (corp-wide): 44.2B **Publicly Held**
SIC: 2087 5149
PA: The Coca-Cola Company
1 Coca Cola Plz Nw
Atlanta GA 30313
404 676-2121

(P-2253)
CREATIVE CONCEPTS HOLDINGS LLC (HQ)
580 Garcia Ave, Pittsburg (94565-4901)
PHONE..................................949 705-6584
Richard N Fischler, *President*
Robert E Murphy, *Corp Secy*
EMP: 11
SALES (est): 2.4MM
SALES (corp-wide): 9.2MM **Privately Held**
WEB: www.creativeflavorconcepts.com
SIC: 2087 Extracts, flavoring
PA: Flavor Producers, Llc
8521 Fllbrook Ave Ste 380
West Hills CA 91304
818 307-4062

(P-2254)
DELANO GROWERS GRAPE PRODUCTS
32351 Bassett Ave, Delano (93215-9699)
PHONE..................................661 725-3255
Jim Cesare, *President*
Piper Hare, *Sales Dir*
▲ **EMP:** 55 **EST:** 1940
SQ FT: 40,000
SALES (est): 29.1MM **Privately Held**
WEB: www.delanocc.com
SIC: 2087 Concentrates, drink

(P-2255)
DISTRIBUTORS PROCESSING INC
Also Called: D P I
17656 Avenue 168, Porterville
(93257-9263)
PHONE..................................559 781-0297
Randy Walker, *President*
Gary Jacinto, *Ch of Bd*
William Blatnick, *Corp Secy*
Kendal Thompson, *Vice Pres*
Lawrence Willey, *Info Tech Mgr*
▼ **EMP:** 17
SQ FT: 23,050
SALES (est): 3.1MM **Privately Held**
WEB: www.dpiglobal.com
SIC: 2087 Extracts, flavoring

(P-2256)
DR SMOOTHIE BRANDS INC
1730 Raymer Ave, Fullerton (92833-2530)
PHONE..................................714 449-9787
Sam Lteif, *CEO*
Cara Anderson, *Human Resources*
Jason Moore, *Opers Mgr*
Ron Garrett, *Mktg Dir*
Russ Cullen, *Sales Dir*
▼ **EMP:** 33
SQ FT: 30,000
SALES (est): 5.4MM
SALES (corp-wide): 50.8MM **Publicly Held**
SIC: 2087 Beverage bases, concentrates, syrups, powders & mixes
PA: Juice Tyme, Inc.
4401 S Oakley Ave
Chicago IL 60609
773 579-1291

(P-2257)
DR SMOOTHIE ENTERPRISES
1730 Raymer Ave, Fullerton (92833-2530)
PHONE..................................714 449-9787
Bill Haugh, *President*
William P Haugh, *Principal*
Jason Moore, *Info Tech Mgr*
Cara Anderson, *Human Resources*
Mike Finch, *Buyer*
▼ **EMP:** 21
SQ FT: 30,000
SALES (est): 4.7MM **Privately Held**
WEB: www.drsmoothie.com
SIC: 2087 Beverage bases, concentrates, syrups, powders & mixes

(P-2258)
DRY CREEK NUTRITION INC
600 Yosemite Blvd, Modesto (95354-2760)
PHONE..................................209 341-5696
Robert J Gallo, *Ch of Bd*
Peter Kovacs, *President*
EMP: 15
SALES (est): 1.3MM **Privately Held**
WEB: www.activin.com
SIC: 2087 Extracts, flavoring

(P-2259)
FELBRO FOOD PRODUCTS INC
5700 W Adams Blvd, Los Angeles
(90016-2402)
PHONE..................................323 936-5266
Michael Feldmar, *CEO*
Barton Feldmar, *President*
Barton J Feldmar, *CEO*
EMP: 49
SQ FT: 35,000
SALES (est): 30MM **Privately Held**
WEB: www.felbro.com
SIC: 2087 Syrups, drink

(P-2260)
FISCHLER INVESTMENTS INC (DH)
Also Called: Affinity Flavors
2026 Cecilia Cir, Corona (92881-3389)
PHONE..................................951 479-4682
Tom Damiano, *CEO*
John Houtenville, *Vice Pres*
Andrea Underhill,
EMP: 10 **EST:** 1998
SQ FT: 38,000

SALES (est): 2.1MM
SALES (corp-wide): 438.5MM **Privately Held**
WEB: www.affinityflavors.com
SIC: 2087 Extracts, flavoring
HQ: T. Hasegawa U.S.A. Inc.
14017 183rd St
Cerritos CA 90703
714 522-1900

(P-2261)
FLAVOR HOUSE INC
16378 Koala Rd, Adelanto (92301-3916)
PHONE..........................760 246-9131
Richard Staley, *President*
◆ EMP: 40
SQ FT: 23,600
SALES (est): 7.6MM **Privately Held**
WEB: www.flavorhouse.com
SIC: 2087 Flavoring extracts & syrups

(P-2262)
FLAVORCHEM CORPORATION
271 Calle Pintoresco, San Clemente
(92672-7506)
PHONE..........................949 369-7900
Baron Zachary, *Branch Mgr*
Rae L Velker, *Manager*
EMP: 30
SALES (est): 5.7MM
SALES (corp-wide): 39.9MM **Privately Held**
WEB: www.flavorchem.com
SIC: 2087 Extracts, flavoring
PA: Flavorchem Corporation
1525 Brook Dr
Downers Grove IL 60515
630 932-8100

(P-2263)
FPG OC INC
24855 Corbit Pl Ste B, Yorba Linda
(92887-5543)
PHONE..........................714 692-2950
Joshua Cua, *CEO*
Priscilla Latter, *President*
Julie Hodson, *Vice Pres*
▲ EMP: 53
SQ FT: 74,300
SALES (est): 6.1MM **Privately Held**
SIC: 2087 Extracts, flavoring

(P-2264)
FROZEN BEAN INC
9238 Bally Ct, Rancho Cucamonga
(91730-5313)
PHONE..........................855 837-6936
John Bae, *CEO*
Delia Zamora, *Natl Sales Mgr*
David Spry, *Regl Sales Mgr*
Thuy Dang, *Director*
Tammy Le, *Manager*
▼ EMP: 30 EST: 2011
SALES (est): 5.6MM **Privately Held**
SIC: 2087 Beverage bases, concentrates,
syrups, powders & mixes

(P-2265)
FRUTAROM
790 E Harrison St, Corona (92879-1348)
PHONE..........................951 734-6620
Imtiaz Syed, *Branch Mgr*
Ericka Perez, *Sales Staff*
EMP: 19
SALES (corp-wide): 1.3B **Privately Held**
SIC: 2087 Extracts, flavoring
PA: Frutarom Industries Ltd
25 Hashaish
Haifa 26291
996 038-00

(P-2266)
GOLDEN STATE FOODS CORP
(PA)
18301 Von Karman Ave # 1100, Irvine
(92612-0133)
PHONE..........................949 247-8000
Mark Wetterau, *Ch of Bd*
William Sanderson, *CFO*
Lisa Gottlieb, *Treasurer*
Frank Listi, *Sr Exec VP*
Steve Becker, *Vice Pres*
◆ EMP: 35

SALES (est): 1.3B **Privately Held**
WEB: www.goldenstatefoods.com
SIC: 2087 5142 5148 5149 Syrups,
drink; packaged frozen goods; vegetables; vegetables, fresh; condiments;
meats, cured or smoked

(P-2267)
HERBALIFE MANUFACTURING
LLC
20481 Crescent Bay Dr, Lake Forest
(92630-8817)
PHONE..........................949 457-0951
Gerry Holly, *Senior VP*
Marilyn Best, *Senior Buyer*
▼ EMP: 75
SQ FT: 145,000
SALES (est): 23.4MM **Privately Held**
SIC: 2087 2023 Beverage bases, concen-
trates, syrups, powders & mixes; dietary
supplements, dairy & non-dairy based
HQ: Herbalife Nutrition Ltd.
800 W Olympic Blvd # 406
Los Angeles CA 90015
310 410-9600

(P-2268)
ICEE COMPANY
6800 Sierra Ct Ste M, Dublin (94568-2644)
PHONE..........................925 828-5807
Mike Fehely, *Manager*
EMP: 13
SALES (corp-wide): 1B **Publicly Held**
WEB: www.theiceecompany.com
SIC: 2087 Beverage bases, concentrates,
syrups, powders & mixes
HQ: The Icee Company
1205 S Dupont Ave
Ontario CA 91761
800 426-4233

(P-2269)
J & J PROCESSING INC
Also Called: Custom Foods
14715 Anson Ave, Santa Fe Springs
(90670-5305)
PHONE..........................562 926-2333
James B Nelson, *CEO*
Paul Nelson, *Exec VP*
Andrea Goettman, *Office Mgr*
Lisa Goldstein, *Research*
Erika Sosa, *QC Mgr*
▲ EMP: 50
SQ FT: 44,000
SALES (est): 15.7MM **Privately Held**
SIC: 2087 2041 2099 Beverage bases;
flour & other grain mill products; season-
ings: dry mixes; spices, including grinding

(P-2270)
JAVO BEVERAGE COMPANY
INC
1311 Specialty Dr, Vista (92081-8521)
PHONE..........................760 560-5286
Dennis Riley, *President*
Gerry Anderson, *CFO*
Chris Johnson, *Exec VP*
Joanne Sheean, *Vice Pres*
David Estes, *Regional Mgr*
▲ EMP: 55
SQ FT: 39,000
SALES (est): 15.4MM **Privately Held**
WEB: www.javobeverage.com
SIC: 2087 Extracts, flavoring

(P-2271)
LA PAZ PRODUCTS INC
345 Oak Pl, Brea (92821-4122)
P.O. Box 459 (92822-0459)
PHONE..........................714 990-0982
Suanne Casey, *CEO*
Dave Alcantar, *Production*
Roy Farhi, *Sales Dir*
▼ EMP: 18
SQ FT: 18,000
SALES (est): 3.6MM **Privately Held**
WEB: www.lapazproducts.com
SIC: 2087 Cocktail mixes, nonalcoholic

(P-2272)
MASTERTASTE INC
Also Called: Kerry Ingredients and Flavours
1916 S Tubeway Ave, Commerce
(90040-1612)
PHONE..........................323 727-2100
Chris Long, *General Mgr*

EMP: 74 **Privately Held**
WEB: www.mastertaste.com
SIC: 2087 Flavoring extracts & syrups
HQ: Mastertaste Inc.
160 Terminal Ave
Clark NJ 07066
732 882-0202

(P-2273)
MISSION FLAVORS
FRAGRANCES INC
25882 Wright, El Toro (92610-3503)
PHONE..........................949 461-3344
Patrick S Imburgia, *CEO*
EMP: 15
SALES (est): 3.7MM **Privately Held**
WEB: www.missionflavors.com
SIC: 2087 Extracts, flavoring; syrups, fla-
voring (except drink)

(P-2274)
NEWPORT FLAVORS &
FRAGRANCES
Also Called: Nature's Flavors
833 N Elm St, Orange (92867-7909)
PHONE..........................714 771-2200
William R Sabo, *CEO*
Jeanne A Rossman, *Admin Sec*
James Thelen, *Accountant*
Lane Melland, *Director*
▲ EMP: 30
SALES (est): 5.6MM **Privately Held**
WEB: www.newportflavours.com
SIC: 2087 Extracts, flavoring

(P-2275)
PACIFIC COAST PRODUCTS LLC
(PA)
Also Called: Perfumer's Apprentice
170 Technology Cir, Scotts Valley
(95066-3520)
PHONE..........................831 316-7137
Linda Andrews,
David Hertzberg, *Prdtn Mgr*
EMP: 15
SQ FT: 50,000
SALES (est): 23.3MM **Privately Held**
SIC: 2087 5141 8741 Extracts, flavoring;
food brokers; administrative management

(P-2276)
PACIFIC COAST PRODUCTS LLC
Also Called: Perfumer's Apprentice
200 Technology Cir, Scotts Valley
(95066-3500)
PHONE..........................831 316-7137
David Hertzberg, *Prdtn Mgr*
EMP: 32
SQ FT: 26,000
SALES (corp-wide): 23.3MM **Privately Held**
SIC: 2087 2844 Extracts, flavoring; con-
centrates, perfume
PA: Pacific Coast Products Llc
170 Technology Cir
Scotts Valley CA 95066
831 316-7137

(P-2277)
PRIMAL ESSENCE INC
1351 Maulhardt Ave, Oxnard (93030-7963)
PHONE..........................805 981-2409
Preman Brady, *President*
Dr Mark Smythe, *CFO*
Susan Smythe, *Treasurer*
Carolyn Brenthel, *Vice Pres*
Stuart Bienstock, *General Mgr*
▲ EMP: 10
SQ FT: 12,780
SALES (est): 1.9MM **Privately Held**
WEB: www.primalessence.com
SIC: 2087 Flavoring extracts & syrups

(P-2278)
QUAKER OATS COMPANY
5625 International Blvd, Oakland
(94621-4403)
PHONE..........................510 261-5800
Joan Parrott Sheffer, *Systems Staff*
Nemesio Dumlao, *Manager*
EMP: 120

SALES (corp-wide): 63.5B **Publicly Held**
WEB: www.quakeroats.com
SIC: 2087 2086 Beverage bases, concentrates, syrups, powders & mixes; bottled
& canned soft drinks
HQ: The Quaker Oats Company
555 W Monroe St Fl 1
Chicago IL 60661
312 821-1000

(P-2279)
R TORRE & COMPANY INC (PA)
Also Called: Torani Syrups & Flavors
233 E Harris Ave, South San Francisco
(94080-6807)
PHONE..........................800 775-1925
Melanie Dulbecco, *CEO*
Julie Garlikov, *Vice Pres*
Lisa Lucheta, *Principal*
Paul Lucheta, *Principal*
Paula McCormack, *Prdtn Mgr*
◆ EMP: 160 EST: 1925
SQ FT: 110,000
SALES (est): 39.8MM **Privately Held**
WEB: www.torani.com
SIC: 2087 Syrups, drink

(P-2280)
R TORRE & COMPANY INC
400 Littlefield Ave, South San Francisco
(94080-6105)
PHONE..........................650 624-2830
Steve Schultz, *Surgery Dir*
EMP: 35
SALES (corp-wide): 39.8MM **Privately Held**
SIC: 2087 Syrups, drink
PA: R. Torre & Company, Inc.
233 E Harris Ave
South San Francisco CA 94080
800 775-1925

(P-2281)
SCISOREK & SON FLAVORS
INC
Also Called: S&S Flavours
2951 Enterprise St, Brea (92821-6212)
PHONE..........................714 524-0550
Mark Tuerffs, *President*
Dan Hart, *Vice Pres*
EMP: 50
SQ FT: 33,000
SALES (est): 4.5MM **Privately Held**
WEB: www.ssflavors.com
SIC: 2087 Extracts, flavoring

(P-2282)
SUNOPTA FRUIT GROUP INC
(DH)
12128 Center St, South Gate (90280-8046)
P.O. Box 2218 (90280-9218)
PHONE..........................323 774-6000
Joseph Stern, *CEO*
Frank Gonzalez, *COO*
Gabriel Rodriguez, *Vice Pres*
Frank Livoti, *General Mgr*
▲ EMP: 26 EST: 1954
SQ FT: 150,000
SALES (est): 14.9MM
SALES (corp-wide): 1.2B **Privately Held**
SIC: 2087 Flavoring extracts & syrups

(P-2283)
SYMRISE INC
332 Forest Ave, Laguna Beach
(92651-2117)
PHONE..........................949 276-4600
Steve Koehr, *Branch Mgr*
EMP: 11
SALES (corp-wide): 3.5B **Privately Held**
WEB: www.flavorinfusion.com
SIC: 2087 Syrups, drink
HQ: Symrise Inc.
300 North St
Teterboro NJ 07608
201 288-3200

(P-2284)
T HASEGAWA USA INC (HQ)
14017 183rd St, Cerritos (90703-7000)
PHONE..........................714 522-1900
Tom Damiano, *CEO*
Tokujiro Hasegawa, *President*
Nasser Dastmalchi, *Vice Pres*
Laura Gibbons, *Executive Asst*
Laura Rossman, *Executive Asst*

▲ EMP: 50
SQ FT: 56,000
SALES (est): 14.6MM
SALES (corp-wide): 438.5MM **Privately Held**
WEB: www.thasegawa.com
SIC: 2087 Extracts, flavoring
PA: T.Hasegawa Co., Ltd.
4-4-14, Nihombashihoncho
Chuo-Ku TKY 103-0
332 411-151

(P-2285)
UNION FLAVORS INC
14145 Proctor Ave Ste 15, City of Industry (91746-2841)
PHONE..................626 333-1612
Nam Duck Kim, *President*
▼ EMP: 10
SQ FT: 4,500
SALES (est): 5MM **Privately Held**
SIC: 2087 Extracts, flavoring

(P-2286)
UNITED BRANDS COMPANY INC
5930 Cornerstone Ct W # 170, San Diego (92121-3772)
PHONE..................619 461-5220
Michael Michail, *President*
Philip W Oneil, *Exec VP*
Alan Neal, *Vice Pres*
Michelle Moore, *Prdtn Mgr*
Brad Dulong, *Natl Sales Mgr*
EMP: 43
SQ FT: 1,800
SALES (est): 13.1MM **Privately Held**
SIC: 2087 2082 Beverage bases; ale (alcoholic beverage)

(P-2287)
WEIDER HEALTH AND FITNESS
21100 Erwin St, Woodland Hills (91367-3772)
PHONE..................818 884-6800
Eric Weider, *President*
Tonja Fuller, *Treasurer*
Lian Katz, *Treasurer*
George Lengvari, *Vice Ch Bd*
Bernard J Cartoon, *Admin Sec*
EMP: 466
SQ FT: 6,000
SALES (est): 47.2MM **Privately Held**
WEB: www.weider.com
SIC: 2087 7991 7999 Beverage bases, concentrates, syrups, powders & mixes; physical fitness facilities; physical fitness instruction

---
2091 Fish & Seafoods, Canned & Cured

(P-2288)
AQUAMAR INC
10888 7th St, Rancho Cucamonga (91730-5421)
PHONE..................909 481-4700
Hugo Yamakawa, *Principal*
Taka Iwasaki, *Vice Pres*
Takahiko Iwasaki, *VP Opers*
Vincent Navarro, *Safety Mgr*
Alice Sheu, *QC Mgr*
◆ EMP: 150
SQ FT: 42,000
SALES (est): 37.8MM **Privately Held**
WEB: www.aquamar.net
SIC: 2091 2092 Shellfish, canned & cured; fresh or frozen packaged fish

(P-2289)
BUMBLE BEE CAPITAL CORP
280 10th Ave, San Diego (92101-7406)
PHONE..................858 715-4000
Christopher Lischew, *Principal*
EMP: 123
SALES (est): 8MM **Privately Held**
SIC: 2091 Tuna fish: packaged in cans, jars, etc.
HQ: Bee Bumble Foods Llc
280 10th Ave
San Diego CA 92101
858 715-4000

(P-2290)
BUMBLE BEE FOODS LLC (DH)
Also Called: Bumble Bee
280 10th Ave, San Diego (92101-7406)
P.O. Box 85362 (92186-5362)
PHONE..................858 715-4000
Jan Tharp, *CEO*
◆ EMP: 277
SALES (est): 177.1MM **Privately Held**
SIC: 2091 Tuna fish: packaged in cans, jars, etc.
HQ: Bee Bumble Holdings Inc
280 10th Ave
San Diego CA 92101
858 715-4000

(P-2291)
BUMBLE BEE SEAFOODS LP
280 10th Ave, San Diego (92101-7406)
P.O. Box 85362 (92186-5362)
PHONE..................858 715-4000
Christopher Lischewsky, *Partner*
Douglas Hines, *Exec VP*
James Badet, *Vice Pres*
Roy Bryant, *Vice Pres*
Tony Costa, *Vice Pres*
▼ EMP: 78
SALES (est): 47.6MM **Privately Held**
SIC: 2091 2047 Tuna fish: packaged in cans, jars, etc.; dog & cat food

(P-2292)
BUMBLE BEE SEAFOODS INC
280 10th Ave, San Diego (92101-7406)
PHONE..................858 715-4000
Gabriela Silva, *CEO*
Patty Chavez, *Manager*
◆ EMP: 23
SALES (est): 2.9MM **Privately Held**
SIC: 2091 Tuna fish: packaged in cans, jars, etc.

(P-2293)
BUMBLE BEE SEAFOODS INC
280 10th Ave, San Diego (92101-7406)
P.O. Box 85362 (92186-5362)
PHONE..................858 715-4068
◆ EMP: 3000
SALES (est): 308.8MM **Privately Held**
SIC: 2091 2047

(P-2294)
BUMBLE BEE SEAFOODS LLC
13100 Arctic Cir, Santa Fe Springs (90670-5508)
PHONE..................562 483-7474
Sheri Glazebrook, *CEO*
John Frenzley, *Info Tech Mgr*
Gloria Castro, *Engineer*
Cindy Devers, *Human Res Dir*
Cindy Slawson, *Human Res Mgr*
EMP: 20
SALES (est): 3MM **Privately Held**
SIC: 2091 Canned & cured fish & seafoods

(P-2295)
COAST SEAFOODS COMPANY
25 Waterfront Dr, Eureka (95501-0370)
PHONE..................707 442-2947
Greg Dale, *Manager*
EMP: 30
SALES (corp-wide): 70.7MM **Privately Held**
WEB: www.coastseafoods.com
SIC: 2091 0913 2092 Oysters: packaged in cans, jars, etc.; oyster beds; fresh or frozen packaged fish
HQ: Coast Seafoods Company
1200 Robert Bush Dr
Bellevue WA 98007

(P-2296)
GLOBAL OCEAN TRADING LLC
430 S Grfield Ave Ste 405, Alhambra (91801)
PHONE..................626 281-0800
▼ EMP: 10
SALES (est): 1.1MM **Privately Held**
SIC: 2091 Canned & cured fish & seafoods

(P-2297)
KEYSOURCE FOODS LLC
2263 W 190th St, Torrance (90504-6001)
PHONE..................310 879-4888
Roger Lin, *Mng Member*

▲ EMP: 23
SALES (est): 4.3MM **Privately Held**
SIC: 2091 Seafood products: packaged in cans, jars, etc.

(P-2298)
OCEAN BEAUTY SEAFOODS LLC
Three Star Smoked Fish Co
629 S Central Ave, Los Angeles (90021-1050)
PHONE..................213 624-2101
Mark Palmer, *President*
EMP: 200
SQ FT: 68,000
SALES (corp-wide): 472.7MM **Privately Held**
WEB: www.oceanbeauty.com
SIC: 2091 5149 Fish, smoked; fish, cured; chocolate
PA: Ocean Beauty Seafoods Llc
1100 W Ewing St
Seattle WA 98119
206 285-6800

(P-2299)
OCEAN FRESH LLC (PA)
Also Called: Ocean Fresh Seafood Products
350 N Main St, Fort Bragg (95437-3406)
PHONE..................707 964-1389
Robert S Juntz, *Mng Member*
Susan Juntz,
▲ EMP: 41
SQ FT: 5,000
SALES (est): 4.7MM **Privately Held**
SIC: 2091 Fish, canned & cured

(P-2300)
PACIFIC PLAZA IMPORTS INC (PA)
Also Called: Plaze De Caviar
3018 Willow Pass Rd # 102, Concord (94519-2598)
PHONE..................925 349-4000
Mark Bolourchi, *President*
Sharon Bolourchi, *Vice Pres*
Ali Bolourchi, *Executive*
Otto Szilagyi, *Sales Staff*
▲ EMP: 30
SQ FT: 24,000
SALES: 15MM **Privately Held**
WEB: www.pacificplaza.net
SIC: 2091 Caviar: packaged in cans, jars, etc.

(P-2301)
RLT SEAFOOD SUPERMARKET INC
Also Called: SM Asian Market
333 S E St, San Bernardino (92401-2010)
PHONE..................909 888-6520
Ronald Loca Tsu, *CEO*
EMP: 10
SALES (est): 974.4K **Privately Held**
SIC: 2091 Seafood products: packaged in cans, jars, etc.

(P-2302)
SAFE CATCH INC
85 Liberty Ship Way, Sausalito (94965-3316)
PHONE..................415 944-4442
Bryan Boches, *CEO*
Sean Wittenberg, *President*
Kevin McCay, *COO*
Kasey Fahey, *Accountant*
Michelle Watson, *Marketing Mgr*
◆ EMP: 12
SQ FT: 4,000
SALES (est): 1.1MM **Privately Held**
SIC: 2091 Tuna fish: packaged in cans, jars, etc.

(P-2303)
SOUTH PACIFIC TUNA CORPORATION
501 W Broadway, San Diego (92101-3536)
PHONE..................619 233-2060
Max Chou, *President*
Annette Schlife, *CFO*
Capt Bobby Virissimo, *Vice Pres*
Capt B Virissimo, *Vice Pres*
EMP: 12 EST: 2007
SALES (est): 1.4MM **Privately Held**
SIC: 2091 Tuna fish, preserved & cured

(P-2304)
TAOKAENOI USA INC
Also Called: Gim Factory
13767 Milroy Pl, Santa Fe Springs (90670-5130)
PHONE..................562 404-9888
Itthipat Peeradechapan, *CEO*
Grace Kim, *Manager*
EMP: 13
SQ FT: 27,000
SALES (est): 1.1MM **Privately Held**
SIC: 2091 Canned & cured fish & seafoods

(P-2305)
THAI UNION INTERNATIONAL INC (HQ)
9330 Scranton Rd Ste 500, San Diego (92121-7706)
PHONE..................858 558-9662
Thiraphong Chansiri, *Principal*
▼ EMP: 11
SALES (est): 74MM
SALES (corp-wide): 4.1B **Privately Held**
SIC: 2091 Tuna fish: packaged in cans, jars, etc.; salmon: packaged in cans, jars, etc.
PA: Thai Union Group Public Company Limited
72/1 Moo 7, Sethakit 1 Road
Muang 74000
348 165-00

(P-2306)
TRI-UNION SEAFOODS LLC
3 Diamond
4510 Executive Dr Ste 300, San Diego (92121-3029)
PHONE..................858 558-9662
Dennis Mussell, *President*
EMP: 10
SALES (corp-wide): 4.1B **Privately Held**
SIC: 2091 Tuna fish: packaged in cans, jars, etc.
HQ: Tri-Union Seafoods, Llc
2150 E Grand Ave
El Segundo CA 90245
858 558-9662

(P-2307)
YAMASA ENTERPRISES
Also Called: Yamasa Fish Cake
515 Stanford Ave, Los Angeles (90013-2189)
PHONE..................213 626-2211
Frank Kawana, *President*
Yuji Kawana, *Vice Pres*
Sachie Kawana, *Admin Sec*
Doug Watanabe, *Sales Mgr*
▲ EMP: 27
SQ FT: 20,000
SALES (est): 4.3MM **Privately Held**
SIC: 2091 Fish & seafood cakes: packaged in cans, jars, etc.

2092 Fish & Seafoods, Fresh & Frozen

(P-2308)
AZUMA FOODS INTL INC USA (HQ)
Also Called: Azuma Foods Internatl
20201 Mack St, Hayward (94545-1224)
PHONE..................510 782-1112
Toshinobu Azuma, *Chairman*
Takahiro Tamura, *President*
Toshie Azuma, *CFO*
Kimiyuki Inamura, *Officer*
◆ EMP: 70
SQ FT: 70,000
SALES (est): 13.6MM
SALES (corp-wide): 25.3MM **Privately Held**
WEB: www.azumafoods.com
SIC: 2092 5146 Fresh or frozen packaged fish; seafoods
PA: Azuma Foods Co.,Ltd.
3095-45, Nagai, Komonocho
Mie-Gun MIE 510-1
593 965-577

(PA)=Parent Co (HQ)=Headquarters (DH)=Div Headquarters
✿ = New Business established in last 2 years

2019 California
Manufacturers Register

107

PRODUCTS & SVCS

(P-2309)
CALIFORNIA SHELLFISH CO INC (PA)
818 E Broadway C, San Gabriel (91776-1902)
P.O. Box 2028, San Francisco (94126-2028)
PHONE....................................415 923-7400
Robin Yuan, *Principal*
Dave Zeller, *CFO*
EMP: 15
SQ FT: 6,000
SALES (est): 105.4MM **Privately Held**
WEB: www.dfeh.ca.gov
SIC: 2092 Fresh or frozen packaged fish

(P-2310)
CHASIN FOODS INC
1855 E 27th St, Vernon (90058-1119)
PHONE....................................323 544-0000
Derek Ben Chasin, *President*
EMP: 22
SALES (est): 4.1MM **Privately Held**
SIC: 2092 Seafoods, frozen: prepared

(P-2311)
DEL MAR SEAFOODS INC (PA)
331 Ford St, Watsonville (95076-4108)
PHONE....................................831 763-3000
Joe Cappuccio, *President*
Joe Roggio, *CFO*
Roseanne Cappuccio, *Vice Pres*
Cesar Durin, *Plant Mgr*
◆ **EMP:** 200
SQ FT: 40,000
SALES (est): 38.3MM **Privately Held**
WEB: www.delmarseafoods.com
SIC: 2092 Seafoods, fresh: prepared

(P-2312)
FISH HOUSE FOODS INC
1263 Linda Vista Dr, San Marcos (92078-3827)
PHONE....................................760 597-1270
Ron Butler, *President*
Ronald J Butler, *CEO*
Rex Butler, *Vice Pres*
Karen Butler, *Admin Sec*
EMP: 430
SQ FT: 52,000
SALES (est): 31.2MM
SALES (corp-wide): 29.5MM **Privately Held**
WEB: www.fishhousefoods.com
SIC: 2092 5149 Seafoods, fresh: prepared; groceries & related products
PA: The Fish House Vera Cruz Inc
3585 Main St Ste 212
Riverside CA 92501
760 744-8000

(P-2313)
FISHERMANS PRIDE PRCESSORS INC
Also Called: Neptune Foods
4510 S Alameda St, Vernon (90058-2011)
PHONE....................................323 232-1980
Howard Choi, *CEO*
Hector Poon, *COO*
Charlene Lau, *Technology*
Martin Tsai, *Controller*
Rich Meyer, *Sales Mgr*
◆ **EMP:** 300
SQ FT: 125,000
SALES (est): 101.1MM **Privately Held**
WEB: www.neptunefoods.com
SIC: 2092 Fresh or frozen packaged fish

(P-2314)
J DELUCA FISH COMPANY INC (PA)
Also Called: Nautilus Seafood
2194 Signal Pl, San Pedro (90731-7225)
PHONE....................................310 684-5180
John Deluca, *President*
◆ **EMP:** 40
SQ FT: 60,000
SALES (est): 18MM **Privately Held**
SIC: 2092 Seafoods, frozen: prepared

(P-2315)
LONG BEACH ENTERPRISE INC (PA)
Also Called: Sea One Seafood
12319 Florence Ave, Santa Fe Springs (90670-3807)
P.O. Box 3048 (90670-0048)
PHONE....................................562 944-8945
Tai Van Tran, *President*
Thanh Thu Nguyen, *Corp Secy*
Norman Nguyen, *Manager*
▲ **EMP:** 27
SQ FT: 6,000
SALES (est): 3.5MM **Privately Held**
WEB: www.seaoneseafoods.com
SIC: 2092 Seafoods, frozen: prepared

(P-2316)
LONG BEACH SEAFOODS CO
4643 Hackett Ave, Lakewood (90713-2632)
PHONE....................................562 432-7300
Tony Delucia, *President*
Star Delucia, *Vice Pres*
EMP: 38
SQ FT: 50,000
SALES (est): 5.8MM **Privately Held**
WEB: www.longbeachseafood.com
SIC: 2092 5146 Fresh or frozen packaged fish; fish & seafoods

(P-2317)
MARUHIDE MARINE PRODUCTS INC
Also Called: M M P
2145 W 17th St, Long Beach (90813-1013)
PHONE....................................562 435-6509
Hideo Kawamura, *President*
EMP: 60
SQ FT: 14,352
SALES (est): 7.3MM **Privately Held**
WEB: www.maruhide.us
SIC: 2092 Shellfish, frozen: prepared

(P-2318)
MS INTERTRADE INC (PA)
Also Called: Sonoma Foods
2221 Bluebell Dr Ste A, Santa Rosa (95403-2545)
PHONE....................................707 837-8057
Matthew J Mariani, *CEO*
Scott A Gray, *President*
Charles Hansen, *Vice Pres*
EMP: 44
SQ FT: 8,000
SALES (est): 4.7MM **Privately Held**
SIC: 2092 Fresh or frozen fish or seafood chowders, soups & stews

(P-2319)
NIKKO ENTERPRISE CORPORATION
Also Called: Hanna Fuji Sushi
13168 Sandoval St, Santa Fe Springs (90670-6600)
PHONE....................................562 941-6080
Tlang T Mawii, *CEO*
Sein Myint, *Shareholder*
Robby Sharma, *Vice Pres*
EMP: 23
SQ FT: 5,000
SALES (est): 4.4MM **Privately Held**
WEB: www.necsushi.com
SIC: 2092 Fresh or frozen fish or seafood chowders, soups & stews

(P-2320)
OCEAN DIRECT LLC (PA)
Also Called: Boardwalk Solutions
13771 Gramercy Pl, Gardena (90249-2470)
PHONE....................................424 266-9300
Neil Kinney,
Matthew Hamel, *Info Tech Mgr*
Michael Schodorf, *Opers Staff*
▼ **EMP:** 47
SQ FT: 20,000
SALES (est): 13MM **Privately Held**
WEB: www.oceandirect.com
SIC: 2092 2022 2037 2033 Fresh or frozen fish or seafood chowders, soups & stews; prepared fish or other seafood cakes & sticks; natural cheese; frozen fruits & vegetables; vegetables & vegetable products in cans, jars, etc.; groceries, general line

(P-2321)
RICH PRODUCTS CORPORATION
320 O St, Fresno (93721-3086)
PHONE....................................559 486-7380
Gary Rogers, *Finance Other*
Louis Mata, *Human Res Dir*
Clay Ory, *Manager*
EMP: 152
SQ FT: 64,413
SALES (corp-wide): 4B **Privately Held**
WEB: www.richs.com
SIC: 2092 2045 2038 Fresh or frozen packaged fish; prepared flour mixes & doughs; frozen specialties
PA: Rich Products Corporation
1 Robert Rich Way
Buffalo NY 14213
716 878-8000

(P-2322)
SEA SNACK FOODS INC (PA)
914 E 11th St, Los Angeles (90021-2091)
P.O. Box 21467 (90021-0467)
PHONE....................................213 622-2204
Fred W Ockrim, *CEO*
Barbara Kahn, *Treasurer*
Jeffrey Kahn, *Vice Pres*
Sheri Ockrim, *Admin Sec*
◆ **EMP:** 50
SQ FT: 2,000
SALES (est): 9.2MM **Privately Held**
SIC: 2092 Fish, frozen: prepared

(P-2323)
SIMPLY FRESH FOODS INC
11215 Knott Ave Ste A, Cypress (90630-5495)
P.O. Box 225, Santa Clara (95052-0225)
PHONE....................................714 562-5000
Dale Jabour, *CEO*
Chris Boyd, *Vice Pres*
Jeff Wagner, *Vice Pres*
Leslie Frausto, *Purch Mgr*
John Molino, *QC Mgr*
▼ **EMP:** 15
SQ FT: 20,000
SALES: 40MM **Privately Held**
WEB: www.spcap.com
SIC: 2092 Fresh or frozen packaged fish
PA: Ancor Holdings, Lp
100 Throckmorton St St
Southlake TX 76092
-

(P-2324)
SUN COAST CALAMARI INC
928 E 3rd St, Oxnard (93030-6119)
P.O. Box 151 (93032-0151)
PHONE....................................805 385-0056
John Borman, *President*
Jeff Reichle, *Vice Pres*
Wayne Reichle, *Vice Pres*
EMP: 150
SQ FT: 15,000
SALES (est): 20.2MM **Privately Held**
SIC: 2092 Fresh or frozen packaged fish

(P-2325)
SUSAN ZADI
Also Called: Revolutionario
4220 Beverly Blvd, Los Angeles (90004-4430)
PHONE....................................424 223-3526
Susan Zadi, *Owner*
EMP: 11
SQ FT: 1,000
SALES (est): 724.5K **Privately Held**
SIC: 2092 Eating places

(P-2326)
TARDIO ENTERPRISES INC
Also Called: Newport Fish
457 S Canal St, South San Francisco (94080-4607)
PHONE....................................650 877-7200
Andrew Tardio, *President*
EMP: 25
SALES (est): 4.6MM **Privately Held**
SIC: 2092 5421 Fresh or frozen packaged fish; fish & seafood markets

2095 Coffee

(P-2327)
APFFELS COFFEE INC
12115 Pacific St, Santa Fe Springs (90670-2989)
P.O. Box 2506 (90670-0506)
PHONE....................................562 309-0400
Darryl Blunk, *CEO*
Alvin Apffel, *President*
Mike Rogers, *Exec VP*
Edward Apffel, *Vice Pres*
Christina De La Paz, *Office Mgr*
◆ **EMP:** 25
SQ FT: 100,000
SALES (est): 5.4MM **Privately Held**
WEB: www.apffels.com
SIC: 2095 5149 Coffee roasting (except by wholesale grocers); coffee, ground: mixed with grain or chicory; coffee, green or roasted; tea

(P-2328)
BAY AREA COFFEE INC
4201 Industrial Way, Benicia (94510-1228)
PHONE....................................707 745-1320
Thomas Waterman, *CEO*
Michael Daugherty, *Manager*
Joseph Lin, *Accounts Mgr*
EMP: 50
SALES (est): 8.4MM **Privately Held**
SIC: 2095 Coffee roasting (except by wholesale grocers)

(P-2329)
BORESHA INTERNATIONAL INC
7041 Koll Center Pkwy # 100, Pleasanton (94566-3192)
PHONE....................................925 676-1400
Tony Drexel Smith, *President*
George Najjar, *President*
EMP: 30
SALES (est): 5.3MM **Privately Held**
SIC: 2095 Coffee extracts

(P-2330)
BRAD BARRY COMPANY LTD
Also Called: Caffe D'Vita
14020 Central Ave Ste 580, Chino (91710-5524)
PHONE....................................909 591-9493
Robert S Greene, *President*
Jerome Greener, *CFO*
Tina Tout, *Accounting Mgr*
April Higbee, *Opers Mgr*
Alan Dossey, *Natl Sales Mgr*
◆ **EMP:** 30
SQ FT: 39,600
SALES (est): 11.5MM **Privately Held**
WEB: www.caffedvita.com
SIC: 2095 Roasted coffee

(P-2331)
CAFE VIRTUOSO LLC
1622 National Ave, San Diego (92113-1009)
PHONE....................................619 550-1830
Laurie Britton, *CEO*
Rigo Hernandez, *Sales Mgr*
EMP: 14
SQ FT: 5,500
SALES (est): 931.7K **Privately Held**
SIC: 2095 5812 Coffee roasting (except by wholesale grocers); coffee shop

(P-2332)
CAFECITO ORGANICO OC LLC
534 N Hoover St, Los Angeles (90004-2309)
PHONE....................................213 537-8367
Jose Angel Orozco, *Principal*
Angel Orozco, *Managing Prtnr*
EMP: 24
SALES (corp-wide): 4.8MM **Privately Held**
SIC: 2095 Roasted coffee
PA: Cafecito Organico Oc, Llc
710 N Heliotrope Dr
Los Angeles CA 90029
213 537-8367

(P-2333)
CAFECITO ORGANICO OC LLC
2916 Heathercliff Rd, Malibu (90265)
PHONE......................................213 537-8367
Jose Angel Orozco, *Principal*
EMP: 19
SALES (corp-wide): 4.8MM **Privately Held**
SIC: 2095 Roasted coffee
PA: Cafecito Organico Oc, Llc
710 N Heliotrope Dr
Los Angeles CA 90029
213 537-8367

(P-2334)
CAFFE CARDINALE COF ROASTING
246 The Crossroads Blvd, Carmel (93923-8651)
P.O. Box 7222 (93921-7222)
PHONE......................................831 626-2095
Gaspher Cardinale, *Partner*
Carmella Cardinale, *Partner*
Rocco Cardinale, *Partner*
EMP: 10 **EST:** 1992
SQ FT: 2,000
SALES (est): 801.3K **Privately Held**
WEB: www.carmelcoffee.com
SIC: 2095 5812 Coffee roasting (except by wholesale grocers); cafe

(P-2335)
CAFFE CLABRIA COF ROASTERS LLC
3933 30th St, San Diego (92104-3004)
PHONE......................................619 683-7787
Arne Holt,
Susan Holt,
▲ **EMP:** 40 **EST:** 2000
SALES (est): 4.3MM **Privately Held**
SIC: 2095 Roasted coffee

(P-2336)
CAFFE CLASSICO FOODS INC
2500 Annalisa Dr, Concord (94520-1178)
PHONE......................................925 602-5400
Tom Heffernan, *President*
▲ **EMP:** 18
SALES (est): 3MM **Privately Held**
WEB: www.caffeclassicofoods.com
SIC: 2095 Roasted coffee

(P-2337)
COFFEE GUYS INC (PA)
Also Called: Calistoga Roastery, The
975 Silverado Trl, Calistoga (94515-1128)
P.O. Box 666 (94515-0666)
PHONE......................................707 942-5747
Terry Rich, *President*
Clive Richardson, *Ch of Bd*
EMP: 21
SQ FT: 1,200
SALES (est): 2.5MM **Privately Held**
WEB: www.calistogaroastery.com
SIC: 2095 5812 5149 5499 Coffee roasting (except by wholesale grocers); coffee shop; caterers; coffee, green or roasted; coffee; food, mail order

(P-2338)
COFFEE WORKS INC
3418 Folsom Blvd, Sacramento (95816-5312)
PHONE......................................916 452-1086
John Shahabian, *President*
EMP: 18
SQ FT: 4,000
SALES (est): 2.2MM **Privately Held**
WEB: www.coffeeworks.com
SIC: 2095 5499 Coffee roasting (except by wholesale grocers); coffee

(P-2339)
DAYMAR CORPORATION
Also Called: Daymar Select Fine Coffees
460 Cypress Ln Ste B, El Cajon (92020-1647)
PHONE......................................619 444-1155
Ricardo L Granados, *President*
Robert Salazar, *Shareholder*
Rogeolio Gallegos, *COO*
Enrique Lizarraga Osuna, *CFO*
Leonardo Rico, *Admin Sec*
EMP: 10
SQ FT: 6,000

SALES (est): 1.2MM **Privately Held**
WEB: www.daymar.net
SIC: 2095 5149 Roasted coffee; coffee, green or roasted

(P-2340)
F GAVINA & SONS INC
Also Called: Gavia
2700 Fruitland Ave, Vernon (90058-2893)
PHONE......................................323 582-0671
Pedro Gavina, *President*
Jose Gavina, *Corp Secy*
Leonor Gavi A-Valls, *Vice Pres*
Francisco M Gavina, *Vice Pres*
Leonora Gavina, *Vice Pres*
▲ **EMP:** 295
SQ FT: 239,000
SALES (est): 72.6MM **Privately Held**
WEB: www.gavina.com
SIC: 2095 Coffee roasting (except by wholesale grocers)

(P-2341)
FARMER BROS CO
Also Called: Farmers Brothers Coffee
1350 Stellar Dr, Oxnard (93033-2411)
PHONE......................................805 483-8406
Andy Juarez, *Branch Mgr*
EMP: 10
SALES (corp-wide): 606.5MM **Publicly Held**
WEB: www.farmerbros.com
SIC: 2095 Coffee roasting (except by wholesale grocers)
PA: Farmer Bros. Co.
1912 Farmer Brothers Dr
Northlake TX 76262
888 998-2468

(P-2342)
FARMER BROS CO
7855 Ostrow St Ste A, San Diego (92111-3634)
PHONE......................................858 292-7578
Albert Moya, *General Mgr*
Mark Bailey, *Branch Mgr*
EMP: 20
SQ FT: 19,036
SALES (corp-wide): 606.5MM **Publicly Held**
WEB: www.farmerbros.com
SIC: 2095 5149 Coffee roasting (except by wholesale grocers); coffee, green or roasted
PA: Farmer Bros. Co.
1912 Farmer Brothers Dr
Northlake TX 76262
888 998-2468

(P-2343)
FARMER BROS CO
Also Called: Farmers Brothers Coffee
20671 Corsair Blvd, Hayward (94545-1007)
PHONE......................................510 638-1660
Dustin Clark, *Branch Mgr*
EMP: 17
SALES (corp-wide): 606.5MM **Publicly Held**
WEB: www.farmerbros.com
SIC: 2095 7389 5149 Coffee roasting (except by wholesale grocers); coffee service; coffee, green or roasted
PA: Farmer Bros. Co.
1912 Farmer Brothers Dr
Northlake TX 76262
888 998-2468

(P-2344)
FARMER BROS CO
Also Called: Farmers Brothers Coffee
11460 Commercial Pkwy, Castroville (95012-3202)
PHONE......................................831 633-6521
Jeff Barber, *Sales/Mktg Mgr*
EMP: 12
SALES (corp-wide): 606.5MM **Publicly Held**
WEB: www.farmerbros.com
SIC: 2095 Coffee roasting (except by wholesale grocers)
PA: Farmer Bros. Co.
1912 Farmer Brothers Dr
Northlake TX 76262
888 998-2468

(P-2345)
FARMER BROS CO
8802 Swigert Ct, Bakersfield (93311-9647)
PHONE......................................661 663-9908
Mike Ward, *Manager*
EMP: 10
SALES (corp-wide): 541.5MM **Publicly Held**
WEB: www.farmerbros.com
SIC: 2095 5149 Coffee roasting (except by wholesale grocers); coffee, green or roasted
PA: Farmer Bros. Co.
1912 Farmer Brothers Dr
Northlake TX 76262
888 998-2468

(P-2346)
FARMER BROS CO
480 Ryan Ave Ste 100, Chico (95973-8899)
PHONE......................................530 343-3165
Tom Santos, *Manager*
EMP: 10
SALES (corp-wide): 541.5MM **Publicly Held**
WEB: www.farmerbros.com
SIC: 2095 5149 Coffee roasting (except by wholesale grocers); coffee, green or roasted
PA: Farmer Bros. Co.
1912 Farmer Brothers Dr
Northlake TX 76262
888 998-2468

(P-2347)
FARMER BROS CO
Also Called: Farmers Brothers Coffee
9373 Remick Ave, Arleta (91331-4222)
PHONE......................................818 767-7649
Jeff Meisell, *Manager*
EMP: 10
SQ FT: 15,004
SALES (corp-wide): 606.5MM **Publicly Held**
WEB: www.farmerbros.com
SIC: 2095 Roasted coffee
PA: Farmer Bros. Co.
1912 Farmer Brothers Dr
Northlake TX 76262
888 998-2468

(P-2348)
FARMER BROS CO
Also Called: Farmers Brothers Coffee
4243 Arch Rd, Stockton (95215-8325)
PHONE......................................209 466-0203
Wade Selpy, *Manager*
EMP: 20
SALES (corp-wide): 606.5MM **Publicly Held**
WEB: www.farmerbros.com
SIC: 2095 7389 5149 5046 Coffee roasting (except by wholesale grocers); coffee service; coffee, green or roasted; coffee brewing equipment & supplies
PA: Farmer Bros. Co.
1912 Farmer Brothers Dr
Northlake TX 76262
888 998-2468

(P-2349)
FUTURE WAVE TECHNOLOGIES INC
Also Called: Caffe Del Mar
1343 Camino Teresa, Solana Beach (92075-1635)
PHONE......................................858 481-1112
Fax: 858 794-4033
▲ **EMP:** 30
SQ FT: 20,000
SALES (est): 3.1MM **Privately Held**
WEB: www.caffedelmar.com
SIC: 2095 2086

(P-2350)
GOURMET COFFEE WAREHOUSE INC
Also Called: Groundwork Coffee Company
11275 Chandler Blvd, North Hollywood (91601-2708)
PHONE......................................818 423-2626
EMP: 67 **Privately Held**
SIC: 2095 Roasted coffee

PA: Gourmet Coffee Warehouse, Inc.
920 N Formosa Ave
Los Angeles CA 90046

(P-2351)
GOURMET COFFEE WAREHOUSE INC (PA)
Also Called: Groundwork Coffee Company
920 N Formosa Ave, Los Angeles (90046-6702)
PHONE......................................323 871-8930
Richard Karno, *President*
EMP: 20
SQ FT: 10,000
SALES (est): 8MM **Privately Held**
SIC: 2095 5149 5499 Coffee roasting (except by wholesale grocers); coffee & tea; coffee

(P-2352)
HERITAGE MISSIONAL COMMUNITY
Also Called: Heritage Roasting Company
4302 Shasta Dam Blvd, Shasta Lake (96019-9420)
PHONE......................................530 605-1990
Stuart Sutherland, *Director*
EMP: 10
SALES (est): 192.5K **Privately Held**
SIC: 2095 5812 5499 Roasted coffee; coffee shop; coffee

(P-2353)
HOT CAN INC
10620 Treena St Ste 230, San Diego (92131-1140)
PHONE......................................707 601-6013
James Scudder, *President*
▲ **EMP:** 50
SQ FT: 1,160
SALES (est): 2MM **Privately Held**
WEB: www.hot-can.com
SIC: 2095 Coffee roasting (except by wholesale grocers)

(P-2354)
INTERCONTINENTAL COF TRDG LLC
Also Called: Intercontinental Coffee Trdg
110 W A St Ste 110 # 110, San Diego (92101-3702)
PHONE......................................619 338-8335
Lisa Colon, *CEO*
Renee Strik, *CFO*
John Danczak, *Controller*
▲ **EMP:** 11
SQ FT: 3,800
SALES (est): 14.7MM **Privately Held**
SIC: 2095 Roasted coffee

(P-2355)
JEREMIAHS PICK COFFEE COMPANY
1495 Evans Ave, San Francisco (94124-1706)
PHONE......................................415 206-9900
Jeremiah Pick, *President*
Mike Ahmadi, *Shareholder*
Krislyn Asagra, *Webmaster*
Ronnie Crabtree, *Human Res Mgr*
▲ **EMP:** 19
SQ FT: 11,000
SALES (est): 3.4MM **Privately Held**
WEB: www.jeremiahspick.com
SIC: 2095 5149 Coffee roasting (except by wholesale grocers); coffee, green or roasted

(P-2356)
KAV AMERICA AG INC
422 Commercial Rd, San Bernardino (92408-3706)
PHONE......................................855 528-8721
Tak Lam, *CEO*
EMP: 25
SALES (est): 4.5MM **Privately Held**
SIC: 2095 Coffee extracts

(P-2357)
KEYSTONE COFFEE COMPANY
2230 Will Wool Dr Ste 100, San Jose (95112-2605)
PHONE......................................408 998-2221
Tim Wright, *President*

Marlena Wright, *Corp Secy*
EMP: 17
SQ FT: 22,000
SALES (est): 1.8MM **Privately Held**
WEB: www.keystonecoffee.com
SIC: 2095 Coffee roasting (except by
wholesale grocers)

(P-2358)
KLATCH COFFEE INC
Also Called: Coffee Klatch
8767 Onyx Ave, Rancho Cucamonga
(91730-4533)
PHONE.....................909 981-4031
Mike Perry, *CEO*
Heather Perry, *Vice Pres*
Cindy Perry, *Admin Sec*
Helene Ingstrom, *Business Mgr*
Holly Perry, *Manager*
EMP: 40
SQ FT: 2,400
SALES: 3.5MM **Privately Held**
SIC: 2095 Roasted coffee

(P-2359)
LINGLE BROS COFFEE INC
6500 Garfield Ave, Bell Gardens
(90201-1897)
PHONE.....................562 927-3317
James B Lingle, *President*
EMP: 30
SQ FT: 24,000
SALES (est): 4.6MM **Privately Held**
SIC: 2095 Coffee roasting (except by
wholesale grocers)

(P-2360)
NAPA VALLEY COFFEE ROASTING CO (PA)
948 Main St, NAPA (94559-3045)
PHONE.....................707 224-2233
Denise Fox, *President*
Leon Sange, *Corp Secy*
EMP: 15
SALES (est): 2MM **Privately Held**
WEB: www.napavalleycoffeeroasting.com
SIC: 2095 5499 Coffee roasting (except by
wholesale grocers); coffee

(P-2361)
NUZEE INC
2865 Scott St Ste 101, Vista (92081-8555)
PHONE.....................858 549-6893
Masa Higashida, *CEO*
Travis Gorney, *President*
EMP: 12
SALES: 1.6MM **Privately Held**
SIC: 2095 Coffee, ground: mixed with grain
or chicory

(P-2362)
PALO ALTO CAFE
2675 Middlefield Rd, Palo Alto
(94306-2516)
PHONE.....................650 322-8644
Kevin Shermanshahi, *Owner*
EMP: 10
SQ FT: 1,800
SALES (est): 526.3K **Privately Held**
SIC: 2095 Coffee roasting (except by
wholesale grocers)

(P-2363)
PEERLESS COFFEE COMPANY INC
Also Called: Peerles Coffee and Tea
260 Oak St, Oakland (94607-4512)
PHONE.....................510 763-1763
George J Vukasin Jr, *CEO*
Mike Pine, *CFO*
Kristina V Brouhard, *Exec VP*
John Ziglar, *Vice Pres*
Lyra Giron, *Administration*
EMP: 85
SQ FT: 65,000
SALES (est): 17.6MM **Privately Held**
WEB: www.peerlesscoffee.com
SIC: 2095 5149 Coffee roasting (except by
wholesale grocers); tea; spices & season-
ings

(P-2364)
PEETS COFFEE & TEA LLC (HQ)
1400 Park Ave, Emeryville (94608-3520)
PHONE.....................510 594-2100
David Burwick, *CEO*

Paul Clayton, *President*
Mark Rudolph, *Treasurer*
Shawn Conway, *Vice Pres*
Paul Yee, *Executive*
▲ **EMP:** 277 **EST:** 1971
SQ FT: 60,000
SALES (est): 1.4B
SALES (corp-wide): 2.2B **Privately Held**
SIC: 2095 5149 Roasted coffee; coffee,
green or roasted

(P-2365)
PLANTATION COFFEE ROASTERS
9583 Elk Grove Florin Rd, Elk Grove
(95624-1803)
PHONE.....................916 714-2633
Dan Davis, *Owner*
EMP: 29
SQ FT: 1,000
SALES (est): 1.6MM **Privately Held**
SIC: 2095 5149 5499 5812 Roasted cof-
fee; coffee & tea; coffee; eating places

(P-2366)
SANTA BARBARA COFFEE LLC
Also Called: Red Star Coffee
6489 Calle Real Ste G, Goleta
(93117-1538)
PHONE.....................805 683-2555
Daniel M Randall, *Mng Member*
Werner Diaz,
Kevin C Donnelly,
EMP: 15
SQ FT: 1,645
SALES (est): 2.6MM **Privately Held**
SIC: 2095 5499 Coffee roasting (except by
wholesale grocers); coffee

(P-2367)
SUPREME BEAN LLC
Also Called: Groundwork Coffee
5457 Cleon Ave, North Hollywood
(91601-2834)
PHONE.....................818 506-6020
Steven Levan, *Partner*
Jeffrey Chean, *Partner*
EMP: 160
SQ FT: 4,650
SALES: 9MM **Privately Held**
SIC: 2095 5812 5149 Roasted coffee;
contract food services; coffee, green or
roasted

(P-2368)
TAYLOR MAID FARMS LLC
6790 Mckinley Ave, Sebastopol
(95472-3496)
PHONE.....................707 824-9110
Christ Martin,
Michael Presley,
EMP: 30 **EST:** 2000
SALES: 3.5MM **Privately Held**
SIC: 2095 Roasted coffee

(P-2369)
TULLYS COFFEE CO INC (HQ)
2455 Fillmore St, San Francisco
(94115-1814)
PHONE.....................415 929-8808
Tom O' Keefe, *President*
Steve Griffin, *CFO*
EMP: 25
SQ FT: 8,000
SALES (est): 8.1MM **Privately Held**
SIC: 2095 5149 5499 5812 Coffee,
ground: mixed with grain or chicory; cof-
fee, green or roasted; coffee; coffee shop

(P-2370)
TULLYS COFFEE CO INC
1509 Sloat Blvd, San Francisco
(94132-1222)
PHONE.....................415 213-8791
Jen Wong, *Manager*
EMP: 10 **Privately Held**
SIC: 2095 5499 Coffee roasting (except by
wholesale grocers); coffee
HQ: Tully's Coffee Co Inc
2455 Fillmore St
San Francisco CA 94115
415 929-8808

2096 Potato Chips & Similar Prdts

(P-2371)
4505 MEATS INC
1246 Howard St, San Francisco
(94103-2712)
PHONE.....................415 255-3094
Ryan Farr, *CEO*
EMP: 20
SQ FT: 3,000
SALES: 394K **Privately Held**
SIC: 2096 Pork rinds

(P-2372)
ACAPULCO MEXICAN DELI INC
929 S Kern Ave, Los Angeles (90022-3013)
PHONE.....................323 266-0267
Rubin Ibarra, *CEO*
Saul Casillas, *Vice Pres*
Acapulco Enrique, *Manager*
EMP: 34
SALES (est): 2.3MM **Privately Held**
SIC: 2096 2032 Tortilla chips; Mexican
foods: packaged in cans, jars, etc.

(P-2373)
ALIVE & RADIANT FOODS INC
2921 Adeline St, Emeryville (94608-4422)
PHONE.....................510 238-0128
Nicholas Taylor Kelley, *President*
Nicholas Kelley, *CEO*
▲ **EMP:** 25
SALES (est): 5.9MM **Privately Held**
SIC: 2096 Potato chips & similar snacks

(P-2374)
ANITAS MEXICAN FOODS CORP (PA)
3454 N Mike Daley Dr, San Bernardino
(92407-1890)
PHONE.....................909 884-8706
Ricardo Alvarez, *President*
Ricardo Robles, *CEO*
Rene Robles, *COO*
Jacqueline Robles, *Admin Sec*
Paul Omness, *Finance*
▲ **EMP:** 121 **EST:** 1936
SQ FT: 330,000
SALES: 50MM **Privately Held**
SIC: 2096 Potato chips & similar snacks

(P-2375)
BOT N BOT INC
13005 Los Nietos Rd, Santa Fe Springs
(90670-3013)
PHONE.....................562 906-4873
Francis E Llado, *President*
Carmencita J Llado, *Med Doctor*
EMP: 10
SQ FT: 6,353
SALES (est): 1.1MM **Privately Held**
SIC: 2096 Pork rinds

(P-2376)
CALIFORNIA NUGGETS INC
23073 S Frederick Rd, Ripon (95366-9616)
PHONE.....................209 599-7131
Steve Gikas, *CEO*
Richard Piercefield, *CFO*
Barbara Bain, *Corp Secy*
Lori Gikas, *Vice Pres*
Chris Ben Groningen, *Controller*
◆ **EMP:** 40
SQ FT: 50,000
SALES (est): 6.7MM **Privately Held**
WEB: www.californianuggets.com
SIC: 2096 2068 Potato chips & similar
snacks; nuts: dried, dehydrated, salted or
roasted

(P-2377)
CORAZONAS FOODS INC
3780 Kilroy Airport Way # 430, Long Beach
(90806-6863)
PHONE.....................800 388-8998
Ramona Cappello, *CEO*
Robert Crumby, *CFO*
Morgan Potter, *Controller*
Wanda James, *Transportation*
▲ **EMP:** 11
SALES (est): 1.9MM **Privately Held**
WEB: www.corazonas.com
SIC: 2096 Tortilla chips

(P-2378)
DON VITO OZUNA FOODS CORP
180 Cochrane Cir, Morgan Hill
(95037-2807)
PHONE.....................408 400-0495
Cevero Ozuna, *President*
EMP: 22
SQ FT: 12,000
SALES (est): 2.3MM **Privately Held**
SIC: 2096 Tortilla chips

(P-2379)
EVANS FOOD WEST INC (PA)
1920 S Augusta Ave, Ontario (91761-5701)
PHONE.....................909 947-3001
Alan F Sussna, *President*
Mauricio Olloqui, *Plant Mgr*
EMP: 10
SALES (est): 1.5MM **Privately Held**
SIC: 2096 Potato chips & similar snacks

(P-2380)
FANTE INC (PA)
Also Called: Casa Sanchez Foods
2898 W Winton Ave, Hayward
(94545-1122)
P.O. Box 12582, San Francisco (94112-
0582)
PHONE.....................650 697-7525
Robert C Sanchez, *President*
Robert Sanchez, *President*
Rosemarie Ramos, *Prdtn Mgr*
Linda Renteria, *Manager*
▲ **EMP:** 30
SALES (est): 16.1MM **Privately Held**
WEB: www.fante.com
SIC: 2096 2099 Tortilla chips; dips, except
cheese & sour cream based

(P-2381)
FLAMOUS BRANDS INC
1801 Highland Ave Ste C, Duarte
(91010-2833)
PHONE.....................626 551-3201
Salman M Shehayeb, *President*
Alejandra Lopez, *Admin Asst*
Yasser Chehayeb, *VP Mfg*
Michelle Whoolery, *Marketing Staff*
EMP: 10 **EST:** 2007
SALES (est): 1.4MM **Privately Held**
SIC: 2096 Potato chips & similar snacks

(P-2382)
FRITO-LAY NORTH AMERICA INC
16701 Trojan Way, La Mirada
(90638-5906)
PHONE.....................714 562-7260
Jino Lerena, *Principal*
EMP: 164
SALES (corp-wide): 63.5B **Publicly Held**
SIC: 2096 Potato chips & similar snacks
HQ: Frito-Lay North America, Inc.
7701 Legacy Dr
Plano TX 75024

(P-2383)
FRITO-LAY NORTH AMERICA INC
1190 Spreckels Rd, Manteca (95336-8962)
PHONE.....................209 824-3700
Keith Prather, *Manager*
EMP: 20
SALES (corp-wide): 63.5B **Publicly Held**
WEB: www.fritolay.com
SIC: 2096 5145 Potato chips & similar
snacks; confectionery
HQ: Frito-Lay North America, Inc.
7701 Legacy Dr
Plano TX 75024

(P-2384)
FRITO-LAY NORTH AMERICA INC
5045 Forni Dr, Concord (94520-1224)
PHONE.....................925 689-4260
Andy Glavich, *Manager*
EMP: 50
SQ FT: 10,792
SALES (corp-wide): 63.5B **Publicly Held**
WEB: www.fritolay.com
SIC: 2096 Potato chips & similar snacks

▲ = Import ▼=Export
◆ =Import/Export

HQ: Frito-Lay North America, Inc.
7701 Legacy Dr
Plano TX 75024

(P-2385)
FRITO-LAY NORTH AMERICA INC
4535 Dupont Ct, Ventura (93003-7735)
PHONE...............................805 658-1668
Terri Livingston, *Manager*
Teri Livingston, *Manager*
EMP: 45
SALES (corp-wide): 63.5B **Publicly Held**
WEB: www.fritolay.com
SIC: 2096 Corn chips & other corn-based snacks
HQ: Frito-Lay North America, Inc.
7701 Legacy Dr
Plano TX 75024

(P-2386)
FRITO-LAY NORTH AMERICA INC
4953 Paramount Dr, San Diego (92123-1446)
PHONE...............................858 576-3300
Pete Rojas, *Manager*
Knick Staley, *Manager*
EMP: 12
SQ FT: 75,896
SALES (corp-wide): 63.5B **Publicly Held**
WEB: www.fritolay.com
SIC: 2096 Potato chips & similar snacks
HQ: Frito-Lay North America, Inc.
7701 Legacy Dr
Plano TX 75024

(P-2387)
FRITO-LAY NORTH AMERICA INC
635 W Valley Blvd, Bloomington (92316-2200)
PHONE...............................909 877-0902
Fred Schmidt, *Branch Mgr*
Rob Smith, *Manager*
EMP: 100
SQ FT: 18,220
SALES (corp-wide): 63.5B **Publicly Held**
WEB: www.fritolay.com
SIC: 2096 5145 5149 4226 Potato chips & similar snacks; confectionery; groceries & related products; special warehousing & storage
HQ: Frito-Lay North America, Inc.
7701 Legacy Dr
Plano TX 75024

(P-2388)
FRITO-LAY NORTH AMERICA INC
600 Garner Rd, Modesto (95357-0514)
PHONE...............................209 544-5400
Bob Schreck, *Manager*
Saul Esqueda, *Sales Staff*
EMP: 450
SALES (corp-wide): 63.5B **Publicly Held**
WEB: www.fritolay.com
SIC: 2096 2099 Potato chips & similar snacks; food preparations
HQ: Frito-Lay North America, Inc.
7701 Legacy Dr
Plano TX 75024

(P-2389)
FRITO-LAY NORTH AMERICA INC
28801 Highway 58, Bakersfield (93314-9000)
PHONE...............................661 328-6000
Jerry Matthews, *Manager*
Randy Brezinski, *Manager*
Edwin Field, *Manager*
Tim King, *Manager*
EMP: 800
SALES (corp-wide): 63.5B **Publicly Held**
WEB: www.fritolay.com
SIC: 2096 2099 Potato chips & similar snacks; food preparations

HQ: Frito-Lay North America, Inc.
7701 Legacy Dr
Plano TX 75024

(P-2390)
GRUMA CORPORATION
Also Called: Mission Foods Dc60
12316 World Trade Dr # 104, San Diego (92128-3795)
PHONE...............................858 673-5780
Armando Romero, *Manager*
EMP: 10 **Privately Held**
WEB: www.missionfoods.com
SIC: 2096 Tortilla chips
HQ: Gruma Corporation
5601 Executive Dr Ste 800
Irving TX 75038
972 232-5000

(P-2391)
GRUMA CORPORATION
Also Called: Mission Foods
2849 E Edgar Ave, Fresno (93706-5454)
PHONE...............................559 498-7820
Kathy Trout, *Plant Mgr*
EMP: 99 **Privately Held**
WEB: www.missionfoods.com
SIC: 2096 Tortilla chips
HQ: Gruma Corporation
5601 Executive Dr Ste 800
Irving TX 75038
972 232-5000

(P-2392)
GRUMA CORPORATION
Also Called: Mission Foods
11559 Jersey Blvd Ste A, Rancho Cucamonga (91730-4924)
PHONE...............................909 980-3566
Victor Cervantes, *Manager*
EMP: 206 **Privately Held**
WEB: www.missionfoods.com
SIC: 2096 Tortilla chips
HQ: Gruma Corporation
5601 Executive Dr Ste 800
Irving TX 75038
972 232-5000

(P-2393)
KING HENRYS INC
29124 Hancock Pkwy 1, Valencia (91355-1066)
PHONE...............................661 295-5566
Trina Davidian, *CEO*
◆ EMP: 45
SQ FT: 44,000
SALES: 19MM **Privately Held**
WEB: www.kinghenrys.com
SIC: 2096 2064 Cheese curls & puffs; breakfast bars

(P-2394)
LAURA SCUDDERS COMPANY LLC
1537 E Mcfadden Ave Ste B, Santa Ana (92705-4317)
PHONE...............................714 444-3700
Micheal Gallegos, *Mng Member*
▼ EMP: 25
SALES (est): 3.7MM **Privately Held**
SIC: 2096 Potato chips & similar snacks

(P-2395)
LOOKOUT ENTERPRISES INC
Also Called: Alto Rey
11468 Dona Teresa Dr, North Hollywood (91604-4271)
PHONE...............................323 969-0178
David Ufberg, *President*
Kelly Hurley, *Vice Pres*
David Richardson, *Manager*
EMP: 15
SALES (est): 1.7MM **Privately Held**
WEB: www.altorey.com
SIC: 2096 Potato chips & similar snacks

(P-2396)
MARQUEZ MARQUEZ INC
Also Called: Marquez & Marquez Food PR
11821 Industrial Ave, South Gate (90280-7914)
PHONE...............................562 408-0960
Elias Marquez, *President*
Adriana Marquez, *VP Sales*
EMP: 29

SALES (est): 5.6MM **Privately Held**
SIC: 2096 2041 Corn chips & other corn-based snacks; flour

(P-2397)
PERSHING FOODS
3680 S Santa Fe Ave, Vernon (90058-1413)
PHONE...............................323 589-1658
Jing Jun Jiang, *President*
Nelson Lee, *General Mgr*
Julia Lee, *Admin Sec*
EMP: 16
SQ FT: 1,500
SALES (est): 1.6MM **Privately Held**
SIC: 2096 Tortilla chips

(P-2398)
POPSALOT LLC
Also Called: Popsalot Gourmet Popcorn
7723 Somerset Blvd, Paramount (90723-4104)
P.O. Box 7040, Beverly Hills (90212-7040)
PHONE...............................213 761-0156
Victoria Ho, *Principal*
Jason Conn, *Sales Mgr*
▲ EMP: 20
SQ FT: 8,400
SALES (est): 1.4MM **Privately Held**
SIC: 2096 Popcorn, already popped (except candy covered)

(P-2399)
PURE NATURE FOODS LLC
700 Santa Anita Dr, Woodland (95776-6102)
P.O. Box 2387 (95776-2387)
PHONE...............................530 723-5269
Miguel Reyna, *President*
Shan Staka, *CFO*
Matt Brabazon, *Vice Pres*
EMP: 25
SQ FT: 60,000
SALES (est): 890.1K **Privately Held**
SIC: 2096 Rice chips

(P-2400)
RODRIGUEZ ISMAEL
Also Called: Lompoc Tortilla Shop
138 N D St, Lompoc (93436-6912)
PHONE...............................805 736-7362
Ismael Rodriguez, *Owner*
Juanita Rodriguez, *Co-Owner*
EMP: 10
SALES: 629K **Privately Held**
SIC: 2096 Tortilla chips

(P-2401)
RUDOLPH FOODS COMPANY INC
920 W Fourth St, Beaumont (92223-2675)
PHONE...............................909 388-2202
Fransico Quirarte, *Manager*
EMP: 75
SALES (corp-wide): 138.3MM **Privately Held**
SIC: 2096 Pork rinds
PA: Rudolph Foods Company, Inc.
6575 Bellefontaine Rd
Lima OH 45804
909 383-7463

(P-2402)
RUHE CORPORATION (PA)
901 S Leslie St, La Habra (90631-6841)
PHONE...............................714 777-8321
Thomas A Ruhe, *President*
Connie Ruhe, *Treasurer*
Scott Ruhe, *Vice Pres*
EMP: 173
SALES (est): 16.8MM **Privately Held**
SIC: 2096 Tortilla chips

(P-2403)
SENOR SNACKS INC
Also Called: Senor Snacks Holdings
2325 Raymer Ave, Fullerton (92833-2514)
PHONE...............................714 739-1073
Javier Ramirez, *CEO*
Robert Drelford, *CFO*
Salvador Diaz, *General Mgr*
EMP: 15
SQ FT: 16,264
SALES (est): 2.4MM **Privately Held**
WEB: www.senorsnacks.com
SIC: 2096

(P-2404)
TACO WORKS INC
3424 Sacramento Dr, San Luis Obispo (93401-7128)
PHONE...............................805 541-1556
Roy D Bayly, *President*
Theresa Bayly, *Admin Sec*
EMP: 20
SQ FT: 9,900
SALES (est): 3.6MM **Privately Held**
SIC: 2096 5145 Tortilla chips; snack foods

(P-2405)
TACUPETO CHIPS & SALSA INC
1330 Distribution Way A, Vista (92081-8837)
PHONE...............................760 597-9400
Gilberto Pablo Fajardo, *President*
Gilberto Ramon Fajardo, *Vice Pres*
EMP: 18
SALES (est): 25K **Privately Held**
SIC: 2096 Corn chips & other corn-based snacks

(P-2406)
WARNOCK FOOD PRODUCTS INC
20237 Masa St, Madera (93638-9457)
PHONE...............................559 661-4845
Donald Warnock, *Principal*
Cathryn Warnock, *Admin Sec*
Gary Long, *Plant Mgr*
Neil Coen, *Maintence Staff*
▲ EMP: 98
SQ FT: 25,000
SALES (est): 35.9MM **Privately Held**
WEB: www.warnockfoods.com
SIC: 2096 2099 2033 Tortilla chips; food preparations; canned fruits & specialties

2097 Ice

(P-2407)
ARCTIC GLACIER CALIFORNIA INC
Also Called: Jack Frost Ice Service
1440 Coldwell Ave, Modesto (95350-5704)
PHONE...............................209 524-3128
Stephen Ward, *Regional Mgr*
EMP: 85
SALES: 950K **Privately Held**
SIC: 2097 Manufactured ice

(P-2408)
ARCTIC GLACIER USA INC
17011 Central Ave, Carson (90746-1303)
PHONE...............................310 638-0321
Sharon Cooper, *Manager*
EMP: 200
SALES (corp-wide): 132MM **Privately Held**
SIC: 2097 Manufactured ice
HQ: Arctic Glacier U.S.A., Inc.
1654 Marthaler Ln
Saint Paul MN 55118
204 784-5873

(P-2409)
CHINO ICE SERVICE LLC
3640 Francis Ave, Chino (91710-1512)
PHONE...............................909 628-2105
Gerald Ades,
EMP: 27 EST: 1950
SQ FT: 6,000
SALES (est): 3.2MM **Privately Held**
WEB: www.chinoice.com
SIC: 2097 Block ice

(P-2410)
COACHELLE VALLEY ICE CO
83796 Date Ave, Indio (92201-4738)
P.O. Box 1256 (92202-1256)
PHONE...............................760 347-3529
Hugh Mason, *President*
EMP: 20
SQ FT: 22,000
SALES (est): 1.8MM **Privately Held**
SIC: 2097 Manufactured ice

PRODUCTS & SVCS

(P-2411)
CV ICE COMPANY INC
83796 Date Ave, Indio (92201-4738)
P.O. Box 1256 (92202-1256)
PHONE.................................760 347-3529
Kevin Mason, *President*
EMP: 29
SALES (est): 3.5MM **Privately Held**
SIC: 2097 Manufactured ice

(P-2412)
FRESH INNOVATIONS LLC
Also Called: Terminal Freezers
908 E 3rd St, Oxnard (93030-6119)
P.O. Box 472 (93032-0472)
PHONE.................................805 483-2265
John Brashear, *Manager*
EMP: 45
SALES (corp-wide): 9.5MM **Privately Held**
WEB: www.terminalfreezers.com
SIC: 2097 4222 Manufactured ice; refrigerated warehousing & storage
PA: Fresh Innovations Llc
1135 Mountain View Ave
Oxnard CA 93030
360 755-9015

(P-2413)
GLACIER VALLEY ICE COMPANY LP (PA)
Also Called: Glacier Ice Company
8580 Laguna Station Rd, Elk Grove
(95758-9550)
PHONE.................................916 394-2939
Sarah Demartini, *Principal*
Angela Aistrup, *Systems Mgr*
Karen Anderson, *Human Resources*
Bob Sikes, *Sales Executive*
EMP: 40
SQ FT: 72,000
SALES (est): 3.8MM **Privately Held**
SIC: 2097 5199 Manufactured ice; ice, manufactured or natural

(P-2414)
GROWERS ICE CO
1124 Abbott St, Salinas (93901-4502)
P.O. Box 298 (93902-0298)
PHONE.................................831 424-5781
Susan Merrill, *Ch of Bd*
Kathy Bullene, *Human Res Dir*
George Mika, *Opers Spvr*
Tom Schmidt, *Safety Mgr*
Scott Jackson, *Plant Mgr*
EMP: 36
SQ FT: 200,000
SALES (est): 12MM **Privately Held**
WEB: www.growersice.com
SIC: 2097 4222 7623 6512 Manufactured ice; warehousing, cold storage or refrigerated; ice making machinery repair service; commercial & industrial building operation

(P-2415)
ICE MAN INC
8710 Park St, Bellflower (90706-5527)
PHONE.................................562 633-4423
Jim Mueller, *President*
Jeff Hendershot, *Corp Secy*
Diane Mueller, *Vice Pres*
EMP: 15
SQ FT: 5,000
SALES (est): 2.3MM **Privately Held**
WEB: www.iceman.com
SIC: 2097 Block ice; ice cubes

(P-2416)
KAR ICE SERVICE INC (PA)
2521 Solar Way, Barstow (92311-3616)
P.O. Box 1197 (92312-1197)
PHONE.................................760 256-2648
Tom Lewis, *President*
Micheal Lewis, *CFO*
Carol Lewis, *Corp Secy*
EMP: 18
SQ FT: 14,400
SALES (est): 1.2MM **Privately Held**
WEB: www.karice.com
SIC: 2097 Ice cubes

(P-2417)
PARTY TIME ICE INC
983 N Pacific Ave, San Pedro
(90731-1633)
PHONE.................................310 833-0187
Ambrose Marchant III, *Ch of Bd*
Marea Marchant, *CFO*
Douglas N Marchant,
EMP: 15
SQ FT: 5,000
SALES (est): 2.3MM **Privately Held**
WEB: www.partytimeice.com
SIC: 2097 Manufactured ice

(P-2418)
PELTON-SHEPHERD INDUSTRIES INC (PA)
812 W Luce St Ste B, Stockton
(95203-4937)
P.O. Box 30218 (95213-0218)
PHONE.................................209 460-0893
Alicia M Shepherd, *President*
▲ **EMP:** 35 **EST:** 1950
SQ FT: 30,000
SALES: 14.4MM **Privately Held**
WEB: www.peltonshepherd.com
SIC: 2097 Manufactured ice

(P-2419)
R&JS BUSINESS GROUP INC
Also Called: Carving Ice
900 S Placentia Ave Ste B, Placentia
(92870-8002)
PHONE.................................714 224-1455
Roland Hernandez, *CEO*
David Sosnowski, *President*
Janice Hernandez, *CFO*
EMP: 17
SQ FT: 12,000
SALES: 1.2MM **Privately Held**
SIC: 2097 Manufactured ice

(P-2420)
REDDY ICE CORPORATION
462 N 8th St, Brawley (92227-1605)
PHONE.................................760 344-0535
Robert Whitted, *CEO*
EMP: 22
SALES (corp-wide): 2.5B **Privately Held**
SIC: 2097 Manufactured ice
HQ: Reddy Ice Corporation
5720 Lyndon B Johnson Fwy # 200
Dallas TX 75240
214 526-6740

(P-2421)
SOUTHERN CALIFORNIA ICE CO
Also Called: Arrowhead Ice
22921 Lockness Ave, Torrance
(90501-5118)
PHONE.................................310 325-1040
Sharon Corbin, *President*
EMP: 13 **EST:** 1935
SQ FT: 11,000
SALES (est): 2.7MM **Privately Held**
WEB: www.sccu.edu
SIC: 2097 Ice cubes

(P-2422)
UNION ICE COMPANY
2970 E 50th St, Vernon (90058-2920)
PHONE.................................323 277-1000
Richard L Burke, *Principal*
EMP: 14
SALES (est): 1.2MM **Privately Held**
SIC: 2097 Manufactured ice

(P-2423)
UNITED STATES COLD STORAGE INC
Also Called: U S Cold Storage
4701 Stine Rd, Bakersfield (93313-2342)
PHONE.................................661 834-2371
Bob West, *Sales/Mktg Mgr*
EMP: 21
SALES (corp-wide): 13.8B **Privately Held**
WEB: www.uscold.com
SIC: 2097 Manufactured ice
HQ: United States Cold Storage, Inc.
2 Aquarium Dr Ste 400
Camden NJ 08103
856 354-8181

(P-2424)
YALDO ENTERPRISES INC
Also Called: Perkins Market
24680 Viejas Grade Rd B, Descanso
(91916-9815)
P.O. Box 262 (91916-0262)
PHONE.................................619 445-2578
Steve Yaldo, *President*
Sean Yaldo, *Vice Pres*
EMP: 12
SQ FT: 4,000
SALES (est): 1.4MM **Privately Held**
SIC: 2097 5199 Manufactured ice; ice, manufactured or natural

---

2098 Macaroni, Spaghetti & Noodles

(P-2425)
C NC NOODLE CO
1787 Sabre St, Hayward (94545-1015)
PHONE.................................510 732-1318
Betty Lim, *Principal*
▲ **EMP:** 12
SALES (est): 1.6MM **Privately Held**
SIC: 2098 Noodles (e.g. egg, plain & water), dry

(P-2426)
FLORENCE MACARONI COMPANY
1312 W 2nd St, San Pedro (90732-3210)
PHONE.................................310 548-5942
Beatrice Esposito, *President*
Pat Peterson, *Treasurer*
Joseph Esposito, *Vice Pres*
EMP: 13
SQ FT: 8,000
SALES (est): 885.5K **Privately Held**
SIC: 2098 Macaroni products (e.g. alphabets, rings & shells), dry; spaghetti, dry

(P-2427)
FUNGS VILLAGE INC
5339 E Washington Blvd, Commerce
(90040-2111)
PHONE.................................323 881-1600
Albert Lee, *President*
▲ **EMP:** 20
SQ FT: 18,000
SALES (est): 3MM **Privately Held**
SIC: 2098 Noodles (e.g. egg, plain & water), dry

(P-2428)
HERSHEY COMPANY
2704 S Maple Ave, Fresno (93725-2109)
P.O. Box 12146 (93776-2146)
PHONE.................................559 485-8110
Thomas Martens, *Branch Mgr*
EMP: 125
SQ FT: 135,000
SALES (corp-wide): 7.5B **Publicly Held**
WEB: www.hersheys.com
SIC: 2098 Macaroni products (e.g. alphabets, rings & shells), dry
PA: Hershey Company
100 Crystal A Dr
Hershey PA 17033
717 534-4200

(P-2429)
MARUCHAN INC
1902 Deere Ave, Irvine (92606-4819)
PHONE.................................949 789-2300
Shino Saki, *Manager*
Jo Kaneko, *Accounting Mgr*
EMP: 250
SALES (corp-wide): 3.6B **Privately Held**
WEB: www.maruchaninc.com
SIC: 2098 5146 Noodles (e.g. egg, plain & water), dry; fish, cured; fish, fresh; fish, frozen, unpackaged
HQ: Maruchan, Inc.
15800 Laguna Canyon Rd
Irvine CA 92618
949 789-2300

(P-2430)
MYOJO USA INC
6220 Prescott Ct, Chino (91710-7111)
PHONE.................................909 464-1411
Yoshie Nakamura, *President*
Takuro Okada, *CFO*

▲ **EMP:** 16
SQ FT: 20,759
SALES (est): 3.6MM
SALES (corp-wide): 4.8B **Privately Held**
SIC: 2098 Noodles (e.g. egg, plain & water), dry
PA: Nissin Foods Holdings Co.,Ltd.
6-28-1, Shinjuku
Shinjuku-Ku TKY 160-0
332 055-111

(P-2431)
NANKA SEIMEN CO
3030 Leonis Blvd, Vernon (90058-2914)
PHONE.................................323 585-9967
Shoichi Sayano, *President*
Kanji Sayano, *Shareholder*
Reigo Sayano, *Shareholder*
Fusako Yoshida, *Treasurer*
Toshiaki Yoshida, *Vice Pres*
▲ **EMP:** 18 **EST:** 1905
SQ FT: 20,000
SALES (est): 3.8MM **Privately Held**
SIC: 2098 Noodles (e.g. egg, plain & water), dry

(P-2432)
NESTLE REFRIGERATED FOOD CO
800 N Brand Blvd Fl 5, Glendale
(91203-4281)
PHONE.................................818 549-6000
Fax: 818 549-6399
EMP: 500
SALES (est): 63.7MM
SALES (corp-wide): 94.6B **Privately Held**
SIC: 2098 2033
HQ: Nestle Usa, Inc.
800 N Brand Blvd
Glendale CA 22209
818 549-6000

(P-2433)
NEW HONG KONG NOODLE CO INC
360 Swift Ave Ste 22, South San Francisco
(94080-6220)
PHONE.................................650 588-6425
Steven Lum, *President*
Wai-Kui England Lum, *Treasurer*
Richard Lum, *Vice Pres*
Lam Wai Lum, *Admin Sec*
◆ **EMP:** 40
SQ FT: 26,000
SALES (est): 8MM **Privately Held**
WEB: www.nhknoodle.com
SIC: 2098 Noodles (e.g. egg, plain & water), dry

(P-2434)
NISSIN FOODS USA COMPANY INC (HQ)
2001 W Rosecrans Ave, Gardena
(90249-2994)
PHONE.................................310 327-8478
Hiroyuki Yoshida, *CEO*
Evelyn Jareno, *President*
Takahiro Enomoto, *Vice Pres*
Leslie Mohr, *Vice Pres*
Fumiko Carney, *Admin Asst*
◆ **EMP:** 200 **EST:** 1970
SQ FT: 200,000
SALES (est): 120.1MM
SALES (corp-wide): 4.8B **Privately Held**
WEB: www.nissinfoods.com
SIC: 2098 2038 Noodles (e.g. egg, plain & water), dry; ethnic foods, frozen
PA: Nissin Foods Holdings Co.,Ltd.
6-28-1, Shinjuku
Shinjuku-Ku TKY 160-0
332 055-111

(P-2435)
NOODLE THEORY
6099 Claremont Ave, Oakland
(94618-1222)
PHONE.................................510 595-6988
Louis KAO, *President*
EMP: 12
SALES (est): 1.3MM **Privately Held**
SIC: 2098 Noodles (e.g. egg, plain & water), dry

▲ = Import ▼=Export
◆ =Import/Export

(P-2436)
PASTA SONOMA LLC
640 Martin Ave Ste 1, Rohnert Park
(94928-7994)
PHONE.....................................707 584-0800
Don Luber,
▲ EMP: 17
SQ FT: 6,500
SALES: 2MM **Privately Held**
WEB: www.pastasonoma.com
SIC: 2098 5812 Macaroni & spaghetti;
eating places

(P-2437)
PEKING NOODLE CO INC
1514 N San Fernando Rd, Los Angeles
(90065-1282)
PHONE.....................................323 223-0897
Frank Tong, *President*
Stephen Tong, *President*
Donna Tong, *Corp Secy*
Derek Tat, *General Mgr*
▲ EMP: 40
SQ FT: 40,000
SALES (est): 9.1MM **Privately Held**
SIC: 2098 2052 Noodles (e.g. egg, plain &
water), dry; cookies & crackers

(P-2438)
SAKURA NOODLE INC
620 E 7th St, Los Angeles (90021-1461)
PHONE.....................................213 623-2396
Shohachi Suzuki, *President*
Taketoshi Inagaki, *Admin Sec*
▲ EMP: 14 EST: 1978
SQ FT: 9,000
SALES (est): 2.1MM **Privately Held**
SIC: 2098 2099 Noodles (e.g. egg, plain &
water), dry; food preparations

(P-2439)
SAMYANG USA INC
3810 Wilshire Blvd # 1212, Los Angeles
(90010-3204)
PHONE.....................................562 946-9977
Mun K Chun, *President*
John Ha, *Admin Sec*
Dongwook Park, *Planning*
◆ EMP: 10
SQ FT: 195,580
SALES: 12MM **Privately Held**
WEB: www.samyang.com
SIC: 2098 Noodles (e.g. egg, plain &
water), dry

(P-2440)
**SANYO FOODS CORP AMERICA
(DH)**
Also Called: Yorba Linda Country Club
11955 Monarch St, Garden Grove
(92841-2194)
PHONE.....................................714 891-3671
Junichiro Ida, *CEO*
Hiroaki Obuchi, *Admin Sec*
Hiratsugu Aiba, *Controller*
K Kumagai, *Manager*
▲ EMP: 30
SQ FT: 130,000
SALES: 20MM
SALES (corp-wide): 71B **Privately Held**
SIC: 2098 7997 Noodles (e.g. egg, plain &
water), dry; golf club, membership; coun-
try club, membership
HQ: Sanyo Foods Co., Ltd.
1-1-1, Higashihama
Ichikawa CHI 272-0
473 290-801

(P-2441)
SENG CHEANG MONG CO
Also Called: Seng Cheang Mong Food
2661 Merced Ave, El Monte (91733-1905)
PHONE.....................................626 442-2899
Chay Ling, *Owner*
EMP: 10
SALES (est): 932.5K **Privately Held**
SIC: 2098 Macaroni & spaghetti

(P-2442)
THAI THAI NOODLE
1400 California St, San Francisco
(94109-4712)
PHONE.....................................415 441-5551
Sineenart Puangpini, *Principal*
EMP: 10

SALES (est): 779.2K **Privately Held**
SIC: 2098 Noodles (e.g. egg, plain &
water), dry

(P-2443)
TM NOODLE
4110 Manzanita Ave, Carmichael
(95608-1726)
PHONE.....................................916 486-2579
Minh Pham, *Principal*
EMP: 13
SALES (est): 670K **Privately Held**
SIC: 2098 Noodles (e.g. egg, plain &
water), dry

(P-2444)
WAH FUNG NOODLES INC
4443 Rowland Ave, El Monte (91731-1121)
PHONE.....................................626 442-0588
Zexiong Liang, *President*
▲ EMP: 13
SALES (est): 1.7MM **Privately Held**
SIC: 2098 Noodles (e.g. egg, plain &
water), dry

(P-2445)
YONG KEE RICE NOODLE CO
Also Called: Young Kee
946 Stockton St Apt 10c, San Francisco
(94108-1643)
PHONE.....................................415 986-3759
Kwok Wong, *Partner*
Ying Wong, *Partner*
EMP: 15 EST: 1952
SQ FT: 1,500
SALES (est): 880K **Privately Held**
SIC: 2098 5411 Noodles (e.g. egg, plain &
water), dry; grocery stores

2099 Food Preparations, NEC

(P-2446)
AB MAURI FOOD INC
Also Called: Fleis Chmanns Vinegar
12604 Hiddencreek Way A, Cerritos
(90703-2137)
PHONE.....................................562 483-4619
Dave Billings, *President*
EMP: 12
SALES (corp-wide): 19.7B **Privately Held**
WEB: www.breadworld.com
SIC: 2099 2087 Vinegar; flavoring extracts
& syrups
HQ: Ab Mauri Food Inc.
4240 Duncan Ave Ste 150
Saint Louis MO 63110
314 392-0800

(P-2447)
**ADELANTO ELEMENTARY
SCHOOL DST**
Also Called: Desert Trils Prpratory Academy
14350 Bellflower St, Adelanto
(92301-4246)
P.O. Box 400880, Hesperia (92340-0880)
PHONE.....................................760 530-7680
Mandy Plantz, *Principal*
EMP: 42
SALES (corp-wide): 102.7MM **Privately
Held**
SIC: 2099 Food preparations
PA: Adelanto Elementary School District
11824 Air Expy
Adelanto CA 92301
760 246-8691

(P-2448)
**ALEXANDER VALLEY GOURMET
LLC**
140 Grove Ct B, Healdsburg (95448-4780)
PHONE.....................................707 473-0116
David Ehreth,
EMP: 20
SALES (est): 2.5MM **Privately Held**
SIC: 2099 Food preparations

(P-2449)
**ALLIED BLNDING INGREDIENTS
INC**
Also Called: Solvaira
5690 Lindbergh Ln, Bell (90201-6411)
PHONE.....................................562 806-7560

Veronica Banuelos, *Purchasing*
EMP: 10
SALES (corp-wide): 112.3MM **Privately
Held**
SIC: 2099 Tortillas, fresh or refrigerated
HQ: Allied Blending & Ingredients, Inc.
121 Royal Rd
Keokuk IA 52632
-

(P-2450)
AMBER FOODS INC
301 N M St, Dinuba (93618-2135)
PHONE.....................................559 591-4782
William Bernstein, *President*
Daryll Bernstein, *Vice Pres*
EMP: 100
SQ FT: 40,000
SALES (est): 14.6MM **Privately Held**
SIC: 2099 Salads, fresh or refrigerated

(P-2451)
**AMERICAN YEAST
CORPORATION**
5455 District Blvd, Bakersfield
(93313-2123)
PHONE.....................................661 834-1050
Lloyd Fry, *Opers-Prdtn-Mfg*
EMP: 30 **Privately Held**
SIC: 2099 Yeast
HQ: American Yeast Corporation
8215 Beachwood Rd
Baltimore MD 21222
410 477-3700

(P-2452)
AMZART INC
Also Called: MARGEAUX AND LINDA'S
VEGAN KIT
3260 Casitas Ave, Los Angeles
(90039-2206)
PHONE.....................................323 404-9372
Aram Zadikian, *President*
Margaux Zadikian, *Vice Pres*
EMP: 10
SQ FT: 3,000
SALES: 604.3K **Privately Held**
SIC: 2099 Ready-to-eat meals, salads &
sandwiches

(P-2453)
ANNIES INC (HQ)
Also Called: Homegrown Naturals
1610 5th St, Berkeley (94710-1715)
PHONE.....................................510 558-7500
John Foraker, *CEO*
Molly F Ashby, *Ch of Bd*
Kelly J Kennedy, *CFO*
Sarah Bird, *Officer*
Amanda K Martinez, *Exec VP*
EMP: 80
SQ FT: 33,500
SALES (est): 68.4MM
SALES (corp-wide): 15.7B **Publicly Held**
WEB: www.annies.com
SIC: 2099 Food preparations
PA: General Mills, Inc.
1 General Mills Blvd
Minneapolis MN 55426
763 764-7600

(P-2454)
APIO INC (HQ)
4575 W Main St, Guadalupe (93434-1659)
P.O. Box 727 (93434-0727)
PHONE.....................................800 454-1355
Ron Midyett, *CEO*
Tim Nykoluk, *President*
Debra Vanhorsen, *President*
Parker Javid, *Officer*
Todd Reece, *Vice Pres*
◆ EMP: 80
SQ FT: 200,000
SALES: 470.5MM
SALES (corp-wide): 524.2MM **Publicly
Held**
WEB: www.apioinc.com
SIC: 2099 0723 Food preparations; veg-
etable packing services
PA: Landec Corporation
5201 Great America Pkwy
Santa Clara CA 95054
650 306-1650

(P-2455)
**ARANDAS TORTILLA COMPANY
INC**
1318 E Scotts Ave, Stockton (95205-6152)
PHONE.....................................209 464-8675
Victor Aranda, *CEO*
Javier Aranda, *Treasurer*
Vicent Aranda, *Vice Pres*
EMP: 48
SQ FT: 20,000
SALES (est): 8.8MM **Privately Held**
SIC: 2099 Tortillas, fresh or refrigerated

(P-2456)
AREVALO TORTILLERIA INC
3033 Supply Ave, Commerce (90040-2709)
P.O. Box 788, Los Angeles (90078-0788)
PHONE.....................................323 888-1711
Edward Arello, *Manager*
EMP: 30
SALES (est): 2MM
SALES (corp-wide): 36.6MM **Privately
Held**
SIC: 2099 Tortillas, fresh or refrigerated
PA: Arevalo Tortilleria, Inc.
1537 W Mines Ave
Montebello CA 90640
323 888-1711

(P-2457)
**AREVALO TORTILLERIA INC
(PA)**
1537 W Mines Ave, Montebello
(90640-5414)
P.O. Box 788 (90640-0788)
PHONE.....................................323 888-1711
Jose Luis Arevalo, *CEO*
Emilia Arevalo, *Admin Sec*
Daniel Arevalo, *Info Tech Mgr*
Luis Arevalo, *Manager*
▲ EMP: 82
SQ FT: 20,000
SALES (est): 36.6MM **Privately Held**
SIC: 2099 Tortillas, fresh or refrigerated

(P-2458)
**ASIANA CUISINE ENTERPRISES
INC**
Also Called: Ace Sushi
22771 S Wstn Ave Ste 100, Torrance
(90501)
PHONE.....................................310 327-2223
Harlan Chin, *President*
Gary Chin, *CFO*
▲ EMP: 560
SQ FT: 6,000
SALES (est): 48.6MM **Privately Held**
WEB: www.acesushi.com
SIC: 2099 5812 8741 Ready-to-eat
meals, salads & sandwiches; fast food
restaurants & stands; management serv-
ices

(P-2459)
BAKEMARK USA LLC
32621 Central Ave, Union City
(94587-2008)
PHONE.....................................510 487-8188
Dean Chavez, *Manager*
EMP: 50
SALES (corp-wide): 615.9MM **Privately
Held**
SIC: 2099 Food preparations
PA: Bakemark Usa Llc
7351 Crider Ave
Pico Rivera CA 90660
562 949-1054

(P-2460)
**BARNEY & CO CALIFORNIA
LLC**
2925 S Elm Ave Ste 101, Fresno
(93706-5465)
PHONE.....................................559 442-1752
Dawn Kelley, *President*
Steve Kelley, *COO*
Tiffany Nguyen, *Accountant*
Dale Killen, *Plant Mgr*
Steven J Luttrell,
EMP: 18 EST: 2006
SQ FT: 37,000
SALES (est): 6.9MM **Privately Held**
SIC: 2099 Almond pastes

(P-2461)
BAY LEAF SPICE COMPANY
21c Orinda Way 363, Orinda (94563-2534)
PHONE.....................................925 330-1918
Mike Lewis, *President*
EMP: 20
SALES: 5MM **Privately Held**
SIC: 2099 Seasonings & spices

(P-2462)
BDS NATURAL PRODUCTS INC (PA)
Also Called: Npms Natural Products Mil Svcs
14824 S Main St, Gardena (90248-1919)
PHONE.....................................310 518-2227
Steven G Brenneis, *CEO*
David Solomon, *Vice Pres*
▲ **EMP:** 65
SQ FT: 80,000
SALES (est): 12.2MM **Privately Held**
WEB: www.bdsnatural.com
SIC: 2099 5149 Seasonings & spices; tea blending; natural & organic foods

(P-2463)
BERBER FOOD MANUFACTURING INC
Also Called: Ml Rancho Tortilla Factory
425 Hester St, San Leandro (94577-1025)
PHONE.....................................510 553-0444
Manuel Berber, *President*
Robert Berber Jr, *Corp Secy*
▼ **EMP:** 150
SQ FT: 85,000
SALES (est): 28.6MM **Privately Held**
SIC: 2099 Tortillas, fresh or refrigerated

(P-2464)
BEST FORMULATIONS INC
17758 Rowland St, City of Industry (91748-1148)
PHONE.....................................626 912-9998
Charles Ung, *Chairman*
Jeffrey Goh, *President*
Eugene Ung, *CEO*
Robin C Koon, *Exec VP*
Nighat Ansari, *Vice Pres*
◆ **EMP:** 200
SQ FT: 50,000
SALES (est): 80.4MM **Privately Held**
WEB: www.bestformulations.com
SIC: 2099 8748 5149 2834 Food preparations; business consulting; health foods; pharmaceutical preparations

(P-2465)
BIMBO BAKERIES USA INC
38960 Trade Center Dr A, Palmdale (93551-3715)
PHONE.....................................661 274-8458
Nenette Bertell, *Manager*
EMP: 16 **Privately Held**
SIC: 2099 Tortillas, fresh or refrigerated
HQ: Bimbo Bakeries Usa, Inc
255 Business Center Dr # 200
Horsham PA 19044
215 347-5500

(P-2466)
BIMBO BAKERIES USA INC
1215 Alek St, Anaheim (92805)
PHONE.....................................714 533-9436
Jesse Delgado, *Manager*
EMP: 50 **Privately Held**
SIC: 2099 Tortillas, fresh or refrigerated
HQ: Bimbo Bakeries Usa, Inc
255 Business Center Dr # 200
Horsham PA 19044
215 347-5500

(P-2467)
BIMBO BAKERIES USA INC
21423 Strathern St, Canoga Park (91304-4135)
PHONE.....................................818 348-9716
Scott Hubert, *Manager*
EMP: 19
SQ FT: 7,920 **Privately Held**
SIC: 2099 Tortillas, fresh or refrigerated
HQ: Bimbo Bakeries Usa, Inc
255 Business Center Dr # 200
Horsham PA 19044
215 347-5500

(P-2468)
BITCHIN INC
Also Called: Bitchin Sauce
6211 Yarrow Dr Ste C, Carlsbad (92011-1539)
PHONE.....................................760 224-7447
Starr Edwards, *CEO*
Harrison Edwards, *Chief Mktg Ofcr*
EMP: 26 **EST:** 2012
SALES (est): 345.4K **Privately Held**
SIC: 2099 Sauces: gravy, dressing & dip mixes

(P-2469)
BLUE DIAMOND GROWERS
1701 C St, Sacramento (95811-1029)
PHONE.....................................916 446-8464
EMP: 191
SALES (corp-wide): 1.6B **Privately Held**
SIC: 2099 Food preparations
PA: Diamond Blue Growers
1802 C St
Sacramento CA 95811
916 442-0771

(P-2470)
BLUE DIAMOND GROWERS
Also Called: Blue Diamond
1300 N Washington Rd, Turlock (95380-9506)
PHONE.....................................209 604-1501
EMP: 100
SALES (corp-wide): 1.6B **Privately Held**
SIC: 2099 Food preparations
PA: Diamond Blue Growers
1802 C St
Sacramento CA 95811
916 442-0771

(P-2471)
BOTANAS MEXICO INC
11122 Rush St, South El Monte (91733)
PHONE.....................................626 279-1512
Carlos Aleman, *President*
Miriam Aleman, *Vice Pres*
▲ **EMP:** 16
SALES (est): 2.4MM **Privately Held**
SIC: 2099 5499 Seasonings & spices; spices, including grinding; spices & herbs

(P-2472)
BRIGHT PEOPLE FOODS INC (PA)
Also Called: Dr McDougall's Right Foods
1640 Tide Ct, Woodland (95776-6210)
P.O. Box 2205 (95776-2205)
PHONE.....................................530 669-6870
Michael L Vinnicombe, *President*
Carolyn Vinnicombe, *Vice Pres*
▼ **EMP:** 25
SQ FT: 30,000
SALES (est): 7MM **Privately Held**
SIC: 2099 Spices, including grinding

(P-2473)
BROWN BAG SANDWICH COMPANY LLC
111 E Garry Ave, Santa Ana (92707-4201)
PHONE.....................................714 444-2126
Jeffrey P Heaurland,
Steve Bogen,
EMP: 140
SQ FT: 27,000
SALES (est): 15.5MM **Privately Held**
SIC: 2099 5812 Sandwiches, assembled & packaged: for wholesale market; sandwiches & submarines shop

(P-2474)
C & F FOODS INC (PA)
15620 E Valley Blvd, City of Industry (91744-3926)
PHONE.....................................626 723-1000
Manuel G Fernandez, *Ch of Bd*
Luis Faura, *President*
Alex Tran, *CFO*
Gloria Riesgo, *Executive Asst*
Werner Schlag, *Info Tech Dir*
▲ **EMP:** 100
SQ FT: 165,000
SALES (est): 255.7MM **Privately Held**
WEB: www.cnf-foods.com
SIC: 2099 Food preparations

(P-2475)
C&S GLOBAL FOODS INC
Also Called: Ojo De Agua Produce
20110 State Highway 33, Dos Palos (93620-9701)
P.O. Box 1209, Los Banos (93635-1209)
PHONE.....................................209 392-2223
Reuben Castaneda, *Owner*
EMP: 13
SALES (est): 1.8MM **Privately Held**
SIC: 2099 4789 Food preparations; freight car loading & unloading

(P-2476)
CACHE CREEK FOODS LLC
411 N Pioneer Ave, Woodland (95776-6122)
P.O. Box 180 (95776-0180)
PHONE.....................................530 662-1764
Matthew Morehart,
Connie Stephens, *Office Mgr*
Layne Lee, *Administration*
Michael Clark, *QC Mgr*
Carl Hartmangruber, *Plant Supt*
▲ **EMP:** 19
SQ FT: 40,000
SALES (est): 5MM **Privately Held**
WEB: www.cachecreek.com
SIC: 2099 2064 Almond pastes; nuts, glace

(P-2477)
CADENCE GOURMET LLC
Also Called: Cadence Gourmet Involve Foods
155 Klug Cir, Corona (92880-5424)
PHONE.....................................951 272-5949
Brian J Wynn, *CEO*
David Wells, *President*
▲ **EMP:** 30
SQ FT: 12,000
SALES (est): 9.7MM **Privately Held**
SIC: 2099 Food preparations

(P-2478)
CALIF FRUT AND TMTO KTCHN LLC
1785 Ashby Rd, Merced (95348-4302)
PHONE.....................................530 666-6600
Chris Rufer, *Mng Member*
Tim Cruise,
▼ **EMP:** 10 **EST:** 1946
SQ FT: 252,212
SALES (est): 1.3MM **Privately Held**
WEB: www.calfruittom.com
SIC: 2099 Food preparations

(P-2479)
CALIFORNIA NATURAL PRODUCTS
Also Called: Power Automation Systems
1250 Lathrop Rd, Lathrop (95330-9709)
P.O. Box 1219 (95330-1219)
PHONE.....................................209 858-2525
Eric Beringause, *CEO*
Timothy Preuninger, *CFO*
Curtis Heffernan, *VP Bus Dvlpt*
David Stott, *Admin Sec*
Lew Webb, *Administration*
▲ **EMP:** 230 **EST:** 1976
SQ FT: 220,000
SALES (est): 80.6MM
SALES (corp-wide): 350.6MM **Privately Held**
SIC: 2099 7389 Food preparations; packaging & labeling services
HQ: Gf Assets Holdings Corporation
N116w15970 Main St
Germantown WI 53022
262 251-8572

(P-2480)
CALIFORNIA NEW FOODS LLC
11165 Commercial Pkwy, Castroville (95012-3207)
PHONE.....................................831 444-1872
Peter Uli,
EMP: 25
SALES (est): 809.2K **Privately Held**
SIC: 2099 Food preparations

(P-2481)
CAMINO REAL FOODS INC (PA)
Also Called: Camino Real Kitchens
2638 E Vernon Ave, Vernon (90058-1825)
P.O. Box 30729, Los Angeles (90030-0729)
PHONE.....................................323 585-6599
Rob Cross, *President*
Richard Lunsford, *CFO*
Yessica Carrillo, *Admin Asst*
Vicky Taylor, *Accountant*
Brian Canny, *Controller*
EMP: 410
SALES (est): 132.8MM **Privately Held**
WEB: www.crfoods.com
SIC: 2099 Food preparations

(P-2482)
CARMEL FOOD GROUP INC
31128 San Clemente St, Hayward (94544-7802)
PHONE.....................................510 471-4889
John Personeni, *President*
Joel Personeni, *Corp Secy*
▲ **EMP:** 31
SQ FT: 18,000
SALES (est): 5.2MM **Privately Held**
WEB: www.carmelfoodgroup.com
SIC: 2099 Pasta, uncooked: packaged with other ingredients

(P-2483)
CEDARLANE NATURAL FOODS NORTH
Also Called: Cedar Lane North
150 Airport Blvd, South San Francisco (94080-4739)
PHONE.....................................650 742-0444
George Hourani, *President*
EMP: 25
SALES (est): 4.1MM **Privately Held**
SIC: 2099

(P-2484)
CFARMS INC
1244 E Beamer St, Woodland (95776-6002)
PHONE.....................................916 375-3000
Baljit Pattar, *Branch Mgr*
EMP: 28
SALES (corp-wide): 4.6MM **Privately Held**
SIC: 2099 5149 Food preparations; flavourings & fragrances
PA: Cfarms, Inc.
1330 N Dutton Ave Ste 100
Santa Rosa CA 95401
916 375-3000

(P-2485)
CHEF MERITO INC (PA)
Also Called: Merito.Com
7915 Sepulveda Blvd, Van Nuys (91405-1032)
PHONE.....................................818 787-0100
Jose J Corugedo, *CEO*
Plinio J Garcia Sr, *Shareholder*
Jose Corugedo, *CFO*
Natt Hasson, *Admin Sec*
Gus Hixson, *Info Tech Mgr*
▲ **EMP:** 84
SQ FT: 30,000
SALES (est): 13.4MM **Privately Held**
WEB: www.chefmerito.com
SIC: 2099 2033 2032 2044 Spices, including grinding; jellies, edible, including imitation: in cans, jars, etc.; soups, except seafood: packaged in cans, jars, etc.; enriched rice (vitamin & mineral fortified); sausages & other prepared meats

(P-2486)
CHEFMASTER
501 Airpark Dr, Fullerton (92833-2501)
PHONE.....................................714 554-4000
Aaron G Byrnes, *President*
▲ **EMP:** 35
SALES: 1.3MM **Privately Held**
SIC: 2099 Sugar powdered from purchased ingredients

(P-2487)
CHH LP
Also Called: Rosa's Cafe & Tortilla Factory
28134 Jefferson Ave, Temecula (92590-6604)
PHONE.....................................951 506-5800

Dale Hackbarth, *Managing Prtnr*
Bobby Cox, *Partner*
Edward Hackbarth, *Partner*
EMP: 35
SQ FT: 5,000
SALES (est): 4.1MM **Privately Held**
SIC: 2099 5812 Tortillas, fresh or refrigerated; caterers

(P-2488)
CJ FOODS MANUFACTURING CORP
500 S State College Blvd, Fullerton (92831-5114)
PHONE 714 888-3500
Joo Hong Shin, *President*
▲ **EMP:** 23 **EST:** 2012
SALES (est): 6.9MM **Privately Held**
SIC: 2099 Seasonings & spices

(P-2489)
CLARMIL MANUFACTURING CORP (PA)
Also Called: Goldilocks
30865 San Clemente St, Hayward (94544-7136)
PHONE 510 476-0700
Mary-Ann Yee Ortiz-Luis, *President*
Mary Ann Yee Ortiz Luis, *President*
Freddie L Go Jr, *COO*
Mannette Roxas, *Treasurer*
Cherrimel Yuzon, *Admin Sec*
▲ **EMP:** 98
SQ FT: 57,000
SALES (est): 21.5MM **Privately Held**
WEB: www.clarmil.com
SIC: 2099 5149 2051 Food preparations; bakery products; bread, cake & related products

(P-2490)
CLASSIC SALADS LLC
100 Harrington Rd, Royal Oaks (95076-5604)
P.O. Box 3800, Salinas (93912-3800)
PHONE 928 726-6196
Lance Batistich, *Mng Member*
Christina Batistich,
▲ **EMP:** 44
SALES (est): 15.4MM **Privately Held**
WEB: www.classicsalads.com
SIC: 2099 Salads, fresh or refrigerated

(P-2491)
CLASSIC WINE VINEGAR CO INC
Also Called: Classic Vinegar
4110 Brew Master Dr, Ceres (95307-7583)
PHONE 209 538-7600
Walter Nicolau,
Donna Nicolau, *Partner*
EMP: 12
SQ FT: 15,000
SALES (est): 2.5MM **Privately Held**
WEB: www.classicwinevinegar.com
SIC: 2099 Vinegar

(P-2492)
CNC NOODLE CORPORATION
325 Fallon St, Oakland (94607-4611)
PHONE 510 835-2269
Betty Lim, *President*
▲ **EMP:** 15
SQ FT: 12,000
SALES (est): 2.6MM **Privately Held**
SIC: 2099 Noodles, fried (Chinese)

(P-2493)
COLLETTE FINE FOODS LLC (PA)
Also Called: Cff
2412 Heinemann Dr, Valley Springs (95252-8853)
P.O. Box 6526, Stockton (95206-0526)
PHONE 209 430-7814
Joseph T Collette,
Taft Metters III, *Vice Pres*
EMP: 100
SQ FT: 5,500
SALES (est): 6.1MM **Privately Held**
SIC: 2099 Seasonings & spices; seasonings: dry mixes

(P-2494)
COSMOS FOOD CO INC
16015 Phoenix Dr, City of Industry (91745-1624)
PHONE 323 221-9142
David Kim, *President*
EMP: 45
SQ FT: 85,000
SALES (est): 8.2MM **Privately Held**
WEB: www.cosmosfood.com
SIC: 2099 5149 Tortillas, fresh or refrigerated; groceries & related products

(P-2495)
CREATIVE FOODS LLC
13132 Poway Rd, Poway (92064-4612)
PHONE 858 748-0070
Frank Interlandi, *Mng Member*
EMP: 25
SALES (est): 860.8K **Privately Held**
SIC: 2099 5812 Food preparations; eating places

(P-2496)
CRISPIN CIDER COMPANY (DH)
1213 S Auburn St Ste A, Colfax (95713-9800)
P.O. Box 753 (95713-0753)
PHONE 530 346-9699
Lesley Heron, *CEO*
Bruce Nissen, *COO*
▼ **EMP:** 35
SALES (est): 6.9MM
SALES (corp-wide): 11B **Publicly Held**
SIC: 2099 Cider, nonalcoholic
HQ: Tenth And Blake Beer Company
250 S Wacker Dr Ste 800
Chicago IL 60606
312 496-2759

(P-2497)
CUAHUTEMOC TORTILLERIA
3455 E 1st St, Los Angeles (90063-2945)
PHONE 323 262-0410
Maria Vasques, *Owner*
EMP: 20
SQ FT: 2,500
SALES (est): 1.2MM **Privately Held**
SIC: 2099 Tortillas, fresh or refrigerated

(P-2498)
CULINARY INTERNATIONAL LLC
3280 E 44th St, Vernon (90058-2426)
PHONE 626 289-3000
Cesar Rodarte,
EMP: 250
SALES (est): 75.4K **Privately Held**
SIC: 2099 2038 5149 Food preparations; ethnic foods, frozen; natural & organic foods; specialty food items

(P-2499)
CULINARY SPECIALTIES INC
1231 Linda Vista Dr, San Marcos (92078-3809)
PHONE 760 744-8220
Chris Schragner, *President*
Patrick O Farrell, *Vice Pres*
Patrick O'Farrell, *Vice Pres*
Patrick Ofarrell, *Vice Pres*
Renee Alford, *Human Res Mgr*
EMP: 53 **EST:** 1997
SQ FT: 6,400
SALES (est): 8.9MM **Privately Held**
SIC: 2099 2038 Emulsifiers, food; frozen specialties

(P-2500)
DEAN DISTRIBUTORS INC
5015 Hallmark Pkwy, San Bernardino (92407-1871)
PHONE 323 587-8147
John D Garinger, *Branch Mgr*
Jay Brown, *General Mgr*
Bill Slay, *Maintence Staff*
Dean Hergenreder, *Manager*
EMP: 20
SALES (corp-wide): 3.8MM **Privately Held**
WEB: www.cambridgedietusa.com
SIC: 2099 2087 2834 Sauces: dry mixes; syrups, flavoring (except drink); pharmaceutical preparations

PA: Dean Distributors, Inc.
1350 Bayshore Hwy Ste 400
Burlingame CA 94010
800 792-0816

(P-2501)
DEAN DISTRIBUTORS INC
5015 Hallmark Pkwy, San Bernardino (92407-1871)
PHONE 323 923-5400
Jerry Vasquez, *Director*
EMP: 14
SALES (corp-wide): 3.8MM **Privately Held**
SIC: 2099 Syrups; seasonings & spices; sauces: gravy, dressing & dip mixes
PA: Dean Distributors, Inc.
1350 Bayshore Hwy Ste 400
Burlingame CA 94010
800 792-0816

(P-2502)
DEL CASTILLO FOODS INC
Also Called: La Campana Tortilla Factory
2346 Maggio Cir, Lodi (95240-8812)
PHONE 209 369-2877
Marciano Del Castillo, *President*
Rosario Del Castillo, *Treasurer*
Bertha Del Castillo, *Vice Pres*
EMP: 40
SQ FT: 16,200
SALES (est): 5.8MM **Privately Held**
SIC: 2099 5461 5411 2096 Tortillas, fresh or refrigerated; bakeries; grocery stores; potato chips & similar snacks

(P-2503)
DELIVERY ZONE LLC
120 S Anderson St, Los Angeles (90033-3220)
PHONE 323 780-0888
Carl Ferro,
John Stewart,
EMP: 80
SQ FT: 4,700
SALES (est): 9.2MM **Privately Held**
WEB: www.sunfare.com
SIC: 2099 4215 Ready-to-eat meals, salads & sandwiches; courier services, except by air

(P-2504)
DELORI PRODUCTS INC
Also Called: Delori Foods
17043 Green Dr, City of Industry (91745-1812)
P.O. Box 92668 (91715-2668)
PHONE 626 965-3006
Jaime Brown, *CEO*
Blanca Brown, *Treasurer*
Albert Valdez, *Purchasing*
Marlene Brown, *Sales Mgr*
▲ **EMP:** 32
SALES (est): 6.8MM **Privately Held**
WEB: www.deloriproducts.com
SIC: 2099 Jelly, corncob (gelatin)

(P-2505)
DIAMOND CRYSTAL BRANDS INC
Also Called: Diamond Crystal Brands-Hormel
8700 W Doe Ave, Visalia (93291-8900)
PHONE 559 651-7782
Robert Elderdice, *Branch Mgr*
EMP: 40
SALES (corp-wide): 264.1MM **Privately Held**
SIC: 2099 Food preparations
PA: Diamond Crystal Brands, Inc
3000 Tremont Rd
Savannah GA 31405
912 651-5112

(P-2506)
DIANAS MEXICAN FOOD PDTS INC (PA)
Also Called: La Bonita
16330 Pioneer Blvd, Norwalk (90650-7042)
P.O. Box 369 (90651-0369)
PHONE 562 926-5802
Samuel Magana, *CEO*
Elmer Guzman, *Chief Mktg Ofcr*
Hortensia Magana, *Vice Pres*
Rosario Zavanero, *Executive*
Lydia Rodriguez, *Purch Mgr*
EMP: 300 **EST:** 1975

SQ FT: 4,068
SALES (est): 56.2MM **Privately Held**
WEB: www.dianas.net
SIC: 2099 5812 Tortillas, fresh or refrigerated; ethnic food restaurants

(P-2507)
DIANAS MEXICAN FOOD PDTS INC
2905 Durfee Ave, El Monte (91732-3517)
PHONE 626 444-0555
Samuel Magana, *Owner*
EMP: 40
SQ FT: 13,530
SALES (corp-wide): 56.2MM **Privately Held**
WEB: www.dianas.net
SIC: 2099 5812 Tortillas, fresh or refrigerated; Mexican restaurant
PA: Diana's Mexican Food Products, Inc.
16330 Pioneer Blvd
Norwalk CA 90650
562 926-5802

(P-2508)
DIVINE PASTA COMPANY (PA)
140 W Providencia Ave, Burbank (91502-2121)
PHONE 213 542-3300
Alexander Palermo, *President*
Maureen Moore, *Purchasing*
Todd Ramsey, *Opers Mgr*
EMP: 49
SQ FT: 30,000
SALES (est): 26.8MM **Privately Held**
WEB: www.divinepasta.com
SIC: 2099 Packaged combination products: pasta, rice & potato

(P-2509)
DOLE FRESH VEGETABLES INC (DH)
2959 Salinas Hwy, Monterey (93940-6400)
P.O. Box 2018 (93942-2018)
PHONE 831 422-8871
Howard Roeder, *CEO*
David H Murdock, *President*
Ray Riggi, *President*
Michael H Solomon, *President*
Roger Billingsly, *Exec VP*
▼ **EMP:** 150
SQ FT: 15,000
SALES (est): 130.8MM
SALES (corp-wide): 11.7B **Privately Held**
SIC: 2099 0723 Food preparations; fruit (fresh) packing services
HQ: Dole Food Company, Inc.
1 Dole Dr
Westlake Village CA 91362
818 874-4000

(P-2510)
EARTHRISE NUTRITIONALS LLC
113 E Hoober Rd, Calipatria (92233-9703)
PHONE 760 348-5027
Jose Perez, *Manager*
EMP: 15
SALES (corp-wide): 7B **Privately Held**
SIC: 2099 Chicory root, dried
HQ: Earthrise Nutritionals Llc
2151 Michelson Dr Ste 258
Irvine CA 92612
949 623-0980

(P-2511)
EL GALLITO MARKET INC
12242 Valley Blvd, El Monte (91732-3108)
PHONE 626 442-1190
Sandra Veisaga, *President*
Mario Rodriguez, *Treasurer*
EMP: 35
SQ FT: 1,200
SALES (est): 4.7MM **Privately Held**
SIC: 2099 5421 5411 Tortillas, fresh or refrigerated; meat & fish markets; grocery stores

(P-2512)
EL INDIO TORTILLERIA
Also Called: El Indio Tortillas Fctry
1502 W 5th St, Santa Ana (92703-2902)
PHONE 714 542-3114
Humberto Sanchez, *President*
Graciela Sanchez, *Treasurer*
EMP: 12
SQ FT: 4,500

SALES: 850K **Privately Held**
WEB: www.elindiotortilleria.com
SIC: 2099 Tortillas, fresh or refrigerated

(P-2513)
ESPERANZAS TORTILLERIA INC
750 Rock Springs Rd, Escondido
(92025-1625)
PHONE...................760 743-5908
Victor Martinez, *President*
Teresa Martinez, *Treasurer*
Hugo Martinez, *Vice Pres*
Leonor Batista, *Office Mgr*
EMP: 46
SALES (est): 7.7MM **Privately Held**
SIC: 2099 Tortillas, fresh or refrigerated

(P-2514)
EVERSON SPICE COMPANY INC
2667 Gundry Ave, Long Beach
(90755-1808)
PHONE...................562 595-4785
Kim Everson, *CEO*
Ken Hopkins, *President*
Thomas Everson, *Admin Sec*
Jerry Keifer, *Info Tech Mgr*
Juan Medina, *Technology*
▲ EMP: 35
SQ FT: 35,000
SALES (est): 8.9MM **Privately Held**
WEB: www.eversonspice.com
SIC: 2099 Spices, including grinding

(P-2515)
F I O IMPORTS INC
Also Called: Contessa Premium Foods
5970 Alcoa Ave, Vernon (90058-3925)
PHONE...................323 263-5100
Dirk Leuenberger, *President*
Bob Nielsen, *CFO*
Adan Hernadez, *Manager*
EMP: 300
SALES (est): 20.7MM
SALES (corp-wide): 207.3MM **Privately Held**
SIC: 2099 Food preparations
PA: Aqua Star (Usa), Corp.
2025 1st Ave Ste 200
Seattle WA 98121
206 448-5400

(P-2516)
FAMILY LOOMPYA CORPORATION
2626 Southport Way Ste F, National City
(91950-8753)
PHONE...................619 477-2125
Alen Enriquez, *President*
▲ EMP: 25
SQ FT: 10,000
SALES (est): 4.3MM **Privately Held**
WEB: www.lumpia.com
SIC: 2099 5149 Food preparations; specialty food items

(P-2517)
FAYES FOODS INC
Also Called: Fay's Foods
10650 Burbank Blvd, North Hollywood
(91601-2511)
PHONE...................818 508-8392
EMP: 37
SQ FT: 15,000
SALES: 5MM **Privately Held**
SIC: 2099 5812 5149 5141

(P-2518)
FINEST FOOD INC
6491 Weathers Pl Ste A, San Diego
(92121-2935)
PHONE...................858 699-4746
Jose Aldo Enrique Landman, *President*
Sylvia Landman, *CFO*
Guillermo Ayan Helmholt, *Vice Pres*
▲ EMP: 12
SQ FT: 18,000
SALES: 200K **Privately Held**
WEB: www.panini.fr
SIC: 2099 Food preparations

(P-2519)
FIORE DI PASTA INC
4776 E Jensen Ave, Fresno (93725-1704)
PHONE...................559 457-0431
Bernadetta Primavera, *President*
Anthony Primavera, *CFO*

Ana Miller, *Controller*
Polo Garcia, *HR Admin*
Jason Preis, *Purch Mgr*
▲ EMP: 49
SQ FT: 59,000
SALES (est): 11.2MM **Privately Held**
SIC: 2099 Pasta, uncooked: packaged with other ingredients

(P-2520)
FISHER NUT COMPANY
137 N Hart Rd, Modesto (95358-9537)
PHONE...................209 527-0108
Ronald Fisher, *President*
▼ EMP: 15
SALES (est): 3.6MM **Privately Held**
WEB: www.fishernut.com
SIC: 2099 Food preparations

(P-2521)
FLORENTYNAS FRESH PASTA
Also Called: Florentynas Fresh Pasta Fctry
1864 E 22nd St, Vernon (90058-1034)
PHONE...................213 742-9374
Yvonne Smulovitz, *President*
Jascha Smulovitz, *Treasurer*
EMP: 17
SQ FT: 5,500
SALES (est): 2.3MM **Privately Held**
WEB: www.freshpasta.com
SIC: 2099 Pasta, uncooked: packaged with other ingredients

(P-2522)
FLORES BROTHERS INC
Also Called: Durango Foods
7777 Scout Ave, Bell (90201-4941)
PHONE...................562 806-9128
David Flores, *President*
Armando Flores, *Vice Pres*
EMP: 20
SALES (est): 2.9MM **Privately Held**
SIC: 2099 Emulsifiers, food

(P-2523)
FOOD-O-MEX CORPORATION
Also Called: El Dorado Mexican Food Pdts
2928 N Main St, Los Angeles (90031-3325)
PHONE...................323 225-1737
Eleanor Lopez, *President*
Elenore Lopez, *President*
Philip Manly, *Vice Pres*
EMP: 60
SQ FT: 18,000
SALES (est): 8.3MM **Privately Held**
WEB: www.eldoradotortillas.com
SIC: 2099 Tortillas, fresh or refrigerated

(P-2524)
FOREVER YOUNG
Also Called: Supernutrition
208 Palmetto Ave, Pacifica (94044-1374)
PHONE...................650 355-5481
Patrick Mooney, *President*
Kathleen Mooney-Dillon, *President*
Lois Stanton, *Treasurer*
Joan Hollrah, *Admin Sec*
EMP: 24
SQ FT: 12,000
SALES (est): 2.9MM **Privately Held**
SIC: 2099 2834

(P-2525)
FORTUNA TORTILLA FACTORY
1425 C St, Livingston (95334-1416)
PHONE...................209 394-3028
Joe Soto, *Owner*
EMP: 18
SQ FT: 7,200
SALES (est): 820K **Privately Held**
SIC: 2099 5411 Tortillas, fresh or refrigerated; grocery stores, independent

(P-2526)
FRESH & READY FOODS LLC
1145 Arroyo St Ste B, San Fernando
(91340-1842)
PHONE...................818 837-7600
Art Sezgin, *President*
John Saladino, *Vice Pres*
EMP: 99
SALES (est): 4.5MM **Privately Held**
SIC: 2099 Salads, fresh or refrigerated

(P-2527)
FRESH EXPRESS INCORPORATED
950 E Blanco Rd, Salinas (93901-4487)
P.O. Box 80599 (93912-0599)
PHONE...................831 424-2921
Mark Drever, *Branch Mgr*
Daniel Kapsalis, *Planning*
Rocio Lozano, *Controller*
Loren Hughes, *Director*
Robert Luquin, *Manager*
EMP: 20
SALES (corp-wide): 3B **Privately Held**
WEB: www.freshexpress.com
SIC: 2099 Food preparations
HQ: Fresh Express Incorporated
4757 The Grove Dr Ste 260
Windermere FL 34786
407 612-5000

(P-2528)
GH FOODS CA LLC (DH)
8425 Carbide Ct, Sacramento
(95828-5609)
PHONE...................916 844-1140
Jim Gibson,
Brianne Goree, *QA Dir*
EMP: 330
SQ FT: 60,000
SALES (est): 72.3MM
SALES (corp-wide): 1B **Publicly Held**
SIC: 2099 Salads, fresh or refrigerated
HQ: Renaissance Food Group, Llc
11020 White Rock Rd # 100
Rancho Cordova CA 95670
916 638-8825

(P-2529)
GHIRINGHLLI SPCIALTY FOODS INC
101 Benicia Rd, Vallejo (94590-7003)
PHONE...................707 561-7670
Mike Ghiringhelli, *President*
Ed Ferrero, *Vice Pres*
EMP: 145
SQ FT: 55,000
SALES (est): 41.2MM **Privately Held**
WEB: www.gfoods.net
SIC: 2099 Ready-to-eat meals, salads & sandwiches; salads, fresh or refrigerated

(P-2530)
GMP MANUFACTURING INC
Also Called: Cytosport
1340 Treat Blvd Ste 350, Walnut Creek
(94597-7581)
PHONE...................707 751-3942
Gregory Pickett, *President*
David Webber, *CFO*
Roberta White, *Vice Pres*
Lauren Jimenez, *Human Resources*
Darren Carter, *VP Sales*
EMP: 25
SQ FT: 67,000
SALES (est): 3.3MM
SALES (corp-wide): 9.1B **Publicly Held**
SIC: 2099 Food preparations
PA: Hormel Foods Corporation
1 Hormel Pl
Austin MN 55912
507 437-5611

(P-2531)
GOLDEN SPECIALTY FOODS LLC
14605 Best Ave, Norwalk (90650-5258)
PHONE...................562 802-2537
Philip Pisciotta, *CEO*
Jeff Chan, *President*
Deryk Howard, *CFO*
◆ EMP: 25
SQ FT: 31,000
SALES (est): 6.8MM **Privately Held**
WEB: www.goldenspecialtyfoods.com
SIC: 2099 2032 Food preparations; canned specialties

(P-2532)
HAIGS DELICACIES LLC
25673 Nickel Pl, Hayward (94545-3221)
PHONE...................510 782-6285
Rita Takvorian, *Mng Member*
Mark Takvorian, *COO*
Steven Cherezian, *VP Sales*
Nadine Takvorian,

EMP: 20
SQ FT: 1,200
SALES (est): 4.1MM **Privately Held**
WEB: www.haigsdelicacies.com
SIC: 2099 Dips, except cheese & sour cream based; ready-to-eat meals, salads & sandwiches; salads, fresh or refrigerated

(P-2533)
HANNIBALS CATRG & EVENTS INC (PA)
8141 37th Ave, Sacramento (95824-2305)
PHONE...................916 638-4363
Philip Paw, *President*
Indra Paw, *Vice Pres*
EMP: 25
SALES (est): 4.6MM **Privately Held**
SIC: 2099 Food preparations

(P-2534)
HARMLESS HARVEST INC (PA)
712 Sansome St, San Francisco
(94111-1704)
PHONE...................347 688-6286
Giannella Alvarez, *CEO*
Justin Guilbert, *President*
Brad Paris, *COO*
Blair Cornish, *Officer*
Mary Azzopardi, *Executive*
▲ EMP: 30
SALES (est): 8MM **Privately Held**
SIC: 2099 Coconut, desiccated & shredded

(P-2535)
HEALTHY TIMES
Also Called: Healty Times Natural Products
225 Broadway Ste 450, San Diego
(92101-5027)
PHONE...................858 513-1550
Rondi Prescott, *CEO*
Richard Prescott, *President*
EMP: 15
SQ FT: 2,800
SALES (est): 2.6MM **Privately Held**
WEB: www.healthytimes.com
SIC: 2099 2844 Food preparations; cosmetic preparations

(P-2536)
HONEY BENNETTS FARM INC
Also Called: Bennett's Honey Farm
3176 Honey Ln, Fillmore (93015-2026)
PHONE...................805 521-1375
Gilebert Vannoy, *President*
Ann Lindsay Bennett, *Principal*
EMP: 25
SQ FT: 20,000
SALES: 4MM **Privately Held**
SIC: 2099 5191 0279 Honey, strained & bottled; farm supplies; apiary (bee & honey farm)

(P-2537)
HONEY OLIVAREZ BEES INC
6398 County Road 20, Orland
(95963-9475)
P.O. Box 847 (95963-0847)
PHONE...................530 865-0298
Ray A Olivarez Jr, *CEO*
EMP: 97
SALES (est): 1.5MM **Privately Held**
SIC: 2099 Honey, strained & bottled

(P-2538)
HUNTER SPICE INC
184 Suburban Rd, San Luis Obispo
(93401-7502)
P.O. Box 8110 (93403-8110)
PHONE...................805 597-8900
Conrad Sauer, *President*
William Uhlik, *CFO*
◆ EMP: 65 EST: 1984
SQ FT: 110,000
SALES: 25.9MM
SALES (corp-wide): 413.2MM **Privately Held**
WEB: www.cfsauer.com
SIC: 2099 Seasonings & spices
PA: The C F Sauer Company
2000 W Broad St
Richmond VA 23220
804 359-5786

(P-2539)
IL PASTAIO FOODS INC
Also Called: IL Pastaio Fresh Pasta Company
1266 E Julian St, San Jose (95116-1009)
PHONE..................................408 753-9220
Francisco Avela, *President*
EMP: 10
SALES (est): 1MM **Privately Held**
SIC: 2099 Pasta, uncooked: packaged with
other ingredients

(P-2540)
INGREDIENTS BY NATURE LLC
5555 Brooks St, Montclair (91763-4547)
PHONE..................................909 230-6200
Matt Outz, *President*
Bo Zhu, *Exec VP*
Xanh T Phan, *QC Mgr*
Lan Zou, *Opers Staff*
EMP: 27 **EST:** 2010
SALES (est): 5MM **Privately Held**
SIC: 2099 Molasses, mixed or blended:
from purchased ingredients

(P-2541)
J W FLOOR COVERING INC
3401 Enterprise Ave, Hayward
(94545-3201)
PHONE..................................858 444-1214
Decklan Donohue, *Manager*
EMP: 59
SALES (corp-wide): 44.1MM **Privately
Held**
WEB: www.jwfloors.com
SIC: 2099 Food preparations
PA: J. W. Floor Covering, Inc.
9881 Carroll Centre Rd
San Diego CA 92126
858 536-8565

(P-2542)
JAYONE FOODS INC
7212 Alondra Blvd, Paramount
(90723-3902)
PHONE..................................562 633-7400
Seung Hoon Lee, *President*
Chil Park, *Vice Pres*
Ik T Kim, *Opers Staff*
Woon Yoo, *Sales Dir*
Donald Han, *Marketing Mgr*
▲ **EMP:** 50
SQ FT: 28,000
SALES (est): 10.2MM **Privately Held**
WEB: www.jayone.com
SIC: 2099 Food preparations

(P-2543)
JBR INC (PA)
Also Called: Jbr Gourmet Foods
1731 Aviation Blvd, Lincoln (95648-9317)
PHONE..................................916 258-8000
Jon B Rogers, *CEO*
Barbara Rogers, *Vice Pres*
◆ **EMP:** 185 **EST:** 1979
SQ FT: 400,000
SALES (est): 73.1MM **Privately Held**
WEB: www.o-coffee.com
SIC: 2099 2095 Tea blending; coffee
roasting (except by wholesale grocers)

(P-2544)
JESUS CABEZAS
Also Called: J C Kitchen
145 Utah Ave, South San Francisco
(94080-6712)
PHONE..................................650 583-0469
Jesus Cabezas, *Owner*
EMP: 17
SALES (est): 1.9MM **Privately Held**
WEB: www.jesuscabezas.com
SIC: 2099 Vegetables, peeled for the trade

(P-2545)
JIMENES FOOD INC
7046 Jackson St, Paramount (90723-4835)
PHONE..................................562 602-2505
Reyna Jimenez, *President*
Juan Jimenez, *Vice Pres*
EMP: 30
SQ FT: 11,000
SALES (est): 6.1MM **Privately Held**
SIC: 2099 Tortillas, fresh or refrigerated

(P-2546)
JOHNS INCREDIBLE PIZZA CO
14766 Bear Valley Rd, Victorville
(92395-9610)
PHONE..................................760 951-1111
John Parlet, *President*
Betty Parlet, *Treasurer*
EMP: 100
SQ FT: 16,000
SALES (est): 7.8MM **Privately Held**
SIC: 2099 5812 7993 Salads, fresh or re-
frigerated; pizza restaurants; Italian
restaurant; video game arcade

(P-2547)
JOY PROCESSED FOODS INC
1330 Seabright Ave, Long Beach
(90813-1189)
PHONE..................................562 435-1106
Alvin Clawson, *President*
EMP: 30 **EST:** 1966
SQ FT: 5,000
SALES (est): 3.3MM **Privately Held**
SIC: 2099 Vegetables, peeled for the trade

(P-2548)
JSL FOODS INC (PA)
3550 Pasadena Ave, Los Angeles
(90031-1946)
PHONE..................................323 223-2484
Teiji Kawana, *President*
Koji Kawana, *Exec VP*
Edwardo Rivas, *Info Tech Mgr*
Steve Lopez, *Purch Mgr*
Jerry Kobayashi, *VP Opers*
▲ **EMP:** 120
SALES (est): 26.4MM **Privately Held**
WEB: www.jslfoods.com
SIC: 2099 5142 2052 Pasta, uncooked:
packaged with other ingredients; pack-
aged frozen goods; cookies

(P-2549)
JSL FOODS INC
2222 1/2 Davie Ave, Commerce
(90040-1708)
PHONE..................................323 727-9999
Teiji Kawana, *President*
EMP: 60
SALES (corp-wide): 26.4MM **Privately
Held**
WEB: www.jslfoods.com
SIC: 2099 2052 Pasta, uncooked: pack-
aged with other ingredients; cookies
PA: Jsl Foods, Inc.
3550 Pasadena Ave
Los Angeles CA 90031
323 223-2484

(P-2550)
KATE FARMS INC
101 Innovation Pl, Santa Barbara
(93108-2268)
P.O. Box 50840 (93150-0840)
PHONE..................................805 845-2446
Richard Laver, *President*
Michelle Laver, *Vice Pres*
Mia Greenstein, *Director*
EMP: 123
SALES: 1.8MM **Privately Held**
SIC: 2099 Ready-to-eat meals, salads &
sandwiches

(P-2551)
KDS INGREDIENTS LLC
3460 Mrron Rd Ste 103-229, Oceanside
(92056)
PHONE..................................760 310-5245
Keri Ross, *CEO*
EMP: 19
SALES (corp-wide): 2.1MM **Privately
Held**
SIC: 2099 Molasses, mixed or blended:
from purchased ingredients
PA: Kds Ingredients Llc
1907 Cheyenne Cir
Oceanside CA 92056
608 469-0866

(P-2552)
**KHYBER FOODS
INCORPORATED**
Also Called: Sun Glo Foods
500 S Acacia Ave, Fullerton (92831-5102)
P.O. Box 4324 (92834-4324)
PHONE..................................714 879-0900

A R Ghafoori, *President*
Larry Ballard, *Corp Secy*
▲ **EMP:** 25 **EST:** 1964
SQ FT: 55,000
SALES (est): 2MM **Privately Held**
SIC: 2099 Food preparations

(P-2553)
KNOTTS BERRY FARM LLC (HQ)
Also Called: Knott's Berry Farm
8039 Beach Blvd, Buena Park
(90620-3225)
P.O. Box 5002 (90622-5002)
PHONE..................................714 827-1776
Jack Falfas, *Partner*
Larry Daniel, *Vice Pres*
Scott Goldberg, *Vice Pres*
Raffi Kaprelyan, *Vice Pres*
Russ Knibbs, *Vice Pres*
▲ **EMP:** 500 **EST:** 1920
SQ FT: 5,000
SALES (est): 121.8MM
SALES (corp-wide): 1.3B **Publicly Held**
WEB: www.knotts.com
SIC: 2099 Syrups
PA: Cedar Fair, L.P.
1 Cedar Point Dr
Sandusky OH 44870
419 626-0830

(P-2554)
**KOZY SHACK ENTERPRISES
LLC**
Also Called: Land O'Lakes
600 S Tegner Rd, Turlock (95380-9475)
PHONE..................................209 634-2131
EMP: 100
SALES (corp-wide): 12.8B **Privately Held**
WEB: www.kozyshack.com
SIC: 2099 Desserts, ready-to-mix; gelatin
dessert preparations
HQ: Kozy Shack Enterprises, Llc
83 Ludy St
Hicksville NY 11801
516 870-3000

(P-2555)
KRAFT HEINZ FOODS COMPANY
1500 E Walnut Ave, Fullerton (92831-4731)
PHONE..................................714 870-8235
Robert Pech, *Branch Mgr*
EMP: 500
SQ FT: 2,878
SALES (corp-wide): 26.2B **Publicly Held**
WEB: www.kraftfoods.com
SIC: 2099 Food preparations
HQ: Kraft Heinz Foods Company
1 Ppg Pl Ste 3200
Pittsburgh PA 15222
412 456-5700

(P-2556)
KRAFT HEINZ FOODS COMPANY
3971 E Airport Dr, Ontario (91761-1538)
PHONE..................................909 605-7201
Tony Iannello, *Manager*
EMP: 10
SALES (corp-wide): 26.2B **Publicly Held**
WEB: www.kraftfoods.com
SIC: 2099 Food preparations
HQ: Kraft Heinz Foods Company
1 Ppg Pl Ste 3200
Pittsburgh PA 15222
412 456-5700

(P-2557)
KTS KITCHENS INC
1065 E Walnut St Ste C, Carson
(90746-1384)
PHONE..................................310 764-0850
Kathleen D Taggares, *CEO*
Joan Paris, *Corp Secy*
EMP: 250
SALES (est): 62.4MM **Privately Held**
WEB: www.ktskitchens.com
SIC: 2099 2035 Pizza, refrigerated: except
frozen; dressings, salad: raw & cooked
(except dry mixes)

(P-2558)
LA BARCA TORTILLERIA INC
3047 Whittier Blvd, Los Angeles
(90023-1651)
P.O. Box 23548 (90023-0548)
PHONE..................................323 268-1744
Jose Luis Arevalo, *CEO*

Antonio Arevalo, *President*
Al Arevalo, *Treasurer*
Alexander Arevalo, *Corp Secy*
EMP: 50
SQ FT: 6,000
SALES (est): 9.8MM **Privately Held**
SIC: 2099 Tortillas, fresh or refrigerated

(P-2559)
LA CARRETA FOOD PRODUCTS
Also Called: La Carreta Mexican Foods
302 S La Cadena Dr, Colton (92324-3420)
PHONE..................................909 825-0737
Celia Cervantes, *Owner*
EMP: 10 **EST:** 1945
SQ FT: 2,500
SALES (est): 708K **Privately Held**
SIC: 2099 Tortillas, fresh or refrigerated

(P-2560)
LA CHAPALITA INC (PA)
1724 Chico Ave, El Monte (91733-2942)
PHONE..................................626 443-8556
Luis E Moya Jr, *President*
Claudia Moya, *Officer*
EMP: 20 **EST:** 1981
SQ FT: 15,000
SALES (est): 3.7MM **Privately Held**
WEB: www.lachapalita.com
SIC: 2099 Tortillas, fresh or refrigerated

(P-2561)
**LA COLONIAL TORTILLA PDTS
INC**
Also Called: La Colonial Mexican Foods
543 Monterey Pass Rd, Monterey Park
(91754-2416)
PHONE..................................626 289-3647
Daniel Robles, *President*
Hector Robles, *Human Res Dir*
EMP: 185 **EST:** 1950
SQ FT: 27,000
SALES (est): 40MM **Privately Held**
WEB: www.lacolonial.com
SIC: 2099 Tortillas, fresh or refrigerated

(P-2562)
**LA ESTRELLITA TIZAPAN
MERCADO**
Also Called: La Estrellita Market & Deli
2387 University Ave, East Palo Alto
(94303-1620)
PHONE..................................650 328-0799
Hector Cornelio, *Branch Mgr*
EMP: 11
SALES (corp-wide): 2.2MM **Privately
Held**
SIC: 2099 5411 5812 Tortillas, fresh or re-
frigerated; grocery stores, independent;
Mexican restaurant
PA: La Estrellita Tizapan Mercado
2205 Middlefield Rd
Redwood City CA 94063
650 369-3877

(P-2563)
**LA FE TORTILLA FACTORY INC
(PA)**
Also Called: La Fe Tortilleria Factory
446 W Mission Rd Ste 126, San Marcos
(92069-6535)
P.O. Box 787 (92079-0787)
PHONE..................................760 752-8350
Hoxsie Smith, *President*
Andrea Smith, *Vice Pres*
EMP: 30
SQ FT: 4,000
SALES (est): 2.6MM **Privately Held**
SIC: 2099 5461 5812 5046 Tortillas,
fresh or refrigerated; bakeries; Mexican
restaurant; bakery equipment & supplies

(P-2564)
LA FORTALEZA INC
525 N Ford Blvd, Los Angeles
(90022-1104)
PHONE..................................323 261-1211
Hermila Josefina Ortiz, *CEO*
David Ortiz, *Vice Pres*
Ramiro Ortiz Jr, *Vice Pres*
Mila Vargas, *Executive*
Sandra Ortiz, *Sales Executive*
EMP: 98
SQ FT: 40,000

PRODUCTS & SVCS

SALES (est): 14.3MM **Privately Held**
WEB: www.lafortaleza.net
SIC: **2099** 2096 Tortillas, fresh or refrigerated; potato chips & similar snacks

(P-2565)
LA GLORIA FOODS CORP (PA)
Also Called: La Gloria Tortilleria
3455 E 1st St, Los Angeles (90063-2945)
PHONE...............................323 262-0410
Maria De La Luz Vera, *CEO*
Luz V De La, *Agent*
▼ EMP: 100 EST: 1954
SQ FT: 8,000
SALES: 7MM **Privately Held**
SIC: **2099** 5461 5812 Tortillas, fresh or refrigerated; bread; Mexican restaurant

(P-2566)
LA GLORIA FOODS CORP
Also Called: La Gloria Flour Tortillas
3285 E Cesar E Chavez Ave, Los Angeles (90063-2853)
PHONE...............................323 263-6755
Daniel Torrez, *Manager*
EMP: 60
SALES (corp-wide): 7MM **Privately Held**
SIC: **2099** 5461 Tortillas, fresh or refrigerated; bakeries
PA: La Gloria Foods Corp.
3455 E 1st St
Los Angeles CA 90063
323 262-0410

(P-2567)
LA MANO TORTILLERIA
9529 Garvey Ave, South El Monte (91733-1015)
PHONE...............................626 350-4229
Vincente Cortez, *Owner*
EMP: 15
SQ FT: 1,755
SALES (est): 1.2MM **Privately Held**
SIC: **2099** Tortillas, fresh or refrigerated

(P-2568)
LA PRINCESITA TORTILLERIA (PA)
Also Called: Abalquiga
3432 E Cesar E Chavez Ave, Los Angeles (90063-4146)
PHONE...............................323 267-0673
Francisco Ramirez, *President*
EMP: 20
SQ FT: 2,195
SALES (est): 3.2MM **Privately Held**
SIC: **2099** Tortillas, fresh or refrigerated

(P-2569)
LA SELVA BEACH SPICE COMPANY
453 Mcquaide Dr, Watsonville (95076-1908)
PHONE...............................831 724-4500
Floyd W Brady, *CEO*
EMP: 20
SALES (est): 671.8K **Privately Held**
SIC: **2099** Seasonings & spices

(P-2570)
LA TAPATIA - NORCAL INC
23423 Cabot Blvd, Hayward (94545-1665)
PHONE...............................510 783-2045
Antonio Chavez, *President*
EMP: 150
SQ FT: 35,000
SALES (est): 16MM **Privately Held**
SIC: **2099** 2096 Tortillas, fresh or refrigerated; tortilla chips

(P-2571)
LA TAPATIA TORTILLERIA INC
104 E Belmont Ave, Fresno (93701-1403)
PHONE...............................559 441-1030
Helen Chavez-Hansen, *Principal*
John Hansen, *Senior VP*
EMP: 170
SQ FT: 40,000
SALES (est): 31.4MM **Privately Held**
WEB: www.tortillas4u.com
SIC: **2099** Tortillas, fresh or refrigerated

(P-2572)
LA TERRA FINA USA INC
1300 Atlantic St, Union City (94587-2004)
PHONE...............................510 404-5888
Peter Molloy, *President*
Stephen Cottrell, *CFO*
Henri Madaj, *Engineer*
Scott Byrnes, *Controller*
Marlene Chavez, *Personnel Assit*
EMP: 70
SQ FT: 24,000
SALES (est): 30.4MM **Privately Held**
SIC: **2099** Seasonings & spices

(P-2573)
LA TORTILLA FACTORY INC
3645 Standish Ave, Santa Rosa (95407-8142)
PHONE...............................707 586-4000
Carlos Tamayo, *President*
Piero Di Manno, *Network Analyst*
Carmen Padilla, *Personnel Assit*
Nathan Wilson, *QC Mgr*
Angel Ybarra, *Marketing Staff*
EMP: 47
SALES (corp-wide): 157.8MM **Privately Held**
WEB: www.latortillafactory.com
SIC: **2099** Tortillas, fresh or refrigerated
PA: La Tortilla Factory Inc.
3300 Westwind Blvd
Santa Rosa CA 95403
707 586-4000

(P-2574)
LAM ENTERPRISES INC
824 S Center St, Stockton (95206-1308)
P.O. Box 640, Ml Wuk Village (95346-0640)
PHONE...............................209 586-2217
Glenn Miller, *President*
Lucia Miller, *Corp Secy*
EMP: 10
SQ FT: 30,000
SALES (est): 1.2MM **Privately Held**
SIC: **2099** 5149 Spices, including grinding; spices & seasonings

(P-2575)
LAMORENITA TORTILLERA & MT MKT
1876 Fremont Blvd, Seaside (93955-3611)
PHONE...............................831 394-3770
Juventino Ibarra Magana, *Partner*
Antonio Moreno, *Partner*
EMP: 17
SALES (est): 2.1MM **Privately Held**
SIC: **2099** Tortillas, fresh or refrigerated

(P-2576)
LANTY INC
9660 Flair Dr, El Monte (91731-3017)
PHONE...............................626 582-8001
Dongmei LI, *CEO*
EMP: 181
SALES (est): 4.2MM **Privately Held**
SIC: **2099** Vegetables, peeled for the trade

(P-2577)
LAPERLA SPICE CO INC
Also Called: Laperla Del Mayab
555 N Fairview St, Santa Ana (92703-1806)
PHONE...............................714 543-0159
Wilbert Marrufo, *President*
EMP: 10
SQ FT: 5,000
SALES (est): 850K **Privately Held**
WEB: www.delmayab.com
SIC: **2099** 5149 Spices, including grinding; spices & seasonings

(P-2578)
LAROSA TORTILLA FACTORY
26 Menker St, Watsonville (95076-4915)
PHONE...............................831 728-5332
Alfonso Solorio, *Owner*
EMP: 98 **Privately Held**
WEB: www.larosatortillafactory.com
SIC: **2099** Tortillas, fresh or refrigerated
PA: Larosa Tortilla Factory
142 2nd St
Watsonville CA 95076

(P-2579)
LASSONDE PAPPAS AND CO INC
1755 E Acacia St, Ontario (91761-7702)
PHONE...............................909 923-4041
Rick Jochums, *Manager*
Anne Novak, *Vice Pres*
Sharon Bangert, *Human Res Dir*
Jarrod Perkins, *Marketing Staff*
Paul Carey, *Manager*
EMP: 85 **Privately Held**
WEB: www.clementpappas.com
SIC: **2099** Food preparations
HQ: Lassonde Pappas And Company, Inc.
1 Collins Dr Ste 200
Carneys Point NJ 08069
856 455-1000

(P-2580)
LAURENT CULINARY SERVICE
Also Called: Jessie A Laurent
1945 Francisco Blvd E # 44, San Rafael (94901-5525)
PHONE...............................415 485-1122
Jessie Laurent Boucher, *Partner*
EMP: 13
SALES (est): 1.5MM **Privately Held**
SIC: **2099** 5812 Ready-to-eat meals, salads & sandwiches; eating places

(P-2581)
LEE KUM KEE (USA) FOODS INC
14455 Don Julian Rd, City of Industry (91746-3102)
PHONE...............................626 709-1888
Simon Wu, *President*
Alan Lui, *CFO*
Dickson Chan, *Treasurer*
Alice Zhou, *Executive*
Maria Sanchez, *Human Res Mgr*
EMP: 99
SQ FT: 54,000
SALES (est): 3.6MM **Privately Held**
SIC: **2099** Sauces: gravy, dressing & dip mixes

(P-2582)
LEHMAN FOODS INC
Also Called: Fresh & Ready
1145 Arroyo St Ste B, San Fernando (91340-1842)
PHONE...............................818 837-7600
Charles Lehman, *CEO*
Art Sezgin, *President*
Harry Iknadosian, *Vice Pres*
Tim Ridgway, *Vice Pres*
Cameron Childs, *Director*
EMP: 25
SQ FT: 15,000
SALES (est): 9.7MM **Privately Held**
WEB: www.freshandreadyfoods.com
SIC: **2099** Salads, fresh or refrigerated; sandwiches, assembled & packaged: for wholesale market

(P-2583)
LEQUIOS JAPAN CO LTD
14241 Firestone Blvd, La Mirada (90638-5530)
PHONE...............................410 629-8694
Ichiro Miyamoto, *CEO*
EMP: 12
SALES (est): 476.9K **Privately Held**
SIC: **2099** Food preparations

(P-2584)
LETS DO LUNCH
Also Called: Integrated Food Service
310 W Alondra Blvd, Gardena (90248-2423)
PHONE...............................310 523-3664
Paul G Giuliano, *President*
Jon Sugimoto, *Vice Pres*
David Watzke, *Director*
▲ EMP: 80
SQ FT: 57,000
SALES (est): 32MM **Privately Held**
WEB: www.integratedfoodservice.com
SIC: **2099** Sandwiches, assembled & packaged: for wholesale market

(P-2585)
LILLY TORTILLERIA
4271 University Ave, San Diego (92105-1536)
PHONE...............................619 281-2890

Delia Amezquita, *Owner*
EMP: 24
SALES (est): 2.4MM **Privately Held**
SIC: **2099** 5411 Tortillas, fresh or refrigerated; grocery stores

(P-2586)
LIVING TREE COMMUNITY FOODS
1455 5th St, Berkeley (94710-1337)
P.O. Box 10082 (94709-5082)
PHONE...............................510 526-7106
Jesse Schwartz, *Owner*
Michael Tapscott, *Opers Mgr*
EMP: 20
SQ FT: 600
SALES (est): 2.5MM **Privately Held**
WEB: www.livingtreecommunity.com
SIC: **2099** Food preparations

(P-2587)
LIVING WELLNESS PARTNERS LLC
Also Called: Buddha Teas
5130 Avenida Encinas, Carlsbad (92008-4372)
PHONE...............................800 642-3754
John Boyd, *CEO*
Nicholas Narier, *CFO*
Tysen Sybesma, *Creative Dir*
Ted Turczyn, *Sales Staff*
EMP: 30
SQ FT: 10,000
SALES: 1MM **Privately Held**
SIC: **2099** Tea blending

(P-2588)
LOS PERICOS FOOD PRODUCTS LLC
2301 Valley Blvd, Pomona (91768-1105)
PHONE...............................909 623-5625
Marcelino Ortega, *Partner*
Guadalupe Ortega, *Partner*
Luis Ortega, *Partner*
EMP: 46
SQ FT: 20,000
SALES (est): 6.8MM **Privately Held**
WEB: www.lospericosfood.com
SIC: **2099** Tortillas, fresh or refrigerated

(P-2589)
LOUIE FOODS INTERNATIONAL
471 S Teilman Ave, Fresno (93706-1315)
PHONE...............................559 264-2745
Jay Louie, *President*
Stephanie Louie, *Admin Sec*
EMP: 15 EST: 1950
SALES: 895.5K **Privately Held**
SIC: **2099** 0182 5199 Noodles, fried (Chinese); tofu, except frozen desserts; bean sprouts grown under cover; packaging materials

(P-2590)
LUCERNE FOODS INC
5918 Stoneridge Mall Rd, Pleasanton (94588-3229)
PHONE...............................925 951-4724
Kenneth Gott, *President*
Peggy Han, *Senior VP*
▼ EMP: 40
SALES: 5.9MM
SALES (corp-wide): 59.9B **Privately Held**
SIC: **2099** Food preparations
HQ: Safeway Inc.
11555 Dublin Canyon Rd
Pleasanton CA 94588
925 226-5000

(P-2591)
M C I FOODS INC
Also Called: Los Cabos Mexican Foods
13013 Molette St, Santa Fe Springs (90670-5521)
PHONE...............................562 977-4000
Alberta Southard, *Ch of Bd*
Daniel Southard, *President*
John M Southard, *Vice Pres*
Cathy Wong, *Research*
Brian Mills, *Plant Mgr*
EMP: 140 EST: 1970
SQ FT: 15,000
SALES (est): 31.7MM **Privately Held**
WEB: www.mcifoods.com
SIC: **2099** Food preparations

(P-2592)
M R S FOODS INC (PA)
Also Called: La Rancherita Tortilla
4408 W 5th St, Santa Ana (92703-3224)
PHONE..............................714 554-2791
Laura Perez, *President*
Roxana Perez, *Treasurer*
Shirley Serna, *Admin Sec*
▲ EMP: 60
SQ FT: 4,000
SALES (est): 5.8MM **Privately Held**
SIC: 2099 5812 Tortillas, fresh or refrigerated; fast-food restaurant, independent

(P-2593)
MAMA SUES GOURMET PASTA INC
2621 Lee Ave, South El Monte (91733-1411)
PHONE..............................626 241-2394
Susan Chiu, *President*
EMP: 25
SQ FT: 8,000
SALES (est): 2.9MM **Privately Held**
SIC: 2099 Noodles, uncooked: packaged with other ingredients

(P-2594)
MAMMA LINAS INCORPORATED
Also Called: Mamma Lina Ravioli Co
10741 Roselle St, San Diego (92121-1507)
PHONE..............................858 535-0620
Checchino Massullo, *Ch of Bd*
Emily Massullo, *CEO*
Lina Massullo, *Director*
EMP: 14 EST: 1959
SALES: 1MM **Privately Held**
SIC: 2099 Pasta, uncooked: packaged with other ingredients

(P-2595)
MAPLEGROVE GLUTEN FREE FOODS
5010 Eucalyptus Ave, Chino (91710-9216)
PHONE..............................909 334-7828
Raj Sukul, *President*
Felix Wong, *VP Finance*
May Wong, *VP Human Res*
EMP: 37
SALES (est): 7MM **Privately Held**
SIC: 2099 Food preparations

(P-2596)
MARINPAK
Also Called: MPK Sonoma
21684 8th St E Ste 100, Sonoma (95476-2816)
PHONE..............................707 996-3931
Fax: 707 996-3999
▲ EMP: 14
SQ FT: 23,000
SALES (est): 1.1MM **Privately Held**
WEB: www.mpksonoma.com
SIC: 2099

(P-2597)
MARUCHAN INC (HQ)
15800 Laguna Canyon Rd, Irvine (92618-3103)
PHONE..............................949 789-2300
Noritaka Sumimoto, *CEO*
Gary Leeper, *Info Tech Mgr*
Daizo Arima, *Research*
Shintaro Matsunaga, *Purch Mgr*
Masaaki Miyashita, *Purch Mgr*
▲ EMP: 450
SQ FT: 300,000
SALES (est): 243MM
SALES (corp-wide): 3.6B **Privately Held**
WEB: www.maruchaninc.com
SIC: 2099 Food preparations
PA: Toyo Suisan Kaisha, Ltd.
2-13-40, Konan
Minato-Ku TKY 108-0
334 585-111

(P-2598)
MARUKAN VINEGAR U S A INC (HQ)
16203 Vermont Ave, Paramount (90723-5042)
PHONE..............................562 630-6060
Yasuo Sasada, *Ch of Bd*
Toshio Takeuchi, *President*
Denzaemon Sasada, *CEO*

Yoshi Tsumura, *CFO*
Junichi Oyama, *Exec VP*
◆ EMP: 105
SQ FT: 20,000
SALES (est): 21.6MM
SALES (corp-wide): 19.9MM **Privately Held**
WEB: www.marukan-usa.com
SIC: 2099 Vinegar
PA: Marukan Vinegar Co.,Ltd.
5-6, Koyochonishi, Higashinada-Ku
Kobe HYO 658-0
788 570-501

(P-2599)
MARUKOME USA INC
17132 Pullman St, Irvine (92614-5524)
PHONE..............................949 863-0110
Shigeru Shirasaka, *President*
Toshio Abe, *Corp Secy*
Yuji Teranishi, *Sales Mgr*
Kazuhiko Fushimi, *Marketing Staff*
Sang Kim, *Sales Staff*
▲ EMP: 17
SQ FT: 134,172
SALES (est): 4.5MM
SALES (corp-wide): 423.1MM **Privately Held**
WEB: www.marukomeusa.com
SIC: 2099 Seasonings & spices
PA: Marukome Co.,Ltd.
883, Amori
Nagano NAG 380-0
262 260-255

(P-2600)
MCCORMICK & COMPANY INC
180 N Riverview Dr, Anaheim (92808-1241)
PHONE..............................714 685-0934
EMP: 95
SALES (corp-wide): 4.8B **Publicly Held**
SIC: 2099 Spices, including grinding
PA: Mccormick & Company Incorporated
24 Schilling Rd Ste 1
Hunt Valley MD 21031
410 771-7301

(P-2601)
MCCORMICK & COMPANY INC
340 El Cam Ste 20, Salinas (93901)
PHONE..............................831 775-3350
David Sasaki, *Branch Mgr*
Joseph Altman, *Mfg Staff*
EMP: 69
SALES (corp-wide): 4.8B **Publicly Held**
WEB: www.mccormick.com
SIC: 2099 Spices, including grinding
PA: Mccormick & Company Incorporated
24 Schilling Rd Ste 1
Hunt Valley MD 21031
410 771-7301

(P-2602)
MCCORMICK & COMPANY INC
340 El Camino Real S # 20, Salinas (93901-4553)
P.O. Box 81311 (93912)
PHONE..............................831 758-2411
Fax: 831 755-0230
EMP: 200
SALES (corp-wide): 4.2B **Publicly Held**
SIC: 2099
PA: Mccormick & Company Incorporated
18 Loveton Cir
Sparks MD 21031
410 771-7301

(P-2603)
MCCORMICK FRESH HERBS LLC
1575 W Walnut Pkwy, Compton (90220-5022)
PHONE..............................323 278-9750
EMP: 75
SALES (est): 5.8MM
SALES (corp-wide): 4.2B **Publicly Held**
SIC: 2099
PA: Mccormick & Company Incorporated
18 Loveton Cir
Sparks MD 21031
410 771-7301

(P-2604)
MI RANCHO TORTILLA INC
801 Purvis Ave, Clovis (93612-2892)
PHONE..............................559 299-3183
Criss K Cruz, *CEO*
Dorothy Cruz, *President*
EMP: 56
SQ FT: 6,000
SALES (est): 11.4MM **Privately Held**
SIC: 2099 Tortillas, fresh or refrigerated

(P-2605)
MILLERS AMERICAN HONEY INC
Also Called: Superior Honey Company
1455 Riverview Dr, San Bernardino (92408-2931)
PHONE..............................909 825-1722
George T Murdock, *CEO*
Steve Smith, *Vice Pres*
◆ EMP: 34
SQ FT: 33,000
SALES (est): 5.7MM **Privately Held**
WEB: www.millershoney.com
SIC: 2099 Honey, strained & bottled

(P-2606)
MINSLEY INC
989 S Monterey Ave, Ontario (91761-3463)
PHONE..............................909 458-1100
Song Tae Jin, *CEO*
Jeff Kim, *General Mgr*
Brian Jung, *Manager*
Jason Park, *Manager*
▲ EMP: 40
SQ FT: 42,000
SALES (est): 8.2MM **Privately Held**
WEB: www.minsley.com
SIC: 2099 Packaged combination products: pasta, rice & potato

(P-2607)
MIZKAN AMERICAS INC
46 Walker St, Watsonville (95076-4925)
PHONE..............................831 728-2061
David Shields, *Manager*
Irma Gonzalez, *Purch Agent*
EMP: 15 **Privately Held**
SIC: 2099 Vinegar
HQ: Mizkan America, Inc.
1661 Feehanville Dr # 200
Mount Prospect IL 60056
847 590-0059

(P-2608)
MIZKAN AMERICAS INC
Also Called: Indian Summer
10037 8th St, Rancho Cucamonga (91730-5210)
PHONE..............................909 484-8743
Pete Marsing, *Branch Mgr*
Antonio Holguin, *QC Mgr*
EMP: 45
SQ FT: 58,500 **Privately Held**
SIC: 2099 Vinegar
HQ: Mizkan America, Inc.
1661 Feehanville Dr # 200
Mount Prospect IL 60056
847 590-0059

(P-2609)
MOJAVE FOODS CORPORATION
6200 E Slauson Ave, Commerce (90040-3012)
PHONE..............................323 890-8900
Richard D Lipka, *CEO*
Craig M Berger, *CFO*
Robert Horn, *General Mgr*
◆ EMP: 200
SQ FT: 110,000
SALES (est): 42.1MM
SALES (corp-wide): 4.8B **Publicly Held**
WEB: www.mccormick.com
SIC: 2099 Butter, renovated & processed
PA: Mccormick & Company Incorporated
24 Schilling Rd Ste 1
Hunt Valley MD 21031
410 771-7301

(P-2610)
MOORE FARMS INC
916 S Derby St, Arvin (93203-2312)
P.O. Box 698 (93203-0698)
PHONE..............................661 854-5588
John Moore, *President*
EMP: 15

SQ FT: 2,000
SALES: 970K **Privately Held**
SIC: 2099 0134 Potatoes, peeled for the trade; Irish potatoes

(P-2611)
MORINAGA NUTRITIONAL FOODS INC
3838 Del Amo Blvd Ste 201, Torrance (90503-7709)
P.O. Box 7969 (90504-9369)
PHONE..............................310 787-0200
Hiroyuki Imanishi, *President*
Tetsuhisa Tato, *Vice Pres*
Akiko Akamatsu, *Administration*
Susan Buch R, *Mktg Dir*
Adrian Cruz, *Marketing Staff*
▼ EMP: 19
SQ FT: 2,782
SALES: 4.3MM
SALES (corp-wide): 5.5B **Privately Held**
WEB: www.morinu.com
SIC: 2099 Food preparations
PA: Morinaga Milk Industry Co., Ltd.
5-33-1, Shiba
Minato-Ku TKY 108-0
337 980-111

(P-2612)
NANCYS SPECIALTY FOODS
2400 Olympic Blvd Ste 8, Walnut Creek (94595-1500)
PHONE..............................510 494-1100
Adam Ferrif, *COO*
Nancy S Mueller, *President*
R Larry Booth, *Vice Pres*
David M Joiner, *Vice Pres*
EMP: 375
SQ FT: 86,000
SALES (est): 34MM
SALES (corp-wide): 26.2B **Publicly Held**
SIC: 2099 Food preparations
HQ: Kraft Heinz Foods Company
1 Ppg Pl Ste 3200
Pittsburgh PA 15222
412 456-5700

(P-2613)
NANCYS TORTILLERIA & MINI MKT
348 S Towne Ave, Pomona (91766-2036)
PHONE..............................909 629-5889
Jose Vergara, *Owner*
Teresa Vergara, *Owner*
EMP: 34
SQ FT: 6,000
SALES (est): 3.2MM **Privately Held**
SIC: 2099 Tortillas, fresh or refrigerated

(P-2614)
NAPA VALLEY KITCHENS INC
Also Called: Consorzio
1610 5th St, Berkeley (94710-1715)
PHONE..............................510 558-7500
John Foraker, *CEO*
Sarah Bird, *Vice Pres*
Stephen Palmer, *Admin Sec*
EMP: 75
SQ FT: 10,000
SALES: 10MM
SALES (corp-wide): 15.7B **Publicly Held**
WEB: www.annies.com
SIC: 2099 Vinegar
HQ: Annie's, Inc.
1610 5th St
Berkeley CA 94710

(P-2615)
NATIONAL STABILIZERS INC
611 S Duggan Ave, Azusa (91702-5139)
PHONE..............................626 969-5700
Lorraine Mancilla, *Bd of Directors*
Robert Burger, *President*
EMP: 10 EST: 1975
SQ FT: 7,000
SALES (est): 1.3MM **Privately Held**
SIC: 2099 Food preparations

(P-2616)
NATIVE KJALII FOODS INC
1474 29th Ave, San Francisco (94122-3234)
P.O. Box 471030 (94147-1030)
PHONE..............................415 592-8670
Julie Jeremy, *CEO*

PRODUCTS & SVCS

Bret Jeremy, *Shareholder*
Fred Levinson, *Vice Pres*
Rory Gallagher, *Director*
Sophia Rosensteel, *Manager*
EMP: 25
SQ FT: 1,000
SALES (est): 3MM **Privately Held**
WEB: www.sfsalsa.com
SIC: 2099 Food preparations

(P-2617)
NATREN INC
3105 Willow Ln, Thousand Oaks
(91361-4919)
PHONE..................805 371-4737
Yordan Trenev, *CEO*
Natasha Trenev, *President*
Edessa Braza, *Executive Asst*
Odessa Braza, *Admin Sec*
Michael Chapovsky, *Info Tech Dir*
EMP: 60
SQ FT: 22,000
SALES (est): 12.3MM **Privately Held**
SIC: 2099 8011 Food preparations; offices
& clinics of medical doctors

(P-2618)
NECTAVE INC
6700 Caballero Blvd, Buena Park
(90620-1134)
PHONE..................714 393-0144
Richard Ellinghausen, *President*
Annalisa Chavez, *CFO*
EMP: 15 **EST:** 2011
SQ FT: 30,000
SALES (est): 693.4K **Privately Held**
SIC: 2099 Sorghum syrups: for sweetening

(P-2619)
NEW GLOBAL FOOD
13577 Larwin Cir, Santa Fe Springs
(90670-5032)
PHONE..................562 404-9953
Duk Kiml, *Principal*
EMP: 12
SALES (est): 1.3MM **Privately Held**
SIC: 2099 Food preparations

(P-2620)
NEW HORIZON FOODS INC
33440 Western Ave, Union City
(94587-3202)
PHONE..................510 489-8600
Kenneth L Crawford, *President*
Elieser Pedroza, *Prdtn Mgr*
EMP: 20
SQ FT: 20,000
SALES (est): 3.9MM
SALES (corp-wide): 14.4MM **Privately Held**
WEB: www.tovaindustries.com
SIC: 2099 Food preparations
PA: Tova Industries, Llc
2902 Blankenbaker Rd
Louisville KY 40299
502 267-7333

(P-2621)
NEWLY WEDS FOODS INC
Also Called: Heller Seasoning
437 S Mcclure Rd, Modesto (95357-0519)
PHONE..................209 491-7777
Allen Holzmen, *Manager*
Hilda Israde, *Human Res Mgr*
Dave Best, *Maintence Staff*
EMP: 50
SALES (corp-wide): 116.5MM **Privately Held**
WEB: www.newlywedsfoods.com
SIC: 2099 Spices, including grinding
PA: Newly Weds Foods, Inc.
4140 W Fullerton Ave
Chicago IL 60639
773 489-7000

(P-2622)
NINA MIA INC
Also Called: Pasta Mia
826 Enterprise Way, Fullerton
(92831-5015)
PHONE..................714 773-5588
Diego Mazza, *President*
Jessica Mazza, *Vice Pres*
Kevin Gruezo, *Purch Mgr*
▲ **EMP:** 80
SQ FT: 32,000

SALES (est): 17.8MM **Privately Held**
WEB: www.pastamiacorp.com
SIC: 2099 Pasta, uncooked: packaged with
other ingredients

(P-2623)
NINAS MEXICAN FOODS INC
20631 Valley Blvd Ste A, Walnut
(91789-2751)
PHONE..................909 468-5888
Ruben Vasquez, *President*
▲ **EMP:** 40
SQ FT: 14,000
SALES (est): 12.3MM **Privately Held**
SIC: 2099 Tortillas, fresh or refrigerated

(P-2624)
NIPPON TRENDS FOOD SERVICE INC
Also Called: Yamachan Ramen
631 Giguere Ct Ste A1, San Jose
(95133-1745)
PHONE..................408 214-0511
Hideyuki Yamashita, *President*
Tomoko Yamashita, *Vice Pres*
▲ **EMP:** 60
SQ FT: 5,000
SALES (est): 3MM **Privately Held**
SIC: 2099 Noodles, uncooked: packaged
with other ingredients

(P-2625)
NUTIVA (PA)
213 W Cutting Blvd, Richmond
(94804-2015)
PHONE..................510 255-2700
John Roulac, *CEO*
Mary Gratol, *General Mgr*
Caroline Hersom, *Planning*
Holly Espiritu, *Financial Analy*
Jeff Moir, *Controller*
▲ **EMP:** 91
SQ FT: 1,300
SALES (est): 20.9MM **Privately Held**
SIC: 2099 Vegetables, peeled for the trade

(P-2626)
NYDR HOLDINGS INC
Also Called: Genesis Natural Products
9525 Cozycroft Ave Ste M, Chatsworth
(91311-0712)
PHONE..................818 626-8174
Helena Belmes, *CEO*
Eli Belmes, *Vice Pres*
▲ **EMP:** 10
SQ FT: 10,000
SALES: 5MM **Privately Held**
SIC: 2099 Food preparations

(P-2627)
OASIS DATE GARDEN INC
59111 Grapefruit Blvd, Thermal
(92274-8813)
P.O. Box 757 (92274-0757)
PHONE..................760 399-5665
James Freimuth, *President*
Dana Emery, *Vice Pres*
Chris Nelsen, *Vice Pres*
Maribel Aguilar, *Personnel*
▲ **EMP:** 45
SQ FT: 14,000
SALES (est): 11.1MM **Privately Held**
WEB: www.oasisdategardens.com
SIC: 2099 5431 5148 0179 Food prepa-
rations; fruit stands or markets; fruits;
date orchard

(P-2628)
OLD PUEBLO RANCH INC (PA)
Also Called: La Reina
316 N Ford Blvd, Los Angeles
(90022-1121)
PHONE..................323 268-2791
Mauro Robles, *Vice Pres*
Ricardo Robles, *President*
Marisela Robles, *Admin Sec*
EMP: 101 **EST:** 1958
SQ FT: 90,000
SALES (est): 24.1MM **Privately Held**
WEB: www.lareinainc.com
SIC: 2099 Tortillas, fresh or refrigerated

(P-2629)
OOGOLOW ENTERPRISES
1608 W 5th St A, Chico (95928-4716)
PHONE..................530 899-9927

Michael Epperson, *President*
EMP: 13
SALES (est): 1.9MM **Privately Held**
SIC: 2099 Food preparations

(P-2630)
ORGANIC SPICES (PA)
4180 Business Center Dr, Fremont
(94538-6354)
PHONE..................510 440-1044
Clara Bonner, *CEO*
Bijan Chansari, *CFO*
Raj Dhillon, *Technology*
Marina Gonzales, *Opers Staff*
Adrian Ruiz, *Production*
▲ **EMP:** 30
SQ FT: 27,000
SALES (est): 3.5MM **Privately Held**
SIC: 2099 Chicory root, dried

(P-2631)
ORGANICGIRL LLC
900 Work St, Salinas (93901-4386)
P.O. Box 5999 (93915-5999)
PHONE..................831 758-7800
Mark Drever,
Tom Browning, *Vice Pres*
Julie Bily, *Business Mgr*
Steve Taylor,
Julie Vanacker, *Director*
EMP: 650
SQ FT: 125,000
SALES (est): 228.8MM **Privately Held**
SIC: 2099 5148 Ready-to-eat meals, sal-
ads & sandwiches; fresh fruits & vegeta-
bles

(P-2632)
OTSUKA AMERICA FOODS INC (DH)
1 Embarcadero Ctr # 2020, San Francisco
(94111-3750)
PHONE..................424 219-9425
Bradley Paris, *President*
Osamu Aizawa, *CFO*
EMP: 10
SQ FT: 5,000
SALES (est): 1.2MM
SALES (corp-wide): 11B **Privately Held**
SIC: 2099 Food preparations
HQ: Otsuka Foods Co.,Ltd.
3-2-27, Otedori, Chuo-Ku
Osaka OSK 540-0
669 437-755

(P-2633)
PACIFIC SPICE COMPANY INC
Also Called: Pacific Natural Spices
6430 E Slauson Ave, Commerce
(90040-3108)
PHONE..................323 726-9190
Gershon D Schlussel, *CEO*
Akiba E Schlussel, *President*
Sharon Schlussel, *Admin Sec*
Elias A Pflaster, *Agent*
◆ **EMP:** 82
SQ FT: 150,000
SALES (est): 21.6MM **Privately Held**
WEB: www.pacspice.com
SIC: 2099 5149 Spices, including grinding;
spices & seasonings

(P-2634)
PAPPYS MEAT COMPANY INC
Also Called: Pappy's Fine Foods
5663 E Fountain Way, Fresno
(93727-7813)
P.O. Box 5257 (93755-5257)
PHONE..................559 291-0218
Marie Papulias, *President*
Edward Papulias, *CEO*
Patricia Papulias, *Corp Secy*
EMP: 23
SQ FT: 10,000
SALES (est): 3.4MM **Privately Held**
WEB: www.pappyschoice.com
SIC: 2099 Seasonings & spices; season-
ings: dry mixes

(P-2635)
PASSPORT FOOD GROUP LLC (PA)
Also Called: Wing Hing Noodle Company
2539 E Philadelphia St, Ontario
(91761-7774)
PHONE..................909 627-7312

Michael Axelrod, *CEO*
Ibeth E Sphr, *Vice Pres*
Steve Chang, *Opers Staff*
Jade Lucas, *Manager*
▲ **EMP:** 150
SQ FT: 103,000
SALES (est): 41.7MM **Privately Held**
WEB: www.winghing.com
SIC: 2099 Packaged combination prod-
ucts: pasta, rice & potato

(P-2636)
PEARL CROP INC
Also Called: Linden Nut
8452 Demartini Ln, Linden (95236-9446)
PHONE..................209 887-3731
Halil Ulas Turkhan, *President*
Chad Temel, *Purchasing*
EMP: 50
SALES (corp-wide): 140MM **Privately Held**
SIC: 2099 2068 Food preparations; salted
& roasted nuts & seeds
PA: Pearl Crop, Inc.
1550 Industrial Dr
Stockton CA 95206
209 808-7575

(P-2637)
PETIT POT INC
158 S Spruce Ave, South San Francisco
(94080-4519)
PHONE..................650 488-7432
Maxime Pouvreau, *CEO*
Anne Lesgourgues, *Director*
EMP: 10
SQ FT: 2,000
SALES (est): 1.2MM **Privately Held**
SIC: 2099 Dessert mixes & fillings

(P-2638)
PGP INTERNATIONAL INC (DH)
351 Hanson Way, Woodland (95776-6224)
P.O. Box 2060 (95776-2060)
PHONE..................530 662-5056
Nicolas J Hanson, *CEO*
Carmen Sciackitano, *Admin Sec*
◆ **EMP:** 180
SALES (est): 70.3MM
SALES (corp-wide): 19.7B **Privately Held**
WEB: www.protient.com
SIC: 2099 Almond pastes

(P-2639)
PHAT N JICY BURGERS BRANDS LLC
Also Called: Phat N Juicy Brands
25876 The Old Rd 305, Stevenson Ranch
(91381-1711)
PHONE..................310 420-7983
Christopher Champion,
Kenya Champion,
EMP: 30
SALES (est): 2.7MM **Privately Held**
SIC: 2099 Food preparations

(P-2640)
PRE-PEELED POTATO CO INC
1585 S Union St, Stockton (95206-2269)
P.O. Box 111 (95201-0111)
PHONE..................209 469-6911
Bart Birt, *President*
EMP: 19
SQ FT: 10,000
SALES: 3MM **Privately Held**
SIC: 2099 Potatoes, peeled for the trade;
vegetables, peeled for the trade

(P-2641)
PRESTIGE CHINESE TEAS CO
Also Called: P C Teas
882 Mahler Rd, Burlingame (94010-1604)
PHONE..................650 697-8989
Sunny Wong, *Owner*
▲ **EMP:** 10
SQ FT: 3,300
SALES (est): 670K **Privately Held**
SIC: 2099 5149 5499 Tea blending; tea;
spices & herbs

(P-2642)
PRO FOOD INC
19431 Bus Center Dr # 35, Northridge
(91324-3507)
PHONE..................818 341-4040
Laurent Caraco, *President*

▲ = Import ▼ =Export
◆ =Import/Export

EMP: 10
SQ FT: 3,000
SALES: 1MM **Privately Held**
SIC: 2099 Food preparations

(P-2643)
PRODUCE WORLD INC
30611 San Antonio St, Hayward
(94544-7103)
PHONE..................510 441-1449
Joseph Fereira, *President*
Dennis Dahlin, *Vice Pres*
EMP: 75
SQ FT: 20,000
SALES (est): 11.3MM **Privately Held**
SIC: 2099 Vegetables, peeled for the trade

(P-2644)
PSW INC
Also Called: Taste Nirvana International
149 Via Trevizio, Corona (92879-1773)
PHONE..................951 371-7100
Jack Wattanaporn, *President*
Mika Williams, *Opers Mgr*
Joyce Chang, *Sales Mgr*
Kris Wattanaporn, *Sales Staff*
▲ EMP: 15
SQ FT: 23,667
SALES (est): 2.4MM **Privately Held**
WEB: www.psw.com
SIC: 2099 2095 5141 Tea blending;
roasted coffee; groceries, general line

(P-2645)
**Q TRADE INTERNATIONAL
CORP (PA)**
Also Called: QTRADE TEAS & HERBS
16205 Distribution Way, Cerritos
(90703-2329)
PHONE..................949 766-0070
Manik Jayakumar, *CEO*
Lisa Schommer, *COO*
Kingsley Alagaratnam, *Senior VP*
Royce Van Twest, *Vice Pres*
Queenie Jayakumar, *Admin Sec*
▲ EMP: 50 EST: 1994
SQ FT: 1,800
SALES: 27.5MM **Privately Held**
SIC: 2099 2086 Tea blending; tea, iced:
packaged in cans, bottles, etc.

(P-2646)
**QST INGREDIENTS AND PACKG
INC**
9734-40 6th St, Rancho Cucamonga
(91730)
PHONE..................909 989-4343
Chris Topps, *President*
Mario Larraga, *Opers Staff*
Jill Mauleon, *Manager*
▲ EMP: 15
SALES (est): 4.3MM **Privately Held**
SIC: 2099 5046 Seasonings & spices;
commercial cooking & food service equipment

(P-2647)
QUEST NUTRITION LLC (PA)
777 S Aviation Blvd, El Segundo
(90245-4806)
PHONE..................888 212-0601
Michael Osborn, *Mng Member*
Ryan Worsham, *Marketing Staff*
Erika Martos, *Sales Staff*
Michelle Minchuk, *Sales Staff*
Emilio Mercado, *Supervisor*
▲ EMP: 50
SALES (est): 28.7MM **Privately Held**
SIC: 2099 1541 Food preparations

(P-2648)
QUEST NUTRITION LLC
2221 Park Pl, El Segundo (90245-4909)
PHONE..................562 446-3321
EMP: 28
SALES (est): 10MM **Privately Held**
SIC: 2099

(P-2649)
**RAMA FOOD MANUFACTURE
CORP**
1486 E Cedar St, Ontario (91761-8300)
PHONE..................909 923-5305
Karen Trang Ving, *CEO*
Michael Yin, *VP Opers*

▲ EMP: 40
SQ FT: 25,000
SALES (est): 9.2MM **Privately Held**
SIC: 2099 Noodles, fried (Chinese)

(P-2650)
READY PAC FOODS INC (HQ)
4401 Foxdale St, Irwindale (91706-2161)
PHONE..................626 856-8686
Tony Sarsam, *CEO*
Peter Laport, *COO*
Dan Redfern, *CFO*
Tristan Simpson, *Chief Mktg Ofcr*
Tim Clark, *Officer*
▲ EMP: 400
SQ FT: 135,000
SALES: 804.2MM **Privately Held**
SIC: 2099 5148 Salads, fresh or refrigerated; vegetables, fresh
PA: Bonduelle
Rue De La Woestyne
Renescure
328 498-228

(P-2651)
RELS FOODS INC (PA)
1814 Franklin St Ste 310, Oakland
(94612-3426)
PHONE..................510 652-2747
P Scott Sorensen, *CEO*
Soren Peder Sorensen, *President*
Peder Scott Sorensen, *Treasurer*
Dick Welch, *Principal*
EMP: 12
SQ FT: 4,000
SALES (est): 5.9MM **Privately Held**
WEB: www.relsfoods.com
SIC: 2099 5142 Sandwiches, assembled
& packaged: for wholesale market; packaged frozen goods

(P-2652)
**RENAISSANCE FOOD GROUP
LLC (HQ)**
Also Called: Garden Highway
11020 White Rock Rd # 100, Rancho Cordova (95670-6402)
PHONE..................916 638-8825
James S Catchot, *President*
Donald Ochoa, *President*
Debbie Vest, *President*
Jim Gibson, *COO*
Allen Bridges, *CFO*
▲ EMP: 48
SQ FT: 12,000
SALES (est): 106.9MM
SALES (corp-wide): 1B **Publicly Held**
SIC: 2099 Salads, fresh or refrigerated
PA: Calavo Growers, Inc.
1141 Cummings Rd Ste A
Santa Paula CA 93060
805 525-1245

(P-2653)
RISVOLDS INC
1234 W El Segundo Blvd, Gardena
(90247-1593)
PHONE..................323 770-2674
Tim Brandon, *CEO*
Ed Scoullar, *President*
Wendy O'Neill, *Vice Pres*
Jenifer Peterson, *Purch Mgr*
EMP: 65
SQ FT: 30,000
SALES: 12MM **Privately Held**
WEB: www.risvolds.com
SIC: 2099 Salads, fresh or refrigerated

(P-2654)
RITAS FINE FOOD
Also Called: Da Vinci Fine Food
8900 Grossmont Blvd Ste 5, La Mesa
(91941-4047)
PHONE..................619 698-3925
Faris Auro, *President*
Basma Shammas, *Vice Pres*
Raad Shammas, *Vice Pres*
EMP: 12
SQ FT: 2,100
SALES: 650K **Privately Held**
SIC: 2099 Salads, fresh or refrigerated;
sandwiches, assembled & packaged: for
wholesale market

(P-2655)
RIVIANA FOODS INC
2704 S Maple Ave, Fresno (93725-2109)
PHONE..................559 485-8110
Tom Martins, *Branch Mgr*
EMP: 100 **Privately Held**
WEB: www.skinnerpasta.com
SIC: 2099 Food preparations
HQ: Riviana Foods Inc.
2777 Allen Pkwy Fl 15
Houston TX 77019
713 529-3251

(P-2656)
ROBEKS CORPORATION
Also Called: Robeks Juice
8905 S Sepulveda Blvd, Los Angeles
(90045-3603)
PHONE..................310 642-7800
Antje Frei, *Manager*
EMP: 15 **Privately Held**
SIC: 2099 5812 Ready-to-eat meals, salads & sandwiches; soft drink stand
PA: Robeks Corporation
5220 Pacific Concourse Dr
Los Angeles CA 90045

(P-2657)
ROBLES BROS INC (PA)
Also Called: La Colonial
1700 Rogers Ave, San Jose (95112-1107)
PHONE..................408 436-5551
George Robles, *President*
Claudia Robles, *Corp Secy*
Hector Robles, *Vice Pres*
EMP: 35
SQ FT: 7,000
SALES (est): 5.3MM **Privately Held**
SIC: 2099 Tortillas, fresh or refrigerated

(P-2658)
**ROMEROS FOOD PRODUCTS
INC (PA)**
15155 Valley View Ave, Santa Fe Springs
(90670-5323)
PHONE..................562 802-1858
Richard Scandalito, *CEO*
Leon Romero Sr, *President*
Leon S Romero, *CEO*
Raul Romero Sr, *Vice Pres*
Robert Romero, *General Mgr*
EMP: 100 EST: 1971
SQ FT: 20,000
SALES: 28MM **Privately Held**
WEB: www.romerosfood.com
SIC: 2099 2096 5461 Tortillas, fresh or refrigerated; tortilla chips; bakeries

(P-2659)
**ROMEROS FOOD PRODUCTS
INC**
Also Called: Distribution Center
993 S Waterman Ave, San Bernardino
(92408-2304)
PHONE..................909 884-5531
David Hernandez, *Branch Mgr*
EMP: 10
SQ FT: 1,260
SALES (corp-wide): 28MM **Privately
Held**
WEB: www.romerosfood.com
SIC: 2099 Tortillas, fresh or refrigerated
PA: Romero's Food Products, Incorporated
15155 Valley View Ave
Santa Fe Springs CA 90670
562 802-1858

(P-2660)
**ROYAL ANGELUS MACARONI
COMPANY**
2539 E Philadelphia St, Ontario
(91761-7774)
PHONE..................909 627-7312
Dave Abrams, *President*
Scott Kraus, *CFO*
▲ EMP: 130 EST: 2008
SALES (est): 150.3K
SALES (corp-wide): 41.7MM **Privately
Held**
SIC: 2099 Pasta, uncooked: packaged with
other ingredients

PA: Passport Food Group, Llc
2539 E Philadelphia St
Ontario CA 91761
909 627-7312

(P-2661)
RUIZ MEXICAN FOODS INC (PA)
Also Called: Ruiz Flour Tortillas
1200 Marlborough Ave A, Riverside
(92507-2158)
PHONE..................909 947-7811
Dolores C Ruiz, *CEO*
Anna Loza, *Finance Mgr*
Dana Warren, *Accountant*
Ed Ruiz, *Director*
▼ EMP: 140
SQ FT: 38,000
SALES (est): 28.8MM **Privately Held**
SIC: 2099 3556 Tortillas, fresh or refrigerated; food products machinery

(P-2662)
S MARTINELLI & COMPANY (PA)
735 W Beach St, Watsonville (95076-5141)
P.O. Box 1868 (95077-1868)
PHONE..................831 724-1126
Stephen C Martinelli, *Chairman*
Stephen John Martinelli, *President*
Gun Ruder, *CFO*
Doris M Brown, *Vice Pres*
Alice M Kett, *Asst Sec*
▲ EMP: 195
SALES (est): 63.2MM **Privately Held**
WEB: www.martinellis.com
SIC: 2099 Cider, nonalcoholic

(P-2663)
**SANTA CRUZ MTN PASTA
FCTRY**
Also Called: Santa Cruz Pasta Factory
5340 Scotts Valley Dr, Scotts Valley
(95066-3568)
PHONE..................831 461-9900
Steven Matthew Simonovich, *President*
Catherine Simonovich, *Admin Sec*
EMP: 12
SQ FT: 2,000
SALES (est): 900K **Privately Held**
SIC: 2099 5149 5812 Pasta, uncooked:
packaged with other ingredients; pasta &
rice; Italian restaurant

(P-2664)
SD DESSERTS LLC
1608 India St Ste 104, San Diego
(92101-2564)
P.O. Box 2146, Rancho Santa Fe (92067-2146)
PHONE..................702 480-9083
Celine Maury,
Jean-Philippe Maury,
EMP: 10
SALES: 800K **Privately Held**
SIC: 2099 7389 Desserts, ready-to-mix;

(P-2665)
SEELECT INC
833 N Elm St, Orange (92867-7909)
PHONE..................714 744-3700
William R Sabo, *CEO*
Bill Sabo, *President*
EMP: 17 EST: 1935
SALES (est): 2.2MM **Privately Held**
WEB: www.seelecttea.com
SIC: 2099 Tea blending

(P-2666)
**SENSIENT TECHNOLOGIES
CORP**
9984 W Walnut Ave, Livingston (95334)
P.O. Box 485 (95334-0485)
PHONE..................209 394-7971
Joe Martins, *Branch Mgr*
EMP: 10
SALES (corp-wide): 1.3B **Publicly Held**
WEB: www.sensient-tech.com
SIC: 2099 2034 2087 Yeast; seasonings
& spices; chili pepper or powder; seasonings: dry mixes; dehydrated fruits, vegetables, soups; beverage bases
PA: Sensient Technologies Corporation
777 E Wisconsin Ave # 1100
Milwaukee WI 53202
414 271-6755

(P-2667)
SILAO TORTILLERIA INC
250 N California Ave, City of Industry
(91744-4323)
PHONE...................................626 961-0761
Leandro Espinosa Sr, *President*
Leandro Espinosa Jr, *Vice Pres*
EMP: 44
SALES (est): 6.1MM **Privately Held**
SIC: 2099 Tortillas, fresh or refrigerated

(P-2668)
SINBAD FOODS LLC
2401 W Almond Ave, Madera (93637-4807)
PHONE...................................559 674-4445
Mike Bizik,
EMP: 54
SALES (est): 1.6MM **Privately Held**
SIC: 2099 Food preparations

(P-2669)
SINCERE ORIENT COMMERCIAL CORP
Also Called: Sincere Orient Food Company
15222 Valley Blvd, City of Industry
(91746-3323)
PHONE...................................626 333-8882
Andy Khun, *President*
▲ **EMP:** 70
SQ FT: 12,000
SALES (est): 6.7MM **Privately Held**
WEB: www.sincereorient.com
SIC: 2099 Packaged combination products: pasta, rice & potato

(P-2670)
SONOMA CIDER MILL
Also Called: Sonoma Sparkler
1083 Vine St, Healdsburg (95448-4830)
PHONE...................................707 433-8212
David Cordtz, *President*
Roger Dumaine, *CFO*
EMP: 10
SQ FT: 15,000
SALES: 2MM **Privately Held**
WEB: www.sonomasparkler.com
SIC: 2099 Cider, nonalcoholic

(P-2671)
SOUTHWEST PRODUCTS LLC
Also Called: Tortilla Land
8411 Siempre Viva Rd, San Diego
(92154-6299)
PHONE...................................619 263-8000
Zeno Santache, *Mng Member*
Eric Brenk,
▲ **EMP:** 250 EST: 1974
SQ FT: 160,000
SALES (est): 58MM
SALES (corp-wide): 40B **Publicly Held**
SIC: 2099 Tortillas, fresh or refrigerated
PA: Tyson Foods, Inc.
    2200 W Don Tyson Pkwy
    Springdale AR 72762
    479 290-4000

(P-2672)
SPICES UNLIMITED INC
2339 Tech Pkwy Ste J, Hollister (95023)
PHONE...................................831 636-3596
Dennis Voechting, *President*
Garron Billick, *Vice Pres*
Connie Voechting, *Admin Sec*
◆ **EMP:** 12 EST: 1948
SQ FT: 4,000
SALES: 500K **Privately Held**
SIC: 2099 Seasonings: dry mixes

(P-2673)
STANESS JONEKOS ENTPS INC
Also Called: Eat Like A Woman
4000 W Magnolia Blvd D, Burbank
(91505-2827)
PHONE...................................818 606-2710
Staness Jonekos, *Owner*
EMP: 27
SALES: 3.1MM **Privately Held**
SIC: 2099 Food preparations

(P-2674)
SUN BASKET INC
1 Clarence Pl Unit 14, San Francisco
(94107-2577)
PHONE...................................408 669-4418
Brett Frazer, *Cust Mgr*
EMP: 60
SALES (corp-wide): 100MM **Privately Held**
SIC: 2099 Almond pastes
PA: Sun Basket, Inc.
    1170 Olinder Ct
    San Jose CA 95122
    408 669-4418

(P-2675)
SUN RICH FOODS INTL CORP
1240 N Barsten Way, Anaheim
(92806-1822)
PHONE...................................714 632-7577
Walid A Barakat, *President*
Shirley Barakat, *CFO*
Alex Barakat, *Vice Pres*
EMP: 17
SQ FT: 6,500
SALES (est): 3.2MM **Privately Held**
SIC: 2099 Food preparations

(P-2676)
SURVIVOR INDUSTRIES INC
1621 Emerson Ave, Oxnard (93033-1846)
PHONE...................................805 385-5560
Howard Wallace, *President*
Linda Wallace, *Corp Secy*
◆ **EMP:** 35
SQ FT: 24,000
SALES (est): 6.3MM **Privately Held**
WEB: www.survivorind.com
SIC: 2099 Food preparations

(P-2677)
SWEET EARTH INC
Also Called: Sweet Earth Natural Foods
3080 Hilltop Rd, Moss Landing
(95039-9692)
PHONE...................................831 375-8673
Kelly Swette, *President*
Brian Swette, *President*
Rob Beitscher, *Finance*
EMP: 80
SQ FT: 30,000
SALES (est): 10MM **Privately Held**
SIC: 2099 Food preparations

(P-2678)
TAMPICO SPICE CO INCORPORATED
Also Called: Tampico Spice Company
5901 S Central Ave 5941, Los Angeles
(90001-1128)
P.O. Box 1229 (90001-0229)
PHONE...................................323 235-3154
George Martinez, *CEO*
Baudelia Martinez, *Treasurer*
Delia Navarro, *Treasurer*
Mario Jaimes, *General Mgr*
Frank Rubin, *Technician*
▲ **EMP:** 40
SQ FT: 150,000
SALES (est): 8.8MM **Privately Held**
WEB: www.tampico.com
SIC: 2099 Spices, including grinding; seasonings: dry mixes

(P-2679)
TARAZI SPECIALTY FOODS LLC
13727 Seminole Dr, Chino (91710-5515)
PHONE...................................909 628-3601
Rocco Fiore, *General Mgr*
Alexandra Vorbeck, *President*
Kirsten Tappan, *Office Mgr*
EMP: 13
SALES (est): 1.7MM **Privately Held**
SIC: 2099 Seasonings: dry mixes

(P-2680)
TEST LABORATORIES INC (PA)
Also Called: Brewster Foods
7121 Canby Ave, Reseda (91335-4304)
PHONE...................................818 881-4251
Gregory L Brewster, *President*
Karen G Brewster, *Corp Secy*
▲ **EMP:** 11
SQ FT: 5,000
SALES (est): 2.2MM **Privately Held**
WEB: www.testlabinc.com
SIC: 2099 Food preparations

(P-2681)
TEVA FOODS INC
4401 S Downey Rd, Vernon (90058-2518)
P.O. Box 58128, Los Angeles (90058-0128)
PHONE...................................323 267-8110
Erik Litmanovich, *President*
EMP: 30
SALES (est): 5.7MM **Privately Held**
SIC: 2099 Salads, fresh or refrigerated

(P-2682)
TOFU SHOP SPECIALTY FOODS INC
65 Frank Martin Ct, Arcata (95521-8930)
PHONE...................................707 822-7401
Matthew Schmit, *President*
EMP: 20
SQ FT: 4,400
SALES (est): 642.2K **Privately Held**
SIC: 2099 Tofu, except frozen desserts

(P-2683)
TOM HARRIS INC
Also Called: Uncle Bum's Gourmet Sauces
5821 Wilderness Ave, Riverside
(92504-1004)
PHONE...................................951 352-5700
Tom Harris, *President*
Richard Harris, *Vice Pres*
EMP: 60
SQ FT: 140,000
SALES (est): 3.9MM **Privately Held**
WEB: www.il.nacdnet.net
SIC: 2099 2035 Food preparations; pickles, sauces & salad dressings

(P-2684)
TOPNOTCH FOODS INC
1988 E 57th St, Vernon (90058-3464)
PHONE...................................323 586-2007
Meyer Luskin, *President*
Anna Arroyo, *Vice Pres*
Anna M Arroyo, *General Mgr*
Joe Giustra, *Manager*
EMP: 11
SQ FT: 20,000
SALES (est): 1.6MM
SALES (corp-wide): 203.7MM **Privately Held**
SIC: 2099 Bread crumbs, not made in bakeries
HQ: Reconserve, Inc.
    2811 Wilshire Blvd # 410
    Santa Monica CA 90403
    310 458-1574

(P-2685)
TORTILLERIA LA CALIFORNIA INC
2241 Cypress Ave, Los Angeles
(90065-1214)
PHONE...................................323 221-8940
Sergio Sanchez, *President*
EMP: 22 EST: 1972
SQ FT: 20,000
SALES (est): 3.3MM **Privately Held**
SIC: 2099 Tortillas, fresh or refrigerated

(P-2686)
TORTILLERIA LA MEJOR
Also Called: La Mejor Restaurant
684 S Farmersville Blvd, Farmersville
(93223-2042)
P.O. Box 657 (93223-0657)
PHONE...................................559 747-0739
Rafael Vasquez, *Owner*
Octaviana Vasquez, *Co-Owner*
EMP: 55
SALES (est): 4.9MM **Privately Held**
SIC: 2099 5411 Tortillas, fresh or refrigerated; grocery stores, independent

(P-2687)
TORTILLERIA SAN MARCOS
Also Called: San Marco's Tortilla & Market
1927 E 1st St, Los Angeles (90033-3412)
PHONE...................................323 263-0208
Gregorio Garcia, *President*
Amparo Garcia, *Vice Pres*
EMP: 27
SQ FT: 8,750
SALES (est): 750K **Privately Held**
SIC: 2099 Tortillas, fresh or refrigerated

(P-2688)
TORTILLERIA SANTA FE
387 Zenith St, Chula Vista (91911-5751)
PHONE...................................619 585-0350
Guillermo Estrada, *Owner*
EMP: 28
SALES (est): 4.4MM **Privately Held**
WEB: www.tortillaflats.net
SIC: 2099 Tortillas, fresh or refrigerated

(P-2689)
TORTILLERIA TEMECULA
28780 Old Town Front St A7, Temecula
(92590-2847)
PHONE...................................951 676-5272
Victor Castillo, *President*
Elizabeth Gonzales, *Controller*
EMP: 14
SALES: 1MM **Privately Held**
WEB: www.temeculainformation.com
SIC: 2099 Tortillas, fresh or refrigerated

(P-2690)
TRADITIONAL MEDICINALS INC (PA)
4515 Ross Rd, Sebastopol (95472-2250)
P.O. Box 239, Cotati (94931-0239)
PHONE...................................707 823-8911
Drake Sadler, *Chairman*
Emily Davydov, *Partner*
Blair Kellison, *CEO*
Teal Tasso, *COO*
Jane C Howard, *CFO*
▲ **EMP:** 150
SQ FT: 20,000
SALES (est): 32.6MM **Privately Held**
WEB: www.traditionalmedicinals.com
SIC: 2099 Tea blending

(P-2691)
TRINIDAD BENHAM HOLDING CO
Also Called: Westlam Foods
5177 Chino Ave, Chino (91710-5110)
PHONE...................................909 627-7535
Gary Fash, *MIS Dir*
Dennis Liptak, *Controller*
EMP: 30
SQ FT: 47,719
SALES (corp-wide): 1.1MM **Privately Held**
WEB: www.trinidadbenham.com
SIC: 2099 2032 Popcorn, packaged: except already popped; beans, without meat: packaged in cans, jars, etc.
PA: Trinidad Benham Holding Company
    3650 S Yosemite St # 300
    Denver CO 80237
    303 220-1400

(P-2692)
TRIPLE H FOOD PROCESSORS LLC
5821 Wilderness Ave, Riverside
(92504-1004)
PHONE...................................951 352-5700
Tom Harris Jr,
Richard J Harris,
▲ **EMP:** 60
SQ FT: 120,000
SALES (est): 17.6MM **Privately Held**
WEB: www.triplehfoods.com
SIC: 2099 2035 2033 Food preparations; pickles, sauces & salad dressings; jams, jellies & preserves: packaged in cans, jars, etc.

(P-2693)
TRUROOTS INC (HQ)
Also Called: Enray Inc.
6999 Southfront Rd, Livermore
(94551-8221)
PHONE...................................925 218-2205
Nimesh Ray, *CEO*
Esha Ray, *President*
▲ **EMP:** 25
SQ FT: 20,000
SALES (est): 2.1MM
SALES (corp-wide): 7.3B **Publicly Held**
SIC: 2099 Rice, uncooked: packaged with other ingredients
PA: The J M Smucker Company
    1 Strawberry Ln
    Orrville OH 44667
    330 682-3000

▲ = Import ▼=Export
◆ =Import/Export

(P-2694)
TRUROOTS INC
37 Speedway Ave, Chico (95928-9554)
PHONE............................925 218-2205
Emily Douglass, *Branch Mgr*
Ricardo Gonzalez, *Plant Mgr*
EMP: 17
SALES (corp-wide): 7.3B **Publicly Held**
SIC: 2099 Rice, uncooked: packaged with other ingredients
HQ: Truroots, Inc.
6999 Southfront Rd
Livermore CA 94551
925 218-2205

(P-2695)
UNCLE LEES TEA INC
Also Called: Ten Fu Company Limited
11020 Rush St, El Monte (91733-3547)
PHONE............................626 350-3309
Kuo-Lin Lee, *President*
Wyatt Kaul, *Natl Sales Mgr*
Heather Nicholson, *Sales Staff*
▲ EMP: 30
SQ FT: 7,772
SALES (est): 4.7MM **Privately Held**
WEB: www.unclelee.com
SIC: 2099 Tea blending

(P-2696)
UNITED FOODS INTL USA INC (HQ)
23447 Cabot Blvd, Hayward (94545-1665)
PHONE............................510 264-5850
Takeo Shimura, *President*
Vikram Kurve, *QA Dir*
Ryan Mewhinney, *Research*
Michael Skinner, *Plant Mgr*
Fumie Sato, *Marketing Staff*
▲ EMP: 49
SQ FT: 24,000
SALES (est): 13.1MM
SALES (corp-wide): 319.9MM **Privately Held**
WEB: www.senbausa.com
SIC: 2099 Seasonings: dry mixes
PA: United Foods International Co., Ltd.
1-5-18, Sarugakucho
Chiyoda-Ku TKY 101-0
332 957-550

(P-2697)
UPPER CRUST ENTERPRISES INC
411 Center St, Los Angeles (90012-3435)
PHONE............................213 625-0038
Gary Kawaguchi, *CEO*
Edward Shelley, *CFO*
Ken Kawaguchi, *Vice Pres*
Lisa Furumoto, *Accountant*
Alex Ruano, *Human Res Mgr*
◆ EMP: 50
SQ FT: 45,000
SALES: 2.5K **Privately Held**
WEB: www.uppercrustent.com
SIC: 2099 Bread crumbs, not made in bakeries

(P-2698)
VIRGINIA PARK LLC
Also Called: Virginia Park Foods
2225 Via Cerro Ste A, Riverside (92509-2440)
P.O. Box 1567, New York NY (10159-1567)
PHONE............................816 592-0776
Manoj Venugopal, *Mng Member*
Brian Rudolf,
Scott Rudolph,
EMP: 15
SQ FT: 35,000
SALES: 1MM
SALES (corp-wide): 4.2MM **Privately Held**
SIC: 2099 Pasta, uncooked: packaged with other ingredients
PA: Banza Llc
1570 Woodward Ave Fl 3
Detroit MI 48226
914 338-8009

(P-2699)
WALKER FOODS INC
Also Called: La Flora Del Sur
237 N Mission Rd, Los Angeles (90033-2103)
PHONE............................323 268-5191
Robert L Walker Jr, *President*
Denise Walker, *Admin Sec*
Gloria Michel, *Manager*
EMP: 65
SQ FT: 150,000
SALES (est): 13.6MM **Privately Held**
WEB: www.walkerfoods.com
SIC: 2099 2033 2032 Canned fruits & specialties; canned specialties; ready-to-eat meals, salads & sandwiches

(P-2700)
WHOLESOME VALLEY FOODS (PA)
Also Called: Barnana
1746 Berkeley St Unit B, Santa Monica (90404-4105)
PHONE............................858 480-1543
Caue Suplicy, *CEO*
Matt Clifford, *COO*
Nicholas Ingersoll, *Chief Mktg Ofcr*
EMP: 13
SALES (est): 2MM **Privately Held**
SIC: 2099 Food preparations

(P-2701)
WOOLERY ENTERPRISES INC
Also Called: Will's Fresh Foods
1991 Republic Ave, San Leandro (94577-4220)
PHONE............................510 357-5700
Daniel C Woolery, *CEO*
Susan Woolery, *Admin Sec*
EMP: 43
SQ FT: 23,000
SALES (est): 8.2MM **Privately Held**
SIC: 2099 Salads, fresh or refrigerated

(P-2702)
WORLDWIDE SPECIALTIES INC
Also Called: California Specialty Farms
2420 Modoc St, Los Angeles (90021-2916)
PHONE............................323 587-2200
Mady Joes, *Manager*
Bernadette Berumen, *Marketing Staff*
EMP: 120 **Privately Held**
SIC: 2099 Almond pastes
PA: Worldwide Specialties, Inc
2421 E 16th St 1
Los Angeles CA 90021

2111 Cigarettes

(P-2703)
AMERAMATIC VTECH LLC
2880 Scott St Ste 106, Vista (92081-8560)
PHONE............................760 688-8561
Kyle Kruger, *Mng Member*
Erik Hutchinson,
EMP: 14
SQ FT: 1,800
SALES: 500K **Privately Held**
SIC: 2111 5063 Cigarettes; electrical apparatus & equipment

(P-2704)
COSMIC FOG VAPORS
3115 Airway Ave, Costa Mesa (92626-4609)
PHONE............................949 266-1730
Robert Crofsey, *Mng Member*
Brant Peto, *Mng Member*
EMP: 60 EST: 2016
SALES: 19.5MM **Privately Held**
SIC: 2111 Cigarettes

(P-2705)
DYNAMIC E-MARKETS LLC
Also Called: Sandi Duty Free
2335 Roll Dr Ste 5, San Diego (92154-7274)
PHONE............................619 327-4777
Michael McVevin,
Michael McNevin, *General Mgr*
EMP: 10

SALES (est): 3MM **Privately Held**
SIC: 2111 5194 Cigarettes; tobacco & tobacco products

(P-2706)
HOOK IT UP
1513 S Grand Ave, Santa Ana (92705-4410)
PHONE............................714 600-0100
Zack Zakari, *CEO*
EMP: 135
SQ FT: 5,000
SALES (est): 6.6MM **Privately Held**
SIC: 2111 Cigarettes

(P-2707)
PHILIP MORRIS USA INC
185 Technology Dr, Irvine (92618-2412)
PHONE............................949 453-3500
EMP: 69
SALES (corp-wide): 25.4B **Publicly Held**
SIC: 2111
HQ: Philip Morris Usa Inc.
6601 W Brd St
Richmond VA 23230
804 274-2000

(P-2708)
R J REYNOLDS TOBACCO COMPANY
8380 Miramar Mall Ste 117, San Diego (92121-2549)
PHONE............................858 625-8453
Ken Stevens, *Principal*
EMP: 226
SALES (corp-wide): 26.8B **Privately Held**
WEB: www.carolinagroup.com
SIC: 2111 Cigarettes
HQ: R. J. Reynolds Tobacco Company
401 N Main St
Winston Salem NC 27101
336 741-5000

(P-2709)
SPACE JAM JUICE LLC
1041 Calle Trepadora, San Clemente (92673-6204)
PHONE............................714 660-7467
Daniel Peykoff, *CEO*
Michael Crawford, *President*
Dylan Spencer, *Exec VP*
Jessica Chae, *Accountant*
Ryan Battaglia, *Marketing Staff*
▲ EMP: 60
SQ FT: 25,000
SALES: 20MM **Privately Held**
SIC: 2111 Cigarettes

(P-2710)
USA SALES INC
Also Called: Statewide Distributors
1560 S Archibald Ave, Ontario (91761-7629)
PHONE............................909 390-9606
Kabiruddin Ali, *CEO*
EMP: 20
SALES (est): 4.6MM **Privately Held**
SIC: 2111 2121 Cigarettes; cigars

(P-2711)
VITACIG INC
433 N Camden Dr Fl 6, Beverly Hills (90210-4416)
PHONE............................310 402-6937
Paul Rosenberg, *CEO*
Mike Hawkins, *CFO*
EMP: 64
SALES (est): 84.3K
SALES (corp-wide): 7MM **Publicly Held**
SIC: 2111 Cigarettes
PA: Mcig, Inc.
2901 S Highland Dr 13b
Las Vegas NV 89109
570 778-6459

2121 Cigars

(P-2712)
BJC
1356 Lomita Blvd Apt 1, Harbor City (90710-2125)
PHONE............................310 977-6068
Brian Buenaventura, *Owner*
EMP: 10

SALES (est): 1MM **Privately Held**
SIC: 2121 Cigars

2131 Tobacco, Chewing & Snuff

(P-2713)
FANTASIA DISTRIBUTION INC
Also Called: Fantasia Hookah Tobacco
1566 W Embassy St, Anaheim (92802-1016)
PHONE............................714 817-8300
Randy Jacob Bahbah, *CEO*
Issa Bahbah, *CFO*
◆ EMP: 24
SALES (est): 7.2MM **Privately Held**
SIC: 2131 Smoking tobacco

(P-2714)
LA EJUICE LLC
Also Called: Five Star Juice
22871 Lockness Ave, Torrance (90501)
PHONE............................310 531-3888
Robert Hummer, *Mng Member*
Dan Cordei,
Fili Moala,
EMP: 27
SQ FT: 10,000
SALES (est): 1.7MM **Privately Held**
SIC: 2131 5194 Chewing & smoking tobacco; tobacco & tobacco products

2211 Cotton, Woven Fabric

(P-2715)
2016 MONTGOMERY INC
Also Called: People For Peace
755 E 14th Pl, Los Angeles (90021-2117)
PHONE............................323 316-6886
▲ EMP: 10
SQ FT: 4,500
SALES (est): 730K **Privately Held**
SIC: 2211

(P-2716)
A ALPHA WAVE GUIDE CO (PA)
Also Called: A Alpha Waveguide Tube Co
1217 E El Segundo Blvd, El Segundo (90245-4203)
PHONE............................310 322-3487
James Kelley Jr, *Owner*
▲ EMP: 12
SQ FT: 2,500
SALES: 3.5MM **Privately Held**
WEB: www.a-alphawaveguide.com
SIC: 2211 Tubing, seamless: cotton

(P-2717)
AIRCRAFT COVERS INC
Also Called: Bruce's Custom Covers
18850 Adams Ct, Morgan Hill (95037-2816)
PHONE............................408 738-3959
Bruce Perlitch, *President*
Heather Perlitch, *Vice Pres*
Javier Uranga, *General Mgr*
Sylvie Windeshausen, *Office Mgr*
Ivan Uranga, *Human Resources*
EMP: 65
SQ FT: 21,909
SALES (corp-wide): 10.2MM **Privately Held**
SIC: 2211 Canvas
PA: Aircraft Covers, Inc.
18850 Adams Ct
Morgan Hill CA 95037
408 738-3959

(P-2718)
ALSTYLE APPAREL LLC
1501 E Cerritos Ave, Anaheim (92805-6400)
PHONE............................714 765-0400
Bonnie Davis, *Human Resources*
EMP: 3765 EST: 2014
SALES (est): 94.8K
SALES (corp-wide): 2.7B **Privately Held**
SIC: 2211 Apparel & outerwear fabrics, cotton

HQ: Alstyle Apparel & Activewear Management Co.
1501 E Cerritos Ave
Anaheim CA 92805
714 765-0400

(P-2719)
AMERICAN APPAREL RETAIL INC (DH)
747 Warehouse St, Los Angeles (90021-1106)
P.O. Box 5129, Brandon MS (39047-5129)
PHONE..................................213 488-0226
Paula Schneider, *CEO*
Maria Aoki, *District Mgr*
Olivia Matson, *District Mgr*
Aja Boyer, *Store Mgr*
Timothy Gebbia, *Store Mgr*
◆ EMP: 29
SALES (est): 5.1MM
SALES (corp-wide): 2.7B **Privately Held**
SIC: 2211 Apparel & outerwear fabrics, cotton
HQ: App Winddown, Llc
747 Warehouse St
Los Angeles CA 90021
213 488-0226

(P-2720)
ANCHOR EXPORTATION USA LLC
11500 W Olympic Blvd 4, Los Angeles (90064-1524)
PHONE..................................310 312-4575
Miguel A Gutierrez,
Carlos I Gonzalez,
◆ EMP: 15
SALES (est): 964.1K **Privately Held**
SIC: 2211 Apparel & outerwear fabrics, cotton

(P-2721)
APPLIED SEWING RESOURCES INC
Also Called: Kiva Designs
6440 Goodyear Rd, Benicia (94510-1219)
PHONE..................................707 748-1614
Tom Koenig, *President*
Margaret Raible, *Vice Pres*
Ramon Koenig, *Admin Sec*
EMP: 25
SALES: 3MM **Privately Held**
SIC: 2211 2393

(P-2722)
APTAN CORP
2000 S Main St, Los Angeles (90007-1420)
PHONE..................................213 748-5271
Ronald Tanzman, *President*
Ron Tanzman, *Manager*
EMP: 12
SQ FT: 10,000
SALES (est): 2.5MM **Privately Held**
WEB: www.aptancorp.com
SIC: 2211 2396 Linings & interlinings, cotton; elastic fabrics, cotton; pads, shoulder: for coats, suits, etc.

(P-2723)
B & M UPHOLSTERY
Also Called: Belmar Company
2525 16th St Ste 201, San Francisco (94103-4246)
PHONE..................................415 621-7447
Markus Melitsky, *Owner*
Bella Miretsky, *President*
Markus Miretsky, *Vice Pres*
EMP: 19
SQ FT: 11,000
SALES (est): 1.9MM **Privately Held**
SIC: 2211 7641 Upholstery, tapestry & wall coverings: cotton; antique furniture repair & restoration

(P-2724)
BELAGIO ENTERPRISES INC
4801 W Jefferson Blvd, Los Angeles (90016-3920)
PHONE..................................323 731-6934
Ruben Melamed, *CEO*
▲ EMP: 20
SALES: 9MM **Privately Held**
SIC: 2211 2269 Decorative trim & specialty fabrics, including twist weave; decorative finishing of narrow fabrics

(P-2725)
BONDED FIBERLOFT INC
2748 Tanager Ave, Commerce (90040-2721)
PHONE..................................323 726-7820
Mark Bidner, *CEO*
Mike Wood, *CFO*
EMP: 350
SQ FT: 96,000
SALES (est): 22.5MM **Privately Held**
SIC: 2211 2823 2299 Broadwoven fabric mills, cotton; cellulosic manmade fibers; batts & batting: cotton mill waste & related material
PA: Western Synthetic Fiber Inc
2 Atlantic Ave Fl 4
Boston MA
-

(P-2726)
BRONCS INC
Also Called: Wct
12691 Pala Dr Ste A, Garden Grove (92841-3936)
PHONE..................................310 637-9100
Joel Chun, *President*
EMP: 165
SQ FT: 140,000
SALES (est): 4MM **Privately Held**
SIC: 2211 7389 Broadwoven fabric mills, cotton; textile & apparel services

(P-2727)
BUILDERS DRAPERY SERVICE INC
1494 Gladding Ct, Milpitas (95035-6831)
PHONE..................................408 263-3300
John A Garden Jr, *CEO*
Lottie Garden, *President*
▲ EMP: 35
SQ FT: 6,000
SALES (est): 5MM **Privately Held**
SIC: 2211 2591 Draperies & drapery fabrics, cotton; window blinds

(P-2728)
CABO INTERNATIONAL
Also Called: Cabo Gear
2345 La Mirada Dr, Vista (92081-7863)
PHONE..................................760 597-9199
Jacquelyn Stuart, *President*
Jim Stuart, *CFO*
James Stuart, *Vice Pres*
Jim Grambow, *Director*
EMP: 15
SQ FT: 14,000
SALES (est): 2MM **Privately Held**
WEB: www.cabogear.net
SIC: 2211 Apparel & outerwear fabrics, cotton

(P-2729)
CALIFORNIA COAST CLOTHING LLC
Also Called: Rd Jean
3690 S Santa Fe Ave, Vernon (90058-1413)
PHONE..................................323 923-3870
Ralph Davis, *Mng Member*
David S Ryan,
▲ EMP: 11 EST: 2007
SQ FT: 10,000
SALES (est): 1.5MM **Privately Held**
SIC: 2211 5131 5699 Denims; trimmings, apparel; caps & gowns (academic vestments)

(P-2730)
COLORMAX INDUSTRIES INC (PA)
1627 Paloma St, Los Angeles (90021-3013)
PHONE..................................213 748-6600
Gholamreza Amighi, *President*
Goodarz Haydarzadeh, *CEO*
EMP: 25
SQ FT: 64,000
SALES (est): 4MM **Privately Held**
SIC: 2211 2269 2261 2254 Broadwoven fabric mills, cotton; finishing plants; finishing plants, cotton; dyeing & finishing knit underwear

(P-2731)
CONTEMPO WINDOW FASHIONS
5721 Newcastle Ave, Encino (91316-1054)
PHONE..................................818 768-1773
Kathleen Bryan, *Owner*
EMP: 10
SQ FT: 1,400
SALES: 500K **Privately Held**
SIC: 2211 5023 5714 Draperies & drapery fabrics, cotton; draperies; draperies

(P-2732)
COTTYON INC
Also Called: Cotty On
2202 E Anderson St, Vernon (90058-3451)
PHONE..................................323 589-1563
EMP: 20
SALES (est): 1.9MM **Privately Held**
SIC: 2211

(P-2733)
DESTINEY GROUP INC
Also Called: Unitex International
4800 District Blvd, Vernon (90058-2727)
PHONE..................................323 581-4477
Raymond Mashian, *President*
Shahriar Hebroni, *Vice Pres*
Kristina Anthony, *Prdtn Mgr*
Velia Gomez, *Marketing Staff*
Chris Hebroni, *Sales Staff*
▲ EMP: 16
SQ FT: 18,000
SALES (est): 2.9MM **Privately Held**
SIC: 2211 Broadwoven fabric mills, cotton

(P-2734)
DOS FASHIONS
2633 Troy Ave, El Monte (91733-1429)
PHONE..................................626 454-4558
Do M Lam, *Owner*
EMP: 40
SALES (est): 2.2MM **Privately Held**
SIC: 2211 Apparel & outerwear fabrics, cotton

(P-2735)
DRAPERY PRODUCTIONS INC
33 E 4th Ave, San Mateo (94401-4001)
PHONE..................................650 340-8555
Gary Smith, *President*
Gary Schmidt, *Vice Pres*
Shirley Show, *Office Mgr*
EMP: 10
SALES (est): 743K **Privately Held**
SIC: 2211 5023 Draperies & drapery fabrics, cotton; draperies

(P-2736)
EXOTIC SILKS INC
Also Called: Thai Silks
1959 Leghorn St Ste B, Mountain View (94043-1797)
PHONE..................................650 948-8611
Rosi Valqui, *Manager*
EMP: 12
SALES (corp-wide): 9MM **Privately Held**
WEB: www.exoticsilks.com
SIC: 2211 5949 Apparel & outerwear fabrics, cotton; fabric stores piece goods
PA: Exotic Silks, Inc.
1959 Leghorn St Ste B
Mountain View CA 94043
650 965-7760

(P-2737)
FACTORY ONE STUDIO INC
6700 Avalon Blvd Ste 101, Los Angeles (90003-1920)
PHONE..................................323 752-1670
Steve C Rhee, *CEO*
EMP: 52
SALES: 10MM **Privately Held**
SIC: 2211 Denims

(P-2738)
FAT QUARTERS QUILT SHOP
728 Civic Center Dr, Vista (92084-6150)
PHONE..................................760 758-8308
Mary Sullivan, *Owner*
Kelly Sullivan, *Co-Owner*
EMP: 10
SALES (est): 688.2K **Privately Held**
WEB: www.fatquartersquiltshop.com
SIC: 2211 2395 5949 Shirting fabrics, cotton; quilting & quilting supplies; fabric stores piece goods

(P-2739)
FIRST FINISH INC
11126 Wright Rd, Lynwood (90262-3122)
PHONE..................................310 631-6717
Keyomars Fard, *President*
Tony Jordan, *Manager*
▲ EMP: 25
SQ FT: 10,000
SALES (est): 3.1MM **Privately Held**
WEB: www.firstfinish.com
SIC: 2211 Jean fabrics

(P-2740)
GOLDEN TEXTILE INC
2922 S Main St, Los Angeles (90007-3336)
PHONE..................................323 620-2612
Bruce Lee, *President*
▲ EMP: 15
SQ FT: 7,000
SALES: 900K **Privately Held**
SIC: 2211 Apparel & outerwear fabrics, cotton

(P-2741)
GREY STUDIO INC
629 S Clarence St, Los Angeles (90023-1107)
PHONE..................................323 780-8111
Kendrick D Kim, *President*
EMP: 50
SALES (est): 7MM **Privately Held**
SIC: 2211 Denims

(P-2742)
HIDDEN JEANS INC (PA)
Also Called: Cello Jeans
1001 Towne Ave Ste 103, Los Angeles (90021-2088)
PHONE..................................213 746-4223
Kenny Jin Park, *CEO*
Adam Lee, *Vice Pres*
▲ EMP: 11 EST: 2007
SQ FT: 4,000
SALES (est): 4.5MM **Privately Held**
SIC: 2211 Denims

(P-2743)
HUGE USA INC
1100 S San Pedro St J02, Los Angeles (90015-2328)
PHONE..................................213 741-1707
Jin Ser Park, *CEO*
EMP: 11 EST: 2012
SALES (est): 370.7K **Privately Held**
SIC: 2211 Denims

(P-2744)
INTEGRATED MARKETING GROUP LLC
528 W Briardale Ave, Orange (92865-4208)
PHONE..................................714 771-2401
Gregory Dahlstrom, *Mng Member*
Colleen Anderson, *VP Sales*
EMP: 19
SALES (est): 3.1MM **Privately Held**
SIC: 2211 Apparel & outerwear fabrics, cotton

(P-2745)
J BRAND INC
Also Called: J Brand Jeans
1318 E 7th St Ste 260, Los Angeles (90021-1131)
PHONE..................................213 749-3500
Jeffrey Rudes, *President*
Efthimios P Sotos, *CFO*
Susie Crippen, *Vice Pres*
Mikey Scott, *Planning*
Veronica Cuevas, *Accounting Mgr*
◆ EMP: 60
SALES (est): 15.2MM
SALES (corp-wide): 19.1B **Privately Held**
SIC: 2211 Denims
PA: Fast Retailing Co., Ltd.
9-7-1, Akasaka
Minato-Ku TKY 107-0
368 650-050

▲ = Import ▼=Export
◆ =Import/Export

(P-2746)
J&COMPANY JEANS LLC
Also Called: J N C O
1501 Rio Vista Ave, Los Angeles
(90023-2619)
P.O. Box 691844, West Hollywood (90069-8844)
PHONE..................................323 260-7329
Haim Revah, *Mng Member*
Jacob Abikzer,
Julien Jarmoune,
Stephen Korn,
▲ EMP: 77
SQ FT: 75,000
SALES (est): 11.7MM **Privately Held**
WEB: www.jnco.com
SIC: 2211 Denims

(P-2747)
JADE SPEC LLC
Also Called: Jadespec
15932 Downey Ave Ste A, Paramount
(90723-5140)
PHONE..................................310 933-4338
Dylan Rodriguez, *Mng Member*
EMP: 15
SALES (est): 221.5K **Privately Held**
SIC: 2211 2591 5021 Draperies & drapery fabrics, cotton; drapery hardware & blinds & shades; shade, curtain & drapery hardware; curtain & drapery rods, poles & fixtures; beds & bedding

(P-2748)
JML TEXTILE INC
Also Called: W & M Textile
5801 S 2nd St, Vernon (90058-3403)
PHONE..................................323 584-2323
Seung Choon Lim, *CEO*
Seung Hoon Lim, *President*
▲ EMP: 60
SQ FT: 350,000
SALES (est): 8.8MM **Privately Held**
WEB: www.wimatex.com
SIC: 2211 Apparel & outerwear fabrics, cotton

(P-2749)
JONDO
10556 Industrial Ave # 100, Roseville
(95678-6232)
PHONE..................................714 394-4344
Fretman Soto, *General Mgr*
EMP: 25 EST: 2016
SALES (est): 2.3MM **Privately Held**
SIC: 2211 Canvas

(P-2750)
KATHRYN M IRELAND INC (PA)
5285 W Washington Blvd, Los Angeles
(90016-1340)
PHONE..................................323 965-9888
Kathryn Ireland, *President*
▲ EMP: 20 EST: 1998
SQ FT: 1,500
SALES (est): 1.5MM **Privately Held**
WEB: www.kathrynireland.com
SIC: 2211 7389 Broadwoven fabric mills, cotton; interior design services

(P-2751)
LOS ANGELES MILLS INC
2331 E 8th St, Los Angeles (90021-1732)
PHONE..................................424 307-0075
William G Meyer, *President*
▲ EMP: 33 EST: 1963
SALES (est): 40MM **Privately Held**
SIC: 2211 2299 2281 2221 Cotton broad woven goods; yarns, specialty & novelty; yarn spinning mills; broadwoven fabric mills, manmade; throwing & winding mills

(P-2752)
MSP GROUP INC
206 W 140th St, Los Angeles (90061-1006)
PHONE..................................310 660-0022
Jong H Lim, *President*
▲ EMP: 35
SQ FT: 1,000
SALES: 7MM **Privately Held**
SIC: 2211 Apparel & outerwear fabrics, cotton

(P-2753)
NIKI-VIKI APPAREL INC
2141 E 52nd St, Vernon (90058-3498)
PHONE..................................323 587-5055
Hey Jung Choi, *CEO*
Kristel Varona, *Sales Associate*
▲ EMP: 18
SQ FT: 6,400
SALES (est): 2.7MM **Privately Held**
SIC: 2211 Apparel & outerwear fabrics, cotton

(P-2754)
NOT ONLY JEANS INC
3004 S Main St, Los Angeles (90007-3825)
PHONE..................................213 765-9725
Lucia Sanchez, *President*
EMP: 20
SALES (est): 2.2MM **Privately Held**
SIC: 2211

(P-2755)
NUTRADE INC
Also Called: Dreamworks Knitting
2808 Willis St, Santa Ana (92705-5714)
PHONE..................................949 477-2300
Alan Hashemian, *CEO*
▲ EMP: 25 EST: 1998
SALES: 3.6MM **Privately Held**
WEB: www.nutrade.com
SIC: 2211 Apparel & outerwear fabrics, cotton

(P-2756)
PACIFIC WEAVING CORPORATION
1068 American St, San Carlos
(94070-5304)
PHONE..................................650 592-9434
Andrew Sommer, *President*
EMP: 20
SALES (est): 1.6MM **Privately Held**
SIC: 2211 2221 Draperies & drapery fabrics, cotton; draperies & drapery fabrics, manmade fiber & silk

(P-2757)
PETUNIA PICKLE BOTTOM CORP
3567 Old Conejo Rd, Newbury Park
(91320-2122)
PHONE..................................805 643-6697
Yann Boulbain, *CEO*
Denai Jones, *President*
Korie Conant, *Chief Mktg Ofcr*
Korie Fergeson, *Vice Pres*
▲ EMP: 10
SQ FT: 26,000
SALES (est): 1.5MM **Privately Held**
WEB: www.petuniapicklebottom.com
SIC: 2211 Bags & bagging, cotton

(P-2758)
PJY INC
Also Called: Intimo Industry
3251 Leonis Blvd, Vernon (90058-3018)
PHONE..................................323 583-7737
Paul Yang, *President*
Jorge Vigil, *Production*
Nicole Weaver, *Marketing Staff*
Wan Suh, *Manager*
▲ EMP: 40
SALES (est): 6.6MM **Privately Held**
WEB: www.intimoindustry.com
SIC: 2211 Long cloth, cotton

(P-2759)
REBELKINGSNUGUS LLC
112 W 9th St, Los Angeles (90015-1510)
PHONE..................................323 667-8565
Semaria Fessahaye, *Vice Pres*
Ajani Wells, *Vice Pres*
EMP: 11
SQ FT: 1,000
SALES (est): 508.8K **Privately Held**
SIC: 2211 Canvas & other heavy coarse fabrics; cotton

(P-2760)
RICHLINE TEXTILE INC
1706 Maple Ave, Los Angeles
(90015-3705)
PHONE..................................323 792-1030
Masoud Omrani, *President*
Ramin Omrani, *Vice Pres*

Mary Jane Galit, *Accounting Mgr*
◆ EMP: 30
SQ FT: 2,400
SALES (est): 8.1MM **Privately Held**
SIC: 2211 Denims

(P-2761)
RNK INDUSTRIES CO
2816 E 11th St, Los Angeles (90023-3406)
PHONE..................................323 446-0777
Rachel Lo, *President*
▲ EMP: 10
SALES (est): 1.5MM **Privately Held**
SIC: 2211 Twills, drills, denims & other ribbed fabrics: cotton

(P-2762)
SKY JEANS INC
6600 Avalon Blvd Ste 102, Los Angeles
(90003-1960)
PHONE..................................323 778-2065
Maria Gonzalez, *President*
EMP: 20
SALES (est): 1.1MM **Privately Held**
SIC: 2211

(P-2763)
SLEEPOW LTD
11706 Darlington Ave, Los Angeles
(90049-5517)
PHONE..................................646 688-0808
EMP: 40
SQ FT: 600
SALES (est): 2.9MM **Privately Held**
SIC: 2211

(P-2764)
STANZINO INC
Also Called: Apparel House USA
16325 S Avalon Blvd, Gardena
(90248-2909)
PHONE..................................213 746-8822
David Ghods, *CEO*
EMP: 145
SALES: 4MM **Privately Held**
SIC: 2211 Apparel & outerwear fabrics, cotton

(P-2765)
TUA FASHION INC (PA)
Also Called: Tua USA
8936 Appian Way, Los Angeles
(90046-7737)
PHONE..................................213 422-2384
Yum Cho, *President*
Mark Cho, *COO*
Andrew Cho, *Principal*
Duck J Cho, *Principal*
EMP: 15
SQ FT: 22,000
SALES (est): 1.9MM **Privately Held**
WEB: www.tuausa.com
SIC: 2211 Apparel & outerwear fabrics, cotton

(P-2766)
UPHOLSTERY BY WAYNE STOEC
3316 E Annadale Ave, Fresno
(93725-1904)
PHONE..................................559 233-1960
Wayne Stoec, *Owner*
EMP: 11
SALES: 900K **Privately Held**
SIC: 2211 Upholstery, tapestry & wall coverings: cotton

(P-2767)
VERATEX INC (PA)
20362 Plummer St, Chatsworth
(91311-5371)
PHONE..................................818 994-6487
AVI Cohen, *CEO*
Bob Scott, *Exec VP*
Jessica Cortez, *Project Mgr*
Mikael Mnstsakanian, *Technology*
Guille O'Campo, *Human Resources*
◆ EMP: 250
SQ FT: 15,000
SALES (est): 32MM **Privately Held**
WEB: www.veratex.com
SIC: 2211 5131 Sheets, bedding & table cloths: cotton; linen piece goods, woven

(P-2768)
WOLFSON KNITTING MILLS INC
2124 Sacramento St, Los Angeles
(90021-1722)
PHONE..................................213 627-8746
Stephanie Wolfson, *President*
EMP: 10
SQ FT: 12,500
SALES (est): 1.5MM **Privately Held**
SIC: 2211 Decorative trim & specialty fabrics, including twist weave

(P-2769)
XCVI LLC (PA)
2311 S Santa Fe Ave, Los Angeles
(90058-1154)
PHONE..................................213 749-2661
Alon Zeltzer,
Mordechia Zelter,
Gita Zeltzer,
▲ EMP: 120
SQ FT: 60,000
SALES (est): 21.9MM **Privately Held**
WEB: www.xcviwearables.com
SIC: 2211 Apparel & outerwear fabrics, cotton; sheets, bedding & table cloths: cotton

(P-2770)
YC TEXTILE INC
1821 E 48th Pl, Vernon (90058-1903)
PHONE..................................323 233-9833
Jae S Yang, *President*
▲ EMP: 10
SQ FT: 40,000
SALES (est): 1.4MM **Privately Held**
WEB: www.yctextile.com
SIC: 2211 7389 Broadwoven fabric mills, cotton; textile & apparel services

2221 Silk & Man-Made Fiber

(P-2771)
3 INK PRODUCTIONS INC
4790 W Jacquelyn Ave, Fresno
(93722-6406)
PHONE..................................559 275-4565
Craig Stidham, *President*
Dianne Stidham, *Partner*
EMP: 14
SALES (est): 1.1MM **Privately Held**
SIC: 2221 5023 Textile warping, on a contract basis; sheets, textile

(P-2772)
AGRICULTURE BAG MFG USA INC (PA)
Also Called: Agriculture Bag Manufacturing,
960 98th Ave, Oakland (94603-2347)
PHONE..................................510 632-5637
Jeff C Kuo, *CEO*
▲ EMP: 44
SALES (est): 6.8MM **Privately Held**
WEB: www.agriculturebag.com
SIC: 2221 2673 2393 Polypropylene broadwoven fabrics; plastic & pliofilm bags; textile bags

(P-2773)
AMERICAN GARMENT FINISHING
17941 Lost Canyon Rd # 6, Canyon Country (91387-8266)
PHONE..................................310 962-1929
Michelle Vital, *President*
EMP: 33
SQ FT: 2,000
SALES: 7.5MM **Privately Held**
WEB: www.finishag.com
SIC: 2221 Textile mills, broadwoven: silk & manmade, also glass

(P-2774)
BELLA NOTTE LINENS INC
60 Galli Dr Ste 2, Novato (94949-5713)
PHONE..................................415 883-3434
Kathleen McCoy, *President*
Bob Gunnell, *Treasurer*
Mitchell Gately, *Vice Pres*
Wayne Ly, *Prdtn Mgr*
Nicole Moreno, *Production*
◆ EMP: 38
SQ FT: 13,000

SALES (est): 5.3MM **Privately Held**
WEB: www.bellanottelinens.com
SIC: 2221 Bedding, manmade or silk fabric

(P-2775)
DAE SHIN USA INC
610 N Gilbert St, Fullerton (92833-2555)
PHONE....................714 578-8900
Jae Weon Lee, *CEO*
▲ **EMP:** 100
SQ FT: 10,000
SALES: 11MM
SALES (corp-wide): 16.9MM **Privately Held**
SIC: 2221 Textile mills, broadwoven: silk & manmade, also glass
PA: Daeshin Textile Co.,Ltd.
Choji-Dong
Ansan 15614
823 149-1084

(P-2776)
DOOL FNA INC
Also Called: Grand Textile
16220 Manning Way, Cerritos (90703-2223)
PHONE....................562 483-4100
Jae Weon Lee, *CEO*
Jaeweon Lee, *Vice Pres*
Justine Lee, *Principal*
▲ **EMP:** 120
SQ FT: 100,000
SALES (est): 18.2MM **Privately Held**
SIC: 2221 Textile mills, broadwoven: silk & manmade, also glass

(P-2777)
FABRITEX INC
2301 E 7th St Ste D102, Los Angeles (90023-1041)
PHONE....................213 747-1417
Kourosh Dayan, *President*
Norick Minisians, *CFO*
▲ **EMP:** 14
SQ FT: 30,000
SALES: 5.7MM **Privately Held**
WEB: www.fabritex.com
SIC: 2221 5131 Linings, rayon or silk; piece goods & other fabrics

(P-2778)
FABTEX INC
Also Called: Ft Textiles
1202 W Struck Ave, Orange (92867-3532)
PHONE....................714 538-0877
William P Friese, *Branch Mgr*
EMP: 105
SALES (corp-wide): 109.6MM **Privately Held**
WEB: www.fabtex.com
SIC: 2221 2515 2392 2391 Draperies & drapery fabrics, manmade fiber & silk; bedding, manmade or silk fabric; mattresses & bedsprings; household furnishings; curtains & draperies
PA: Fabtex, Inc.
29 Woodbine Ln
Danville PA 17821
570 275-7500

(P-2779)
JUICY COUTURE INC
12723 Wentworth St, Arleta (91331-4330)
PHONE....................888 824-8826
Pamela Levy, *CEO*
Ellen Rodriguez, *Senior VP*
Lisa Rodericks, *Admin Sec*
Elva Gonzales, *Manager*
Veronica Perez, *Manager*
EMP: 160
SALES (est): 56.2K
SALES (est): 5.8B **Publicly Held**
WEB: www.juicycouture.com
SIC: 2221 Broadwoven fabric mills, manmade
HQ: Kate Spade & Company Llc
2 Park Ave Fl 8
New York NY 10016
212 354-4900

(P-2780)
OPULENCE INTERNATIONAL
Also Called: Austin Horn Collection
30085 Comercio, Rcho STA Marg (92688-2106)
PHONE....................949 360-7611

Douglas B Fencl, *CEO*
EMP: 35
SALES (est): 281.7K **Privately Held**
SIC: 2221 Bedding, manmade or silk fabric

(P-2781)
POP 82 INC
8211 Orangethorpe Ave, Buena Park (90621-3811)
PHONE....................714 523-8500
Steven North, *CEO*
Bill Blandin, *Vice Pres*
Marisela Ramos, *Admin Sec*
EMP: 15
SQ FT: 15,000
SALES: 1.2MM **Privately Held**
SIC: 2221 7389 Acrylic broadwoven fabrics; printing broker

(P-2782)
SCRIMCO INC
2377 S Orange Ave, Fresno (93725-1021)
PHONE....................559 237-7442
Todd J Stevens, *President*
▲ **EMP:** 10
SQ FT: 54,000
SALES (est): 2.4MM **Privately Held**
WEB: www.scrimco.com
SIC: 2221 Polyester broadwoven fabrics; fiberglass fabrics

(P-2783)
SURPRISESILKCOM
628 Madre St, Pasadena (91107-5661)
PHONE....................626 568-9889
EMP: 10
SALES (est): 400K **Privately Held**
SIC: 2221

(P-2784)
TEXTILE PRODUCTS INC
2512-2520 W Woodland Dr, Anaheim (92801)
PHONE....................714 761-0401
Piyush A Shah, *CEO*
Richard Murillo, *Plant Mgr*
Benny Amesquita, *Supervisor*
▲ **EMP:** 26
SQ FT: 16,000
SALES (est): 7.7MM
SALES (corp-wide): 3.6B **Privately Held**
WEB: www.textileproducts.com
SIC: 2221 Manmade & synthetic broadwoven fabrics
HQ: Kordsa Teknik Tekstil Anonim Sirketi
No:90 Alikahya Fatih Mahalelsi
Kocaeli 41310
262 316-7000

(P-2785)
TOMASINI INC
1001 E 60th St, Los Angeles (90001-1018)
PHONE....................323 231-2349
Angela Brown, *President*
EMP: 20
SQ FT: 5,500
SALES (est): 1.9MM **Privately Held**
WEB: www.tomasini.com
SIC: 2221 5719 Bedding, manmade or silk fabric; comforters & quilts, manmade fiber & silk; bedding (sheets, blankets, spreads & pillows)

(P-2786)
VALLEY DRAPERY INC
Also Called: Valley Drapery and Upholstery
16616 Schoenborn St, North Hills (91343-6106)
PHONE....................818 892-7744
Norman Sewitz, *President*
Michael Sewitz, *Vice Pres*
David Sewitz, *Admin Sec*
Jana Nearman, *Consultant*
▲ **EMP:** 62 **EST:** 1977
SQ FT: 15,000
SALES (est): 7.8MM **Privately Held**
WEB: www.valleydrapery.com
SIC: 2221 Draperies & drapery fabrics, manmade fiber & silk

(P-2787)
WIND & SHADE SCREENS INC
1223 Linda Vista Dr, San Marcos (92078-3809)
PHONE....................760 761-4994
Paul Leathem, *President*

Patricia Somerville, *Vice Pres*
EMP: 17
SQ FT: 2,500
SALES: 650K **Privately Held**
SIC: 2221 2399 Polypropylene broadwoven fabrics; banners, made from fabric

---

2231 Wool, Woven Fabric

(P-2788)
A AND G INC
Also Called: Alstyle Dyeing & Finishing
1501 E Cerritos Ave, Anaheim (92805-6400)
PHONE....................714 756-0400
Jim Gordon, *Manager*
EMP: 131
SALES (corp-wide): 2.7B **Privately Held**
WEB: www.murina.com
SIC: 2231 Dyeing & finishing: wool or similar fibers
HQ: A And G, Inc.
11296 Harrel St
Mira Loma CA 91752
714 765-0400

(P-2789)
AMERICAN AP DYG & FINSHG INC
747 Warehouse St, Los Angeles (90021-1106)
P.O. Box 5129, Brandon MS (39047-5129)
PHONE....................310 644-4001
Sang Ho Lim, *President*
Joe Yi, *Office Mgr*
▲ **EMP:** 70
SALES (est): 7.1MM
SALES (corp-wide): 2.7B **Privately Held**
WEB: www.americanapparel.net
SIC: 2231 Dyeing & finishing: wool or similar fibers
HQ: App Winddown, Llc
747 Warehouse St
Los Angeles CA 90021
213 488-0226

(P-2790)
CALIFORNIA INDUSTRIAL FABRICS
2325 Marconi Ct, San Diego (92154-7241)
PHONE....................619 661-7166
Michael Lindsey, *CEO*
Erin McNamara, *CFO*
Patrick Dickey, *Vice Pres*
Jt Lawson, *Manager*
Melissa Ledezma, *Manager*
◆ **EMP:** 30 **EST:** 1978
SQ FT: 24,000
SALES (est): 2.5MM **Privately Held**
WEB: www.ci-fabrics.com
SIC: 2231 Broadwoven fabric mills, wool

(P-2791)
COMFORT INDUSTRIES INC
12266 Rooks Rd, Whittier (90601-1613)
PHONE....................562 692-8288
Kevin Do, *CEO*
Ken Quach, *Vice Pres*
Kevin Deal, *Admin Sec*
◆ **EMP:** 35 **EST:** 1998
SQ FT: 18,000
SALES (est): 5.3MM **Privately Held**
SIC: 2231 Upholstery fabrics, wool

(P-2792)
ICON APPAREL GROUP LLC
2989 Promenade St Ste 100, West Sacramento (95691-6419)
PHONE....................916 372-4266
Juan C Ceja, *Mng Member*
Alberto Rivera, *Portfolio Mgr*
Jerrad Fiore,
Ronnie Leavitt,
EMP: 35
SQ FT: 10,000
SALES: 1.7MM **Privately Held**
WEB: www.iconapparel.com
SIC: 2231 7389 2759 Apparel & outerwear broadwoven fabrics; apparel designers, commercial; screen printing

(P-2793)
LEKOS DYE & FINISHING INC
3131 E Harcourt St, Compton (90221-5505)
PHONE....................310 763-0900
Ilgun Lee, *President*
Daniel Lee, *Executive*
Petra Perez, *Telecom Exec*
▲ **EMP:** 65
SQ FT: 72,000
SALES (est): 10.2MM **Privately Held**
SIC: 2231 Dyeing & finishing: wool or similar fibers

(P-2794)
PACIFIC DRY GOODS INC
1085 Essex Ave, Richmond (94801-2112)
P.O. Box 3879, San Leandro (94578-0879)
PHONE....................925 288-2929
Brian W Hudsono, *President*
Phillip Brown, *Treasurer*
▲ **EMP:** 10
SQ FT: 20,000
SALES (est): 1.3MM **Privately Held**
WEB: www.pacificdrygoods.com
SIC: 2231 3291 Sponging cloth: wool, mohair or similar fabric; cloth, abrasive: garnet, emery, aluminum oxide coated

(P-2795)
TRI-STAR DYEING & FINSHG INC
15125 Marquardt Ave, Santa Fe Springs (90670-5705)
PHONE....................562 483-0123
Jang You, *Principal*
◆ **EMP:** 63
SQ FT: 60,000
SALES: 22.3MM **Privately Held**
SIC: 2231 Dyeing & finishing: wool or similar fibers
PA: Jangyou Co., Ltd.
Rm 12b-22
Ansan
823 149-2117

2241 Fabric Mills, Cotton, Wool, Silk & Man-Made

(P-2796)
ALL AMERICAN LABEL
Also Called: Label Gallery
1700 Wall St, Los Angeles (90015-3719)
PHONE....................213 622-2222
Steve Firouz, *President*
EMP: 22
SALES (est): 246.1K **Privately Held**
SIC: 2241 Labels, woven

(P-2797)
AX II INC
Also Called: Gin'l Fabrics
13921 S Figueroa St, Los Angeles (90061-1027)
PHONE....................310 292-6523
Anthony Xepolis, *President*
Ginny Xepolis, *Vice Pres*
EMP: 26
SALES (est): 2.8MM **Privately Held**
SIC: 2241 2396 Narrow fabric mills; automotive & apparel trimmings

(P-2798)
CHUA & SONS INC
Also Called: Reliable Tape Products
3300 E 50th St, Vernon (90058-3004)
P.O. Box 58261, Los Angeles (90058-0261)
PHONE....................323 588-8044
Shirley Chua, *President*
▲ **EMP:** 23
SQ FT: 67,000
SALES (est): 3.6MM **Privately Held**
SIC: 2241 Fabric tapes

(P-2799)
FAIRWAY TRADING INC
5717 Ferguson Dr, Commerce (90022-5101)
PHONE....................323 582-8111
Sam Farmanara, *President*
▲ **EMP:** 10

SALES (est): 2MM **Privately Held**
WEB: www.fairwaytrading.com
SIC: 2241 Trimmings, textile

(P-2800)
HANAH SILK INC
5155 Myrtle Ave, Eureka (95503-9506)
PHONE................................707 442-0886
Brooke Exley, *President*
▲ EMP: 10
SALES (est): 905.4K **Privately Held**
SIC: 2241 Ribbons

(P-2801)
INDUSTRIAL WIPER & SUPPLY INC
1025 98th Ave A, Oakland (94603-2356)
PHONE................................408 286-4752
Mitchell Tobin, *CEO*
Robert Tobin, *President*
▲ EMP: 29
SQ FT: 10,000
SALES (est): 4.8MM **Privately Held**
WEB: www.industrialwiper.com
SIC: 2241 Narrow fabric mills

(P-2802)
MAKO INC
736 Monterey Pass Rd, Monterey Park (91754-3607)
PHONE................................323 262-2168
John Chaing, *President*
Jenney Tsung, *Vice Pres*
▲ EMP: 50
SALES (est): 4.3MM **Privately Held**
SIC: 2241 Trimmings, textile

(P-2803)
MAXSTRAPS INC
925 Gravenstein Ave, Sebastopol (95472-4573)
P.O. Box 63 (95473-0063)
PHONE................................707 829-3000
Steven Williams, *President*
Elaine Williams, *Vice Pres*
EMP: 68
SALES (est): 5.8MM **Privately Held**
WEB: www.maxstraps.com
SIC: 2241 5013 Strapping webs; automotive supplies & parts

(P-2804)
RIVERA YARN PRODUCTS INC
1690 Cactus Rd, San Diego (92154-8101)
PHONE................................619 661-6306
Chris Rivera, *President*
Gloria Rivera, *Corp Secy*
Bill Rivera, *Vice Pres*
Rosemarie Huddleston, *Principal*
EMP: 20
SQ FT: 8,000
SALES (est): 2.3MM **Privately Held**
SIC: 2241 2298

(P-2805)
ROCKY LABEL MILLS INC
1930 Doreen Ave, South El Monte (91733-3332)
PHONE................................323 278-0080
Frank Lin, *President*
▲ EMP: 23
SALES (est): 1.6MM **Privately Held**
SIC: 2241 Labels, woven

(P-2806)
SANTA FE TEXTILES INC
17370 Mount Herrmann St, Fountain Valley (92708-4104)
PHONE................................949 251-1960
Fax: 949 251-9006
EMP: 18
SQ FT: 25,000
SALES (est): 1.4MM **Privately Held**
SIC: 2241 3496

(P-2807)
SILVER TEXTILE INCORPORATED
Also Called: Olympia Trading
2101 S Flower St, Los Angeles (90007-2051)
PHONE................................213 747-2221
Sam Tehrani, *CEO*
Susan Tehrani, *Treasurer*
Shiva Tehrani, *Admin Sec*

▲ EMP: 12
SQ FT: 4,000
SALES (est): 2.1MM **Privately Held**
SIC: 2241 2221 5131 Narrow fabric mills; broadwoven fabric mills, manmade; silk piece goods, woven

(P-2808)
TRIMKNIT INC
7542 San Fernando Rd, Sun Valley (91352-4344)
PHONE................................818 768-7878
Peter Krausz, *President*
EMP: 21
SQ FT: 12,000
SALES (est): 2.1MM **Privately Held**
SIC: 2241 Trimmings, textile

(P-2809)
VEGA TEXTILE INC
2751 S Alameda St, Los Angeles (90058-1311)
PHONE................................323 923-0600
Linchun Liu, *President*
Zengle Wang, *Admin Sec*
▲ EMP: 10
SALES (est): 990K **Privately Held**
SIC: 2241 Bindings, textile

2251 Hosiery, Women's Full & Knee Length

(P-2810)
CALISON INC
2447 Leef Ave, South El Monte (91733)
PHONE................................626 448-3328
Tina Wu, *Vice Pres*
EMP: 25
SQ FT: 7,000
SALES: 800K **Privately Held**
SIC: 2251 Women's hosiery, except socks

2252 Hosiery, Except Women's

(P-2811)
DRYMAX TECHNOLOGIES INC
9900 El Camino Real, Atascadero (93422-5573)
P.O. Box 2500 (93423-2500)
PHONE................................805 239-2555
William Blythe, *CEO*
Robert Macgillivray, *Principal*
Bob Macgillivray, *Manager*
EMP: 15 EST: 2014
SALES (est): 1.8MM **Privately Held**
SIC: 2252 Socks

(P-2812)
GOLDEN GATE HOSIERY INC
14095 Laurelwood Pl, Chino (91710-5495)
PHONE................................909 464-0805
Sang Hoon Moon, *President*
SAE Yang Chang, *Corp Secy*
▲ EMP: 25
SQ FT: 13,000
SALES (est): 3.3MM **Privately Held**
SIC: 2252 Socks

(P-2813)
RICHER POORER INC
27132 Paseo Espada B1225, San Juan Capistrano (92675-6721)
PHONE................................949 388-9994
Iva Pawling, *CEO*
Trevor Gray, *Opers Staff*
Sean Fleuriau, *Sales Dir*
▲ EMP: 19
SALES (est): 2.6MM **Privately Held**
SIC: 2252 5632 Socks; hosiery

(P-2814)
SOCKSMITH DESIGN INC (PA)
1515 Pacific Ave, Santa Cruz (95060-3911)
PHONE................................831 426-6416
Eric W Gil, *President*
Ryan Dineen, *Sales Staff*
▲ EMP: 24
SQ FT: 10,000
SALES (est): 3.3MM **Privately Held**
SIC: 2252 Socks

(P-2815)
SOXNET INC
235 S 6th Ave, La Puente (91746-2916)
PHONE................................626 855-3200
Miri Ryu, *CEO*
Linda Ryu, *CFO*
Paige Stenanchuk, *Vice Pres*
Suzanne Kang, *Sales Associate*
Yadira Jardon, *Sales Staff*
▲ EMP: 17
SQ FT: 30,434
SALES: 100K **Privately Held**
SIC: 2252 Men's, boys' & girls' hosiery

(P-2816)
THIRTY THREE THREADS INC
1330 Park Center Dr, Vista (92081-8300)
PHONE................................877 486-3769
Joe Patterson, *CEO*
▲ EMP: 35 EST: 2009
SALES (est): 5.8MM **Privately Held**
SIC: 2252 Socks

(P-2817)
UNIVERSAL HOSIERY INC
28337 Constellation Rd, Valencia (91355-5048)
PHONE................................661 702-8444
Johnathan Ekizian, *President*
▲ EMP: 75
SQ FT: 44,000
SALES: 45MM **Privately Held**
SIC: 2252 Socks

(P-2818)
US HOSIERY INC
1415 S Main St, Los Angeles (90015-2501)
PHONE................................213 742-0101
Chong S Won, *CEO*
◆ EMP: 13
SALES (est): 1.6MM **Privately Held**
SIC: 2252 Socks

(P-2819)
VM PROVIDER INC (PA)
1135 1/2 N Berendo St, Los Angeles (90029-1705)
PHONE................................800 674-3233
Vahe Mkhitaryan, *President*
EMP: 10
SALES (est): 871.9K **Privately Held**
SIC: 2252 Socks

2253 Knit Outerwear Mills

(P-2820)
ALPHA SOURCE INC
2415 S Sequoia Dr, Compton (90220-5442)
PHONE................................310 515-5560
Stephan Kim, *President*
Debora Simon, *Representative*
EMP: 50
SQ FT: 40,000
SALES (est): 8.3MM **Privately Held**
WEB: www.alphasource.com
SIC: 2253 Shirts (outerwear), knit

(P-2821)
ALSTYLE AP & ACTIVEWEAR MGT CO (HQ)
1501 E Cerritos Ave, Anaheim (92805-6400)
PHONE................................714 765-0400
Rauf Gajiani, *CEO*
Rick Travis, *CFO*
Amin Amdani, *Vice Pres*
Xxtodd Scarborough, *Executive Asst*
Scott Bloom, *Sales Mgr*
◆ EMP: 1800 EST: 2001
SQ FT: 715,000
SALES (est): 659MM
SALES (corp-wide): 2.7B **Privately Held**
WEB: www.alstyle.com
SIC: 2253 Shirts (outerwear), knit
PA: Gildan Activewear Inc
600 Boul De Maisonneuve O 33eme etage
Montreal QC H3A 3
514 735-2023

(P-2822)
ALSTYLE AP & ACTIVEWEAR MGT CO
Also Called: Alstyle Dyeing & Finishing
1501 E Cerritos Ave, Anaheim (92805-6400)
PHONE................................714 765-0400
Rauf Gajiani, *Manager*
EMP: 10
SALES (corp-wide): 2.7B **Privately Held**
WEB:
SIC: 2253 T-shirts & tops, knit
HQ: Alstyle Apparel & Activewear Management Co.
1501 E Cerritos Ave
Anaheim CA 92805
714 765-0400

(P-2823)
BALBOA MANUFACTURING CO LLC (PA)
Also Called: Bobster Eyewear
9401 Waples St Ste 120, San Diego (92121-3909)
PHONE................................858 715-0060
John Smaller, *Mng Member*
Jennifer Struebing, *COO*
Mike Maxwell, *Admin Mgr*
Lorena Aguilar, *Office Mgr*
Gina Lozano, *Admin Asst*
▲ EMP: 26
SQ FT: 40,000
SALES (est): 3.9MM **Privately Held**
WEB: www.balboawholesale.com
SIC: 2253 2211 Hats & headwear, knit; apparel & outerwear fabrics, cotton

(P-2824)
BALL OF COTTON INC
6400 E Washington Blvd, Commerce (90040-1820)
PHONE................................323 888-9448
Eddy Park, *President*
Elizabeth Park, *Vice Pres*
EMP: 45
SQ FT: 7,000
SALES: 5MM **Privately Held**
WEB: www.ballofcotton.com
SIC: 2253 Sweaters & sweater coats, knit

(P-2825)
BROADWAY KNITTING MILLS CORP
1766 N Helm Ave Ste 101, Fresno (93727-1627)
PHONE................................559 456-0955
Jan Mattlin, *Manager*
EMP: 30
SALES (est): 1.3MM
SALES (corp-wide): 2.3MM **Privately Held**
WEB: www.broadwayalbion.com
SIC: 2253 Knit outerwear mills
PA: Broadway Knitting Mills Corp
2152 Sacramento St
Los Angeles CA
213 680-9694

(P-2826)
BYER CALIFORNIA
Alfred Paquette Division
1201 Rio Vista Ave, Los Angeles (90023-2609)
PHONE................................323 780-7615
Jan Shostak, *Manager*
EMP: 380
SQ FT: 10,000
SALES (corp-wide): 372.3MM **Privately Held**
WEB: www.byer.com
SIC: 2253 2339 2335 Dresses, knit; women's & misses' outerwear; women's, juniors' & misses' dresses
PA: Byer California
66 Potrero Ave
San Francisco CA 94103
415 626-7844

(P-2827)
C A N ENTERPRISES
Also Called: C M Sport
291 Kinross Dr, Walnut Creek (94598-2105)
PHONE................................925 939-9736
Chereen Makhlouf, *Owner*

Hania Makhlouf, *Co-Owner*
▲ **EMP:** 70
SALES (est): 3MM **Privately Held**
WEB: www.canenterprises.com
SIC: 2253 Knit outerwear mills

(P-2828)
CARE TEX INDUSTRIES INC (PA)
4583 Firestone Blvd, South Gate
(90280-3343)
PHONE..................323 567-5074
Richard Kang, *President*
Charles Kang, *CEO*
Dan Kang, *Admin Sec*
EMP: 60
SQ FT: 27,000
SALES (est): 7.4MM **Privately Held**
SIC: 2253 Dyeing & finishing knit outer-
wear, excl. hosiery & glove

(P-2829)
CASMARI INC
9035 Eton Ave Ste C, Canoga Park
(91304-6521)
PHONE..................818 727-1856
Maria Carter, *CEO*
Rita Ragusa, *CFO*
EMP: 10
SALES (est): 1.1MM **Privately Held**
SIC: 2253 Sweaters & sweater coats, knit

(P-2830)
COLOR IMAGE APPAREL INC
Also Called: Bellacanvas
860 S Los Angeles St, Los Angeles
(90014-3311)
PHONE..................855 793-3100
Daniel Harris, *Owner*
EMP: 23 **Privately Held**
SIC: 2253 2396 T-shirts & tops, knit;
screen printing on fabric articles
PA: Color Image Apparel, Inc.
6670 Flotilla St
Commerce CA 90040

(P-2831)
COMPLETE GARMENT INC
2101 E 38th St, Vernon (90058-1616)
PHONE..................323 846-3731
Steven Shaul, *CEO*
EMP: 33
SQ FT: 40,000
SALES (est): 4MM **Privately Held**
SIC: 2253 Dyeing & finishing knit outer-
wear, excl. hosiery & glove

(P-2832)
DELTA PACIFIC ACTIVEWEAR INC
331 S Hale Ave, Fullerton (92831-4805)
PHONE..................714 871-9281
Imran Parekh, *President*
▲ **EMP:** 80
SALES (est): 15.6MM **Privately Held**
SIC: 2253 2331 2321 T-shirts & tops, knit;
women's & misses' blouses & shirts;
men's & boys' furnishings

(P-2833)
DM COLLECTIVE INC
4536 District Blvd, Vernon (90058-2712)
PHONE..................323 923-2400
Daniel S Lee, *CEO*
Monica Lee, *CFO*
▲ **EMP:** 30
SALES (est): 5.6MM **Privately Held**
SIC: 2253 5131 Warm weather knit outer-
wear, including beachwear; knit fabrics

(P-2834)
EMA TEXTILES INC
Also Called: Sworn Virgins
2947 E 44th St, Vernon (90058-2429)
PHONE..................323 589-9800
Ali Amini, *President*
Alex Amini, *President*
Essi Faraji, *Treasurer*
EMP: 12
SQ FT: 10,000
SALES (est): 1.7MM **Privately Held**
WEB: www.ematex.com
SIC: 2253

(P-2835)
FANTASY ACTIVEWEAR INC (PA)
Also Called: Fantasy Manufacturing
5383 Alcoa Ave, Vernon (90058-3734)
PHONE..................213 705-4111
Anwar Gajiani, *CEO*
Yassmin Gajiani, *Vice Pres*
▲ **EMP:** 45
SQ FT: 20,000
SALES (est): 36.1MM **Privately Held**
WEB: www.fantasyincgroup.com
SIC: 2253 2331 2321 T-shirts & tops, knit;
women's & misses' blouses & shirts;
men's & boys' furnishings

(P-2836)
FANTASY ACTIVEWEAR INC
5383 Alcoa Ave, Vernon (90058-3734)
PHONE..................323 983-9988
Aziz Mohammed, *Branch Mgr*
EMP: 34
SALES (corp-wide): 36.1MM **Privately Held**
WEB: www.fantasyincgroup.com
SIC: 2253 T-shirts & tops, knit
PA: Fantasy Activewear, Inc.
5383 Alcoa Ave
Vernon CA 90058
213 705-4111

(P-2837)
FANTASY DYEING & FINISHING INC
5383 Alcoa Ave, Vernon (90058-3734)
PHONE..................323 983-9988
Anwar M Gajiani, *CEO*
Aziz Ahmad, *Controller*
EMP: 100
SALES (est): 15MM **Privately Held**
SIC: 2253 Dyeing & finishing knit outer-
wear, excl. hosiery & glove

(P-2838)
FORTUNE SWIMWEAR LLC (HQ)
Also Called: Palisades Beach Club
2340 E Olympic Blvd Ste A, Los Angeles
(90021-2544)
PHONE..................310 733-2130
Fred Kayne, *Mng Member*
Alan Shamma, *Engineer*
Adeline Kevorkian, *Controller*
Julie Goldmeier, *Sales Staff*
Stephen Soller,
▲ **EMP:** 30
SQ FT: 10,000
SALES (est): 7.6MM **Privately Held**
WEB: www.fortuneswimwear.com
SIC: 2253 2335 Bathing suits & swimwear,
knit; women's, juniors' & misses' dresses

(P-2839)
FRESH PEACHES INCORPORATED (PA)
Also Called: Fresh Peaches Swimwear
8423 Rochester Ave # 103, Rancho Cuca-
monga (91730-3995)
PHONE..................909 980-0172
Jeanette M Love, *President*
James M Love Jr, *Treasurer*
Lannette Love, *Corp Secy*
▲ **EMP:** 12
SQ FT: 6,650
SALES (est): 1.3MM **Privately Held**
WEB: www.fresh-peaches.com
SIC: 2253 5699 5632 Bathing suits &
swimwear, knit; body stockings, knit;
bathing suits; dancewear

(P-2840)
GARDENA TEXTILE INC
245 W 135th St, Los Angeles (90061-1625)
PHONE..................310 327-5060
EMP: 18
SQ FT: 22,000
SALES (est): 106K **Privately Held**
SIC: 2253

(P-2841)
GRAND WEST INC (PA)
Also Called: Crown Fashion
1441 E Adams Blvd, Los Angeles
(90011-1819)
PHONE..................323 235-2700
Dae Hyun Kim, *President*

EMP: 10
SQ FT: 52,000
SALES (est): 1.3MM **Privately Held**
WEB: www.grandwest.com
SIC: 2253 Jerseys, knit

(P-2842)
HIGH-END KNITWEAR INC
Also Called: T Q M Apparel Group
1100 S Hope St Ph 202, Los Angeles
(90015-2197)
PHONE..................323 582-6061
Michael Hong, *President*
Juliane Hong, *CFO*
Abby Dejoya, *Manager*
EMP: 35
SQ FT: 30,000
SALES (est): 3.9MM **Privately Held**
SIC: 2253

(P-2843)
ISIQALO LLC
Also Called: Spectra USA
5521 Schaefer Ave, Chino (91710-9070)
PHONE..................714 683-2820
Thomas Fenchel,
Nick Agakanian,
EMP: 350 **EST:** 2012
SQ FT: 350,000
SALES: 75MM **Privately Held**
SIC: 2253 5136 5137 2321 T-shirts &
tops, knit; jackets, knit; men's & boys'
clothing; women's & children's clothing;
sport shirts, men's & boys': from pur-
chased materials; T-shirts & tops,
women's: made from purchased materials

(P-2844)
JBS PRIVATE LABEL INC
Also Called: J B'S Private Label
4383 Irvine Ave, Studio City (91604-2705)
PHONE..................818 762-3736
Jackie Bender, *President*
EMP: 28
SQ FT: 2,500
SALES: 700K **Privately Held**
SIC: 2253 5199 2339 2337 Warm
weather knit outerwear, including beach-
wear; dresses & skirts; blouses, shirts,
pants & suits; knit goods; women's &
misses' outerwear; women's & misses'
suits & coats

(P-2845)
KOAM KNITECH INC
18118 S Broadway, Gardena (90248-3536)
PHONE..................310 515-1121
James Park, *President*
▲ **EMP:** 49 **EST:** 1998
SQ FT: 20,000
SALES (est): 5MM **Privately Held**
SIC: 2253 2339 Sweaters & sweater
coats, knit; women's & misses' outerwear

(P-2846)
LA SWIM LLC
Also Called: S Howard Hirsh
719 S Los Angeles St # 400, Los Angeles
(90014-2133)
PHONE..................213 689-4575
Ilan Blumenfeld, *Mng Member*
▲ **EMP:** 14
SALES (est): 1.4MM **Privately Held**
SIC: 2253 Bathing suits & swimwear, knit

(P-2847)
LIALEE INC
Also Called: Two Hands
525 E 87th Pl, Los Angeles (90003-3501)
PHONE..................213 765-7788
Lia Seungeun Lee, *CEO*
Seung Eun Lee, *President*
▲ **EMP:** 15
SQ FT: 4,310
SALES (est): 3.2MM **Privately Held**
SIC: 2253 T-shirts & tops, knit

(P-2848)
M & M SPORTSWEAR MANUFACTURING
18267 4th Ave, Jamestown (95327-9760)
P.O. Box 1429 (95327-1429)
PHONE..................209 984-5632
Denny Minners, *President*
EMP: 10
SQ FT: 4,800

SALES (est): 620K **Privately Held**
WEB: www.mmsportswear.com
SIC: 2253 7336 2339 Jerseys, knit; commercial art & graphic design; women's &
misses' outerwear

(P-2849)
MAXIT DESIGNS INC
4044 Wayside Ln Ste A, Carmichael
(95608-1756)
P.O. Box 1052 (95609-1052)
PHONE..................916 489-1023
Gail Ellison, *President*
Mike Ellison, *Vice Pres*
EMP: 10
SQ FT: 6,500
SALES (est): 1.1MM **Privately Held**
WEB: www.headgator.com
SIC: 2253 Knit outerwear mills

(P-2850)
MILL 42 INC
5331 Production Dr, Huntington Beach
(92649-1522)
PHONE..................714 979-4200
Kevin Dunlap, *CEO*
Mike Dunlap, *CFO*
Brad Bleick, *VP Sales*
◆ **EMP:** 11
SQ FT: 2,000
SALES (est): 5.6MM **Privately Held**
SIC: 2253 T-shirts & tops, knit

(P-2851)
MJ BLANKS INC
Also Called: Blanks Plus
1155 S Grand Ave Apt 614, Los Angeles
(90015-2780)
PHONE..................213 629-0006
Sung Ho Hong, *President*
EMP: 30
SQ FT: 12,000
SALES (est): 3MM **Privately Held**
SIC: 2253 T-shirts & tops, knit

(P-2852)
MJCK CORPORATION
Also Called: Xzavier
3222 E Washington Blvd, Vernon
(90058-8022)
PHONE..................888 992-8437
Tae Y Choi, *President*
EMP: 30 **EST:** 2010
SALES (est): 3MM **Privately Held**
SIC: 2253 2361 T-shirts & tops, knit; t-
shirts & tops: girls', children's & infants'

(P-2853)
PRO TAG CORP
8122 Maie Ave Unit C, Los Angeles
(90001-3855)
PHONE..................213 272-9606
Sujung Choi, *President*
Jae S Park, *CEO*
Charlie Choi, *Vice Pres*
EMP: 20
SALES (est): 989.9K **Privately Held**
SIC: 2253 Shirts (outerwear), knit

(P-2854)
SNOWFLAKE DESIGNS
2893 Larkin Ave, Clovis (93612-3908)
PHONE..................559 291-6234
Ladonna Snow, *Co-Owner*
Richard L Snow, *Co-Owner*
EMP: 22
SQ FT: 7,100
SALES (est): 1.2MM **Privately Held**
WEB: www.snowleotards.com
SIC: 2253 5632 Leotards, knit; dancewear

(P-2855)
ST JOHN KNITS INTL INC
17622 Armstrong Ave, Irvine (92614-5728)
PHONE..................949 399-8200
Philip Miller, *CEO*
EMP: 439

SALES (corp-wide): 703.3MM **Privately Held**
WEB: www.stjohnknits.com
SIC: 2253 2339 2335 3961 Dresses, knit; skirts, knit; pants, slacks or trousers, knit; T-shirts & tops, knit; sportswear, women's; scarves, hoods, headbands, etc.: women's; jackets, untailored: women's, misses' & juniors'; slacks: women's, misses' & juniors'; women's, juniors' & misses' dresses; bridal & formal gowns; costume jewelry; apparel belts
HQ: St John Knits International Incorporated
17622 Armstrong Ave
Irvine CA 92614
949 863-1171

(P-2856)
STUDIO9D8 INC
9743 Alesia St, South El Monte (91733-3008)
PHONE....................626 350-0832
Ann Lem, *CEO*
EMP: 30 **EST:** 2011
SALES (est): 1.5MM **Privately Held**
SIC: 2253 2515 T-shirts & tops, knit; studio couches

(P-2857)
STYLE KNITS INC
1745 Chapin Rd, Montebello (90640-6609)
PHONE....................323 890-9080
Patrick Quinn, *President*
EMP: 60
SALES (est): 3MM **Privately Held**
SIC: 2253 Knit outerwear mills

(P-2858)
SUN DYEING AND FINISHING CO
15621 Broadway Center St, Gardena (90248-2138)
PHONE....................310 329-0844
Ronald Nam, *President*
Nam Chul Kim, *Director*
EMP: 15
SQ FT: 23,000
SALES (est): 1.7MM **Privately Held**
SIC: 2253 Dyeing & finishing knit outerwear, excl. hosiery & glove

(P-2859)
SUN TRADE GROUP INC (PA)
Also Called: Sun Dog International
1251 Burton St, Fullerton (92831-5211)
PHONE....................714 525-4888
Lori Gulsvig, *President*
Stuart Nichols, *COO*
EMP: 15
SQ FT: 45,000
SALES (est): 7MM **Privately Held**
WEB: www.sundoginternational.com
SIC: 2253 T-shirts & tops, knit

(P-2860)
SWIMWEAR EXPERT INC
4025 Spencer St Ste 401, Torrance (90503-2450)
PHONE....................310 941-4880
John Daneshrad, *CEO*
EMP: 10
SALES (est): 780.6K **Privately Held**
SIC: 2253 Bathing suits & swimwear, knit

(P-2861)
THIENES APPAREL INC
1811 Floradale Ave, South El Monte (91733-3605)
PHONE....................626 575-2818
Chao Wen Chang, *Principal*
▲ **EMP:** 130
SQ FT: 17,500
SALES (est): 13.1MM **Privately Held**
SIC: 2253 Blouses, knit

(P-2862)
TIEN-HU KNITTING CO (US) INC
3996 San Pablo Ave Ste A, Emeryville (94608-3885)
P.O. Box 629, Oakland (94604-0629)
PHONE....................510 268-8833
Tim Shing Chan, *President*
Jane Wm Chan, *Vice Pres*
▲ **EMP:** 80
SQ FT: 30,000

SALES (est): 6.5MM **Privately Held**
SIC: 2253 2339 Sweaters & sweater coats, knit; women's & misses' outerwear

(P-2863)
YOUNG KNITTING MILLS
3499 E 15th St, Los Angeles (90023-3833)
PHONE....................323 980-8677
Fax: 323 980-5198
EMP: 21
SQ FT: 25,000
SALES (est): 961.3K **Privately Held**
SIC: 2253

2254 Knit Underwear Mills

(P-2864)
RICKS AMERICA INC
2828 Stanford Ave, Los Angeles (90011-2018)
PHONE....................323 232-6800
Byung C Yoo, *President*
Jackelyn Rivera, *Admin Sec*
▲ **EMP:** 10
SALES (est): 895.7K **Privately Held**
WEB: www.ricksamerica.com
SIC: 2254 Shirts & t-shirts (underwear), knit

(P-2865)
VAN TISSE INC
2565 3rd St Ste 319, San Francisco (94107-3155)
PHONE....................415 543-2404
Andres Van Dam, *President*
Diane Lee Van Dam, *Corp Secy*
EMP: 15
SQ FT: 12,000
SALES: 1MM **Privately Held**
SIC: 2254 2339 2322 2341 Nightwear (nightgowns, negligees, pajamas), knit; women's & misses' outerwear; women's & misses' athletic clothing & sportswear; men's & boys' underwear & nightwear; women's & children's underwear

2257 Circular Knit Fabric Mills

(P-2866)
MATCHMASTER DYG & FINSHG INC
Antex Knitting Mills
3750 Broadway Pl, Los Angeles (90007-4400)
PHONE....................323 232-2061
EMP: 65
SALES (corp-wide): 123.1MM **Privately Held**
SIC: 2257 5199
PA: Matchmaster Dyeing & Finishing, Inc.
3750 S Broadway
Los Angeles CA 90007
323 232-2061

(P-2867)
SHARA-TEX INC
3338 E Slauson Ave, Vernon (90058-3915)
PHONE....................323 587-7200
Shahram Fahimian, *Ch of Bd*
S Tony Souferian, *President*
▲ **EMP:** 45
SQ FT: 55,000
SALES (est): 9.6MM **Privately Held**
WEB: www.shara-tex.com
SIC: 2257 Weft knit fabric mills

(P-2868)
TENENBLATT CORPORATION
Also Called: Antex Knitting Mills
3750 Broadway Pl, Los Angeles (90007-4400)
PHONE....................323 232-2061
William Tenenblatt, *President*
Anna Tenenblatt, *Vice Pres*
◆ **EMP:** 200 **EST:** 1973
SQ FT: 60,000

SALES (est): 18.3MM
SALES (corp-wide): 53.8MM **Privately Held**
WEB: www.antexknitting.com
SIC: 2257 Dyeing & finishing circular knit fabrics
PA: Matchmaster Dyeing & Finishing, Inc.
3750 S Broadway
Los Angeles CA 90007
323 232-2061

2258 Lace & Warp Knit Fabric Mills

(P-2869)
PIERCE TEXTILE INC
13984 Orange Ave, Paramount (90723-2029)
PHONE....................562 220-1177
Frank Choy, *President*
Joon K Kim, *Admin Sec*
EMP: 20
SQ FT: 43,000
SALES (est): 1.1MM **Privately Held**
SIC: 2258 Cloth, warp knit

(P-2870)
PRIME ALLIANCE LLC
360 W Victoria St, Compton (90220-6061)
PHONE....................310 764-1000
EMP: 50
SQ FT: 60,000
SALES (est): 7.2MM **Privately Held**
SIC: 2258

(P-2871)
TUBE RAGS
4382 Bandini Blvd, Vernon (90058-4323)
PHONE....................323 264-7770
AVI Mor, *CEO*
◆ **EMP:** 10
SALES (est): 68.7K **Privately Held**
SIC: 2258 Dyeing & finishing lace goods & warp knit fabric

2259 Knitting Mills, NEC

(P-2872)
AZITEX TRADING CORP
Also Called: Azitex Knitting Mills
1850 E 15th St, Los Angeles (90021-2820)
PHONE....................213 745-7072
Michael Azizi, *President*
Andrew Azizi, *Corp Secy*
Mozie Azizi, *Vice Pres*
▲ **EMP:** 60
SQ FT: 50,000
SALES (est): 13.3MM **Privately Held**
SIC: 2259 2253 Convertors, knit goods; knit outerwear mills

(P-2873)
COTTON KNITS TRADING
3097 E Ana St, Compton (90221-5604)
PHONE....................310 884-9600
Ali Farid, *President*
Hadi E Farid, *Vice Pres*
▲ **EMP:** 35
SQ FT: 110,000
SALES (est): 4.8MM **Privately Held**
WEB: www.natureusa.net
SIC: 2259 Bags & bagging, knit

(P-2874)
MIDTHRUST IMPORTS INC
830 E 14th Pl, Los Angeles (90021-2120)
PHONE....................213 749-6651
Kamran Noman, *CEO*
▲ **EMP:** 20
SALES (est): 4.1MM **Privately Held**
WEB: www.midthrust.com
SIC: 2259 Convertors, knit goods

(P-2875)
SAS TEXTILES INC
3100 E 44th St, Vernon (90058-2406)
PHONE....................323 277-5555
Sohrab Sassounian, *President*
Albert Sassounian, *Treasurer*
Soheil Sassounian, *Vice Pres*
▲ **EMP:** 70
SQ FT: 40,000

SALES (est): 13.4MM **Privately Held**
SIC: 2259 2257 7389 Convertors, knit goods; weft knit fabric mills; textile & apparel services

(P-2876)
SW SAFETY SOLUTIONS INC
33278 Central Ave Ste 102, Union City (94587-2016)
PHONE....................510 429-8692
Belle Chou, *CEO*
Lilly Yao, *Controller*
Russell Silver, *Sales Staff*
EMP: 26
SALES: 9.5MM **Privately Held**
SIC: 2259 Gloves & mittens, knit

2261 Cotton Fabric Finishers

(P-2877)
AS MATCH DYEING CO INC
Also Called: National Dyeing
2522 E 37th St, Vernon (90058-1725)
PHONE....................323 277-0470
Geun Jo Cha, *President*
Young C Kim, *Admin Sec*
▲ **EMP:** 109
SQ FT: 60,000
SALES (est): 16.4MM **Privately Held**
SIC: 2261 2262 2269 Finishing plants, cotton; finishing plants, manmade fiber & silk fabrics; finishing plants

(P-2878)
BIG STUDIO INC
1247 E Hill St, Long Beach (90755-3523)
PHONE....................562 989-2444
Mitchell Kron, *President*
Chris Carder, *Assistant*
EMP: 15
SQ FT: 11,424
SALES (est): 1.7MM **Privately Held**
WEB: www.bigstudio.com
SIC: 2261 Screen printing of cotton broadwoven fabrics

(P-2879)
CAITAC GARMENT PROCESSING INC
14725 S Broadway, Gardena (90248-1813)
PHONE....................310 217-9888
Muneyuki Ishii, *CEO*
Azusa Sahara, *CFO*
Hiroyuki Shigenai, *CIO*
Terry Valenciano, *Human Res Mgr*
Griselda Contreras, *Personnel Assit*
▲ **EMP:** 250
SQ FT: 200,000
SALES (est): 37.8MM
SALES (corp-wide): 179.3MM **Privately Held**
WEB: www.caitacgarment.com
SIC: 2261 2339 2325 5651 Screen printing of cotton broadwoven fabrics; bleaching cotton broadwoven fabrics; dyeing cotton broadwoven fabrics; women's & misses' outerwear; men's & boys' trousers & slacks; jeans stores; embroidery kits
PA: Caitac Holdings Corp.
3-12, Showacho, Kita-Ku
Okayama OKA 700-0
862 553-555

(P-2880)
ESTEPHANIAN ORIGINALS INC
1550 E Mountain St, Pasadena (91104-3909)
PHONE....................626 358-7265
Mark Derestephanian, *President*
EMP: 30
SQ FT: 11,000
SALES (est): 2.8MM **Privately Held**
WEB: www.eodye.com
SIC: 2261 Screen printing of cotton broadwoven fabrics

(P-2881)
FULCRUM INTERNATIONAL INC
993 S Firefly Dr, Anaheim (92808-1504)
PHONE....................310 763-6823
Marcus J Reza, *President*
EMP: 48

PRODUCTS & SVCS

SQ FT: 12,080
SALES (est): 4.2MM **Privately Held**
SIC: 2261 Dyeing cotton broadwoven fabrics

(P-2882)
HARRYS DYE AND WASH INC
1015 E Orangethorpe Ave, Anaheim (92801-1135)
PHONE...............................714 446-0300
Harry Choung, *President*
Kang Ho Lee, *Vice Pres*
EMP: 30
SQ FT: 20,000
SALES (est): 3MM **Privately Held**
SIC: 2261 2269 Finishing plants, cotton; finishing plants

(P-2883)
L A AIR LINE INC
3844 S Santa Fe Ave, Vernon (90058-1713)
PHONE...............................323 585-1088
Dennis Maroney, *President*
Sandy Maroney, *Treasurer*
EMP: 27
SQ FT: 20,600
SALES (est): 3.3MM **Privately Held**
WEB: www.laairline.com
SIC: 2261 2396 2269 Dyeing cotton broadwoven fabrics; printing & embossing on plastics fabric articles; screen printing on fabric articles; finishing plants

(P-2884)
LORBER INDUSTRIES CALIFORNIA
Also Called: Lorber Industries of Claif
823 N Roxbury Dr, Beverly Hills (90210-3017)
PHONE...............................310 275-1568
Tom Lorber, *President*
John Robertson, *CFO*
Michael Gruener, *Vice Pres*
Greg Lorber, *Vice Pres*
Michael Painter, *Vice Pres*
EMP: 435
SALES (est): 28MM **Privately Held**
SIC: 2261 2262 2253 2257 Screen printing of cotton broadwoven fabrics; bleaching cotton broadwoven fabrics; shrinking cotton cloth; napping of cotton broadwoven fabrics; screen printing: manmade fiber & silk broadwoven fabrics; bleaching: manmade fiber & silk broadwoven fabrics; shrinking: manmade fiber & silk cloth; napping: manmade fiber & silk broadwoven fabrics; knit outerwear mills; weft knit fabric mills

(P-2885)
MAD ENGINE LLC (PA)
6740 Cobra Way Ste 100, San Diego (92121-4102)
PHONE...............................858 558-5270
Danish Gajrani, *CEO*
Faizan Bakali, *President*
Bill Bussiere, *CFO*
▲ **EMP:** 50
SQ FT: 50,000
SALES (est): 158.1MM **Privately Held**
WEB: www.madengine.com
SIC: 2261 Screen printing of cotton broadwoven fabrics

(P-2886)
MANDEGO INC
Also Called: Mandego Apparel
2300 Tech Pkwy Ste 2, Hollister (95023)
PHONE...............................831 637-5241
Dean Machado, *President*
Kelly Machado, *Admin Sec*
EMP: 17
SQ FT: 4,000
SALES (est): 1.2MM **Privately Held**
WEB: www.mandego.com
SIC: 2261 Screen printing of cotton broadwoven fabrics

(P-2887)
PACIFIC CONTNTL TEXTILES INC
Pacific Contntl Dyne & Finshg
2880 E Ana St, E Rncho Dmngz (90221-5602)
PHONE...............................310 639-1500

Thomas MA, *Manager*
Edmund Kim, *CEO*
John Yi, *Opers Mgr*
EMP: 10
SQ FT: 80,850
SALES (corp-wide): 41.9MM **Privately Held**
SIC: 2261 2262 2269 2759 Dyeing cotton broadwoven fabrics; dyeing: manmade fiber & silk broadwoven fabrics; printing of narrow fabrics; dyeing: raw stock yarn & narrow fabrics; textile printing rolls: engraving
HQ: Pacific Continental Textiles, Inc.
18737 S Reyes Ave
Compton CA 90221
310 604-1100

(P-2888)
PACIFIC IMPRESSIONS INC
3494 Edward Ave, Santa Clara (95054-2130)
PHONE...............................408 727-4200
John Kaveny, *President*
Diane Kaveny, *Corp Secy*
EMP: 10
SQ FT: 12,000
SALES: 500K **Privately Held**
WEB: www.pacimp.com
SIC: 2261 2759 2395 Screen printing of cotton broadwoven fabrics; screen printing; embroidery products, except schiffli machine

(P-2889)
PADILLA REMBERTO
Also Called: High Fidelity Textiles
3524 Union Pacific Ave, Los Angeles (90023-3922)
PHONE...............................323 268-1111
Remberto Padilla, *Owner*
EMP: 14
SQ FT: 7,000
SALES (est): 1.1MM **Privately Held**
SIC: 2261 Dyeing cotton broadwoven fabrics

(P-2890)
PRIMA-TEX INDUSTRIES CAL INC
6237 Descanso Cir, Buena Park (90620-1018)
PHONE...............................714 521-6104
Pienita S Tio, *President*
Josie Inouye, *CFO*
Richard Greer, *Vice Pres*
Nacho Varela, *Systems Dir*
▲ **EMP:** 59
SQ FT: 40,000
SALES (est): 8.9MM **Privately Held**
SIC: 2261 2396 2299 2331 Printing of cotton broadwoven fabrics; automotive & apparel trimmings; textile mill waste & remnant processing; women's & misses' blouses & shirts

(P-2891)
RAINBOW NOVELTY CREATIONS CO
3431 E Olympic Blvd, Los Angeles (90023-3030)
PHONE...............................323 855-9464
Ja Yun, *Owner*
EMP: 25
SALES (est): 1.2MM **Privately Held**
SIC: 2261 Screen printing of cotton broadwoven fabrics

(P-2892)
RAOULS PRINTWORKS
110 Los Aguajes Ave, Santa Barbara (93101-3818)
PHONE...............................805 965-1694
Sally Mc Quillan, *Owner*
EMP: 10
SALES (est): 640.9K **Privately Held**
WEB: www.textile.com
SIC: 2261 Screen printing of cotton broadwoven fabrics

(P-2893)
SCREEN WORKS
320 E Alton Ave, Santa Ana (92707-4419)
PHONE...............................714 432-7900
Robert Wolsshagen, *Owner*
▲ **EMP:** 50

SALES (est): 5.1MM **Privately Held**
WEB: www.screenwerks.com
SIC: 2261 Screen printing of cotton broadwoven fabrics

(P-2894)
SILK SCREEN SHIRTS INC
Also Called: SSS
6185 El Camino Real, Carlsbad (92009-1602)
PHONE...............................760 233-3900
Stephen H Taylor, *President*
William Regan, *CEO*
Laura D Wile, *Vice Pres*
◆ **EMP:** 30 **EST:** 1969
SQ FT: 20,000
SALES (est): 7.7MM **Privately Held**
WEB: www.silkscreenshirtsinc.com
SIC: 2261 2396 Screen printing of cotton broadwoven fabrics; automotive & apparel trimmings

(P-2895)
SRL APPAREL INC
Also Called: Printed Image, The
2209 Park Ave, Chico (95928-6704)
PHONE...............................530 898-9525
Scott Laursen, *President*
Marie Halvorsen, *Shareholder*
David Bryant, *Accounts Exec*
EMP: 26
SQ FT: 14,130
SALES (est): 4.7MM **Privately Held**
WEB: www.smokeybearproducts.com
SIC: 2261 5137 5136 2396 Screen printing of cotton broadwoven fabrics; women's & children's sportswear & swimsuits; men's & boys' sportswear & work clothing; automotive & apparel trimmings

(P-2896)
SUNSET ISLANDWEAR
Also Called: Just For Kids
601 Mary Ann Dr, Redondo Beach (90278-5306)
PHONE...............................310 372-7960
David Faolridia, *President*
EMP: 18
SALES (est): 1.7MM **Privately Held**
SIC: 2261 2759 Screen printing of cotton broadwoven fabrics; screen printing

(P-2897)
SUPERIOR PANORAMIC HAND PRNTS
840 Via Alondra, Camarillo (93012-8045)
PHONE...............................805 445-7770
Bob Strem, *President*
Janet Strem, *Vice Pres*
EMP: 60
SALES (est): 7.1MM **Privately Held**
WEB: www.superiorpanoramic.com
SIC: 2261 Printing of cotton broadwoven fabrics

(P-2898)
TOMORROWS LOOK INC
Also Called: Dimensions In Screen Printing
17462 Von Karman Ave, Irvine (92614-6206)
PHONE...............................949 596-8400
Steven E Mellgren, *CEO*
Torrey Mellgren, *Admin Sec*
EMP: 70
SQ FT: 36,000
SALES (est): 8MM **Privately Held**
SIC: 2261 Screen printing of cotton broadwoven fabrics

(P-2899)
WASHINGTON GARMENT DYEING
1332 E 18th St, Los Angeles (90021-3027)
PHONE...............................213 747-1111
Pradip Shah, *Manager*
EMP: 23
SALES (corp-wide): 6.9MM **Privately Held**
WEB: www.washingtongarments.com
SIC: 2261 2262 Finishing plants, cotton; finishing plants, manmade fiber & silk fabrics

PA: Washington Garment Dyeing & Finishing, Inc.
1341 E Washington Blvd
Los Angeles CA 90021
213 747-1111

2262 Silk & Man-Made Fabric Finishers

(P-2900)
ALVAREZ REFINISHING INC
23 W Romneya Dr, Anaheim (92801)
P.O. Box 407, Fulton (95439-0407)
PHONE...............................714 780-0171
Juan Rivera, *President*
EMP: 25 **EST:** 1998
SALES (est): 1.6MM **Privately Held**
SIC: 2262 Refinishing: manmade fiber & silk broadwoven fabrics

(P-2901)
CALIFORNIA SWATCH DYERS INC
776 E Washington Blvd, Los Angeles (90021-3042)
PHONE...............................213 748-8425
Delia Pineda, *President*
EMP: 30
SALES (est): 3.2MM **Privately Held**
SIC: 2262 Dyeing: manmade fiber & silk broadwoven fabrics

(P-2902)
FINAL FINISH INC
10910 Norwalk Blvd, Santa Fe Springs (90670-3828)
PHONE...............................562 777-7774
Luis Ibarria, *President*
EMP: 25
SQ FT: 20,000
SALES: 3.7MM **Privately Held**
WEB: www.finalfinish.com
SIC: 2262 Preshrinking: manmade fiber & silk broadwoven fabrics; dyeing: manmade fiber & silk broadwoven fabrics

(P-2903)
INX PRINTS INC
1802 Kettering, Irvine (92614-5618)
PHONE...............................949 660-9190
Harold A Haase Jr, *CEO*
David Van Steenhuyse, *Owner*
Don Moos, *Technology*
▼ **EMP:** 100
SQ FT: 26,000
SALES (est): 17.7MM **Privately Held**
SIC: 2262 Screen printing: manmade fiber & silk broadwoven fabrics

(P-2904)
REID & CLARK SCREEN ARTS CO
722 33rd St, San Diego (92102-3338)
PHONE...............................619 233-7541
Alejandro Melero, *President*
EMP: 12
SQ FT: 17,500
SALES (est): 1.8MM **Privately Held**
SIC: 2262 Screen printing: manmade fiber & silk broadwoven fabrics

(P-2905)
SPREADCO INC
803 Us Highway 78, Brawley (92227-9514)
PHONE...............................760 351-0747
Mario Valenzuela, *President*
Roque Valenzuela, *Admin Sec*
EMP: 20
SALES (est): 3.1MM **Privately Held**
SIC: 2262 Chemical coating or treating: manmade broadwoven fabrics

(P-2906)
UNIVERSAL DYEING & PRINTING
2303 E 11th St, Los Angeles (90021-2846)
PHONE...............................213 746-0818
Kee Sung Hwang, *President*
Betty Hwang, *Admin Sec*
▲ **EMP:** 100
SQ FT: 95,000

▲ = Import ▼=Export
◆ =Import/Export

SALES (est): 7.1MM **Privately Held**
SIC: **2262** Printing: manmade fiber & silk broadwoven fabrics

(P-2907)
WASHINGTON GARMENT DYEING (PA)
1341 E Washington Blvd, Los Angeles (90021-3037)
PHONE..........................213 747-1111
Vijay Shah, *President*
Pradip Shah, *Vice Pres*
EMP: 60
SQ FT: 20,000
SALES (est): 6.9MM **Privately Held**
WEB: www.washingtongarments.com
SIC: **2262 2261 2269** Dyeing: manmade fiber & silk broadwoven fabrics; dyeing cotton broadwoven fabrics; finishing plants

2269 Textile Finishers, NEC

(P-2908)
ALMORE DYE HOUSE INC
6850 Tujunga Ave, North Hollywood (91605-6324)
PHONE..........................818 506-5444
Jeffery Teichner, *President*
Don Kishner, *COO*
Donald Teichner, *Vice Pres*
Stuart Teichner, *Admin Sec*
Joel Romero, *Technology*
EMP: 45
SQ FT: 20,000
SALES (est): 6.6MM **Privately Held**
SIC: **2269** Dyeing: raw stock yarn & narrow fabrics

(P-2909)
CAL PACIFIC DYEING & FINISHING
233 E Gardena Blvd, Gardena (90248-2800)
PHONE..........................310 327-3792
Russell C Shoemaker, *President*
Price Shoemaker, *CFO*
Brian Vieweg, *VP Finance*
EMP: 64
SQ FT: 100,000
SALES (est): 4.2MM **Privately Held**
SIC: **2269** Dyeing: raw stock yarn & narrow fabrics; finishing: raw stock, yarn & narrow fabrics

(P-2910)
DP PRINT SERVICES INC
2331 Walling Ave, La Habra (90631-4267)
PHONE..........................310 600-5250
David Ponzio, *President*
EMP: 15
SALES: 6MM **Privately Held**
SIC: **2269** Labels, cotton: printed

(P-2911)
EXPO DYEING & FINISHING INC
1365 N Knollwood Cir, Anaheim (92801-1312)
PHONE..........................714 220-9583
Eduardo J Kim, *President*
▲ EMP: 170
SQ FT: 86,000
SALES (est): 25.9MM **Privately Held**
SIC: **2269** Dyeing: raw stock yarn & narrow fabrics

(P-2912)
FREEDOM WOOD FINISHING INC
Also Called: Freedom Finishing
600 Wilshire Blvd # 1200, Los Angeles (90017-3212)
PHONE..........................213 534-6620
Dean Schlaufman, *CFO*
Richard Pack, *Partner*
Maya Jackson, *Vice Pres*
EMP: 88 EST: 1995
SQ FT: 10,000
SALES: 5.4MM **Privately Held**
SIC: **2269** Finishing plants

(P-2913)
GREEN MATTRESS INC
6827 Mckinley Ave, Los Angeles (90001-1525)
PHONE..........................323 752-2026
Luis Ponce, *CEO*
Raquel Vizcarra, *Vice Pres*
EMP: 15
SQ FT: 28,000
SALES: 10MM **Privately Held**
SIC: **2269** Finishing: raw stock, yarn & narrow fabrics

(P-2914)
MATCHMASTER DYG & FINSHG INC (PA)
Also Called: Antex Knitting Mills
3750 S Broadway, Los Angeles (90007-4436)
PHONE..........................323 232-2061
William Tenenblatt, *President*
◆ EMP: 250
SQ FT: 66,000
SALES (est): 53.8MM **Privately Held**
SIC: **2269** Dyeing: raw stock yarn & narrow fabrics

(P-2915)
PACIFIC COAST BACH LABEL CO
3015 S Grand Ave, Los Angeles (90007-3814)
PHONE..........................213 612-0314
Dan Finnegan, *President*
▲ EMP: 23
SALES (est): 3.3MM **Privately Held**
WEB: www.bachlabel.net
SIC: **2269 2679** Labels, cotton: printed; labels, paper: made from purchased material

(P-2916)
PACIFIC CONTNTL TEXTILES INC (HQ)
Also Called: Pct
18737 S Reyes Ave, Compton (90221-5609)
PHONE..........................310 604-1100
Edmund Kim, *CEO*
Matt Nasab, *Director*
▲ EMP: 47
SQ FT: 80,000
SALES (est): 40.3MM
SALES (corp-wide): 41.9MM **Privately Held**
SIC: **2269 2329** Finishing plants; men's & boys' sportswear & athletic clothing
PA: Edmund Kim International, Inc.
18737 S Reyes Ave
Compton CA 90221
310 604-1100

(P-2917)
REZEX CORPORATION
Also Called: Geltman Industries
1901 Sacramento St, Los Angeles (90021-1608)
PHONE..........................213 622-2015
Shari Rezai, *President*
Amir R Rezai, *Vice Pres*
Mary Bejines, *Finance Mgr*
EMP: 25 EST: 1981
SQ FT: 41,000
SALES (est): 3.8MM **Privately Held**
WEB: www.geltman.com
SIC: **2269** Finishing plants

(P-2918)
STARR DESIGN FABRICS INC
440 Pig Aly, Etna (96027)
PHONE..........................530 467-5121
Kathleen Starr, *President*
Shelly Starr, *Vice Pres*
EMP: 14
SQ FT: 3,500
SALES: 600K **Privately Held**
WEB: www.starrfabrics.com
SIC: **2269** Linen fabrics: dyeing, finishing & printing

(P-2919)
TAG-IT PACIFIC INC
21900 Burbank Blvd # 270, Woodland Hills (91367-7461)
PHONE..........................818 444-4100
Colin Dyne, *CEO*
Steven Forte, *CEO*
Cornelia Boylston, *Info Tech Dir*
▲ EMP: 50
SALES (est): 7MM **Publicly Held**
WEB: www.tag-it.com
SIC: **2269** Labels, cotton: printed
PA: Talon International, Inc.
21900 Burbank Blvd # 270
Woodland Hills CA 91367

(P-2920)
TAGTRENDS INC
Also Called: Tagtrends USA
1340 Reynolds Ave Ste 101, Irvine (92614-5502)
PHONE..........................714 903-7792
Robert Haroutoonian, *President*
Sunshine Haroutoonian, *Vice Pres*
▲ EMP: 15
SQ FT: 2,000
SALES (est): 1.2MM **Privately Held**
WEB: www.tagtrends.com
SIC: **2269** Labels, cotton: printed

(P-2921)
VALERIE TRADING INC
870 E 59th St, Los Angeles (90001-1006)
PHONE..........................323 231-4255
Josefina Perez, *President*
▼ EMP: 32
SALES (est): 2.2MM **Privately Held**
SIC: **2269 5651** Cloth mending, for the trade; unisex clothing stores

(P-2922)
WATTS LIQUIDATION CORPORATION
555 Van Ness Ave, Torrance (90501-1424)
PHONE..........................310 328-5999
Kenneth E Watts, *CEO*
Jindas Shah, *Ch of Bd*
▲ EMP: 17
SQ FT: 36,000
SALES (est): 3.8MM
SALES (corp-wide): 11.2MM **Privately Held**
WEB: www.coatedfabrics.com
SIC: **2269** Finishing plants
HQ: Coated Fabrics Company
12658 Cisneros Ln
Santa Fe Springs CA 90670

(P-2923)
WESTERN YARN DYEING INC
2011 Raymer Ave, Fullerton (92833-2664)
PHONE..........................714 578-9500
Chong Kim, *President*
Byeng C Ahn, *Admin Sec*
▲ EMP: 42
SQ FT: 60,000
SALES (est): 5MM **Privately Held**
SIC: **2269** Dyeing: raw stock yarn & narrow fabrics

2273 Carpets & Rugs

(P-2924)
ATLAS CARPET MILLS INC
2200 Saybrook Ave, Commerce (90040-1720)
P.O. Box 11467, Mobile AL (36671-0467)
PHONE..........................323 724-7930
James Horwich, *President*
Ada Horwich, *Vice Pres*
Markos Varpas, *Vice Pres*
Stan Dunford, *Executive*
Mark Hesther, *Executive*
▲ EMP: 229
SQ FT: 350,000
SALES (est): 990.7K
SALES (corp-wide): 412.4MM **Publicly Held**
WEB: www.atlascarpetmills.com
SIC: **2273** Rugs, tufted
HQ: Tdg Operations, Llc
716 Bill Myles Dr
Saraland AL 36571
251 675-9080

(P-2925)
BENTLEY MILLS INC
315 S 7th Ave, City of Industry (91746-3117)
PHONE..........................800 423-4709
Maria Gonzalez, *Manager*
Tom Mee, *President*
Jim Harley, *COO*
Tim Sellers, *Database Admin*
Noelle Novak, *Marketing Staff*
EMP: 10
SALES (corp-wide): 218.1MM **Privately Held**
SIC: **2273** Carpets & rugs
PA: Bentley Mills, Inc.
14641 Don Julian Rd
City Of Industry CA 91746
626 333-4585

(P-2926)
BENTLEY MILLS INC (PA)
14641 Don Julian Rd, City of Industry (91746-3106)
PHONE..........................626 333-4585
Ralph Grogan, *President*
Jim Harley, *COO*
Eric Petty, *CFO*
Sherry Dreger, *Vice Pres*
Tom Mee, *Vice Pres*
◆ EMP: 250
SQ FT: 390,000
SALES (est): 218.1MM **Privately Held**
SIC: **2273 2299** Carpets, textile fiber; batting, wadding, padding & fillings

(P-2927)
CAROUSEL CARPET MILLS INC
19 Bryan Dr, Novato (94945-2275)
PHONE..........................415 892-8207
Joan Nussbaum, *CEO*
Debra Galli, *CFO*
Laura Whiting, *Vice Pres*
Denice Spencer, *Admin Sec*
EMP: 55
SQ FT: 98,000
SALES (est): 6MM **Privately Held**
WEB: www.carouselcpt.com
SIC: **2273** Finishers of tufted carpets & rugs; rugs, braided & hooked; rugs, machine woven; carpets, textile fiber

(P-2928)
CATALINA CARPET MILLS INC (PA)
Also Called: Catalina Home
14418 Best Ave, Santa Fe Springs (90670-5133)
PHONE..........................562 926-5811
Duane Jensen, *President*
Jack Heinrich, *Vice Pres*
Jennifer Yaeger, *Production*
Frank Johnson, *Sales Staff*
Ginny Figueras, *Manager*
▲ EMP: 58
SQ FT: 60,000
SALES (est): 11.8MM **Privately Held**
WEB: www.catalinahome.com
SIC: **2273 5023** Finishers of tufted carpets & rugs; floor coverings

(P-2929)
FABRICA INTERNATIONAL INC
Also Called: Fabrica Fine Carpet
3201 S Susan St, Santa Ana (92704-6838)
PHONE..........................949 261-7181
Greg Uttecht, *President*
Tim Skwarek, *Partner*
Jon A Faulkner, *CEO*
Rosa Licea, *General Mgr*
Gene Farnell, *Technology*
◆ EMP: 167
SQ FT: 107,000
SALES (est): 35.6MM
SALES (corp-wide): 412.4MM **Publicly Held**
SIC: **2273** Carpets, hand & machine made; rugs, braided & hooked
PA: The Dixie Group Inc
475 Reed Rd
Dalton GA 30720
706 876-5800

PRODUCTS & SVCS

(P-2930)
LAND N TOP CLEANING SERVICES
20953 Sioux Rd, Apple Valley (92308-4232)
PHONE..................................760 624-8845
Nichole Duran, *Principal*
EMP: 25
SALES (est): 1.4MM **Privately Held**
SIC: 2273 Axminster carpets

(P-2931)
LLOYD DESIGN CORPORATION
Also Called: Lloyd Mats
19731 Nordhoff St, Northridge (91324-3330)
PHONE..................................818 768-6001
Lloyd S Levine, *CEO*
Brendan Dooley, *President*
Gary Lavender, *Vice Pres*
Marvin Rios, *Opers Mgr*
Mary Freeman, *Manager*
▲ EMP: 55
SALES (est): 8.2MM **Privately Held**
WEB: www.lloydmats.com
SIC: 2273 Automobile floor coverings, except rubber or plastic

(P-2932)
MARSPRING CORPORATION (PA)
Also Called: Marflex
4920 S Boyle Ave, Vernon (90058-3017)
P.O. Box 58643 (90058-0643)
PHONE..................................323 589-5637
Ronald J Greitzer, *President*
Stan Greitzer, *Vice Pres*
▲ EMP: 34
SQ FT: 54,008
SALES (est): 10.3MM **Privately Held**
WEB: www.marflex.com
SIC: 2273 Carpets, textile fiber

(P-2933)
MAT CACTUS MFG CO
930 W 10th St, Azusa (91702-1936)
PHONE..................................626 969-0444
Debra Hartranft-Dering, *President*
Cailey Dering, *Treasurer*
Micheal Armstrong, *Info Tech Mgr*
John Armstrong, *Manager*
Debbie Hartranft, *Manager*
▲ EMP: 20 EST: 1934
SQ FT: 35,000
SALES (est): 3.9MM **Privately Held**
WEB: www.cactusmat.com
SIC: 2273 5023 3069 Carpets & rugs; floor coverings; mats or matting, rubber

(P-2934)
MOHAWK INDUSTRIES INC
9687 Transportation Way, Fontana (92335-2604)
PHONE..................................909 357-1064
Lisa Gomez, *Branch Mgr*
Mathew Witte, *Opers Dir*
EMP: 80
SALES (corp-wide): 9.4B **Publicly Held**
SIC: 2273 3253 Finishers of tufted carpets & rugs; smyrna carpets & rugs, machine woven; ceramic wall & floor tile
PA: Mohawk Industries, Inc.
160 S Industrial Blvd
Calhoun GA 30701
706 629-7721

(P-2935)
MOHAWK INDUSTRIES INC
41490 Boyce Rd, Fremont (94538-3113)
PHONE..................................510 440-8790
Don Cruz, *Branch Mgr*
EMP: 140
SALES (corp-wide): 9.4B **Publicly Held**
SIC: 2273 Finishers of tufted carpets & rugs
PA: Mohawk Industries, Inc.
160 S Industrial Blvd
Calhoun GA 30701
706 629-7721

(P-2936)
NEXT SYSTEM INC
20605 Soledad Canyon Rd # 222, Canyon Country (91351-2438)
PHONE..................................661 257-1600

Daniel Pharo, *President*
Alex Hembree, *Vice Pres*
EMP: 26
SQ FT: 8,600
SALES (est): 3.3MM **Privately Held**
WEB: www.nextsystem.net
SIC: 2273 Mats & matting

(P-2937)
OHNO AMERICA INC
Also Called: Soho Carpet & Rugs
18781 Winnwood Ln, Santa Ana (92705-1215)
PHONE..................................770 773-3820
Akio Tabata, *President*
▲ EMP: 20
SQ FT: 36,000
SALES (est): 1.6MM
SALES (corp-wide): 47.9MM **Privately Held**
SIC: 2273
PA: Ohno Inc.
5-15-1, Harayamadai, Minami-Ku
Sakai OSK 590-0
722 970-566

(P-2938)
SAVNIK & COMPANY INC
601 Mcclary Ave, Oakland (94621-1915)
PHONE..................................510 568-4628
Berry Savnik, *General Mgr*
Kathryn Savnik, *Corp Secy*
Kurt Savnik, *Manager*
EMP: 11
SQ FT: 15,000
SALES (est): 400K **Privately Held**
SIC: 2273 Carpets, hand & machine made; rugs, tufted

(P-2939)
SHAW INDUSTRIES GROUP INC
Also Called: Tuftex Carpet Mills
15305 Valley View Ave, Santa Fe Springs (90670-5325)
PHONE..................................562 921-7209
Jim Cusack, *Director*
Ed Lutterloh, *Vice Pres*
Edward Zaldana, *Info Tech Mgr*
Michael Arai, *Accounting Mgr*
Chuck Dryer, *Sales Mgr*
EMP: 271
SALES (corp-wide): 242.1B **Publicly Held**
SIC: 2273 Dyeing & finishing of tufted rugs & carpets
HQ: Shaw Industries Group, Inc.
616 E Walnut Ave
Dalton GA 30721
800 446-9332

(P-2940)
SHAW INDUSTRIES GROUP INC
11411 Valley View St, Cypress (90630-5368)
PHONE..................................562 430-4445
Stan Diehl, *Manager*
Holly Carter, *President*
Robin Worsham, *Manager*
Nancy Landeros, *Supervisor*
EMP: 140
SALES (corp-wide): 242.1B **Publicly Held**
SIC: 2273 5713 5023 Finishers of tufted carpets & rugs; floor covering stores; home furnishings
HQ: Shaw Industries Group, Inc.
616 E Walnut Ave
Dalton GA 30721
800 446-9332

(P-2941)
SOEX WEST TEX RECYCL USA LLC
2360 S Orange Ave, Fresno (93725-1014)
PHONE..................................559 233-1765
Roubik Aftandilians,
▼ EMP: 65
SALES (est): 10.2MM **Privately Held**
SIC: 2273 Carpets & rugs

(P-2942)
STANTON CARPET CORP
Also Called: Hibernia Woolen Mills
2209 Pine Ave, Manhattan Beach (90266-2832)
PHONE..................................562 945-8711

Debbie Dearo, *Manager*
Eric Scharff, *Admin Sec*
EMP: 16
SALES (corp-wide): 58MM **Privately Held**
WEB: www.hiberniawoolenmills.com
SIC: 2273 Carpets & rugs
PA: Stanton Carpet Corp.
211 Robbins Ln
Syosset NY 11791
516 822-5878

(P-2943)
STUDENT SPORTS
23954 Madison St, Torrance (90505-6011)
PHONE..................................310 791-1142
Andy Bark, *Principal*
Laura Tamilin, *CFO*
Zack Greer, *Officer*
Miya Malauulu, *Opers Staff*
Patrick Bark, *Director*
EMP: 10
SALES (est): 1MM **Privately Held**
SIC: 2273 Carpets & rugs

(P-2944)
TDG OPERATIONS LLC
340 S Avenue 17, Los Angeles (90031-2505)
PHONE..................................323 724-9000
Charles Jones, *Manager*
EMP: 52
SALES (corp-wide): 412.4MM **Publicly Held**
WEB: www.atlascarpetmills.com
SIC: 2273 Rugs, tufted
HQ: Tdg Operations, Llc
716 Bill Myles Dr
Saraland AL 36571
251 675-9080

(P-2945)
TDG OPERATIONS LLC
6433 Gayhart St, Commerce (90040-2505)
PHONE..................................323 724-9000
Pancha Vega, *Manager*
EMP: 15
SALES (corp-wide): 412.4MM **Publicly Held**
WEB: www.atlascarpetmills.com
SIC: 2273 Rugs, tufted
HQ: Tdg Operations, Llc
716 Bill Myles Dr
Saraland AL 36571
251 675-9080

2281 Yarn Spinning Mills

(P-2946)
PHARR-PALOMAR INC
6781 8th St, Buena Park (90620-1097)
P.O. Box 1939, Mc Adenville NC (28101-1939)
PHONE..................................714 522-4811
H W Gosney, *President*
Jim Howard, *Corp Secy*
Walt Davenport, *Vice Pres*
EMP: 1600
SQ FT: 52,000
SALES (est): 115.1MM
SALES (corp-wide): 12MM **Privately Held**
WEB: www.pharryarns.com
SIC: 2281 2282 Yarn spinning mills; carpet yarn: twisting, winding or spooling
HQ: Pharr Yarns, Llc
100 Main St
Mc Adenville NC 28101
704 824-3551

(P-2947)
TDG OPERATIONS LLC
Also Called: Candlewick-Porterville
600 S E St, Porterville (93257-5318)
PHONE..................................559 781-4116
Dennis Johnson, *Branch Mgr*
Darryl Tamashiro, *Technology*
Harry Gloth, *Marketing Staff*
EMP: 60
SQ FT: 144,964
SALES (corp-wide): 412.4MM **Publicly Held**
WEB: www.royaltycarpetmills.com
SIC: 2281 2221 Yarn spinning mills; broadwoven fabric mills, manmade

HQ: Tdg Operations, Llc
475 Reed Rd
Dalton GA 30720
706 876-5851

(P-2948)
WINDSOR TEXTILE CORPORATION
13122 S Normandie Ave, Gardena (90249-2128)
PHONE..................................310 323-3997
EMP: 12
SALES: 1MM **Privately Held**
SIC: 2281

2282 Yarn Texturizing, Throwing, Twisting & Winding Mills

(P-2949)
C S AMERICA INC (HQ)
13365 Estelle St, Corona (92879-1881)
PHONE..................................323 583-7627
SOO Bong Joo, *President*
◆ EMP: 45
SQ FT: 50,000
SALES (est): 11.1MM
SALES (corp-wide): 44.7MM **Privately Held**
SIC: 2282 Throwing & winding mills
PA: Cs Fibertech Co., Ltd
471 Busong 1-Gil, Jiksan-Eup Seobuk-Gu
Cheonan 31038
824 155-7621

(P-2950)
MUSTANG HILLS LLC
16409 K St, Mojave (93501-1215)
PHONE..................................661 888-5810
James Spencer, *CEO*
Andrew Golembeski, *COO*
Charlie Williams, *CFO*
Christopher Shears, *Exec VP*
Kevin Sheen, *Vice Pres*
EMP: 24
SALES (est): 1.5MM
SALES (corp-wide): 352.2K **Privately Held**
SIC: 2282 Throwing & winding mills
HQ: Everpower Wind Holdings, Inc.
1251 Waterfront Pl Fl 3
Pittsburgh PA 15222

2284 Thread Mills

(P-2951)
AMERICAN & EFIRD LLC
6098 Rickenbacker Rd, Commerce (90040-3030)
PHONE..................................323 724-6884
Juan Anbric, *Manager*
EMP: 93
SALES (corp-wide): 151.9MM **Privately Held**
SIC: 2284 Thread mills
PA: American & Efird Llc
22 American St
Mount Holly NC 28120
704 827-4311

(P-2952)
G R J FASHIONS
6750 Foster Bridge Blvd B, Bell Gardens (90201-2052)
PHONE..................................323 537-5814
Gabriel Carranza, *Partner*
Ricardo Hernandez, *Partner*
EMP: 14
SALES (est): 1.3MM **Privately Held**
SIC: 2284 Embroidery thread

(P-2953)
INSTATHREADS LLC
238 Lakeview Dr, Palmdale (93551-7933)
PHONE..................................661 470-7841
Pamela Foster, *President*
EMP: 10
SALES (est): 631.3K **Privately Held**
SIC: 2284 Needle & handicraft thread

(P-2954)
MEDRANO RAYMUNDO
Also Called: Best Ink and Thread
1752 S Bon View Ave, Ontario
(91761-4411)
PHONE.............................909 947-5507
Raymundo Medrano, *Owner*
EMP: 20
SALES: 500K **Privately Held**
SIC: 2284 2759 Embroidery thread;
screen printing

(P-2955)
POLYTEX MANUFACTURING INC (PA)
1140 S Hope St, Los Angeles (90015-2119)
PHONE.............................323 726-0140
Men Tao, *President*
▲ EMP: 15
SQ FT: 8,000
SALES (est): 19.6MM **Privately Held**
SIC: 2284 Thread mills

2295 Fabrics Coated Not Rubberized

(P-2956)
AOC LLC
Also Called: AOC California Plant
19991 Seaton Ave, Perris (92570-8724)
PHONE.............................951 657-5161
John Mulrine, *Manager*
Eric Padilla, *Engineer*
Greg Ralston, *Safety Mgr*
Tim Maxman, *Plant Mgr*
EMP: 100
SALES (corp-wide): 296.8MM **Privately Held**
WEB: www.aoc-resins.com
SIC: 2295 2821 5169 Resin or plastic
coated fabrics; plastics materials & resins;
synthetic resins, rubber & plastic materials
HQ: Aoc, Llc
955 Highway 57
Collierville TN 38017

(P-2957)
CALIFORNIA COMBINING CORP
5607 S Santa Fe Ave, Vernon
(90058-3525)
PHONE.............................323 589-5727
Charlette Heller, *CEO*
Vincent Rosato, *President*
Kathy Diaz, *Corp Secy*
▲ EMP: 37
SQ FT: 68,000
SALES (est): 6.3MM **Privately Held**
SIC: 2295 Coated fabrics, not rubberized

(P-2958)
CYTEC AEROSPACE MTLS CA INC
Also Called: Cytec Engineered Materials
851 W 18th St, Costa Mesa (92627-4410)
PHONE.............................714 899-0400
David Drillock, *CEO*
Hisham Alameddine, *President*
Chris Jouppi, *President*
Jim Davis, *CEO*
Guillaume Gignac, *Vice Pres*
▲ EMP: 140
SQ FT: 51,300
SALES (est): 20.1MM
SALES (corp-wide): 10MM **Privately Held**
WEB: www.jdlincoln.com
SIC: 2295 2891 Coated fabrics, not rubberized; adhesives & sealants
HQ: Cytec Industries Inc.
250 Pehle Ave Ste 306
Saddle Brook NJ 07663

(P-2959)
FLEXFIRM HOLDINGS LLC
2300 Chico Ave, El Monte (91733-1611)
PHONE.............................323 283-1173
Barry Eichorn, *President*
EMP: 15
SQ FT: 10,000

SALES (est): 2.4MM **Privately Held**
WEB: www.flexfirmproducts.com
SIC: 2295 Resin or plastic coated fabrics

(P-2960)
HEXCEL CORPORATION
11711 Dublin Blvd, Dublin (94568-2898)
PHONE.............................925 551-4900
Robert Petrisko, *Branch Mgr*
John Bonema, *General Mgr*
Justin Crudale, *Project Mgr*
Tyler Blohm, *Engineer*
Ricky Carr, *Engineer*
EMP: 59
SALES (corp-wide): 1.9B **Publicly Held**
WEB: www.hexcel.com
SIC: 2295 Plastic coated yarns or fabrics
PA: Hexcel Corporation
281 Tresser Blvd Ste 1503
Stamford CT 06901
203 969-0666

(P-2961)
NANOSTONE WATER INC
2463 Impala Dr, Carlsbad (92010-7227)
PHONE.............................442 232-2595
EMP: 17
SALES (corp-wide): 9.6MM **Privately Held**
SIC: 2295 Chemically coated & treated
fabrics
PA: Solecta Inc
4113 Avenida De La Plata
Oceanside CA 92056
760 630-9643

(P-2962)
SHERWIN-WILLIAMS COMPANY
5501 E Slauson Ave, Commerce
(90040-2920)
PHONE.............................323 726-7272
Eric Westerman, *Branch Mgr*
EMP: 30
SALES (corp-wide): 14.9B **Publicly Held**
SIC: 2295 Resin or plastic coated fabrics
PA: The Sherwin-Williams Company
101 W Prospect Ave # 1020
Cleveland OH 44115
216 566-2000

(P-2963)
SOLECTA INC (PA)
4113 Avenida De La Plata, Oceanside
(92056-6002)
PHONE.............................760 630-9643
Michael Ahearn, *CEO*
▲ EMP: 33 EST: 2014
SALES (est): 9.6MM **Privately Held**
SIC: 2295 Chemically coated & treated
fabrics

(P-2964)
SPECILTY MTALS FABRICATION INC
11222 Woodside Ave N, Santee
(92071-4716)
PHONE.............................619 937-6100
Richard Buxton, *President*
Tom Buxton, *CFO*
Larry Hendry, *Admin Sec*
Sandy Fousek, *Manager*
EMP: 16
SALES (est): 1.9MM **Privately Held**
SIC: 2295 Metallizing of fabrics

2297 Fabrics, Nonwoven

(P-2965)
APPARELWAY INC
4516 Loma Vista Ave, Vernon
(90058-2602)
PHONE.............................323 581-5888
Don X Ho, *CEO*
▲ EMP: 15
SALES (est): 2MM **Privately Held**
WEB: www.apparelway.com
SIC: 2297 Nonwoven fabrics

(P-2966)
IOU INTERNATIONAL INC
2624 Geraldine St, Los Angeles
(90011-1829)
PHONE.............................323 846-0056
Hee Ja Cha, *President*

EMP: 25 EST: 2009
SALES (est): 3.7MM **Privately Held**
SIC: 2297 Nonwoven fabrics

(P-2967)
TEXOLLINI INC
2575 E El Presidio St, Long Beach
(90810-1114)
PHONE.............................310 537-3400
Daniel Kadisha, *President*
Kathy Pond, *Manager*
▲ EMP: 250
SQ FT: 200,000
SALES (est): 45.1MM **Privately Held**
WEB: www.texollini.com
SIC: 2297 2262 2269 2221 Nonwoven
fabrics; dyeing: manmade fiber & silk
broadwoven fabrics; finishing plants;
broadwoven fabric mills, manmade

2298 Cordage & Twine

(P-2968)
ASSOCIATED WIRE ROPE & RIGGING
910 Mahar Ave, Wilmington (90744-3829)
PHONE.............................310 448-5444
Scott Fishfader, *President*
Bob Levy, *VP Opers*
▲ EMP: 30
SALES (est): 5.2MM **Privately Held**
SIC: 2298 3315 5051 3536 Wire rope
centers; wire, steel: insulated or armored;
rope, wire (not insulated); hoists, cranes
& monorails; miscellaneous fabricated
wire products; industrial machinery &
equipment

(P-2969)
BAY ASSOCIATES WIRE TECH CORP (DH)
46840 Lakeview Blvd, Fremont
(94538-6543)
PHONE.............................510 988-3800
Harry Avonti, *CEO*
Amy King, *CFO*
Jack Sanford, *Treasurer*
Mark Rotner, *Admin Sec*
Darlene Overton, *Technology*
▲ EMP: 67
SQ FT: 45,000
SALES (est): 63MM
SALES (corp-wide): 75MM **Privately Held**
WEB: www.newenglandwire.com
SIC: 2298 3351 3357 Cable, fiber; copper
rolling & drawing; nonferrous wiredrawing
& insulating
HQ: New England Wire Technologies Corporation
130 N Main St
Lisbon NH 03585
603 838-6624

(P-2970)
CABLE BUILDERS INC
2380 Camino Vida, Carlsbad (92011)
P.O. Box 230872, Encinitas (92023-0872)
PHONE.............................760 308-0042
Cliff Robert Renison, *President*
▲ EMP: 10
SALES (est): 951.9K **Privately Held**
SIC: 2298 Ropes & fiber cables

(P-2971)
CABLE MANUFACTURING TECH
Also Called: Cmt
2455 Bates Ave Ste E, Concord
(94520-8520)
P.O. Box 343, Walnut Creek (94597-0343)
PHONE.............................925 687-3700
Andrew Enriquez, *Owner*
▲ EMP: 12
SQ FT: 3,500
SALES (est): 945.7K **Privately Held**
WEB: www.cmtcables.com
SIC: 2298 Blasting mats, rope

(P-2972)
CABLECO
13100 Firestone Blvd, Santa Fe Springs
(90670-5517)
PHONE.............................562 942-8076
Greg Bailey, *Principal*

James Currie, *Sales Mgr*
▲ EMP: 23
SALES (est): 4.9MM **Privately Held**
SIC: 2298 Cable, fiber

(P-2973)
COORDNTED WIRE ROPE RGGING INC
Also Called: Coordinated Wire Rope No. Ca.
790 139th Ave Ste 1, San Leandro
(94578-3214)
PHONE.............................510 569-6911
Ron Kutzman, *Branch Mgr*
EMP: 13
SALES (corp-wide): 2.2MM **Privately Held**
SIC: 2298 5251 Wire rope centers; hardware
HQ: Coordinated Wire Rope & Rigging, Inc.
1707 E Anaheim St
Wilmington CA 90744
310 834-8535

(P-2974)
DYNAMEX CORPORATION
155 E Albertoni St, Carson (90746-1405)
PHONE.............................310 329-0399
Ben Bravin, *President*
◆ EMP: 20
SALES (est): 3.3MM **Privately Held**
WEB: www.dynamexcorp.com
SIC: 2298 Cable, fiber

(P-2975)
MANUFACTURE RESOURCE PDTS INC
19907 E Walnut Dr S Ste C, Walnut
(91789-2854)
PHONE.............................909 839-2988
Mark Lu, *President*
Roger Pritchard, *Representative*
▲ EMP: 20
SALES (est): 3MM **Privately Held**
SIC: 2298 Cable, fiber

(P-2976)
PACIFIC FIBRE & ROPE CO INC
903 Flint Ave 927, Wilmington
(90744-3740)
PHONE.............................310 834-4567
Mark Goldman, *President*
Allen Goldman, *President*
Michael Goldman, *Treasurer*
Ronald Goldman, *Vice Pres*
EMP: 15
SQ FT: 45,000
SALES (est): 1.5MM **Privately Held**
WEB: www.pacificfibre.com
SIC: 2298 5085 Cordage: abaca, sisal,
henequen, hemp, jute or other fiber; rope,
except wire rope

(P-2977)
PELICAN ROPE WORKS
1600 E Mcfadden Ave, Santa Ana
(92705-4310)
PHONE.............................714 545-0116
Gaylord C Whipple, *President*
Terry Walker, *Financial Exec*
Paul Ottone, *Opers Staff*
Roderick Woods, *VP Sls/Mktg*
Malena Michota, *Sales Associate*
▲ EMP: 15
SQ FT: 20,000
SALES (est): 2.5MM **Privately Held**
WEB: www.pelicanrope.com
SIC: 2298 Ropes & fiber cables

(P-2978)
RIP-TIE INC
883 San Leandro Blvd, San Leandro
(94577-1530)
P.O. Box 549 (94577-0549)
PHONE.............................510 577-0200
Michael P Fennell, *President*
Suzanne Elliott, *Opers Mgr*
Marsha Duffie, *Sales Staff*
▲ EMP: 18
SQ FT: 45,000
SALES (est): 1.8MM **Privately Held**
WEB: www.riptie.com
SIC: 2298 Cordage & twine

PRODUCTS & SVCS

(P-2979)
RJ MFG
1201 S Blaker Rd, Turlock (95380-8305)
PHONE.....................................209 632-9708
Richard Jones, *President*
▲ EMP: 10
SQ FT: 10,000
SALES: 1MM **Privately Held**
WEB: www.rjmanufacturing.com
SIC: 2298 Ropes & fiber cables; rope, except asbestos & wire

(P-2980)
STRAND PRODUCTS INC
721 E Yanonali St, Santa Barbara
(93103-3235)
P.O. Box 4610 (93140-4610)
PHONE.....................................805 568-0304
Kelly Allin, *Branch Mgr*
EMP: 20
SALES (corp-wide): 4MM **Privately Held**
WEB: www.strandproducts.com
SIC: 2298 Wire rope centers
PA: Strand Products Inc.
    725 E Yanonali St
    Santa Barbara CA 93103
    805 568-0304

(P-2981)
TNT ASSEMBLY LLC
Also Called: TNT Cable Industries
1331 Specialty Dr, Vista (92081-8521)
PHONE.....................................760 410-1750
Carlos Navarro, *Mng Member*
Chris Rutman, *COO*
Everardo Sagamaga, *Opers Mgr*
Zoltan Vidakovics, *Sales Staff*
EMP: 42
SQ FT: 7,000
SALES: 5MM **Privately Held**
SIC: 2298 3355 3357 Ropes & fiber cables; aluminum wire & cable; automotive wire & cable, except ignition sets: nonferrous

(P-2982)
TRADE MARKER INTERNATIONAL
Also Called: TMI
445 Ryan Dr Ste 101, San Marcos
(92078-4072)
PHONE.....................................760 602-4864
Peter Nyari, *President*
Klara Nyari, *CFO*
▲ EMP: 10
SALES: 3.5MM **Privately Held**
SIC: 2298 0139 Cordage: abaca, sisal, henequen, hemp, jute or other fiber; hard fiber cordage & twine; soft fiber cordage & twine; twine, cord & cordage;

(P-2983)
TSF CONSTRUCTION SERVICES INC
Also Called: Dvbe Supply
4805 Mercury St Ste E, San Diego
(92111-2110)
PHONE.....................................619 202-7615
Theodore Foster, *President*
EMP: 11 EST: 2015
SALES (est): 466.6K **Privately Held**
SIC: 2298 5099 3845 7359 Ropes & fiber cables; lifesaving & survival equipment (non-medical); respiratory analysis equipment, electromedical; work zone traffic equipment (flags, cones, barrels, etc.)

2299 Textile Goods, NEC

(P-2984)
AGRIBAG INC
3925 Alameda Ave, Oakland (94601-3931)
PHONE.....................................510 533-2388
Hsieh Liang, *President*
Wen-Ping Liang, *Vice Pres*
Annie Chang, *General Mgr*
Belle Chang, *Graphic Designe*
Mike Garner, *Sales Mgr*
▲ EMP: 25
SQ FT: 20,000
SALES (est): 3.9MM **Privately Held**
SIC: 2299 2673 Bagging, jute; bags: plastic, laminated & coated

(P-2985)
ALMAC FIXTURE & SUPPLY CO
Also Called: Almac Felt Co
12932 Jolette Ave, Granada Hills
(91344-1068)
PHONE.....................................818 360-1706
Al K Friedman, *President*
EMP: 20 EST: 1965
SQ FT: 55,000
SALES (est): 2.1MM **Privately Held**
WEB: www.almacfelt.com
SIC: 2299 2824 Garnetting of textile waste & rags; organic fibers, noncellulosic

(P-2986)
AMERICAN DAWN INC (PA)
Also Called: ADI
401 W Artesia Blvd, Compton
(90220-5518)
PHONE.....................................310 223-2000
Adnan Rawjee, *President*
Mahmud G Rawjee, *Ch of Bd*
Lillian Huang, *CFO*
Vyto Tozer, *Exec VP*
Steve Berg, *Vice Pres*
◆ EMP: 60 EST: 1980
SQ FT: 212,000
SALES (est): 27.9MM **Privately Held**
WEB: www.americandawn.com
SIC: 2299 5023 5131 2393 Linen fabrics; linens & towels; textiles, woven; cushions, except spring & carpet: purchased materials; pillows, bed: made from purchased materials

(P-2987)
AMERICAN FOAM FIBER & SUPS INC
Also Called: Foam Depot
13280 Amar Rd, City of Industry
(91746-1202)
PHONE.....................................626 969-7268
Jack Hung, *President*
Irene Hung, *Vice Pres*
▲ EMP: 75
SALES (est): 13MM **Privately Held**
SIC: 2299 Hair, curled: for upholstery, pillow & quilt filling

(P-2988)
AMRAPUR OVERSEAS INCORPORATED (PA)
Also Called: Colonial Home Textiles
1560 E 6th St Ste 101, Corona
(92879-1712)
PHONE.....................................714 893-8808
Chandru H Wadhwani, *CEO*
Laxmi Wadhwani, *Admin Sec*
Ann Varallo, *Planning*
Danny Nguyen, *Info Tech Mgr*
Jiame A Chan, *Purch Mgr*
▲ EMP: 25
SQ FT: 130,000
SALES (est): 5.4MM **Privately Held**
WEB: www.amrapur.com
SIC: 2299 2269 5023 Linen fabrics; linen fabrics: dyeing, finishing & printing; linens & towels

(P-2989)
ASHFORD TEXTILES LLC
1535 W 139th St, Gardena (90249-2603)
PHONE.....................................310 327-4670
Jack Burns,
Allen Guo,
▲ EMP: 40
SQ FT: 32,000
SALES (est): 5.2MM **Privately Held**
WEB: www.ashfordtextiles.com
SIC: 2299 Hemp yarn, thread, roving & textiles

(P-2990)
B&F FEDELINI INC (PA)
1301 S Main St Ste 226, Los Angeles
(90015-2452)
PHONE.....................................213 628-3901
Farhad Sadian, *President*
EMP: 24
SQ FT: 15,000
SALES: 50MM **Privately Held**
SIC: 2299 Apparel filling: cotton waste, kapok & related material

(P-2991)
B&F FEDELINI INC
305 E 9th St, Los Angeles (90015-1850)
PHONE.....................................213 628-3901
Ben Aronoff, *Branch Mgr*
EMP: 24
SALES (corp-wide): 50MM **Privately Held**
SIC: 2299 Apparel filling: cotton waste, kapok & related material
PA: B&F Fedelini Inc.
    1301 S Main St Ste 226
    Los Angeles CA 90015
    213 628-3901

(P-2992)
BRK GROUP LLC
Also Called: Silve Rest Innov Sleep Produ
8357 Loch Lomond Dr, Pico Rivera
(90660-2507)
PHONE.....................................562 949-4394
Vy Nguyen, *Mng Member*
Tramy Nguyen, *Marketing Mgr*
Carter Bucklin, *Sales Staff*
Jeff Miller, *Mng Member*
▲ EMP: 39 EST: 2004
SALES (est): 7.6MM **Privately Held**
SIC: 2299 Textile mill waste & remnant processing

(P-2993)
CAL FIBER INC
1360 S Beverly Glen Blvd # 401, Los Angeles (90024-5254)
PHONE.....................................323 268-0191
Peter S Kahn III, *President*
EMP: 10
SQ FT: 30,000
SALES (est): 940K **Privately Held**
SIC: 2299 Pillow fillings: curled hair, cotton waste, moss, hemp tow

(P-2994)
CALIFORNIA WEBBING MILLS INC
6920 Stanford Ave, Los Angeles
(90001-1544)
PHONE.....................................323 753-0260
Albert Bakhshizaeeh, *President*
Aram Khayatpour, *Office Mgr*
▲ EMP: 16
SALES (est): 2.3MM **Privately Held**
WEB: www.calwebmills.com
SIC: 2299 Acoustic felts

(P-2995)
DECCOFELT CORPORATION
555 S Vermont Ave, Glendora
(91741-6206)
P.O. Box 156 (91740-0156)
PHONE.....................................626 963-8511
Gerald L Heinrich, *CEO*
Art Jones, *Technology*
Gary Smith, *Engineer*
Ashley Strader, *Purch Dir*
Petrzilek Eric, *Sales Staff*
▲ EMP: 24
SQ FT: 33,000
SALES: 4.7MM **Privately Held**
WEB: www.deccofelt.com
SIC: 2299 Felts & felt products

(P-2996)
EVEREST GROUP USA INC
1885 S Vineyard Ave Ste 3, Ontario
(91761-7760)
PHONE.....................................909 923-1818
Peter Ho, *CEO*
Niko Peng, *President*
▲ EMP: 20
SALES (est): 6.8MM **Privately Held**
WEB: www.everestgroupusa.com
SIC: 2299 Broadwoven fabrics: linen, jute, hemp & ramie

(P-2997)
F R INDUSTRIES INC
Also Called: Villa Firenze
3157 Dona Susana Dr, Studio City
(91604-4357)
PHONE.....................................818 503-9143
Florence Keller, *President*
▲ EMP: 18
SQ FT: 8,900

SALES (est): 2MM **Privately Held**
WEB: www.frindustries.com
SIC: 2299 Upholstery filling, textile

(P-2998)
FASHION CAMP
2477 Park Ave, Tustin (92782-2705)
PHONE.....................................714 259-0946
Erin Blanchi, *Owner*
Perin Patel, *Consultant*
EMP: 20
SALES (est): 262.5K **Privately Held**
SIC: 2299 Textile goods

(P-2999)
GANAR INDUSTRIES INC
13721 Harvard Pl, Gardena (90249-2594)
PHONE.....................................310 515-5683
Gary Balbach, *President*
EMP: 10
SQ FT: 11,000
SALES (est): 1.1MM **Privately Held**
SIC: 2299 Fabrics: linen, jute, hemp, ramie

(P-3000)
INFINITY TEXTILE
11023 Shoemaker Ave, Santa Fe Springs
(90670-4636)
PHONE.....................................562 777-9770
Steve Kim, *Owner*
EMP: 15
SALES (est): 600K **Privately Held**
SIC: 2299 Linen fabrics

(P-3001)
IQ TEXTILE IND INC
3003 S Hill St, Los Angeles (90007-3824)
PHONE.....................................213 745-2290
Zia Abhari, *President*
Fathima Gharibdoost, *Vice Pres*
Behnaz Dibai, *Admin Sec*
▲ EMP: 10
SQ FT: 20,000
SALES: 8MM **Privately Held**
SIC: 2299 Fabrics: linen, jute, hemp, ramie

(P-3002)
J H TEXTILES INC
2301 E 55th St, Vernon (90058-3435)
PHONE.....................................323 585-4124
Jong Soon Hur, *CEO*
▲ EMP: 25
SQ FT: 80,000
SALES: 10.2MM **Privately Held**
SIC: 2299 Textile mill waste & remnant processing

(P-3003)
LASANI-FELT CO
830 E 59th St, Los Angeles (90001-1086)
PHONE.....................................323 233-5278
Melvyn Goodman, *President*
Lynn Goodman, *Corp Secy*
John Cioffi, *Vice Pres*
EMP: 40 EST: 1969
SQ FT: 55,000
SALES (est): 5.5MM **Privately Held**
SIC: 2299 2282 Batts & batting: cotton mill waste & related material; polypropylene filament yarn: twisting, winding, etc.

(P-3004)
LAVINDER INC
Also Called: Thomas Lavin
8687 Melrose Ave Ste B310, West Hollywood (90069-5724)
PHONE.....................................310 278-2456
Thomas Patrick Lavin, *CEO*
EMP: 14
SALES (est): 1.9MM **Privately Held**
SIC: 2299 Linen fabrics

(P-3005)
LAWRENCE O LAWRENCE LTD
Also Called: Lawrence of La Brea
8104 Beverly Blvd, Los Angeles
(90048-4508)
PHONE.....................................323 935-1100
David Nourasshan, *Branch Mgr*
EMP: 10
SALES (corp-wide): 1MM **Privately Held**
SIC: 2299 Scouring & carbonizing of textile fibers

▲ = Import ▼=Export
◆ =Import/Export

PA: Lawrence O Lawrence Ltd
1408 Montana Ave
Santa Monica CA
-

(P-3006)
LAYNE LABORATORIES INC
Also Called: Patina Products
4303 Huasna Rd, Arroyo Grande
(93420-6175)
P.O. Box 1259 (93421-1259)
PHONE..................................805 242-7918
John Waterman, *CEO*
Patricia Moffitt, *President*
Eric Reifinger, *Office Mgr*
▲ EMP: 19
SQ FT: 40,000
SALES: 3MM **Privately Held**
WEB: www.laynelabs.com
SIC: 2299 Batting, wadding, padding & fillings

(P-3007)
LF VISUALS INC
Also Called: Little Folk Visuals
39620 Entrepreneur Ln, Palm Desert
(92211-0400)
P.O. Box 14243 (92255-4243)
PHONE..................................760 345-5571
Michael Firman, *President*
▲ EMP: 15
SQ FT: 7,300
SALES (est): 1.4MM **Privately Held**
WEB: www.littlefolkvisuals.com
SIC: 2299 Felts & felt products

(P-3008)
LINENS EXCHANGE INC
Also Called: Coachella Valley Rag Company
3148 Martin Luther King, Lynwood
(90262-1858)
PHONE..................................310 638-5507
Cenk Mesta, *President*
Estella Navarro, *General Mgr*
EMP: 12 EST: 1991
SQ FT: 80,000
SALES (est): 1.4MM **Privately Held**
SIC: 2299 Carbonized rags

(P-3009)
MFB WORLDWIDE INC (PA)
4901 Patata St 201-204, Cudahy
(90201-5942)
PHONE..................................323 562-2339
Daniel Holmes, *CEO*
Pedro Garcia, *COO*
Robert Harrison, *Chief Mktg Ofcr*
EMP: 15
SQ FT: 20,000
SALES: 2.9MM **Privately Held**
SIC: 2299 Fabrics: linen, jute, hemp, ramie

(P-3010)
NEW HAVEN COMPANIES INC
13571 Vaughn St Unit E, San Fernando
(91340-3006)
PHONE..................................213 749-8181
James P Levine, *CEO*
EMP: 55
SALES (corp-wide): 59.8MM **Privately Held**
SIC: 2299 3537 2298 2273 Batting, wadding, padding & fillings; industrial trucks & tractors; cordage & twine; nets, seines, slings & insulator pads; cargo nets; carpets & rugs
PA: The New Haven Companies Inc
4820 Suthpoint Dr Ste 102
Fredericksburg VA 22407
540 898-2354

(P-3011)
NEXTRADE INC (PA)
Also Called: NEXTEX INTERNATIONAL
12411 Industrial Ave, South Gate
(90280-8221)
PHONE..................................562 944-9950
Jang R Cho, *President*
▲ EMP: 25
SQ FT: 40,000
SALES: 10.2MM **Privately Held**
SIC: 2299 Batting, wadding, padding & fillings

(P-3012)
PACESETTER FABRICS LLC (HQ)
11450 Sheldon St, Sun Valley
(91352-1121)
PHONE..................................213 741-9999
Ramin Namvar,
Sean Namvar,
◆ EMP: 17
SQ FT: 36,000
SALES (est): 2.6MM **Privately Held**
SIC: 2299 Tops & top processing, manmade or other fiber

(P-3013)
PROGRESSIVE PRODUCTS INC
1650 7th St, Riverside (92507-4455)
PHONE..................................951 784-9930
Todd Schmidt, *President*
Jacqueline Schmidt, *Vice Pres*
Todd M Schmidt, *Admin Sec*
▲ EMP: 13
SQ FT: 30,000
SALES (est): 2.4MM **Privately Held**
WEB: www.progressiveproduct.com
SIC: 2299 Fabrics: linen, jute, hemp, ramie; padding & wadding, textile

(P-3014)
QUIVERA MARKETING INC
Also Called: Quivera Hospitality
611 S Palm Canyon Dr, Palm Springs
(92264-7213)
PHONE..................................213 746-8200
D Michael Painter, *CEO*
Ali Rizvi, *Vice Pres*
Matt Yagiz, *Vice Pres*
Donna Levine, *Director*
▲ EMP: 17 EST: 2000
SQ FT: 2,000
SALES: 5.2MM **Privately Held**
SIC: 2299 Towels & towelings, linen & linen-and-cotton mixtures

(P-3015)
RELIANCE UPHOLSTERY SUPPLY INC
Also Called: Reliance Carpet Cushion
4920 S Boyle Ave, Vernon (90058-3017)
PHONE..................................800 522-5252
Ronald J Greitzer, *President*
EMP: 10
SALES (est): 1.3MM **Privately Held**
SIC: 2299 Carpet cushions, felt

(P-3016)
S J STERILIZED WIPING RAGS
201 San Jose Ave, San Jose (95125-1009)
P.O. Box 5486 (95150-5486)
PHONE..................................408 287-2512
Richard Veccio, *Owner*
EMP: 17
SALES (est): 1.3MM **Privately Held**
SIC: 2299 Textile mill waste & remnant processing

(P-3017)
SOLUTIONS SAFETY SERVICES INC
16182 Gothard St Ste J, Huntington Beach
(92647-3642)
PHONE..................................714 843-5653
Harley Haase, *President*
EMP: 70
SALES (est): 4.3MM **Privately Held**
WEB: www.solutionssafety.com
SIC: 2299 Textile mill waste & remnant processing

(P-3018)
SPRINGS INDUSTRIES INC
5770 Peachtree St, Commerce
(90040-4095)
PHONE..................................323 887-3920
Mark Peterson, *Plt & Fclts Mgr*
EMP: 120 **Privately Held**
SIC: 2299 Batts & batting: cotton mill waste & related material; pillow fillings: curled hair, cotton waste, moss, hemp tow; upholstery filling, textile
HQ: Springs Industries, Inc.
7549 Graber Rd
Middleton WI 53562
608 836-1011

(P-3019)
STONE HARBOR INC
5015 District Blvd, Vernon (90058-2719)
PHONE..................................323 277-2777
Marvin Jacob, *President*
Michael Balaban, *Vice Pres*
▲ EMP: 18
SQ FT: 60,000
SALES: 5MM **Privately Held**
SIC: 2299 Textile mill waste & remnant processing

(P-3020)
WELMARK TEXTILE INC
14824 S Main St, Gardena (90248-1919)
PHONE..................................310 516-7289
Min-Yu Hung, *President*
Irene Hung, *Vice Pres*
▲ EMP: 13
SALES (est): 1.1MM **Privately Held**
SIC: 2299 7389 Padding & wadding, textile; textile & apparel services

(P-3021)
WILDFLOWER LINEN INC (PA)
6901 8th St, Buena Park (90620-1024)
PHONE..................................714 522-2777
Young Martin, *President*
▲ EMP: 40
SQ FT: 22,502
SALES (est): 5.5MM **Privately Held**
SIC: 2299 Linen fabrics

(P-3022)
ZOO ZOO WHAM WHAMS BLIP BLOPS
645 W Rosecrans Ave, Compton
(90222-3945)
PHONE..................................213 248-9591
Bernard Miller,
EMP: 10
SALES: 200K **Privately Held**
SIC: 2299 Batting, wadding, padding & fillings

2311 Men's & Boys' Suits, Coats & Overcoats

(P-3023)
2BB UNLIMITED INC
Also Called: Mimo
724 E 1st St Ste 300, Los Angeles
(90012-4349)
PHONE..................................213 253-9810
K Y Lee, *President*
▲ EMP: 20
SQ FT: 6,000
SALES (est): 1.3MM **Privately Held**
SIC: 2311 Men's & boys' suits & coats

(P-3024)
ANGELS YOUNG INC
Also Called: Young Angels Children's Wear
514 S Broadway, Los Angeles
(90013-2302)
PHONE..................................213 614-0742
Blanca Duran, *President*
Sandor Duran, *Vice Pres*
EMP: 20
SQ FT: 3,500
SALES (est): 2.1MM **Privately Held**
SIC: 2311 2335 Tuxedos: made from purchased materials; bridal & formal gowns

(P-3025)
BARCO UNIFORMS INC
350 W Rosecrans Ave, Gardena
(90248-1728)
PHONE..................................310 323-7315
Michael Kenneth Donner, *CEO*
David Donner, *President*
Danny Robertson, *President*
David Ayers, *CFO*
David Aquino, *Exec VP*
◆ EMP: 150 EST: 1929
SQ FT: 74,000
SALES (est): 30.4MM **Privately Held**
WEB: www.barcouniforms.com
SIC: 2311 2326 2337 Men's & boys' uniforms; men's & boys' work clothing; uniforms, except athletic: women's, misses' & juniors'

(P-3026)
BLUE SPHERE INC
Also Called: Lucky-13 Apparel
215 Baker St Ste 100, Costa Mesa
(92626-4547)
PHONE..................................714 953-7555
Robert Kloetzly, *President*
▲ EMP: 45
SQ FT: 18,000
SALES (est): 5.9MM **Privately Held**
SIC: 2311 2331 2369 Men's & boys' suits & coats; women's & misses' blouses & shirts; girls' & children's outerwear

(P-3027)
CROSSPORT MOCEAN
1611 Babcock St, Newport Beach
(92663-2805)
PHONE..................................949 646-1701
Bill Levitt, *President*
Pamela Green, *Treasurer*
Tim Hindman, *Admin Sec*
▲ EMP: 18
SQ FT: 3,000
SALES: 2.5MM **Privately Held**
WEB: www.mocean.net
SIC: 2311 Policemen's uniforms: made from purchased materials

(P-3028)
DESIGNS BY BATYA INC
1200 Santee St Ste 208, Los Angeles
(90015-2553)
PHONE..................................213 746-7844
Victoria Haiavy, *Owner*
EMP: 11
SQ FT: 2,000
SALES (est): 1MM **Privately Held**
SIC: 2311 2331 2321 2337 Men's & boys' suits & coats; women's & misses' blouses & shirts; men's & boys' furnishings; women's & misses' suits & coats; leather & sheep-lined coats & hats

(P-3029)
FIRST TACTICAL LLC
4335 N Star Way, Modesto (95356-8624)
PHONE..................................855 665-3410
Dan J Costa,
Denise L Costa,
EMP: 901 EST: 2015
SALES (est): 43.5MM **Privately Held**
SIC: 2311 Military uniforms, men's & youths': purchased materials

(P-3030)
HUGO BOSS USA INC
395 Santa Monica Pl # 162, Santa Monica
(90401-3478)
PHONE..................................310 260-0109
Patrick Maini, *Branch Mgr*
EMP: 238
SALES (corp-wide): 3.2B **Privately Held**
SIC: 2311 Men's & boys' suits & coats
HQ: Hugo Boss Usa, Inc.
55 Water St Fl 48
New York NY 10041
212 940-0600

(P-3031)
J R U D E S HOLDINGS LLC
9200 W Sunset Blvd Ph 2, West Hollywood
(90069-3607)
PHONE..................................310 281-0800
Jeffrey Rudesk, *Mng Member*
Ruth Inouye, *Executive Asst*
EMP: 19 EST: 2014
SALES: 4MM **Privately Held**
SIC: 2311 Men's & boys' suits & coats

(P-3032)
LANSHON INC
Also Called: IL Canto
12995 Los Nietos Rd, Santa Fe Springs
(90670-3011)
PHONE..................................562 777-1688
Howey Chiang, *President*
▲ EMP: 20 EST: 1973
SQ FT: 2,200
SALES (est): 1.2MM **Privately Held**
WEB: www.ilcanto.com
SIC: 2311 2337 Suits, men's & boys': made from purchased materials; suits: women's, misses' & juniors'

(P-3033)
LITO CHILDRENS WEAR INC
3730 Union Pacific Ave, Los Angeles
(90023-3773)
PHONE..........................323 260-4692
Tom Lee, *Ch of Bd*
▼ EMP: 42 EST: 1974
SQ FT: 13,000
SALES (est): 3.8MM **Privately Held**
WEB: www.litoonline.com
SIC: 2311 2361 2369 Suits, men's &
boys': made from purchased materials;
dresses: girls', children's & infants'; girls'
& children's outerwear

(P-3034)
MARSHA VICKI ORIGINALS INC
Also Called: Vicki Marsha Uniforms
5292 Production Dr, Huntington Beach
(92649-1521)
PHONE..........................714 895-6371
Diane Cologne, *President*
Timothy Cologne, *Vice Pres*
Francesca Becker, *Exec Dir*
EMP: 45
SQ FT: 14,500
SALES (est): 5.8MM **Privately Held**
SIC: 2311 Men's & boys' uniforms

(P-3035)
MEDELITA LLC
23456 S Pointe Dr Ste A, Laguna Hills
(92653-1587)
PHONE..........................949 542-4100
Lara Manchik,
Lauren Reinzuch, *Design Engr*
Dean Valerio, *Accounting Mgr*
Jen Moffroid, *Buyer*
Ryan Sabia, *Opers Staff*
▲ EMP: 10 EST: 2008
SALES (est): 1.5MM **Privately Held**
SIC: 2311 Topcoats, men's & boys': made
from purchased materials

(P-3036)
NEW CHEF FASHION INC
3223 E 46th St, Vernon (90058-2407)
PHONE..........................323 581-0300
G Lucien Salama, *President*
Chantal Salama, *Vice Pres*
◆ EMP: 89
SALES (est): 21MM **Privately Held**
WEB: www.newchef.com
SIC: 2311 2339 2326 5137 Men's &
boys' uniforms; women's & misses' outer-
wear; men's & boys' work clothing; uni-
forms, women's & children's

(P-3037)
NO SECOND THOUGHTS INC
Also Called: Nst
1333 30th St Ste D, San Diego
(92154-3487)
PHONE..........................619 428-5992
Audrey Swirsky, *President*
Onnie Ramos, *General Mgr*
EMP: 52 EST: 1999
SALES (est): 1.2MM **Privately Held**
SIC: 2311 2329 2326 Men's & boys' uni-
forms; men's & boys' sportswear & ath-
letic clothing; medical & hospital uniforms,
men's

(P-3038)
ORIGINAL WATERMEN INC
1198 Joshua Way, Vista (92081-7836)
PHONE..........................760 599-0990
Ken Miller, *CEO*
Jennifer Miller, *President*
▲ EMP: 10
SQ FT: 10,000
SALES (est): 2.5MM **Privately Held**
WEB: www.originalwatermen.com
SIC: 2311 Men's & boys' uniforms

(P-3039)
RDD ENTERPRISES INC
Also Called: Americawear
4638 E Washinton Blvd, Commerce
(90040)
PHONE..........................213 746-0020
Tony Lomeli, *Branch Mgr*
Golan Friedman, *Marketing Staff*
EMP: 13

SALES (corp-wide): 5MM **Privately Held**
SIC: 2311 Military uniforms, men's &
youths': purchased materials
PA: R.D.D. Enterprises, Inc.
4638 E Washington Blvd
Commerce CA
213 742-0666

(P-3040)
ROBERT TALBOTT INC (PA)
Also Called: Talbott Ties
24560 Silver Cloud Ct, Monterey
(93940-6560)
PHONE..........................831 649-6000
Robert J Corliss, *CEO*
Robert Corliss II, *President*
Shelby Corliss, *Vice Pres*
Joann Chinn, *Credit Mgr*
Michael Weber, *Controller*
◆ EMP: 28
SQ FT: 77,000
SALES (est): 33.2MM **Privately Held**
WEB: www.talbottvineyards.com
SIC: 2311 2321 2322 2323 Men's &
boys' suits & coats; men's & boys' furnish-
ings; men's & boys' underwear & night-
wear; men's & boys' neckwear; men's &
boys' trousers & slacks; men's & boys'
work clothing

(P-3041)
ROBINSON TEXTILES INC
24532 Woodward Ave, Lomita
(90717-1110)
PHONE..........................310 527-8110
Gary Lovemark, *President*
◆ EMP: 20
SALES (est): 2.7MM **Privately Held**
WEB: www.robinsontextiles.com
SIC: 2311 Men's & boys' uniforms

(P-3042)
SAMPAV INC
Also Called: Valley Department Store
1394 W 7th St, Upland (91786-7086)
PHONE..........................909 984-8646
Kamal Hassamal, *President*
Pavan Hassamal, *Vice Pres*
▲ EMP: 18
SQ FT: 25,000
SALES (est): 2.7MM **Privately Held**
SIC: 2311 5136 5699 Men's & boys' uni-
forms; uniforms, men's & boys'; uniforms

(P-3043)
SAMS TAILORING
18120 Brookhurst St, Fountain Valley
(92708-6727)
PHONE..........................714 963-6776
EMP: 12
SALES (est): 1.3MM **Privately Held**
SIC: 2311 5949 Coats, tailored, men's &
boys': from purchased materials; sewing
supplies

(P-3044)
**SANTANA FORMAL
ACCESSORIES INC**
707 Arroyo St B, San Fernando
(91340-2248)
P.O. Box 2248, Agoura Hills (91376-2248)
PHONE..........................818 898-3677
Delores Tennant, *President*
Doug Freed, *CFO*
EMP: 107
SQ FT: 18,000
SALES (est): 8.1MM **Privately Held**
WEB: www.santanaapparel.com
SIC: 2311 2339 2323 2389 Vests: made
from purchased materials; women's &
misses' outerwear; bow ties, men's &
boys': made from purchased materials;
cummerbunds

(P-3045)
TRUMAKER INC
Also Called: Trumaker & Co.
228 Grant Ave Fl 2, San Francisco
(94108-4647)
PHONE..........................415 662-3836
Mark Lovas, *CEO*
Michael Zhang, *President*
Wes Goddard, *Vice Pres*
Adam Sidney, *Vice Pres*
Bobby Niers, *Opers Staff*
▲ EMP: 50

SALES (est): 5.2MM **Privately Held**
SIC: 2311 2321 2325 Men's & boys' suits
& coats; men's & boys' furnishings; men's
& boys' trousers & slacks

(P-3046)
TYLER TRAFFICANTE INC (PA)
Also Called: Richard Tyler
700 S Palm Ave, Alhambra (91803-1528)
PHONE..........................323 869-9299
Lisa Trafficante, *President*
Richard Tyler, *Vice Pres*
EMP: 60
SQ FT: 30,000
SALES: 9MM **Privately Held**
SIC: 2311 2335 5611 5621 Tailored suits
& formal jackets; gowns, formal; suits,
men's; dress shops; women's & misses'
outerwear

(P-3047)
UNIVERSAL MERCHANDISE INC
Also Called: Mds
5422 Aura Ave, Tarzana (91356-3004)
P.O. Box 572152 (91357-2152)
PHONE..........................818 344-2044
Itender Singh, *President*
Jasbir Singh, *Vice Pres*
▲ EMP: 16 EST: 1994
SQ FT: 4,000
SALES (est): 1.1MM **Privately Held**
SIC: 2311 5049 2339 5136 Men's &
boys' uniforms; religious supplies; uni-
forms, athletic; women's, misses' & jun-
iors'; uniforms, men's & boys'; uniforms,
women's & children's

(P-3048)
**WARRENS DEPARTMENT
STORE INC**
Also Called: House of Uniforms
9800 De Soto Ave, Chatsworth
(91311-4411)
PHONE..........................888 577-2735
Warren F Ackerman, *Chairman*
Cheryl Clough, *President*
Fred Kemmerling, *Vice Pres*
EMP: 47
SALES (est): 3MM **Privately Held**
SIC: 2311 2337 Men's & boys' uniforms;
uniforms, except athletic: women's,
misses' & juniors'

2321 Men's & Boys' Shirts

(P-3049)
101 APPAREL INC (PA)
1017 S Hathaway St, Santa Ana
(92705-4127)
PHONE..........................714 454-8988
Eric Crandell, *Owner*
EMP: 13
SALES (est): 2.1MM **Privately Held**
SIC: 2321 2353 Sport shirts, men's &
boys': from purchased materials; hats &
caps

(P-3050)
ALLIED DVBE INC
Also Called: Allied Dvbe Supply
260 Bonita Glen Dr Apt V3, Chula Vista
(91910-3178)
P.O. Box 182091, Coronado (92178-2091)
PHONE..........................619 690-4900
Steve Deorlow, *President*
EMP: 15
SALES (est): 440.1K **Privately Held**
SIC: 2321 Polo shirts, men's & boys':
made from purchased materials

(P-3051)
BENIGNA
4630 Floral Dr, Los Angeles (90022-1244)
PHONE..........................323 262-2484
Al Rangel, *Owner*
EMP: 10 EST: 1971
SQ FT: 10,000
SALES (est): 390K **Privately Held**
SIC: 2321 Men's & boys' dress shirts

(P-3052)
BPS TACTICAL INC
2165 E Colton Ave, Mentone (92359-9657)
P.O. Box 868 (92359-0868)
PHONE..........................909 794-2435
William F Blankenship Jr, *President*
EMP: 13
SQ FT: 1,800
SALES (est): 424.1K **Privately Held**
WEB: www.policemag.com
SIC: 2321 5699 Uniform shirts: made from
purchased materials; uniforms

(P-3053)
CREATIVE DESIGN INDUSTRIES
2587 Otay Center Dr, San Diego
(92154-7612)
PHONE..........................619 710-2525
Sylvia Habchi, *Partner*
Elie Habchi, *Partner*
▲ EMP: 125
SQ FT: 15,000
SALES (est): 9.4MM **Privately Held**
SIC: 2321 5137 Men's & boys' furnishings;
sportswear, women's & children's

(P-3054)
EI-LO INC
2102 Alton Pkwy Ste B, Irvine
(92606-4947)
PHONE..........................949 200-6626
Edward Chavez, *CEO*
EMP: 14
SALES (est): 1.5MM **Privately Held**
SIC: 2321 Sport shirts, men's & boys': from
purchased materials

(P-3055)
**FRESH JIVE MANUFACTURING
INC**
Also Called: Gonz's
1317 S Olive St, Los Angeles
(90015-3018)
P.O. Box 7847, Northridge (91327-7847)
PHONE..........................213 748-0129
Richard Klotz, *President*
▲ EMP: 20
SQ FT: 10,000
SALES (est): 2.3MM **Privately Held**
WEB: www.freshjive.net
SIC: 2321 2311 2325 Men's & boys' fur-
nishings; coats, overcoats & vests; shorts
(outerwear): men's, youths' & boys'

(P-3056)
GINO CORPORATION
Also Called: Shaka Wear
555 E Jefferson Blvd, Los Angeles
(90011-2430)
PHONE..........................323 234-7979
Sung Uk Park, *CEO*
▲ EMP: 18
SALES (est): 2.9MM **Privately Held**
SIC: 2321 5136 Men's & boys' dress
shirts; shirts, men's & boys'

(P-3057)
JL DESIGN ENTERPRISES INC
Also Called: Jl Racing.com
1821 Newport Cir, Santa Ana (92705-5113)
PHONE..........................714 479-0240
Jolene Sparza, *President*
Kenneth Mills, *Vice Pres*
▲ EMP: 63
SALES (est): 6MM **Privately Held**
WEB: www.jlracing.com
SIC: 2321 Sport shirts, men's & boys': from
purchased materials

(P-3058)
JUST FOR FUN
Also Called: Jff Uniforms
557 Van Ness Ave, Torrance (90501-1424)
PHONE..........................310 320-1327
Corinne Stolz, *President*
Gary Stolz, *Vice Pres*
▲ EMP: 24 EST: 1975
SQ FT: 11,000
SALES (est): 2.6MM **Privately Held**
WEB: www.jffuniforms.com
SIC: 2321 2337 2339 2326 Uniform
shirts: made from purchased materials;
uniforms, except athletic: women's,
misses' & juniors'; women's & misses'
outerwear; men's & boys' work clothing

▲ = Import ▼=Export
◆ =Import/Export

(P-3059)
SEAMAID MANUFACTURING CORP
960 Mission St, San Francisco (94103-2911)
PHONE..............................415 777-9978
Freda Lau, *President*
Jian Xiu Zhen, *Vice Pres*
▲ EMP: 50
SQ FT: 11,000
SALES: 2.5MM **Privately Held**
SIC: 2321 2325 2331 2335 Men's & boys' furnishings; men's & boys' trousers & slacks; women's & misses' blouses & shirts; women's, juniors' & misses' dresses; women's & misses' suits & coats; women's & misses' outerwear

(P-3060)
STARLION INC
Also Called: Star Lion
706 E 32nd St, Los Angeles (90011-2406)
PHONE..............................323 233-8823
Mike Lim, *President*
Moon Lim, *Principal*
EMP: 22
SQ FT: 11,000
SALES (est): 750K **Privately Held**
WEB: www.starlion.com
SIC: 2321 2331 Men's & boys' dress shirts; women's & misses' blouses & shirts

(P-3061)
TEXTILE UNLIMITED CORPORATION (PA)
20917 Higgins Ct, Torrance (90501-1723)
PHONE..............................310 263-7400
James Y Kim, *CEO*
Stanley Kim, *President*
Sam Lee, *President*
James Chung, *Vice Pres*
Yumi Park, *Admin Sec*
▲ EMP: 36
SQ FT: 135,000
SALES (est): 56.9MM **Privately Held**
WEB: www.tuc.net
SIC: 2321 2339 2329 2331 Men's & boys' furnishings; women's & misses' athletic clothing & sportswear; men's & boys' athletic uniforms; women's & misses' blouses & shirts

(P-3062)
TOP HEAVY CLOTHING COMPANY INC (PA)
28381 Vincent Moraga Dr, Temecula (92590-3653)
PHONE..............................951 442-8839
Tadd D Chilcott, *President*
Douglas Lo, *Vice Pres*
▲ EMP: 65
SQ FT: 40,000
SALES (est): 11.8MM **Privately Held**
WEB: www.topheavyclothing.com
SIC: 2321 Men's & boys' dress shirts; men's & boys' sports & polo shirts

(P-3063)
UNITED UNIFORM MFRS INC
1096 W Rialto Ave, San Bernardino (92410-2376)
P.O. Box 7298 (92411-0298)
PHONE..............................909 381-2682
Kambiz Zinati, *CEO*
James Russell, *President*
Winnie Chen, *CFO*
Kami Zaniti, *CFO*
▲ EMP: 14
SQ FT: 45,000
SALES (est): 1.7MM **Privately Held**
WEB: www.uumfg.com
SIC: 2321 Uniform shirts: made from purchased materials
PA: Amwear International Group, Inc
   250 Benjamin Dr Ste B
   Corona CA 92879

(P-3064)
VAN HEUSEN FACTORY OUTLET
17600 Collier Ave D134, Lake Elsinore (92530-2633)
PHONE..............................951 674-1190
Tina Hoel, *Manager*

EMP: 10
SALES (est): 554.6K **Privately Held**
SIC: 2321 Men's & boys' dress shirts

2322 Men's & Boys' Underwear & Nightwear

(P-3065)
MAKERS USA INC
Also Called: Mu Gallery Makers
5000 District Blvd, Vernon (90058-2720)
PHONE..............................323 582-1800
Sangwoo Samuel Kim, *President*
EMP: 16
SQ FT: 130,000
SALES (est): 1.4MM **Privately Held**
WEB: www.makersusa.com
SIC: 2322 2389 Men's & boys' underwear & nightwear; men's miscellaneous accessories

(P-3066)
STATESIDE MERCHANTS LLC
Also Called: Pair of Thieves
5813 Washington Blvd, Culver City (90232-7330)
PHONE..............................424 251-5190
David Ehrenberg,
Alan Stuart,
Cash Warren,
EMP: 20
SQ FT: 3,000
SALES: 10MM **Privately Held**
SIC: 2322 2341 Men's & boys' underwear & nightwear; women's & children's undergarments

2323 Men's & Boys' Neckwear

(P-3067)
PVH NECKWEAR INC (HQ)
1735 S Santa Fe Ave, Los Angeles (90021-2904)
PHONE..............................213 688-7970
Marc Schneider, *CEO*
Lynn Sarver, *Merchandising*
▲ EMP: 520 EST: 1873
SQ FT: 210,000
SALES (est): 132.3MM
SALES (corp-wide): 8.9B **Publicly Held**
WEB: www.superba.com
SIC: 2323 Men's & boys' neckwear
PA: Pvh Corp.
   200 Madison Ave Bsmt 1
   New York NY 10016
   212 381-3500

2325 Men's & Boys' Separate Trousers & Casual Slacks

(P-3068)
CORDOVAN & GREY LTD
4826 Gregg Rd, Pico Rivera (90660-2107)
PHONE..............................562 699-8300
Fax: 213 699-9910
EMP: 22
SALES (est): 1.3MM **Privately Held**
SIC: 2325

(P-3069)
DRY AGED DENIM LLC (PA)
Also Called: James Jeans
1545 Rio Vista Ave, Los Angeles (90023-2619)
P.O. Box 76019 (90076-0019)
PHONE..............................323 780-6206
Seun Lim,
Michael Chung,
▲ EMP: 10
SALES (est): 3.7MM **Privately Held**
SIC: 2325 2369 5651 Jeans: men's, youths' & boys'; leggings: girls', children's & infants'; jeans stores

---

(P-3070)
GUESS INC (PA)
1444 S Alameda St, Los Angeles (90021-2433)
PHONE..............................213 765-3100
Victor Herrero, *CEO*
Paul Marciano, *Ch of Bd*
Sandeep Reddy, *CFO*
Felix Wong, *Project Mgr*
Jason Chen, *Technology*
EMP: 700
SQ FT: 341,700
SALES: 2.3B **Publicly Held**
WEB: www.guess.com
SIC: 2325 2339 5611 5621 Men's & boys' jeans & dungarees; women's & misses' outerwear; clothing, sportswear, men's & boys'; women's sportswear; children's & infants' wear stores

(P-3071)
GUESS INC
358 Plaza Dr, West Covina (91790-2848)
PHONE..............................626 856-5555
EMP: 25
SALES (corp-wide): 2.3B **Publicly Held**
SIC: 2325 Men's & boys' jeans & dungarees
PA: Guess , Inc.
   1444 S Alameda St
   Los Angeles CA 90021
   213 765-3100

(P-3072)
GUESS INC
Also Called: G By Guess
820 State St, Santa Barbara (93101-3256)
PHONE..............................805 963-9490
EMP: 10
SALES (corp-wide): 2.2B **Publicly Held**
SIC: 2325
PA: Guess , Inc.
   1444 S Alameda St
   Los Angeles CA 90021
   213 765-3100

(P-3073)
GUESS INC
1 Mills Cir Ste 313, Ontario (91764-5209)
PHONE..............................909 987-7776
Yesenia Rodriguez, *Manager*
EMP: 25
SALES (corp-wide): 2.3B **Publicly Held**
WEB: www.guess.com
SIC: 2325 Men's & boys' jeans & dungarees
PA: Guess , Inc.
   1444 S Alameda St
   Los Angeles CA 90021
   213 765-3100

(P-3074)
INDU FASHIONS
220 W 25th St Ste B, National City (91950-6680)
PHONE..............................619 336-4638
Shashi Pal, *Owner*
EMP: 30
SQ FT: 7,000
SALES: 1.2MM **Privately Held**
WEB: www.indufashions.com
SIC: 2325 Shorts (outerwear): men's, youths'

(P-3075)
J & C APPAREL
757 Towne Ave Unit B, Los Angeles (90021-1419)
PHONE..............................323 490-8260
Cipriano Serrano, *President*
EMP: 40
SALES (est): 906.5K **Privately Held**
SIC: 2325 Men's & boys' trousers & slacks

(P-3076)
JAMES WEST INC (PA)
13344 S Main St Ste B, Los Angeles (90061-1638)
PHONE..............................310 380-1510
James Ahn, *President*
Bobby Ahn, *Vice Pres*
Youn OK Ahn, *Vice Pres*
EMP: 10
SQ FT: 2,500

SALES: 295.9K **Privately Held**
SIC: 2325 2339 7389 Men's & boys' trousers & slacks; slacks: women's, misses' & juniors'; sewing contractor

(P-3077)
JB BRITCHES INC
2279 Ward Ave, Simi Valley (93065-1863)
PHONE..............................818 898-4046
Asdghik Bedrosian, *President*
Ohannes Bedrosian, *Vice Pres*
EMP: 100 EST: 1978
SQ FT: 20,000
SALES (est): 18.5MM **Privately Held**
WEB: www.jbbritches.com
SIC: 2325 Men's & boys' trousers & slacks

(P-3078)
LEVI STRAUSS & CO (PA)
1155 Battery St, San Francisco (94111-1264)
PHONE..............................415 501-6000
Charles V Bergh, *President*
Stephen C Neal, *Ch of Bd*
Carrie Ask, *President*
Roy Bagattini, *President*
James Curleigh, *President*
◆ EMP: 1600
SALES: 4.9B **Privately Held**
WEB: www.levistrauss.com
SIC: 2325 2339 2321 2331 Jeans: men's, youths' & boys'; slacks, dress: men's, youths' & boys'; jeans: women's, misses' & juniors'; slacks: women's, misses' & juniors'; athletic clothing: women's, misses' & juniors'; men's & boys' furnishings; shirts, women's & juniors': made from purchased materials; T-shirts & tops, women's: made from purchased materials; skirts, separate: women's, misses' & juniors'; jackets (suede, leatherette, etc.), sport: men's & boys'; athletic (warmup, sweat & jogging) suits: men's & boys'

(P-3079)
LEVI STRAUSS & CO
1155 Battery St, San Francisco (94111-1264)
PHONE..............................415 677-9927
Kofi Johnson, *Bd of Directors*
Ray Bolin, *Manager*
EMP: 19
SALES (corp-wide): 4.9B **Privately Held**
SIC: 2325 Jeans: men's, youths' & boys'
PA: Levi Strauss & Co.
   1155 Battery St
   San Francisco CA 94111
   415 501-6000

(P-3080)
LEVI STRAUSS & CO
316 N Beverly Dr, Beverly Hills (90210-4701)
PHONE..............................310 246-9044
EMP: 13
SALES (corp-wide): 4.4B **Privately Held**
SIC: 2325
PA: Levi Strauss & Co.
   1155 Battery St
   San Francisco CA 94111
   415 501-6000

(P-3081)
LEVI STRAUSS & CO
17600 Collier Ave, Lake Elsinore (92530-2633)
PHONE..............................951 674-2694
Leslie Gollihar, *Manager*
EMP: 19
SALES (corp-wide): 4.9B **Privately Held**
SIC: 2325 Jeans: men's, youths' & boys'
PA: Levi Strauss & Co.
   1155 Battery St
   San Francisco CA 94111
   415 501-6000

(P-3082)
LUCKY BRAND DUNGAREES LLC
1427 3rd S, Santa Monica (90401-2326)
PHONE..............................310 587-3515
Ralph Rivera, *Asst Mgr*
EMP: 38

SALES (corp-wide): 3.7B **Privately Held**
SIC: **2325** Dungarees: men's, youths' &
boys'
HQ: Lucky Brand Dungarees, Llc
540 S Santa Fe Ave
Los Angeles CA 90013
213 443-5700

(P-3083)
LUCKY BRAND DUNGAREES LLC (HQ)
540 S Santa Fe Ave, Los Angeles
(90013-2233)
PHONE...................213 443-5700
Carlos Alberini,
Stephanie Cotsifas, *Store Mgr*
Bre"ann Davert, *Store Mgr*
Stacy Paluskiewicz, *Store Mgr*
Julie Ryberg, *Store Mgr*
◆ **EMP:** 67
SQ FT: 21,000
SALES (est): 410.8MM
SALES (corp-wide): 3.5B **Privately Held**
SIC: **2325** 2339 Dungarees: men's,
youths' & boys'; jeans: men's, youths' &
boys'; jeans: women's, misses' & juniors'
PA: Leonard Green & Partners, L.P.
11111 Santa Monica Blvd # 2000
Los Angeles CA 90025
310 954-0444

(P-3084)
NEW RISE BRAND HOLDINGS LLC
801 S Figueroa St # 1000, Los Angeles
(90017-5508)
PHONE...................323 233-9005
John Inn, *President*
Ryan Crenshaw, *Vice Pres*
Kevin Kok Leong Yap,
▲ **EMP:** 20
SALES (est): 4.3MM **Privately Held**
SIC: **2325** Men's & boys' trousers & slacks

(P-3085)
RED ENGINE INC
Also Called: Red Engine Jeans
1850 E 15th St, Los Angeles (90021-2820)
PHONE...................213 742-8858
James Boldes, *President*
Kristy Harlan, *Director*
▲ **EMP:** 11
SQ FT: 10,000
SALES (est): 1.3MM **Privately Held**
WEB: www.redenginejeans.com
SIC: **2325** Jeans: men's, youths' & boys'

(P-3086)
ROB INC (PA)
Also Called: Robin's Jeans
6760 Foster Bridge Blvd, Bell Gardens
(90201-2030)
PHONE...................562 806-5589
Robert Chretien, *CEO*
Gilberto Jimenez, *Vice Pres*
Morsan McSweeney, *Controller*
Will Parseghian, *Sales Executive*
Gilles Bendenoun, *Mktg Dir*
▲ **EMP:** 70
SQ FT: 26,000
SALES (est): 14MM **Privately Held**
WEB: www.rob.com
SIC: **2325** 2339 2369 Jeans: men's,
youths' & boys'; men's & boys' dress
slacks & shorts; trousers, dress (separate): men's, youths' & boys'; women's &
misses' culottes, knickers & shorts; knickers: women's, misses' & juniors'; jeans:
women's, misses' & juniors'; shorts (outerwear): girls' & children's; jackets: girls',
children's & infants'; jeans: girls', children's & infants'

(P-3087)
SEMORE INC
Also Called: Nubile
1437 Santee St Ste 201, Los Angeles
(90015-2590)
PHONE...................213 746-4122
Fax: 213 746-2426
▲ **EMP:** 18
SQ FT: 10,000
SALES (est): 1.6MM **Privately Held**
WEB: www.solosemore.com
SIC: **2325** 2321 2331

(P-3088)
SEVEN FOR ALL MANKIND LLC-(DH)
Also Called: 7 For All Mankind
777 S Alameda St, Los Angeles
(90021-1656)
PHONE...................323 406-5300
Paula Schneider, *CEO*
Brittani Beasley, *Store Mgr*
Chad Dodson, *Store Mgr*
James Dyson, *Store Mgr*
Rita Sanchez, *Store Mgr*
▲ **EMP:** 350
SQ FT: 141,774
SALES (est): 105.3MM
SALES (corp-wide): 1.3B **Privately Held**
WEB: www.vfc.com
SIC: **2325** Men's & boys' jeans & dungarees
HQ: Delta Galil Usa Inc.
1 Harmon Plz Fl 5
Secaucus NJ 07094
201 902-0055

(P-3089)
THREE GUYS HOLDING CO LLC
430 Pacific Ave, San Francisco
(94133-4607)
PHONE...................855 711-7686
Kyle G Hency, *Mng Member*
EMP: 17 EST: 2011
SALES (est): 2.1MM **Privately Held**
SIC: **2325** Shorts (outerwear): men's,
youths' & boys'

(P-3090)
VF CONTEMPORARY BRANDS INC
777 S Alameda St Bldg 1, Los Angeles
(90021-1633)
PHONE...................213 747-7002
EMP: 11
SALES (est): 1.3MM
SALES (corp-wide): 12.3B **Publicly Held**
SIC: **2325** 2321
PA: V.F. Corporation
105 Corporate Center Blvd
Greensboro NC 27408
336 424-6000

2326 Men's & Boys' Work Clothing

(P-3091)
ADWEAR INC (PA)
Also Called: Tutti
850 S Broadway Ste 400, Los Angeles
(90014-3235)
PHONE...................213 629-2535
Dairi Hariri, *President*
Louesette Cohen, *Treasurer*
EMP: 15 EST: 1993
SQ FT: 20,000
SALES (est): 5MM **Privately Held**
WEB: www.baseballjacket.com
SIC: **2326** Work pants

(P-3092)
ALPINESTARS USA
2780 W 237th St, Torrance (90505-5270)
PHONE...................310 891-0222
Giovanni Mazzarolo, *CEO*
George Trelut, *Sales Mgr*
Katrina Lavender, *Manager*
◆ **EMP:** 10
SQ FT: 28,380
SALES (est): 2.5MM
SALES (corp-wide): 1.3MM **Privately Held**
WEB: www.alpinestars.com
SIC: **2326** 2331 Men's & boys' work clothing; women's & misses' blouses & shirts
HQ: Alpinestars Spa
Viale Enrico Fermi 5
Asolo TV 31011
042 352-86

(P-3093)
ALVARADO DYE & KNITTING MILL
30542 Union City Blvd, Union City
(94587-1598)
PHONE...................510 324-8892

Raymond Chan, *President*
▲ **EMP:** 50
SALES (est): 3.5MM **Privately Held**
WEB: www.alvaradomills.com
SIC: **2326** Men's & boys' work clothing

(P-3094)
AMERICAN GIANT INC
161 Natoma St Fl 2, San Francisco
(94105-3746)
PHONE...................415 529-2429
Bayard Winthrop, *President*
Pete Dinh, *CFO*
Don Pillsbury, *Vice Pres*
Brian Droz, *Office Mgr*
Tate Huffard, *Opers Mgr*
EMP: 10
SALES (est): 1.3MM **Privately Held**
SIC: **2326** Work uniforms

(P-3095)
BEN F DAVIS COMPANY (PA)
Also Called: Ben Davis
3140 Kerner Blvd, San Rafael
(94901-5441)
PHONE...................415 382-1000
Frank L Davis, *President*
Mike Davis, *Manager*
▲ **EMP:** 10
SALES (est): 19.1MM **Privately Held**
WEB: www.bendavis.com
SIC: **2326** Work pants; overalls & coveralls; jackets, overall & work

(P-3096)
BUNKERHILL INDUS GROUP INC
Also Called: Big Front Uniforms
4535 Huntington Dr S, Los Angeles
(90032-1940)
PHONE...................323 227-4222
EMP: 15
SALES: 950K **Privately Held**
SIC: **2326**

(P-3097)
BUY INSTA SLIM INC
Also Called: Instantfigure
17662 Armstrong Ave, Irvine (92614-5728)
PHONE...................949 263-2301
Eeman Jalili, *CEO*
Monir Jalili, *President*
Ehsan Jalili, *Vice Pres*
Houshang Jalili, *Vice Pres*
Sonia Silva, *Manager*
▲ **EMP:** 14
SALES: 5MM **Privately Held**
SIC: **2326** 5961 7389 Men's & boys' work
clothing; women's apparel, mail order;

(P-3098)
CINTAS CORPORATION
1679 Entp Blvd Ste 10, West Sacramento
(95691)
PHONE...................916 375-8633
Ken Eslick, *Branch Mgr*
EMP: 15
SALES (corp-wide): 6.4B **Publicly Held**
WEB: www.cintas-corp.com
SIC: **2326** Work uniforms
PA: Cintas Corporation
6800 Cintas Blvd
Cincinnati OH 45262
513 459-1200

(P-3099)
COH-FB LLC
Also Called: Fabric Brand
5715 Bickett St, Huntington Park
(90255-2624)
PHONE...................323 923-1240
Christine Soh, *Director*
Amy William, *President*
Simon Miller,
EMP: 50 EST: 2015
SQ FT: 500
SALES (est): 1.7MM **Privately Held**
SIC: **2326** Work garments, except raincoats: waterproof

(P-3100)
COOL JAMS INC
11206 Spencerport Way, San Diego
(92131-2912)
PHONE...................858 566-6165
Anita Mahaffey, *President*
▲ **EMP:** 15

SALES (est): 935.8K **Privately Held**
SIC: **2326** 5651 5136 Men's & boys' work
clothing; family clothing stores; men's &
boys' clothing

(P-3101)
DAVID GARMENT CUTNG FUSING SVC
5008 S Boyle Ave, Vernon (90058-3904)
PHONE...................323 583-9885
David Alvarado, *President*
Mario Alvarado, *Vice Pres*
▲ **EMP:** 15
SQ FT: 15,000
SALES (est): 1.4MM **Privately Held**
WEB: www.davidsclothier.com
SIC: **2326** 2339 Men's & boys' work clothing; women's & misses' athletic clothing &
sportswear

(P-3102)
DEIST ENGINEERING INC
Also Called: Deist Safety Equipment
2623 N San Fernando Rd, Los Angeles
(90065-1316)
PHONE...................818 240-7866
Jim F Deist, *President*
Kirk Miller, *CFO*
Marian Deist, *Vice Pres*
Sean Sousa, *Admin Sec*
Joe Hasen, *Purch Mgr*
▲ **EMP:** 32
SQ FT: 15,000
SALES (est): 2.5MM **Privately Held**
WEB: www.deist.com
SIC: **2326** 3545 Overalls & coveralls; machine tool accessories

(P-3103)
GOLD BELT LINE INC
1547 Jayken Way Ste C, Chula Vista
(91911-4677)
PHONE...................619 424-5544
Jonnie Simon, *CEO*
Alan Simon, *President*
Simon Al, *Manager*
EMP: 10
SQ FT: 6,000
SALES (est): 670K **Privately Held**
WEB: www.goldbeltline.com
SIC: **2326** Industrial garments, men's &
boys'

(P-3104)
HAUS OF GREY LLC
Also Called: Matte Grey
10641 Calle Lee Ste 161, Los Alamitos
(90720-8503)
PHONE...................562 270-4739
Travis Johnson, *President*
Kimberly Miller, *Vice Pres*
Jeff Berokoff, *Sales Staff*
Steve Hurtig, *Sales Staff*
Kelli Marie Riley,
EMP: 10
SALES (est): 1.5MM **Privately Held**
SIC: **2326** 2335 5136 Men's & boys' work
clothing; women's, juniors' & misses'
dresses; men's & boys' clothing

(P-3105)
IMAGE APPAREL FOR BUSINESS INC
1618 E Edinger Ave, Santa Ana
(92705-5019)
PHONE...................714 541-5247
Keith Knerr, *CEO*
Robert Duffield, *Controller*
Mike Gilber, *Manager*
EMP: 25
SALES (est): 1.3MM **Privately Held**
SIC: **2326** 2339 2353 7213 Men's &
boys' work clothing; uniforms, athletic:
women's, misses' & juniors'; uniform hats
& caps; linen supply

(P-3106)
IMAGE SOLUTIONS APPAREL INC
19571 Magellan Dr, Torrance (90502-1136)
PHONE...................310 464-8991
Chris Kelley, *President*
Tom Fitzpatrick, *General Mgr*
Danielle Sorge, *Executive Asst*
Alana Owens, *Opers Staff*

▲ = Import ▼=Export
◆ =Import/Export

Ramon Pradera, *Director*
▲ EMP: 35
SQ FT: 4,500
SALES (est): 10MM **Privately Held**
WEB: www.eimagesolutions.com
SIC: 2326 Work uniforms

(P-3107)
INDIE SOURCE INC
1933 S Broadway Ste 1168, Los Angeles
(90007-4501)
PHONE.....................................424 200-2027
Jesse Dombrowiak, *Officer*
EMP: 20
SALES: 750K **Privately Held**
SIC: 2326 7336 Men's & boys' work clothing; graphic arts & related design

(P-3108)
KIM & ROY CO INC
Also Called: Cnc Clothing
2924 E Ana St, Compton (90221-5603)
PHONE.....................................310 762-1896
Hahn J Kim, *President*
▲ EMP: 10
SALES: 9.5MM **Privately Held**
SIC: 2326 Industrial garments, men's & boys'

(P-3109)
KNK APPAREL INC
223 W Rosecrans Ave, Gardena
(90248-1831)
PHONE.....................................310 768-3333
John Kang, *President*
EMP: 250
SQ FT: 90,000
SALES (est): 14.4MM **Privately Held**
WEB: www.knktreasures.com
SIC: 2326 2339 Men's & boys' work clothing; women's & misses' outerwear

(P-3110)
LA TRIUMPH INC
Also Called: Medgear
13336 Alondra Blvd, Cerritos (90703-2205)
PHONE.....................................562 404-7657
Hasina Lakhani, *CEO*
Amin Lakhani, *President*
▲ EMP: 24
SQ FT: 40,000
SALES (est): 2.8MM **Privately Held**
WEB: www.medgear.com
SIC: 2326 Medical & hospital uniforms, men's; work uniforms

(P-3111)
MATSUN AMERICA CORP
4070 Greystone Dr Ste B, Ontario
(91761-3103)
PHONE.....................................909 930-0779
Yo R Song, *President*
Bob Wang, *General Mgr*
EMP: 14 EST: 2011
SQ FT: 40,000
SALES (est): 728.9K **Privately Held**
SIC: 2326 5136 Men's & boys' work clothing; men's & boys' clothing

(P-3112)
MENS WEARHOUSE
6100 Stevenson Blvd, Fremont
(94538-2490)
PHONE.....................................510 657-9821
EMP: 48
SALES (est): 9MM **Privately Held**
SIC: 2326

(P-3113)
MEXAPPAREL INC (PA)
2344 E 38th St, Vernon (90058-1627)
PHONE.....................................323 364-8600
Maria Maniatis, *President*
Fred Kalmar, *CFO*
Hubert Guez, *Vice Pres*
Nomaan Yousef, *Controller*
Becky Ruiz, *Director*
EMP: 14
SQ FT: 277,000
SALES (est): 2.3MM **Privately Held**
SIC: 2326 Service apparel (baker, barber, lab, etc.), washable: men's

(P-3114)
MINACHEE INC
1248 S Flower St, Los Angeles
(90015-2117)
PHONE.....................................213 745-8100
EMP: 15
SALES (corp-wide): 2.5MM **Privately Held**
SIC: 2326 Men's & boys' work clothing
PA: Minachee, Inc.
    832 S Los Angeles St A
    Los Angeles CA 90014
    310 989-3535

(P-3115)
NICEWELL INC
2411 Loma Ave, South El Monte
(91733-1415)
PHONE.....................................626 455-0099
Min-Fu Wang, *President*
▲ EMP: 16
SQ FT: 10,000
SALES (est): 1.1MM **Privately Held**
WEB: www.nicewell.com
SIC: 2326 Men's & boys' work clothing

(P-3116)
PAIGE LLC (PA)
Also Called: Paige Premium Denim
10119 Jefferson Blvd, Culver City
(90232-3519)
PHONE.....................................310 733-2100
Michael Geller, *President*
Walt Lacher, *CFO*
Alan Shamma, *Info Tech Dir*
Randy Peinado, *Credit Staff*
Jaime Godinez, *Buyer*
▲ EMP: 90
SQ FT: 40,000
SALES (est): 31MM **Privately Held**
SIC: 2326 5621 2329 Men's & boys' work clothing; women's clothing stores; shirt & slack suits: men's, youths' & boys'

(P-3117)
PROVIDENCE INDUSTRIES LLC
Also Called: Mydyer.com
3833 Mcgowen St, Long Beach
(90808-1702)
PHONE.....................................562 420-9091
Daniel S Kang, *President*
Dan Kang, *President*
James Lee, *CFO*
Jennifer Gim, *Vice Pres*
Sue Eklof, *Executive*
◆ EMP: 60
SQ FT: 10,000
SALES (est): 27.3MM **Privately Held**
WEB: www.mydyer.com
SIC: 2326 2331 Men's & boys' work clothing; blouses, women's & juniors': made from purchased material

(P-3118)
PURE COTTON INCORPORATED
2221 S Main St Fl 2, Los Angeles
(90007-1427)
PHONE.....................................213 507-3270
Kyung H Choi, *CEO*
EMP: 100 EST: 2006
SALES (est): 3.9MM **Privately Held**
SIC: 2326 Industrial garments, men's & boys'

(P-3119)
ROF LLC
Also Called: Ring of Fire
7800 Arprt Bus Pkwy Ste B, Van Nuys
(91406)
PHONE.....................................818 933-4000
Isaac Bitton,
Eran Bitton,
EMP: 45
SQ FT: 60,000
SALES (est): 24.3MM **Privately Held**
SIC: 2326 Men's & boys' work clothing

(P-3120)
SECURA INC
Also Called: Suttini
6965 El Camino Re Ste 105, Oceanside
(92054)
PHONE.....................................760 804-7313
EMP: 70
SQ FT: 4,000

SALES (est): 4.9MM **Privately Held**
SIC: 2326

(P-3121)
SEW FORTH INC
2350 Central Ave, Duarte (91010-2919)
PHONE.....................................323 725-3500
Samuel Androus, *CEO*
◆ EMP: 25
SQ FT: 26,000
SALES (est): 4.4MM **Privately Held**
WEB: www.sewforth.com
SIC: 2326 Men's & boys' work clothing

(P-3122)
SKIRT INC
Also Called: Sofi Clothing
2600 E 8th St, Los Angeles (90023-2104)
PHONE.....................................213 553-1134
Susan Miller, *President*
Kari Spitz, *Vice Pres*
EMP: 12 EST: 2001
SQ FT: 3,000
SALES: 1.5MM **Privately Held**
SIC: 2326 Men's & boys' work clothing

(P-3123)
STRATEGIC DISTRIBUTION L P
9800 De Soto Ave, Chatsworth
(91311-4411)
PHONE.....................................818 671-2100
Michael Singer, *CEO*
Dan Hosch, *Accounts Exec*
◆ EMP: 240 EST: 2003
SALES (est): 44.2MM **Privately Held**
SIC: 2326 2337 3143 3144 Work uniforms; medical & hospital uniforms, men's; uniforms, except athletic: women's, misses' & juniors'; men's footwear, except athletic; women's footwear, except athletic; uniforms & work clothing; shoes
PA: Strategic Partners, Inc.
    9800 De Soto Ave
    Chatsworth CA 91311

(P-3124)
TECHNICHE SOLUTIONS
Also Called: Techniche International
2575 Pioneer Ave Ste 101, Vista
(92081-8450)
PHONE.....................................619 818-0071
Doug Frost, *CEO*
Scott Kimball, *Opers Mgr*
Lauren Hennessey, *Accounts Mgr*
◆ EMP: 25
SALES (est): 2.5MM **Privately Held**
SIC: 2326 Men's & boys' work clothing

(P-3125)
US GARMENT LLC
4440 E 26th St, Vernon (90058-4318)
P.O. Box 23368, Los Angeles (90023-0368)
PHONE.....................................323 415-6464
Jae Ki Chung, *Mng Member*
Wesley J Chung,
▲ EMP: 35
SALES (est): 3.8MM **Privately Held**
SIC: 2326 Men's & boys' work clothing

(P-3126)
WAY OUT WEST INC
1440 W 135th St, Gardena (90249-2218)
PHONE.....................................310 769-6937
Michael C Goldberg, *President*
Mark J Goldberg, *President*
Michael Goldberg, *CEO*
Josh Goldberg, *Human Res Dir*
▲ EMP: 40 EST: 1979
SQ FT: 11,000
SALES (est): 6.4MM **Privately Held**
WEB: www.wayoutwestinc.com
SIC: 2326 2385 Industrial garments, men's & boys'; waterproof outerwear

(P-3127)
WEST COAST GARMENT MFG
70 Elmira St, San Francisco (94124-1911)
PHONE.....................................415 896-1772
Katherine Ng, *President*
Erica Ku, *Admin Sec*
▲ EMP: 38
SQ FT: 10,000

SALES: 9.2MM **Privately Held**
SIC: 2326 2369 2339 Industrial garments, men's & boys'; girls' & children's outerwear; women's & misses' outerwear

---

2329 Men's & Boys' Clothing, NEC

(P-3128)
3 POINT DISTRIBUTION LLC
Also Called: Ezekiel
170 Technology Dr, Irvine (92618-2401)
PHONE.....................................949 266-2700
Steven A Kurtzman,
Ryan Mark, *Marketing Staff*
Daniel Kurtzman,
▲ EMP: 20
SQ FT: 42,000
SALES (est): 3.4MM **Privately Held**
WEB: www.3-point.org
SIC: 2329 Men's & boys' sportswear & athletic clothing

(P-3129)
A AND G INC (HQ)
Also Called: Alstyle Apparel
11296 Harrel St, Mira Loma (91752-3715)
PHONE.....................................714 765-0400
Keith S Walters, *President*
Gloria Del Mundo, *Administration*
Aziz Kazi, *Purchasing*
Kevin Potter, *VP Mfg*
Aaron Moreno, *Opers Staff*
◆ EMP: 627
SALES (est): 179.4MM
SALES (corp-wide): 2.7B **Privately Held**
WEB: www.murina.com
SIC: 2329 2253 Athletic (warmup, sweat & jogging) suits: men's & boys'; T-shirts & tops, knit
PA: Gildan Activewear Inc
    600 Boul De Maisonneuve O 33eme etage
    Montreal QC H3A 3
    514 735-2023

(P-3130)
ACTIVEAPPAREL INC (PA)
11076 Venture Dr, Mira Loma
(91752-3234)
PHONE.....................................951 361-0060
Wasif M Siddique, *President*
Khan Baloch, *Admin Sec*
▲ EMP: 19
SQ FT: 30,000
SALES (est): 11.4MM **Privately Held**
WEB: www.activeapparel.net
SIC: 2329 2339 7389 Men's & boys' sportswear & athletic clothing; women's & misses' athletic clothing & sportswear; sewing contractor

(P-3131)
ADIDAS NORTH AMERICA INC
Also Called: Adidas Outlet Store Vacaville
378 Nut Tree Rd, Vacaville (95687-3233)
PHONE.....................................707 446-1070
Wibur Grapes, *Manager*
Nick Clinton, *Manager*
EMP: 20
SALES (corp-wide): 25B **Privately Held**
WEB: www.role.noris.net
SIC: 2329 Athletic (warmup, sweat & jogging) suits: men's & boys'; men's & boys' athletic uniforms; knickers, dress (separate): men's & boys'
HQ: Adidas North America, Inc.
    3449 N Anchor St Ste 500
    Portland OR 97217
    971 234-2300

(P-3132)
ALONA APPAREL INC
Also Called: Positano
1651 Mateo St, Los Angeles (90021-2854)
PHONE.....................................323 232-1548
Ofer Kashanian, *President*
Eitan Kashanian, *Vice Pres*
EMP: 10
SALES (est): 976.4K **Privately Held**
SIC: 2329 2321

(P-3133)
AMERICAN FASHION GROUP INC (PA)
1430 E Washington Blvd, Los Angeles (90021-3040)
P.O. Box 15755 (90015-0755)
PHONE..................................213 748-2100
Ali Saleh, *President*
Mohamad Saleh, *CFO*
▲ EMP: 12
SQ FT: 24,000
SALES (est): 1.4MM **Privately Held**
SIC: 2329 Men's & boys' sportswear & athletic clothing

(P-3134)
ANDARI FASHION INC
9626 Telstar Ave, El Monte (91731-3004)
PHONE..................................626 575-2759
WEI Chen Wang, *President*
Lillian Wang, *President*
Charles Chang, *Vice Pres*
▲ EMP: 120
SQ FT: 50,000
SALES (est): 15.2MM **Privately Held**
WEB: www.andari.com
SIC: 2329 2339 5199 2253 Sweaters & sweater jackets: men's & boys'; women's & misses' outerwear; knit goods; sweaters & sweater coats, knit

(P-3135)
ANGELS GARMENTS
Also Called: Angel Manufacturing
525 E 12th St Ste 107, Los Angeles (90015-2645)
PHONE..................................213 748-0581
Jae R Kim, *Owner*
Susan Cockrell, *Opers Mgr*
EMP: 15
SALES (est): 1.2MM **Privately Held**
WEB: www.angelsgarment.com
SIC: 2329 2339 2361 Men's & boys' sportswear & athletic clothing; women's & misses' outerwear; girls' & children's dresses, blouses & shirts

(P-3136)
ANTAEUS FASHIONS GROUP INC
2400 Chico Ave, South El Monte (91733-1613)
PHONE..................................626 452-0797
Yungchieh Lin, *CEO*
Peter Lin, *CFO*
Michael Lin, *General Mgr*
Shangwen Lin, *Admin Sec*
▲ EMP: 35
SQ FT: 10,000
SALES (est): 4.3MM **Privately Held**
SIC: 2329 2339 Men's & boys' sportswear & athletic clothing; women's & misses' athletic clothing & sportswear

(P-3137)
ARIES 33 LLC
3400 S Main St, Los Angeles (90007-4412)
PHONE..................................310 355-8330
Daniel Guez, *CEO*
Robin Saeks, *CFO*
EMP: 20 EST: 2017
SQ FT: 28,000
SALES: 15MM **Privately Held**
SIC: 2329 7389 2339 Men's & boys' sportswear & athletic clothing; apparel designers, commercial; women's & misses' outerwear

(P-3138)
B O A INC
580 W Lambert Rd Ste L, Brea (92821-3913)
PHONE..................................714 256-8960
David Fleming, *President*
Pamela Fleming, *Vice Pres*
▲ EMP: 34
SQ FT: 6,000
SALES (est): 3.1MM **Privately Held**
SIC: 2329 2337 2339 Men's & boys' sportswear & athletic clothing; women's & misses' suits & coats; women's & misses' outerwear

(P-3139)
BOARDRIDERS INC (DH)
5600 Argosy Ave Ste 100, Huntington Beach (92649-1063)
PHONE..................................714 889-2200
Dave Tanner, *CEO*
Thomas Chambolle, *President*
Greg Healy, *President*
Nate Smith, *President*
Danny Kwock, *Exec VP*
◆ EMP: 200
SALES (est): 257.4MM **Publicly Held**
WEB: www.quiksilverusa.com
SIC: 2329 2339 3949 5136 Men's & boys' sportswear & athletic clothing; women's & misses' athletic clothing & sportswear; sporting & athletic goods; winter sports equipment; skateboards; windsurfing boards (sailboards) & equipment; sportswear, men's & boys'; sportswear, women's & children's

(P-3140)
BODY GLOVE INTERNATIONAL LLC
504 N Broadway, Redondo Beach (90277-2101)
PHONE..................................310 374-3441
Robbie Meistrell, *CEO*
Russ Lesser, *President*
◆ EMP: 17
SALES (est): 843.4K **Privately Held**
SIC: 2329 2339 2369 3069 Bathing suits & swimwear: men's & boys'; bathing suits: women's, misses' & juniors'; bathing suits & swimwear: girls', children's & infants'; wet suits, rubber; shorts (outerwear): men's, youths' & boys'; men's & boys' clothing; apparel belts, men's & boys'; men's & boys' outerwear; shirts, men's & boys'

(P-3141)
CORAL HEAD INC (PA)
Also Called: Hawaiian Island Creations
1988 W 169th St, Gardena (90247-5254)
PHONE..................................310 366-7712
Ronald Yoshida, *Partner*
Clarence Hara, *Vice Pres*
Craig Hara, *Vice Pres*
▲ EMP: 10
SQ FT: 6,600
SALES (est): 1.6MM **Privately Held**
SIC: 2329 Men's & boys' sportswear & athletic clothing

(P-3142)
COTTON PALM INC
12410 Foothill Blvd Ste R, Sylmar (91342-8662)
PHONE..................................818 890-3037
Edward Petros, *Owner*
EMP: 20
SALES (est): 1.2MM **Privately Held**
WEB: www.cottonpalm.com
SIC: 2329 2339 Men's & boys' sportswear & athletic clothing; women's & misses' outerwear

(P-3143)
DC SHOES INC (DH)
5600 Argosy Ave Ste 100, Huntington Beach (92649-1063)
PHONE..................................714 889-4206
Charles Exon, *CEO*
Brad Holman, *CFO*
Scott Fullerton, *Vice Pres*
Jeff Shine, *Vice Pres*
Erika Barajas, *Executive*
◆ EMP: 81
SQ FT: 100,000
SALES (est): 31.2MM **Publicly Held**
WEB: www.dcshoes.com
SIC: 2329 5136 5137 5139 Men's & boys' sportswear & athletic clothing; ski & snow clothing: men's & boys'; men's & boys' clothing; women's & children's clothing; footwear
HQ: Boardriders, Inc.
5600 Argosy Ave Ste 100
Huntington Beach CA 92649
714 889-2200

(P-3144)
DHY INC
Also Called: Darrow
922 Duncan Ave, Manhattan Beach (90266-6626)
PHONE..................................310 376-7512
David Yates, *President*
Betty Yates, *Corp Secy*
Tracy Vanpelt, *Admin Sec*
EMP: 40
SQ FT: 24,000
SALES (est): 1.5MM **Privately Held**
SIC: 2329 2339 2369 2331 Men's & boys' sportswear & athletic clothing; sportswear, women's; girls' & children's outerwear; women's & misses' blouses & shirts; men's & boys' furnishings

(P-3145)
DRIVEN CONCEPTS INC
4040 W Carriage Dr, Santa Ana (92704-6303)
PHONE..................................714 549-2170
Brian Hirth, *CEO*
Gary Hunt, *President*
Harish Naran, *CFO*
Leila Drager, *Exec VP*
Justin McKibben, *Mktg Dir*
EMP: 10
SQ FT: 50,000
SALES (est): 1.8MM **Privately Held**
WEB: www.drivenconcepts.com
SIC: 2329 2253 Men's & boys' sportswear & athletic clothing; T-shirts & tops, knit

(P-3146)
E8 DENIM HOUSE LLC
309 E 8th St Fl 5, Los Angeles (90014-2200)
PHONE..................................310 386-4413
Carlo Ghailian, *CEO*
Mark Davis, *President*
Steve Ajamian, *CFO*
▲ EMP: 10
SQ FT: 10,000
SALES (est): 141.7K
SALES (corp-wide): 35MM **Privately Held**
SIC: 2329 2339 Men's & boys' sportswear & athletic clothing; women's & misses' athletic clothing & sportswear
PA: Castma, Inc.
309 E 8th St Fl 5
Los Angeles CA 90014
213 769-4545

(P-3147)
EDMUND KIM INTERNATIONAL INC (PA)
18737 S Reyes Ave, Compton (90221-5609)
PHONE..................................310 604-1100
Edmund K Kim, *President*
Reza Farmehr, *CFO*
Jay Choi, *Controller*
◆ EMP: 20
SQ FT: 120,000
SALES (est): 41.9MM **Privately Held**
WEB: www.ekii.com
SIC: 2329 2261 7218 2253 Athletic (warmup, sweat & jogging) suits: men's & boys'; dyeing cotton broadwoven fabrics; industrial launderers; dresses & skirts; blouses, shirts, pants & suits; commercial printing, lithographic

(P-3148)
ELEGANCE EMBROIDERY LTD
4077 Emery St, Emeryville (94608-3601)
PHONE..................................510 654-0788
Sandra Chan, *President*
Kam Hoi Chan, *Vice Pres*
Thomas Wong, *Manager*
▲ EMP: 25 EST: 1986
SQ FT: 8,000
SALES (est): 2MM **Privately Held**
WEB: www.elegance-embdy.com
SIC: 2329 2339 2395 Ski & snow clothing: men's & boys'; ski jackets & pants: women's, misses' & juniors'; pleating & stitching

(P-3149)
ELITE SPORTS INC
2120 E Howell Ave Ste 502, Anaheim (92806-6030)
PHONE..................................714 634-3835
Carlos G Vega, *President*
▲ EMP: 14
SALES (est): 1.2MM **Privately Held**
SIC: 2329 Men's & boys' athletic uniforms

(P-3150)
FEAR OF GOD LLC
1200 S Santa Fe Ave Ste A, Los Angeles (90021-1789)
PHONE..................................310 466-9751
EMP: 36 **Privately Held**
SIC: 2329 Sweaters & sweater jackets: men's & boys'
PA: Fear Of God, Llc
3940 Laurel Canyon Blvd
Studio City CA 91604
-

(P-3151)
FEAR OF GOD LLC (PA)
3940 Laurel Canyon Blvd, Studio City (91604-3709)
PHONE..................................213 235-7985
Jerry Manuel, *Mng Member*
Glenn Milus, *CFO*
Lao Lee, *Manager*
EMP: 12
SALES (est): 4.2MM **Privately Held**
SIC: 2329 Sweaters & sweater jackets: men's & boys'

(P-3152)
FETISH GROUP INC (PA)
Also Called: Tag Rag
1013 S Los Angeles St # 700, Los Angeles (90015-1793)
PHONE..................................323 587-7873
Raphael Sabbah, *CEO*
Orly Dahan, *Vice Pres*
▲ EMP: 47
SQ FT: 28,000
SALES (est): 5MM **Privately Held**
WEB: www.tagrag.com
SIC: 2329 2339 2369 Men's & boys' sportswear & athletic clothing; women's & misses' athletic clothing & sportswear; girls' & children's outerwear

(P-3153)
FIERRA DESIGN INC
Also Called: Fierra Design CL Manufactures
1359 Channing St, Los Angeles (90021-2410)
PHONE..................................213 622-2426
Haim Iber, *President*
EMP: 30
SQ FT: 35,000
SALES (est): 1.3MM **Privately Held**
SIC: 2329 Men's & boys' sportswear & athletic clothing

(P-3154)
FIVE KEYS INC
Also Called: Mount Seven
150 E Broadway Ave, Atwater (95301-4562)
PHONE..................................209 358-7971
Mohan Johal, *Officer*
Bob Johal, *Controller*
EMP: 40
SQ FT: 21,000
SALES (est): 3.8MM **Privately Held**
WEB: www.fivekeys.com
SIC: 2329 5632 7389 Men's & boys' sportswear & athletic clothing; women's accessory & specialty stores; sewing contractor

(P-3155)
FOURBRO INC
13772 A Better Way, Garden Grove (92843-3906)
PHONE..................................714 277-3858
Rasheed Hussain, *President*
Mohamed Abuthahir, *Corp Secy*
▲ EMP: 14
SQ FT: 34,000

SALES (est): 1.3MM **Privately Held**
WEB: www.fourbro.com
SIC: 2329 2331 2321 Men's & boys' sportswear & athletic clothing; women's & misses' blouses & shirts; men's & boys' furnishings

(P-3156)
FUNNY-BUNNY INC (PA)
Also Called: Cachcach
1513b E Saint Gertrude Pl, Santa Ana (92705-5309)
PHONE.....................714 957-1114
Paul Kohne, *President*
▲ EMP: 95
SQ FT: 25,000
SALES (est): 8.7MM **Privately Held**
WEB: www.cachcach.com
SIC: 2329 2369 Men's & boys' sportswear & athletic clothing; slacks: girls' & children's

(P-3157)
GLOBAL CASUALS INC
18505 S Broadway, Gardena (90248-4632)
PHONE.....................310 817-2828
Jack Tsao, *General Mgr*
▲ EMP: 15
SQ FT: 2,000
SALES (est): 1.2MM
SALES (corp-wide): 101.6MM **Privately Held**
WEB: www.unionbay.com
SIC: 2329 Men's & boys' sportswear & athletic clothing
PA: Seattle Pacific Industries, Inc.
1633 Westlake Ave N Ste 3
Seattle WA 98109
253 872-8822

(P-3158)
GUESS INC
Guess Factory Store 3122
8300 Arroyo Cir Ste 270, Gilroy (95020-7335)
PHONE.....................408 847-3400
May Satsain, *Manager*
EMP: 20
SALES (corp-wide): 2.3B **Publicly Held**
WEB: www.guess.com
SIC: 2329 2331 Men's & boys' sportswear & athletic clothing; women's & misses' blouses & shirts
PA: Guess , Inc.
1444 S Alameda St
Los Angeles CA 90021
213 765-3100

(P-3159)
HOT SHOPPE DESIGNS INC
1323 Calle Avanzado, San Clemente (92673-6351)
PHONE.....................949 487-2828
David Marietti, *CEO*
Max Frost, *Opers Staff*
▲ EMP: 15
SQ FT: 4,800
SALES (est): 135.9K **Privately Held**
WEB: www.hotshoppedesigns.com
SIC: 2329 5136 7336 7389 Riding clothes:, men's, youths' & boys'; shirts, men's & boys'; package design; lettering & sign painting services

(P-3160)
HURLEY INTERNATIONAL LLC
100 Citadel Dr Ste 433, Commerce (90040-1595)
PHONE.....................323 728-1821
Oscar Gomez, *Branch Mgr*
Juanita Altamirano, *Prdtn Mgr*
Terri Palmer, *Director*
EMP: 11
SALES (corp-wide): 36.4B **Publicly Held**
SIC: 2329 5621 5611 Men's & boys' sportswear & athletic clothing; women's clothing stores; men's & boys' clothing stores
HQ: Hurley International Llc
1945g Placentia Ave
Costa Mesa CA 92627
949 548-9375

(P-3161)
HURLEY INTERNATIONAL LLC
321 Nut Tree Rd, Vacaville (95687-3242)
PHONE.....................707 446-6300
EMP: 105
SALES (corp-wide): 36.4B **Publicly Held**
SIC: 2329 Men's & boys' sportswear & athletic clothing
HQ: Hurley International Llc
1945g Placentia Ave
Costa Mesa CA 92627
949 548-9375

(P-3162)
HURLEY INTERNATIONAL LLC (HQ)
1945g Placentia Ave, Costa Mesa (92627-3420)
PHONE.....................949 548-9375
Robert W Coombes, *Mng Member*
Alex Hawkins, *Vice Pres*
Ryan Hurley, *Vice Pres*
Ryan Mangan, *Vice Pres*
Sean Vali, *Vice Pres*
◆ EMP: 200
SALES (est): 99MM
SALES (corp-wide): 36.4B **Publicly Held**
WEB: www.hurley.com
SIC: 2329 5137 Knickers, dress (separate): men's & boys'; women's & children's clothing
PA: Nike, Inc.
1 Sw Bowerman Dr
Beaverton OR 97005
503 671-6453

(P-3163)
IMAGE STAR LLC
Also Called: Reflective Images
42 Digital Dr Ste 10, Novato (94949-5762)
PHONE.....................415 883-5815
Angelika Sultan,
Kristen Gregoriev,
EMP: 11
SQ FT: 2,640
SALES (est): 411.2K **Privately Held**
SIC: 2329 2759 Men's & boys' sportswear & athletic clothing; screen printing

(P-3164)
INTERNATIONAL TREND - 3 CORP
Also Called: Trinity - 4
7103 Marcelle St, Paramount (90723-4840)
PHONE.....................562 360-5185
Steve Shin, *President*
EMP: 20
SQ FT: 15,000
SALES (est): 1.6MM **Privately Held**
SIC: 2329 2339 Men's & boys' sportswear & athletic clothing; athletic clothing: women's, misses' & juniors'

(P-3165)
J K STAR CORP
1123 N Stanford Ave, Los Angeles (90059-3516)
PHONE.....................310 538-0185
Jae K Yoo, *President*
Ock Yoo, *Admin Sec*
▲ EMP: 80
SQ FT: 50,000
SALES: 3.7MM **Privately Held**
SIC: 2329 2339

(P-3166)
JEFFREY RUDES LLC
9550 Heather Rd, Beverly Hills (90210-1739)
PHONE.....................310 281-0800
Jeffrey Rudes, *Mng Member*
EMP: 10 EST: 2014
SQ FT: 2,900
SALES (est): 1.9MM **Privately Held**
SIC: 2329 Knickers, dress (separate): men's & boys'

(P-3167)
JS APPAREL INC
1751 E Del Amo Blvd, Carson (90746-2938)
PHONE.....................310 631-6333
Ki S Kim, *CEO*
▲ EMP: 99

SALES (est): 17.4MM **Privately Held**
WEB: www.jsapparel.net
SIC: 2329 2339 Men's & boys' sportswear & athletic clothing; women's & misses' outerwear

(P-3168)
KOKATAT INC
5350 Ericson Way, Arcata (95521-9277)
PHONE.....................707 822-7621
Stephen O Meara, *President*
Kit Mann, *Vice Pres*
Jordan Jones, *Technology*
Michele Bisgrove, *Human Res Mgr*
John McGibbon, *Production*
◆ EMP: 100
SQ FT: 30,000
SALES (est): 11.7MM **Privately Held**
WEB: www.kokatat.com
SIC: 2329 2339 Men's & boys' sportswear & athletic clothing; women's & misses' athletic clothing & sportswear

(P-3169)
KORAL LLC
Also Called: Koral Active Wear
5124 Pacific Blvd, Vernon (90058-2218)
PHONE.....................323 391-1060
Marcelo Kugel, *Mng Member*
Liz Hampshire,
Peter Koral,
Ilana Kugel,
EMP: 36
SALES: 7MM **Privately Held**
SIC: 2329 2339 Men's & boys' sportswear & athletic clothing; women's & misses' athletic clothing & sportswear

(P-3170)
KRISSY OP SHINS USA INC
Also Called: International Baggyz
2408 S Broadway, Los Angeles (90007-2716)
PHONE.....................213 747-2591
Hae Shin, *President*
Donna Shin, *Vice Pres*
Julie Yoon, *Manager*
EMP: 80
SALES: 2.7MM **Privately Held**
WEB: www.kos-usa.com
SIC: 2329 Men's & boys' sportswear & athletic clothing

(P-3171)
LA JOLLA SPORT USA INC (HQ)
Also Called: O'Neill Sportswear
14350 Myford Rd, Irvine (92606-1002)
PHONE.....................855 554-5930
Daniel Neukomm, *CEO*
Cristy Abella, *CFO*
Rich Brown, *Admin Sec*
◆ EMP: 60
SQ FT: 1,500,000
SALES (est): 13MM **Privately Held**
SIC: 2329 Men's & boys' sportswear & athletic clothing
PA: La Jolla Sportswear Inc
17 Pasteur
Irvine CA 92618
949 428-2800

(P-3172)
LEEMARC INDUSTRIES LLC
Also Called: Canari
2471 Coral St, Vista (92081-8431)
PHONE.....................760 598-0505
Christopher Robinson, *Mng Member*
▲ EMP: 55
SQ FT: 40,000
SALES (est): 8MM **Privately Held**
WEB: www.canari.com
SIC: 2329 2339 Athletic (warmup, sweat & jogging) suits: men's & boys'; women's & misses' outerwear

(P-3173)
LEEMAX INTERNATIONAL INC
Also Called: Ranboy Sportswear
1182 Via Escalante, Chula Vista (91910-8141)
PHONE.....................619 208-2355
David L Shen, *President*
Juan Jose, *Manager*
EMP: 30
SQ FT: 3,000

SALES: 2MM **Privately Held**
SIC: 2329 Men's & boys' sportswear & athletic clothing

(P-3174)
LEVI STRAUSS INTERNATIONAL (HQ)
1155 Battery St, San Francisco (94111-1264)
PHONE.....................415 501-6000
Michael Howard, *President*
John Anderson, *President*
S Lindsay Webbe, *President*
Robert Friedman, *Principal*
Doug Stetter, *Technical Staff*
▲ EMP: 10 EST: 1965
SQ FT: 25,000
SALES (est): 1.8MM
SALES (corp-wide): 4.9B **Privately Held**
SIC: 2329 2339 Men's & boys' sportswear & athletic clothing; women's & misses' outerwear
PA: Levi Strauss & Co.
1155 Battery St
San Francisco CA 94111
415 501-6000

(P-3175)
LIQUID GRAPHICS INC
2701 S Harbor Blvd Unit A, Santa Ana (92704-5839)
PHONE.....................949 486-3588
Josh Merrell, *President*
Mark Hyman, *CFO*
▲ EMP: 130 EST: 1997
SQ FT: 100,000
SALES: 25MM **Privately Held**
SIC: 2329 Men's & boys' sportswear & athletic clothing

(P-3176)
LOST INTERNATIONAL LLC
170 Technology Dr, Irvine (92618-2401)
PHONE.....................949 600-6950
Mike Reola, *Mng Member*
Matt Biolos,
Joel Cooper,
▲ EMP: 15
SALES (est): 1.8MM **Privately Held**
SIC: 2329 Athletic (warmup, sweat & jogging) suits: men's & boys'

(P-3177)
MAD APPAREL INC
Also Called: Athos Works
201 Arch St, Redwood City (94062-1305)
PHONE.....................800 714-9697
Dhananja Jayalath, *CEO*
Don Faul, *COO*
Lindsey Cruz, *Principal*
Julie Desjardins, *Marketing Mgr*
James Berg, *Manager*
EMP: 33 EST: 2012
SQ FT: 5,800
SALES (est): 4.4MM **Privately Held**
SIC: 2329 2339 Men's & boys' sportswear & athletic clothing; women's & misses' athletic clothing & sportswear

(P-3178)
MELAMED INTERNATIONAL INC (PA)
Also Called: Phantom
113 N Palm Dr, Beverly Hills (90210-5506)
PHONE.....................310 271-8585
Shahram Melamed, *President*
Dr Ruben Melamed, *Ch of Bd*
Farshad Melamed, *Director*
Michelle Melamed, *Director*
EMP: 12
SALES (est): 910.4K **Privately Held**
WEB: www.melamedinternational.com
SIC: 2329 2339 2369 5136 Men's & boys' sportswear & athletic clothing; women's & misses' athletic clothing & sportswear; girls' & children's outerwear; men's & boys' clothing; women's & children's clothing

(P-3179)
MELMARC PRODUCTS INC
752 S Campus Ave, Ontario (91761-1728)
PHONE.....................714 460-6691
Miguel Delgato, *President*
EMP: 15
SQ FT: 15,000

SALES (corp-wide): 89MM **Privately Held**
SIC: 2329 2339 2396 2395 Men's & boys' sportswear & athletic clothing; women's & misses' athletic clothing & sportswear; automotive & apparel trimmings; pleating & stitching
PA: Melmarc Products, Inc.
752 S Campus Ave
Ontario CA 91761
714 549-2170

(P-3180)
MIHOLIN INC
Also Called: Spikey Wear
1500 S Bradshawe Ave, Monterey Park (91754-5426)
PHONE...................213 820-8225
Peter Yoo, *President*
MI Young Song, *Vice Pres*
EMP: 10 **EST:** 2001
SQ FT: 7,600
SALES: 800K **Privately Held**
SIC: 2329 Men's & boys' sportswear & athletic clothing

(P-3181)
NORQUIST SALVAGE CORP INC
Also Called: Thrift Town
5005 Stockton Blvd Ste B, Sacramento (95820-5424)
PHONE...................916 454-0435
Rita Cheshire, *Manager*
EMP: 25
SALES (corp-wide): 109.8MM **Privately Held**
WEB: www.thrifttown.com
SIC: 2329 5932 3944 2731 Men's & boys' sportswear & athletic clothing; used merchandise stores; games, toys & children's vehicles; book publishing; women's & misses' outerwear
PA: Norquist Salvage Corporation, Inc.
2151 Prof Dr Ste 200
Roseville CA 95661
916 787-1070

(P-3182)
NORQUIST SALVAGE CORP INC
Also Called: Thrift Town
410 El Camino Ave, Sacramento (95815-2937)
PHONE...................916 922-9942
Donna Lunquist, *Manager*
EMP: 30
SALES (corp-wide): 109.8MM **Privately Held**
WEB: www.thrifttown.com
SIC: 2329 5932 Men's & boys' sportswear & athletic clothing; clothing, secondhand
PA: Norquist Salvage Corporation, Inc.
2151 Prof Dr Ste 200
Roseville CA 95661
916 787-1070

(P-3183)
OLAES ENTERPRISES INC
Also Called: Olaes Design & Marketing
13860 Stowe Dr, Poway (92064-8800)
PHONE...................858 679-4450
Anthony Olaes, *President*
Kathy Buie, *CFO*
▲ **EMP:** 20
SQ FT: 28,000
SALES: 23.5MM **Privately Held**
WEB: www.olaesdesign.com
SIC: 2329 Men's & boys' athletic uniforms

(P-3184)
PEOPLE TREND INC
4801 Staunton Ave, Vernon (90058-1944)
PHONE...................213 995-5555
Shahram Sharafian, *President*
EMP: 12 **EST:** 2011
SALES: 3.9MM **Privately Held**
SIC: 2329 Down-filled clothing: men's & boys'; men's & boys' sportswear & athletic clothing; athletic (warmup, sweat & jogging) suits: men's & boys'; riding clothes:, men's, youths' & boys'

(P-3185)
PRINT INK INC
Also Called: Build Your Own Garment
6918 Sierra Ct, Dublin (94568-2641)
PHONE...................925 829-3950

Cathileen Marchese, *President*
Jacqui Peters, *Sales Staff*
Michele Deering, *Manager*
EMP: 24
SALES (est): 3.1MM **Privately Held**
WEB: www.byologo.com
SIC: 2329 Men's & boys' sportswear & athletic clothing

(P-3186)
QOR LLC
775 Baywood Dr Ste 312, Petaluma (94954-5500)
P.O. Box 1020 (94953-1020)
PHONE...................707 658-2539
Joe Teno, *Mng Member*
Kelly Cooper, *Officer*
Heidi Massey, *Creative Dir*
Lori Overton, *Info Tech Dir*
Susie Brockley, *Manager*
▲ **EMP:** 11
SALES (est): 1.9MM **Privately Held**
SIC: 2329 Athletic (warmup, sweat & jogging) suits: men's & boys'

(P-3187)
SAUVAGE INC (PA)
7717 Formula Pl, San Diego (92121-2419)
PHONE...................858 408-0100
Elizabeth Southwood, *President*
Simon Southwood, *Corp Secy*
EMP: 18
SQ FT: 10,000
SALES (est): 1.6MM **Privately Held**
WEB: www.sauvagewear.com
SIC: 2329 2339 Men's & boys' sportswear & athletic clothing; bathing suits & swimwear: men's & boys'; bathing suits: women's, misses' & juniors'; sportswear, women's

(P-3188)
SPORTSROBE INC (PA)
8654 Hayden Pl, Culver City (90232-2902)
PHONE...................310 559-3999
Allen Ruegsegger, *President*
Mary Ann Ruegsegger, *Vice Pres*
EMP: 25
SQ FT: 14,000
SALES (est): 3MM **Privately Held**
SIC: 2329 Baseball uniforms: men's, youths' & boys'; football uniforms: men's, youths' & boys'

(P-3189)
ST CYCLEWEAR/GALLOP LLC
Also Called: S T Cycle Wear
1200 Billy Mitchell Dr D, El Cajon (92020-1184)
PHONE...................619 449-9191
Bruce Powell, *Mng Member*
Elan Powell, *General Mgr*
▲ **EMP:** 13 **EST:** 1981
SQ FT: 3,700
SALES (est): 1.5MM **Privately Held**
WEB: www.stcyclewear.com
SIC: 2329 Athletic (warmup, sweat & jogging) suits: men's & boys'; men's & boys' leather, wool & down-filled outerwear

(P-3190)
STEADY CLOTHING INC
1711 Newport Cir, Santa Ana (92705-5111)
PHONE...................714 444-2058
Eric Anthony, *President*
Joshua Brownfield, *Vice Pres*
Genesis Prizmic, *Marketing Staff*
▲ **EMP:** 17
SQ FT: 10,000
SALES (est): 2.3MM **Privately Held**
WEB: www.steadyclothing.com
SIC: 2329 2339 Men's & boys' sportswear & athletic clothing; sportswear, women's

(P-3191)
STRAIGHT DOWN SPORTSWEAR (PA)
Also Called: Straight Down Clothing Co
625 Clarion Ct, San Luis Obispo (93401-8177)
PHONE...................805 543-3086
Mike Rowley, *President*
Steve Petterson, *Vice Pres*
▲ **EMP:** 20
SQ FT: 21,000

SALES (est): 2.6MM **Privately Held**
WEB: www.straightdown.com
SIC: 2329 2339 Men's & boys' sportswear & athletic clothing; women's & misses' outerwear

(P-3192)
STREAMLINE DSIGN SLKSCREEN INC (PA)
Also Called: Old Guys Rule
1299 S Wells Rd, Ventura (93004-1901)
PHONE...................805 884-1025
Thom Hill, *CEO*
▲ **EMP:** 54
SQ FT: 33,000
SALES (est): 13.9MM **Privately Held**
SIC: 2329 5136 5611 Men's & boys' sportswear & athletic clothing; men's & boys' clothing; men's & boys' clothing stores

(P-3193)
SUNFLOWER IMPORTS INC
412 W Pico Blvd, Los Angeles (90015-2404)
PHONE...................213 748-3444
Premkumar Sakhrani, *Principal*
▲ **EMP:** 11
SQ FT: 15,000
SALES (est): 902.4K **Privately Held**
WEB: www.sunflowerimports.com
SIC: 2329 2339 Shirt & slack suits: men's, youths' & boys'; women's & misses' athletic clothing & sportswear

(P-3194)
SURF RIDE
1609 Ord Way, Oceanside (92056-3599)
PHONE...................760 433-4020
John Ennis, *Principal*
Taylor Stahl, *Manager*
EMP: 16 **EST:** 2007
SALES (est): 2MM **Privately Held**
SIC: 2329 5941 Men's & boys' sportswear & athletic clothing; skateboarding equipment

(P-3195)
TARTAN FASHION INC
4357 Rowland Ave, El Monte (91731-1119)
PHONE...................626 575-2828
Joann Sun, *President*
◆ **EMP:** 20
SQ FT: 20,363
SALES (est): 1.8MM **Privately Held**
WEB: www.tartan168.com
SIC: 2329 Men's & boys' sportswear & athletic clothing

(P-3196)
TOAD & CO INTERNATIONAL INC (PA)
Also Called: TOAd&co
2020 Alameda Padre Serra, Santa Barbara (93103-1756)
P.O. Box 21508 (93121-1508)
PHONE...................805 957-1474
Gordon Seabury, *President*
Sunny Shrestha, *Accountant*
Lindsay Faulding, *Buyer*
Steven McCann, *Marketing Mgr*
Kate Larramendy, *Director*
▲ **EMP:** 30
SQ FT: 7,000
SALES (est): 11.2MM **Privately Held**
SIC: 2329 2339 Men's & boys' sportswear & athletic clothing; women's & misses' athletic clothing & sportswear

(P-3197)
TOP QUALITY SPORTSWEAR
Also Called: Top Quality Sports Wear
4740 E Olympic Blvd, Los Angeles (90022-3729)
PHONE...................323 262-0399
Raquel Hernandez, *Partner*
EMP: 18 **EST:** 1999
SALES: 94K **Privately Held**
SIC: 2329 Jackets (suede, leatherette, etc.), sport: men's & boys'

(P-3198)
TRAVISMATHEW LLC
15202 Graham St, Huntington Beach (92649-1109)
PHONE...................562 799-6900

Travis Brasher, *CEO*
John Kruger,
Chris Rossassen,
▲ **EMP:** 17
SALES (est): 2.4MM
SALES (corp-wide): 1B **Publicly Held**
SIC: 2329 5699 Athletic (warmup, sweat & jogging) suits: men's & boys'; sports apparel
PA: Callaway Golf Company
2180 Rutherford Rd
Carlsbad CA 92008
760 931-1771

(P-3199)
TRUWEST INC
5592 Engineer Dr, Huntington Beach (92649-1122)
P.O. Box 1855 (92647-1855)
PHONE...................714 895-2444
Lee Westwell, *President*
Gil Westwell, *Treasurer*
Gary Westwell, *Vice Pres*
Norm Westwell, *Vice Pres*
EMP: 28
SQ FT: 13,000
SALES (est): 3MM **Privately Held**
WEB: www.truwest.com
SIC: 2329 2339 Men's & boys' sportswear & athletic clothing; women's & misses' athletic clothing & sportswear

(P-3200)
UNDER ARMOUR INC
321 Nut Tree Rd, Vacaville (95687-3242)
PHONE...................707 451-4736
EMP: 29
SALES (corp-wide): 4.9B **Publicly Held**
SIC: 2329 Men's & boys' sportswear & athletic clothing
PA: Under Armour, Inc.
1020 Hull St Ste 300
Baltimore MD 21230
410 454-6428

(P-3201)
UNILETE INC
18774 Ashford Ln, Huntington Beach (92648-7032)
P.O. Box 1520 (92647-1520)
PHONE...................714 557-1271
Jonathan Oe, *President*
EMP: 10 **EST:** 2000
SALES: 300K **Privately Held**
SIC: 2329 2339 Athletic (warmup, sweat & jogging) suits: men's & boys'; athletic clothing: women's, misses' & juniors'

(P-3202)
UV SKINZ INC
13775 Mono Way Ste A, Sonora (95370-8857)
PHONE...................209 536-9200
Rhonda R Sparks, *President*
Sarah Owsley, *Office Mgr*
Chris Fort, *Graphic Designe*
Megan Holloway, *Graphic Designe*
Rafael Cruz, *Controller*
▲ **EMP:** 10
SQ FT: 3,500
SALES (est): 960.4K **Privately Held**
SIC: 2329 Men's & boys' sportswear & athletic clothing

(P-3203)
VF OUTDOOR LLC (HQ)
Also Called: North Face, The
2701 Harbor Bay Pkwy, Alameda (94502-3041)
PHONE...................510 618-3500
Scott Baxter, *President*
Lindsey Fischer, *Partner*
WEI-En Chang, *Vice Pres*
Jim Gerson, *Vice Pres*
Douglas L Hassman, *Vice Pres*
▲ **EMP:** 250 **EST:** 1994
SQ FT: 151,085

▲ = Import ▼=Export
◆ =Import/Export

SALES (est): 799.8MM
SALES (corp-wide): 11.8B **Publicly Held**
WEB: www.thenorthface.com
SIC: **2329** 2339 3949 2394 Men's & boys' leather, wool & down-filled outerwear; ski & snow clothing: men's & boys'; women's & misses' outerwear; camping equipment & supplies; tents: made from purchased materials; sleeping bags; camping & backpacking equipment; skiing equipment
PA: V.F. Corporation
105 Corporate Center Blvd
Greensboro NC 27408
336 424-6000

(P-3204)
WARNACO SWIMWEAR INC (DH)
Also Called: Warnaco Swimwear Products
1201 W 5th St Ste 1200, Los Angeles (90017-2019)
PHONE....................213 481-4300
Linda J Wachner, *Ch of Bd*
Kathy Van Ness, *President*
Roger Williams, *President*
Antonio Alvarez, *CEO*
Stanley S Lerstein, *CEO*
▲ EMP: 50
SQ FT: 10,000
SALES (est): 62.3MM
SALES (corp-wide): 8.9B **Publicly Held**
SIC: **2329** 2339 2321 3949
HQ: Warnaco Inc.
501 Fashion Ave Fl 14
New York NY 10018
212 287-8000

(P-3205)
WATT ENTERPRISE INC
Also Called: Pacific Coast Sportswear
10575 Bechler River Ave, Fountain Valley (92708-6908)
PHONE....................714 963-0781
Al Watt Jr, *President*
Lisa Hahn, *Manager*
EMP: 12
SALES (est): 1.5MM **Privately Held**
WEB: www.pcsportswear.com
SIC: **2329** 2339 Men's & boys' sportswear & athletic clothing; women's & misses' athletic clothing & sportswear

(P-3206)
ZEENI INC
Also Called: Prieto Sports
9536 Gidley St, Temple City (91780-4213)
PHONE....................626 350-1024
Hassan Zeenni, *President*
Mercedes Zeenni, *Treasurer*
Darryl Hill, *Director*
▲ EMP: 15
SQ FT: 11,000
SALES (est): 1.9MM **Privately Held**
WEB: www.prietosports.com
SIC: **2329** Baseball uniforms: men's, youths' & boys'

(P-3207)
ZK ENTERPRISES INC
Also Called: Unique Sales
4368 District Blvd, Vernon (90058-3124)
PHONE....................213 622-7012
Ron Kelfer, *President*
Kathy Kelfer, *Vice Pres*
Edwin Rosales, *Graphic Designe*
Ralph Barragan, *Prdtn Mgr*
EMP: 40
SQ FT: 13,000
SALES (est): 5MM **Privately Held**
WEB: www.uniquesalesco.com
SIC: **2329** 2339 Athletic (warmup, sweat & jogging) suits: men's & boys'; jogging & warmup suits: women's, misses' & juniors'

2331 Women's & Misses' Blouses

(P-3208)
ACTIVE KNITWEAR RESOURCES INC
Also Called: Gypsy Heart
322 S Date Ave, Alhambra (91803-1404)
PHONE....................626 308-1328
Aaron Lam, *President*

Michael Oconnor, *Sales Mgr*
▲ EMP: 19
SQ FT: 22,000
SALES (est): 2.4MM **Privately Held**
WEB: www.activeknitwear.com
SIC: **2331** 7389

(P-3209)
AIMEZ CLOSET INC
3499 S Main St, Los Angeles (90007-4413)
PHONE....................213 744-1222
Eunkyung Amy Joung, *President*
Hangil Kim, *Vice Pres*
▲ EMP: 12
SALES (est): 1MM **Privately Held**
SIC: **2331** T-shirts & tops, women's: made from purchased materials

(P-3210)
ALL ACCESS APPAREL INC (PA)
Also Called: Self Esteem
1515 Gage Rd, Montebello (90640-6613)
PHONE....................323 889-4300
Richard Clareman, *CEO*
Michael Conway, *CFO*
Andrea Rankin, *Exec VP*
Kazi Alam, *Controller*
◆ EMP: 130
SQ FT: 122,000
SALES (est): 119.3MM **Privately Held**
WEB: www.selfesteemclothing.com
SIC: **2331** 2361 2335 Women's & misses' blouses & shirts; girls' & children's dresses, blouses & shirts; women's, juniors' & misses' dresses

(P-3211)
ALL STAR CLOTHING INC
Also Called: Big Bang Clothing
4507 Staunton Ave, Vernon (90058-1936)
PHONE....................323 233-7773
Sam Lee, *Principal*
EMP: 12
SQ FT: 6,000
SALES (est): 788.2K **Privately Held**
SIC: **2331** 5137 Women's & misses' blouses & shirts; women's & children's clothing

(P-3212)
ALLIANCE APPAREL INC
Also Called: Blu Heaven
3422 Garfield Ave, Commerce (90040-3104)
PHONE....................323 888-8900
Tae Hoo Shin, *President*
Michael Park, *Vice Pres*
▲ EMP: 40 EST: 1999
SQ FT: 17,500
SALES (est): 4.9MM **Privately Held**
WEB: www.bluheaven.net
SIC: **2331** Blouses, women's & juniors': made from purchased material

(P-3213)
AMERTEX INTERNATIONAL INC
2108 Orange St, Alhambra (91803-1427)
PHONE....................626 570-9409
Amy Wong, *President*
Victor Wong, *CFO*
▲ EMP: 50
SQ FT: 25,000
SALES (est): 12.5MM **Privately Held**
WEB: www.amertex.net
SIC: **2331** 2335 2337 2339 Women's & misses' blouses & shirts; women's, juniors' & misses' dresses; women's & misses' suits & coats; sportswear, women's

(P-3214)
ATREVETE INC
Also Called: Staccato
2055 E 51st St, Vernon (90058-2818)
PHONE....................323 277-5551
Sarah Moon, *Owner*
▲ EMP: 17
SALES (est): 1.4MM **Privately Held**
SIC: **2331** Women's & misses' blouses & shirts

(P-3215)
BAILEY 44 LLC
4700 S Boyle Ave, Vernon (90058-3000)
PHONE....................213 228-1930
Shelli Segal, *Mng Member*

Joe Traboulsi, *COO*
Linda Heiman, *Buyer*
Carlos Leiva, *Prdtn Mgr*
Amanda Santoro, *Sales Mgr*
EMP: 22
SALES (est): 3.3MM **Privately Held**
SIC: **2331** 5621 Blouses, women's & juniors': made from purchased material; shirts, women's & juniors': made from purchased materials; T-shirts & tops, women's: made from purchased materials; boutiques

(P-3216)
BERESHITH INC (PA)
Also Called: Love In
1100 S San Pedro St G09, Los Angeles (90015-2328)
PHONE....................213 935-8086
Kyung Hae Lee Chang, *CEO*
Helen Chang, *Director*
EMP: 10 EST: 2010
SALES (est): 1.5MM **Privately Held**
SIC: **2331** 2335 2361 Women's & misses' blouses & shirts; women's, juniors' & misses' dresses; girls' & children's blouses & shirts

(P-3217)
BLTEE LLC
7101 Telegraph Rd, Montebello (90640-6511)
P.O. Box 2762, Santa Fe Springs (90670-0762)
PHONE....................213 802-1736
Elano Miguel Elias, *Mng Member*
EMP: 45
SQ FT: 4,900
SALES (est): 10.5MM **Privately Held**
SIC: **2331** 5136 Women's & misses' blouses & shirts; shirts, men's & boys'

(P-3218)
BLUPRINT CLOTHING CORP
5600 Bandini Blvd, Bell (90201-6407)
PHONE....................323 780-4347
Ju Hyun Kim, *CEO*
Liz Lee, *Vice Pres*
Juan Corona, *Technology*
Ginalyn Balag, *Controller*
Karen Robertson, *VP Sales*
▲ EMP: 75
SQ FT: 16,000
SALES (est): 30MM **Privately Held**
SIC: **2331** Women's & misses' blouses & shirts; blouses, women's & juniors': made from purchased material; shirts, women's & juniors': made from purchased materials

(P-3219)
BOULEVARD STYLE INC
1680 E 40th Pl, Los Angeles (90011-2223)
PHONE....................213 749-1551
EMP: 26 **Privately Held**
SIC: **2331** Women's & misses' blouses & shirts
PA: Boulevard Style, Inc.
1015 Crocker St Ste 27
Los Angeles CA 90021
-

(P-3220)
BOULEVARD STYLE INC (PA)
Also Called: In Style
1015 Crocker St Ste 27, Los Angeles (90021-2051)
PHONE....................213 749-1551
Joseph Huh, *CEO*
EMP: 15
SALES (est): 2.7MM **Privately Held**
SIC: **2331** Women's & misses' blouses & shirts

(P-3221)
BYER CALIFORNIA (PA)
66 Potrero Ave, San Francisco (94103-4800)
PHONE....................415 626-7844
Allan G Byer, *CEO*
Ed Manburg, *CFO*
Marian Byer, *Corp Secy*
Barbara Berling, *Vice Pres*
Janis Byer, *Vice Pres*
▲ EMP: 575
SQ FT: 230,000

SALES (est): 372.3MM **Privately Held**
WEB: www.byer.com
SIC: **2331** Women's & misses' blouses & shirts

(P-3222)
BYER CALIFORNIA
3740 Livermore Outlets Dr, Livermore (94551-4215)
PHONE....................925 245-0184
EMP: 67
SALES (corp-wide): 372.3MM **Privately Held**
SIC: **2331**
PA: Byer California
66 Potrero Ave
San Francisco CA 94103
415 626-7844

(P-3223)
C-QUEST INC
Also Called: Ava James
1439 S Herbert Ave, Commerce (90023-4047)
PHONE....................323 980-1400
Nam Paik, *CEO*
Sung C Choi, *Admin Sec*
◆ EMP: 55
SQ FT: 100,000
SALES (est): 8.1MM **Privately Held**
WEB: www.chereamie.com
SIC: **2331** Women's & misses' blouses & shirts

(P-3224)
CAVERN CLUB LLC
Also Called: Liverpool Jeans
1708 Aeros Way, Montebello (90640-6504)
PHONE....................323 837-9800
Doron Kadosh,
Benjamin Goldstein,
Ronald Perilman,
PA: 10 EST: 2012
SQ FT: 65,000
SALES (est): 1MM **Privately Held**
SIC: **2331** Women's & misses' blouses & shirts

(P-3225)
CLOTHING BY FRENZII INC
905 Mateo St, Los Angeles (90021-1713)
PHONE....................213 670-0265
Sung-Kyu William Kang, *CEO*
William Kang, *COO*
EMP: 16 EST: 2001
SQ FT: 8,950
SALES (est): 1.7MM **Privately Held**
SIC: **2331** 5137 Women's & misses' blouses & shirts; women's & children's clothing; women's & children's dresses, suits, skirts & blouses

(P-3226)
COLON MANUFACTURING INC (PA)
Also Called: Coc Inc
1100 S San Pedro St, Los Angeles (90015-2328)
PHONE....................213 749-6149
Thomas T Byun, *President*
Julia Anna Byun, *Admin Sec*
EMP: 19
SALES (est): 1.7MM **Privately Held**
WEB: www.healthwear.org
SIC: **2331** 2335 2337 Women's & misses' blouses & shirts; women's, juniors' & misses' dresses; women's & misses' suits & coats

(P-3227)
CURE APPAREL LLC
Also Called: Liberty Love
3338 S Malt Ave, Commerce (90040-3126)
PHONE....................562 927-7460
Mohammad R Seilabi, *Mng Member*
Amir Seilabi, *Vice Pres*
▲ EMP: 15
SQ FT: 5,000
SALES (est): 1.9MM **Privately Held**
SIC: **2331** Blouses, women's & juniors': made from purchased material

(P-3228)
CUT & TRIM INC
20847 Betron St, Woodland Hills
(91364-3351)
PHONE...............................818 264-0101
Jon Bernstein, *President*
Janet Bernstein, *Vice Pres*
EMP: 11
SQ FT: 10,000
SALES: 1.2MM **Privately Held**
SIC: 2331 Women's & misses' blouses & shirts

(P-3229)
D & R BROTHERS INC
Also Called: Visage Ladies Fashions
952 S Broadway 2, Los Angeles
(90015-1610)
PHONE...............................213 747-4309
Rafi Khosrow Shaoulian, *President*
Danny Shaoulian, *Vice Pres*
EMP: 45
SQ FT: 40,000
SALES (est): 3.7MM **Privately Held**
WEB: www.drbrothers.com
SIC: 2331 8741 5136 T-shirts & tops, women's: made from purchased materials; management services; shirts, men's & boys'

(P-3230)
DELTA SPORTSWEAR INC
331 S Hale Ave, Fullerton (92831-4805)
PHONE...............................714 568-1102
Imran Parekh, *President*
Muhamed Y Wadalawala, *CFO*
EMP: 10
SQ FT: 30,000
SALES (est): 1.2MM **Privately Held**
WEB: www.delpacific.com
SIC: 2331 T-shirts & tops, women's: made from purchased materials

(P-3231)
DIDI OF CALIFORNIA INC
5816 Piedmont Ave, Los Angeles
(90042-4244)
PHONE...............................323 256-4514
Aldo Garrolini, *President*
EMP: 25
SQ FT: 10,000
SALES (est): 1.9MM **Privately Held**
SIC: 2331 2339 Blouses, women's & juniors': made from purchased material; women's & misses' outerwear

(P-3232)
DRESS TO KILL INC
Also Called: Jane Mohr Design
15500 Erwin St Ste 1089, Van Nuys
(91411-1027)
PHONE...............................818 994-3890
Jane Mohr, *CEO*
▲ **EMP:** 12
SQ FT: 1,400
SALES (est): 955.2K **Privately Held**
SIC: 2331 Women's & misses' blouses & shirts

(P-3233)
EASTWEST CLOTHING INC (PA)
Also Called: Language Los Angeles
40 E Verdugo Ave, Burbank (91502-1931)
PHONE...............................323 980-1177
Michael Schreier, *CEO*
Arvril Ozen, *COO*
▲ **EMP:** 22
SQ FT: 10,000
SALES (est): 5.2MM **Privately Held**
SIC: 2331 Women's & misses' blouses & shirts

(P-3234)
ERGE DESIGNS LLC
4770 E 48th St, Vernon (90058-2702)
PHONE...............................310 614-9197
David Berg, *Mng Member*
Frank Quijada, *Partner*
EMP: 10
SQ FT: 30,000
SALES (est): 1.5MM **Privately Held**
SIC: 2331 Blouses, women's & juniors': made from purchased material

(P-3235)
FIESTA FASHION CO INC (PA)
1100 Wall St Ste 106, Los Angeles
(90015-2326)
PHONE...............................213 748-5775
Myung J Kim, *President*
Peter Choi, *Vice Pres*
▲ **EMP:** 18
SQ FT: 1,000
SALES: 10MM **Privately Held**
SIC: 2331 Women's & misses' blouses & shirts

(P-3236)
FORTUNE CASUALS LLC (PA)
Also Called: Judy Ann
10119 Jefferson Blvd, Culver City
(90232-3519)
PHONE...............................310 733-2100
Fred Kayne, *Mng Member*
Michael Geller,
Walt Lacher,
◆ **EMP:** 110 **EST:** 1999
SQ FT: 40,000
SALES (est): 9.5MM **Privately Held**
WEB: www.fortunecasuals.com
SIC: 2331 2339 2321 T-shirts & tops, women's: made from purchased materials; slacks: women's, misses' & juniors'; men's & boys' furnishings

(P-3237)
GIANNO CO LTD
13546 Vintage Pl, Chino (91710-5243)
PHONE...............................909 628-6928
Peter Chang, *President*
▲ **EMP:** 10
SALES (est): 949.3K **Privately Held**
WEB: www.giannousa.com
SIC: 2331 Women's & misses' blouses & shirts

(P-3238)
GLORIA LANCE INC (PA)
Also Called: Electric Designs
15616 S Broadway, Gardena (90248-2211)
PHONE...............................310 767-4400
Robert Hempling, *President*
Michael Kazden, *CFO*
Gloria Lopez, *Treasurer*
Zvia Hempling, *Vice Pres*
Miguel Lopez, *Admin Sec*
◆ **EMP:** 90
SQ FT: 25,000
SALES (est): 18.3MM **Privately Held**
SIC: 2331 2339 2335 Blouses, women's & juniors': made from purchased material; sportswear, women's; bridal & formal gowns

(P-3239)
GRAU DESIGN INC
1133 N Highland Ave, Los Angeles (90038)
P.O. Box 93156 (90093-0156)
PHONE...............................323 461-4462
Claudia Marie Grau, *President*
Mel Grau, *Treasurer*
Ann Grau, *Vice Pres*
EMP: 10
SQ FT: 2,000
SALES (est): 590.8K **Privately Held**
SIC: 2331 2335 2337 Women's & misses' blouses & shirts; women's, juniors' & misses' dresses; women's & misses' suits & coats

(P-3240)
GROUP MARTIN LLC JOHNATHON
3400 S Main St, Los Angeles (90007-4412)
PHONE...............................323 235-1555
Yaniv Dirman,
Eli Cohen,
EMP: 30
SALES (est): 1.2MM **Privately Held**
SIC: 2331 Women's & misses' blouses & shirts

(P-3241)
GURU KNITS INC
Also Called: Antex Knitting Mills
225 W 38th St, Los Angeles (90037-1405)
PHONE...............................323 235-9424
Kevin Port, *CEO*
▲ **EMP:** 60

SALES (est): 8MM **Privately Held**
SIC: 2331 Women's & misses' blouses & shirts; blouses: girls', children's & infants'

(P-3242)
GUSB INC
219 E 32nd St, Los Angeles (90011-1917)
PHONE...............................323 233-0044
Scott Changsup Lee, *CEO*
▲ **EMP:** 15
SQ FT: 10,000
SALES (est): 1.1MM **Privately Held**
SIC: 2331 2335 2337 2339 Women's & misses' blouses & shirts; women's, juniors' & misses' dresses; women's & misses' suits & coats; women's & misses' outerwear

(P-3243)
H & L APPAREL ENTERPRISE INC
2202 E Anderson St, Vernon (90058-3451)
PHONE...............................323 589-1563
EMP: 11 **EST:** 2013
SQ FT: 20,000
SALES (est): 1MM **Privately Held**
SIC: 2331

(P-3244)
HARKHAM INDUSTRIES INC (PA)
Also Called: Jonathan Martin
857 S San Pedro St # 300, Los Angeles
(90014-2432)
PHONE...............................323 586-4600
Uri Harkham, *President*
◆ **EMP:** 50
SQ FT: 140,000
SALES (est): 5.5MM **Privately Held**
SIC: 2331 2335 2337 2339 Blouses, women's & juniors': made from purchased material; women's, juniors' & misses' dresses; skirts, separate: women's, misses' & juniors'; women's & misses' outerwear

(P-3245)
HEARTBREAKER FASHION
Also Called: Heart of Haute
1925 Mckinley Ave Ste H, La Verne
(91750-5800)
PHONE...............................909 599-0715
Teresa Becker, *Partner*
EMP: 16
SQ FT: 8,000
SALES: 1.4MM **Privately Held**
SIC: 2331 Women's & misses' blouses & shirts

(P-3246)
J HEYRI INC
Also Called: Everleigh
6900 S Alameda St, Huntington Park
(90255-3619)
PHONE...............................323 588-1234
Tiffany Lin, *President*
Sunny Choi, *CEO*
Alexis Kwak, *Vice Pres*
▲ **EMP:** 20
SQ FT: 3,000
SALES (est): 2.4MM **Privately Held**
SIC: 2331 Women's & misses' blouses & shirts

(P-3247)
K TOO
Also Called: K-Too
800 E 12th St Ste 117, Los Angeles
(90021-2199)
PHONE...............................213 747-7766
Jae Hee Kim, *CEO*
Erik Kim, *Vice Pres*
Kelley Kim, *Principal*
Audrey Kim, *Exec Dir*
◆ **EMP:** 41
SALES (est): 20MM **Privately Held**
SIC: 2331 Women's & misses' blouses & shirts

(P-3248)
KAMIRAN INC
Also Called: Mesmerize
1415 Maple Ave Ste 220, Los Angeles
(90015-3103)
PHONE...............................213 746-9161

Kamram Hakimi, *President*
Kambi Hakimi, *Vice Pres*
▲ **EMP:** 13
SQ FT: 6,000
SALES (est): 1.6MM **Privately Held**
WEB: www.kamikam.com
SIC: 2331 Women's & misses' blouses & shirts

(P-3249)
KATHY IRELAND WORLDWIDE
39 Princeton Dr, Rancho Mirage
(92270-3115)
P.O. Box 1410 (92270-1052)
PHONE...............................310 557-2700
Kathy Ireland, *CEO*
Stephen Roseberry, *President*
Erik Sterling, *CFO*
Steve Glick, *Exec VP*
Bialik Benjamin, *Vice Pres*
EMP: 11
SALES (est): 1.3MM **Privately Held**
SIC: 2331 2335 2337 5023 Women's & misses' blouses & shirts; women's, juniors' & misses' dresses; women's & misses' suits & coats; rugs

(P-3250)
KOMEX INTERNATIONAL INC
Also Called: Bubblegum USA
736 E 29th St, Los Angeles (90011-2014)
PHONE...............................323 233-9005
John J Inn, *President*
Laura Hong, *Vice Pres*
Paul Sanghyon Inn, *Vice Pres*
◆ **EMP:** 40
SQ FT: 60,000
SALES (est): 4.4MM **Privately Held**
WEB: www.bubblegumusa.com
SIC: 2331 2329 2339 2325 Women's & misses' blouses & shirts; men's & boys' sportswear & athletic clothing; women's & misses' outerwear; men's & boys' trousers & slacks

(P-3251)
LA MAMBA LLC
242 S Anderson St, Los Angeles
(90033-3205)
PHONE...............................323 526-3526
Vera Campbell,
Stephen Brown,
Denni Kopelan,
▲ **EMP:** 25
SALES (est): 2.5MM **Privately Held**
SIC: 2331 Blouses, women's & juniors': made from purchased material

(P-3252)
LF SPORTSWEAR INC (PA)
Also Called: Furst
5333 Mcconnell Ave, Los Angeles
(90066-7025)
PHONE...............................310 437-4100
Phillip L Furst, *CEO*
Marsha Furst, *Vice Pres*
Steve Katz, *Vice Pres*
Karina Jaramillo, *Graphic Designe*
▲ **EMP:** 30
SQ FT: 35,000
SALES (est): 16.2MM **Privately Held**
WEB: www.lfstores.com
SIC: 2331 5137 2211 Women's & misses' blouses & shirts; women's & children's dresses, suits, skirts & blouses; denims

(P-3253)
LILI BUTLER STUDIO INC
Also Called: The Rupp Butler Studio
7950 Redwood Dr Ste 16, Cotati
(94931-3054)
PHONE...............................707 793-0222
Lili Butler, *President*
EMP: 17
SALES (est): 1.8MM **Privately Held**
WEB: www.lilibutler.com
SIC: 2331 2335 2337 5621 Women's & misses' blouses & shirts; women's, juniors' & misses' dresses; women's & misses' suits & coats; women's clothing stores

▲ = Import ▼=Export
◆ =Import/Export

(P-3254)
LOVE MARKS INC (PA)
Also Called: Kiddo By Katie
2050 E 51st St, Vernon (90058-2819)
PHONE.....................................323 859-8770
Samuel Paik, *President*
▲ EMP: 17 EST: 2012
SALES (est): 6.2MM Privately Held
SIC: 2331 Women's & misses' blouses & shirts

(P-3255)
LSPACE AMERICA LLC
Also Called: L Space
9821 Irvine Center Dr, Irvine (92618-4307)
PHONE.....................................949 596-8726
Paul Carr, *Mng Member*
Lauren Kula, *CFO*
▲ EMP: 20
SALES (est): 1.5MM Privately Held
SIC: 2331 2253 Women's & misses' blouses & shirts; bathing suits & swimwear, knit

(P-3256)
LYRIC CULTURE LLC
2520 W 6th St Ste 250, Los Angeles (90057-3199)
PHONE.....................................323 581-3511
Jason Schutzer, *Mng Member*
Elliot Schutzer,
EMP: 10 EST: 2014
SQ FT: 53,000
SALES (est): 857.5K Privately Held
SIC: 2331 T-shirts & tops, women's: made from purchased materials

(P-3257)
MAKING IT BIG INC
525 Portal St, Cotati (94931-3062)
PHONE.....................................707 795-1995
Tracy Amiral, *President*
Carson Amiral, *General Mgr*
EMP: 24
SQ FT: 17,500
SALES (est): 3.6MM Privately Held
WEB: www.amiral.org
SIC: 2331 2335 2337 2339 Women's & misses' blouses & shirts; women's, juniors' & misses' dresses; women's & misses' suits & coats; women's & misses' outerwear; women's apparel, mail order; women's clothing stores

(P-3258)
MF INC
Also Called: Welovefine
2010 E 15th St, Los Angeles (90021-2823)
PHONE.....................................213 627-2498
Danish Gajiani, *CEO*
Faizan Bakali, *President*
Bill Bussiere, *CFO*
Dean Allen, *Chief Mktg Ofcr*
Jan Sussman, *Vice Pres*
▲ EMP: 120
SQ FT: 700,000
SALES (est): 25MM
SALES (corp-wide): 158.1MM Privately Held
WEB: www.rubygloom.com
SIC: 2331 2253 T-shirts & tops, women's: made from purchased materials; shirts, women's & juniors': made from purchased materials; T-shirts & tops, knit
PA: Mad Engine, Llc
6740 Cobra Way Ste 100
San Diego CA 92121
858 558-5270

(P-3259)
MONROW INC
1404 S Main St Ste C, Los Angeles (90015-2566)
PHONE.....................................213 741-6007
Megan George, *President*
EMP: 29
SALES: 12.1MM Privately Held
SIC: 2331 T-shirts & tops, women's: made from purchased materials

(P-3260)
MXF DESIGNS INC
Also Called: Nally & Millie
1601 Perrino Pl Ste A, Los Angeles (90023-2662)
PHONE.....................................323 266-1451

James Park, *President*
Nally Park, *Shareholder*
▼ EMP: 95
SQ FT: 64,000
SALES: 11MM Privately Held
SIC: 2331 Blouses, women's & juniors': made from purchased material; T-shirts & tops, women's: made from purchased materials

(P-3261)
MYMICHELLE COMPANY LLC (HQ)
Also Called: My Michelle
13077 Temple Ave, La Puente (91746-1418)
PHONE.....................................626 934-4166
Arthur Gordon, *President*
Caren Belair, *President*
Perri Cohen, *President*
Susan Stokes, *President*
Roger D Joseph, *Treasurer*
▲ EMP: 300 EST: 1948
SQ FT: 600,000
SALES (est): 21.4MM
SALES (corp-wide): 350.8MM Privately Held
WEB: www.kellwoodco.com
SIC: 2331 2337 2335 2361 Blouses, women's & juniors': made from purchased material; shirts, women's & juniors': made from purchased materials; skirts, separate: women's, misses' & juniors'; dresses, paper: cut & sewn; blouses: girls', children's & infants'; shirts: girls', children's & infants'; girls' & children's outerwear; women's & misses' athletic clothing & sportswear
PA: Kellwood Company, Llc
600 Kellwood Pkwy Ste 200
Chesterfield MO 63017
314 576-3100

(P-3262)
NOAHS ARK INTERNATIONAL INC
Also Called: Cheol Lee
2319 E 8th St, Los Angeles (90021-1732)
PHONE.....................................714 521-1235
Cheol Woo Lee, *President*
EMP: 12
SQ FT: 3,000
SALES: 2.9MM Privately Held
SIC: 2331 Blouses, women's & juniors': made from purchased material

(P-3263)
NORTH BAY RHBLITATION SVCS INC
Also Called: North Bay Industries
875 Airport Rd, Monterey (93940)
PHONE.....................................831 372-4094
Robert Hutt, *Branch Mgr*
EMP: 30
SALES (corp-wide): 15MM Privately Held
WEB: www.nbrs.org
SIC: 2331 8331 2399 7389 Shirts, women's & juniors': made from purchased materials; community service employment training program; flags, fabric; sewing contractor
PA: North Bay Rehabilitation Services, Inc.
649 Martin Ave
Rohnert Park CA 94928
707 585-1991

(P-3264)
NOTHING TO WEAR INC (PA)
Also Called: Figure 8
630 Maple Ave, Torrance (90503-5001)
PHONE.....................................310 328-0408
Cindy Nunes Freeman, *President*
Darrin Freeman, *CFO*
Julie L Santiago, *Production*
◆ EMP: 35
SQ FT: 18,000
SALES (est): 7.7MM Privately Held
WEB: www.subtletones.com
SIC: 2331 2335 2339 Women's & misses' blouses & shirts; women's, juniors' & misses' dresses; women's & misses' accessories

(P-3265)
OAKLEY INC (DH)
1 Icon, Foothill Ranch (92610-3000)
PHONE.....................................949 951-0991
Colin Baden, *President*
Jim Jannard, *Ch of Bd*
D Scott Olivet, *Ch of Bd*
Don Krause, *President*
Gianluca Tagliabue, *CFO*
◆ EMP: 900
SQ FT: 550,000
SALES (est): 1B Privately Held
WEB: www.oakley.com
SIC: 2331 2339 3021 3873 Women's & misses' blouses & shirts; women's & misses' outerwear; rubber & plastics footwear; watches, clocks, watchcases & parts; men's footwear, except athletic; glasses, sun or glare

(P-3266)
ONE WORLD APPAREL INC
13071 Temple Ave, La Puente (91746-1418)
PHONE.....................................213 222-1010
▲ EMP: 40
SQ FT: 15,000
SALES (est): 3.8MM Privately Held
SIC: 2331 Women's & misses' blouses & shirts

(P-3267)
OUTDOOR LFSTYLE COLLECTIVE LLC
Also Called: Mad Hueys, The
829 Windcrest Dr, Carlsbad (92011-3715)
PHONE.....................................858 336-5580
Patrick J Connell, *Mng Member*
▲ EMP: 12
SQ FT: 5,000
SALES: 500K Privately Held
SIC: 2331 2329 5136 5137 Women's & misses' blouses & shirts; shirt & slack suits: men's, youths' & boys'; men's & boys' clothing; women's & children's clothing

(P-3268)
PROJECT SOCIAL T LLC
615 S Clarence St, Los Angeles (90023-1107)
PHONE.....................................323 266-4500
Mike Chodler, *Mng Member*
EMP: 30
SALES: 15MM Privately Held
SIC: 2331 5137 5621 Women's & misses' blouses & shirts; women's & children's clothing; women's clothing stores

(P-3269)
REBECCA BEESON INC
Also Called: Rebecca Beeson Collection Tees
1345 Howard St, San Francisco (94103-2616)
P.O. Box 411719 (94141-1719)
PHONE.....................................415 865-0471
Rebecca Beeson, *President*
Jeffery Mullun, *Vice Pres*
EMP: 10
SQ FT: 7,000
SALES (est): 1.1MM Privately Held
WEB: www.rebeccabeeson.com
SIC: 2331 T-shirts & tops, women's: made from purchased materials

(P-3270)
SANCTUARY CLOTHING INC
3611 N San Fernando Blvd, Burbank (91505-1043)
PHONE.....................................818 505-0018
Ken Polanco, *President*
Debra Polanco, *Vice Pres*
EMP: 40
SALES (est): 3.3MM Privately Held
WEB: www.sanctuaryclothing.com
SIC: 2331 Women's & misses' blouses & shirts

(P-3271)
SENSE FASHION CORPORATION
Also Called: Sense Fashions
2415 Merced Ave, South El Monte (91733-1921)
PHONE.....................................626 454-3381
June Ho, *President*
Charles Loh, *Vice Pres*

◆ EMP: 30
SQ FT: 14,000
SALES: 2.1MM Privately Held
SIC: 2331 2339 2329 Blouses, women's & juniors': made from purchased material; shirts, women's & juniors': made from purchased materials; sportswear, women's; men's & boys' sportswear & athletic clothing

(P-3272)
SEWING EXPERTS INC
227 Lincoln St, Calexico (92231-2257)
PHONE.....................................760 357-8525
Mike Fletes, *President*
EMP: 35
SALES (est): 2.8MM Privately Held
SIC: 2331 2329 Women's & misses' blouses & shirts; shirt & slack suits: men's, youths' & boys'

(P-3273)
SHIMMER FASHION
555 Broadway Ste 134, Chula Vista (91910-5382)
PHONE.....................................619 426-7781
Joy Lafond, *Owner*
EMP: 15
SALES (est): 784.7K Privately Held
SIC: 2331

(P-3274)
STYLE PLUS INC (PA)
Also Called: Wanna B
2807 S Olive St, Los Angeles (90007-3339)
PHONE.....................................213 205-8408
Eun Kyoung Shin, *CEO*
Kenny Kim, *CFO*
EMP: 12
SALES (est): 3.3MM Privately Held
SIC: 2331 Women's & misses' blouses & shirts

(P-3275)
TEAM FASHION
2303 E 55th St, Vernon (90058-3435)
PHONE.....................................323 589-3388
EMP: 15
SQ FT: 80,000
SALES (est): 1.6MM Privately Held
SIC: 2331

(P-3276)
THREE BROTHERS CUTTING
8416 Otis St, South Gate (90280-2515)
PHONE.....................................323 564-4774
Jose Hernandez, *Owner*
EMP: 15
SALES (est): 677.2K Privately Held
SIC: 2331 Blouses, women's & juniors': made from purchased material

(P-3277)
THREE DOTS LLC
7340 Lampson Ave, Garden Grove (92841-2902)
PHONE.....................................714 799-6333
Sharon Lebon,
Bruno Lenon,
▲ EMP: 72
SALES (est): 9.1MM
SALES (corp-wide): 15.3MM Privately Held
WEB: www.threedots.net
SIC: 2331 T-shirts & tops, women's: made from purchased materials
PA: Three Dots, Inc.
7340 Lampson Ave
Garden Grove CA 92841
714 799-6333

(P-3278)
THREE PLUS ONE INC
Also Called: Audrey 3plus1
3007 Fruitland Ave, Vernon (90058-3626)
PHONE.....................................213 623-3070
Kim Yon MI, *President*
Audrey Kim, *General Mgr*
Durey Kim,
EMP: 14 EST: 2007
SALES (est): 1.1MM Privately Held
SIC: 2331 Women's & misses' blouses & shirts

(PA)=Parent Co (HQ)=Headquarters (DH)=Div Headquarters
✪ = New Business established in last 2 years

2019 California
Manufacturers Register

145

PRODUCTS & SVCS

(P-3279)
TIANELLO INC
Also Called: Tianello By Steve Barraza
138 W 38th St, Los Angeles (90037-1404)
PHONE................................323 231-0599
Steven Barraza, *President*
Kent Bailey, *CFO*
Brianna Barraza, *Sales Mgr*
Sharon Santiago, *Sales Staff*
Angel Orellana, *Cust Mgr*
▲ EMP: 185
SQ FT: 25,000
SALES (est): 23.5MM Privately Held
WEB: www.tianello.com
SIC: 2331 5621 2339 Women's & misses'
blouses & shirts; women's clothing stores;
women's & misses' outerwear

(P-3280)
TRIXXI CLOTHING COMPANY
INC (PA)
6817 E Acco St, Commerce (90040-1901)
PHONE................................323 585-4200
Annette Soufrine, *CEO*
Leslie Flores, *President*
▲ EMP: 47
SQ FT: 35,000
SALES (est): 50MM Privately Held
WEB: www.trixxigirl.com
SIC: 2331 Blouses, women's & juniors':
made from purchased material

(P-3281)
TWO STAR DOG INC (PA)
Also Called: Body Dope
1329 9th St, Berkeley (94710-1502)
PHONE................................510 525-1100
Steven Boutrous, *President*
Jeff Fenigstein, *COO*
Allan Boutrous, *Vice Pres*
Attas Boutrous, *Vice Pres*
Stella Boutrous Carakasi, *Vice Pres*
▲ EMP: 31
SQ FT: 25,000
SALES (est): 4.4MM Privately Held
SIC: 2331 Women's & misses' blouses &
shirts

(P-3282)
UBST INC
373 Van Ness Ave, Torrance (90501-1484)
PHONE................................424 222-9908
Ju Chun, *CEO*
EMP: 11
SALES: 7.9MM Privately Held
SIC: 2331 Shirts, women's & juniors':
made from purchased materials

(P-3283)
UMGEE USA INC
500 S Anderson St, Los Angeles
(90033-4222)
PHONE................................323 526-9138
Boyng Ki GI, *President*
▼ EMP: 18
SQ FT: 12,600
SALES (est): 763.5K Privately Held
SIC: 2331 2335 Women's & misses'
blouses & shirts; women's, juniors' &
misses' dresses

(P-3284)
UNGER FABRIK LLC (PA)
13071 Temple Ave, La Puente
(91746-1418)
PHONE................................213 222-1010
Yongbin Luo, *CEO*
Celso Ong, *Controller*
▲ EMP: 110
SQ FT: 300,000
SALES (est): 61.2MM Privately Held
WEB: www.ungerfab.com
SIC: 2331 Women's & misses' blouses &
shirts

(P-3285)
US PREMIER INC
624 S Clarence St, Los Angeles
(90023-1108)
PHONE................................323 267-4463
Tae Lee, *President*
EMP: 12 EST: 2015
SQ FT: 8,000

SALES: 2.5MM Privately Held
SIC: 2331 2329 Women's & misses'
blouses & shirts; knickers, dress (separate): men's & boys'

(P-3286)
VEEZEE INC
Also Called: Honulua Surf Co
121 Waterworks Way, Irvine (92618-7719)
PHONE................................949 265-0800
Paul Naude, *President*
▲ EMP: 20
SALES (est): 1.6MM Publicly Held
SIC: 2331 5099 Women's & misses'
blouses & shirts; sunglasses
HQ: Billabong International Limited
1 Billabong Pl
Burleigh Heads QLD 4220

(P-3287)
W5 CONCEPTS INC
2049 E 38th St, Vernon (90058)
PHONE................................323 231-2415
Kyung Eun Kim, *CEO*
Maritza Orozco, *Manager*
EMP: 25
SALES (est): 2.6MM Privately Held
SIC: 2331 Women's & misses' blouses &
shirts

2335 Women's & Misses'
Dresses

(P-3288)
4 YOU APPAREL INC
Also Called: Egen
2944 E 44th St, Vernon (90058-2430)
PHONE................................323 583-4242
Joo Sung Son, *President*
▲ EMP: 15 EST: 2000
SQ FT: 53,420
SALES (est): 1.3MM Privately Held
WEB: www.4youapparel.com
SIC: 2335 Women's, juniors' & misses'
dresses

(P-3289)
ADRIENNE DRESSES INC
719 S Los Angeles St # 827, Los Angeles
(90014-2129)
PHONE................................213 622-8557
Miriam G Rosa, *President*
EMP: 16
SQ FT: 1,796
SALES (est): 1.2MM Privately Held
SIC: 2335 Women's, juniors' & misses'
dresses

(P-3290)
AGS USA LLC
Also Called: American Garment Sewing
1210 Rexford Ave, Pasadena (91107-1713)
PHONE................................323 588-2200
Anton Pavel, *Mng Member*
Michael Rublevich,
▲ EMP: 150
SQ FT: 21,000
SALES: 8.3MM Privately Held
WEB: www.agsconstruction.com
SIC: 2335 2325 2326 2339 Women's,
juniors' & misses' dresses; jeans: men's,
youths' & boys'; men's & boys' work cloth-
ing; jeans: women's, misses' & juniors';
women's & misses' blouses & shirts

(P-3291)
ALMACK LINERS INC
9541 Cozycroft Ave, Chatsworth
(91311-5102)
PHONE................................818 718-5878
Susana Almack, *President*
EMP: 25
SQ FT: 3,000
SALES (est): 3.2MM Privately Held
WEB: www.almackliners.com
SIC: 2335 2329 Women's, juniors' &
misses' dresses; men's & boys' sports-
wear & athletic clothing

(P-3292)
ANAYAS CUTTING INC
3130 Leonis Blvd Ste 204, Vernon
(90058-3012)
PHONE................................323 582-5758
Martin Anaya, *President*
EMP: 55
SQ FT: 70,000
SALES: 3MM Privately Held
SIC: 2335 Dresses, paper: cut & sewn

(P-3293)
AQUARIUS RAGS LLC (PA)
Also Called: ABS By Allen Schwartz
1218 S Santa Fe Ave, Los Angeles
(90021-1745)
PHONE................................213 895-4400
Allen Schwartz, *Mng Member*
Kirk Foster,
Armand Marciano,
▲ EMP: 15
SQ FT: 50,000
SALES (est): 16.1MM Privately Held
SIC: 2335 Women's, juniors' & misses'
dresses

(P-3294)
AWAKE INC
Also Called: Jem Sportswear
10711 Walker St, Cypress (90630-4720)
PHONE................................818 365-9361
Jeffrey A Marine, *CEO*
Orna Stark, *President*
▲ EMP: 100
SQ FT: 65,000
SALES (est): 11.5MM Privately Held
SIC: 2335 Women's, juniors' & misses'
dresses

(P-3295)
AZAZIE INC
148 E Brokaw Rd, San Jose (95112-4203)
PHONE................................650 963-9420
Qi Zhong, *CEO*
Gary Zhao, *Opers Mgr*
Karen Luo, *Marketing Staff*
Rachel Hogue, *Manager*
EMP: 11
SALES (est): 1.1MM Privately Held
SIC: 2335 Gowns, formal

(P-3296)
B & Y GLOBAL SOURCING LLC
801 S Grand Ave Ste 475, Los Angeles
(90017-4622)
PHONE................................213 891-1112
Norbert Baroukh,
Jack Remoke,
Eddie Yuen,
▲ EMP: 13
SQ FT: 2,000
SALES (est): 1.2MM Privately Held
SIC: 2335 Women's, juniors' & misses'
dresses

(P-3297)
BD IMPOTEX LLC
Also Called: Sweet Girl
2623 S San Pedro St, Los Angeles
(90011-1521)
PHONE................................323 521-1500
Shaiful Alam, *Mng Member*
Shoyebul Islam,
▲ EMP: 10
SQ FT: 18,000
SALES: 25MM Privately Held
SIC: 2335 5137 Women's, juniors' &
misses' dresses; women's & children's
clothing

(P-3298)
BEE DARLIN INC (PA)
Also Called: Bee Darlin and Be Smart
1875 E 22nd St, Los Angeles (90058-1033)
PHONE................................213 749-2116
Steve Namm, *President*
Jill Namm, *Corp Secy*
Edwina Von Bjorn, *Principal*
▲ EMP: 100
SQ FT: 30,000
SALES (est): 20.2MM Privately Held
SIC: 2335 Dresses, paper: cut & sewn

(P-3299)
BELLASPOSA WEDDING
CENTER
11450 4th St Ste 103, Rancho Cucamonga
(91730-9024)
PHONE................................909 758-0176
Hsin Hung Lu, *Principal*
EMP: 11
SALES (est): 1MM Privately Held
SIC: 2335 Wedding gowns & dresses

(P-3300)
CAROL ANDERSON INC (PA)
Also Called: Carol Anderson By Invitation
18700 S Laurel Park Rd, Rancho
Dominguez (90220-6003)
PHONE................................310 638-3333
Jan Janura, *President*
Carol M Anderson, *President*
Jan A Janura, *President*
◆ EMP: 25 EST: 1977
SQ FT: 50,000
SALES (est): 8.7MM Privately Held
SIC: 2335 2339 Women's, juniors' &
misses' dresses; shorts (outerwear):
women's, misses' & juniors'

(P-3301)
CENTURY SEWING CO
421 S Raymond Ave, Alhambra
(91803-1532)
PHONE................................626 289-0533
Margaret Fong, *Partner*
EMP: 30
SQ FT: 5,000
SALES (est): 1.8MM Privately Held
SIC: 2335 Dresses, paper: cut & sewn

(P-3302)
CHOON INC (PA)
Also Called: Pezeme
520 Mateo St, Los Angeles (90013-2243)
PHONE................................213 225-2500
Choon S Nakamura, *President*
Daniel Nakamura, *Vice Pres*
Paul Avila, *General Mgr*
▲ EMP: 32 EST: 1972
SQ FT: 35,000
SALES (est): 4.8MM Privately Held
WEB: www.choon.com
SIC: 2335 Women's, juniors' & misses'
dresses

(P-3303)
COMPLETE CLOTHING
COMPANY (PA)
Also Called: Willow & Clay
4950 E 49th St, Vernon (90058-2736)
PHONE................................323 277-1470
Eleanor M Sanchez, *President*
John Meyer, *COO*
▲ EMP: 60
SQ FT: 30,000
SALES (est): 12.4MM Privately Held
WEB: www.originalzinc.com
SIC: 2335 2339 2337 2331 Women's,
juniors' & misses' dresses; sportswear,
women's; women's & misses' suits &
coats; women's & misses' blouses &
shirts

(P-3304)
DANBEE INC
3360 E Pico Blvd, Los Angeles
(90023-3729)
PHONE................................323 780-0077
Hae MI Choi, *President*
Ann Choi, *Admin Sec*
EMP: 12
SALES (est): 1.1MM Privately Held
SIC: 2335 Women's, juniors' & misses'
dresses

(P-3305)
DIAMOND TREE INVESTMENTS
LLC
2841 Octavia St, San Francisco
(94123-4305)
PHONE................................415 627-7730
Michael Thaler,
EMP: 50
SQ FT: 5,000
SALES: 6MM Privately Held
SIC: 2335 Women's, juniors' & misses'
dresses

(P-3306)
DJ BRONSON INC (PA)
Also Called: Sugar Free
8427 Secura Way, Santa Fe Springs
(90670-2215)
PHONE..................562 945-9609
Justin Ding, *CEO*
Bruce Bronson, *President*
Debbie Grossberg-Nudelman, *Vice Pres*
▲ **EMP:** 14
SQ FT: 28,000
SALES (est): 5.9MM **Privately Held**
SIC: 2335 5621 Women's, juniors' &
misses' dresses; women's specialty cloth-
ing stores

(P-3307)
DONNA KARAN COMPANY LLC
1 Mills Cir, Ontario (91764-5207)
PHONE..................909 484-1201
Karan Murphy, *Branch Mgr*
EMP: 157
SALES (corp-wide): 2.8B **Publicly Held**
SIC: 2335 Women's, juniors' & misses'
dresses
HQ: The Donna Karan Company Llc
240 W 40th St
New York NY 10018
212 789-1500

(P-3308)
ELLE BOUTIQUE
200 E Garvey Ave Ste 105, Monterey Park
(91755-1859)
PHONE..................626 307-9882
Danny Kiang, *Owner*
EMP: 12
SQ FT: 2,000
SALES (est): 550K **Privately Held**
SIC: 2335 5621 Ensemble dresses:
women's, misses' & juniors'; dress shops

(P-3309)
GAZE USA INC
1665 Mateo St, Los Angeles (90021-2854)
PHONE..................213 622-0022
EMP: 18
SALES: 12MM **Privately Held**
SIC: 2335

(P-3310)
**GINZA COLLECTION DESIGN
INC**
6015 Obispo Ave, Long Beach
(90805-3756)
PHONE..................562 531-1116
Ty Yeh, *President*
WEI Chen Yeh, *Admin Sec*
EMP: 40
SALES (est): 2.5MM
SALES (corp-wide): 6.2MM **Privately
Held**
WEB: www.avantidesign.net
SIC: 2335 Wedding gowns & dresses
PA: Private Label By G Inc
6015 Obispo Ave
Long Beach CA 90805
562 531-1116

(P-3311)
GLS APPAREL USA INC
1125 San Julian St C, Los Angeles
(90015-2313)
PHONE..................213 749-8484
EMP: 11
SALES (corp-wide): 3.9MM **Privately
Held**
SIC: 2335 Wedding gowns & dresses
PA: Gls Apparel Usa, Inc.
3833 S Hill St
Los Angeles CA 90037
213 226-8484

(P-3312)
GREEN MOCHI LLC
Also Called: 12th Street By Cynthia Vincent
834 S Broadway Ste Mezz, Los Angeles
(90014-3501)
PHONE..................213 225-2250
Cynthia Vincent,
Armen Gregorian,
▲ **EMP:** 12
SALES (est): 1.2MM **Privately Held**
SIC: 2335 3144 Women's, juniors' &
misses' dresses; dress shoes, women's

(P-3313)
HUANG QI
4700 Miller Dr Ste H, Temple City
(91780-3757)
PHONE..................626 442-6808
Hung Yuk See, *Owner*
EMP: 15
SALES (est): 640.5K **Privately Held**
SIC: 2335

(P-3314)
IRENE KASMER INC
315 S Bedford Dr, Beverly Hills
(90212-3724)
PHONE..................310 553-8986
Irene Kasmer, *President*
Gerald Kasmer, *Vice Pres*
EMP: 15 **EST:** 1967
SALES (est): 1.2MM **Privately Held**
SIC: 2335 2331 Dresses, paper: cut &
sewn; blouses, women's & juniors': made
from purchased material

(P-3315)
JADE APPAREL INC
1625 S Greenwood Ave, Montebello
(90640-6534)
PHONE..................323 867-9800
Joe H Cho, *President*
Jason Kim, *Vice Pres*
▲ **EMP:** 32 **EST:** 2000
SQ FT: 25,000
SALES (est): 5.5MM **Privately Held**
WEB: www.jadeapparel.net
SIC: 2335 Women's, juniors' & misses'
dresses

(P-3316)
JAY-CEE BLOUSE CO INC
Also Called: La Rose of California
823 Maple Ave Ste 200, Los Angeles
(90014-2232)
PHONE..................213 622-0116
Stephen Roseman, *President*
Edith Roseman, *Vice Pres*
Richard Roseman, *Vice Pres*
EMP: 108
SALES (est): 7.1MM **Privately Held**
SIC: 2335 2331 Women's, juniors' &
misses' dresses; blouses, women's & jun-
iors': made from purchased material

(P-3317)
JC TRIMMING COMPANY INC
Also Called: JC Industries
3800 S Hill St, Los Angeles (90037-1416)
PHONE..................323 235-4458
Eric Shin, *CEO*
Dawn Woods, *Manager*
▲ **EMP:** 90
SQ FT: 40,088
SALES (est): 13.5MM **Privately Held**
SIC: 2335 2326 Women's, juniors' &
misses' dresses; men's & boys' work
clothing

(P-3318)
JODI KRISTOPHER LLC (PA)
Also Called: City Triangles
1950 Naomi Ave, Los Angeles
(90011-1342)
PHONE..................323 890-8000
Ira Rosenberg, *President*
Ellen Delosh-Bacher, *Shareholder*
Jan Smith, *Shareholder*
Ira Fogelman, *CFO*
Alice Rosenberg, *Admin Sec*
▲ **EMP:** 200
SQ FT: 100,000
SALES (est): 29.4MM **Privately Held**
SIC: 2335 Women's, juniors' & misses'
dresses

(P-3319)
**JOHNNY WAS COLLECTION INC
(PA)**
Also Called: Johnny Was Showroom
2423 E 23rd St, Los Angeles (90058-1201)
PHONE..................323 231-8222
Eli Levite, *President*
▼ **EMP:** 26
SQ FT: 30,000
SALES (est): 3.6MM **Privately Held**
SIC: 2335 Women's, juniors' & misses'
dresses

(P-3320)
**KATHRINE BAUMANN BEVERLY
HILLS**
Also Called: Katherine Baumann Collectibles
9040 W Sunset Blvd # 208, West Holly-
wood (90069-1851)
PHONE..................310 274-7441
Kathrine Baumann, *President*
EMP: 37
SQ FT: 6,000
SALES (est): 3.4MM **Privately Held**
SIC: 2335 Women's, juniors' & misses'
dresses

(P-3321)
LA SICILIANA INC
Also Called: La Siciliana Dressmaking
8674 Washington Blvd, Culver City
(90232-7460)
PHONE..................323 870-4155
Tindara Mollica, *President*
Anthony Mollica, *Admin Sec*
EMP: 40 **EST:** 1967
SQ FT: 10,000
SALES (est): 2.6MM **Privately Held**
WEB: www.lasiciliana.com
SIC: 2335 2339 Women's, juniors' &
misses' dresses; women's & misses' out-
erwear

(P-3322)
LAVISH CLOTHING INC
245 W 28th St, Los Angeles (90007-3312)
PHONE..................213 745-5400
Song Kyung Choi, *President*
EMP: 15
SQ FT: 25,000
SALES: 4.5MM **Privately Held**
SIC: 2335 Women's, juniors' & misses'
dresses

(P-3323)
LAYERED LUXE INC
1443 S Lorena St, Los Angeles
(90023-3718)
PHONE..................323 513-8200
Karen Gutierrez, *President*
EMP: 25
SQ FT: 10,000
SALES (est): 976K **Privately Held**
SIC: 2335 2339 2331 Women's, juniors' &
misses' dresses; athletic clothing:
women's, misses' & juniors'; jogging &
warmup suits: women's, misses' & juniors'; sportswear, women's; scarves,
hoods, headbands, etc.: women's;
blouses, women's & juniors': made from
purchased material

(P-3324)
LCI LAUNDRY INC
Also Called: Laundry By Shelli Segal
5835 S Eastrn Ave Ste 100, Commerce
(90040)
PHONE..................323 767-1900
Paul Sharron, *Ch of Bd*
Paula Schneider, *President*
▲ **EMP:** 125 **EST:** 1976
SQ FT: 58,000
SALES (est): 8.3MM
SALES (corp-wide): 5.8B **Publicly Held**
SIC: 2335 2339 2331 Dresses, paper: cut
& sewn; women's & misses' athletic cloth-
ing & sportswear; women's & misses'
blouses & shirts
HQ: Kate Spade & Company Llc
2 Park Ave Fl 8
New York NY 10016
212 354-4900

(P-3325)
LEES FASHIONS INC
1157 Monterey Pl, Encinitas (92024-1340)
PHONE..................760 753-2408
Lee Torti, *President*
Loretta Torti, *Vice Pres*
EMP: 25
SQ FT: 5,000
SALES (est): 1.8MM **Privately Held**
SIC: 2335 2331 2339 Women's, juniors' &
misses' dresses; blouses, women's & jun-
iors': made from purchased material;
slacks: women's, misses' & juniors'

(P-3326)
LOTUS ORIENT CORP (PA)
Also Called: Venus Bridal Gowns
411 S California St, San Gabriel
(91776-2527)
P.O. Box 280 (91778-0280)
PHONE..................626 285-5796
Eugene Wu, *President*
▲ **EMP:** 14
SQ FT: 6,400
SALES (est): 1.5MM **Privately Held**
SIC: 2335 5621 Wedding gowns &
dresses; bridal shops

(P-3327)
MISS KIM INC
Also Called: Miss Cristina
1015 San Julian St, Los Angeles
(90015-2311)
PHONE..................213 747-4011
Leticia Alvarez, *CEO*
Sung H Kim, *CFO*
EMP: 16
SALES (est): 2.5MM **Privately Held**
SIC: 2335 5137 Ensemble dresses:
women's, misses' & juniors'; dresses

(P-3328)
NIGHT FASHION INC
Also Called: Fashion 1001 Nights
628 W 30th St Ofc C, Los Angeles
(90007-4629)
PHONE..................213 747-8740
David Kahenassa, *President*
▲ **EMP:** 34
SQ FT: 30,000
SALES (est): 2.2MM **Privately Held**
WEB: www.fashion1001nights.com
SIC: 2335 Bridal & formal gowns

(P-3329)
NOVA PRINT INC
2100 S Fairview St, Santa Ana
(92704-4516)
PHONE..................951 525-4040
Douglas Gay, *CEO*
Michelle Gay, *COO*
EMP: 12
SQ FT: 4,000
SALES: 600K **Privately Held**
SIC: 2335 2262 Dresses, paper: cut &
sewn; roller printing: manmade fiber & silk
broadwoven fabrics

(P-3330)
ONEWORLD APPAREL LLC (HQ)
Also Called: Live and Let Live
13071 Temple Ave, La Puente
(91746-1418)
PHONE..................213 222-1010
Arthur Gordon, *CEO*
Clay Medley, *President*
Robert Burns,
Wong Tak Fong,
▲ **EMP:** 26
SQ FT: 14,000
SALES (est): 18.7MM
SALES (corp-wide): 330.1MM **Privately
Held**
WEB: www.oneworldapparel.com
SIC: 2335 Women's, juniors' & misses'
dresses
PA: Shangying Global Co., Ltd.
3/F,Shangying Group Building, No. 8
Xuhong Middle Road, Xuhui Di
Shanghai 20023
216 469-8868

(P-3331)
PACIFIC BOULEVARD INC
Also Called: Verde
5075 Pacific Blvd, Vernon (90058-2215)
PHONE..................323 581-1656
Joe Ramos, *President*
EMP: 15
SALES (est): 853.7K **Privately Held**
SIC: 2335 Women's, juniors' & misses'
dresses

(P-3332)
**PALIHUSE HLLWAY RSIDENCES
ASSN**
8465 Holloway Dr, West Hollywood
(90069-4258)
PHONE..................323 656-4100
Kirsten Leigh Pratt, *CEO*

Kazu Namise, *Comms Dir*
Matt Fisher, *Principal*
Nicole Castaneda, *Director*
Bryan Westbrook, *Manager*
EMP: 10
SALES (est): 1MM **Privately Held**
SIC: 2335 Housedresses

(P-3333)
PRIVATE BRAND MDSG CORP
Also Called: Jody of California
214 W Olympic Blvd, Los Angeles
(90015-1605)
PHONE....................213 749-0191
William Berman, *President*
Rochelle Berman, *Corp Secy*
John Berman, *VP Sales*
EMP: 23
SQ FT: 6,000
SALES (est): 2.7MM **Privately Held**
WEB: www.jodyca.com
SIC: 2335 2339 Women's, juniors' &
misses' dresses; sportswear, women's

(P-3334)
PRIVATE LABEL BY G INC (PA)
6015 Obispo Ave, Long Beach
(90805-3756)
PHONE....................562 531-1116
Ty Yeh, *President*
WEI Chen Yeh, *Treasurer*
Ken Yeh, *Marketing Staff*
▲ **EMP:** 25
SQ FT: 5,000
SALES (est): 6.2MM **Privately Held**
WEB: www.privatelabelbyg.com
SIC: 2335 Wedding gowns & dresses

(P-3335)
PROMISES PROMISES INC
Also Called: Broadway Pl
3121 S Grand Ave, Los Angeles
(90007-3816)
PHONE....................213 749-7725
Eugene M Hardy, *President*
▲ **EMP:** 29 **EST:** 1978
SALES (est): 3.9MM **Privately Held**
WEB: www.promisespromises.com
SIC: 2335 Women's, juniors' & misses'
dresses

(P-3336)
PROTREND LTD (HQ)
6001 E Washington Blvd, Commerce
(90040-2451)
PHONE....................323 832-9323
Peter Kim, *President*
Eunice Kim, *CEO*
▲ **EMP:** 13
SQ FT: 22,000
SALES (est): 2MM
SALES (corp-wide): 2MM **Privately Held**
WEB: www.saymeekinc.com
SIC: 2335 Women's, juniors' & misses'
dresses
PA: K Saymee Inc
6409 Gayhart St
Commerce CA 90040
323 832-9323

(P-3337)
STOP STARING DESIGNS
1151 Goodrick Dr, Tehachapi (93561-1517)
PHONE....................213 627-1480
Alicia Estrada, *CEO*
James Atyeo, *CFO*
EMP: 27
SQ FT: 2,500
SALES (est): 942.4K **Privately Held**
WEB: www.stopstaringclothing.com
SIC: 2335 Women's, juniors' & misses'
dresses

(P-3338)
STUDIO KRP LLC
6133 Bonsall Dr, Malibu (90265-3824)
PHONE....................310 589-5777
Carol Rosenstein, *CEO*
EMP: 13
SQ FT: 1,500
SALES: 3MM **Privately Held**
SIC: 2335 Women's, juniors' & misses'
dresses

(P-3339)
SUBLITEX INC
Also Called: Sublitex Sublimation Tech
1515 E 15th St, Los Angeles (90021-2711)
PHONE....................323 582-9596
Serge Esebag, *President*
Alvin Goldfarb, *Corp Secy*
Jacob Esebag, *Vice Pres*
EMP: 35
SQ FT: 22,000
SALES (est): 8.1MM **Privately Held**
SIC: 2335 7389 Women's, juniors' &
misses' dresses; printing broker

(P-3340)
SWEET INSPIRATIONS INC
17770 Ridgeway Rd, Granada Hills
(91344-2131)
PHONE....................310 886-9010
Chieko Kamisato, *President*
Bebe Ganaja, *Corp Secy*
EMP: 30
SQ FT: 30,000
SALES (est): 1.4MM **Privately Held**
WEB: www.sweetinspiration.com
SIC: 2335 Women's, juniors' & misses'
dresses

(P-3341)
TADASHI SHOJI & ASSOCIATES INC (PA)
3016 E 44th St, Vernon (90058-2428)
PHONE....................213 627-7145
Tadashi Shoji, *CEO*
Maria Dirmandzhyan, *Store Mgr*
Ruben Epong, *Info Tech Mgr*
Martin Chang, *Technology*
Laura Davis, *Graphic Designe*
◆ **EMP:** 100
SQ FT: 36,000
SALES (est): 18.8MM **Privately Held**
SIC: 2335 Dresses, paper: cut & sewn

(P-3342)
TONY MARTERIE & ASSOCIATES (PA)
Also Called: North Coast Industries
28 Liberty Ship Way Fl 2, Sausalito
(94965-3320)
P.O. Box 2018 (94966-2018)
PHONE....................415 331-7150
Tony Marterie, *President*
Roxanne Marterie, *Vice Pres*
▲ **EMP:** 22
SQ FT: 27,000
SALES (est): 1.9MM **Privately Held**
SIC: 2335 2339 Women's, juniors' &
misses' dresses; women's & misses' out-
erwear

(P-3343)
TWO STAR DOG INC
Also Called: Stella Carakasi
1329 9th St, Berkeley (94710-1502)
PHONE....................510 525-1100
EMP: 19 **Privately Held**
SIC: 2335 Women's, juniors' & misses'
dresses
PA: Two Star Dog Inc.
1329 9th St
Berkeley CA 94710

(P-3344)
URBAN OUTFITTERS INC
Also Called: Urban Outfitters Store 18
139 W Colorado Blvd, Pasadena
(91105-1924)
PHONE....................626 449-1818
Allie Enoch, *Manager*
EMP: 30
SALES (corp-wide): 3.6B **Publicly Held**
WEB: www.urbanoutfittersinc.com
SIC: 2335 5611 5719 Women's, juniors' &
misses' dresses; men's & boys' clothing
stores; kitchenware
PA: Urban Outfitters, Inc.
5000 S Broad St
Philadelphia PA 19112
215 454-5500

(P-3345)
URU BY KRISTINE ST RRIK INC
Also Called: U R U
622 Aero Way, Escondido (92029-1201)
PHONE....................760 745-1800
Ken Brown, *President*
Kristine Garrett, *Admin Sec*
▲ **EMP:** 16
SQ FT: 7,700
SALES (est): 2.1MM **Privately Held**
SIC: 2335 2384 2339 2331 Women's,
juniors' & misses' dresses; robes & dress-
ing gowns; women's & misses' outerwear;
women's & misses' blouses & shirts

(P-3346)
VALMAS INC
Also Called: Sam & Lavi
1233 S Boyle Ave, Los Angeles
(90023-2601)
PHONE....................323 677-2211
Sam Arasteh, *President*
▲ **EMP:** 20
SALES (est): 1.5MM **Privately Held**
SIC: 2335 Women's, juniors' & misses'
dresses

(P-3347)
YMI JEANSWEAR INC (PA)
1155 S Boyle Ave, Los Angeles
(90023-2109)
PHONE....................323 581-7700
Moshe Moshezaga, *CEO*
David Vered, *President*
Michael Godigian, *Vice Pres*
Michael Silvestri, *Vice Pres*
Moshe Zaga, *Vice Pres*
▲ **EMP:** 15
SALES (est): 13.1MM **Privately Held**
WEB: www.ymijeans.com
SIC: 2335 Women's, juniors' & misses'
dresses

2337 Women's & Misses' Suits, Coats & Skirts

(P-3348)
ANN LILLI CORP (PA)
1010 B St Ste 209, San Rafael
(94901-2919)
PHONE....................415 482-9444
Don Kamler, *Principal*
Jo Schuman, *Principal*
EMP: 63
SALES (est): 5.7MM **Privately Held**
SIC: 2337 Women's & misses' suits &
coats

(P-3349)
CALIFORNIA FASHION CLUB INC (PA)
Also Called: Lisa & ME
207 S 9th Ave, La Puente (91746-3310)
P.O. Box 880, San Gabriel (91778-0880)
PHONE....................626 575-1838
Sandy Wai Nga Chen, *President*
William Chen, *Vice Pres*
▲ **EMP:** 11
SQ FT: 1,100
SALES: 2MM **Privately Held**
SIC: 2337 2331 Women's & misses' suits
& coats; women's & misses' blouses &
shirts

(P-3350)
DANOC MANUFACTURING CORP INC
Also Called: Danoc Embroidery
6015 Power Inn Rd Ste A, Sacramento
(95824-2336)
PHONE....................916 455-2876
Tom Land, *President*
EMP: 16
SQ FT: 1,500
SALES (est): 1.3MM **Privately Held**
WEB: www.danoc.com
SIC: 2337 2326 Uniforms, except athletic:
women's, misses' & juniors'; industrial
garments, men's & boys' work garments,
except raincoats: waterproof

(P-3351)
DBG SUBSIDIARY INC
Also Called: Joe's Jeans
1500 N El Centro Ave # 150, Los Angeles
(90028-9223)
PHONE....................323 837-3700
Marc B Crossman, *President*
Elena Pickett, *Vice Pres*
Dmitry Brezhnev, *Info Tech Dir*
Sal Lopez, *Director*
Robert Muzingo, *Director*
▲ **EMP:** 150
SALES (est): 58.4MM
SALES (corp-wide): 164MM **Publicly Held**
SIC: 2337 Women's & misses' suits &
coats
PA: Centric Brands Inc.
350 5th Ave Lbby 6
New York NY 10118
323 890-1800

(P-3352)
FASHION QUEEN MANIA INC
800 E 12th St Ste 428, Los Angeles
(90021-2245)
PHONE....................213 788-7310
Hee Young Moon, *CEO*
EMP: 20 **EST:** 2017
SALES (est): 615.4K **Privately Held**
SIC: 2337 Skirts, separate: women's,
misses' & juniors'

(P-3353)
KAYO OF CALIFORNIA (PA)
161 W 39th St, Los Angeles (90037-1080)
PHONE....................323 233-6107
Jack Ostrovsky, *Ch of Bd*
Jeffrey Michaels, *CEO*
Annabelle Wall, *CFO*
Janis Dardick, *Vice Pres*
Jonathan Kaye, *Vice Pres*
◆ **EMP:** 45 **EST:** 1968
SQ FT: 24,000
SALES (est): 8.4MM **Privately Held**
WEB: www.kayo.com
SIC: 2337 2339 Skirts, separate:
women's, misses' & juniors'; sportswear,
women's; shorts (outerwear): women's,
misses' & juniors'; slacks: women's,
misses' & juniors'

(P-3354)
KELLER CLASSICS INC (PA)
Also Called: Nannette Keller
19628 Country Oaks St, Tehachapi
(93561-8490)
PHONE....................805 524-1322
Nannette Keller, *President*
Roger Keller, *CFO*
Richard Scott, *Admin Sec*
EMP: 35
SQ FT: 12,000
SALES (est): 3.6MM **Privately Held**
WEB: www.kellerclassics.com
SIC: 2337 5621 Women's & misses' suits
& skirts; women's clothing stores

(P-3355)
KOMAROV ENTERPRISES INC
Also Called: Kisca
1936 Mateo St, Los Angeles (90021-2833)
PHONE....................213 244-7000
Dimitri Komarov, *President*
Dimitri Leiberman, *Vice Pres*
Jose Rojas, *Accounting Mgr*
Rita Husak, *Controller*
Shelley Komvarov, *Director*
▲ **EMP:** 75
SQ FT: 25,000
SALES (est): 8.7MM **Privately Held**
WEB: www.komarovinc.com
SIC: 2337 2331 Women's & misses' suits
& coats; women's & misses' blouses &
shirts

(P-3356)
NINE WEST HOLDINGS INC
Also Called: Kasper
232 Great Mall Dr, Milpitas (95035-8026)
PHONE....................408 946-2570
EMP: 10
SALES (corp-wide): 2.2B **Privately Held**
WEB: www.kasper.net
SIC: 2337 Women's & misses' suits &
coats

HQ: Nine West Holdings, Inc.
180 Rittenhouse Cir
Bristol PA 19007
215 785-4000

(P-3357)
NORTH HOLLYWOOD UNIFORM INC
Also Called: North Hollywood Uniform Group
7328 Laurel Canyon Blvd, North Hollywood (91605-3710)
PHONE....................818 503-5931
Virginia Gray, *President*
EMP: 15
SALES (est): 1MM **Privately Held**
SIC: 2337 2329 5137 Uniforms, except athletic: women's, misses' & juniors'; men's & boys' athletic uniforms; uniforms, women's & children's

(P-3358)
OFF PRICE NETWORK LLC
10544 Dunleer Dr, Los Angeles (90064-4318)
PHONE....................213 477-8205
Diana Murray,
EMP: 30
SQ FT: 56,500
SALES (est): 2.6MM **Privately Held**
WEB: www.offprice.net
SIC: 2337 Women's & misses' suits & coats

(P-3359)
POETRY CORPORATION (PA)
2111 Long Beach Ave, Los Angeles (90058-1023)
PHONE....................213 765-8957
Seong H Lee, *CEO*
▲ **EMP:** 24 **EST:** 1998
SQ FT: 50,000
SALES (est): 4.1MM **Privately Held**
SIC: 2337 Women's & misses' suits & coats

(P-3360)
R B III ASSOCIATES INC
Also Called: Teamwork Athletic Apparel
166 Newport Dr, San Marcos (92069-1467)
PHONE....................760 471-5370
Matthew Lehrer, *CEO*
Dave Caserta, *President*
Andy Lehrer, *Vice Pres*
Violet Lehrer, *Executive*
Jan Kruger, *Admin Asst*
▲ **EMP:** 150
SQ FT: 110,000
SALES (est): 22.9MM **Privately Held**
WEB: www.fcsite1.com
SIC: 2337 2329 Uniforms, except athletic: women's, misses' & juniors'; men's & boys' athletic uniforms

(P-3361)
RENEE C
127 E 9th St Ste 506, Los Angeles (90015-1735)
PHONE....................213 741-0095
Jin Young Song, *Principal*
EMP: 17
SALES (est): 661K **Privately Held**
SIC: 2337 Women's & misses' suits & coats

(P-3362)
RUBEL MARGUERITE MFG CO
27 Pier, San Francisco (94111-1038)
PHONE....................415 362-2626
EMP: 12 **EST:** 1952
SQ FT: 20,000
SALES (est): 1MM **Privately Held**
SIC: 2337

(P-3363)
S STUDIO INC
Also Called: Sue Wong
3030 W 6th St, Los Angeles (90020-1506)
PHONE....................213 388-7400
Dieter Raabe, *President*
Sue Wong, *Ch of Bd*
Mark Ishak, *Graphic Designe*
Josh Homann, *Manager*
▲ **EMP:** 60
SQ FT: 28,000

SALES (est): 22.5MM **Privately Held**
WEB: www.suewong.com
SIC: 2337 Women's & misses' suits & skirts

(P-3364)
SCHOOL APPAREL INC (PA)
Also Called: A Career Apparel
838 Mitten Rd, Burlingame (94010-1304)
PHONE....................650 777-4500
Kenneth Knoss, *Principal*
Ryan Knoss, *Ch of Bd*
Dave Weil, *CFO*
Bernice B Knoss, *Treasurer*
Vincent Knoss, *Chief Mktg Ofcr*
◆ **EMP:** 152
SALES (est): 65.2MM **Privately Held**
WEB: www.schoolapparel.com
SIC: 2337 2311 2326 Uniforms, except athletic: women's, misses' & juniors'; men's & boys' uniforms; work uniforms

(P-3365)
TOPSON DOWNS CALIFORNIA INC
3545 Motor Ave, Los Angeles (90034-4806)
PHONE....................310 558-0300
Kris Scott, *Manager*
EMP: 35
SALES (corp-wide): 238.7MM **Privately Held**
SIC: 2337 5621 Women's & misses' suits & coats; ready-to-wear apparel, women's
PA: Topson Downs Of California, Inc.,
3840 Watseka Ave
Culver City CA 90232
310 558-0300

2339 Women's & Misses' Outerwear, NEC

(P-3366)
AARON CORPORATION
Also Called: J P Sportswear
1820 E 41st St, Vernon (90058-1534)
PHONE....................323 235-5959
Paul Shechet, *President*
Francisco Balleste, *Vice Pres*
Francisco Ballester, *Vice Pres*
Paco Ballester, *Opers Mgr*
Anna Almeida, *Manager*
▲ **EMP:** 170 **EST:** 1955
SQ FT: 41,000
SALES (est): 22.9MM **Privately Held**
WEB: www.jpsportswear.net
SIC: 2339 Women's & misses' athletic clothing & sportswear

(P-3367)
AB&R INC
Also Called: Billy Blues
5849 Smithway St, Commerce (90040-1605)
PHONE....................323 727-0007
Rene Allison Thomas, *President*
William Scott Curtis, *Vice Pres*
▲ **EMP:** 22
SQ FT: 10,500
SALES (est): 2.1MM **Privately Held**
SIC: 2339 Women's & misses' outerwear

(P-3368)
ABS BY ALLEN SCHWARTZ LLC (HQ)
1218 S Santa Fe Ave, Los Angeles (90021-1745)
PHONE....................213 895-4400
Allen Schwartz, *Mng Member*
Kirk Foster, *CFO*
▲ **EMP:** 37
SQ FT: 50,000
SALES (est): 13.4MM
SALES (corp-wide): 16.1MM **Privately Held**
WEB: www.harmonycollection.com
SIC: 2339 5621 Women's & misses' outerwear; women's clothing stores
PA: Aquarius Rags, Llc
1218 S Santa Fe Ave
Los Angeles CA 90021
213 895-4400

(P-3369)
ABS CLOTHING COLLECTION INC
Also Called: A.B.S. By Allen Schwartz
1218 S Santa Fe Ave, Los Angeles (90021-1745)
PHONE....................213 895-4400
Allen Schwartz, *President*
EMP: 15
SALES (est): 1.9MM **Privately Held**
SIC: 2339 5621 Women's & misses' outerwear; women's clothing stores

(P-3370)
ALBION KNITTING MILLS INC
2152 Sacramento St, Los Angeles (90021-1722)
PHONE....................213 624-7740
George Ainslie, *President*
EMP: 28 **EST:** 1923
SQ FT: 15,000
SALES (est): 2.2MM **Privately Held**
SIC: 2339 2329 2253 Uniforms, athletic: women's, misses' & juniors'; jackets (suede, leatherette, etc.), sport: men's & boys'; knit outerwear mills

(P-3371)
ALEGIO FASHIONS INC
25634 Amber Leaf Rd, Torrance (90505-7102)
PHONE....................310 539-0981
Francis Mejia, *President*
Lucia Mejia, *Vice Pres*
EMP: 30
SQ FT: 9,100
SALES (est): 408.6K **Privately Held**
SIC: 2339 Bathing suits: women's, misses' & juniors'

(P-3372)
AMBIANCE USA INC (PA)
Also Called: Ambiance Apparel
2415 E 15th St, Los Angeles (90021-2936)
PHONE....................323 587-0007
Sang B Noh, *CEO*
◆ **EMP:** 12
SALES (est): 3.5MM **Privately Held**
SIC: 2339 Women's & misses' outerwear

(P-3373)
APPAREL ENTERPRISES CO INC
1900 Wilson Ave Ste B, National City (91950-5532)
PHONE....................619 474-6916
Duy Nguyentran, *President*
Uyen Dao, *Vice Pres*
◆ **EMP:** 20 **EST:** 2001
SALES (est): 1.9MM **Privately Held**
SIC: 2339 Women's & misses' outerwear

(P-3374)
APPAREL LIMITED INC
Also Called: Kangol
3011 E Pico Blvd, Los Angeles (90023-3611)
PHONE....................323 859-2430
Masud Sarshar, *CEO*
Maryam Toofer, *President*
Vickie Barich, *Webmaster*
▼ **EMP:** 90
SQ FT: 71,000
SALES (est): 8.1MM **Privately Held**
SIC: 2339 Women's & misses' athletic clothing & sportswear

(P-3375)
APPAREL PROD SVCS GLOBL LLC
8954 Lurline Ave, Chatsworth (91311-6103)
PHONE....................818 700-3700
Clayton Medley, *President*
Paul Stanley, *Vice Pres*
◆ **EMP:** 42
SQ FT: 15,000
SALES (est): 6.8MM **Privately Held**
WEB: www.apscorp.org
SIC: 2339 2329 Women's & misses' athletic clothing & sportswear; men's & boys' sportswear & athletic clothing

(P-3376)
ASSOLUTO INC
Also Called: Molly Max
215 S Santa Fe Ave Apt 5, Los Angeles (90012-4350)
PHONE....................213 748-1116
Ugo Capasso, *CEO*
▲ **EMP:** 16
SQ FT: 2,600
SALES (est): 1.8MM **Privately Held**
WEB: www.gigigirl.com
SIC: 2339 Women's & misses' athletic clothing & sportswear

(P-3377)
AVID LYFE INC
990 Park Center Dr Ste C, Vista (92081-8352)
PHONE....................888 510-2517
Lindsey Hunziker, *CEO*
EMP: 12
SALES (est): 1.2MM **Privately Held**
SIC: 2339 3498 2326 Athletic clothing: women's, misses' & juniors'; fabricated pipe & fittings; men's & boys' work clothing

(P-3378)
AZTECA JEANS INC
6600 Avalon Blvd, Los Angeles (90003-1959)
PHONE....................323 758-7721
Manuel Sanchez, *Principal*
EMP: 50
SALES (est): 3.4MM **Privately Held**
SIC: 2339

(P-3379)
BABETTE (PA)
867 Isabella St, Oakland (94607-3429)
PHONE....................510 625-8500
Babette Pinsky, *President*
Steven Pinsky, *CFO*
Elfriede Griffey, *Admin Sec*
▲ **EMP:** 37
SQ FT: 28,000
SALES (est): 6.8MM **Privately Held**
WEB: www.babettesf.com
SIC: 2339 2369 Sportswear, women's; women's & misses' jackets & coats, except sportswear; girls' & children's outerwear

(P-3380)
BARE NOTHINGS INC (PA)
17705 Sampson Ln, Huntington Beach (92647-6790)
PHONE....................714 848-8532
Ann Mase, *President*
Ronald Mase, *Vice Pres*
EMP: 22
SALES (est): 2.4MM **Privately Held**
WEB: www.barenothings.com
SIC: 2339 Bathing suits: women's, misses' & juniors'

(P-3381)
BB CO INC
Also Called: Wild Lizard
1753 E 21st St, Los Angeles (90058-1006)
PHONE....................213 747-4701
Kyoung K Frazier, *President*
▲ **EMP:** 30
SQ FT: 22,000
SALES (est): 4.6MM **Privately Held**
SIC: 2339 Women's & misses' athletic clothing & sportswear

(P-3382)
BCBG MAXAZRIA ENTRMT LLC
2761 Fruitland Ave, Vernon (90058-3607)
PHONE....................323 277-4713
Max Azria,
Charles Cohenm,
EMP: 10
SALES (est): 791.4K **Privately Held**
SIC: 2339 5137 5621 Women's & misses' outerwear; women's & children's clothing; women's clothing stores

(P-3383)
BEACH PATROL INC (HQ)
3771 Lockland Dr Apt 2, Carson (90745)
PHONE....................310 522-2700
John Wickham, *President*
Ronald Stern, *Ch of Bd*

PRODUCTS & SVCS

Robert Silver, *CEO*
Gail Rhodes, *Senior VP*
▲ **EMP:** 12
SQ FT: 107,000
SALES (est): 5.6MM **Privately Held**
SIC: 2339 2329 Athletic clothing: women's, misses' & juniors'; bathing suits: women's, misses' & juniors'; athletic (warmup, sweat & jogging) suits: men's & boys'; bathing suits & swimwear: men's & boys'
PA: Western Glove Works
555 Logan Ave
Winnipeg MB R3A 0
204 788-4249

(P-3384)
BIDU INC
756 E Wash Blvd Ste B, Los Angeles (90021-3017)
PHONE....................213 748-4433
Walter Shim, *President*
EMP: 11
SALES (est): 1.3MM **Privately Held**
WEB: www.bidu.com
SIC: 2339 7389 Women's & misses' outerwear; sewing contractor

(P-3385)
BIG BANG CLOTHING INC (PA)
Also Called: Big Bang Clothing Co
4507 Staunton Ave, Vernon (90058-1936)
PHONE....................323 233-7773
Sam Seungwoo Lee, *President*
EMP: 10
SQ FT: 9,000
SALES (est): 1.5MM **Privately Held**
WEB: www.bigbangclothing.com
SIC: 2339 Women's & misses' athletic clothing & sportswear

(P-3386)
BLACK SILVER ENTERPRISES INC (PA)
Also Called: Gracie Collection
6024 Paseo Delicias, Rancho Santa Fe (92067)
PHONE....................858 623-9220
Un MI Lee, *President*
Seya Mahvi, *CEO*
EMP: 11
SQ FT: 1,500
SALES (est): 802.8K **Privately Held**
SIC: 2339 Women's & misses' outerwear

(P-3387)
BURNING TORCH INC
1738 Cordova St, Los Angeles (90007-1129)
PHONE....................323 733-7700
Karyn Craven, *President*
Gracie Minijarez, *Bookkeeper*
Rose Marron, *Prdtn Mgr*
▲ **EMP:** 20
SQ FT: 5,000
SALES (est): 2.5MM **Privately Held**
WEB: www.burningtorchinc.com
SIC: 2339 Sportswear, women's

(P-3388)
C & Y INVESTMENT INC
Also Called: Girl Talk Clothing
946 E 29th St, Los Angeles (90011-2034)
PHONE....................323 267-9000
Carrie Jooyon Yi, *CEO*
Michael Yi, *CFO*
EMP: 11
SQ FT: 8,000
SALES (est): 2.5MM **Privately Held**
SIC: 2339 Aprons, except rubber or plastic: women's, misses', juniors'

(P-3389)
C P SHADES INC (PA)
403 Coloma St, Sausalito (94965-2827)
PHONE....................415 331-4581
David Weinstein, *President*
Denise Weinstein, *Treasurer*
Alison Pownall, *Vice Pres*
Bianca Chui, *Executive*
Cyndi Pettibone, *Office Mgr*
▲ **EMP:** 17
SQ FT: 40,405

SALES (est): 101.8MM **Privately Held**
SIC: 2339 5621 Women's & misses' athletic clothing & sportswear; sportswear, women's; women's sportswear

(P-3390)
CAMP SMIDGEMORE INC (DH)
Also Called: Renee Claire Inc
3641 10th Ave, Los Angeles (90018-4114)
PHONE....................323 634-0333
Wendy Luttrel, *CEO*
Renee Bertrand, *President*
Rafael Vega, *Controller*
▲ **EMP:** 22
SQ FT: 13,000
SALES (est): 5.3MM
SALES (corp-wide): 310.7MM **Privately Held**
SIC: 2339 2341 Women's & misses' outerwear; pajamas & bedjackets: women's & children's
HQ: Komar Intimates, Llc
90 Hudson St
Jersey City NJ 07302
212 725-1500

(P-3391)
CAROL WIOR INC
Also Called: Slimsuit
7533 Garfield Ave, Bell (90201-4817)
PHONE....................562 927-0052
Carol Wior, *President*
Troy Berg, *CEO*
Lucy Weddell, *Treasurer*
Niki Wior, *Vice Pres*
Julie Wilson, *Admin Sec*
▲ **EMP:** 70
SQ FT: 77,000
SALES (est): 6.7MM **Privately Held**
SIC: 2339 5699 Bathing suits: women's, misses' & juniors'; sportswear, women's; beachwear: women's, misses' & juniors'; bathing suits

(P-3392)
CEE SPORTSWEAR
6409 Gayhart St, Commerce (90040-2505)
PHONE....................323 726-8158
Paul Bogner, *President*
▲ **EMP:** 20 **EST:** 1958
SQ FT: 57,000
SALES (est): 2.4MM **Privately Held**
SIC: 2339 Maternity clothing

(P-3393)
CITIZENS OF HUMANITY LLC (PA)
Also Called: Goldsign
5715 Bickett St, Huntington Park (90255-2624)
PHONE....................323 923-1240
Jerome Dahan, *CEO*
Amy Williams, *President*
Melissa Means, *Executive Asst*
Daniel Pulido, *Administration*
Jared Freedman, *CTO*
▲ **EMP:** 70
SQ FT: 70,000
SALES (est): 81MM **Privately Held**
WEB: www.citizensofhumanity.com
SIC: 2339 Jeans: women's, misses' & juniors'

(P-3394)
CLASSIC TEES INC
4915 Walnut Grove Ave, San Gabriel (91776-2021)
PHONE....................626 607-0255
Paul Chauderson, *President*
Connie Lam, *Vice Pres*
EMP: 35
SQ FT: 15,000
SALES (est): 3.2MM **Privately Held**
WEB: www.classic-tees.com
SIC: 2339 Women's & misses' athletic clothing & sportswear

(P-3395)
CLOTHING ILLUSTRATED INC (PA)
Also Called: Love Stitch
2014 E 15th St, Los Angeles (90021-2823)
PHONE....................213 403-9950
Danny Forouzesh, *President*
Cyrous Forouzesh, *CFO*
▲ **EMP:** 40

SALES (est): 6.2MM **Privately Held**
SIC: 2339 Women's & misses' outerwear

(P-3396)
CLOVER GARMENTS INC
2565 3rd St Ste 232, San Francisco (94107-3160)
PHONE....................415 826-6909
Florence Lo, *President*
▲ **EMP:** 70
SQ FT: 10,000
SALES (est): 5.9MM **Privately Held**
SIC: 2339 2329 Sportswear, women's; men's & boys' sportswear & athletic clothing

(P-3397)
CONNECTED APPAREL COMPANY LLC (PA)
Also Called: Next Up
6015 Bandini Blvd, Commerce (90040-2904)
PHONE....................323 890-8000
Jay Balaban, *Mng Member*
Ira Fogelman, *CFO*
Ellen Delloshbacher,
Alice Rosenberg,
Jan Smith,
▲ **EMP:** 25
SQ FT: 50,000
SALES (est): 4.7MM **Privately Held**
WEB: www.connectedapparel.com
SIC: 2339 Athletic clothing: women's, misses' & juniors'

(P-3398)
CREW KNITWEAR LLC (PA)
Also Called: Hiatus
660 S Myers St, Los Angeles (90023-1015)
PHONE....................323 526-3888
Peter Jung, *CEO*
Chris Y Jung, *President*
▲ **EMP:** 51
SQ FT: 39,000
SALES (est): 17MM **Privately Held**
WEB: www.crewknitwear.com
SIC: 2339 Women's & misses' outerwear

(P-3399)
CUT LOOSE (PA)
101 Williams Ave, San Francisco (94124-2619)
PHONE....................415 822-2031
Will Wenham, *President*
Rosemarie Ovian, *Vice Pres*
◆ **EMP:** 55
SQ FT: 17,000
SALES (est): 8.7MM **Privately Held**
WEB: www.cutloose.com
SIC: 2339 5621 2331 Sportswear, women's; women's clothing stores; women's blouses & shirts

(P-3400)
D&A UNLIMITED INC
111 W Victoria St, Long Beach (90805-2162)
PHONE....................562 336-1528
David Anthony, *CEO*
Anna Anthony, *President*
EMP: 25
SQ FT: 4,400
SALES: 300K **Privately Held**
SIC: 2339 Women's & misses' athletic clothing & sportswear

(P-3401)
DARBO MANUFACTURING COMPANY
363 Glenoaks St, Brea (92821-2117)
PHONE....................714 529-7693
Scott Silber, *President*
EMP: 25
SQ FT: 7,500
SALES: 1.2MM **Privately Held**
WEB: www.dancewearforyou.com
SIC: 2339 2369 2389

(P-3402)
DASH SPORTSWEAR
Also Called: Dash Sportwear
2624 Geraldine St, Los Angeles (90011-1829)
PHONE....................323 846-2640
Ho Suk Kim, *Owner*
EMP: 20

SQ FT: 13,000
SALES (est): 1.3MM **Privately Held**
SIC: 2339 5131 Women's & misses' outerwear; piece goods & other fabrics

(P-3403)
DDA HOLDINGS INC
Also Called: A Commom Thread
834 S Broadway Ste 1100, Los Angeles (90014-3510)
PHONE....................213 624-5200
Anthony Graham, *CEO*
Sandra Balestier, *President*
▲ **EMP:** 18
SQ FT: 15,000
SALES (est): 2.7MM **Privately Held**
SIC: 2339 Women's & misses' athletic clothing & sportswear

(P-3404)
DE SOTO CLOTHING INC
Also Called: De Soto Sport
7584 Trade St, San Diego (92121-2412)
PHONE....................858 578-6672
Emilio De Soto II, *President*
Dan Neyenhuis, *Shareholder*
Marta Lundgren, *Admin Sec*
Vinti Mehra, *Prdtn Mgr*
Richard Dimaano, *Associate*
▲ **EMP:** 15
SQ FT: 5,600
SALES (est): 1.4MM **Privately Held**
WEB: www.desotosport.com
SIC: 2339 2329 Women's & misses' athletic clothing & sportswear; men's & boys' sportswear & athletic clothing

(P-3405)
DESIGN CONCEPTS INC
4625 E 50th St, Vernon (90058-3223)
P.O. Box 58512, Los Angeles (90058-0512)
PHONE....................323 277-4771
Michael Park, *President*
EMP: 15
SALES (est): 121.3K **Privately Held**
SIC: 2339 Women's & misses' athletic clothing & sportswear

(P-3406)
DESIGN TODAYS INC (PA)
725 E Wash Blvd Fl 2nd, Los Angeles (90021-3069)
PHONE....................213 745-3091
Sung OK Hong, *President*
EMP: 53
SQ FT: 12,000
SALES (est): 4MM **Privately Held**
WEB: www.designtodays.com
SIC: 2339 Women's & misses' outerwear

(P-3407)
DHM INTERNATIONAL CORP
Also Called: Sunshine Enterprises
901 Monterey Pass Rd, Monterey Park (91754-3610)
PHONE....................323 263-3888
Scott Yuen, *President*
Joe Yuen, *Vice Pres*
Ross Yuen, *Vice Pres*
▲ **EMP:** 90
SQ FT: 28,000
SALES (est): 9.2MM **Privately Held**
SIC: 2339 2326 Women's & misses' outerwear; men's & boys' work clothing

(P-3408)
DMBM LLC
2445 E 12th St Ste C, Los Angeles (90021-2954)
PHONE....................714 321-6032
David Chong, *Owner*
EMP: 25 **Privately Held**
WEB: www.dmbmla.com
SIC: 2339 2369 Women's & misses' outerwear; girls' & children's outerwear
PA: Dmbm, Llc
2701 S Santa Fe Ave
Vernon CA

(P-3409)
DOSA INC
850 S Broadway Ste 700, Los Angeles (90014-3238)
PHONE....................213 627-3672
Christina Kim, *President*

▲ = Import ▼=Export
◆ =Import/Export

Meghan Murphy, *Prdtn Mgr*
▲ **EMP:** 30
SQ FT: 15,000
SALES (est): 2.8MM **Privately Held**
SIC: 2339 Sportswear, women's

(P-3410)
ELECOCO INC
Also Called: Shinestar
4553 Seville Ave, Vernon (90058-2307)
PHONE....................213 627-2377
Young Kuk Chang, *CEO*
EMP: 40 **EST:** 2001
SALES (est): 14.3MM **Privately Held**
WEB: www.otl.com
SIC: 2339 Athletic clothing: women's, misses' & juniors'

(P-3411)
EQUESTRIAN DESIGNS LLC
91 2nd St Ste A, Buellton (93427-9471)
PHONE....................805 686-4455
Iona Marshall, *Mng Member*
EMP: 25
SQ FT: 6,000
SALES (est): 2.4MM **Privately Held**
WEB: www.equestriandesigns.net
SIC: 2339 Women's & misses' outerwear

(P-3412)
ESKA INC
Also Called: Event Spice Wear
3631 Union Pacific Ave, Los Angeles
(90023-3255)
PHONE....................323 268-2134
Suk Eun Cho, *President*
▲ **EMP:** 25
SQ FT: 1,660
SALES (est): 3.4MM **Privately Held**
WEB: www.eska.com
SIC: 2339 Athletic clothing: women's, misses' & juniors'

(P-3413)
EUNINA INC
1100 S San Pedro St J09, Los Angeles
(90015-2366)
PHONE....................213 747-1672
Jenny Lee, *Manager*
EMP: 20
SALES (corp-wide): 6.7MM **Privately Held**
SIC: 2339 Slacks: women's, misses' & juniors'
PA: Eunina, Inc.
     3398 Leonis Blvd
     Vernon CA 90058
     323 588-6914

(P-3414)
EVER-GLORY INTL GROUP INC
1009 Becklee Rd, Glendora (91741-2201)
P.O. Box 855 (91740-0855)
PHONE....................626 859-6638
Jessie Hsu, *Manager*
EMP: 10 **Privately Held**
SIC: 2339 Women's & misses' outerwear
HQ: Ever-Glory International Group Apparel Inc.
     No. 509, Chengxin Ave., Jiangning Technical Economic Development Nanjing
     255 209-6879

(P-3415)
FASHION TODAY INC
Also Called: Mon Amie
1100 S San Pedro St Ste A, Los Angeles
(90015-2328)
PHONE....................213 744-1636
John Sung, *CFO*
EMP: 22 **Privately Held**
SIC: 2339 Women's & misses' jackets & coats, except sportswear
PA: Fashion Today, Inc.
     3100 S Grand Ave Fl 3
     Los Angeles CA 90007

(P-3416)
FASHION TODAY INC (PA)
Also Called: Mon Amie
3100 S Grand Ave Fl 3, Los Angeles
(90007-3815)
PHONE....................213 744-1636
Kwang Pyo Hong, *CEO*

Sung Hwan Hong, *President*
EMP: 11
SQ FT: 10,000
SALES (est): 10MM **Privately Held**
SIC: 2339 Athletic clothing: women's, misses' & juniors'; women's & misses' jackets & coats, except sportswear

(P-3417)
FAST SPORTSWEAR INC
6400 E Washington Blvd, Commerce
(90040-1820)
PHONE....................323 720-1078
Young Kuen Kim, *President*
Sook In Kim, *Vice Pres*
EMP: 70
SQ FT: 200,000
SALES (est): 4.9MM **Privately Held**
SIC: 2339 Sportswear, women's

(P-3418)
FELLYR INTERNATIONAL INC
Also Called: Fenini
13453 Brooks Dr Ste B, Baldwin Park
(91706-2255)
PHONE....................626 960-5111
Sandra Yang, *President*
EMP: 14
SQ FT: 10,000
SALES (est): 1.9MM **Privately Held**
SIC: 2339 5085 Women's & misses' athletic clothing & sportswear; commercial containers

(P-3419)
FINESSE APPAREL INC (PA)
815 Fairview Ave Unit 101, South
Pasadena (91030-2490)
PHONE....................213 747-7077
▲ **EMP:** 40
SQ FT: 60,000
SALES (est): 24.3MM **Privately Held**
SIC: 2339

(P-3420)
GAZE USA INC
1665 Mateo St, Los Angeles (90021-2854)
PHONE....................213 622-0022
Ji S Hong, *CEO*
Stephen S Whang, *President*
EMP: 25 **EST:** 2010
SALES (est): 2.9MM **Privately Held**
SIC: 2339 5651 3999 Women's & misses' athletic clothing & sportswear; unisex clothing stores; bristles, dressing of

(P-3421)
GLIMA INC
11133 Vanowen St Ste A, North Hollywood
(91605-6379)
PHONE....................818 980-9686
AVI Levy, *CEO*
EMP: 12
SALES (est): 1.1MM **Privately Held**
WEB: www.glima.com
SIC: 2339 Athletic clothing: women's, misses' & juniors'

(P-3422)
GOLDEN COAST SPORTSWEAR INC
1140 E Howell Ave, Anaheim (92805-6452)
P.O. Box 3370 (92803-3370)
PHONE....................714 704-4655
Mark Casale, *President*
Katy Kunzweiler, *President*
EMP: 50 **EST:** 1982
SALES (est): 5.4MM **Privately Held**
SIC: 2339 2329 Sportswear, women's; men's & boys' sportswear & athletic clothing

(P-3423)
GOLF APPAREL BRANDS INC
Also Called: La Mode
13621 S Main St, Los Angeles
(90061-2163)
PHONE....................310 327-5188
Edward J Kahn, *President*
W Barry Kahn, *Vice Pres*
▲ **EMP:** 140
SQ FT: 108,000
SALES (est): 9.7MM **Privately Held**
WEB: www.golf-apparel-brands.com
SIC: 2339 Women's & misses' outerwear

(P-3424)
GYPSY 05 INC
3200 Union Pacific Ave, Los Angeles
(90023-4203)
PHONE....................323 265-2700
Dotan Shoham, *President*
Catalina Dado, *Accounting Mgr*
▲ **EMP:** 20
SALES (est): 2.2MM **Privately Held**
SIC: 2339 Women's & misses' athletic clothing & sportswear

(P-3425)
H STARLET LLC
3447 S Main St, Los Angeles (90007-4413)
PHONE....................323 235-8777
Brad Zions,
Heidi Cornell,
▲ **EMP:** 10
SALES (est): 1.5MM **Privately Held**
SIC: 2339 Women's & misses' athletic clothing & sportswear

(P-3426)
HANK PLAYER INC
4303 Lemp Ave, Studio City (91604-2814)
PHONE....................818 856-6079
EMP: 10
SQ FT: 6,000
SALES (est): 76.4K **Privately Held**
WEB: www.hank.com
SIC: 2339 5136

(P-3427)
HEARTS DELIGHT
4035 N Ventura Ave, Ventura (93001-1163)
PHONE....................805 648-7123
Deborah Mesker, *Owner*
EMP: 27
SQ FT: 2,000
SALES (est): 2.1MM **Privately Held**
SIC: 2339 5621 Women's & misses' outerwear; boutiques

(P-3428)
HEY BABY OF CALIFORNIA
11238 Peoria St C, Sun Valley
(91352-1632)
PHONE....................818 504-2060
Pam Lengua, *Partner*
Anita Lengua, *Partner*
Rick Lengua, *Partner*
EMP: 42
SQ FT: 3,500
SALES: 1.5MM **Privately Held**
SIC: 2339 Bathing suits: women's, misses' & juniors'

(P-3429)
HIP & HIP INC (PA)
Also Called: Angels
1100 S San Pedro St D07, Los Angeles
(90015-2328)
PHONE....................310 494-6742
Jung Ae Park, *President*
EMP: 20 **EST:** 1997
SQ FT: 30,000
SALES (est): 1.4MM **Privately Held**
SIC: 2339 Women's & misses' outerwear

(P-3430)
HONEY PUNCH INC (PA)
1535 Rio Vista Ave, Los Angeles
(90023-2619)
PHONE....................323 800-3812
Tae Sung Kang, *President*
Huyon Kang, *Vice Pres*
▲ **EMP:** 15
SALES (est): 2.2MM **Privately Held**
SIC: 2339 5621 Women's & misses' athletic clothing & sportswear; women's clothing stores

(P-3431)
I JOAH (PA)
1721 Wall St, Los Angeles (90015-3718)
PHONE....................213 742-0500
Peter Song, *President*
▲ **EMP:** 10
SALES (est): 3.2MM **Privately Held**
WEB: www.ms1-misopeusa.com
SIC: 2339 Women's & misses' athletic clothing & sportswear

(P-3432)
J & F DESIGN INC
Also Called: Next Generation
5578 Bandini Blvd, Bell (90201-6404)
PHONE....................323 526-4444
Jack Farshi, *President*
Richard Howard, *Vice Pres*
▲ **EMP:** 67
SQ FT: 100,000
SALES (est): 10.1MM **Privately Held**
SIC: 2339 Sportswear, women's

(P-3433)
JAMES KIM YOUNG
1215 W Walnut St, Compton (90220-5009)
PHONE....................310 605-5328
James Young, *Principal*
EMP: 40
SALES (est): 1.7MM **Privately Held**
SIC: 2339 Women's & misses' outerwear

(P-3434)
JAMM INDUSTRIES CORP
Also Called: Bordeaux
2425 E 12th St, Los Angeles (90021-2906)
PHONE....................213 622-0555
Atshin Raminfar, *CEO*
▲ **EMP:** 39
SQ FT: 15,000
SALES (est): 4.6MM **Privately Held**
SIC: 2339 Service apparel, washable: women's

(P-3435)
JAPANESE WEEKEND INC (PA)
496 S Airport Blvd, South San Francisco
(94080-6911)
PHONE....................415 621-0555
Barbara White, *President*
▲ **EMP:** 25
SQ FT: 6,000
SALES (est): 4.6MM **Privately Held**
WEB: www.japaneseweekend.com
SIC: 2339 5621 Maternity clothing; maternity wear

(P-3436)
JAYA APPAREL GROUP LLC (PA)
5175 S Soto St, Vernon (90058-3620)
PHONE....................323 584-3500
Jane Siskin, *CEO*
Don Lewis, *Officer*
Holly Morgan, *Vice Pres*
Rachel Cashman, *Graphic Designe*
Luis Gutierrez, *Engineer*
▲ **EMP:** 80
SQ FT: 170,000
SALES (est): 23.8MM **Privately Held**
SIC: 2339 2337 Women's & misses' jackets & coats, except sportswear; shorts (outerwear): women's, misses' & juniors'; women's & misses' suits & skirts

(P-3437)
JNJ APPAREL INC
3838 S Santa Fe Ave, Vernon
(90058-1713)
PHONE....................323 584-9700
Chan Hyoung Park, *President*
▲ **EMP:** 30
SQ FT: 10,000
SALES (est): 3.4MM **Privately Held**
SIC: 2339 Women's & misses' athletic clothing & sportswear

(P-3438)
JOLYN CLOTHING COMPANY LLC
150 5th St Ste 100, Huntington Beach
(92648-5139)
PHONE....................714 794-2149
Warren Lief Pedersen, *President*
Brandon Molina, *COO*
Ann Dawson, *Vice Pres*
EMP: 30
SALES (est): 1.9MM **Privately Held**
SIC: 2339 5621 Women's & misses' athletic clothing & sportswear; women's sportswear

(P-3439)
JOY ACTIVE
13324 Estrella Ave, Gardena (90248-1519)
PHONE....................310 660-0022
Jong Lim, *President*

EMP: 85
SALES (est): 3.1MM **Privately Held**
SIC: 2339 Women's & misses' outerwear

(P-3440)
JT DESIGN STUDIO INC (PA)
Also Called: 860, Shameless, Hot Wire
860 S Los Angeles St # 912, Los Angeles
(90014-3319)
PHONE..............................213 891-1500
Ted Cooper, *President*
Jan Grossman, *Vice Pres*
Robert Grossman, *Vice Pres*
▲ EMP: 24 EST: 1998
SALES (est): 4MM **Privately Held**
WEB: www.shamelessclothing.com
SIC: 2339 Women's & misses' athletic
clothing & sportswear

(P-3441)
JUST FOR WRAPS INC (PA)
Also Called: A-List
5745 Rickenbacker Rd, Commerce
(90040-3052)
PHONE..............................213 239-0503
Vrajesh Lal, *CEO*
Rakesh Lal, *Vice Pres*
Edna Asuncion, *Accounting Mgr*
Alba Miro, *Human Res Mgr*
Alyssa Knowlton, *Sales Staff*
▲ EMP: 130
SQ FT: 105,000
SALES (est): 24.8MM **Privately Held**
WEB: www.wrapper.com
SIC: 2339 2335 2337 Sportswear,
women's; women's, juniors' & misses'
dresses; women's & misses' suits & coats

(P-3442)
KAREN KANE INC (PA)
2275 E 37th St, Vernon (90058-1435)
PHONE..............................323 588-0000
Lonnie Kane, *President*
Cecelia Jenkins, *Treasurer*
Karen Kane, *Vice Pres*
Cindy Tseng, *Graphic Designe*
Donna Ancheta, *Accountant*
▲ EMP: 130 EST: 1981
SQ FT: 96,000
SALES (est): 58MM **Privately Held**
SIC: 2339 Sportswear, women's; women's
& misses' jackets & coats, except sports-
wear

(P-3443)
KAYO OF CALIFORNIA
11854 Alameda St, Lynwood (90262-4019)
PHONE..............................310 605-2693
Sandra Salgado, *Branch Mgr*
EMP: 10
SALES (corp-wide): 8.4MM **Privately
Held**
SIC: 2339 Women's & misses' accessories
PA: Kayo Of California
161 W 39th St
Los Angeles CA 90037
323 233-6107

(P-3444)
KC EXCLUSIVE INC (PA)
Also Called: Zenana
1100 S San Pedro St, Los Angeles
(90015-2328)
PHONE..............................213 749-0088
Seok Jun Choi, *CEO*
▼ EMP: 73
SALES (est): 12.5MM **Privately Held**
SIC: 2339 Women's & misses' athletic
clothing & sportswear

(P-3445)
**KENNETH MILLER CLOTHING
INC**
210 E Olympic Blvd # 208, Los Angeles
(90015-1775)
P.O. Box 79293 (90079-0293)
PHONE..............................213 746-8866
Rabin Babazadeh, *CEO*
◆ EMP: 22
SQ FT: 6,000
SALES: 2.2MM **Privately Held**
SIC: 2339 Women's & misses' jackets &
coats, except sportswear

(P-3446)
KIM & CAMI PRODUCTIONS INC
Also Called: Kim and Cami
2950 Leonis Blvd, Vernon (90058-2916)
PHONE..............................323 584-1300
Kimberly A Hiatt, *President*
Cami Gasmer, *Vice Pres*
▲ EMP: 22
SQ FT: 1,000
SALES (est): 3.6MM **Privately Held**
SIC: 2339 Sportswear, women's

(P-3447)
KITTY TEXTILE INC (PA)
2812 S Grand Ave, Los Angeles
(90007-3303)
PHONE..............................213 749-7278
Gye S NA, *President*
▲ EMP: 18
SQ FT: 2,000
SALES (est): 2MM **Privately Held**
WEB: www.kittyfashion.com
SIC: 2339 Sportswear, women's

(P-3448)
KLK FORTE INDUSTRY INC (PA)
Also Called: Honey Punch
1535 Rio Vista Ave, Los Angeles
(90023-2619)
PHONE..............................323 415-9181
Katherine Kim, *CEO*
◆ EMP: 45 EST: 2012
SQ FT: 30,000
SALES: 100K **Privately Held**
SIC: 2339 Women's & misses' outerwear

(P-3449)
KORAL INDUSTRIES LLC (PA)
Also Called: Koral Los Angeles
5124 Pacific Blvd, Vernon (90058-2218)
PHONE..............................323 585-5343
David Koral,
Peter Koral,
▲ EMP: 52
SQ FT: 60,000
SALES (est): 6.2MM **Privately Held**
SIC: 2339 Service apparel, washable:
women's

(P-3450)
KYMSTA CORP
1506 W 12th St, Los Angeles (90015-2013)
PHONE..............................213 380-8118
Roxanne Heptner, *President*
Arthur Pereira, *CFO*
EMP: 30
SQ FT: 25,000
SALES (est): 2.3MM **Privately Held**
WEB: www.kymsta.com
SIC: 2339 Women's & misses' athletic
clothing & sportswear

(P-3451)
L Y A GROUP INC
1317 S Grand Ave, Los Angeles
(90015-3008)
PHONE..............................213 683-1123
Claudia L Blanco, *CEO*
Augustin Ramirez, *President*
▲ EMP: 18
SALES (est): 4.2MM **Privately Held**
SIC: 2339 Jeans: women's, misses' & jun-
iors'

(P-3452)
LAC BLEU INC
3817 S Santa Fe Ave, Vernon
(90058-1712)
PHONE..............................213 973-5335
Kevin Chong, *Branch Mgr*
EMP: 10
SALES (corp-wide): 5.5MM **Privately
Held**
SIC: 2339 Women's & misses' outerwear
PA: Lac Bleu, Inc.
1145 Towne Ave Ste 9
Los Angeles CA 90021
213 973-5335

(P-3453)
LAT LLC
Also Called: G Girl
2052 E Vernon Ave, Vernon (90058-1613)
PHONE..............................323 233-3017
Simon Cho, *Mng Member*
Sung H Cho,

▲ EMP: 40
SQ FT: 20,000
SALES: 12MM **Privately Held**
SIC: 2339 Women's & misses' outerwear

(P-3454)
LEE THOMAS INC (PA)
13800 S Figueroa St, Los Angeles
(90061-1026)
PHONE..............................310 532-7560
Lee Opolinsky, *President*
Thomas Mahoney, *Vice Pres*
EMP: 30
SQ FT: 45,000
SALES (est): 1.9MM **Privately Held**
SIC: 2339 Women's & misses' athletic
clothing & sportswear

(P-3455)
LISA AND LESLEY CO
Also Called: Lisa & Lesley Fashion ACC
14140 Ventura Blvd # 101, Sherman Oaks
(91423-2750)
P.O. Box 1958, Studio City (91614-0958)
PHONE..............................323 877-9878
Lisa Rosson, *Partner*
Lesley Rosson, *Partner*
EMP: 10
SALES (est): 966.8K **Privately Held**
SIC: 2339 Women's & misses' athletic
clothing & sportswear

(P-3456)
LORNA JANE USA INC (HQ)
1674 20th St, Santa Monica (90404-3818)
PHONE..............................310 828-0022
Howell Amanda, *Principal*
▲ EMP: 41 EST: 2012
SALES (est): 9.3MM **Privately Held**
SIC: 2339 Women's & misses' athletic
clothing & sportswear

(P-3457)
LUGOS OF CALIFORNIA INC
Also Called: Lynn Lugo
7719 Cecilia St, Downey (90241-2103)
PHONE..............................323 582-5164
Pedro Lugo, *President*
Domingo Lugo, *Treasurer*
George Lugo, *Office Mgr*
Fernando Lugo, *Admin Sec*
Jorge Lugo, *Prdtn Mgr*
EMP: 40
SQ FT: 12,000
SALES (est): 3.3MM **Privately Held**
WEB: www.lugocutting.com
SIC: 2339 Women's & misses' outerwear

(P-3458)
M STEVENS INC
Also Called: Stevens, M Dancewear & Design
1925 Blake Ave, Los Angeles (90039-3807)
PHONE..............................323 661-2147
Norma Winner, *President*
Gayle Davis, *Vice Pres*
Sonya Cohen, *Manager*
EMP: 10
SQ FT: 3,500
SALES (est): 1.2MM **Privately Held**
WEB: www.solipsist.org
SIC: 2339 Women's & misses' athletic
clothing & sportswear

(P-3459)
**MANHATTAN BEACHWEAR INC
(PA)**
Also Called: La Blanca Swimwear
10700 Valley View St, Cypress
(90630-4835)
PHONE..............................714 892-7354
Allan Colvin, *CEO*
Brenda West, *President*
Lindsey Shumlas, *CFO*
Jennifer Berger, *Vice Pres*
Susan Dick, *Vice Pres*
◆ EMP: 200 EST: 1977
SQ FT: 81,000
SALES (est): 161.7MM **Privately Held**
SIC: 2339 Bathing suits: women's, misses'
& juniors'; beachwear: women's, misses'
& juniors'; athletic clothing: women's,
misses' & juniors'; sportswear, women's

(P-3460)
MANHATTAN BEACHWEAR INC
10700 Valley View St, Cypress
(90630-4835)
PHONE..............................714 892-7354
EMP: 100
SALES (corp-wide): 229.8MM **Privately
Held**
SIC: 2339
PA: Manhattan Beachwear, Inc.
10700 Valley View St
Cypress CA 90630
714 892-7354

(P-3461)
MAR & COMPANY INC (PA)
Also Called: Side Effects of California
1763 Flower St, Glendale (91201-2022)
P.O. Box 5939 (91221-5939)
PHONE..............................818 241-8882
Jean L Mar, *Owner*
Anna Mar, *Corp Secy*
Johnny Mar, *Vice Pres*
▼ EMP: 30
SQ FT: 40,000
SALES (est): 3MM **Privately Held**
SIC: 2339 2337 Women's & misses' outer-
wear; skirts, separate: women's, misses'
& juniors'; suits: women's, misses' & jun-
iors'

(P-3462)
MARCEA INC
1742 Crenshaw Blvd, Torrance
(90501-3311)
P.O. Box 48317, Los Angeles (90048-0317)
PHONE..............................213 746-5191
Marcia D Lane, *President*
EMP: 12
SQ FT: 2,500
SALES (est): 154.6K **Privately Held**
WEB: www.marcea.com
SIC: 2339 Sportswear, women's

(P-3463)
MARGARET OLEARY INC (PA)
50 Dorman Ave, San Francisco
(94124-1807)
PHONE..............................415 354-6663
Margaret O'Leary, *CEO*
Melvin TSE, *Planning Mgr*
Monica Scholes, *Store Mgr*
Joya Choudhuri, *Production*
Julie Benson, *Director*
▲ EMP: 70
SQ FT: 16,000
SALES (est): 16MM **Privately Held**
WEB: www.moleary.com
SIC: 2339 2253 Sportswear, women's; knit
outerwear mills

(P-3464)
MARIKA LLC
5553-B Bandini Blvd, Bell (90201)
PHONE..............................323 888-7755
Frank M Zarabi, *Mng Member*
Patrick Shaowl,
▲ EMP: 100
SQ FT: 160,000
SALES (est): 109.3MM **Privately Held**
SIC: 2339 Athletic clothing: women's,
misses' & juniors'; women's & misses
athletic clothing & sportswear

(P-3465)
MARINA SPORTSWEAR INC
Also Called: Marina Industries
3766 S Main St, Los Angeles (90007-4419)
PHONE..............................323 232-2012
Marina Galdamez, *President*
Mondie Saenz, *Opers Staff*
EMP: 70
SQ FT: 12,000
SALES: 2MM **Privately Held**
SIC: 2339 2329 Sportswear, women's;
men's & boys' sportswear & athletic cloth-
ing

(P-3466)
MAX LEON INC (PA)
Also Called: Max Studio.com
3100 New York Dr, Pasadena
(91107-1524)
P.O. Box 70879 (91117-7879)
PHONE..............................626 797-6886
Leon Max, *President*

▲ = Import ▼=Export
◆ =Import/Export

Jolene Abercromby, *Manager*
Jesse Munoz, *Manager*
▲ **EMP:** 100
SQ FT: 65,000
SALES (est): 118.6MM **Privately Held**
WEB: www.maxstudio.com
SIC: 2339 5632 Sportswear, women's; apparel accessories

(P-3467)
MGT INDUSTRIES INC (PA)
Also Called: California Dynasty
13889 S Figueroa St, Los Angeles
(90061-1025)
PHONE....................310 516-5900
Jeffrey P Mirvis, *CEO*
Alessandra Strahl, *President*
Phil Nathanson, *CFO*
Mike Brooks, *Vice Pres*
Joseph Ende, *Info Tech Mgr*
▲ **EMP:** 115
SQ FT: 82,000
SALES (est): 63.5MM **Privately Held**
SIC: 2339 Women's & misses' outerwear

(P-3468)
MONTEREY CANYON LLC (PA)
1515 E 15th St, Los Angeles (90021-2711)
PHONE....................213 741-0209
Fabian Oberfeld,
Richard Sneider,
▲ **EMP:** 70 **EST:** 1977
SALES (est): 4.7MM **Privately Held**
WEB: www.canyon-sports.com
SIC: 2339 Sportswear, women's

(P-3469)
NEXXEN APPAREL INC (PA)
Also Called: Check It Out
1555 Los Palos St, Los Angeles
(90023-3218)
PHONE....................323 267-9900
Jai Sim, *President*
Carol Chang, *Vice Pres*
Billy Sim, *Vice Pres*
EMP: 18
SQ FT: 10,000
SALES (est): 2.9MM **Privately Held**
SIC: 2339 Women's & misses' outerwear

(P-3470)
NILS INC (PA)
Also Called: Nils Skiwear
3151 Airway Ave Ste V, Costa Mesa
(92626-4627)
PHONE....................714 755-1600
Nils Andersson, *CEO*
Richard Leffler, *President*
▲ **EMP:** 15 **EST:** 1953
SALES (est): 3.1MM **Privately Held**
WEB: www.nilsskiwear.com
SIC: 2339 Women's & misses' athletic clothing & sportswear; ski jackets & pants: women's, misses' & juniors'; snow suits: women's, misses' & juniors'

(P-3471)
NOOSHIN INC
Also Called: Nooshin Blanque
555 Chalette Dr, Beverly Hills
(90210-1915)
PHONE....................310 559-5766
Nooshin Malakzad, *President*
Newsha Malakzad, *Admin Sec*
EMP: 10
SQ FT: 8,000
SALES (est): 1.4MM **Privately Held**
SIC: 2339 Sportswear, women's

(P-3472)
OAK APPAREL INC
Also Called: Jemstone
1363 Elwood St, Los Angeles
(90021-2412)
PHONE....................213 489-9766
Eun S Kim, *CEO*
▲ **EMP:** 10
SQ FT: 5,000
SALES (est): 5MM **Privately Held**
SIC: 2339 Women's & misses' outerwear

(P-3473)
ODETTE CHRISTIANE LLC
Also Called: Dresses.com
21521 Blythe St, Canoga Park
(91304-4910)
PHONE....................818 883-0410
Joseph Sweeney,
Odette Sweeney,
Tor Sweeney,
EMP: 12
SQ FT: 5,000
SALES: 3MM **Privately Held**
WEB: www.oscardresses.com
SIC: 2339 Sportswear, women's

(P-3474)
PACE SPORTSWEAR INC
12781 Monarch St, Garden Grove
(92841-3920)
PHONE....................714 891-8716
Leonor Saavedra, *CEO*
Maria Marsh, *President*
▲ **EMP:** 13
SQ FT: 6,500
SALES: 785.8K **Privately Held**
WEB: www.pacesportswear.com
SIC: 2339 2329 Athletic clothing: women's, misses' & juniors'; athletic (warmup, sweat & jogging) suits: men's & boys'

(P-3475)
PACIFIC ATHLETIC WEAR INC
1545 Macarthur Blvd, Costa Mesa
(92626-1407)
PHONE....................714 751-8006
John Hillenbrand, *President*
Gabriela Hillenbrand, *Executive*
▲ **EMP:** 70
SQ FT: 10,000
SALES (est): 7.9MM **Privately Held**
WEB: www.pawman.com
SIC: 2339 Uniforms, athletic: women's, misses' & juniors'

(P-3476)
PATTERSON KINCAID LLC
5175 S Soto St, Vernon (90058-3620)
PHONE....................323 584-3559
Jane Siskin, *Mng Member*
Jilali Elbasri,
◆ **EMP:** 12
SQ FT: 35,000
SALES (est): 783K
SALES (corp-wide): 23.8MM **Privately Held**
SIC: 2339 Women's & misses' outerwear
PA: Jaya Apparel Group Llc
5175 S Soto St
Vernon CA 90058
323 584-3500

(P-3477)
PEEP INC
Also Called: Peep Studio
720 Towne Ave, Los Angeles (90021-1418)
PHONE....................213 748-5500
Kamran Samooha, *President*
▲ **EMP:** 20
SQ FT: 2,000
SALES (est): 2MM **Privately Held**
WEB: www.marshmallowpeeps.com
SIC: 2339 Sportswear, women's

(P-3478)
PERFORMANCE APPAREL CORP
Also Called: Hot Chillys
4145 Santa Fe Rd Ste 1, San Luis Obispo
(93401-8103)
PHONE....................805 541-0989
Guy N Wells, *President*
Shirley Skinner, *Human Res Dir*
▲ **EMP:** 10
SALES (est): 2MM **Privately Held**
WEB: www.hotchillys.com
SIC: 2339 Athletic clothing: women's, misses' & juniors'; bathing suits: women's, misses' & juniors'

(P-3479)
PETER K INC (PA)
Also Called: Next ERA
5175 S Soto St, Vernon (90058-3620)
PHONE....................323 585-5343
Peter Koral, *President*

▲ **EMP:** 41 **EST:** 1982
SALES (est): 8.4MM **Privately Held**
SIC: 2339 2369 Sportswear, women's; girls' & children's outerwear

(P-3480)
PICCONE APPAREL CORP
3740 Motor Ave, Los Angeles
(90034-6404)
PHONE....................310 559-6702
Robin Piccone, *President*
Roy Schwartz, *Senior VP*
Rita Piccone, *Vice Pres*
Anthony Dubey, *Production*
▲ **EMP:** 35
SQ FT: 10,000
SALES (est): 5.5MM **Privately Held**
WEB: www.dominioncorde.com
SIC: 2339 Bathing suits: women's, misses' & juniors'

(P-3481)
PIERRE MITRI (PA)
Also Called: Watch L A.
1138 Wall St, Los Angeles (90015-2320)
PHONE....................213 747-1838
Pierre D Mitri, *Owner*
▲ **EMP:** 17
SQ FT: 6,000
SALES (est): 2.9MM **Privately Held**
WEB: www.watchla.com
SIC: 2339 Jeans: women's, misses' & juniors'; women's & misses' athletic clothing & sportswear

(P-3482)
PIET RETIEF INC
Also Called: Peter Cohen Companies
1914 6th Ave, Los Angeles (90018-1124)
PHONE....................323 732-8312
Peter Cohen, *President*
Anna Cohen, *Treasurer*
Lee Stuart Cox, *Vice Pres*
EMP: 34
SQ FT: 4,800
SALES (est): 3.5MM **Privately Held**
WEB: www.petercohen.net
SIC: 2339 Sportswear, women's

(P-3483)
POINT CONCEPTION INC
Also Called: Kechika
23121 Arroyo Vis Ste A, Rcho STA Marg
(92688-2609)
PHONE....................949 589-6890
Jeff Jung, *CEO*
Jamie Jung, *President*
Victoria Jung, *Corp Secy*
◆ **EMP:** 35
SQ FT: 20,000
SALES (est): 3.8MM **Privately Held**
WEB: www.pointconception.com
SIC: 2339 Bathing suits: women's, misses' & juniors'; sportswear, women's

(P-3484)
POLYMOND DK INC
777 E 10th St Ste 110, Los Angeles
(90021-2083)
PHONE....................213 327-0771
EMP: 30
SALES (corp-wide): 2.3MM **Privately Held**
SIC: 2339 5136 Women's & misses' athletic clothing & sportswear; men's & boys' clothing
PA: Polymond Dk, Inc.
655 S Santa Fe Ave
Los Angeles CA 90021
213 327-0771

(P-3485)
PRODUCE APPAREL INC
23383 Saint Andrews, Mission Viejo
(92692-1538)
PHONE....................949 472-9434
Scott Machock, *President*
Helen Machock, *Vice Pres*
▲ **EMP:** 15
SQ FT: 5,000
SALES (est): 2.1MM **Privately Held**
WEB: www.produceapparel.com
SIC: 2339 5621 Sportswear, women's; women's clothing stores

(P-3486)
PURE ALLURE INC
Also Called: Pure Allure Accessories
4005 Avenida De La Plata, Oceanside
(92056-5843)
PHONE....................760 966-3650
Dale A Grose, *President*
Daylene Grose, *Vice Pres*
▲ **EMP:** 100
SQ FT: 6,000
SALES (est): 6.7MM **Privately Held**
WEB: www.pureallure.com
SIC: 2339 5137 3961 Women's & misses' accessories; women's & children's accessories; costume jewelry

(P-3487)
Q&A7 LLC
Also Called: Accuracy
2155 E 7th St Ste 150, Los Angeles
(90023-1032)
PHONE....................323 364-4250
Aaron Zoref,
◆ **EMP:** 19
SQ FT: 10,000
SALES (est): 9.2MM **Privately Held**
SIC: 2339 5137 Women's & misses' athletic clothing & sportswear; athletic clothing: women's, misses' & juniors'; women's & children's clothing

(P-3488)
RAJ MANUFACTURING LLC
2692 Dow Ave, Tustin (92780-7208)
PHONE....................714 838-3110
Joseph Binotto,
EMP: 17
SALES (est): 2.2MM **Privately Held**
SIC: 2339 Bathing suits: women's, misses' & juniors'

(P-3489)
RHAPSODY CLOTHING INC
Also Called: Epilogue and Arrested
3140 E Pico Blvd Unit A, Los Angeles
(90023-3604)
PHONE....................213 614-8887
Bryan Kang, *CEO*
Yoon MI Kang, *Vice Pres*
Joi Dela Rama, *Manager*
▲ **EMP:** 65
SQ FT: 47,000
SALES (est): 7.9MM **Privately Held**
WEB: www.rhapsodyclothing.com
SIC: 2339 Shorts (outerwear): women's, misses' & juniors'; jeans: women's, misses' & juniors'

(P-3490)
RIAH FASHION INC
1820 E 46th St, Vernon (90058-1948)
PHONE....................323 325-7308
Jose Alejandro Kim, *CEO*
Eunice Jung, *CFO*
EMP: 10
SQ FT: 4,550
SALES: 1MM **Privately Held**
SIC: 2339 5122 5944 5621 Women's & misses' accessories; cosmetics; jewelry stores; women's clothing stores

(P-3491)
ROTAX INCORPORATED
Also Called: Gamma
2940 Leonis Blvd, Vernon (90058-2916)
PHONE....................323 589-5999
Arthur Torssien, *President*
Ripsick Kepenekian, *Vice Pres*
▲ **EMP:** 40
SALES (est): 210.1K **Privately Held**
WEB: www.rotax.com
SIC: 2339 2329 Women's & misses' outerwear; men's & boys' sportswear & athletic clothing

(P-3492)
ROYAL APPAREL INC
4331 Baldwin Ave, El Monte (91731-1103)
PHONE....................626 579-5168
Kung-Shih Yang, *President*
Sheena Yang, *Corp Secy*
Michael Hsu, *Vice Pres*
▲ **EMP:** 70
SQ FT: 24,000

PRODUCTS & SVCS

SALES (est): 5.6MM **Privately Held**
WEB: www.royalapparel.com
SIC: 2339 Leotards: women's, misses' &
juniors'; women's & misses' athletic clothing & sportswear

(P-3493)
SESSIONS
60 Old El Pueblo Rd, Scotts Valley
(95066-3540)
PHONE..............................831 461-5080
Joel Gomez, *CEO*
Cindy Busenhart, *President*
▲ EMP: 40
SQ FT: 20,000
SALES (est): 4.6MM **Privately Held**
WEB: www.sessions.com
SIC: 2339 5941 2329 Ski jackets & pants:
women's, misses' & juniors'; snow suits:
women's, misses' & juniors'; sporting
goods & bicycle shops; ski & snow cloth-
ing: men's & boys'

(P-3494)
SEW SPORTY
2215 La Mirada Dr, Vista (92081-8828)
PHONE..............................760 599-0585
Loralynn Williams, *Partner*
David Sheeron, *Partner*
▲ EMP: 20
SQ FT: 8,000
SALES: 1MM **Privately Held**
WEB: www.sewsporty.com
SIC: 2339 2329 Uniforms, athletic:
women's, misses' & juniors'; men's &
boys' athletic uniforms

(P-3495)
SFO APPAREL
41 Park Pl 43, Brisbane (94005-1306)
PHONE..............................415 468-8816
Peter Mou, *President*
▲ EMP: 140
SQ FT: 20,000
SALES (est): 16.3MM **Privately Held**
SIC: 2339 Women's & misses' athletic
clothing & sportswear; beachwear:
women's, misses' & juniors'

(P-3496)
SIHO CORPORATION
Also Called: Annianna
5750 Grace Pl, Commerce (90022-4121)
PHONE..............................323 721-4000
Hanni Hilman, *President*
Jason Teng, *CFO*
EMP: 15
SQ FT: 3,000
SALES (est): 5MM **Privately Held**
SIC: 2339 Women's & misses' outerwear

(P-3497)
SILVER STAR EXCHANGE
Also Called: Wilson Garment
240 S Raymond Ave, Alhambra
(91801-3168)
PHONE..............................626 300-6668
Benson TSE, *Owner*
EMP: 40 EST: 1998
SALES (est): 3MM **Privately Held**
SIC: 2339 2369 Sportswear, women's;
girls' & children's outerwear

(P-3498)
SKY LUXURY CORP
3001 Humboldt St, Los Angeles
(90031-1830)
PHONE..............................323 940-0111
Peter Kane, *President*
EMP: 21
SQ FT: 8,000
SALES (est): 2.3MM **Privately Held**
SIC: 2339 5661 Women's & misses' outer-
wear; shoes, orthopedic

(P-3499)
SLEDGE USA INC
940 W Washington Blvd, Los Angeles
(90015-3312)
PHONE..............................213 747-4400
Albert Elkouby, *Ch of Bd*
Philippe Teboul, *Vice Pres*
EMP: 30
SQ FT: 18,000

SALES (est): 2.5MM **Privately Held**
WEB: www.jhdesigngroup.net
SIC: 2339 2311 5136 Women's & misses'
athletic clothing & sportswear; men's &
boys' suits & coats; men's & boys' clothing

(P-3500)
SMB CLOTHING INC
Also Called: Top Ten
1016 Towne Ave Unit 104, Los Angeles
(90021-2078)
PHONE..............................213 489-4949
Yong Koo Hyung, *President*
EMP: 10
SALES (est): 1.2MM **Privately Held**
SIC: 2339 5137 Sportswear, women's;
sportswear, women's & children's

(P-3501)
SOLE SURVIVOR
CORPORATION
Also Called: Gramicci Comfort Engineered
28632 Roadside Dr Ste 200, Agoura Hills
(91301-6088)
PHONE..............................818 338-3760
Donald N Love, *CEO*
Sandra Arellano, *Controller*
▲ EMP: 145
SQ FT: 46,000
SALES (est): 9.6MM **Privately Held**
SIC: 2339 2329 5137 5136 Sportswear,
women's; men's & boys' sportswear &
athletic clothing; women's & children's
clothing; men's & boys' clothing

(P-3502)
SOLOW
2907 Glenview Ave, Los Angeles
(90039-2823)
PHONE..............................323 664-7772
Sarah Siegel,
▼ EMP: 30
SQ FT: 20,000
SALES (est): 3.3MM **Privately Held**
SIC: 2339 Sportswear, women's

(P-3503)
SPIRIT CLOTHING COMPANY
Also Called: Spirit Activewear
2211 E 37th St, Vernon (90058-1427)
PHONE..............................213 784-0251
Jake Pitaszink, *President*
◆ EMP: 25
SQ FT: 19,000
SALES (est): 3.8MM **Privately Held**
WEB: www.spiritactivewear.com
SIC: 2339 2329 Athletic clothing:
women's, misses' & juniors'; men's &
boys' sportswear & athletic clothing

(P-3504)
ST JOHN KNITS INC (DH)
17522 Armstrong Ave, Irvine (92614-5726)
PHONE..............................949 863-1171
Bruce Fetter, *CEO*
George Sharp, *Vice Pres*
EMP: 111
SALES (est): 170.1MM
SALES (corp-wide): 703.3MM **Privately
Held**
SIC: 2339 2253 2389 Women's & misses'
accessories; knit outerwear mills; men's
miscellaneous accessories
HQ: St John Knits International Incorpo-
rated
17622 Armstrong Ave
Irvine CA 92614
949 863-1171

(P-3505)
ST JOHN KNITS INTL INC (HQ)
17622 Armstrong Ave, Irvine (92614-5728)
PHONE..............................949 863-1171
Geoffroy Van Raemdonck, *CEO*
James Kelley, *Partner*
Bernd Beetz, *Ch of Bd*
Glenn McMahon, *CEO*
Bruce Fetter, *COO*
◆ EMP: 150 EST: 1962
SQ FT: 71,100

SALES (est): 703.3MM **Privately Held**
WEB: www.stjohnknits.com
SIC: 2339 Sportswear, women's; scarves,
hoods, headbands, etc.: women's; jackets, untailored: women's, misses' & juniors'; slacks: women's, misses' & juniors'
PA: Gray Vestar Investors Llc
17622 Armstrong Ave
Irvine CA 92614
949 863-1171

(P-3506)
STAPLES INC
731 S Spring St Ste 300, Los Angeles
(90014-2922)
PHONE..............................213 623-4395
Gary Brownstein, *President*
EMP: 15
SALES (est): 852.3K **Privately Held**
SIC: 2339 2335 Sportswear, women's;
women's, juniors' & misses' dresses

(P-3507)
STAR AVE
514 E 8th St Ste 500, Los Angeles
(90014-2335)
PHONE..............................213 623-5799
Hyon Seun Kim, *Owner*
EMP: 25 EST: 1998
SALES (est): 1.1MM **Privately Held**
SIC: 2339 Athletic clothing: women's,
misses' & juniors'

(P-3508)
STELLA FASHIONS INC
1015 Crocker St Ste Q04, Los Angeles
(90021-2063)
PHONE..............................213 746-6889
Yun Lee, *President*
Jung Lee, *Treasurer*
EMP: 20 EST: 1998
SQ FT: 5,000
SALES: 6MM **Privately Held**
SIC: 2339 Athletic clothing: women's,
misses' & juniors'; women's & misses'
athletic clothing & sportswear

(P-3509)
STEPS APPAREL GROUP INC
(PA)
Also Called: Bcnu
1105 S Boyle Ave, Los Angeles
(90023-2109)
PHONE..............................323 261-2233
Young Chu, *President*
Key Chu, *Vice Pres*
Ke Yoon, *Admin Sec*
▲ EMP: 45
SQ FT: 30,000
SALES (est): 8.4MM **Privately Held**
WEB: www.stepsdancecenter.com
SIC: 2339 Service apparel, washable:
women's

(P-3510)
STONY APPAREL CORP (PA)
Also Called: Eyeshadow
1500 S Evergreen Ave, Los Angeles
(90023-3618)
PHONE..............................323 981-9080
Tony Litman, *CEO*
Ben Quan, *Vice Pres*
Dean Wiener, *Vice Pres*
Stephen B Maiman, *Admin Sec*
Henry Silva, *Graphic Designe*
▲ EMP: 200
SQ FT: 200,000
SALES (est): 52.9MM **Privately Held**
SIC: 2339 Women's & misses' athletic
clothing & sportswear

(P-3511)
SUSY CLOTHING CO
2256 Hollister Ter, Glendale (91206-3031)
PHONE..............................818 500-7879
Gevork Koshkakaryan, *Owner*
EMP: 27
SALES: 650K **Privately Held**
SIC: 2339 Athletic clothing: women's,
misses' & juniors'

(P-3512)
SWIMWEAR
Also Called: T. H. E. Swimwear
1961 Hawkins Cir, Los Angeles
(90001-2255)
PHONE..............................323 584-7536
Thomas J Hartigan, *President*
Mary E Hartigan, *Vice Pres*
Michael V Hartigan, *Vice Pres*
EMP: 35
SQ FT: 30,000
SALES: 1.5MM **Privately Held**
WEB: www.theswimwear.com
SIC: 2339 Bathing suits: women's, misses'
& juniors'

(P-3513)
T BAGS LLC
1530 E 25th St, Los Angeles (90011-1814)
PHONE..............................323 225-9525
Shadi Askari, *Principal*
EMP: 10
SALES (est): 1.4MM **Privately Held**
SIC: 2339 Athletic clothing: women's,
misses' & juniors'

(P-3514)
TCJ MANUFACTURING LLC
Also Called: Velvet Heart
2744 E 11th St, Los Angeles (90023-3404)
PHONE..............................213 488-8400
Gabrielle Tsabag, *Mng Member*
Moshe Tsabag,
▲ EMP: 22
SALES (est): 3.4MM **Privately Held**
SIC: 2339 Athletic clothing: women's,
misses' & juniors'

(P-3515)
TCW TRENDS INC
2886 Columbia St, Torrance (90503-3808)
PHONE..............................310 533-5177
Charanjiv S Mansingh, *President*
Prerana Sachdev Khanna, *Vice Pres*
Gurvinder Singh Sandhu, *Vice Pres*
Rohaidah Chehassan, *Finance Dir*
Yamini Patel, *Production*
▲ EMP: 18
SQ FT: 10,000
SALES (est): 28MM **Privately Held**
SIC: 2339 2326 5137 Aprons, except rub-
ber or plastic: women's, misses', juniors';
men's & boys' work clothing; coordinate
sets: women's, children's & infants'

(P-3516)
TEAZE OF CALIFORNIA INC
Also Called: CIT
9900 Bell Ranch Dr # 105, Santa Fe
Springs (90670-2985)
PHONE..............................562 944-8995
Josh Bradbury, *CEO*
Kristen Lantz, *President*
Hector Loza, *VP Prdtn*
▲ EMP: 230
SQ FT: 87,000
SALES (est): 16.7MM **Privately Held**
WEB: www.teazeofca.com
SIC: 2339 2369 Sportswear, women's;
girls' & children's outerwear

(P-3517)
TEMPTED APPAREL CORP
4516 Loma Vista Ave, Vernon
(90058-2602)
PHONE..............................323 859-2480
Steven Schoenholz, *President*
Donna Ericastillo, *Executive*
Moy Valentin, *Controller*
Regina Pugliese, *Opers Staff*
Rose Huber, *Sales Staff*
▲ EMP: 50
SALES (est): 5.8MM **Privately Held**
SIC: 2339 Women's & misses' outerwear

(P-3518)
THIRD DEGREE SPORTSWEAR
INC
Also Called: Valuable Market
5402 Commercial Dr, Huntington Beach
(92649-1232)
P.O. Box 4229 (92605-4229)
PHONE..............................714 890-9828
Steve Laszlo, *President*
Terry Laszlo, *Vice Pres*
Daniel Gomez, *Graphic Designe*

Jodie Chapman, *Marketing Staff*
Jeanne Smith, *Accounts Mgr*
EMP: 15
SQ FT: 4,000
SALES (est): 2.4MM **Privately Held**
WEB: www.thirddegreesportswear.com
SIC: 2339 Sportswear, women's

(P-3519)
TOSKA INC
Also Called: Tz
1100 S San Pedro St I06, Los Angeles
(90015-2387)
PHONE..................213 746-0088
Nancy Choi, *President*
▲ **EMP:** 15
SALES (est): 1.4MM **Privately Held**
SIC: 2339 5137 Women's & misses' outer-
wear; women's & children's clothing

(P-3520)
TOUCH ME FASHION INC
Also Called: Teen Bell
906 E 60th St, Los Angeles (90001-1017)
PHONE..................323 234-9200
Hyun Soon Chung, *President*
▲ **EMP:** 29
SALES (est): 3.5MM **Privately Held**
SIC: 2339 Women's & misses' outerwear

(P-3521)
TRANSGLOBAL APPAREL GROUP INC
12362 Knott St, Garden Grove
(92841-2802)
PHONE..................714 890-9200
Andrew Su, *President*
Timmic Su, *CFO*
EMP: 10
SALES (est): 10.5MM **Privately Held**
SIC: 2339 Women's & misses' outerwear

(P-3522)
TRES BIEN INC (PA)
1016 Towne Ave Unit 113, Los Angeles
(90021-2078)
PHONE..................213 747-3366
Daejae Kim, *CEO*
▲ **EMP:** 12
SALES (est): 1.5MM **Privately Held**
SIC: 2339 Athletic clothing: women's,
misses' & juniors'

(P-3523)
UNIQUE APPAREL INC
3777 S Main St, Los Angeles (90007-4420)
PHONE..................213 321-8192
Suzie Kang, *President*
▲ **EMP:** 80
SALES (est): 4.7MM **Privately Held**
SIC: 2339 Jeans: women's, misses' & jun-
iors'

(P-3524)
VICTORY CUSTOM ATHLETICS
2001 Anchor Ct Ste A, Newbury Park
(91320-1615)
PHONE..................818 349-8476
Mike Le Cocq, *Partner*
Carlos Yniguez, *Partner*
Tommy Kimmerle, *Graphic Designe*
Ron Mouzis, *Sales Mgr*
EMP: 54
SQ FT: 5,500
SALES (est): 5.6MM **Privately Held**
WEB: www.victory-la.com
SIC: 2339 2329 Athletic clothing:
women's, misses' & juniors'; athletic
(warmup, sweat & jogging) suits: men's &
boys'

(P-3525)
VICTORY PROFESSIONAL PRODUCTS
Also Called: Victory Koredrry
5601 Engineer Dr, Huntington Beach
(92649-1123)
PHONE..................714 887-0621
Marc Spitaleri, *President*
▲ **EMP:** 28
SQ FT: 8,500

SALES: 3MM **Privately Held**
WEB: www.victorywetsuits.com
SIC: 2339 2329 2393 Women's & misses'
athletic clothing & sportswear; men's &
boys' sportswear & athletic clothing; textile bags

(P-3526)
VISIONMAX INC
Also Called: Ficcare
17232 Railroad St, City of Industry
(91748-1021)
PHONE..................626 839-1602
Janet Lau, *President*
Lau Janet, *Administration*
▲ **EMP:** 10
SALES (est): 1.1MM **Privately Held**
SIC: 2339 Women's & misses' accessories

(P-3527)
W & W CONCEPT INC
Also Called: Perseption
4890 S Alameda St, Vernon (90058-2806)
PHONE..................323 233-9202
Wonsook Chong, *President*
Jay Joo, *CEO*
▲ **EMP:** 55
SQ FT: 45,000
SALES (est): 17.3MM **Privately Held**
WEB: www.perseption.com
SIC: 2339 Sportswear, women's

(P-3528)
WEARABLE INTEGRITY INC
Also Called: Barbara Lesser
1360 E 17th St, Los Angeles (90021-3024)
PHONE..................213 748-6044
Mark Lesser, *President*
Barbara Lesser, *Vice Pres*
▲ **EMP:** 22
SQ FT: 20,000
SALES (est): 2.5MM **Privately Held**
WEB: www.barbaralesser.com
SIC: 2339 5137 2335 Women's & misses'
outerwear; women's & children's sports-
wear & swimsuits; women's, juniors' &
misses' dresses

(P-3529)
YH TEXPERT CORPORATION
Also Called: Urbanista
5052 Cecelia St, South Gate (90280-3511)
PHONE..................323 562-8800
Alexander Han, *CEO*
John Park, *Vice Pres*
Yoon Lee, *Accounts Mgr*
▲ **EMP:** 11
SQ FT: 6,000
SALES: 7MM **Privately Held**
WEB: www.texpert.net
SIC: 2339 5137 Women's & misses' ath-
letic clothing & sportswear; athletic cloth-
ing: women's, misses' & juniors';
maternity clothing; women's & children's
clothing

(P-3530)
YMI JEANSWEAR INC
1015 Wall St Ste 115, Los Angeles
(90015-2392)
PHONE..................213 746-6681
Ronan Vered, *Branch Mgr*
EMP: 55
SALES (corp-wide): 13.1MM **Privately Held**
WEB: www.ymijeans.com
SIC: 2339 2325 Jeans: women's, misses'
& juniors'; men's & boys' jeans & dunga-
rees
PA: Y.M.I. Jeanswear, Inc,
1155 S Boyle Ave
Los Angeles CA 90023
323 581-7700

**2341 Women's, Misses' &
Children's Underwear &
Nightwear**

(P-3531)
402 SHOES INC
Also Called: Trashy Lingerie
402 N La Cienega Blvd, West Hollywood
(90048-1907)
PHONE..................323 655-5437
Mitchell Shrier, *President*
Deirdre Miller, *CFO*
Tracy Shrier, *Admin Sec*
Randy Shrier,
EMP: 23
SQ FT: 6,000
SALES (est): 1.9MM **Privately Held**
SIC: 2341 5632 2322 Women's & chil-
dren's nightwear; lingerie & corsets (un-
derwear); men's & boys' underwear &
nightwear

(P-3532)
ADVANCE LATEX PRODUCTS INC
Also Called: International Molders
6915 Woodley Ave B, Van Nuys
(91406-4844)
PHONE..................310 559-8300
Blanch Howard, *CEO*
Michael Wellman, *President*
▲ **EMP:** 30
SQ FT: 40,000
SALES (est): 2.6MM **Privately Held**
SIC: 2341 Women's & children's under-
wear

(P-3533)
AFR APPAREL INTERNATIONAL INC
Also Called: Parisa Lingerie & Swim Wear
19401 Business Center Dr, Northridge
(91324-3506)
PHONE..................818 773-5000
Amir Moghadam, *President*
Brenda J Moghadam, *Exec VP*
Frank Waks, *Exec VP*
Brenda Moghadam, *Vice Pres*
Armond Aghakhani, *Graphic Designe*
▲ **EMP:** 60
SQ FT: 46,000
SALES: 25MM **Privately Held**
WEB: www.parisausa.com
SIC: 2341 2342 2369 5137 Women's &
children's nightwear; bras, girdles & allied
garments; bathing suits & swimwear:
girls', children's & infants'; lingerie

(P-3534)
CALOR APPAREL GROUP INTL CORP
Also Called: True Grit
884 W 16th St, Newport Beach
(92663-2802)
PHONE..................949 548-9095
Bruce W Bennett III, *CEO*
John R Provine, *Treasurer*
▲ **EMP:** 28
SQ FT: 7,000
SALES (est): 2.8MM **Privately Held**
SIC: 2341 2329 2342 5961 Women's &
children's underwear; men's & boys'
sportswear & athletic clothing; bras, gir-
dles & allied garments; mail order house;
women's apparel, mail order

(P-3535)
CHARLES KOMAR & SONS INC
Also Called: Komar Distribution Services
11850 Riverside Dr, Mira Loma
(91752-1001)
PHONE..................951 934-1377
Lisa Casillas, *Branch Mgr*
EMP: 307
SALES (corp-wide): 310.7MM **Privately Held**
WEB: www.komar-ny.com
SIC: 2341 Women's & children's nightwear
PA: Charles Komar & Sons, Inc.
90 Hudson St Fl 9
Jersey City NJ 07302
212 725-1500

(P-3536)
FARR WEST FASHIONS
580 Cathedral Dr, Aptos (95003-3407)
PHONE..................831 661-5039
Charles Farr, *President*
John E Farr Jr, *Chairman*
Iris Farr, *Corp Secy*
EMP: 13
SQ FT: 9,600
SALES: 720.1K **Privately Held**
WEB: www.farrwest.com
SIC: 2341 Chemises, camisoles & teddies:
women's & children's; nightgowns & neg-
ligees: women's & children's; women's &
children's nightwear

(P-3537)
HONEST COMPANY INC (PA)
12130 Millennium Ste 500, Playa Vista
(90094-2946)
PHONE..................310 917-9199
Nick Vlahos, *CEO*
Jessica Alba, *President*
David Parker, *COO*
Christopher Gavigan, *Officer*
Janis Hoyt, *Officer*
▲ **EMP:** 187
SALES (est): 108.4MM **Privately Held**
SIC: 2341 2833 Panties: women's,
misses', children's & infants'; vitamins,
natural or synthetic: bulk, uncompounded

(P-3538)
LITO
3730 Union Pacific Ave, Los Angeles
(90023-3229)
PHONE..................323 260-4692
Lee Garvin, *Manager*
▲ **EMP:** 40 **EST:** 2013
SALES (est): 1.4MM **Privately Held**
SIC: 2341 Women's & children's undergar-
ments

(P-3539)
MAIDENFORM LLC
100 Citadel Dr Ste 323, Commerce
(90040-1592)
PHONE..................323 724-9558
EMP: 178
SALES (corp-wide): 5.7B **Publicly Held**
SIC: 2341
HQ: Maidenform Llc
1000 E Hanes Mill Rd
Winston Salem NC 27105
336 519-8080

(P-3540)
NATIONAL CORSET SUPPLY HOUSE (PA)
Also Called: Louden Madelon
3240 E 26th St, Vernon (90058-8008)
PHONE..................323 261-0265
Roy Schlobohm, *CEO*
Larry Hiscock, *Technology*
Kirk Schlobohm, *Controller*
Dora Schlobohm, *Persnl Mgr*
Al Saenz, *Plant Mgr*
▲ **EMP:** 65 **EST:** 1948
SQ FT: 25,000
SALES (est): 11.1MM **Privately Held**
WEB: www.shirleyofhollywood.com
SIC: 2341 5137 Women's & children's un-
dergarments; corsets

(P-3541)
NEFFUL USA INC
18563 Gale Ave, City of Industry
(91748-1339)
PHONE..................626 839-6657
Toshiya Kanijo, *President*
Akira Mori, *Vice Pres*
Chia WEI, *Master*
▲ **EMP:** 10
SALES (est): 1.2MM **Privately Held**
WEB: www.neffulusa.com
SIC: 2341 Women's & children's undergar-
ments

(P-3542)
PACOIMA CLOTHING LLC
Also Called: Fantansty Lingerie
21345 Lassen St, Chatsworth
(91311-6841)
PHONE..................818 897-8009
Michael F Savage, *Mng Member*
EMP: 30

SALES (est): 1.5MM **Privately Held**
SIC: 2341 Women's & children's undergarments

(P-3543)
SAN FRANCISCO NETWORK
Also Called: Sunday Brunch
2171 Francisco Blvd E G, San Rafael
(94901-5542)
PHONE...................415 468-1110
Leonard Eber, *Ch of Bd*
Karen Neuberger, *President*
Richard N Compton, *CFO*
▲ **EMP:** 33
SQ FT: 3,000
SALES (est): 1.9MM **Privately Held**
SIC: 2341 Women's & children's nightwear

(P-3544)
SELECTRA INDUSTRIES CORP
5166 Alcoa Ave, Vernon (90058-3110)
PHONE...................323 581-8500
John Neman, *President*
Malek Neman, *CFO*
Mark Neman, *Admin Sec*
▲ **EMP:** 85 **EST:** 2000
SQ FT: 30,000
SALES (est): 10.9MM **Privately Held**
WEB: www.selectraindustries.com
SIC: 2341 2339 Women's & children's underwear; sportswear, women's

(P-3545)
SUNNYSIDE LLC
Also Called: Sundry Clothing
3763 S Hill St, Los Angeles (90007-4339)
PHONE...................213 745-3070
Matthieu Leblan, *Mng Member*
EMP: 10 **EST:** 2014
SALES (est): 1.5MM **Privately Held**
SIC: 2341 Women's & children's undergarments

(P-3546)
T L CARE INC
1459 San Mateo Ave, South San Francisco
(94080-6504)
P.O. Box 77087, San Francisco (94107-0087)
PHONE...................650 589-3659
Estelle Lee, *CEO*
R Timothy Leister, *CFO*
Diane Leister, *Admin Sec*
▲ **EMP:** 10
SQ FT: 5,000
SALES: 5MM **Privately Held**
WEB: www.tlcare.com
SIC: 2341 2342 2385 5137 Women's & children's undergarments; maternity bras & corsets; waterproof outerwear; bibs, waterproof: made from purchased materials; diaper covers, waterproof: made from purchased materials; baby goods; diapers; infants' wear; infant furnishings & equipment

2342 Brassieres, Girdles & Garments

(P-3547)
BRAGEL INTERNATIONAL INC
Also Called: Brava
3383 Pomona Blvd, Pomona (91768-3297)
PHONE...................909 598-8808
Clotilde Chen, *CEO*
Kenny Chen, *Shareholder*
Alice Chen, *Treasurer*
▲ **EMP:** 45
SQ FT: 30,000
SALES (est): 6.9MM **Privately Held**
WEB: www.bragel.com
SIC: 2342 Brassieres

(P-3548)
FOH GROUP INC (PA)
Also Called: Movie Star
6255 W Sunset Blvd # 2212, Los Angeles
(90028-7423)
PHONE...................323 466-5151
Thomas J Lynch, *Ch of Bd*
Thomas Rende, *CFO*
◆ **EMP:** 41
SQ FT: 23,000

SALES: 86.5MM **Privately Held**
SIC: 2342 2339 5621 5632 Bras, girdles & allied garments; women's & misses' outerwear; women's & misses' athletic clothing & sportswear; jeans: women's, misses' & juniors'; women's clothing stores; ready-to-wear apparel, women's; teenage apparel; women's accessory & specialty stores; apparel accessories; women's dancewear, hosiery & lingerie; handbags; women's & children's nightwear

(P-3549)
INSTYLE PRINTING INC
2115 Central Ave, South El Monte
(91733-2117)
PHONE...................626 575-2725
Vicky Yang, *President*
EMP: 30
SALES (est): 1.5MM **Privately Held**
SIC: 2342 2326 Foundation garments, women's; industrial garments, men's & boys'

(P-3550)
METRIC PRODUCTS INC (PA)
4630 Leahy St, Culver City (90232-3515)
PHONE...................310 815-9000
Shirley Magidson, *President*
Rita Haft, *Vice Pres*
Debra Magidson, *Admin Sec*
▲ **EMP:** 20
SQ FT: 25,000
SALES (est): 9.8MM **Privately Held**
WEB: www.metric-products.com
SIC: 2342 3496 Brassieres; fabrics, woven wire

(P-3551)
MSA WEST LLC
16161 Ventura Blvd C326, Encino
(91436-2522)
PHONE...................213 536-9880
ARI Aalfon, *Mng Member*
◆ **EMP:** 20 **EST:** 2016
SALES (est): 2MM **Privately Held**
SIC: 2342 Bras, girdles & allied garments

(P-3552)
OFFLINE INC (PA)
2250 Maple Ave, Los Angeles
(90011-1190)
PHONE...................213 742-9001
Charles Park, *President*
Nina Kim, *Creative Dir*
Karen Park, *Admin Sec*
▲ **EMP:** 45
SQ FT: 50,000
SALES (est): 6.2MM **Privately Held**
WEB: www.offlineinc.com
SIC: 2342 2326 Foundation garments, women's; industrial garments, men's & boys'

(P-3553)
ORANGE CORPORATION
1430 S Grande Vista Ave, Los Angeles
(90023-3717)
PHONE...................323 266-0700
OK Kyung Lee, *President*
EMP: 10 **EST:** 1997
SQ FT: 20,000
SALES (est): 1MM **Privately Held**
SIC: 2342 Foundation garments, women's

(P-3554)
SOFTMAX INC
Also Called: Greige Gods Boking PO AP
Group
2341 E 49th St Fl 2, Vernon (90058-2820)
PHONE...................213 718-2100
David Jung, *CEO*
EMP: 12
SQ FT: 6,000
SALES: 500K **Privately Held**
SIC: 2342 5137 Foundation garments, women's; women's & children's clothing

(P-3555)
SUGARED + BRONZED LLC
13033 Ventura Blvd, Studio City
(91604-2219)
PHONE...................747 264-0477
EMP: 127

SALES (corp-wide): 5.5MM **Privately Held**
SIC: 2342 Bras, girdles & allied garments
PA: Sugared + Bronzed, Llc
34241 Pacific Coast Hwy
Dana Point CA 92629
410 493-3467

2353 Hats, Caps & Millinery

(P-3556)
AGRON INC
2440 S Sepulveda Blvd # 201, Los Angeles
(90064-1748)
PHONE...................310 473-7223
Wade Siegel, *President*
Anton Schiff, *CFO*
Greg Thomse, *Managing Dir*
Jack Urner, *Admin Sec*
David Hall, *Info Tech Mgr*
▲ **EMP:** 60
SQ FT: 10,000
SALES (est): 9.5MM **Privately Held**
WEB: www.agron.com
SIC: 2353 2393 3949 3171 Hats, caps & millinery; canvas bags; sporting & athletic goods; women's handbags & purses

(P-3557)
AUGUST HAT COMPANY INC (PA)
Also Called: August Accessories
850 Calle Plano Ste M, Camarillo
(93012-8570)
PHONE...................805 983-4651
Roque Valladares, *President*
Ann Valladares, *Corp Secy*
Trent Valladares, *Vice Pres*
Scott Beebe, *Admin Mgr*
Tracy Gonzales, *Technology*
▲ **EMP:** 23
SQ FT: 11,000
SALES (est): 3.7MM **Privately Held**
WEB: www.augustacc.com
SIC: 2353 2381 2339 Hats, caps & millinery; fabric dress & work gloves; scarves, hoods, headbands, etc.: women's

(P-3558)
BAAM INC
Also Called: Logos Unlimited
20847 Betron St, Woodland Hills
(91364-3351)
PHONE...................818 716-1818
Jon Bernstein, *President*
Peter Newhouse, *Vice Pres*
▲ **EMP:** 25 **EST:** 1970
SQ FT: 7,200
SALES (est): 2.2MM **Privately Held**
SIC: 2353 2395 3993 Hats & caps; embroidery & art needlework; signs & advertising specialties

(P-3559)
CALI-FAME LOS ANGELES INC
Also Called: Kennedy Athletics
20934 S Santa Fe Ave, Carson
(90810-1131)
PHONE...................310 747-5263
Michael G Kennedy, *CEO*
Brian Kennedy, *President*
Linelle Kennedy, *Corp Secy*
Tim Kennedy, *Vice Pres*
Timothy Kennedy, *Vice Pres*
▲ **EMP:** 92
SQ FT: 30,000
SALES (est): 11.2MM **Privately Held**
WEB: www.califame.com
SIC: 2353 Uniform hats & caps

(P-3560)
CALIFORNIA CUSTOM CAPS
2319 Sastre Ave, South El Monte
(91733-2655)
PHONE...................626 454-1766
Robn Trung Tran, *Principal*
EMP: 25
SALES (est): 2.1MM **Privately Held**
WEB: www.californiacustomcaps.com
SIC: 2353 Hats & caps

(P-3561)
CAREER CAP CORPORATION
1680 Industrial Blvd, Chula Vista
(91911-3922)
PHONE...................619 575-2277
Jim Ghashghaee, *President*
Jack Frise, *Vice Pres*
EMP: 48
SQ FT: 5,100
SALES: 1.6MM **Privately Held**
WEB: www.careercap.com
SIC: 2353 Baseball caps

(P-3562)
GOORIN BROS INC (PA)
1890 Bryant St Ste 208, San Francisco
(94110-7410)
PHONE...................415 431-9196
Benjamin T Goorin, *CEO*
Jim Curly, *CFO*
Keith Agcaoili, *Graphic Designe*
Karen Wong, *Financial Exec*
Glenn Ramit, *Manager*
▲ **EMP:** 30 **EST:** 1895
SALES (est): 10.7MM **Privately Held**
WEB: www.goorin.com
SIC: 2353 Hats & caps

(P-3563)
GOORIN BROSINC
23787 Eichler St Ste E, Hayward
(94545-2760)
EMP: 15
SALES (corp-wide): 6MM **Privately Held**
SIC: 2353
PA: Goorin Bros.Inc.
1269 Howard St
San Francisco CA 94110
415 431-9196

(P-3564)
HEADMASTER INC (PA)
3000 S Croddy Way, Santa Ana
(92704-6305)
PHONE...................714 556-5244
Dong J Park, *President*
Jimmy J Park, *Vice Pres*
▲ **EMP:** 21
SQ FT: 35,000
SALES (est): 1.9MM **Privately Held**
WEB: www.headmaster.com
SIC: 2353 Hats: cloth, straw & felt

(P-3565)
LEGENDARY HOLDINGS INC
Also Called: Legendary Headwear
2295 Paseo De Las America, San Diego
(92154-7909)
PHONE...................619 872-6100
Thomas Smith, *CEO*
Stephen Cunliffe, *Treasurer*
Legendary Lample, *Production*
Carolyn Wang, *Director*
▲ **EMP:** 38
SQ FT: 13,300
SALES (est): 5MM **Privately Held**
WEB: www.legendaryholdings.com
SIC: 2353 Hats, caps & millinery

(P-3566)
LIDS CORPORATION
357 Sun Valley Mall Ste C, Concord
(94520-5811)
PHONE...................925 609-9516
Kevin Baker, *Branch Mgr*
Josh Gould, *Manager*
EMP: 15
SALES (corp-wide): 2.9B **Publicly Held**
WEB: www.hatworld.com
SIC: 2353 Hats & caps
HQ: Lids Corporation
7555 Woodland Dr
Indianapolis IN 46278

(P-3567)
LOUISE GREEN MILLINERY CO INC
1616 Cotner Ave, Los Angeles
(90025-3304)
PHONE...................310 479-1881
Lawrence Green, *President*
Louise Green, *Partner*
▲ **EMP:** 12
SQ FT: 9,000

SALES (est): 1.3MM **Privately Held**
WEB: www.louisegreen.com
SIC: 2353 5137 Millinery; women's & children's clothing

(P-3568)
NIKE INC
20001 Ellipse, Foothill Ranch
(92610-3001)
PHONE..............................949 768-4000
Matt Ross, *Manager*
Alexander Willson, *Manager*
EMP: 15
SALES (corp-wide): 36.4B **Publicly Held**
WEB: www.nike.com
SIC: 2353 5137 5136 Baseball caps; women's & children's clothing; men's & boys' clothing
PA: Nike, Inc.
1 Sw Bowerman Dr
Beaverton OR 97005
503 671-6453

(P-3569)
ONE HAT ONE HAND LLC
1335 Yosemite Ave, San Francisco
(94124-3319)
PHONE..............................415 822-2020
Chrisray Collins,
Marcus Guillard,
EMP: 42 EST: 2008
SQ FT: 19,000
SALES (est): 3.7MM **Privately Held**
SIC: 2353 Hats, caps & millinery

2361 Children's & Infants' Dresses & Blouses

(P-3570)
A THANKS MILLION INC
8195 Mercury Ct Ste 140, San Diego
(92111-1231)
PHONE..............................858 432-7744
Lowell J Cohen, *CEO*
Peter Mouostaos, *President*
Ian Barrow, *COO*
Greg Dona, *General Mgr*
Terry Sarver, *Opers Staff*
◆ EMP: 19
SALES (est): 2.6MM **Privately Held**
SIC: 2361 2329 T-shirts & tops: girls', children's & infants'; shirt & slack suits: men's, youths' & boys'

(P-3571)
AST SPORTSWEAR INC
2701 E Imperial Hwy, Brea (92821-6713)
P.O. Box 17219, Anaheim (92817-7219)
PHONE..............................714 223-2030
Shoaib Dadabhoy, *CEO*
Abdul Rashid, *COO*
Taher Dadabhoy, *Admin Sec*
▲ EMP: 480
SQ FT: 42,000
SALES (est): 59.1MM **Privately Held**
WEB: www.astsportswear.com
SIC: 2361 2331 5699 T-shirts & tops: girls', children's & infants'; T-shirts & tops, women's: made from purchased materials; sports apparel

(P-3572)
AVALON APPAREL LLC (PA)
Also Called: Disorderly Kids, LLC
2520 W 6th St, Los Angeles (90057-3174)
PHONE..............................323 581-3511
Elliot Schutzer, *Mng Member*
Terri Cohen,
Jill Grossman,
Jason Schutzer,
EMP: 165
SQ FT: 5,000
SALES (est): 14.4MM **Privately Held**
SIC: 2361 Girls' & children's dresses, blouses & shirts

(P-3573)
BABE HOLLYWOOD INC
Also Called: Broadway Babe
113 E Arrow Hwy, San Dimas
(91773-3305)
PHONE..............................626 859-7700
Brian Setoodeh, *President*
Yolanda Romero, *Vice Pres*

EMP: 13
SQ FT: 6,000
SALES (est): 1.2MM **Privately Held**
WEB: www.broadwaybabe.com
SIC: 2361 2389 5137 Dresses: girls', children's & infants'; theatrical costumes; children's goods

(P-3574)
COTTON GENERATION INC
Also Called: Trouble At The Mill
6051 Maywood Ave, Huntington Park
(90255-3211)
PHONE..............................323 581-8555
Mohamad Toluee, *President*
Masoud Parvinjah, *Vice Pres*
Shadi Toloueenia, *Technology*
EMP: 50
SQ FT: 45,000
SALES (est): 4.6MM **Privately Held**
SIC: 2361 2339 7389 T-shirts & tops: girls', children's & infants'; sportswear, women's; textile & apparel services

(P-3575)
CRESTONE LLC
Also Called: Hazel Clothes
1852 E 46th St, Vernon (90058-1948)
PHONE..............................323 588-8857
Robert Cho, *Mng Member*
Maria Madriz, *Production*
Ruben Romero, *Sales Mgr*
Janet Cho, *Mng Member*
▲ EMP: 30
SQ FT: 10,000
SALES (est): 4MM **Privately Held**
SIC: 2361 2331 Girls' & children's dresses, blouses & shirts; women's & misses' blouses & shirts

(P-3576)
EVY OF CALIFORNIA INC (HQ)
Also Called: La Touch
2042 Garfield Ave, Commerce
(90040-1804)
P.O. Box 812030, Los Angeles (90081-0018)
PHONE..............................213 746-4647
Kurt Krieser, *President*
Kevin Krieser, *COO*
Checrag Peer, *CFO*
Cheryl Kimble, *Software Engr*
Esther Aguire, *Human Res Dir*
▲ EMP: 136
SQ FT: 50,000
SALES (est): 16.5MM
SALES (corp-wide): 685.7MM **Privately Held**
WEB: www.evy.com
SIC: 2361 2369 Dresses: girls', children's & infants'; warm-up, jogging & sweat suits: girls' & children's
PA: Hybrid Promotions, Llc
10711 Walker St
Cypress CA 90630
714 952-3866

(P-3577)
EVY OF CALIFORNIA INC
Also Called: Fleurish Clothing Company
1875 E 22nd St, Los Angeles (90058-1033)
PHONE..............................213 746-4647
Amy Powers, *Branch Mgr*
EMP: 10
SALES (corp-wide): 672.7MM **Privately Held**
WEB: www.evy.com
SIC: 2361 Girls' & children's dresses, blouses & shirts
HQ: Evy Of California, Inc.
2042 Garfield Ave
Commerce CA 90040
213 746-4647

(P-3578)
JESSICA MCCLINTOCK INC (PA)
2307 Broadway St, San Francisco
(94115-1291)
PHONE..............................415 553-8200
Jessica Mc Clintock, *President*
▲ EMP: 150 EST: 1970
SQ FT: 120,000

SALES (est): 58.9MM **Privately Held**
WEB: www.jessicamclintock.com
SIC: 2361 2335 2844 Dresses: girls', children's & infants'; women's, juniors' & misses' dresses; perfumes, natural or synthetic

(P-3579)
KENNETH CRONON INC
10413 Haines Canyon Ave, Tujunga
(91042-2031)
PHONE..............................818 632-4972
Kenneth Cronon, *President*
EMP: 12 EST: 2016
SALES (est): 401.9K **Privately Held**
SIC: 2361 Girls' & children's dresses, blouses & shirts

(P-3580)
KWDZ MANUFACTURING LLC (PA)
337 S Anderson St, Los Angeles
(90033-3742)
PHONE..............................323 526-3526
Vera Campbell,
Gene Bonilla,
▲ EMP: 75
SQ FT: 45,000
SALES (est): 19.5MM **Privately Held**
SIC: 2361 T-shirts & tops: girls', children's & infants'

(P-3581)
L A S A M INC
Also Called: Natural Elements
3844 S Santa Fe Ave, Vernon
(90058-1713)
PHONE..............................323 586-8717
Sandy Maroney, *President*
Dennis Maroney, *Admin Sec*
EMP: 14 EST: 1981
SQ FT: 5,000
SALES (est): 1MM **Privately Held**
WEB: www.lasam.net
SIC: 2361 Girls' & children's dresses, blouses & shirts

(P-3582)
LIDA CHILDRENS WEAR INC
3113 E California Blvd, Pasadena
(91107-5352)
PHONE..............................626 967-8868
John Yong-Shon Yu, *President*
Nien Tsu Yu, *Vice Pres*
Jason Yu, *Manager*
◆ EMP: 50
SALES (est): 3.7MM **Privately Held**
WEB: www.lidachildren.com
SIC: 2361 2311 2369 2335

(P-3583)
MARNA RO LLC
818 S Broadway Ste 800, Los Angeles
(90014-3228)
PHONE..............................310 801-5788
Dee Drexler, *CEO*
EMP: 10
SALES (est): 1.2MM **Privately Held**
SIC: 2361 2335 3171 3151 Girls' & children's dresses, blouses & shirts; women's, juniors' & misses' dresses; women's handbags & purses; leather gloves & mittens; shirt & slack suits: men's, youths' & boys'

(P-3584)
MISYD CORP (PA)
Also Called: Ruby Rox
30 Fremont Pl, Los Angeles (90005-3858)
PHONE..............................213 742-1800
Robert Borman, *President*
Joseph Hanasab, *CFO*
▲ EMP: 79
SQ FT: 35,000
SALES (est): 11.3MM **Privately Held**
SIC: 2361 Shirts: girls', children's & infants'

(P-3585)
PEEK ARENT YOU CURIOUS INC (PA)
425 2nd St Ste 405, San Francisco
(94107-1420)
PHONE..............................415 512-7335
Maria Cristina Canales, *CEO*
Jason Klein, *CFO*
Gregory Onken, *Admin Sec*

▲ EMP: 86
SQ FT: 2,000
SALES (est): 7.8MM **Privately Held**
SIC: 2361 2369 5641 5661 Girls' & children's dresses, blouses & shirts; girls' & children's outerwear; children's & infants' wear stores; children's shoes

(P-3586)
ROSE GENUINE INC
Also Called: Jinelle
834 S Broadway Ste 1100, Los Angeles
(90014-3510)
P.O. Box 555970 (90055-0970)
PHONE..............................213 747-4120
John Golshan, *President*
Mike Golshan, *Admin Sec*
▲ EMP: 15
SQ FT: 15,000
SALES (est): 2.1MM **Privately Held**
SIC: 2361 Dresses: girls', children's & infants'

(P-3587)
RSDG INTERNATIONAL INC
2127 Aralia St, Newport Beach
(92660-4131)
P.O. Box 4032, Diamond Bar (91765-0032)
PHONE..............................626 256-4190
Ralph Silva, *President*
▲ EMP: 24
SQ FT: 9,000
SALES: 6MM **Privately Held**
SIC: 2361 Girls' & children's dresses, blouses & shirts

(P-3588)
S SEDGHI INC (PA)
Also Called: Lavender Alley
2416 W 7th St, Los Angeles (90057-3904)
P.O. Box 361338 (90036-9330)
PHONE..............................213 745-2019
Shohreh Sedghi, *Principal*
▲ EMP: 22
SALES (est): 2.2MM **Privately Held**
SIC: 2361 Girls' & children's dresses, blouses & shirts

(P-3589)
WILDTHINGS SNAP-ONS INC
4 De Luca Pl, San Rafael (94901-3909)
P.O. Box 3635 (94912-3635)
PHONE..............................415 457-0112
Patricia Phillips, *President*
▲ EMP: 10
SQ FT: 1,500
SALES: 500K **Privately Held**
SIC: 2361 T-shirts & tops: girls', children's & infants'

(P-3590)
WINSTAR TEXTILE INC
16815 E Johnson Dr, City of Industry
(91745-2417)
PHONE..............................626 357-1133
Der Yeu Lu, *CEO*
Davis Lu, *President*
Huimin Dou, *Principal*
Alan KAO, *Prdtn Mgr*
▲ EMP: 20 EST: 1999
SQ FT: 3,400
SALES (est): 3.2MM **Privately Held**
WEB: www.winstartextile.com
SIC: 2361 2325 Blouses: girls', children's & infants'; men's & boys' trousers & slacks

---

2369 Girls' & Infants' Outerwear, NEC

(P-3591)
BABY GUESS INC
1444 S Alameda St, Los Angeles
(90021-2433)
PHONE..............................213 765-3100
Maurice Marciano, *Ch of Bd*
EMP: 50
SALES (est): 356.1K
SALES (corp-wide): 2.3B **Publicly Held**
WEB: www.guess.com
SIC: 2369 Jackets: girls', children's & infants'; skirts: girls', children's & infants'; slacks: girls' & children's

---

PA: Guess , Inc.
1444 S Alameda St
Los Angeles CA 90021
213 765-3100

(P-3592)
FLAP HAPPY INC
2857 E 11th St, Los Angeles (90023-3405)
PHONE..........................310 453-3527
Laurie Snyder, *President*
Walter Snyder, *Vice Pres*
EMP: 20
SQ FT: 12,000
SALES (est): 3MM **Privately Held**
WEB: www.flaphappy.com
SIC: 2369 2353 Girls' & children's outer-
wear; hats & caps

(P-3593)
MACK & REISS INC
Also Called: Biscotti and Kate Mack
5601 San Leandro St Ste 3, Oakland
(94621-4433)
PHONE..........................510 434-9122
Bernadette Reiss, *President*
Robert Mack, *Corp Secy*
Carrie Martin, *Officer*
Janise Ftaton, *Persnl Mgr*
Judy Beall, *Mktg Dir*
▲ **EMP:** 85
SQ FT: 75,000
SALES (est): 9.5MM **Privately Held**
WEB: www.biscottiinc.com
SIC: 2369 Girls' & children's outerwear

(P-3594)
RMLA INC
Also Called: La Chic
1972 E 20th St, Vernon (90058-1005)
PHONE..........................213 749-4333
Ralph Maya, *CEO*
Jan Adamcyk, *Bd of Directors*
Jack Maya, *Vice Pres*
▲ **EMP:** 55
SALES (est): 7.2MM **Privately Held**
WEB: www.rmla.com
SIC: 2369 Girls' & children's outerwear

(P-3595)
**SOUTH COAST SEWING
COMPANY INC**
2009 S Grand Ave, Santa Ana
(92705-5202)
PHONE..........................310 350-0535
Damion Roberson, *CEO*
Preechar Sullivan, *Vice Pres*
EMP: 30
SQ FT: 6,600
SALES: 1.7MM **Privately Held**
SIC: 2369 2326 Bathing suits &
swimwear; girls', children's & infants';
men's & boys' work clothing

(P-3596)
**TRLG INTERMEDIATE
HOLDINGS LLC (PA)**
1888 Rosecrans Ave, Manhattan Beach
(90266-3712)
PHONE..........................323 266-3072
John Ermatinger, *CEO*
Dalli Snyder, *CFO*
Alan Weiss, *Vice Pres*
Eugene Davis, *Director*
Tony Di Paolo, *Director*
◆ **EMP:** 11
SQ FT: 119,000
SALES: 350MM **Privately Held**
SIC: 2369 2325 2339 Girls' & children's
outerwear; men's & boys' trousers &
slacks; women's & misses' outerwear

(P-3597)
**TRUE RELIGION APPAREL INC
(HQ)**
Also Called: True Religion Brand Jeans
1888 Rosecrans Ave # 1000, Manhattan
Beach (90266-3795)
PHONE..........................323 266-3072
Chelsea A Grayson, *CEO*
Lynne Koplin, *President*
Eric Bauer, *CFO*
Peter F Collins, *CFO*
David Chiovetti, *Senior VP*
▲ **EMP:** 300
SQ FT: 119,000

SALES (est): 529.2MM
SALES (corp-wide): 350MM **Privately
Held**
WEB: www.truereligionbrandjeans.com
SIC: 2369 2325 2339 Men's & boys'
trousers & slacks; jeans: men's, youths' &
boys'; women's & misses' outerwear;
jeans: women's, misses' & juniors'; jeans:
girls', children's & infants'
PA: Trlg Intermediate Holdings, Llc
1888 Rosecrans Ave
Manhattan Beach CA 90266
323 266-3072

(P-3598)
**VESTURE GROUP
INCORPORATED**
Also Called: Pinky Los Angeles
3405 W Pacific Ave, Burbank (91505-1555)
PHONE..........................818 842-0200
Robert Galishoff, *CEO*
Gail Lupacchini, *Vice Pres*
Kathy Fortner, *Production*
▲ **EMP:** 48
SQ FT: 3,500
SALES (est): 7.1MM **Privately Held**
SIC: 2369 2335 Skirts: girls', children's &
infants'; women's, juniors' & misses'
dresses

2371 Fur Goods

(P-3599)
BOND FURS INC
114 W Lime Ave, Monrovia (91016-2841)
PHONE..........................626 471-9912
Steven Zaslaw, *President*
EMP: 12
SQ FT: 3,000
SALES (est): 1MM **Privately Held**
WEB: www.bondfurs.com
SIC: 2371 5632 3999 Coats, fur; fur ap-
parel, made to custom order; furs

(P-3600)
FUR ACCENTS LLC
1425 E Lincoln Ave Ste O, Anaheim
(92805-2210)
PHONE..........................714 403-5286
Steven Goodyear, *Mng Member*
EMP: 15
SALES: 2MM **Privately Held**
SIC: 2371 5632 Fur goods; fur apparel

(P-3601)
LARRY B LLC
Also Called: Dicker & Dicker Beverly Hills
215 S Robertson Blvd, Beverly Hills
(90211-2810)
PHONE..........................310 652-3877
Lawrence Charles Becker,
EMP: 11
SQ FT: 1,200
SALES (est): 942K **Privately Held**
SIC: 2371 5199 5632 Apparel, fur;
leather, leather goods & furs; fur apparel

2381 Dress & Work Gloves

(P-3602)
MECHANIX WEAR INC (PA)
28525 Witherspoon Pkwy, Valencia
(91355-5417)
PHONE..........................800 222-4296
Michael Hale, *CEO*
Jordan Dull, *Partner*
Kevin Reynolds, *President*
Bari Waalk, *COO*
Jamie Mearns, *CFO*
▲ **EMP:** 98
SQ FT: 24,000
SALES (est): 26.2MM **Privately Held**
WEB: www.mechanixwear.com
SIC: 2381 7218 Fabric dress & work
gloves; safety glove supply

(P-3603)
ORBITA CORP (PA)
Also Called: Estam
1136 Crocker St, Los Angeles
(90021-2014)
PHONE..........................213 746-4783
Dae Seung Park, *President*

▲ **EMP:** 15
SALES (est): 4.5MM **Privately Held**
SIC: 2381 Fabric dress & work gloves

2384 Robes & Dressing Gowns

(P-3604)
TERRY TOWN CORPORATION
1440 Innov Dr 200&, San Diego (92154)
PHONE..........................619 421-5354
Saip Ereren, *CEO*
Jeff Erdogmus, *COO*
Aaron Bradley, *Natl Sales Mgr*
Chip Harlow, *Sales Mgr*
Esmeralda Anaya, *Marketing Staff*
◆ **EMP:** 19
SQ FT: 25,000
SALES: 16.7MM **Privately Held**
SIC: 2384 5023 5719 Bathrobes, men's &
women's: made from purchased materi-
als; linens & towels; bedding (sheets,
blankets, spreads & pillows)

(P-3605)
VICTOIRE LLC
Also Called: Robeworks
955 S Meridian Ave, Alhambra
(91803-1249)
PHONE..........................323 225-0101
Vincent Rojas,
Kenneth Nim,
EMP: 12
SQ FT: 5,000
SALES (est): 1MM **Privately Held**
SIC: 2384 Robes & dressing gowns

2386 Leather & Sheep Lined Clothing

(P-3606)
AJG INC
Also Called: Astrologie California
7220 E Slauson Ave, Commerce
(90040-3625)
PHONE..........................323 346-0171
Angelo Ghailian, *CEO*
▲ **EMP:** 20
SALES (est): 9.9MM **Privately Held**
SIC: 2386 5131 5199 Leather & sheep-
lined clothing; knit fabrics; fabrics, yarns &
knit goods

(P-3607)
AWCC CORPORATION
434 N Coast Hwy, Laguna Beach
(92651-1630)
PHONE..........................949 497-6313
Bob Turner, *President*
▲ **EMP:** 10 **EST:** 1995
SALES (est): 1MM **Privately Held**
WEB: www.pacificrimdirect.com
SIC: 2386 Garments, leather

(P-3608)
BARRY COSTELLO
319 Broad St, Nevada City (95959-2405)
PHONE..........................530 265-3300
Margaret Costello, *Manager*
EMP: 14
SALES (corp-wide): 1.7MM **Privately
Held**
WEB: www.furtraders.com
SIC: 2386 Leather & sheep-lined clothing
PA: Barry Costello
233 Broad St
Nevada City CA
530 265-3300

(P-3609)
BATES INDUSTRIES INC
Also Called: Bates Leathers
3671 Industry Ave Ste C5, Lakewood
(90712-4159)
PHONE..........................562 426-8668
Dana L Grindle, *President*
Dawn Grindle, *President*
Lori Montez, *Treasurer*
▲ **EMP:** 10 **EST:** 1939
SQ FT: 4,300

SALES (est): 660K **Privately Held**
WEB: www.batesleathers.com
SIC: 2386 Garments, leather

(P-3610)
CHROME HEARTS LLC (PA)
921 N Mansfield Ave, Los Angeles
(90038-2311)
PHONE..........................323 957-7544
Richard Stark, *Mng Member*
Adrian Taylor, *CFO*
Peter Struthers, *Office Mgr*
Eric Kachadoorian, *Engineer*
Monica Venegas, *Prdtn Mgr*
▲ **EMP:** 50
SQ FT: 50,000
SALES (est): 17.9MM **Privately Held**
WEB: www.chromehearts.com
SIC: 2386 3911 2511 2371 Leather &
sheep-lined clothing; jewelry, precious
metal; wood household furniture; fur
goods

(P-3611)
COLLOQUY LLC
Also Called: Golden Bear Sportswear
200 Potrero Ave, San Francisco
(94103-4815)
P.O. Box 411317 (94141-1317)
PHONE..........................415 863-6171
Matthew Peters Ehlen,
EMP: 20
SQ FT: 17,000
SALES (est): 2.5MM **Privately Held**
SIC: 2386 5136 Coats & jackets, leather &
sheep-lined; leather & sheep lined cloth-
ing, men's & boys'

(P-3612)
CORONADO LEATHER CO INC
1961 Main St, San Diego (92113-2129)
PHONE..........................619 238-0265
Brent Laulom, *President*
EMP: 15
SQ FT: 2,100
SALES (est): 2MM **Privately Held**
WEB: www.coronadoleather.com
SIC: 2386 3111 Garments, leather; hand-
bag leather

(P-3613)
DISTINCTIVE INDS TEXAS INC
Also Called: Roadwire Distinctive Inds
10618 Shoemaker Ave, Santa Fe Springs
(90670-4038)
PHONE..........................512 491-3500
Dwight Forrester, *Principal*
EMP: 28
SALES (corp-wide): 13.6MM **Privately
Held**
SIC: 2386 Leather & sheep-lined clothing
PA: Distinctive Industries Of Texas, Inc.
4516 Seton Pkwy 135
Austin TX 78752
512 491-3500

(P-3614)
EURO BELLO USA
10660 Wilshire Blvd, Los Angeles
(90024-4522)
PHONE..........................213 446-2818
Bijan Israel, *President*
Natalio Oscar, *Manager*
EMP: 46 **EST:** 2014
SQ FT: 20,000
SALES: 18MM **Privately Held**
SIC: 2386 2211 Garments, leather; ap-
parel & outerwear fabrics, cotton

(P-3615)
HD GARMENT SOLUTIONS INC
13351 Riverside Dr, Sherman Oaks
(91423-2542)
PHONE..........................323 581-6000
Ron Mansuri, *President*
EMP: 20 **EST:** 2011
SQ FT: 2,000
SALES (est): 1.7MM **Privately Held**
SIC: 2386 Garments, leather

(P-3616)
JEJOMI DESIGNS INC
Also Called: Long Pine Leathers
2626 Fruitland Ave, Vernon (90058-2220)
PHONE..........................323 584-4211
Jorge Castellon, *President*

▲ = Import ▼=Export
◆ =Import/Export

Cecilia Polanco, *Treasurer*
Susan Castellon, *Vice Pres*
▲ EMP: 35
SQ FT: 9,200
SALES: 3.6MM **Privately Held**
SIC: 2386 Coats & jackets, leather &
sheep-lined

(P-3617)
JOHNSON LEATHER
CORPORATION (PA)
1833 Polk St, San Francisco (94109-3003)
PHONE.................................415 775-7393
Johnson Tam, *President*
▲ EMP: 12
SQ FT: 3,000
SALES (est): 1MM **Privately Held**
WEB: www.johnsonleather.com
SIC: 2386 5699 5136 5137 Garments,
leather; leather garments; leather &
sheep lined clothing, men's & boys';
leather & sheep lined clothing, women's &
children's

(P-3618)
JOHNSON LEATHER
CORPORATION
3265 17th St Ste 204, San Francisco
(94110-1258)
PHONE.................................415 863-8819
Johnson Tam, *President*
EMP: 15
SALES (corp-wide): 1MM **Privately Held**
WEB: www.johnsonleather.com
SIC: 2386 Garments, leather
PA: Johnson Leather Corporation
1833 Polk St
San Francisco CA 94109
415 775-7393

(P-3619)
KRASNES INC
Also Called: Cop Shopper
2222 Commercial St, San Diego
(92113-1111)
PHONE.................................619 232-2066
Jerry Krasne, *President*
Gail Wilson, *CFO*
Kurt Krasne, *Vice Pres*
James Wells, *General Mgr*
Susie Godinez, *Sales Staff*
▲ EMP: 90
SQ FT: 28,000
SALES (est): 10.6MM **Privately Held**
WEB: www.triplek.com
SIC: 2386 3484 Leather & sheep-lined
clothing; small arms

(P-3620)
MR S LEATHER
Also Called: Fetters U.S.A.
385 8th St, San Francisco (94103-4423)
PHONE.................................415 863-7764
Richard Hunter, *President*
Tchukon Hunter, *Vice Pres*
▲ EMP: 45
SQ FT: 15,000
SALES (est): 4.8MM **Privately Held**
WEB: www.mr-s-leather-fetters.com
SIC: 2386 5699 5136 Garments, leather;
leather garments; men's & boys' clothing;
men's & boys' furnishings

(P-3621)
OHECK LLC
5830 Bickett St, Huntington Park
(90255-2627)
PHONE.................................323 923-2700
Eric Jweon, *Mng Member*
EMP: 250 EST: 2012
SQ FT: 52,000
SALES (est): 25MM **Privately Held**
SIC: 2386 Garments, leather

(P-3622)
SCULLY SPORTSWEAR INC
Also Called: Oakridge
1701 Pacific Ave, Oxnard (93033-2745)
PHONE.................................805 483-6339
Daniel J Scully III, *CEO*
Robert Swink, *Vice Pres*
Linda Hansen, *Admin Asst*
Ernesto Quintanilla, *Info Tech Mgr*
Linda Hanson, *Human Res Mgr*
▲ EMP: 60
SQ FT: 80,000

SALES (est): 8.2MM **Privately Held**
SIC: 2386 5099 Coats & jackets, leather &
sheep-lined; garments, leather; luggage;
cases, carrying

(P-3623)
SUPERLAMB INC
Also Called: Sheepskin Specialties
8026 Miramar Rd, San Diego
(92126-4320)
PHONE.................................858 566-2031
Lindsay Gulliver, *CEO*
Elizabeth Gulliver, *Vice Pres*
▼ EMP: 15
SQ FT: 7,000
SALES (est): 1.6MM **Privately Held**
WEB: www.superlambfootwear.com
SIC: 2386 Leather & sheep-lined clothing

(P-3624)
TEX SHOEMAKER & SON INC
19034 E Donington St, Glendora
(91741-1900)
PHONE.................................909 592-2071
Douglas Shoemaker, *President*
John Zubiate, *CFO*
EMP: 10
SQ FT: 32,000
SALES: 300K **Privately Held**
WEB: www.texshoemaker.com
SIC: 2386 5941 3172

(P-3625)
WALZ CAPS INC
2215 La Mirada Dr, Vista (92081-8828)
PHONE.................................760 683-9259
Michael Gilstrap, *President*
Michael R Gilstrap, *President*
EMP: 30
SALES (est): 289.8K **Privately Held**
SIC: 2386 Hats & caps, leather

2387 Apparel Belts

(P-3626)
BELTS BY SIMON INC
14382 Chambers Rd, Tustin (92780-6912)
PHONE.................................714 573-0303
Saeed Tavassoli, *President*
▲ EMP: 65
SQ FT: 4,000
SALES (est): 6.3MM **Privately Held**
SIC: 2387 Apparel belts

(P-3627)
BRIGHTON COLLECTIBLES LLC
10250 Santa Monica Blvd, Los Angeles
(90067-6482)
PHONE.................................626 961-9381
EMP: 32
SALES (corp-wide): 375.3MM **Privately
Held**
SIC: 2387 Apparel belts
PA: Brighton Collectibles, Llc
14022 Nelson Ave
City Of Industry CA 91746
626 961-9381

(P-3628)
CABORCA LEATHER LLC
4275 Peaceful Glen Rd, Vacaville
(95688-9507)
PHONE.................................707 463-7607
Paul L Clapham,
Paul Clapham, *President*
Ron Davis, *Vice Pres*
Jim Hess, *VP Finance*
▲ EMP: 35
SALES (est): 2.7MM **Privately Held**
SIC: 2387 5136 Apparel belts; apparel
belts, men's & boys'

(P-3629)
ELITE FASHION ACCESSORIES
INC
7141 N Warren Ave, Fresno (93711-7150)
PHONE.................................559 435-0225
Diane Daddian, *President*
Laurie Sivas, *Treasurer*
Paul Sivas, *Vice Pres*
Jeanet Sivas, *Director*
EMP: 10 EST: 1977
SQ FT: 20,000

SALES: 3.5MM **Privately Held**
WEB: www.warehouseexpress.com
SIC: 2387 Apparel belts

(P-3630)
LEJON OF CALIFORNIA INC
Also Called: Lejon Tulliani
1229 Railroad St, Corona (92882-1838)
PHONE.................................951 736-1229
John W Shirinian, *President*
Jack Shirinian, *Admin Sec*
▲ EMP: 40
SQ FT: 33,000
SALES: 6MM **Privately Held**
WEB: www.lejon.com
SIC: 2387 3172 Apparel belts; personal
leather goods

(P-3631)
MARKAP INC
20382 Hermana Cir, Lake Forest
(92630-8701)
PHONE.................................949 240-1418
Gavin Kaplan, *CEO*
Mark Naude, *CFO*
▲ EMP: 48
SQ FT: 27,000
SALES (est): 3.5MM **Privately Held**
WEB: www.anotherline.com
SIC: 2387 Apparel belts

(P-3632)
SAWHNEY GARCIA HERNANDEZ
401 B St Ste 2210, San Diego
(92101-4298)
PHONE.................................619 564-8400
Bonifacio Bonny Garcia, *Managing Prtnr*
EMP: 13
SALES (est): 1.4MM **Privately Held**
SIC: 2387 8111 Apparel belts; specialized
law offices, attorneys

(P-3633)
STREETS AHEAD INC
Also Called: Hyde
5510 S Soto St Unit B, Vernon
(90058-3623)
PHONE.................................323 277-0860
David Sack, *CEO*
Michael Fructuoso, *Controller*
Michelle Sack, *Sales Dir*
▲ EMP: 20
SQ FT: 28,000
SALES (est): 3.8MM **Privately Held**
SIC: 2387 Apparel belts

(P-3634)
WESTSIDE ACCESSORIES INC
(PA)
8920 Vernon Ave Ste 128, Montclair
(91763-1663)
PHONE.................................626 858-5452
Carol Cantagallo, *President*
▲ EMP: 21
SALES (est): 2MM **Privately Held**
WEB: www.westsideaccessories.com
SIC: 2387 Apparel belts

2389 Apparel &
Accessories, NEC

(P-3635)
32 BAR BLUES LLC
1015 Cindy Ln B, Carpinteria (93013-2905)
PHONE.................................805 962-6665
Steve Meronk, *Mng Member*
Bruce Willard, *Managing Dir*
Sondra Williamson, *Assistant*
▲ EMP: 13 EST: 2011
SALES (est): 1.8MM **Privately Held**
SIC: 2389 Men's miscellaneous acces-
sories

(P-3636)
ACADEMIC CH CHOIR GWNS
MFG INC
Also Called: Academic Cap & Gown
20644 Superior St, Chatsworth
(91311-4414)
PHONE.................................818 886-8697
Mike Cronan, *President*
Evelyn Cronan, *Vice Pres*
Mark Cronan, *Vice Pres*
▲ EMP: 30 EST: 1947

SQ FT: 13,000
SALES: 24.3MM **Privately Held**
WEB: www.academicapparel.com
SIC: 2389 2353 Clergymen's vestments;
academic vestments (caps & gowns); uni-
forms & vestments; hats, caps & millinery

(P-3637)
ALEXANDERS TEXTILE PDTS
INC
Also Called: Alexander's Costumes
200 N D St, San Bernardino (92401-1702)
PHONE.................................951 276-2500
Scott Alexander, *President*
Kay A Young, *Corp Secy*
Leslie Fournier, *Vice Pres*
▲ EMP: 15
SQ FT: 16,000
SALES (est): 2.2MM **Privately Held**
WEB: www.merseyworld.com
SIC: 2389 2299 5099 2339

(P-3638)
AMERICAN APPAREL (USA)
LLC
747 Warehouse St, Los Angeles
(90021-1106)
P.O. Box 5129, Brandon MS (39047-5129)
PHONE.................................213 488-0226
Dov Charney,
▲ EMP: 18
SALES (est): 2.6MM **Privately Held**
WEB: www.americanapparel.net
SIC: 2389 5961 Men's miscellaneous ac-
cessories; women's apparel, mail order

(P-3639)
AMERICAN COSTUME CORP
12980 Raymer St, North Hollywood
(91605-4276)
PHONE.................................818 432-4350
Luster Bayless, *Chairman*
Diana Foster, *President*
EMP: 10
SQ FT: 30,000
SALES (est): 1.2MM **Privately Held**
SIC: 2389 Costumes

(P-3640)
AMERICAN GARMENT
COMPANY
Also Called: Laila Jayde Dda
16230 Manning Way, Cerritos
(90703-2223)
PHONE.................................562 483-8300
Justin Lee, *CEO*
David Laduke, *President*
EMP: 10
SALES (est): 5MM **Privately Held**
SIC: 2389 Men's miscellaneous acces-
sories

(P-3641)
ANDREA BIJOUX
1001 Crocker St Ste 8, Los Angeles
(90021-2050)
PHONE.................................213 236-0747
Andrea Bijoux, *Owner*
EMP: 16
SALES (est): 828.5K **Privately Held**
SIC: 2389 Apparel & accessories

(P-3642)
APP WINDDOWN LLC
16400 Trojan Way, La Mirada
(90638-5630)
PHONE.................................213 272-1669
John Kuwano, *Manager*
EMP: 10
SALES (corp-wide): 2.7B **Privately Held**
SIC: 2389 Men's miscellaneous acces-
sories
HQ: App Winddown, Llc
747 Warehouse St
Los Angeles CA 90021
213 488-0226

(P-3643)
APP WINDDOWN LLC (HQ)
Also Called: American Apparel
747 Warehouse St, Los Angeles
(90021-1106)
P.O. Box 5129, Brandon MS (39047-5129)
PHONE.................................213 488-0226
Chelsea Grayson, *CEO*

(PA)=Parent Co (HQ)=Headquarters (DH)=Div Headquarters
✿ = New Business established in last 2 years

2019 California
Manufacturers Register

159

PRODUCTS & SVCS

Alma Amaya, *President*
David Wynne, *Vice Pres*
Jasmine Bracamontes, *Store Mgr*
Jeffery Crawford, *Store Mgr*
◆ **EMP:** 21
SALES: 608.8MM
SALES (corp-wide): 2.7B **Privately Held**
WEB: www.americanapparel.net
SIC: 2389 2311 2331 Men's miscellaneous accessories; men's & boys' suits & coats; women's & misses' blouses & shirts
PA: Gildan Activewear Inc
600 Boul De Maisonneuve O 33eme etage
Montreal QC H3A 3
514 735-2023

(P-3644)
B2 APPAREL INC
Also Called: Bb Apparel
219 E 32nd St, Los Angeles (90011-1917)
PHONE..............................323 233-0044
Scott Lee, *President*
EMP: 15
SQ FT: 20,000
SALES (est): 10MM **Privately Held**
SIC: 2389 Footlets

(P-3645)
BRIGHTON COLLECTIBLES LLC
1195 Broadway Plz, Walnut Creek (94596-5130)
PHONE..............................925 932-1500
Jerry Kohl, *Branch Mgr*
EMP: 24
SALES (corp-wide): 375.3MM **Privately Held**
SIC: 2389 Men's miscellaneous accessories
PA: Brighton Collectibles, Llc
14022 Nelson Ave
City Of Industry CA 91746
626 961-9381

(P-3646)
CALIFRNIA CSTUME CLLCTIONS INC (PA)
Also Called: California Costume Int'l
210 S Anderson St, Los Angeles (90033-3205)
PHONE..............................323 262-8383
Tak Kwan Woo, *CEO*
Peter Woo, *President*
Charles Woo, *Treasurer*
Alec Saatjian, *Executive*
Quinton Young, *Info Tech Mgr*
◆ **EMP:** 47
SQ FT: 300,000
SALES (est): 39.3MM **Privately Held**
WEB: www.californiacostumes.com
SIC: 2389 5092 Costumes; toys

(P-3647)
CENTER THTRE GROUP LOS ANGELES
Also Called: Center Thatre Group Costume Sp
2856 E 11th St, Los Angeles (90023-3406)
PHONE..............................213 972-3751
Michael Thompson, *Branch Mgr*
Dawn Holiski, *Director*
EMP: 30
SALES (corp-wide): 48.8MM **Privately Held**
WEB: www.ctgla.org
SIC: 2389 Theatrical costumes
PA: Center Theatre Group Of Los Angeles
601 W Temple St
Los Angeles CA 90012
213 972-7344

(P-3648)
CHAGALL DESIGN LIMITED
20625 Belshaw Ave, Carson (90746-3507)
PHONE..............................310 537-9530
Jacques De Groot, *President*
Mannix Delfino-De Groot, *Vice Pres*
EMP: 12
SQ FT: 8,000
SALES (est): 1.1MM **Privately Held**
WEB: www.chagalldesign.com
SIC: 2389 Clergymen's vestments

(P-3649)
CHARADES LLC (PA)
14438 Don Julian Rd, City of Industry (91746-3101)
PHONE..............................626 435-0077
Jerry B Beck,
Howard Beige,
Mark Beige,
▲ **EMP:** 240
SQ FT: 100,000
SALES (est): 34.8MM **Privately Held**
WEB: www.charadescostumes.com
SIC: 2389 Costumes

(P-3650)
COMPUTERIZED FASHION SVCS INC
Also Called: Pride Sash
3341 Jack Northrop Ave, Hawthorne (90250-4426)
PHONE..............................310 973-0106
Louis Boksenbaum, *President*
Joelle Boksenbaum, *Vice Pres*
Stephanie Aviv, *VP Mktg*
▲ **EMP:** 13
SALES: 1MM **Privately Held**
SIC: 2389 Uniforms & vestments

(P-3651)
CREATIVE COSTUMING DESIGNS INC
15402 Electronic Ln, Huntington Beach (92649-1334)
PHONE..............................714 895-0982
Noreen Roberts, *Owner*
Kevin Roberts, *CFO*
EMP: 35
SQ FT: 5,300
SALES (est): 3.3MM **Privately Held**
SIC: 2389 Academic vestments (caps & gowns)

(P-3652)
CUSTOM CHARACTERS INC
621 Thompson Ave, Glendale (91201-2032)
PHONE..............................818 507-5940
Ryan Rhodes, *President*
Drew Herron, *Treasurer*
Victoria Arcenale, *Accounting Mgr*
EMP: 18
SQ FT: 5,200
SALES (est): 1.7MM **Privately Held**
WEB: www.customcharacters.com
SIC: 2389 3999 Costumes; stage hardware & equipment, except lighting

(P-3653)
DECKERS OUTDOOR CORPORATION (PA)
250 Coromar Dr, Goleta (93117-3697)
PHONE..............................805 967-7611
David Powers, *President*
John M Gibbons, *Ch of Bd*
Stefano Caroti, *President*
Andrea O'Donnell, *President*
David E Lafitte, *COO*
EMP: 277
SQ FT: 185,000
SALES: 1.9B **Publicly Held**
WEB: www.deckers.com
SIC: 2389 2339 3021 Men's miscellaneous accessories; women's & misses' accessories; sandals, rubber

(P-3654)
DISGUISE INC (HQ)
12120 Kear Pl, Poway (92064-7132)
PHONE..............................858 391-3600
Stephen Berman, *CEO*
Benoit Pousset, *President*
◆ **EMP:** 33
SQ FT: 206,000
SALES (est): 13.6MM **Publicly Held**
WEB: www.disguise.com
SIC: 2389 7299 Costumes; costume rental

(P-3655)
DISNEY ENTERPRISES INC
1313 S Harbor Blvd, Anaheim (92802-2309)
PHONE..............................407 397-6000
Marlene Madrid, *Manager*
EMP: 100 **Publicly Held**
SIC: 2389 Theatrical costumes

HQ: Disney Enterprises, Inc.
500 S Buena Vista St
Burbank CA 91521
818 560-1000

(P-3656)
FABFAD LLC
1901 E 7th Pl, Los Angeles (90021-1601)
PHONE..............................213 488-0456
Lolita Mejia, *Vice Pres*
EMP: 19 EST: 2017
SALES (est): 487.3K **Privately Held**
SIC: 2389 Men's miscellaneous accessories

(P-3657)
GILLI INC
1100 S San Pedro St C07, Los Angeles (90015-2385)
PHONE..............................213 744-9808
Hae Yun Suh, *Branch Mgr*
EMP: 15
SALES (corp-wide): 7MM **Privately Held**
SIC: 2389 5137 Uniforms & vestments; women's & children's clothing
PA: Gilli, Inc.
2939 Bandini Blvd
Vernon CA 90058
323 235-3722

(P-3658)
HQ BRANDS LLC
Also Called: House of Quirky
860 S Los Angeles St # 706, Los Angeles (90014-3333)
PHONE..............................213 627-7922
Melissa Tong, *Mng Member*
EMP: 10
SQ FT: 5,000
SALES (est): 906.7K **Privately Held**
SIC: 2389 Disposable garments & accessories

(P-3659)
INCHARACTER COSTUMES LLC
4560 Alvarado Canyon Rd 1d, San Diego (92120-4309)
PHONE..............................858 552-3600
Robert S Pickens, *Mng Member*
Joanne Cochran, *COO*
Robert Emmerman, *Vice Pres*
Tippy Larkin, *Accountant*
Robert Torre, *Controller*
▲ **EMP:** 50
SQ FT: 46,800
SALES: 17MM **Privately Held**
WEB: www.incharacter.com
SIC: 2389 Costumes

(P-3660)
IRONHEAD STUDIOS INC
7616 Ventura Canyon Ave, Van Nuys (91402-6372)
PHONE..............................818 901-7561
Jose Fernandez, *CEO*
EMP: 19
SALES: 670K **Privately Held**
SIC: 2389 7922 Costumes; costume & scenery design services

(P-3661)
J&C TAPOCIK INC
Also Called: Express ID
2941 Mcallister St, Riverside (92503-6111)
PHONE..............................951 351-4333
Claudette Tapocik, *President*
John C Tapocik, *Corp Secy*
Mike Tapocik, *Vice Pres*
▲ **EMP:** 10
SQ FT: 30,000
SALES (est): 1MM **Privately Held**
SIC: 2389 2321 Men's miscellaneous accessories; men's & boys' furnishings

(P-3662)
JUST SAYING INC
800 S Date Ave, Alhambra (91803-1414)
PHONE..............................888 512-5007
Tony Lau, *President*
EMP: 10
SALES (est): 702K **Privately Held**
SIC: 2389 Apparel & accessories

(P-3663)
KATIE K INC
5601 Bickett St, Vernon (90058-3605)
PHONE..............................323 589-3030
Mimi Kim, *President*
▲ **EMP:** 10
SQ FT: 4,000
SALES (est): 1.6MM **Privately Held**
SIC: 2389 Uniforms & vestments

(P-3664)
KINARY INC
2542 Troy Ave, South El Monte (91733-1428)
PHONE..............................626 575-7873
Kim Chung, *President*
EMP: 30
SALES (est): 1.5MM **Privately Held**
SIC: 2389 Uniforms & vestments

(P-3665)
LAKEVIEW INNOVATIONS INC
7777 Greenback Ln Ste 100, Citrus Heights (95610-5800)
PHONE..............................212 502-6702
Scott Colquitt, *President*
Harry Mull, *CFO*
▲ **EMP:** 10
SQ FT: 2,500
SALES (est): 2.5MM **Privately Held**
SIC: 2389 Cummerbunds

(P-3666)
LE CHEF COSTUMIER INC
825 Western Ave Ste 21, Glendale (91201-2385)
PHONE..............................818 242-0868
Jason Vaughan, *CEO*
EMP: 20
SALES: 1.3MM **Privately Held**
SIC: 2389 Costumes

(P-3667)
LETS GO APPAREL INC (PA)
Also Called: Uptown
1729 E Washington Blvd, Los Angeles (90021-3124)
PHONE..............................213 863-1767
Chang Wha Yoon, *President*
▼ **EMP:** 17
SQ FT: 30,000
SALES: 8.5MM **Privately Held**
SIC: 2389 5661 5632 Academic vestments (caps & gowns); shoes, custom; apparel accessories

(P-3668)
LLC MARSH PERKINS
80080 Via Pessaro, La Quinta (92253-7581)
PHONE..............................760 880-4558
Diane Lohman,
EMP: 15
SALES (est): 400.1K **Privately Held**
SIC: 2389 Apparel & accessories

(P-3669)
MASK U S INC
3121 Main St Ste F, Chula Vista (91911-5765)
PHONE..............................619 476-9041
David P Bragg, *CEO*
Martha Bragg, *Treasurer*
▲ **EMP:** 14
SQ FT: 8,000
SALES (est): 1.3MM **Privately Held**
WEB: www.maskus.com
SIC: 2389 Costumes

(P-3670)
MAURY RAZON
Also Called: L R Associates
74 W Cochran St Ste A, Simi Valley (93065-6268)
PHONE..............................818 989-6246
Maury Razon, *Owner*
EMP: 15
SQ FT: 5,000
SALES (est): 1.2MM **Privately Held**
SIC: 2389 2353 Uniforms & vestments; hats & caps

▲ = Import ▼=Export
◆ =Import/Export

(P-3671)
MDC INTERIOR SOLUTIONS LLC
Also Called: Komar Apparel Supply
6900 E Washington Blvd, Los Angeles
(90040-1908)
PHONE....................................800 621-4006
Gary Rothschild, *Manager*
EMP: 75
SALES (corp-wide): 89MM **Privately Held**
SIC: 2389 Men's miscellaneous accessories
PA: Mdc Interior Solutions, Llc
400 High Grove Blvd
Glendale Heights IL 60139
847 437-4000

(P-3672)
ML KISHIGO MFG CO LLC
2901 Daimler St, Santa Ana (92705-5810)
P.O. Box 1526, Costa Mesa (92628-1526)
PHONE....................................949 852-1963
Loren H Wall, *CEO*
Karen Wall, *Vice Pres*
▲ **EMP:** 86
SQ FT: 24,000
SALES (est): 15.7MM
SALES (corp-wide): 11.3B **Privately Held**
WEB: www.mlkishigo.com
SIC: 2389 Men's miscellaneous accessories
PA: Bunzl Public Limited Company
York House, 45 Seymour Street
London W1H 7
207 725-5000

(P-3673)
NICOLE FULLERTON
Also Called: Pendragon Costumes
27821 Pine Crest Pl, Castaic (91384-4129)
PHONE....................................661 257-0406
Nicole Fullerton, *Owner*
EMP: 12
SALES: 500K **Privately Held**
SIC: 2389 5621 Costumes; women's clothing stores

(P-3674)
PARADISE RANCH
Also Called: Molly's Custom Silver
2900 Adams St Ste C8, Riverside
(92504-7915)
PHONE....................................951 776-7736
Randy Rush, *CEO*
Molly Rush, *President*
EMP: 12
SQ FT: 2,000
SALES: 4MM **Privately Held**
SIC: 2389 Men's miscellaneous accessories

(P-3675)
POLERAX USA
909 S Greenwood Ave Ste K, Montebello
(90640-5836)
PHONE....................................323 477-1866
Kyung J Lee, *President*
EMP: 18
SALES (est): 1MM **Privately Held**
SIC: 2389 Apparel & accessories

(P-3676)
R & R INDUSTRIES INC
204 Avenida Fabricante, San Clemente
(92672-7538)
PHONE....................................949 361-9238
Robert Pare, *President*
Roger Poulin, *Treasurer*
Neil Samuels, *Vice Pres*
◆ **EMP:** 30
SQ FT: 8,150
SALES (est): 3.6MM **Privately Held**
SIC: 2389 Uniforms & vestments

(P-3677)
RG COSTUMES & ACCESSORIES INC
726 Arrow Grand Cir, Covina (91722-2147)
PHONE....................................626 858-9559
Roger Lee, *President*
Michael Lee, *Vice Pres*
▲ **EMP:** 30
SQ FT: 21,000

SALES: 1.9MM **Privately Held**
SIC: 2389 7299 Costumes; costume rental

(P-3678)
RM 518 MANAGEMENT LLC
Also Called: S M U
719 S Los Angeles St, Los Angeles
(90014-2109)
PHONE....................................213 624-6788
Randall Beatty,
Victor Kaplan,
Mike Price,
MEI Price,
▲ **EMP:** 23
SQ FT: 3,000
SALES (est): 1.3MM **Privately Held**
SIC: 2389 Men's miscellaneous accessories

(P-3679)
SHAFTON INC
6932 Tujunga Ave, North Hollywood
(91605-6212)
PHONE....................................818 985-5025
David Janzow, *President*
Becky Allen, *Corp Secy*
EMP: 17 EST: 1975
SQ FT: 7,000
SALES (est): 1.6MM **Privately Held**
WEB: www.shaftoninc.com
SIC: 2389 Theatrical costumes

(P-3680)
SHANE HUNTER LLC
Also Called: Auqa Blues
1013 S Los Angeles St # 1000, Los Angeles
(90015-1789)
PHONE....................................213 749-9390
Michael H Thaler,
Deborah Ford,
▲ **EMP:** 35
SALES (est): 4.5MM **Privately Held**
SIC: 2389

(P-3681)
SILVIAS COSTUMES
4964 Hollywood Blvd, Los Angeles
(90027-6108)
PHONE....................................323 661-2142
Silvia Tchakmakjian, *CEO*
Micheal Majian, *President*
EMP: 20
SQ FT: 6,000
SALES (est): 1.8MM **Privately Held**
SIC: 2389 Masquerade costumes

(P-3682)
SKATE GROUP INC
830 E 14th Pl, Los Angeles (90021-2120)
PHONE....................................213 749-6651
Kevin Neman, *President*
EMP: 10
SALES (est): 1.1MM **Privately Held**
SIC: 2389 Disposable garments & accessories

(P-3683)
SUSPENDER FACTORY INC
Also Called: Suspender Factory of S F
1425 63rd St, Emeryville (94608-2188)
PHONE....................................510 547-5400
John Nemec, *President*
▲ **EMP:** 35
SQ FT: 6,000
SALES (est): 5.3MM **Privately Held**
SIC: 2389 2387 Suspenders; apparel belts

(P-3684)
TRUE WARRIOR LLC
21226 Lone Star Way, Santa Clarita
(91390-4226)
PHONE....................................661 237-6588
Edward Luster,
EMP: 20 EST: 2017
SALES (est): 508.6K **Privately Held**
SIC: 2389 3069 Apparel & accessories; boot or shoe products, rubber

(P-3685)
UNDERWRAPS COSTUME CORPORATION
Also Called: Underwraps Costumes Inc.
9600 Irondale Ave, Chatsworth
(91311-5008)
P.O. Box 9603, Canoga Park (91309-0603)
PHONE....................................818 349-5300

Payman Shaffa, *CEO*
Irene Shaffa, *Vice Pres*
▲ **EMP:** 16
SQ FT: 45,000
SALES (est): 6.8MM **Privately Held**
SIC: 2389 Costumes

(P-3686)
WALT DISNEY IMAGINEERING
1200 N Miller St Unit D, Anaheim
(92806-1954)
PHONE....................................714 781-3152
Mark Hollingworth, *Branch Mgr*
EMP: 150 **Publicly Held**
SIC: 2389 Masquerade costumes; theatrical costumes
HQ: Walt Disney Imagineering Research & Development, Inc.
1401 Flower St
Glendale CA 91201
818 544-6500

(P-3687)
X SUBLIMATION INC
2837 S Olive St, Los Angeles
(90007-3339)
PHONE....................................213 700-1024
Terry Park, *President*
EMP: 10
SALES (est): 660.3K **Privately Held**
SIC: 2389 Disposable garments & accessories

2391 Curtains & Draperies

(P-3688)
ALLIED DRAPERY SERVICES INC
365 Lincoln Ave, San Jose (95126-3413)
PHONE....................................408 293-1600
Randy C Peters, *President*
EMP: 12
SQ FT: 3,000
SALES: 1MM **Privately Held**
WEB: www.allieddrapery.com
SIC: 2391 Draperies, plastic & textile: from purchased materials

(P-3689)
AMERICAN BLINDS AND DRAP INC
30776 Huntwood Ave, Hayward
(94544-7002)
P.O. Box 56267 (94545-6267)
PHONE....................................510 487-3500
Paul Russo, *President*
EMP: 50 EST: 1961
SQ FT: 30,000
SALES (est): 5.6MM **Privately Held**
WEB: www.americandrape.com
SIC: 2391 2591 Draperies, plastic & textile: from purchased materials; mini blinds

(P-3690)
AMTEX CALIFORNIA INC
Also Called: Ameritex International
113 S Utah St, Los Angeles (90033-3213)
PHONE....................................323 859-2200
Saq Hafeez, *President*
Alia Hafeez, *Vice Pres*
▲ **EMP:** 45 EST: 1991
SQ FT: 40,000
SALES (est): 5.4MM **Privately Held**
WEB: www.ameritexinternational.com
SIC: 2391 2392 5023 Draperies, plastic & textile: from purchased materials; bedspreads & bed sets: made from purchased materials; curtains; bedspreads

(P-3691)
ANTISTA DRAPERIES INC
Also Called: Antista's Draperies
4048 Tivoli Ave, Los Angeles (90066-5104)
PHONE....................................323 935-1912
Vincent Antista, *President*
Anna Antista, *Treasurer*
EMP: 12
SQ FT: 5,000
SALES (est): 1.1MM **Privately Held**
SIC: 2391 Draperies, plastic & textile: from purchased materials

(P-3692)
D & M DRAPERIES INC
Also Called: Dan-Mar Custom Draperies
323 W Maple Ave, Monrovia (91016-3331)
PHONE....................................626 256-1993
Marcos Barron, *President*
Danny Luna, *Vice Pres*
EMP: 15
SALES (est): 880K **Privately Held**
SIC: 2391 Curtains & draperies

(P-3693)
DRAPERY ENTERPRISES
1334 Brommer St Ste B5, Santa Cruz
(95062-2955)
PHONE....................................831 458-2578
Dave Byus, *Owner*
EMP: 12 EST: 1970
SQ FT: 3,000
SALES (est): 1.1MM **Privately Held**
SIC: 2391 Curtains & draperies

(P-3694)
ILONA DRAPERIES INC
3130 N Clybourn Ave, Burbank
(91505-1081)
PHONE....................................818 840-8811
Fred Winter, *President*
Keith Winter, *Treasurer*
Carol Winter, *Vice Pres*
EMP: 30
SQ FT: 8,000
SALES (est): 2.9MM **Privately Held**
WEB: www.ilonadraperies.com
SIC: 2391 2392 Draperies, plastic & textile: from purchased materials; comforters & quilts: made from purchased materials

(P-3695)
M L INTERIORS INC
Also Called: Mark Levine Window Coverings
151 Shipyard Way Ste 4, Newport Beach
(92663-4460)
PHONE....................................949 723-5001
Mark Levine, *President*
Debby Levine, *Corp Secy*
EMP: 23
SQ FT: 6,000
SALES (est): 1.7MM **Privately Held**
SIC: 2391 7389 2392 Curtains & draperies; interior decorating; bedspreads & bed sets: made from purchased materials

(P-3696)
MANZER CORPORATION
Also Called: Pacific Drapery
3801 30th St, San Diego (92104-3609)
PHONE....................................619 295-6031
Kathleen McAveney, *Owner*
EMP: 20
SQ FT: 2,000
SALES (est): 1.4MM **Privately Held**
SIC: 2391 2221 Draperies, plastic & textile: from purchased materials; broadwoven fabric mills, manmade

(P-3697)
MBF INTERIORS INC
Also Called: Modern Blind Factory
7831 Ostrow St, San Diego (92111-3602)
PHONE....................................858 565-2944
Behrooz Farhood, *President*
EMP: 25
SQ FT: 24,000
SALES: 3MM **Privately Held**
SIC: 2391 2591 5714 5719 Draperies, plastic & textile: from purchased materials; blinds vertical; draperies; vertical blinds

(P-3698)
MCCARTHYS DRAPERIES INC
Also Called: Rubio Fabrics
6955 Luther Dr, Sacramento (95823-1805)
PHONE....................................916 422-0155
Vern McCarthy, *President*
Eugenia McCarthy, *Vice Pres*
EMP: 35 EST: 1958
SQ FT: 10,000
SALES (est): 2.7MM **Privately Held**
SIC: 2391 5131 2591 Draperies, plastic & textile: from purchased materials; piece goods & notions; drapery hardware & blinds & shades

(P-3699)
PATS DECORATING SERVICE INC
2532 Strozier Ave, South El Monte (91733-2020)
PHONE..............................323 585-5073
Maria Lopez, *President*
Patricia L Prole, *President*
EMP: 15
SQ FT: 36,000
SALES (est): 1.7MM **Privately Held**
WEB: www.patsdecorator.com
SIC: 2391 2392 5714 5719 Draperies, plastic & textile: from purchased materials; bedspreads & bed sets: made from purchased materials; draperies; bedding (sheets, blankets, spreads & pillows)

(P-3700)
ROYAL DRAPERY MANUFACTURING
Also Called: Royal Drapery and Interiors
3149 California Blvd K, NAPA (94558-3334)
PHONE..............................707 226-2022
Peter Lomonaco, *Partner*
Sharon Lomonaco, *Partner*
EMP: 13
SALES (est): 450K **Privately Held**
SIC: 2391 5714 Draperies, plastic & textile: from purchased materials; draperies

(P-3701)
S & K THEATRICAL DRAP INC
Also Called: Sk Drapes
7313 Varna Ave, North Hollywood (91605-4009)
PHONE..............................818 503-0596
Carmela Skogman, *President*
Damian Schmidt, *Prdtn Mgr*
EMP: 16
SALES (est): 2.2MM **Privately Held**
WEB: www.sktheatricaldraperies.com
SIC: 2391 Draperies, plastic & textile: from purchased materials

(P-3702)
SANDYS DRAPERY INC
48374 Milmont Dr Bldg A, Fremont (94538-7324)
PHONE..............................510 445-0112
Donald L Yauger, *President*
Harry Yauger, *Treasurer*
Cindy Yauger, *Admin Sec*
EMP: 35
SQ FT: 27,500
SALES (est): 2.9MM **Privately Held**
SIC: 2391 2591 2211 Draperies, plastic & textile: from purchased materials; drapery hardware & blinds & shades; draperies & drapery fabrics, cotton

(P-3703)
SEW WHAT INC
Also Called: Rent What
1978 E Gladwick St, Compton (90220-6201)
PHONE..............................310 639-6000
Megan Duckett, *President*
Adam Duckett, *Vice Pres*
Lynda Vaughn, *General Mgr*
◆ EMP: 35
SQ FT: 15,000
SALES (est): 4.5MM **Privately Held**
WEB: www.sewwhat.com
SIC: 2391 5049 Curtains & draperies; theatrical equipment & supplies

(P-3704)
SUPERIOR WINDOW COVERINGS INC
7683 N San Fernando Rd, Burbank (91505-1073)
PHONE..............................818 762-6685
Marco Bonilla, *President*
Mario Murillo, *Info Tech Dir*
▲ EMP: 35
SQ FT: 4,000
SALES (est): 3.5MM **Privately Held**
WEB: www.superiorshades.com
SIC: 2391 2591 Draperies, plastic & textile: from purchased materials; blinds vertical

---

2392 House furnishings: Textile

(P-3705)
AMERICA ASIA TRADE PROMOTION
Also Called: A A Trader
4633 Old Ironsides Dr # 400, Santa Clara (95054-1807)
P.O. Box 3331 (95055-3331)
PHONE..............................408 970-8868
EMP: 10
SALES (est): 580K **Privately Held**
SIC: 2392 2511 2512 2834

(P-3706)
ANATOMIC GLOBAL INC
1241 Old Temescal Rd # 103, Corona (92881-7266)
PHONE..............................800 874-7237
David Farley, *CEO*
▲ EMP: 115
SQ FT: 55,000
SALES (est): 29.9MM **Privately Held**
WEB: www.anatomicconcepts.com
SIC: 2392 Bedspreads & bed sets: made from purchased materials

(P-3707)
ART MASTERPIECE GALLERY
4950 S Santa Fe Ave, Vernon (90058-2106)
PHONE..............................323 277-9448
Peter Leogrande, *President*
Randy Greenberg, *CEO*
Glenn Knecht, *Vice Pres*
▲ EMP: 14
SQ FT: 120,000
SALES (est): 1.1MM **Privately Held**
SIC: 2392 Household furnishings

(P-3708)
BELLAS PILLOW INSERTS INC
150 E Slauson Ave, Los Angeles (90011-5338)
PHONE..............................323 235-3898
Gerardo Luis, *President*
Evelyn Luis, *Vice Pres*
EMP: 16
SQ FT: 13,200
SALES (est): 990K **Privately Held**
SIC: 2392 5131 Cushions & pillows; upholstery fabrics, woven

(P-3709)
BEME INTERNATIONAL LLC
7333 Ronson Rd, San Diego (92111-1404)
PHONE..............................858 751-0580
Peisheng Qian,
Ed File, *Engineer*
Kristina Johnson, *Sales Mgr*
Mike Cruz, *Sales Staff*
Brian Graves,
▲ EMP: 21 EST: 1998
SALES (est): 3MM **Privately Held**
WEB: www.beme.net
SIC: 2392 Household furnishings

(P-3710)
BOJER INC
177 S Peckham Rd, Azusa (91702-3237)
PHONE..............................626 334-1711
Doris Gabai, *President*
Joey Gabai, *Vice Pres*
EMP: 20
SQ FT: 12,974
SALES (est): 1.6MM **Privately Held**
WEB: www.bojerinc.com
SIC: 2392 Cushions & pillows

(P-3711)
BRENTWOOD ORIGINALS INC (PA)
20639 S Fordyce Ave, Carson (90810-1019)
PHONE..............................310 637-6804
Loren H Sweet, *President*
Bill Bronstein, *Senior VP*
Tom Rose, *Senior VP*
Craig Torrey, *Senior VP*
Sigrid Simonson, *Vice Pres*
◆ EMP: 650
SQ FT: 1,200,000

SALES (est): 150.1MM **Privately Held**
WEB: www.brentwoodoriginals.com
SIC: 2392 Cushions & pillows

(P-3712)
BURTON CHING LTD
432 N Canal St Ste 5, South San Francisco (94080-4666)
PHONE..............................415 522-5520
Sen Ching, *Owner*
Tony Ching, *Partner*
John Cerney, *Manager*
EMP: 14
SALES (est): 650K **Privately Held**
WEB: www.burtonching.com
SIC: 2392 5932 Household furnishings; used merchandise stores

(P-3713)
CALIFORNIA FEATHER INDS INC
2241 E 49th St, Vernon (90058-2822)
PHONE..............................323 585-5800
Jeff Goldman, *President*
Paras Jain, *Vice Pres*
Anhil Mehta, *Vice Pres*
EMP: 11
SQ FT: 45,000
SALES (est): 810K **Privately Held**
SIC: 2392 Cushions & pillows

(P-3714)
CLASSIC SLIPCOVER INC
4300 District Blvd, Vernon (90058-3110)
PHONE..............................323 583-0804
David Illulian, *CEO*
Chris Wroolie, *President*
▲ EMP: 20
SQ FT: 15,000
SALES (est): 2.1MM **Privately Held**
WEB: www.classicslipcovers.com
SIC: 2392 5714 Slipcovers: made of fabric, plastic etc.; slip covers

(P-3715)
COTTON TALE DESIGNS INC
16291 Sierra Ridge Way, Hacienda Heights (91745-5545)
PHONE..............................714 435-9558
Larry D Aspegren, *President*
Nina Selby, *President*
Larry Aspegren, *Vice Pres*
▲ EMP: 20
SQ FT: 16,500
SALES (est): 2.2MM **Privately Held**
WEB: www.cottontaledesigns.com
SIC: 2392 2361 2211 Household furnishings; girls' & children's dresses, blouses & shirts; bed sheeting, cotton

(P-3716)
CUSHION WORKS
68929 Perez Rd Ste B, Cathedral City (92234-7283)
PHONE..............................760 321-7808
Dia Davis, *President*
EMP: 10
SALES (est): 430.3K **Privately Held**
SIC: 2392 Cushions & pillows

(P-3717)
CUSTOM QUILTING INC
2832 Walnut Ave Ste D, Tustin (92780-7002)
PHONE..............................949 455-7337
Alfredo Zermeno, *Owner*
EMP: 13
SALES (corp-wide): 2.1MM **Privately Held**
SIC: 2392 Bedspreads & bed sets: made from purchased materials
PA: Custom Quilting, Inc
     2832 Walnut Ave Ste D
     Tustin CA 92780
     714 731-7271

(P-3718)
CUSTOM QUILTING INC (PA)
2832 Walnut Ave Ste D, Tustin (92780-7002)
PHONE..............................714 731-7271
Alfredo Zermeno, *Owner*
Elda Zermeno, *Vice Pres*
EMP: 15

SALES (est): 2.1MM **Privately Held**
SIC: 2392 5719 Bedspreads & bed sets: made from purchased materials; bedding (sheets, blankets, spreads & pillows)

(P-3719)
DRAPES 4 SHOW INC
12811 Foothill Blvd, Sylmar (91342-5316)
PHONE..............................818 838-0852
Karen Honigberg, *President*
Jason Honigberg, *Sales Mgr*
▲ EMP: 25
SQ FT: 3,500
SALES (est): 3.8MM **Privately Held**
WEB: www.drapes.com
SIC: 2392 Tablecloths & table settings

(P-3720)
DREAMS DUVETS & BED LINENS
Also Called: Dreams Duvets & Linens
921 Howard St, San Francisco (94103-4108)
PHONE..............................415 543-1800
Kusum Jain, *President*
EMP: 11
SQ FT: 17,000
SALES: 900K **Privately Held**
SIC: 2392 5719 7699 Comforters & quilts: made from purchased materials; beddings & linens; general household repair services

(P-3721)
DV KAP INC
Also Called: Canaan Company
426 W Bedford Ave, Fresno (93711-6858)
PHONE..............................559 435-5575
Dan Sivas, *CEO*
◆ EMP: 50
SQ FT: 25,000
SALES (est): 7.5MM **Privately Held**
WEB: www.canaancompany.com
SIC: 2392 Cushions & pillows

(P-3722)
FABRIC WALLS INC
322 Harriet St, San Francisco (94103-4716)
PHONE..............................415 863-2711
Donald Piermarini, *President*
Ray Bollinger, *Vice Pres*
Mitchell Dietson, *Manager*
EMP: 11 EST: 1974
SQ FT: 2,000
SALES (est): 1.3MM **Privately Held**
SIC: 2392 2391 Household furnishings; curtains, window: made from purchased materials

(P-3723)
FARALLON BRANDS INC (PA)
Also Called: Peanut Shell
33300 Central Ave, Union City (94587-2044)
PHONE..............................510 550-4299
Michael Roach, *CEO*
William T Tauscher, *Ch of Bd*
Laura Tauscher, *COO*
Yvonne Ortiz, *Vice Pres*
Diane Nesom, *Comms Mgr*
▲ EMP: 17
SQ FT: 27,000
SALES (est): 2.3MM **Privately Held**
SIC: 2392 3944 Blankets, comforters & beddings; baby carriages & restraint seats

(P-3724)
HOMETEX CORPORATION
1743 Continental Ln, Escondido (92029-4328)
PHONE..............................619 661-0400
Shoaib Kothawala, *President*
James Houlihan, *Vice Pres*
EMP: 30
SALES (est): 1.9MM **Privately Held**
SIC: 2392 Towels, fabric & nonwoven: made from purchased materials

(P-3725)
HUDSON & COMPANY LLC
Also Called: Spirit Throws
100 Irene Ave, Roseville (95678-3226)
P.O. Box 968 (95678-0968)
PHONE..............................916 774-6465

▲ = Import ▼=Export
◆ =Import/Export

Shannon Hudson, *Mng Member*
▼ EMP: 23
SQ FT: 984
SALES (est): 1.1MM **Privately Held**
SIC: 2392 Blankets, comforters & beddings

(P-3726)
JR WATKINS LLC
101 Mission St, San Francisco
(94105-1705)
PHONE..................415 477-8500
Michael Fox, *CEO*
Dan Swander, *Partner*
Chris Folena, *CFO*
EMP: 22
SALES (est): 617.7K **Privately Held**
SIC: 2392 5963 Household furnishings;
home related products, direct sales

(P-3727)
KIDS LINE LLC
10541 Humbolt St, Los Alamitos
(90720-5401)
P.O. Box 16712, Irvine (92623-6712)
PHONE..................310 660-0110
▲ EMP: 140
SQ FT: 275,000
SALES (est): 11.8MM **Privately Held**
SIC: 2392

(P-3728)
KLEEN MAID INC
11450 Sheldon St, Sun Valley
(91352-1121)
PHONE..................323 581-3000
Sean Solouki, *CEO*
Kamyar Solouki, *President*
Hamid Moghaven, *Vice Pres*
▲ EMP: 27
SALES (est): 12.4MM **Privately Held**
WEB: www.kleenmaidinc.com
SIC: 2392 3991 Mops, floor & dust;
brushes, household or industrial

(P-3729)
KUMI KOOKOON
18018 S Western Ave, Gardena
(90248-3624)
PHONE..................310 515-8811
Jennifer S Chang, *Owner*
▲ EMP: 13
SALES (est): 1.2MM **Privately Held**
WEB: www.kumikookoon.com
SIC: 2392 Blankets, comforters & beddings

(P-3730)
LAMBS & IVY INC
Also Called: Bed Time Originals
2042 E Maple Ave, El Segundo
(90245-5008)
PHONE..................310 322-3800
Barbara Laiken, *President*
Cathy Ravdin, *Vice Pres*
Cristina Muresean, *Production*
Karin Kerylow, *Sales Staff*
Stephanie Elias, *Director*
◆ EMP: 60
SQ FT: 30,000
SALES (est): 7.2MM **Privately Held**
WEB: www.lambsandivy.com
SIC: 2392 Blankets, comforters & beddings

(P-3731)
MAGNOLIA LANE SOFT HM FURN INC
Also Called: Designs With Fabric
187 Utah Ave, South San Francisco
(94080-6712)
PHONE..................650 624-0700
Kathleen Redmond, *President*
Mary McWilliams, *Admin Sec*
Judy Powers, *Marketing Staff*
EMP: 20
SQ FT: 5,000
SALES (est): 1.8MM **Privately Held**
WEB: www.designswithfabric.com
SIC: 2392 2391 Cushions & pillows; blankets, comforters & beddings; draperies, plastic & textile: from purchased materials

(P-3732)
MATTEO LLC
1000 E Cesar E Chavez Ave, Los Angeles
(90033-1204)
PHONE..................213 617-2813
Matthew Lenoci, *Mng Member*

▲ EMP: 50
SQ FT: 25,000
SALES (est): 8.1MM **Privately Held**
WEB: www.matteohome.com
SIC: 2392 Blankets, comforters & beddings

(P-3733)
MAX FISCHER & SONS INC
Also Called: Acme Wiping Materials
1327 Palmetto St, Los Angeles
(90013-2228)
PHONE..................213 624-8756
Marilyn Fischer, *President*
Marla Fischer, *Vice Pres*
EMP: 20
SQ FT: 50,000
SALES (est): 2MM **Privately Held**
SIC: 2392 Towels, fabric & nonwoven: made from purchased materials

(P-3734)
MICRONOVA MANUFACTURING INC
3431 Lomita Blvd, Torrance (90505-5010)
PHONE..................310 784-6990
Audrey J Reynolds Lowman, *CEO*
Bridgett Butler, *Executive Asst*
Debra Southard, *Finance*
Phillip Lecompte, *Mfg Spvr*
Travis Hunsucker, *Pub Rel Dir*
▲ EMP: 30
SQ FT: 28,310
SALES (est): 5.6MM **Privately Held**
WEB: www.micronova-mfg.com
SIC: 2392 Mops, floor & dust

(P-3735)
OMNIA LEATHER MOTION INC
Also Called: Cathy Ireland Home
4950 Edison Ave, Chino (91710-5713)
PHONE..................909 393-4400
Peter Zolferino, *President*
Luie Nastri, *Vice Pres*
David Weigel, *Natl Sales Mgr*
Murray Eastern, *VP Sales*
Katherine Skinner, *Merchandising*
▲ EMP: 200
SALES (est): 23.6MM **Privately Held**
WEB: www.omnialeather.com
SIC: 2392 Household furnishings

(P-3736)
ONE BELLA CASA INC
Also Called: Artehouse
101 Lucas Valley Rd # 130, San Rafael
(94903-1791)
PHONE..................707 746-8300
Gary Sattin, *CEO*
▲ EMP: 24 **EST:** 2013
SQ FT: 10,000
SALES (est): 22MM **Privately Held**
SIC: 2392 3952 Pillows, bed: made from purchased materials; canvas, prepared on frames: artists'

(P-3737)
PACIFIC COAST FEATHER LLC
8500 Rex Rd, Pico Rivera (90660-3779)
PHONE..................562 222-5560
Rudy Garza, *Branch Mgr*
EMP: 150
SALES (corp-wide): 943.4MM **Privately Held**
WEB: www.pacificcoast.com
SIC: 2392 Cushions & pillows
HQ: Pacific Coast Feather, Llc
1964 4th Ave S
Seattle WA 98134
206 624-1057

(P-3738)
PACIFIC COAST FEATHER CUSHION (DH)
7600 Industry Ave, Pico Rivera
(90660-4302)
PHONE..................562 801-9995
Neil Puro, *President*
Eric Moen, *Treasurer*
Cristina Kopecky, *Vice Pres*
Joseph Crawford, *Admin Sec*
Joseph Leikin, *Sales Executive*
▲ EMP: 110
SQ FT: 100,000

SALES (est): 28.8MM
SALES (corp-wide): 943.4MM **Privately Held**
WEB: www.pcfcushion.com
SIC: 2392 Cushions & pillows
HQ: Pacific Coast Feather, Llc
1964 4th Ave S
Seattle WA 98134
206 624-1057

(P-3739)
PACIFIC COAST HOME FURN INC (PA)
Also Called: Sherry Kline
2424 Saybrook Ave, Commerce
(90040-2510)
PHONE..................323 838-7808
Parviz Banafshe, *President*
Shahrokh Samani, *CFO*
▲ EMP: 19
SQ FT: 35,000
SALES (est): 3.7MM **Privately Held**
SIC: 2392 3261 Cushions & pillows; bathroom accessories/fittings, vitreous china or earthenware

(P-3740)
PACIFIC URETHANES LLC
1671 Champagne Ave Ste A, Ontario
(91761-3660)
PHONE..................909 390-8400
Darrell Nance, *Mng Member*
Neil Silverman,
▲ EMP: 200
SQ FT: 250,000
SALES (est): 120MM **Privately Held**
SIC: 2392 5021 Blankets, comforters & beddings; beds & bedding

(P-3741)
PALERMO PRODUCTS LLC
16935 Saticoy St, Van Nuys (91406-2128)
PHONE..................949 201-9066
James Hoseini, *CEO*
Ali Hahseni, *Vice Pres*
Alex Araeloui, *Manager*
EMP: 15
SALES (est): 1.5MM **Privately Held**
SIC: 2392 Household furnishings

(P-3742)
PAVILION PRODUCTS INC
4520 Azalia Dr, Tarzana (91356-5310)
PHONE..................818 345-4841
Jack Adelstein, *President*
Gary Adelstein, *Treasurer*
Rick Roberts, *Vice Pres*
▼ EMP: 15
SALES (est): 760K **Privately Held**
SIC: 2392 Shower curtains: made from purchased materials

(P-3743)
PRO-MART INDUSTRIES INC (PA)
Also Called: Promart Dazz
17421 Von Karman Ave, Irvine
(92614-6205)
PHONE..................949 428-7700
Azad Sabounjian, *CEO*
▲ EMP: 40
SQ FT: 120,000
SALES (est): 8.9MM **Privately Held**
WEB: www.deltanovaltd.com
SIC: 2392 Bags, laundry: made from purchased materials

(P-3744)
QUILTING HOUSE
16872 Millikan Ave, Irvine (92606-5012)
PHONE..................949 476-7090
Richard Shields, *Owner*
Sheri Shields, *Co-Owner*
EMP: 40
SQ FT: 16,000
SALES (est): 3.6MM **Privately Held**
WEB: www.quiltinghouse.com
SIC: 2392 2391 Cushions & pillows; bedspreads & bed sets: made from purchased materials; pillows, bed: made from purchased materials; curtains & draperies

(P-3745)
RELIANCE UPHOLSTERY SUP CO INC
Also Called: Reliance Carpet Cushion
5942 Santa Fe Ave, Huntington Park
(90255-2733)
P.O. Box 58584, Vernon (90058-0584)
PHONE..................323 321-2300
Ronald J Greitzer, *CEO*
Stanley Grietzer, *President*
Sheldon P Wallach, *CFO*
Doug Williams, *Vice Pres*
EMP: 95
SQ FT: 360,000
SALES (est): 9MM **Privately Held**
SIC: 2392 Linings, carpet: textile, except felt; cushions & pillows

(P-3746)
ROYAL BLUE INC
9025 Wilshire Blvd # 301, Beverly Hills
(90211-1831)
PHONE..................310 888-0156
Diana Moinian, *President*
▲ EMP: 21
SALES (est): 2MM **Privately Held**
WEB: www.royalblueintl.com
SIC: 2392 2299 Household furnishings; towels & towelings, linen & linen-and-cotton mixtures

(P-3747)
SIBYL SHEPARD INC
Also Called: Sarris Interiors
8225 Alondra Blvd, Paramount
(90723-4401)
PHONE..................562 531-8612
C Nicholas Sarris, *President*
Chris Andrew Sarris, *Vice Pres*
Byron Sarris, *Director*
Nick Sarris, *Manager*
EMP: 20 **EST:** 1957
SQ FT: 15,000
SALES (est): 2MM **Privately Held**
WEB: www.sarrisinteriors.com
SIC: 2392 Bedspreads & bed sets: made from purchased materials; towels, fabric & nonwoven: made from purchased materials; washcloths & bath mitts: made from purchased materials; shower curtains: made from purchased materials

(P-3748)
SILVER EAGLE CORPORATION
Also Called: Woodmark Manufacturing
2655 Land Ave, Sacramento (95815-2383)
PHONE..................916 925-6843
Mark E Bristow, *President*
Bill Bristow, *Vice Pres*
Pat Bristow, *Admin Sec*
EMP: 30
SQ FT: 40,000
SALES (est): 3.8MM **Privately Held**
SIC: 2392 Household furnishings

(P-3749)
SLEEP-N-AIRE MATTRESS CO INC
5101 White Ln Ste F, Bakersfield
(93309-8941)
PHONE..................661 835-0200
Jeffrey B Sherley, *CEO*
EMP: 12
SQ FT: 15,000
SALES (est): 1.1MM **Privately Held**
SIC: 2392 5712 Mattress pads; furniture stores; mattresses

(P-3750)
SPENCER N ENTERPRISES LLC (DH)
Also Called: Spencer Home Decor
425 S Lemon Ave, City of Industry
(91789-2911)
PHONE..................909 895-8495
Jeffrey Werner, *President*
Charles F Kuehne, *CFO*
▲ EMP: 100
SQ FT: 100,000
SALES (est): 22.9MM **Privately Held**
SIC: 2392 Cushions & pillows

(P-3751)
SUNRISE PILLOW CO INC
2215 Merced Ave, El Monte (91733-2622)
PHONE..................................626 401-9283
Adnan K Hermas, *President*
EMP: 16
SQ FT: 11,500
SALES (est): 1.3MM **Privately Held**
SIC: 2392 5719 Pillows, bed: made from purchased materials; bedding (sheets, blankets, spreads & pillows)

(P-3752)
THOMAS WEST INC (PA)
Also Called: T W I
470 Mercury Dr, Sunnyvale (94085-4706)
PHONE..................................408 481-3850
Tom West, *CEO*
Dr Steve Kirtley, *COO*
Martin Wohlert, *Info Tech Dir*
Meredith Holley, *Controller*
Nhu Tieu, *Production*
▲ EMP: 27
SQ FT: 43,000
SALES (est): 4.9MM **Privately Held**
WEB: www.thomaswest.com
SIC: 2392 Towels, dishcloths & dust cloths

(P-3753)
THOREEN DESIGNS INC
930 W 16th St Ste C1, Costa Mesa (92627-4337)
PHONE..................................949 645-0981
Cheryl Thoreen, *President*
Nicole Coffey, *Prgrmr*
EMP: 32
SQ FT: 2,500
SALES: 1MM **Privately Held**
SIC: 2392 5023 5719 Pillows, bed: made from purchased materials; bedspreads; bedding (sheets, blankets, spreads & pillows)

(P-3754)
UNIVERSAL CUSHION COMPANY INC (PA)
Also Called: Cloud Nine Comforts
3121 Fujita St, Torrance (90505-4006)
PHONE..................................323 887-8000
Sharyl Bloom, *President*
EMP: 34
SQ FT: 17,000
SALES (est): 4.9MM **Privately Held**
WEB: www.universalcushion.com
SIC: 2392 2221 2211 Cushions & pillows; comforters & quilts: made from purchased materials; pillowcases: made from purchased materials; comforters & quilts, manmade fiber & silk; sheets & sheetings, cotton; pillowcases; piques, cotton

(P-3755)
VFT INC
Also Called: Vertical Fiber Technologies
1040 S Vail Ave, Montebello (90640-6020)
PHONE..................................323 728-2280
John Chang, *President*
Joyce Chien, *Sales Mgr*
Diane Bighead, *Manager*
▲ EMP: 40 EST: 1998
SQ FT: 70,000
SALES (est): 6.4MM **Privately Held**
WEB: www.bedtimelinens.com
SIC: 2392 Household furnishings

(P-3756)
WASATCH CO
Also Called: Wasatch Import
11000 Wright Rd, Lynwood (90262-3153)
PHONE..................................310 637-6160
Abdul Wahab, *President*
Yosuf Haroon, *Vice Pres*
▲ EMP: 12
SQ FT: 50,000
SALES (est): 6.7MM **Privately Held**
SIC: 2392 Towels, dishcloths & dust cloths; tablecloths & table settings; bedspreads & bed sets: made from purchased materials; mattress pads

(P-3757)
WOOF & POOF INC
388 Orange St, Chico (95928-5091)
PHONE..................................530 895-0693
Debra Headley, *President*
▲ EMP: 30

SQ FT: 14,000
SALES (est): 2.3MM **Privately Held**
WEB: www.woofpoof.com
SIC: 2392 Pillows, bed: made from purchased materials

(P-3758)
XIMENEZ ICONS
Also Called: Goddess of Gadgets
1107 Fair Oaks Ave Ste 11, South Pasadena (91030-3311)
PHONE..................................310 344-6670
Lisa Rodgers, *CEO*
Lisa N Rodgers, *Principal*
EMP: 10
SALES (est): 493K **Privately Held**
SIC: 2392 Household furnishings

2393 Textile Bags

(P-3759)
ACTION BAG & COVER INC
18401 Mount Langley St, Fountain Valley (92708-6904)
PHONE..................................714 965-7777
Byung Ki Lee, *President*
▲ EMP: 80 EST: 1978
SQ FT: 15,000
SALES (est): 8.1MM **Privately Held**
WEB: www.actionbaginc.com
SIC: 2393 Canvas bags

(P-3760)
AMERICAN SPORT BAGS INC
1485 E Warner Ave, Santa Ana (92705-5434)
PHONE..................................714 547-8013
Camacho Alvarez, *President*
Mary Ann Alvarez, *Treasurer*
EMP: 35
SQ FT: 5,000
SALES (est): 3.2MM **Privately Held**
SIC: 2393 3949 3161 Textile bags; sporting & athletic goods; luggage

(P-3761)
CHICOECO INC
Also Called: Chicobag
747 Fortress St, Chico (95973-9012)
PHONE..................................530 342-4426
Andrew Keller, *President*
Angela Heiden, *Exec VP*
Martha Mathern, *Administration*
Samantha Luger, *Human Resources*
Sierra Norton, *Pub Rel Mgr*
▲ EMP: 30
SALES (est): 4.5MM **Privately Held**
WEB: www.chicobag.com
SIC: 2393 Textile bags

(P-3762)
CTA MANUFACTURING INC
Also Called: Bagmasters
1160 California Ave, Corona (92881-3324)
PHONE..................................951 280-2400
Richard Gayne Whittier, *President*
Gayne Whittier, *Vice Pres*
Scott Conk, *Manager*
Kimica Bleckert, *Accounts Mgr*
▲ EMP: 40 EST: 1922
SQ FT: 23,000
SALES (est): 6.1MM **Privately Held**
WEB: www.ctamfg.com
SIC: 2393 Textile bags

(P-3763)
CUSHION WORKS INC
3320 18th St, San Francisco (94110-1905)
PHONE..................................415 552-6220
Susan Schroeder, *President*
EMP: 10
SQ FT: 15,000
SALES (est): 1.2MM **Privately Held**
WEB: www.cushionworks.net
SIC: 2393 Cushions, except spring & carpet: purchased materials

(P-3764)
GLEASON CORPORATION (PA)
10474 Santa Monica Blvd # 400, Los Angeles (90025-6932)
PHONE..................................310 470-6001
Harry Kotler, *President*
Howard Seinman, *COO*

Jeff Leggat, *Treasurer*
Shirley Kotler, *Vice Pres*
◆ EMP: 11 EST: 1946
SQ FT: 8,000
SALES (est): 17MM **Privately Held**
WEB: www.gleasoncorporation.com
SIC: 2393 2399 5083 Textile bags; hammocks & other net products; lawn machinery & equipment

(P-3765)
GOLD CREST INDUSTRIES INC
1018 E Acacia St, Ontario (91761-4553)
P.O. Box 3280 (91761-0928)
PHONE..................................909 930-9069
Jose Garcia, *President*
Frank Castillo, *Manager*
Denise Keeler, *Manager*
EMP: 40
SQ FT: 14,000
SALES (est): 3.6MM **Privately Held**
WEB: www.goldcrestind.com
SIC: 2393 3999 2392 Cushions, except spring & carpet: purchased materials; garden umbrellas; household furnishings

(P-3766)
JANSPORT INC (HQ)
2601 Harbor Bay Pkwy, Alameda (94502-3042)
PHONE..................................510 814-7400
Mackey McDonald, *President*
Alexandra Reveles, *Mktg Coord*
Genevieve Peterson, *Manager*
Scott Wareham, *Manager*
▲ EMP: 10
SALES (est): 1.2MM
SALES (corp-wide): 11.8B **Publicly Held**
WEB: www.vfc.com
SIC: 2393 Bags & containers, except sleeping bags: textile
PA: V.F. Corporation
105 Corporate Center Blvd
Greensboro NC 27408
336 424-6000

(P-3767)
NEW AMERICAN INDUSTRIES INC
5475 E Hedges Ave # 102, Fresno (93727-2252)
P.O. Box 8059 (93747-8059)
PHONE..................................559 251-1581
Nanci Mathers, *General Mgr*
Ralph G Victor, *President*
Andrew Victor, *Treasurer*
Polly N Victor, *Vice Pres*
EMP: 21
SQ FT: 8,000
SALES (est): 2.9MM **Privately Held**
SIC: 2393 3949 Textile bags; sporting & athletic goods

(P-3768)
OUTDOOR RECREATION GROUP (PA)
Also Called: Outdoor Products
3450 Mount Vernon Dr, View Park (90008-4936)
PHONE..................................323 226-0830
Joel Altshule, *Ch of Bd*
Andrew Altshule, *CEO*
Robert Guzman, *Sr Associate*
▲ EMP: 37
SQ FT: 90,000
SALES (est): 15.5MM **Privately Held**
WEB: www.fieldline.com
SIC: 2393 3949 Textile bags; camping equipment & supplies

(P-3769)
RICKSHAW BAGWORKS INC
904 22nd St, San Francisco (94107-3427)
PHONE..................................415 904-8368
Mark Dwight, *CEO*
Joseph Montana, *Marketing Staff*
Christopher Schroeder, *Sales Staff*
Caroline Ikeji, *Manager*
Ashley Loth, *Manager*
▲ EMP: 26
SALES (est): 3.5MM **Privately Held**
SIC: 2393 Textile bags

(P-3770)
RIVERSIDE TENT & AWNING CO
231 E Alcandro Blvd Ste A, Riverside (92508)
PHONE..................................951 683-1925
Chilton E Burt, *President*
Betty Burt, *Vice Pres*
▲ EMP: 12 EST: 1919
SQ FT: 20,000
SALES: 1.5MM **Privately Held**
SIC: 2393 2394 Canvas bags; canvas & related products

(P-3771)
SPECIAL FORCES CUSTOM GEAR INC
2949 Hoover Ave, National City (91950)
PHONE..................................619 241-5453
Juan Vazquez, *President*
EMP: 38
SQ FT: 18,500
SALES (est): 1.2MM **Privately Held**
SIC: 2393 Bags & containers, except sleeping bags: textile

(P-3772)
TIMBUK2 DESIGNS INC (PA)
583 Shotwell St, San Francisco (94110-1915)
PHONE..................................415 252-4300
Patricia Cazzato, *CEO*
Tony Meneghetti, *CFO*
Jesse Gillingham, *Business Mgr*
Kevin Rogers, *Opers Staff*
Claire Petersen, *Sales Staff*
▲ EMP: 60
SQ FT: 30,000
SALES (est): 13.4MM **Privately Held**
WEB: www.timbuk2.com
SIC: 2393 Canvas bags

(P-3773)
WESSCO INTERNATIONAL LTD A C (PA)
11400 W Olympic Blvd # 450, Los Angeles (90064-1550)
PHONE..................................310 477-4272
Robert Bregman, *President*
Nick Bregman, *COO*
Tyler Shepodd, *CFO*
Alex Silva, *Creative Dir*
Tony Bregman, *Controller*
▲ EMP: 30
SQ FT: 7,000
SALES (est): 60.3MM **Privately Held**
WEB: www.wessco.net
SIC: 2393 Textile bags

(P-3774)
WORLD TEXTILE AND BAG INC
1627 Main Ave Ste 4, Sacramento (95838-2451)
PHONE..................................916 922-9222
Richard Quinley, *CEO*
EMP: 28
SALES (est): 3.6MM **Privately Held**
SIC: 2393 Textile bags

(P-3775)
YAMAMOTO OF ORIENT INC
Also Called: Yamamotoyama of America
12475 Mills Ave, Chino (91710-2078)
PHONE..................................909 591-7654
Willy Gomez, *Branch Mgr*
EMP: 10
SALES (corp-wide): 64.4MM **Privately Held**
SIC: 2393 Tea bags, fabric: made from purchased materials
HQ: Yamamoto Of Orient, Inc.
122 Voyager St
Pomona CA 91768
909 594-7356

2394 Canvas Prdts

(P-3776)
A&R TARPAULINS INC
Also Called: AR Tech Aerospace
16246 Valley Blvd, Fontana (92335-7831)
P.O. Box 1400 (92334-1400)
PHONE..................................909 829-3828
Carmen Weisbart, *President*
Charles Rosselet, *Corp Secy*

▲ = Import ▼ = Export
◆ = Import/Export

Bud Weisbart, *Vice Pres*
Lizeth Ponce, *Admin Asst*
Albert Greggen, *Info Tech Mgr*
EMP: 34
SQ FT: 15,000
SALES (est): 6MM **Privately Held**
WEB: www.artech2000.com
SIC: 2394 Awnings, fabric: made from purchased materials

(P-3777)
A-AZTEC RENTS & SELLS INC (PA)
Also Called: Aztec Tents
2665 Columbia St, Torrance (90503-3801)
PHONE..........................310 347-3010
Chuck Miller, *CEO*
Alex Kouzmanoff, *Vice Pres*
Dave Bradley, *General Mgr*
Phil Teer, *Administration*
Eric Vanderploeg, *Financial Exec*
◆ **EMP:** 125
SQ FT: 70,000
SALES (est): 16.9MM **Privately Held**
WEB: www.aztectent.com
SIC: 2394 Canvas & related products

(P-3778)
ABC SUN CONTROL LLC
7241 Ethel Ave, North Hollywood (91605-4215)
PHONE..........................818 982-6989
Donald B Smallwood,
Martina Smallwood, *Vice Pres*
Martina H Smallwood,
▲ **EMP:** 16
SQ FT: 30,000
SALES (est): 2.5MM **Privately Held**
WEB: www.abcsuncontrol.com
SIC: 2394 Awnings, fabric: made from purchased materials

(P-3779)
BAY AREA CANVAS INC
2362 De La Cruz Blvd, Santa Clara (95050-2921)
PHONE..........................408 727-4314
Chris Ferretti, *CEO*
Kevin Zierman, *Partner*
EMP: 12
SQ FT: 4,000
SALES (est): 1.3MM **Privately Held**
WEB: www.bayareaawning.com
SIC: 2394 Awnings, fabric: made from purchased materials

(P-3780)
BRAMPTON MTHESEN FABR PDTS INC
Also Called: Sullivan & Brampton
1688 Abram Ct, San Leandro (94577-3227)
PHONE..........................510 483-7771
Fax: 510 483-7723
EMP: 20
SQ FT: 40,000
SALES (est): 1.9MM **Privately Held**
WEB: www.sullivanandbrampton.com
SIC: 2394 2519 2393

(P-3781)
CANVAS AWNING CO INC
325 W Main St, Ontario (91762-3843)
PHONE..........................909 447-5100
Mark Burg, *President*
Roseanna Burg, *Vice Pres*
EMP: 18
SALES (est): 1.6MM **Privately Held**
WEB: www.apexstructures.com
SIC: 2394 Awnings, fabric: made from purchased materials

(P-3782)
CANVAS CONCEPTS INC
649 Anita St Ste A2, Chula Vista (91911-4658)
PHONE..........................619 424-3428
Robert A Mackenzie, *President*
Olivia Appel, *Corp Secy*
Anton Silvernagel, *Vice Pres*
Dale Kalar, *VP Sales*
EMP: 18
SQ FT: 9,600

SALES: 1.3MM **Privately Held**
WEB: www.canvasstore.com
SIC: 2394 Awnings, fabric: made from purchased materials

(P-3783)
CANVAS SPECIALTY INC
1309 S Eastern Ave, Commerce (90040-5610)
P.O. Box 22268, Los Angeles (90022-0268)
PHONE..........................323 722-1156
Gregory Naiman, *President*
Richard P Naiman, *Exec VP*
▲ **EMP:** 25
SQ FT: 84,000
SALES (est): 3.2MM **Privately Held**
WEB: www.can-spec.com
SIC: 2394 5199 Tarpaulins, fabric: made from purchased materials; canvas products

(P-3784)
CITY CANVAS
1381 N 10th St, San Jose (95112-2804)
PHONE..........................408 287-2688
John M Cerrito, *President*
EMP: 13
SQ FT: 10,000
SALES: 1.5MM **Privately Held**
WEB: www.citycanvas.com
SIC: 2394 7699 Awnings, fabric: made from purchased materials; awning repair shop

(P-3785)
E-Z UP DIRECTCOM
Also Called: EZ Up Factory Store
1900 2nd St, Colton (92324)
PHONE..........................909 426-0060
Rose Kilstrom,
EMP: 25
SALES (est): 2.5MM **Privately Held**
WEB: www.ezupdirect.com
SIC: 2394 Shades, canvas: made from purchased materials

(P-3786)
EIDE INDUSTRIES INC
16215 Piuma Ave, Cerritos (90703-1528)
PHONE..........................562 402-8335
Don Araiza, *President*
Jesus Borrego, *Vice Pres*
Dan Neill, *Vice Pres*
Joe Belli, *Admin Sec*
Edgar Cervantes, *Project Mgr*
◆ **EMP:** 80
SQ FT: 41,000
SALES (est): 14MM **Privately Held**
WEB: www.eideindustries.com
SIC: 2394 Tents: made from purchased materials; awnings, fabric: made from purchased materials

(P-3787)
FRAMETENT INC
Also Called: Central Tent
26480 Summit Cir, Santa Clarita (91350-2991)
PHONE..........................661 290-3375
Nattha Chunapongse, *President*
Joe Chunapongse, *General Mgr*
◆ **EMP:** 30
SALES (est): 5.4MM **Privately Held**
WEB: www.centraltent.com
SIC: 2394 5999 Tents: made from purchased materials; tents

(P-3788)
GOLDEN FLEECE DESIGNS INC
441 S Victory Blvd, Burbank (91502-2353)
PHONE..........................323 849-1901
Antoinette Argyropoulos, *President*
Symeon Argyropoulos, *Chairman*
Maria Argyropoulos, *Vice Pres*
EMP: 15
SQ FT: 16,000
SALES (est): 1.5MM **Privately Held**
SIC: 2394 5199 Canvas & related products; advertising specialties

(P-3789)
GUARDIAN CORPORATE SERVICES
Also Called: Acme Awning & Canvas Co
2814 University Ave Frnt, San Diego (92104-2993)
PHONE..........................619 295-2646
EMP: 25
SQ FT: 1,000
SALES: 3.2MM
SALES (corp-wide): 156.9MM **Privately Held**
SIC: 2394
HQ: Reassure Companies Services Limited
Windsor House Ironmasters Way
Telford TF3 4
843 372-9142

(P-3790)
HARBOR CUSTOM CANVAS
733 W Anaheim St, Long Beach (90813-2819)
PHONE..........................562 436-7708
Daniel Loggans, *CEO*
EMP: 10
SQ FT: 7,500
SALES (est): 1.1MM **Privately Held**
WEB: www.harborcustomcanvas.com
SIC: 2394 Liners & covers, fabric: made from purchased materials

(P-3791)
INTERNATIONAL E-Z UP INC (PA)
1900 2nd St, Norco (92860-2803)
PHONE..........................800 457-4233
William Bradford Smith, *CEO*
Mark Carter, *Ch of Bd*
Brad Smith, *President*
▲ **EMP:** 100
SQ FT: 115,000
SALES (est): 18.7MM **Privately Held**
WEB: www.ezup.com
SIC: 2394 Shades, canvas: made from purchased materials

(P-3792)
INTERNATIONAL TENTS & SUPPLIES
1720 1st St, San Fernando (91340-2711)
PHONE..........................818 599-6258
▲ **EMP:** 10 **EST:** 2008
SALES (est): 530K **Privately Held**
SIC: 2394

(P-3793)
KENSINGTON PROTECTIVE PRODUCTS
151 N Reservoir St, Pomona (91767-5709)
PHONE..........................909 469-1240
Anthony Gatto, *President*
Becky Hasbach, *Marketing Staff*
▲ **EMP:** 12
SALES (est): 907.2K **Privately Held**
WEB: www.kensingtonproducts.com
SIC: 2394 3199 Awnings, fabric: made from purchased materials; saddles or parts

(P-3794)
KEVINS AWNINGS INC
Also Called: Kevin's San Lorenzo Awnings
907 River St, Santa Cruz (95060-1707)
PHONE..........................831 423-7918
Sydnie Smith, *President*
David Schwartz, *Corp Secy*
EMP: 10
SALES (est): 576.5K **Privately Held**
WEB: www.kevinsawnings.com
SIC: 2394 Awnings, fabric: made from purchased materials

(P-3795)
LARSENS INC
1041 17th Ave Ste A, Santa Cruz (95062-3070)
PHONE..........................831 476-3009
Kurt W Larsen, *President*
Susan Larsen, *Vice Pres*
EMP: 15 **EST:** 1972
SQ FT: 6,000
SALES (est): 2MM **Privately Held**
WEB: www.larsensails.com
SIC: 2394 Sails: made from purchased materials

(P-3796)
MODESTO TENT AND AWNING INC
Also Called: Mid-Valley Tarp Service
4448 Sisk Rd, Modesto (95356-8729)
PHONE..........................209 545-1607
Robert Valk, *President*
Leonard Rigg, *Corp Secy*
▲ **EMP:** 12
SQ FT: 26,000
SALES (est): 1.4MM **Privately Held**
WEB: www.modestotentandawning.com
SIC: 2394 2399 7359 5999 Awnings, fabric: made from purchased materials; tarpaulins, fabric: made from purchased materials; banners, made from fabric; tent & tarpaulin rental; tents; signs, not made in custom sign painting shops; truck equipment & parts

(P-3797)
N J P SPORTS INC
548 Arden Ave, Glendale (91203-1012)
P.O. Box 1469 (91209-1469)
PHONE..........................818 247-3914
Norman J Perry, *President*
Regina Perry, *Vice Pres*
EMP: 15 **EST:** 1969
SALES (est): 1.7MM **Privately Held**
WEB: www.njpsports.com
SIC: 2394 5999 3949 2298 Canvas & related products; canvas products; sporting & athletic goods; cordage & twine

(P-3798)
NATHAN KIMMEL COMPANY LLC
1213 S Santa Fe Ave, Los Angeles (90021-1753)
PHONE..........................213 627-8556
Carol J Schary, *Mng Member*
Dat Trust,
EMP: 13
SQ FT: 20,000
SALES (est): 2.3MM **Privately Held**
WEB: www.nathankimmel.com
SIC: 2394 5085 Tarpaulins, fabric: made from purchased materials; industrial supplies

(P-3799)
NORTH SAILS GROUP LLC
Also Called: North Sails One Design
4630 Santa Fe St, San Diego (92109-1601)
PHONE..........................619 226-1415
Vince Brun, *Owner*
Ian Pouliot, *Bd of Directors*
Celeste Palumbo, *Office Mgr*
Tyler Vanicek, *Graphic Designe*
Dawn Morgan, *Human Resources*
EMP: 60
SQ FT: 11,592 **Privately Held**
WEB: www.northsails.com
SIC: 2394 Sails: made from purchased materials
HQ: North Sails Group, Llc
125 Old Gate Ln Ste 7
Milford CT 06460
203 874-7548

(P-3800)
PACIFIC PLAY TENTS INC
2801 E 12th St, Los Angeles (90023-3621)
PHONE..........................323 269-0431
Victor Preisler, *CEO*
Brian Jablan, *Vice Pres*
▲ **EMP:** 13
SQ FT: 75,000
SALES (est): 1.6MM **Privately Held**
WEB: www.pacificplaytents.com
SIC: 2394 5941 5092 3944 Tents: made from purchased materials; sporting goods & bicycle shops; toys; games, toys & children's vehicles

(P-3801)
PACIFIC TENT AND AWNING
Also Called: Awnings
7295 N Palm Bluffs Ave, Fresno (93711-5737)
PHONE..........................559 436-8147
Ken Bricker, *Partner*
Michael Mygind, *Partner*
EMP: 10

SQ FT: 3,000
SALES (est): 1MM **Privately Held**
SIC: 2394 Awnings, fabric: made from purchased materials

(P-3802)
PALO ALTO AWNING INC
1381 N 10th St, San Jose (95112-2804)
PHONE..................................650 968-4270
John M Cerrito, *President*
Robert Terry, *General Mgr*
EMP: 16 EST: 1993
SQ FT: 4,800
SALES: 1MM **Privately Held**
SIC: 2394 5999 Awnings, fabric: made from purchased materials; awnings

(P-3803)
PARADISE MANUFACTURING CO INC
Also Called: Arden/Paradise Manufacturing
13364 Aerospace Dr 100, Victorville (92394-7902)
PHONE..................................909 477-3460
Robert Sachs, *President*
Michael Sachs, *Vice Pres*
Jose Sanabria, *Maintence Staff*
EMP: 150
SALES (est): 12.2MM **Privately Held**
SIC: 2394 Air cushions & mattresses, canvas; canvas awnings & canopies

(P-3804)
PHILIP A STITT AGENCY
Also Called: Capitol Tarpaulin Co
3900 Stockton Blvd, Sacramento (95820-2913)
PHONE..................................916 451-2801
Martin Stitt, *President*
Philip L Stitt, *Corp Secy*
Richard Pechal, *Vice Pres*
EMP: 15
SQ FT: 13,000
SALES (est): 1.1MM **Privately Held**
WEB: www.captarp.com
SIC: 2394 Tarpaulins, fabric: made from purchased materials; tents: made from purchased materials; awnings, fabric: made from purchased materials

(P-3805)
POLYAIR INTER PACK INC
1692 Jenks Dr Ste 102, Corona (92880-2513)
PHONE..................................951 737-7125
Jim Higgins, *Branch Mgr*
EMP: 80
SALES (corp-wide): 898.1MM **Privately Held**
SIC: 2394 5199 Tarpaulins, fabric: made from purchased materials; liners & covers, fabric: made from purchased materials; packaging materials
HQ: Polyair Inter Pack Inc
330 Humberline Dr
Etobicoke ON M9W 1
416 679-6600

(P-3806)
REDWOOD EMPIRE AWNG & FURN CO
3547 Santa Rosa Ave, Santa Rosa (95407-8270)
PHONE..................................707 633-8156
Marilyn Lenney, *President*
Gregory Lenney, *Treasurer*
Leon Lenney, *Vice Pres*
Micheal Lenney, *Admin Sec*
EMP: 11
SQ FT: 8,000
SALES: 1.5MM **Privately Held**
WEB: www.reaco.com
SIC: 2394 5999 8742 Awnings, fabric: made from purchased materials; awnings; industrial consultant

(P-3807)
S A FIELDS INC
Also Called: Tent City Canvas House
3328 N Duke Ave, Fresno (93727-7803)
PHONE..................................559 292-1221
Stephen A Fields, *President*
Susan Fields, *Admin Sec*
EMP: 16
SQ FT: 10,000

SALES (est): 1.6MM **Privately Held**
WEB: www.tentcitycanvashouse.com
SIC: 2394 Canvas & related products

(P-3808)
SAN JOSE AWNING COMPANY INC
755 Chestnut St Ste E, San Jose (95110-1832)
PHONE..................................408 350-7000
Michael Yaholkovsky, *President*
Susan Pham, *CFO*
EMP: 14
SQ FT: 8,800
SALES (est): 2MM **Privately Held**
WEB: www.sanjoseawning.com
SIC: 2394 Awnings, fabric: made from purchased materials

(P-3809)
SCHULZ LEATHER CO INC
Also Called: Schulz Industries
16247 Minnesota Ave, Paramount (90723-4915)
PHONE..................................562 633-1081
Robert Schulz, *President*
Lillian Schulz, *Corp Secy*
Bob Schulz, *General Mgr*
EMP: 25
SQ FT: 12,000
SALES (est): 2.7MM **Privately Held**
WEB: www.fodbuster.com
SIC: 2394 2393 3161 2273 Liners & covers, fabric: made from purchased materials; bags & containers, except sleeping bags: textile; luggage; carpets & rugs; narrow fabric mills; broadwoven fabric mills, manmade

(P-3810)
SEMCO AEROSPACE
9637 Owensmouth Ave, Chatsworth (91311-4804)
PHONE..................................818 678-9381
Joseph Sember, *President*
EMP: 10
SALES (est): 650.6K **Privately Held**
SIC: 2394 3357 Air cushions & mattresses, canvas; aluminum wire & cable

(P-3811)
SHELTER SYSTEMS
224 Walnut St, Menlo Park (94025-2613)
PHONE..................................650 323-6202
Robert Gillis, *Owner*
EMP: 10
SALES (est): 946.2K **Privately Held**
WEB: www.shelter-systems.com
SIC: 2394 Tents: made from purchased materials

(P-3812)
STARK MFG CO
Also Called: Stark Awning & Canvas
76 Broadway, Chula Vista (91910-1422)
PHONE..................................619 425-5880
Turner Stark, *Chairman*
Stephan Hegyi, *General Mgr*
EMP: 29 EST: 1953
SQ FT: 3,500
SALES (est): 3.9MM **Privately Held**
WEB: www.starkmfgco.com
SIC: 2394 3444 Awnings, fabric: made from purchased materials; sheet metalwork

(P-3813)
SUPERIOR AWNING INC
14555 Titus St, Panorama City (91402-4920)
PHONE..................................818 780-7200
Brian Hotchkiss, *President*
Julie Hotchkiss, *Vice Pres*
Jeff Robert, *Sales Mgr*
EMP: 40
SQ FT: 11,776
SALES (est): 3.9MM **Privately Held**
WEB: www.superiorawning.com
SIC: 2394 5999 3444 Awnings, fabric: made from purchased materials; awnings; sheet metalwork

(P-3814)
TARPS & TIE-DOWNS INC (PA)
24967 Huntwood Ave, Hayward (94544-1814)
PHONE..................................510 782-8772
David Lee, *President*
Todd Stiles, *VP Bus Dvlpt*
Cindy C Cortes, *Branch Mgr*
Michael Chun, *General Mgr*
Rebecca Martinez, *Office Admin*
▲ EMP: 10
SQ FT: 12,000
SALES (est): 8.7MM **Privately Held**
SIC: 2394 Tarpaulins, fabric: made from purchased materials

(P-3815)
TEMPTROL INDUSTRIES INC
3909 Onawa Ct, Antelope (95843-2412)
PHONE..................................916 344-4457
Richard D Koscinski, *President*
EMP: 12
SQ FT: 11,000
SALES (est): 3.5MM **Privately Held**
SIC: 2394 Canvas & related products

(P-3816)
TRANSPORTATION EQUIPMENT INC (PA)
Also Called: Pulltarps Manufacturing
1404 N Marshall Ave, El Cajon (92020-1521)
PHONE..................................619 449-8860
Nathan Lynn Chenowth, *President*
Rodger Hubbard, *Information Mgr*
▲ EMP: 48
SQ FT: 20,000
SALES (est): 10MM **Privately Held**
WEB: www.pulltarps.com
SIC: 2394 3479 Tarpaulins, fabric: made from purchased materials; bonderizing of metal or metal products

(P-3817)
ULLMAN SAILS INC (PA)
2710 S Croddy Way, Santa Ana (92704-5206)
PHONE..................................714 432-1860
Bruce Cooper, *President*
EMP: 15
SQ FT: 10,900
SALES (est): 2.7MM **Privately Held**
WEB: www.ullmansails.com
SIC: 2394 Sails: made from purchased materials

(P-3818)
VINYL FABRICATIONS INC
2690 5th Ave, Oroville (95965-5824)
PHONE..................................530 532-1236
Michael G Smith, *President*
Bonita Charron, *Treasurer*
EMP: 10
SQ FT: 12,000
SALES (est): 409.1K **Privately Held**
WEB: www.vinylfabricators.com
SIC: 2394 Liners & covers, fabric: made from purchased materials

(P-3819)
WEST COAST CANVAS (PA)
14900 W Highway 12 Ste C, Lodi (95242-9523)
PHONE..................................209 333-0243
Curtis G Page, *Owner*
EMP: 15
SQ FT: 5,000
SALES (est): 1.4MM **Privately Held**
WEB: www.westcoastcanvas.com
SIC: 2394 Liners & covers, fabric: made from purchased materials; convertible tops, canvas or boat: from purchased materials; awnings, fabric: made from purchased materials

(P-3820)
WESTCOAST COMPANIES INC
Also Called: Westcoast Elevator Pads
725-729 E Washington Blvd, Pasadena (91104)
PHONE..................................626 794-9330
Leslie Malloy, *President*
EMP: 10
SQ FT: 8,000

SALES: 1.5MM **Privately Held**
SIC: 2394 Air cushions & mattresses, canvas

(P-3821)
WINDTAMER TARPS
13704 Hanford Armona Rd B2, Hanford (93230-9263)
P.O. Box 645, Lemoore (93245-0645)
PHONE..................................559 584-2080
Bobby Lee, *Owner*
EMP: 15
SQ FT: 10,000
SALES: 720K **Privately Held**
SIC: 2394 Tarpaulins, fabric: made from purchased materials

2395 Pleating & Stitching For The Trade

(P-3822)
AAA GARMENTS & LETTERING INC
Also Called: Competitor Golf & Tennis AP
9309 La Riviera Dr Ste C, Sacramento (95826-2437)
PHONE..................................916 363-4590
James L Lortz, *President*
Barbara Beringer, *Office Mgr*
EMP: 14
SQ FT: 5,600
SALES (est): 1.1MM **Privately Held**
SIC: 2395 Emblems, embroidered; embroidery & art needlework

(P-3823)
AAA PRINTING BY WIZARD
8961 W Sunset Blvd Ste 1d, West Hollywood (90069-1886)
PHONE..................................310 285-0505
Michael Norman, *Owner*
EMP: 30
SALES (est): 1.9MM **Privately Held**
SIC: 2395 Embroidery products, except schiffli machine

(P-3824)
ACADEMY AWNING INC
1501 Beach St, Montebello (90640-5431)
PHONE..................................800 422-9646
James D Richman, *President*
Maury Rice, *Corp Secy*
Tom Shapiro, *Vice Pres*
EMP: 25
SALES (est): 3.7MM **Privately Held**
WEB: www.academyawning.com
SIC: 2395 5999 Quilted fabrics or cloth; awnings

(P-3825)
ACE PLEATING & STITCHING INC
2351 E 49th St, Vernon (90058-2820)
PHONE..................................323 582-8213
Jorge Nevarez Sr, *President*
Jorge Nevarez Jr, *Vice Pres*
EMP: 25
SALES (est): 1.9MM **Privately Held**
WEB: www.acepleatinginc.com
SIC: 2395 Pleating & tucking, for the trade

(P-3826)
ALL-STAR MKTG & PROMOTIONS INC
Also Called: All-Star Logo
8715 Aviation Blvd, Inglewood (90301-2003)
PHONE..................................323 582-4880
Edmond Moossighi, *Vice Pres*
▲ EMP: 10
SQ FT: 10,000
SALES: 2MM **Privately Held**
WEB: www.allstarlogo.com
SIC: 2395 Embroidery & art needlework

(P-3827)
AMERICAN QUILTING COMPANY INC
Also Called: Antaky Quilting Company
1540 Calzona St, Los Angeles (90023-3254)
PHONE..................................323 233-2500
Derek Antaky, *CEO*

Elias Antaky Jr, *Vice Pres*
▲ **EMP:** 30
SALES (est): 2.5MM **Privately Held**
WEB: www.antakyquilting.com
SIC: 2395 Quilting, for the trade

(P-3828)
ANAHEIM EMBROIDERY INC
Also Called: KB Design Enterprises
1230 N Jefferson St Ste C, Anaheim
(92807-1631)
PHONE..........................714 563-5220
Kent D Brush, *President*
Kent Brush, *President*
Catherine Brush, *Vice Pres*
EMP: 30
SQ FT: 10,000
SALES (est): 3.9MM **Privately Held**
WEB: www.anaheimembroidery.com
SIC: 2395 2396 Embroidery products, ex-
cept schiffli machine; automotive & ap-
parel trimmings

(P-3829)
B J EMBROIDERY &
SCREENPRINT
272 E Smith St, Ukiah (95482-4411)
PHONE..........................707 463-2767
Walt Richey, *Owner*
EMP: 12 **EST:** 2000
SALES (est): 601.2K **Privately Held**
SIC: 2395 Emblems, embroidered

(P-3830)
BEST- IN- WEST
Also Called: Best-In-West Emblem Co
2279 Eagle Glen Pkwy, Corona
(92883-0790)
PHONE..........................909 947-6507
Eric Roberts, *President*
Heriberto Perez, *Treasurer*
Beatriz Roberts, *Admin Sec*
EMP: 50
SQ FT: 15,000
SALES (est): 4.1MM **Privately Held**
WEB: www.bestinwest.net
SIC: 2395 2759 Embroidery products, ex-
cept schiffli machine; commercial printing

(P-3831)
CADEN CONCEPTS LLC
13412 Ventura Blvd # 300, Sherman Oaks
(91423-6201)
PHONE..........................323 651-1190
Lori Caden, *Mng Member*
Kari Caden,
Warren Friedman,
Caroline Hick, *Account Dir*
▲ **EMP:** 12
SQ FT: 3,900
SALES (est): 1.6MM **Privately Held**
WEB: www.cadenconcepts.com
SIC: 2395 Embroidery products, except
schiffli machine

(P-3832)
CAL NOR EMBROIDERY & SPC
4208 Douglas Blvd Ste 100, Granite Bay
(95746-5909)
PHONE..........................916 786-3131
Jim Thyken, *Partner*
Dana Thyken, *Partner*
Amy Schneider, *Mktg Dir*
EMP: 10
SALES (est): 700K **Privately Held**
WEB: www.norcallogos.com
SIC: 2395 Embroidery products, except
schiffli machine

(P-3833)
CAL STITCH EMBROIDERY INC
2057 Hunter Rd, Chino Hills (91709-5219)
PHONE..........................909 465-5448
Johnny Ko, *President*
Judy Ko, *Vice Pres*
EMP: 18
SQ FT: 8,000
SALES (est): 1.1MM **Privately Held**
WEB: www.calsportswear.com
SIC: 2395 Embroidery products, except
schiffli machine

(P-3834)
CECILIAS DESIGNS INC
6862 Vanscoy Ave, North Hollywood
(91605-5330)
PHONE..........................323 584-6151
Edgar Miron, *President*
Julio Miron, *Vice Pres*
Marlyn Mendenhall, *Admin Sec*
EMP: 30
SQ FT: 10,000
SALES (est): 2.2MM **Privately Held**
SIC: 2395 Embroidery products, except
schiffli machine

(P-3835)
CHRISTINE ALEXANDER INC
110 E 9th St Ste B336, Los Angeles
(90079-3336)
PHONE..........................213 488-1114
EMP: 24 **Privately Held**
SIC: 2395

(P-3836)
CLASSIC GRAPHIX
12152 Woodruff Ave, Downey
(90241-5606)
PHONE..........................562 940-0806
Judy Bathurst, *President*
Jeff Bathurst, *Corp Secy*
Scott Bathurst, *Vice Pres*
EMP: 12
SQ FT: 15,000
SALES (est): 1MM **Privately Held**
WEB: www.classicgraphix.com
SIC: 2395 2759 Emblems, embroidered;
screen printing

(P-3837)
CLASSIC QUILTING
1471 E Warner Ave, Santa Ana
(92705-5434)
PHONE..........................714 558-8312
Rosa Aceves, *Owner*
EMP: 10
SALES (est): 390K **Privately Held**
SIC: 2395 2211 Quilted fabrics or cloth;
sheets, bedding & table cloths: cotton

(P-3838)
COLORSTITCH INC
3100 S Croddy Way, Santa Ana
(92704-6346)
PHONE..........................714 754-4220
Federico P Garcia, *President*
Abby Diaz, *Prdtn Mgr*
Sarahi Diaz, *Cust Mgr*
EMP: 10
SALES (est): 807.8K **Privately Held**
WEB: www.colorstitch.biz
SIC: 2395 Embroidery products, except
schiffli machine

(P-3839)
COMPUTERIZED EMBROIDERY
CO
Also Called: C.E.C.
673 E Cooley Dr Ste 101, Colton
(92324-4016)
PHONE..........................909 825-3841
Ruben Duran Jr, *Owner*
Karen Duran, *Co-Owner*
▲ **EMP:** 10
SQ FT: 200
SALES (est): 590K **Privately Held**
WEB: www.cecembroidery.com
SIC: 2395 2759 5699 Embroidery prod-
ucts, except schiffli machine; commercial
printing; customized clothing & apparel

(P-3840)
DCL PRODUCTIONS
1284 Missouri St, San Francisco
(94107-3310)
PHONE..........................415 826-2200
David Christopher Long, *Owner*
EMP: 12 **EST:** 1995
SQ FT: 7,500
SALES (est): 1.4MM **Privately Held**
WEB: www.dclproductions.com
SIC: 2395 2759 Embroidery & art needle-
work; promotional printing; screen printing

(P-3841)
DOUBLE V INDUSTRIES
Also Called: Bluefrog Embroidery
717 Whitney St, San Leandro (94577-1117)
PHONE..........................510 347-3764
Michael P Givvin, *President*
Lesa Schultz, *Office Mgr*
Raia Arteaga, *Project Mgr*
Laney Joaquin, *Project Mgr*
Manuel Perez, *Graphic Designe*
EMP: 40
SQ FT: 10,000
SALES (est): 4.3MM **Privately Held**
WEB: www.bluefrogemb.com
SIC: 2395 Embroidery & art needlework

(P-3842)
DUDEN ENTERPRISES INC
Also Called: Bryngelson Prints
2025 W Park Ave Ste 4, Redlands
(92373-6274)
P.O. Box 1690, Yucaipa (92399-1438)
PHONE..........................909 795-0160
Harlan Duden, *President*
Frank Wisener, *Treasurer*
Lisa Duden, *Admin Sec*
▲ **EMP:** 10
SQ FT: 5,000
SALES (est): 955K **Privately Held**
SIC: 2395 2396 Embroidery & art needle-
work; screen printing on fabric articles

(P-3843)
E J Y CORPORATION
Also Called: Dlt Co
151 W 33rd St, Los Angeles (90007-4106)
PHONE..........................213 748-1700
Eun Kim, *President*
▲ **EMP:** 35
SQ FT: 8,250
SALES (est): 2.3MM **Privately Held**
WEB: www.dltco.com
SIC: 2395 Embroidery products, except
schiffli machine

(P-3844)
EMBROIDERTEX WEST LTD (PA)
435 E 16th St, Los Angeles (90015-3726)
PHONE..........................213 749-4319
Leonard Kleiderman, *President*
EMP: 15 **EST:** 1977
SQ FT: 13,000
SALES (est): 5.3MM **Privately Held**
SIC: 2395 2397 Embroidery products, ex-
cept schiffli machine; schiffli machine em-
broideries

(P-3845)
EMBROIDERY BY P & J INC
301 E Arrow Hwy Ste 104, San Dimas
(91773-3364)
PHONE..........................909 592-2622
Pat Smith, *President*
EMP: 10
SALES (est): 841K **Privately Held**
WEB: www.embbypj.com
SIC: 2395 Embroidery products, except
schiffli machine; embroidery & art needle-
work

(P-3846)
EMBROIDERY ONE CORP
1359 Channing St, Los Angeles
(90021-2410)
PHONE..........................213 572-0280
Danny Yektafar, *President*
John Mora, *Manager*
EMP: 20
SQ FT: 4,600
SALES (est): 1.1MM **Privately Held**
WEB: www.embroidery-one.com
SIC: 2395 Embroidery products, except
schiffli machine; embroidery & art needle-
work

(P-3847)
EMBROIDERY OUTLET
Also Called: Discount Outlet
10460 Magnolia Ave, Riverside
(92505-1812)
PHONE..........................951 687-1750
Yong Jeon, *Owner*
EMP: 10

SALES (est): 323.2K **Privately Held**
SIC: 2395 5699 Embroidery products, except schiffli machine; uniforms & work
clothing

(P-3848)
EQUIPMENT DE SPORT USA
INC
Also Called: Elan Blanc
39301 Badger St Ste 500, Palm Desert
(92211-1162)
PHONE..........................760 772-5544
Sharon Elaine Burr, *President*
Brian Burr, *Vice Pres*
▼ **EMP:** 17
SQ FT: 2,500
SALES (est): 960.6K **Privately Held**
SIC: 2395 Embroidery & art needlework

(P-3849)
HOLCOMB PRODUCTS INC
Also Called: California Embroidery
6751 N Blackstone Ave # 103, Fresno
(93710-3500)
PHONE..........................559 822-2067
Gary Holcomb, *President*
Wilma Holcomb, *Vice Pres*
EMP: 10
SALES (est): 882.4K **Privately Held**
WEB: www.californiaembroidery.com
SIC: 2395 Embroidery products, except
schiffli machine; embroidery & art needle-
work

(P-3850)
KINGS SILK EMBROIDERY ART
14321 Franklin Ave, Tustin (92780-7016)
PHONE..........................714 505-0731
Emily Wang, *Manager*
▲ **EMP:** 10
SALES (est): 437K **Privately Held**
SIC: 2395 Embroidery & art needlework

(P-3851)
M AND M SPORTS
Also Called: M and M Apparel
14288 Central Ave Ste A, Chino
(91710-5779)
PHONE..........................909 548-3371
Edward J Martin, *Owner*
EMP: 11
SALES: 800K **Privately Held**
WEB: www.mandmapparel.com
SIC: 2395 2261 2262 2396 Embroidery
products, except schiffli machine; screen
printing of cotton broadwoven fabrics;
screen printing: manmade fiber & silk
broadwoven fabrics; screen printing on
fabric articles; athletic (warmup, sweat &
jogging) suits: men's & boys'

(P-3852)
MELMARC PRODUCTS INC (PA)
752 S Campus Ave, Ontario (91761-1728)
PHONE..........................714 549-2170
Brian Hirth, *President*
Leila Drager, *COO*
Harish Naran, *CFO*
Migel Delgato, *Vice Pres*
Eddie Mejia, *Vice Pres*
▲ **EMP:** 330
SQ FT: 85,000
SALES (est): 89MM **Privately Held**
WEB: www.melmarc.com
SIC: 2395 2396 Pleating & stitching;
screen printing on fabric articles

(P-3853)
N STITCHES PRINTS INC
16009 S Broadway, Gardena (90248-2417)
PHONE..........................310 323-7777
Ali Amir Nanji, *President*
Ali Amir, *President*
EMP: 11
SQ FT: 3,800
SALES: 800K **Privately Held**
SIC: 2395 Embroidery products, except
schiffli machine

(P-3854)
NATIONAL EMBLEM INC (PA)
3925 E Vernon St, Long Beach
(90815-1727)
P.O. Box 15680 (90815-0680)
PHONE..........................310 515-5055
Milton H Lubin Sr, *President*

PRODUCTS & SVCS

Milton H Lubin Jr, *Vice Pres*
Rose Atkinson, *Admin Dir*
Alicia Diasanz, *Human Res Dir*
▲ **EMP:** 250
SQ FT: 60,000
SALES (est): 46.9MM **Privately Held**
WEB: www.nationalemblem.com
SIC: 2395 2396 Emblems, embroidered;
automotive & apparel trimmings

(P-3855)
NATIONAL PREMIUM MERCHANDISING (PA)
Also Called: La Palm Furniture and ACC
1650 W Artesia Blvd, Gardena
(90248-3217)
PHONE..............................310 217-2700
Dorra Ngan, *CEO*
Donna Sada, *Vice Pres*
Shawn Morse, *Sales Staff*
Gino Lam, *Director*
John Lee, *Director*
▲ **EMP:** 70
SQ FT: 30,000
SALES (est): 5.7MM **Privately Held**
WEB: www.apolloemb.com
SIC: 2395 Embroidery products, except
schiffli machine

(P-3856)
OUTLOOK RESOURCES INC
Also Called: Leftbank Art
14930 Alondra Blvd, La Mirada
(90638-5752)
PHONE..............................714 522-2452
Chris Hyun, *President*
Quinn Blackman, *Office Mgr*
Janell Jernigan, *Administration*
▲ **EMP:** 100
SALES (est): 11.6MM **Privately Held**
WEB: www.leftbankart.com
SIC: 2395 5999 Pleating & stitching; art
dealers

(P-3857)
PRODUCTION EMBROIDERY INC
1235 Activity Dr Ste D, Vista (92081-8562)
PHONE..............................760 727-7407
Andy Cao, *President*
EMP: 13
SALES (est): 500K **Privately Held**
WEB: www.proembroidery.net
SIC: 2395 Emblems, embroidered

(P-3858)
R & R INDUSTRIES INC
1923 S Santa Fe Ave, Los Angeles
(90021-2917)
PHONE..............................323 581-6000
Ron Mansuri, *President*
EMP: 29
SALES: 1.8MM **Privately Held**
SIC: 2395 Embroidery & art needlework

(P-3859)
REBECCA INTERNATIONAL INC
4587 E 48th St, Vernon (90058-3201)
PHONE..............................323 973-2602
Eli Kahen, *Owner*
EMP: 25
SQ FT: 1,500
SALES: 2MM **Privately Held**
SIC: 2395 2759 7299 Embroidery products, except schiffli machine; screen printing; stitching services

(P-3860)
RPM EMBROIDERY INC
1614 Babcock St, Costa Mesa
(92627-4330)
P.O. Box 11847 (92627-0847)
PHONE..............................949 650-0085
Bekki Prather, *Vice Pres*
Doug Prather, *Owner*
EMP: 12
SALES (est): 84.7K **Privately Held**
SIC: 2395 Embroidery products, except
schiffli machine

(P-3861)
SAN FRANSTITCHCO INC
6819 Redwood Dr Ste E, Cotati
(94931-3003)
PHONE..............................707 795-6891
Darrel Kolse, *President*
EMP: 15

SALES (est): 1.3MM **Privately Held**
SIC: 2395 Embroidery products, except
schiffli machine

(P-3862)
SKY SIGNS & GRAPHICS
15340 San Fernnd Missn Bl, Mission Hills
(91345-1122)
PHONE..............................818 898-3802
Alvarez Rene, *Owner*
EMP: 18
SALES (est): 1.2MM **Privately Held**
SIC: 2395 3479 5699 1799 Embroidery products, except schiffli machine; engraving jewelry silverware, or metal; miscellaneous apparel & accessories; sign installation & maintenance; signs & advertising specialties

(P-3863)
STITCH FACTORY
Also Called: Stitch Service
120 W 131st St, Los Angeles (90061-1616)
PHONE..............................310 523-3337
Luis Salguero, *Owner*
EMP: 15
SALES: 222K **Privately Held**
SIC: 2395 2396 Embroidery products, except schiffli machine; automotive & apparel trimmings

(P-3864)
SUNDANCE UNIFORM & EMBROIDERY
Also Called: Sundance Uniforms & Embroidery
4050 Durock Rd Ste 13, Shingle Springs
(95682-8450)
PHONE..............................530 676-6900
Laurie Oliver, *CEO*
Danny Oliver, *President*
Lori Oliver, *Vice Pres*
EMP: 13 **EST:** 1995
SALES (est): 1MM **Privately Held**
SIC: 2395 5699 2759 Embroidery products, except schiffli machine; uniforms & work clothing; screen printing

(P-3865)
SUPERIOR EMBLEM & EMBROIDERY
2601 S Hill St, Los Angeles (90007-2705)
PHONE..............................213 747-4103
David Park, *President*
Young Park, *Treasurer*
Cathy Hong, *Vice Pres*
H E Park, *Admin Sec*
John Park, *Manager*
EMP: 45
SQ FT: 9,500
SALES (est): 2.4MM **Privately Held**
SIC: 2395 Emblems, embroidered

(P-3866)
TAIGA EMBROIDERY INC
12368 Valley Blvd Ste 114, El Monte
(91732-3668)
PHONE..............................626 448-4812
Tomoko Ishida, *President*
EMP: 15
SALES: 508K **Privately Held**
SIC: 2395 Embroidery products, except
schiffli machine

(P-3867)
TSS EMBROIDERY INC
3432 Royal Ridge Rd, Chino Hills
(91709-1422)
PHONE..............................909 590-1383
EMP: 10
SALES: 300K **Privately Held**
SIC: 2395

(P-3868)
VFLY CORPORATION
Also Called: V Fly
4137 Peck Rd, El Monte (91732-2249)
PHONE..............................626 575-3115
LI Shiu Yu, *President*
▲ **EMP:** 10
SALES (est): 735.1K **Privately Held**
SIC: 2395 2396 Embroidery & art needlework; automotive & apparel trimmings

(P-3869)
WINNING TEAM INC
24922 Anza Dr Ste E, Valencia
(91355-1228)
P.O. Box 802197 (91380-2197)
PHONE..............................661 295-1428
Harris G Birken, *President*
EMP: 12
SQ FT: 6,000
SALES (est): 1MM **Privately Held**
WEB: www.thewinningteam.com
SIC: 2395 2253 Embroidery products, except schiffli machine; jackets, knit

---

2396 Automotive Trimmings, Apparel Findings, Related Prdts

(P-3870)
ABSOLUTE SCREEN GRAPHICS INC
2131 S Hellman Ave Ste A, Ontario
(91761-8004)
PHONE..............................909 923-1227
Ernest Ferraras, *President*
EMP: 11
SALES (est): 660K **Privately Held**
SIC: 2396 Screen printing on fabric articles

(P-3871)
ABSOLUTE SCREENPRINT INC
333 Cliffwood Park St, Brea (92821-4104)
P.O. Box 9069 (92822-9069)
PHONE..............................714 529-2120
Steven Restivo, *CEO*
Andrea Restivo, *CFO*
Robert Bargelski, *General Mgr*
Heather Uden, *Admin Asst*
Jamie Davis,
▲ **EMP:** 250
SQ FT: 65,000
SALES (est): 41.4MM **Privately Held**
WEB: www.absolutescreenprint.com
SIC: 2396 3993 2759 Screen printing on fabric articles; signs & advertising specialties; screen printing

(P-3872)
ACCURATE SCREEN PROCESSING
3538 Foothill Blvd, La Crescenta
(91214-1828)
PHONE..............................818 957-3965
Fax: 818 957-6445
EMP: 15
SQ FT: 2,320
SALES (est): 1.1MM
SALES (corp-wide): 2.8MM **Privately Held**
SIC: 2396
PA: Accurate Dial & Nameplate Inc
329 Mira Loma Ave
Glendale CA 91204
323 245-9181

(P-3873)
AD SPECIAL TS EMB SCREEN PRTG
202 Bella Vista Rd Ste B, Vacaville
(95687-5412)
PHONE..............................707 452-7272
Mike Anderson, *President*
Donald McKimmy, *Vice Pres*
Lela Anderson, *Admin Sec*
EMP: 12
SQ FT: 6,300
SALES: 900K **Privately Held**
WEB: www.adspecialts.com
SIC: 2396 2395 5941 5699 Screen printing on fabric articles; embroidery & art needlework; sporting goods & bicycle shops; sports apparel

(P-3874)
ALPHA IMPRESSIONS INC
4161 S Main St, Los Angeles (90037-2297)
P.O. Box 3156 (90051-1156)
PHONE..............................323 234-8221
Joseph H Dudas, *President*
Linda I Dudas, *Admin Sec*
Kathleen Reed, *Manager*
EMP: 13

SQ FT: 3,000
SALES (est): 1.1MM **Privately Held**
WEB: www.alphaimpressions.com
SIC: 2396 2752 Fabric printing & stamping; commercial printing, lithographic

(P-3875)
APPLECORE
1200 Harkness St, Manhattan Beach
(90266-4218)
PHONE..............................310 567-6768
Roberta Schannep, *Owner*
EMP: 18
SALES (est): 936.6K **Privately Held**
WEB: www.applecore.net
SIC: 2396 Screen printing on fabric articles

(P-3876)
ATOMIC MONKEY INDUSTRIES INC
946 Calle Amanecer, San Clemente
(92673-6221)
PHONE..............................949 415-8846
Michael P Lynn, *Principal*
James R Lynn, *Principal*
EMP: 10
SQ FT: 2,000
SALES (est): 580K **Privately Held**
SIC: 2396 Automotive trimmings, fabric

(P-3877)
BANDMERCH LLC
3120 W Empire Ave, Burbank
(91504-3107)
PHONE..............................818 736-4800
Joseph Bongiovi, *President*
▲ **EMP:** 33
SALES (est): 18MM **Privately Held**
SIC: 2396 Fabric printing & stamping
HQ: Aeg Presents Llc
425 W 11th St
Los Angeles CA 90015
323 930-5700

(P-3878)
BEL AIRE BRIDAL INC
Also Called: Bel Aire Bridal Accessories
23002 Mariposa Ave, Torrance
(90502-2605)
PHONE..............................310 325-8160
Joyce Smith, *President*
Stephanie Smith, *Shareholder*
Eric D Smith, *Vice Pres*
Eric Smith, *VP Sls/Mktg*
▲ **EMP:** 22 **EST:** 1960
SQ FT: 12,000
SALES (est): 2.3MM **Privately Held**
WEB: www.belairebridal.com
SIC: 2396 2353 Veils & veiling: bridal, funeral, etc.; hats, caps & millinery

(P-3879)
BRUCK BRAID COMPANY
1200 S Santa Fe Ave, Los Angeles
(90021-1789)
PHONE..............................213 627-7611
Gino Nasear, *Owner*
Ronald Jacobs, *President*
Ellen Jacobs, *Vice Pres*
EMP: 40
SQ FT: 90,000
SALES (est): 3.1MM **Privately Held**
SIC: 2396 Trimming, fabric

(P-3880)
C S DASH COVER INC
14020 Paramount Blvd, Paramount
(90723-2606)
PHONE..............................562 790-8300
Cameron Zada, *President*
Karsten Berg, *General Mgr*
▲ **EMP:** 16
SQ FT: 3,200
SALES (est): 1.7MM **Privately Held**
WEB: www.csdashcovers.com
SIC: 2396 5521 Automotive trimmings, fabric; used car dealers

(P-3881)
CALIBER SCREENPRINTING INC
1101 S Hope St, El Centro (92243-3452)
PHONE..............................760 353-3499
Oscar Quintero, *CEO*
EMP: 10
SQ FT: 2,400

SALES (est): 981.6K **Privately Held**
SIC: 2396 Screen printing on fabric articles

(P-3882)
CALIFORNIA CSTM FURN & UPHL CO
Also Called: Andrew Morgan Furniture
2835 La Mirada Dr Ste C, Vista
(92081-8457)
PHONE......................760 727-1444
Marie Cunning, *Owner*
EMP: 20
SQ FT: 19,000
SALES (est): 1.5MM **Privately Held**
WEB: www.andrewmorganfurniture.com
SIC: 2396 2514 2512 2511 Furniture trimmings, fabric; metal household furniture; upholstered household furniture; wood household furniture; household furnishings; curtains & draperies

(P-3883)
CALIFORNIA SILKSCREEN
Also Called: Calif Silk Screen
1507 Plaza Del Amo, Torrance
(90501-4935)
PHONE......................310 320-5111
Beverly Collins, *Vice Pres*
EMP: 14 **EST:** 1976
SQ FT: 7,400
SALES: 900K **Privately Held**
SIC: 2396 Screen printing on fabric articles

(P-3884)
CKCC INC
Also Called: Nissi Trim
2125 Bay St, Los Angeles (90021-1707)
PHONE......................213 629-0939
Thuong T Nguyen, *CEO*
EMP: 20 **EST:** 2014
SALES (est): 22.9MM **Privately Held**
WEB: www.nissi-inc.com
SIC: 2396 Trimming, fabric

(P-3885)
CLEARLAKE CAPITAL GROUP LP (PA)
233 Wilshire Blvd Ste 800, Santa Monica
(90401-1207)
PHONE......................310 400-8800
Behdad Eghbali, *Partner*
Jose Feliciano, *Partner*
Lisa Flanigan, *Admin Asst*
Fred Ebrahemi, *General Counsel*
EMP: 258
SALES (est): 935.5MM **Privately Held**
SIC: 2396 Automotive & apparel trimmings

(P-3886)
CONTAINER DECORATING INC
12 Homestead Ct, Danville (94506-1410)
PHONE......................510 489-9212
Joe Gallegos, *President*
Vickie Gallegos, *Treasurer*
EMP: 10
SALES: 350K **Privately Held**
SIC: 2396 Printing & embossing on plastics fabric articles

(P-3887)
D AND J MARKETING INC
Also Called: DJM Suspension
580 W 184th St, Gardena (90248-4202)
PHONE......................310 538-1583
Jeffery J Ullmann, *President*
Mark Dunham, *Vice Pres*
Juan Juarez, *Facilities Mgr*
▲ **EMP:** 32
SQ FT: 18,000
SALES (est): 3.3MM **Privately Held**
WEB: www.djmsuspension.com
SIC: 2396 2531 3714 Automotive trimmings, fabric; public building & related furniture; motor vehicle parts & accessories

(P-3888)
DECOR AUTO INC
1709 W Washington Blvd, Los Angeles
(90007-1121)
PHONE......................323 733-9025
Susan K Wheaton, *President*
Susan Wheaton, *President*
Moon Wheaton, *Vice Pres*
EMP: 11
SQ FT: 4,930

SALES (est): 700K **Privately Held**
WEB: www.decorauto.com
SIC: 2396 Automotive & apparel trimmings

(P-3889)
DISTINCTIVE INDUSTRIES
Also Called: Specialty Division
10618 Shoemaker Ave, Santa Fe Springs
(90670-4038)
PHONE......................800 421-9777
Dwight Forrister, *CEO*
Aaron Forrister, *Vice Pres*
▲ **EMP:** 410
SQ FT: 110,000
SALES (est): 34MM **Privately Held**
WEB: www.distinctiveindustries.com
SIC: 2396 3086 Automotive trimmings, fabric; plastics foam products

(P-3890)
DJ SAFETY INC
2623 N San Fernando Rd, Los Angeles
(90065-1316)
PHONE......................323 221-0000
Joe Hansen, *President*
Sandra Hansen, *Shareholder*
Darlene Hansen, *Shareholder*
Dee Hansen, *Vice Pres*
Sandy Andres, *General Mgr*
▲ **EMP:** 20 **EST:** 1996
SQ FT: 11,000
SALES (est): 2.5MM **Privately Held**
WEB: www.dj-ltd.com
SIC: 2396 Automotive & apparel trimmings

(P-3891)
FOUR SEASONS DESIGN INC (PA)
2451 Britannia Blvd, San Diego
(92154-7405)
PHONE......................619 761-5151
John Borsini, *President*
▲ **EMP:** 200
SALES (est): 28.6MM **Privately Held**
WEB: www.rudeboyz.net
SIC: 2396 Screen printing on fabric articles

(P-3892)
FULTON ACRES INC
Also Called: Headgear Plus Promo
1330 Commerce St Ste A, Petaluma
(94954-7493)
PHONE......................707 762-2280
David Trisko, *Office Mgr*
Kristine Trisko, *Managing Prtnr*
Katy Bussey, *Technology*
Jose Rodriguez, *Technology*
Amanda Anderson, *Bookkeeper*
EMP: 10
SQ FT: 9,000
SALES: 2MM **Privately Held**
WEB: www.headgearplus.com
SIC: 2396 2395 5136 Screen printing on fabric articles; embroidery & art needlework; sportswear, men's & boys'

(P-3893)
FUTURIS AUTOMOTIVE (CA) LLC
6601 Overlake Pl, Newark (94560-1009)
PHONE......................510 771-2300
Merv Dunn, *CEO*
Mark Lepech, *Engineer*
Colin Stevens, *Engineer*
Richard Steele, *Consultant*
▲ **EMP:** 280
SQ FT: 22,000
SALES (est): 9.2MM **Privately Held**
SIC: 2396 Automotive trimmings, fabric
HQ: Futuris Automotive (Us) Inc.
    14925 W 11 Mile Rd
    Oak Park MI 48237
    248 439-7800

(P-3894)
G&A APPAREL GROUP
Also Called: G&A Bias Les
3610 S Broadway, Los Angeles
(90007-4430)
PHONE......................323 234-1746
German Amaya, *President*
EMP: 30
SQ FT: 4,000
SALES (est): 2.4MM **Privately Held**
SIC: 2396

(P-3895)
GP DESIGN INC
1185 W Mahalo Pl, Compton (90220-5444)
PHONE......................310 638-8737
Glenn Aoyama, *President*
Margaret Aoyama, *Treasurer*
EMP: 15
SQ FT: 8,000
SALES: 1MM **Privately Held**
SIC: 2396 Screen printing on fabric articles

(P-3896)
GRAPHIC PRINTS INC
Also Called: Pipeline
1200 Kona Dr, Compton (90220-5405)
PHONE......................310 768-0474
Alan Greenberg, *CEO*
Tamotsu Inouye, *COO*
Richard Greenberg, *Corp Secy*
Caroline Buan, *Accounts Mgr*
EMP: 45
SQ FT: 22,000
SALES (est): 5.9MM **Privately Held**
WEB: www.graphicprints.net
SIC: 2396 2339 2329 Screen printing on fabric articles; women's & misses' athletic clothing & sportswear; men's & boys' sportswear & athletic clothing

(P-3897)
HAMBLY STUDIOS INC
23980 Spalding Ave, Los Altos
(94024-6349)
PHONE......................408 496-1100
Harry Hambly, *President*
EMP: 40 **EST:** 1959
SQ FT: 16,000
SALES (est): 3.5MM **Privately Held**
SIC: 2396 2672 Screen printing on fabric articles; coated & laminated paper

(P-3898)
HI FASHION PRODUCTIONS INC
2850 Tanager Ave, Commerce
(90040-2716)
PHONE......................323 722-8200
Ali Honari, *President*
▲ **EMP:** 27
SQ FT: 20,000
SALES (est): 2.8MM **Privately Held**
WEB: www.shoulderpads.com
SIC: 2396 5137 Pads, shoulder: for coats, suits, etc.; lingerie

(P-3899)
JAMES GANG COMPANY
4851 Newport Ave, San Diego
(92107-3110)
PHONE......................619 225-1283
Leigh Ann Bearce, *Partner*
James Berdeguez, *Partner*
Elizabeth Berdeguez, *CFO*
Paul Bearce, *Vice Pres*
EMP: 13 **EST:** 2011
SALES (est): 1.3MM **Privately Held**
SIC: 2396 2752 2261 Screen printing on fabric articles; commercial printing, offset; business form & card printing, lithographic; screen printing of cotton broadwoven fabrics

(P-3900)
KAPAN - KENT COMPANY INC
2675 Vista Pacific Dr, Oceanside
(92056-3500)
PHONE......................760 631-1716
Arnold Kapen Sr, *President*
Stefanie Baird, *Vice Pres*
Caroline Papo, *Office Mgr*
Myrna Vandeveld, *Prdtn Mgr*
Kipp Anders, *Sales Staff*
▲ **EMP:** 35
SQ FT: 30,023
SALES (est): 4.6MM **Privately Held**
WEB: www.kapankent.com
SIC: 2396 3231 Screen printing on fabric articles; decorated glassware: chipped, engraved, etched, etc.

(P-3901)
KNIT FIT INC
112 W 9th St Ste 230, Los Angeles
(90015-1636)
PHONE......................213 673-4731
Barry Wolin, *President*
▲ **EMP:** 18

SQ FT: 8,500
SALES (est): 1.2MM **Privately Held**
SIC: 2396 7389 Apparel & other linings, except millinery; textile & apparel services

(P-3902)
LEMOR TRIMS INC
830 Venice Blvd, Los Angeles
(90015-3228)
PHONE......................213 741-1646
Romel Acosta, *President*
▲ **EMP:** 15
SALES (est): 1.3MM **Privately Held**
SIC: 2396 Apparel findings & trimmings

(P-3903)
LOGOS PLUS INC
Also Called: Original Letterman Jacket Co
8130 Rosecrans Ave, Paramount
(90723-2754)
PHONE......................562 634-3009
Attorney Frenzel, *Owner*
Michael Jessick, *President*
Murray Gardner, *Treasurer*
Maria Jessick, *Director*
EMP: 12
SQ FT: 11,000
SALES (est): 440K **Privately Held**
SIC: 2396 2395 Screen printing on fabric articles; embroidery & art needlework

(P-3904)
LUNA MORA LLC
Also Called: Blur Leather
1240 S Corning St Apt 306, Los Angeles
(90035-2481)
PHONE......................310 550-6979
Farshid Javaheri, *CEO*
▲ **EMP:** 11
SQ FT: 2,000
SALES (est): 772.6K **Privately Held**
SIC: 2396 Apparel & other linings, except millinery

(P-3905)
MAGNA CHARGER INC
1990 Knoll Dr Ste A, Ventura (93003-7309)
PHONE......................805 642-8833
Jerry Magnuson, *President*
Edward Tresback, *Vice Pres*
Maureen Magnuson, *Admin Sec*
EMP: 65
SALES (est): 3.7MM **Privately Held**
WEB: www.magnacharger.net
SIC: 2396 Automotive & apparel trimmings

(P-3906)
METRO NOVELTY & PLEATING CO
906 Thayer Ave, Los Angeles
(90024-3314)
PHONE......................213 748-1201
Manny Fingson, *President*
Martin Telleria, *Vice Pres*
Nader Pakravan, *Principal*
▲ **EMP:** 80
SQ FT: 52,000
SALES (est): 5.1MM **Privately Held**
SIC: 2396 2387 5099 Trimming, fabric; apparel belts; novelties, durable

(P-3907)
MIKE FELLOWS
28913 Arnold Dr, Sonoma (95476-9738)
PHONE......................707 938-0278
Mike Fellows, *Principal*
EMP: 20
SALES (est): 1.1MM **Privately Held**
WEB: www.inmotion.net
SIC: 2396 2759 Screen printing on fabric articles; screen printing

(P-3908)
MONICA BRUCE DESIGNS INC
Also Called: Inmotion
28913 Arnold Dr, Sonoma (95476-9738)
PHONE......................707 938-0277
T Michael Fellows, *President*
Nick Castro, *Vice Pres*
Doug Scott, *Art Dir*
EMP: 17 **EST:** 1974
SQ FT: 9,000
SALES (est): 1.9MM **Privately Held**
SIC: 2396 2395 Screen printing on fabric articles; embroidery & art needlework

(P-3909)
NEXT DAY PRINTED TEES
Also Called: Swim Cap Company , The
3523 Main St Ste 601, Chula Vista
(91911-0803)
PHONE.....................................619 420-8618
Timothy B Lewis, *President*
Carmen Nichols, *CFO*
Mary Jane Lewis, *Senior VP*
Christopher Lewis, *Vice Pres*
Jane Lewis, *Vice Pres*
EMP: 16
SQ FT: 9,000
SALES (est): 2.2MM **Privately Held**
WEB: www.ndpt.com
SIC: 2396 5699 Screen printing on fabric
    articles; customized clothing & apparel

(P-3910)
NORTH AMERICAN TEXTILE CO LLC (PA)
Also Called: N A T C O
346 W Cerritos Ave, Glendale
(91204-2704)
PHONE.....................................818 409-0019
Esteban E Arslanian Sr,
Armine Madanyan, *Graphic Designe*
Andrea Toledo, *Prdtn Mgr*
Armando Arslanian,
Carlos Arslanian,
▲ EMP: 35
SQ FT: 18,000
SALES (est): 7.3MM **Privately Held**
WEB: www.natcolabel.com
SIC: 2396 7389 Apparel findings & trim-
    mings; textile & apparel services

(P-3911)
OSUMO INC
Also Called: Fabrix
1933 Republic Ave, San Leandro
(94577-4220)
PHONE.....................................510 346-6888
M Sung, *President*
Michael Sung, *President*
EMP: 10 EST: 1978
SALES: 500K **Privately Held**
WEB: www.osumo.com
SIC: 2396 Screen printing on fabric articles

(P-3912)
PANGEA SILKSCREEN
110 Howard St Ste A, Petaluma
(94952-2922)
PHONE.....................................707 778-0110
Richard Nakagawa, *President*
Michelle Caldwell, *Vice Pres*
EMP: 25
SQ FT: 10,500
SALES (est): 2.5MM **Privately Held**
WEB: www.pangeapromo.com
SIC: 2396 2395 Screen printing on fabric
    articles; embroidery & art needlework

(P-3913)
PLASTECH SPECIALTIES COMPANY (PA)
4645 Portofino Cir, Cypress (90630-6806)
PHONE.....................................626 357-6839
Mike Delaney, *CEO*
Patrick L Delaney, *President*
EMP: 12
SQ FT: 14,000
SALES (est): 782.3K **Privately Held**
WEB: www.plastechspec.com
SIC: 2396 Printing & embossing on plas-
    tics fabric articles

(P-3914)
R B T INC
Also Called: Ink Throwers
2240 Encinitas Blvd, Encinitas
(92024-4345)
PHONE.....................................619 781-8802
Tom Butler, *CEO*
EMP: 14 EST: 1999
SALES (est): 1.7MM **Privately Held**
SIC: 2396 Screen printing on fabric articles

(P-3915)
RC APPAREL INC
3104 Markridge Rd, La Crescenta
(91214-1332)
PHONE.....................................818 541-1994
▲ EMP: 12

SALES: 2MM **Privately Held**
SIC: 2396

(P-3916)
ROYAL TRIM
2529 Chambers St, Vernon (90058-2107)
PHONE.....................................323 583-2121
Farzad Pakravan, *President*
▲ EMP: 25
SQ FT: 30,000
SALES (est): 2.2MM **Privately Held**
SIC: 2396 2395 Apparel findings & trim-
    mings; pleating & stitching

(P-3917)
SEA & SUN GRAPHICS INC
11721 Seaboard Cir, Stanton (90680-3444)
PHONE.....................................714 897-4020
Beatriz Caballero, *President*
Hugo Flores, *President*
Milton Flores, *Treasurer*
Sigfred Flores, *Vice Pres*
EMP: 12
SQ FT: 10,000
SALES (est): 1.2MM **Privately Held**
SIC: 2396 Screen printing on fabric articles

(P-3918)
SECURITY TEXTILE CORPORATION
1457 E Washington Blvd, Los Angeles
(90021-3039)
PHONE.....................................213 747-2673
Doug Weitman, *CEO*
Brian Weitman, *President*
Mary Larimore, *Human Res Mgr*
Jeff Waldman, *Sales Dir*
▲ EMP: 80
SQ FT: 85,000
SALES (est): 7MM **Privately Held**
SIC: 2396 5131 Automotive & apparel
    trimmings; sewing supplies & notions

(P-3919)
SIMSO TEX SUBLIMATION (PA)
3028 E Las Hermanas St, E Rncho Dmngz
(90221-5511)
PHONE.....................................310 885-9717
Joe Simsoly, *CEO*
Eli Simsollo, *President*
Kaden Simsollo, *Admin Sec*
▲ EMP: 59 EST: 2001
SQ FT: 38,000
SALES (est): 14.3MM **Privately Held**
WEB: www.simsotex.com
SIC: 2396 Fabric printing & stamping

(P-3920)
SJ&L BIAS BINDING & TEX CO INC
Also Called: Superior Bias Trims
1950 E 20th St, Vernon (90058-1005)
PHONE.....................................213 747-5271
Lynn Menichiwi, *CEO*
Joseph Menichini, *Vice Pres*
▲ EMP: 50
SQ FT: 11,000
SALES (est): 5.5MM **Privately Held**
SIC: 2396 Pads, shoulder: for coats, suits,
    etc.

(P-3921)
SMOOTHREADS INC
Also Called: 2.95 Guys
13750 Stowe Dr Ste A, Poway
(92064-8828)
PHONE.....................................800 536-5959
Lance Beesley, *President*
Johnny Beifus, *Director*
Jorge Morales, *Manager*
▲ EMP: 28
SQ FT: 12,000
SALES (est): 3.6MM **Privately Held**
WEB: www.295guys.com
SIC: 2396 2395 Screen printing on fabric
    articles; embroidery products, except
    schiffli machine

(P-3922)
STANDARD BIAS BINDING CO INC
4621 Pacific Blvd, Vernon (90058-2221)
P.O. Box 58025, Los Angeles (90058-0025)
PHONE.....................................323 277-9763
Rex Bollar, *President*

Loree Bollar, *Treasurer*
EMP: 36
SQ FT: 20,800
SALES (est): 2.6MM **Privately Held**
SIC: 2396 Automotive & apparel trimmings

(P-3923)
STAR FISH INC
410 Talbert St, Daly City (94014-1623)
PHONE.....................................415 468-6688
Sieu Khac, *Administration*
Sieu MA, *President*
Susan Shaw, *Director*
EMP: 10
SALES: 1MM **Privately Held**
SIC: 2396 Screen printing on fabric articles

(P-3924)
SUPER VIAS & TRIM
3651 S Main St E, Los Angeles
(90007-4417)
PHONE.....................................323 233-2556
Alex Rodriguez, *President*
EMP: 12
SALES (est): 1.1MM **Privately Held**
SIC: 2396 7389

(P-3925)
TEAM COLOR INC
Also Called: Team Color Screen Printing
837 W 18th St, Costa Mesa (92627-4410)
PHONE.....................................949 646-6486
William Andrew Wolfe, *President*
Julie Wolfe, *Vice Pres*
EMP: 40
SALES (est): 4.9MM **Privately Held**
SIC: 2396 2759 Screen printing on fabric
    articles; screen printing

(P-3926)
UNIQUE SCREEN PRINTING INC
Also Called: Yang's Screen Printing
2115 Central Ave, South El Monte
(91733-2117)
PHONE.....................................626 575-2725
Lu Hui-Chin Yang, *President*
EMP: 30
SQ FT: 2,000
SALES: 400K **Privately Held**
SIC: 2396 Screen printing on fabric articles

(P-3927)
VALLEY IMAGES
1925 Kyle Park Ct, San Jose (95125-1029)
PHONE.....................................408 279-6777
Carlo Strangis, *Partner*
Robert Malik, *Partner*
EMP: 17
SQ FT: 10,201
SALES (est): 1.3MM **Privately Held**
WEB: www.valleyimages.com
SIC: 2396 Screen printing on fabric articles

(P-3928)
VOELKER SENSORS INC
3790 El Camino Real, Palo Alto
(94306-3314)
PHONE.....................................650 361-0570
Joe Hedges, *President*
Paul Voelker, *CEO*
EMP: 15
SQ FT: 1,000
SALES (est): 1.3MM **Privately Held**
WEB: www.vsi-oil.com
SIC: 2396 Automotive & apparel trimmings

(P-3929)
WESTSIDE RESEARCH INC
4293 County Road 99w, Orland
(95963-9153)
PHONE.....................................530 330-0085
Tim Dexter, *President*
Karen Dexter, *Vice Pres*
▲ EMP: 15
SALES (est): 1.5MM **Privately Held**
WEB: www.westsideresearch.com
SIC: 2396 Automotive & apparel trimmings

(P-3930)
WORLD UPHOLSTERY & TRIM INC
1320 E Main St, Santa Paula (93060-2926)
PHONE.....................................805 921-0100
Michael May, *President*
Fran Adler, *Vice Pres*
EMP: 11

SALES: 800K **Privately Held**
WEB: www.worlduph.com
SIC: 2396 Automotive trimmings, fabric

2399 Fabricated Textile Prdts, NEC

(P-3931)
A LOT TO SAY INC
1541 S Vineyard Ave, Ontario
(91761-7717)
PHONE.....................................925 964-5079
Armando Herrera, *Branch Mgr*
EMP: 15 **Privately Held**
SIC: 2399 2361 Banners, made from fab-
    ric; girls' & children's blouses & shirts
PA: A Lot To Say, Inc.
    4155 Blackhawk
    Danville CA 94506
    -

(P-3932)
A LOT TO SAY INC (PA)
4155 Blackhawk Ste 110, Danville (94506)
PHONE.....................................877 366-8448
Jennifer Spannich Danmiller, *CEO*
Alisson Spannich Powers, *COO*
EMP: 15
SALES (est): 2.6MM **Privately Held**
SIC: 2399 Banners, made from fabric

(P-3933)
AAA FLAG & BANNER MFG CO INC
Also Called: A A A Sign & Banner Mfg Co
8966 National Blvd, Los Angeles
(90034-3308)
PHONE.....................................310 836-3341
Howard Furst, *President*
Rick Puleo, *Branch Mgr*
EMP: 200
SALES (corp-wide): 29MM **Privately Held**
WEB: www.aaaflag.com
SIC: 2399 3993 Banners, pennants &
    flags; signs & advertising specialties
PA: Aaa Flag & Banner Mfg Co Inc
    8937 National Blvd
    Los Angeles CA 90034
    310 836-3200

(P-3934)
ACTION EMBROIDERY CORP (PA)
1315 Brooks St, Ontario (91762-3612)
PHONE.....................................909 983-1359
Ira Newman, *President*
Steven Mendelow, *Treasurer*
Connie Sanchez, *Manager*
▲ EMP: 120
SQ FT: 12,000
SALES (est): 28.1MM **Privately Held**
WEB: www.actionemb.com
SIC: 2399 2395 Emblems, badges & in-
    signia: from purchased materials; pleating
    & stitching

(P-3935)
AIRBORNE SYSTEMS N AMER CA INC
3100 W Segerstrom Ave, Santa Ana
(92704-5812)
PHONE.....................................714 662-1400
Bryce Wiedeman, *President*
Sean P Maroney, *Treasurer*
Terrance M Paradie, *Principal*
Halle F Terrion, *Admin Sec*
Patrick Sheridan, *Controller*
▼ EMP: 161
SQ FT: 160,000
SALES: 49.1MM
SALES (corp-wide): 3.5B **Publicly Held**
WEB: www.irvinaerospace.com
SIC: 2399 Parachutes
HQ: Airborne Systems North America Inc.
    5800 Magnolia Ave
    Pennsauken NJ 08109
    856 663-1275

▲ = Import ▼=Export
◆ =Import/Export

(P-3936)
AMERICAN HORSE PRODUCTS
Also Called: Inerfab
31896 Plaza Dr Ste C4, San Juan Capistrano (92675-3736)
PHONE..................................949 248-5300
James Carter, *CEO*
Diane Carter, *Vice Pres*
EMP: 12
SQ FT: 12,000
SALES: 3.5MM **Privately Held**
SIC: 2399 5699 Horse & pet accessories, textile; riding apparel

(P-3937)
AMZR INC
Also Called: Adco Products
29115 Avenue Valleyview, Valencia (91355-5443)
PHONE..................................800 541-2326
Alan Ein, *President*
▲ **EMP:** 150 **EST:** 1955
SQ FT: 250,000
SALES (est): 70.9MM
SALES (corp-wide): 110.2MM **Privately Held**
WEB: www.adcoprod.com
SIC: 2399 Automotive covers, except seat & tire covers
PA: Covercraft Industries, Llc
100 Enterprise
Pauls Valley OK 73075
405 238-9651

(P-3938)
AUTOLIV SAFETY TECHNOLOGY INC
2475 Paseo D Las Amrcs, San Diego (92154)
PHONE..................................619 662-8000
Bradley J Murray, *President*
Raymond B Pekar, *Treasurer*
Anthony J Nellis, *Admin Sec*
EMP: 1003
SALES (est): 17.8K
SALES (corp-wide): 10.3B **Publicly Held**
SIC: 2399 Seat belts, automobile & aircraft
PA: Autoliv, Inc.
3350 Airport Rd
Ogden UT 84405
801 629-9800

(P-3939)
CABEAU INC
21700 Oxnard St Ste 900, Woodland Hills (91367-7569)
PHONE..................................877 962-2232
David Sternlight, *CEO*
Troy Grabow, *Vice Pres*
Ryan Hilterbran, *Vice Pres*
Connie Colin, *Executive Asst*
Ricky Helland, *Finance*
▲ **EMP:** 25
SALES (est): 1.5MM **Privately Held**
WEB: www.completesupportpillow.com
SIC: 2399 Emblems, badges & insignia

(P-3940)
CAL TRENDS ACCESSORIES LLC
Also Called: Cal Trend Automotive Products
2121 S Anne St, Santa Ana (92704-4408)
PHONE..................................714 708-5115
Roger Loomis,
Mike Wadhera, *CIO*
EMP: 22
SALES (est): 2.5MM **Privately Held**
WEB: www.caltrend.com
SIC: 2399 3751 3714 Automotive covers, except seat & tire covers; motorcycle accessories; motor vehicle parts & accessories

(P-3941)
DISPLAY FABRICATION GROUP INC
1231 N Miller St Ste 100, Anaheim (92806-1950)
PHONE..................................714 373-2100
Luis Ocampo, *President*
Lindsey Johnson, *Executive Asst*
Javier Villegas, *Purchasing*
Craig Moloney, *VP Opers*
◆ **EMP:** 50
SQ FT: 100,000

SALES (est): 274.4K **Privately Held**
SIC: 2399 Belting, fabric: made from purchased materials

(P-3942)
DRAKE ENTERPRISES INCORPORATED
Also Called: Big D Products
490 Watt Dr, Fairfield (94534-1663)
PHONE..................................707 864-3077
Glenn Drake, *President*
Pilar Pena, *Bookkeeper*
▲ **EMP:** 67
SQ FT: 55,000
SALES (est): 6.4MM **Privately Held**
WEB: www.bigdblankets.com
SIC: 2399 Horse blankets; horse & pet accessories, textile

(P-3943)
DSY EDUCATIONAL CORPORATION
Also Called: Main Street Banner
525 Maple St, Carpinteria (93013-2070)
P.O. Box 41829, Santa Barbara (93140-1829)
PHONE..................................805 684-8111
David Yothers, *President*
Sharon Yothers, *Corp Secy*
Jeannie Dominguez, *Office Admin*
EMP: 11
SQ FT: 15,000
SALES (est): 1.1MM **Privately Held**
WEB: www.mainstreetbanner.com
SIC: 2399 7336 Banners, made from fabric; flags, fabric; commercial art & graphic design

(P-3944)
EEVELLE LLC
2270 Cosmos Ct Ste 100, Carlsbad (92011-1558)
PHONE..................................760 434-2231
Charles McKee, *Mng Member*
▲ **EMP:** 24
SALES (est): 1.5MM **Privately Held**
WEB: www.eevelle.com
SIC: 2399 Automotive covers, except seat & tire covers

(P-3945)
EXXEL OUTDOORS INC
343 Baldwin Park Blvd, City of Industry (91746-1406)
PHONE..................................626 369-7278
EMP: 249
SALES (corp-wide): 126.5MM **Privately Held**
SIC: 2399 Sleeping bags
PA: Exxel Outdoors, Inc.
300 American Blvd
Haleyville AL 35565
205 486-5258

(P-3946)
FALCON AUTOMOTIVE INC
1305 E Wakeham Ave, Santa Ana (92705-4145)
PHONE..................................714 569-1085
Peter Eberhardt, *President*
▲ **EMP:** 30
SQ FT: 16,000
SALES (est): 2.5MM **Privately Held**
SIC: 2399 2273 3714 Automotive covers, except seat & tire covers; seat covers, automobile; automobile floor coverings, except rubber or plastic; motor vehicle parts & accessories

(P-3947)
FLAGCRAFTERS INC
1120 Bay Blvd Ste E, Chula Vista (91911-7169)
PHONE..................................619 585-1044
Janet Crowe, *CEO*
Robert Crowe, *President*
Barbara Ayers, *Vice Pres*
EMP: 20
SALES (est): 1.6MM **Privately Held**
WEB: www.flagcrafters.com
SIC: 2399 Banners, made from fabric; flags, fabric

(P-3948)
FLEXSYSTEMS USA INC
1308 N Magnolia Ave Ste J, El Cajon (92020-1646)
PHONE..................................619 401-1858
Diane Chapman, *President*
▲ **EMP:** 25
SALES (est): 3.4MM **Privately Held**
WEB: www.flexsystems.com
SIC: 2399 2396 Emblems, badges & insignia; pet collars, leashes, etc.: non-leather; apparel findings & trimmings

(P-3949)
FXC CORPORATION
Guardian Parachute Division
3050 Red Hill Ave, Costa Mesa (92626-4524)
PHONE..................................714 557-8032
Frank X Chevrier, *Manager*
EMP: 75
SALES (corp-wide): 14.7MM **Privately Held**
WEB: www.fxcguardian.com
SIC: 2399 3429 Parachutes; parachute hardware
PA: Fxc Corporation
3050 Red Hill Ave
Costa Mesa CA 92626
714 556-7400

(P-3950)
HIGH ENERGY SPORTS INC
1081 N Shepard St Ste A, Anaheim (92806-2819)
PHONE..................................714 632-3323
Elizabeth Rothman, *President*
EMP: 15
SQ FT: 3,600
SALES (est): 1.4MM **Privately Held**
WEB: www.highenergysports.com
SIC: 2399 Parachutes

(P-3951)
HITEX DYEING & FINISHING INC
355 Vineland Ave, City of Industry (91746-2321)
PHONE..................................626 363-0160
Young C Kim, *President*
▲ **EMP:** 40
SALES (est): 458.8K **Privately Held**
SIC: 2399 2257 Nets, launderers & dyers; dyeing & finishing circular knit fabrics

(P-3952)
JESSIE STEELE INC
2112 Adams Ave, San Leandro (94577-1010)
PHONE..................................510 204-0991
Helena J Steele, *President*
Larry Philipps, *COO*
Larry Phillipes, *COO*
Mitchell Merrick, *VP Sales*
▲ **EMP:** 11
SALES (est): 1.5MM **Privately Held**
WEB: www.jessiesteele.com
SIC: 2399 Aprons, breast (harness)

(P-3953)
MADDOX DEFENSE INC
Also Called: Stinger Solar Kits
6549 Mission Gorge Rd # 112, San Diego (92120-2306)
PHONE..................................818 378-8246
Jason Maddox, *CEO*
EMP: 15
SALES (est): 1.4MM **Privately Held**
SIC: 2399 2394 5099 Military insignia, textile; convertible tops, canvas or boat: from purchased materials; lifesaving & survival equipment (non-medical)

(P-3954)
MARIE JOANN DESIGNS INC
630 S Jefferson St Ste H, Placentia (92870-6639)
PHONE..................................714 996-0550
Fred Hughes, *Partner*
Joann Marie Dextradeur, *Partner*
▲ **EMP:** 13
SQ FT: 2,000
SALES: 1.2MM **Privately Held**
WEB: www.jmdinc.net
SIC: 2399 5199 Emblems, badges & insignia; gifts & novelties

(P-3955)
MOTORLAMB INTERNATIONAL ACC
Also Called: Blue Ribbon Sheepskin
8055 Clairemont Mesa Blvd # 108, San Diego (92111-1620)
PHONE..................................858 569-8111
Selwyn Klein, *President*
EMP: 10 **EST:** 1979
SQ FT: 4,400
SALES (est): 628K **Privately Held**
SIC: 2399 5531 Seat covers, automobile; automotive accessories

(P-3956)
NORTH BAY RHBLITATION SVCS INC (PA)
Also Called: North Bay Industries
649 Martin Ave, Rohnert Park (94928-2050)
PHONE..................................707 585-1991
Robert Hutt, *CEO*
William Stewart, *Ch of Bd*
Bella Hutt, *CFO*
EMP: 230
SQ FT: 18,000
SALES: 15MM **Privately Held**
WEB: www.nbrs.org
SIC: 2399 0782 8331 Banners, pennants & flags; lawn services; community service employment training program; vocational rehabilitation agency

(P-3957)
PATCH PLACE
1724 S Grove Ave Ste A, Ontario (91761-4564)
PHONE..................................909 947-3023
Eric Roberts, *Owner*
EMP: 50
SALES (est): 3.7MM **Privately Held**
WEB: www.thepatchplace.com
SIC: 2399 Emblems, badges & insignia

(P-3958)
PRESTIGE FLAG & BANNER CO
591 Camino Dela Reina 917, San Diego (92108)
PHONE..................................619 497-2220
Mike Roberts, *President*
Dave Fenimore, *COO*
Stuart Fried, *Vice Pres*
Tiffany Rogers, *Accounting Mgr*
Barbara Carlton, *Accounts Mgr*
▼ **EMP:** 100
SQ FT: 8,000
SALES (est): 9.9MM **Privately Held**
WEB: www.prestigeflag.com
SIC: 2399 Flags, fabric

(P-3959)
RANKS BIG DATA
2453 Naglee Rd, Tracy (95304-7324)
PHONE..................................510 830-6926
Nathan Sharma, *CEO*
EMP: 149 **EST:** 2010
SQ FT: 2,000
SALES (est): 6.9MM **Privately Held**
SIC: 2399 8748 Hand woven apparel; business consulting; energy conservation consultant

(P-3960)
REFLEX CORPORATION
1825 Aston Ave Ste A, Carlsbad (92008-7341)
PHONE..................................760 931-9009
John C Levy Jr, *President*
Annika Risher, *COO*
Kathleen Coawn, *CFO*
▲ **EMP:** 20
SQ FT: 20,000
SALES (est): 2.1MM **Privately Held**
WEB: www.premiumtufflock.com
SIC: 2399 Horse & pet accessories, textile; pet collars, leashes, etc.: non-leather

(P-3961)
ROYAL RIDERS
120 Mast St Ste B, Morgan Hill (95037-5154)
PHONE..................................408 779-1997
Janet Graham, *Owner*
▲ **EMP:** 11
SQ FT: 5,500

SALES (est): 836.5K **Privately Held**
SIC: 2399 Horse blankets

(P-3962)
RUTH TRAINING CENTER SEW MCHS
328 E 24th St, Los Angeles (90011-1029)
PHONE.................................213 748-8033
Lilian Herrera, *President*
EMP: 10
SALES (est): 560K **Privately Held**
SIC: 2399 7999 Fabricated textile products; sewing instruction

(P-3963)
SAMPLING INTERNATIONAL LLC
Also Called: Levolor
28 Hammond Ste C, Irvine (92618-1663)
PHONE.................................949 305-5333
Dean Treister, *Managing Dir*
Richard Sternberg, *VP Opers*
▲ **EMP:** 11
SQ FT: 2,000
SALES (est): 2.1MM **Privately Held**
SIC: 2399 Book covers, fabric

(P-3964)
SCOTTEX INC
12828 S Broadway, Los Angeles (90061-1116)
PHONE.................................310 516-1411
Stanley Jung, *President*
▲ **EMP:** 11
SQ FT: 19,000
SALES (est): 1.8MM **Privately Held**
WEB: www.scottex.net
SIC: 2399 Hand woven & crocheted products

(P-3965)
SEABORN CANVAS
435 N Harbor Blvd Ste B1, San Pedro (90731-2271)
PHONE.................................310 519-1208
Juanita Wade, *Owner*
▼ **EMP:** 25
SQ FT: 5,000
SALES (est): 1.1MM **Privately Held**
SIC: 2399 2394 Banners, pennants & flags; flags, fabric; canvas & related products

(P-3966)
SEVENTH HEAVEN INC
Also Called: Western Mountaineering
1025 S 5th St, San Jose (95112-3927)
PHONE.................................408 287-8945
Gary Schaezlein, *Director*
Gary Peterson, *Prdtn Mgr*
▲ **EMP:** 30
SQ FT: 12,000
SALES (est): 3.7MM **Privately Held**
WEB: www.westernmountaineering.com
SIC: 2399 2392 2329 Sleeping bags; comforters & quilts: made from purchased materials; down-filled clothing: men's & boys'

(P-3967)
SONMEZ EMRE
Also Called: Sofi Enterprises
1370 E Washington Blvd, Los Angeles (90021-3038)
PHONE.................................323 589-6000
Emre Sonmez, *Owner*
EMP: 15 **EST:** 2012
SQ FT: 1,000
SALES (est): 1.3MM **Privately Held**
SIC: 2399 2221 Emblems, badges & insignia; dress fabrics, manmade fiber & silk

(P-3968)
TB KAWASHIMA USA INC
19200 Von Karman Ave # 870, Irvine (92612-8523)
PHONE.................................714 389-5310
Masanori Sawa, *Branch Mgr*
EMP: 10
SALES (corp-wide): 13.1B **Privately Held**
SIC: 2399 Aprons, breast (harness)
HQ: Tb Kawashima Usa, Inc.
    412 Groves St
    Lugoff SC 29078
    803 421-0033

(P-3969)
UNIVERSITY BLANKET & FLAG CORP (PA)
1111 Orange Ave Ste C, Coronado (92118-3432)
PHONE.................................619 435-4100
Carroll Gerbel, *President*
Linda Gerbel, *Vice Pres*
▲ **EMP:** 10
SQ FT: 1,000
SALES (est): 2.2MM **Privately Held**
WEB: www.ubflag.com
SIC: 2399 2392 Flags, fabric; blankets: made from purchased materials

(P-3970)
USA PRODUCTS GROUP INC (PA)
Also Called: Progrip Cargo Control
1300 E Vine St, Lodi (95240-3148)
P.O. Box 1750 (95241-1750)
PHONE.................................209 334-1460
Stephen D Jackson, *President*
Yolanda Bernasconi, *Executive*
Shirley Callaham, *Buyer*
David Jackson, *Marketing Mgr*
Seth Talbot, *Marketing Staff*
▲ **EMP:** 30
SALES (est): 8.4MM **Privately Held**
SIC: 2399 3949 Seat covers, automobile; bags, golf; golf equipment

(P-3971)
VANGUARD INDUSTRIES EAST INC
2440 Impala Dr, Carlsbad (92010-7226)
PHONE.................................800 433-1334
William M Gershen, *Branch Mgr*
Melinda Kindred, *Purchasing*
Brian Robertson, *Purch Agent*
Glenn Deans, *Natl Sales Mgr*
Rochelle Debicki, *Sales Staff*
EMP: 73
SALES (corp-wide): 13.4MM **Privately Held**
SIC: 2399 Military insignia, textile
PA: Vanguard Industries East, Inc.
    1172 Azalea Garden Rd
    Norfolk VA 23502
    800 221-1264

(P-3972)
VANGUARD INDUSTRIES WEST INC (PA)
2440 Impala Dr, Carlsbad (92010-7226)
PHONE.................................760 438-4437
William M Gershen, *President*
Michael Harrison, *Vice Pres*
Bill Gershen, *Principal*
Cindy Mortrud, *General Mgr*
David Thomas, *Info Tech Dir*
▲ **EMP:** 107
SQ FT: 36,000
SALES (est): 14.2MM **Privately Held**
SIC: 2399 2395 Military insignia, textile; pleating & stitching

(P-3973)
WEST COAST SHEEPSKIN IMPORT
14056 Whittier Blvd, Whittier (90605-2041)
PHONE.................................562 945-5151
Fax: 562 698-3946
EMP: 10
SQ FT: 6,000
SALES (est): 245K **Privately Held**
SIC: 2399 5013 5531

(P-3974)
YOUNG SUNG USA INC
1122 S Alvarado St, Los Angeles (90006-4110)
PHONE.................................213 427-2580
Pyung Kwon, *President*
Gonzalo Arita, *Sales Mgr*
▲ **EMP:** 15
SQ FT: 15,600
SALES (est): 1.6MM **Privately Held**
SIC: 2399 Seat covers, automobile

2411 Logging

(P-3975)
A&M TIMBER INC
4002 Alta Mesa Dr, Redding (96002-3732)
PHONE.................................530 515-1740
Joseph D Atchley III, *President*
Clay Montgomery, *Corp Secy*
EMP: 11
SALES (est): 730K **Privately Held**
SIC: 2411 Logging

(P-3976)
ALDERMAN TIMBER COMPANY INC
Also Called: Alderman Logging
17180 Alderman Rd, Sonora (95370-8909)
P.O. Box 127, Soulsbyville (95372-0127)
PHONE.................................209 532-9636
Keith Alderman, *President*
Linda Alderman, *Corp Secy*
Roger Alderman, *Vice Pres*
EMP: 14
SQ FT: 12,020
SALES (est): 1.8MM **Privately Held**
SIC: 2411 Logging camps & contractors

(P-3977)
AMUNDSON TOM TMBER FLLING CNTR
14615 River Oaks Dr, Red Bluff (96080-9338)
PHONE.................................530 529-0504
Thomas Amundson, *Owner*
EMP: 10
SALES (est): 720K **Privately Held**
SIC: 2411 Timber, cut at logging camp

(P-3978)
ANDERSON LOGGING INC
1296 N Main St, Fort Bragg (95437-8407)
P.O. Box 1266 (95437-1266)
PHONE.................................707 964-2770
Michael Anderson, *President*
Joseph Anderson, *Vice Pres*
Maribelle Anderson, *Admin Sec*
EMP: 100 **EST:** 1977
SQ FT: 3,000
SALES (est): 10.1MM **Privately Held**
SIC: 2411 4212 Logging camps & contractors; lumber (log) trucking, local

(P-3979)
AUBERRY FOREST PRODUCTS INC
32177 Auberry Rd, Auberry (93602-9603)
PHONE.................................559 855-6255
Darlene Allen, *President*
Matthew Allen, *President*
EMP: 17
SQ FT: 600
SALES (est): 1.5MM **Privately Held**
WEB: www.auberryforestproducts.com
SIC: 2411 Logging

(P-3980)
BIG HILL LOGGING & RD BUILDING (PA)
680 Sutter St, Yuba City (95991-4218)
PHONE.................................530 673-4155
Macarthur Siller, *President*
McArthur Siller, *President*
Janet Siller, *Vice Pres*
Dane Siller, *Admin Sec*
EMP: 26
SQ FT: 1,726
SALES (est): 2.6MM **Privately Held**
SIC: 2411 1611 Logging camps & contractors; highway & street construction

(P-3981)
BUNDY AND SONS INC
15196 Mountain Shadows Dr, Redding (96001-9544)
PHONE.................................530 246-3868
William J Bundy, *President*
Terrice Bundy, *Vice Pres*
EMP: 22
SQ FT: 2,000
SALES (est): 3.7MM **Privately Held**
SIC: 2411 Logging camps & contractors

(P-3982)
CHUCK L LOGGING INC
6527 Big Springs Rd, Montague (96064-9105)
PHONE.................................530 459-3842
Charles Hedin, *President*
Sandy Hedin, *Corp Secy*
EMP: 45
SALES: 4MM **Privately Held**
SIC: 2411 Logging camps & contractors

(P-3983)
D L STOY LOGGING CO
17302 Mountain View Rd, Greenville (95947-9750)
PHONE.................................530 283-3292
Douglas L Stoy, *Owner*
EMP: 11
SALES: 1.4MM **Privately Held**
SIC: 2411 Logging camps & contractors

(P-3984)
DAN ARENS AND SON INC
Also Called: Arens Brothers Logging
5780 Ridgeway Dr, Pollock Pines (95726-9533)
P.O. Box 1142 (95726-1142)
PHONE.................................530 644-6307
Dan Arens, *CEO*
Jerry Arens, *CFO*
Levi Arens, *Admin Sec*
EMP: 12
SQ FT: 2,000
SALES (est): 1.8MM **Privately Held**
WEB: www.danarensi.com
SIC: 2411 Logging camps & contractors

(P-3985)
DAVE RICHARDSON TRUCKING
Also Called: R & B Logging
8817 Lwer Lttle Shasta Rd, Montague (96064-9699)
PHONE.................................530 459-5088
Dave Richardson, *Owner*
Deborah Richardson, *Co-Owner*
EMP: 18 **EST:** 1974
SALES: 2MM **Privately Held**
SIC: 2411 4212 Logging camps & contractors; lumber (log) trucking, local

(P-3986)
DEL LOGGING INC
101 Punkin Center Rd, Bieber (96009)
P.O. Box 246 (96009-0246)
PHONE.................................530 294-5492
Russ Hawkins, *President*
Helen Hawkins, *Corp Secy*
EMP: 42 **EST:** 1971
SQ FT: 450
SALES (est): 2.4MM **Privately Held**
SIC: 2411 Logging camps & contractors

(P-3987)
FORD LOGGING INC
Also Called: Pacific Earthscape
1225 Central Ave Ste 11, McKinleyville (95519-5301)
PHONE.................................707 840-9442
Delman Ford, *President*
Heath Ford, *Treasurer*
Glenn Ford, *Vice Pres*
Derek Ford, *Admin Sec*
EMP: 20
SALES (est): 600K **Privately Held**
SIC: 2411 1611 Logging camps & contractors; gravel or dirt road construction

(P-3988)
FRANKLIN LOGGING INC
11906 Wilson Way, Redding (96003-7589)
P.O. Box 1303, Bella Vista (96008-1303)
PHONE.................................530 549-4924
Dianne Franklin, *President*
Bruce Olsen, *Vice Pres*
EMP: 25 **EST:** 1950
SQ FT: 1,700
SALES (est): 3.5MM **Privately Held**
SIC: 2411 Logging

(P-3989)
FRAY LOGGING INC
10619 Jim Brady Rd, Jamestown (95327-9518)
PHONE.................................209 984-5968
Richard N Fray, *President*
Susan Fray, *Treasurer*

EMP: 20
SALES (est): 2.1MM **Privately Held**
SIC: 2411 Logging camps & contractors

(P-3990)
H&M LOGGING
442 S Franklin St, Fort Bragg
(95437-4803)
PHONE..................707 964-2340
Richard Hautala, *President*
EMP: 10
SALES (est): 820K **Privately Held**
SIC: 2411 Logging camps & contractors

(P-3991)
HOOPA FOREST INDUSTRIES
778 Marshall Ln, Hoopa (95546-9762)
P.O. Box 759 (95546-0759)
PHONE..................530 625-4281
Merwin Clark, *CEO*
EMP: 29
SALES (est): 2.5MM **Privately Held**
SIC: 2411 Logging
PA: Hoopa Valley Tribal Council
Hwy 96
Hoopa CA 95546
530 625-4211

(P-3992)
HUFFMAN LOGGING CO INC
1155 Huffman Dr, Fortuna (95540-3337)
PHONE..................707 725-4335
Kenneth E Huffman, *President*
Jacqueline J Huffman, *Corp Secy*
James L Huffman, *Vice Pres*
EMP: 45
SALES (est): 2.9MM **Privately Held**
SIC: 2411

(P-3993)
IVERSON & LOGGING INC
41575 Little Lake Rd, Mendocino
(95460-9784)
PHONE..................707 937-0028
Walter R Iverson, *President*
Marlene E Iverson, *Corp Secy*
Donald Iverson, *Bd of Directors*
EMP: 13
SALES (est): 900K **Privately Held**
SIC: 2411 1629 Logging camps & contractors; land preparation construction

(P-3994)
IVES INC
Also Called: Lord's Light Logging
1918 Highland Cir, Eureka (95501-2715)
P.O. Box 1037 (95502-1037)
PHONE..................707 498-0311
David Ives, *President*
EMP: 10
SALES (est): 820K **Privately Held**
SIC: 2411 Logging

(P-3995)
J W BAMFORD INC
Also Called: Bamford Equipment
4288 State Highway 70, Oroville
(95965-8340)
PHONE..................530 533-0732
Joel Bamford, *President*
James W Bamford, *Trustee*
James Bamford, *Vice Pres*
Nathan Bamford, *Admin Sec*
Kelly McDaniels, *Bookkeeper*
EMP: 16
SQ FT: 8,000
SALES (est): 4MM **Privately Held**
WEB: www.bamfordequipment.com
SIC: 2411 Logging

(P-3996)
JAMES A HEADRICK II/ELIZABETH
Also Called: Headrick Logging
7194 Bridge St, Anderson (96007-9496)
PHONE..................530 247-8000
James Headrick, *Owner*
Elizabeth Headrick, *Co-Owner*
EMP: 55
SQ FT: 4,500
SALES (est): 6.3MM **Privately Held**
SIC: 2411 Logging camps & contractors

(P-3997)
JOHN WHEELER LOGGING INC
13570 State Highway 36 E, Red Bluff
(96080-8878)
P.O. Box 339 (96080-0339)
PHONE..................530 527-2993
Dave Holder, *President*
Vern Mc Coshum, *Vice Pres*
EMP: 105 **EST:** 1966
SQ FT: 3,500
SALES (est): 13.6MM **Privately Held**
SIC: 2411 4212 Logging camps & contractors; local trucking, without storage

(P-3998)
LIVING WATERS LOGGING INC
1159 Stromberg Ave, Arcata (95521-5121)
PHONE..................707 822-3955
Kim Vanden Plas, *President*
Saundra Vanden Plas, *Admin Sec*
EMP: 12
SALES (est): 1.1MM **Privately Held**
SIC: 2411 Logging camps & contractors

(P-3999)
M & M LOGGING INC
Also Called: Contract Logging
7800 N Old Stage Rd, Weed (96094-9510)
P.O. Box 429 (96094-0429)
PHONE..................530 938-0745
Timothy E Miller, *Principal*
EMP: 10
SALES (est): 1MM **Privately Held**
SIC: 2411 Logging

(P-4000)
MARK CRAWFORD LOGGING INC
26 Walker Creek Rd, Seiad Valley (96086)
P.O. Box 720 (96086-0720)
PHONE..................530 496-3272
Mark Crawford, *President*
Sherry Crawford, *Admin Sec*
EMP: 10
SALES (est): 3MM **Privately Held**
SIC: 2411 Logging

(P-4001)
MARTIN FISCHER LOGGING INC
1165 Skull Flat Rd, West Point (95255)
P.O. Box 146 (95255-0146)
PHONE..................209 293-4847
Martin M Fischer, *President*
Lillian Fischer, *Admin Sec*
EMP: 11
SALES (est): 1.1MM **Privately Held**
SIC: 2411 Logging camps & contractors

(P-4002)
MATTHEWS SKYLINE LOGGING INC
10100 East Rd, Potter Valley (95469-9773)
P.O. Box 419, Calpella (95418-0419)
PHONE..................707 743-2890
Cecil Matthews, *President*
Betty Matthews, *Admin Sec*
EMP: 32 **EST:** 1977
SQ FT: 20,000
SALES: 3MM **Privately Held**
SIC: 2411 Logging camps & contractors

(P-4003)
MESSER LOGGING INC
32111 Rock Hill Ln, Auberry (93602-9771)
PHONE..................559 855-3160
Timothy Messer, *President*
Tery Messer, *CFO*
Hayley Ferguson, *Corp Secy*
EMP: 20
SALES (est): 3.3MM **Privately Held**
SIC: 2411 Logging camps & contractors

(P-4004)
NORTHWEST SKYLINE LOGGING INC
725 Lower Airport Rd, Happy Camp
(96039)
P.O. Box 144, Round Mountain (96084-0144)
PHONE..................530 493-5150
Tom Forcher, *President*
Anton Forcher, *Corp Secy*
Elena Norman, *Admin Sec*
EMP: 10

SALES (est): 610K **Privately Held**
SIC: 2411 Logging

(P-4005)
PACIFIC TIMBER CONTRACTING
690 Jacobsen Way, Ferndale (95536)
P.O. Box 44 (95536-0044)
PHONE..................707 498-1374
David Walters, *Owner*
EMP: 10
SALES: 950K **Privately Held**
SIC: 2411 Logging

(P-4006)
PHILBRICK INC
Also Called: Philbrick Logging & Trucking
32180 Airport Rd, Fort Bragg (95437-9509)
P.O. Box 1288 (95437-1288)
PHONE..................707 964-2277
Jerry D Philbrick, *President*
EMP: 48
SQ FT: 500
SALES: 4MM **Privately Held**
WEB: www.philbrick.com
SIC: 2411 Logging camps & contractors

(P-4007)
ROACH BROS INC (PA)
23550 Shady Ln, Fort Bragg (95437-8421)
PHONE..................707 964-9240
Leroy Roach, *President*
Sybil Roach, *Treasurer*
Gary Roach, *Vice Pres*
Sally Roach, *Admin Sec*
EMP: 50
SALES (est): 3.6MM **Privately Held**
WEB: www.roachbros.com
SIC: 2411 Logging camps & contractors

(P-4008)
ROUNDS LOGGING COMPANY
4350 Lynbrook Loop Apt 1, Redding
(96003-6853)
PHONE..................530 247-0517
Roger Rounds, *President*
Stacie Rounds, *Admin Sec*
EMP: 45
SQ FT: 1,200
SALES (est): 5.3MM **Privately Held**
SIC: 2411 Logging camps & contractors

(P-4009)
SANDERS PRCSION TIMBER FALLING
9509 N Old Stage Rd, Weed (96094-9516)
PHONE..................530 938-4120
Ross Sanders, *Owner*
Bernard Cilione, *Treasurer*
Forest Sanders, *Vice Pres*
Tom Midget, *Admin Sec*
EMP: 30
SALES (est): 1.4MM **Privately Held**
SIC: 2411 Logging

(P-4010)
SHASTA GREEN INC
Also Called: Franklin Logging
35586a State Hwy 299 E, Burney
(96013-4048)
PHONE..................530 335-4924
Diane Franklin, *President*
Keith Tiner, *Vice Pres*
EMP: 50
SQ FT: 1,500
SALES (est): 7.3MM **Privately Held**
WEB: www.shastagreen.com
SIC: 2411 Logging

(P-4011)
SHUSTERS LOGGING INC
750 E Valley St, Willits (95490-9749)
PHONE..................707 459-4131
Steve Shuster, *President*
Marv Lawrence, *Corp Secy*
Phillip L Shuster, *Vice Pres*
EMP: 75
SQ FT: 2,300
SALES (est): 6.1MM **Privately Held**
SIC: 2411 Logging

(P-4012)
SIERRA RESOURCE MANAGEMENT INC
12015 La Grange Rd, Jamestown
(95327-9724)
PHONE..................209 984-1146
Mike Albrecht, *President*
Stacy Dodge, *Vice Pres*
EMP: 25
SQ FT: 4,500
SALES (est): 2.7MM **Privately Held**
WEB: www.sierraresource.org
SIC: 2411 Logging

(P-4013)
SILLER BROTHERS INC (PA)
Also Called: Siller Aviation
1250 Smith Rd, Yuba City (95991-6948)
P.O. Box 1585 (95992-1585)
PHONE..................530 673-0734
Tom Siller, *President*
Hunt Norris, *CFO*
Jack Parnell, *Chairman*
Andrew Jansen, *Vice Pres*
Andy Jansen, *Vice Pres*
EMP: 55
SALES (est): 9.5MM **Privately Held**
SIC: 2411 2421 Logging camps & contractors; sawmills & planing mills, general

(P-4014)
SOPER-WHEELER COMPANY LLC (PA)
19855 Barton Hill Rd, Strawberry Valley
(95981-9700)
PHONE..................530 675-2343
David Westcott, *CEO*
Daniel Krueger, *President*
Paul Violet, *Vice Pres*
Paul Violett, *Vice Pres*
Daniel Kruger, *Info Tech Dir*
EMP: 30
SQ FT: 30,000
SALES: 10MM **Privately Held**
SIC: 2411 Logging camps & contractors

(P-4015)
STEVE MORRIS
Also Called: Steve Morris Logging & Contg
1500 Glendale Dr, McKinleyville
(95519-9208)
PHONE..................707 822-8537
Steve Morris, *Owner*
EMP: 10
SALES: 3MM **Privately Held**
SIC: 2411 Logging camps & contractors

(P-4016)
TS LOGGING
18121 Rays Rd, Philo (95466)
P.O. Box 31 (95466-0031)
PHONE..................707 895-3751
Timothy Slotte, *Owner*
EMP: 11
SALES (est): 1.4MM **Privately Held**
SIC: 2411 Logging camps & contractors

(P-4017)
TUBIT ENTERPRISES INC
21640 S Vallejo St, Burney (96013-9778)
P.O. Box 1019 (96013-1019)
PHONE..................530 335-5085
Douglas Lindgren, *CEO*
Richard Lindgren, *President*
EMP: 40
SQ FT: 3,000
SALES: 1MM **Privately Held**
SIC: 2411 Logging

(P-4018)
US DOOR AND FENCE LLC
3880 Garner Rd, Riverside (92501-1066)
PHONE..................951 300-0010
Gang Wu, *Mng Member*
Nick Anis, *Vice Pres*
Aizhen Chen, *Mng Member*
Chunjie Sun, *Mng Member*
Yicheng Sun, *Mng Member*
▲ **EMP:** 15
SQ FT: 30,000

PRODUCTS & SVCS

SALES (est): 1.7MM
SALES (corp-wide): 14.1MM **Privately Held**
SIC: 2411 3089 3315 3442 Rails, fence: round or split; fences, gates & accessories: plastic; fence gates posts & fittings: steel; screen & storm doors & windows; screen doors, metal; storm doors or windows, metal; metal doors; fences, gates, posts & flagpoles; metal doors, sash & trim
PA: Ningbo Win Success Machinery Co.,Ltd
No. 228 Jinchuan Road , Zhenhai Economic Development Zone.
Ningbo 31520
574 863-0767

(P-4019)
WARNER ENTERPRISES INC
1577 Beltline Rd, Redding (96003-1407)
PHONE..................530 241-4000
Paul Warner, *President*
Gary Warner, *Vice Pres*
EMP: 30
SQ FT: 9,000
SALES (est): 3.8MM **Privately Held**
WEB: www.wagner-webworks.com
SIC: 2411 Wood chips, produced in the field; logging camps & contractors

(P-4020)
WASHBURN GROVE MANAGEMENT INC
27781 Fairview Ave, Hemet (92544-8521)
PHONE..................909 322-4690
Dennis Washburn, *President*
David Washburn, *Vice Pres*
EMP: 25
SALES (est): 2.7MM **Privately Held**
SIC: 2411 0783 Logging; ornamental shrub & tree services

(P-4021)
WELL ANALYSIS CORPORATION INC (PA)
Also Called: Welaco
5500 Woodmere Dr, Bakersfield (93313-2776)
P.O. Box 20008 (93390-0008)
PHONE..................661 283-9510
Judy L Bebout, *CEO*
Dan Bebout, *Treasurer*
Brenda Muniozguren, *Vice Pres*
Robert Muniozguren, *Admin Sec*
Chuck O'Brien, *Safety Mgr*
▲ **EMP:** 28
SQ FT: 1,400
SALES (est): 4.4MM **Privately Held**
WEB: www.welaco.com
SIC: 2411 1389 Logging; oil field services

(P-4022)
WEST COAST TIMBER CORP
6221 Apache Rd, Westminster (92683-1919)
PHONE..................714 893-4374
Bette Herkins, *President*
Robert Herkins, *Vice Pres*
EMP: 15
SALES (est): 700K **Privately Held**
SIC: 2411

(P-4023)
WHEELER LUMBER CO INC
Also Called: Jim Wheeler Logging
2407 Cathy Rd, Miranda (95553)
P.O. Box 294 (95553-0294)
PHONE..................707 943-3424
Jimmie Wheeler, *President*
H D Wheeler, *Vice Pres*
EMP: 10 **EST:** 1969
SALES (est): 815.9K **Privately Held**
SIC: 2411 5211 Logging camps & contractors; planing mill products & lumber

(P-4024)
WILLIAM R SCHMITT
Also Called: Schmitt Superior Classics
18135 Clear Creek Rd, Redding (96001-5233)
PHONE..................530 243-3069
William R Schmitt, *Owner*
Sylvia Schmitt, *Co-Owner*
EMP: 20

SALES (est): 1.6MM **Privately Held**
SIC: 2411 4212 5521 Logging; lumber (log) trucking, local; automobiles, used cars only; antique automobiles

(P-4025)
WIRTA LOGGING INC
970 Kandy Ln, Portola (96122-9631)
PHONE..................928 440-3446
Mike Wirta, *President*
EMP: 20
SALES (est): 1.1MM **Privately Held**
SIC: 2411 Logging camps & contractors

(P-4026)
WITTEN LOGGING
4600 Kelso Creek Rd, Weldon (93283-9687)
PHONE..................760 378-3640
Jess Witten, *Owner*
EMP: 10
SALES (est): 718.7K **Privately Held**
SIC: 2411 Logging camps & contractors

(P-4027)
WYLATTI RESOURCE MGT INC
23601 Cemetery Ln, Covelo (95428-9773)
P.O. Box 575 (95428-0575)
PHONE..................707 983-8135
Brian K Hurt, *President*
EMP: 20
SALES (est): 3MM **Privately Held**
SIC: 2411 1611 1622 1442 Logging; general contractor, highway & street construction; bridge construction; construction sand & gravel; dump truck haulage; heavy machinery transport, local

2421 Saw & Planing Mills

(P-4028)
AMERICAN WOOD FIBERS INC
4560 Skyway Dr, Marysville (95901)
P.O. Box 788 (95901-0021)
PHONE..................530 741-3700
Mark Medearis, *Manager*
EMP: 12 **Privately Held**
WEB: www.awf.com
SIC: 2421 Sawdust & shavings
PA: American Wood Fibers, Inc.
9841 Broken Land Pkwy # 302
Columbia MD 21046

(P-4029)
ARTESIA SAWDUST PRODUCTS INC
13434 S Ontario Ave, Ontario (91761-7956)
PHONE..................909 947-5983
Brigitte De Laura-Espinoza, *President*
Anthony Espinoza, *Vice Pres*
John Carmona, *Accountant*
EMP: 35
SQ FT: 2,700
SALES (est): 5.8MM **Privately Held**
WEB: www.artesiasawdust.com
SIC: 2421 Sawdust & shavings; wood chips, produced at mill

(P-4030)
AUTUMN MILLING CO INC
20930 S Alameda St, Long Beach (90810-1111)
PHONE..................310 635-0703
Charles E Jordan, *President*
Janet Jordan, *Treasurer*
Craig Jordan, *Vice Pres*
EMP: 20
SALES (est): 2.3MM
SALES (corp-wide): 2.4MM **Privately Held**
SIC: 2421 Sawmills & planing mills, general
PA: C E Jordan Hardwood Co Inc
20930 S Alameda St
Long Beach CA 90810
310 635-0703

(P-4031)
B P JOHN RECYCLE INC
Also Called: B P John Hauling
38875 Avenida La Cresta, Murrieta (92563-9155)
PHONE..................951 696-1144
Edward F Metzler, *President*
Lynda Metzler, *Admin Sec*
EMP: 20
SALES: 5MM **Privately Held**
SIC: 2421 4212 Fuelwood, from mill waste; light haulage & cartage, local

(P-4032)
BLASTED WOOD PRODUCTS INC
Also Called: Insignia
7108 Santa Rita Cir, Buena Park (90620-3189)
PHONE..................714 237-1600
Joseph L Westbrook, *CEO*
Joseph Westbrook, *President*
EMP: 10
SALES (est): 1.9MM **Privately Held**
SIC: 2421 Lumber: rough, sawed or planed

(P-4033)
CHAPMAN DESIGNS INC
8333 Secura Way, Santa Fe Springs (90670-2213)
P.O. Box 2155, Whittier (90610-2155)
PHONE..................562 698-4600
Michael Chapman, *President*
John Chapman, *Vice Pres*
EMP: 25
SQ FT: 16,000
SALES (est): 3.5MM **Privately Held**
WEB: www.chapmandesignsinc.com
SIC: 2421 Specialty sawmill products

(P-4034)
COLLINS PINE COMPANY
500 Main St, Chester (96020)
P.O. Box 796 (96020-0796)
PHONE..................530 258-2111
Chris Verderber, *Branch Mgr*
Steve Ackley, *Manager*
EMP: 262
SALES (corp-wide): 139MM **Privately Held**
WEB: www.collinswood.com
SIC: 2421 Sawmills & planing mills, general
PA: Collins Pine Company
29190 Sw Town Center Loop
Wilsonville OR 97070
503 227-1219

(P-4035)
CROSSROADS RECYCLED LUMBER LLC
58500 Hancock Way, North Fork (93643)
P.O. Box 928 (93643-0928)
PHONE..................559 877-3645
Toll Free:..................888 -
Marc Mandell, *Mng Member*
EMP: 10
SQ FT: 30,000
SALES (est): 627K **Privately Held**
WEB: www.crossroadslumber.com
SIC: 2421 5932 Lumber: rough, sawed or planed; building materials, secondhand

(P-4036)
D LAURENCE GATES LTD
2671 Crow Canyon Rd, San Ramon (94583-1519)
PHONE..................925 736-8176
David Gates, *CEO*
Vanessa Lindores, *Associate*
EMP: 25
SQ FT: 3,500
SALES (est): 812.9K **Privately Held**
SIC: 2421 3272 5031 Building & structural materials, wood; building materials, except block or brick: concrete; concrete stuctural support & building material; building materials, interior; building materials, exterior

(P-4037)
HAGLE LUMBER COMPANY INC
3100 Somis Rd, Somis (93066-9549)
P.O. Box 120 (93066-0120)
PHONE..................805 987-3887

Ralph Hagle, *CEO*
Rick Hagle, *President*
Joe Ferreira, *Vice Pres*
Benjamin G Hagle, *Opers Mgr*
John Hagle, *Sales Staff*
EMP: 30
SQ FT: 3,000
SALES (est): 10.2MM **Privately Held**
WEB: www.haglelumber.com
SIC: 2421 Sawmills & planing mills, general

(P-4038)
HAMAR WOOD PARQUET COMPANY
Also Called: Royal Custom Parquet
9303 Greenleaf Ave, Santa Fe Springs (90670-3029)
PHONE..................562 944-8885
Jeffrey Hamar, *President*
EMP: 20
SALES (est): 1.4MM **Privately Held**
SIC: 2421 Flooring (dressed lumber), softwood

(P-4039)
HMR BUILDING SYSTEMS LLC
620 Newport Center Dr # 12, Newport Beach (92660-6420)
PHONE..................951 749-4700
Ronald Simon,
RSI Holding LLC,
▲ **EMP:** 15
SQ FT: 90,000
SALES (est): 2.7MM **Privately Held**
SIC: 2421 Building & structural materials, wood
PA: Rsi Holding Llc
620 Nwport Ctr Dr Fl 12 Flr 12
Newport Beach CA 92660

(P-4040)
I & E LATH MILL INC
8701 School Rd, Philo (95466)
P.O. Box 9 (95466-0009)
PHONE..................707 895-3380
Rodney Island, *President*
Virginia Island, *Corp Secy*
EMP: 35
SQ FT: 40,000
SALES (est): 5.3MM **Privately Held**
SIC: 2421 2411 Lumber: rough, sawed or planed; snow fence lath; logging

(P-4041)
JACK MCMAHON LANDSCAPE
Also Called: Jack McMahon Landscaping Svcs
21 Miriam Dr, Calistoga (94515-1335)
PHONE..................707 942-1122
Jack McMahon, *Owner*
EMP: 10
SALES (est): 550K **Privately Held**
SIC: 2421 0781 Flooring (dressed lumber), softwood; landscape services

(P-4042)
LINDGREN LUMBER CO
3851 W End Ct, Arcata (95521)
PHONE..................707 822-6519
Joe Lindgren, *Owner*
EMP: 10
SQ FT: 8,400
SALES (est): 824.2K **Privately Held**
WEB: www.lindgrenlumber.com
SIC: 2421 Lath, made in sawmills & lath-mills

(P-4043)
NORTH CAL WOOD PRODUCTS INC
700 Kunzler Ranch Rd, Ukiah (95482-3264)
P.O. Box 1534 (95482-1534)
PHONE..................707 462-0686
Frank Van Vranken, *President*
Tony Fernandez, *Vice Pres*
Charles Currey, *Admin Sec*
EMP: 50
SQ FT: 8,000
SALES: 4MM **Privately Held**
SIC: 2421 2431 2435 Lumber: rough, sawed or planed; lath, made in sawmills & lathmills; panel work, wood; hardwood veneer & plywood

(P-4044)
PEW FOREST PRODUCTS INC
Also Called: Pew Forestry
390 Arlington Rd, Crescent Mills
(95934-9709)
PHONE..................530 284-7882
Randy A Pew, *President*
EMP: 25
SALES (est): 3.2MM **Privately Held**
SIC: 2421 Sawmills & planing mills, general

(P-4045)
PLUM CREEK TIMBERLANDS LP
615 N Benson Ave, Upland (91786-5076)
PHONE..................909 949-2255
EMP: 117
SALES (corp-wide): 7.2B **Publicly Held**
SIC: 2421
HQ: Plum Creek Timberlands, L.P.
601 Union St Ste 3100
Seattle WA 98101
206 467-3600

(P-4046)
PLUM VALLEY INC
Also Called: Pacific Wood Milling Reload
3308 Cyclone Ct Cttonwood Cottonwood,
Cottonwood (96022)
P.O. Box 1485 (96022-1485)
PHONE..................530 262-6262
Donald E Frank, *CEO*
Jackie Tonner, *Manager*
Mary Victor, *Manager*
EMP: 20
SQ FT: 5,000
SALES (est): 254.8K **Privately Held**
WEB: www.plumvalley.com
SIC: 2421 Lumber: rough, sawed or planed

(P-4047)
PREFERRED MILLING INC
3151 Airway Ave Ste A1, Costa Mesa
(92626-4620)
PHONE..................714 754-4230
James Ferreira, *President*
James Ferreira, *President*
Celia Ferriera, *Treasurer*
EMP: 30
SQ FT: 51,000
SALES (est): 4.2MM **Privately Held**
SIC: 2421 2426 Sawmills & planing mills,
general; hardwood dimension & flooring
mills

(P-4048)
RAFAEL SANDOVAL
Also Called: Lathrop Woodworks
16175 Mckinley Ave, Lathrop (95330-9703)
PHONE..................209 858-4173
Rafael Sandoval, *Owner*
Richard Sandoval, *Manager*
▲ EMP: 45
SQ FT: 1,000
SALES (est): 5.5MM **Privately Held**
WEB: www.dmv.ca.gov
SIC: 2421 Outdoor wood structural products; specialty sawmill products

(P-4049)
REGAL CUSTOM MILLWORK INC
301 E Santa Ana St, Anaheim
(92805-3954)
P.O. Box 879 (92815-0879)
PHONE..................714 632-2488
Shirley Reel, *President*
Don Reel, *Shareholder*
Gilbert Reel, *CFO*
EMP: 17
SALES: 2.6MM **Privately Held**
SIC: 2421 5211 Custom sawmill; millwork
& lumber

(P-4050)
REUSER INC
370 Santana Dr, Cloverdale (95425-4224)
PHONE..................707 894-4224
Bruce Reuser, *President*
John Reuser, *Vice Pres*
EMP: 15
SQ FT: 5,000

SALES (est): 3.1MM **Privately Held**
WEB: www.reuserinc.com
SIC: 2421 2875 Sawdust & shavings;
wood chips, produced at mill; fertilizers,
mixing only

(P-4051)
SAMSGAZEBOSCOM INC
Also Called: Sams Crftsman Style Pfab
Gzbos
132 E 163rd St, Gardena (90248-2804)
PHONE..................310 523-3778
Sam Goeku, *President*
EMP: 10
SQ FT: 12,320
SALES (est): 1.6MM **Privately Held**
WEB: www.samsgazebos.com
SIC: 2421 5211 Outdoor wood structural
products; lumber products

(P-4052)
SCHMIDBAUER LUMBER INC (PA)
Also Called: Pacific Clears
1099 W Waterfront Dr, Eureka
(95501-0170)
P.O. Box 152 (95502-0152)
PHONE..................707 443-7024
Frank Schmidbauer, *Principal*
Duane Martin, *Treasurer*
Mary Schmidbauer, *Vice Pres*
▲ EMP: 210
SQ FT: 200,000
SALES (est): 47.6MM **Privately Held**
SIC: 2421 5211 Sawmills & planing mills,
general; lumber & other building materials

(P-4053)
SCHMIDBAUER LUMBER INC
Pacific Clears
1017 Samoa Blvd, Arcata (95521-6605)
P.O. Box 1141 (95518-1141)
PHONE..................707 822-7607
Lee Iorg, *Sales/Mktg Mgr*
Lee Liorg, *Plant Mgr*
EMP: 30
SQ FT: 3,000
SALES (corp-wide): 47.6MM **Privately Held**
SIC: 2421 5211 Resawing lumber into
smaller dimensions; planing mill products
& lumber
PA: Schmidbauer Lumber, Inc.
1099 W Waterfront Dr
Eureka CA 95501
707 443-7024

(P-4054)
SELL LUMBER CORPORATION
7887 Eastside Rd, Redding (96001-8307)
P.O. Box 990788 (96099-0788)
PHONE..................530 241-2085
Robert H Sell Sr, *CEO*
Verleen Rath, *Vice Pres*
EMP: 12
SQ FT: 2,000
SALES (est): 2.2MM **Privately Held**
WEB: www.selllumber.com
SIC: 2421 Sawmills & planing mills, general

(P-4055)
SETZER FOREST PRODUCTS INC
Also Called: Millwork Div
1980 Kusel Rd, Oroville (95966-9528)
PHONE..................530 534-8100
Terry Dunn, *Manager*
Brian Hoyle, *Purch Dir*
EMP: 115
SALES (corp-wide): 45.9MM **Privately Held**
WEB: www.setzerforest.com
SIC: 2421 2431 Cut stock, softwood; millwork
PA: Forest Setzer Products Inc
2555 3rd St Ste 200
Sacramento CA 95818
916 442-2555

(P-4056)
SIERRA PACIFIC INDUSTRIES
2771 Bechelli Ln, Redding (96002-1924)
PHONE..................530 226-5181
EMP: 13

SALES (corp-wide): 1.2B **Privately Held**
SIC: 2421 Lumber: rough, sawed or planed
PA: Sierra Pacific Industries
19794 Riverside Ave
Anderson CA 96007
530 378-8000

(P-4057)
SIERRA PACIFIC INDUSTRIES (PA)
19794 Riverside Ave, Anderson
(96007-4908)
P.O. Box 496028, Redding (96049-6028)
PHONE..................530 378-8000
George Emmerson, *President*
Mark Emmerson, *Chairman*
Kendall Pierson, *Vice Pres*
Aaron Sulzer, *Vice Pres*
Dominic Truniger, *Vice Pres*
◆ EMP: 100
SQ FT: 37,000
SALES (est): 1.2B **Privately Held**
WEB: www.sierrapacificind.com
SIC: 2421 2431 Lumber: rough, sawed or
planed; millwork; windows, wood

(P-4058)
SIERRA PACIFIC INDUSTRIES
36336 Highway 299 E, Burney (96013)
PHONE..................530 378-8301
Ed Fischer, *Branch Mgr*
EMP: 13
SALES (corp-wide): 1.2B **Privately Held**
SIC: 2421 Sawmills & planing mills, general
PA: Sierra Pacific Industries
19794 Riverside Ave
Anderson CA 96007
530 378-8000

(P-4059)
SIERRA PACIFIC INDUSTRIES
3025 S 5th Ave, Oroville (95965-5855)
P.O. Box 2198 (95965-2198)
PHONE..................530 532-6630
Scott Meek, *Branch Mgr*
Mike Vinum, *Plant Mgr*
EMP: 161
SALES (corp-wide): 1.2B **Privately Held**
WEB: www.sierrapacificind.com
SIC: 2421 2431 Lumber: rough, sawed or
planed; millwork; windows, wood
PA: Sierra Pacific Industries
19794 Riverside Ave
Anderson CA 96007
530 378-8000

(P-4060)
SIERRA PACIFIC INDUSTRIES
Hwy 299 E, Burney (96013)
P.O. Box 2677 (96013-2677)
PHONE..................530 335-3681
Ed Fisher, *Branch Mgr*
Chris Skinner, *Plant Mgr*
EMP: 150
SQ FT: 1,000
SALES (corp-wide): 1.2B **Privately Held**
WEB: www.sierrapacificind.com
SIC: 2421 Lumber: rough, sawed or planed
PA: Sierra Pacific Industries
19794 Riverside Ave
Anderson CA 96007
530 378-8000

(P-4061)
SIERRA PACIFIC INDUSTRIES
3735 El Cajon Ave, Shasta Lake
(96019-9211)
PHONE..................530 275-8851
Darrell Dearman, *Branch Mgr*
John Phillips, *Plant Mgr*
EMP: 120
SALES (corp-wide): 1.2B **Privately Held**
WEB: www.sierrapacificind.com
SIC: 2421 2426 Lumber: rough, sawed or
planed; hardwood dimension & flooring
mills
PA: Sierra Pacific Industries
19794 Riverside Ave
Anderson CA 96007
530 378-8000

(P-4062)
SIERRA PACIFIC INDUSTRIES
19758 Riverside Ave, Anderson
(96007-4908)
P.O. Box 10939 (96007-1939)
PHONE..................530 365-3721
Shane Young, *Division Mgr*
Erin Swezey, *Programmer Anys*
Larry Ostman, *Engineer*
EMP: 420
SALES (corp-wide): 1.2B **Privately Held**
WEB: www.sierrapacificind.com
SIC: 2421 Lumber: rough, sawed or planed
PA: Sierra Pacific Industries
19794 Riverside Ave
Anderson CA 96007
530 378-8000

(P-4063)
SIERRA PACIFIC INDUSTRIES
3950 Carson Rd, Camino (95709-9347)
P.O. Box 680 (95709-0680)
PHONE..................530 644-2311
Brian Coyle, *Branch Mgr*
EMP: 300
SALES (corp-wide): 1.2B **Privately Held**
WEB: www.sierrapacificind.com
SIC: 2421 Lumber: rough, sawed or planed
PA: Sierra Pacific Industries
19794 Riverside Ave
Anderson CA 96007
530 378-8000

(P-4064)
SIERRA PACIFIC INDUSTRIES
1440 Lincoln Blvd, Lincoln (95648-9105)
PHONE..................916 645-1631
Dan Quarton, *Branch Mgr*
Rick Sage, *Maint Spvr*
Alan Gulko, *Manager*
EMP: 300
SALES (corp-wide): 1.2B **Privately Held**
WEB: www.sierrapacificind.com
SIC: 2421 Lumber: rough, sawed or planed
PA: Sierra Pacific Industries
19794 Riverside Ave
Anderson CA 96007
530 378-8000

(P-4065)
SIERRA PACIFIC INDUSTRIES
Window Division
11605 Reading Rd, Red Bluff (96080-6702)
P.O. Box 8489 (96080-8489)
PHONE..................530 527-9620
Bob Taylor, *Manager*
Jan Stephens, *Research*
Kevin Butcher, *Production*
EMP: 500
SALES (corp-wide): 1.2B **Privately Held**
WEB: www.sierrapacificind.com
SIC: 2421 Sawmills & planing mills, general
PA: Sierra Pacific Industries
19794 Riverside Ave
Anderson CA 96007
530 378-8000

(P-4066)
SIMPSON TIMBER COMPANY
1165 Maple Creek Rd, Korbel
(95550-9613)
P.O. Box 68 (95550-0068)
PHONE..................707 668-4566
Garry Anderson, *President*
Gary Anderson, *President*
EMP: 12
SALES (est): 1.5MM **Privately Held**
WEB: www.simpsoncalifornia.com
SIC: 2421

(P-4067)
STRATA FOREST PRODUCTS INC (PA)
Also Called: Profile Planing Mill
2600 S Susan St, Santa Ana (92704-5816)
PHONE..................714 751-0800
Richard W Hormuth, *President*
John Hormuth, *President*
Jenna Hormuth, *Marketing Staff*
Michelle Grohnke, *Sales Staff*
▲ EMP: 50
SQ FT: 38,000
SALES (est): 8.1MM **Privately Held**
WEB: www.strataforest.com
SIC: 2421 Planing mills

PRODUCTS & SVCS

(P-4068)
SUNSET MOULDING CO (PA)
2231 Paseo Rd, Live Oak (95953-9721)
P.O. Box 326, Yuba City (95992-0326)
PHONE.............................530 790-2700
John A Morrison, *CEO*
Wendy Forren, *CFO*
Michel Morrison, *Vice Pres*
Mark Westlake, *Vice Pres*
▲ EMP: 50
SALES (est): 24.3MM Privately Held
WEB: www.sunsetmoulding.com
SIC: 2421 2431 Cut stock, softwood;
moldings, wood: unfinished & prefinished

(P-4069)
TRINITY RIVER LUMBER COMPANY (PA)
1375 Main St, Weaverville (96093)
P.O. Box 249 (96093-0249)
PHONE.............................530 623-5561
Frank A Schmidbauer, *CEO*
Dee Sanders, *Vice Pres*
▲ EMP: 150
SQ FT: 10,000
SALES (est): 26.1MM Privately Held
SIC: 2421 Lumber: rough, sawed or planed

(P-4070)
WEYERHAEUSER COMPANY
2700 S California St, Stockton
(95206-3223)
PHONE.............................209 942-1825
John Copenhever, *Manager*
EMP: 12
SALES (corp-wide): 7.2B Publicly Held
SIC: 2421 Lumber: rough, sawed or planed
PA: Weyerhaeuser Company
220 Occidental Ave S
Seattle WA 98104
206 539-3000

(P-4071)
WILLITS REDWOOD COMPANY INC
220 Franklin Ave, Willits (95490-4132)
PHONE.............................707 459-4549
Bruce Burton, *President*
Chris Baldo, *Vice Pres*
EMP: 24 EST: 1975
SQ FT: 500
SALES (est): 3.7MM Privately Held
WEB: www.willitsredwood.com
SIC: 2421 Custom sawmill

2426 Hardwood Dimension & Flooring Mills

(P-4072)
AGED TIMBER CO INC
12432 Foothill Blvd, Sylmar (91342-6004)
PHONE.............................818 897-9663
Timothy Sheldon, *General Mgr*
Chantel Piper, *Bookkeeper*
Jim Scott, *Opers Mgr*
EMP: 50
SALES (est): 5.3MM Privately Held
SIC: 2426 Hardwood dimension & flooring mills

(P-4073)
B&M NOBLE CO (PA)
Also Called: Duchateau Floors
8480 Miralani Dr, San Diego (92126-4349)
PHONE.............................619 793-5899
Benjamin Buzali, *CEO*
Scott Campbell, *CFO*
John Sandoval, *Office Mgr*
▲ EMP: 45 EST: 2006
SALES (est): 12.8MM Privately Held
SIC: 2426 Flooring, hardwood

(P-4074)
BAXSTRA INC
Also Called: Martin Erattrud Co
1224 W 132nd St, Gardena (90247-1506)
PHONE.............................323 770-4171
Patrick Baxter, *Vice Pres*
Allan Stratford, *Owner*
EMP: 100

SALES (est): 6MM Privately Held
WEB: www.martinbrattrud.com
SIC: 2426 Frames for upholstered furniture, wood

(P-4075)
BECKER WOODWORKING
847 E 108th St, Los Angeles (90059-1005)
PHONE.............................323 564-2441
Boyd Becker, *Owner*
EMP: 12
SQ FT: 11,500
SALES: 550K Privately Held
SIC: 2426 2499 Hardwood dimension & flooring mills; decorative wood & woodwork

(P-4076)
CALIFORNIA PRO-SPECS INC
Also Called: Production Specialties
2240 15th Ave, Sacramento (95822-1504)
PHONE.............................916 455-9890
Stephen J Luther, *President*
Nancy Luther, *Vice Pres*
EMP: 25
SQ FT: 31,000
SALES (est): 2.5MM Privately Held
SIC: 2426 2511 2435 2434 Furniture dimension stock, hardwood; novelty furniture: wood; hardwood veneer & plywood; wood kitchen cabinets

(P-4077)
DELTA COMMERCE CORPORATION
Also Called: Delta Floors
1363 S State College Blvd, Anaheim (92806-5728)
PHONE.............................714 758-0030
Natalie Sunghee Kwon, *President*
Joseph Kwon, *Vice Pres*
▲ EMP: 12
SQ FT: 10,000
SALES (est): 2.2MM Privately Held
WEB: www.jamminlink.com
SIC: 2426 5731 5713 Flooring, hardwood; radio, television & electronic stores; floor covering stores

(P-4078)
DESERT SHUTTERS INC
33907 Robles Dr, Dana Point (92629-2268)
PHONE.............................949 388-8344
Tom Schuster, *President*
EMP: 20
SQ FT: 3,500
SALES (est): 2.4MM Privately Held
WEB: www.desertshutters.com
SIC: 2426 2431 Shuttle blocks, hardwood; millwork

(P-4079)
EXCAVO LLC
13428 Maxella Ave Ste 409, Marina Del Rey (90292-5620)
PHONE.............................310 823-7670
Tristan Klobas,
EMP: 15
SQ FT: 2,250
SALES (est): 1.4MM Privately Held
WEB: www.excavofurniture.com
SIC: 2426

(P-4080)
FURNITURE TECHNOLOGIES INC
17227 Columbus St, Adelanto (92301)
P.O. Box 1076 (92301-1076)
PHONE.............................760 246-9180
Kenneth Drum, *CEO*
Peggy Ball, *Manager*
EMP: 24
SQ FT: 31,000
SALES (est): 4.6MM Privately Held
SIC: 2426 Furniture stock & parts, hardwood

(P-4081)
HALLMARK FLOORS INC (PA)
2360 S Archibald Ave, Ontario (91761-8520)
PHONE.............................909 947-7736
Zheng Qing Pan, *President*
Sylvia Bulanek, *Marketing Mgr*
▲ EMP: 28

SALES (est): 3.5MM Privately Held
SIC: 2426 Flooring, hardwood

(P-4082)
HV INDUSTRIES INC
13688 Newhope St, Garden Grove (92843-3712)
PHONE.............................651 233-5676
Vu Ho, *Manager*
John Ho, *Manager*
EMP: 10
SALES (est): 518.4K Privately Held
SIC: 2426 3569 3069 3542 Textile machinery accessories, hardwood; lubrication machinery, automatic; reclaimed rubber (reworked by manufacturing processes); presses: hydraulic & pneumatic, mechanical & manual

(P-4083)
LA HARDWOOD FLOORING INC (PA)
Also Called: Eternity Flooring
9880 San Fernando Rd, Pacoima (91331-2603)
PHONE.............................818 361-0099
Doron Gal, *President*
Eliyahu Shuat, *Principal*
▲ EMP: 17
SQ FT: 12,000
SALES (est): 5.1MM Privately Held
SIC: 2426 5211 Flooring, hardwood; flooring, wood

(P-4084)
MCMURTRIE & MCMURTRIE INC
Also Called: Tru-Wood Products
915 W 5th St, Azusa (91702-3311)
P.O. Box 1940, Monrovia (91017-5940)
PHONE.............................626 815-0177
Richard McMurtrie, *CEO*
Bill Cherry, *Corp Secy*
▲ EMP: 70
SQ FT: 97,000
SALES (est): 8.4MM Privately Held
SIC: 2426 2431 5031 Frames for upholstered furniture, wood; trim, wood; lumber, plywood & millwork

(P-4085)
MONTCLAIR WOOD CORPORATION
545 N Mountain Ave # 104, Upland (91786-5054)
PHONE.............................909 985-0302
John Slavek Grey, *President*
Louis Jimenez, *Vice Pres*
Melissa Lee, *Director*
EMP: 106
SQ FT: 70,000
SALES (est): 16.7MM Privately Held
SIC: 2426 5031 Furniture stock & parts, hardwood; lumber: rough, dressed & finished

(P-4086)
N M FLOOR COVERINGS INC
Also Called: Pacific Coast Coml Interiors
5651 Palmer Way Ste D, Carlsbad (92010-7244)
P.O. Box 6017, Oceanside (92052-6017)
PHONE.............................760 931-8274
Nathan Mallory, *President*
Krista A Mallory, *CEO*
EMP: 15
SALES (est): 3.8MM Privately Held
SIC: 2426 2599 Hardwood dimension & flooring mills; factory furniture & fixtures

(P-4087)
O INDUSTRIES CORPORATION
1930 W 139th St, Gardena (90249-2408)
P.O. Box 779, Dana Point (92629-0779)
PHONE.............................310 719-2289
Rhonda Oerding, *CEO*
William Oerding, *COO*
▼ EMP: 15
SALES: 3MM Privately Held
SIC: 2426 Flooring, hardwood

(P-4088)
PARQUET BY DIAN INC
16601 S Main St, Gardena (90248-2722)
PHONE.............................310 527-3779
Anatoli Efros, *CEO*
Dima Efros, *President*

EMP: 92
SALES (est): 12MM Privately Held
WEB: www.parquet.com
SIC: 2426 Parquet flooring, hardwood

(P-4089)
QEP CO INC
Also Called: Qep
4200 Santa Ana St, Ontario (91761-1539)
PHONE.............................909 622-3537
Marco Garcia, *Branch Mgr*
EMP: 15
SALES (corp-wide): 309.2MM Publicly Held
SIC: 2426 5023 Hardwood dimension & flooring mills; floor coverings
PA: Q.E.P. Co., Inc.
1001 Brkn Snd Pkwy Nw A
Boca Raton FL 33487
561 994-5550

(P-4090)
RONALD D TESON INC
Also Called: California Frames
13945 Mckinley Ave, Los Angeles (90059-3501)
P.O. Box 869, Sunset Beach (90742-0869)
PHONE.............................310 532-5987
Ronald D Teson, *President*
EMP: 34
SQ FT: 18,000
SALES (est): 2.6MM Privately Held
WEB: www.californiaframes.com
SIC: 2426 Frames for upholstered furniture, wood

(P-4091)
RTMEX INC
Also Called: Best Redwood
1202 Piper Ranch Rd, San Diego (92154-7714)
P.O. Box 8662, Chula Vista (91912-8662)
PHONE.............................619 391-9913
Jorje Sampietro, *President*
Charlie Burgas, *Sales Mgr*
EMP: 108
SQ FT: 15,000
SALES: 50K Privately Held
SIC: 2426 Carvings, furniture: wood

2429 Special Prdt Sawmills, NEC

(P-4092)
CHARLOIS COOPERAGE USA
1285 S Foothill Blvd, Cloverdale (95425-3254)
PHONE.............................707 224-2377
Sylvain Charlois, *CEO*
▲ EMP: 14
SALES (est): 2.3MM Privately Held
SIC: 2429 Heading, barrel (cooperage stock): sawed or split

(P-4093)
TONELERIA NACIONAL USA INC
Also Called: Tncoopers
21481 8th St E Ste 20c, Sonoma (95476-9292)
P.O. Box 1815 (95476-1815)
PHONE.............................707 501-8728
Alejandro Fantoni, *CEO*
Ron Goss, *General Mgr*
Alexander Schnaidt, *General Mgr*
Eric Hansen, *Prdtn Mgr*
EMP: 17
SALES (est): 1.8MM Privately Held
SIC: 2429 Barrels & barrel parts

2431 Millwork

(P-4094)
A & R DOORS INC
Also Called: A & R Pre-Hung Door
41 5th St Frnt, Hollister (95023-3975)
PHONE.............................831 637-8139
Ruben L Rodriguez, *President*
Albert Rodriguez, *Vice Pres*
EMP: 14
SQ FT: 8,000

▲ = Import ▼=Export
◆ =Import/Export

SALES: 2.2MM **Privately Held**
WEB: www.aandrdoors.com
SIC: 2431 Doors, wood

(P-4095)
A WORLD OF MOULDING
3041 S Main St, Santa Ana (92707-4250)
PHONE..................................714 361-9308
Michael Leymon, *President*
EMP: 20
SQ FT: 12,000
SALES (est): 1.8MM **Privately Held**
WEB: www.worldofmoulding.com
SIC: 2431 Moldings, wood: unfinished &
prefinished

(P-4096)
AAB GARAGE DOOR INC
25333 Pennsylvania Ave, Lomita
(90717-2025)
PHONE..................................310 530-3637
Fatih Qeblwy, *President*
EMP: 11
SALES (est): 1.2MM **Privately Held**
SIC: 2431 Garage doors, overhead: wood

(P-4097)
ABC CUSTOM WOOD
SHUTTERS INC
Also Called: Golden West Shutters
20561 Pascal Way, Lake Forest
(92630-8119)
PHONE..................................949 595-0300
David Harris, *Vice Pres*
John Stahman, *Vice Pres*
EMP: 35
SALES (est): 2.2MM **Privately Held**
SIC: 2431 Door shutters, wood; window
shutters, wood

(P-4098)
ANDERCO INC
540 Airpark Dr, Fullerton (92833-2503)
PHONE..................................714 446-9508
Peter Johnson, *President*
Ralph Johnson, *Vice Pres*
Sandra Feenstra, *Info Tech Mgr*
▲ EMP: 50
SQ FT: 70,000
SALES (est): 8.3MM **Privately Held**
SIC: 2431 5031 Door frames, wood; doors
& windows

(P-4099)
ANLIN INDUSTRIES
Also Called: Anlin Window Systems
1665 Tollhouse Rd, Clovis (93611-0523)
PHONE..................................800 287-7996
Thomas Anton Vidmar, *Principal*
Harry Parisi, *CFO*
Eric Vidmar, *Corp Secy*
Stan Fikes, *Vice Pres*
Greg Vidmar, *Vice Pres*
EMP: 250
SQ FT: 188,000
SALES (est): 51MM **Privately Held**
SIC: 2431 Windows & window parts & trim,
wood; doors & door parts & trim, wood

(P-4100)
APEX INTERIOR SOURCE INC
30555 Roseview Ln, Thousand Palms
(92276-2916)
PHONE..................................760 343-1919
Dennis Silva, *President*
EMP: 20
SQ FT: 3,000
SALES (est): 1.7MM **Privately Held**
SIC: 2431 Windows & window parts & trim,
wood

(P-4101)
APEX SPECIALTY CNSTR ENTPS
Also Called: Apex Door & Frame
17461 Poplar St, Hesperia (92345-6563)
PHONE..................................714 334-1118
Oscar Gonzalez, *President*
Virgina Gonzalez, *Vice Pres*
EMP: 16
SQ FT: 2,500
SALES (est): 1.3MM **Privately Held**
WEB: www.apexdoorandframe.com
SIC: 2431 Door frames, wood

(P-4102)
ARCH-RITE INC
1062 N Armando St, Anaheim
(92806-2605)
P.O. Box 6207, Fullerton (92834-6207)
PHONE..................................714 630-9305
Michael Barry, *President*
George Goodwin, *Vice Pres*
EMP: 14
SQ FT: 15,000
SALES (est): 1.2MM **Privately Held**
WEB: www.arch-rite.com
SIC: 2431 Windows & window parts & trim,
wood; doors & door parts & trim, wood

(P-4103)
ARCHITCTRAL MLLWK
SLUTIONS INC
2565 Progress St, Vista (92081-8423)
PHONE..................................760 510-6440
Ricardo E Alcantara, *President*
Terry Alcantara, *CFO*
EMP: 15
SQ FT: 8,850
SALES: 1MM **Privately Held**
SIC: 2431 Millwork

(P-4104)
ARCHITCTRAL MLLWK SNTA
BARBARA
Also Called: Manufacturers of Wood Products
8 N Nopal St, Santa Barbara (93103-3317)
P.O. Box 4699 (93140-4699)
PHONE..................................805 965-7011
Thomas G Mathews, *President*
Ronald Mathews, *Shareholder*
Glenice Mathews, *CEO*
Joseph J Mathews, *Vice Pres*
Lisa Mathews, *Accounting Mgr*
EMP: 40
SQ FT: 10,000
SALES (est): 7.5MM **Privately Held**
WEB: www.archmill.com
SIC: 2431 Millwork

(P-4105)
ARCHITECTURAL WOOD
DESIGN INC
Also Called: Carpentry Millwork
5672 E Dayton Ave, Fresno (93727-7801)
PHONE..................................559 292-9104
Phillip D Farnsworth, *President*
Corey Farnsworth, *Vice Pres*
Riley Farnsworth, *Project Mgr*
Caleb Adams, *Engineer*
Jason Terry, *Engineer*
EMP: 40
SQ FT: 16,000
SALES: 8MM **Privately Held**
SIC: 2431 Millwork

(P-4106)
ART GLASS ETC INC
Also Called: AG Millworks
3111 Golf Course Dr, Ventura
(93003-7604)
PHONE..................................805 644-4494
Rachid El Etel, *President*
Aida El Etel, *CFO*
Tony Mansour, *Vice Pres*
Laura Graybill, *Manager*
▲ EMP: 50
SALES (est): 7.4MM **Privately Held**
WEB: www.artglassandmetal.com
SIC: 2431 Doors & door parts & trim,
wood; windows & window parts & trim,
wood

(P-4107)
AVALON SHUTTERS INC
3407 N Perris Blvd, Perris (92571-3100)
PHONE..................................909 937-4900
Douglas Noel Serbin, *CEO*
Joe Martinez, *Regional Mgr*
Tammy Vincent, *Accountant*
Jody Strickland, *Safety Mgr*
Reece Clough, *Sales Staff*
▲ EMP: 150
SQ FT: 85,000
SALES (est): 51.1MM **Privately Held**
WEB: www.avalonshutters.net
SIC: 2431 Window shutters, wood; door
shutters, wood; blinds (shutters), wood

(P-4108)
B & G MILLWORKS
12522 Lakeland Rd, Santa Fe Springs
(90670-3940)
PHONE..................................562 944-4599
Gene Harden, *Partner*
Brad Simons, *Partner*
Catalina Montezuma, *Office Mgr*
Tom Borba, *Project Mgr*
EMP: 14
SALES (est): 1.9MM **Privately Held**
WEB: www.bgmillworks.com
SIC: 2431 1751 5084 Millwork; carpentry
work; woodworking machinery

(P-4109)
BAKERSFIELD WOODWORKS
INC
3416 Big Trail Ave, Bakersfield
(93313-5071)
PHONE..................................661 282-8492
EMP: 10
SALES (est): 1.1MM **Privately Held**
WEB: www.bakersfieldwoodworksinc.com
SIC: 2431

(P-4110)
BLOSSOM APPLE MOULDING &
MLLWK
Also Called: Apple Blossom Mould Mill Work
2411 Old Crow Canyon Rd L, San Ramon
(94583-1240)
PHONE..................................925 820-2345
Donald Utley, *Owner*
EMP: 22
SALES (est): 3.2MM **Privately Held**
SIC: 2431 5031 Millwork; lumber, plywood
& millwork

(P-4111)
BMC EAST LLC
Also Called: Precision Milling
161 W Cypress Ave, Burbank
(91502-1739)
PHONE..................................818 842-8139
Todd Righplery, *Manager*
EMP: 18
SQ FT: 2,092 **Publicly Held**
WEB: www.stockbuildingsupply.com
SIC: 2431 Millwork
HQ: Bmc East, Llc
8020 Arco Corp Dr Ste 400
Raleigh NC 27617
919 431-1000

(P-4112)
BROOKS MILLWORK COMPANY
17308 1/2 Woodruff Ave, Bellflower
(90706-6745)
PHONE..................................562 920-3000
Michael B Brooks, *Owner*
EMP: 11
SQ FT: 12,000
SALES (est): 1.5MM **Privately Held**
SIC: 2431 5211 Moldings, wood: unfin-
ished & prefinished; millwork & lumber

(P-4113)
CA SKYHOOK INC
4149 Cartagena Dr Ste B, San Diego
(92115-6724)
PHONE..................................619 229-2169
John Reinhold, *President*
Gaye Reinhold, *CFO*
Sharon Pendergrass, *Manager*
EMP: 23
SQ FT: 12,500
SALES: 2.2MM **Privately Held**
SIC: 2431 Staircases, stairs & railings

(P-4114)
CALIFORNIA CAB & STORE FIX
8472 Carbide Ct, Sacramento
(95828-5609)
PHONE..................................916 386-1340
Bruce D Nicolson, *President*
EMP: 45
SQ FT: 20,640
SALES: 5MM **Privately Held**
SIC: 2431 2541 Millwork; table or counter
tops, plastic laminated

(P-4115)
CALIFORNIA DECOR
Also Called: Salon Brandy
541 E Pine St, Compton (90222-2817)
PHONE..................................310 603-9944
James Lee Jenkins, *President*
Richard Mars, *Corp Secy*
EMP: 23
SQ FT: 36,000
SALES: 1.4MM **Privately Held**
WEB: www.californiadecor.com
SIC: 2431 7359 2522 2512 Woodwork,
interior & ornamental; equipment rental &
leasing; office furniture, except wood; up-
holstered household furniture; wood
household furniture

(P-4116)
CALIFORNIA DELUXE WINDOW
INDUS (PA)
20735 Superior St, Chatsworth
(91311-4416)
PHONE..................................818 349-5566
Aaron Adirim, *President*
Patricia Karen, *Controller*
Leoni Paez, *Controller*
EMP: 50
SQ FT: 60,000
SALES (est): 12.7MM **Privately Held**
SIC: 2431 2824 Windows & window parts
& trim, wood; vinyl fibers

(P-4117)
CALIFORNIA KIT CAB DOOR
CORP
Also Called: Cal Door
1800 Abbott St, Salinas (93901-4534)
PHONE..................................831 784-5142
Jorg Bruckner, *Principal*
Kim Mancera, *Sales Mgr*
EMP: 200
SALES (corp-wide): 65.3MM **Privately
Held**
SIC: 2431 Doors & door parts & trim, wood
PA: California Kitchen Cabinet Door Corpo-
ration
400 Cochrane Cir
Morgan Hill CA 95037
408 782-5700

(P-4118)
CALIFORNIA MILLWORKS CORP
Also Called: California Classics
27772 Avenue Scott, Santa Clarita
(91355-3417)
PHONE..................................661 294-2345
Steven Gadol, *President*
Lay Cho, *President*
Steven Godol, *President*
Edmond Cho, *Vice Pres*
EMP: 22
SQ FT: 149,000
SALES (est): 417.4K
SALES (corp-wide): 4.5MM **Privately
Held**
WEB: www.california-classics.com
SIC: 2431 Doors, wood; windows & win-
dow parts & trim, wood
PA: Old English Milling And Woodworks,
Inc
27772 Avenue Scott
Santa Clarita CA 91355
661 294-9171

(P-4119)
CALIFRNIA MANTEL FIREPLACE
INC (PA)
4141 N Freeway Blvd, Sacramento
(95834-1209)
P.O. Box 340037 (95834-0037)
PHONE..................................916 925-5775
Stephen Casey, *President*
Spencer Lowe, *Sales Dir*
EMP: 45
SQ FT: 7,000
SALES (est): 7.5MM **Privately Held**
SIC: 2431 3272 Mantels, wood; mantels,
concrete

(P-4120)
CAMELIA CITY MILLWORK INC
7831 Clifton Rd, Sacramento (95826-4324)
PHONE..................................916 451-2454
Angelo Bertagnini, *President*
Karen Bertagnini, *Vice Pres*

EMP: 11 EST: 1978
SQ FT: 7,000
SALES (est): 1.5MM Privately Held
SIC: 2431 2434 Millwork; wood kitchen
cabinets

(P-4121)
CANYON GRAPHICS INC
6680 Cobra Way, San Diego (92121-4107)
PHONE..................................858 646-0444
Scott Moncrieff, *CEO*
Chet Hecht, *Administration*
Jesus Castro, *QA Dir*
Joseph Holland, *Software Dev*
Mack Meler, *Engineer*
EMP: 60
SQ FT: 34,500
SALES (est): 11MM Privately Held
WEB: www.canyongraphics.com
SIC: 2431 2754 Moldings & baseboards,
ornamental & trim; labels: gravure printing

(P-4122)
CARL NERSESIAN
Also Called: California Blind Company
13415 Saticoy St, North Hollywood
(91605-3413)
PHONE 818 888-0111
Carl Nersesian, *Owner*
Lisa Kianoun, *Executive Asst*
EMP: 15
SQ FT: 6,000
SALES (est): 2MM Privately Held
WEB: www.californiablinds.com
SIC: 2431 2591 5023 5714 Blinds (shut-
ters), wood; window blinds; vertical blinds;
drapery & upholstery stores; window fur-
nishings

(P-4123)
CASA GRANDE WOODWORKS
4230 Cloud Way, Paso Robles
(93446-8378)
PHONE 805 226-2040
Jeff Casagrande, *Principal*
EMP: 20 EST: 2011
SALES (est): 2MM Privately Held
SIC: 2431 Millwork

(P-4124)
CHARLES GEMEINER CABINETS
3225 Exposition Pl, Los Angeles
(90018-4032)
PHONE 323 299-8696
Charles Gemeiner, *Owner*
EMP: 27
SQ FT: 20,000
SALES (est): 800K Privately Held
SIC: 2431 1751 Millwork; cabinet building
& installation

(P-4125)
COMMERCIAL CASEWORK INC
(PA)
Also Called: Madera Fina
41780 Christy St, Fremont (94538-5106)
PHONE 510 657-7933
William M Palmer, *CEO*
Nick Palmer, *Executive*
Renee Hildebrant, *Project Mgr*
Richard Topete, *Engineer*
Randall Williams, *Engineer*
EMP: 58
SQ FT: 35,000
SALES (est): 10.1MM Privately Held
WEB: www.commercialcasework.com
SIC: 2431 2541 Millwork; office fixtures,
wood

(P-4126)
COMMERCIAL MTL & DOOR SUP
INC
Also Called: Commercial Mill & Builders Sup
1210 Ames Ave, Milpitas (95035-6306)
P.O. Box 612708, San Jose (95161-2708)
PHONE 408 432-3383
Gerald Zisch, *President*
Dennis Henslye, *Treasurer*
Ronald Bowron, *Vice Pres*
EMP: 12
SQ FT: 30,000
SALES (est): 1.7MM Privately Held
SIC: 2431 5031 Doors, wood; lumber, ply-
wood & millwork

(P-4127)
COMPOSITE TECHNOLOGY INTL
INC
Also Called: Composite Technology Intl
1730 I St Ste 100, Sacramento
(95811-3015)
PHONE..................................916 551-1850
J Griffin Reid, *CEO*
Cynthia Reid, *Corp Secy*
Griffin Reid, *Vice Pres*
Joseph Falmer, *VP Finance*
◆ EMP: 46
SQ FT: 3,000
SALES (est): 9.3MM Privately Held
SIC: 2431 5023 8711 3999 Moldings,
wood: unfinished & prefinished; frames &
framing, picture & mirror; sanitary engi-
neers; barber & beauty shop equipment

(P-4128)
COPPA WOODWORKING INC
1231 Paraiso St, San Pedro (90731-1334)
PHONE..................................310 548-4142
Ciro C Coppa, *President*
Carol Coppa, *Vice Pres*
▼ EMP: 10
SQ FT: 9,000
SALES (est): 1.4MM Privately Held
WEB: www.coppawoodworking.com
SIC: 2431 2511 5712 5211 Door screens,
wood frame; wood lawn & garden furni-
ture; outdoor & garden furniture; screens,
door & window

(P-4129)
CPS WOOD WORKS INC
1257 E 9th St, Pomona (91766-3830)
PHONE..................................909 326-1102
Oscar Gomez, *CEO*
EMP: 13
SALES (est): 159.3K Privately Held
SIC: 2431 Millwork

(P-4130)
CREATIVE CONCEPTS AND
DESIGN
8460 Freedom Ln, Winters (95694-9681)
PHONE..................................707 812-9320
William Nylander, *Owner*
EMP: 10 EST: 2013
SALES (est): 427.8K Privately Held
SIC: 2431 7389 Millwork;

(P-4131)
CRESTMARK
ARCHITRACTURAL MILL
5640 West End Rd, Arcata (95521-9202)
PHONE..................................707 822-4034
Scott David Olsen, *Principal*
Tio Escarda, *Project Mgr*
Rick Hani, *Project Mgr*
EMP: 45
SALES (est): 1.7MM Privately Held
WEB: www.crestmarkam.com
SIC: 2431 Millwork

(P-4132)
CUSTOM MULDINGS SASH
DOORS INC
7732 Densmore Ave Ste A, Van Nuys
(91406-1919)
PHONE..................................818 787-7367
Peter Montano Jr, *President*
Antonio Jose Garcia, *Vice Pres*
Jose I Garcia, *Vice Pres*
EMP: 11
SQ FT: 4,800
SALES (est): 950K Privately Held
SIC: 2431 Door sashes, wood

(P-4133)
CUSTOM QUALITY DOOR &
TRIM INC
1116 Bradford Cir, Corona (92882-1874)
PHONE..................................951 278-0066
Michael Leroy Hughes, *CEO*
Shawn Hughes, *President*
Dennis Brenenstall, *Purch Agent*
EMP: 13
SALES (est): 3.2MM Privately Held
SIC: 2431 Doors & door parts & trim, wood

(P-4134)
CUSTOM WINDOW DESIGN INC
3242 Production Ave, Oceanside
(92058-1308)
PHONE..................................760 439-6213
Mark Alvey, *President*
Andrew Alvey, *Admin Sec*
EMP: 30
SQ FT: 30,000
SALES (est): 3.9MM Privately Held
WEB: www.customwindowdesign.com
SIC: 2431 Doors, wood; door frames,
wood; windows, wood; window frames,
wood

(P-4135)
CUTTING EDGE WOOD TECH
INC
130 N Gilbert St, Fullerton (92833-2505)
PHONE..................................714 447-3667
Steve Ardis, *President*
Lori Ardis, *Admin Sec*
EMP: 26
SQ FT: 4,900
SALES (est): 4MM Privately Held
WEB: www.tcedoors.com
SIC: 2431

(P-4136)
D & L MOULDING AND LUMBER
CO
1044 N Soldano Ave, Azusa (91702-2135)
PHONE..................................626 444-0134
EMP: 11
SQ FT: 6,000
SALES (est): 820.5K Privately Held
SIC: 2431

(P-4137)
D S MCGEE ENTERPRISES INC
3240 Trade Center Dr, Riverside
(92507-3432)
PHONE..................................951 378-8473
Dennis McGee, *President*
Sherrie McGee, *Corp Secy*
EMP: 45
SQ FT: 4,500
SALES (est): 8MM Privately Held
SIC: 2431 Woodwork, interior & ornamen-
tal; moldings, wood: unfinished & prefin-
ished

(P-4138)
DAVID L LONG
Also Called: Valid Woodworks
16317 Piuma Ave, Cerritos (90703-1529)
PHONE..................................562 809-5740
David L Long, *Owner*
EMP: 18
SQ FT: 10,000
SALES: 900K Privately Held
SIC: 2431 Millwork

(P-4139)
DAY STAR INDUSTRIES
13727 Excelsior Dr, Santa Fe Springs
(90670-5104)
PHONE..................................562 926-8800
Dan R Prigmore, *President*
Anne Prigmore, *Treasurer*
Christine Robertson, *Project Mgr*
EMP: 19
SALES (est): 2.9MM Privately Held
SIC: 2431 Millwork

(P-4140)
DE LARSHE CABINETRY LLC
Also Called: L-G Wood Products
2000 S Reservoir St, Pomona
(91766-5545)
PHONE..................................909 627-2757
Scott League, *Mng Member*
Jeff Cregger,
EMP: 40
SQ FT: 19,500
SALES (est): 6.2MM Privately Held
SIC: 2431 2448 Staircases & stairs, wood;
wood pallets & skids

(P-4141)
DECORE-ATIVE SPECIALTIES
4414 Azusa Canyon Rd, Irwindale
(91706-2740)
PHONE..................................626 960-7731
David Thompson, *Branch Mgr*

Alejandro Martinez, *Engineer*
EMP: 230
SALES (corp-wide): 182.1MM Privately
Held
SIC: 2431 Millwork
PA: Decore-Ative Specialties
2772 Peck Rd
Monrovia CA 91016
626 254-9191

(P-4142)
DECORE-ATIVE SPECIALTIES
104 Gate Eats Stock Blvd, Elk Grove
(95624)
PHONE..................................916 686-4700
Jack Albright, *Manager*
EMP: 240
SALES (corp-wide): 182.1MM Privately
Held
WEB: www.decore.com
SIC: 2431 Doors, wood
PA: Decore-Ative Specialties
2772 Peck Rd
Monrovia CA 91016
626 254-9191

(P-4143)
DESIGN WOODWORKING INC
(PA)
709 N Sacramento St, Lodi (95240-1255)
PHONE..................................209 334-6674
David Worfolk, *President*
Stefan I Sekula, *Admin Sec*
EMP: 35
SQ FT: 22,000
SALES (est): 4.6MM Privately Held
WEB: www.deswood.com
SIC: 2431 Millwork

(P-4144)
DIAMOND WOODCRAFT
Also Called: Diamond Doors
2197 Ruth Ave Ste 1, South Lake Tahoe
(96150-4340)
PHONE..................................530 541-0866
Robert Beaty, *Owner*
EMP: 12 EST: 1958
SQ FT: 9,000
SALES (est): 1.2MM Privately Held
WEB: www.diamondwoodcraft.com
SIC: 2431 Millwork

(P-4145)
DOOR & HARDWARE
INSTALLERS INC
Also Called: Cabinet & Millwork Installers
14300 Davenport Rd Ste 1a, Santa Clarita
(91390-5004)
PHONE..................................661 298-9383
Arthur Benson, *President*
EMP: 30 EST: 1995
SQ FT: 15,000
SALES (est): 4.6MM Privately Held
SIC: 2431 Doors & door parts & trim, wood

(P-4146)
DOORS PLUS INC
314 N Main St, Lodi (95240-0604)
PHONE..................................209 463-3667
Douglas Larsson, *President*
Susie Larsson, *Treasurer*
▲ EMP: 14
SQ FT: 16,000
SALES (est): 2.4MM Privately Held
WEB: www.doorsplusonline.com
SIC: 2431 Doors, wood; window frames,
wood

(P-4147)
DORRIS LUMBER AND
MOULDING CO (PA)
2601 Redding Ave, Sacramento
(95820-2155)
PHONE..................................916 452-7531
Joshua Tyler, *President*
Nels Israelson, *Shareholder*
E Chase Israelson, *Ch of Bd*
Dennis Murcko, *CFO*
Larry White, *Vice Pres*
▲ EMP: 145
SQ FT: 2,000
SALES (est): 22MM Privately Held
WEB: www.dorrismoulding.com
SIC: 2431 Moldings, wood: unfinished &
prefinished

(P-4148)
DPC WOODWORK INC
5714 W Pico Blvd, Los Angeles
(90019-3708)
PHONE............................323 935-4828
Dennis Parry, *President*
EMP: 50
SQ FT: 400
SALES (est): 2.1MM **Privately Held**
SIC: 2431 Millwork

(P-4149)
DREES WOOD PRODUCTS INC
14020 Orange Ave, Paramount
(90723-2018)
PHONE............................562 633-7337
Ed Drees, *Manager*
EMP: 50
SALES (corp-wide): 16.4MM **Privately
Held**
WEB: www.dreeswood.com
SIC: 2431 Doors, wood
PA: Drees Wood Products, Inc.
14003 Orange Ave
Paramount CA 90723
562 633-7337

(P-4150)
**DREES WOOD PRODUCTS INC
(PA)**
14003 Orange Ave, Paramount
(90723-2017)
PHONE............................562 633-7337
Ed Drees, *CEO*
EMP: 50
SALES (est): 16.4MM **Privately Held**
WEB: www.dreeswood.com
SIC: 2431 Doors, wood

(P-4151)
DYNAMIC SHUTTERS INC
Also Called: Dynamic Finishing
9310 Corbin Ave, Northridge (91324-2405)
PHONE............................818 407-6310
Jerome Lavorante, *President*
EMP: 22
SALES (est): 2.3MM **Privately Held**
SIC: 2431 Window shutters, wood

(P-4152)
**EAGLE MOULDING COMPANY 1
(PA)**
1625 Tierra Buena Rd, Yuba City
(95993-8854)
PHONE............................530 673-6517
Constance Mc Cool, *President*
Kevin P Mc Cool, *Vice Pres*
▲ **EMP:** 28
SQ FT: 44,000
SALES (est): 3.2MM **Privately Held**
WEB: www.eagleco.en.alibaba.com
SIC: 2431 Moldings, wood: unfinished &
prefinished

(P-4153)
ESCO WOODWORKS
2894 Aiello Dr C, San Jose (95111-2154)
PHONE............................408 225-2777
Richard Mannina, *Principal*
EMP: 10
SALES (est): 790K **Privately Held**
SIC: 2431 Millwork

(P-4154)
**EUROPEAN ELEGANCE
WOODWORK**
8019 Haskell Ave Unit 102, Van Nuys
(91406-1302)
PHONE............................818 570-9401
Laszlo Balazs, *Principal*
EMP: 10
SALES (est): 1.2MM **Privately Held**
SIC: 2431 Millwork

(P-4155)
FINELINE WOODWORKING INC
1139 Baker St, Costa Mesa (92626-4114)
PHONE............................714 540-5468
Marc Butman, *President*
EMP: 28
SQ FT: 20,000
SALES (est): 5.8MM **Privately Held**
SIC: 2431 Millwork

(P-4156)
G A DOORS INC
Also Called: Grand American Millwork
15140 Desman Rd, La Mirada
(90638-5737)
P.O. Box 805 (90637-0805)
PHONE............................714 739-1144
Norman Nilsen, *President*
John Nilsen, *Vice Pres*
EMP: 56
SQ FT: 16,000
SALES (est): 5.6MM **Privately Held**
SIC: 2431 Doors, wood; window shutters,
wood

(P-4157)
G AND S MILLING CO
Also Called: Island Mountain Lumber
23205 Live Oak Rd, Willits (95490-9707)
PHONE............................707 459-0294
Fred Galten, *Owner*
Christine Galten, *Principal*
EMP: 30
SALES (est): 1.7MM **Privately Held**
SIC: 2431 2421 2426 Millwork; sawmills
& planing mills, general; hardwood dimen-
sion & flooring mills

(P-4158)
**GARAGE DOORS
INCORPORATED**
147 Martha St, San Jose (95112-5814)
PHONE............................408 293-7443
Scott Jensen, *President*
Nancy Jensen, *Treasurer*
EMP: 60
SQ FT: 45,000
SALES (est): 9.5MM **Privately Held**
WEB: www.garagedoorsinc.com
SIC: 2431 5031 Garage doors, overhead:
wood; doors, garage

(P-4159)
GLOBAL DOORS CORP
1340 E 6th St, Los Angeles (90021-1272)
PHONE............................213 622-2003
Tal Hassid, *President*
EMP: 48
SALES (est): 3.5MM **Privately Held**
SIC: 2431 Doors, wood

(P-4160)
GMJ WOODWORKING
2365 Mountain View Dr, Escondido
(92027-4951)
PHONE............................760 294-7428
Christopher Laughton, *Owner*
EMP: 10 EST: 2007
SALES (est): 738.2K **Privately Held**
SIC: 2431 Millwork

(P-4161)
GONZALEZ FELICIANO
Also Called: Paradise Kitchen Doors
1583 E Grand Ave, Pomona (91766-3808)
PHONE............................909 236-1372
Feliciano Gonzalez, *Owner*
EMP: 15 EST: 2015
SALES (est): 1.5MM **Privately Held**
SIC: 2431 Doors, wood

(P-4162)
HALEY BROS INC (HQ)
6291 Orangethorpe Ave, Buena Park
(90620-1339)
PHONE............................714 670-2112
Thomas J Cobb, *CEO*
Barry Reynolds, *General Mgr*
Thomas Cobb, *Admin Sec*
Pierre Klein, *Controller*
Ingrid Bradford, *Human Res Dir*
▲ **EMP:** 200
SQ FT: 24,000
SALES (est): 31MM
SALES (corp-wide): 92.5MM **Privately
Held**
WEB: www.haleybros.com
SIC: 2431 Doors, wood; moldings, wood:
unfinished & prefinished
PA: T. M. Cobb Company
500 Palmyrita Ave
Riverside CA 92507
951 248-2400

(P-4163)
HALLE-HOPPER LLC
Also Called: Trim Quick Co
630 Parkridge Ave, Norco (92860-3124)
PHONE............................951 284-7373
Richard Hopper,
John Halle,
EMP: 20 EST: 2001
SQ FT: 70,000
SALES (est): 3.8MM **Privately Held**
SIC: 2431 Window trim, wood

(P-4164)
**HAND CRFTED DUTCHMAN
DOORS INC**
770 Stonebridge Dr, Tracy (95376-2812)
PHONE............................209 833-7378
Larry B Vis, *President*
Donna Vis, *CFO*
EMP: 40
SQ FT: 16,000
SALES (est): 6.6MM **Privately Held**
WEB: www.dutchmandoors.com
SIC: 2431 2434 Doors, wood; wood
kitchen cabinets

(P-4165)
**HOSPITALITY WOOD
PRODUCTS INC**
7206 E Gage Ave, Commerce
(90040-3813)
PHONE............................562 806-5564
Michael Romero, *President*
Carlos Escalante, *Treasurer*
Victor Garcia, *Vice Pres*
EMP: 17 EST: 2001
SALES (est): 2.4MM **Privately Held**
SIC: 2431 Interior & ornamental woodwork
& trim

(P-4166)
HOWIES MOULDING INC
8032 Allport Ave, Santa Fe Springs
(90670-2102)
PHONE............................562 698-0261
Howard F Holmes, *President*
Michael Holmes, *Shareholder*
Phyllis Holmes, *Treasurer*
▲ **EMP:** 10 EST: 1963
SQ FT: 8,000
SALES (est): 1.4MM **Privately Held**
SIC: 2431 Moldings, wood: unfinished &
prefinished

(P-4167)
**ICI ARCHITECTURAL MILLWORK
INC**
6820 Brynhurst Ave, Los Angeles
(90043-4664)
PHONE............................323 759-4993
Izhak Korin, *CEO*
Robert A Babayan, *President*
Byron Bailey, *Project Mgr*
EMP: 15 EST: 2007
SALES (est): 2.1MM **Privately Held**
SIC: 2431 Millwork

(P-4168)
IDX LOS ANGELES LLC
Also Called: Universal Forest Products
5005 E Philadelphia St, Ontario
(91761-2816)
PHONE............................909 212-8333
Graham Fownes, *General Mgr*
◆ **EMP:** 109
SALES (est): 10.2MM
SALES (corp-wide): 3.9B **Publicly Held**
SIC: 2431 Millwork
PA: Universal Forest Products, Inc.
2801 E Beltline Ave Ne
Grand Rapids MI 49525
616 364-6161

(P-4169)
J & J QUALITY DOOR INC
Also Called: Quality Door & Trim
741 S Airport Way, Stockton (95205-6126)
PHONE............................209 948-5013
Jeffery Dean Cannon, *CEO*
Steve Cantrell, *President*
Debbie Sue Cantrell, *CFO*
Jeff JC, *General Mgr*
EMP: 35

SALES (est): 6.9MM **Privately Held**
WEB: www.qualitydoor.net
SIC: 2431 Doors, wood

(P-4170)
J RS WOODWORKS INC
300 W Robles Ave Ste B, Santa Rosa
(95407-8168)
P.O. Box 9491 (95405-1491)
PHONE............................707 588-8255
Richard Hoffman, *President*
EMP: 10
SQ FT: 5,750
SALES (est): 1.7MM **Privately Held**
SIC: 2431 Millwork

(P-4171)
J SUMMITT INC
Also Called: Summit Forest Products
13834 Bettencourt St, Cerritos
(90703-1010)
PHONE............................562 236-5744
Jim Summit, *Branch Mgr*
EMP: 27 **Privately Held**
WEB: www.jmsummitt.net
SIC: 2431 Millwork
PA: J. Summitt, Inc.
13834 Bettencourt St
Cerritos CA 90703

(P-4172)
JELD-WEN INC
Also Called: International Wood Products
3760 Convoy St Ste 111, San Diego
(92111-3743)
PHONE............................800 468-3667
Hugo Hernadez, *Manager*
EMP: 23 **Publicly Held**
SIC: 2431 Doors, wood
HQ: Jeld-Wen, Inc.
2645 Silver Crescent Dr
Charlotte NC 28273
800 535-3936

(P-4173)
JELD-WEN INC
Jeld-Wen Doors
3901 Cincinnati Ave, Rocklin (95765-1303)
PHONE............................916 782-4900
Roald Pederson, *Manager*
EMP: 115 **Publicly Held**
WEB: www.jeld-wen.com
SIC: 2431 5211 Doors, wood; door & win-
dow products
HQ: Jeld-Wen, Inc.
2645 Silver Crescent Dr
Charlotte NC 28273
800 535-3936

(P-4174)
JENSEN DOOR SYSTEMS INC
160 Vallecitos De Oro, San Marcos
(92069-1435)
PHONE............................760 736-4036
Tim Jensen, *President*
Lisa Jensen, *Vice Pres*
EMP: 11
SALES (est): 1.3MM **Privately Held**
WEB: www.jensendoorsystems.com
SIC: 2431 Doors, wood

(P-4175)
JOHN L STATON INC
1214 5th St, Berkeley (94710-1306)
PHONE............................510 527-3114
Loretta Penning, *President*
John L Staton, *Shareholder*
EMP: 70
SALES (est): 6.4MM **Privately Held**
SIC: 2431 Doors, wood; window frames,
wood; window shutters, wood

(P-4176)
**KARLS CUSTOM SASH AND
DOORS**
Also Called: Karl's Sash & Doors
18292 Gothard St, Huntington Beach
(92648-1225)
PHONE............................714 842-7877
Anton Seitz, *Managing Prtnr*
EMP: 23 EST: 1980
SQ FT: 9,900
SALES (est): 2.2MM **Privately Held**
SIC: 2431 Door sashes, wood; doors,
wood

PRODUCTS & SVCS

(P-4177)
KASTLE STAIR INC (PA)
7422 Mountjoy Dr, Huntington Beach
(92648-1231)
PHONE....................714 596-2600
Rose Phillips, *President*
EMP: 20
SALES (est): 6.4MM **Privately Held**
WEB: www.kastlestair.com
SIC: 2431 Staircases, stairs & railings

(P-4178)
KATZIRS FLOOR & HM DESIGN INC
Also Called: National Hardwood Flooring & M
14742 Calvert St, Van Nuys (91411-2705)
PHONE....................818 988-9663
Omer Katzir, *President*
EMP: 15
SQ FT: 13,310
SALES (corp-wide): 10.8MM **Privately Held**
WEB: www.nationalhardwood.com
SIC: 2431 Millwork
PA: Katzir's Floor And Home Design, Inc.
14959 Delano St
Van Nuys CA 91411
818 988-9663

(P-4179)
KLS DOORS LLC
Chaparral A Division Kls Door
501 Kettering Dr, Ontario (91761-8150)
PHONE....................909 605-6468
Varry Methvin, *Branch Mgr*
EMP: 29
SALES (corp-wide): 3.8MM **Privately Held**
SIC: 2431 Doors & door parts & trim, wood
PA: Kls Doors Llc
501 Kettering Dr
Ontario CA 91761
909 605-6468

(P-4180)
L & L CUSTOM SHUTTERS INC
3133 Yukon Ave, Costa Mesa
(92626-2921)
PHONE....................714 996-9539
Larry Allen, *President*
Lillian Allen, *Treasurer*
Ralph Gerardo, *Vice Pres*
EMP: 135
SQ FT: 9,000
SALES (est): 12.4MM **Privately Held**
SIC: 2431 Window shutters, wood

(P-4181)
L J SMITH INC
25956 Commercentre Dr, Lake Forest
(92630-8815)
PHONE....................949 609-0544
Danny Umemoto, *Manager*
EMP: 15
SALES (corp-wide): 238.4MM **Privately Held**
WEB: www.ljsmith.com
SIC: 2431 Millwork
HQ: L. J. Smith, Inc.
35280 Scio Bowerston Rd
Bowerston OH 44695
740 269-2221

(P-4182)
L&F WOOD LLC
Also Called: Boardhouse
416 E Alondra Blvd, Gardena
(90248-2902)
PHONE....................310 400-5569
Russell Walker, *Mng Member*
Marcia Kirschbaum, *Sales Associate*
Michael Dutko,
Christine A Meyer,
▲ EMP: 15
SQ FT: 20,000
SALES: 3.7MM **Privately Held**
SIC: 2431 5211 5031 Millwork; millwork & lumber; millwork

(P-4183)
LEEPERS WOOD TURNING CO INC (PA)
Also Called: Leeper's Stair Products
341 Bonnie Cir Ste 104, Corona
(92880-2895)
PHONE....................562 422-6525
Michael Skinner, *President*
Barbara Skinner, *Ch of Bd*
Molly Rubio, *Treasurer*
▲ EMP: 95 EST: 1946
SQ FT: 29,000
SALES (est): 10MM **Privately Held**
WEB: www.stairproducts.com
SIC: 2431 Staircases & stairs, wood; staircases, stairs & railings

(P-4184)
LOWPENSKY MOULDING
900 Palou Ave, San Francisco
(94124-3429)
PHONE....................415 822-7422
Theodore M Lowpensky, *Owner*
Todd Lowpensky, *Office Mgr*
EMP: 15
SQ FT: 13,000
SALES (est): 1.8MM **Privately Held**
WEB: www.lowpensky.com
SIC: 2431 Moldings, wood: unfinished & prefinished

(P-4185)
LUXOR INDUSTRIES INTERNATIONAL
1250 E Franklin Ave, Pomona
(91766-5449)
PHONE....................909 469-4757
Randy Rodriguez, *President*
EMP: 30
SQ FT: 36,000
SALES (est): 2.9MM **Privately Held**
SIC: 2431 Millwork

(P-4186)
MABREY PRODUCTS INC
200 Ryan Ave, Chico (95973-9032)
PHONE....................530 895-3799
Douglas Tobey, *President*
EMP: 12
SQ FT: 5,000
SALES: 600K **Privately Held**
WEB: www.mabreyproducts.com
SIC: 2431 Woodwork, interior & ornamental

(P-4187)
MAR VISTA WOOD PRODUCTS INC
7343 Pierce Ave, Whittier (90602-1112)
PHONE....................562 698-2024
Judy Wu, *President*
EMP: 10
SALES (est): 1.1MM **Privately Held**
SIC: 2431 Moldings & baseboards, ornamental & trim

(P-4188)
MASONITE ENTRY DOOR CORP
25100 Globe St, Moreno Valley
(92551-9528)
PHONE....................951 243-2261
Lawrence Repar, *President*
Felipe Lopera, *Plant Mgr*
▲ EMP: 11
SALES (est): 1.8MM **Privately Held**
SIC: 2431 Doors, wood

(P-4189)
MASONITE INTERNATIONAL CORP
Also Called: Delta Door Company
433 W Scotts Ave, Stockton (95203-3320)
PHONE....................209 948-0637
Steve Beckham, *Manager*
EMP: 50
SALES (corp-wide): 2B **Publicly Held**
WEB: www.masoniteinternational.com
SIC: 2431 5211 Doors, wood; doors, wood or metal, except storm
PA: Masonite International Corporation
201 N Franklin St Ste 300
Tampa FL 33602
800 895-2723

(P-4190)
MATRIX CAB PARTS INC
Also Called: Matrix Millwork
7950 Woodley Ave Ste B, Van Nuys
(91406-1261)
PHONE....................818 782-7022
Anthony Abiad, *CEO*
Julie Antunez, *Office Mgr*
EMP: 11
SQ FT: 9,000
SALES: 2MM **Privately Held**
WEB: www.matrixcabparts.com
SIC: 2431 5251 Millwork; hardware

(P-4191)
METAL TEK ENGINEERING INC
7426 Cherry Ave Ste 210, Fontana
(92336-4263)
PHONE....................909 821-4158
Moises Lopez, *President*
EMP: 20
SQ FT: 2,000
SALES: 1.2MM **Privately Held**
SIC: 2431 Staircases, stairs & railings

(P-4192)
MILLCRAFT INC
2850 E White Star Ave, Anaheim
(92806-2517)
PHONE....................714 632-9621
Lars Eppick, *President*
Philip De Marco, *Treasurer*
Reginald Skipcott, *Vice Pres*
Ray Pfeifer, *Admin Sec*
EMP: 70
SQ FT: 34,000
SALES (est): 10MM **Privately Held**
WEB: www.millcraft.info
SIC: 2431 2434 Doors, wood; wood kitchen cabinets

(P-4193)
MILLWORK CO
607 Brazos St Ste C, Ramona
(92065-1884)
PHONE....................760 788-1533
Gregory J Lucas, *CEO*
EMP: 16
SALES (est): 2.2MM **Privately Held**
SIC: 2431 Millwork

(P-4194)
MILLWORKS BY DESIGN INC
2248 Townsgate Rd Ste 1, Westlake Village
(91361-2441)
PHONE....................818 597-1326
Daniel S Parish, *CEO*
Zachary D Eglit, *President*
Susan Morrissey, *Office Mgr*
Jeremy Beauchamp, *Project Mgr*
Adam Henninger, *Project Mgr*
▲ EMP: 37
SALES (est): 7.3MM **Privately Held**
SIC: 2431 Millwork

(P-4195)
MOLDINGS PLUS INC
1856 S Grove Ave, Ontario (91761-5613)
PHONE....................909 947-3310
Robert Bryant, *President*
Steve Totri, *Vice Pres*
Brandon Casto, *Sales Mgr*
▲ EMP: 20 EST: 1972
SQ FT: 13,500
SALES (est): 4.2MM **Privately Held**
WEB: www.moldingsplusinc.com
SIC: 2431 Moldings, wood: unfinished & prefinished; doors & door parts & trim, wood; moldings & baseboards, ornamental & trim

(P-4196)
MONTY VENTSAM INC
Also Called: Ventsam Sash & Door Mfg Co
9495 San Fernando Rd, Sun Valley
(91352-1421)
PHONE....................818 768-6424
Monty Ventsam, *President*
EMP: 12
SQ FT: 8,000
SALES: 1.5MM **Privately Held**
SIC: 2431 5211 Door sashes, wood; door trim, wood; door & window products

(P-4197)
MRR MOULDING INDUSTRIES INC
Also Called: Accurate Moulding Mirror Work
125 N Mary Ave Spc 42, Sunnyvale
(94086-4819)
PHONE....................510 794-8116
Deborah Daughtrey, *President*
EMP: 12
SQ FT: 22,000
SALES (est): 1.5MM **Privately Held**
WEB: www.accuratemoulding.com
SIC: 2431

(P-4198)
NEST ENVIRONMENTS INC
530 E Dyer Rd, Santa Ana (92707-3737)
PHONE....................714 979-5500
Staci Bina, *Principal*
EMP: 10
SALES (est): 1MM **Privately Held**
SIC: 2431 Millwork

(P-4199)
NEVADA WINDOW SUPPLY INC
Also Called: ATI Windows
1455 Columbia Ave, Riverside
(92507-2013)
PHONE....................951 300-0100
Stephan Schwartz, *CEO*
Daniel Schwartz, *President*
Stephen Schwartz, *CEO*
EMP: 13 EST: 2005
SALES (est): 3.6MM **Privately Held**
SIC: 2431 Window frames, wood

(P-4200)
NEWMAN BROS CALIFORNIA INC (PA)
Also Called: A-1 Grit Co
1901 Massachusetts Ave, Riverside
(92507-2618)
P.O. Box 5675 (92517-5675)
PHONE....................951 782-0102
Harold Newman, *CEO*
EMP: 20
SALES (est): 3.6MM **Privately Held**
SIC: 2431 3291 5199 8711 Millwork; grit, steel; architects' supplies (non-durable); consulting engineer

(P-4201)
NEWPORT CUSTOM WOODWORKING
1835 Whittier Ave Ste C10, Costa Mesa
(92627-4576)
PHONE....................949 631-6397
Norman E Johnson, *Partner*
John Ferraiolo, *Partner*
EMP: 12
SQ FT: 2,000
SALES (est): 1.3MM **Privately Held**
SIC: 2431 Millwork

(P-4202)
NICKS DOORS INC
Also Called: Nick's Cabinet Doors
1052 W Kirkwall Rd, Azusa (91702-5126)
PHONE....................626 812-6491
Nicolas Huizar, *President*
Anna Huizar, *Treasurer*
Sal Huizar, *Vice Pres*
Socorro Huizar, *Admin Sec*
EMP: 15
SQ FT: 32,000
SALES (est): 2MM **Privately Held**
SIC: 2431 5211 Doors, wood; door & window products

(P-4203)
NORTH BAY PLYWOOD INC
510 Northbay Dr, NAPA (94559-1426)
P.O. Box 2338 (94558-0518)
PHONE....................707 224-7849
Thomas H Lowenstein, *President*
Janice Leann Lowenstein, *Treasurer*
EMP: 39
SQ FT: 24,000
SALES (est): 10MM **Privately Held**
WEB: www.northbayplywood.com
SIC: 2431 2599 5211 2434 Doors, wood; cabinets, factory; cabinets, kitchen; doors, wood or metal, except storm; wood kitchen cabinets

▲ = Import ▼=Export
◆ =Import/Export

(P-4204)
NORTHERN CALIFORNIA STAIR
Also Called: California Stairs
7150 Alexander St, Gilroy (95020-6609)
P.O. Box 536 (95021-0536)
PHONE..........................408 847-0106
Warner Gartner, *President*
EMP: 10
SALES (est): 1.1MM **Privately Held**
SIC: 2431 Staircases & stairs, wood

(P-4205)
OAK-IT INC
143 Business Center Dr, Corona
(92880-1757)
PHONE..........................951 735-5973
Lori Barrett, *President*
EMP: 31
SALES (est): 5.6MM **Privately Held**
SIC: 2431 Millwork

(P-4206)
**OLD ENGLISH MIL &
WOODWORKS (PA)**
Also Called: Old English Mil & Woodworks
27772 Avenue Scott, Santa Clarita
(91355-3417)
PHONE..........................661 294-9171
Lay Cho, *President*
Edmond Cho, *Vice Pres*
EMP: 30 **EST:** 1977
SQ FT: 30,000
SALES: 4.5MM **Privately Held**
WEB: www.valencialumber.com
SIC: 2431 2439 1751 Staircases & stairs,
wood; window frames, wood; door
frames, wood; structural wood members;
carpentry work

(P-4207)
**PACIFIC ARCHTECTURAL
MLLWK INC (PA)**
Also Called: Reveal Windows & Doors
1435 Pioneer St, Brea (92821-3721)
PHONE..........................562 905-3200
John Higman, *CEO*
Roy Gustin, *Vice Pres*
Skip McDonald, *Vice Pres*
Alice Vanberpool, *Vice Pres*
Betty Kekuna, *Office Mgr*
▲ **EMP:** 100
SQ FT: 31,000
SALES (est): 19MM **Privately Held**
WEB: www.pacmillwork.com
SIC: 2431 Planing mill, millwork

(P-4208)
**PACIFIC DOOR & CABINET
COMPANY**
7050 N Harrison Ave, Pinedale
(93650-1008)
PHONE..........................559 439-3822
Duane Failla, *President*
Gail Baker, *Executive*
Janet Failla, *Human Resources*
Terry Freeman, *Sales Executive*
EMP: 30
SQ FT: 16,000
SALES (est): 5.6MM **Privately Held**
WEB: www.pacificdoorinc.com
SIC: 2431 3442 Doors, wood; windows,
wood; metal doors, sash & trim

(P-4209)
**PACIFIC MDF PRODUCTS INC
(PA)**
Also Called: Pac Trim
4312 Anthony Ct Ste A, Rocklin
(95677-2174)
PHONE..........................916 660-1882
Clifford Stokes, *President*
Geri Grommett, *General Mgr*
Scott Clapp, *Controller*
Rick Miller, *Safety Mgr*
Joel Dahlgren, *Plant Mgr*
▲ **EMP:** 59
SQ FT: 55,000
SALES (est): 21.9MM **Privately Held**
WEB: www.pactrim.com
SIC: 2431 Moldings, wood: unfinished &
prefinished

(P-4210)
PAULA KELLER
Also Called: San Pedro Garage Door and
Repr
1044 S Gaffey St, San Pedro (90731-4072)
PHONE..........................310 833-1894
Paula Keller, *Owner*
EMP: 16
SALES (est): 1.5MM **Privately Held**
SIC: 2431 Garage doors, overhead: wood

(P-4211)
PERFECT PLANK CO
2850 S 5th Ave, Oroville (95965-5851)
PHONE..........................530 533-7606
Terry Horne, *Systems Mgr*
Diana Kelley, *Director*
EMP: 14
SQ FT: 10,000
SALES (corp-wide): 3MM **Privately Held**
WEB: www.perfectplank.com
SIC: 2431 Millwork
PA: Perfect Plank Co.
2850 S 5th Ave
Oroville CA
530 533-7606

(P-4212)
**PHILLIPS LOBUE & WILSON
MLLWK**
300 E Santa Ana St, Anaheim
(92805-3953)
PHONE..........................951 331-5714
Richard Phillips, *Vice Pres*
Ken Lobue, *President*
Randy Wilson, *Admin Sec*
EMP: 15
SQ FT: 2,000
SALES (est): 1.3MM **Privately Held**
SIC: 2431 Millwork

(P-4213)
**PINECRAFT CUSTOM
SHUTTERS INC**
Also Called: Sterling Shutters
946 W 17th St, Costa Mesa (92627-4403)
P.O. Box 2417, Newport Beach (92659-
1417)
PHONE..........................949 642-9317
Frank L Gerardo Sr, *President*
Anthony Gerardo, *Vice Pres*
EMP: 50 **EST:** 1964
SQ FT: 12,000
SALES (est): 5MM **Privately Held**
SIC: 2431 Door shutters, wood

(P-4214)
PRECISION COMPANIES INC
Also Called: Precision Doors & Millwork
15088 La Palma Dr, Chino (91710-9669)
PHONE..........................909 548-2700
Joseph J Felix, *President*
Marcia Felix, *Corp Secy*
Melodee Kroll, *Sales Staff*
EMP: 15
SQ FT: 5,000
SALES: 4.5MM **Privately Held**
WEB: www.predoor.com
SIC: 2431 3441 3442 Millwork; fabricated
structural metal; metal doors, sash & trim

(P-4215)
PRECISION MILLWORK LLC
14300 Davenport Rd Ste 4a, Agua Dulce
(91390-5000)
PHONE..........................661 402-5021
Ardith Swanger, *Mng Member*
Miguel Pena,
Michelle St John,
EMP: 15 **EST:** 2012
SQ FT: 5,000
SALES: 8MM **Privately Held**
SIC: 2431 Millwork

(P-4216)
RAU RESTORATION
Also Called: Rau William Automotive Wdwrk
2027 Pontius Ave, Los Angeles
(90025-5613)
PHONE..........................310 445-1128
William Rau, *President*
EMP: 15
SQ FT: 4,000

SALES: 1.2MM **Privately Held**
WEB: www.rau-autowood.com
SIC: 2431 Interior & ornamental woodwork
& trim

(P-4217)
**REDWOOD MILLING COMPANY
LLC**
12055 Old Redwood Hwy, Healdsburg
(95448-9238)
PHONE..........................707 433-1343
Steven I Pankowski, *Partner*
Ronald Pankowski, *Partner*
EMP: 20
SALES (est): 1.7MM **Privately Held**
SIC: 2431 Moldings, wood: unfinished &
prefinished

(P-4218)
**RENAISSANCE WDWRK &
DESIGN INC**
7605 Hazeltine Ave Unit B, Van Nuys
(91405-1423)
PHONE..........................818 787-7238
Will Windrow, *Branch Mgr*
EMP: 15
SALES (corp-wide): 8MM **Privately Held**
SIC: 2431 Millwork
PA: Renaissance Woodwork & Design, Inc.
22531 Ventura Blvd
Woodland Hills CA 91364
818 222-2771

(P-4219)
**RENAISSNCE FRNCH DORS
SASH INC (PA)**
Also Called: Renaissance Doors & Windows
38 Segada, Rcho STA Marg (92688-2744)
PHONE..........................714 578-0090
Michael Jenkins, *President*
James Jenkins, *Corp Secy*
Thomas Jenkins, *Vice Pres*
EMP: 129
SQ FT: 75,000
SALES (est): 7.1MM **Privately Held**
WEB: www.renaissancedoors.com
SIC: 2431 Doors, wood

(P-4220)
RITESCREEN INC
33444 Western Ave, Union City
(94587-3202)
P.O. Box 965 (94587-0965)
PHONE..........................800 949-4174
Art Lucero, *General Mgr*
EMP: 13
SALES (est): 810K **Privately Held**
SIC: 2431 Door screens, wood frame

(P-4221)
RIVER CITY MILLWORK INC
3045 Fite Cir, Sacramento (95827-1814)
PHONE..........................916 364-8981
Paul Parks, *President*
Valerie Parks, *Corp Secy*
Doug Parker, *General Mgr*
Scott Penley, *Project Mgr*
Eriq Perrault, *Project Mgr*
EMP: 33
SQ FT: 24,000
SALES (est): 7.5MM **Privately Held**
SIC: 2431 2434 Moldings, wood: unfin-
ished & prefinished; wood kitchen cabi-
nets

(P-4222)
RTA SALES INC
Also Called: Shutters By Angel Co
210 E Avenue L Ste A, Lancaster
(93535-4613)
PHONE..........................661 942-3553
Ralph Arellano, *President*
EMP: 17
SQ FT: 22,000
SALES (est): 2.2MM **Privately Held**
SIC: 2431 Window shutters, wood

(P-4223)
**SADDLEBACK STAIR &
MILLWORK**
23291 Peralta Dr Ste B4, Laguna Hills
(92653-1426)
PHONE..........................949 460-0384
Miles Densmore, *President*
Irene Densmore, *Vice Pres*

EMP: 13
SALES (est): 1.4MM **Privately Held**
SIC: 2431 Staircases & stairs, wood

(P-4224)
**SAN FRANCISCO VICTORIANA
INC**
2070 Newcomb Ave, San Francisco
(94124-1615)
PHONE..........................415 648-0313
Gary Root, *President*
▲ **EMP:** 10 **EST:** 1971
SQ FT: 25,000
SALES (est): 1.1MM **Privately Held**
WEB: www.sfvictoriana.com
SIC: 2431 Exterior & ornamental wood-
work & trim

(P-4225)
SBS AMERICA LLC (PA)
Also Called: San Benito Shutter
1600 Lana Way, Hollister (95023-2532)
PHONE..........................831 637-8700
Jordan Bastable, *Mng Member*
Jillian Shaw, *Accountant*
Michele Lee, *Opers Mgr*
Michelle Lee,
William S Lee,
▲ **EMP:** 70
SQ FT: 112,000
SALES (est): 18MM **Privately Held**
WEB: www.sanbenitoshutter.com
SIC: 2431 Blinds (shutters), wood

(P-4226)
**SETZER FOREST PRODUCTS
INC (PA)**
2555 3rd St Ste 200, Sacramento
(95818-1196)
PHONE..........................916 442-2555
D Mark Kable, *CEO*
Hardie Setzer, *Shareholder*
Garner Setzer, *President*
Jeff Setzer, *Vice Pres*
Joseph Hwang, *Administration*
▲ **EMP:** 160 **EST:** 1927
SALES (est): 45.9MM **Privately Held**
WEB: www.setzerforest.com
SIC: 2431 2441 Moldings, wood: unfin-
ished & prefinished; box shook, wood

(P-4227)
**SIERRA LUMBER
MANUFACTURERS**
375 W Hazelton Ave, Stockton
(95203-3306)
P.O. Box 6216 (95206-0216)
PHONE..........................209 943-7777
Bob Long, *President*
▼ **EMP:** 190 **EST:** 1965
SQ FT: 65,000
SALES (est): 18.9MM
SALES (corp-wide): 2B **Publicly Held**
WEB: www.sierralumber.com
SIC: 2431 2421 2435 Doors, wood; cut
stock, softwood; hardwood veneer & ply-
wood
HQ: Masonite Corporation
201 N Franklin St Ste 300
Tampa FL 33602
813 877-2726

(P-4228)
SIERRA PACIFIC INDUSTRIES
Alameda Rd, Corning (96021)
PHONE..........................530 824-2474
Kendall Pierson, *Vice Pres*
Troi Shilts, *Sales Staff*
Bill Carroll, *Manager*
EMP: 400
SALES (corp-wide): 1.2B **Privately Held**
WEB: www.sierrapacificind.com
SIC: 2431 2426 2421 Millwork; hardwood
dimension & flooring mills; sawmills &
planing mills, general
PA: Sierra Pacific Industries
19794 Riverside Ave
Anderson CA 96007
530 378-8000

(P-4229)
SIERRA WOODWORKING INC
960 6th St Ste 101a, Norco (92860-1440)
PHONE..........................714 538-8440
Maurice Kendall, *President*

EMP: 22
SQ FT: 10,000
SALES (est): 3.9MM **Privately Held**
WEB: www.sierrawoodworking.com
SIC: 2431 2541 2521 2439 Millwork;
cabinets, except refrigerated: show, display, etc.: wood; wood office furniture;
structural wood members; wood kitchen
cabinets; decorative wood & woodwork

(P-4230)
SIGNATURE WOODWORKS
7334 Hollister Ave Ste B, Goleta
(93117-2866)
PHONE.............................805 685-4080
David Starks, *Owner*
EMP: 11
SQ FT: 4,600
SALES (est): 1MM **Privately Held**
SIC: 2431 Millwork

(P-4231)
SIMMONS STAIRWAYS INC
Also Called: Stair Service
830 Jury Ct Ste 4, San Jose (95112-2816)
PHONE.............................408 920-0105
Howard Simmons, *CEO*
Charles Simmons, *Vice Pres*
Nichole Montrouil, *Accounting Mgr*
EMP: 48
SQ FT: 15,000
SALES (est): 7.5MM **Privately Held**
WEB: www.stairservice.com
SIC: 2431 Staircases, stairs & railings

(P-4232)
SISKIYOU FOREST PRODUCTS (PA)
6275 State Highway 273, Anderson
(96007)
PHONE.............................530 378-6980
Fred Duchi, *President*
Bill Duchi, *Vice Pres*
Monte Acquistapace, *Sales Associate*
▲ **EMP:** 48 **EST:** 1974
SQ FT: 2,280
SALES (est): 10.4MM **Privately Held**
WEB: www.siskiyouforestproducts.com
SIC: 2431 5031 Millwork; lumber, plywood
& millwork

(P-4233)
SKYCO SHADING SYSTEMS INC
3411 W Fordham Ave, Santa Ana
(92704-4422)
PHONE.............................714 708-3038
Sandra Young, *President*
▲ **EMP:** 28
SQ FT: 16,000
SALES (est): 5.2MM **Privately Held**
WEB: www.skycoshade.com
SIC: 2431 Awnings, blinds & shutters,
wood

(P-4234)
SOUTH COAST STAIRS INC
30251 Tomas, Rcho STA Marg
(92688-2123)
PHONE.............................949 858-1685
Chris Galloway, *President*
Mary Galloway, *Vice Pres*
Tamera Selchau, *Admin Sec*
EMP: 40
SQ FT: 2,000
SALES (est): 4.8MM **Privately Held**
SIC: 2431 2439 5211 Staircases & stairs,
wood; structural wood members; millwork
& lumber

(P-4235)
STEINER & MATEER INC
Also Called: Shuttercraft of California
8333 Secura Way, Santa Fe Springs
(90670-2299)
PHONE.............................562 464-9082
Richard K Oliver, *President*
EMP: 30
SQ FT: 20,000
SALES (est): 3.8MM **Privately Held**
SIC: 2431 Louver doors, wood; window
shutters, wood

(P-4236)
STEVE BRUNER
Also Called: Tali Pak Lumber Milling
81 Hwy 175, Hopland (95449)
PHONE.............................707 744-1103
Steve Bruner, *Owner*
EMP: 20
SQ FT: 1,000
SALES (est): 1.7MM **Privately Held**
SIC: 2431 Millwork

(P-4237)
SUMMIT WINDOW PRODUCTS INC
6336 Patterson Pass Rd F, Livermore
(94550-9577)
PHONE.............................408 526-1600
Ron Clementi, *President*
Nick Sabic, *Vice Pres*
EMP: 54
SQ FT: 15,000
SALES (est): 5.7MM **Privately Held**
WEB: www.summitwindowproducts.com
SIC: 2431 Window shutters, wood

(P-4238)
SUN MOUNTAIN INC
2 Henry Adams St Ste 150, San Francisco
(94103-5045)
PHONE.............................415 852-2320
EMP: 25
SALES (corp-wide): 12.1MM **Privately Held**
SIC: 2431 Millwork
PA: Sun Mountain, Inc.
140 Commerce Rd
Berthoud CO 80513
970 532-2105

(P-4239)
SUNRISE WOOD PRODUCTS INC
Also Called: Sunrise Shutters
6701 11th Ave, Los Angeles (90043-4729)
P.O. Box 43998 (90043-0998)
PHONE.............................323 971-6540
Detlef Guttke, *President*
Erika Guttke, *Corp Secy*
EMP: 25
SQ FT: 11,000
SALES (est): 3.2MM **Privately Held**
SIC: 2431 Window shutters, wood

(P-4240)
SUNWOOD DOORS INC
1143 N Stanford Ave, Los Angeles
(90059-3516)
PHONE.............................562 951-9401
Oscar Alvarez, *President*
▲ **EMP:** 31
SQ FT: 11,000
SALES (est): 3.6MM **Privately Held**
SIC: 2431 5211 Millwork; garage doors,
sale & installation

(P-4241)
SURE GUARD SOCAL
Also Called: Sure Guard Windows
11702 Anabel Ave, Garden Grove
(92843-3711)
PHONE.............................714 556-5497
Charles Nguyen, *Partner*
EMP: 10
SALES (est): 546.8K **Privately Held**
SIC: 2431 Windows & window parts & trim,
wood

(P-4242)
T M COBB COMPANY (PA)
Also Called: Haley Bros
500 Palmyrita Ave, Riverside (92507-1196)
PHONE.............................951 248-2400
Jeffrey Cobb, *President*
Thomas J Cobb, *Vice Pres*
Peter Bonilla, *Administration*
Yoshiko Miyazaki, *Administration*
Vince French, *Controller*
▲ **EMP:** 23
SALES (est): 92.5MM **Privately Held**
WEB: www.tmcobbco.com
SIC: 2431 3442 Door frames, wood; win-
dow & door frames

(P-4243)
T M COBB COMPANY
Also Called: Haley Brothers
2651 E Roosevelt St, Stockton
(95205-3825)
PHONE.............................209 948-5358
John Jenkins, *Branch Mgr*
Carlos Vizcarra, *Purchasing*
EMP: 55
SQ FT: 1,200
SALES (corp-wide): 92.5MM **Privately Held**
WEB: www.tmcobbco.com
SIC: 2431 Doors, wood
PA: T. M. Cobb Company
500 Palmyrita Ave
Riverside CA 92507
951 248-2400

(P-4244)
T M COBB COMPANY
Haley Bros Inc A Div T M Cobb
6291 Orangethorpe Ave, Buena Park
(90620-1339)
PHONE.............................714 670-2112
Thomas J Cobb, *President*
Raymond Pickering, *COO*
Gary Erickson, *General Mgr*
Oscar Caicedo, *Sales Mgr*
EMP: 40
SQ FT: 7,966
SALES (corp-wide): 92.5MM **Privately Held**
WEB: www.tmcobbco.com
SIC: 2431 Doors, wood; moldings, wood:
unfinished & prefinished
PA: T. M. Cobb Company
500 Palmyrita Ave
Riverside CA 92507
951 248-2400

(P-4245)
TAIT CABINETRY WOODWORKS
6572 Whitman Ct, Riverside (92506-4905)
PHONE.............................951 776-1192
Bruce Tait, *Principal*
EMP: 10
SALES (est): 710K **Privately Held**
SIC: 2431 Millwork

(P-4246)
THOMAS TELLEZ
Also Called: Wallace
100 Taylor Way, Blue Lake (95525)
PHONE.............................707 668-1825
Thomas Tellez, *Owner*
EMP: 20
SALES (est): 1.7MM **Privately Held**
SIC: 2431 3547 8712 Millwork; bar mills;
architectural services

(P-4247)
TMR EXECUTIVE INTERIORS INC
2677 N Argyle Ave, Fresno (93727-1304)
PHONE.............................559 346-0631
Jamie Russell, *President*
Timothy Russell, *Vice Pres*
EMP: 19
SQ FT: 1,700
SALES (est): 2.4MM **Privately Held**
SIC: 2431 1751 Millwork; cabinet & finish
carpentry

(P-4248)
TRAVIS AMERICAN GROUP LLC
Also Called: Travis Industries
11450 Sheldon St, Sun Valley
(91352-1121)
PHONE.............................714 258-1200
Thomas D Bell, *President*
Stephen Saponaro, *VP Finance*
Lyle Zastrow, *VP Opers*
Robert Kincaid,
Robert Levine,
EMP: 150
SQ FT: 5,300
SALES (est): 10.7MM **Privately Held**
SIC: 2431 2499 2426 2591 Moldings,
wood: unfinished & prefinished; veneer
work, inlaid; furniture stock & parts, hard-
wood; venetian blinds; paints, varnishes &
supplies

(P-4249)
TRINITY WOODWORKS INC
2620 Temple Heights Dr, Oceanside
(92056-3512)
PHONE.............................760 639-5351
Jeffrey D Hollenbeck, *CEO*
Deanna Hollenbeck, *Vice Pres*
Brian Franks, *Project Mgr*
Mel Dix, *Prdtn Mgr*
Oscar Espinoza, *Production*
EMP: 23
SALES (est): 4.2MM **Privately Held**
SIC: 2431 Millwork

(P-4250)
UNION PLANING MILL (PA)
965 Oakhurst Way, Stockton (95209-2028)
P.O. Box 348 (95201-0348)
PHONE.............................209 466-9617
Richard Mc Clure, *President*
Mathew Brodie, *Corp Secy*
EMP: 40
SQ FT: 42,000
SALES (est): 2.8MM **Privately Held**
WEB: www.unionplaningmill.com
SIC: 2431 Planing mill, millwork

(P-4251)
UNITY FOREST PRODUCTS INC
1162 Putman Ave, Yuba City (95991-7216)
P.O. Box 1849 (95992-1849)
PHONE.............................530 671-7152
Enita Elphick, *President*
Ryan Smith, *Treasurer*
Michael Smith, *Vice Pres*
Mike Smith, *Vice Pres*
Shawn Nelson, *Admin Sec*
EMP: 48
SQ FT: 4,200
SALES: 11MM **Privately Held**
WEB: www.unityforest.com
SIC: 2431 Millwork

(P-4252)
VICTORIAN SHUTTERS INC (PA)
Also Called: Golden State Shutters
305 Industrial Way Frnt, Dixon
(95620-9769)
PHONE.............................707 678-1776
Richard Scholten, *President*
Cornelius J Scholten, *Vice Pres*
Melinda Scholten, *Admin Sec*
EMP: 13 **EST:** 1931
SQ FT: 20,000
SALES: 750K **Privately Held**
WEB: www.goldenstateshutters.com
SIC: 2431 5211 Window shutters, wood;
door & window products

(P-4253)
W B POWELL INC
630 Parkridge Ave, Norco (92860-3124)
PHONE.............................951 270-0095
Charles G Mayhew, *CEO*
Chuck Mayhew, *President*
Doug Westra, *CFO*
Jack Bacon, *Vice Pres*
Sean Gingras, *Project Mgr*
EMP: 30
SALES (est): 5.5MM
SALES (corp-wide): 7MM **Privately Held**
WEB: www.foldcraft.com
SIC: 2431 2439 Millwork; structural wood
members
PA: Foldcraft Co.
14400 Southcross Dr W
Burnsville MN 55306
507 789-5111

(P-4254)
WESTERN INTEGRATED MTLS INC (PA)
3310 E 59th St, Long Beach (90805-4504)
PHONE.............................562 634-2823
Larry Farrah, *President*
Edward G Farrah, *Vice Pres*
Jim Halbrook, *Principal*
Debra Price, *Principal*
Alex Rojas, *Principal*
▲ **EMP:** 30
SQ FT: 20,000
SALES (est): 4.4MM **Privately Held**
WEB: www.western-integrated.com
SIC: 2431 3442 Millwork; window & door
frames

▲ = Import ▼=Export
◆ =Import/Export

(P-4255)
WESTGATE HARDWOODS INC (PA)
9296 Midway, Durham (95938-9779)
PHONE..................................530 892-0300
Ivan Hoath, *President*
Becky Hoath, *Corp Secy*
Ivan Hoath III, *Vice Pres*
Tom Greminger, *Executive*
Craig Jones, *Draft/Design*
EMP: 22
SQ FT: 10,000
SALES (est): 6MM **Privately Held**
WEB: www.westgatehardwoods.com
SIC: 2431 5031 Millwork; lumber: rough, dressed & finished

(P-4256)
WHOLESALE SHUTTER COMPANY INC
411 Olive Ave, Beaumont (92223-2640)
PHONE..................................951 845-8786
Sabiha Patel, *CEO*
▲ **EMP:** 11
SQ FT: 10,000
SALES (est): 920K **Privately Held**
WEB: www.wholesaleshutter.com
SIC: 2431 Door shutters, wood; blinds (shutters), wood

(P-4257)
WINDOW & DOOR SHOP INC (PA)
185 Industrial St, San Francisco (94124-1927)
PHONE..................................415 282-6192
Javier Garcia, *President*
Fred Ochoa, *Treasurer*
Jose Ochoa, *Admin Sec*
Diane Larson, *Project Mgr*
Steve Robertson, *Project Mgr*
EMP: 14
SQ FT: 9,000
SALES (est): 1.6MM **Privately Held**
WEB: www.windowanddoorshop.com
SIC: 2431 5211 Doors, wood; windows, wood; door & window products

(P-4258)
WINDOW PRODUCTS MANAGEMENT INC
Also Called: Wpm
5917 Olivas Park Dr Ste F, Ventura (93003-7613)
PHONE..................................805 677-6800
John Norman Edwards, *President*
EMP: 10
SALES (est): 1.3MM **Privately Held**
SIC: 2431 2591 Windows & window parts & trim, wood; window shutters, wood; window shades

(P-4259)
WINDSOR WILLITS COMPANY (PA)
Also Called: Windsor Mill
7950 Redwood Dr Ste 4, Cotati (94931-3054)
PHONE..................................707 665-9663
Craig Flynn, *President*
Douglas Sherer, *CFO*
Alrene Flynn, *Admin Sec*
Charlie Holum, *Technology*
Brian Bunt, *Mktg Dir*
▲ **EMP:** 29
SQ FT: 50,000
SALES (est): 13.8MM **Privately Held**
WEB: www.windsorone.com
SIC: 2431 Moldings, wood: unfinished & prefinished

(P-4260)
WINDSOR WILLITS COMPANY
Also Called: Windsor Mill
661 Railroad Ave, Willits (95490-3942)
PHONE..................................707 459-8568
John Hankins, *Opers-Prdtn-Mfg*
EMP: 40
SALES (corp-wide): 13.8MM **Privately Held**
WEB: www.windsorone.com
SIC: 2431 2439 Moldings, wood: unfinished & prefinished; moldings & baseboards, ornamental & trim; structural wood members

PA: Windsor Willits Company
7950 Redwood Dr Ste 4
Cotati CA 94931
707 665-9663

(P-4261)
WOOD CONNECTION INC
4701 N Star Way, Modesto (95356-9567)
PHONE..................................209 577-1044
William W Fenstermacher, *President*
Judy L Fenstermacher, *Admin Sec*
EMP: 25
SQ FT: 11,400
SALES (est): 4.3MM **Privately Held**
SIC: 2431 2434 Millwork; wood kitchen cabinets

(P-4262)
WTI JKB INC (PA)
Also Called: Woodtech Industries
405 Aldo Ave, Santa Clara (95054-2302)
PHONE..................................408 297-8579
Joe Becher, *President*
◆ **EMP:** 10
SQ FT: 10,000
SALES (est): 1.4MM **Privately Held**
SIC: 2431 2541 Millwork; cabinets, except refrigerated: show, display, etc.: wood

(P-4263)
YOUNG & FAMILY INC
Also Called: Quality Doors & Trim
64 Soda Bay Rd, Lakeport (95453-5609)
P.O. Box 897 (95453-0897)
PHONE..................................707 263-8877
Hilary Young, *President*
Andrew Young, *Vice Pres*
EMP: 25
SQ FT: 11,400
SALES (est): 3.2MM **Privately Held**
SIC: 2431 2434 Doors, wood; wood kitchen cabinets

(P-4264)
YUBA RIVER MOULDING MLLWK INC (PA)
Also Called: Cal Yuba Investments
3757 Feather River Blvd, Olivehurst (95961-9615)
P.O. Box 1078, Yuba City (95992-1078)
PHONE..................................530 742-2168
Thomas C Williams Sr, *Ch of Bd*
Thomas C Williams Jr, *President*
Jolyne Williams, *Corp Secy*
Damon Munsee, *Vice Pres*
Andrea Watson, *Department Mgr*
▲ **EMP:** 41 **EST:** 1977
SQ FT: 200,000
SALES (est): 10.7MM **Privately Held**
SIC: 2431 6512 Moldings, wood: unfinished & prefinished; commercial & industrial building operation

---

2434 Wood Kitchen

(P-4265)
3D REMODELING INC
111 Lindbergh Ave Ste D, Livermore (94551-9526)
P.O. Box 2812 (94551-2812)
PHONE..................................925 449-5477
James Alexander, *President*
Michelle Faria, *Office Mgr*
Marie Alexander, *Admin Sec*
EMP: 25
SQ FT: 3,500
SALES: 2.5MM **Privately Held**
WEB: www.3dremodeling.com
SIC: 2434 Wood kitchen cabinets

(P-4266)
ACCRACUTT CABINETS
4744 Felspar St, Riverside (92509-3068)
PHONE..................................951 685-7322
William Ball, *Owner*
EMP: 10
SQ FT: 8,000
SALES (est): 1MM **Privately Held**
WEB: www.accracutt.com
SIC: 2434 Wood kitchen cabinets

(P-4267)
AGAN WOODCRAFTERS
175 W Radio Rd, Palm Springs (92262-1629)
PHONE..................................760 322-1310
Renee Agular, *Owner*
Alex Agular, *Co-Owner*
EMP: 12
SALES (est): 1.1MM **Privately Held**
SIC: 2434 Wood kitchen cabinets

(P-4268)
ALEX DESIGN INC
8541 Younger Creek Dr # 400, Sacramento (95828-1037)
PHONE..................................916 386-8020
Lazaro Martinez, *Branch Mgr*
EMP: 12
SALES (corp-wide): 827.6K **Privately Held**
SIC: 2434 Wood kitchen cabinets
PA: Alex Design, Inc.
8517 Florin Rd
Sacramento CA 95828
916 706-0059

(P-4269)
AMBERWOOD PRODUCTS INC
Also Called: Amberwood Installation
1555 S 7th St Bldg 7, San Jose (95112-5926)
PHONE..................................408 938-1600
Frank Guidace, *CEO*
Josephine Guidace, *Treasurer*
Terrie Dudley, *Vice Pres*
Terrie Field, *Vice Pres*
Maryann Cervelli, *Admin Sec*
EMP: 150
SQ FT: 100,000
SALES (est): 17.1MM **Privately Held**
WEB: www.amberwoodproducts.com
SIC: 2434 Vanities, bathroom: wood

(P-4270)
ARANDAS WOODCRAFT INC
137 W 157th St, Gardena (90248-2225)
P.O. Box 3954 (90247-7507)
PHONE..................................310 538-9945
EMP: 40
SQ FT: 19,000
SALES (est): 4.7MM **Privately Held**
WEB: www.arandaswoodcraft.com
SIC: 2434 2541

(P-4271)
ARTCRAFTERS CABINETS INC
5446 Cleon Ave, North Hollywood (91601-2897)
PHONE..................................818 752-8960
Jack R Walter, *President*
Sharon E Walter, *Vice Pres*
Sharon Walter, *Vice Pres*
Dawn Kunihiro, *Office Mgr*
Mike Boyle, *Project Mgr*
EMP: 50
SQ FT: 20,000
SALES (est): 5.5MM **Privately Held**
WEB: www.artcrafter.com
SIC: 2434 2521 Wood kitchen cabinets; wood office furniture; millwork

(P-4272)
BARBOSA CABINETS INC
2020 E Grant Line Rd, Tracy (95304-8525)
PHONE..................................209 836-2501
Edward Barbosa, *President*
Ron Barbosa, *Exec VP*
Dawn Mounsey, *Administration*
Christina Sena, *Administration*
Johnny Horton, *Project Mgr*
▲ **EMP:** 346
SQ FT: 300,000
SALES (est): 57.1MM **Privately Held**
WEB: www.barcab.com
SIC: 2434 Wood kitchen cabinets

(P-4273)
BELLATERRA HOME LLC
8372 Tiogawoods Dr # 180, Sacramento (95828-5066)
PHONE..................................916 896-3188
Betty Cheung, *President*
Alpha Cheung, *Principal*
▲ **EMP:** 10

SALES (est): 1.5MM **Privately Held**
SIC: 2434 5719 5211 Vanities, bathroom: wood; mirrors; counter tops

(P-4274)
BIRCHWOOD CABINETS OF CAL
2 Iwanuma Dr, NAPA (94558-3561)
PHONE..................................209 523-2323
Thad Erickson, *President*
Margot Roen, *Vice Pres*
EMP: 35
SQ FT: 8,000
SALES (est): 3.4MM **Privately Held**
SIC: 2434 Vanities, bathroom: wood

(P-4275)
BIRCHWOOD CABINETS SONORA INC
Also Called: Bcsi
14375 Cuesta Ct, Sonora (95370-8223)
PHONE..................................209 532-1417
Lee F Erickson, *President*
Carrie Erickson, *Vice Pres*
EMP: 19
SQ FT: 10,000
SALES (est): 2.1MM **Privately Held**
SIC: 2434 Vanities, bathroom: wood

(P-4276)
BLUEGATE SURFACE WORKS INC
15936 Downey Ave, Paramount (90723-5116)
PHONE..................................562 630-9005
Charles Anthony Gallagher, *Owner*
EMP: 11
SALES (est): 995K **Privately Held**
SIC: 2434 5031 5211 Wood kitchen cabinets; kitchen cabinets; cabinets, kitchen; counter tops

(P-4277)
BURMAN CABINET CORPORATION
864 S Mcglincy Ln B, Campbell (95008-5411)
PHONE..................................408 377-6652
Joseph Burman, *President*
Rochelle Burman Greenfield, *Vice Pres*
Bernard Greenfield, *Admin Sec*
EMP: 20
SQ FT: 15,000
SALES (est): 1.7MM **Privately Held**
WEB: www.burmancabinets.com
SIC: 2434 Wood kitchen cabinets

(P-4278)
C & C BUILT-IN INC
Also Called: Build-In C & C
2000 Lana Way, Hollister (95023-2500)
PHONE..................................831 635-5880
Hyung Ki Han, *President*
EMP: 20
SALES (est): 2MM **Privately Held**
SIC: 2434 Wood kitchen cabinets

(P-4279)
CABINET CONCEPTS
950 W Cienega Ave, San Dimas (91773-2454)
PHONE..................................909 599-9191
Joe Arnold, *President*
EMP: 10
SALES: 800K **Privately Held**
SIC: 2434 Wood kitchen cabinets

(P-4280)
CABINETS & DOORS DIRECT INC
858 E 1st St, Pomona (91766-2004)
PHONE..................................909 629-3388
Sam Ho, *President*
EMP: 12
SALES: 1MM **Privately Held**
SIC: 2434 Wood kitchen cabinets

(P-4281)
CABINETS 2000 INC
11100 Firestone Blvd, Norwalk (90650-2269)
PHONE..................................562 868-0909
Frank Hamadani, *Chairman*
Nematollah Abdollahi, *President*
Sherwood Prusso, *President*
Sue Abdollahi, *CFO*

PRODUCTS & SVCS

Azam Abdollahi, *Officer*
EMP: 180
SQ FT: 103,000
SALES (est): 39.3MM **Privately Held**
WEB: www.cabinets2000.com
SIC: 2434 1751 Wood kitchen cabinets;
cabinet & finish carpentry

(P-4282)
CABINETS BY ANDY INC
2411 Central Ave, McKinleyville
(95519-3615)
PHONE.................707 839-0220
Andy Dickey, *President*
EMP: 15
SQ FT: 10,000
SALES (est): 1.2MM **Privately Held**
WEB: www.cabinetsbyandy.com
SIC: 2434 Wood kitchen cabinets

(P-4283)
CALIFORNIA KIT CAB DOOR CORP (PA)
Also Called: California Door
400 Cochrane Cir, Morgan Hill
(95037-2859)
PHONE.................408 782-5700
Edward Joseph Rossi, *Principal*
Amber Linse, *Executive*
Melissa Naranjo, *Executive*
Kathryn Therrien, *Executive*
Tu Nduyen, *Info Tech Dir*
◆ **EMP:** 100
SQ FT: 260,000
SALES (est): 65.3MM **Privately Held**
WEB: www.caldoor.com
SIC: 2434 2431 Wood kitchen cabinets;
millwork

(P-4284)
CALIFORNIA WOODWORKING INC
1726 Ives Ave, Oxnard (93033-4072)
PHONE.................805 982-9090
Edward Vickery, *President*
Lucas Vickery, *Vice Pres*
Luke Vickery, *Vice Pres*
Rj Pranski, *General Mgr*
Susan Vickery, *Admin Sec*
EMP: 30
SQ FT: 8,000
SALES (est): 3.1MM **Privately Held**
WEB: www.calwoodinc.com
SIC: 2434 Wood kitchen cabinets

(P-4285)
CENTRAL VALLEY CABINET MFG
Also Called: Vern Lackey
10739 14th Ave, Armona (93202)
P.O. Box 1211 (93202-1211)
PHONE.................559 584-8441
Vern Lackey, *President*
EMP: 10
SALES (est): 954.2K **Privately Held**
SIC: 2434 Wood kitchen cabinets

(P-4286)
CLASSIC MILL & CABINET
Also Called: Classic Innovations
590 Santana Dr, Cloverdale (95425-4296)
PHONE.................707 894-9800
Tony Mertes, *President*
Ms Billie Siemsen, *Manager*
Chad Stephens, *Accounts Mgr*
▲ **EMP:** 37
SQ FT: 35,000
SALES (est): 3.8MM **Privately Held**
SIC: 2434 Wood kitchen cabinets

(P-4287)
CLIFF BARTLETT
Also Called: Bartlett Fine Cabinetry Mllwk
250 Industrial Way Ste B, Buellton
(93427-9505)
PHONE.................805 693-1617
Cliff R Barlett, *Owner*
Joseph Franklin, *General Mgr*
Karyn Wortendyke, *Accounting Mgr*
EMP: 12
SQ FT: 3,000
SALES: 650K **Privately Held**
SIC: 2434 Wood kitchen cabinets

(P-4288)
CORONA MILLWORKS COMPANY (PA)
5572 Edison Ave, Chino (91710-6936)
PHONE.................909 606-3288
Jose Corona, *CEO*
Catherine Medina, *Controller*
Frances Young, *Human Resources*
Cindy Struck, *Purchasing*
Darren Dean, *Sales Mgr*
▲ **EMP:** 81
SQ FT: 8,700
SALES: 12MM **Privately Held**
WEB: www.coronamillworks.com
SIC: 2434 Wood kitchen cabinets

(P-4289)
CUSTOM FURNITURE DESIGN INC
Also Called: Entertainment Centers Plus
3340 Sunrise Blvd Ste F, Rancho Cordova
(95742-7316)
PHONE.................916 631-6300
Dan Gwiazdon, *President*
EMP: 20
SQ FT: 13,000
SALES (est): 1.8MM **Privately Held**
WEB: www.cfdsacto.com
SIC: 2434 Wood kitchen cabinets

(P-4290)
CUSTOM INSTALLATIONS
1452 Hawks Vista Ln, Alpine (91901-3338)
P.O. Box 550 (91903-0550)
PHONE.................619 445-0692
Dale Hinriths, *Owner*
EMP: 13
SALES (est): 870.2K **Privately Held**
WEB: www.custominstallations.com
SIC: 2434 Wood kitchen cabinets

(P-4291)
D & D CBNETS - SVAGE DSGNS INC
1478 Sky Harbor Dr, Olivehurst
(95961-7418)
PHONE.................530 634-9713
Peter D Giordano, *President*
EMP: 30
SALES (est): 7.3MM **Privately Held**
SIC: 2434 Wood kitchen cabinets

(P-4292)
DAVID BEARD
Also Called: Beards Custom Cabinets
821 Twin View Blvd, Redding (96003-2002)
PHONE.................530 244-1248
David Beard, *Owner*
EMP: 16
SQ FT: 8,550
SALES (est): 1.6MM **Privately Held**
WEB: www.davidbeard.com
SIC: 2434 2521 2541 Wood kitchen cabi-
nets; cabinets, office: wood; cabinets,
lockers & shelving

(P-4293)
DECORE-ATIVE SPECIALTIES (PA)
2772 Peck Rd, Monrovia (91016-5005)
PHONE.................626 254-9191
Jack Lansford Sr, *CEO*
Jack Lansford Jr, *President*
Billie Lansford, *Treasurer*
Eric Lansford, *Senior VP*
Lori Golden, *Finance*
▲ **EMP:** 1100
SALES (est): 182.1MM **Privately Held**
WEB: www.decore.com
SIC: 2434 Wood kitchen cabinets

(P-4294)
DOORS UNLIMITED
Also Called: Timberline Molding
1316 Armorlite Dr, San Marcos
(92069-1342)
PHONE.................760 744-5590
Marvin Wait, *Partner*
Susan Wait, *Partner*
EMP: 12
SQ FT: 7,500
SALES (est): 1.5MM **Privately Held**
SIC: 2434 Wood kitchen cabinets

(P-4295)
DREAMS CLOSETS
13030 Ramona Blvd Unit 9, Baldwin Park
(91706-3759)
PHONE.................626 641-5070
Armando Padilla, *Owner*
EMP: 11
SALES: 200K **Privately Held**
SIC: 2434 Vanities, bathroom: wood

(P-4296)
DYNAMIC CABINET DESIGNS INC
10215 Canoga Ave, Chatsworth
(91311-3008)
PHONE.................818 700-1658
Stephan Schwartz, *President*
Natalie Schwartz, *Vice Pres*
Stephan Shvarts, *Sales Executive*
EMP: 33
SQ FT: 12,000
SALES (est): 4.6MM **Privately Held**
WEB: www.cabinetsinc.com
SIC: 2434 2521 2431 Wood kitchen cabi-
nets; cabinets, office: wood; millwork

(P-4297)
ENCORE FINE CABINETRY INC
14748 Highway 41 Ste B, Madera
(93636-8904)
PHONE.................559 822-4333
Edward Fenton, *President*
EMP: 14 EST: 2000
SQ FT: 32,000
SALES (est): 1.7MM **Privately Held**
WEB: www.encorefinecabinetry.com
SIC: 2434 Wood kitchen cabinets

(P-4298)
EUROPEAN WOODWORK
7531 Suzi Ln, Westminster (92683-4359)
PHONE.................714 892-8831
Anthony Dunatov, *Owner*
EMP: 10
SQ FT: 4,800
SALES (est): 1MM **Privately Held**
WEB: www.europeanwoodworksinc.com
SIC: 2434 Wood kitchen cabinets

(P-4299)
EXCEL CABINETS INC
225 Jason Ct, Corona (92879-6199)
PHONE.................951 279-4545
Charles W Ketzel, *CEO*
Sandra Ketzel, *Corp Secy*
Kevin Ketzel, *Vice Pres*
Amber Lukes, *Technology*
Carl Nielsen, *Controller*
▲ **EMP:** 35
SALES (est): 6MM **Privately Held**
WEB: www.excelcabinetsinc.com
SIC: 2434 Wood kitchen cabinets

(P-4300)
FINELINE CARPENTRY INC
1297 Old County Rd, Belmont
(94002-3920)
PHONE.................650 592-2442
Mac Bean, *President*
Cheryl Bean, *Vice Pres*
EMP: 25
SQ FT: 15,000
SALES (est): 4MM **Privately Held**
WEB: www.finelinecarpentry.com
SIC: 2434 Wood kitchen cabinets

(P-4301)
FINISHING TOUCH MOULDING INC
6190 Corte Del Cedro, Carlsbad
(92011-1515)
PHONE.................760 444-1019
Roland Chaney, *President*
EMP: 55
SALES (est): 4.1MM **Privately Held**
SIC: 2434 1751 Wood kitchen cabinets;
carpentry work

(P-4302)
FITUCCI LLC
14753 Oxnard St, Van Nuys (91411-3122)
PHONE.................818 785-3841
Eric Fituci, *Mng Member*
EMP: 11

SALES (est): 1.1MM **Privately Held**
SIC: 2434 Wood kitchen cabinets

(P-4303)
FRANKS CABINET SHOP INC
11204 San Diego St, Lamont (93241-2453)
PHONE.................661 845-0781
Ronnie Jung, *President*
Doris Jung, *Treasurer*
Anetta Jung, *Admin Sec*
EMP: 15
SQ FT: 32,000
SALES (est): 1.5MM **Privately Held**
SIC: 2434 2541 5211 Wood kitchen cabi-
nets; wood partitions & fixtures; lumber
products

(P-4304)
GALLERY CABINET CONNECTION
5783 E Shields Ave, Fresno (93727-7821)
PHONE.................559 294-7007
Herb Falk, *President*
EMP: 11
SALES (est): 1.2MM **Privately Held**
SIC: 2434 Wood kitchen cabinets

(P-4305)
GALLEYS PLUS CUSTOM CABINETS
1432 E 6th St, Corona (92879-1713)
PHONE.................951 278-4596
Bob Ballenger, *President*
EMP: 10
SQ FT: 5,000
SALES (est): 1.2MM **Privately Held**
SIC: 2434 2599 2521 2541 Wood kitchen
cabinets; cabinets, factory; cabinets, of-
fice: wood; cabinets, except refrigerated:
show, display, etc.: wood; cabinets: show,
display or storage: except wood

(P-4306)
HEART WOOD MANUFACTURING INC
Also Called: Heartwood Cabinets
5860 Obata Way, Gilroy (95020-7038)
PHONE.................408 848-9750
David Boll, *President*
Eileen Boll, *Vice Pres*
EMP: 55
SQ FT: 25,000
SALES (est): 8.3MM **Privately Held**
SIC: 2434 2511 2431 Wood kitchen cabi-
nets; wood household furniture; millwork

(P-4307)
HERITAGE WOODWORKING CO INC
4633 Mountain Lakes Blvd, Redding
(96003-1450)
PHONE.................530 243-7215
James Boisselle, *President*
Nora Boisselle, *Corp Secy*
EMP: 20
SQ FT: 14,720
SALES: 2.5MM **Privately Held**
SIC: 2434 Vanities, bathroom: wood

(P-4308)
HILKERS CUSTOM CABINETS INC
504 N Greco Ct, San Jacinto (92582-3877)
PHONE.................951 487-7640
Daniel D Hilker, *President*
EMP: 10
SALES (est): 895.6K **Privately Held**
SIC: 2434 Wood kitchen cabinets

(P-4309)
HIS LIFE WOODWORKS
15107 S Main St, Gardena (90248-1923)
PHONE.................310 756-0170
John Johnson Jr, *President*
Garrett Brim, *President*
EMP: 40
SQ FT: 15,000
SALES: 2.8MM **Privately Held**
WEB: www.hislifewoodworks.com
SIC: 2434 Wood kitchen cabinets

▲ = Import ▼=Export
◆ =Import/Export

(P-4310)
HOLLANDS CUSTOM CABINETS INC
14511 Olde Highway 80, El Cajon
(92021-2877)
PHONE....................................619 443-6081
Robert Holland, *President*
Jed Richard, *Vice Pres*
EMP: 25
SQ FT: 10,000
SALES (est): 3.7MM **Privately Held**
SIC: 2434 Wood kitchen cabinets

(P-4311)
I AND E CABINETS INC
14660 Raymer St, Van Nuys (91405-1217)
PHONE....................................818 933-6480
Israel Chlomovitz, *CEO*
Ettie Chlomovitz, *Treasurer*
EMP: 34
SQ FT: 9,000
SALES: 5MM **Privately Held**
SIC: 2434 Wood kitchen cabinets

(P-4312)
IDO CABINET INC
1551 Minnesota St, San Francisco
(94107-3521)
PHONE....................................415 282-1683
James Yu, *President*
Jenny Kong, *Vice Pres*
EMP: 13
SQ FT: 10,000
SALES (est): 1.2MM **Privately Held**
SIC: 2434 Wood kitchen cabinets

(P-4313)
INDIGO DESIGNS
16607 Reed St, Fontana (92336-2528)
PHONE....................................909 997-0854
George Ramirez, *Partner*
EMP: 10
SALES (est): 531.3K **Privately Held**
SIC: 2434 Wood kitchen cabinets

(P-4314)
JKF CONSTRUCTION INC
460 E Easy St Ste 102, Simi Valley
(93065-1868)
PHONE....................................805 583-4228
Jon Flugum, *President*
EMP: 14
SALES (est): 1.4MM **Privately Held**
SIC: 2434 Wood kitchen cabinets

(P-4315)
JM KITCHEN CABINETS
702 E Gage Ave, Los Angeles
(90001-1514)
PHONE....................................323 752-6520
Jose Maltonado, *Owner*
▲ EMP: 13
SALES (est): 1.1MM **Privately Held**
SIC: 2434 Wood kitchen cabinets

(P-4316)
JR STEPHENS COMPANY
5208 Boyd Rd, Arcata (95521-4410)
PHONE....................................707 825-0100
Jim Stephens, *President*
Bryan Stephens, *CFO*
Josh Stephens, *Vice Pres*
Rosalie Stephens, *Admin Sec*
EMP: 40
SALES: 6MM **Privately Held**
WEB: www.jrsco.net
SIC: 2434 Wood kitchen cabinets

(P-4317)
K & Z CABINET CO INC
1450 S Grove Ave, Ontario (91761-4523)
PHONE....................................909 947-3567
Dennis Chan, *President*
Mike Twyford, *Plant Mgr*
Troy Zerillo, *Sr Project Mgr*
EMP: 60
SQ FT: 59,000
SALES: 12.2MM **Privately Held**
SIC: 2434 2431 Wood kitchen cabinets;
millwork

(P-4318)
KENEY MANUFACTURING CO (PA)
Also Called: Keney's Cabinets
586 Broadway Ave, Atwater (95301-4408)
P.O. Box 518 (95301-0518)
PHONE....................................209 358-6474
Robert Hernandez, *Partner*
Rodney Haygood, *Partner*
EMP: 16
SALES (est): 1.5MM **Privately Held**
SIC: 2434 Wood kitchen cabinets

(P-4319)
KEYSTONE CABINETRY INC
3110 N Clybourn Ave, Burbank
(91505-1050)
PHONE....................................818 565-3330
Julian Sahagun, *CEO*
Amber Sahagun, *COO*
EMP: 10
SQ FT: 8,000
SALES (est): 1.3MM **Privately Held**
WEB: www.keystonecabinetry.com
SIC: 2434 Wood kitchen cabinets

(P-4320)
KINGSBURG CABINET INC
Also Called: Kingsbury Cabinets
1000 14th Ave Ste A, Kingsburg
(93631-2475)
PHONE....................................559 897-7716
Michael J Harder, *President*
Tammy Harder, *CFO*
Esther Harder, *Admin Sec*
EMP: 12
SQ FT: 7,800
SALES (est): 1.3MM **Privately Held**
SIC: 2434 Vanities, bathroom: wood

(P-4321)
KITCHENS NOW INC
20 Blue Sky Ct, Sacramento (95828-1015)
PHONE....................................916 229-8222
Douglas Carl Schubert, *CEO*
Kevin Sexton, *COO*
Daniel Rodriguez, *Project Mgr*
Xavier Salazar, *Project Mgr*
EMP: 17
SALES (est): 2.5MM **Privately Held**
SIC: 2434 Wood kitchen cabinets

(P-4322)
KOBIS WINDOWS & DOORS MFG INC
7326 Laurel Canyon Blvd, North Hollywood
(91605-3710)
PHONE....................................818 764-6400
Kobi Louria, *CEO*
Kathleen Joseph, *Sales Staff*
▲ EMP: 25 EST: 1999
SALES (est): 6.1MM **Privately Held**
SIC: 2434 2431 1522 Vanities, bathroom:
wood; millwork; residential construction

(P-4323)
LA BATH VANITY INC
2222 Davie Ave, Commerce (90040-1708)
PHONE....................................909 303-3323
EMP: 16 **Privately Held**
SIC: 2434 Vanities, bathroom: wood
PA: La Bath Vanity Inc.
1071 W 9th St
Upland CA 91786

(P-4324)
LA HABRA CABINET INC
540 S Cypress St, La Habra (90631-6127)
PHONE....................................562 691-0681
Ralph Clifton, *President*
John Clifton, *Corp Secy*
John Hanscom, *Vice Pres*
EMP: 210 EST: 1963
SQ FT: 60,000
SALES (est): 1.1MM **Privately Held**
SIC: 2434 Wood kitchen cabinets

(P-4325)
LACKEY WOODWORKING INC
2730 Chanticleer Ave, Santa Cruz
(95065-1812)
PHONE....................................831 462-0528
John E Lackey, *President*
Kathy Lackey, *Principal*

EMP: 13 EST: 1974
SQ FT: 6,000
SALES: 750K **Privately Held**
WEB: www.lackeywoodworking.com
SIC: 2434 2541 2431 2511 Wood kitchen
cabinets; cabinets, except refrigerated:
show, display, etc.: wood; doors, wood;
wood household furniture; signboards,
wood

(P-4326)
M AND M CABINETS INC
33238 Central Ave, Union City
(94587-2010)
PHONE....................................510 324-4034
Mark Mc Gee, *President*
Tim Mc Gee, *Treasurer*
Shirley Milburn, *Vice Pres*
EMP: 10
SQ FT: 2,500
SALES (est): 1.4MM **Privately Held**
SIC: 2434 Wood kitchen cabinets

(P-4327)
MASTERBRAND CABINETS INC
3700 S Riverside Ave, Colton
(92324-3329)
PHONE....................................951 686-3614
Michael Mejia, *Manager*
EMP: 50
SALES (corp-wide): 5.2B **Publicly Held**
WEB: www.mbcabinets.com
SIC: 2434 Wood kitchen cabinets
HQ: Masterbrand Cabinets, Inc.
1 Masterbrand Cabinets Dr
Jasper IN 47546
812 482-2527

(P-4328)
MILLBROOK KITCHENS INC
15960 Downey Ave, Paramount
(90723-5116)
PHONE....................................310 684-3366
▲ EMP: 15
SQ FT: 450,000
SALES: 450K **Privately Held**
SIC: 2434 1799

(P-4329)
MILLWOOD CABINET CO INC
2321 Virginia Ave, Bakersfield
(93307-2545)
PHONE....................................661 327-0371
David T Millwood Jr, *President*
Sandra Millwood, *Treasurer*
Diana Shackelford, *Admin Sec*
EMP: 23
SQ FT: 18,000
SALES (est): 4.3MM **Privately Held**
SIC: 2434 2541 Wood kitchen cabinets;
wood partitions & fixtures

(P-4330)
MISSION BELL MFG CO INC
25656 Schulte Ct, Tracy (95377-8643)
PHONE....................................209 229-7280
Terry Silva, *Manager*
EMP: 25
SALES (corp-wide): 19.1MM **Privately
Held**
SIC: 2434 2431 Wood kitchen cabinets;
millwork
PA: Mission Bell Mfg. Co., Inc.
16100 Jacqueline Ct
Morgan Hill CA 95037
408 778-2036

(P-4331)
MITCHELL DEAN COLLINS
12771 Monarch St, Garden Grove
(92841-3920)
P.O. Box 48, Sunset Beach (90742-0048)
PHONE....................................714 894-6767
Mitchell Collins, *Owner*
Sophia Staveley, *Office Mgr*
Jason Guthrie, *Project Mgr*
Phil Staveley, *Project Mgr*
Bob Staveley, *Sales Staff*
EMP: 10
SALES (est): 1.1MM **Privately Held**
SIC: 2434 Wood kitchen cabinets

(P-4332)
NORM TESSIER CABINETS INC
11989 6th St, Rancho Cucamonga
(91730-6133)
PHONE....................................909 987-8955
David L Beavers, *President*
Denise Beavers, *Vice Pres*
EMP: 35
SQ FT: 20,000
SALES: 2MM **Privately Held**
WEB: www.normtessiercabinets.com
SIC: 2434 Wood kitchen cabinets

(P-4333)
PACIFIC HARDWOOD CABINETRY
2811 Dowd Dr, Santa Rosa (95407-7897)
PHONE....................................707 528-8627
Daniel G Bauman, *Owner*
EMP: 30
SQ FT: 41,000
SALES (est): 2.4MM **Privately Held**
SIC: 2434 Wood kitchen cabinets

(P-4334)
PATRICKS CABINETS
10160 Redwood Ave, Fontana
(92335-6237)
P.O. Box 787, Yucaipa (92399-0787)
PHONE....................................909 823-2524
Chris Dyer, *Owner*
EMP: 12
SQ FT: 10,000
SALES (est): 1.4MM **Privately Held**
SIC: 2434 Vanities, bathroom: wood

(P-4335)
PELICAN WOODWORKS
560 Birch St Ste 2, Lake Elsinore
(92530-2726)
PHONE....................................951 674-7821
Richard Mancuso, *Partner*
Frank Mc Whirt, *Partner*
EMP: 25
SQ FT: 11,000
SALES (est): 2.5MM **Privately Held**
SIC: 2434 2541 Wood kitchen cabinets;
counters or counter display cases, wood

(P-4336)
PROGRESSIVE WOODWORK
2255 Ceanothus Ave, Chico (95926-1661)
P.O. Box 1371 (95927-1371)
PHONE....................................530 343-2211
Gary Mc Connell, *Owner*
EMP: 15 EST: 1992
SQ FT: 10,000
SALES: 500K **Privately Held**
SIC: 2434 Vanities, bathroom: wood

(P-4337)
QUALITY CABINET AND FIXTURE CO (HQ)
7955 Saint Andrews Ave, San Diego
(92154-8224)
PHONE....................................619 266-1011
Michael J Floyd, *CEO*
Donald Paradise, *Ch of Bd*
Tim Paradise, *President*
Andrew Meek, *CFO*
Nicholas P Willems, *CFO*
▲ EMP: 24
SQ FT: 55,000
SALES (est): 3.9MM
SALES (corp-wide): 25.4MM **Privately
Held**
WEB: www.qcfc.com
SIC: 2434 Wood kitchen cabinets
PA: Glenn Rieder, Inc.
6520 W Becher Pl
Milwaukee WI 53219
414 449-2888

(P-4338)
QUALITY CRAFT CABINETS INC
504 E Duarte Rd, Monrovia (91016-4604)
PHONE....................................626 358-2021
Andrew Riccardo, *President*
Steve Riccardo, *Vice Pres*
EMP: 14 EST: 1966
SQ FT: 8,000
SALES (est): 1.4MM **Privately Held**
SIC: 2434 Wood kitchen cabinets

(P-4339)
QUALITY WOODWORKS INC
261a Redel Rd, San Marcos (92078-4347)
PHONE................................760 744-4748
Greg Durmer, *President*
Charles Somers, *Vice Pres*
EMP: 28
SQ FT: 10,000
SALES (est): 3.2MM **Privately Held**
SIC: 2434 Wood kitchen cabinets

(P-4340)
R A JENSON MANUFACTURING CO
1337 Van Dyke Ave, San Francisco (94124-3312)
PHONE................................415 822-2732
Richard A Jenson, *President*
Rita Jenson, *Vice Pres*
Ron Smith, *Vice Pres*
Laura Jenson, *Admin Sec*
Richard Bailen,
EMP: 15 EST: 1960
SQ FT: 7,500
SALES (est): 1.7MM **Privately Held**
SIC: 2434 Vanities, bathroom: wood

(P-4341)
RAWSON CUSTOM CABINETS INC (PA)
16890 Church St Bldg 1a, Morgan Hill (95037-5114)
PHONE................................408 779-9838
Dennis Rawson, *President*
Patricia Rawson, *Admin Sec*
EMP: 24 EST: 1975
SQ FT: 19,300
SALES (est): 1.6MM **Privately Held**
WEB: www.rawson-cabinets.com
SIC: 2434 Wood kitchen cabinets

(P-4342)
REGAL KITCHENS LLC
3480 Sunset Ln, Oxnard (93035-4129)
PHONE................................786 953-6578
Tony Pace, *President*
George Flack, *CFO*
Robert Sweeney,
◆ EMP: 200 EST: 1957
SQ FT: 168,000
SALES (est): 21.7MM **Privately Held**
WEB: www.regalkitchensinc.com
SIC: 2434 Wood kitchen cabinets

(P-4343)
ROCHAS CABINETS
108 Industrial Park Dr # 17, Manteca (95337-6128)
PHONE................................209 239-2367
Anthony Rocha, *Partner*
Jared Rocha, *Partner*
Joe Rocha, *Partner*
EMP: 10
SQ FT: 10,500
SALES: 1MM **Privately Held**
SIC: 2434 Vanities, bathroom: wood

(P-4344)
ROYAL CABINETS INC
1299 E Phillips Blvd, Pomona (91766-5429)
PHONE................................909 629-8565
Clay Smith, *President*
Bill Roan, *COO*
▲ EMP: 600
SQ FT: 70,000
SALES (est): 89.6MM **Privately Held**
WEB: www.royalcabinets.com
SIC: 2434 2511 Wood kitchen cabinets; wood household furniture

(P-4345)
ROYAL INDUSTRIES INC
Also Called: Royal Cabinets
1299 E Phillips Blvd, Pomona (91766-5429)
PHONE................................909 629-8565
Clay R Smith, *CEO*
Dan McGinn, *President*
Gus Danjoi, *CFO*
Kathy Goodrow, *Admin Sec*
EMP: 130
SALES (est): 17.5MM **Privately Held**
SIC: 2434 Vanities, bathroom: wood

(P-4346)
RUCKER MILL & CABINET WORKS
5828 Mother Lode Dr, Placerville (95667-8233)
PHONE................................530 621-0236
John Rucker, *President*
Janice Rucker, *Admin Sec*
EMP: 12
SQ FT: 8,800
SALES (est): 1.1MM **Privately Held**
SIC: 2434 2431 1751 Wood kitchen cabinets; millwork; cabinet & finish carpentry

(P-4347)
S M G CUSTOM CABINETS INC
5750 Alder Ave, Sacramento (95828-1112)
PHONE................................916 381-5999
Stephen M Gelasakis, *President*
Mike Gelasakis, *Vice Pres*
Maria Gelasakis, *Admin Sec*
EMP: 20
SQ FT: 22,000
SALES (est): 2MM **Privately Held**
SIC: 2434 Wood kitchen cabinets

(P-4348)
SAGE INTERIOR INC
9 Aspen Tree Ln, Irvine (92612-2202)
PHONE................................949 654-0184
Majid Kiani, *President*
EMP: 12
SALES (est): 2MM **Privately Held**
SIC: 2434 Wood kitchen cabinets

(P-4349)
SAN DIEGO CABINETS INC
2001 Lendee Dr, Escondido (92025-6351)
PHONE................................760 747-3100
Sky Polselli, *President*
EMP: 30
SALES (est): 2.8MM **Privately Held**
SIC: 2434 Wood kitchen cabinets

(P-4350)
SE INDUSTRIES INC
300 W Collins Ave, Orange (92867-5506)
PHONE................................714 744-3200
Jan Schaffer, *President*
EMP: 12
SQ FT: 27,000
SALES (est): 1.3MM **Privately Held**
WEB: www.seindustries.net
SIC: 2434 Wood kitchen cabinets

(P-4351)
SLIGH CABINETS INC
105 Calle Propano, Paso Robles (93446-3929)
PHONE................................805 239-2550
Steve Sligh, *President*
Lynndell Sligh, *Admin Sec*
Jordan Sligh, *Production*
EMP: 14
SQ FT: 30,000
SALES (est): 2.1MM **Privately Held**
WEB: www.slighcabinets.com
SIC: 2434 Vanities, bathroom: wood

(P-4352)
SOUTHCOAST CABINET INC (PA)
755 Pinefalls Ave, Walnut (91789-3027)
PHONE................................909 594-3089
Dante M Senese, *CEO*
John Lopez, *President*
Ron St Jean, *Safety Mgr*
Scott Fibrow, *Opers Mgr*
Craig Creese, *Foreman/Supr*
EMP: 50
SQ FT: 108,000
SALES (est): 12.6MM **Privately Held**
WEB: www.southcoastcabinet.com
SIC: 2434 Wood kitchen cabinets

(P-4353)
STEVE AND CYNTHIA KIZANIS
Also Called: Kizanis Custom Cabinets
2483 Washington Ave, San Leandro (94577-5920)
PHONE................................510 352-2832
Steve Kizanis, *Owner*
Cynthia Kizanis, *Co-Owner*
John Fillipucci, *Sales Associate*
EMP: 13

SQ FT: 10,000
SALES (est): 740K **Privately Held**
SIC: 2434 Wood kitchen cabinets

(P-4354)
SUPERIOR MILLWORK OF SB INC
7330 Hollister Ave Ste B, Goleta (93117-2868)
PHONE................................805 685-1744
Joseph Morin, *President*
Diana Morin, *CFO*
EMP: 24
SQ FT: 10,000
SALES (est): 2MM **Privately Held**
SIC: 2434 2431 Wood kitchen cabinets; millwork

(P-4355)
T L CLARK CO INC
Also Called: Orion Woodcraft
3430 Kurtz St, San Diego (92110-4429)
PHONE................................619 230-1400
Thomas Clark, *President*
Matt Moody, *Manager*
EMP: 18
SQ FT: 8,000
SALES (est): 1MM **Privately Held**
WEB: www.orionwoodcraft.com
SIC: 2434 2499 Wood kitchen cabinets; laundry products, wood

(P-4356)
TARA ENTERPRISES INC
27023 Mack Bean Pkwy, Valencia (91355)
PHONE................................661 510-2206
EMP: 15
SALES (est): 1.2MM **Privately Held**
SIC: 2434

(P-4357)
TAYLOR COMPANY
Also Called: Taylor Cabinet Door Company
4646 Qantas Ln Ste B14, Stockton (95206-4981)
P.O. Box 567, Byron (94514-0567)
PHONE................................209 933-9747
Michael A Taylor, *Owner*
EMP: 18
SQ FT: 30,000
SALES (est): 1.6MM **Privately Held**
WEB: www.taylorcabinetdoor.com
SIC: 2434 Wood kitchen cabinets

(P-4358)
TONUSA LLC
Also Called: Contemporary Bath.com
16770 E Johnson Dr, City of Industry (91745-2414)
PHONE................................626 961-8700
Yin Ming Ng,
Christine Hsu, *Opers Staff*
Raymond Kovacs, *Opers Staff*
James Ng,
Dan Yu Chan Tseng,
◆ EMP: 15
SQ FT: 4,000
SALES (est): 2.3MM **Privately Held**
SIC: 2434 Vanities, bathroom: wood

(P-4359)
TRUE DESIGN INC
9427 Norwalk Blvd, Santa Fe Springs (90670-2943)
PHONE................................562 699-2001
Hani ABI Naked, *CEO*
Thomas Cavelti, *CFO*
EMP: 15 EST: 2014
SQ FT: 17,000
SALES (est): 3MM **Privately Held**
SIC: 2434 Wood kitchen cabinets

(P-4360)
TURLOCK CABINET SHOP INC
1475 West Ave S, Turlock (95380-5740)
PHONE................................209 632-1311
Richard Lopes, *President*
Carolyn Lopes, *Admin Sec*
EMP: 11
SQ FT: 8,600
SALES (est): 1.1MM **Privately Held**
SIC: 2434 Wood kitchen cabinets

(P-4361)
ULTRA BUILT KITCHENS INC
1814 E 43rd St, Los Angeles (90058-1517)
PHONE................................323 232-3362
Iris Yanes, *President*
Eduardo Yanes, *Treasurer*
Daisy Blanco, *Vice Pres*
EMP: 28
SQ FT: 18,000
SALES (est): 3.7MM **Privately Held**
WEB: www.ultrabuiltkitchens.net
SIC: 2434 Vanities, bathroom: wood

(P-4362)
UNITED GRANITE & CABINETS LLC
5225 Central Ave, Richmond (94804-5805)
PHONE................................510 558-8999
Paul Yu, *Owner*
Simon Yu CHI Ao, *Principal*
▲ EMP: 13
SALES (est): 630K **Privately Held**
SIC: 2434 Wood kitchen cabinets

(P-4363)
VAKNIN JUDA
Also Called: Juda's Custom Cabinets
7359 Fulton Ave, North Hollywood (91605-4114)
PHONE................................818 503-8872
Juda Vaknin, *Owner*
EMP: 10
SALES (est): 510.6K **Privately Held**
SIC: 2434 2517 Wood kitchen cabinets; wood television & radio cabinets

(P-4364)
VALLEY CASEWORK INC
1112 Cleghorn Way, Alpine (91901-2907)
PHONE................................619 579-6886
Fax: 619 579-0701
EMP: 60
SQ FT: 15,000
SALES (est): 5.9MM **Privately Held**
WEB: www.valleycasework.com
SIC: 2434

(P-4365)
VCSD INC
Also Called: Valley Cabinet
585 Vernon Way, El Cajon (92020-1934)
PHONE................................619 579-6886
Larry Doyle, *President*
Susan Raymond, *CFO*
EMP: 49 EST: 2011
SALES (est): 6.9MM **Privately Held**
SIC: 2434 Wood kitchen cabinets

(P-4366)
VILLAGE COLLECTION INC
1303 Elmer St A, Belmont (94002-4010)
PHONE................................650 594-1635
Martin Phelps, *President*
Debbie Janssen, *Vice Pres*
EMP: 11
SQ FT: 18,000
SALES: 2MM **Privately Held**
WEB: www.thevillagecollection.net
SIC: 2434 5211 1521 Wood kitchen cabinets; cabinets, kitchen; counter tops; single-family housing construction

(P-4367)
W L RUBOTTOM CO
320 W Lewis St, Ventura (93001-1335)
PHONE................................805 648-6943
Gary McCoy, *President*
Lawrence Rubottom, *Vice Pres*
Dene Hawthorne, *Accounting Dir*
EMP: 55 EST: 1946
SQ FT: 40,000
SALES (est): 7.9MM **Privately Held**
WEB: www.rubottomco.com
SIC: 2434 Wood kitchen cabinets

(P-4368)
WEST PACIFIC CABINET MFG
3121 Swetzer Rd Ste A, Loomis (95650-9586)
PHONE................................916 652-6840
Steven Dietz, *President*
Cindy Dietz, *Vice Pres*
EMP: 19
SQ FT: 7,200

SALES (est): 1.8MM **Privately Held**
WEB: www.westpacificcabinets.com
SIC: 2434 2521 Wood kitchen cabinets;
cabinets, office: wood

(P-4369)
WILLIAMS CABINETS INC
2011 Frontier Trl, Anderson (96007-3008)
P.O. Box 915 (96007-0915)
PHONE..................................530 365-8421
Ronald E Raab, *President*
EMP: 10
SQ FT: 7,000
SALES (est): 600K **Privately Held**
SIC: 2434 Vanities, bathroom: wood

(P-4370)
WOODEN BRIDGE INC
483 Reynolds Cir, San Jose (95112-1122)
PHONE..................................408 436-9663
David Baeza, *President*
Dave Toubrn, *Co-Owner*
EMP: 15
SALES (est): 2MM **Privately Held**
WEB: www.woodenbridge.com
SIC: 2434 Wood kitchen cabinets

(P-4371)
WOODLINE PARTNERS INC
Also Called: Woodline Cabinets
5165 Fulton Dr, Fairfield (94534-1638)
PHONE..................................707 864-5445
Grant Paxton, *President*
Paul Mc Kay, *CFO*
Lloyd Alexander, *Opers Mgr*
EMP: 49
SQ FT: 37,500
SALES (est): 4.8MM **Privately Held**
SIC: 2434 Wood kitchen cabinets

(P-4372)
WOODPECKER CABINET INC
21512 Nordhoff St, Chatsworth
(91311-5822)
PHONE..................................310 404-4805
Izaac Sananes, *CEO*
River Cook, *Manager*
EMP: 20
SALES: 1.2MM **Privately Held**
SIC: 2434 1799 Wood kitchen cabinets;
kitchen cabinet installation

(P-4373)
WYNDHAM COLLECTION LLC
1175 Aviation Pl, San Fernando
(91340-1460)
PHONE..................................888 522-8476
Martin Symes, *Mng Member*
Christophe Blondeau, *Vice Pres*
Harry Parsamyan,
Sammy Parsamyan,
Monica Madeja, *Clerk*
EMP: 26 EST: 2011
SQ FT: 100,000
SALES (est): 306K **Privately Held**
SIC: 2434 Vanities, bathroom: wood

(P-4374)
YOUNGS CUSTOM CABINET INC
1760 Yosemite Ave, San Francisco
(94124-2622)
PHONE..................................415 822-8313
Yong X Xiao, *President*
EMP: 10
SALES (est): 905.3K **Privately Held**
SIC: 2434 Vanities, bathroom: wood

(P-4375)
ZIETHING CABINETS INC
200 Briggs Ave, Costa Mesa (92626-4510)
PHONE..................................949 642-6344
James F Zeithing, *President*
EMP: 10
SQ FT: 6,500
SALES (est): 1.4MM **Privately Held**
SIC: 2434 Wood kitchen cabinets

2435 Hardwood Veneer & Plywood

(P-4376)
ARCHITECTURAL PLYWOOD INC
Also Called: API
7104 Case Ave, North Hollywood
(91605-6301)
PHONE..................................818 255-1900
Ernie Huber, *President*
EMP: 20
SQ FT: 35,000
SALES (est): 2.2MM **Privately Held**
WEB: www.apiply.com
SIC: 2435 Plywood, hardwood or hard-
wood faced

(P-4377)
GENERAL VENEER MFG CO
8652 Otis St, South Gate (90280-3292)
P.O. Box 1607 (90280-1607)
PHONE..................................323 564-2661
William Dewitt, *President*
Ed Bewitt, *Treasurer*
Ed Witt, *Treasurer*
Doug Bradley, *Vice Pres*
Douglas Bradley, *Vice Pres*
EMP: 50 EST: 1942
SQ FT: 200,000
SALES (est): 9.8MM **Privately Held**
WEB: www.generalveneer.com
SIC: 2435 3365 Hardwood veneer & ply-
wood; aerospace castings, aluminum

(P-4378)
JC HANSCOM INC
Also Called: Panel Works
11830 Wakeman St, Santa Fe Springs
(90670-2129)
PHONE..................................562 789-9955
John C Hanscom, *President*
Marsha Hanscom, *Vice Pres*
EMP: 16
SQ FT: 23,000
SALES (est): 2.5MM **Privately Held**
WEB: www.panelworks.com
SIC: 2435 Panels, hardwood plywood

(P-4379)
MADRID INC
7800 Industry Ave, Pico Rivera
(90660-4306)
PHONE..................................562 404-9941
Bob Ellis, *President*
EMP: 10
SQ FT: 25,000
SALES (est): 1.7MM **Privately Held**
WEB: www.madridinc.com
SIC: 2435 2511 Hardwood veneer & ply-
wood; wood household furniture

(P-4380)
MALAKAN INC
307 W Broadway Apt 6, Glendale
(91204-1341)
PHONE..................................818 915-0014
Radik Khachatryan, *President*
▲ EMP: 25
SQ FT: 8,000
SALES (est): 1.7MM **Privately Held**
SIC: 2435 Hardwood veneer & plywood

(P-4381)
PACIFIC PANEL PRODUCTS CORP
15601 Arrow Hwy, Irwindale (91706-2004)
P.O. Box 2204 (91706-1126)
PHONE..................................626 851-0444
Jon R Dickey, *CEO*
Sandra Dickey, *Finance Mgr*
Cory Dickey, *Plant Mgr*
Jeff Elliot, *Sales Staff*
Renee Valencia,
▲ EMP: 39
SQ FT: 79,800
SALES (est): 8.2MM **Privately Held**
WEB: www.pacificpanel.com
SIC: 2435 Panels, hardwood plywood

(P-4382)
PLYCRAFT INDUSTRIES INC
Also Called: Concepts & Wood
2100 E Slauson Ave, Huntington Park
(90255-2727)
PHONE..................................323 587-8101
Ashley Joffe, *President*
Nathan Joffe, *CFO*
Donald R Greenberg, *Exec VP*
George Samoya, *CIO*
▲ EMP: 180
SQ FT: 71,187
SALES: 56MM **Privately Held**
SIC: 2435 Plywood, hardwood or hard-
wood faced; veneer stock, hardwood

(P-4383)
SONORA FACE CO
5233 Randolph St, Maywood (90270-3448)
PHONE..................................323 560-8188
Ossiel Calvillo, *President*
▲ EMP: 24
SQ FT: 20,000
SALES (est): 3.8MM **Privately Held**
SIC: 2435 Veneer stock, hardwood

(P-4384)
SPACEWALL INC
Also Called: Spacewall West Slotwall Mfg
350 E Crowther Ave, Placentia
(92870-6419)
PHONE..................................714 961-1300
Terry Sexton, *Manager*
EMP: 12
SQ FT: 15,605
SALES (corp-wide): 3.9MM **Privately
Held**
WEB: www.spacewall.com
SIC: 2435 5046 Hardwood veneer & ply-
wood; store fixtures & display equipment
PA: Spacewall, Inc.
4509 Stonegate Indus Blvd
Stone Mountain GA 30083
404 294-9564

(P-4385)
SWANER HARDWOOD CO INC (PA)
5 W Magnolia Blvd, Burbank (91502-1776)
PHONE..................................818 953-5350
Keith M Swaner, *CEO*
Gary Swaner, *President*
Stephen Haag, *Treasurer*
Beverly Swaner, *Admin Sec*
David Layland, *Administration*
▲ EMP: 70
SQ FT: 4,500
SALES: 83MM **Privately Held**
WEB: www.swanerhardwood.com
SIC: 2435 5031 Hardwood veneer & ply-
wood; lumber: rough, dressed & finished;
plywood

(P-4386)
TIMBER PRODUCTS CO LTD PARTNR
Also Called: Yreka Division
130 N Phillipe Ln, Yreka (96097-9014)
P.O. Box 766 (96097-0766)
PHONE..................................530 842-2310
Pete Himmel, *Branch Mgr*
EMP: 116
SALES (corp-wide): 357.7MM **Privately
Held**
WEB: www.sor.teamtp.com
SIC: 2435 2436 Veneer stock, hardwood;
softwood veneer & plywood
PA: Timber Products Co. Limited Partner-
ship
305 S 4th St
Springfield OR 97477
541 995-0780

(P-4387)
WOODSOURCE INTERNATIONAL
2201 Dominguez St, Torrance
(90501-1418)
P.O. Box 153, Saint James MO (65559-
0153)
PHONE..................................310 328-9663
Chris Margetis, *Partner*
Dennis Prock, *General Ptnr*
EMP: 10

SALES (est): 111K **Privately Held**
SIC: 2435 Hardwood veneer & plywood

2439 Structural Wood Members, NEC

(P-4388)
ADVANTAGE TRUSS COMPANY LLC
2025 San Juan Rd, Hollister (95023-9601)
PHONE..................................831 635-0377
Jennifer Pfeiffer, *CEO*
Chuck Mullaney,
EMP: 25 EST: 2000
SALES: 3.4MM **Privately Held**
SIC: 2439 1522 Trusses, wooden roof;
residential construction

(P-4389)
ALL-TRUSS INC
22700 Broadway, Sonoma (95476-8233)
PHONE..................................707 938-5595
Robert L Biggs, *President*
EMP: 20
SALES (est): 3.4MM **Privately Held**
WEB: www.alltruss.netfirms.com
SIC: 2439 Trusses, wooden roof

(P-4390)
AMERICAN PACIFIC TRUSS INC
Also Called: American Truss
24265 Rue De Cezanne, Laguna Niguel
(92677-6107)
PHONE..................................949 363-1691
Nouraddin Kharazmi, *CEO*
EMP: 25
SALES (est): 2.3MM **Privately Held**
SIC: 2439 Trusses, wooden roof

(P-4391)
AUTOMATED BLDG COMPONENTS INC
2853 S Orange Ave, Fresno (93725-1921)
PHONE..................................559 485-8232
David Cervantes, *President*
Violet Cervantes, *Treasurer*
Gabriel Cervantes, *Vice Pres*
EMP: 13
SQ FT: 15,669
SALES (est): 1.8MM **Privately Held**
WEB: www.automatedbuildingcompo-
nents.com
SIC: 2439 Trusses, wooden roof

(P-4392)
BETTER BUILT TRUSS INC
251 E 4th St, Ripon (95366-2774)
P.O. Box 1319 (95366-1319)
PHONE..................................209 869-4545
Jeff Qualle, *CEO*
David Sanders, *President*
Andrea Baer, *Planning*
Mariana Cardoso, *Controller*
Melissa Dugan, *Controller*
EMP: 50 EST: 2010
SALES (est): 9.4MM **Privately Held**
SIC: 2439 Trusses, wooden roof

(P-4393)
BROWN & HONEYCUTT TRUSS SYSTMS
16775 Smoke Tree St, Hesperia
(92345-6165)
P.O. Box 401804 (92340-1804)
PHONE..................................760 244-8887
Michael Hough, *President*
EMP: 45
SQ FT: 1,800
SALES (est): 4.7MM **Privately Held**
WEB: www.bhtruss.com
SIC: 2439 Trusses, wooden roof

(P-4394)
CAL-ASIA TRUSS INC
10547 E Stockton Blvd, Elk Grove
(95624-9743)
PHONE..................................916 685-5648
Richard Avery, *Manager*
EMP: 46
SALES (corp-wide): 5MM **Privately Held**
WEB: www.cal-asia.com
SIC: 2439 Trusses, wooden roof

PA: Cal-Asia Truss, Inc.
2300 Clayton Rd Ste 1400
Concord CA 94520
925 680-7701

(P-4395)
CALIFORNIA TRUSFRAME LLC
144 Commerce Way, Sanger (93657)
PHONE...................................951 657-7491
EMP: 595 **Privately Held**
SIC: 2439 Trusses, wooden roof
PA: California Trusframe, Llc
23665 Cajalco Rd
Perris CA 92570

(P-4396)
CALIFORNIA TRUSFRAME LLC (PA)
Also Called: C T F
23665 Cajalco Rd, Perris (92570-8181)
PHONE...................................951 657-7491
Steve Stroder, *CEO*
Susan Engquist, *CFO*
Kenneth Cloyd, *Chairman*
Jason Walsh, *VP Sales*
EMP: 90
SQ FT: 5,000
SALES: 110MM **Privately Held**
SIC: 2439 Trusses, wooden roof

(P-4397)
CALIFORNIA TRUSS COMPANY (PA)
23665 Cajalco Rd, Perris (92570-8181)
PHONE...................................951 657-7491
Kennenth M Cloyd, *President*
Jim Butler, *CFO*
Mike Ruede, *Vice Pres*
Jim Swan, *Engineer*
Martha Lara, *Foreman/Supr*
EMP: 65
SQ FT: 5,000
SALES (est): 41.1MM **Privately Held**
SIC: 2439 Trusses, wooden roof

(P-4398)
CALIFORNIA TRUSS COMPANY
2800 Tully Rd, Hughson (95326-9640)
PHONE...................................209 883-8000
Kenneth Cloyd, *President*
EMP: 30
SALES (corp-wide): 41.1MM **Privately Held**
SIC: 2439 Trusses, wooden roof
PA: California Truss Company
23665 Cajalco Rd
Perris CA 92570
951 657-7491

(P-4399)
COMMERCIAL TRUSS CO
Also Called: Alliance Trutrus
10731 Treena St Ste 207, San Diego (92131-1041)
PHONE...................................858 693-1771
Dan Hershey, *President*
EMP: 50
SALES: 20MM **Privately Held**
SIC: 2439 Structural wood members

(P-4400)
COMPU TECH LUMBER PRODUCTS
1980 Huntington Ct, Fairfield (94533-9753)
PHONE...................................707 437-6683
Walter L Young, *President*
Michael Blazer, *CFO*
Greg Young, *Vice Pres*
EMP: 80
SQ FT: 94,657
SALES (est): 11.9MM **Privately Held**
SIC: 2439 2431 1742 Trusses, wooden roof; doors & door parts & trim, wood; plastering, plain or ornamental

(P-4401)
CY TRUSS
10715 E American Ave, Del Rey (93616-9703)
P.O. Box 188 (93616-0188)
PHONE...................................559 888-2160
Dave Campos, *Owner*
EMP: 30

SALES: 1MM **Privately Held**
SIC: 2439 Trusses, wooden roof

(P-4402)
DIAMOND TRUSS
12462 Charles Dr, Grass Valley (95945-9371)
PHONE...................................530 477-1477
Joseph C Droivold, *Principal*
EMP: 12
SALES (est): 1.5MM **Privately Held**
SIC: 2439 Trusses, wooden roof

(P-4403)
EL DORADO TRUSS COINC
300 Industrial Dr, Placerville (95667-6828)
PHONE...................................530 622-1264
Steve Stewart, *President*
Edith Stewart, *Corp Secy*
EMP: 45
SQ FT: 15,000
SALES (est): 5.9MM **Privately Held**
SIC: 2439 Trusses, wooden roof

(P-4404)
ENTRUSSED LLC
5065 Commercial Pl, Sheridan (95681-9601)
PHONE...................................916 753-5406
Dale Ebberts, *Mng Member*
EMP: 10
SQ FT: 720
SALES (est): 546.4K **Privately Held**
SIC: 2439 Trusses, except roof: laminated lumber

(P-4405)
GENERAL TRUSS COMPANY INC
6947 Power Inn Rd, Sacramento (95828-2402)
PHONE...................................916 388-9300
Dieter Jurgens, *President*
Rosa Miramontes, *Office Mgr*
EMP: 18
SALES (est): 3.3MM **Privately Held**
WEB: www.generaltruss.com
SIC: 2439 Trusses, wooden roof

(P-4406)
GOLDENWOOD TRUSS CORPORATION
11032 Nardo St, Ventura (93004-3210)
PHONE...................................805 659-2520
Kevin Tollefson, *President*
Darin Ranson, *Vice Pres*
Myron Hodgson, *Admin Sec*
EMP: 80
SALES (est): 12.9MM **Privately Held**
WEB: www.goldenwoodtruss.com
SIC: 2439 Trusses, wooden roof

(P-4407)
HAISCH CONSTRUCTION CO INC
Also Called: Systems Plus Lumber
1800 S Barney Rd, Anderson (96007-9703)
PHONE...................................530 378-6800
Matthew C Haisch, *CEO*
Bill Ivey, *Corp Secy*
Douglas C Haisch, *Principal*
Tony Lobue, *Program Mgr*
EMP: 18 **EST:** 1968
SQ FT: 10,000
SALES (est): 3.9MM **Privately Held**
WEB: www.systplus.com
SIC: 2439 3441 Trusses, wooden roof; fabricated structural metal

(P-4408)
HANSON TRUSS INC (PA)
13950 Yorba Ave, Chino (91710-5520)
PHONE...................................909 591-9256
Donald R Hanson, *President*
Tom Hanson, *Corp Secy*
EMP: 110
SQ FT: 4,000
SALES (est): 37.6MM **Privately Held**
SIC: 2439 Trusses, wooden roof

(P-4409)
HANSON TRUSS COMPONENTS INC
4476 Skyway Dr, Olivehurst (95961-7477)
P.O. Box 31, Marysville (95901-0001)
PHONE...................................530 740-7750
Steven L Hanson, *President*
EMP: 60
SALES: 6MM **Privately Held**
SIC: 2439 Trusses, except roof: laminated lumber

(P-4410)
HIGH SIERRA TRUSS COMPANY INC
1201 S K St, Tulare (93274-6424)
PHONE...................................559 688-6611
Oral E Micham, *President*
Jerry Kramlich, *General Mgr*
EMP: 14
SQ FT: 800
SALES (est): 1.9MM **Privately Held**
SIC: 2439 Arches, laminated lumber

(P-4411)
HOMEWOOD COMPONENTS INC
Also Called: Homewood Truss
5033 Feather River Blvd, Marysville (95901)
PHONE...................................530 743-8855
Hamid Noorani, *President*
Lain Moss, *Treasurer*
Adam Noorani, *Director*
EMP: 65
SQ FT: 120,000
SALES (est): 7MM **Privately Held**
SIC: 2439 Trusses, wooden roof; trusses, except roof: laminated lumber

(P-4412)
INLAND EMPIRE TRUSS INC (PA)
275 W Rider St, Perris (92571-3225)
PHONE...................................951 300-1758
Daniel W Irwin, *President*
EMP: 24
SALES (est): 4.1MM **Privately Held**
WEB: www.ietruss.com
SIC: 2439 Trusses, wooden roof

(P-4413)
INLAND TRUSS INC (PA)
275 W Rider St, Perris (92571-3225)
PHONE...................................951 300-1758
Dan Irwin, *President*
Ernie Castro, *Treasurer*
Daniel Irwin, *Executive*
Debbie Meier, *Office Mgr*
Jason Irwin, *Sales Mgr*
EMP: 66
SQ FT: 1,200
SALES (est): 5.1MM **Privately Held**
SIC: 2439 Trusses, wooden roof

(P-4414)
INLAND VALLEY TRUSS INC
150 N Sinclair Ave, Stockton (95215-5132)
PHONE...................................209 943-4710
Daniel Irwin, *President*
Dan Irwin, *President*
EMP: 11
SALES (est): 1.4MM **Privately Held**
WEB: www.inlandvalleytruss.com
SIC: 2439 Trusses, wooden roof
PA: Inland Empire Truss, Inc.
275 W Rider St
Perris CA 92571

(P-4415)
INTER MOUNTAIN TRUSS & GIRDER
596 Armstrong Way, Oakdale (95361-9367)
PHONE...................................209 847-9184
Paul Girard, *President*
Lance B Lester, *Treasurer*
EMP: 18
SQ FT: 1,632
SALES (est): 2.4MM **Privately Held**
SIC: 2439 Trusses, wooden roof

(P-4416)
JIM ELLIS
Also Called: Ellis Truss Company
16797 Live Oak St, Hesperia (92345-6209)
PHONE...................................760 244-8566
Jim Ellis, *Owner*
Sherry Vanillo, *CFO*
EMP: 15
SQ FT: 4,328
SALES (est): 1.3MM **Privately Held**
SIC: 2439 Trusses, wooden roof

(P-4417)
KATERRA INC
2302 Paradise Rd, Tracy (95304-8530)
PHONE...................................623 236-5322
Matt Ryan, *Branch Mgr*
EMP: 703
SALES (corp-wide): 125MM **Privately Held**
SIC: 2439 2421 2434 Trusses, wooden roof; lumber: rough, sawed or planed; wood kitchen cabinets
PA: Katerra Inc.
2494 Sand Hill Rd Ste 100
Menlo Park CA 94025
650 422-3572

(P-4418)
LASSEN FOREST PRODUCTS INC
22829 Casale Rd, Red Bluff (96080)
P.O. Box 8520 (96080-8520)
PHONE...................................530 527-7677
Peter Brunello Jr, *President*
EMP: 42
SQ FT: 30,000
SALES (est): 5.8MM **Privately Held**
SIC: 2439 5031 Structural wood members; lumber, plywood & millwork

(P-4419)
PACIFIC COAST SUPPLY LLC
Also Called: Pacific Supply
5550 Roseville Rd, North Highlands (95660-5038)
PHONE...................................916 339-8100
Wayne Tibke, *Branch Mgr*
Heather Miller, *Administration*
Leslie Blomquist, *Tax Mgr*
Robert Hollis, *Manager*
EMP: 18
SALES (corp-wide): 1.7B **Privately Held**
SIC: 2439 Structural wood members
HQ: Pacific Coast Supply, Llc
4290 Roseville Rd
North Highlands CA 95660
916 971-2301

(P-4420)
SAN DIEGO COUNTY TRUSS INC
7462 Mission Gorge Rd, San Diego (92120-1302)
PHONE...................................619 286-8787
Gary Farrar, *President*
EMP: 10
SALES: 1.2MM **Privately Held**
WEB: www.sandiegocountytruss.com
SIC: 2439 Trusses, wooden roof

(P-4421)
SIMPSON STRONG-TIE COMPANY INC
12246 Holly St, Riverside (92509-2314)
PHONE...................................714 871-8373
Dave Bastian, *Branch Mgr*
EMP: 250
SQ FT: 40,845
SALES (corp-wide): 977MM **Publicly Held**
SIC: 2439 3429 Structural wood members; manufactured hardware (general)
HQ: Simpson Strong-Tie Company Inc.
5956 W Las Positas Blvd
Pleasanton CA 94588
925 560-9000

(P-4422)
SOUTHERN CALIFORNIA COMPONENTS
9927 C Ave, Hesperia (92345-6048)
P.O. Box 401550 (92340-1550)
PHONE...................................760 949-5144
James Mc Cabe, *President*
EMP: 62 **EST:** 1978

▲ = Import ▼=Export
◆ =Import/Export

SQ FT: 2,000
SALES (est): 5MM **Privately Held**
WEB: www.socalcomp.com
SIC: 2439 Trusses, wooden roof

(P-4423)
SPATES FABRICATORS INC
85435 Middleton, Thermal (92274-9619)
PHONE..................................760 397-4122
Tom Spates, *President*
David Spates, *Vice Pres*
Frankie Spates, *Admin Sec*
EMP: 51 EST: 1976
SQ FT: 40,000
SALES (est): 20.2MM **Privately Held**
WEB: www.spates.com
SIC: 2439 Trusses, except roof: laminated
  lumber; trusses, wooden roof

(P-4424)
SPS INC
3000 E Miraloma Ave, Anaheim
(92806-1808)
PHONE..................................714 632-7131
EMP: 12
SALES (est): 1.7MM **Privately Held**
SIC: 2439 Trusses, wooden roof

(P-4425)
STONE TRUSS LLC (PA)
507 Jones Rd, Oceanside (92058-1217)
PHONE..................................951 255-6958
Valerie Thomas, *Mng Member*
Steven Hall, *Principal*
Charles Signorino, *Principal*
Christopher Thomas, *Principal*
Richard Thomas, *General Mgr*
EMP: 10
SQ FT: 80
SALES: 621.5K **Privately Held**
SIC: 2439 Trusses, wooden roof

(P-4426)
STRUCTURAL WOOD SYSTEMS
505 San Bernardino Blvd, Ridgecrest
(93555-8236)
PHONE..................................760 375-2772
Gary Allred, *Owner*
EMP: 10
SQ FT: 1,000
SALES (est): 897.2K **Privately Held**
SIC: 2439 Trusses, except roof: laminated
  lumber

(P-4427)
**T L TIMMERMAN
CONSTRUCTION**
Also Called: Timco
9845 Santa Fe Ave E, Hesperia
(92345-6216)
P.O. Box 402563 (92340-2563)
PHONE..................................760 244-2532
Timothy L Timmerman, *President*
Anita Timmerman, *Vice Pres*
EMP: 30 EST: 1976
SQ FT: 7,700
SALES (est): 3.7MM **Privately Held**
SIC: 2439 Trusses, wooden roof

(P-4428)
**TRI STATE TRUSS
CORPORATION**
600 River Rd, Needles (92363)
P.O. Box 628 (92363-0628)
PHONE..................................760 326-3868
Richard C Huebner, *CEO*
Mike Terry, *President*
EMP: 18 EST: 1978
SQ FT: 1,500
SALES (est): 2.4MM **Privately Held**
SIC: 2439 Trusses, wooden roof; trusses,
  except roof: laminated lumber

(P-4429)
TRI-CO BUILDING SUPPLY INC
Also Called: Truspro
695 Obispo St, Guadalupe (93434-1631)
P.O. Box 850 (93434-0850)
PHONE..................................805 343-2555
Patrick A Herring Sr, *President*
Memory Herring, *Corp Secy*
Steve Herring, *Vice Pres*
EMP: 51 EST: 1975
SQ FT: 2,500
SALES (est): 7.3MM **Privately Held**
SIC: 2439 Trusses, wooden roof

(P-4430)
TRI-K TRUSS COMPANY
453 S Main St, Porterville (93257-5323)
PHONE..................................559 784-8511
Larry Hansen, *President*
Ginger Hansen, *Vice Pres*
EMP: 16 EST: 2000
SQ FT: 2,200
SALES (est): 2.5MM **Privately Held**
WEB: www.tri-k-truss.com
SIC: 2439 Trusses, wooden roof

(P-4431)
TRUSS ENGINEERING INC
477 Zeff Rd, Modesto (95351-3943)
P.O. Box 580210 (95358-0005)
PHONE..................................209 527-6387
Lawrence O Brien, *President*
EMP: 20
SQ FT: 14,000
SALES (est): 3MM **Privately Held**
WEB: www.trussengineering.com
SIC: 2439 Trusses, wooden roof

2441 Wood Boxes

(P-4432)
A & J INDUSTRIES INC
Also Called: A & J Manufacturing
1430 240th St, Harbor City (90710-1307)
P.O. Box 90596, Los Angeles (90009-0596)
PHONE..................................310 216-2170
Patrick Doucette, *CEO*
Keith Bell, *Admin Sec*
◆ EMP: 18
SQ FT: 40,000
SALES: 3MM **Privately Held**
WEB: www.ajcases.com
SIC: 2441 Chests & trunks, wood; tool
  chests, wood; shipping cases, wood:
  nailed or lock corner; packing cases,
  wood: nailed or lock corner

(P-4433)
ARBO BOX INC
2900 Supply Ave, Commerce (90040-2708)
PHONE..................................562 404-2726
Robert Wharton, *CEO*
EMP: 45
SQ FT: 14,200
SALES: 2.4MM **Privately Held**
WEB: www.arbobox.com
SIC: 2441 Nailed wood boxes & shook

(P-4434)
ARMORED GROUP INC
Also Called: Innerspace Cases
11555 Cantara St, North Hollywood
(91605-1652)
PHONE..................................818 767-3030
Louis Kaye, *President*
Loretta Kaye, *Corp Secy*
EMP: 25 EST: 1986
SQ FT: 15,000
SALES (est): 4.5MM **Privately Held**
WEB: www.innerspacecases.com
SIC: 2441 Cases, wood

(P-4435)
**BASAW MANUFACTURING INC
(PA)**
7300 Varna Ave, North Hollywood
(91605-4008)
PHONE..................................818 765-6650
Robert Allen, *President*
Hugh Mullen, *Treasurer*
Eleazar Padilla, *Vice Pres*
Jorge Cea,
Martha Rivera,
▲ EMP: 32
SQ FT: 63,165
SALES (est): 8.6MM **Privately Held**
WEB: www.basaw.com
SIC: 2441 7389 Shipping cases, wood:
  nailed or lock corner; packaging & label-
  ing services

(P-4436)
BASAW SERVICES INC
7300 Varna Ave, North Hollywood
(91605-4008)
PHONE..................................818 765-6650
Robert Allen, *Vice Pres*
EMP: 50

SALES (corp-wide): 8.6MM **Privately
Held**
WEB: www.basaw.com
SIC: 2441 Shipping cases, wood: nailed or
  lock corner
PA: Basaw Manufacturing Inc
  7300 Varna Ave
  North Hollywood CA 91605
  818 765-6650

(P-4437)
BASAW SERVICES INC
13340 Raymer St, North Hollywood
(91605-4101)
PHONE..................................818 765-6650
Robert Allen, *Manager*
EMP: 40
SALES (corp-wide): 8.6MM **Privately
Held**
WEB: www.basaw.com
SIC: 2441 Shipping cases, wood: nailed or
  lock corner
PA: Basaw Manufacturing Inc
  7300 Varna Ave
  North Hollywood CA 91605
  818 765-6650

(P-4438)
**CAL-COAST PKG & CRATING
INC**
2040 E 220th St, Carson (90810-1603)
PHONE..................................310 518-7215
Dale Loughry, *President*
▲ EMP: 35 EST: 1957
SQ FT: 58,000
SALES (est): 3.9MM **Privately Held**
WEB: www.calcoastpacking.com
SIC: 2441 2449 Shipping cases, wood:
  nailed or lock corner; wood containers

(P-4439)
CASE HARDIGG CENTER
651 Barrington Ave Ste A, Ontario
(91764-5115)
PHONE..................................413 665-2163
Natalie Cohen, *Manager*
EMP: 10
SALES (est): 943K **Privately Held**
SIC: 2441 Shipping cases, wood: nailed or
  lock corner

(P-4440)
EL CAMINO WOOD PRODUCTS
16816 S Broadway, Gardena (90248-3110)
PHONE..................................310 768-3447
Donald Bailey Jr, *Owner*
EMP: 10
SQ FT: 4,000
SALES (est): 716.9K **Privately Held**
SIC: 2441 Boxes, wood

(P-4441)
FCA LLC
3810 Transport St, Ventura (93003-5126)
PHONE..................................805 477-9901
Carol S Kilburg, *President*
EMP: 18 **Privately Held**
SIC: 2441 Cases, wood
PA: Fca, Llc
  7601 John Deere Pkwy
  Moline IL 61265
  -

(P-4442)
ICM PACKAGING INC
1604 W Collins Ave, Orange (92867-5421)
PHONE..................................714 744-4836
Jon M Trefethen, *President*
EMP: 22
SQ FT: 20,000
SALES (est): 3.9MM **Privately Held**
WEB: www.icmpackaging.com
SIC: 2441 Boxes, wood

(P-4443)
MEZA PALLET INC
14619 Merrill Ave, Fontana (92335-4219)
PHONE..................................909 829-0223
Leodegario G Meza, *President*
Michael Meza, *President*
EMP: 15
SALES (est): 3MM **Privately Held**
SIC: 2441 Ammunition boxes, wood

(P-4444)
NEFAB PACKAGING INC
8477 Central Ave, Newark (94560-3431)
PHONE..................................408 678-2500
Ana Gonzales, *Branch Mgr*
EMP: 98
SALES (corp-wide): 454.3MM **Privately
Held**
SIC: 2441 5113 5199 Shipping cases,
  wood: nailed or lock corner; cardboard &
  products; packaging materials
HQ: Nefab Packaging, Inc.
  204 Airline Dr Ste 100
  Coppell TX 75019
  469 444-5264

(P-4445)
NELSON CASE CORPORATION
650 S Jefferson St Ste A, Placentia
(92870-6640)
PHONE..................................714 528-2215
Edward Bobadilla, *CEO*
John Bovadilla Jr, *CEO*
Virginia Sandburg, *CFO*
Scott Mana, *Sales Associate*
Stephanie Hiser, *Accounts Exec*
EMP: 19
SALES (est): 3.9MM **Privately Held**
WEB: www.nelsoncasecorp.com
SIC: 2441 5199 5099 2449 Packing
  cases, wood: nailed or lock corner; ship-
  ping cases, wood: nailed or lock corner;
  bags, baskets & cases; cases, carrying;
  shipping cases, wood: wirebound

(P-4446)
PROCASES INC
Also Called: Az-Iz Case Co
4626 E 48th St, Vernon (90058-3228)
PHONE..................................323 585-4447
Afshin Zakhor, *President*
▲ EMP: 10
SQ FT: 10,080
SALES: 1.5MM **Privately Held**
WEB: www.procases.com
SIC: 2441 Shipping cases, wood: nailed or
  lock corner

(P-4447)
UNIQUE DRAWER BOXES INC
9435 Bond Ave, El Cajon (92021-2874)
PHONE..................................619 873-4240
Mark Plas, *President*
Margaret Plas, *Vice Pres*
EMP: 14
SALES (est): 2.4MM **Privately Held**
WEB: www.quickdrawer.com
SIC: 2441 Boxes, wood

2448 Wood Pallets & Skids

(P-4448)
**AAA PALLET RECYCLING &
MFG INC**
23120 Oleander Ave, Perris (92570-5662)
PHONE..................................951 681-7748
Tyson Paulis, *CEO*
EMP: 22
SQ FT: 152,460
SALES: 5MM **Privately Held**
SIC: 2448 Wood pallets & skids

(P-4449)
**ALL BAY PALLET COMPANY INC
(PA)**
24993 Tarman Ave, Hayward (94544-2119)
PHONE..................................510 636-4131
Eladio Garcia Padilla, *President*
EMP: 36
SQ FT: 50,000
SALES: 2.1MM **Privately Held**
SIC: 2448 2449 Wood pallets & skids;
  wood containers

(P-4450)
ALL GOOD PALLETS INC
1055 Diamond St, Stockton (95205-7020)
PHONE..................................209 467-7000
Jack Nagra, *Manager*
EMP: 20
SALES (corp-wide): 3.2MM **Privately
Held**
SIC: 2448 Wood pallets & skids

PA: All Good Pallets, Inc.
6756 Central Ave Ste E
Newark CA 94560
510 794-4700

(P-4451)
ARNIES SUPPLY SERVICE LTD (PA)
1541 N Ditman Ave, Los Angeles (90063-2501)
P.O. Box 26, Monterey Park (91754-0026)
PHONE..................................323 263-1696
Arnold Espino, *President*
Madeline Espino, *Treasurer*
Maria Espino, *Admin Sec*
EMP: 25 **EST:** 1975
SALES (est): 6.6MM **Privately Held**
SIC: 2448 Pallets, wood & wood with metal

(P-4452)
ATLAS PALLET CORP
600 Industry Rd, Pittsburg (94565-2767)
P.O. Box 1363 (94565-0136)
PHONE..................................925 432-6261
La Sang Lim, *Principal*
EMP: 12 **EST:** 1969
SQ FT: 6,000
SALES (est): 1.9MM **Privately Held**
SIC: 2448 Pallets, wood; pallets, wood & wood with metal

(P-4453)
AZTEC TECHNOLOGY CORPORATION
14022 Slover Ave, Fontana (92337-7039)
PHONE..................................909 350-8830
Dale Aldey, *Manager*
EMP: 12
SALES (corp-wide): 9.5MM **Privately Held**
WEB: www.azteccontainer.com
SIC: 2448 Cargo containers, wood & wood with metal
PA: Aztec Technology Corporation
2550 S Santa Fe Ave
Vista CA 92084
760 727-2300

(P-4454)
BIG GZ PALLETS
1181 S Wilson Way, Stockton (95205-7053)
P.O. Box 55140 (95205-8640)
PHONE..................................209 465-0351
Ronal Grijalva, *Owner*
EMP: 10
SALES (est): 1.7MM **Privately Held**
SIC: 2448 Pallets, wood; pallets, wood & wood with metal

(P-4455)
BIG VALLEY PALLET
2512 Paulson Rd, Turlock (95380-9757)
P.O. Box 1998 (95381-1998)
PHONE..................................209 632-7687
Mike Atwood, *President*
Jim Atwood, *Vice Pres*
Janice Atwood, *Office Mgr*
EMP: 30
SQ FT: 3,000
SALES (est): 4.7MM **Privately Held**
SIC: 2448 Pallets, wood

(P-4456)
BRUCE IVERSEN
Also Called: B&B Pallet Company
439 E Carlin Ave, Compton (90222-2309)
PHONE..................................310 537-4168
Bruce Iversen, *Owner*
EMP: 42
SQ FT: 20,000
SALES: 5MM **Privately Held**
SIC: 2448 2421 Pallets, wood; sawdust & shavings

(P-4457)
C PALLETS FROM BKERSFIELD CALL
2508 E Brundage Ln, Bakersfield (93307-2812)
P.O. Box 367, Delano (93216-0367)
PHONE..................................661 833-2801
Isaias Correa, *Owner*
C Pallets, *Owner*
EMP: 12

SALES (est): 960K **Privately Held**
SIC: 2448 5085 4789 Pallets, wood & wood with metal; plastic pallets; cargo loading & unloading services

(P-4458)
CELERINOS PALLETS
1320 Mateo St, Los Angeles (90021-1747)
PHONE..................................626 923-4182
Edgar Reyes, *Owner*
EMP: 15 **EST:** 2011
SALES (est): 1.2MM **Privately Held**
SIC: 2448 Pallets, wood & wood with metal

(P-4459)
CENTRAL PALLETS
1002 Navy Dr, Stockton (95206-1166)
PHONE..................................209 462-3019
Rene Torres, *Owner*
EMP: 15
SALES (est): 1.4MM **Privately Held**
SIC: 2448 Pallets, wood & wood with metal

(P-4460)
CHEP (USA) INC
Also Called: Bay Area Pallette Company
2276 Wilbur Ln, Antioch (94509-8510)
PHONE..................................925 234-4970
Vince Sheldon, *Manager*
EMP: 55 **Privately Held**
WEB: www.ifcosystems.com
SIC: 2448 5085 Wood pallets & skids; industrial supplies
HQ: Chep (U.S.A.) Inc.
5897 Windward Pkwy
Alpharetta GA 30005
770 379-6900

(P-4461)
COMMERCIAL LBR & PALLET CO INC (PA)
135 Long Ln, City of Industry (91746-2633)
PHONE..................................626 968-0631
Raymond Gutierrez, *President*
EMP: 150
SQ FT: 10,000
SALES (est): 87.2MM **Privately Held**
SIC: 2448 5031 Pallets, wood; lumber: rough, dressed & finished

(P-4462)
CORREA PALLET INC (PA)
13036 Avenue 76, Pixley (93256-9458)
PHONE..................................559 757-1790
Martin Correa, *President*
EMP: 50
SALES (est): 9.1MM **Privately Held**
SIC: 2448 Pallets, wood

(P-4463)
CROWN PALLET COMPANY INC
15151 Salt Lake Ave, La Puente (91746-3316)
PHONE..................................626 937-6565
Robert Miller, *President*
▲ **EMP:** 20
SQ FT: 400
SALES (est): 2.7MM **Privately Held**
SIC: 2448 2441 Pallets, wood; nailed wood boxes & shook

(P-4464)
CUTTER LUMBER PRODUCTS
4004 S El Dorado St, Stockton (95206-3759)
PHONE..................................209 982-4477
Tony Palma, *Manager*
EMP: 50
SALES (est): 4.8MM
SALES (corp-wide): 11.3MM **Privately Held**
WEB: www.cutterlumber.com
SIC: 2448 Pallets, wood
PA: Cutter Lumber Products
10 Rickenbacker Cir
Livermore CA 94551
925 443-5959

(P-4465)
D L B PALLETS (PA)
4510 Rutile St, Riverside (92509-2649)
P.O. Box 10513, San Bernardino (92423-0513)
PHONE..................................951 360-9896
Daniel Bodbyl, *President*
Anna Bodbyl, *Treasurer*

EMP: 15
SALES (est): 3.3MM **Privately Held**
SIC: 2448 5031 Pallets, wood; pallets, wood

(P-4466)
DEL RIO WEST PALLETS
3845 S El Dorado St, Stockton (95206-3760)
PHONE..................................209 983-8215
Candy Villalobos, *Owner*
EMP: 24
SALES (est): 3.9MM **Privately Held**
SIC: 2448 Pallets, wood & wood with metal

(P-4467)
E & R PALLETS INC
4247 Campbell St, Riverside (92509-2618)
PHONE..................................951 790-1212
Ronnie Cortez, *Administration*
EMP: 10
SALES (est): 1.2MM **Privately Held**
SIC: 2448 Pallets, wood & wood with metal

(P-4468)
E VASQUEZ DISTRIBUTORS INC
Also Called: Oxnard Pallet Company
4524 E Pleasant Valley Rd, Oxnard (93033-2309)
P.O. Box 1748 (93032-1748)
PHONE..................................805 487-8458
Elias Vasquez Jr, *President*
Beatrice Vasquez, *CFO*
Vannessa Vasquez, *Vice Pres*
EMP: 30
SQ FT: 480
SALES: 5.8MM **Privately Held**
SIC: 2448 4214 Pallets, wood; local trucking with storage

(P-4469)
EL PELADO LLC
Also Called: Sonoma Pacific Company
1180 Fremont Dr, Sonoma (95476-9257)
PHONE..................................707 938-2877
Tommy Thompson, *Owner*
EMP: 44
SQ FT: 326,699
SALES: 5MM **Privately Held**
SIC: 2448 Wood pallets & skids

(P-4470)
FIVE STAR LUMBER COMPANY LLC
655 Brunken Ave, Salinas (93901-4362)
PHONE..................................831 422-4493
Gary Beasley, *Manager*
EMP: 20
SALES (corp-wide): 18.5MM **Privately Held**
SIC: 2448 Pallets, wood
PA: Five Star Lumber Company Llc
6899 Smith Ave
Newark CA 94560
510 795-7204

(P-4471)
FIVE STAR LUMBER COMPANY LLC (PA)
Also Called: Five Star Pallet Co
6899 Smith Ave, Newark (94560-4223)
PHONE..................................510 795-7204
Marco Beretta, *President*
Bruce Beretta,
David Beretta,
Sandra Beretta,
▲ **EMP:** 25 **EST:** 1981
SQ FT: 20,000
SALES: 18.5MM **Privately Held**
SIC: 2448 5031 Pallets, wood; lumber: rough, dressed & finished

(P-4472)
FRUIT GROWERS SUPPLY COMPANY
229 S Phillipe Ln, Yreka (96097-9043)
PHONE..................................530 842-4530
Rick Hopper, *Manager*
EMP: 25
SALES (corp-wide): 220.6MM **Privately Held**
SIC: 2448 Pallets, wood

PA: Fruit Growers Supply Company Inc
27770 N Entrmt Dr Fl 3 Flr 3
Valencia CA 91355
818 986-6480

(P-4473)
G O PALLETS INC
15642 Slover Ave, Fontana (92337-7362)
PHONE..................................909 823-4663
Guatalupe Ojeda, *President*
Lina Montes, *Office Mgr*
EMP: 22
SALES (est): 3.4MM **Privately Held**
SIC: 2448 Pallets, wood

(P-4474)
HANNIBAL LAFAYETTE
Also Called: D & L Pallet Company
10758 Fremont Ave, Ontario (91762-3909)
PHONE..................................909 322-0600
Lafayette Hannibal, *Branch Mgr*
EMP: 11
SALES (corp-wide): 200K **Privately Held**
SIC: 2448 Wood pallets & skids
PA: Lafayette Hannibal
1554 W Holt Ave
Pomona CA 91768
909 322-0600

(P-4475)
HARDING CONTAINERS INTL INC
4000 Santa Fe Ave, Long Beach (90810-1832)
PHONE..................................310 549-7272
Victor Hsing, *President*
Keith R Mayer, *Vice Pres*
▲ **EMP:** 20
SQ FT: 1,000
SALES (est): 3.4MM **Privately Held**
SIC: 2448 Cargo containers, wood & wood with metal

(P-4476)
HAYWARD PALLET COMPANY INC
4324 Rose Ln, Concord (94518-1821)
P.O. Box 1553, San Leandro (94577-0155)
PHONE..................................510 538-3127
Gary G Medeiros Sr, *President*
EMP: 15
SALES (est): 1.6MM **Privately Held**
SIC: 2448 Pallets, wood & wood with metal

(P-4477)
IDEAL PALLET SYSTEM INC
7422 Cedar Dr, Huntington Beach (92647-5498)
PHONE..................................714 847-9657
Toll Free:..................................877 -
Melvin Mermelstein, *President*
Edie Mermelstein, *CFO*
Mark Flippin, *General Mgr*
EMP: 15
SQ FT: 3,500
SALES (est): 2MM **Privately Held**
WEB: www.idealpallet.com
SIC: 2448 Pallets, wood

(P-4478)
IFCO SYSTEMS NORTH AMERICA INC
14750 Miller Ave, Fontana (92336-1685)
PHONE..................................909 356-0697
EMP: 46 **Privately Held**
SIC: 2448
HQ: Ifco Systems North America, Inc.
13100 Nw Fwy Ste 625
Houston TX 77040

(P-4479)
IFCO SYSTEMS US LLC
8950 Rochester Ave # 150, Rancho Cucamonga (91730-5541)
PHONE..................................909 484-4332
Mike Ellis, *Principal*
Chris Taylor, *Managing Dir*
Bob Ellsworth, *General Mgr*
Cindy Sanchez, *Office Mgr*
Michael McCracken, *Site Mgr*
EMP: 47 **Privately Held**
SIC: 2448 Pallets, wood

▲ = Import ▼=Export
◆ =Import/Export

HQ: Ifco Systems Us, Llc
3030 N Rocky Point Dr W # 300
Tampa FL 33607

(P-4480)
INCA PALLETS SUPPLY INC
1349 S East End Ave, Pomona
(91766-5412)
PHONE..................................909 622-1414
Zuleica Quimones, *President*
EMP: 29
SALES (est): 4.3MM **Privately Held**
SIC: 2448 7699 Pallets, wood; pallet re-
pair

(P-4481)
J & A PALLET ACCESSORY INC
6607 Doolittle Ave Ste A, Riverside
(92503-1471)
PHONE..................................951 785-1594
Omar Sosa, *President*
Sonia Sanchez-Sosa, *Vice Pres*
Sonya Sanchez-Sosa, *Vice Pres*
EMP: 12
SALES (est): 2.1MM **Privately Held**
SIC: 2448 Pallets, wood

(P-4482)
JC PALLET CO
5800 State Rd Spc 13, Bakersfield
(93308-3039)
P.O. Box 81196 (93380-1196)
PHONE..................................661 393-2229
Jack Chalmers, *Owner*
EMP: 10
SQ FT: 6,000
SALES (est): 730K **Privately Held**
SIC: 2448 2449 Pallets, wood & wood with
metal; wood containers

(P-4483)
LARSON PACKAGING COMPANY LLC
1000 Yosemite Dr, Milpitas (95035-5410)
PHONE..................................408 946-4971
Mark A Hoffman, *Mng Member*
Tom Moore, *Design Engr*
Manuel Perez, *Design Engr*
Angelo Gochangco, *Sales Staff*
Arnold Hoffman,
EMP: 48 EST: 1967
SQ FT: 30,000
SALES (est): 10.2MM **Privately Held**
SIC: 2448 2421 2441 Pallets, wood;
sawmills & planing mills, general; nailed
wood boxes & shook

(P-4484)
LONG BEACH WOODWORKS LLC
Also Called: Pacific Pallet Co
1261 Highland Ave, Glendale (91202-2055)
PHONE..................................562 437-2293
Steven P Amato,
John Ryder, *Opers Staff*
Sam Amato,
Pam Amato, *Manager*
EMP: 14
SQ FT: 2,000
SALES (est): 2.4MM **Privately Held**
WEB: www.pacificpallet.com
SIC: 2448 Pallets, wood

(P-4485)
LOPEZ PALLETS INC
11080 Redwood Ave, Fontana
(92337-7130)
P.O. Box 847, Rancho Cucamonga (91729-
0847)
PHONE..................................909 823-0865
Jesus M Lopez, *President*
EMP: 16
SQ FT: 700
SALES (est): 1.5MM **Privately Held**
SIC: 2448 7699 Pallets, wood; skids,
wood; pallet repair

(P-4486)
M C WOODWORK
747 E 60th St, Los Angeles (90001-1030)
PHONE..................................323 233-0954
Mario Contreares, *Owner*
EMP: 18
SALES (est): 1.1MM **Privately Held**
SIC: 2448 Wood pallets & skids

(P-4487)
MARTINEZ PALLET SERVICES LLC
671 Mariposa Rd, Modesto (95354-4145)
P.O. Box 2854, Turlock (95381-2854)
PHONE..................................209 968-1393
Jose Martinez,
Oscar Barcelo,
Rafael Palomino, *Manager*
EMP: 14 EST: 2014
SALES (est): 818.4K **Privately Held**
SIC: 2448 Pallets, wood

(P-4488)
MEDINA WOOD PRODUCTS INC
26342 S Banta Rd, Tracy (95304-8157)
P.O. Box 1037 (95378-1037)
PHONE..................................209 832-4523
Salvador David Medina, *President*
Irene Medina, *CFO*
EMP: 14
SQ FT: 700
SALES (est): 2.1MM **Privately Held**
SIC: 2448 Pallets, wood

(P-4489)
MOBIL PALLETS EXCHANGE
140 Villa Pacheco Ct, Hollister
(95023-6331)
PHONE..................................831 758-5203
Brian Pina, *Owner*
EMP: 18
SALES (est): 1.6MM **Privately Held**
SIC: 2448 Wood pallets & skids

(P-4490)
P & R PALLETS INC
2301 Porter St, Los Angeles (90021-2509)
PHONE..................................213 327-1104
Juan Reyes, *President*
Mary Ruelas, *CFO*
Mary luelas, *Manager*
EMP: 25
SQ FT: 5,520
SALES (est): 1.7MM **Privately Held**
WEB: www.prpallets.com
SIC: 2448 Pallets, wood

(P-4491)
P T M INC
10842 Road 28 1/2, Madera (93637-8504)
P.O. Box 602 (93639-0602)
PHONE..................................559 673-1552
John Gonzales, *President*
Beatrice Gonzales, *Admin Sec*
EMP: 15
SALES (est): 1.4MM **Privately Held**
SIC: 2448 7699 Pallets, wood; pallet re-
pair

(P-4492)
PACIFIC COAST PALLETS INC
15151 Salt Lake Ave, La Puente
(91746-3316)
PHONE..................................626 937-6565
Richard Reeves, *President*
EMP: 20 EST: 1979
SQ FT: 600
SALES: 1MM **Privately Held**
WEB: www.pacificcoastpallets.com
SIC: 2448 7699 Pallets, wood; pallet re-
pair

(P-4493)
PACIFIC PALLET EXCHANGE INC
3350 51st Ave, Sacramento (95823)
PHONE..................................916 448-5589
Ricardo Zepeda, *President*
Douglas Schnabel, *President*
Glenna Schnabel, *CFO*
EMP: 30
SQ FT: 77,537
SALES: 3MM **Privately Held**
SIC: 2448 Pallets, wood

(P-4494)
PACKAGING SPECIALISTS INC
Also Called: PSI
3663 Feather River Blvd, Plumas Lake
(95961-9616)
P.O. Box 10, Olivehurst (95961-0010)
PHONE..................................530 742-8441
Gary Allen, *CEO*
David Allen, *President*

Mary Allen, *Admin Sec*
EMP: 14
SALES (est): 2.7MM **Privately Held**
SIC: 2448 Pallets, wood

(P-4495)
PALETTE UNLIMITED
2390 Athens Ave, Lincoln (95648-9508)
P.O. Box 1656 (95648-1443)
PHONE..................................916 408-1914
Jamie Anderson, *Principal*
EMP: 23 EST: 2007
SALES (est): 3.9MM **Privately Held**
SIC: 2448 Pallets, wood & wood with metal

(P-4496)
PALLET DEPOT INC (PA)
19049 Avenue 242, Lindsay (93247-9698)
PHONE..................................916 645-0490
Jamie Anderson, *President*
Mike Anderson, *Vice Pres*
Sharon Anderson, *Director*
EMP: 20
SALES (est): 3.8MM **Privately Held**
SIC: 2448 Wood pallets & skids

(P-4497)
PALLET MASTERS INC
655 E Florence Ave, Los Angeles
(90001-2319)
PHONE..................................323 758-1713
Stephen H Anderson, *President*
Tim Hwang, *Controller*
Jerry Kelly, *Marketing Mgr*
EMP: 55
SQ FT: 105,000
SALES (est): 8.8MM **Privately Held**
SIC: 2448 2441 2439 Pallets, wood;
skids, wood; boxes, wood; structural
wood members

(P-4498)
PALLET RECOVERY SERVICE INC
3401 Gaffery Rd, Tracy (95304-9345)
P.O. Box 35, Westley (95387-0035)
PHONE..................................209 496-5074
Lisa E Kilcoyne, *President*
Matt Haugrud, *Vice Pres*
Edward Gonzales, *Manager*
EMP: 14 EST: 2008
SALES (est): 2.6MM **Privately Held**
SIC: 2448 Pallets, wood

(P-4499)
PALLETS 4 LESS INC
750 Ceres Ave, Los Angeles (90021-1516)
P.O. Box 21096 (90021-0096)
PHONE..................................213 377-7813
Gabriel Diaz, *President*
Oralia Tarra, *Admin Sec*
EMP: 10
SALES (est): 1MM **Privately Held**
SIC: 2448 Pallets, wood

(P-4500)
PREFERRED PALLETS INC
288 E Santa Ana Ave, Bloomington
(92316-2918)
P.O. Box 1652, Rancho Cucamonga
(91729-1652)
PHONE..................................909 875-7540
Laura Gonzalez, *President*
EMP: 12
SQ FT: 2,000
SALES (est): 1.9MM **Privately Held**
SIC: 2448 7699 Pallets, wood; pallet re-
pair

(P-4501)
PREMIUM PALLET INC
2000 Pomona Blvd, Pomona (91768-3323)
PHONE..................................909 868-9621
Agusting Perez, *President*
EMP: 10
SALES (est): 1.6MM **Privately Held**
SIC: 2448 Pallets, wood & wood with metal

(P-4502)
PRIORITY PALLET INC
1060 E Third St, Beaumont (92223-3020)
PHONE..................................951 769-9399
Raymond Guiterrez, *President*
EMP: 150
SALES (est): 16.2MM **Privately Held**
SIC: 2448 Pallets, wood

(P-4503)
RH PRODUCTS INC
Also Called: Rh Wood Products
6756 Central Ave Ste E, Newark
(94560-5923)
P.O. Box 1188 (94560-6188)
PHONE..................................510 794-6676
Richard Huetteman, *President*
EMP: 30
SQ FT: 23,000
SALES: 1.5MM **Privately Held**
SIC: 2448 Pallets, wood & metal combina-
tion

(P-4504)
ROGER R CARUSO ENTERPRISES INC
Also Called: Century Pallets
2911 Norton Ave, Lynwood (90262-1810)
PHONE..................................714 778-6006
Roger R Caruso, *President*
Rose Caruso, *Admin Sec*
▲ EMP: 20
SQ FT: 92,000
SALES (est): 3.2MM **Privately Held**
WEB: www.centurypallet.com
SIC: 2448 Pallets, wood

(P-4505)
SATCO INC (PA)
1601 E El Segundo Blvd, El Segundo
(90245-4334)
PHONE..................................310 322-4719
Peter Frasier Looker, *CEO*
Robert Looker, *President*
Peter Looker, *CEO*
Mary Looker, *Corp Secy*
Rob L Looker, *Vice Pres*
▲ EMP: 125 EST: 1968
SQ FT: 27,000
SALES (est): 61.3MM **Privately Held**
WEB: www.satco-inc.com
SIC: 2448 Cargo containers, wood & metal
combination

(P-4506)
SELMA PALLET INC
1651 Pacific St, Selma (93662-9336)
P.O. Box 615 (93662-0615)
PHONE..................................559 896-7171
Lupe Romero, *President*
Vera Romero, *Vice Pres*
Lynette Wilson, *Office Mgr*
Lynette Romero Wilson, *Admin Sec*
EMP: 50
SQ FT: 1,000
SALES (est): 9.5MM **Privately Held**
SIC: 2448 Pallets, wood; skids, wood

(P-4507)
SONOMA PACIFIC COMPANY LLC
1180 Fremont Dr, Sonoma (95476-9257)
P.O. Box 1251 (95476-1251)
PHONE..................................707 938-2877
Scott Gillum, *Branch Mgr*
EMP: 60
SQ FT: 10,000
SALES (est): 8.3MM
SALES (corp-wide): 8.2MM **Privately Held**
WEB: www.sonpac.com
SIC: 2448 Pallets, wood
PA: Sonoma Pacific Company, Llc
100 W Canyon Crest Rd # 204
Alpine UT 84004
972 899-5980

(P-4508)
STANDARD LUMBER COMPANY INC (HQ)
Also Called: United Wholesale Lumber Co
8009 W Doe Ave, Visalia (93291-9284)
PHONE..................................559 651-2037
Thomas J Thayer, *CEO*
EMP: 35
SQ FT: 10,000
SALES: 15.1MM
SALES (corp-wide): 220.6MM **Privately Held**
WEB: www.uwlco.com
SIC: 2448 2441 Pallets, wood; nailed
wood boxes & shook

PRODUCTS & SVCS

PA: Fruit Growers Supply Company Inc
27770 N Entrmt Dr Fl 3 Flr 3
Valencia CA 91355
818 986-6480

(P-4509)
TRIPLE A PALLETS INC
Also Called: Ayala and Son Pallets
3555 S Academy Ave, Sanger
(93657-9566)
P.O. Box 1380 (93657-1380)
PHONE......................559 313-7636
Arturo Ayala, *Principal*
EMP: 15
SALES (est): 710.2K **Privately Held**
SIC: 2448 Pallets, wood

(P-4510)
UNITED PALLET SERVICES INC
4043 Crows Landing Rd, Modesto
(95358-9404)
PHONE......................209 538-5844
Wayne Randall, *President*
Darrel Roberson, *Vice Pres*
Darrell Roberson, *Vice Pres*
Mike Tobin, *Office Mgr*
Amber McMahon, *Admin Sec*
EMP: 150
SQ FT: 46,884
SALES (est): 26.3MM **Privately Held**
WEB: www.palts4u.com
SIC: 2448 7699 Pallets, wood; pallet repair

(P-4511)
VILLA PALLET LLC
6756 Central Ave, Hayward (94544)
PHONE......................510 794-6676
Pati Patrick, *Office Mgr*
EMP: 14 **EST:** 2010
SALES (est): 903.2K **Privately Held**
SIC: 2448 Wood pallets & skids

(P-4512)
WALKER STREET PALLETS LLC
801 Ohlone Pkwy, Watsonville
(95076-7016)
P.O. Box 2568 (95077-2568)
PHONE......................831 724-6088
Rick Thayer,
EMP: 15
SQ FT: 1,200
SALES: 4MM **Privately Held**
SIC: 2448 Pallets, wood

(P-4513)
WESTSIDE PALLET INC
2138 L St, Newman (95360)
P.O. Box 786 (95360-0786)
PHONE......................209 862-3941
Bernadine Rocha, *President*
Carolyn Beach, *Vice Pres*
EMP: 55
SQ FT: 10,000
SALES (est): 7MM **Privately Held**
SIC: 2448 Pallets, wood; skids, wood

(P-4514)
WILMINGTON WOODWORKS INC
318 E C St, Wilmington (90744-6614)
P.O. Box 581 (90748-0581)
PHONE......................310 834-1015
Ronald Young, *President*
Pat Mace, *Shareholder*
EMP: 25
SALES (est): 2.9MM **Privately Held**
WEB: www.wilmwoodworks.com
SIC: 2448 Pallets, wood

2449 Wood Containers, NEC

(P-4515)
ADVANCED PACKAGING & CRATING
15432 Electronic Ln, Huntington Beach
(92649-1334)
PHONE......................714 892-1702
Tippi Longo, *President*
EMP: 10
SQ FT: 6,000
SALES (est): 1.3MM **Privately Held**
SIC: 2449 4783 Containers, plywood & veneer wood; packing goods for shipping

(P-4516)
APEX DRUM COMPANY INC
Also Called: Apex Container Services
6226 Ferguson Dr, Commerce
(90022-5399)
PHONE......................323 721-8994
Abe Michlin, *CEO*
Sybil Flom, *Admin Sec*
Joshua Flom, *Asst Mgr*
EMP: 19
SQ FT: 40,000
SALES (est): 3.5MM **Privately Held**
WEB: www.apexdrum.com
SIC: 2449 5085 Containers, plywood & veneer wood; shipping cases & drums, wood: wirebound & plywood; cooperage stock; drums, new or reconditioned

(P-4517)
BACKYARD UNLIMITED (PA)
4765 Pacific St, Rocklin (95677-2407)
PHONE......................916 630-7433
Nathan Martin, *Principal*
Jerry Wenger, *Sales Staff*
EMP: 13
SALES (est): 1.9MM **Privately Held**
SIC: 2449 Chicken coops (crates), wood: wirebound

(P-4518)
BROWN WOOD PRODUCTS INC
310 Devonshire Blvd, San Carlos
(94070-1633)
PHONE......................650 593-9875
Richard Russell, *President*
Bonnie Russell, *Vice Pres*
EMP: 32
SQ FT: 35,000
SALES (est): 1.4MM **Privately Held**
SIC: 2449 5084 2441 Shipping cases & drums, wood: wirebound & plywood; industrial machinery & equipment; nailed wood boxes & shook

(P-4519)
CORRWOOD CONTAINERS
7182 Rasmussen Ave, Visalia
(93291-9405)
P.O. Box 670, Goshen (93227-0670)
PHONE......................559 651-0335
Don Nepinsky, *President*
Candace Nepinsky, *Corp Secy*
▲ **EMP:** 31
SQ FT: 70,000
SALES: 16MM **Privately Held**
SIC: 2449 Shipping cases, wood: wirebound

(P-4520)
DEMPTOS NAPA COOPERAGE (HQ)
1050 Soscol Ferry Rd, NAPA (94558-6228)
PHONE......................707 257-2628
Jerome Francois, *President*
William Jamieson, *Vice Pres*
Angie Martinez, *Manager*
◆ **EMP:** 32 **EST:** 1982
SQ FT: 27,500
SALES (est): 7.3MM
SALES (corp-wide): 46MM **Privately Held**
WEB: www.demptosusa.com
SIC: 2449 5085 Barrels, wood: coopered; barrels, new or reconditioned
PA: Tonnellerie Francois Freres

Saint Romain 21190
380 212-333

(P-4521)
FRANK KAMS & ASSOCIATES INC
Also Called: California Redwood Products
242 W Hanna St, Colton (92324-2772)
PHONE......................909 382-0047
Frank L Kams, *CEO*
Eleanor Kams, *Corp Secy*
▲ **EMP:** 32 **EST:** 1976
SQ FT: 44,700
SALES (est): 4.5MM **Privately Held**
SIC: 2449 5083 Rectangular boxes & crates, wood; lawn & garden machinery & equipment

(P-4522)
GLOBAL PACKING SOLUTIONS INC
2139 S 10th St, San Jose (95112-4113)
PHONE......................408 279-4196
Jeffrey D Brooks, *CEO*
Jeff Brooks, *CEO*
EMP: 14 **EST:** 2011
SALES (est): 2.3MM **Privately Held**
SIC: 2449 Rectangular boxes & crates, wood

(P-4523)
INDUSTRIAL MDFICATION REPR INC
1323 W 132nd St, Gardena (90247-1507)
PHONE......................310 516-7992
Dana B Thomas, *President*
EMP: 10
SQ FT: 5,000
SALES (est): 537.2K **Privately Held**
SIC: 2449 Wood containers

(P-4524)
INNERSTAVE LLC
Also Called: Custom Cooperage Innerstave
21660 8th St E Ste B, Sonoma
(95476-2828)
PHONE......................707 996-8781
Brian Daw,
Carl Dillon, *General Mgr*
Alicia McBride, *General Mgr*
Candy Hemert, *Controller*
Candy Vanhemert, *Controller*
◆ **EMP:** 28
SALES (est): 5.4MM **Privately Held**
WEB: www.innerstave.com
SIC: 2449 5085 5182 Wood containers; commercial containers; wine & distilled beverages

(P-4525)
JDC DEVELOPMENT GROUP INC
Also Called: Dggr Packaging Crating & Foam
1321 N Blue Gum St, Anaheim
(92806-1750)
PHONE......................714 575-1108
Joseph Dibenedetto Jr, *President*
Joseph Di Benedetto Jr, *President*
EMP: 35
SALES (est): 3.7MM **Privately Held**
WEB: www.jdpack.com
SIC: 2449 2631 Rectangular boxes & crates, wood; container, packaging & boxboard

(P-4526)
JOHN DANIEL GONZALEZ
Also Called: Custom Wood Products
13458 E Industrial Dr, Parlier (93648-9678)
P.O. Box 783 (93648-0783)
PHONE......................559 646-6621
John Daniel Gonzalez, *Owner*
Jennifer Gonzalez, *Co-Owner*
EMP: 43
SQ FT: 14,000
SALES (est): 2.9MM **Privately Held**
SIC: 2449 Wood containers

(P-4527)
JOHNSTONS TRADING POST INC
11 N Pioneer Ave, Woodland (95776-5907)
PHONE......................530 661-6152
James B Johnston, *CEO*
Cary Johnston, *Vice Pres*
Gloria Johnston, *Admin Sec*
EMP: 50
SQ FT: 112,000
SALES (est): 8.4MM **Privately Held**
SIC: 2449 4225 Wood containers; general warehousing & storage

(P-4528)
LESTER BOX INC
Also Called: Lester Box & Manufacturing
1470 Seabright Ave, Long Beach
(90813-1152)
PHONE......................562 437-5123
Steven S Amato, *President*
EMP: 12
SQ FT: 10,360

SALES (est): 2.1MM **Privately Held**
WEB: www.lesterbox.com
SIC: 2449 Boxes, wood: wirebound

(P-4529)
MARIBA CORPORATION
158 N Glendora Ave Ste W, Glendora
(91741-3352)
PHONE......................626 963-6775
Ray Malki, *CEO*
Richard Malki, *President*
EMP: 10
SQ FT: 10,000
SALES (est): 820K **Privately Held**
WEB: www.mariba.com
SIC: 2449 Wood containers

(P-4530)
OBENTEC INC (PA)
Also Called: Laptop Lunches
500 Chestnut St Ste 225, Santa Cruz
(95060-3675)
PHONE......................831 457-0301
Tammy Pelstring, *President*
Amy Hemmert, *President*
Summer Cornish, *Marketing Staff*
Kelly Davies, *Sales Staff*
▲ **EMP:** 10
SQ FT: 1,000
SALES (est): 987.8K **Privately Held**
SIC: 2449 2731 Food containers, wood: wirebound; book publishing

(P-4531)
OMEGA CASE COMPANY INC
2231 N Hollywood Way, Burbank
(91505-1113)
PHONE......................818 238-9263
Omar Gonzales, *Owner*
Cris Vargas, *Opers Mgr*
Randy Velasquez, *Sales Staff*
EMP: 30
SALES (est): 4MM **Privately Held**
WEB: www.omegacase.com
SIC: 2449 Shipping cases & drums, wood: wirebound & plywood

(P-4532)
PICNIC AT ASCOT INC
3237 W 131st St, Hawthorne (90250-5514)
PHONE......................310 674-3098
Paul Whitlock, *President*
Jill Brown, *Vice Pres*
Karen Burke, *Finance Mgr*
Elsa Laguna, *Marketing Staff*
◆ **EMP:** 30
SQ FT: 20,000
SALES (est): 6.1MM **Privately Held**
WEB: www.picnicatascot.com
SIC: 2449 5947 Baskets: fruit & vegetable, round stave, till, etc.; gift, novelty & souvenir shop

(P-4533)
RED RIVER LUMBER CO
Also Called: Barrel Merchants
2959 Saint Helena Hwy N, Saint Helena
(94574-9703)
PHONE......................707 963-1251
Richard M Heckert, *President*
EMP: 20
SQ FT: 1,200
SALES (est): 1.6MM **Privately Held**
SIC: 2449

(P-4534)
SAN JUAN SPECIALTY PDTS INC
4149 Avenida De La Plata, Oceanside
(92056-6002)
PHONE......................888 342-8262
Barney Rigney, *President*
Kathryn Rigney, *Admin Sec*
EMP: 11
SQ FT: 1,900
SALES (est): 51.8K **Privately Held**
SIC: 2449 Wood containers

(P-4535)
SEGUIN MOREAU HOLDINGS INC (PA)
151 Camino Dorado, NAPA (94558-6213)
PHONE......................707 252-3408
Thomas Martin, *President*
▲ **EMP:** 57

SALES (est): 6.5MM **Privately Held**
SIC: 2449 5085 Barrels, wood: coopered; barrels, new or reconditioned

(P-4536)
SPECILIZED PACKG SOLUTIONS INC
Also Called: Specilzed Packg Solutions-Wood
38505 Cherry St Ste H, Newark (94560-4700)
P.O. Box 3042, Fremont (94539-0304)
PHONE..............................510 494-5670
Karen Besso, *CEO*
Terrence Besso, *Vice Pres*
▲ EMP: 50
SQ FT: 63,000
SALES (est): 11.8MM **Privately Held**
SIC: 2449 2653 5113 3086 Rectangular boxes & crates, wood; sheets, corrugated: made from purchased materials; corrugated & solid fiber boxes; plastics foam products

(P-4537)
T & R LUMBER COMPANY (PA)
8685 Etiwanda Ave, Rancho Cucamonga (91739-9611)
P.O. Box 2484 (91729-2484)
PHONE..............................909 899-2383
Cheryl L Guardia, *President*
Philip Guardia, *Vice Pres*
Dennis Anderson, *Opers Staff*
Nicole Jackson, *Sales Associate*
Steve Reynolds, *Associate*
▲ EMP: 73
SQ FT: 4,600
SALES (est): 11.9MM **Privately Held**
SIC: 2449 2499 2441 Boxes, wood: wirebound; handles, poles, dowels & stakes: wood; nailed wood boxes & shook

(P-4538)
TONNELLERIE FRANCAISE FRENCH C
Also Called: Nadalie USA
1401 Tubbs Ln, Calistoga (94515-9726)
P.O. Box 798 (94515-0798)
PHONE..............................707 942-9301
Jean Jacques Nadalie, *CEO*
Alain Poisson, *Vice Pres*
Kevin Andre, *Marketing Staff*
April Moulton, *Sales Staff*
▲ EMP: 18
SQ FT: 12,000
SALES (est): 3.8MM
SALES (corp-wide): 32.4MM **Privately Held**
WEB: www.nadalieusa.com
SIC: 2449 Barrels, wood: coopered
PA: Tonnellerie Ludonnaise
   99 Rue Lafont
   Ludon Medoc 33290
   557 884-593

(P-4539)
TONNELLERIE RADOUX USA INC
480 Aviation Blvd, Santa Rosa (95403-1069)
PHONE..............................707 284-2888
Christen Liarg, *President*
Phillip Doray, *Corp Secy*
Maria Ortiz, *Admin Asst*
Maria Vigil, *Admin Asst*
Maud Fitzpatrick, *Technology*
▲ EMP: 17
SQ FT: 25,000
SALES (est): 3.2MM
SALES (corp-wide): 46MM **Privately Held**
WEB: www.tonnellerieradoux.com
SIC: 2449 Vats, wood: coopered
HQ: Tonnelerie Radoux
   10 Avenue Faidherbe
   Jonzac 17500
   546 480-065

(P-4540)
WINE COUNTRY CASES INC
621 Airpark Rd, NAPA (94558-6272)
PHONE..............................707 967-4805
Dan C Pina, *President*
EMP: 87
SQ FT: 5,500

SALES (est): 6.7MM **Privately Held**
WEB: www.winecountrycases.com
SIC: 2449 2657 Butter crates, wood: wirebound; folding paperboard boxes

(P-4541)
WOOD BOX SPECIALTIES INC
23308 Kidder St, Hayward (94545-1633)
PHONE..............................510 786-1600
Terry Tressell, *President*
EMP: 10
SALES: 500K **Privately Held**
WEB: www.woodboxspecialties.com
SIC: 2449 5199 2541 Wood containers; gift baskets; store & office display cases & fixtures

(P-4542)
WOOD-N-WOOD PRODUCTS CAL INC (PA)
2247 W Birch Ave, Fresno (93711-0442)
PHONE..............................559 896-3636
Rodney Allen Scary, *CEO*
Susan Scarry, *Treasurer*
EMP: 38
SQ FT: 15,000
SALES (est): 3.9MM **Privately Held**
SIC: 2449 Wood containers

(P-4543)
WOOD-N-WOOD PRODUCTS CAL INC
13598 S Golden State Blvd, Selma (93662)
PHONE..............................559 896-3636
Rick Murillo, *Manager*
EMP: 20
SALES (corp-wide): 3.9MM **Privately Held**
SIC: 2449 Containers, plywood & veneer wood
PA: Wood-N-Wood Products Of California, Inc.
   2247 W Birch Ave
   Fresno CA 93711
   559 896-3636

(P-4544)
WOOD-N-WOOD PRODUCTS INC
Also Called: Wood-N-Wood Products Cal
2247 W Birch Ave, Fresno (93711-0442)
PHONE..............................559 896-3636
Allen Scarry, *Branch Mgr*
EMP: 15
SALES (corp-wide): 5.3MM **Privately Held**
SIC: 2449 Rectangular boxes & crates, wood
PA: Wood-N-Wood Products Inc
   3750 S Hwy 287
   Corsicana TX

2451 Mobile Homes

(P-4545)
10100 HOLDINGS INC (PA)
10100 Santa Monica Blvd # 1050, Los Angeles (90067-4003)
PHONE..............................310 552-0705
Ernest L Thesman, *President*
EMP: 12
SALES (est): 20.7MM **Privately Held**
SIC: 2451 6515 Mobile homes; mobile home site operators

(P-4546)
CASTAIC LAKE R V PARK INC
Also Called: Castaic R V Park
31540 Ridge Route Rd, Castaic (91384-3358)
PHONE..............................661 257-3340
Arthur Staudigel, *President*
C Dan Foote, *Treasurer*
Clyde Widrig, *Vice Pres*
Robert C Tallent, *Admin Sec*
EMP: 15
SALES (est): 1.7MM **Privately Held**
WEB: www.castaiclakervpark.com
SIC: 2451 5411 7011 5921 Mobile homes; grocery stores, independent; hotels & motels; liquor stores

(P-4547)
CAVCO INDUSTRIES INC
7007 Jurupa Ave, Riverside (92504-1015)
PHONE..............................951 351-0378
Mike Hayes, *Branch Mgr*
EMP: 70
SALES (corp-wide): 773.8MM **Publicly Held**
SIC: 2451 Mobile homes
PA: Cavco Industries, Inc.
   1001 N Central Ave # 800
   Phoenix AZ 85004
   602 256-6263

(P-4548)
CAVCO INDUSTRIES INC
Also Called: Fleetwood Homes
7007 Jurupa Ave, Riverside (92504-1015)
PHONE..............................951 688-5353
Mike Hayes, *Branch Mgr*
EMP: 215
SALES (corp-wide): 773.8MM **Publicly Held**
SIC: 2451 2452 Mobile homes; prefabricated buildings, wood
PA: Cavco Industries, Inc.
   1001 N Central Ave # 800
   Phoenix AZ 85004
   602 256-6263

(P-4549)
CLAYTON HOMES INC
Also Called: CMH Manufacturing West
9998 Old Placerville Rd, Sacramento (95827-3557)
PHONE..............................916 363-2681
Alen Limley, *Branch Mgr*
Doug Rogers, *Materials Mgr*
Paul Furtsch, *Manager*
EMP: 13
SALES (corp-wide): 242.1B **Publicly Held**
SIC: 2451 Mobile homes, personal or private use
HQ: Clayton Homes, Inc.
   5000 Clayton Rd
   Maryville TN 37804
   865 380-3000

(P-4550)
CLAYTON HOMES INC
Also Called: Golden West Homes
3100 N Perris Blvd, Perris (92571-3242)
PHONE..............................951 657-1611
John Drean, *Branch Mgr*
Jesse Carrasco, *Branch Mgr*
Tania Rowland, *Human Res Mgr*
John Brean, *Purch Agent*
EMP: 150
SALES (corp-wide): 242.1B **Publicly Held**
WEB: www.clayton.net
SIC: 2451 Mobile homes, personal or private use
HQ: Clayton Homes, Inc.
   5000 Clayton Rd
   Maryville TN 37804
   865 380-3000

(P-4551)
D-MAC INC
1105 E Discovery Ln, Anaheim (92801-1121)
PHONE..............................714 808-3918
David A Wade, *Principal*
Leo Hernandez, *Controller*
Mike Marks, *Sales Associate*
EMP: 26
SALES (est): 4.4MM **Privately Held**
WEB: www.d-mac.com
SIC: 2451 5039 5032 Mobile home frames; structural assemblies, prefabricated: non-wood; paving materials; plastering materials

(P-4552)
DVELE INC
25525 Redlands Blvd, Loma Linda (92354-2009)
PHONE..............................909 796-2561
EMP: 45
SALES (corp-wide): 2.6MM **Privately Held**
SIC: 2451 2452 Mobile homes, except recreational; prefabricated buildings, wood

PA: Dvele, Inc.
   2201 Market St
   San Francisco CA
   -

(P-4553)
DVELE OMEGA CORPORATION
Also Called: Hallmark Southwest
25525 Redlands Blvd, Loma Linda (92354-2009)
P.O. Box 1710 (92354-0150)
PHONE..............................909 796-2561
Luca Brammer, *President*
EMP: 100
SQ FT: 5,000
SALES (est): 6.6MM **Privately Held**
SIC: 2451 2452 Mobile homes, personal or private use; mobile homes, industrial or commercial use; prefabricated wood buildings; modular homes, prefabricated, wood; panels & sections, prefabricated, wood

(P-4554)
FLEETWOOD ENTERPRISES INC
351 Corporate Terrace Cir, Corona (92879-6028)
PHONE..............................951 750-1971
Kent Wemsel, *Branch Mgr*
EMP: 402
SALES (corp-wide): 2.3B **Privately Held**
SIC: 2451 Mobile homes, personal or private use
HQ: Fleetwood Enterprises, Inc.
   1351 Pomona Rd Ste 230
   Corona CA 92882
   951 354-3000

(P-4555)
FLEETWOOD HOMES ARIZONA INC
7007 Jurupa Ave, Riverside (92504-1015)
PHONE..............................623 939-2600
Irv Hill, *Manager*
EMP: 400
SALES (corp-wide): 2.3B **Privately Held**
SIC: 2451 3448 2452 Mobile homes, except recreational; prefabricated metal buildings; modular homes, prefabricated, wood
HQ: Fleetwood Homes Of Arizona, Inc.
   3125 Myers St
   Riverside CA 92503

(P-4556)
FLEETWOOD HOMES ARIZONA INC (DH)
3125 Myers St, Riverside (92503-5527)
PHONE..............................951 351-3000
Elden L Smith, *President*
Leonard McGill, *Senior VP*
Roger L Howsmon, *Vice Pres*
Lyle N Larkin, *Vice Pres*
Boyd R Plowman, *Vice Pres*
▲ EMP: 498
SQ FT: 262,900
SALES (est): 45.7MM
SALES (corp-wide): 2.3B **Privately Held**
SIC: 2451 Mobile homes, except recreational
HQ: Fleetwood Enterprises, Inc.
   1351 Pomona Rd Ste 230
   Corona CA 92882
   951 354-3000

(P-4557)
FLEETWOOD HOMES CALIFORNIA INC (DH)
7007 Jurupa Ave, Riverside (92504-1015)
P.O. Box 7638 (92513-7638)
PHONE..............................951 351-2494
Elvin Smith, *President*
Lyle N Larkin, *Treasurer*
Boyd R Plowman, *Exec VP*
Roger L Howsmon, *Senior VP*
Forrest D Theobald, *Senior VP*
▲ EMP: 28
SQ FT: 262,900
SALES (est): 30.5MM
SALES (corp-wide): 2.3B **Privately Held**
SIC: 2451 Mobile homes

(PA)=Parent Co (HQ)=Headquarters (DH)=Div Headquarters
♻ = New Business established in last 2 years

HQ: Fleetwood Enterprises, Inc.
  1351 Pomona Rd Ste 230
  Corona CA 92882
  951 354-3000

(P-4558)
FLEETWOOD HOMES OF FLORIDA (DH)
3125 Myers St, Riverside (92503-5527)
P.O. Box 7638 (92513-7638)
PHONE.................................909 261-4274
Edward B Caudill, *President*
Boyd R Plowman, *CFO*
Lyle N Larkin, *Treasurer*
Forrest D Theobald, *Senior VP*
▲ **EMP:** 16
SQ FT: 262,900
SALES (est): 6.2MM
SALES (corp-wide): 2.3B **Privately Held**
SIC: 2451 Mobile homes, except recreational
HQ: Fleetwood Enterprises, Inc.
  1351 Pomona Rd Ste 230
  Corona CA 92882
  951 354-3000

(P-4559)
FLEETWOOD HOMES OF IDAHO INC
3125 Myers St, Riverside (92503-5527)
P.O. Box 7698 (92513-7698)
PHONE.................................951 354-3000
Edward B Caudill, *President*
Boyd R Plowman, *CFO*
Lyle Larkin, *Treasurer*
Roger L Howsmon, *Senior VP*
Forrest D Theobald, *Senior VP*
EMP: 200
SQ FT: 262,900
SALES (est): 15.4MM
SALES (corp-wide): 2.3B **Privately Held**
SIC: 2451 Mobile homes
HQ: Fleetwood Enterprises, Inc.
  1351 Pomona Rd Ste 230
  Corona CA 92882
  951 354-3000

(P-4560)
FLEETWOOD HOMES OF KENTUCKY (DH)
1351 Pomona Rd Ste 230, Corona (92882-7165)
PHONE.................................800 688-1745
Elden L Smith, *Principal*
Boyd R Plowman, *CFO*
Roger L Howsmon, *Treasurer*
Forrest D Theobald, *Senior VP*
Lyle N Larkin, *Vice Pres*
EMP: 13 **EST:** 1998
SALES (est): 10.9MM
SALES (corp-wide): 2.3B **Privately Held**
SIC: 2451 Mobile homes
HQ: Fleetwood Enterprises, Inc.
  1351 Pomona Rd Ste 230
  Corona CA 92882
  951 354-3000

(P-4561)
FLEETWOOD HOMES OF VIRGINIA
3125 Myers St, Riverside (92503-5527)
P.O. Box 7638 (92513-7638)
PHONE.................................951 351-3500
Elden L Smith, *Principal*
Edward B Caudill, *President*
Boyd R Plowman, *CFO*
Lyle N Larkin, *Vice Pres*
Roger L Howsmon, *Senior VP*
EMP: 180 **EST:** 1968
SQ FT: 262,900
SALES (est): 12MM
SALES (corp-wide): 2.3B **Privately Held**
SIC: 2451 Mobile homes
HQ: Fleetwood Enterprises, Inc.
  1351 Pomona Rd Ste 230
  Corona CA 92882
  951 354-3000

(P-4562)
INCEPTION HOMES INC
Also Called: Advantage Homes
12640 Beach Blvd, Stanton (90680-4008)
PHONE.................................714 890-1883
Tom Randall, *Branch Mgr*
EMP: 10

SALES (corp-wide): 6.6MM **Privately Held**
SIC: 2451 Mobile homes
PA: Inception Homes, Inc.
  2890 Monterey Hwy
  San Jose CA 95111
  408 239-4859

(P-4563)
SKYLINE HOMES INC
499 W Esplanade Ave, San Jacinto (92583-5001)
P.O. Box 670 (92581-0670)
PHONE.................................951 654-9321
Jim Claverie, *General Mgr*
Bethany Faulkner, *Administration*
Bill Metzger, *Train & Dev Mgr*
Eric Brown, *Purchasing*
Brad Clark, *Purchasing*
EMP: 115
SALES (corp-wide): 1.5B **Publicly Held**
WEB: www.skylinerv.com
SIC: 2451 Mobile homes
HQ: Skyline Homes, Inc.
  2520 Bypass Rd
  Elkhart IN 46514
  574 294-6521

(P-4564)
SKYLINE HOMES INC
Also Called: Buddy Homes 355
1720 E Beamer St, Woodland (95776-6218)
P.O. Box 1870 (95776-1870)
PHONE.................................530 666-0974
Tim Howard, *Principal*
Steve Mac Intosh, *Manager*
EMP: 200
SALES (corp-wide): 1.5B **Publicly Held**
WEB: www.skylinerv.com
SIC: 2451 Mobile homes, except recreational
HQ: Skyline Homes, Inc.
  2520 Bypass Rd
  Elkhart IN 46514
  574 294-6521

2452 Prefabricated Wood Buildings & Cmpnts

(P-4565)
ALAMEDA VIDEO STATION
1929 Broadway, Alameda (94501-1512)
PHONE.................................510 523-5200
Ken Dorrance, *Owner*
EMP: 50
SALES: 11.8MM **Privately Held**
SIC: 2452 Prefabricated wood buildings

(P-4566)
ALAN PRE-FAB BUILDING CORP (PA)
17817 Evelyn Ave, Gardena (90248-3735)
PHONE.................................310 538-0333
Toll Free:.................................888 -
John W Andrus, *President*
Bill Andrus, *Vice Pres*
Bret Andrus, *Vice Pres*
Ann Andrus, *Admin Sec*
EMP: 13
SQ FT: 49,000
SALES (est): 1.8MM **Privately Held**
WEB: www.alanprefab.com
SIC: 2452 7359 Prefabricated wood buildings; equipment rental & leasing

(P-4567)
AMERICAN MODULAR SYSTEMS INC
Also Called: AMS
787 Spreckels Ave, Manteca (95336-6002)
PHONE.................................209 825-1921
Daniel Sarich, *President*
Tony Sarich, *Vice Pres*
EMP: 100
SQ FT: 85,000
SALES (est): 41.3MM **Privately Held**
SIC: 2452 1542 Modular homes, prefabricated, wood; nonresidential construction

(P-4568)
APPLIED POLYTECH SYSTEMS INC
Also Called: A P S
26000 Springbrook Ave # 102, Santa Clarita (91350-2592)
PHONE.................................818 504-9261
Christine Wagner, *President*
Chris Wagner, *Data Proc Dir*
EMP: 30
SQ FT: 6,000
SALES (est): 4.1MM **Privately Held**
SIC: 2452 Prefabricated wood buildings

(P-4569)
BLU HOMES INC (PA)
1015 Walnut Ave, Vallejo (94592-1190)
PHONE.................................866 887-7997
William Haney, *President*
Gary Martell, *CFO*
Trevor Huffard, *Vice Pres*
Maura McCarthy, *Vice Pres*
Dennis Michaud, *Vice Pres*
EMP: 59
SALES (est): 44.3MM **Privately Held**
SIC: 2452 Prefabricated wood buildings

(P-4570)
CALIFORNIA LEISURE PRODUCTS
265 Thomas St, Ukiah (95482-5823)
PHONE.................................707 462-2106
Greg Farmer, *Owner*
EMP: 13
SALES (est): 1.2MM **Privately Held**
WEB: www.califleisureproducts.com
SIC: 2452 5999 Prefabricated buildings, wood; spas & hot tubs

(P-4571)
CUORA CORPORATION
Also Called: Sequoia Works
2401 Q St, Rio Linda (95673-2823)
PHONE.................................916 991-3028
Fred Hobbs, *President*
Kurt Peterson, *Exec VP*
▼ **EMP:** 20
SQ FT: 15,000
SALES (est): 3.2MM **Privately Held**
WEB: www.sequoiaworks.com
SIC: 2452 2499 Prefabricated wood buildings; fencing, wood

(P-4572)
CURRENT MODULAR INC
Also Called: Current Enterprises Modular
141 S Lake Ave Fl 2, Pasadena (91101-4759)
PHONE.................................909 792-9207
Robert Allison, *President*
Gerald Payte, *Managing Prtnr*
Rick Shepard, *Vice Pres*
EMP: 32 **EST:** 2005
SQ FT: 60,000
SALES (est): 2MM **Privately Held**
WEB: www.currentmodular.com
SIC: 2452 Modular homes, prefabricated, wood

(P-4573)
GARY DOUPNIK MANUFACTURING INC
3237 Rippey Rd, Loomis (95650-7654)
PHONE.................................916 652-9291
Sherie Edgar, *President*
Gary Doupnik Sr, *Treasurer*
Gary Doupnik Jr, *Vice Pres*
Jt Doupnik, *Vice Pres*
Kirtus Doupnik, *Vice Pres*
EMP: 60
SQ FT: 4,000
SALES (est): 6.4MM **Privately Held**
WEB: www.gdmfg.com
SIC: 2452 3448 Prefabricated buildings, wood; prefabricated metal buildings

(P-4574)
GLOBAL DIVERSIFIED INDS INC (PA)
1200 Airport Dr, Chowchilla (93610-9344)
P.O. Box 32, Atwater (95301-0032)
PHONE.................................559 665-5800
Phillip Hamilton, *President*
Adam N Debard, *Corp Secy*
Jeffrey Chan-Lugay, *Engineer*

Robert Cronin, *Opers Mgr*
EMP: 50
SQ FT: 100,000
SALES (est): 5.3MM **Privately Held**
WEB: www.gdvi.net
SIC: 2452 Modular homes, prefabricated, wood

(P-4575)
GLOBAL MODULAR INC (HQ)
1200 Airport Dr, Chowchilla (93610-9344)
P.O. Box 369 (93610-0369)
PHONE.................................559 665-5800
Adam De Bard, *President*
Milo King, *Admin Sec*
EMP: 30
SALES (est): 4.8MM
SALES (corp-wide): 5.3MM **Privately Held**
WEB: www.gdvi.net
SIC: 2452 Prefabricated wood buildings
PA: Global Diversified Industries, Inc.
  1200 Airport Dr
  Chowchilla CA 93610
  559 665-5800

(P-4576)
JET CUTTING SOLUTIONS INC
10853 Bell Ct, Rancho Cucamonga (91730-4835)
PHONE.................................909 948-2424
Louis Mammooito, *CEO*
Thomas Ribas, *President*
EMP: 10
SALES (est): 2.1MM **Privately Held**
SIC: 2452 Prefabricated wood buildings

(P-4577)
MCCARTHY RANCH
15425 Los Gatos Blvd # 102, Los Gatos (95032-2541)
PHONE.................................408 356-2300
Joe McCarthy, *Owner*
EMP: 12
SALES (est): 2.1MM **Privately Held**
SIC: 2452 Farm & agricultural buildings, prefabricated wood

(P-4578)
PLH PRODUCTS INC
6655 Knott Ave, Buena Park (90620-1129)
PHONE.................................714 739-6622
Seung Woo Lee, *Ch of Bd*
Kyung Min Park, *President*
Won Yong Lee, *CFO*
Logan Ross, *Business Dir*
◆ **EMP:** 29
SALES: 38.5MM **Privately Held**
WEB: www.healthmatesauna.com
SIC: 2452 2449 5999 Sauna rooms, prefabricated, wood; hot tubs, wood; sauna equipment & supplies

(P-4579)
TUFF SHED INC
2431 Sarah Dr, Fresno (93706)
PHONE.................................559 268-8833
Greg Torrecillas, *Manager*
Mark Kaljumagi, *Sales Staff*
Gregorio Torrecillas, *Manager*
EMP: 30
SALES (corp-wide): 289.8MM **Privately Held**
SIC: 2452 Prefabricated wood buildings
PA: Tuff Shed, Inc.
  1777 S Harrison St # 600
  Denver CO 80210
  303 753-8833

(P-4580)
TUFF SHED INC
850 W Foothill Blvd, Azusa (91702-2800)
PHONE.................................626 334-0748
Tom Saurey, *Branch Mgr*
EMP: 13
SALES (corp-wide): 289.8MM **Privately Held**
SIC: 2452 Prefabricated wood buildings
PA: Tuff Shed, Inc.
  1777 S Harrison St # 600
  Denver CO 80210
  303 753-8833

▲ = Import ▼=Export
◆ =Import/Export

(P-4581)
TUFF SHED INC
931 Cadillac Ct, Milpitas (95035-3053)
PHONE..............................408 935-8833
Rod Miller, *Manager*
EMP: 11
SALES (corp-wide): 289.8MM **Privately Held**
SIC: 2452 Prefabricated wood buildings
PA: Tuff Shed, Inc.
1777 S Harrison St # 600
Denver CO 80210
303 753-8833

(P-4582)
TUFF SHED INC
1401 Franquette Ave, Concord (94520-7956)
PHONE..............................925 681-3492
Penny Gerald, *Branch Mgr*
EMP: 13
SALES (corp-wide): 289.8MM **Privately Held**
SIC: 2452 Prefabricated wood buildings
PA: Tuff Shed, Inc.
1777 S Harrison St # 600
Denver CO 80210
303 753-8833

(P-4583)
UNITED PARTITION SYSTEMS INC
2180 S Hellman Ave, Ontario (91761-7700)
PHONE..............................909 947-1077
Mike Kaminski, *CEO*
Robert Kaminski, *CFO*
Bryan Leisure, *Regional Mgr*
Sue Kaminski, *Admin Sec*
EMP: 10
SQ FT: 13,000
SALES (est): 2MM **Privately Held**
WEB: www.unitedpartition.com
SIC: 2452 3448 2541 1542 Prefabricated metal buildings; partitions for floor attachment, prefabricated: wood; commercial & office buildings, prefabricated erection; panels & sections, prefabricated, wood

(P-4584)
US CONTAINER AND HOUSING CO
22320 Fthill Blvd Ste 450, Hayward (94541)
PHONE..............................844 762-8242
Terry Keeney, *CEO*
Jerrold Johnson, *CFO*
EMP: 20 EST: 2014
SALES: 10MM **Privately Held**
SIC: 2452 1522 3444 1542 Panels & sections, prefabricated, wood; residential construction; metal housings, enclosures, casings & other containers; commercial & office building, new construction

(P-4585)
WALDEN STRUCTURES INC (PA)
1000 Bristol St N 126, Newport Beach (92660-8916)
PHONE..............................909 389-9100
Charlie Walden, *Owner*
Curtis H Claire, *COO*
Michael J Dominici, *CFO*
EMP: 89
SQ FT: 150,000
SALES (est): 68.9MM **Privately Held**
WEB: www.waldenstructures.com
SIC: 2452 Modular homes, prefabricated, wood

(P-4586)
WEST COAST LAMINATING LLC
13833 Borate St, Santa Fe Springs (90670-5311)
PHONE..............................562 906-2489
Ramon Ramontes, *Manager*
EMP: 10
SALES (corp-wide): 94.5MM **Privately Held**
SIC: 2452 Panels & sections, prefabricated, wood
HQ: West Coast Laminating, Llc
5602 Bickett St
Vernon CA 90058
323 585-9201

2491 Wood Preserving

(P-4587)
BLUE LAKE ROUNDSTOCK CO LLC
19195 Latona Rd, Anderson (96007-9421)
PHONE..............................530 515-7007
Robert Hambrecht,
Glenn Zane,
EMP: 12 EST: 2009
SQ FT: 500
SALES (est): 1.4MM **Privately Held**
SIC: 2491 Poles, posts & pilings: treated wood

(P-4588)
CALIFORNIA CASCADE INDUSTRIES
7512 14th Ave, Sacramento (95820-3539)
P.O. Box 130026 (95853-0026)
PHONE..............................916 736-3353
Stuart D Heath, *President*
Stu Heath, *President*
Richard Rose, *CFO*
Kyle Keaton, *Corp Secy*
Cheryl Kaufenberg, *Human Resources*
EMP: 200
SQ FT: 6,500
SALES (est): 67.7MM
SALES (corp-wide): 889.9MM **Privately Held**
WEB: www.californiacascade.com
SIC: 2491 2421 Wood preserving; sawmills & planing mills, general
PA: Canwel Building Materials Group Ltd
1055 Georgia St W Suite 1100
Vancouver BC V6E 3
604 432-1400

(P-4589)
CALIFORNIA CASCADE-WOODLAND
Also Called: Western Wood Treating
1492 Churchill Downs Ave, Woodland (95776-6113)
P.O. Box 1443 (95776-1443)
PHONE..............................530 666-1261
Henry Feenstra, *President*
EMP: 15
SQ FT: 1,000
SALES (est): 3MM **Privately Held**
SIC: 2491 Structural lumber & timber, treated wood

(P-4590)
CHARLES JJ INC
Also Called: Used Pellet Co
4115 S Orange Ave, Fresno (93725-9367)
PHONE..............................559 264-6664
Jeffrey Seib, *President*
EMP: 40
SALES (est): 3.9MM **Privately Held**
SIC: 2491 Wood preserving

(P-4591)
COAST WOOD PRESERVING INC (PA)
600 W Glenwood Ave, Turlock (95380-6232)
P.O. Box 1805 (95381-1805)
PHONE..............................209 632-9931
Micheal Logsdon, *President*
Gene Piepila, *Corp Secy*
EMP: 13
SQ FT: 13,200
SALES (est): 1.5MM **Privately Held**
SIC: 2491 Wood preserving

(P-4592)
CONRAD WOOD PRESERVING CO
7085 Eddy Rd Unit C, Arbuckle (95912-9789)
PHONE..............................530 476-2894
Fred Noah, *Branch Mgr*
EMP: 14
SALES (corp-wide): 40.3MM **Privately Held**
SIC: 2491 Wood preserving
PA: Conrad Wood Preserving Co.
68765 Wildwood Rd
North Bend OR 97459
800 356-7146

(P-4593)
EAST BAY FIXTURE COMPANY
941 Aileen St, Oakland (94608-2805)
PHONE..............................510 652-4421
Richard Laible, *President*
Frances Laible, *Corp Secy*
EMP: 50
SQ FT: 32,000
SALES (est): 7.6MM **Privately Held**
WEB: www.ebfc.com
SIC: 2491 2541 Millwork, treated wood; office fixtures, wood

(P-4594)
JH BAXTER A CAL LTD PARTNR (PA)
1700 S El Camino Real, San Mateo (94402-3047)
PHONE..............................650 349-0201
Georgia B Krause, *Managing Prtnr*
Richard Keeley, *Partner*
Sandra Lavino, *Partner*
Robert Stockton, *Partner*
Paul Krotts, *Controller*
EMP: 50
SQ FT: 2,000
SALES (est): 7.4MM **Privately Held**
WEB: www.acza.com
SIC: 2491 Poles & pole crossarms, treated wood

(P-4595)
PACIFIC STATES TREATING INC
422 Mill St, Weed (96094-2261)
PHONE..............................530 938-4408
Roger A Burch, *President*
EMP: 12
SALES (est): 1.8MM **Privately Held**
SIC: 2491 Wood preserving

(P-4596)
PACIFIC WD PRSERVING-NEW STINE
5601 District Blvd, Bakersfield (93313-2129)
PHONE..............................661 617-6385
Richard Jackson, *President*
EMP: 19
SALES (est): 2.8MM **Privately Held**
SIC: 2491 Preserving (creosoting) of wood

(P-4597)
SC BLUWOOD INC
2604 El Camino Real Ste B, Carlsbad (92008-1205)
PHONE..............................909 519-5470
Stephen Conboy, *President*
EMP: 30
SALES (est): 1.6MM **Privately Held**
SIC: 2491 Structural lumber & timber, treated wood

(P-4598)
THUNDERBOLT SALES INC
3400 Patterson Rd, Riverbank (95367-2998)
P.O. Box 890 (95367-0890)
PHONE..............................209 869-4561
T W Ted Seybold, *President*
T W Seybold, *President*
Don De Vries, *Vice Pres*
Leonard Lovalvo, *Vice Pres*
EMP: 20
SALES (est): 2.1MM
SALES (corp-wide): 7.3MM **Privately Held**
SIC: 2491 Wood preserving
PA: Thunderbolt Wood Treating Co., Inc.
3400 Patterson Rd
Riverbank CA 95367
209 869-4561

(P-4599)
THUNDERBOLT WD TREATING CO INC (PA)
3400 Patterson Rd, Riverbank (95367-2998)
P.O. Box 890 (95367-0890)
PHONE..............................209 869-4561
T W Seybold, *President*
Donald De Vries, *Vice Pres*
Miguel Gutierrez, *Sales Staff*
EMP: 25 EST: 1977
SQ FT: 1,500

SALES (est): 7.3MM **Privately Held**
SIC: 2491 Structural lumber & timber, treated wood

2493 Reconstituted Wood Prdts

(P-4600)
PANOLAM INDUSTRIES INTL INC
Also Called: Pionite
8535 Oakwood Pl Ste A, Rancho Cucamonga (91730-4864)
PHONE..............................909 581-1970
John Fulkerson, *Manager*
EMP: 20 **Privately Held**
SIC: 2493 Particleboard products
PA: Panolam Industries International, Inc.
1 Corporate Dr Ste 725
Shelton CT 06484

(P-4601)
REGARDS ENTERPRISES INC
Also Called: Quality Marble & Granite
731 S Taylor Ave, Ontario (91761-1847)
PHONE..............................909 983-0655
Evan Cohen, *CEO*
▲ EMP: 19
SQ FT: 95,000
SALES (est): 2.3MM **Privately Held**
SIC: 2493 3281 Marbleboard (stone face hard board); granite, cut & shaped

(P-4602)
STANDARD INDUSTRIES INC
Also Called: GAF Materials
3301 Navone Rd, Stockton (95215-9312)
PHONE..............................209 931-1277
Maria Lewis, *Opers-Prdtn-Mfg*
EMP: 65
SQ FT: 50,000
SALES (corp-wide): 2.7B **Privately Held**
SIC: 2493 Insulation & roofing material, reconstituted wood
HQ: Standard Industries Inc.
1 Campus Dr
Parsippany NJ 07054

2499 Wood Prdts, NEC

(P-4603)
A E T C O INC
2825 Metropolitan Pl, Pomona (91767-1853)
P.O. Box 458, San Dimas (91773-0458)
PHONE..............................909 593-2521
Anthony Taylor, *President*
Jeanne Shinogle, *Vice Pres*
Barbara Taylor, *Admin Sec*
EMP: 35
SQ FT: 12,500
SALES (est): 4.5MM **Privately Held**
WEB: www.aetcoinc.com
SIC: 2499 3429 3842 2326 Policemen's clubs, wood; handcuffs & leg irons; surgical appliances & supplies; men's & boys' work clothing

(P-4604)
ALACO LADDER COMPANY
5167 G St, Chino (91710-5143)
PHONE..............................909 591-7561
Gil Jacobs, *President*
Mario Garcia, *Vice Pres*
▼ EMP: 25
SQ FT: 26,000
SALES (est): 2.1MM
SALES (corp-wide): 3.2MM **Privately Held**
SIC: 2499 3354 3499 Ladders, wood; aluminum extruded products; metal ladders; ladders, portable: metal
PA: B, E & P Enterprises, Llc
5167 G St
Chino CA 91710
909 591-7561

(P-4605)
APPLIED SILVER INC
26254 Eden Landing Rd, Hayward (94545-3717)
PHONE..............................888 939-4747

P R O D U C T S & S V C S

Sean Morham, *CEO*
Elizabeth Hutt Pollard, *Ch of Bd*
Paul McCabe, *CFO*
Robert B Babcock, *Engineer*
EMP: 11
SALES (est): 1.1MM **Privately Held**
SIC: 2499 5719 Laundry products, wood;
  linens

(P-4606)
ART DREAMS HOME INC
1834 Palma Dr Ste G, Ventura
(93003-3700)
PHONE.............................805 642-6444
Donald Koszyk, *CEO*
Kathleen Koszyk, *President*
▲ **EMP:** 100
SQ FT: 90,000
SALES (est): 9.6MM **Privately Held**
WEB: www.artdreams.com
SIC: 2499 2752 Picture & mirror frames,
  wood; commercial printing, lithographic

(P-4607)
B E & P ENTERPRISES LLC (PA)
Also Called: Alaco Ladder Company
5167 G St, Chino (91710-5143)
PHONE.............................909 591-7561
Mario Garcia,
Sue Ritchey, *Sales Executive*
Stephen Bernstein,
Fred Evans,
Gil Jacobs,
EMP: 25
SALES (est): 3.2MM **Privately Held**
SIC: 2499 3499 3354 Ladders, wood; lad-
  ders, portable: metal; aluminum extruded
  products

(P-4608)
BK SEMS USA INC
4 Executive Park Ste 270, Irvine (92614)
PHONE.............................949 390-7120
EMP: 19 EST: 2002
SALES (est): 3MM **Privately Held**
SIC: 2499

(P-4609)
BRENT-WOOD PRODUCTS INC
777 E Rosecrans Ave Ste D, Los Angeles
(90059-3563)
P.O. Box 59178 (90059-0178)
PHONE.............................800 400-7335
Lawrence D Hobbs, *CEO*
Birgitta Olin, *President*
Anna Pinili, *Corp Secy*
Larry Hobbs, *VP Bus Dvlpt*
Jordan Hobbs, *Consultant*
▼ **EMP:** 30 EST: 1963
SQ FT: 26,000
SALES (est): 6.7MM **Privately Held**
SIC: 2499 Reels, plywood

(P-4610)
CALIFORNIA BIO-MASS INC (PA)
20055 Shay Rd, Victorville (92394-8501)
PHONE.............................760 246-7946
Dave Hardy, *President*
Michael Hardy, *Vice Pres*
EMP: 37
SQ FT: 2,000
SALES (est): 4.5MM **Privately Held**
WEB: www.californiabiomass.com
SIC: 2499 4953 Mulch, wood & bark; recy-
  cling, waste materials

(P-4611)
CALIFORNIA CEDAR PRODUCTS CO (PA)
2385 Arch Airport Rd # 500, Stockton
(95206-4405)
PHONE.............................209 932-5002
Charles Berolzheimer, *President*
Paula Sullivan, *President*
Susan Macintyre, *CFO*
Dave Morgali, *Info Tech Mgr*
Troy White, *VP Finance*
▲ **EMP:** 50 EST: 1920
SQ FT: 10,000
SALES (est): 87MM **Privately Held**
WEB: www.calcedar.com
SIC: 2499 Pencil slats, wood; logs of saw-
  dust & wood particles, pressed

(P-4612)
CALIFORNIA CEDAR PRODUCTS CO
2385 Arch Airport Rd # 500, Stockton
(95206-4405)
PHONE.............................209 944-5800
Mike Hume, *Manager*
EMP: 150
SALES (corp-wide): 87MM **Privately
Held**
WEB: www.calcedar.com
SIC: 2499 Pencil slats, wood; logs of saw-
  dust & wood particles, pressed
PA: California Cedar Products Company
  2385 Arch Airport Rd # 500
  Stockton CA 95206
  209 932-5002

(P-4613)
CARRIS REELS CALIFORNIA INC (HQ)
2100 W Almond Ave, Madera (93637-5203)
P.O. Box 88 (93639-0088)
PHONE.............................559 674-0804
William Carris, *Ch of Bd*
Dave Ferraro, *President*
David Fitzgerald, *CFO*
David Ferraro, *Vice Pres*
Dwight Harder, *General Mgr*
▲ **EMP:** 30 EST: 1966
SALES (est): 3.5MM **Privately Held**
SIC: 2499 2448 Spools, reels & pulleys:
  wood; reels, plywood; pallets, wood

(P-4614)
CONROS CORP
Also Called: American Texas Firelog
6001 Power Inn Rd, Sacramento
(95824-2320)
PHONE.............................916 381-8511
William Trayner, *Branch Mgr*
EMP: 23
SALES (est): 1.3MM **Privately Held**
SIC: 2499 Logs of sawdust & wood parti-
  cles, pressed
HQ: Conros Corporation
  41 Lesmill Rd
  North York ON M3B 2
  416 751-4343

(P-4615)
CONTINENTAL COMPONENTS LLC
243 S Escondido Blvd, Escondido
(92025-4116)
PHONE.............................760 480-4420
Judd Lafountain, *Branch Mgr*
EMP: 15
SALES (corp-wide): 1.5MM **Privately
Held**
SIC: 2499 Applicators, wood
PA: Continental Components, L.L.C.
  5617 Ne Portland Hwy
  Portland OR 97218
  503 281-8700

(P-4616)
COOLING TOWER RESOURCES INC (PA)
Also Called: C T R
1470 Grove St, Healdsburg (95448-4700)
P.O. Box 159 (95448-0159)
PHONE.............................707 433-3900
Gordon Martin, *CEO*
Terri Martin, *Corp Secy*
Brad Pirrung, *Sales Executive*
Justin Davis, *Marketing Staff*
◆ **EMP:** 20
SQ FT: 1,200
SALES (est): 6.1MM **Privately Held**
WEB: www.cooltower.com
SIC: 2499 Cooling towers, wood or wood &
  sheet metal combination

(P-4617)
CRI 2000 LP (PA)
Also Called: Lso
2245 San Diego Ave # 125, San Diego
(92110-2072)
PHONE.............................619 542-1975
Mitchell G Lynn, *Partner*
Mitchel Lynn, *Managing Prtnr*
Luis Torres, *General Mgr*
Debi Siegel, *Controller*
Kristina Au, *Human Res Dir*

◆ **EMP:** 50
SQ FT: 10,000
SALES (est): 18MM **Privately Held**
SIC: 2499 5112 5049 5092 Picture frame
  molding, finished; office supplies; school
  supplies; arts & crafts equipment & supplies; photographic equipment & supplies

(P-4618)
DELGADO BROTHERS LLC
647 E 59th St, Los Angeles (90001-1001)
PHONE.............................323 233-9793
Felipe Delgado, *Partner*
Antonio Delgado, *Partner*
Rafael Delgado Jr, *Partner*
Ramiro Delgado, *Partner*
▲ **EMP:** 25
SQ FT: 105,000
SALES (est): 3.4MM **Privately Held**
WEB: www.delgadobrothers.com
SIC: 2499 Picture frame molding, finished;
  picture & mirror frames, wood

(P-4619)
FAITH INDUSTRIES INC
Also Called: Western Wood
4117 Pearl St, Lake Elsinore (92530-2023)
PHONE.............................951 351-1486
Jeff Loupe, *President*
Dan Morgan, *CFO*
EMP: 25 EST: 1962
SQ FT: 86,000
SALES (est): 1.8MM **Privately Held**
SIC: 2499 Decorative wood & woodwork

(P-4620)
FORMSOLVER INC
Also Called: Framatic Company
3041 N North Coolidge Ave, Los Angeles
(90039-3413)
PHONE.............................323 664-7888
David Dedlow, *President*
Dwayne Johnson, *Officer*
Edwina Dedlow, *Vice Pres*
Vicente Diaz, *Technology*
Donna Ruckman, *Controller*
▲ **EMP:** 33
SQ FT: 12,500
SALES (est): 4.5MM **Privately Held**
WEB: www.framatic.com
SIC: 2499 Picture frame molding, finished

(P-4621)
FOSTER PLANING MILL CO
1258 W 58th St, Los Angeles (90037-3917)
PHONE.............................323 759-9156
Robert Stanley, *President*
EMP: 14
SQ FT: 15,000
SALES (est): 1.5MM **Privately Held**
SIC: 2499 2431 Picture & mirror frames,
  wood; venetian blind slats, wood

(P-4622)
GL WOODWORKING INC
Also Called: Millers Woodworking
14341 Franklin Ave, Tustin (92780-7010)
PHONE.............................949 515-2192
Grant Miller, *Owner*
EMP: 63
SALES (est): 6.7MM **Privately Held**
SIC: 2499 Decorative wood & woodwork

(P-4623)
GLC GENERAL INC
Also Called: Linen Liners
100 W Walnut Ave, Fullerton (92832-2345)
PHONE.............................714 870-9825
Gary L Cox, *President*
Garrison Cox, *Buyer*
▲ **EMP:** 12 EST: 1962
SQ FT: 1,000
SALES (est): 2.1MM **Privately Held**
WEB: www.linenliners.com
SIC: 2499 Picture frame molding, finished;
  picture & mirror frames, wood

(P-4624)
GOLDEN VANTAGE LLC
8807 Rochester Ave, Rancho Cucamonga
(91730-4913)
PHONE.............................626 255-3362
Canlin Chen, *Mng Member*
Anfeng Huang, *Mng Member*
▲ **EMP:** 10
SQ FT: 55,000

SALES: 8MM **Privately Held**
SIC: 2499 5074 Kitchen, bathroom &
  household ware: wood; plumbing & hydronic heating supplies

(P-4625)
J & S STAKES INC
3157 Greenwood Heights Dr, Kneeland
(95549-8912)
PHONE.............................707 668-5647
Larry A Johnson, *President*
Mary L Johnson, *Treasurer*
EMP: 18
SQ FT: 21,000
SALES: 2MM **Privately Held**
SIC: 2499

(P-4626)
JERRY SOLOMON ENTERPRISES INC
Also Called: Jerry Slmon Cstm Picture Frmng
5221 W Jefferson Blvd, Los Angeles
(90016-3815)
PHONE.............................323 556-2265
Jerry Solomon, *President*
Arlyn Solomon, *Corp Secy*
Fred Solomon, *Vice Pres*
▲ **EMP:** 50
SQ FT: 60,000
SALES (est): 4.7MM **Privately Held**
WEB: www.solomonframe.com
SIC: 2499 5999 3231 Picture & mirror
  frames, wood; picture frames, ready
  made; products of purchased glass

(P-4627)
JIMO ENTERPRISES
6001 Santa Monica Blvd, Los Angeles
(90038-1807)
PHONE.............................323 469-0805
Larry Neuberg, *Owner*
▲ **EMP:** 20
SALES (est): 1MM **Privately Held**
SIC: 2499 Picture & mirror frames, wood

(P-4628)
JUST JOHNSONS INC
5850 District Blvd Ste 1, Bakersfield
(93313-2136)
PHONE.............................661 396-0200
John Johnson, *CEO*
Ryan Johnson, *President*
Kelly Confair, *CFO*
Debra Johnson, *Vice Pres*
▲ **EMP:** 64
SQ FT: 4,800
SALES (est): 9.8MM **Privately Held**
WEB: www.justjohnsons.com
SIC: 2499 Carved & turned wood

(P-4629)
KENS STAKES & SUPPLIES
193 S Mariposa Ave, Visalia (93292-9242)
PHONE.............................559 747-1313
Joseph Hallmeyer, *President*
Barbara Hallmeyer, *Vice Pres*
EMP: 10
SQ FT: 12,000
SALES (est): 1.5MM **Privately Held**
SIC: 2499 5049 Handles, poles, dowels &
  stakes: wood; surveyors' instruments

(P-4630)
KUTZIN & KUTZIN INC
Also Called: Custom Framing Service
14726 Oxnard St, Van Nuys (91411-3121)
P.O. Box 57438, Sherman Oaks (91413-
2438)
PHONE.............................818 994-0242
Matthew Kutzin, *President*
Karen Kutzin, *Corp Secy*
EMP: 11
SALES: 900K **Privately Held**
SIC: 2499 3952 Picture & mirror frames,
  wood; frames for artists' canvases

(P-4631)
LARSON-JUHL US LLC
Also Called: Larson Picture Frames
12206 Bell Ranch Dr, Santa Fe Springs
(90670-3361)
PHONE.............................562 946-6873
Anthony Eikenberry, *Manager*
EMP: 24

SALES (corp-wide): 242.1B **Publicly Held**
SIC: **2499** Picture & mirror frames, wood
HQ: Larson-Juhl Us Llc
3900 Steve Reynolds Blvd
Norcross GA 30093
770 279-5200

(P-4632)
LARSON-JUHL US LLC
5365 Industrial Way, Benicia (94510-1026)
PHONE................................707 747-0555
Donna Hugel, *Sales Staff*
EMP: 20
SALES (corp-wide): 242.1B **Publicly Held**
SIC: **2499** 3231 Picture & mirror frames, wood; products of purchased glass
HQ: Larson-Juhl Us Llc
3900 Steve Reynolds Blvd
Norcross GA 30093
770 279-5200

(P-4633)
LUCKY PICTURE FRAME CO INC
1948 Mairemont Dr, Walnut (91789-3527)
PHONE................................323 583-6710
Hyun K Lee, *President*
▲ EMP: 20
SALES (est): 1.8MM **Privately Held**
SIC: **2499** Picture & mirror frames, wood

(P-4634)
MADERA CONCEPTS
Also Called: Absolute Woods Products
55b Depot Rd, Goleta (93117)
PHONE................................805 692-0053
Jeffrey A Wayco, *Partner*
Antonio G Gonzales, *Partner*
▲ EMP: 15
SALES: 800K **Privately Held**
WEB: www.maderaconcepts.com
SIC: **2499** Decorative wood & woodwork

(P-4635)
MAGIC-FLIGHT GENERAL MFG INC
3417 Hancock St, San Diego (92110-4307)
P.O. Box 3758, Rancho Santa Fe (92067-3758)
PHONE................................619 288-4638
Forrest Landry, *CEO*
Tamara Ward, *CFO*
EMP: 130
SQ FT: 35,000
SALES (est): 10MM **Privately Held**
SIC: **2499** Woodenware, kitchen & household

(P-4636)
MOLDING COMPANY
1987 Russell Ave, Santa Clara (95054-2035)
PHONE................................408 748-6968
Doug Randall, *President*
EMP: 25
SALES (est): 2.4MM **Privately Held**
SIC: **2499** Decorative wood & woodwork

(P-4637)
MONARCH ART & FRAME INC
7700 Gloria Ave, Van Nuys (91406-1819)
PHONE................................818 373-6180
Jaime V Mizrahi, *CEO*
EMP: 50
SQ FT: 16,000
SALES (est): 6.2MM **Privately Held**
WEB: www.themonarchcollection.com
SIC: **2499** Picture & mirror frames, wood; picture frame molding, finished

(P-4638)
MWW INC
Also Called: Modern Woodworks
7945 Deering Ave, Canoga Park (91304-5009)
PHONE................................800 575-3475
George Mekhtarian, *CEO*
Allen Mekhtarian, *Vice Pres*
▲ EMP: 35
SQ FT: 10,000
SALES (est): 6.1MM **Privately Held**
SIC: **2499** Carved & turned wood

(P-4639)
OUTDOOR DIMENSIONS LLC
5325 E Hunter Ave, Anaheim (92807-2054)
PHONE................................714 578-9555
Donald Pickler, *President*
Brian Pickler, *Vice Pres*
Pam Rogers, *Executive*
Angel Luna, *Project Mgr*
Rose Johnson, *Asst Controller*
EMP: 160
SQ FT: 80,000
SALES (est): 34.4MM **Privately Held**
WEB: www.outdoordimensions.com
SIC: **2499** 3993 3281 Signboards, wood; signs & advertising specialties; cut stone & stone products

(P-4640)
OVERHOLTZER ELVAN
Also Called: Micawrap Moulding Company
3142 Talbot Ave, Riverbank (95367-2842)
PHONE................................209 869-2536
Elvan Overholtzer, *Owner*
EMP: 30
SQ FT: 90,000
SALES: 3MM **Privately Held**
WEB: www.americanlaminates.com
SIC: **2499** 2511 2512 Picture frame molding, finished; chairs, household, except upholstered; wood; chairs: upholstered on wood frames

(P-4641)
PICTURE THIS FRAMING INC
631 S State College Blvd, Fullerton (92831-5115)
PHONE................................714 447-8749
Neil Oleary, *President*
Neil O'Leary, *President*
Ginger Greenleaf, *Vice Pres*
EMP: 15
SQ FT: 8,000
SALES (est): 2MM **Privately Held**
WEB: www.picturethisframing.com
SIC: **2499** Picture & mirror frames, wood

(P-4642)
PORTOCORK AMERICA INC
560 Technology Way, NAPA (94558-7513)
PHONE................................707 258-3930
Dustin Mowe, *President*
Jose Santos, *Vice Pres*
Isabelle Sodini, *Director*
▼ EMP: 12
SQ FT: 26,000
SALES (est): 2.6MM **Privately Held**
WEB: www.portocork.com
SIC: **2499** Corks, bottle
HQ: Amorim - ServiCos E GestAo, S.A.
Rua De Meladas, 380
Mozelos Vfr 4535-
227 475-400

(P-4643)
PRO TOUR MEMORABILIA LLC
Also Called: Ptm Images
700 N San Vicente Blvd G696, West Hollywood (90069-5073)
P.O. Box 15084, Beverly Hills (90209-1084)
PHONE................................424 303-7200
Jonathan Bass,
▲ EMP: 25
SQ FT: 8,000
SALES (est): 7.4MM **Privately Held**
WEB: www.ptmimages.com
SIC: **2499** Picture & mirror frames, wood

(P-4644)
QUALITY FIRST WOODWORKS INC
1264 N Lakeview Ave, Anaheim (92807-1831)
PHONE................................714 632-0480
Mark Nappy, *President*
Chad Nappy, *Corp Secy*
Randy Dell, *Vice Pres*
EMP: 115
SQ FT: 30,000
SALES: 14MM **Privately Held**
WEB: www.qualityfirstwoodworks.com
SIC: **2499** 1751 Decorative wood & woodwork; cabinet building & installation

(P-4645)
RAPHAELS INC
2780 Sweetwater Spgs Blvd, Spring Valley (91977-7136)
PHONE................................619 670-7999
Scott Brummitt, *CEO*
Richard J Hennen, *President*
▲ EMP: 17 EST: 1976
SQ FT: 300,000
SALES (est): 2.8MM **Privately Held**
WEB: www.raphaelstoday.com
SIC: **2499** Picture & mirror frames, wood

(P-4646)
REDWORKS INDUSTRIES LLC
23986 Aliso Creek Rd, Laguna Niguel (92677-3908)
PHONE................................949 334-7081
Melissa Soto,
EMP: 35
SQ FT: 15,000
SALES: 950K **Privately Held**
SIC: **2499** Applicators, wood

(P-4647)
RICH XIBERTA USA INC
450 Aaron St, Cotati (94931-3068)
PHONE................................707 795-1800
Ferran Botifoll, *General Mgr*
Andrea Fishbein, *Accounts Mgr*
Steven Rome, *Accounts Mgr*
▲ EMP: 10
SQ FT: 11,000
SALES (est): 1.9MM **Privately Held**
WEB: www.xiberta.com
SIC: **2499** 5085 Cork & cork products; bottler supplies
HQ: Rich Xiberta Sa
Travesia Taronja, S/N
Caldes De Malavella 17455
972 472-727

(P-4648)
ROMA MOULDING INC
6230 N Irwindale Ave, Irwindale (91702-3208)
PHONE................................626 334-2539
Jon Mathews, *Manager*
EMP: 20 **Privately Held**
SIC: **2499** 5023 Picture frame molding, finished; frames & framing, picture & mirror
PA: Roma Moulding Inc
360 Hanlan Rd
Woodbridge ON L4L 3
905 850-1500

(P-4649)
ROSS FABRICATION & WELDING INC
1154 Basta Ave, Bakersfield (93308-4477)
PHONE................................661 393-1242
Jeffrey Ross, *President*
Julie Ross, *CFO*
EMP: 14
SALES (est): 1.6MM **Privately Held**
SIC: **2499** Food handling & processing products, wood

(P-4650)
S & S WOODCARVER INC
Also Called: American Carousel
13 San Rafael Pl, Laguna Niguel (92677-7623)
PHONE................................714 258-2222
Sid Askari, *CEO*
Sy Vakhsourpour, *President*
EMP: 28
SALES: 2.5MM **Privately Held**
WEB: www.americancarousel.com
SIC: **2499** Decorative wood & woodwork; carved & turned wood

(P-4651)
S&S SIGNATURE MILL WORKS INC
5951 Jetton Ln Ste C6, Loomis (95650-9593)
PHONE................................916 652-1046
Gary Stephens, *Owner*
EMP: 15
SQ FT: 4,000
SALES: 1MM **Privately Held**
SIC: **2499** 1751 Decorative wood & woodwork; cabinet & finish carpentry

(P-4652)
SEVEN WELLS LLC
Also Called: I.E. Distribution
14801 Able Ln Ste 102, Huntington Beach (92647-2059)
PHONE................................213 305-4775
John Dickenson, *Manager*
Barry Lublin, *CFO*
▲ EMP: 14
SALES (est): 1.5MM **Privately Held**
SIC: **2499** Shoe & boot products, wood

(P-4653)
SHASTA FOREST PRODUCTS INC (PA)
1412 Montague Rd, Yreka (96097-9659)
P.O. Box 777 (96097-0777)
PHONE................................530 842-0527
Richard W Conroy, *President*
William Hall, *Vice Pres*
Karen Cunningham, *Admin Sec*
EMP: 42
SQ FT: 3,500
SALES: 10.7MM **Privately Held**
WEB: www.shastabark.com
SIC: **2499** Mulch, wood & bark

(P-4654)
SHASTA FOREST PRODUCTS INC
1423 Montague Rd, Yreka (96097-9659)
P.O. Box 777 (96097-0777)
PHONE................................530 842-2787
Bill Hall, *Manager*
EMP: 30
SALES (corp-wide): 10.7MM **Privately Held**
WEB: www.shastabark.com
SIC: **2499** 2421 Mulch, wood & bark; sawmills & planing mills, general
PA: Shasta Forest Products, Inc.
1412 Montague Rd
Yreka CA 96097
530 842-0527

(P-4655)
SHELTER INTERNATIONAL INC
6310 Corsair St, Commerce (90040-2504)
PHONE................................323 888-8856
Shawn Arshad, *President*
EMP: 50
SALES (est): 105.1K **Privately Held**
SIC: **2499** Decorative wood & woodwork

(P-4656)
SHINE COMPANY INC
3535 Philadelphia St, Chino (91710-2089)
PHONE................................909 590-5005
Wallace Chen, *President*
Margarita Chen, *Vice Pres*
Gideon Yambot, *Accounts Mgr*
▲ EMP: 10
SQ FT: 50,000
SALES (est): 870K **Privately Held**
WEB: www.shineco.com
SIC: **2499** Decorative wood & woodwork

(P-4657)
SOUTHERN CALIFORNIA MULCH INC
30141 Antelope Rd 116, Menifee (92584-7001)
PHONE................................951 352-5355
Elisabeth Michelle Brownton, *CEO*
EMP: 12
SALES (est): 266K **Privately Held**
SIC: **2499** 5999 Mulch or sawdust products, wood; rock & stone specimens

(P-4658)
SURVEY STAKE AND MARKER INC
Also Called: Nichols Lumber
13470 Dalewood St, Baldwin Park (91706-5834)
PHONE................................626 960-4802
Judith A Nichols, *President*
Evelyn M Rumsey, *Vice Pres*
Charles F Nichols, *Admin Sec*
Charles Nichols, *Admin Sec*
EMP: 18
SQ FT: 3,000
SALES (est): 1.5MM **Privately Held**
SIC: **2499** Surveyors' stakes, wood

(P-4659)
SYBMAN INC
Also Called: Picture Source of California
9911 Gidley St, El Monte (91731-1111)
PHONE..............................626 579-9911
Angky Dharmosetio, *President*
Kusno Wongsodirdjo, *Vice Pres*
Ferry Soendjojo, *Admin Sec*
Angel Kusumah, *Director*
◆ **EMP:** 10
SQ FT: 6,000
SALES: 495K **Privately Held**
WEB: www.hotelart.com
SIC: 2499 Picture frame molding, finished

(P-4660)
TIMMONS WOOD PRODUCTS INC
4675 Wade Ave, Perris (92571-7494)
PHONE..............................951 940-4700
Eddie Timmons, *President*
EMP: 13
SQ FT: 45,000
SALES (est): 1.3MM **Privately Held**
SIC: 2499 Handles, poles, dowels & stakes: wood

(P-4661)
TREND MARKETING CORPORATION
Also Called: Trend Frames
3025 Beyer Blvd Ste 102, San Diego (92154-3432)
PHONE..............................800 468-7363
Sam Ceci, *President*
EMP: 100 **EST:** 1976
SQ FT: 7,512
SALES (est): 10.8MM **Privately Held**
WEB: www.go-trend.com
SIC: 2499 3999 Picture & mirror frames, wood; novelties, bric-a-brac & hobby kits

(P-4662)
UNIVERSITY FRAMES INC
3060 E Miraloma Ave, Anaheim (92806-1810)
PHONE..............................714 575-5100
John G Winn, *CEO*
Tom Biehn, *Exec VP*
Diane Winn, *Vice Pres*
Danny Winn, *Opers Mgr*
Andrea Arczynski, *Director*
▲ **EMP:** 50
SQ FT: 20,000
SALES (est): 9.6MM **Privately Held**
WEB: www.universityframes.com
SIC: 2499 5999 Picture frame molding, finished; picture frames, ready made

(P-4663)
WALTON COMPANY INC
17900 Sampson Ln, Huntington Beach (92647-7149)
PHONE..............................714 847-8800
Don Walton, *President*
▼ **EMP:** 15
SQ FT: 12,000
SALES (est): 1.3MM **Privately Held**
SIC: 2499 Cork & cork products

(P-4664)
WILDLIFE IN WOOD INC
165 E Liberty Ave, Anaheim (92801-1014)
PHONE..............................714 773-5816
Devra Robledo, *President*
EMP: 18 **EST:** 1976
SQ FT: 12,000
SALES (est): 2.2MM **Privately Held**
SIC: 2499 8011 Decorative wood & woodwork; novelties, wood fiber; furniture inlays (veneers); engraved wood products; offices & clinics of medical doctors

(P-4665)
YTI ENTERPRISES INC
Also Called: Laminating Technologies
1260 S State College Pkwy, Anaheim (92806-5240)
PHONE..............................714 632-8696
Judith Rochverger, *President*
Jair N Rochverger, *CFO*
EMP: 15
SQ FT: 16,500
SALES (est): 2MM **Privately Held**
SIC: 2499 Seats, toilet

2511 Wood Household Furniture

(P-4666)
ALDER & CO LLC
412 Wallace St, Bakersfield (93307-1447)
PHONE..............................661 326-0320
Bryan Shimp,
Adriana Caceres, *Vice Pres*
Jose Luis Garcia,
Adan Perez,
Humberto Cobian, *Mng Member*
EMP: 16
SQ FT: 10,000
SALES: 800K **Privately Held**
WEB: www.alderandco.com
SIC: 2511 Wood household furniture

(P-4667)
AMERICAN CRAFTSMEN CORPORATION
273 N Hill Ave, Pasadena (91106-1531)
PHONE..............................626 793-3329
James L Key, *President*
EMP: 10
SQ FT: 3,301
SALES (est): 1.1MM **Privately Held**
SIC: 2511 2434 Wood household furniture; wood kitchen cabinets

(P-4668)
AMISH COUNTRY GAZEBOS INC
739 E Francis St, Ontario (91761-5514)
PHONE..............................800 700-1777
Chet Beiler, *President*
EMP: 12
SALES: 1.6MM **Privately Held**
SIC: 2511 5031 1521 Garden furniture: wood; structural assemblies, prefabricated: wood; patio & deck construction & repair

(P-4669)
ART OF MUSE
Also Called: Oly
2222 5th St, Berkeley (94710-2217)
PHONE..............................510 644-1870
Brad Huntzinger, *President*
Kate McIntyre, *Vice Pres*
▲ **EMP:** 25
SALES (est): 3.9MM **Privately Held**
SIC: 2511 2521 Wood household furniture; wood office furniture

(P-4670)
ARTS CUSTOM CABINETS INC
897 E Tulare Rd, Lindsay (93247-2244)
P.O. Box 218 (93247-0218)
PHONE..............................559 562-2766
Art Serna, *President*
Leonor Dela Fuente Serna, *Admin Sec*
EMP: 19
SQ FT: 45,000
SALES (est): 2.2MM **Privately Held**
WEB: www.artscc.com
SIC: 2511 2434 Kitchen & dining room furniture; vanities, bathroom: wood

(P-4671)
ASHLEY FURNITURE INDS INC
Also Called: Ashley Furnishing Homestore
5055 S Montclair Plaza Ln, Montclair (91763-1512)
PHONE..............................909 652-6840
EMP: 480
SALES (corp-wide): 4.7B **Privately Held**
SIC: 2511 Wood household furniture
PA: Ashley Furniture Industries, Inc.
1 Ashley Way
Arcadia WI 54612
608 323-3377

(P-4672)
ASHLEY FURNITURE INDS INC
2250 W Lugonia Ave, Redlands (92374-5050)
PHONE..............................909 825-4900
Kurt Haines, *Manager*
Dan Aiman, *Vice Pres*
Norman L Blemaster, *Vice Pres*
George Gesualdo, *Vice Pres*
Chris M Seneca, *Vice Pres*
EMP: 800

(P-4673)
ASPEN BRANDS CORPORATION
1305 E Wakeham Ave, Santa Ana (92705-4145)
PHONE..............................702 946-9430
Michael Rocha, *CEO*
▲ **EMP:** 14
SALES (est): 427.5K **Privately Held**
SIC: 2511 3231 3641 5021 Chairs, household, except upholstered: wood; tables, household: wood; products of purchased glass; electric light bulbs, complete; tables, occasional; chairs; glassware; lighting fixtures

(P-4674)
AW INDUSTRIES INC
Also Called: Skog Furniture
1810 S Reservoir St, Pomona (91766-5541)
PHONE..............................909 629-1500
Ted Wong, *President*
Beatrice Wong, *Admin Sec*
EMP: 55
SQ FT: 46,000
SALES (est): 6.4MM **Privately Held**
WEB: www.awindustries.com
SIC: 2511 Wood household furniture

(P-4675)
BAU FURNITURE MANUFACTURING (PA)
23811 Aliso Creek Rd # 134, Laguna Niguel (92677-3902)
PHONE..............................949 643-2729
Thomas Bau, *President*
Linda Bau, *President*
EMP: 40
SQ FT: 43,000
SALES (est): 3.4MM **Privately Held**
WEB: www.baufurniture.com
SIC: 2511 2512 2521 Tables, household: wood; chairs, household, except upholstered: wood; upholstered household furniture; tables, office: wood; chairs, office: padded, upholstered or plain: wood

(P-4676)
BEAUTY CRAFT FURNITURE CORP
Also Called: California House
3316 51st Ave, Sacramento (95823-1089)
PHONE..............................916 428-2238
Steven Start, *President*
Dee Start, *Ch of Bd*
▲ **EMP:** 44
SQ FT: 65,000
SALES (est): 7MM **Privately Held**
SIC: 2511 Wood game room furniture

(P-4677)
BENT FIR COMPANY
3598 Manzanita Ave, Nice (95464)
P.O. Box 506 (95464-0506)
PHONE..............................707 274-6628
Robert Alvord, *Owner*
EMP: 11 **EST:** 1952
SQ FT: 6,000
SALES: 600K **Privately Held**
SIC: 2511 2431 Screens, privacy: wood; doors, wood

(P-4678)
BERKELEY MLLWK & FURN CO INC
Also Called: Berkeley Mills
2830 7th St, Berkeley (94710-2703)
PHONE..............................510 549-2854
Eugene Agress, *President*
Luong Lee Dinh, *Vice Pres*
Scott Pew, *Vice Pres*
EMP: 43
SQ FT: 18,000
SALES (est): 4.6MM **Privately Held**
WEB: www.berkeleymills.com
SIC: 2511 2541 2434 Wood household furniture; wood partitions & fixtures; wood kitchen cabinets

(P-4679)
BIG TREE FURNITURE & INDS INC (PA)
760 S Vail Ave, Montebello (90640-4954)
PHONE..............................310 894-7500
Joe Ho, *CEO*
▲ **EMP:** 44
SALES (est): 8.8MM **Privately Held**
SIC: 2511 Wood household furniture

(P-4680)
BLANK AND CABLES INC
3100 E 10th St, Oakland (94601-2914)
P.O. Box 23563 (94623-0563)
PHONE..............................415 648-3842
Walter Craven, *President*
EMP: 10
SQ FT: 11,000
SALES (est): 1.7MM **Privately Held**
WEB: www.blankandcables.com
SIC: 2511 2514 Wood household furniture; metal household furniture

(P-4681)
BRADSHAW KIRCHOFER HOME FURN
22926 Mariposa Ave, Torrance (90502-2603)
PHONE..............................310 325-0010
John Kirchofer, *Co-Owner*
Ann Kirchofer, *Co-Owner*
EMP: 12 **EST:** 1995
SQ FT: 10,000
SALES: 1.3MM **Privately Held**
WEB: www.bradshawkirchofer.com
SIC: 2511 Wood household furniture

(P-4682)
CABINETS GALORE ORANGE COUNTY
Also Called: Cabinets Galore Oc
9279 Cabot Dr Ste D, San Diego (92126-4364)
PHONE..............................858 586-0555
Barry Jacobs, *President*
ADI Jacobs, *Vice Pres*
EMP: 20
SQ FT: 10,000
SALES: 1.8MM **Privately Held**
SIC: 2511 5722 2514 3088 Furniture dimension stock, softwood; cabinet & finish carpentry

(P-4683)
CALIFORNIA BEDROOMS INC
95 Santa Fe Ave, Fresno (93721-3034)
PHONE..............................559 233-7050
Elias Serrano, *President*
▲ **EMP:** 40
SALES (est): 4.8MM **Privately Held**
SIC: 2511 Wood bedroom furniture

(P-4684)
CB MILL INC
1232 Connecticut St, San Francisco (94107-3352)
PHONE..............................415 386-5309
David Wickum, *President*
EMP: 19 **EST:** 2001
SQ FT: 16,000
SALES: 2.2MM **Privately Held**
WEB: www.cbmill.net
SIC: 2511

(P-4685)
CONCEPTS BY J INC
834 E 108th St, Los Angeles (90059-1006)
P.O. Box 88249 (90009-8249)
PHONE..............................323 564-9988
Jay Meepos, *President*
EMP: 20 **EST:** 1979
SQ FT: 12,100
SALES (est): 2MM **Privately Held**
WEB: www.conceptsbyq.com
SIC: 2511 Wood household furniture

(P-4686)
CRESCENT WOODWORKING CO LTD
Also Called: Ayca Furniture
400 Ramona Ave Ste 212, Corona (92879-1443)
PHONE..................................909 673-9955
▲ EMP: 12
SQ FT: 32,000
SALES (est): 1.5MM
SALES (corp-wide): 10.3MM **Privately Held**
WEB: www.crescentwoodworking.com
SIC: 2511
PA: Tianjin Sayca Wood Co., Ltd.
In Hailong Warehousing And Transportation Center, No.5035, Jinta
Tianjin 30045
222 532-3876

(P-4687)
CYPRESS FURNITURE INC
26602 Corporate Ave, Hayward (94545-3919)
PHONE..................................510 723-4890
James Berrens, *President*
Charles Oliver, *Admin Sec*
EMP: 10
SQ FT: 15,000
SALES (est): 700K **Privately Held**
WEB: www.cypressfurniture.com
SIC: 2511 Bed frames, except water bed frames: wood

(P-4688)
DATELINE PRODUCTS LLC
1375 E Base Line St Ste B, San Bernardino (92410-4063)
PHONE..................................909 888-9785
Robert Prescaro, *CFO*
Joe Garofalo, *President*
Rodger Reynoso, *Vice Pres*
◆ EMP: 12
SQ FT: 20,000
SALES (est): 1.3MM **Privately Held**
WEB: www.datelineproducts.com
SIC: 2511 Wood household furniture

(P-4689)
DOUG MOCKETT & COMPANY INC
1915 Abalone Ave, Torrance (90501-3706)
P.O. Box 3333, Manhattan Beach (90266-1333)
PHONE..................................310 318-2491
Susan Darby Gordon, *President*
Sonia Marie H Mockett, *Admin Sec*
Martha Gonzales, *Human Res Dir*
Melissa Punch, *Purchasing*
Jamaul Teague, *Purch Agent*
▲ EMP: 40
SALES (est): 9.3MM **Privately Held**
WEB: www.mockett.com
SIC: 2511 Unassembled or unfinished furniture, household: wood

(P-4690)
DR TEAK INC
13726 Harvard Pl, Gardena (90249-2527)
PHONE..................................310 527-2675
Chris Putrimas, *CEO*
Mike Smith, *General Mgr*
EMP: 31
SQ FT: 7,576
SALES (est): 2.4MM **Privately Held**
SIC: 2511 7641 Wood household furniture; reupholstery & furniture repair

(P-4691)
EDMONS UNQUE FURN STONE GLLERY (PA)
5174 Melrose Ave, Los Angeles (90038-4117)
PHONE..................................323 462-5787
Edmon Simonian, *President*
EMP: 10
SQ FT: 10,000
SALES (est): 1MM **Privately Held**
SIC: 2511 Wood household furniture

(P-4692)
ELEMENTS BY GRAPEVINE INC
18251 N Highway 88, Lockeford (95237-9716)
P.O. Box 1458 (95237-1458)
PHONE..................................209 727-3711
Isaac Kubryk, *President*
Renee Kubryk, *Vice Pres*
▲ EMP: 45 EST: 1979
SQ FT: 60,000
SALES (est): 15MM **Privately Held**
WEB: www.wizkids.com
SIC: 2511 2519 Tables, household: wood; lawn & garden furniture, except wood & metal

(P-4693)
EMANUEL MOREZ INC
Also Called: Amos Art Studio
8754 Yolanda Ave, Northridge (91324-3831)
PHONE..................................818 780-2787
Amos Stockfish, *President*
▲ EMP: 30
SQ FT: 26,000
SALES (est): 3MM **Privately Held**
WEB: www.emanuelmorez.com
SIC: 2511 2499 1751 Wood household furniture; decorative wood & woodwork; carved & turned wood; cabinet & finish carpentry

(P-4694)
ENVIRONMENT FURNITURE INC (HQ)
Also Called: ERA Furniture
785 Holmby Ave, Los Angeles (90024-3319)
PHONE..................................323 782-0296
Davide Berruto, *CEO*
Natalie Mata, *Manager*
▲ EMP: 21
SQ FT: 3,000
SALES (est): 2.5MM **Privately Held**
WEB: www.environment-furniture.com
SIC: 2511 Wood household furniture

(P-4695)
EURODESIGN LTD (PA)
62 Chester Cir, Los Altos (94022-1246)
PHONE..................................650 948-5160
Edward G Wildanger, *President*
Paula P Wildanger, *Corp Secy*
Linda Rios, *Bookkeeper*
EMP: 15
SALES (est): 3MM **Privately Held**
SIC: 2511 5712 Wood household furniture; furniture stores

(P-4696)
FEDERAL PRISON INDUSTRIES
Also Called: Unicor
3600 Guard Rd, Lompoc (93436-2705)
PHONE..................................805 736-4154
Steve Southall, *Superintendent*
EMP: 245 **Publicly Held**
WEB: www.unicor.gov
SIC: 2511 2759 3993 9223 Wood household furniture; commercial printing; signs & advertising specialties; correctional institutions
HQ: Federal Prison Industries, Inc
320 1st St Nw
Washington DC 20534
202 305-3500

(P-4697)
FREMARC INDUSTRIES INC (PA)
Also Called: Fremarc Designs
18810 San Jose Ave, City of Industry (91748-1325)
PHONE..................................626 965-0802
Maurice M Donenfeld, *President*
Harriette Donenfeld, *Corp Secy*
▲ EMP: 82
SQ FT: 45,000
SALES (est): 10.5MM **Privately Held**
WEB: www.fremarc.com
SIC: 2511 Wood household furniture

(P-4698)
FRENCH TRADITION (PA)
13700 Crenshaw Blvd, Gardena (90249-2348)
PHONE..................................310 719-9977
Franck Valles, *President*
Julie Valles, *Vice Pres*
Jerry Boshear, *Project Mgr*
EMP: 15
SQ FT: 7,000
SALES (est): 2.1MM **Privately Held**
WEB: www.thefrenchtradition.com
SIC: 2511 Wood household furniture

(P-4699)
FURNITURE ACCESSORY RET GROUP
180 Knoll Rd, San Marcos (92069-1529)
PHONE..................................619 591-1150
Richard Huffman, *Branch Mgr*
EMP: 25
SALES (corp-wide): 14.5MM **Privately Held**
SIC: 2511 Wood household furniture
PA: Furniture & Accessory Retail Group
180 Knoll Rd
San Marcos CA 92069
760 744-2335

(P-4700)
FURNITURE TECHNICS INC
Also Called: Furniture Techniques
2900 Supply Ave, Commerce (90040-2708)
PHONE..................................562 802-0261
Cesar Rousseau, *President*
Ricardo Flores, *Admin Sec*
EMP: 25
SALES (est): 266.4K **Privately Held**
SIC: 2511 2426 Wood household furniture; furniture stock & parts, hardwood

(P-4701)
HANSENS OAK INC (PA)
166 E Broadway Ave, Atwater (95301-4562)
PHONE..................................209 357-3424
Michael Hansen, *President*
Robert Glenney, *Vice Pres*
▲ EMP: 14
SALES (est): 1.3MM **Privately Held**
SIC: 2511 Dining room furniture: wood; chairs, household, except upholstered: wood; desks, household: wood

(P-4702)
HANSON BRASS INC
7530 San Fernando Rd, Sun Valley (91352-4344)
PHONE..................................818 767-3501
Tom Hanson Jr, *President*
Thomas Hanson Sr, *Chairman*
James Hanson, *Vice Pres*
EMP: 10
SQ FT: 6,000
SALES (est): 1MM **Privately Held**
WEB: www.hansonbrass.com
SIC: 2511 3648 Buffets (furniture); infrared lamp fixtures

(P-4703)
HOLLYWOOD CHAIRS
Also Called: Totally Bamboo
1810 Diamond St, San Marcos (92078-5100)
PHONE..................................818 720-9946
Joanne Chen, *President*
Tom Sullivan, *CEO*
◆ EMP: 12
SQ FT: 10,000
SALES (est): 2.2MM **Privately Held**
WEB: www.totallybamboo.com
SIC: 2511 Wood household furniture

(P-4704)
I M GINSBURG FURNITURE INC
Also Called: David Furniture
1441 W 130th St, Gardena (90249-2101)
PHONE..................................310 243-1260
Irving Ginsburg, *President*
Davene Ginsburg, *Vice Pres*
EMP: 43
SQ FT: 20,000
SALES (est): 3.8MM **Privately Held**
WEB: www.imdavid.com
SIC: 2511 Wood game room furniture; dining room furniture: wood

(P-4705)
IMPERIAL CUSTOM CABINET INC
8093 Lemon Grove Way, Lemon Grove (91945-1913)
PHONE..................................619 461-4093
Art Schiele, *President*
EMP: 15 EST: 1971
SQ FT: 10,000
SALES (est): 1.8MM **Privately Held**
SIC: 2511 2434 Wood household furniture; wood kitchen cabinets

(P-4706)
INTERIOR WOOD DESIGN INC
334 Sacramento St Ste 1, Auburn (95603-5510)
PHONE..................................530 888-7707
Tim Hanson, *President*
Tim Fariss, *Vice Pres*
EMP: 10
SQ FT: 5,000
SALES (est): 1.1MM **Privately Held**
WEB: www.interiorwooddesign.com
SIC: 2511 2521 Wood household furniture; cabinets, office: wood

(P-4707)
JOES CUSTOM FURN & FRAMES
6402 Whittier Blvd, Los Angeles (90022-4604)
PHONE..................................323 721-1881
Joe Cypert Jr, *Partner*
Manuel Cypert, *Partner*
EMP: 10
SQ FT: 2,000
SALES (est): 1.3MM **Privately Held**
SIC: 2511 5932 7641 Wood household furniture; furniture, secondhand; furniture repair & maintenance

(P-4708)
JP PRODUCTS LLC
2054 Davie Ave, Commerce (90040-1705)
PHONE..................................310 237-6237
Patrick Mooney, *Mng Member*
Jacqueline Mooney, *Mng Member*
EMP: 46
SQ FT: 35,000
SALES (est): 3.5MM **Privately Held**
SIC: 2511 Wood household furniture

(P-4709)
JUAN BRAMBILA SR
Also Called: Brambila's Draperies
5018 Venice Blvd, Los Angeles (90019-5308)
PHONE..................................323 939-8312
Juan Brambila Sr, *Owner*
Ana Brambila, *Co-Owner*
EMP: 16
SQ FT: 8,000
SALES (est): 1.8MM **Privately Held**
SIC: 2511 2392 2391 5023 Bed frames, except water bed frames: wood; bedspreads & bed sets: made from purchased materials; draperies, plastic & textile: from purchased materials; draperies

(P-4710)
KEHOE CUSTOM WOOD DESIGNS
1320 N Miller St Ste D, Anaheim (92806-1414)
PHONE..................................714 993-0444
Joseph T Kehoe, *President*
EMP: 10
SQ FT: 5,000
SALES (est): 819K **Privately Held**
SIC: 2511 2517 2521 Wood household furniture; wood television & radio cabinets; cabinets, office: wood

(P-4711)
KERROCK COUNTERTOPS INC (PA)
Also Called: Lisac Construction
33220 Western Ave, Union City (94587-2209)
PHONE..................................510 441-2300
William G Lisac, *President*
▲ EMP: 20
SQ FT: 18,000

PRODUCTS & SVCS

SALES: 1.6MM **Privately Held**
WEB: www.kerrock.com
SIC: 2511 5211 1799 Wood household
furniture; cabinets, kitchen; counter top installation

(P-4712)
KINWAI USA INC
2265 Davis Ct, Hayward (94545-1113)
PHONE..................................510 780-9388
Chongwei Zhao, *President*
Daniel Murphy, *Project Mgr*
▲ EMP: 20
SALES (est): 2.3MM **Privately Held**
SIC: 2511 5021 Wood household furniture;
household furniture

(P-4713)
KUSHWOOD CHAIR INC
1290 E Elm St, Ontario (91761-4025)
PHONE..................................909 930-2100
Daniel Kusvhinikov, *President*
Roger Douglas, *Vice Pres*
EMP: 250 EST: 1979
SQ FT: 450,000
SALES (est): 18.9MM **Privately Held**
SIC: 2511 2521 Wood office furniture;
unassembled or unfinished furniture,
household: wood

(P-4714)
**LA CANDELARIA
MANUFACTURING**
Also Called: La Candelaria Furniture Mfr
2790 M L King Jr Blvd, Lynwood (90262)
PHONE..................................310 763-0112
Felipe Contreras, *Owner*
Antonio Garcia, *Co-Owner*
EMP: 10
SQ FT: 1,200
SALES (est): 675.8K **Privately Held**
SIC: 2511 Wood stands & chests, except
bedside stands; wood bedroom furniture

(P-4715)
LANPAR INC
Also Called: Oakwood Interiors
1333 S Bon View Ave, Ontario
(91761-4404)
PHONE..................................541 484-1962
Nick Lanphier, *Ch of Bd*
EMP: 255
SQ FT: 180,000
SALES (est): 19.8MM **Privately Held**
WEB: www.fineoak.com
SIC: 2511 Wood bedroom furniture

(P-4716)
M F G EUROTEC INC
Also Called: BV WILMS
84464 Cabazon Center Dr, Indio
(92201-6200)
PHONE..................................760 863-0033
Jody R Williams, *President*
A R Williams, *Treasurer*
William Vinton Williams, *Principal*
Jason Williams, *Admin Sec*
EMP: 20
SQ FT: 18,500
SALES: 755.2K **Privately Held**
WEB: www.bvwilms.com
SIC: 2511 5211 1751 Wood household
furniture; cabinets, kitchen; cabinet & fin-
ish carpentry

(P-4717)
**MAGNUSSEN HOME
FURNISHINGS INC**
2155 Excise Ave Ste B, Ontario
(91761-8536)
PHONE..................................336 841-4424
Jeff Cook, *Branch Mgr*
EMP: 11 **Privately Held**
SIC: 2511 Wood household furniture
HQ: Magnussen Home Furnishings, Inc.
4523 Green Point Dr # 109
Greensboro NC 27410
336 841-4424

(P-4718)
**MCGUNAGLE WILLIAM H &
SONS MFG (PA)**
Also Called: Mack Wall Bed Systems
971 Transport Way Ste B, Petaluma
(94954-1402)
PHONE..................................707 762-7900
William H Mc Gunagle, *President*
Nancy Mc Gunagle, *Vice Pres*
EMP: 10
SALES: 225K **Privately Held**
WEB: www.mackwallbedsystems.com
SIC: 2511 5712 Bedspring frames: wood;
furniture stores

(P-4719)
**MICHAELS FURNITURE
COMPANY INC**
15 Koch Rd Ste J, Corte Madera
(94925-1231)
PHONE..................................916 381-9086
Gary Friedman, *CEO*
Mike Bollum, *General Mgr*
▲ EMP: 300
SQ FT: 150,000
SALES (est): 25.6MM
SALES (corp-wide): 2.4B **Publicly Held**
WEB: www.restorationhardware.com
SIC: 2511 Wood household furniture
HQ: Restoration Hardware, Inc.
15 Koch Rd Ste K
Corte Madera CA 94925
415 924-1005

(P-4720)
MID CENTURY IMPORTS INC
5333 Cahuenga Blvd, North Hollywood
(91601-3431)
PHONE..................................818 509-3050
David Pierce, *President*
▲ EMP: 10
SALES (est): 901.6K **Privately Held**
SIC: 2511 Wood household furniture

(P-4721)
MIKHAIL DARAFEEV INC (PA)
5075 Edison Ave, Chino (91710-5716)
PHONE..................................909 613-1818
Antonina Darafeev, *President*
Paul Darafeev, *Treasurer*
George Darafeev, *Admin Sec*
▲ EMP: 50 EST: 1957
SALES (est): 18.2MM **Privately Held**
WEB: www.darafeev.com
SIC: 2511 Stools, household: wood

(P-4722)
**MILLER & PIDSKALNY CSTM
WDWRK**
1940 Blair Ave, Santa Ana (92705-5707)
PHONE..................................949 250-8508
Lawrence P Miller, *President*
EMP: 15
SQ FT: 3,500
SALES (est): 1.3MM **Privately Held**
WEB: www.millerpid.com
SIC: 2511 2512 2431 Wood household
furniture; upholstered household furniture;
staircases, stairs & railings

(P-4723)
MINTON-SPIDELL INC (PA)
8467 Steller Dr, Culver City (90232-2424)
PHONE..................................310 836-0403
Maurice N Spidell, *President*
Rick Nelson, *Sales Executive*
Rick A Nelson, *Agent*
EMP: 19 EST: 1959
SQ FT: 9,000
SALES (est): 1.5MM **Privately Held**
WEB: www.minton-spidell.com
SIC: 2511 Wood household furniture

(P-4724)
MOD SHOP
15610 S Main St, Gardena (90248-2219)
PHONE..................................310 523-1008
John Bernard, *Owner*
▲ EMP: 50
SALES (est): 4MM **Privately Held**
SIC: 2511 Wood household furniture

(P-4725)
**MODERN BAMBOO
INCORPORATED**
5853 Virmar Ave, Oakland (94618-1536)
PHONE..................................925 820-2804
Anthony Marschak, *President*
Rod Suzuki, *CFO*
EMP: 12
SALES (est): 842.7K **Privately Held**
SIC: 2511 Wood household furniture

(P-4726)
**NELSON ADAMS NACO
CORPORATION**
160 N Cactus Ave, Rialto (92376-5725)
PHONE..................................909 256-8938
Rafael Rangel, *President*
Jesus Bojorquez, *Accounting Mgr*
Juan Gutierrez, *Sls & Mktg Exec*
Luis Vega, *Marketing Staff*
EMP: 20
SQ FT: 40,000
SALES (est): 3.6MM **Privately Held**
SIC: 2511 Coffee tables: wood

(P-4727)
NEWCO INTERNATIONAL INC
Also Called: Harmony Kids
13600 Vaughn St, San Fernando
(91340-3017)
PHONE..................................818 834-7100
Howard Napolske, *President*
Ernest Johnston, *Vice Pres*
▲ EMP: 350
SQ FT: 20,000
SALES (est): 36.2MM **Privately Held**
WEB: www.harmonykids.com
SIC: 2511 Children's wood furniture

(P-4728)
NOVA LIFESTYLE INC (PA)
6565 E Washington Blvd, Commerce
(90040-1821)
PHONE..................................323 888-9999
Tawny Lam, *Ch of Bd*
Thanh H Lam, *Ch of Bd*
Sammy Ho, *CFO*
Yuen Ching Ho, *CFO*
Huy La, *Bd of Directors*
EMP: 22
SALES: 106.4MM **Publicly Held**
SIC: 2511 2512 Wood household furniture;
upholstered household furniture; chairs:
upholstered on wood frames

(P-4729)
OAK TREE FURNITURE INC
13615 Excelsior Dr, Santa Fe Springs
(90670-5103)
PHONE..................................562 944-0754
Tim Sopp, *President*
Elaine Sopp, *Vice Pres*
▲ EMP: 70 EST: 1977
SQ FT: 55,000
SALES (est): 7.2MM **Privately Held**
WEB: www.otfinc.net
SIC: 2511 Wood household furniture

(P-4730)
**P J MILLIGAN COMPANY LLC
(PA)**
Also Called: P J Milligan & Associates
436 E Gutierrez St, Santa Barbara
(93101-1709)
PHONE..................................805 963-4038
Patrick Milligan, *CEO*
▲ EMP: 13
SQ FT: 18,000
SALES: 2.5MM **Privately Held**
WEB: www.pjmilligan.com
SIC: 2511 5712 Wood household furniture;
furniture stores

(P-4731)
PLUSH HOME INC
8323 Melrose Ave, Los Angeles
(90069-5403)
PHONE..................................323 852-1912
Steven Ho, *President*
EMP: 24
SALES (est): 1.7MM **Privately Held**
WEB: www.plushhome.com
SIC: 2511 7389 Wood household furniture;
interior designer

(P-4732)
QUALITY SHEDS INC
33210 Bailey Park Blvd, Menifee
(92584-9584)
PHONE..................................951 672-6750
Matt Poturich, *Owner*
Jack Roy, *Administration*
EMP: 11
SQ FT: 3,700
SALES (est): 1.5MM **Privately Held**
SIC: 2511 Storage chests, household:
wood

(P-4733)
RADFORD CABINETS INC
216 E Avenue K8, Lancaster (93535-4527)
PHONE..................................661 729-8931
Steven Radford, *President*
Robert Mendoza, *Vice Pres*
Sharon Radford, *Admin Sec*
EMP: 70
SQ FT: 20,000
SALES (est): 9.1MM **Privately Held**
WEB: www.radfordcabinets.com
SIC: 2511 2434 2521 Kitchen & dining
room furniture; wood kitchen cabinets;
cabinets, office: wood

(P-4734)
RANDOLPH & HEIN
720 E 59th St, Los Angeles (90001-1004)
PHONE..................................323 233-6010
Mohammad Ali Karbalai, *Administration*
Katie Razavi, *Sales Mgr*
▲ EMP: 10
SALES (est): 1MM **Privately Held**
SIC: 2511 5712 Wood household furniture;
furniture stores

(P-4735)
RODS UNFINISHED FURNITURE
1121 S Meridian Ave, Alhambra
(91803-1218)
PHONE..................................626 281-9855
Juan C Rodriguez Sr, *President*
Ann Rodriguez, *Corp Secy*
John Rodriguez Jr, *Vice Pres*
EMP: 20 EST: 1982
SQ FT: 25,000
SALES (est): 1.8MM **Privately Held**
SIC: 2511 Unassembled or unfinished fur-
niture, household: wood

(P-4736)
**ROSETTI GENNARO
FURNITURE**
6833 Brynhurst Ave, Los Angeles
(90043-4665)
PHONE..................................323 750-7794
Gennaro Rosetti, *Owner*
EMP: 33
SQ FT: 15,000
SALES (est): 2.4MM **Privately Held**
SIC: 2511 2426 2521 Wood household
furniture; hardwood dimension & flooring
mills; wood office furniture

(P-4737)
S D M FURNITURE CO INC
Also Called: Sdm
4620 W Jefferson Blvd, Los Angeles
(90016-4007)
PHONE..................................323 936-0295
Victor Cohen, *President*
Martha Cohen, *Treasurer*
Michael Cohen, *Vice Pres*
EMP: 14
SQ FT: 6,000
SALES (est): 1.5MM **Privately Held**
SIC: 2511 Wood household furniture

(P-4738)
**SAN DIEGO ARCFT INTERIORS
INC**
2940 Hoover Ave, National City
(91950-7218)
PHONE..................................619 474-1997
Juan Carlos Vasquez, *President*
Juan Vazquez, *Executive*
Erick Muschenheim, *General Mgr*
Carlos Vazquez, *General Mgr*
▲ EMP: 23
SALES: 1MM **Privately Held**
SIC: 2511 Chairs, household, except up-
holstered: wood

▲ = Import ▼=Export
◆ =Import/Export

(P-4739)
SANDBERG FURNITURE MFG CO INC (PA)
5705 Alcoa Ave, Vernon (90058-3794)
P.O. Box 58291, Los Angeles (90058-0291)
PHONE...................................323 582-0711
John Sandberg, *CEO*
Mark Nixon, *Senior VP*
Linda Hart, *Credit Mgr*
▲ EMP: 225
SALES (est): 75MM Privately Held
SIC: 2511 Wood bedroom furniture

(P-4740)
STUART DAVID INC (PA)
Also Called: Stuart's Fine Furniture
3419 Railroad Ave, Ceres (95307-3623)
P.O. Box 1009 (95307-1009)
PHONE...................................209 537-7449
David Neilson, *President*
Della Maria Nielson, *Accounts Mgr*
EMP: 35
SQ FT: 79,000
SALES (est): 4.7MM Privately Held
WEB: www.stuarts.net
SIC: 2511 Wood household furniture

(P-4741)
SUMMERTREE INTERIORS INC
4111 Buchanan St, Riverside (92503-4812)
PHONE...................................951 549-0590
Pockets Alvarez, *President*
EMP: 10
SALES (est): 1.2MM Privately Held
SIC: 2511 Wood household furniture

(P-4742)
SUMMIT FURNITURE INC (PA)
5 Harris Ct Bldg W, Monterey (93940-5755)
PHONE...................................831 375-7811
Jane Sieberts, *President*
Patty Parker, *CFO*
Patricia Parker, *Corp Secy*
Omattie Luedtke, *Controller*
Hilary Gustafsson, *Sales Dir*
▲ EMP: 13
SQ FT: 30,000
SALES (est): 1.6MM Privately Held
SIC: 2511 Wood household furniture

(P-4743)
TEXTURED DESIGN FURNITURE
Also Called: Texture Design
1303 S Claudina St, Anaheim (92805-6235)
PHONE...................................714 502-9121
J Luis Gonzales, *President*
▲ EMP: 40
SQ FT: 34,000
SALES: 4MM Privately Held
WEB: www.texturedesign.com
SIC: 2511 Wood household furniture

(P-4744)
TOSCANELLA INC
9935 Toluca Lake Ave, Toluca Lake (91602-2921)
PHONE...................................818 506-7283
Fiorenzo Tirinnanzi, *President*
Kathy Tirinnanzi, *Corp Secy*
EMP: 22
SQ FT: 20,000
SALES: 2MM Privately Held
SIC: 2511 2499 2512 2426 Unassembled or unfinished furniture, household: wood; decorative wood & woodwork; uphol-stered household furniture; hardwood dimension & flooring mills

(P-4745)
TREND MANOR FURN MFG CO INC
17047 Gale Ave, City of Industry (91745-1808)
PHONE...................................626 964-6493
Theodore Vecchione, *President*
▲ EMP: 42 EST: 1946
SQ FT: 63,000
SALES (est): 6MM Privately Held
SIC: 2511 Wood household furniture

(P-4746)
UNIVERSAL INTERIOR INDUSTRIES
4111 Buchanan St, Riverside (92503-4812)
PHONE...................................951 743-5446
Pockets Alvarez, *President*
Marvella Garcia, *Vice Pres*
Pockets Alarez, *Principal*
EMP: 12
SALES (est): 1MM Privately Held
SIC: 2511 Wood household furniture

(P-4747)
WALMSLEY DESIGN
3825 Willat Ave Bldg A, Culver City (90232-2306)
PHONE...................................310 836-0772
Ian Walmsley, *Owner*
EMP: 10
SQ FT: 3,000
SALES: 500K Privately Held
SIC: 2511 Wood household furniture

(P-4748)
WEST COAST CATRG TRCKS MFG INC
1217 Goodrich Blvd, Commerce (90022-5124)
PHONE...................................323 278-1279
Juan Gomez, *President*
Jesus Gomez, *Director*
EMP: 12
SQ FT: 18,000
SALES (est): 1.2MM Privately Held
WEB: www.westcoastcateringtrucks.com
SIC: 2511 Stands, household, wood

(P-4749)
WEST WORLD MANUFACTURING INC
Also Called: West-World Co
6420 Federal Blvd Ste F, Lemon Grove (91945-1339)
P.O. Box 152780, San Diego (92195-2780)
PHONE...................................619 287-4403
Richard Mossay, *President*
EMP: 12 EST: 1977
SQ FT: 6,000
SALES: 1MM Privately Held
SIC: 2511 3083 2541 3089 Wood household furniture; plastic finished products, laminated; cabinets, except refrigerated: show, display, etc.: wood; plastic kitchenware, tableware & houseware; wood kitchen cabinets

(P-4750)
WESTERN DOVETAIL INCORPORATED
1101 Nimitz Ave Ste 209, Vallejo (94592-1034)
P.O. Box 1592 (94590-0159)
PHONE...................................707 556-3683
Maxfield Hunter, *Principal*
Joshua Hunter, *Director*
EMP: 22
SQ FT: 1,000
SALES: 3.3MM Privately Held
WEB: www.drawer.com
SIC: 2511 Wood household furniture

(P-4751)
WHALEN FURNITURE MFG INC
1578 Air Wing Rd, San Diego (92154-7706)
PHONE...................................619 423-9948
Kenneth J Whalen, *CEO*
◆ EMP: 38
SALES (est): 7.1MM Privately Held
SIC: 2511 Wood household furniture

(P-4752)
WHALEN LLC (DH)
Also Called: Whalen Furniture Manufacturing
1578 Air Wing Rd, San Diego (92154-7706)
PHONE...................................619 423-9948
Dow Famulak, *President*
Paul Coscarelli, *President*
Paul Jones, *Vice Pres*
Scott Knauss, *Vice Pres*
David Levinson, *Vice Pres*
◆ EMP: 110
SQ FT: 100,000

SALES (est): 30.3MM Privately Held
WEB: www.whalenfurniture.com
SIC: 2511 Wood household furniture
HQ: Li & Fung Development (China) Limited
11/F Lifung Twr
Cheung Sha Wan KLN
230 023-00

(P-4753)
WILD WOOD DESIGNS INC
Also Called: Wildwood Designs
1607 E Edinger Ave Ste P, Santa Ana (92705-5017)
PHONE...................................714 543-6549
Matthew Taylor, *President*
EMP: 10
SQ FT: 1,600
SALES: 500K Privately Held
WEB: www.wildwooddesigns.com
SIC: 2511 2434 Wood household furniture; wood kitchen cabinets

(P-4754)
WOOD TECH INC
4611 Malat St, Oakland (94601-4903)
PHONE...................................510 534-4930
Juan D Figueroa, *CEO*
Herbert Vega, *Controller*
EMP: 70
SQ FT: 92,000
SALES (est): 9.2MM Privately Held
WEB: www.woodtechonline.com
SIC: 2511 2521 Wood household furniture; wood office furniture

(P-4755)
WOODLAND BEDROOMS INC
3423 Merced St, Los Angeles (90065-1660)
PHONE...................................562 408-1558
Gustavo Loza, *President*
Delia Loza, *Vice Pres*
▲ EMP: 75
SQ FT: 60,000
SALES (est): 6.6MM Privately Held
SIC: 2511 Wood household furniture

(P-4756)
WOODWORKS
107 Nunes Rd, Watsonville (95076-9627)
P.O. Box 227, Freedom (95019-0227)
PHONE...................................831 688-8420
Christopher Holmstrom, *Owner*
EMP: 10
SALES (est): 602.9K Privately Held
SIC: 2511 2431 Wood household furniture; door frames, wood

2512 Wood Household Furniture, Upholstered

(P-4757)
A P SMILEY & SONS INC
5460 W Washington Blvd, Los Angeles (90016-1135)
PHONE...................................323 937-2244
Felipe Bautispa, *Owner*
EMP: 26
SALES (est): 1MM Privately Held
SIC: 2512 7641 Upholstered household furniture; reupholstery & furniture repair

(P-4758)
A RUDIN INC (PA)
Also Called: A Rudin Designs
6062 Alcoa Ave, Vernon (90058-3902)
PHONE...................................323 589-5547
Arnold Rudin, *President*
Ralph Rudin, *Vice Pres*
Lauraa Smith, *Manager*
▲ EMP: 92
SQ FT: 117,000
SALES (est): 12.5MM Privately Held
SIC: 2512 5021 Upholstered household furniture; household furniture

(P-4759)
AMERASIA FURNITURE COMPONENTS
2772 Norton Ave, Lynwood (90262-1835)
PHONE...................................310 638-0570
Khue Van Cao, *CEO*
Alfred Varela Jr, *President*

▲ EMP: 29
SQ FT: 55,000
SALES (est): 3.3MM Privately Held
SIC: 2512 Upholstered household furniture

(P-4760)
BEST QUALITY FURNITURE MFG INC
5400 E Francis St, Ontario (91761-3603)
P.O. Box 310795, Fontana (92331-0795)
PHONE...................................909 230-6440
Khoa Van Ta, *President*
Craig Alford, *Vice Pres*
▲ EMP: 100 EST: 1996
SALES (est): 9.5MM Privately Held
WEB: www.bestqualityfurniture.com
SIC: 2512 5021 2511 Upholstered household furniture; household furniture; wood household furniture

(P-4761)
BURTON JAMES INC
428 Turnbull Canyon Rd, City of Industry (91745-1011)
PHONE...................................626 961-7221
Raymond Zoref, *CEO*
Harry Robbins, *CFO*
Brandy Wong, *Director*
EMP: 80
SQ FT: 28,000
SALES (est): 12.4MM Privately Held
WEB: www.burtonjames.com
SIC: 2512 Upholstered household furniture

(P-4762)
CISCO BROS CORP
938 E 60th St, Los Angeles (90001-1017)
PHONE...................................323 778-8612
Ysenia Mota, *Manager*
EMP: 15 Privately Held
SIC: 2512 Upholstered household furniture
PA: Cisco Bros. Corp.
5955 S Western Ave
Los Angeles CA 90047

(P-4763)
CISCO BROS CORP (PA)
Also Called: Cisco & Brothers Designs
5955 S Western Ave, Los Angeles (90047-1124)
PHONE...................................323 778-8612
Francisco Pinedo, *CEO*
Alba E Pinedo, *Exec VP*
David Cuevas, *Info Tech Dir*
Jose Pinedo, *Plant Mgr*
◆ EMP: 145
SQ FT: 100,000
SALES (est): 49.8MM Privately Held
WEB: www.ciscobrothers.com
SIC: 2512 Upholstered household furniture

(P-4764)
COMMERCIAL INTR RESOURCES INC
Also Called: Contract Resources
6077 Rickenbacker Rd, Commerce (90040-3031)
PHONE...................................562 926-5885
Roberta Tuchman, *CEO*
Stanley Rice, *President*
Barbara Rice, *Corp Secy*
Stephanie Lesko, *Vice Pres*
Juan Morales, *Vice Pres*
EMP: 65
SQ FT: 28,000
SALES (est): 8.9MM Privately Held
WEB: www.bprco.com
SIC: 2512 Upholstered household furniture

(P-4765)
CORTEZ FURNITURE MFG INC
2423 E 58th St, Los Angeles (90058-3511)
PHONE...................................323 581-5935
Antonio Flores, *President*
EMP: 15
SALES (corp-wide): 800K Privately Held
SIC: 2512 Upholstered household furniture
PA: Cortez Furniture Manufacturing, Inc.
2444 E 57th St
Vernon CA 90058
323 581-5935

(P-4766)
CORTEZ FURNITURE MFG INC (PA)
2444 E 57th St, Vernon (90058-3510)
PHONE....................323 581-5935
Antonio Flores, *President*
Maria Guadalupe, *Corp Secy*
Jose Flores, *Vice Pres*
EMP: 30
SQ FT: 37,500
SALES: 2.1MM **Privately Held**
SIC: 2512 Upholstered household furniture

(P-4767)
CUSTOM UPHOLSTERED FURN INC
Also Called: Upholstery Workroom
5000 W Jefferson Blvd, Los Angeles (90016-3925)
PHONE....................323 731-3033
EMP: 14
SALES (est): 982.6K **Privately Held**
SIC: 2512

(P-4768)
DAVES INTERIORS INC
Also Called: Life Style West
1579 N Main St, Orange (92867-3439)
PHONE....................714 998-5554
David Navarro, *President*
Denise Navarro, *Treasurer*
Rachel Navarro, *Vice Pres*
Kay Ames, *Admin Sec*
▲ **EMP:** 25
SQ FT: 12,500
SALES (est): 3.1MM **Privately Held**
WEB: www.davesinteriors.com
SIC: 2512 7641 2511 Upholstered household furniture; reupholstery; wood household furniture

(P-4769)
DECOR FABRICS INC
Also Called: Decor International
6515 Mckinley Ave, Los Angeles (90001-1519)
PHONE....................323 752-2200
Freshath Kashani, *President*
EMP: 25
SQ FT: 25,000
SALES: 2MM **Privately Held**
SIC: 2512 2521 Upholstered household furniture; wood office furniture

(P-4770)
DELLAROBBIA INC (PA)
119 Waterworks Way, Irvine (92618-3110)
PHONE....................949 251-9532
David Soonlan, *President*
Sunee Soonlan, *Admin Sec*
▲ **EMP:** 48
SQ FT: 27,000
SALES (est): 3.7MM **Privately Held**
WEB: www.dellarobbiausa.com
SIC: 2512 Upholstered household furniture

(P-4771)
EBANISTA INC (PA)
2015 Newport Blvd, Costa Mesa (92627-2161)
PHONE....................949 650-6397
Abby Menhenett, *Principal*
EMP: 20
SALES (est): 9MM **Privately Held**
SIC: 2512 Living room furniture: upholstered on wood frames

(P-4772)
EJ LAUREN LLC
Also Called: Ejl
9400 Hall Rd, Downey (90241-5365)
PHONE....................562 803-1113
Antonio Ocampo, *Mng Member*
▲ **EMP:** 50
SQ FT: 20,000
SALES (est): 7.2MM **Privately Held**
SIC: 2512 Upholstered household furniture

(P-4773)
ELITE LEATHER LLC
3131 E Maria St, Compton (90221-5805)
PHONE....................909 548-8600
Jeff Lazar, *CEO*
John Contreras, *Business Mgr*
Tony Piro, *Finance Mgr*

Greg Rickabus, *Natl Sales Mgr*
Sherry Nguyen, *Marketing Mgr*
▲ **EMP:** 100 **EST:** 1959
SALES (est): 16.8MM
SALES (corp-wide): 85MM **Privately Held**
WEB: www.eliteleather.com
SIC: 2512 Living room furniture: upholstered on wood frames
PA: J L Furnishings Llc
　　19007 S Reyes Ave
　　Compton CA 90221
　　310 605-6600

(P-4774)
FLORES DESIGN FINE FURN INC
4618 Pacific Blvd, Vernon (90058-2210)
PHONE....................323 585-3200
Jose Guerra, *CEO*
▲ **EMP:** 35
SQ FT: 30,000
SALES (est): 5.2MM **Privately Held**
SIC: 2512 Upholstered household furniture

(P-4775)
FUTON EXPRESS
10309 Vacco St, South El Monte (91733-3315)
PHONE....................626 443-8684
GI Cheng LI, *Owner*
▲ **EMP:** 10
SALES (est): 576.3K **Privately Held**
WEB: www.futonexpress.net
SIC: 2512 Upholstered household furniture

(P-4776)
GARDENA FURNITURE MFG
11330 Markon Dr, Garden Grove (92841-1403)
PHONE....................714 441-8436
Henry Vuu, *Vice Pres*
Peter Lee, *President*
▲ **EMP:** 12
SQ FT: 10,000
SALES (est): 1.2MM **Privately Held**
WEB: www.gardenasofa.com
SIC: 2512 Couches, sofas & davenports: upholstered on wood frames

(P-4777)
GARDENA SOFA LLC
11330 Markon Dr, Garden Grove (92841-1403)
PHONE....................714 441-8436
Henry Vuu,
EMP: 10
SALES: 500K **Privately Held**
SIC: 2512 Couches, sofas & davenports: upholstered on wood frames

(P-4778)
GENESIS TC INC
Also Called: Genesis 2000
524 Hofgaarden St, La Puente (91744-5529)
PHONE....................626 968-4455
Anthony Moreno, *President*
EMP: 12
SALES (est): 1.6MM **Privately Held**
SIC: 2512 Wood upholstered chairs & couches

(P-4779)
GOMEN FURNITURE MFG INC
11612 Wright Rd, Lynwood (90262-3945)
PHONE....................310 635-4894
Leonardo Gonzalez, *President*
▲ **EMP:** 30
SALES (est): 4MM **Privately Held**
WEB: www.gomenfurniture.com
SIC: 2512 7641 Upholstered household furniture; upholstery work

(P-4780)
GUY CHADDOCK & COMPANY (PA)
1100 La Avenida St, Mountain View (94043-1452)
PHONE....................408 907-9200
EMP: 230
SQ FT: 75,000
SALES (est): 21.9MM **Privately Held**
SIC: 2512 2521 2511

(P-4781)
HAMMER COLLECTION INC
14427 S Main St, Gardena (90248-1913)
P.O. Box 2458, Manhattan Beach (90267-2458)
PHONE....................310 515-0276
Frank Hammer, *President*
Eva Hammer, *Vice Pres*
▲ **EMP:** 41
SQ FT: 30,000
SALES (est): 4.2MM **Privately Held**
SIC: 2512 2511 Upholstered household furniture; wood household furniture

(P-4782)
HARBOR FURNITURE MANUFACTURING (PA)
Also Called: Harbor House
12508 Center St, South Gate (90280-8079)
PHONE....................323 636-1201
Malcolm Tuttleton Jr, *President*
Brent Tuttleton, *Vice Pres*
▲ **EMP:** 40 **EST:** 1929
SQ FT: 40,000
SALES (est): 2MM **Privately Held**
SIC: 2512 2511 6514 2521 Upholstered household furniture; wood household furniture; dwelling operators, except apartments; wood office furniture

(P-4783)
HILE STUDIO INC
310 N Sunnyside Ave, Sierra Madre (91024-1017)
PHONE....................626 359-7210
Warren Hile, *President*
Gillian Hile, *CFO*
EMP: 25
SQ FT: 12,000
SALES (est): 2.4MM **Privately Held**
SIC: 2512 2511 2426 Upholstered household furniture; wood household furniture; hardwood dimension & flooring mills

(P-4784)
J F FITZGERALD COMPANY INC
Also Called: Fitzgerald Designers & Mfrs
2750 19th St, San Francisco (94110-2124)
PHONE....................415 648-6161
Charles James Willin Jr, *President*
Michael Willin, *Vice Pres*
EMP: 19
SQ FT: 15,000
SALES: 1.5MM **Privately Held**
SIC: 2512 Upholstered household furniture

(P-4785)
JENSON CUSTOM FURNITURE INC
Also Called: Infiniti
2161 S Dupont Dr, Anaheim (92806-6102)
PHONE....................714 634-8145
Florence Simpson, *President*
Mary Anne Simpson, *Treasurer*
Anthony Simpson, *Vice Pres*
EMP: 75
SQ FT: 27,000
SALES (est): 7.6MM **Privately Held**
SIC: 2512 Upholstered household furniture

(P-4786)
JGA INC
Also Called: Taylor Scott Collection, The
1123 E Redondo Blvd, Inglewood (90302-1735)
PHONE....................310 672-4000
Jeffrey Gold, *President*
EMP: 15
SQ FT: 12,000
SALES (est): 1.7MM **Privately Held**
SIC: 2512 Couches, sofas & davenports: upholstered on wood frames

(P-4787)
JONATHAN LOUIS INTL LTD
12919 S Figueroa St, Los Angeles (90061-1134)
PHONE....................213 622-6114
EMP: 492
SALES (corp-wide): 190.5MM **Privately Held**
SIC: 2512 Upholstered household furniture

PA: Jonathan Louis International Ltd.
　　544 W 130th St
　　Gardena CA 90248
　　323 770-3330

(P-4788)
JONATHAN LOUIS INTL LTD (PA)
544 W 130th St, Gardena (90248-1502)
PHONE....................323 770-3330
Juan Valle, *CEO*
Javier Sanchez, *Partner*
Maribel Corona, *Office Admin*
Ushan Dalwis, *Technology*
Maximo Moreno, *Engineer*
▲ **EMP:** 118
SQ FT: 55,000
SALES (est): 190.5MM **Privately Held**
WEB: www.jonathanlouis.net
SIC: 2512 Upholstered household furniture

(P-4789)
KAY CHESTERFIELD INC
6365 Coliseum Way, Oakland (94621-3719)
PHONE....................510 533-5565
Kriss Kokoefer, *President*
Kevelynne Ely, *Sr Project Mgr*
EMP: 14
SQ FT: 10,000
SALES (est): 2.1MM **Privately Held**
WEB: www.reupholster.com
SIC: 2512 7641 Upholstered household furniture; upholstery work

(P-4790)
LA FAMOSA MANUFACTURE INC
6600 Mckinley Ave, Los Angeles (90001-1522)
PHONE....................323 241-3100
Gabriela Dalvamez, *President*
EMP: 14
SALES (est): 698.6K **Privately Held**
SIC: 2512 Couches, sofas & davenports: upholstered on wood frames

(P-4791)
LITTLE CASTLE FURNITURE CO INC
301 Todd Ct, Oxnard (93030-5192)
P.O. Box 4254, Westlake Village (91359-1254)
PHONE....................805 278-4646
Kayvan Torabian, *President*
▲ **EMP:** 45
SQ FT: 9,000
SALES (est): 10.7MM **Privately Held**
WEB: www.littlecastleinc.com
SIC: 2512 Upholstered household furniture

(P-4792)
LOCKHART FURNITURE MFG INC
Also Called: Lockhart Collection
13710 Milroy Pl, Santa Fe Springs (90670-5131)
PHONE....................562 404-0561
Joseph Lockhart, *President*
Daniel Lockhart, *Vice Pres*
EMP: 75
SQ FT: 10,000
SALES (est): 8.1MM **Privately Held**
WEB: www.lockhartcollection.com
SIC: 2512 Upholstered household furniture

(P-4793)
MARCO FINE FURNITURE INC
650 Potrero Ave, San Francisco (94110-2117)
P.O. Box 590659 (94159-0659)
PHONE....................415 285-3235
Marco Martin II, *President*
Chuck Martin, *Manager*
◆ **EMP:** 20
SQ FT: 23,000
SALES (est): 1.9MM **Privately Held**
WEB: www.marcofinefurniture.com
SIC: 2512

(P-4794)
MARGE CARSON INC (PA)
1260 E Grand Ave, Pomona (91766-3801)
P.O. Box 1283 (91769-1283)
PHONE....................626 571-1111
James Labarge, *CEO*

▲ = Import ▼=Export
◆ =Import/Export

Dominic Ching, *CFO*
Mike Elliott, *Vice Pres*
Jim Barge, *Info Tech Dir*
Maria Campos, *Buyer*
▲ **EMP:** 82 **EST:** 1951
SQ FT: 88,000
SALES (est): 20.7MM **Privately Held**
WEB: www.margecarson.com
SIC: 2512 2511 Living room furniture: upholstered on wood frames; wood household furniture

(P-4795)
MARLIN DESIGNS LLC
1900 E Warner Ave Ste J, Santa Ana (92705-5549)
PHONE...................................949 637-7257
Ronald Whitlock, *Mng Member*
EMP: 120
SALES (est): 10.1MM **Privately Held**
WEB: www.marlin-designs.com
SIC: 2512 Upholstered household furniture

(P-4796)
MARTIN/BRATTRUD INC
1224 W 132nd St, Gardena (90247-1566)
PHONE...................................323 770-4171
Allan G Stratford, *President*
Patrick Baxter, *Vice Pres*
EMP: 95
SQ FT: 38,000
SALES (est): 15.9MM **Privately Held**
SIC: 2512 2511 Upholstered household furniture; tables, household: wood

(P-4797)
MASTER DESIGNS SOFA INC
9800 Rush St, South El Monte (91733-2642)
PHONE...................................626 444-1477
David P Nguyen, *President*
EMP: 15
SALES (est): 900K **Privately Held**
SIC: 2512 Upholstered household furniture

(P-4798)
MINSON CORPORATION
Also Called: Mallin Casual Furniture
1 Minson Way, Montebello (90640-6744)
PHONE...................................323 513-1041
Jennifer Chen, *Ch of Bd*
Kenneth Chen, *President*
Andy Chen, *Vice Pres*
Henry Chen, *Vice Pres*
Merv Conn, *Vice Pres*
▲ **EMP:** 300
SQ FT: 380,000
SALES (est): 37.1MM **Privately Held**
WEB: www.mallinfurniture.com
SIC: 2512 2514 Wood upholstered chairs & couches; lawn furniture: metal; backs & seats for metal household furniture; household furniture: upholstered on metal frames; bookcases, household: metal

(P-4799)
MONTE ALLEN INTERIORS INC
1505 W 139th St, Gardena (90249-2603)
PHONE...................................310 380-4640
ESA Maki, *Owner*
ESA Yla-Soininmaki, *Partner*
Timo Yla-Soininmaki, *Partner*
EMP: 40
SALES (est): 4.7MM **Privately Held**
WEB: www.monteallen.com
SIC: 2512 7641 2211 2511 Upholstered household furniture; reupholstery & furniture repair; slip cover fabrics, cotton; wood household furniture

(P-4800)
MPB FURNITURE CORPORATION
414 W Ridgecrest Blvd, Ridgecrest (93555-4015)
PHONE...................................760 375-4800
Mike McGee, *President*
Bill Farris, *General Mgr*
EMP: 12
SQ FT: 18,000
SALES (est): 1.3MM **Privately Held**
SIC: 2512 Upholstered household furniture

(P-4801)
MULHOLLAND BROTHERS (PA)
1710 4th St, Berkeley (94710-1711)
PHONE...................................415 824-5995
Jay Holland, *President*
Guy Holland, *Vice Pres*
▲ **EMP:** 29
SALES (est): 9MM **Privately Held**
WEB: www.mulhollandbrothers.com
SIC: 2512 5199 3161 Upholstered household furniture; leather, leather goods & furs; cases, carrying

(P-4802)
OLD BONES CO
Also Called: Old Bones Company
641 Paularino Ave, Costa Mesa (92626-3033)
PHONE...................................714 641-2800
Sheia Jalalvand, *Owner*
EMP: 12
SQ FT: 3,800
SALES (est): 732.6K **Privately Held**
SIC: 2512 Living room furniture: upholstered on wood frames

(P-4803)
R J VINCENT INC
Also Called: Devon Furniture
1030 Abbot Ave, San Gabriel (91776-2902)
PHONE...................................626 448-1509
Sanh Phung, *President*
Luu Nguyen, *Treasurer*
▲ **EMP:** 25
SQ FT: 17,000
SALES (est): 1.3MM **Privately Held**
WEB: www.rjvincent.com
SIC: 2512 2511 Living room furniture: upholstered on wood frames; wood household furniture

(P-4804)
RAMON LOPEZ
Also Called: G R Furniture Manufacturing
9729 Alpaca St, South El Monte (91733-3028)
PHONE...................................626 575-3891
Ramon Lopez, *Owner*
EMP: 14
SQ FT: 9,000
SALES (est): 690K **Privately Held**
WEB: www.ramonlopez.com
SIC: 2512 Living room furniture: upholstered on wood frames

(P-4805)
RC FURNITURE INC
1111 Jellick Ave, City of Industry (91748-1212)
PHONE...................................626 964-4100
Rene Cazares, *President*
Nora Pineda, *Human Res Mgr*
Rick Cazares, *Opers Mgr*
▲ **EMP:** 81
SQ FT: 25,000
SALES (est): 16.3MM **Privately Held**
WEB: www.rcfurniture.com
SIC: 2512 5021 Upholstered household furniture; furniture

(P-4806)
REGAL FURNITURE MANUFACTURING
6007 S St Andrews Pl # 2, Los Angeles (90047-1335)
PHONE...................................323 971-9185
Harvey Jacobson, *President*
Ron Jacobson, *Vice Pres*
EMP: 17 **EST:** 1945
SQ FT: 20,000
SALES (est): 1.9MM **Privately Held**
SIC: 2512 2426 Living room furniture: upholstered on wood frames; frames for upholstered furniture, wood

(P-4807)
REPUBLIC FURNITURE MFG INC
2241 E 49th St, Vernon (90058-2822)
PHONE...................................323 235-2144
Karen Rosen-Hirsch, *President*
Judy Rosen, *Vice Pres*
EMP: 42
SQ FT: 38,000

SALES (est): 5MM **Privately Held**
SIC: 2512 2515 Living room furniture: upholstered on wood frames; mattresses & bedsprings

(P-4808)
ROMAN EMPIRE FURN PARTS MFG
Also Called: Regency Fine Furniture
4466 Worth St, Los Angeles (90063-2538)
PHONE...................................323 264-8857
Roman Amezquita, *President*
Elisa Amezquita, *Corp Secy*
Carlos Amezquita, *Vice Pres*
EMP: 25
SQ FT: 125,000
SALES (est): 3MM **Privately Held**
SIC: 2512 2511 2426 Upholstered household furniture; wood household furniture; hardwood dimension & flooring mills

(P-4809)
ROMAN UPHOLSTERY MANUFACTURING
2008 Cotner Ave, Los Angeles (90025-5604)
PHONE...................................310 479-3252
Steven Hipsman, *President*
Arthur J Hipsman, *Treasurer*
EMP: 11 **EST:** 1963
SQ FT: 5,000
SALES (est): 900K **Privately Held**
SIC: 2512 7641 Upholstered household furniture; reupholstery

(P-4810)
ROYAL CUSTOM DESIGNS INC
13951 Monte Vista Ave, Chino (91710-5536)
PHONE...................................909 591-8990
Raya Trietsch, *President*
Darius Panah, *CEO*
George Trietsch, *Treasurer*
Martha Clark, *Project Dir*
Jeff Illingworth, *Engineer*
▲ **EMP:** 120 **EST:** 1970
SQ FT: 35,000
SALES (est): 19.5MM **Privately Held**
WEB: www.royalcustomdesigns.com
SIC: 2512 Upholstered household furniture

(P-4811)
SOFA U LOVE (PA)
Also Called: Factory Showroom Exchange
1207 N Western Ave, Los Angeles (90029-1018)
PHONE...................................323 464-3397
Varougan Karapetian, *President*
EMP: 22
SQ FT: 22,000
SALES (est): 5.6MM **Privately Held**
WEB: www.sofaulove.com
SIC: 2512 5712 Upholstered household furniture; furniture stores

(P-4812)
SOLE DESIGNS INC
11685 Mcbean Dr, El Monte (91732-1104)
PHONE...................................626 452-8642
Linda Le, *CEO*
Lam Tran, *President*
▲ **EMP:** 17
SQ FT: 8,000
SALES (est): 2.2MM **Privately Held**
WEB: www.soledesigns.com
SIC: 2512 Upholstered household furniture

(P-4813)
STITCH INDUSTRIES INC
Also Called: Joybird
6055 E Wash Blvd Ste 900, Commerce (90040-2453)
PHONE...................................310 977-5556
Josh Stellin, *Principal*
Chris Stormer, *Shareholder*
Alex Del Toro, *Principal*
Andres Hinostroza, *Principal*
EMP: 50
SALES (est): 9.8MM **Privately Held**
SIC: 2512 Upholstered household furniture

(P-4814)
SUNRISE LUXURY LIVING ROOM INC
12160 Woodruff Ave, Downey (90241-5606)
P.O. Box 956 (90241-0956)
PHONE...................................562 803-1301
Frank Garcia, *CEO*
EMP: 30
SALES (est): 4.2MM **Privately Held**
SIC: 2512 Couches, sofas & davenports: upholstered on wood frames

(P-4815)
SUPERB CHAIR CORPORATION
Also Called: Patricia Edwards
6861 Watcher St, Commerce (90040-3715)
PHONE...................................562 776-1771
Audrey Smith, *President*
James E Smith, *Vice Pres*
Julie Smith, *Vice Pres*
EMP: 35
SQ FT: 36,000
SALES (est): 4.5MM **Privately Held**
WEB: www.patriciaedwards.com
SIC: 2512 Living room furniture: upholstered on wood frames; chairs: upholstered on wood frames; couches, sofas & davenports: upholstered on wood frames

(P-4816)
TERRA FURNITURE INC
549 E Edna Pl, Covina (91723-1311)
PHONE...................................626 912-8523
Gary Stafford, *President*
▲ **EMP:** 41
SQ FT: 57,600
SALES (est): 5.4MM **Privately Held**
WEB: www.terrafurniture.com
SIC: 2512 2514 2522 2511 Upholstered household furniture; metal household furniture; office furniture, except wood; wood lawn & garden furniture

(P-4817)
VAN SARK INC (PA)
Also Called: Dependable Furniture Mfg Co
888 Doolittle Dr, San Leandro (94577-1020)
PHONE...................................510 635-1111
Kevin Sarkisian, *President*
Eniko Sarkisian, *Treasurer*
Shant Kevorkian, *General Mgr*
Doug Tong, *Engineer*
Baltazar Garcia, *Prdtn Mgr*
▲ **EMP:** 50
SQ FT: 75,000
SALES (est): 13.4MM **Privately Held**
WEB: www.dfmonline.com
SIC: 2512 Wood upholstered chairs & couches

(P-4818)
VIOSKI INC
1625 S Magnolia Ave, Monrovia (91016-4509)
PHONE...................................626 359-4571
Douglas Desantis, *CEO*
EMP: 13
SALES (est): 1.3MM **Privately Held**
SIC: 2512 Couches, sofas & davenports: upholstered on wood frames

(P-4819)
YEN-NHAI INC
Also Called: Nathan Anthony Furniture
4940 District Blvd, Vernon (90058-2718)
PHONE...................................323 584-1315
Khai MAI, *President*
Lizbeth Estrada, *Office Mgr*
Randy Gleckman, *Natl Sales Mgr*
EMP: 40
SALES (est): 5.8MM **Privately Held**
SIC: 2512 Upholstered household furniture

2514 Metal Household Furniture

(P-4820)
A A CATER TRUCK MFG CO INC
Also Called: Hizco Truck Body
750 E Slauson Ave, Los Angeles (90011-5236)
PHONE...................................323 233-2343

Vahe Karapetian, *President*
EMP: 75
SQ FT: 60,000
SALES (est): 8MM **Privately Held**
SIC: 2514 7538 Metal household furniture; general truck repair

(P-4821)
AIRFLEX5D LLC
Also Called: ADVANING
12282 Knott St, Garden Grove (92841-2825)
PHONE...................714 622-2600
Wendy Lin, *Exec VP*
EMP: 10
SQ FT: 20,000
SALES (est): 685.3K **Privately Held**
SIC: 2514 Garden furniture, metal

(P-4822)
ALL AMERICAN FRAME & BEDG CORP
4641 Ardine St, Cudahy (90201-5801)
PHONE...................323 773-7415
Don Diep, *President*
Suzuyo Diep, *Admin Sec*
▲ **EMP:** 24
SQ FT: 10,600
SALES (est): 3MM **Privately Held**
SIC: 2514 5047 Beds, including folding & cabinet, household: metal; frames for box springs or bedsprings: metal

(P-4823)
ANVIL ARTS INC
1137 N Fountain Way, Anaheim (92806-2009)
P.O. Box 4445, Orange (92863-4445)
PHONE...................714 630-2870
Gary Benson, *President*
EMP: 10 EST: 1974
SQ FT: 7,000
SALES (est): 1MM **Privately Held**
SIC: 2514 3646 Metal household furniture; ornamental lighting fixtures, commercial

(P-4824)
ATLANTIC REPRESENTATIONS INC
Also Called: Snowsound USA
10018 Santa Fe Springs Rd, Santa Fe Springs (90670-2922)
P.O. Box 2399 (90670-0399)
PHONE...................562 903-9550
Shahriar Dardashti, *President*
Farnaz Dardashti, *Vice Pres*
Mari Garibaldi, *Controller*
▲ **EMP:** 30
SQ FT: 150,000
SALES (est): 28.9MM **Privately Held**
WEB: www.atlantic-inc.com
SIC: 2514 2511 Metal household furniture; wood household furniture

(P-4825)
ATLAS SURVIVAL SHELTERS LLC
7407 Telegraph Rd, Montebello (90640-6515)
PHONE...................323 727-7084
Ronal D Hubbard, *Mng Member*
EMP: 25
SQ FT: 30,000
SALES (est): 3MM **Privately Held**
SIC: 2514 Beds, including folding & cabinet, household: metal

(P-4826)
BEST LIVING INTERNATIONAL INC
12234 Florence Ave, Santa Fe Springs (90670-3806)
PHONE...................626 625-2911
Wenjie Kuang, *Principal*
EMP: 10
SQ FT: 40,000
SALES (est): 355.2K **Privately Held**
SIC: 2514 Metal lawn & garden furniture

(P-4827)
BULTHAUP CORP
153 S Robertson Blvd, Los Angeles (90048-3207)
PHONE...................310 288-3875
Fax: 310 288-3885

EMP: 11
SALES (est): 1.1MM
SALES (corp-wide): 157.6MM **Privately Held**
SIC: 2514
PA: Bulthaup Gmbh & Co Kg
Werkstr. 4-6
Bodenkirchen 84155
874 180-0

(P-4828)
CASUALWAY USA LLC
Also Called: Casualway Home & Garden
1623 Lola Way, Oxnard (93030-5080)
PHONE...................805 660-7408
Guoxiang Wu,
Jian He, *Co-Owner*
Ralph Ybarra, *Vice Pres*
EMP: 99
SALES (est): 2.1MM **Privately Held**
SIC: 2514 Garden furniture, metal

(P-4829)
COSMO IMPORT & EXPORT LLC (PA)
3919 Channel Dr, West Sacramento (95691-3431)
PHONE...................916 209-5500
Jennifer Hayes, *CEO*
EMP: 20
SQ FT: 100,000
SALES (est): 60MM **Privately Held**
SIC: 2514 Garden furniture, metal

(P-4830)
EARTHLITE LLC (DH)
990 Joshua Way, Vista (92081-7855)
P.O. Box 51245, Los Angeles (90051-5545)
PHONE...................760 599-1112
James Chenevey, *CEO*
Philippe Barret, *CFO*
Bill Martin, *Vice Pres*
Ronnie Lemar, *General Mgr*
David Stricko, *Info Tech Dir*
▲ **EMP:** 97
SQ FT: 68,000
SALES (est): 41.4MM
SALES (corp-wide): 12.1MM **Privately Held**
WEB: www.earthlite.com
SIC: 2514 5091 2531 Tables, household: metal; spa equipment & supplies; chairs, portable folding
HQ: Earthlite Holdings, Llc
150 E 58th St Fl 37
New York NY 10155
212 317-2004

(P-4831)
INNOVATIVE DESIGNS & MFG INC
1067 W 5th St, Azusa (91702-3313)
PHONE...................626 812-4422
Ted Koroghlian, *CEO*
Peter Koroghlian, *General Mgr*
EMP: 10
SQ FT: 15,000
SALES (est): 686.4K **Privately Held**
WEB: www.idmifurnishings.com
SIC: 2514 1542 Metal household furniture; commercial & office building contractors

(P-4832)
J - ART CO INC
Also Called: J-Art Ornamental Iron
9435 Jefferson Blvd, Culver City (90232-2915)
PHONE...................310 202-1126
Michael Putman, *President*
Jefferey Putman, *Vice Pres*
EMP: 12 EST: 1955
SQ FT: 5,600
SALES (est): 1.4MM **Privately Held**
WEB: www.jartiron.com
SIC: 2514 Metal household furniture

(P-4833)
JBI LLC
Also Called: Buchbinder, Jay Industries
18521 S Santa Fe Ave, Compton (90221-5624)
PHONE...................310 537-2910
Claudio Luna, *Manager*
EMP: 36

SALES (corp-wide): 52.9MM **Privately Held**
WEB: www.jbiindustries.com
SIC: 2514 2221 2511 Tables, household: metal; fiberglass fabrics; wood household furniture
PA: Jbi, Llc
2650 E El Presidio St
Long Beach CA 90810
310 886-8034

(P-4834)
KOLKKA JOHN
Also Called: Kolkka Furniture Design & Mfg
1300 Green Island Rd, Vallejo (94503-9658)
PHONE...................707 554-3660
Fernando Flores, *Manager*
EMP: 29
SALES (corp-wide): 5.4MM **Privately Held**
SIC: 2514 Metal household furniture
PA: Kolkka, John
871 Charter St
Redwood City CA 94063
650 327-5001

(P-4835)
LEE SANDUSKY CORPORATION
16125 Widmere Rd, Arvin (93203-9307)
P.O. Box 517 (93203-0517)
PHONE...................661 854-5551
Jim Coontz, *Branch Mgr*
EMP: 50
SALES (corp-wide): 22.8MM **Privately Held**
WEB: www.sanduskycabinets.com
SIC: 2514 2522 Metal household furniture; office furniture, except wood
PA: Lee Sandusky Corporation
80 Keystone St
Littlestown PA 17340
717 359-4111

(P-4836)
LUIS WTKINS CSTM WRUGHT IR LLC
Also Called: Watkins, Luis
3737 S Durango Ave, Los Angeles (90034-3314)
PHONE...................310 836-5655
Ines Madison,
Freddy Fuentes,
EMP: 24 EST: 1969
SQ FT: 5,000
SALES (est): 3.1MM **Privately Held**
SIC: 2514 3645 Metal household furniture; residential lighting fixtures

(P-4837)
OAK LAND FURNITURE
Also Called: Oak Land Company
2462 Main St Ste D, Chula Vista (91911-4694)
PHONE...................619 424-8758
Sasan Moazzam, *President*
EMP: 17
SQ FT: 8,000
SALES (est): 2MM **Privately Held**
SIC: 2514 2515 Metal bedroom furniture; mattresses & bedsprings

(P-4838)
PACIFIC CASUAL LLC
1060 Avenida Acaso, Camarillo (93012-8712)
PHONE...................805 445-8310
Rick Stephens, *Mng Member*
Dale C Boles, *CEO*
Doug Phillips, *Exec Dir*
Tracy Moats, *VP Mfg*
Peter Schultz, *VP Sales*
▲ **EMP:** 35
SQ FT: 29,000
SALES (est): 5.1MM **Privately Held**
SIC: 2514 Metal lawn & garden furniture

(P-4839)
PEREZ BROTHERS
Also Called: Perez Bros Ornamental Iron
19607 Prairie St, Northridge (91324-2426)
PHONE...................818 780-8482
Juan A Perez, *Owner*
Raul Perez, *Manager*
EMP: 10

SALES (est): 1.1MM **Privately Held**
SIC: 2514 Metal kitchen & dining room furniture; chairs, household: metal; cabinets, radio & television: metal; garden furniture, metal

(P-4840)
RSI HOME PRODUCTS INC (HQ)
400 E Orangethorpe Ave, Anaheim (92801-1046)
PHONE...................714 449-2200
Alex Calabrese, *CEO*
David Lowrie, *CFO*
Jeff Hoeft, *Exec VP*
Kreig Rugh, *Vice Pres*
John Garneau, *Regional Mgr*
▲ **EMP:** 700
SQ FT: 675,000
SALES (est): 1B
SALES (corp-wide): 1.2B **Publicly Held**
SIC: 2514 2541 3281 2434 Kitchen cabinets: metal; medicine cabinets & vanities: metal; counter & sink tops; cut stone & stone products; wood kitchen cabinets
PA: American Woodmark Corporation
561 Shady Elm Rd
Winchester VA 22602
540 665-9100

(P-4841)
RSI HOME PRODUCTS INC
620 Newport Center Dr # 1200, Newport Beach (92660-8012)
PHONE...................949 720-1116
Terri Stevens, *Branch Mgr*
EMP: 1000
SALES (corp-wide): 1.2B **Publicly Held**
SIC: 2514 2541 1751 Metal household furniture; wood partitions & fixtures; cabinet & finish carpentry
HQ: Rsi Home Products, Inc.
400 E Orangethorpe Ave
Anaheim CA 92801
714 449-2200

(P-4842)
RSI HOME PRODUCTS MFG INC
400 E Orangethorpe Ave, Anaheim (92801-1046)
P.O. Box 4120 (92803-4120)
PHONE...................714 449-2200
Thomas Chieffe, *CEO*
Jeff Hoeft, *President*
▲ **EMP:** 100
SALES (est): 25.8MM
SALES (corp-wide): 1.2B **Publicly Held**
SIC: 2514 2541 3281 2434 Kitchen cabinets: metal; medicine cabinets & vanities: metal; counter & sink tops; cut stone & stone products; wood kitchen cabinets
HQ: Rsi Home Products, Inc.
400 E Orangethorpe Ave
Anaheim CA 92801
714 449-2200

(P-4843)
SURROUNDING ELEMENTS LLC
33051 Calle Aviador Ste A, San Juan Capistrano (92675-4780)
PHONE...................949 582-9000
Moss Shacter, *Mng Member*
Anthony C Geach,
EMP: 20
SQ FT: 15,000
SALES (est): 2.2MM **Privately Held**
WEB: www.surroundingelements.com
SIC: 2514 Lawn furniture: metal

(P-4844)
THOMAS LUNDBERG
Also Called: Lundberg Designs
2620 3rd St, San Francisco (94107-3115)
PHONE...................415 695-0110
Thomas Lundberg, *Owner*
EMP: 12
SQ FT: 5,000
SALES (est): 1.2MM **Privately Held**
WEB: www.lundbergdesign.com
SIC: 2514 Metal household furniture

(P-4845)
TK CLASSICS LLC
3771 Channel Dr 100, West Sacramento (95691-3421)
PHONE...................916 209-5500
Jennifer Hayes, *CEO*

▲ = Import ▼=Export
◆ =Import/Export

EMP: 20
SQ FT: 100,000
SALES: 60MM **Privately Held**
SIC: 2514 Garden furniture, metal
PA: Cosmo Import & Export, Llc
   3919 Channel Dr
   West Sacramento CA 95691
   916 209-5500

(P-4846)
TROPITONE FURNITURE CO INC (HQ)
5 Marconi, Irvine (92618-2594)
PHONE..................................949 595-2000
Randy Danielson, CFO
Chris Magana, Executive
Rebecca Cotogno, General Mgr
Richard Rivera, CTO
Kevin Poirrier, QA Dir
◆ EMP: 45 EST: 1954
SALES (est): 109.6MM **Privately Held**
WEB: www.tropitone.com
SIC: 2514 2522 Garden furniture, metal;
   camp furniture: metal; office furniture, ex-
   cept wood

(P-4847)
VICTOR MARTIN INC
Also Called: Corsican Furniture
1640 W 132nd St, Gardena (90249-2006)
PHONE..................................323 587-3101
Martin Perfit, President
Marvin Alperin, Principal
EMP: 140
SQ FT: 100,000
SALES (est): 7.5MM **Privately Held**
WEB: www.victormartin.com
SIC: 2514 Beds, including folding & cabi-
   net, household: metal

(P-4848)
WESLEY ALLEN INC (PA)
Also Called: Iron Beds of America
1001 E 60th St, Los Angeles (90001-1098)
PHONE..................................323 231-4275
Victor Sawan, CEO
Earlene Marbury, Office Mgr
Daniel Molina, Purchasing
Francoise Chesaux, Mktg Dir
Wesley Allen, Agent
▲ EMP: 140
SQ FT: 100,000
SALES (est): 20.2MM **Privately Held**
WEB: www.wesleyallen.com
SIC: 2514 Metal household furniture

2515 Mattresses & Bedsprings

(P-4849)
AIR DREAMS MATTRESSES
3266 Rosemead Blvd, El Monte
(91731-2807)
PHONE..................................626 573-5733
Felipe Carlos, Owner
EMP: 12
SQ FT: 12,000
SALES (est): 1MM **Privately Held**
SIC: 2515 2512 5712 5021 Mattresses,
   innerspring or box spring; upholstered
   household furniture; mattresses; mat-
   tresses

(P-4850)
AMERICAN NATIONAL MFG INC
252 Mariah Cir, Corona (92879-1751)
PHONE..................................951 273-7888
Eve Miller, President
Craig Miller, Vice Pres
▲ EMP: 110
SQ FT: 75,000
SALES (est): 20.5MM **Privately Held**
WEB: www.americannationalmfg.com
SIC: 2515 5712 Mattresses & bedsprings;
   furniture stores

(P-4851)
AMF SUPPORT SURFACES INC (DH)
1691 N Delilah St, Corona (92879-1885)
PHONE..................................951 549-6800
Fredrick Kohnke, CEO
Carole A Wyatt, President
Charles C Wyatt, President

Curt Wyatt, CEO
▲ EMP: 162 EST: 1932
SQ FT: 40,000
SALES (est): 32.2MM
SALES (corp-wide): 2.7B **Publicly Held**
WEB: www.amfsupport.com
SIC: 2515 Mattresses, containing felt, foam
   rubber, urethane, etc.
HQ: Anodyne Medical Device, Inc.
   4200 Nw 120th Ave
   Coral Springs FL 33065
   954 340-0500

(P-4852)
BANNER MATTRESS INC (PA)
1501 E Cooley Dr Ste B, Colton
(92324-3991)
PHONE..................................909 835-4200
Lisa Scorziell, President
Eugene Scorziell, CEO
Bob Forrest, CFO
Bryan Pollock, Info Tech Mgr
▲ EMP: 24 EST: 1926
SQ FT: 50,000
SALES: 19MM **Privately Held**
WEB: www.bannermattress.net
SIC: 2515 5021 Bedsprings, assembled;
   mattresses

(P-4853)
BIG SLEEP FUTON INC
Also Called: Big Tree Big Sleep
760 S Vail Ave, Montebello (90640-4954)
PHONE..................................800 647-2671
Ying He, CEO
Robert Pecorara, President
▲ EMP: 22
SALES (est): 3.2MM **Privately Held**
SIC: 2515 Sleep furniture

(P-4854)
BRENTWOOD HOME LLC (PA)
Also Called: Silverrest
701 Burning Tree Rd Ste A, Fullerton
(92833-1451)
PHONE..................................562 949-3759
Vy Nguyen, President
Tramy Nguyen, Vice Pres
EMP: 128 EST: 2015
SQ FT: 80,000
SALES (est): 30MM **Privately Held**
SIC: 2515 5021 5712 Mattresses, con-
   taining felt, foam rubber, urethane, etc.;
   mattresses; mattresses

(P-4855)
BRENTWOOD HOME LLC
2301 E 7th St Ste 417, Los Angeles
(90023-1035)
PHONE..................................213 457-7626
Vy Nguyen, President
Laxman Ghimire, Accountant
Oscar Ruiz, Opers Staff
Makenzie McNeill, Manager
EMP: 12
SALES (corp-wide): 30MM **Privately Held**
SIC: 2515 5021 5712 Mattresses, con-
   taining felt, foam rubber, urethane, etc.;
   mattresses; mattresses
PA: Brentwood Home, Llc
   701 Burning Tree Rd Ste A
   Fullerton CA 92833
   562 949-3759

(P-4856)
COMFORT-PEDIC MATTRESS USA
Also Called: Resta Mattress
9080 Charles Smith Ave, Rancho Cuca-
monga (91730-5566)
PHONE..................................909 810-2600
Raouf Ghobrial, President
EMP: 10
SALES: 2MM **Privately Held**
WEB: www.comfortpedicmattress.com
SIC: 2515 5021 5712 Mattresses & bed-
   springs; mattresses; mattresses

(P-4857)
CRISTAL MATERIALS INC
6825 Mckinley Ave, Los Angeles
(90001-1525)
PHONE..................................323 855-1688
Luis Ponce, CEO
EMP: 10

SALES (est): 1.7MM **Privately Held**
SIC: 2515 5999 3086 Mattresses, containing felt, foam rubber, urethane, etc.;
   foam & foam products; plastics foam
   products

(P-4858)
CUEVAS MATTRESS INC
Also Called: Springpudic
3504 E Olympic Blvd, Los Angeles
(90023-3924)
PHONE..................................310 631-8382
Isabel Cuevas, President
EMP: 14
SALES (corp-wide): 1.1MM **Privately Held**
SIC: 2515 Mattresses & bedsprings
PA: Cuevas Mattress Inc.
   5843 S Broadway
   Los Angeles CA 90003
   310 631-8382

(P-4859)
DELLA ROBBIA INC
796 E Harrison St, Corona (92879-1348)
PHONE..................................951 372-9199
David Soonlan, President
▲ EMP: 20
SQ FT: 72,000
SALES (est): 5MM **Privately Held**
SIC: 2515 Sofa beds (convertible sofas)

(P-4860)
ES KLUFT & COMPANY INC (PA)
11096 Jersey Blvd Ste 101, Rancho Cuca-
monga (91730-5158)
PHONE..................................909 373-4211
David Binke, CEO
Ron Bruneau, COO
Alan Docherty, CFO
Alwyna Luceno, Office Mgr
Luciano Saldana, VP Opers
◆ EMP: 156
SALES (est): 73.1MM **Privately Held**
WEB: www.kluftmattress.com
SIC: 2515 Mattresses & bedsprings

(P-4861)
GOLDEN MATTRESS CO INC
4231 Firestone Blvd, South Gate
(90280-3223)
PHONE..................................323 887-1888
San Dang, CEO
Phuc Nguyen, Vice Pres
▲ EMP: 52
SQ FT: 33,000
SALES (est): 7.1MM **Privately Held**
SIC: 2515 5021 Mattresses & foundations;
   mattresses

(P-4862)
HANDCRAFT MATTRESS COMPANY
1131 Baker St, Costa Mesa (92626-4114)
PHONE..................................714 241-8316
Dave Ogle, CEO
EMP: 12
SQ FT: 16,000
SALES: 1.6MM **Privately Held**
WEB: www.hmcwest.com
SIC: 2515 Mattresses & foundations

(P-4863)
HOSPITALITY SLEEP SYSTEMS INC
107 E Rialto Ave, San Bernardino
(92408-1128)
PHONE..................................909 387-9779
Cristiana Solorio, CEO
EMP: 11
SALES (est): 1.3MM **Privately Held**
SIC: 2515 Mattresses & foundations; mat-
   tresses, innerspring or box spring

(P-4864)
INNOVATIVE R ADVANCED (PA)
Also Called: Smart Foam Pads
23101 Lake Center Dr # 100, Lake Forest
(92630-2801)
PHONE..................................949 273-8100
Robert Doherty, CEO
Timothy G Woodward, COO
Michael Seffer, CFO
EMP: 15
SQ FT: 4,000

SALES: 1.2MM **Privately Held**
SIC: 2515 Mattresses, containing felt, foam
   rubber, urethane, etc.

(P-4865)
INNOVATIVE R ADVANCED
3401 Etiwanda Ave, Mira Loma
(91752-1128)
PHONE..................................949 273-8100
Brad Bannister, Manager
EMP: 30
SALES (corp-wide): 1.2MM **Privately Held**
SIC: 2515 Mattresses, containing felt, foam
   rubber, urethane, etc.
PA: Advanced Innovative Recovery Tech-
   nologies, Inc.
   23101 Lake Center Dr # 100
   Lake Forest CA 92630
   949 273-8100

(P-4866)
JONA GLOBAL TRADING INC
Also Called: Foam Depot
245 S 8th Ave, La Puente (91746-3210)
PHONE..................................626 855-2588
Jack Hung, Principal
▲ EMP: 10 EST: 2012
SALES (est): 942.2K **Privately Held**
SIC: 2515 Mattresses, containing felt, foam
   rubber, urethane, etc.

(P-4867)
KINGDOM MATTRESS INC
Also Called: Kingdom Matress Company
17920 S Figueroa St, Gardena
(90248-4211)
PHONE..................................562 630-5531
Jose Flores, President
EMP: 35
SALES (est): 4.3MM **Privately Held**
SIC: 2515 Mattresses & bedsprings

(P-4868)
LEGGETT & PLATT INCORPORATED
Also Called: Lpcc 6008
1050 S Dupont Ave, Ontario (91761-1578)
PHONE..................................909 937-1010
Barry Kubasak, Manager
EMP: 96
SALES (corp-wide): 3.9B **Publicly Held**
SIC: 2515 Mattresses, innerspring or box
   spring
PA: Leggett & Platt, Incorporated
   1 Leggett Rd
   Carthage MO 64836
   417 358-8131

(P-4869)
LEGGETT & PLATT INCORPORATED
Whittier 0e00
12352 Whittier Blvd, Whittier (90602-1015)
PHONE..................................562 945-2641
Ray Wolven, Branch Mgr
Peter Lee, Technology
Jim Dibelka, Purch Mgr
EMP: 73
SQ FT: 226,000
SALES (corp-wide): 3.9B **Publicly Held**
WEB: www.leggett.com
SIC: 2515 2511 Mattresses & bedsprings;
   wood household furniture
PA: Leggett & Platt, Incorporated
   1 Leggett Rd
   Carthage MO 64836
   417 358-8131

(P-4870)
MARSPRING CORPORATION
4920 S Boyle Ave, Vernon (90058-3017)
PHONE..................................800 522-5252
Ronald Greitzer, Manager
EMP: 34
SALES (corp-wide): 10.3MM **Privately Held**
WEB: www.marflex.com
SIC: 2515 Spring cushions
PA: Marspring Corporation
   4920 S Boyle Ave
   Vernon CA 90058
   323 589-5637

(P-4871)
MARSPRING CORPORATION
Also Called: Los Angeles Fiber Co
4920 S Boyle Ave, Vernon (90058-3017)
P.O. Box 58643, Los Angeles (90058-0643)
PHONE.............................310 484-6849
Ronald Greitzer, *President*
EMP: 34
SALES (corp-wide): 10.3MM **Privately
Held**
WEB: www.marflex.com
SIC: 2515 Spring cushions
PA: Marspring Corporation
4920 S Boyle Ave
Vernon CA 90058
323 589-5637

(P-4872)
MAXIMS MATTRESS INC
2553 Garfield Ave, Commerce
(90040-2605)
PHONE.............................323 721-5616
Connie Yip, *CEO*
Robin Diep, *Principal*
▲ EMP: 11
SALES (est): 1.5MM **Privately Held**
SIC: 2515 Mattresses & bedsprings

(P-4873)
MBC MATTRESS CO INC
19270 Envoy Ave, Corona (92881-3839)
PHONE.............................951 371-8044
Charles H Mumford, *President*
Micheal Gargaliss, *Vice Pres*
EMP: 25
SALES (est): 3.2MM **Privately Held**
SIC: 2515 Mattresses, innerspring or box
spring

(P-4874)
**MIRACLE BEDDING
CORPORATION**
3700 Capitol Ave, City of Industry
(90601-1731)
PHONE.............................562 908-2370
CAM Hua, *President*
CAM Tu Hua, *President*
Quyen Lieu, *Treasurer*
▲ EMP: 50
SQ FT: 100,000
SALES (est): 5.3MM **Privately Held**
SIC: 2515 5719 5712 Mattresses, con-
taining felt, foam rubber, urethane, etc.;
mattresses, innerspring or box spring;
bedding (sheets, blankets, spreads & pil-
lows); mattresses

(P-4875)
**NATIONAL BEDDING COMPANY
LLC**
Also Called: Serta International
6818 Patterson Pass Rd, Livermore
(94550-4230)
PHONE.............................925 373-1350
Michael Traub, *President*
EMP: 200
SALES (est): 5.9MM **Privately Held**
SIC: 2515 Mattresses & bedsprings
PA: Serta Simmons Bedding, Llc
3560 Lenox Rd Ne Ste 1100
Atlanta GA 30326

(P-4876)
ORGANIC MATTRESSES INC
Also Called: OMI
1335 Harter Pkwy, Yuba City (95993-2604)
PHONE.............................530 790-6723
Walt Bader, *President*
Jeri Kemmer, *Opers Spvr*
▲ EMP: 35
SQ FT: 60,000
SALES (est): 6.4MM **Privately Held**
WEB: www.omimattress.com
SIC: 2515 Mattresses & foundations

(P-4877)
PARAMOUNT MATTRESS INC
2900 E Olympic Blvd, Los Angeles
(90023-3431)
PHONE.............................323 264-3451
Hector Hernandez, *President*
▼ EMP: 10
SQ FT: 10,000

SALES: 650K **Privately Held**
WEB: www.paramountmatt.com
SIC: 2515 Mattresses, innerspring or box
spring

(P-4878)
PLEASANT MATTRESS INC
Also Called: McRoskey Mattress
1400 Minnesota St, San Francisco
(94107-3520)
PHONE.............................415 874-7540
Paul Deming, *Branch Mgr*
EMP: 14
SALES (corp-wide): 23.6MM **Privately
Held**
WEB: www.mcroskey.com
SIC: 2515 Mattresses & foundations
PA: Pleasant Mattress, Inc.
375 S West Ave
Fresno CA 93706
559 268-6446

(P-4879)
PLEASANT MATTRESS INC (PA)
Also Called: Cannon Sleep Products
375 S West Ave, Fresno (93706-1341)
PHONE.............................559 268-6446
Herbert Morgenstern, *President*
Stephanie Aguilar, *Treasurer*
Judy Davis, *Vice Pres*
Rion Morgenstern, *Vice Pres*
Pao Vang, *MIS Mgr*
▲ EMP: 78 EST: 1948
SQ FT: 100,000
SALES (est): 23.6MM **Privately Held**
WEB: www.cannonsleep.com
SIC: 2515 Mattresses & foundations

(P-4880)
PLEASANT MATTRESS INC
Also Called: McRoskey Mattress
1400 Minnesota St, San Francisco
(94107-3520)
PHONE.............................415 861-4532
EMP: 39
SALES (corp-wide): 23.6MM **Privately
Held**
SIC: 2515 Mattresses & foundations
PA: Pleasant Mattress, Inc.
375 S West Ave
Fresno CA 93706
559 268-6446

(P-4881)
PURA NATURALS INC
3401 Etiwanda Ave, Mira Loma
(91752-1128)
PHONE.............................949 273-8100
Brad Bannister, *Manager*
EMP: 30
SALES (corp-wide): 1.2MM **Privately
Held**
SIC: 2515 Mattresses, containing felt, foam
rubber, urethane, etc.
HQ: Pura Naturals, Inc.
23101 Lake Center Dr # 100
Lake Forest CA 92630
949 273-8100

(P-4882)
**RGR DIVERSIFIED SERVICES
INC**
5635 Panorama Dr, Whittier (90601-2428)
PHONE.............................562 522-0028
Arthur G Rios, *President*
EMP: 15
SALES (est): 1.2MM **Privately Held**
SIC: 2515 Mattresses & bedsprings

(P-4883)
**ROYAL-PEDIC MATTRESS MFG
LLC**
Also Called: Royalpedic Mattress Mfg
331 N Fries Ave, Wilmington (90744-5624)
PHONE.............................310 518-5420
Tony E Keleman, *Manager*
EMP: 25
SALES (est): 2.2MM
SALES (corp-wide): 4.6MM **Privately
Held**
WEB: www.royalpedic.com
SIC: 2515 5021 5712 Mattresses & bed-
springs; mattresses, innerspring or box
spring; mattresses; mattresses

PA: Royal-Pedic Mattress Manufacturing,
Llc
341 N Robertson Blvd
Beverly Hills CA 90211
310 278-9594

(P-4884)
SEALY MATTRESS MFG CO INC
4361 Firestone Blvd, South Gate
(90280-3340)
PHONE.............................323 567-7781
Janie Womack, *Branch Mgr*
Yvonne Garcia, *COO*
Victoria Clavijo, *Human Res Dir*
Sharon Macias, *Purch Agent*
Michael Reilly, *Sales Staff*
EMP: 120
SQ FT: 185,000
SALES (corp-wide): 2.7B **Publicly Held**
SIC: 2515 Mattresses, containing felt, foam
rubber, urethane, etc.
HQ: Sealy Mattress Manufacturing Com-
pany, Llc
1 Office Parkway Rd
Trinity NC 27370
336 861-3500

(P-4885)
SEALY MATTRESS MFG CO INC
1130 7th St, Richmond (94801-2103)
PHONE.............................510 235-7171
Curt Maszun, *Branch Mgr*
Kurt Mason, *Executive*
EMP: 200
SQ FT: 238,000
SALES (corp-wide): 2.7B **Publicly Held**
SIC: 2515 Mattresses, innerspring or box
spring
HQ: Sealy Mattress Manufacturing Com-
pany, Llc
1 Office Parkway Rd
Trinity NC 27370
336 861-3500

(P-4886)
SKY RIDER EQUIPMENT CO INC
1180 N Blue Gum St, Anaheim
(92806-2409)
PHONE.............................714 632-6890
Martin Villegas, *CEO*
Carl Gray, *President*
Dev Donnelley, *Vice Pres*
Karl Keranen, *Vice Pres*
Desiree Avila, *Executive Asst*
▲ EMP: 30
SQ FT: 12,000
SALES (est): 6MM **Privately Held**
WEB: www.sky-rider.com
SIC: 2515 7349 5719 Foundations & plat-
forms; window cleaning; window shades

(P-4887)
SLEEPRITE INDUSTRIES INC
Also Called: Restonic/San Francisco
1492 Rollins Rd, Burlingame (94010-2307)
P.O. Box 814 (94011-0710)
PHONE.............................650 344-1980
Jeffrey S Karp, *President*
Elaine Karp, *Corp Secy*
Randall H Karp, *Vice Pres*
Bob Homerski, *Manager*
Michael Stineman, *Manager*
▼ EMP: 25 EST: 1968
SQ FT: 30,000
SALES (est): 4.2MM **Privately Held**
SIC: 2515 Mattresses, containing felt, foam
rubber, urethane, etc.; mattresses, inner-
spring or box spring

(P-4888)
**SOUTH BAY INTERNATIONAL
INC**
13169 Slover Ave Ste B, Fontana
(92337-6923)
PHONE.............................909 718-5000
Guohai Tang, *President*
Daniella Serven, *CEO*
Wendiao Hou, *CFO*
Weijun She, *Admin Sec*
▲ EMP: 25
SQ FT: 69,000
SALES: 32.2MM **Privately Held**
SIC: 2515 Mattresses & bedsprings

(P-4889)
SPECFOAM LLC
13215 Marlay Ave, Fontana (92337-6942)
P.O. Box 310159 (92331-0159)
PHONE.............................951 685-3626
Hector Jimenez,
EMP: 18
SQ FT: 26,000
SALES (est): 2.1MM **Privately Held**
SIC: 2515 Mattresses, containing felt, foam
rubber, urethane, etc.

(P-4890)
**SQUARE DEAL MATTRESS
FACTORY**
Also Called: Square Deal Mat Fctry & Uphl
1354 Humboldt Ave, Chico (95928-5952)
PHONE.............................530 342-2510
Lois Lash, *President*
Richard Lash, *President*
EMP: 24
SQ FT: 6,000
SALES (est): 2.6MM **Privately Held**
WEB: www.squaredealmattress.com
SIC: 2515 5712 Mattresses & bedsprings;
furniture stores

(P-4891)
**SSB MANUFACTURING
COMPANY**
20100 S Alameda St, Compton
(90221-6208)
PHONE.............................770 512-7700
Tito Lampon, *General Mgr*
EMP: 108 **Privately Held**
WEB: www.simmonscompany.com
SIC: 2515 5021 Bedsprings, assembled;
box springs, assembled; mattresses
HQ: Ssb Manufacturing Company
1 Concourse Pkwy Ste 800
Atlanta GA 30328
770 512-7700

(P-4892)
VISIONARY SLEEP LLC
2060 S Wineville Ave A, Ontario
(91761-3633)
PHONE.............................909 605-2010
Carter Gronbach, *Manager*
EMP: 58
SALES (corp-wide): 3.3MM **Privately
Held**
SIC: 2515 Mattresses, innerspring or box
spring
PA: Visionary Sleep, Llc
Moon Lake Blvd Ste 205
Hoffman Estates IL 60169
812 945-4155

(P-4893)
**WICKLINE BEDDING ENTP
CORP**
Also Called: Sleep Therapy
455 N Quince St, Escondido (92025-2521)
PHONE.............................760 747-7761
Kuan-Yu Chen, *Principal*
Jack Chen, *CEO*
▲ EMP: 30
SALES (est): 5MM **Privately Held**
SIC: 2515 Mattresses, innerspring or box
spring

(P-4894)
WILLIAMS FOAM INC
12961 San Fernando Rd, Sylmar
(91342-3656)
PHONE.............................818 833-4343
William Ramirez, *President*
▲ EMP: 12
SQ FT: 30,000
SALES: 2MM **Privately Held**
WEB: www.williamsfoam.com
SIC: 2515 3069 3086 Mattresses, con-
taining felt, foam rubber, urethane, etc.;
foam rubber; plastics foam products

(P-4895)
ZINUS INC (HQ)
1951 Fairway Dr Ste A, San Leandro
(94577-5643)
PHONE.............................925 417-2100
Youn Jae Lee, *President*
Lee Soojin, *Accounting Mgr*
Jiyun Jeong, *Finance*
Stephanie TSO, *Accountant*

▲ = Import ▼=Export
◆ =Import/Export

Min Yang, *Marketing Staff*
▲ **EMP:** 70
SQ FT: 155,000
SALES: 123.8MM
SALES (corp-wide): 273.6MM **Privately Held**
WEB: www.zinus.com
SIC: 2515 Chair & couch springs, assembled
PA: Zinus Inc.
10 Yatap-Ro 81beon-Gil, Bundang-Gu
Seongnam 13497
823 162-2170

2517 Wood T V, Radio, Phono & Sewing Cabinets

(P-4896)
ANA GLOBAL LLC
2360 Marconi Ct, San Diego (92154-7241)
PHONE..................................619 482-9990
MD Anwarul Hoque,
Yesenia Rivera, *Purchasing*
Mamoru Kojima, *Marketing Staff*
Hasan Khan, *Sales Staff*
Yoshiaki Nishiba,
▲ **EMP:** 800
SALES (est): 149.3MM **Privately Held**
SIC: 2517 5999 Television cabinets, wood; medical apparatus & supplies

(P-4897)
GILBERT MARTIN WDWKG CO INC (PA)
Also Called: Martin Furniture
2345 Britannia Blvd, San Diego
(92154-8313)
PHONE..................................800 268-5669
Gilbert Martin, *President*
Mark Mitchell, *Vice Pres*
George Dosch, *Sales Staff*
Alberto Enriquez, *Manager*
Alma Ahumada, *Receptionist*
◆ **EMP:** 30 **EST:** 1980
SQ FT: 210,000
SALES (est): 51.5MM **Privately Held**
WEB: www.martinfurniture.com
SIC: 2517 2511 2521 5021 Home entertainment unit cabinets, wood; stereo cabinets, wood; television cabinets, wood; wood household furniture; wood office furniture; furniture; furniture stores

(P-4898)
PARKER HOUSE MFG CO INC
Also Called: Parker House International
6300 Providence Way, Eastvale
(92880-9636)
PHONE..................................800 628-1319
John E Lupo, *CEO*
Chris Lupo, *President*
Arlene M Zonni, *COO*
Maria R Lupo, *Corp Secy*
Judy Watson, *Bookkeeper*
▲ **EMP:** 30
SQ FT: 135,000
SALES (est): 13.8MM **Privately Held**
SIC: 2517 2511 Wood television & radio cabinets; bookcases, household: wood

(P-4899)
SPARTAK ENTERPRISES INC
11186 Venture Dr, Mira Loma (91752-1194)
PHONE..................................951 360-0610
Armen Babayan, *President*
EMP: 30
SQ FT: 40,000
SALES (est): 4.4MM **Privately Held**
WEB: www.spartakent.com
SIC: 2517 2522 Wood television & radio cabinets; office furniture, except wood

(P-4900)
TOCABI AMERICA CORPORATION
333 H St Ste 5007, Chula Vista
(91910-5561)
P.O. Box 5397 (91912-5397)
PHONE..................................619 661-6136
Katsumi Sayama, *President*
Kahori Yutani, *Accounting Mgr*
Carlos Moreno, *Mfg Staff*
▲ **EMP:** 23

SALES (est): 2MM **Privately Held**
WEB: www.tocabi.com
SIC: 2517 2542 2521 2511

(P-4901)
WEBB MASSEY CO INC
201 W Carleton Ave, Orange (92867-3678)
P.O. Box 4969 (92863-4969)
PHONE..................................714 639-6012
Webb Massey, *President*
Jeanne Massey, *Treasurer*
EMP: 32
SALES (est): 1.7MM **Privately Held**
SIC: 2517

(P-4902)
ZELCO CABINET MFG INC
298 W Robles Ave, Santa Rosa
(95407-8118)
PHONE..................................707 584-1121
Zelco Cecich-Karuzic, *President*
Paula Cecich-Karuzic, *Vice Pres*
Margo Abraham, *Admin Sec*
EMP: 10
SQ FT: 12,000
SALES: 1MM **Privately Held**
SIC: 2517 2434 Home entertainment unit cabinets, wood; wood kitchen cabinets

---

2519 Household Furniture, NEC

(P-4903)
ACRYLIC DISTRIBUTION CORP
8511 Lankershim Blvd, Sun Valley
(91352-3127)
PHONE..................................818 767-8448
Shlomi Haziza, *Principal*
Soli Amor, *Treasurer*
Nick Enriques, *General Mgr*
Richard Wetters, *Chief Engr*
▲ **EMP:** 75
SQ FT: 12,000
SALES (est): 10.8MM **Privately Held**
WEB: www.hstudio.com
SIC: 2519 Furniture, household: glass, fiberglass & plastic

(P-4904)
ALVARADO ALTA CALIDAD LLC
Also Called: Alvarado Alta Clidad Cstm Furn
2907 Humboldt St, Los Angeles
(90031-1828)
PHONE..................................323 222-0038
Robert Alvarado,
EMP: 12
SQ FT: 10,000
SALES: 1.5MM **Privately Held**
SIC: 2519 Household furniture, except wood or metal: upholstered

(P-4905)
AMERICAN FURNITURE ALIANCE INC
9141 Arrow Rte, Rancho Cucamonga
(91730-4414)
PHONE..................................323 804-5242
John Chang, *CEO*
Paul Chien, *Director*
EMP: 10
SQ FT: 1,000
SALES: 2MM **Privately Held**
SIC: 2519 3291 ; tripoli

(P-4906)
ARKTURA LLC (PA)
18225 S Figueroa St, Gardena
(90248-4216)
PHONE..................................310 532-1050
Chris Kabatsi, *CEO*
▲ **EMP:** 30
SALES: 9MM **Privately Held**
SIC: 2519 Furniture, household: glass, fiberglass & plastic

(P-4907)
BAKER INTERIORS FURNITURE CO
Also Called: McGuire Furniture
101 Henry Adams St # 350, San Francisco
(94103-5222)
PHONE..................................415 626-1414
EMP: 45

SALES (corp-wide): 487.5MM **Privately Held**
SIC: 2519 2511 2512 Rattan furniture: padded or plain; wood household furniture; upholstered household furniture
HQ: Baker Interiors Furniture Company
1105 22nd St Se
Hickory NC 28602
828 624-7000

(P-4908)
CALIFRNIA FURN COLLECTIONS INC
Also Called: Artifacts International
150 Reed Ct Ste A, Chula Vista
(91911-5890)
PHONE..................................619 621-2455
Eric Vogt, *President*
Kian Manzanilla, *Info Tech Dir*
Monica Reyes, *Accounting Mgr*
EMP: 114
SQ FT: 40,000
SALES (est): 11MM **Privately Held**
WEB: www.artifactsinternational.com
SIC: 2519 2514 2511 2512 Household furniture, except wood or metal: upholstered; metal household furniture; household furniture: upholstered on metal frames; wood household furniture; upholstered household furniture

(P-4909)
DWELL HOME INC
39962 Cedar Blvd Ste 277, Newark
(94560-5326)
PHONE..................................877 864-5752
EMP: 10
SALES (est): 840K **Privately Held**
SIC: 2519

(P-4910)
HADES PERFORMANCE
3481 Euclid Ave, Concord (94519-2320)
PHONE..................................925 671-9197
D Rodriguez, *Owner*
EMP: 16
SALES (est): 1.1MM **Privately Held**
SIC: 2519 Fiberglass & plastic furniture

(P-4911)
KOMFY KINGS INC
10445 Glenoaks Blvd, Pacoima
(91331-1609)
PHONE..................................818 899-8929
Howard Napolske, *President*
EMP: 100
SQ FT: 75,000
SALES: 12MM **Privately Held**
SIC: 2519 Household furniture, except wood or metal: upholstered

(P-4912)
MEADOW DECOR INC
1477 E Cedar St Ste A, Ontario
(91761-8330)
PHONE..................................909 923-2558
Jun Chen, *CEO*
David Mok, *Ch of Bd*
John Chen, *President*
Jiali Zhang, *Principal*
▲ **EMP:** 13
SQ FT: 24,000
SALES (est): 4MM **Privately Held**
SIC: 2519 2392 Lawn & garden furniture, except wood & metal; cushions & pillows

(P-4913)
NEXT DAY FRAME INC
11560 Wright Rd, Lynwood (90262-3944)
PHONE..................................310 886-0851
Nancy Abelar, *CEO*
EMP: 65
SALES (est): 5MM **Privately Held**
SIC: 2519 Household furniture, except wood or metal: upholstered

(P-4914)
NICHOLAS MICHAEL DESIGNS INC
2330 Raymer Ave, Fullerton (92833-2515)
PHONE..................................714 562-8101
Michael A Cimarueti, *CEO*
Alison Diaz, *Account Dir*
▲ **EMP:** 120

SALES (est): 18.7MM **Privately Held**
SIC: 2519 Household furniture, except wood or metal: upholstered

(P-4915)
PATIO & DOOR OUTLET INC (PA)
Also Called: Patio Outlet
410 W Fletcher Ave, Orange (92865-2612)
PHONE..................................714 974-9900
Christopher Lyons, *President*
▲ **EMP:** 23
SQ FT: 200,000
SALES (est): 2.6MM **Privately Held**
SIC: 2519 5712 2514 5031 Garden furniture, except wood, metal, stone or concrete; outdoor & garden furniture; garden furniture, metal; lumber, plywood & millwork; furniture

(P-4916)
PF PLASTICS INC
Also Called: Crystal Craft
2044 Wright Ave, La Verne (91750-5821)
PHONE..................................909 392-4488
Parviz Youssefy, *President*
EMP: 13
SQ FT: 10,300
SALES (est): 1.5MM **Privately Held**
WEB: www.crystalcraft.com
SIC: 2519 2541 Household furniture, except wood or metal: upholstered; display fixtures, wood; store fixtures, wood

(P-4917)
PRC COMPOSITES LLC
1400 S Campus Ave, Ontario (91761-4330)
PHONE..................................909 391-2006
John Upsher, *Mng Member*
Gene Gregory,
EMP: 99 **EST:** 2014
SALES (est): 17.7MM **Privately Held**
SIC: 2519 Furniture, household: glass, fiberglass & plastic

(P-4918)
RECYCLED SPACES INC
Also Called: High Camp Home
10191 Donner Pass Rd # 1, Truckee
(96161-0408)
P.O. Box 10358 (96162-0358)
PHONE..................................530 587-3394
Diana Vincent, *CEO*
Teresa Mersky, *President*
Amy Trehal, *Opers Mgr*
Laurel Meyer, *Marketing Staff*
▲ **EMP:** 15
SALES (est): 2.1MM **Privately Held**
WEB: www.highcamphome.com
SIC: 2519 5712 Lawn & garden furniture, except wood & metal; furniture stores

(P-4919)
SEATING COMPONENT MFG INC
3951 E Miraloma Ave, Anaheim
(92806-6201)
PHONE..................................714 693-3376
Daryl Fossier, *President*
EMP: 12
SQ FT: 12,000
SALES (est): 1.5MM **Privately Held**
SIC: 2519 Fiberglass furniture, household: padded or plain

(P-4920)
STONE YARD INC
Also Called: Carlsbad Manufacturing
8980 Crestmar Pt, San Diego
(92121-3222)
PHONE..................................858 586-1580
Mitchell Brean, *President*
◆ **EMP:** 45
SQ FT: 35,500
SALES (est): 4MM **Privately Held**
WEB: www.stoneyardinc.com
SIC: 2519 Household furniture, except wood or metal: upholstered

(P-4921)
TAZI DESIGNS
2660 Bridgeway, Sausalito (94965-1482)
PHONE..................................415 503-0013
Hicham Tazi, *Owner*
▲ **EMP:** 10
SALES (est): 1.1MM **Privately Held**
SIC: 2519 Household furniture

PRODUCTS & SVCS

(P-4922)
TRIMEK INC (HQ)
900 Lane Ave Ste 170, Chula Vista
(91914-4559)
PHONE.................................858 571-7475
Gyung Jae Lee, *CEO*
Jong P Woo, *CFO*
SOO N Joe, *Controller*
▲ EMP: 12
SQ FT: 2,000
SALES (est): 38.5MM
SALES (corp-wide): 78MM **Privately
Held**
SIC: 2519 Television cabinets, plastic
PA: Samjin Lnd Co., Ltd.
64-17 Dongtangiheung-Ro, Dongtan-
Myeon
Hwaseong 18487
823 137-9205

(P-4923)
VINOTEMP INTERNATIONAL CORP (PA)
16782 Von Karman Ave # 15, Irvine
(92606-2417)
PHONE.................................310 886-3332
India Hynes, *CEO*
Karen Philvin, *General Mgr*
Marcela Salinas, *Office Mgr*
David Satter, *Info Tech Mgr*
Raul Arias, *Technical Staff*
▲ EMP: 70
SQ FT: 70,000
SALES (est): 13.1MM **Privately Held**
WEB: www.vinotemp.com
SIC: 2519 Household furniture, except
wood or metal: upholstered

(P-4924)
WISE LIVING INC
2001 W 60th St, Los Angeles (90047-1037)
PHONE.................................323 541-0410
Jose A Pinedo, *CEO*
EMP: 35
SALES (est): 5.1MM **Privately Held**
SIC: 2519 Household furniture, except
wood or metal: upholstered

2521 Wood Office Furniture

(P-4925)
A M CABINETS INC (PA)
239 E Gardena Blvd, Gardena
(90248-2813)
PHONE.................................310 532-1919
Alex H Mc Kay Jr, *President*
Alex H McKay, *COO*
Travis McKay, *General Mgr*
Nancy Wolfinger, *Admin Sec*
Janette Preciado, *Admin Asst*
EMP: 90
SQ FT: 35,000
SALES (est): 20.4MM **Privately Held**
WEB: www.amcabinets.com
SIC: 2521 2434 2541 Wood office furni-
ture; wood kitchen cabinets; counters or
counter display cases, wood

(P-4926)
ACTION LAMINATES LLC
3400 Investment Blvd, Hayward
(94545-3811)
PHONE.................................510 259-6217
Daniel Johnston,
EMP: 13
SQ FT: 12,000
SALES (est): 2.1MM **Privately Held**
WEB: www.actionlaminates.com
SIC: 2521 Wood office furniture

(P-4927)
AMERICON
900 Flynn Rd, Camarillo (93012-8703)
PHONE.................................805 987-0412
Bill Farrah, *President*
Billy Farah, *Purchasing*
Dan Moro, *Sales Staff*
Danielle Maria, *Manager*
Jerry Herrington, *Consultant*
EMP: 17
SQ FT: 30,000
SALES: 4MM **Privately Held**
WEB: www.americon-usa.com
SIC: 2521 3663 Wood office furniture;
radio & TV communications equipment

(P-4928)
AMPINE LLC
11610 Ampine Fibreform Rd, Sutter Creek
(95685-9686)
PHONE.................................209 223-1690
Terry Velasco, *General Mgr*
EMP: 112
SALES (corp-wide): 357.7MM **Privately
Held**
SIC: 2521 Wood office furniture
HQ: Ampine, Llc
11300 Ridge Rd
Martell CA 95654
209 223-6091

(P-4929)
AMQ SOLUTIONS LLC (HQ)
764 Walsh Ave, Santa Clara (95050-2613)
PHONE.................................877 801-0370
James P Keane, *President*
Jennifer Maciel, *Sales Mgr*
Tyler Silva, *Sales Mgr*
Sarah Gaballah, *Sales Staff*
Kenny Jackson, *Facilities Mgr*
◆ EMP: 14
SALES (est): 2.9MM
SALES (corp-wide): 3B **Publicly Held**
SIC: 2521 2522 5021 Wood office desks
& tables; office chairs, benches & stools,
except wood; office furniture
PA: Steelcase Inc.
901 44th St Se
Grand Rapids MI 49508
616 247-2710

(P-4930)
ANDERSON DESK INC
7510 Airway Rd Ste 7, San Diego
(92154-8303)
PHONE.................................619 671-1040
Mark Baker, *President*
Jose Campos, *Info Tech Mgr*
Rogelio A Meza, *Purch Mgr*
Olga Gomez, *Manager*
▲ EMP: 300
SALES (est): 27.9MM
SALES (corp-wide): 3B **Publicly Held**
SIC: 2521 Wood office furniture
PA: Steelcase Inc.
901 44th St Se
Grand Rapids MI 49508
616 247-2710

(P-4931)
ANTIQUE DESIGNS LTD INC
916 W Hyde Park Blvd, Inglewood
(90302-3308)
PHONE.................................310 671-5400
Ann J Lockie, *President*
Thomas R Lockie, *Vice Pres*
Deborah Lockie, *Admin Sec*
▲ EMP: 31
SQ FT: 6,000
SALES: 120K **Privately Held**
WEB: www.antiquedesigns.net
SIC: 2521 2426 2511

(P-4932)
ARTISTIC CONCEPTS
3293 N San Fernando Rd, Los Angeles
(90065-1414)
PHONE.................................323 257-8101
Oscar Mejia, *President*
EMP: 10
SQ FT: 3,000
SALES (est): 808.1K **Privately Held**
WEB: www.laform.com
SIC: 2521 Cabinets, office: wood

(P-4933)
BAUSMAN AND COMPANY INC (PA)
1500 Crafton Ave Bldg 124, Mentone
(92359-1304)
PHONE.................................909 947-0139
Craig L Johnson, *CEO*
Craig Johnson, *CEO*
Robert Williams, *Vice Pres*
EMP: 249 EST: 1971

SALES (est): 38.5MM **Privately Held**
WEB: www.bausman.net
SIC: 2521 2511 Wood office furniture;
wood household furniture

(P-4934)
BKON INTERIOR SOUTION
15330 Allen St, Paramount (90723-4012)
PHONE.................................562 408-1655
Jong Lee, *Owner*
Terry Kim, *Co-Owner*
EMP: 10
SQ FT: 10,000
SALES (est): 1.1MM **Privately Held**
SIC: 2521 2431 Cabinets, office: wood; in-
terior & ornamental woodwork & trim

(P-4935)
CAPITOL STORE FIXTURES
Also Called: Capitol Components
4220 Pell Dr Ste C, Sacramento
(95838-2575)
PHONE.................................916 646-9096
Toll Free:.................................888
Jim Pelc, *President*
Vicki Pelc, *Vice Pres*
EMP: 25
SQ FT: 24,000
SALES (est): 3.6MM **Privately Held**
WEB: www.csfixtures.com
SIC: 2521 5046 Cabinets, office: wood;
shelving, commercial & industrial

(P-4936)
CASEWORX INC
1130 Research Dr, Redlands (92374-4562)
PHONE.................................909 799-8550
Bruce Humphrey, *President*
Melissa Fletcher, *Office Mgr*
Gregg Schneider, *Admin Sec*
Angel Salgado, *Opers Mgr*
▲ EMP: 37
SQ FT: 28,000
SALES (est): 6.4MM **Privately Held**
SIC: 2521 Cabinets, office: wood

(P-4937)
CENTRAL COAST CABINETS
111a Lee Rd, Watsonville (95076-9422)
PHONE.................................831 724-2992
Kelly Souza, *Co-Owner*
Todd Souza, *Co-Owner*
EMP: 10
SQ FT: 34,000
SALES (est): 1.2MM **Privately Held**
SIC: 2521 2434 Cabinets, office: wood;
wood kitchen cabinets

(P-4938)
COLOMBARAS CABINET & MLLWK INC
421 4th St, Woodland (95695-4011)
PHONE.................................530 662-2665
Craig Colombara, *President*
Eileen Colombara, *CFO*
Raymond Colombara, *Vice Pres*
Elaine Scarlett, *Admin Sec*
EMP: 10
SQ FT: 11,000
SALES (est): 1.5MM **Privately Held**
WEB: www.colombaras.com
SIC: 2521 5251 2541 2434 Cabinets, of-
fice: wood; builders' hardware; sink tops,
plastic laminated; table or counter tops,
plastic laminated; vanities, bathroom:
wood

(P-4939)
COMMERCIAL FURNITURE
1261 N Lakeview Ave, Anaheim
(92807-1834)
PHONE.................................714 350-7045
Bob Gomez, *President*
Helen Masterson, *Accounting Mgr*
EMP: 20
SQ FT: 8,500
SALES (est): 2MM **Privately Held**
WEB: www.commfurn.com
SIC: 2521 7641 Wood office furniture; up-
holstery work

(P-4940)
CREATIVE WOOD PRODUCTS INC
900 77th Ave, Oakland (94621-2526)
P.O. Box 14367 (94614-2367)
PHONE.................................510 635-5399
Jose Mendes, *President*
Polly Peggs Mendes, *CFO*
Polly Mendes, *Safety Mgr*
Josh Halsey, *Sales Staff*
▲ EMP: 120 EST: 1964
SQ FT: 85,000
SALES (est): 21.1MM **Privately Held**
WEB: www.creativewood.net
SIC: 2521 Desks, office: wood

(P-4941)
CRI SUB 1 (DH)
Also Called: E O C
1715 S Anderson Ave, Compton
(90220-5005)
PHONE.................................310 537-1657
Ken Bodger, *CEO*
Richard L Sinclair Jr, *President*
Charles Hess, *Vice Pres*
▲ EMP: 32
SQ FT: 120,000
SALES (est): 3.5MM
SALES (corp-wide): 70.7MM **Privately
Held**
WEB: www.eoccorp.com
SIC: 2521 Cabinets, office: wood; chairs,
office: padded, upholstered or plain:
wood; panel systems & partitions (free-
standing), office: wood

(P-4942)
DESKMAKERS INC
6525 Flotilla St, Commerce (90040-1713)
PHONE.................................323 264-2260
Philip K Polishook, *CEO*
Daniel Boiles, *Vice Pres*
John Bornstein, *Vice Pres*
April Simental, *Administration*
Jose Bugarin, *Opers Staff*
◆ EMP: 50
SQ FT: 105,000
SALES (est): 10.2MM **Privately Held**
SIC: 2521 Desks, office: wood

(P-4943)
FAUSTINOS CHAIR FACTORY INC
2425 S Malt Ave, Commerce (90040-3201)
P.O. Box 911515, Los Angeles (90091-
1239)
PHONE.................................323 724-8055
Faustino Limon, *President*
▲ EMP: 50
SQ FT: 90,000
SALES (est): 7.3MM **Privately Held**
WEB: www.faustinoschairfactory.com
SIC: 2521 Wood office furniture

(P-4944)
FORTRESS INC
Also Called: Off Broadway
1721 Wright Ave, La Verne (91750-5841)
PHONE.................................909 593-8600
Donald I Wolper, *President*
Shanon Wolper, *Purch Mgr*
▲ EMP: 35
SQ FT: 100
SALES (est): 6.1MM **Privately Held**
WEB: www.fortresseating.com
SIC: 2521 2522 Chairs, office: padded,
upholstered or plain: wood; chairs, office:
padded or plain, except wood

(P-4945)
GALTECH COMPUTER CORPORATION
Also Called: Galtech International
501 Flynn Rd, Camarillo (93012-8756)
P.O. Box 305, Newbury Park (91319-0305)
PHONE.................................805 376-1060
Fei Lin Ko, *CEO*
Jim Lai, *Shareholder*
Robert Ko, *President*
▲ EMP: 20
SQ FT: 32,000
SALES: 11.9MM **Privately Held**
WEB: www.galtechcorp.com
SIC: 2521 Benches, office: wood

(P-4946)
GARFIELD COMMERCIAL ENTPS
15977 Heron Ave, La Mirada (90638-5512)
PHONE..................................714 690-5959
Simon Yao, *President*
EMP: 49 EST: 2015
SALES (est): 3.7MM **Privately Held**
SIC: 2521 2531 2519 2512 Wood office
furniture; school furniture; household fur-
niture; chairs: upholstered on wood
frames

(P-4947)
GRAHAM LEE ASSOCIATES INC
8674 Atlantic Ave, South Gate
(90280-3502)
PHONE..................................323 581-8203
Charles Graham, *President*
Michael Chu, *Shareholder*
Brian Krueger, *Shareholder*
Ywart Lee, *Vice Pres*
EMP: 17
SQ FT: 11,000
SALES (est): 1.4MM **Privately Held**
WEB: www.grahamlee.com
SIC: 2521 Cabinets, office: wood

(P-4948)
HERMAN MILLER INC
2740 Zanker Rd Ste 150, San Jose
(95134-2132)
PHONE..................................408 432-5730
Marcus Lohela, *Principal*
EMP: 24
SALES (corp-wide): 2.3B **Publicly Held**
SIC: 2521 Wood office furniture
PA: Herman Miller, Inc.
855 E Main Ave
Zeeland MI 49464
616 654-3000

(P-4949)
HPL CONTRACT INC
525 Baldwin Rd, Patterson (95363-8859)
PHONE..................................209 892-1717
Frank Stratiotis, *President*
Jim Robertson, *Vice Pres*
EMP: 17
SQ FT: 7,200
SALES (est): 3.9MM **Privately Held**
WEB: www.hplcontract.com
SIC: 2521 Wood office furniture

(P-4950)
INTERIOR WOOD OF SAN DIEGO
1215 W Nutmeg St, San Diego
(92101-1230)
PHONE..................................619 295-6469
Alan Marshall, *President*
Dan O'Brien, *Exec VP*
Cheryl Dubois, *Manager*
EMP: 32
SQ FT: 10,000
SALES (est): 3.9MM **Privately Held**
WEB: www.interiorwood.com
SIC: 2521 Cabinets, office: wood

(P-4951)
IRONIES LLC
2222 5th St, Berkeley (94710-2217)
PHONE..................................510 644-2100
Kathleen McIntyre, *President*
EMP: 35
SALES (est): 6.2MM **Privately Held**
WEB: www.ironies.com
SIC: 2521 Wood office furniture

(P-4952)
J & C CUSTOM CABINETS INC
11451 Elks Cir, Rancho Cordova
(95742-7355)
PHONE..................................916 638-3400
Chris Christie, *Ch of Bd*
James E Farrell, *President*
EMP: 20
SQ FT: 20,000
SALES (est): 2.8MM **Privately Held**
SIC: 2521 2434 Cabinets, office: wood;
wood kitchen cabinets

(P-4953)
KINGS CABINET SYSTEMS
426 Park Ave, Hanford (93230-4440)
PHONE..................................559 584-9662
Fax: 559 584-9670
EMP: 13 EST: 1977
SQ FT: 12,500
SALES (est): 1.2MM **Privately Held**
SIC: 2521

(P-4954)
LIGNUM VITAE CABINET
1625 16th St, Oakland (94607-1541)
PHONE..................................510 444-2030
James Martin, *Owner*
EMP: 10 EST: 1976
SALES (est): 1MM **Privately Held**
WEB: www.lignumvitae.com
SIC: 2521 2511 5712 7389 Wood office
furniture; wood household furniture; cabi-
net work, custom;

(P-4955)
MONTBLEAU & ASSOCIATES INC (PA)
555 Raven St, San Diego (92102-4523)
PHONE..................................619 263-5550
Ron P Montbleau, *President*
Barton Ward, *Exec VP*
David Zammit, *Vice Pres*
Marti Montbleau, *Admin Sec*
Kim Zimlich, *Administration*
EMP: 90
SQ FT: 32,000
SALES (est): 17.7MM **Privately Held**
WEB: www.montbleau.com
SIC: 2521 1751 2434 Wood office furni-
ture; cabinet building & installation; wood
kitchen cabinets

(P-4956)
NAKAMURA-BEEMAN INC
8520 Wellsford Pl, Santa Fe Springs
(90670-2226)
PHONE..................................562 696-1400
Mike Beeman, *President*
Jack Loudermill, *Opers Mgr*
EMP: 40 EST: 1978
SQ FT: 20,000
SALES (est): 6.3MM **Privately Held**
WEB: www.nbifixtures.com
SIC: 2521 3429 2541 Wood office furni-
ture; cabinet hardware; display fixtures,
wood

(P-4957)
NEW MAVERICK DESK INC
15100 S Figueroa St, Gardena
(90248-1724)
PHONE..................................310 217-1554
John Long, *CEO*
Rich Mealey, *President*
Ted Jaroszewicz, *CEO*
Donald Clark, *Purchasing*
▲ EMP: 150
SQ FT: 1,000
SALES (est): 19.8MM **Privately Held**
SIC: 2521 Wood office furniture
HQ: Workstream Inc.
3158 Production Dr
Fairfield OH 45014

(P-4958)
NICHOLAS R HYLAND
Also Called: Hyland & Associates
227 San Jose Ave, San Jose (95125-1009)
PHONE..................................408 392-0600
Michele Hyland, *Owner*
Dan Hyland, *Manager*
EMP: 16
SQ FT: 12,000
SALES (est): 1.2MM **Privately Held**
WEB: www.gworkshop.com
SIC: 2521 1521 Cabinets, office: wood;
general remodeling, single-family houses

(P-4959)
NORSTAR OFFICE PRODUCTS INC (PA)
Also Called: Boss
5353 Jillson St, Commerce (90040-2115)
PHONE..................................323 262-1919
William W Huang, *President*
Kari Brown, *Executive*
Kathy Yi, *Branch Mgr*
Faith Bishop, *Opers Staff*
Vanessa Gutierrez, *Sales Staff*
◆ EMP: 40
SQ FT: 150,000
SALES (est): 247.7MM **Privately Held**
WEB: www.bosschair.com
SIC: 2521 2522 Chairs, office: padded,
upholstered or plain: wood; chairs, office:
padded or plain, except wood

(P-4960)
NORTHWOOD DESIGN PARTNERS INC
1550 Atlantic St, Union City (94587-2006)
PHONE..................................510 731-6505
Michael Hayes, *CEO*
Josh Michael Hayes, *President*
Brian Wong, *Engineer*
Patrick Palme, *Manager*
EMP: 38
SQ FT: 2,000
SALES (est): 7.4MM **Privately Held**
SIC: 2521 2431 Wood office furniture; mill-
work

(P-4961)
OAK DESIGN CORPORATION
13272 6th St, Chino (91710-4108)
PHONE..................................909 628-9597
Ismaell Castellanos, *President*
Julio Salas, *President*
EMP: 25
SALES (est): 3.1MM **Privately Held**
WEB: www.oakdesigns.net
SIC: 2521 2434 2511 Wood office furni-
ture; wood kitchen cabinets; wood bed-
room furniture

(P-4962)
OFFICE CHAIRS INC
Also Called: Oci
14815 Radburn Ave, Santa Fe Springs
(90670-5319)
PHONE..................................562 802-0464
Sharon Klapper, *President*
Joseph J Klapper Jr, *Corp Secy*
Donald J Simek, *Exec VP*
▲ EMP: 60 EST: 1974
SQ FT: 60,000
SALES (est): 10.3MM **Privately Held**
WEB: www.officechairs.net
SIC: 2521 2512 Wood office furniture;
chairs: upholstered on wood frames

(P-4963)
OHIO INC
630 Treat Ave, San Francisco
(94110-2016)
PHONE..................................415 647-6446
David Pierce, *President*
EMP: 13 EST: 1996
SQ FT: 7,000
SALES (est): 500K **Privately Held**
SIC: 2521 Wood office furniture

(P-4964)
RAINBOW MANUFACTURING CO INC
1504 W 58th St, Los Angeles (90062-2824)
PHONE..................................323 778-2093
David Azari, *President*
Rachel Azari, *Vice Pres*
Moshe Azari, *Admin Sec*
▲ EMP: 10
SQ FT: 9,000
SALES (est): 1.3MM **Privately Held**
SIC: 2521 Wood office furniture

(P-4965)
RBF GROUP INTERNATIONAL
Also Called: Rbf Lifestyle Holdings
1441 W 2nd St, Pomona (91766-1202)
P.O. Box 1094 (91769-1094)
PHONE..................................626 333-5700
Robert Brown, *CEO*
▲ EMP: 15
SALES (est): 1.7MM **Privately Held**
SIC: 2521 Chairs, office: padded, uphol-
stered or plain: wood

(P-4966)
S & H CABINETS AND MFG INC
10860 Mulberry Ave, Fontana
(92337-7027)
PHONE..................................909 357-0551
Michael Hansen, *CEO*
EMP: 40 EST: 1954
SQ FT: 22,000

SALES (est): 6.2MM **Privately Held**
WEB: www.shcabinets.com
SIC: 2521 2541 2431 Cabinets, office:
wood; table or counter tops, plastic laminated; millwork

(P-4967)
SARDO BUS & COACH UPHOLSTERY
512 W Rosecrans Ave, Gardena
(90248-1515)
PHONE..................................800 654-3824
Jim Kemme, *Manager*
EMP: 60
SALES (est): 950K **Privately Held**
SIC: 2521 2512 Chairs, office: padded,
upholstered or plain: wood; couches,
sofas & davenports: upholstered on wood
frames

(P-4968)
STARSHIP WORLDWIDE LLC
Also Called: Jazzyexpo.com
3030 Enterprise Ct Ste C, Vista
(92081-8361)
PHONE..................................760 727-1190
Allen Weiss, *Sales Mgr*
Jenny Ficklin, *Mng Member*
▲ EMP: 10
SQ FT: 95,000
SALES (est): 900K **Privately Held**
WEB: www.jazzyexpo.com
SIC: 2521 Wood office furniture

(P-4969)
STEELCASE INC
7510 Airway Rd Ste 7, San Diego
(92154-8303)
PHONE..................................619 671-1040
Mark Baker, *Manager*
Luke Rumley, *Exec VP*
Adrian Sanchez, *Info Tech Dir*
Juan Mendoza, *Purch Mgr*
EMP: 300
SALES (corp-wide): 3B **Publicly Held**
SIC: 2521 Wood office furniture
PA: Steelcase Inc.
901 44th St Se
Grand Rapids MI 49508
616 247-2710

(P-4970)
STOLO CABINETS INC (PA)
Also Called: Stolo Custom Cabinets
860 Challenger St, Brea (92821-2946)
PHONE..................................714 529-7303
Gary Stolo, *Vice Pres*
Robert F Stolo, *Corp Secy*
Donald J Stolo, *Vice Pres*
Justin Stolo, *Vice Pres*
Jo Nagel, *Admin Asst*
EMP: 45
SQ FT: 15,000
SALES (est): 7.9MM **Privately Held**
WEB: www.stolocabinets.com
SIC: 2521 Cabinets, office: wood

(P-4971)
TRADEINCOM INC
Also Called: Office Furniture Solutions
28441 Rancho Cal Rd Ste Z, Temecula
(92590-3677)
PHONE..................................951 296-5566
Jon Driscoll, *President*
EMP: 12
SALES (est): 1.5MM **Privately Held**
SIC: 2521 Wood office desks & tables

(P-4972)
TRINITY OFFICE FURNITURE INC
1050 W Rialto Ave, San Bernardino
(92410-2376)
P.O. Box 1526, Wildomar (92595-1526)
PHONE..................................909 888-5551
James B Kesterson, *President*
Marci Kesterson, *Admin Sec*
▲ EMP: 70
SQ FT: 135,000
SALES (est): 5.4MM **Privately Held**
SIC: 2521 2511 5021 Wood office furni-
ture; wood household furniture; office fur-
niture

(P-4973)
VALLEY OAKS INDUSTRIES
Also Called: Valley Oak Cabinets
3550 E Highway 246 Ste Ae, Santa Ynez
(93460-9480)
P.O. Box 1097 (93460-1097)
PHONE..............................805 688-2754
Tom Carlson, *President*
Kim Carlson, *Vice Pres*
Travis Whitney, *Sales Staff*
EMP: 17
SALES (est): 2.5MM **Privately Held**
WEB: www.valleyoakindustries.com
SIC: 2521 2511 Wood office furniture;
wood household furniture

(P-4974)
**ZUO MODERN CONTEMPORARY
INC (PA)**
80 Swan Way Ste 300, Oakland
(94621-1440)
PHONE..............................510 777-1030
Luis Ruesga, *CEO*
Steven Poon, *COO*
Terry Tam, *CFO*
Cristy Maxwell, *Sales Staff*
◆ EMP: 26
SQ FT: 64,000
SALES: 25.4MM **Privately Held**
WEB: www.zuomod.com
SIC: 2521 3645 Wood office furniture; res-
idential lighting fixtures

2522 Office Furniture,
Except Wood

(P-4975)
**AMERICAN FURNITURE
SYSTEMS INC**
Also Called: Advantage Custom Fixtures
14105 Avalon Blvd, Los Angeles
(90061-2637)
PHONE..............................626 457-9900
Allen Sterris, *President*
EMP: 34
SQ FT: 50,000
SALES: 2.5MM **Privately Held**
WEB: www.americanfurnituresys.com
SIC: 2522 5411 Office furniture, except
wood; convenience stores

(P-4976)
ANGELL & GIROUX INC
2727 Alcazar St, Los Angeles (90033-1196)
PHONE..............................323 269-8596
Richard M Hart, *CEO*
Carol A Hart, *Vice Pres*
Kenneth Hart, *Vice Pres*
Rosemary Vazquez, *Executive*
EMP: 52
SQ FT: 13,000
SALES (est): 9.9MM **Privately Held**
WEB: www.angellandgiroux.com
SIC: 2522 3479 Cabinets, office: except
wood; painting, coating & hot dipping;
enameling, including porcelain, of metal
products

(P-4977)
ARTE DE MEXICO INC (PA)
1000 Chestnut St, Burbank (91506-1623)
PHONE..............................818 753-4559
Gerald J Stoffers, *CEO*
Thea Stoffers, *Director*
▲ EMP: 90
SQ FT: 103,000
SALES (est): 22.5MM **Privately Held**
WEB: www.artedemexico.com
SIC: 2522 3645 Office furniture, except
wood; residential lighting fixtures

(P-4978)
BENCH-TEK SOLUTIONS LLC
525 Aldo Ave, Santa Clara (95054-2205)
P.O. Box 640818, San Jose (95164-0818)
PHONE..............................408 653-1100
Maria Castellon,
Jorge Castellon,
Ha Phung, *Manager*
▼ EMP: 13
SQ FT: 8,000

SALES: 4MM **Privately Held**
WEB: www.bench-tek.com
SIC: 2522 2599 Benches, office: except
wood; work benches, factory

(P-4979)
BERTOLINI CORPORATION
2605 E Cedar St, Ontario (91761-8511)
PHONE..............................909 613-1393
Jim Bertolini, *CEO*
Chuck Horn, *Exec VP*
Charles Bertolini, *Director*
◆ EMP: 125
SQ FT: 80,000
SALES (est): 29.8MM **Privately Held**
WEB: www.bertolinidirect.com
SIC: 2522 2531 Office chairs, benches &
stools, except wood; public building & re-
lated furniture

(P-4980)
COLORLINE INC
Also Called: Counter Fitters, The
6239 San Ricardo Way, Buena Park
(90620-2845)
PHONE..............................714 373-9500
Dave G Naslund, *President*
Betty Cook, *Vice Pres*
Kim Naslund, *Vice Pres*
EMP: 15
SQ FT: 13,000
SALES: 1MM **Privately Held**
SIC: 2522 Office furniture, except wood

(P-4981)
D3 INC (PA)
Also Called: 9 To 5 Seating
3211 Jack Northrop Ave, Hawthorne
(90250-4424)
PHONE..............................310 223-2200
Darius Mir, *CEO*
Jerry Long, *Vice Pres*
Susan Mir, *Vice Pres*
Mike Heazlitt, *General Mgr*
Matthew Mills, *Info Tech Mgr*
◆ EMP: 95
SQ FT: 50,000
SALES (est): 19.6MM **Privately Held**
WEB: www.9to5seating.com
SIC: 2522 Chairs, office: padded or plain,
except wood

(P-4982)
ELITE MFG CORP
12143 Altamar Pl, Santa Fe Springs
(90670-2501)
PHONE..............................888 354-8356
Peter Luong, *CEO*
Robinson Ho, *Vice Pres*
◆ EMP: 102
SQ FT: 62,000
SALES (est): 19.2MM **Privately Held**
SIC: 2522 2514 Office furniture, except
wood; metal household furniture

(P-4983)
ENCORE SEATING INC
13747 Midway St, Cerritos (90703-2330)
PHONE..............................562 926-1969
Casey Journigan, *President*
Chris Burgess, *Vice Pres*
▲ EMP: 30
SQ FT: 53,000
SALES (est): 6.8MM **Privately Held**
WEB: www.encoreseating.com
SIC: 2522 Chairs, office: padded or plain,
except wood

(P-4984)
ERGODIRECT INC
1601 Old County Rd, San Carlos
(94070-5204)
PHONE..............................650 654-4300
Nasser M Moshiri, *President*
Nazan Meysami, *General Mgr*
Nikki Moshiri, *Info Tech Mgr*
EMP: 10
SALES (est): 1.3MM **Privately Held**
SIC: 2522 Office furniture, except wood

(P-4985)
**ERGONONMIC COMFORT
DESIGN INC**
9140 Stellar Ct Ste B, Corona
(92883-4902)
P.O. Box 79018 (92877-0167)
PHONE..............................951 277-1558
Aldolfo Agramonte, *President*
Patricia Agramonte, *Vice Pres*
▲ EMP: 18
SQ FT: 22,000
SALES (est): 3.6MM **Privately Held**
WEB: www.ecdonline.net
SIC: 2522 Office chairs, benches & stools,
except wood

(P-4986)
EXEMPLIS LLC
Also Called: Sit On It
6280 Artesia Blvd, Buena Park
(90620-1004)
PHONE..............................714 995-4800
Paul Devries, *Manager*
EMP: 35 **Privately Held**
SIC: 2522 2521 2512 Chairs, office:
padded or plain, except wood; wood of-
fice furniture; upholstered household fur-
niture
PA: Exemplis Llc
6415 Katella Ave
Cypress CA 90630
-

(P-4987)
EXEMPLIS LLC
Also Called: Ideon
6280 Artesia Blvd, Buena Park
(90620-1004)
PHONE..............................714 898-5500
Craig Dumity, *Director*
EMP: 260 **Privately Held**
SIC: 2522 5021 Chairs, office: padded or
plain, except wood; furniture
PA: Exemplis Llc
6415 Katella Ave
Cypress CA 90630

(P-4988)
EXEMPLIS LLC (PA)
Also Called: Sitonit
6415 Katella Ave, Cypress (90630-5245)
PHONE..............................714 995-4800
Paul Devries, *CEO*
Mike Mekjian, *President*
Chip Brown, *CFO*
Mike Phelan, *CFO*
Patrick Sommerfield, *Exec VP*
◆ EMP: 40
SQ FT: 20,000
SALES (est): 113.5MM **Privately Held**
SIC: 2522 Chairs, office: padded or plain,
except wood

(P-4989)
HAWORTH INC
144 N Robertson Blvd # 202, West Holly-
wood (90048-3109)
PHONE..............................310 854-7633
EMP: 17
SALES (corp-wide): 1.2B **Privately Held**
SIC: 2522 5021
HQ: Haworth, Inc.
1 Haworth Ctr
Holland MI 49423
616 393-3000

(P-4990)
HNI CORPORATION
3780 Pell Cir, Sacramento (95838-2528)
PHONE..............................916 927-0400
EMP: 318
SALES (corp-wide): 2.1B **Publicly Held**
SIC: 2522 Office furniture, except wood
PA: Hni Corporation
600 E 2nd St
Muscatine IA 52761
563 272-7400

(P-4991)
KIMBALL OFFICE INC
330 Pine St, San Francisco (94104-3202)
PHONE..............................415 397-1557
Michael Donahue, *Vice Pres*
Tom Bryant, *Project Engr*
Pedro Ayala, *Manager*

Kristen Maddas, *Manager*
EMP: 19
SALES (corp-wide): 685.6MM **Publicly
Held**
SIC: 2522 Office furniture, except wood
HQ: Kimball Office Inc.
1600 Royal St
Jasper IN 47549

(P-4992)
KORDEN INC
611 S Palmetto Ave, Ontario (91762-4124)
PHONE..............................909 988-8979
Barjona S Meek, *Principal*
Thomas Mc Cormick, *President*
Jim Ethridge, *Exec VP*
EMP: 13 EST: 1949
SQ FT: 75,000
SALES (est): 3MM **Privately Held**
WEB: www.korden.com
SIC: 2522 Stools, office: except wood

(P-4993)
MARK RESOURCES LLC (PA)
1962 22nd Ave, San Francisco
(94116-1209)
PHONE..............................415 515-5540
Lloyd Mark,
David Mark,
EMP: 10
SQ FT: 2,500
SALES (est): 840.4K **Privately Held**
SIC: 2522 7221 8742 8711 Office furni-
ture, except wood; photographer, still or
video; business planning & organizing
services; designing: ship, boat, machine
& product

(P-4994)
**MC-DOWELL-CRAIG MFGCO
(PA)**
Also Called: McDowell Craig
13146 Firestone Blvd, Santa Fe Springs
(90670-5517)
PHONE..............................714 521-7170
Brent McDowell, *Admin Sec*
EMP: 12
SQ FT: 125,000
SALES (est): 2.3MM **Privately Held**
WEB: www.mcdowell-craig.com
SIC: 2522 Cabinets, office: except wood

(P-4995)
**MCDOWELL & CRAIG OFF
SYSTEMS**
Also Called: McDowell-Craig Office Furn
13146 Firestone Blvd, Norwalk (90650)
PHONE..............................562 921-4441
Brent G McDowell, *President*
Jeffrey C McDowell, *Admin Sec*
EMP: 70
SQ FT: 117,000
SALES (est): 8.4MM **Privately Held**
WEB: www.mcdowellcraig.com
SIC: 2522 Office furniture, except wood

(P-4996)
**MODULAR OFFICE SOLUTIONS
INC**
11701 6th St, Rancho Cucamonga
(91730-6030)
PHONE..............................909 476-4200
Daniel G Coelho, *CEO*
Jorge E Robles, *President*
▲ EMP: 100 EST: 1999
SQ FT: 173,000
SALES (est): 9.8MM **Privately Held**
SIC: 2522 2521 Office furniture, except
wood; wood office furniture

(P-4997)
OFFICE MASTER INC
1110 Mildred St, Ontario (91761-3512)
PHONE..............................909 392-5678
William Chow, *CEO*
Wallace Hwang, *Vice Pres*
Omar Lee, *Purch Mgr*
John Bueno, *Plant Mgr*
Richard Chou, *Natl Sales Mgr*
◆ EMP: 60
SQ FT: 70,000

▲ = Import ▼=Export
◆ =Import/Export

SALES (est): 12.7MM **Privately Held**
WEB: www.office-master.com
SIC: **2522** Office chairs, benches & stools, except wood

(P-4998)
RDM INDUSTRIAL PRODUCTS INC
1652 Watson Ct, Milpitas (95035-6822)
PHONE..................................408 945-8400
Ricky Vigil, *President*
Kristi Cubillo, *Info Tech Mgr*
Kristi Ehrhorn, *Manager*
Michele Gomez, *Manager*
Victor Gomez, *Manager*
EMP: 18 EST: 1976
SQ FT: 17,000
SALES: 3MM **Privately Held**
WEB: www.rdm-ind.com
SIC: **2522** 5712 2521 Cabinets, office: except wood; cabinet work, custom; custom made furniture, except cabinets; office furniture; cabinets, office: wood

(P-4999)
RUSS BASSETT CORP
Also Called: Group Five, Inc.
8189 Byron Rd, Whittier (90606-2615)
PHONE..................................562 945-2445
Mike Dressendorfer, *CEO*
Peter Fink, *President*
Sasha Johnson, *President*
Andy Tripicchio, *Sales Engr*
◆ EMP: 115
SQ FT: 112,000
SALES (est): 25.7MM **Privately Held**
WEB: www.russbassett.com
SIC: **2522** Desks, office: except wood

(P-5000)
SISNEROS INC
Also Called: Sisneros Office Furntiure
12717 Los Nietos Rd, Santa Fe Springs (90670-3007)
PHONE..................................562 777-9797
Luis Sisneros, *President*
Margarita Sisneros, *Vice Pres*
EMP: 20
SQ FT: 20,000
SALES (est): 2.7MM **Privately Held**
SIC: **2522** Office furniture, except wood

(P-5001)
STEELCASE INC
111 Rhode Island St, San Francisco (94103-5200)
PHONE..................................415 865-0261
EMP: 263
SALES (corp-wide): 3B **Publicly Held**
SIC: **2522** Office furniture, except wood
PA: Steelcase Inc.
901 44th St Se
Grand Rapids MI 49508
616 247-2710

(P-5002)
UNITED CABINET COMPANY INC
1510 S Mountain View Ave, San Bernardino (92408-3134)
PHONE..................................909 796-3015
Dennis Rice, *President*
Gayle L Rice, *Shareholder*
Doris Rice, *Corp Secy*
Jeffery Westrom, *Vice Pres*
EMP: 19
SQ FT: 10,000
SALES (est): 1.5MM **Privately Held**
SIC: **2522** Office cabinets & filing drawers: except wood

(P-5003)
Z-LINE DESIGNS INC (PA)
2410 San Ramon Valley Blv, San Ramon (94583-1791)
PHONE..................................925 743-4000
James Sexton, *President*
John Negovetich, *Treasurer*
Rick Lamb, *Vice Pres*
Pauleen Sexton, *Admin Sec*
Jason Peralta, *Administration*
▲ EMP: 90
SQ FT: 13,000
SALES (est): 9.9MM **Privately Held**
WEB: www.z-linedesigns.com
SIC: **2522** Office furniture, except wood

2531 Public Building & Related Furniture

(P-5004)
AERO SEATING TECHNOLOGIES LLC (HQ)
5795 Martin Rd, Irwindale (91706-6211)
PHONE..................................626 286-1130
Pete Perera,
James Foresi, *President*
Gabe Ruvalcaba, *Program Mgr*
Norick Avanessian,
Hossein Motlagh,
▲ EMP: 48
SQ FT: 16,000
SALES (est): 14.9MM **Privately Held**
WEB: www.aeroseating.com
SIC: **2531** Seats, aircraft

(P-5005)
AEROFOAM INDUSTRIES INC
Also Called: QUALITY FOAM PACKAGING
31855 Corydon St, Lake Elsinore (92530-8501)
PHONE..................................951 245-4429
Noel Castellon Jr, *President*
Ruth Castellon, *Treasurer*
Jim Barrett, *Vice Pres*
Darlene Garay, *Finance Mgr*
Vicki Figueroa, *Human Res Mgr*
▲ EMP: 80
SQ FT: 150,000
SALES (est): 21.2MM **Privately Held**
SIC: **2531** Seats, aircraft

(P-5006)
AIRO INDUSTRIES COMPANY
429 Jessie St, San Fernando (91340-2541)
PHONE..................................818 838-1008
Bahram Salem, *President*
Mike Salem, *Vice Pres*
Adam Lari, *Materials Mgr*
Shakila Ardakani, *Marketing Staff*
Kasunthika Ilippuli, *Marketing Staff*
▲ EMP: 25
SQ FT: 20,000
SALES (est): 4.1MM **Privately Held**
WEB: www.airoindustries.com
SIC: **2531** 4581 Seats, aircraft; aircraft upholstery repair

(P-5007)
ALUMINUM SEATING INC
555 Tennis Court Ln, San Bernardino (92408-1615)
P.O. Box 1462, Loma Linda (92354-1462)
PHONE..................................909 884-9449
Sakorn Sirirat, *President*
Quy Van Dang, *Vice Pres*
EMP: 10
SQ FT: 15,000
SALES (est): 753.3K **Privately Held**
SIC: **2531** Stadium seating

(P-5008)
COD USA INC
Also Called: Creative Outdoor Distrs USA
25954 Commercentre Dr, Lake Forest (92630-8815)
PHONE..................................949 381-7367
Heather Smulson, *President*
Brian Horowitz, *CEO*
Barbara Tolbert, *COO*
EMP: 23
SQ FT: 34,000
SALES: 4.6MM **Privately Held**
SIC: **2531** Chairs, portable folding; chairs, table & arm

(P-5009)
COUNTY OF MARIN
Also Called: Parks and Open Space
1600 Los Gamos Dr Ste 200, San Rafael (94903-1807)
PHONE..................................415 446-4414
Linda Dahl, *Director*
EMP: 70 **Privately Held**
SIC: **2531** 9111 Picnic tables or benches, park; county supervisors' & executives' offices

PA: County Of Marin
3501 Civic Center Dr # 258
San Rafael CA 94903
415 473-6358

(P-5010)
DANG THA
Also Called: Skyline Seating
13050 Hoover St, Westminster (92683-2388)
PHONE..................................714 898-0989
Tha Dang, *Owner*
EMP: 15
SQ FT: 3,000
SALES (est): 1.1MM **Privately Held**
SIC: **2531** Seats, automobile

(P-5011)
DEFOE FURNITURE FOR KIDS INC
910 S Grove Ave, Ontario (91761-3435)
PHONE..................................909 947-4459
John G Defoe, *President*
Narcisa Defoe, *Treasurer*
EMP: 16
SQ FT: 17,000
SALES (est): 2.2MM **Privately Held**
SIC: **2531** School furniture

(P-5012)
ECR4KIDS LP
Also Called: Early Childhood Resources
4370 Jutland Dr, San Diego (92117-3642)
PHONE..................................619 323-2005
Mitchell Lynn,
Steve McMahon, *Purch Mgr*
Jamie Lasky, *Purchasing*
Ashley West, *Marketing Mgr*
Megan Clow, *Sales Staff*
◆ EMP: 23
SALES (est): 11.5MM **Privately Held**
WEB: www.ecr4kids.com
SIC: **2531** 3944 2511 5021 Chairs, table & arm; craft & hobby kits & sets; children's wood furniture; chairs; public building furniture; arts & crafts equipment & supplies
PA: Cri 2000, L.P.
2245 San Diego Ave # 125
San Diego CA 92110

(P-5013)
ERA PRODUCTS INC
1130 Benedict Canyon Dr, Beverly Hills (90210-2726)
PHONE..................................310 324-4908
Marlene Alter, *President*
Roy H Alter, *Vice Pres*
EMP: 16
SQ FT: 56,792
SALES (est): 4MM **Privately Held**
WEB: www.eraproducts.com
SIC: **2531** Vehicle furniture

(P-5014)
FUTUREFLITE INC
28895 Industry Dr, La Crescenta (91214)
PHONE..................................818 957-0316
Andrew S Kanigowski, *CEO*
EMP: 15
SALES (est): 2MM **Privately Held**
WEB: www.futureflite.com
SIC: **2531** Seats, aircraft

(P-5015)
IJOT DEVELOPMENT INC
11360b Pleasant Valley Rd, Penn Valley (95946-9000)
P.O. Box 2136, Orinda (94563-6536)
PHONE..................................925 258-9909
Michael Gompertz, *President*
▲ EMP: 1600
SQ FT: 12,000
SALES (est): 89.4MM **Privately Held**
SIC: **2531** 2599 Public building & related furniture; work benches, factory

(P-5016)
J L FURNISHINGS LLC (PA)
Also Called: J L F/Lone Meadow
19007 S Reyes Ave, Compton (90221-5813)
PHONE..................................310 605-6600
Jeffrey Lazar,
◆ EMP: 300

SQ FT: 200,000
SALES (est): 85MM **Privately Held**
WEB: www.jlfurnishings.com
SIC: **2531** 2521 Chairs, table & arm; wood office chairs, benches & stools; chairs, office: padded, upholstered or plain: wood; tables, office: wood

(P-5017)
J L FURNISHINGS LLC
3145 E Maria St, Compton (90221-5805)
PHONE..................................310 856-0412
Jeffrey Lazar, *Branch Mgr*
EMP: 12
SALES (corp-wide): 85MM **Privately Held**
SIC: **2531** 2521 Chairs, table & arm; wood office chairs, benches & stools
PA: J L Furnishings Llc
19007 S Reyes Ave
Compton CA 90221
310 605-6600

(P-5018)
JOHNSON CONTROLS INC
5770 Warland Dr Ste A, Cypress (90630-5047)
PHONE..................................562 799-8882
Dough Beebe, *Manager*
EMP: 150 **Privately Held**
SIC: **2531** 1711 5075 5065 Seats, automobile; heating systems repair & maintenance; warm air heating & air conditioning; electronic parts & equipment
HQ: Johnson Controls, Inc.
5757 N Green Bay Ave
Milwaukee WI 53209
414 524-1200

(P-5019)
KINGS RIVER CASTING INC
1350 North Ave, Sanger (93657-3742)
PHONE..................................559 875-8250
Patrick Henry, *President*
Merry Henry, *Corp Secy*
▼ EMP: 15
SQ FT: 30,000
SALES (est): 1.8MM **Privately Held**
SIC: **2531** 3648 2599 Benches for public buildings; street lighting fixtures; bar furniture

(P-5020)
LOUIS SARDO UPHOLSTERY INC (PA)
Also Called: Sardo Bus & Coach Upholstery
512 W Rosecrans Ave, Gardena (90248-1515)
PHONE..................................310 327-0532
Louis Sardo, *President*
Jeanie Sardo, *Vice Pres*
Kathy Cruse, *Natl Sales Mgr*
Sandy Follis, *VP Sales*
Betty Sahranavard, *Director*
EMP: 55
SQ FT: 10,000
SALES (est): 8.1MM **Privately Held**
SIC: **2531** 3713 7641 Seats, automobile; truck & bus bodies; reupholstery & furniture repair

(P-5021)
MORTECH MANUFACTURING CO INC
411 N Aerojet Dr, Azusa (91702-3253)
PHONE..................................626 334-1471
Gino Joseph, *CEO*
Christy Haines, *CFO*
Paul Joseph, *Vice Pres*
Michael Kubacik, *Vice Pres*
John Joseph, *Marketing Mgr*
◆ EMP: 42
SQ FT: 43,000
SALES (est): 9.9MM **Privately Held**
WEB: www.mortechmfg.com
SIC: **2531** 5087 Altars & pulpits; funeral directors' equipment & supplies

(P-5022)
NELSON ADAMS INC
160 N Cactus Ave, Rialto (92376-5725)
PHONE..................................909 256-8938
Rafael Rangel, *President*
Eric Adler, *CEO*
▲ EMP: 20
SQ FT: 40,000

SALES (est): 3.3MM **Privately Held**
SIC: 2531 Chairs, table & arm

(P-5023)
NEWHOUSE UPHOLSTERY
Also Called: Newhouse Upholstery Mfg
2309 Edwards Ave, El Monte (91733-2041)
P.O. Box 3201 (91733-0201)
PHONE..................................626 444-1370
Ed Stevenson, *President*
Maria Stevenson, *Corp Secy*
EMP: 20 EST: 1953
SQ FT: 18,000
SALES (est): 3.1MM **Privately Held**
WEB: www.newhouserv.com
SIC: 2531 Vehicle furniture

(P-5024)
ORBO CORPORATION
Also Called: Eurotec Seating
1000 S Euclid St, La Habra (90631-6806)
PHONE..................................562 806-6171
Oscar Galvez, *President*
Ricardo Galvez, *Vice Pres*
EMP: 50
SALES (est): 2.4MM **Privately Held**
SIC: 2531 Seats, automobile

(P-5025)
PRIMED PRODUCTIONS INC
1443 E Washington Blvd, Pasadena
(91104-2650)
PHONE..................................626 216-5822
Jax Pascua, *President*
EMP: 18
SALES (est): 1.6MM **Privately Held**
SIC: 2531 Bleacher seating, portable

(P-5026)
REDART CORPORATION
Also Called: Beard Seats
2549 Eastbluff Dr, Newport Beach
(92660-3500)
PHONE..................................714 774-9444
Tim Sousamian, *President*
▲ EMP: 14
SQ FT: 10,000
SALES (est): 1.5MM **Privately Held**
WEB: www.redart.com
SIC: 2531 2298 Seats, automobile; cargo
nets

(P-5027)
SEATING CONCEPTS LLC
4229 Ponderosa Ave Ste B, San Diego
(92123-1519)
PHONE..................................619 491-3159
Juan Carlos Letayf, *Mng Member*
Craig Nichols, *Natl Sales Mgr*
Jose Letayf,
Bill Overton,
◆ EMP: 30
SALES (est): 6.8MM **Privately Held**
WEB: www.seatingconcepts.com
SIC: 2531 5021 Theater furniture; chairs

(P-5028)
SERIOUS ENERGY INC (PA)
Also Called: Serious Windows
1250 Elko Dr, Sunnyvale (94089-2213)
PHONE..................................408 541-8000
Kevin Surace, *CEO*
Mark Mitchell, *COO*
Russ Lampert, *CFO*
Sandra Vaughan, *Chief Mktg Ofcr*
Scott Morgan, *Senior VP*
▲ EMP: 55
SALES (est): 12.6MM **Privately Held**
WEB: www.quietsolution.com
SIC: 2531 Public building & related furni-
ture

(P-5029)
STEARNS PARK
Also Called: Long Beach City of
4520 E 23rd St, Long Beach (90815-1806)
PHONE..................................562 570-1685
Garcia Elyse, *Principal*
EMP: 30
SALES: 400K **Privately Held**
SIC: 2531 Picnic tables or benches, park

(P-5030)
TALIMAR SYSTEMS INC
3105 W Alpine St, Santa Ana (92704-6911)
PHONE..................................714 557-4884

David Wesdell, *President*
David G Wesdell, *President*
Jason Thies, *Vice Pres*
Rosario Hernandez, *Purchasing*
Mike Lee, *Mktg Dir*
▲ EMP: 37
SQ FT: 11,000
SALES (est): 6.2MM **Privately Held**
WEB: www.talimarsystems.com
SIC: 2531 5712 7389 5932 Public build-
ing & related furniture; furniture stores;
merchandise liquidators; office furniture,
secondhand

(P-5031)
VILLA FURNITURE MFG CO
Also Called: Villa International
13760 Midway St, Cerritos (90703-2331)
PHONE..................................714 535-7272
Andrew M Greenthal, *President*
John Hermosillo, *Plant Mgr*
▲ EMP: 125
SQ FT: 75,000
SALES (est): 24.2MM **Privately Held**
SIC: 2531 2522 Vehicle furniture; office
furniture, except wood

(P-5032)
VIRCO MFG CORPORATION (PA)
2027 Harpers Way, Torrance (90501-1524)
P.O. Box 44846, Los Angeles (90044-0846)
PHONE..................................310 533-0474
Robert A Virtue, *Ch of Bd*
Douglas A Virtue, *President*
J Scott Bell, *COO*
Robert E Dose, *CFO*
James D Johnson, *Chief Mktg Ofcr*
◆ EMP: 277
SQ FT: 560,000
SALES (est): 189.2MM **Publicly Held**
WEB: www.virco.com
SIC: 2531 2522 2511 School furniture;
chairs, portable folding; chairs, table &
arm; office furniture, except wood; chairs,
office: padded or plain, except wood; ta-
bles, office: except wood; wood house-
hold furniture

(P-5033)
YANFENG US AUTOMOTIVE
30559 San Antonio St, Hayward
(94544-7101)
PHONE..................................616 886-3622
Phillip George, *Branch Mgr*
EMP: 20 **Privately Held**
SIC: 2531 Seats, automobile
HQ: Yanfeng Us Automotive Interior Sys-
tems I Llc
41935 W 12 Mile Rd
Novi MI 48377
248 319-7333

┌─────────────────────────────┐
│ **2541 Wood, Office & Store** │
│ **Fixtures** │
└─────────────────────────────┘

(P-5034)
ALEMAD INC
2061 Freeway Dr Ste C, Woodland
(95776-9506)
PHONE..................................530 661-1697
Mike Ware, *President*
EMP: 40
SQ FT: 20,000
SALES (est): 3.5MM **Privately Held**
WEB: www.weretops.com
SIC: 2541 5999 1799 Counter & sink
tops; monuments & tombstones; counter
top installation

(P-5035)
ALL AMERICAN CABINETRY INC
Also Called: All American Sterile Coat
13901 Saticoy St, Van Nuys (91402-6521)
PHONE..................................818 376-0500
Chris Zepatos, *President*
EMP: 60
SALES (est): 6.3MM **Privately Held**
SIC: 2541 Cabinets, lockers & shelving

(P-5036)
AMTREND CORPORATION
1458 Manhattan Ave, Fullerton
(92831-5222)
PHONE..................................714 630-2070
Hamid A Malik, *President*
Javeeda Malik, *CEO*
Waseem Malik, *Officer*
Luis Orozco, *Plant Mgr*
Robert Flores, *Manager*
EMP: 85 EST: 1980
SQ FT: 45,000
SALES (est): 16.8MM **Privately Held**
WEB: www.amtrend.com
SIC: 2541 2521 7641 2512 Wood parti-
tions & fixtures; wood office furniture; up-
holstery work; upholstered household
furniture

(P-5037)
ARCHITECTURAL WOODWORKING CO
582 Monterey Pass Rd, Monterey Park
(91754-2417)
PHONE..................................626 570-4125
John K Heydorff, *President*
John F Heydorff, *Shareholder*
Thomas C Heydorff, *CFO*
Richard A Schaub, *Admin Sec*
Edward Illig, *Director*
EMP: 100 EST: 1963
SQ FT: 60,000
SALES (est): 14.4MM **Privately Held**
WEB: www.architecturalwoodwork.com
SIC: 2541 1751 Office fixtures, wood; cab-
inets, except refrigerated: show, display,
etc.: wood; display fixtures, wood; parti-
tions for floor attachment, prefabricated:
wood; carpentry work

(P-5038)
ARNOLD & EGAN MANUFACTURING CO
1515 Griffith St, San Francisco
(94124-3412)
PHONE..................................415 822-2700
Kenneth Egan, *CEO*
Rose Egan, *CFO*
Donna Egan, *Admin Sec*
EMP: 20
SQ FT: 10,000
SALES (est): 3.8MM **Privately Held**
SIC: 2541 2521 2434 2431 Wood parti-
tions & fixtures; wood office furniture;
wood kitchen cabinets; millwork

(P-5039)
ATLAS GRANITE & STONE
2560 Grennan Ct, Rancho Cordova
(95742-6318)
PHONE..................................916 638-7100
Steve Zabetian, *Owner*
▲ EMP: 10 EST: 2000
SQ FT: 7,000
SALES (est): 1.7MM **Privately Held**
WEB: www.atlasgranite.com
SIC: 2541 5722 Counter & sink tops;
kitchens, complete (sinks, cabinets, etc.)

(P-5040)
BLOCK TOPS INC (PA)
1321 S Sunkist St, Anaheim (92806-5614)
PHONE..................................714 978-5080
Vanessa Bates, *CEO*
Nate Kolenski, *President*
▲ EMP: 34 EST: 1977
SQ FT: 10,000
SALES (est): 8.2MM **Privately Held**
WEB: www.blocktops.com
SIC: 2541 2519 3281 2821 Table or
counter tops, plastic laminated; furniture,
household: glass, fiberglass & plastic; cut
stone & stone products; plastics materials
& resins

(P-5041)
BRIGGS & SONS
1225 E Macarthur St, Sonoma
(95476-3811)
P.O. Box 1469 (95476-1469)
PHONE..................................707 938-4325
Mike Briggs, *Owner*
Patricia Briggs, *Principal*
EMP: 11
SQ FT: 8,000

SALES: 1.3MM **Privately Held**
SIC: 2541 1751 Store fixtures, wood; cabinets, except refrigerated: show, display,
etc.: wood; cabinet & finish carpentry

(P-5042)
BRISTOL OMEGA INC
9441 Opal Ave Ste 2, Mentone
(92359-9900)
PHONE..................................909 794-6862
Ralf G Zacky, *CEO*
EMP: 27
SALES (est): 1.2MM **Privately Held**
SIC: 2541 1611 Wood partitions & fixtures;
general contractor, highway & street con-
struction

(P-5043)
CABINET COMPANY INC
Also Called: Complete Kitchen & Bath
416 Crown Point Cir Ste 7, Grass Valley
(95945-9558)
PHONE..................................530 273-7533
Joshua L Emrich, *President*
EMP: 10
SALES (est): 750K **Privately Held**
WEB: www.thecabinetcompany.com
SIC: 2541 2521 5211 1799 Cabinets,
lockers & shelving; office: wood; closets, interiors
& accessories; counter top installation;
cabinet & finish carpentry

(P-5044)
CALIFORNIA MFG CABINETRY INC
Also Called: C M C
1474 E Francis St, Ontario (91761-5791)
PHONE..................................909 930-3632
Miguel Jimenez, *President*
Mike Jimmez, *Vice Pres*
EMP: 15
SALES (est): 2MM **Privately Held**
SIC: 2541 2434 2431 Cabinets, except
refrigerated: show, display, etc.: wood;
wood kitchen cabinets; millwork

(P-5045)
CCM ENTERPRISES
9366 Abraham Way, Santee (92071-2861)
PHONE..................................619 562-2605
Cody Nosko, *Manager*
EMP: 10 **Privately Held**
WEB: www.ccmmfg.com
SIC: 2541 3083 Counter & sink tops; lami-
nated plastics plate & sheet
PA: Ccm Enterprises
10848 Wheatlands Ave
Santee CA 92071

(P-5046)
CCM ENTERPRISES (PA)
10848 Wheatlands Ave, Santee
(92071-2855)
PHONE..................................619 562-2605
Cody L Nosko, *CEO*
Duane Nosco, *Vice Pres*
Virginia Jaggi, *Admin Sec*
EMP: 60
SQ FT: 67,543
SALES (est): 7.6MM **Privately Held**
WEB: www.ccmmfg.com
SIC: 2541 1799 Counter & sink tops;
kitchen & bathroom remodeling; kitchen
cabinet installation

(P-5047)
CHICO CUSTOM COUNTER
3080 Thorntree Dr Ste 45, Chico
(95973-9503)
PHONE..................................530 894-8123
Shane Barker, *Owner*
EMP: 12
SQ FT: 6,000
SALES (est): 1MM **Privately Held**
SIC: 2541 Counters or counter display
cases, wood

▲ = Import ▼=Export
◆ =Import/Export

(P-5048)
CK MANUFACTURING AND TRADING
Also Called: Kosakura Associates
6 Piedmont, Trabuco Canyon
(92679-4219)
P.O. Box 1190, Sulphur Springs TX
(75483-1190)
PHONE...................................949 529-3400
Mark Bradley, *CEO*
Justin Becker, *President*
▲ EMP: 35 EST: 1999
SQ FT: 53,500
SALES (est): 5.8MM **Privately Held**
WEB: www.kosakura.com
SIC: 2541 Display fixtures, wood

(P-5049)
CLOSETS BY DESIGN INC
3860 Capitol Ave, City of Industry
(90601-1733)
PHONE...................................562 699-9945
Frank Melkonian, *President*
Gerard Thompson, *CFO*
EMP: 185
SALES (est): 20.7MM **Privately Held**
SIC: 2541 2521 Lockers, except refrigerated: wood; wood office filing cabinets & bookcases

(P-5050)
COLUMBIA SHOWCASE & CAB CO INC
11034 Sherman Way Ste A, Sun Valley
(91352-4915)
PHONE...................................818 765-9710
Samuel M Patterson Jr, *CEO*
James E Barnett, *Co-COB*
Samuel M Patterson Sr, *Co-COB*
Joe Patterson, *Senior VP*
James Haley, *Project Mgr*
▲ EMP: 125
SQ FT: 170,000
SALES (est): 26.5MM **Privately Held**
WEB: www.columbiashowcase.com
SIC: 2541 1542 Cabinets, except refrigerated: show, display, etc.: wood; commercial & office building contractors

(P-5051)
CTA FIXTURES INC
5721 Santa Ana St Ste B, Ontario
(91761-8617)
PHONE...................................909 390-6744
Carlos Gutierrez, *CEO*
▲ EMP: 62
SQ FT: 90,000
SALES (est): 9.6MM **Privately Held**
WEB: www.ctafixtures.com
SIC: 2541 Wood partitions & fixtures

(P-5052)
CUSTOM DISPLAYS INC
411 W 157th St, Gardena (90248-2118)
PHONE...................................323 770-8074
Thomas Otani, *President*
Ben Hasuike, *Vice Pres*
EMP: 30
SQ FT: 16,000
SALES (est): 3.7MM **Privately Held**
WEB: www.customdisplays.com
SIC: 2541 3827 3993 Display fixtures, wood; triplet magnifying instruments, optical; signs & advertising specialties

(P-5053)
DENNIS REEVES INC
Also Called: Reeves Enterprises
1350 Palomares St Ste A, La Verne
(91750-5230)
PHONE...................................909 392-9999
Dennis L Reeves, *President*
Denise Reeves, *CFO*
Brad Reeves, *Vice Pres*
EMP: 10
SQ FT: 20,000
SALES (est): 1.8MM **Privately Held**
SIC: 2541 1751 Store fixtures, wood; cabinet building & installation

(P-5054)
DESIGN WORKSHOPS
486 Lesser St, Oakland (94601-4902)
PHONE...................................510 434-0727
Richard G Bourdon, *President*

David Keystone, *CFO*
EMP: 10
SQ FT: 45,000
SALES (est): 1.8MM **Privately Held**
WEB: www.design-workshops.com
SIC: 2541 2521 2517 2434 Cabinets, except refrigerated: show, display, etc.: wood; wood office furniture; wood television & radio cabinets; wood kitchen cabinets

(P-5055)
DIMENSIONS UNLIMITED
1080 Nimitz Ave Ste 400, Vallejo
(94592-1009)
PHONE...................................707 552-6800
John Ewer, *President*
Jane Ewer, *Admin Sec*
EMP: 15
SQ FT: 9,300
SALES: 1.4MM **Privately Held**
WEB: www.dimensions-unlimited.com
SIC: 2541 1751 Cabinets, except refrigerated: show, display, etc.: wood; lockers, except refrigerated: wood; cabinet & finish carpentry; customized furniture & cabinets

(P-5056)
EL CERRITO WOODWORKING
4443 Carson St, Oakland (94619-2954)
PHONE...................................510 647-3767
Jack Moore, *President*
John Bray, *Treasurer*
Wes Richardson, *Vice Pres*
EMP: 10
SALES (est): 1MM **Privately Held**
SIC: 2541 Cabinets, except refrigerated: show, display, etc.: wood

(P-5057)
ELEMENTS MANUFACTURING INC
115 Harvey West Blvd C, Santa Cruz
(95060-2168)
PHONE...................................831 421-9440
Ken Ketch, *President*
Kristy Stormes, *Partner*
Alan Stormes, *Admin Sec*
EMP: 20
SQ FT: 15,000
SALES (est): 1.3MM **Privately Held**
WEB: www.elementsmfg.com
SIC: 2541 Cabinets, lockers & shelving; counter & sink tops

(P-5058)
EMERZIAN WOODWORKING INC
2555 N Argyle Ave, Fresno (93727-1378)
PHONE...................................559 292-2448
Tom Emerzian, *Owner*
EMP: 40
SQ FT: 46,000
SALES (est): 5.6MM **Privately Held**
WEB: www.emerzianwoodworking.com
SIC: 2541 2434 Showcases, except refrigerated: wood; wood kitchen cabinets

(P-5059)
EUROPEAN WHOLESALE COUNTER
10051 Prospect Ave, Santee (92071-4321)
PHONE...................................619 562-0565
Pete Sciarrino, *CEO*
EMP: 150
SQ FT: 40,000
SALES (est): 14.6MM **Privately Held**
SIC: 2541 1799 Counter & sink tops; cabinets, lockers & shelving; counter top installation

(P-5060)
F-J-E INC
Also Called: JF FIXTURES & DESIGN
546 W Esther St, Long Beach
(90813-1529)
PHONE...................................562 437-7466
Frank Ernandes, *President*
Barbara Ernandes, *Admin Sec*
EMP: 25
SQ FT: 26,000

SALES: 3.1MM **Privately Held**
WEB: www.jffixtures.com
SIC: 2541 2542 Store fixtures, wood; fixtures, store: except wood

(P-5061)
FAIRMONT GLOBAL LLC (PA)
Also Called: Fairmont Designs
2010 Jimmy Durante Blvd, Del Mar
(92014-2237)
PHONE...................................415 320-2929
Robert Shapiro,
Michael Shapiro,
Tery Young,
EMP: 10
SALES (est): 5.6MM **Privately Held**
SIC: 2541 7389 Store & office display cases & fixtures; design services

(P-5062)
FIXTURES BY DESIGN LLC
2951 Saturn St Ste Unitb, Brea
(92821-6206)
PHONE...................................714 572-5406
Lorrain Sandoval Obrien, *CEO*
Mark Cooper, *Vice Pres*
EMP: 15
SQ FT: 5,900
SALES: 1.4MM
SALES (corp-wide): 2.5MM **Privately Held**
SIC: 2541 Store fixtures, wood
PA: Obrien Systems Llc
21123 Via Santiago
Yorba Linda CA 92887
714 485-2179

(P-5063)
GOLDEN STATE GRANITE INC
1001 Shary Cir Ste 9, Concord
(94518-2419)
PHONE...................................925 825-5888
Henry Oscar Benning, *CEO*
Michael Lopez, *Principal*
EMP: 13
SALES (est): 1.5MM **Privately Held**
SIC: 2541 Counter & sink tops

(P-5064)
GREG IAN ISLANDS INC
Also Called: Igi
123b E Montecito Ave B, Sierra Madre
(91024-1923)
PHONE...................................626 355-0019
Greg Jorgenson, *President*
EMP: 20
SALES (est): 1.8MM **Privately Held**
SIC: 2541

(P-5065)
GRENEKER FURNITURE
3110 E 12th St, Los Angeles (90023-3616)
PHONE...................................323 263-9000
Erik Johnson, *Owner*
EMP: 30
SQ FT: 100,000
SALES (est): 3.4MM **Privately Held**
SIC: 2541 2542 Display fixtures, wood; fixtures: display, office or store: except wood

(P-5066)
H & M CABINET COMPANY
1565 La Mirada Dr, San Marcos
(92078-2425)
PHONE...................................760 744-0559
Hamilton L Hawkins Jr, *Owner*
EMP: 10
SALES (est): 640K **Privately Held**
SIC: 2541

(P-5067)
H AND M INDUSTRIES LLC
Also Called: Specialty Science Counter Tops
855 Rancho Conejo Blvd, Newbury Park
(91320-1714)
PHONE...................................805 499-5100
Steve Coats,
Mike Downey,
Mary Fields,
Gloria Kaiser,
EMP: 12
SQ FT: 15,000
SALES (est): 990K **Privately Held**
SIC: 2541 Table or counter tops, plastic laminated

(P-5068)
HEMISPHERE DESIGN & MFG LLC
25215 Rye Canyon Rd, Valencia
(91355-1203)
PHONE...................................661 294-9500
Timothy Arnold, *Mng Member*
EMP: 15 EST: 2013
SQ FT: 3,500
SALES: 3MM **Privately Held**
SIC: 2541 7389 Store & office display cases & fixtures; design services

(P-5069)
HERITAGE CABINET CO INC
21740 Marilla St, Chatsworth (91311-4125)
PHONE...................................818 786-4900
Robert Geyer, *Owner*
Kathy Geyer, *Corp Secy*
EMP: 12
SQ FT: 12,000
SALES (est): 1.4MM **Privately Held**
WEB: www.heritagecabinet.com
SIC: 2541 5211 2521 2517 Cabinets, except refrigerated: show, display, etc.: wood; lumber & other building materials; wood office furniture; wood television & radio cabinets; wood kitchen cabinets; millwork

(P-5070)
IDEAL PRODUCTS INC
4501 Etiwanda Ave, Mira Loma
(91752-1445)
P.O. Box 4090, Ontario (91761-1006)
PHONE...................................951 727-8600
Robert L Martin Jr, *CEO*
Virginia Martin, *Vice Pres*
Matt Hopkins, *Sales Staff*
Ruth Lomeli, *Cust Mgr*
EMP: 35
SQ FT: 20,000
SALES (est): 7MM **Privately Held**
WEB: www.idealockers.com
SIC: 2541 Lockers, except refrigerated: wood

(P-5071)
IVARS CABINET SHOP INC (PA)
Also Called: Ivar's Displays
2314 E Locust St, Ontario (91761-7637)
PHONE...................................909 923-2761
Ivan Gundersen, *President*
Karl Gundersen, *CEO*
Jason Gundersen, *CFO*
Linda Pulice, *Vice Pres*
Rose Marie Aunario, *Accounts Mgr*
▲ EMP: 109
SQ FT: 95,000
SALES: 16.3MM **Privately Held**
WEB: www.ivarsdisplay.com
SIC: 2541 2542 Store fixtures, wood; shelving, office & store: except wood

(P-5072)
J P B JEWELRY BOX CO (PA)
2428 Dallas St, Los Angeles (90031-1013)
PHONE...................................323 225-0500
Jerry Borodian, *Partner*
Josephine Borodian, *Partner*
▲ EMP: 15
SQ FT: 14,000
SALES: 1MM **Privately Held**
SIC: 2541 2441 3172 Wood partitions & fixtures; nailed wood boxes & shook; cases, jewelry

(P-5073)
JUDITH VON HOPF INC
8750 Prestige Ct, Rancho Cucamonga
(91730-5138)
PHONE...................................909 481-1884
Judith P Hopf, *CEO*
Shana Wardle, *Creative Dir*
Marsha Whitehead, *Sales Staff*
▲ EMP: 25
SQ FT: 7,500
SALES (est): 3.6MM **Privately Held**
WEB: www.judithvonhopf.com
SIC: 2541 Display fixtures, wood

(P-5074)
KALANICO INC
Also Called: Salsam Manufacturing Co
1036 Chantilly Cir, Santa Ana
(92705-6108)
PHONE....................714 532-5770
Carl Eisler, *President*
Donna Eisler, *Admin Sec*
EMP: 15 EST: 1971
SQ FT: 20,000
SALES: 750K Privately Held
WEB: www.salsam.com
SIC: 2541 Cabinets, except refrigerated:
show, display, etc.: wood; showcases, ex-
cept refrigerated: wood

(P-5075)
KEYS CABINETRY INC
20 Pimentel Ct Ste B14, Novato
(94949-5688)
PHONE....................415 382-1466
Steven Cheavacci, *President*
EMP: 10
SQ FT: 4,000
SALES (est): 730K Privately Held
SIC: 2541 Cabinets, except refrigerated:
show, display, etc.: wood

(P-5076)
KILLION INDUSTRIES INC (PA)
1380 Poinsettia Ave, Vista (92081-8504)
PHONE....................760 727-5102
Richard W Killion, *President*
Larry Edward, *Vice Pres*
▲ EMP: 80 EST: 1981
SQ FT: 185,000
SALES (est): 36.8MM Privately Held
SIC: 2541 Store & office display cases &
fixtures; display fixtures, wood; counters
or counter display cases, wood

(P-5077)
L & N FIXTURES INC
2214 Tyler Ave, El Monte (91733-2710)
PHONE....................323 686-0041
Louis Pierotti, *President*
EMP: 31 EST: 1970
SQ FT: 16,000
SALES: 2MM Privately Held
SIC: 2541 1799 2521 2434 Store fix-
tures, wood; office furniture installation;
wood office furniture; wood kitchen cabi-
nets

(P-5078)
LA CABINET & MILLWORK INC
Also Called: Bromack
3005 Humboldt St, Los Angeles
(90031-1830)
PHONE....................323 227-5000
Leonard Lumpkin, *President*
Kurt Webster, *Treasurer*
Oscar Gonzalez, *Vice Pres*
Robert Rieger, *Vice Pres*
Margie Esquivel, *Admin Sec*
EMP: 25
SQ FT: 17,000
SALES: 1MM Privately Held
SIC: 2541 1799 2434 1751 Counters or
counter display cases, wood; counter top
installation; wood kitchen cabinets; car-
pentry work

(P-5079)
LEGGETT & PLATT INCORPORATED
Also Called: Leggett & Platt 0302
29120 Commerce Center Dr # 1, Valencia
(91355-5404)
PHONE....................661 775-8500
EMP: 30
SALES (corp-wide): 3.7B Publicly Held
SIC: 2541
PA: Leggett & Platt, Incorporated
1 Leggett Rd
Carthage MO 64836
417 358-8131

(P-5080)
LEONARDS CARPET SERVICE INC (PA)
Also Called: Xgrass Turf Direct
1121 N Red Gum St, Anaheim
(92806-2582)
PHONE....................714 630-1930

Leonard Nagel, *President*
Joel Nagel, *CEO*
▲ EMP: 75
SQ FT: 52,000
SALES (est): 35.3MM Privately Held
WEB: www.lcsdesign.com
SIC: 2541 1771 1799 Table or counter
tops, plastic laminated; flooring contrac-
tor; artificial turf installation

(P-5081)
LRB MILLWORK & CASEWORK INC
2760 S Iowa Ave, Colton (92324-5801)
PHONE....................951 328-0105
Rene Alberto Bernhardt, *President*
EMP: 16
SQ FT: 34,979
SALES (est): 2.6MM Privately Held
SIC: 2541 Cabinets, except refrigerated:
show, display, etc.: wood

(P-5082)
MEYER & REEDER INC
1255 N Patt St, Anaheim (92801-2550)
PHONE....................714 388-0148
Jeff Oskin, *President*
Linda Oskin, *Corp Secy*
EMP: 13
SQ FT: 8,000
SALES (est): 2.6MM Privately Held
SIC: 2541 Bar fixtures, wood

(P-5083)
NETWORK TELEPHONE SERVICES INC (PA)
Also Called: N T S
21135 Erwin St, Woodland Hills
(91367-3713)
PHONE....................800 742-5687
Joseph Preston, *Ch of Bd*
Gary Passon, *President*
Dan Coleman, *Vice Pres*
Marlene Tanner, *Vice Pres*
Robert Juarez, *Supervisor*
EMP: 500
SQ FT: 70,000
SALES (est): 72MM Privately Held
WEB: nts.net/index.php
SIC: 2541 4813 Telephone booths, wood;

(P-5084)
NICO NAT MFG CORP
Also Called: Niconat Manufacturing
2624 Yates Ave, Commerce (90040-2622)
PHONE....................323 721-1900
Jose Valdez, *CEO*
Francisco Valdez, *Shareholder*
Valerie Castillo, *Assistant*
EMP: 45 EST: 2008
SALES (est): 8.7MM Privately Held
SIC: 2541 Store & office display cases &
fixtures

(P-5085)
NORTHBAY STONE WRKS CNTERTOPS
849 Sweetser Ave, Novato (94945-2428)
PHONE....................415 898-0200
Greg Palmer, *Partner*
Mark Miltenberger, *Partner*
EMP: 13
SQ FT: 5,000
SALES (est): 1.2MM Privately Held
WEB: www.nbstoneworks.com
SIC: 2541 5211 Counter & sink tops;
counter tops

(P-5086)
NYCETEK INC
Also Called: Rack Master
555 W Lambert Rd Ste F, Brea
(92821-3917)
PHONE....................714 671-3860
Nelson Chang, *President*
Yvonne Chang, *CFO*
▲ EMP: 10
SALES (est): 780K Privately Held
WEB: www.nycetek.com
SIC: 2541 Display fixtures, wood

(P-5087)
OAK-IT INC
845 Sandhill Ave, Carson (90746-1210)
P.O. Box 4733, Downey (90241-1733)
PHONE....................310 719-3999
Lori Barrett, *President*
Sean Kittiko, *Treasurer*
◆ EMP: 40
SQ FT: 8,000
SALES (est): 5.3MM Privately Held
SIC: 2541 2431 5046 Store fixtures,
wood; cabinets, except refrigerated:
show, display, etc.: wood; millwork; store
fixtures

(P-5088)
OLDE WORLD CORPORATION
Also Called: Great Spaces USA
360 Grogan Ave, Merced (95341-6446)
PHONE....................209 384-1337
Richard T Conas, *President*
Jan Conas, *Vice Pres*
Tom Siverly, *Accounts Mgr*
EMP: 20
SQ FT: 35,000
SALES (est): 3.9MM Privately Held
SIC: 2541 Store & office display cases &
fixtures

(P-5089)
OMNI ENCLOSURES INC
Also Called: Omni Pacific
505 Raleigh Ave, El Cajon (92020-3139)
PHONE....................619 579-6664
Thomas P Burke, *President*
Amber Frye, *Vice Pres*
Tara Burke, *General Mgr*
Tracey Mendoza, *Info Tech Mgr*
Jorge Frayre, *Production*
▲ EMP: 27
SQ FT: 20,000
SALES (est): 4.3MM Privately Held
WEB: www.omnipacific.com
SIC: 2541 Office fixtures, wood

(P-5090)
OTANEZ NEW CREATIONS
7179 E Columbus Dr, Anaheim
(92807-4530)
PHONE....................951 808-9663
Joe Otanez, *President*
Olga Otanez, *Treasurer*
EMP: 13
SQ FT: 10,000
SALES (est): 1.1MM Privately Held
SIC: 2541 1751 Wood partitions & fixtures;
cabinet & finish carpentry

(P-5091)
PACIFIC WESTLINE INC
1536 W Embassy St, Anaheim
(92802-1016)
PHONE....................714 956-2442
Daniel G McLeith, *CEO*
John Lara, *Office Mgr*
EMP: 90
SQ FT: 62,000
SALES (est): 13.2MM Privately Held
WEB: www.pacificwestline.com
SIC: 2541 2431 Cabinets, except refriger-
ated: show, display, etc.: wood; millwork

(P-5092)
PAZZULLA PLASTICS INC
165 Emilia Ln, Fallbrook (92028-2686)
PHONE....................714 847-2541
Sam Pazzulla, *Owner*
EMP: 20
SQ FT: 7,800
SALES (est): 1.4MM Privately Held
WEB: www.pazzullaplastics.com
SIC: 2541 Table or counter tops, plastic
laminated

(P-5093)
PG EMMINGER INC
4036 Pacheco Blvd A, Martinez
(94553-2224)
PHONE....................925 313-5830
Philip G Emminger, *President*
Mike Graham, *Project Mgr*
Rod Hoffman, *Project Mgr*
Herb Deegroot, *Foreman/Supr*
EMP: 22
SQ FT: 10,000

SALES (est): 3.8MM Privately Held
SIC: 2541 Wood partitions & fixtures

(P-5094)
PLANET ONE PRODUCTS INC (PA)
Also Called: Le Cache Premium Wine Cabi-
nets
1445 N Mcdowell Blvd, Petaluma
(94954-6516)
PHONE....................707 794-8000
Ben Z Argov, *President*
Bruce Kirsten, *Treasurer*
Keith Sedwick, *Vice Pres*
Doug McAlpine, *Engineer*
▲ EMP: 27
SQ FT: 18,000
SALES (est): 4.8MM Privately Held
WEB: www.lecache.com
SIC: 2541 Cabinets, except refrigerated:
show, display, etc.: wood

(P-5095)
PRECISION SURFACES INC
8081 Orangethorpe Ave, Buena Park
(90621-3801)
PHONE....................951 680-9279
Marc Salveson, *President*
EMP: 30
SALES (est): 3.6MM Privately Held
SIC: 2541 1799 Counters or counter dis-
play cases, wood; counter top installation

(P-5096)
PYRAMID SYSTEMS INC
10105 8 3/4 Ave, Hanford (93230-4769)
PHONE....................559 582-9345
David Gunter, *President*
Lori Pollard, *Exec VP*
Amber Ratt, *Admin Sec*
EMP: 25
SQ FT: 12,000
SALES (est): 3.5MM Privately Held
SIC: 2541 Wood partitions & fixtures

(P-5097)
QUALITY COUNTERTOPS INC
17853 Santiago Blvd # 107, Villa Park
(92861-4113)
PHONE....................909 597-6888
Rick Rambo, *President*
Tammy Rambo, *Vice Pres*
EMP: 15
SQ FT: 14,000
SALES (est): 2MM Privately Held
SIC: 2541 1799 Wood partitions & fixtures;
counter top installation

(P-5098)
RON & DIANA VANATTA
Also Called: R C I
332 Sacramento St, Auburn (95603-5510)
PHONE....................530 888-0200
Ron Vannatta, *Owner*
Diana Vannatta, *Co-Owner*
EMP: 14
SQ FT: 5,000
SALES (est): 1.6MM Privately Held
WEB: www.rcitops.com
SIC: 2541 5211 1799 1751 Table or
counter tops, plastic laminated; cabinets,
kitchen; counter top installation; cabinet &
finish carpentry

(P-5099)
SCIENTIFIC SURFACE INDS INC
Also Called: Ssi Surfaces
855 Rancho Conejo Blvd, Newbury Park
(91320-1714)
PHONE....................805 499-5100
David Marquez, *Vice Pres*
EMP: 18
SQ FT: 10,000
SALES (est): 1MM Privately Held
SIC: 2541 Counter & sink tops

(P-5100)
SHASTA WOOD PRODUCTS
19751 Hirsch Ct, Anderson (96007-4945)
P.O. Box 1101, Cottonwood (96022-1101)
PHONE....................530 378-6880
Jeff Aboud, *President*
Tamara Aboud, *CEO*
Cheryl Aboud, *Treasurer*
Thomas Aboud, *Vice Pres*
EMP: 20 EST: 1986

▲ = Import ▼=Export ◆ =Import/Export

SQ FT: 12,000
SALES (est): 3.9MM **Privately Held**
WEB: www.shastawoodproducts.com
SIC: 2541 2499 2434 Cabinets, lockers &
shelving; counter & sink tops; kitchen,
bathroom & household ware: wood; wood
kitchen cabinets

(P-5101)
SHOW OFFS
1696 W Mill St Unit 10, Colton
(92324-1074)
PHONE..................................909 885-5223
Dave Snavely, *Owner*
EMP: 23
SQ FT: 18,000
SALES (est): 2.4MM **Privately Held**
WEB: www.showoffsdisplay.com
SIC: 2541 2542 5046 Display fixtures,
wood; racks, merchandise display or stor-
age: except wood; store fixtures

(P-5102)
SISTONE INC
15530 Lanark St, Van Nuys (91406-1411)
PHONE..................................818 988-9918
Yair Sisso, *President*
Sharon Sisso, *CFO*
Arthur Sistone, *Technology*
Angelo Nuguid, *Safety Dir*
EMP: 30
SALES (est): 4.3MM **Privately Held**
WEB: www.sistoneinc.com-.gif
SIC: 2541 Counter & sink tops

(P-5103)
SPALINGER ENTERPRISES INC
Also Called: Skyline Cabinet & Millworks
800 S Mount Vernon Ave, Bakersfield
(93307-2889)
PHONE..................................661 834-4550
David Spalinger, *President*
Melody Spalinger, *Treasurer*
J W Spalinger, *Vice Pres*
▲ EMP: 12
SQ FT: 8,500
SALES (est): 1.5MM **Privately Held**
SIC: 2541 Cabinets, except refrigerated:
show, display, etc.: wood

(P-5104)
SPOONERS WOODWORKS INC
12460 Kirkham Ct, Poway (92064-6819)
PHONE..................................858 679-9086
Tom Spooner, *President*
Thomas Spooner, *CEO*
Valerie Spooner, *Treasurer*
Stephen Spooner, *Vice Pres*
Rosemary Spooner, *Admin Sec*
EMP: 85
SQ FT: 22,000
SALES (est): 17.3MM **Privately Held**
WEB: www.spoonerwoodworks.com
SIC: 2541 Store fixtures, wood

(P-5105)
SUBA MFG INC
921 Bayshore Rd, Benicia (94510-2990)
PHONE..................................707 745-0358
Jack Bell, *President*
Sue Bell, *Admin Sec*
Scott Cody, *Marketing Staff*
EMP: 23
SQ FT: 40,000
SALES (est): 3.8MM **Privately Held**
SIC: 2541 3083 Table or counter tops,
plastic laminated; laminated plastics plate
& sheet

(P-5106)
SULLIVAN COUNTER TOPS INC
1189 65th St, Oakland (94608-1108)
PHONE..................................510 652-2337
Thomas C Sullivan, *President*
Stacey Steele, *Opers Mgr*
EMP: 26
SQ FT: 10,000
SALES (est): 4.4MM **Privately Held**
WEB: www.sullivancountertops.com
SIC: 2541 2821 Counter & sink tops; table
or counter tops, plastic laminated; plastics
materials & resins

(P-5107)
SURFACE TECHNIQUES CORPORATION (PA)
Also Called: Surface Technology
25673 Nickel Pl, Hayward (94545-3221)
PHONE..................................510 887-6000
Howard Berger, *President*
EMP: 30
SQ FT: 13,000
SALES (est): 21.7MM **Privately Held**
SIC: 2541 Counters or counter display
cases, wood

(P-5108)
SW FIXTURES INC
3940 Valley Blvd Ste C, Walnut
(91789-1541)
PHONE..................................909 595-2506
Daniel Zachary, *President*
Daniel Farinella, *Design Engr*
Brian Welsh, *Opers Mgr*
EMP: 18
SQ FT: 22,500
SALES (est): 3.4MM **Privately Held**
SIC: 2541 2431 Display fixtures, wood;
planing mill, millwork

(P-5109)
T M COBB COMPANY
Also Called: Haley Brothers
1592 E San Bernardino Ave, San
Bernardino (92408-2929)
PHONE..................................909 796-6969
Thomas J Cobb, *Branch Mgr*
Bob Filter, *Manager*
EMP: 150
SQ FT: 1,000
SALES (corp-wide): 92.5MM **Privately Held**
WEB: www.tmcobbco.com
SIC: 2541 2431 5211 Wood partitions &
fixtures; millwork; door & window products
PA: T. M. Cobb Company
500 Palmyrita Ave
Riverside CA 92507
951 248-2400

(P-5110)
TAMALPAIS COML CABINETRY INC
200 9th St, Richmond (94801-3146)
P.O. Box 2169 (94802-1169)
PHONE..................................510 231-6800
John Kenner, *President*
EMP: 30
SQ FT: 23,000
SALES (est): 5.2MM **Privately Held**
WEB: www.tamcab.com
SIC: 2541 Cabinets, lockers & shelving

(P-5111)
TECHNIQUE DESIGNS INC
63665 19th Ave, North Palm Springs
(92258)
P.O. Box 550, Morongo Valley (92256-
0550)
PHONE..................................760 904-6223
Bruce Watts, *President*
Danelle Watts, *Admin Sec*
EMP: 14
SQ FT: 6,000
SALES (est): 3.2MM **Privately Held**
SIC: 2541 Wood partitions & fixtures

(P-5112)
TEMEKA ADVERTISING INC
Also Called: Temeka Group
9073 Pulsar Ct, Corona (92883-7357)
PHONE..................................951 277-2525
Michael D Wilson, *CEO*
Paul Mieboer, *Shareholder*
Marlene Kelly, *CFO*
EMP: 55
SQ FT: 24,000
SALES: 10MM **Privately Held**
SIC: 2541 Store & office display cases &
fixtures

(P-5113)
TONY GLAZING SPECIALTIES CO
Also Called: Fixtures Unlimited
13011 S Normandie Ave, Gardena
(90249-2125)
PHONE..................................323 770-8400

Tony Bressickello Sr, *President*
Anthony Bressickello Jr, *Corp Secy*
EMP: 10 EST: 1946
SQ FT: 15,000
SALES (est): 1.1MM **Privately Held**
SIC: 2541 1542 7922 Store fixtures,
wood; commercial & office building, new
construction; commercial & office build-
ings, renovation & repair; theatrical rental
services

(P-5114)
TROSAK CABINETS INC
1478 Alpine Pl, San Marcos (92078-3801)
PHONE..................................760 744-9042
Matthew Trosak, *President*
Richard Trosak, *Vice Pres*
EMP: 16
SQ FT: 9,500
SALES (est): 2.3MM **Privately Held**
WEB: www.trosak.com
SIC: 2541 1751 Cabinets, except refriger-
ated: show, display, etc.: wood; cabinet &
finish carpentry

(P-5115)
V TWEST INC
16222 Phoebe Ave, La Mirada
(90638-5610)
PHONE..................................714 521-2167
Douglas Edward Clausen, *Branch Mgr*
EMP: 12
SALES (corp-wide): 197.8MM **Privately Held**
SIC: 2541 Counter & sink tops
HQ: V T.West Inc.
1000 Industrial Park
Holstein IA 51025

(P-5116)
VIEW RITE MANUFACTURING
455 Allan St, Daly City (94014-1627)
PHONE..................................415 468-3856
Brad Somberg, *President*
Nha Nguyen, *Vice Pres*
EMP: 50
SQ FT: 78,000
SALES (est): 8MM **Privately Held**
SIC: 2541 2542 Store fixtures, wood; fix-
tures, store: except wood

(P-5117)
VSS COUNTERTOPS INC
7640 Wilbur Way, Sacramento
(95828-4928)
PHONE..................................916 681-8677
Duane Tucker, *President*
Marcia S Tucker, *Corp Secy*
Maria Dodson, *Manager*
Terry Koh, *Manager*
▲ EMP: 25
SQ FT: 16,000
SALES (est): 5MM **Privately Held**
WEB: www.vsscountertops.com
SIC: 2541 Counter & sink tops

(P-5118)
WALLACE WOOD PRODUCTS
Also Called: Corte Custom Case
1247 S Buena Vista St C, San Jacinto
(92583-4664)
PHONE..................................951 654-9311
Roy Wallace, *Owner*
EMP: 12 **Privately Held**
SIC: 2541 Wood partitions & fixtures
PA: Wallace Wood Products
1247 S Buena Vista St C
San Jacinto CA 92583

(P-5119)
WEST COAST FIXTURES INC (PA)
511 Stone Rd, Benicia (94510-1113)
PHONE..................................707 752-6373
Rick D Dade, *President*
Barry Nash, *Vice Pres*
EMP: 45
SQ FT: 12,500
SALES: 12MM **Privately Held**
SIC: 2541 Display fixtures, wood

(P-5120)
WOODLAND PRODUCTS CO INC
10825 7th St Ste C, Rancho Cucamonga
(91730-5402)
PHONE..................................909 622-3456
Frank Robertson, *President*
Judith Louise Robertson, *Treasurer*
EMP: 10 EST: 1959
SQ FT: 50,000
SALES (est): 1.2MM **Privately Held**
SIC: 2541 Wood partitions & fixtures

(P-5121)
WOODSMITHS ARCHITECTURAL CASEW
2709 Del Monte St, West Sacramento
(95691-3811)
PHONE..................................916 456-8871
Eric Smith, *CEO*
Anthony Anderson, *Principal*
EMP: 13
SALES (est): 2.2MM **Privately Held**
WEB: www.woodsmiths.biz
SIC: 2541 Cabinets, except refrigerated:
show, display, etc.: wood

(P-5122)
YOSHIMASA DISPLAY CASE INC
108 Pico St, Pomona (91766-2137)
PHONE..................................213 637-9999
Toro Hayashi, *President*
Michael Y Yoo, *Principal*
Alma Kim, *Manager*
▲ EMP: 35 EST: 2011
SQ FT: 15,000
SALES: 2.5MM **Privately Held**
SIC: 2541 3564 Store & office display
cases & fixtures; aircurtains (blower)

2542 Partitions & Fixtures, Except Wood

(P-5123)
ABTECH INCORPORATED
3420 W Fordham Ave, Santa Ana
(92704-4422)
PHONE..................................714 550-9961
James Herr, *CEO*
Cheryl Herr, *Treasurer*
▲ EMP: 21
SQ FT: 11,000
SALES (est): 4.1MM **Privately Held**
WEB: www.abtech.net
SIC: 2542 3448 Partitions & fixtures, ex-
cept wood; prefabricated metal buildings;
buildings, portable: prefabricated metal;
panels for prefabricated metal buildings

(P-5124)
ACCURATE LAMINATED PDTS INC
1826 Dawns Way, Fullerton (92831-5323)
PHONE..................................714 632-2773
Daniel Dunn, *President*
Patricia Dunn, *Vice Pres*
Karen Evans, *Project Mgr*
Brian Vigneault, *Project Mgr*
Michael Clark, *Project Engr*
EMP: 30
SQ FT: 5,000
SALES (est): 5.1MM **Privately Held**
WEB: www.accuratelaminated.com
SIC: 2542 Bar fixtures, except wood; cabi-
nets: show, display or storage: except
wood

(P-5125)
ADVANCED EQUIPMENT CORPORATION (PA)
2401 W Commonwealth Ave, Fullerton
(92833-2999)
PHONE..................................714 635-5350
Wesley B Dickson, *Owner*
W Dickson, *President*
W Scott Dickson, *CEO*
Lynn Stanco, *Corp Secy*
Frank Manning, *Senior VP*
◆ EMP: 50
SQ FT: 51,000

SALES (est): 10.9MM **Privately Held**
SIC: **2542** Partitions for floor attachment, prefabricated: except wood; wood partitions & fixtures

(P-5126)
ALFRED PICON
Also Called: Superior Manufacturing
7644 Emil Ave, Bell (90201-4940)
PHONE..............................562 928-2561
Alfred Picon, *Owner*
EMP: 14
SQ FT: 7,000
SALES (est): 810K **Privately Held**
SIC: **2542** Showcases (not refrigerated): except wood; stands, merchandise display: except wood

(P-5127)
BRIAN KLAAS INC
11101 Tuxford St, Sun Valley (91352-2632)
PHONE..............................818 394-9881
Brian Klaas, *President*
EMP: 10
SALES (est): 951.2K **Privately Held**
SIC: **2542** Cabinets: show, display or storage: except wood

(P-5128)
BRITCAN INC
Also Called: Rich Limited
3809 Ocean Ranch Blvd # 110, Oceanside (92056-8606)
PHONE..............................760 722-2300
James B Hollen, *CEO*
◆ EMP: 20
SQ FT: 23,000
SALES (est): 5.1MM **Privately Held**
WEB: www.richltd.com
SIC: **2542** 3089 Racks, merchandise display or storage: except wood; air mattresses, plastic

(P-5129)
BURKE DISPLAY SYSTEMS INC
55 S Peak, Laguna Niguel (92677-2903)
PHONE..............................949 248-0091
Robert Burke, *President*
EMP: 35
SQ FT: 1,000
SALES (est): 400.2K **Privately Held**
WEB: www.burkedisplays.us
SIC: **2542** Fixtures, store: except wood

(P-5130)
CAL PARTITIONS INC
23814 President Ave, Harbor City (90710-1390)
PHONE..............................310 539-1911
Alan Anderson, *President*
Sarah Anderson, *Treasurer*
Keith Peckham, *VP Sls/Mktg*
EMP: 19 EST: 1959
SQ FT: 13,000
SALES (est): 2.3MM **Privately Held**
WEB: www.calpartitions.com
SIC: **2542** 5046 3231 2631 Partitions for floor attachment, prefabricated: except wood; partitions; products of purchased glass; paperboard mills; wood partitions & fixtures; office furniture, except wood

(P-5131)
CALIFORNIA COUNTERTOP INC (PA)
7811 Alvarado Rd, La Mesa (91942-0665)
PHONE..............................619 460-0205
Wayne J Krumenacker, *President*
Christine Mori, *Sales Staff*
EMP: 20
SQ FT: 8,300
SALES (est): 2.7MM **Privately Held**
WEB: www.californiacountertop.com
SIC: **2542** 1799 2541 5211 Counters or counter display cases: except wood; counter top installation; wood partitions & fixtures; cabinets, kitchen

(P-5132)
CARDENAS ENTERPRISES INC
Also Called: J C Rack Systems
5232 Alcoa Ave, Vernon (90058-3710)
PHONE..............................323 588-0137
John Cardenas, *President*
Maria Cardenas, *Vice Pres*
EMP: 17 EST: 1977

SQ FT: 19,992
SALES (est): 1MM **Privately Held**
WEB: www.versatilegunrack.com
SIC: **2542** Garment racks: except wood

(P-5133)
CCI MAIL & SHIPPING SYSTEMS
Also Called: C C I Mling-Shipping Eqp Suppl
369 Estrella St, Ventura (93003)
PHONE..............................805 658-9123
Annette Klein, *Partner*
Paul Klein, *Partner*
EMP: 10
SALES (est): 1.1MM **Privately Held**
SIC: **2542** 5044 Postal lock boxes, mail racks & related products; mailing machines

(P-5134)
COIN GLLERY OF SAN FRNCSCO INC
Also Called: Presentation Systems
951 Hensley St, Richmond (94801-2114)
PHONE..............................510 236-8882
Cory Marcus, *President*
Jim Blake, *Vice Pres*
Fancisco Mejia, *Vice Pres*
EMP: 19
SQ FT: 25,000
SALES (est): 10MM **Privately Held**
SIC: **2542** 3999 3131 Stands, merchandise display: except wood; coins & tokens, non-currency; inner parts for shoes

(P-5135)
CRYSTOLON INC
7223 Sycamore St, Commerce (90040-2713)
P.O. Box 58323, Los Angeles (90058-0323)
PHONE..............................323 725-3482
Marki Leonard, *President*
Russell R Moore, *Corp Secy*
EMP: 50
SQ FT: 13,000
SALES (est): 4.3MM **Privately Held**
SIC: **2542** 5046 Fixtures, store: except wood; store fixtures

(P-5136)
CUTTING EDGE CREATIVE LLC
8155 Byron Rd, Whittier (90606-2615)
PHONE..............................562 907-7007
Jennifer Franklin, *Mng Member*
Daniel Esquer, *Prdtn Mgr*
Ward Lookabaugh,
Jennifer Stark, *Manager*
▲ EMP: 75
SQ FT: 40,000
SALES (est): 12.3MM **Privately Held**
WEB: www.weldedfixtures.com
SIC: **2542** 3496 7319 Racks, merchandise display or storage: except wood; miscellaneous fabricated wire products; display advertising service

(P-5137)
DESIGN IMAGERY
3621 Ortega St, San Francisco (94122-4033)
PHONE..............................650 589-6464
Jordan Kwan, *Owner*
EMP: 10
SQ FT: 7,000
SALES: 1MM **Privately Held**
WEB: www.designimagery.com
SIC: **2542**

(P-5138)
DURACITE
Also Called: Mark One Counter Top Designs
2636 N Argyle Ave, Fresno (93727-1303)
PHONE..............................559 346-1181
Fadi Halabi, *CEO*
EMP: 10
SQ FT: 2,700
SALES (est): 609K **Privately Held**
SIC: **2542** Counters or counter display cases: except wood

(P-5139)
FELBRO INC
3666 E Olympic Blvd, Los Angeles (90023-3147)
PHONE..............................323 263-8686
Howard Feldner, *Ch of Bd*
Norman Feldner, *CEO*

Conrad Natac, *Controller*
Jeffrey Feldner, *VP Mfg*
Maria Sotelo, *Traffic Mgr*
▲ EMP: 180
SQ FT: 75,000
SALES (est): 39.6MM **Privately Held**
WEB: www.felbro-inc.com
SIC: **2542** Racks, merchandise display or storage: except wood

(P-5140)
FOX MERCHANDISING INTL INC
Also Called: Fox Marble & Granite
1315 Armstrong Ave, San Francisco (94124-3608)
PHONE..............................415 671-0635
Charles McLaughlin, *President*
Raquel Jones, *General Mgr*
◆ EMP: 122
SQ FT: 16,613
SALES (est): 22.1MM **Privately Held**
WEB: www.fox-marble.com
SIC: **2542** 5032 Counters or counter display cases: except wood; marble building stone

(P-5141)
GEO A DIACK INC
1250 S Johnson Dr, City of Industry (91745-2481)
PHONE..............................626 961-2491
Thomas Gonzalez, *President*
Consuelo Diack, *Vice Pres*
EMP: 32
SQ FT: 30,000
SALES (est): 5.3MM **Privately Held**
WEB: www.showcasesbydiack.com
SIC: **2542** Fixtures: display, office or store: except wood

(P-5142)
GIANNELLI CABINET MFG CO
8835 Shirley Ave, Northridge (91324-3412)
PHONE..............................818 882-9787
John Giannelli, *President*
EMP: 10
SQ FT: 17,000
SALES (est): 1.5MM **Privately Held**
SIC: **2542** 1751 2541 2434 Cabinets: show, display or storage: except wood; cabinet & finish carpentry; wood partitions & fixtures; wood kitchen cabinets

(P-5143)
GLOBAL STEEL PRODUCTS CORP
Also Called: Global Specialties Direct
936 61st St, Oakland (94608-1307)
PHONE..............................510 652-2060
Steve Allen, *Manager*
Jill Morley, *Technology*
EMP: 25
SQ FT: 13,600
SALES (corp-wide): 201.6MM **Privately Held**
WEB: www.globalpartitions.com
SIC: **2542** 5023 5021 5046 Partitions for floor attachment, prefabricated: except wood; home furnishings; furniture; partitions
HQ: Global Steel Products Corp
    95 Marcus Blvd
    Deer Park NY 11729
    631 586-3455

(P-5144)
HANNIBAL MATERIAL HANDLING
2230 E 38th St, Vernon (90058-1629)
PHONE..............................323 587-4060
Blanton Bartlett, *President*
Heidy Moon, *Vice Pres*
Steve Roger, *Vice Pres*
▼ EMP: 214
SQ FT: 163,000
SALES (est): 40.4MM
SALES (corp-wide): 62.9MM **Privately Held**
WEB: www.hannibalindustries.com
SIC: **2542** Partitions & fixtures, except wood
PA: Hannibal Industries, Inc.
    3851 S Santa Fe Ave
    Vernon CA 90058
    323 513-1200

(P-5145)
HUFCOR CALIFORNIA INC (HQ)
Also Called: Hufcor Airwall Since 1900
2380 E Artesia Blvd, Long Beach (90805-1708)
PHONE..............................562 634-3116
Andy Espineira, *President*
J Michael Borden, *CEO*
Mike Borden, *Chairman*
Frank Scott, *Treasurer*
Scott Goza, *Sales Mgr*
EMP: 56
SQ FT: 87,000
SALES (est): 49.2MM
SALES (corp-wide): 233MM **Privately Held**
SIC: **2542** 5046 Partitions & fixtures, except wood; partitions
PA: Hufcor, Inc.
    2101 Kennedy Rd
    Janesville WI 53545
    608 756-1241

(P-5146)
IDX CORPORATION
5655 Silver Creek Vly Rd, San Jose (95138-2473)
PHONE..............................408 270-8094
Carl Vitale, *Principal*
EMP: 122
SALES (corp-wide): 394.6MM **Privately Held**
SIC: **2542** Office & store showcases & display fixtures
PA: Idx Corporation
    1 Rider Trail Plaza Dr
    Earth City MO 63045
    314 739-4120

(P-5147)
IMPERIAL SHADE VENETIAN BLIND
Also Called: Imperial Shade Venetian Blind
909 E 59th St, Los Angeles (90001-1007)
PHONE..............................323 233-4391
Sue Joe, *Branch Mgr*
EMP: 10
SALES (corp-wide): 9.2MM **Privately Held**
SIC: **2542** 1541 Counters or counter display cases: except wood; industrial buildings & warehouses
PA: Imperial Shade And Venetian Blind Co.
    4362 S Broadway
    Los Angeles CA 90037
    323 232-4901

(P-5148)
INTERIOR CORNER USA INC
2714 Stingle Ave, Rosemead (91770-3329)
PHONE..............................626 452-8833
Jacob Tsang-CHI Poon, *President*
▲ EMP: 10 EST: 2003
SQ FT: 10,052
SALES (est): 1.1MM **Privately Held**
SIC: **2542** Fixtures, office: except wood

(P-5149)
JCM INDUSTRIES INC (PA)
Also Called: Advance Storage Products
15302 Pipeline Ln, Huntington Beach (92649-1138)
PHONE..............................714 902-9000
John V Krummell, *President*
Ken Blankenhorn, *President*
Charles Kish, *CFO*
Tj Imholte, *Vice Pres*
Chris Krummell, *Info Tech Mgr*
▼ EMP: 21
SQ FT: 10,000
SALES (est): 34.9MM **Privately Held**
WEB: www.rackbargains.com
SIC: **2542** Racks, merchandise display or storage: except wood

(P-5150)
JOHNS FORMICA SHOP INC
2439 Piner Rd, Santa Rosa (95403-2356)
PHONE..............................707 544-8585
John Deas, *President*
Ellen Deas, *Vice Pres*
EMP: 15
SQ FT: 4,500

SALES (est): 2.5MM **Privately Held**
WEB: www.johnsformicashop.com
SIC: 2542 2434 Counters or counter display cases: except wood; wood kitchen cabinets

(P-5151)
M S F INC
1100 Industrial Rd Ste 18, San Carlos (94070-4131)
PHONE...................................650 592-0239
Sabino F Madariaga, *President*
Mike Jaca, *Vice Pres*
Brian Madariaga, *Vice Pres*
EMP: 12
SALES: 3MM **Privately Held**
WEB: www.msf.net
SIC: 2542 Partitions & fixtures, except wood

(P-5152)
M3 PRODUCTS INC
Also Called: J Roberts Design
335 N Puente St Ste E, Brea (92821-5274)
PHONE...................................626 371-1900
Heejung Yu, *President*
EMP: 15
SALES (est): 1.9MM **Privately Held**
SIC: 2542 Fixtures, store: except wood

(P-5153)
MAGNA-POLE PRODUCTS INC (PA)
Also Called: Hang-UPS Unlimited
1904 14th St Ste 107, Santa Monica (90404-4600)
PHONE...................................310 453-3806
Scott Freeman, *President*
◆ EMP: 16 EST: 1962
SQ FT: 15,000
SALES (est): 2.6MM **Privately Held**
WEB: www.hangups.com
SIC: 2542 Partitions & fixtures, except wood

(P-5154)
MERCHANDISING SYSTEMS INC
31801 Hayman St, Hayward (94544-7924)
P.O. Box 2423, Union City (94587-7423)
PHONE...................................510 477-9100
Kyle Robinson, *President*
Mary Lynn Robinson, *Treasurer*
▲ EMP: 50
SALES (est): 5.8MM **Privately Held**
WEB: www.msmdisplays.com
SIC: 2542 Partitions & fixtures, except wood

(P-5155)
MICHAEL T MINGIONE
Also Called: 2 Spec Mfg
2885 Aiello Dr Ste D, San Jose (95111-2188)
PHONE...................................408 365-1544
Michael Mingione, *Owner*
EMP: 10
SQ FT: 34,000
SALES: 1MM **Privately Held**
SIC: 2542 Postal lock boxes, mail racks & related products

(P-5156)
MULTIMEDIA OPERATIONS DESIGN (PA)
Also Called: Castle Design & Fabrication
3816 Medford St, Los Angeles (90063-1941)
PHONE...................................818 848-1303
Stefan Castle, *Mng Member*
Tanja Serpieri, *Mng Member*
EMP: 20 EST: 2006
SQ FT: 6,000
SALES (est): 3.2MM **Privately Held**
SIC: 2542 Bar fixtures, except wood

(P-5157)
NEW GREENSCREEN INCORPORATED
Also Called: Impac International
5500 Jurupa St, Ontario (91761-3668)
PHONE...................................800 767-9378
Kory Levoy, *Branch Mgr*
EMP: 20 **Privately Held**
WEB: www.pmpwest.com

SIC: 2542 3444 Cabinets: show, display or storage: except wood; sheet metalwork
PA: New Greenscreen, Incorporated
5500 Jurupa St
Ontario CA 91761

(P-5158)
ONQ SOLUTIONS INC (PA)
24540 Clawiter Rd, Hayward (94545-2222)
PHONE...................................650 262-4150
Paul Chapuis, *President*
Alan Garrison, *CFO*
Laura Metz, *Vice Pres*
EMP: 31
SQ FT: 1,700
SALES (est): 5MM **Privately Held**
SIC: 2542 Stands, merchandise display: except wood

(P-5159)
PACIFIC FIXTURE COMPANY INC
12860 San Fernando Rd B1, Sylmar (91342-3786)
PHONE...................................818 362-2130
Keith Stark, *President*
EMP: 14
SQ FT: 15,000
SALES: 2.6MM **Privately Held**
WEB: www.pacificfixture.com
SIC: 2542 Partitions & fixtures, except wood

(P-5160)
PACIFIC MANUFACTURING MGT INC
Also Called: Greneker Solutions
3110 E 12th St, Los Angeles (90023-3616)
PHONE...................................323 263-9000
Erik Johnson, *President*
Steven Beckman, *Exec VP*
David Naranjo, *Vice Pres*
Gerry Clark, *Project Mgr*
Steve Beckman, *Human Res Mgr*
▲ EMP: 60
SQ FT: 60,000
SALES (est): 13.7MM **Privately Held**
WEB: www.grenekersolutions.com
SIC: 2542 2541 Fixtures: display, office or store: except wood; display fixtures, wood

(P-5161)
PALOMAR CASEWORK INC
4275 Clearview Dr, Carlsbad (92008-3632)
PHONE...................................760 941-9860
Mel Dix, *President*
EMP: 18
SQ FT: 15,000
SALES (est): 2.1MM **Privately Held**
SIC: 2542 2541

(P-5162)
PLASTIC TOPS INC (PA)
521 E Jamie Ave, La Habra (90631-6842)
PHONE...................................714 738-8128
Paul Ackerman, *President*
Gene Versluys, *Vice Pres*
Don Gauthier, *Sales Mgr*
EMP: 14
SQ FT: 9,500
SALES (est): 2.1MM **Privately Held**
SIC: 2542 8011 Counters or counter display cases: except wood; offices & clinics of medical doctors

(P-5163)
RAP SECURITY INC
4630 Cecilia St, Cudahy (90201-5814)
PHONE...................................323 560-3493
Angelo Palmer, *President*
Tina Martinez, *COO*
Bob Palmer, *Vice Pres*
Marki Leonard, *General Mgr*
▲ EMP: 55
SQ FT: 40,000
SALES (est): 8.8MM **Privately Held**
WEB: www.rapstfx.com
SIC: 2542 Fixtures, store: except wood

(P-5164)
REEVE STORE EQUIPMENT COMPANY (PA)
9131 Bermudez St, Pico Rivera (90660-4507)
P.O. Box 276 (90660-0276)
PHONE...................................562 949-2535

John Frackelton, *President*
Mary Ann Crysler, *CFO*
Mary Crysler, *CFO*
Robert Frackelton, *Vice Pres*
Maynor Ruano, *Info Tech Dir*
▲ EMP: 100 EST: 1932
SQ FT: 170,000
SALES (est): 18.6MM **Privately Held**
SIC: 2542 3471 Counters or counter display cases: except wood; electroplating of metals or formed products

(P-5165)
SALSBURY INDUSTRIES INC (PA)
1010 E 62nd St, Los Angeles (90001-1510)
PHONE...................................323 846-6700
Dennis Fraher, *President*
Michael N Lobasso, *CFO*
John Fraher, *Chairman*
Brian Fraher, *Vice Pres*
Stefanie Cruz, *Accountant*
◆ EMP: 222
SQ FT: 600,000
SALES (est): 68.5MM **Privately Held**
WEB: www.mailboxes.com
SIC: 2542 Locker boxes, postal service: except wood; postal lock boxes, mail racks & related products

(P-5166)
SAMSON PRODUCTS INC
Also Called: J L Industries
6285 Randolph St, Commerce (90040-3514)
PHONE...................................323 726-9070
John Reissner, *President*
Robert Dunn, *President*
EMP: 480
SQ FT: 20,000
SALES (est): 54.3MM
SALES (corp-wide): 154.2MM **Privately Held**
WEB: www.samsonproducts.com
SIC: 2542 Cabinets: show, display or storage: except wood
PA: Activar, Inc.
9700 Newton Ave S
Bloomington MN 55431
952 944-3533

(P-5167)
SANTA CRUZ INDUSTRIES INC
129 Bulkhead, Santa Cruz (95060-2701)
P.O. Box 37 (95063-0037)
PHONE...................................831 423-9211
Walter Poterbin, *President*
Marvin Christie, *Vice Pres*
Cathy Poterbin, *Vice Pres*
▲ EMP: 10 EST: 1954
SALES (est): 960K **Privately Held**
WEB: www.santacruzind.com
SIC: 2542 Office & store showcases & display fixtures

(P-5168)
STEVES PLATING CORPORATION
3111 N San Fernando Blvd, Burbank (91504-2527)
PHONE...................................818 842-2184
Terry Knezevich, *CEO*
Roger C Knezevich, *Corp Secy*
EMP: 140 EST: 1956
SQ FT: 80,000
SALES (est): 20.3MM **Privately Held**
WEB: www.stevesplating.com
SIC: 2542 3446 3471 7692 Fixtures, store: except wood; ladders, for permanent installation: metal; railings, prefabricated metal; plating of metals or formed products; welding repair; fabricated pipe & fittings

(P-5169)
STRAFFORD INTL GROUP INC
Also Called: Sig
877 Island Ave Unit 704, San Diego (92101-7152)
PHONE...................................619 446-6960
Keith S Robinson, *President*
▲ EMP: 17
SQ FT: 2,000
SALES: 3.2MM **Privately Held**
SIC: 2542 8742 Fixtures, office: except wood; business consultant

(P-5170)
TEAMMATE BUILDERS INC
Also Called: Formatop
281 E Mcglincy Ln Frnt, Campbell (95008-4946)
PHONE...................................408 377-9000
Toll Free:...................................888 -
Fax: 408 377-6972
EMP: 19
SQ FT: 12,000
SALES (est): 1.9MM **Privately Held**
WEB: www.formatopusa.com
SIC: 2542

(P-5171)
TEICHMAN ENTERPRISES INC
Also Called: T & H Store Fixtures
6100 Bandini Blvd, Commerce (90040-3112)
PHONE...................................323 278-9000
Ruth Teichman, *President*
Alan Teichman, *Treasurer*
Sol Teichman, *Corp Secy*
Bernard Teichman, *Vice Pres*
Sidney Teichman, *Vice Pres*
▲ EMP: 50
SALES (est): 9.5MM **Privately Held**
WEB: www.teichman.net
SIC: 2542 Fixtures: display, office or store: except wood

(P-5172)
TRINITY ENGINEERING
583 Martin Ave, Rohnert Park (94928-2060)
PHONE...................................707 585-2959
Bruce D Omholt, *CEO*
Michael Johnston, *President*
Ronald R Milard, *President*
Denise R Palmer, *CFO*
Ellen Tackett, *Executive Asst*
EMP: 23
SQ FT: 18,000
SALES: 3.5MM **Privately Held**
WEB: www.trinityengineering.com
SIC: 2542 8711 Fixtures: display, office or store: except wood; designing: ship, boat, machine & product

(P-5173)
TURTLE STORAGE LTD
Also Called: American Bicycle Security Co
401 S Beckwith Rd, Santa Paula (93060-3047)
P.O. Box 7359, Ventura (93006-7359)
PHONE...................................805 933-3688
Thomas Volk, *President*
Thomas M Volk, *CEO*
Ron Reynolds, *Administration*
EMP: 20
SQ FT: 16,000
SALES: 2.7MM **Privately Held**
WEB: www.ameribike.com
SIC: 2542 1799 Lockers (not refrigerated): except wood; fiberglass work

(P-5174)
UNIWEB INC (PA)
222 S Promenade Ave, Corona (92879-1743)
PHONE...................................951 279-7999
Karl F Weber, *CEO*
Charles Montou, *Design Engr*
Dianna Manship, *Project Mgr*
Marty Deland, *Engineer*
Delia Guerrero, *Human Res Dir*
▲ EMP: 90 EST: 1979
SQ FT: 170,000
SALES (est): 14.2MM **Privately Held**
WEB: www.uniwebinc.com
SIC: 2542 Fixtures: display, office or store: except wood

(P-5175)
VERLO INDUSTRIES INC
10762 Chestnut Ave, Stanton (90680-2434)
PHONE...................................714 236-2191
Kreig Lopour, *President*
EMP: 40
SQ FT: 16,000
SALES (est): 6.5MM **Privately Held**
SIC: 2542 2522 Racks, merchandise display or storage: except wood; office furniture, except wood

PRODUCTS & SVCS

(P-5176)
WBP ASSOCIATES INC
2017 Seaman Ave, South El Monte
(91733-2626)
PHONE..............................626 575-0747
William Pope, *President*
Robert Pope, *Vice Pres*
EMP: 19
SQ FT: 6,500
SALES: 1MM **Privately Held**
SIC: 2542 1799 Counters or counter display cases: except wood; counter top installation

(P-5177)
WESTERN PCF STOR SOLUTIONS INC (PA)
300 E Arrow Hwy, San Dimas
(91773-3339)
PHONE..............................909 451-0303
Tom Rogers, *President*
Peter G Dunn, *Ch of Bd*
Mike Guerrero, *VP Engrg*
EMP: 100
SQ FT: 165,000
SALES (est): 23MM **Privately Held**
WEB: www.wpss.com
SIC: 2542 Shelving, office & store: except wood

2591 Drapery Hardware, Window Blinds & Shades

(P-5178)
ALL STRONG INDUSTRY (USA) INC (PA)
326 Paseo Tesoro, Walnut (91789-2725)
PHONE..............................909 598-6494
Pei-Hsiang Hsu, *Ch of Bd*
Frank Hsu, *Vice Pres*
▲ EMP: 30
SQ FT: 52,000
SALES (est): 5.8MM **Privately Held**
WEB: www.allstrongusa.com
SIC: 2591 Mini blinds; window shades

(P-5179)
ALRO CSTM DRAPERY INSTALLATION
809 San Antonio Rd Ste 1, Palo Alto
(94303-4626)
PHONE..............................650 847-4343
Alfred Robledo, *Admin Sec*
Mar Y Sol Alvarado, *President*
EMP: 10 EST: 2016
SALES (est): 416.1K **Privately Held**
SIC: 2591 5714 Drapery hardware & blinds & shades; curtains

(P-5180)
AMBASSADOR INDUSTRIES (PA)
2754 W Temple St, Los Angeles
(90026-4795)
PHONE..............................213 383-1171
Mike Lahav, *Owner*
EMP: 10
SQ FT: 20,000
SALES (est): 952.8K **Privately Held**
WEB: www.ambassadorindustries.com
SIC: 2591 5719 5023 Window blinds; blinds vertical; window shades; window furnishings; vertical blinds

(P-5181)
BLIND MAN INC
814 S State St, San Jacinto (92583-4907)
PHONE..............................951 654-5938
John Ennes, *President*
Dawn Ennes, *Corp Secy*
Laura Welsh, *Manager*
EMP: 12
SQ FT: 7,000
SALES: 700K **Privately Held**
SIC: 2591 5719 5714 Window blinds; window shades; draperies

(P-5182)
BONDED WINDOW COVERINGS INC
7831 Ostrow St, San Diego (92111-3602)
P.O. Box 710130 (92171-0130)
PHONE..............................858 974-7700
Lee Howard Tandet, *President*
Mitch Adler, *Info Tech Dir*
EMP: 40
SALES (est): 4.4MM **Privately Held**
WEB: www.bondedwindowcoverings.com
SIC: 2591 Drapery hardware & blinds & shades

(P-5183)
C & M WOOD INDUSTRIES
17229 Lemon St Ste D, Hesperia
(92345-5125)
PHONE..............................760 949-3292
Calvin Lam, *President*
Roger McCarvel, *Vice Pres*
▲ EMP: 155
SQ FT: 55,000
SALES (est): 13.1MM **Privately Held**
WEB: www.cmwood.com
SIC: 2591 Venetian blinds

(P-5184)
CAROLS ROMAN SHADES INC (PA)
130 Mason Cir Ste K, Concord
(94520-1246)
PHONE..............................925 674-9622
Carol Krystoff Lawton, *President*
EMP: 20
SQ FT: 4,033
SALES (est): 6.5MM **Privately Held**
WEB: www.carolsromanshades.com
SIC: 2591 Window shades

(P-5185)
CAROLS ROMAN SHADES INC
130 Mason Cir Ste K, Concord
(94520-1246)
PHONE..............................925 674-9622
Linda Ling, *Manager*
EMP: 10
SALES (corp-wide): 6.5MM **Privately Held**
WEB: www.carolsromanshades.com
SIC: 2591 Window shades
PA: Carol's Roman Shades, Inc.
   130 Mason Cir Ste K
   Concord CA 94520
   925 674-9622

(P-5186)
CENTURY BLINDS INC
451 N Cota St, Corona (92880-2008)
PHONE..............................951 734-3762
Mitch Shapiro, *CEO*
Natalie Zaro, *Office Mgr*
Eugenia Sierra, *Controller*
Jim Quemada, *VP Sales*
Alan Kramer, *Sales Mgr*
▲ EMP: 100
SQ FT: 71,000
SALES (est): 19.9MM **Privately Held**
WEB: www.centuryblindsinc.com
SIC: 2591 3429 5719 5023 Blinds vertical; manufactured hardware (general); vertical blinds; vertical blinds
HQ: Hunter Douglas Scandinavia Ab
   Kristineholmsvagen 14a
   Alingsas 441 3
   322 775-00

(P-5187)
DISCOUNT BLIND CENTER
16074 Grand Ave, Lake Elsinore
(92530-1418)
PHONE..............................951 678-3980
Richard M Caty, *Owner*
John Caty, *Partner*
EMP: 10
SALES: 250K **Privately Held**
SIC: 2591 1799 Window blinds; window treatment installation

(P-5188)
DOUGLAS HUNTER INC
2080 Enterprise Blvd, West Sacramento
(95691-5051)
PHONE..............................916 288-4464
Bryan Claveaux, *Branch Mgr*

Jenny Porter, *QC Mgr*
Karin Hart, *Mktg Mgr*
Scott Klinger, *Director*
Tony Sterns, *Manager*
EMP: 191 **Privately Held**
SIC: 2591 Window blinds
HQ: Hunter Douglas Inc.
   1 Blue Hill Plz Ste 1569
   Pearl River NY 10965
   845 664-7000

(P-5189)
GGC ADMINISTRATION LLC (PA)
Also Called: Golden Gate Capital
1 Embarcadero Ctr Fl 39, San Francisco
(94111-3714)
PHONE..............................415 983-2700
Stephan Scholl, *President*
Robert Little, *COO*
Sue Breedlove, *CFO*
Nick Stangl, *Vice Pres*
Pat Stone, *Executive*
EMP: 27
SALES (est): 1.4B **Privately Held**
SIC: 2591 Curtain & drapery rods, poles & fixtures

(P-5190)
HADCO PRODUCTS INC
Also Called: Sierra Sunscreens
3345 Sunrise Blvd Ste 5, Rancho Cordova
(95742-7309)
PHONE..............................916 966-2409
Daniel A Wilmoth, *President*
EMP: 11
SQ FT: 3,800
SALES (est): 1.2MM **Privately Held**
SIC: 2591 1799 5211 1521 Window shade rollers & fittings; window treatment installation; screens, door & window; patio & deck construction & repair

(P-5191)
HAUSER & SONS INC
Also Called: Hauser Shade
150 S 2nd St, Richmond (94804-2110)
PHONE..............................510 234-8850
Ken Hauser, *President*
Susan Hauser, *Treasurer*
Robert Hauser, *Vice Pres*
Marilyn Hauser, *Admin Sec*
Victoria Jones, *Marketing Mgr*
▲ EMP: 13 EST: 1910
SQ FT: 18,000
SALES (est): 1.9MM **Privately Held**
WEB: www.hausershade.com
SIC: 2591 Window shades

(P-5192)
HD WINDOW FASHIONS INC (DH)
Also Called: M & B Window Fashions
1818 Oak St, Los Angeles (90015-3302)
PHONE..............................213 749-6333
Wayne Gourlay, *President*
Dominique Au Yeung, *General Mgr*
Isha Garcia, *Human Res Mgr*
▲ EMP: 500
SQ FT: 200,000
SALES (est): 57.7MM **Privately Held**
SIC: 2591 Mini blinds; venetian blinds; window shades; blinds vertical
HQ: Hunter Douglas Inc.
   1 Blue Hill Plz Ste 1569
   Pearl River NY 10965
   845 664-7000

(P-5193)
HT WINDOW FASHIONS CORPORATION (PA)
Also Called: Richview By Tehdex
770 Epperson Dr, City of Industry
(91748-1336)
PHONE..............................626 839-8866
Lynne Lee, *President*
Greg Miles, *Vice Pres*
Grace Wong, *Accountant*
William Liu, *Mktg Dir*
▲ EMP: 60
SQ FT: 34,000
SALES (est): 9.6MM **Privately Held**
WEB: www.richview.com
SIC: 2591 Blinds vertical; window blinds

(P-5194)
HUNTER DOUGLAS FABRICATIONS
Also Called: Win-Glo Window Coverings
842 Charcot Ave, San Jose (95131-2210)
PHONE..............................408 435-8844
Jerry Fuchs, *President*
Ajit Mehra, *Treasurer*
Steve Pirylis, *Vice Pres*
Tom Hill, *Admin Sec*
Barry Gilbert, *Info Tech Mgr*
EMP: 275 EST: 1930
SQ FT: 76,000
SALES (est): 31.4MM **Privately Held**
SIC: 2591 Window blinds; blinds vertical; venetian blinds; window shades
HQ: Hunter Douglas N.V.
   Piekstraat 2
   Rotterdam 3071
   104 869-911

(P-5195)
HUNTER DOUGLAS INC
17100 Pioneer Blvd # 170, Artesia
(90701-2713)
PHONE..............................562 207-0800
Steve Swidarski, *Branch Mgr*
John Anthony, *Executive*
EMP: 191 **Privately Held**
SIC: 2591 Drapery hardware & blinds & shades
HQ: Hunter Douglas Inc.
   1 Blue Hill Plz Ste 1569
   Pearl River NY 10965
   845 664-7000

(P-5196)
HUNTER DOUGLAS INC
Hunter Douglas Window Fashions
2080 Enterprise Blvd, West Sacramento
(95691-5051)
PHONE..............................425 430-6110
Paul Fergen, *Branch Mgr*
EMP: 191 **Privately Held**
SIC: 2591 Window shades
HQ: Hunter Douglas Inc.
   1 Blue Hill Plz Ste 1569
   Pearl River NY 10965
   845 664-7000

(P-5197)
JC WINDOW FASHIONS INC
6400 Fleet St, Commerce (90040-1710)
PHONE..............................909 364-8888
Jennifer Chiao, *CEO*
▲ EMP: 28
SALES (est): 4.2MM **Privately Held**
SIC: 2591 Drapery hardware & blinds & shades

(P-5198)
JENARDS WINDOW COVERINGS
Also Called: Je Nard's Window Covering
2299 Ringwood Ave Ste C2, San Jose
(95131-1732)
PHONE..............................408 434-5937
Danny Jensen, *Partner*
Patti Jensen, *Partner*
EMP: 11
SALES (est): 1MM **Privately Held**
SIC: 2591 Window blinds

(P-5199)
KITTRICH CORPORATION (PA)
1585 W Mission Blvd, Pomona
(91766-1233)
PHONE..............................714 736-1000
Robert Friedland, *CEO*
◆ EMP: 130
SQ FT: 237,000
SALES (est): 189.6MM **Privately Held**
WEB: www.kittrich.com
SIC: 2591 2392 2381 Blinds vertical; household furnishings; fabric dress & work gloves

(P-5200)
L C PRINGLE SALES INC (PA)
Also Called: Pringle's Draperies
12020 Western Ave, Garden Grove
(92841-2913)
PHONE..............................714 892-1524
Larry C Pringle, *President*
Pamela Pringle Skinner, *Corp Secy*
Susan Pringle Kusinsky, *Vice Pres*
Carolyn Pringle, *Vice Pres*

Curtis L Pringle, *Vice Pres*
EMP: 30 **EST:** 1968
SQ FT: 11,000
SALES (est): 3MM **Privately Held**
SIC: 2591 7216 2391 7211 Blinds vertical; mini blinds; curtain cleaning & repair; draperies, plastic & textile: from purchased materials; power laundries, family & commercial

(P-5201)
LA VOIES OF SAN JOSE
Also Called: Donald La Voie
2096 Lincoln Ave, San Jose (95125-3539)
PHONE..........................408 297-1285
Donald La Voie, *Owner*
EMP: 10
SQ FT: 4,867
SALES (est): 1.5MM **Privately Held**
WEB: www.lavoiesofsj.com
SIC: 2591 5231 5719 5714 Window shades; wallpaper; window furnishings; upholstery materials

(P-5202)
MES ENTERPRISES
10096 6th St Ste L, Rancho Cucamonga (91730-5750)
PHONE..........................909 484-6863
Mitchell Schliebs, *President*
EMP: 12
SQ FT: 16,800
SALES (est): 1.2MM **Privately Held**
SIC: 2591 Window shades

(P-5203)
MILLER MANUFACTURING INC
Also Called: Silent Servant
165 Cascade Ct, Rohnert Park (94928-1601)
PHONE..........................707 584-9528
Tom Miller, *President*
Joanne Miller, *Vice Pres*
Steve Miller, *Admin Sec*
Jim Miller, *Foreman/Supr*
▲ **EMP:** 10
SQ FT: 10,400
SALES (est): 1.4MM **Privately Held**
WEB: www.silentservant.com
SIC: 2591 3534 3442 3479 Curtain & drapery rods, poles & fixtures; dumbwaiters; metal doors, sash & trim; etching & engraving

(P-5204)
MILLERTON BUILDERS INC
Also Called: Vinyl Specialties
4714 E Home Ave, Fresno (93703-4509)
PHONE..........................559 252-0490
Frank Spencer, *President*
Matthew Carlton, *Treasurer*
Matt Carlton, *Corp Secy*
EMP: 25
SQ FT: 20,000
SALES (est): 3MM **Privately Held**
SIC: 2591 Drapery hardware & blinds & shades

(P-5205)
PHASE II PRODUCTS INC (PA)
501 W Broadway Ste 2090, San Diego (92101-8563)
PHONE..........................619 236-9699
Charles Hunt, *CEO*
John Bowie, *CFO*
Gordon Peiper, *Vice Pres*
▲ **EMP:** 30
SQ FT: 4,800
SALES (est): 4.8MM **Privately Held**
SIC: 2591 Drapery hardware & blinds & shades

(P-5206)
PLASTIC VIEW ATC INC
4585 Runway St Ste B, Simi Valley (93063-3479)
PHONE..........................805 520-9390
Ryan Voges, *President*
EMP: 10
SQ FT: 5,400
SALES: 1.4MM **Privately Held**
WEB: www.pvatc.com
SIC: 2591 Window shades

(P-5207)
REMEDY BLINDS INC
220 W Central Ave, Santa Ana (92707-3416)
PHONE..........................714 245-0186
Craig Briggs, *President*
Grace Briggs, *Corp Secy*
◆ **EMP:** 55
SQ FT: 21,000
SALES (est): 7.1MM **Privately Held**
SIC: 2591 2431 Window blinds; window shades; window shutters, wood

(P-5208)
ROLL-A-SHADE INC (PA)
12101 Madera Way, Riverside (92503-4849)
PHONE..........................951 245-5077
Tyrone Pereira, *President*
Ric Berg, *Vice Pres*
▲ **EMP:** 22
SQ FT: 10,000
SALES (est): 6.9MM **Privately Held**
SIC: 2591 1799 Window shades; window treatment installation

(P-5209)
SHADES UNLIMITED INC
Also Called: Redi Shades
361 Blodgett St, Cotati (94931-8700)
PHONE..........................707 285-2233
Kevin D Wohlert, *CEO*
Joe Militello, *CEO*
Joe Metger, *CFO*
Christine Zabaneh, *CFO*
Richard Konopelski, *VP Sales*
▲ **EMP:** 18
SALES (est): 3.7MM **Privately Held**
WEB: www.redishade.com
SIC: 2591 Window shades

(P-5210)
SHOWDOGS INC
Also Called: Wholesale Shade
168 S Pacific St, San Marcos (92078-2527)
PHONE..........................760 603-3269
Patrick Howe, *President*
EMP: 30
SQ FT: 10,000
SALES: 1MM **Privately Held**
SIC: 2591 Blinds vertical

(P-5211)
SKAGFIELD CORPORATION
Also Called: Skandia Industries
2225 Avenida Costa Este, San Diego (92154-6238)
PHONE..........................858 635-7777
Larry Sack, *Branch Mgr*
Dana Kissie, *Human Res Dir*
Sarah Sharp, *Manager*
EMP: 300
SALES (corp-wide): 19.8MM **Privately Held**
SIC: 2591 Window blinds
PA: Skagfield Corporation
270 Crossway Rd
Tallahassee FL 32305
850 878-1144

(P-5212)
SPEED-O-PIN INTERNATIONAL
1401 Freeman Ave, Long Beach (90804-2518)
PHONE..........................562 433-4911
Jeffrey Jacobson, *President*
EMP: 12
SQ FT: 20,000
SALES (est): 1.2MM **Privately Held**
SIC: 2591 2672 Drapery hardware & blinds & shades; coated & laminated paper

(P-5213)
STONESIDE LLC
228 Hamilton Ave Ste 300, Palo Alto (94301-2583)
PHONE..........................650 422-2154
EMP: 40
SALES (est): 1.7MM **Privately Held**
SIC: 2591 Window blinds
PA: Stoneside Llc
1801 Broadway Ste 800
Denver CO 80202

(P-5214)
VERTICAL DOORS INC
Also Called: Vdi Motor Sports
542 3rd St, Lake Elsinore (92530-2729)
PHONE..........................951 273-1069
Rob Baum, *President*
Autumn Baum, *Purch Mgr*
Steve Mora, *Mfg Staff*
EMP: 18
SALES (est): 3.5MM **Privately Held**
WEB: www.verticaldoors.com
SIC: 2591 Blinds vertical

(P-5215)
WEBB DESIGNS INC
Also Called: Webbshade
40300 Greenwood Way, Oakhurst (93644-9566)
P.O. Box 215 (93644-0215)
PHONE..........................559 641-5400
Mike Benbrook, *President*
Natalie Webb, *Treasurer*
Allison Benbrook, *Vice Pres*
Barbara Magoon, *Office Mgr*
▼ **EMP:** 18
SQ FT: 9,000
SALES: 1.8MM **Privately Held**
SIC: 2591 Window shades

(P-5216)
XENTRIC DRAPERY HARDWARE INC
11001 Sutter Ave, Pacoima (91331-2457)
PHONE..........................818 897-0444
Carlos Contreras, *President*
Erika Luna Contreras, *Vice Pres*
▲ **EMP:** 10
SALES (est): 1.4MM **Privately Held**
SIC: 2591 Blinds vertical

2599 Furniture & Fixtures, NEC

(P-5217)
ACCENT MANUFACTURING INC
105 Leavesley Rd Bldg 3d, Gilroy (95020-3688)
PHONE..........................408 846-9993
Joe Catanzaro, *President*
Esther Catanzaro, *Corp Secy*
Frank Catanzaro, *Vice Pres*
EMP: 20
SQ FT: 30,000
SALES (est): 2.9MM **Privately Held**
WEB: www.accentmfg.com
SIC: 2599 2431 5031 2434 Cabinets, factory; doors & door parts & trim, wood; lumber, plywood & millwork; wood kitchen cabinets

(P-5218)
AFN SERVICES LLC
Also Called: Socialight, The
368 E Campbell Ave, Campbell (95008-2029)
PHONE..........................408 364-1564
EMP: 40
SQ FT: 2,200
SALES: 250K **Privately Held**
SIC: 2599 5813 7929

(P-5219)
ALEGACY FOODSERVICE PRODUCTS
12683 Corral Pl, Santa Fe Springs (90670-4748)
PHONE..........................562 320-3100
Jesse Gross, *Principal*
Brett Gross, *President*
Eric Gross, *Vice Pres*
Christine Trujillo, *Accountant*
Les Palmer, *Sales Dir*
◆ **EMP:** 60
SQ FT: 130,000
SALES (est): 9.7MM **Privately Held**
WEB: www.alegacy.com
SIC: 2599 3263 Carts, restaurant equipment; cookware, fine earthenware

(P-5220)
AMKO RESTAURANT FURNITURE INC
5833 Avalon Blvd, Los Angeles (90003-1307)
PHONE..........................323 234-0388
Seong Gyun Shin, *President*
Soon Jo Shin, *CFO*
Shin Tae, *Info Tech Dir*
Woogie Park, *Manager*
▲ **EMP:** 23
SQ FT: 18,000
SALES (est): 3.5MM **Privately Held**
WEB: www.chairimports.com
SIC: 2599 Restaurant furniture, wood or metal

(P-5221)
BAY VALVE SERVICE & ENGRG LLC
3948 Teal Ct, Benicia (94510-1202)
PHONE..........................707 748-7166
Rob Sterry, *Branch Mgr*
EMP: 25
SALES (corp-wide): 35.9MM **Privately Held**
SIC: 2599 Bar, restaurant & cafeteria furniture
PA: Bay Valve Service & Engineering, Llc
4385 S 133rd St
Tukwila WA 98168
206 782-7800

(P-5222)
BENCH-CRAFT INC
4005 Artesia Ave, Fullerton (92833-2519)
PHONE..........................714 523-3322
Theodor Steinhilber, *President*
John Boyd, *CFO*
David Spivy, *CFO*
EMP: 10 **EST:** 1985
SQ FT: 35,000
SALES (est): 1.8MM
SALES (corp-wide): 4.6MM **Privately Held**
WEB: www.bench-craft.com
SIC: 2599 Work benches, factory
PA: Stein Industries, Inc.
4005 Artesia Ave
Fullerton CA 92833
714 522-4560

(P-5223)
BENCHPRO INC
Also Called: Bench Depot
23949 Tecate Mission Rd, Tecate (91980)
P.O. Box G (91980-0958)
PHONE..........................619 478-9400
Jay David Lissner, *President*
Coy Marchino, *Info Tech Mgr*
Susengno Sutijo, *Info Tech Mgr*
Danielle Wence, *Sales Staff*
▲ **EMP:** 188
SQ FT: 155,000
SALES (est): 34.2MM **Privately Held**
WEB: www.benchpro.com
SIC: 2599 Work benches, factory

(P-5224)
COMMERCIAL CSTM STING UPHL INC
12601 Western Ave, Garden Grove (92841-4014)
PHONE..........................714 850-0520
Robert Francis, *CEO*
▲ **EMP:** 90
SQ FT: 50,000
SALES (est): 20.5MM **Privately Held**
WEB: www.commercialcustomseating.com
SIC: 2599 Restaurant furniture, wood or metal

(P-5225)
CUSTOM INTERIORS DESIGN FIXS
Also Called: Custom Interior Designs
7800 Industry Ave, Pico Rivera (90660-4306)
PHONE..........................562 942-7969
Thomas Ego, *President*
Salvadore Romero, *Vice Pres*
EMP: 35
SQ FT: 19,000

PRODUCTS & SVCS

SALES (est): 4.2MM **Privately Held**
WEB: www.cidf.com
SIC: 2599 5046 Restaurant furniture,
wood or metal; restaurant equipment &
supplies

(P-5226)
DAVID HAID
8619 Crocker St, Los Angeles
(90003-3516)
PHONE.....................323 752-8096
EMP: 20 **Privately Held**
WEB: www.oasisfurniture.net
SIC: 2599 5199 Factory furniture & fix-
tures; advertising specialties
PA: David Haid
3931 Topanga Canyon Blvd
Malibu CA 90265

(P-5227)
DIVISADERO 500 LLC
Also Called: Mad Zone
502 Divisadero St, San Francisco
(94117-2213)
PHONE.....................415 572-6062
Michael J Krouse, *President*
EMP: 18 EST: 2010
SALES (est): 1MM **Privately Held**
SIC: 2599 Bar, restaurant & cafeteria furni-
ture

(P-5228)
ELEGANCE UPHOLSTERY INC
11803 Slauson Ave Unit A, Ontario (91762)
PHONE.....................562 698-2584
Ricardo Vargas, *CEO*
Maria Arroyo, *Office Mgr*
EMP: 16
SALES (est): 2.2MM **Privately Held**
SIC: 2599 7641 Bar, restaurant & cafeteria
furniture; restaurant furniture, wood or
metal; bowling establishment furniture; re-
upholstery & furniture repair; reupholstery

(P-5229)
ELITE CABINETRY INC
25755 Jefferson Ave, Murrieta
(92562-6903)
PHONE.....................951 698-5050
Paul Silva, *President*
EMP: 14
SQ FT: 8,200
SALES (est): 1.8MM **Privately Held**
WEB: www.elitecabinetry.com
SIC: 2599 Cabinets, factory

(P-5230)
ELKAY INTERIOR SYSTEMS INC
225 Santa Monica Blvd, Santa Monica
(90401-2207)
PHONE.....................800 837-8373
Laurie Schmidt, *Branch Mgr*
EMP: 10
SALES (corp-wide): 1.3B **Privately Held**
WEB: www.isiamerica.com
SIC: 2599 2511 Restaurant furniture,
wood or metal; wood household furniture
HQ: Elkay Interior Systems Inc.
241 N Broadway Ste 600
Milwaukee WI 53202
414 224-0957

(P-5231)
ERGONOM CORPORATION
Also Called: E R G International
361 Bernoulli Cir, Oxnard (93030-5164)
PHONE.....................805 981-9978
George Zaki, *CEO*
Roy Zaki, *President*
▲ EMP: 90
SALES (est): 25.4MM **Privately Held**
WEB: www.erginternational.com
SIC: 2599 2531 Hospital furniture, except
beds; hotel furniture; school furniture

(P-5232)
FIXTURE DESIGN & MFG CO
Also Called: F D M
4848 Lakeview Ave Ste E, Yorba Linda
(92886-3452)
P.O. Box 819, Anaheim (92815-0819)
PHONE.....................714 776-3104
David T Carlson, *President*
Judy McArthur, *Corp Secy*
Doreen Carlson, *Vice Pres*

EMP: 30
SQ FT: 40,000
SALES: 6MM **Privately Held**
WEB: www.fixturedesign.com
SIC: 2599 Bar, restaurant & cafeteria furni-
ture

(P-5233)
FORBES INDUSTRIES DIV
1933 E Locust St, Ontario (91761-7608)
PHONE.....................909 923-4559
Tim Sweetland, *President*
Peter Sweetland, *Vice Pres*
Van Bennett, *Regl Sales Mgr*
▼ EMP: 210
SQ FT: 110,000
SALES (est): 26.3MM
SALES (corp-wide): 41.8MM **Privately
Held**
WEB: www.forbesindustries.com
SIC: 2599 Carts, restaurant equipment
PA: The Winsford Corporation
1933 E Locust St
Ontario CA 91761
909 923-4559

(P-5234)
GLP DESIGNS INC
Also Called: Antique Designs
916 W Hyde Park Blvd, Inglewood
(90302-3308)
PHONE.....................310 652-6800
Keith G Hudson, *Vice Pres*
Keith Hudson, *Vice Pres*
EMP: 15
SALES: 950K **Privately Held**
SIC: 2599 Furniture & fixtures

(P-5235)
HARMONY INFINITE INC
Also Called: Best Slip Cover Company
12918 Bloomfield St, Studio City
(91604-1401)
PHONE.....................818 780-4569
Stuart Dones, *CEO*
Joan Dones, *Corp Secy*
Joshua Siegel, *Vice Pres*
EMP: 16
SALES (est): 3.6MM **Privately Held**
SIC: 2599 Factory furniture & fixtures

(P-5236)
HIRE ELEGANCE
8333 Arjons Dr Ste E, San Diego
(92126-6320)
PHONE.....................858 740-7862
Stuart Simble, *Principal*
EMP: 10
SALES (est): 1.4MM **Privately Held**
SIC: 2599 Furniture & fixtures

(P-5237)
HURLEYS LP
Also Called: Hurleys Restaurant & Bar
1516 King Ave, NAPA (94559-1524)
PHONE.....................707 944-2345
Robert Hurley, *Owner*
EMP: 60
SALES (est): 6.9MM **Privately Held**
WEB: www.hurleysrestaurant.com
SIC: 2599 Bar, restaurant & cafeteria furni-
ture

(P-5238)
J&T DESIGNS LLC
1463 W El Segundo Blvd, Compton
(90222-1144)
PHONE.....................310 868-5190
Joe Galindo,
EMP: 35
SQ FT: 15,000
SALES (est): 3.6MM **Privately Held**
WEB: www.jtdesigns.net
SIC: 2599 Factory furniture & fixtures

(P-5239)
JAY EDWARD GROUP LLC
Also Called: Jay Edward Hospitality Furn
12250 El Camino Real # 200, San Diego
(92130-3091)
PHONE.....................858 799-1227
Michael Shapiro, *President*
Jimmy Wong, *COO*
Robert Shapiro, *Managing Dir*
Lindy Torribio, *Administration*
EMP: 23 EST: 2012

SQ FT: 1,500
SALES (est): 3MM **Privately Held**
SIC: 2599 Hotel furniture

(P-5240)
JBI LLC (PA)
Also Called: Jbi Interiors
2650 E El Presidio St, Long Beach
(90810-1142)
PHONE.....................310 886-8034
Pete Jensen, *Manager*
Andy Braddy, *Exec VP*
Joseph Parisi, *Senior VP*
Robert Rivas, *Business Dir*
Gregg Buchbinder, *CTO*
◆ EMP: 200
SQ FT: 270,000
SALES (est): 52.9MM **Privately Held**
WEB: www.jbiindustries.com
SIC: 2599 5046 Restaurant furniture,
wood or metal; restaurant equipment &
supplies

(P-5241)
K&K WORLD INC
721 W Wedgewood Ln, La Habra
(90631-7664)
PHONE.....................714 234-6237
Sun Suk Kang, *President*
▲ EMP: 35
SALES: 950K **Privately Held**
SIC: 2599 Furniture & fixtures

(P-5242)
**KOUZOUIANS FINE CUSTOM
FURN**
Also Called: Kouzouian Custom Furniture
18586 Caspian Ct, Granada Hills
(91344-2010)
PHONE.....................818 772-1212
Hartyoun Kouzouian, *President*
Diana Kouzouian, *Vice Pres*
EMP: 25
SQ FT: 20,000
SALES (est): 2.8MM **Privately Held**
SIC: 2599 Hotel furniture

(P-5243)
LEOS CABINETS
7007 Avalon Blvd, Los Angeles
(90003-2207)
PHONE.....................323 759-7649
Leo Romeraz, *Owner*
EMP: 10
SALES (est): 639K **Privately Held**
SIC: 2599 Cabinets, factory

(P-5244)
M DAMICO INC
Also Called: Mjd Cabinets
12650 Highway 67 Ste E, Lakeside
(92040-1132)
PHONE.....................619 390-5858
Mark D'Amico, *President*
Maryanne D'Amico, *Treasurer*
Nick D'Amico, *Vice Pres*
EMP: 20
SQ FT: 6,000
SALES (est): 1.6MM **Privately Held**
SIC: 2599 Cabinets, factory

(P-5245)
**MAKE BEVERAGE HOLDINGS
LLC**
2569 Tea Leaf Ln, Tustin (92782-2001)
PHONE.....................949 923-8238
Jeffrey Duggan, *Principal*
EMP: 20
SALES (est): 685.6K **Privately Held**
SIC: 2599 Bar, restaurant & cafeteria furni-
ture

(P-5246)
MASHINDUSTRIES INC
1700 E Via Burton, Anaheim (92806-1211)
PHONE.....................714 736-9600
Bernard Brucha, *CEO*
Michelle Blemel, *Admin Sec*
EMP: 47
SQ FT: 30,000
SALES: 3MM **Privately Held**
SIC: 2599 Factory furniture & fixtures

(P-5247)
**NLP FURNITURE INDUSTRIES
INC**
1425 Corporate Center Dr # 200, San
Diego (92154-6629)
P.O. Box 530659 (92153-0659)
PHONE.....................619 661-5170
Joseph B Cabrera, *President*
Louis J Rodriguez, *Vice Pres*
▲ EMP: 134
SQ FT: 9,000
SALES (est): 12.6MM **Privately Held**
WEB: www.nlpfurniture.com
SIC: 2599 Hospital furniture, except beds

(P-5248)
PANDA BOWL
11940 Edinger Ave, Fountain Valley
(92708-1211)
PHONE.....................714 418-0299
Victor Cheng, *Owner*
EMP: 12
SALES (est): 1.4MM **Privately Held**
SIC: 2599 Food wagons, restaurant

(P-5249)
**PRODUCTION SYSTEMS GROUP
INC**
Also Called: Production Industries
895 Beacon St, Brea (92821-2905)
PHONE.....................714 990-8997
EMP: 40
SQ FT: 50,000
SALES: 5MM
SALES (corp-wide): 12.6MM **Privately
Held**
SIC: 2599
PA: Iac Industries
895 Beacon St
Brea CA 85338
714 990-8997

(P-5250)
R & J FABRICATORS INC
1121 Railroad St Ste 102, Corona
(92882-8219)
PHONE.....................951 817-0300
James Ciarletta, *CEO*
Jay Warren Ciarletta, *Vice Pres*
EMP: 20
SQ FT: 20,000
SALES (est): 3.8MM **Privately Held**
SIC: 2599 Restaurant furniture, wood or
metal

(P-5251)
RICHTER FURNITURE MFG 2002
Also Called: Richter Furniture Mfr Rfm
28720 Canwood St Ste 108, Agoura Hills
(91301-9745)
PHONE.....................323 588-7900
EMP: 150
SALES (est): 10.1MM **Privately Held**
SIC: 2599 Factory furniture & fixtures

(P-5252)
RIVER CITY
Also Called: River City Restaurant
505 Lincoln Ave, NAPA (94558-3610)
P.O. Box 2553 (94558-0255)
PHONE.....................707 253-1111
Assaad Barazi, *President*
EMP: 45
SQ FT: 6,000
SALES (est): 5.1MM **Privately Held**
SIC: 2599 5812 Bar, restaurant & cafeteria
furniture; eating places

(P-5253)
ROTH WOOD PRODUCTS LTD
2260 Canoas Garden Ave, San Jose
(95125-2007)
PHONE.....................408 723-8888
Robert E Roth, *CEO*
Marilyn Roth, *Treasurer*
EMP: 40 EST: 1974
SQ FT: 12,800
SALES (est): 5.6MM **Privately Held**
WEB: www.rothwoodproducts.com
SIC: 2599 2434 Cabinets, factory; wood
kitchen cabinets

(P-5254)
SAMMONS EQUIPMENT MFG CORP
Also Called: Shammi Industries
390 Meyer Cir Ste A, Corona (92879-6617)
PHONE..................................951 340-3419
Bhupinder Saggu, *President*
David Duke, *Manager*
▲ EMP: 14 EST: 1932
SQ FT: 39,000
SALES (est): 2.6MM **Privately Held**
WEB: www.sammonsequipment.com
SIC: 2599 Carts, restaurant equipment

(P-5255)
STAINLESS FIXTURES INC
1250 E Franklin Ave, Pomona (91766-5449)
PHONE..................................909 622-1615
Randy Rodriguez, *President*
Daniel Briones, *Project Mgr*
Armando Gonzalez, *Project Mgr*
Lana Hammerton, *Controller*
EMP: 35
SQ FT: 36,000
SALES (est): 11.7MM **Privately Held**
SIC: 2599 Restaurant furniture, wood or metal; hotel furniture

(P-5256)
STANFORD FURNITURE MFG INC
5851 Alder Ave Ste A, Sacramento (95828-1126)
PHONE..................................916 387-5300
Alireza Angha, *Owner*
EMP: 28
SALES (est): 4.1MM **Privately Held**
SIC: 2599 Factory furniture & fixtures

(P-5257)
TAHITI CABINETS INC
5419 E La Palma Ave, Anaheim (92807-2022)
PHONE..................................714 693-0618
Mark Ramsey, *President*
Doreen Ramsey, *Admin Sec*
Eric Neff, *Project Mgr*
Carrie Olson, *Project Mgr*
Jessica Parra, *Purch Mgr*
EMP: 58
SQ FT: 32,000
SALES (est): 12.3MM **Privately Held**
WEB: www.tahiticabinets.com
SIC: 2599 2431 2434 Cabinets, factory; millwork; wood kitchen cabinets

(P-5258)
THOMAS CRAVEN WOOD FINISHERS
15746 W Arminta St, Simi Valley (93065)
PHONE..................................805 341-7713
Thomas Craven, *President*
EMP: 11
SALES: 600K **Privately Held**
SIC: 2599 2491 7641 Furniture & fixtures; wood preserving; furniture repair & maintenance

(P-5259)
TRATTORIA AMICI/AMERICANA LLC
783 Americana Way, Glendale (91210-1507)
PHONE..................................818 502-1220
Tancredi Deluca, *CEO*
EMP: 10
SALES (est): 1.4MM **Privately Held**
SIC: 2599 Food wagons, restaurant

(P-5260)
ULTIMATE JUMPERS INC
14924 Arrow Hwy Ste A, Baldwin Park (91706-1849)
PHONE..................................626 337-3086
Tigran Thenteretshyan, *President*
Vazgen Melikyan, *Vice Pres*
EMP: 15
SQ FT: 11,500
SALES: 1.1MM **Privately Held**
SIC: 2599 Inflatable beds

(P-5261)
VISIBILITY SOLUTIONS INC
320 E Dyer Rd, Santa Ana (92707-3740)
PHONE..................................714 434-7040
Jeffrey Jacobson, *President*
Marty Jacobson, *Vice Pres*
EMP: 13
SALES (est): 860K **Privately Held**
WEB: www.visibilitysolutions.com
SIC: 2599 Inflatable beds

(P-5262)
VITALITY FURNITURE GROUP INC
5042 Wilshire Blvd # 265, Los Angeles (90036-4305)
PHONE..................................323 937-4900
George Shamu, *CEO*
Felecia Fisher, *President*
Geisha Petina, *Vice Pres*
EMP: 15
SQ FT: 22,000
SALES (est): 1.4MM **Privately Held**
SIC: 2599 Hotel furniture

(P-5263)
WESTERN MILL FABRICATORS INC
615 Fee Ana St, Placentia (92870-6704)
PHONE..................................714 993-3667
Kimball Boyack, *CEO*
EMP: 30
SQ FT: 25,000
SALES (est): 4.9MM **Privately Held**
WEB: www.wmfinc.com
SIC: 2599 Bar, restaurant & cafeteria furniture

(P-5264)
WORKSTATION INDUSTRIES INC
1938 E Pomona St, Santa Ana (92705-5120)
PHONE..................................714 258-7535
Albert Cappello, *President*
Christine Cappello, *CFO*
EMP: 32
SQ FT: 20,000
SALES: 3.3MM **Privately Held**
WEB: www.workstationindustries.com
SIC: 2599 Factory furniture & fixtures

2611 Pulp Mills

(P-5265)
ARNA TRADING INC (PA)
Also Called: Simba Recycling
2892 S Santa Fe Ave # 109, San Marcos (92069-6022)
PHONE..................................760 940-2775
Ash Shah, *President*
▼ EMP: 15
SQ FT: 20,000
SALES (est): 3.7MM **Privately Held**
WEB: www.simbaint.com
SIC: 2611 Pulp mills, mechanical & recycling processing; kraft (sulfate) pulp

(P-5266)
BEYOND ULTIMATE LLC
360 S 9th Ave, City of Industry (91746-3311)
PHONE..................................626 330-9777
Janak Patel,
Dipak Patel,
EMP: 10
SALES (est): 1.3MM **Privately Held**
SIC: 2611 Pulp manufactured from waste or recycled paper

(P-5267)
CENCAL RECYCLING LLC
501 Port Road 22, Stockton (95203-2909)
PHONE..................................209 546-8000
Steve Sutta, *Mng Member*
EMP: 16
SQ FT: 104,400
SALES (est): 2.2MM **Privately Held**
WEB: www.cencalrecycling.com
SIC: 2611 Pulp mills, mechanical & recycling processing

(P-5268)
INLAND PCF RESOURCE RECOVERY
12650 Slughter Hse Cyn Rd, Lakeside (92040)
P.O. Box 123 (92040-0123)
PHONE..................................619 390-1418
Lloyd Maynard, *President*
Ralph Esquivel, *Vice Pres*
EMP: 32
SALES (est): 2.5MM **Privately Held**
SIC: 2611 Pulp manufactured from waste or recycled paper

(P-5269)
NEW GREEN DAY LLC
1710 E 111th St, Los Angeles (90059-1910)
P.O. Box 72147 (90002-0147)
PHONE..................................323 566-7603
Brian Kelly, *CEO*
Virgialeo San Victors, *Accountant*
Randi Yamamoto, *Accountant*
David Holt,
Kirk Sanford, *Mng Member*
EMP: 25
SQ FT: 25,000
SALES (est): 6.1MM **Privately Held**
SIC: 2611 Pulp manufactured from waste or recycled paper

(P-5270)
WESTERN PACIFIC PULP AND PAPER (HQ)
9400 Hall Rd, Downey (90241-5365)
PHONE..................................562 803-4401
Ralph Ho, *Ch of Bd*
Kevin Duncombe, *CEO*
Jim Forkey, *Vice Pres*
Kyle Duncombe, *General Mgr*
Jill Jensen, *General Mgr*
▼ EMP: 51
SALES (est): 15.6MM **Privately Held**
SIC: 2611 5093 Pulp manufactured from waste or recycled paper; waste paper
PA: Y. F. International
180 Park Rd
Burlingame CA 94010
650 342-6560

2621 Paper Mills

(P-5271)
ACME UNITED CORPORATION
630 Young St, Santa Ana (92705-5633)
PHONE..................................714 557-2001
EMP: 22
SALES (corp-wide): 130.5MM **Publicly Held**
SIC: 2621 Absorbent paper
PA: Acme United Corporation
55 Walls Dr Ste 201
Fairfield CT 06824
203 254-6060

(P-5272)
ALLEN REED COMPANY INC
Also Called: Chicwrap
23823 Malibu Rd Ste 50275, Malibu (90265-4628)
PHONE..................................310 575-8704
Ian Kaiser, *President*
Michael Kaiser, *Ch of Bd*
Garry Pearson, *CEO*
Sean Allen Neiberger, *Vice Pres*
John Lutz, *Sales Dir*
EMP: 10
SQ FT: 10,000
SALES (est): 1MM **Privately Held**
SIC: 2621 3353 Parchment paper; foil, aluminum

(P-5273)
ATTENDS HEALTHCARE PDTS INC
1941 N White Ave, La Verne (91750-5663)
P.O. Box 1060 (91750-0960)
PHONE..................................909 392-1200
Dave Franklin, *Branch Mgr*
EMP: 190
SALES (corp-wide): 5.1B **Privately Held**
SIC: 2621 Sanitary tissue paper; absorbent paper; tissue paper
HQ: Attends Healthcare Products Inc.
8020 Arco Corp Dr Ste 200
Raleigh NC 27617
252 752-1100

(P-5274)
BESTWALL LLC
Also Called: Georgia-Pacific
1988 Marina Blvd, San Leandro (94577-3207)
PHONE..................................510 483-7580
Fred Curcio, *Branch Mgr*
Michelle Decastro, *Safety Mgr*
EMP: 107
SALES (corp-wide): 42.9B **Privately Held**
WEB: www.gp.com
SIC: 2621 3275 Paper mills; gypsum products
HQ: Georgia-Pacific Llc
133 Peachtree St Nw
Atlanta GA 30303
404 652-4000

(P-5275)
BOISE CASCADE COMPANY
12030 S Harlan Rd, Lathrop (95330-8768)
PHONE..................................209 983-4114
Brad Terrell, *Branch Mgr*
EMP: 40
SALES (corp-wide): 4.4B **Publicly Held**
SIC: 2621 2679 Paper mills; building paper, laminated: made from purchased material
PA: Boise Cascade Company
1111 W Jefferson St # 300
Boise ID 83702
208 384-6161

(P-5276)
BOISE HEXACOMB
9700 Bell Ranch Dr, Santa Fe Springs (90670-2950)
PHONE..................................562 944-0052
Mark W Kowlzan, *CEO*
Carlos Ruiz, *Plant Mgr*
Ray Kowalski, *Manager*
EMP: 14
SALES (est): 2.1MM **Privately Held**
SIC: 2621 Packaging paper

(P-5277)
CLEARWATER PAPER CORPORATION
1320 Willow Pass Rd # 550, Concord (94520-5244)
PHONE..................................925 947-4700
Mark Ohleyer, *Principal*
EMP: 600 **Publicly Held**
SIC: 2621 2631 Paper mills; paperboard mills
PA: Clearwater Paper Corporation
601 W Riverside Ave # 1100
Spokane WA 99201

(P-5278)
D D OFFICE PRODUCTS INC
Also Called: Liberty Paper
5025 Hampton St, Vernon (90058-2133)
P.O. Box 58026 (90058-0026)
PHONE..................................323 582-3400
Alex Ismail, *CEO*
Anwar Lalani, *President*
Benazir Ismael *CFO*
Abdul Ismail, *Vice Pres*
Celia Goldman, *Human Resources*
▲ EMP: 25
SQ FT: 22,000
SALES: 36.6MM **Privately Held**
WEB: www.libertypp.com
SIC: 2621 5112 5044 5045 Printing paper; stationery & office supplies; office equipment; computers & accessories, personal & home entertainment; hardware; furniture

(P-5279)
DOCUMENT PROC SOLUTIONS INC
535 Main St Ste 317, Martinez (94553-1102)
PHONE..................................925 839-1182
EMP: 35
SALES (corp-wide): 8.8MM **Privately Held**
SIC: 2621 Paper mills

PRODUCTS & SVCS

PA: Document Processing Solutions, Inc.
590 W Lambert Rd
Brea CA 92821
714 482-2060

(P-5280)
EAGLE RIDGE PAPER LTD (HQ)
Also Called: Eagleridge Paper CA
100 S Anaheim Blvd # 250, Anaheim
(92805-3872)
PHONE..................714 780-1799
Yeoh Khai Sun, *President*
▲ EMP: 20
SALES (est): 2.8MM **Privately Held**
SIC: 2621 Printing paper
PA: Eagle Ridge Paper Ltd
20 Hereford St Unit 15
Brampton ON
888 324-5399

(P-5281)
ENVELOPE PRODUCTS CO (PA)
Also Called: Epco
2882 W Cromwell Ave, Fresno
(93711-0353)
PHONE..................925 939-5173
Alex Macdonald, *Chairman*
Darlene Macdonald, *President*
Janine Eldred, *Vice Pres*
EMP: 26
SQ FT: 23,000
SALES (est): 3.5MM **Privately Held**
WEB: www.epco-envelopes.com
SIC: 2621 2761 Envelope paper; manifold
business forms

(P-5282)
FLEENOR COMPANY INC
4201 E Fremont St, Stockton (95215-4814)
P.O. Box 14438, Oakland (94614-2438)
PHONE..................209 932-0329
Ramon Cavares, *Branch Mgr*
EMP: 50
SALES (corp-wide): 21.3MM **Privately Held**
WEB: www.fleenorpaper.com
SIC: 2621 Paper mills
PA: Fleenor Company, Inc
2225 Harbor Bay Pkwy
Alameda CA 94502
800 433-2531

(P-5283)
GEORGIA-PACIFIC LLC
2800 Alvarado St, San Leandro
(94577-5704)
PHONE..................510 352-8269
Ron Huff, *Principal*
Alejandro Reyes, *Plant Supt*
EMP: 23
SALES (corp-wide): 42.9B **Privately Held**
WEB: www.gp.com
SIC: 2621 Paper mills
HQ: Georgia-Pacific Llc
133 Peachtree St Nw
Atlanta GA 30303
404 652-4000

(P-5284)
GLOBAL PAPER SOLUTIONS INC
100 S Anaheim Blvd # 250, Anaheim
(92805-3872)
PHONE..................714 687-6102
CHI MI Chung, *President*
◆ EMP: 30
SALES (est): 8.9MM **Privately Held**
SIC: 2621 Paper mills

(P-5285)
GRAPHIC PACKAGING INTL LLC
Also Called: International Paper
1600 Kelsey Rd, Visalia (93291)
P.O. Box 4349 (93278-4349)
PHONE..................559 651-3535
Robert E Eades, *Opers-Prdtn-Mfg*
EMP: 150 **Publicly Held**
WEB: www.internationalpaper.com
SIC: 2621 Paper mills
HQ: Graphic Packaging International, Llc
1500 Riveredge Pkwy # 100
Atlanta GA 30328

(P-5286)
HARVARD LABEL LLC
Also Called: Harvard Card Systems
111 Baldwin Park Blvd, City of Industry
(91746-1402)
PHONE..................626 333-8881
Michael Tang, *CEO*
David Banducci, *President*
▲ EMP: 115
SQ FT: 125,000
SALES (est): 33MM **Privately Held**
WEB: www.harvardlabel.com
SIC: 2621 2675 2752 Greeting card
paper; stencil cards, die-cut: made from
purchased materials; cards, lithographed
PA: Plasticard - Locktech International, Llp
1220 Trade Dr
North Las Vegas NV 89030

(P-5287)
IMAGE SQUARE INC
Also Called: Image Square Copy & Print
1627 Stanford St, Santa Monica
(90404-4113)
PHONE..................310 586-2333
Kavian Soudbakhsh, *President*
Ashkan Soudbakhsh, *President*
Jacquelyn Cubas, *Exec Dir*
Sepideh Soudbakhsh, *Admin Sec*
Thomas Allison, *Mktg Dir*
EMP: 11
SQ FT: 2,400
SALES (est): 2.6MM **Privately Held**
WEB: www.imagesquare.com
SIC: 2621 Printing paper

(P-5288)
INTERNATIONAL PAPER COMPANY
42305 Albrae St, Fremont (94538-3392)
PHONE..................510 490-5887
Jay Casos, *Manager*
EMP: 50
SQ FT: 60,805
SALES (corp-wide): 21.7B **Publicly Held**
WEB: www.internationalpaper.com
SIC: 2621 Paper mills
PA: International Paper Company
6400 Poplar Ave
Memphis TN 38197
901 419-9000

(P-5289)
INTERNATIONAL PAPER COMPANY
900 N Plaza Dr, Visalia (93291-8826)
PHONE..................559 651-1416
Derek Miller, *Branch Mgr*
EMP: 133
SALES (corp-wide): 21.7B **Publicly Held**
WEB: www.internationalpaper.com
SIC: 2621 Paper mills
PA: International Paper Company
6400 Poplar Ave
Memphis TN 38197
901 419-9000

(P-5290)
INTERNATIONAL PAPER COMPANY
1111 N Anderson Rd, Exeter (93221-9370)
PHONE..................559 592-7279
Rick Goddard, *Branch Mgr*
EMP: 60
SALES (corp-wide): 21.7B **Publicly Held**
WEB: www.internationalpaper.com
SIC: 2621 Paper mills
PA: International Paper Company
6400 Poplar Ave
Memphis TN 38197
901 419-9000

(P-5291)
INTERNATIONAL PAPER COMPANY
10268 Waterman Rd, Elk Grove
(95624-9403)
PHONE..................916 685-9000
Dave Carpenter, *Branch Mgr*
Ted Maloney, *Sales Executive*
EMP: 100
SALES (corp-wide): 21.7B **Publicly Held**
WEB: www.internationalpaper.com
SIC: 2621 Paper mills

PA: International Paper Company
6400 Poplar Ave
Memphis TN 38197
901 419-9000

(P-5292)
INTERNATIONAL PAPER COMPANY
6211 Descanso Ave, Buena Park
(90620-1012)
PHONE..................714 736-0296
Brian Evans, *Branch Mgr*
EMP: 168
SALES (corp-wide): 21.7B **Publicly Held**
SIC: 2621 Paper mills
PA: International Paper Company
6400 Poplar Ave
Memphis TN 38197
901 419-9000

(P-5293)
INTERNATIONAL PAPER COMPANY
6791 Alexander St, Gilroy (95020-6679)
PHONE..................408 846-2060
David Washer, *General Mgr*
EMP: 65
SALES (corp-wide): 21.7B **Publicly Held**
SIC: 2621 Printing paper
PA: International Paper Company
6400 Poplar Ave
Memphis TN 38197
901 419-9000

(P-5294)
INTERNATIONAL PAPER COMPANY
2000 Pleasant Valley Rd, Camarillo
(93010-8543)
PHONE..................805 933-4347
EMP: 11
SALES (corp-wide): 21.7B **Publicly Held**
SIC: 2621 Paper mills
PA: International Paper Company
6400 Poplar Ave
Memphis TN 38197
901 419-9000

(P-5295)
INTERNATIONAL PAPER COMPANY
19615 S Susana Rd, Compton
(90221-5717)
PHONE..................310 639-2310
Joseph Winters, *General Mgr*
EMP: 13
SALES (corp-wide): 21.7B **Publicly Held**
SIC: 2621 Paper mills
PA: International Paper Company
6400 Poplar Ave
Memphis TN 38197
901 419-9000

(P-5296)
INTERNATIONAL PAPER COMPANY
1000 Muscat Ave, Sanger (93657-4001)
PHONE..................559 875-3311
EMP: 16
SALES (corp-wide): 21.7B **Publicly Held**
SIC: 2621 Paper mills
PA: International Paper Company
6400 Poplar Ave
Memphis TN 38197
901 419-9000

(P-5297)
INTERNATIONAL PAPER COMPANY
14150 Artesia Blvd, Cerritos (90703-7032)
PHONE..................562 404-1856
Manuel Gutierrez, *Branch Mgr*
EMP: 10
SALES (corp-wide): 21.7B **Publicly Held**
SIC: 2621 Paper mills
PA: International Paper Company
6400 Poplar Ave
Memphis TN 38197
901 419-9000

(P-5298)
INTERNATIONAL PAPER COMPANY
11205 Knott Ave Ste A, Cypress
(90630-5489)
PHONE..................714 889-4900
EMP: 10
SALES (corp-wide): 21.7B **Publicly Held**
SIC: 2621 Paper mills
PA: International Paper Company
6400 Poplar Ave
Memphis TN 38197
901 419-9000

(P-5299)
INTERNATIONAL PAPER COMPANY
12851 Alondra Blvd, Norwalk (90650-6838)
PHONE..................562 483-6680
John Faraci, *President*
EMP: 13
SALES (corp-wide): 21.7B **Publicly Held**
SIC: 2621 Paper mills
PA: International Paper Company
6400 Poplar Ave
Memphis TN 38197
901 419-9000

(P-5300)
INTERNATIONAL PAPER COMPANY
1345 Harkins Rd, Salinas (93901-4408)
PHONE..................831 755-2100
Rosamaria Alcaraz, *Human Res Mgr*
MO Sepulveda, *Maintence Staff*
EMP: 11
SALES (corp-wide): 21.7B **Publicly Held**
SIC: 2621 Paper mills
PA: International Paper Company
6400 Poplar Ave
Memphis TN 38197
901 419-9000

(P-5301)
INTERNATIONAL PAPER COMPANY
6400 Jamieson Way, Gilroy (95020-6620)
PHONE..................408 847-6400
Michael Hayford, *Branch Mgr*
EMP: 92
SALES (corp-wide): 21.7B **Publicly Held**
WEB: www.tin.com
SIC: 2621 Paper mills
PA: International Paper Company
6400 Poplar Ave
Memphis TN 38197
901 419-9000

(P-5302)
INTERNATIONAL PAPER COMPANY
1714 Cebrian St, West Sacramento
(95691-3819)
PHONE..................916 371-4634
Clark Weiss, *Opers Staff*
EMP: 40
SALES (corp-wide): 21.7B **Publicly Held**
WEB: www.internationalpaper.com
SIC: 2621 Paper mills
PA: International Paper Company
6400 Poplar Ave
Memphis TN 38197
901 419-9000

(P-5303)
INTERNATIONAL PAPER COMPANY
9211 Norwalk Blvd, Santa Fe Springs
(90670-2923)
PHONE..................562 692-9465
Lee Bekiarian, *Branch Mgr*
Brian Perez, *Safety Mgr*
EMP: 150
SALES (corp-wide): 21.7B **Publicly Held**
WEB: www.tin.com
SIC: 2621 Paper mills
PA: International Paper Company
6400 Poplar Ave
Memphis TN 38197
901 419-9000

▲ = Import ▼=Export
◆ =Import/Export

(P-5304)
INTERNATIONAL PAPER COMPANY
1350 E 223rd St, Carson (90745-4381)
PHONE....................................310 549-5525
Melanie Kastner, *Branch Mgr*
John Berry, *Plant Mgr*
EMP: 150
SALES (corp-wide): 21.7B **Publicly Held**
WEB: www.internationalpaper.com
SIC: 2621 Paper mills
PA: International Paper Company
6400 Poplar Ave
Memphis TN 38197
901 419-9000

(P-5305)
INTERNATIONAL PAPER COMPANY
6485 Descanso Ave, Buena Park (90620-1016)
PHONE....................................562 868-2246
Bob Dickens, *General Mgr*
Robert Dickens, *General Mgr*
Stuard Putzeys, *Engineer*
EMP: 84
SQ FT: 74,826
SALES (corp-wide): 21.7B **Publicly Held**
WEB: www.internationalpaper.com
SIC: 2621 Paper mills
PA: International Paper Company
6400 Poplar Ave
Memphis TN 38197
901 419-9000

(P-5306)
J R C INDUSTRIES INC
11804 Wakeman St, Santa Fe Springs (90670-2129)
PHONE....................................562 698-0171
Leonard Fishelberg, *CEO*
EMP: 67
SQ FT: 32,000
SALES (est): 14.2MM **Privately Held**
SIC: 2621 Stationery, envelope & tablet papers

(P-5307)
KIMBERLY-CLARK CORPORATION
2001 E Orangethorpe Ave, Fullerton (92831-5396)
PHONE....................................714 578-0705
Rick Tucker, *Branch Mgr*
John Cisneros, *Planning*
Gary Hardesty, *Safety Mgr*
Joanne Han, *Manager*
EMP: 410
SQ FT: 3,000
SALES (corp-wide): 18.2B **Publicly Held**
WEB: www.kimberly-clark.com
SIC: 2621 2676 Sanitary tissue paper; sanitary paper products
PA: Kimberly-Clark Corporation
351 Phelps Dr
Irving TX 75038
972 281-1200

(P-5308)
KIMBERLY-CLARK CORPORATION
15260 Ventura Blvd # 1410, Van Nuys (91403-5307)
PHONE....................................818 986-2430
Troy Moore, *Branch Mgr*
EMP: 10
SQ FT: 3,000
SALES (corp-wide): 18.2B **Publicly Held**
WEB: www.kimberly-clark.com
SIC: 2621 2676 Sanitary tissue paper; infant & baby paper products
PA: Kimberly-Clark Corporation
351 Phelps Dr
Irving TX 75038
972 281-1200

(P-5309)
KUI CO INC
266 Calle Pintoresco, San Clemente (92672-7504)
PHONE....................................949 369-7949
Terry Daum, *President*
Sandy Daum, *CFO*
EMP: 40
SQ FT: 14,800

SALES: 3.5MM **Privately Held**
WEB: www.kuico.com
SIC: 2621 3089 Molded pulp products; plastic processing

(P-5310)
MAILWORKS INC
2513 Folex Way, Spring Valley (91978-2038)
PHONE....................................619 670-2365
Robert Hodges, *President*
EMP: 30
SALES (est): 5.6MM **Privately Held**
SIC: 2621 Printing paper

(P-5311)
METHOD HOME PRODUCTS
637 Commercial St Fl 3, San Francisco (94111-6515)
PHONE....................................415 568-4600
Steve Jurvetson, *Owner*
Stephanie Mann, *Director*
EMP: 13
SALES (est): 2.5MM **Privately Held**
SIC: 2621 Cleansing paper

(P-5312)
NAKAGAWA MANUFACTURING USA INC
8652 Thornton Ave, Newark (94560-3330)
PHONE....................................510 782-0197
Yuzuru Isshiki, *CEO*
Shinji Aoki, *President*
Tetsuya Isshiki, *President*
Teppei Tokura, *Controller*
Fumihiro Fujimaki, *Marketing Staff*
◆ EMP: 40
SQ FT: 40,000
SALES (est): 9.1MM
SALES (corp-wide): 113.6MM **Privately Held**
WEB: www.nakagawa-usa.com
SIC: 2621 Specialty papers
PA: Nakagawa Mfg.Co., Ltd.
2-5-21, Nishikicho
Warabi STM 335-0
484 448-211

(P-5313)
NASHUA CORPORATION
Rittenhouse
13341 Cambridge St, Santa Fe Springs (90670-4903)
PHONE....................................323 583-8828
EMP: 80
SQ FT: 57,600
SALES (corp-wide): 1.9B **Publicly Held**
SIC: 2621
HQ: Nashua Corporation
59 Daniel Webster Hwy A
Merrimack NH 03054
603 880-1100

(P-5314)
NATIONAL SALES INC
825 F St Ste 600, West Sacramento (95605-2389)
PHONE....................................916 912-2894
Majid Pasha, *President*
EMP: 12
SALES (est): 1.1MM **Privately Held**
SIC: 2621 Toilet tissue stock

(P-5315)
NEW-INDY CONTAINERBOARD LLC (DH)
Also Called: International Paper
3500 Porsche Way Ste 150, Ontario (91764-4969)
P.O. Box 519, Port Hueneme (93044-0519)
PHONE....................................909 296-3400
Richard Hartman, *CEO*
Mike Conkey, *Vice Pres*
Zhen Han, *Engineer*
Jeff Branch, *Purch Mgr*
Robyn Lebrilla, *Manager*
▲ EMP: 95
SALES: 332.3K
SALES (corp-wide): 36.5MM **Privately Held**
SIC: 2621 Paper mills
HQ: New-Indy Containerboard Hold Co Llc
5100 Jurupa St
Foxboro MA 02035
508 384-4230

(P-5316)
NEW-INDY ONTARIO LLC
Also Called: New-Indy Containerboard
5100 Jurupa St, Ontario (91761-3618)
PHONE....................................909 390-1055
Richard Hartman, *CEO*
Mike Conkey, *Vice Pres*
Scott Conant, *General Mgr*
George Johnston, *Maint Spvr*
EMP: 110
SALES: 345MM
SALES (corp-wide): 36.5MM **Privately Held**
SIC: 2621 Paper mills
HQ: New-Indy Containerboard Llc
3500 Porsche Way Ste 150
Ontario CA 91764
909 296-3400

(P-5317)
NEW-INDY OXNARD LLC
Also Called: New-Indy Containerboard
5936 Perkins Rd, Oxnard (93033-9044)
P.O. Box 519, Port Hueneme (93044-0519)
PHONE....................................805 986-3881
Richard Hartman, *CEO*
Mike Conkey, *Vice Pres*
Rudy Rehbein, *Plant Mgr*
▲ EMP: 224 EST: 2012
SALES: 345MM
SALES (corp-wide): 36.5MM **Privately Held**
SIC: 2621 Paper mills
HQ: New-Indy Containerboard Llc
3500 Porsche Way Ste 150
Ontario CA 91764
909 296-3400

(P-5318)
NOVACART
Also Called: Novacart USA
510 W Ohio Ave, Richmond (94804-2040)
P.O. Box 70579 (94807-0579)
PHONE....................................510 215-8999
Toll Free:........................877   -
Giorgio Angahileri, *President*
Guadalupe Gonzalez, *Accounting Mgr*
Patrick Wilson, *Opers Mgr*
Rick Botoff, *Natl Sales Mgr*
Jennie Doyle, *Manager*
▲ EMP: 10
SQ FT: 35,000
SALES: 7MM
SALES (corp-wide): 107.3K **Privately Held**
WEB: www.novacartusa.com
SIC: 2621 Molded pulp products
HQ: Novacart Spa
Via Europa 1
Garbagnate Monastero LC 23846
031 858-611

(P-5319)
OEM MATERIALS & SUPPLIES INC
1500 Ritchey St, Santa Ana (92705-4731)
PHONE....................................714 564-9600
Randall K Johnson, *CEO*
Wendy R King, *President*
Ana Garcia, *Manager*
EMP: 20
SALES (est): 7.9MM **Privately Held**
SIC: 2621 2631 5084 2671 Wrapping & packaging papers; container, packaging & boxboard; processing & packaging equipment; packaging paper & plastics film, coated & laminated

(P-5320)
PACIFIC MILLENNIUM US CORP
12526 High Bluff Dr # 300, San Diego (92130-2064)
PHONE....................................858 450-1505
Richard Tan, *President*
EMP: 17
SALES (est): 2MM **Privately Held**
SIC: 2621 Writing paper

(P-5321)
PACIFIC PULP MOLDING INC
11285 Forestview Ln, San Diego (92131-1359)
PHONE....................................619 977-5617
John McNeil, *CEO*
Christine Elliot, *Principal*
Armando Aguiar, *Plant Mgr*

EMP: 45
SQ FT: 25,000
SALES: 3MM **Privately Held**
SIC: 2621 Wrapping & packaging papers

(P-5322)
PAPER GROUP COMPANY LLC
15201 Woodlawn Ave # 200, Tustin (92780-6449)
PHONE....................................714 566-0025
Marie Van Vugt, *Mng Member*
▲ EMP: 40
SQ FT: 42,000
SALES (est): 7.8MM **Privately Held**
SIC: 2621 Facial tissue stock

(P-5323)
PAPER MAX INC (PA)
Also Called: Charta Global
100 S Anaheim Blvd # 250, Anaheim (92805-3872)
PHONE....................................714 780-0595
Rizal Setiadi, *CEO*
William Cho, *Principal*
▲ EMP: 10
SALES (est): 3.2MM **Privately Held**
SIC: 2621 Stationery, envelope & tablet papers

(P-5324)
PAPER SURCE CONVERTING MFG INC
Also Called: Soft-Touch Tissue
4800 S Santa Fe Ave, Vernon (90058-2104)
PHONE....................................323 583-3800
Jacob Khobian, *CEO*
Jonathan Khodabakhsh, *Vice Pres*
▲ EMP: 50
SQ FT: 55,000
SALES (est): 21.1MM **Privately Held**
WEB: www.papersourcemfg.com
SIC: 2621 Tissue paper; napkin stock, paper; facial tissue stock; toilet tissue stock

(P-5325)
PPS PACKAGING COMPANY
Also Called: Continental Enterprises
3189 E Manning Ave, Fowler (93625-9749)
P.O. Box 427 (93625-0427)
PHONE....................................559 834-1641
Thomas Wilson, *Ch of Bd*
Ray Casuga, *President*
Joni Hill, *CEO*
Jeff Thorp, *Purch Mgr*
Galen Van Aalsburg, *Manager*
▲ EMP: 75
SQ FT: 108,000
SALES (est): 19.2MM **Privately Held**
WEB: www.ppspackaging.com
SIC: 2621 Packaging paper

(P-5326)
PRATT INDUSTRIES INC
2643 Industrial Pkwy Ofc, Santa Maria (93455-1536)
PHONE....................................805 348-1097
Robert Mann, *President*
Larry Garcia, *Accounts Mgr*
EMP: 20
SALES (corp-wide): 2.5B **Privately Held**
WEB: www.rmp.com
SIC: 2621 Paper mills
PA: Pratt Industries, Inc.
1800 Sarasota Busin Ste C
Conyers GA 30013
770 918-5678

(P-5327)
PRATT INDUSTRIES INC
Also Called: Robert Mann Packaging
3931 Oceanic Dr, Oceanside (92056-5846)
PHONE....................................760 966-9170
Steve Clarke, *Branch Mgr*
EMP: 26
SQ FT: 13,000
SALES (corp-wide): 2.5B **Privately Held**
SIC: 2621 Packaging paper
PA: Pratt Industries, Inc.
1800 Sarasota Busin Ste C
Conyers GA 30013
770 918-5678

PRODUCTS & SVCS

(P-5328)
PRATT INDUSTRIES INC
2131 E Louise Ave, Lathrop (95330-9607)
PHONE.................................770 922-0117
Ron McComas, *General Mgr*
EMP: 110
SALES (corp-wide): 2.5B **Privately Held**
SIC: 2621 Packaging paper
PA: Pratt Industries, Inc.
1800 Sarasota Busin Ste C
Conyers GA 30013
770 918-5678

(P-5329)
PRATT INDUSTRIES INC
3931 Oceanic Dr, Oceanside (92056-5846)
PHONE.................................760 966-9170
Steve Clarke, *Manager*
Maria Chavez,
Richard Armstrong, *Accounts Mgr*
Joe Cannon, *Accounts Mgr*
Joe Fleskoski, *Accounts Mgr*
EMP: 10
SALES (corp-wide): 2.5B **Privately Held**
WEB: www.rmp.com
SIC: 2621 Packaging paper
PA: Pratt Industries, Inc.
1800 Sarasota Busin Ste C
Conyers GA 30013
770 918-5678

(P-5330)
PRATT INDUSTRIES INC
223 W Riverside Dr, Watsonville
(95076-5101)
PHONE.................................831 763-0630
Jeff Diciccico, *President*
EMP: 20
SALES (corp-wide): 2.5B **Privately Held**
WEB: www.rmp.com
SIC: 2621 Packaging paper
PA: Pratt Industries, Inc.
1800 Sarasota Busin Ste C
Conyers GA 30013
770 918-5678

(P-5331)
PRATT INDUSTRIES INC
1051 S Rose Ave, Oxnard (93030-5180)
PHONE.................................805 483-5331
Richard Meyers, *Manager*
EMP: 50
SALES (corp-wide): 2.5B **Privately Held**
WEB: www.rmp.com
SIC: 2621 Packaging paper
PA: Pratt Industries, Inc.
1800 Sarasota Busin Ste C
Conyers GA 30013
770 918-5678

(P-5332)
RONPAK INC
10900 San Sevaine Way, Mira Loma
(91752-1138)
PHONE.................................951 685-3800
Paul Warg, *Opers-Prdtn-Mfg*
Valerie Casas, *QA Dir*
Charlotte Reese, *Manager*
EMP: 49
SALES (corp-wide): 73.2MM **Privately Held**
WEB: www.ronpak.com
SIC: 2621 2673 2671 Bag paper; bags:
plastic, laminated & coated; packaging
paper & plastics film, coated & laminated
PA: Ronpak, Inc
1 Nathan Sedley Rd
Shreveport LA 71115
318 219-4300

(P-5333)
SAN DIEGO DAILY TRANSCRIPT
34 Emerald Gln, Laguna Niguel
(92677-9379)
PHONE.................................619 232-4381
Ed Frederickson, *President*
EMP: 63 **EST:** 1886
SQ FT: 30,000
SALES (est): 11.3MM
SALES (corp-wide): 13.4MM **Privately Held**
WEB: www.sddt.com
SIC: 2621 4813 Printing paper;

PA: Calcomco, Inc.
5544 S Red Pine Cir
Kalamazoo MI 49009
313 885-9228

(P-5334)
SIERRA HYGIENE PRODUCTS LLC
4749 Bennett Dr Ste B, Livermore
(94551-4806)
PHONE.................................925 371-7173
Doug Johnson,
John Perterson,
▼ **EMP:** 10
SQ FT: 1,600
SALES (est): 1.9MM **Privately Held**
WEB: www.sierrahygiene.com
SIC: 2621 Tissue paper

(P-5335)
SMALL PAPER CO INC
2559 E 56th St, Huntington Park
(90255-2516)
PHONE.................................323 277-0525
Federico Rodriguez, *President*
Gracia Rodriguez, *Principal*
EMP: 10
SALES (est): 1.6MM **Privately Held**
SIC: 2621 Paper mills

(P-5336)
SMITHCORP INC
Also Called: Green Field Paper Company
7196 Clairemont Mesa Blvd, San Diego
(92111-1005)
PHONE.................................888 402-9979
Frederick Smith, *President*
Shari Smith, *CEO*
EMP: 10
SALES (est): 1.9MM **Privately Held**
SIC: 2621 Wrapping & packaging papers

(P-5337)
SPILL MAGIC INC
630 Young St, Santa Ana (92705-5633)
PHONE.................................714 557-2001
Susan Wampler, *President*
David Wampler, *Vice Pres*
▲ **EMP:** 22
SQ FT: 30,000
SALES (est): 950.4K **Privately Held**
WEB: www.spillmagic.com
SIC: 2621 Absorbent paper

(P-5338)
ZIP NOTES LLC
2822 Van Ness Ave, San Francisco
(94109-1426)
PHONE.................................415 931-8020
Maurice Kanbar,
EMP: 10
SQ FT: 6,800
SALES (est): 900K **Privately Held**
SIC: 2621 Stationery, envelope & tablet papers

2631 Paperboard Mills

(P-5339)
ALL STARS PACKAGING INC
Also Called: All Stars Packaging & Display
13851 Roswell Ave Ste H, Chino
(91710-5471)
PHONE.................................626 664-3797
Elizabeth Pereyra, *Principal*
EMP: 12
SALES (est): 800K **Privately Held**
SIC: 2631 Container, packaging & boxboard

(P-5340)
AMIMON INC
2350 Mission College Blvd # 190, Santa
Clara (95054-1542)
PHONE.................................650 641-3191
Yoav Nissan Cohen, *President*
EMP: 13
SALES (est): 1.8MM **Privately Held**
SIC: 2631
PA: Amimon Ltd
26 Zarchin Alexander
Raanana
996 292-00

(P-5341)
BUZZ CONVERTING INC
4343 E Fremont St, Stockton (95215-4032)
PHONE.................................209 948-1341
Merlin Davis Jr, *President*
Jeff Vandan Baum, *General Mgr*
EMP: 17
SQ FT: 35,000
SALES (est): 2.5MM **Privately Held**
SIC: 2631 Chip board

(P-5342)
C B SHEETS INC
13901 Carmenita Rd, Santa Fe Springs
(90670-4916)
PHONE.................................562 921-1223
John Widera, *CEO*
Mackey Davis, *President*
EMP: 21 **EST:** 2001
SALES (est): 3.2MM
SALES (corp-wide): 21.7MM **Privately Held**
SIC: 2631 Cardboard
PA: California Box Company
13901 Carmenita Rd
Santa Fe Springs CA 90670
562 921-1223

(P-5343)
CALIFORNIA TRADE CONVERTERS
13299 Louvre St, Pacoima (91331-2319)
PHONE.................................818 899-1455
Carlos Martinez, *President*
EMP: 25
SALES (est): 1.7MM **Privately Held**
SIC: 2631 2675 Paperboard mills; paper die-cutting

(P-5344)
CARAUSTAR INDUSTRIES INC
Newark Recovery & Recycling
800b W Church St, Stockton (95203-3206)
P.O. Box 58044, Santa Clara (95052-8044)
PHONE.................................209 464-6590
Mark Vincent, *Opers-Prdtn-Mfg*
Ronald Lewis, *MIS Staff*
Sam Franco, *Persnl Mgr*
EMP: 250
SQ FT: 480,000
SALES (corp-wide): 1.7B **Privately Held**
WEB: www.newarkgroup.com
SIC: 2631 Paperboard mills
PA: Caraustar Industries, Inc.
5000 Astell Pwdr Sprng Rd
Austell GA 30106
770 948-3101

(P-5345)
CARAUSTAR INDUSTRIES INC
Also Called: California Paperboard
525 Mathew St, Santa Clara (95050-3001)
P.O. Box 58044 (95052-8044)
PHONE.................................408 845-7600
Stephen G Blankenship, *Manager*
Larry Lacotti, *Marketing Staff*
EMP: 120
SQ FT: 61,005
SALES (corp-wide): 1.7B **Privately Held**
WEB: www.newarkgroup.com
SIC: 2631 Paperboard mills
PA: Caraustar Industries, Inc.
5000 Astell Pwdr Sprng Rd
Austell GA 30106
770 948-3101

(P-5346)
DERIK PLASTICS INDUSTRIES INC
2540 Corp Pl Ste B100, Monterey Park
(91754)
PHONE.................................626 371-7799
Derik Zhang, *President*
EMP: 700
SALES (est): 35.3MM **Privately Held**
SIC: 2631 Container, packaging & boxboard

(P-5347)
EDWIN T SEKI INC
Also Called: Arco Industries-Western
14711 Sinclair Cir, Tustin (92780-7225)
P.O. Box 62497, Irvine (92602-6083)
PHONE.................................714 838-1177
Edwin T Seki, *President*

EMP: 18
SQ FT: 11,800
SALES (est): 3.2MM **Privately Held**
SIC: 2631 Binders' board

(P-5348)
FINN INDUSTRIES INC
2000 Chota Rd, La Habra Heights
(90631-8406)
PHONE.................................909 930-1500
William L Finn, *CEO*
Bruce Altshuler, *Corp Secy*
▲ **EMP:** 50 **EST:** 1931
SQ FT: 80,000
SALES (est): 11.4MM **Privately Held**
WEB: www.finnindustriesinc.com
SIC: 2631 Folding boxboard; setup boxboard

(P-5349)
FIRST CLASS PACKAGING INC
280 Cypress Ln Ste D, El Cajon
(92020-1662)
PHONE.................................619 579-7166
Sandra L Brock, *President*
EMP: 22
SQ FT: 18,500
SALES (est): 6.4MM **Privately Held**
WEB: www.firstclasspack.com
SIC: 2631 2449 3086 5085 Packaging
board; rectangular boxes & crates, wood;
plastics foam products; bins & containers,
storage; corrugated & solid fiber boxes;
nailed wood boxes & shook

(P-5350)
GRAPHIC PACKAGING INTL INC
1600 Barranca Pkwy, Irvine (92606-4823)
PHONE.................................949 250-0900
Wendy Shute, *Sales Staff*
Ottie Gamboz, *Telecom Exec*
Cheryl Kennard, *Controller*
Mike Croft, *Foreman/Supr*
Wayne Reichenthaler, *Manager*
EMP: 240 **Publicly Held**
SIC: 2631 Folding boxboard
HQ: Graphic Packaging International, Llc
1500 Riveredge Pkwy # 100
Atlanta GA 30328

(P-5351)
INTERNATIONAL PAPER COMPANY
660 Mariposa Rd, Modesto (95354-4130)
P.O. Box 3171 (95353-3171)
PHONE.................................209 526-4700
Rick Fritz, *Branch Mgr*
Kelly Huhn, *Engineer*
Paul Edds, *Human Res Dir*
EMP: 130
SQ FT: 165,196
SALES (corp-wide): 21.7B **Publicly Held**
WEB: www.internationalpaper.com
SIC: 2631 2653 Corrugating medium; corrugated & solid fiber boxes
PA: International Paper Company
6400 Poplar Ave
Memphis TN 38197
901 419-9000

(P-5352)
INTERNATIONAL PAPER COMPANY
3551 E Francis St, Ontario (91761-2926)
PHONE.................................909 605-2540
Jim Elder, *Opers-Prdtn-Mfg*
EMP: 61
SALES (corp-wide): 21.7B **Publicly Held**
WEB: www.internationalpaper.com
SIC: 2631 2672 2621 Setup boxboard;
coated & laminated paper; paper mills
PA: International Paper Company
6400 Poplar Ave
Memphis TN 38197
901 419-9000

(P-5353)
INTERPRESS TECHNOLOGIES INC (HQ)
1120 Del Paso Rd, Sacramento
(95834-7737)
PHONE.................................916 929-9771
Roderick W Miner, *President*
Peter Fox, *President*

◆ EMP: 50
SQ FT: 20,000
SALES: 30MM Privately Held
WEB: www.interpresstechnologies.com
SIC: 2631 Folding boxboard
PA: R. W. Miner Corporation
260 California St Ste 300
San Francisco CA 94111
415 781-2626

(P-5354)
LOS ANGELES BOARD MILLS INC
Also Called: Los Angeles Ppr Box & Bd Mills
6027 S Eastern Ave, Commerce
(90040-3413)
PHONE.................................323 685-8900
William H Kewell III, President
Carol A Kewell, Corp Secy
EMP: 150
SQ FT: 300,000
SALES (est): 28.9MM Privately Held
WEB: www.lapb.com
SIC: 2631 2652 2653 5113 Folding
boxboard; packaging board; setup
boxboard; setup paperboard boxes;
boxes, corrugated: made from purchased
materials; industrial & personal service
paper; folding paperboard boxes

(P-5355)
MAXCO SUPPLY INC
2059 E Olsen Ave, Reedley (93654)
P.O. Box 814, Parlier (93648-0814)
PHONE.................................559 638-8449
Roy Ortega, Manager
EMP: 60
SQ FT: 50,550
SALES (corp-wide): 151.4MM Privately Held
SIC: 2631 Cardboard
PA: Maxco Supply, Inc.
605 S Zediker Ave
Parlier CA 93648
559 646-8449

(P-5356)
ONE UP MANUFACTURING LLC
2555 E Del Amo Blvd, Compton
(90221-6001)
PHONE.................................310 749-8347
Nielson Ballon, Mng Member
Kavish Mehta,
Nathan Miller,
EMP: 25
SQ FT: 15,000
SALES: 500K Privately Held
SIC: 2631 Container, packaging &
boxboard

(P-5357)
ORGANIC BOTTLE DCTG CO LLC
Also Called: Zion Packaging
575 Alcoa Cir Ste B, Corona (92880-9203)
PHONE.................................951 335-4600
Gary Martin,
EMP: 20 EST: 2013
SALES: 2MM Privately Held
SIC: 2631 2759 Container, packaging &
boxboard; screen printing

(P-5358)
PACKAGING DIST ASSEMBLY GROUP
Also Called: Pda Group
24730 Avenue Rockefeller, Valencia
(91355-3465)
PHONE.................................661 607-0600
▲ EMP: 13
SALES (est): 2MM Privately Held
SIC: 2631 Container, packaging &
boxboard

(P-5359)
SANTA ANA PACKAGING INC
14655 Firestone Blvd, La Mirada
(90638-5916)
PHONE.................................714 670-6397
Ning Yen, CEO
Michael Nguyen, General Mgr
Sean Cumby, Warehouse Mgr
Peter Yen, Manager
▲ EMP: 10

SALES (est): 2.5MM Privately Held
SIC: 2631 Container, packaging &
boxboard

(P-5360)
SIMPLE CONTAINER SOLUTIONS INC
Also Called: Insulated Products
250 W Artesia Blvd, Rancho Dominguez
(90220-5500)
PHONE.................................310 638-0900
Charles Veiseh, President
▲ EMP: 27
SQ FT: 100,000
SALES: 21MM Privately Held
SIC: 2631 Container, packaging &
boxboard

(P-5361)
SONOCO PRODUCTS COMPANY
Also Called: Sonoco Industrial Products Div
166 Baldwin Park Blvd, City of Industry
(91746-1498)
PHONE.................................626 369-6611
Dhamo Srinivasan, Opers-Prdtn-Mfg
EMP: 100
SALES (corp-wide): 5B Publicly Held
WEB: www.sonoco.com
SIC: 2631 2611 Paperboard mills; pulp
mills
PA: Sonoco Products Company
1 N 2nd St
Hartsville SC 29550
843 383-7000

(P-5362)
SONOCO PRODUCTS COMPANY
12851 Leyva St, Norwalk (90650-6853)
PHONE.................................562 921-0881
Jeff Blaine, Opers-Prdtn-Mfg
EMP: 55
SQ FT: 164,934
SALES (corp-wide): 5B Publicly Held
WEB: www.sonoco.com
SIC: 2631 2655 Paperboard mills; fiber
cans, drums & similar products
PA: Sonoco Products Company
1 N 2nd St
Hartsville SC 29550
843 383-7000

(P-5363)
UNION CARBIDE CORPORATION
19206 Hawthorne Blvd, Torrance
(90503-1590)
PHONE.................................310 214-5300
Patrick E Gottschalk, Principal
EMP: 60
SQ FT: 15,269
SALES (corp-wide): 62.4B Publicly Held
SIC: 2631 Latex board
HQ: Union Carbide Corporation
1254 Enclave Pkwy
Houston TX 77077
281 966-2727

(P-5364)
WALLY INTERNATIONAL INC (PA)
20520 E Walnut Dr N, Walnut
(91789-2925)
PHONE.................................805 444-7764
Yibin Gu, CEO
Fend Zhou, Vice Pres
EMP: 200 EST: 2015
SALES: 2.6MM Privately Held
SIC: 2631 3423 Container, packaging &
boxboard; hand & edge tools

(P-5365)
WESTROCK CP LLC
2710 O St, Bakersfield (93301-2446)
PHONE.................................661 327-3841
Judy Walker, Office Mgr
EMP: 10
SALES (corp-wide): 14.8B Publicly Held
WEB: www.sto.com
SIC: 2631 Paperboard mills
HQ: Westrock Cp, Llc
504 Thrasher St
Norcross GA 30071

(P-5366)
WESTROCK CP LLC
205 E Alma Ave, San Jose (95112-5902)
PHONE.................................770 448-2193
David Blavin, Controller
EMP: 35
SALES (corp-wide): 14.8B Publicly Held
WEB: www.sto.com
SIC: 2631 Paperboard mills
HQ: Westrock Cp, Llc
504 Thrasher St
Norcross GA 30071

(P-5367)
WESTROCK CP LLC
24 S Thorne Ave, Fresno (93706-1460)
P.O. Box 12303 (93777-2303)
PHONE.................................559 441-1166
Bob Kuhn, Manager
EMP: 19
SALES (corp-wide): 14.8B Publicly Held
WEB: www.sto.com
SIC: 2631 Paperboard mills
HQ: Westrock Cp, Llc
504 Thrasher St
Norcross GA 30071

(P-5368)
WESTROCK CP LLC
Also Called: Corpak of Tulare
701 E Continental Ave, Tulare
(93274-6813)
PHONE.................................559 685-1102
Eric Miller, Branch Mgr
EMP: 70
SALES (corp-wide): 14.8B Publicly Held
SIC: 2631 Paperboard mills
HQ: Westrock Cp, Llc
504 Thrasher St
Norcross GA 30071

(P-5369)
WESTROCK CP LLC
4800 Florin Perkins Rd, Sacramento
(95826-4813)
PHONE.................................916 379-2200
Richard Garmsen, Manager
EMP: 50
SALES (corp-wide): 14.8B Publicly Held
WEB: www.sto.com
SIC: 2631 2611 Paperboard mills; pulp
mills
HQ: Westrock Cp, Llc
504 Thrasher St
Norcross GA 30071

(P-5370)
WESTROCK CP LLC
2540 S Main St, Santa Ana (92707-3430)
PHONE.................................714 641-8891
Rob Allen, General Mgr
EMP: 20
SALES (corp-wide): 14.8B Publicly Held
WEB: www.sto.com
SIC: 2631 Paperboard mills
HQ: Westrock Cp, Llc
504 Thrasher St
Norcross GA 30071

(P-5371)
WESTROCK CP LLC
Smurfit Stone Container
15300 Marquardt Ave, Santa Fe Springs
(90670)
PHONE.................................714 523-3550
Robert Simonds, Manager
EMP: 55
SALES (corp-wide): 14.8B Publicly Held
WEB: www.sto.com
SIC: 2631 Paperboard mills
HQ: Westrock Cp, Llc
504 Thrasher St
Norcross GA 30071

(P-5372)
WESTROCK CP LLC
3003 N San Fernando Blvd, Burbank
(91504-2525)
PHONE.................................818 557-1500
Sue Woldanski, Manager

EMP: 25
SALES (corp-wide): 14.8B Publicly Held
WEB: www.smurfit-stone.com
SIC: 2631 Container board
HQ: Westrock Cp, Llc
504 Thrasher St
Norcross GA 30071

(P-5373)
WESTROCK MWV LLC
15750 Mountain Ave, Chino (91708-9120)
PHONE.................................909 597-2197
Pete Miller, COO
EMP: 300
SALES (corp-wide): 14.8B Publicly Held
WEB: www.meadwestvaco.com
SIC: 2631 Paperboard mills
HQ: Westrock Mwv, Llc
501 S 5th St
Richmond VA 23219
804 444-1000

```
2652 Set-Up Paperboard
Boxes
```

(P-5374)
CORRU-KRAFT IV
1911 E Rosslynn Ave, Fullerton
(92831-5141)
PHONE.................................714 773-0124
Bob Dunford, Principal
Ron Crawford, Plant Mgr
Ron Vivian, Sales Mgr
EMP: 15
SALES (est): 5.3MM Privately Held
SIC: 2652 Setup paperboard boxes

(P-5375)
CUSTOM PAPER PRODUCTS
2360 Teagarden St, San Leandro
(94577-4341)
PHONE.................................510 352-6880
Robert W Field Jr, President
Frank Leyva, COO
Mona Bano, Manager
EMP: 70
SQ FT: 100,000
SALES (est): 16.1MM Privately Held
WEB: www.custompaperproducts.com
SIC: 2652 3089 Filing boxes, paperboard:
made from purchased materials; boxes,
plastic

(P-5376)
DAVID DULEY
700 La Cresta Blvd, San Marcos (92079)
PHONE.................................619 449-8556
David Daley, Owner
EMP: 55
SALES (est): 4.1MM Privately Held
SIC: 2652 Setup paperboard boxes

(P-5377)
JAMACO ENTERPRISES INC
Also Called: Westcoast Business Solutions
5331 Derry Ave Ste L, Agoura Hills
(91301-3386)
PHONE.................................818 991-2050
Bradley C Schwartz, President
EMP: 10
SQ FT: 2,500
SALES (est): 2.2MM Privately Held
WEB: www.solutionspartner.com
SIC: 2652 2754 2759 2761 Filing boxes,
paperboard: made from purchased materials; business forms: gravure printing;
seals: gravure printing; stationery:
gravure printing; financial note & certificate printing & engraving; continuous
forms, office & business; embossing
seals, corporate & official; value-added
resellers, computer systems

(P-5378)
MOZAIK LLC
2330 Artesia Ave Ste B, Fullerton
(92833-2566)
PHONE.................................562 207-1900
Paul Bellamy, Mng Member
Laurie Hilton,
Kevin Stein,
▲ EMP: 12
SQ FT: 27,000

SALES: 12MM **Privately Held**
SIC: 2652 Filing boxes, paperboard: made
from purchased materials

(P-5379)
PACIFIC PAPER BOX COMPANY (PA)
3928 Encino Hills Pl, Encino (91436-3804)
PHONE....................................323 771-7733
Craig T Harrison, *CEO*
Bud Erhardt, *President*
EMP: 31
SQ FT: 70,000
SALES (est): 5.6MM **Privately Held**
WEB: www.pacificpaperbox.com
SIC: 2652 Boxes, newsboard, metal
edged: made from purchased materials

(P-5380)
WESTROCK RKT LLC
1854 E Home Ave, Fresno (93703-3636)
PHONE....................................559 441-1181
Wes Gentles, *General Mgr*
EMP: 11
SQ FT: 50,000
SALES (corp-wide): 14.8B **Publicly Held**
WEB: www.rocktenn.com
SIC: 2652 2631 Setup paperboard boxes;
paperboard mills
HQ: Westrock Rkt, Llc
1000 Abernathy Rd Ste 125
Atlanta GA 30328
770 448-2193

2653 Corrugated & Solid Fiber Boxes

(P-5381)
ABEX DISPLAY SYSTEMS INC (PA)
Also Called: Abex Exhibit Systems
355 Parkside Dr, San Fernando
(91340-3036)
PHONE....................................800 537-0231
Robbie Blumenfeld, *President*
Peter Blumenfeld, *Vice Pres*
Max Candiotty, *Vice Pres*
Keri Negosian, *Human Resources*
Alex Soto, *VP Opers*
▲ EMP: 105
SQ FT: 85,000
SALES (est): 17.7MM **Privately Held**
WEB: www.abex.com
SIC: 2653 2541 Display items, solid fiber:
made from purchased materials; store &
office display cases & fixtures

(P-5382)
ADVANCE PAPER BOX COMPANY
Also Called: Packaging Spectrum
6100 S Gramercy Pl, Los Angeles
(90047-1397)
PHONE....................................323 750-2550
Martin Gardner, *CEO*
Carlo Mendoza, *CFO*
Nick Silk, *Treasurer*
Devan Gardner, *Vice Pres*
Evan Gardner, *Administration*
▲ EMP: 250
SQ FT: 500,000
SALES (est): 80.9MM **Privately Held**
WEB: www.packagingspectrum.com
SIC: 2653 3082 Boxes, corrugated: made
from purchased materials; boxes, solid
fiber: made from purchased materials; un-
supported plastics profile shapes

(P-5383)
AMERICAN CONTAINERS INC
813 W Luce St Ste B, Stockton
(95203-4937)
PHONE....................................209 460-1127
Robert Calverly, *Branch Mgr*
EMP: 25
SALES (corp-wide): 33.8MM **Privately Held**
SIC: 2653 Corrugated boxes, partitions,
display items, sheets & pad
PA: American Containers, Inc
2526 Western Ave
Plymouth IN 46563
574 936-4068

(P-5384)
ANDROP PACKAGING INC
Also Called: Ontario Foam Products
4400 E Francis St, Ontario (91761-2327)
PHONE....................................909 605-8842
Cesar Flores, *President*
Larry Urane, *VP Sls/Mktg*
▲ EMP: 23
SQ FT: 52,000
SALES (est): 6.3MM **Privately Held**
WEB: www.androppackaging.com
SIC: 2653 3086 Boxes, corrugated: made
from purchased materials; plastics foam
products

(P-5385)
AWARD PACKAGING SPC CORP
12855 Midway Pl, Cerritos (90703-2141)
PHONE....................................323 727-1200
Alfred Espinoza, *CEO*
Virginia S Espinoza, *Treasurer*
EMP: 40
SQ FT: 800
SALES (est): 10.3MM **Privately Held**
SIC: 2653 Boxes, corrugated: made from
purchased materials

(P-5386)
BAY CITIES CONTAINER CORP (PA)
5138 Industry Ave, Pico Rivera
(90660-2550)
PHONE....................................562 948-3751
Greg A Tucker, *CEO*
Brett Kirkpatrick, *COO*
Patrick Donohoe, *CFO*
Jen Chen, *Admin Sec*
Lizette Pineda, *Controller*
▲ EMP: 143
SALES (est): 59.6MM **Privately Held**
WEB: www.bay-cities.com
SIC: 2653 3993 5113 Boxes, corrugated:
made from purchased materials; display
items, corrugated: made from purchased
materials; signs & advertising specialties;
corrugated & solid fiber boxes; folding pa-
perboard boxes

(P-5387)
BAYCORR PACKAGING INC (PA)
Also Called: Heritage Paper Co
6850 Brisa St, Livermore (94550-2521)
P.O. Box 44441, San Francisco (94144-0001)
PHONE....................................925 449-1148
John Tatum, *CEO*
Richard Heinz, *President*
Dick Heinz, *Personnel Exec*
▲ EMP: 130
SQ FT: 129,000
SALES (est): 35.1MM **Privately Held**
WEB: www.heritagepaper.com
SIC: 2653 5113 Boxes, corrugated: made
from purchased materials; corrugated &
solid fiber boxes

(P-5388)
BEST BOX COMPANY INC
Also Called: A1 Carton Co
8011 Beach St, Los Angeles (90001-3424)
PHONE....................................323 589-6088
Jay Kim, *President*
EMP: 15
SQ FT: 38,000
SALES (est): 1MM **Privately Held**
WEB: www.best-box.com
SIC: 2653 Boxes, corrugated: made from
purchased materials

(P-5389)
BESTWALL LLC
Also Called: Georgia-Pacific
15500 Valley View Ave, La Mirada
(90638-5230)
PHONE....................................714 521-4270
David Rieser, *Sales/Mktg Mgr*
Sergio Morales, *Manager*
Victor Vicuna, *Manager*
EMP: 225
SALES (corp-wide): 42.9B **Privately Held**
WEB: www.gp.com
SIC: 2653 5113 Boxes, corrugated: made
from purchased materials; corrugated &
solid fiber boxes

HQ: Georgia-Pacific Llc
133 Peachtree St Nw
Atlanta GA 30303
404 652-4000

(P-5390)
BLOWER-DEMPSAY CORPORATION
Also Called: Pacific Western Container
4044 W Garry Ave, Santa Ana
(92704-6300)
PHONE....................................714 547-9266
Ken Ito, *Manager*
EMP: 100
SQ FT: 30,000
SALES (corp-wide): 156.9MM **Privately Held**
SIC: 2653 5199 5113 Boxes, corrugated:
made from purchased materials; packag-
ing materials; corrugated & solid fiber
boxes
PA: Blower-Dempsay Corporation
4042 W Garry Ave
Santa Ana CA 92704
714 481-3800

(P-5391)
BLUE RIBBON CONT & DISPLAY INC
11106 Shoemaker Ave, Santa Fe Springs
(90670-4647)
PHONE....................................562 944-1217
Kenneth G Overfield, *President*
EMP: 15
SQ FT: 32,000
SALES (est): 3.3MM **Privately Held**
WEB: www.brcbox.com
SIC: 2653 5199 5113 Boxes, corrugated:
made from purchased materials; packag-
ing materials; boxes & containers

(P-5392)
CAL SHEETS LLC
1212 Performance Dr, Stockton
(95206-4925)
P.O. Box 30370 (95213-0370)
PHONE....................................209 234-3300
Rick Goddard, *CEO*
Scott Sherman, *President*
Pete Brodie, *CFO*
Bill Cullers, *Plant Mgr*
Joe Escobar, *Mng Member*
▲ EMP: 68
SQ FT: 203,000
SALES (est): 27.3MM
SALES (corp-wide): 20.5MM **Privately Held**
WEB: www.calsheets.com
SIC: 2653 Sheets, corrugated: made from
purchased materials
PA: Golden West Packaging Group Llc
8333 24th Ave
Sacramento CA 95826
404 345-8365

(P-5393)
CALIFORNIA BOX II
8949 Toronto Ave, Rancho Cucamonga
(91730-5412)
PHONE....................................909 944-9202
John Widera, *CEO*
Mackey Davis, *Vice Pres*
EMP: 45
SQ FT: 100,000
SALES (est): 9.4MM **Privately Held**
WEB: www.calbox.com
SIC: 2653 5113 Boxes, corrugated: made
from purchased materials; corrugated &
solid fiber boxes

(P-5394)
CAPITAL CORRUGATED LLC
Also Called: Capital Corrugated and Carton
8333 24th Ave, Sacramento (95826-4809)
P.O. Box 278060 (95827-8060)
PHONE....................................916 388-7848
Dennis D Watson, *President*
▲ EMP: 80
SQ FT: 124,000

SALES (est): 26.9MM
SALES (corp-wide): 20.5MM **Privately Held**
WEB: www.capitalcorrugated.com
SIC: 2653 Boxes, corrugated: made from
purchased materials; display items, corrugated: made from purchased materials;
sheets, corrugated: made from purchased
materials; partitions, corrugated: made
from purchased materials
PA: Golden West Packaging Group Llc
8333 24th Ave
Sacramento CA 95826
404 345-8365

(P-5395)
CD CONTAINER INC
Also Called: Carton Design
7343 Paramount Blvd, Pico Rivera
(90660-3713)
PHONE....................................562 948-1910
Juan De La Cruz, *President*
Jose De La Cruz, *CFO*
▲ EMP: 70
SQ FT: 46,000
SALES (est): 16.3MM **Privately Held**
SIC: 2653 Boxes, corrugated: made from
purchased materials

(P-5396)
CITY PAPER BOX CO
652 E 61st St, Los Angeles (90001-1021)
PHONE....................................323 231-5990
Stanley Goodrich, *President*
Maurey Friedman, *Vice Pres*
Frieda Goodrich, *Vice Pres*
Michael Goodrich, *Vice Pres*
Abe Friedman, *Executive*
EMP: 16
SQ FT: 9,000
SALES (est): 2.9MM **Privately Held**
SIC: 2653 Boxes, corrugated: made from
purchased materials

(P-5397)
COASTAL CONTAINER INC
8455 Loch Lomond Dr, Pico Rivera
(90660-2508)
PHONE....................................562 801-4595
Richard Rudell, *President*
Roberta Noble, *Treasurer*
EMP: 30
SQ FT: 3,000
SALES (est): 5.8MM **Privately Held**
WEB: www.coastalcontainer.com
SIC: 2653 5113 Boxes, corrugated: made
from purchased materials; corrugated &
solid fiber boxes

(P-5398)
COLOR-BOX LLC
Also Called: Georgia-Pacific
1275 S Granada Dr, Madera (93637-4803)
PHONE....................................559 674-1049
Tim McCoy, *Manager*
EMP: 50
SQ FT: 107,424
SALES (corp-wide): 42.9B **Privately Held**
WEB: www.gp.com
SIC: 2653 2657 Corrugated & solid fiber
boxes; folding paperboard boxes
HQ: Color-Box Llc
623 S G St
Richmond IN 47374
765 966-7588

(P-5399)
COMMANDER PACKAGING WEST INC
602 S Rockefeller Ave D, Ontario
(91761-8191)
PHONE....................................714 921-9350
Joseph F Kindlon, *Ch of Bd*
Brian R Webber, *President*
Emilia Diaz, *Office Mgr*
EMP: 37
SQ FT: 48,000
SALES (est): 8MM
SALES (corp-wide): 10.8MM **Privately Held**
WEB: www.commanderpackagingwest.com
SIC: 2653 7389 5113 Boxes, corrugated:
made from purchased materials; packag-
ing & labeling services; corrugated & solid
fiber boxes

PA: Cano Container Corporation
3920 Enterprise Ct Ste A
Aurora IL 60504
630 585-7500

(P-5400)
COMPRO PACKAGING LLC
Also Called: Bayline
1600 Atlantic St, Union City (94587-2017)
PHONE..................510 475-0118
Michael Ramelot, *President*
John Roberts, *Ch of Bd*
Donald Cook, *Vice Pres*
EMP: 50
SQ FT: 75,000
SALES (est): 4.2MM Privately Held
SIC: 2653 2679 5113 Boxes, corrugated:
made from purchased materials; corrugated paper: made from purchased material; industrial & personal service paper

(P-5401)
**CORRUGADOS DE BAJA
CALIFORNIA**
2475 Paseo De Las A, San Diego (92154)
PHONE..................619 662-8672
Smurfit Kappa, *Owner*
Eduardo Lopez, *Manager*
EMP: 900
SALES (est): 228.8MM Privately Held
SIC: 2653 Corrugated & solid fiber boxes

(P-5402)
**CORRUGATED PACKAGING
PDTS INC**
27403 Industrial Blvd, Hayward
(94545-3348)
PHONE..................650 615-9180
Christopher Grandov, *President*
Linda Grandov, *Admin Sec*
EMP: 25
SQ FT: 2,000
SALES (est): 7MM Privately Held
SIC: 2653 2631 Corrugated & solid fiber
boxes; paperboard mills

(P-5403)
CROCKETT GRAPHICS INC (PA)
Also Called: Folding Cartons
980 Avenida Acaso, Camarillo
(93012-8759)
PHONE..................805 987-8577
Edward Randall Crockett, *President*
Rod K Rieth, *Treasurer*
Ed Fuentes, *General Mgr*
Russ Collins, *Human Res Dir*
Glen Brown, *Sales Staff*
▲ EMP: 60
SALES (est): 19MM Privately Held
WEB: www.garedgraphics.com
SIC: 2653 Corrugated boxes, partitions,
display items, sheets & pad

(P-5404)
**CROWN CARTON COMPANY
INC**
1820 E 48th Pl, Vernon (90058-1946)
PHONE..................323 582-3053
Jeffrey P Marks, *President*
Kyle Johnson, *Vice Pres*
EMP: 20
SQ FT: 28,000
SALES (est): 4MM Privately Held
WEB: www.crowncarton.com
SIC: 2653 Boxes, corrugated: made from
purchased materials

(P-5405)
**CUSTOM PAD AND PARTITION
INC**
1100 Richard Ave, Santa Clara
(95050-2800)
PHONE..................408 970-9711
James L Jones, *CEO*
Janice Jones, *Treasurer*
Cathy Crowder, *Purchasing*
Chip Peto, *Purchasing*
Gina Bence, *Cust Mgr*
EMP: 65
SQ FT: 60,000

SALES (est): 22.6MM Privately Held
WEB: www.custompad.com
SIC: 2653 Pads, corrugated: made from
purchased materials; partitions, corrugated: made from purchased materials;
boxes, corrugated: made from purchased
materials

(P-5406)
ECKO PRODUCTS GROUP LLC
Also Called: Ecko Print & Packaging
740 S Milliken Ave Ste C, Ontario
(91761-7842)
PHONE..................909 628-5678
Eric Rogers, *CFO*
Christopher Hively, *President*
Eric Martinez, *Vice Pres*
Brandon Dinovo, *Graphic Designe*
Jennifer Pearce, *Accountant*
▲ EMP: 23
SQ FT: 17,000
SALES (est): 9.6MM Privately Held
SIC: 2653 5085 2759 Boxes, corrugated:
made from purchased materials; abrasives & adhesives; commercial printing

(P-5407)
**EMPIRE CONTAINER
CORPORATION**
1161 E Walnut St, Carson (90746-1382)
PHONE..................310 537-8190
Donald Simmons, *President*
Patrick Fox, *Shareholder*
Gregory V Hall, *Principal*
Peter Salazar, *Project Mgr*
Jerry Liess, *QC Mgr*
▲ EMP: 66 EST: 1970
SQ FT: 61,000
SALES (est): 25.6MM Privately Held
WEB: www.empirecontainercorp.com
SIC: 2653 3578 Boxes, corrugated: made
from purchased materials; point-of-sale
devices

(P-5408)
EXPRESS CONTAINER INC
560 Iowa St, Redlands (92373-8060)
PHONE..................909 798-3857
Gilles Roy, *President*
EMP: 22
SQ FT: 25,000
SALES (est): 5.2MM Privately Held
WEB: www.expresscontainer.com
SIC: 2653 Boxes, corrugated: made from
purchased materials

(P-5409)
**FRUIT GROWERS SUPPLY
COMPANY (PA)**
27770 N Entrmt Dr Fl 3 Flr 3, Valencia
(91355)
PHONE..................818 986-6480
Mark H Lindgren, *CEO*
Charles Boyce, *CFO*
William O Knox, *Vice Pres*
Mark Lindgren, *President*
John W Eacker, *Regional Mgr*
◆ EMP: 50
SQ FT: 10,000
SALES (est): 220.6MM Privately Held
WEB: www.fruitgrowers.com
SIC: 2653 0811 5191 2448 Boxes, corrugated: made from purchased materials;
timber tracts; farm supplies; fertilizer &
fertilizer materials; pallets, wood; cardboard & products

(P-5410)
**FRUIT GROWERS SUPPLY
COMPANY**
225 S Wineville Ave, Ontario (91761-7891)
PHONE..................909 390-0190
Steve Moore, *Sales/Mktg Mgr*
Stephen Moore, *General Mgr*
Reagan Foley, *Manager*
EMP: 80
SALES (corp-wide): 220.6MM Privately
Held
SIC: 2653 Corrugated & solid fiber boxes
PA: Fruit Growers Supply Company Inc
27770 N Entrmt Dr Fl 3 Flr 3
Valencia CA 91355
818 986-6480

(P-5411)
**FRUIT GROWERS SUPPLY
COMPANY**
Also Called: F G S Packing Services
674 E Myer Ave, Exeter (93221-9644)
PHONE..................559 592-6550
Bruce Adams, *Manager*
EMP: 12
SQ FT: 5,240
SALES (corp-wide): 220.6MM Privately
Held
SIC: 2653 Boxes, corrugated: made from
purchased materials
PA: Fruit Growers Supply Company Inc
27770 N Entrmt Dr Fl 3 Flr 3
Valencia CA 91355
818 986-6480

(P-5412)
GABRIEL CONTAINER CO (PA)
Also Called: Recycled Paper Products
8844 Millergrove Dr, Santa Fe Springs
(90670-2013)
P.O. Box 3188 (90670-0188)
PHONE..................562 699-1051
Ronald H Gabriel, *President*
Agnes Gabriel, *Admin Sec*
▲ EMP: 199 EST: 1935
SQ FT: 72,000
SALES (est): 38.2MM Privately Held
WEB: www.gabrielcontainer.com
SIC: 2653 2621 Boxes, corrugated: made
from purchased materials; paper mills

(P-5413)
GEM BOX OF WEST
2430 S Hill St, Los Angeles (90007-2720)
PHONE..................213 748-4875
Sang Up Park, *President*
Suizie Park, *Admin Sec*
▲ EMP: 26
SQ FT: 135,000
SALES (est): 3.8MM Privately Held
SIC: 2653 5094 Solid fiber boxes, partitions, display items & sheets; jewelers'
findings

(P-5414)
GENERAL CONTAINER
5450 Dodds Ave, Buena Park
(90621-1209)
PHONE..................714 562-8700
Tim Black, *President*
Tim G Black, *President*
Jerry Monroe, *Vice Pres*
Patty Black, *Admin Sec*
Debbie McMillen, *Accounting Mgr*
EMP: 75 EST: 1976
SQ FT: 62,000
SALES (est): 21.8MM Privately Held
SIC: 2653 Boxes, corrugated: made from
purchased materials

(P-5415)
GEORGIA-PACIFIC LLC
2400 Lapham Dr, Modesto (95354-4003)
PHONE..................209 522-5201
David Rieser, *General Mgr*
Dan Brasher, *Manager*
Tenley Paxiao, *Representative*
EMP: 150
SALES (corp-wide): 42.9B Privately Held
WEB: www.gp.com
SIC: 2653 Boxes, corrugated: made from
purchased materials
HQ: Georgia-Pacific Llc
133 Peachtree St Nw
Atlanta GA 30303
404 652-4000

(P-5416)
GEORGIA-PACIFIC LLC
249 E Grand Ave, South San Francisco
(94080-4804)
P.O. Box 2407 (94083)
PHONE..................650 873-7800
Ron Huff, *Branch Mgr*
EMP: 225
SALES (corp-wide): 42.9B Privately Held
WEB: www.gp.com
SIC: 2653 5113 Boxes, corrugated: made
from purchased materials; corrugated &
solid fiber boxes

HQ: Georgia-Pacific Llc
133 Peachtree St Nw
Atlanta GA 30303
404 652-4000

(P-5417)
GEORGIA-PACIFIC LLC
24600 Avenue 13, Madera (93637-9019)
P.O. Box 1327 (93639-1327)
PHONE..................559 674-4685
Steve Mindt, *General Mgr*
Joe Antonino, *Sales Staff*
EMP: 150
SALES (corp-wide): 42.9B Privately Held
WEB: www.gp.com
SIC: 2653 5113 Boxes, corrugated: made
from purchased materials; corrugated &
solid fiber boxes
HQ: Georgia-Pacific Llc
133 Peachtree St Nw
Atlanta GA 30303
404 652-4000

(P-5418)
**GLOBAL PACKAGING
SOLUTIONS INC**
6259 Progressive Dr # 200, San Diego
(92154-6644)
PHONE..................619 710-2661
Jawed Ghias, *CEO*
Henry Romo, *Shareholder*
Rajnikanth Parikh, *Treasurer*
Anila Parikh, *Principal*
Tariq Butt, *Admin Sec*
▲ EMP: 280
SALES (est): 6.4MM Privately Held
SIC: 2653 3089 Corrugated & solid fiber
boxes; injection molding of plastics
PA: Global Packaging Solutions, S.A. De
C.V.
Calle 7 Norte No.108
Tijuana B.C. 22444

(P-5419)
GOLDENCORR SHEETS LLC
13890 Nelson Ave, City of Industry
(91746-2050)
P.O. Box 90968 (91715-0968)
PHONE..................626 369-6446
Tom Anderson, *Mng Member*
John Perullo, *President*
Jeffrey Erseluis, *Mng Member*
Glen Tucker, *Mng Member*
John Webb, *Mng Member*
▲ EMP: 150
SALES (est): 44.6MM Privately Held
SIC: 2653 Corrugated boxes, partitions,
display items, sheets & pad

(P-5420)
GRAPHICPAK CORPORATION
760 S Vail Ave, Montebello (90640-4954)
PHONE..................323 306-3054
Robert Berger, *CEO*
EMP: 10
SQ FT: 33,000
SALES (est): 2.8MM Privately Held
WEB: www.graphicpak.com
SIC: 2653 Corrugated & solid fiber boxes

(P-5421)
**HARVEST CONTAINER
COMPANY**
24476 Road 216, Lindsay (93247-8222)
P.O. Box 697 (93247-0697)
PHONE..................559 562-1394
Dennis A Del Rio, *Principal*
Fred Lo Bue, *President*
Robert Reniers, *Corp Secy*
Phil Enghusen, *Executive*
Dennis Del Rio, *General Mgr*
▲ EMP: 45
SQ FT: 104,000
SALES (est): 12.9MM Privately Held
WEB: www.harvestcontainer.com
SIC: 2653 Boxes, corrugated: made from
purchased materials

(P-5422)
HERITAGE CONTAINER INC
4777 Felspar St, Riverside (92509-3040)
P.O. Box 605, Mira Loma (91752-0605)
PHONE..................951 360-1900
Richard Gabriel, *CEO*
Thomas Gabriel, *President*

Nancy Zuniga, *Vice Pres*
Tom Gabriel, *Executive*
Charlie Cashen, *Purchasing*
EMP: 55
SQ FT: 95,000
SALES: 15MM **Privately Held**
WEB: www.heritagecontainer.com
SIC: 2653 5199 Boxes, corrugated: made from purchased materials; boxes, solid fiber: made from purchased materials; packaging materials

(P-5423)
HERITAGE PAPER CO (HQ)
2400 S Grand Ave, Santa Ana (92705-5211)
PHONE....................714 540-9737
Ron Scagliotti, *CEO*
Lenet Derksen, *CFO*
Terri Sloane, *Department Mgr*
Hugh Lovelace, *Sales Mgr*
Mike Singleton, *Sales Staff*
▲ **EMP:** 75
SQ FT: 150,000
SALES (est): 24.6MM
SALES (corp-wide): 158.2MM **Privately Held**
WEB: www.heritage-paper.net
SIC: 2653 5199 Boxes, corrugated: made from purchased materials; packaging materials
PA: Pioneer Packing, Inc.
2430 S Grand Ave
Santa Ana CA 92705
714 540-9751

(P-5424)
HOLLINGER METAL EDGE INC
6340 Bandini Blvd, Commerce (90040-3116)
PHONE....................323 721-7800
Robert J Henderson, *CEO*
Annie Riddle, *Vice Pres*
▼ **EMP:** 20
SQ FT: 31,500
SALES: 3.8MM **Privately Held**
WEB: www.metaledgeinc.com
SIC: 2653 Boxes, corrugated: made from purchased materials; boxes, solid fiber: made from purchased materials

(P-5425)
INTERNATIONAL PAPER COMPANY
601 E Ball Rd, Anaheim (92805-5910)
PHONE....................714 776-6060
Terry Tockey, *Branch Mgr*
Herman Martinez, *Purchasing*
Ryan Arensdorf, *Accounts Mgr*
EMP: 140
SALES (corp-wide): 21.7B **Publicly Held**
WEB: www.internationalpaper.com
SIC: 2653 Boxes, corrugated: made from purchased materials
PA: International Paper Company
6400 Poplar Ave
Memphis TN 38197
901 419-9000

(P-5426)
INTERNATIONAL PAPER COMPANY
11211 Greenstone Ave, Santa Fe Springs (90670-4616)
PHONE....................323 946-6100
Marc Bailey, *General Mgr*
EMP: 145
SALES (corp-wide): 21.7B **Publicly Held**
SIC: 2653 Boxes, corrugated: made from purchased materials
PA: International Paper Company
6400 Poplar Ave
Memphis TN 38197
901 419-9000

(P-5427)
INTERNATIONAL PAPER COMPANY
3550 Bozzano Rd, Stockton (95215-9100)
PHONE....................209 931-9005
Doc Parris, *Manager*
EMP: 40
SALES (corp-wide): 21.7B **Publicly Held**
WEB: www.internationalpaper.com
SIC: 2653 Boxes, corrugated: made from purchased materials

PA: International Paper Company
6400 Poplar Ave
Memphis TN 38197
901 419-9000

(P-5428)
INTERNATIONAL PAPER COMPANY
5110 E Jurupa Ave, Ontario (91761)
PHONE....................323 724-5010
Anrie Keppler, *Manager*
EMP: 92
SALES (corp-wide): 21.7B **Publicly Held**
WEB: www.tin.com
SIC: 2653 Boxes, corrugated: made from purchased materials
PA: International Paper Company
6400 Poplar Ave
Memphis TN 38197
901 419-9000

(P-5429)
INTERNATIONAL PAPER COMPANY
1950 Marina Blvd, San Leandro (94577-3207)
PHONE....................510 614-1600
Will Rauch, *General Mgr*
Rick Godinez, *Purch Agent*
EMP: 2000
SQ FT: 106,000
SALES (corp-wide): 21.7B **Publicly Held**
SIC: 2653 Boxes, corrugated: made from purchased materials
PA: International Paper Company
6400 Poplar Ave
Memphis TN 38197
901 419-9000

(P-5430)
JACKS BOX & CRATE LLC
6301 Industrial Ave, Riverside (92504-1121)
PHONE....................951 343-1790
John Schumaker, *CEO*
EMP: 20 EST: 2012
SQ FT: 30,000
SALES (est): 1.7MM **Privately Held**
SIC: 2653 5199 Boxes, corrugated: made from purchased materials; packaging materials

(P-5431)
JELLCO CONTAINER INC
1151 N Tustin Ave, Anaheim (92807-1736)
PHONE....................714 666-2728
Jeff Erselius, *President*
Rick Leininger, *CFO*
Mike Carmichael, *Manager*
EMP: 72
SQ FT: 42,000
SALES (est): 24.6MM **Privately Held**
WEB: www.jellco.com
SIC: 2653 Boxes, corrugated: made from purchased materials

(P-5432)
JSJ INC CORRUGATED
10700 Jersey Blvd, Rancho Cucamonga (91730-5116)
PHONE....................909 987-4746
Joseph G Alba, *President*
EMP: 12
SALES (est): 1MM **Privately Held**
SIC: 2653 Boxes, corrugated: made from purchased materials

(P-5433)
KAWEAH CONTAINER INC (HQ)
7101 Avenue 304, Visalia (93291-9479)
P.O. Box 6940 (93290-6940)
PHONE....................559 651-7850
Robert J Reeves, *CEO*
Joe Edwards, *Plant Mgr*
Rene Cabanilla, *Director*
Ken Weisenberger, *Accounts Mgr*
▲ **EMP:** 75
SQ FT: 30,000
SALES (est): 21.1MM
SALES (corp-wide): 100.4MM **Privately Held**
SIC: 2653 Boxes, corrugated: made from purchased materials

PA: Wileman Bros. & Elliott, Inc.
40232 Road 128
Cutler CA 93615
559 651-8378

(P-5434)
LIBERTY CONTAINER COMPANY
Also Called: Key Container
4224 Santa Ana St, South Gate (90280-2557)
P.O. Box 71 (90280-0071)
PHONE....................323 564-4211
Robert J Watts, *President*
William J Watts, *Vice Pres*
▲ **EMP:** 110
SQ FT: 300,000
SALES (est): 25.8MM **Privately Held**
WEB: www.keycontainer.com
SIC: 2653 Boxes, corrugated: made from purchased materials

(P-5435)
LIBERTY DIVERSIFIED INTL INC
Also Called: Harbor Packaging
13100 Danielson St, Poway (92064-6840)
PHONE....................858 391-7302
Luis Cook, *Info Tech Mgr*
Lauren De-Cerbo, *Accountant*
Jeannette Sebastiano, *Purch Mgr*
Dane Rittmiller, *Opers Mgr*
David Alvarado, *Plant Mgr*
EMP: 245
SALES (corp-wide): 499.3MM **Privately Held**
SIC: 2653 5199 Boxes, corrugated: made from purchased materials; packaging materials
PA: Liberty Diversified International, Inc.
5600 Highway 169 N
New Hope MN 55428
763 536-6600

(P-5436)
MENASHA PACKAGING COMPANY LLC
305 Resource Dr Ste 100, Bloomington (92316-3528)
PHONE....................951 374-5281
EMP: 30
SALES (corp-wide): 1.7B **Privately Held**
SIC: 2653 Boxes, corrugated: made from purchased materials
HQ: Menasha Packaging Company, Llc
1645 Bergstrom Rd
Neenah WI 54956
920 751-1000

(P-5437)
MENASHA PACKAGING COMPANY LLC
8110 Sorensen Ave, Santa Fe Springs (90670-2122)
PHONE....................562 698-3705
Ann Barraza, *Human Res Mgr*
Hector Gonzalez, *Prdtn Mgr*
Minerva Gonzalez, *Assistant*
EMP: 84
SALES (corp-wide): 1.7B **Privately Held**
WEB: www.menasha.com
SIC: 2653 Boxes, corrugated: made from purchased materials
HQ: Menasha Packaging Company, Llc
1645 Bergstrom Rd
Neenah WI 54956
920 751-1000

(P-5438)
MONTEBELLO CONTAINER CO LLC
14333 Macaw St, La Mirada (90638-5208)
PHONE....................714 994-2351
Al Perez, *CFO*
EMP: 100 **Privately Held**
WEB: www.montcc.com
SIC: 2653 5113 Boxes, corrugated: made from purchased materials; corrugated & solid fiber boxes
HQ: Montebello Container Company Llc
13220 Molette St
Santa Fe Springs CA 90670
562 404-6221

(P-5439)
MONTEBELLO CONTAINER CO LLC
13220 Molette St, Santa Fe Springs (90670-5526)
PHONE....................562 948-3483
David Gutierrez, *Manager*
EMP: 30
SQ FT: 30,000 **Privately Held**
WEB: www.montcc.com
SIC: 2653 Boxes, corrugated: made from purchased materials
HQ: Montebello Container Company Llc
13220 Molette St
Santa Fe Springs CA 90670
562 404-6221

(P-5440)
NUMATECH WEST (KMP) LLC
Also Called: Kmp Numatech Pacific
1201 E Lexington Ave, Pomona (91766-5520)
PHONE....................909 706-3627
John Neate, *Mng Member*
Robert Sliter, *General Mgr*
Rodelieta Clavin, *Director*
▲ **EMP:** 100
SQ FT: 65,000
SALES (corp-wide): 45.3MM **Privately Held**
SIC: 2653 Boxes, corrugated: made from purchased materials
PA: Nw Packaging Llc
1201 E Lexington Ave
Pomona CA 91766
909 706-3627

(P-5441)
ORANGE CONTAINER INC
1984 E Mcfadden Ave, Santa Ana (92705-4706)
PHONE....................714 547-9617
Harold Bankhead, *President*
Terry Schnabel, *Vice Pres*
EMP: 60
SQ FT: 25,000
SALES (est): 7MM **Privately Held**
WEB: www.orangecontainer.com
SIC: 2653 Boxes, corrugated: made from purchased materials

(P-5442)
PACIFIC QUALITY PACKAGING CORP
660 Neptune Ave, Brea (92821-2909)
PHONE....................714 257-1234
Frederick H Chau, *President*
Chris Chau, *Project Mgr*
▲ **EMP:** 65
SQ FT: 44,000
SALES (est): 14.2MM **Privately Held**
SIC: 2653 3993 Boxes, corrugated: made from purchased materials; signs & advertising specialties

(P-5443)
PACIFIC SOUTHWEST CONT LLC
Also Called: PSC
9525 W Nicholas Ct, Visalia (93291-9468)
PHONE....................559 651-5500
Don Mayol,
Palmira Crane, *Opers Staff*
EMP: 74
SALES (corp-wide): 145.9MM **Privately Held**
SIC: 2653 Boxes, corrugated: made from purchased materials
PA: Pacific Southwest Container, Llc
4530 Leckron Rd
Modesto CA 95357
209 526-0444

(P-5444)
PACIFIC SOUTHWEST CONT LLC
4530 Leckron Rd, Modesto (95357-0517)
PHONE....................209 373-2900
John Mayol, *Branch Mgr*
EMP: 37
SALES (corp-wide): 145.9MM **Privately Held**
SIC: 2653 Corrugated & solid fiber boxes

PA: Pacific Southwest Container, Llc
4530 Leckron Rd
Modesto CA 95357
209 526-0444

(P-5445)
PACKAGEONE INC (PA)
Also Called: All West Container
1100 Union St, San Francisco
(94109-2019)
PHONE..................................650 761-3339
Richard Pfaff, *President*
Christopher Grandov, *Vice Pres*
▼ EMP: 44 EST: 1958
SQ FT: 129,000
SALES (est): 7MM **Privately Held**
WEB: www.allwestcontainer.com
SIC: 2653 Boxes, corrugated: made from
purchased materials

(P-5446)
**PACKAGING CORPORATION
AMERICA**
Also Called: PCA/Los Angeles 349
4240 Bandini Blvd, Vernon (90058-4207)
PHONE..................................323 263-7581
Mark Beyma, *Branch Mgr*
Win Tan, *Info Tech Mgr*
Jose Jimenez, *Technician*
Margie Latorre, *Human Res Dir*
Margie De La Torre, *Persnl Mgr*
EMP: 100
SALES (corp-wide): 6.4B **Publicly Held**
WEB: www.packagingcorp.com
SIC: 2653 Boxes, corrugated: made from
purchased materials
PA: Packaging Corporation Of America
1955 W Field Ct
Lake Forest IL 60045
847 482-3000

(P-5447)
**PACKAGING CORPORATION
AMERICA**
Also Called: PCA/South Gate 378
9700 E Frontage Rd Ste 20, South Gate
(90280-5421)
PHONE..................................562 927-7741
Eric Thorntoon, *Branch Mgr*
Margie D Torre, *Human Res Dir*
Michael Hinton, *Safety Mgr*
Ron De-La-Torre, *Plant Mgr*
EMP: 230
SALES (corp-wide): 6.4B **Publicly Held**
WEB: www.packagingcorp.com
SIC: 2653 Boxes, corrugated: made from
purchased materials
PA: Packaging Corporation Of America
1955 W Field Ct
Lake Forest IL 60045
847 482-3000

(P-5448)
PACKAGING PLUS
3816 S Willow Ave Ste 102, Fresno
(93725-9241)
PHONE..................................209 858-9200
Robert Crossman, *President*
Alecia Crossman, *Vice Pres*
Michelle Reid, *Manager*
▲ EMP: 32
SQ FT: 60,000
SALES (est): 6.1MM **Privately Held**
SIC: 2653 Sheets, corrugated: made from
purchased materials

(P-5449)
PACTIV LLC
4545 Qantas Ln, Stockton (95206-3982)
PHONE..................................209 983-1930
Steve McNeal, *Controller*
Trena Huerta, *HR Admin*
John Chamberlain, *Plant Engr*
Jeff Frese, *Manager*
Russ Stanley, *Manager*
EMP: 1300 **Privately Held**
SIC: 2653 2656 2652 Boxes, corrugated:
made from purchased materials; sanitary
food containers; setup paperboard boxes
HQ: Pactiv Llc
1900 W Field Ct
Lake Forest IL 60045
847 482-2000

(P-5450)
**PCA CENTRAL CAL
CORRUGATED LLC**
Also Called: Packaging America - Sacra-
mento
4841 Urbani Ave, McClellan (95652-2025)
PHONE..................................916 614-0580
EMP: 162
SALES (corp-wide): 6.4B **Publicly Held**
SIC: 2653 Corrugated & solid fiber boxes
HQ: Pca Central California Corrugated, Llc
1955 W Field Ct
Lake Forest IL 60045
847 482-3000

(P-5451)
PK1 INC (HQ)
Also Called: American River Packaging
4225 Pell Dr, Sacramento (95838-2533)
PHONE..................................916 858-1300
Thomas Kandris, *CEO*
Ronald Frederick, *CFO*
Ron Frederick, *Vice Pres*
Matt Lerwill, *Vice Pres*
Ken Bales, *Info Tech Mgr*
▲ EMP: 100
SQ FT: 240,000
SALES (est): 23.5MM
SALES (corp-wide): 20.5MM **Privately
Held**
WEB: www.arpkg.com
SIC: 2653 5113 4783 Boxes, corrugated:
made from purchased materials; industrial
& personal service paper; packing goods
for shipping
PA: Golden West Packaging Group Llc
8333 24th Ave
Sacramento CA 95826
404 345-8365

(P-5452)
**PNC PROACTIVE NTHRN CONT
LLC**
602 S Rockefeller Ave A, Ontario
(91761-8190)
PHONE..................................909 390-5624
Gary Hartog, *Mng Member*
▲ EMP: 50
SQ FT: 362,000
SALES (est): 8.7MM **Privately Held**
SIC: 2653 Boxes, corrugated: made from
purchased materials
PA: Fourth Third Llc
375 Park Ave Ste 3304
New York NY

(P-5453)
**PROACTIVE PACKG & DISPLAY
INC (PA)**
602 S Rockefeller Ave, Ontario
(91761-8190)
PHONE..................................909 390-5624
Gary Hartog, *CEO*
▲ EMP: 72
SQ FT: 164,000
SALES (est): 28.8MM **Privately Held**
WEB: www.proactivepkg.com
SIC: 2653 Boxes, corrugated: made from
purchased materials

(P-5454)
**PROGRESSIVE PACKG GROUP
INC (PA)**
18931 Portola Dr Ste C, Salinas
(93908-1295)
P.O. Box 2268 (93902-2268)
PHONE..................................831 424-2942
Eli Riddle, *President*
Barry Jhonston, *CFO*
EMP: 22
SQ FT: 1,700
SALES (est): 5.7MM **Privately Held**
SIC: 2653 Boxes, corrugated: made from
purchased materials

(P-5455)
RICARDO OCHOA
Also Called: Northwest Pallets
281 N Pioneer Ave, Woodland (95776)
PHONE..................................530 668-1152
Ricardo Ochoa, *Owner*
EMP: 17
SQ FT: 17,500

SALES: 2.1MM **Privately Held**
SIC: 2653 2448 Pallets, corrugated: made
from purchased materials; wood pallets &
skids

(P-5456)
SAN DIEGO CRATING & PKG INC
12678 Brookprinter Pl, Poway
(92064-6809)
PHONE..................................858 748-0100
Jacqueline H Peterson, *CEO*
Lee Peterson, *President*
EMP: 17
SQ FT: 12,000
SALES (est): 1.1MM **Privately Held**
WEB: www.sdcrate.com
SIC: 2653 4783 Boxes, corrugated: made
from purchased materials; crating goods
for shipping; packing goods for shipping

(P-5457)
SCOPE PACKAGING INC
Also Called: Sp
13400 Nelson Ave, City of Industry
(91746-2331)
P.O. Box 3768, Orange (92857-0768)
PHONE..................................714 998-4411
Mike E Flinn, *CEO*
Cindy Baker, *Vice Pres*
Christine Maple, *Project Mgr*
Margaret Stewart, *Human Resources*
Doug Hall, *Opers Mgr*
▲ EMP: 45
SQ FT: 70,000
SALES (est): 13.6MM **Privately Held**
WEB: www.kraftdesigns.com
SIC: 2653 7389 Boxes, corrugated: made
from purchased materials; packaging &
labeling services

(P-5458)
**SMURFIT KAPPA NORTH AMER
LLC**
13400 Nelson Ave, City of Industry
(91746-2331)
PHONE..................................626 333-6363
Michael Feterik, *Principal*
EMP: 450 **Privately Held**
SIC: 2653 2671 Boxes, corrugated: made
from purchased materials; packaging
paper & plastics film, coated & laminated
HQ: Smurfit Kappa North America Llc
13400 Nelson Ave
City Of Industry CA 91746
626 333-6363

(P-5459)
**SMURFIT KAPPA NORTH AMER
LLC (HQ)**
Also Called: Coi Graphics
13400 Nelson Ave, City of Industry
(91746-2331)
PHONE..................................626 333-6363
Greg Hall, *President*
David Ortiz, *Senior VP*
David Capanash, *Principal*
Forest Felvey, *Principal*
Michael Feterik, *Principal*
▲ EMP: 300 EST: 1974
SQ FT: 270,000
SALES (est): 935.2MM **Privately Held**
SIC: 2653 2671 2657 Boxes, corrugated:
made from purchased materials; packag-
ing paper & plastics film, coated & lami-
nated; folding paperboard boxes

(P-5460)
**SMURFIT KAPPA NORTH AMER
LLC**
440 Baldwin Park Blvd, City of Industry
(91746-1407)
PHONE..................................626 322-2123
EMP: 413 **Privately Held**
SIC: 2653 2671 2657
HQ: Smurfit Kappa North America Llc
13400 Nelson Ave
City Of Industry CA 91746
626 333-6363

(P-5461)
SONOCO CORRFLEX LLC
1225 Grand Central Ave, Glendale
(91201-2425)
PHONE..................................818 507-7477
John Kack, *Regl Sales Mgr*

EMP: 17
SALES (corp-wide): 5B **Publicly Held**
SIC: 2653 Display items, corrugated: made
from purchased materials
HQ: Sonoco Display & Packaging, Llc
555 Aureole St
Winston Salem NC 27107

(P-5462)
**SONOCO PRTECTIVE
SOLUTIONS INC**
3466 Enterprise Ave, Hayward
(94545-3219)
PHONE..................................510 785-0220
Rob Hazelton, *Manager*
EMP: 60
SQ FT: 125,975
SALES (corp-wide): 5B **Publicly Held**
WEB: www.tuscarora.com
SIC: 2653 3086 Boxes, corrugated: made
from purchased materials; plastics foam
products
HQ: Sonoco Protective Solutions, Inc.
1 N 2nd St
Hartsville SC 29550
843 383-7000

(P-5463)
SOUTHLAND CONTAINER CORP
Also Called: Concept Packaging Group
1600 Champagne Ave, Ontario
(91761-3612)
PHONE..................................909 937-9781
Tom Heinz, *Branch Mgr*
EMP: 15
SALES (corp-wide): 1.2B **Privately Held**
WEB: www.concept-pkg.com
SIC: 2653 Boxes, corrugated: made from
purchased materials
PA: Southland Container Corporation
60 Fairview Church Rd
Spartanburg SC 29303
864 578-0085

(P-5464)
SOVEREIGN PACKAGING INC
8420 Kass Dr, Buena Park (90621-3808)
PHONE..................................714 670-6811
David Pittman, *President*
Sheryl Dreiling, *Vice Pres*
Doug Herr, *Office Mgr*
Duncan Kiddle, *Marketing Staff*
EMP: 24
SQ FT: 25,000
SALES (est): 2.8MM **Privately Held**
WEB: www.sovereignpackaging.com
SIC: 2653 7336 5113 Boxes, corrugated:
made from purchased materials; package
design; corrugated & solid fiber boxes

(P-5465)
**WESTERN CORRUGATED
DESIGN INC**
8741 Pioneer Blvd, Santa Fe Springs
(90670-2021)
PHONE..................................562 695-5718
John Brendlinger, *CEO*
▲ EMP: 50
SALES (est): 888K **Privately Held**
SIC: 2653 Boxes, corrugated: made from
purchased materials

(P-5466)
**WESTROCK CONVERTING
COMPANY**
16110 Cosmos St, Moreno Valley
(92551-7308)
PHONE..................................951 601-4164
Tony Rangel, *General Mgr*
EMP: 18
SALES (corp-wide): 14.8B **Publicly Held**
SIC: 2653 Partitions, solid fiber: made from
purchased materials
HQ: Westrock Converting, Llc
1000 Abernathy Rd Ste 125
Atlanta GA 30328
770 246-9982

(P-5467)
WESTROCK CP LLC
Also Called: Smurfit-Stone Container
201 S Hillview Dr, Milpitas (95035-5417)
PHONE..................................408 946-3600
Derek Bonner, *Branch Mgr*

Don Steele, *Engineer*
EMP: 146
SALES (corp-wide): 14.8B **Publicly Held**
WEB: www.smurfit-stone.com
SIC: 2653 5113 Boxes, corrugated: made from purchased materials; corrugated & solid fiber boxes
HQ: Westrock Cp, Llc
504 Thrasher St
Norcross GA 30071
-

(P-5468)
WESTROCK CP LLC
Also Called: Smurfit-Stone Container
13833 Freeway Dr, Santa Fe Springs (90670-5701)
PHONE.................714 523-3550
Manny Loera, *Branch Mgr*
EMP: 125
SQ FT: 265,000
SALES (corp-wide): 14.8B **Publicly Held**
WEB: www.smurfit-stone.com
SIC: 2653 Boxes, corrugated: made from purchased materials
HQ: Westrock Cp, Llc
504 Thrasher St
Norcross GA 30071

(P-5469)
WESTROCK CP LLC
1078 Merrill St, Salinas (93901-4409)
PHONE.................831 424-1831
Jimmy Murkison, *General Mgr*
EMP: 120
SALES (corp-wide): 14.8B **Publicly Held**
WEB: www.smurfit-stone.com
SIC: 2653 Boxes, corrugated: made from purchased materials
HQ: Westrock Cp, Llc
504 Thrasher St
Norcross GA 30071

(P-5470)
WESTROCK CP LLC
185 N Smith Ave, Corona (92880-1739)
PHONE.................951 734-1870
David Tichchch, *Branch Mgr*
EMP: 117
SALES (corp-wide): 14.8B **Publicly Held**
WEB: www.smurfit-stone.com
SIC: 2653 5113 Boxes, corrugated: made from purchased materials; corrugated & solid fiber boxes
HQ: Westrock Cp, Llc
504 Thrasher St
Norcross GA 30071

(P-5471)
WESTROCK CP LLC
Also Called: West Rock
201 S Hillview Dr, Milpitas (95035-5417)
PHONE.................408 946-3600
Russell Asp, *Branch Mgr*
EMP: 150
SALES (corp-wide): 14.8B **Publicly Held**
WEB: www.sto.com
SIC: 2653 Boxes, corrugated: made from purchased materials
HQ: Westrock Cp, Llc
504 Thrasher St
Norcross GA 30071

(P-5472)
WESTROCK CP LLC
3366 E Muscat Ave, Fresno (93725-2624)
PHONE.................559 519-7240
Bernardo Thomas,
EMP: 101
SALES (corp-wide): 14.8B **Publicly Held**
SIC: 2653 2631 2655 Boxes, corrugated: made from purchased materials; partitions, corrugated: made from purchased materials; partitions, solid fiber: made from purchased materials; container board; boxboard; folding boxboard; linerboard; tubes, fiber or paper: made from purchased material; fiber cores, reels & bobbins; drums, fiber: made from purchased material

HQ: Westrock Cp, Llc
504 Thrasher St
Norcross GA 30071

(P-5473)
WESTROCK RKT COMPANY
749 N Poplar St, Orange (92868-1013)
PHONE.................714 978-2895
Bob Appoloney, *Branch Mgr*
EMP: 161
SALES (corp-wide): 14.8B **Publicly Held**
SIC: 2653 Boxes, corrugated: made from purchased materials
HQ: Westrock Rkt, Llc
1000 Abernathy Rd Ste 125
Atlanta GA 30328
770 448-2193

(P-5474)
WESTROCK RKT COMPANY
3366 E Muscat Ave, Fresno (93725-2624)
PHONE.................559 497-1662
Thomas Bernardo, *Branch Mgr*
EMP: 161
SALES (corp-wide): 14.8B **Publicly Held**
SIC: 2653 Hampers, solid fiber: made from purchased materials; boxes, corrugated: made from purchased materials
HQ: Westrock Rkt, Llc
1000 Abernathy Rd Ste 125
Atlanta GA 30328
770 448-2193

(P-5475)
WESTROCK RKT COMPANY
Also Called: Alliance Display & Packaging
100 E Tujunga Ave Ste 102, Burbank (91502-1963)
PHONE.................818 729-0610
Allen Kinder, *Branch Mgr*
EMP: 20
SALES (corp-wide): 14.8B **Publicly Held**
WEB: www.rocktenn.com
SIC: 2653 Boxes, corrugated: made from purchased materials
HQ: Westrock Rkt, Llc
1000 Abernathy Rd Ste 125
Atlanta GA 30328
770 448-2193

(P-5476)
WESTROCK RKT COMPANY
536 S 2nd Ave, Covina (91723-3043)
PHONE.................626 859-7633
EMP: 161
SALES (corp-wide): 16B **Publicly Held**
SIC: 2653 2679
HQ: Westrock Rkt Company
504 Thrasher St
Norcross GA 30328
770 448-2193

(P-5477)
WESTROCK USC INC
13833 Freeway Dr, Santa Fe Springs (90670-5701)
PHONE.................562 282-4200
David Weissberg, *CEO*
EMP: 11
SALES (corp-wide): 14.8B **Publicly Held**
SIC: 2653 Boxes, corrugated: made from purchased materials
HQ: Westrock Usc, Inc.
1000 Abernathy Rd
Atlanta GA 30328
770 448-2193

(P-5478)
WEYERHAEUSER COMPANY
Also Called: Los Angeles Sales Office-North
543 Country Club Dr, Simi Valley (93065-0637)
PHONE.................800 238-3676
Ralph Hathaway, *Branch Mgr*
EMP: 147
SALES (corp-wide): 7.2B **Publicly Held**
SIC: 2653 Corrugated boxes, partitions, display items, sheets & pad
PA: Weyerhaeuser Company
220 Occidental Ave S
Seattle WA 98104
206 539-3000

2655 Fiber Cans, Tubes & Drums

(P-5479)
ADMAIL WEST INC
800 N 10th St Ste F, Sacramento (95811-0342)
PHONE.................916 554-5755
Mike Mc Bride, *Manager*
EMP: 95
SALES (corp-wide): 12.3MM **Privately Held**
SIC: 2655 Fiber shipping & mailing containers
PA: Admail West, Inc.
521 N 10th St
Sacramento CA 95811
916 442-3613

(P-5480)
BIOMATRICA INC
5627 Oberlin Dr Ste 120, San Diego (92121-3748)
PHONE.................858 550-0308
Nick Ecos, *President*
Pankaj Singhal, *Development*
EMP: 28
SALES (est): 8.2MM
SALES (corp-wide): 265.9MM **Publicly Held**
SIC: 2655 Tubes, for chemical or electrical uses: paper or fiber
PA: Exact Sciences Corporation
441 Charmany Dr
Madison WI 53719
608 284-5700

(P-5481)
CALIFORNIA COMPOSITE CONT CORP
22770 Perry St, Perris (92570-9725)
PHONE.................951 940-9343
Jerry Martin, *President*
Richard Hull, *Vice Pres*
Mary Martin, *Sales Executive*
▲ **EMP:** 25
SQ FT: 18,000
SALES (est): 6.2MM **Privately Held**
SIC: 2655 Cans, fiber: made from purchased material

(P-5482)
CARAUSTAR INDUSTRIES INC
4502 E Airport Dr, Ontario (91761-7820)
PHONE.................951 685-5544
D Wever Paul Potter, *Manager*
EMP: 43
SALES (corp-wide): 1.7B **Privately Held**
WEB: www.newarkpaperboardproducts.com
SIC: 2655 Tubes, fiber or paper: made from purchased material
PA: Caraustar Industries, Inc.
5000 Astell Pwdr Sprng Rd
Austell GA 30106
770 948-3101

(P-5483)
COMPOSITE SUPPORT AND SLTNS IN
767 W Channel St, San Pedro (90731-1411)
PHONE.................310 514-3162
Clem Hill, *President*
Hilde Hiel, *Admin Sec*
EMP: 16
SALES (est): 1.4MM **Privately Held**
SIC: 2655 Cans, composite: foil-fiber & other: from purchased fiber

(P-5484)
D & T FIBERGLASS INC
8900 Osage Ave D, Sacramento (95828-1124)
P.O. Box 293330 (95829-3330)
PHONE.................916 383-9012
Donald R Stommel, *CEO*
EMP: 37
SQ FT: 35,000
SALES (est): 8.9MM **Privately Held**
WEB: www.dtfiberglass.com
SIC: 2655 Cans, composite: foil-fiber & other: from purchased fiber

(P-5485)
DORCO ELECTRONICS INC
Also Called: Dorco Fiberglass Products
13540 Larwin Cir, Santa Fe Springs (90670-5031)
PHONE.................562 623-1133
Ted Casmer, *President*
Gary Dexter, *Vice Pres*
EMP: 16 EST: 1958
SQ FT: 7,000
SALES (est): 3MM **Privately Held**
WEB: www.dorco.com
SIC: 2655 Bobbins, fiber: made from purchased material

(P-5486)
GREIF INC
2400 Cooper Ave, Merced (95348-4310)
P.O. Box 2146 (95344-0146)
PHONE.................209 383-4396
Farrell Smith, *Manager*
Mitch Swinderman, *Engineer*
Mark Recasens, *Human Res Mgr*
Larry Allen, *Sales Executive*
Ron Hickman, *Maintence Staff*
EMP: 75
SALES (corp-wide): 3.6B **Publicly Held**
WEB: www.greif.com
SIC: 2655 Fiber cans, drums & similar products
PA: Greif, Inc.
425 Winter Rd
Delaware OH 43015
740 549-6000

(P-5487)
GREIF INC
Also Called: Western Division
235 San Pedro Ave, Morgan Hill (95037-5236)
PHONE.................408 779-2161
John Saldate, *Plant Mgr*
Fran Sorci, *Manager*
EMP: 72
SQ FT: 105,731
SALES (corp-wide): 3.6B **Publicly Held**
WEB: www.greif.com
SIC: 2655 Drums, fiber: made from purchased material
PA: Greif, Inc.
425 Winter Rd
Delaware OH 43015
740 549-6000

(P-5488)
GREIF INC
Western Division
5701 Fresca Dr, La Palma (90623-1009)
PHONE.................714 523-9580
George Grace, *Manager*
Tom Newman, *Vice Pres*
George Gray, *Manager*
EMP: 60
SQ FT: 72,000
SALES (corp-wide): 3.6B **Publicly Held**
WEB: www.greif.com
SIC: 2655 5085 3412 2674 Drums, fiber: made from purchased material; commercial containers; metal barrels, drums & pails; bags: uncoated paper & multiwall
PA: Greif, Inc.
425 Winter Rd
Delaware OH 43015
740 549-6000

(P-5489)
HITCO CARBON COMPOSITES INC
1551 W 139th St, Gardena (90249-2603)
PHONE.................424 329-5250
Jeff Schade, *Vice Pres*
Les Cohen, *Vice Pres*
David Lamb, *Vice Pres*
Eric Sorenson, *Vice Pres*
Gerard Taccini, *Vice Pres*
▲ **EMP:** 90
SALES: 40MM
SALES (corp-wide): 1B **Privately Held**
SIC: 2655 Fiber cans, drums & similar products
HQ: Sgl Carbon, Llc
10715 David Taylor Dr # 460
Charlotte NC 28262
704 593-5100

(P-5490)
HUHTAMAKI INC
8450 Gerber Rd, Sacramento
(95828-3712)
PHONE..................916 688-4938
Michael Pacheco, *Opers Staff*
EMP: 12
SALES (corp-wide): 35.2B **Privately Held**
SIC: 2655 Fiber cans, drums & similar
products
HQ: Huhtamaki, Inc.
9201 Packaging Dr
De Soto KS 66018
913 583-3025

(P-5491)
ICSH PARENT INC
1540 S Greenwood Ave, Montebello
(90640-6536)
P.O. Box 2067 (90640-1467)
PHONE..................323 724-8507
Charles Veniez, *President*
EMP: 98
SALES (est): 8.9MM **Privately Held**
SIC: 2655 5085 Fiber cans, drums & con-
tainers; drums, fiber: made from pur-
chased material; drums, new or
reconditioned

(P-5492)
PACIFIC PAPER TUBE INC (PA)
4343 E Fremont St, Stockton (95215-4032)
PHONE..................510 562-8823
Toll Free:..................888   -
Patrick Wallace, *President*
Colleen Wallace, *Vice Pres*
Nancy Wallace, *Admin Sec*
▲ **EMP:** 50
SQ FT: 85,000
SALES (est): 23.4MM **Privately Held**
WEB: www.pacificpapertube.com
SIC: 2655 Tubes, fiber or paper: made
from purchased material

(P-5493)
RECTANGULAR TUBING INC
Also Called: Rti
333 Newquist Pl, City of Industry
(91745-1027)
PHONE..................626 333-7884
Dennis Sherlin, *President*
Emily Sherlin, *CFO*
Perry Regf,
EMP: 10
SQ FT: 6,000
SALES (est): 1.5MM **Privately Held**
WEB: www.rectube.com
SIC: 2655 3496 Tubes, fiber or paper:
made from purchased material; miscella-
neous fabricated wire products

(P-5494)
**SPIRAL PPR TUBE & CORE CO
INC**
5200 Industry Ave, Pico Rivera
(90660-2506)
PHONE..................562 801-9705
George Hibard, *CEO*
Summer Hibard, *Vice Pres*
▲ **EMP:** 45
SQ FT: 40,000
SALES (est): 11MM **Privately Held**
SIC: 2655 Fiber cans, drums & similar
products

(P-5495)
STABLCOR TECHNOLOGY INC
17011 Beach Blvd Ste 900, Huntington
Beach (92647-5998)
PHONE..................714 375-6644
Doug S Schneider, *President*
EMP: 10
SQ FT: 3,000
SALES (est): 985.7K **Privately Held**
SIC: 2655 Cans, composite: foil-fiber &
other: from purchased fiber

(P-5496)
TUBE-TAINER INC
8174 Byron Rd, Whittier (90606-2616)
PHONE..................562 945-3711
Mike Mundia, *President*
▲ **EMP:** 45
SQ FT: 44,000

SALES (est): 2.1MM **Privately Held**
WEB: www.tubetainer.com
SIC: 2655 Tubes, fiber or paper: made
from purchased material

2656 Sanitary Food Containers

(P-5497)
AMSCAN INC
Ampro
804 W Town And Country Rd, Orange
(92868-4712)
PHONE..................714 972-2626
James Bell, *Branch Mgr*
EMP: 52
SALES (corp-wide): 2.3B **Publicly Held**
SIC: 2656 Cups, paper: made from pur-
chased material
HQ: Amscan Inc.
80 Grasslands Rd Ste 3
Elmsford NY 10523
914 345-2020

(P-5498)
BESTWALL LLC
Also Called: Georgia-Pacific
3630 E Wawona Ave Ste 104, Fresno
(93725-9028)
PHONE..................559 485-4900
Daniel August, *General Mgr*
EMP: 225
SALES (corp-wide): 42.9B **Privately Held**
WEB: www.gp.com
SIC: 2656 Sanitary food containers
HQ: Georgia-Pacific Llc
133 Peachtree St Nw
Atlanta GA 30303
404 652-4000

(P-5499)
LOLLICUP USA INC (PA)
Also Called: Lollicup Tea Zone
6185 Kimball Ave, Chino (91708-9126)
PHONE..................626 965-8882
Alan Yu, *President*
Marvin Cheng, *Vice Pres*
Joanne Wang, *Vice Pres*
Candy Yu, *CTO*
Betty Kong, *Purch Mgr*
◆ **EMP:** 33 **EST:** 2000
SQ FT: 9,800
SALES (est): 20.9MM **Privately Held**
WEB: www.lollicupstore.com
SIC: 2656 Paper cups, plates, dishes &
utensils

(P-5500)
S W C GROUP INC
Also Called: Carryoutsupplies.com
750 Royal Oaks Dr Ste 108, Monrovia
(91016-6356)
PHONE..................888 982-1628
Jimmy Chan, *CEO*
◆ **EMP:** 30
SQ FT: 18,000
SALES: 8MM **Privately Held**
SIC: 2656 Sanitary food containers

(P-5501)
YOCUP COMPANY
13711 S Main St, Los Angeles
(90061-2165)
PHONE..................310 884-9888
Jian Yin Liang, *President*
▲ **EMP:** 14 **EST:** 2009
SALES (est): 619.6K **Privately Held**
SIC: 2656 Cups, paper: made from pur-
chased material

(P-5502)
ZOO PIKS INTERNATIONAL
5951 Rickenbacker Rd, Commerce
(90040-3029)
PHONE..................323 724-0503
Nathan Long, *Manager*
EMP: 35
SALES (est): 3.3MM **Privately Held**
SIC: 2656 Straws, drinking: made from
purchased material

2657 Folding Paperboard Boxes

(P-5503)
ARIZONA PAPER BOX CO INC
10605 Jamacha Blvd, Spring Valley
(91978-2002)
PHONE..................619 660-9566
Sidney B Chapman, *President*
EMP: 20
SQ FT: 47,000
SALES (est): 1.5MM **Privately Held**
WEB: www.arizonapaperbox.com
SIC: 2657 Folding paperboard boxes

(P-5504)
BOXES R US INC
Also Called: Ultimate Paper Box Company
15051 Don Julian Rd, City of Industry
(91746-3302)
PHONE..................626 820-5410
Janak P Patel, *President*
Dipak Patel, *Vice Pres*
Eric Haikara, *Sales Mgr*
Geeta Radia, *Manager*
Damon Francis, *Accounts Mgr*
▲ **EMP:** 70
SQ FT: 38,000
SALES (est): 24.2MM **Privately Held**
SIC: 2657 Folding paperboard boxes

(P-5505)
CRAFTON CARTON
31790 Hayman St, Hayward (94544-7934)
PHONE..................510 441-5985
Glenn Boatley, *President*
Diane Boatley, *Vice Pres*
EMP: 20
SQ FT: 20,000
SALES (est): 3.3MM **Privately Held**
WEB: www.sierrapack.com
SIC: 2657 Folding paperboard boxes

(P-5506)
EVERETT GRAPHICS INC
7300 Edgewater Dr, Oakland (94621-3006)
PHONE..................510 577-6777
Munson Wittman Everett, *President*
Mark Carlson, *CFO*
Tara Saba, *Officer*
John F Everett, *Vice Pres*
John Everett, *Admin Sec*
▲ **EMP:** 75
SQ FT: 100,000
SALES (est): 34.9MM **Privately Held**
WEB: www.everettgraphics.com
SIC: 2657 Folding paperboard boxes

(P-5507)
**IMPERIAL PRTG PPR BOX MFG
INC**
Also Called: Abdalian Carton
1622 W 130th St, Gardena (90249-2002)
PHONE..................310 323-7300
John Setareh, *President*
David Setareh, *CEO*
Gloria Setareh,
▲ **EMP:** 24
SQ FT: 22,000
SALES (est): 3.5MM **Privately Held**
WEB: www.abdaliancarton.com
SIC: 2657 Folding paperboard boxes

(P-5508)
**ROYAL PAPER BOX CO
CALIFORNIA (PA)**
1105 S Maple Ave, Montebello
(90640-6007)
P.O. Box 458 (90640-0458)
PHONE..................323 728-7041
Jim Hodges, *CEO*
Darryl Carlson, *Vice Pres*
Scott Larson, *Vice Pres*
Steve Perez, *Vice Pres*
Andy Polanco, *Vice Pres*
▲ **EMP:** 117
SQ FT: 172,500
SALES (est): 50MM **Privately Held**
WEB: www.royalpaperbox.com
SIC: 2657 Folding paperboard boxes

(P-5509)
SAN DIEGO PAPER BOX CO INC
10605 Jamacha Blvd, Spring Valley
(91978-2098)
PHONE..................619 660-9566
Richard D Chapman, *President*
EMP: 30 **EST:** 1906
SQ FT: 100,000
SALES (est): 8.2MM **Privately Held**
WEB: www.sdpbc.com
SIC: 2657 Folding paperboard boxes

(P-5510)
T & T BOX COMPANY INC
Also Called: Thomas Container & Packaging
1353 Philadelphia St, Pomona
(91766-5554)
PHONE..................909 465-0848
Thomas Murphy, *CEO*
Andy Murphy, *Vice Pres*
EMP: 22
SQ FT: 60,000
SALES (est): 4.7MM **Privately Held**
WEB: www.thomascontainer.com
SIC: 2657 2653 Folding paperboard
boxes; corrugated & solid fiber boxes

(P-5511)
THERMAL BAGS BY INGRID INC
5801 Skylab Rd, Huntington Beach
(92647-2051)
PHONE..................847 836-4400
Ingrid Kosar, *Owner*
Mary Denicolo, *Sales Mgr*
▲ **EMP:** 18
SALES (est): 3.9MM **Privately Held**
WEB: www.thermalbags.com
SIC: 2657 Food containers, folding: made
from purchased material

(P-5512)
THORO—PACKAGING (DH)
1467 Davril Cir, Corona (92880-6957)
PHONE..................951 278-2100
Janet Dabek Steiner, *President*
EMP: 130
SQ FT: 56,000
SALES (est): 24.2MM
SALES (corp-wide): 3.1MM **Privately
Held**
WEB: www.thoropkg.com
SIC: 2657 Folding paperboard boxes
HQ: Autajon Cs
Autajon Packaging Montelimar Pt Pel-
ica Petit Pelican
Montelimar
475 002-000

(P-5513)
TWPM INC
Also Called: 3 Ball Co
15320 Valley View Ave, La Mirada
(90638-5236)
PHONE..................714 522-8881
Seon H Sohn, *Principal*
Nancy Hwang, *CFO*
EMP: 11
SQ FT: 10,000
SALES: 1MM **Privately Held**
SIC: 2657 Food containers, folding: made
from purchased material

(P-5514)
UNITED PAPER BOX INC
Also Called: California Button
1530 Lakeview Loop, Anaheim
(92807-1819)
PHONE..................714 777-8383
Ron Silverstein, *President*
John Hynes, *Exec VP*
H Rosie Silverstein, *Admin Sec*
EMP: 20
SALES (est): 1.7MM **Privately Held**
WEB: www.californiabutton.com
SIC: 2657 3544 7389 5113 Folding pa-
perboard boxes; special dies, tools, jigs &
fixtures; laminating service; bags, paper &
disposable plastic

(P-5515)
**YAVAR MANUFACTURING CO
INC**
Also Called: National Packaging Products
1900 S Tubeway Ave, Commerce
(90040-1612)
PHONE..................323 722-2040

Massoud Afari, *CEO*
Ben Afari, *Vice Pres*
▲ **EMP:** 23
SQ FT: 50,000
SALES (est): 5.9MM **Privately Held**
SIC: 2657 Folding paperboard boxes

2671 Paper Coating & Laminating for Packaging

(P-5516)
AMCOR FLEXIBLES LLC
5425 Broadway St, American Canyon
(94503-9678)
PHONE....................707 257-6481
Richard Evans, *Branch Mgr*
EMP: 135
SALES (corp-wide): 9.1B **Privately Held**
SIC: 2671 2621 2821 3081 Plastic film,
coated or laminated for packaging; packaging paper; plastics materials & resins;
packing materials, plastic sheet; closures,
stamped metal
HQ: Amcor Flexibles Llc
2150 E Lake Cook Rd
Buffalo Grove IL 60089
224 313-7000

(P-5517)
AMCOR FLEXIBLES LLC
5416 Union Pacific Ave, Commerce
(90022-5117)
PHONE....................323 721-6777
Graeme Liebelt, *Branch Mgr*
EMP: 135
SALES (corp-wide): 9.1B **Privately Held**
SIC: 2671 2621 2821 3081 Plastic film,
coated or laminated for packaging; packaging paper; plastics materials & resins;
packing materials, plastic sheet; closures,
stamped metal
HQ: Amcor Flexibles Llc
2150 E Lake Cook Rd
Buffalo Grove IL 60089
224 313-7000

(P-5518)
ATRA INTERNATIONAL TRADERS INC
3301 Leonis Blvd, Vernon (90058-3013)
PHONE....................562 864-3885
Alex Patel, *President*
▼ **EMP:** 30
SALES (est): 4.7MM **Privately Held**
SIC: 2671 Packaging paper & plastics film,
coated & laminated

(P-5519)
AUDIO VIDEO COLOR CORPORATION (PA)
Also Called: Avc
17707 S Santa Fe Ave, Compton
(90221-5419)
PHONE....................424 213-7500
Kali J Limath, *CEO*
Jim Hardiman, *President*
Guy Marrom, *Exec VP*
▲ **EMP:** 78
SQ FT: 78,000
SALES (est): 75.6MM **Privately Held**
WEB: www.avccorp.com
SIC: 2671 Packaging paper & plastics film,
coated & laminated

(P-5520)
BEU INDUSTRIES INC
2937 E Maria St, E Rncho Dmngz
(90221-5801)
PHONE....................310 885-9626
Jeffrey Beu, *President*
Ken Beu Jr, *Vice Pres*
EMP: 30
SALES (est): 3.8MM **Privately Held**
SIC: 2671 Packaging paper & plastics film,
coated & laminated

(P-5521)
ESHIELDS LLC
2307 Country Clb Vista St, Glendora
(91741-4060)
PHONE....................909 305-8848
Andrew Mason, *Mng Member*
Theani Davis, *Opers Staff*
Derek Lopez, *Marketing Staff*

David Clifford,
Eleanora Clifford,
▲ **EMP:** 32 **EST:** 2006
SQ FT: 1,500
SALES (est): 5.6MM **Privately Held**
SIC: 2671 Plastic film, coated or laminated
for packaging

(P-5522)
FREE-FLOW PACKAGING INTL INC
Also Called: FP International
34175 Ardenwood Blvd, Fremont
(94555-3653)
PHONE....................302 737-2413
Kenneth Johnson, *Plant Mgr*
Christina Giles, *Administration*
EMP: 30
SQ FT: 4,000
SALES (corp-wide): 4.7B **Privately Held**
WEB: www.fpintl.com
SIC: 2671 2821 Packaging paper & plastics film, coated & laminated; plastics materials & resins
HQ: Free-Flow Packaging International,
Inc.
34175 Ardenwood Blvd
Fremont CA 94555
650 261-5300

(P-5523)
GLOBAL LINK SOURCING INC
41690 Corporate Center Ct, Murrieta
(92562-7084)
PHONE....................951 698-1977
Jullie Annet, *President*
Mike Deigan, *VP Bus Dvlpt*
Lanette Johnson, *Office Mgr*
Brittany Reed, *Mktg Coord*
Ashley Glenn, *Manager*
▲ **EMP:** 70
SQ FT: 80,000
SALES: 15MM **Privately Held**
SIC: 2671 Packaging paper & plastics film,
coated & laminated

(P-5524)
GREAT NORTHERN CORPORATION
Laminations West
12075 Cabernet Dr, Fontana (92337-7703)
PHONE....................951 361-4770
Josh Coldiron, *Plant Mgr*
Sally Brewer, *Executive*
EMP: 35
SALES (corp-wide): 392.5MM **Privately Held**
SIC: 2671 Paper coated or laminated for
packaging
PA: Great Northern Corporation
395 Stroebe Rd
Appleton WI 54914
920 739-3671

(P-5525)
LIFE LINE PACKAGING INC
Also Called: Life Line Products
1250 Pierre Way, El Cajon (92021-4608)
PHONE....................619 444-2737
Miguel Lackenbacher, *President*
EMP: 15
SQ FT: 16,000
SALES (est): 907.5K **Privately Held**
WEB: www.lifelinepackaging.com
SIC: 2671 3089 5113 7336 Thermoplastic coated paper for packaging; thermoformed finished plastic products; shipping
supplies; package design

(P-5526)
MICHELSEN PACKAGING CO CAL
Also Called: Michelsen Packaging California
4165 S Cherry Ave, Fresno (93706-5709)
P.O. Box 10109 (93745-0109)
PHONE....................559 237-3819
Dan Keck, *President*
Debbie Falcon, *Office Mgr*
Jason Cline, *Plant Mgr*
Falcon Debbie, *Marketing Staff*
Tyke Mederios, *Sales Staff*
EMP: 25

SALES (corp-wide): 68MM **Privately Held**
SIC: 2671 2674 Packaging paper & plastics film, coated & laminated; paper bags:
made from purchased materials
PA: Michelsen Packaging Company Of California
202 N 2nd Ave
Yakima WA 98902
509 248-6270

(P-5527)
NORMAN PAPER AND FOAM CO INC
Also Called: Norman International
4501 S Santa Fe Ave, Vernon
(90058-2129)
PHONE....................323 582-7132
Norman Levine, *President*
Christopher Werner, *CFO*
Ellen Levine, *Corp Secy*
Dawnn Winter, *Executive*
▲ **EMP:** 23 **EST:** 1980
SQ FT: 40,000
SALES (est): 5.8MM **Privately Held**
SIC: 2671 3086 2673 Packaging paper &
plastics film, coated & laminated; packaging & shipping materials, foamed plastic;
bags: plastic, laminated & coated

(P-5528)
OSIO INTERNATIONAL INC
2550 E Cerritos Ave, Anaheim
(92806-5627)
PHONE....................714 935-9700
Don H Kwon, *CEO*
Rick Whipple, *Vice Pres*
Matthew Hendricks, *General Mgr*
Carol Blackwell, *Accounting Mgr*
▲ **EMP:** 11
SQ FT: 7,500
SALES: 12MM **Privately Held**
WEB: www.osiopack.com
SIC: 2671 8711 Paper coated or laminated
for packaging; industrial engineers

(P-5529)
PACIFIC SOUTHWEST CONT LLC (PA)
4530 Leckron Rd, Modesto (95357-0517)
PHONE....................209 526-0444
John W Mayol, *Mng Member*
Bryan Smith, *President*
Lester H Mangold, *CFO*
Darin Jones, *Exec VP*
Robert Nagle, *Senior VP*
▲ **EMP:** 347
SQ FT: 129,600
SALES (est): 145.9MM **Privately Held**
SIC: 2671 2657 3086 2653 Packaging
paper & plastics film, coated & laminated;
folding paperboard boxes; packaging &
shipping materials, foamed plastic; boxes,
corrugated: made from purchased materials; commercial printing, lithographic

(P-5530)
PAPERBOARD PACKAGING CORP (HQ)
Also Called: Deluxe Pckges An Amcor Flexble
800 N Walton Ave, Yuba City (95993-9352)
P.O. Box 3057 (95992-3057)
PHONE....................530 671-9000
Mark S Williams, *President*
▲ **EMP:** 75
SQ FT: 100,000
SALES: 37MM
SALES (corp-wide): 9.1B **Privately Held**
WEB: www.deluxepackages.com
SIC: 2671 2759 Packaging paper & plastics film, coated & laminated; flexographic
printing
PA: Amcor Ltd
L11 60 City Rd
Southbank VIC 3006
392 269-000

(P-5531)
PAPERCUTTERS INC
6023 Bandini Blvd, Los Angeles
(90040-2904)
PHONE....................323 888-1330
Susan Feinstein, *President*
Joyce Feinstein, *Corp Secy*
Beth Feinstein, *Vice Pres*
Beth Thurber, *VP Mktg*

▲ **EMP:** 21
SQ FT: 20,000
SALES (est): 4.9MM **Privately Held**
WEB: www.papercutters.net
SIC: 2671 5113 Packaging paper & plastics film, coated & laminated; paper &
products, wrapping or coarse

(P-5532)
PGAC CORP (PA)
9630 Ridgehaven Ct Ste B, San Diego
(92123-5605)
PHONE....................858 560-8213
Mark Grantham, *President*
Florentina Shields, *Vice Pres*
EMP: 75
SALES (est): 86.8MM **Privately Held**
SIC: 2671 Paper coated or laminated for
packaging

(P-5533)
POUCHES INCORPORATED
1901 S Bon View Ave, Ontario
(91761-5601)
PHONE....................909 923-1135
David A Nagy Jr, *CEO*
▲ **EMP:** 15 **EST:** 1990
SQ FT: 9,200
SALES (est): 3.1MM **Privately Held**
WEB: www.pouchesinc.com
SIC: 2671 Plastic film, coated or laminated
for packaging

(P-5534)
PRECISION LABEL INC
659 Benet Rd, Oceanside (92058-1208)
P.O. Box 766, Solana Beach (92075-0766)
PHONE....................760 757-7533
Robert A Wilcox, *President*
EMP: 30 **EST:** 1991
SQ FT: 7,000
SALES (est): 7.8MM **Privately Held**
SIC: 2671 2759 Packaging paper & plastics film, coated & laminated; labels &
seals: printing

(P-5535)
PREMIER BAG COMPANY LLC
Also Called: Premier Packaging Group, LLC
1603 Commerce Way, Paso Robles
(93446-3644)
P.O. Box 2180 (93447-2180)
PHONE....................805 237-1910
Harry T Greenhouse, *CFO*
Peter K Tur, *Mng Member*
EMP: 42
SALES (corp-wide): 20MM **Privately Held**
SIC: 2671 Packaging paper & plastics film,
coated & laminated
PA: Columbia Burlap And Bag Company,
Inc.
999 Bedford Rd
North Kansas City MO 64116
816 421-4121

(P-5536)
QUALITY CONTAINER CORP
866 Towne Center Dr, Pomona
(91767-5902)
P.O. Box 1297, Claremont (91711-1297)
PHONE....................909 482-1850
Edward J Kaleff, *CEO*
EMP: 18
SALES (est): 5.7MM **Privately Held**
SIC: 2671 Packaging paper & plastics film,
coated & laminated

(P-5537)
SAMCO PLASTICS INC
Also Called: Sambrailo Packaging
1260 W Beach St, Watsonville (95076)
P.O. Box 50090 (95077-5090)
PHONE....................831 761-1392
William Sambrailo, *President*
Mark Sambrailo, *President*
Michael Sambrailo, *Vice Pres*
EMP: 12
SQ FT: 30,000
SALES (est): 1.4MM **Privately Held**
SIC: 2671 Plastic film, coated or laminated
for packaging

▲ = Import ▼=Export
◆ =Import/Export

(P-5538)
STERIPAX INC
5412 Research Dr, Huntington Beach
(92649-1542)
PHONE.....................714 892-8811
Steve Pearce, *President*
Linda Pearce, *Vice Pres*
John Pearce, *Opers Mgr*
Steve Marmion, *Sales Staff*
▲ EMP: 47
SQ FT: 10,000
SALES: 27.9MM **Privately Held**
WEB: www.steripaxinc.com
SIC: 2671 Packaging paper & plastics film,
    coated & laminated

(P-5539)
SUMMIT INTERNATIONAL PACKG INC
Also Called: Western Summit Manufacturing
30200 Cartier Dr, Rancho Palos Verdes
(90275-5722)
PHONE.....................626 333-3333
Donald Clark, *President*
EMP: 85
SQ FT: 58,000
SALES (est): 11.3MM **Privately Held**
SIC: 2671 Plastic film, coated or laminated
    for packaging

(P-5540)
SUSTAINABLE FIBR SOLUTIONS LLC (PA)
30950 Rancho Viejo Rd, San Juan Capis-
trano (92675-1764)
PHONE.....................949 265-8287
Raymond Taccolini, *President*
EMP: 11
SALES (est): 1.5MM **Privately Held**
SIC: 2671 Packaging paper & plastics film,
    coated & laminated

(P-5541)
TECHFLEX PACKAGING LLC
Also Called: Xsential
13771 Gramercy Pl, Gardena
(90249-2470)
PHONE.....................424 266-9400
Burt Siegelman,
Lucas Van Winkle, *Engineer*
Mike Serrano, *Sales Executive*
Neil Kinney,
▲ EMP: 52
SALES (est): 15MM **Privately Held**
SIC: 2671 Plastic film, coated or laminated
    for packaging

(P-5542)
TETRA PAK PROCESSING EQUIP
1408 W Main St Ste E, Ripon
(95366-3013)
PHONE.....................209 599-4634
Brad Clark, *Branch Mgr*
EMP: 88
SALES (corp-wide): 7.5B **Privately Held**
WEB: www.tetrapak.com
SIC: 2671 Paper coated or laminated for
    packaging
HQ: Tetra Pak Processing Equipment Inc.
    801 Kingsley St S
    Winsted MN 55395

(P-5543)
THERMECH CORPORATION
Also Called: Thermech Engineering
1773 W Lincoln Ave Ste I, Anaheim
(92801-6713)
PHONE.....................714 533-3183
Jim Shah, *CEO*
Richard Gorman, *President*
Casey Patelski, *Sales Staff*
EMP: 23
SQ FT: 24,000
SALES (est): 4.7MM **Privately Held**
WEB: www.thermech.com
SIC: 2671 3083 Packaging paper & plas-
    tics film, coated & laminated; plastic fin-
    ished products, laminated

(P-5544)
TRIUNE ENTERPRISES INC
Also Called: Triune Enterprises Mfg
13711 S Normandie Ave, Gardena
(90249-2609)
PHONE.....................310 719-1600
John Christman, *CEO*
Sidney Arouh, *Vice Pres*
Donald Alhanati, *Admin Sec*
◆ EMP: 23
SQ FT: 29,000
SALES (est): 6.7MM **Privately Held**
SIC: 2671 5162 Plastic film, coated or
    laminated for packaging; resinous impreg-
    nated paper for packaging; plastics mate-
    rials & basic shapes

(P-5545)
UOP LLC
2100 E Orangethorpe Ave, Anaheim
(92806-1227)
PHONE.....................714 870-7590
Lorraine Manandik, *Manager*
EMP: 30
SALES (corp-wide): 40.5B **Publicly Held**
SIC: 2671 Packaging paper & plastics film,
    coated & laminated
HQ: Uop Llc
    25 E Algonquin Rd
    Des Plaines IL 60016
    847 391-2000

(P-5546)
VINYL TECHNOLOGY INC
200 Railroad Ave, Monrovia (91016-4643)
PHONE.....................626 443-5257
Carlos A Mollura, *Ch of Bd*
Daniel Mullora, *CEO*
Haydee Mollura, *Corp Secy*
Rodney Mollura, *Exec VP*
Carlos Mollura Jr, *Vice Pres*
▲ EMP: 200
SQ FT: 68,000
SALES (est): 72.3MM **Privately Held**
WEB: www.vinyltechnology.com
SIC: 2671 7389 Plastic film, coated or
    laminated for packaging; sewing contrac-
    tor

2672 Paper Coating & Laminating, Exc for Packaging

(P-5547)
AUTOMATED TAPE AND LABEL INC
7702 Kester Ave, Van Nuys (91405-1156)
PHONE.....................818 908-4400
Arthur Rosenblum, *President*
Shelly Rosenblum, *Corp Secy*
Bruce Rosenblum, *Vice Pres*
EMP: 20
SQ FT: 10,000
SALES (est): 4.2MM **Privately Held**
SIC: 2672 Labels (unprinted), gummed:
    made from purchased materials

(P-5548)
AVERY DENNISON CORPORATION (PA)
207 N Goode Ave Ste 500, Glendale
(91203-1301)
PHONE.....................626 304-2000
Mitchell R Butier, *President*
Dean A Scarborough, *Ch of Bd*
Georges Gravanis, *President*
Gregory S Lovins, *CFO*
Anne Hill, *Officer*
EMP: 277
SALES: 6.6B **Publicly Held**
WEB: www.avery.com
SIC: 2672 3081 3497 2678 Adhesive pa-
    pers, labels or tapes: from purchased ma-
    terial; gummed paper: made from
    purchased materials; coated paper, ex-
    cept photographic, carbon or abrasive;
    unsupported plastics film & sheet; metal
    foil & leaf; notebooks: made from pur-
    chased paper

(P-5549)
AVERY DENNISON CORPORATION
50 Pointe Dr, Brea (92821-3652)
PHONE.....................714 674-8500
Rick Alonzo, *Manager*
Tony Hill, *Facilities Mgr*
Colwin Chan, *Senior Mgr*
EMP: 400
SALES (corp-wide): 6.6B **Publicly Held**
WEB: www.avery.com
SIC: 2672 3081 3497 2678 Adhesive pa-
    pers, labels or tapes: from purchased ma-
    terial; unsupported plastics film & sheet;
    metal foil & leaf; stationery products; pens
    & mechanical pencils; adhesives &
    sealants
PA: Avery Dennison Corporation
    207 N Goode Ave Ste 500
    Glendale CA 91203
    626 304-2000

(P-5550)
AVERY DENNISON CORPORATION
751 N Todd Ave, Azusa (91702-2244)
PHONE.....................626 938-7239
EMP: 115
SALES (corp-wide): 6.6B **Publicly Held**
SIC: 2672 3081 3497 2678 Adhesive pa-
    pers, labels or tapes: from purchased ma-
    terial; gummed paper: made from
    purchased materials; coated paper, ex-
    cept photographic, carbon or abrasive;
    unsupported plastics film & sheet; metal
    foil & leaf; notebooks: made from pur-
    chased paper
PA: Avery Dennison Corporation
    207 N Goode Ave Ste 500
    Glendale CA 91203
    626 304-2000

(P-5551)
AVERY DENNISON CORPORATION
11195 Eucalyptus St, Rancho Cucamonga
(91730-3836)
PHONE.....................909 987-4631
Marta E Corfaelb, *Manager*
Desean Jackson, *Manager*
Dario Soto, *Manager*
EMP: 125
SALES (corp-wide): 6.6B **Publicly Held**
WEB: www.avery.com
SIC: 2672 Tape, pressure sensitive: made
    from purchased materials
PA: Avery Dennison Corporation
    207 N Goode Ave Ste 500
    Glendale CA 91203
    626 304-2000

(P-5552)
AVERY DENNISON CORPORATION
10721 Jasmine St, Fontana (92337-8200)
PHONE.....................909 428-4238
Bruce Elliott, *Manager*
EMP: 115
SALES (corp-wide): 6.6B **Publicly Held**
WEB: www.avery.com
SIC: 2672 Coated paper, except photo-
    graphic, carbon or abrasive
PA: Avery Dennison Corporation
    207 N Goode Ave Ste 500
    Glendale CA 91203
    626 304-2000

(P-5553)
AVERY DENNISON CORPORATION
2900 Bradley St, Pasadena (91107-1560)
PHONE.....................626 304-2000
Dave Edwards, *Vice Pres*
Paul Germeraad, *Network Mgr*
Liviu Dinescu, *Research*
Herman Hartono, *Engineer*
Hal Hatfield, *Manager*
EMP: 120
SQ FT: 67,580

(P-5554)
AVERY DENNISON CORPORATION
5819 Telegraph Rd, Commerce
(90040-1515)
PHONE.....................323 728-8888
Justman Morley, *Branch Mgr*
EMP: 115
SALES (corp-wide): 6.6B **Publicly Held**
SIC: 2672 Adhesive backed films, foams &
    foils
PA: Avery Dennison Corporation
    207 N Goode Ave Ste 500
    Glendale CA 91203
    626 304-2000

(P-5555)
AVERY DENNISON CORPORATION
2743 Thompson Creek Rd, Pomona
(91767-1861)
PHONE.....................626 304-2000
Jeffrey Stites, *Branch Mgr*
EMP: 115
SALES (corp-wide): 6.6B **Publicly Held**
SIC: 2672 Adhesive backed films, foams &
    foils
PA: Avery Dennison Corporation
    207 N Goode Ave Ste 500
    Glendale CA 91203
    626 304-2000

(P-5556)
BECKERS FABRICATION INC
Also Called: B F I Labels
22465 La Palma Ave, Yorba Linda
(92887-3803)
PHONE.....................714 692-1600
Mark Becker, *CEO*
Dan Becker, *President*
David Beilfuss, *General Mgr*
Sergio Serrano, *Purch Mgr*
James Steven, *Sales Staff*
EMP: 24
SQ FT: 6,500
SALES (est): 6.5MM **Privately Held**
WEB: www.beckersfab.com
SIC: 2672 2759 Coated & laminated
    paper; screen printing

(P-5557)
CINTON
Also Called: West Coast Labels
620 Richfield Rd, Placentia (92870-6727)
PHONE.....................714 961-8808
Salvatore Scaffide, *President*
Romona Scaffide, *Vice Pres*
Cindi Montgomery, *Admin Sec*
Mark Trahanovski, *Mktg Dir*
Vanessa Garcia, *Sales Staff*
EMP: 46
SQ FT: 23,000
SALES (est): 10.4MM **Privately Held**
WEB: www.westcoastlabels.com
SIC: 2672 2679 Coated & laminated
    paper; labels, paper: made from pur-
    chased material

(P-5558)
CLARIANT CORPORATION
926 S 8th St, Colton (92324-3500)
P.O. Box 610 (92324-0610)
PHONE.....................909 825-1793
Kenneth Golder, *President*
EMP: 32
SALES (corp-wide): 665.7MM **Privately Held**
SIC: 2672 7389 5199 Coated & laminated
    paper; packaging & labeling services;
    packaging materials
HQ: Clariant Corporation
    4000 Monroe Rd
    Charlotte NC 28205
    704 331-7000

(P-5559)
EDWARDS ASSOC CMMNICATIONS INC (PA)
Also Called: Edwards Label
2277 Knoll Dr Ste A, Ventura (93003-5878)
PHONE..................................805 658-2626
Joel Horacio Gomez-Avila, *President*
John Edwards, *President*
Jessica Sujo, *Executive Asst*
Garrett Boys, *Human Resources*
Melyssa Ho, *Mfg Staff*
EMP: 300
SQ FT: 44,000
SALES (est): 67.9MM Privately Held
SIC: 2672 Labels (unprinted), gummed: made from purchased materials; adhesive papers, labels or tapes: from purchased material

(P-5560)
EXCEL GRAPHIX INTERNATIONAL
11 Autry Ste B, Irvine (92618-2766)
PHONE..................................949 582-5970
Gary Larsen, *President*
M Hawkner, *Vice Pres*
EMP: 30
SQ FT: 4,000
SALES (est): 3.4MM Privately Held
WEB: www.thermaprint.com
SIC: 2672 2395 2396 Chemically treated papers: made from purchased materials; appliqueing, for the trade; automotive & apparel trimmings

(P-5561)
HARRIS INDUSTRIES INC (PA)
5181 Argosy Ave, Huntington Beach (92649-1058)
P.O. Box 3269 (92605-3269)
PHONE..................................714 898-8048
William Helzer, *President*
Gail Helzer, *Corp Secy*
▲ EMP: 50
SQ FT: 25,000
SALES (est): 10.7MM Privately Held
SIC: 2672 Tape, pressure sensitive: made from purchased materials

(P-5562)
HIS COMPANY INC
Precision Converting
400 E Parkridge Ave # 101, Corona (92879-6618)
PHONE..................................951 493-0200
George Cailloueepe, *Director*
EMP: 18
SALES (corp-wide): 202.9MM Privately Held
SIC: 2672 Adhesive backed films, foams & foils
PA: His Company, Inc.
6650 Concord Park Dr
Houston TX 77040
713 934-1600

(P-5563)
KIERAN LABEL CORP
2321 Siempre Viva Ct # 101, San Diego (92154-6301)
PHONE..................................619 449-4457
Denis Vanier, *CEO*
William Walker, *President*
Bill Walker, *Sr Corp Ofcr*
Karl Morgan, *Controller*
Cynthia Johnson, *Human Res Mgr*
▲ EMP: 44 EST: 1979
SALES (est): 13.8MM Privately Held
SIC: 2672 Labels (unprinted), gummed: made from purchased materials

(P-5564)
KING ABRASIVES INC
1942 National Ave, Hayward (94545-1710)
PHONE..................................510 785-8100
David D, *Co-CEO*
◆ EMP: 12
SALES: 200K Privately Held
SIC: 2672 3291 Adhesive papers, labels or tapes: from purchased material; abrasive wheels & grindstones, not artificial

(P-5565)
LABEL SERVICE INC
20008 Normandie Ave, Torrance (90502-1210)
PHONE..................................310 329-5605
Russell Nakada, *President*
Minoru Nakada, *Shareholder*
Peter Nakada, *Shareholder*
Kanji Yasutomi, *Shareholder*
EMP: 13
SQ FT: 7,700
SALES: 1.2MM Privately Held
SIC: 2672 2752 2679 Labels (unprinted), gummed: made from purchased materials; commercial printing, offset; labels, paper: made from purchased material

(P-5566)
LABELING HURST SYSTEMS LLC
Also Called: Hurst International
20747 Dearborn St, Chatsworth (91311-5914)
P.O. Box 5169 (91313-5169)
PHONE..................................818 701-0710
Aron Lichtenberg, *President*
▲ EMP: 18
SQ FT: 12,875
SALES (est): 5.3MM Privately Held
SIC: 2672 Book paper, coated: made from purchased materials

(P-5567)
LOCKWOOD INDUSTRIES LLC
Also Called: Fralock
28525 Industry Dr, Valencia (91355-5424)
PHONE..................................661 702-6999
Marcelo Norona, *CEO*
Bobbi Booher, *CFO*
Kc Calderon, *Project Mgr*
Daniel Lehan, *Technology*
Sejal Shah, *Engineer*
EMP: 200 EST: 1966
SQ FT: 62,500
SALES (est): 83.8MM Privately Held
WEB: www.fralock.com
SIC: 2672 2821 3644 3559 Adhesive backed films, foams & foils; polyimides (skybond, kaplon); insulators & insulation materials, electrical; electronic component making machinery

(P-5568)
LOGIC TECHNOLOGY INC (PA)
1138 W Evelyn Ave, Sunnyvale (94086-5742)
PHONE..................................408 530-1007
Henry Tan, *President*
Jerry Robinson, *Sales/Mktg Mgr*
EMP: 12 EST: 1971
SQ FT: 7,500
SALES (est): 2.1MM Privately Held
SIC: 2672 Coated & laminated paper

(P-5569)
LOHMANN PRCISION DIE CUTNG LLC
Also Called: G&L Precision Die Cutting
1766 Junction Ave, San Jose (95112-1021)
PHONE..................................408 453-9400
Steven J De Jong, *Mng Member*
EMP: 18
SALES (est): 3MM
SALES (corp-wide): 589.5MM Privately Held
SIC: 2672 3363 3364 Tape, pressure sensitive: made from purchased materials; aluminum die-castings; nonferrous die-castings except aluminum
HQ: Lohmann Technologies Corporation
3000 Earhart Ct
Hebron KY 41048
859 334-4900

(P-5570)
MARCAFLEX INC
2 Seville Dr, San Rafael (94903-1561)
PHONE..................................415 472-4423
Mario Cataldi, *President*
EMP: 15
SALES (est): 2.2MM Privately Held
WEB: www.marcaflex.com
SIC: 2672 3961 Labels (unprinted), gummed: made from purchased materials; keychains, except precious metal

(P-5571)
MILLER PRODUCTS INC
Also Called: Mpi Label Systems
2315 Station Dr, Stockton (95215-7928)
PHONE..................................209 467-2470
Spencer Cser, *Principal*
EMP: 60
SALES (corp-wide): 33MM Privately Held
SIC: 2672 2679 2759 Adhesive papers, labels or tapes: from purchased material; labels, paper: made from purchased material; commercial printing
PA: Miller Products, Inc.
450 Courtney Rd
Sebring OH 44672
330 938-2134

(P-5572)
MPS LANSING INC
Also Called: John Henry Packaging West
101 H St Ste M, Petaluma (94952-5100)
PHONE..................................707 778-1250
Dan Welty, *President*
EMP: 30
SALES (corp-wide): 14.8B Publicly Held
WEB: www.thejohnhenrycompany.com
SIC: 2672 2754 Coated & laminated paper; commercial printing, gravure
HQ: Lansing Mps Inc
5800 W Grand River Ave
Lansing MI 48906
517 323-9000

(P-5573)
NITTO AMERICAS INC (HQ)
Also Called: Permacel-Automotive
48500 Fremont Blvd, Fremont (94538-6579)
PHONE..................................510 445-5400
Toru Takeuchi, *Ch of Bd*
Yoichiro Sakuma, *President*
Steve Evans, *CFO*
Matt Altieri, *Vice Pres*
Bob Vath, *Info Tech Dir*
◆ EMP: 125 EST: 1968
SQ FT: 168,000
SALES (est): 350MM
SALES (corp-wide): 8B Privately Held
SIC: 2672 3589 5162 5065 Tape, pressure sensitive: made from purchased materials; water treatment equipment, industrial; plastics products; electronic parts
PA: Nitto Denko Corporation
4-20, Ofukacho, Kita-Ku
Osaka OSK 530-0
676 322-101

(P-5574)
PACIFIC LABEL INC
1511 E Edinger Ave, Santa Ana (92705-4907)
PHONE..................................714 237-1276
Nick Valestrino, *President*
EMP: 98 EST: 1998
SQ FT: 22,000
SALES (est): 11.2MM Privately Held
WEB: www.lable.com
SIC: 2672 Adhesive papers, labels or tapes: from purchased material

(P-5575)
PRECISION DYNAMICS CORPORATION (HQ)
Also Called: PDC
27770 N Entmt Dr Ste 200, Valencia (91355)
PHONE..................................818 897-1111
J Michael Nauman, *CEO*
Robin Barber, *Vice Pres*
Robert Case, *Vice Pres*
John Park, *Vice Pres*
Sherry Johnston, *Executive Asst*
◆ EMP: 200 EST: 1956
SQ FT: 75,000
SALES (est): 96.4MM
SALES (corp-wide): 1.1B Publicly Held
WEB: www.pdcorp.com
SIC: 2672 2754 5047 3069 Adhesive papers, labels or tapes: from purchased material; labels (unprinted), gummed: made from purchased materials; labels: gravure printing; instruments, surgical & medical; tape, pressure sensitive: rubber

PA: Brady Corporation
6555 W Good Hope Rd
Milwaukee WI 53223
414 358-6600

(P-5576)
RICHARDS LABEL CO INC
17291 Mount Herrmann St, Fountain Valley (92708-4117)
PHONE..................................714 529-1791
Kyle Richards, *President*
Leigh Richards, *Treasurer*
Gary Richards, *Vice Pres*
Julie Sagat - Ofc, *Manager*
EMP: 12
SQ FT: 6,300
SALES: 1.4MM Privately Held
WEB: www.richardslabel.com
SIC: 2672 Labels (unprinted), gummed: made from purchased materials

(P-5577)
SCAPA TAPES NORTH AMERICA LLC
540 N Oak St, Inglewood (90302-2942)
PHONE..................................310 419-0567
Kevin Ryan, *Branch Mgr*
EMP: 42
SALES (corp-wide): 408.3MM Privately Held
SIC: 2672 Adhesive papers, labels or tapes: from purchased material
HQ: Scapa Tapes North America Llc
111 Great Pond Dr
Windsor CT 06095
860 688-8000

(P-5578)
SEAL METHODS INC (PA)
11915 Shoemaker Ave, Santa Fe Springs (90670-4717)
P.O. Box 2604 (90670-0604)
PHONE..................................562 944-0291
Eugene Welter, *Principal*
Geri Welter, *Admin Sec*
Ramon Cardenas, *Prdtn Mgr*
Paul Serna, *Sales Staff*
Darin Welter, *Sales Staff*
▲ EMP: 90 EST: 1974
SQ FT: 75,000
SALES (est): 31.2MM Privately Held
WEB: www.sealmethodsinc.com
SIC: 2672 3053 5085 Masking tape: made from purchased materials; tape, pressure sensitive: made from purchased materials; gaskets, all materials; packing, rubber; gaskets; seals, industrial

(P-5579)
TAPE & LABEL CONVERTERS INC
8231 Allport Ave, Santa Fe Springs (90670-2105)
P.O. Box 398, Pico Rivera (90660-0398)
PHONE..................................562 945-3486
Toll Free:..................................888 -
Robert Varela Jr, *President*
Jeanette Verela, *Admin Sec*
EMP: 20
SQ FT: 3,625
SALES (est): 3.7MM Privately Held
SIC: 2672 2782 2752 2671 Labels (unprinted), gummed: made from purchased materials; blankbooks & looseleaf binders; commercial printing, lithographic; packaging paper & plastics film, coated & laminated

(P-5580)
TAPE FACTORY INC
Also Called: American Decal Company
11899 Lotus Ave, Fountain Valley (92708-2637)
PHONE..................................714 979-7742
Paul Riccobon, *President*
EMP: 20
SQ FT: 17,000
SALES (est): 5.2MM Privately Held
SIC: 2672 Tape, pressure sensitive: made from purchased materials

(P-5581)
UPM RAFLATAC INC
1105 Auto Center Dr, Ontario (91761-2213)
PHONE..................................909 390-4657
Alan Punch, *Manager*

▲ = Import ▼=Export
◆ =Import/Export

EMP: 20
SALES (corp-wide): 11.8B Privately Held
WEB: www.raflatac.com
SIC: 2672 2679 Coated & laminated paper; labels, paper: made from purchased material
HQ: Upm Raflatac, Inc.
400 Broadpointe Dr
Mills River NC 28759
828 651-4800

(P-5582)
VINTAGE 99 LABEL MFG INC
611 Enterprise Ct, Livermore (94550-5200)
PHONE..................................925 294-5270
Mark Gonzales, CEO
Kathy Gonzales, President
Samantha Gomez, Creative Dir
Brian Lloyd, Sales Dir
Greg Mackie, Regl Sales Mgr
EMP: 21
SALES (est): 5.7MM Privately Held
WEB: www.vintage99.com
SIC: 2672 2752 Adhesive papers, labels or tapes: from purchased material; commercial printing, lithographic

(P-5583)
WESTROCK CP LLC
2363 Boulevard Cir Ste 4, Walnut Creek (94595-1173)
PHONE..................................925 946-0842
Robert Scheer, Manager
EMP: 88
SALES (corp-wide): 14.8B Publicly Held
WEB: www.smurfit-stone.com
SIC: 2672 Coated & laminated paper
HQ: Westrock Cp, Llc
504 Thrasher St
Norcross GA 30071

2673 Bags: Plastics, Laminated & Coated

(P-5584)
ADAMANT ENTERPRISE INC
2326 Jurado Ave, Hacienda Heights (91745-4423)
PHONE..................................626 934-3399
Angie WEI, CEO
Yung C WEI, Vice Pres
Teresa WEI, Admin Sec
▲ EMP: 35
SQ FT: 40,000
SALES (est): 7.3MM Privately Held
SIC: 2673 Plastic & pliofilm bags

(P-5585)
ADVANCED ADBAG PACKAGING INC
597 Quarry Rd, San Carlos (94070-6222)
P.O. Box 1048 (94070-1048)
PHONE..................................650 591-1625
Carmen Nevaro, President
Dan Bridgeman, Vice Pres
Kevin Neadeau, Vice Pres
▲ EMP: 10 EST: 1981
SALES (est): 2.3MM Privately Held
WEB: www.adbag-inc.com
SIC: 2673 Cellophane bags, unprinted: made from purchased materials

(P-5586)
ALLSTATE PLASTICS LLC
1763 Sabre St, Hayward (94545-1015)
PHONE..................................510 783-9600
Angela Leung, Mng Member
Yau CHI Leung,
◆ EMP: 17
SQ FT: 26,538
SALES (est): 4.2MM Privately Held
SIC: 2673 Plastic & pliofilm bags

(P-5587)
ASIA PLASTICS INC
9347 Rush St, South El Monte (91733-2544)
PHONE..................................626 448-8100
Kent Ung, CEO
Hung Tran, CFO
Tracy Ung, Corp Secy
▲ EMP: 20 EST: 1982
SQ FT: 11,000
SALES (est): 3.9MM Privately Held
WEB: www.asiaplastics.com
SIC: 2673 Plastic bags: made from purchased materials

(P-5588)
C H K MANUFACTURING INC
960 98th Ave, Oakland (94603-2347)
PHONE..................................510 632-5637
Chio-Hsiung Kuo, President
EMP: 50
SQ FT: 30,000
SALES: 10.8MM Privately Held
SIC: 2673 Plastic bags: made from purchased materials

(P-5589)
CALIFORNIA PLASTIX INC
Also Called: Sierra Plastic
1319 E 3rd St, Pomona (91766-2212)
PHONE..................................909 629-8288
Danny Farshadfar, President
Touraj Tour, Vice Pres
▲ EMP: 42
SALES (est): 9.1MM Privately Held
SIC: 2673 3089 Garment & wardrobe bags, (plastic film); extruded finished plastic products

(P-5590)
CALTEX PLASTICS INC (PA)
2380 E 51st St, Vernon (90058-2813)
PHONE..................................800 584-7303
Ruth Rosenfeld, CEO
Rafael Rosenfeld, CFO
Stephen Graves, Executive
Jin Kim, Executive
Fred Movey, Controller
▲ EMP: 50
SQ FT: 35,000
SALES (est): 8.5MM Privately Held
WEB: www.caltexplastics.com
SIC: 2673 Trash bags (plastic film): made from purchased materials

(P-5591)
CENTRAL VALLEY PROFESSIONAL SE
Also Called: Central Valley Prof Svcs
8207 Mondo Ln, Oakdale (95361-8135)
PHONE..................................209 847-7832
David A Racher, President
John Hassapakis, Vice Pres
▲ EMP: 13
SQ FT: 12,400
SALES (est): 1.8MM Privately Held
SIC: 2673 2385 3423 3089 Pliofilm bags: made from purchased materials; aprons, waterproof: made from purchased materials; knives, agricultural or industrial; injection molding of plastics

(P-5592)
CF&B MANUFACTURING INC
Also Called: Cleanroom Film & Bags
1405 N Manzanita St, Orange (92867-3603)
P.O. Box 807, Atwood (92811-0807)
PHONE..................................714 744-8361
James Fruth, President
Brad Mello, General Mgr
Peggy Pearce, Sales Staff
EMP: 20
SQ FT: 10,000
SALES (est): 3MM Privately Held
SIC: 2673 Plastic bags: made from purchased materials

(P-5593)
CLEAR IMAGE INC (PA)
Also Called: Clearbags
4949 Windplay Dr Ste 100, El Dorado Hills (95762-9318)
PHONE..................................916 933-4700
Benny Dyal Wilkins, President
Dave Pavao, General Mgr
Laura Wilkins, Admin Sec
Aaron Johnson, Administration
Dave Deppner, Info Tech Mgr
◆ EMP: 41
SQ FT: 35,000
SALES (est): 7.6MM Privately Held
WEB: www.clearbags.com
SIC: 2673 5112 Bags: plastic, laminated & coated; envelopes

(P-5594)
CLW PLASTIC BAG MFG CO INC
13060 Park St, Santa Fe Springs (90670-4032)
PHONE..................................562 903-8878
Yo Fu Lee, President
Wen-CHI Wu, Vice Pres
▲ EMP: 10
SALES (est): 2MM Privately Held
SIC: 2673 Plastic bags: made from purchased materials

(P-5595)
COMMAND PACKAGING LLC
3840 E 26th St, Vernon (90058-4107)
PHONE..................................323 980-0918
Dhu Thompson,
Avelino Garcia, Engineer
Mahesh Narkhede, Engineer
Michael Manville, Controller
Cristina Ehlert, VP Human Res
▲ EMP: 200
SQ FT: 170,000
SALES (est): 83.5MM Privately Held
WEB: www.restaurantbags.com
SIC: 2673 Bags: plastic, laminated & coated
PA: Delta Plastics Of The South, Llc
8801 Frazier Pike
Little Rock AR 72206

(P-5596)
CROWN POLY INC
Also Called: Pull-N-Pac
5700 Bickett St, Huntington Park (90255-2625)
PHONE..................................323 268-1298
Ebrahim Simhaee, CEO
David Simhaee, Vice Pres
Derek Perreira, Info Tech Mgr
Sandeep Cherukuri, Electrical Engi
Frerick Widjaja, Engineer
◆ EMP: 150
SQ FT: 40,000
SALES (est): 93.5MM Privately Held
WEB: www.crownpoly.com
SIC: 2673 Plastic bags: made from purchased materials

(P-5597)
DURABAG COMPANY INC
1432 Santa Fe Dr, Tustin (92780-6417)
PHONE..................................714 259-8811
Frank C S Huang, Vice Pres
Daniel Huang, Vice Pres
Frank Pannier, Plant Mgr
Wendy SOO, Marketing Mgr
Feng Jung Huang, Director
▲ EMP: 70
SQ FT: 150,000
SALES (est): 28.9MM Privately Held
WEB: www.durabag.net
SIC: 2673 Food storage & frozen food bags, plastic; trash bags (plastic film): made from purchased materials; plastic bags: made from purchased materials

(P-5598)
E-Z PLASTIC PACKAGING CORP
2051 Garfield Ave, Commerce (90040-1803)
PHONE..................................323 887-0123
Sui TAC LI, President
Nam LI, Vice Pres
EMP: 25 EST: 1996
SQ FT: 75,000
SALES: 5MM Privately Held
SIC: 2673 Bags: plastic, laminated & coated

(P-5599)
EMERALD PACKAGING INC
Also Called: E P
33050 Western Ave, Union City (94587-2157)
P.O. Box 5038 (94587-8538)
PHONE..................................510 429-5700
Kevin Kelly, CEO
James P Kelly Sr, Ch of Bd
James M Kelly Jr, Exec VP
Maura Kelly Koberlein, Vice Pres
Mary Anne Lothrop, Admin Asst
▲ EMP: 250
SQ FT: 80,000

SALES (est): 100.9MM Privately Held
SIC: 2673 Plastic bags: made from purchased materials

(P-5600)
EPSILON PLASTICS INC
3100 E Harcourt St, Compton (90221-5506)
PHONE..................................310 609-1320
Jim Gifford, Manager
Tracie Castillo, Executive
Luz Franco, Office Mgr
Fred Stabile, Mfg Staff
Tamayo Covarrubias, Mfg Staff
EMP: 75
SQ FT: 39,963 Privately Held
SIC: 2673 Bags: plastic, laminated & coated
HQ: Epsilon Plastics Inc.
Page & Schuyler Ave 8
Lyndhurst NJ 07071
201 933-6000

(P-5601)
GREAT AMERICAN PACKAGING
4361 S Soto St, Vernon (90058-2311)
PHONE..................................323 582-2247
Greg Gurewitz, President
Bruce Carter, President
Marlene Gurewitz, CFO
David Vogel, Finance
Bob Clarke, Sales Mgr
EMP: 50
SQ FT: 40,000
SALES (est): 13.4MM Privately Held
WEB: www.greatampack.com
SIC: 2673 3081 3082 Plastic bags: made from purchased materials; plastic film & sheet; unsupported plastics profile shapes

(P-5602)
HEAT FACTORY INC
2793 Loker Ave W, Carlsbad (92010-6601)
PHONE..................................760 734-5300
Chris Treptow, CEO
Chris Parks, COO
Deron Degraw, Design Engr
Marian Strohmeyer, Finance
Jeff Imray, Director
▲ EMP: 35
SQ FT: 40,000
SALES (est): 8.4MM Privately Held
SIC: 2673 2381 Bags: plastic, laminated & coated; fabric dress & work gloves

(P-5603)
HERITAGE BAG COMPANY
12320 4th St, Rancho Cucamonga (91730-6123)
PHONE..................................909 899-5554
John Eberhard, Manager
Victor Garibay, Plant Mgr
EMP: 10
SALES (corp-wide): 2.9B Privately Held
WEB: www.heritage-bag.com
SIC: 2673 Plastic bags: made from purchased materials
HQ: Heritage Bag Company
501 Gateway Pkwy
Roanoke TX 76262
972 241-5525

(P-5604)
LIBERTY PACKG & EXTRUDING INC
3015 Supply Ave, Commerce (90040-2709)
PHONE..................................323 722-5124
Derek De Heras, CEO
Bonnie Hudson, CEO
Mary Anne Bove, Treasurer
Mary Hudson, Vice Pres
Lola Jones, Principal
EMP: 40
SQ FT: 25,000
SALES (est): 9.1MM Privately Held
WEB: www.libertypkg.com
SIC: 2673 7389 Plastic & pliofilm bags; packaging & labeling services

(P-5605)
LIZAL INC
19503 Stevens Creek Blvd, Cupertino (95014-2466)
PHONE..................................408 252-5200
Lisa Nolan, President

PRODUCTS & SVCS

Alan Zoltie, *Shareholder*
▲ EMP: 23
SQ FT: 1,000
SALES: 3.4MM **Privately Held**
WEB: www.lizalinc.com
SIC: 2673 Bags: plastic, laminated &
coated

(P-5606)
M & M PRINTED BAG INC
5651 Kimball Ct, Chino (91710-9121)
PHONE..................909 393-5537
Ernest N Taylor, *CEO*
Jeff Taylor, *President*
Gay Taylor, *Corp Secy*
▲ EMP: 32
SQ FT: 24,000
SALES (est): 8.5MM **Privately Held**
SIC: 2673 Plastic bags: made from pur-
chased materials

(P-5607)
MERCURY PLASTICS INC (PA)
14825 Salt Lake Ave, City of Industry
(91746-3131)
PHONE..................626 961-0165
Benjamin Deutsch, *CEO*
Stanley Tzenkov, *Exec VP*
Kamyar Mirdamadi, *Vice Pres*
Zachary Deutsch, *VP Admin*
Cecilia Rojas, *Human Res Mgr*
▲ EMP: 415
SQ FT: 140,000
SALES (est): 135.7MM **Privately Held**
SIC: 2673 2759 3089 Plastic bags: made
from purchased materials; bags, plastic:
printing; plastic containers, except foam

(P-5608)
METRO POLY CORPORATION
1651 Aurora Dr, San Leandro
(94577-3101)
PHONE..................510 357-9898
Peter Kung, *Principal*
▲ EMP: 48
SQ FT: 40,000
SALES: 17.6MM **Privately Held**
SIC: 2673 Plastic bags: made from pur-
chased materials

(P-5609)
MIXED BAG DESIGNS INC
1744 Rollins Rd, Burlingame (94010-2208)
PHONE..................650 239-5358
Jan E Mercer, *CEO*
▲ EMP: 100
SALES (est): 7.6MM **Privately Held**
SIC: 2673 Cellophane bags, unprinted:
made from purchased materials

(P-5610)
MOHAWK WESTERN PLASTICS INC
1496 Arrow Hwy, La Verne (91750-5219)
P.O. Box 463 (91750-0463)
PHONE..................909 593-7547
John R Mordoff, *CEO*
J Christopher Mordoff, *President*
Dale Long, *Marketing Staff*
EMP: 40 EST: 1965
SQ FT: 28,000
SALES (est): 10.1MM **Privately Held**
WEB: www.mohawkwestern.com
SIC: 2673 3081 Plastic bags: made from
purchased materials; unsupported plas-
tics film & sheet

(P-5611)
NELSON BANNER INC
5720 Labath Ave, Rohnert Park
(94928-2039)
PHONE..................707 585-9942
A J Nelson, *President*
C R Nelson, *Vice Pres*
EMP: 28
SQ FT: 3,500
SALES: 1.3MM **Privately Held**
SIC: 2673 Bags: plastic, laminated &
coated

(P-5612)
OMEGA PLASTICS CORP
Also Called: Omega Extruding
9614 Lucas Ranch Rd Ste D, Rancho Cucamonga (91730-5787)
PHONE..................909 987-8716

EMP: 125 **Privately Held**
SIC: 2673 Plastic bags: made from pur-
chased materials
HQ: Omega Plastics Corp.
Page & Schuyler Ave Ste 5
Lyndhurst NJ 07071
201 507-9100

(P-5613)
PACKIT LLC
875 S Westlake Blvd, Westlake Village
(91361-2902)
PHONE..................805 496-2999
Melissa Kieling, *Mng Member*
Vivian Meneses, *COO*
Melissa Zuk, *Graphic Designe*
Paula Service, *Controller*
Frank Rosales, *Opers Mgr*
▲ EMP: 10 EST: 2009
SALES (est): 3.1MM **Privately Held**
SIC: 2673 Food storage & trash bags
(plastic)

(P-5614)
PANIC PLASTICS
1652 W 11th St, Upland (91786-3511)
PHONE..................909 946-5529
Miles Bruce, *Principal*
EMP: 19
SALES (est): 3.1MM **Privately Held**
SIC: 2673 Bags: plastic, laminated &
coated

(P-5615)
PRINTPACK INC
5870 Stoneridge Mall Rd # 200, Pleasanton
(94588-3704)
PHONE..................925 469-0601
Doug Brow, *Manager*
EMP: 188
SALES (corp-wide): 1.3B **Privately Held**
WEB: www.printpack.com
SIC: 2673 3081 Bags: plastic, laminated &
coated; plastic film & sheet
HQ: Printpack, Inc.
2800 Overlook Pkwy Ne
Atlanta GA 30339
404 460-7000

(P-5616)
PURFECT PACKAGING
5420 Brooks St, Montclair (91763-4520)
PHONE..................909 460-7363
Marlene Froechlich, *President*
Roland Blazys, *Vice Pres*
▲ EMP: 15
SQ FT: 7,000
SALES (est): 2MM **Privately Held**
SIC: 2673 Bags: plastic, laminated &
coated

(P-5617)
RCRV INC
Also Called: Rock Revival
4619 S Alameda St, Vernon (90058-2012)
PHONE..................323 235-7332
EMP: 17
SALES (corp-wide): 66.6MM **Privately Held**
SIC: 2673 5137 Garment & wardrobe
bags, (plastic film); women's & children's
clothing
PA: Rcrv, Inc.
4715 S Alameda St
Vernon CA 90058
323 235-7354

(P-5618)
REPUBLIC BAG INC (PA)
580 E Harrison St, Corona (92879-1344)
PHONE..................951 734-9740
Richard Schroeder, *CEO*
Chris Mayer, *Senior VP*
Steven Fritz, *Vice Pres*
Mark Teo, *Principal*
Oscar Arias, *Plant Mgr*
▲ EMP: 130
SQ FT: 59,000
SALES (est): 33.9MM **Privately Held**
SIC: 2673 Plastic bags: made from pur-
chased materials

(P-5619)
ROPLAST INDUSTRIES INC
3155 S 5th Ave, Oroville (95965-5858)
PHONE..................530 532-9500

Robert C Berman, *Chairman*
Robert Bateman, *President*
◆ EMP: 110
SQ FT: 160,000
SALES (est): 47.6MM **Privately Held**
WEB: www.roplast.com
SIC: 2673 Plastic bags: made from pur-
chased materials

(P-5620)
SANTA FE PACKAGING CORP
9614 Lucas Ranch Rd Ste D, Rancho Cu-
camonga (91730-5787)
PHONE..................562 921-8991
Alfred Teo, *CEO*
Cheryl Odonnell, *Executive*
EMP: 45
SALES (est): 6.2MM **Privately Held**
SIC: 2673 Plastic bags: made from pur-
chased materials

(P-5621)
SAVENSEALCOM LTD
Also Called: Shieldnseal
15478 Applewood Ln, Nevada City
(95959-9712)
PHONE..................530 478-0238
Larry Heiniemi, *President*
▲ EMP: 10 EST: 2011
SALES: 1.6MM **Privately Held**
SIC: 2673 Food storage & frozen food
bags, plastic

(P-5622)
SEALED AIR CORPORATION
16201 Commerce Way, Cerritos
(90703-2324)
PHONE..................201 791-7600
Brian Duncan, *Branch Mgr*
Greg Beauregard, *Regl Sales Mgr*
EMP: 20
SALES (corp-wide): 4.4B **Publicly Held**
WEB: www.sealedair.com
SIC: 2673 Food storage & frozen food
bags, plastic
PA: Sealed Air Corporation
2415 Cascade Pointe Blvd
Charlotte NC 28208
980 221-3235

(P-5623)
SEALED AIR CORPORATION
Also Called: Special Products Group
2311 Boswell Rd Ste 8, Chula Vista
(91914-3512)
PHONE..................619 421-9003
David Rader, *Manager*
Michael Wilson, *Production*
EMP: 25
SALES (corp-wide): 4.4B **Publicly Held**
WEB: www.sealedair.com
SIC: 2673 Bags: plastic, laminated &
coated
PA: Sealed Air Corporation
2415 Cascade Pointe Blvd
Charlotte NC 28208
980 221-3235

(P-5624)
SIUS PRODUCTS-DISTRIBUTOR INC (PA)
700 Kevin Ct, Oakland (94621-4040)
PHONE..................510 382-1700
Kuai Cheong Siu, *CEO*
Peter Siu, *Vice Pres*
▲ EMP: 18
SQ FT: 45,000
SALES (est): 3.7MM **Privately Held**
WEB: www.siusproducts.com
SIC: 2673 Plastic bags: made from pur-
chased materials

(P-5625)
SORMA USA LLC
9810 W Ferguson Ave, Visalia
(93291-2450)
PHONE..................559 651-1269
Rick Goddard, *Vice Pres*
Tracy Hart, *General Mgr*
Donna Dee, *Controller*
Laura Pena, *Production*
Kelvin Farris, *Sales Staff*
▲ EMP: 350

SALES (est): 61.9MM
SALES (corp-wide): 29.3MM **Privately Held**
SIC: 2673 3565 Bags: plastic, laminated &
coated; packaging machinery
PA: Sorma Spa
Via Don Federico Tosatto 8
Venezia VE 30174

(P-5626)
SUN PLASTICS INC
7140 E Slauson Ave, Commerce
(90040-3663)
PHONE..................323 888-6999
Vahan Bagamian, *President*
Movses Shrikian, *Admin Sec*
EMP: 50
SQ FT: 60,000
SALES (est): 11.5MM **Privately Held**
WEB: www.sunplastics.com
SIC: 2673 Plastic bags: made from pur-
chased materials

(P-5627)
TDI2 CUSTOM PACKAGING INC
3400 W Fordham Ave, Santa Ana
(92704-4422)
PHONE..................714 751-6782
Stephen Deniger, *CEO*
Catharina Deniger, *Admin Sec*
EMP: 17
SQ FT: 19,000
SALES (est): 3.9MM **Privately Held**
SIC: 2673 Trash bags (plastic film): made
from purchased materials

(P-5628)
TRANS WESTERN POLYMERS INC
7539 Las Positas Rd, Livermore
(94551-8202)
P.O. Box 2399, Appleton WI (54912-2399)
PHONE..................925 449-7800
Joon B Bai, *Ch of Bd*
Stephen Bai, *President*
Matthew Kim, *Vice Pres*
Rosemary Jiang, *Controller*
Joe Lagana, *Sales Executive*
▲ EMP: 400
SQ FT: 100,000
SALES (est): 148.9MM **Privately Held**
SIC: 2673 5023 3089 Plastic bags: made
from purchased materials; kitchen tools &
utensils; tableware, plastic

(P-5629)
TRANSCONTINENTAL US LLC
Also Called: Coveris
10801 Iona Ave, Hanford (93230-9415)
PHONE..................559 585-2040
Walter Gerst, *Branch Mgr*
EMP: 140
SALES (corp-wide): 1.6B **Privately Held**
WEB: www.exopack.com
SIC: 2673 Bags: plastic, laminated &
coated
HQ: Transcontinental Us Llc
50 International Dr # 100
Greenville SC 29615
773 877-3300

(P-5630)
TRANSCONTINENTAL US LLC
Also Called: Coveris
5601 Santa Ana St, Ontario (91761-8622)
PHONE..................909 390-8866
EMP: 20
SALES (corp-wide): 1.6B **Privately Held**
WEB: www.exopack.com
SIC: 2673 Bags: plastic, laminated &
coated
HQ: Transcontinental Us Llc
50 International Dr # 100
Greenville SC 29615
773 877-3300

(P-5631)
TUNG FEI PLASTIC INC
Also Called: Wheaton International
1859 Sabre St, Hayward (94545-1023)
PHONE..................510 783-9688
Rick Liu, *President*
Ming Liu, *Admin Sec*
▲ EMP: 10
SQ FT: 20,000

▲ = Import ▼=Export
◆ =Import/Export

SALES (est): 1.8MM **Privately Held**
WEB: www.tfplastic.com
SIC: 2673 Plastic bags: made from purchased materials

(P-5632)
UC PLASTIC MANUFACTURE INC
3202 Diablo Ave, Hayward (94545-2780)
PHONE..................................510 785-6777
Jesse K Tseng, *President*
▲ EMP: 30
SQ FT: 10,000
SALES (est): 4.4MM **Privately Held**
SIC: 2673 Bags: plastic, laminated & coated

(P-5633)
UNI-POLY INC
2040 Williams St, San Leandro (94577-2306)
PHONE..................................510 357-9898
Alex Eduardo, *Manager*
EMP: 18
SALES (corp-wide): 8.7MM **Privately Held**
SIC: 2673 Plastic & pliofilm bags
PA: Uni-Poly, Inc.
1651 Aurora Dr
San Leandro CA 94577
510 357-9898

(P-5634)
WESTERN STATES PACKAGING INC
13276 Paxton St, Pacoima (91331-2356)
PHONE..................................818 686-6045
Richard Joyce, *President*
Mark Pickrell, *Vice Pres*
Rocco Loosbrock, *Marketing Staff*
▲ EMP: 50
SQ FT: 35,000
SALES (est): 12.4MM **Privately Held**
WEB: www.westernstatespackaging.com
SIC: 2673 5113 5162 Plastic bags: made from purchased materials; bags, paper & disposable plastic; plastics materials

(P-5635)
ZENITH SPECIALTY BAG CO INC (PA)
Also Called: Zs Bag
17625 Railroad St, City of Industry (91748-1195)
P.O. Box 8445, Rowland Heights (91748-0445)
PHONE..................................626 912-2481
Scott Anderson, *President*
Betty Anderson, *Ch of Bd*
Ron Anderson, *Vice Pres*
Susan Washle, *Admin Sec*
▲ EMP: 176
SQ FT: 80,000
SALES (est): 46.8MM **Privately Held**
WEB: www.zsb.com
SIC: 2673 2674 Bags: plastic, laminated & coated; bags: uncoated paper & multiwall

2674 Bags: Uncoated Paper & Multiwall

(P-5636)
ACME BAG CO INC (PA)
Also Called: California Bag
440 N Pioneer Ave Ste 300, Woodland (95776-6139)
P.O. Box 1788 (95776-1788)
PHONE..................................530 662-6130
David Rosenberg, *CEO*
EMP: 15
SQ FT: 40,000
SALES (est): 2.2MM **Privately Held**
WEB: www.sacbag.com
SIC: 2674 5199 5191 2673 Bags: uncoated paper & multiwall; bags, textile; greenhouse equipment & supplies; bags: plastic, laminated & coated; textile bags; broadwoven fabric mills, cotton

(P-5637)
BAGCRAFTPAPERCON I LLC
Also Called: Papercon Packaging Division
515 Turnbull Canyon Rd, City of Industry (91745-1118)
PHONE..................................626 961-6766
Hector Lourido, *Manager*
EMP: 100
SALES (corp-wide): 2.9B **Privately Held**
WEB: www.packaging-dynamics.com
SIC: 2674 2671 Bags: uncoated paper & multiwall; packaging paper & plastics film, coated & laminated
HQ: Bagcraftpapercon I, Llc
3900 W 43rd St
Chicago IL 60632
620 856-2800

(P-5638)
CALIFORNIA PAPER BAG INC
1829 Dana St Ste A, Glendale (91201-2026)
PHONE..................................818 240-6717
Felix Perez, *President*
Olga Perez, *Corp Secy*
Tony Perez, *Vice Pres*
▲ EMP: 10
SQ FT: 22,000
SALES (est): 1.4MM **Privately Held**
SIC: 2674 Bags: uncoated paper & multiwall

(P-5639)
CTS CEMENT MANUFACTURING CORP
13846 Firestone Blvd, Santa Fe Springs (90670-5807)
PHONE..................................562 802-2660
Jim Scanlan, *Manager*
EMP: 34
SALES (corp-wide): 43MM **Privately Held**
WEB: www.ctscement.com
SIC: 2674 Cement bags: made from purchased materials
PA: Cts Cement Manufacturing Corporation
12442 Knott St
Garden Grove CA 92841
714 379-8260

(P-5640)
E-Z MIX INC
3355 Industrial Dr, Bloomington (92316-3534)
PHONE..................................909 874-7686
Bobbie Telcamp, *Principal*
EMP: 28
SALES (est): 3.7MM **Privately Held**
WEB: www.e-zmix.com
SIC: 2674 3241 Bags: uncoated paper & multiwall; cement, hydraulic
PA: E-Z Mix Inc.
11450 Tuxford St
Sun Valley CA 91352

(P-5641)
E-Z MIX INC (PA)
11450 Tuxford St, Sun Valley (91352-2638)
PHONE..................................818 768-0568
William Frenzel, *CEO*
Sunjiv Parekh, *CEO*
Joel Castellanos, *Sales Staff*
Refugio Mercado, *Sales Staff*
Frank Maggio, *Transportation*
EMP: 33
SQ FT: 50,000
SALES (est): 14.1MM **Privately Held**
WEB: www.e-zmix.com
SIC: 2674 Cement bags: made from purchased materials

(P-5642)
E-Z MIX INC
4125 Breakwater Ave Ste E, Hayward (94545-3600)
PHONE..................................510 782-8010
Richard Vega, *Branch Mgr*
EMP: 31 **Privately Held**
WEB: www.e-zmix.com
SIC: 2674 Bags: uncoated paper & multiwall
PA: E-Z Mix Inc.
11450 Tuxford St
Sun Valley CA 91352

(P-5643)
ENDPAK PACKAGING INC
9101 Perkins St, Pico Rivera (90660-4512)
PHONE..................................562 801-0281
Edgar A Garcia, *CEO*
Carlos Garcia, *President*
EMP: 90
SQ FT: 45,600
SALES (est): 30.1MM **Privately Held**
WEB: www.endpak.com
SIC: 2674 5199 Paper bags: made from purchased materials; packaging materials

(P-5644)
LANGSTON COMPANIES INC
2500 S K St, Tulare (93274-6874)
PHONE..................................559 688-3839
Joe Hart, *Branch Mgr*
EMP: 25
SQ FT: 26,000
SALES (corp-wide): 68.2MM **Privately Held**
SIC: 2674 Shipping bags or sacks, including multiwall & heavy duty
PA: Langston Companies, Inc.
1760 S 3rd St
Memphis TN 38109
901 774-4440

(P-5645)
MAHIVR
5405 Alton Pkwy, Irvine (92604-3717)
PHONE..................................949 559-5470
Carlynn Cassidy, *Manager*
EMP: 10
SALES (est): 980.2K **Privately Held**
SIC: 2674 Shipping & shopping bags or sacks

(P-5646)
PACOBOND INC
9800 Glenoaks Blvd, Sun Valley (91352-1041)
PHONE..................................818 768-5002
Arsine Seraydarian, *CEO*
Gerard Seradarian, *President*
Arsi Seradarian, *CFO*
Ronnie Wong, *General Mgr*
▲ EMP: 50
SQ FT: 45,000
SALES (est): 9.1MM **Privately Held**
SIC: 2674 5162 Shopping bags: made from purchased materials; plastics materials

(P-5647)
ROMEO PACKING COMPANY
106 Princeton Ave, Half Moon Bay (94019-4035)
PHONE..................................650 728-3393
Charles Romeo, *President*
Frank Romeo, *Treasurer*
Joey Romeo, *Vice Pres*
Constance Romeo, *Admin Sec*
Joan Chalmers, *Manager*
EMP: 22
SQ FT: 40,000
SALES (est): 5MM **Privately Held**
WEB: www.romeopacking.com
SIC: 2674 2873 Paper bags: made from purchased materials; fertilizers: natural (organic), except compost

(P-5648)
SILICON 360 LLC
801 Buckeye Ct, Milpitas (95035-7408)
PHONE..................................408 432-1790
Zafar Malik,
EMP: 10
SALES (est): 979.5K **Privately Held**
SIC: 2674 Bags: uncoated paper & multiwall

(P-5649)
WOLFPACK GEAR INC
3765 S Higuera St Ste 150, San Luis Obispo (93401-1569)
P.O. Box 2538, Paso Robles (93447-2538)
PHONE..................................805 439-1911
Michael Oberndorfer, *President*
Ronald Darin Sanders, *Vice Pres*
Mike Oberndorfer, *General Mgr*
Theresa Sanders, *Technology*
Jake Mallory, *Manager*
EMP: 11
SQ FT: 1,700

SALES (est): 2.8MM **Privately Held**
SIC: 2674 Bags: uncoated paper & multiwall

2675 Die-Cut Paper & Board

(P-5650)
APEX DIE CORPORATION
840 Cherry Ln, San Carlos (94070-3394)
PHONE..................................650 592-6350
Thomas J Cullen, *Chairman*
Kevin Cullen, *President*
Eva Cummings, *CFO*
Chris J Cullen, *Vice Pres*
Judy Grilli, *Accountant*
EMP: 55
SQ FT: 33,800
SALES (est): 11.4MM **Privately Held**
WEB: www.apexdie.com
SIC: 2675 2759 2672 Die-cut paper & board; embossing on paper; coated & laminated paper

(P-5651)
ARCHITECTURAL FOAMSTONE INC
9757 Glenoaks Blvd, Sun Valley (91352-1013)
PHONE..................................818 767-4500
Ruben Jimenez, *President*
EMP: 17
SQ FT: 9,000
SALES (est): 3.2MM **Privately Held**
SIC: 2675 3086 Die-cut paper & board; plastics foam products

(P-5652)
IMPERIAL DIE CUTTING INC
800 Richards Blvd, Sacramento (95811-0315)
PHONE..................................916 443-6142
Brent Rabe, *President*
Jennifer Rabe, *Vice Pres*
EMP: 35
SQ FT: 13,000
SALES (est): 6.4MM **Privately Held**
WEB: www.imperialdie.com
SIC: 2675 3469 2759 Die-cut paper & board; metal stampings; commercial printing

(P-5653)
J J FOIL COMPANY INC
650 W Freedom Ave, Orange (92865-2537)
PHONE..................................714 998-9920
Tiffany Dang, *President*
Michael Wang, *Vice Pres*
EMP: 45
SQ FT: 18,000
SALES (est): 10.2MM **Privately Held**
WEB: www.jjfoil.com
SIC: 2675 2759 Paper die-cutting; embossing on paper

(P-5654)
K & D GRAPHICS
Also Called: K & D Graphics Prtg & Packg
1432 N Main St Ste C, Orange (92867-3450)
PHONE..................................714 639-8900
Don Chew, *CEO*
Montri Chew, *CFO*
Bebe Chew, *Vice Pres*
Gus Chew, *Vice Pres*
Kim Chew, *Admin Sec*
EMP: 48
SQ FT: 75,500
SALES: 7.9MM **Privately Held**
WEB: www.kdpp.com
SIC: 2675 2752 Die-cut paper & board; commercial printing, offset

(P-5655)
PRESENTATION FOLDER INC
1130 N Main St, Orange (92867-3421)
PHONE..................................714 289-7000
Joseph Tardie Jr, *President*
Joseph Tardie Sr, *Vice Pres*
▲ EMP: 45
SQ FT: 70,000

SALES (est): 11MM **Privately Held**
WEB: www.presentationfolder.com
SIC: 2675 2759 2672 Folders, filing, die-cut: made from purchased materials; paper die-cutting; embossing on paper; coated & laminated paper

(P-5656)
R & J RULE & DIE INC
Also Called: R & J Paper Box
701 Sturbridge Dr, La Habra (90631-6324)
PHONE.................................562 945-7535
Jim Fuller, *President*
Ray Fuller, *Shareholder*
Vera Fuller, *Shareholder*
EMP: 10
SQ FT: 10,000
SALES: 800K **Privately Held**
SIC: 2675 Paper die-cutting

(P-5657)
RAINBOW SYMPHONY INC
6860 Canby Ave Ste 120, Reseda (91335-8710)
PHONE.................................818 708-8400
Mark Margolis, *President*
▲ EMP: 12
SQ FT: 2,100
SALES (est): 1.7MM **Privately Held**
WEB: www.rainbowsymphony.com
SIC: 2675 Paper die-cutting

(P-5658)
SHAMROCK DIE CUTTING COMPANY
3020 Meyerloa Ln, Pasadena (91107-1133)
PHONE.................................323 266-4556
Carole Lorenzini, *President*
Sean M Lorenzini, *Treasurer*
Sadie Chism, *Vice Pres*
EMP: 40
SQ FT: 12,000
SALES (est): 3.3MM **Privately Held**
SIC: 2675 3544 2789 Die-cut paper & board; special dies, tools, jigs & fixtures; bookbinding & related work

(P-5659)
TOPS SLT INC
8550 Chetle Ave Ste B, Whittier (90606-2662)
PHONE.................................562 968-2000
EMP: 148
SALES (corp-wide): 10.4B **Publicly Held**
SIC: 2675
HQ: Tops Slt, Inc.
225 Broadhollow Rd 184w
Melville NY 11747
631 675-5700

(P-5660)
WINDSOR HOUSE INVESTMENTS INC
Also Called: Colortone
12250 Coast Dr, Whittier (90601-1607)
PHONE.................................323 261-0231
Carl Price, *President*
EMP: 25 EST: 1938
SALES (est): 6MM **Privately Held**
WEB: www.colortonegrafx.com
SIC: 2675 2752 2843 2796 Paper die-cutting; decals, lithographed; surface active agents; platemaking services; bookbinding & related work; automotive & apparel trimmings

2676 Sanitary Paper Prdts

(P-5661)
ALLIED WEST PAPER CORP
11101 Etiwanda Ave # 100, Fontana (92337-6984)
PHONE.................................909 349-0710
Ray Ovanessian, *CEO*
Eric Ovanessian, *Vice Pres*
Mike Ovanessian, *Vice Pres*
▲ EMP: 95
SQ FT: 300,000

SALES (est): 51MM **Privately Held**
WEB: www.alliedwestpaper.com
SIC: 2676 Napkins, paper: made from purchased paper; towels, paper: made from purchased paper; facial tissues: made from purchased paper; toilet paper: made from purchased paper

(P-5662)
AXENT CORPORATION LIMITED (PA)
Also Called: Axent USA
3 Musick, Irvine (92618-1638)
PHONE.................................949 900-4349
LI Feiyu, *Principal*
▲ EMP: 13 EST: 2008
SALES (est): 7.8MM **Privately Held**
SIC: 2676 2499 Sanitary paper products; seats, toilet

(P-5663)
BABY BOX COMPANY INC (PA)
733 Seward St, Los Angeles (90038-3503)
PHONE.................................844 422-2926
Jennifer Clary-Haberer, *CEO*
Michelle Vick, *Principal*
Kevin Haberer, *CTO*
▲ EMP: 13
SALES (est): 8.1MM **Privately Held**
SIC: 2676 5137 5113 Infant & baby paper products; baby goods; boxes & containers

(P-5664)
DEPENDBLE INCONTINENCE SUP INC
Also Called: Dis
590 S Vincent Ave, Azusa (91702-5130)
PHONE.................................626 812-0044
Mike Cholakian, *CEO*
Harry Kemangian, *CFO*
▼ EMP: 15
SQ FT: 25,000
SALES: 16MM **Privately Held**
WEB: www.disbriefs.com
SIC: 2676 Diapers, paper (disposable): made from purchased paper

(P-5665)
GEORGIA PACIFIC HOLDINGS INC
13208 Hadley St Apt 1, Whittier (90601-4531)
PHONE.................................626 926-1474
Jorge Arroyo, *CEO*
EMP: 860
SQ FT: 1,000
SALES (corp-wide): 166.8MM
SALES (corp-wide): 42.9B **Privately Held**
SIC: 2676 2656 2435 2821 Sanitary paper products; sanitary food containers; hardwood veneer & plywood; plastics materials & resins
PA: Koch Industries, Inc.
4111 E 37th St N
Wichita KS 67220
316 828-5500

(P-5666)
IDEAL BRANDS INC
16060 Ventura Blvd, Encino (91436-2761)
PHONE.................................213 489-5557
Danny BEK, *CEO*
Djamshid Berhrad, *President*
▲ EMP: 50
SALES (est): 14.1MM **Privately Held**
WEB: www.idealbrands.com
SIC: 2676 Cleansing tissues: made from purchased paper

(P-5667)
JOHNSON & JOHNSON
3509 Langdon Cmn, Fremont (94538-5403)
PHONE.................................650 237-4878
Phil Palin, *Principal*
EMP: 80
SALES (corp-wide): 76.4B **Publicly Held**
SIC: 2676 Feminine hygiene paper products
PA: Johnson & Johnson
1 Johnson And Johnson Plz
New Brunswick NJ 08933
732 524-0400

(P-5668)
PRINCESS PAPER INC
4455 Fruitland Ave, Vernon (90058-3222)
PHONE.................................323 588-4777
Abraham Hakimi, *President*
▲ EMP: 45
SQ FT: 150,000
SALES: 12MM **Privately Held**
WEB: www.princesspaper.com
SIC: 2676 Towels, napkins & tissue paper products; toilet paper: made from purchased paper

(P-5669)
PROCTER & GAMBLE PAPER PDTS CO
800 N Rice Ave, Oxnard (93030-8910)
PHONE.................................805 485-8871
Shirley Boone, *Manager*
John Zaragoza, *Project Leader*
Martin Boyd, *Technology*
Joe Santos, *Engineer*
Sokny Ea, *Human Res Mgr*
EMP: 500
SALES (corp-wide): 66.8B **Publicly Held**
SIC: 2676 Towels, paper: made from purchased paper
HQ: The Procter & Gamble Paper Products Company
1 Procter And Gamble Plz
Cincinnati OH 45202
513 983-1100

(P-5670)
RAEL INC
6940 Beach Blvd Unit D608, Buena Park (90621-6850)
PHONE.................................800 573-1516
Aness Han, *CEO*
Yanghee Park, *President*
EMP: 20 EST: 2017
SALES (est): 3.4MM **Privately Held**
SIC: 2676 Feminine hygiene paper products

(P-5671)
ROCHESTER MIDLAND CORPORATION
7275 Sycamore Canyon Blvd # 101, Riverside (92508-2326)
PHONE.................................800 388-4762
Brenda Barr, *Branch Mgr*
EMP: 22
SALES (corp-wide): 125.6MM **Privately Held**
WEB: www.rochestermidland.com
SIC: 2676 5087 8732 2899 Feminine hygiene paper products; cleaning & maintenance equipment & supplies; commercial nonphysical research; chemical preparations; floor waxes
PA: Rochester Midland Corporation
155 Paragon Dr
Rochester NY 14624
585 336-2200

2677 Envelopes

(P-5672)
CENVEO WORLDWIDE LIMITED
150 N Myers St, Los Angeles (90033-2109)
PHONE.................................323 261-7171
Ed Binder, *Plant Mgr*
Kirk Bennett, *Sales Staff*
EMP: 65
SQ FT: 156,100
SALES (corp-wide): 685.5MM **Privately Held**
WEB: www.mail-well.com
SIC: 2677 2752 2759 Envelopes; commercial printing, lithographic; labels & seals: printing
HQ: Cenveo Worldwide Limited
200 First Stamford Pl # 2
Stamford CT 06902
303 790-8023

(P-5673)
CLEANSMART SOLUTIONS INC
Also Called: San Francisco Envelope
47422 Kato Rd, Fremont (94538-7319)
PHONE.................................650 871-9123
Don Clark, *Branch Mgr*
EMP: 30

SALES (corp-wide): 49MM **Privately Held**
WEB: www.jcpaper.com
SIC: 2677 Envelopes
PA: Cleansmart Solutions Inc.
47422 Kato Rd
Fremont CA 94538
510 413-4700

(P-5674)
GOLDEN WEST ENVELOPE CORP
1009 Morton St, Alameda (94501-3904)
PHONE.................................510 452-5419
Raymond Mazur, *President*
Gert Mazur, *Vice Pres*
Kathy Ito, *Manager*
EMP: 25
SQ FT: 17,000
SALES: 1MM **Privately Held**
WEB: www.goldenwestenvelope.com
SIC: 2677 2752 Envelopes; commercial printing, offset

(P-5675)
INLAND ENVELOPE COMPANY
150 N Park Ave, Pomona (91768-3835)
PHONE.................................909 622-2016
Bernard Kloenne, *CEO*
Otilia Kloenne, *Admin Sec*
EMP: 55
SQ FT: 45,000
SALES (est): 20.4MM **Privately Held**
WEB: www.inlandenvelope.com
SIC: 2677 Envelopes

(P-5676)
LA ENVELOPE INCORPORATED
1053 S Vail Ave, Montebello (90640-6019)
PHONE.................................323 838-9300
Gary T Earls, *President*
Louise Earls, *Admin Sec*
EMP: 35
SQ FT: 25,000
SALES (est): 9MM **Privately Held**
WEB: www.laenvelope.com
SIC: 2677 2752 Envelopes; commercial printing, offset

(P-5677)
SEABOARD ENVELOPE CO INC
15601 Cypress Ave, Irwindale (91706-2120)
P.O. Box 2225, Baldwin Park (91706-1134)
PHONE.................................626 960-4559
Ronald Neidringhaus, *President*
Richard Riggle, *Vice Pres*
Stacie Mendias, *Office Admin*
Daniel Gant, *Sales Staff*
EMP: 25
SQ FT: 72,000
SALES (est): 7.5MM **Privately Held**
WEB: www.seaboardenvelope.com
SIC: 2677 Envelopes

(P-5678)
SOUTHLAND ENVELOPE COMPANY INC
10111 Riverford Rd, Lakeside (92040-2741)
PHONE.................................619 449-3553
Dianne Gonzalez, *CEO*
Frank Soloman Jr, *President*
Rita Soloman, *Vice Pres*
Chris Jackson, *Technician*
Ernie Bennett, *Technology*
EMP: 115 EST: 1970
SQ FT: 80,000
SALES (est): 45.2MM **Privately Held**
WEB: www.southlandenvelope.com
SIC: 2677 Envelopes

(P-5679)
TENSION ENVELOPE CORPORATION
40750 County Center Dr, Temecula (92591-6018)
PHONE.................................951 296-0500
Stanley Moskovitz, *Vice Pres*
EMP: 115
SALES (corp-wide): 234MM **Privately Held**
WEB: www.tension.com
SIC: 2677 Envelopes

▲ = Import ▼=Export
◆ =Import/Export

PA: Tension Envelope Corporation
819 E 19th St
Kansas City MO 64108
816 471-3800

(P-5680)
VISION ENVELOPE & PRTG CO INC (PA)
13707 S Figueroa St, Los Angeles
(90061-1045)
PHONE....................310 324-7062
Mark Fisher, *Principal*
Michael J Leeny, *Vice Pres*
EMP: 50
SQ FT: 45,000
SALES (est): 7.9MM **Privately Held**
SIC: 2677 2752 Envelopes; commercial printing, offset

(P-5681)
WESTERN STATES ENVELOPE CORP
2301 Raymer Ave, Fullerton (92833-2514)
PHONE....................714 449-0909
Lisa Hoehle, *President*
Giovanni Portanova, *Maintence Staff*
Jing Zaide, *Maintence Staff*
EMP: 60
SQ FT: 24,000
SALES (est): 16.3MM **Privately Held**
SIC: 2677 Envelopes

2678 Stationery Prdts

(P-5682)
AVERY PRODUCTS CORPORATION (DH)
50 Pointe Dr, Brea (92821-3652)
PHONE....................714 675-8500
Geoff Martin, *President*
Mark Cooper, *Vice Pres*
Kathleen Kuhn, *Vice Pres*
Jeff Lattanzio, *Vice Pres*
Jeffery Jett, *Regional Mgr*
EMP: 277
SALES (est): 278.9MM
SALES (corp-wide): 3.7B **Privately Held**
SIC: 2678 3951 2672 2891 Notebooks: made from purchased paper; markers, soft tip (felt, fabric, plastic, etc.); labels (unprinted), gummed: made from purchased materials; adhesives
HQ: Ccl Industries Corporation
15 Controls Dr
Shelton CT 06484
203 926-1253

(P-5683)
CARDIOMART INC
11715 Avenida Del Sol, Northridge (91326-1501)
P.O. Box 8224 (91327-8224)
PHONE....................818 516-6875
Alex Tajyar, *President*
▲ **EMP:** 50
SALES (est): 3.7MM **Privately Held**
SIC: 2678 Stationery products

(P-5684)
ETERNAL STAR CORPORATION
17813 S Main St Ste 101, Gardena (90248-3542)
PHONE....................310 768-1945
Jeewon Choi, *President*
Hung Choi, *CEO*
Hee Choi, *Director*
▲ **EMP:** 30
SQ FT: 250,000
SALES (est): 4.1MM **Privately Held**
SIC: 2678 2782

(P-5685)
LADY JAYNE LP
10833 Valley View St # 420, Cypress (90630-5045)
▲ **EMP:** 10
SQ FT: 28,000
SALES (est): 1.5MM
SALES (corp-wide): 380.1MM **Privately Held**
WEB: www.ladyjayneltd.com
SIC: 2678

PA: R.A.F. Industries, Inc.
165 Township Line Rd # 2100
Jenkintown PA 19046
215 572-0738

(P-5686)
MILLS ASAP REPROGRAPHICS (PA)
495 Morro Bay Blvd, Morro Bay (93442-2143)
PHONE....................805 772-2019
Roger R Marlin, *Owner*
EMP: 18
SQ FT: 4,000
SALES (est): 2.1MM **Privately Held**
WEB: www.asapreprographics.com
SIC: 2678 5943 5999 Memorandum books, notebooks & looseleaf filler paper; office forms & supplies; writing supplies; artists' supplies & materials

(P-5687)
MRS GROSSMANS PAPER COMPANY
Also Called: Paragon Label
3810 Cypress Dr, Petaluma (94954-5613)
PHONE....................707 763-1700
Fax: 707 763-7121
▲ **EMP:** 100 **EST:** 1975
SQ FT: 11,000
SALES (est): 22.9MM **Privately Held**
WEB: www.paragonlabel.com
SIC: 2678 2679 2759 2752

(P-5688)
PENCIL GRIP INC (PA)
21200 Superior St Ste A, Chatsworth (91311-4324)
P.O. Box 3787 (91313-3787)
PHONE....................310 315-3545
Alexander Provda, *CEO*
Asher Provda, *CEO*
Julia Boyle, *Vice Pres*
Theresa Baker, *Finance*
Teresa Briggs, *Sales Staff*
▲ **EMP:** 17
SQ FT: 12,000
SALES (est): 2.8MM **Privately Held**
WEB: www.pencilgrip.com
SIC: 2678 Stationery products

(P-5689)
TREE HOUSE PAD & PAPER INC
2341 Pomona Rd Ste 108, Corona (92880-6973)
PHONE....................800 213-4194
David Moncrief, *President*
Darrin Monroe, *Vice Pres*
Rebekah Radford, *Finance Mgr*
EMP: 55
SQ FT: 50,000
SALES (est): 16MM **Privately Held**
WEB: www.treehousepaper.com
SIC: 2678 Stationery products

(P-5690)
VIVA HOLDINGS LLC (PA)
Also Called: Viva Concepts
1025 N Brand Blvd Ste 300, Glendale (91202-3633)
PHONE....................818 243-1363
Farid Tabibzadeh,
Eiman Rahnama, *Director*
EMP: 18
SQ FT: 30,000
SALES (est): 12.1MM **Privately Held**
SIC: 2678 Memorandum books, except printed: purchased materials

(P-5691)
VIVA PRINT LLC (HQ)
1025 N Brand Blvd Ste 300, Glendale (91202-3633)
PHONE....................818 243-1363
Greg Hughes Sr, *CEO*
Greg Hughes Jr, *COO*
EMP: 10
SQ FT: 28,000
SALES (est): 2.1MM
SALES (corp-wide): 12.1MM **Privately Held**
SIC: 2678 Memorandum books, except printed: purchased materials

PA: Viva Holdings, Llc
1025 N Brand Blvd Ste 300
Glendale CA 91202
818 243-1363

2679 Converted Paper Prdts, NEC

(P-5692)
A A LABEL INC (PA)
Also Called: All American Label
6958 Sierra Ct, Dublin (94568-2641)
PHONE....................925 803-5709
Bradley Brown, *CEO*
Cynthia Brown, *Vice Pres*
Irene George, *Sales Staff*
Ken Wickman, *Sales Staff*
Brandon Warren, *Manager*
▲ **EMP:** 25
SQ FT: 25,000
SALES (est): 5.2MM **Privately Held**
WEB: www.allamericanlabel.net
SIC: 2679 Labels, paper: made from purchased material

(P-5693)
A PLUS LABEL INCORPORATED
3215 W Warner Ave, Santa Ana (92704-5314)
PHONE....................714 229-9811
Nick Phan, *President*
Jeff Pioch, *Accounts Exec*
EMP: 40
SQ FT: 6,400
SALES (est): 2.5MM **Privately Held**
WEB: www.apluslabel.com
SIC: 2679 Tags & labels, paper

(P-5694)
ALL LABEL INC
Also Called: K1 Packaging
17989 Arenth Ave, City of Industry (91748-1126)
PHONE....................626 964-6744
Jui Yun Tsai, *President*
▲ **EMP:** 10
SQ FT: 36,876
SALES (est): 1.8MM **Privately Held**
SIC: 2679 Labels, paper: made from purchased material

(P-5695)
AMERICAN GRAPHIC BOARD INC
5880 E Slauson Ave, Commerce (90040-3018)
PHONE....................323 721-0585
Don Zeccola, *President*
Michael Carmody, *CFO*
Peter Kang, *Admin Sec*
▲ **EMP:** 35
SQ FT: 135,000
SALES (est): 6.9MM **Privately Held**
SIC: 2679 Paperboard products, converted

(P-5696)
AMERICAN INDEX AND FILES LLC
2900 E Miraloma Ave Bc, Anaheim (92806-1827)
PHONE....................714 630-3360
Peggy Alvardo, *CEO*
Eddie Alvarado,
Jesse Alvizar,
EMP: 12
SQ FT: 6,600
SALES (est): 1.1MM **Privately Held**
SIC: 2679 Cardboard products, except die-cut

(P-5697)
APPLE PAPER CONVERTING INC
3800 E Miraloma Ave, Anaheim (92806-2108)
P.O. Box 768, Atwood (92811-0768)
PHONE....................714 632-3195
Jorge Daniel Podboj, *President*
Louis Salavar, *President*
George Podboj, *Vice Pres*
EMP: 20
SALES (est): 2.5MM **Privately Held**
SIC: 2679 Paper products, converted

(P-5698)
ARTISSIMO DESIGNS LLC (HQ)
2100 E Grand Ave Ste 400, El Segundo (90245-5055)
PHONE....................310 906-3700
Ravi Bhagavatula, *CEO*
▲ **EMP:** 50
SQ FT: 13,000
SALES: 73MM **Privately Held**
SIC: 2679 Wallboard, decorated: made from purchased material
PA: Excelsior Capital Partners, Llc
4695 Macarthur Ct Ste 370
Newport Beach CA 92660
949 566-8110

(P-5699)
ARTISTRY IN MOTION INC
19411 Londelius St, Northridge (91324-3512)
PHONE....................818 994-7388
Roger Wachtell, *CEO*
Richard Graves, *President*
EMP: 22
SALES (est): 2.9MM **Privately Held**
WEB: www.artistryinmotion.com
SIC: 2679 5947 Confetti: made from purchased material; gifts & novelties

(P-5700)
BOWEN PRINTING INC
Also Called: Bowen Enterprises
380 Coogan Way, El Cajon (92020-1976)
PHONE....................619 440-8605
Newell B Bowen, *President*
EMP: 12
SQ FT: 8,000
SALES (est): 1.3MM **Privately Held**
WEB: www.bowenprinting.com
SIC: 2679 2752 Labels, paper: made from purchased material; commercial printing, offset

(P-5701)
BRUSH DANCE INC
165 N Redwood Dr Ste 200, San Rafael (94903-1971)
PHONE....................415 491-4950
Marc A Lesser, *CEO*
Johanna Malen, *President*
Karma Spore, *Admin Asst*
◆ **EMP:** 14
SQ FT: 7,000
SALES (est): 1.9MM **Privately Held**
SIC: 2679 Paper products, converted

(P-5702)
CALPACO PAPERS INC (PA)
3155 Universe Dr, Mira Loma (91752-3252)
PHONE....................323 767-2800
Paul Maier, *President*
Francis A Maier, *Chairman*
▲ **EMP:** 136
SQ FT: 606,000
SALES (est): 8.1MM **Privately Held**
WEB: www.calpaco.com
SIC: 2679 5111 Paper products, converted; printing & writing paper

(P-5703)
CENVEO WORLDWIDE LIMITED
6250 S Boyle Ave, Vernon (90058-3937)
PHONE....................323 262-6000
Kevin Johnson, *Sales/Mktg Mgr*
Susan Torres, *Hum Res Coord*
Susan Peters, *Purch Mgr*
Larry Lindwall, *Purch Agent*
John Steinman, *Accounts Exec*
EMP: 125
SQ FT: 135,212
SALES (corp-wide): 685.5MM **Privately Held**
WEB: www.mail-well.com
SIC: 2679 5112 Tags & labels, paper; envelopes
HQ: Cenveo Worldwide Limited
200 First Stamford Pl # 2
Stamford CT 06902
303 790-8023

PRODUCTS & SVCS

(P-5704)
COAST TO COAST LABEL INC (PA)
18401 Bandilier Cir, Fountain Valley (92708-7012)
PHONE..................................657 203-2583
Renee Anastasia, *CEO*
Dana Anastasia, *President*
Bryce Littlejohn, *Sales Staff*
▼ EMP: 12
SQ FT: 3,000
SALES (est): 1.5MM **Privately Held**
WEB: www.coasttocoastlabel.com
SIC: 2679 Labels, paper: made from purchased material

(P-5705)
COLORTECH LABEL INC
1230 S Sherman St, Anaheim (92805-6455)
PHONE..................................714 999-5545
Randy Montram, *President*
EMP: 13
SALES (est): 1.1MM **Privately Held**
SIC: 2679 Labels, paper: made from purchased material

(P-5706)
CONTINENTAL DATALABEL INC
Also Called: American Single Sheets
211 Business Center Ct, Redlands (92373-4404)
PHONE..................................909 307-3600
Patrick Flynn, *Branch Mgr*
Jean Hess, *Manager*
EMP: 30
SALES (corp-wide): 31.5MM **Privately Held**
WEB: www.compulabel.com
SIC: 2679 2672 Labels, paper: made from purchased material; coated & laminated paper
PA: Continental Datalabel, Inc.
1855 Fox Ln
Elgin IL 60123
847 742-1600

(P-5707)
CROWN PAPER CONVERTING INC
1380 S Bon View Ave, Ontario (91761-4403)
P.O. Box 3277 (91761-0928)
PHONE..................................909 923-5226
Bruce Hale, *Principal*
Lisa Hale, *Vice Pres*
EMP: 40
SQ FT: 34,000
SALES (est): 11.4MM **Privately Held**
SIC: 2679 Paper products, converted

(P-5708)
DATA LABEL PRODUCTS INC
840 N Cummings Rd, Covina (91724-2505)
PHONE..................................626 915-6478
David Jensen, *President*
EMP: 10 EST: 1964
SALES (est): 1.2MM **Privately Held**
WEB: www.datalabelproducts.com
SIC: 2679 2752 Labels, paper: made from purchased material; commercial printing, lithographic

(P-5709)
DIETZGEN CORPORATION
1522 E Bentley Dr, Corona (92879-1741)
PHONE..................................951 278-3259
Darren A Letang, *President*
Alfonso Herrera, *Manager*
EMP: 22
SALES (corp-wide): 44.6MM **Privately Held**
SIC: 2679 Paper products, converted
PA: Dietzgen Corporation
121 Kelsey Ln Ste G
Tampa FL 33619
813 286-4767

(P-5710)
DIGITAL LABEL SOLUTIONS INC
22745 Old Canal Rd, Yorba Linda (92887-4603)
PHONE..................................714 982-5000

Joel H Mark, *CEO*
Sandy Petersen, *Vice Pres*
Suzie Dobyns, *Admin Sec*
EMP: 29
SQ FT: 14,000
SALES: 6.3MM **Privately Held**
SIC: 2679 Tags & labels, paper

(P-5711)
FDS MANUFACTURING COMPANY (PA)
2200 S Reservoir St, Pomona (91766-6408)
P.O. Box 3120 (91769-3120)
PHONE..................................909 591-1733
Robert B Stevenson, *CEO*
Samuel B Stevenson, *Chairman*
Chuck O'Connor, *Vice Pres*
Kevin Stevenson, *Vice Pres*
Todd Lawrence, *Controller*
▲ EMP: 100
SQ FT: 240,000
SALES (est): 24.3MM **Privately Held**
WEB: www.fdsmfg.com
SIC: 2679 3089 Corrugated paper: made from purchased material; plastic containers, except foam

(P-5712)
FLEENOR COMPANY INC (PA)
Also Called: Fleenor Paper Company
2225 Harbor Bay Pkwy, Alameda (94502-3026)
P.O. Box 14438, Oakland (94614-2438)
PHONE..................................800 433-2531
Rebecca Fleenor, *President*
Janine Rochex, *CFO*
Zoe Rose, *Info Tech Mgr*
Kathy Jimenez, *Personnel Assit*
Doug Hollowell, *Opers Mgr*
▲ EMP: 40
SALES (est): 21.3MM **Privately Held**
WEB: www.fleenorpaper.com
SIC: 2679 Paper products, converted; paperboard products, converted

(P-5713)
GM NAMEPLATE INC
2095 Otoole Ave, San Jose (95131-1374)
PHONE..................................408 435-1666
Bruce Cleckley, *Sales Mgr*
Mike Bogle, *Program Mgr*
John Perez, *Purch Mgr*
Jason Righter, *Buyer*
EMP: 127
SQ FT: 24,600
SALES (corp-wide): 311.3MM **Privately Held**
SIC: 2679 3479 3993 2752 Labels, paper: made from purchased material; name plates: engraved, etched, etc.; signs & advertising specialties; commercial printing, lithographic; packaging paper & plastics film, coated & laminated
PA: Gm Nameplate, Inc.
2040 15th Ave W
Seattle WA 98119
206 284-2200

(P-5714)
GOLDEN KRAFT INC
15500 Valley View Ave, La Mirada (90638-5230)
PHONE..................................562 926-8888
Dan August, *General Mgr*
EMP: 92 EST: 1982
SQ FT: 63,200
SALES: 15MM
SALES (corp-wide): 42.9B **Privately Held**
SIC: 2679 2631 Corrugated paper: made from purchased material; paperboard mills
HQ: Georgia-Pacific Corrugated Iii Llc
5645 W 82nd St
Indianapolis IN 46278

(P-5715)
INSULATED PRODUCTS CORPORATION
250 W Artesia Blvd, Compton (90220-5500)
PHONE..................................323 838-0900
Charles Veiseh, *President*
EMP: 26
SQ FT: 47,000

SALES (est): 8.8MM **Privately Held**
SIC: 2679 Building, insulating & packaging paper

(P-5716)
MAIN STREET KITCHENS
37 Quail Ct Ste 200, Walnut Creek (94596-8722)
PHONE..................................925 944-0153
Scott J Westby, *Owner*
EMP: 15
SALES: 1.3MM **Privately Held**
WEB: www.mainstreetkitchens.com
SIC: 2679 5031 1799 Building paper, laminated: made from purchased material; building materials, interior; kitchen & bathroom remodeling

(P-5717)
NATIONAL RECYCLING CORPORATION
1312 Kirkham St, Oakland (94607-2257)
PHONE..................................510 268-1022
Richard Wang, *President*
▼ EMP: 18
SQ FT: 80,000
SALES (est): 3.2MM **Privately Held**
SIC: 2679 4953 Paper products, converted; recycling, waste materials

(P-5718)
NCLA INC
16031 Carmenita Rd, Cerritos (90703-2208)
PHONE..................................562 926-6252
John McGee, *President*
EMP: 19
SALES (est): 4.5MM **Privately Held**
WEB: www.ncla.net
SIC: 2679 3083 Paper products, converted; plastic finished products, laminated

(P-5719)
NOVIPAX INC (DH)
Also Called: Paper-Pak Industries
1941 N White Ave, La Verne (91750-5663)
PHONE..................................909 392-1750
Ron Leach, *CEO*
Rich Beu, *President*
Jeffrey Williams, *CFO*
Maria Valdez, *Executive Asst*
Sophia Smeragliuolo, *Research*
◆ EMP: 100
SQ FT: 100,000
SALES (est): 46.6MM
SALES (corp-wide): 2.3B **Privately Held**
WEB: www.paperpakindustries.com
SIC: 2679 Building, insulating & packaging paper
HQ: Novipax Llc
2215 York Rd Ste 504
Oak Brook IL 60523
630 686-2735

(P-5720)
ONE STOP LABEL CORPORATION
1641 S Baker Ave, Ontario (91761-8025)
PHONE..................................909 230-9380
Maria Navarro, *President*
Jorge Navarro, *Vice Pres*
EMP: 19
SQ FT: 12,000
SALES (est): 4.1MM **Privately Held**
WEB: www.onestoplabel.com
SIC: 2679 Labels, paper: made from purchased material

(P-5721)
P & R PAPER SUPPLY CO INC
1350 Piper Ranch Rd, San Diego (92154-7708)
PHONE..................................619 671-2400
Bruce Overmeyer, *Manager*
EMP: 19
SALES (corp-wide): 102.2MM **Privately Held**
SIC: 2679 2621 Paper products, converted; paper mills
PA: P. & R. Paper Supply Company, Inc.
1898 E Colton Ave
Redlands CA 92374
909 389-1811

(P-5722)
PACIFIC PPRBD CONVERTING LLC (PA)
8865 Utica Ave Ste A, Rancho Cucamonga (91730-5144)
PHONE..................................909 476-6466
Bill Donahue, *CEO*
EMP: 25
SALES (est): 5.1MM **Privately Held**
WEB: www.bmxpaper.com
SIC: 2679 Paper products, converted

(P-5723)
PACTIV CORPORATION
9700 Bell Ranch Dr, Santa Fe Springs (90670-2950)
PHONE..................................562 944-0052
Carlos Ruiz, *Branch Mgr*
Ray Kowalski, *Manager*
EMP: 35 **Privately Held**
WEB: www.pactiv.com
SIC: 2679 2671 2631 Honeycomb core & board: made from purchased material; packaging paper & plastics film, coated & laminated; paperboard mills
HQ: Pactiv Llc
1900 W Field Ct
Lake Forest IL 60045
847 482-2000

(P-5724)
PAPER PULP & FILM
Also Called: Fresno Paper Express
2822 S Maple Ave, Fresno (93725-2207)
PHONE..................................559 233-1151
G Carol Jones, *CEO*
Tal Cloud, *President*
Meredith Orman, *Admin Sec*
▲ EMP: 40
SQ FT: 120,000
SALES (est): 21.5MM **Privately Held**
WEB: www.paperconverter.com
SIC: 2679 4213 Wrappers, paper (unprinted): made from purchased material; heavy hauling

(P-5725)
PARADIGM LABEL INC
10258 Birtcher Dr, Mira Loma (91752-1827)
PHONE..................................951 372-9212
Curtis Harton, *CEO*
EMP: 15
SQ FT: 15,000
SALES (est): 3.9MM **Privately Held**
SIC: 2679 Labels, paper: made from purchased material

(P-5726)
POSITIVE CONCEPTS INC (PA)
Also Called: Ameri-Fax
2021 N Glassell St, Orange (92865-3305)
PHONE..................................714 685-5800
Lambert C Thom, *CEO*
George Manzur, *President*
Susan Lindsey, *Manager*
Brittney Fierro, *Accounts Exec*
Rocio Guridi, *Accounts Exec*
▼ EMP: 22
SQ FT: 20,000
SALES (est): 5.2MM **Privately Held**
WEB: www.posconcepts.com
SIC: 2679 5084 Paper products, converted; machine tools & accessories

(P-5727)
PRIME CONVERTING CORPORATION
9121 Pttsbrgh Ave Ste 100, Rancho Cucamonga (91730)
P.O. Box 3207 (91729-3207)
PHONE..................................909 476-9500
Robert J Nielsen, *President*
▲ EMP: 24
SALES (est): 12MM **Privately Held**
WEB: www.primeconvertingcorp.com
SIC: 2679 Paper products, converted

(P-5728)
PROGRESSIVE LABEL INC
2545 Yates Ave, Commerce (90040-2619)
P.O. Box 911430, Los Angeles (90091-1238)
PHONE..................................323 415-9770
Gus Garcia, *President*

▲ = Import ▼=Export
◆ =Import/Export

David Lawrence, *Shareholder*
Adam Flores, *Vice Pres*
Julie Lawrence, *Admin Sec*
Regina Sitt, *Purchasing*
▲ **EMP:** 39
SQ FT: 18,000
SALES (est): 8.9MM **Privately Held**
WEB: www.progressivelabel.com
SIC: 2679 2672 2671 2241 Tags & labels, paper; coated & laminated paper; packaging paper & plastics film, coated & laminated; narrow fabric mills

(P-5729)
RO GENERATION INC
1528 Highland Ave, Duarte (91010-2831)
PHONE..................323 771-5416
Derrick Ro, *President*
EMP: 10
SALES (est): 88.4K **Privately Held**
WEB: www.thelabelfactory.com
SIC: 2679 Tags & labels, paper

(P-5730)
RTS PACKAGING LLC
1900 Wardrobe Ave, Merced (95341-6447)
PHONE..................209 722-2787
Mike Myer, *Manager*
EMP: 71
SQ FT: 32,400
SALES (corp-wide): 14.8B **Publicly Held**
WEB: www.rtspackaging.com
SIC: 2679 2631 Paperboard products, converted; paperboard mills
HQ: Rts Packaging, Llc
504 Thrasher St
Norcross GA 30071
800 558-6984

(P-5731)
SACHS INDUSTRIES INC
Also Called: Custom Label
801 Kate Ln, Woodland (95776-5733)
PHONE..................631 242-9000
EMP: 18
SQ FT: 12,000
SALES (est): 2.3MM **Privately Held**
SIC: 2679 5113

(P-5732)
SAKURA PAPER INC
1683 Sunflower Ave # 103, Costa Mesa (92626-1540)
PHONE..................714 886-3791
Joe C Wen, *CEO*
▲ **EMP:** 16 EST: 2013
SALES (est): 3.3MM **Privately Held**
SIC: 2679 Paper products, converted

(P-5733)
SALINAS VALLEY WAX PAPER CO
1111 Abbott St, Salinas (93901-4501)
P.O. Box 68 (93902-0068)
PHONE..................831 424-2747
Charles Nelson, *CEO*
Bill Zimmerman, *Vice Pres*
Chris Zimmerman, *Admin Sec*
▲ **EMP:** 49
SQ FT: 50,000
SALES (est): 10.2MM **Privately Held**
WEB: www.salinasvalleywaxpapercompany.com
SIC: 2679 2672 Paper products, converted; coated & laminated paper

(P-5734)
SAPPI NORTH AMERICA INC
333 S Anita Dr Ste 840, Orange (92868-3320)
PHONE..................714 456-0600
Brent Demichael, *Branch Mgr*
Brad Fisher, *Manager*
EMP: 60
SALES (corp-wide): 5.3B **Privately Held**
SIC: 2679 Paper products, converted
HQ: Sappi North America, Inc.
255 State Fl 4
Boston MA 02109
617 423-7300

(P-5735)
SIGN OF TIMES INC
4950 S Santa Fe Ave, Vernon (90058-2106)
PHONE..................323 826-9766

Mark Roginson, *President*
▲ **EMP:** 20
SALES (est): 1.8MM **Privately Held**
WEB: www.signofthetimes.com
SIC: 2679 Wallboard, decorated: made from purchased material

(P-5736)
SUNRISE MFG INC (PA)
2665 Mercantile Dr, Rancho Cordova (95742-6521)
PHONE..................916 635-6262
James Sewell, *CEO*
Michael Ritz, *COO*
Justin Sewell, *General Mgr*
Jessica Morris, *Office Mgr*
Dawn Beermann, *Marketing Staff*
▲ **EMP:** 25
SQ FT: 72,000
SALES (est): 8.7MM **Privately Held**
WEB: www.sunrisemfg.com
SIC: 2679 Building, insulating & packaging paper

(P-5737)
SUPERIOR RADIANT INSUL INC
451 W Covina Blvd, San Dimas (91773-2909)
P.O. Box 247 (91773-0247)
PHONE..................909 305-1450
David Dittemore, *President*
Linda Dittemore, *Admin Sec*
EMP: 10
SQ FT: 17,000
SALES (est): 1.8MM **Privately Held**
SIC: 2679 Insulating paper: batts, fills & blankets

(P-5738)
TAB LABEL INC
21 Hegenberger Ct, Oakland (94621-1321)
P.O. Box 6266 (94603-0266)
PHONE..................510 638-4411
EMP: 17
SQ FT: 11,000
SALES (est): 223.8K **Privately Held**
WEB: www.tablabel.com
SIC: 2679

(P-5739)
TAGS & LABELS
Also Called: Label Art of California
290 27th St, Oakland (94612-3821)
PHONE..................510 465-1125
David Masri, *President*
EMP: 30 EST: 1965
SALES (est): 4.5MM **Privately Held**
SIC: 2679 Tags, paper (unprinted): made from purchased paper

(P-5740)
TAGTIME U S A INC
4601 District Blvd, Vernon (90058-2731)
PHONE..................323 587-1555
Cort Johnson, *President*
Mindy Knox, *Vice Pres*
Darryl Rudnick, *Vice Pres*
Kaare Breitung, *MIS Dir*
Dan Whitney, *VP Sales*
▲ **EMP:** 480
SQ FT: 23,000
SALES (est): 59MM **Privately Held**
WEB: www.tagtimeusa.com
SIC: 2679 Labels, paper: made from purchased material

(P-5741)
TAPP LABEL INC (HQ)
161 S Vasco Rd L, Livermore (94551-5130)
PHONE..................707 252-8300
John Attayek, *CEO*
Brian Sharpe, *Vice Pres*
Brooks Denny, *Business Dir*
Kristina Garrett, *Business Dir*
Tim Miles, *Business Dir*
EMP: 10
SALES (est): 2.3MM **Privately Held**
SIC: 2679 Labels, paper: made from purchased material
PA: Tltc Holdings Inc
6270 205 St
Langley BC V2Y 1
604 533-3294

(P-5742)
TEKNI-PLEX INC
Also Called: Natvar
19555 Arenth Ave, City of Industry (91748-1403)
PHONE..................909 589-4366
Joleen Kennelley, *Branch Mgr*
Jerry Wombold, *Marketing Staff*
EMP: 163
SALES (corp-wide): 1.1B **Privately Held**
WEB: www.dolco.net
SIC: 2679 Egg cartons, molded pulp: made from purchased material
PA: Tekni-Plex, Inc.
460 E Swedesford Rd # 3000
Wayne PA 19087
484 690-1520

(P-5743)
TLC LOGISTICS INC
Also Called: Western Die Cutting and Prtg
3109 Casitas Ave, Los Angeles (90039-2410)
PHONE..................323 665-0474
Jerry Lavinsky, *President*
EMP: 10
SQ FT: 7,000
SALES (est): 1.4MM **Privately Held**
SIC: 2679 Paper products, converted

(P-5744)
TOTAL PAPER AND PACKAGING INC
2175 Agate Ct Unit A, Simi Valley (93065-1839)
PHONE..................818 885-1072
Rajiv Kaushal, *President*
▲ **EMP:** 13
SALES: 5MM **Privately Held**
SIC: 2679 Paper products, converted

(P-5745)
U S LABEL CORPORATION
3100 W Vanowen St, Burbank (91505-1237)
PHONE..................818 558-3703
John Mindle, *CEO*
EMP: 12
SQ FT: 3,000
SALES (est): 2.9MM **Privately Held**
WEB: www.uslabelcorp.com
SIC: 2679 Labels, paper: made from purchased material

(P-5746)
W/S PACKAGING GROUP INC
W/S Packaging Fullerton
531 Airpark Dr, Fullerton (92833-2501)
PHONE..................714 992-2574
William Harper, *Manager*
Christopher Failla, *Design Engr*
Gabbie Moran, *Manager*
EMP: 81
SALES (corp-wide): 760.8MM **Privately Held**
WEB: www.wspackaging.com
SIC: 2679 2671 2759 Labels, paper: made from purchased material; packaging paper & plastics film, coated & laminated; labels & seals: printing
PA: W/S Packaging Group, Inc.
2571 S Hemlock Rd
Green Bay WI 54229
920 866-6300

(P-5747)
WORLD CENTRIC
617 2nd St Ste C, Petaluma (94952-5160)
PHONE..................707 241-9190
Aseem Das, *CEO*
Xing Jin, *Research*
Bill Biggar, *VP Sales*
Greg Zitzer, *Director*
Janae Lloyd, *Manager*
◆ **EMP:** 17
SALES (est): 7.5MM **Privately Held**
SIC: 2679 2675 5113 Plates, pressed & molded pulp: from purchased material; die-cut paper & board; industrial & personal service paper

(P-5748)
Z B P INC
Also Called: Z-Barten Productions
2871 E Pico Blvd, Los Angeles (90023-3609)
PHONE..................323 266-3363
Dale Zabel, *President*
Nancy Andersen, *Principal*
Jane Berse, *Principal*
Paula Greenberg, *Principal*
Howard Kuykendall, *Principal*
▲ **EMP:** 12
SQ FT: 20,000
SALES (est): 1.3MM **Privately Held**
WEB: www.confetti.com
SIC: 2679 2678 Novelties, paper: made from purchased material; stationery products

---

2711 Newspapers: Publishing & Printing

(P-5749)
2100 FREEDOM INC (HQ)
625 N Grand Ave, Santa Ana (92701-4347)
PHONE..................714 796-7000
Richard E Mirman, *CEO*
Aaron Kushner, *CEO*
EMP: 100
SALES: 371.7MM
SALES (corp-wide): 2.5B **Privately Held**
SIC: 2711 2721 7313 2741 Newspapers, publishing & printing; periodicals; newspaper advertising representative; miscellaneous publishing; newspapers, home delivery, not by printers or publishers;
PA: 2100 Trust, Llc
625 N Grand Ave
Santa Ana CA 92701
877 469-7344

(P-5750)
5800 SUNSET PRODUCTIONS INC
Also Called: Tribune Studios
5800 W Sunset Blvd, Los Angeles (90028-6607)
PHONE..................323 460-3987
EMP: 13
SALES (est): 3.4MM
SALES (corp-wide): 2B **Publicly Held**
SIC: 2711
PA: Tribune Media Company
435 N Michigan Ave Fl 2
Chicago IL 60654
212 210-2786

(P-5751)
ACORN NEWSPAPER INC
30423 Canwood St Ste 108, Agoura Hills (91301-4313)
PHONE..................818 706-0266
Jim Rule, *President*
EMP: 30
SQ FT: 3,000
SALES (est): 1.7MM **Privately Held**
WEB: www.theacorn.com
SIC: 2711 Newspapers: publishing only, not printed on site

(P-5752)
ADVERTISER PERCEPTIONS
3009 Deer Meadow Dr, Danville (94506-2134)
PHONE..................925 648-3902
Kenneth M Pearl, *CEO*
Frank Papsadore, *Programmer Anys*
Claire Jones, *Director*
Michele Laprade, *Director*
EMP: 20 EST: 2008
SALES (est): 1.2MM **Privately Held**
SIC: 2711 Newspapers: publishing only, not printed on site

(P-5753)
ALAMEDA NEWSPAPERS INC (DH)
Also Called: Times Herald
22533 Foothill Blvd, Hayward (94541-4109)
PHONE..................510 783-6111
Joh Schueler, *President*
P Scott McKibben, *President*

EMP: 250
SQ FT: 50,000
SALES (est): 65.1MM
SALES (corp-wide): 4.3B Privately Held
WEB: www.newsschool.com
SIC: 2711 Newspapers, publishing & printing

(P-5754)
ALAMEDA NEWSPAPERS INC
Also Called: San Mateo Times
1080 S Amphlett Blvd, San Mateo
(94402-1802)
PHONE..................................650 348-4321
Dan Cruey, *Manager*
EMP: 80
SALES (corp-wide): 4.3B Privately Held
WEB: www.newsschool.com
SIC: 2711 Newspapers: publishing only, not printed on site; newspapers, publishing & printing
HQ: Alameda Newspapers, Inc
22533 Foothill Blvd
Hayward CA 94541
510 783-6111

(P-5755)
ALAMEDA NEWSPAPERS INC
Also Called: Tri-Valley Herald
127 Spring St, Pleasanton (94566-6623)
PHONE..................................209 832-6144
P Scott, *CEO*
EMP: 300
SALES (corp-wide): 4.3B Privately Held
WEB: www.newsschool.com
SIC: 2711 2752 Newspapers, publishing & printing; commercial printing, lithographic
HQ: Alameda Newspapers, Inc
22533 Foothill Blvd
Hayward CA 94541
510 783-6111

(P-5756)
ALPENHORN CRESTLINE CHRONICLE
23570 Knapps Cutoff, Crestline (92325)
PHONE..................................909 338-8484
Dennis Labadie, *Principal*
Tiffany O'Hare, *Publisher*
EMP: 20
SALES (est): 1MM Privately Held
SIC: 2711 Newspapers

(P-5757)
AMERICAN CITY BUS JOURNALS INC
Also Called: Sacramento Business Journal
555 Capitol Mall Ste 200, Sacramento
(95814-4557)
P.O. Box 189249 (95818-9249)
PHONE..................................916 447-7661
Mike Trainor, *General Mgr*
EMP: 29
SALES (corp-wide): 1.4B Privately Held
SIC: 2711 Newspapers: publishing only, not printed on site
HQ: American City Business Journals, Inc.
120 W Morehead St Ste 400
Charlotte NC 28202
704 973-1000

(P-5758)
AMMI PUBLISHING INC
Also Called: Ark Newspaper, The
1550 Tiburon Blvd Ste D, Belvedere
Tiburon (94920-2537)
P.O. Box 1054 (94920-4054)
PHONE..................................415 435-2652
Allison Kern, *President*
Emily Lavin, *Production*
Jeff Dempsey, *Editor*
EMP: 10
SQ FT: 1,000
SALES (est): 618.8K Privately Held
WEB: www.thearknewspaper.com
SIC: 2711 Newspapers: publishing only, not printed on site

(P-5759)
AMPERSAND PUBLISHING LLC (PA)
Also Called: Santa Barbara News-Press Info
715 Anacapa St, Santa Barbara
(93101-2203)
P.O. Box 1359 (93102-1359)
PHONE..................................805 564-5200
Wendy McCaw,
Sharon Moore, *President*
Yolanda Apodaca, *Executive*
Rick Merrick, *Administration*
Peg Mueting, *Sales Staff*
EMP: 30
SQ FT: 65,000
SALES (est): 27.2MM Privately Held
WEB: www.newspress.com
SIC: 2711 Newspapers: publishing only, not printed on site

(P-5760)
ANG NEWSPAPER GROUP INC (DH)
Also Called: Pacifica Tribune
1301 Grant Ave B, Novato (94945-3143)
PHONE..................................650 359-6666
Cynthia Caldwell, *Manager*
Dean Singelton, *President*
Chris Hunter, *Principal*
Victoria Monroe, *Production*
Barbara Pagan, *Manager*
EMP: 14
SQ FT: 4,500
SALES: 1.4MM
SALES (corp-wide): 4.3B Privately Held
WEB: www.pacificatribune.com
SIC: 2711 Commercial printing & newspaper publishing combined

(P-5761)
ANTELOPE VALLEY NEWSPAPERS INC
Also Called: Antelope Valley Press
44939 10th St W, Lancaster (93534-2313)
PHONE..................................661 940-1000
Tammy Valdes, *Manager*
EMP: 42
SALES (est): 1MM
SALES (corp-wide): 12.7MM Privately Held
SIC: 2711 7313 2741 Newspapers: publishing only, not printed on site; newspaper advertising representative; miscellaneous publishing
PA: Antelope Valley Newspapers Inc.
37404 Sierra Hwy
Palmdale CA
661 273-2700

(P-5762)
ARGONAUT
5355 Mcconnell Ave, Los Angeles
(90066-7025)
PHONE..................................310 822-1629
David Asper Johnson, *President*
George Drury Smith, *CFO*
EMP: 27 EST: 1971
SQ FT: 10,000
SALES: 2MM Privately Held
WEB: www.argonautnewspaper.com
SIC: 2711 Newspapers: publishing only, not printed on site

(P-5763)
ASIA PACIFIC CALIFORNIA INC (PA)
Also Called: China Press, The
1648 Gilbreth Rd, Burlingame
(94010-1408)
PHONE..................................650 513-6189
Yining Xie, *President*
▲ EMP: 47
SQ FT: 13,000
SALES (est): 2.4MM Privately Held
SIC: 2711 Newspapers, publishing & printing

(P-5764)
ASIA PACIFIC CALIFORNIA INC
Also Called: The China Press
2121 W Micaion Rd Ste 207, Alhambra
(91803)
PHONE..................................626 281-8500
Non Hiand, *General Mgr*
Mark Lam, *Manager*

EMP: 35 Privately Held
SIC: 2711 Newspapers
PA: Asia Pacific California Inc
1648 Gilbreth Rd
Burlingame CA 94010

(P-5765)
ASIAN WEEK (PA)
809 Sacramento St, San Francisco
(94108-2116)
PHONE..................................415 397-0220
James Fang, *President*
EMP: 10
SQ FT: 10,000
SALES (est): 3.3MM Privately Held
WEB: www.asianweek.com
SIC: 2711 2721 Newspapers; television schedules: publishing & printing

(P-5766)
ASSOCIATED DESERT NEWSPAPER (DH)
Also Called: Imperial Valley Press
205 N 8th St, El Centro (92243-2301)
P.O. Box 2641 (92244-2641)
PHONE..................................760 337-3400
Mayer Malone, *President*
David Leone, *President*
Teresa Zimmer, *CFO*
John Yanni, *Treasurer*
Clifford James, *Admin Sec*
EMP: 40
SQ FT: 30,000
SALES (est): 5.3MM
SALES (corp-wide): 882.7MM Publicly Held
WEB: www.ivpressonline.com
SIC: 2711 Newspapers, publishing & printing; commercial printing & newspaper publishing combined
HQ: Schurz Communications, Inc.
1301 E Douglas Rd Ste 200
Mishawaka IN 46545
574 247-7237

(P-5767)
ASSOCIATED STUDENTS UCLA
Also Called: Asucla Publications
308 Westwood Plz Ste 118, Los Angeles
(90095-8355)
PHONE..................................310 825-2787
Arvli Ward, *Manager*
Miriam Bribiesca, *Editor*
EMP: 200
SALES (corp-wide): 42.7MM Privately Held
SIC: 2711 2741 2721 Newspapers: publishing only, not printed on site; miscellaneous publishing; periodicals
PA: Associated Students U.C.L.A.
308 Westwood Plz
Los Angeles CA 90095
310 825-4321

(P-5768)
AUBURN JOURNAL INC (HQ)
1030 High St, Auburn (95603-4707)
P.O. Box 5910 (95604-5910)
PHONE..................................530 885-5656
Craig Dennis, *President*
Tony Hazarian, *Owner*
Martin Cody, *President*
William J Brehm Sr, *Vice Pres*
Christina Moneypenny, *Executive*
EMP: 23
SQ FT: 18,000
SALES (est): 38.3MM
SALES (corp-wide): 224.9MM Privately Held
SIC: 2711 Commercial printing & newspaper publishing combined; newspapers, publishing & printing
PA: Brehm Communications, Inc.
16644 W Bernardo Dr # 300
San Diego CA 92127
858 451-6200

(P-5769)
AUBURN JOURNAL INC
Also Called: Colfax Record
1030 High St, Auburn (95603-4707)
PHONE..................................530 346-2232
Todd Frantz, *Principal*
EMP: 100

SALES (corp-wide): 224.9MM Privately Held
SIC: 2711 7313 Newspapers: publishing only, not printed on site; newspaper advertising representative
HQ: Auburn Journal Inc
1030 High St
Auburn CA 95603
530 885-5656

(P-5770)
AUBURN TRADER INC (DH)
1115 Grass Valley Hwy, Auburn
(95603-3439)
P.O. Box 5910 (95604-5910)
PHONE..................................530 888-7653
Bill Brehm, *President*
Kim Christen, *Manager*
EMP: 20
SALES (est): 37.8MM
SALES (corp-wide): 224.9MM Privately Held
SIC: 2711 Newspapers, publishing & printing
HQ: Auburn Journal Inc
1030 High St
Auburn CA 95603
530 885-5656

(P-5771)
AZTECA NEWS
1532 E Wellington Ave, Santa Ana
(92701-3235)
PHONE..................................714 972-9912
Rosana Romano, *Owner*
EMP: 10
SALES (est): 462.1K Privately Held
WEB: www.aztecanews.com
SIC: 2711 Newspapers

(P-5772)
BAKERSFIELD CALIFORNIAN (PA)
1707 Eye St, Bakersfield (93301-5299)
P.O. Box 440 (93302-0440)
PHONE..................................661 322-5627
Richard Beene, *President*
Logan Molen, *COO*
Michelle Hirst, *CFO*
Virginia Fritts Moorhouse, *Chairman*
John Arthur, *Vice Pres*
EMP: 190
SQ FT: 53,000
SALES (est): 21.8MM Privately Held
WEB: www.bakersfield.net
SIC: 2711 Commercial printing & newspaper publishing combined; newspapers, publishing & printing

(P-5773)
BALITA MEDIA INC
Also Called: Weekend Balita
2629 Foothill Blvd, La Crescenta
(91214-3511)
PHONE..................................818 552-4503
Luchie Allen, *CEO*
Ruby Allen, *Principal*
Ramonsito Mendoza, *Admin Sec*
Gary Escarilla, *Sales Mgr*
EMP: 22
SALES: 2MM Privately Held
WEB: www.balita.com
SIC: 2711 Newspapers, publishing & printing

(P-5774)
BAR MEDIA INC
Also Called: Bay Area Reporter
44 Gough St Ste 204, San Francisco
(94103-5424)
PHONE..................................415 861-5019
Michael Yamashita, *President*
Thomas E Horn, *Ch of Bd*
Patrick Brown, *CFO*
Todd Vogt, *Admin Sec*
EMP: 15
SQ FT: 1,258
SALES (est): 103.8K Privately Held
SIC: 2711 Newspapers: publishing only, not printed on site

(P-5775)
BAY GUARDIAN COMPANY
Also Called: San Francisco Bay Guardian
135 Micaicaippi St, San Francisco (94107)
PHONE..................................415 255-3100

▲ = Import ▼=Export
◆ =Import/Export

Bruce Brugman, *President*
Jean Brugman, *President*
EMP: 70
SQ FT: 28,000
SALES (est): 3.6MM **Privately Held**
SIC: 2711 Newspapers, publishing & printing

(P-5776)
BEACON MEDIA INC
125 E Chestnut Ave, Monrovia (91016-3411)
PHONE.................................626 301-1010
Jesse Dillon, *CEO*
Andrea Olivas, *COO*
Fred Bankston, *Accounts Mgr*
Jose Correa, *Accounts Mgr*
Terry Miller, *Editor*
EMP: 10
SALES (est): 848.7K **Privately Held**
SIC: 2711 2759 Newspapers: publishing only, not printed on site; commercial printing

(P-5777)
BEVERLY HILLS COURIER INC
499 N Canon Dr Ste 100, Beverly Hills (90210-6192)
PHONE.................................310 278-1322
Clifton Smith, *President*
March Schwartz, *President*
EMP: 20
SQ FT: 10,000
SALES (est): 1.3MM **Privately Held**
WEB: www.bhcourier.com
SIC: 2711 Newspapers, publishing & printing

(P-5778)
BIOCENTURY PUBLICATIONS INC (PA)
1235 Radio Rd Ste 100, Redwood City (94065-1315)
P.O. Box 1246, San Carlos (94070-1246)
PHONE.................................650 595-5333
David Flores, *President*
Meredith Durkin Wolfe, *Research*
Jaime De Leon, *Research Analys*
Chris Lieu, *Research Analys*
Manal Tawashi, *Director*
EMP: 35
SALES (est): 3.7MM **Privately Held**
SIC: 2711 2721 Newspapers; periodicals

(P-5779)
BREHM COMMUNICATIONS INC
Also Called: Folsom Telegraph
921 Sutter St, Folsom (95630-2441)
PHONE.................................916 985-2581
Jeff Royce, *Manager*
Susan Morin, *Manager*
EMP: 12
SALES (corp-wide): 224.9MM **Privately Held**
WEB: www.brehmcommunications.com
SIC: 2711 Newspapers, publishing & printing
PA: Brehm Communications, Inc.
16644 W Bernardo Dr # 300
San Diego CA 92127
858 451-6200

(P-5780)
BRENTWOOD PRESS & PUBG LLC
Also Called: Brentwood Yellow Pages
248 Oak St, Brentwood (94513-1337)
PHONE.................................925 516-4757
Jimmy Chamores Mg Mem, *Principal*
Sonia Beasley, *Sales Mgr*
Jimmy Chamores, *Mng Member*
EMP: 45
SQ FT: 3,500
SALES (est): 1MM **Privately Held**
SIC: 2711 Newspapers: publishing only, not printed on site

(P-5781)
BUENA PARK ANAHEIM INDEPENDENT
9551 Valley View St, Cypress (90630)
PHONE.................................714 952-8505
Eddie Verdugo, *President*
EMP: 20

SALES (est): 553.6K **Privately Held**
SIC: 2711 Newspapers, publishing & printing

(P-5782)
BULLDOG REPORTER
124 Linden St, Oakland (94607-2538)
PHONE.................................510 596-9300
EMP: 16
SALES (est): 3MM **Privately Held**
SIC: 2711

(P-5783)
BUSINESS JRNL PUBLICATIONS INC
125 S Market St 11, San Jose (95113-2292)
PHONE.................................408 295-3800
Italo Jimenez, *Manager*
EMP: 43
SALES (corp-wide): 1.4B **Privately Held**
WEB: www.tampabaybusinessjournal.com
SIC: 2711 Newspapers: publishing only, not printed on site
HQ: Business Journal Publications, Inc.
4350 W Cypress St Ste 800
Tampa FL 33607

(P-5784)
BUSINESS JRNL PUBLICATIONS INC
Also Called: San Francisco Business Time
275 Battery St Ste 600, San Francisco (94111-3376)
PHONE.................................415 989-2522
Mary Huss, *Principal*
Corinne Crncich, *Accounts Exec*
EMP: 45
SALES (corp-wide): 1.4B **Privately Held**
WEB: www.tampabaybusinessjournal.com
SIC: 2711 Newspapers: publishing only, not printed on site
HQ: Business Journal Publications, Inc.
4350 W Cypress St Ste 800
Tampa FL 33607

(P-5785)
CALAVERAS FIRST CO INC
Also Called: Calaveras Enterprise
15 Main St, San Andreas (95249)
P.O. Box 1197 (95249-1197)
PHONE.................................209 754-3861
Ralph Alldredge, *President*
Buz Engleton, *General Mgr*
Dana Gray, *Manager*
EMP: 30
SQ FT: 8,000
SALES (est): 1.8MM **Privately Held**
SIC: 2711 Newspapers: publishing only, not printed on site

(P-5786)
CALI TODAY DAILY NEWSPAPER
1310 Tully Rd Ste 105, San Jose (95122-3054)
PHONE.................................408 297-8271
Nan Nguyen, *President*
EMP: 14
SALES (est): 590.9K **Privately Held**
SIC: 2711 Newspapers, publishing & printing

(P-5787)
CALIFORNIA COMMUNITY NEWS LLC (HQ)
5091 4th St, Irwindale (91706-2173)
PHONE.................................626 472-5297
Eddy Hartenstein, *President*
Judy Kendall, *Vice Pres*
Julie Xanders, *Admin Sec*
Julia Morgan, *Director*
EMP: 349
SQ FT: 324,000
SALES (est): 65.5MM
SALES (corp-wide): 1.5B **Publicly Held**
SIC: 2711 Newspapers, publishing & printing; commercial printing & newspaper publishing combined
PA: Tribune Publishing Company
435 N Michigan Ave
Chicago IL 60611
312 222-9100

(P-5788)
CALIFORNIA NEWSPAPERS INC
Also Called: Marin Independent Journal
150 Alameda Del Prado, Novato (94949-6665)
PHONE.................................415 883-8600
Roger Grossman, *President*
Mario Bendingan, *President*
Carolyn Ware, *Executive*
EMP: 526
SQ FT: 60,000
SALES (est): 26MM
SALES (corp-wide): 4.3B **Privately Held**
WEB: www.marinij.com
SIC: 2711 Commercial printing & newspaper publishing combined; newspapers, publishing & printing
HQ: California Newspapers Limited Partnership
605 E Huntington Dr # 100
Monrovia CA 91016
626 962-8811

(P-5789)
CALIFORNIA NEWSPAPERS PARTNR (PA)
Also Called: Mng Newspapers
4 N 2nd St Ste 800, San Jose (95113-1317)
PHONE.................................408 920-5333
Steven B Rossi, *President*
Linda Roatch, *Advt Staff*
EMP: 149
SALES (est): 9.3MM **Privately Held**
SIC: 2711 Newspapers: publishing only, not printed on site

(P-5790)
CALIFRNIA NWSPAPERS LTD PARTNR (DH)
Also Called: Inland Valley Daily Bulletin
605 E Huntington Dr # 100, Monrovia (91016-6352)
P.O. Box 1259, Covina (91722-0259)
PHONE.................................626 962-8811
Ron Hasse, *President*
Mark Welches, *Vice Pres*
Grace Reaza, *Office Mgr*
Michelle Vielma, *Sales Staff*
Rich Archbold, *Director*
EMP: 450
SALES (est): 237.9MM
SALES (corp-wide): 4.3B **Privately Held**
WEB: www.sgvtribune.com
SIC: 2711 Newspapers: publishing only, not printed on site

(P-5791)
CALIFRNIA NWSPAPERS LTD PARTNR
Also Called: Inland Valley Daily Bulletin
9616 Archibald Ave # 100, Rancho Cucamonga (91730-7939)
PHONE.................................909 987-6397
Bob Balzer, *Manager*
Snezana Tomasevic, *Executive*
Christine Burt, *Executive Asst*
Curt Annett, *Sales Mgr*
EMP: 275
SQ FT: 88,304
SALES (corp-wide): 4.3B **Privately Held**
WEB: www.sgvtribune.com
SIC: 2711 Newspapers, publishing & printing
HQ: California Newspapers Limited Partnership
605 E Huntington Dr # 100
Monrovia CA 91016
626 962-8811

(P-5792)
CALIFRNIA NWSPAPERS LTD PARTNR
Also Called: Redlands Daily Facts
19 E Citrus Ave Ste 102, Redlands (92373-4763)
PHONE.................................909 793-3221
Peggy Del Torro, *Manager*
EMP: 35
SQ FT: 8,301
SALES (corp-wide): 4.3B **Privately Held**
WEB: www.sgvtribune.com
SIC: 2711 7313 Newspapers, publishing & printing; newspaper advertising representative

HQ: California Newspapers Limited Partnership
605 E Huntington Dr # 100
Monrovia CA 91016
626 962-8811

(P-5793)
CALIFRNIA NWSPAPERS LTD PARTNR
5399 Clark Rd, Paradise (95969-6325)
P.O. Box 70 (95967-0070)
PHONE.................................530 877-4413
Steve McCormick, *Controller*
EMP: 185
SALES (corp-wide): 4.3B **Privately Held**
WEB: www.sgvtribune.com
SIC: 2711 2796 2791 2789 Newspapers: publishing only, not printed on site; platemaking services; typesetting; bookbinding & related work; commercial printing, lithographic
HQ: California Newspapers Limited Partnership
605 E Huntington Dr # 100
Monrovia CA 91016
626 962-8811

Also Called: Media News

(P-5794)
CALIMESA NEWS MIRROR
1007 Calimesa Blvd Ste D, Calimesa (92320-1143)
PHONE.................................909 795-8145
Jerry Bean, *CEO*
EMP: 20
SALES (est): 568.7K **Privately Held**
SIC: 2711 Newspapers

(P-5795)
CARMEL COMMUNICATIONS INC
Also Called: Carmel Pine Cone, The
734 Lighthouse Ave, Pacific Grove (93950-2522)
PHONE.................................831 274-8593
Paul Miller, *Treasurer*
Nicholas Shaw, *Vice Pres*
EMP: 14
SALES (est): 312.5K **Privately Held**
SIC: 2711 Commercial printing & newspaper publishing combined

(P-5796)
CHAMPION PBLICATIONS CHINO INC
Also Called: Champion Newspapers
13179 9th St, Chino (91710-4216)
P.O. Box 607 (91708-0607)
PHONE.................................909 628-5501
Allen P McCombs, *President*
Bill McCombs, *Treasurer*
Gretchen McCombs, *Vice Pres*
Suzanne White, *Advt Staff*
Linda Fenner, *Sales Staff*
EMP: 21
SQ FT: 6,500
SALES (est): 1.5MM **Privately Held**
WEB: www.chinochampion.com
SIC: 2711 Newspapers, publishing & printing
PA: Golden State Newspapers Llc
95 W 11th St Ste 101
Tracy CA 95376
209 835-3030

(P-5797)
CHICO COMMUNITY PUBLISHING (PA)
Also Called: Reno News & Review
353 E 2nd St, Chico (95928-5469)
PHONE.................................530 894-2300
Jeff Von Kaenel, *CEO*
Jeff Vonkaenel, *President*
Charles Marcks, *CFO*
Valentina Flynn, *Vice Pres*
Deborah Redmond, *Admin Sec*
EMP: 40
SQ FT: 7,200
SALES (est): 9.6MM **Privately Held**
WEB: www.newsreview.com
SIC: 2711 Newspapers, publishing & printing

PRODUCTS & SVCS

(P-5798)
CHICO COMMUNITY PUBLISHING
Also Called: Sacramento News & Review
1124 Del Paso Blvd, Sacramento
(95815-3607)
PHONE..................916 498-1234
Angela Hanson, *Manager*
Deborah Redmond, *General Mgr*
Dax Strane, *Consultant*
Melissa Daugherty, *Editor*
Rachel Leibrock, *Relations*
EMP: 60
SALES (corp-wide): 9.6MM **Privately Held**
WEB: www.newsreview.com
SIC: 2711 Newspapers, publishing & printing
PA: Chico Community Publishing Inc
353 E 2nd St
Chico CA 95928
530 894-2300

(P-5799)
CHINA PRESS
2121 W Mission Rd Ste 103, Alhambra
(91803-1433)
PHONE..................626 281-8500
Fax: 626 281-8400
▲ EMP: 10
SALES (est): 799.2K **Privately Held**
SIC: 2711

(P-5800)
CHINA TIMES PRINTING INC
445 Madera St, San Gabriel (91776-2411)
P.O. Box 970 (91778-0970)
PHONE..................626 576-7006
Franklin C Yu, *President*
Rosalind Yu, *Treasurer*
EMP: 60 EST: 1981
SQ FT: 30,000
SALES (est): 3.2MM **Privately Held**
SIC: 2711 2752 2741 2721 Newspapers, publishing & printing; commercial printing, lithographic; miscellaneous publishing; periodicals; commercial printing

(P-5801)
CHRISTIAN HERALD INC
520 S La Fayette Park Pl # 520, Los Angeles (90057-1600)
PHONE..................213 353-0777
Myong Kim, *President*
EMP: 10
SALES: 964.1K **Privately Held**
SIC: 2711 Newspapers, publishing & printing

(P-5802)
CHRISTIAN MUSIC TODAY INC
Also Called: Spirit West Coast
80 Gilman Ave Ste 2, Campbell
(95008-3013)
PHONE..................408 377-9232
John Robertson, *President*
Allan Stark, *Treasurer*
David Martinez, *Admin Sec*
Jon Robberson, *Relg Ldr*
EMP: 12
SQ FT: 1,200
SALES: 751.7K **Privately Held**
WEB: www.spiritwestcoast.org
SIC: 2711 Newspapers: publishing only, not printed on site

(P-5803)
CHRISTIAN SCIENCE CHURCH
Also Called: First Church Christ, Scientist
120 E Valerio St, Santa Barbara
(93101-1914)
PHONE..................805 966-6661
Fredrick Hunter, *Pastor*
Ann Flury, *Representative*
EMP: 20
SALES (est): 861.3K **Privately Held**
WEB: www.christiansciencechurch.com
SIC: 2711 Newspapers

(P-5804)
CHRISTIAN TODAY INC
354 S Normandie Ave # 101, Los Angeles (90020-3183)
PHONE..................323 931-0505
Jong Chun Suh, *CEO*
Young Bin Lee, *President*

Irene Suh, *Editor*
▲ EMP: 10
SQ FT: 2,000
SALES: 160K **Privately Held**
SIC: 2711 Newspapers

(P-5805)
CITY WIDE PRINTING INC
Also Called: Citywide Printing
5100 Lankershim Blvd, North Hollywood
(91601-3717)
PHONE..................818 752-9300
Albert Hakakha, *CEO*
Albert Hak, *President*
Robert Hak, *CFO*
EMP: 12
SQ FT: 5,000
SALES (est): 860.9K **Privately Held**
WEB: www.citywideprinting.com
SIC: 2711 Commercial printing & newspaper publishing combined

(P-5806)
CIVIC CENTER NEWS INC
Also Called: Los Angeles Downtown News
1264 W 1st St, Los Angeles (90026-5831)
PHONE..................213 481-1448
Susan R Laris, *President*
Claudia Hernandez, *Production*
EMP: 20
SQ FT: 2,366
SALES (est): 1.3MM **Privately Held**
SIC: 2711 Newspapers: publishing only, not printed on site

(P-5807)
CLAREMONT COURIER
114 Olive St, Claremont (91711-4924)
PHONE..................909 621-4761
Peter Weinberger, *Owner*
EMP: 20
SQ FT: 4,000
SALES (est): 1.3MM **Privately Held**
WEB: www.claremontcourier.com
SIC: 2711 Newspapers: publishing only, not printed on site

(P-5808)
COAST NEWS
315 S Coast Highway 101 W, Encinitas
(92024-3543)
PHONE..................760 436-9737
James Kydd, *CEO*
Phyllis Mitchell, *Graphic Designe*
Sue Otto, *Sales Staff*
Savannah Lang, *Manager*
Brad Rollins, *Manager*
EMP: 30
SALES (est): 1.4MM **Privately Held**
WEB: www.thecoastnews.com
SIC: 2711 2741 Newspapers; miscellaneous publishing

(P-5809)
COMMUNITY CLOSE-UP WESTMINSTER
1771 S Lewis St, Anaheim (92805-6439)
PHONE..................714 704-5811
EMP: 61
SALES (est): 6.6MM
SALES (corp-wide): 2.3B **Privately Held**
SIC: 2711
HQ: Freedom Communications, Inc.
625 N Grand Ave
Santa Ana CA 92701
714 796-7000

(P-5810)
COMMUNITY MEDIA CORPORATION
Also Called: Event Newspapers
5119 Ball Rd, Cypress (90630-3645)
PHONE..................714 220-0292
Kathy Verdugo, *President*
Daniel Verdugo, *COO*
Linda Townson, *Vice Pres*
Franco Te, *Director*
Eddie Verdugo, *Publisher*
EMP: 80
SQ FT: 4,000
SALES (est): 3.8MM **Privately Held**
WEB: www.community-media.com
SIC: 2711 Newspapers, publishing & printing

(P-5811)
CONTRA COSTA NEWSPAPERS INC (DH)
Also Called: Contra Costa Times
175 Lennon Ln Ste 100, Walnut Creek
(94598-2466)
P.O. Box 5088 (94596-0088)
PHONE..................925 935-2525
George Riggs, *CEO*
John Armstrong, *President*
Chris Boisvert, *Info Tech Dir*
Betty Brown, *Consultant*
EMP: 1000
SQ FT: 180,000
SALES (est): 195.3MM
SALES (corp-wide): 4.3B **Privately Held**
WEB: www.contracostatimes.com
SIC: 2711 Newspapers, publishing & printing

(P-5812)
CONTRA COSTA NEWSPAPERS INC
1516 Oak St, Alameda (94501-2947)
PHONE..................510 748-1683
John Kawomoto, *Branch Mgr*
EMP: 273
SALES (corp-wide): 4.3B **Privately Held**
SIC: 2711 Newspapers, publishing & printing
HQ: Contra Costa Newspapers, Inc.
175 Lennon Ln Ste 100
Walnut Creek CA 94598
925 935-2525

(P-5813)
CONTRA COSTA NEWSPAPERS INC
127 Spring St, Pleasanton (94566-6623)
PHONE..................925 847-2123
Kelly Gust, *Principal*
EMP: 91
SALES (corp-wide): 4.3B **Privately Held**
SIC: 2711 Newspapers, publishing & printing
HQ: Contra Costa Newspapers, Inc.
175 Lennon Ln Ste 100
Walnut Creek CA 94598
925 935-2525

(P-5814)
CONTRA COSTA NEWSPAPERS INC
2800 Camino Diablo, Walnut Creek
(94597-3951)
PHONE..................925 943-3925
EMP: 273
SALES (corp-wide): 4.3B **Privately Held**
SIC: 2711 Newspapers
HQ: Contra Costa Newspapers, Inc.
175 Lennon Ln Ste 100
Walnut Creek CA 94598
925 935-2525

(P-5815)
CONTRA COSTA NEWSPAPERS INC
2205 Dean Lesher Dr, Concord (94520)
PHONE..................925 977-8520
Gary Gomes, *Manager*
EMP: 140
SALES (corp-wide): 4.3B **Privately Held**
WEB: www.contracostatimes.com
SIC: 2711 Newspapers, publishing & printing
HQ: Contra Costa Newspapers, Inc.
175 Lennon Ln Ste 100
Walnut Creek CA 94598
925 935-2525

(P-5816)
CONTRA COSTA NEWSPAPERS INC
Also Called: Brentwood News
1700 Cavallo Rd, Antioch (94509-1930)
PHONE..................925 634-2125
EMP: 10
SALES (corp-wide): 4.3B **Privately Held**
SIC: 2711
HQ: Contra Costa Newspapers, Inc.
175 Lennon Ln Ste 100
Walnut Creek CA 94598
925 935-2525

(P-5817)
CONTRA COSTA NEWSPAPERS INC
Also Called: Roseville Press-Tribune
188 Cirby Way, Roseville (95678-6481)
PHONE..................916 786-6500
Mike Giangreco, *General Mgr*
EMP: 100
SALES (corp-wide): 4.3B **Privately Held**
WEB: www.contracostatimes.com
SIC: 2711 Newspapers
HQ: Contra Costa Newspapers, Inc.
175 Lennon Ln Ste 100
Walnut Creek CA 94598
925 935-2525

(P-5818)
COPLEY PRESS INC
Also Called: Union Tribune
1152 Armorlite Dr, San Marcos
(92069-1441)
P.O. Box 120191, San Diego (92112-0191)
PHONE..................760 752-6700
EMP: 16
SQ FT: 44,044
SALES (corp-wide): 92.6MM **Privately Held**
SIC: 2711 7383 7313
PA: The Copley Press Inc
7776 Ivanhoe Ave
La Jolla CA 92037
858 454-0411

(P-5819)
CYCLE NEWS INC (PA)
Also Called: CN Publishing Group
17771 Mitchell N, Irvine (92614-6028)
P.O. Box 930, North Bend OR (97459-0073)
PHONE..................949 863-7082
Sharon Clayton, *President*
Michelle Baird, *Editor*
EMP: 32
SQ FT: 10,000
SALES (est): 1.7MM **Privately Held**
WEB: www.watercraft.com
SIC: 2711 Newspapers, publishing & printing

(P-5820)
DAILY COMPUTING SOLUTIONS INC
3521 Foxglove Rd, Glendale (91206-4817)
PHONE..................818 240-5400
Artin Kasparian, *President*
Andre Keshishyan, *Software Dev*
EMP: 10
SALES (est): 161.7K **Privately Held**
SIC: 2711 Newspapers, publishing & printing

(P-5821)
DAILY JOURNAL
1720 S Amphlett Blvd # 123, San Mateo
(94402-2710)
PHONE..................650 344-5200
Jerry Lee, *Owner*
EMP: 20
SALES (est): 645.7K **Privately Held**
SIC: 2711 Newspapers, publishing & printing

(P-5822)
DAILY JOURNAL CORPORATION (PA)
915 E 1st St, Los Angeles (90012-4042)
PHONE..................213 229-5300
Gerald L Salzman, *President*
Charles T Munger, *Ch of Bd*
John Patrick Guerin, *Vice Ch Bd*
Peter Kaufman, *Bd of Directors*
Gary Wilcox, *Bd of Directors*
EMP: 101
SQ FT: 34,000
SALES: 41.3MM **Publicly Held**
WEB: www.dailyjournal.com
SIC: 2711 2721 7313 7372 Newspapers, publishing & printing; magazines: publishing & printing; newspaper advertising representative; prepackaged software

(P-5823)
DAILY JOURNAL CORPORATION
Also Called: San Francisco Daily Journal
44 Montgomery St Ste 500, San Francisco
(94104-4607)
PHONE.............................415 296-2400
Ray Reynolds, *Branch Mgr*
EMP: 80
SALES (corp-wide): 41.3MM **Publicly Held**
WEB: www.dailyjournal.com
SIC: 2711 2721 Newspapers, publishing & printing; periodicals
PA: Daily Journal Corporation
    915 E 1st St
    Los Angeles CA 90012
    213 229-5300

(P-5824)
DAILY RECORDER
901 H St Ste 312, Sacramento
(95814-1808)
PHONE.............................916 444-2355
Chris Nofuente, *Manager*
EMP: 12
SALES (est): 456K **Privately Held**
SIC: 2711 Newspapers

(P-5825)
DAILY REVIEW
Also Called: A and G News Papers
3317 Arden Rd, Hayward (94545-3903)
PHONE.............................510 783-6111
Steve Cressoub, *CFO*
Tiffany Towner, *Manager*
EMP: 30
SALES (est): 1.3MM **Privately Held**
WEB: www.thedailyreview.com
SIC: 2711 Newspapers, publishing & printing

(P-5826)
DAILY SPORTS SEOUL USA INC
626 S Kingsley Dr, Los Angeles
(90005-2318)
PHONE.............................213 487-9331
Jang Hee Lee, *President*
Austin Park, *Marketing Mgr*
EMP: 30
SALES (est): 1.9MM **Privately Held**
SIC: 2711 Commercial printing & newspaper publishing combined; newspapers, publishing & printing

(P-5827)
DAKOTA PRESS INC
14400 Doolittle Dr, San Leandro
(94577-5546)
PHONE.............................510 895-1300
Mary Reid, *President*
Gary Reid, *Vice Pres*
EMP: 15
SALES (est): 4MM **Privately Held**
SIC: 2711 Commercial printing & newspaper publishing combined

(P-5828)
DESERT SUN PUBLISHING CO (HQ)
750 N Gene Autry Trl, Palm Springs
(92262-5463)
P.O. Box 2734 (92263-2734)
PHONE.............................760 322-8889
Robert J Dickey, *President*
EMP: 200 EST: 1974
SQ FT: 30,621
SALES (est): 22MM
SALES (corp-wide): 3.1B **Publicly Held**
WEB: www.thedesertsun.com
SIC: 2711 Newspapers, publishing & printing
PA: Gannett Co., Inc.
    7950 Jones Branch Dr
    Mc Lean VA 22102
    703 854-6000

(P-5829)
DIGITAL FIRST MEDIA LLC
Also Called: Orange County Register, The
625 N Grand Ave, Santa Ana (92701-4347)
P.O. Box 61056, Anaheim (92803-6156)
PHONE.............................714 796-7000
Toll Free:.............................877 -
Chris Anderson, *Manager*
N Christian Anderson, *President*
Jon Merendino, *Vice Pres*

Niko Houston, *Executive*
Melissa English, *Business Anlyst*
EMP: 900
SQ FT: 144,000
SALES (corp-wide): 4.3B **Privately Held**
WEB: www.freedom.com
SIC: 2711 Commercial printing & newspaper publishing combined
PA: Digital First Media, Llc
    101 W Colfax Ave Fl 11
    Denver CO 80202
    212 257-7212

(P-5830)
DISPATCHER NEWSPAPER
1188 Franklin St Fl 4, San Francisco
(94109-6800)
PHONE.............................415 775-0533
Robert McEllreth, *President*
EMP: 25
SALES (est): 863.3K **Privately Held**
SIC: 2711 Newspapers

(P-5831)
DIXON TRIBUNE
145 E A St, Dixon (95620-3599)
PHONE.............................707 678-5594
David Payne, *Owner*
EMP: 17
SALES (est): 773.5K **Privately Held**
SIC: 2711 Newspapers, publishing & printing

(P-5832)
DOW JONES & COMPANY INC
201 California St Fl 13, San Francisco
(94111-5002)
PHONE.............................415 765-6131
Steve Yoder, *Chief*
Mason Nikfarjam, *Info Tech Mgr*
EMP: 20
SALES (corp-wide): 9B **Publicly Held**
SIC: 2711 Newspapers, publishing & printing
HQ: Dow Jones & Company, Inc.
    1211 Avenue Of The Americ
    New York NY 10036
    609 627-2999

(P-5833)
DOW JONES LMG STOCKTON INC
Also Called: Record The
530 E Market St, Stockton (95202-3009)
PHONE.............................209 943-6397
Deitra Kenoly, *President*
Roger Coover, *President*
Stewart Willis, *Info Tech Mgr*
Kenneth Damilano, *Technical Staff*
Sylvia Rivas, *Sales Staff*
EMP: 208
SALES (est): 11.7MM
SALES (corp-wide): 1.3B **Publicly Held**
SIC: 2711 Newspapers, publishing & printing
HQ: Local Media Group, Inc.
    40 Mulberry St
    Middletown NY 10940
    845 341-1100

(P-5834)
DOWNEY PATRIOT
8301 Florence Ave Ste 100, Downey
(90240-3946)
PHONE.............................562 904-3668
Jennifer Dekay-Gibins, *Owner*
EMP: 10
SALES (est): 637.5K **Privately Held**
SIC: 2711 Newspapers

(P-5835)
E Z BUY E Z SELL RECYCLER CORP (HQ)
Also Called: Recycler Classified
4954 Van Nuys Blvd # 201, Sherman Oaks
(91403-1719)
PHONE.............................310 886-7808
Niki Ruokosuo, *President*
Jim Fullmer, *VP Finance*
EMP: 200
SQ FT: 13,000

SALES (est): 36.3MM
SALES (corp-wide): 1.8B **Publicly Held**
WEB: www.recycler.com
SIC: 2711 2741 Newspapers: publishing only, not printed on site; miscellaneous publishing
PA: Tribune Media Company
    515 N State St Ste 2400
    Chicago IL 60654
    312 222-3394

(P-5836)
EAGLE NEWSPAPERS LLC
Also Called: Coronado Eagle
1224 10th St Ste 103, Coronado
(92118-3419)
PHONE.............................619 437-8800
Dean Eckenroth,
EMP: 20
SQ FT: 1,350
SALES (est): 1.2MM **Privately Held**
WEB: www.eaglenewsca.com
SIC: 2711 Newspapers: publishing only, not printed on site

(P-5837)
EAST COUNTY GAZETTE
Also Called: Alcine Gazette
270 E Douglas Ave, El Cajon (92020-4514)
PHONE.............................619 444-5774
Debbie Norman, *Owner*
EMP: 10
SALES (est): 587.9K **Privately Held**
SIC: 2711 Newspapers: publishing only, not printed on site; newspapers, publishing & printing

(P-5838)
EASTBAY PUBLISHING CORP
Also Called: Castro Valley Forum
2117 San Jose Ave, Alameda
(94501-4915)
PHONE.............................510 537-1792
Fred Zinder, *Owner*
Greg Benson, *Art Dir*
Howard Morrison, *Manager*
EMP: 12
SALES (est): 638.6K **Privately Held**
SIC: 2711 Newspapers

(P-5839)
EASY AD INCORPORATED
155 S Harvard St, Hemet (92543-4233)
PHONE.............................951 658-2244
Winston Greene Jr, *President*
EMP: 35
SALES (est): 1.7MM **Privately Held**
SIC: 2711 2741 Newspapers: publishing only, not printed on site; miscellaneous publishing

(P-5840)
EASY READER INC
832 Hermosa Ave, Hermosa Beach
(90254-4116)
P.O. Box 427 (90254-0427)
PHONE.............................310 372-4611
Kevin Cody, *President*
Richard Budman, *COO*
Amy Berg, *Executive*
Jared Thompson, *Director*
Tamar Gillotti, *Accounts Mgr*
EMP: 30
SQ FT: 3,400
SALES (est): 1.7MM **Privately Held**
WEB: www.hermosawave.net
SIC: 2711 Newspapers: publishing only, not printed on site

(P-5841)
EL AVISADOR MAGAZINE
400 Bremerton Ct, Roseville (95661-5106)
PHONE.............................916 903-7490
Orlando Ruiz, *Owner*
Jamil Martinez, *Editor*
EMP: 10
SALES (est): 554.5K **Privately Held**
SIC: 2711 2721 5994 Newspapers, publishing & printing; periodicals: publishing only; magazine stand

(P-5842)
EL DORADO GOLD PANNER INC
Also Called: Gold Panner, The
247 Placerville Dr, Placerville (95667-3911)
PHONE.............................530 626-5057

Jerry Moore, *President*
EMP: 10
SALES (est): 490K **Privately Held**
SIC: 2711 Newspapers: publishing only, not printed on site

(P-5843)
EL DORADO NEWSPAPERS INC (DH)
Also Called: Clovis Independent
2100 Q St, Sacramento (95816-6816)
P.O. Box 15779 (95852-0779)
PHONE.............................916 321-1826
Karole Morgan-Prager, *Admin Sec*
Anna Ramseier, *Prdtn Mgr*
EMP: 200
SALES (est): 18.5MM
SALES (corp-wide): 903.5MM **Publicly Held**
WEB: www.clovisindependent.com
SIC: 2711 Commercial printing & newspaper publishing combined; newspapers, publishing & printing
HQ: Mcclatchy Newspapers, Inc.
    2100 Q St
    Sacramento CA 95816
    916 321-1855

(P-5844)
EL OBSERVADOR PUBLICATIONS INC
1042 W Hedding St Ste 250, San Jose
(95126-1206)
PHONE.............................408 938-1700
Hilbert Morales, *President*
Monica Amador, *Vice Pres*
Elizabeth J Rose-Morales, *Vice Pres*
Justin Rossi, *Advt Staff*
EMP: 10
SQ FT: 1,400
SALES (est): 765.1K **Privately Held**
WEB: www.el-observador.com
SIC: 2711 Newspapers: publishing only, not printed on site

(P-5845)
EL POPULAR SPANISH NEWSPAPER
404 Truxtun Ave, Bakersfield (93301-5316)
PHONE.............................661 325-7725
George Camacho, *Partner*
EMP: 10 EST: 1983
SALES (est): 586.4K **Privately Held**
WEB: www.elpopularnews.com
SIC: 2711 Newspapers: publishing only, not printed on site

(P-5846)
EMBARCADERO PUBLISHING COMPANY (PA)
Also Called: Country Almanac
450 Cambridge Ave, Palo Alto
(94306-1507)
P.O. Box 1610 (94302-1610)
PHONE.............................650 964-6300
William Johnson, *President*
Peter Beller, *CFO*
Shannon Corey, *Creative Dir*
Doris Taylor, *Admin Asst*
Frank Bravo, *Info Tech Dir*
EMP: 132
SQ FT: 4,500
SALES (est): 12.3MM **Privately Held**
WEB: www.paweekly.com
SIC: 2711 Commercial printing & newspaper publishing combined; newspapers, publishing & printing

(P-5847)
EXIN LLC
1213 Evans Ave, San Francisco
(94124-1717)
PHONE.............................415 359-2600
Ted Fang, *President*
Florence Fang, *Ch of Bd*
Simon Smith, *CFO*
James Fang, *Treasurer*
EMP: 120
SQ FT: 27,526
SALES (est): 4.2MM **Privately Held**
SIC: 2711 Newspapers: publishing only, not printed on site

(P-5848)
FEATHER PUBLISHING COMPANY INC (PA)
Also Called: Feather River Bulletin
287 Lawrence St, Quincy (95971-9477)
P.O. Box B (95971-3586)
PHONE..............................530 283-0800
Michael C Taborski, *President*
Keri B Taborski, *Vice Pres*
EMP: 30
SALES (est): 7.5MM **Privately Held**
WEB: www.plumasnews.com
SIC: 2711 2752 Newspapers, publishing & printing; lithographing on metal

(P-5849)
FEATHER PUBLISHING COMPANY INC
Also Called: Lassen County Times
100 Grand Ave, Susanville (96130-4451)
PHONE..............................530 257-5321
Sam Williams, *Manager*
Jill Atkinson, *Manager*
Laura Tew, *Consultant*
Teresa Mossinger, *Relations*
EMP: 15
SALES (corp-wide): 7.5MM **Privately Held**
WEB: www.plumasnews.com
SIC: 2711 2759 Newspapers, publishing & printing; newspapers: printing
PA: Feather Publishing Company, Incorporated
287 Lawrence St
Quincy CA 95971
530 283-0800

(P-5850)
FOOTHILLS SUN-GAZETTE
Also Called: Foothills Advertiser
120 N E St, Exeter (93221-1729)
P.O. Box 7 (93221-0007)
PHONE..............................559 592-3171
Katie Byrne, *President*
Wsley Byrne, *Treasurer*
Reggie Ellis, *Vice Pres*
William Brown, *Principal*
EMP: 20
SQ FT: 5,000
SALES (est): 1.2MM **Privately Held**
WEB: www.theexetersun.com
SIC: 2711 Newspapers: publishing only, not printed on site

(P-5851)
FREEDOM COMMUNICATIONS INC
Also Called: Orange County Register
22481 Aspan St, El Toro (92630-1630)
PHONE..............................949 454-7300
EMP: 50
SALES (corp-wide): 2.5B **Privately Held**
SIC: 2711
HQ: Freedom Communications Inc
625 N Grand Ave
Santa Ana CA 92701
714 796-7000

(P-5852)
GANNETT CO INC
U S A Today
10960 Wilshire Blvd # 1000, Los Angeles (90024-3702)
PHONE..............................310 444-2120
Gary Pietsch, *Director*
EMP: 20
SALES (corp-wide): 3.1B **Publicly Held**
WEB: www.gannett.com
SIC: 2711 Newspapers
PA: Gannett Co., Inc.
7950 Jones Branch Dr
Mc Lean VA 22102
703 854-6000

(P-5853)
GANNETT CO INC
Also Called: Tulare Advance Register
330 N West St, Tulare (93274)
PHONE..............................559 688-0521
Amy Pack, *Manager*
EMP: 120
SALES (corp-wide): 3.1B **Publicly Held**
WEB: www.gannett.com
SIC: 2711 Newspapers, publishing & printing

PA: Gannett Co., Inc.
7950 Jones Branch Dr
Mc Lean VA 22102
703 854-6000

(P-5854)
GANNETT CO INC
Also Called: Desert Sun, The
750 N Gene Autry Trl, Palm Springs (92262-5463)
PHONE..............................760 322-8889
Robert Dickey, *Branch Mgr*
EMP: 77
SALES (corp-wide): 3.1B **Publicly Held**
WEB: www.gannett.com
SIC: 2711 Newspapers
PA: Gannett Co., Inc.
7950 Jones Branch Dr
Mc Lean VA 22102
703 854-6000

(P-5855)
GARDENA VALLEY NEWS INC (PA)
Also Called: Valley News Gardens
15005 S Vermont Ave, Gardena (90247-3004)
P.O. Box 219 (90248-0219)
PHONE..............................310 329-6351
George D Algie, *President*
Ruriko Yatabe, *Corp Secy*
Carlos Bueno, *Plant Mgr*
Robert Von Gorres, *Sales Mgr*
EMP: 15
SQ FT: 8,200
SALES (est): 3.5MM **Privately Held**
WEB: www.gardenavalleynews.com
SIC: 2711 Commercial printing & newspaper publishing combined

(P-5856)
GARDENA VALLEY NEWS INC
15005 S Vermont Ave, Gardena (90247-3004)
PHONE..............................310 532-4882
George Algie, *President*
EMP: 20
SALES (est): 452K
SALES (corp-wide): 3.5MM **Privately Held**
WEB: www.gardenavalleynews.com
SIC: 2711 Commercial printing & newspaper publishing combined
PA: Gardena Valley News, Inc.
15005 S Vermont Ave
Gardena CA 90247
310 329-6351

(P-5857)
GATEHOUSE MEDIA LLC
Also Called: Fort Bragg Advocate-News
690 S Main St, Fort Bragg (95437-5108)
P.O. Box 1188 (95437-1188)
PHONE..............................707 964-5642
Stan Andreson, *Enginr/R&D Mgr*
EMP: 19
SQ FT: 3,500
SALES (corp-wide): 1.3B **Publicly Held**
WEB: www.fortsmith.com
SIC: 2711 Newspapers, publishing & printing
HQ: Gatehouse Media, Llc
175 Sullys Trl Ste 300
Pittsford NY 14534
585 598-0030

(P-5858)
GATEHOUSE MEDIA LLC
Also Called: Siskiyou Daily News
309 S Broadway St, Yreka (96097-2905)
P.O. Box 129 (96097-0129)
PHONE..............................530 842-5777
Rod Ows, *Branch Mgr*
EMP: 24
SALES (corp-wide): 1.3B **Publicly Held**
WEB: www.gatehousemedia.com
SIC: 2711 Newspapers, publishing & printing
HQ: Gatehouse Media, Llc
175 Sullys Trl Ste 300
Pittsford NY 14534
585 598-0030

(P-5859)
GATEHOUSE MEDIA LLC
Also Called: Chico Enterprise Record
400 E Park Ave, Chico (95928-7127)
P.O. Box 9 (95927-0009)
PHONE..............................530 891-1234
Wolf Rosenburg, *Branch Mgr*
EMP: 70
SALES (corp-wide): 1.3B **Publicly Held**
WEB: www.fortsmith.com
SIC: 2711 Newspapers, publishing & printing
HQ: Gatehouse Media, Llc
175 Sullys Trl Ste 300
Pittsford NY 14534
585 598-0030

(P-5860)
GAZETTE MEDIA CO LLC
Also Called: Sacramento Gazette, The
770 L St Ste 950, Sacramento (95814-3361)
P.O. Box 293956 (95829-3956)
PHONE..............................916 567-9654
David Fong, *Mng Member*
EMP: 10
SALES (est): 545.6K **Privately Held**
SIC: 2711 Newspapers: publishing only, not printed on site

(P-5861)
GAZETTE NEWSPAPERS
Also Called: Grunion Gazette
5225 E 2nd St, Long Beach (90803-5326)
PHONE..............................562 433-2000
Simmon Grief, *Principal*
Julie McKibbin, *Assistant*
EMP: 20
SQ FT: 2,600
SALES (est): 1.3MM **Privately Held**
WEB: www.gazettes.com
SIC: 2711 Newspapers, publishing & printing

(P-5862)
GIBSON PRINTING & PUBLISHING
Also Called: Benicia Herald
820 1st St, Benicia (94510-3216)
P.O. Box 65 (94510-0065)
PHONE..............................707 745-0733
Pam Poppee, *Manager*
EMP: 18
SALES (corp-wide): 4.3MM **Privately Held**
SIC: 2711 7313 Newspapers: publishing only, not printed on site; newspaper advertising representative
PA: Gibson Printing & Publishing
544 Curtola Pkwy
Vallejo CA 94590
707 643-2552

(P-5863)
GIBSON PRINTING & PUBLISHING (PA)
Also Called: Martinez News Gazette
544 Curtola Pkwy, Vallejo (94590-6925)
PHONE..............................707 643-2552
David L Payne, *President*
Jeanne M Payne, *Vice Pres*
Heloise C Di Ricco, *Admin Sec*
EMP: 20
SQ FT: 40,000
SALES (est): 4.3MM **Privately Held**
SIC: 2711 2752 Commercial printing & newspaper publishing combined; commercial printing, lithographic

(P-5864)
GIBSON PRINTING & PUBLISHING
Also Called: Martinez News Gazette
802 Alhambra Ave, Martinez (94553-1604)
P.O. Box 151 (94553-0015)
PHONE..............................925 228-6400
Dale Lorren, *Manager*
Stephen Shores, *Adv Dir*
EMP: 10
SALES (corp-wide): 4.3MM **Privately Held**
SIC: 2711 Newspapers: publishing only, not printed on site

PA: Gibson Printing & Publishing
544 Curtola Pkwy
Vallejo CA 94590
707 643-2552

(P-5865)
GIBSON PRINTING & PUBLISHING
Also Called: Dixon Tribune
145 E A St, Dixon (95620-3531)
PHONE..............................707 678-5594
David Payne, *Owner*
EMP: 10
SALES (corp-wide): 4.3MM **Privately Held**
SIC: 2711 Commercial printing & newspaper publishing combined
PA: Gibson Printing & Publishing
544 Curtola Pkwy
Vallejo CA 94590
707 643-2552

(P-5866)
GRACE COMMUNICATIONS INC (PA)
Also Called: Metropolitan News Company
210 S Spring St, Los Angeles (90012-3710)
P.O. Box 60859 (90060-0859)
PHONE..............................213 628-4384
Joann W Grace, *President*
Roger M Grace, *Vice Pres*
Veronica Lopez, *Advt Staff*
EMP: 43 EST: 1901
SQ FT: 21,000
SALES (est): 7.2MM **Privately Held**
SIC: 2711 Newspapers, publishing & printing; newspapers: publishing only, not printed on site

(P-5867)
GREAT NORTHERN WHEELS DEALS
Also Called: Wheels and Deals
810 Lake Blvd Ste C, Redding (96003-2200)
PHONE..............................530 533-2134
Fax: 530 533-1531
EMP: 33
SQ FT: 2,400
SALES: 2MM **Privately Held**
WEB: www.wheelsanddeals.com
SIC: 2711 7313

(P-5868)
GUM SUN TIMES INC (PA)
Also Called: Chinese Times
625 Kearny St, San Francisco (94108-1849)
PHONE..............................415 379-6788
Michael Lamm, *President*
See B Hom, *President*
Harrison Lim, *President*
EMP: 30
SQ FT: 9,000
SALES (est): 1.3MM **Privately Held**
SIC: 2711 Newspapers: publishing only, not printed on site

(P-5869)
HANFORD SENTINEL INC
Also Called: Pulitzer Community Newspapers
300 W 6th St, Hanford (93230-4518)
P.O. Box 9 (93232-0009)
PHONE..............................559 582-0471
Randy Rickman, *President*
Mark Daniel, *Vice Pres*
Davis Taylor, *Admin Sec*
Joyce Chambers, *Manager*
Jennifer Vikjord, *Manager*
EMP: 90
SQ FT: 16,000
SALES (est): 5.2MM
SALES (corp-wide): 566.9MM **Publicly Held**
WEB: www.newzcentral.com
SIC: 2711 Commercial printing & newspaper publishing combined; newspapers, publishing & printing
HQ: Pulitzer Inc
900 N Tucker Blvd
Saint Louis MO 63101
314 340-8000

▲ = Import ▼=Export
◆ =Import/Export

(P-5870)
HEARST COMMUNICATIONS INC
7916 Arcade Lake Ln, Citrus Heights (95610-5165)
PHONE..................916 725-8694
EMP: 251
SALES (corp-wide): 6.6B Privately Held
SIC: 2711 Newspapers, publishing & printing
HQ: Hearst Communications, Inc.
300 W 57th St
New York NY 10019
212 649-2000

(P-5871)
HEARST COMMUNICATIONS INC
1350 16th St, Oakland (94607-2248)
PHONE..................510 645-4250
Cheryl Ruiz, *Manager*
EMP: 251
SALES (corp-wide): 6.6B Privately Held
SIC: 2711 Newspapers, publishing & printing
HQ: Hearst Communications, Inc.
300 W 57th St
New York NY 10019
212 649-2000

(P-5872)
HEARST COMMUNICATIONS INC
Chronicle Books
680 2nd St, San Francisco (94107-2015)
PHONE..................415 537-4200
Nion McEvoy, *Manager*
EMP: 160
SALES (corp-wide): 6.6B Privately Held
WEB: www.telegram.com
SIC: 2711 Newspapers, publishing & printing
HQ: Hearst Communications, Inc.
300 W 57th St
New York NY 10019
212 649-2000

(P-5873)
HEARST CORPORATION
Also Called: HEARST CORPORATION THE
224 Reindollar Ave, Marina (93933-3857)
PHONE..................831 582-9605
Joel Doss, *Manager*
EMP: 247
SALES (corp-wide): 6.6B Privately Held
WEB: www.hearstcorp.com
SIC: 2711 Newspapers
PA: The Hearst Corporation
300 W 57th St Fl 42
New York NY 10019
212 649-2000

(P-5874)
HEARST CORPORATION
Sunical Land and Livestock Div
5 3rd St Ste 200, San Francisco (94103-3299)
PHONE..................415 777-0600
Stephen Hurst, *Manager*
Michael Duncan, *Manager*
EMP: 13
SALES (corp-wide): 6.6B Privately Held
WEB: www.hearstcorp.com
SIC: 2711 Newspapers
PA: The Hearst Corporation
300 W 57th St Fl 42
New York NY 10019
212 649-2000

(P-5875)
HEARTS FOR LONG BEACH INC
5225 E 2nd St, Long Beach (90803-5326)
PHONE..................562 433-2000
Simmon Grief, *Principal*
EMP: 20 EST: 1977
SALES: 4.3K Privately Held
WEB: www.heartsforhounds.com
SIC: 2711 Newspapers, publishing & printing

(P-5876)
HERBURGER PUBLICATIONS INC (PA)
Also Called: Galt Herald
604 N Lincoln Way, Galt (95632-8601)
PHONE..................916 685-5533
Roy Herburger, *President*
David Herburger, *Vice Pres*
EMP: 60 EST: 1903
SQ FT: 10,000
SALES (est): 6.8MM Privately Held
WEB: www.herburger.net
SIC: 2711 Commercial printing & newspaper publishing combined

(P-5877)
HERBURGER PUBLICATIONS INC
Also Called: Elk Grove Citizen
8970 Elk Grove Blvd, Elk Grove (95624-1971)
P.O. Box 1777 (95759-1777)
PHONE..................916 685-3945
Cameron Macdonald, *Principal*
EMP: 10
SALES (corp-wide): 6.8MM Privately Held
WEB: www.herburger.net
SIC: 2711 7313 Newspapers, publishing & printing; newspaper advertising representative
PA: Herburger Publications, Inc
604 N Lincoln Way
Galt CA 95632
916 685-5533

(P-5878)
HESPERIA RESORTER
Also Called: Apple Valley News
16925 Main St Ste A, Hesperia (92345-6038)
P.O. Box 400937 (92340-0937)
PHONE..................760 244-0021
Ray Pryke, *Owner*
EMP: 25
SALES (est): 1.3MM Privately Held
SIC: 2711 Newspapers

(P-5879)
HI-DESERT PUBLISHING COMPANY
Also Called: Yuciapa & Calimesa News Mirror
35154 Yucaipa Blvd, Yucaipa (92399-4339)
P.O. Box 760 (92399-0760)
PHONE..................909 797-9101
Fax: 909 797-0502
EMP: 27
SALES (corp-wide): 213.8MM Privately Held
SIC: 2711
HQ: Hi-Desert Publishing Company
56445 29 Palms Hwy
Yucca Valley CA 92284
760 365-3315

(P-5880)
HI-DESERT PUBLISHING COMPANY
Also Called: Mountain News & Shopper
28200 Highway 189 O-1, Lake Arrowhead (92352-9700)
P.O. Box 2410 (92352-2410)
PHONE..................909 336-3555
Harry Bradley, *Sales/Mktg Mgr*
EMP: 23
SALES (corp-wide): 224.9MM Privately Held
WEB: www.hidesertstar.com
SIC: 2711 Commercial printing & newspaper publishing combined
HQ: Hi-Desert Publishing Company
56445 29 Palms Hwy
Yucca Valley CA 92284

(P-5881)
HI-DESERT PUBLISHING COMPANY (HQ)
56445 29 Palms Hwy, Yucca Valley (92284-2861)
PHONE..................760 365-3315
Cindy Melland, *Publisher*
Jay Thomas, *Director*
Stacy Moore, *Editor*
EMP: 70

SALES (est): 24.6MM
SALES (corp-wide): 224.9MM Privately Held
WEB: www.hidesertstar.com
SIC: 2711 Newspapers, publishing & printing
PA: Brehm Communications, Inc.
16644 W Bernardo Dr # 300
San Diego CA 92127
858 451-6200

(P-5882)
HORIZON CAL PUBLICATIONS
Also Called: Mammoth Times
452 Old Mammoth Rd, Mammoth Lakes (93546-2013)
P.O. Box 3929 (93546-3929)
PHONE..................760 934-3929
David J Radler, *President*
EMP: 15
SQ FT: 2,100
SALES: 2MM Privately Held
WEB: www.mammothtimes.com
SIC: 2711 Newspapers

(P-5883)
HORIZON PUBLICATIONS INC
Also Called: Inyo Register, The
407 W Line St Ste 8, Bishop (93514-3321)
PHONE..................760 873-3535
Bob Reitz, *Branch Mgr*
Carol Ross, *Admin Mgr*
Darcy Ellis, *Editor*
Rena Mlodecki, *Publisher*
EMP: 16
SALES (corp-wide): 83.1MM Privately Held
WEB: www.malvern-online.com
SIC: 2711 Newspapers
PA: Horizon Publications, Inc.
1120 N Carbon St Ste 100
Marion IL 62959
618 993-1711

(P-5884)
HUMBOLDT NEWSPAPER INC
Also Called: Times-Standard
930 6th St, Eureka (95501-1112)
P.O. Box 3580 (95502-3580)
PHONE..................707 442-1711
Stephan J Sosinski, *Publisher*
Catherine Wong, *Internal Med*
Ron Maloney, *Manager*
Ryan Hoffman, *Accounts Exec*
Patrick Bonitatibus, *Supervisor*
EMP: 526
SQ FT: 49,872
SALES (est): 20.9MM Privately Held
WEB: www.times-standard.com
SIC: 2711 Newspapers: publishing only, not printed on site

(P-5885)
INDEPENDENT BERKELEY STUDENT
Also Called: Daily Californian
2483 Hearst Ave, Berkeley (94709-1320)
P.O. Box 1949 (94701-1949)
PHONE..................510 548-8300
Karim Doumar, *President*
Nicole Lee, *Natl Sales Mgr*
Pressly Pratt, *Editor*
EMP: 100
SQ FT: 4,100
SALES: 266.5K Privately Held
SIC: 2711 7372 Newspapers: publishing only, not printed on site; application computer software

(P-5886)
INDEPENDENT COAST OBSERVER
Also Called: I. C. O.
38500 S Highway 1, Gualala (95445-8592)
P.O. Box 1200 (95445-1200)
PHONE..................707 884-3501
Stephen McLaughlin, *President*
EMP: 15
SQ FT: 2,000
SALES (est): 862.2K Privately Held
WEB: www.independentcoastobserver.com
SIC: 2711 Commercial printing & newspaper publishing combined

(P-5887)
INDIA-WEST PUBLICATIONS INC (PA)
933 Macarthur Blvd, San Leandro (94577-3062)
PHONE..................510 383-1140
Ramesh Murarka, *President*
Bina Murarka, *Corp Secy*
EMP: 21
SQ FT: 7,000
SALES (est): 2MM Privately Held
SIC: 2711 Newspapers: publishing only, not printed on site

(P-5888)
INLAND EMPIRE CMNTY NEWSPAPERS
Also Called: Rialto Record
1809 Commercenter W, San Bernardino (92408-3303)
P.O. Box 110, Colton (92324-0110)
PHONE..................909 381-9898
William B Harrison, *President*
EMP: 25
SQ FT: 4,000
SALES (est): 1.2MM Privately Held
SIC: 2711 Newspapers: publishing only, not printed on site

(P-5889)
INLAND VALLEY NEWS INC
2009 Porter Field Way C, Upland (91786-2196)
PHONE..................909 949-3099
Gloria Morrow, *President*
Tommy Morrow, *Admin Sec*
▲ EMP: 15
SALES: 105.4K Privately Held
WEB: www.inlandvalleynews.com
SIC: 2711 Newspapers: publishing only, not printed on site

(P-5890)
INLAND VALLEY PUBLISING CO
Also Called: Independent, The
2250 1st St, Livermore (94550-3143)
P.O. Box 1198 (94551-1198)
PHONE..................925 243-8000
Joan Seppala, *President*
Gale Marshall, *Tech/Comp Coord*
EMP: 12
SQ FT: 5,000
SALES: 850K Privately Held
WEB: www.independentnews.com
SIC: 2711 Newspapers: publishing only, not printed on site

(P-5891)
INTERNATIONAL DAILY NEWS INC (PA)
870 Monterey Pass Rd, Monterey Park (91754-3688)
PHONE..................323 265-1317
Jessica G Elnitiarta, *President*
Yopie Sioeng, *Manager*
▲ EMP: 20
SQ FT: 10,000
SALES (est): 3.7MM Privately Held
WEB: www.chinesetoday.com
SIC: 2711 Newspapers, publishing & printing

(P-5892)
INVESTORS BUSINESS DAILY INC (HQ)
12655 Beatrice St, Los Angeles (90066-7303)
PHONE..................310 448-6000
William O'Neil, *President*
Kathy Sherman, *Vice Pres*
▲ EMP: 200
SQ FT: 180,000
SALES (est): 30.3MM
SALES (corp-wide): 231.5MM Privately Held
WEB: www.investors.com
SIC: 2711 Newspapers, publishing & printing
PA: Data Analysis Inc.
12655 Beatrice St
Los Angeles CA 90066
310 448-6800

PRODUCTS & SVCS

(P-5893)
JOBS & CAREERS NEWSPAPERS INC
1480 Oddstad Dr, Redwood City (94063-2607)
PHONE..................................650 367-6885
Michael Mainiero, *President*
EMP: 13
SALES (est): 5.3MM
SALES (corp-wide): 903.5MM **Publicly Held**
SIC: 2711 Job printing & newspaper publishing combined
PA: The Mcclatchy Company
2100 Q St
Sacramento CA 95816
916 321-1844

(P-5894)
JOONG-ANG DAILY NEWS CAL INC (HQ)
Also Called: Korea Daily
690 Wilshire Pl, Los Angeles (90005-3930)
PHONE..................................213 368-2500
Kae Hong Ko, *CEO*
In Taek Park, *President*
Yoonsoo Kim, *General Mgr*
Jung Lee, *General Mgr*
Charlie Lee, *Administration*
▲ EMP: 200
SQ FT: 70,000
SALES (est): 89.1MM
SALES (corp-wide): 244.9MM **Privately Held**
WEB: www.joongangusa.com
SIC: 2711 Commercial printing & newspaper publishing combined
PA: Joongang Ilbo
100 Seosomun-Ro, Jung-Gu
Seoul 04513
822 751-9114

(P-5895)
JOONG-ANG DAILY NEWS CAL INC
Also Called: Korea Central
8269 Garden Grove Blvd, Garden Grove (92844-1010)
PHONE..................................714 638-2341
Chung Park, *Manager*
EMP: 10
SALES (corp-wide): 244.9MM **Privately Held**
WEB: www.joongangusa.com
SIC: 2711 Newspapers, publishing & printing
HQ: The Joong-Ang Daily News California Inc
690 Wilshire Pl
Los Angeles CA 90005
213 368-2500

(P-5896)
JOURNAL OF BOCOMMUNICATION INC
2772 Woodwardia Dr, Los Angeles (90077-2121)
PHONE..................................310 475-4708
Robert C Turner, *Principal*
EMP: 15
SALES: 0 **Privately Held**
SIC: 2711 Newspapers, publishing & printing

(P-5897)
KAAR DRECT MAIL FLFILLMENT LLC
1225 Expo Way Ste 160, San Diego (92154)
PHONE..................................619 382-3670
Sohela Aragon, *CEO*
EMP: 25
SALES (est): 2.2MM **Privately Held**
SIC: 2711 5963 Commercial printing & newspaper publishing combined; direct sales, telemarketing

(P-5898)
KING RUSTLER
522 Broadway St Ste A, King City (93930-3243)
P.O. Box 710 (93930-0710)
PHONE..................................831 385-4880
Tom Cross, *Partner*
EMP: 15

SALES (est): 544.9K **Privately Held**
SIC: 2711 5812 Newspapers, publishing & printing; eating places

(P-5899)
KOREA CENTRAL DAILY NEWS
Also Called: Joongang Dily Nwssan Francisco
33288 Central Ave, Union City (94587-2010)
PHONE..................................213 368-2500
Kim Pansoo, *President*
Yeon T Lee, *President*
Sunny Ui Lee, *Treasurer*
▲ EMP: 17
SQ FT: 23,000
SALES: 2MM **Privately Held**
SIC: 2711 Newspapers

(P-5900)
KOREA DAILY NEWS & KOREA TIMES
8134 Capwell Dr, Oakland (94621-2110)
PHONE..................................510 777-1111
Jae Chang, *President*
EMP: 30
SALES (est): 1.3MM **Privately Held**
SIC: 2711 Newspapers, publishing & printing

(P-5901)
KOREA TIMES LOS ANGELES INC
Also Called: Korea Times San Francisco, The
8134 Capwell Dr, Oakland (94621-2110)
PHONE..................................510 777-1111
Sung CHI, *Manager*
EMP: 30
SALES (corp-wide): 83.9MM **Privately Held**
WEB: www.koreatimeshawaii.com
SIC: 2711 Newspapers, publishing & printing
PA: The Korea Times Los Angeles Inc
3731 Wilshire Blvd
Los Angeles CA 90010
323 692-2000

(P-5902)
KOREA TIMES LOS ANGELES INC
9572 Garden Grove Blvd, Garden Grove (92844-1514)
PHONE..................................714 530-6001
Cangy Lee, *Manager*
EMP: 10
SALES (corp-wide): 83.9MM **Privately Held**
WEB: www.koreatimeshawaii.com
SIC: 2711 Newspapers, publishing & printing
PA: The Korea Times Los Angeles Inc
3731 Wilshire Blvd
Los Angeles CA 90010
323 692-2000

(P-5903)
KYOCHARO USA LLC
3807 Wilshire Blvd # 518, Los Angeles (90010-3113)
PHONE..................................213 383-1236
Im Kyu Sim, *Owner*
▲ EMP: 15
SALES: 1MM **Privately Held**
SIC: 2711 Newspapers, publishing & printing

(P-5904)
LA OPINION LP (HQ)
Also Called: Lozano Enterprises
915 Wilshire Blvd Ste 800, Los Angeles (90017-3488)
PHONE..................................213 896-2196
Monica C Lozano, *CEO*
Lozano Communications, *General Ptnr*
La Opini N, *Vice Pres*
Noe Magana, *Administration*
Justin Leao, *Info Tech Mgr*
EMP: 54
SQ FT: 45,000

SALES (est): 31.1MM
SALES (corp-wide): 66.1MM **Privately Held**
WEB: www.laopinion.com
SIC: 2711 Newspapers, publishing & printing
PA: Impremedia, Llc
1 Metrotech Ctr Fl 18
Brooklyn NY 11201
212 807-4600

(P-5905)
LA TIMES
202 W 1st St Ste 500, Los Angeles (90012-4401)
PHONE..................................213 237-2279
Raymond Jansen, *CEO*
EMP: 13
SALES (est): 1.1MM **Privately Held**
SIC: 2711 Newspapers, publishing & printing

(P-5906)
LA WEEKLY
Also Called: L A Weekly
724 S Spring St Ste 700, Los Angeles (90014-2943)
P.O. Box 5052, Culver City (90231-5052)
PHONE..................................310 574-7100
Mike Sigman, *President*
Joel Lara, *Sales Staff*
EMP: 150
SALES (est): 9.4MM
SALES (corp-wide): 24.3MM **Privately Held**
WEB: www.laweekly.com
SIC: 2711 Newspapers, publishing & printing
PA: Village Voice Media Llc
36 Cooper Sq Fl 433333
New York NY
212 475-3300

(P-5907)
LAKE COUNTY PUBLISHING CO (DH)
Also Called: Lake County Record-Bee
2150 S Main St, Lakeport (95453-5620)
PHONE..................................707 263-5636
Edward Mead, *President*
EMP: 69
SALES (est): 5.2MM
SALES (corp-wide): 4.3B **Privately Held**
SIC: 2711 Newspapers, publishing & printing

(P-5908)
LAPRENSA SAN DIEGO
220 Glover Ave Apt E, Chula Vista (91910-2657)
PHONE..................................619 425-7400
Daniel Munoz, *Principal*
EMP: 10
SALES (est): 379.5K **Privately Held**
SIC: 2711 Newspapers, publishing & printing

(P-5909)
LATINA & ASSOCIATES INC (PA)
Also Called: El Latino Newspaper
1105 Broadway, Chula Vista (91911-2767)
P.O. Box 120550, San Diego (92112-0550)
PHONE..................................619 426-1491
Fanny Miller, *CEO*
EMP: 38 EST: 1985
SQ FT: 2,500
SALES (est): 2.3MM **Privately Held**
WEB: www.ellatino.net
SIC: 2711 Newspapers: publishing only, not printed on site

(P-5910)
LEE CENTRAL CAL NEWSPAPERS
Also Called: Selma Enterprise
2045 Grant St, Selma (93662-3508)
P.O. Box 100 (93662-0100)
PHONE..................................559 896-1976
Manuel Collazo, *Director*
EMP: 50

SALES (est): 2.2MM
SALES (corp-wide): 566.9MM **Publicly Held**
WEB: www.selmaenterprise.com
SIC: 2711 2752 Commercial printing & newspaper publishing combined; lithographing on metal
PA: Lee Enterprises, Incorporated
201 N Harrison St Ste 600
Davenport IA 52801
563 383-2100

(P-5911)
LEE ENTERPRISES INCORPORATED
Also Called: Santa Maria Times
3200 Skyway Dr, Santa Maria (93455-1824)
PHONE..................................805 925-2691
Cynthia Schur, *Manager*
Claudio Delgado, *General Mgr*
Danyelle Chavez, *Accounts Exec*
EMP: 140
SALES (corp-wide): 566.9MM **Publicly Held**
WEB: www.lee.net
SIC: 2711 Commercial printing & newspaper publishing combined
PA: Lee Enterprises, Incorporated
201 N Harrison St Ste 600
Davenport IA 52801
563 383-2100

(P-5912)
LELAND STANFORD JUNIOR UNIV
Also Called: Stanford University Press
500 Broadway St, Redwood City (94063-3199)
PHONE..................................650 723-9434
Geoffrey Burn, *Director*
Jean Kim, *Finance*
Jessica Ling, *Production*
Kendra Schynert, *Marketing Staff*
Linda Stewart, *Marketing Staff*
EMP: 30
SALES (corp-wide): 5.6B **Privately Held**
SIC: 2711 2731 Newspapers; book publishing
PA: Leland Stanford Junior University
450 Serra Mall
Stanford CA 94305
650 723-2300

(P-5913)
LITTLE SAIGON NEWS INC
Also Called: Saigon Nho
13861 Seaboard Cir, Garden Grove (92843-3908)
PHONE..................................714 265-0800
Brigitte L Huynh, *CEO*
Brigitte Huynh, *President*
EMP: 18
SQ FT: 16,370
SALES (est): 1.6MM **Privately Held**
SIC: 2711 Newspapers

(P-5914)
LIVE JOURNAL INC
430 Main St, San Francisco (94105-2006)
PHONE..................................415 230-3600
Andrew Paulson, *President*
Steffanie Gravelle, *CFO*
Brenden Delzer, *Editor*
EMP: 33
SALES (est): 2.3MM **Privately Held**
SIC: 2711 Newspapers, publishing & printing

(P-5915)
LMG NATIONAL PUBLISHING INC
Also Called: Daily Press
13891 Park Ave, Victorville (92392-2435)
PHONE..................................760 241-7744
Albert Frattura, *Manager*
David Schrimpf, *Webmaster*
Mike Sipe, *Prdtn Mgr*
Cynthia McMeans, *Advt Staff*
Angela Callahan, *Director*
EMP: 100
SALES (corp-wide): 1.3B **Publicly Held**
SIC: 2711 2752 Newspapers, publishing & printing; commercial printing, lithographic

▲ = Import ▼=Export
◆ =Import/Export

HQ: Lmg National Publishing, Inc.
350 Willowbrook Office Pa
Fairport NY 14450
585 598-6874

(P-5916)
LODI NEWS SENTINEL
Also Called: Lodi Mail Express
125 N Church St, Lodi (95240-2197)
P.O. Box 1360 (95241-1360)
PHONE..................................209 369-2761
Frederick E Weybret, *Ch of Bd*
Alcyon Weybret, *Shareholder*
James Weybret, *Shareholder*
Martin Weybret, *President*
Matt Wilson, *Editor*
▲ EMP: 90
SQ FT: 19,000
SALES (est): 5.5MM **Privately Held**
WEB: www.lodinews.com
SIC: 2711 Commercial printing & newspa-
per publishing combined; newspapers,
publishing & printing

(P-5917)
LOS ANGELES SENTINEL INC
Also Called: La Sentinel Newspaper
3800 Crenshaw Blvd, Los Angeles
(90008-1813)
PHONE..................................323 299-3800
Jennifer Thomas, *President*
Brik Booker, *CEO*
EMP: 51 EST: 1933
SALES (est): 4.2MM **Privately Held**
WEB: www.losangelessentinel.com
SIC: 2711 Newspapers: publishing only,
not printed on site

(P-5918)
**LOS ANGLES TMES
CMMNCTIONS LLC (PA)**
2300 E Imperial Hwy, El Segundo
(90245-2813)
PHONE..................................213 237-5000
Ross Levinsohn, *CEO*
Don Reis, *Officer*
Crane Kenney, *Vice Pres*
Scott McKibben,
▲ EMP: 190
SQ FT: 162,000
SALES (est): 769.2MM **Privately Held**
WEB: www.latimes.com
SIC: 2711 Newspapers, publishing & print-
ing

(P-5919)
**LOS ANGLES TMES
CMMNCTIONS LLC**
1717 4th St Ste 100, Santa Monica
(90401-3319)
PHONE..................................310 450-6666
Greg Bertness, *Manager*
Karen Melick, *Project Mgr*
EMP: 100
SQ FT: 4,000
SALES (corp-wide): 769.2MM **Privately
Held**
SIC: 2711 Newspapers
PA: Los Angeles Times Communications,
Llc
2300 E Imperial Hwy
El Segundo CA 90245
213 237-5000

(P-5920)
**LOS ANGLES TMES
CMMNCTIONS LLC**
1245 S Longwood Ave, Los Angeles
(90019-1759)
PHONE..................................213 237-7203
John Madigan, *Branch Mgr*
EMP: 115
SALES (corp-wide): 769.2MM **Privately
Held**
SIC: 2711 Newspapers, publishing & print-
ing
PA: Los Angeles Times Communications,
Llc
2300 E Imperial Hwy
El Segundo CA 90245
213 237-5000

(P-5921)
**LOS ANGLES TMES
CMMNCTIONS LLC**
10540 Talbert Ave 300w, Fountain Valley
(92708-6027)
P.O. Box 2008, Costa Mesa (92628-2008)
PHONE..................................714 966-5600
Judith L Sweeney, *President*
Ronald Nickerson, *Opers Staff*
EMP: 411
SQ FT: 60,000
SALES (corp-wide): 769.2MM **Privately
Held**
SIC: 2711 Newspapers: publishing only,
not printed on site
PA: Los Angeles Times Communications,
Llc
2300 E Imperial Hwy
El Segundo CA 90245
213 237-5000

(P-5922)
**LOS ANGLES TMES
CMMNCTIONS LLC**
Also Called: Glendale Times
1011 E Wilson Ave Fl 2, Glendale
(91206-4535)
PHONE..................................818 637-3203
Judee Kendall, *General Mgr*
EMP: 65
SALES (corp-wide): 769.2MM **Privately
Held**
SIC: 2711 Newspapers, publishing & print-
ing
PA: Los Angeles Times Communications,
Llc
2300 E Imperial Hwy
El Segundo CA 90245
213 237-5000

(P-5923)
**LOS ANGLES TMES
CMMNCTIONS LLC**
705 Pine St, Paso Robles (93446-2860)
PHONE..................................805 238-2720
EMP: 37
SALES (corp-wide): 769.2MM **Privately
Held**
SIC: 2711 Newspapers
PA: Los Angeles Times Communications,
Llc
2300 E Imperial Hwy
El Segundo CA 90245
213 237-5000

(P-5924)
**LOS ANGLES TMES
CMMNCTIONS LLC**
388 Market St Ste 1550, San Francisco
(94111-5355)
PHONE..................................415 274-9000
EMP: 13
SALES (corp-wide): 769.2MM **Privately
Held**
SIC: 2711
PA: Los Angeles Times Communications,
Llc
2300 E Imperial Hwy
El Segundo CA 90245
213 237-5000

(P-5925)
**LOS ANGLES TMES
CMMNCTIONS LLC**
Also Called: La Canada Valley Sun
1061 Valley Sun Ln, La Canada Flintridge
(91011-3283)
P.O. Box 38, La Canada (91012-0038)
PHONE..................................818 790-8774
Carol Cormacie, *Manager*
Olga Albarado, *Controller*
Elaine Zinngrabe, *Publisher*
EMP: 35
SALES (corp-wide): 769.2MM **Privately
Held**
SIC: 2711 Newspapers: publishing only,
not printed on site
PA: Los Angeles Times Communications,
Llc
2300 E Imperial Hwy
El Segundo CA 90245
213 237-5000

(P-5926)
**LOS ANGLES TMES
CMMNCTIONS LLC**
10427 San Sevaine Way E, Mira Loma
(91752-1151)
PHONE..................................951 683-6066
Darlene Masi, *Branch Mgr*
EMP: 38
SALES (corp-wide): 769.2MM **Privately
Held**
SIC: 2711 Newspapers
PA: Los Angeles Times Communications,
Llc
2300 E Imperial Hwy
El Segundo CA 90245
213 237-5000

(P-5927)
**LOS ANGLES TMES
CMMNCTIONS LLC**
Also Called: Lats International
145 S Spring St, Los Angeles
(90012-4053)
PHONE..................................213 237-7987
Jesse E Levine, *President*
EMP: 30
SALES (corp-wide): 769.2MM **Privately
Held**
SIC: 2711 2741
PA: Los Angeles Times Communications,
Llc
2300 E Imperial Hwy
El Segundo CA 90245
213 237-5000

(P-5928)
**LOS ANGLES TMES
CMMNCTIONS LLC**
Also Called: L A Times Olympic Plant
2000 E 8th St, Los Angeles (90021-2474)
PHONE..................................213 237-5691
EMP: 240
SALES (corp-wide): 769.2MM **Privately
Held**
SIC: 2711 Newspapers, publishing & print-
ing
PA: Los Angeles Times Communications,
Llc
2300 E Imperial Hwy
El Segundo CA 90245
213 237-5000

(P-5929)
**LOS ANGLES TMES
CMMNCTIONS LLC**
5091 4th St, Baldwin Park (91706-2173)
PHONE..................................909 980-3707
Victor Depalma, *Sales/Mktg Mgr*
John Silver, *Project Mgr*
EMP: 20
SALES (corp-wide): 769.2MM **Privately
Held**
SIC: 2711 2741 Newspapers, publishing &
printing; miscellaneous publishing
PA: Los Angeles Times Communications,
Llc
2300 E Imperial Hwy
El Segundo CA 90245
213 237-5000

(P-5930)
**LOS ANGLES TMES
CMMNCTIONS LLC**
Also Called: Donald Tyler Latimes Agency 14
5555 Ontario Mills Pkwy F, Ontario
(91764-5102)
P.O. Box 265, Claremont (91711-0265)
PHONE..................................909 980-3707
Don Tyler, *Manager*
EMP: 42
SALES (corp-wide): 769.2MM **Privately
Held**
SIC: 2711 2741 Newspapers, publishing &
printing; miscellaneous publishing
PA: Los Angeles Times Communications,
Llc
2300 E Imperial Hwy
El Segundo CA 90245
213 237-5000

(P-5931)
**LOS ANGLES TMES
CMMNCTIONS LLC**
2001 E Cashdan St, Compton
(90220-6438)
PHONE..................................310 638-9414
Sandy Sao, *Manager*
EMP: 14
SALES (corp-wide): 769.2MM **Privately
Held**
SIC: 2711 Newspapers, publishing & print-
ing
PA: Los Angeles Times Communications,
Llc
2300 E Imperial Hwy
El Segundo CA 90245
213 237-5000

(P-5932)
**MADERA PRINTING & PUBG CO
INC**
2890 Falcon Dr, Madera (93637-9287)
PHONE..................................559 674-2424
Charles P Doud, *President*
EMP: 35
SQ FT: 15,000
SALES (est): 1.7MM **Privately Held**
WEB: www.maderatribune.net
SIC: 2711 Newspapers

(P-5933)
**MAINSTREET MEDIA GROUP
LLC**
6400 Monterey Rd, Gilroy (95020-6628)
P.O. Box 516 (95021-0516)
PHONE..................................408 842-6400
Anthony A Allegretti, *CEO*
Stephen P Staloch, *COO*
Christopher L Lake, *CFO*
Dana Arvig, *Vice Pres*
EMP: 180
SQ FT: 25,000
SALES (est): 10.5MM **Privately Held**
WEB: www.mainstreetmediagroup.com
SIC: 2711 Newspapers, publishing & print-
ing

(P-5934)
MALIBU ENTERPRISES INC
Also Called: Surfside News
28990 Pacific Coast Hwy # 108, Malibu
(90265-3952)
P.O. Box 6854 (90264-6854)
PHONE..................................310 457-2112
Anne C Soble, *President*
EMP: 24
SQ FT: 2,100
SALES (est): 108.9K **Privately Held**
SIC: 2711 5994 Newspapers: publishing
only, not printed on site; news dealers &
newsstands

(P-5935)
MALIBU TIMES INC
3864 Las Flores Canyon Rd, Malibu
(90265-5295)
P.O. Box 1127 (90265-1127)
PHONE..................................310 456-5507
Arnold York, *President*
Karen York, *Vice Pres*
Bridget Gungoren, *Assistant*
EMP: 15
SQ FT: 2,000
SALES (est): 1.1MM **Privately Held**
WEB: www.malibutimes.com
SIC: 2711 Newspapers: publishing only,
not printed on site

(P-5936)
MAMMOTH MEDIA INC
1447 2nd St, Santa Monica (90401-3404)
PHONE..................................310 393-3024
Benoit Vatere, *CEO*
Mike Jones, *Chairman*
EMP: 64 EST: 2016
SALES (est): 1.9MM **Privately Held**
SIC: 2711 Newspapers

(P-5937)
MANNIS COMMUNICATIONS INC
Also Called: The Beacon
1621 Grand Ave Ste C, San Diego
(92109-4458)
PHONE..................................858 270-3103
Julie M Hoisington, *CEO*

(PA)=Parent Co (HQ)=Headquarters (DH)=Div Headquarters
✿ = New Business established in last 2 years

2019 California
Manufacturers Register

249

P R O D U C T S & S V C S

David Mannis, *President*
EMP: 25
SALES (est): 1.4MM **Privately Held**
SIC: 2711 Newspapers

(P-5938)
MANNIS COMMUNICATIONS INC
Also Called: San Diego Cmnty Newsppr Group
4645 Caca St Fl 2 Flr 2, San Diego (92109)
PHONE..................858 270-3103
David Mannis, *President*
Julie Mannis, *Vice Pres*
EMP: 35
SQ FT: 3,000
SALES (est): 1.9MM **Privately Held**
WEB: www.sdnews.com
SIC: 2711 Newspapers: publishing only, not printed on site

(P-5939)
MARIN SCOPE INCORPORATED
Also Called: Marin Scope Newspapers
1301b Grant Ave, Novato (94945-3143)
P.O. Box 8 (94948-0008)
PHONE..................415 892-1516
Dijay Mallya, *Principal*
Vijay Mallya, *President*
EMP: 20
SQ FT: 3,400
SALES (est): 1.2MM **Privately Held**
WEB: www.marinscope.com
SIC: 2711 Newspapers, publishing & printing

(P-5940)
MARIN SCOPE INCORPORATED
Also Called: San Rfl-Trra Linda Newspointer
700 Larkspur Landing Cir, Larkspur (94939-1715)
P.O. Box 1689, Sausalito (94966-1689)
PHONE..................415 892-1516
Paul A Anderson, *President*
John Igan, *Principal*
EMP: 29 **EST:** 1971
SQ FT: 6,000
SALES (est): 1.4MM **Privately Held**
SIC: 2711 Newspapers, publishing & printing

(P-5941)
MARIPOSA GAZETTE & MINER
Also Called: Mountain Life
5180 Hwy 140 Ste B, Mariposa (95338)
PHONE..................209 966-2500
Robert Daniel Tucker, *Owner*
Nicole Little, *Office Mgr*
Shantel Sojka, *Sales Staff*
Greg Little, *Editor*
Dan Tucker, *Publisher*
EMP: 12
SQ FT: 3,000
SALES (est): 612.4K **Privately Held**
SIC: 2711 Newspapers, publishing & printing

(P-5942)
MARKETING BULLETIN BOARD
639 Olive Rd, Santa Barbara (93108-1442)
PHONE..................805 455-2255
Walter E Owen III, *Principal*
Walter Owen, *Principal*
EMP: 10 **EST:** 2008
SALES (est): 634.3K **Privately Held**
SIC: 2711 Newspapers, publishing & printing

(P-5943)
MCCLATCHY COMPANY (PA)
2100 Q St, Sacramento (95816-6816)
P.O. Box 15779 (95852-0779)
PHONE..................916 321-1844
Craig I Forman, *President*
Kevin S McClatchy, *Ch of Bd*
Elaine Lintecum, *CFO*
Terrance Geiger, *Vice Pres*
Tim Grieve, *Vice Pres*
EMP: 209
SALES: 903.5MM **Publicly Held**
WEB: www.mcclatchy.com
SIC: 2711 Newspapers: publishing only, not printed on site

(P-5944)
MCCLATCHY NEWSPAPERS INC (HQ)
Also Called: Sacramento Bee
2100 Q St, Sacramento (95816-6899)
P.O. Box 15779 (95852-0779)
PHONE..................916 321-1855
Erwin Potts, *Ch of Bd*
James P Smith, *Treasurer*
Jamileh Smith, *Controller*
Betty Lou Maloney, *Asst Sec*
William Ellery Mc Clatchy, *Asst Sec*
▲ **EMP:** 2500
SALES (est): 1.1B
SALES (corp-wide): 903.5MM **Publicly Held**
WEB: www.sacbee.com
SIC: 2711 2759 7375 Newspapers, publishing & printing; commercial printing; online data base information retrieval
PA: The Mcclatchy Company
2100 Q St
Sacramento CA 95816
916 321-1844

(P-5945)
MCCLATCHY NEWSPAPERS INC
Fresno Bee, The
1626 E St, Fresno (93706-2006)
P.O. Box 11016 (93771-1016)
PHONE..................559 441-6111
William Fleet, *Publisher*
Ken Hatfield, *Vice Pres*
Keith Buchanan, *Info Tech Mgr*
Carlos Davidson, *Technology*
Frank Lamonski, *Engineer*
EMP: 300
SQ FT: 80,000
SALES (corp-wide): 903.5MM **Publicly Held**
WEB: www.sacbee.com
SIC: 2711 Newspapers, publishing & printing
HQ: Mcclatchy Newspapers, Inc.
2100 Q St
Sacramento CA 95816
916 321-1855

(P-5946)
MCCLATCHY NEWSPAPERS INC
Also Called: Modesto Bee, The
948 11th St Ste 30, Modesto (95354-2340)
P.O. Box 11986, Fresno (93776-1986)
PHONE..................209 578-2007
Karen Ruho, *Branch Mgr*
Juanita Toth, *Natl Sales Mgr*
Kyndal Dunbar, *Consultant*
EMP: 18
SALES (corp-wide): 903.5MM **Publicly Held**
SIC: 2711 Newspapers, publishing & printing
HQ: Mcclatchy Newspapers, Inc.
2100 Q St
Sacramento CA 95816
916 321-1855

(P-5947)
MCCLATCHY NEWSPAPERS INC
Also Called: El Sol
1325 H St, Modesto (95354-2427)
P.O. Box 3928 (95352-3928)
PHONE..................209 238-4636
Olivia Ruiz, *Manager*
EMP: 500
SALES (corp-wide): 903.5MM **Publicly Held**
WEB: www.sacbee.com
SIC: 2711 Newspapers, publishing & printing
HQ: Mcclatchy Newspapers, Inc.
2100 Q St
Sacramento CA 95816
916 321-1855

(P-5948)
MCCLATCHY NEWSPAPERS INC
Also Called: Los Banos Enterprise
907 6th St, Los Banos (93635-4215)
PHONE..................209 826-3831
Gene Lieb, *Manager*
EMP: 95
SALES (corp-wide): 903.5MM **Publicly Held**
WEB: www.sacbee.com
SIC: 2711 Newspapers, publishing & printing

HQ: Mcclatchy Newspapers, Inc.
2100 Q St
Sacramento CA 95816
916 321-1855

(P-5949)
MCCLATCHY NEWSPAPERS INC
Also Called: Merced Sun Star
3033 G St, Merced (95340-2108)
PHONE..................209 722-1511
Allen Portman, *Manager*
EMP: 140
SALES (corp-wide): 903.5MM **Publicly Held**
WEB: www.sacbee.com
SIC: 2711 2759 7375 Newspapers, publishing & printing; commercial printing; online data base information retrieval
HQ: Mcclatchy Newspapers, Inc.
2100 Q St
Sacramento CA 95816
916 321-1855

(P-5950)
MCCLATCHY NEWSPAPERS INC
Also Called: Modesto Bee Circulation
948 11th St Ste 30, Modesto (95354-2340)
P.O. Box 5256 (95352-5256)
PHONE..................209 587-2250
Wes Horan, *Manager*
EMP: 300
SALES (corp-wide): 903.5MM **Publicly Held**
WEB: www.sacbee.com
SIC: 2711 2721 Newspapers, publishing & printing; periodicals
HQ: Mcclatchy Newspapers, Inc.
2100 Q St
Sacramento CA 95816
916 321-1855

(P-5951)
MCCLATCHY NEWSPAPERS INC
Also Called: Cambrian
2068 Main St, Cambria (93428-3014)
PHONE..................805 927-8652
Bert Etling, *Branch Mgr*
EMP: 95
SALES (corp-wide): 903.5MM **Publicly Held**
WEB: www.sacbee.com
SIC: 2711 Newspapers, publishing & printing
HQ: Mcclatchy Newspapers, Inc.
2100 Q St
Sacramento CA 95816
916 321-1855

(P-5952)
MCCLATCHY NEWSPAPERS INC
Also Called: Silicon Vly Cmnty Newspapers
4 N 2nd St Ste 800, San Jose (95113-1317)
PHONE..................408 200-1000
David Cohen, *Principal*
EMP: 68
SALES (corp-wide): 903.5MM **Publicly Held**
WEB: www.sacbee.com
SIC: 2711 Newspapers, publishing & printing
HQ: Mcclatchy Newspapers, Inc.
2100 Q St
Sacramento CA 95816
916 321-1855

(P-5953)
MCCLATCHY NEWSPAPERS INC
Also Called: San Luis Tribune
3825 S Higuera St, San Luis Obispo (93401-7438)
P.O. Box 112 (93406-0112)
PHONE..................805 781-7800
Paso Robles, *Branch Mgr*
James Morgan, *Manager*
EMP: 180
SALES (corp-wide): 903.5MM **Publicly Held**
WEB: www.sacbee.com
SIC: 2711 Newspapers, publishing & printing
HQ: Mcclatchy Newspapers, Inc.
2100 Q St
Sacramento CA 95816
916 321-1855

(P-5954)
MCNAUGHTON NEWSPAPERS
Also Called: D Davis Enterprise
315 G St, Davis (95616-4119)
P.O. Box 1470 (95617-1470)
PHONE..................530 756-0800
Foy McNaughton, *Owner*
Richard B Mc Naughton, *Admin Sec*
Linda Dubois, *Accounting Dir*
Shelley Butler, *Human Resources*
Debbie Kennedy, *Sales Staff*
EMP: 60
SALES (est): 3.8MM **Privately Held**
WEB: www.davisenterprise.com
SIC: 2711 Commercial printing & newspaper publishing combined; newspapers, publishing & printing

(P-5955)
MCNAUGHTON NEWSPAPERS INC (PA)
Also Called: Daily Republic
1250 Texas St, Fairfield (94533-5748)
P.O. Box 47 (94533-0747)
PHONE..................707 425-4646
Foy Mc Naughton, *President*
R Burt Mc Naughton, *Corp Secy*
▲ **EMP:** 99 **EST:** 1855
SQ FT: 35,000
SALES (est): 13MM **Privately Held**
WEB: www.dailyrepublic.com
SIC: 2711 Commercial printing & newspaper publishing combined; newspapers, publishing & printing

(P-5956)
MEDIA NEWS GROUP
Also Called: Willits News
77 W Commercial St, Willits (95490-3021)
P.O. Box 628 (95490-0628)
PHONE..................707 459-4643
Kevin McConnell, *President*
Edward Burton, *Vice Pres*
Dan McKee, *Editor*
EMP: 10
SQ FT: 4,000
SALES (est): 659K
SALES (corp-wide): 4.3B **Privately Held**
WEB: www.willitsnews.com
SIC: 2711 Commercial printing & newspaper publishing combined; newspapers, publishing & printing
HQ: Medianews Group, Inc.
101 W Colfax Ave Ste 1100
Denver CO 80202

(P-5957)
MEDIANEWS GROUP INC
Long Beach Press-Telegram
300 Oceangate Ste 150, Long Beach (90802-6801)
PHONE..................562 435-1161
Barbie Brodeur, *Branch Mgr*
Tom Kelly, *Officer*
Tom Moore, *Executive*
EMP: 99
SALES (corp-wide): 4.3B **Privately Held**
SIC: 2711 Newspapers
HQ: Medianews Group, Inc.
101 W Colfax Ave Ste 1100
Denver CO 80202

(P-5958)
MEDIANEWS GROUP INC
Also Called: Daily News
21860 Burbank Blvd # 200, Woodland Hills (91367-6477)
P.O. Box 4200 (91365-4200)
PHONE..................818 713-3000
Douglas Hanes, *Publisher*
Gloria Arango, *Vice Pres*
Jim Vita, *Opers Mgr*
Carin Coonrod, *Sales Staff*
Mike Mariano, *Sales Staff*
EMP: 700
SALES (corp-wide): 4.3B **Privately Held**
SIC: 2711 Newspapers
HQ: Medianews Group, Inc.
101 W Colfax Ave Ste 1100
Denver CO 80202

(P-5959)
MEDIANEWS GROUP INC
Also Called: Daily Breeze
5215 Torrance Blvd, Torrance
(90503-4009)
PHONE...................310 540-5511
Michael J Koren, *Vice Pres*
Sean McHugh, *Vice Pres*
EMP: 157
SALES (corp-wide): 4.3B Privately Held
SIC: 2711 Newspapers
HQ: Medianews Group, Inc.
    101 W Colfax Ave Ste 1100
    Denver CO 80202

(P-5960)
MEDIANEWS GROUP INC
Also Called: Convertly
4 N 2nd St Ste 800, San Jose
(95113-1317)
PHONE...................408 920-5713
Michael Koren, *CFO*
EMP: 500
SALES (corp-wide): 4.3B Privately Held
SIC: 2711 Newspapers, publishing & print-
ing
HQ: Medianews Group, Inc.
    101 W Colfax Ave Ste 1100
    Denver CO 80202

(P-5961)
MEDIANEWS GROUP INC
Also Called: Daily News
255 Constitution Dr, Menlo Park
(94025-1108)
PHONE...................650 391-1000
Nisook Lee, *Branch Mgr*
EMP: 157
SALES (corp-wide): 4.3B Privately Held
WEB: www.sacbee.com
SIC: 2711 Newspapers
HQ: Medianews Group, Inc.
    101 W Colfax Ave Ste 1100
    Denver CO 80202

(P-5962)
MEDIANEWS GROUP INC
Also Called: Daily Democrat, The
711 Main St, Woodland (95695-3406)
P.O. Box 730 (95776-0730)
PHONE...................530 662-5421
John Fenric, *General Mgr*
EMP: 30
SALES (corp-wide): 4.3B Privately Held
WEB: www.fortsmith.com
SIC: 2711 Newspapers, publishing & print-
ing
HQ: Medianews Group, Inc.
    101 W Colfax Ave Ste 1100
    Denver CO 80202

(P-5963)
MEDIANEWS GROUP INC
Also Called: Daily News
24800 Ave Rockefeller, Valencia
(91355-3467)
P.O. Box 4200, Woodland Hills (91365-
4200)
PHONE...................661 257-5200
Gene Janski, *Manager*
EMP: 200
SALES (corp-wide): 4.3B Privately Held
SIC: 2711 2752
HQ: Medianews Group, Inc.
    101 W Colfax Ave Ste 1100
    Denver CO 80202

(P-5964)
MEDIANEWS GROUP INC
14913 Lakeshore Dr, Clearlake
(95422-8503)
PHONE...................707 994-6656
EMP: 157
SALES (corp-wide): 4.3B Privately Held
SIC: 2711 Newspapers
HQ: Medianews Group, Inc.
    101 W Colfax Ave Ste 1100
    Denver CO 80202

(P-5965)
MEDIANEWS GROUP INC
Also Called: Red Bluff Daily News
728 Main St, Red Bluff (96080-3342)
PHONE...................530 527-2151
Jay Harn, *Principal*
EMP: 35
SALES (corp-wide): 4.3B Privately Held
WEB: www.fortsmith.com
SIC: 2711 2752 Newspapers, publishing &
printing; commercial printing, lithographic
HQ: Medianews Group, Inc.
    101 W Colfax Ave Ste 1100
    Denver CO 80202

(P-5966)
MEDLEYCOM INCORPORATED
Also Called: Adultfriendfinder
910 E Hamilton Ave Fl 6, Campbell
(95008-0655)
PHONE...................408 745-5418
Anthony Previte, *CEO*
Marlene Flores, *Opers Staff*
EMP: 19
SALES (est): 1.5MM Privately Held
SIC: 2711 Newspapers, publishing & print-
ing

(P-5967)
METRO PUBLISHING INC
Also Called: Metro Santa Cruz Newspaper
1205 Pacific Ave Ste 301, Santa Cruz
(95060-3936)
PHONE...................831 457-9000
Debra Whizin, *Manager*
EMP: 15
SALES (corp-wide): 10MM Privately
Held
WEB: www.metcruz.com
SIC: 2711 Newspapers, publishing & print-
ing
PA: Metro Publishing, Inc.
    380 S 1st St
    San Jose CA
    408 298-8000

(P-5968)
METRO PUBLISHING INC
Also Called: Metrosa
847 5th St, Santa Rosa (95404-4526)
PHONE...................707 527-1200
Rosemary Olson, *Manager*
EMP: 13
SALES (corp-wide): 10MM Privately
Held
WEB: www.metcruz.com
SIC: 2711 8611 Newspapers, publishing &
printing; business associations
PA: Metro Publishing, Inc.
    380 S 1st St
    San Jose CA
    408 298-8000

(P-5969)
METROPOLITAN NEWS COMPANY
Also Called: Riverside Bulletin & Jurupa Th
3540 12th St, Riverside (92501-3802)
P.O. Box 60859, Los Angeles (90060-0859)
PHONE...................951 369-5890
Roger Gray, *President*
EMP: 29 EST: 1998
SALES (est): 536.6K Privately Held
SIC: 2711 Newspapers

(P-5970)
MID VALLEY PUBLICATION
Also Called: Merced County Times
2221 K St, Merced (95340-3868)
PHONE...................209 383-0433
John Derby, *President*
EMP: 25
SQ FT: 1,238
SALES (est): 732.3K Privately Held
SIC: 2711 Newspapers, publishing & print-
ing

(P-5971)
MIDVALLEY PUBLISHING INC
Also Called: Orange Cove Mountain Times
1130 G St, Reedley (93654-3004)
P.O. Box 432 (93654-0432)
PHONE...................559 638-2244
Fred Hall, *President*
Janie Lucio, *Advt Staff*

Beth Warmerdam, *Editor*
EMP: 35
SALES (est): 2.1MM Privately Held
SIC: 2711 Newspapers, publishing & print-
ing

(P-5972)
MIDVALLEY PUBLISHING INC
Also Called: Fowler Ensinger
740 N St, Sanger (93657-3114)
PHONE...................559 875-2511
Fred Hall, *President*
Pete Penner, *Ch of Bd*
Floyd Barsoon, *Treasurer*
Norma Hage, *Vice Pres*
Rosemary Kallio, *Admin Sec*
EMP: 25
SQ FT: 5,650
SALES (est): 1.4MM Privately Held
SIC: 2711 2752 Newspapers, publishing &
printing; commercial printing, lithographic

(P-5973)
MILPITAS POST NEWSPAPERS INC
59 Marylinn Dr, Milpitas (95035-4311)
PHONE...................408 262-2454
Rob Devincenzi, *Principal*
EMP: 13
SALES (est): 672.7K Privately Held
SIC: 2711 Newspapers

(P-5974)
MLIM LLC
350 Camino De La Reina, San Diego
(92108-3003)
PHONE...................619 299-3131
Douglas Manchester, *Chairman*
John Lynch, *CEO*
Ryan Kiesel, *CFO*
EMP: 766
SALES (est): 143.3MM
SALES (corp-wide): 1.5B Publicly Held
SIC: 2711 Newspapers, publishing & print-
ing
PA: Tribune Publishing Company
    435 N Michigan Ave
    Chicago IL 60611
    312 222-9100

(P-5975)
MODERN TIMES BEER
3000 Upas St Ste 102, San Diego
(92104-4221)
PHONE...................619 269-5222
E Mondola, *General Mgr*
Elizabeth Mondola, *General Mgr*
EMP: 45
SALES (est): 535K Privately Held
SIC: 2711 Newspapers

(P-5976)
MONTEREY COUNTY HERALD COMPANY (DH)
Also Called: Monterey Herald
2200 Garden Rd, Monterey (93940-5329)
P.O. Box 271 (93942-0271)
PHONE...................831 372-3311
Gary Omerick, *Publisher*
Mardi Browning, *Director*
Davide V Leal, *Manager*
Larry Parsons, *Relations*
Mike Hale, *Publisher*
EMP: 30
SQ FT: 60,000
SALES (est): 11.2MM
SALES (corp-wide): 4.3B Privately Held
SIC: 2711 Commercial printing & newspa-
per publishing combined; newspapers,
publishing & printing

(P-5977)
MONTEREY COUNTY WEEKLY
Also Called: Exchange, The
668 Williams Ave, Seaside (93955-5736)
PHONE...................831 393-3348
Bradley Zeve, *President*
Arno Featherstone, *Executive*
George Kassal, *Executive*
Kevin Smith, *Director*
Susan Diallo, *Manager*
EMP: 22
SQ FT: 3,300

SALES (est): 1.5MM Privately Held
WEB: www.montereycountyweekly.com
SIC: 2711 2791 Newspapers: publishing
only, not printed on site; typesetting

(P-5978)
MOONSHINE INK
10137 Riverside Dr, Truckee (96161-0303)
P.O. Box 4003 (96160-4403)
PHONE...................530 587-3607
Mayumi Elegado, *Owner*
Kara Fox, *Assoc Editor*
Ally Gravina, *Assoc Editor*
Melissa V Siig, *Assoc Editor*
Jeremy Jensen, *Editor*
EMP: 20
SALES (est): 615.9K Privately Held
SIC: 2711 Newspapers

(P-5979)
MORRIS MULTIMEDIA INC
Also Called: Signal Newspaper, The
24000 Creekside Rd, Santa Clarita
(91355-1726)
P.O. Box 801870 (91380-1870)
PHONE...................661 259-1234
Jay Harn, *Branch Mgr*
EMP: 100
SALES (corp-wide): 313.5MM Privately
Held
WEB: www.morrismultimedia.com
SIC: 2711 Newspapers: publishing only,
not printed on site
PA: Morris Multimedia, Inc.
    27 Abercorn St
    Savannah GA 31401
    912 233-1281

(P-5980)
MORRIS NEWSPAPER CORP CAL (HQ)
Also Called: Manteca Bulletin
531 E Yosemite Ave, Manteca
(95336-5806)
P.O. Box 1958 (95336-1156)
PHONE...................209 249-3500
Jennifer Merrick, *Director*
Dennis Wyatt, *Director*
EMP: 65
SQ FT: 8,000
SALES (est): 5.8MM
SALES (corp-wide): 313.5MM Privately
Held
WEB: www.mantecabulletin.com
SIC: 2711 6531 Newspapers, publishing &
printing; real estate agents & managers
PA: Morris Multimedia, Inc.
    27 Abercorn St
    Savannah GA 31401
    912 233-1281

(P-5981)
MORRIS PUBLICATIONS (PA)
Also Called: Advertiser, The
122 S 3rd Ave, Oakdale (95361-3935)
P.O. Box 278 (95361-0278)
PHONE...................209 847-3021
Drew Savage, *General Mgr*
EMP: 40 EST: 1888
SQ FT: 5,000
SALES (est): 3.1MM Privately Held
WEB: www.oakdaleleader.com
SIC: 2711 2752 8999 Commercial printing
& newspaper publishing combined; photo-
offset printing; newspaper column writing

(P-5982)
MOTHER LODE PRINTING & PUBG CO
Also Called: Mountain Democrat
2889 Ray Lawyer Dr, Placerville
(95667-3914)
PHONE...................530 344-5030
James Webb, *Publisher*
Richard Esposito, *General Mgr*
Susie Graunstadt, *Advt Staff*
Jon Meyer, *Sales Staff*
Letty Baumgardner, *Manager*
EMP: 74 EST: 1851
SQ FT: 19,400
SALES (est): 3.8MM Privately Held
WEB: www.mtdemocrat.com
SIC: 2711 Commercial printing & newspa-
per publishing combined

(P-5983)
MOUNT ROSE PUBLISHING CO INC
Also Called: Sierra Sun Newspaper
10775 Pioneer Trl, Truckee (96161-0232)
P.O. Box 2973 (96160-2973)
PHONE..................................530 587-6061
Jody Poe, *Manager*
Ben Rogers, *Advt Staff*
EMP: 10
SALES (est): 468.7K
SALES (corp-wide): 808.7K **Privately Held**
WEB: www.tahoeworld.com
SIC: 2711 Newspapers: publishing only, not printed on site
PA: Mount Rose Publishing Co Inc
395 N Lake Blvd Ste A
Tahoe City CA 96145
530 583-3487

(P-5984)
MOUNT ROSE PUBLISHING CO INC (PA)
Also Called: Tahoe World
395 N Lake Blvd Ste A, Tahoe City (96145)
PHONE..................................530 583-3487
Scott McElhaney, *President*
EMP: 12
SQ FT: 1,350
SALES (est): 808.7K **Privately Held**
WEB: www.tahoeworld.com
SIC: 2711 Newspapers: publishing only, not printed on site

(P-5985)
MOUNTAIN VIEW VOICE
450 Cambridge Ave, Palo Alto (94306-1507)
P.O. Box 405, Mountain View (94042-0405)
PHONE..................................650 326-8210
William Johnson, *President*
EMP: 40
SALES (est): 1.1MM **Privately Held**
WEB: www.mv-voice.com
SIC: 2711 Newspapers, publishing & printing

(P-5986)
MY BURBANKCOM INC
10061 Rverside Dr Ste 520, Toluca Lake (91602)
PHONE..................................818 842-2140
Craig Sherwood, *President*
EMP: 10
SALES (est): 130.6K **Privately Held**
SIC: 2711 Newspapers, publishing & printing

(P-5987)
NAPA VALLEY PUBLISHING CO
Also Called: NAPA Valley Register
1615 Soscol Ave, NAPA (94559-1901)
PHONE..................................707 226-3711
Carson Pierce, *Director*
Tracy Hardee, *Data Proc Staff*
Michael Donnelly, *Editor*
Sean Scully, *Editor*
Jl Sousa, *Editor*
EMP: 74
SALES (corp-wide): 10.1MM **Privately Held**
SIC: 2711 Newspapers: publishing only, not printed on site
PA: Napa Valley Publishing Co
1615 Soscol Ave
Napa CA 94559
707 226-3711

(P-5988)
NAPA VALLEY PUBLISHING CO (PA)
Also Called: NAPA Register
1615 Soscol Ave, NAPA (94559-1901)
PHONE..................................707 226-3711
E W Scripps, *Ch of Bd*
Betty Knight Scripps, *Vice Chairman*
EMP: 26 EST: 1958
SALES (est): 10.1MM **Privately Held**
SIC: 2711 Newspapers: publishing only, not printed on site

(P-5989)
NATIONAL HOT ROD ASSOCIATION
Also Called: National Dragster Magazine
2035 E Financial Way, Glendora (91741-4602)
PHONE..................................626 250-2300
Adrian Pierson, *Manager*
EMP: 50
SALES (corp-wide): 99.2MM **Privately Held**
WEB: www.nhra.com
SIC: 2711 2721 Newspapers: publishing only, not printed on site; periodicals
PA: National Hot Rod Association
2035 E Financial Way
Glendora CA 91741
626 914-4761

(P-5990)
NATIONAL MEDIA INC (HQ)
Also Called: Beach Reporter
609 Deep Valley Dr # 200, Rllng HLS Est (90274-3629)
P.O. Box 2609, Pls Vrds Pnsl (90274-8609)
PHONE..................................310 377-6877
Stephen C Laxineta, *President*
Simon M Tam, *President*
William Dean Singleton, *CEO*
EMP: 30
SQ FT: 12,000
SALES (est): 5.4MM
SALES (corp-wide): 4.3B **Privately Held**
WEB: www.pvnews.com
SIC: 2711 Newspapers: publishing only, not printed on site
PA: Digital First Media, Llc
101 W Colfax Ave Fl 11
Denver CO 80202
212 257-7212

(P-5991)
NATIONAL MEDIA INC
Also Called: Beach Reporter, The
2615 Pcf Cast Hwy Ste 329, Hermosa Beach (90254)
PHONE..................................310 372-0388
Richard Frank, *Publisher*
Lisa Jacobs, *General Mgr*
Caren Weiner, *Sales Staff*
Michael Hixon, *Editor*
Jenifer Lemon, *Accounts Exec*
EMP: 24
SALES (corp-wide): 4.3B **Privately Held**
WEB: www.pvnews.com
SIC: 2711 Newspapers: publishing only, not printed on site
HQ: National Media, Inc.
609 Deep Valley Dr # 200
Rllng Hls Est CA 90274
310 377-6877

(P-5992)
NEVADA COUNTY PUBLISHING CO
Also Called: Union, The
464 Sutton Way, Grass Valley (95945-4102)
PHONE..................................530 273-9561
Jeff Akerman, *Publisher*
Becky Dirk, *CFO*
Mary Davis, *Social Dir*
Nathalia Carroll, *Design Engr*
Scott Coffey, *Opers Staff*
▼ EMP: 650
SQ FT: 13,000
SALES (est): 24.8MM
SALES (corp-wide): 137.7MM **Privately Held**
WEB: www.sierrasun.com
SIC: 2711 Newspapers, publishing & printing
PA: Swift Communications, Inc.
580 Mallory Way
Carson City NV 89701
775 850-7676

(P-5993)
NEW INCORPORATION NOW
12323 Imperial Hwy, Norwalk (90650-8304)
PHONE..................................562 484-3020
Lee Cantafio, *CEO*
EMP: 18
SALES (est): 663.6K **Privately Held**
SIC: 2711 8231 Newspapers, publishing & printing; documentation center

(P-5994)
NEWLON ROUGE LLC
Also Called: Santa Monica Daily Press
1640 5th St Ste 218, Santa Monica (90401-3325)
PHONE..................................310 458-7737
Ross Furukawa,
Jenny Medina, *Executive*
David Ganforth,
Carolyn Sackariason,
Matthew Hall, *Editor*
EMP: 12
SALES (est): 724.5K **Privately Held**
WEB: www.smdp.com
SIC: 2711 Commercial printing & newspaper publishing combined; newspapers, publishing & printing

(P-5995)
NEWS MEDIA CORPORATION
Also Called: Watsonvlle Register-Pajaronian
100 Westridge Dr, Watsonville (95076-6602)
PHONE..................................831 761-7300
Tom Cross, *Principal*
EMP: 55 **Privately Held**
WEB: www.newsmediacorporation.com
SIC: 2711 Newspapers, publishing & printing
PA: News Media Corporation
211 E Il Route 38
Rochelle IL 61068

(P-5996)
NEWS MEDIA INC
Also Called: Paso Robles Press
502 First St, Paso Robles (93446-3742)
P.O. Box 427 (93447-0427)
PHONE..................................805 237-6060
Richard D Reddick, *President*
Brian Williams, *General Mgr*
Sheri Potruch, *Marketing Staff*
Doug Monn, *Director*
Rachel Fox, *Manager*
EMP: 20 EST: 2000
SALES (est): 846.9K **Privately Held**
WEB: www.darlastephenson.com
SIC: 2711 Newspapers, publishing & printing

(P-5997)
NGUOI VIETNAMESE PEOPLE INC (PA)
Also Called: Nguoi Viet Newspaper
14771 Moran St, Westminster (92683-5553)
PHONE..................................714 892-9414
Dat Pham, *Chairman*
Hoang Tong, *CEO*
Dieu Le, *Vice Pres*
▲ EMP: 30
SQ FT: 10,000
SALES (est): 4.8MM **Privately Held**
WEB: www.nguoi-viet.com
SIC: 2711 5994 2741 Newspapers: publishing only, not printed on site; news dealers & newsstands; miscellaneous publishing

(P-5998)
NORTH COAST JOURNAL INC
310 F St, Eureka (95501-1006)
PHONE..................................707 442-1400
Judy Hodgson, *President*
Carolyn Fernandez, *Vice Pres*
Chuck Leifhman, *General Mgr*
Carmen England, *Bookkeeper*
Holly Harvey, *Production*
EMP: 18
SALES (est): 1.3MM **Privately Held**
WEB: www.northcoastjournal.com
SIC: 2711 Newspapers

(P-5999)
NORTH COUNTY TIMES (DH)
Also Called: Californian, The
350 Camino De La Reina, San Diego (92108-3003)
PHONE..................................800 533-8830
▲ EMP: 250
SQ FT: 45,000

SALES (est): 24.8MM
SALES (corp-wide): 566.9MM **Publicly Held**
WEB: www.nctimes.com
SIC: 2711 Newspapers, publishing & printing
HQ: Lee Publications, Inc.
201 N Harrison St Ste 600
Davenport IA 52801
563 383-2100

(P-6000)
NORTH COUNTY TIMES
28441 Rancho California R, Temecula (92590-3618)
PHONE..................................951 676-4315
Claude Reinke, *Manager*
EMP: 50
SALES (corp-wide): 566.9MM **Publicly Held**
WEB: www.nctimes.com
SIC: 2711 Newspapers, publishing & printing
HQ: North County Times
350 Camino De La Reina
San Diego CA 92108
800 533-8830

(P-6001)
NORTH VALLEY NEWSPAPERS INC
Also Called: Valley Post
2676 Gateway Dr, Anderson (96007-3530)
P.O. Box 492397, Redding (96049-2397)
PHONE..................................530 365-2797
Douglas Hirsch, *President*
EMP: 15
SALES (est): 817.8K **Privately Held**
SIC: 2711 Newspapers, publishing & printing

(P-6002)
NOTICIERO SEMANAL ADVERTISING
Also Called: Porterville Recorder
115 E Oak Ave, Porterville (93257-3807)
P.O. Box 151 (93258-0151)
PHONE..................................559 784-5000
Paul Mauney, *Principal*
Robert Foster, *Graphic Designe*
Terry Feagin, *Accounting Mgr*
Alex Larson, *Consultant*
EMP: 65
SALES (est): 1.8MM **Privately Held**
SIC: 2711 7313 Newspapers, publishing & printing; newspaper advertising representative

(P-6003)
OAKLAND TRIBUNE INC
Also Called: Tribune, The
600 Grand Ave 308, Oakland (94610-3548)
PHONE..................................510 208-6300
John Armstrong, *President*
Doug Van Sant, *Producer*
◆ EMP: 800
SALES (est): 20.6MM
SALES (corp-wide): 4.3B **Privately Held**
SIC: 2711 Newspapers, publishing & printing
HQ: Medianews Group, Inc.
101 W Colfax Ave Ste 1100
Denver CO 80202

(P-6004)
OBSERVER NEWSPAPER
1844 Lincoln Blvd, Santa Monica (90404-4506)
P.O. Box 5652 (90409-5652)
PHONE..................................310 452-9900
David Ganezer, *President*
EMP: 20
SALES: 500K **Privately Held**
SIC: 2711 Newspapers, publishing & printing

(P-6005)
OLYMPIC CASCADE PUBLISHING (DH)
Also Called: Puyallup Herald
2100 Q St, Sacramento (95816-6816)
P.O. Box 15779 (95852-0779)
PHONE..................................916 321-1000
Steven Robinson, *Vice Pres*

▲ = Import ▼=Export
◆ =Import/Export

Marion Dodd, *Corp Secy*
EMP: 45
SQ FT: 5,100
SALES (est): 4.6MM
SALES (corp-wide): 903.5MM **Publicly Held**
WEB: www.puyallupherald.com
SIC: 2711 Commercial printing & newspaper publishing combined; newspapers, publishing & printing
HQ: Mcclatchy Newspapers, Inc.
2100 Q St
Sacramento CA 95816
916 321-1855

(P-6006)
OUTWORD NEWS MAGAZINE
Also Called: Outword Newsmagazine
1 Ebbtide Ct, Sacramento (95831-2406)
PHONE..................916 329-9280
Fred Palmer, *President*
EMP: 45
SALES (est): 1.7MM **Privately Held**
WEB: www.outwordmagazine.com
SIC: 2711 Newspapers

(P-6007)
PACIFIC COAST BUS TIMES INC
14 E Carrillo St Ste A, Santa Barbara (93101-2769)
PHONE..................805 560-6950
Henry Dubroff, *President*
Debra Giles, *Office Mgr*
Glenn Rabinowitz, *Manager*
Marlize Van Romburgh, *Editor*
Linda Le Brock, *Publisher*
EMP: 13
SQ FT: 2,200
SALES (est): 898.6K **Privately Held**
WEB: www.pacbiztimes.com
SIC: 2711 Newspapers, publishing & printing

(P-6008)
PACIFIC NORTHWEST PUBG CO INC
2100 Q St, Sacramento (95816-6816)
PHONE..................916 321-1828
Patrick Talmantes, *Director*
EMP: 300 EST: 1905
SQ FT: 100,000
SALES (est): 26.7MM
SALES (corp-wide): 3.1B **Publicly Held**
WEB: www.tallahassee.com
SIC: 2711 Newspapers, publishing & printing
HQ: Gannett River States Publishing Corporation
7950 Jones Branch Dr
Mc Lean VA 22102
703 284-6000

(P-6009)
PACIFIC PRESS CORPORATION
Also Called: Viet Nam Daily Newspaper
2350 S 10th St, San Jose (95112-4109)
PHONE..................408 292-3422
Can Nguyen, *President*
Giang Nguyen, *Corp Secy*
EMP: 30
SQ FT: 10,000
SALES (est): 1.6MM **Privately Held**
SIC: 2711 2752 Newspapers: publishing only, not printed on site; commercial printing, lithographic

(P-6010)
PASADENA NEWSPAPERS INC (PA)
Also Called: Pasadena Star-News
2 N Lake Ave Ste 150, Pasadena (91101-1896)
PHONE..................626 578-6300
Dean Singleton, *President*
▲ EMP: 190
SQ FT: 80,000
SALES (est): 32.5MM **Privately Held**
WEB: www.pasadenastarnews.com
SIC: 2711 7313 Commercial printing & newspaper publishing combined; newspaper advertising representative

(P-6011)
PASADENA NEWSPAPERS INC
Also Called: Eureka Times-Standard
930 6th St, Eureka (95501-1112)
P.O. Box 3580 (95502-3580)
PHONE..................707 442-1711
Gerry Adolph, *Manager*
EMP: 135
SQ FT: 49,872
SALES (corp-wide): 32.5MM **Privately Held**
WEB: www.pasadenastarnews.com
SIC: 2711 2752 Newspapers: publishing only, not printed on site; commercial printing, lithographic
PA: Pasadena Newspapers Inc
2 N Lake Ave Ste 150
Pasadena CA 91101
626 578-6300

(P-6012)
PENNYSAVER
Also Called: Harthanks
1520 N Mountain Ave # 121, Ontario (91762-1132)
PHONE..................909 467-8500
Mike Paulsin, *President*
EMP: 50
SALES (est): 2MM **Privately Held**
WEB: www.hhshoppers.com
SIC: 2711 Newspapers, publishing & printing

(P-6013)
PERIODICO EL VIDA
Also Called: Vida Newspaper
130 Palm Dr, Oxnard (93030-4979)
PHONE..................805 483-1008
Manuel Munoz, *Owner*
EMP: 37
SALES (est): 1.2MM **Privately Held**
SIC: 2711 Newspapers, publishing & printing

(P-6014)
PHIL BLAZER ENTERPRISES INC
Also Called: Jewish News
15315 Magnolia Blvd # 101, Sherman Oaks (91403-1100)
PHONE..................818 786-4000
Phil Blazer, *President*
Adam Blazer, *CFO*
Craig Durst, *Vice Pres*
Joyce Sachartoff, *Executive Asst*
Hanan Druker, *Graphic Designe*
EMP: 10 EST: 1972
SQ FT: 3,000
SALES: 823.3K **Privately Held**
SIC: 2711 7812 Newspapers: publishing only, not printed on site; television film production

(P-6015)
POLITEZER NEWSPAERS INC
Also Called: Grover City Press
260 Station Way Ste F, Arroyo Grande (93420-3359)
PHONE..................805 929-3864
Emily Slater, *Manager*
Cynthia Schur, *President*
Vern Ahrendes, *Manager*
EMP: 13 EST: 1963
SQ FT: 12,000
SALES (est): 670K **Privately Held**
WEB: www.timespressrecorder.com
SIC: 2711 Newspapers, publishing & printing

(P-6016)
POPULAR TV NETWORKS LLC
8307 Rugby Pl, Los Angeles (90046-1527)
PHONE..................323 822-3324
Marvin Jarrett, *Principal*
Jaclynn Jarrett, *Principal*
EMP: 10 EST: 2014
SALES (est): 409.5K **Privately Held**
SIC: 2711 7389 Newspapers, publishing & printing;

(P-6017)
PRECINCT REPORTER
Also Called: Precinct Reporter Newsprs
357 W 2nd St Ste 1a, San Bernardino (92401-1824)
PHONE..................909 889-0597

Brian Townsend, *Partner*
Mary Townsend, *Partner*
EMP: 10
SALES (est): 631.1K **Privately Held**
SIC: 2711 7313 Job printing & newspaper publishing combined; newspaper advertising representative

(P-6018)
PREMIER MEDIA INC
Also Called: India Journal
13353 Alondra Blvd # 115, Santa Fe Springs (90670-5545)
PHONE..................562 802-9720
Navneet Chugh, *President*
Parminder Singh, *General Mgr*
Neha Sarin, *Producer*
EMP: 11
SQ FT: 2,100
SALES (est): 540K **Privately Held**
WEB: www.indiajournal.com
SIC: 2711 8732 Newspapers: publishing only, not printed on site; commercial nonphysical research

(P-6019)
PRESS-ENTERPRISE COMPANY (PA)
3450 14th St, Riverside (92501-3878)
P.O. Box 792 (92502-0792)
PHONE..................951 684-1200
Ronald Redfern, *President*
Ed Lasak, *CFO*
Sue Barry, *Vice Pres*
Kathy Weiermiller, *Vice Pres*
Wayne Raspberry, *Foreman/Supr*
▲ EMP: 700
SQ FT: 190,000
SALES (est): 158.4MM **Privately Held**
SIC: 2711 Commercial printing & newspaper publishing combined; newspapers, publishing & printing

(P-6020)
PRESS-ENTERPRISE COMPANY
3450 14th St, Riverside (92501-3878)
PHONE..................951 684-1200
Deniene Husted, *Sales/Mktg Mgr*
EMP: 15
SALES (corp-wide): 158.4MM **Privately Held**
SIC: 2711 Newspapers, publishing & printing
PA: Press-Enterprise Company
3450 14th St
Riverside CA 92501
951 684-1200

(P-6021)
PULITZER INC
Also Called: Lompoc Record
115 N H St, Lompoc (93436-6818)
P.O. Box 578 (93438-0578)
PHONE..................805 735-1132
Kevin Pankey, *Manager*
Gaila Anderson, *Sales Staff*
John Fragosa, *Sales Staff*
Marie Schaefer, *Sales Staff*
Marga Cooley, *Manager*
EMP: 40
SALES (corp-wide): 566.9MM **Publicly Held**
WEB: www.postnet.com
SIC: 2711 7313 Newspapers: publishing only, not printed on site; newspaper advertising representative
HQ: Pulitzer Inc
900 N Tucker Blvd
Saint Louis MO 63101
314 340-8000

(P-6022)
RAFU SHIMPO
Also Called: L A Japanese Daily News
701 E 3rd St Ste 130, Los Angeles (90013-1789)
PHONE..................213 629-2231
Michael M Komai, *President*
George Johnston, *Business Dir*
Bryce Umemoto, *Admin Asst*
Gail Miyasaka, *Manager*
EMP: 20
SQ FT: 20,000

SALES: 52K **Privately Held**
WEB: www.rafu.com
SIC: 2711 Newspapers, publishing & printing

(P-6023)
RAMONA HOME JOURNAL
726 D St, Ramona (92065-2330)
PHONE..................760 788-8148
Carol Kinney, *Owner*
EMP: 10 EST: 1998
SALES (est): 451.3K **Privately Held**
SIC: 2711 Newspapers, publishing & printing

(P-6024)
RANCHO CUCAMONGA MAVERICK
Also Called: Rancho Cucamonga Today
7349 Milliken Ave Ste 110, Rancho Cucamonga (91730-7435)
PHONE..................909 466-6445
Rex Gutierrez, *Owner*
EMP: 10 EST: 1997
SALES (est): 350K **Privately Held**
SIC: 2711 Newspapers

(P-6025)
REED PRINT INC (PA)
Also Called: Arvin Tiller Printing
5409 Aldrin Ct, Bakersfield (93313-2104)
PHONE..................661 845-3704
Frank W Reed, *President*
Janice Reed, *Treasurer*
Donald Reed, *Vice Pres*
Kathy Reed, *Admin Sec*
EMP: 50
SQ FT: 16,000
SALES (est): 5.2MM **Privately Held**
SIC: 2711 2752 Commercial printing & newspaper publishing combined; commercial printing, lithographic

(P-6026)
REPORTER
Also Called: Media News Groups
916 Cotting Ln, Vacaville (95688-9338)
PHONE..................707 448-6401
Jody Lodevick, *President*
Eric Chappell, *Officer*
Shauna Manina, *VP Bus Dvlpt*
Ron Tilson, *Prdtn Dir*
Rowena Nguyen, *Sales Staff*
EMP: 91
SQ FT: 40,000
SALES (est): 5.6MM **Privately Held**
WEB: www.thereporter.com
SIC: 2711 Commercial printing & newspaper publishing combined; newspapers, publishing & printing

(P-6027)
RICHARD MATZ
Also Called: Military Press Newspaper
6780 Miramar Rd Ste 202, San Diego (92121-2639)
PHONE..................858 537-2280
Richard T Matz Sr, *Owner*
Richard Matz Sr, *Owner*
Tom Chambers, *Production*
Carol Williams, *Cust Mgr*
EMP: 20
SALES (est): 920K **Privately Held**
SIC: 2711 Newspapers: publishing only, not printed on site

(P-6028)
RIDER CIRCULATION SERVICES
Also Called: Rcs
1324 Cypress Ave, Los Angeles (90065-1220)
PHONE..................323 344-1200
John Dorman, *President*
Michael Werner, *Vice Pres*
▲ EMP: 10
SQ FT: 8,500
SALES: 4.4MM **Privately Held**
WEB: www.gorcs.com
SIC: 2711 Newspapers, publishing & printing

PRODUCTS & SVCS

(P-6029)
RJ MEDIA
Also Called: India Post
1860 Mowry Ave Ste 200, Fremont
(94538-1730)
PHONE.....................510 938-8667
Romesh K Japra, *President*
Naresh Sodhi, *General Mgr*
EMP: 10 EST: 2005
SALES (est): 241.5K Privately Held
SIC: 2711 Newspapers

(P-6030)
SAIGON TIMES INC
9234 Valley Blvd, Rosemead (91770-1922)
P.O. Box 428 (91770-0428)
PHONE.....................626 288-2696
Hap Tu Thai, *President*
EMP: 10
SQ FT: 3,285
SALES (est): 437.4K Privately Held
WEB: www.saigontimes.net
SIC: 2711 Commercial printing & newspaper publishing combined

(P-6031)
SALINAS NEWSPAPERS LLC
Also Called: Salinas Newspapers Inc
1093 S Main St Ste 101, Salinas
(93901-2362)
P.O. Box 81091 (93912-1000)
PHONE.....................831 424-2221
Paula Goudraw, *President*
Charlene Clark, *Adv Mgr*
EMP: 150
SQ FT: 8,000
SALES (est): 6.3MM
SALES (corp-wide): 3.1B Publicly Held
WEB: www.californianprepress.com
SIC: 2711 Newspapers, publishing & printing
PA: Gannett Co., Inc.
7950 Jones Branch Dr
Mc Lean VA 22102
703 854-6000

(P-6032)
SAN CLEMENTE TIMES LLC
34932 Calle Del Sol Ste B, Capistrano
Beach (92624-1664)
PHONE.....................949 388-7700
Norb Garrett,
Fiat Luxe MGT,
EMP: 10
SALES (est): 736.6K Privately Held
SIC: 2711 Commercial printing & newspaper publishing combined; newspapers, publishing & printing

(P-6033)
SAN DIEGO UNION-TRIBUNE LLC
San Diego Union Tribune
600 B St Ste 1201, San Diego
(92101-4505)
P.O. Box 120191 (92112-0191)
PHONE.....................619 299-3131
Roy E Gene Bell, *CEO*
EMP: 99
SQ FT: 400,000 Privately Held
WEB: www.copleynewspapers.com
SIC: 2711 7313 Newspapers: publishing only, not printed on site; newspaper advertising representative
PA: The San Diego Union-Tribune Llc
600 B St Ste 1201
San Diego CA 92101
-

(P-6034)
SAN DIEGO UNION-TRIBUNE LLC (PA)
Also Called: San Diego Union Tribune, The
600 B St Ste 1201, San Diego
(92101-4505)
P.O. Box 120191 (92112-0191)
PHONE.....................619 299-3131
Jeff Light, *President*
Patty Rangel, *Accounts Exec*
EMP: 600

SALES (est): 155MM Privately Held
SIC: 2711 7313 7383 Newspapers: publishing only, not printed on site; newspaper advertising representative; news reporting services for newspapers & periodicals

(P-6035)
SAN JOSE BUSINESS JOURNAL
125 S Market St Ste 1100, San Jose
(95113-2286)
PHONE.....................408 295-3800
Dick Kruez, *Publisher*
Jason Sherry, *Graphic Designe*
Italo Jimenez, *Business Mgr*
EMP: 45
SALES (est): 2.2MM
SALES (corp-wide): 1.4B Privately Held
SIC: 2711 2741 Newspapers, publishing & printing; miscellaneous publishing
HQ: American City Business Journals, Inc.
120 W Morehead St Ste 400
Charlotte NC 28202
704 973-1000

(P-6036)
SAN JOSE MERCURY-NEWS LLC (DH)
4 N 2nd St Ste 8008800, San Jose
(95113-1308)
PHONE.....................408 920-5000
Michael Hopkins,
Bud Geracie, *Executive*
Astrid Garcia, *Principal*
Mindy Kiernan, *Principal*
Joseph T Natoli, *Principal*
EMP: 1000
SQ FT: 400,000
SALES (est): 128.7MM
SALES (corp-wide): 4.3B Privately Held
WEB: www.mercurynews.com
SIC: 2711 Commercial printing & newspaper publishing combined; newspapers, publishing & printing

(P-6037)
SAN MATEO DAILY NEWS
255 Constitution Dr, Menlo Park
(94025-1108)
PHONE.....................650 327-9090
Dave Price, *President*
EMP: 50
SALES (est): 2.3MM Privately Held
SIC: 2711 Newspapers, publishing & printing

(P-6038)
SANTA BARBARA INDEPENDENT INC
12 E Figueroa St, Santa Barbara
(93101-2709)
PHONE.....................805 965-5205
Randy Campbell, *President*
Tanya Guiliacci, *Opers Mgr*
Megan Hillegas, *Prdtn Mgr*
Emily Cosentino, *Marketing Staff*
Marion Partridge, *Chief*
EMP: 40
SQ FT: 5,000
SALES (est): 2.9MM Privately Held
WEB: www.independant.com
SIC: 2711 Newspapers: publishing only, not printed on site

(P-6039)
SANTA MARIA TIMES INC
3200 Skyway Dr, Santa Maria
(93455-1896)
P.O. Box 400 (93456-0400)
PHONE.....................805 925-2691
Dan Cotter, *Manager*
Adrienne Yracheta, *Graphic Designe*
Marga Cooley, *Editor*
Len Wood, *Editor*
EMP: 120
SALES (corp-wide): 5.4MM Privately Held
SIC: 2711 Newspapers, publishing & printing
PA: Santa Maria Times, Inc
7701 Forsyth Blvd # 1000
Saint Louis MO 63105
314 340-8890

(P-6040)
SANTA ROSA PRESS DEMOCRAT INC (HQ)
Also Called: Press Democrat, The
427 Mendocino Ave, Santa Rosa
(95401-6313)
P.O. Box 569 (95402-0569)
PHONE.....................707 546-2020
Michael J Parman, *President*
EMP: 270
SALES (est): 75MM Privately Held
WEB: www.sonomatraveler.com
SIC: 2711 Newspapers, publishing & printing
PA: Sonoma Media Investments, Llc
427 Mendocino Ave
Santa Rosa CA 95401
707 546-2020

(P-6041)
SCRIPPS MEDIA INC
Also Called: Ventura County Star
550 Camarillo Center Dr, Camarillo
(93010-7700)
PHONE.....................805 437-0000
Shanna Cannon,
EMP: 175
SALES (est): 8.3MM
SALES (corp-wide): 3.1B Publicly Held
WEB: www.scripps.com
SIC: 2711 Newspapers
HQ: Journal Media Group, Inc.
333 W State St
Milwaukee WI 53203
414 224-2000

(P-6042)
SENTINEL PRINTING & PUBLISHING
Also Called: Dinuba Sentinel
145 S L St, Dinuba (93618-2324)
PHONE.....................559 591-4632
Bob Raison, *Manager*
Margarita Moreno, *Accountant*
EMP: 17 EST: 1909
SQ FT: 7,500
SALES (est): 800K Privately Held
WEB: www.dinubasentinel.com
SIC: 2711 Commercial printing & newspaper publishing combined

(P-6043)
SEREECHAI NEWSPAPER INC
4904 Fountain Ave, Los Angeles
(90029-1502)
PHONE.....................323 465-7550
Teck Sanguporn, *President*
Boonyalak Charoenkitkan, *Admin Sec*
EMP: 10
SALES: 350K Privately Held
SIC: 2711 5994 Newspapers, publishing & printing; magazine stand

(P-6044)
SIERRA VIEW INC
Also Called: News Review, The
109 N Sanders St, Ridgecrest
(93555-3848)
PHONE.....................760 371-4301
Patricia Farris, *President*
Rebecca Neipp, *Bd of Directors*
Allison Aubin,
EMP: 25
SQ FT: 2,800
SALES: 450K Privately Held
SIC: 2711 Newspapers: publishing only, not printed on site

(P-6045)
SIGNAL
Also Called: Newhall Signal
26330 Diamond Pl Ste 100, Santa Clarita
(91350-5819)
PHONE.....................661 259-1234
Charles Morris, *President*
Dawn Begley, *Executive*
Monica Jaffe, *Executive*
Christy Packard, *Creative Dir*
Emily Lyman, *Graphic Designe*
EMP: 98
SQ FT: 32,000

SALES (est): 5.3MM
SALES (corp-wide): 313.5MM Privately Held
WEB: www.sclarita.com
SIC: 2711 Newspapers, publishing & printing
PA: Morris Multimedia, Inc.
27 Abercorn St
Savannah GA 31401
912 233-1281

(P-6046)
SING TAO NEWSPAPERS (HQ)
Also Called: Sing Tao Daily
1818 Gilbreth Rd Ste 108, Burlingame
(94010-1217)
PHONE.....................650 808-8800
Robin Mui, *CEO*
Charles Fu, *CFO*
Florence TSO, *General Mgr*
Kelvin Yeung, *Info Tech Mgr*
Angel Law, *Accountant*
▲ EMP: 75
SQ FT: 22,000
SALES (est): 14.8MM Privately Held
WEB: www.singtaousa.com
SIC: 2711 Commercial printing & newspaper publishing combined

(P-6047)
SING TAO NEWSPAPERS LTD
Also Called: Sing Tao Nwspapers Los Angeles
17059 Green Dr, City of Industry
(91745-1812)
PHONE.....................626 839-8200
Sau K Cheung, *Manager*
Dennis Hsiao, *Adv Mgr*
Vivian Chao, *Advt Staff*
Esther Fung, *Advt Staff*
EMP: 52 Privately Held
WEB: www.singtao.com
SIC: 2711 Newspapers, publishing & printing
PA: Sing Tao Limited
Sing Tao News Corporation Bldg
Tseung Kwan O NT
279 823-23

(P-6048)
SLO NEW TIMES INC
Also Called: New Times Media Group
1010 Marsh St, San Luis Obispo
(93401-3630)
PHONE.....................805 546-8208
Bob Rucker, *CEO*
Jason Gann, *Adv Dir*
Rhonda Odell, *Advt Staff*
Giselle Armstrong, *Marketing Staff*
James Parsons, *Manager*
EMP: 30
SALES (est): 1.9MM Privately Held
WEB: www.newtimesslo.com
SIC: 2711 Newspapers: publishing only, not printed on site

(P-6049)
SONOMA INDEX-TRIBUNE
Also Called: Sonoma Valley Publishing
117 W Napa St Ste A, Sonoma
(95476-6691)
P.O. Box C (95476-0209)
PHONE.....................707 938-2111
William Lynch, *President*
James Lynch, *Corp Secy*
Jean Lynch, *Vice Pres*
EMP: 55
SQ FT: 17,000
SALES (est): 2.9MM Privately Held
WEB: www.sonomanews.com
SIC: 2711 Commercial printing & newspaper publishing combined

(P-6050)
SONOMA WEST PUBLISHERS INC (PA)
Also Called: Sonoma West Times & News
135 S Main St, Sebastopol (95472-4258)
P.O. Box 518, Healdsburg (95448-0518)
PHONE.....................707 823-7845
Jeff Mays, *President*
Sandra M Mays, *Treasurer*
Sarah Bradbury, *Vice Pres*
EMP: 12

SALES (est): 1.9MM **Privately Held**
WEB: www.sonomawest.com
SIC: 2711 Newspapers: publishing only,
not printed on site

(P-6051)
SOUTH COAST PUBLISHING INC
Also Called: Long Beach Business Journal
2599 E 28th St Ste 212, Long Beach
(90755-2139)
PHONE.............................562 988-1222
George Economides, *President*
Heather Dann, *Sales Staff*
Samantha Mehlinger, *Assoc Editor*
▲ EMP: 10
SALES (est): 742.8K **Privately Held**
WEB: www.lbbj.com
SIC: 2711 Newspapers, publishing & print-
ing

(P-6052)
SOUTH COUNTY NEWSPAPERS LLC
Also Called: Soledad Bee
522 Broadway St Ste B, King City
(93930-3243)
PHONE.............................831 385-4880
Tricia Bergeron, *General Mgr*
Jeremy Burke, *Mng Member*
EMP: 10
SALES (est): 607.2K **Privately Held**
WEB: www.newsmediacorporation.com
SIC: 2711 Newspapers, publishing & print-
ing
PA: News Media Corporation
211 E II Route 38
Rochelle IL 61068

(P-6053)
SOUTHLAND PUBLISHING INC
Also Called: Ventura County Reporter
50 S Delacey Ave Ste 200, Pasadena
(91105)
PHONE.............................626 584-1500
Michael Flannery, *President*
David Comden, *Vice Pres*
Chris Jay, *Author*
EMP: 20
SALES (est): 72K **Privately Held**
WEB: www.vcreporter.com
SIC: 2711 Newspapers: publishing only,
not printed on site

(P-6054)
SPORTS MEDICINE INFO NETWORK
8737 Beverly Blvd Ste 303, West Hollywood
(90048-1839)
PHONE.............................310 659-6889
Robert Carp, *Owner*
EMP: 10 EST: 2001
SALES (est): 320.6K **Privately Held**
WEB: www.sportsmedinfo.net
SIC: 2711 Newspapers

(P-6055)
SR3 SOLUTIONS LLC
Also Called: S R 3´
13136 Saticoy St, North Hollywood
(91605-3438)
PHONE.............................818 255-3131
Richard Kaltman, *Mng Member*
Jon Kaltman, *Mng Member*
EMP: 10
SQ FT: 24,000
SALES (est): 713.2K **Privately Held**
SIC: 2711 Commercial printing & newspa-
per publishing combined

(P-6056)
ST LOUIS POST-DISPATCH LLC
Also Called: Novato Advance Newspaper
1068 Machin Ave, Novato (94945-2458)
P.O. Box 8 (94948-0008)
PHONE.............................415 892-1516
William C Haigwood, *Manager*
EMP: 43
SALES (corp-wide): 566.9MM **Publicly Held**
SIC: 2711 Newspapers, publishing & print-
ing
HQ: St. Louis Post-Dispatch Llc
900 N Tucker Blvd
Saint Louis MO 63101
314 340-8000

(P-6057)
ST LOUIS POST-DISPATCH LLC
Also Called: Argus Courier
830 Petaluma Blvd N, Petaluma
(94952-2109)
P.O. Box 1091 (94953-1091)
PHONE.............................707 762-4541
John Burnes, *Branch Mgr*
EMP: 25
SQ FT: 10,000
SALES (corp-wide): 566.9MM **Publicly Held**
SIC: 2711 Newspapers, publishing & print-
ing
HQ: St. Louis Post-Dispatch Llc
900 N Tucker Blvd
Saint Louis MO 63101
314 340-8000

(P-6058)
ST LOUIS POST-DISPATCH LLC
Also Called: Daily Midway Driller
800 Center St, Taft (93268-3129)
PHONE.............................661 763-3171
John Watkins, *Branch Mgr*
EMP: 10
SALES (corp-wide): 566.9MM **Publicly Held**
SIC: 2711 Newspapers, publishing & print-
ing
HQ: St. Louis Post-Dispatch Llc
900 N Tucker Blvd
Saint Louis MO 63101
314 340-8000

(P-6059)
STANFORD DAILY PUBLISHING CORP
Also Called: Stanford Daily, The
456 Panama Mall, Stanford (94305-5294)
PHONE.............................650 723-2555
Alice Brown, *President*
Wes Radez, *Vice Pres*
Michael Ramadan, *Vice Pres*
EMP: 40 EST: 1973
SQ FT: 2,300
SALES: 699.1K **Privately Held**
SIC: 2711 Newspapers: publishing only,
not printed on site

(P-6060)
STAR NEWS PUBLISHING CO INC
296 Third Ave, Chula Vista (91910-2701)
PHONE.............................619 427-3000
Margo Griebel, *Principal*
EMP: 10
SALES (est): 634.4K **Privately Held**
SIC: 2711 Newspapers, publishing & print-
ing

(P-6061)
STATE HORNET
6000 J St, Sacramento (95819-2605)
PHONE.............................916 278-6583
Layla Bohm, *Principal*
EMP: 70
SALES (est): 3MM **Privately Held**
WEB: www.statehornet.com
SIC: 2711 Newspapers

(P-6062)
SUN COMPANY SAN BERNARDINO CAL (PA)
Also Called: San Bernardino County Sun, The
4030 Georgia Blvd, San Bernardino
(92407-1847)
PHONE.............................909 889-9666
Bob Balzer, *President*
Douglass H McCorkindale, *Principal*
Gustavo Ortiz, *MIS Dir*
Theresa Almanza, *Technology*
Louise Kopitch, *VP Human Res*
EMP: 400
SQ FT: 110,000
SALES (est): 42MM **Privately Held**
SIC: 2711 Newspapers, publishing & print-
ing

(P-6063)
SUN REPORTER PUBLISHING INC
Also Called: Sun Reporter Newspaper
1286 Fillmore St, San Francisco
(94115-4111)
PHONE.............................415 671-1000
Amelia Ward, *President*
EMP: 15
SALES (est): 1.1MM **Privately Held**
WEB: www.sunreporter.com
SIC: 2711 8661 Newspapers: publishing
only, not printed on site; religious organi-
zations

(P-6064)
TACOMA NEWS INC (DH)
2100 Q St, Sacramento (95816-6816)
PHONE.............................916 321-1846
Elizabeth F Brenner, *President*
Elaine Lintecum, *Treasurer*
Robert J Weil, *Vice Pres*
Karole Morgan-Prager, *Admin Sec*
EMP: 500
SALES (est): 48.8MM
SALES (corp-wide): 903.5MM **Publicly Held**
WEB: www.tacomanews.com
SIC: 2711 Newspapers, publishing & print-
ing
HQ: Mcclatchy Newspapers, Inc.
2100 Q St
Sacramento CA 95816
916 321-1855

(P-6065)
TAKE A BREAK PAPER
263 W Olive Ave 307, Burbank
(91502-1825)
PHONE.............................323 333-7773
Albert Moran, *Partner*
EMP: 30 EST: 2013
SALES (est): 474.8K **Privately Held**
SIC: 2711 Newspapers, publishing & print-
ing

(P-6066)
TAKUYO CORPORATION
Also Called: Light House
2958 Columbia St, Torrance (90503-3806)
PHONE.............................310 782-6927
Yoichi Komiyama, *President*
Yuzo Komiyama, *Vice Pres*
Hiromi Komiyama, *Accounting Mgr*
Yui Nakade, *Accounts Exec*
EMP: 15
SQ FT: 6,647
SALES (est): 1.2MM **Privately Held**
WEB: www.takuyo.com
SIC: 2711 Newspapers

(P-6067)
TARGET MEDIA PARTNERS OPER LLC
5900 Wilshire Blvd # 550, Los Angeles
(90036-5013)
PHONE.............................323 930-3123
Mark Schiffmacher, *CEO*
EMP: 40
SALES (est): 1MM **Privately Held**
SIC: 2711 Newspapers

(P-6068)
TEHACHAPI NEWS INC (PA)
Also Called: Southeast Kern Weekender
411 N Mill St, Tehachapi (93561-1351)
P.O. Box 1840 (93581-1840)
PHONE.............................661 822-6828
Al Criseli, *President*
William J Mead, *President*
Elizabeth S Mead, *Corp Secy*
Carol Barrett, *Controller*
EMP: 17 EST: 1943
SQ FT: 2,400
SALES (est): 1.1MM **Privately Held**
WEB: www.tehachapinews.com
SIC: 2711 Newspapers, publishing & print-
ing

(P-6069)
THE VALLEY BUSINESS JURNL INC
40335 Winchester Rd # 128, Temecula
(92591-5500)
PHONE.............................951 461-0400

Linda Wunderlich, *President*
EMP: 15
SALES (est): 699.8K **Privately Held**
WEB: www.valleybusinessjournal.com
SIC: 2711 Newspapers, publishing & print-
ing

(P-6070)
TIDINGS
Also Called: VIDA NUEVA
3424 Wilshire Blvd, Los Angeles
(90010-2263)
PHONE.............................213 637-7360
Roger Mahoney, *President*
EMP: 30
SALES: 2MM **Privately Held**
WEB: www.the-tidings.com
SIC: 2711 Newspapers: publishing only,
not printed on site

(P-6071)
TIMES MEDIA INC
Also Called: Bellou Publishing
1900 Camden Ave, San Jose (95124-2942)
PHONE.............................408 494-7000
William D Bellou, *CEO*
Sandy Bellou, *Human Res Mgr*
Brigitte Jones, *Manager*
Jeanne Carbone, *Editor*
EMP: 14
SALES (est): 897.5K **Privately Held**
WEB: www.almadentimes.com
SIC: 2711 Newspapers: publishing only,
not printed on site

(P-6072)
TRACY PRESS INC
145 W 10th St, Tracy (95376-3903)
P.O. Box 419 (95378-0419)
PHONE.............................209 835-3030
Robert S Matthews, *President*
Tom Matthews, *Vice Pres*
Maggie Jauregui, *Graphic Designe*
Will Fleet, *VP Mktg*
Michael Langley, *Editor*
EMP: 30
SQ FT: 20,000
SALES (est): 2.2MM **Privately Held**
WEB: www.tracypress.com
SIC: 2711 Commercial printing & newspa-
per publishing combined; newspapers,
publishing & printing

(P-6073)
TRIBE MEDIA CORP
Also Called: JEWISH JOURNAL, THE
3250 Wilshire Blvd, Los Angeles
(90010-1577)
PHONE.............................213 368-1661
Rob Eshman, *Publisher*
Amanda Epstein, *Admin Asst*
Ginger Vick, *Admin Asst*
Sara Budisantoso, *Traffic Mgr*
Lynn Pelkey, *Art Dir*
EMP: 27
SQ FT: 4,500
SALES: 4.3MM **Privately Held**
WEB: www.jewishjournal.com
SIC: 2711 Newspapers, publishing & print-
ing

(P-6074)
TRIBUNE LOS ANGELES INC
202 W 1st St Ste 500, Los Angeles
(90012-4401)
PHONE.............................213 237-5000
EMP: 13
SALES (est): 773.5K
SALES (corp-wide): 1.8B **Publicly Held**
WEB: www.tribune.com
SIC: 2711 Newspapers, publishing & print-
ing
PA: Tribune Media Company
515 N State St Ste 2400
Chicago IL 60654
312 222-3394

(P-6075)
TURLOCK JOURNAL
138 S Center St, Turlock (95380-4508)
P.O. Box 800 (95381-0800)
PHONE.............................209 634-9141
Olaf Frandsen, *Principal*
EMP: 11

PRODUCTS & SVCS

SALES (est): 722.3K **Privately Held**
SIC: **2711** Commercial printing and newspaper publishing combined; newspapers, publishing & printing

(P-6076)
TXD INTERNATIONAL USA INC
2336 S Vineyard Ave A, Ontario
(91761-7767)
PHONE..................................909 947-6568
Rodolfo J Galvez Cordova, *CEO*
Francisco Galvez Vernis, *Vice Pres*
Armando Herrera, *Admin Sec*
▲ EMP: 15
SQ FT: 8,500
SALES (est): 1.7MM **Privately Held**
SIC: **2711 2752 2211 2262** Commercial printing & newspaper publishing combined; promotional printing, lithographic; print cloths, cotton; printing: manmade fiber & silk broadwoven fabrics; printing of narrow fabrics

(P-6077)
VALLEY COMMUNITY NEWSPAPER
1109 Markham Way, Sacramento
(95818-2913)
PHONE..................................916 429-9901
George Macko, *President*
EMP: 10
SALES (est): 716.6K **Privately Held**
WEB: www.valcomnews.com
SIC: **2711** Newspapers: publishing only, not printed on site

(P-6078)
VANGIE L CORTES
Also Called: Asian America Business Journal
9466 Black Mountain Rd, San Diego
(92126-4550)
PHONE..................................858 578-6807
Vangie L Cortes, *Owner*
EMP: 21
SALES (est): 70K **Privately Held**
SIC: **2711** Newspapers: publishing only, not printed on site

(P-6079)
VENTURA COUNTY STAR
151 Factory Stores Dr, Camarillo
(93010-7511)
P.O. Box 6006 (93011-6006)
PHONE..................................805 437-0138
George H Cogswell III, *President*
EMP: 16
SALES (est): 1.2MM **Privately Held**
WEB: www.vcstar.com
SIC: **2711** Newspapers: publishing only, not printed on site

(P-6080)
VIETNMESE AMRCN MDIA CORP VAMC
Also Called: Vien Dong Daily News
14891 Moran St, Westminster
(92683-5535)
PHONE..................................714 379-2851
Hoang Tong, *Exec Dir*
EMP: 19
SALES: 950K **Privately Held**
SIC: **2711** Newspapers: publishing only, not printed on site

(P-6081)
VILLAGE VOICE MEDIA
Also Called: Eastbay Express
318 Harrison St Ste 302, Oakland
(94607-4134)
PHONE..................................510 879-3700
Josh Fromson, *Principal*
Danielle Flax, *Accounts Exec*
Linda Snider, *Accounts Exec*
EMP: 54
SQ FT: 7,400
SALES (est): 3MM **Privately Held**
WEB: www.eastbayexpress.com
SIC: **2711 5812** Newspapers: publishing & printing; eating places

(P-6082)
VILLLAGE NEWS INC
Also Called: Fallbrook Bonsall Village News
41740 Enterprise Cir S, Temecula
(92590-4881)
PHONE..................................760 451-3488

Julie Reeder, *President*
Darren McDowell, *General Mgr*
Michelle Howard, *Advt Staff*
Terry Morrow, *Editor*
EMP: 23 EST: 1997
SQ FT: 1,500
SALES (est): 1.4MM **Privately Held**
WEB: www.thevillagenews.com
SIC: **2711** Newspapers: publishing only, not printed on site

(P-6083)
WAVE COMMUNITY NEWSPAPERS INC (PA)
Also Called: The Wave
3731 Wilshire Blvd # 840, Los Angeles
(90010-2830)
PHONE..................................323 290-3000
Pluria Marshall, *President*
▲ EMP: 30
SQ FT: 15,000
SALES (est): 2MM **Privately Held**
SIC: **2711** Commercial printing & newspaper publishing combined; newspapers, publishing & printing

(P-6084)
WESTERN HELLENIC JOURNAL INC
1839 Ygnacio Valley Rd, Walnut Creek
(94598-3214)
PHONE..................................925 939-3900
Fanis Economidis, *President*
EMP: 34
SALES (est): 162.2K **Privately Held**
SIC: **2711** Newspapers, publishing & printing

(P-6085)
WESTERN OUTDOORS PUBLICATIONS (PA)
Also Called: Western Outdoor News
901 Calle Amanecer # 300, San Clemente
(92673-6278)
P.O. Box 73370 (92673-0113)
PHONE..................................949 366-0030
Robert Twilegar, *President*
Lori Twilegar, *Admin Sec*
Gloria Sievers, *Graphic Designe*
Chuck Buhagiar, *Sls & Mktg Exec*
Bill Egan, *Director*
EMP: 42
SQ FT: 6,000
SALES (est): 3.2MM **Privately Held**
WEB: www.wonews.com
SIC: **2711 2721** Newspapers: publishing only, not printed on site; periodicals

(P-6086)
WESTERN STATES WEEKLIES INC
Also Called: Long Beach Navy Dispatch
6312 Riverdale St, San Diego
(92120-3310)
P.O. Box 600600 (92160-0600)
PHONE..................................619 280-2988
Sara Hagerty, *President*
EMP: 10
SALES (est): 520K **Privately Held**
WEB: www.navynews.com
SIC: **2711 2721** Newspapers: publishing only, not printed on site; periodicals

(P-6087)
WICK COMMUNICATIONS CO
Also Called: Kern Valley Sun
6404 Lake Isabella Blvd, Lake Isabella
(93240-9475)
P.O. Box 3074 (93240-3074)
PHONE..................................760 379-3667
Cliff Urfeth, *Manager*
EMP: 31
SALES (corp-wide): 79.4MM **Privately Held**
WEB: www.hmbreview.com
SIC: **2711** Newspapers, publishing & printing
HQ: Wick Communications Co.
333 W Wilcox Dr Ste 302
Sierra Vista AZ 85635
520 458-0200

(P-6088)
WICK COMMUNICATIONS CO
Also Called: Half Moon Bay Review
714 Kelly St, Half Moon Bay (94019-1919)
P.O. Box 68 (94019-0068)
PHONE..................................650 726-4424
Debra Godshall, *Principal*
EMP: 25
SALES (corp-wide): 79.4MM **Privately Held**
WEB: www.hmbreview.com
SIC: **2711 6531** Newspapers, publishing & printing; real estate agents & managers
HQ: Wick Communications Co.
333 W Wilcox Dr Ste 302
Sierra Vista AZ 85635
520 458-0200

(P-6089)
WINTON TIMES
Also Called: Mid Valley Publications
6950 Gerard Ave, Winton (95388)
P.O. Box 65 (95388-0065)
PHONE..................................209 358-5311
John M Derby, *Owner*
EMP: 25
SQ FT: 5,000
SALES (est): 1.1MM **Privately Held**
SIC: **2711 2752** Newspapers, publishing & printing; commercial printing, lithographic

(P-6090)
WORLD JOURNAL INC (PA)
231 Adrian Rd, Millbrae (94030-3102)
PHONE..................................650 692-9936
PI Ly Wang, *President*
Shiun Yi Hsia, *CEO*
Ming Dai, *Executive*
May Shen, *Mktg Dir*
Monica Liu, *Marketing Staff*
▲ EMP: 98
SQ FT: 15,000
SALES (est): 14.6MM **Privately Held**
WEB: www.chinesenews.com
SIC: **2711** Newspapers, publishing & printing

(P-6091)
WORLD JOURNAL INC
1588 Corporate Center Dr, Monterey Park
(91754-7624)
PHONE..................................323 261-6972
Lily Chueh, *Admin Sec*
Yaongan Yio, *Graphic Designe*
Michelle Han, *Accounts Exec*
▲ EMP: 21
SALES (est): 1.8MM **Privately Held**
SIC: **2711 5994** Commercial printing & newspaper publishing combined; newsstand

(P-6092)
WORLD JOURNAL LA LLC (HQ)
1588 Corporate Center Dr, Monterey Park
(91754-7624)
PHONE..................................323 268-4982
James Guon, *CEO*
▲ EMP: 170 EST: 1981
SQ FT: 45,000
SALES (est): 24.4MM **Privately Held**
WEB: www.chinesedailynews.com
SIC: **2711** Newspapers, publishing & printing: publishing only, not printed on site
PA: United Daily News
369, Datong Rd., Sec. 1,
New Taipei City
286 925-588

(P-6093)
YNEZ CORPORATION
432 2nd St, Solvang (93463)
P.O. Box 647 (93464-0647)
PHONE..................................805 688-5522
Peggy Johnson, *President*
EMP: 16 EST: 1974
SQ FT: 8,000
SALES (est): 1.1MM
SALES (corp-wide): 566.9MM **Publicly Held**
SIC: **2711** Newspapers, publishing & printing
PA: Lee Enterprises, Incorporated
201 N Harrison St Ste 600
Davenport IA 52801
563 383-2100

2721 Periodicals: Publishing & Printing

(P-6094)
18 MEDIA INC (PA)
Also Called: Gentry Magazine
873 Santa Cruz Ave # 206, Menlo Park
(94025-4635)
PHONE..................................650 324-1818
Elsie Sloriani, *Ch of Bd*
Sloan Citron, *President*
Brenda Beck, *Vice Pres*
Tiffany Birch, *Executive*
Collier Granberry, *Executive*
EMP: 13
SQ FT: 2,500
SALES (est): 1.8MM **Privately Held**
WEB: www.18media.com
SIC: **2721** Magazines: publishing only, not printed on site

(P-6095)
909 MEDIA GROUP INC
Also Called: 909 Magazine
100 N Euclid Ave Ste 202, Upland
(91786-8315)
PHONE..................................909 608-7426
Marc Grossman, *Branch Mgr*
EMP: 15
SALES (corp-wide): 700K **Privately Held**
SIC: **2721 7389** Magazines: publishing only, not printed on site; advertising, promotional & trade show services
PA: 909 Media Group Inc.
100 N Euclid Ave Ste 202
Upland CA 91786
909 252-7224

(P-6096)
ACTIVE INTEREST MEDIA INC (PA)
Also Called: A I M
300 Continental Blvd # 650, El Segundo
(90245-5067)
PHONE..................................310 356-4100
Efrem Zimbalist, *President*
Mitchell H Faigen, *Senior VP*
EMP: 91
SALES (est): 132MM **Privately Held**
WEB: www.activeinterestmedia.com
SIC: **2721** Magazines: publishing only, not printed on site

(P-6097)
ADAMS TRADE PRESS LP (PA)
Also Called: Adams Business Media
420 S Palm Canyon Dr, Palm Springs
(92262-7304)
PHONE..................................760 318-7000
Mark Adams, *Partner*
EMP: 30
SQ FT: 2,000
SALES (est): 2.2MM **Privately Held**
WEB: www.adamsbevgroup.com
SIC: **2721** Periodicals: publishing only

(P-6098)
AEROTECH NEWS AND REVIEW INC (PA)
Also Called: Bullseye
220 E Avenue K4 Ste 7, Lancaster
(93535-4687)
PHONE..................................520 623-9321
Paul Kinison, *President*
EMP: 45
SQ FT: 2,000
SALES: 3.7MM **Privately Held**
SIC: **2721 2741 2752** Trade journals: publishing only, not printed on site; miscellaneous publishing; commercial printing, lithographic

(P-6099)
AFFLUENT TARGET MARKETING INC
Also Called: Affluent Living Publication
3855 E La Palma Ave # 250, Anaheim
(92807-1765)
P.O. Box 18507 (92817-8507)
PHONE..................................714 446-6280
Wally Hicks, *President*
David Marchand, *Prdtn Mgr*
Debbie Tarnoff, *Clerk*

▲ = Import ▼=Export
◆ =Import/Export

EMP: 26
SQ FT: 3,500
SALES (est): 3.8MM Privately Held
SIC: 2721 Magazines: publishing only, not printed on site

(P-6100)
AKN HOLDINGS LLC (PA)
10250 Constellation Blvd, Los Angeles (90067-6200)
PHONE..................................310 432-7100
Andrew Nikou,
Daniel Abrams, *Senior VP*
Matthias Gundlach, *Principal*
EMP: 11
SALES (est): 751.9MM Privately Held
WEB: www.opengatecapital.com
SIC: 2721 6799 8621 Magazines: publishing & printing; investors; professional membership organizations

(P-6101)
ALM MEDIA HOLDINGS INC
Also Called: American Lawyer Media
1035 Market St Ste 500, San Francisco (94103-1650)
PHONE..................................415 490-1054
Chirstopher Braun, *Manager*
Judy Weiss, *Manager*
Jason Doiy, *Editor*
EMP: 30
SALES (corp-wide): 177.1MM Privately Held
SIC: 2721 Periodicals: publishing & printing
PA: Alm Media Holdings, Inc.
    120 Broadway Fl 5
    New York NY 10271
    212 457-9400

(P-6102)
APPAREL NEWS GROUP
Also Called: California Apparel News
110 E 9th St Ste A777, Los Angeles (90079-1777)
PHONE..................................213 327-1002
Terry Fellman, *CEO*
Terry Martinez, *Sales Executive*
Lousie Amberg, *Marketing Staff*
Daniella Platt, *Editor*
Molly Rhodes, *Publisher*
EMP: 40
SALES (est): 3.7MM
SALES (corp-wide): 4.5MM Privately Held
WEB: www.apparelnews.net
SIC: 2721
PA: Mnm Corporation
    110 E 9th St Ste A777
    Los Angeles CA 90079
    213 627-3737

(P-6103)
APPLIED MATERIALS INC
3330 Scott Blvd Bldg 6, Santa Clara (95054-3101)
PHONE..................................408 727-5555
Debbie Noris, *Branch Mgr*
Inna Louneva, *Sr Software Eng*
Thorsten Kril, *Technical Staff*
Chris Blank, *Engineer*
Hanish Kumar, *Engineer*
EMP: 14
SALES (corp-wide): 14.5B Publicly Held
WEB: www.appliedmaterials.com
SIC: 2721 3559 Periodicals; semiconductor manufacturing machinery
PA: Applied Materials, Inc.
    3050 Bowers Ave
    Santa Clara CA 95054
    408 727-5555

(P-6104)
APRESS L P
Also Called: Appress
2588 Telegraph Ave, Berkeley (94704-2920)
PHONE..................................510 549-5930
Gary Cornell, *CEO*
EMP: 12
SALES (est): 131.2K Privately Held
WEB: www.apress.com
SIC: 2721 Magazines: publishing & printing

(P-6105)
ARSENIC INC
530 S Hewitt St Unit 119, Los Angeles (90013-2290)
PHONE..................................310 701-7559
Amanda Micallef, *President*
EMP: 15
SALES (est): 1MM Privately Held
SIC: 2721 Magazines: publishing only, not printed on site

(P-6106)
AUTO CLUB ENTERPRISES
Also Called: Westway Magazine
3333 Fairview Rd, Costa Mesa (92626-1610)
PHONE..................................714 885-2376
Tamara Hill, *Principal*
Larene Grisom, *Regional Mgr*
EMP: 278
SALES (corp-wide): 3.4B Privately Held
WEB: www.aaa-newmexico.com
SIC: 2721 Periodicals
PA: Auto Club Enterprises
    3333 Fairview Rd Msa451
    Costa Mesa CA 92626
    714 850-5111

(P-6107)
AVIATION PUBLISHING CORP
El Monte Airport, El Monte (91733)
PHONE..................................626 618-4000
Michael Higgins, *President*
EMP: 100 EST: 1993
SALES: 75MM Privately Held
SIC: 2721 Magazines: publishing only, not printed on site

(P-6108)
BACKSTAGE WEST
5055 Wilshire Blvd 5, Los Angeles (90036-6100)
PHONE..................................323 525-2356
Jamie Young, *Principal*
EMP: 20
SALES (est): 695.4K Privately Held
WEB: www.backstagewest.com
SIC: 2721 Magazines: publishing only, not printed on site

(P-6109)
BASS ANGLER
Also Called: Bass Angler Magazine
2500 Shadow Mountain Ct, San Ramon (94583-1823)
P.O. Box 2805 (94583-7805)
PHONE..................................925 362-3190
Mark Lassagne, *President*
EMP: 11
SALES: 500K Privately Held
SIC: 2721 7311 Magazines: publishing only, not printed on site; advertising agencies

(P-6110)
BEAR BROTHERS ENTERPRISES LTD
777 E Tahqtz Cyn Way # 200, Palm Springs (92262-6797)
PHONE..................................914 588-6885
Steve Harris, *President*
Michael Goldberg, *Vice Pres*
EMP: 30
SQ FT: 800
SALES (est): 1.8MM Privately Held
SIC: 2721 Magazines: publishing & printing

(P-6111)
BELMONT PUBLICATIONS INC
Also Called: Dimensions of Dental Hygiene
3621 S Harbor Blvd # 265, Santa Ana (92704-8905)
PHONE..................................714 825-1234
Lorene G Kent, *President*
EMP: 10
SALES (est): 1.3MM Privately Held
WEB: www.dimensionsofdentalhygiene.com
SIC: 2721 Magazines: publishing only, not printed on site

(P-6112)
BENTLEY MANAGEMENT CORPORATION
Also Called: Players International Publ
8060 Melrose Ave Ste 210, Los Angeles (90046-7037)
PHONE..................................323 653-8060
Bentley Morris, *Vice Pres*
Bentley Morriss, *Vice Pres*
Tom Morney, *Director*
EMP: 10
SQ FT: 3,000
SALES (est): 581.2K Privately Held
SIC: 2721 Magazines: publishing & printing

(P-6113)
BONNIER CORPORATION
15255 Alton Pkwy, Irvine (92618-2367)
PHONE..................................760 707-0100
Jeremy Thompson, *Owner*
Andy Leisner, *Vice Pres*
Jordan Mastagni, *Editor*
EMP: 88
SALES (corp-wide): 3.1B Privately Held
SIC: 2721 Magazines: publishing only, not printed on site
HQ: Bonnier Corporation
    460 N Orlando Ave Ste 200
    Winter Park FL 32789

(P-6114)
BOWTIE INC (HQ)
Also Called: Global Distribution Services
500 N Brand Blvd Ste 600, Glendale (91203-4704)
PHONE..................................213 385-2222
Norman Ridker, *CEO*
Nicole Fabian, *CFO*
Jeffrey Scharf, *Vice Pres*
▲ EMP: 45
SQ FT: 10,000
SALES (est): 55.6MM
SALES (corp-wide): 56.1MM Privately Held
WEB: www.bowtieinc.com
SIC: 2721 Magazines: publishing & printing
PA: I-5 Publishing, Llc
    5151 California Ave # 100
    Irvine CA 92617
    949 855-8822

(P-6115)
BOWTIE INC
Also Called: Pet Product News
3 Burroughs, Irvine (92618-2804)
P.O. Box 6050, Mission Viejo (92690-6050)
PHONE..................................949 855-8822
Peter Bullhagen, *President*
EMP: 80
SALES (corp-wide): 56.1MM Privately Held
WEB: www.bowtieinc.com
SIC: 2721 0752 2731 Magazines: publishing & printing; animal specialty services; book publishing
HQ: Bowtie, Inc.
    500 N Brand Blvd Ste 600
    Glendale CA 91203
    213 385-2222

(P-6116)
BRIDGE USA INC
20817 S Western Ave, Torrance (90501-1804)
PHONE..................................310 532-5921
Yoshihiro Ishii, *President*
EMP: 20
SQ FT: 6,000
SALES (est): 2.3MM Privately Held
SIC: 2721 7311 Magazines: publishing only, not printed on site; advertising agencies

(P-6117)
BRIGHT BUSINESS MEDIA LLC
Also Called: Smart Meetings
475 Gate 5 Rd Ste 235, Sausalito (94965-2877)
PHONE..................................415 339-9355
Marin Bright,
John Decesare, *Vice Pres*
Luc Troussieux, *Principal*
EMP: 10

SALES (est): 2MM Privately Held
WEB: www.smartmtgs.com
SIC: 2721 Magazines: publishing only, not printed on site

(P-6118)
BUILDER & DEVELOPER MAGAZINES
Also Called: Peninsula Publishing
1602 Monrovia Ave, Newport Beach (92663-2808)
PHONE..................................949 631-0308
Nick Slevin, *Partner*
Stuart Cochrane, *Partner*
Leslie Hearne, *Business Mgr*
Nicole Feenstra, *Marketing Staff*
Robert Hamud, *Art Dir*
EMP: 10
SALES (est): 966.2K Privately Held
WEB: www.bdmag.com
SIC: 2721 Trade journals: publishing only, not printed on site

(P-6119)
BUISNESS LEADER MEDIA
Also Called: Inside Tennis Associates
2907 Claremont Ave # 220, Berkeley (94705-2410)
PHONE..................................510 665-9600
William G Simons, *Manager*
EMP: 43 Privately Held
SIC: 2721 Magazines: publishing only, not printed on site
PA: Buisness Leader Media
    3801 Wake Forest Rd # 205
    Raleigh NC

(P-6120)
BUSINESS EXTENSION BUREAU
Also Called: Western Real Estate News
500 S Airport Blvd, South San Francisco (94080-6912)
PHONE..................................650 737-5700
Gil Chin, *President*
Aleatha Farr, *Assoc Editor*
EMP: 20 EST: 1927
SQ FT: 7,000
SALES: 1MM Privately Held
SIC: 2721 7331 2752 Trade journals: publishing & printing; direct mail advertising services; commercial printing, lithographic

(P-6121)
BUSINESS JOURNAL
Also Called: Fresno Business Journal
1315 Van Ness Ave Ste 200, Fresno (93721-1729)
P.O. Box 126 (93707-0126)
PHONE..................................559 490-3400
Gordon M Webster Jr, *President*
Brandie Carpenter, *Marketing Staff*
Kaysi Curtin, *Sales Staff*
EMP: 24 EST: 1886
SALES (est): 2.8MM Privately Held
WEB: www.thebusinessjournal.com
SIC: 2721 2711 Trade journals: publishing only, not printed on site; newspapers

(P-6122)
BUTANE PROPANE NEWS INC
338 E Foothill Blvd, Arcadia (91006-2542)
P.O. Box 660698 (91066-0698)
PHONE..................................626 357-2168
Natalia Peal, *President*
Nanette Dougall, *Vice Pres*
EMP: 10
SQ FT: 1,750
SALES (est): 790K Privately Held
WEB: www.bpnews.com
SIC: 2721 2741 Magazines: publishing & printing; business service newsletters: publishing & printing

(P-6123)
CBJ LP
Also Called: San Fernando Valley Bus Jurnl
21550 Oxnard St, Woodland Hills (91367-7100)
PHONE..................................818 676-1750
Pegi Matsuda, *Manager*
EMP: 12

PRODUCTS & SVCS

SALES (est): 1.2MM
SALES (corp-wide): 31.5MM **Privately Held**
WEB: www.ocbj.com
SIC: 2721 Magazines: publishing only, not printed on site
PA: Cbj, L.P.
　7101 College Blvd # 1100
　Shawnee Mission KS
　913 451-9000

(P-6124)
CBJ LP
Also Called: Los Angeles Business Journal
5700 Wilshire Blvd # 170, Los Angeles (90036-7205)
PHONE...................................323 549-5225
Matt Toledo, *Branch Mgr*
Rosz Murray, *Advt Staff*
Helya Askari, *Manager*
Jim Slater, *Manager*
Eva Juse, *Accounts Mgr*
EMP: 40
SALES (corp-wide): 31.5MM **Privately Held**
WEB: www.ocbj.com
SIC: 2721 2711 8742 Periodicals: publishing only; trade journals: publishing only, not printed on site; newspapers; general management consultant
PA: Cbj, L.P.
　7101 College Blvd # 1100
　Shawnee Mission KS
　913 451-9000

(P-6125)
CBJ LP
Also Called: San Diego Business Journal
4909 Murphy Canyon Rd # 200, San Diego (92123-4349)
PHONE...................................858 277-6359
Armon Mills, *Principal*
Jeffrey Blease, *Partner*
EMP: 25
SQ FT: 10,000
SALES (corp-wide): 31.5MM **Privately Held**
WEB: www.ocbj.com
SIC: 2721 2741 2711 Trade journals: publishing & printing; miscellaneous publishing; newspapers
PA: Cbj, L.P.
　7101 College Blvd # 1100
　Shawnee Mission KS
　913 451-9000

(P-6126)
CBJ LP
Also Called: Orange County Business Journal
18500 Von Karman Ave # 150, Irvine (92612-0504)
PHONE...................................949 833-8373
Janet Cox, *Manager*
Cynthia Newcomb, *Executive Asst*
Wendy Stremel, *Executive Asst*
Martin Nilchian, *Technology*
Brette Miller, *Graphic Designe*
EMP: 40
SALES (corp-wide): 31.5MM **Privately Held**
WEB: www.ocbj.com
SIC: 2721 2711 7313 Trade journals: publishing only, not printed on site; newspapers; newspaper advertising representative
PA: Cbj, L.P.
　7101 College Blvd # 1100
　Shawnee Mission KS
　913 451-9000

(P-6127)
CHALLENGE PUBLICATIONS INC
21835 Nordhoff St, Chatsworth (91311-5712)
PHONE...................................818 700-6868
Edwin A Schnepf, *President*
Susan Duprey, *Mng Officer*
EMP: 20
SQ FT: 30,000
SALES (est): 2MM **Privately Held**
WEB: www.challengeweb.com
SIC: 2721 Magazines: publishing & printing

(P-6128)
CHET COOPER
Also Called: C2 Publishing
1001 W 17th St, Costa Mesa (92627-4512)
P.O. Box 10878 (92627-0271)
PHONE...................................949 854-8700
Chet Cooper, *Owner*
EMP: 12
SALES (est): 968.8K **Privately Held**
WEB: www.abilitymagazine.com
SIC: 2721 Magazines: publishing only, not printed on site

(P-6129)
CHURM PUBLISHING INC (PA)
Also Called: O.C. Metro Magazine
1451 Quail St Ste 201, Newport Beach (92660-2741)
PHONE...................................714 796-7000
Steve Churm, *President*
Brian O'Neill, *CFO*
Peter Churm, *Vice Pres*
EMP: 47
SQ FT: 7,000
SALES (est): 3MM **Privately Held**
WEB: www.ocfamily.com
SIC: 2721 Trade journals: publishing & printing

(P-6130)
CLIQUE BRANDS INC (PA)
Also Called: Who What Wear
750 N San Vicnte Blvd Re800, West Hollywood (90069-5788)
PHONE...................................323 648-5619
Katherine Power, *CEO*
Hilary Kerr, *President*
Mika Onishi, *COO*
Shayna Kossove, *Vice Pres*
Stacy Macklin, *Director*
EMP: 32
SQ FT: 2,200
SALES (est): 5MM **Privately Held**
SIC: 2721 Magazines: publishing only, not printed on site

(P-6131)
COIN DEALER NEWSLETTER INC
2034 262nd St, Lomita (90717-3416)
PHONE...................................310 515-7369
Pauline Miladin, *President*
EMP: 12
SALES (est): 1.5MM **Privately Held**
WEB: www.greysheet.com
SIC: 2721 Periodicals: publishing only

(P-6132)
COMPETITOR GROUP INC (HQ)
Also Called: Competitor Magazine
6420 Sequence Dr, San Diego (92121-4313)
PHONE...................................858 450-6510
David Abeles, *CEO*
Scott Dickey, *President*
Steve Gintowt, *COO*
Barrett Garrison, *CFO*
Keith Kendrick, *Chief Mktg Ofcr*
▲ EMP: 191
SQ FT: 56,796
SALES (est): 126.4MM
SALES (corp-wide): 127MM **Privately Held**
SIC: 2721 7941 Magazines: publishing & printing; sports promotion
PA: Calera Capital Management, Inc.
　580 California St # 2200
　San Francisco CA 94104
　415 632-5200

(P-6133)
COMPETITOR MAGAZINE
10179 Hudiken St Ste 100, San Diego (92121)
PHONE...................................858 768-6800
Bob Babbitt, *President*
Lois Schwartz, *Vice Pres*
EMP: 20
SQ FT: 2,500
SALES (est): 2.3MM **Privately Held**
SIC: 2721 Magazines: publishing only, not printed on site

(P-6134)
COMSTOCK PUBLISHING INC
Also Called: Comstock's Magazine
2335 American River Dr # 301, Sacramento (95825-7088)
PHONE...................................916 364-1000
Comstockca Exc, *Vice Pres*
Winnie Comstockcarlson, *Exec VP*
Thomas Hanns, *Business Mgr*
Jason Balangue, *Advt Staff*
Ashley Wilborn, *Assoc Editor*
EMP: 15
SQ FT: 1,600
SALES (est): 1.6MM **Privately Held**
SIC: 2721 Magazines: publishing only, not printed on site

(P-6135)
CONTINENTAL FEATURE/ NEWS SVC
501 W Broadway Ste C, San Diego (92101-3520)
PHONE...................................858 492-8696
Gary P Salamone, *Owner*
EMP: 50
SALES (est): 2.5MM **Privately Held**
SIC: 2721 4899 7383 7389 Periodicals: publishing & printing; data communication services; news syndicates; personal service agents, brokers & bureaus

(P-6136)
COYNE & BLANCHARD INC
Also Called: Communication Arts
110 Constitution Dr, Menlo Park (94025-1107)
PHONE...................................650 326-6040
Patrick Coyne, *President*
Martha Coyne, *Corp Secy*
Eric Coyne, *Vice Pres*
Marti Coyne, *Admin Sec*
Mike Hoyt, *MIS Dir*
EMP: 20
SQ FT: 7,500
SALES (est): 2.4MM **Privately Held**
WEB: www.creativehotlist.com
SIC: 2721 Magazines: publishing only, not printed on site

(P-6137)
CREATIVE AGE PUBLICATIONS INC
Also Called: Nailpro
7628 Densmore Ave, Van Nuys (91406-2042)
PHONE...................................818 782-7328
Deborah Carver, *President*
Mindy Rosiejka, *CFO*
Jeff Black, *Vice Pres*
Breanna Armstrong, *Manager*
Jennifer Carofano, *Manager*
EMP: 50
SQ FT: 14,000
SALES (est): 7.1MM **Privately Held**
WEB: www.creativeage.com
SIC: 2721 2731 Magazines: publishing only, not printed on site; book publishing

(P-6138)
CURTCO MEDIA GROUP LLC
29160 Heathercliff Rd # 1, Malibu (90265-6310)
P.O. Box 6934 (90264-6934)
PHONE...................................310 589-7700
Samantha Brooks, *Principal*
EMP: 12 EST: 2010
SALES (est): 1.3MM **Privately Held**
SIC: 2721 Magazines: publishing & printing

(P-6139)
CURTCO ROBB MEDIA LLC (PA)
29160 Heathercliff Rd # 1, Malibu (90265-6310)
PHONE...................................310 589-7700
Stephen Colvin, *CEO*
William J Curtis, *Vice Ch Bd*
David Arnold, *Senior VP*
Christopher Fabian,
Kristy Bauer, *Director*
EMP: 30
SALES (est): 17.4MM **Privately Held**
WEB: www.curtco.com
SIC: 2721 Magazines: publishing & printing

(P-6140)
DAILY GRAPHS INC
Also Called: Daily Graphics
12655 Beatrice St, Los Angeles (90066-7306)
PHONE...................................310 448-6843
William Oneil, *President*
William O'Neil, *President*
Don Drake, *Treasurer*
EMP: 20
SALES (est): 971.1K
SALES (corp-wide): 231.5MM **Privately Held**
WEB: www.dailygraphs.com
SIC: 2721 7371 Magazines: publishing only, not printed on site; custom computer programming services
HQ: O'neil Securities, Incorporated
　12655 Beatrice St Ste 2b
　Los Angeles CA 90066
　310 448-6800

(P-6141)
DAISY PUBLISHING COMPANY INC
Also Called: Hi-Torque Publications
25233 Anza Dr, Santa Clarita (91355-1289)
PHONE...................................661 295-1910
Roland Hinz, *President*
Lila Hinz, *Vice Pres*
Carl Husfeld, *Safety Mgr*
Robb Mesecher, *Adv Dir*
Greg Flanagan, *Adv Mgr*
EMP: 55 EST: 1969
SQ FT: 16,000
SALES (est): 11.5MM **Privately Held**
WEB: www.dirtbikemagazine.com
SIC: 2721 Magazines: publishing & printing

(P-6142)
DAN M SWOFFORD
728 Cherry St, Chico (95928-5143)
PHONE...................................530 343-9994
EMP: 10
SALES (est): 480K **Privately Held**
SIC: 2721

(P-6143)
DESERT PUBLICATIONS INC (PA)
Also Called: Desert Grafics
303 N Indian Canyon Dr, Palm Springs (92262-6015)
P.O. Box 2724 (92263-2724)
PHONE...................................760 325-2333
Franklin Jones, *Principal*
Stuart Funk, *Creative Dir*
Todd May, *Info Tech Dir*
Kelly Oconnor, *Opers Mgr*
Julie Rogers, *Accounts Mgr*
EMP: 49
SQ FT: 25,000
SALES (est): 7.5MM **Privately Held**
WEB: www.jonesagency.com
SIC: 2721 7311 Magazines: publishing only, not printed on site; advertising agencies

(P-6144)
DESIGN JOURNAL INC
Also Called: Design La
1720 20th St Ste 201, Santa Monica (90404-3944)
P.O. Box 993, Pacific Palisades (90272-0993)
PHONE...................................310 394-4394
John Platter, *President*
John Moses, *Admin Sec*
EMP: 15
SALES (est): 1.8MM **Privately Held**
WEB: www.adexawards.com
SIC: 2721 7311 8742 Magazines: publishing only, not printed on site; advertising agencies; marketing consulting services

(P-6145)
DIABLO COUNTRY MAGAZINE INC
Also Called: Diablo Custom Publishing
2520 Camino Diablo, Walnut Creek (94597-3939)
PHONE...................................925 943-1111
Steven J Rivera, *President*
Eileen Cunningham, *COO*
Dave Bergeron, *Creative Dir*

Jodie Aranda, *Project Mgr*
Angela Noel, *Manager*
▲ **EMP:** 40 **EST:** 1979
SQ FT: 7,640
SALES (est): 6.9MM **Privately Held**
WEB: www.dcpubs.com
SIC: 2721 2741 Magazines: publishing only, not printed on site; miscellaneous publishing

(P-6146)
DISNEY PUBLISHING WORLDWIDE (DH)
500 S Buena Vista St, Burbank (91521-0001)
PHONE.................................212 633-4400
R Russell Hampton Jr, *Chairman*
Robert W Hernandez, *Senior VP*
▲ **EMP:** 100
SALES (est): 31MM **Publicly Held**
SIC: 2721 Periodicals
HQ: Disney Enterprises, Inc.
     500 S Buena Vista St
     Burbank CA 91521
     818 560-1000

(P-6147)
DISTINCTIVE PRPTS NAPA VLY
1615 2nd St, NAPA (94559-2818)
PHONE.................................707 256-2251
Randy Principe, *Director*
Priscilla Lara, *Manager*
EMP: 100 **EST:** 1984
SALES: 2MM **Privately Held**
WEB: www.napanews.com
SIC: 2721 Periodicals

(P-6148)
DIVERSITYCOMM INC
Also Called: Diversity In Steam
18 Technology Dr Ste 170, Irvine (92618-2313)
PHONE.................................949 825-5777
Mona Lisa Faris, *President*
Richard Abboud, *General Mgr*
Erica Sabino, *Executive Asst*
Melissa Simmons, *Admin Sec*
Rosario Diaz, *Research*
EMP: 12
SQ FT: 1,700
SALES (est): 1.5MM **Privately Held**
WEB: www.hnmagazine.com
SIC: 2721 Magazines: publishing only, not printed on site

(P-6149)
DMH MEDIA NETWORK CORP
1801 Avenue Of The Stars, Los Angeles (90067)
PHONE.................................818 732-4217
David Hill, *Ch of Bd*
EMP: 17
SQ FT: 1,000
SALES (est): 831.5K **Privately Held**
SIC: 2721 Magazines: publishing & printing

(P-6150)
DOW THEORY LETTERS INC
7590 Fay Ave Ste 404, La Jolla (92037-4872)
P.O. Box 1759 (92038-1759)
PHONE.................................858 454-0481
Richard Russell, *President*
Daria Doering, *Vice Pres*
Fay Russell, *Vice Pres*
EMP: 10 **EST:** 1958
SQ FT: 1,500
SALES (est): 1MM **Privately Held**
WEB: www.dowtheoryletters.com
SIC: 2721 Statistical reports (periodicals): publishing only

(P-6151)
DREAM COMMUNICATIONS INC
Also Called: Dream Homes Magazine
2431 Morena Blvd, San Diego (92110-4139)
PHONE.................................619 275-9100
Michael Vlassis, *President*
EMP: 15
SQ FT: 4,732
SALES (est): 1.6MM **Privately Held**
WEB: www.dreamhomesmagazine.com
SIC: 2721 Magazines: publishing & printing

(P-6152)
DUB PUBLISHING INC
Also Called: Dub Custom Auto Show
11803 Smith Ave, Santa Fe Springs (90670-3226)
P.O. Box 91471, City of Industry (91715-1471)
PHONE.................................626 336-3821
Myles Kovacs, *President*
Haythem Haddad, *Art Dir*
Herman Flores, *Director*
▲ **EMP:** 10
SQ FT: 5,000
SALES (est): 2.6MM **Privately Held**
WEB: www.dubmagazine.com
SIC: 2721 Magazines: publishing & printing

(P-6153)
DUNCAN MCINTOSH COMPANY INC (PA)
Also Called: Sea Magazine
18475 Bandilier Cir, Fountain Valley (92708-7000)
PHONE.................................949 660-6150
Duncan R McIntosh, *CEO*
Teresa McIntosh, *Corp Secy*
Dave Kelsen, *Info Tech Dir*
Rick Avila, *Opers Staff*
Janette Hood, *Adv Dir*
EMP: 35
SQ FT: 15,728
SALES (est): 5.1MM **Privately Held**
WEB: www.seamag.com
SIC: 2721 7389 Magazines: publishing & printing; trade show arrangement

(P-6154)
DWELL LIFE INC (PA)
595 Pacific Ave 4, San Francisco (94133-4669)
PHONE.................................415 373-5100
Michela Abrams, *CEO*
Amy Lloyd, *Partner*
Jenna Page, *Marketing Mgr*
Lara H Deam,
David Morin,
EMP: 40
SALES (est): 20MM **Privately Held**
WEB: www.dwellmag.com
SIC: 2721 7389 Magazines: publishing & printing; advertising, promotional & trade show services

(P-6155)
E H PUBLISHING INC
Also Called: Security Sales & Integration
3520 Challenger St, Torrance (90503-1640)
PHONE.................................310 533-2400
Scott Goldfine, *Editor*
EMP: 24 **Privately Held**
SIC: 2721 Magazines: publishing & printing
PA: E H Publishing, Inc.
     111 Speen St Ste 200
     Framingham MA 01701

(P-6156)
ELISID MAGAZINE
1450 University Ave F168, Riverside (92507-4467)
PHONE.................................619 990-9999
EMP: 20
SALES (est): 1.2MM **Privately Held**
SIC: 2721

(P-6157)
EMERALD EXPOSITIONS LLC
Also Called: Vnu Business
31910 Del Obispo St # 200, San Juan Capistrano (92675-3182)
PHONE.................................949 226-5754
Denise Bashem, *Branch Mgr*
Alicia Keith, *Opers Staff*
EMP: 70
SALES (corp-wide): 348.2MM **Publicly Held**
SIC: 2721 7389 Trade journals: publishing only, not printed on site; promoters of shows & exhibitions
HQ: Emerald Expositions, Llc
     31910 Del Obispo St # 200
     San Juan Capistrano CA 92675

(P-6158)
EMERALD EXPOSITIONS LLC
5055 Wilshire Blvd # 600, Los Angeles (90036-6100)
PHONE.................................323 525-2000
Eric Mika, *Branch Mgr*
EMP: 60
SALES (corp-wide): 348.2MM **Publicly Held**
SIC: 2721 Trade journals: publishing only, not printed on site
HQ: Emerald Expositions, Llc
     31910 Del Obispo St # 200
     San Juan Capistrano CA 92675

(P-6159)
ENTER MUSIC PUBLISHING INC
Also Called: Drum Magazine
1346 The Alameda Ste 7, San Jose (95126-5006)
PHONE.................................408 971-9794
Phillip Hood, *President*
Connie Hood, *Treasurer*
Andrew Doerschuk, *Vice Pres*
EMP: 14
SQ FT: 3,000
SALES (est): 1.8MM **Privately Held**
WEB: www.drummagazine.com
SIC: 2721 Magazines: publishing only, not printed on site

(P-6160)
ENTREPRENEUR MEDIA INC (PA)
Also Called: Entrepeneur Magazine
18061 Fitch, Irvine (92614-6018)
P.O. Box 19787 (92623-9787)
PHONE.................................949 261-2325
Ryan Shea, *CEO*
Neil Perlman, *President*
Joe Goodman, *CFO*
Ronald Young, *Admin Sec*
Angel Cool, *Web Dvlpr*
▲ **EMP:** 80
SQ FT: 30,000
SALES (est): 16.5MM **Privately Held**
SIC: 2721 Magazines: publishing only, not printed on site

(P-6161)
EXCELLENCE MAGAZINE INC
Also Called: Ross Periodicals
42 Digital Dr Ste 5, Novato (94949-5762)
PHONE.................................415 382-0582
Tom Toldrian, *President*
EMP: 14
SQ FT: 2,850
SALES (est): 1.4MM **Privately Held**
WEB: www.rossperiodicals.com
SIC: 2721 Magazines: publishing only, not printed on site

(P-6162)
FIVE STAR MEDIA INC
155 12th St, San Francisco (94103-2520)
PHONE.................................415 298-2510
Christopher R Guido, *President*
EMP: 12
SQ FT: 2,500
SALES (est): 700K **Privately Held**
SIC: 2721 Magazines: publishing & printing

(P-6163)
FLAUNT MAGAZINE
1422 N Highland Ave, Los Angeles (90028-7611)
PHONE.................................323 836-1044
Luis A Barajas Jr, *President*
Angus Donohoo, *Senior Editor*
▲ **EMP:** 18 **EST:** 1998
SQ FT: 8,500
SALES (est): 903.5K **Privately Held**
WEB: www.flauntmagazine.com
SIC: 2721 Magazines: publishing & printing

(P-6164)
FORESTER COMMUNICATIONS INC
Also Called: Grading and Excavating Mag
2946 De La Vina St, Santa Barbara (93105-3310)
P.O. Box 3100 (93130-3100)
PHONE.................................805 682-1300
Daniel Waldman, *President*
Judith Donlon, *Administration*
John Richardson, *Info Tech Dir*
John Pasini, *Finance Mgr*
Doug Mlyn, *Prdtn Mgr*
EMP: 30
SQ FT: 4,500
SALES (est): 3.8MM **Privately Held**
WEB: www.forester.net
SIC: 2721 Magazines: publishing only, not printed on site

(P-6165)
FORTY-NINERS PUBLICATION
1250 Bellflower Blvd Csul, Long Beach (90840-0001)
PHONE.................................562 985-5568
Dr William A Mulligan, *Owner*
Beverly Munson, *Manager*
EMP: 10
SALES (est): 549.7K **Privately Held**
SIC: 2721 Magazines: publishing & printing

(P-6166)
FOUNDATION FOR NAT PROGRESS
Also Called: MOTHER JONES MAGAZINE
222 Sutter St Ste 600, San Francisco (94108-4457)
PHONE.................................415 321-1700
Madeleine Buckingham, *CFO*
EMP: 39 **EST:** 1975
SQ FT: 13,500
SALES (est): 16.5MM **Privately Held**
SIC: 2721 Magazines: publishing & printing

(P-6167)
FRANCHISE UPDATE INC
Also Called: Franchise Update Media Group
6489 Camden Ave Ste 204, San Jose (95120-2851)
P.O. Box 20547 (95160-0547)
PHONE.................................408 402-5681
Therese Thilgen, *CEO*
Jamie N Hage, *Partner*
Andrew P Loewinger, *Partner*
Carolyn G Nussbaum, *Partner*
Arthur L Pressman, *Partner*
EMP: 15
SALES (est): 1.8MM **Privately Held**
WEB: www.franchise-update.com
SIC: 2721 Magazines: publishing only, not printed on site

(P-6168)
FREEDOM OF PRESS FOUNDATION
601 Van Ness Ave Ste E731, San Francisco (94102-3200)
PHONE.................................415 321-1760
Trevor Timm, *Exec Dir*
EMP: 16
SALES: 2MM **Privately Held**
SIC: 2721 Periodicals

(P-6169)
FUTURE US INC (HQ)
1390 Market St Ste 200, San Francisco (94102-5404)
PHONE.................................650 238-2400
Rachelle Considine, *CEO*
Charlie Speight, *Senior VP*
Rhoda Bueno, *Vice Pres*
Stacy Gaines, *Vice Pres*
Isaac Ugay, *Vice Pres*
EMP: 76
SALES (est): 37.6MM
SALES (corp-wide): 108.3MM **Privately Held**
WEB: www.futurenetworkusa.com
SIC: 2721 Magazines: publishing only, not printed on site
PA: Future Plc
     Quay House
     Bath BA1 1
     122 544-2244

(P-6170)
GAMMON LLC
Also Called: Sonoma Business Magazine
1410 Neotomas Ave Ste 200, Santa Rosa (95405-7533)
PHONE.................................707 575-8282
Norman Rosinski,
John Dennis,
Joni Rosinski,
EMP: 12 **EST:** 2000

(P-6171)
GANNETT CO INC
Also Called: Nurseweek Publishing
1156 Aster Ave Ste C, Sunnyvale
(94086-6810)
PHONE....................800 859-2091
Andy Baldwin, *Manager*
EMP: 30
SALES (corp-wide): 3.1B **Publicly Held**
WEB: www.gannett.com
SIC: 2721 Magazines: publishing only, not printed on site
PA: Gannett Co., Inc.
7950 Jones Branch Dr
Mc Lean VA 22102
703 854-6000

(P-6172)
GOLD PROSPECTORS ASSN OF AMER
Also Called: Gold Prospectors Assn Amer
43445 Bus Pk Dr Ste 113, Temecula
(92590-3671)
P.O. Box 891509 (92589-1509)
PHONE....................951 699-4749
Thomas H Massie, *President*
Richard Dixon, *Admin Sec*
Dominick Ricci, *Opers Staff*
Kevin Hoagland, *Manager*
Jeremy Jefferson, *Manager*
EMP: 20
SQ FT: 35,000
SALES (est): 2.5MM **Privately Held**
WEB: www.goldprospectors.com
SIC: 2721 4833 Magazines: publishing only, not printed on site; television broadcasting stations

(P-6173)
GRAPHIC FILM GROUP LLC (PA)
1901 Avenue Of The Stars, Los Angeles
(90067-6001)
PHONE....................310 887-6330
Scott Walterschied, *Chairman*
Ranford Schlei, *Chairman*
Randy Mendhlsohn, *Principal*
EMP: 15
SALES (est): 1MM **Privately Held**
SIC: 2721 7812 Television schedules: publishing & printing; video production

(P-6174)
GREATDAD LLC
Also Called: Pregnancy Magazine
2337 Vallejo St, San Francisco
(94123-4711)
PHONE....................415 572-8181
Paul Banas, *Owner*
EMP: 10
SALES (est): 686.5K **Privately Held**
SIC: 2721 Magazines: publishing & printing

(P-6175)
H S N CONSULTANTS INC
Also Called: Nilson Report, The
1110 Eugenia Pl Ste 100, Carpinteria
(93013-2080)
PHONE....................805 684-8800
David Robertson, *President*
Logan Carr, *Sales Staff*
Monica Dalto, *Sales Staff*
Deborah Hillesland, *Director*
Alistair Mills, *Director*
EMP: 10 EST: 1970
SALES: 2MM **Privately Held**
WEB: www.nilsonreport.com
SIC: 2721 Periodicals

(P-6176)
HARTLE MEDIA VENTURES LLC
Also Called: 7x7
680 2nd St, San Francisco (94107-2015)
PHONE....................415 362-7797
EMP: 20
SQ FT: 2,000
SALES (est): 2.1MM **Privately Held**
WEB: www.allegiscapital.com
SIC: 2721

(P-6177)
HAYMARKET WORLDWIDE INC
17030 Red Hill Ave, Irvine (92614-5626)
PHONE....................949 417-6700

Peter Foubister, *CEO*
Paul Simpson, *Chief*
▲ EMP: 30
SQ FT: 4,000
SALES (est): 2.8MM
SALES (corp-wide): 223.6MM **Privately Held**
WEB: www.haymarketworldwide.com
SIC: 2721 Magazines: publishing only, not printed on site
HQ: Haymarket Media, Inc.
275 7th Ave Fl 10
New York NY 10001
646 638-6000

(P-6178)
HEARST CORPORATION
Also Called: Examiner Special Projects Div
3000 Ocean Park Blvd, Santa Monica
(90405-3020)
PHONE....................310 752-1040
Amory Jack Cooke, *Manager*
Liz Manley, *Sales Staff*
Sandy Adamski, *Director*
Kelly Beres, *Manager*
EMP: 14
SALES (corp-wide): 6.6B **Privately Held**
WEB: www.hearstcorp.com
SIC: 2721 Magazines: publishing only, not printed on site
PA: The Hearst Corporation
300 W 57th St Fl 42
New York NY 10019
212 649-2000

(P-6179)
HEARST CORPORATION
Also Called: Cycle World Magazine
15255 Alton Pkwy Ste 300, Irvine
(92618-2603)
PHONE....................760 707-0100
Nancy Laporte, *Manager*
Alex Nunez, *Site Mgr*
Jason Nikic, *Adv Dir*
EMP: 60
SALES (corp-wide): 6.6B **Privately Held**
WEB: www.popphoto.com
SIC: 2721 Magazines: publishing & printing
PA: The Hearst Corporation
300 W 57th St Fl 42
New York NY 10019
212 649-2000

(P-6180)
HEARST CORPORATION
1 Wyntoon Rd, Mccloud (96057)
P.O. Box 1600, McCloud (96057-1600)
PHONE....................530 964-3131
Pat Patterson, *Manager*
EMP: 25
SALES (corp-wide): 6.6B **Privately Held**
WEB: www.hearstcorp.com
SIC: 2721 Magazines: publishing only, not printed on site
PA: The Hearst Corporation
300 W 57th St Fl 42
New York NY 10019
212 649-2000

(P-6181)
HELEN NOBLE
Also Called: Military Magazine
2120 28th St, Sacramento (95818-1910)
PHONE....................916 457-8990
Armond Nobel, *Owner*
Helen Nobel, *Owner*
EMP: 11
SALES (est): 595.8K **Privately Held**
WEB: www.milmag.com
SIC: 2721 Magazines: publishing only, not printed on site

(P-6182)
HIC CORPORATION (PA)
Also Called: Heavy Duty Trucking
38 Executive Park Ste 300, Irvine
(92614-6755)
PHONE....................949 261-1636
Doug Condra, *President*
EMP: 15
SALES (est): 2.3MM **Privately Held**
WEB: www.heavydutytrucking.com
SIC: 2721 Magazines: publishing only, not printed on site

(P-6183)
HISPANIC BUSINESS INC
Also Called: Hispanic Business Magazine
5385 Hollister Ave # 204, Santa Barbara
(93111-2389)
PHONE....................805 964-4554
Jesus Chavarria, *President*
Bonnie Chavarria, *Corp Secy*
EMP: 13
SQ FT: 40,000
SALES (est): 1.9MM **Privately Held**
WEB: www.hirediversity.com
SIC: 2721 7375 7389 Magazines: publishing only, not printed on site; data base information retrieval; trade show arrangement

(P-6184)
HITS MAGAZINE INC
Also Called: Music Market Update
6906 Hollywood Blvd Fl 2, Los Angeles
(90028-6104)
PHONE....................323 946-7600
Dennis Lavinthal, *President*
Lenny Beer, *Principal*
Simon Glickman, *Senior Editor*
EMP: 60
SALES (est): 38.1K **Privately Held**
WEB: www.hitsmagazine.com
SIC: 2721 Magazines: publishing only, not printed on site

(P-6185)
HW HOLDCO LLC
555 Anton Blvd Ste 950, Costa Mesa
(92626-7811)
PHONE....................714 540-8500
Jeff Meyers, *Manager*
Dave Macintosh, *VP Sales*
Anthony Crocco, *Director*
EMP: 50
SALES (corp-wide): 164.8MM **Privately Held**
WEB: www.toolsofthetrade.org
SIC: 2721 Trade journals: publishing only, not printed on site
PA: Hw Holdco, Llc
1 Thomas Cir Nw Ste 600
Washington DC 20005
202 452-0800

(P-6186)
HWF CONSTRUCTION INC
3685 Fruitvale Ave, Bakersfield
(93308-5107)
PHONE....................661 587-3590
Robert Hinelsy, *President*
EMP: 15
SALES: 32.2MM **Privately Held**
SIC: 2721 Magazines: publishing only, not printed on site

(P-6187)
I-5 PUBLISHING LLC (PA)
Also Called: Global Distribution Svcs
5151 California Ave # 100, Irvine
(92617-3205)
PHONE....................949 855-8822
Mark Harris, *Mng Member*
David Katzoff, *CFO*
David Fry,
Liliana Estep, *Art Dir*
Gary Bernard, *Director*
▲ EMP: 130
SALES (est): 56.1MM **Privately Held**
SIC: 2721 2731 Magazines: publishing only, not printed on site; book publishing

(P-6188)
IDG CONSUMER & SMB INC (DH)
Also Called: PC World Online
501 2nd St, San Francisco (94107-1469)
PHONE....................415 243-0500
Colin Crawford, *President*
Michael Kisseberth, *President*
Edward B Bloom, *Vice Pres*
Kevin C Krull, *Vice Pres*
Miriam Karlin, *Admin Sec*
EMP: 116
SQ FT: 21,000

SALES (est): 14.2MM
SALES (corp-wide): 2.1B **Privately Held**
WEB: www.pcworld.com
SIC: 2721 Magazines: publishing only, not printed on site; periodicals: publishing only
HQ: Idg Communications, Inc.
5 Speen St
Framingham MA 01701
508 872-8200

(P-6189)
IDG GAMES MEDIA GROUP INC
Also Called: Gamepro Magazine
555 12th St, Oakland (94607-4046)
PHONE....................510 768-2700
John Rousseau, *President*
EMP: 50
SALES (est): 3.1MM
SALES (corp-wide): 2.1B **Privately Held**
WEB: www.gamepro.com
SIC: 2721 Trade journals: publishing only, not printed on site
HQ: Idg Communications, Inc.
5 Speen St
Framingham MA 01701
508 872-8200

(P-6190)
IMAGE MAGAZINE INC
5001 Birch St, Newport Beach
(92660-2116)
PHONE....................949 608-5188
Dean Dingman, *President*
EMP: 26
SALES (est): 1.8MM **Privately Held**
SIC: 2721 5994 Periodicals; magazine stand

(P-6191)
INFOFAX INC
305 Nord Ave, Chico (95926-4710)
P.O. Box 4191 (95927-4191)
PHONE....................530 895-0431
John Scott, *President*
EMP: 12
SQ FT: 2,041
SALES: 500K **Privately Held**
SIC: 2721 Statistical reports (periodicals): publishing only

(P-6192)
INFOKOREA INC
Also Called: Radio Korea USA
626 S Kingsley Dr, Los Angeles
(90005-2318)
PHONE....................213 487-1580
Fax: 213 487-7744
▲ EMP: 30
SALES (est): 2.3MM **Privately Held**
SIC: 2721 4832

(P-6193)
INFORMA MEDIA INC
Also Called: Enviormental Business Intl
4452 Park Blvd Ste 306, San Diego
(92116-4049)
PHONE....................619 295-7685
Grant Ferrier, *Principal*
EMP: 20 **Privately Held**
WEB: www.penton.com
SIC: 2721 Magazines: publishing & printing
HQ: Informa Media, Inc.
605 3rd Ave Fl 22
New York NY 10158
212 204-4200

(P-6194)
INFORMA MEDIA INC
11500 W Olympic Blvd, Los Angeles
(90064-1524)
PHONE....................301 755-0162
EMP: 62 **Privately Held**
SIC: 2721 Periodicals
HQ: Informa Media, Inc.
605 3rd Ave Fl 22
New York NY 10158
212 204-4200

(P-6195)
INFOWORLD MEDIA GROUP INC (DH)
501 2nd St Ste 500, San Francisco
(94107-4133)
PHONE....................415 243-4344
Robert Ostrow, *CEO*

Patrick J Mc Govern, *Ch of Bd*
William P Murphy, *Treasurer*
Virginia Hines, *Vice Pres*
Derek Butcher, *Engineer*
▲ **EMP:** 75
SQ FT: 50,000
SALES (est): 8.3MM
SALES (corp-wide): 2.1B **Privately Held**
WEB: www.infoworld.com
SIC: 2721 2741 7389 Magazines: publishing only, not printed on site; newsletter publishing; trade show arrangement
HQ: Idg Communications, Inc.
    5 Speen St
    Framingham MA 01701
    508 872-8200

(P-6196)
INLAND EMPIRE MEDIA GROUP INC
Also Called: Inland Empire Magazine
3400 Central Ave Ste 160, Riverside (92506-2183)
PHONE.................................951 682-3026
Don Lorenzi, *President*
Richard Lorenzi, *Admin Sec*
Lesleyanne Daniels, *Regl Sales Mgr*
Brenda Lorenzi, *Sales Staff*
Robert Smith, *Manager*
EMP: 15 EST: 1972
SQ FT: 1,700
SALES (est): 1.9MM **Privately Held**
WEB: www.inlandempiremagazine.com
SIC: 2721 Magazines: publishing & printing; magazines: publishing only, not printed on site

(P-6197)
INTERNET INDUSTRY PUBLISHING
315 Pacific Ave, San Francisco (94111-1701)
PHONE.................................415 733-5400
Jonathan Wright, *Executive*
EMP: 50
SALES (est): 1.8MM
SALES (corp-wide): 2.1B **Privately Held**
WEB: www.workscape.net
SIC: 2721 Magazines: publishing only, not printed on site
PA: International Data Group, Inc.
    1 Exeter Plz Fl 15
    Boston MA 02116
    617 534-1200

(P-6198)
IRONMAN MAGAZINE
562 Pacific Cove Dr, Port Hueneme (93041-2164)
PHONE.................................805 385-3500
John Balik, *Partner*
EMP: 20
SQ FT: 5,000
SALES (est): 3MM **Privately Held**
SIC: 2721 Magazines: publishing only, not printed on site

(P-6199)
KELLEY BLUE BOOK CO INC (DH)
217 Technology Dr, Irvine (92618-2400)
P.O. Box 19691 (92623-9691)
PHONE.................................949 770-7704
Jared Rowe, *CEO*
John Morrison, *CFO*
Susan Brown, *Vice Pres*
Andrea Suh, *Comms Mgr*
Sherry Peters, *Executive Asst*
EMP: 92
SQ FT: 23,000
SALES (est): 82.4MM
SALES (corp-wide): 32.8B **Privately Held**
WEB: www.kbb.com
SIC: 2721 Trade journals: publishing only, not printed on site
HQ: Autotrader.Com, Inc.
    3003 Summit Blvd Fl 200
    Brookhaven GA 30319
    404 568-8000

(P-6200)
KNIGHT PUBLISHING CORP
8060 Melrose Ave Ste 210, Los Angeles (90046-7037)
PHONE.................................323 653-8060
Bentley Morriss, *President*

EMP: 20
SQ FT: 3,000
SALES (est): 1.5MM **Privately Held**
SIC: 2721 2759 Magazines: publishing only, not printed on site; periodicals: printing

(P-6201)
L F P INC (PA)
Also Called: Flynt, Larry Publishing
8484 Wilshire Blvd # 900, Beverly Hills (90211-3218)
PHONE.................................323 651-3525
Larry Flynt, *Ch of Bd*
Michael H Klein, *President*
Alexander Behrens, *Vice Pres*
Philip Del Rio, *Vice Pres*
Erik Horacek, *Vice Pres*
▲ **EMP:** 100 EST: 1976
SQ FT: 10,000
SALES (est): 29MM **Privately Held**
SIC: 2721 Magazines: publishing & printing

(P-6202)
LA PARENT MAGAZINE (PA)
5855 Topanga Canyon Blvd # 150, Woodland Hills (91367-4685)
PHONE.................................818 264-2222
Madelyn Calabrese, *Manager*
Cara Natterson, *Med Doctor*
Carolyn Richardson, *Assistant*
EMP: 20
SQ FT: 2,500
SALES (est): 1.1MM **Privately Held**
SIC: 2721 Magazines: publishing only, not printed on site

(P-6203)
LANDSCAPE COMMUNICATIONS INC
Also Called: Landscape Contract National
14771 Plaza Dr Ste A, Tustin (92780-2779)
P.O. Box 1126 (92781-1126)
PHONE.................................714 979-5276
George Schmok, *President*
Amy Deane, *Admin Asst*
Cynthia McCarthy, *Admin Asst*
Kip Ongstad, *Sales Staff*
Kyle Cavaness, *Assistant*
EMP: 25
SQ FT: 1,618
SALES (est): 2.8MM **Privately Held**
WEB: www.landscapeonline.com
SIC: 2721 Trade journals: publishing only, not printed on site

(P-6204)
LATINO AMERICANOS REVISTA
82723 Miles Ave, Indio (92201-4229)
PHONE.................................760 342-2312
Patricia Parrilla, *Owner*
EMP: 10
SALES (est): 702.3K **Privately Held**
WEB: www.latinoamericanos.com
SIC: 2721 8721 Magazines: publishing & printing; certified public accountant

(P-6205)
LATITUDE 38 PUBLISHING COMPANY
15 Locust Ave, Mill Valley (94941-2899)
PHONE.................................415 383-8200
Richard L Spindler, *President*
Penny Clayton, *Bookkeeper*
Mitch Perkins, *Advt Staff*
Mike Zwiebach, *Representative*
EMP: 10
SQ FT: 2,000
SALES (est): 1.1MM **Privately Held**
WEB: www.latitude38.com
SIC: 2721 Magazines: publishing only, not printed on site

(P-6206)
LAUFER MEDIA INC
Also Called: Tiger Beat Magazine
330 N Brand Blvd Ste 1150, Glendale (91203-2339)
PHONE.................................818 291-8408
Scott D Laufer, *President*
EMP: 11
SALES (est): 2.5MM **Privately Held**
SIC: 2721 Periodicals

(P-6207)
LIFE MEDIA INC
Also Called: Black Media News
7657 Winnetka Ave Ste 504, Winnetka (91306-2677)
PHONE.................................800 201-9440
Phil Tucker, *President*
Art Allen, *CFO*
EMP: 50
SALES (est): 10MM **Privately Held**
WEB: www.lifemedia.ca
SIC: 2721 Magazines: publishing only, not printed on site

(P-6208)
LINE PUBLICATIONS INC
Also Called: Movieline Magazine
9800 S La Cienega Blvd # 10, Inglewood (90301-4440)
PHONE.................................310 234-9501
John Evans, *President*
Anne Volokh, *Chief*
EMP: 15
SALES (est): 1.4MM **Privately Held**
WEB: www.movieline.com
SIC: 2721

(P-6209)
LOS ANGELES BUS JURNL ASSOC
5700 Wilshire Blvd # 170, Los Angeles (90036-7205)
PHONE.................................323 549-5225
Matt Toledo, *President*
EMP: 45
SALES (est): 3.8MM **Privately Held**
SIC: 2721 Magazines: publishing only, not printed on site

(P-6210)
LUNDBERG SURVEY INC
911 Via Alondra, Camarillo (93012-8048)
PHONE.................................805 383-2400
Trilby Lundberg, *President*
EMP: 35
SALES (est): 3.2MM **Privately Held**
WEB: www.lundbergsurvey.com
SIC: 2721 8748 2741 Statistical reports (periodicals): publishing only; business consulting; miscellaneous publishing

(P-6211)
LUTHER E GIBSON INC
Also Called: Gibson Radio and Publishing Co
544 Curtola Pkwy, Vallejo (94590-6925)
P.O. Box 3067 (94590-0674)
PHONE.................................707 643-6104
David Payne, *President*
Maggie Keane, *General Mgr*
Toni Kirsch, *Director*
EMP: 25
SALES (est): 1.6MM **Privately Held**
SIC: 2721 Periodicals

(P-6212)
MAC PUBLISHING LLC (HQ)
Also Called: Macworld Magazine
501 2nd St Ste 500, San Francisco (94107-4133)
PHONE.................................415 243-0505
Colin Crawford, *President*
Stephen Daniels, *President*
Kevin Greene, *Sales Executive*
Jason Thach, *Sales Mgr*
Niki Stranz, *Manager*
EMP: 20
SALES (est): 2.9MM
SALES (corp-wide): 2.1B **Privately Held**
WEB: www.macworld.com
SIC: 2721 Magazines: publishing only, not printed on site
PA: International Data Group, Inc.
    1 Exeter Plz Fl 15
    Boston MA 02116
    617 534-1200

(P-6213)
MAGAZINE PUBLISHERS SVC INC
350 E St, Santa Rosa (95404-4437)
PHONE.................................707 571-7610
Ronald E Allen Jr, *President*
EMP: 99
SALES (est): 5.8MM **Privately Held**
SIC: 2721 Magazines: publishing & printing

(P-6214)
MARIN MAGAZINE INC
1 Harbor Dr Ste 208, Sausalito (94965-1434)
PHONE.................................415 332-4800
Nikki Wood, *President*
Maeve Walsh, *Controller*
Michele Johnson, *Adv Dir*
Daniel Jewett, *Assoc Editor*
Leah Bronson, *Manager*
EMP: 12
SQ FT: 2,500
SALES (est): 1.6MM **Privately Held**
WEB: www.marinmagazine.com
SIC: 2721 7311 Magazines: publishing only, not printed on site; printed media advertising representatives

(P-6215)
MCKINNON ENTERPRISES
Also Called: San Dego HM Grdn Lfestyles Mag
4577 Viewridge Ave, San Diego (92123-1623)
P.O. Box 719001 (92171-9001)
PHONE.................................858 571-1818
Michael Dean McKinnon, *Partner*
EMP: 20
SALES (est): 2MM **Privately Held**
WEB: www.mediaza.com
SIC: 2721 Magazines: publishing only, not printed on site

(P-6216)
MEYERS PUBLISHING INC
799 Camarillo Springs Rd, Camarillo (93012-9468)
PHONE.................................805 445-8881
Len Meyers, *CEO*
Andrew Meyers, *President*
Lana Meyers, *CFO*
Lee Denton, *Controller*
Mark Horowitz, *Adv Dir*
EMP: 12
SALES (est): 1.6MM **Privately Held**
WEB: www.meyerspublishing.com
SIC: 2721 Magazines: publishing only, not printed on site

(P-6217)
MINGO ENTERPRISES INC
Also Called: Ad Review
1209b Solano Ave, Albany (94706-1724)
P.O. Box 6071 (94706-0071)
PHONE.................................510 528-3044
Liz Tellefsen, *President*
EMP: 16
SQ FT: 500
SALES (est): 1.4MM **Privately Held**
SIC: 2721 Trade journals: publishing only, not printed on site

(P-6218)
MINORITY SUCCESS PUBG GROUP
Also Called: Minorities & Success
3711 Lomita Blvd Ste 196, Torrance (90505-3886)
PHONE.................................310 373-2868
Farimah Farahpour, *President*
Parviz Nasseri, *Officer*
Ali F Chegini, *Vice Pres*
EMP: 20
SQ FT: 1,500
SALES (est): 2.4MM **Privately Held**
WEB: www.mspg.org
SIC: 2721 Magazines: publishing only, not printed on site

(P-6219)
MNM CORPORATION (PA)
Also Called: Apparel Newsgroup, The
110 E 9th St Ste A777, Los Angeles (90079-1777)
PHONE.................................213 627-3737
Martin Wernicke, *CEO*
Jim Patel, *CPA*
Alison Nieder, *Editor*
Amy Valencia, *Accounts Exec*
Marsha Ross, *Publisher*
▲ **EMP:** 60
SQ FT: 11,000

SALES (est): 4.5MM **Privately Held**
WEB: www.singnet.com.sg
SIC: 2721 8721 Magazines: publishing only, not printed on site; accounting, auditing & bookkeeping

(P-6220)
MOBILE HOME BOARD
Also Called: Mobile Home Park Magazines
1240 Mountain Vw Alviso C, Sunnyvale (94089)
PHONE..................................408 744-1011
Elizabeth Tripp, *President*
Clifford Shores, *Shareholder*
Dana Sketchley, *Shareholder*
Rosemary Walsh, *Shareholder*
EMP: 25
SQ FT: 3,500
SALES (est): 2.7MM **Privately Held**
WEB: www.mobilehomeparkmagazines.com
SIC: 2721 6531 Trade journals: publishing & printing; real estate listing services

(P-6221)
MODERN LUXURY MEDIA LLC (HQ)
Also Called: Angeleno Magazine
243 Vallejo St, San Francisco (94111-1511)
PHONE..................................404 443-0004
Michael B Kong, *Mng Member*
John Carroll, *President*
Michael Dickey, *President*
Leslie Wolfson, *President*
Hunter Lane, *Vice Pres*
▲ EMP: 40
SALES (est): 13MM
SALES (corp-wide): 41MM **Privately Held**
SIC: 2721 Magazines: publishing only, not printed on site
PA: Dickey Publishing, Inc.
3280 Peachtree Rd Ne S
Atlanta GA 30305
404 949-0700

(P-6222)
MUSIC CONNECTION INC
Also Called: Music Connection Magazine
16130 Ventura Blvd # 540, Encino (91436-2503)
PHONE..................................818 995-0101
J Michael Dolan, *President*
Eric Bettelli, *CEO*
EMP: 11
SALES (est): 1.1MM **Privately Held**
WEB: www.musicconnection.com
SIC: 2721 Magazines: publishing only, not printed on site

(P-6223)
NATIVE AMERICAN MEDIA
Also Called: Native Canadian Media
10806 1/2 Wilshire Blvd, Los Angeles (90024)
PHONE..................................310 475-6845
Mike Roberts, *President*
EMP: 12
SALES (est): 1.3MM **Privately Held**
SIC: 2721 Magazines: publishing only, not printed on site

(P-6224)
OMICS GROUP INC
731 Gull Ave, Foster City (94404-1329)
PHONE..................................650 268-9744
Srinu B Gedela, *Branch Mgr*
EMP: 460
SALES (corp-wide): 46.3MM **Privately Held**
SIC: 2721 Trade journals: publishing & printing
PA: Omics Group Inc
2360 Corp Cir Ste 400
Henderson NV 89074
888 843-8169

(P-6225)
ORANGE CNTY MLT-HSING SVC CORP
525 Cabrillo Park Dr # 125, Santa Ana (92701-5017)
PHONE..................................714 245-9500
Alan Daugher, *President*
EMP: 12

SALES (est): 1.1MM **Privately Held**
WEB: www.aaoc.com
SIC: 2721 Magazines: publishing only, not printed on site
PA: Apartment Association Of Orange County
525 Cabrillo Park Dr # 125
Santa Ana CA 92701
714 245-9500

(P-6226)
ORANGE COAST KOMMUNICATIONS
Also Called: Orange Coast Magazine
1124 Main St Ste A, Irvine (92614-6757)
PHONE..................................949 862-1133
Gary Thoe, *President*
Chivan Wang, *Marketing Staff*
Sofia Gutierrez, *Mktg Coord*
Randy Bilsley, *Manager*
Ed Estrada, *Accounts Exec*
EMP: 26
SQ FT: 14,000
SALES (est): 3.2MM
SALES (corp-wide): 148.4MM **Publicly Held**
WEB: www.orangecoastmagazine.com
SIC: 2721 5812 Magazines: publishing only, not printed on site; eating places
HQ: Emmis Publishing, L.P.
40 Monument Cir Ste 100
Indianapolis IN 46204
-

(P-6227)
PACIFIC SUN
847 5th St, Santa Rosa (95404-4526)
PHONE..................................415 488-8100
Gina Channell-Allen, *Principal*
EMP: 12
SALES (est): 908.4K **Privately Held**
SIC: 2721 Periodicals

(P-6228)
PAISANO PUBLICATIONS LLC (PA)
Also Called: V Twin Magazine
28210 Dorothy Dr, Agoura Hills (91301-2693)
PHONE..................................818 889-8740
John Lagana, *CEO*
Joseph Teresi, *Chairman*
Beverly Barragan, *Exec VP*
Dave Nichols, *Vice Pres*
Cary Brobeck, *Technology*
EMP: 113
SQ FT: 40,000
SALES (est): 13.2MM **Privately Held**
WEB: www.paisanopub.com
SIC: 2721 Magazines: publishing only, not printed on site

(P-6229)
PAISANO PUBLICATIONS INC
Also Called: V/ Twins
28210 Dorothy Dr, Agoura Hills (91301-2693)
P.O. Box 3000 (91376-3000)
PHONE..................................818 889-8740
Bill Prather, *President*
Robert Davis, *Treasurer*
Allen Ribakoff, *Vice Pres*
Joseph Teresi, *Admin Sec*
Beverly Jermyn, *Human Res Dir*
EMP: 65
SALES: 30MM
SALES (corp-wide): 13.2MM **Privately Held**
WEB: www.paisanopub.com
SIC: 2721 7812 Magazines: publishing & printing; commercials, television: tape or film
PA: Paisano Publications, Llc
28210 Dorothy Dr
Agoura Hills CA 91301
818 889-8740

(P-6230)
PENHOUSE MEDIA GROUP INC
11601 Wilshire Blvd Fl 5, Los Angeles (90025-1995)
PHONE..................................310 575-4835
Harlan Baum, *Principal*
EMP: 32

SALES (corp-wide): 11.5MM **Privately Held**
SIC: 2721 Magazines: publishing only, not printed on site
PA: Penhouse Media Group Incorporated
11 Penn Plz Fl 12
New York NY 10001
212 702-6000

(P-6231)
PENINSULA PUBLISHING INC
1602 Monrovia Ave, Newport Beach (92663-2808)
PHONE..................................949 631-1307
Nick Slevin, *President*
Nick Kosan, *Natl Sales Mgr*
Rona Fiedler, *Sales Mgr*
Georgina Slim, *Sales Mgr*
EMP: 50 EST: 1998
SALES (est): 1.8MM **Privately Held**
WEB: www.optionsmag.com
SIC: 2721 Magazines: publishing & printing

(P-6232)
PFANNER COMMUNICATIONS INC
Also Called: Sportscar
3334 E Coast Hwy Ste 162, Corona Del Mar (92625-2328)
PHONE..................................714 227-3579
Paul Pfanner, *President*
EMP: 17
SQ FT: 4,000
SALES (est): 1.3MM **Privately Held**
SIC: 2721 8742 Magazines: publishing & printing; marketing consulting services

(P-6233)
PINPOINT MEDIA GROUP INC
Also Called: The Orgnal Los Angeles APT Mag
3188 Airway Ave Ste L, Costa Mesa (92626-4652)
PHONE..................................714 545-5640
EMP: 15 EST: 1991
SQ FT: 900
SALES (est): 1.1MM **Privately Held**
SIC: 2721

(P-6234)
PLAYBOY JAPAN INC
9346 Civic Center Dr # 200, Beverly Hills (90210-3604)
PHONE..................................310 424-1800
Katy Omahony, *Human Res Dir*
Tamar Aprahamian, *Director*
Magnolia Nguyen, *Manager*
Kristi Beck, *Assistant*
EMP: 14
SALES (est): 806.4K
SALES (corp-wide): 45.3MM **Privately Held**
SIC: 2721 Periodicals
PA: Playboy Enterprises, Inc.
9346 Civic Center Dr # 200
Beverly Hills CA 90210
310 424-1800

(P-6235)
POLLSTAR LLC (PA)
Also Called: Pollstar.com
4697 W Jacquelyn Ave, Fresno (93722-6443)
PHONE..................................559 271-7900
Gary Bongiovanni, *President*
Gary Smith, *CEO*
Agustin Rivera, *Technology*
EMP: 58
SQ FT: 16,500
SALES (est): 8.4MM **Privately Held**
WEB: www.pollstar.com
SIC: 2721 Trade journals: publishing only, not printed on site

(P-6236)
PRIMEDIA ENTHSAST PBLCTONS INC (HQ)
831 S Douglas St Ste 100, El Segundo (90245-4956)
PHONE..................................717 657-9555
Tom Rogers, *Chairman*
John Loughlin, *President*
EMP: 125
SQ FT: 32,000

SALES (est): 21.5MM
SALES (corp-wide): 781MM **Privately Held**
WEB: www.flyfisherman.com
SIC: 2721 5961 Magazines: publishing only, not printed on site; magazines, mail order
PA: The Enthusiast Network Inc
2221 Rosecrans Ave # 195
El Segundo CA 90245
310 531-9900

(P-6237)
PROMEDIA COMPANIES
Also Called: National Mustang Racers Assn
3518 W Lake Center Dr D, Santa Ana (92704-6979)
PHONE..................................714 444-2426
Steve Wolcott, *Partner*
James Lawrence, *Partner*
Judy Keaton, *Executive*
Camee Edelbrock, *Mktg Dir*
Jim Campisano, *Sales Dir*
EMP: 13
SQ FT: 3,000
SALES (est): 2MM **Privately Held**
WEB: www.fasteststreetcar.com
SIC: 2721 Magazines: publishing only, not printed on site

(P-6238)
PUBLISHERS DEVELOPMENT CORP
Also Called: American Handgunner and Guns
12345 World Trade Dr, San Diego (92128-3743)
PHONE..................................858 605-0200
Thomas Von Rosen, *CEO*
Thomas M Hollander, *Vice Pres*
EMP: 40 EST: 1941
SQ FT: 7,135
SALES (est): 7.3MM **Privately Held**
WEB: www.fmgnews.com
SIC: 2721 Magazines: publishing only, not printed on site

(P-6239)
QG PRINTING CORP
6688 Box Springs Blvd, Riverside (92507-0726)
PHONE..................................951 571-2500
Ken Eazell, *Manager*
EMP: 230
SALES (corp-wide): 4.1B **Publicly Held**
WEB: www.qwdys.com
SIC: 2721 2752 Periodicals; commercial printing, lithographic
HQ: Qg Printing Corp.
N61w23044 Harrys Way
Sussex WI 53089

(P-6240)
QUALITY CIRCLE INSTITUTE INC
Also Called: Quality Digest
555 East Ave, Chico (95926-1204)
PHONE..................................530 893-4095
Mike Richman, *Manager*
Dirk Dusharme, *Chief*
Taran March, *Director*
April Johnson, *Manager*
EMP: 14
SALES (corp-wide): 1.6MM **Privately Held**
WEB: www.qualitydigest.com
SIC: 2721 8742 Periodicals; management consulting services
PA: Quality Circle Institute, Inc
633 Orange St Ste 3
Chico CA
530 893-4095

(P-6241)
R T C GROUP
Also Called: Cots Journal Magazine
905 Calle Amanecer # 250, San Clemente (92673-6274)
PHONE..................................949 226-2000
John Reardon, *Owner*
Rolando Trujillo, *Executive*
John Koon, *Business Dir*
Jim Bell, *Art Dir*
Jeff Child, *Editor*
EMP: 20

SALES (est): 2.3MM **Privately Held**
WEB: www.rtcgroup.com
SIC: 2721 Magazines: publishing only, not printed on site

(P-6242)
RACER MEDIA & MARKETING INC
17030 Red Hill Ave, Irvine (92614-5626)
PHONE......................949 417-6700
William Sparks, *COO*
Paul Pfanner, *President*
EMP: 14
SQ FT: 4,500
SALES (est): 1.4MM **Privately Held**
SIC: 2721 Magazines: publishing only, not printed on site

(P-6243)
RANGEFINDER PUBLISHING CO INC
Also Called: After Capture
11835 W Olympic Blvd 550e, Los Angeles (90064-5001)
PHONE......................310 846-4770
Stephen Sheanin, *President*
EMP: 18
SQ FT: 12,000
SALES (est): 1.7MM
SALES (corp-wide): 348.2MM **Publicly Held**
WEB: www.rfpublishing.com
SIC: 2721 Magazines: publishing only, not printed on site
HQ: Emerald Expositions, Llc
 31910 Del Obispo St # 200
 San Juan Capistrano CA 92675
 -

(P-6244)
READER MAGAZINE
108 Orange St Ste 11, Redlands (92373-4719)
PHONE......................909 335-8100
Chris Theater, *President*
EMP: 11
SALES (est): 823.5K **Privately Held**
SIC: 2721 Magazines: publishing only, not printed on site

(P-6245)
RECRUITMENT SERVICES INC
Also Called: Working Nurse
3600 Wilshire Blvd Ste 15, Los Angeles (90010-2603)
PHONE......................213 364-1960
Randy Goldring, *President*
EMP: 12
SALES: 950K **Privately Held**
SIC: 2721 Periodicals

(P-6246)
RELX INC
Also Called: Lexisnexis Matthew Bender
201 Mission St Fl 26, San Francisco (94105-1831)
PHONE......................415 908-3200
Isabela Sonnenberg, *Principal*
EMP: 49
SALES (corp-wide): 9.7B **Privately Held**
SIC: 2721 2731 7389 Trade journals: publishing only, not printed on site; books: publishing only; trade show arrangement
HQ: Relx Inc.
 230 Park Ave Ste 700
 New York NY 10169
 212 309-8100

(P-6247)
RHODES PUBLICATIONS INC
Also Called: Working World
3600 Wilshire Blvd # 1526, Los Angeles (90010-2619)
PHONE......................213 385-4781
Catherine Rhodes, *President*
Richard Rhodes, *President*
EMP: 12
SALES (est): 1.1MM **Privately Held**
SIC: 2721 Magazines: publishing & printing

(P-6248)
ROADRACING WORLD PUBLISHING
Also Called: .com
581 Birch St Ste C, Lake Elsinore (92530-2746)
P.O. Box 1428 (92531-1428)
PHONE......................951 245-6411
Trudy Ulrich, *President*
John Ulrich, *Vice Pres*
Chris Ulrich,
▲ EMP: 10
SQ FT: 1,500
SALES (est): 2MM **Privately Held**
WEB: www.roadracingworld.com
SIC: 2721 Magazines: publishing & printing

(P-6249)
ROBB CURTCO MEDIA LLC
29160 Heathercliff Rd # 200, Malibu (90265-6306)
PHONE......................310 589-7700
EMP: 33
SALES (corp-wide): 17.4MM **Privately Held**
SIC: 2721 Magazines: publishing & printing
PA: Curtco Robb Media Llc
 29160 Heathercliff Rd # 1
 Malibu CA 90265
 310 589-7700

(P-6250)
RUNNERS WORLD MAGAZINE
2101 Rosecrans Ave # 6200, El Segundo (90245-4749)
PHONE......................310 615-4567
Steve Murphy, *President*
EMP: 17 EST: 1966
SALES (est): 552.6K **Privately Held**
SIC: 2721 Magazines: publishing only, not printed on site

(P-6251)
S & J ADVERTISING INC (PA)
Also Called: Monthly Grapevine, The
555 Mason St Ste 250, Vacaville (95688-4637)
PHONE......................707 448-6446
Judy Mena, *President*
Suzanne Clark, *Vice Pres*
Liz Clark, *Sales Associate*
EMP: 10
SALES (est): 791.8K **Privately Held**
WEB: www.sandjadvertising.com
SIC: 2721 Magazines: publishing only, not printed on site

(P-6252)
SAN DIEGO FAMILY MAGAZINE LLC
1475 6th Ave Ste 500, San Diego (92101-3200)
P.O. Box 23960 (92193-3960)
PHONE......................619 685-6970
Sharon Bay,
Larry Bay,
EMP: 11
SQ FT: 4,000
SALES (est): 1.3MM **Privately Held**
WEB: www.sandiegofamily.com
SIC: 2721 Magazines: publishing & printing

(P-6253)
SAN DIEGO MAGAZINE PUBG CO
707 Broadway Ste 1100, San Diego (92101-5315)
PHONE......................619 230-9292
James Fitzpatrick, *CEO*
EMP: 30
SQ FT: 10,000
SALES (est): 8.1MM
SALES (corp-wide): 3.2MM **Privately Held**
WEB: www.sandiegomag.com
SIC: 2721 Magazines: publishing only, not printed on site
PA: Curtco Publishing Llc
 29160 Heathercliff Rd # 1
 Malibu CA 90265
 310 589-7700

(P-6254)
SCI PUBLISHING INC
Also Called: Sportscar International
42 Digital Dr Ste 5, Novato (94949-5762)
P.O. Box 1529, Ross (94957-1529)
PHONE......................415 382-0580
Thomas Toldrian, *President*
Eric Gustafson, *Editor*
Aaron Jenkins, *Editor*
EMP: 11
SALES (est): 775.5K
SALES (corp-wide): 1.5MM **Privately Held**
SIC: 2721 Magazines: publishing only, not printed on site
PA: Ross Periodicals, Inc
 42 Digital Dr Ste 5
 Novato CA
 415 382-0580

(P-6255)
SELECT COMMUNICATIONS INC
Also Called: Los Altos Town Crier
138 Main St, Los Altos (94022-2905)
PHONE......................650 948-9000
Paul D Nyberg, *President*
Elizabeth Nyberg, *Vice Pres*
Howard Bischoff, *MIS Dir*
Kathy Lera, *Sales Dir*
Chris Redden, *Director*
EMP: 20
SQ FT: 3,600
SALES: 1.5MM **Privately Held**
WEB: www.losaltosonline.com
SIC: 2721 2711 Magazines: publishing only, not printed on site; newspapers, publishing & printing

(P-6256)
SERBIN COMMUNICATIONS INC
Also Called: Photographer's Forum
813 Reddick St, Santa Barbara (93103-3124)
PHONE......................805 564-7636
Glen Serbin, *President*
Susan Baraz, *Director*
▲ EMP: 15
SQ FT: 3,000
SALES (est): 1.7MM **Privately Held**
WEB: www.serbin.com
SIC: 2721 7335 Magazines: publishing only, not printed on site; commercial photography

(P-6257)
SIDNEY MILLERS BLACK RADIO EX
Also Called: Black Radio Exclusive Magazine
15030 Ventura Blvd # 864, Sherman Oaks (91403-5470)
PHONE......................818 907-9959
Susan Miller, *President*
EMP: 27 EST: 1978
SQ FT: 4,600
SALES (est): 1.9MM **Privately Held**
WEB: www.bremagazine.com
SIC: 2721 Magazines: publishing only, not printed on site

(P-6258)
SMITH PUBLISHING INC
Also Called: Santa Barbara Magazine
2064 Alameda Padre Serra # 120, Santa Barbara (93103-1704)
PHONE......................805 965-5999
Jennifer Smithhale, *President*
Jennifer Smith-Hale, *President*
EMP: 10
SALES (est): 1.1MM **Privately Held**
WEB: www.sbmag.com
SIC: 2721 Magazines: publishing only, not printed on site

(P-6259)
SOCCER LEARNING SYSTEMS INC
17610 Murphy Pkwy, Lathrop (95330-8629)
P.O. Box 765, Salida (95368-0765)
PHONE......................209 858-4300
Patrick Mc Quaid, *President*
Patrick McQuaid, *Managing Prtnr*
EMP: 10
SALES (est): 1MM **Privately Held**
WEB: www.soccerbooks.com
SIC: 2721 Periodicals

(P-6260)
SOCIETY FOR THE ADVANCEMENT OF
Also Called: Sampe
21680 Gateway Center Dr # 300, Diamond Bar (91765-2453)
PHONE......................626 521-9460
Gregg Balko, *CEO*
Priscilla Heredia, *Manager*
CJ James, *Manager*
EMP: 12 EST: 1944
SQ FT: 5,789
SALES: 258K **Privately Held**
SIC: 2721 Periodicals: publishing only

(P-6261)
SPIRITUAL COUNTERFEITS PRJ INC
Also Called: S C P
2606 Dwight Way, Berkeley (94704-3029)
P.O. Box 40015, Pasadena (91114-7015)
PHONE......................510 540-0300
Tal Brooke, *President*
EMP: 10
SQ FT: 3,284
SALES: 101.7K **Privately Held**
WEB: www.scp-inc.org
SIC: 2721 2741 Trade journals: publishing only, not printed on site; newsletter publishing

(P-6262)
STYLE MEDIA GROUP INC
120 Blue Ravine Rd Ste 5, Folsom (95630-4752)
P.O. Box 925 (95763-0925)
PHONE......................916 988-9888
Terence Carroll, *CEO*
Wendy Sipple, *COO*
Mark Mendelsohn, *VP Sales*
Siobhn Pritt, *Marketing Staff*
Bettie Cosby-Grijalva, *Manager*
EMP: 22
SALES (est): 2.1MM **Privately Held**
SIC: 2721 Magazines: publishing only, not printed on site

(P-6263)
SUBDIRECT LLC
Also Called: Subco
653 W Fallbrook Ave # 101, Fresno (93711-5503)
PHONE......................559 321-0449
Kelly Vucovich,
Michael Sheehy, *President*
Brian Knowles, *Chief Mktg Ofcr*
Scott Porterfield, *Division Mgr*
Kristina Rivera, *General Mgr*
EMP: 20
SQ FT: 10,000
SALES (est): 2.8MM **Privately Held**
SIC: 2721 Magazines: publishing & printing

(P-6264)
SUNSET PUBLISHING CORPORATION (HQ)
Also Called: Sunset Magazine
55 Harrison St Ste 150, Oakland (94607-3772)
P.O. Box 62375, Tampa FL (33662-2375)
PHONE......................650 324-5558
Kevin Lynch, *Vice Pres*
Christopher Kevorkian, *Vice Pres*
Mark Okean, *Vice Pres*
Christina Olsen, *Vice Pres*
Lorinda Reichert, *Vice Pres*
EMP: 150 EST: 1928
SQ FT: 56,000
SALES (est): 14.4MM
SALES (corp-wide): 21.6MM **Privately Held**
WEB: www.sunset.com
SIC: 2721 2731 Magazines: publishing only, not printed on site; books: publishing only
PA: Regent, Lp
 9720 Wilshire Blvd
 Beverly Hills CA 90212
 310 299-4100

(P-6265)
SYNTHESIS
210 W 6th St, Chico (95928-5510)
PHONE......................530 899-7708
William Fishkin, *Owner*

EMP: 25
SQ FT: 1,600
SALES (est): 1.8MM **Privately Held**
WEB: www.synthesis.net
SIC: 2721 Periodicals

(P-6266)
T C MEDIA INC
Also Called: Pacific Rim Publishing
40748 Encyclopedia Cir, Fremont
(94538-2473)
PHONE.................510 656-5100
Thomas OH, *President*
Joan Chien, *Admin Sec*
Gene Ching, *Publisher*
Gigi C OH, *Publisher*
EMP: 10
SQ FT: 40,000
SALES (est): 992K **Privately Held**
WEB: www.martialartsmart.com
SIC: 2721 7812 5941 8743 Magazines:
publishing only, not printed on site; video
tape production; martial arts equipment &
supplies; promotion service

(P-6267)
TEN ENTHUSIAST NETWORK LLC
Transworld Snowboarding
2052 Corte Del Nogal # 100, Carlsbad
(92011-1498)
PHONE.................760 722-7777
Scott Dickey, *CEO*
Courtney Owyeong, *CFO*
Ashley Otte, *General Mgr*
Mozelle Martinez, *Office Mgr*
Paul Kobriger, *Mktg Dir*
EMP: 125 **Privately Held**
SIC: 2721 Periodicals
PA: Ten Publishing Media, Llc
831 S Douglas St Ste 100
El Segundo CA 90245

(P-6268)
TENNIS MEDIA CO LLC
814 S Westgate Ave # 100, Los Angeles
(90049-5678)
PHONE.................310 966-8182
Jeffrey Williams, *Mng Member*
Steve Furgals, *President*
Michael Sultan, *CFO*
EMP: 10
SALES: 7MM **Privately Held**
SIC: 2721 Magazines: publishing & printing

(P-6269)
THEATER PUBLICATIONS INC
Also Called: Pisani Printing II
3485 Victor St, Santa Clara (95054-2319)
P.O. Box 4743 (95056-4743)
PHONE.................408 748-1600
Michael Pisani, *President*
Gail Pisani, *Vice Pres*
EMP: 10
SQ FT: 3,000
SALES (est): 1.2MM **Privately Held**
WEB: www.theaterpublications.com
SIC: 2721 2752 Magazines: publishing &
printing; commercial printing, lithographic

(P-6270)
THOMSON REUTERS (MARKETS) LLC
Also Called: THOMSON REUTERS (MARKETS) LLC
1 Sansome St Lbby 3, San Francisco
(94104-4448)
PHONE.................415 344-6000
Andrea Lavoie, *Principal*
EMP: 345 **Privately Held**
WEB: www.tfn.com
SIC: 2721 Periodicals
HQ: Thomson Reuters (Markets) Llc
3 Times Sq
New York NY 10036
646 223-4000

(P-6271)
TIME INC
2 Embarcadero Ctr # 1900, San Francisco
(94111-3914)
PHONE.....:.................415 434-5244
Tim Richards, *Manager*
EMP: 33

SALES (corp-wide): 1.7B **Publicly Held**
SIC: 2721 Magazines: publishing only, not
printed on site
HQ: Time Inc.
225 Liberty St Ste C2
New York NY 10281
212 522-1212

(P-6272)
TL ENTERPRISES LLC (DH)
Also Called: Highways Magazine
2750 Park View Ct Ste 240, Oxnard
(93036-5458)
PHONE.................805 981-8393
Marcus Lemonis, *President*
Thomas Wolfe, *CFO*
Stephen Adams, *Chairman*
Laurie James, *Vice Pres*
Chuck Gregory, *Opers Staff*
EMP: 27
SALES (est): 25.1MM
SALES (corp-wide): 488.7MM **Privately Held**
WEB: www.motorhomemagazine.com
SIC: 2721 Magazines: publishing only, not
printed on site

(P-6273)
TOURISM DEVELOPMENT CORP (PA)
Also Called: Where Orange County Magazine
3679 Motor Ave Ste 300, Los Angeles
(90034-5762)
PHONE.................310 280-2880
Jeff Levy, *President*
Leanne Killian, *Executive*
Amina Karwa, *Admin Asst*
Dawn Cheng, *Prdtn Mgr*
Benjamin Epstein, *Chief*
▲ EMP: 10
SQ FT: 3,000
SALES (est): 2.1MM **Privately Held**
SIC: 2721 Magazines: publishing only, not
printed on site

(P-6274)
TRANSFORMATIONNET MEDIA LLC
Also Called: Realtalkla
1640 N Spring St, Los Angeles
(90012-1927)
PHONE.................310 476-5259
Jay M Levin, *CEO*
Karen Fund,
Sridhar RAO,
EMP: 35 EST: 1999
SQ FT: 7,200
SALES (est): 2.1MM **Privately Held**
WEB: www.realtalkla.com
SIC: 2721 Magazines: publishing & printing

(P-6275)
TWELVE SIGNS INC
Also Called: Starscroll
3369 S Robertson Blvd, Los Angeles
(90034)
PHONE.................310 553-8000
Richard W Housman, *President*
H Kim, *Vice Pres*
EMP: 100
SQ FT: 25,000
SALES (est): 9.1MM **Privately Held**
WEB: www.starmatch.com
SIC: 2721 Magazines: publishing only, not
printed on site

(P-6276)
UBM CANON LLC (DH)
2901 28th St Ste 100, Santa Monica
(90405-2975)
PHONE.................310 445-4200
Sally Shankland, *CEO*
Scott Schulman, *CEO*
Brian Field, *COO*
Rudolf Hotter, *COO*
David Cox, *CFO*
EMP: 122
SQ FT: 50,000
SALES (est): 60.3MM
SALES (corp-wide): 1B **Privately Held**
WEB: www.cancom.com
SIC: 2721 7389 Magazines: publishing
only, not printed on site; trade show
arrangement

HQ: Ubm, Llc
1983 Marcus Ave Ste 250
New Hyde Park NY 11042
516 562-7800

(P-6277)
UBM LLC
18301 Von Karman Ave # 920, Irvine
(92612-1009)
PHONE.................415 947-6770
Sharon Fibelkorn, *Manager*
Steve Weitzner, *President*
Jennifer Reidy, *Training Spec*
R C Johnson, *Editor*
EMP: 55
SALES (corp-wide): 1B **Privately Held**
WEB: www.cmp.com
SIC: 2721 2741 Periodicals: publishing
only; miscellaneous publishing
HQ: Ubm, Llc
1983 Marcus Ave Ste 250
New Hyde Park NY 11042
516 562-7800

(P-6278)
UBM LLC
Also Called: Cmp Healthcare Media
303 2nd St Ste 900s, San Francisco
(94107-1375)
PHONE.................415 947-6488
Armand Derhacobian, *Director*
EMP: 128
SALES (corp-wide): 1B **Privately Held**
WEB: www.cmp.com
SIC: 2721 Magazines: publishing & printing
HQ: Ubm, Llc
1983 Marcus Ave Ste 250
New Hyde Park NY 11042
516 562-7800

(P-6279)
UBM TECHWEB (DH)
303 Secon St Tower Fl 9 9 Stower, San
Francisco (94107)
PHONE.................415 947-6000
Paul Miller, *CEO*
Marco Pardi, *President*
John Dennehy, *CFO*
Lenny Heymann, *Exec VP*
Fred S Knight, *Vice Pres*
EMP: 14
SALES (est): 9.1MM
SALES (corp-wide): 1B **Privately Held**
SIC: 2721 Magazines: publishing only, not
printed on site
HQ: Ubm, Llc
1983 Marcus Ave Ste 250
New Hyde Park NY 11042
516 562-7800

(P-6280)
UNION PUBLICATIONS INC
653 Wellesley Ave, Kensington
(94708-1009)
PHONE.................510 525-6300
Hoda Perry, *President*
Douglas Perry, *Corp Secy*
EMP: 11
SALES (est): 1MM **Privately Held**
SIC: 2721 2759

(P-6281)
UNITED ADVG PUBLICATIONS INC
Also Called: For Rent
3017 Douglas Blvd, Roseville
(95661-3848)
PHONE.................916 746-2300
Dee Dahl, *Exec Dir*
Heather Jones, *Admin Asst*
EMP: 21 **Privately Held**
WEB: www.traderonline.com
SIC: 2721 Magazines: publishing & printing
HQ: United Advertising Publications, Inc.
1331 L St Nw Ste 2
Washington DC 20005
210 377-3116

(P-6282)
UNITED ADVG PUBLICATIONS INC
Also Called: For Rent
8250 White Oak Ave # 101, Rancho Cuca-
monga (91730-7679)
PHONE.................909 466-1480
Melanie Frances, *Manager*

EMP: 19 **Privately Held**
WEB: www.traderonline.com
SIC: 2721 Magazines: publishing & printing
HQ: United Advertising Publications, Inc.
1331 L St Nw Ste 2
Washington DC 20005
210 377-3116

(P-6283)
UNIVERSAL MEDICAL PRESS INC
2443 Fillmore St, San Francisco
(94115-1814)
PHONE.................415 436-9790
Thomas F Laszlo, *President*
EMP: 12
SALES (est): 944.3K **Privately Held**
SIC: 2721 8011 Trade journals: publishing
only, not printed on site; offices & clinics
of medical doctors

(P-6284)
VIDEOMAKER INC
Also Called: Smart TV & Sound
645 Mangrove Ave, Chico (95926-3946)
P.O. Box 4591 (95927-4591)
PHONE.................530 891-8410
Matthew York, *President*
Patrice York, *Treasurer*
Terra Yurkovic, *Business Dir*
Jennifer O'Rourke, *General Mgr*
Jill Lutge, *Web Dvlpr*
EMP: 36
SQ FT: 8,000
SALES (est): 4MM **Privately Held**
WEB: www.litewheels.com
SIC: 2721 7812 Magazines: publishing
only, not printed on site; motion picture &
video production

(P-6285)
VISTANOMICS INC
3450 Ocean View Blvd Frnt, Glendale
(91208-3301)
PHONE.................818 249-1236
Gary W Short, *President*
EMP: 10
SQ FT: 800
SALES (est): 1.2MM **Privately Held**
SIC: 2721 3829 Periodicals: publishing
only; measuring & controlling devices

(P-6286)
VIZ MEDIA LLC
Also Called: Viz Media Music
1355 Market St Ste 200, San Francisco
(94103-1460)
P.O. Box 77010 (94107-0010)
PHONE.................415 546-7073
Hidemi Fukuhara, *CEO*
Brad Woods, *Chief Mktg Ofcr*
Hyoe Narita, *Exec VP*
Akane Matsuo, *Vice Pres*
Keith Beasley, *Web Dvlpr*
▲ EMP: 153
SALES (est): 37.5MM
SALES (corp-wide): 850.9MM **Privately Held**
WEB: www.viz.com
SIC: 2721 2731 7819 6794 Comic books:
publishing only, not printed on site; books:
publishing only; video tape or disk repro-
duction; copyright buying & licensing; pre-
recorded records & tapes
PA: Shogakukan Inc.
2-3-1, Hitotsubashi
Chiyoda-Ku TKY 101-0
332 305-211

(P-6287)
WEIDER LEASING INC
21100 Erwin St, Woodland Hills
(91367-3712)
PHONE.................818 884-6800
EMP: 100
SQ FT: 32,000
SALES (est): 4.7MM **Privately Held**
SIC: 2721

(P-6288)
WEIDER PUBLICATIONS LLC (HQ)
Also Called: Muscle & Fitness Flex M&F Hers
3699 Wilshire Blvd # 1220, Los Angeles
(90010-2732)
PHONE.................818 884-6800

▲ = Import ▼=Export
◆ =Import/Export

David Pecker,
Rebecca Schramm, *Info Tech Dir*
Robert Wynn, *Agent*
EMP: 65
SQ FT: 48,000
SALES (est): 49.2MM
SALES (corp-wide): 300MM **Privately Held**
WEB: www.fitnessonline.com
SIC: 2721 Magazines: publishing only, not printed on site
PA: American Media, Inc.
1350 E Newport
Deerfield Beach FL 33442
212 545-4800

(P-6289)
WELLS PUBLISHING INC (PA)
Also Called: Insurance Journal
3570 Camino Delrio N 20, San Diego (92108)
PHONE..............................619 584-1100
Mark Wells, *President*
Mindy Trammell, *Sales Staff*
Don Jergler, *Editor*
EMP: 22 **EST:** 1923
SQ FT: 3,600
SALES (est): 2.2MM **Privately Held**
WEB: www.insurancejrnl.com
SIC: 2721 8111 Magazines: publishing & printing; legal services

(P-6290)
WENNER MEDIA LLC
5700 Wilshire Blvd # 345, Los Angeles (90036-3626)
PHONE..............................323 930-3300
Dawn Rice, *Manager*
EMP: 20
SALES (est): 1.2MM
SALES (corp-wide): 63.3MM **Privately Held**
SIC: 2721 Magazines: publishing & printing
PA: Wenner Media Llc
1290 Ave Of The Amer Fl 2
New York NY 10104
212 484-1616

(P-6291)
WEST WORLD PRODUCTIONS INC
420 N Camden Dr, Beverly Hills (90210-4507)
PHONE..............................310 273-9874
Yuri Spiro, *President*
EMP: 21 **EST:** 1980
SQ FT: 9,000
SALES (est): 2.4MM **Privately Held**
WEB: www.wwpi.com
SIC: 2721 Trade journals: publishing only, not printed on site

(P-6292)
WINE COMMUNICATIONS GROUP
Also Called: Wine Business Monthly
35 Maple St, Sonoma (95476-7014)
PHONE..............................707 939-0822
Eric Jorgensen, *President*
Liz Netherton, *Social Dir*
Jacki Kardum, *Office Mgr*
Curtis Phillips, *Technical Staff*
EMP: 15
SALES: 2MM **Privately Held**
WEB: www.winebusinessmonthly.com
SIC: 2721 Magazines: publishing only, not printed on site

(P-6293)
WIRED VENTURES INC
520 3rd St Ste 305, San Francisco (94107-6805)
PHONE..............................415 276-8400
Louis Rossetto, *Ch of Bd*
Kimberly Kelleher, *Officer*
Sally Lyon, *Business Dir*
Jane Metcalfe, *Principal*
Ron Licata, *Prdtn Dir*
EMP: 175
SALES (est): 37.8MM **Privately Held**
SIC: 2721 6719 Magazines: publishing only, not printed on site; investment holding companies, except banks

(P-6294)
WORLD TARIFF LIMITED
Also Called: Worldtariff
220 Montgomery St Ste 448, San Francisco (94104-3536)
PHONE..............................415 391-7501
G Edmund Clark, *President*
EMP: 25
SQ FT: 5,335
SALES (est): 1.6MM
SALES (corp-wide): 65.4B **Publicly Held**
WEB: www.worldtariff.com
SIC: 2721 Statistical reports (periodicals): publishing & printing
HQ: Fedex Trade Networks, Inc.
6075 Poplar Ave Ste 300
Memphis TN 38119
901 684-4800

(P-6295)
WORLDRADIO INC
Also Called: Worldradio News
2120 28th St, Sacramento (95818-1910)
PHONE..............................916 457-3655
Armond Noble, *President*
EMP: 12
SALES (est): 1MM **Privately Held**
WEB: www.wr6wr.com
SIC: 2721 Magazines: publishing only, not printed on site

(P-6296)
WRITE THOUGHT INC
1254 Commerce Way, Sanger (93657-8731)
PHONE..............................559 876-2170
Stephen B Mettee, *President*
EMP: 15
SALES (est): 1MM **Privately Held**
SIC: 2721 2731 Magazines: publishing & printing; books: publishing & printing

(P-6297)
WSR PUBLISHING INC (PA)
Also Called: Widescreen Review
27645 Commerce Center Dr, Temecula (92590-2521)
P.O. Box 2587 (92593-2587)
PHONE..............................951 676-4914
Gary Reber, *President*
Mary M Reber, *Exec VP*
Tricia Spears, *Assoc Editor*
EMP: 14
SQ FT: 7,000
SALES: 1.9MM **Privately Held**
WEB: www.surroundmusic.net
SIC: 2721 2731 Periodicals: publishing only; radio, television & electronic stores

(P-6298)
XPLAIN CORPORATION
Also Called: Mactech Magazine
705 Lakefield Rd Ste I, Westlake Village (91361-5903)
P.O. Box 5200 (91359-5200)
PHONE..............................805 494-9797
Neil Ticktin, *President*
Andrea Sniderman, *Ch of Bd*
EMP: 15
SALES (est): 1.1MM **Privately Held**
WEB: www.xplain.com
SIC: 2721 5994 Magazines: publishing only, not printed on site; magazine stand

(P-6299)
ZOASIS CORPORATION
1960 E Grand Ave Ste 555, El Segundo (90245-5099)
PHONE..............................800 745-4725
Douglas Drew, *CEO*
David Aucoin, *President*
Lisa Moise, *Vice Pres*
EMP: 39
SQ FT: 7,000
SALES (est): 3.1MM **Privately Held**
WEB: www.zoasis.com
SIC: 2721 8742 7375 Periodicals: publishing only; marketing consulting services; information retrieval services

---

2731 Books: Publishing & Printing

(P-6300)
5 BALL INC
Also Called: Bikernet.com
200 Broad Ave, Wilmington (90744-5812)
PHONE..............................310 830-0630
Keith Ball, *CEO*
Jason Douglass, *Vice Pres*
Ladd Terry, *Vice Pres*
Ben Lamboeuf, *Adv Dir*
EMP: 12 **EST:** 1995
SQ FT: 2,000
SALES: 34.4K **Privately Held**
WEB: www.bikernet.com
SIC: 2731 Book publishing

(P-6301)
A B C-CLIO INC (PA)
Also Called: ABC-Clio
130 Cremona Dr Ste C, Santa Barbara (93117-5505)
P.O. Box 1911 (93116-1911)
PHONE..............................805 968-1911
Ronald Boehm, *CEO*
Marlys Boehm, *Admin Sec*
Mark Lacommare, *Info Tech Mgr*
Chris Martinich, *Software Dev*
Roblyn Hartsfield, *IT/INT Sup*
EMP: 115 **EST:** 1955
SQ FT: 25,000
SALES (est): 15.8MM **Privately Held**
WEB: www.abc-clio.com
SIC: 2731 Books: publishing only

(P-6302)
ABC - CLIO LLC
130 Cremona Dr Ste C, Santa Barbara (93117-5505)
P.O. Box 1911 (93116-1911)
PHONE..............................800 368-6868
Becky A Snyder,
Vince Burns, *Vice Pres*
Jimi Derouen, *Business Anlyst*
Jennifer Pfau, *Opers Staff*
Mike Florman, *Production*
EMP: 13
SALES (est): 1MM **Privately Held**
SIC: 2731 Book publishing

(P-6303)
ALAN WOFSY FINE ARTS LLC
Also Called: Dow Frosini
1109 Geary Blvd, San Francisco (94109-6815)
P.O. Box 2210 (94126-2210)
PHONE..............................415 292-6500
Alan Wofsy, *Principal*
EMP: 10
SQ FT: 500
SALES (est): 19.1K **Privately Held**
WEB: www.art-books.com
SIC: 2731 5192 8412 Books: publishing only; books; art gallery

(P-6304)
ALFRED MUSIC GROUP INC (PA)
16320 Roscoe Blvd Ste 100, Van Nuys (91406-1216)
PHONE..............................818 891-5999
Steven Manus, *CEO*
Ron Manus, *President*
Christina Cohen, *General Mgr*
Robin Wolff, *Admin Asst*
Dan Otoole, *CTO*
EMP: 20
SALES (est): 1.6MM **Privately Held**
SIC: 2731 Book music: publishing & printing

(P-6305)
ALLAN BORUSHEK & ASSOC INC
16360 Pacific Coast Hwy # 216, Huntington Beach (92649-1819)
PHONE..............................949 642-8500
Allan Borushek, *CEO*
▲ **EMP:** 10
SQ FT: 3,000
SALES (est): 740K **Privately Held**
WEB: www.calorieking.com
SIC: 2731 Books: publishing only

(P-6306)
ALPHA PUBLISHING CORPORATION
Also Called: McDowell Publishers
337 N Vineyard Ave # 240, Ontario (91764-4453)
PHONE..............................909 464-0500
Taki Khan, *President*
EMP: 35
SQ FT: 4,500
SALES: 9MM **Privately Held**
SIC: 2731 5961 Book publishing; books, mail order (except book clubs)

(P-6307)
AMAZING FACTS INC
Also Called: Amazing Facts Ministries
1203 W Sunset Blvd, Rocklin (95765-1305)
P.O. Box 1058, Roseville (95678-8058)
PHONE..............................916 434-3880
Doug Batchelor, *President*
Richard Marker, *Partner*
Todd Parrish, *Partner*
Boyd Brod, *President*
Pam Lascoe, *COO*
EMP: 70
SQ FT: 28,000
SALES (est): 9.1MM **Privately Held**
WEB: www.bibleuniverse.com
SIC: 2731 4832 4833 Pamphlets: publishing & printing; religious; television broadcasting stations

(P-6308)
AMERICAN PUBLISHING CORP
2143 E Convention Center, Ontario (91764-5635)
PHONE..............................909 390-7548
Taki Khan, *President*
EMP: 26
SQ FT: 11,000
SALES: 8MM **Privately Held**
SIC: 2731 Book publishing

(P-6309)
ANTHEM MUSIC & MEDIA FUND LLC
Also Called: Bicycle Music Co, The
100 N Crescent Dr Ste 323, Beverly Hills (90210-5453)
PHONE..............................310 286-6600
Jake Wisely, *CEO*
Michael Pizzuto, *Senior VP*
Steve Toland, *Vice Pres*
Maeline Younger, *Manager*
EMP: 14
SALES (est): 1.3MM **Privately Held**
SIC: 2731 Book music: publishing & printing

(P-6310)
AVN MEDIA NETWORK INC
Also Called: Adult Video News
9400 Penfield Ave, Chatsworth (91311-6549)
PHONE..............................818 718-5788
Tony Rios, *CEO*
Roy Karch, *Bd of Directors*
Roy Salter, *Vice Pres*
Jesse Dena, *Creative Dir*
Bonnie Leblanc, *Prdtn Mgr*
EMP: 30
SQ FT: 15,000
SALES (est): 3.9MM **Privately Held**
SIC: 2731 2721 Book publishing; periodicals

(P-6311)
BERRETT-KOEHLER PUBLISHERS INC (PA)
1333 Broadway Ste 1000, Oakland (94612-1926)
PHONE..............................510 817-2277
Steven Piersanti, *President*
Richard Wilson, *Vice Pres*
▲ **EMP:** 20
SQ FT: 5,400
SALES (est): 3MM **Privately Held**
WEB: www.bkpub.com
SIC: 2731 Books: publishing only

P R O D U C T S & S V C S

(P-6312)
BERTELSMANN INC
Also Called: Arvato Services
29011 Commerce Center Dr, Valencia
(91355-4195)
PHONE...................661 702-2700
Janet Adams, *Manager*
EMP: 400
SALES (corp-wide): 82.3MM **Privately Held**
WEB: www.bertelsmann.com
SIC: 2731 Book publishing
HQ: Bertelsmann, Inc.
1745 Broadway Fl 20
New York NY 10019
212 782-1000

(P-6313)
BEST VALUE TEXTBOOKS LLC
Also Called: BVT Publishing
410 Hemsted Dr Ste 100, Redding
(96002-0164)
P.O. Box 492831 (96049-2831)
PHONE...................530 222-5980
Jason James, *Mng Member*
Richard Schofield, *Business Dir*
Erik Lineback, *Software Dev*
Tim Gerlach, *Graphic Designe*
Shannon Conley, *Business Mgr*
EMP: 22
SQ FT: 2,000
SALES (est): 4.6MM **Privately Held**
WEB: www.bestvaluetextbooks.com
SIC: 2731 Textbooks: publishing & printing

(P-6314)
BETTER CHINESE LLC
150 W Iowa Ave Ste 104, Sunnyvale
(94086-6179)
P.O. Box 695, Palo Alto (94302-0695)
PHONE...................650 384-0902
James Lin, *Mng Member*
Xuqing Zan, *Assoc Editor*
▲ EMP: 10 EST: 2005
SALES (est): 1.1MM **Privately Held**
SIC: 2731 Book publishing

(P-6315)
BHAKTIVEDANTA BOOK TR INTL INC
Also Called: Bbt
9701 Venus Blvd Ste A, Los Angeles
(90034)
PHONE...................310 837-5284
Emil Beca, *President*
Stuart Kadetz, *Treasurer*
Gil Sanchez, *Admin Sec*
▲ EMP: 12
SQ FT: 5,000
SALES: 652.3K **Privately Held**
WEB: www.mcremo.com
SIC: 2731 Books: publishing only

(P-6316)
BLUE MTN CTR OF MEDITATION INC
Also Called: Nilgiri Press
3600 Tomales Rd, Tomales (94971)
P.O. Box 256 (94971-0256)
PHONE...................707 878-2369
Christine Easwaran, *President*
Joan Barnicle, *Manager*
John Suerstedt, *Manager*
EMP: 20
SQ FT: 1,800
SALES: 1.3MM **Privately Held**
WEB: www.bluemountaincenter.org
SIC: 2731 8661 Books: publishing & printing; religious organizations

(P-6317)
BLURB INC
580 California St Fl 3, San Francisco
(94104-1024)
PHONE...................415 364-6300
Eileen Gittins, *CEO*
Elizabeth Allen, *Chief Mktg Ofcr*
Kelly Leach, *General Mgr*
Jennifer Alderete, *Sr Software Eng*
Krista Jackson, *Software Engr*
EMP: 54
SALES (est): 11.8MM **Privately Held**
SIC: 2731 Books: publishing only

(P-6318)
BRIDGE PUBLICATIONS INC (PA)
Also Called: Bpi Records
5600 E Olympic Blvd, Commerce
(90022-5128)
PHONE...................323 888-6200
Blake Silber, *CEO*
Lis Astrupgaard, *President*
Sisel Lan, *Exec VP*
Helen Lumbroso, *Vice Pres*
Irma Macias, *Vice Pres*
▲ EMP: 40
SQ FT: 15,000
SALES (est): 18.4MM **Privately Held**
SIC: 2731 3652 Books: publishing only; pre-recorded records & tapes

(P-6319)
BRYAN EDWARDS PUBLISHING CO
Also Called: Flash Anatomy
2185 N Orange Olive Rd # 3, Orange
(92865-3300)
PHONE...................714 634-0264
Bryan Edward Nash, *President*
EMP: 10
SALES (est): 994K **Privately Held**
SIC: 2731 Books: publishing only

(P-6320)
C&T PUBLISHING INC
1651 Challenge Dr, Concord (94520-5206)
PHONE...................925 677-0377
J Todd Hensley, *CEO*
Tony Hensley, *CFO*
▲ EMP: 43
SQ FT: 12,250
SALES (est): 5.5MM **Privately Held**
WEB: www.ctpub.com
SIC: 2731 Books: publishing only

(P-6321)
CENGAGE LEARNING INC
Also Called: Thomson Higher Education
303 2nd St Ste S500, San Francisco
(94107-1373)
PHONE...................415 839-2300
Frank Talamantez, *Manager*
Frank Messina, *Exec Dir*
Ilya Aronov, *Info Tech Mgr*
Steve Lee, *Financial Analy*
Cynthia Hernandez, *Human Resources*
EMP: 315 **Privately Held**
WEB: www.thomsonlearning.com
SIC: 2731 Textbooks: publishing & printing
PA: Cengage Learning, Inc.
20 Channel Ctr St
Boston MA 02210

(P-6322)
CENGAGE LEARNING INC
Education To Go
40880 County Center Dr G, Temecula
(92591-6024)
P.O. Box 760 (92593-0760)
PHONE...................951 719-1878
Jerry Weissberg, *Branch Mgr*
EMP: 35 **Privately Held**
WEB: www.thomsonlearning.com
SIC: 2731 Textbooks: publishing & printing
PA: Cengage Learning, Inc.
20 Channel Ctr St
Boston MA 02210

(P-6323)
CENTER FOR CLLBRTIVE CLASSROOM
1001 Marina Village Pkwy # 110, Alameda
(94501-1092)
PHONE...................510 533-0213
Jacqueline Frankle, *Administration*
Victor Young, *President*
Brent Welling, *CFO*
Peter Brunn, *Vice Pres*
Kelly Stuart, *Vice Pres*
▲ EMP: 99
SQ FT: 15,000
SALES: 14.2MM **Privately Held**
WEB: www.devstu.org
SIC: 2731 8299 Book publishing; personal development school

(P-6324)
CENTERSOURCE SYSTEMS LLC
60 Commerce Ln Ste D, Cloverdale
(95425-4230)
PHONE...................707 838-1061
David Gibbs, *General Mgr*
Jeanne Gibbs, *Software Dev*
Carolyn Rankin,
Susan Rankin,
Michele McAhall, *Consultant*
▲ EMP: 10
SQ FT: 4,000
SALES (est): 1MM **Privately Held**
WEB: www.centersourcesystems.com
SIC: 2731 8748 Book publishing; business consulting

(P-6325)
CEQUAL PRODUCTS INC
1328 16th St, Santa Monica (90404-1804)
PHONE...................310 458-0441
▲ EMP: 10
SALES (est): 840K **Privately Held**
WEB: www.cequal.com
SIC: 2731 7812 8741

(P-6326)
CHICK PUBLICATIONS INC
8780 Archibald Ave, Rancho Cucamonga
(91730-4697)
P.O. Box 3500, Ontario (91761-1019)
PHONE...................909 987-0771
Jack T Chick, *President*
Ronald Rockney, *Treasurer*
George A Collins, *Vice Pres*
◆ EMP: 35 EST: 1961
SQ FT: 10,000
SALES (est): 4.3MM **Privately Held**
WEB: www.chick.com
SIC: 2731 5961 Books: publishing only; mail order house

(P-6327)
CHRONICLE BOOKS LLC
680 2nd St, San Francisco (94107-2015)
PHONE...................415 537-4200
Nion McEvoy,
John Carlson, *Exec Dir*
Daria Harper, *Admin Sec*
Gerry Kong, *Info Tech Mgr*
David Thompson, *Info Tech Mgr*
▲ EMP: 160
SALES (est): 22.1MM
SALES (corp-wide): 30.2MM **Privately Held**
WEB: www.chroniclebooks.com
SIC: 2731 Books: publishing only
PA: The Mcevoy Group Llc
680 2nd St
San Francisco CA 94107
415 537-4200

(P-6328)
CLP APG LLC
Also Called: Clp Apg, Inc.
1700 4th St, Berkeley (94710-1711)
PHONE...................510 528-1444
Charles B Winton, *Ch of Bd*
Susan Reich, *President*
EMP: 90
SQ FT: 14,000
SALES (est): 3.9MM
SALES (corp-wide): 173.4MM **Privately Held**
SIC: 2731 Books: publishing only
PA: Clp Pb, Llc
1290 Ave Of The Amrcas
New York NY 10104
212 340-8100

(P-6329)
COGNELLA INC
Also Called: University Readers
3970 Sorrento Valley Blvd # 500, San Diego
(92121-1416)
PHONE...................858 552-1120
Bassin Hamadeh, *CEO*
Ryan Bailey, *Vice Pres*
Mike Simpson, *Vice Pres*
Jennifer Bowen, *Admin Asst*
David Wilson, *Info Tech Dir*
EMP: 65
SQ FT: 8,000
SALES (est): 7.8MM **Privately Held**
WEB: www.universityreaders.com
SIC: 2731 Textbooks: publishing only, not printed on site

(P-6330)
CONCORD MUSIC GROUP INC
100 N Crescent Dr Ste 275, Beverly Hills
(90210-5412)
PHONE...................310 385-4455
Glen Barros, *CEO*
John Burk, *President*
Edward Ginis, *President*
Gene Rumsey, *President*
Bob Valentine, *CFO*
▲ EMP: 160
SQ FT: 8,000
SALES (est): 25.1MM **Privately Held**
SIC: 2731 Book music: publishing & printing

(P-6331)
CORWIN PRESS INC
2455 Teller Rd, Newbury Park
(91320-2218)
PHONE...................805 499-9734
Douglas Rife, *President*
Melissa Mirkovich, *Vice Chairman*
Johnnie A James, *Senior VP*
Elena Nikitina, *Vice Pres*
Leigh Peake, *Vice Pres*
EMP: 19
SALES (est): 2.1MM
SALES (corp-wide): 117.8MM **Privately Held**
WEB: www.corwinpress.com
SIC: 2731 Books: publishing only
PA: Sage Publications, Inc.
2455 Teller Rd
Thousand Oaks CA 91320
805 499-0721

(P-6332)
CPP/BELWIN INC
16320 Roscoe Blvd Ste 100, Van Nuys
(91406-1216)
PHONE...................818 891-5999
Steven Manus, *President*
▲ EMP: 31
SQ FT: 142,000
SALES (est): 1.9MM **Privately Held**
SIC: 2731 Book music: publishing only, not printed on site
PA: Alfred Music Group Inc.
16320 Roscoe Blvd Ste 100
Van Nuys CA 91406

(P-6333)
CREATIVE TEACHING PRESS INC (PA)
6262 Katella Ave, Cypress (90630-5204)
PHONE...................714 799-2100
James M Connelly, *CEO*
Luella Connelly, *Chairman*
Patrick Connelly, *Treasurer*
Susan Connelly, *Admin Sec*
Mike Kennedy, *Administration*
◆ EMP: 66
SQ FT: 85,000
SALES (est): 13.4MM **Privately Held**
WEB: www.creativeteaching.com
SIC: 2731 Books: publishing only

(P-6334)
DAWN SIGN PRESS INC
6130 Nancy Ridge Dr, San Diego
(92121-3223)
PHONE...................858 625-0600
Joe Dannis, *CEO*
Wendy McNair, *CFO*
Tina Jo Breindel, *Treasurer*
Brianna Guzman, *Vice Pres*
Rebecca Ryan, *Vice Pres*
◆ EMP: 28
SQ FT: 16,500
SALES: 7.7MM **Privately Held**
WEB: www.dawnsign.com
SIC: 2731 Books: publishing only

(P-6335)
DHARMA MUDRANALAYA (PA)
Also Called: Dharma Publishing
35788 Hauser Bridge Rd, Cazadero
(95421-9611)
PHONE...................707 847-3380

▲ = Import ▼=Export
◆ =Import/Export

Arnaud Maitland, *CEO*
Tarthang Tulku, *President*
Debbie Black, *Vice Pres*
Andreea Mosila, *Managing Dir*
Matthew Breit, *Technology*
▲ **EMP:** 21
SQ FT: 16,000
SALES: 376.1K **Privately Held**
WEB: www.dharmapublishing.com
SIC: 2731 7336 Books: publishing & printing; commercial art & graphic design

(P-6336)
DISNEY BOOK GROUP LLC (HQ)
Also Called: Hyperion Books For Children
500 S Buena Vista St, Burbank
(91521-0001)
PHONE.....................818 560-1000
Russell R Hampton Jr, *President*
Marsha L Reed, *Admin Sec*
EMP: 14
SALES (est): 1.3MM **Publicly Held**
SIC: 2731 Book publishing

(P-6337)
EDUCATIONAL IDEAS INCORPORATED
Also Called: Ballard & Tighe Publishers
471 Atlas St, Brea (92821-3118)
P.O. Box 219 (92822-0219)
PHONE.....................714 990-4332
Dorothy Roberts, *Ch of Bd*
Mark Espinola, *CEO*
Kent Roberts, *Admin Sec*
▲ **EMP:** 30
SQ FT: 12,000
SALES (est): 3.2MM **Privately Held**
WEB: www.ballard-tighe.com
SIC: 2731 Textbooks: publishing only, not printed on site

(P-6338)
ELAINE GILL INC
Also Called: Crossing Press, The
6001 Shellmound St Fl 4th, Emeryville
(94608-1968)
PHONE.....................510 559-1600
Philip Wood, *President*
Joann Deck, *Vice Pres*
EMP: 15 EST: 1966
SQ FT: 14,800
SALES (est): 960K **Privately Held**
SIC: 2731 Books: publishing only

(P-6339)
EVAN-MOOR CORPORATION (HQ)
Also Called: Evan-Moor Educational Publr
18 Lower Ragsdale Dr, Monterey
(93940-5746)
PHONE.....................831 649-5901
William E Evans, *President*
Joellen Moore, *Vice Pres*
Dave Miller, *Finance*
James F O'Donnell III, *VP Sales*
▲ **EMP:** 30
SQ FT: 20,000
SALES (est): 10MM
SALES (corp-wide): 15.2MM **Privately Held**
WEB: www.evan-moor.com
SIC: 2731 Books: publishing & printing
PA: Lincoln Learning Solutions, Inc.
294 Massachusetts Ave
Rochester PA 15074
724 764-7200

(P-6340)
FONDO DE CULTURA ECONOMICA
2293 Verus St, San Diego (92154-4704)
PHONE.....................619 429-0455
Rovolso Pataky, *Manager*
EMP: 10
SQ FT: 7,822 **Privately Held**
WEB: www.fondodeculturaeconomica.com
SIC: 2731 Textbooks: publishing only, not printed on site; books: publishing only
HQ: Fondo De Cultura Economica
Carr. Picacho - Ajusco No. 227
Ciudad De Mexico CDMX 14738

(P-6341)
FOUR M STUDIOS
Also Called: Meredith Publishing
201 Mission St Fl 12, San Francisco
(94105-1888)
PHONE.....................415 249-2362
Tamara Marcsisak, *Manager*
EMP: 80
SALES (corp-wide): 2.2B **Publicly Held**
WEB: www.meredith.com
SIC: 2731 2721 Book publishing; periodicals
PA: Meredith Corporation
1716 Locust St
Des Moines IA 50309
515 284-3000

(P-6342)
GALAXY PRESS INC
6115-6121 Malburg Way, Vernon (90058)
PHONE.....................323 399-3433
Mich Breuer, *General Mgr*
EMP: 25
SALES (est): 904.5K **Privately Held**
SIC: 2731 Book publishing

(P-6343)
GANDER PUBLISHING INC
450 Front St, Avila Beach (93424)
P.O. Box 780 (93424-0780)
PHONE.....................805 541-5523
Nanci L Bell, *CEO*
▲ **EMP:** 18
SQ FT: 5,000
SALES (est): 1.8MM **Privately Held**
WEB: www.ganderpublishing.net
SIC: 2731 Books: publishing only

(P-6344)
GAULT MILLAU INC
4311 Wilshire Blvd # 405, Los Angeles
(90001-3713)
PHONE.....................323 617-3982
Andre Gayot, *President*
Christian Millau, *Shareholder*
Alain Gayot, *Vice Pres*
EMP: 10
SQ FT: 2,000
SALES (est): 871.2K **Privately Held**
WEB: www.gayot.net
SIC: 2731 2741 2711 Pamphlets: publishing & printing; newsletter publishing; newspapers: publishing only, not printed on site

(P-6345)
GOFF CORPORATION
Also Called: Palace Press International
10 Paul Dr, San Rafael (94903-2102)
PHONE.....................415 526-1370
Raoul Goff, *President*
▲ **EMP:** 30
SALES (est): 2.5MM **Privately Held**
WEB: www.palacepress.com
SIC: 2731 2796 Books: publishing & printing; color separations for printing

(P-6346)
HARPERCOLLINS PUBLISHERS LLC
353 Sacramento St Ste 500, San Francisco
(94111-3637)
PHONE.....................415 477-4400
Diane Gedymin, *Manager*
Katy Hamilton, *Editor*
EMP: 35
SALES (corp-wide): 9B **Publicly Held**
WEB: www.harpercollins.com
SIC: 2731 Book publishing
HQ: Harpercollins Publishers L.L.C.
195 Broadway Fl 2
New York NY 10007
212 207-7000

(P-6347)
HESPERIAN HEALTH GUIDES (PA)
1919 Addison St Ste 304, Berkeley
(94704-1143)
PHONE.....................510 845-1447
Sarah Shannon, *Director*
Mary A Buckley, *Business Mgr*
Rosemary Jason, *Production*
Edith Friedman, *Manager*
Tawnia Litwin, *Manager*

EMP: 24
SQ FT: 1,600
SALES: 1.8MM **Privately Held**
WEB: www.hesperian.org
SIC: 2731 2741 8399 8641 Books: publishing only; miscellaneous publishing; community development groups; civic social & fraternal associations

(P-6348)
HEYDAY
Also Called: Heyday Books
2120 University Ave, Berkeley
(94704-1026)
P.O. Box 9145 (94709-0145)
PHONE.....................510 549-3564
Malcolm Margolin, *Exec Dir*
Steve Wasserman, *Exec Dir*
Madeline Hemingway, *Project Dir*
Ashley Ingram, *Graphic Designe*
Diane Lee, *Prdtn Dir*
▲ **EMP:** 12
SQ FT: 2,500
SALES: 1.2MM **Privately Held**
WEB: www.heydaybooks.com
SIC: 2731 2721 Books: publishing only; magazines: publishing only, not printed on site

(P-6349)
HOLLOWAY HOUSE PUBLISHING CO
8060 Melrose Ave Fl 3, Los Angeles
(90046-7039)
PHONE.....................323 653-8060
Bentley Morris, *President*
Mark Marsh, *Manager*
EMP: 15 EST: 1961
SQ FT: 5,000
SALES (est): 1.3MM **Privately Held**
SIC: 2731 Books: publishing only

(P-6350)
HOMESTEAD PUBLISHING INC
4388 17th St, San Francisco (94114-1888)
PHONE.....................307 733-6248
Carl A Schreier, *President*
EMP: 20
SALES (est): 1.2MM **Privately Held**
SIC: 2731 Books: publishing only

(P-6351)
HOUGHTON MIFFLIN HARCOURT PUBG
Also Called: Harcourt Trade Publishers
525 B St Ste 1900, San Diego
(92101-4495)
PHONE.....................617 351-5000
Barbara Fisch, *Branch Mgr*
EMP: 17
SALES (corp-wide): 1.4B **Publicly Held**
SIC: 2731 Textbooks: publishing only, not printed on site
HQ: Houghton Mifflin Harcourt Publishing Company
125 High St Ste 900
Boston MA 02110
617 351-5000

(P-6352)
INSIGHT EDITIONS LP (PA)
800 A St Ste B, San Rafael (94901-3011)
P.O. Box 3088 (94912-3088)
PHONE.....................415 526-1370
Raoul Goff, *CEO*
Michael Madden, *COO*
Jason Smalridge, *Accounting Mgr*
Eric Chang, *Marketing Staff*
Julie Hamilton, *Marketing Staff*
▲ **EMP:** 30
SALES (est): 14.8MM **Privately Held**
SIC: 2731 2721 Books: publishing only; comic books: publishing only, not printed on site

(P-6353)
INSPIRED PROPERTIES LLC
14320 Ventura Blvd 181, Sherman Oaks
(91423-2717)
PHONE.....................818 430-9634
Ron Belk, *Mng Member*
EMP: 27
SALES (est): 2.3MM **Privately Held**
SIC: 2731 Book publishing

(P-6354)
J S PALUCH CO INC
9400 Norwalk Blvd, Santa Fe Springs
(90670-6105)
PHONE.....................562 692-0484
Lee Corbasque, *Manager*
EMP: 50
SQ FT: 47,232
SALES (corp-wide): 88.3MM **Privately Held**
WEB: www.jspaluch.com
SIC: 2731 8743 2721 Book publishing; sales promotion; periodicals
PA: J. S. Paluch Co., Inc.
3708 River Rd Ste 400
Franklin Park IL 60131
847 678-9300

(P-6355)
JASPER SINCLAIRE MEDIA MGT INC
505 Montgomery St Fl 11, San Francisco
(94111-2585)
PHONE.....................559 380-7853
Debra K Kanagaki, *CEO*
Robert S Hunt, *Ch of Bd*
Vivlene M Edwards, *Corp Secy*
EMP: 125
SALES: 2.3MM **Privately Held**
SIC: 2731 5149 3861 5199 Books: publishing only; specialty food items; motion picture film; clothes hangers

(P-6356)
JO SONJAS FOLK ART STUDIO
2136 3rd St, Eureka (95501-0814)
P.O. Box 9080 (95502-9080)
PHONE.....................707 445-9306
Jerry Jansen, *President*
Jo Sonja Jansen, *Vice Pres*
Mark Jansen, *Manager*
▲ **EMP:** 10 EST: 1975
SQ FT: 10,000
SALES (est): 690K **Privately Held**
SIC: 2731 8299 2721 Books: publishing only; art school, except commercial; periodicals

(P-6357)
JOHN WILEY & SONS INC
Also Called: Jossey-Bass Publishers
1 Montgomery St Ste 1200, San Francisco
(94104-4594)
PHONE.....................415 433-1740
Steve Robinson, *Manager*
Lenny Friedman, *Exec Dir*
Michael Damore, *Marketing Staff*
Lynn Honrado, *Marketing Staff*
Rebecca Middleton, *Sales Staff*
EMP: 154
SALES (corp-wide): 1.8B **Publicly Held**
WEB: www.wiley.com
SIC: 2731 2741 Textbooks: publishing only, not printed on site; miscellaneous publishing
PA: John Wiley & Sons, Inc.
111 River St Ste 2000
Hoboken NJ 07030
201 748-6000

(P-6358)
JUDY O PRODUCTIONS INC
4858 W Pico Blvd Ste 331, Los Angeles
(90019-4225)
PHONE.....................323 938-8513
Judy Ostarch, *President*
▲ **EMP:** 28 EST: 1999
SALES (est): 182.7K **Privately Held**
WEB: www.judyoproductions.com
SIC: 2731 Book publishing

(P-6359)
LITTLE EINSTEINS LLC
Also Called: Baby Einstein Co Llc, The
500 S Buena Vista St, Burbank
(91521-0001)
P.O. Box 25020, Glendale (91221-5020)
PHONE.....................818 560-1000
Julie Aigner-Clark,
Susan McLain, *Vice Pres*
EMP: 13
SQ FT: 6,000
SALES (est): 811.6K **Publicly Held**
SIC: 2731 3695 Books: publishing & printing; video recording tape, blank

PRODUCTS & SVCS

PA: The Walt Disney Company
500 S Buena Vista St
Burbank CA 91521

(P-6360)
MARSHALL & SWIFT/BOECKH LLC
777 S Figueroa St Fl 12, Los Angeles (90017-5878)
PHONE..................213 683-9000
Tony Reisz, *CEO*
Norrine Brydon, *Vice Pres*
David Rice, *Administration*
Mike Fisher, *Info Tech Dir*
Ed Martinez, *Technical Mgr*
EMP: 16
SALES (corp-wide): 1.8B **Publicly Held**
SIC: 2731 2741 Pamphlets: publishing & printing; miscellaneous publishing
HQ: Marshall & Swift/Boeckh, Llc
10001 W Innovation Dr # 100
Milwaukee WI 53226
262 780-2800

(P-6361)
MCEVOY PROPERTIES LLC
680 2nd St, San Francisco (94107-2015)
PHONE..................415 537-4200
Nion McEvoy,
EMP: 163
SALES (est): 985.2K **Privately Held**
SIC: 2731 Book publishing

(P-6362)
MCKEAGUE PATPATRICK
Also Called: XYZ Text Book
1339 Marsh St, San Luis Obispo (93401-3315)
PHONE..................805 541-4593
Patpatrick McKeague, *Owner*
Richard Jones, *Marketing Staff*
EMP: 10
SALES (est): 530K **Privately Held**
SIC: 2731 Textbooks: publishing only, not printed on site

(P-6363)
MERIDIAN TECHNICAL SALES INC
520 Alder Dr, Milpitas (95035-7443)
PHONE..................408 526-2000
David Dilling, *President*
Ray Bautista, *Vice Pres*
Jeff Waldman, *Sales Mgr*
Brandy Thomas, *Marketing Staff*
Deondra Bicknell, *Sales Staff*
EMP: 20
SALES (est): 2MM **Privately Held**
SIC: 2731 7313 Books: publishing only; electronic media advertising representatives

(P-6364)
MIKE MURACH & ASSOCIATES
4340 N Knoll Ave, Fresno (93722-7825)
PHONE..................559 440-9071
Michael Murach, *President*
Georgia Murach, *Admin Sec*
Joel Murach, *Technical Staff*
Judy Taylor, *Sls & Mktg Exec*
Kelly Slivkoff, *Cust Mgr*
EMP: 12 **EST:** 1972
SALES (est): 1.5MM **Privately Held**
WEB: www.murach.com
SIC: 2731 Textbooks: publishing only, not printed on site

(P-6365)
NARCOTICS ANONYMOUS WORLD SERV
Also Called: World Service Office
19737 Nordhoff Pl, Chatsworth (91311-6606)
P.O. Box 9999, Van Nuys (91409-9099)
PHONE..................818 773-9999
Anthony Edmondson, *CEO*
▲ **EMP:** 45
SQ FT: 35,000
SALES: 7.9MM **Privately Held**
SIC: 2731 Books: publishing only; pamphlets: publishing only, not printed on site

(P-6366)
NATIONAL DIRECTORY SERVICES
19698 View Forever Ln, Grass Valley (95945-8883)
PHONE..................530 268-8636
Mario Plough, *President*
Mario Cloegh, *Principal*
EMP: 20 **EST:** 1989
SALES (est): 1.4MM **Privately Held**
WEB: www.lucchesivineyards.com
SIC: 2731 2741

(P-6367)
NATIONAL LAW DIGEST INC
Also Called: Times Publishing
23844 Hawthorne Blvd # 200, Torrance (90505-5945)
PHONE..................310 791-9975
Vijay Fadia, *President*
EMP: 20
SALES (est): 1.8MM **Privately Held**
WEB: www.timespublishing.com
SIC: 2731 2721 Books: publishing only; periodicals: publishing only

(P-6368)
NATURAL STD RES COLLABORATION
3120 W March Ln Fl 1, Stockton (95219-2368)
PHONE..................617 591-3300
Catherine M Ulbricht, *CEO*
Ethan M Basch MD, *President*
EMP: 20
SQ FT: 2,000
SALES: 2.5MM **Privately Held**
SIC: 2731

(P-6369)
NEW HARBINGER PUBLICATIONS INC (PA)
5674 Shattuck Ave, Oakland (94609-1662)
PHONE..................510 652-0215
Matt McKay, *President*
Heather Garnos, *Vice Pres*
Catharine Meyers, *Vice Pres*
Minoo Irvani, *Executive*
Jesse Burson, *Project Mgr*
▲ **EMP:** 33
SQ FT: 6,500
SALES: 14.6MM **Privately Held**
WEB: www.newharbinger.com
SIC: 2731 3652 Books: publishing only; master records or tapes, preparation of

(P-6370)
NO STARCH PRESS INC
245 8th St, San Francisco (94103-3910)
PHONE..................415 863-9900
William Pollock, *President*
Serena Yang, *Prdtn Mgr*
Siobhan Robinson, *Marketing Staff*
Ming Choi,
Jan Cash, *Assoc Editor*
▲ **EMP:** 18
SQ FT: 8,000
SALES (est): 1.8MM **Privately Held**
WEB: www.nostarch.com
SIC: 2731 Books: publishing only

(P-6371)
NOLO
950 Parker St, Berkeley (94710-2524)
PHONE..................510 549-1976
Bob Dubow, *CEO*
Chelsey Langan, *Vice Pres*
Laurence Nathanson, *Vice Pres*
John Plessas, *Vice Pres*
Mark Stuhr, *Vice Pres*
EMP: 120
SQ FT: 25,000
SALES (est): 11MM
SALES (corp-wide): 257.9MM **Privately Held**
WEB: www.nolo.com
SIC: 2731 8111 8742 Books: publishing only; legal services; marketing consulting services
PA: Internet Brands, Inc.
909 N Pacific Coast Hwy # 11
El Segundo CA 90245
310 280-4000

(P-6372)
NORMAN & GLOBUS INC
Also Called: Science Wiz Summer Camp
5215 Central Ave Ste A, Richmond (94804-5802)
P.O. Box 20533, El Sobrante (94820-0533)
PHONE..................510 222-2638
Penelope A Norman, *CEO*
▲ **EMP:** 12
SQ FT: 4,000
SALES (est): 1.7MM **Privately Held**
WEB: www.electrowiz.com
SIC: 2731 Books: publishing only

(P-6373)
OREILLY MEDIA INC (PA)
Also Called: Safari Books Online
1005 Gravenstein Hwy N, Sebastopol (95472-2811)
PHONE..................707 827-7000
Timothy F O'Reilly, *President*
Mark Jacobsen, *Managing Prtnr*
Maria Manrique, *CFO*
Karen Hebert-Maccaro, *Officer*
Mark Jacobs, *Officer*
▲ **EMP:** 150
SQ FT: 90,000
SALES (est): 117.5MM **Privately Held**
WEB: www.oreilly.com
SIC: 2731 2741 8231 Books: publishing only; ; libraries

(P-6374)
OWEN WELDON INC (HQ)
Also Called: Weldonowen
1045 Sansome St Ste 100, San Francisco (94111-1313)
PHONE..................415 291-0100
Roger Shaw, *President*
▲ **EMP:** 36
SALES (est): 6MM **Privately Held**
WEB: www.weldonowen.com
SIC: 2731 Books: publishing only

(P-6375)
OWEN WELDON PUBLISHING INC (DH)
1045 Sansome St Ste 100, San Francisco (94111-1313)
PHONE..................415 291-0100
Weldon Owen, *President*
EMP: 10
SALES (est): 4.5MM **Privately Held**
SIC: 2731 Books: publishing only
HQ: Weldon Owen Inc.
1045 Sansome St Ste 100
San Francisco CA 94111
415 291-0100

(P-6376)
PALACE PRINTING & DESIGN LP
800 A St, San Rafael (94901-3011)
PHONE..................415 526-1370
Raoul Goff, *President*
Jason Smalridge, *Accountant*
Sreed Haran, *Sales Staff*
▲ **EMP:** 20
SALES (est): 1.2MM **Privately Held**
SIC: 2731 Books: publishing & printing

(P-6377)
PAM DEE PUBLISHING
303 Talbot Ave, Santa Rosa (95405-4534)
PHONE..................707 542-1528
Pamela Atchison, *Owner*
EMP: 10
SALES (est): 500.6K **Privately Held**
SIC: 2731 Book publishing

(P-6378)
PEARSON EDUCATION INC
Also Called: Scott Foresman Pearson Educatn
3700 Inland Empire Blvd, Ontario (91764-4906)
PHONE..................800 653-1918
Mark Moyer, *Branch Mgr*
EMP: 10
SALES (corp-wide): 5.9B **Privately Held**
WEB: www.phgenit.com
SIC: 2731 Book publishing

HQ: Pearson Education, Inc.
221 River St
Hoboken NJ 07030
201 236-7000

(P-6379)
PEARSON EDUCATION INC
1301 Sansome St, San Francisco (94111-1122)
PHONE..................415 402-2500
Benjamin Cummings, *Manager*
Richard Harrington, *Vice Pres*
Donae Viertel, *Technology*
Sheryl Jett, *Security Mgr*
EMP: 20
SALES (corp-wide): 5.9B **Privately Held**
WEB: www.phgenit.com
SIC: 2731 Book publishing
HQ: Pearson Education, Inc.
221 River St
Hoboken NJ 07030
201 236-7000

(P-6380)
PENGUIN RANDOM HOUSE LLC
Also Called: Prima Games
3000 Lava Ridge Ct # 100, Roseville (95661-2802)
PHONE..................916 787-7000
Richard Sarnoff, *President*
Ken Silva, *Vice Pres*
EMP: 31
SALES (corp-wide): 82.3MM **Privately Held**
WEB: www.anchorbooks.com
SIC: 2731 Books: publishing only
HQ: Penguin Random House Llc
1745 Broadway
New York NY 10019
212 782-9000

(P-6381)
PLAYERS PRESS INC
Fulton Ave, Studio City (91604)
PHONE..................818 789-4980
William Landes, *President*
June Heal, *President*
Sharon Gorrell, *Senior VP*
Marjorie Clapper, *Admin Sec*
EMP: 33
SALES (est): 2.6MM **Privately Held**
SIC: 2731 Books: publishing & printing

(P-6382)
PLURAL PUBLISHING INC
5521 Ruffin Rd, San Diego (92123-1314)
PHONE..................858 492-1555
Sadanand Singh, *President*
Brian Summerville, *Controller*
Marty Lew, *Sales Mgr*
Lindsey Burcham, *Marketing Staff*
Tim Kelehan, *Warehouse Mgr*
▲ **EMP:** 15
SALES (est): 2MM **Privately Held**
WEB: www.pluralpublishing.com
SIC: 2731 Textbooks: publishing only, not printed on site

(P-6383)
PRACTICE MANAGEMENT INFO CORP (PA)
Also Called: Pmic
4727 Wilshire Blvd # 302, Los Angeles (90010-3806)
PHONE..................323 954-0224
James B Davis, *President*
Michelle Cuevas, *Opers Mgr*
Richard Uyeno, *Manager*
Charles Ekin, *Representative*
◆ **EMP:** 35
SQ FT: 6,000
SALES (est): 4.4MM **Privately Held**
WEB: www.medicalbookstore.com
SIC: 2731 7372 Book publishing; business oriented computer software

(P-6384)
PRIMA GAMES INC
Also Called: Prima Publishing
2990 Lava Ridge Ct # 120, Roseville (95661-3076)
PHONE..................916 787-7000
Richard Sarnoff, *President*
Jeff Barton, *Sales Mgr*
Mark Hughes, *Sales Staff*
Julie Asbury, *Director*

▲ = Import ▼=Export
◆ =Import/Export

EMP: 180
SALES (est): 12.6MM Privately Held
WEB: www.primagames.com
SIC: 2731 Books: publishing only

(P-6385)
QUEENSHIP PUBLISHING COMPANY
5951 Encina Rd Ste 100, Goleta
(93117-6251)
P.O. Box 220 (93116-0220)
PHONE...................................805 692-0043
David Schaeffer, President
EMP: 12
SALES: 129.7K Privately Held
WEB: www.queenship.org
SIC: 2731 Books: publishing only

(P-6386)
RICKY READER LLC
6715 Mckinley Ave Unit B, Los Angeles
(90001-1591)
PHONE...................................323 231-4322
Dennis Brown, President
EMP: 10
SALES (est): 292.2K Privately Held
SIC: 2731 Books: publishing only

(P-6387)
ROBERT W CAMERON & CO INC
Also Called: Cameron & Company
149 Kentucky St Ste 7, Petaluma
(94952-2940)
PHONE...................................707 769-1617
Christopher Roger Gruener, CEO
Robert Cameron, Ch of Bd
Tracy Davis, Treasurer
Nina Gruener, Vice Pres
Linda Henry, Admin Sec
▲ EMP: 10
SQ FT: 8,000
SALES (est): 660K Privately Held
WEB: www.rwcameronlaw.ca
SIC: 2731 Books: publishing only

(P-6388)
SADDLEBACK EDUCATIONAL INC
151 Kalmus Dr Ste J-1, Costa Mesa
(92626-5973)
PHONE...................................949 860-2500
Arianne M McHugh, President
Print Isenberg, Purch Mgr
Amber Dormanesh, Prdtn Mgr
Tim McHugh, Sales Mgr
Carol Pizer, Director
▲ EMP: 20
SQ FT: 5,000
SALES (est): 3.1MM Privately Held
WEB: www.sdlback.com
SIC: 2731 5192

(P-6389)
SCHOLASTIC INC
4821 Charter St, Baldwin Park
(91706-2195)
PHONE...................................626 337-9996
Karen Stearn, Branch Mgr
EMP: 28
SALES (corp-wide): 1.6B Publicly Held
WEB: www.scholasticdealer.com
SIC: 2731 Textbooks: publishing only, not printed on site
HQ: Scholastic Inc.
    557 Broadway Lbby 1
    New York NY 10012
    800 724-6527

(P-6390)
SECRET ROAD MUSIC PUBG INC
5850 Foothill Dr, Los Angeles
(90068-3622)
PHONE...................................323 464-1234
Lynn Grossman, CEO
EMP: 15 EST: 2010
SALES (est): 657.9K Privately Held
SIC: 2731 Books: publishing & printing

(P-6391)
SHREDDING PAPER
75 Plum Tree Ln Apt 3, San Rafael
(94901-2059)
PHONE...................................415 454-2242

Mel Cheplowitz, Owner
EMP: 15
SALES (est): 478.3K Privately Held
SIC: 2731 Book clubs: publishing & printing

(P-6392)
SMILEY GROUP INC
4434 Crenshaw Blvd, Los Angeles
(90043-1208)
PHONE...................................323 290-4690
Tavis Smiley, President
Kimberly McFarland, Executive Asst
Vanessa Rumbles, Producer
Joe Zefran, Producer
EMP: 10
SALES (est): 1.3MM Privately Held
WEB: www.tavistalks.com
SIC: 2731 Book publishing

(P-6393)
SOCIETY FOR THE STUDY O
Also Called: NORTH ATLANTIC BOOKS
2526 M Luthr King Jr Way, Berkeley
(94704)
PHONE...................................510 549-4270
Douglas Reil, CEO
Lindy Hough, Treasurer
Richard Grossinger, Exec Dir
Alla Spector, Finance Dir
Minda Armstrong, Prdtn Mgr
▲ EMP: 25
SQ FT: 6,000
SALES: 4.2MM Privately Held
WEB: www.northatlanticbooks.com
SIC: 2731 Books: publishing only

(P-6394)
STAMATS COMMUNICATIONS INC
Also Called: Stamats Travel Group
550 Montgomery St Ste 750, San Francisco
(94111-2557)
PHONE...................................800 358-0388
Peters Stamats, Branch Mgr
EMP: 20
SALES (corp-wide): 21.8MM Privately Held
WEB: www.stamatsinfo.com
SIC: 2731 2721 Pamphlets: publishing only, not printed on site; magazines: publishing only, not printed on site
PA: Stamats Communications, Inc.
    615 5th St Se
    Cedar Rapids IA 52401
    319 364-6167

(P-6395)
STONEYBROOK PUBLISHING INC
16772 W Bernardo Dr, San Diego
(92127-1904)
PHONE...................................858 674-4600
Aaron Combs, President
Dave Stone, CEO
Jordan Stone, Creative Dir
EMP: 21
SQ FT: 7,500
SALES (est): 2.1MM Privately Held
WEB: www.dcmspec.com
SIC: 2731 2741 7331 Pamphlets: publishing only, not printed on site; newsletter publishing; direct mail advertising services

(P-6396)
TASCHEN AMERICA LLC (PA)
6671 W Sunset Blvd, Los Angeles
(90028-7175)
PHONE...................................323 463-4441
Elissa Gomez, Director
Rosemarie Falotico, Store Mgr
Abbey Golden, Admin Asst
Iris Ploetzer, Admin Asst
Erin Uehara, Finance
▲ EMP: 13
SQ FT: 5,000
SALES (est): 2.2MM Privately Held
SIC: 2731 Books: publishing only

(P-6397)
TEACHER CREATED MATERIALS INC
5301 Oceanus Dr, Huntington Beach
(92649-1030)
P.O. Box 1040 (92647-1040)
PHONE...................................714 891-2273
Rachelle Cracchiolo, CEO
Corinne Burton, President
Rich Levitt, COO
Kimberly Carlton, Officer
Lynda McKelvey, Officer
▲ EMP: 110
SQ FT: 10,000
SALES (est): 21.2MM Privately Held
WEB: www.tcmpub.com
SIC: 2731 Textbooks: publishing only, not printed on site

(P-6398)
TEACHER CREATED RESOURCES INC
12621 Western Ave, Garden Grove
(92841-4014)
PHONE...................................714 230-7060
Mary Diane Smith, CEO
Kristine Lapena, Sales Staff
Dianne Kelly, Director
Sara Connolly, Editor
Karen Goldfuss, Editor
◆ EMP: 100
SALES (est): 14.8MM Privately Held
SIC: 2731 Textbooks: publishing only, not printed on site

(P-6399)
TEACHERS CURRICULUM INST LLC (PA)
2440 W El Cam, Mountain View (94040)
P.O. Box 1327, Rancho Cordova (95741-1327)
PHONE...................................800 497-6138
Bert Bower, Mng Member
Michael Hall, Admin Asst
Gabriel Redig, Software Engr
Michael Avalos, Technology
Matt Moorman, Natl Sales Mgr
EMP: 24
SQ FT: 7,994
SALES: 28MM Privately Held
WEB: www.teachtci.com
SIC: 2731 8748 Books: publishing only; educational consultant

(P-6400)
THE MICROFILM COMPANY OF CAL
Also Called: Library Reproduction Service
14214 S Figueroa St, Los Angeles
(90061-1034)
PHONE...................................310 354-2610
Joan Miller, President
Peter Jones, Vice Pres
EMP: 15 EST: 1946
SQ FT: 7,000
SALES (est): 1.5MM Privately Held
WEB: www.lrs-largeprint.com
SIC: 2731 7389 Books: publishing & printing; microfilm recording & developing service

(P-6401)
TOKYOPOP INC
5200 W Century Blvd Fl 7, Los Angeles
(90045-5926)
PHONE...................................323 920-5967
Stuart J Levy, President
John Parker, Vice Pres
Victor Chin, Admin Sec
◆ EMP: 90
SQ FT: 8,699
SALES (est): 5.9MM Privately Held
WEB: www.tokyopop.com
SIC: 2731 3652 7812 7371 Books: publishing only; compact laser discs, prerecorded; video tape production; custom computer programming services; periodicals; entertainment promotion

(P-6402)
TORAH-AURA PRODUCTIONS INC
2710 Supply Ave, Commerce (90040-2704)
PHONE...................................323 585-1847
▲ EMP: 13 EST: 1982

SQ FT: 15,000
SALES (est): 1.3MM Privately Held
WEB: www.torahaura.com
SIC: 2731

(P-6403)
TRUCK CLUB PUBLISHING INC
7807 Telegraph Rd Ste H, Montebello
(90640-6528)
PHONE...................................323 726-8620
Miguel A Machuca, President
EMP: 20
SALES (est): 1.9MM Privately Held
WEB: www.truckclubmagazine.com
SIC: 2731 Book publishing

(P-6404)
UNIVERSITY CAL PRESS FUNDATION (PA)
155 Grand Ave Ste 400, Oakland
(94612-3764)
PHONE...................................510 642-4247
Lynne Withey, President
Richard C Atkinson, President
Alma Yee, Accounting Mgr
Armine Hacoupian, Accountant
Angela Chen, Production
EMP: 100
SALES (est): 10.7MM Privately Held
SIC: 2731 Books: publishing only

(P-6405)
UNIVERSITY CAL PRESS FUNDATION
2000 Center St Ste 303, Berkeley
(94704-1200)
PHONE...................................510 642-4247
Rebecca Symon, Principal
Rebecca Simon, Principal
EMP: 25
SALES (corp-wide): 10.7MM Privately Held
SIC: 2731 Books: publishing only
PA: University Of California Press Foundation
    155 Grand Ave Ste 400
    Oakland CA 94612
    510 642-4247

(P-6406)
UNIVERSITY CALIFORNIA BERKELEY
Also Called: University of California Press
155 Grand Ave Ste 400, Oakland
(94612-3764)
PHONE...................................510 642-4247
Allison Mudditt, Branch Mgr
Brendan Tinney, Officer
Shachar Kariv, Pharmacy Dir
Michael Sumner, Research
Dylan Mendonca, Engineer
EMP: 20 Privately Held
WEB: www.law.berkeley.edu
SIC: 2731 8221 9411 Book publishing; university; administration of educational programs;
HQ: The University California Berkeley
    200 Clfrnia Hall Spc 1500
    Berkeley CA 94720
    510 642-6000

(P-6407)
WEST PUBLISHING CORPORATION
Also Called: The Rutter Group
633 W 5th St Ste 2300, Los Angeles
(90071-2049)
PHONE...................................800 747-3161
William Rutter, Branch Mgr
Bruce E Cooperman, Partner
Robert H Fairbank, Partner
Dennis L Greenwald, Partner
Mark Hagarty, Partner
EMP: 50 Publicly Held
WEB: www.ruttergroup.com
SIC: 2731 8111 Book publishing; general practice attorney, lawyer
HQ: West Publishing Corporation
    610 Opperman Dr
    Eagan MN 55123
    651 687-7000

(P-6408)
WHATEVER PUBLISHING INC
Also Called: New World Library
14 Pamaron Way Ste 1, Novato
(94949-6215)
PHONE..................415 884-2100
Marc Allen, *President*
Victoria Clarke, *CEO*
▲ EMP: 18
SQ FT: 6,000
SALES (est): 2.2MM **Privately Held**
WEB: www.newworldlibrary.com
SIC: 2731 Books: publishing only

(P-6409)
WILSHIRE BOOK COMPANY INC
22647 Ventura Blvd, Woodland Hills
(91364-1416)
PHONE..................818 700-1522
Melvin Powers, *President*
EMP: 22
SQ FT: 15,000
SALES: 5MM **Privately Held**
WEB: www.mpowers.com
SIC: 2731 5961 Textbooks: publishing
only, not printed on site; mail order house

(P-6410)
WINE APPRECIATION GUILD LTD
Also Called: Vintage Image
360 Swift Ave Ste 34, South San Francisco
(94080-6220)
PHONE..................650 866-3020
Donna Bottrell, *CEO*
Maurice Sullivan, *Vice Pres*
▲ EMP: 18
SQ FT: 29,000
SALES (est): 746.5K **Privately Held**
WEB: www.winehardware.com
SIC: 2731 2542 5149 Books: publishing
only; racks, merchandise display or storage: except wood; wine makers' equipment & supplies

(P-6411)
WIXEN MUSIC PUBLISHING INC
24025 Park Sorrento # 130, Calabasas
(91302-4018)
PHONE..................818 591-7355
Randall Wixen, *President*
EMP: 15
SALES (est): 1.8MM **Privately Held**
WEB: www.wixenmusic.com
SIC: 2731 8111 Book music: publishing &
printing; legal services

(P-6412)
WORKBOOK INC
110 N Doheny Dr, Beverly Hills
(90211-1811)
PHONE..................323 856-0008
Alexis Scott, *Principal*
Allan Gallant, *CFO*
Stephen Chiang, *IT/INT Sup*
Marie Oley, *Opers Staff*
Heidi Goverman, *Sales Staff*
▲ EMP: 20
SALES (est): 2.2MM **Privately Held**
SIC: 2731 Book publishing

(P-6413)
WORLD HARMONY ORGANIZATION
World Harmony Institute
514 Arballo Dr, San Francisco
(94132-2163)
PHONE..................415 246-6886
Francis Cw Fung, *President*
EMP: 10 **Privately Held**
SIC: 2731 Book publishing
PA: World Harmony Organization
24301 Suthland Dr Ste 405
Hayward CA 94545

(P-6414)
WORLDVIEW PROJECT
2445 Morena Blvd Ste 210, San Diego
(92110-4157)
PHONE..................858 964-0709
Thomas Johnston O Neill, *President*
Chris Bengs, *Principal*
William James, *Principal*
Shari Johnston-O'neill, *Principal*
EMP: 15
SALES (est): 13.6K **Privately Held**
WEB: www.worldviewpress.org
SIC: 2731 Book publishing

(P-6415)
YOSEMITE NATURAL HISTORY ASSN
Also Called: Yosemite Association
5020 El Portal Rd, El Portal (95318)
P.O. Box 230 (95318-0230)
PHONE..................209 379-2646
Steven P Medley, *President*
Beth Pratt, *CFO*
Patricia Wight, *Admin Sec*
▲ EMP: 63
SQ FT: 1,500
SALES (est): 2.5MM **Privately Held**
WEB: www.yosemite.org
SIC: 2731 5942 Books: publishing only;
book stores

(P-6416)
ZOOM BOOKZ LLC
10000 Fairway Dr Ste 140, Roseville
(95678-3553)
PHONE..................800 662-9982
Viktor Oleynik, *Mng Member*
EMP: 10
SALES (est): 276.7K **Privately Held**
SIC: 2731 Book publishing

2732 Book Printing, Not Publishing

(P-6417)
CONSOLIDATED PRINTERS INC
2630 8th St, Berkeley (94710-2588)
PHONE..................510 843-8524
Lawrence A Hawkins, *CEO*
Jim Fassett, *Vice Pres*
Paula Dudley, *Human Resources*
Ken Thorsen, *VP Mfg*
Mike Fave, *Mktg Dir*
EMP: 50
SQ FT: 60,000
SALES (est): 11.5MM **Privately Held**
WEB: www.consoprinters.com
SIC: 2732 2752 Books: printing & binding;
commercial printing, lithographic

(P-6418)
COREFACT CORPORATION
20936 Cabot Blvd, Hayward (94545-1129)
PHONE..................866 777-3986
Christopher Burnley, *President*
Arnold Shurin, *President*
Jim Hammarstrom, *Vice Pres*
Cynthia Kwok, *Vice Pres*
Chio Saelee, *Creative Dir*
EMP: 10
SQ FT: 16,000
SALES (est): 2.1MM **Privately Held**
SIC: 2732 7371 Book printing; computer
software development

(P-6419)
HAMPTON-BROWN COMPANY LLC
1 Lower Ragsdale Dr # 1200, Monterey
(93940-5749)
PHONE..................831 620-6001
EMP: 10 EST: 2011
SALES (est): 510K **Privately Held**
SIC: 2732

(P-6420)
MICHAEL MARTELLA
Also Called: Heritage Printing
9955 Black Mountain Rd, San Diego
(92126-4514)
P.O. Box 509100 (92150-9100)
PHONE..................858 695-9600
Michael Martella, *Owner*
EMP: 104 EST: 1986
SQ FT: 21,500
SALES (est): 15MM **Privately Held**
SIC: 2732 Book printing

2741 Misc Publishing

(P-6421)
ACCEPTED CO
2229 S Canfield Ave, Los Angeles
(90034-1114)
PHONE..................310 815-9553
Linda Abraham, *President*
Jen Weld, *Regl Sales Mgr*
Cydney Foote, *Sr Consultant*
Michelle Stockman, *Consultant*
Judy Gruen, *Editor*
EMP: 14
SALES (est): 881.9K **Privately Held**
WEB: www.accepted.com
SIC: 2741 Miscellaneous publishing

(P-6422)
ADVANCED PUBLISHING TECH INC
1105 N Hollywood Way, Burbank
(91505-2528)
PHONE..................818 557-3035
D Kraai, *Owner*
EMP: 18 **Privately Held**
SIC: 2741 Miscellaneous publishing
PA: Advanced Publishing Technology, Inc.
123 S Victory Blvd
Burbank CA 91502

(P-6423)
AGI PUBLISHING INC (PA)
Also Called: Valley Yellow Pages
1850 N Gateway Blvd # 152, Fresno
(93727-1600)
PHONE..................559 251-8888
Sieg A Fischer, *CEO*
Michael Schilling, *Treasurer*
Dominic D'Innocenti, *Senior VP*
Mike Schilling, *Vice Pres*
Candice Rasmussen, *Executive*
EMP: 50
SQ FT: 19,000
SALES (est): 128.2MM **Privately Held**
WEB: www.valleyyellowpages.com
SIC: 2741 Directories, telephone: publishing only, not printed on site

(P-6424)
AGI PUBLISHING INC
Also Called: Valley Yellow Pages
1850 N Gateway Blvd # 152, Fresno
(93727-1600)
PHONE..................559 251-8888
Karen Donner, *Human Res Mgr*
EMP: 136
SALES (corp-wide): 128.2MM **Privately Held**
WEB: www.valleyyellowpages.com
SIC: 2741 Directories, telephone: publishing only, not printed on site
PA: Agi Publishing, Inc.
1850 N Gateway Blvd # 152
Fresno CA 93727
559 251-8888

(P-6425)
AIR MARKETING
516 E 7th St, Long Beach (90813-4504)
PHONE..................562 208-3990
Francisco Dominguez, *President*
EMP: 10
SALES (est): 261K **Privately Held**
SIC: 2741

(P-6426)
AIRCRAFT TECHNICAL PUBLISHERS (PA)
Also Called: Atp
2000 Sierra Point Pkwy # 501, Brisbane
(94005-1874)
PHONE..................415 330-9500
Rick Noble, *CEO*
Stephen Gray, *CFO*
Mark Culpepper,
Ken Aubrey, *Officer*
Ted Haugner, *Vice Pres*
EMP: 65
SQ FT: 28,000
SALES (est): 12.8MM **Privately Held**
WEB: www.atp.com
SIC: 2741 Miscellaneous publishing

(P-6427)
ALAMEDA DIRECTORY INC
Also Called: Oakland Magazine
1416 Park Ave, Alameda (94501-4520)
PHONE..................510 747-1060
Tracy McKean, *President*
EMP: 16
SALES (est): 834.2K **Privately Held**
WEB: www.oaklandmagazine.com
SIC: 2741 Directories, telephone: publishing only, not printed on site

(P-6428)
ALPHA I PUBLISHING INC
28400 Coachman Ln, Highland
(92346-2721)
PHONE..................909 862-9572
John Tillman, *President*
Shirley Hirst, *Vice Pres*
Roberta Tillman, *Vice Pres*
EMP: 11
SQ FT: 3,400
SALES (est): 825K **Privately Held**
WEB: www.alpha1pub.com
SIC: 2741 7311 Directories, telephone:
publishing only, not printed on site; advertising agencies

(P-6429)
AMERICAN CLUBS LLC
Also Called: American Cellar Wine Club
4550 E Thousand Oaks Blvd, Westlake Village (91362-3820)
PHONE..................805 496-1218
Larry Dutra,
James Perdue,
EMP: 16 EST: 1997
SQ FT: 2,500
SALES (est): 1.4MM **Privately Held**
WEB: www.acwc.com
SIC: 2741 7331 Atlas, map & guide publishing; direct mail advertising services

(P-6430)
AMERICAN HISTORIC INNS INC
249 Forest Ave, Laguna Beach
(92651-2104)
P.O. Box 669, Dana Point (92629-0669)
PHONE..................949 499-8070
Deborah Sakach, *CEO*
Jamee Danihels, *Office Mgr*
Diane Ringler, *Marketing Staff*
EMP: 16
SQ FT: 1,800
SALES (est): 1.3MM **Privately Held**
SIC: 2741 7011 Directories: publishing
only, not printed on site; hotels & motels

(P-6431)
AMERICAN SECURITY EDUCATORS
8734 Cleta St Ste E, Downey
(90241-5279)
P.O. Box 1337 (90240-0337)
PHONE..................562 928-1847
Georgia Gonos Ananias, *President*
Dean Ananias, *Exec VP*
EMP: 10
SALES (est): 630K **Privately Held**
WEB: www.americansecurityeducators.com
SIC: 2741 8322 Miscellaneous publishing;
individual & family services

(P-6432)
AMERICAN SYSTEM PUBLICATIONS
3018 Carmel St, Los Angeles
(90065-1401)
P.O. Box 476, Pasadena (91102-0476)
PHONE..................323 259-1867
Maureen Calney, *President*
EMP: 49
SALES (est): 3.4MM **Privately Held**
SIC: 2741 Miscellaneous publishing

(P-6433)
APARTMENT DIRECTORY OF L A
Also Called: Apartment Drctry L A-South Bay
2515 S Western Ave Ste 13, San Pedro
(90732-4643)
PHONE..................310 832-0354
Glenn Kurtz, *Partner*
Armida Kurtz, *Partner*
EMP: 14

SALES (est): 953.8K **Privately Held**
SIC: 2741 7331 Directories: publishing & printing; mailing list compilers

(P-6434)
ART BRAND STUDIOS LLC (PA)
18715 Madrone Pkwy, Morgan Hill (95037-2876)
PHONE.....................408 201-5000
Steve Loveless,
EMP: 50
SQ FT: 40,000
SALES (est): 12MM **Privately Held**
SIC: 2741 6794 Art copy & poster publishing; copyright buying & licensing

(P-6435)
ART IMPRESSIONS INC
23586 Calabasas Rd # 210, Calabasas (91302-1319)
PHONE.....................818 591-0105
Cindy Bailey, *President*
Alison Kenney, *Vice Pres*
▲ **EMP:** 12
SALES (est): 1.2MM **Privately Held**
SIC: 2741

(P-6436)
ASSOC STUDENTS UNIVERSITY CA
Also Called: Bsr
112 Hearst Gym Rm 4520, Berkeley (94720-3611)
PHONE.....................510 590-7874
Asako Miyakawa, *Branch Mgr*
EMP: 40
SALES (corp-wide): 1.9MM **Privately Held**
SIC: 2741 8299 Miscellaneous publishing; educational services
PA: Associated Students Of The University Of California
Bancroft Way 400 Eshleman St Bancroft W
Berkeley CA 94704
510 642-5420

(P-6437)
ASSOCIATED DESERT SHOPPERS (DH)
Also Called: The White Sheet
73400 Highway 111, Palm Desert (92260-3908)
PHONE.....................760 346-1729
Harold Paradis, *President*
Esperanza Barrett, *Treasurer*
Rey Verdugo Sr, *Vice Pres*
EMP: 75
SQ FT: 4,000
SALES (est): 14.1MM
SALES (corp-wide): 882.7MM **Publicly Held**
WEB: www.desertshoppers.net
SIC: 2741 7313 Shopping news: publishing & printing; newspaper advertising representative
HQ: Schurz Communications, Inc.
1301 E Douglas Rd Ste 200
Mishawaka IN 46545
574 247-7237

(P-6438)
AT&T CORP
Also Called: Advertising Solutions
8954 Rio San Diego Dr # 604, San Diego (92108-1659)
PHONE.....................619 521-6100
Vanita Thurston, *Manager*
Phil Dunn, *General Mgr*
EMP: 222
SALES (corp-wide): 160.5B **Publicly Held**
SIC: 2741 Miscellaneous publishing
HQ: At&T Corp.
1 At&T Way
Bedminster NJ 07921
800 403-3302

(P-6439)
AT&T CORP
1610 W Yosemite Ave Ste 2, Manteca (95337-5189)
PHONE.....................209 275-3075
Carl Berndt, *Principal*
EMP: 222

SALES (corp-wide): 160.5B **Publicly Held**
SIC: 2741 Miscellaneous publishing
HQ: At&T Corp.
1 At&T Way
Bedminster NJ 07921
800 403-3302

(P-6440)
AT&T CORP
Also Called: SBC
370 3rd St Rm 714, San Francisco (94107-1250)
PHONE.....................415 542-9000
Tom Miller, *Manager*
EMP: 500
SALES (corp-wide): 160.5B **Publicly Held**
WEB: www.swbell.com
SIC: 2741 4812 4813 Directories, telephone: publishing only, not printed on site; cellular telephone services; paging services; radio pager (beeper) communication services; data telephone communications; local telephone communications; long distance telephone communications
HQ: At&T Corp.
1 At&T Way
Bedminster NJ 07921
800 403-3302

(P-6441)
AUDIENCE INC
5670 Wilshire Blvd # 100, Los Angeles (90036-5686)
PHONE.....................323 413-2370
Oliver Luckett, *CEO*
Kate McLean, *President*
Jeffery Pressman, *COO*
Mike Drath, *CFO*
William Petersen, *Vice Pres*
EMP: 45
SALES (est): 4.5MM **Privately Held**
SIC: 2741 Miscellaneous publishing
PA: Al Ahli Holding Group
Dubai Al-Ain Road Route 66, Dubai
Outlet City, Blue Glasses
Dubai
442 346-66

(P-6442)
AUTOMOTIVE LEASE GUIDE ALG INC
120 Broadway Ste 200, Santa Monica (90401-2385)
P.O. Box 61207, Santa Barbara (93160-1207)
PHONE.....................424 258-8026
James Nguyen, *President*
Michael Guthrie, *CFO*
Oliver Strauss, *Vice Pres*
Valeri Tompkins, *Vice Pres*
Jeff Swart, *Admin Sec*
EMP: 44
SALES (est): 4.2MM
SALES (corp-wide): 323.1MM **Publicly Held**
WEB: www.dealertrack.com
SIC: 2741 Directories: publishing only, not printed on site
PA: Truecar, Inc.
120 Broadway Ste 200
Santa Monica CA 90401
800 200-2000

(P-6443)
B C YELLOW PAGES
1001 Bille Rd, Paradise (95969-3319)
PHONE.....................530 876-8616
Marco Orlando, *President*
EMP: 10
SALES (est): 420.8K **Privately Held**
SIC: 2741 Telephone & other directory publishing

(P-6444)
B-FLAT PUBLISHING LLC
Also Called: Royce Records
9616 Macarthur Blvd, Oakland (94605-4748)
PHONE.....................510 639-7170
EMP: 13
SALES (est): 1MM **Privately Held**
SIC: 2741

(P-6445)
BAY AR YELLOW PAGES
46292 Warm Springs Blvd, Fremont (94539-7997)
PHONE.....................650 558-8888
Hua Su, *Manager*
EMP: 10
SALES (est): 366.1K **Privately Held**
SIC: 2741 Telephone & other directory publishing

(P-6446)
BINGO PUBLISHERS INCORPORATED
24881 Alicia Pkwy Ste E, Laguna Hills (92653-4617)
PHONE.....................949 581-5410
Charles Sloan, *President*
EMP: 20
SQ FT: 3,000
SALES (est): 1.5MM **Privately Held**
SIC: 2741 Miscellaneous publishing

(P-6447)
BIRDCAGE PRESS LLC
2320 Bowdoin St, Palo Alto (94306-1216)
PHONE.....................650 462-6300
Wanda O Reilly, *Manager*
Maureen Kravitz, *Vice Pres*
Kelly Davis, *Graphic Designe*
Jen Minto, *Art Dir*
EMP: 12
SALES (est): 1MM **Privately Held**
WEB: www.birdcagepress.com
SIC: 2741 Miscellaneous publishing

(P-6448)
BIRDEYE INC
2479 E Bayshore Rd # 100, Palo Alto (94303-3233)
PHONE.....................800 561-3357
Navee Gupta, *CEO*
Rachel Randall, *Partner*
Chris Aker, *Officer*
Janelle Johnson, *Vice Pres*
Ameya Virkar, *VP Engrg*
EMP: 110
SALES (est): 1.9MM **Privately Held**
SIC: 2741

(P-6449)
BLUE BOOK PUBLISHERS INC (PA)
Also Called: Coastal Graphics
9820 Willow Creek Rd # 410, San Diego (92131-1115)
P.O. Box 561, La Jolla (92038-0561)
PHONE.....................858 454-7939
Richard L Levin, *President*
Stephen Milne, *Exec VP*
Susan Davidson, *Vice Pres*
Brian Husebye, *Vice Pres*
Scott Levin, *Vice Pres*
EMP: 55
SQ FT: 13,000
SALES (est): 3.9MM **Privately Held**
WEB: www.lajollabluebook.com
SIC: 2741 Directories, telephone: publishing only, not printed on site; guides: publishing only, not printed on site

(P-6450)
BLUEWATER PUBLISHING LLC
9040 Brentwood Blvd Ste B, Brentwood (94513-4052)
P.O. Box 1598 (94513-3598)
PHONE.....................925 634-0880
Karen J Spann,
James Spann,
Karen Spann,
EMP: 10
SQ FT: 2,000
SALES (est): 869.6K **Privately Held**
SIC: 2741 Miscellaneous publishing

(P-6451)
BOOKPACK INC
Also Called: Ulysses Press
3286 Adeline St Ste 1, Berkeley (94703-2484)
P.O. Box 3440 (94703-0440)
PHONE.....................510 601-8301
Ray Riegert, *President*
Leslie Henriques, *Corp Secy*
Claire Chun, *Prdtn Mgr*

Bryce Willett, *Sales Staff*
Lindsay Tamura, *Assistant*
▲ **EMP:** 10
SQ FT: 1,250
SALES (est): 1.1MM **Privately Held**
WEB: www.ulyssespress.com
SIC: 2741 2731 Guides: publishing only, not printed on site; book clubs: publishing only, not printed on site

(P-6452)
BROADVISION RCAO BROADVISI
585 Broadway St, Redwood City (94063-3122)
PHONE.....................650 261-5100
Asher Kotz, *Partner*
Neil Pisane, *President*
Renee Huber, *Executive*
Ricky Nguyen, *CTO*
Steven Gilbert, *Engineer*
EMP: 13 **EST:** 2008
SALES (est): 1.2MM **Privately Held**
SIC: 2741 Miscellaneous publishing

(P-6453)
BROWNTROUT PUBLISHERS INC
4977 Allison Pkwy Ste C, Vacaville (95688-8799)
PHONE.....................707 451-8593
William Michael Brown, *CEO*
EMP: 11
SALES (corp-wide): 23.6MM **Privately Held**
SIC: 2741 Miscellaneous publishing
PA: Browntrout Publishers Inc.
201 Continental Blvd # 200
El Segundo CA 90245
424 290-6122

(P-6454)
BROWNTROUT PUBLISHERS INC (PA)
201 Continental Blvd # 200, El Segundo (90245-4514)
PHONE.....................424 290-6122
William Michael Brown, *CEO*
Gray Peterson, *Vice Pres*
Adeline Digby, *Managing Dir*
Neal Potter, *Finance*
Chuck Loeser, *Manager*
▲ **EMP:** 40
SQ FT: 11,000
SALES (est): 23.6MM **Privately Held**
SIC: 2741 Miscellaneous publishing

(P-6455)
BUY AND SELL PRESS INC
605 Broadway, Jackson (95642-2420)
PHONE.....................209 223-3333
Emilio Prunetti, *President*
Craig Murphy, *Treasurer*
Dan Barnett, *Vice Pres*
Hazel Prunetti, *Admin Sec*
Donna Murphy, *Director*
EMP: 18
SQ FT: 2,000
SALES (est): 1.3MM **Privately Held**
WEB: www.buynsel.com
SIC: 2741 6512 Shopping news: publishing & printing; nonresidential building operators

(P-6456)
C PUBLISHING LLC
Also Called: C Magazine
1543 7th St Ste 202, Santa Monica (90401-2645)
PHONE.....................310 393-3800
Jennifer Smith Hale,
Nick Hale, *CFO*
Sandy Hubbard, *Info Tech Dir*
Molly Downing, *Sales Staff*
Autumn Okeefe, *Director*
EMP: 25
SALES (est): 3.1MM **Privately Held**
SIC: 2741 Miscellaneous publishing

(P-6457)
CASUAL FRIDAYS INC
Also Called: Social Media Day San Diego
3990 Old Town Ave A203, San Diego (92110-2905)
PHONE.....................858 433-1442

Tyler Anderson, *CEO*
William Vieux, *Vice Pres*
Michael Crump, *Principal*
Staci Semper, *Graphic Designe*
EMP: 25 **EST:** 2010
SALES (est): 1.3MM **Privately Held**
SIC: 2741

(P-6458)
CELEBRITY PUBLISHING LLC
17320 Woodentree Ln, Riverside
(92503-6798)
PHONE..................714 914-4635
Brenda Villegas, *Mng Member*
EMP: 10 **EST:** 2011
SALES (est): 491.6K **Privately Held**
SIC: 2741 Miscellaneous publishing

(P-6459)
CHI-AM COMICS DAILY INC
Also Called: Katherine Shih
673 Monterey Pass Rd, Monterey Park
(91754-2418)
PHONE..................626 281-2989
Katherine Shih, *President*
EMP: 10
SALES (est): 523.3K **Privately Held**
SIC: 2741 6531 Miscellaneous publishing;
real estate agents & managers

(P-6460)
CHINESE OVERSEAS MKTG SVC CORP
33420 Alvarado Niles Rd, Union City
(94587-3110)
PHONE..................510 476-0880
Alan KAO, *President*
EMP: 50
SALES (corp-wide): 1.5MM **Privately Held**
WEB: www.ccyp.com
SIC: 2741 7389 Directories, telephone:
publishing only, not printed on site; trade
show arrangement
PA: Chinese Overseas Marketing Service
Corporation
3940 Rosemead Blvd
Rosemead CA 91770
626 280-8588

(P-6461)
CHINESE OVERSEAS MKTG SVC CORP
Also Called: Chinese Consumer Yellow
Pages
46292 Warm Springs Blvd, Fremont
(94539-7997)
PHONE..................626 280-8588
Gorden KAO, *Branch Mgr*
EMP: 40
SALES (corp-wide): 1.5MM **Privately Held**
WEB: www.ccyp.com
SIC: 2741 7389 8742 Directories, tele-
phone: publishing only, not printed on
site; trade show arrangement; marketing
consulting services
PA: Chinese Overseas Marketing Service
Corporation
3940 Rosemead Blvd
Rosemead CA 91770
626 280-8588

(P-6462)
CHINESE OVERSEAS MKTG SVC CORP (PA)
Also Called: Chinese Consumer Yellow
Pages
3940 Rosemead Blvd, Rosemead
(91770-1952)
PHONE..................626 280-8588
Alan KAO, *President*
Kimo Gao, *Prgrmr*
Gorden KAO, *Director*
Ruby Lei, *Manager*
▲ **EMP:** 60
SQ FT: 9,298
SALES: 1.5MM **Privately Held**
WEB: www.ccyp.com
SIC: 2741 7389 8742 Directories, tele-
phone: publishing only, not printed on
site; trade show arrangement; marketing
consulting services

(P-6463)
COBRA SYSTEMS
Reminderstickers Div
3521 E Enterprise Dr, Anaheim
(92807-1604)
PHONE..................714 688-7992
Wendy Mazurier, *Branch Mgr*
EMP: 10
SALES (corp-wide): 4MM **Privately Held**
SIC: 2741 Miscellaneous publishing
PA: Cobra Systems
3521 E Enterprise Dr
Anaheim CA 92807
714 688-7999

(P-6464)
CRITTENDEN PUBLISHING INC (HQ)
45 Leveroni Ct Ste 204, Novato
(94949-5721)
P.O. Box 1150 (94948-1150)
PHONE..................415 475-1522
Alan Crittenden, *CEO*
Allen Crittenden, *President*
David Berger, *Principal*
Teresa Moody, *Principal*
Eva Nickel-Raudio, *Human Res Mgr*
EMP: 19 **EST:** 1980
SQ FT: 9,500
SALES (est): 1.8MM
SALES (corp-wide): 6.6MM **Privately Held**
WEB: www.crittendenonline.com
SIC: 2741 2721 Newsletter publishing; pe-
riodicals
PA: Crittenden Research Inc
45 Leveroni Ct
Novato CA 94949
415 475-1576

(P-6465)
CRITTENDEN RESEARCH INC (PA)
45 Leveroni Ct, Novato (94949-5721)
P.O. Box 1150 (94948-1150)
PHONE..................415 475-1576
Alan Crittenden, *President*
Michelle Watson,
EMP: 30
SQ FT: 9,500
SALES (est): 6.6MM **Privately Held**
WEB: www.crittendenconferences.com
SIC: 2741 Newsletter publishing

(P-6466)
CTG I LLC
Also Called: Cleantech Group
600 California St Fl 11, San Francisco
(94108-2727)
PHONE..................415 233-9700
Richard Youngman, *CEO*
Nicholas Parker, *Co-Founder*
Keith Raab, *Co-Founder*
Jules Besnainou, *Director*
Stephen Marcus, *Director*
EMP: 12
SALES (est): 573.3K **Privately Held**
SIC: 2741 Miscellaneous publishing

(P-6467)
DAISY SCOUT PUBLISHING
1200 N Barsten Way, Anaheim
(92806-1822)
PHONE..................714 630-6611
Athena Cox, *Owner*
Athena Cox-Hayes, *CFO*
EMP: 10
SALES (est): 656.4K **Privately Held**
SIC: 2741 Miscellaneous publishing

(P-6468)
DANIELS INC (PA)
Also Called: Big Nickel
74745 Leslie Ave, Palm Desert
(92260-2030)
PHONE..................801 621-3355
Daniel Murphy, *President*
Dennis Porter, *Corp Secy*
EMP: 23
SQ FT: 10,000
SALES: 1.5MM **Privately Held**
SIC: 2741 Shopping news: publishing &
printing

(P-6469)
DINNER ON A DOLLAR INC
10249 Caminito Pitaya, San Diego
(92131-2010)
PHONE..................858 693-3939
EMP: 11
SALES (est): 730K **Privately Held**
SIC: 2741

(P-6470)
DIVERSIFIED PRINTERS INC
12834 Maxwell Dr, Tustin (92782-0914)
PHONE..................714 994-3400
Kenneth Bittner, *President*
Paul R Nassar, *CFO*
Jerry Tominaga, *Exec VP*
EMP: 51
SQ FT: 105,000
SALES (est): 9.8MM **Privately Held**
WEB: www.diversifiedprinters.com
SIC: 2741 2759 2789 Directories: publish-
ing & printing; commercial printing; book-
binding & related work

(P-6471)
DLIVE INC
675 Mariners Island Blvd # 108, San Mateo
(94404-1062)
PHONE..................650 397-1777
Yinghan Wang, *CEO*
EMP: 20
SALES (est): 465.3K **Privately Held**
SIC: 2741

(P-6472)
ECONODAY INC
3730 Mt Diablo Blvd # 340, Lafayette
(94549-3641)
P.O. Box 954 (94549-0954)
PHONE..................925 299-5350
Cynthia Parker, *President*
June Moberg, *Admin Sec*
Anne Picker, *Deputy Dir*
EMP: 17
SQ FT: 1,200
SALES: 1MM **Privately Held**
WEB: www.econoday.com
SIC: 2741 Miscellaneous publishing

(P-6473)
EDIRECT PUBLISHING INC
Also Called: Resumemailman
3451 Via Montebello # 192, Carlsbad
(92009-8492)
PHONE..................760 602-8300
Lee Marc, *CEO*
Spencer Greenwald, *Vice Pres*
Melisa Cochran, *Opers Staff*
EMP: 12
SALES (est): 964.2K **Privately Held**
WEB: www.execs-direct.com
SIC: 2741 5961 ;

(P-6474)
EL CLASIFICADO
1125 Goodrich Blvd, Commerce
(90022-5104)
P.O. Box 227310, Los Angeles (90022-
0750)
PHONE..................323 278-5310
EMP: 100
SALES (corp-wide): 11.2MM **Privately Held**
SIC: 2741
PA: El Clasificado
11205 Imperial Hwy
Norwalk CA 90650
323 837-4095

(P-6475)
ELSEVIER INC
525 B St Ste 1650, San Diego
(92101-4497)
PHONE..................619 231-6616
Kristen Chrisman, *Branch Mgr*
EMP: 67
SALES (corp-wide): 9.7B **Privately Held**
SIC: 2741 Miscellaneous publishing
HQ: Elsevier Inc.
230 Park Ave Fl 8
New York NY 10169
212 989-5800

(P-6476)
EMI MUSIC PUBLISHING INC
2700 Colorado Ave Ste 100, Santa Monica
(90404-3581)
PHONE..................310 586-2700
Martin Bandier, *Principal*
Andre Pacheco, *Marketing Staff*
EMP: 40
SALES (est): 1.9MM **Privately Held**
WEB: www.emimusicpublishing.com
SIC: 2741 Music, sheet: publishing & print-
ing

(P-6477)
EMPLOYERWARE LLC
Also Called: Poster Compliance Center
3687 Mt Diablo Blvd 100a, Lafayette
(94549-3777)
PHONE..................925 283-9735
Maurice Levich,
Rick Donley, *Controller*
Angel Tims, *Manager*
Margaret Lennon, *Accounts Mgr*
Lisa Parker, *Accounts Mgr*
EMP: 33
SQ FT: 2,500
SALES (est): 3.1MM **Privately Held**
WEB: www.employerware.com
SIC: 2741 8748 Miscellaneous publishing;
publishing consultant

(P-6478)
EQUITY FORD RESEARCH
11722 Sorrento Valley Rd I, San Diego
(92121-1021)
PHONE..................858 755-1327
Timothy R Alward, *President*
Jonathan Worrall, *Chairman*
Stephen Cicero, *Software Dev*
Albert Chan, *Financial Analy*
William Neill, *VP Opers*
EMP: 18
SQ FT: 5,500
SALES (est): 1.3MM **Privately Held**
WEB: www.fordupdate.com
SIC: 2741 6282 Miscellaneous publishing;
investment advice

(P-6479)
EXPRESS CHIPPING
418 Goetz Ave, Santa Ana (92707-3710)
PHONE..................562 789-8058
Mike Pla, *Owner*
John Pla, *President*
EMP: 12
SALES (est): 1.1MM **Privately Held**
SIC: 2741 Miscellaneous publishing

(P-6480)
EXPRESS FOLDING
21250 Hawthorne Blvd, Torrance
(90503-5506)
PHONE..................310 316-6762
Mark Nelson, *Owner*
EMP: 45
SALES (est): 1.4MM **Privately Held**
SIC: 2741 Miscellaneous publishing

(P-6481)
EXPRESS IT DELIVERS
168 Mason Way Ste B5, City of Industry
(91746-2339)
PHONE..................626 855-1294
Paul Grassia, *Owner*
EMP: 50
SALES (est): 1.3MM **Privately Held**
SIC: 2741 Miscellaneous publishing

(P-6482)
EXTREME REACH INC
1048 N Lake St, Burbank (91502-1624)
PHONE..................818 588-3635
Kris Estrella, *Branch Mgr*
EMP: 10 **Privately Held**
SIC: 2741 Miscellaneous publishing
PA: Extreme Reach, Inc.
75 2nd Ave Ste 720
Needham Heights MA 02494

▲ = Import ▼=Export
◆ =Import/Export

(P-6483)
FEDERAL BUYERS GUIDE INC (PA)
Also Called: Government Travel Directory
324 Palm Ave, Santa Barbara
(93101-1727)
PHONE..................................805 963-7470
Stuart Miller, *President*
Cory Oltmer, *CFO*
Afzal Hussain, *Exec VP*
EMP: 12
SQ FT: 3,500
SALES (est): 1.2MM **Privately Held**
WEB: www.federalbuyersguideinc.com
SIC: 2741 Guides: publishing & printing

(P-6484)
FINAL DATA INC
5950 Canoga Ave Ste 220, Woodland Hills
(91367-5066)
PHONE..................................818 835-9560
Chae Lee, *President*
Akira Katanosaka, *Vice Pres*
EMP: 30
SALES: 2.7MM **Privately Held**
SIC: 2741 Miscellaneous publishing

(P-6485)
FINDDOCTR INC
9550 Bolsa Ave Ste 213, Westminster
(92683-5947)
PHONE..................................657 888-2629
Thu Thai, *President*
EMP: 10
SALES (est): 261K **Privately Held**
SIC: 2741

(P-6486)
FIRST DATABANK INC (DH)
Also Called: First Data Bank
701 Gateway Blvd Ste 600, South San
Francisco (94080-7084)
PHONE..................................800 633-3453
Gregory H Dorn, *President*
Don Nielsen, *President*
James Schultz, *Treasurer*
Bob Katter, *Exec VP*
Clifton Louie, *Exec VP*
EMP: 74
SALES (est): 27.5MM
SALES (corp-wide): 6.6B **Privately Held**
WEB: www.firstdatabank.com
SIC: 2741 7375 Technical manuals: publishing only, not printed on site; micropublishing; information retrieval services; data base information retrieval
HQ: Hearst Business Media Corp
2620 Barrett Rd
Gainesville GA 30507
770 532-4111

(P-6487)
FRANKLIN COVEY CO
3333 Michelson Dr Ste 400, Irvine
(92612-1684)
PHONE..................................949 788-8102
Maryann Bothers, *Manager*
EMP: 23
SALES (corp-wide): 209.7MM **Publicly Held**
SIC: 2741 Miscellaneous publishing
PA: Franklin Covey Co.
2200 W Parkway Blvd
Salt Lake City UT 84119
801 817-1776

(P-6488)
FRONTIERS MEDIA LLC
Also Called: Frontiers Magazine
5657 Wilshire Blvd # 470, Los Angeles
(90036-3736)
PHONE..................................323 930-3220
David Stern,
Jacci Ybarra, *Adv Dir*
EMP: 50
SALES: 3.7MM **Privately Held**
SIC: 2741

(P-6489)
FULL VOID 2 INC (PA)
Also Called: Alfred Music Publishing
16320 Roscoe Blvd Ste 100, Van Nuys
(91406-1216)
P.O. Box 10003 (91410-0003)
PHONE..................................818 891-5999
Ron Manus, *Ch of Bd*

Jeannette Delisa, *President*
Morton Manus, *President*
Paul Vindigni, *CFO*
Andrew Surmani, *Vice Pres*
▲ EMP: 125 EST: 1922
SQ FT: 20,000
SALES (est): 59.1MM **Privately Held**
WEB: www.alfred.com
SIC: 2741 Miscellaneous publishing

(P-6490)
FUNDX INVESTMENT GROUP
Also Called: Fundex Investment Group
235 Montgomery St # 1049, San Francisco
(94104-3008)
PHONE..................................415 986-7979
Janet Brown, *President*
Bernie Burke, *Ch Credit Ofcr*
Jeffrey Smith, *Principal*
Dannielle Kimpel, *Executive Asst*
Jason Browne, *Portfolio Mgr*
EMP: 18
SQ FT: 2,000
SALES (est): 2MM **Privately Held**
WEB: www.dal-investment.com
SIC: 2741 6282 Newsletter publishing; investment advisory service

(P-6491)
GAYOT PUBLICATIONS
1744 Sunset Ave, Santa Monica
(90405-5920)
PHONE..................................323 965-3529
Andry Gayot, *Owner*
Jeremy Jeffers, *Business Mgr*
Jana Montgomery, *Personnel*
Laurie Hartzell, *Assoc Editor*
Becky Sauer, *Assoc Editor*
EMP: 20
SALES (est): 996.9K **Privately Held**
SIC: 2741 Miscellaneous publishing

(P-6492)
GLOBAL COMPLIANCE INC
Also Called: Compliance Poster
438 W Chestnut Ave Ste A, Monrovia
(91016-1129)
P.O. Box 607 (91017-0607)
PHONE..................................626 303-6855
Patricia A Blum, *President*
Irene Golding, *Credit Mgr*
Tom Simmons, *QC Mgr*
John Nielsen, *Corp Comm Staff*
EMP: 25
SALES (est): 3.4MM **Privately Held**
WEB: www.complianceposter.com
SIC: 2741 Posters: publishing & printing

(P-6493)
GMM INC
Also Called: Creative Industry Handbooks
10152 Riverside Dr, Toluca Lake
(91602-2532)
PHONE..................................323 874-1600
Carl Rovsek, *President*
Blythe Rovsek, *Vice Pres*
EMP: 20
SALES (est): 1.7MM **Privately Held**
WEB: www.creativehandbook.com
SIC: 2741 Newsletter publishing

(P-6494)
GOFF INVESTMENT GROUP LLC
Also Called: Global Printing Sourcing & Dev
980 Lincoln Ave Ste 200b, San Rafael
(94901-8802)
PHONE..................................415 456-2934
Steven Goff, *Managing Dir*
▲ EMP: 11
SQ FT: 3,000
SALES (est): 1.9MM **Privately Held**
WEB: www.globalpsd.com
SIC: 2741 Miscellaneous publishing

(P-6495)
GOOD WORLDWIDE LLC
6380 Wilshire Blvd # 1500, Los Angeles
(90048-5015)
PHONE..................................323 206-6495
Ben Goldhirsh,
Michelle Medlock, *Manager*
EMP: 44
SALES: 950K **Privately Held**
SIC: 2741 Miscellaneous publishing

(P-6496)
GRAPHIQ LLC
101a Innovation Pl, Santa Barbara
(93108-2268)
P.O. Box 1259, Summerland (93067-1259)
PHONE..................................805 335-2433
Kevin Oconnor, *President*
Ivan Bercovich, *President*
Scott Leonard, *CTO*
Chad Goldberg, *Manager*
Alex Rosenberg, *Manager*
EMP: 120 EST: 2009
SALES: 9.9MM **Publicly Held**
SIC: 2741 4813 ;
PA: Amazon.Com, Inc.
410 Terry Ave N
Seattle WA 98109

(P-6497)
GUADALUPE ASSOCIATES INC (PA)
Also Called: Ignatius Press
1348 10th Ave, San Francisco
(94122-2304)
PHONE..................................415 387-2324
Mark Brumley, *CEO*
Jack Gergurich, *Accountant*
Carolyn Lemon, *Production*
Vivian Dudro, *Assoc Editor*
Penelope Boldrick, *Director*
▲ EMP: 15
SQ FT: 1,500
SALES (est): 2.9MM **Privately Held**
WEB: www.catecheticalresources.com
SIC: 2741 2731 Miscellaneous publishing; books: publishing only

(P-6498)
HADLEY MEDIA INC
1665 S Ranch Santa Fe Rd, San Marcos
(92078)
PHONE..................................800 270-2084
Patrick Hadley, *President*
Katherine Hadley, *Project Mgr*
EMP: 15
SALES (est): 1.1MM **Privately Held**
WEB: www.hadleymedia.com
SIC: 2741 Catalogs: publishing only, not printed on site

(P-6499)
HIGHWIRE PRESS INC (PA)
973 University Ave, Los Gatos
(95032-7636)
PHONE..................................650 721-6388
Dan Filby, *CEO*
John Sack, *Director*
Kevin-John Black, *Manager*
EMP: 22
SALES (est): 2.7MM **Privately Held**
SIC: 2741 Miscellaneous publishing

(P-6500)
HOMEFACTS MANAGEMENT LLC
Also Called: Homefacts.com
1 Venture Ste 300, Irvine (92618-7416)
PHONE..................................949 502-8300
Cabell Cobbs, *Principal*
EMP: 15
SQ FT: 3,750
SALES (est): 545.6K **Privately Held**
SIC: 2741

(P-6501)
IBISWORLD INC
11755 Wilshire Blvd # 1100, Los Angeles
(90025-1506)
PHONE..................................212 626-6794
Justin Ruthven, *President*
EMP: 50
SALES (est): 1.4MM **Privately Held**
WEB: www.ibisworld.com
SIC: 2741 Miscellaneous publishing

(P-6502)
INFORMA BUSINESS MEDIA INC
Sourceesb
16815 Von Karman Ave # 150, Irvine
(92606-2406)
PHONE..................................949 252-1146
Tam Nguyen, *Branch Mgr*
EMP: 30 **Privately Held**

SIC: 2741 Directories: publishing only, not printed on site
HQ: Informa Business Media, Inc.
605 3rd Ave
New York NY 10158
212 204-4200

(P-6503)
INGROOVES FONTANA
15821 Ventura Blvd # 420, Encino
(91436-2915)
PHONE..................................818 212-2550
Jason Rowlands, *Principal*
EMP: 12
SALES (est): 1.2MM **Privately Held**
SIC: 2741 Miscellaneous publishing

(P-6504)
INSTITUTIONAL REAL ESTATE (PA)
1475 N Broadway Ste 300, Walnut Creek
(94596-4643)
PHONE..................................925 933-4040
Geoffrey Dohrmann, *CEO*
Nyia Dohrman, *President*
Erika Cohen, *COO*
Jonathan A Schein, *Senior VP*
Bridgite Thompson, *Marketing Staff*
EMP: 22
SQ FT: 3,000
SALES (est): 1.4MM **Privately Held**
WEB: www.irei.com
SIC: 2741 8742 8748 2721 Newsletter publishing; real estate consultant; business consulting; periodicals

(P-6505)
JACK BRAIN AND ASSOCIATES INC
20819 Nunes Ave, Castro Valley
(94546-5741)
PHONE..................................510 889-1360
Jack Brain, *President*
Karrie Brain Marsh, *Treasurer*
Shirley Brain, *Admin Sec*
EMP: 10
SQ FT: 4,000
SALES (est): 820K **Privately Held**
WEB: www.jackbrain.com
SIC: 2741 6513 Newsletter publishing; apartment building operators

(P-6506)
JENNIS GROUP LLC
Also Called: Pinecone Press
1631 Placentia Ave, Costa Mesa
(92627-4311)
PHONE..................................714 227-7972
Debra Jennis, *President*
Alex Jennis, *Principal*
Walter Jennis, *Principal*
EMP: 11
SALES (est): 700K **Privately Held**
SIC: 2741 2621 Miscellaneous publishing; magazine paper

(P-6507)
JIGSAW DATA CORPORATION
900 Concar Dr, San Mateo (94402-2600)
PHONE..................................650 235-8400
James Fowler, *President*
Barry Friefield, *Partner*
Steven Klei, *CFO*
Garth Moulton, *Vice Pres*
Shaun Flaherty, *Admin Sec*
EMP: 16
SALES (est): 1.5MM
SALES (corp-wide): 10.4B **Publicly Held**
SIC: 2741 Telephone & other directory publishing
PA: Salesforce.Com, Inc.
1 Market Ste 300
San Francisco CA 94105
415 901-7000

(P-6508)
JONES GLYN PRODUCTIONS INC
1945 Camino Vida Roble M, Carlsbad
(92008-6529)
PHONE..................................760 431-8955
Glyn Jones, *President*
EMP: 10
SQ FT: 4,500

SALES (est): 879.8K Privately Held
WEB: www.glynjones.com
SIC: 2741

(P-6509)
JOSEPH CHARLES WHITSON
Also Called: Adventures In Personal Cmpt
154 Auburn Way, Vacaville (95688-3561)
PHONE..............................707 694-8806
Joseph C Whitson, *Principal*
EMP: 10
SALES (est): 65.1K Privately Held
SIC: 2741 Miscellaneous publishing

(P-6510)
JOURNEYWORKS PUBLISHING
763 Chestnut St, Santa Cruz (95060-3751)
P.O. Box 8466 (95061-8466)
PHONE..............................831 423-1400
Steven Bignell, *President*
Judith Carey, *Vice Pres*
Mary Bignell, *Admin Sec*
EMP: 16
SQ FT: 5,200
SALES (est): 2MM Privately Held
WEB: www.journeyworks.com
SIC: 2741 Miscellaneous publishing

(P-6511)
KAN GROUP CORP
3807 Wilshire Blvd # 518, Los Angeles
(90010-3101)
PHONE..............................213 383-1236
Michelle Parks, *President*
EMP: 15
SALES (est): 691.4K Privately Held
SIC: 2741 Miscellaneous publishing

(P-6512)
KPI AGENCY INC
32 Via Jacobea, San Clemente
(92673-7201)
PHONE..............................949 232-0220
Nico Coutzee,
Chad Childress,
EMP: 15
SALES (est): 589.5K Privately Held
SIC: 2741

(P-6513)
KUDOS&CO INC
470 Ramona St, Palo Alto (94301-1707)
PHONE..............................650 799-9104
Ole Vidar Hestaas, *CEO*
EMP: 25
SALES (est): 616.5K Privately Held
SIC: 2741

(P-6514)
LA XPRESS AIR & HEATING SVCS
6400 E Wash Blvd Ste 121, Commerce
(90040-1820)
PHONE..............................310 856-9678
Jesus A Chavez, *CEO*
EMP: 67
SALES (est): 108.4K Privately Held
SIC: 2741 Miscellaneous publishing

(P-6515)
LARSON BROTHERS
5665 E Westover Ave # 101, Fresno
(93727-8650)
PHONE..............................559 292-8161
Jeff Larson, *Partner*
Tom Larson, *Partner*
Luz Ehrastom, *Office Mgr*
EMP: 12
SQ FT: 2,500
SALES (est): 1.2MM Privately Held
WEB: www.larsonbrothers.com
SIC: 2741 7221 Yearbooks: publishing & printing; school photographer

(P-6516)
LEE & FIELDS PUBLISHING INC
3731 Wilshire Blvd # 940, Los Angeles
(90010-2827)
PHONE..............................213 380-5858
Edward Y Lee, *President*
EMP: 12
SALES (est): 820K Privately Held
SIC: 2741 Miscellaneous publishing

(P-6517)
LELAND STANFORD JUNIOR UNIV
Also Called: Stanford University Libraries
557 Escondido Mall, Stanford
(94305-6001)
PHONE..............................650 723-5553
Robert Phillips, *Branch Mgr*
Susan Cabral, *COO*
Diane Meyer, *Officer*
Michelle Heeseman, *Associate Dir*
Colin Stewart, *Associate Dir*
EMP: 106
SQ FT: 10,000
SALES (corp-wide): 5.6B Privately Held
SIC: 2741 8221 Miscellaneous publishing; university
PA: Leland Stanford Junior University
450 Serra Mall
Stanford CA 94305
650 723-2300

(P-6518)
LELAND STANFORD JUNIOR UNIV
Also Called: Stanford Humanities Review
424 Matison Ave, Stanford (94305)
PHONE..............................650 723-3052
Stefano Franch, *Editor*
EMP: 103
SALES (corp-wide): 5.6B Privately Held
SIC: 2741 8221 Miscellaneous publishing; university
PA: Leland Stanford Junior University
450 Serra Mall
Stanford CA 94305
650 723-2300

(P-6519)
LELAND STANFORD JUNIOR UNIV
Also Called: Institute For Intl Studies
559 Nathan Abbott Way, Stanford
(94305-8602)
PHONE..............................650 723-4455
Larry Kramer, *Principal*
EMP: 100
SALES (corp-wide): 5.6B Privately Held
SIC: 2741 8221 2721 Technical manuals: publishing & printing; colleges universities & professional schools; periodicals
PA: Leland Stanford Junior University
450 Serra Mall
Stanford CA 94305
650 723-2300

(P-6520)
LOG(N) LLC
564 Market St Ste 500, San Francisco
(94104-5402)
PHONE..............................415 500-2558
Jinal Jhaveri, *Mng Member*
Forum Desai, *COO*
Abigail Beckwith, *Human Resources*
EMP: 14
SQ FT: 3,939
SALES (est): 918.5K Privately Held
SIC: 2741 7379 ; computer related consulting services

(P-6521)
LYRA CORPORATION
Also Called: M & H Type Composition & Fndry
1802 Hays St, San Francisco (94129-1197)
PHONE..............................415 668-2546
Andrew Hoyem, *President*
Barry Traub, *Admin Sec*
EMP: 11 EST: 1961
SQ FT: 10,000
SALES (est): 1.4MM Privately Held
WEB: www.arionpress.com
SIC: 2741 Miscellaneous publishing

(P-6522)
M G A INVESTMENT CO INC
Also Called: Easy Ad Magazine
3211 Broad St Ste 201, San Luis Obispo
(93401-6770)
PHONE..............................805 543-9050
Jackie Koda, *Administration*
EMP: 15
SQ FT: 2,000
SALES (est): 1.6MM Privately Held
WEB: www.photo-ad.com
SIC: 2741 2721 Shopping news: publishing only, not printed on site; magazines: publishing only, not printed on site

(P-6523)
MARCOA MEDIA LLC (PA)
9955 Black Mountain Rd, San Diego
(92126-4514)
P.O. Box 509100 (92150-9100)
PHONE..............................858 635-9627
Michael Martella, *Mng Member*
Scott Ogan, *Exec Dir*
Anthony Kuh, *Project Mgr*
Carolina Ruiz, *Graphic Designe*
Zury Luevanos, *Advt Staff*
EMP: 40
SQ FT: 40,000
SALES (est): 13MM Privately Held
WEB: www.marcoa.com
SIC: 2741 Atlas, map & guide publishing

(P-6524)
MARCOA QUALITY PUBLISHING LLC
9955 Black Mountain Rd, San Diego
(92126-4514)
P.O. Box 509100 (92150-9100)
PHONE..............................858 695-9600
Quinn Smith,
Forrest Smith, *Info Tech Dir*
EMP: 99
SALES (est): 950K Privately Held
SIC: 2741 Miscellaneous publishing

(P-6525)
MCCORMACKS GUIDES INC
3211 Elmquist Ct, Martinez (94553-3150)
PHONE..............................925 229-1869
Don McCormack, *President*
EMP: 10
SALES (est): 83.4K Privately Held
SIC: 2741 Guides: publishing only, not printed on site

(P-6526)
MEETVILLE INC
1465 Civic Ct, Concord (94520-7914)
PHONE..............................415 755-0822
Mark Fedin, *CEO*
EMP: 120
SALES: 12MM Privately Held
SIC: 2741

(P-6527)
MESGONA CORPORATION
12534 Moorpark St Apt H, Studio City
(91604-1357)
PHONE..............................310 926-3238
Seyedrasool Sadrieh, *President*
EMP: 10
SALES (est): 261K Privately Held
SIC: 2741

(P-6528)
MID MICHIGAN TRADING POST LTD
Also Called: Wheeler Deeler
5200 Lankershim Blvd # 350, North Hollywood (91601-3155)
P.O. Box 389, Dimondale MI (48821-0389)
PHONE..............................517 323-9020
Patrick D Karslake, *President*
Gretchen Karslake, *Admin Sec*
EMP: 90
SQ FT: 3,200
SALES (est): 6.3MM Privately Held
WEB: www.wheelerdeeler.com
SIC: 2741 2752 2721 Shopping news: publishing only, not printed on site; commercial printing, offset; periodicals

(P-6529)
MITCHELL REPAIR INFO CO LLC (HQ)
Also Called: Mitchell1
14145 Danielson St Ste A, Poway
(92064-8827)
PHONE..............................858 391-5000
David Ellingen,
Ken Young, *Exec VP*
Scott Degiorgio, *General Mgr*
David Rady, *General Mgr*
Lon Mok, *Admin Asst*
EMP: 20 EST: 1996
SALES (est): 34.1MM
SALES (corp-wide): 3.6B Publicly Held
WEB: www.mitchellrepair.com
SIC: 2741 2731 5251 Technical manuals: publishing only, not printed on site; book publishing; hardware
PA: Snap-On Incorporated
2801 80th St
Kenosha WI 53143
262 656-5200

(P-6530)
MODERNPRO LLC
15 Woodcrest Ln, Aliso Viejo (92656-2125)
PHONE..............................949 232-2148
Scott Esposto, *President*
EMP: 10
SALES (est): 615.9K Privately Held
SIC: 2741 7812 7221 8748 ; motion picture & video production; music video production; photographer, still or video; business consulting

(P-6531)
MONGABAY ORG CORPORATION
15 Clinton St, Redwood City (94062-1596)
PHONE..............................209 315-5573
Rhett Butler, *President*
EMP: 24 EST: 2011
SALES (est): 1.3MM Privately Held
SIC: 2741

(P-6532)
MOTHERLY INC
1725 Oakdell Dr, Menlo Park (94025-5735)
PHONE..............................917 860-9926
Christina Cubeta, *COO*
EMP: 24
SALES: 600K Privately Held
SIC: 2741

(P-6533)
MPC NETWORKCOM INC
440 Fair Dr Ste 233, Costa Mesa
(92626-6294)
PHONE..............................949 873-1002
Rich D'Alessio, *CEO*
Dennis D'Alessio, *Ch of Bd*
EMP: 10
SALES (est): 843.6K Privately Held
SIC: 2741 Directories: publishing only, not printed on site

(P-6534)
MYERS-BRIGGS COMPANY (PA)
Also Called: Cpp
185 N Wolfe Rd, Sunnyvale (94086-5212)
PHONE..............................650 969-8901
Jeffrey Hayes, *President*
Marion McGovern, *Ch of Bd*
Carl Thoresen, *Ch of Bd*
Calvin W Finch, *Senior VP*
Andrew Bell, *Vice Pres*
EMP: 100
SQ FT: 16,000
SALES (est): 34.2MM Privately Held
SIC: 2741 Miscellaneous publishing

(P-6535)
MYVOICEGIG LLC
12517 Wedgwood Cir, Tustin (92780-2879)
PHONE..............................714 702-6006
D Elery Werner, *CEO*
EMP: 11 EST: 2014
SALES (est): 650K Privately Held
SIC: 2741

(P-6536)
NEIL A KJOS MUSIC COMPANY (PA)
4382 Jutland Dr, San Diego (92117-3642)
P.O. Box 178270 (92177-8270)
PHONE..............................858 270-9800
Ryan Nowlin, *President*
Neil A Kjos Jr, *Ch of Bd*
Barbara G Kjos, *Chairman*
◆ EMP: 40
SQ FT: 72,000
SALES (est): 6.8MM Privately Held
WEB: www.kjos.com
SIC: 2741 Music books: publishing & printing; music, sheet: publishing & printing

▲ = Import ▼=Export
◆ =Import/Export

(P-6537)
NEIL A KJOS MUSIC COMPANY
4382 Jutland Dr, San Diego (92117-3642)
P.O. Box 178270 (92177-8270)
PHONE..................................619 225-6710
Chris Callipari - Controller, *Branch Mgr*
EMP: 18
SALES (corp-wide): 6.8MM **Privately Held**
SIC: 2741 Music books: publishing & printing; music, sheet: publishing & printing
PA: Neil A Kjos Music Company
4382 Jutland Dr
San Diego CA 92117
858 270-9800

(P-6538)
NEIL PATEL DIGITAL LLC
750 B St Ste 2600, San Diego (92101-8175)
PHONE..................................619 356-8119
Mike Kamo,
EMP: 25
SALES (est): 560.4K **Privately Held**
SIC: 2741

(P-6539)
NETMARBLE US INC
6131 Orangethorpe Ave # 160, Buena Park (90620-4906)
PHONE..................................714 276-1196
Chul Min Sim, *CEO*
Joon Yoon, *Marketing Mgr*
Nicole Kim, *Marketing Staff*
EMP: 15
SQ FT: 2,500
SALES: 10MM
SALES (corp-wide): 1.5B **Privately Held**
SIC: 2741 5734 Miscellaneous publishing; software, computer games
PA: Netmarble Corporation
20/F G-Valley Biz Plaza
Seoul 08379
821 588-5180

(P-6540)
NEXTAG INC (PA)
555 Twin Dolphin Dr # 370, Redwood City (94065-2133)
PHONE..................................650 645-4700
Chris Hart, *CEO*
EMP: 97
SALES (est): 66.3MM **Privately Held**
WEB: www.nextag.com
SIC: 2741 Shopping news: publishing & printing

(P-6541)
NEXTCLIENTCOM INC
25012 Avenue Kearny, Valencia (91355-1253)
PHONE..................................818 550-8989
Lawrence J Tjan, *CEO*
David Morelli, *CFO*
Karen E Sugihara, *Admin Sec*
Enrique Aguilar, *Web Dvlpr*
Jonathan Tjan, *Web Dvlpr*
EMP: 14
SALES: 1.7MM **Privately Held**
SIC: 2741 Newsletter publishing

(P-6542)
NYABENGA LLC
Also Called: Thehomemag Bay Area
9020 Brentwood Blvd Ste A, Brentwood (94513-4048)
PHONE..................................925 418-4221
David Pritchett, *President*
Mark Pistor, *Shareholder*
Rachel Pritchett, *Principal*
EMP: 10
SQ FT: 1,200
SALES (est): 553K **Privately Held**
SIC: 2741 7311 5963 Miscellaneous publishing; advertising agencies

(P-6543)
OCEAN WAYNE MEDIA INC
100 N Citrus St Ste 530, West Covina (91791-6601)
PHONE..................................626 966-8808
WEI Zhang, *President*
Daoji LI, *Administration*
EMP: 10
SALES (est): 577.6K **Privately Held**
SIC: 2741

(P-6544)
ONNET USA INC
2870 Zanker Rd Ste 205, San Jose (95134-2133)
PHONE..................................408 457-3992
Kyongwan Son, *CEO*
Yeon Pak, *Office Mgr*
EMP: 26
SALES (est): 2MM
SALES (corp-wide): 145.6MM **Privately Held**
SIC: 2741 Miscellaneous publishing
HQ: Onnet Co., Ltd.
Sampyung-Dong
Seongnam 13488
822 568-5765

(P-6545)
ORB MEDIA BROADCASTING INC
3125 W Beverly Blvd, Montebello (90640-2216)
PHONE..................................323 246-4524
Yoel Berrios, *CEO*
Wendell Frohwein, *Shareholder*
Adrian Mendoza, *Shareholder*
EMP: 10
SALES (est): 200K **Privately Held**
SIC: 2741 Miscellaneous publishing

(P-6546)
OUTREACH SLUTIONS AS A SVC LLC
980 9th St Fl 16, Sacramento (95814-2736)
PHONE..................................800 824-8573
William Molina,
EMP: 10
SALES (est): 304.1K **Privately Held**
SIC: 2741

(P-6547)
PARROT COMMUNICATIONS INTL INC
Also Called: Parrot Media Network
26321 Ferry Ct, Santa Clarita (91350-2998)
PHONE..................................818 567-4700
Robert W Mertz, *CEO*
▲ EMP: 50
SQ FT: 60,000
SALES (est): 5.8MM **Privately Held**
WEB: www.parrotmedia.com
SIC: 2741 7331 4822 7375 Directories: publishing only, not printed on site; direct mail advertising services; facsimile transmission services; information retrieval services; prepackaged software

(P-6548)
PEACHPIT PRESS
1301 Sansome St, San Francisco (94111-1122)
PHONE..................................415 336-6831
M Carreiro, *Director*
Jenny Collins, *Production*
Tracey Croom, *Editor*
EMP: 40
SALES (est): 141.3K **Privately Held**
SIC: 2741 Miscellaneous publishing

(P-6549)
PENROSE STUDIOS INC
223 Mississippi St Ste 3, San Francisco (94107-2501)
PHONE..................................703 354-1801
Eugene Chung, *CEO*
EMP: 15
SALES (est): 402.6K **Privately Held**
SIC: 2741

(P-6550)
PERSONAL AWARENESS SYSTEMS
Also Called: Persona International
767 Bridgeway Ste 3b, Sausalito (94965-2193)
P.O. Box 100 (94966-0100)
PHONE..................................415 331-3900
Jon Gornstein, *Ch of Bd*
Leah Rosenthal, *President*
Quan Lieu Keongam, *Vice Pres*
EMP: 15

SALES (est): 1.3MM **Privately Held**
WEB: www.personaglobal.com
SIC: 2741 8742 Technical manual & paper publishing; management consulting services

(P-6551)
PLANNED PARENTHOOD LOS ANGELES
1578 Colorado Blvd Ste 13, Los Angeles (90041-1452)
PHONE..................................323 256-1717
Sheri Bonner, *CEO*
EMP: 48
SALES (corp-wide): 63.9MM **Privately Held**
SIC: 2741 Miscellaneous publishing
PA: Planned Parenthood Los Angeles, Inc
400 W 30th St
Los Angeles CA 90007
213 284-3200

(P-6552)
PLAYBOY ENTERPRISES INTL INC
Also Called: Peei
10960 Wilshire Blvd # 2200, Los Angeles (90024-3808)
PHONE..................................310 424-1800
Christopher Pachler, *Exec VP*
Hugh Heffner, *Officer*
EMP: 100
SALES: 3MM
SALES (corp-wide): 45.3MM **Privately Held**
SIC: 2741 Miscellaneous publishing
PA: Playboy Enterprises, Inc.
9346 Civic Center Dr # 200
Beverly Hills CA 90210
310 424-1800

(P-6553)
POPSUGAR INC (PA)
111 Sutter St Fl 16, San Francisco (94104-4541)
PHONE..................................415 391-7576
Brian Sugar, *CEO*
Lisa Sugar, *President*
Sean Macnew, *CFO*
Anna Fieler, *Chief Mktg Ofcr*
Geoff Schiller, *Officer*
EMP: 117
SALES (est): 35.4MM **Privately Held**
SIC: 2741 Miscellaneous publishing

(P-6554)
POSITIVE PUBLISHING INC
449 Nautilus St, La Jolla (92037-5968)
P.O. Box 8648 (92038-8648)
PHONE..................................858 551-0889
Anthony Kampmann, *CEO*
Rose Kampmann, *Vice Pres*
Patricia Kampmann, *Admin Sec*
▲ EMP: 18
SALES (est): 1.4MM **Privately Held**
WEB: www.pospub.com
SIC: 2741 Miscellaneous publishing

(P-6555)
PPL ENTERTAINMENT GROUP INC (PA)
Also Called: Pollybyrd Publications Limited
468 N Camden Dr, Beverly Hills (90210-4507)
P.O. Box 261488, Encino (91426-1488)
PHONE..................................310 860-7499
Jaeson James Jarrett, *CEO*
Suzette L Cuseo, *President*
Maximus Z Diamond, *Exec VP*
Michael J Hochberg, *Vice Pres*
Jake Q Montana, *Vice Pres*
EMP: 25
SQ FT: 3,000
SALES (est): 1.3MM **Privately Held**
SIC: 2741 7389 3652 Music book & sheet music publishing; recording studio, non-commercial records; compact laser discs, prerecorded

(P-6556)
PRIORITY POSTING AND PUBG INC
17501 Irvine Blvd Ste 1, Tustin (92780-3147)
PHONE..................................714 338-2568

Thomas Haacker, *President*
Maureen Haacker, *Vice Pres*
EMP: 25
SQ FT: 3,000
SALES (est): 2.5MM **Privately Held**
WEB: www.priorityposting.com
SIC: 2741 Miscellaneous publishing

(P-6557)
PRISON RIDE SHARE NETWORK
Also Called: Prison Rideshare Network
1541 S California Ave, Compton (90221-4924)
PHONE..................................314 703-5245
Keisha Joseph-Beard, *Owner*
EMP: 20
SALES (est): 492.2K **Privately Held**
SIC: 2741 8742 4729 Telephone & other directory publishing; transportation consultant; carpool/vanpool arrangement

(P-6558)
PROFORMATIVE INC
99 Almaden Blvd Ste 975, San Jose (95113-1616)
PHONE..................................408 400-3993
John Kogan, *Principal*
Dave Cowan, *Vice Pres*
EMP: 17
SALES (est): 1.7MM **Privately Held**
SIC: 2741 Miscellaneous publishing

(P-6559)
PROTOTYPE INDUSTRIES INC (PA)
1545 26th St Ste 200, Santa Monica (90404-3554)
PHONE..................................310 255-0021
Irene Grigoriadis, *President*
EMP: 16
SQ FT: 4,000
SALES (est): 1.7MM **Privately Held**
WEB: www.prototypeindustries.com
SIC: 2741 2752 Miscellaneous publishing; commercial printing, offset

(P-6560)
PROVIDENCE PUBLICATIONS LLC
1620 Santa Clara Dr, Roseville (95661-3558)
PHONE..................................916 774-4000
J Dale Debber, *Managing Dir*
Janet M Debber,
EMP: 30
SQ FT: 7,904
SALES (est): 171.4K **Privately Held**
SIC: 2741 Miscellaneous publishing

(P-6561)
QUADRIGA AMERICAS LLC
17800 S Main St Ste 113, Gardena (90248-3511)
PHONE..................................424 634-4900
EMP: 21 **Privately Held**
SIC: 2741
HQ: Quadriga Americas, Llc
480 Olde Worthington Rd # 350
Westerville OH 43082
614 890-6090

(P-6562)
RANGEME INC
665 3rd St Ste 415, San Francisco (94107-1968)
PHONE..................................415 351-9268
Nicky Jackson, *CEO*
EMP: 12
SALES (est): 334.3K **Privately Held**
SIC: 2741
PA: Efficient Collaborative Retail Marketing Company, Llc
27070 Miles Rd Ste A
Solon OH 44139

(P-6563)
RASPADOXPRESS
8610 Van Nuys Blvd, Panorama City (91402-7205)
PHONE..................................818 892-6969
Oscar Limon, *Branch Mgr*
EMP: 16
SALES (corp-wide): 1MM **Privately Held**
SIC: 2741 Miscellaneous publishing

PRODUCTS & SVCS

PA: Raspadoxpress
9765 Laurel Canyon Blvd
Pacoima CA 91331
818 890-4111

(P-6564)
RATEBEER LLC
Also Called: Ratebeer.com
1381 Velma Ave, Santa Rosa
(95403-7218)
PHONE..................................302 476-2337
Joseph Tucker, *Principal*
EMP: 95
SALES (est): 2.7MM **Privately Held**
SIC: 2741

(P-6565)
REAL MARKETING
9955 Black Mountain Rd, San Diego
(92126-4514)
PHONE..................................858 847-0335
David Collins, *President*
John Princic, *Prdtn Mgr*
▼ **EMP:** 28
SQ FT: 4,000
SALES (est): 3.7MM **Privately Held**
SIC: 2741 2759 2721 Newsletter publishing; promotional printing; magazines: publishing & printing

(P-6566)
REDDIT INC
420 Taylor St, San Francisco (94102-1702)
PHONE..................................415 666-2330
Steve Huffman, *Founder*
Alexis Ohanian, *Founder*
Zubair Jandali, *Senior VP*
Alex Le, *Vice Pres*
Ashley Dawkins, *Comms Dir*
EMP: 20 **EST:** 2011
SQ FT: 50,000
SALES (est): 3.8MM **Privately Held**
SIC: 2741

(P-6567)
REGENT PUBLISHING SERVICES
5355 Mira Sorrento Pl # 100, San Diego
(92121-3803)
PHONE..................................760 510-1936
Valerie Harwell, *Principal*
EMP: 40
SALES (corp-wide): 14.9MM **Privately Held**
SIC: 2741 Miscellaneous publishing
PA: Regent Publishing Services Limited
Rm B&C 7/F Genesis
Wong Chuk Hang HK
289 778-03

(P-6568)
REMBA PARTNERS LLC
1419 E Adams Blvd, Los Angeles
(90011-1819)
PHONE..................................310 858-8495
Luis Remba,
EMP: 10
SALES: 900K **Privately Held**
WEB: www.mixografia.com
SIC: 2741 8748 Art copy: publishing & printing; business consulting

(P-6569)
RJW & ASSOC
31700 Dunraven Ct Ste 100, Thousand Oaks (91361-4513)
PHONE..................................818 706-0289
Ron Weilbacher, *Owner*
EMP: 12
SALES (est): 587.2K **Privately Held**
SIC: 2741 Miscellaneous publishing

(P-6570)
ROCK RAG INC
913 N Highland Ave, Los Angeles
(90038-2412)
P.O. Box 827, Burbank (91503-0827)
PHONE..................................818 919-9364
Kimberly Fields, *President*
EMP: 12
SALES (est): 496K **Privately Held**
SIC: 2741 Miscellaneous publishing

(P-6571)
RONDOR MUSIC INTERNATIONAL (PA)
2440 S Sepulveda Blvd # 119, Los Angeles
(90064-1784)
PHONE..................................310 235-4800
Lance Freed, *President*
Kevin Hall, *Exec VP*
EMP: 12
SQ FT: 25,000
SALES (est): 6.1MM **Privately Held**
SIC: 2741 Music, sheet: publishing only, not printed on site

(P-6572)
ROSS PUBLICATIONS INC
113 W Amerige Ave, Fullerton
(92832-1875)
P.O. Box 873, La Habra (90633-0873)
PHONE..................................562 691-5013
Shelly Hupp, *Vice Pres*
June Wankier, *President*
Shelly Wankier, *Vice Pres*
EMP: 20 **EST:** 1959
SALES (est): 1.5MM **Privately Held**
SIC: 2741 Directories, telephone: publishing only, not printed on site

(P-6573)
SAMUEL FRENCH INC
Also Called: French Saml
7623 W Sunset Blvd, Los Angeles
(90046-2795)
PHONE..................................323 876-0570
Leon Embry, *Director*
EMP: 28
SALES (corp-wide): 6.7MM **Privately Held**
WEB: www.samuelfrench.com
SIC: 2741 Miscellaneous publishing
PA: Samuel French, Inc.
235 Park Ave S Fl 5
New York NY 10003
212 206-8990

(P-6574)
SAN DEGO GOGRAPHIC INFO SOURCE
Also Called: Sangis
5510 Overland Ave Ste 230, San Diego
(92123-1239)
PHONE..................................858 874-7000
Brad Lind, *Exec Dir*
Frank Jessie, *Technology*
EMP: 14 **EST:** 1997
SQ FT: 4,000
SALES: 1.3MM **Privately Held**
WEB: www.sangis.com
SIC: 2741 Maps: publishing & printing

(P-6575)
SAN DIEGO GUIDE INC
Also Called: San Diegan
6370 Lusk Blvd Ste F202, San Diego
(92121-2755)
PHONE..................................858 877-3217
Barry M Berndes, *President*
EMP: 20
SQ FT: 2,500
SALES (est): 1.7MM **Privately Held**
WEB: www.sandiegan.com
SIC: 2741 Guides: publishing only, not printed on site

(P-6576)
SANTA BARBARA MUSIC PUBLISHING
260 Loma Media Rd, Santa Barbara
(93103-2154)
PHONE..................................805 962-5800
Barbara Harlow, *President*
David Harlow, *Vice Pres*
EMP: 20
SALES (est): 1.5MM **Privately Held**
WEB: www.sbmp.com
SIC: 2741 Music book & sheet music publishing

(P-6577)
SCRIBBLE PRESS INC
1109 Montana Ave, Santa Monica
(90403-1609)
P.O. Box 20743, New York NY (10021-0075)
PHONE..................................212 288-2928

EMP: 30
SALES (est): 2.2MM
SALES (corp-wide): 5.2MM **Privately Held**
SIC: 2741
PA: Make Meaning, Inc.
1100 La Avenida St Ste A
Mountain View CA 94043
646 307-5906

(P-6578)
SELFOPTIMA INC
1601 S De Anza Blvd # 255, Cupertino
(95014-5347)
P.O. Box 3502, Saratoga (95070-1502)
PHONE..................................408 217-8667
Nader Vasseghi, *CEO*
Bill Gray, *Chief Mktg Ofcr*
EMP: 11
SQ FT: 3,500
SALES (est): 684.1K **Privately Held**
SIC: 2741

(P-6579)
SHORES PRESS
1100 Industrial Rd Ste 2, San Carlos
(94070-4131)
PHONE..................................650 593-2802
Homayoon Pejooh, *Partner*
Stewart Ghazvini, *Partner*
Kayvan Pejooh, *Partner*
EMP: 13
SQ FT: 7,350
SALES (est): 1.3MM **Privately Held**
WEB: www.rspfunding.com
SIC: 2741 7334 2752 Miscellaneous publishing; photocopying & duplicating services; commercial printing, offset

(P-6580)
SIXTEEN RIVERS PRESS INC
1195 Green St, San Francisco
(94109-2060)
P.O. Box 640663 (94164-0663)
PHONE..................................415 273-1303
Margaret Kaufman, *President*
Sharon Olson, *Treasurer*
EMP: 14
SALES: 23.5K **Privately Held**
SIC: 2741 Miscellaneous publishing

(P-6581)
SOCIALWISE INC
Also Called: Rallio
300 Spectrum Center Dr # 950, Irvine
(92618-4925)
PHONE..................................949 861-3900
Chuck Goetschel, *CEO*
EMP: 10
SALES: 1MM **Privately Held**
SIC: 2741

(P-6582)
SODAMAIL LLC
1300 Valley House Dr # 100, Rohnert Park
(94928-4927)
PHONE..................................707 794-1289
Lauren R Elliott,
Cliff Allen, *Vice Pres*
EMP: 11 **EST:** 1997
SALES (est): 657.9K **Privately Held**
WEB: www.sodamail.com
SIC: 2741 Newsletter publishing

(P-6583)
SONGS MUSIC PUBLISHING LLC
7656 W Sunset Blvd, Los Angeles
(90046-2724)
PHONE..................................323 939-3511
Carianne Marshall, *Manager*
EMP: 15 **Privately Held**
SIC: 2741 Miscellaneous publishing
PA: Songs Music Publishing, Llc
307 7th Ave Rm 904
New York NY 10001

(P-6584)
SONY/ATV MUSIC PUBLISHING LLC
10635 Santa Monica Blvd # 300, Los Angeles (90025-8314)
PHONE..................................310 441-1300
Irwin Robinson, *Manager*
EMP: 30

SALES (corp-wide): 80.1B **Privately Held**
SIC: 2741 5736 Music book & sheet music publishing; sheet music
HQ: Sony/Atv Music Publishing Llc
25 Madison Ave Fl 24
New York NY 10010
212 833-7730

(P-6585)
SOUTHLAND PUBLISHING
Also Called: Pasadena Weekly
50 S De Lacey Ave Ste 200, Pasadena
(91105-3806)
PHONE..................................626 584-1500
Bruce Bolkin, *Owner*
David Comden, *Principal*
EMP: 30
SALES (est): 116.7K **Privately Held**
SIC: 2741 Miscellaneous publishing

(P-6586)
SPARKCENTRAL INC (PA)
650 California St # 1850, San Francisco
(94108-2702)
PHONE..................................866 559-6229
Joe Gagnon, *CEO*
Matthew Finneran, *Principal*
Gemma Williams, *Executive Asst*
Sophie Vu, *VP Mktg*
Cameron Halstead, *Marketing Staff*
EMP: 20
SQ FT: 1,400
SALES: 790.2K **Privately Held**
SIC: 2741 4899 Miscellaneous publishing; data communication services

(P-6587)
SPIDELL PUBLISHING INC
1134 N Gilbert St, Anaheim (92801-1401)
P.O. Box 61044 (92803-6144)
PHONE..................................714 776-7850
Lynn Freer, *President*
Tim Hilger, *CPA*
Austin Lewis, *Manager*
Renee Rodda, *Editor*
Kathryn Zdan, *Editor*
EMP: 20
SQ FT: 2,500
SALES (est): 2.4MM **Privately Held**
WEB: www.spidell.com
SIC: 2741 Guides: publishing only, not printed on site

(P-6588)
SPINMEDIA GROUP INC
6464 W Sunset Blvd # 650, Los Angeles
(90028-8001)
PHONE..................................323 203-1333
Stephen Blackwell, *CEO*
EMP: 125
SQ FT: 13,000
SALES (est): 7.1MM **Privately Held**
SIC: 2741 Miscellaneous publishing

(P-6589)
SPROUT INC
475 Brannan St Ste 410, San Francisco
(94107-5421)
PHONE..................................415 894-9629
Carnet Williams, *CEO*
Matthew McNeely, *Vice Pres*
Adam Taisch, *Vice Pres*
Kevin Hughes, *CTO*
Leo Santana, *Controller*
EMP: 10
SALES (est): 575.1K **Privately Held**
SIC: 2741 7311 Miscellaneous publishing; advertising agencies
PA: Inmobi Technologies Private Limited
7th Floor, Embassy Tech Square,
Bengaluru KA

(P-6590)
STAFFING INDUSTRY ANALYSTS INC
Also Called: Staffing Industry Report
1975 W El Cmno Rl 304, Mountain View
(94040)
PHONE..................................650 390-6200
Ron Mester, *CEO*
Barry Asin, *President*
Philip Grabfield, *Marketing Staff*
EMP: 35
SQ FT: 4,307

SALES (est): 3.1MM
SALES (corp-wide): 225MM **Privately Held**
WEB: www.staffingindustry.com
SIC: 2741 Newsletter publishing
PA: Crain Communications, Inc.
1155 Gratiot Ave
Detroit MI 48207
313 446-6000

(P-6591)
STONE PUBLISHING INC (PA)
Also Called: Almaden Press
2549 Scott Blvd, Santa Clara (95050-2508)
PHONE............................408 450-7910
Eric T Stern, *President*
Manny Cuevas, *President*
H Gene Timmons, *CFO*
Almos Adorjan, *Vice Pres*
Jodi Romkee, *Office Admin*
EMP: 70
SQ FT: 100,000
SALES (est): 22.3MM **Privately Held**
WEB: www.almadenpress.com
SIC: 2741 Miscellaneous publishing

(P-6592)
STREETWISE REPORTS LLC
755 Baywood Dr Fl 2, Petaluma
(94954-5510)
P.O. Box 1099, Kenwood (95452-1099)
PHONE............................707 981-8999
Karen Roche, *President*
Ron Tomassini, *Web Dvlpr*
Kevin Jaillet, *Marketing Staff*
Paul Guedes, *Contractor*
Patrice Fusillo, *Editor*
EMP: 25 **EST:** 2011
SALES (est): 1.5MM **Privately Held**
SIC: 2741

(P-6593)
STRING LETTER PUBLISHING INC
Also Called: Acoustic Guitar Magazine
501 Canal Blvd Ste J, Richmond
(94804-3505)
PHONE............................510 215-0010
David Lusterman, *President*
Cindi Kazarian, *Sales Dir*
Cindi Olwell, *Sales Dir*
Greg Sutton, *Sales Mgr*
Tricia Baxter, *Marketing Staff*
EMP: 25
SQ FT: 6,500
SALES: 3.8MM **Privately Held**
SIC: 2741 Miscellaneous publishing

(P-6594)
STUDIO SYSTEMS INC (PA)
5700 Wilshire Blvd # 600, Los Angeles
(90036-3659)
PHONE............................323 634-3400
Gary Hiller, *President*
EMP: 20
SQ FT: 13,000
SALES (est): 2.5MM **Privately Held**
SIC: 2741 Miscellaneous publishing

(P-6595)
SUPERMEDIA LLC
1215 W Center St Ste 102, Manteca
(95337-4280)
PHONE............................209 472-6011
Renee Fink, *Branch Mgr*
EMP: 254
SALES (corp-wide): 1.8B **Privately Held**
SIC: 2741 Directories, telephone: publish-
ing only, not printed on site
HQ: Supermedia Llc
2200 W Airfield Dr
Dfw Airport TX 75261
972 453-7000

(P-6596)
SUPERMEDIA LLC
3401 Centre Lake Dr # 500, Ontario
(91761-1217)
PHONE............................909 390-5000
Shelly Long, *General Mgr*
Florence Leigh, *Executive*
Gerardo Coronado, *Marketing Staff*
EMP: 254
SALES (corp-wide): 1.8B **Privately Held**
SIC: 2741 Directories, telephone: publish-
ing only, not printed on site

HQ: Supermedia Llc
2200 W Airfield Dr
Dfw Airport TX 75261
972 453-7000

(P-6597)
SUPERMEDIA LLC
1270 E Garvey St, Covina (91724-3658)
PHONE............................626 331-9440
EMP: 254
SALES (corp-wide): 1.8B **Privately Held**
SIC: 2741
HQ: Supermedia Llc
2200 W Airfield Dr
Dfw Airport TX 75261
972 453-7000

(P-6598)
SUPERMEDIA LLC
Also Called: Verizon
3131 Katella Ave, Los Alamitos
(90720-2335)
P.O. Box 3770 (90720-0377)
PHONE............................562 594-5101
Del Humenik, *Manager*
EMP: 400
SQ FT: 150,078
SALES (corp-wide): 1.8B **Privately Held**
WEB: www.verizon.superpages.com
SIC: 2741 7372 2791 Directories, tele-
phone: publishing only, not printed on
site; prepackaged software; typesetting
HQ: Supermedia Llc
2200 W Airfield Dr
Dfw Airport TX 75261
972 453-7000

(P-6599)
SUPERMEDIA LLC
Also Called: Verizon
1200 Melody Ln Ste 100, Roseville
(95678-5189)
PHONE............................916 782-6866
Robert Collins, *Branch Mgr*
EMP: 254
SALES (corp-wide): 1.8B **Privately Held**
WEB: www.verizon.superpages.com
SIC: 2741 Telephone & other directory
publishing
HQ: Supermedia Llc
2200 W Airfield Dr
Dfw Airport TX 75261
972 453-7000

(P-6600)
TABOR COMMUNICATIONS INC
Also Called: Hpcwire
8445 Camino Santa Fe # 101, San Diego
(92121-2649)
PHONE............................858 625-0070
Debra Goldfarb, *President*
Thomas Taber, *Ch of Bd*
EMP: 20
SQ FT: 15,000
SALES: 1.7MM **Privately Held**
WEB: www.hpcwire.com
SIC: 2741 Miscellaneous publishing

(P-6601)
TELLME NETWORKS INC
1065 La Avenida St, Mountain View
(94043-1421)
PHONE............................650 693-1009
John Lamacchia, *Chairman*
Robert Komin, *CFO*
Joseph Blackburn, *Administration*
Rich Schultz, *Engineer*
▲ **EMP:** 330 **EST:** 1999
SALES (est): 24.2MM
SALES (corp-wide): 110.3B **Publicly Held**
WEB: www.tellme.com
SIC: 2741 4812 Telephone & other direc-
tory publishing; radio telephone communi-
cation
PA: Microsoft Corporation
1 Microsoft Way
Redmond WA 98052
425 882-8080

(P-6602)
THOMSON REUTERS CORPORATION
163 Albert Pl, Costa Mesa (92627-1744)
PHONE............................949 400-7782
EMP: 325 **Publicly Held**

SIC: 2741 Miscellaneous publishing
HQ: Thomson Reuters Corporation
3 Times Sq
New York NY 10036
646 223-4000

(P-6603)
TOP ART LLC
8830 Rehco Rd Ste G, San Diego
(92121-3263)
PHONE............................858 554-0102
Keith Circosta, *Mng Member*
▲ **EMP:** 13
SQ FT: 2,600
SALES (est): 1.3MM **Privately Held**
WEB: www.ericwaugh.com
SIC: 2741 Art copy & poster publishing

(P-6604)
TOTAL MEDIA ENTERPRISES INC
Also Called: The Hispanic News
16235 Montbrook St, La Puente
(91744-3231)
PHONE............................626 961-7887
Patricia Rago, *Principal*
EMP: 15 **EST:** 1995
SQ FT: 2,475
SALES (est): 876.1K **Privately Held**
SIC: 2741 Newsletter publishing

(P-6605)
TOUCANED INC
1716 Brommer St, Santa Cruz
(95062-3002)
PHONE............................831 464-0508
Kathleen Middleton, *President*
Mary Cunningham, *Marketing Staff*
EMP: 15 **EST:** 2002
SALES (est): 1.5MM **Privately Held**
WEB: www.toucaned.com
SIC: 2741 8742 Miscellaneous publishing;
hospital & health services consultant

(P-6606)
TRAYLOR MANAGEMENT INC (PA)
Also Called: Map Masters
12120 Tech Center Dr B, Poway
(92064-7149)
P.O. Box 720699, San Diego (92172-0699)
PHONE............................858 486-7700
Natalie Carlson, *CEO*
Dana Ertley, *President*
EMP: 12
SQ FT: 3,200
SALES (est): 1MM **Privately Held**
WEB: www.century-publishing.com
SIC: 2741 Maps: publishing only, not
printed on site; directories: publishing
only, not printed on site; guides: publish-
ing only, not printed on site

(P-6607)
TSE WORLDWIDE PRESS INC
Also Called: United Yearbook Printing Svcs
9830 6th St Ste 101, Rancho Cucamonga
(91730-7969)
PHONE............................909 989-8282
Sarah TSE, *CEO*
Jayde Porte, *Admin Asst*
▲ **EMP:** 20
SQ FT: 4,000
SALES (est): 1.6MM **Privately Held**
SIC: 2741 Miscellaneous publishing

(P-6608)
TYLOON MEDIA CORPORATION
15713 E Valley Blvd, City of Industry
(91744-3932)
PHONE............................626 330-5838
Bary Su, *CEO*
EMP: 10
SALES (est): 287.1K **Privately Held**
SIC: 2741

(P-6609)
UNITED REPORTING PUBG CORP
1835 Iron Point Rd # 100, Folsom
(95630-8771)
P.O. Box 41037, Sacramento (95841-0037)
PHONE............................916 542-7501
Paul Curry, *CEO*
Christopher M Thompson, *President*

Brieann Tilford, *Opers Mgr*
EMP: 35
SQ FT: 3,399
SALES: 1MM **Privately Held**
SIC: 2741 Miscellaneous publishing

(P-6610)
UNIVERSAL DIRECTORY PUBLISHING
Also Called: Elson Alexander
2995 E White Star Ave, Anaheim
(92806-2630)
PHONE............................714 994-6025
Stanley Pesner, *President*
Lila Pesner, *Vice Pres*
EMP: 40
SQ FT: 4,000
SALES (est): 2.4MM **Privately Held**
SIC: 2741 Directories: publishing only, not
printed on site

(P-6611)
UNIVERSAL MUSIC PUBG GROUP
2100 Colorado Ave, Santa Monica
(90404-3504)
PHONE............................310 235-4700
Rakesh Nigam, *Senior VP*
Kevin Cady, *Vice Pres*
Hector Rivera, *Sales Dir*
EMP: 14
SALES (est): 912.8K **Privately Held**
SIC: 2741 Miscellaneous publishing

(P-6612)
UNIVOCITY MEDIA INC
2901 E Alejo Rd Bldg 4, Palm Springs
(92262-6251)
P.O. Box 2086 (92263-2086)
PHONE............................760 904-5200
John McMullen, *President*
Haddon Libby, *CFO*
Haddon Lebby, *Officer*
Blake Stubbs, *Vice Pres*
Chad Benson, *Social Dir*
EMP: 11 **EST:** 2015
SALES: 170K **Privately Held**
SIC: 2741 7372 ; application computer
software

(P-6613)
UPPER DECK COMPANY
5830 El Camino Real, Carlsbad
(92008-8816)
PHONE............................800 873-7332
Jason Masherah, *President*
Don Utic, *Treasurer*
EMP: 120
SQ FT: 33,424
SALES (est): 11.9MM **Privately Held**
SIC: 2741 Music books: publishing & print-
ing

(P-6614)
VALLEY PUBLICATIONS
27259 One Half Camp Plnty, Canyon Coun-
try (91351)
PHONE............................661 298-5330
Douglas D Sutton, *Partner*
Doug Sutton,
Darren Watson,
EMP: 15
SQ FT: 1,500
SALES: 1.3MM **Privately Held**
SIC: 2741 Newsletter publishing

(P-6615)
VANISHING VISTAS
Also Called: Richard E Cox Interprizes
5043 Midas Ave, Rocklin (95677-2200)
P.O. Box 1491 (95677-7491)
PHONE............................916 624-1237
Richard Cox, *President*
EMP: 37
SALES (est): 862.3K **Privately Held**
SIC: 2741 Miscellaneous publishing

(P-6616)
VEREDATECH LLC
4645 Vereda Mar Del Sol, San Diego
(92130-8628)
PHONE............................858 342-6468
Raja Habir,
EMP: 10
SALES (est): 261K **Privately Held**
SIC: 2741

(P-6617)
VIDEO REPORTER INC
Also Called: National Advertising Centre
21107 Vanowen St, Canoga Park
(91303-2822)
PHONE.....................800 266-9104
Itzhak Bejerano, *President*
Marty Hecht, *Exec VP*
EMP: 30
SQ FT: 5,000
SALES (est): 4.6MM **Privately Held**
WEB: www.videoreporter.com
SIC: 2741 Miscellaneous publishing

(P-6618)
VIPOLOGY INC
1278 Center Court Dr, Covina
(91724-3601)
PHONE.....................626 502-8661
Chris Peaslee, *CEO*
Brian Pinkus, *CFO*
Thomas Pinkus, *Admin Sec*
EMP: 10 EST: 2013
SQ FT: 10,000
SALES (est): 315.9K **Privately Held**
SIC: 2741 4813 7371 ; ; software pro-
gramming applications

(P-6619)
VISION PUBLICATIONS INC
Also Called: Vision Design Studio
1342 Coronado Ave, Long Beach
(90804-2807)
PHONE.....................562 597-4000
Carl Patrick Dene, *President*
Carl Dene, *Principal*
Beverly Wurth, *Director*
EMP: 28 EST: 2000
SALES (est): 353.4K **Privately Held**
SIC: 2741 7311 Miscellaneous publishing;
advertising agencies

(P-6620)
VOTEBLAST INC
8478 Hollywood Blvd, Los Angeles
(90069-1511)
PHONE.....................650 387-9147
Ardeshir Falaki, *Principal*
EMP: 21
SALES (est): 811K **Privately Held**
SIC: 2741

(P-6621)
VOXARA LLC
5737 Kanan Rd Ste 700, Agoura Hills
(91301-1601)
PHONE.....................844 869-2721
Alec R Nakashima,
EMP: 12
SALES: 850K **Privately Held**
SIC: 2741

(P-6622)
VOYAGER LEARNING COMPANY
2060 Lynx Pl Unit G, Ontario (91761)
PHONE.....................909 923-3120
EMP: 16 **Publicly Held**
SIC: 2741
HQ: Voyager Learning Company
17855 Dallas Pkwy Ste 400
Dallas TX 75287
214 932-9500

(P-6623)
WARNER/CHAPPELL MUSIC INC (DH)
10585 Santa Monica Blvd # 300, Los Ange-
les (90025-0349)
PHONE.....................310 441-8600
Cameron Strang, *CEO*
Scott Francis, *President*
Ira Pianko, *COO*
Brian Roberts, *CFO*
Edgar Miles Bronfman, *Chairman*
EMP: 110 EST: 1984
SQ FT: 35,000
SALES (est): 106.7MM **Privately Held**
SIC: 2741 Music book & sheet music pub-
lishing

(P-6624)
WCITIESCOM INC
1212 Broadway Ste 910, Oakland
(94612-1811)
PHONE.....................415 495-8090

Fraser Campbell, *CEO*
Amir Khan, *CTO*
Fraser Find, *Sales Staff*
Simone Da'silva, *Director*
Eliza Lamson, *Editor*
EMP: 12 EST: 2003
SQ FT: 5,000
SALES (est): 319.1K **Privately Held**
WEB: www.wcities.com
SIC: 2741 Telephone & other directory
publishing

(P-6625)
WEDDINGCHANNELCOM INC
5757 Wilshire Blvd # 504, Los Angeles
(90036-5810)
PHONE.....................213 599-4100
Adam Berger, *President*
Donald Drapkin, *Chairman*
Lee Essmer, *Vice Pres*
Greg Franchina, *CIO*
EMP: 125 EST: 1996
SQ FT: 18,000
SALES (est): 7.3MM **Publicly Held**
SIC: 2741 5621 Miscellaneous publishing;
women's clothing stores
PA: Xo Group Inc.
195 Broadway Fl 25
New York NY 10007

(P-6626)
WILSON IMAGING AND PUBLISHING
305 N 2nd Ave Pmb 324, Upland
(91786-6064)
PHONE.....................909 931-1818
Kent Wilson, *President*
EMP: 11
SALES (est): 1MM **Privately Held**
SIC: 2741 Miscellaneous publishing

(P-6627)
XOMV MEDIA CORPORATION
9465 Wilshire Blvd, Beverly Hills
(90212-2612)
PHONE.....................424 284-4024
Marissa Webber, *President*
EMP: 20 EST: 2015
SALES (est): 868.3K **Privately Held**
SIC: 2741

(P-6628)
YAMAGATA AMERICA INC
3760 Convoy St Ste 219, San Diego
(92111-3744)
PHONE.....................858 751-1010
Yasuhide Fujimoto, *President*
Annelies De Vliegher, *Senior Mgr*
EMP: 19
SQ FT: 4,630
SALES: 8.4MM
SALES (corp-wide): 34.3MM **Privately
Held**
WEB: www.yamagataamerica.com
SIC: 2741 Technical manuals: publishing &
printing
HQ: Yamagata Holdings America, Inc.
3760 Convoy St Ste 219
San Diego CA 92111
619 889-4566

(P-6629)
YB MEDIA LLC
1534 Plaza Ln 146, Burlingame
(94010-3204)
PHONE.....................310 467-5804
Benjamin Maggin, *CEO*
EMP: 20
SALES (est): 611.7K **Privately Held**
SIC: 2741

(P-6630)
YELLOW PAGES INC
24931 Nellie Gail Rd, Laguna Hills
(92653-5821)
PHONE.....................714 776-0534
Maria Salivar, *Branch Mgr*
John Wurth, *CIO*
EMP: 20
SALES (corp-wide): 7.3MM **Privately
Held**
WEB: www.ypinc.net
SIC: 2741 Miscellaneous publishing

PA: Yellow Pages, Inc.
222 N Main St
New City NY 10956
845 639-6060

2752 Commercial Printing: Lithographic

(P-6631)
365 PRINTING INC
14747 Artesia Blvd Ste 3a, La Mirada
(90638-6003)
PHONE.....................714 752-6990
Chang Lee, *President*
EMP: 15
SQ FT: 3,300
SALES (est): 1.2MM **Privately Held**
SIC: 2752 Commercial printing, litho-
graphic

(P-6632)
A & J ENTERPRISES INC
Also Called: USA Printing
7925 Santa Monica Blvd, West Hollywood
(90046-5181)
PHONE.....................323 654-5902
Amir Shirian, *President*
Steve Ordyke, *Prdtn Mgr*
EMP: 12 EST: 1968
SQ FT: 12,000
SALES (est): 2.4MM **Privately Held**
SIC: 2752 Commercial printing, offset

(P-6633)
ABACUS PRINTING & GRAPHICS INC
Also Called: Abacus Prtg & Digital Graphics
23806 Strathern St, Canoga Park
(91304-6133)
PHONE.....................818 929-6740
Robert D Posard, *President*
Ricki Posard, *Vice Pres*
EMP: 10
SALES: 1.6MM **Privately Held**
SIC: 2752 Color lithography

(P-6634)
ABC PRINTING INC
1090 S Milpitas Blvd, Milpitas
(95035-6307)
PHONE.....................408 263-1118
Danny Luong, *President*
Diana Wong, *Treasurer*
EMP: 15
SQ FT: 8,000
SALES: 1.6MM **Privately Held**
SIC: 2752 Commercial printing, offset

(P-6635)
ABLE CARD LLC
1300 W Optical Dr Ste 600, Irwindale
(91702-3285)
PHONE.....................626 969-1888
Herman Ho, *President*
Donny Yu, *Vice Pres*
EMP: 20
SALES (est): 3.4MM **Privately Held**
SIC: 2752 Calendar & card printing, litho-
graphic

(P-6636)
ACE COMMERCIAL INC
Also Called: Press Colorcom
10310 Pioneer Blvd Ste 1, Santa Fe
Springs (90670-3737)
PHONE.....................562 946-6664
Andrew H Choi, *CEO*
Juan Garcia, *Prdtn Mgr*
Ozzie Villalobos, *Manager*
Jeff Morgan, *Accounts Mgr*
Eugene Yoo, *Accounts Mgr*
EMP: 40
SQ FT: 22,000
SALES (est): 10.6MM **Privately Held**
WEB: www.acecommercial.com
SIC: 2752 2791 2789 Commercial
printing, offset; direct mail advertising
services; typesetting; bookbinding & re-
lated work; die-cut paper & board

(P-6637)
ACE GRAPHICS INC
5351 Bonsai Ave, Moorpark (93021-1785)
PHONE.....................213 746-5100

Ricardo Huambachano, *President*
EMP: 13
SQ FT: 11,000
SALES (est): 184.7K **Privately Held**
WEB: www.acegraphicsinc.com
SIC: 2752 Commercial printing, offset

(P-6638)
ACI POSTAL SYSTEM
Also Called: Michael Somers Attorney At Law
3245 E 59th St, Long Beach (90805-4501)
PHONE.....................562 987-2200
Robert Summers, *President*
EMP: 100
SQ FT: 6,000
SALES (est): 7.3MM **Privately Held**
SIC: 2752 7375 7331 7371 Commercial
printing, offset; circulars, lithographed; in-
formation retrieval services; direct mail
advertising services; custom computer
programming services

(P-6639)
ACME PRESS INC
Also Called: California Lithographers
2312 Stanwell Dr, Concord (94520-4809)
P.O. Box 5698 (94524-0698)
PHONE.....................925 682-1111
Mardjan Taheripour, *CEO*
Bahman Taheri, *Vice Pres*
Bahman Taheripour, *Vice Pres*
Rob Rutan, *Business Dir*
Kenneth Vonberg, *Info Tech Dir*
EMP: 87
SQ FT: 36,000
SALES (est): 23.9MM **Privately Held**
WEB: www.calitho.com
SIC: 2752 Commercial printing, offset

(P-6640)
ACP VENTURES
Also Called: Allegro Copy & Print
3340 Mt Diablo Blvd Ste B, Lafayette
(94549-4076)
PHONE.....................925 297-0100
Peter Smyth, *President*
Karen Smyth, *Vice Pres*
Paulette States, *Technology*
EMP: 19
SQ FT: 6,300
SALES (est): 2.6MM **Privately Held**
WEB: www.allegrocp.com
SIC: 2752 2791 2789 7331 Commercial
printing, offset; typesetting; bookbinding &
related work; mailing service

(P-6641)
ADMAIL-EXPRESS INC
31640 Hayman St, Hayward (94544-7122)
PHONE.....................510 471-6200
Brian M Schott, *CEO*
EMP: 45
SQ FT: 55,000
SALES (est): 8.2MM **Privately Held**
WEB: www.admail.com
SIC: 2752 Commercial printing, offset

(P-6642)
ADVANCED COLOR GRAPHICS
Also Called: Acg Ecopack
1921 S Business Pkwy, Ontario
(91761-8539)
PHONE.....................909 930-1500
Steve Thompson, *President*
Mike Mullens, *Vice Pres*
EMP: 60
SQ FT: 70,000
SALES: 8MM **Privately Held**
WEB: www.acg-online.com
SIC: 2752 Commercial printing, offset

(P-6643)
ADVERTISING SERVICES
Also Called: Menu Services
7697 9th St, Buena Park (90621-2898)
PHONE.....................714 522-2781
Orris Abbott, *Owner*
EMP: 25
SQ FT: 30,000 **Privately Held**
WEB: www.advertisingservices.com
SIC: 2752 Menus, lithographed

(P-6644)
AKIDO PRINTING INC
Also Called: Promotion Xpress Prtg Graphics
2096 Merced St, San Leandro
(94577-3230)
PHONE..................................510 357-0238
Thanh Do, *President*
Stella Phan, *CFO*
EMP: 11
SQ FT: 12,000
SALES (est): 1.9MM **Privately Held**
SIC: 2752 Commercial printing, offset

(P-6645)
ALAN HAMILTON INDUSTRIES
Also Called: Hamilton & Associates
21020 Lassen St, Chatsworth
(91311-4241)
PHONE..................................818 885-5121
Richard A Hamilton, *Ch of Bd*
EMP: 85
SQ FT: 14,700
SALES (est): 749.1K **Privately Held**
WEB: www.hamilton-inc.com
SIC: 2752 2759 Commercial printing, lithographic; commercial printing

(P-6646)
ALEXANDER BUSINESS SUPPLIES
Also Called: Alexander Color Printing
21500 Wyandotte St # 110, Canoga Park
(91303-1566)
PHONE..................................818 346-1820
Alexander Frankel, *President*
Diane Frankel, *Vice Pres*
EMP: 10
SQ FT: 3,000
SALES (est): 1.5MM **Privately Held**
SIC: 2752 5734 5943 Commercial printing, offset; modems, monitors, terminals & disk drives: computers; office forms & supplies

(P-6647)
ALL CITY PRINTING INC
1061 Howard St, San Francisco
(94103-2822)
PHONE..................................415 861-8088
Tony Ngi, *President*
Helen Lei, *Office Mgr*
EMP: 10
SQ FT: 7,000
SALES (est): 1.7MM **Privately Held**
WEB: www.allcityprinting.com
SIC: 2752 Commercial printing, offset

(P-6648)
ALL VALLEY PRINTING INC
Also Called: Agency At All Valley, The
110 W 7th St, Hanford (93230-4522)
PHONE..................................559 584-5444
Pauline Hershey, *President*
EMP: 10
SQ FT: 6,500
SALES (est): 810K **Privately Held**
WEB: www.avprint.com
SIC: 2752 Commercial printing, lithographic

(P-6649)
ALLEGRA
434 9th St, San Francisco (94103-4411)
PHONE..................................415 824-9610
Takashi Yomshmu, *President*
To Chuk Kong, *Vice Pres*
▲ **EMP:** 15
SQ FT: 6,000
SALES (est): 1.9MM **Privately Held**
WEB: www.goldendragonprint.com
SIC: 2752 Commercial printing, offset

(P-6650)
ALLIED PRINTING COMPANY
1912 O St, Sacramento (95811-5210)
PHONE..................................916 442-1373
Matthew G Zellmer, *Owner*
EMP: 10
SQ FT: 4,200
SALES (est): 720K **Privately Held**
SIC: 2752 2759 Commercial printing, offset; letters, circular or form: lithographed; letterpress printing

(P-6651)
ALLURA PRINTING INC
185 Paularino Ave Ste B, Costa Mesa
(92626-3324)
PHONE..................................714 433-0200
David Gagnon, *CEO*
Rene Gagnon, *Vice Pres*
EMP: 12
SALES: 500K **Privately Held**
SIC: 2752 Commercial printing, offset

(P-6652)
ALLYN JAMES INC
6575 Trinity Ct Ste B, Dublin (94568-2643)
PHONE..................................925 828-5530
Mark Cady, *President*
Mark W Cady, *President*
Curtis J Mc Carthy, *Vice Pres*
EMP: 16
SALES: 1.8MM **Privately Held**
WEB: www.jamesallyn.com
SIC: 2752 Commercial printing, offset

(P-6653)
ALMADEN VALLEY PRINTING CO
16570 Church St Ste 105, Morgan Hill
(95037-5175)
PHONE..................................408 288-6886
Steven Johnson, *President*
EMP: 10
SQ FT: 3,000
SALES (est): 1.2MM **Privately Held**
WEB: www.avprinting.com
SIC: 2752 Commercial printing, offset; lithographing on metal

(P-6654)
ALPHA PRINTING & GRAPHICS INC
12758 Schabarum Ave, Irwindale
(91706-6801)
PHONE..................................626 851-9800
Stacey Chen, *President*
Kelly Ngo, *CEO*
▲ **EMP:** 20
SQ FT: 5,000
SALES (est): 4.8MM **Privately Held**
WEB: www.alphaprinting.com
SIC: 2752 Commercial printing, offset

(P-6655)
AMERICAN LITHOGRAPHERS INC
Also Called: Pacific Standard Print
2629 5th St, Sacramento (95818-2802)
PHONE..................................916 441-5392
Joe R Davis, *CEO*
Tom Mueller, *President*
John Pappas, *Sales Staff*
Peter Bachelor, *Accounts Exec*
EMP: 70
SQ FT: 60,000
SALES (est): 13.8MM
SALES (corp-wide): 6.9B **Publicly Held**
WEB: www.printpsp.com/
SIC: 2752 2759 Commercial printing, offset; commercial printing
HQ: Consolidated Graphics, Inc.
　　5858 Westheimer Rd # 400
　　Houston TX 77057
　　713 787-0977

(P-6656)
AMERICAN PCF PRTRS COLLEGE INC
Also Called: Kenny The Printer
17931 Sky Park Cir, Irvine (92614-6312)
PHONE..................................949 250-3212
David Smith, *CEO*
Cal Laird, *CFO*
EMP: 36 **EST:** 1981
SQ FT: 22,000
SALES (est): 7.8MM **Privately Held**
WEB: www.kennytheprinter.com
SIC: 2752 Commercial printing, offset

(P-6657)
AMERICAN PRINTING & COPY INC
1100 Obrien Dr, Menlo Park (94025-1411)
PHONE..................................650 325-2322
Kamran Motamedi, *President*
Cynthia Motamedi, *Vice Pres*

Brady Hopkins, *Principal*
Kanak Sesha, *Principal*
Dan Tamada, *Principal*
EMP: 14
SQ FT: 1,400
SALES (est): 2.6MM **Privately Held**
SIC: 2752 7334 Commercial printing, offset; photocopying & duplicating services

(P-6658)
AMERICAN PRINTING & DESIGN
14622 Ventura Blvd # 102, Sherman Oaks
(91403-3600)
PHONE..................................310 287-0460
Michael Kenner, *President*
EMP: 20 **EST:** 1981
SQ FT: 40,000
SALES (est): 2MM **Privately Held**
SIC: 2752 Commercial printing, offset; catalogs, lithographed

(P-6659)
AMERICHIP INC (PA)
19032 S Vermont Ave, Gardena
(90248-4412)
PHONE..................................310 323-3697
Timothy Clegg, *CEO*
Keven Clegg, *President*
Primoz Samardzija, *Exec VP*
John Clegg, *Vice Pres*
Nicole Reid, *Graphic Designe*
▲ **EMP:** 56
SQ FT: 30,000
SALES (est): 13.3MM **Privately Held**
WEB: www.americhip.com
SIC: 2752 Promotional printing, lithographic

(P-6660)
AMPLIGRAPHIX
Also Called: Central Printing & Graphics
1768 Glenwood Dr, Bakersfield
(93306-4230)
PHONE..................................661 321-3150
Sherry Darke, *President*
Craig C Combs, *Admin Sec*
Christie Meinke, *Sales Staff*
EMP: 10 **EST:** 1957
SQ FT: 4,500
SALES (est): 760K **Privately Held**
WEB: www.central-printing.com
SIC: 2752 Commercial printing, offset

(P-6661)
ANGELUS PACIFIC COMPANY INC
700 E Walnut Ave, Fullerton (92831-4530)
P.O. Box 111 (92836-0111)
PHONE..................................714 871-1610
Barbara Waddell, *Ch of Bd*
Timothy H Waddell, *President*
Alison Waddell, *Sales Mgr*
EMP: 18 **EST:** 1932
SQ FT: 16,600
SALES (est): 1.5MM **Privately Held**
WEB: www.angeluspacific.com
SIC: 2752 Decals, lithographed

(P-6662)
ANIN CO (PA)
Also Called: PIP Printing
2041 Powell St, San Francisco
(94133-2336)
PHONE..................................415 433-1341
Mancy Chen, *President*
Jerry Jen, *Vice Pres*
EMP: 13
SQ FT: 2,000
SALES (est): 1.4MM **Privately Held**
SIC: 2752 7334 Commercial printing, offset; photocopying & duplicating services

(P-6663)
ANTO OFFSET PRINTING
1101 5th St, Berkeley (94710-1201)
PHONE..................................510 843-8454
Alexder Cingoz, *Partner*
Antrenge Cingoz, *Partner*
EMP: 11 **EST:** 1977
SQ FT: 10,000
SALES (est): 1.1MM **Privately Held**
SIC: 2752 Commercial printing, offset

(P-6664)
ANY BUDGET PRINTING & MAILING
8170 Ronson Rd Ste L, San Diego
(92111-2008)
PHONE..................................858 278-3151
Charlie Silveria, *Owner*
Terry Silveria, *Co-Owner*
Ron Watt, *General Mgr*
EMP: 14
SQ FT: 1,500
SALES (est): 1.3MM **Privately Held**
WEB: www.anybudget.com
SIC: 2752 Commercial printing, offset

(P-6665)
API MARKETING
Also Called: Auburn Printers and Mfg
13020 Earhart Ave, Auburn (95602-9536)
PHONE..................................916 632-1946
Merrill Kagan-Weston, *President*
Brad Weston, *Vice Pres*
Kelley Buxton, *Opers Mgr*
Steven Reynolds, *Sales Staff*
Richard Neal,
EMP: 17
SQ FT: 10,000
SALES (est): 1.7MM **Privately Held**
WEB: www.auburnprint.com
SIC: 2752 Commercial printing, offset; catalogs, lithographed; circulars, lithographed

(P-6666)
ARDEN & HOWE PRINTING INC
Also Called: Signature Press
430 17th St, Sacramento (95811-1004)
PHONE..................................916 444-7154
Chris Martinez, *President*
EMP: 10 **EST:** 1978
SQ FT: 8,000
SALES (est): 1.2MM **Privately Held**
SIC: 2752 2759 Commercial printing, offset; letterpress printing

(P-6667)
ARROWHEAD PRESS INC
220 W Maple Ave Ste B, Monrovia
(91016-3393)
PHONE..................................626 358-1168
Diana Marie Sims, *CEO*
Ken Shannon, *Marketing Staff*
Charlie Hodge, *Manager*
EMP: 28 **EST:** 1973
SQ FT: 9,000
SALES (est): 6.2MM **Privately Held**
WEB: www.arrowheadpress.com
SIC: 2752 2789 Commercial printing, offset; bookbinding & related work

(P-6668)
ARSH INCORPORATED
Also Called: Copyland /Zip2print
2300 Stevens Creek Blvd, San Jose
(95128-1650)
PHONE..................................408 971-2722
Frank Ettefgh, *President*
EMP: 10 **EST:** 1995
SALES: 1.5MM **Privately Held**
SIC: 2752 5099 5999 Commercial printing, offset; signs, except electric; banners

(P-6669)
ASIA AMERICA ENTERPRISE INC
Also Called: America Printing
1321 N Carolan Ave, Burlingame
(94010-2401)
PHONE..................................650 348-2333
Macy Mak, *CEO*
Ryan Mak, *Corp Secy*
EMP: 20
SQ FT: 27,000
SALES (est): 3.3MM **Privately Held**
WEB: www.americaprinting.com
SIC: 2752 Commercial printing, offset

(P-6670)
ASML INC
150 Paularino Ave, Costa Mesa
(92626-3301)
PHONE..................................714 754-1912
EMP: 17

P R O D U C T S & S V C S

SALES (est): 1.5MM **Privately Held**
SIC: **2752** Commercial printing, lithographic

(P-6671)
ATLAS LITHOGRAPH COMPANY
13561 Elderberry Way, San Diego (92130-5648)
PHONE................................858 560-8273
William E Cary, *President*
Christopher Cary, *Corp Secy*
Frank K Poehlman, *Vice Pres*
EMP: 22 EST: 1954
SQ FT: 10,800
SALES (est): 3.9MM **Privately Held**
WEB: www.atlaslitho.com
SIC: **2752** Commercial printing, offset

(P-6672)
AUTUMN PRESS INC (PA)
Also Called: Autumn Express
945 Camelia St, Berkeley (94710-1437)
PHONE................................510 654-4545
Miguel Alson, *President*
Gordon Empey, *Exec VP*
Theresa Thornton, *Vice Pres*
Emily Tong,
EMP: 20
SQ FT: 15,000
SALES (est): 2.6MM **Privately Held**
WEB: www.autumnpress.com
SIC: **2752** Commercial printing, offset

(P-6673)
AVION GRAPHICS INC
27192 Burbank, Foothill Ranch (92610-2503)
PHONE................................949 472-0438
Craig Greiner, *President*
Mary Kay Swanson, *Shareholder*
Michele Morris, *Vice Pres*
Mark Macdonald, *Prdtn Mgr*
Marc Oberman, *VP Sales*
EMP: 33
SQ FT: 6,800
SALES (est): 8.8MM **Privately Held**
WEB: www.aviongraphics.com
SIC: **2752** 7336 3993 5999 Decals, lithographed; commercial art & graphic design; signs & advertising specialties; decals; aircraft & parts

(P-6674)
AZPIRE PRINT & MEDIAWORKS LLC
10555 Clarkson Rd, Los Angeles (90064-4315)
PHONE................................310 736-5952
Hardat N Pariag, *President*
EMP: 19
SALES (est): 500K **Privately Held**
SIC: **2752** 7389 Commercial printing, offset;

(P-6675)
B & D LITHO GROUP INC
325 N Ponderosa Ave, Ontario (91761-1530)
PHONE................................909 390-0903
Steve Gaynor, *Principal*
Christine Van Empel, *Engineer*
Anel-Mary Gomez, *Accounting Mgr*
EMP: 22
SALES (corp-wide): 370.1MM **Publicly Held**
SIC: **2752** Commercial printing, offset
HQ: B & D Litho Group, Inc.
    3820 N 38th Ave
    Phoenix AZ 85019
    602 269-2526

(P-6676)
B AND Z PRINTING INC
1300 E Wakeham Ave B, Santa Ana (92705-4145)
PHONE................................714 892-2000
Frank Buono, *President*
James Zimmer, *Admin Sec*
EMP: 45
SQ FT: 40,000
SALES (est): 7.3MM **Privately Held**
WEB: www.bandzprinting.com
SIC: **2752** 2789 Commercial printing, offset; bookbinding & related work

(P-6677)
B BRAYS CARD INC
12053 Mariposa Rd, Victorville (92394)
PHONE................................760 265-4720
Melvin Bray, *Principal*
EMP: 12 EST: 2013
SALES (est): 1MM **Privately Held**
SIC: **2752** Business form & card printing, lithographic

(P-6678)
B R PRINTERS INC (PA)
665 Lenfest Rd, San Jose (95133-1615)
PHONE................................408 929-5403
Adam Demaestri, *President*
Richard Brown, *President*
Chris Rooney, *Vice Pres*
Carlee Harder-Brown, *Admin Sec*
EMP: 80
SQ FT: 90,000
SALES (est): 20.6MM **Privately Held**
WEB: www.brprinters.com
SIC: **2752** Commercial printing, offset

(P-6679)
B3DIGIGRAFX
8759 Lion St, Rancho Cucamonga (91730-4428)
PHONE................................909 259-0153
Peter W Gomez, *President*
Adrian P Gomez, *Vice Pres*
EMP: 20
SALES (est): 2.9MM **Privately Held**
SIC: **2752** 2399 Commercial printing, offset; banners, made from fabric

(P-6680)
BABYLON PRINTING INC
Also Called: Medius
1800 Dobbin Dr, San Jose (95133-1701)
PHONE................................408 519-5000
Daisy Zaia, *CEO*
George Zaia, *Vice Pres*
Torres Tom, *Sales Executive*
Miruna Williams, *Marketing Staff*
Ranjit Kumar,
▲ EMP: 43
SQ FT: 110,000
SALES: 9MM **Privately Held**
WEB: www.mediuscorp.com
SIC: **2752** Commercial printing, offset

(P-6681)
BACCHUS PRESS INC (PA)
1287 66th St, Emeryville (94608-1198)
PHONE................................510 420-5800
Monsoor Assadi, *President*
Karen Schreiber, *Sales Staff*
Sue Kent, *Manager*
Jerry Blueford, *Supervisor*
EMP: 20
SQ FT: 10,000
SALES (est): 3.7MM **Privately Held**
WEB: www.bacchuspress.com
SIC: **2752** Commercial printing, offset

(P-6682)
BACHUR & ASSOCIATES
1950 Homestead Rd, Santa Clara (95050-6936)
PHONE................................408 988-5861
Jerry Bachur, *Owner*
EMP: 12
SALES: 600K **Privately Held**
WEB: www.bachur-n-associates.com
SIC: **2752** 8748 Photolithographic printing; systems analysis & engineering consulting services

(P-6683)
BAISE ENTERPRISES INC
Also Called: Sutter Printing
3258 Stockton Blvd, Sacramento (95820-1418)
PHONE................................916 446-0167
Craig Baise, *President*
EMP: 13
SALES (est): 1.2MM **Privately Held**
WEB: www.sutterprinting.com
SIC: **2752** 7334 2791 2759 Commercial printing, offset; photocopying & duplicating services; typesetting, computer controlled; commercial printing; commercial art & graphic design

(P-6684)
BARLOW AND SONS PRINTING INC
Also Called: Barlow Printing
481 Aaron St, Cotati (94931-3081)
PHONE................................707 664-9773
Patrick Barlow, *President*
Ken Reed, *Vice Pres*
EMP: 15
SQ FT: 20,000
SALES (est): 3.2MM **Privately Held**
WEB: www.barlowprinting.com
SIC: **2752** Letters, circular or form: lithographed; commercial printing, offset

(P-6685)
BARRYS PRINTING INC
Also Called: All About Printing
20936 Devonshire St Ste E, Chatsworth (91311-8232)
PHONE................................818 998-8600
Barry Shapiro, *CEO*
EMP: 30
SQ FT: 1,500
SALES (est): 4.9MM **Privately Held**
WEB: www.dotgraphics.net
SIC: **2752** 7334 Commercial printing, offset; photocopying & duplicating services

(P-6686)
BATCHLDER BUS CMMNICATIONS INC
Also Called: AlphaGraphics
2900 Standiford Ave Ste 5, Modesto (95350-6575)
PHONE................................209 577-2222
Ardem Batchelder, *President*
EMP: 12
SALES (est): 1.5MM **Privately Held**
SIC: **2752** 7331 Commercial printing, offset; mailing list compilers

(P-6687)
BATIDA INC
Also Called: Western Lithographics
3187 Airway Ave Ste B, Costa Mesa (92626-4603)
PHONE................................714 557-4597
George Petty, *Vice Pres*
Parie Petty, *President*
Phyllis Petty, *Treasurer*
Allen Bacon, *Project Mgr*
Monica Garza,
EMP: 11 EST: 1970
SQ FT: 4,200
SALES (est): 2MM **Privately Held**
WEB: www.westernlithographics.com
SIC: **2752** Commercial printing, offset

(P-6688)
BAY CENTRAL PRINTING INC
33401 Western Ave, Union City (94587-3201)
PHONE................................510 429-9111
Michael H Mahmoudi, *President*
Bob Popolizio, *Sales Staff*
Patrick Hartman, *Accounts Exec*
EMP: 14
SQ FT: 2,500
SALES (est): 2.5MM **Privately Held**
WEB: www.baycentralprinting.com
SIC: **2752** Commercial printing, offset

(P-6689)
BBC CORP
Also Called: Enterprise Printing
4286 N Star Dr, Shingle Springs (95682-5003)
PHONE................................530 677-4009
Chris K Mulligan, *President*
Bertha J Mulligan, *Treasurer*
EMP: 29
SALES (est): 2.4MM **Privately Held**
SIC: **2752** Commercial printing, lithographic

(P-6690)
BENJAMIN LEWIS INC
Also Called: Studio Two Black Diamond Prtg
23042 Alcalde Dr Ste C, Laguna Hills (92653-1326)
PHONE................................949 859-5119
Jeff Benjamin, *President*
Eddie Chung, *Cust Mgr*
EMP: 13

SALES (est): 1.4MM **Privately Held**
SIC: **2752** Commercial printing, offset

(P-6691)
BENJAMIN LITHO INC
1810 Oakland Rd Ste F, San Jose (95131-2316)
PHONE................................408 232-3800
Ronald Habit, *President*
Matt Bonnett, *Production*
Jim Bowen, *VP Sales*
▲ EMP: 10
SQ FT: 1,040
SALES (est): 1.2MM **Privately Held**
WEB: www.benjaminlitho.com
SIC: **2752** 5199 2759 Commercial printing, lithographic; gifts & novelties; screen printing

(P-6692)
BENNETT INDUSTRIES INC
Also Called: Graphic Source, The
4304 Redwood Hwy 200, San Rafael (94903-2103)
PHONE................................415 482-9000
Christie Lo, *President*
Jeffrey Lo, *Vice Pres*
Terri Adams,
Jay McKeown, *Manager*
Joann Brandis, *Accounts Mgr*
▲ EMP: 13
SQ FT: 2,500
SALES (est): 2.4MM **Privately Held**
WEB: www.graphic-source.com
SIC: **2752** Commercial printing, offset

(P-6693)
BENTLEY PRTG & GRAPHICS INC
12800 Garden Grove Blvd C, Garden Grove (92843-2008)
PHONE................................714 636-1622
Thomas Bentley, *President*
Donna Aigner, *Manager*
EMP: 11
SQ FT: 3,500
SALES: 1.2MM **Privately Held**
WEB: www.bentleyprint.com
SIC: **2752** 2791 Commercial printing, offset; typesetting

(P-6694)
BERT-CO INDUSTRIES INC (PA)
2150 S Parco Ave, Ontario (91761-5768)
P.O. Box 4150 (91761-1068)
PHONE................................323 669-5700
Charles F Stay, *CEO*
Rose Vanderzanden, *CFO*
▲ EMP: 106 EST: 1984
SQ FT: 120,000
SALES: 50MM **Privately Held**
WEB: www.bert-co.com
SIC: **2752** Commercial printing, lithographic

(P-6695)
BETTER INSTANT COPY
512 S San Vicente Blvd # 1, Los Angeles (90048-4645)
P.O. Box 17734, Beverly Hills (90209-3734)
PHONE................................323 782-6934
Boaz Rasael, *Owner*
EMP: 10
SALES (est): 1.1MM **Privately Held**
SIC: **2752** Commercial printing, offset

(P-6696)
BIBBERO SYSTEMS INC (HQ)
1300 N Mcdowell Blvd, Petaluma (94954-1180)
PHONE................................800 242-2376
Michael Buckley, *President*
Joan Buckley, *Corp Secy*
EMP: 32 EST: 1953
SQ FT: 60,000
SALES (est): 4.1MM
SALES (corp-wide): 7.9MM **Privately Held**
WEB: www.bibbero.com
SIC: **2752** 2759 Offset & photolithographic printing; business forms: printing
PA: Professional Filing Systems, Inc.
    5076 Winters Chapel Rd # 200
    Atlanta GA 30360
    770 396-4994

▲ = Import ▼=Export
◆ =Import/Export

(P-6697)
BIG INK PRINTING
1711 Branham Ln Ste A5, San Jose
(95118-5223)
PHONE..............................408 624-1204
Dion Berry, *Principal*
EMP: 10 EST: 2013
SALES (est): 905.8K Privately Held
SIC: 2752 Commercial printing, offset

(P-6698)
BIG TIME DIGITAL
6935 Hermosa Cir, Buena Park
(90620-1151)
PHONE..............................310 329-1383
Jeanette F Reale, *Mng Member*
EMP: 11
SALES (est): 1.4MM Privately Held
SIC: 2752 Commercial printing, litho-
graphic

(P-6699)
BLUEBARRY ENTERPRISES INC
Also Called: PIP Printing
16525 Sherman Way Ste C11, Van Nuys
(91406-3786)
PHONE..............................818 956-0912
Michael Bluestein, *President*
EMP: 10
SQ FT: 1,200
SALES (est): 1.1MM Privately Held
SIC: 2752 Commercial printing, offset

(P-6700)
BOHNS PRINTING
656 W Lancaster Blvd, Lancaster
(93534-3127)
PHONE..............................661 948-8081
Roger Hemme, *Owner*
Shirley Hemme, *Co-Owner*
EMP: 10
SQ FT: 6,500
SALES (est): 1MM Privately Held
SIC: 2752 Commercial printing, offset

(P-6701)
BOSS LITHO INC
2380 Peck Rd, City of Industry
(90601-1601)
PHONE..............................626 912-7088
Jean P Nataf, *President*
Kathy Greil, *Project Dir*
Scott Jensen, *Project Dir*
Tim Chen, *Marketing Staff*
EMP: 42
SALES (est): 9.4MM Privately Held
WEB: www.bosslitho.com
SIC: 2752 Commercial printing, offset

(P-6702)
BOSS PRINTING INC
3403 W Macarthur Blvd, Santa Ana
(92704-6805)
PHONE..............................714 545-2677
Todd Gibb, *President*
George Turlis, *Prdtn Mgr*
EMP: 10
SQ FT: 11,500
SALES (est): 968K Privately Held
SIC: 2752 Commercial printing, litho-
graphic

(P-6703)
BOX CO INC
7575 Britannia Park Pl, San Diego
(92154-7418)
PHONE..............................619 661-8090
Richard Barragan, *President*
Maggie Barragan, *Corp Secy*
▲ EMP: 16
SQ FT: 16,000
SALES (est): 3.8MM Privately Held
WEB: www.theboxcoinc.com
SIC: 2752 2657 Commercial printing, litho-
graphic; folding paperboard boxes

(P-6704)
BRAND IDENTITY INC
9520 Flintridge Way, Orangevale
(95662-5713)
PHONE..............................916 553-0000
Peter Stelmaszczyk, *CEO*
Kasia Stelmaszczyk, *Vice Pres*
EMP: 11 EST: 1994
SQ FT: 6,000

SALES: 1.1MM Privately Held
WEB: www.thebrandidentity.com
SIC: 2752 Commercial printing, offset

(P-6705)
BREHM COMMUNICATIONS INC (PA)
Also Called: B C I
16644 W Bernardo Dr # 300, San Diego
(92127-1901)
P.O. Box 28429 (92198-0429)
PHONE..............................858 451-6200
Bill Brehm Jr, *President*
W J Brehm, *Chairman*
Tom Kirk, *Vice Pres*
Tom Taylor, *Vice Pres*
Mona Brehm, *Admin Sec*
EMP: 47 EST: 1919
SQ FT: 6,000
SALES (est): 224.9MM Privately Held
WEB: www.brehmcommunications.com
SIC: 2752 2711 Commercial printing, off-
set; commercial printing & newspaper
publishing combined

(P-6706)
BRUCE PARKER
Also Called: Colour Impressions
5323 Lupine St, Yorba Linda (92886-4439)
PHONE..............................714 970-2307
Bruce Parker, *President*
EMP: 10
SQ FT: 6,000
SALES (est): 860K Privately Held
WEB: www.bruceparker.com
SIC: 2752 Commercial printing, offset

(P-6707)
BRUNETTES PRINTING SERVICE
Also Called: Brunette Printing
742 E Washington Blvd, Los Angeles
(90021-3077)
PHONE..............................213 749-7441
Ed Volen, *President*
Mark Volen, *Vice Pres*
Renee Volen, *Admin Sec*
EMP: 10
SQ FT: 5,200
SALES (est): 1.4MM Privately Held
SIC: 2752 2759 Commercial printing, off-
set; letterpress printing

(P-6708)
BRYAN PRESS INC
1011 S Stimson Ave, City of Industry
(91745-1630)
PHONE..............................626 961-9257
K Bryan, *President*
Brad Bryan, *Sales Mgr*
EMP: 18
SALES (est): 2.6MM Privately Held
SIC: 2752 Commercial printing, litho-
graphic

(P-6709)
BULLFROG PRINTING AND GRAPHICS
1261 S Wright St, Santa Ana (92705-4511)
P.O. Box 11402 (92711-1402)
PHONE..............................714 641-0220
Steven Sealy, *Owner*
EMP: 10
SALES (est): 1.1MM Privately Held
SIC: 2752 Commercial printing, offset

(P-6710)
BUSINESS PRINTING AND COPIES
1565 River Park Dr Ste A, Sacramento
(95815-4618)
PHONE..............................916 920-1412
Gregory Hurst, *CEO*
Brenda Hurst, *President*
EMP: 11
SQ FT: 3,000
SALES (est): 700K Privately Held
SIC: 2752 Commercial printing, offset

(P-6711)
BUSINESS WITH PLEASURE
1 Victor Sq, Scotts Valley (95066-3575)
PHONE..............................831 430-9711
Marcelo Siero, *Owner*
EMP: 10
SQ FT: 5,500

SALES (est): 1MM Privately Held
SIC: 2752 5943 5947 Commercial printing, offset; office forms & supplies; gift,
novelty & souvenir shop

(P-6712)
C T V INC
Also Called: Imperial Printing
481 Vandell Way, Campbell (95008-6907)
PHONE..............................408 378-1606
Melvin Cardoza, *President*
Ron Cardoza, *Vice Pres*
Sharon Cardoza, *Vice Pres*
Kris Salazar, *Vice Pres*
Christina Rodriguez, *Bookkeeper*
EMP: 13
SALES (est): 2MM Privately Held
SIC: 2752 Commercial printing, offset

(P-6713)
C4 LITHO
27020 Daisy Cir, Yorba Linda (92887-4233)
PHONE..............................714 259-1073
Su T Dang,
Stacey Dang,
EMP: 17
SALES (est): 3.5MM Privately Held
SIC: 2752 Commercial printing, offset

(P-6714)
CAL SOUTHERN GRAPHICS CORP
8432 Steller Dr, Culver City (90232-2425)
PHONE..............................310 559-3600
Timothy Toomey, *CEO*
Dorie Fullerton, *President*
Crystal Zuniga, *Administration*
Amir Saeed, *Controller*
Mark Armstrong, *Sales Staff*
▲ EMP: 82
SQ FT: 32,000
SALES: 20MM Privately Held
WEB: www.socalgraph.com
SIC: 2752 2759 2754 Lithographing on
metal; commercial printing; commercial
printing, gravure

(P-6715)
CALIFORNIA MASTER PRINTERS
Also Called: Gold Leaf Cigar Co
796 N Todd Ave, Azusa (91702-2227)
PHONE..............................626 812-8930
Tony Lazzeri, *President*
Arthur Lazzeri, *Vice Pres*
Beverly Lazzeri, *Vice Pres*
EMP: 10
SQ FT: 8,000
SALES (est): 847K Privately Held
SIC: 2752 Commercial printing, offset

(P-6716)
CALIFORNIA OFFSET PRINTERS INC
Also Called: Cop Communications
620 W Elk Ave, Glendale (91204-1494)
PHONE..............................631 274-9530
John Hedlund, *Ch of Bd*
William R Rittwage, *President*
Jeff Victor, *Admin Asst*
Mirek Paluch, *Sales Staff*
Lisa Neely, *Publisher*
EMP: 100 EST: 1962
SQ FT: 55,000
SALES (est): 34.4MM Privately Held
WEB: www.copcomm.com
SIC: 2752 2741 2721 Commercial print-
ing, offset; miscellaneous publishing; peri-
odicals

(P-6717)
CALIFORNIA SCENE PUBLISHING
8360 Juniper Creek Ln, San Diego
(92126-1072)
PHONE..............................858 635-9400
Leo Sismanis, *President*
▲ EMP: 10
SQ FT: 6,200
SALES (est): 1.1MM Privately Held
WEB: www.calscene.com
SIC: 2752 Post cards, picture: lithographed

(P-6718)
CAMPBELL GRAPHICS INC
156 N 2nd St, Campbell (95008-2024)
PHONE..............................408 371-6411
Laverne G Lamar, *President*
Jean Lamar, *Treasurer*
EMP: 24
SQ FT: 10,000
SALES (est): 2.9MM Privately Held
WEB: www.cgprint.com
SIC: 2752 Commercial printing, offset

(P-6719)
CANDLELIGHT PRESS INC
26752 Oak Ave Ste F, Canyon Country
(91351-6675)
PHONE..............................323 299-3798
Richard E Rice, *President*
EMP: 20
SQ FT: 15,000
SALES: 1.8MM Privately Held
WEB: www.candlelightpress.com
SIC: 2752 Commercial printing, litho-
graphic

(P-6720)
CANDU GRAPHICS
5737 Kanan Rd Ste 132, Agoura Hills
(91301-1601)
PHONE..............................310 822-1620
Michael Dutra, *President*
EMP: 10 EST: 2013
SALES: 1.3MM Privately Held
SIC: 2752 Commercial printing, offset

(P-6721)
CARL & IRVING PRINTERS INC
161 N N St, Tulare (93274-4226)
P.O. Box 627 (93275-0627)
PHONE..............................559 686-8354
James Gonsalves, *President*
Arlene Gonsalves, *Corp Secy*
EMP: 10
SQ FT: 11,000
SALES (est): 933.6K Privately Held
SIC: 2752 2759 Commercial printing, litho-
graphic; letterpress printing

(P-6722)
CASEY PRINTING INC
398 E San Antonio Dr, King City
(93930-2509)
PHONE..............................831 385-3221
Richard Casey, *President*
Bill Casey, *Vice Pres*
Sharon Casey, *Admin Sec*
Candace Popper, *Consultant*
EMP: 48
SQ FT: 31,000
SALES (est): 7MM Privately Held
WEB: www.caseyprinting.com
SIC: 2752 Commercial printing, offset

(P-6723)
CEC PRINT SOLUTIONS INC
30971 San Benito St, Hayward
(94544-7936)
PHONE..............................510 670-0160
Amit Chokshi, *President*
Mary Beth Cahill, *Office Mgr*
Pratik Dakwala, *Mktg Dir*
Richard Fish, *Accounts Exec*
▲ EMP: 12 EST: 1976
SQ FT: 26,000
SALES (est): 2.8MM Privately Held
WEB: www.cecprinting.com
SIC: 2752 Commercial printing, offset;
business forms, lithographed

(P-6724)
CENTRAL BUSINESS FORMS INC
Also Called: Central Printing Group
289 Foster City Blvd B, Foster City
(94404-1100)
PHONE..............................650 548-0918
Jeanine M Morgan, *President*
Michelle L Cabral, *Corp Secy*
EMP: 18
SQ FT: 22,800
SALES (est): 3.5MM Privately Held
WEB: www.cpgusa.com
SIC: 2752 Commercial printing, offset

(P-6725)
CENVEO WORLDWIDE LIMITED
888 Tennessee St, San Francisco
(94107-3034)
PHONE..............................415 821-7171
Coleen Schoenatide, *Manager*
EMP: 80
SALES (corp-wide): 685.5MM **Privately Held**
SIC: 2752 Commercial printing, offset
HQ: Cenveo Worldwide Limited
200 First Stamford Pl # 2
Stamford CT 06902
303 790-8023

(P-6726)
CH IMAGE INC
Also Called: Cater Line , The
15350 Valley Blvd, City of Industry
(91746-3335)
PHONE..............................626 336-6063
▲ EMP: 15 EST: 1999
SALES (est): 1.2MM **Privately Held**
SIC: 2752

(P-6727)
CHALLENGE GRAPHICS INC
16611 Roscoe Pl, North Hills (91343-6104)
PHONE..............................818 892-0123
Robert F Ritter, *President*
Kathy Burtoft, *Treasurer*
Sally A Ritter, *Vice Pres*
Tara Curtis, *Admin Sec*
EMP: 25
SQ FT: 17,000
SALES: 2.5MM **Privately Held**
WEB: www.challenge-graphics.com
SIC: 2752 Commercial printing, offset

(P-6728)
CHECCHI ENTERPRISES INC
Also Called: Harvest Printing Company
19849 Riverside Ave, Anderson
(96007-4909)
PHONE..............................530 378-1207
Tom Watega, *President*
Lois Rohlf, *General Mgr*
Joni Sargent, *Manager*
EMP: 15
SQ FT: 10,200
SALES (est): 2.4MM **Privately Held**
WEB: www.harvestprinting.com
SIC: 2752 Commercial printing, offset

(P-6729)
CHILD EVNGELISM FELLOWSHIP INC
2201 Mount Vernon Ave, Bakersfield
(93306-3341)
P.O. Box 60735 (93386-0735)
PHONE..............................661 873-9032
EMP: 41
SALES (corp-wide): 24.4MM **Privately Held**
SIC: 2752 Commercial printing, lithographic
PA: Child Evangelism Fellowship Incorporated
17482 Highway M
Warrenton MO 63383
636 456-4321

(P-6730)
CHIMES PRINTING INCORPORATED
1065 Hensley St, Richmond (94801-2116)
PHONE..............................510 235-2388
Thomas C Pimm, *President*
EMP: 12 EST: 1989
SALES (est): 1.7MM **Privately Held**
SIC: 2752 Commercial printing, offset

(P-6731)
CHROMATIC INC LITHOGRAPHERS
127 Concord St, Glendale (91203-2456)
PHONE..............................818 242-5785
Keith Sevigny, *President*
Mary Gene Sevigny, *CEO*
Michael Sevigny, *Vice Pres*
Marlene Lunn, *Administration*
▲ EMP: 32
SQ FT: 30,000
SALES (est): 7.2MM **Privately Held**
SIC: 2752 Commercial printing, offset

(P-6732)
CHUP CORPORATION
Also Called: Color Digit
2990 Airway Ave Ste A, Costa Mesa
(92626-6037)
PHONE..............................949 455-0676
Mohsen Kaeni, *President*
Hadi Kaeni, *Vice Pres*
Hamid Kaeni, *Admin Sec*
EMP: 15
SQ FT: 11,000
SALES (est): 4.1MM **Privately Held**
SIC: 2752 2796 Commercial printing, offset; color separations for printing

(P-6733)
CLASSIC LITHO & DESIGN INC
340 Maple Ave, Torrance (90503-2600)
PHONE..............................310 224-5200
Masoud Nikravan, *CEO*
Firouzeh Nikravan, *President*
Bill Obr, *Project Mgr*
Craig Elferdink, *Manager*
EMP: 30 EST: 1976
SQ FT: 12,500
SALES: 5.2MM **Privately Held**
WEB: www.classiclitho.com
SIC: 2752 Commercial printing, offset

(P-6734)
CLEAR IMAGE PRINTING INC
12744 San Fernando Rd # 200, Sylmar
(91342-3856)
PHONE..............................818 547-4684
Anthony Toven, *President*
Jessica Slepicka, *Executive*
Daniele Toven, *Admin Sec*
Dejirlene Concha, *Bookkeeper*
Jason Byers, *Plant Mgr*
EMP: 28
SQ FT: 18,000
SALES (est): 7.7MM **Privately Held**
SIC: 2752 Commercial printing, offset

(P-6735)
CLIC LLC
Also Called: Andresen
601 20th St, San Francisco (94107-3116)
PHONE..............................415 421-2900
Michael Hicks, *Mng Member*
Andresen Family Trust, *Mng Member*
EMP: 18
SQ FT: 7,500
SALES (est): 3.5MM **Privately Held**
WEB: www.andresen.com
SIC: 2752 7374 Commercial printing, lithographic; computer graphics service

(P-6736)
CMYK ENTERPRISE INC
Also Called: Cmyk Prints and Promotions.com
25653 Gateway Blvd, Tracy (95377-8645)
PHONE..............................209 229-7230
Nick Michael Pappas, *President*
Amy Gephart, *Accountant*
▲ EMP: 12
SQ FT: 30,000
SALES (est): 2.8MM **Privately Held**
SIC: 2752 7389 8743 Commercial printing, lithographic; packaging & labeling services; promotion service

(P-6737)
CO-COLOR
Also Called: Co/Color Division
650 W Terrace Dr, San Dimas
(91773-2908)
PHONE..............................909 394-7888
Fax: 909 394-7897
EMP: 12 EST: 1969
SQ FT: 12,000
SALES (est): 3.6MM **Privately Held**
SIC: 2752

(P-6738)
COAST COLOR PRINTING INC
Also Called: Sunset Printing
16301 S Broadway, Gardena (90248-2709)
PHONE..............................310 352-3560
Dennis Lanfre, *CEO*
Michael Lanfre, *Vice Pres*
Kimberly Lanfre-Brubaker, *Vice Pres*
Kim Pritchard, *Manager*
EMP: 10
SQ FT: 6,000

SALES: 1.7MM **Privately Held**
SIC: 2752 Commercial printing, lithographic

(P-6739)
COLE PRINT & MARKETING
2001 Salvio St Ste 25, Concord
(94520-2059)
PHONE..............................925 276-2344
Chris Cole, *Owner*
EMP: 11 EST: 2010
SALES (est): 1.3MM **Privately Held**
SIC: 2752 Commercial printing, lithographic

(P-6740)
COLOR INC
1600 Flower St, Glendale (91201-2319)
PHONE..............................818 240-1350
Barry D Hamm, *President*
James E Hamm, *Vice Pres*
Karen Fiorenza, *Technology*
Alan Forney, *Production*
EMP: 35
SQ FT: 16,000
SALES (est): 6MM **Privately Held**
SIC: 2752 2796 Color lithography; publication printing, lithographic; platemaking services

(P-6741)
COLORCOM INC
2437 S Eastern Ave, Commerce
(90040-1414)
PHONE..............................323 246-4640
John Youn, *President*
Young Kim, *Shareholder*
Paul Yoo, *General Mgr*
Aaron Azmi, *Marketing Mgr*
EMP: 16
SALES (est): 3.4MM **Privately Held**
WEB: www.colorcom.net
SIC: 2752 Commercial printing, offset

(P-6742)
COLORFAST DYE & PRINT HSE INC
5075 Pacific Blvd, Vernon (90058-2215)
PHONE..............................323 581-1656
Enrique Ruiz, *President*
Jose Ramos, *Vice Pres*
EMP: 107
SQ FT: 30,000
SALES (est): 9.3MM **Privately Held**
SIC: 2752 2396 2269 Commercial printing, lithographic; screen printing on fabric articles; dyeing: raw stock yarn & narrow fabrics

(P-6743)
COLORFX INC
11050 Randall St, Sun Valley (91352-2621)
P.O. Box 12357, La Crescenta (91224-5357)
PHONE..............................818 767-7671
Razmik Avedissian, *CEO*
Arby Avedissan, *Vice Pres*
Yolanda Avedissan, *Admin Sec*
EMP: 50
SQ FT: 28,000
SALES (est): 8.4MM **Privately Held**
WEB: www.colorfxweb.com
SIC: 2752 Commercial printing, offset

(P-6744)
COLORMARX CORPORATION (PA)
Also Called: PIP Printing
4825 Auburn Blvd, Sacramento
(95841-3603)
PHONE..............................916 334-0334
Kabrina K McNaught, *President*
Ray McNaught, *Vice Pres*
EMP: 11
SQ FT: 5,600
SALES (est): 1.9MM **Privately Held**
SIC: 2752 Commercial printing, offset

(P-6745)
COLORPRINT
1570 Gilbreth Rd, Burlingame
(94010-1605)
PHONE..............................650 697-7611
Mark Jaffe, *Owner*
Irene Jhin, *Partner*
Genevieve Soriano, *Technology*

Madsen Lorraine, *VP Sales*
Gino Saccuman, *Sales Dir*
EMP: 10
SQ FT: 3,200
SALES (est): 900K **Privately Held**
WEB: www.colorprint.com
SIC: 2752 7334 Commercial printing, offset; photocopying & duplicating services

(P-6746)
COLOUR CONCEPTS INC
Also Called: Partner Printing
1225 Los Angeles St, Glendale
(91204-2403)
PHONE..............................951 787-9988
Mark S Sears, *President*
EMP: 150
SQ FT: 36,000
SALES (est): 28.8MM **Privately Held**
SIC: 2752 7371 Commercial printing, lithographic; computer software development

(P-6747)
COMMERCE PRINTERS INC
3201 Halladay St, Santa Ana (92705-5628)
PHONE..............................714 549-5002
Cheryl Toscas, *CEO*
Thomas Toscas, *Owner*
Jayson Toscas, *Engineer*
Jay Toscas, *Manager*
▲ EMP: 20
SQ FT: 8,000
SALES (est): 3.5MM **Privately Held**
SIC: 2752 Commercial printing, offset

(P-6748)
COMMERCIAL CLEAR PRINT INC
9025 Fullbright Ave, Chatsworth
(91311-6126)
PHONE..............................818 709-1220
Geoffrey Pick, *President*
Colleen Pick, *Vice Pres*
Blaine Waldman, *Project Mgr*
Bob Palmer, *Manager*
EMP: 10
SQ FT: 4,900
SALES (est): 2.1MM **Privately Held**
WEB: www.clearprint.com
SIC: 2752 7336 2759 Commercial printing, offset; commercial art & graphic design; commercial printing

(P-6749)
COMMUNICART
1589 Laurelwood Rd, Santa Clara
(95054-2744)
PHONE..............................408 970-0922
Ken Azebu, *President*
Diane Ogami, *CEO*
Chiyo Ogami, *Treasurer*
Richard Ogami, *Vice Pres*
EMP: 10
SQ FT: 6,300
SALES (est): 870K **Privately Held**
WEB: www.communicart.com
SIC: 2752 2791 Commercial printing, offset; typesetting

(P-6750)
COMMUNITY PRINTERS INC
1827 Soquel Ave, Santa Cruz
(95062-1385)
PHONE..............................831 426-4682
Joe Chavez, *President*
Shelly D'Amour, *CFO*
Mischa Kandinksy, *Treasurer*
Brian Lorentz, *Sales Mgr*
Dan Vannatter, *Manager*
EMP: 32
SQ FT: 10,000
SALES: 4.9MM
SALES (corp-wide): 316.3K **Privately Held**
WEB: www.comprinters.com
SIC: 2752 Commercial printing, offset
PA: Eschaton Foundation
612 Ocean St
Santa Cruz CA 95060
831 423-1626

(P-6751)
COMSTOCK PRESS
2117 San Jose Ave, Alameda
(94501-4915)
PHONE..............................510 522-4115

▲ = Import ▼=Export
◆ =Import/Export

Fritz Zehender, *Owner*
EMP: 22
SALES: 1.5MM **Privately Held**
SIC: 2752 Commercial printing, lithographic

(P-6752)
CONTINENTAL GRAPHICS CORP
Also Called: Continental Engineering Svcs
6910 Carroll Rd, San Diego (92121-2211)
PHONE.................................858 552-6520
Manuel Defaria, *Branch Mgr*
EMP: 500
SALES (corp-wide): 93.3B **Publicly Held**
WEB: www.cdgnow.com
SIC: 2752 7336 Promotional printing, lithographic; graphic arts & related design
HQ: Continental Graphics Corporation
4060 N Lakewood Blvd
Long Beach CA 90808
714 503-4200

(P-6753)
CONTINENTAL GRAPHICS CORP
Also Called: Continental Data Graphics
4060 N Lakewood Blvd 8015fl, Long Beach
(90808-1700)
PHONE.................................714 827-1752
Warren Smith, *Manager*
Stephen Page, *Senior VP*
EMP: 1080
SALES (corp-wide): 93.3B **Publicly Held**
WEB: www.cdgnow.com
SIC: 2752 7336 Promotional printing, lithographic; graphic arts & related design
HQ: Continental Graphics Corporation
4060 N Lakewood Blvd
Long Beach CA 90808
714 503-4200

(P-6754)
CONTINENTAL GRAPHICS CORP
9302 Pttsbrgh Ave Ste 100, Rancho Cucamonga (91730)
PHONE.................................909 758-9800
Adrienne Yates, *Senior Engr*
EMP: 30
SALES (corp-wide): 93.3B **Publicly Held**
WEB: www.cdgnow.com
SIC: 2752 7336 Promotional printing, lithographic; graphic arts & related design
HQ: Continental Graphics Corporation
4060 N Lakewood Blvd
Long Beach CA 90808
714 503-4200

(P-6755)
CONTINENTAL GRAPHICS CORP
Also Called: Continental Data Graphics
222 N Pacific Coast Hwy # 300, El Segundo (90245-5648)
PHONE.................................310 662-2307
Mike Parvin, *Manager*
Dolores Pickler, *Technical Mgr*
Scott Gauss, *Human Res Mgr*
Peggy Maluia, *Purch Mgr*
Brad Morrison, *Sales Engr*
EMP: 20
SALES (corp-wide): 93.3B **Publicly Held**
WEB: www.cdgnow.com
SIC: 2752 7336 Promotional printing, lithographic; graphic arts & related design
HQ: Continental Graphics Corporation
4060 N Lakewood Blvd
Long Beach CA 90808
714 503-4200

(P-6756)
CONTINENTAL GRAPHIX
166 Riviera Dr, San Rafael (94901-1554)
PHONE.................................415 864-2345
Barry Schwartz, *President*
EMP: 25
SALES (est): 2.2MM **Privately Held**
WEB: www.continentalgraphix.com
SIC: 2752 7334 Commercial printing, lithographic; photocopying & duplicating services

(P-6757)
CONTINENTAL LITHO INC
1360 Park Center Dr, Vista (92081-8300)
PHONE.................................760 598-0291
Stephen Tomacelli, *President*
EMP: 80
SQ FT: 37,000

SALES (est): 7.2MM **Privately Held**
WEB: www.continental-litho.com
SIC: 2752 Commercial printing, offset

(P-6758)
COPY 1 INC
Also Called: Digital One Legal Solutions
77 Battery St Fl 2, San Francisco
(94111-5544)
PHONE.................................415 986-0111
Young Park, *President*
EMP: 25
SALES (est): 3.6MM **Privately Held**
SIC: 2752 Commercial printing, offset

(P-6759)
COPYMAT SALINAS LLC
44 W Gabilan St, Salinas (93901-2731)
PHONE.................................831 753-0471
Barbara Mazzei,
Robert Gerholdt, *Vice Pres*
EMP: 12
SQ FT: 4,000
SALES (est): 1.6MM **Privately Held**
SIC: 2752 Commercial printing, offset

(P-6760)
CORPORATE GRAPHICS & PRINTING
335 Science Dr, Moorpark (93021-2092)
PHONE.................................805 529-5333
Harry A Stidham, *President*
Harry Stidham, *President*
John Bird, *Vice Pres*
EMP: 17
SQ FT: 20,000
SALES: 3MM **Privately Held**
WEB: www.corp-graphics.com
SIC: 2752 Commercial printing, offset

(P-6761)
CORPORATE GRAPHICS INTL INC
Also Called: Corporate Graphics West
4909 Alcoa Ave, Vernon (90058-3022)
PHONE.................................323 826-3440
Robert Gonynor, *General Mgr*
Cory Hanna, *General Mgr*
EMP: 85
SALES (corp-wide): 3.4B **Privately Held**
SIC: 2752 2759 Commercial printing, offset; lithographing on metal; embossing on paper
HQ: Corporate Graphics International, Inc.
1885 Northway Dr
North Mankato MN 56003
507 625-4400

(P-6762)
COYLE REPRODUCTIONS INC (PA)
2850 Orbiter St, Brea (92821-6224)
PHONE.................................866 269-5373
Frank T Cutrone Jr, *CEO*
Frank T Cutrone, *Ch of Bd*
Jason De Soto, *Exec VP*
Rosa Hernandez, *Office Mgr*
Hannah Wilson, *Office Mgr*
EMP: 140 **EST:** 1963
SQ FT: 18,000
SALES (est): 34.3MM **Privately Held**
WEB: www.coylerepro.com
SIC: 2752 Commercial printing, offset

(P-6763)
CPRINT HOLDINGS LLC
1901 E 7th Pl, Los Angeles (90021-1601)
PHONE.................................213 488-0456
Sean Saberi, *President*
EMP: 15 **EST:** 2015
SALES: 2MM **Privately Held**
SIC: 2752 Commercial printing, offset

(P-6764)
CPS PRINTING
Also Called: Zuza
2304 Faraday Ave, Carlsbad (92008-7216)
PHONE.................................760 494-9000
Philip M Lurie, *President*
Martin Solarish, *Vice Pres*
EMP: 72
SQ FT: 23,000
SALES (est): 16.7MM **Privately Held**
WEB: www.cpsprinting.com
SIC: 2752 Commercial printing, offset

(P-6765)
CREAMER PRINTING CO
1413 N La Brea Ave, Inglewood
(90302-1218)
PHONE.................................310 671-9491
Fred John Creamer III, *President*
Lawrence Creamer, *CFO*
Edmund J Creamer, *Corp Secy*
EMP: 15 **EST:** 1924
SQ FT: 10,000
SALES (est): 2.2MM **Privately Held**
SIC: 2752 2759 Commercial printing, offset; flexographic printing

(P-6766)
CREATIVE COLOR PRINTING INC
1605 Railroad St, Corona (92880-2503)
PHONE.................................951 737-4551
Rudy Resner, *President*
Steve Rebel, *Sales Staff*
EMP: 11 **EST:** 1982
SQ FT: 8,000
SALES (est): 1.8MM **Privately Held**
WEB: www.creativecolorprinting.com
SIC: 2752 Commercial printing, offset

(P-6767)
CREATIVE PRESS LLC
1600 E Ball Rd, Anaheim (92805-5990)
PHONE.................................714 774-5060
Michael L Patton, *President*
Tina Seybert, *Technology*
Tom Spence, *Prdtn Mgr*
Kevin McHugh, *Foreman/Supr*
Steve Bergman, *Sales Executive*
EMP: 65
SQ FT: 31,000
SALES (est): 21.6MM **Privately Held**
WEB: www.creativepressinc.net
SIC: 2752 2791 2789 Commercial printing; offset; typesetting; bookbinding & related work

(P-6768)
CRESCENT INC
1196 N Osprey Cir, Anaheim (92807-1709)
PHONE.................................714 992-6030
Reza Mohkami, *President*
Tahereh Mohkami, *Treasurer*
Ira Heshmati, *Vice Pres*
EMP: 25
SQ FT: 10,000
SALES (est): 3.9MM **Privately Held**
WEB: www.printprinting.com
SIC: 2752 7549 Commercial printing, offset; do-it-yourself garages

(P-6769)
CRESTEC USA INC
Also Called: Crestec Los Angeles
2410 Mira Mar Ave, Long Beach
(90815-1756)
PHONE.................................310 327-9000
Tsuyoshi Kaneko, *CEO*
Mike Burk, *Vice Pres*
Rene Isip, *Executive*
Isabel Bocanegra, *Admin Sec*
Peter Tang, *Production*
▲ **EMP:** 50 **EST:** 1967
SALES (est): 10.2MM
SALES (corp-wide): 132.8MM **Privately Held**
WEB: www.crestecla.com
SIC: 2752 Commercial printing, offset
PA: Crestec Inc.
676, Kasaishindencho, Higashi-Ku
Hamamatsu SZO 431-3
534 353-553

(P-6770)
CRT COLOR PRINTING INC
Also Called: C R T
13201 Barton Cir, Santa Fe Springs
(90670)
PHONE.................................562 906-1517
Rosanna Tung, *President*
Roger Tung, *Vice Pres*
EMP: 15
SQ FT: 14,000
SALES: 3MM **Privately Held**
SIC: 2752 Commercial printing, offset

(P-6771)
CTS PRINTING
9920 Jordan Cir, Santa Fe Springs
(90670-3346)
PHONE.................................562 941-8420
EMP: 10
SALES (est): 580K **Privately Held**
WEB: www.ctsll.com
SIC: 2752

(P-6772)
CUSTOM ART SERVICES CORP
Also Called: Colorplak.com
37110 Mesa Rd, Temecula (92592-8650)
PHONE.................................951 302-9889
Marvin Ellerby Farr, *CEO*
Melodie Faith Farr, *President*
EMP: 10 **EST:** 2008
SALES: 750K **Privately Held**
SIC: 2752 7699 Photo-offset printing; picture framing, custom

(P-6773)
CUSTOM LITHOGRAPH
7006 Stanford Ave, Los Angeles
(90001-1583)
PHONE.................................323 778-7751
Robert D Hanel, *President*
John Sebourn, *CFO*
Pamela Sebourn, *Admin Sec*
EMP: 20 **EST:** 1958
SQ FT: 92,000
SALES (est): 3.1MM **Privately Held**
WEB: www.customlithograph.com
SIC: 2752 Commercial printing, offset

(P-6774)
CYU LITHOGRAPHICS INC
Also Called: Choice Lithographics
6951 Oran Cir, Buena Park (90621-3305)
PHONE.................................888 878-9898
Michael Wang, *President*
▲ **EMP:** 25
SQ FT: 13,000
SALES: 3MM **Privately Held**
WEB: www.choicelitho.com
SIC: 2752 2721 Color lithography; magazines: publishing only, not printed on site

(P-6775)
D & J PRINTING INC
Also Called: Sinclair Printing Company
600 W Technology Dr, Palmdale
(93551-3748)
PHONE.................................661 775-4586
Donna Beltran, *Branch Mgr*
Roger Butzen, *Representative*
Jess Gallegos, *Representative*
EMP: 100
SALES (corp-wide): 68.5MM **Privately Held**
SIC: 2752 Commercial printing, offset
HQ: D. & J. Printing, Inc.
3323 Oak St
Brainerd MN 56401
218 829-2877

(P-6776)
D BENHAM CORPORATION
Also Called: KEBERT REPROGRAPHICS
10969 Wheatlands Ave A, Santee
(92071-5619)
PHONE.................................619 448-8079
Dewey Kebert, *President*
Sandra Kebert, *Admin Sec*
Ryan Morse, *Web Dvlpr*
EMP: 10
SQ FT: 8,000
SALES: 850K **Privately Held**
WEB: www.kebertreprographics.com
SIC: 2752 Offset & photolithographic printing

(P-6777)
DAKOTA PRESS
14400 Doolittle Dr, San Leandro
(94577-5546)
PHONE.................................510 895-1300
Mary Reid, *President*
Perry Mundorff, *Vice Pres*
EMP: 15
SQ FT: 11,000

SALES (est): 1.4MM **Privately Held**
WEB: www.dakotapress.com
SIC: 2752 2791 2789 2761 Typesetting; bookbinding & related work; manifold business forms; commercial printing, offset

(P-6778)
DARE LITHOWORKS INC
Also Called: Rabbit Lithographics
13512 Vintage Pl A, Chino (91710-5243)
PHONE..................................213 250-9062
Armand Dabuet, *President*
Ernand Dabuet, *Treasurer*
Reine Dabuet, *Vice Pres*
Renwick Dabuet, *Admin Sec*
EMP: 10
SQ FT: 6,000
SALES (est): 1.6MM **Privately Held**
WEB: www.rabbitlitho.com
SIC: 2752 Commercial printing, lithographic

(P-6779)
DAVID B ANDERSON
Also Called: Central Coast Printing
921 Huston St, Grover Beach (93433-3108)
PHONE..................................805 489-0661
David B Anderson, *Owner*
Gail Speer, *Admin Sec*
Doug Speer, *Plant Mgr*
EMP: 26 EST: 1978
SQ FT: 17,000
SALES (est): 3.6MM **Privately Held**
SIC: 2752 Commercial printing, offset

(P-6780)
DBC PRINTING INCORPORATED
Also Called: Vanguard Printing
220 Bernoulli Cir, Oxnard (93030-8012)
PHONE..................................805 988-8855
Jeff D Cox, *CEO*
Justin Cox, *Sales Staff*
EMP: 14
SQ FT: 14,000
SALES (est): 2.5MM **Privately Held**
SIC: 2752 Offset & photolithographic printing

(P-6781)
DENNIS BOLTON ENTERPRISES INC
7285 Coldwater Canyon Ave, North Hollywood (91605-4204)
PHONE..................................818 982-1800
Dennis Bolton, *President*
Osvaldo Acosta, *Treasurer*
Max Guerrero, *Vice Pres*
Carlo Bernal, *Admin Sec*
EMP: 23
SQ FT: 14,780
SALES (est): 3.1MM **Privately Held**
WEB: www.printingbydbe.com
SIC: 2752 7334 7311 Commercial printing, offset; photocopying & duplicating services; advertising consultant

(P-6782)
DESIGNER PRINTING INC
Also Called: Igraphix
638 Washington St, San Francisco (94111-2106)
PHONE..................................415 989-0008
Wade Lai, *President*
▲ EMP: 17
SQ FT: 8,500
SALES (est): 1.7MM **Privately Held**
WEB: www.designerprinting.com
SIC: 2752 Commercial printing, offset

(P-6783)
DF GRAFIX INC
13871 Danielson St, Poway (92064-6891)
PHONE..................................858 866-0858
David P Fox, *President*
◆ EMP: 10
SALES (est): 2MM **Privately Held**
SIC: 2752 Commercial printing, offset

(P-6784)
DIEGO & SON PRINTING INC
2104 National Ave, San Diego (92113-2209)
P.O. Box 13100 (92170-3100)
PHONE..................................619 233-5373
Nicholas Aguilera, *President*
Isabelle Aguilera, *Corp Secy*
Rebecca Aguilera, *Vice Pres*
Rebecca Aguilera-Gardin, *Vice Pres*
Clara Aguilera, *Project Mgr*
EMP: 22
SQ FT: 13,500
SALES (est): 4.4MM **Privately Held**
WEB: www.diegoandson.com
SIC: 2752 2759 Commercial printing, offset; commercial printing

(P-6785)
DIGI PRINT PLUS
9670 Research Dr, Irvine (92618-4666)
PHONE..................................949 770-5000
Farhad Omidvar, *CEO*
Miguel Castellanos, *Business Mgr*
Fariba Shirmo, *Manager*
EMP: 11
SALES (est): 1.4MM **Privately Held**
SIC: 2752 Commercial printing, offset

(P-6786)
DIGITAL MANIA INC
Also Called: Copymat
455 Market St Ste 180, San Francisco (94105-2476)
PHONE..................................415 896-0500
Darius Meykadah, *President*
EMP: 20
SALES (est): 4.5MM **Privately Held**
SIC: 2752 Commercial printing, offset

(P-6787)
DIGITAL PRINTING SYSTEMS INC (PA)
777 N Georgia Ave, Azusa (91702-2207)
PHONE..................................626 815-1888
Donald J Nores, *CEO*
Peter Young, *CEO*
Doug Gabriel, *CFO*
Joyce Nores, *Treasurer*
Jim Nores, *Vice Pres*
◆ EMP: 75
SQ FT: 30,640
SALES (est): 12.4MM **Privately Held**
WEB: www.dpstickets.com
SIC: 2752 Tickets, lithographed

(P-6788)
DIRECT LABEL & TAG LLC
11909 Telegraph Rd, Santa Fe Springs (90670-3785)
PHONE..................................562 948-4499
Edward Rosen, *Mng Member*
Jeffrey Gampel,
▲ EMP: 21
SQ FT: 2,700
SALES (est): 1.2MM **Privately Held**
SIC: 2752 2754 3577 5131 Tags, lithographed; labels: gravure printing; bar code (magnetic ink) printers; labels

(P-6789)
DISCOUNT INSTANT PRINTING
175 S Thurston Ave, Los Angeles (90049-3128)
PHONE..................................213 622-4347
Kamran Nazarian, *Partner*
Kiu Nazarian, *Partner*
EMP: 12
SQ FT: 3,400
SALES (est): 1.1MM **Privately Held**
SIC: 2752 Commercial printing, lithographic

(P-6790)
DLA DOCUMENT SERVICES
4231 San Pedro Rd, Port Hueneme (93043-4308)
PHONE..................................805 982-4310
Mark Shadinger, *Manager*
EMP: 28 **Publicly Held**
SIC: 2752 9711 Commercial printing, lithographic; national security;
HQ: Dla Document Services
5450 Carlisle Pike Bldg 9
Mechanicsburg PA 17050
717 605-2362

(P-6791)
DOCUMOTION RESEARCH INC
2020 S Eastwood Ave, Santa Ana (92705-5208)
PHONE..................................714 662-3800
Joel Van Boom, *President*
EMP: 17
SQ FT: 10,000
SALES (est): 3.2MM **Privately Held**
SIC: 2752 Commercial printing, lithographic

(P-6792)
DOT COPY INC
Also Called: DOT Graphics
9655 De Soto Ave, Chatsworth (91311-5013)
PHONE..................................818 341-6666
Brian Whiteman, *CEO*
Jamie Gordon, *Executive*
Crystal Sessions, *Purchasing*
Mike Trudeau, *Sales Executive*
Jessica Laskey, *Accounts Exec*
EMP: 49
SALES (est): 10.9MM **Privately Held**
SIC: 2752 Commercial printing, offset

(P-6793)
DOT PRINTER INC (PA)
2424 Mcgaw Ave, Irvine (92614-5834)
PHONE..................................949 474-1100
Bruce M Carson, *President*
Stan Lowe, *COO*
James Voss, *CFO*
Jim Voss, *CFO*
Laura Parker, *Senior VP*
▲ EMP: 170
SQ FT: 40,000
SALES (est): 56.5MM **Privately Held**
WEB: www.dotprinter.com
SIC: 2752 2732 3555 Commercial printing, lithographic; book printing; printing trades machinery

(P-6794)
DSJ PRINTING INC
1703 Stewart St, Santa Monica (90404-4021)
PHONE..................................310 828-8051
Jeffrey L Vaughan, *President*
Ed Molina, *Vice Pres*
Jeffrey Vaughan Jr, *Vice Pres*
Stacie Vaughan, *Graphic Designe*
Brandon Vaughan, *Prdtn Mgr*
EMP: 13
SQ FT: 3,000
SALES (est): 2MM **Privately Held**
WEB: www.dsjprinting.com
SIC: 2752 2759 Commercial printing, offset; letterpress printing

(P-6795)
DUMONT PRINTING INC
Also Called: Dumont Printing & Mailing
1333 G St, Fresno (93706-1634)
P.O. Box 12726 (93779-2726)
PHONE..................................559 485-6311
Susan Denise Moore, *CEO*
Susan Moore, *President*
▼ EMP: 42
SQ FT: 21,000
SALES (est): 10.4MM **Privately Held**
WEB: www.dumontprinting.com
SIC: 2752 2759 7331 7334 Commercial printing, offset; commercial printing; letterpress & screen printing; direct mail advertising services; mailing service; photocopying & duplicating services; signs & advertising specialties; subscription fulfillment services: magazine, newspaper, etc.; printers' services: folding, collating; document embossing; presorted mail service

(P-6796)
DUNCAN PRESS INC
25 W Lockeford St, Lodi (95240-2125)
P.O. Box 1627 (95241-1627)
PHONE..................................209 462-5245
Michael Bedford, *President*
Steven Bedford, *Corp Secy*
Sally D Press, *Graphic Designe*
EMP: 13
SALES (est): 1MM **Privately Held**
SIC: 2752 Commercial printing, offset

(P-6797)
DUNN BROS COMMERCIAL PRTRS INC
1239 W 130th St, Gardena (90247-1591)
PHONE..................................323 321-2211
Robert Dunn, *President*
▲ EMP: 21
SQ FT: 12,500
SALES (est): 2.5MM **Privately Held**
SIC: 2752 Commercial printing, offset

(P-6798)
EARTH PRINT INC
Also Called: Cr Print
31115 Via Colinas Ste 301, Westlake Village (91362-4507)
PHONE..................................818 879-6050
Jim Friedl, *President*
Edward Corridori, *Admin Sec*
EMP: 19
SQ FT: 7,500
SALES (est): 3.4MM **Privately Held**
WEB: www.crprint.com
SIC: 2752 7334 Commercial printing, offset; photocopying & duplicating services

(P-6799)
EAST WEST PRINTING
7433 Lampson Ave, Garden Grove (92841-2903)
PHONE..................................714 899-7885
Fax: 714 899-7886
EMP: 11
SQ FT: 1,200
SALES (est): 1.4MM **Privately Held**
SIC: 2752

(P-6800)
ECLIPSE PRTG & GRAPHICS LLC
Also Called: James Litho
4462 E Airport Dr, Ontario (91761-7804)
PHONE..................................909 390-2452
Jeff James, *Mng Member*
Sue James,
EMP: 20 EST: 1999
SQ FT: 25,000
SALES (est): 5.3MM **Privately Held**
SIC: 2752 Commercial printing, offset

(P-6801)
ECON-O-PLATE INC
Also Called: Pacific Rim Printers & Mailers
5760 Hannum Ave, Culver City (90230-6501)
PHONE..................................310 342-5900
Robert Brothers, *President*
Brad Carl, *Treasurer*
Yana Shmuliver, *Executive*
Leslie Rice, *Office Mgr*
Frank Tellez, *Programmer Anys*
EMP: 15
SQ FT: 15,000
SALES (est): 3.9MM **Privately Held**
WEB: www.pacificrimprinters.com
SIC: 2752 7331 Commercial printing, offset; mailing service

(P-6802)
ECONOMY PRINT & IMAGE INC
Also Called: Economy Printing
7515 Metropolitan Dr, San Diego (92108-4403)
PHONE..................................619 295-4455
John Ferrari, *President*
Susanne Gustavsson, *Accountant*
Greg Hunt, *Accounts Mgr*
EMP: 16
SQ FT: 7,200
SALES (est): 2.3MM **Privately Held**
WEB: www.economyprint.com
SIC: 2752 Commercial printing, offset

(P-6803)
ECONOMY PRINTING
Also Called: Economy Printing Image
12642 Stoutwood St, Poway (92064-6430)
PHONE..................................858 679-8630
Robert Baird, *Owner*
EMP: 15
SALES (est): 1MM **Privately Held**
SIC: 2752 Commercial printing, lithographic

(P-6804)
EDGEWOOD PRESS INC
1130 N Main St, Orange (92867-3421)
PHONE..................................714 516-2455
Carol Altvater, *President*
Ernest Altvater Jr, *Corp Secy*
John M Atwell, *Vice Pres*

▲ = Import ▼=Export
◆ =Import/Export

EMP: 14
SQ FT: 12,000
SALES (est): 1.2MM **Privately Held**
WEB: www.folderfacts.com
SIC: 2752 Commercial printing, offset

(P-6805)
EDITION ONE GROUP
2080 2nd St, Berkeley (94710-1907)
PHONE...............................510 705-1930
Ben Zlotkin, *Owner*
EMP: 10 EST: 2010
SALES (est): 905.7K **Privately Held**
SIC: 2752 Commercial printing, lithographic

(P-6806)
ELITE 4 PRINT INC
851 E Walnut St, Carson (90746-1214)
PHONE...............................310 366-1344
Keith Kyong, *Principal*
▲ EMP: 20
SALES (est): 3.9MM **Privately Held**
SIC: 2752 Commercial printing, offset

(P-6807)
ELLEGRA PRINT & IMAGING
1419 Santa Fe Ave, Long Beach
(90813-1236)
PHONE...............................562 432-2931
Connie Bucks, *President*
Richard W Mc Hale Jr, *Shareholder*
Mike Bucks, *Vice Pres*
EMP: 10
SQ FT: 7,000
SALES (est): 926.5K **Privately Held**
SIC: 2752 Commercial printing, offset

(P-6808)
EPAC TECHNOLOGIES INC (PA)
2561 Grant Ave, San Leandro
(94579-2501)
PHONE...............................510 317-7979
Sasha Dobrovolsky, *CEO*
James Gentilcore, *President*
Pete Baldwin, *Vice Pres*
Sean Scott, *Vice Pres*
Kathy Torru, *Executive*
▲ EMP: 105 EST: 1998
SALES (est): 26.8MM **Privately Held**
WEB: www.epac.com
SIC: 2752 Commercial printing, lithographic

(P-6809)
ESCHATON FOUNDATION (PA)
Also Called: Resource Ctr For Nonviolence
612 Ocean St, Santa Cruz (95060-4006)
PHONE...............................831 423-1626
Barbara Hayes,
Peter Klotz-Chamberlin, *Corp Secy*
Jane Weed, *Vice Pres*
Tom Helman, *Exec Dir*
Robert Muller, *Admin Sec*
EMP: 60
SQ FT: 2,000
SALES: 316.3K **Privately Held**
WEB: www.rcnv.org
SIC: 2752 8399 Commercial printing, lithographic; council for social agency

(P-6810)
ESSENCE PRINTING INC (PA)
270 Oyster Point Blvd, South San Francisco (94080-1911)
PHONE...............................650 952-5072
Sue WEI, *President*
Herbert WEI, *CEO*
Edwin WEI Jr, *Vice Pres*
Hanson Shiu, *Project Mgr*
Alan Quale, *Prdtn Mgr*
EMP: 82 EST: 1988
SQ FT: 40,000
SALES (est): 13.5MM **Privately Held**
WEB: www.essenceprinting.com
SIC: 2752 Commercial printing, offset

(P-6811)
FALLBROOK PRINTING CORP
Also Called: Fallbrook Communications
504 E Alvarado St Ste 110, Fallbrook
(92028-2363)
PHONE...............................760 731-2020
Randall C Folin, *President*
Randall Folin, *Officer*
Cheryl Henderson, *Prdtn Mgr*

EMP: 10
SQ FT: 8,000
SALES (est): 1.7MM **Privately Held**
WEB: www.fallbrookprinting.com
SIC: 2752 Commercial printing, offset

(P-6812)
FAUST PRINTING INC
8656 Utica Ave Ste 100, Rancho Cucamonga (91730-4860)
P.O. Box 721713, Pinon Hills (92372-1713)
PHONE...............................909 980-1577
Donald F Faust Jr, *President*
Greg Faust, *Shareholder*
Tom Faust, *Shareholder*
Rosemary Faust, *Ch of Bd*
Jim Buccholz, *CFO*
EMP: 30
SQ FT: 20,000
SALES (est): 5.5MM **Privately Held**
WEB: www.faustprinting.com
SIC: 2752 2796 Commercial printing, offset; letterpress plates, preparation of; embossing plates for printing

(P-6813)
FBPRODUCTIONS INC
12722 Rverside Dr Ste 204, Valley Village
(91607)
PHONE...............................818 773-9337
Frank Barbarino, *President*
David Wohl, *CEO*
Jerry Cheney, *Vice Pres*
EMP: 100
SQ FT: 60,000
SALES (est): 13.2MM **Privately Held**
WEB: www.fbonline.com
SIC: 2752 2675 Commercial printing, offset; die-cut paper & board

(P-6814)
FED EX KINKOS OFC & PRINT CTR
255 W Stanley Ave, Ventura (93001-1313)
PHONE...............................805 604-6000
Robin Jo Ann, *Vice Pres*
EMP: 15
SALES (est): 2MM **Privately Held**
SIC: 2752 Commercial printing, lithographic

(P-6815)
FIREBRAND MEDIA LLC
Also Called: Laguna Beach Magazine
580 Broadway St Ste 301, Laguna Beach
(92651-4328)
PHONE...............................949 715-4100
Vincent Zepezauer, *Mng Member*
Steve Zepezauer, *CEO*
Sonia Chung, *Creative Dir*
Cindy Mendaros, *Office Mgr*
Scott Sanchez, *CTO*
EMP: 25
SQ FT: 5,000
SALES: 2MM **Privately Held**
SIC: 2752 Commercial printing, lithographic

(P-6816)
FIRST IMPRESSIONS PRINTING
25030 Viking St, Hayward (94545-2704)
PHONE...............................510 784-0811
Gary E Stang, *President*
Nancy Stang, *Treasurer*
Jennifer Stang, *Admin Sec*
EMP: 20
SQ FT: 10,000
SALES (est): 3MM **Privately Held**
SIC: 2752 Commercial printing, offset

(P-6817)
FISHER PRINTING INC (PA)
2257 N Pacific St, Orange (92865-2615)
PHONE...............................714 998-9200
Thomas Fischer, *Chairman*
Will Fischer, *CEO*
Tom Scarpati, *COO*
Brad Fischer, *Vice Pres*
Mario Urquizo, *Info Tech Mgr*
EMP: 150 EST: 1933
SQ FT: 60,000
SALES (est): 60.1MM **Privately Held**
WEB: www.fisherprinting.com
SIC: 2752 Commercial printing, offset

(P-6818)
FIVE-STAR GRAPHICS INC
2628 Woodbury Dr, Torrance (90503-7374)
PHONE...............................310 325-6881
Shirley Fuerst, *President*
Barry Fuerst, *President*
Robert Fuerst, *President*
EMP: 18
SQ FT: 11,000
SALES (est): 2.2MM **Privately Held**
SIC: 2752 Commercial printing, offset

(P-6819)
FIZZY COLOR LLC
3561 Homestead Rd Ste 231, Santa Clara
(95051-5161)
PHONE...............................408 623-6705
Joseph Zojaji, *Owner*
EMP: 10
SALES (est): 761K **Privately Held**
SIC: 2752 Commercial printing, lithographic

(P-6820)
FONG BROTHERS PRINTING INC (PA)
320 Valley Dr, Brisbane (94005-1208)
PHONE...............................415 467-1050
Tony D Fong, *President*
Susie Woo, *CFO*
Eugene Fong, *Vice Pres*
Paul Fong, *Vice Pres*
Peter Fong, *Vice Pres*
▲ EMP: 150
SQ FT: 105,000
SALES (est): 47.4MM **Privately Held**
WEB: www.fbp.com
SIC: 2752 Commercial printing, offset

(P-6821)
FONG FONG PRTRS LTHGRPHERS INC
3009 65th St, Sacramento (95820-2021)
PHONE...............................916 739-1313
Karen Cotton, *CEO*
Marsha Fong, *Corp Secy*
May L Fong, *Vice Pres*
Michael Raschack, *Production*
Curtis Fong, *Sales Mgr*
EMP: 43
SQ FT: 50,000
SALES: 8MM **Privately Held**
SIC: 2752 Commercial printing, offset

(P-6822)
FOOTHILL PRITNIG & GRAPHICS/ C (PA)
2245 Highway 49, Angels Camp
(95222-9579)
P.O. Box 338 (95222-0338)
PHONE...............................209 736-4332
James D Klann, *President*
▲ EMP: 12
SQ FT: 5,000
SALES (est): 1.9MM **Privately Held**
WEB: www.foothillprinting.com
SIC: 2752 Commercial printing, offset

(P-6823)
FOREST INVESTMENT GROUP INC
Also Called: Unicorn Group
83 Hamilton Dr Ste 100, Novato
(94949-5674)
PHONE...............................415 459-2330
David A Brooks, *CEO*
Mark Schmidt, *Vice Pres*
EMP: 15
SQ FT: 8,000
SALES (est): 1.7MM **Privately Held**
SIC: 2752 2791 2789 7334 Commercial printing, offset; typesetting; bookbinding & related work; photocopying & duplicating services

(P-6824)
FOSTER PRINTING COMPANY INC
700 E Alton Ave, Santa Ana (92705-5610)
PHONE...............................714 731-2000
Dennis M Blackburn, *CEO*
Steve Gutmann, *Plant Mgr*
Mike Pointer, *General Counsel*
Chad Goldfarb, *Representative*

EMP: 65
SQ FT: 35,000
SALES (est): 12.6MM **Privately Held**
WEB: www.fosterprint.com
SIC: 2752 Commercial printing, offset

(P-6825)
FOUR COLORCOM
Also Called: Cal Printing
2300 Stevens Creek Blvd, San Jose
(95128-1650)
PHONE...............................408 436-7574
Shawn Malakiman, *President*
Manuela Malakiman, *Treasurer*
EMP: 16
SQ FT: 10,000
SALES (est): 2.7MM **Privately Held**
SIC: 2752 7374 Commercial printing, offset; computer graphics service; optical scanning data service

(P-6826)
FPC GRAPHICS INC
2682 Market St, Riverside (92501-2126)
P.O. Box 192 (92502-0192)
PHONE...............................951 686-0232
Michael S Vaughan, *President*
EMP: 35 EST: 1955
SQ FT: 35,000
SALES (est): 4.3MM **Privately Held**
WEB: www.fpcgraphics.com
SIC: 2752 7336 7311 2791 Commercial printing, offset; commercial art & graphic design; advertising agencies; typesetting

(P-6827)
FRICKE-PARKS PRESS INC
Also Called: F-P Press
33250 Transit Ave, Union City
(94587-2035)
PHONE...............................510 489-6543
Robert C Parks, *Ch of Bd*
David Brown, *President*
Patti Parks, *Vice Pres*
Lupe Girgis, *Human Resources*
EMP: 60
SQ FT: 50,000
SALES (est): 11.9MM **Privately Held**
WEB: www.fricke-parks.com
SIC: 2752 Commercial printing, offset

(P-6828)
FRUITRIDGE PRTG LITHOGRAPH INC (PA)
3258 Stockton Blvd, Sacramento
(95820-1418)
PHONE...............................916 452-9213
Susan Hausmann, *President*
Karen Young, *Vice Pres*
EMP: 39 EST: 1965
SQ FT: 28,500
SALES (est): 7.6MM **Privately Held**
WEB: www.fruitridge.com
SIC: 2752 2796 Color lithography; platemaking services

(P-6829)
FULL COLOR BUSINESS
Also Called: Full Color Bus Cds & Flyers
2620 El Camino Ave, Sacramento
(95821-5902)
PHONE...............................916 218-7845
William Lewis, *Owner*
EMP: 10
SALES (est): 1.6MM **Privately Held**
SIC: 2752 Business form & card printing, lithographic

(P-6830)
FULLERTON PRINTING INC
Also Called: Bixby Knolls Prtg & Graphics
315 N Lemon St, Fullerton (92832-2030)
PHONE...............................714 870-7500
Donald Moreland, *President*
Bryan D Moreland, *Officer*
EMP: 12
SQ FT: 3,737
SALES (est): 1.3MM **Privately Held**
WEB: www.fullertonprinting.com
SIC: 2752 Commercial printing, offset

(P-6831)
GENESIS PRINTING
5872 W Pico Blvd, Los Angeles
(90019-3715)
PHONE...............................323 965-7935

(PA)=Parent Co (HQ)=Headquarters (DH)=Div Headquarters
✿ = New Business established in last 2 years

Liborio Lozano, *Owner*
EMP: 15
SQ FT: 6,864
SALES (est): 1.4MM **Privately Held**
SIC: 2752 Commercial printing, offset

(P-6832)
GEORGE CORIATY
Also Called: Sir Speedy
7240 Greenleaf Ave, Whittier (90602-1312)
PHONE..................................562 698-7513
George Coriaty, *Owner*
Dustin Speakman, *Sales Staff*
EMP: 32
SQ FT: 12,000
SALES: 12.4MM **Privately Held**
WEB: www.sswhittier.com
SIC: 2752 7334 Commercial printing, off-
set; photocopying & duplicating services

(P-6833)
GIANT HORSE PRINTING INC
1336 San Mateo Ave, South San Francisco
(94080-6501)
PHONE..................................650 875-7137
Steve MA, *President*
EMP: 15
SQ FT: 15,000
SALES (est): 1.9MM **Privately Held**
WEB: www.gianthorse.com
SIC: 2752 2732 2791 Commercial print-
ing, offset; books: printing only; typo-
graphic composition, for the printing trade

(P-6834)
**GLENDALE ROTARY OFFSET
PRTG CO (PA)**
Also Called: B J'S Printing Emporium
434 Fernando Ct, Glendale (91204-2724)
P.O. Box 2694, Ventura (93002-2694)
PHONE..................................818 548-1847
Robert G Deal, *President*
Gerald L Deal, *Treasurer*
Gerald DEA, *Treasurer*
Gerald L Bir, *Vice Pres*
EMP: 30
SQ FT: 12,000
SALES (est): 6.2MM **Privately Held**
WEB: www.bjsprinting.com
SIC: 2752 Commercial printing, offset

(P-6835)
GOLDEN COLOR PRINTING INC
9353 Rush St, South El Monte
(91733-2544)
PHONE..................................626 455-0850
Deng-Muh Yen, *President*
EMP: 21
SQ FT: 11,000
SALES (est): 3.5MM **Privately Held**
SIC: 2752 Color lithography

(P-6836)
GOLDEN GATE LITHO
11144 Golf Links Rd, Oakland
(94605-5799)
PHONE..................................510 568-5335
Don Asher, *President*
Scott Stanko, *Business Dir*
EMP: 10
SQ FT: 13,000
SALES: 1.3MM **Privately Held**
WEB: www.goldengatelitho.com
SIC: 2752 Cards, lithographed; commercial
printing, offset

(P-6837)
GRAPHIC COLOR SYSTEMS INC
Also Called: Continental Colorcraft
1166 W Garvey Ave, Monterey Park
(91754-2511)
PHONE..................................323 283-3000
Andy Scheidegger, *President*
Maria Donhauser, *Treasurer*
Linda Clarke, *Vice Pres*
Dale Drake, *VP Opers*
Eric Osborn, *Opers Mgr*
EMP: 52
SQ FT: 28,000
SALES (est): 13MM **Privately Held**
WEB: www.continentalcolorcraft.com
SIC: 2752 2796 2791 2759 Commercial
printing, offset; color separations for print-
ing; typesetting; commercial printing

(P-6838)
GRAPHIC FOX INC
3124 Thorntree Dr, Chico (95973-9068)
PHONE..................................530 895-1359
Larry Laney, *President*
Michael Ritsch, *Sales Mgr*
EMP: 14
SQ FT: 5,000
SALES (est): 1.9MM **Privately Held**
SIC: 2752 Commercial printing, offset

(P-6839)
GRAPHIC VISIONS INC
7119 Fair Ave, North Hollywood
(91605-6304)
PHONE..................................818 845-8393
Randall Avazian, *CEO*
Kenneth Langer, *President*
Steven Milne, *Sales Mgr*
▲ **EMP:** 23
SALES (est): 5.7MM **Privately Held**
SIC: 2752 Commercial printing, offset

(P-6840)
GRAPHIX PRESS INC
13814 Del Sur St, San Fernando
(91340-3440)
PHONE..................................818 834-8520
Steve Reder, *President*
James Cohen, *Exec VP*
EMP: 50
SQ FT: 35,000
SALES (est): 5.2MM **Privately Held**
SIC: 2752 Commercial printing, litho-
graphic

(P-6841)
GRIFFITHS SERVICES INC
Also Called: Griffiths Printing
121 S Old Springs Rd, Anaheim
(92808-1247)
PHONE..................................714 685-7700
Ron Griffith, *President*
Allison Griffiths, *Opers Mgr*
Evan Brown, *Plant Mgr*
EMP: 30
SQ FT: 6,600
SALES (est): 4MM **Privately Held**
SIC: 2752 Commercial printing, offset

(P-6842)
GSG LLC (PA)
Also Called: Golden State Graphics
177 Vallecitos De Oro, San Marcos
(92069-1436)
PHONE..................................760 752-9500
Alan Katz,
David Hyman, *CFO*
Lori Spucces, *Executive*
Deborah Allen, *Technology*
Joe Geimer, *Plant Mgr*
▲ **EMP:** 32 **EST:** 2000
SQ FT: 24,000
SALES (est): 4.9MM **Privately Held**
WEB: www.goldenstategraphics.com
SIC: 2752 Commercial printing, offset

(P-6843)
GSL FINE LITHOGRAPHERS
8386 Rovana Cir, Sacramento
(95828-2527)
PHONE..................................916 231-1410
Joe R Davis, *Ch of Bd*
Darian Koberl, *President*
Chanel Decker, *Principal*
Donna Oakley, *Planning Mgr*
EMP: 38
SQ FT: 24,000
SALES: 6.1MM
SALES (corp-wide): 6.9B **Publicly Held**
WEB: www.gslitho.com
SIC: 2752 Commercial printing, offset
HQ: Consolidated Graphics, Inc.
5858 Westheimer Rd # 400
Houston TX 77057
713 787-0977

(P-6844)
GUEST CHEX INC
Also Called: Guestchex
7697 9th St, Buena Park (90621-2898)
PHONE..................................714 522-1860
EMP: 10
SALES (est): 840K **Privately Held**
SIC: 2752

(P-6845)
H J S GRAPHICS
Also Called: Printing Connection , The
6825 Valjean Ave, Van Nuys (91406-4713)
PHONE..................................818 782-5490
Henry Steenackers, *President*
Erik Steenackers, *Technology*
EMP: 15
SQ FT: 6,000
SALES (est): 2.9MM **Privately Held**
WEB: www.printcnx.net
SIC: 2752 Commercial printing, offset

(P-6846)
H&H IMAGING INC
Also Called: H&H Platemakers
375 Alabama St Ste 150, San Francisco
(94110-7333)
PHONE..................................415 431-4731
Kenneth Mitchell, *President*
EMP: 10 **EST:** 1964
SQ FT: 10,000
SALES (est): 2MM **Privately Held**
SIC: 2752 Commercial printing, offset

(P-6847)
HALL LETTER SHOP INC
5200 Rosedale Hwy, Bakersfield
(93308-6000)
PHONE..................................661 327-3228
Catherine A Dounies, *President*
Greg Dounies, *General Mgr*
EMP: 13
SALES (est): 1.3MM **Privately Held**
WEB: www.hallprintmail.com
SIC: 2752 7331 2791 2789 Commercial
printing, offset; mailing service; typeset-
ting, computer controlled; binding only:
books, pamphlets, magazines, etc.

(P-6848)
HANDBILL PRINTERS LP
820 E Parkridge Ave, Corona (92879-6611)
PHONE..................................951 547-5910
Don J Messick, *President*
Dane Messick, *Partner*
Kenneth Messick, *Partner*
Mark Messick, *Partner*
Michael Messick, *Partner*
EMP: 45
SQ FT: 62,500
SALES (est): 31.4MM **Privately Held**
WEB: www.hbprinters.com
SIC: 2752 7336 Commercial printing, off-
set; graphic arts & related design

(P-6849)
HARMAN PRESS
Also Called: Harman Envelopes
6840 Vineland Ave, North Hollywood
(91605-6409)
PHONE..................................818 432-0570
Jay Goldner, *President*
Phillip Goldner, *Vice Pres*
Deborah Goldner-Watson, *Admin Sec*
Nicole Palmquist, *Project Mgr*
David Wardlow, *Marketing Staff*
EMP: 38 **EST:** 1963
SQ FT: 10,000
SALES (est): 10.6MM **Privately Held**
WEB: www.harmanpress.com
SIC: 2752 Lithographing on metal

(P-6850)
HAVANA GRAPHIC CENTER INC
Also Called: Zada International Printing
301 S Flower St, Burbank (91502-2104)
PHONE..................................818 841-3774
George Zada, *CEO*
Kenarique Zada, *Treasurer*
Shaunt Berberian, *Art Dir*
EMP: 20
SQ FT: 14,770
SALES (est): 2.8MM **Privately Held**
SIC: 2752 2759 Lithographing on metal;
flexographic printing

(P-6851)
HELENS PLACE INC
Also Called: Printing Rsources Southern Cal
893 W 9th St, Upland (91786-4541)
PHONE..................................909 981-5715
Nancy De Diemar Jones, *President*
Patrick C Jones, *Corp Secy*
James Dilonardo, *Manager*
EMP: 15

SQ FT: 5,400
SALES (est): 2MM **Privately Held**
WEB: www.printingresources.com
SIC: 2752 7331 Commercial printing, off-
set; mailing service

(P-6852)
HENRY L HUDSON (PA)
Also Called: Graphic Systems
403 N G St, Lompoc (93436-5317)
PHONE..................................805 736-2737
Henry L Hudson, *Owner*
Ryan Bruemmer, *Department Mgr*
Michael Hudson, *Systems Staff*
EMP: 12
SQ FT: 3,200
SALES (est): 1.4MM **Privately Held**
WEB: www.gsprinters.com
SIC: 2752 2791 7334 Commercial print-
ing, offset; typesetting; blueprinting serv-
ice

(P-6853)
HERALD PRINTING LTD (PA)
1242 Los Angeles Ave, Ventura
(93004-1920)
PHONE..................................805 647-1870
Eric Linquist, *President*
Cathy Linquist, *Corp Secy*
EMP: 10
SQ FT: 1,500
SALES (est): 1.3MM **Privately Held**
WEB: www.heraldprinting.net
SIC: 2752 Commercial printing, offset;
color lithography

(P-6854)
**HERDELL PRINTING &
LITHOGRAPHY**
340 Mccormick St, Saint Helena
(94574-1457)
P.O. Box 72 (94574-0072)
PHONE..................................707 963-3634
Michael Herdell, *President*
Patricia A Herdell, *Admin Sec*
Patty Ditomaso, *Controller*
EMP: 26
SQ FT: 22,200
SALES (est): 6.1MM **Privately Held**
SIC: 2752 Commercial printing, offset; lith-
ographing on metal

(P-6855)
HERITAGE PAPER CO
17740 Shideler Pkwy, Lathrop
(95330-9356)
PHONE..................................925 449-1148
EMP: 13
SALES (est): 1.7MM **Privately Held**
SIC: 2752 Commercial printing, litho-
graphic

(P-6856)
**HERRICK RETAIL
CORPORATION TH**
Also Called: AlphaGraphics
2923 Saturn St Ste D, Brea (92821-6260)
PHONE..................................714 256-9543
Bill Herrik, *Owner*
Janet Herrik, *Co-Owner*
EMP: 10
SALES (est): 851.2K **Privately Held**
SIC: 2752 Commercial printing, offset

(P-6857)
HI REZ DIGITAL SOLUTIONS
1235 Activity Dr Ste E, Vista (92081-8562)
PHONE..................................760 597-2650
Drew Hendricks, *Owner*
Jonathan Connelly, *Prdtn Mgr*
EMP: 10
SQ FT: 2,900
SALES (est): 580K **Privately Held**
WEB: www.hirezdigital.com
SIC: 2752 Commercial printing, offset

(P-6858)
HIGH FIVE INC
Also Called: Printech
1452 Manhattan Ave, Fullerton
(92831-5222)
PHONE..................................714 847-2200
Steve Kramer, *President*
Alan Kramer, *CFO*
Katherine Kramer, *Corp Secy*
Tina Kramer, *Office Mgr*

▼ **EMP:** 27
SQ FT: 12,800
SALES (est): 4.9MM **Privately Held**
WEB: www.printechusa.com
SIC: 2752 Commercial printing, offset

(P-6859)
HILLIS PRINTING CO INC
525 Parrott St, San Jose (95112-4121)
PHONE..................................408 450-7910
Charles B Hillis II, *President*
EMP: 13 **EST:** 1901
SQ FT: 10,000
SALES: 2MM **Privately Held**
WEB: www.hillisprinting.com
SIC: 2752 Commercial printing, lithographic

(P-6860)
HNC PRINTING SERVICES LLC
Also Called: Business Point Impressions
5125 Port Chicago Hwy, Concord
(94520-1216)
PHONE..................................925 689-1716
EMP: 17
SALES (est): 1.5MM **Privately Held**
SIC: 2752

(P-6861)
HO TAI PRINTING CO INC
Also Called: Ho Tai Printing & Book Store
723 Clay St Ste 725, San Francisco
(94108-1802)
PHONE..................................415 421-4218
Tak Pui TSE, *President*
Christy Ng, *Admin Sec*
▲ **EMP:** 10 **EST:** 1974
SQ FT: 1,000
SALES (est): 1MM **Privately Held**
SIC: 2752 5942 5943 Commercial printing, offset; book stores; stationery stores

(P-6862)
HOUSE OF PRINT & COPY
1501 E Main St, Grass Valley
(95945-5229)
PHONE..................................530 273-1000
Patti Ferree, *Owner*
EMP: 11
SQ FT: 2,000
SALES (est): 1.5MM **Privately Held**
SIC: 2752 7334 Commercial printing, offset; photocopying & duplicating services

(P-6863)
HOUSE OF PRINTING INC
3336 E Colorado Blvd, Pasadena
(91107-3885)
PHONE..................................626 793-7034
Eugene F Pittroff Sr, *President*
Marguerite Pittroff, *Treasurer*
Walter E Pittroff, *Vice Pres*
Edna Pittroff, *Admin Sec*
EMP: 22
SQ FT: 6,500
SALES (est): 3MM **Privately Held**
SIC: 2752 2791 2789 Commercial printing, offset; typesetting; bookbinding & related work

(P-6864)
HUNTFORD PRINTING
Also Called: Huntford Printing & Graphics
275 Dempsey Rd, Milpitas (95035-5556)
PHONE..................................408 957-5000
George Loughborough, *President*
Charles H Loughborough, *Vice Pres*
Larry Nadeau, *Admin Sec*
EMP: 24
SQ FT: 10,000
SALES: 3.5MM **Privately Held**
WEB: www.huntford.com
SIC: 2752 Commercial printing, offset

(P-6865)
HYDE PRINTING AND GRAPHICS
2748 Willow Pass Rd, Concord
(94519-2546)
PHONE..................................925 686-4933
Patrick Hyde, *President*
AVI Ben-ARI, *Vice Pres*
Heidi Cheary, *Office Mgr*
Craig Levine, *Sales Mgr*
EMP: 12
SQ FT: 6,000

SALES (est): 1.4MM **Privately Held**
WEB: www.hydeprinting.com
SIC: 2752 Commercial printing, offset

(P-6866)
I COLOR PRINTING & MAILING INC
1450 W 228th St Ste 12, Torrance
(90501-5081)
PHONE..................................310 947-1452
Sameer Khan, *Branch Mgr*
EMP: 10 **Privately Held**
SIC: 2752 Commercial printing, offset
PA: I Color Printing & Mailing Inc.
13000 S Broadway
Los Angeles CA 90061

(P-6867)
I COLOR PRINTING & MAILING INC (PA)
Also Called: Icolorprinting.net
13000 S Broadway, Los Angeles
(90061-1120)
PHONE..................................310 997-1452
Mohammed Adil Khan, *CEO*
EMP: 10
SALES (est): 4.3MM **Privately Held**
SIC: 2752 Commercial printing, offset

(P-6868)
ICLAVIS LLC
8222 Allport Ave, Santa Fe Springs
(90670-2106)
PHONE..................................310 503-6847
David Chavez, *Principal*
EMP: 10 **EST:** 2014
SQ FT: 20,000
SALES (est): 580.1K **Privately Held**
SIC: 2752 Tag, ticket & schedule printing: lithographic

(P-6869)
IDEA PRINTING & GRAPHICS INC
1921 E Main St, Visalia (93292-6714)
PHONE..................................559 733-4149
James Laber, *President*
Beckie Boswell, *Graphic Designe*
Ruby Laber, *Cust Mgr*
EMP: 11
SQ FT: 8,000
SALES (est): 1.7MM **Privately Held**
WEB: www.ideaprinting.net
SIC: 2752 7334 Commercial printing, offset; photocopying & duplicating services

(P-6870)
IDEAL GRAPHICS INC
1458 N Hundley St, Anaheim (92806-1322)
PHONE..................................714 632-3398
Patric Fung, *President*
Frank Liang, *Vice Pres*
EMP: 17
SQ FT: 7,500
SALES (est): 2.2MM **Privately Held**
SIC: 2752 Offset & photolithographic printing

(P-6871)
IDEAL PRINTING CO INC
17855 Maclaren St, City of Industry
(91744-5799)
PHONE..................................626 964-2019
Richard Mancino, *President*
Yolanda Mancino, *Vice Pres*
Bob James, *Prdtn Mgr*
Joey Tosta, *Sales Staff*
EMP: 20
SQ FT: 30,000
SALES (est): 2.5MM **Privately Held**
WEB: www.idealprintingcompany.com
SIC: 2752 Commercial printing, offset

(P-6872)
IMAGE DISTRIBUTION SERVICES
3191 W Temple Ave Ste 180, Pomona
(91768-3254)
PHONE..................................909 599-7680
EMP: 16
SALES (corp-wide): 8.1MM **Privately Held**
SIC: 2752 Commercial printing, offset

PA: Image Distribution Services Inc
60 Bunsen
Irvine CA 92618
949 754-9000

(P-6873)
IMAGE DISTRIBUTION SERVICES (PA)
Also Called: Image Printing Solutions
60 Bunsen, Irvine (92618-4210)
PHONE..................................949 754-9000
Joe Fries, *CEO*
William Kaszton, *President*
Chris Paul, *CFO*
Ron Smith, *Opers Staff*
EMP: 48
SQ FT: 15,000
SALES (est): 8.1MM **Privately Held**
SIC: 2752 5943 Commercial printing, offset; office forms & supplies

(P-6874)
IMAGEMOVER INC
10051 Bradley Ave, Pacoima (91331-2202)
PHONE..................................818 485-8840
Ben Taylor, *President*
EMP: 17
SALES (est): 3.1MM **Privately Held**
SIC: 2752 Commercial printing, lithographic

(P-6875)
IMAGEX INC
5990 Stoneridge Dr # 112, Pleasanton
(94588-4517)
PHONE..................................925 474-8100
Stan Poitras, *President*
Karen Merrigan, *Business Dir*
Cindy Knabe, *Info Tech Mgr*
Glen Douglas, *Manager*
Kaitlyn Camargo, *Accounts Exec*
EMP: 17
SALES (est): 3.3MM **Privately Held**
SIC: 2752 Commercial printing, offset; advertising posters, lithographed; business form & card printing, lithographic

(P-6876)
IMPERIAL PRINTERS INC (PA)
Also Called: Imperial Printers Rocket Copy
430 W Main St, El Centro (92243-3019)
PHONE..................................760 352-4374
Rudy Rodrguegos, *President*
Rodolfo Rodriguez, *Vice Pres*
Marvin Wieben Jr, *Vice Pres*
Manuel Perez, *Plant Mgr*
EMP: 18
SQ FT: 8,725
SALES (est): 2MM **Privately Held**
WEB: www.imperialprinters.com
SIC: 2752 2796 Commercial printing, offset; letterpress plates, preparation of

(P-6877)
IMPRESS COMMUNICATIONS INC
9320 Lurline Ave, Chatsworth
(91311-6041)
PHONE..................................818 701-8800
Paul Marino, *President*
Stefanie Cogger, *Executive Asst*
Jeff Park, *Info Tech Mgr*
Toba Oluyide, *Technology*
Any Tosounian, *Controller*
▲ **EMP:** 92
SQ FT: 50,000
SALES: 15MM **Privately Held**
WEB: www.impress1.com
SIC: 2752 7336 7319 Commercial printing, offset; commercial art & graphic design; display advertising service

(P-6878)
IN TO INK
6959 Colorado Ave, La Mesa (91942-1107)
PHONE..................................858 271-6363
Larry Pyle, *Partner*
Theresa Pyle, *Partner*
EMP: 12
SQ FT: 3,250
SALES (est): 1.7MM **Privately Held**
WEB: www.intoink.com
SIC: 2752 Commercial printing, offset

(P-6879)
INDEPENDENT PRINTING CO INC (PA)
Also Called: Ipco Printing
1530 Franklin Canyon Rd, Martinez
(94553-9607)
PHONE..................................925 229-5050
Kurt Brombacher, *President*
Lisa Brombacher, *Admin Sec*
Lisa Olson, *Admin Sec*
Linda Peterson, *Manager*
EMP: 40 **EST:** 1910
SQ FT: 7,000
SALES (est): 5.5MM **Privately Held**
SIC: 2752 Commercial printing, offset

(P-6880)
INDUSTRY COLOR PRINTING INC
11642 Washington Blvd, Whittier
(90606-2425)
PHONE..................................626 961-2403
Rafael Osorio, *President*
Miriam Osorio, *Treasurer*
EMP: 20
SALES (est): 2MM **Privately Held**
WEB: www.icpprint.com
SIC: 2752 Commercial printing, offset

(P-6881)
INK & COLOR INC
Also Called: Acuprint
5920 Bowcroft St, Los Angeles
(90016-4302)
PHONE..................................310 280-6060
Saman Sowlaty, *CEO*
Mojgan Sowalty, *Vice Pres*
Cris Zabka, *Marketing Staff*
Rafael Medina, *Sales Staff*
Fletcher Anduiza,
▲ **EMP:** 30
SQ FT: 17,000
SALES (est): 6.2MM **Privately Held**
WEB: www.acuprint.net
SIC: 2752 Commercial printing, offset

(P-6882)
INK SPOT INC
9737 Bell Ranch Dr, Santa Fe Springs
(90670-2951)
PHONE..................................626 338-4500
Somsak Reuanglith, *CEO*
Mark Diaz, *Controller*
EMP: 26
SALES (est): 4.8MM **Privately Held**
SIC: 2752 Commercial printing, offset

(P-6883)
INKOVATION INC (PA)
13659 Excelsior Dr, Santa Fe Springs
(90670-5103)
PHONE..................................800 465-4174
Janak Savaliya, *President*
Carl Friesen, *Project Mgr*
EMP: 22
SALES (est): 5.6MM **Privately Held**
SIC: 2752 Commercial printing, offset

(P-6884)
INKOVATION INC
14906 Spring Ave, Santa Fe Springs
(90670-5112)
PHONE..................................800 465-4174
Janak Savaliya, *Branch Mgr*
EMP: 26
SALES (corp-wide): 5.6MM **Privately Held**
SIC: 2752 Commercial printing, lithographic
PA: Inkovation, Inc.
13659 Excelsior Dr
Santa Fe Springs CA 90670
800 465-4174

(P-6885)
INKWRIGHT LLC
5822 Research Dr, Huntington Beach
(92649-1348)
PHONE..................................714 892-3300
Danny Nichols, *Principal*
EMP: 30
SALES (est): 6.1MM **Privately Held**
SIC: 2752 Offset & photolithographic printing

(P-6886)
INLAND LITHO LLC
Also Called: Inland Group
4305 E La Palma Ave, Anaheim
(92807-1843)
PHONE.................714 993-6000
Steve Urbanovitch, *Marketing Mgr*
Kathy Urbanovitch,
EMP: 60
SQ FT: 40,000
SALES (est): 19.3MM **Privately Held**
SIC: 2752 Lithographing on metal

(P-6887)
INLAND MAILING SERVICES INC
Also Called: Advanced Mktg Print & Mail
160 W Fthill Pkwy Ste 105, Corona
(92882)
PHONE.................951 371-6245
Phillip K Adishian, *President*
Michelle Adishian, *Vice Pres*
EMP: 60
SQ FT: 38,500
SALES (est): 6.4MM **Privately Held**
WEB: www.ampm2.com
SIC: 2752 7331 Commercial printing, lithographic; direct mail advertising services

(P-6888)
INSTANT IMPRINTS FRANCHISING
6615 Flanders Dr Ste B, San Diego
(92121-2963)
PHONE.................858 642-4848
Leo Kats, *President*
Lev Kats, *CEO*
EMP: 22
SQ FT: 20,000
SALES (est): 2.4MM **Privately Held**
SIC: 2752 Commercial printing, lithographic

(P-6889)
INSTANT WEB LLC
Also Called: Iwco Direct - Downey
7300 Flores St, Downey (90242-4010)
PHONE.................562 658-2020
Jake Hertel, *Branch Mgr*
EMP: 240
SALES (corp-wide): 436.6MM **Publicly Held**
SIC: 2752 Commercial printing, lithographic
HQ: Instant Web, Llc
7951 Powers Blvd
Chanhassen MN 55317
952 474-0961

(P-6890)
INSUA GRAPHICS INCORPORATED
9121 Glenoaks Blvd, Sun Valley
(91352-2612)
PHONE.................818 767-7007
Jose Miguel Insua, *CEO*
Albert Insua, *Treasurer*
Eric Insua, *Vice Pres*
▲ EMP: 35
SQ FT: 28,000
SALES (est): 7MM **Privately Held**
SIC: 2752 Commercial printing, offset

(P-6891)
INTEGRATED COMMUNICATIONS INC
1411 W 190th St Ste 110, Gardena
(90248-4370)
PHONE.................310 851-8066
Peter Levshin, *CEO*
David Humphrey, *President*
▲ EMP: 24
SQ FT: 5,000
SALES: 4.1MM **Privately Held**
WEB: www.icla.com
SIC: 2752 Commercial printing, lithographic

(P-6892)
INTELICARE DIRECT INC
Also Called: Instant Checkmate
9596 Chesapeake Dr Ste A, San Diego
(92123-1346)
PHONE.................702 765-0867
Kristian Kibak, *CEO*

Katharine Payne, *Info Tech Mgr*
Karen Horais, *Finance Mgr*
Brandon Wright, *Mng Member*
EMP: 17 EST: 2014
SALES (est): 3.6MM **Privately Held**
SIC: 2752 Commercial printing, lithographic

(P-6893)
INTER-CITY PRINTING CO INC
Also Called: Madison Street Press
614 Madison St, Oakland (94607-4726)
PHONE.................510 451-4775
Paul Murai, *President*
Miok Murai, *Admin Sec*
Marlene Cornelius, *VP Sales*
Christopher Dougherty, *Marketing Mgr*
Diane Duppman, *Consultant*
EMP: 17
SQ FT: 6,500
SALES (est): 3.9MM **Privately Held**
WEB: www.madison-st-press.com
SIC: 2752 Commercial printing, offset

(P-6894)
INTERLINK INC
Also Called: Precision Plastics Printing
3845 E Coronado St, Anaheim
(92807-1649)
PHONE.................714 905-7700
Bob Bhagat, *President*
Hathin Bhagat, *Principal*
▲ EMP: 85
SQ FT: 50,000
SALES (est): 20MM **Privately Held**
SIC: 2752 Commercial printing, lithographic

(P-6895)
INTERNATIONAL PRINTING & TYPSG
14535 Hamlin St, Van Nuys (91411-1608)
PHONE.................818 787-6804
Todd M Wallace, *President*
Joyce Wallace, *CFO*
EMP: 15
SQ FT: 3,000
SALES (est): 1.2MM **Privately Held**
SIC: 2752 2791 Commercial printing, offset; typesetting, computer controlled

(P-6896)
IPS PRINTING INC
2020 K St, Sacramento (95811-4217)
PHONE.................916 442-8961
Richard Peterson, *President*
Ken Peterson, *Vice Pres*
EMP: 31
SQ FT: 9,000
SALES (est): 3.9MM **Privately Held**
SIC: 2752 2791 Photolithographic printing; typesetting

(P-6897)
ISLAND COLOR INC
3972 Barranca Pkwy J521, Irvine
(92606-1204)
PHONE.................714 352-5888
David E Pauley, *President*
EMP: 10
SALES (est): 1.2MM **Privately Held**
SIC: 2752 Commercial printing, lithographic

(P-6898)
J & D BUSINESS FORMS INC
Also Called: JD Printing and Mailing
650 W Terrace Dr, San Dimas
(91773-2908)
PHONE.................626 914-1777
John Longtin, *CEO*
EMP: 11
SQ FT: 20,000
SALES (est): 1.5MM **Privately Held**
SIC: 2752 3577

(P-6899)
J & K RESOURCES INC
Also Called: Metro Print
5205 E Ocean Blvd Apt 10, Long Beach
(90803-6920)
PHONE.................503 252-4009
Jeff Seid, *President*
Kim Seid, *Vice Pres*
EMP: 20

SALES (est): 2.8MM **Privately Held**
WEB: www.metroprint.net
SIC: 2752 2791 Commercial printing, offset; typesetting

(P-6900)
J & M PRINTING INC
Also Called: River City Lithography
4321 Anthony Ct Ste 1, Rocklin
(95677-2150)
PHONE.................916 652-4600
William Utley, *President*
Joan Michael, *Vice Pres*
EMP: 10
SQ FT: 2,000
SALES (est): 1.7MM **Privately Held**
WEB: www.jandm-printing.com
SIC: 2752 Lithographing on metal; commercial printing, offset

(P-6901)
J E J PRINT INC
673 Monterey Pass Rd, Monterey Park
(91754-2418)
PHONE.................626 281-8989
Catherine Shih, *Manager*
EMP: 18
SALES (est): 1.8MM **Privately Held**
SIC: 2752 Commercial printing, lithographic

(P-6902)
J R RAPID PRINT INC
909 S Cucamonga Ave # 104, Ontario
(91761-1973)
PHONE.................909 947-4868
Rita Wong, *President*
EMP: 10
SQ FT: 1,200
SALES (est): 1.4MM **Privately Held**
SIC: 2752 Commercial printing, offset

(P-6903)
J S M PRODUCTIONS INC
Also Called: PIP Printing
537 E Florida Ave, Hemet (92543-4333)
PHONE.................951 929-5771
John E Mullany, *President*
EMP: 13
SQ FT: 3,500
SALES (est): 2MM **Privately Held**
SIC: 2752 Commercial printing, offset

(P-6904)
J&L PRESS INC (PA)
1218 W 163rd St, Gardena (90247-4432)
PHONE.................818 549-8344
Mark Iwakiri, *CEO*
John Iwakiri, *Vice Pres*
EMP: 15
SQ FT: 6,700
SALES (est): 2.2MM **Privately Held**
SIC: 2752 Commercial printing, offset

(P-6905)
JA FERRARI PRINT IMAGING LLC
Also Called: Allegra Print & Imaging
7515 Metro Dr Ste 405, San Diego (92108)
PHONE.................619 295-8307
John Ferrari, *Mng Member*
EMP: 15
SALES (est): 2.3MM **Privately Held**
SIC: 2752 Commercial printing, offset

(P-6906)
JAMES GANG CUSTOM PRINTING
Also Called: James Gang Graphics & Printing
4851 Newport Ave, San Diego
(92107-3110)
PHONE.................619 225-1283
Pat James, *President*
EMP: 12 EST: 1964
SQ FT: 5,000
SALES (est): 1.1MM **Privately Held**
SIC: 2752 7331 Commercial printing, offset; direct mail advertising services

(P-6907)
JAPAN GRAPHICS CORP
1820 W 220th St Ste 210, Torrance
(90501-0697)
PHONE.................310 222-8639
Tai Makino, *President*

Hatsue Makino, *Vice Pres*
EMP: 21
SQ FT: 3,800
SALES (est): 2.9MM **Privately Held**
WEB: www.japangraphics.com
SIC: 2752 Commercial printing, offset

(P-6908)
JAY BREWER
Also Called: Jawen Enterprises
926 Turquoise St Ste A, San Diego
(92109-1186)
PHONE.................858 488-4871
Jay Brewer, *Owner*
EMP: 10
SQ FT: 7,780
SALES (est): 1.5MM **Privately Held**
WEB: www.jaybrewer.com
SIC: 2752 Commercial printing, offset

(P-6909)
JD BUSINESS SOLUTIONS INC
Also Called: Printing Impressions
1351 Holiday Hill Rd, Goleta (93117-1815)
PHONE.................805 962-8193
James Denion, *President*
Michael Gregory, *Principal*
Jeannine Denion, *Admin Sec*
James Capitola, *Technician*
Lori Dalton, *Sales Staff*
EMP: 20
SQ FT: 9,000
SALES (est): 3.8MM **Privately Held**
SIC: 2752 Commercial printing, offset

(P-6910)
JEB-PHI INC
Also Called: PIP Printing
10417 Lakewood Blvd, Downey
(90241-2744)
PHONE.................562 861-0863
Bruce Pansky, *President*
Belinda Pansky, *Corp Secy*
Phillip Pansky, *Vice Pres*
Landy Pansky, *Sales Mgr*
Danny Schneider, *Marketing Staff*
EMP: 22
SQ FT: 2,900
SALES (est): 3.4MM **Privately Held**
SIC: 2752 Commercial printing, offset

(P-6911)
JENSEN GRAPHICS & PRINTING
Also Called: D I Printing
18270 Spyglass Rd, Hidden Valley Lake
(95467-8655)
P.O. Box 7295, Clearlake (95422-7295)
PHONE.................707 987-8966
William Jensen, *President*
Linda Jensen, *Corp Secy*
Jack Jensen, *Vice Pres*
EMP: 10
SQ FT: 3,400
SALES (est): 932.3K **Privately Held**
SIC: 2752 Commercial printing, offset

(P-6912)
JJ LITHOGRAPHICS INC
Also Called: Jj Printing
8607 Dice Rd, Santa Fe Springs
(90670-2511)
PHONE.................562 698-0280
Shulin Chiu, *CEO*
Hung-Nan Chen, *President*
Derek Lee, *General Mgr*
Edward Chen, *Prdtn Mgr*
Leo Tsai, *Marketing Mgr*
▲ EMP: 10
SQ FT: 4,000
SALES (est): 2.2MM **Privately Held**
SIC: 2752 Commercial printing, lithographic

(P-6913)
JORLIND ENTERPRISES INC
Also Called: Kwik Kopy Printing
28570 Marguerite Pkwy # 108, Mission Viejo (92692-3713)
PHONE.................949 364-2309
David Leckness, *President*
▲ EMP: 10
SQ FT: 1,100
SALES (est): 1.4MM **Privately Held**
SIC: 2752 Commercial printing, offset

(P-6914)
JOSEF MENDELOVITZ
Also Called: Power Printing
11240 Explorer Rd, La Mesa (91941-7276)
PHONE...........................619 231-3555
Josef Mendelovitz, *Owner*
EMP: 12
SALES (est): 940K **Privately Held**
SIC: 2752 Commercial printing, lithographic

(P-6915)
JP GRAPHICS INC
3310 Woodward Ave, Santa Clara
(95054-2627)
PHONE...........................408 235-8821
Joan Escover, *CEO*
Mike Day, *Technology*
Barbara Gasman, *Graphic Designe*
Rodney Keane, *Cust Mgr*
Bill Grizzle, *Accounts Mgr*
▲ EMP: 40
SQ FT: 14,000
SALES (est): 7MM **Privately Held**
SIC: 2752 Commercial printing, offset

(P-6916)
JSL PARTNERS INC
Also Called: AlphaGraphics
1294 Anvilwood Ct, Sunnyvale
(94089-2200)
PHONE...........................408 747-9000
Jeff Lerner, *President*
Jill Learner, *Vice Pres*
Melissa Bright, *Office Mgr*
Chris Riggs, *Project Mgr*
Michael Garner, *Graphic Designe*
EMP: 12 EST: 1997
SQ FT: 7,500
SALES (est): 2.2MM **Privately Held**
SIC: 2752 Commercial printing, lithographic

(P-6917)
JUNO GRAPHICS
16334 S Avalon Blvd, Gardena
(90248-2910)
PHONE...........................310 329-0126
Chang Kim, *Owner*
▲ EMP: 14
SQ FT: 11,000
SALES (est): 1.5MM **Privately Held**
SIC: 2752 7389 Commercial printing, offset; printing broker

(P-6918)
K-1 PACKAGING GROUP
2001 W Mission Blvd, Pomona
(91766-1020)
PHONE...........................626 964-9384
EMP: 29 **Privately Held**
SIC: 2752 Offset & photolithographic printing
PA: K-1 Packaging Group
17989 Arenth Ave
City Of Industry CA 91748

(P-6919)
K-1 PACKAGING GROUP (PA)
17989 Arenth Ave, City of Industry
(91748-1126)
PHONE...........................626 964-9384
Mike Tsai, *President*
Angela Hsu, *Controller*
Frank Tsai, *Mktg Dir*
Robert Ruddell, *Sales Staff*
▲ EMP: 91
SALES (est): 19.9MM **Privately Held**
WEB: www.k1packaging.com
SIC: 2752 Offset & photolithographic printing

(P-6920)
KELMSCOTT COMMUNICATIONS LLC
Also Called: Orange County Printing
2485 Da Vinci, Irvine (92614-5844)
PHONE...........................949 475-1900
Paz Calaci, *Branch Mgr*
EMP: 11
SALES (corp-wide): 6.9B **Publicly Held**
WEB: www.ocpc.com
SIC: 2752 Commercial printing, offset

HQ: Kelmscott Communications Llc
5858 Westheimer Rd # 410
Houston TX 77057
713 787-0977

(P-6921)
KEYLINE LITHOGRAPHY INC
Also Called: Key Line Litho
1726 W 180th St, Gardena (90248-3600)
PHONE...........................310 538-8618
Danny Wong, *President*
EMP: 10
SQ FT: 4,000
SALES (est): 1.4MM **Privately Held**
WEB: www.keylinelitho.com
SIC: 2752 Commercial printing, offset

(P-6922)
KINDRED LITHO INCORPORATED
10833 Bell Ct, Rancho Cucamonga
(91730-4835)
PHONE...........................909 944-4015
Kurt Kindred, *President*
Cherie Kindred, *Admin Sec*
EMP: 13
SQ FT: 8,000
SALES (est): 2MM **Privately Held**
SIC: 2752 Commercial printing, offset

(P-6923)
KINGS PRINTING CORP
Also Called: King's Printing
5401 Linda Vista Rd # 401, San Diego
(92110-2402)
PHONE...........................619 297-6000
Sabbel Aguilar, *President*
Tony Capulong, *Treasurer*
Michael Wong, *Vice Pres*
EMP: 20
SQ FT: 5,200
SALES (est): 2.3MM **Privately Held**
SIC: 2752 Commercial printing, offset

(P-6924)
KJ AERO HOLDINGS LLC
Also Called: Pac Litho
5142 Argosy Ave, Huntington Beach
(92649-1067)
PHONE...........................714 891-6060
Jack Chalabian, *CEO*
Ronald Anderson,
EMP: 13
SALES (est): 2MM **Privately Held**
WEB: www.paclithollc.com
SIC: 2752 Commercial printing, offset

(P-6925)
KK-GRAPHICS PRINTING
1336 San Mateo Ave, South San Francisco
(94080-6501)
PHONE...........................415 468-1057
Moon MA, *Owner*
Julie MA, *Finance*
Jack Szeto, *Production*
EMP: 10 EST: 1979
SQ FT: 5,000
SALES (est): 2.6MM **Privately Held**
SIC: 2752 Commercial printing, offset

(P-6926)
KKP - ROSEVILLE INC
Also Called: Avalon Graphics
106 N Sunrise Ave Ste B2, Roseville
(95661-2915)
PHONE...........................916 786-8573
Kenneth Frank, *President*
Sandra Frank, *Vice Pres*
EMP: 12
SQ FT: 4,500
SALES (est): 2MM **Privately Held**
WEB: www.avalongraphics.com
SIC: 2752 Commercial printing, offset

(P-6927)
KM PRINTING PRODUCTION INC
218 Longden Ave, Irwindale (91706-1328)
PHONE...........................626 821-0008
Chim Moon Ming, *President*
Kerwin Ngo, *Vice Pres*
Wendy Lui, *Accounting Mgr*
EMP: 18
SQ FT: 600

SALES (est): 2.6MM **Privately Held**
WEB: www.kmppi.com
SIC: 2752 Offset & photolithographic printing

(P-6928)
KORE PRINT SOLUTIONS INC
46711 Fremont Blvd, Fremont
(94538-6539)
PHONE...........................510 445-1638
Ken Chapman, *President*
EMP: 10
SALES (est): 1.4MM **Privately Held**
SIC: 2752 Commercial printing, offset

(P-6929)
KOVIN CORPORATION INC
Also Called: Neb Cal Printing
9240 Mira Este Ct, San Diego
(92126-6336)
PHONE...........................858 558-0100
Mervin Kodesh, *President*
Sandra Kodesh, *Vice Pres*
EMP: 30
SQ FT: 10,000
SALES (est): 5.5MM **Privately Held**
WEB: www.nebcal.com
SIC: 2752 2789 Commercial printing, offset; bookbinding & related work

(P-6930)
KP LLC (PA)
13951 Washington Ave, San Leandro
(94578-3220)
PHONE...........................510 346-0729
Joe Atturio, *CEO*
Steve Bottomley, *Business Dir*
Heather Burroughs, *Program Mgr*
Darcy Fisher, *Program Mgr*
Rachel Lee, *Program Mgr*
▲ EMP: 300 EST: 1929
SQ FT: 12,000
SALES (est): 120MM **Privately Held**
WEB: www.kpcorporation.com
SIC: 2752 7334 7331 7374 Commercial printing, offset; photocopying & duplicating services; direct mail advertising services; computer graphics service; subscription fulfillment services: magazine, newspaper, etc.; marketing consulting services

(P-6931)
KP LLC
K/P Graphics-Salem Division
13951 Washington Ave, San Leandro
(94578-3220)
PHONE...........................510 346-0729
Keith Whittier, *Manager*
David Gibson, *Systems Admin*
Amee Adair, *Accounting Mgr*
EMP: 25
SALES (est): 2.1MM
SALES (corp-wide): 120MM **Privately Held**
WEB: www.kpcorporation.com
SIC: 2752 8742 7331 2796 Commercial printing, offset; management consulting services; direct mail advertising services; platemaking services; partitions & fixtures, except wood
PA: Kp Llc
13951 Washington Ave
San Leandro CA 94578
510 346-0729

(P-6932)
KYUNG IN PRINTING INC
Also Called: Printing Manufacturer
7920 Airway Rd Ste A8, San Diego
(92154-8311)
PHONE...........................619 662-3920
Sung Hwan Lee, *President*
Kay Park, *CFO*
▲ EMP: 198
SQ FT: 36,000
SALES: 33.4MM **Privately Held**
WEB: www.pl-america.com
SIC: 2752 Commercial printing, offset

(P-6933)
L & L PRINTERS CARLSBAD LLC
Also Called: Specialist Media Group
6200 Yarrow Dr, Carlsbad (92011-1537)
PHONE...........................760 438-3456

William Anderson, *President*
Frank Scorzelli, *Info Tech Mgr*
Gabrielle Hathorn, *Prdtn Mgr*
Joel Green, *Sales Executive*
EMP: 50
SALES (est): 13.6MM **Privately Held**
SIC: 2752 Commercial printing, offset

(P-6934)
L & L PRINTERS INC
6200 Yarrow Dr, Carlsbad (92011-1537)
PHONE...........................858 278-4300
William Anderson, *President*
Nancy Byron, *CFO*
Sally Anderson, *Vice Pres*
Michael Kennev, *Vice Pres*
Dirk Williams, *Vice Pres*
EMP: 13
SQ FT: 7,500
SALES (est): 3.8MM **Privately Held**
WEB: www.llprinters.com
SIC: 2752 Commercial printing, offset

(P-6935)
L T LITHO & PRINTING CO
16811 Noyes Ave, Irvine (92606-5122)
PHONE...........................949 863-1340
Fax: 949 724-0732
EMP: 26
SQ FT: 16,000
SALES (est): 4.8MM **Privately Held**
WEB: www.ltlitho.net
SIC: 2752 2759

(P-6936)
LA BROTHERS ENTERPRISE INC
Also Called: Oscar Printing
57 Columbia Sq, San Francisco
(94103-4015)
PHONE...........................415 626-8818
Jeffrey La, *President*
Steve La, *Corp Secy*
▲ EMP: 24
SQ FT: 8,000
SALES (est): 3.8MM **Privately Held**
WEB: www.oscarprinting.com
SIC: 2752 2759 Commercial printing, offset; letterpress printing

(P-6937)
LA PRINTING & GRAPHICS INC
Also Called: L A PRESS
13951 S Main St, Los Angeles
(90061-2151)
PHONE...........................310 527-4526
Kevin Sheu Chhim Kaing, *CEO*
Sheu C Kevin Kaing, *President*
Lor Yik, *Admin Sec*
EMP: 26
SQ FT: 32,000
SALES: 4.8MM **Privately Held**
SIC: 2752 Commercial printing, offset

(P-6938)
LAHLOUH INC
1649 Adrian Rd, Burlingame (94010-2103)
P.O. Box 4345 (94011-4345)
PHONE...........................650 692-6600
John Lahlouh, *President*
Fadi Lahlouh, *Vice Pres*
Michael Lahlouh, *Admin Sec*
▲ EMP: 185
SALES (est): 64MM **Privately Held**
WEB: www.colorcopyprinting.com
SIC: 2752 Commercial printing, offset

(P-6939)
LAVA PRODUCTS INC
3168 Airway Ave, Costa Mesa
(92626-4608)
PHONE...........................949 951-7191
Michael Freitas, *CEO*
David Howard, *Vice Pres*
Dean Passaglia, *Creative Dir*
Rhonda Stutz, *General Mgr*
Chris Joyce, *Sales Dir*
▲ EMP: 22
SQ FT: 13,500
SALES (est): 5.5MM **Privately Held**
WEB: www.lavaproducts.com
SIC: 2752 Commercial printing, offset

PRODUCTS & SVCS

(P-6940)
LEE AUGUSTYN INC
9390 7th St Ste A, Rancho Cucamonga
(91730-5669)
PHONE....................909 483-0688
Kevin Brown, *President*
EMP: 10 EST: 1991
SQ FT: 1,600
SALES (est): 1MM **Privately Held**
SIC: 2752 Commercial printing, lithographic

(P-6941)
LEE MAXTON INC
Also Called: Minuteman Press
10844 Edison Ct, Rancho Cucamonga
(91730-3868)
PHONE....................909 483-0688
Kevin Browm, *President*
EMP: 12
SALES (est): 1.6MM **Privately Held**
SIC: 2752 Commercial printing, lithographic

(P-6942)
LEEWOOD PRESS INC
1407 Indiana St, San Francisco
(94107-3515)
PHONE....................415 896-0513
Tom W Lee, *President*
John Villa, *Representative*
EMP: 20
SQ FT: 19,000
SALES (est): 3.9MM **Privately Held**
WEB: www.leewoodpress.com
SIC: 2752 Commercial printing, offset

(P-6943)
LEO LAM INC
Also Called: A & M Printing
3589 Nevada St Ste A, Pleasanton
(94566-6323)
PHONE....................925 484-3690
Leo Lam, *President*
Amy Chan, *CEO*
Patricia Lau, *Supervisor*
EMP: 30
SQ FT: 13,000
SALES (est): 5.9MM **Privately Held**
WEB: www.anmprinting.com
SIC: 2752 7331 2789 Commercial printing, offset; direct mail advertising services; bookbinding & related work

(P-6944)
LESTER LITHOGRAPH INC
1128 N Gilbert St, Anaheim (92801-1412)
PHONE....................714 491-3981
Robert Miller, *CEO*
Larry Lester, *COO*
Larita Miller, *CFO*
James Witt, *Vice Pres*
Georgiana Lester, *Admin Sec*
EMP: 50
SQ FT: 25,000
SALES (est): 10MM **Privately Held**
WEB: www.lesterlitho.com
SIC: 2752 Commercial printing, offset

(P-6945)
LETTERHEAD FACTORY INC
1007 E Dominguez St Ste H, Carson
(90746-7252)
PHONE....................310 538-3321
Richard W Rice, *CEO*
Jerry Loukatos, *Manager*
Jeff Prizler, *Accounts Exec*
EMP: 15
SQ FT: 5,000
SALES (est): 2.8MM **Privately Held**
WEB: www.letterheadfactory.com
SIC: 2752 Commercial printing, offset

(P-6946)
LIBERTY PRINTING INC
2601 Teepee Dr, Stockton (95205-2421)
P.O. Box 275, Clements (95227-0275)
PHONE....................209 467-8800
Dorothy Baker, *President*
Dan Mossbarger, *Vice Pres*
Jim Mossbarger, *Vice Pres*
EMP: 20
SQ FT: 40,000
SALES (est): 2.1MM **Privately Held**
WEB: www.libertyprinting.net
SIC: 2752 2789 Commercial printing, lithographic; bookbinding & related work

(P-6947)
LICHER DIRECT MAIL INC
980 Seco St, Pasadena (91103-2816)
PHONE....................626 795-3333
Wayne Licher Sr, *President*
Besse Licher, *Corp Secy*
Wayne Licher Jr, *Vice Pres*
Tony Huynh, *Prdtn Mgr*
Lupa Chang, *Advt Staff*
EMP: 20
SQ FT: 17,000
SALES (est): 3.4MM **Privately Held**
SIC: 2752 7331 Commercial printing, offset; direct mail advertising services

(P-6948)
LIGHTS FANTASTIC
Also Called: Screen Machine
2408 Lincoln Village Dr, San Jose
(95125-2741)
PHONE....................408 266-2787
Clay Wescott, *President*
EMP: 24 EST: 2003
SQ FT: 1,200
SALES: 175K **Privately Held**
SIC: 2752 1799 7389 Offset & photolithographic printing; screening contractor: window, door, etc.;

(P-6949)
LITHOGRAPH REPRODUCTIONS
4120 Martin Luther King J, Oakland
(94609-2320)
PHONE....................510 658-2367
Lance Green, *President*
Mireille Green, *Admin Sec*
EMP: 10 EST: 1947
SQ FT: 5,000
SALES: 1MM **Privately Held**
WEB: www.lithographinc.com
SIC: 2752 Commercial printing, offset

(P-6950)
LITHOGRAPHIX INC (PA)
12250 Crenshaw Blvd, Hawthorne
(90250-3332)
PHONE....................323 770-1000
Herbert Zebrack, *President*
Victor Wolfe, *CFO*
Jeffrey Zebrack, *Corp Secy*
Ariel Minguez, *Vice Pres*
Layne Morey, *Vice Pres*
▲ EMP: 305
SQ FT: 250,000
SALES (est): 117.2MM **Privately Held**
WEB: www.lithoxprep.com
SIC: 2752 2759 Commercial printing, offset; commercial printing

(P-6951)
LITHOTYPE COMPANY INC (PA)
333 Point San Bruno Blvd, South San Francisco (94080-4917)
PHONE....................650 871-1750
Aphos Ikonomou, *President*
Penelope Rich, *CEO*
Linda Sartori, *CFO*
Bob Shoreen, *Senior VP*
Greg Edwall, *Vice Pres*
▲ EMP: 65
SQ FT: 41,000
SALES: 39MM **Privately Held**
WEB: www.lithotype.com
SIC: 2752 Wrappers, lithographed

(P-6952)
LL BAKER INC
Also Called: Printing Solutions
431 N Hale Ave, Escondido (92029-1421)
PHONE....................760 741-9899
Monika Baker, *President*
Mike Baker, *Vice Pres*
EMP: 10
SQ FT: 3,000
SALES (est): 1.7MM **Privately Held**
WEB: www.printing-solutions.biz
SIC: 2752 Commercial printing, offset

(P-6953)
LOMA LINDA UNIVERSITY
Also Called: University Printing
24951 Stewart St, Loma Linda
(92350-1712)
PHONE....................909 558-4552
Jennifer Rowland, *Manager*
Billy Hughes, *Education*
EMP: 25
SALES (corp-wide): 301.3MM **Privately Held**
WEB: www.llu.edu
SIC: 2752 Commercial printing, lithographic
PA: Loma Linda University
11060 Anderson St
Loma Linda CA 92350
909 558-4540

(P-6954)
LOMBARD ENTERPRISES INC
Also Called: Lombard Graphics
3619 San Gbriel Rver Pkwy, Pico Rivera
(90660-1403)
PHONE....................562 692-7070
Stephen R Lombard, *President*
Ross Lombard, *Vice Pres*
EMP: 20
SQ FT: 10,000
SALES (est): 3.6MM **Privately Held**
WEB: www.lombardgraphics.com
SIC: 2752 Commercial printing, offset

(P-6955)
LOUIS ROESCH COMPANY
289 Foster City Blvd B, Foster City
(94404-1100)
PHONE....................650 212-2052
EMP: 10
SALES (est): 860K **Privately Held**
SIC: 2752

(P-6956)
LUCE COMMUNICATIONS LLC
Also Called: ABG Communications
3810 Wabash Dr, Mira Loma (91752-1143)
PHONE....................951 361-7404
Joel Luce, *CEO*
Dan Ablett, *President*
Vicki Ruff, *Vice Pres*
Humberto Quintanar, *Principal*
Brian Suggs, *Exec Dir*
EMP: 40
SQ FT: 50,000
SALES (est): 12.7MM **Privately Held**
WEB: www.abgonline.com
SIC: 2752 2899 4822 7331 Business forms, lithographed; ; electronic mail; mailing service

(P-6957)
MAILRITE PRINT & MAIL INC
834 Striker Ave Ste C, Sacramento
(95834-1169)
PHONE....................916 927-6245
Reimah Reinert, *CEO*
Robyn Christensen, *Administration*
Shannon Jerrett, *Project Mgr*
Richard Reed, *Accounts Exec*
EMP: 22
SQ FT: 20,000
SALES (est): 3.8MM **Privately Held**
SIC: 2752 Commercial printing, offset

(P-6958)
MAJOR FULFILLMENT INC
13707 S Figueroa St, Los Angeles
(90061-1024)
PHONE....................310 323-2326
Lewis Schuver, *President*
Alberto Rodriguez, *Plant Mgr*
EMP: 12
SQ FT: 25,000
SALES (est): 1.9MM **Privately Held**
WEB: www.majorfulfillment.com
SIC: 2752 Commercial printing, offset

(P-6959)
MAN-GROVE INDUSTRIES INC
Also Called: Lithocraft Co
1201 N Miller St, Anaheim (92806-1933)
PHONE....................714 630-3020
Bradley L Thurman, *President*
Colleen Cosgrove, *Vice Pres*
John Cosgrove, *Admin Sec*
Todd Phillips, *Information Mgr*

Patty Marshall, *Purch Mgr*
EMP: 64
SQ FT: 45,000
SALES (est): 18.5MM **Privately Held**
SIC: 2752 Commercial printing, offset

(P-6960)
MARIN COUNTY COPY SHOPS INC
Also Called: Copy Shop & Printing Co, The
901 C St, San Rafael (94901-2805)
PHONE....................415 457-5600
Richard Goldstein, *President*
Howard Goldstein, *Treasurer*
Edythe Goldstein, *Admin Sec*
EMP: 10
SQ FT: 5,000
SALES (est): 1.1MM **Privately Held**
SIC: 2752 7334 Commercial printing, offset; photocopying & duplicating services

(P-6961)
MARRS PRINTING INC
Also Called: Mars Printing and Packaging
860 Tucker Ln, City of Industry
(91789-2914)
PHONE....................909 594-9459
Walter H Marrs, *CEO*
Jackie Marrs, *Treasurer*
Teresa Grigsby, *Vice Pres*
Teresa Grisby, *Vice Pres*
Scott Marrs, *Vice Pres*
EMP: 82
SQ FT: 27,000
SALES (est): 16.9MM **Privately Held**
WEB: www.marrsprint.net
SIC: 2752 Commercial printing, offset

(P-6962)
MASKLESS LITHOGRAPHY INC
2550 Zanker Rd, San Jose (95131-1127)
P.O. Box 641537 (95164-1537)
PHONE....................408 433-1864
William D Meisburger, *President*
William Wr Elder, *CEO*
William Pappani, *CFO*
▲ EMP: 14
SALES (est): 2.1MM **Privately Held**
WEB: www.maskless.com
SIC: 2752 Commercial printing, offset

(P-6963)
MASS GROUP
Also Called: Mass Press
1959 Kingsdale Ave, Redondo Beach
(90278-3417)
PHONE....................310 214-2000
Michael Davoudian, *President*
EMP: 25
SQ FT: 4,500
SALES (est): 3.1MM **Privately Held**
WEB: www.masspress.com
SIC: 2752 Commercial printing, offset

(P-6964)
MASTER PRODUCTIONS INC
8310 Miramar Mall Ste A, San Diego
(92121-2576)
PHONE....................858 677-0037
David Ekeroth, *President*
Joy Ekeroth, *Treasurer*
George Ekeroth, *Vice Pres*
Joshua Miskovsky, *Information Mgr*
EMP: 10
SQ FT: 7,600
SALES (est): 1.4MM **Privately Held**
WEB: www.master4printing.com
SIC: 2752 Commercial printing, offset

(P-6965)
MATSUDA HOUSE PRINTING INC
Also Called: B & G House of Printing
1825 W 169th St Ste A, Gardena
(90247-5270)
PHONE....................310 532-1533
Benjamin Matsuda, *CEO*
Patsy Matsuda, *Corp Secy*
Darren Matsuda, *Vice Pres*
▲ EMP: 31
SALES (est): 5.3MM **Privately Held**
SIC: 2752 Lithographing on metal; commercial printing, offset

(P-6966)
MEGAPRINT DIGITAL PRTG CORP
1404 Old County Rd, Belmont (94002-3928)
PHONE.................................650 517-0200
Lee R Browner, *CEO*
Dick Stas, *Accountant*
EMP: 13
SALES (est): 1.9MM **Privately Held**
SIC: 2752 Commercial printing, offset

(P-6967)
MEKONG PRINTING INC
Also Called: Mk Printing
2421 W 1st St, Santa Ana (92703-3509)
PHONE.................................714 558-9595
Hoan Truong, *President*
Nancy Luu, *Vice Pres*
EMP: 22
SQ FT: 20,000
SALES (est): 3.5MM **Privately Held**
WEB: www.mekongprinting.com
SIC: 2752 Commercial printing, offset

(P-6968)
MENDOCINO LITHOGRAPHERS
Also Called: Mendo Litho
100 N Franklin St, Fort Bragg (95437-3603)
PHONE.................................707 964-0062
Phil Sharples, *Owner*
EMP: 10
SQ FT: 3,525
SALES (est): 1MM **Privately Held**
WEB: www.mendolitho.com
SIC: 2752 Commercial printing, offset

(P-6969)
MERIDIAN GRAPHICS INC
2652 Dow Ave, Tustin (92780-7208)
PHONE.................................949 833-3500
Paul Valencia, *President*
David Melin, *President*
Craig Miller, *Corp Secy*
George Mathews, *Technology*
Brian Schkeryantz, *Technology*
▲ **EMP:** 65
SQ FT: 40,000
SALES (est): 24.3MM **Privately Held**
WEB: www.mglitho.com
SIC: 2752 2759 Commercial printing, offset; letterpress printing

(P-6970)
MERILIZ INCORPORATED (PA)
Also Called: Dome Printing and Lithograph
2031 Dome Ln, McClellan (95652-2033)
PHONE.................................916 923-3663
Tim Poole, *President*
Timothy M Poole, *President*
Bob Poole, *Chief Mktg Ofcr*
Dave Baker, *Vice Pres*
Eric Carle, *Vice Pres*
EMP: 120
SQ FT: 65,000
SALES (est): 32.3MM **Privately Held**
WEB: www.domeprinting.com
SIC: 2752 Commercial printing, offset

(P-6971)
METRO DIGITAL PRINTING INC
3311 W Macarthur Blvd, Santa Ana (92704-6803)
PHONE.................................714 545-8400
Mike Jafari, *President*
Sherri Taheri, *Treasurer*
EMP: 30
SQ FT: 15,000
SALES (est): 3.6MM **Privately Held**
SIC: 2752 Commercial printing, lithographic

(P-6972)
MGX COPY (PA)
8840 Kenamar Dr Ste 405, San Diego (92121-2450)
PHONE.................................877 649-5463
Lawrence Chou, *Owner*
EMP: 15
SALES (est): 2.6MM **Privately Held**
SIC: 2752 Commercial printing, lithographic

(P-6973)
MICROPRINT INC
133 Puente Ave, City of Industry (91746-2302)
PHONE.................................626 369-1950
Stone Liu, *President*
Chung Chien Peng, *Shareholder*
Teresa Peng, *Shareholder*
TSE Hung Liu, *CEO*
Judy Cheng, *Office Mgr*
▲ **EMP:** 20
SQ FT: 10,000
SALES (est): 3.2MM **Privately Held**
SIC: 2752 Commercial printing, offset

(P-6974)
MICROSCALE INDUSTRIES INC
18435 Bandilier Cir, Fountain Valley (92708-7012)
PHONE.................................714 593-1422
David Williams, *President*
David Khai-Vu, *Info Tech Dir*
Kathy Williams, *Webmaster*
Spencer Bartsch, *Graphic Designe*
Jay Peterson, *Purchasing*
EMP: 18
SQ FT: 10,626
SALES (est): 1.4MM **Privately Held**
WEB: www.microscale.com
SIC: 2752 5945 Decals, lithographed; hobby, toy & game shops

(P-6975)
MIKE PRINTER INC
6933 Woodley Ave, Van Nuys (91406-4844)
PHONE.................................818 902-9922
Mike Domash, *President*
Roy Shirakata, *Manager*
EMP: 10
SQ FT: 12,000
SALES (est): 1.5MM **Privately Held**
WEB: www.miketheprinter.com
SIC: 2752 Commercial printing, offset

(P-6976)
MINUTE MAN ENVMTL SYSTEMS INC
830 W 16th St, Costa Mesa (92627-4331)
PHONE.................................949 637-5446
John Agamalian, *President*
EMP: 21 **EST:** 2010
SALES (est): 1.6MM **Privately Held**
SIC: 2752 Commercial printing, lithographic

(P-6977)
MIR PRINTING & GRAPHICS
21333 Deering Ct, Canoga Park (91304-5018)
PHONE.................................818 313-9333
Robert Mirzakhaian, *CEO*
EMP: 10
SALES (est): 1.2MM **Privately Held**
SIC: 2752 Commercial printing, offset

(P-6978)
MOJAVE COPY & PRINTING INC
12402 Industrial Blvd E10, Victorville (92395-5875)
PHONE.................................760 241-7898
Howard Kack, *President*
EMP: 14
SQ FT: 5,500
SALES (est): 3.1MM **Privately Held**
SIC: 2752 Commercial printing, offset

(P-6979)
MOLINO COMPANY
Also Called: Melcast
13712 Alondra Blvd, Cerritos (90703-2316)
PHONE.................................323 726-1000
Melchor Castano, *President*
EMP: 85
SQ FT: 200,000
SALES (est): 13.3MM **Privately Held**
SIC: 2752 Lithographing on metal

(P-6980)
MONARCH LITHO INC (PA)
1501 Date St, Montebello (90640-6324)
PHONE.................................323 727-0300
Robert Lopez, *President*
Victor Neri, *Treasurer*
George Lopez, *Vice Pres*

Jose Badia, *General Mgr*
Mariano Balbuena, *Info Tech Dir*
EMP: 50 **EST:** 1974
SQ FT: 153,000
SALES (est): 55.5MM **Privately Held**
WEB: www.monarchlitho.com
SIC: 2752 Commercial printing, offset; advertising posters, lithographed

(P-6981)
MONTEREY GRAPHICS INC
23505 Crenshaw Blvd # 137, Torrance (90505-5225)
P.O. Box 3398 (90510-3398)
PHONE.................................310 787-3370
Larry Bird, *President*
Tami Bird, *Vice Pres*
Garrett Bird, *Sales Staff*
EMP: 10
SQ FT: 2,400
SALES (est): 3.2MM **Privately Held**
WEB: www.montereygraphics.com
SIC: 2752 7336 Commercial printing, offset; graphic arts & related design

(P-6982)
MONTEREY SIGNS INC
555 Broadway Ave, Seaside (93955-4250)
PHONE.................................831 632-0490
Shawn Adams, *President*
Anjanette Adams, *CFO*
EMP: 12
SQ FT: 28,000
SALES: 450K **Privately Held**
SIC: 2752 7389 Commercial printing, lithographic; lettering & sign painting services

(P-6983)
MONTERO PRINTING INC
Also Called: Economy Printing Service
2 Harris Ct Ste A6, Monterey (93940-7817)
PHONE.................................831 655-5511
Francisco Montero, *President*
Diane Montero, *CFO*
EMP: 20
SQ FT: 2,600
SALES (est): 800K **Privately Held**
WEB: www.economyprintingservice.com
SIC: 2752 Commercial printing, offset

(P-6984)
MOQUIN PRESS INC
555 Harbor Blvd, Belmont (94002-4020)
PHONE.................................650 592-0575
Gregory A Mocquin, *Founder*
EMP: 60
SQ FT: 22,000
SALES (est): 14.6MM **Privately Held**
WEB: www.moquinpress.com
SIC: 2752 Commercial printing, offset

(P-6985)
MULTI PACKAGING SOLUTIONS INC
1212 S Flower St Ste 100, Los Angeles (90015-2123)
PHONE.................................818 638-0216
Rick Dickson, *Vice Pres*
EMP: 35
SALES (corp-wide): 14.8B **Publicly Held**
WEB: www.ivyhill-cinram.com
SIC: 2752 Color lithography
HQ: Multi Packaging Solutions, Inc.
  150 E 52nd St Fl 28
  New York NY 10022

(P-6986)
MY SIGN DESIGN LLC
4821 Lankershim Blvd F145, North Hollywood (91601-4538)
PHONE.................................818 384-0800
Alan Nudel, *CEO*
EMP: 10
SQ FT: 25,000
SALES (est): 399.7K **Privately Held**
SIC: 2752 5999 3993 Commercial printing, offset; banners, flags, decals & posters; advertising artwork

(P-6987)
N M H INC
Also Called: MGF Graphics
19426 Londelius St, Northridge (91324-3511)
PHONE.................................818 843-8522

Michael Fitleberg, *President*
EMP: 12
SQ FT: 5,100
SALES (est): 1.4MM **Privately Held**
WEB: www.mgfgraphics.com
SIC: 2752 2791 2789 Commercial printing, offset; typesetting; bookbinding & related work

(P-6988)
NAPA PRINTING & GRAPHICS CTR (PA)
Also Called: NAPA Desktop Publishing
630 Airpark Rd Ste D, NAPA (94558-7528)
PHONE.................................707 257-6555
John Dunbar, *President*
Jeff Gerlomes, *Vice Pres*
Dennis Burdick, *Executive Asst*
Don Thiess, *Administration*
Kristi Hanan, *Sales Mgr*
▲ **EMP:** 13 **EST:** 1981
SQ FT: 4,000
SALES (est): 1.8MM **Privately Held**
WEB: www.napaprinting.com
SIC: 2752 7334 2791 7331 Commercial printing, offset; photocopying & duplicating services; typesetting; direct mail advertising services

(P-6989)
NATIONAL GRAPHICS LLC
Also Called: Jano Graphics
4893 Mcgrath St, Ventura (93003-7719)
PHONE.................................805 644-9212
Mike Scher, *President*
John Armstrong, *Administration*
Ginna Caskey, *Accounts Mgr*
Junior Gaona, *Accounts Mgr*
EMP: 40
SQ FT: 15,000
SALES (est): 9.2MM **Privately Held**
WEB: www.janographics.com
SIC: 2752 Commercial printing, offset

(P-6990)
NETWORK PRINTING & COPY CENTER
12155 Flint Pl, Poway (92064-7107)
PHONE.................................858 695-8221
Henry Cook, *Partner*
Bob Cook, *Partner*
EMP: 10
SQ FT: 5,000
SALES: 900K **Privately Held**
WEB: www.nwp1.com
SIC: 2752 7336 7334 Photo-offset printing; graphic arts & related design; photocopying & duplicating services

(P-6991)
NEWPORT MESA USD CAMPUS C
2985 Bear St, Costa Mesa (92626-4300)
PHONE.................................714 424-8939
Mellissia Christensen, *Principal*
EMP: 13 **EST:** 2013
SALES (est): 3.1MM **Privately Held**
SIC: 2752 Commercial printing, lithographic

(P-6992)
NEYENESCH PRINTERS INC
2750 Kettner Blvd, San Diego (92101-1295)
P.O. Box 81184 (92138-1184)
PHONE.................................619 297-2281
Carl A Bentley, *CEO*
Clifford Neyenesch, *Ch of Bd*
Dave Pauley, *President*
Kandy Neyenesch, *CFO*
Keith Spencer, *Director*
EMP: 70 **EST:** 1899
SQ FT: 30,000
SALES (est): 16.9MM **Privately Held**
WEB: www.neyenesch.com
SIC: 2752 Commercial printing, offset

(P-6993)
NG JOHN
Also Called: Copy Mill
780 Van Ness Ave, San Francisco (94102-3218)
PHONE.................................415 929-7188
John Ng, *Owner*
▲ **EMP:** 10

SALES (est): 1MM **Privately Held**
SIC: 2752 Commercial printing, offset

(P-6994)
NIKNEJAD INC
Also Called: Colornet
6855 Hayvenhurst Ave, Van Nuys
(91406-4718)
PHONE.....................310 478-8363
Kamran Niknejad, *President*
Sima Fouladi, *Vice Pres*
Rashid Yassamy, *Vice Pres*
EMP: 40 EST: 1981
SQ FT: 5,000
SALES (est): 7.7MM **Privately Held**
SIC: 2752 7336 2791 Commercial print-
ing, offset; graphic arts & related design;
typesetting

(P-6995)
NO BOUNDARIES INC
Also Called: Greenbox Art and Culture
789 Gateway Center Way, San Diego
(92102-4539)
PHONE.....................619 266-2349
Thomas Capp, *CEO*
Karen Capp, *Vice Pres*
Jessica Nicholson, *Graphic Designe*
▲ EMP: 50
SQ FT: 3,500
SALES (est): 9.1MM **Privately Held**
WEB: www.oopsydaisy.com
SIC: 2752 Commercial printing, offset

(P-6996)
NONSTOP PRINTING INC
6226 Santa Monica Blvd, Los Angeles
(90038-1704)
PHONE.....................323 464-1640
Kenneth Chan, *Partner*
Leiman Chan, *Manager*
EMP: 11
SQ FT: 8,000
SALES (est): 1.4MM **Privately Held**
SIC: 2752 7334 Commercial printing, off-
set; photocopying & duplicating services

(P-6997)
NORCAL PRINTING INC (PA)
1555 Yosemite Ave Ste 28, San Francisco
(94124-3272)
PHONE.....................415 282-8856
MEI Lee, *President*
Tim Anderer, *Vice Pres*
Kim Lee, *Vice Pres*
Joe Ambrus, *Sales Mgr*
▲ EMP: 13
SQ FT: 12,400
SALES (est): 1.6MM **Privately Held**
WEB: www.norcalprinting.com
SIC: 2752 Commercial printing, offset

(P-6998)
NORSAL PRINTING INC
20255 Prairie St, Chatsworth (91311-6025)
PHONE.....................818 886-4164
Salvatore Dapello, *President*
Eric Floyd, *Vice Pres*
Patricia V Dapello, *Admin Sec*
EMP: 13
SQ FT: 4,500
SALES (est): 1.4MM **Privately Held**
SIC: 2752 2759 Commercial printing, off-
set; commercial printing

(P-6999)
OAKMEAD PRTG & REPRODUCTION
233 E Weddell Dr Ste G, Sunnyvale
(94089-1659)
PHONE.....................408 734-5505
Toll Free:.....................888 -
Tony Ngo, *President*
EMP: 50
SQ FT: 2,000
SALES (est): 2.7MM **Privately Held**
WEB: www.oakmead.com
SIC: 2752 2791 Commercial printing, off-
set; typesetting, computer controlled

(P-7000)
OCPC INC
Also Called: The Orange County Printing Co
2485 Da Vinci, Irvine (92614-5844)
PHONE.....................949 475-1900
Miguel Jacobowitz, *COO*

Matt Schwartz, *Technology*
Luis Delgadillo, *Production*
Lac Pham, *Production*
John Coyle Jr, *Sales Staff*
EMP: 60
SQ FT: 18,000
SALES (est): 11.3MM **Privately Held**
SIC: 2752 Commercial printing, offset

(P-7001)
ODCOMBE PRESS (NASHVILLE)
Also Called: Haynes Publications
859 Lawrence Dr, Newbury Park
(91320-2232)
PHONE.....................615 793-5414
John H Haynes, *Ch of Bd*
▲ EMP: 30
SALES (est): 4.3MM
SALES (corp-wide): 38.1MM **Privately Held**
WEB: www.hays.plc.uk
SIC: 2752 Commercial printing, litho-
graphic
PA: Haynes Publishing Group Public Lim-
ited Company
Sparkford
Yeovil BA22
196 344-0635

(P-7002)
OKI GRAPHICS INC
2148 Zanker Rd, San Jose (95131-2113)
PHONE.....................408 451-9294
Yoon OH Kim, *President*
EMP: 16
SALES (est): 2.1MM **Privately Held**
WEB: www.okigraphics.com
SIC: 2752 Commercial printing, offset

(P-7003)
OMEGA GRAPHICS PRINTING HOLLYW
6000 Fountain Ave, Los Angeles
(90028-8311)
PHONE.....................213 784-5200
MAI Vong, *CEO*
EMP: 10
SQ FT: 1,100
SALES: 150K **Privately Held**
SIC: 2752 Commercial printing, litho-
graphic

(P-7004)
ON PRESS PRINTING SERVICE INC
1440 Richardson St, San Bernardino
(92408-2962)
PHONE.....................909 799-9599
Grant Rumary, *President*
Annie Boyd, *Treasurer*
EMP: 14
SQ FT: 15,000
SALES (est): 1.1MM **Privately Held**
SIC: 2752 2759 Commercial printing, off-
set; commercial printing

(P-7005)
ONEIL DIGITAL SOLUTIONS LLC
12655 Beatrice St, Los Angeles
(90066-7300)
PHONE.....................310 448-6407
David Woodley, *Controller*
EMP: 201
SALES (corp-wide): 231.5MM **Privately Held**
SIC: 2752 5045 7389 Commercial print-
ing, lithographic; computer software; mail-
box rental & related service
HQ: O'neil Digital Solutions, Llc
3100 E Plano Pkwy
Plano TX 75074
972 881-1282

(P-7006)
ORANGE COAST REPROGRAPHICS INC
Also Called: Mouse Graphics
659 W 19th St, Costa Mesa (92627-2715)
PHONE.....................949 548-5571
Constance Mary Lane, *CEO*
EMP: 22
SQ FT: 9,000

SALES (est): 4.5MM **Privately Held**
WEB: www.sendmouse.com
SIC: 2752 7336 2789 2759 Commercial
printing, lithographic; commercial art &
graphic design; bookbinding & related
work; commercial printing

(P-7007)
ORCHARD PRINTING
325 Aleut Ct, Fremont (94539-6871)
PHONE.....................510 490-1736
Steven T Karris, *Owner*
EMP: 11
SQ FT: 6,700
SALES (est): 530K **Privately Held**
SIC: 2752 Publication printing, lithographic

(P-7008)
OWENS PRINTING CO
9170 Independence Ave, Chatsworth
(91311-5902)
PHONE.....................818 773-8900
Owen L Lee, *President*
EMP: 18
SALES (est): 1.4MM **Privately Held**
SIC: 2752 Commercial printing, offset

(P-7009)
PACFUL INC (PA)
11311 White Rock Rd # 100, Rancho Cor-
dova (95742-6876)
PHONE.....................916 233-1488
Jennifer Jo Hudek, *CEO*
Minnetta McAdams, *CFO*
◆ EMP: 57
SALES (est): 19.9MM **Privately Held**
SIC: 2752 7389 Commercial printing, off-
set; rug binding

(P-7010)
PACFUL INC
131 Glenn Way Ste 4, San Carlos
(94070-6259)
PHONE.....................650 200-4252
Rhonda Lepera, *Controller*
Pete Brewer, *Cust Mgr*
Sue Kent, *Manager*
EMP: 72 **Privately Held**
SIC: 2752 7389 Commercial printing, litho-
graphic; rug binding
PA: Pacful, Inc.
11311 White Rock Rd # 100
Rancho Cordova CA 95742

(P-7011)
PACIFIC IMAGING
Also Called: Pacific Printing
9687 Distribution Ave, San Diego
(92121-2307)
PHONE.....................858 536-2600
Steve Cook, *President*
EMP: 17
SQ FT: 8,250
SALES (est): 1.4MM **Privately Held**
WEB: www.pac-print.com
SIC: 2752 7336 Commercial printing, off-
set; graphic arts & related design

(P-7012)
PACIFIC WEST LITHO INC
3291 E Miraloma Ave, Anaheim
(92806-1910)
PHONE.....................714 579-0868
Chang Che Chou, *CEO*
Raymond Lai, *Info Tech Mgr*
Johnny Tu, *Production*
John Bruccheri, *Sales Mgr*
Eric Chou, *Sales Staff*
EMP: 70
SQ FT: 24,000
SALES (est): 11.7MM **Privately Held**
WEB: www.pacificwestlitho.com
SIC: 2752 Lithographing on metal; com-
mercial printing, offset

(P-7013)
PAR GLOBAL RESOURCES INC
2005 De La Cruz Blvd # 111, Santa Clara
(95050-3030)
PHONE.....................408 982-5515
Paul Craft Hathaway, *President*
Jane Hathaway, *Admin Sec*
EMP: 12

SALES (est): 2.2MM **Privately Held**
WEB: www.par-global.com
SIC: 2752 Commercial printing, offset

(P-7014)
PARADISE PRINTING INC
13474 Pumice St, Norwalk (90650-5247)
PHONE.....................714 228-9628
Paul B Pistone, *CEO*
William Psinka, *Technology*
EMP: 25
SQ FT: 48,000
SALES (est): 5.4MM **Privately Held**
SIC: 2752 Commercial printing, offset

(P-7015)
PARKER PRINTING INC
11240 Young River Ave, Fountain Valley
(92708-4109)
PHONE.....................714 444-4550
Marie Colacchio, *President*
Bernie P Colacchio, *Vice Pres*
EMP: 12
SQ FT: 12,000
SALES (est): 2.4MM **Privately Held**
WEB: www.parkerprinting.com
SIC: 2752 Commercial printing, offset

(P-7016)
PARS PUBLISHING CORP
Also Called: Grapheex
4485 Runway St, Simi Valley (93063-3436)
PHONE.....................818 280-0540
Mehran Kiankarimi, *President*
Mike Kian, *President*
Allan Yegani, *Treasurer*
Mahnaz Shidfar, *Vice Pres*
Vincent Fisher, *Admin Sec*
EMP: 54
SQ FT: 40,000
SALES (est): 7.2MM **Privately Held**
WEB: www.grapheex.com
SIC: 2752 Commercial printing, offset

(P-7017)
PATSONS PRESS
Also Called: Patsons Media Group
831 Martin Ave, Santa Clara (95050-2903)
PHONE.....................408 567-0911
Patricia Dellamano, *President*
Pat Dellamano, *CFO*
Joseph Dellamano, *Corp Secy*
Mark Dellamano, *Vice Pres*
George Crawford, *Office Mgr*
EMP: 50
SQ FT: 25,000
SALES (est): 9MM **Privately Held**
WEB: www.patsons.com
SIC: 2752 Commercial printing, offset

(P-7018)
PAUL BAKER PRINTING INC
220 Riverside Ave, Roseville (95678-3146)
PHONE.....................916 969-8317
Kasey Cotulla, *President*
James Davis, *Vice Pres*
EMP: 32
SQ FT: 8,500
SALES (est): 5.9MM **Privately Held**
WEB: www.pbaker.com
SIC: 2752 Commercial printing, offset

(P-7019)
PAUL SILVER ENTERPRISES INC
Also Called: Quick Silver Prtg & Graphics
9155 Alabama Ave Ste F, Chatsworth
(91311-5873)
PHONE.....................818 998-9900
Paul Silver, *President*
Ava Silver, *Vice Pres*
▲ EMP: 10
SALES (est): 1.6MM **Privately Held**
WEB: www.quicksilverprint.com
SIC: 2752 8743 2759 Commercial print-
ing, offset; promotion service; advertising
literature: printing

(P-7020)
PDF PRINT COMMUNICATIONS INC (PA)
2630 E 28th St, Long Beach (90755-2202)
PHONE.....................562 426-6978
Robert Albert Mullaney, *CEO*
Shirley Mullaney, *Treasurer*
Kevin J Mullaney, *Vice Pres*
Jeff Keller, *Production*

▲ = Import ▼=Export
◆ =Import/Export

EMP: 52
SQ FT: 23,000
SALES (est): 16.3MM **Privately Held**
WEB: www.pacificdataforms.com
SIC: 2752 2761 Commercial printing, off-set; manifold business forms

(P-7021)
PEGASUS INTERPRINT
7111 Hayvenhurst Ave, Van Nuys
(91406-3807)
PHONE.............................800 926-9873
Donald A Faber, *Principal*
▲ **EMP:** 24
SALES (est): 4MM **Privately Held**
SIC: 2752

(P-7022)
PEGASUS PRESS 2010 LLC
7111 Hayvenhurst Ave, Van Nuys
(91406-3807)
PHONE.............................818 989-3600
Michael Jacobs, *Mng Member*
EMP: 75
SALES (est): 9.2MM **Privately Held**
SIC: 2752 7374 Commercial printing, litho-graphic; data processing service

(P-7023)
PERFORMANCE PRINTING CENTER
4380 Redwood Hwy Ste B8, San Rafael
(94903-2110)
P.O. Box 3675 (94912-3675)
PHONE.............................415 485-5878
Barbara Echo, *President*
Mike Murnin, *Sales Mgr*
EMP: 25
SALES (est): 2.5MM **Privately Held**
WEB: www.printingcenter.com
SIC: 2752 Commercial printing, offset

(P-7024)
PFANSTIEL PUBLISHERS & PRTRS
Also Called: Pfanstiel Printing
3010 E Anaheim St, Long Beach
(90804-3802)
PHONE.............................562 438-5641
Craig Pfanstiel, *President*
Charlotte J Pfanstiel, *Treasurer*
Denise Pfanstiel, *Corp Secy*
EMP: 10
SQ FT: 6,000
SALES (est): 1.2MM **Privately Held**
WEB: www.pfanstielprinters.com
SIC: 2752 2711 Commercial printing, off-set; newspapers, publishing & printing

(P-7025)
PGI PACIFIC GRAPHICS INTL
14938 Nelson Ave, City of Industry
(91744-4330)
PHONE.............................626 336-7707
Yvonne Castillo Wasson, *CEO*
John D Stone, *Exec VP*
Ricardo Wasson, *Vice Pres*
EMP: 25
SQ FT: 17,000
SALES (est): 4.5MM **Privately Held**
SIC: 2752 2759 8742 7331 Commercial printing, offset; commercial printing; mar-keting consulting services; mailing service

(P-7026)
PHOTONIC CORP
5800 Uplander Way Ste 100, Culver City
(90230-6608)
PHONE.............................310 642-7975
Birendra Dutt, *President*
Marco Ramirez, *Technology*
Al Lucero, *Manager*
EMP: 12
SALES (est): 1.5MM **Privately Held**
SIC: 2752 Commercial printing, litho-graphic

(P-7027)
PINE GROVE INDUSTRIES INC
Also Called: Custom Printing
2001 Cabot Pl, Oxnard (93030-2666)
PHONE.............................805 485-3700
Charles Utts, *President*
Becky Utts, *Vice Pres*
Kristen Utts, *Accounting Mgr*
Michael Jones, *Prdtn Mgr*

Bryon Frovarp, *Marketing Mgr*
EMP: 39
SQ FT: 10,000
SALES (est): 8.9MM **Privately Held**
SIC: 2752 Commercial printing, offset

(P-7028)
PIPNSV INC
Also Called: PIP Printing
8422 Sunland Blvd, Sun Valley
(91352-3436)
P.O. Box 10426, Burbank (91510-0426)
PHONE.............................818 768-0550
Carol Silver, *President*
EMP: 10
SQ FT: 2,700
SALES (est): 1.3MM **Privately Held**
SIC: 2752 7334 7336 2789 Commercial printing, offset; photocopying & duplicat-ing services; graphic arts & related de-sign; bookbinding & related work

(P-7029)
PM CORPORATE GROUP INC
Also Called: PM Packaging
6425 Randolph St, Commerce
(90040-3511)
PHONE.............................619 498-9199
Ramona Schmidt, *President*
Gayle Cronin, *Vice Pres*
Steve Reder, *Vice Pres*
EMP: 240
SALES (est): 24.8MM **Privately Held**
SIC: 2752 Commercial printing, offset

(P-7030)
PM LITHOGRAPHERS INC
Also Called: Promedia Printers
7600 Linley Ln, Canoga Park (91304-5224)
PHONE.............................818 704-2626
Victor J Gelfo, *President*
Holly Gelfo, *Treasurer*
EMP: 14
SQ FT: 4,000
SALES (est): 1.3MM **Privately Held**
SIC: 2752 Commercial printing, offset

(P-7031)
PMRCA INC (PA)
Also Called: Witts Everything For Office
20437 Brian Way Ste B, Tehachapi
(93561-6764)
P.O. Box 1334 (93581-1334)
PHONE.............................661 822-6760
Mika Amato, *President*
Paul M Amato, *Vice Pres*
Paul Amato, *Vice Pres*
Laura Coaly, *Executive*
EMP: 11
SQ FT: 8,000
SALES (est): 2.7MM **Privately Held**
WEB: www.governmentauction.com
SIC: 2752 5943 Offset & photolithographic printing; office forms & supplies

(P-7032)
PRE-PRESS INTERNATIONAL
Also Called: Digital Pre-Press Intl
20 S Linden Ave Ste 4a, South San Fran-cisco (94080-6425)
PHONE.............................415 216-0031
Sanjay Sakhuja, *President*
EMP: 37
SQ FT: 20,710
SALES: 6MM **Privately Held**
SIC: 2752 Commercial printing, litho-graphic

(P-7033)
PRECISION LITHO INC
1185 Joshua Way, Vista (92081-7892)
PHONE.............................760 727-9400
Bill Anderson, *President*
Mike Gacnik, *President*
John Krebs, *Vice Pres*
Kent Wright, *Vice Pres*
EMP: 35 **EST:** 1981
SQ FT: 40,000
SALES (est): 5.8MM
SALES (corp-wide): 6.9B **Publicly Held**
WEB: www.plitho.com
SIC: 2752 Commercial printing, litho-graphic

HQ: Consolidated Graphics, Inc.
5858 Westheimer Rd # 400
Houston TX 77057
713 787-0977

(P-7034)
PRECISION OFFSET INC
Also Called: Precision Services Group
15201 Woodlawn Ave, Tustin (92780-6449)
PHONE.............................949 752-1714
Lawrence Smith, *President*
Greg Cocroft, *Vice Pres*
Heather Parker, *Project Mgr*
Kevin Smith, *Sales Mgr*
Lydia Avina, *Manager*
EMP: 75
SQ FT: 15,000
SALES (est): 21.1MM **Privately Held**
WEB: www.precisionoffset.net
SIC: 2752 Commercial printing, offset

(P-7035)
PREMIER COLOR GRAPHICS INC
1899 N Helm Ave, Fresno (93727-1612)
PHONE.............................559 625-8606
Wayne Yada, *President*
Mary J Yada, *Treasurer*
Ed Caz, *Vice Pres*
Justina Gonzalez, *Manager*
EMP: 23
SQ FT: 11,000
SALES (est): 3MM **Privately Held**
WEB: www.printingonline.com
SIC: 2752 2789 2759 Commercial print-ing, offset; bookbinding & related work; commercial printing

(P-7036)
PRESSNET EXPRESS INC
7283 Engineer Rd Ste Ab, San Diego
(92111-1414)
PHONE.............................858 694-0070
Sam Levine, *CEO*
Yoav Levine, *President*
Jose Garcia, *Prdtn Mgr*
EMP: 15
SQ FT: 5,000
SALES (est): 2.4MM **Privately Held**
WEB: www.pressnetexpress.com
SIC: 2752 Commercial printing, offset

(P-7037)
PRIMARY COLOR SYSTEMS CORP (PA)
11130 Holder St, Cypress (90630-5162)
PHONE.............................949 660-7080
Daniel Hirt, *President*
Ronald Hirt, *Shareholder*
David Dalessandro, *COO*
Michael Hirt, *Vice Pres*
Paul Wartman, *Vice Pres*
▲ **EMP:** 292 **EST:** 1984
SQ FT: 40,000
SALES: 61MM **Privately Held**
WEB: www.primarycolor.com
SIC: 2752 2759 Commercial printing, off-set; commercial printing

(P-7038)
PRINT & MAIL SOLUTIONS INC
Also Called: AlphaGraphics
1322 Blue Oaks Blvd # 100, Roseville
(95678-7051)
PHONE.............................916 782-5489
Guy Vasconcellos, *CEO*
Linda Vasconcellos, *Vice Pres*
Kent Walters, *Regl Sales Mgr*
Cecilia Clark, *Sales Staff*
EMP: 12
SQ FT: 4,500
SALES (est): 2.2MM **Privately Held**
SIC: 2752 Commercial printing, offset

(P-7039)
PRINT N SAVE INC
2120 E Howell Ave Ste 414, Anaheim
(92806-6029)
PHONE.............................714 634-1133
Roy Anderson, *Vice Pres*
Maud Anderson, *President*
EMP: 10
SQ FT: 3,845
SALES (est): 1MM **Privately Held**
SIC: 2752 Commercial printing, litho-graphic

(P-7040)
PRINT SMITH INC
8047 Soquel Dr, Aptos (95003-3928)
PHONE.............................831 688-1538
Peter Truman, *President*
Kimberly Ann Truman, *Admin Sec*
EMP: 10
SQ FT: 3,200
SALES (est): 1MM **Privately Held**
WEB: www.printsmith.com
SIC: 2752 7334 7338 7374 Commercial printing, offset; photocopying & duplicat-ing services; word processing service; data processing & preparation

(P-7041)
PRINT-N-STUFF INC
Also Called: Galaxy Press
1300 Galaxy Way Ste 3, Concord
(94520-4922)
PHONE.............................925 798-3212
Tom J Meyer, *President*
Robert Meyer, *Vice Pres*
EMP: 10
SQ FT: 6,900
SALES (est): 1.7MM **Privately Held**
WEB: www.galaxypress.net
SIC: 2752 Commercial printing, offset

(P-7042)
PRINTCOM INC
Also Called: Minuteman Press
14675 Titus St, Van Nuys (91402-4922)
PHONE.............................818 891-8282
Pamela K Berg, *President*
Kevin Berg, *Vice Pres*
EMP: 13
SQ FT: 5,100
SALES (est): 1.4MM **Privately Held**
WEB: www.minutemanpressla.com
SIC: 2752 Commercial printing, litho-graphic

(P-7043)
PRINTEFEX INC
401 W Los Feliz Rd Ste C, Glendale
(91204-2772)
PHONE.............................818 240-2400
Rouben Ovanespour, *Co-Owner*
Seth Ovanespour, *Co-Owner*
EMP: 10
SQ FT: 1,150
SALES (est): 1.5MM **Privately Held**
WEB: www.printefex.com
SIC: 2752 7384 2759 Commercial print-ing, offset; photofinishing laboratory; com-mercial printing

(P-7044)
PRINTERY INC
1762 Kaiser Ave, Irvine (92614-5706)
PHONE.............................949 757-1930
Massis Chahbazian, *CEO*
Holly Acocello, *Admin Mgr*
Emma Macmillan, *Graphic Designe*
Denise Acosta, *Finance Mgr*
Mike Wilson, *Manager*
▲ **EMP:** 15
SQ FT: 10,000
SALES (est): 3.9MM **Privately Held**
SIC: 2752 Commercial printing, offset

(P-7045)
PRINTING DIVISION INC
1933 N Main St, Orange (92865-4101)
PHONE.............................714 685-0111
Richard Baca, *CEO*
Sam Nooriala, *CFO*
EMP: 13
SQ FT: 6,800
SALES (est): 2MM **Privately Held**
WEB: www.printdivinc.com
SIC: 2752 Commercial printing, offset

(P-7046)
PRINTING ISLAND CORPORATION
11535 Martens River Cir, Fountain Valley
(92708-4201)
PHONE.............................714 668-1000
Philip Wang, *President*
Denise Pham, *Admin Sec*
EMP: 11
SALES (est): 1.2MM **Privately Held**
WEB: www.printingisland.com
SIC: 2752 Commercial printing, offset

(P-7047)
PRINTING MANAGEMENT ASSOCIATES (PA)
17128 Edwards Rd, Cerritos (90703-2424)
PHONE..................................562 407-9977
Jeffrey Brady, *CEO*
Michael Lane, *President*
Clif McDougall, *Exec VP*
Rich Russell, *Vice Pres*
Steve Doerr, *Executive*
▲ EMP: 19
SQ FT: 12,600
SALES (est): 3MM Privately Held
WEB: www.printmgt.com
SIC: 2752 5111 Commercial printing, off-set; printing paper

(P-7048)
PRINTING PALACE INC
2300 Lincoln Blvd, Santa Monica (90405-2530)
PHONE..................................310 451-5151
Eli Albek, *President*
EMP: 20
SQ FT: 8,000
SALES (est): 3.3MM Privately Held
WEB: www.printingpalace.com
SIC: 2752 Commercial printing, offset

(P-7049)
PRINTING SAFARI CO
Also Called: Safari Signs
9855 Topanga Canyon Blvd, Chatsworth (91311-4044)
PHONE..................................818 709-3752
Doris Potvin, *Partner*
Ingrid Lindquist, *Partner*
Rick Carranza, *General Mgr*
EMP: 12
SQ FT: 3,800
SALES (est): 1.4MM Privately Held
WEB: www.printingsafari.com
SIC: 2752 Commercial printing, offset

(P-7050)
PRINTOGRAPH INC
7625 N San Fernando Rd, Burbank (91505-1073)
PHONE..................................818 252-3000
Kristina Keshishyan, *Principal*
EMP: 13
SALES (est): 2.4MM Privately Held
SIC: 2752 Commercial printing, litho-graphic

(P-7051)
PRINTS CHARMN INC (PA)
11560 Tennessee Ave, Los Angeles (90064-1513)
PHONE..................................310 312-0904
Maxine Elster-Pearlman, *President*
Maxine A Elster, *Owner*
EMP: 11
SQ FT: 1,000
SALES (est): 1MM Privately Held
WEB: www.printscharmn.com
SIC: 2752 Commercial printing, litho-graphic

(P-7052)
PRO DOCUMENT SOLUTIONS INC (PA)
1760 Commerce Way, Paso Robles (93446-3620)
PHONE..................................805 238-6680
George Phillips, *President*
Zac Alvarez, *Supervisor*
▲ EMP: 92
SQ FT: 35,000
SALES (est): 31.2MM Privately Held
WEB: www.prodocumentsolutions.com
SIC: 2752 Business forms, lithographed

(P-7053)
PROCESSORS MAILING INC
Also Called: Processors The
761 N Dodsworth Ave, Covina (91724-2408)
PHONE..................................626 358-5075
Fax: 626 358-5607
EMP: 30 EST: 1974
SQ FT: 8,000
SALES (est): 4MM Privately Held
WEB: www.theprocessors.com
SIC: 2752 7331 2791

(P-7054)
PROFESSIONAL PRINT & MAIL INC
2818 E Hamilton Ave, Fresno (93721-3209)
PHONE..................................559 237-7468
Doug Carlile, *President*
Mike Carlile, *Vice Pres*
Roberta L Carlile, *Admin Sec*
Jennifer Her, *Graphic Designe*
Justin Serrano, *Prdtn Mgr*
EMP: 30 EST: 1985
SQ FT: 20,000
SALES: 3.4MM Privately Held
WEB: www.printfresno.com
SIC: 2752 7331 Commercial printing, off-set; mailing service

(P-7055)
PROGRAPHICS INC
9200 Lower Azusa Rd, Rosemead (91770-1593)
PHONE..................................626 287-0417
Christina Stevens, *CEO*
Timothy Stevens, *President*
Jaime Colacio, *Vice Pres*
EMP: 39
SQ FT: 23,000
SALES (est): 13.7MM Privately Held
WEB: www.prographicsllc.com
SIC: 2752 Commercial printing, offset

(P-7056)
PYRAMID GRAPHICS
Also Called: Pyramid Printing and Graphics
325 Harbor Way, South San Francisco (94080-6919)
PHONE..................................650 871-0290
Kingman Leung, *President*
Nancy Tam, *Treasurer*
Katrina Qiu, *Graphic Designe*
Jay Leung, *Prdtn Mgr*
EMP: 16
SQ FT: 4,000
SALES (est): 2.2MM Privately Held
WEB: www.pyramidgraphics.net
SIC: 2752 7374 7336 Commercial print-ing, offset; data processing & preparation; commercial art & graphic design

(P-7057)
Q TEAM
Also Called: Ryan Press
6400 Dale St, Buena Park (90621-3115)
PHONE..................................714 228-4465
Donna Quibodeaux, *President*
James Quibodeaux, *Treasurer*
Mike Quibodeaux, *Vice Pres*
Ken Dobbins, *Sales Dir*
EMP: 16
SQ FT: 13,000
SALES (est): 4.1MM Privately Held
WEB: www.ryanpress.com
SIC: 2752 Commercial printing, offset

(P-7058)
QG LLC
Worldcolor Merced
2201 Cooper Ave, Merced (95348-4307)
PHONE..................................209 384-0444
EMP: 611
SALES (corp-wide): 4.1B Publicly Held
WEB: www.qwdys.com
SIC: 2752 Commercial printing, offset
HQ: Qg, Llc
    N61w23044 Harrys Way
    Sussex WI 53089

(P-7059)
QG PRINTING II CORP
1221 California Ave, Pittsburg (94565-4112)
PHONE..................................925 432-9740
EMP: 519
SALES (corp-wide): 4.1B Publicly Held
SIC: 2752 Commercial printing, offset
HQ: Qg Printing Ii Corp.
    N61w23044 Harrys Way
    Sussex WI 53089

(P-7060)
QG PRINTING II CORP
Also Called: Quad Graphics
6688 Box Springs Blvd, Riverside (92507-0726)
PHONE..................................951 571-2500
Georg Decker, *Branch Mgr*
Daniel Piedra, *Technology*
Johnny Sutton, *Technology*
Steve Lund, *Maintence Staff*
Matthew Desantis, *Manager*
EMP: 519
SALES (corp-wide): 4.1B Publicly Held
SIC: 2752 Commercial printing, offset
HQ: Qg Printing Ii Corp.
    N61w23044 Harrys Way
    Sussex WI 53089

(P-7061)
QUAD EXPRESS PRINTING INC
3324 Investment Blvd, Hayward (94545-3809)
PHONE..................................415 861-3433
Jose S Garcia, *CEO*
Jose Z Garcia Jr, *President*
JB Garcia, *Vice Pres*
Anthony Garcia, *Marketing Staff*
Connie Ugarte, *Accounts Mgr*
▲ EMP: 10
SQ FT: 2,000
SALES (est): 2.6MM Privately Held
WEB: www.quadexpress.com
SIC: 2752 Commercial printing, offset

(P-7062)
QUAD/GRAPHICS INC
17871 Park Plaza Dr # 150, Cerritos (90703-9317)
PHONE..................................310 751-3900
Jeff Wunrow, *Managing Dir*
Lisa Eddy, *Sales Mgr*
EMP: 12
SALES (corp-wide): 4.1B Publicly Held
WEB: www.qg.com
SIC: 2752 Commercial printing, litho-graphic
PA: Quad/Graphics Inc.
    N61w23044 Harrys Way
    Sussex WI 53089
    414 566-6000

(P-7063)
QUAD/GRAPHICS INC
7190 Jurupa Ave, Riverside (92504-1016)
PHONE..................................951 689-1122
Uli Oels, *General Mgr*
EMP: 250
SQ FT: 30,000
SALES (corp-wide): 4.1B Publicly Held
WEB: www.vertisinc.com
SIC: 2752 7336 Commercial printing, off-set; commercial art & graphic design
PA: Quad/Graphics Inc.
    N61w23044 Harrys Way
    Sussex WI 53089
    414 566-6000

(P-7064)
QUAD/GRAPHICS INC
350 Rhode Island St # 110, San Francisco (94103-5188)
PHONE..................................415 267-3700
Bruce Vogen, *Manager*
EMP: 509
SALES (corp-wide): 4.1B Publicly Held
SIC: 2752 Commercial printing, offset
PA: Quad/Graphics Inc.
    N61w23044 Harrys Way
    Sussex WI 53089
    414 566-6000

(P-7065)
QUAD/GRAPHICS INC
100 North Pt Ste 105, San Francisco (94133-1551)
PHONE..................................415 398-0624
EMP: 509
SALES (corp-wide): 4.1B Publicly Held
SIC: 2752 Commercial printing, offset
PA: Quad/Graphics Inc.
    N61w23044 Harrys Way
    Sussex WI 53089
    414 566-6000

(P-7066)
QUAD/GRAPHICS INC
2201 Cooper Ave, Merced (95348-4307)
PHONE..................................209 384-0444
Freider Debiasi, *Branch Mgr*
Susan Grofe, *Buyer*
Dave Hall, *Maintence Staff*
Marc Kulick, *Director*
EMP: 463
SALES (corp-wide): 4.1B Publicly Held
SIC: 2752 Commercial printing, offset
PA: Quad/Graphics Inc.
    N61w23044 Harrys Way
    Sussex WI 53089
    414 566-6000

(P-7067)
QUADCO PRINTING INC
2535 Zanella Way, Chico (95928-7146)
PHONE..................................530 894-4061
Richard Braak, *President*
Dick Braak, *President*
Sherryl Garcia Braak, *CFO*
EMP: 18 EST: 1978
SQ FT: 15,000
SALES: 1.5MM Privately Held
WEB: www.quadcoprinting.com
SIC: 2752 Commercial printing, offset

(P-7068)
QUEEN BEACH PRINTERS INC
937 Pine Ave, Long Beach (90813-4375)
P.O. Box 540 (90801-0540)
PHONE..................................562 436-8201
Nicholas W Edwards, *CEO*
William L Edwards Sr, *President*
Bill Edwards Jr, *COO*
William L Edwards Jr, *COO*
Virginia Noyes, *Vice Pres*
EMP: 30 EST: 1944
SQ FT: 25,000
SALES (est): 4.8MM Privately Held
WEB: www.qbprinters.com
SIC: 2752 7336 Commercial printing, off-set; commercial art & graphic design

(P-7069)
R GOODLOE & ASSOCIATES INC
Also Called: Rga
25602 Alicia Pkwy, Laguna Hills (92653-5309)
PHONE..................................714 380-3900
Robert A Goodloe, *President*
Robert Goodloe, *President*
Lavinia Goodloe, *Vice Pres*
EMP: 11
SALES (est): 1.5MM Privately Held
SIC: 2752 Commercial printing, offset

(P-7070)
R R DONNELLEY & SONS COMPANY
Also Called: Moore Business Forms
1050 Aviator Dr, Vacaville (95688-8900)
PHONE..................................707 446-6195
Mark George, *Branch Mgr*
EMP: 15
SALES (corp-wide): 6.9B Publicly Held
WEB: www.moore.com
SIC: 2752 Commercial printing, litho-graphic
PA: R. R. Donnelley & Sons Company
    35 W Wacker Dr Ste 3650
    Chicago IL 60601
    312 326-8000

(P-7071)
RAINBOW MAGNETICS INCORPORATED
1 Whatney, Irvine (92618-2806)
PHONE..................................714 540-4777
Robert Knapp, *President*
Jennifer Knapp, *CFO*
▲ EMP: 25 EST: 1974
SQ FT: 13,174
SALES (est): 3.5MM Privately Held
WEB: www.rainbowmagnetics.com
SIC: 2752 3993 Commercial printing, off-set; advertising novelties

▲ = Import ▼=Export
◆ =Import/Export

(P-7072)
RAINTREE BUSINESS PRODUCTS
Also Called: B C T
23101 Terra Dr, Laguna Hills (92653-1320)
PHONE..................................949 859-0801
Joseph H Rachal Jr, *President*
Donna C Rachal, *Vice Pres*
EMP: 20
SQ FT: 7,000
SALES (est): 2.5MM **Privately Held**
WEB: www.bctlaguna.com
SIC: 2752 Commercial printing, lithographic

(P-7073)
RANCHO BERNARDO PRINTING INC
1519 Industrial Ave Ste D, Escondido (92029-1363)
P.O. Box 461101 (92046-1101)
PHONE..................................858 486-4540
Steve Swadell, *President*
Loyd Beth Swadell, *Shareholder*
EMP: 11
SALES (est): 1.6MM **Privately Held**
WEB: www.rbprinting.com
SIC: 2752 Commercial printing, offset

(P-7074)
RANROY COMPANY
8320 Camino Santa Fe # 200, San Diego (92121-2659)
PHONE..................................858 571-8800
Randall S Roy, *President*
Steve Levon, *Sales Staff*
Jennifer San Nicolas, *Accounts Mgr*
Ana Anderson, *Relations*
EMP: 25
SQ FT: 20,000
SALES (est): 1.4MM **Privately Held**
WEB: www.ranroy.com
SIC: 2752 5112 Commercial printing, offset; envelopes

(P-7075)
RAPID PRINTERS OF MONTEREY
201 Foam St, Monterey (93940-1400)
PHONE..................................831 373-1822
Mike Djubasak, *President*
Jean Angley, *President*
Jean Djubasak, *Vice Pres*
Rapid Printers, *Sales Staff*
EMP: 20 EST: 1981
SQ FT: 6,900
SALES (est): 2.9MM **Privately Held**
WEB: www.rapidprinters.com
SIC: 2752 2791 2789 Commercial printing, offset; typesetting; bookbinding & related work

(P-7076)
RAYMERT PRESS INCORPORATED
1604 Sunburst Dr, El Cajon (92021-1541)
PHONE..................................858 576-0880
Dan Jones Jr, *President*
Gloria Jones, *Vice Pres*
EMP: 22 EST: 1930
SQ FT: 10,000
SALES (est): 2.8MM **Privately Held**
WEB: www.raymertpress.com
SIC: 2752 2759 Commercial printing, offset; letterpress printing

(P-7077)
RAYMONDS LITTLE PRINT SHOP INC
Also Called: Jim Little Raymonds Print Shop
41454 Christy St, Fremont (94538-5105)
PHONE..................................510 353-3608
Raymond Lei, *President*
EMP: 450
SQ FT: 100,000
SALES: 10MM
SALES (corp-wide): 165.8MM **Privately Held**
SIC: 2752 Commercial printing, lithographic
PA: Ooshirts Inc.
41454 Christy St
Fremont CA 94538
866 660-8667

(P-7078)
RDS GROUP INC
Also Called: RDS Printing and Graphics Ctr
1714 E Grevillea Ct, Ontario (91761-8035)
PHONE..................................909 923-8831
Robert Saiz, *President*
Theresa Saiz, *Vice Pres*
EMP: 10
SQ FT: 10,000
SALES (est): 1.6MM **Privately Held**
WEB: www.rdsprinting.com
SIC: 2752 Commercial printing, offset

(P-7079)
READY INDUSTRIES INC
Also Called: Ready Reproductions
1520 E 15th St, Los Angeles (90021-2712)
PHONE..................................213 749-2041
E H Reitz, *CEO*
Chuck Nix, *Treasurer*
EMP: 16
SQ FT: 15,000
SALES (est): 1.7MM **Privately Held**
WEB: www.readyrepro.com
SIC: 2752 Photolithographic printing

(P-7080)
RED BRICK CORPORATION
Also Called: Design Printing
5364 Venice Blvd, Los Angeles (90019-5240)
PHONE..................................323 549-9444
Parviz Bina, *CEO*
Bijan Bina, *Vice Pres*
Wendy Galope, *Accountant*
Bob Hart, *Prdtn Mgr*
EMP: 18
SQ FT: 8,000
SALES (est): 3.8MM **Privately Held**
SIC: 2752 Commercial printing, offset

(P-7081)
REDDING PRINTING CO INC (PA)
1130 Continental St, Redding (96001-0799)
PHONE..................................530 243-0525
Ken Peterson, *President*
Richard Peterson, *Corp Secy*
EMP: 30
SQ FT: 14,000
SALES (est): 2.6MM **Privately Held**
WEB: www.reddingprinting.com
SIC: 2752 Commercial printing, offset

(P-7082)
REDSHARK GROUP INC
166 Saint Helena Ct, Danville (94526-5523)
PHONE..................................925 837-3490
Gregory Sharkey, *President*
Kevin Kurbenknabe, *Vice Pres*
EMP: 11
SALES (est): 1.9MM **Privately Held**
WEB: www.redsharkgroup.com
SIC: 2752 Commercial printing, lithographic

(P-7083)
REPRO MAGIC
8585 Miramar Pl, San Diego (92121-2529)
PHONE..................................858 277-2488
Ali Rashidi, *President*
Kia Talai, *Marketing Staff*
Rick Webster, *Representative*
Joe Sigurdson, *Accounts Exec*
EMP: 12 EST: 1997
SQ FT: 6,000
SALES (est): 3.1MM **Privately Held**
WEB: www.repromagic.com
SIC: 2752 Commercial printing, offset

(P-7084)
REY NELSON PRINTING INC
1955 S Starfire Ave, Corona (92879-2946)
PHONE..................................909 947-3505
Reynold Nelson, *President*
Steve Dickerson, *Treasurer*
Teri Dickerson, *Admin Sec*
Terri Dickerson, *Admin Sec*
Charles Contreras, *Manager*
EMP: 13
SQ FT: 6,000
SALES (est): 2.2MM **Privately Held**
WEB: www.rnprint.com
SIC: 2752 Commercial printing, offset

(P-7085)
RIVAS INDUSTRIES INC
Also Called: Omega Graphics
6687 Havenhurst St, Corona (92880-3797)
PHONE..................................951 880-8638
Ricardo Rivas, *President*
Luz Rivas, *Vice Pres*
EMP: 16
SQ FT: 18,000
SALES (est): 1.5MM **Privately Held**
SIC: 2752 Color lithography

(P-7086)
RIVER CITY PRINT AND MAIL INC
2431 Mercantile Dr Ste G, Rancho Cordova (95742-6252)
PHONE..................................916 638-8400
Michael S Hagen, *President*
EMP: 11
SALES (est): 1.7MM **Privately Held**
SIC: 2752 Commercial printing, lithographic

(P-7087)
RIVER CITY PRINTERS LLC
2431 Mercantile Dr Ste G, Rancho Cordova (95742-6252)
PHONE..................................916 638-8400
Kasey Cotulla, *Mng Member*
Eric Fields, *Vice Pres*
Jim Davis,
EMP: 35
SQ FT: 14,000
SALES (est): 9.5MM **Privately Held**
SIC: 2752 Commercial printing, offset

(P-7088)
RMS PRINTING LLC
5331 Derry Ave Ste N, Agoura Hills (91301-3384)
PHONE..................................818 707-2625
EMP: 15
SALES (est): 2MM **Privately Held**
SIC: 2752 Commercial printing, offset

(P-7089)
RNJ PRINTING CORPORATION
16005 S Broadway, Gardena (90248-2417)
PHONE..................................310 638-7768
John Samuel Osten, *President*
Rose Cecola Osten, *CFO*
Yvette Barnett, *General Mgr*
Alfredo Jimenez, *Manager*
EMP: 16
SQ FT: 8,000
SALES (est): 2.6MM **Privately Held**
WEB: www.rnjprinting.com
SIC: 2752 2796 Commercial printing, offset; letterpress plates, preparation of

(P-7090)
RR DONNELLEY & SONS COMPANY
3837 Producers Dr, Stockton (95206-4217)
PHONE..................................209 983-6700
EMP: 389
SALES (corp-wide): 6.9B **Publicly Held**
SIC: 2752 Commercial printing, lithographic
PA: R. R. Donnelley & Sons Company
35 W Wacker Dr Ste 3650
Chicago IL 60601
312 326-8000

(P-7091)
RUSH PRESS INC
Also Called: Arts & Crafts Press
955 Gateway Center Way, San Diego (92102-4542)
PHONE..................................619 296-7874
Joe R Davis, *CEO*
Gene Valles, *President*
Jim Art, *Vice Pres*
Tony Fowler, *Marketing Mgr*
Edward Gonzales, *Sales Staff*
EMP: 48
SALES (est): 7MM
SALES (corp-wide): 6.9B **Publicly Held**
WEB: www.rushpress.com
SIC: 2752 Commercial printing, offset
HQ: Consolidated Graphics, Inc.
5858 Westheimer Rd # 400
Houston TX 77057
713 787-0977

(P-7092)
S & S PRINTERS
2100 W Lincoln Ave Ste A, Anaheim (92801-5641)
PHONE..................................714 535-5592
Bann Ratankee, *President*
EMP: 32
SQ FT: 10,000
SALES (est): 1.2MM **Privately Held**
SIC: 2752 2759 Commercial printing, offset; letterpress printing

(P-7093)
SACRAMENTO ENVELOPE CO INC
773 Northport Dr Ste C-A, West Sacramento (95691-2176)
PHONE..................................916 371-4747
Dominic Tringali, *President*
Lisa Tringali, *Corp Secy*
Lisa Cofield, *Admin Sec*
EMP: 10
SQ FT: 8,000
SALES (est): 2.7MM **Privately Held**
WEB: www.sacenvelope.com
SIC: 2752 Commercial printing, offset

(P-7094)
SAN DIEGUITO PUBLISHERS INC
Also Called: San Dieguito Printers
1880 Diamond St, San Marcos (92078-5100)
P.O. Box 885, Solana Beach (92075-0885)
PHONE..................................760 593-5139
Mary Lapham, *CEO*
Richard Lapham, *President*
Chris Lapham, *Vice Pres*
▲ EMP: 59 EST: 1964
SALES (est): 16.1MM **Privately Held**
WEB: www.sd-print.com
SIC: 2752 Commercial printing, offset

(P-7095)
SAN FRANCISCO PRINT MEDIA CO (PA)
835 Market St Ste 550, San Francisco (94103-1906)
PHONE..................................415 487-2594
David Black, *CEO*
Jay Curran, *Officer*
Aaron Barbero, *VP Opers*
David Lee, *Sales Staff*
EMP: 23
SALES (est): 8.4MM **Privately Held**
SIC: 2752 Commercial printing, lithographic

(P-7096)
SARI ART & PRINTING INC
720 N Todd Ave, Azusa (91702-2227)
PHONE..................................626 305-0888
Theresa MEI Ching Tan, *CEO*
▲ EMP: 10
SALES (est): 2.3MM **Privately Held**
SIC: 2752 Commercial printing, lithographic

(P-7097)
SCHOLASTIC SPORTS INC
4878 Ronson Ct Ste Kl, San Diego (92111-1806)
PHONE..................................858 496-9221
Jill Spindle, *President*
Sam Spindlee, *Vice Pres*
Reggie Segal, *Manager*
EMP: 90
SQ FT: 5,500
SALES (est): 867.6K **Privately Held**
SIC: 2752 Commercial printing, lithographic

(P-7098)
SEASIDE PRINTING CO
1220 E 4th St, Long Beach (90802-1893)
PHONE..................................562 437-6437
Mark Cochrane, *President*
Jack Cochrane, *Shareholder*
John Eastin, *Shareholder*
John La Combe, *Shareholder*
EMP: 30
SQ FT: 15,000

(PA)=Parent Co (HQ)=Headquarters (DH)=Div Headquarters
✿ = New Business established in last 2 years

2019 California
Manufacturers Register

295

PRODUCTS & SVCS

SALES (est): 6MM **Privately Held**
WEB: www.seasideprinting.com
SIC: 2752 2796 2721 Commercial printing, offset; platemaking services; periodicals

(P-7099)
SEDAS PRINTING INC
5335 Santa Monica Blvd, Los Angeles (90029-1105)
PHONE....................323 469-1034
John Rashidi, *President*
Seda Rashidi, *Vice Pres*
EMP: 15
SQ FT: 8,000
SALES (est): 1.4MM **Privately Held**
WEB: www.sedasprinting.com
SIC: 2752 Commercial printing, offset

(P-7100)
SEEGERS INDUSTRIES INC
Also Called: Seeger's Printing
210 N Center St, Turlock (95380-4003)
PHONE....................209 667-2750
Arthur W Seeger, *President*
Richard Berger, *Treasurer*
Mark Grossi, *Sales Staff*
Toni Jevert,
Karollee Seeger, *Consultant*
EMP: 15
SQ FT: 7,100
SALES (est): 2.1MM **Privately Held**
WEB: www.seegersprinting.com
SIC: 2752 Photo-offset printing; commercial printing, offset

(P-7101)
SELECT GRAPHICS
11931 Euclid St, Garden Grove (92840-2200)
PHONE....................714 537-5250
Yung Phan, *Principal*
Laura Reeves, *Graphic Designe*
Christina Pham, *Accountant*
Jennifer Pham, *Marketing Staff*
Leah Beardsley, *Representative*
EMP: 12
SQ FT: 2,703
SALES: 1.5MM **Privately Held**
SIC: 2752 2759 Commercial printing, offset; commercial printing

(P-7102)
SERVICE PRESS INC
935 Tanklage Rd, San Carlos (94070-3222)
PHONE....................650 592-3484
Keith Thompson, *President*
Tom Hawkins, *Technology*
▲ **EMP:** 10
SQ FT: 2,000
SALES (est): 1.7MM **Privately Held**
WEB: www.servicepressinc.com
SIC: 2752 Commercial printing, offset

(P-7103)
SHIFT CALENDARS INC
Also Called: Graphics United
809 N Glendora Ave, Covina (91724-2529)
PHONE....................626 967-5862
Robert Breaux Jr, *President*
Brenda Moreno, *Office Mgr*
EMP: 15
SQ FT: 6,500
SALES (est): 2.9MM **Privately Held**
WEB: www.graphicsunited.com
SIC: 2752 Commercial printing, offset

(P-7104)
SHORETT PRINTING INC
Also Called: Crown Printers Anaheim
250 W Rialto Ave, San Bernardino (92408-1017)
PHONE....................714 956-9001
Charles D Shorett Jr, *Branch Mgr*
EMP: 10
SALES (est): 558.3K
SALES (corp-wide): 6.7MM **Privately Held**
WEB: www.crownconnect.com
SIC: 2752 Commercial printing, offset
PA: Shorett Printing, Inc.
  250 W Rialto Ave
  San Bernardino CA 92408
  714 545-4689

(P-7105)
SIERRA OFFICE SYSTEMS PDTS INC (PA)
Also Called: Sierra Office Supplies & Prtg
9950 Horn Rd Ste 5, Sacramento (95827-1905)
PHONE....................916 369-0491
Michael Kipp, *CEO*
Jason Gallivan, *COO*
Mary Theis, *Admin Sec*
Paul Grahma, *Info Tech Mgr*
Debbie Williams, *Technology*
EMP: 100
SQ FT: 28,000
SALES (est): 30.5MM **Privately Held**
WEB: www.sierrabg.com
SIC: 2752 5712 5943 Commercial printing, offset; office furniture; office forms & supplies

(P-7106)
SORENSON PUBLISHING INC
Also Called: Prestige Printing
12925 Alcosta Blvd Ste 6, San Ramon (94583-1341)
PHONE....................925 866-1514
Fax: 925 866-0533
EMP: 10
SQ FT: 3,200
SALES (est): 990K **Privately Held**
WEB: www.prestigeprinting.com
SIC: 2752

(P-7107)
SOURCE PRINT MEDIA SOLUTIONS
29108 Summer Oak Ct, Santa Clarita (91390-4192)
PHONE....................661 263-1880
Matthew L Pearson, *CEO*
Anthony Wright, *General Ptnr*
Mary K Pearson, *Vice Pres*
EMP: 12
SALES (est): 1.9MM **Privately Held**
WEB: www.sourceprintmedia.com
SIC: 2752 Commercial printing, offset

(P-7108)
SOURCING GROUP LLC
1672 Delta Ct, Hayward (94544-7043)
PHONE....................510 471-4749
EMP: 30
SALES (corp-wide): 60MM **Privately Held**
SIC: 2752 2761
PA: Sourcing Group The Llc
  77 Water St Ste 902
  New York NY 10005
  646 572-7520

(P-7109)
SOURCING GROUP LLC
148 Whitcomb Ave, Colfax (95713-9036)
PHONE....................530 346-1280
Gerry Knoll, *Branch Mgr*
EMP: 12
SALES (corp-wide): 60MM **Privately Held**
SIC: 2752 7371 Business forms, lithographed; custom computer programming services
PA: Sourcing Group The Llc
  77 Water St Ste 902
  New York NY 10005
  646 572-7520

(P-7110)
SOUTHWEST OFFSET PRTG CO INC (PA)
13650 Gramercy Pl, Gardena (90249-2453)
PHONE....................310 965-9154
Greg McDonald, *CEO*
Dutch Greve, *COO*
Art Spear, *CFO*
Jennifer McDonald, *Vice Pres*
Stephen Rogers, *Vice Pres*
▲ **EMP:** 300
SQ FT: 45,000
SALES (est): 115.9MM **Privately Held**
WEB: www.southwestoffset.com
SIC: 2752 Commercial printing, offset

(P-7111)
SPECTRATEK TECHNOLOGIES INC (PA)
9834 Jordan Cir, Santa Fe Springs (90670-3303)
PHONE....................310 822-2400
Michael Foster, *CEO*
Terry Conway, *CFO*
Tamika Gordon, *Vice Pres*
Michael Wanlass, *Principal*
▲ **EMP:** 53
SQ FT: 74,000
SALES (est): 21MM **Privately Held**
WEB: www.spectratek.net
SIC: 2752 Commercial printing, offset

(P-7112)
SPECTRUM GRAFIX INC
141 10th St, San Francisco (94103-2604)
P.O. Box 884961 (94188-4961)
PHONE....................415 648-2400
Bill Forman, *President*
John Shea, *General Mgr*
Bart Forman, *Sales Staff*
EMP: 10
SQ FT: 2,500
SALES (est): 1.6MM **Privately Held**
WEB: www.spectrumgrafix.com
SIC: 2752 2789 5112 Offset & photolithographic printing; binding only: books, pamphlets, magazines, etc.; envelopes

(P-7113)
SPECTRUM LITHOGRAPH INC
4300 Business Center Dr, Fremont (94538-6358)
PHONE....................510 438-9192
Fernandino Pereira, *President*
Fernanda Pereira, *CFO*
EMP: 27 EST: 2006
SQ FT: 46,000
SALES (est): 7MM **Privately Held**
WEB: www.spectrumlithograph.com
SIC: 2752 Commercial printing, offset

(P-7114)
SPRINT COPY CENTER INC
175 N Main St, Sebastopol (95472-3448)
PHONE....................707 823-3900
Ron Hudelson, *President*
EMP: 11
SALES (est): 500K **Privately Held**
SIC: 2752 7334 Commercial printing, offset; photocopying & duplicating services

(P-7115)
STADIUM PRINTING INC
3700 Temescal Ave, Norco (92860-1459)
PHONE....................951 371-3890
Larry Tarpley, *President*
Jacquie Tarpley, *Corp Secy*
EMP: 10
SQ FT: 6,500
SALES (est): 960K **Privately Held**
WEB: www.stadiumchiropractic.com
SIC: 2752 Lithographing on metal; commercial printing, offset

(P-7116)
STOCKON MAILING & PRINTING
4133 Postal Ave, Stockton (95204-2318)
P.O. Box 8374 (95208-0374)
PHONE....................209 466-6741
James S Huiras Jr, *President*
James Huiras Sr, *Shareholder*
Nancy Huiras, *Shareholder*
Kelly Hartemann, *Treasurer*
EMP: 18
SQ FT: 12,000
SALES (est): 1.5MM **Privately Held**
SIC: 2752 7331 Lithographing on metal; addressing service; mailing service

(P-7117)
STOUGHTON PRINTING CO
130 N Sunset Ave, City of Industry (91744-3595)
PHONE....................626 961-3678
Jack Stoughton Jr, *President*
Clay Stoughton, *Vice Pres*
Rob Maushund,
EMP: 27
SQ FT: 21,000
SALES (est): 5.6MM **Privately Held**
WEB: www.stoughtonprinting.com
SIC: 2752 Commercial printing, offset

(P-7118)
STRAHMCOLOR
3000 Kerner Blvd, San Rafael (94901-5413)
P.O. Box 9445 (94912-9445)
PHONE....................415 459-5409
Jason Strahm, *President*
EMP: 12
SQ FT: 10,000
SALES (est): 1.7MM **Privately Held**
WEB: www.strahmcom.com
SIC: 2752 Commercial printing, offset

(P-7119)
STREETER PRINTING
Also Called: Goodway Printing
13865 Sagewood Dr Ste C, Poway (92064-1403)
PHONE....................858 278-6611
Adrienne Streeter, *Partner*
EMP: 20
SQ FT: 5,000
SALES (est): 1.8MM **Privately Held**
SIC: 2752 7336 Lithographing on metal; commercial art & graphic design

(P-7120)
STREETER PRINTING INC
9880 Via Pasar Ste C, San Diego (92126-4575)
PHONE....................858 566-0866
Adrienne Streeter, *President*
Jack Streeter, *Vice Pres*
Jon Streeter, *Vice Pres*
Ingrid Nehmitz, *Accounting Mgr*
Darryl Diruscio, *Opers Mgr*
EMP: 16 EST: 1980
SQ FT: 11,000
SALES (est): 3.5MM **Privately Held**
WEB: www.streeterprinting.com
SIC: 2752 Commercial printing, offset

(P-7121)
STUDIO TWO PRINTING INC
Also Called: Studio Two Graphics and Prtg
23042 Alcalde Dr Ste C, Laguna Hills (92653-1326)
PHONE....................949 859-5119
Thomas Lewis, *President*
Dori Lewis, *Corp Secy*
Jeff Benjamin, *Vice Pres*
EMP: 28
SALES (est): 3.9MM **Privately Held**
SIC: 2752 7336 Commercial printing, offset; commercial art & graphic design; graphic arts & related design

(P-7122)
SUMI PRINTING & BINDING INC
Also Called: Sumi Office Services
1139 E Janis St, Carson (90746-1306)
PHONE....................310 769-1600
Roland Sumi, *President*
John Castillo, *Manager*
EMP: 14
SALES: 2.8MM **Privately Held**
WEB: www.sumiprinting.com
SIC: 2752 Commercial printing, lithographic

(P-7123)
SUPERIOR GRAPHIC PACKAGING INC
Also Called: Superior Lithographics
3055 Bandini Blvd, Vernon (90058-4109)
PHONE....................323 263-8400
Douglas Rawson, *CEO*
Carol Rawson, *President*
Jeff Ku, *Vice Pres*
Alex Rabino, *Admin Mgr*
Carla Drago, *Purchasing*
▲ **EMP:** 90
SQ FT: 60,000
SALES: 22.7MM **Privately Held**
SIC: 2752 Commercial printing, offset

(P-7124)
SUPERPRINT LITHOGRAPHICS INC
8332 Secura Way, Santa Fe Springs (90670-2204)
PHONE....................562 698-8001
Chao-Tung Chen, *CEO*
Roy Chen, *President*
Michael Chen, *General Mgr*

2019 California
Manufacturers Register

▲ = Import ▼=Export
◆ =Import/Export

Erika Delun, *Accountant*
Sal Dipasquale, *Sales Staff*
EMP: 15
SQ FT: 30,000
SALES (est): 3.4MM **Privately Held**
WEB: www.roychen.com
SIC: 2752 Commercial printing, offset

(P-7125)
SUPREME GRAPHICS INC
3403 Jack Northrop Ave, Hawthorne
(90250-4428)
PHONE......................310 531-8300
Ramin Kohanteb, *President*
EMP: 18
SALES (est): 3.2MM **Privately Held**
WEB: www.supremegraphic.com
SIC: 2752 Commercial printing, offset

(P-7126)
T & V PRINTING INC
7101 Jurupa Ave Ste 3, Riverside
(92504-1029)
PHONE......................951 353-8470
Vince A Castelluccio, *CEO*
EMP: 11
SQ FT: 5,000
SALES (est): 1.4MM **Privately Held**
SIC: 2752 Commercial printing, offset

(P-7127)
TAJEN GRAPHICS INC
Also Called: Apollo Printing & Graphics
2100 W Lincoln Ave Ste B, Anaheim
(92801-5642)
PHONE......................714 527-3122
Dhansukhlal Ratanjee, *President*
Ken Ratanjee, *Vice Pres*
Gary Radig, *Accounts Exec*
EMP: 30
SQ FT: 1,800
SALES (est): 5.7MM **Privately Held**
WEB: Www.apganaheim.com
SIC: 2752 2791 Commercial printing, offset; typesetting, computer controlled

(P-7128)
TAM PRINTING INC
2961 E White Star Ave, Anaheim
(92806-2630)
PHONE......................714 224-4488
Tam Bui, *President*
Debbie Trinh, *Director*
Bee Trinh, *Manager*
CHI Trinh, *Manager*
EMP: 19
SQ FT: 10,000
SALES (est): 2.7MM **Privately Held**
WEB: www.tamprinting.com
SIC: 2752 Commercial printing, lithographic

(P-7129)
TAPP LABEL INC
580 Gateway Dr, NAPA (94558-7517)
PHONE......................707 253-8250
Gerald Haudirch, *General Mgr*
Paul Sturgis, *Purchasing*
EMP: 10 **Privately Held**
SIC: 2752 Commercial printing, offset
HQ: Tapp Label, Inc.
161 S Vasco Rd L
Livermore CA 94551
707 252-8300

(P-7130)
TECHNOLOGY TRAINING CORP
Also Called: Avalon Communications
3238 W 131st St, Hawthorne (90250-5517)
PHONE......................310 644-7777
Richard D Lytle, *President*
EMP: 80
SALES (corp-wide): 8MM **Privately Held**
WEB: www.ttcus.com
SIC: 2752 7331 3577 Commercial printing, offset; direct mail advertising services; computer peripheral equipment
PA: Technology Training Corp
369 Van Ness Way Ste 735
Torrance CA 90501
310 320-8110

(P-7131)
TEEFOR 2 INC
5460 Vine St, Ontario (91710-5247)
PHONE......................909 613-0055

Larry Lazalde, *CEO*
EMP: 16 **EST:** 2012
SALES (est): 2.7MM **Privately Held**
SIC: 2752 Commercial printing, lithographic

(P-7132)
TEK LABELS AND PRINTING INC
472 Vista Way, Milpitas (95035-5406)
PHONE......................408 586-8107
Jim Dibona, *President*
David Hinds, *Vice Pres*
EMP: 25
SALES (est): 2.7MM **Privately Held**
WEB: www.teklabel.com
SIC: 2752 Commercial printing, lithographic

(P-7133)
THE LIGATURE INC (HQ)
Also Called: Echelon Fine Printing
4909 Alcoa Ave, Vernon (90058-3022)
PHONE......................323 585-6000
Tom Clifford, *Vice Pres*
Dave Meyer, *Vice Pres*
Linda H Pennell, *Admin Sec*
Denyse Owens, *VP Finance*
Carol Lewis, *Accounts Mgr*
EMP: 50 **EST:** 1920
SQ FT: 47,415
SALES (est): 12.6MM
SALES (corp-wide): 3.4B **Privately Held**
WEB: www.theligature.com
SIC: 2752 2759 Commercial printing, offset; invitation & stationery printing & engraving
PA: Taylor Corporation
1725 Roe Crest Dr
North Mankato MN 56003
507 625-2828

(P-7134)
THOMAS BURT
Also Called: Ink Spots
5095 Brooks St, Montclair (91763-4804)
P.O. Box 2086, Arcadia (91077-2086)
PHONE......................626 301-9065
Thomas Burt, *Owner*
EMP: 15
SQ FT: 15,000
SALES (est): 2.3MM **Privately Held**
WEB: www.inkspotsprinting.com
SIC: 2752 Commercial printing, lithographic

(P-7135)
TIME PRTG SOLUTIONS PROVIDER
1614 D St, Sacramento (95814-1014)
PHONE......................916 446-6152
Andy Poole, *President*
Dena Poole, *CFO*
EMP: 10
SALES (est): 120K **Privately Held**
SIC: 2752 Commercial printing, offset

(P-7136)
TIMES LITHO INC
300 S Grand Ave Ste 1200, Los Angeles
(90071-3122)
PHONE......................503 359-0300
William T Beckwith, *President*
Richard Bunker, *Vice Pres*
EMP: 49
SQ FT: 70,000
SALES (est): 2.7MM **Privately Held**
SIC: 2752 0752 Animal specialty services; color lithography

(P-7137)
TOMS PRINTING INC
1819 E St, Sacramento (95811-1018)
PHONE......................916 444-7788
Daniel Tom, *President*
Mel Tom, *Treasurer*
Robert Tom, *Vice Pres*
Rebecca Tom, *Admin Sec*
EMP: 16
SQ FT: 9,600
SALES (est): 2.1MM **Privately Held**
WEB: www.toms-printing.com
SIC: 2752 Lithographing on metal; commercial printing, offset

(P-7138)
TOUCH LITHO COMPANY
7215 E Gage Ave, Commerce
(90040-3812)
PHONE......................562 927-8899
Michael Wu, *President*
Jimmy Magpayo, *Manager*
Alex Wu, *Accounts Mgr*
▲ **EMP:** 15
SQ FT: 6,000
SALES (est): 2.9MM **Privately Held**
SIC: 2752 Commercial printing, offset

(P-7139)
TRACKSTAR PRINTING INC
1140 W Mahalo Pl, Compton (90220-5443)
PHONE......................310 216-1275
Larry Migliazzo, *President*
Patricia A Migliazzo, *Admin Sec*
▲ **EMP:** 12
SQ FT: 2,600
SALES (est): 2MM **Privately Held**
WEB: www.trackstarla.com
SIC: 2752 Commercial printing, offset

(P-7140)
TRADE PRINTING SERVICES LLC
2080 Las Palmas Dr, Carlsbad
(92011-1570)
PHONE......................760 496-0230
Jim Simpson,
Jason Karches,
EMP: 24
SALES (est): 3.1MM **Privately Held**
WEB: www.tradeprintingsvc.com
SIC: 2752 Commercial printing, lithographic

(P-7141)
TREND OFFSET PRINTING SVCS INC
3701 Catalina St, Los Alamitos
(90720-2402)
PHONE......................859 449-2900
Jason Hummer, *Manager*
Randy Ginsberg, *Vice Pres*
Bill Hall, *Production*
Norman Webster, *Cust Mgr*
Sylvia Kenney, *Manager*
EMP: 110
SALES (corp-wide): 329.2MM **Privately Held**
SIC: 2752 Commercial printing, offset
PA: Trend Offset Printing Services, Inc.
3701 Catalina St
Los Alamitos CA 90720
562 598-2446

(P-7142)
TREND OFFSET PRINTING SVCS INC (PA)
3701 Catalina St, Los Alamitos
(90720-2402)
P.O. Box 3008 (90720-1308)
PHONE......................562 598-2446
Anthony Jacob Lienau, *Ch of Bd*
Richard Carter, *President*
Todd Nelson, *CEO*
Munir Ahmed, *COO*
Thomas Balutis, *CFO*
▲ **EMP:** 650
SQ FT: 300,000
SALES (est): 329.2MM **Privately Held**
WEB: www.trendoffset.com
SIC: 2752 Commercial printing, offset

(P-7143)
TREND OFFSET PRINTING SVCS INC
3791 Catalina St, Los Alamitos
(90720-2402)
PHONE......................562 598-2446
Paul Rhilindger, *Manager*
Jim Alaimo, *Purch Dir*
Clark King, *Sales Executive*
Mike Day, *Director*
Robert Cervantes, *Manager*
EMP: 425
SALES (corp-wide): 329.2MM **Privately Held**
WEB: www.trendoffset.com
SIC: 2752 2732 Commercial printing, offset; books: printing & binding

PA: Trend Offset Printing Services, Inc.
3701 Catalina St
Los Alamitos CA 90720
562 598-2446

(P-7144)
TREND OFFSET PRINTING SVCS INC
3722 Catalina St, Los Alamitos
(90720-2403)
PHONE......................714 826-2360
Robert Lienau, *Manager*
Peter Thiemthat, *Purchasing*
Alicia Beltran, *Education*
EMP: 100
SALES (corp-wide): 329.2MM **Privately Held**
WEB: www.trendoffset.com
SIC: 2752 Commercial printing, offset
PA: Trend Offset Printing Services, Inc.
3701 Catalina St
Los Alamitos CA 90720
562 598-2446

(P-7145)
TRI PRINT LLC
Also Called: Hangtags.com
7573 Slater Ave Ste C, Huntington Beach
(92647-7754)
PHONE......................714 847-1400
Ronald P Herrema,
▲ **EMP:** 16
SALES (est): 2.7MM **Privately Held**
WEB: www.triprint.com
SIC: 2752 Commercial printing, offset

(P-7146)
TRIALGRAPHIX INC
600 Wilshire Blvd Ste 700, Los Angeles
(90017-3219)
PHONE......................213 621-4400
Edward Myles, *Principal*
EMP: 19
SALES (est): 408.8K **Privately Held**
SIC: 2752 Business form & card printing, lithographic
PA: Resonant Legal Media, Llc
1 Penn Plz Ste 1514
New York NY 10119

(P-7147)
TRIBAL PRINT SOURCE
36146 Pala Temecula Rd, Pala (92059)
PHONE......................760 597-2650
Drew Hendricks, *Director*
EMP: 12 **EST:** 2011
SALES (est): 1.1MM **Privately Held**
SIC: 2752 Commercial printing, lithographic

(P-7148)
TRINITY MARKETING LLC
Also Called: Prestige Printing & Graphics
12925 Alcosta Blvd Ste 6, San Ramon
(94583-1341)
PHONE......................925 866-1514
Rose Maloney, *Mng Member*
Chris Maloney,
EMP: 10 **EST:** 2015
SALES (est): 1.5MM **Privately Held**
SIC: 2752 Commercial printing, offset

(P-7149)
TULIP PUBG & GRAPHICS INC
Also Called: Greener Printer
1003 Canal Blvd, Richmond (94804-3549)
PHONE......................510 898-0000
Mario Assadi, *Principal*
Michael Schifter, *Info Tech Mgr*
Andrea Larson, *Accounting Mgr*
Sarah Marth, *Controller*
David Grant, *Opers Mgr*
EMP: 28
SQ FT: 40,000
SALES (est): 6.1MM **Privately Held**
WEB: www.tulipnet.com
SIC: 2752 Commercial printing, offset

(P-7150)
TYPECRAFT INC
Also Called: Typecraft Wood & Jones
2040 E Walnut St, Pasadena (91107-5804)
PHONE......................626 795-8093
D Harry Montgomery, *President*
Jeffrey J Gish, *Vice Pres*

Mark Burks, *Plant Mgr*
Ashley Gish, *Manager*
Tim Silverlake, *Manager*
EMP: 38
SQ FT: 19,000
SALES (est): 6.6MM **Privately Held**
WEB: www.typecraft.com
SIC: 2752 Commercial printing, offset; circulars, lithographed; posters, lithographed

(P-7151)
TYT LLC (HQ)
Also Called: PS Print, LLC
2861 Mandela Pkwy, Oakland
(94608-4011)
PHONE...................510 444-3933
Andy Comly, *Mng Member*
Carol Leung, *Accountant*
Miguel Rodriguez, *Prdtn Mgr*
Sonia Mansfield, *Marketing Staff*
Frank Young, *Mng Member*
▼ **EMP:** 110
SQ FT: 55,000
SALES (est): 8MM
SALES (corp-wide): 1.9B **Publicly Held**
WEB: www.psprint.com
SIC: 2752 Commercial printing, offset
PA: Deluxe Corporation
3680 Victoria St N
Shoreview MN 55126
651 483-7111

(P-7152)
UBS PRINTING GROUP INC
2577 Research Dr, Corona (92882-7607)
PHONE...................951 273-7900
Gene Hamrick, *Principal*
Laura Bradshaw, *Controller*
Alex Castro, *Plant Mgr*
Gilbert Ashdown, *Opers Staff*
Dan Entzminger, *Sales Executive*
▲ **EMP:** 64
SQ FT: 78,000
SALES (est): 17.7MM **Privately Held**
WEB: www.ubsprint.com
SIC: 2752 Commercial printing, offset

(P-7153)
ULTIMATE PRINT SOURCE INC
Also Called: PRINTING 4HIM
2070 S Hellman Ave, Ontario (91761-8018)
PHONE...................909 947-5292
Jeffrey J Ferrazzano, *CEO*
Edith Le Leux, *Treasurer*
Desiree Ferrazzano, *Vice Pres*
Jon Le Leux, *Admin Sec*
EMP: 30
SQ FT: 20,000
SALES: 5.5MM **Privately Held**
WEB: www.ultimateprintsource.com
SIC: 2752 Commercial printing, offset

(P-7154)
UNI SPORT INC
16933 Gramercy Pl, Gardena
(90247-5207)
PHONE...................310 217-4587
Thomas Hebert, *President*
EMP: 25
SQ FT: 10,000
SALES (est): 3.2MM **Privately Held**
SIC: 2752 Commercial printing, lithographic

(P-7155)
UNIQUE IMAGE INC
19365 Bus Center Dr Ste 4, Northridge
(91324-3581)
PHONE...................818 727-7785
Wafa Kanan, *President*
Jeff Reed, *Manager*
EMP: 17 **EST:** 1993
SQ FT: 15,400
SALES (est): 3.1MM **Privately Held**
SIC: 2752 2741 7311 7331 Commercial printing, lithographic; miscellaneous publishing; advertising agencies; direct mail advertising services; commercial art & graphic design; public relations services

(P-7156)
UNITED CRAFTSMEN PRINITING
Also Called: Craftsman Printing
6660 Via Del Oro, San Jose (95119-1392)
PHONE...................408 224-6464
Joan Falkenstein, *President*

EMP: 30
SQ FT: 17,900
SALES (est): 6.7MM **Privately Held**
SIC: 2752 Commercial printing, lithographic

(P-7157)
UNIVERSAL PRINTING SERVICES
Also Called: Color Tech Commercial Printing
26012 Atlantic Ocean Dr, Lake Forest
(92630-8843)
PHONE...................951 788-1500
Gregg Baxter, *President*
Sharon Baxter, *Vice Pres*
EMP: 14
SQ FT: 2,800
SALES (est): 3.8MM **Privately Held**
WEB: www.colortechprinting.com
SIC: 2752 Commercial printing, lithographic

(P-7158)
UPPER DECK COMPANY LLC
5830 El Camino Real, Carlsbad
(92008-8816)
PHONE...................800 873-7332
Richard Mc William, *CEO*
Jason Masherah, *President*
Roz Nowicki, *Exec VP*
Dianne Hatley, *Executive*
Richard Bonora, *Business Dir*
▲ **EMP:** 400
SQ FT: 247,000
SALES (est): 113.7MM **Privately Held**
SIC: 2752 5947 Souvenir cards, lithographed; gift, novelty & souvenir shop

(P-7159)
USA PRINTER COMPANY
Also Called: USA Printer Guy
41571 Corning Pl Ste 115, Murrieta
(92562-7066)
PHONE...................800 279-7768
Gordon Wood, *President*
▲ **EMP:** 10 **EST:** 2010
SALES (est): 1.4MM **Privately Held**
SIC: 2752 Commercial printing, offset

(P-7160)
UTAP PRINTING CO INC
1423 San Mateo Ave, South San Francisco
(94080-6504)
PHONE...................650 588-2818
Patrick Y Chin, *President*
Kyi Khin, *Controller*
EMP: 13
SQ FT: 5,200
SALES (est): 2MM **Privately Held**
WEB: www.utap.com
SIC: 2752 Commercial printing, offset

(P-7161)
V3 PRINTING CORPORATION
Also Called: V 3
200 N Elevar St, Oxnard (93030-7969)
PHONE...................805 981-2600
David Wilson, *President*
Michael Szanger, *Vice Pres*
EMP: 80
SQ FT: 4,000
SALES (est): 21.7MM **Privately Held**
WEB: www.venturaprint.com
SIC: 2752 Lithographing on metal; commercial printing, offset

(P-7162)
VALLEY BUSINESS PRINTERS INC
Also Called: Valley Printers
16230 Filbert St, Sylmar (91342-1039)
PHONE...................818 362-7771
Michael Flannery, *CEO*
Bruce Bolkin, *President*
Karen S Flannery, *Corp Secy*
▲ **EMP:** 92
SQ FT: 110,000
SALES (est): 16.4MM **Privately Held**
SIC: 2752 2759 Commercial printing, offset; commercial printing

(P-7163)
VANARD LITHOGRAPHERS INC
3220 Kurtz St, San Diego (92110-4426)
PHONE...................619 291-5571
Annette Fritzenkotter, *President*

Ted Jingling, *Software Engr*
EMP: 28
SQ FT: 25,000
SALES (est): 3.5MM **Privately Held**
WEB: www.vanard.com
SIC: 2752 Commercial printing, offset

(P-7164)
VANS INSTANT PRINTERS INC
221 E San Bernardino Rd, Covina
(91723-1624)
PHONE...................626 966-1708
William J Hammnett, *Owner*
EMP: 11
SALES (est): 605.7K **Privately Held**
SIC: 2752 Commercial printing, offset

(P-7165)
VARIABLE IMAGE PRINTING
16540 Aston Ste A, Irvine (92606-4805)
PHONE...................949 296-1444
Paul O Brien, *President*
Bob Stewart, *Vice Pres*
EMP: 18 **EST:** 2000
SQ FT: 12,400
SALES (est): 2.4MM **Privately Held**
WEB: www.variableimageprinting.com
SIC: 2752 Commercial printing, offset

(P-7166)
VARIABLE IMAGE PRINTING
9020 Kenamar Dr Ste 204, San Diego
(92121-2431)
PHONE...................858 530-2443
Paul O'Brien, *President*
Paul Obrien, *President*
Bob Stewart, *Vice Pres*
EMP: 30
SALES (est): 2.2MM **Privately Held**
SIC: 2752 Commercial printing, offset

(P-7167)
VDP DIRECT LLC (PA)
5520 Ruffin Rd Ste 111, San Diego
(92123-1320)
PHONE...................858 300-4510
Jimmy Lakdwala,
Janice Lakdawala,
EMP: 25
SQ FT: 12,500
SALES (est): 5.5MM **Privately Held**
SIC: 2752 Commercial printing, offset

(P-7168)
VELO3D INC
511 Division St, Campbell (95008-6905)
PHONE...................408 666-5309
Benny Buller, *CEO*
EMP: 120
SQ FT: 17,000
SALES (est): 351.7K **Privately Held**
SIC: 2752 Commercial printing, lithographic

(P-7169)
VILLAGE INSTANT PRINTING INC
Also Called: Park's Prtg & Lithographic Co
1515 10th St, Modesto (95354-0726)
PHONE...................209 576-2568
Austin E Parks, *President*
Michelle Neilsen, *Corp Secy*
Frank Parks, *Vice Pres*
Terry Jacob, *Analyst*
Jeffrey Wright, *Sales Executive*
EMP: 40 **EST:** 1974
SQ FT: 10,000
SALES (est): 8.3MM **Privately Held**
SIC: 2752 Commercial printing, offset

(P-7170)
VOMELA SPECIALTY COMPANY
9810 Bell Ranch Dr, Santa Fe Springs
(90670-2952)
PHONE...................562 944-3853
Loren Maxwell, *Branch Mgr*
EMP: 23
SALES (corp-wide): 148.4MM **Privately Held**
SIC: 2752 7336 Poster & decal printing, lithographic; commercial art & graphic design
PA: Vomela Specialty Company
274 Fillmore Ave E
Saint Paul MN 55107
651 228-2200

(P-7171)
WALKER LITHOGRAPH
Also Called: Walker Printing
20869 Walnut St, Red Bluff (96080-9704)
PHONE...................530 527-2142
Neal Gagliano, *Partner*
Chris Gagliano, *Partner*
EMP: 14 **EST:** 1996
SQ FT: 5,000
SALES (est): 2.1MM **Privately Held**
WEB: www.walkerlitho.com
SIC: 2752 Commercial printing, offset

(P-7172)
WANDA MATRANGA
Also Called: Printing Place, The
41651 Corporate Way Ste 5, Palm Desert
(92260-1987)
P.O. Box 12827 (92255-2827)
PHONE...................760 773-4701
Wanda Matranga, *Owner*
Larry Espinola, *Project Mgr*
Scott Brooks, *Marketing Staff*
Karen Schroeder, *Accounts Exec*
EMP: 12
SQ FT: 7,000
SALES (est): 1.4MM **Privately Held**
WEB: www.theprintingplace.net
SIC: 2752 Commercial printing, offset

(P-7173)
WARREN PRINTING & MAILING INC
5000 Eagle Rock Blvd, Los Angeles
(90041-1908)
PHONE...................323 258-2621
Robert H Warren, *President*
Victoria Warren, *Vice Pres*
EMP: 10
SQ FT: 5,661
SALES (est): 1.4MM **Privately Held**
WEB: www.print-mail.com
SIC: 2752 7331 2759 Commercial printing, offset; direct mail advertising services; commercial printing

(P-7174)
WE DO GRAPHICS INC
1150 N Main St, Orange (92867-3421)
PHONE...................714 997-7390
Douglas K Le Mieux, *President*
Heidi G Le Mieux, *CFO*
Steven I Lehrer, *Vice Pres*
Kevin Magula, *Director*
Laura Lehrer, *Manager*
▲ **EMP:** 25
SQ FT: 23,000
SALES (est): 4.3MM **Privately Held**
WEB: www.wedographics.com
SIC: 2752 Commercial printing, offset

(P-7175)
WEBER PRINTING COMPANY INC
1124 E Del Amo Blvd, Carson
(90746-3180)
PHONE...................310 639-5064
Richard M Weber, *President*
Lynda Slack, *CFO*
Steven Weber, *Vice Pres*
Ron Lamantia, *Technology*
EMP: 35
SQ FT: 30,000
SALES (est): 6.6MM **Privately Held**
SIC: 2752 Photo-offset printing; commercial printing, offset

(P-7176)
WEISER LITHO INC
9025 Owensmouth Ave, Canoga Park
(91304-1417)
PHONE...................818 707-2708
Paula Weiser, *President*
EMP: 19
SQ FT: 7,700
SALES: 1.5MM **Privately Held**
WEB: www.weiserlitho.com
SIC: 2752 Commercial printing, offset

(P-7177)
WELLPRINT INC
380 E 1st St Ste B, Tustin (92780-3211)
PHONE...................714 838-3962
Rick Mandell, *President*
EMP: 10 **EST:** 1971

▲ = Import ▼=Export
◆ =Import/Export

SQ FT: 3,300
SALES (est): 780K **Privately Held**
WEB: www.wellprint.com
SIC: 2752 7334 Commercial printing, offset; photocopying & duplicating services

(P-7178)
WEST COAST BUSINESS PRTRS INC
Also Called: West Coast Digital
9822 Independence Ave, Chatsworth (91311-4319)
PHONE..................818 709-4980
Arthur Worthington, *President*
Patricia Worthington, *Admin Sec*
EMP: 13
SQ FT: 10,000
SALES (est): 1.4MM **Privately Held**
WEB: www.wcdigital.com
SIC: 2752 5112 2759 Commercial printing, lithographic; envelopes; commercial printing

(P-7179)
WESTCOTT PRESS INC
1121 W Isabel St, Burbank (91506-1405)
PHONE..................626 794-7716
Jeffrey W Carpenter, *President*
Mila Carpenter, *Treasurer*
Neil W Carpenter, *Vice Pres*
Neil Carpenter, *Vice Pres*
EMP: 12
SQ FT: 10,000
SALES: 1.8MM **Privately Held**
WEB: www.westcottpress.com
SIC: 2752 Commercial printing, offset

(P-7180)
WESTERN METAL DCTG CO COIL DIV
Also Called: Cucamonga Division
8875 Industrial Ln, Rancho Cucamonga (91730-4529)
PHONE..................909 987-2506
Scott Brotzman, *CEO*
EMP: 11
SQ FT: 95,000
SALES: 1MM **Privately Held**
WEB: www.western-metal.com
SIC: 2752 Lithographing on metal

(P-7181)
WESTERN PAD
391 Thor Pl, Brea (92821-4133)
PHONE..................714 671-1900
William Guerra, *CEO*
Gloria Guerra, *Corp Secy*
Steven Medina, *General Mgr*
EMP: 21
SQ FT: 1,000
SALES (est): 4.7MM **Privately Held**
WEB: www.westernpad.com
SIC: 2752 2678 Commercial printing, offset; stationery products

(P-7182)
WESTERN PRTG & GRAPHICS LLC (PA)
Also Called: Western Printing and Label
17931 Sky Park Cir, Irvine (92614-6312)
PHONE..................714 532-3946
Aaron David Smith,
Cynthia Joan Smith,
EMP: 23 EST: 1981
SQ FT: 11,000
SALES (est): 3MM **Privately Held**
WEB: www.westprint.com
SIC: 2752 2791 2759 2741 Commercial printing, offset; typesetting; commercial printing; miscellaneous publishing

(P-7183)
WESTERN TRADE PRINTING INC
5695 E Shields Ave, Fresno (93727-7819)
PHONE..................559 251-8595
Claude Teisinger, *President*
Christine Langney, *Corp Secy*
Erlinda Teisinger, *Vice Pres*
▲ EMP: 14
SQ FT: 19,000
SALES (est): 2.6MM **Privately Held**
WEB: www.westerntradeprinting.com
SIC: 2752 Commercial printing, lithographic

(P-7184)
WESTERN WEB INC
1900 Bendixsen St Ste 2, Samoa (95564-9525)
P.O. Box 278 (95564-0278)
PHONE..................707 444-6236
Stephen Jackson, *President*
Michael Morris, *Vice Pres*
EMP: 21 EST: 2010
SQ FT: 25,400
SALES: 3MM **Privately Held**
SIC: 2752 Commercial printing, lithographic

(P-7185)
WESTMINSTER PRESS INC
4906 W 1st St, Santa Ana (92703-3110)
PHONE..................714 210-2881
Gary Tang, *CEO*
Thoai Tang, *Vice Pres*
Tri Tang, *Vice Pres*
EMP: 50
SQ FT: 10,000
SALES (est): 8MM **Privately Held**
SIC: 2752 Color lithography

(P-7186)
WILLEY PRINTING COMPANY INC
1405 10th St, Modesto (95354-0724)
P.O. Box 886 (95353-0886)
PHONE..................209 524-4811
Jerry Sauls, *President*
Mary Alice Willey, *Vice Pres*
Barbara Haynes, *Bookkeeper*
EMP: 30 EST: 1946
SQ FT: 20,000
SALES (est): 5.2MM **Privately Held**
SIC: 2752 Commercial printing, offset

(P-7187)
WILLIAM J HAMMETT INC
Also Called: Grand Printing
221 E San Bernardino Rd, Covina (91723-1624)
PHONE..................626 966-1708
William Hammett, *President*
EMP: 10
SQ FT: 4,500
SALES: 600K **Privately Held**
WEB: www.grandprinting.com
SIC: 2752 Commercial printing, offset; lithographing on metal

(P-7188)
WIRZ & CO
444 Colton Ave, Colton (92324-3019)
PHONE..................909 825-6970
Charles Fred Wirz, *Owner*
Kelly Gettings, *Marketing Staff*
EMP: 18
SQ FT: 8,000
SALES (est): 1.8MM **Privately Held**
SIC: 2752 Commercial printing, offset

(P-7189)
WISSINGS INC
Also Called: Printing Shoppe, The
9906 Mesa Rim Rd, San Diego (92121-2910)
PHONE..................858 625-4111
Jerry Wissing, *President*
Nancy Wissing, *CFO*
Paul De Graaf, *Prdtn Mgr*
Chelsea Wissing, *Sales Staff*
EMP: 14 EST: 1981
SQ FT: 8,600
SALES (est): 2.4MM **Privately Held**
WEB: www.printingshoppe.com
SIC: 2752 Commercial printing, offset

(P-7190)
WS PACKAGING-BLAKE PRINTERY (HQ)
2222 Beebee St, San Luis Obispo (93401-5505)
PHONE..................805 543-6843
Michael P Glavin, *President*
Jay K Tomcheck, *VP Finance*
EMP: 19 EST: 1949
SQ FT: 40,000
SALES (est): 6.6MM
SALES (corp-wide): 760.8MM **Privately Held**
SIC: 2752 Commercial printing, offset

PA: W/S Packaging Group, Inc.
2571 S Hemlock Rd
Green Bay WI 54229
920 866-6300

(P-7191)
WS PACKAGING-BLAKE PRINTERY
Also Called: Poor Richards Press
2224 Beebee St, San Luis Obispo (93401-5505)
PHONE..................805 543-6844
Bruce Dickinson, *Branch Mgr*
EMP: 30
SQ FT: 3,500
SALES (corp-wide): 760.8MM **Privately Held**
SIC: 2752 2621 2791 Commercial printing, offset; wrapping paper; typesetting, computer controlled
HQ: Ws Packaging-Blake Printery
2222 Beebee St
San Luis Obispo CA 93401
805 543-6843

(P-7192)
X-IGENT PRINTING INC
1001 Goodrich Blvd, Commerce (90022-5102)
PHONE..................323 837-9779
Omar Rodriguez, *President*
Norma Cerzanges, *Office Mgr*
Hugo Cervantes, *Admin Sec*
Isabel Serrano, *Technology*
Ivan Cervantes, *Accounts Mgr*
EMP: 15
SQ FT: 6,000
SALES (est): 2.3MM **Privately Held**
WEB: www.xigentsolutions.com
SIC: 2752 Commercial printing, offset

(P-7193)
ZADA GRAPHICS INC
Also Called: Micro-DOT
13009 S Broadway, Los Angeles (90061-1119)
PHONE..................323 321-8940
Helen Zada, *President*
Sam H Zada, *Corp Secy*
Allan Zada, *Vice Pres*
John Cameron, *General Mgr*
EMP: 12
SQ FT: 5,500
SALES: 1.2MM **Privately Held**
WEB: www.zadagraphics.com
SIC: 2752 2759 Commercial printing, offset; letterpress printing

(P-7194)
ZAP PRINTING INCORPORATED
Also Called: Zap Printing and Graphics
127 Radio Rd, Corona (92879-1724)
P.O. Box 1208 (92878-1208)
PHONE..................951 734-8181
Paula A Montanez, *CEO*
Eugene Montanez, *President*
Lina Limbach, *Marketing Staff*
Aimee Silletto, *Marketing Staff*
Wendy Herzog, *Sales Staff*
EMP: 11
SQ FT: 7,000
SALES (est): 2MM **Privately Held**
SIC: 2752 3993 2759 Commercial printing, offset; signs & advertising specialties; commercial printing

(P-7195)
ZIP PRINT INC (PA)
Also Called: Valprint
1257 G St, Fresno (93706-1610)
P.O. Box 12332 (93777-2332)
PHONE..................559 486-3112
Jack Emerian, *President*
Darryl Hanoian, *Vice Pres*
Keith Cappelluti, *Graphic Designe*
Becky Prettyman, *Sales Staff*
Lori Sharp, *Sales Staff*
EMP: 50
SQ FT: 7,500
SALES (est): 8.5MM **Privately Held**
SIC: 2752 7334 7331 2791 Commercial printing, offset; photocopying & duplicating services; direct mail advertising services; typesetting; bookbinding & related work; commercial printing

(P-7196)
ZOO PRINTING INC (PA)
Also Called: Zoo Printing Trade Printer
4730 Eastern Ave, Bell (90201-6400)
PHONE..................310 253-7751
Dan Doron, *President*
Maria Camins, *Vice Pres*
Mark Russell, *QA Dir*
Michael Claire, *Info Tech Mgr*
Sako Sahaghian, *Info Tech Mgr*
▲ EMP: 93
SQ FT: 25,000
SALES (est): 21MM **Privately Held**
SIC: 2752 Commercial printing, offset

2754 Commercial Printing: Gravure

(P-7197)
ALNA ENVELOPE COMPANY INC
1567 E 25th St, Los Angeles (90011-1887)
PHONE..................323 235-3161
Al Azus, *President*
Hedi Azus, *Treasurer*
Max Candiotty, *Vice Pres*
Jose Caldera, *General Mgr*
EMP: 35 EST: 1955
SQ FT: 14,000
SALES (est): 3.7MM **Privately Held**
WEB: www.alnaenvelope.com
SIC: 2754 2759 Envelopes: gravure printing; commercial printing

(P-7198)
COORSTEK INC
Also Called: Tetrafluor
2051 E Maple Ave, El Segundo (90245-5009)
PHONE..................310 322-2545
Louis Sobo, *Branch Mgr*
Tim Nelson, *Manager*
EMP: 18
SALES (corp-wide): 909.3MM **Privately Held**
SIC: 2754 Seals: gravure printing
HQ: Coorstek, Inc.
14143 Denver West Pkwy # 400
Lakewood CO 80401
303 271-7000

(P-7199)
COSMOJET INC
9601 Cozycroft Ave Ste 2, Chatsworth (91311-5183)
PHONE..................818 773-6544
Serge Kapustin, *President*
Olga Kapustin, *CFO*
▲ EMP: 10 EST: 1999
SQ FT: 10,000
SALES (est): 442.8K **Privately Held**
SIC: 2754 8742 Labels: gravure printing; marketing consulting services

(P-7200)
FERNQVIST RETAIL SYSTEMS INC (HQ)
Also Called: Fernqvist Labeling Solutions
2544 Leghorn St, Mountain View (94043-1614)
PHONE..................650 428-0330
Tom Vargas, *CEO*
Jim Clark, *President*
Teresa Caputo, *Officer*
EMP: 16
SQ FT: 6,100
SALES: 3.8MM **Privately Held**
WEB: www.fernqvist.com
SIC: 2754 5734 Labels: gravure printing; printers & plotters: computers
PA: Epic Labeling Solutions, Inc.
2544 Leghorn St
Mountain View CA 94043
650 428-0330

(P-7201)
FILET MENU INC
1830 S La Cienega Blvd, Los Angeles (90035-4652)
P.O. Box 352161 (90035-0256)
PHONE..................310 202-8000
Michael R Levine, *President*
EMP: 22
SQ FT: 28,000

(PA)=Parent Co (HQ)=Headquarters (DH)=Div Headquarters
✿ = New Business established in last 2 years

2019 California
Manufacturers Register

PRODUCTS & SVCS

299

SALES (est): 163.1K **Privately Held**
SIC: 2754 2759 Commercial printing, gravure; commercial printing

(P-7202)
FONGS GRAPHICS & PRINTING INC
7743 Garvey Ave, Rosemead (91770-3068)
PHONE..................626 307-1898
Chak M Fong, *President*
Annie Ng, *Art Dir*
Daphne Fong, *Manager*
▲ EMP: 20
SQ FT: 1,300
SALES (est): 1.9MM **Privately Held**
WEB: www.fongsmenu.com
SIC: 2754 7336 Menus: gravure printing; commercial art & graphic design

(P-7203)
INSTITUTE OF ELECTRICAL AND EL
Also Called: Ieee Computer Society
10662 Los Vaqueros Cir, Los Alamitos (90720-2513)
P.O. Box 3014 (90720)
PHONE..................714 821-8380
Linda Ashworth, *Administration*
Anabell St Vincent, *Database Admin*
Osvaldo Perez, *Transptn Dir*
Christine Anthony, *Editor*
EMP: 85
SALES (corp-wide): 496.6MM **Privately Held**
SIC: 2754 Publication printing, gravure
PA: The Institute Of Electrical And Electronics Engineers Incorporated
445 Hoes Ln
Piscataway NJ 08854
212 419-7900

(P-7204)
JERRY V JOHNSON & ASSOC INC
Also Called: J J and A
720 S Glendale Ave, Glendale (91205-2318)
PHONE..................818 543-6710
Jerry V Johnson, *Ch of Bd*
Robert Rembert, *President*
Linda Rice, *Treasurer*
Brad Starkey, *Vice Pres*
Jennifer Rojo, *Office Mgr*
EMP: 11 EST: 1974
SQ FT: 14,000
SALES (est): 1.6MM **Privately Held**
SIC: 2754 Commercial printing, gravure

(P-7205)
KMR LABEL LLC
Also Called: Axiom Label Group
1360 W Walnut Pkwy, Compton (90220-5029)
PHONE..................310 603-8910
Kieron Delahunt, *General Mgr*
Keith McHugh, *CFO*
Dave Puopolo, *Vice Pres*
Connie Hui, *Controller*
V Story, *Production*
EMP: 50
SQ FT: 24,000
SALES (est): 8.6MM **Privately Held**
WEB: www.axiomlabel.com
SIC: 2754 2752 Labels: gravure printing; commercial printing, lithographic

(P-7206)
MC ALLISTER INDUSTRIES INC (PA)
731 S Highway 101 Ste 2, Solana Beach (92075-2629)
PHONE..................858 755-0683
Robert Mc Allister, *President*
▲ EMP: 20
SQ FT: 2,500
SALES (est): 1.9MM **Privately Held**
WEB: www.mcallisterindustries.com
SIC: 2754 Cards, except greeting: gravure printing

(P-7207)
MILLENNIUM GRAPHICS INC
3443 Park Pl, Pleasanton (94588-2936)
PHONE..................925 602-0635

Frank Baltazar, *President*
Christine Baltazar, *Vice Pres*
EMP: 11
SALES: 400K **Privately Held**
SIC: 2754 Commercial printing, gravure

(P-7208)
MONTEREY BAY OFFICE PDTS INC
1700 Wyatt Dr, Santa Clara (95054-1526)
PHONE..................408 727-4627
Kellie S Murphy, *Branch Mgr*
EMP: 12
SALES (corp-wide): 10.8MM **Privately Held**
SIC: 2754 Business form & card printing, gravure
PA: Monterey Bay Office Products Inc.
325 Victor St Ste A
Salinas CA 93907
831 646-8080

(P-7209)
ONEIL CAPITAL MANAGEMENT
Also Called: O'Neil Data Systems, Inc.
12655 Beatrice St, Los Angeles (90066-7300)
PHONE..................310 448-6400
William O Neil, *CEO*
Jason O'Brien, *Human Res Mgr*
Christine Canerdy, *Manager*
William Stirling, *Manager*
▲ EMP: 92
SQ FT: 70,000
SALES (est): 28.3MM
SALES (corp-wide): 231.5MM **Privately Held**
WEB: www.oneildata.com
SIC: 2754 2732 2741 2711 Catalogs: gravure printing, not published on site; book printing; miscellaneous publishing; newspapers
PA: Data Analysis Inc.
12655 Beatrice St
Los Angeles CA 90066
310 448-6800

(P-7210)
QPE INC
Also Called: Quality Packaging and Engrg
1372 Mcgaw Ave, Irvine (92614-5539)
PHONE..................949 263-0381
Kirk WEI, *President*
Rachel Lee, *CFO*
Joseph S Chiang, *Corp Secy*
◆ EMP: 18
SQ FT: 10,000
SALES: 6MM **Privately Held**
SIC: 2754 7389 Labels: gravure printing; packaging & labeling services

(P-7211)
R R DONNELLEY & SONS COMPANY
Also Called: Donnelley Financial
1 Embarcadero Ctr Ste 200, San Francisco (94111-3644)
PHONE..................415 362-2300
Joyce Battisite, *Manager*
EMP: 40
SALES (corp-wide): 6.9B **Publicly Held**
WEB: www.rrdonnelley.com
SIC: 2754 2752 Directories: gravure printing, not published on site; commercial printing, lithographic
PA: R. R. Donnelley & Sons Company
35 W Wacker Dr Ste 3650
Chicago IL 60601
312 326-8000

(P-7212)
SOLUTION BOX INC
Also Called: Ideal Print Solutions
1923 Avenida Plaza Real, Oceanside (92056-6024)
PHONE..................949 387-3223
Larry Corrado, *President*
Amber Ramsey, *Office Mgr*
EMP: 11
SQ FT: 6,000
SALES: 3.5MM **Privately Held**
SIC: 2754 Labels: gravure printing

(P-7213)
TAYLOR COMMUNICATIONS INC
330 E Lambert Rd Ste 100, Brea (92821-4100)
PHONE..................866 541-0937
EMP: 14
SALES (corp-wide): 3.4B **Privately Held**
SIC: 2754 Commercial printing, gravure
HQ: Taylor Communications, Inc.
4205 S 96th St
Omaha NE 68127
402 898-6422

(P-7214)
TRANSWORLD PRINTING SVCS INC
Also Called: T P S
2857 Transworld Dr, Stockton (95206-3950)
PHONE..................209 982-1511
Edwin McClenton, *CEO*
Daphyne Brown, *President*
Dennis Vera, *Manager*
EMP: 15
SALES (est): 2.2MM **Privately Held**
SIC: 2754 Commercial printing, gravure

(P-7215)
WESTERN SHELD ACQUISITIONS LLC
Also Called: Western Shield Label
2146 E Gladwick St, Rancho Dominguez (90220-6203)
PHONE..................310 527-6212
Graham C Weaver, *Mng Member*
Thomas Moyer, *President*
Frank Connelly, *CEO*
Lori McLain, *Sales Executive*
Dan Stadler, *Mktg Dir*
EMP: 28 EST: 1970
SQ FT: 17,000
SALES (est): 5MM **Privately Held**
WEB: www.westernshield.com
SIC: 2754 3172 2752 Labels: gravure printing; tobacco pouches; coupons, lithographed

2759 Commercial Printing

(P-7216)
4 OVER LLC (HQ)
5900 San Fernando Rd D, Glendale (91202-2773)
PHONE..................818 246-1170
Zarik Megerdichian, *CEO*
Armond Sarkisian, *Shareholder*
Tina Hartounian, *President*
Renee Hanneken, *Admin Asst*
Amber Solorzano, *Admin Asst*
▲ EMP: 277 EST: 2001
SALES (est): 190.6MM **Privately Held**
WEB: www.4over.com
SIC: 2759 7336 Commercial printing; commercial art & graphic design

(P-7217)
4 OVER LLC
1225 Los Angeles St, Glendale (91204-2403)
PHONE..................818 246-1170
Erika Takenaka, *Principal*
EMP: 15
SALES (corp-wide): 190.6MM **Privately Held**
SIC: 2759 Screen printing
HQ: 4 Over, Llc
5900 San Fernando Rd D
Glendale CA 91202
818 246-1170

(P-7218)
A F E INDUSTRIES INC (PA)
13233 Barton Cir, Whittier (90605-3255)
P.O. Box 3303, Santa Fe Springs (90670-1303)
PHONE..................562 944-6889
Fred Elhami, *President*
Ruth Elhami, *Corp Secy*
EMP: 94
SQ FT: 27,000
SALES (est): 13MM **Privately Held**
SIC: 2759 Screen printing; imprinting; letterpress printing

(P-7219)
ABLE CARD CORPORATION LLC
1300 W Optical Dr Ste 600, Irwindale (91702-3285)
PHONE..................626 969-1888
Herman Ho, *CEO*
Donny Yu, *CFO*
Hector Dominguez, *Vice Pres*
EMP: 70
SQ FT: 45,000
SALES (est): 7.4MM **Privately Held**
WEB: www.ablecard.com
SIC: 2759 Commercial printing
PA: First Nations Capital Partners, Llc
7676 Hazard Center Dr # 5
San Diego CA 92108

(P-7220)
ADAMS LABEL COMPANY LLC (PA)
6052 Industrial Way Ste G, Livermore (94551-9711)
PHONE..................925 371-5393
David Bowyer, *CEO*
Patty Hassett, *Administration*
EMP: 14 EST: 2014
SALES (est): 2.9MM **Privately Held**
SIC: 2759 3565 Labels & seals: printing; labeling machines, industrial

(P-7221)
ADCRAFT PRODUCTS CO INC
1230 S Sherman St, Anaheim (92805-6455)
PHONE..................714 776-1230
Randy C Mottram, *President*
Keith A Mottram, *Vice Pres*
Sal Reyna, *Plant Mgr*
Mike Flynn, *Manager*
Laural Gadison, *Manager*
EMP: 27
SALES (est): 5.6MM **Privately Held**
SIC: 2759 Screen printing

(P-7222)
ADVANCE SCREEN GRAPHIC
5720 Union Pacific Ave, Commerce (90022-5135)
PHONE..................323 724-9910
Raymundo Alcaraz, *President*
Umberto Contreras, *Treasurer*
Jose Luis Contreras, *Vice Pres*
Juan Felix, *Admin Sec*
EMP: 15
SQ FT: 22,000
SALES (est): 1.7MM **Privately Held**
SIC: 2759 Screen printing

(P-7223)
ADVANCED VSUAL IMAGE DSIGN LLC
Also Called: Avid Ink
229 N Sherman Ave, Irvine (92614)
PHONE..................951 279-2138
Robert D Davis, *CEO*
Jennie Enholm,
▲ EMP: 200
SQ FT: 20,000
SALES (est): 31.4MM **Privately Held**
SIC: 2759 Screen printing

(P-7224)
ADVANCED WEB OFFSET INC
Also Called: Awo
2260 Oak Ridge Way, Vista (92081-8341)
PHONE..................760 727-1700
Stephen F Shoemaker, *President*
Dan Armstrong, *General Mgr*
David Altomare, *Admin Sec*
Laura McGowan, *Human Res Mgr*
Rob Tanner, *Purchasing*
EMP: 75
SQ FT: 65,000
SALES (est): 14.4MM **Privately Held**
WEB: www.awoink.com
SIC: 2759 2752 Newspapers: printing; periodicals: printing; offset & photolithographic printing

(P-7225)
ADVANTAGE BUSINESS FORMS INC
102 N Riverside Ave, Rialto (92376-5922)
PHONE.........................909 875-7163
Kevin M Danko, *CEO*
Victor Maglio, *Sales Staff*
Keith Sabo, *Sales Staff*
Debi Southern, *Supervisor*
EMP: 12
SQ FT: 10,000
SALES (est): 1.2MM **Privately Held**
WEB: www.abfprints.com
SIC: 2759 7323 Commercial printing; credit reporting services

(P-7226)
ALHAMBRA REPROGRAPHICS INC (PA)
Also Called: A & I Reprographics
3939 E Guasti Rd Ste B, Ontario (91761-1574)
PHONE.........................909 390-4839
Gary Moylan, *President*
Kathy Moylan, *Vice Pres*
EMP: 17
SQ FT: 1,200
SALES (est): 2.7MM **Privately Held**
WEB: www.alhambrareprographics.com
SIC: 2759 Business forms: printing

(P-7227)
ALL FORMS EXPRESS
17572 Griffin Ln, Huntington Beach (92647-6791)
PHONE.........................714 596-8641
Brent Millville, *President*
EMP: 11
SALES (est): 642.2K **Privately Held**
SIC: 2759 Commercial printing

(P-7228)
ALL SPORTS SERVICES INC
Also Called: Sportsco
765 S Gifford Ave Ste 1, San Bernardino (92408-2461)
PHONE.........................909 885-4626
Ray C Imbriana, *President*
Bob Forrest, *Corp Secy*
David Epperson, *Vice Pres*
EMP: 11
SQ FT: 6,000
SALES (est): 1.1MM **Privately Held**
WEB: www.teamsportsco.com
SIC: 2759 Screen printing

(P-7229)
ALL-STAR LETTERING INC
9419 Ann St, Santa Fe Springs (90670-2613)
PHONE.........................562 404-5995
Paul Possemato, *President*
Palma Possemato, *Treasurer*
Susan Possemato, *Vice Pres*
Arcadio Aguayo, *General Mgr*
Tania Martinez,
EMP: 45 EST: 1969
SALES (est): 6.3MM **Privately Held**
WEB: www.allstarlettering.com
SIC: 2759 3555 2396 Screen printing; printing trades machinery; automotive & apparel trimmings

(P-7230)
ALLIANCE MULTIMEDIA LLC
2033 San Elijo Ave Ste 20, Cardiff (92007-1726)
PHONE.........................760 522-3455
Bill McCaffrey, *Mng Member*
Bradlee Rutledge, *Assoc Editor*
EMP: 12
SALES: 1.5MM **Privately Held**
SIC: 2759 7374 7812 7941 Publication printing; computer graphics service; video production; sports promotion

(P-7231)
ALLIANCE TAGS
9235 Trade Pl, San Diego (92126-6313)
P.O. Box 537, La Jolla (92038-0537)
PHONE.........................858 549-7297
Bricks Keifer, *General Mgr*
Tessie Mills, *Administration*
EMP: 22

SALES (est): 1.9MM **Privately Held**
WEB: www.alliancetag.com
SIC: 2759 3993 2671 Labels & seals: printing; signs & advertising specialties; packaging paper & plastics film, coated & laminated

(P-7232)
ALROS LABEL CO INC
Also Called: Alros Lebel Co
14200 Aetna St, Van Nuys (91401-3433)
PHONE.........................818 781-2403
Alfredo Rosales, *President*
Dalia Masjuam, *Corp Secy*
Maria L Rosales, *Vice Pres*
Maria Rosales, *Vice Pres*
Dalia Masjuan, *Office Mgr*
EMP: 12 EST: 1976
SQ FT: 5,000
SALES: 900K **Privately Held**
SIC: 2759 Labels & seals: printing

(P-7233)
AMERICAN FOIL & EMBOSING INC
35 Musick, Irvine (92618-1638)
PHONE.........................949 580-0080
Abdul A Hussain, *President*
EMP: 10
SQ FT: 3,600
SALES (est): 1.4MM **Privately Held**
WEB: www.americanfoil.com
SIC: 2759 Commercial printing

(P-7234)
AMERICAN NON STOP LABEL CORP
Also Called: American Label Co
16221 Arthur St, Cerritos (90703-2130)
PHONE.........................562 921-9437
George Loayza, *CEO*
John Lincoln, *Shareholder*
▲ EMP: 19
SQ FT: 20,000
SALES (est): 3.7MM **Privately Held**
WEB: www.americanlabelco.com
SIC: 2759 Flexographic printing

(P-7235)
AMERICAN ZABIN INTL INC
3933 S Hill St, Los Angeles (90037-1313)
PHONE.........................213 746-3770
Alan Faiola, *CEO*
Steven Garfinkle, *President*
Eric Sedso, *Vice Pres*
Stephanie Zavala, *Sales Staff*
▲ EMP: 32
SQ FT: 18,000
SALES: 10MM **Privately Held**
SIC: 2759 Tags: printing

(P-7236)
AMIGO CUSTOM SCREEN PRINTS LLC
6351 Yarrow Dr Ste A&B, Carlsbad (92011-1545)
PHONE.........................760 452-7964
Robert Lusitana,
EMP: 30
SALES (est): 4MM **Privately Held**
SIC: 2759

(P-7237)
APPAREL UNIFIED LLC
12136 Del Vista Dr, La Mirada (90638-1402)
PHONE.........................562 639-7233
Richard Bermejo,
EMP: 10
SQ FT: 10,000
SALES (est): 334.8K **Privately Held**
SIC: 2759 Letterpress & screen printing

(P-7238)
AQUA PRIETA TEES LLC
102 Via Murcia, San Clemente (92672-3859)
PHONE.........................714 719-2000
Jamey Darter, *Mng Member*
EMP: 12
SALES (est): 1.5MM **Privately Held**
SIC: 2759 Screen printing

(P-7239)
ARACA MERCHANDISE LP
Araca Ink
459 Park Ave, San Fernando (91340-2525)
PHONE.........................818 743-5400
Judy Courney, *Manager*
EMP: 20 **Privately Held**
SIC: 2759 Screen printing
HQ: Araca Merchandise L.P.
545 W 45th St Fl 10
New York NY 10036

(P-7240)
ARTEEZ
Also Called: J & J Screen Printing
3600 Sunrise Blvd Ste 4, Rancho Cordova (95742-7340)
PHONE.........................916 631-0473
John Kim, *Owner*
EMP: 10
SQ FT: 5,000
SALES (est): 1.2MM **Privately Held**
WEB: www.arteez.com
SIC: 2759 2396 Screen printing; automotive & apparel trimmings

(P-7241)
ARTISAN NAMEPLATE AWARDS CORP
Also Called: Weber Precision Graphics
2730 S Shannon St, Santa Ana (92704-5232)
PHONE.........................714 556-6222
Henry G Weber, *President*
Margaret Weber, *Corp Secy*
Jeff Johnson, *Exec VP*
Manny Estrada, *General Mgr*
Nacho Cuevas, *Purch Mgr*
EMP: 33
SQ FT: 12,160
SALES (est): 6.3MM **Privately Held**
WEB: www.weberpg.com
SIC: 2759 3479 Labels & seals: printing; coating of metals with plastic or resins

(P-7242)
ARTISAN SCREEN PRINTING INC
1055 W 5th St, Azusa (91702-3313)
PHONE.........................626 815-2700
Vasant N Doabria, *President*
C P Kheni, *Corp Secy*
Praful Bajaria, *Vice Pres*
▲ EMP: 120
SQ FT: 90,000
SALES (est): 16.2MM **Privately Held**
SIC: 2759 Screen printing

(P-7243)
ASHKA PRINT LLC
600 E Wash Blvd Ste W4, Los Angeles (90015-3731)
PHONE.........................323 980-6008
Sung Lee,
EMP: 30
SALES (est): 836.9K **Privately Held**
SIC: 2759 Screen printing

(P-7244)
B & B LABEL INC
2357 Thompson Way, Santa Maria (93455-1050)
PHONE.........................805 922-0332
Stephen Brookshire, *President*
Brian McCormick, *Vice Pres*
Cathy Brookshire, *Admin Sec*
EMP: 12
SQ FT: 6,000
SALES (est): 1.3MM **Privately Held**
WEB: www.bblabel.com
SIC: 2759 Flexographic printing

(P-7245)
B K HARRIS INC
Also Called: Presstime
3574 E Enterprise Dr, Anaheim (92807-1627)
PHONE.........................714 630-8780
Bryan Kerl, *President*
Marcelle Kerl, *Admin Sec*
EMP: 10
SALES (est): 890K **Privately Held**
WEB: www.presstimeprinters.com
SIC: 2759 Commercial printing

(P-7246)
BASIC BUSINESS FORMS INC
561 Kinetic Dr Ste A, Oxnard (93030-7947)
PHONE.........................805 278-4551
Helen Ingerd, *President*
EMP: 30
SALES (est): 2.7MM **Privately Held**
SIC: 2759 2761

(P-7247)
BERT-CO INDUSTRIES INC
2150 S Parco Ave, Ontario (91761-5768)
PHONE.........................323 669-5700
Vince Savasta, *Branch Mgr*
EMP: 11
SQ FT: 89,149
SALES (corp-wide): 50MM **Privately Held**
WEB: www.bert-co.com
SIC: 2759 2752 Commercial printing; commercial printing, lithographic
PA: Bert-Co Industries, Inc.
2150 S Parco Ave
Ontario CA 91761
323 669-5700

(P-7248)
BEST LABEL COMPANY INC (PA)
Also Called: Imperial Marking Systems
13260 Moore St, Cerritos (90703-2252)
PHONE.........................562 926-1452
Ernest Wong, *President*
Timothy Koontz, *CFO*
Donald Ingle, *Admin Sec*
Pat Ortiz, *Persnl Dir*
Gary Ingle, *Opers Mgr*
EMP: 120
SQ FT: 60,000
SALES (est): 21.2MM **Privately Held**
WEB: www.bestlabel.com
SIC: 2759

(P-7249)
BIZINKCOM LLC
9330 Eton Ave, Chatsworth (91311-5809)
PHONE.........................818 676-0766
Tom Pelino,
James Elwell, *Prdtn Mgr*
EMP: 12 EST: 1995
SQ FT: 11,000
SALES: 1.5MM **Privately Held**
SIC: 2759 Commercial printing

(P-7250)
BJS UKIAH EMBROIDERY
272 E Smith St, Ukiah (95482-4411)
PHONE.........................707 463-2767
Walt Richey, *Owner*
EMP: 10
SALES (est): 550K **Privately Held**
SIC: 2759 Screen printing

(P-7251)
BLACKBURN ALTON INVSTMENTS LLC
Also Called: Foster Print
700 E Alton Ave, Santa Ana (92705-5610)
PHONE.........................714 731-2000
Dennis M Blackburn,
EMP: 34 EST: 2011
SALES (est): 1.7MM **Privately Held**
SIC: 2759 Commercial printing

(P-7252)
BOONE PRINTING & GRAPHICS INC
70 S Kellogg Ave Ste 8, Goleta (93117-6408)
PHONE.........................805 683-2349
Andrew Ochsner, *President*
Rob Grayson, *Creative Dir*
Dave Tanner, *General Mgr*
Scott Tate, *Info Tech Dir*
Steve Dorf, *Graphic Designe*
EMP: 52
SQ FT: 15,000
SALES (est): 9.7MM **Privately Held**
WEB: www.boonegraphics.net
SIC: 2759 Screen printing

(P-7253)
BORDEN DECAL COMPANY INC
870 Harrison St Unit 101, San Francisco
(94107-2254)
PHONE..................................415 431-1587
Richard Parmelee, *President*
Sharon Parmelee, *Treasurer*
Mark Flagg, *Vice Pres*
Christina Lau, *QC Mgr*
EMP: 20 EST: 1923
SQ FT: 15,000
SALES (est): 2.3MM **Privately Held**
WEB: www.bordendecal.com
SIC: 2759 2396 Decals: printing; automotive & apparel trimmings

(P-7254)
BRAND INK INC
3801 Oceanic Dr Ste 103, Oceanside
(92056-5850)
P.O. Box 4007, Carlsbad (92018-4007)
PHONE..................................760 721-4465
Todd Liotine, *President*
EMP: 30
SQ FT: 12,000
SALES (est): 4.3MM **Privately Held**
SIC: 2759 Screen printing

(P-7255)
BRAVO DESIGN INC
150 E Olive Ave Ste 304, Burbank
(91502-1850)
PHONE..................................818 563-1385
Dan Arriola, *CEO*
Ramon Buensuceso, *COO*
John Jurado, *Graphic Designe*
EMP: 12 EST: 2001
SALES (est): 1MM **Privately Held**
WEB: www.bravodesigninc.com
SIC: 2759 Advertising literature: printing

(P-7256)
BREAKAWAY PRESS INC
9620 Topanga Canyon Pl A, Chatsworth
(91311-0868)
PHONE..................................818 727-7388
Cynthia Friedman, *President*
Marc Friedman, *Vice Pres*
Mark Baril, *Sales Mgr*
EMP: 21
SQ FT: 3,000
SALES (est): 3.5MM **Privately Held**
WEB: www.breakawaypress.com
SIC: 2759 Commercial printing

(P-7257)
BRETT CORP
Also Called: So Cal Graphics
8316 Clairemont Mesa Blvd # 105, San
Diego (92111-1316)
PHONE..................................858 292-4919
Bret Catcott, *President*
Jessi Catcott, *Office Mgr*
Keri Catcott, *Admin Sec*
Lee Evans, *Manager*
EMP: 20
SQ FT: 4,500
SALES (est): 2.8MM **Privately Held**
WEB: www.socalgraphics.com
SIC: 2759 7336 Commercial printing;
graphic arts & related design

(P-7258)
BRIXEN & SONS INC
2100 S Fairview St, Santa Ana
(92704-4516)
PHONE..................................714 566-1444
Martin Corey Brixen, *President*
Son Nguyen, *Treasurer*
▲ EMP: 27
SQ FT: 32,000
SALES (est): 5.3MM **Privately Held**
WEB: www.brixen.com
SIC: 2759 3993 Screen printing; signs &
advertising specialties

(P-7259)
C & H LETTERPRESS INC
3400 W Castor St, Santa Ana
(92704-3910)
PHONE..................................714 438-1350
Hernan A Pineda, *President*
Suzanne Harrison, *Treasurer*
EMP: 14
SQ FT: 8,600

SALES: 7.2MM **Privately Held**
WEB: www.chletterpress.com
SIC: 2759 Letterpress printing

(P-7260)
C T L PRINTING INDS INC
Also Called: Cal Tape & Label
1741 W Lincoln Ave Ste A, Anaheim
(92801-6716)
PHONE..................................714 635-2980
James Edward Hudson, *CEO*
J J Hudson, *Ch of Bd*
Dave Adams, *Principal*
EMP: 25
SQ FT: 8,950
SALES (est): 4.9MM **Privately Held**
WEB: www.caltapeandlabel.com
SIC: 2759 Labels & seals: printing; decals:
printing

(P-7261)
CAL SPRINGS LLC
6250 N Irwindale Ave, Irwindale
(91702-3208)
PHONE..................................562 943-5599
Steven Finch, *Mng Member*
▲ EMP: 54
SALES (est): 4.6MM **Privately Held**
SIC: 2759 3069 3751 5149

(P-7262)
CALICO TAG & LABEL INC
13233 Barton Cir, Whittier (90605-3255)
P.O. Box 3303, Santa Fe Springs (90670-
1303)
PHONE..................................562 944-6889
Fred Elhami, *President*
Ruth Elhami, *Vice Pres*
EMP: 13
SQ FT: 15,012
SALES (est): 966.5K **Privately Held**
WEB: www.calicotag.com
SIC: 2759 Tags: printing; labels & seals:
printing
PA: A F E Industries Inc.
13233 Barton Cir
Whittier CA 90605

(P-7263)
CALIFORNIA PRTG SOLUTIONS
INC
1950 W Park Ave, Redlands (92373-3133)
P.O. Box 11451, San Bernardino (92423-
1451)
PHONE..................................909 307-2032
Mark Smith, *President*
▲ EMP: 22
SQ FT: 20,000
SALES (est): 2.9MM **Privately Held**
WEB: www.printingsolutions.net
SIC: 2759 Promotional printing

(P-7264)
CAMEO CRAFTS
Also Called: York Label
4995 Hillsdale Cir, El Dorado Hills
(95762-5707)
PHONE..................................513 381-1480
John McKernan, *CEO*
Scott Grigsby, *VP Opers*
Kevin Grigsby, *VP Sales*
EMP: 21
SQ FT: 30,000
SALES (est): 1.9MM **Privately Held**
WEB: www.yorklabel.com
SIC: 2759 Flexographic printing

(P-7265)
CASA MEXICO ENTERPRISES
INC
3156 Foothill Blvd Ste G, La Crescenta
(91214-4258)
PHONE..................................888 411-9530
Eric Leyva Buccio, *President*
EMP: 10
SALES (est): 368.3K **Privately Held**
SIC: 2759 Promotional printing

(P-7266)
CCL LABEL INC
Pharmaceutical Label Systems
576 College Commerce Way, Upland
(91786-4377)
PHONE..................................909 608-2655
Kieorn Delahunt, *Branch Mgr*

Chuck Gilland, *Maintence Staff*
Jan Burnett, *Manager*
EMP: 130
SQ FT: 43,000
SALES: 14.9MM
SALES (corp-wide): 3.7B **Privately Held**
SIC: 2759 Labels & seals: printing
HQ: Ccl Label, Inc.
161 Worcester Rd Ste 504
Framingham MA 01701
508 872-4511

(P-7267)
CCL LABEL (DELAWARE) INC
576 College Commerce Way, Upland
(91786-4377)
PHONE..................................909 608-2260
Kieron Delahunt, *Manager*
Susan Wood, *Human Res Mgr*
EMP: 150
SALES (corp-wide): 3.7B **Privately Held**
SIC: 2759 Labels & seals: printing
HQ: Ccl Label (Delaware), Inc.
15 Controls Dr
Shelton CT 06484
203 926-1253

(P-7268)
CEE -JAY RESEARCH & SALES
LLC
920 W 10th St, Azusa (91702-1936)
PHONE..................................626 815-1530
Bert Banta, *Mng Member*
EMP: 30
SALES (est): 4.3MM **Privately Held**
WEB: www.cee-jay.com
SIC: 2759 2679 3429 Tags: printing; tags,
paper (unprinted): made from purchased
paper; manufactured hardware (general)

(P-7269)
CENTURY PUBLISHING
Also Called: Community Adviser Newspaper
218 N Murray St, Banning (92220-5512)
P.O. Box 727 (92220-0018)
PHONE..................................951 849-4586
Gerald Bean, *Owner*
Art Reyes, *General Mgr*
Virginia Bradford, *Office Mgr*
Ana Rivera, *Manager*
EMP: 15
SALES (est): 1.7MM **Privately Held**
WEB: www.recordgazette.net
SIC: 2759 7313 2711 Commercial printing; newspaper advertising representative; newspapers

(P-7270)
CHEMTEX PRINT USA INC
3061 E Maria St, Compton (90221-5803)
PHONE..................................310 900-1818
Carolyn Tan, *President*
Dominic Tan, *Vice Pres*
▲ EMP: 25
SQ FT: 50,000
SALES (est): 2.2MM **Privately Held**
WEB: www.ctxprint.com
SIC: 2759 7389 Textile printing rolls: engraving; textile & apparel services

(P-7271)
CHURCH SCIENTOLOGY INTL
Freedon Publishing
6331 Hollywood Blvd # 801, Los Angeles
(90028-4698)
PHONE..................................323 960-3500
Aron Mason, *Principal*
EMP: 100
SALES (corp-wide): 114.6MM **Privately
Held**
SIC: 2759 7313 Publication printing; magazine advertising representative
PA: Church Of Scientology International
6331 Hollywood Blvd # 801
Los Angeles CA 90028
323 960-3500

(P-7272)
CITY & COUNTY OF SAN
FRANCISCO
Also Called: Administrative Services
875 Stevenson St Ste 125, San Francisco
(94103-0952)
PHONE..................................415 557-5251
David German, *Manager*
EMP: 20 **Privately Held**

SIC: 2759 9199 Commercial printing; general government administration; ;
PA: City & County Of San Francisco
1 Dr Carlton B Goodlett P
San Francisco CA 94102
415 554-7500

(P-7273)
CLAREMONT INSTITUTE
STATESMANS (PA)
Also Called: Claremont Institute, The
1317 W Foothill Blvd # 120, Upland
(91786-3675)
PHONE..................................909 981-2200
Michael Pack, *President*
Ana Collisson, *President*
Ryan Williams, *COO*
John Marini, *Bd of Directors*
Daniel C Palm, *Admin Sec*
EMP: 21
SQ FT: 3,600
SALES: 6.1MM **Privately Held**
SIC: 2759 8733 Publication printing; research institute

(P-7274)
CLIFF DIGITAL
14700 S Main St, Gardena (90248-1959)
PHONE..................................310 323-5600
David Thomas, *President*
EMP: 11
SQ FT: 4,500
SALES (est): 896.5K **Privately Held**
SIC: 2759 7374 Screen printing; computer graphics service

(P-7275)
COASTAL TAG & LABEL INC
13233 Barton Cir, Whittier (90605-3255)
P.O. Box 3303, Santa Fe Springs (90670-
1303)
PHONE..................................562 946-4318
Fred Elhami, *President*
Ruth Elhami, *Admin Sec*
EMP: 94
SALES (est): 11.1MM **Privately Held**
WEB: www.afeindustries.com
SIC: 2759 2672 2671 Labels & seals:
printing; tags: printing; coated & laminated paper; packaging paper & plastics
film, coated & laminated
PA: A F E Industries Inc.
13233 Barton Cir
Whittier CA 90605

(P-7276)
COASTWIDE TAG & LABEL CO
7647 Industry Ave, Pico Rivera
(90660-4301)
PHONE..................................323 721-1501
Jay Sullivan, *President*
Jerry Sullivan, *Vice Pres*
EMP: 25 EST: 1946
SQ FT: 6,000
SALES (est): 3.5MM **Privately Held**
SIC: 2759 Labels & seals: printing; tags:
printing

(P-7277)
COLLOTYPE LABELS USA INC
(HQ)
21 Executive Way, NAPA (94558-6271)
PHONE..................................707 603-2500
Nigel Vinecombe, *CEO*
David Buse, *President*
Mike Huntsinger, *Vice Pres*
▲ EMP: 91
SQ FT: 14,500
SALES (est): 23MM
SALES (corp-wide): 1.3B **Publicly Held**
WEB: www.collotype.com
SIC: 2759 Labels & seals: printing
PA: Multi-Color Corporation
4053 Clough Woods Dr
Batavia OH 45103
513 381-1480

(P-7278)
COLLOTYPE LABELS USA INC
Also Called: Multicolor
21684 8th St E, Sonoma (95476-2815)
PHONE..................................707 931-7400
Ann Herron, *Sales Executive*
Joseph Maurer, *Manager*
EMP: 20

▲ = Import ▼=Export
◆ =Import/Export

SALES (corp-wide): 1.3B **Publicly Held**
SIC: 2759 Labels & seals: printing
HQ: Collotype Labels Usa Inc.
   21 Executive Way
   Napa CA 94558
   707 603-2500

(P-7279)
COLMOL INC
Also Called: King Graphics
8517 Production Ave, San Diego
(92121-2204)
PHONE..................................858 693-7575
Sean P Mundy, CEO
▲ EMP: 45
SQ FT: 14,000
SALES (est): 10.7MM **Privately Held**
WEB: www.kinggraph.com
SIC: 2759 Screen printing

(P-7280)
COLOR DEPOT INC
512 State St, Glendale (91203-1524)
PHONE..................................818 500-9033
Thomas Hovsepian, President
Anna Hovsepian, CFO
EMP: 14
SQ FT: 2,800
SALES (est): 1MM **Privately Held**
SIC: 2759 7336 2732 2752 Commercial
   printing; commercial art & graphic design;
   book printing; commercial printing, litho-
   graphic

(P-7281)
COLORMAX GRAPHICS INC
1243 Via Del Rey, South Pasadena
(91030-3628)
PHONE..................................626 299-1289
Linda Siew, President
EMP: 15
SQ FT: 11,520
SALES (est): 1.6MM **Privately Held**
WEB: www.i-max.com
SIC: 2759 Screen printing; laser printing

(P-7282)
COLOUR DROP
1388 Sutter St Ste 508, San Francisco
(94109-5452)
PHONE..................................415 353-5720
Tipu Barber, Owner
EMP: 10
SALES: 1MM **Privately Held**
WEB: www.colourdrop.com
SIC: 2759 Commercial printing

(P-7283)
CONSOLIDATED GRAPHICS INC
Anderson La
3550 Tyburn St, Los Angeles (90065-1427)
PHONE..................................323 460-4115
Luke Westlake, Vice Pres
Tuan Pham, Vice Pres
Kevin Polley, VP Bus Dvlpt
Ann Lydecker, Executive
Tim Hanley, Director
EMP: 95
SALES (corp-wide): 6.9B **Publicly Held**
SIC: 2759 2752 Commercial printing; let-
   terpress printing; screen printing; com-
   mercial printing, offset
HQ: Consolidated Graphics, Inc.
   5858 Westheimer Rd # 400
   Houston TX 77057
   713 787-0977

(P-7284)
CONTENT MANAGEMENT CORPORATION
Also Called: C M C
4287 Technology Dr, Fremont
(94538-6339)
PHONE..................................510 505-1100
Tom Pipkin, CEO
Zack Tsuji, President
Beverly Veloza, Project Mgr
Jennifer Jones-Boyd, Accounting Mgr
David Trinidad, Opers Mgr
EMP: 17
SQ FT: 8,000
SALES (est): 3MM **Privately Held**
WEB: www.cmcondemand.com
SIC: 2759 Commercial printing

(P-7285)
CORPORATE IMPRESSIONS LA INC
Also Called: Dorado Pkg
10742 Burbank Blvd, North Hollywood
(91601-2516)
PHONE..................................818 761-9295
Jennifer L Freund, President
Gary Gonzales, Project Mgr
Tim Atwell, Technology
Sandy Benson, Business Mgr
Robert Moore, Finance
EMP: 27 EST: 1982
SQ FT: 10,000
SALES (est): 4.7MM **Privately Held**
WEB: www.corporateimpressions.com
SIC: 2759 7389 Screen printing; packag-
   ing & labeling services

(P-7286)
CORPRINT INCORPORATED
Also Called: Total Brand Delivery
4235 Mission Oaks Blvd, Camarillo
(93010)
PHONE..................................818 839-5316
Marc Lewis, President
EMP: 15
SALES (est): 3.5MM **Privately Held**
WEB: www.corprintinc.com
SIC: 2759 Business forms: printing

(P-7287)
COSMO FIBER CORPORATION (PA)
1802 Santo Domingo Ave, Duarte
(91010-2933)
PHONE..................................626 256-6098
Sidney Ru, President
Sissy Ru, Admin Sec
Salina Brill, Accounts Mgr
▲ EMP: 33
SQ FT: 4,000
SALES (est): 6.3MM **Privately Held**
WEB: www.cosmofiber.com
SIC: 2759 7389 Promotional printing; ad-
   vertising, promotional & trade show serv-
   ices

(P-7288)
COUNTY OF MONTEREY
Also Called: Monterey Coun Graphic Comm
855 E Laurel Dr Ste C, Salinas
(93905-1300)
PHONE..................................831 755-4790
Virgil Schwab, Branch Mgr
EMP: 10 **Privately Held**
WEB: www.montereycountyfarmbureau.org
SIC: 2759 9111 2752 Commercial print-
   ing; county supervisors' & executives' of-
   fices; commercial printing, lithographic
PA: County Of Monterey
   168 W Alisal St Fl 2
   Salinas CA 93901
   831 755-5040

(P-7289)
CR & A CUSTOM APPAREL INC
Also Called: Cr & A Custom
312 W Pico Blvd, Los Angeles
(90015-2437)
PHONE..................................213 749-4440
Masoud RAD, COO
Carmen RAD, President
Dino Maquiddang, Controller
Scott Kurosaki, VP Sales
◆ EMP: 30
SQ FT: 26,500
SALES: 6.5MM **Privately Held**
WEB: www.cracustom.com
SIC: 2759 Posters, including billboards:
   printing

(P-7290)
CREO INC
Also Called: Screaming Squeegee
50 Fullerton Ct Ste 107, Sacramento
(95825-6205)
PHONE..................................530 756-1477
Greg Garcia, President
Claire Impens, Graphic Designe
EMP: 11
SQ FT: 2,400
SALES (est): 1.2MM **Privately Held**
WEB: www.squeegee.com
SIC: 2759 Screen printing

(P-7291)
CUSTOM DECALS & EMBLEMS INC
Also Called: Custom Deacals & Emblems
1900 Weld Blvd Ste 120, El Cajon
(92020-0503)
PHONE..................................619 449-5611
Matthew Schmoke, President
Pearley Wells, Vice Pres
Susan Well, Admin Sec
EMP: 25
SQ FT: 8,500
SALES (est): 3.8MM **Privately Held**
WEB: www.customdecal.com
SIC: 2759 2752 2395 Decals: printing;
   commercial printing, lithographic; pleating
   & stitching

(P-7292)
CUSTOM LABEL AND DECAL LLC
3392 Investment Blvd, Hayward
(94545-3809)
PHONE..................................510 876-0000
Colin Ho-Tseung Jr, Mng Member
Connie Gouveia, Vice Pres
Wade Ignacio, Sales Mgr
Scott Dickes,
Dick Parmelee,
EMP: 20
SQ FT: 25,000
SALES (est): 3.5MM **Privately Held**
WEB: www.customlabel.com
SIC: 2759 2752 2672 Labels & seals:
   printing; commercial printing, lithographic;
   coated & laminated paper

(P-7293)
CUSTOMPLANETCOM INC
12180 Ridgecrest Rd # 314, Victorville
(92395-7798)
PHONE..................................760 508-2648
Chris Taylor, Principal
Hannah Taylor, Manager
EMP: 15
SALES (est): 1.9MM **Privately Held**
SIC: 2759 Screen printing

(P-7294)
DATAPAGE INC
5577 Sheila St, Commerce (90040-1424)
P.O. Box 911188, Los Angeles (90091-1188)
PHONE..................................323 725-7500
Barbara Martine, President
Thirkield Thomas, Opers Spvr
EMP: 10
SALES (est): 990K **Privately Held**
WEB: www.datapageinc.com
SIC: 2759 Laser printing

(P-7295)
DELTA WEB PRINTING INC
Also Called: Delta Web Printing & Bindery
1871 Enterprise Blvd, West Sacramento
(95691-3423)
PHONE..................................916 375-0044
James Davis, President
Kasey Cotulla, Vice Pres
Eric Cormier, Plant Mgr
Peggy Foley, Prdtn Mgr
Jody Montgomery,
EMP: 22
SQ FT: 30,000
SALES (est): 4.3MM **Privately Held**
SIC: 2759 2789 Screen printing; binding &
   repair of books, magazines & pamphlets

(P-7296)
DIGITAL ONE PRINTING INC
13367 Kirkham Way 110, Poway
(92064-7118)
PHONE..................................858 278-2228
Micheal Clark, President
Dave Picinich, Vice Pres
EMP: 10
SALES (est): 1.2MM **Privately Held**
SIC: 2759 Commercial printing

(P-7297)
DIGITAL ROOM HOLDINGS INC (PA)
Also Called: New Printing
8000 Haskell Ave, Van Nuys (91406-1321)
PHONE..................................310 575-4440
Michael Turner, CEO
Brett Zane, CFO
Joel Ancheta, Sr Ntwrk Engine
Steven Carlson, Network Mgr
Mervin Rodelas, Plant Mgr
▲ EMP: 101
SALES (est): 82.4MM **Privately Held**
WEB: www.digitalroom.com
SIC: 2759 7336 Commercial printing;
   graphic arts & related design

(P-7298)
DIGITALPRO INC
Also Called: Dpi Direct
13257 Kirkham Way, Poway (92064-7116)
PHONE..................................858 874-7750
Sam Mousavi, President
Mohammed Khaki, Vice Pres
Paul Moebius, Vice Pres
Paula Cross, Manager
EMP: 65
SQ FT: 38,000
SALES (est): 9.4MM **Privately Held**
WEB: www.digitalpro.com
SIC: 2759 Screen printing

(P-7299)
DIRECT EDGE SCREENWORKS INC
430 W Collins Ave, Orange (92867-5508)
PHONE..................................714 579-3686
Ryan Clark, President
Ryan Brueckenru, Vice Pres
Nicksharo Oshiro, Vice Pres
Tim Standon, Vice Pres
EMP: 19
SQ FT: 20,000
SALES: 3MM **Privately Held**
SIC: 2759 Screen printing

(P-7300)
DISPLAY ADVERTISING INC
1837 Van Ness Ave, Fresno (93721-1190)
PHONE..................................559 266-0231
Dave O' Brien, President
EMP: 10
SQ FT: 16,000
SALES: 900K **Privately Held**
SIC: 2759 Screen printing

(P-7301)
DIVERSIFIED IMAGES INC
27955 Beale Ct, Valencia (91355-1211)
PHONE..................................661 702-0003
Robert W Waycott, President
Barbara Waycott, Vice Pres
Bill Waycott, General Mgr
EMP: 12
SQ FT: 16,000
SALES (est): 880K **Privately Held**
WEB: www.diversifiedimages.com
SIC: 2759 2752 3479 Screen printing; de-
   cals, lithographed; etching & engraving

(P-7302)
DM LUXURY LLC
875 Prospect St Ste 300, La Jolla
(92037-4264)
PHONE..................................858 366-9721
EMP: 267
SALES (corp-wide): 79.5MM **Privately Held**
SIC: 2759 Advertising literature: printing
PA: Dm Luxury, Llc
   3414 Peachtree Rd Ne # 480
   Atlanta GA 30326
   404 443-1180

(P-7303)
DOLPHIN PRESS INC
264 S Maple Ave, South San Francisco
(94080-6304)
PHONE..................................650 873-9092
Gary Swanson, President
Marsha Fontes, Vice Pres
EMP: 14
SQ FT: 4,200
SALES (est): 2MM **Privately Held**
SIC: 2759 Letterpress printing

(P-7304)
DREAMTEAM BUSINESS GROUP LLC
Also Called: Rlf Print Shop
5261 E Kings Canyon Rd # 101, Fresno (93727-4083)
PHONE..................................559 430-7676
Nehemiah Fane,
Dwayne Taylor,
EMP: 10
SQ FT: 5,000
SALES (est): 971.1K Privately Held
SIC: 2759 Commercial printing

(P-7305)
DYNAMIC SERVICES INC
27091 Burbank, El Toro (92610-2505)
PHONE..................................949 458-2553
Zoltan F Csik, President
EMP: 10
SQ FT: 8,500
SALES: 1.4MM Privately Held
WEB: www.dynamicservice.com
SIC: 2759 5734 3565 2679 Labels & seals: printing; printers & plotters: computers; labeling machines, industrial; labels, paper: made from purchased material

(P-7306)
E Z MARTIN STICK LABELS INC
12921 Sunnyside Pl, Santa Fe Springs (90670-4645)
PHONE..................................562 906-1577
Francisco Martinez, President
Sylvia Martinez, Treasurer
Moncia Martinez, Admin Sec
EMP: 18
SQ FT: 14,800
SALES (est): 2MM Privately Held
WEB: www.ezstick.com
SIC: 2759 Labels & seals: printing

(P-7307)
EARL HAYS PRESS
10707 Sherman Way, Sun Valley (91352-5155)
PHONE..................................818 765-0700
Rafael Hernandez Jr, Partner
Paul Crumrine, Partner
EMP: 16
SQ FT: 8,000
SALES: 1.5MM Privately Held
SIC: 2759 7829 Card printing & engraving, except greeting; motion picture distribution services

(P-7308)
EAS SENSORSENSE INC
13351 Riverside Dr Ste D, Sherman Oaks (91423-2542)
PHONE..................................818 763-9186
Arthur Fuss, President
EMP: 28
SQ FT: 16,000
SALES (est): 2.7MM Privately Held
SIC: 2759 Tags: printing

(P-7309)
ELECTRONIC PRTG SOLUTIONS LLC
4879 Ronson Ct Ste C, San Diego (92111-1811)
PHONE..................................858 576-3000
Grant Freeman, Mng Member
Joanne Chau, Accountant
Brian Bell,
Janice Freeman,
EMP: 20
SQ FT: 7,600
SALES: 3.2MM Privately Held
WEB: www.epsolution.com
SIC: 2759 2732 Magazines: printing; book printing

(P-7310)
ELITE COLOR TECHNOLOGIES INC
851 E Walnut St, Carson (90746-1214)
PHONE..................................310 324-3040
Ki Kyong, President
▲ EMP: 12
SQ FT: 15,000
SALES (est): 2.1MM Privately Held
SIC: 2759 Commercial printing

(P-7311)
EPICSON INC
Also Called: Candroy Embroidery
8250 Cmino Santa Fe Ste A, San Diego (92121)
P.O. Box 131, La Jolla (92038-0131)
PHONE..................................858 558-5757
Miranda R Amid, Principal
EMP: 15
SALES (est): 1.6MM Privately Held
SIC: 2759 Screen printing

(P-7312)
EUROSTAMPA NORTH AMERICA INC
2545 Napa Vly, NAPA (94558)
PHONE..................................707 927-4848
Pat Hoe, Plant Mgr
Shannon Bezold, Cust Mgr
EMP: 18
SALES (corp-wide): 156.4K Privately Held
SIC: 2759 Labels & seals: printing
HQ: Eurostampa North America Inc.
1440 Seymour Ave
Cincinnati OH 45237

(P-7313)
EXCALIBER SYSTEMS INC
185 Los Vientos Dr, Newbury Park (91320-2810)
PHONE..................................805 376-1366
Mark Bliskel, President
Mark Sponsler, President
George Sponsler, Vice Pres
EMP: 40
SALES (est): 8MM Privately Held
SIC: 2759 Souvenir cards: printing

(P-7314)
EXECUPRINT INC
9650 Topanga Canyon Pl E, Chatsworth (91311-4104)
PHONE..................................818 993-8184
Amin Farag, Partner
Bassem Farag, Partner
Esther Farag, Partner
Michael Farag, Partner
B Farag, Managing Prtnr
EMP: 10 EST: 1975
SQ FT: 6,000
SALES (est): 2.1MM Privately Held
WEB: www.execuprint.com
SIC: 2759 7374 2752 Ready prints; computer graphics service; commercial printing, offset

(P-7315)
EXPRESS BUSINESS SYSTEMS INC
9155 Trade Pl, San Diego (92126-4377)
P.O. Box 537, La Jolla (92038-0537)
PHONE..................................858 549-9828
Briggs Keiffer, President
Maureen O'Malley, Corp Secy
EMP: 37
SQ FT: 7,000
SALES (est): 3.8MM Privately Held
WEB: www.expresscorp.com
SIC: 2759 3993 2672 2671 Labels & seals: printing; signs & advertising specialties; coated & laminated paper; packaging paper & plastics film, coated & laminated; labels, paper: made from purchased material

(P-7316)
FACE FIRST SCREEN PRINT INC
33049 Calle Aviador Ste C, San Juan Capistrano (92675-4785)
PHONE..................................949 443-9895
John Theaders, President
▲ EMP: 23
SQ FT: 4,800
SALES (est): 2.4MM Privately Held
SIC: 2759 5699 Screen printing; customized clothing & apparel

(P-7317)
FISHER PRINTING & STAMPING CO
5038 Venice Blvd, Los Angeles (90019-5310)
PHONE..................................323 933-9193

John E Becca, Owner
EMP: 10
SQ FT: 2,000
SALES: 900K Privately Held
SIC: 2759 2752 Embossing on paper; letterpress printing; commercial printing, lithographic

(P-7318)
FLANNIGANS MERCHANDISING INC
15803 Stagg St, Van Nuys (91406-1922)
PHONE..................................818 785-7428
Nathan Boles, President
Tara Guerin, Office Mgr
Arturo Verdin, Prdtn Mgr
EMP: 20
SQ FT: 10,000
SALES: 750K Privately Held
SIC: 2759 Screen printing

(P-7319)
FLOYD DENNEE
Also Called: A B C Press
2780 Walnut Ave, Signal Hill (90755-1832)
PHONE..................................562 595-6024
Floyd Dennee, Owner
Ruth Denee, Co-Owner
EMP: 10
SQ FT: 5,000
SALES: 1.2MM Privately Held
WEB: www.abcpres.com
SIC: 2759 Announcements: engraved; envelopes: printing; stationery: printing; visiting cards (including business): printing

(P-7320)
FOILFLEX PRODUCTS INC
24963 Avenue Tibbitts, Valencia (91355-3427)
PHONE..................................661 702-0775
Michael Dekel, President
Ned Washburn, Vice Pres
▲ EMP: 14
SQ FT: 17,000
SALES (est): 3.5MM Privately Held
WEB: www.foilflex.com
SIC: 2759 Flexographic printing

(P-7321)
FORWARD PRINTING & DESIGN
9331 Burr St, Oakland (94605-4313)
PHONE..................................510 535-2222
Daniel Corcoran, Principal
Joyce Corcoran, CFO
Daniel Phelan, Project Mgr
EMP: 16
SALES (est): 2.1MM Privately Held
SIC: 2759 Screen printing

(P-7322)
FRANKLIN LEE ENTERPRISES LLC
Also Called: Conveyor Group
2419 Imprl Bus Park Dr, Imperial (92251-4004)
PHONE..................................760 355-1500
Aaron Popejoy,
Hartnoll Nicholson,
EMP: 10
SALES (est): 1.1MM Privately Held
WEB: www.conveyorgroup.com
SIC: 2759 5734 7335 7375 Commercial printing; computer software & accessories; commercial photography; on-line data base information retrieval

(P-7323)
G PRINTING INC
456 W Broadway, Glendale (91204-1209)
PHONE..................................818 246-1156
George Ouzounian, President
John Melkonian, Vice Pres
Gary Worth, Manager
EMP: 11 EST: 1974
SQ FT: 8,000
SALES: 952.7K Privately Held
SIC: 2759 Catalogs: printing; business forms: printing; menus: printing; letterpress printing

(P-7324)
G2 GRAPHIC SERVICE INC
5510 Cleon Ave, North Hollywood (91601-2835)
PHONE..................................818 623-3100

John C Beard, CEO
Joe Cotrupe, President
Pamela Beard-Cotrupe, CEO
Rob Cashman, Vice Pres
Scott Dewinkeleer, Vice Pres
◆ EMP: 52
SQ FT: 35,000
SALES (est): 12.5MM Privately Held
WEB: www.g2online.com
SIC: 2759 7331 Commercial printing; direct mail advertising services

(P-7325)
GACHUPIN ENTERPRISES LLC
Also Called: Speedwear.com
5671 Engineer Dr, Huntington Beach (92649-1123)
PHONE..................................714 375-4111
Kai Gachupin, Owner
Tony Bustamante, Graphic Designe
Mike Thomas, Accounting Mgr
David Thomas, Manager
▲ EMP: 40
SQ FT: 11,000
SALES: 1.9MM Privately Held
SIC: 2759 7389 3949 Screen printing; embroidering of advertising on shirts, etc.; sporting & athletic goods

(P-7326)
GC LABELS LLC
Also Called: Gold Coast Label
11927 Burke St, Santa Fe Springs (90670-2507)
P.O. Box 4242 (90670-1242)
PHONE..................................951 270-1664
Steve Stong,
Dave Hobson, Manager
EMP: 12
SALES: 3MM
SALES (corp-wide): 55.8MM Privately Held
SIC: 2759 Labels & seals: printing
PA: Steven Label Corporation
11926 Burke St
Santa Fe Springs CA 90670
562 698-9971

(P-7327)
GEO LABELS INC
1180 E Francis St Ste G, Ontario (91761-4802)
P.O. Box 3009 (91761-0901)
PHONE..................................909 923-6832
George Contreras, President
Elena Conteras, Admin Sec
EMP: 12
SQ FT: 16,000
SALES (est): 1.5MM Privately Held
SIC: 2759 Labels & seals: printing

(P-7328)
GOLDEN APPLEXX CO INC
19805 Harrison Ave, Walnut (91789-2849)
PHONE..................................909 594-9788
Peter Lee, President
Jeff Lee, Vice Pres
Shio R Lee, Vice Pres
Shio-Ru Lee, Vice Pres
▲ EMP: 40
SALES (est): 4.8MM Privately Held
WEB: www.goldenapplexx.com
SIC: 2759 2396 Promotional printing; automotive & apparel trimmings

(P-7329)
GRAPHIC PACKAGING INTL LLC
Also Called: Sierra Pacific Packaging
525 Airport Pkwy, Oroville (95965-9248)
PHONE..................................530 533-1058
Allen Ennis, Branch Mgr
Vincent Geiger, Engineer
Alyson Lazarus, Safety Mgr
Josh Rasmussen, Manager
EMP: 160 Publicly Held
SIC: 2759 2752 2671 2631 Commercial printing; commercial printing, lithographic; packaging paper & plastics film, coated & laminated; paperboard mills
HQ: Graphic Packaging International, Llc
1500 Riveredge Pkwy # 100
Atlanta GA 30328

▲ = Import ▼=Export
◆ =Import/Export

(P-7330)
GRAPHIC SYSTEMS
1693 Mission Dr Ste C101, Solvang (93463-3608)
PHONE.....................805 686-0705
Heather Bedford, *Owner*
EMP: 16 **EST:** 1981
SALES (est): 856.5K **Privately Held**
SIC: 2759 Commercial printing

(P-7331)
GRAPHIC TRENDS INCORPORATED
7301 Adams St, Paramount (90723-4007)
PHONE.....................562 531-2339
Kieu V Tran, *Principal*
Allen Gasper, *Info Tech Mgr*
Chris Dang, *Project Mgr*
Chris Jackson, *Project Mgr*
Albert Beserra, *Purch Dir*
EMP: 40
SQ FT: 20,984
SALES (est): 7.6MM **Privately Held**
WEB: www.graphictrends.net
SIC: 2759 7336 Screen printing; graphic arts & related design

(P-7332)
GRAPHICS 2000 LLC
1600 E Valencia Dr, Fullerton (92831-4735)
PHONE.....................714 879-1188
Jim Hamel, *CEO*
Jim Blee, *COO*
Mark Schwartz, *CFO*
Donnie Voltz, *Maintenance Dir*
EMP: 54
SALES (est): 6.6MM **Privately Held**
WEB: www.graphic2k.com
SIC: 2759 2396 Letterpress & screen printing; automotive & apparel trimmings

(P-7333)
GRAPHICS FACTORY INC
21344 Superior St, Chatsworth (91311-4312)
PHONE.....................818 727-9040
Jeffrey Hampsten, *President*
Lisa Hampsten, *CFO*
EMP: 10
SQ FT: 5,000
SALES (est): 1.2MM **Privately Held**
SIC: 2759 Commercial printing

(P-7334)
GRAPHICS INK LITHOGRAPHY LLC
5531 Foxtail Loop, Carlsbad (92010-7153)
PHONE.....................760 438-9052
EMP: 10 **EST:** 1998
SQ FT: 4,000
SALES: 1.2MM **Privately Held**
SIC: 2759

(P-7335)
GREAT WESTERN PACKAGING LLC
8230-8240 Haskell Ave, Van Nuys (91406)
PHONE.....................818 464-3800
Michael C Warner, *Mng Member*
Denise Beilowitz, *Project Mgr*
Charles Wesley, *Purch Mgr*
Jim Crowfoot, *Plant Mgr*
Victoria Warner Kaplan,
EMP: 68 **EST:** 1970
SALES (est): 11.2MM **Privately Held**
SIC: 2759 Commercial printing

(P-7336)
GREATHOUSE SCREEN PRINTING
Also Called: Gsp
5644 Kearny Mesa Rd Ste E, San Diego (92111-1311)
PHONE.....................858 279-4939
Shawn Greathouse, *Owner*
EMP: 12
SQ FT: 5,000
SALES (est): 1.2MM **Privately Held**
SIC: 2759 Screen printing

(P-7337)
GREEN SHEET INC
5830 Commerce Blvd Ste B, Rohnert Park (94928-1666)
P.O. Box 750878, Petaluma (94975-0878)
PHONE.....................707 284-1684
Paul Green, *President*
Wolf D Stiles, *Administration*
Danielle Thorpe, *Director*
Kat Stiles, *Manager*
Ann Train, *Relations*
EMP: 10
SQ FT: 2,300
SALES (est): 1.4MM **Privately Held**
WEB: www.thegreensheet.com
SIC: 2759 Magazines: printing

(P-7338)
GUANO RECORDS LLC
26298 Jaylene St, Murrieta (92563-4940)
PHONE.....................714 263-5398
Breian Russell, *CEO*
EMP: 10
SALES (est): 368.3K **Privately Held**
SIC: 2759 7389 Music sheet: printing;

(P-7339)
GUTIERREZ GRADING
1505 E Phillips Blvd, Pomona (91766-5435)
PHONE.....................909 397-8717
Geronimo Gutierrez, *Owner*
EMP: 10
SALES (est): 946.4K **Privately Held**
SIC: 2759 Commercial printing

(P-7340)
H & H ENTERPRISES INC
Also Called: Grafix Screen Printing
681 Portal St, Cotati (94931-3019)
PHONE.....................707 794-9988
Larry Hebert, *President*
EMP: 10 **EST:** 1972
SQ FT: 10,000
SALES (est): 1.1MM **Privately Held**
WEB: www.grafixscreenprinting.com
SIC: 2759 2752 Screen printing; commercial printing, lithographic

(P-7341)
H2 CARDS INC
Also Called: Igraphix
638 Washington St, San Francisco (94111-2106)
PHONE.....................415 788-7888
Wade Lai, *President*
Opal Tsui, *Executive*
Peter Tam, *Creative Dir*
▲ **EMP:** 10
SALES (est): 1.8MM **Privately Held**
SIC: 2759 7336 7313 7312 Commercial printing; commercial art & graphic design; radio advertising representative; printed media advertising representatives; outdoor advertising services; billboard advertising

(P-7342)
HB PRODUCTS LLC
5671 Engineer Dr, Huntington Beach (92649-1123)
PHONE.....................714 799-6967
Robert Mannarelli,
John Abramson, *Vice Pres*
EMP: 20
SALES (est): 3MM **Privately Held**
SIC: 2759 Screen printing

(P-7343)
HI-TECH LABELS INCORPORATED (PA)
Also Called: Hi-Tech Products
8530 Roland St, Buena Park (90621-3124)
PHONE.....................714 670-2150
Jeffrey T Ruch, *CEO*
Damian Craig, *Vice Pres*
Jerry Oswald, *Engineer*
Mike Lohman, *Sales Staff*
▲ **EMP:** 34
SQ FT: 24,000
SALES (est): 7.6MM **Privately Held**
WEB: www.hi-tech-products.com
SIC: 2759 Labels & seals: printing

(P-7344)
HUDSON PRINTING INC
2780 Loker Ave W, Carlsbad (92010-6611)
PHONE.....................760 602-1260
James Fairweather, *President*
Anne Fairweather, *Treasurer*
Tom Fairweather, *Vice Pres*
Ashley Fairweather, *Production*
Ben Fairweather, *Sales Staff*
EMP: 23
SQ FT: 6,000
SALES (est): 5.5MM **Privately Held**
SIC: 2759 2752 Screen printing; commercial printing, offset

(P-7345)
HYX TECH CORP
13620 Benson Ave Ste B, Chino (91710-5201)
PHONE.....................951 907-3386
Yaxian Huang, *President*
EMP: 12
SALES (est): 549.4K **Privately Held**
SIC: 2759 Commercial printing

(P-7346)
I E P FULL SERVICE PRINTING
1501 Cortland Ave, San Francisco (94110-5769)
PHONE.....................415 648-6002
Michael Kim, *Principal*
EMP: 14 **EST:** 2000
SALES (est): 861.3K **Privately Held**
SIC: 2759 Commercial printing

(P-7347)
IC INK IMAGE CO INC
Also Called: Legends Apparel & I C Ink
4627 E Fremont St, Stockton (95215-4010)
P.O. Box 4487 (95204-0487)
PHONE.....................209 931-3040
Tom Sousa, *President*
Debbie Dolin, *Purchasing*
EMP: 20
SQ FT: 25,000
SALES (est): 3.6MM **Privately Held**
SIC: 2759 2396 2395 Screen printing; automotive & apparel trimmings; pleating & stitching

(P-7348)
ICON SCREENING INC
Also Called: Icon Screen Printing
1108 W Grove Ave, Orange (92865-4131)
PHONE.....................714 630-4266
Bryan Huber, *CEO*
EMP: 13 **EST:** 2011
SALES (est): 674.4K **Privately Held**
SIC: 2759 Screen printing

(P-7349)
IGRAPHICS (PA)
Also Called: Precision Printers
165 Spring Hill Dr, Grass Valley (95945-5936)
PHONE.....................530 273-2200
James G Clay, *Mng Member*
David Clay, *Mng Member*
EMP: 25
SQ FT: 15,000
SALES (est): 1.7MM **Privately Held**
WEB: www.igraphicspp.com
SIC: 2759 7389 3993 2671 Screen printing; printing broker; signs & advertising specialties; packaging paper & plastics film, coated & laminated; automotive & apparel trimmings

(P-7350)
ILLINOIS TOOL WORKS INC
ITW Labels
1980 Lundy Ave, San Jose (95131-1831)
PHONE.....................408 468-1230
EMP: 14
SALES (corp-wide): 14.3B **Publicly Held**
SIC: 2759 Commercial printing
PA: Illinois Tool Works Inc.
155 Harlem Ave
Glenview IL 60025
847 724-7500

(P-7351)
IMPACT PRINTING & GRAPHICS
15150 Sierra Bonita Ln, Chino (91710-8903)
PHONE.....................909 614-1678
Bill McGinley, *President*
Sarah Jensen, *Human Resources*
EMP: 25
SQ FT: 14,000
SALES (est): 3.6MM **Privately Held**
WEB: www.impact-printing.com
SIC: 2759 Commercial printing

(P-7352)
IN HOUSE CUSTOM DECALS
Also Called: In House Stickers
2300 S Reservoir St # 308, Pomona (91766-6458)
PHONE.....................909 613-1403
Frank Caldron, *Owner*
▲ **EMP:** 13 **EST:** 1996
SALES (est): 240.3K **Privately Held**
SIC: 2759 Decals: printing

(P-7353)
INDEX PRINTING INC
Also Called: Tuesday Review, The
1021 Fresno St, Newman (95360-1303)
P.O. Box 878 (95360-0878)
PHONE.....................209 862-2222
Susan Mattos, *President*
Dean Harris, *Editor*
EMP: 13
SALES (est): 685.2K **Privately Held**
SIC: 2759 Commercial printing

(P-7354)
INDIAN INK SCREEN PRINT
1351 Logan Ave Ste A, Costa Mesa (92626-4096)
PHONE.....................714 437-0882
Doug Winbury, *President*
Paul Schmitt, *Vice Pres*
Mark Oblow, *Admin Sec*
EMP: 40
SQ FT: 25,000
SALES (est): 2MM **Privately Held**
WEB: www.giantsk8dist.com
SIC: 2759 2396 Screen printing; automotive & apparel trimmings

(P-7355)
INFOIMAGE OF CALIFORNIA INC (PA)
141 Jefferson Dr, Menlo Park (94025-1114)
PHONE.....................650 473-6388
Howard Lee, *President*
Rose Lee, *COO*
Lilly Fong, *CFO*
Tomas Lee, *Officer*
David Trang, *Program Mgr*
EMP: 85
SALES (est): 16MM **Privately Held**
WEB: www.infoimageinc.com
SIC: 2759 7331 3374 Laser printing; mailing service; data processing service

(P-7356)
INK FX CORPORATION
2031 S Lynx Ave, Ontario (91761-8011)
PHONE.....................909 673-1950
Joe Metz, *President*
Mike Machrone, *CEO*
Lydia Matz, *Financial Exec*
EMP: 25
SQ FT: 12,000
SALES (est): 3.5MM **Privately Held**
WEB: www.inkfx.net
SIC: 2759 Screen printing

(P-7357)
INNOPACK USA INC
238 W Taft Ave, Orange (92865-4220)
PHONE.....................714 637-4091
Edward J McCrink, *President*
John Johnston, *Vice Pres*
Jon Johnston, *Vice Pres*
Mary McCrink, *Admin Sec*
▲ **EMP:** 10
SALES (est): 978.5K **Privately Held**
WEB: www.innopackusa.com
SIC: 2759 Promotional printing

(P-7358)
INTEGRATED BUSINESS NETWORK
28310 Roadside Dr Ste 136, Agoura Hills (91301-4950)
PHONE.....................818 879-0670
EMP: 10

SALES (est): 612.8K **Privately Held**
SIC: 2759

(P-7359)
INTER COLOR PLUS INTER
13234 Sherman Way Ste 6, North Holly-
wood (91605-7711)
PHONE..............................818 764-5034
Oscar Moleno, *Owner*
Patricia Abrim, *Admin Sec*
EMP: 28
SALES: 38K **Privately Held**
SIC: 2759 Commercial printing

(P-7360)
**INTERNTIONAL COLOR
POSTERS INC**
Also Called: ICP West
8081 Orangethorpe Ave, Buena Park
(90621-3801)
PHONE..............................949 768-1005
Eric Guerineau, *President*
▲ EMP: 50
SQ FT: 26,000
SALES (est): 5.9MM **Privately Held**
WEB: www.icpwest.com
SIC: 2759 Screen printing

(P-7361)
**INVESTMENT ENTERPRISES
INC (PA)**
Also Called: Great Western Litho
8230 Haskell Ave Ste 8240, Van Nuys
(91406-1322)
PHONE..............................818 464-3800
Michael Warner, *President*
Denise Scanlon, *Vice Pres*
Jack Wickson, *Vice Pres*
EMP: 43 EST: 1970
SALES (est): 12.3MM **Privately Held**
SIC: 2759 Magazines: printing

(P-7362)
IRIS GROUP INC
Also Called: Modern Postcard
1675 Faraday Ave, Carlsbad (92008-7314)
PHONE..............................760 431-1103
Steve Hoffman, *CEO*
EMP: 250
SQ FT: 75,000
SALES (est): 66.8MM **Privately Held**
WEB: www.modernpostcard.com
SIC: 2759 5961 Commercial printing; mail
order house

(P-7363)
J & J TAPE & LABEL INC
189 Whirlaway St, Perris (92571-2567)
PHONE..............................951 657-6631
Jess Kinney, *President*
Jane Kinney, *CFO*
EMP: 10
SQ FT: 3,200
SALES (est): 1.3MM **Privately Held**
SIC: 2759 Labels & seals: printing

(P-7364)
JAVA PRINTING INC
5754 Grace Pl, Commerce (90022-4121)
PHONE..............................323 888-1601
Aris Sihono, *CEO*
Aries Sihono, *CEO*
▲ EMP: 20
SALES (est): 304.1K **Privately Held**
SIC: 2759 Commercial printing

(P-7365)
JOHN LOMPA
Also Called: Trade Lithography
720 Harbour Way S Ste A, Richmond
(94804-3631)
PHONE..............................510 965-6501
John Lompa, *Owner*
EMP: 15
SQ FT: 14,000
SALES (est): 2.5MM **Privately Held**
SIC: 2759 Commercial printing

(P-7366)
JONDO LTD
22700 Savi Ranch Pkwy, Yorba Linda
(92887-4608)
PHONE..............................714 279-2300
John S DOE, *CEO*
Dave Murray, *CFO*

Elayne Rogers, *Buyer*
Justin DOE, *Production*
Jenny Coulston, *Marketing Staff*
EMP: 40
SQ FT: 50,000
SALES (est): 13MM **Privately Held**
WEB: www.harvestpro.com
SIC: 2759 2741 Commercial printing; mis-
cellaneous publishing

(P-7367)
JP GRAPHICS INC
3310 Woodward Ave, Santa Clara
(95054-2627)
PHONE..............................408 235-8821
Joan Denise Escover, *CEO*
EMP: 30
SALES: 5MM **Privately Held**
SIC: 2759 2752 Commercial printing;
commercial printing, lithographic; pho-
tolithographic printing

(P-7368)
K S PRINTING INC
710 E Parkridge Ave # 105, Corona
(92879-1097)
PHONE..............................951 268-5180
Ralph Azar, *President*
▲ EMP: 12
SQ FT: 20,000
SALES: 100K **Privately Held**
WEB: www.ksprintingonline.com
SIC: 2759 Commercial printing

(P-7369)
KJM ENTERPRISES INC
8148 Auberge Cir, San Diego
(92127-4204)
PHONE..............................858 537-2490
Kevin Murray, *President*
▲ EMP: 40
SQ FT: 16,000
SALES (est): 8.3MM **Privately Held**
WEB: www.kjmscreenprints.com
SIC: 2759 Screen printing

(P-7370)
KP LLC
Also Called: K P Graphics
1134 Enterprise St, Stockton (95204-2316)
P.O. Box 8900 (95208-0900)
PHONE..............................209 466-6761
Roberta Morris, *Manager*
Dave Skinner, *Manager*
EMP: 20
SQ FT: 10,000
SALES (corp-wide): 120MM **Privately
Held**
WEB: www.kpcorporation.com
SIC: 2759 Business forms: printing
PA: Kp Llc
13951 Washington Ave
San Leandro CA 94578
510 346-0729

(P-7371)
L A SUPPLY CO
Also Called: Label House
18005 Sky Park Cir Ste A, Irvine
(92614-6514)
P.O. Box 14876 (92623-4876)
PHONE..............................949 470-9900
Randolph William Austin, *CEO*
▲ EMP: 31 EST: 1947
SQ FT: 35,000
SALES (est): 5.4MM **Privately Held**
SIC: 2759 2752 2672 2396 Labels &
seals: printing; commercial printing, litho-
graphic; coated & laminated paper; auto-
motive & apparel trimmings; service
establishment equipment

(P-7372)
LABEL ART-EASY STIK LABELS
Also Called: Label Art of California
290 27th St, Oakland (94612-3821)
PHONE..............................510 465-1125
David S Masri, *President*
Daniel Masri, *Vice Pres*
Elizabeth Masri, *Admin Sec*
EMP: 25
SALES (est): 4.2MM **Privately Held**
WEB: www.instantlabel.com
SIC: 2759 Labels & seals: printing

(P-7373)
LABEL ID TECHNOLOGIES INC
2275 Michael Faraday Dr, San Diego
(92154-7927)
PHONE..............................619 661-5566
Ricardo Tamborrell, *President*
Alex Nieves, *CFO*
▲ EMP: 15
SQ FT: 12,000
SALES (est): 2MM **Privately Held**
WEB: www.dclabel.com
SIC: 2759 Labels & seals: printing

(P-7374)
LABEL IMPRESSIONS INC
1831 W Sequoia Ave, Orange
(92868-1017)
PHONE..............................714 634-3466
Jeffrey Salisbury, *CEO*
Carolyn Deyoe, *Vice Pres*
EMP: 42
SQ FT: 15,000
SALES (est): 8.1MM **Privately Held**
WEB: www.labelimpressions.com
SIC: 2759 Labels & seals: printing

(P-7375)
LABEL MASTERS INC
3188 N Marks Ave Ste 112, Fresno
(93722-4940)
PHONE..............................559 445-1208
Roger A Cooper, *President*
Kathleen Cooper, *Vice Pres*
EMP: 12 EST: 1979
SQ FT: 10,000
SALES (est): 1.5MM **Privately Held**
WEB: www.labelmastersinc.com
SIC: 2759 2752 Flexographic printing;
commercial printing, offset

(P-7376)
LABEL PRODUCTIONS OF CAL
42068 Winchester Rd, Temecula
(92590-4804)
PHONE..............................951 296-1881
Steven Hamelback, *President*
Susanna F Hamelback, *Vice Pres*
EMP: 12
SQ FT: 17,425
SALES (est): 2.9MM **Privately Held**
SIC: 2759 Commercial printing

(P-7377)
LABEL SPECIALTIES INC
704 Dunn Way, Placentia (92870-6805)
PHONE..............................714 961-8074
Michael A Gyure, *President*
Tom Wetterhus, *Vice Pres*
EMP: 18
SQ FT: 11,000
SALES (est): 3.8MM **Privately Held**
WEB: www.labelspec.com
SIC: 2759 Labels & seals: printing

(P-7378)
LABEL TECHNOLOGY INC
2050 Wardrobe Ave, Merced (95341-6409)
PHONE..............................209 384-1000
John Bankson, *Ch of Bd*
David Bankson, *President*
Vinton Thengvall, *CFO*
Dennis Deisenroth, *Vice Pres*
Michael Russell, *Info Tech Mgr*
▲ EMP: 105
SQ FT: 60,000
SALES (est): 23.1MM **Privately Held**
SIC: 2759 Labels & seals: printing

(P-7379)
LABELTRONIX LLC
Also Called: Rethink Label Systems
2419 E Winston Rd, Anaheim
(92806-5544)
PHONE..............................800 429-4321
Daniel Blair,
Gail Senna, *Human Res Mgr*
Christina Castillo, *Purchasing*
Khristopher Maiquez, *Purchasing*
Candice Charbonneau, *Production*
▲ EMP: 73
SQ FT: 48,000
SALES (est): 19MM **Privately Held**
WEB: www.labeltronix.com
SIC: 2759 Labels & seals: printing

(P-7380)
**LANDMARK LABEL
MANUFACTURING**
39611 Eureka Dr, Newark (94560-4806)
PHONE..............................510 651-5551
Peter Offerman, *President*
Peter Offermann, *President*
EMP: 48
SQ FT: 24,000
SALES (est): 4.5MM
SALES (corp-wide): 236.4MM **Privately
Held**
WEB: www.landmarklabel.com
SIC: 2759 2672 Labels & seals: printing;
coated & laminated paper
HQ: Cellotape, Inc.
39611 Eureka Dr
Newark CA 94560
510 651-5551

(P-7381)
LAWEB OFFSET PRINTING INC
Also Called: Chinese-La Daily News
9639 Telstar Ave, El Monte (91731-3003)
PHONE..............................626 454-2469
Walter Chang, *President*
Ya-Tang Fu, *Shareholder*
CHI-Kwang Chiang, *Treasurer*
▲ EMP: 165
SQ FT: 29,730
SALES (est): 18MM **Privately Held**
WEB: www.laweboffset.com
SIC: 2759 2752 Newspapers: printing;
commercial printing, offset

(P-7382)
LAYTON PRINTING & MAILING
1538 Arrow Hwy, La Verne (91750-5318)
PHONE..............................909 592-4419
Michael Layton, *President*
Mary Ellen Layton, *Admin Sec*
EMP: 18
SQ FT: 20,000
SALES (est): 4.1MM **Privately Held**
WEB: www.laytonprinting.com
SIC: 2759 Commercial printing

(P-7383)
LCA PROMOTIONS INC
9545 Cozycroft Ave, Chatsworth
(91311-5102)
PHONE..............................818 773-9170
Terrence R Aleck, *President*
EMP: 20
SQ FT: 6,200
SALES (est): 2.8MM **Privately Held**
WEB: www.lcapromotions.com
SIC: 2759 Screen printing

(P-7384)
LEGACY GRAPHICS LLC
1120 Bay Blvd Ste E, Chula Vista
(91911-7169)
PHONE..............................619 585-1044
Janet Crowe, *Mng Member*
EMP: 10
SALES: 950K **Privately Held**
SIC: 2759 2399 3993 5999 Commercial
printing; banners, pennants & flags; banners, made from fabric; signs & advertising specialties; banners, flags, decals &
posters; commercial art & graphic design

(P-7385)
LEGION CREATIVE GROUP
1680 Vine St Ste 700, Los Angeles
(90028-8833)
PHONE..............................323 498-1100
Kathleen Fliller, *Owner*
EMP: 25
SALES: 40MM **Privately Held**
SIC: 2759 Advertising literature: printing

(P-7386)
LIMPUS PRINTS INC
Also Called: Insight System Exchange
1820 S Santa Fe St, Santa Ana
(92705-4815)
PHONE..............................714 545-5078
Pat Pester, *President*
EMP: 14
SALES (est): 2MM **Privately Held**
SIC: 2759 Screen printing

▲ = Import ▼=Export
◆ =Import/Export

(P-7387)
LITHOGRAPHIX INC
6200 Yarrow Dr, Carlsbad (92011-1537)
PHONE..................760 438-3456
Carl Davenport, *Manager*
EMP: 75
SALES (corp-wide): 117.2MM **Privately Held**
WEB: www.lithoxprep.com
SIC: 2759 2796 2789 2752 Screen printing; platemaking services; bookbinding & related work; commercial printing, lithographic
PA: Lithographix, Inc.
12250 Crenshaw Blvd
Hawthorne CA 90250
323 770-1000

(P-7388)
LITHOTECH INTERNATIONAL LLC
9950 Baldwin Pl, El Monte (91731-2204)
PHONE..................626 443-4210
Shen Yen,
Shih-Yi Yang,
▲ EMP: 42
SALES (est): 4.1MM **Privately Held**
WEB: www.pop-international.com
SIC: 2759 Commercial printing

(P-7389)
LITHOTECHS INC
9950 Baldwin Pl, El Monte (91731-2204)
PHONE..................626 433-1333
Shen Yen, *CEO*
EMP: 12
SQ FT: 16,000
SALES: 2.3MM **Privately Held**
SIC: 2759 Commercial printing

(P-7390)
LPS AGENCY SALES AND POSTING
3210 El Camino Real # 200, Irvine (92602-1368)
PHONE..................714 247-7500
Richard Teal, *Branch Mgr*
Danny Laughlin, *Info Tech Mgr*
EMP: 21
SALES (corp-wide): 500K **Privately Held**
SIC: 2759 Publication printing
PA: Lps Agency Sales And Posting Inc
3210 El Camino Real # 200
Irvine CA 92602
714 247-7503

(P-7391)
LUCKY DEVIL LLC
431 Atlas St, Brea (92821-3118)
PHONE..................714 990-2237
Timothy J Worcester,
EMP: 10
SALES (est): 1.2MM **Privately Held**
SIC: 2759 Screen printing

(P-7392)
LUCKY STAR SILKSCREEN LLC
Also Called: Golden Star Silk Screen
5767 E Washington Blvd, Commerce (90040-2228)
PHONE..................323 728-4071
Timmy Trieu, *Mng Member*
Dino Ha,
EMP: 41
SALES (est): 1.2MM **Privately Held**
SIC: 2759 Screen printing

(P-7393)
M B C REPROGRAPHICS INC
Also Called: Mesa Reprographics
5560 Ruffin Rd Ste 5, San Diego (92123-1332)
PHONE..................858 541-1500
Michael Atkins, *President*
Phyllis Atkins, *Admin Sec*
Karen Atkins, *Prdtn Mgr*
Jim Chavarria, *VP Sales*
Olsen Greg, *Sales Mgr*
EMP: 22
SQ FT: 4,500
SALES (est): 3.8MM **Privately Held**
WEB: www.mesablueprint.com
SIC: 2759 7334 Commercial printing; blueprinting service

(P-7394)
MAINETTI USA INC
5350 Zambrano St, Commerce (90040-3036)
PHONE..................562 741-2920
Gabino Banuelos, *Branch Mgr*
Adonis Vancampen, *Controller*
Irma Mendoza, *Sales Staff*
Santiago Rangel, *Manager*
Marc Richardson, *Manager*
EMP: 15
SALES (corp-wide): 12.5MM **Privately Held**
SIC: 2759 3089 Bag, wrapper & seal printing & engraving; clothes hangers, plastic
HQ: Mainetti Usa Inc.
300 Mac Ln
Keasbey NJ 08832
201 215-2900

(P-7395)
MARCO FINE ARTS
4860 W 147th St, Hawthorne (90250-6706)
PHONE..................310 615-1818
Al Marco, *Principal*
Gabriella Carlstroem, *Manager*
▲ EMP: 80
SQ FT: 10,000
SALES (est): 12.5MM **Privately Held**
WEB: www.marcofinearts.com
SIC: 2759 5199 5023 Commercial printing; art goods; frames & framing, picture & mirror

(P-7396)
MARIA CORPORATION
Also Called: Reprodox
2760 S Harbor Blvd Ste C, Santa Ana (92704-5827)
PHONE..................714 751-2460
Maria Cutler, *CEO*
Kevin David Cutler, *CFO*
Ulises Lopez, *Admin Sec*
EMP: 10
SQ FT: 3,200
SALES (est): 955.2K **Privately Held**
SIC: 2759 Commercial printing

(P-7397)
MATRIX DOCUMENT IMAGING INC
527 E Rowland St Ste 214, Covina (91723-3267)
PHONE..................626 966-9959
Thomas Smith, *President*
Mercedes Uribe, *Vice Pres*
Michael Murray, *Manager*
EMP: 51
SALES (est): 5.9MM **Privately Held**
SIC: 2759 8111 Laser printing; legal services

(P-7398)
MEPCO LABEL SYSTEMS
1313 S Stockton St, Lodi (95240-5942)
PHONE..................209 946-0201
Jennifer Tracy, *CEO*
Tom Gassner, *President*
Alfred M Gassner, *CEO*
Carol Gassner, *CEO*
Karl Gassner, *Exec VP*
EMP: 96
SQ FT: 83,000
SALES (est): 18.7MM **Privately Held**
WEB: www.mepcolabel.com
SIC: 2759 Publication printing; labels & seals: printing

(P-7399)
MERRILL CORPORATION
350 S Grand Ave Ste 3000, Los Angeles (90071-3424)
PHONE..................213 253-5900
William Brahos, *Director*
EMP: 88
SALES (corp-wide): 566.6MM **Privately Held**
SIC: 2759 Commercial printing
PA: Merrill Corporation
1 Merrill Cir
Saint Paul MN 55108
651 646-4501

(P-7400)
MERRILL CORPORATION
10716 Reagan St, Los Alamitos (90720-2431)
PHONE..................714 690-2200
Brian Merrill, *President*
EMP: 88
SALES (corp-wide): 566.6MM **Privately Held**
SIC: 2759 Commercial printing
PA: Merrill Corporation
1 Merrill Cir
Saint Paul MN 55108
651 646-4501

(P-7401)
MERRILL CORPORATION
1731 Embarcadero Rd # 100, Palo Alto (94303-3339)
PHONE..................650 493-1400
Don Conception, *Manager*
EMP: 30
SALES (corp-wide): 566.6MM **Privately Held**
WEB: www.merrillcorp.com
SIC: 2759 Commercial printing
PA: Merrill Corporation
1 Merrill Cir
Saint Paul MN 55108
651 646-4501

(P-7402)
MERRILL CORPORATION
8899 University Center Ln # 200, San Diego (92122-1065)
PHONE..................858 623-0300
Jon Silgester, *Manager*
Anthony Liccardo, *Manager*
EMP: 87
SALES (corp-wide): 566.6MM **Privately Held**
WEB: www.merrillcorp.com
SIC: 2759 Commercial printing
PA: Merrill Corporation
1 Merrill Cir
Saint Paul MN 55108
651 646-4501

(P-7403)
MERRILL CORPORATION
14500 Reservation Rd, Salinas (93908-9251)
PHONE..................831 759-9300
Brian Merrill, *Branch Mgr*
EMP: 15
SALES (corp-wide): 566.6MM **Privately Held**
WEB: www.merrillcorp.com
SIC: 2759 Commercial printing
PA: Merrill Corporation
1 Merrill Cir
Saint Paul MN 55108
651 646-4501

(P-7404)
MERRILL CORPORATION
Also Called: Merrill/Orange County
1900 Avenue Of The Stars # 1200, Los Angeles (90067-4403)
PHONE..................949 252-9449
Nancy Dagostino, *Manager*
Paul Saiki, *Sr Project Mgr*
EMP: 12
SALES (corp-wide): 566.6MM **Privately Held**
WEB: www.merrillcorp.com
SIC: 2759 Financial note & certificate printing & engraving
PA: Merrill Corporation
1 Merrill Cir
Saint Paul MN 55108
651 646-4501

(P-7405)
MERRILL CORPORATION INC
10635 Santa Monica Blvd # 350, Los Angeles (90025-8300)
PHONE..................310 552-5288
Fax: 310 552-5299
EMP: 25
SALES (corp-wide): 691.4MM **Privately Held**
SIC: 2759

PA: Merrill Corporation
1 Merrill Cir
Saint Paul MN 55108
651 646-4501

(P-7406)
MESA LABEL EXPRESS INC
13257 Kirkham Way, Poway (92064-7116)
PHONE..................858 668-2820
James Teeter, *President*
Mary Ellen Teeter, *Treasurer*
EMP: 14
SQ FT: 10,000
SALES (est): 2.7MM **Privately Held**
WEB: www.mesalabel.com
SIC: 2759 2672 Labels & seals: printing; adhesive papers, labels or tapes: from purchased material

(P-7407)
MIDONNA INC
Also Called: Blue Engravers
1375 Caspian Ave, Long Beach (90813-2649)
PHONE..................562 983-5140
Michael Leonar, *President*
EMP: 14
SALES: 700K **Privately Held**
SIC: 2759 Engraving

(P-7408)
MIXONIC
1145 Polk St Ste A, San Francisco (94109-5541)
PHONE..................866 838-5067
Robert Jacobson, *CEO*
EMP: 12 EST: 2001
SALES (est): 27.1K **Privately Held**
WEB: www.mixonic.com
SIC: 2759 Commercial printing

(P-7409)
MORRISSEY BROS PRINTERS INC
929 E Slauson Ave, Los Angeles (90011-5239)
PHONE..................323 233-7197
Donisle R Morrissey Jr, *President*
John B Jones, *Treasurer*
D R Morrisey III, *Vice Pres*
Jeanne Morrissey, *Admin Sec*
EMP: 25
SQ FT: 15,000
SALES (est): 2.9MM **Privately Held**
SIC: 2759 2752 7389 5111 Flexographic printing; commercial printing, lithographic; brokers' services; printing & writing paper; stationery stores; packaging paper & plastics film, coated & laminated

(P-7410)
NATIONALS ELITE ATHLETICS INC (PA)
5000 Birch St, Newport Beach (92660-2127)
PHONE..................866 253-6614
Harold Hicks Jr, *President*
EMP: 10 EST: 2016
SQ FT: 820
SALES: 125K **Privately Held**
SIC: 2759 8699 8741 Screen printing; athletic organizations; administrative management

(P-7411)
NATIONWIDE PRINTING SVCS INC
400 Camino Vista Verde, San Clemente (92673-6815)
PHONE..................714 258-7899
Lewis Gray, *President*
EMP: 10
SALES (est): 630K **Privately Held**
SIC: 2759 Commercial printing

(P-7412)
NELSON NAME PLATE COMPANY (PA)
Also Called: Nelson-Miller
2800 Casitas Ave, Los Angeles (90039-2942)
PHONE..................323 663-3971
Hosmel Galan, *CEO*
Jim Kaldem, *President*
David Balce, *CFO*

PRODUCTS & SVCS

Thomas Cassutt, *Co-President*
David Lazier, *Co-President*
▲ **EMP:** 182
SQ FT: 87,000
SALES (est): 62MM **Privately Held**
WEB: www.nelsonusa.com
SIC: 2759 3479 3993 2796 Screen print-
ing; name plates: engraved, etched, etc.;
signs & advertising specialties; platemak-
ing services

(P-7413)
NEW DIRECTION SILK SCREEN
Also Called: Screenprintit
2328 Auburn Blvd Ste 2, Sacramento
(95821-1706)
PHONE....................................916 971-3939
Ray Wise, *Owner*
EMP: 18
SQ FT: 18,000
SALES (est): 1.9MM **Privately Held**
WEB: www.screenprintit.com
SIC: 2759 5199 7389 Screen printing; ad-
vertising specialties; embroidering of ad-
vertising on shirts, etc.

(P-7414)
NORMEL INC
Also Called: Edward's Industries
9983 Glenoaks Blvd, Sun Valley
(91352-1023)
PHONE....................................818 504-4041
Milton Friedman, *President*
Norma Friedman, *Admin Sec*
▲ **EMP:** 18
SQ FT: 14,000
SALES (est): 1.6MM **Privately Held**
WEB: www.edwardsindustries.com
SIC: 2759 Commercial printing

(P-7415)
NORTHERN CALIFORNIA LABELS INC
12809 Marquardt Ave, Santa Fe Springs
(90670-4827)
P.O. Box 1693, La Mirada (90637-1693)
PHONE....................................562 802-8528
Ron Broussard, *President*
Alice Broussard, *Corp Secy*
EMP: 10
SQ FT: 6,000
SALES (est): 1.2MM **Privately Held**
WEB: www.nclabels.com
SIC: 2759 2752 Labels & seals: printing;
commercial printing, lithographic

(P-7416)
NSS ENTERPRISES
Also Called: Cyber Press
3380 Viso Ct, Santa Clara (95054-2625)
PHONE....................................408 970-9200
Chuck Nijmeh, *President*
Adam Zeno, *Vice Pres*
EMP: 22
SALES: 3.6MM **Privately Held**
WEB: www.cyber-press.net
SIC: 2759 Commercial printing

(P-7417)
ODDBOX HOLDINGS INC
Also Called: Purple Platypus
17332 Von, Irvine (92614)
PHONE....................................714 602-8864
Mark Swart, *Principal*
Matthew Degroat, *Manager*
EMP: 11
SALES (est): 1.1MM **Privately Held**
SIC: 2759 Flexographic printing

(P-7418)
OLYMPIC PRESS INC
461 Nelo St, Santa Clara (95054-2145)
PHONE....................................408 496-6222
Becky Bayot, *President*
Oliver Bayot, *Vice Pres*
EMP: 16
SALES (est): 1.6MM **Privately Held**
WEB: www.olympicpress.com
SIC: 2759 Letterpress printing

(P-7419)
OMEGA GRAPHICS PRINTING INC
7710 Kester Ave, Van Nuys (91405-1104)
PHONE....................................818 374-9189
Peter Smith, *President*

EMP: 12 **EST:** 2012
SALES (est): 1MM **Privately Held**
SIC: 2759 7336 Commercial printing;
commercial art & graphic design

(P-7420)
OOSHIRTS INC (PA)
41454 Christy St, Fremont (94538-5105)
PHONE....................................866 660-8667
Raymond Lei, *President*
Debi Hinson, *Accountant*
Rick Barger, *Facilities Mgr*
◆ **EMP:** 450
SALES (est): 165.8MM **Privately Held**
SIC: 2759 Screen printing

(P-7421)
OPTEC LASER SYSTEMS LLC
11622 El Camino Real, San Diego
(92130-2049)
PHONE....................................858 220-1070
John Roy,
EMP: 25
SALES (est): 1.1MM **Privately Held**
SIC: 2759 Laser printing

(P-7422)
ORANGE CIRCLE STUDIO CORP
8687 Research Dr Ste 150, Irvine
(92618-4290)
PHONE....................................949 727-0800
Scott Whang, *CEO*
▲ **EMP:** 30 **EST:** 2009
SQ FT: 10,000
SALES (est): 5.4MM **Privately Held**
SIC: 2759 Calendars: printing

(P-7423)
ORANGE COUNTY LABEL CO INC
301 W Dyer Rd Ste D, Santa Ana
(92707-3450)
PHONE....................................714 437-1010
Jerome Mattert, *President*
EMP: 13 **EST:** 1995
SQ FT: 3,500
SALES (est): 805.2K **Privately Held**
WEB: www.oclabel.com
SIC: 2759 Labels & seals: printing

(P-7424)
ORORA VISUAL LLC
1600 E Valencia Dr, Fullerton (92831-4735)
PHONE....................................714 879-2400
James R Hamel, *President*
Lisa Freeman, *Project Mgr*
Wendy Petitjean, *Prdtn Mgr*
Laura Tennis, *Manager*
▲ **EMP:** 100
SALES (est): 9MM **Privately Held**
WEB: www.graphictech.net
SIC: 2759 Screen printing

(P-7425)
ORORA VISUAL TX LLC
3116 W Avenue 32, Los Angeles
(90065-2317)
PHONE....................................323 258-4111
EMP: 70 **Privately Held**
SIC: 2759 Commercial printing
HQ: Orora Visual Tx Llc
3210 Innovative Way
Mesquite TX 75149
972 289-0705

(P-7426)
P E N INC
Also Called: News Publishers' Press
215 Allen Ave, Glendale (91201-2803)
PHONE....................................818 954-0775
Richard E Jutras, *CEO*
Jeffrey Jutras, *President*
Joven Calingo, *Info Tech Dir*
Cindy Morrison, *Controller*
Robert Garcia, *Plant Mgr*
EMP: 30 **EST:** 1978
SQ FT: 11,000
SALES (est): 3.3MM **Privately Held**
WEB: www.newspublisherspress.com
SIC: 2759 Newspapers: printing

(P-7427)
PACIFIC COLOR GRAPHICS INC
6336 Patterson Pass Rd A, Livermore
(94550-9577)
PHONE....................................925 600-3006

David A Rekart, *President*
Lynette Rekart, *CFO*
Rob Edwards, *Sales Mgr*
Cindy Davis, *Director*
Chris Grimes, *Manager*
EMP: 14
SQ FT: 1,200
SALES (est): 2.8MM **Privately Held**
WEB: www.pacificcolor.net
SIC: 2759 Screen printing

(P-7428)
PACIFIC CONTAINERPRINT INC
5951 Riverside Dr Apt 4, Chino
(91710-4477)
PHONE....................................909 465-0365
Michael E Wever, *President*
Debra Wever, *Treasurer*
Daniel P Wever, *Vice Pres*
EMP: 28
SQ FT: 9,300
SALES (est): 700K **Privately Held**
SIC: 2759 3993 Screen printing; signs &
advertising specialties

(P-7429)
PACIFIC THERMOGRAPHY
9550 Jellico Ave, Northridge (91325-2029)
PHONE....................................323 938-3349
Chang C Pak, *Owner*
Steven Pak, *Owner*
EMP: 20
SQ FT: 4,500
SALES (est): 1.7MM **Privately Held**
WEB: www.ptcprint.com
SIC: 2759 2752 Thermography; commer-
cial printing, offset

(P-7430)
PADYWELL CORP
835 Meridian St, Duarte (91010-3587)
PHONE....................................626 359-9149
Larry Chang, *President*
▲ **EMP:** 20
SQ FT: 7,825
SALES (est): 1.4MM **Privately Held**
SIC: 2759

(P-7431)
PAPER WORKS CORPORATION
19168 Van Ness Ave, Torrance
(90501-1101)
PHONE....................................310 781-9400
Matt Kim, *President*
EMP: 10
SQ FT: 7,500
SALES (est): 689.3K **Privately Held**
SIC: 2759 Commercial printing

(P-7432)
PAW PRINTS INC
3166 Bay Rd, Redwood City (94063-3907)
PHONE....................................650 365-4077
John Garibaldi, *President*
Antionette Garibaldi, *Vice Pres*
EMP: 11
SALES: 800K **Privately Held**
WEB: www.pawprints.org
SIC: 2759 5199 3993 Screen printing; ad-
vertising specialties; signs & advertising
specialties

(P-7433)
PERFECT IMAGE PRINTING INC
3223 Monier Cir, Rancho Cordova
(95742-6807)
PHONE....................................916 631-8350
James Van Hill, *CEO*
Anita Van Hill, *CFO*
EMP: 10
SQ FT: 7,500
SALES (est): 1.6MM **Privately Held**
SIC: 2759 Screen printing

(P-7434)
PERFORMANCE LABEL INTL INC
6825 Gateway Park Dr # 1, San Diego
(92154-7530)
PHONE....................................619 429-6870
Harold Dreis, *President*
EMP: 12
SQ FT: 8,400
SALES (est): 1.9MM **Privately Held**
WEB: www.performancelabel.com
SIC: 2759 Screen printing

(P-7435)
PHEONICIA INC
710 E Parkridge Ave # 105, Corona
(92879-1097)
PHONE....................................951 268-5180
Ralph Azar, *CEO*
EMP: 10
SALES (est): 1.6MM **Privately Held**
SIC: 2759 Commercial printing

(P-7436)
PINNACLE DIVERSIFIED INC
Also Called: Pinnacle Press
1248 San Luis Obispo St, Hayward
(94544-7916)
PHONE....................................408 562-0111
Jason Kim, *President*
Rui Wang, *Vice Pres*
William Furr, *General Mgr*
David Fok, *Manager*
EMP: 17
SQ FT: 13,000
SALES (est): 3MM **Privately Held**
SIC: 2759 Commercial printing

(P-7437)
PIXSCAN
Also Called: Scanart
1259 Park Ave, Emeryville (94608-3630)
PHONE....................................510 595-2222
Frederic Lompa, *President*
Kathy Lompa, *CFO*
EMP: 10
SQ FT: 5,000
SALES (est): 2.1MM **Privately Held**
WEB: www.scanart.com
SIC: 2759 Commercial printing

(P-7438)
PLASTI-PRINT INC
1620 Gilbreth Rd, Burlingame
(94010-1405)
PHONE....................................650 652-4950
Peter Vigil, *President*
Helen Vigil, *Corp Secy*
Adolf Vigil, *Vice Pres*
Rodney Vigil, *Vice Pres*
EMP: 10
SALES (est): 700K **Privately Held**
WEB: www.plasti-print.com
SIC: 2759 7389 2672 2396 Screen print-
ing; letterpress printing; laminating serv-
ice; coated & laminated paper;
automotive & apparel trimmings

(P-7439)
POLYCRAFT INC
42075 Avenida Alvarado, Temecula
(92590-3486)
PHONE....................................951 296-0860
William D Verstegen, *President*
Bryan Nealy, *Principal*
Patricia Verstegen, *Principal*
EMP: 20
SQ FT: 21,000
SALES (est): 1.6MM **Privately Held**
WEB: www.polycraftinc.com
SIC: 2759 2671 Screen printing; labels &
seals: printing; decals: printing; flexo-
graphic printing; packaging paper & plas-
tics film, coated & laminated

(P-7440)
POPULAR PRINTERS INC
3210 San Gabriel Blvd, Rosemead
(91770-2540)
PHONE....................................626 307-4281
Lihung Wang, *President*
Timothy Chu, *Vice Pres*
EMP: 10
SQ FT: 5,000
SALES (est): 1MM **Privately Held**
SIC: 2759 Commercial printing

(P-7441)
POSTCARD PRESS INC (PA)
Also Called: Next Day Flyers
8000 Haskell Ave, Van Nuys (91406-1321)
PHONE....................................310 747-3800
David Handmaker, *President*
◆ **EMP:** 31 **EST:** 1996
SALES (est): 9.5MM **Privately Held**
WEB: www.nextdayflyers.com
SIC: 2759 Visiting cards (including busi-
ness): printing

(P-7442)
PRESIDENT ENTERPRISE INC
Also Called: Lotus Labels
700 Columbia St, Brea (92821-2914)
PHONE....................714 671-9577
George Wu, *President*
Shu-Feng T Wu, *Vice Pres*
Lindsey Hand, *Sales Staff*
▲ EMP: 20
SQ FT: 22,000
SALES (est): 3.6MM **Privately Held**
WEB: www.lotuslabels.net
SIC: 2759 Labels & seals: printing

(P-7443)
PRESTIGE FOIL INC
13531 Fairmont Way, Tustin (92780-1808)
PHONE....................714 556-1431
Charles Wingard, *President*
Anne Considine Wingard, *Corp Secy*
Mike Wingard, *Vice Pres*
Phil Wingard, *Vice Pres*
Phillip Wingard, *Principal*
EMP: 10
SQ FT: 5,000
SALES (est): 1.1MM **Privately Held**
SIC: 2759 Embossing on paper

(P-7444)
PRIMARY COLOR SYSTEMS CORP
401 Coral Cir, El Segundo (90245-4622)
PHONE....................310 841-0250
Ed Philipps, *Branch Mgr*
Tim Gillham, *Supervisor*
EMP: 100
SALES (corp-wide): 61MM **Privately Held**
WEB: www.primarycolor.com
SIC: 2759 2752 Commercial printing; commercial printing, lithographic
PA: Primary Color Systems Corporation
11130 Holder St
Cypress CA 90630
949 660-7080

(P-7445)
PRINTFIRM INC
21333 Deering Ct, Canoga Park (91304-5018)
PHONE....................818 992-1005
Masis Artounian, *President*
Alex Vartanian, *Manager*
EMP: 13
SALES (est): 1.7MM **Privately Held**
SIC: 2759 Screen printing

(P-7446)
PRINTING AND MARKETING INC
33200 Transit Ave, Union City (94587-2035)
PHONE....................510 931-7000
Stacy Mudd, *President*
Stacy Pena, *Accountant*
Francisco Quiteno, *Manager*
EMP: 10
SALES (est): 856K **Privately Held**
SIC: 2759 5699 2754 Commercial printing; T-shirts, custom printed; promotional printing, gravure

(P-7447)
PRINTRUNNER LLC
Also Called: U-Nited Printing and Copy Ctr
8000 Haskell Ave, Van Nuys (91406-1321)
PHONE....................888 296-5760
Dean Rabbani, *Principal*
Mike Zaya, *President*
Adam Berger, *CEO*
Kamie Davison, *Controller*
EMP: 30 EST: 1999
SQ FT: 50,000
SALES (est): 445.9K **Privately Held**
WEB: www.printrunner.com
SIC: 2759 Commercial printing

(P-7448)
PRINTYOURCOMPANY
2661 Dow Ave, Tustin (92780-7207)
PHONE....................714 380-3900
Robert Goodloe, *Owner*
EMP: 12
SALES (est): 185.4K **Privately Held**
SIC: 2759 Commercial printing

(P-7449)
PRODIGY PRESS INC
1136 W Evelyn Ave, Sunnyvale (94086-5742)
PHONE....................408 962-0396
Alireza Azadan, *President*
EMP: 10
SALES (est): 1.9MM **Privately Held**
WEB: www.prodigypress.com
SIC: 2759 Advertising literature: printing

(P-7450)
PROFESSNAL RPRGRAPHIC SVCS INC
Also Called: Pro Group
17731 Cowan, Irvine (92614-6009)
PHONE....................949 748-5400
Cindy Kennedy, *President*
Thomas Brian Kennedy, *CFO*
EMP: 25
SALES (est): 8MM **Privately Held**
SIC: 2759 Commercial printing

(P-7451)
PROGRAPHICS SCREENPRINTING INC
1975 Diamond St, San Marcos (92078-5122)
PHONE....................760 744-4555
Bruce Heid, *President*
Barbara Heid, *Vice Pres*
Janeen Duncan, *Manager*
EMP: 41
SQ FT: 18,000
SALES (est): 6.4MM **Privately Held**
SIC: 2759 3993 2396 5112 Screen printing; signs & advertising specialties; automotive & apparel trimmings; pens &/or pencils; embroidery products, except schiffli machine

(P-7452)
PROGRSSIVE INTGRATED SOLUTIONS
Also Called: Progressive Manufacturing
3700 E Miraloma Ave, Anaheim (92806-2107)
PHONE....................714 237-0980
Rodney Dean Boehme, *President*
Victor Roth, *Director*
EMP: 76
SQ FT: 30,000
SALES (est): 10.1MM **Privately Held**
SIC: 2759 2752 Envelopes: printing; commercial printing, offset

(P-7453)
PRPCO
Also Called: Poor Richard's Press
2226 Beebee St, San Luis Obispo (93401-5505)
PHONE....................805 543-6844
Todd P Ventura, *President*
Mary Monroe, *CFO*
Richard C Blake, *Vice Pres*
Karen Evans, *Project Mgr*
Jon McCoid, *Project Mgr*
EMP: 35
SALES (est): 3.3MM **Privately Held**
SIC: 2759 Screen printing

(P-7454)
QINGMU INTERNATIONAL INC
1055 Park View Dr Ste 119, Covina (91724-3735)
PHONE....................626 965-7277
EMP: 50
SALES (est): 2.1MM **Privately Held**
SIC: 2759

(P-7455)
QUADRIGA USA ENTERPRISES INC
Also Called: Commercial and Security Labels
28410 Witherspoon Pkwy, Valencia (91355-4167)
PHONE....................888 669-9994
Aram Mehrabyan, *CEO*
Ashot Mehrabyan, *CFO*
Vahan Arakelyan, *General Mgr*
Mher Mehrabyan, *Admin Sec*
EMP: 14
SQ FT: 18,200

SALES (est): 366.7K **Privately Held**
SIC: 2759 2679 5131 7389 Tags & labels, paper; labels; packaging & labeling services; adhesive papers, labels or tapes: from purchased material; labels & seals: printing

(P-7456)
QUANTUM CHROMODYNAMICS INC
3703 W 190th St, Torrance (90504-5706)
PHONE....................310 329-5000
David Hills, *President*
EMP: 15
SALES (est): 960K **Privately Held**
WEB: www.hillslasermarking.com
SIC: 2759 7389 Laser printing; engraving service

(P-7457)
QUEST INDUSTRIES LLC
Also Called: Quest Inds - Stockton Plant
2518 Boeing Way, Stockton (95206-3937)
PHONE....................209 234-0202
Ryan Reid, *Branch Mgr*
EMP: 18
SALES (corp-wide): 19.4MM **Privately Held**
WEB: www.questllc.com
SIC: 2759 Labels & seals: printing
PA: Quest Industries Llc
15 Bleeker St Ste 202
Millburn NJ 07041
908 851-9070

(P-7458)
QUIKTURN PROF SCRNPRINTING INC
567 S Melrose St, Placentia (92870-6305)
PHONE....................800 784-5419
Bill Allen, *CEO*
Victor Carlos, *Exec VP*
Gian Emanuele, *Exec VP*
EMP: 15
SALES (est): 2.5MM **Privately Held**
SIC: 2759 Commercial printing

(P-7459)
R R DONNELLEY & SONS COMPANY
Also Called: RR Donnelley
1600 Proforma Ave, Ontario (91761-7605)
PHONE....................909 930-1605
Kyle Mankowski, *Branch Mgr*
EMP: 20
SALES (corp-wide): 6.9B **Publicly Held**
WEB: www.rrdonnelley.com
SIC: 2759 Screen printing
PA: R. R. Donnelley & Sons Company
35 W Wacker Dr Ste 3650
Chicago IL 60601
312 326-8000

(P-7460)
R R DONNELLEY & SONS COMPANY
Also Called: R R Donnelley Financial
1888 Century Park E # 1650, Los Angeles (90067-1734)
PHONE....................310 789-4100
Summer Carmichael, *Manager*
EMP: 11
SALES (corp-wide): 6.9B **Publicly Held**
WEB: www.rrdonnelley.com
SIC: 2759 Financial note & certificate printing & engraving
PA: R. R. Donnelley & Sons Company
35 W Wacker Dr Ste 3650
Chicago IL 60601
312 326-8000

(P-7461)
R R DONNELLEY & SONS COMPANY
Also Called: R R Donnelley Financial
333 S Grand Ave Ste 4350, Los Angeles (90071-1595)
PHONE....................213 928-0967
Dave Oslin, *Manager*
EMP: 40
SALES (corp-wide): 6.9B **Publicly Held**
WEB: www.rrdonnelley.com
SIC: 2759 Financial note & certificate printing & engraving

PA: R. R. Donnelley & Sons Company
35 W Wacker Dr Ste 3650
Chicago IL 60601
312 326-8000

(P-7462)
R R DONNELLEY & SONS COMPANY
Also Called: R R Donnelley
955 Gateway Center Way, San Diego (92102-4542)
PHONE....................619 527-4600
Boyd Richardson, *Branch Mgr*
EMP: 204
SALES (corp-wide): 6.9B **Publicly Held**
SIC: 2759 Commercial printing
PA: R. R. Donnelley & Sons Company
35 W Wacker Dr Ste 3650
Chicago IL 60601
312 326-8000

(P-7463)
R R DONNELLEY & SONS COMPANY
Also Called: R R Donnelley Coml Press Plant
960 Gateway Center Way, San Diego (92102-4542)
PHONE....................619 527-4600
Jim Rosenberg, *Manager*
EMP: 150
SALES (corp-wide): 6.9B **Publicly Held**
WEB: www.rrdonnelley.com
SIC: 2759 Commercial printing
PA: R. R. Donnelley & Sons Company
35 W Wacker Dr Ste 3650
Chicago IL 60601
312 326-8000

(P-7464)
RAINBOW SUBLYMATION INC
2438 E 11th St, Los Angeles (90021-2938)
PHONE....................213 489-5001
Hyuk Jun Yoon, *President*
▲ EMP: 37
SALES (est): 2.7MM **Privately Held**
SIC: 2759

(P-7465)
RAOUL TEXTILES INC
Also Called: Raoul's Hand-Screened Yardage
110 Los Aguajes Ave, Santa Barbara (93101-3818)
PHONE....................805 965-1694
Salley McQuillan, *President*
EMP: 16 EST: 2004
SALES (est): 1.9MM **Privately Held**
WEB: www.raoultextiles.com
SIC: 2759 Screen printing

(P-7466)
RESOURCE LABEL GROUP LLC
30803 San Clemente St, Hayward (94544-7136)
PHONE....................510 477-0707
EMP: 49
SALES (est): 1.2MM
SALES (corp-wide): 236.4MM **Privately Held**
SIC: 2759 Flexographic printing
PA: Resource Label Group, Llc
147 Seaboard Ln
Franklin TN 37067
615 661-5900

(P-7467)
RESPONSE ENVELOPE INC (PA)
1340 S Baker Ave, Ontario (91761-7742)
PHONE....................909 923-5855
Jonas Ulrich, *CEO*
Wendy Antrim, *Vice Pres*
Philip Ulrich, *Vice Pres*
▲ EMP: 104
SQ FT: 85,000
SALES (est): 19MM **Privately Held**
WEB: www.response-envelope.com
SIC: 2759 2677 Envelopes: printing; envelopes

(P-7468)
RESPONSE GRAPHICS IN PRINT
1065 La Mirada St, Laguna Beach (92651-3569)
PHONE....................949 376-8701
▲ EMP: 12
SALES (est): 450K **Privately Held**
SIC: 2759

(P-7469)
RETAIL PRINT MEDIA INC
2355 Crenshaw Blvd # 135, Torrance
(90501-3341)
PHONE..................424 488-6950
Raymond Young, *CEO*
Karli Sikich, *COO*
Erika Whitmore, *Director*
Angelina Jungo, *Account Dir*
EMP: 35
SALES (est): 3.6MM **Privately Held**
SIC: 2759 7371 Advertising literature:
printing; computer software writing services

(P-7470)
RHEETECH SALES & SERVICES INC
2401 S Main St, Los Angeles (90007-2727)
PHONE..................213 749-9111
Brian Rhee, *President*
▲ EMP: 10
SQ FT: 10,000
SALES (est): 1.2MM **Privately Held**
WEB: www.prinsupply.com
SIC: 2759 Screen printing

(P-7471)
RJ ACQUISITION CORP (PA)
Also Called: Ad Art Company
3260 E 26th St, Vernon (90058-8008)
PHONE..................323 318-1107
Joe M Demarco, *President*
Roger Keech, *CEO*
Eddie Leon, *General Mgr*
Jonathan Gonzalez, *Project Mgr*
Robin Abrams Auarte, *Controller*
▲ EMP: 215
SQ FT: 200,000
SALES (est): 75.7MM **Privately Held**
WEB: www.adartco.com
SIC: 2759 Screen printing

(P-7472)
ROBERT R WIX INC (PA)
Also Called: Valley Printing
2140 Pine St, Ceres (95307-3620)
PHONE..................209 537-4561
Robert R Wix, *President*
Linny Goodrich, *Vice Pres*
Tom Mink, *Vice Pres*
Mia Wix, *Manager*
EMP: 32 EST: 1959
SQ FT: 31,000
SALES (est): 5.5MM **Privately Held**
WEB: www.valleyptg.com
SIC: 2759 2752 2672 2671 Letterpress
printing; flexographic printing; commercial
printing, offset; coated & laminated paper;
packaging paper & plastics film, coated &
laminated

(P-7473)
ROBINSON PRINTING INC
42685 Rio Nedo, Temecula (92590-3711)
PHONE..................951 296-0300
David Robinson, *CEO*
Mike Robinson, *President*
▲ EMP: 25
SQ FT: 24,000
SALES (est): 4.4MM **Privately Held**
WEB: www.robinsonprinting.com
SIC: 2759 2621 Screen printing; packaging paper

(P-7474)
RR DONNELLEY & SONS COMPANY
Also Called: Donnelley Financial
19200 Von Karman Ave # 700, Irvine
(92612-8518)
PHONE..................949 852-1933
Ben Puente, *General Mgr*
Gosch Karen, *Technology*
EMP: 40
SALES (corp-wide): 6.9B **Publicly Held**
WEB: www.rrdonnelley.com
SIC: 2759 Commercial printing
PA: R. R. Donnelley & Sons Company
35 W Wacker Dr Ste 3650
Chicago IL 60601
312 326-8000

(P-7475)
RR DONNELLEY & SONS COMPANY
Los Angeles Manufacturing Div
19681 Pacific Gateway Dr, Torrance
(90502-1116)
PHONE..................310 516-3100
Barbara Dowell, *Data Proc Dir*
Edee Del Negro, *Purch Mgr*
EMP: 600
SQ FT: 80,000
SALES (corp-wide): 6.9B **Publicly Held**
WEB: www.rrdonnelley.com
SIC: 2759 2752 Publication printing; commercial printing, lithographic
PA: R. R. Donnelley & Sons Company
35 W Wacker Dr Ste 3650
Chicago IL 60601
312 326-8000

(P-7476)
SAFE PUBLISHING COMPANY
5775 Lindero Canyon Rd, Westlake Village
(91362-4013)
PHONE..................805 973-1300
John Gooden, *President*
EMP: 70 EST: 1976
SQ FT: 96,000
SALES (est): 5.4MM **Privately Held**
WEB: www.inside12x12.com
SIC: 2759 8748 8742 8741 Promotional
printing; business consulting; management consulting services; management
services; information retrieval services;
special warehousing & storage

(P-7477)
SAN BRNRDINO CMNTY COLLEGE DST
Also Called: Print Shop
701 S Mount Vernon Ave, San Bernardino
(92410-2705)
PHONE..................909 888-6511
Louie Chavira, *Supervisor*
EMP: 163
SALES (corp-wide): 11.5MM **Privately Held**
WEB: www.sbvc.sbccd.cc.ca.us
SIC: 2759 Commercial printing
PA: San Bernardino Community College
District
114 S Del Rosa Dr
San Bernardino CA 92408
909 382-4000

(P-7478)
SCREEN ART INC
15162 Triton Ln, Huntington Beach
(92649-1041)
PHONE..................714 891-4185
James K Proctor, *President*
Kathie Proctor, *Vice Pres*
Kathryn Proctor, *Vice Pres*
EMP: 17
SQ FT: 8,400
SALES (est): 2.2MM **Privately Held**
WEB: www.screenartinc.com
SIC: 2759 Screen printing

(P-7479)
SCREEN PRINTERS RESOURCE INC (PA)
1251 Burton St, Fullerton (92831-5211)
PHONE..................714 441-1155
Frank Sator, *President*
◆ EMP: 16
SQ FT: 20,000
SALES (est): 3MM **Privately Held**
WEB: www.spresource.com
SIC: 2759 Screen printing

(P-7480)
SCREENWORKS CO TIM
Also Called: Tcth Screenworks
1705 W 134th St, Gardena (90249-2032)
PHONE..................310 532-7239
Cheryl Hughes, *President*
EMP: 20
SALES (est): 1.8MM **Privately Held**
SIC: 2759 Screen printing

(P-7481)
SHIHS PRINTING
673 Monterey Pass Rd, Monterey Park
(91754-2418)
PHONE..................626 281-2989
Catherine Shih, *Owner*
EMP: 15 EST: 1989
SALES (est): 934.2K **Privately Held**
SIC: 2759 Magazines: printing

(P-7482)
SHORETT PRINTING INC (PA)
Also Called: Crown Printers
250 W Rialto Ave, San Bernardino
(92408-1017)
PHONE..................714 545-4689
Charles D Shorett Jr, *CEO*
John Shorett, *Vice Pres*
Mike Brusig, *Exec Dir*
Erin Franco, *Business Mgr*
Ken Martin, *VP Opers*
EMP: 40 EST: 1970
SALES (est): 6.7MM **Privately Held**
WEB: www.crownconnect.com
SIC: 2759 2752 Commercial printing;
commercial printing, offset

(P-7483)
SINCLAIR SYSTEMS INTL LLC
3115 S Willow Ave, Fresno (93725-9349)
PHONE..................559 233-4500
Erik A Gregerson, *President*
Edward Clapp, *CFO*
Paula Cooke, *Bd of Directors*
Pam Reddin, *Administration*
David Miller, *Info Tech Mgr*
▲ EMP: 11
SQ FT: 4,100
SALES (est): 2.9MM
SALES (corp-wide): 93.8MM **Privately Held**
WEB: www.sinclair-intl.com
SIC: 2759 7389 2672 Decals: printing;
packaging & labeling services; coated &
laminated paper
HQ: Sinclair International Limited
Jarrold Way Bowthorpe Employment
Area
Norwich NR5 9

(P-7484)
SINE-TIFIC SOLUTIONS INC
1701 Fortune Dr Ste C, San Jose
(95131-1702)
PHONE..................408 432-3434
Bruce McGuire, *President*
Franklin Pennell, *Vice Pres*
Jennifer Guerra, *Executive Asst*
EMP: 12 EST: 1963
SQ FT: 6,000
SALES (est): 2.1MM **Privately Held**
WEB: www.engravers.com
SIC: 2759 7389 Screen printing; engraving service

(P-7485)
SIRENA INCORPORATED
Also Called: Los Angeles Wraps
22717 S Western Ave, Torrance
(90501-4952)
PHONE..................866 548-5353
Brandon Park, *CEO*
EMP: 16
SQ FT: 10,000
SALES (est): 1.5MM **Privately Held**
SIC: 2759 Commercial printing

(P-7486)
SKIVA GRAPHICS SCREEN PRTG INC
2258 Rutherford Rd Ste A, Carlsbad
(92008-8824)
PHONE..................760 602-9124
Leon Monfort, *President*
EMP: 40
SQ FT: 42,078
SALES (est): 14.5MM **Privately Held**
WEB: www.skivagraphics.com
SIC: 2759 7336 3993 Screen printing;
commercial art & graphic design; signs &
advertising specialties

(P-7487)
SOCIAL IMPRINTS LLC
969 Folsom St, San Francisco
(94107-1020)
PHONE..................415 956-0269
Jeff Sheinbein, *CEO*
Kevin McCraeken, *COO*
Loie Maxwell, *Chief Mktg Ofcr*
Chris Stanley, *Accounting Mgr*
Daniel Phifer, *Opers Mgr*
EMP: 21
SQ FT: 10,000
SALES (est): 7.3MM **Privately Held**
SIC: 2759 Screen printing

(P-7488)
SOFT TOUCH INC
Also Called: Mojado Bros
1830 E Miraloma Ave Ste C, Placentia
(92870-6744)
PHONE..................714 524-3382
Mike Rodriguez, *President*
EMP: 10
SQ FT: 7,300
SALES (est): 885.6K **Privately Held**
SIC: 2759 Screen printing

(P-7489)
SONOMA PINS ETC CORPORATION
Also Called: Sonoma Promotional Solutions
841 W Napa St, Sonoma (95476-6414)
PHONE..................707 996-9956
Bernard Friedman, *President*
Judy Friedman, *Exec VP*
Tonya Edwards, *Vice Pres*
Barb Wendel, *Graphic Designe*
Nickolai Mathison, *VP Sales*
▲ EMP: 99
SQ FT: 600
SALES (est): 11.6MM **Privately Held**
WEB: www.sonoma88188.com
SIC: 2759 Promotional printing

(P-7490)
SOUTH SWELL SCREEN ARTS
8440 Production Ave, San Diego
(92121-2203)
PHONE..................858 566-3095
Allen Repashy, *Owner*
EMP: 10
SQ FT: 6,000
SALES (est): 910.2K **Privately Held**
WEB: www.southswellcorp.com
SIC: 2759 3993 2396 Screen printing;
signs & advertising specialties; automotive & apparel trimmings

(P-7491)
SOUTHWEST OFFSET PRTG CO INC
Also Called: San Francisco Offset Printing
587 Charcot Ave, San Jose (95131-2202)
PHONE..................408 232-5160
Ed Tervol, *Branch Mgr*
Warren Weinzoff, *Business Dir*
Sonny Fritz, *Safety Mgr*
Kevin Campau, *Sales Executive*
EMP: 85
SALES (corp-wide): 115.9MM **Privately Held**
WEB: www.southwestoffset.com
SIC: 2759 2789 2752 Commercial printing; bookbinding & related work; commercial printing, lithographic
PA: Southwest Offset Printing Co., Inc.
13650 Gramercy Pl
Gardena CA 90249
310 965-9154

(P-7492)
SPARTAN
444 E Taylor St, San Jose (95112-3137)
PHONE..................800 743-6950
EMP: 22 EST: 2014
SALES (est): 800.5K **Privately Held**
SIC: 2759 Screen printing

(P-7493)
SPECIALIZED SCREEN PRINTING
18435 Bandilier Cir, Fountain Valley
(92708-7012)
PHONE..................714 964-1230
David Williams, *CEO*

▲ = Import ▼=Export
◆ =Import/Export

Jim Keisker, *President*
EMP: 32
SQ FT: 20,000
SALES (est): 4.2MM **Privately Held**
WEB: www.specializedscreenprinting.com
SIC: 2759 2752 2396 Screen printing;
commercial printing, lithographic; automotive & apparel trimmings

(P-7494)
SPECTRAPRINT INC
24 Moody Ct, San Rafael (94901-1029)
PHONE..................................415 460-1228
Kim Magaline, *President*
EMP: 16
SQ FT: 12,800
SALES (est): 1.8MM **Privately Held**
WEB: www.spectraprintinc.com
SIC: 2759

(P-7495)
SPINELLI GRAPHIC INC
10631 Bloomfield St Ste 2, Los Alamitos
(90720-6765)
P.O. Box 397 (90720-0397)
PHONE..................................562 431-3232
Joseph Spinelli, *President*
Renee Spinelli, *Admin Sec*
EMP: 11
SQ FT: 9,500
SALES: 1.2MM **Privately Held**
WEB: www.spinelligraphics.com
SIC: 2759 2752 Screen printing; commercial printing, lithographic

(P-7496)
STEVEN LABEL CORPORATION
9046 Sorensen Ave, Santa Fe Springs
(90670-2641)
PHONE..................................562 906-2612
John McCullough, *Controller*
EMP: 10
SALES (corp-wide): 55.8MM **Privately
Held**
WEB: www.stevenlabel.com
SIC: 2759 Letterpress printing; screen
printing; flexographic printing
PA: Steven Label Corporation
11926 Burke St
Santa Fe Springs CA 90670
562 698-9971

(P-7497)
STEVEN LABEL CORPORATION
11926 Burke St, Santa Fe Springs
(90670-2546)
PHONE..................................562 698-9971
John McCullough, *Manager*
EMP: 10
SALES (corp-wide): 55.8MM **Privately
Held**
WEB: www.stevenlabel.com
SIC: 2759 Letterpress printing; screen
printing; flexographic printing
PA: Steven Label Corporation
11926 Burke St
Santa Fe Springs CA 90670
562 698-9971

(P-7498)
STICKER HUB INC
Also Called: Plush Printing
1452 Manhattan Ave, Fullerton
(92831-5222)
PHONE..................................714 912-8457
Sean W Wigand, *CEO*
EMP: 11 **EST:** 2010
SALES (est): 1.1MM **Privately Held**
SIC: 2759 Commercial printing

(P-7499)
**STRATEGIC PRTG SOLUTION
INC**
12110 Slauson Ave Ste 9, Santa Fe Springs
(90670-8649)
PHONE..................................562 242-5880
Sarabjit Singh Bedi, *CEO*
EMP: 11
SALES (est): 129.8K **Privately Held**
SIC: 2759 Publication printing
PA: Strategic Designs Private Limited
46/6,
New Delhi DL

(P-7500)
**STREAMLINE DSIGN
SLKSCREEN INC**
Also Called: Iron and Resin
1328 N Ventura Ave, Ventura (93001-1546)
PHONE..................................805 884-1025
Tom Hill, *President*
EMP: 10 **Privately Held**
SIC: 2759 Screen printing
PA: Streamline Design & Silkscreen, Inc.
1299 S Wells Rd
Ventura CA 93004

(P-7501)
SUN TEES
310 S Main St, Templeton (93465-5300)
P.O. Box 1493 (93465-1493)
PHONE..................................805 434-0074
Tad Thompkins, *Owner*
EMP: 10
SALES (est): 718.5K **Privately Held**
WEB: www.suntees.com
SIC: 2759 Screen printing

(P-7502)
SUNSET SIGNS AND PRINTING
2981 E White Star Ave, Anaheim
(92806-2630)
PHONE..................................714 255-9104
Tracy Eschenbrenner, *CEO*
EMP: 16
SALES (est): 2.9MM **Privately Held**
SIC: 2759 Commercial printing

(P-7503)
SUNWEST PRINTING INC
118 E Airport Dr Ste 209, San Bernardino
(92408-3419)
PHONE..................................909 890-3898
Nick Lopez, *President*
John Lopez, *Vice Pres*
EMP: 12
SQ FT: 8,500
SALES (est): 1.8MM **Privately Held**
WEB: www.sunwestprint.com
SIC: 2759 2789 Screen printing; bookbinding & related work

(P-7504)
**SUPER COLOR DIGITAL LLC
(PA)**
16761 Hale Ave, Irvine (92606-5006)
PHONE..................................949 622-0010
Peyman Rashtchi, *Mng Member*
Arman Rashtchi, *Mng Member*
▲ **EMP:** 250
SQ FT: 48,043
SALES (est): 50.5MM **Privately Held**
SIC: 2759 Commercial printing

(P-7505)
SUPERIOR PRINTING INC
Also Called: Superior Press
9440 Norwalk Blvd, Santa Fe Springs
(90670-2928)
PHONE..................................562 368-1700
Robert Traut, *President*
Jason Traut, *Treasurer*
Kevin Traut, *Admin Sec*
EMP: 95
SQ FT: 32,000
SALES (est): 22.9MM **Privately Held**
WEB: www.superior-press.com
SIC: 2759 5112 Commercial printing; business forms

(P-7506)
SYNECTIC PACKAGING INC
1201 San Luis Obispo St, Hayward
(94544-7915)
PHONE..................................650 474-0132
Joe Iskander, *President*
Gil Dulong, *Vice Pres*
Dave Hoydal, *Vice Pres*
Andy Pena, *Vice Pres*
▲ **EMP:** 10
SQ FT: 10,000
SALES (est): 1.3MM **Privately Held**
SIC: 2759 5999 Flexographic printing;
packaging materials: boxes, padding, etc.

(P-7507)
TACKETT VOLUME PRESS INC
1348 Terminal St, West Sacramento
(95691-3515)
PHONE..................................916 374-8991
Ron Tackett, *President*
EMP: 28
SQ FT: 45,000
SALES (est): 6.5MM **Privately Held**
WEB: www.volumepress.com
SIC: 2759 Commercial printing

(P-7508)
TAG PAX & LABEL INC
9528 Rush St Ste C, El Monte
(91733-1551)
PHONE..................................626 579-2000
Michael Brown, *President*
EMP: 20
SQ FT: 10,000
SALES (est): 2MM **Privately Held**
WEB: www.paxtag.com
SIC: 2759 2679 Tags: printing; tags, paper
(unprinted): made from purchased paper

(P-7509)
TAILGATE PRINTING INC
2930 S Fairview St, Santa Ana
(92704-6503)
PHONE..................................714 966-3035
Maria C Vega, *President*
Colleen Madrid, *Executive*
EMP: 147
SQ FT: 80,000
SALES: 8.8MM **Privately Held**
SIC: 2759 Letterpress printing

(P-7510)
TAYLOR GRAPHICS INC
1582 Browning, Irvine (92606-4807)
PHONE..................................949 752-5200
Dean S Taylor, *CEO*
Carla Spicer, *Admin Sec*
EMP: 23
SQ FT: 7,500
SALES (est): 4.1MM **Privately Held**
SIC: 2759 Screen printing

(P-7511)
TEC COLOR CRAFT (PA)
Also Called: TEC Color Craft Products
1860 Wright Ave, La Verne (91750-5824)
PHONE..................................909 392-9000
Edgar A Frenkiel, *CEO*
Blake Frenkiel, *Project Mgr*
Dave Marsh, *Purchasing*
Martin Serrano, *Prdtn Mgr*
Jim Evans, *VP Sales*
▲ **EMP:** 40
SQ FT: 8,000
SALES (est): 6.2MM **Privately Held**
WEB: www.teccolorcraft.com
SIC: 2759 Screen printing

(P-7512)
**TECHNICAL SCREEN PRINTING
INC**
677 N Hariton St, Orange (92868-1311)
PHONE..................................714 541-8590
Robert Golino, *President*
Barbara Golino, *Vice Pres*
EMP: 35
SQ FT: 18,000
SALES: 3.5MM **Privately Held**
SIC: 2759 2752 2396 Screen printing;
commercial printing, lithographic; automotive & apparel trimmings

(P-7513)
TELECARD LLC
220 Bingham Dr Ste 101, San Marcos
(92069-1482)
PHONE..................................760 752-1700
Alan Saloner, *Mng Member*
Cheryl King, *Opers Mgr*
EMP: 15
SALES (est): 570K **Privately Held**
SIC: 2759 Visiting cards (including business): printing

(P-7514)
**TEMECULA T-SHIRT PRINTERS
INC**
41607 Enterprise Cir N A, Temecula
(92590-5684)
PHONE..................................951 296-0184
Kenneth Dawkins, *President*
EMP: 15
SALES (est): 469.5K **Privately Held**
SIC: 2759 Screen printing

(P-7515)
TERRAMAR GRAPHICS INC
5345 Townsgate Rd Ste 330, Westlake Village (91361)
PHONE..................................805 529-8845
Elaine Mc Coy, *Owner*
EMP: 14
SQ FT: 4,000
SALES (est): 1.5MM **Privately Held**
SIC: 2759 5112 Business forms: printing;
business forms

(P-7516)
**TEXTILE 2000 SCREEN
PRINTING**
Also Called: Frontline Military Apparel
8675 Miralani Dr, San Diego (92126-4355)
PHONE..................................858 735-8521
Keith Gentry, *Owner*
EMP: 23 **EST:** 1999
SALES (est): 1.5MM **Privately Held**
SIC: 2759 Screen printing

(P-7517)
THE LIGATURE INC
Also Called: Echelon Fine Printing
4909 Alcoa Ave, Vernon (90058-3022)
PHONE..................................800 421-8703
Richard Moffitt, *Branch Mgr*
EMP: 15
SALES (corp-wide): 3.4B **Privately Held**
WEB: www.theligature.com
SIC: 2759 Commercial printing
HQ: The Ligature Inc
4909 Alcoa Ave
Vernon CA 90058
323 585-6000

(P-7518)
THE LIGATURE INC
Echelon Fine Printing
750 Gilmore St, Berkeley (94710)
PHONE..................................510 526-5181
Baird Conner, *General Mgr*
EMP: 30
SALES (corp-wide): 3.4B **Privately Held**
WEB: www.theligature.com
SIC: 2759 2752 Commercial printing;
commercial printing, lithographic
HQ: The Ligature Inc
4909 Alcoa Ave
Vernon CA 90058
323 585-6000

(P-7519)
THERMCRAFT INC
3762 Bradview Dr, Sacramento
(95827-9702)
PHONE..................................916 363-9411
Ray Summers, *President*
Maurine Summers, *Vice Pres*
EMP: 16
SQ FT: 4,600
SALES (est): 2.1MM **Privately Held**
WEB: www.thermcraft.com
SIC: 2759 Thermography

(P-7520)
THREE MAN CORPORATION
Also Called: San Diego Printers
10025 Huennekens St, San Diego
(92121-2957)
PHONE..................................858 684-5200
John Barros, *President*
Wayne Ihms, *Vice Pres*
EMP: 20
SQ FT: 14,000
SALES (est): 3.7MM **Privately Held**
WEB: www.sdprinters.com
SIC: 2759 2752 Commercial printing;
commercial printing, lithographic

P
R
O
D
U
C
T
S

&

S
V
C
S

(P-7521)
TJ GIANT LLC
12623 Cisneros Ln, Santa Fe Springs
(90670-3373)
PHONE..............................562 906-1060
Peter D Ahn,
EMP: 900
SQ FT: 1,500
SALES: 5.1MM **Privately Held**
SIC: 2759 Screen printing

(P-7522)
TOP PRINTING & GRAPHIC INC
1210 N Knollwood Cir, Anaheim
(92801-1309)
PHONE..............................714 484-9200
Kyu H Yoon, *President*
EMP: 10
SQ FT: 14,000
SALES (est): 500K **Privately Held**
SIC: 2759 Commercial printing

(P-7523)
TOTTY PRINTING
1208 W Collins Ave, Orange (92867-5413)
PHONE..............................714 633-7081
Thomas Totty, *Owner*
EMP: 10
SQ FT: 1,800
SALES (est): 1.1MM **Privately Held**
WEB: www.tottyprinting.com
SIC: 2759 Screen printing

(P-7524)
TRADE ONLY SCREEN PRINTING INC
Also Called: Curry Graphics
23482 Foley St, Hayward (94545-5308)
P.O. Box 5698, Concord (94524-0698)
PHONE..............................510 887-2020
Patrick T Bryson, *President*
Richard Ayres, *President*
EMP: 20
SQ FT: 15,000
SALES (est): 2.5MM **Privately Held**
SIC: 2759 2396 Screen printing; promotional printing; automotive & apparel trimmings

(P-7525)
TRANSCONTINENTAL NRTHERN CA 20
47540 Kato Rd, Fremont (94538-7303)
PHONE..............................510 580-7700
Brian Reid, *CEO*
Francois Olivier, *Principal*
Vivian Marzin McKay, *Finance*
▲ **EMP:** 200
SALES (est): 42MM
SALES (corp-wide): 1.6B **Privately Held**
SIC: 2759 Magazines: printing
PA: Transcontinental Inc
    1 Place Ville-Marie Bureau 3240
    Montreal QC H3B 0
    514 954-4000

(P-7526)
TRI-CITY TECHNOLOGIES INC
Also Called: Tri-City Print & Mail
2615 Del Monte St, West Sacramento
(95691-3809)
PHONE..............................916 503-5300
Charles F Sievers Jr, *President*
John English, *Marketing Staff*
Lupe Murillo, *Marketing Staff*
Crystal Fitch, *Sales Staff*
Jonny Billings,
EMP: 16
SQ FT: 10,000
SALES (est): 1.5MM **Privately Held**
WEB: www.tricitytech.net
SIC: 2759 7331 Advertising literature: printing; direct mail advertising services

(P-7527)
TRISAR INC
950 W Town And Country Rd, Orange
(92868-4714)
PHONE..............................714 972-2626
James Bell, *President*
▲ **EMP:** 40
SALES (est): 4.4MM
SALES (corp-wide): 2.3B **Publicly Held**
SIC: 2759 2261 Screen printing; screen printing of cotton broadwoven fabrics

HQ: Amscan Inc.
    80 Grasslands Rd Ste 3
    Elmsford NY 10523
    914 345-2020

(P-7528)
TURNER GROUP PUBLICATIONS INC
27788 Klaus Ct, Hayward (94542-2366)
PHONE..............................408 297-3299
EMP: 11
SALES: 2MM **Privately Held**
SIC: 2759

(P-7529)
UNITECH DECO INC
Also Called: Unitech Industries
19731 Bahama St, Northridge
(91324-3304)
PHONE..............................818 700-1373
Merle Wurm, *President*
Tina Wurm-Donikian, *Treasurer*
EMP: 34
SQ FT: 9,000
SALES (est): 3.8MM **Privately Held**
SIC: 2759 2789 2396 Bag, wrapper & seal printing & engraving; bookbinding & related work; automotive & apparel trimmings

(P-7530)
UNIVERSAL LABEL PRINTERS INC
Also Called: Unilabel
13003 Los Nietos Rd, Santa Fe Springs
(90670-3348)
PHONE..............................562 944-0234
John Walsh, *President*
Patricia Walsh, *Treasurer*
Jack Walsh, *Vice Pres*
Kathleen Mulcahey, *Admin Sec*
Paul Mulcahey, *Human Res Mgr*
EMP: 22
SQ FT: 30,000
SALES (est): 3MM **Privately Held**
WEB: www.universallabel.com
SIC: 2759 Labels & seals: printing; tags: printing

(P-7531)
US DIRECT LLC
1700 Barranca Pkwy, Irvine (92606-4824)
PHONE..............................949 491-3342
Brian Hauck, *Mng Member*
EMP: 22
SALES (est): 3.9MM **Privately Held**
SIC: 2759 Commercial printing

(P-7532)
US1COM INC
715 Southpoint Blvd Ste D, Petaluma
(94954-6836)
P.O. Box 3303, Santa Fe Springs (90670-1303)
PHONE..............................707 781-2560
Farid Elhami, *President*
Jose Chavez, *Opers Mgr*
EMP: 17
SQ FT: 5,417
SALES (est): 614.2K **Privately Held**
WEB: www.us1com.com
SIC: 2759
PA: A F E Industries Inc.
    13233 Barton Cir
    Whittier CA 90605

(P-7533)
VENTURA PRINTING INC (PA)
Also Called: V3
200 N Elevar St, Oxnard (93030-7969)
PHONE..............................805 981-2600
David Wilson, *President*
Neal Soper, *Manager*
David Ballantyne, *Accounts Exec*
▲ **EMP:** 55
SALES (est): 14.3MM **Privately Held**
SIC: 2759 Commercial printing

(P-7534)
VITACHROME GRAPHICS INC (PA)
3710 Park Pl, Montrose (91020-1623)
PHONE..............................818 957-0900
Gary Durbin, *President*

Tony Won, *Vice Pres*
Jeanne De Guzman, *Opers Mgr*
Lisa Beach, *Cust Mgr*
EMP: 25
SQ FT: 43,000
SALES (est): 3.5MM **Privately Held**
WEB: www.vitachrome.com
SIC: 2759 Decals: printing; screen printing; labels & seals: printing

(P-7535)
VOMAR PRODUCTS INC
7800 Deering Ave, Canoga Park
(91304-5005)
P.O. Box 11105 (91309-2105)
PHONE..............................818 610-5115
Paul Van Ostrand, *CEO*
Herbert Paul Van Ostrand, *President*
Jason Van Ostrand, *Vice Pres*
Srdjan Kovacevic, *General Mgr*
Anh Nguyen, *Info Tech Mgr*
EMP: 38
SQ FT: 29,000
SALES (est): 5.9MM **Privately Held**
WEB: www.vomarproducts.com
SIC: 2759 3993 Commercial printing; name plates: except engraved, etched, etc.: metal

(P-7536)
WAY OF THE WORLD INC
170 Commercial St, Sunnyvale
(94086-5201)
PHONE..............................408 616-7700
Mark Johnson, *President*
Karen Thomas, *Vice Pres*
EMP: 10
SQ FT: 5,000
SALES (est): 1.2MM **Privately Held**
SIC: 2759 Commercial printing

(P-7537)
WES GO INC
Also Called: GP Color Imaging Group
8211 Lankershim Blvd, North Hollywood
(91605-1614)
PHONE..............................818 504-1200
Wesley Adams, *CEO*
Thomas Wilhelm, *President*
Wes Adams, *Info Tech Mgr*
Jorge Galvez, *Prdtn Mgr*
▲ **EMP:** 24
SALES (est): 3.6MM **Privately Held**
WEB: www.gpcolor.com
SIC: 2759 Posters, including billboards: printing

(P-7538)
WESTERN DIE & PRINTING CORP
3109 Casitas Ave, Los Angeles
(90039-2410)
PHONE..............................323 665-0474
Saied Toobian, *President*
▲ **EMP:** 12
SALES (est): 1.5MM **Privately Held**
SIC: 2759 Commercial printing

(P-7539)
WESTERN ROTO ENGRAVERS INC
Also Called: W R E Colortech
1225 6th St, Berkeley (94710-1488)
PHONE..............................510 525-2950
Bill Mackay, *Manager*
John Comerford, *President*
Kathleen Harrelson, *CFO*
Daniel Comerford, *Vice Pres*
Chris Mackay, *Manager*
EMP: 12
SALES (corp-wide): 13.8MM **Privately Held**
WEB: www.wrecolor.com
SIC: 2759 2796 Engraving; plates & cylinders for rotogravure printing
PA: Western Roto Engravers, Incorporated
    533 Banner Ave
    Greensboro NC 27401
    336 275-9821

(P-7540)
WESTERN YANKEE INC
13233 Barton Cir, Whittier (90605-3255)
PHONE..............................562 944-6889
Fred Elhami, *President*
EMP: 30

SQ FT: 18,000
SALES: 2.2MM **Privately Held**
WEB: www.westernyankee.com
SIC: 2759 Letterpress & screen printing; imprinting; letterpress printing
PA: A F E Industries Inc.
    13233 Barton Cir
    Whittier CA 90605

(P-7541)
WHATS HAPPENING TRI CITY
Also Called: Tri City Voice
39120 Argonaut Way # 335, Fremont
(94538-1304)
PHONE..............................510 494-1999
William Marshak, *President*
Sharon Marshak, *Co-Owner*
EMP: 30
SALES (est): 2.1MM **Privately Held**
SIC: 2759 5192 Magazines: printing; newspapers: printing; newspapers

(P-7542)
WILSONS ART STUDIO INC
Also Called: Solutions Unlimited
501 S Acacia Ave, Fullerton (92831-5101)
PHONE..............................714 870-7030
William L Goetsch, *President*
Roberta C Goetsch, *Corp Secy*
N Jim Goetsch, *Vice Pres*
EMP: 63 **EST:** 1958
SQ FT: 50,000
SALES (est): 8.1MM **Privately Held**
SIC: 2759 2396 Screen printing; automotive & apparel trimmings

(P-7543)
WINTFLASH INC
Also Called: Print Shop, The
13720 De Alcala Dr, La Mirada
(90638-3622)
PHONE..............................562 944-6548
Scott Flasher, *President*
Joy Flasher, *Corp Secy*
EMP: 11 **EST:** 1997
SQ FT: 3,000
SALES (est): 600K **Privately Held**
SIC: 2759 Commercial printing

(P-7544)
WIZARD GRAPHICS INC
411 Otterson Dr Ste 20, Chico
(95928-8241)
P.O. Box 7650 (95927-7650)
PHONE..............................530 893-3636
Merlin Newkirk, *President*
EMP: 15
SQ FT: 10,000
SALES (est): 1.1MM **Privately Held**
SIC: 2759 Commercial printing

(P-7545)
XYZ GRAPHICS INC (PA)
190 Lombard St, San Francisco
(94111-1111)
PHONE..............................415 227-9972
Steven Waterloo, *President*
Charlie Boyle, *Exec VP*
Sean Mc Glynn, *Vice Pres*
John Gatewood, *Project Mgr*
Steve Gomez, *Project Mgr*
EMP: 29
SQ FT: 8,500
SALES (est): 4.1MM **Privately Held**
WEB: www.xygraphics.com
SIC: 2759 Commercial printing

(P-7546)
YENOR INC
Also Called: Library Mosacis
5640 W 63rd St, Los Angeles
(90056-2013)
PHONE..............................310 410-1573
Raymond Rony, *President*
EMP: 10
SALES: 175K **Privately Held**
SIC: 2759 Magazines: printing

(P-7547)
ZUZA
2304 Faraday Ave, Carlsbad (92008-7216)
PHONE..............................760 438-9411
EMP: 50 **EST:** 2011
SALES (est): 4.3MM **Privately Held**
SIC: 2759

▲ = Import ▼=Export
◆ =Import/Export

2761 Manifold Business Forms

(P-7548)
APPERSON INC (PA)
17315 Studebaker Rd # 211, Cerritos
(90703-2508)
PHONE......................562 356-3333
Kelly Doherty, *CEO*
William Apperson, *Ch of Bd*
Brian Apperson, *Vice Pres*
▲ **EMP:** 70
SQ FT: 80,080
SALES (est): 22MM **Privately Held**
WEB: www.appersonprint.com
SIC: 2761 Continuous forms, office & business

(P-7549)
COMPLYRIGHT DISTRIBUTION SVCS
3451 Jupiter Ct, Oxnard (93030-8957)
PHONE......................805 981-0992
Richard Roddis, *CEO*
Nancy Melton, *Manager*
EMP: 44
SALES (est): 822.5K
SALES (corp-wide): 3.4B **Privately Held**
SIC: 2761 Manifold business forms
PA: Taylor Corporation
1725 Roe Crest Dr
North Mankato MN 56003
507 625-2828

(P-7550)
ENNIS INC
298 Sherwood Rd, Paso Robles
(93446-3546)
PHONE......................805 238-1144
Terry Reynolds, *Manager*
EMP: 113
SALES (corp-wide): 370.1MM **Publicly Held**
WEB: www.ennis.com
SIC: 2761 3955 2621 Manifold business forms; carbon paper for typewriters, sales books, etc.; writing paper
PA: Ennis, Inc.
2441 Presidential Pkwy
Midlothian TX 76065
972 775-9801

(P-7551)
PRINTEGRA CORP
379 Earhart Way, Livermore (94551-9509)
PHONE......................925 373-6368
Vinny Dinicola, *Manager*
Kevin Stanton, *General Mgr*
EMP: 22
SALES (corp-wide): 370.1MM **Publicly Held**
WEB: www.printegra.com
SIC: 2761 2782 Continuous forms, office & business; blankbooks & looseleaf binders
HQ: Printegra Corp
5040 Highlands Pkwy Se
Smyrna GA 30082
770 487-5151

(P-7552)
RR DONNELLEY & SONS COMPANY
1765 Challenge Way # 220, Sacramento
(95815-5000)
PHONE......................916 929-8632
Steve Sherbondy, *Branch Mgr*
EMP: 10
SALES (corp-wide): 6.9B **Publicly Held**
WEB: www.moore.com
SIC: 2761 Computer forms, manifold or continuous
PA: R. R. Donnelley & Sons Company
35 W Wacker Dr Ste 3650
Chicago IL 60601
312 326-8000

(P-7553)
RR DONNELLEY & SONS COMPANY
Also Called: Forms Division
19200 Von Karman Ave # 700, Irvine
(92612-8518)
PHONE......................949 476-0505
Gordon Gaudett, *Branch Mgr*
EMP: 40
SALES (corp-wide): 6.9B **Publicly Held**
WEB: www.moore.com
SIC: 2761 Computer forms, manifold or continuous
PA: R. R. Donnelley & Sons Company
35 W Wacker Dr Ste 3650
Chicago IL 60601
312 326-8000

(P-7554)
TAYLOR COMMUNICATIONS INC
8972 Cuyamaca St, Corona (92883-2102)
PHONE......................951 203-9011
Edward Arminta, *Branch Mgr*
EMP: 24
SALES (corp-wide): 3.4B **Privately Held**
SIC: 2761 Manifold business forms
HQ: Taylor Communications, Inc.
4205 S 96th St
Omaha NE 68127
402 898-6422

(P-7555)
TAYLOR COMMUNICATIONS INC
1300 Ethan Way Ste 675, Sacramento
(95825-2295)
P.O. Box 255366 (95865-5366)
PHONE......................916 927-1891
Pegge Kiszely, *Branch Mgr*
EMP: 14
SALES (corp-wide): 3.4B **Privately Held**
WEB: www.stdreg.com
SIC: 2761 Manifold business forms
HQ: Taylor Communications, Inc.
4205 S 96th St
Omaha NE 68127
402 898-6422

(P-7556)
TAYLOR COMMUNICATIONS INC
5151 Murphy Canyon Rd # 100, San Diego
(92123-4440)
PHONE......................866 541-0937
Steven Wickman, *Branch Mgr*
EMP: 10
SALES (corp-wide): 3.4B **Privately Held**
WEB: www.stdreg.com
SIC: 2761 Manifold business forms
HQ: Taylor Communications, Inc.
4205 S 96th St
Omaha NE 68127
402 898-6422

(P-7557)
TAYLOR COMMUNICATIONS INC
3885 Seaport Blvd Ste 40, West Sacramento (95691-3527)
PHONE......................916 340-0200
John Joyce, *Branch Mgr*
Wendell Lapinig, *Production*
EMP: 75
SALES (corp-wide): 3.4B **Privately Held**
WEB: www.stdreg.com
SIC: 2761 Manifold business forms
HQ: Taylor Communications, Inc.
4205 S 96th St
Omaha NE 68127
402 898-6422

(P-7558)
TAYLOR COMMUNICATIONS INC
535 Anton Blvd Ste 530, Costa Mesa
(92626-1947)
PHONE......................714 708-2005
EMP: 20
SALES (corp-wide): 3.4B **Privately Held**
WEB: www.stdreg.com
SIC: 2761 Manifold business forms
HQ: Taylor Communications, Inc.
4205 S 96th St
Omaha NE 68127
402 898-6422

(P-7559)
TAYLOR COMMUNICATIONS INC
400 N Tustin Ave Ste 275, Santa Ana
(92705-3885)
PHONE......................714 664-8865
Don Chelius, *Manager*
EMP: 22
SALES (corp-wide): 3.4B **Privately Held**
WEB: www.stdreg.com
SIC: 2761 Manifold business forms
HQ: Taylor Communications, Inc.
4205 S 96th St
Omaha NE 68127
402 898-6422

(P-7560)
TAYLOR COMMUNICATIONS INC
10390 Coloma Rd Ste 7, Rancho Cordova
(95670-2152)
PHONE......................916 368-1200
John Miller, *Manager*
EMP: 13
SALES (corp-wide): 3.4B **Privately Held**
WEB: www.stdreg.com
SIC: 2761 Manifold business forms
HQ: Taylor Communications, Inc.
4205 S 96th St
Omaha NE 68127
402 898-6422

(P-7561)
TST/IMPRESO CALIFORNIA INC
10589 Business Dr, Fontana (92337-8223)
PHONE......................909 357-7190
Marshall Sorokwasz, *President*
▲ **EMP:** 15
SQ FT: 30,000
SALES (est): 1.9MM
SALES (corp-wide): 83.3MM **Publicly Held**
SIC: 2761 Continuous forms, office & business
HQ: Tst/Impreso, Inc.
652 Southwestern Blvd
Coppell TX 75019
972 462-0100

(P-7562)
WRIGHT BUSINESS FORMS INC
Also Called: Wright Business Graphics Calif
13602 11th St Ste A, Chino (91710-5200)
P.O. Box 20489, Portland OR (97294-0489)
PHONE......................909 614-6700
Gene Snitker, *Principal*
Steve Dupas, *Cust Mgr*
EMP: 50
SALES (corp-wide): 90.4MM **Privately Held**
WEB: www.wrightbg.com
SIC: 2761 Manifold business forms
PA: Wright Business Forms, Inc.
18440 Ne San Rafael St
Portland OR 97230
503 661-2525

2771 Greeting Card Publishing

(P-7563)
FOUND IMAGE PRESS INC
5225 Riley St, San Diego (92110-2620)
PHONE......................619 282-3452
Barry Bell, *Co-Owner*
Catherine Bell, *Co-Owner*
EMP: 13
SQ FT: 6,250
SALES: 1MM **Privately Held**
WEB: www.foundimage.com
SIC: 2771 5199 Greeting cards; calendars

(P-7564)
HALLMARK LABS LLC
3130 Wilshire Blvd # 400, Santa Monica
(90403-2346)
PHONE......................424 210-3600
Steven Hawn, *President*
Paul Wang, *CFO*
Jeff McMillen, *Treasurer*
Kevin M Hartley, *Officer*
Albert Lai, *Senior VP*
EMP: 117
SQ FT: 22,831
SALES (est): 15.9MM
SALES (corp-wide): 6.7B **Privately Held**
SIC: 2771 2741 8999 Greeting cards; ; personal services
PA: Hallmark Cards, Incorporated
2501 Mcgee St
Kansas City MO 64108
816 274-5111

(P-7565)
JUMPING CRACKER BEANS LLC
1588 Camden Village Cir, San Jose
(95124-6582)
PHONE......................408 265-0658
Judith Dugan,
Julia Dugan,
EMP: 10
SALES (est): 1.2MM **Privately Held**
SIC: 2771 Greeting cards

(P-7566)
PUNKPOST INC
41 Federal St Unit 4, San Francisco
(94107-4199)
PHONE......................415 818-7677
Alexis Monson, *CEO*
Santiago Prieto, *President*
EMP: 27
SALES: 100K **Privately Held**
SIC: 2771 7389 Greeting cards;

(P-7567)
SCHURMAN FINE PAPERS
22500 Town Cir, Moreno Valley
(92553-7509)
PHONE......................951 653-1934
EMP: 158
SALES (corp-wide): 265.8MM **Privately Held**
SIC: 2771
PA: Schurman Retail Group
500 Chadbourne Rd
Fairfield CA 37072
707 428-0200

(P-7568)
SPS STUDIOS INC
7917 Ivanhoe Ave, La Jolla (92037-4512)
P.O. Box 1046 (92038-1046)
PHONE......................858 456-2336
EMP: 33 **Privately Held**
SIC: 2771
PA: Sps Studios, Inc.
2905 Wilderness Pl # 100
Boulder CO 80301
303 449-0536

(P-7569)
STAR ROUTE LLC
4522 Henley Ct, Westlake Village
(91361-4307)
P.O. Box 6101, Thousand Oaks (91359-6101)
PHONE......................805 405-8510
Tom Jankowski, *President*
Don Ko, *Director*
EMP: 12
SQ FT: 2,000
SALES: 600K **Privately Held**
SIC: 2771 Greeting cards

2782 Blankbooks & Looseleaf Binders

(P-7570)
ABISCO PRODUCTS CO
5925 E Washington Blvd, Commerce
(90040-2412)
PHONE......................562 906-9330
Angel Munoz, *President*
Julian Carrasco, *Shareholder*
EMP: 25
SQ FT: 10,000
SALES (est): 2.7MM **Privately Held**
WEB: www.abiscoproducts.com
SIC: 2782 2675

(P-7571)
AD INDUSTRIES LLC (PA)
Also Called: California Calendar
14071 Peyton Dr Unit 2170, Chino Hills
(91709-7195)
P.O. Box 3316, Basalt CO (81621-3316)
PHONE......................818 765-4200

Steven Anderson, *Mng Member*
Karen Anderson, *Partner*
Rob Rose, *Partner*
▲ **EMP:** 10
SQ FT: 50,000
SALES (est): 1.7MM **Privately Held**
WEB: www.adind.com
SIC: 2782 Looseleaf binders & devices

(P-7572)
BINDERS EXPRESS INC
13800 Gramercy Pl, Gardena
(90249-2457)
PHONE..........................310 329-4811
Moti Taragano, *President*
Frank Naranjo, *Vice Pres*
EMP: 10
SALES (est): 1.4MM **Privately Held**
WEB: www.bindersexpress.com
SIC: 2782 Checkbooks

(P-7573)
BLAZAR COMMUNICATIONS CORP
Also Called: Blazar Mailing Solutions
17951 Sky Park Cir Ste K, Irvine
(92614-4353)
PHONE..........................949 336-7115
Jay Rajcevich, *President*
David Haimes, *COO*
Marilyn Norman, *Treasurer*
Raegan Hart, *Vice Pres*
EMP: 11
SALES (est): 1.5MM **Privately Held**
SIC: 2782 3589 7374 8748 Account books; shredders, industrial & commercial; data entry service; communications consulting

(P-7574)
CACHE PHLOW ENTERPRISE
1894 Lynwood Dr Apt D, Concord
(94519-1158)
P.O. Box 415 (94522-0415)
PHONE..........................925 609-8649
Aaron Morris, *Partner*
EMP: 10
SALES (est): 478.4K **Privately Held**
SIC: 2782 Record albums

(P-7575)
CHAMELEON LIKE INC
Also Called: Chameleon Books & Journals
345 Kishimura Dr, Gilroy (95020-3653)
PHONE..........................408 847-3661
Pierre Martichoux, *President*
Daniel Busatto, *Vice Pres*
Sophia Corona, *Sales Associate*
Mark Strauss, *Accounts Exec*
▲ **EMP:** 34
SQ FT: 12,000
SALES (est): 6.4MM **Privately Held**
WEB: www.chameleonlike.com
SIC: 2782 Blankbooks & looseleaf binders

(P-7576)
CHECKWORKS INC
315 Cloverleaf Dr Ste J, Baldwin Park
(91706-6510)
P.O. Box 60065, City of Industry (91716-0065)
PHONE..........................626 333-1444
Aloysious J Uniack, *President*
Aloysius J Uniack, *President*
Christen Mc Kiernan, *Admin Sec*
Rodica Bohm, *Controller*
Bryan Cambra, *Mktg Dir*
EMP: 55
SQ FT: 15,000
SALES (est): 7.6MM **Privately Held**
WEB: www.checkworks.com
SIC: 2782 Checkbooks

(P-7577)
CONTINENTAL BDR SPECIALTY CORP (PA)
407 W Compton Blvd, Gardena
(90248-1703)
PHONE..........................310 324-8227
Andrew Lisardi, *CEO*
Jack Gray, *Vice Pres*
▼ **EMP:** 120 **EST:** 1978
SQ FT: 31,000

SALES (est): 11.9MM **Privately Held**
SIC: 2782 2759 2675 2396 Looseleaf binders & devices; commercial printing; die-cut paper & board; automotive & apparel trimmings

(P-7578)
DELUXE CORPORATION
Also Called: Deluxe Financial Services
1551 Dell Ave, Campbell (95008-6903)
P.O. Box 328800, Los Gatos (95032)
PHONE..........................408 370-8801
Randy Bueford, *Manager*
EMP: 100
SALES (corp-wide): 1.9B **Publicly Held**
SIC: 2782 Checkbooks
PA: Deluxe Corporation
3680 Victoria St N
Shoreview MN 55126
651 483-7111

(P-7579)
DELUXE CORPORATION
2861 Mandela Pkwy, Oakland
(94608-4011)
PHONE..........................651 483-7100
EMP: 278
SALES (corp-wide): 1.9B **Publicly Held**
SIC: 2782 Checkbooks
PA: Deluxe Corporation
3680 Victoria St N
Shoreview MN 55126
651 483-7111

(P-7580)
DELUXE CORPORATION
Also Called: Deluxe Check Printers
42933 Business Ctr Pkwy, Lancaster
(93535-4515)
PHONE..........................661 942-1144
Shannon Holcomb, *General Mgr*
EMP: 460
SQ FT: 67,253
SALES (corp-wide): 1.9B **Publicly Held**
WEB: www.dlx.com
SIC: 2782 2761 2759 Checkbooks; manifold business forms; commercial printing
PA: Deluxe Corporation
3680 Victoria St N
Shoreview MN 55126
651 483-7111

(P-7581)
DOCUPAK INC
17515 Valley View Ave, Cerritos
(90703-7002)
PHONE..........................714 670-7944
William Lyons, *President*
John Flores, *CFO*
Pat Lyons, *Vice Pres*
EMP: 50
SQ FT: 27,000
SALES (est): 5.8MM **Privately Held**
SIC: 2782 Looseleaf binders & devices

(P-7582)
LIFETOUCH NAT SCHL STUDIOS INC
2860 Fair St, Chico (95928-8804)
PHONE..........................530 345-3993
Robert Evans, *Manager*
Phil Lawry, *Technology*
Ryan Cranney, *Engineer*
Mark Pereira, *Senior Mgr*
EMP: 100
SQ FT: 53,000
SALES (corp-wide): 1.1B **Publicly Held**
SIC: 2782 7221 Account books; photographer, still or video
HQ: Lifetouch National School Studios Inc.
11000 Viking Dr Ste 300
Eden Prairie MN 55344
952 826-4000

(P-7583)
PIONEER PHOTO ALBUMS INC (PA)
9801 Deering Ave, Chatsworth
(91311-4398)
P.O. Box 2497 (91313-2497)
PHONE..........................818 882-2161
Shell Plutsky, *CEO*
Jason Reubens, *President*
Eric Bisquera, *COO*
Tiffany Boxer, *Vice Pres*
Rick Collies, *Vice Pres*

▲ **EMP:** 170
SQ FT: 100,000
SALES (est): 18.3MM **Privately Held**
WEB: www.pioneerphotoalbums.com
SIC: 2782 Albums

(P-7584)
RR DONNELLEY & SONS COMPANY
Also Called: RR Donnelley Financial
855 N California Ave A, Palo Alto (94303)
PHONE..........................650 845-6600
James Alley, *General Mgr*
EMP: 50
SALES (corp-wide): 6.9B **Publicly Held**
WEB: www.rrdonnelley.com
SIC: 2782 2759 Blankbooks & looseleaf binders; commercial printing
PA: R. R. Donnelley & Sons Company
35 W Wacker Dr Ste 3650
Chicago IL 60601
312 326-8000

(P-7585)
SONG BEOUNG
Also Called: Viva Photo Albums Company
501 Murphy Ranch Rd # 148, Milpitas
(95035-7930)
PHONE..........................510 670-8788
Beoung Song, *Owner*
▲ **EMP:** 13
SALES (est): 987.9K **Privately Held**
SIC: 2782 Scrapbooks, albums & diaries

(P-7586)
SUNNY PRODUCTS INC
Also Called: Pacific Trendz
1989 S Campus Ave, Ontario (91761-5410)
PHONE..........................909 947-5028
Seungsik Jang, *CEO*
SOO Chang, *President*
Rock Chon, *Vice Pres*
▲ **EMP:** 15
SQ FT: 12,000
SALES (est): 1.6MM **Privately Held**
WEB: www.sunnyproducts.com
SIC: 2782 Albums

(P-7587)
ULTRA PRO ACQUISITION LLC
6049 E Slauson Ave, Commerce
(90040-3007)
PHONE..........................323 725-1975
▲ **EMP:** 120
SALES (est): 6.1MM **Privately Held**
SIC: 2782 Library binders, looseleaf
PA: Marlin Equity Partners, Llc
338 Pier Ave
Hermosa Beach CA 90254

(P-7588)
ULTRA PRO INTERNATIONAL LLC (PA)
Also Called: Jolly Roger Games
6049 E Slauson Ave, Commerce
(90040-3007)
PHONE..........................323 890-2100
Sheldon Rosenberg, *Mng Member*
Jay Kuo, *Vice Pres*
Dave Wise, *QA Dir*
Justin Cole, *Project Mgr*
Ray Lei, *Accountant*
▲ **EMP:** 62
SALES (est): 17.8MM **Privately Held**
SIC: 2782 Scrapbooks, albums & diaries

(P-7589)
US PACKAGERS INC
Also Called: West Coast Binders
13620 Crenshaw Blvd, Gardena
(90249-2347)
PHONE..........................310 327-7721
Policarpio Adriano, *President*
Juvenal Chiwawa, *Vice Pres*
EMP: 25 **EST:** 2011
SQ FT: 10,000
SALES (est): 1.2MM **Privately Held**
SIC: 2782 Blankbooks & looseleaf binders

(P-7590)
VAGRANT RECORDS INC
6351 Wilshire Blvd # 101, Los Angeles
(90048-5021)
PHONE..........................323 302-0100

Richard A Egan, *President*
Jon Cohen, *Vice Pres*
Dan Gill, *General Mgr*
Jake Lowry, *Opers Mgr*
EMP: 20
SALES (est): 2.5MM **Privately Held**
WEB: www.vagrantrecords.com
SIC: 2782 5735 Record albums; records

(P-7591)
VIATECH PUBG SOLUTIONS INC
5668 E 61st St, Commerce (90040-3408)
PHONE..........................323 721-3629
Erik Treutlein, *Manager*
EMP: 56
SALES (corp-wide): 55MM **Privately Held**
SIC: 2782 2741 Blankbooks & looseleaf binders; miscellaneous publishing
PA: Viatech Publishing Solutions, Inc.
11935 N Stemmons Fwy
Dallas TX 75234
214 827-8151

2789 Bookbinding

(P-7592)
ACE BINDERY INC
10549 Dale Ave, Stanton (90680-2641)
PHONE..........................714 220-0232
Soon Chang, *President*
EMP: 13
SQ FT: 10,000
SALES (est): 1.1MM **Privately Held**
SIC: 2789 Bookbinding & related work

(P-7593)
B J BINDERY
833 S Grand Ave, Santa Ana (92705-4117)
PHONE..........................714 835-7342
Naresh Arya, *CEO*
Renu Arya, *Vice Pres*
▲ **EMP:** 80 **EST:** 1970
SQ FT: 29,000
SALES (est): 9.3MM **Privately Held**
WEB: www.bjbindery.com
SIC: 2789 Binding only: books, pamphlets, magazines, etc.

(P-7594)
BARGAS BINDERY
1658 Scenicview Dr, San Leandro
(94577-5333)
PHONE..........................510 357-7901
Bernard Richard Wade, *Owner*
EMP: 10 **EST:** 1958
SQ FT: 9,500
SALES (est): 602.5K **Privately Held**
SIC: 2789 Binding only: books, pamphlets, magazines, etc.

(P-7595)
CAL BIND
Also Called: Mechanical Bookbinding
4700 Littlejohn St, Baldwin Park
(91706-2274)
PHONE..........................626 338-3699
Chris Stern, *President*
Mary Ellen Nardoza, *Vice Pres*
EMP: 50 **EST:** 1949
SQ FT: 21,000
SALES (est): 4.4MM **Privately Held**
WEB: www.calbind.com
SIC: 2789 Bookbinding & repairing: trade, edition, library, etc.

(P-7596)
D A M BINDERY INC
Also Called: Bindery , The
7949 Stromesa Ct Ste B, San Diego
(92126-6338)
PHONE..........................858 621-7000
Sarah Sabor, *President*
Richard Sabor, *Treasurer*
Laurel Smith, *Vice Pres*
EMP: 10
SQ FT: 13,700
SALES (est): 1MM **Privately Held**
WEB: www.thebinderyinc.com
SIC: 2789 Bookbinding & related work

▲ = Import ▼=Export
◆ =Import/Export

(P-7597)
DGCC INC
Also Called: Unique Bindery
14745 Keswick St, Van Nuys (91405-1206)
PHONE..................................818 787-5007
Linus Kim, *President*
▲ EMP: 13 EST: 2006
SALES (est): 1.6MM **Privately Held**
SIC: 2789 Binding only: books, pamphlets, magazines, etc.

(P-7598)
DYNAMIC BINDERY INC
170 S Arrowhead Ave, San Bernardino (92408-1303)
PHONE..................................909 884-1296
James Jameson, *President*
Lewane Stephenson, *Vice Pres*
EMP: 18
SQ FT: 12,000
SALES (est): 2MM **Privately Held**
SIC: 2789 Binding only: books, pamphlets, magazines, etc.

(P-7599)
GOLDEN RULE BINDERY INC
Also Called: Golden Rule Packaging
242 Bingham Dr Ste 101, San Marcos (92069-1483)
PHONE..................................760 471-2013
Jerry Kiley, *President*
Fred Antor, *Treasurer*
EMP: 22
SQ FT: 6,400
SALES (est): 3.1MM **Privately Held**
WEB: www.goldenrulebindery.com
SIC: 2789 Bookbinding & related work

(P-7600)
GRAPHICS BINDERY
16611 Roscoe Pl, North Hills (91343-6104)
PHONE..................................818 886-2463
Steve Silverman, *Owner*
EMP: 16
SQ FT: 5,000
SALES (est): 1.1MM **Privately Held**
SIC: 2789 Trade binding services

(P-7601)
HONG FAT DYE CUTTING CO
2103 Sastre Ave, South El Monte (91733-2651)
PHONE..................................626 452-0382
Shing Koo, *Owner*
▲ EMP: 10 EST: 1993
SALES: 650K **Privately Held**
SIC: 2789 Paper cutting

(P-7602)
INVESTMENT LAND APPRAISERS
Also Called: Supreme Bindery
333 E 157th St, Gardena (90248-2512)
PHONE..................................310 819-8831
EMP: 11
SALES (corp-wide): 699.3K **Privately Held**
SIC: 2789
PA: Investment Land Appraisers, Inc
4208 W 175th Pl
Torrance CA
310 532-3850

(P-7603)
JAMES CLARK
Also Called: Fresno Trade Bindery & Mailing
1766 N Helm Ave Ste 105, Fresno (93727-1627)
PHONE..................................559 456-3893
James Clark, *Owner*
Michael Clark, *General Mgr*
Jim Lockwood, *General Mgr*
Corey Clark, *Consultant*
EMP: 10
SQ FT: 7,500
SALES: 500K **Privately Held**
WEB: www.jamesclark.com
SIC: 2789 Bookbinding & related work

(P-7604)
JIM PERRY
Also Called: Action Color Card
13611 Northlands Rd, Corona (92880-0769)
PHONE..................................909 947-0747

Jim Perry, *Owner*
EMP: 30
SALES (est): 1.9MM **Privately Held**
SIC: 2789 2782 Swatches & samples; blankbooks & looseleaf binders

(P-7605)
JS TRADE BINDERY SERVICES INC
435 Harbor Blvd, Belmont (94002-4019)
PHONE..................................650 486-1475
Jai Kumar, *President*
Raj Lal, *Human Res Mgr*
Armando Puente, *Production*
Debbie Carter, *Cust Mgr*
EMP: 61
SQ FT: 40,000
SALES (est): 7.8MM **Privately Held**
WEB: www.jsbindery.com
SIC: 2789 Trade binding services

(P-7606)
KATER-CRAFTS INCORPORATED
Also Called: Book Binders
4860 Gregg Rd, Pico Rivera (90660-2107)
PHONE..................................562 692-0665
Bruce Kavin, *President*
Richard Kavin, *Vice Pres*
EMP: 40
SQ FT: 20,000
SALES (est): 4MM **Privately Held**
WEB: www.katercrafts.com
SIC: 2789 Bookbinding & repairing: trade, edition, library, etc.

(P-7607)
M M BOOK BINDERY
1826 W 169th St, Gardena (90247-5252)
P.O. Box 3307, Torrance (90510-3307)
PHONE..................................310 532-0780
Stephen M Goodman, *Administration*
EMP: 16
SALES (est): 2.7MM **Privately Held**
SIC: 2789 Bookbinding & related work

(P-7608)
MISSION BINDERY INC
7140 Via Solana, San Jose (95135-1376)
PHONE..................................510 623-8260
Joe Gobert, *President*
EMP: 23
SQ FT: 12,000
SALES (est): 1.4MM **Privately Held**
SIC: 2789 Binding only: books, pamphlets, magazines, etc.

(P-7609)
ONTARIO BINDING COMPANY INC
15951 Promontory Rd, Chino Hills (91709-2371)
PHONE..................................909 947-7866
Maria Doerzapf, *President*
Luis Sanchez, *Treasurer*
EMP: 67
SQ FT: 25,000
SALES (est): 6.5MM **Privately Held**
WEB: www.ontariobinding.com
SIC: 2789 2675 Binding only: books, pamphlets, magazines, etc.; die-cut paper & board

(P-7610)
PACIFIC COAST BINDERY INC
12250 Coast Dr, Whittier (90601-1607)
PHONE..................................562 908-5900
OK K Chang, *President*
EMP: 35
SQ FT: 20,000
SALES (est): 1.3MM **Privately Held**
SIC: 2789 Binding & repair of books, magazines & pamphlets

(P-7611)
PACIFICO BINDERY INC
544 W Angus Ave, Orange (92868-1302)
PHONE..................................714 744-1510
Richard G Zinke, *President*
EMP: 20
SALES (est): 2.2MM **Privately Held**
WEB: www.pacificobindery.com
SIC: 2789 Binding only: books, pamphlets, magazines, etc.

(P-7612)
PEL MANUFACTURING LEASNG CORP
Also Called: Pel Mfg & Leasing
3200 Kashiwa St, Torrance (90505-4021)
PHONE..................................310 530-7145
Phillis Pelezzare, *President*
Joseph A Pelezzare, *President*
EMP: 16
SQ FT: 9,000
SALES (est): 1.8MM **Privately Held**
SIC: 2789 Bookbinding & related work

(P-7613)
ROBERT A KERL
Also Called: Southwest Trade Bindery
8930 Quartz Ave, Northridge (91324-3339)
PHONE..................................818 341-9281
Robert A Kerl Jr, *Owner*
EMP: 22
SALES (est): 1.5MM **Privately Held**
SIC: 2789 Trade binding services

(P-7614)
ROSS BINDERY INC
15310 Spring Ave, Santa Fe Springs (90670-5644)
PHONE..................................562 623-4565
George Jackson, *CEO*
Jaime Cerda, *Manager*
Alisa Sanchez, *Receptionist*
▲ EMP: 120
SQ FT: 65,000
SALES (est): 17.3MM **Privately Held**
WEB: www.rossbindery.com
SIC: 2789 Pamphlets, binding

(P-7615)
S & S BINDERY INC
2366 1st St, La Verne (91750-5545)
PHONE..................................909 596-2213
Steve Thompson, *President*
Scott Fehrensen, *Vice Pres*
▼ EMP: 20
SQ FT: 13,750
SALES (est): 2.6MM **Privately Held**
SIC: 2789 Bookbinding & related work

(P-7616)
S K DIGITAL IMAGING INC
7686 Miramar Rd Ste A, San Diego (92126-4236)
PHONE..................................858 408-0732
Sean E Kaye, *President*
Gerald Kaye, *CFO*
EMP: 13
SALES (est): 1.8MM **Privately Held**
SIC: 2789 2752 Trade binding services; commercial printing, lithographic

(P-7617)
SACRAMENTAL COLOR COIL
Also Called: D Bindery
8541 Thys Ct, Sacramento (95828-1006)
PHONE..................................916 383-9588
Darrell Johnston, *President*
May Johnston, *Vice Pres*
EMP: 20
SQ FT: 2,880
SALES: 750K **Privately Held**
SIC: 2789 Binding & repair of books, magazines & pamphlets

(P-7618)
SILVER PRESS INC
940 Rincon Cir, San Jose (95131-1313)
PHONE..................................408 435-0449
Chin U Kim, *President*
Yoon Kim, *Vice Pres*
EMP: 10
SQ FT: 9,996
SALES (est): 1MM **Privately Held**
SIC: 2789 Bookbinding & related work

(P-7619)
SOMERSET TRAVELLER INC
Also Called: Somerset Printing
2765 Comstock Cir, Belmont (94002-2904)
PHONE..................................650 593-7350
Allan W Jaffe, *President*
Isac Gutfreund, *Treasurer*
EMP: 16
SQ FT: 8,000

SALES: 2.8MM **Privately Held**
SIC: 2789 2752 Bookbinding & related work; commercial printing, offset

(P-7620)
SOUTHERN CAL BNDERY MILING INC
10661 Business Dr, Fontana (92337-8212)
PHONE..................................909 829-1949
Rex Miller, *President*
EMP: 75
SQ FT: 51,000
SALES (est): 6.8MM **Privately Held**
SIC: 2789 7331 Binding & repair of books, magazines & pamphlets; mailing service

(P-7621)
SPECIALTY GRAPHICS INC
1998 Republic Ave, San Leandro (94577-4224)
PHONE..................................510 351-7705
Angela Plowman, *President*
Deborah Waltmire, *Admin Sec*
EMP: 15
SQ FT: 37,000
SALES (est): 2.2MM **Privately Held**
WEB: www.sgica.com
SIC: 2789 2732 Trade binding services; books: printing only

(P-7622)
SPEEDY BINDERY INC
4386 Jutland Dr, San Diego (92117-3642)
PHONE..................................619 275-0261
Fozi Awad Khouri, *President*
Victor Khouri, *Vice Pres*
EMP: 26
SQ FT: 20,000
SALES (est): 2.8MM **Privately Held**
SIC: 2789 7389 2675 Binding only: books, pamphlets, magazines, etc.; laminating service; die-cut paper & board

(P-7623)
THREE CHIEFS & NO INDIANS LLC
Also Called: California Sample Services
4200 E Mission Blvd, Ontario (91761-2952)
PHONE..................................909 465-6314
Raymond Paul Gaytan,
Andrew Kallman,
▲ EMP: 190
SALES (est): 23.8MM **Privately Held**
SIC: 2789 Swatches & samples

(P-7624)
WESCO MOUNTING & FINISHING INC
5450 Dodds Ave, Buena Park (90621-1209)
PHONE..................................714 562-0122
Tim Black, *President*
EMP: 25
SQ FT: 32,000
SALES (est): 2.6MM **Privately Held**
SIC: 2789 Paper cutting

(P-7625)
YOUNG AMERICAN BINDERY
2157 E Del Amo Blvd, Compton (90220-6301)
PHONE..................................310 898-1212
Art Solano, *President*
Gordon Hollick, *Vice Pres*
Iris Hollick, *Admin Sec*
EMP: 20 EST: 1963
SQ FT: 25,000
SALES (est): 2.2MM **Privately Held**
SIC: 2789 Binding only: books, pamphlets, magazines, etc.

2791 Typesetting

(P-7626)
AUTOMATION PRINTING CO (PA)
1230 Long Beach Ave, Los Angeles (90021-2320)
PHONE..................................213 488-1230
David Tobman, *President*
Ann Tobman, *Corp Secy*
Jesse Lobato, *Executive*
Dylan Gaines, *Chief Engr*
Art Tolentino, *Opers Mgr*
EMP: 39

SQ FT: 30,000
SALES (est): 5.7MM **Privately Held**
WEB: www.automationtaft.com
SIC: **2791** 2796 2759 2732 Typesetting;
platemaking services; commercial printing; book printing; commercial printing,
offset

(P-7627)
BARKERBLUE INC
363 N Amphlett Blvd, San Mateo
(94401-1806)
PHONE..................................650 696-2100
Eugene A Klein, *CEO*
Michael Callaghan, *CFO*
Konstantin Koshelev, *Senior VP*
Eric Gee, *Production*
Pat Booker, *Cust Mgr*
EMP: 35
SQ FT: 15,000
SALES (est): 5.1MM **Privately Held**
WEB: www.barkerblue.com
SIC: **2791** 7334 Typesetting; blueprinting
service

(P-7628)
FOLGERGRAPHICS INC
21093 Forbes Ave, Hayward (94545-1115)
PHONE..................................510 293-2294
Richard L Folger, *CEO*
Matthew Revak, *President*
Patricia A Folger, *Vice Pres*
Lee Jensen, *Executive*
Brianna Parker, *Project Mgr*
EMP: 40
SQ FT: 16,000
SALES (est): 6.7MM **Privately Held**
WEB: www.folgergraphics.com
SIC: **2791** 2752 Typesetting; commercial
printing, offset

(P-7629)
GOLDING PUBLICATIONS
Also Called: Friday Flier
31558 Railroad Canyon Rd, Canyon Lake
(92587-9427)
PHONE..................................951 244-1966
Charles G Golding, *Owner*
Dona Jessup, *Executive*
Marti Norris, *Executive*
Greg Golding, *Opers Mgr*
Kailey Barnes, *Manager*
EMP: 11
SALES (est): 1.1MM **Privately Held**
WEB: www.goldingpublications.com
SIC: **2791** Typesetting

(P-7630)
NORCO PRINTING INC
440 Hester St, San Leandro (94577-1024)
PHONE..................................510 569-2200
Ricky C Damiani, *President*
Rick C Damiani, *President*
Rose Damiani, *Vice Pres*
Catherine Simi, *Sales Executive*
EMP: 15
SALES (est): 2.1MM **Privately Held**
WEB: www.norcoprint.com
SIC: **2791** 2759 2752 2789 Typesetting;
letterpress & screen printing; commercial
printing, offset; bookbinding & related
work; manifold business forms

(P-7631)
RAPID LASERGRAPHICS (HQ)
836 Harrison St, San Francisco
(94107-1125)
PHONE..................................415 957-5840
Bent Kjolby, *President*
John Perkins, *Vice Pres*
EMP: 13
SALES (est): 1.3MM
SALES (corp-wide): 3.3MM **Privately
Held**
SIC: **2791** 2752 7336 Typesetting; color li-
thography; graphic arts & related design
PA: Rapid Typographers Company Inc
836 Harrison St
San Francisco CA 94107
415 957-5840

(P-7632)
RAPID TYPOGRAPHERS COMPANY (PA)
Also Called: Rapid Lasergraphics
836 Harrison St, San Francisco
(94107-1125)
PHONE..................................415 957-5840
Bent Kjolby, *President*
John Perkins, *Vice Pres*
EMP: 45
SQ FT: 12,000
SALES (est): 3.3MM **Privately Held**
WEB: www.rapidgraphics.com
SIC: **2791** 2752 7336 2759 Typesetting;
color lithography; graphic arts & related
design; commercial printing

(P-7633)
SYSTEMS PRINTING INC
14311 Chambers Rd, Tustin (92780-6911)
PHONE..................................714 832-4677
Kevin Williams, *President*
EMP: 11
SQ FT: 3,600
SALES (est): 1MM **Privately Held**
WEB: www.allegraprint.com
SIC: **2791** 7334 2752 Typesetting; photo-
copying & duplicating services; commer-
cial printing, lithographic

(P-7634)
TAS GROUP INC
Also Called: Vision Press
2333 San Ramon Vly Blvd, San Ramon
(94583-1763)
PHONE..................................925 551-3700
Andy Lion, *President*
Robert Carda, *CFO*
Steve Commerford, *Vice Pres*
EMP: 10
SALES (est): 910K **Privately Held**
SIC: **2791** Typesetting

(P-7635)
THOMPSON TYPE INC
3687 Voltaire St, San Diego (92106-1297)
PHONE..................................619 224-3137
John Pierce, *President*
Alma Bell, *Production*
EMP: 24
SQ FT: 12,000
SALES (est): 2.4MM **Privately Held**
WEB: www.thompsontype.com
SIC: **2791** Hand composition typesetting

(P-7636)
ULTRATYPE & GRAPHICS
1929 Hancock St Ste D, San Diego
(92110-2062)
PHONE..................................858 541-1894
EMP: 10
SQ FT: 2,800
SALES (est): 746.2K **Privately Held**
SIC: **2791** 7336

(P-7637)
WILSTED & TAYLOR PUBG SVCS
430 40th St, Oakland (94609-2691)
PHONE..................................510 428-9087
Christine Taylor, *Partner*
Leroy Wilsted, *Partner*
Jennifer Brown, *Office Mgr*
EMP: 10 EST: 1979
SQ FT: 1,000
SALES (est): 1.1MM **Privately Held**
WEB: www.wilstedandtaylor.com
SIC: **2791** 7389 2731 Typesetting; design,
commercial & industrial; book publishing

2796 Platemaking & Related Svcs

(P-7638)
ACTION GRAPHIC ARTS INC
13065 Raintree Pl, Chino (91710-4637)
PHONE..................................626 443-3113
Dennis Ward, *President*
Clyde Bergman, *Vice Pres*
Francy Ward, *Admin Sec*
EMP: 10 EST: 1960
SQ FT: 5,000

SALES (est): 790K **Privately Held**
SIC: **2796** Color separations for printing

(P-7639)
AFT CORPORATION
Also Called: Andresen Digital Pre-Press
1815c Centinela Ave, Santa Monica
(90404-4203)
PHONE..................................310 576-1007
William Andresen, *President*
Ann Verkuilen, *CFO*
Chuck Henk, *Treasurer*
Glen Rosuck, *Vice Pres*
EMP: 21
SQ FT: 4,200
SALES (est): 2.3MM **Privately Held**
SIC: **2796** Color separations for printing

(P-7640)
COAST ENGRAVING COMPANIES
Also Called: Coast Creative Nameplates
1097 N 5th St, San Jose (95112-4449)
PHONE..................................408 297-2555
Ida Wool, *President*
Fred A Wool Jr, *CFO*
EMP: 40 EST: 1970
SQ FT: 10,000
SALES (est): 4.7MM **Privately Held**
WEB: www.coaste.com
SIC: **2796** 2752 2759 Engraving on cop-
per, steel, wood or rubber: printing plates;
lithographic plates, positives or negatives;
commercial printing, lithographic; com-
mercial printing

(P-7641)
COLOR SERVICE INC
40 E Verdugo Ave, Burbank (91502-1931)
PHONE..................................323 283-4793
Patrick F Seeholzer, *President*
Patrick Seeholzer, *Bd of Directors*
Michael Mahoney, *Vice Pres*
EMP: 42
SQ FT: 30,000
SALES (est): 4.3MM **Privately Held**
WEB: www.colorservice.com
SIC: **2796** Color separations for printing

(P-7642)
EFFECTIVE GRAPHICS INC
40 E Verdugo Ave, Burbank (91502-1931)
PHONE..................................310 323-2223
Roger Sanders, *CEO*
David Curtis, *President*
Michael Vascellaro, *CFO*
EMP: 55
SQ FT: 47,970
SALES (est): 6.6MM **Privately Held**
WEB: www.effectivegraphics.com
SIC: **2796** 2752 Color separations for
printing; commercial printing, lithographic

(P-7643)
FLEXLINE INC
15405 Cornet St, Santa Fe Springs
(90670-5533)
PHONE..................................562 921-4141
John Bateman, *President*
William Hall, *Vice Pres*
Steve Valenzuela, *Sales Mgr*
Dave Saguin, *Art Dir*
EMP: 28
SALES (est): 3.1MM **Privately Held**
WEB: www.flexlineinc.com
SIC: **2796** 2759 3555 Platemaking serv-
ices; commercial printing; printing plates

(P-7644)
GEMINI - G E L
8365 Melrose Ave, Los Angeles
(90069-5419)
PHONE..................................323 651-0513
Sidney B Felsen, *President*
Stanley Grinstein, *Treasurer*
EMP: 20
SQ FT: 6,000
SALES (est): 2.2MM **Privately Held**
WEB: www.geminigel.com
SIC: **2796** 2752 Etching on copper, steel,
wood or rubber: printing plates; commer-
cial printing, lithographic

(P-7645)
GRAFICO INC
15320 Cornet St, Santa Fe Springs
(90670-5532)
PHONE..................................562 404-4976
Dan Koon, *CEO*
Daniel Koon, *President*
Meredith Dugan, *CFO*
Spencer Koon, *Creative Dir*
▲ EMP: 15
SQ FT: 23,500
SALES (est): 1.7MM **Privately Held**
WEB: www.grafico.com
SIC: **2796** 7336 2791 Color separations
for printing; commercial art & graphic de-
sign; typesetting

(P-7646)
GRAPHIC DIES INC
12335 Florence Ave, Santa Fe Springs
(90670-3807)
P.O. Box 4343 (90670-1355)
PHONE..................................562 946-1802
Paul Bushaw, *President*
Estelle Bushaw, *Treasurer*
Janice Bushaw, *Admin Sec*
EMP: 10 EST: 1967
SQ FT: 5,129
SALES (est): 400K **Privately Held**
WEB: www.graphicdiesinc.com
SIC: **2796** Photoengraving plates, linecuts
or halftones

(P-7647)
HEADLINE GRAPHICS INC
131 Aberdeen Dr, Cardiff By The Sea
(92007-1821)
P.O. Box 1177, Cardiff (92007-7177)
PHONE..................................760 436-0133
Gerald Anderson, *President*
Debra Anderson, *Vice Pres*
EMP: 30
SQ FT: 4,000
SALES (est): 3MM **Privately Held**
WEB: www.headlinegraphics.com
SIC: **2796** 7336 2791 Color separations
for printing; graphic arts & related design;
commercial art & illustration; typesetting,
computer controlled

(P-7648)
HEINZ WEBER INCORPORATED
13025 Park Pl Unit 402, Hawthorne
(90250-0995)
PHONE..................................310 477-3561
Heinz Weber, *President*
EMP: 45
SQ FT: 5,000
SALES (est): 5MM **Privately Held**
WEB: www.heinzweber.com
SIC: **2796** Color separations for printing

(P-7649)
INLAND COLOR GRAPHICS
2054 Tandem, Norco (92860-3609)
PHONE..................................951 493-2999
Carl J Vitolo, *President*
EMP: 10
SQ FT: 10,000
SALES (est): 1.6MM **Privately Held**
WEB: www.icgcolor.com
SIC: **2796** Color separations for printing

(P-7650)
JAGUAR LITHO INCORPORATED
Also Called: J & L Imaging Center
1500 S Sunkist St Ste I, Anaheim
(92806-5815)
PHONE..................................714 978-1821
Joe Vitolo, *President*
Sue Vitolo, *Treasurer*
EMP: 10
SQ FT: 6,500
SALES (est): 1.1MM **Privately Held**
WEB: www.jaguarlitho.com
SIC: **2796** Color separations for printing

(P-7651)
MASTER ARTS INC
Also Called: Master Arts Engraving
3737 E Miraloma Ave, Anaheim
(92806-2100)
PHONE..................................714 240-4550
Elgin Chalayan, *President*
Mike Liberto, *Cust Mgr*

EMP: 15
SQ FT: 10,000
SALES (est): 2.3MM **Privately Held**
SIC: 2796 3555 Platemaking services; printing plates

(P-7652)
MIKA COLOR
6000 Monterey Rd, Los Angeles (90042-4327)
PHONE..................323 254-1450
Wen Che Huang, *President*
Kathy Huang, *Treasurer*
EMP: 11 **EST:** 1978
SQ FT: 4,700
SALES (est): 1.2MM **Privately Held**
SIC: 2796 Color separations for printing

(P-7653)
MOEBIUS DESIGN
Also Called: Moebius Color
9770 Carroll Centre Rd, San Diego (92126-6504)
PHONE..................858 450-4486
Peter K Moebius, *President*
Paul O Moebius, *Shareholder*
EMP: 20
SQ FT: 6,000
SALES (est): 3MM **Privately Held**
WEB: www.moebiuscolor.com
SIC: 2796 7373 2759 Color separations for printing; computer-aided design (CAD) systems service; commercial printing

(P-7654)
ONE COLOR COMMUNICATIONS LLC
Also Called: One Color Communications
1851 Harbor Bay Pkwy, Alameda (94502-3010)
PHONE..................510 263-1840
Stephen Kozel, *Mng Member*
Tim Wilson, *Branch Mgr*
Kim Fogarty,
Tom Kozel,
EMP: 75
SQ FT: 40,000
SALES (est): 5.6MM **Privately Held**
SIC: 2796 Color separations for printing

(P-7655)
PRESSLINE INK AND SUP CO INC
Also Called: Graphicom Digital
12117 Slauson Ave, Santa Fe Springs (90670-2603)
PHONE..................562 907-1891
Rafael Garcia, *President*
Salvador Garcia, *Vice Pres*
George Chiu, *Manager*
EMP: 21
SQ FT: 16,000
SALES (est): 4.4MM **Privately Held**
WEB: www.graphicomdigital.com
SIC: 2796 Color separations for printing

(P-7656)
SGK LLC
Also Called: Schawk
650 Townsend St Ste 160, San Francisco (94103-6258)
PHONE..................415 438-6700
Leslie Ungar, *Manager*
EMP: 100
SALES (corp-wide): 1.5B **Publicly Held**
WEB: www.schawk.com
SIC: 2796 7374 Color separations for printing; computer graphics service
HQ: Sgk, Llc
1600 Sherwin Ave
Des Plaines IL 60018
847 827-9494

(P-7657)
SGK LLC
Also Called: Schawk
3116 W Avenue 32, Los Angeles (90065-2317)
PHONE..................323 258-4111
Joe Kellenberger, *Principal*
EMP: 150
SQ FT: 75,850
SALES (corp-wide): 1.5B **Publicly Held**
WEB: www.schawk.com
SIC: 2796 Lithographic plates, positives or negatives

HQ: Sgk, Llc
1600 Sherwin Ave
Des Plaines IL 60018
847 827-9494

2812 Alkalies & Chlorine

(P-7658)
ARKEMA INC
Also Called: Arkema Coating Resins
19206 Hawthorne Blvd, Torrance (90503-1505)
PHONE..................310 214-5327
EMP: 124
SALES (corp-wide): 77.8MM **Privately Held**
SIC: 2812 2819 2869 2899 Chlorine, compressed or liquefied; caustic soda, sodium hydroxide; industrial inorganic chemicals; sodium compounds or salts, inorg., ex. refined sod. chloride; sodium sulfate, glauber's salt, salt cake; peroxides, hydrogen peroxide; industrial organic chemicals; solvents, organic; formaldehyde (formalin); metal treating compounds; plastics pipe
HQ: Arkema Inc.
900 First Ave
King Of Prussia PA 19406
610 205-7000

(P-7659)
CHURCH & DWIGHT CO INC
31266 Avenue 12, Madera (93638-8328)
PHONE..................559 661-2790
David Johnston, *Manager*
EMP: 20
SALES (corp-wide): 3.7B **Publicly Held**
WEB: www.churchdwight.com
SIC: 2812 Sodium bicarbonate
PA: Church & Dwight Co., Inc.
500 Charles Ewing Blvd
Ewing NJ 08628
609 806-1200

(P-7660)
CLOROX COMPANY VOLUNTARY
1221 Broadway Ste 1300, Oakland (94612-1871)
P.O. Box 24305 (94623-1305)
PHONE..................510 271-7000
EMP: 15
SALES (est): 3.5MM **Privately Held**
SIC: 2812 Chlorine, compressed or liquefied

(P-7661)
CLOROX SALES COMPANY
530 Idaho Ave, Escondido (92025-5226)
PHONE..................760 432-8362
EMP: 25
SALES (corp-wide): 5.5B **Publicly Held**
SIC: 2812
HQ: The Clorox Sales Company
1221 Broadway Ste 13
Oakland CA 94612
510 271-7000

(P-7662)
FMC CORPORATION
201 Cousteau Pl, Davis (95618-5412)
PHONE..................530 753-6718
Chris Cencula, *Engineer*
Jason Kinney, *Senior Buyer*
EMP: 95
SALES (corp-wide): 2.8B **Publicly Held**
SIC: 2812 Soda ash, sodium carbonate (anhydrous)
PA: Fmc Corporation
2929 Walnut St
Philadelphia PA 19104
215 299-6000

(P-7663)
HASA INC
1251 Loveridge Rd, Pittsburg (94565-2803)
PHONE..................661 259-5848
Lisa Wilson, *Manager*
EMP: 30

SALES (corp-wide): 65.7MM **Privately Held**
WEB: www.hasapool.com
SIC: 2812 Chlorine, compressed or liquefied
PA: Hasa, Inc.
23119 Drayton St
Santa Clarita CA 91350
661 259-5848

(P-7664)
HILL BROTHERS CHEMICAL COMPANY
Also Called: Desert Brand
15017 Clark Ave, City of Industry (91745-1409)
PHONE..................626 333-2251
Ron Hill, *President*
Toni Dakovich, *Purch Mgr*
Pedro Lozano, *QC Dir*
Bobby Conrad, *Sales Staff*
Jason Kowanetz, *Sales Staff*
EMP: 18
SQ FT: 17,203
SALES (est): 5MM
SALES (corp-wide): 110.9MM **Privately Held**
WEB: www.durafiber.com
SIC: 2812 2851 2819 Chlorine, compressed or liquefied; paints & allied products; industrial inorganic chemicals
PA: Hill Brothers Chemical Company
1675 N Main St
Orange CA 92867
714 998-8800

(P-7665)
JCI JONES CHEMICALS INC
1401 Del Amo Blvd, Torrance (90501-1630)
PHONE..................310 523-1629
Mike Reddinton, *Manager*
EMP: 35
SALES (corp-wide): 179MM **Privately Held**
WEB: www.jcichem.com
SIC: 2812 2899 Alkalies; chlorine, compressed or liquefied; chemical preparations
PA: Jci Jones Chemicals, Inc.
1765 Ringling Blvd
Sarasota FL 34236
941 330-1537

(P-7666)
OLIN CHLOR ALKALI LOGISTICS
Also Called: Chlor Alkali Products & Vinyls
11600 Pike St, Santa Fe Springs (90670-2938)
PHONE..................562 692-0510
John Bilac, *Branch Mgr*
EMP: 136
SALES (corp-wide): 6.2B **Publicly Held**
SIC: 2812 Alkalies & chlorine
HQ: Olin Chlor Alkali Logistics Inc
490 Stuart Rd Ne
Cleveland TN 37312
423 336-4850

(P-7667)
OLIN CHLOR ALKALI LOGISTICS
Also Called: Chlor Alkali Products & Vinyls
26700 S Banta Rd, Tracy (95304-8157)
PHONE..................209 835-5424
George Karscig, *Manager*
EMP: 20
SALES (corp-wide): 6.2B **Publicly Held**
WEB: www.olin.com
SIC: 2812 Alkalies & chlorine
HQ: Olin Chlor Alkali Logistics Inc
490 Stuart Rd Ne
Cleveland TN 37312
423 336-4850

2813 Industrial Gases

(P-7668)
AIR LIQUID HEALTHCARE
12460 Arrow Rte, Rancho Cucamonga (91739-9682)
PHONE..................909 899-4633
Gerald Berger, *Principal*
EMP: 26

SALES (est): 4.8MM **Privately Held**
SIC: 2813 8099 Oxygen, compressed or liquefied; health & allied services

(P-7669)
AIR LIQUIDE USA LLC
5121 Brandin Ct, Fremont (94538-5109)
PHONE..................510 659-0162
Gita Parobek, *Manager*
Eric Kleinschmidt, *Plant Engr*
EMP: 50
SQ FT: 24,000
SALES (corp-wide): 164.2MM **Privately Held**
WEB: www.asgemail.com
SIC: 2813 Industrial gases
HQ: Air Liquide Usa Llc
9811 Kepy Fwy Ste 100
Houston TX 77024
713 402-2221

(P-7670)
AIR PRODUCTS AND CHEMICALS INC
1515 Norman Ave Frnt, Santa Clara (95054-2029)
PHONE..................408 988-2142
John McLaine, *CEO*
EMP: 20
SALES (corp-wide): 8.1B **Publicly Held**
WEB: www.airproducts.com
SIC: 2813 Industrial gases
PA: Air Products And Chemicals, Inc.
7201 Hamilton Blvd
Allentown PA 18195
610 481-4911

(P-7671)
AIR PRODUCTS AND CHEMICALS INC
8934 Dice Rd, Santa Fe Springs (90670-2518)
PHONE..................562 944-3873
EMP: 50
SALES (corp-wide): 8.1B **Publicly Held**
WEB: www.airproducts.com
SIC: 2813 2869 Oxygen, compressed or liquefied; amines, acids, salts, esters
PA: Air Products And Chemicals, Inc.
7201 Hamilton Blvd
Allentown PA 18195
610 481-4911

(P-7672)
AIR PRODUCTS AND CHEMICALS INC
23300 S Alameda St, Carson (90810-1921)
PHONE..................310 847-7300
Matt Pitcher, *Manager*
EMP: 10
SALES (corp-wide): 8.1B **Publicly Held**
WEB: www.airproducts.com
SIC: 2813 Industrial gases
PA: Air Products And Chemicals, Inc.
7201 Hamilton Blvd
Allentown PA 18195
610 481-4911

(P-7673)
AIR PRODUCTS AND CHEMICALS INC
901 W 12th St, Long Beach (90813-2813)
PHONE..................562 437-0462
Shelly Stuart, *Branch Mgr*
EMP: 25
SALES (corp-wide): 8.1B **Publicly Held**
WEB: www.airproducts.com
SIC: 2813 Industrial gases
PA: Air Products And Chemicals, Inc.
7201 Hamilton Blvd
Allentown PA 18195
610 481-4911

(P-7674)
AIR PRODUCTS AND CHEMICALS INC
400 Macarthur Blvd, Newport Beach (92660)
PHONE..................949 474-1860
Max Monestime, *Branch Mgr*
EMP: 11
SALES (corp-wide): 8.1B **Publicly Held**
WEB: www.airproducts.com
SIC: 2813 5169 Industrial gases; industrial gases

PA: Air Products And Chemicals, Inc.
7201 Hamilton Blvd
Allentown PA 18195
610 481-4911

(P-7675)
AIR PRODUCTS AND CHEMICALS INC
1969 Palomar Oaks Way, Carlsbad
(92011-1307)
PHONE...............................760 931-9555
Ileen Turner, *Site Mgr*
EMP: 175
SALES (corp-wide): 8.1B **Publicly Held**
WEB: www.airproducts.com
SIC: 2813 3625 2899 2865 Industrial
gases; relays & industrial controls; chemi-
cal preparations; cyclic crudes & interme-
diates
PA: Air Products And Chemicals, Inc.
7201 Hamilton Blvd
Allentown PA 18195
610 481-4911

(P-7676)
AIR PRODUCTS AND CHEMICALS INC
700 N Henry Ford Ave, Wilmington
(90744-6717)
PHONE...............................310 952-9172
Jim Click, *Branch Mgr*
EMP: 20
SALES (corp-wide): 8.1B **Publicly Held**
WEB: www.airproducts.com
SIC: 2813 Industrial gases
PA: Air Products And Chemicals, Inc.
7201 Hamilton Blvd
Allentown PA 18195
610 481-4911

(P-7677)
AIR SOURCE INDUSTRIES
3976 Cherry Ave, Long Beach
(90807-3727)
PHONE...............................562 426-4017
Robert L Bowers, *CEO*
Richard Smith, *Vice Pres*
EMP: 14
SALES (est): 3.6MM **Privately Held**
WEB: www.air-source.com
SIC: 2813 5999 Industrial gases; conva-
lescent equipment & supplies

(P-7678)
AIRGAS USA LLC
315 Harbor Way, South San Francisco
(94080-6919)
PHONE...............................650 873-4212
Dennis Byron, *Manager*
EMP: 12
SALES (corp-wide): 164.2MM **Privately Held**
SIC: 2813 5999 5169
HQ: Airgas Usa, Llc
259 N Radnor Chester Rd # 100
Radnor PA 19087
610 687-5253

(P-7679)
AIRGAS USA LLC
1415 Grand Ave, San Marcos
(92078-2405)
PHONE...............................760 744-1472
Fernando Anzaldua, *Branch Mgr*
EMP: 25
SQ FT: 22,032
SALES (corp-wide): 164.2MM **Privately Held**
WEB: www.airgas.com
SIC: 2813 5084 3443 Industrial gases;
welding machinery & equipment; weld-
ments
HQ: Airgas Usa, Llc
259 N Radnor Chester Rd # 100
Radnor PA 19087
610 687-5253

(P-7680)
AIRGAS USA LLC
9810 Jordan Cir, Santa Fe Springs
(90670-3303)
PHONE...............................562 946-8394
Ruthie Cox, *Manager*
Lisa Watson, *Human Res Mgr*
EMP: 50

SALES (corp-wide): 164.2MM **Privately Held**
SIC: 2813 5999 5169 Industrial gases;
ice; dry ice
HQ: Airgas Usa, Llc
259 N Radnor Chester Rd # 100
Radnor PA 19087
610 687-5253

(P-7681)
AIRGAS USA LLC
700 Decoto Rd, Union City (94587-3513)
PHONE...............................510 429-4200
Bob Oconnor, *Manager*
EMP: 56
SQ FT: 35,886
SALES (corp-wide): 164.2MM **Privately Held**
WEB: www.airliquide.com
SIC: 2813 5084 Industrial gases; industrial
machinery & equipment
HQ: Airgas Usa, Llc
259 N Radnor Chester Rd # 100
Radnor PA 19087
610 687-5253

(P-7682)
AIRGAS USA LLC
1750 Clinton Dr, Concord (94521-2015)
PHONE...............................925 969-0419
EMP: 17
SALES (corp-wide): 164.2MM **Privately Held**
SIC: 2813 Industrial gases
HQ: Airgas Usa, Llc
259 N Radnor Chester Rd # 100
Radnor PA 19087
610 687-5253

(P-7683)
AIRGAS USA LLC
8832 Dice Rd, Santa Fe Springs
(90670-2516)
PHONE...............................562 945-1383
Rafael Motta, *Branch Mgr*
Cynthia Aragundi, *Plant Mgr*
EMP: 44
SQ FT: 29,887
SALES (corp-wide): 164.2MM **Privately Held**
WEB: www.airliquide.com
SIC: 2813 5084 Industrial gases; industrial
machinery & equipment
HQ: Airgas Usa, Llc
259 N Radnor Chester Rd # 100
Radnor PA 19087
610 687-5253

(P-7684)
AIRGAS USA LLC
46409 Landing Pkwy, Fremont
(94538-6496)
PHONE...............................510 624-4000
Scott Anderson, *Branch Mgr*
EMP: 40
SQ FT: 10,000
SALES (corp-wide): 164.2MM **Privately Held**
WEB: www.airliquide.com
SIC: 2813 Industrial gases
HQ: Airgas Usa, Llc
259 N Radnor Chester Rd # 100
Radnor PA 19087
610 687-5253

(P-7685)
AIRGAS USA LLC
9756 Santa Fe Springs Rd, Santa Fe
Springs (90670-2920)
PHONE...............................562 906-8700
Cynthia Aragundi, *Manager*
EMP: 30
SALES (corp-wide): 164.2MM **Privately Held**
WEB: www.airliquide.com
SIC: 2813 5169 Industrial gases; oxygen
HQ: Airgas Usa, Llc
259 N Radnor Chester Rd # 100
Radnor PA 19087
610 687-5253

(P-7686)
AIRGAS USA LLC
311 Kentucky St, Bakersfield (93305-4229)
PHONE...............................661 201-8107
Roy Neal, *Branch Mgr*

EMP: 20
SALES (corp-wide): 164.2MM **Privately Held**
WEB: www.airliquide.com
SIC: 2813 2911 5084 Industrial gases;
petroleum refining; materials handling
machinery
HQ: Airgas Usa, Llc
259 N Radnor Chester Rd # 100
Radnor PA 19087
610 687-5253

(P-7687)
AIRGAS USA LLC
352 W 133rd St, Los Angeles (90061-1110)
PHONE...............................310 329-4390
Arturo Garcia, *Manager*
EMP: 10
SALES (corp-wide): 164.2MM **Privately Held**
WEB: www.airgaswest.com
SIC: 2813 Acetylene
HQ: Airgas Usa, Llc
259 N Radnor Chester Rd # 100
Radnor PA 19087
610 687-5253

(P-7688)
AIRGAS USA LLC
12550 Arrow Rte, Rancho Cucamonga
(91739-9683)
PHONE...............................909 899-4670
Dave Erickson, *Branch Mgr*
EMP: 17
SALES (corp-wide): 164.2MM **Privately Held**
SIC: 2813 Industrial gases
HQ: Airgas Usa, Llc
259 N Radnor Chester Rd # 100
Radnor PA 19087
610 687-5253

(P-7689)
AMERICAN AIR LIQUIDE INC (DH)
46409 Landing Pkwy, Fremont
(94538-6496)
PHONE...............................510 624-4000
Benoit Potier, *Chairman*
Pierre Dufour, *President*
Scott Krapf, *CFO*
Gregory Alexander, *Treasurer*
Jean-Pierre Duprieu, *Exec VP*
◆ **EMP:** 90
SQ FT: 40,000
SALES (est): 314.8MM
SALES (corp-wide): 164.2MM **Privately Held**
SIC: 2813 5084 3533 4931 Industrial
gases; welding machinery & equipment;
oil & gas drilling rigs & equipment; electric
& other services combined
HQ: Air Liquide International
75 Quai D Orsay
Paris
140 625-555

(P-7690)
FLEXCUBE INC
1861 Spring Mountain Rd, Saint Helena
(94574-1736)
PHONE...............................707 738-4001
Peter Graham Steer, *CEO*
▲ **EMP:** 12
SALES (est): 230.1K **Privately Held**
SIC: 2813 Oxygen, compressed or lique-
fied

(P-7691)
FOLLMER DEVELOPMENT INC
Also Called: Fd
840 Tourmaline Dr, Newbury Park
(91320-1205)
PHONE...............................805 498-4531
Christopher H Follmer, *CEO*
Garrett Follmer, *President*
Helen Follmer, *Treasurer*
David McKenzie, *Vice Pres*
Dan Follmer, *Principal*
▼ **EMP:** 41
SQ FT: 35,000
SALES (est): 20.7MM **Privately Held**
WEB: www.follmerdevelopment.com
SIC: 2813 Aerosols

(P-7692)
KMG ELECTRONIC CHEMICALS INC
2340 Bert Dr, Hollister (95023-2510)
PHONE...............................831 636-5151
Brad Clark, *Branch Mgr*
EMP: 11
SALES (corp-wide): 465.5MM **Publicly Held**
SIC: 2813 Industrial gases
HQ: Kmg Electronic Chemicals, Inc.
300 Throckmorton St # 1900
Fort Worth TX 76102
-

(P-7693)
LINDE GAS NORTH AMERICA LLC
Also Called: Lifegas
614 S Glenwood Pl, Burbank (91506-2820)
PHONE...............................626 855-8344
Kevin Johnston, *Branch Mgr*
EMP: 19
SALES (corp-wide): 20.1B **Privately Held**
SIC: 2813
HQ: Linde Gas North America Llc
200 Somerset Corp Blvd # 7000
Bridgewater NJ 08807

(P-7694)
LINDE GAS NORTH AMERICA LLC
Also Called: Lifegas
680 Baldwin Park Blvd, City of Industry
(91746-1501)
PHONE...............................626 780-3104
Alan Underwood, *Principal*
EMP: 19
SALES (corp-wide): 20.1B **Privately Held**
SIC: 2813 Nitrogen; oxygen, compressed
or liquefied
HQ: Linde Gas North America Llc
200 Somerset Corp Blvd # 7000
Bridgewater NJ 08807
-

(P-7695)
LINDE LLC
Also Called: Cryostar USA
13117 Meyer Rd, Whittier (90605-3555)
PHONE...............................562 903-1290
Mark Sutton, *Branch Mgr*
EMP: 17
SALES (corp-wide): 20.1B **Privately Held**
SIC: 2813 3561 Oxygen, compressed or
liquefied; pumps & pumping equipment
HQ: Linde Llc
200 Somerset Corporate Bl
Bridgewater NJ 08807
908 464-8100

(P-7696)
LINDE LLC
2535 Del Amo Blvd, Torrance (90503-1706)
PHONE...............................310 533-8394
Jason Lacasella, *Manager*
EMP: 20
SALES (corp-wide): 20.1B **Privately Held**
SIC: 2813 Carbon dioxide
HQ: Linde Llc
200 Somerset Corporate Bl
Bridgewater NJ 08807
908 464-8100

(P-7697)
LINDE LLC
Also Called: Boc Gases
731 W Cutting Blvd, Richmond
(94804-2023)
PHONE...............................510 233-8911
Ken Marquardt, *Opers-Prdtn-Mfg*
EMP: 18
SALES (corp-wide): 20.1B **Privately Held**
SIC: 2813 Oxygen, compressed or lique-
fied
HQ: Linde Llc
200 Somerset Corporate Bl
Bridgewater NJ 08807
908 464-8100

(P-7698)
LINDE LLC
5858 88th St, Sacramento (95828-1104)
PHONE...............................916 381-1606

▲ = Import ▼=Export
◆ =Import/Export

Steve Morgan, *Branch Mgr*
EMP: 20
SALES (corp-wide): 20.1B **Privately Held**
SIC: 2813 Nitrogen; oxygen, compressed
or liquefied
HQ: Linde Llc
200 Somerset Corporate Bl
Bridgewater NJ 08807
908 464-8100

(P-7699)
LINDE LLC
B O C Edwards/Temescal
4569 Las Positas Rd Ste C, Livermore
(94551-8865)
PHONE..................925 371-4170
Gregg S Wallace, *Manager*
EMP: 33
SALES (corp-wide): 20.1B **Privately Held**
SIC: 2813 Oxygen, compressed or lique-
fied
HQ: Linde Llc
200 Somerset Corporate Bl
Bridgewater NJ 08807
908 464-8100

(P-7700)
LINDE LLC
660 Baldwin Park Blvd, City of Industry
(91746-1501)
PHONE..................626 855-8366
Mike Colvin, *Branch Mgr*
EMP: 60
SALES (corp-wide): 20.1B **Privately Held**
SIC: 2813 Nitrogen; oxygen, compressed
or liquefied
HQ: Linde Llc
200 Somerset Corporate Bl
Bridgewater NJ 08807
908 464-8100

(P-7701)
MATHESON TRI-GAS INC
16125 Ornelas St, Irwindale (91706-2037)
PHONE..................626 334-2905
Fermin Reyes, *Manager*
Michael Yeargan, *Executive*
Mike Berkof, *Project Engr*
Joe Cassidy, *Engineer*
Kathy Hart, *Purch Agent*
EMP: 25
SQ FT: 19,472
SALES (corp-wide): 34.9B **Privately Held**
WEB: www.matheson-trigas.com
SIC: 2813 5169 Industrial gases; industrial
gases
HQ: Matheson Tri-Gas, Inc.
150 Allen Rd Ste 302
Basking Ridge NJ 07920
908 991-9200

(P-7702)
MATHESON TRI-GAS INC
6925 Central Ave, Newark (94560-3940)
PHONE..................510 714-3026
Tae-Byung Park, *Finance*
EMP: 16
SALES (corp-wide): 34.9B **Privately Held**
SIC: 2813 Industrial gases
HQ: Matheson Tri-Gas, Inc.
150 Allen Rd Ste 302
Basking Ridge NJ 07920
908 991-9200

(P-7703)
MATHESON TRI-GAS INC
8800 Utica Ave, Rancho Cucamonga
(91730-5104)
PHONE..................909 758-5464
Gary Harper, *Branch Mgr*
EMP: 20
SQ FT: 5,560
SALES (corp-wide): 34.9B **Privately Held**
WEB: www.matheson-trigas.com
SIC: 2813 5084 3494 Industrial gases;
welding machinery & equipment; valves &
pipe fittings
HQ: Matheson Tri-Gas, Inc.
150 Allen Rd Ste 302
Basking Ridge NJ 07920
908 991-9200

(P-7704)
MATHESON TRI-GAS INC
6775 Central Ave, Newark (94560-3936)
PHONE..................510 793-2559

Rob Peetz, *Division Mgr*
Scott Kallman, *COO*
Richard White, *Div Sub Head*
EMP: 90
SQ FT: 19,281
SALES (corp-wide): 34.9B **Privately Held**
WEB: www.matheson-trigas.com
SIC: 2813 5084 3494 Industrial gases;
welding machinery & equipment; valves &
pipe fittings
HQ: Matheson Tri-Gas, Inc.
150 Allen Rd Ste 302
Basking Ridge NJ 07920
908 991-9200

(P-7705)
MATHESON TRI-GAS INC
5555 District Blvd, Vernon (90058-4017)
PHONE..................323 773-2777
Robin Reynolds, *Manager*
EMP: 15
SALES (corp-wide): 34.9B **Privately Held**
SIC: 2813 5084 5169 Industrial gases;
welding machinery & equipment; indus-
trial gases
HQ: Matheson Tri-Gas, Inc.
150 Allen Rd Ste 302
Basking Ridge NJ 07920
908 991-9200

(P-7706)
PRAXAIR INC
2430 Camino Ramon Ste 310, San Ramon
(94583-4321)
PHONE..................925 866-6800
Mark Plant, *Director*
D L Pierce, *Marketing Mgr*
EMP: 12
SALES (corp-wide): 11.4B **Privately Held**
SIC: 2813 Industrial gases
PA: Praxair, Inc.
10 Riverview Dr
Danbury CT 06810
203 837-2000

(P-7707)
PRAXAIR INC
2000 Loveridge Rd, Pittsburg (94565-4114)
PHONE..................925 427-1051
Sturt Becker, *Manager*
EMP: 60
SALES (corp-wide): 11.4B **Privately Held**
SIC: 2813 Industrial gases
PA: Praxair, Inc.
10 Riverview Dr
Danbury CT 06810
203 837-2000

(P-7708)
PRAXAIR INC
2006 E 223rd St, Long Beach
(90810-1609)
PHONE..................310 816-1066
Stu Lehmann, *Manager*
EMP: 20
SALES (corp-wide): 11.4B **Privately Held**
SIC: 2813 Industrial gases
PA: Praxair, Inc.
10 Riverview Dr
Danbury CT 06810
203 837-2000

(P-7709)
PRAXAIR INC
10728 Prospect Ave Ste A, Santee
(92071-4558)
PHONE..................619 596-4558
Wayne Yakich, *Owner*
EMP: 20
SALES (corp-wide): 11.4B **Privately Held**
SIC: 2813 Industrial gases
PA: Praxair, Inc.
10 Riverview Dr
Danbury CT 06810
203 837-2000

(P-7710)
PRAXAIR INC
3481 Yeager Rd, Madera (93637-8749)
PHONE..................559 674-7306
Jimmy Schulte, *Branch Mgr*
EMP: 20
SALES (corp-wide): 11.4B **Privately Held**
SIC: 2813 Industrial gases

PA: Praxair, Inc.
10 Riverview Dr
Danbury CT 06810
203 837-2000

(P-7711)
PRAXAIR INC
2995 Atlas Rd, San Pablo (94806-1167)
PHONE..................510 223-9593
EMP: 20
SALES (corp-wide): 11.9B **Publicly Held**
SIC: 2813
PA: Praxair, Inc.
39 Old Ridgebury Rd
Danbury CT 06810
203 837-2000

(P-7712)
PRAXAIR INC
305 E Haley St Ste A, Santa Barbara
(93101-1723)
PHONE..................805 966-0829
Karl Grimm, *Manager*
EMP: 16
SALES (corp-wide): 11.4B **Privately Held**
SIC: 2813 Industrial gases
PA: Praxair, Inc.
10 Riverview Dr
Danbury CT 06810
203 837-2000

(P-7713)
PRAXAIR INC
8300 Atlantic Ave, Cudahy (90201-5808)
PHONE..................323 562-5200
Don Hamric, *Manager*
EMP: 14
SALES (corp-wide): 11.4B **Privately Held**
SIC: 2813 Industrial gases
PA: Praxair, Inc.
10 Riverview Dr
Danbury CT 06810
203 837-2000

(P-7714)
PRAXAIR INC
3331 Buck Owens Blvd, Bakersfield
(93308-6323)
PHONE..................661 861-6421
Mark Cooper, *Manager*
EMP: 20
SALES (corp-wide): 11.4B **Privately Held**
SIC: 2813 Industrial gases
PA: Praxair, Inc.
10 Riverview Dr
Danbury CT 06810
203 837-2000

(P-7715)
PRAXAIR INC
3505 Buck Owens Blvd, Bakersfield
(93308-4919)
PHONE..................661 327-5336
Mark Cooper, *General Mgr*
EMP: 25
SALES (corp-wide): 11.4B **Privately Held**
SIC: 2813 Industrial gases
PA: Praxair, Inc.
10 Riverview Dr
Danbury CT 06810
203 837-2000

(P-7716)
PRAXAIR INC
1011 W Collins Ave, Orange (92867-5535)
PHONE..................515 963-3872
EMP: 23
SALES (corp-wide): 11.4B **Privately Held**
SIC: 2813 Industrial gases
PA: Praxair, Inc.
10 Riverview Dr
Danbury CT 06810
203 837-2000

(P-7717)
PRAXAIR INC
3994 Bayshore Blvd, Brisbane
(94005-1404)
PHONE..................415 657-9880
EMP: 21
SALES (corp-wide): 11.4B **Privately Held**
SIC: 2813 Oxygen, compressed or lique-
fied

PA: Praxair, Inc.
10 Riverview Dr
Danbury CT 06810
203 837-2000

(P-7718)
PRAXAIR INC
5700 S Alameda St, Vernon (90058-3430)
PHONE..................323 588-8181
Rob Riedel, *Manager*
EMP: 30
SQ FT: 25,661
SALES (corp-wide): 11.4B **Privately Held**
SIC: 2813 Industrial gases
PA: Praxair, Inc.
10 Riverview Dr
Danbury CT 06810
203 837-2000

(P-7719)
PRAXAIR INC
5705 E Airport Dr, Ontario (91761-8611)
PHONE..................909 390-0283
M M Stenberg, *Branch Mgr*
EMP: 65
SALES (corp-wide): 11.4B **Privately Held**
SIC: 2813 Industrial gases
PA: Praxair, Inc.
10 Riverview Dr
Danbury CT 06810
203 837-2000

(P-7720)
PRAXAIR INC
7501 Foothills Blvd, Roseville
(95747-6504)
PHONE..................916 786-3900
EMP: 15
SALES (corp-wide): 11.4B **Privately Held**
SIC: 2813 Industrial gases
PA: Praxair, Inc.
10 Riverview Dr
Danbury CT 06810
203 837-2000

(P-7721)
PRAXAIR INC
331 E Channel Rd, Benicia (94510-1127)
PHONE..................707 745-5328
John Alford, *Manager*
EMP: 20
SALES (corp-wide): 11.4B **Privately Held**
SIC: 2813 Industrial gases
PA: Praxair, Inc.
10 Riverview Dr
Danbury CT 06810
203 837-2000

(P-7722)
PRAXAIR DISTRIBUTION INC
2771 S Maple Ave, Fresno (93725-2117)
PHONE..................559 237-5521
Keith Martinez, *Branch Mgr*
EMP: 33
SQ FT: 11,800
SALES (corp-wide): 11.4B **Privately Held**
SIC: 2813 Acetylene
HQ: Praxair Distribution, Inc.
10 Riverview Dr
Danbury CT 06810
203 837-2000

(P-7723)
PRAXAIR DISTRIBUTION INC
500 Harrington St Ste G, Corona
(92880-6735)
PHONE..................951 736-8113
Laura Johnston, *Principal*
EMP: 47
SALES (corp-wide): 11.4B **Privately Held**
SIC: 2813 Industrial gases
HQ: Praxair Distribution, Inc.
10 Riverview Dr
Danbury CT 06810
203 837-2000

(P-7724)
PRAXAIR DISTRIBUTION INC
305 E Haley St, Santa Barbara
(93101-1723)
PHONE..................805 966-0829
Bret Glasspoole, *Manager*
EMP: 47
SALES (corp-wide): 11.4B **Privately Held**
SIC: 2813 Industrial gases

PRODUCTS & SVCS

HQ: Praxair Distribution, Inc.
10 Riverview Dr
Danbury CT 06810
203 837-2000

(P-7725)
PRAXAIR DISTRIBUTION INC
5508 Vineland Ave, North Hollywood
(91601-2729)
PHONE..................................818 760-2011
Stephen Schultz, *Manager*
EMP: 13
SALES (corp-wide): 11.4B **Privately Held**
SIC: 2813 Industrial gases
HQ: Praxair Distribution, Inc.
10 Riverview Dr
Danbury CT 06810
203 837-2000

(P-7726)
PRAXAIR DISTRIBUTION INC
455 E Wooley Rd, Oxnard (93030-7224)
PHONE..................................805 487-2742
Craig Haggmark, *Manager*
John Whitt, *Manager*
EMP: 12
SALES (corp-wide): 11.4B **Privately Held**
SIC: 2813 Industrial gases
HQ: Praxair Distribution, Inc.
10 Riverview Dr
Danbury CT 06810
203 837-2000

(P-7727)
PRAXAIR DISTRIBUTION INC
2205 Newton Ave, San Diego
(92113-3619)
PHONE..................................619 232-7341
Sal Tena, *Manager*
Sal Pena, *Plant Mgr*
Christine Raymond, *Manager*
Nelly Perez, *Clerk*
EMP: 10
SALES (corp-wide): 11.4B **Privately Held**
SIC: 2813 Industrial gases
HQ: Praxair Distribution, Inc.
10 Riverview Dr
Danbury CT 06810
203 837-2000

(P-7728)
PRAXAIR DISTRIBUTION INC
215 San Jose Ave, San Jose (95125-1009)
PHONE..................................408 995-6089
Brian Anderson, *Manager*
EMP: 12
SALES (corp-wide): 11.4B **Privately Held**
SIC: 2813 Industrial gases
HQ: Praxair Distribution, Inc.
10 Riverview Dr
Danbury CT 06810
203 837-2000

(P-7729)
PRAXAIR DISTRIBUTION INC
1545 E Edinger Ave, Santa Ana
(92705-4907)
PHONE..................................714 547-6684
Janice Webber, *Manager*
Debbie Anderson, *Senior VP*
EMP: 50
SALES (corp-wide): 11.4B **Privately Held**
SIC: 2813 Oxygen, compressed or lique-
fied
HQ: Praxair Distribution, Inc.
10 Riverview Dr
Danbury CT 06810
203 837-2000

(P-7730)
PRAXAIR DISTRIBUTION INC
2020 De La Cruz Blvd, Santa Clara
(95050-3038)
PHONE..................................408 748-1722
Pete Krieger, *Branch Mgr*
EMP: 47
SALES (corp-wide): 11.4B **Privately Held**
SIC: 2813 Industrial gases
HQ: Praxair Distribution, Inc.
10 Riverview Dr
Danbury CT 06810
203 837-2000

(P-7731)
PRAXAIR DISTRIBUTION INC
19200 Hawthorne Blvd, Torrance
(90503-1505)
PHONE..................................310 371-1254
Fred Casey, *Branch Mgr*
Len Kajimoto, *Plant Mgr*
O'Neal Summers, *Plant Mgr*
EMP: 70
SALES (corp-wide): 11.4B **Privately Held**
SIC: 2813 Industrial gases
HQ: Praxair Distribution, Inc.
10 Riverview Dr
Danbury CT 06810
203 837-2000

(P-7732)
**SHIELD REALTY CALIFORNIA
INC (PA)**
Also Called: Shield CA
5165 G St, Chino (91710-5143)
P.O. Box 190, Canton MA (02021-0190)
PHONE..................................909 628-4707
George P Bates, *President*
Todd A Johnston, *Vice Pres*
A Bruce Simpson, *Vice Pres*
Troy D Wilson, *Vice Pres*
Louis A Sgarzi, *Admin Sec*
▲ EMP: 43
SQ FT: 30,000
SALES (est): 21.9MM **Privately Held**
SIC: 2813 Aerosols

(P-7733)
TECH AIR NORTHERN CAL LLC
Also Called: Alliance Welding Supplies
140 S Montgomery St, San Jose
(95110-2520)
PHONE..................................408 293-9353
Chris Gremich, *Manager*
EMP: 11
SALES (corp-wide): 4.8MM **Privately
Held**
SIC: 2813 Industrial gases
PA: Tech Air Of Northern California, Llc
50 Mill Plain Rd
Danbury CT 06811
203 792-1834

(P-7734)
TECH AIR NORTHERN CAL LLC
Also Called: Alliance Welding Supplies
800 Greenville Rd, Livermore
(94550-9241)
PHONE..................................925 449-9353
Mark Harrill, *Manager*
EMP: 11
SALES (corp-wide): 4.8MM **Privately
Held**
SIC: 2813 Industrial gases
PA: Tech Air Of Northern California, Llc
50 Mill Plain Rd
Danbury CT 06811
203 792-1834

(P-7735)
TECH AIR NORTHERN CAL LLC
1224 6th St, Berkeley (94710-1402)
PHONE..................................510 524-9353
Larry McDonnell, *Manager*
EMP: 11
SALES (corp-wide): 4.8MM **Privately
Held**
SIC: 2813 Industrial gases
PA: Tech Air Of Northern California, Llc
50 Mill Plain Rd
Danbury CT 06811
203 792-1834

(P-7736)
TECH AIR NORTHERN CAL LLC
1135 Erickson Rd, Concord (94520-3799)
PHONE..................................925 568-9353
Mike Jones, *Manager*
EMP: 11
SALES (corp-wide): 4.8MM **Privately
Held**
SIC: 2813 Industrial gases
PA: Tech Air Of Northern California, Llc
50 Mill Plain Rd
Danbury CT 06811
203 792-1834

(P-7737)
TECH AIR NORTHERN CAL LLC
820 Industrial Rd, San Carlos
(94070-3319)
PHONE..................................650 593-9353
Juan Aguirre, *Manager*
EMP: 11
SALES (corp-wide): 4.8MM **Privately
Held**
SIC: 2813 Industrial gases
PA: Tech Air Of Northern California, Llc
50 Mill Plain Rd
Danbury CT 06811
203 792-1834

(P-7738)
TECH AIR NORTHERN CAL LLC
Also Called: Alliance Welding Supplies
4445 Jensen St, Oakland (94601-3939)
PHONE..................................510 533-9353
Chris Calegari, *Manager*
EMP: 11
SALES (corp-wide): 4.8MM **Privately
Held**
SIC: 2813 Industrial gases
PA: Tech Air Of Northern California, Llc
50 Mill Plain Rd
Danbury CT 06811
203 792-1834

(P-7739)
TECH AIR OF CALIFORNIA INC
Also Called: California Dental Group
7254 Coldwater Canyon Ave, North Holly-
wood (91605-4203)
PHONE..................................818 787-6010
Jack Storm, *Branch Mgr*
EMP: 10
SALES (corp-wide): 108.7MM **Privately
Held**
SIC: 2813 Industrial gases
HQ: Tech Air Of California, Inc.
50 Mill Plain Rd
Danbury CT 06811
203 792-1834

2816 Inorganic Pigments

(P-7740)
**COLORWEN INTERNATIONAL
CORP**
951 Lawson St, City of Industry
(91748-1121)
PHONE..................................626 363-8855
Chin Huang, *Principal*
Gloria Lin, *Office Mgr*
▲ EMP: 10
SALES (est): 1MM **Privately Held**
SIC: 2816 Color pigments

(P-7741)
DAY-GLO COLOR CORP
4615 Ardine St, Cudahy (90201-5821)
PHONE..................................323 560-2000
Joe Cummings, *Opers-Prdtn-Mfg*
EMP: 19
SQ FT: 100,000
SALES (corp-wide): 5.3B **Publicly Held**
WEB: www.dayglo.com
SIC: 2816 5169 2865 2851 Inorganic pig-
ments; synthetic resins, rubber & plastic
materials; color pigments, organic; paints
& allied products
HQ: Day-Glo Color Corp.
4515 Saint Clair Ave
Cleveland OH 44103
216 391-7070

(P-7742)
GENERAL CARBON COMPANY
7542 Maie Ave, Los Angeles (90001-2637)
PHONE..................................323 588-9291
Renee Aukers, *President*
Julio Negrete, *Vice Pres*
▲ EMP: 12
SQ FT: 10,000
SALES (est): 3.1MM **Privately Held**
WEB: www.generalcarboncompany.com
SIC: 2816 Lamp black

(P-7743)
PLASTIC COLOR TECHNOLOGY
3010 Spyglass Ct, Chino Hills
(91709-2488)
PHONE..................................909 597-9230
Xavier Benegas, *Owner*
EMP: 15
SQ FT: 9,500
SALES (est): 1.8MM **Privately Held**
SIC: 2816 Metallic & mineral pigments

(P-7744)
RYVEC INC
251 E Palais Rd, Anaheim (92805-6239)
PHONE..................................714 520-5592
Michael Ryan, *CEO*
Steve Ryan, *Sales Mgr*
Phil Ellis, *Maintence Staff*
▲ EMP: 26
SQ FT: 43,000
SALES (est): 6.4MM **Privately Held**
WEB: www.ryvec.com
SIC: 2816 2865 2821 Color pigments;
dyes & pigments; polyurethane resins

(P-7745)
SOLOMON COLORS INC
1371 Laurel Ave, Rialto (92376-3011)
PHONE..................................909 484-9156
Jeff Bowers, *Branch Mgr*
Larry Parish, *Vice Pres*
Steve Laforce, *Info Tech Mgr*
Cecilia Lenihan, *Purchasing*
Tanya Bryant, *Marketing Staff*
EMP: 37
SQ FT: 80,000
SALES (corp-wide): 35.7MM **Privately
Held**
WEB: www.solomoncolors.com
SIC: 2816 Inorganic pigments
PA: Solomon Colors, Inc.
4050 Color Plant Rd
Springfield IL 62702
217 522-3112

(P-7746)
SPECTRA COLOR INC
9116 Stellar Ct, Corona (92883-4923)
PHONE..................................951 277-0200
Robert Shedd, *President*
John Shedd, *Admin Sec*
Maria Conner, *Accountant*
▲ EMP: 42
SQ FT: 40,000
SALES (est): 14.4MM **Privately Held**
SIC: 2816 3089 2821 Color pigments;
coloring & finishing of plastic products;
plastics materials & resins

(P-7747)
**STANFORD MATERIALS
CORPORATION**
23661 Birtcher Dr, Lake Forest
(92630-1770)
PHONE..................................949 380-7362
▲ EMP: 13
SALES (est): 2.1MM **Privately Held**
SIC: 2816

(P-7748)
VENATOR AMERICAS LLC
Davis Colors
3700 E Olympic Blvd, Los Angeles
(90023-3123)
P.O. Box 23100 (90023-0100)
PHONE..................................323 269-7311
Nick Paris, *Vice Pres*
Miguel Cortez, *Manager*
EMP: 70
SQ FT: 540,000
SALES (corp-wide): 8.3B **Publicly Held**
WEB: www.rockwoodpigments.com
SIC: 2816 2865 Inorganic pigments; cyclic
crudes & intermediates
HQ: Venator Americas Llc
7011 Muirkirk Rd
Beltsville MD 20705
301 210-3400

▲ = Import ▼=Export
◆ =Import/Export

2819 Indl Inorganic Chemicals, NEC

(P-7749)
ADVANCED CHEMICAL TECH INC
8728 Utica Ave, Rancho Cucamonga (91730-5115)
PHONE..................................800 527-9607
Daniel Anthony Earley, *CEO*
EMP: 40 **EST:** 1996
SQ FT: 18,698
SALES (est): 11.4MM **Privately Held**
SIC: 2819 2899 5169 Industrial inorganic chemicals; antiscaling compounds, boiler; water treating compounds; anti-corrosion products; industrial chemicals

(P-7750)
AIR LIQUIDE ELECTRONICS US LP
Also Called: Aloha
46401 Landing Pkwy, Fremont (94538-6496)
PHONE..................................510 624-4338
Don Swetnam, *Branch Mgr*
EMP: 45
SALES (corp-wide): 164.2MM **Privately Held**
HQ: Air Liquide Electronics U.S. Lp
9101 Lyndon B Johnson Fwy # 800
Dallas TX 75243
972 301-5200

(P-7751)
AMCOR MANUFACTURING INC
500 Winmoore Way, Modesto (95358-5750)
PHONE..................................209 581-9687
Michael Harvey, *President*
Michael Archibald, *Vice Pres*
EMP: 22
SQ FT: 36,000
SALES: 2.9MM **Privately Held**
SIC: 2819 Industrial inorganic chemicals

(P-7752)
AMERICAN LITHIUM ENERGY CORP
2261 Rutherford Rd, Carlsbad (92008-8815)
PHONE..................................760 599-7388
Jiang Fan, *President*
Robert Spotnitz, *CTO*
▲ **EMP:** 15
SALES (est): 1.5MM **Privately Held**
SIC: 2819 3692 5063 Lithium compounds, inorganic; dry cell batteries, single or multiple cell; storage batteries, industrial

(P-7753)
BD BISCNCES SYSTEMS RGENTS INC
2350 Qume Dr, San Jose (95131-1812)
PHONE..................................408 518-5024
EMP: 103
SALES (corp-wide): 1.2MM **Privately Held**
SIC: 2819
PA: Bd Biosciences, Systems And Reagents, Inc.
1 Becton Dr
Franklin Lakes NJ 07417
201 847-6800

(P-7754)
BETTERBILT CHEMICALS
3137 E 26th St, Vernon (90058-8006)
PHONE..................................323 266-7111
Gayl Swinehart, *President*
Mona Swinehart, *Treasurer*
EMP: 10
SQ FT: 10,000
SALES: 800K **Privately Held**
SIC: 2819 Industrial inorganic chemicals

(P-7755)
BIOLARGO INC (PA)
Also Called: BIO2
14921 Chestnut St, Westminster (92683-5215)
P.O. Box 3950, Laguna Hills (92654-3950)
PHONE..................................949 643-9540
Dennis P Calvert, *Ch of Bd*
Charles K Dargan II, *CFO*
Joseph L Provenzano, *Vice Pres*
Kenneth R Code, *Security Dir*
EMP: 19
SQ FT: 9,000
SALES: 516.2K **Publicly Held**
SIC: 2819 Iodine, elemental

(P-7756)
CAL-PAC CHEMICAL CO INC
6231 Maywood Ave, Huntington Park (90255-4530)
PHONE..................................323 585-2178
Charles F Duane, *President*
EMP: 17
SQ FT: 37,000
SALES (est): 3.9MM **Privately Held**
SIC: 2819 Industrial inorganic chemicals

(P-7757)
CALGON CARBON CORPORATION
501 Hatchery Rd, Blue Lake (95525)
P.O. Box 857 (95525-0857)
PHONE..................................707 668-5637
Lee Brown, *Manager*
EMP: 13
SALES (corp-wide): 4.6B **Privately Held**
WEB: www.calgoncarbon.com
SIC: 2819 Charcoal (carbon), activated
HQ: Calgon Carbon Corporation
3000 Gsk Dr
Moon Township PA 15108
412 787-6700

(P-7758)
CALIFORNIA CARBON COMPANY INC
2825 E Grant St, Wilmington (90744-4033)
PHONE..................................562 436-1962
Franklin Liu, *President*
Rita L Wu, *Treasurer*
Richard Liu, *Vice Pres*
▲ **EMP:** 17 **EST:** 1962
SQ FT: 10,000
SALES (est): 3.5MM **Privately Held**
WEB: www.californiacarbon.com
SIC: 2819 Carbides

(P-7759)
CALIFORNIA SILICA PRODUCTS LLC
12808 Rancho Rd, Adelanto (92301-2719)
PHONE..................................909 947-0028
Randall Humphreys, *Branch Mgr*
EMP: 19
SALES (corp-wide): 866K **Privately Held**
SIC: 2819 Silica compounds
PA: California Silica Products, Llc
1420 S Bon View Ave
Ontario CA 91761
760 885-5358

(P-7760)
CALIFORNIA SULPHUR COMPANY
2250 E Pacific Coast Hwy, Wilmington (90744-2917)
P.O. Box 176 (90748-0176)
PHONE..................................562 437-0768
John Babbitt, *Principal*
▼ **EMP:** 28
SQ FT: 900
SALES (est): 6.4MM **Privately Held**
WEB: www.calsulco.com
SIC: 2819 Industrial inorganic chemicals

(P-7761)
CAR SOUND EXHAUST SYSTEM INC
Environmental Catalyst Tech
1901 Corporate Ctr, Oceanside (92056-5831)
PHONE..................................949 888-1625
Steve Kasprisin,
EMP: 20

(P-7762)
CARBOMER INC
6324 Ferris Sq Ste B, San Diego (92121-3238)
P.O. Box 261026 (92196-1026)
PHONE..................................858 552-0992
Manssur Yalpani, *President*
EMP: 85
SALES (est): 17.3K **Privately Held**
SIC: 2819 Industrial inorganic chemicals

(P-7763)
CDTI ADVANCED MATERIALS INC (PA)
1700 Fiske Pl, Oxnard (93033-1863)
PHONE..................................805 639-9458
Matthew Beale, *President*
Lon E Bell, *Ch of Bd*
Peter J Chase, *COO*
Tracy A Kern, *CFO*
Stephen J Golden, *Vice Pres*
EMP: 47
SQ FT: 52,000
SALES: 28.3MM **Publicly Held**
WEB: www.cdti.com
SIC: 2819 3823 Catalysts, chemical; industrial instrmnts msrmnt display/control process variable

(P-7764)
CHEMTRADE CHEMICALS US LLC
501 Nichols Rd, Bay Point (94565-1002)
PHONE..................................925 458-7300
Brad Klock, *General Mgr*
Kip Catanese, *Executive*
EMP: 30
SALES (corp-wide): 1.1B **Privately Held**
SIC: 2819 Industrial inorganic chemicals
HQ: Chemtrade Chemicals Us Llc
90 E Halsey Rd
Parsippany NJ 07054

(P-7765)
CHEMTRADE CHEMICALS US LLC
525 Castro St, Richmond (94801-2104)
PHONE..................................510 232-7193
Thomas Brafford, *Manager*
Larry Landry, *Executive*
Tom Bradford, *Plant Mgr*
Tom Bradford, *Plant Mgr*
EMP: 37
SALES (corp-wide): 1.1B **Privately Held**
SIC: 2819 Sulfuric acid, oleum
HQ: Chemtrade Chemicals Us Llc
90 E Halsey Rd
Parsippany NJ 07054

(P-7766)
CLEARCHEM DIAGNOSTICS INC
1710 E Grevillea Ct, Ontario (91761-8035)
PHONE..................................714 734-8041
Robert Stone, *President*
Kent Fleck, *Vice Pres*
EMP: 12
SQ FT: 12,000
SALES (est): 2.7MM **Privately Held**
SIC: 2819 3559 8711 Chemicals, reagent grade: refined from technical grade; chemical machinery & equipment; electrical or electronic engineering

(P-7767)
CRITERION CATALYSTS & TECH LP
2840 Willow Pass Rd, Bay Point (94565-3237)
P.O. Box 5159, Pittsburg (94565-0659)
PHONE..................................925 458-9045
William Howell, *Manager*
EMP: 100

SALES (corp-wide): 97.1MM **Privately Held**
SIC: 2819 Catalysts, chemical
PA: Car Sound Exhaust System, Inc.
1901 Corporate Ctr
Oceanside CA 92056
949 858-5900

SALES (corp-wide): 305.1B **Privately Held**
WEB: www.criterioncatalysts.com
SIC: 2819 Catalysts, chemical
HQ: Criterion Catalysts & Technologies L.P.
910 Louisiana St Ste 2900
Houston TX 77002
713 241-3000

(P-7768)
DOW CHEMICAL COMPANY
14445 Alondra Blvd, La Mirada (90638-5504)
PHONE..................................714 228-4700
Jim Ryan, *Branch Mgr*
EMP: 200
SQ FT: 29,287
SALES (corp-wide): 62.4B **Publicly Held**
SIC: 2819 2821 Industrial inorganic chemicals; plastics materials & resins
HQ: The Dow Chemical Company
25500 Whitesell St
Hayward CA 94545
510 786-0100

(P-7769)
DUPONT ELECTRONIC TECHNOLOGIES
2520 Barrington Ct, Hayward (94545-1133)
PHONE..................................510 784-9105
Ellen Kullman, *CEO*
Patricia Adamcek, *Pharmacy Dir*
John Nakanishi, *Engineer*
Eric Finson, *Mktg Dir*
▲ **EMP:** 11
SALES (est): 1.9MM **Privately Held**
SIC: 2819 Industrial inorganic chemicals

(P-7770)
ECO SERVICES OPERATIONS CORP
100 Mococo Rd, Martinez (94553-1314)
PHONE..................................925 313-8224
Darrel Hodge, *Plant Mgr*
Colby Fletcher, *Engineer*
James Jordan, *Engineer*
Jim Tatum, *Purchasing*
Ross Denicola, *Opers Mgr*
EMP: 42
SALES (corp-wide): 1.4B **Publicly Held**
WEB: www.food.us.rhodia.com
SIC: 2819 Sulfuric acid, oleum
HQ: Eco Services Operations Corp.
300 Lindenwood Dr
Malvern PA 19355
610 251-9118

(P-7771)
ECO SERVICES OPERATIONS CORP
20720 S Wilmington Ave, Long Beach (90810-1034)
PHONE..................................310 885-6719
Stephen Caro, *Branch Mgr*
EMP: 51
SALES (corp-wide): 1.4B **Publicly Held**
SIC: 2819 Sulfuric acid, oleum
HQ: Eco Services Operations Corp.
300 Lindenwood Dr
Malvern PA 19355
610 251-9118

(P-7772)
ELEMENT SIX TECH US CORP
3901 Burton Dr, Santa Clara (95054-1583)
PHONE..................................408 986-8184
Adrian Wilson, *President*
EMP: 17
SALES (est): 3.2MM **Privately Held**
SIC: 2819 Industrial inorganic chemicals
PA: Element Six Sa
Rue Charles Martel 58
Luxembourg
268 647-08

(P-7773)
ENKI TECHNOLOGY INC
1035 Walsh Ave, Santa Clara (95050-2645)
PHONE..................................408 383-9034
Kevin Kopczynski, *CEO*
Tom Colson, *COO*
Paul Kidman, *Vice Pres*
Brenor Brophy, *CTO*
Sina Maghsoodi, *Engineer*

P
R
O
D
U
C
T
S

&

S
V
C
S

▲ EMP: 13
SQ FT: 8,000
SALES (est): 2.4MM **Privately Held**
SIC: 2819 Silica compounds

(P-7774)
ENVIRNMENTAL CATALYST TECH LLC
3937 Ocean Ranch Blvd, Oceanside (92056-2670)
PHONE..................................949 459-3870
Steve Kasprisin,
Gennaro Paolone, *President*
Bindu Nair, *QC Mgr*
Kathy Paolone,
Laurie Paolone,
▲ EMP: 20
SALES (est): 5.8MM
SALES (corp-wide): 97.1MM **Privately Held**
SIC: 2819 Catalysts, chemical
PA: Car Sound Exhaust System, Inc.
1901 Corporate Ctr
Oceanside CA 92056
949 858-5900

(P-7775)
ERG AEROSPACE CORPORATION
Also Called: Erg Materials and Aerospace
964 Stanford Ave, Oakland (94608-2323)
PHONE..................................510 658-9785
Mitchell Hall, *CEO*
Evelyn Ford, *Director*
EMP: 70
SQ FT: 60,000
SALES (est): 6.8MM **Privately Held**
WEB: www.ergaerospace.com
SIC: 2819 Aluminum compounds

(P-7776)
ERNEST PACKAGING SOLUTIONS (PA)
2825 S Elm Ave Ste 103, Fresno (93706-5460)
PHONE..................................800 757-4968
Tim Wilson, *President*
A Charles Wilson, *Chairman*
Brian Porter, *Vice Pres*
Kenny Briggs, *General Mgr*
Edward Cho, *Manager*
EMP: 45
SQ FT: 50,000
SALES (est): 8.3MM **Privately Held**
SIC: 2819 5191 5087 Industrial inorganic chemicals; chemicals, agricultural; cleaning & maintenance equipment & supplies; janitors' supplies

(P-7777)
FERRO CORPORATION
1395 Aspen Way, Vista (92081-8350)
PHONE..................................442 224-6100
Mike Steele, *Manager*
EMP: 10
SALES (corp-wide): 1.4B **Publicly Held**
WEB: www.ferro.com
SIC: 2819 Industrial inorganic chemicals
PA: Ferro Corporation
6060 Parkland Blvd # 250
Mayfield Heights OH 44124
216 875-5600

(P-7778)
FLORIDE PRODUCTS LLC (PA)
2867 Vail Ave, Commerce (90040-2613)
PHONE..................................323 201-4363
EMP: 23
SALES (est): 19.1MM **Privately Held**
SIC: 2819

(P-7779)
GE-HITACHI NUCLEAR ENERGY
Also Called: GE Vallecitos Nuclear Center
6705 Vallecitos Rd, Sunol (94586-9524)
PHONE..................................925 862-4382
David Turner, *Manager*
EMP: 72
SALES (corp-wide): 122B **Publicly Held**
SIC: 2819 Nuclear fuel & cores, inorganic
HQ: Ge-Hitachi Nuclear Energy America Llc
3901 Castle Hayne Rd
Wilmington NC 28401

(P-7780)
HALDOR TOPSOE INC
Also Called: Refining Technology Division
770 The Cy Dr S Ste 8400, Orange (92868)
PHONE..................................714 621-3800
F Emmett Bingham, *President*
EMP: 10
SALES (corp-wide): 794.2MM **Privately Held**
SIC: 2819 8711 Catalysts, chemical; chemical engineering
HQ: Haldor Topsoe, Inc.
17629 El Cam
Houston TX 77058
281 228-5000

(P-7781)
HONEYWELL INTERNATIONAL INC
3500 Garrett Dr, Santa Clara (95054-2827)
PHONE..................................408 962-2000
Paul Raymond, *Vice Pres*
EMP: 100
SALES (corp-wide): 40.5B **Publicly Held**
WEB: www.honeywell.com
SIC: 2819 3674 Chemicals, reagent grade: refined from technical grade; semiconductors & related devices
PA: Honeywell International Inc.
115 Tabor Rd
Morris Plains NJ 07950
973 455-2000

(P-7782)
HYDRITE CHEMICAL CO
1603 Clancy Ct, Visalia (93291-9253)
PHONE..................................559 651-3450
Steve Reid, *Manager*
EMP: 25
SALES (corp-wide): 1B **Privately Held**
SIC: 2819 Industrial inorganic chemicals
PA: Hydrite Chemical Co.
300 N Patrick Blvd Fl 2
Brookfield WI 53045
262 792-1450

(P-7783)
JVIC CATALYST SERVICES LLC
18025 S Broadway, Carson (90745)
PHONE..................................310 327-0991
Rodney Woody, *Manager*
EMP: 40 **Privately Held**
WEB: www.cat-tech.com
SIC: 2819 Catalysts, chemical
HQ: Jvic Catalyst Services, Llc
4040 Red Bluff Rd
Pasadena TX 77503
713 568-2600

(P-7784)
KEMIRA WATER SOLUTIONS INC
14000 San Bernardino Ave, Fontana (92335-5258)
PHONE..................................909 350-5678
Keith Heasley, *Manager*
Adam Tonzi, *Regional Mgr*
Heriberto Barros, *Director*
EMP: 21
SALES (corp-wide): 2.9B **Privately Held**
WEB: www.kemiron.com
SIC: 2819 Industrial inorganic chemicals
HQ: Kemira Water Solutions, Inc.
1000 Parkwood Cir Se # 500
Atlanta GA 30339
770 436-1542

(P-7785)
MATERIA INC (PA)
60 N San Gabriel Blvd, Pasadena (91107-3748)
PHONE..................................626 584-8400
Christopher Murphy, *President*
Scott Krog, *CFO*
Mark S Trimmer, *Vice Pres*
Dr Richard L Pederson, *Research*
Dr Nicholas J Rodak, *Mfg Staff*
▲ EMP: 120
SQ FT: 30,000
SALES (est): 27.1MM **Privately Held**
WEB: www.materia-inc.com
SIC: 2819 Catalysts, chemical

(P-7786)
MATTERHORN FILTER CORPORATION
125 W Victoria St, Gardena (90248-3522)
PHONE..................................310 329-8073
Joseph Silva, *President*
▲ EMP: 11
SALES (est): 1.6MM **Privately Held**
SIC: 2819 Charcoal (carbon), activated

(P-7787)
MERELEX CORPORATION
Also Called: American Elements
10884 Weyburn Ave, Los Angeles (90024-2917)
PHONE..................................310 208-0551
Michael Silver, *President*
Gabriel Leis, *Buyer*
Brian Lim, *Opers Staff*
Laura Lovekin, *Marketing Staff*
Scott Michel, *Manager*
▲ EMP: 22 EST: 1996
SALES (est): 6.2MM **Privately Held**
SIC: 2819 Chemicals, high purity: refined from technical grade

(P-7788)
MONOLITH MATERIALS INC
1700 Seaport Blvd Ste 110, Redwood City (94063-5572)
PHONE..................................650 933-4957
Pete Johnson, *CEO*
Bill Brady, *Chairman*
Rob Hanson, *Officer*
Brian Allison, *Vice Pres*
Jose Bahury, *Vice Pres*
EMP: 26
SQ FT: 3,500
SALES (est): 10.8MM **Privately Held**
SIC: 2819 Chemicals, high purity: refined from technical grade

(P-7789)
MORAVEK BIOCHEMICALS INC (PA)
577 Mercury Ln, Brea (92821-4831)
PHONE..................................714 990-2018
Paul Moravek, *President*
Joseph Moravek, *President*
Helen Moravek, *Corp Secy*
Ivana Moravek, *Info Tech Mgr*
Daniel Retz, *Research*
▲ EMP: 25
SQ FT: 6,000
SALES (est): 4.1MM **Privately Held**
SIC: 2819 Industrial inorganic chemicals

(P-7790)
MORGAN ADVANCED CERAMICS INC
13079 Earhart Ave, Auburn (95602-9536)
PHONE..................................530 823-3401
John Stang, *CEO*
James A West, *President*
Chester Chiu, *Info Tech Mgr*
Frank Ravera, *Maintence Staff*
▲ EMP: 167
SQ FT: 80,000
SALES (est): 29.9MM
SALES (corp-wide): 1.3B **Privately Held**
SIC: 2819 3356 3264 Aluminum oxide; zirconium & zirconium alloy bars, sheets, strip, etc.; porcelain electrical supplies
HQ: Morganite Industries Inc.
4000 Westchase Blvd # 170
Raleigh NC 27607
919 821-1253

(P-7791)
NUGEN TECHNOLOGIES INC
900 Chesapeake Dr, Redwood City (94063-4727)
PHONE..................................650 590-3600
Nitin Sood, *CEO*
Dan Benetz, *CFO*
Nancy Pecota, *CFO*
Doug Amorese, *Officer*
Nurith Kurn, *Officer*
EMP: 22
SALES (est): 8.2MM **Privately Held**
WEB: www.nugeninc.com
SIC: 2819 Industrial inorganic chemicals

(P-7792)
OHP INC (DH)
4695 Macarthur Ct # 1200, Newport Beach (92660-1882)
P.O. Box 746, Bluffton SC (29910-0746)
PHONE..................................800 659-6745
Dan Stahl, *Vice Pres*
Terry Higgins, *VP Sales*
Ryan Boehm, *Marketing Mgr*
Tobey Barr, *Regl Sales Mgr*
EMP: 27
SQ FT: 2,000
SALES (est): 4.3MM
SALES (corp-wide): 355MM **Publicly Held**
WEB: www.ohp.com
SIC: 2819 Industrial inorganic chemicals
HQ: Amvac Chemical Corporation
4695 Macarthur Ct # 1200
Newport Beach CA 92660
323 264-3910

(P-7793)
OMYA CALIFORNIA INC
Also Called: O M Y A
7299 Crystal Creek Rd, Lucerne Valley (92356-8646)
PHONE..................................760 248-7306
Anthony Colak, *CEO*
James Reddy, *President*
James Rogers, *General Mgr*
Leonard Eisenberg, *Admin Sec*
Richard Bushart, *Technical Staff*
▲ EMP: 100
SQ FT: 6,000
SALES (est): 25MM
SALES (corp-wide): 3.9B **Privately Held**
SIC: 2819 8741 3281 Calcium compounds & salts, inorganic; management services; cut stone & stone products
HQ: Omya Industries, Inc
9987 Carver Rd Ste 300
Blue Ash OH 45242
513 387-4600

(P-7794)
OXBOW ACTIVATED CARBON LLC
2535 Jason Ct, Oceanside (92056-3592)
PHONE..................................760 630-5724
Mark McCormick, *Vice Pres*
EMP: 25
SALES (corp-wide): 602.2MM **Privately Held**
SIC: 2819 Charcoal (carbon), activated
HQ: Oxbow Activated Carbon Llc
1601 Forum Pl Ste 1400
West Palm Beach FL 33401
561 907-5400

(P-7795)
PCT-GW CARBIDE TOOLS USA INC
13701 Excelsior Dr, Santa Fe Springs (90670-5104)
PHONE..................................562 921-7898
Shamir Seth, *President*
▲ EMP: 50
SALES (est): 758.8K **Privately Held**
SIC: 2819 Carbides

(P-7796)
PERIMETER SOLUTIONS LP
Wildfire Control Division
10667 Jersey Blvd, Rancho Cucamonga (91730-5110)
PHONE..................................909 983-0772
Vinayak Sharma, *Manager*
Jeffrey L James, *Systems Mgr*
EMP: 20 **Privately Held**
SIC: 2819 Industrial inorganic chemicals
HQ: Perimeter Solutions Lp
373 Marshall Ave
Saint Louis MO 63119
314 983-7500

(P-7797)
PHIBRO-TECH INC
8851 Dice Rd, Santa Fe Springs (90670-2515)
PHONE..................................562 698-8036
Mark Alling, *Manager*
Alonso Alatorre, *Lab Dir*
Jeff Dorfman, *MIS Dir*
Jim Ferguson, *Maintence Staff*

▲ = Import ▼=Export
◆ =Import/Export

Jerry Mesinger, *Manager*
EMP: 50
SALES (corp-wide): 764.2MM **Publicly Held**
WEB: www.phibrochem.com
SIC: 2819 2899 Inorganic metal compounds or salts; chemical preparations
HQ: Phibro-Tech, Inc.
    300 Frank W Burr Blvd # 21
    Teaneck NJ 07666

(P-7798)
PICKERING LABORATORIES INC
1280 Space Park Way, Mountain View (94043-1434)
PHONE................................650 694-6700
Michael Pickering, *President*
James Murphy, *Vice Pres*
Jim Murphy, *Vice Pres*
Mike Gottschalk, *Principal*
David Mazawa, *Principal*
EMP: 22
SQ FT: 17,000
SALES (est): 6.5MM **Privately Held**
WEB: www.pickeringlabs.com
SIC: 2819 3826 2899 Chemicals, reagent grade; refined from technical grade; liquid chromatographic instruments; chemical preparations

(P-7799)
PQ CORPORATION
8401 Quartz Ave, South Gate (90280-2536)
PHONE................................323 326-1100
Jim Olivier, *Manager*
Maia A Hensley, *Administration*
Leanna Rudell, *Director*
Tim Olivier, *Manager*
EMP: 11
SALES (corp-wide): 1.4B **Publicly Held**
WEB: www.pqcorp.com
SIC: 2819 Industrial inorganic chemicals
HQ: Pq Corporation
    300 Lindenwood Dr
    Malvern PA 19355
    610 651-4200

(P-7800)
QUALITY CAR CARE PRODUCTS INC
2734 Huntington Dr, Duarte (91010-2301)
PHONE................................626 359-9174
Edward R Justice Jr, *President*
EMP: 30
SQ FT: 25,000
SALES (est): 6.2MM **Privately Held**
SIC: 2819 Industrial inorganic chemicals

(P-7801)
REAGENT CHEMICAL & RES INC
Also Called: White Fire Tagets
1454 S Sunnyside Ave, San Bernardino (92408-2810)
PHONE................................909 796-4059
Dan Sumnter, *Branch Mgr*
EMP: 20
SQ FT: 99,400
SALES (corp-wide): 375MM **Privately Held**
WEB: www.biotarget.com
SIC: 2819 3949 Sulfur, recovered or refined, incl. from sour natural gas; targets, archery & rifle shooting
PA: Reagent Chemical & Research, Inc.
    115 Rte 202
    Ringoes NJ 08551
    908 284-2800

(P-7802)
SHELL CHEMICAL LP
10 Mococo Rd, Martinez (94553-1340)
PHONE................................925 313-8601
Marj Leeds, *Manager*
EMP: 65
SALES (corp-wide): 305.1B **Privately Held**
SIC: 2819 Catalysts, chemical
HQ: Shell Chemical Lp
    910 Louisiana St
    Houston TX 77002
    855 697-4355

(P-7803)
SIGNA CHEMISTRY INC
720 Olive Dr Ste Cd, Davis (95616-4740)
PHONE................................212 933-4101
EMP: 25
SALES (corp-wide): 8.9MM **Privately Held**
SIC: 2819 3511
PA: Signa Chemistry, Inc.
    445 Park Ave Ste 937
    New York NY 10017
    212 933-4101

(P-7804)
SILA NANOTECHNOLOGIES INC
2450 Mariner Square Loop, Alameda (94501-1010)
PHONE................................408 475-7452
Gene Berdichevsky, *CEO*
Michelle Chang, *Administration*
Sergei Klochkov, *Research*
Justin Yen, *Engineer*
EMP: 23
SQ FT: 31,000
SALES (est): 5.4MM **Privately Held**
SIC: 2819 Industrial inorganic chemicals

(P-7805)
SMARTWASH SOLUTIONS LLC
1129 Harkins Rd, Salinas (93901-4407)
PHONE................................831 676-9750
Bruce Taylor,
▲ EMP: 15
SALES (est): 4.2MM **Privately Held**
SIC: 2819 Chemicals, high purity: refined from technical grade
PA: Taylor Fresh Foods, Inc
    150 Main St Ste 400
    Salinas CA 93901

(P-7806)
SOLVAY USA INC
Also Called: Marchem Solvay Group
20851 S Santa Fe Ave, Long Beach (90810-1130)
PHONE................................310 669-5300
Maria Johnson, *Manager*
EMP: 17
SALES (corp-wide): 10MM **Privately Held**
SIC: 2819 Industrial inorganic chemicals
HQ: Solvay Usa Inc.
    504 Carnegie Ctr
    Princeton NJ 08540
    609 860-4000

(P-7807)
TESSENDERLO KERLEY INC
5247 E Central Ave, Fresno (93725-9336)
PHONE................................559 485-0114
Vince Roggentine, *General Mgr*
EMP: 40
SALES (corp-wide): 449.8MM **Privately Held**
WEB: www.mprserve.com
SIC: 2819 Industrial inorganic chemicals
HQ: Tessenderlo Kerley, Inc.
    2255 N 44th St Ste 300
    Phoenix AZ 85008
    602 889-8300

(P-7808)
TIGER-SUL PRODUCTS LLC
61 Stork Rd, Stockton (95203-8200)
PHONE................................209 451-2725
EMP: 13 EST: 2008
SALES (est): 3MM **Privately Held**
SIC: 2819 Industrial inorganic chemicals

(P-7809)
TOKYO OHKA KOGYO AMERICA INC
Also Called: Tok America
190 Topaz St, Milpitas (95035-5429)
PHONE................................408 956-9901
Yoshi Arai, *Manager*
EMP: 13
SQ FT: 12,560
SALES (corp-wide): 824.7MM **Privately Held**
WEB: www.ohka.com
SIC: 2819 3674 Industrial inorganic chemicals; semiconductors & related devices

HQ: Tokyo Ohka Kogyo America, Inc.
    4600 Ne Brookwood Pkwy
    Hillsboro OR 97124

(P-7810)
US BORAX INC
14486 Borax Rd, Boron (93516-2017)
PHONE................................760 762-7000
Joe A Carrabba, *Branch Mgr*
Doug Batchelor, *MIS Dir*
Saman Naerges, *Analyst*
Tod Jones, *Production*
EMP: 900
SALES (corp-wide): 40B **Privately Held**
WEB: www.borax.com
SIC: 2819 Industrial inorganic chemicals
HQ: U.S. Borax Inc.
    8051 E Maplewood Ave # 100
    Greenwood Village CO 80111
    303 713-5000

(P-7811)
US BORAX INC
300 Falcon St, Wilmington (90744-6407)
PHONE................................310 522-5300
Robert F Shaw, *President*
EMP: 182
SALES (corp-wide): 40B **Privately Held**
WEB: www.borax.com
SIC: 2819 2899 Industrial inorganic chemicals; chemical preparations
HQ: U.S. Borax Inc.
    8051 E Maplewood Ave # 100
    Greenwood Village CO 80111
    303 713-5000

(P-7812)
VACUUM ENGRG & MTLS CO INC
390 Reed St, Santa Clara (95050-3108)
PHONE................................408 871-9900
John S Kavanaugh Jr, *Ch of Bd*
Robert T Kavanaugh, *President*
Stephanie McConnell, *CFO*
EMP: 30
SQ FT: 16,500
SALES (est): 8.4MM **Privately Held**
WEB: www.vem-co.com
SIC: 2819 3399 3499 Chemicals, high purity: refined from technical grade; powder, metal; friction material, made from powdered metal

(P-7813)
VENUS LABORATORIES INC
Earth Friendly Products
11150 Hope St, Cypress (90630-5236)
PHONE................................714 891-3100
Firas Jamal, *Manager*
Mike Palmatier, *CFO*
Adelisa Robles, *Officer*
Jesse Herrera, *Office Admin*
Belinda Diaz, *Purch Agent*
EMP: 70
SALES (corp-wide): 83MM **Privately Held**
SIC: 2819 2844 2842 2841 Industrial inorganic chemicals; toilet preparations; specialty cleaning, polishes & sanitation goods; soap & other detergents
PA: Venus Laboratories, Inc.
    111 S Rohlwing Rd
    Addison IL 60101
    630 595-1900

(P-7814)
W R GRACE & CO
Also Called: W R Grace Construction Pdts
7237 E Gage Ave, Commerce (90040-3812)
PHONE................................562 927-8513
Suzanne Parsons, *Manager*
EMP: 15
SQ FT: 18,595
SALES (corp-wide): 1.7B **Publicly Held**
WEB: www.grace.com
SIC: 2819 Industrial inorganic chemicals
PA: W. R. Grace & Co.
    7500 Grace Dr
    Columbia MD 21044
    410 531-4000

(P-7815)
W R GRACE & CO
252 W Larch Rd Ste H, Tracy (95304-1638)
PHONE................................209 839-2800
EMP: 164
SALES (corp-wide): 3.1B **Publicly Held**
SIC: 2819
PA: W. R. Grace & Co.
    7500 Grace Dr
    Columbia MD 21044
    410 531-4000

(P-7816)
ZI CHEMICALS
8605 Santa Monica Blvd, Los Angeles (90069-4109)
PHONE................................818 827-1301
Barnaby L Zelman, *Owner*
▼ EMP: 11
SALES (est): 1.3MM **Privately Held**
WEB: www.zichemicals.com
SIC: 2819 Industrial inorganic chemicals

2821 Plastics, Mtrls & Nonvulcanizable Elastomers

(P-7817)
ACP NOXTAT INC
1112 E Washington Ave, Santa Ana (92701-4221)
PHONE................................714 547-5477
Anthony Floyd Richard, *President*
Tracee Huwe, *COO*
EMP: 20
SALES (est): 4.5MM **Privately Held**
WEB: www.noxtat.com
SIC: 2821 Plastics materials & resins

(P-7818)
ALPHA CORPORATION OF TENNESSEE
Also Called: Alpha-Owens Corning
19991 Seaton Ave, Perris (92570-8724)
PHONE................................951 657-5161
John Mulrine, *Enginr/R&D Mgr*
EMP: 60
SALES (corp-wide): 296.8MM **Privately Held**
WEB: www.glasteel.com
SIC: 2821 Polyethylene resins
PA: The Alpha Corporation Of Tennessee
    955 Highway 57
    Collierville TN 38017
    901 854-2800

(P-7819)
AMERICAN LIQUID PACKAGING SYST (PA)
Also Called: Chemtex International
440 N Wolfe Rd, Sunnyvale (94085-3869)
PHONE................................408 524-7474
Saeed Amidhozour, *President*
Rahim Amidhozour, *CFO*
▼ EMP: 40
SQ FT: 25,000
SALES (est): 117.8MM **Privately Held**
SIC: 2821 Plastics materials & resins

(P-7820)
APTCO LLC
31381 Pond Rd Bldg 2, Mc Farland (93250-9795)
PHONE................................661 792-2107
Jim Banuelos, *Mng Member*
Scott Hakl,
▼ EMP: 100
SALES (est): 23.4MM **Privately Held**
WEB: www.aptcollc.com
SIC: 2821 Thermoplastic materials

(P-7821)
BAMBERGER POLYMERS INC
145 S State College Blvd # 100, Brea (92821-5824)
PHONE................................714 672-4740
Chris Landis, *Branch Mgr*
EMP: 10 **Privately Held**
WEB: www.bambergerpolymers.com
SIC: 2821 Plastics materials & resins

HQ: Bamberger Polymers, Inc.
2 Jericho Plz Ste 109
Jericho NY 11753

(P-7822)
BD CLASSIC ENTERPRIZES INC
12903 Sunshine Ave, Santa Fe Springs (90670-4732)
P.O. Box 2445 (90670-0445)
PHONE..................562 944-6177
Fred S Benson, *CEO*
Frederick Benson, *Info Tech Dir*
▲ EMP: 16
SQ FT: 15,000
SALES (est): 6.9MM **Privately Held**
WEB: www.bdcepoxysystems.com
SIC: 2821 Epoxy resins

(P-7823)
BJB ENTERPRISES INC
14791 Franklin Ave, Tustin (92780-7215)
PHONE..................714 734-8450
Brian Stransky, *President*
Troy Peterson, *Technical Staff*
Joel Severin, *Technical Staff*
Michael Richard, *Marketing Staff*
Theresa Jeffers,
EMP: 27
SQ FT: 38,000
SALES (est): 7.1MM **Privately Held**
WEB: www.bjbenterprises.com
SIC: 2821 3087 5162 Polyurethane resins; custom compound purchased resins; plastics materials & basic shapes

(P-7824)
COASTAL ENTERPRISES
1925 W Collins Ave, Orange (92867-5426)
P.O. Box 4875 (92863-4875)
PHONE..................714 771-4969
Chuck Miller, *Owner*
Sheila Miller, *General Mgr*
Krystle Rhodes, *Office Admin*
Kristin Love, *Admin Sec*
Chip Going, *Technical Staff*
▲ EMP: 20
SQ FT: 25,000
SALES (est): 3.5MM **Privately Held**
WEB: www.precisionboard.com
SIC: 2821 Plastics materials & resins

(P-7825)
COSMIC PLASTICS INC (PA)
28410 Industry Dr, Valencia (91355-4108)
PHONE..................661 257-3274
George Luh, *CEO*
Edwin Luh, *Vice Pres*
Eddie Cantrell, *Manager*
◆ EMP: 30
SQ FT: 846,000
SALES: 5MM **Privately Held**
WEB: www.cosmicplastics.com
SIC: 2821 Plastics materials & resins

(P-7826)
CP FILMS INC
Also Called: Cpfilms Distribution Center
4110 E La Palma Ave, Anaheim (92807-1814)
PHONE..................714 634-0900
Greg McKay, *Branch Mgr*
EMP: 20 **Publicly Held**
SIC: 2821 Plastics materials & resins
HQ: Cp Films Inc
4210 The Great Rd
Fieldale VA 24089
276 627-3000

(P-7827)
CROSSFIELD PRODUCTS CORP (PA)
Also Called: Dex-O-Tex Division
3000 E Harcourt St, Compton (90221-5589)
PHONE..................310 886-9100
Richard Watt, *Ch of Bd*
W Brad Watt, *President*
Ronald Borum, *Exec VP*
▲ EMP: 95
SQ FT: 23,000
SALES (est): 28.8MM **Privately Held**
WEB: www.crossfieldproducts.com
SIC: 2821 Plastics materials & resins

(P-7828)
CYTEC ENGINEERED MATERIALS INC
1191 N Hawk Cir, Anaheim (92807-1723)
PHONE..................714 632-8444
George Slayton, *Branch Mgr*
EMP: 20
SALES (corp-wide): 10MM **Privately Held**
WEB: www.cytecengineeredmaterials.com
SIC: 2821 2822 Plastics materials & resins; synthetic rubber
HQ: Cytec Engineered Materials Inc.
2085 E Tech Cir Ste 300
Tempe AZ 85284

(P-7829)
CYTEC ENGINEERED MATERIALS INC
645 N Cypress St, Orange (92867-6603)
PHONE..................714 630-9400
Ron Martin, *Branch Mgr*
Rechelle Swing, *Admin Asst*
Manuel Duchement, *Technology*
Paul Pleskacz, *Manager*
EMP: 130
SQ FT: 300,000
SALES (corp-wide): 10MM **Privately Held**
WEB: www.cytecengineeredmaterials.com
SIC: 2821 Molding compounds, plastics
HQ: Cytec Engineered Materials Inc.
2085 E Tech Cir Ste 300
Tempe AZ 85284

(P-7830)
DOW CHEMICAL COMPANY
901 Loveridge Rd, Pittsburg (94565-2811)
P.O. Box 1398 (94565-0398)
PHONE..................925 432-3165
Larry Reeves, *Branch Mgr*
EMP: 75
SQ FT: 17,280
SALES (corp-wide): 62.4B **Publicly Held**
WEB: www.dow.com
SIC: 2821 2879 2851 Thermoplastic materials; agricultural chemicals; paints & allied products
HQ: The Dow Chemical Company
2211 H H Dow Way
Midland MI 48642
989 636-1000

(P-7831)
DOW CHEMICAL INTERNATIONAL
11266 Jersey Blvd, Rancho Cucamonga (91730-5114)
P.O. Box 748 (91729-0748)
PHONE..................909 987-6261
Steve Rynders, *Principal*
EMP: 36
SALES (corp-wide): 62.4B **Publicly Held**
SIC: 2821 Thermoplastic materials
HQ: The Dow Chemical Company Foundation
2030 Dow Ctr
Midland MI 48674
989 636-1000

(P-7832)
EEZER PRODUCTS INC
4734 E Home Ave, Fresno (93703-4509)
PHONE..................559 255-4140
Leighton Sjostrand, *President*
Cyndi Alcoser, *Vice Pres*
▲ EMP: 21
SQ FT: 20,000
SALES: 1.8MM **Privately Held**
WEB: www.eezer.com
SIC: 2821 Plastics materials & resins

(P-7833)
ELASCO INC
Also Called: E Sales
11377 Markon Dr, Garden Grove (92841-1402)
PHONE..................714 373-4767
Henry Larrucea, *President*
David Schindler, *President*
Gary Stull, *CFO*
Janet Lurrucea, *Vice Pres*
▲ EMP: 100

SQ FT: 28,000
SALES (est): 20.6MM **Privately Held**
WEB: www.elascourethane.com
SIC: 2821 2891 2822 Polyurethane resins; adhesives & sealants; synthetic rubber

(P-7834)
ELITE GLOBAL SOLUTIONS INC
19732 Descartes, Foothill Ranch (92610-2621)
PHONE..................949 709-4872
Garry Mazzone, *President*
Christine Mazzone, *Treasurer*
Alexis Morgan, *Creative Dir*
Tracie Mazzone, *Project Mgr*
Rhett Boyer, *Purchasing*
◆ EMP: 14
SALES (est): 3.7MM **Privately Held**
SIC: 2821 5023 Melamine resins, melamine-formaldehyde; kitchenware

(P-7835)
ENVIRONMENTAL TECHNOLOGY INC
300 S Bay Depot Rd, Fields Landing (95537)
P.O. Box 365 (95537-0365)
PHONE..................707 443-9323
David C Fonsen, *President*
Deborah Fonsen, *Treasurer*
Carol Miller, *Office Mgr*
Andrew Cranfill, *Production*
◆ EMP: 25
SQ FT: 3,000
SALES (est): 6.9MM **Privately Held**
WEB: www.eti-usa.com
SIC: 2821 Thermoplastic materials

(P-7836)
FARAD INDUSTRIES INC
20435 Gramercy Pl Ste 104, Torrance (90501-1536)
PHONE..................310 320-4260
Frederick F Bayer, *President*
Judith H Bayer, *Admin Sec*
EMP: 10
SQ FT: 6,000
SALES: 500K **Privately Held**
WEB: www.faradindustries.com
SIC: 2821 Elastomers, nonvulcanizable (plastics)

(P-7837)
FERCO COLOR INC
Also Called: Ferco Plastic Products
5498 Vine St, Chino (91710-5247)
PHONE..................909 548-2092
Jennifer Thaw, *President*
Barbara Roepke, *Vice Pres*
EMP: 48
SQ FT: 20,000
SALES: 16.9MM **Privately Held**
WEB: www.fercocolor.com
SIC: 2821 2865 Polyethylene resins; polypropylene resins; color pigments, organic

(P-7838)
HENNIS ENTERPRISES INC
2646 Palma Dr Ste 430, Ventura (93003-7798)
PHONE..................805 477-0257
Rodney Hennis, *President*
Christopher Hennis, *Treasurer*
EMP: 20 EST: 1975
SQ FT: 10,000
SALES (est): 3.6MM **Privately Held**
WEB: www.hennisenterprises.com
SIC: 2821 Polyurethane resins

(P-7839)
HOFFMAN PLASTIC COMPOUNDS INC
16616 Garfield Ave, Paramount (90723-5305)
PHONE..................323 636-3346
Ronald P Hoffman, *President*
Susan Hoffman, *Corp Secy*
Larry Czyz, *Plant Mgr*
▲ EMP: 66
SQ FT: 46,000
SALES (est): 18.9MM **Privately Held**
SIC: 2821 3087 Polyvinyl chloride resins (PVC); custom compound purchased resins

(P-7840)
HUNTSMAN ADVANCED MATERIALS AM
5121 W San Fernando Rd, Los Angeles (90039-1011)
PHONE..................818 265-7221
Glenn Bauernschmidt, *Manager*
Marlene Stirbys, *Vice Pres*
Maggie Escriva, *Office Mgr*
Gary Chapman, *Director*
Paul Hu, *Manager*
EMP: 120
SALES (corp-wide): 8.3B **Publicly Held**
SIC: 2821 Plastics materials & resins
HQ: Huntsman Advanced Materials Americas Llc
10003 Woodloch Forest Dr # 260
The Woodlands TX 77380
281 719-6000

(P-7841)
INDUSPAC CALIFORNIA INC
Also Called: Pacific Foam
1550 Champagne Ave, Ontario (91761-3600)
PHONE..................909 390-4422
Keith Tatum, *General Mgr*
EMP: 11 **Privately Held**
SIC: 2821 Polyethylene resins
HQ: Induspac California, Inc.
21062 Forbes Ave
Hayward CA 94545

(P-7842)
INDUSPAC CALIFORNIA INC (HQ)
Also Called: Western Foam
21062 Forbes Ave, Hayward (94545-1116)
PHONE..................510 324-3626
John McAuslan, *CEO*
EMP: 46
SQ FT: 200,000
SALES (est): 10.3MM **Privately Held**
WEB: www.macfarlanegroup.net
SIC: 2821 Polyethylene resins
PA: Groupe Emballage Specialise S.E.C.
1805 50e Av
Lachine QC H8T 3
514 636-7951

(P-7843)
INTERPLASTIC CORPORATION
Also Called: Silmar Division
12335 S Van Ness Ave, Hawthorne (90250-3320)
PHONE..................323 757-1801
Doug Johnson, *Branch Mgr*
EMP: 50
SQ FT: 56,425
SALES (corp-wide): 272.6MM **Privately Held**
WEB: www.interplastic.com
SIC: 2821 5169 Plastics materials & resins; synthetic resins, rubber & plastic materials
PA: Interplastic Corporation
1225 Willow Lake Blvd
Saint Paul MN 55110
651 481-6860

(P-7844)
INTERPLASTIC CORPORATION
Also Called: North American Composites
611 Gilmore Ave Ste C, Stockton (95203-4910)
PHONE..................209 932-0396
Jeremy Locke, *Manager*
EMP: 10
SALES (corp-wide): 272.6MM **Privately Held**
WEB: www.interplastic.com
SIC: 2821 Plastics materials & resins
PA: Interplastic Corporation
1225 Willow Lake Blvd
Saint Paul MN 55110
651 481-6860

(P-7845)
IPP PLASTICS PRODUCTS INC
4610 Littlejohn St, Baldwin Park (91706-2267)
PHONE..................626 357-1178
Russell Wayne King, *President*
EMP: 10

SALES (est): 931.5K **Privately Held**
SIC: 2821 Molding compounds, plastics

(P-7846)
ITW PLYMERS SALANTS N AMER INC
Pacific Polymers
12271 Monarch St, Garden Grove
(92841-2906)
PHONE....................714 898-0025
Robert Seiple, *Branch Mgr*
EMP: 25
SALES (corp-wide): 14.3B **Publicly Held**
SIC: 2821 2822 2851 2891 Plastics materials & resins; synthetic rubber; paints & allied products; adhesives & sealants; asphalt felts & coatings
HQ: Itw Polymers Sealants North America Inc.
111 S Nursery Rd
Irving TX 75060
972 438-9111

(P-7847)
IVEX PROTECTIVE PACKAGING INC
Also Called: IVEX Ontario
1550 Champagne Ave, Ontario
(91761-3600)
PHONE....................909 390-4422
Steve Darby, *General Mgr*
EMP: 29 **Privately Held**
SIC: 2821 Polyethylene resins
HQ: Ivex Protective Packaging Inc.
2600 Campbell Rd
Sidney OH 45365
937 498-9298

(P-7848)
J-M MANUFACTURING COMPANY INC
Also Called: JM Eagle
23711 Rider St, Perris (92570-7114)
PHONE....................951 657-7400
Robert Johnson, *Manager*
EMP: 70
SALES (corp-wide): 1B **Privately Held**
SIC: 2821 Polyvinyl chloride resins (PVC)
PA: J-M Manufacturing Company, Inc.
5200 W Century Blvd
Los Angeles CA 90045
800 621-4404

(P-7849)
J-M MANUFACTURING COMPANY INC
10990 Hemlock Ave, Fontana
(92337-7250)
PHONE....................909 822-3009
Stephen Yang, *Manager*
Sharon Steuck, *Human Res Dir*
EMP: 84
SQ FT: 72,000
SALES (corp-wide): 1B **Privately Held**
SIC: 2821 3084 5051 3085 Polyvinyl chloride resins (PVC); plastics pipe; pipe & tubing, steel; plastics bottles
PA: J-M Manufacturing Company, Inc.
5200 W Century Blvd
Los Angeles CA 90045
800 621-4404

(P-7850)
J-M MANUFACTURING COMPANY INC
1051 Sperry Rd, Stockton (95206-3931)
PHONE....................209 982-1500
David Chen, *Manager*
Jaime Ramirez, *Executive*
EMP: 110
SALES (corp-wide): 1B **Privately Held**
SIC: 2821 3084 Polyvinyl chloride resins (PVC); plastics pipe
PA: J-M Manufacturing Company, Inc.
5200 W Century Blvd
Los Angeles CA 90045
800 621-4404

(P-7851)
K C A ENGINEERED PLASTICS INC (PA)
580 California St Ste 22, San Francisco
(94104-1000)
PHONE....................415 433-4494
C Sedgwick Dienst, *CEO*

Sedgwick Dienst, *CEO*
EMP: 100
SQ FT: 32,000
SALES (est): 6.2MM **Privately Held**
SIC: 2821 3089 Plastics materials & resins; injection molding of plastics

(P-7852)
KURARAY AMERICA INC
2 Park Plz Ste 480, Irvine (92614-3512)
PHONE....................949 476-9600
EMP: 18
SALES (corp-wide): 4.6B **Privately Held**
SIC: 2821 Vinyl resins
HQ: Kuraray America, Inc.
2625 Bay Area Blvd # 600
Houston TX 77058

(P-7853)
MADESOLID INC
2340 Powell St 298, Emeryville
(94608-1738)
PHONE....................510 858-5567
Lance Pickens, *CEO*
EMP: 10
SALES (est): 1.6MM **Privately Held**
SIC: 2821 Plastics materials & resins

(P-7854)
MAPEI CORPORATION
5415 Industrial Pkwy, San Bernardino
(92407-1803)
PHONE....................909 475-4100
Jose Granillo, *Manager*
Ron Pickinpaugh, *Purch Mgr*
EMP: 40 **Privately Held**
SIC: 2821 Acrylic resins
HQ: Mapei Corporation
1144 E Newport Center Dr
Deerfield Beach FL 33442
954 246-8888

(P-7855)
MOLDING ACQUISITION CORP
Also Called: Rotoplas
2651 Cooper Ave, Merced (95348-4315)
PHONE....................209 723-5000
Juan Negrete, *Branch Mgr*
EMP: 15 **Privately Held**
SIC: 2821 Molding compounds, plastics
HQ: Molding Acquisition Corp.
685 John B Sias Mem
Fort Worth TX 76134
209 723-5000

(P-7856)
NATURAL ENVMTL PROTECTION CO
Also Called: Nepco
750 S Reservoir St, Pomona (91766-3815)
PHONE....................909 620-8028
Young Su Shin, *President*
▲ EMP: 31
SQ FT: 3,600
SALES (est): 6.8MM
SALES (corp-wide): 2.3MM **Privately Held**
SIC: 2821 Polystyrene resins
PA: Gum Sung Industry Co., Ltd.
57-6 Gubong-Gil, Donghwa-Myeon
Jangseong 57242
826 139-2966

(P-7857)
NEW TECHNOLOGY PLASTICS INC
12989 Los Nietos Rd, Santa Fe Springs
(90670-3011)
PHONE....................562 941-6034
Gregory A Nelson, *President*
EMP: 35
SQ FT: 8,700
SALES (est): 9MM **Privately Held**
SIC: 2821 5162 Molding compounds, plastics; plastics materials & basic shapes

(P-7858)
NO LIFT NAILS INC
3211 S Shannon St, Santa Ana
(92704-6352)
PHONE....................714 897-0070
Laurence H Gaertner, *President*
Thomas A Gaertner, *Vice Pres*
EMP: 12

SALES (est): 1MM **Privately Held**
WEB: www.noliftnails.com
SIC: 2821 2844 Acrylic resins; manicure preparations

(P-7859)
NORTH AMERICAN COMPOSITES CO
Also Called: Interplastic
4990 Vanderbilt St, Ontario (91761-2202)
PHONE....................909 605-8977
Mark Prost, *Vice Pres*
David Englesgard, *Vice Pres*
ARA Berberian, *Sales Staff*
▲ EMP: 20
SALES (est): 2.3MM **Privately Held**
SIC: 2821 Plastics materials & resins

(P-7860)
NORTH AMRCN SPECIALTY PDTS LLC
300 S Beckman Rd, Lodi (95240-3103)
PHONE....................209 365-7500
Joseph Bondi,
EMP: 11 **Publicly Held**
SIC: 2821 Plastics materials & resins
HQ: North American Specialty Products Llc
993 Old Eagle School Rd
Wayne PA 19087
484 253-4545

(P-7861)
NUSIL TECHNOLOGY LLC
Also Called: Nusil Silicone Technology
1000 Cindy Ln, Carpinteria (93013-2906)
PHONE....................805 684-8780
Giavonnie Jones, *Manager*
Dawn Powered, *Human Res Dir*
Evan Jenkins, *Associate*
EMP: 100
SALES (corp-wide): 574.8MM **Privately Held**
SIC: 2821 Silicone resins
HQ: Nusil Technology Llc
1050 Cindy Ln
Carpinteria CA 93013
805 684-8780

(P-7862)
ORION PLASTICS CORPORATION
700 W Carob St, Compton (90220-5225)
PHONE....................310 223-0370
Patricia Conkling, *Principal*
Wayne Moore, *Business Dir*
Luis Suarez, *Plant Mgr*
Daniel Gitzke, *Accounts Mgr*
▲ EMP: 75 EST: 2000
SQ FT: 60,000
SALES: 26MM **Privately Held**
WEB: www.orionplastics.net
SIC: 2821 Plastics materials & resins

(P-7863)
PACTIV PACKAGING INC (DH)
Also Called: Pwp
3751 Seville Ave, Vernon (90058-1741)
PHONE....................323 513-9000
Ira Maroofion, *President*
Peter J Lazaredes, *President*
John Morrison, *Info Tech Dir*
David Bents, *Purchasing*
◆ EMP: 66
SALES (est): 65.8MM **Privately Held**
WEB: www.pwpc.com
SIC: 2821 Plastics materials & resins
HQ: Pactiv Llc
1900 W Field Ct
Lake Forest IL 60045
847 482-2000

(P-7864)
PERFORMANCE MATERIALS CORP (PA)
Also Called: Tencate Performance Composite
1150 Calle Suerte, Camarillo (93012-8051)
PHONE....................805 482-1722
Thomas W Smith, *President*
Marty Ramirez, *Vice Pres*
Mark Lang, *General Mgr*
Michelle Larios, *Admin Asst*
Niran Perera, *Engineer*
▲ EMP: 100
SQ FT: 50,000

SALES (est): 22.8MM **Privately Held**
WEB: www.performancematerials.com
SIC: 2821 Plastics materials & resins

(P-7865)
PHARMAPACK NORTH AMERICA CORP
5095 E Airport Dr, Ontario (91761-4701)
PHONE....................909 390-1888
Xianjun Qi, *President*
Douglas Powanda, *Vice Pres*
▲ EMP: 10 EST: 2014
SQ FT: 10,000
SALES (est): 2.1MM
SALES (corp-wide): 29.5MM **Privately Held**
SIC: 2821 5162 Plastics materials & resins; plastics materials & basic shapes
PA: Pharmapack Technologies Corporation
No.16,Huangqishan Rd,Yonghe Economic Zone, Getdd
Guangzhou 51135
208 222-0577

(P-7866)
PLASKOLITE WEST LLC
Also Called: Plaskolite West, Inc.
2225 E Del Amo Blvd, Compton
(90220-6303)
PHONE....................310 637-2103
Mitch Grindley, *President*
Rick Larkin, *CFO*
▲ EMP: 30
SALES (est): 11.9MM
SALES (corp-wide): 201.1MM **Privately Held**
SIC: 2821 Acrylic resins
PA: Plaskolite, Llc
400 W Nationwide Blvd # 400
Columbus OH 43215
614 294-3281

(P-7867)
PLASTIC MART INC
43535 Gadsden Ave Ste F, Lancaster
(93534-6147)
PHONE....................310 268-1404
James Nahigian, *President*
Ralph Kafesjian, *Vice Pres*
Gary Phillips, *Admin Sec*
EMP: 30
SALES (est): 4.7MM **Privately Held**
WEB: www.plasticmart.net
SIC: 2821 5211 5162 Plastics materials & resins; lumber & other building materials; plastics materials & basic shapes

(P-7868)
PLEXI FAB INC
1142 E Elm Ave, Fullerton (92831-5024)
PHONE....................714 447-8494
Abol Fazli, *President*
Mike Hall, *President*
Venis Hall, *Vice Pres*
◆ EMP: 17
SQ FT: 20,000
SALES (est): 2.6MM **Privately Held**
WEB: www.plexifab.com
SIC: 2821 Plastics materials & resins

(P-7869)
POLY PROCESSING COMPANY LLC
8055 Ash St, French Camp (95231-9667)
PHONE....................209 982-4904
Dixon Abell, *President*
EMP: 279
SQ FT: 75,000
SALES (est): 35.2MM
SALES (corp-wide): 297.4MM **Privately Held**
SIC: 2821 3443 Molding compounds, plastics; fabricated plate work (boiler shop)
PA: Abell Corporation
2500 Sterlington Rd
Monroe LA 71203
318 343-7565

(P-7870)
POLYNT COMPOSITES USA INC
2801 Lynwood Rd, Lynwood (90262-4009)
PHONE....................310 886-1070
Jason Webb, *Branch Mgr*
Michael Gardea, *Manager*
EMP: 12

SALES (corp-wide): 1.3B **Privately Held**
SIC: 2821 Plastics materials & resins
HQ: Polynt Composites Usa Inc.
99 E Cottage Ave
Carpentersville IL 60110

(P-7871)
POLYONE CORPORATION
2104 E 223rd St, Carson (90810-1611)
P.O. Box 9077, Long Beach (90810-0077)
PHONE...................................310 513-7100
Rod Myers, *Branch Mgr*
EMP: 60 **Publicly Held**
WEB: www.polyone.com
SIC: 2821 Polyvinyl chloride resins (PVC);
vinyl resins
PA: Polyone Corporation
33587 Walker Rd
Avon Lake OH 44012

(P-7872)
POLYONE CORPORATION
11400 Newport Dr Ste A, Rancho Cuca-
monga (91730-5511)
PHONE...................................909 987-0253
Tim Lee, *Manager*
EMP: 40 **Publicly Held**
WEB: www.polyone.com
SIC: 2821 Plastics materials & resins
PA: Polyone Corporation
33587 Walker Rd
Avon Lake OH 44012

(P-7873)
POLYVISION INC (PA)
Also Called: Polycore Optical - USA
9830 Norwalk Blvd Ste 174, Santa Fe
Springs (90670-6115)
PHONE...................................562 944-3924
Chris Soenarjo Jangus, *President*
Hashim Osman, *Admin Sec*
▲ EMP: 24
SQ FT: 45,000
SALES (est): 5.3MM **Privately Held**
WEB: www.polycore-usa.com
SIC: 2821 5049 Polycarbonate resins; op-
tical goods

(P-7874)
PPG ARCHITECTURAL FINISHES INC
Also Called: Glidden Professional Paint Ctr
4388 Vandever Ave, San Diego
(92120-3314)
PHONE...................................619 284-2772
Darin Persinger, *Manager*
EMP: 19
SALES (corp-wide): 14.7B **Publicly Held**
WEB: www.gliddenpaint.com
SIC: 2821 Acrylic resins
HQ: Ppg Architectural Finishes, Inc.
1 Ppg Pl
Pittsburgh PA 15272
412 434-3131

(P-7875)
PPP LLC
5991 Alcoa Ave, Vernon (90058-3920)
PHONE...................................323 581-6058
Tim Guth,
EMP: 10
SQ FT: 81,000
SALES (est): 1.4MM **Privately Held**
SIC: 2821 Polyethylene resins

(P-7876)
PRIME CONDUIT INC
1776 E Beamer St, Woodland
(95776-6218)
PHONE...................................530 669-0160
Tom Godosky, *Branch Mgr*
EMP: 27 **Privately Held**
SIC: 2821 Polyvinyl chloride resins (PVC)
PA: Prime Conduit, Inc.
23240 Chagrin Blvd # 405
Beachwood OH 44122

(P-7877)
QUALITY IMAGE INC
15130 Illinois Ave, Paramount
(90723-4107)
PHONE...................................562 259-9872

Susie Alofaituli, *President*
Robert Cabrera, *Vice Pres*
Roberto Cabrera, *Vice Pres*
EMP: 20
SQ FT: 9,000
SALES (est): 1.8MM **Privately Held**
WEB: www.qualityimageinc.com
SIC: 2821 Plastics materials & resins

(P-7878)
R K FABRICATION INC
1283 N Grove St, Anaheim (92806-2114)
PHONE...................................714 630-9654
Roger King, *CEO*
Sarah King, *Treasurer*
EMP: 18
SQ FT: 10,000
SALES (est): 4.8MM **Privately Held**
WEB: www.rkfabrication.com
SIC: 2821 3714 1799 Plastics materials &
resins; exhaust systems & parts, motor
vehicle; fiberglass work

(P-7879)
REICHHOLD INDUSTRIES INC
Also Called: Reichhold Chemicals
237 S Motor Ave, Azusa (91702-3228)
PHONE...................................626 334-4974
Steward Fletcher, *Branch Mgr*
Keith Arnold, *Purch Agent*
EMP: 14
SALES (corp-wide): 284.3MM **Privately Held**
WEB: www.reichhold.com
SIC: 2821 2851 Plastics materials &
resins; paints & allied products
HQ: Reichhold Industries, Inc.
1035 Swabia Ct
Durham NC 27703

(P-7880)
ROA PACIFIC INC
1225 Exposition Way, San Diego
(92154-6663)
PHONE...................................619 565-2800
Cristina Thalia Mulligan, *CEO*
EMP: 11
SALES (est): 1.8MM **Privately Held**
SIC: 2821 Molding compounds, plastics

(P-7881)
RONCELLI PLASTICS INC
330 W Duarte Rd, Monrovia (91016-4584)
PHONE...................................626 359-2551
Gino Roncelli, *CEO*
Riley Cole, *President*
Bingo Roncelli, *Corp Secy*
EMP: 61 EST: 1970
SQ FT: 11,000
SALES (est): 16.8MM **Privately Held**
WEB: www.roncelliplastics.com
SIC: 2821 Plastics materials & resins

(P-7882)
S R S M INC
Also Called: Vm International
945 E Church St, Riverside (92507-1103)
PHONE...................................310 952-9000
Roya Vazin, *CEO*
Moe II Afsari, *Manager*
◆ EMP: 120 EST: 1996
SQ FT: 250,000
SALES (est): 37.7MM **Privately Held**
WEB: www.srsm.com
SIC: 2821 5023 Plastics materials &
resins; kitchenware

(P-7883)
SAINT-GOBAIN PRFMCE PLAS CORP
7301 Orangewood Ave, Garden Grove
(92841-1411)
PHONE...................................714 893-0470
Greg Maki, *Branch Mgr*
John Leary, *Manager*
EMP: 190
SALES (corp-wide): 213.5MM **Privately Held**
SIC: 2821 Plastics materials & resins
HQ: Saint-Gobain Performance Plastics
Corporation
31500 Solon Rd
Solon OH 44139
440 836-6900

(P-7884)
SENTRY INDUSTRIES INC
1245 Brooks St, Ontario (91762-3609)
PHONE...................................909 986-3642
William Dubble, *President*
Aileen Dubble, *Treasurer*
▲ EMP: 10
SQ FT: 10,000
SALES: 1MM **Privately Held**
SIC: 2821 Acrylic resins

(P-7885)
SHOCKING TECHNOLOGIES INC
5870 Hellyer Ave, San Jose (95138-1004)
PHONE...................................831 331-4558
Lex A Kosowsky, *President*
▼ EMP: 42
SQ FT: 52,000
SALES (est): 6MM **Privately Held**
SIC: 2821 Polymethyl methacrylate resins
(plexiglass)

(P-7886)
SILFINE AMERICA INC
1750 Cleveland Ave, San Jose
(95126-1903)
PHONE...................................408 823-8663
Seung Yong Lim, *President*
Jeffrey Harte, *Exec VP*
▲ EMP: 65
SQ FT: 1,600
SALES: 7MM **Privately Held**
SIC: 2821 Silicone resins

(P-7887)
SOUTHERN CALIFORNIA PLAS INC
3122 Maple St, Santa Ana (92707-4408)
PHONE...................................714 751-7084
Anthony Codet, *President*
Janet Rodriguez, *Manager*
▲ EMP: 54
SQ FT: 240,000
SALES (est): 12.1MM **Privately Held**
SIC: 2821 Plastics materials & resins

(P-7888)
SOUTHLAND POLYMERS INC
14030 Gannet St, Santa Fe Springs
(90670-5314)
PHONE...................................562 921-0444
Henry Hsi, *President*
Pantoja Robert, *Sales Engr*
◆ EMP: 20
SQ FT: 64,000
SALES (est): 7.4MM **Privately Held**
WEB: www.plasticresins.com
SIC: 2821 Plastics materials & resins

(P-7889)
SPHERE ALLIANCE INC
Also Called: Advanced Aircraft Seal
3051 Myers St, Riverside (92503-5525)
PHONE...................................951 352-2400
Daryl Silva, *CEO*
EMP: 37
SALES (est): 9.9MM **Privately Held**
SIC: 2821 Plastics materials & resins

(P-7890)
STEPAN COMPANY
Also Called: Anaheim Plant
1208 N Patt St, Anaheim (92801-2549)
PHONE...................................714 776-9870
Tom Szczeblowski, *Manager*
Eric Ball, *Maintence Staff*
EMP: 32
SQ FT: 10,412
SALES (corp-wide): 1.9B **Publicly Held**
WEB: www.stepan.com
SIC: 2821 2843 Plastics materials &
resins; surface active agents
PA: Stepan Company
22 W Frontage Rd
Northfield IL 60093
847 446-7500

(P-7891)
STOROPACK INC
Strap-Lok
12007 Woodruff Ave, Downey
(90241-5643)
P.O. Box 7007 (90242-8007)
PHONE...................................562 803-1584
Randy Nicholson, *Vice Pres*

EMP: 40
SALES (corp-wide): 443.7MM **Privately Held**
WEB: www.storopack.com
SIC: 2821 5113 3086 2671 Plastics materials & resins; industrial & personal
service paper; plastics foam products;
packaging paper & plastics film, coated &
laminated; packaging materials
HQ: Storopack, Inc.
4758 Devitt Dr
West Chester OH 45246
513 874-0314

(P-7892)
TA AEROSPACE CO
Also Called: Ta Division
28065 Franklin Pkwy, Valencia
(91355-4117)
PHONE...................................661 702-0448
Jim Sweeney, *President*
Hemant Gupta, *Research*
EMP: 180
SQ FT: 78,124
SALES (corp-wide): 2B **Publicly Held**
WEB: www.kirkhill.com
SIC: 2821 3429 Elastomers, nonvulcaniz-
able (plastics); clamps, metal
HQ: Ta Aerospace Co.
28065 Franklin Pkwy
Valencia CA 91355
661 775-1100

(P-7893)
TAMMY TAYLOR NAILS INC
2001 E Deere Ave, Santa Ana
(92705-5724)
PHONE...................................949 250-9287
Tammy Taylor, *Manager*
▼ EMP: 45
SQ FT: 11,500
SALES (est): 8.7MM **Privately Held**
SIC: 2821 7231 5087 Acrylic resins;
beauty shops; beauty parlor equipment &
supplies

(P-7894)
TAP PLASTICS INC A CAL CORP (PA)
3011 Alvarado St Ste A, San Leandro
(94577-5707)
PHONE...................................510 357-3755
David Freeberg, *President*
Carole L Bremer, *CFO*
Robert J Wilson, *Vice Pres*
Janie Faiola, *Administration*
Debra Kawano, *Human Resources*
EMP: 15 EST: 1952
SQ FT: 4,000
SALES (est): 62.3MM **Privately Held**
WEB: www.tapplastics.com
SIC: 2821 5162 Acrylic resins; resins, syn-
thetic

(P-7895)
TECHMER PM INC
18420 S Laurel Park Rd, Compton
(90220-6015)
PHONE...................................310 632-9211
John R Manuck, *President*
◆ EMP: 500
SQ FT: 40,000
SALES (est): 128.2MM **Privately Held**
WEB: www.techmerpm.com
SIC: 2821 Plastics materials & resins

(P-7896)
TEKNOR APEX COMPANY
Maclin Company
420 S 6th Ave, City of Industry
(91746-3128)
P.O. Box 2307, La Puente (91746-0307)
PHONE...................................626 968-4656
Tony Patrizio, *Manager*
Bahman Dariush, *Executive*
James Wynne, *Info Tech Mgr*
Rolo Rios, *Technician*
Brian Sofley, *Design Engr*
EMP: 199
SALES (corp-wide): 964.7MM **Privately Held**
SIC: 2821 3081 3089 Vinyl resins; unsup-
ported plastics film & sheet; plastic pro-
cessing

▲ = Import ▼=Export
◆ =Import/Export

PA: Teknor Apex Company
505 Central Ave
Pawtucket RI 02861
401 725-8000

(P-7897)
TUFF STUFF PRODUCTS
9600 Road 256, Terra Bella (93270-9732)
PHONE.................................559 535-5778
Maximilian B Lee, *President*
▲ EMP: 500 EST: 1999
SALES (est): 68.2MM Privately Held
WEB: www.tufftubs.com
SIC: 2821 Plastics materials & resins

(P-7898)
UREMET CORPORATION
3026 Orange Ave, Santa Ana (92707-4248)
PHONE.................................714 641-8813
Steve Zamollo, *CEO*
Mark Moore, *President*
John Cockriel, *Vice Pres*
▲ EMP: 26
SQ FT: 9,500
SALES (est): 6.6MM Privately Held
WEB: www.uremet.com
SIC: 2821 Polyurethane resins

(P-7899)
US BLANKS LLC (PA)
14700 S San Pedro St, Gardena
(90248-2001)
P.O. Box 486 (90248-0486)
PHONE.................................310 225-6774
Jeff Holtby, *Vice Pres*
Kimberly Thress,
▲ EMP: 48
SALES (est): 8.8MM Privately Held
SIC: 2821 Plastics materials & resins

(P-7900)
VIRTUAL COMPOSITES CO INC
584 Explorer St, Brea (92821-3108)
PHONE.................................714 256-8850
Wayne R Howard, *President*
EMP: 10
SALES (est): 1.6MM Privately Held
SIC: 2821 Plastics materials & resins

(P-7901)
XERXES CORPORATION
1210 N Tustin Ave, Anaheim (92807-1617)
PHONE.................................714 630-0012
Rudy Tapia, *Manager*
EMP: 100
SALES (corp-wide): 147.4MM Privately
Held
WEB: www.xerxescorp.com
SIC: 2821 5999 3444 Polystyrene resins;
fiberglass materials, except insulation;
sheet metalwork
HQ: Xerxes Corporation
7901 Xerxes Ave S Ste 201
Minneapolis MN 55431
952 887-1890

**2822 Synthetic Rubber
(Vulcanizable Elastomers)**

(P-7902)
**CALIFORNIA INDUSTRIAL RBR
CO**
1690 Sierra Ave, Yuba City (95993-8981)
PHONE.................................530 674-2444
Andy Campos, *Branch Mgr*
Hugh Powell, *Manager*
EMP: 20
SQ FT: 4,800
SALES (corp-wide): 56.5MM Privately
Held
SIC: 2822 2891 3496 3241 Synthetic
rubber; adhesives; conveyor belts; ce-
ment, hydraulic; agricultural chemicals
PA: California Industrial Rubber Co, Inc
2539 S Cherry Ave
Fresno CA 93706
559 268-7321

(P-7903)
COI RUBBER PRODUCTS INC
19255 San Jose Ave, City of Industry
(91748-1418)
PHONE.................................626 965-9966
David Chao, *CEO*

EMP: 450
SQ FT: 2,500
SALES (est): 627.1K Privately Held
SIC: 2822 Butadiene-acrylonitrile, nitrile
rubbers, NBR

(P-7904)
CRITICALPOINT CAPITAL LLC
Arlon Materials For Elec Div
9433 Hyssop Dr, Rancho Cucamonga
(91730-6107)
PHONE.................................909 987-9533
Roy Baulmer, *Branch Mgr*
EMP: 100
SALES (corp-wide): 18MM Privately
Held
WEB: www.arlon.com
SIC: 2822 3672 2821 Silicone rubbers;
printed circuit boards; plastics materials &
resins
PA: Criticalpoint Capital, Llc
2121 Rosecrans Ave # 2330
El Segundo CA 90245
310 321-4400

(P-7905)
**HANDY SERVICE
CORPORATION**
1043 S Melrose St Ste A, Placentia
(92870-7133)
PHONE.................................714 632-7832
Sandra Sherman, *President*
Anne Didion, *Corp Secy*
Sandy Sherman, *Administration*
EMP: 10
SQ FT: 6,700
SALES (est): 1.5MM Privately Held
SIC: 2822 Silicone rubbers

(P-7906)
KIRKHILL INC (HQ)
Also Called: Sfs
300 E Cypress St, Brea (92821-4007)
PHONE.................................714 529-4901
Annette Oneal, *President*
Annette O'Neal, *President*
EMP: 23
SALES: 95MM
SALES (corp-wide): 3.5B Publicly Held
SIC: 2822 Synthetic rubber
PA: Transdigm Group Incorporated
1301 E 9th St Ste 3000
Cleveland OH 44114
216 706-2960

(P-7907)
LTI HOLDINGS INC (HQ)
Also Called: Boyd
600 S Mcclure Rd, Modesto (95357-0520)
PHONE.................................209 236-1111
Mitch Aiello, *President*
Kurt Wetzel, *CFO*
▲ EMP: 15
SALES (est): 753.1MM
SALES (corp-wide): 874.5MM Privately
Held
SIC: 2822 3069 Synthetic rubber; hard
rubber & molded rubber products; rubber
automotive products
PA: Snow Phipps Group, Llc
667 Madison Ave Fl 18
New York NY 10065
212 508-3300

(P-7908)
SILPAK INC (PA)
470 E Bonita Ave, Pomona (91767-1928)
PHONE.................................909 625-0056
Philip Galarneau, *President*
Janice A Galarneau, *Vice Pres*
EMP: 15
SQ FT: 13,850
SALES (est): 1.8MM Privately Held
WEB: www.silpak.com
SIC: 2822 Synthetic rubber

(P-7909)
WCE PRODUCTS INC
Also Called: West Coast Enterprizes
7542 Santa Rita Cir, Stanton (90680-3433)
PHONE.................................714 895-4381
Van G Zeitz, *President*
▲ EMP: 13
SQ FT: 12,000
SALES (est): 2.4MM Privately Held
SIC: 2822 Synthetic rubber

**2824 Synthetic Organic
Fibers, Exc Cellulosic**

(P-7910)
DAL-TILE CORPORATION
7865 Ostrow St, San Diego (92111-3602)
PHONE.................................858 565-7767
Scott Hambor, *Manager*
Denise Mediavilla, *Manager*
EMP: 10
SALES (corp-wide): 9.4B Publicly Held
WEB: www.mohawk.com
SIC: 2824 5032 Organic fibers, noncellu-
losic; ceramic wall & floor tile
HQ: Dal-Tile Corporation
7834 C F Hawn Fwy
Dallas TX 75217
214 398-1411

(P-7911)
DAL-TILE CORPORATION
16201 Stagg St, Van Nuys (91406-1716)
PHONE.................................818 787-3224
Scott Phiser, *Branch Mgr*
EMP: 20
SALES (corp-wide): 9.4B Publicly Held
WEB: www.mohawk.com
SIC: 2824 5032 Organic fibers, noncellu-
losic; ceramic wall & floor tile
HQ: Dal-Tile Corporation
7834 C F Hawn Fwy
Dallas TX 75217
214 398-1411

(P-7912)
DAL-TILE CORPORATION
3550 Tyburn St, Los Angeles (90065-1427)
P.O. Box 170730, Dallas TX (75217-0730)
PHONE.................................323 257-7553
Dan Bargreen, *Branch Mgr*
EMP: 12
SALES (corp-wide): 9.4B Publicly Held
WEB: www.mohawk.com
SIC: 2824 5032 1743 Organic fibers, non-
cellulosic; ceramic wall & floor tile; tile in-
stallation; ceramic
HQ: Dal-Tile Corporation
7834 C F Hawn Fwy
Dallas TX 75217
214 398-1411

(P-7913)
ENERGY LANE INC
Also Called: Pitbull Energy Bar
6767 W Sunset Blvd 8152, Los Angeles
(90028-7177)
PHONE.................................323 962-5020
Bobby Robertson, *President*
Biviana Carillo, *COO*
EMP: 10
SALES (est): 1.1MM Privately Held
SIC: 2824 Protein fibers

(P-7914)
LAGIER RANCHES INC
16161 Murphy Rd, Escalon (95320-9755)
P.O. Box 89, Ripon (95366-0089)
PHONE.................................209 982-5618
John E Lagier, *President*
Casey Havre, *Corp Secy*
EMP: 12
SQ FT: 6,000
SALES (est): 2.2MM Privately Held
WEB: www.lagierranches.com
SIC: 2824 Organic fibers, noncellulosic

(P-7915)
PROBACTIVE BIOTECH INC
Also Called: St Paul Brands
11555 Monarch St Ste B, Garden Grove
(92841-1814)
PHONE.................................714 903-1000
Jimmy Ngo, *President*
Henry Smith, *Vice Pres*
Dennis Ngo, *VP Opers*
Giang Tran, *Export Mgr*
Tracy Nguyen, *Marketing Staff*
▲ EMP: 25
SALES: 2MM Privately Held
SIC: 2824 Protein fibers

(P-7916)
SANDERS INDUSTRIES (HQ)
3701 E Conant St, Long Beach
(90808-1783)
PHONE.................................562 354-2920
Larry O'Toole, *CEO*
Rick Ginsburgh, *CFO*
Adam Gilbert, *Vice Pres*
Tim Shanahan, *Vice Pres*
▲ EMP: 15
SQ FT: 55,000
SALES (est): 126.2MM
SALES (corp-wide): 182.4MM Privately
Held
WEB: www.sandersind.com
SIC: 2824 Elastomeric fibers
PA: Igp Industries, Llc
101 Mission St Ste 1500
San Francisco CA 94105
415 882-4550

(P-7917)
TURNER FIBERFILL INC
1600 Date St, Montebello (90640-6371)
P.O. Box 460 (90640-0460)
PHONE.................................323 724-7957
Paul Turner, *President*
▲ EMP: 35
SALES (est): 13.1MM Privately Held
SIC: 2824 Polyester fibers

(P-7918)
UNIQUE PLEX INC
2900 Adams St Ste C130, Riverside
(92504-4364)
PHONE.................................951 653-2500
Andrea N Milner, *President*
Floyd Milner, *CFO*
EMP: 10
SQ FT: 3,000
SALES: 300K Privately Held
SIC: 2824 Acrylic fibers

(P-7919)
VYBION INC
584 Oak St, Monterey (93940-1321)
PHONE.................................607 227-2502
Lee A Henderson, *Ch of Bd*
EMP: 16
SQ FT: 2,500
SALES (est): 856.4K Privately Held
SIC: 2824 Protein fibers

**2833 Medicinal Chemicals &
Botanical Prdts**

(P-7920)
ALLERMED LABORATORIES INC
7203 Convoy Ct, San Diego (92111-1020)
PHONE.................................858 292-1060
H S Nielsen, *President*
EMP: 30
SQ FT: 20,000
SALES (est): 2.7MM Privately Held
WEB: www.allermed.com
SIC: 2833 2836 Medicinals & botanicals;
biological products, except diagnostic

(P-7921)
AMERICAN INGREDIENTS INC
2929 E White Star Ave, Anaheim
(92806-2628)
PHONE.................................714 630-6000
Howard Simon, *President*
Andrea Bauer, *Treasurer*
▲ EMP: 14
SALES (est): 3.1MM
SALES (corp-wide): 3.2B Publicly Held
WEB: www.amer-ing.com
SIC: 2833 Medicinals & botanicals
HQ: Pharmachem Laboratories, Llc
265 Harrison Tpke
Kearny NJ 07032
201 246-1000

(P-7922)
ANIMAL NUTRITION INDS INC
Also Called: Interntnal Veterinary Sciences
5602 E La Palma Ave, Anaheim
(92807-2110)
PHONE.................................949 583-2920
ARA Bohchalian, *CEO*
Norma Wilson, *Office Mgr*
EMP: 10

SQ FT: 4,000
SALES: 300K **Privately Held**
SIC: 2833 Medicinal chemicals

(P-7923)
BAXTER BIOSCIENCE
1700 Rancho Conejo Blvd, Newbury Park (91320-1424)
PHONE..................805 498-8988
Sue Brown, *Manager*
Camille Denoga, *Social Dir*
Shawn Galastian, *Project Engr*
Thomas Golden, *Engineer*
Sarosh Guzder, *Engineer*
EMP: 600
SALES (est): 44.8MM **Privately Held**
SIC: 2833 5122 Medicinals & botanicals; pharmaceuticals

(P-7924)
BIO-RAD LABORATORIES INC
Bio-RAD E C S
9500 Jeronimo Rd, Irvine (92618-2017)
PHONE..................949 598-1200
Kelly Knapps, *Branch Mgr*
EMP: 140
SALES (corp-wide): 2.1B **Publicly Held**
WEB: www.bio-rad.com
SIC: 2833 2835 Medicinals & botanicals; in vitro & in vivo diagnostic substances
PA: Bio-Rad Laboratories, Inc.
1000 Alfred Nobel Dr
Hercules CA 94547
510 724-7000

(P-7925)
CARGILL INCORPORATED
600 N Gilbert St, Fullerton (92833-2555)
PHONE..................714 449-6708
Steve Hoemoller, *Manager*
EMP: 56
SALES (corp-wide): 51.2B **Privately Held**
WEB: www.cargill.com
SIC: 2833 2079 5199 Vegetable oils, medicinal grade: refined or concentrated; edible fats & oils; oils, animal or vegetable
PA: Cargill, Incorporated
15407 Mcginty Rd W
Wayzata MN 55391
952 742-7575

(P-7926)
CHROMADEX CORPORATION (PA)
10005 Muirlands Blvd G, Irvine (92618-2538)
PHONE..................949 419-0288
Stephen R Allen, *Ch of Bd*
Frank L Jaksch Jr, *CEO*
Troy Rhonemus, *COO*
Kevin Farr, *CFO*
Thomas Varvaro, *CFO*
EMP: 65 EST: 2000
SQ FT: 15,000
SALES: 21.2MM **Publicly Held**
SIC: 2833 Botanical products, medicinal: ground, graded or milled

(P-7927)
CHULADA INC
Also Called: Chulada Spices Herbs & Snacks
640 S Flower St, Burbank (91502-2011)
PHONE..................818 841-6536
Hector D Alvarez, *President*
Rey Sanchez, *Director*
EMP: 30
SQ FT: 12,000
SALES (est): 4.4MM **Privately Held**
SIC: 2833 2099 Drugs & herbs: grading, grinding & milling; seasonings & spices

(P-7928)
COSMO - PHARM INC
Also Called: Nature's Glory
11751 Vose St Ste 53, North Hollywood (91605-5736)
PHONE..................818 764-0246
Ashwin Patel, *President*
Urmila Patel, *Corp Secy*
Rajen Patel, *Exec VP*
▼ EMP: 40
SQ FT: 45,000
SALES (est): 7.1MM **Privately Held**
WEB: www.naturesglory.com
SIC: 2833 2048 Vitamins, natural or synthetic: bulk, uncompounded; prepared feeds

(P-7929)
CREATIONS GRDN NATURAL FD MKTS
Also Called: Cgnfm
24849 Anza Dr, Valencia (91355-1259)
PHONE..................661 877-4280
Dino Guglielmelli, *CEO*
EMP: 250 EST: 1999
SALES: 3.3MM **Privately Held**
SIC: 2833 Medicinals & botanicals

(P-7930)
CUSTOM FORMULATIONS CORP
1243 W 130th St, Gardena (90247-1501)
P.O. Box 3279 (90247-1479)
PHONE..................310 516-8273
Jay Daly, *President*
Monica Baez, *Admin Sec*
EMP: 15
SQ FT: 20,000
SALES (est): 2.3MM **Privately Held**
SIC: 2833 5499 5122 Vitamins, natural or synthetic: bulk, uncompounded; health & dietetic food stores; cosmetics

(P-7931)
CV SCIENCES INC
10070 Barnes Canyon Rd, San Diego (92121-2722)
PHONE..................866 290-2157
EMP: 15
SALES (est): 2.9MM
SALES (corp-wide): 20.6MM **Privately Held**
SIC: 2833 Medicinals & botanicals
PA: Cv Sciences, Inc.
2688 S Rainbow Blvd Ste B
Las Vegas NV 89146
866 290-2157

(P-7932)
CYTOMX THERAPEUTICS INC
151 Oyster Point Blvd, South San Francisco (94080-1840)
PHONE..................650 515-3185
Sean A McCarthy, *CEO*
Debanjan Ray, *CFO*
Neil Exter, *Bd of Directors*
Charles Fuchs, *Bd of Directors*
Frederick Gluck, *Bd of Directors*
EMP: 79
SALES: 71.6MM **Privately Held**
SIC: 2833 2834 Antibiotics; antiseptics, medicinal

(P-7933)
DOCTORS SIGNATURE SALES
Also Called: Life Force International
495 Raleigh Ave, El Cajon (92020-3137)
PHONE..................800 531-4877
Ron Hillman, *President*
Geraldine L Hillman, *Ch of Bd*
Kathleen Meadows, *Vice Pres*
Marjorie Lynn, *Admin Sec*
▲ EMP: 23
SQ FT: 24,000
SALES (est): 15.6MM **Privately Held**
WEB: www.lifeforce.net
SIC: 2833 2048 Drugs & herbs: grading, grinding & milling; prepared feeds

(P-7934)
ELYPTOL INC
2500 Broadway Ste F125, Santa Monica (90404-3080)
PHONE..................424 500-8099
Timothy O'Connor, *CEO*
EMP: 10
SALES (est): 846.7K **Privately Held**
SIC: 2833 2834 Medicinals & botanicals; ointments

(P-7935)
EMMAUS MEDICAL INC (HQ)
21250 Hawthorne Blvd # 800, Torrance (90503-5513)
PHONE..................310 214-0065
Yutaka Niihara, *President*
Willis Lee, *COO*
Lan Tran, *Officer*
Yasushi Nagasaki, *Vice Pres*
CUC Tran, *Executive Asst*
EMP: 13
SQ FT: 4,500
SALES (est): 2.5MM
SALES (corp-wide): 513.4K **Privately Held**
WEB: www.emmausmedical.com
SIC: 2833 Medicinals & botanicals
PA: Emmaus Life Sciences Inc.
21250 Hawthorne Blvd B
Torrance CA 90503
310 214-0065

(P-7936)
ENVITA LABS LLC
Also Called: Hero Nutritional
1900 Carnegie Ave Ste A, Santa Ana (92705-5557)
PHONE..................800 500-4376
Jennifer Hodges, *CEO*
Ben Bratcher,
Stephanie Magill,
Estela Schnelle,
Kelly Springer,
EMP: 30
SQ FT: 15,953
SALES (est): 9.5MM **Privately Held**
WEB: www.heronutritionals.com
SIC: 2833 Vitamins, natural or synthetic: bulk, uncompounded

(P-7937)
ERBAVIVA INC
Also Called: Erba Organics
19831 Nordhoff Pl Ste 116, Chatsworth (91311-6614)
PHONE..................818 998-7112
Robin Brown, *CEO*
Anna C Brown, *Vice Pres*
Jason Lee, *Opers Mgr*
Carolina Orozco, *Prdtn Mgr*
Hector Alaniz, *Warehouse Mgr*
◆ EMP: 20
SQ FT: 10,000
SALES (est): 5.9MM **Privately Held**
WEB: www.erbaviva.com
SIC: 2833 Organic medicinal chemicals: bulk, uncompounded

(P-7938)
ETHICAL NATURALS INC
2731 Fair Oaks Ave, Redwood City (94063-3506)
PHONE..................650 336-1190
Cal Bewicke, *Branch Mgr*
EMP: 13
SALES (corp-wide): 1.7MM **Privately Held**
SIC: 2833 Medicinals & botanicals
PA: Ethical Naturals Inc.
18 Commercial Blvd
Novato CA 94949
415 459-4393

(P-7939)
ETHOS NATURAL MEDICINE LLC
Also Called: Etha Natural Medicine
1950 Cordell Ct Ste 105, El Cajon (92020-0923)
PHONE..................858 267-7599
Victor Chung, *Mng Member*
Kendra Price, *General Mgr*
Alexander Karp,
EMP: 10
SQ FT: 2,727
SALES: 1.1MM **Privately Held**
SIC: 2833 Alkaloids & other botanical based products

(P-7940)
FITPRO USA LLC
1911 2nd St, Livermore (94550-4426)
PHONE..................877 645-5776
Kostandinos Malliarodakis, *CEO*
Ericca Hoffman, *COO*
Michael Zumpano, *CFO*
Kevin Cruz, *CIO*
Barbara Harrington, *Controller*
EMP: 10
SALES: 865K **Privately Held**
SIC: 2833 2026 Botanical products, medicinal: ground, graded or milled; milk drinks, flavored

(P-7941)
FUJISAWA BRISTOL CORPORATION
69848 Highway 111, Rancho Mirage (92270-2837)
P.O. Box 2040 (92270-1054)
PHONE..................760 324-1488
Gregory Ackerman, *President*
Maureen Kelly, *Corp Secy*
Nancy Lane, *Exec VP*
EMP: 60
SQ FT: 35,000
SALES: 20MM **Privately Held**
SIC: 2833 2844 Vitamins, natural or synthetic: bulk, uncompounded; face creams or lotions

(P-7942)
GE HEALTHCARE INC
Also Called: GE Health Care
4877 Mercury St, San Diego (92111-2104)
PHONE..................858 279-9382
George Starks, *Manager*
EMP: 20
SALES (corp-wide): 122B **Publicly Held**
SIC: 2833 Medicinals & botanicals
HQ: Ge Healthcare Inc.
100 Results Way
Marlborough MA 01752
800 292-8514

(P-7943)
GE NUTRIENTS INC
Also Called: Gencor
19700 Fairchild Ste 380, Irvine (92612-2523)
PHONE..................949 502-5760
Jith Veeravalli, *CEO*
Kimberly McCallum, *Admin Asst*
Gita Kasiri, *Manager*
▲ EMP: 10 EST: 2014
SALES (est): 179K **Privately Held**
SIC: 2833 Drugs & herbs: grading, grinding & milling

(P-7944)
GREEN ACRES CANNABIS LLC
6256 3rd St, San Francisco (94124-3110)
PHONE..................415 657-3484
Ramona Davis, *Mng Member*
Janiece Addison,
Tiya Addison,
Claudia Smith,
EMP: 26
SALES (est): 2.3MM **Privately Held**
SIC: 2833 Medicinals & botanicals

(P-7945)
GREEN CURES INC
20201 Sherman Way Ste 101, Winnetka (91306-3269)
PHONE..................818 773-3929
Julio Cubillas, *Principal*
EMP: 34
SALES (est): 3MM **Privately Held**
SIC: 2833

(P-7946)
HALL HEALTH AND LONGEVITY CNTR
916 Main St, Venice (90291-3376)
PHONE..................310 566-6690
Longevity Center, *Principal*
EMP: 14
SALES (corp-wide): 1.7MM **Privately Held**
SIC: 2833 Hormones or derivatives
PA: Hall Health And Longevity Center, A Professional Corporation
406 Wilshire Blvd
Santa Monica CA 90401
310 566-6688

(P-7947)
HERBAL SCIENCE INTERNATIONAL
205 Russell St, City of Industry (91744-3940)
PHONE..................626 333-9998
William Chang, *President*
▲ EMP: 15
SALES (est): 1.2MM **Privately Held**
WEB: www.hsusa.net
SIC: 2833 5499 Medicinals & botanicals; spices & herbs

(P-7948)
IMP INTERNATIONAL INC (PA)
Also Called: Unichem Enterprises
1905 S Lynx Ave, Ontario (91761-8055)
PHONE..................................909 321-1000
Chentao Hang, *President*
Ashley Cao, *Purch Mgr*
▲ EMP: 41
SQ FT: 40,000
SALES (est): 6.5MM Privately Held
SIC: 2833 2869 Vitamins, natural or synthetic: bulk, uncompounded; sweeteners, synthetic

(P-7949)
INTERHEALTH NUTRACEUTICALS INC
5451 Industrial Way, Benicia (94510-1010)
PHONE..................................800 783-4636
Paul Dijkstra, *CEO*
Navpreet Singh, *COO*
Mary Helen Lucero, *CFO*
Robert Worsena, *Director*
◆ EMP: 30
SQ FT: 33,000
SALES (est): 8.2MM
SALES (corp-wide): 5.1B Privately Held
WEB: www.interhealthusa.com
SIC: 2833 Vitamins, natural or synthetic: bulk, uncompounded
PA: Lonza Group Ag
    Munchensteinerstrasse 38
    Basel BS 4002
    613 168-111

(P-7950)
INTERNTNAL MDCTION SYSTEMS LTD
Also Called: IMS
10642 El Poche St, South El Monte (91733-3408)
PHONE..................................626 459-5586
EMP: 13
SALES (corp-wide): 210.4MM Publicly Held
SIC: 2833
HQ: International Medication Systems, Ltd.
    1886 Santa Anita Ave
    South El Monte CA 91733
    626 442-6757

(P-7951)
INTIMATE GROOMING ESCENUSALS
Also Called: Sweetspot Labs
15332 Antioch St 418, Pacific Palisades (90272-3628)
PHONE..................................310 230-4544
Shari Creed, *President*
Thomas S Creed, *Vice Pres*
EMP: 10
SQ FT: 1,600
SALES (est): 809.9K Privately Held
WEB: www.sweetspotlabs.com
SIC: 2833 Botanical products, medicinal: ground, graded or milled

(P-7952)
J & D LABORATORIES INC
2710 Progress St, Vista (92081-8449)
PHONE..................................844 453-5227
David Wood, *CEO*
Fon Wong, *CFO*
Joseph English, *Accountant*
Wyatt Humphrey, *Plant Mgr*
Juan Torres, *QC Mgr*
▲ EMP: 300
SQ FT: 32,000
SALES (est): 102.9MM Privately Held
WEB: www.jdlaboratories.com
SIC: 2833 2834 Vitamins, natural or synthetic: bulk, uncompounded; pharmaceutical preparations
PA: Captek Softgel International, Inc.
    16218 Arthur St
    Cerritos CA 90703

(P-7953)
JOHN A THOMSON PHD
Also Called: Huntington Company
12610 Saticoy St S, North Hollywood (91605-4313)
PHONE..................................323 877-5186
John A Thomson, *Owner*

▼ EMP: 22 EST: 1936
SALES (est): 3.8MM Privately Held
WEB: www.superthrive.com
SIC: 2833 Medicinals & botanicals

(P-7954)
MULTIVITAMIN DIRECT INC
2178 Paragon Dr, San Jose (95131-1305)
PHONE..................................408 573-7276
▲ EMP: 21
SQ FT: 5,000
SALES: 3.5MM Privately Held
SIC: 2833

(P-7955)
NATURAL WONDERS CA INC
Also Called: Nature Creation
7240 Eton Ave, Canoga Park (91303-1505)
PHONE..................................818 593-2001
Hagay Mizrahi, *President*
▲ EMP: 15
SQ FT: 20,000
SALES (est): 2.6MM Privately Held
SIC: 2833 5122 Medicinals & botanicals; botanical products, medicinal: ground, graded or milled

(P-7956)
NATURES BOUNTY CO
901 E 233rd St, Carson (90745-6204)
PHONE..................................310 952-7107
Colleen Davis, *Branch Mgr*
Cesar Cortez, *Info Tech Mgr*
EMP: 19 Publicly Held
WEB: www.nbty.com
SIC: 2833 Medicinals & botanicals
HQ: The Nature's Bounty Co
    2100 Smithtown Ave
    Ronkonkoma NY 11779
    631 200-2000

(P-7957)
NATURES BOUNTY CO
7366 Orangewood Ave, Garden Grove (92841-1412)
PHONE..................................714 898-9936
Lily Mu, *Branch Mgr*
EMP: 19 Publicly Held
WEB: www.nbty.com
SIC: 2833 Vitamins, natural or synthetic: bulk, uncompounded
HQ: The Nature's Bounty Co
    2100 Smithtown Ave
    Ronkonkoma NY 11779
    631 200-2000

(P-7958)
NITRO 2 GO INC
1420 Richardson St, San Bernardino (92408-2962)
PHONE..................................909 864-4886
Jeff Diehl, *President*
▲ EMP: 35
SQ FT: 6,000
SALES (est): 7.3MM Privately Held
WEB: www.nitro2go.com
SIC: 2833 Drugs & herbs: grading, grinding & milling

(P-7959)
NORTH WEST PHARMANATURALS, INC
Also Called: Vitamins Unlimited
1000 Beacon St, Brea (92821-2938)
PHONE..................................714 529-0980
▲ EMP: 20
SQ FT: 25,000
SALES (est): 4.5MM Privately Held
WEB: www.northwestpn.com
SIC: 2833 Vitamins, natural or synthetic: bulk, uncompounded

(P-7960)
NU-HEALTH PRODUCTS CO
Also Called: Nu Health Products
20875 Currier Rd, Walnut (91789-3081)
PHONE..................................909 869-0666
Lynn Leung, *President*
Amanda Fu, *Purch Mgr*
Daniel Fu, *Purchasing*
▲ EMP: 25
SQ FT: 12,000

SALES (est): 4MM Privately Held
WEB: www.nu-health.com
SIC: 2833 2048 5149 Vitamins, natural or synthetic: bulk, uncompounded; drugs & herbs: grading, grinding & milling; prepared feeds; organic & diet foods

(P-7961)
ONE LAMBDA INC (HQ)
21001 Kittridge St, Canoga Park (91303-2801)
PHONE..................................818 702-0042
Seth H Hoogasian, *CEO*
George M Ayoub, *President*
James Keegan, *CFO*
Don Arii, *Vice Pres*
Emiko Terasaki, *Admin Sec*
EMP: 102
SQ FT: 53,000
SALES (est): 81.7MM
SALES (corp-wide): 20.9B Publicly Held
WEB: www.onelambda.com
SIC: 2833 Medicinals & botanicals
PA: Thermo Fisher Scientific Inc.
    168 3rd Ave
    Waltham MA 02451
    781 622-1000

(P-7962)
OPTIMUM BIOENERGY INTL CORP
2463 Pomona Rd, Corona (92880-6931)
PHONE..................................714 903-8872
Louis LI, *President*
Judy LI, *Vice Pres*
▲ EMP: 15
SQ FT: 5,000
SALES: 1.2MM Privately Held
SIC: 2833 Vitamins, natural or synthetic: bulk, uncompounded

(P-7963)
PHARMAVITE LLC
1150 Aviation Pl, San Fernando (91340-1460)
PHONE..................................818 221-6200
Jim Jordan, *Exec VP*
Frank Menchaca, *QA Dir*
Octavio Padilla, *Technician*
Manmeet Salh, *Research*
Haik Parkahni, *Engineer*
EMP: 300
SALES (corp-wide): 11B Privately Held
WEB: www.pharmavite.com
SIC: 2833 Vitamins, natural or synthetic: bulk, uncompounded
HQ: Pharmavite Llc
    8510 Balboa Blvd Ste 300
    Northridge CA 91325
    818 221-6200

(P-7964)
PHARMAVITE LLC (DH)
8510 Balboa Blvd Ste 300, Northridge (91325-3582)
P.O. Box 9606, Mission Hills (91346-9606)
PHONE..................................818 221-6200
Jeff Boutelle, *CEO*
Bob McQuillan, *President*
Brian Beams, *Vice Pres*
Christine Burdick-Bell JD, *Vice Pres*
Daniel Grahek, *Administration*
▲ EMP: 172 EST: 2002
SQ FT: 45,000
SALES (est): 277.6MM
SALES (corp-wide): 11B Privately Held
WEB: www.pharmavite.com
SIC: 2833 2834 Vitamins, natural or synthetic: bulk, uncompounded; pharmaceutical preparations
HQ: Otsuka America, Inc.
    1 Embarcadero Ctr # 2020
    San Francisco CA 94111
    415 986-5300

(P-7965)
PROMEGA BIOSCIENCES LLC
277 Granada Dr, San Luis Obispo (93401-7396)
PHONE..................................805 544-8524
Kristen Yetter, *Finance*
Sergiy Levin, *Research*
Poncho Meisenheimer, *Research*
Ce Shi, *Research*
Joel Walker, *Research*
EMP: 55

SQ FT: 40,000
SALES (est): 13MM
SALES (corp-wide): 420.8MM Privately Held
WEB: www.promega.com
SIC: 2833 2835 Medicinal chemicals; in vitro & in vivo diagnostic substances
PA: Promega Corporation
    2800 Woods Hollow Rd
    Fitchburg WI 53711
    608 274-4330

(P-7966)
PROTHENA CORP PUB LTD CO
331 Oyster Point Blvd, South San Francisco (94080-1913)
PHONE..................................650 837-8550
Gene Kinney, *CEO*
Tran Nguyen, *CFO*
Bill Homan, *Officer*
David McNinch, *Officer*
Ingrid Paulson, *Associate Dir*
EMP: 11
SALES (est): 1.8MM Privately Held
SIC: 2833 Medicinals & botanicals

(P-7967)
RADIANT GENOMICS INC
5980 Horton St Ste 105, Emeryville (94608-2056)
PHONE..................................646 450-7332
Jeffrey Kim, *CEO*
Maritza Duarte, *Research*
EMP: 12 EST: 2012
SALES (est): 2.1MM Privately Held
SIC: 2833 Medicinals & botanicals

(P-7968)
RON TEEGUARDEN ENTERPRISES INC (PA)
Also Called: Dragon Herbs
5670 Wilshire Blvd # 1500, Los Angeles (90036-5660)
PHONE..................................323 556-8188
Ron Teagarden, *President*
Yanlin Teeguarden, *Principal*
◆ EMP: 29
SQ FT: 13,000
SALES (est): 4.7MM Privately Held
WEB: www.dragonherbs.com
SIC: 2833 5122 Drugs & herbs: grading, grinding & milling; medicinals & botanicals

(P-7969)
S&B PHARMA INC
Also Called: Norac Pharma
405 S Motor Ave, Azusa (91702-3232)
PHONE..................................626 334-2908
Dr Daniel Levin, *President*
Duran Alex, *Business Mgr*
Lee Miller, *Director*
▲ EMP: 61
SALES (est): 14.2MM Privately Held
SIC: 2833 8731 2834 Medicinals & botanicals; commercial physical research; pharmaceutical preparations

(P-7970)
SABRE SCIENCES INC
2233 Faraday Ave Ste K, Carlsbad (92008-7214)
PHONE..................................760 448-2750
Victor Salerno, *President*
Anna Salerno, *Treasurer*
Michael Borkin, *Principal*
Jennifer Lewis, *Mng Member*
EMP: 18
SQ FT: 8,000
SALES (est): 3.6MM Privately Held
WEB: www.sabresciences.com
SIC: 2833 8731 Hormones or derivatives; commercial physical research

(P-7971)
SAPPHIRE ENERGY INC
10996 Torreyana Rd # 280, San Diego (92121-1161)
PHONE..................................858 768-4700
James Levine, *CEO*
Thomas Willardson, *CFO*
Mike Mendez, *Vice Pres*
Sara Hummel, *Research*
Raechel Roberts, *Research*
EMP: 55
SALES (est): 23.1MM Privately Held
SIC: 2833 Medicinals & botanicals

(P-7972)
SELECT SUPPLEMENTS INC
2390 Oak Ridge Way, Vista (92081-8345)
PHONE......................................760 431-7509
Joar A Opheim, *CEO*
Hector Gudino, *COO*
▲ EMP: 32
SQ FT: 36,000
SALES (est): 12.3MM Privately Held
SIC: 2833 Medicinals & botanicals

(P-7973)
STAUBER PRFMCE INGREDIENTS (HQ)
4120 N Palm St, Fullerton (92835-1026)
PHONE......................................714 441-3900
Patrick Hawkins, *President*
Shirley Rozeboom, *Senior VP*
Sheri Esswein, *VP Bus Dvlpt*
Corina Ramirez, *Info Tech Mgr*
Kathleen Isenberg, *Controller*
EMP: 139
SALES (est): 6.4MM
SALES (corp-wide): 504.1MM Publicly Held
SIC: 2833 Medicinals & botanicals
PA: Hawkins, Inc.
　　2381 Rosegate
　　Roseville MN 55113
　　612 331-6910

(P-7974)
THRESHOLD ENTERPRISES LTD
165 Technology Dr, Watsonville (95076-2448)
PHONE......................................831 425-3955
EMP: 12
SALES (corp-wide): 172MM Privately Held
SIC: 2833 2099 Medicinals & botanicals; food preparations
PA: Threshold Enterprises Ltd.
　　23 Janis Way
　　Scotts Valley CA 95066
　　831 438-6851

(P-7975)
THRESHOLD ENTERPRISES LTD (PA)
Also Called: Vanguard Marketing
23 Janis Way, Scotts Valley (95066-3546)
PHONE......................................831 438-6851
Tom Grillea, *CEO*
Ira L Goldberg, *CEO*
Daniel Goldberg, *Managing Dir*
Matt McNair, *Admin Asst*
Nancy Utley, *Admin Asst*
◆ EMP: 277
SQ FT: 100,000
SALES (est): 172MM Privately Held
WEB: www.planetaryformulas.com
SIC: 2833 Vitamins, natural or synthetic: bulk, uncompounded

(P-7976)
THRESHOLD ENTERPRISES LTD
11 Janis Way, Scotts Valley (95066-3537)
PHONE......................................831 461-6413
Scott Laforce, *Controller*
James Loveless, *Manager*
EMP: 56
SALES (corp-wide): 172MM Privately Held
WEB: www.planetaryformulas.com
SIC: 2833 5122 Vitamins, natural or synthetic: bulk, uncompounded; vitamins & minerals
PA: Threshold Enterprises Ltd.
　　23 Janis Way
　　Scotts Valley CA 95066
　　831 438-6851

(P-7977)
THRESHOLD ENTERPRISES LTD
19 Janis Way Scotts Vly Scotts Valle, Scotts Valley (95066)
PHONE......................................831 461-6343
EMP: 31
SALES (corp-wide): 172MM Privately Held
WEB: www.planetaryformulas.com
SIC: 2833 Vitamins, natural or synthetic: bulk, uncompounded

PA: Threshold Enterprises Ltd.
　　23 Janis Way
　　Scotts Valley CA 95066
　　831 438-6851

(P-7978)
THRESHOLD ENTERPRISES LTD
2280 Delaware Ave, Santa Cruz (95060-5707)
PHONE......................................831 466-4014
Charles Powell, *General Mgr*
EMP: 37
SALES (corp-wide): 172MM Privately Held
SIC: 2833 Vitamins, natural or synthetic: bulk, uncompounded
PA: Threshold Enterprises Ltd.
　　23 Janis Way
　　Scotts Valley CA 95066
　　831 438-6851

(P-7979)
UNI-CAPS LLC
540 Lambert Rd, Brea (92821)
PHONE......................................714 529-8400
Sang H Kim, *Mng Member*
▲ EMP: 30
SALES (est): 14.4MM Privately Held
SIC: 2833 Vitamins, natural or synthetic: bulk, uncompounded

(P-7980)
VISION SMART CENTER INC
123 Astronaut E S Onizuka, Los Angeles (90012-3864)
PHONE......................................213 625-1740
Eddie Shiojima, *CEO*
Yuya Aoyama, *Opers Mgr*
EMP: 10
SQ FT: 2,000
SALES (est): 730K Privately Held
SIC: 2833 Vitamins, natural or synthetic: bulk, uncompounded

(P-7981)
VITAJOY USA INC
14165 Ramona Ave, Chino (91710-5753)
PHONE......................................626 965-8830
Dan Gu, *CEO*
Charles Kuo, *Vice Pres*
Li Hongbin, *Sales Dir*
▲ EMP: 10
SALES (est): 2.5MM Privately Held
SIC: 2833 Vitamins, natural or synthetic: bulk, uncompounded

(P-7982)
WESTAR NUTRITION CORP
350 Paularino Ave, Costa Mesa (92626-4616)
PHONE......................................949 645-6100
David Fan, *President*
Lucy Fan, *Vice Pres*
Joe Ramos, *Manager*
▼ EMP: 240
SQ FT: 55,000
SALES (est): 34.3MM Privately Held
SIC: 2833 2834 2844 7389 Vitamins, natural or synthetic: bulk, uncompounded; pharmaceutical preparations; cosmetic preparations; packaging & labeling services

(P-7983)
WINNING LABORATORIES INC
Also Called: Natutac
16218 Arthur St, Cerritos (90703-2131)
PHONE......................................562 921-6880
James Hao, *President*
Lydia Hao, *Vice Pres*
▲ EMP: 16
SQ FT: 90,000
SALES: 9.2MM Privately Held
WEB: www.silverspurcorp.com
SIC: 2833 Medicinals & botanicals
PA: Silver Spur Corporation
　　16010 Shoemaker Ave
　　Cerritos CA 90703
　　562 921-6880

2834 Pharmaceuticals

(P-7984)
3M COMPANY
19901 Nordhoff St, Northridge (91324-3213)
P.O. Box 1001 (91328-1001)
PHONE......................................818 341-1300
Carol Beesley, *Branch Mgr*
Lora Grant, *Director*
EMP: 400
SALES (corp-wide): 31.6B Publicly Held
WEB: www.mmm.com
SIC: 2834 Pharmaceutical preparations
PA: 3m Company
　　3m Center
　　Saint Paul MN 55144
　　651 733-1110

(P-7985)
A Q PHARMACEUTICALS INC
11555 Monarch St Ste C, Garden Grove (92841-1814)
PHONE......................................714 903-1000
Tracy Nguyen, *President*
Henry Smith, *Vice Pres*
▲ EMP: 30
SQ FT: 3,000
SALES (est): 5.5MM Privately Held
WEB: www.aqpharmaceuticals.com
SIC: 2834 Pharmaceutical preparations

(P-7986)
ABBOTT LABORATORIES
41888 Motor Car Pkwy, Temecula (92591-4651)
P.O. Box 9018 (92589-9018)
PHONE......................................951 914-3000
Matthew Holmes, *Branch Mgr*
Brent Pelletier, *President*
EMP: 45
SALES (corp-wide): 27.3B Publicly Held
SIC: 2834 Pharmaceutical preparations
PA: Abbott Laboratories
　　100 Abbott Park Rd
　　Abbott Park IL 60064
　　224 667-6100

(P-7987)
ABBOTT NUTRITION MFG INC (HQ)
2351 N Watney Way Ste C, Fairfield (94533-6726)
PHONE......................................707 399-1100
Mark Shaffar, *Vice Pres*
Mel Williamson, *Principal*
▼ EMP: 183
SALES (est): 54.8MM
SALES (corp-wide): 27.3B Publicly Held
WEB: www.abbott.com
SIC: 2834 Vitamin, nutrient & hematinic preparations for human use
PA: Abbott Laboratories
　　100 Abbott Park Rd
　　Abbott Park IL 60064
　　224 667-6100

(P-7988)
ABBOTT VASCULAR INC
26531 Ynez Rd, Temecula (92591-4630)
PHONE......................................951 941-2400
Ronald Dollens, *Branch Mgr*
EMP: 500
SALES (corp-wide): 27.3B Publicly Held
SIC: 2834 Pharmaceutical preparations
HQ: Abbott Vascular Inc.
　　3200 Lakeside Dr
　　Santa Clara CA 95054
　　408 845-3000

(P-7989)
ABCO LABORATORIES INC (PA)
Also Called: Baron Brand Spices
2450 S Watney Way, Fairfield (94533-6730)
P.O. Box 2519 (94533-0251)
PHONE......................................707 427-1818
Allen Baron, *President*
Greg Northam, *President*
Eric Whitaker, *Exec VP*
Hamed Malekan, *Research*
Bill Murphy, *Purch Agent*
▲ EMP: 100
SQ FT: 29,000

SALES (est): 22.6MM Privately Held
WEB: www.abcolabs.com
SIC: 2834 2099 Vitamin preparations; spices, including grinding

(P-7990)
ABRAXIS BIOSCIENCE INC
Also Called: American Bioscience
2730 Wilshire Blvd # 110, Santa Monica (90403-4743)
PHONE......................................310 883-1300
EMP: 75
SALES (corp-wide): 13B Publicly Held
SIC: 2834 Pharmaceutical preparations
HQ: Abraxis Bioscience, Inc.
　　86 Morris Ave
　　Summit NJ 07901

(P-7991)
ABRAXIS BIOSCIENCE LLC (DH)
11755 Wilshire Blvd Fl 20, Los Angeles (90025-1543)
PHONE......................................800 564-0216
Leon O Moulder Jr,
Rick Rodgers Sr,
Patrick Soon-Shiong MD,
EMP: 232
SALES (est): 98MM
SALES (corp-wide): 13B Publicly Held
SIC: 2834 Pharmaceutical preparations

(P-7992)
ACADIA PHARMACEUTICALS INC (PA)
3611 Valley Centre Dr # 300, San Diego (92130-3331)
PHONE......................................858 558-2871
Stephen R Davis, *President*
Stephen R Biggar, *Ch of Bd*
Elena Ridloff, *CFO*
Michael J Yang, *Ch Credit Ofcr*
Edmund Harrigan, *Bd of Directors*
▲ EMP: 425
SQ FT: 78,000
SALES: 124.9MM Publicly Held
WEB: www.acadia-pharm.com
SIC: 2834 8731 Pharmaceutical preparations; medical research, commercial

(P-7993)
ACELRX PHARMACEUTICALS INC
351 Galveston Dr, Redwood City (94063-4736)
PHONE......................................650 216-3500
Howard B Rosen, *CEO*
Adrian Adams, *Ch of Bd*
Timothy E Morris, *CFO*
Stephen J Hoffman, *Bd of Directors*
Pamela P Palmer, *Chief Mktg Ofcr*
EMP: 36
SQ FT: 25,893
SALES: 8MM Privately Held
WEB: www.acelrx.com
SIC: 2834 Druggists' preparations (pharmaceuticals)

(P-7994)
ACHAOGEN INC (PA)
1 Tower Pl Ste 300, South San Francisco (94080-1835)
PHONE......................................650 800-3636
Kenneth J Hillan, *President*
Bryan E Roberts, *Ch of Bd*
Liz Bhatt, *COO*
Blake Wise, *COO*
Zeryn Sarpangal, *CFO*
EMP: 160
SQ FT: 16,000
SALES: 11.1MM Publicly Held
WEB: www.achaogen.com
SIC: 2834 Pharmaceutical preparations

(P-7995)
ACOLOGIX INC
3960 Point Eden Way, Hayward (94545-3719)
PHONE......................................510 512-7200
Yoshinari Kumagai, *President*
R Scott Greer, *Ch of Bd*
John J Buckley, *CFO*
Dawn McGuire, *Chief Mktg Ofcr*
David M Rosen, *Senior VP*

▲ = Import ▼=Export
◆ =Import/Export

EMP: 37
SQ FT: 5,244
SALES (est): 5.3MM **Privately Held**
WEB: www.acologix.com
SIC: 2834 Drugs acting on the gastrointestinal or genitourinary system

(P-7996)
ACTAVALON INC
3210 Merryfield Row, San Diego (92121-1126)
PHONE..................................949 244-5684
Gail Wesley Hatfield, *CEO*
G Wesley Hatfield, *CEO*
EMP: 12
SALES (est): 1.5MM **Privately Held**
SIC: 2834 Proprietary drug products

(P-7997)
ACTAVIS LLC
132 Business Center Dr, Corona (92880-1724)
PHONE..................................951 493-5582
Luis Torres, *Exec Dir*
EMP: 13 **Privately Held**
SIC: 2834 Pharmaceutical preparations
HQ: Allergan Finance, Llc
400 Interpace Pkwy
Parsippany NJ 07054
862 261-7000

(P-7998)
ACTELION PHRMACEUTICALS US INC (DH)
5000 Shoreline Ct Ste 200, South San Francisco (94080-1956)
PHONE..................................650 624-6900
Bill Fairey, *President*
Simon Buckingham, *President*
Rajiv Patni, *Senior VP*
Douglas B Snyder, *Senior VP*
Jean Marc Bellemin, *Vice Pres*
EMP: 26 **EST:** 1998
SALES (est): 21.4MM
SALES (corp-wide): 76.4B **Publicly Held**
SIC: 2834 Pharmaceutical preparations
HQ: Actelion Pharmaceuticals Ltd
Gewerbestrasse 16
Allschwil BL 4123
615 656-565

(P-7999)
ADAMAS PHARMACEUTICALS INC (PA)
1900 Powell St Ste 1000, Emeryville (94608-1839)
PHONE..................................510 450-3500
Gregory T Went, *Ch of Bd*
Alfred G Merriweather, *CFO*
Jennifer J Rhodes, *Ch Credit Ofcr*
Rajiv Patni, *Chief Mktg Ofcr*
Christopher B Prentiss,
EMP: 92
SQ FT: 37,626
SALES: 571K **Publicly Held**
WEB: www.adamaspharma.com
SIC: 2834 Drugs acting on the central nervous system & sense organs

(P-8000)
ADAMIS PHARMACEUTICALS CORP (PA)
11682 El Camino Real # 300, San Diego (92130-2092)
PHONE..................................858 997-2400
Dennis J Carlo, *President*
Richard C Williams, *Ch of Bd*
Eddie W Glover, *CEO*
Robert O Hopkins, *CFO*
Robert Rothermel, *Bd of Directors*
EMP: 32
SQ FT: 7,525
SALES: 13MM **Publicly Held**
WEB: www.cellegy.com
SIC: 2834 Pharmaceutical preparations

(P-8001)
ADIANA INC
1240 Elko Dr, Sunnyvale (94089-2212)
PHONE..................................650 421-2900
Paul Goeld, *CEO*
EMP: 30
SQ FT: 12,000

SALES (est): 2.4MM
SALES (corp-wide): 3B **Publicly Held**
WEB: www.adiana.com
SIC: 2834 8731 Pharmaceutical preparations; commercial physical research
HQ: Cytyc Corporation
250 Campus Dr
Marlborough MA 01752
508 263-2900

(P-8002)
ADURO BIOTECH INC (PA)
740 Heinz Ave, Berkeley (94710-2748)
PHONE..................................510 848-4400
Stephen T Isaacs, *Ch of Bd*
Gregory W Schafer, *COO*
Jennifer Lew, *CFO*
Gerald Chan, *Bd of Directors*
William Greenman, *Bd of Directors*
EMP: 85
SQ FT: 25,000
SALES: 17.2MM **Publicly Held**
SIC: 2834 8731 Pharmaceutical preparations; commercial physical research

(P-8003)
ADVANCED CHEMBLOCKS INC
Also Called: A Chemblock
849 Mitten Rd Ste 101, Burlingame (94010-1308)
PHONE..................................650 692-2368
Robert Du, *President*
EMP: 10 **EST:** 2009
SQ FT: 500
SALES (est): 3.5MM **Privately Held**
SIC: 2834 8711 Pharmaceutical preparations; chemical engineering

(P-8004)
ADVANTAGE PHARMACEUTICALS
4363 Pacific St, Rocklin (95677-2117)
PHONE..................................916 630-4960
Arthur Whitney, *President*
EMP: 10
SALES (est): 1.4MM **Privately Held**
SIC: 2834 Pharmaceutical preparations

(P-8005)
AGOURON PHARMACEUTICALS INC (HQ)
10777 Science Center Dr, San Diego (92121-1111)
PHONE..................................858 622-3000
Catherine Mackey PHD, *Senior VP*
Levon Fendekian, *Manager*
EMP: 50
SALES (est): 54.6MM
SALES (corp-wide): 52.5B **Publicly Held**
WEB: www.agouron.com
SIC: 2834 5122 8731 Pharmaceutical preparations; pharmaceuticals; commercial physical research
PA: Pfizer Inc.
235 E 42nd St
New York NY 10017
212 733-2323

(P-8006)
AIMMUNE THERAPEUTICS INC
8000 Marina Blvd Ste 300, Brisbane (94005-1884)
PHONE..................................650 614-5220
Jayson Dallas, *CEO*
Mark D McDade, *Ch of Bd*
Eric H Bjerkholt, *CFO*
Daniel C Adelman, *Chief Mktg Ofcr*
Douglas T Sheehy, *Admin Sec*
EMP: 131
SQ FT: 26,355
SALES (est): 19.7MM **Privately Held**
SIC: 2834 Pharmaceutical preparations

(P-8007)
AKARANTA INC
Also Called: Sierra Pharmacy
8661 Baseline Rd, Rancho Cucamonga (91730-1111)
PHONE..................................909 989-9800
Pradeep K Amin, *CEO*
EMP: 10
SALES (est): 1.8MM **Privately Held**
SIC: 2834 5999 Pharmaceutical preparations; medical apparatus & supplies

(P-8008)
ALCON MANUFACTURING LTD
15800 Alton Pkwy, Irvine (92618-3818)
PHONE..................................949 753-1393
Ken Lickel, *Principal*
▲ **EMP:** 48
SALES (est): 12.7MM
SALES (corp-wide): 49.1B **Privately Held**
SIC: 2834 8011 Veterinary pharmaceutical preparations; eyes, ears, nose & throat specialist: physician/surgeon
HQ: Alcon Laboratories, Inc.
6201 South Fwy
Fort Worth TX 76134
817 293-0450

(P-8009)
ALEXZA PHARMACEUTICALS INC (HQ)
2091 Stierlin Ct, Mountain View (94043-4655)
PHONE..................................650 944-7000
Thomas B King, *President*
Edwin S Kamemoto, *Exec VP*
Edwin Kamemoto, *Vice Pres*
Wenxiang Zeng, *Associate Dir*
Tatyana Naranda, *Business Dir*
EMP: 27
SQ FT: 65,604
SALES: 5MM
SALES (corp-wide): 107.4MM **Privately Held**
WEB: www.alexza.com
SIC: 2834 Druggists' preparations (pharmaceuticals)
PA: Grupo Ferrer Internacional Sa
Avenida Diagonal, 549 - 5 Planta
Barcelona 08029
936 003-700

(P-8010)
ALIOS BIOPHARMA INC
260 E Grand Ave, South San Francisco (94080-4811)
PHONE..................................650 635-5500
Lawrence Blatt MD, *President*
Leonid Beigelman MD, *Security Dir*
Derrick De Leon, *Info Tech Dir*
Humaira Sarker, *Research*
EMP: 26
SALES (est): 9.5MM
SALES (corp-wide): 76.4B **Publicly Held**
SIC: 2834 Pharmaceutical preparations
PA: Johnson & Johnson
1 Johnson And Johnson Plz
New Brunswick NJ 08933
732 524-0400

(P-8011)
ALLAKOS INC
75 Shoreway Rd Ste A, San Carlos (94070-2727)
PHONE..................................650 597-5002
Robert Alexander, *President*
Daniel Janney, *Ch of Bd*
Adam Tomasi, *COO*
Henrik Rasmussen, *Chief Mktg Ofcr*
EMP: 44 **EST:** 2012
SQ FT: 10,142
SALES (est): 15.5MM **Privately Held**
SIC: 2834 Pharmaceutical preparations

(P-8012)
ALLERGAN INC
735 Workman Mill Rd, Whittier (90601-1106)
PHONE..................................512 527-6688
EMP: 194 **Privately Held**
SIC: 2834 Drugs acting on the central nervous system & sense organs
HQ: Allergan, Inc.
5 Giralda Farms
Madison NJ 07940
862 261-7000

(P-8013)
ALLERGAN SPCLTY THRPEUTICS INC
2525 Dupont Dr, Irvine (92612-1599)
PHONE..................................714 246-4500
David Pyott, *President*
Robert Gaskin, *Vice Pres*
John Hartmann, *Vice Pres*
Lily Tu, *Vice Pres*
Jr F Tunney, *Admin Sec*

EMP: 1500 **EST:** 1997
SALES (est): 208.5MM **Privately Held**
WEB: www.allergan.com
SIC: 2834 Pharmaceutical preparations
HQ: Allergan, Inc.
5 Giralda Farms
Madison NJ 07940
862 261-7000

(P-8014)
ALLERGAN USA INC
Also Called: Pacific Communications
18581 Teller Ave, Irvine (92612-1627)
P.O. Box 19534 (92623-9534)
PHONE..................................714 427-1900
David E I Pyott, *CEO*
Craig Sullivan, *President*
Jeffrey L Edwards, *CFO*
James M Hindman, *Treasurer*
Douglas S Ingram, *Admin Sec*
EMP: 2000
SALES (est): 228.8MM **Privately Held**
WEB: www.espritpharma.com
SIC: 2834 Druggists' preparations (pharmaceuticals)
HQ: Allergan, Inc.
5 Giralda Farms
Madison NJ 07940
862 261-7000

(P-8015)
ALLERGY RESEARCH GROUP INC
Also Called: Nutricology
2300 N Loop Rd, Alameda (94502-8009)
PHONE..................................510 263-2000
Stephen Levine, *Ch of Bd*
Manfred Salomon, *CEO*
Susan Levine, *Vice Pres*
Bianca Vasvani, *Marketing Mgr*
Jill Salomon, *Sales Staff*
▲ **EMP:** 50
SQ FT: 29,821
SALES (est): 12.3MM **Privately Held**
WEB: www.allergyresearchgroup.com
SIC: 2834 Vitamin, nutrient & hematinic preparations for human use

(P-8016)
ALPHASCRIPT INC
1160 Industrial Rd Ste 17, San Carlos (94070-4128)
PHONE..................................650 654-2103
Russell Zukin, *CEO*
EMP: 12 **EST:** 2011
SALES (est): 1.7MM **Privately Held**
SIC: 2834 Pharmaceutical preparations

(P-8017)
ALTAVIZ LLC (PA)
13766 Alton Pkwy Ste 143, Irvine (92618-1619)
PHONE..................................949 656-4003
John Huculak, *Mng Member*
Steve Ziemba, *Exec VP*
Jack Auld, *Principal*
Paul Heckler, *Project Engr*
EMP: 10
SALES (est): 1.6MM **Privately Held**
SIC: 2834 8731 Pharmaceutical preparations; biotechnical research, commercial

(P-8018)
ALTURA PHARMACEUTICALS INC
Also Called: Cardinal Pharmaceutical
12540 Mccann Dr, Santa Fe Springs (90670-3337)
PHONE..................................562 906-9000
Primo Cabral, *President*
Cindy Cabral, *CFO*
Ralph Guirago, *Exec VP*
EMP: 25
SQ FT: 15,000
SALES (est): 5.6MM **Privately Held**
WEB: www.cardinalphar.com
SIC: 2834 Pharmaceutical preparations

(P-8019)
ALZA CORPORATION (HQ)
Also Called: Alza Pharmaceuticals
700 Eubanks Dr, Vacaville (95688-9470)
PHONE..................................707 453-6400
Brian Putney, *Mfg Staff*
▲ **EMP:** 800
SQ FT: 74,500

SALES (est): 349.5MM
SALES (corp-wide): 76.4B Publicly Held
WEB: www.alza.com
SIC: 2834 Pharmaceutical preparations
PA: Johnson & Johnson
    1 Johnson And Johnson Plz
    New Brunswick NJ 08933
    732 524-0400

(P-8020)
AMBIT BIOSCIENCES CORPORATION
10201 Wtridge Cir Ste 200, San Diego (92121)
PHONE..................................858 334-2100
Michael A Martino, *President*
Faheem Hasnain, *Ch of Bd*
Alan Fuhrman, *CFO*
Annette North, *Senior VP*
Mario Orlando, *Senior VP*
EMP: 53
SQ FT: 20,000
SALES: 27MM
SALES (corp-wide): 9B Privately Held
WEB: www.ambitbio.com
SIC: 2834 Pharmaceutical preparations
PA: Daiichi Sankyo Company, Limited
    3-5-1, Nihombashihoncho
    Chuo-Ku TKY 103-0
    362 251-111

(P-8021)
AMBRX INC
10975 N Torrey Pines Rd # 100, La Jolla (92037-1051)
PHONE..................................858 875-2400
Tiecheng Qiao, *CEO*
John D Diekman, *Ch of Bd*
Simon Allen, *Officer*
Yong-Jiang HEI, *Officer*
Peter Kiener, *Officer*
EMP: 56
SALES: 20.4MM Privately Held
SIC: 2834 Druggists' preparations (pharmaceuticals)

(P-8022)
AMF PHARMA LLC
1931 S Lynx Ave, Ontario (91761-8055)
PHONE..................................909 930-9599
Zi Meng, *COO*
Trung Bui, *CTO*
Teng Yan, *Engineer*
Huan Pham, *Production*
EMP: 23
SALES (est): 4.9MM Privately Held
SIC: 2834 Pharmaceutical preparations

(P-8023)
AMGEN INC
1909 Oak Terrace Ln, Newbury Park (91320-1732)
PHONE..................................805 499-0512
Sarah Westwood, *Administration*
Carole Mendoza, *Exec Dir*
Jeff Weisiger, *Exec Dir*
Chris Clarke, *Senior Mgr*
Sandhya Patel, *Associate*
EMP: 16
SALES (corp-wide): 22.8B Publicly Held
SIC: 2834 Pharmaceutical preparations
PA: Amgen Inc.
    1 Amgen Center Dr
    Thousand Oaks CA 91320
    805 447-1000

(P-8024)
AMGEN INC
1120 Veterans Blvd, South San Francisco (94080-1985)
PHONE..................................650 244-2000
David V Goeddel, *Site Mgr*
Janis Naeve, *Managing Dir*
Kim Gabel, *District Mgr*
Bruce Eu, *Engrg Dir*
Brandon Ason, *Research*
EMP: 25
SALES (corp-wide): 22.8B Publicly Held
WEB: www.amgen.com
SIC: 2834 Pharmaceutical preparations
PA: Amgen Inc.
    1 Amgen Center Dr
    Thousand Oaks CA 91320
    805 447-1000

(P-8025)
AMGEN INC
1840 De Havilland Dr, Newbury Park (91320-1789)
PHONE..................................805 447-1000
Gordon M Binder, *Manager*
Tia Bush, *Vice Pres*
Scott J Foraker, *Vice Pres*
Barry Cherney, *Exec Dir*
Sandra Ferguson, *Administration*
EMP: 60
SALES (corp-wide): 22.8B Publicly Held
WEB: www.amgen.com
SIC: 2834 Pharmaceutical preparations
PA: Amgen Inc.
    1 Amgen Center Dr
    Thousand Oaks CA 91320
    805 447-1000

(P-8026)
AMPAC FINE CHEMICALS LLC (HQ)
Highway 50 And Hazel Ave, Rancho Cordova (95741)
P.O. Box 1718 (95741-1718)
PHONE..................................916 357-6880
Aslam Malik, *President*
John Sobchak, *CFO*
Richard Beatty, *Vice Pres*
William Dubay, *Vice Pres*
Patrick Park, *Vice Pres*
▲ EMP: 277
SQ FT: 235,000
SALES (est): 152.5MM
SALES (corp-wide): 2.2B Privately Held
WEB: www.apfc.com
SIC: 2834 Pharmaceutical preparations
PA: Sk Holdings Co., Ltd.
    26 Jong-Ro, Jongno-Gu
    Seoul 03188
    822 640-0011

(P-8027)
AMPAC FINE CHEMICALS LLC
Also Called: Ampac Analytical
1100 Windfield Way, El Dorado Hills (95762-9622)
PHONE..................................916 245-6500
Renato Murrer, *Branch Mgr*
EMP: 18
SALES (corp-wide): 2.2B Privately Held
SIC: 2834 Digitalis pharmaceutical preparations
HQ: Ampac Fine Chemicals Llc
    Highway 50 And Hazel Ave
    Rancho Cordova CA 95741
    916 357-6880

(P-8028)
AMPHASTAR PHARMACEUTICALS INC (PA)
11570 6th St, Rancho Cucamonga (91730-6025)
PHONE..................................909 980-9484
Jack Yongfeng Zhang, *CEO*
Mary Ziping Luo, *Ch of Bd*
Jason B Shandell, *President*
William J Peters, *CFO*
Rong Zhou, *Exec VP*
▲ EMP: 140 EST: 1996
SQ FT: 267,674
SALES: 240.1MM Publicly Held
WEB: www.amphastar.com
SIC: 2834 Pharmaceutical preparations

(P-8029)
AMYLIN PHARMACEUTICALS LLC
9373 Twn Cntr Dr 150, San Diego (92101)
PHONE..................................858 552-2200
Fax: 858 552-2212
EMP: 70
SALES (corp-wide): 16.5B Publicly Held
SIC: 2834 8731
HQ: Amylin Pharmaceuticals, Llc
    1800 Concord Pike
    Wilmington DE 19897
    858 552-2200

(P-8030)
ANABOLIC INCORPORATED
Also Called: Vitamer Laboratories
17802 Gillette Ave, Irvine (92614-6502)
P.O. Box 19516 (92623-9516)
PHONE..................................949 863-0340

Steven R Brown, *President*
Jane Drinkwalter, *Vice Pres*
▲ EMP: 95
SALES (est): 11.8MM Privately Held
WEB: www.anabolicabs.com
SIC: 2834 Vitamin preparations

(P-8031)
ANACOR PHARMACEUTICALS INC
1020 E Meadow Cir, Palo Alto (94303-4230)
PHONE..................................650 543-7500
EMP: 20
SALES (corp-wide): 20.6MM Publicly Held
SIC: 2834
PA: Anacor Pharmaceuticals, Inc.
    1020 E Meadow Cir
    Palo Alto CA 10017
    650 543-7500

(P-8032)
ANCHEN PHARMACEUTICALS INC
5 Goodyear, Irvine (92618-2000)
PHONE..................................949 639-8100
Phillip Brancazio, *Owner*
Steve Randazzo, *Mktg Dir*
Maria Santiago, *Senior Mgr*
EMP: 10 Privately Held
SIC: 2834 Druggists' preparations (pharmaceuticals)
HQ: Anchen Pharmaceuticals, Inc.
    9601 Jeronimo Rd
    Irvine CA 92618
    949 639-8100

(P-8033)
ANIVIVE LIFESCIENCES INC
3750 Schaufele Ave # 100, Long Beach (90808-1778)
PHONE..................................714 931-7810
Kwansun Ahn, *CEO*
Warren Rickard, *Principal*
Dylan Balsz, *Exec Dir*
EMP: 10
SALES (est): 366K Privately Held
SIC: 2834 Pharmaceutical preparations

(P-8034)
ANTHERA PHARMACEUTICALS INC
25801 Industrial Blvd B, Hayward (94545-2223)
PHONE..................................510 856-5600
Craig Thompson, *President*
Paul F Truex, *Ch of Bd*
Brent Furse, *Bd of Directors*
Brian Mueller, *Bd of Directors*
Philip Sager, *Bd of Directors*
EMP: 33
SQ FT: 14,000
SALES (est): 145K Privately Held
SIC: 2834 Druggists' preparations (pharmaceuticals)

(P-8035)
AOXING PHARMACEUTICAL CO INC
1098 Foster City Blvd, Foster City (94404-2300)
PHONE..................................646 367-1747
Zhenjiang Yue, *Ch of Bd*
Guirong Zhou, *President*
Zheng James Chen, *CFO*
Guoan Zhang, *Senior VP*
EMP: 346 EST: 2006
SALES: 32.3MM Privately Held
SIC: 2834 Pharmaceutical preparations

(P-8036)
APEXIGEN INC
75 Shoreway Rd Ste C, San Carlos (94070-2727)
PHONE..................................650 931-6236
Xiaodong Yang, *President*
Mark Nevins, *President*
Frances Rena Bahjat, *Vice Pres*
Ovid Trifan, *Vice Pres*
Ovid C Trifan, *Vice Pres*
EMP: 23
SALES (est): 4.8MM Privately Held
SIC: 2834 Pharmaceutical preparations

(P-8037)
APRICUS BIOSCIENCES INC (PA)
11975 El Camino Real, San Diego (92130-2540)
PHONE..................................858 222-8041
Richard W Pascoe, *CEO*
Kleanthis G Xanthopoulos, *Ch of Bd*
Brian T Dorsey, *Senior VP*
Neil Morton, *Senior VP*
EMP: 11
SQ FT: 9,000
SALES (est): 4.2MM Publicly Held
WEB: www.nexmed.com
SIC: 2834 Pharmaceutical preparations

(P-8038)
ARADIGM CORPORATION (PA)
3929 Point Eden Way, Hayward (94545-3720)
PHONE..................................510 265-9000
Igor Gonda, *President*
Virgil D Thompson, *Ch of Bd*
Nancy E Pecota, *CFO*
Juergen Froehlich, *Chief Mktg Ofcr*
Rita Mateo, *Executive Asst*
EMP: 23
SQ FT: 72,000
SALES: 14.4MM Publicly Held
WEB: www.aradigm.com
SIC: 2834 Drugs acting on the respiratory system

(P-8039)
ARDELYX INC
34175 Ardenwood Blvd, Fremont (94555-3653)
PHONE..................................510 745-1700
Michael Raab, *President*
David Mott, *Ch of Bd*
Mark Kaufmann, *CFO*
Bryan Shaw, *CFO*
Robert Bazemore, *Bd of Directors*
EMP: 61
SQ FT: 39,781
SALES: 42MM Privately Held
SIC: 2834 8731 Pharmaceutical preparations; biotechnical research, commercial

(P-8040)
ARENA PHARMACEUTICALS INC (PA)
6154 Nancy Ridge Dr, San Diego (92121-3223)
PHONE..................................858 453-7200
Amit D Munshi, *President*
Kevin R Lind, *CFO*
Scott H Bice, *Bd of Directors*
Jayson Dallas, *Bd of Directors*
Oliver Fetzer, *Bd of Directors*
EMP: 66
SQ FT: 131,000
SALES: 21.3MM Publicly Held
WEB: www.arenapharm.com
SIC: 2834 Pharmaceutical preparations

(P-8041)
ARETE THERAPEUTICS INC
52 Buena Vista Ter, San Francisco (94117-4111)
PHONE..................................650 737-4600
Garrett Roper, *Principal*
EMP: 12
SALES (est): 2.1MM Privately Held
SIC: 2834 Druggists' preparations (pharmaceuticals)

(P-8042)
ARIDIS PHARMACEUTICALS INC
5941 Optical Ct, San Jose (95138-1410)
PHONE..................................408 385-1742
Vu Truong, *CEO*
Eric Patzer, *Ch of Bd*
Fred Kurland, *CFO*
Isaac Blech, *Vice Ch Bd*
Wolfgang Dummer, *Chief Mktg Ofcr*
EMP: 30
SQ FT: 4,500
SALES: 860K Privately Held
WEB: www.aridispharma.com
SIC: 2834 Pharmaceutical preparations

▲ = Import ▼=Export
◆ =Import/Export

(P-8043)
ARMO BIOSCIENCES INC
575 Chesapeake Dr, Redwood City
(94063-4724)
PHONE..................................650 779-5075
Peter Van Vlasselaer, *President*
Herb Cross, *CFO*
Joseph Leveque, *Chief Mktg Ofcr*
Russell Kawahata, *Vice Pres*
Clinton Musil, *Vice Pres*
EMP: 21 **EST:** 2010
SQ FT: 11,388
SALES (est): 2.7MM
SALES (corp-wide): 22.8B **Publicly Held**
SIC: 2834 Pharmaceutical preparations
PA: Eli Lilly And Company
Lilly Corporate Ctr
Indianapolis IN 46285
317 276-2000

(P-8044)
ARROWHEAD
PHARMACEUTICALS INC (PA)
225 S Lake Ave Ste 1050, Pasadena
(91101-4820)
PHONE..................................626 304-3400
Christopher Anzalone, *President*
Douglass Given, *Ch of Bd*
Bruce Given, *COO*
Ken Myszkowski, *CFO*
Kenneth A Myszkowski, *CFO*
EMP: 11
SQ FT: 8,500
SALES (est): 31.4MM **Publicly Held**
WEB: www.arrowres.com
SIC: 2834 8731 Pharmaceutical preparations; biological research

(P-8045)
ASCENDIS PHARMA INC
500 Emerson St, Palo Alto (94301-1607)
PHONE..................................650 352-8389
Jan Mller Mikkelsen, *President*
Flemming Steen Jensen, *President*
Scott T Smith, *CFO*
Michael Wolff Jensen, *Chairman*
Jonathan Leff MD, *Officer*
EMP: 16 **EST:** 2013
SALES (est): 78.8K **Privately Held**
SIC: 2834 Pharmaceutical preparations

(P-8046)
ASCLEMED USA INC
379 Van Ness Ave Ste 1403, Torrance
(90501-7211)
PHONE..................................310 218-4146
Robert Nickell, *President*
Joseph J Dekellis, *Admin Sec*
▲ **EMP:** 10
SQ FT: 8,500
SALES (est): 1.6MM **Privately Held**
SIC: 2834 Pharmaceutical preparations

(P-8047)
ASKGENE PHARMA INC
5217 Verdugo Way Ste A, Camarillo
(93012-8642)
PHONE..................................805 807-9868
Robert Wynner, *Principal*
Yuefeng Lu, *Vice Pres*
EMP: 11 **EST:** 2013
SALES (est): 2.4MM **Privately Held**
SIC: 2834 Pharmaceutical preparations

(P-8048)
ASTEX PHARMACEUTICALS
INC (DH)
4420 Rosewood Dr Ste 200, Pleasanton
(94588-3008)
PHONE..................................925 560-0100
James S J Manuso, *Ch of Bd*
Harren Jhoti, *President*
Michael Molkentin, *CFO*
Mohammad Azab, *Officer*
Martin Buckland, *Officer*
EMP: 78
SQ FT: 37,000
SALES (est): 17.5MM
SALES (corp-wide): 11B **Privately Held**
WEB: www.supergen.com
SIC: 2834 Pharmaceutical preparations
HQ: Otsuka Pharmaceutical Co., Ltd.
2-16-4, Konan
Minato-Ku TKY 108-0
367 171-400

(P-8049)
ASTRAZENECA
PHARMACEUTICALS LP
200 Cardinal Way, Redwood City
(94063-4756)
PHONE..................................650 305-2600
Ed Louie, *Branch Mgr*
EMP: 26
SALES (corp-wide): 22.4B **Privately Held**
SIC: 2834 Druggists' preparations (pharmaceuticals)
HQ: Astrazeneca Pharmaceuticals Lp
1 Medimmune Way
Gaithersburg MD 20878

(P-8050)
AURITEC PHARMACEUTICALS
INC
3200 Santa Monica Blvd # 201, Santa Monica (90404-2639)
PHONE..................................424 272-9501
Thomas Smith, *President*
Frederic Ransom, *President*
Amanda Malone, *Vice Pres*
Meredith Blake, *General Mgr*
Sarjan Shah, *Project Mgr*
EMP: 13
SQ FT: 250
SALES (est): 1.9MM **Privately Held**
WEB: www.auritecpharma.com
SIC: 2834 Proprietary drug products

(P-8051)
AURO PHARMACEUTICALS INC
511 S Harbor Blvd Ste F, La Habra
(90631-9375)
PHONE..................................562 352-9630
Nayan Patel, *President*
Ashwin Patel, *Treasurer*
Yogesh Patel, *Admin Sec*
EMP: 15 **EST:** 2013
SALES (est): 886.8K **Privately Held**
SIC: 2834 Druggists' preparations (pharmaceuticals)

(P-8052)
AURO PHARMACIES INC
Also Called: Central Drugs
511 S Harbor Blvd Ste F, La Habra
(90631-9375)
PHONE..................................562 352-9630
Nayan Patel, *Branch Mgr*
EMP: 30
SALES (corp-wide): 15MM **Privately Held**
SIC: 2834 Pharmaceutical preparations
PA: Auro Pharmacies, Inc.
520 W La Habra Blvd
La Habra CA 90631
562 691-6754

(P-8053)
AUSPEX PHARMACEUTICALS
INC
3333 N Torrey Pines Ct, La Jolla
(92037-1023)
P.O. Box 49272, Los Angeles (90049-0272)
PHONE..................................858 558-2400
Larry Downey, *President*
Deborah A Griffin, *CFO*
Tadimeti RAO, *Vice Pres*
Austin D Kim, *Admin Sec*
Jim Kerr, *Engineer*
EMP: 30
SALES (est): 8MM
SALES (corp-wide): 22.3B **Privately Held**
WEB: www.auspexpharma.com
SIC: 2834 Pharmaceutical preparations
PA: Teva Pharmaceutical Industries Limited
5 Bazel
Petah Tikva 49510
392 672-67

(P-8054)
AVANIR PHARMACEUTICALS
INC (DH)
30 Enterprise Ste 400, Aliso Viejo
(92656-7106)
PHONE..................................949 389-6700
Rohan Palekar, *President*
Gregory J Flesher, *Senior VP*
Richard Malamut, *Senior VP*
Joao Siffert, *Senior VP*
Christine G Ocampo,

EMP: 164
SQ FT: 69,000
SALES (est): 125.7MM
SALES (corp-wide): 11B **Privately Held**
SIC: 2834 Pharmaceutical preparations
HQ: Otsuka Pharmaceutical Co., Ltd.
2-16-4, Konan
Minato-Ku TKY 108-0
367 171-400

(P-8055)
AVID BIOSERVICES INC (PA)
2642 Michelle Dr Ste 200, Tustin
(92780-7019)
PHONE..................................714 508-6000
Roger J Lias, *President*
Joseph Carleone, *Ch of Bd*
Daniel Hart, *CFO*
Mark R Ziebell, *Vice Pres*
EMP: 151
SQ FT: 183,000
SALES: 53.6MM **Publicly Held**
WEB: www.peregrineinc.com
SIC: 2834 Pharmaceutical preparations

(P-8056)
AVID BIOSERVICES INC
14191 Myford Rd, Tustin (92780-7020)
PHONE..................................714 508-6000
Steven W King, *President*
EMP: 21
SALES (corp-wide): 53.6MM **Publicly Held**
SIC: 2834 Pharmaceutical preparations
PA: Avid Bioservices, Inc.
2642 Michelle Dr Ste 200
Tustin CA 92780
714 508-6000

(P-8057)
AXM PHARMA INC
20955 Pathfinder Rd # 100, Diamond Bar
(91765-4029)
PHONE..................................909 843-6338
Linda L Forster, *CEO*
Wang WEI Shi, *Ch of Bd*
Baozhong Zhang, *President*
EMP: 150
SALES (est): 11.4MM **Privately Held**
WEB: www.axmpharma.com
SIC: 2834 Antacids

(P-8058)
BACHEM AMERICAS INC
Also Called: Bachem Vista BSD
1271 Avenida Chelsea, Vista (92081-8315)
PHONE..................................888 422-2436
Brian Gregg, *President*
Sean Prorak, *Engineer*
EMP: 17 **Privately Held**
SIC: 2834 Pharmaceutical preparations
HQ: Bachem Americas, Inc.
3132 Kashiwa St
Torrance CA 90505
310 784-4440

(P-8059)
BAUSCH & LOMB
INCORPORATED
50 Technology Dr, Irvine (92618-2301)
PHONE..................................949 788-6000
EMP: 75
SALES (corp-wide): 5.7B **Privately Held**
SIC: 2834
HQ: Bausch & Lomb Incorporated
1 Bausch And Lomb Pl
Rochester NY 14609
585 338-5442

(P-8060)
BAXALTA INCORPORATED
4501 Colorado Blvd, Los Angeles
(90039-1103)
PHONE..................................818 240-5600
Raul Navarro, *Branch Mgr*
Linda Wong, *Lab Dir*
Frank Ross, *Info Tech Mgr*
John Laux, *Engng Exec*
John Swenson, *Research*
EMP: 1000
SALES (corp-wide): 15.1B **Privately Held**
SIC: 2834 Pharmaceutical preparations
HQ: Baxalta Incorporated
1200 Lakeside Dr
Bannockburn IL 60015
224 940-2000

(P-8061)
BAXTER HEALTHCARE
CORPORATION
Baxter Hospital Supply
4551 E Philadelphia St, Ontario
(91761-2316)
PHONE..................................303 222-6837
Richard S Justin, *Opers-Prdtn-Mfg*
EMP: 150
SALES (corp-wide): 10.5B **Publicly Held**
SIC: 2834 Pharmaceutical preparations
HQ: Baxter Healthcare Corporation
1 Baxter Pkwy
Deerfield IL 60015
224 948-2000

(P-8062)
BAXTER HEALTHCARE
CORPORATION
2024 W Winton Ave, Hayward
(94545-1208)
PHONE..................................510 723-2000
Elden Naea, *Manager*
Joe Stewart, *CTO*
Zachary Fletcher, *Research*
Grace Gallagher, *Research*
Lei Wong, *Engineer*
EMP: 11
SALES (est): 1.7MM **Privately Held**
SIC: 2834 Pharmaceutical preparations

(P-8063)
BAYER HEALTHCARE LLC
455 Mission Bay Blvd S # 493, San Francisco (94158-2158)
PHONE..................................415 437-5800
Douglas Schneider, *Manager*
Arnel Agapito, *Manager*
EMP: 252
SALES (corp-wide): 41.2B **Privately Held**
SIC: 2834 Pharmaceutical preparations
HQ: Bayer Healthcare Llc
100 Bayer Blvd
Whippany NJ 07981
862 404-3000

(P-8064)
BAYER HEALTHCARE LLC
5885 Hollis St, Emeryville (94608-2404)
PHONE..................................510 597-6150
Anita Bawa, *Branch Mgr*
EMP: 104
SALES (corp-wide): 41.2B **Privately Held**
SIC: 2834 Pharmaceutical preparations
HQ: Bayer Healthcare Llc
100 Bayer Blvd
Whippany NJ 07981
862 404-3000

(P-8065)
BAYER HEALTHCARE LLC
800 Dwight Way, Berkeley (94710-2428)
PHONE..................................510 705-7545
Paul Heiden, *Branch Mgr*
Shachi Sharma, *Associate Dir*
John Dang, *General Mgr*
Laura Yee, *Project Mgr*
Vijay Adda, *Senior Engr*
EMP: 134
SALES (corp-wide): 41.2B **Privately Held**
SIC: 2834 Pharmaceutical preparations
HQ: Bayer Healthcare Llc
100 Bayer Blvd
Whippany NJ 07981
862 404-3000

(P-8066)
BAYER HEALTHCARE LLC
Biological Products Division
717 Potter St Street-2, Berkeley
(94710-2722)
PHONE..................................510 705-7539
Jay Keasling, *Branch Mgr*
EMP: 252
SALES (corp-wide): 41.2B **Privately Held**
SIC: 2834 Pharmaceutical preparations
HQ: Bayer Healthcare Llc
100 Bayer Blvd
Whippany NJ 07981
862 404-3000

PRODUCTS & SVCS

(P-8067)
BAYER HEALTHCARE LLC
747 Grayson St, Berkeley (94710-2615)
P.O. Box 6314, Wheeling WV (26003-0734)
PHONE..................................510 705-4421
EMP: 134
SQ FT: 1,964
SALES (corp-wide): 41.2B **Privately Held**
SIC: 2834 Pharmaceutical preparations
HQ: Bayer Healthcare Llc
    100 Bayer Blvd
    Whippany NJ 07981
    862 404-3000

(P-8068)
BAYER HEALTHCARE LLC
2448 6th St, Berkeley (94710-2414)
PHONE..................................510 705-4914
Stan Pinder, *President*
EMP: 134
SALES (corp-wide): 41.2B **Privately Held**
SIC: 2834 Pharmaceutical preparations
HQ: Bayer Healthcare Llc
    100 Bayer Blvd
    Whippany NJ 07981
    862 404-3000

(P-8069)
BAYER HEALTHCARE LLC
Also Called: Bayer Diabetes Care
510 Oakmead Pkwy, Sunnyvale (94085-4022)
PHONE..................................408 499-0606
Joseph Ruggiero, *Manager*
EMP: 60
SALES (corp-wide): 41.2B **Privately Held**
SIC: 2834 Pharmaceutical preparations
HQ: Bayer Healthcare Llc
    100 Bayer Blvd
    Whippany NJ 07981
    862 404-3000

(P-8070)
BAYER HLTHCARE PHRMCTICALS INC
Also Called: Berlex Bioscience
455 Mission Bay Blvd S, San Francisco (94158-2158)
P.O. Box 4099, Richmond (94804-0099)
PHONE..................................510 262-5000
David A Scrimger, *Manager*
Cr Willis Jr, *Vice Pres*
EMP: 400
SALES (corp-wide): 41.2B **Privately Held**
SIC: 2834 8731 Pharmaceutical preparations; commercial physical research
HQ: Bayer Healthcare Pharmaceuticals Inc.
    100 Bayer Blvd
    Whippany NJ 07981
    862 404-3000

(P-8071)
BAYLISS BOTANICALS LLC
17 W Rio Bonito Rd, Biggs (95917)
PHONE..................................530 868-5466
Pedro Convalez, *Mng Member*
EMP: 10 EST: 2010
SALES (est): 46K **Privately Held**
SIC: 2834 Extracts of botanicals: powdered, pilular, solid or fluid

(P-8072)
BEAUTY & HEALTH INTERNATIONAL (PA)
7541 Anthony Ave, Garden Grove (92841-4005)
P.O. Box 890, Westminster (92684-0890)
PHONE..................................714 903-9730
Charles G Myung, *President*
John Myuong, *Manager*
▲ EMP: 20
SQ FT: 12,000
SALES (est): 5.5MM **Privately Held**
WEB: www.nutriwell.net
SIC: 2834 2844 5122 5149 Vitamin preparations; cosmetic preparations; vitamins & minerals; cosmetics; health foods; health & dietetic food stores

(P-8073)
BERKELEY NUTRITIONAL MFG CORP
Also Called: Protein Research
1852 Rutan Dr, Livermore (94551-7635)
PHONE..................................925 243-6300
Robert Matheson, *President*
Ashley Matheson, *Vice Pres*
Gary Troxel, *Vice Pres*
Joy Stanton, *Manager*
▲ EMP: 60
SQ FT: 53,900
SALES (est): 19.1MM **Privately Held**
WEB: www.proteinresearch.com
SIC: 2834 Vitamin preparations

(P-8074)
BIMEDA INC
5539 Ayon Ave, Irwindale (91706-2057)
PHONE..................................626 815-1680
Tim Tynan, *Branch Mgr*
EMP: 14 **Privately Held**
WEB: www.bimeda.com
SIC: 2834 3841 Veterinary pharmaceutical preparations; surgical & medical instruments
HQ: Bimeda Inc.
    1 Tower Ln Ste 2250
    Oakbrook Terrace IL 60181
    630 928-0361

(P-8075)
BIO-NUTRACEUTICALS INC
Also Called: Bni
21820 Marilla St, Chatsworth (91311-4127)
PHONE..................................818 727-0246
Gerald Farris, *President*
Yesenia Ortega, *Admin Asst*
Samad Mridha, *Research*
Denise Ruiz, *Human Res Mgr*
Dawn Hernandez, *Purchasing*
EMP: 64
SALES (est): 17.4MM **Privately Held**
SIC: 2834 Tablets, pharmaceutical

(P-8076)
BIOCALTH INTERNATIONAL INC
1920 Wright Ave, La Verne (91750-5819)
PHONE..................................909 267-3988
Jackson Wen, *CEO*
▲ EMP: 12
SQ FT: 22,000
SALES (est): 1.6MM **Privately Held**
SIC: 2834 Vitamin, nutrient & hematinic preparations for human use

(P-8077)
BIOKEY INC
44370 Old Warm Springs Bl, Fremont (94538-6148)
PHONE..................................510 668-0881
San-Laung Chow, *President*
George Lee, *President*
Paul Dickinson, *QC Mgr*
▼ EMP: 20 EST: 2000
SQ FT: 28,000
SALES (est): 2MM **Privately Held**
SIC: 2834 Pharmaceutical preparations

(P-8078)
BIOMARIN PHARMACEUTICAL INC (PA)
770 Lindaro St, San Rafael (94901-3991)
PHONE..................................415 506-6700
Jean-Jacques Bienaime, *Ch of Bd*
Daniel Spiegelman, *CFO*
Jeff Ajer, *Ch Credit Ofcr*
Robert A Baffi, *Exec VP*
G Eric Davis, *Exec VP*
EMP: 350
SQ FT: 391,700
SALES: 1.3B **Publicly Held**
WEB: www.biomarinpharm.com
SIC: 2834 2835 Pharmaceutical preparations; enzyme & isoenzyme diagnostic agents

(P-8079)
BIOMARIN PHARMACEUTICAL INC
79 Digital Dr, Novato (94949-5788)
PHONE..................................415 218-7386
Rachel Foreman, *Research*
EMP: 16

SALES (corp-wide): 1.3B **Publicly Held**
SIC: 2834 Pharmaceutical preparations
PA: Biomarin Pharmaceutical Inc.
    770 Lindaro St
    San Rafael CA 94901
    415 506-6700

(P-8080)
BIONORICA LLC
903 Calle Amanecer # 110, San Clemente (92673-6253)
PHONE..................................949 361-4900
Scott C Bukow, *Mng Member*
Amy Bukow,
EMP: 12
SALES (est): 1.9MM **Privately Held**
SIC: 2834 Cough medicines

(P-8081)
BIOPHARMX CORPORATION (PA)
1505 Adams Dr Ste D, Menlo Park (94025-1451)
PHONE..................................650 889-5020
David S Tierney, *CEO*
Michael Hubbard, *Ch of Bd*
Anja Krammer, *President*
Greg Kitchener, *CFO*
Kin F Chan, *Exec VP*
EMP: 21
SQ FT: 12,203
SALES: 73K **Publicly Held**
SIC: 2834 Pharmaceutical preparations

(P-8082)
BIOVAIL TECHNOLOGIES LTD
1 Enterprise, Aliso Viejo (92656-2606)
PHONE..................................703 995-2400
David Tierney, *President*
EMP: 125
SQ FT: 55,000
SALES (est): 20.5MM
SALES (corp-wide): 8.7B **Privately Held**
SIC: 2834 8731 3841 2087 Pharmaceutical preparations; commercial physical research; surgical & medical instruments; flavoring extracts & syrups
PA: Bausch Health Companies Inc
    2150 Boul Saint-Elzear O
    Sainte-Rose QC H7L 4
    514 744-6792

(P-8083)
BIOZONE LABORATORIES INC (DH)
Also Called: Bio-Zone Laboratories
580 Garcia Ave, Pittsburg (94565-4901)
PHONE..................................925 473-1000
Richard Fischler, *Mng Member*
Jim Casey, *COO*
Christian Oertle, *Managing Dir*
Stacey Laneve, *Sales Staff*
Tung Ngo, *Asst Director*
◆ EMP: 13
SQ FT: 52,000
SALES (est): 3MM
SALES (corp-wide): 5.6MM **Publicly Held**
WEB: www.biozonelabs.com
SIC: 2834 Pharmaceutical preparations

(P-8084)
BIOZONE LABORATORIES INC
701 Willow Pass Rd Ste 8, Pittsburg (94565-1803)
PHONE..................................925 431-1010
Amhed Shaikh, *Manager*
EMP: 40
SALES (corp-wide): 5.6MM **Publicly Held**
SIC: 2834 5122 8071 Pharmaceutical preparations; drugs, proprietaries & sundries; biological laboratory
HQ: Biozone Laboratories, Inc.
    580 Garcia Ave
    Pittsburg CA 94565
    925 473-1000

(P-8085)
BOIRON INC
4145 Guardian St, Simi Valley (93063-3382)
PHONE..................................805 527-9883
Daniel Derseser, *Manager*
EMP: 11

SALES (corp-wide): 576.4MM **Privately Held**
WEB: www.boiron.com
SIC: 2834 Pharmaceutical preparations
HQ: Boiron, Inc.
    6 Campus Blvd
    Newtown Square PA 19073
    610 325-7464

(P-8086)
BRIGHT HORIZONS AT GILEAD
301 Velocity Way, Foster City (94404-4803)
PHONE..................................650 312-1895
Christina Enerio, *Director*
EMP: 21 EST: 2013
SALES (est): 5.9MM **Privately Held**
SIC: 2834 Pharmaceutical preparations

(P-8087)
BRISTOL - MYERS SQIBB SNNYVALE
700 Bay Rd, Redwood City (94063-2477)
PHONE..................................609 897-2110
Shrikant Deshpande, *Principal*
EMP: 13
SALES (est): 2.4MM **Privately Held**
SIC: 2834 Pharmaceutical preparations

(P-8088)
C S BIO CO
20 Kelly Ct, Menlo Park (94025-1418)
PHONE..................................650 322-1111
Heng WEI Chang, *CEO*
Dario Slavazza, *President*
Bill Dong, *Info Tech Mgr*
Jason Chang, *VP Opers*
Zoe Liang, *Director*
▲ EMP: 10
SQ FT: 5,000
SALES (est): 4.1MM **Privately Held**
WEB: www.csbio.com
SIC: 2834 Pharmaceutical preparations

(P-8089)
C3 BIOSCIENCES INC
3 Grassy Knoll Ln, Rcho STA Marg (92688-5567)
PHONE..................................949 635-9963
David Rose, *CEO*
Bryan Hoynak, *COO*
Gary Mecca, *CFO*
EMP: 15
SALES (est): 1MM **Privately Held**
SIC: 2834 Pharmaceutical preparations

(P-8090)
C8 MEDISENSORS INC
6375 San Ignacio Ave, San Jose (95119-1200)
PHONE..................................408 623-7281
John B Kaiser, *CEO*
Fred Toney, *CFO*
Rudy Hofmeister, *Exec VP*
Viet Ngo, *Vice Pres*
EMP: 30
SQ FT: 50,000
SALES (est): 10.8MM **Privately Held**
SIC: 2834 Pharmaceutical preparations

(P-8091)
CALIFORNIA NATURAL VITAMINS
Also Called: The Vitamin Barn
9044 Independence Ave, Canoga Park (91304-1742)
PHONE..................................818 772-8441
Gene Arnold, *President*
EMP: 22
SALES (est): 3MM **Privately Held**
WEB: www.thevitaminbarn.com
SIC: 2834 Vitamin preparations

(P-8092)
CALIFORNIA PHARMACEUTICALS LLC
768 Calle Plano, Camarillo (93012-8555)
PHONE..................................805 482-3737
Edgar Lozano, *Manager*
EMP: 19 EST: 2008
SALES (est): 3.1MM **Privately Held**
SIC: 2834 Pharmaceutical preparations

▲ = Import ▼=Export
◆ =Import/Export

(P-8093)
CALIMMUNE INC
129 N Hill Ave Ste 105, Pasadena (91106-1961)
PHONE...................................310 806-6240
Mary Santos, *Manager*
EMP: 14 **Privately Held**
SIC: 2834 Pharmaceutical preparations
HQ: Calimmune, Inc.
5151 E Brdwy Blvd Ste 700
Tucson AZ 85711
-

(P-8094)
CALITHERA BIOSCIENCES INC
343 Oyster Point Blvd, South San Francisco (94080-1913)
PHONE...................................650 870-1000
Susan M Molineaux, *President*
William D Waddill, *CFO*
Mark K Bennett, *Senior VP*
Christopher J Molineaux, *Senior VP*
Sumita Ray, *Senior VP*
EMP: 44
SALES: 25.9MM **Privately Held**
SIC: 2834 8731 Pharmaceutical preparations; biotechnical research, commercial

(P-8095)
CALMOSEPTINE INC
16602 Burke Ln, Huntington Beach (92647-4536)
PHONE...................................714 848-2949
Gregory Dixon, *CEO*
Kim Saeng, *Admin Asst*
▲ **EMP:** 10
SQ FT: 5,368
SALES (est): 2.9MM **Privately Held**
WEB: www.calmoseptine.com
SIC: 2834 Ointments

(P-8096)
CAMTEK LLC
2645 Nina St, Pasadena (91107-3710)
PHONE...................................626 508-1700
Delbert White, *President*
EMP: 10
SQ FT: 15,000
SALES: 900K **Privately Held**
SIC: 2834 1541 Pharmaceutical preparations; pharmaceutical manufacturing plant construction

(P-8097)
CANTABIO PHARMACEUTICALS INC
1250 Oakmead Pkwy Ste 210, Sunnyvale (94085-4035)
PHONE...................................408 501-8893
Gergely Toth, *CEO*
EMP: 12 **EST:** 2016
SQ FT: 3,800
SALES (est): 579.9K **Privately Held**
SIC: 2834 Pharmaceutical preparations

(P-8098)
CAPRICOR THERAPEUTICS INC (PA)
8840 Wilshire Blvd Fl 2, Beverly Hills (90211-2606)
PHONE...................................310 358-3200
Linda Marban, *President*
Frank Litvack, *Ch of Bd*
Anthony Bergmann, *CFO*
Deborah Ascheim, *Chief Mktg Ofcr*
Karen G Krasney, *Exec VP*
EMP: 19
SALES: 2.6MM **Publicly Held**
SIC: 2834 Pharmaceutical preparations

(P-8099)
CAPS CORPORATE OFFICE
10370 Slusher Dr Ste 3, Santa Fe Springs (90670-6070)
PHONE...................................562 941-9515
Gary Grandfield, *Director*
EMP: 30
SALES (est): 3.6MM **Privately Held**
SIC: 2834 Pharmaceutical preparations

(P-8100)
CARDINAL HEALTH 414 LLC
640 S Jefferson St, Placentia (92870-6600)
PHONE...................................714 572-9900
Shanam Biglari, *Manager*

Van Tran, *Pharmacy Dir*
Rachi Pichon, *Pharmacist*
EMP: 35
SALES (corp-wide): 136.8B **Publicly Held**
WEB: www.syncor.com
SIC: 2834 5912 Pharmaceutical preparations; drug stores & proprietary stores
HQ: Cardinal Health 414, Llc
7000 Cardinal Pl
Dublin OH 43017
614 757-5000

(P-8101)
CARLSBAD TECHNOLOGY INC
5928 Farnsworth Ct, Carlsbad (92008-7303)
PHONE...................................760 431-8284
Angie Hsu, *Principal*
WEI Yung Lee, *CEO*
Wan Jung Hsu, *Associate*
EMP: 15
SALES (corp-wide): 220MM **Privately Held**
SIC: 2834 Pharmaceutical preparations
HQ: Carlsbad Technology Inc.
5922 Farnsworth Ct # 102
Carlsbad CA 92008

(P-8102)
CARLSBAD TECHNOLOGY INC (DH)
5922 Farnsworth Ct # 102, Carlsbad (92008-7398)
PHONE...................................760 431-8284
WEI Yung Lee, *CEO*
Andy Cheng, *COO*
Trevor Whitehead, *Executive*
Ben Ching, *CIO*
Erin Greenwell, *Project Mgr*
▲ **EMP:** 100
SQ FT: 27,000
SALES (est): 17.1MM
SALES (corp-wide): 220MM **Privately Held**
WEB: www.carlsbadtech.com
SIC: 2834 Druggists' preparations (pharmaceuticals)
HQ: Yung Shin Pharm. Ind. Co., Ltd.
1191, Chung Shan Rd., Sec. 1,
Taichung City 43744
426 875-100

(P-8103)
CARLSBAD TECHNOLOGY INC
5923 Balfour Ct, Carlsbad (92008-7304)
PHONE...................................760 431-8284
Kwok Wan Robert Wan, *President*
WEI Yung Lee, *CEO*
Cheong Yik, *Technology*
Emily Lee, *Supervisor*
Wan Jung Hsu, *Associate*
EMP: 58
SALES (corp-wide): 220MM **Privately Held**
SIC: 2834 Druggists' preparations (pharmaceuticals)
HQ: Carlsbad Technology Inc.
5922 Farnsworth Ct # 102
Carlsbad CA 92008
-

(P-8104)
CATALINA LIFESCIENCES INC
Also Called: A Division of Metagenics
25 Enterprise Ste 200, Aliso Viejo (92656-2713)
PHONE...................................800 898-6888
Thomas Kinder, *President*
▼ **EMP:** 26
SQ FT: 7,800
SALES (est): 5MM
SALES (corp-wide): 8.7B **Privately Held**
SIC: 2834 Vitamin, nutrient & hematinic preparations for human use
HQ: Metagenics, Inc.
25 Enterprise Ste 200
Aliso Viejo CA 92656
949 366-0818

(P-8105)
CATALYST BIOSCIENCES INC (PA)
611 Gateway Blvd Ste 710, South San Francisco (94080)
PHONE...................................650 266-8674
Nassim Usman, *President*
Augustine Lawlor, *Ch of Bd*
Fletcher Payne, *CFO*
Errol De Souza, *Bd of Directors*
Stephen Hill, *Bd of Directors*
EMP: 13
SQ FT: 12,965
SALES: 1MM **Publicly Held**
WEB: www.targacept.com
SIC: 2834 Pharmaceutical preparations

(P-8106)
CELGENE CORPORATION
10300 Campus Point Dr # 100, San Diego (92121-1504)
PHONE...................................858 558-7500
Alan Louis, *President*
Thu Thai, *Executive*
Paul Ryan, *Associate Dir*
Reagan West, *District Mgr*
Alyse Faraone, *Technician*
EMP: 100
SALES (corp-wide): 13B **Publicly Held**
WEB: www.celgene.com
SIC: 2834 Pharmaceutical preparations
PA: Celgene Corporation
86 Morris Ave
Summit NJ 07901
908 673-9000

(P-8107)
CENTRAL ADMXTURE PHRM SVCS INC (DH)
Also Called: Caps
2525 Mcgaw Ave, Irvine (92614-5841)
P.O. Box 19791 (92623-9791)
PHONE...................................949 660-2000
Tom Wilverding, *President*
Lisa Segal, *Controller*
Michael Koch, *VP Mktg*
EMP: 10
SALES (est): 92.5MM **Privately Held**
WEB: www.capspharmacy.com
SIC: 2834 5122 Pharmaceutical preparations; pharmaceuticals
HQ: B. Braun Medical Inc.
824 12th Ave
Bethlehem PA 18018
610 691-5400

(P-8108)
CENTRAL ADMXTURE PHRM SVCS INC
Also Called: C A P S
10370 Slusher Dr Ste 6, Santa Fe Springs (90670-6067)
PHONE...................................562 941-9595
Gary Grandfield, *Branch Mgr*
Peter Huang, *Prdtn Mgr*
Juanita A Harris, *Manager*
EMP: 30 **Privately Held**
WEB: www.capspharmacy.com
SIC: 2834 5122 Pharmaceutical preparations; pharmaceuticals
HQ: Central Admixture Pharmacy Services, Inc.
2525 Mcgaw Ave
Irvine CA 92614

(P-8109)
CENTRAL ADMXTURE PHRM SVCS INC
7935 Dunbrook Rd Ste C, San Diego (92126-6322)
PHONE...................................858 578-1380
Mike Rainey, *Owner*
EMP: 24 **Privately Held**
WEB: www.capspharmacy.com
SIC: 2834 Pharmaceutical preparations
HQ: Central Admixture Pharmacy Services, Inc.
2525 Mcgaw Ave
Irvine CA 92614

(P-8110)
CH LABORATORIES INC
1243 W 130th St, Gardena (90247-1501)
PHONE...................................310 516-8273
Brid Nolan, *President*
EMP: 25
SQ FT: 30,000
SALES (est): 5.3MM **Privately Held**
WEB: www.chlaboratories.com
SIC: 2834 Vitamin preparations

(P-8111)
CHA BIO & DIOSTECH CO LTD
3731 Wilshire Blvd # 850, Los Angeles (90010-2830)
PHONE...................................213 487-3211
Kyung Rae Kim, *Director*
EMP: 95 **EST:** 2011
SALES (est): 5.3MM **Privately Held**
SIC: 2834 Pharmaceutical preparations

(P-8112)
CHEMOCENTRYX INC (PA)
850 Maude Ave, Mountain View (94043-4022)
PHONE...................................650 210-2900
Thomas J Schall, *Ch of Bd*
William C Fairey Jr, *COO*
Markus J Cappel, *Treasurer*
Thomas Edwards, *Bd of Directors*
Joseph Feczko, *Bd of Directors*
EMP: 66
SQ FT: 35,755
SALES: 82.5MM **Publicly Held**
WEB: www.chemocentryx.com
SIC: 2834 Drugs affecting parasitic & infective diseases

(P-8113)
CITRAGEN PHARMACEUTICALS INC
3789 Spinnaker Ct, Fremont (94538-6537)
PHONE...................................510 249-9066
Ravichandran Mahalingam, *CEO*
Ravi Jayapal, *Vice Pres*
EMP: 10
SALES (est): 1.6MM **Privately Held**
SIC: 2834 Pharmaceutical preparations

(P-8114)
CLINICAL FORMULA LLC
888 W 16th St, Newport Beach (92663-2802)
PHONE...................................949 631-0149
Ken Kutanakit, *CEO*
▲ **EMP:** 10
SALES (est): 990K **Privately Held**
SIC: 2834 Dermatologicals

(P-8115)
COHERUS BIOSCIENCES INC (PA)
333 Twin Dolphin Dr # 600, Redwood City (94065-1442)
PHONE...................................650 649-3530
Dennis M Lanfear, *Ch of Bd*
Jean-Frederic Viret, *CFO*
Barbara K Finck, *Chief Mktg Ofcr*
Alan C Herman, *Officer*
Peter K Watler, *Senior VP*
EMP: 79
SALES: 1.5MM **Publicly Held**
SIC: 2834 Pharmaceutical preparations

(P-8116)
COLBY PHARMACEUTICAL COMPANY (PA)
1095 Colby Ave Ste C, Menlo Park (94025-2334)
PHONE...................................650 333-3150
David A Zarling, *CEO*
EMP: 13
SQ FT: 1,623
SALES (est): 1.6MM **Privately Held**
SIC: 2834 Pharmaceutical preparations

(P-8117)
COLLIDION INC (PA)
1770 Corporate Cir, Petaluma (94954-6924)
PHONE...................................707 668-7600
Hoji Alimi, *Ch of Bd*
William Watson, *President*
Sameer Harish, *Finance Dir*
EMP: 10

SALES (est): 1.2MM **Privately Held**
SIC: 2834 Pharmaceutical preparations

(P-8118)
COMPRHNSIVE CRDVSCLAR SPCALIST (PA)
220 S 1st St Ste 101, Alhambra (91801-3705)
PHONE..............................626 281-8663
Peter Fung, *President*
Michael Yeh, *Cardiology*
Annie Saovalaksakul, *Assistant*
EMP: 34
SALES (est): 6.1MM **Privately Held**
SIC: 2834 8111 Drugs acting on the cardiovascular system, except diagnostic; legal services

(P-8119)
CONCENTRIC ANALGESICS INC
1824 Jackson St Apt A, San Francisco (94109-2871)
PHONE..............................415 771-5129
John F Donovan, *Owner*
Mike A Royal, *Officer*
EMP: 10
SALES (est): 411.9K **Privately Held**
SIC: 2834 Analgesics

(P-8120)
CONTINENTAL VITAMIN CO INC
Also Called: Cvc Specialties
4510 S Boyle Ave, Vernon (90058-2418)
PHONE..............................323 581-0176
Ron Beckenfeld, *President*
Lillian Beckenfeld, *Vice Pres*
Tito Marquez, *Technology*
Luis Castro, *VP Human Res*
Steve Slack, *Opers Mgr*
EMP: 60
SQ FT: 80,000
SALES: 8MM **Privately Held**
WEB: www.cvc4health.com
SIC: 2834 5122 Vitamin preparations; vitamins & minerals

(P-8121)
CORCEPT THERAPEUTICS INC
149 Commonwealth Dr, Menlo Park (94025-1133)
PHONE..............................650 327-3270
Joseph K Belanoff, *President*
James N Wilson, *Ch of Bd*
G Charles Robb, *CFO*
David Penake, *Treasurer*
George Baker, *Bd of Directors*
EMP: 103
SQ FT: 20,831
SALES: 159.2MM **Privately Held**
WEB: www.corcept.com
SIC: 2834 Pharmaceutical preparations

(P-8122)
CORE SUPPLEMENT TECHNOLOGY
4665 North Ave, Oceanside (92056-3511)
P.O. Box 3010, La Mesa (91944-3010)
PHONE..............................760 452-7364
EMP: 11
SALES (est): 1.8MM **Privately Held**
SIC: 2834 Pharmaceutical preparations

(P-8123)
CORIUM INTERNATIONAL INC (PA)
235 Constitution Dr, Menlo Park (94025-1108)
PHONE..............................650 298-8255
Peter D Staple, *President*
Robert S Breuil, *CFO*
Robert Thomas, *Bd of Directors*
Joseph J Sarret, *Officer*
Parminder Singh, *Vice Pres*
EMP: 150
SQ FT: 25,000
SALES: 31.8MM **Publicly Held**
WEB: www.coriumintl.com
SIC: 2834 8731 2836 Pharmaceutical preparations; biological research; biological products, except diagnostic

(P-8124)
CORVUS PHARMACEUTICALS INC
863 Mitten Rd Ste 102, Burlingame (94010-1311)
PHONE..............................650 900-4520
Richard A Miller, *Ch of Bd*
Leiv Lea, *CFO*
Ian Clark, *Bd of Directors*
Elisha Gould, *Bd of Directors*
Steve Krognes, *Bd of Directors*
EMP: 55
SQ FT: 28,633
SALES (est): 12.7MM **Privately Held**
SIC: 2834 Pharmaceutical preparations

(P-8125)
COUGAR BIOTECHNOLOGY INC
10990 Wilshire Blvd # 1200, Los Angeles (90024-3913)
PHONE..............................310 943-8040
Alan H Auerbach, *President*
Arie S Belldegrun MD, *Ch of Bd*
Charles Eyler, *Treasurer*
Gloria Lee MD, *Vice Pres*
EMP: 58
SQ FT: 7,300
SALES (est): 7.9MM
SALES (corp-wide): 76.4B **Publicly Held**
WEB: www.cougarbiotechnology.com
SIC: 2834 Drugs affecting neoplasms & endrocrine systems
PA: Johnson & Johnson
1 Johnson And Johnson Plz
New Brunswick NJ 08933
732 524-0400

(P-8126)
CREEKSIDE MANAGED CARE
879 2nd St, Santa Rosa (95404-4621)
PHONE..............................707 578-0399
David Medina, *Owner*
EMP: 17
SALES (est): 1.3MM **Privately Held**
SIC: 2834 Pharmaceutical preparations

(P-8127)
CRINETICS PHARMACEUTICALS INC
10222 Barnes Canyon Rd # 200, San Diego (92121-2711)
PHONE..............................858 450-6464
R Scott Struthers, *President*
Wendell Wierenga, *Ch of Bd*
Marc Wilson, *CFO*
Alan Krasner, *Chief Mktg Ofcr*
Stephen F Betz, *Vice Pres*
EMP: 36
SQ FT: 29,499
SALES: 2MM **Privately Held**
SIC: 2834 Pharmaceutical preparations

(P-8128)
CRISI MEDICAL SYSTEMS INC
9191 Towne Centre Dr # 330, San Diego (92122-6243)
PHONE..............................858 754-8640
Michael Perry, *CEO*
EMP: 12
SALES (est): 1.6MM
SALES (corp-wide): 12B **Publicly Held**
SIC: 2834 3061 Intravenous solutions; medical & surgical rubber tubing (extruded & lathe-cut)
PA: Becton, Dickinson And Company
1 Becton Dr
Franklin Lakes NJ 07417
201 847-6800

(P-8129)
CURE PHARMACEUTICAL CORP
1620 Beacon Pl, Oxnard (93033-2433)
PHONE..............................805 487-7163
Robert Davidson, *CEO*
Edward Maliski, *President*
Wayne Nasby, *COO*
Mark Udell, *CFO*
Rob Davidson, *Controller*
EMP: 24
SALES (est): 4.8MM **Privately Held**
SIC: 2834 Medicines, capsuled or ampuled

(P-8130)
CV SCIENCES INC
5121 Santa Fe St Ste F, La Jolla (92037)
PHONE..............................619 546-8112
Theo Smith, *Manager*
EMP: 10
SALES (corp-wide): 20.6MM **Privately Held**
SIC: 2834 Pharmaceutical preparations
PA: Cv Sciences, Inc.
2688 S Rainbow Blvd Ste B
Las Vegas NV 89146
866 290-2157

(P-8131)
CYMABAY THERAPEUTICS INC (PA)
7999 Gateway Blvd Ste 100, Newark (94560-1144)
PHONE..............................510 293-8800
Robert J Wills, *Ch of Bd*
Sujal Shah, *President*
Robert Booth, *Bd of Directors*
Caroline Loewy, *Bd of Directors*
Paul Truex, *Bd of Directors*
EMP: 21
SALES: 10MM **Publicly Held**
WEB: www.metabolex.com
SIC: 2834 Druggists' preparations (pharmaceuticals)

(P-8132)
CYTOKINETICS INCORPORATED (PA)
280 E Grand Ave, South San Francisco (94080-4808)
PHONE..............................650 624-3000
Robert I Blum, *President*
L Patrick Gage, *Ch of Bd*
Ching Jaw, *CFO*
Fady I Malik, *Exec VP*
David W Cragg, *Senior VP*
EMP: 137
SQ FT: 81,587
SALES: 13.3MM **Publicly Held**
WEB: www.cytokinetics.com
SIC: 2834 8731 Pharmaceutical preparations; biotechnical research, commercial

(P-8133)
DARE BIOSCIENCE INC
3655 Nobel Dr Ste 260, San Diego (92122-1050)
PHONE..............................858 926-7655
Sabrina Johnson, *President*
Sabrina Martucci Johnson, *President*
David Friend, *Officer*
Alejandra V Carvajal, *Vice Pres*
EMP: 19
SALES (est): 1MM **Privately Held**
WEB: www.tempopharmaceuticals.com
SIC: 2834 Pharmaceutical preparations; druggists' preparations (pharmaceuticals)

(P-8134)
DAVITA RX LLC (HQ)
Also Called: Davita Dialysis Center
1178 Cherry Ave, San Bruno (94066-2302)
PHONE..............................650 344-2319
Joshua M Golomb, *Mng Member*
Rick Hagan, *Opers Staff*
H W Guy Seay,
EMP: 38
SALES (est): 7.2MM **Publicly Held**
SIC: 2834 Druggists' preparations (pharmaceuticals)

(P-8135)
DELMAR PHARMACEUTICAL INC
3475 Edison Way Ste R, Menlo Park (94025-1821)
PHONE..............................650 269-1984
Saiid Zarrabian, *President*
Jeffrey Bacha, *President*
Scott Praill, *CFO*
Erich Mohr, *Chairman*
Dennis M Brown, *Principal*
EMP: 10
SALES (est): 1MM **Privately Held**
SIC: 2834 Druggists' preparations (pharmaceuticals)

(P-8136)
DENDREON PHARMACEUTICALS INC
1700 Saturn Way, Seal Beach (90740-5618)
PHONE..............................562 253-3931
EMP: 13
SALES (corp-wide): 215.7MM **Privately Held**
SIC: 2834
HQ: Dendreon Pharmaceuticals Llc
1700 Saturn Way
Seal Beach CA 90740
562 252-7500

(P-8137)
DENDREON PHARMACEUTICALS LLC (HQ)
1700 Saturn Way, Seal Beach (90740-5618)
PHONE..............................562 252-7500
James Caggiano, *CEO*
Christina Yi, *COO*
Chris Carr, *CFO*
Matthew Kemp, *Officer*
Kevin Helmbacher, *Senior VP*
EMP: 50
SALES (est): 153.1MM
SALES (corp-wide): 215.7MM **Privately Held**
SIC: 2834 Pharmaceutical preparations
PA: Sanpower Group Co., Ltd.
No.68, Ruanjian Avenue, Yuhuatai District
Nanjing 21001
258 327-4887

(P-8138)
DERMIRA INC
275 Middlefield Rd # 150, Menlo Park (94025-4008)
PHONE..............................650 421-7200
Thomas G Wiggans, *Ch of Bd*
Andrew L Guggenhime, *COO*
Lori Lyons-Williams, *Ch Credit Ofcr*
Eugene A Bauer, *Chief Mktg Ofcr*
Christopher M Griffith, *Senior VP*
EMP: 162
SQ FT: 68,990
SALES: 4.5MM **Privately Held**
SIC: 2834 Pharmaceutical preparations

(P-8139)
DESIGNERX PHARMACEUTICALS INC
4941 Allison Pkwy Ste B, Vacaville (95688-8794)
PHONE..............................707 451-0441
Bor-Wen Wu, *CEO*
WEI-Jen Kung, *President*
▲ EMP: 14
SQ FT: 18,000
SALES (est): 4MM **Privately Held**
WEB: www.drxpharma.com
SIC: 2834 Pharmaceutical preparations

(P-8140)
DGA INC
Also Called: Pro Form Labs
5325 Industrial Way, Benicia (94510-1026)
PHONE..............................925 299-9000
Melinda Gillespie, *CEO*
EMP: 29 **Privately Held**
SIC: 2834 5499 5149 Vitamin preparations; health & dietetic food stores; organic & diet foods
PA: Dga, Inc.
5001 Industrial Way
Benicia CA 94510

(P-8141)
DIABLO CLINICAL RESEARCH INC
2255 Ygnacio Valley Rd M, Walnut Creek (94598-3347)
PHONE..............................925 930-7267
Richard Weinstein, *President*
EMP: 22
SQ FT: 2,200
SALES: 600K **Privately Held**
WEB: www.diabloclin.com
SIC: 2834 8011 Pharmaceutical preparations; offices & clinics of medical doctors

▲ = Import ▼=Export
◆ =Import/Export

(P-8142)
DLC LABORATORIES INC
Also Called: De La Cruz Products
7008 Marcelle St, Paramount
(90723-4839)
PHONE...................................562 602-2184
Spero Kessaris, President
Judy De Rocha, Purchasing
▲ EMP: 14 EST: 1963
SQ FT: 16,000
SALES (est): 5.9MM Privately Held
WEB: www.dlclaboratories.com
SIC: 2834 2844 Vitamin preparations;
  shampoos, rinses, conditioners: hair

(P-8143)
DR J SKINCLINIC INC
Also Called: Drj Organics
13834 Bettencourt St, Cerritos
(90703-1010)
PHONE...................................714 282-2290
Young Min Choi, CEO
▲ EMP: 11
SQ FT: 15,000
SALES: 3MM
SALES (corp-wide): 49MM Privately
Held
SIC: 2834 5122 Pharmaceutical prepara-
  tions; cosmetics
PA: Pharma Research Products Co.,Ltd.
  Daejun-Dong
  Gangneung 25452
  233 645-7640

(P-8144)
DURECT CORPORATION (PA)
10260 Bubb Rd, Cupertino (95014-4166)
PHONE...................................408 777-1417
James E Brown, President
Felix Theeuwes, Ch of Bd
Matthew J Hogan, CFO
Judy R Joice, Senior VP
Jaymin Shah, Exec Dir
EMP: 93
SALES: 49.1MM Publicly Held
WEB: www.durect.com
SIC: 2834 Drugs acting on the central
  nervous system & sense organs

(P-8145)
DURECT CORPORATION
10240 Bubb Rd, Cupertino (95014-4166)
PHONE...................................408 777-1417
James Brown, CEO
Jian LI. Vice Pres
EMP: 10
SALES (est): 1MM Privately Held
SIC: 2834 Pharmaceutical preparations

(P-8146)
ELI LILLY AND COMPANY
Also Called: Elanco Animal Health
63 Via Ricardo, Newbury Park
(91320-7000)
PHONE...................................805 499-5475
Robert Reingold, Branch Mgr
EMP: 144
SALES (corp-wide): 22.8B Publicly Held
WEB: www.lilly.com
SIC: 2834 Pharmaceutical preparations
PA: Eli Lilly And Company
  Lilly Corporate Ctr
  Indianapolis IN 46285
  317 276-2000

(P-8147)
**EMMAUS LIFE SCIENCES INC
(PA)**
21250 Hawthorne Blvd B, Torrance
(90503-5506)
PHONE...................................310 214-0065
Yutara Nihara, President
Willis C Lee, COO
Kurt Kruger, CFO
Peter Ludlum, Officer
Lan Tran, Officer
EMP: 13 EST: 2008
SALES: 513.4K Privately Held
SIC: 2834 Pharmaceutical preparations

(P-8148)
ENVY MEDICAL INC (PA)
9414 Eton Ave, Chatsworth (91311-5862)
PHONE...................................818 874-2700
Arash A Khazei, CEO
Ken Karasiuk, President

Sona Tolani, Senior VP
Curt Hanson, Vice Pres
Felipe Jimenez PHD, Vice Pres
▲ EMP: 15
SALES (est): 2.1MM Privately Held
SIC: 2834 Dermatologicals

(P-8149)
**ESCIENT PHARMACEUTICALS
INC**
3033 Science Park Rd # 230, San Diego
(92121-1167)
PHONE...................................858 617-8236
Alain Baron, CEO
EMP: 14
SALES (est): 732K Privately Held
SIC: 2834 Pharmaceutical preparations

(P-8150)
**ESSENTIAL PHARMACEUTICAL
CORP**
1906 W Holt Ave, Pomona (91768-3351)
PHONE...................................909 623-4565
Bruce Lin, CEO
PO Chia Lin, Treasurer
▲ EMP: 20
SQ FT: 7,642
SALES (est): 5.1MM Privately Held
SIC: 2834 Vitamin preparations; vitamin,
  nutrient & hematinic preparations for
  human use

(P-8151)
**EVOFEM BIOSCIENCES INC
(PA)**
12400 High Bluff Dr, San Diego
(92130-3077)
PHONE...................................858 550-1900
Saundra Pelletier, CEO
Thomas Lynch, Ch of Bd
Justin J File, CFO
Russ Barrans, Ch Credit Ofcr
Martha Demski, Bd of Directors
EMP: 18
SALES (est): 2.2MM Publicly Held
SIC: 2834 Pharmaceutical preparations

(P-8152)
EVOLUS INC (DH)
17901 Von Karman Ave, Irvine
(92614-6297)
PHONE...................................949 284-4555
David Moatazedi, President
Vikram Malik, Ch of Bd
Murthy Simhambhatla, President
J Christopher Marmo, COO
Lauren Silvernail, CFO
EMP: 22
SQ FT: 3,639
SALES (est): 5.1MM
SALES (corp-wide): 38MM Publicly Held
SIC: 2834 Pharmaceutical preparations
HQ: Alphaeon Corporation
  17901 Von Karman Ave # 150
  Irvine CA 92614
  949 284-4555

(P-8153)
EXELIXIS INC
169 Harbor Way, South San Francisco
(94080-6109)
PHONE...................................650 837-8254
EMP: 200 Publicly Held
SIC: 2834
PA: Exelixis, Inc.
  210 E Grand Ave
  South San Francisco CA 94502

(P-8154)
EXELIXIS INC
1851 Harbor Bay Pkwy, Alameda
(94502-3016)
PHONE...................................650 837-7000
EMP: 129 Publicly Held
SIC: 2834
PA: Exelixis, Inc.
  210 E Grand Ave
  South San Francisco CA 94502

(P-8155)
EXELIXIS INC (PA)
1851 Harbor Bay Pkwy, Alameda
(94502-3010)
PHONE...................................650 837-7000
Michael M Morrissey, President
Stelios Papadopoulos, Ch of Bd
Gisela M Schwab, President
Christopher J Senner, CFO
Charles Cohen, Bd of Directors
EMP: 57
SALES: 452.4MM Publicly Held
WEB: www.exelixis.com
SIC: 2834 Pharmaceutical prepara-
  tions; commercial physical research; bio-
  logical research

(P-8156)
**FAMILY MEDICINE CENTER
TORR**
2841 Lomita Blvd Ste 220, Torrance
(90505-5111)
PHONE...................................310 326-8600
Terence M Hammer, Principal
EMP: 15
SALES (est): 3.1MM Privately Held
SIC: 2834 Medicines, capsuled or ampuled

(P-8157)
**FARMA PHARMACEUTICALS
INC (PA)**
5240 San Fernando Rd, Glendale
(91203-2439)
PHONE...................................818 638-3113
Mr Stephen Cobos, President
EMP: 12
SALES (est): 2.8MM Privately Held
SIC: 2834 5122 Pharmaceutical prepara-
  tions; pharmaceuticals

(P-8158)
**FARMHOUSE CULTURE INC
(PA)**
182 Lewis Rd, Royal Oaks (95076-5352)
P.O. Box 2049, Watsonville (95077-2049)
PHONE...................................831 466-0499
John Tucker, CEO
John Wells, CFO
Heather Dean, Sales Dir
EMP: 45
SALES: 18MM Privately Held
SIC: 2834 Vitamin, nutrient & hematinic
  preparations for human use

(P-8159)
FIBROGEN INC (PA)
409 Illinois St, San Francisco (94158-2509)
PHONE...................................415 978-1200
Thomas B Neff, Ch of Bd
Pat Cotroneo, CFO
Toshinari Tamura, Bd of Directors
K Peony Yu, Chief Mktg Ofcr
Wayne Frost, Vice Pres
EMP: 196
SQ FT: 234,000
SALES: 125.6MM Publicly Held
WEB: www.fibrogen.com
SIC: 2834 Pharmaceutical preparations

(P-8160)
FILMAGIC INC
Also Called: Natures Dream
120 N Fairway Ln, West Covina
(91791-1729)
PHONE...................................626 339-0120
Frank Wong, President
▲ EMP: 12
SQ FT: 6,000
SALES (est): 1.9MM Privately Held
WEB: www.naturesdream.net
SIC: 2834 3842 2023 Pharmaceutical
  preparations; cosmetic restorations; di-
  etary supplements, dairy & non-dairy
  based

(P-8161)
**FIVE PRIME THERAPEUTICS
INC**
111 Oyster Point Blvd, South San Francisco
(94080-1910)
PHONE...................................415 365-5600
Lewis T Williams, Ch of Bd
EMP: 24
SALES (est): 5.5MM Privately Held
SIC: 2834 Pharmaceutical preparations

(P-8162)
**FIVE PRIME THERAPEUTICS
INC**
2 Corporate Dr, South San Francisco
(94080-7047)
PHONE...................................415 365-5600
Lewis T Williams, Ch of Bd
Aron M Knickerbocker, COO
Marc L Belsky, CFO
Franklin Berger, Bd of Directors
Sheila Gujrathi, Bd of Directors
EMP: 195
SQ FT: 81,235
SALES: 39.5MM Privately Held
WEB: www.fiveprime.com
SIC: 2834 8733 Pharmaceutical prepara-
  tions; biotechnical research, noncommer-
  cial

(P-8163)
FOREST LABORATORIES LLC
12021 Dolly Way, Moreno Valley
(92555-2007)
PHONE...................................951 941-0024
Garrett R Campbell, Branch Mgr
EMP: 75 Privately Held
SIC: 2834 Pharmaceutical preparations
HQ: Forest Laboratories, Llc
  909 3rd Ave Fl 23
  New York NY 10022
  212 421-7850

(P-8164)
FORMEX LLC
11011 Torreyana Rd # 100, San Diego
(92121-1104)
PHONE...................................858 529-6600
Cyrus K Mirsaidi, President
Ian Wisenberg, CFO
J Blair West, Security Dir
Armand Amin, Marketing Staff
EMP: 32
SQ FT: 44,000
SALES (est): 6.4MM
SALES (corp-wide): 23.1MM Privately
Held
SIC: 2834 8731 8071 Tablets, pharma-
  ceutical; biological research; testing labo-
  ratories
HQ: Bioduro Llc
  11011 Torreyana Rd
  San Diego CA 92121
  858 529-6600

(P-8165)
**FORMULATION TECHNOLOGY
INC**
571 Armstrong Way, Oakdale
(95361-9367)
P.O. Box 1895 (95361-1895)
PHONE...................................209 847-0331
Keith W Hensley, President
Mary G Hangley, Shareholder
April Houck, Shareholder
Celia Meese, Corp Secy
Jed Meese, Vice Pres
▲ EMP: 49 EST: 1981
SQ FT: 15,000
SALES (est): 11.9MM Privately Held
WEB: www.formulationtech.com
SIC: 2834 Vitamin preparations

(P-8166)
FORMUREX INC
2470 Wilcox Rd, Stockton (95215-2319)
PHONE...................................209 931-2040
Dongxiao Tony Zhang, President
Ravi Mahalingam, Vice Pres
Sreenath Konanki, Info Tech Mgr
Sunny Sun, Analyst
Bhaskara Jasti, Director
EMP: 10
SQ FT: 8,000
SALES (est): 1.5MM Privately Held
WEB: www.formurex.com
SIC: 2834 Pharmaceutical preparations

(P-8167)
FREMONT AMGEN INC
6397 Kaiser Dr, Fremont (94555-3602)
PHONE...................................510 284-6500
Kevin Sharer, President
R Scott Greer, Ch of Bd
H Ward Wolff, CFO
Gisela M Schwab, Officer

Kristen M Anderson, *Senior VP*
▲ **EMP:** 375
SQ FT: 516,000
SALES (est): 52.7MM
SALES (corp-wide): 22.8B **Publicly Held**
SIC: 2834 Extracts of botanicals: powdered, pilular, solid or fluid; antibiotics, packaged
PA: Amgen Inc.
　1 Amgen Center Dr
　Thousand Oaks CA 91320
　805 447-1000

(P-8168)
FRESENIUS USA INC (DH)
Also Called: Fresenius Medical Care
4040 Nelson Ave, Concord (94520-1200)
PHONE...................925 288-4218
Ronald J Kuerbitz, *CEO*
Mark Costanzo, *President*
Ben Lipps, *President*
Angelo Moesslang, *CFO*
Mark Fawcett, *Treasurer*
▲ **EMP:** 220 **EST:** 1974
SQ FT: 85,000
SALES (est): 771.7MM
SALES (corp-wide): 20.9B **Privately Held**
SIC: 2834 3841 2835 3842 Intravenous solutions; solutions, pharmaceutical; hemodialysis apparatus; IV transfusion apparatus; blood transfusion equipment; blood derivative diagnostic agents; surgical appliances & supplies; biological products, except diagnostic

(P-8169)
GB006 INC
3013 Science Park Rd, San Diego (92121-1101)
PHONE.................858 684-1300
Sheila Gujrathi, *President*
Lisa Evans, *Executive Asst*
Christian Waage, *Admin Sec*
EMP: 70
SQ FT: 22,000
SALES (est): 2.4MM
SALES (corp-wide): 17.9MM **Privately Held**
SIC: 2834 Pharmaceutical preparations
PA: Gossamer Bio, Inc.
　3013 Science Park Rd # 200
　San Diego CA 92121
　858 684-1300

(P-8170)
GENELABS TECHNOLOGIES INC (HQ)
505 Penobscot Dr, Redwood City (94063-4737)
P.O. Box 13398, Durham NC (27709-3398)
PHONE...................415 297-2901
Frederick W Driscoll, *President*
Gerald Suh, *Owner*
Irene A Chow, *Ch of Bd*
Ronald C Griffith PHD, *Officer*
Heather Criss Keller, *Vice Pres*
EMP: 18
SQ FT: 50,000
SALES (est): 4.7MM
SALES (corp-wide): 39.8B **Privately Held**
WEB: www.genelabs.com
SIC: 2834 Proprietary drug products
PA: Glaxosmithkline Plc
　980 Great West Road
　Brentford MIDDX TW8 9
　208 047-5000

(P-8171)
GENENTECH INC
1000 New Horizons Way, Vacaville (95688-9431)
PHONE...................707 454-1000
Frank Jackson, *General Mgr*
Jody Rosen, *Partner*
Elkins Cindy, *Vice Pres*
Thomas Civik, *Vice Pres*
Jose Goin, *Associate Dir*
EMP: 25
SALES (corp-wide): 53.9B **Privately Held**
WEB: www.gene.com
SIC: 2834 Pharmaceutical preparations
HQ: Genentech, Inc.
　1 Dna Way
　South San Francisco CA 94080
　650 225-1000

(P-8172)
GENENTECH INC
800 Forbes Blvd, South San Francisco (94080-2010)
PHONE...................650 225-3639
Art Lezenson, *CEO*
Kristina Brumbaugh, *Admin Asst*
Karen Ervin, *Research*
Jenny Jiang, *Research*
EMP: 12
SALES (corp-wide): 53.9B **Privately Held**
WEB: www.gene.com
SIC: 2834 Pharmaceutical preparations
HQ: Genentech, Inc.
　1 Dna Way
　South San Francisco CA 94080
　650 225-1000

(P-8173)
GENENTECH INC (DH)
1 Dna Way, South San Francisco (94080-4990)
P.O. Box 4354, Portland OR (97208-4354)
PHONE...................650 225-1000
Ian Clark, *CEO*
Pascal Soriot, *COO*
Steve Krognes, *CFO*
Hal Barron, *Chief Mktg Ofcr*
Rick Kentz, *Officer*
◆ **EMP:** 2000 **EST:** 1987
SQ FT: 140,000
SALES (est): 3.6B
SALES (corp-wide): 53.9B **Privately Held**
WEB: www.gene.com
SIC: 2834 Hormone preparations

(P-8174)
GENENTECH INC
465 E Grand Ave Ms432, South San Francisco (94080-6225)
PHONE...................408 963-8759
Liane Johnson, *Manager*
EMP: 19
SALES (corp-wide): 53.9B **Publicly Held**
SIC: 2834 Pharmaceutical preparations
HQ: Genentech, Inc.
　1 Dna Way
　South San Francisco CA 94080
　650 225-1000

(P-8175)
GENENTECH INC
1 Antibody Way, Oceanside (92056-5701)
PHONE...................760 231-2440
AMR Elkhayat, *Director*
Don Fitzgerald, *Vice Pres*
Jami Debrango-Palumb, *Associate Dir*
Tracey Harris, *Admin Asst*
Cheryl Mata, *Admin Asst*
EMP: 300
SALES (corp-wide): 53.9B **Privately Held**
WEB: www.gene.com
SIC: 2834 Pharmaceutical preparations
HQ: Genentech, Inc.
　1 Dna Way
　South San Francisco CA 94080
　650 225-1000

(P-8176)
GENENTECH INC
550 Broadway St, Redwood City (94063-3115)
PHONE...................650 216-2900
Kinney Horn, *Associate Dir*
Greg Casey, *Division Mgr*
Lee Gong, *Admin Asst*
Bill Husson, *Administration*
Lily Chou, *Planning*
EMP: 300
SALES (corp-wide): 53.9B **Publicly Held**
WEB: www.gene.com
SIC: 2834 Pharmaceutical preparations
HQ: Genentech, Inc.
　1 Dna Way
　South San Francisco CA 94080
　650 225-1000

(P-8177)
GENENTECH INC
431 Grandview Dr Bldg 27, South San Francisco (94080)
PHONE...................650 225-3214
Rick Rouleau, *Manager*
Tania Ayala, *Director*
David Jennings, *Manager*
EMP: 15

SALES (corp-wide): 53.9B **Publicly Held**
WEB: www.gene.com
SIC: 2834 Pharmaceutical preparations
HQ: Genentech, Inc.
　1 Dna Way
　South San Francisco CA 94080
　650 225-1000

(P-8178)
GENENTECH INC
1 Dna Way, South San Francisco (94080-4990)
PHONE...................650 225-1000
Severin Schwan, *Branch Mgr*
EMP: 193
SALES (corp-wide): 53.9B **Publicly Held**
WEB: www.gene.com
SIC: 2834 Pharmaceutical preparations
HQ: Genentech, Inc.
　1 Dna Way
　South San Francisco CA 94080
　650 225-1000

(P-8179)
GENENTECH USA INC
1 Dna Way, South San Francisco (94080-4990)
PHONE...................650 225-1000
Ian T Clark, *Principal*
Leonard Kanavy, *Principal*
Frederick C Kentz III, *Principal*
Steve Krognes, *Principal*
Maureen Sharkey, *Info Tech Mgr*
▲ **EMP:** 2695
SALES (est): 222MM
SALES (corp-wide): 53.9B **Privately Held**
WEB: www.gene.com
SIC: 2834 Hormone preparations
HQ: Genentech, Inc.
　1 Dna Way
　South San Francisco CA 94080
　650 225-1000

(P-8180)
GENOPIS INC
10390 Pacific Center Ct, San Diego (92121-4340)
PHONE...................858 875-4700
Sun Young Kim, *CEO*
Keith Hall, *COO*
EMP: 24
SQ FT: 68,400
SALES: 500K **Privately Held**
SIC: 2834 Pharmaceutical preparations

(P-8181)
GENSIA SICOR INC (HQ)
19 Hughes, Irvine (92618-1902)
PHONE...................949 455-4700
Carlo Salvi, *Vice Chairman*
▲ **EMP:** 800
SQ FT: 170,000
SALES (est): 99.6MM
SALES (corp-wide): 22.3B **Privately Held**
WEB: www.sicorinc.com
SIC: 2834 8731 Drugs acting on the cardiovascular system, except diagnostic; medical research, commercial
PA: Teva Pharmaceutical Industries Limited
　5 Bazel
　Petah Tikva　49510
　392 672-67

(P-8182)
GENZYME CORPORATION
Also Called: Genzyme Genetics
655 E Huntington Dr, Monrovia (91016-3636)
PHONE...................800 255-1616
Jane Willis, *Branch Mgr*
James Bartley, *Director*
EMP: 80
SALES (corp-wide): 609.6MM **Privately Held**
WEB: www.genzyme.com
SIC: 2834 Pharmaceutical preparations
HQ: Genzyme Corporation
　50 Binney St
　Cambridge MA 02142
　617 252-7500

(P-8183)
GERON CORPORATION (PA)
149 Commonwealth Dr # 2070, Menlo Park (94025-1133)
PHONE...................650 473-7700

SALES (corp-wide): 53.9B **Publicly Held**
WEB: www.gene.com
SIC: 2834 Pharmaceutical preparations
HQ: Genentech, Inc.
　1 Dna Way
　South San Francisco CA 94080
　650 225-1000

John A Scarlett, *President*
Hoyoung Huh, *Ch of Bd*
Olivia K Bloom, *CFO*
Daniel Bradbury, *Bd of Directors*
Karin Eastham, *Bd of Directors*
EMP: 20
SQ FT: 14,500
SALES: 1MM **Publicly Held**
WEB: www.geron.com
SIC: 2834 Pharmaceutical preparations

(P-8184)
GILEAD COLORADO INC
333 Lakeside Dr, Foster City (94404-1147)
PHONE...................650 574-3000
J William Freytag, *President*
John Milligan, *President*
Joseph L Turner, *CFO*
Michael R Bristow, *Officer*
Richard J Gorczynski, *Senior VP*
EMP: 110
SQ FT: 40,000
SALES (est): 15.3MM
SALES (corp-wide): 26.1B **Publicly Held**
WEB: www.myogen.com
SIC: 2834 Pharmaceutical preparations
PA: Gilead Sciences, Inc.
　333 Lakeside Dr
　Foster City CA 94404
　650 574-3000

(P-8185)
GILEAD PALO ALTO INC
Also Called: Gilead Scientist
650 Cliffside Dr, San Dimas (91773-2957)
PHONE...................909 394-4000
Chris Beley, *CEO*
EMP: 300
SALES (corp-wide): 26.1B **Publicly Held**
SIC: 2834 Drugs acting on the cardiovascular system, except diagnostic
HQ: Alto Gilead Palo Inc
　333 Lakeside Dr
　Foster City CA 94404

(P-8186)
GILEAD PALO ALTO INC (HQ)
333 Lakeside Dr, Foster City (94404-1147)
PHONE...................650 384-8500
John C Martin, *Chairman*
Louis Lange PHD, *Ch of Bd*
John F Milligan, *President*
Daniel K Spiegelman, *CFO*
Brent K Blackburn PHD, *Senior VP*
EMP: 70
SALES (est): 67.3MM
SALES (corp-wide): 26.1B **Publicly Held**
WEB: www.cvt.com
SIC: 2834 8731 Drugs acting on the cardiovascular system, except diagnostic; commercial physical research
PA: Gilead Sciences, Inc.
　333 Lakeside Dr
　Foster City CA 94404
　650 574-3000

(P-8187)
GILEAD SCIENCES INC (PA)
333 Lakeside Dr, Foster City (94404-1394)
PHONE...................650 574-3000
John C Martin, *Ch of Bd*
John F Milligan, *President*
Kevin Young, *COO*
Robin L Washington, *CFO*
Kevin Lofton, *Bd of Directors*
▲ **EMP:** 289
SALES: 26.1B **Publicly Held**
WEB: www.gilead.com
SIC: 2834 Pharmaceutical preparations

(P-8188)
GILEAD SCIENCES INC
542 W Covina Blvd, San Dimas (91773-2955)
PHONE...................909 394-4090
Arthur Chiles, *Manager*
EMP: 19
SALES (corp-wide): 26.1B **Publicly Held**
WEB: www.gilead.com
SIC: 2834 Pharmaceutical preparations
PA: Gilead Sciences, Inc.
　333 Lakeside Dr
　Foster City CA 94404
　650 574-3000

▲ = Import ▼=Export
◆ =Import/Export

(P-8189)
GILEAD SCIENCES INC
Also Called: Nexstar Pharmaceutical
650 Cliffside Dr, San Dimas (91773-2957)
PHONE..............................909 394-4000
Christin Eley, *Principal*
Chun Wong, *Manager*
EMP: 183
SALES (corp-wide): 26.1B **Publicly Held**
WEB: www.gilead.com
SIC: 2834 Drugs affecting parasitic & infective diseases
PA: Gilead Sciences, Inc.
 333 Lakeside Dr
 Foster City CA 94404
 650 574-3000

(P-8190)
GLAXOSMITHKLINE CONSUMER
2020 E Vine Ave, Fresno (93706-5458)
PHONE..............................559 650-1550
Mark Bullard, *Branch Mgr*
Rajeev Malhotra, *Director*
EMP: 99
SALES (corp-wide): 39.8B **Privately Held**
SIC: 2834 Pharmaceutical preparations
HQ: Glaxosmithkline Consumer Healthcare, L.P.
 184 Libery Corner Rd
 Warren NJ 07059
 -

(P-8191)
GLAXOSMITHKLINE LLC
11205 Creekside Ct, Dublin (94568-3511)
PHONE..............................925 833-1551
Mary Lewis, *Branch Mgr*
EMP: 26
SALES (corp-wide): 39.8B **Privately Held**
SIC: 2834 Pharmaceutical preparations
HQ: Glaxosmithkline Llc
 5 Crescent Dr
 Philadelphia PA 19112
 215 751-4000

(P-8192)
GLAXOSMITHKLINE LLC
2399 Hummingbird St, Chula Vista (91915-2420)
PHONE..............................619 863-0399
EMP: 26
SALES (corp-wide): 39.8B **Privately Held**
SIC: 2834 Pharmaceutical preparations
HQ: Glaxosmithkline Llc
 5 Crescent Dr
 Philadelphia PA 19112
 215 751-4000

(P-8193)
GLOBAL BLOOD THERAPEUTICS INC
Also Called: Gbt
171 Oyster Point Blvd, South San Francisco (94080-1910)
PHONE..............................650 741-7700
Ted W Love, *President*
Jeffrey Farrow, *CFO*
David L Johnson, *Ch Credit Ofcr*
Tricia Suvari,
Jung E Choi, *Officer*
EMP: 147
SQ FT: 67,185
SALES (est): 45.2MM **Privately Held**
SIC: 2834 8731 Pharmaceutical preparations; biological research

(P-8194)
GLOBAL FUTURE CITY HOLDING INC
2 Park Plz Ste 400, Irvine (92614-8514)
PHONE..............................949 769-3550
Michael R Dunn, *Ch of Bd*
EMP: 10
SQ FT: 5,824
SALES: 3.5MM **Privately Held**
SIC: 2834 2087 Pharmaceutical preparations; concentrates, drink

(P-8195)
GMP LABORATORIES AMERICA INC
2931 E La Jolla St, Anaheim (92806-1306)
PHONE..............................714 630-2467
Mohammad Ishaq, *CEO*
Suhail Ishaq, *President*

Yusuf Ishaq, *COO*
Victor Wilson, *QA Dir*
Jason Rogers, *Human Res Mgr*
▲ EMP: 92
SQ FT: 90,000
SALES (est): 22.1MM **Privately Held**
WEB: www.gmplabs.com
SIC: 2834 Pharmaceutical preparations

(P-8196)
GOLDEN STATE MEDICAL SUP INC
5187 Camino Ruiz, Camarillo (93012-8601)
PHONE..............................805 477-9866
Benjamin Hall, *CEO*
Shiela Curran, *COO*
Thomas S Weaver, *CFO*
Dave Arnold, *Senior VP*
Jim McManimie, *Senior VP*
EMP: 150
SQ FT: 95,500
SALES (est): 36.9MM **Privately Held**
WEB: www.gsms.us
SIC: 2834 Pharmaceutical preparations
PA: Gsms, Inc.
 301 Commerce St Ste 1600
 Fort Worth TX 76102
 805 477-9866

(P-8197)
GRAND MEADOWS INC
1607 W Orange Grove Ave E, Orange (92868-1128)
PHONE..............................714 628-1690
Nicholas Hartog, *President*
Angela Slater, *CFO*
▲ EMP: 10
SQ FT: 8,260
SALES: 2.8MM **Privately Held**
WEB: www.grandmeadows.com
SIC: 2834 Veterinary pharmaceutical preparations

(P-8198)
GREENWICH BIOSCIENCES INC (HQ)
5750 Fleet St Ste 200, Carlsbad (92008-4709)
PHONE..............................760 795-2200
Julian Gangolli, *President*
Justin Gover, *CEO*
Scott Giacobello, *CFO*
Richard Potts, *Opers Staff*
Stephen Wright, *Director*
EMP: 32 EST: 2013
SQ FT: 4,911
SALES (est): 9.7MM
SALES (corp-wide): 10.5MM **Privately Held**
SIC: 2834 Pharmaceutical preparations
PA: Gw Pharmaceuticals Plc
 Sovereign House
 Cambridge CAMBS
 122 326-6800

(P-8199)
GU
1204 10th St, Berkeley (94710-1509)
PHONE..............................510 527-4664
Bill Vaughn, *Owner*
EMP: 27
SALES (est): 6.6MM **Privately Held**
SIC: 2834 Vitamin, nutrient & hematinic preparations for human use

(P-8200)
H J HARKINS COMPANY INC
Also Called: Pharma Pac
1400 W Grand Ave Ste F, Grover Beach (93433-4221)
PHONE..............................805 929-1333
Norma Jean Erenius, *CEO*
Charles Smith, *President*
Norma Erenius, *Officer*
Mary Graham, *Administration*
Dale Gregory, *Info Tech Dir*
EMP: 50
SQ FT: 10,000
SALES (est): 9.5MM **Privately Held**
SIC: 2834 Pharmaceutical preparations

(P-8201)
HAHNEMANN LABORTORIES INC
Also Called: Hahnemann Homeopathic Pharmacy
1940 4th St, San Rafael (94901-2671)
PHONE..............................415 451-6978
April Eya, *President*
Susanne Kessler, *Admin Asst*
Roslyn Ball, *Manager*
EMP: 15
SALES (est): 1.4MM **Privately Held**
WEB: www.hahnemannlabs.com
SIC: 2834 Medicines, capsuled or ampuled

(P-8202)
HANDA PHARMACEUTICALS LLC
1732 N 1st St Ste 200, San Jose (95112-4518)
PHONE..............................510 354-2888
Stephen D Cary, *Principal*
EMP: 13
SALES (est): 2.2MM
SALES (corp-wide): 17.8MM **Privately Held**
SIC: 2834 Pharmaceutical preparations
PA: Handa Pharmaceuticals, Inc.
 3f-2, 3f-1, 23, Nanke 3rd Rd.,
 Tainan City 74147
 650 575-08

(P-8203)
HARBOR BIOSCIENCES INC (PA)
Also Called: (A DEVELOPMENT STAGE COMPANY)
9191 Towne Centre Dr # 409, San Diego (92122-1225)
PHONE..............................858 587-9333
James M Frincke PHD, *CEO*
Daniel Burgess, *CFO*
Robert W Weber, *CFO*
Christopher L Reading PHD, *Officer*
Dwight R Stickney MD, *Officer*
EMP: 19
SALES: 146K **Publicly Held**
WEB: www.holliseden.com
SIC: 2834 Pharmaceutical preparations

(P-8204)
HARMONY FOODS CORPORATION (PA)
Also Called: Santa Cruz Nutritionals
2200 Delaware Ave, Santa Cruz (95060-5707)
PHONE..............................831 457-3200
Michael Westhusing, *CEO*
Randy Bridges, *COO*
Doug Hopkinson, *Exec VP*
Matt Kemme, *Senior VP*
Merit Herman, *Info Tech Dir*
▲ EMP: 215
SQ FT: 200,000
SALES (est): 153.4MM **Privately Held**
WEB: www.harmonyfoods.com
SIC: 2834 2064 Vitamin, nutrient & hematinic preparations for human use; candy & other confectionery products

(P-8205)
HEALTH NATURALS INC
13 Navarre, Irvine (92612-7700)
PHONE..............................714 259-1821
Ruby Ableman, *President*
Steven Jacobson, *Principal*
◆ EMP: 15
SALES (est): 1.4MM **Privately Held**
SIC: 2834 Vitamin preparations

(P-8206)
HEALTH PLUS INC
13837 Magnolia Ave, Chino (91710-7028)
PHONE..............................909 627-9393
Rita Mediratta, *President*
Sunil Kohli, *Vice Pres*
Shelly Kohli, *Admin Sec*
◆ EMP: 50
SQ FT: 24,000
SALES (est): 13.5MM **Privately Held**
WEB: www.healthplusinc.com
SIC: 2834 Vitamin, nutrient & hematinic preparations for human use

(P-8207)
HEALTHSPORT INC
1620 Beacon Pl, Oxnard (93033-2433)
PHONE..............................818 593-4880
Kevin Taheri, *CEO*
Robert S Davidson, *Ch of Bd*
Thomas Beckett, *COO*
EMP: 13
SQ FT: 25,000
SALES: 2.6MM **Privately Held**
WEB: www.healthsportinc.com
SIC: 2834 Druggists' preparations (pharmaceuticals)

(P-8208)
HERON THERAPEUTICS INC (PA)
4242 Campus Point Ct # 200, San Diego (92121-1513)
PHONE..............................858 251-4400
Barry D Quart, *CEO*
Kevin C Tang, *Ch of Bd*
Robert H Rosen, *President*
Robert E Hoffman, *CFO*
Craig Johnson, *Bd of Directors*
EMP: 139
SQ FT: 28,275
SALES: 30.7MM **Publicly Held**
WEB: www.appharma.com
SIC: 2834 Pharmaceutical preparations

(P-8209)
ICU MEDICAL FLEET SERVICES LLC
5729 Fontanoso Way, San Jose (95138-1015)
PHONE..............................408 229-0560
Joe Belloah, *Manager*
Julio Javier Duclos, *Director*
Brent Cossairt, *Manager*
EMP: 100
SALES (corp-wide): 1.2B **Publicly Held**
WEB: www.abbotthpd.com
SIC: 2834 Pharmaceutical preparations
HQ: Icu Medical Fleet Services, Llc
 3900 Howard Ln
 Austin TX 78728
 512 255-2000

(P-8210)
IGENICA INC
863 Mitten Rd Ste 102, Burlingame (94010-1311)
PHONE..............................650 231-4320
Mary Haak-Frendscho, *CEO*
David Goeddel, *Ch of Bd*
Mike Rothe, *President*
Hans V Houte, *CFO*
Hans Van Houte, *CFO*
EMP: 40
SALES (est): 12.7MM **Privately Held**
SIC: 2834 Druggists' preparations (pharmaceuticals)

(P-8211)
IGNYTA INC (PA)
4545 Towne Centre Ct, San Diego (92121-1900)
PHONE..............................858 255-5959
Jonathan E Lim, *Ch of Bd*
Zachary Hornby, *COO*
Jacob Chacko, *CFO*
James Bristol, *Bd of Directors*
Heiner Dreismann, *Bd of Directors*
EMP: 99
SQ FT: 44,000
SALES (est): 24.4MM **Privately Held**
SIC: 2834 Pharmaceutical preparations

(P-8212)
IMMUNCELLULAR THERAPEUTICS LTD
23622 Calabasas Rd # 300, Calabasas (91302-1549)
PHONE..............................818 264-2300
Anthony Gringeri, *CEO*
Gary S Titus, *Ch of Bd*
Andrew Gengos, *President*
David Fractor, *CFO*
Gregg Lapointe, *Bd of Directors*
EMP: 10
SALES (est): 1.7MM **Privately Held**
WEB: www.immunocellular.com
SIC: 2834 Pharmaceutical preparations

PRODUCTS & SVCS

(P-8213)
IMMUNE DESIGN CORP
601 Gateway Blvd Ste 250, South San Francisco (94080-7403)
PHONE.................................650 225-0214
Christopher Whitmore, *Vice Pres*
EMP: 19
SALES (est): 4.6MM
SALES (corp-wide): 7.2MM **Publicly Held**
SIC: 2834 8731 Pharmaceutical preparations; commercial physical research; biotechnical research, commercial
PA: Immune Design Corp.
    1616 Eastlake Ave E
    Seattle WA 98102
    206 682-0645

(P-8214)
IMPAX LABORATORIES INC
31047 Genstar Rd, Hayward (94544-7831)
PHONE.................................510 240-6000
Larry Hsu, *CEO*
EMP: 58
SALES (corp-wide): 1B **Publicly Held**
SIC: 2834 Pharmaceutical preparations
HQ: Impax Laboratories, Llc
    30831 Huntwood Ave
    Hayward CA 94544
    510 240-6000

(P-8215)
IMPAX LABORATORIES LLC (DH)
30831 Huntwood Ave, Hayward (94544-7003)
PHONE.................................510 240-6000
Paul M Bisaro, *President*
Robert L Burr, *Ch of Bd*
Douglas S Boothe, *President*
Michael J Nestor, *President*
Bryan M Reasons, *CFO*
EMP: 600
SQ FT: 45,000
SALES: 775.7MM
SALES (corp-wide): 1B **Publicly Held**
WEB: www.impaxlabs.com
SIC: 2834 Pharmaceutical preparations

(P-8216)
IMPAX LABORATORIES USA LLC
30831 Huntwood Ave, Hayward (94544-7003)
PHONE.................................510 240-6000
Larry Hsu PHD, *CEO*
EMP: 11
SALES (est): 238.1K
SALES (corp-wide): 1B **Publicly Held**
SIC: 2834 Pharmaceutical preparations
HQ: Impax Laboratories, Llc
    30831 Huntwood Ave
    Hayward CA 94544
    510 240-6000

(P-8217)
IMPRIMIS PHARMACEUTICALS INC (PA)
12264 El Camino Real # 350, San Diego (92130-0001)
PHONE.................................858 704-4040
Mark L Baum, *CEO*
Robert J Kammer, *Ch of Bd*
John P Saharek, *Ch Credit Ofcr*
Steven Austin, *Bd of Directors*
Anthony Principi, *Bd of Directors*
EMP: 37
SQ FT: 7,600
SALES: 26.7MM **Publicly Held**
SIC: 2834 Pharmaceutical preparations

(P-8218)
INCARDA THERAPEUTICS INC
39899 Balentine Dr # 185, Newark (94560-5361)
PHONE.................................510 422-5522
Grace Colon, *President*
Carlos Schuler, *COO*
Luiz Belardinelli, *Chief Mktg Ofcr*
Robert L Roden, *Vice Pres*
EMP: 20
SALES (est): 321K **Privately Held**
SIC: 2834 Pharmaceutical preparations

(P-8219)
INCLINE THERAPEUTICS INC
900 Saginaw Dr Ste 200, Redwood City (94063-4701)
PHONE.................................650 241-6800
Alan Levy, *CEO*
David Socks, *President*
John Tucker, *Officer*
Patti Oto, *Senior VP*
Brad Phipps, *Senior VP*
EMP: 14
SALES (est): 2.4MM
SALES (corp-wide): 44.7MM **Publicly Held**
SIC: 2834 Pharmaceutical preparations
PA: The Medicines Company
    8 Sylvan Way
    Parsippany NJ 07054
    973 290-6000

(P-8220)
INNOVIVA INC (PA)
2000 Sierra Point Pkwy # 500, Brisbane (94005-1830)
PHONE.................................650 238-9600
Geoffrey Hulme, *CEO*
Marianne Zhen,
EMP: 12 EST: 1997
SQ FT: 8,427
SALES: 217.2MM **Publicly Held**
WEB: www.theravance.com
SIC: 2834 Drugs acting on the respiratory system

(P-8221)
INSITE VISION INCORPORATED (DH)
965 Atlantic Ave, Alameda (94501-6449)
PHONE.................................510 865-8800
Timothy Ruane, *CEO*
Louis Drapeau, *CFO*
Kamran Hosseini, *Chief Mktg Ofcr*
Lyle M Bowman, *Vice Pres*
Surendra Patel, *Vice Pres*
EMP: 33
SQ FT: 39,123
SALES: 8.2MM
SALES (corp-wide): 1.1B **Privately Held**
WEB: www.insitevision.com
SIC: 2834 Pharmaceutical preparations
HQ: Ranbaxy Inc.
    2 Independence Way
    Princeton NJ 08540
    609 720-9200

(P-8222)
INSTACURE HEALING PRODUCTS
235 N Moorpark Rd # 2022, Thousand Oaks (91358-7001)
PHONE.................................818 222-9600
David Traub, *Owner*
EMP: 33 EST: 2015
SQ FT: 6,000
SALES: 3MM **Privately Held**
SIC: 2834 Lip balms

(P-8223)
INTEGRITY BIO INC
820 Calle Plano, Camarillo (93012-8557)
PHONE.................................805 445-8422
Byeong Chang, *President*
Dorota Dabek, *Officer*
Kisoon Kim, *Office Mgr*
Mariko Finnley, *Project Mgr*
Ann Snyder, *Project Mgr*
EMP: 47
SALES (est): 15.2MM **Privately Held**
SIC: 2834 Pharmaceutical preparations

(P-8224)
INTERCEPT PHARMACEUTICALS INC
4760 Eastgate Mall, San Diego (92121-1970)
PHONE.................................646 747-1005
Mark Pruzanski, *CEO*
Greg Wong, *President*
EMP: 14 **Publicly Held**
SIC: 2834 Pharmaceutical preparations
PA: Intercept Pharmaceuticals, Inc.
    10 Hudson Yards Fl 37
    New York NY 10001

(P-8225)
INTERMUNE INC (DH)
1 Dna Way, South San Francisco (94080-4918)
PHONE.................................415 466-4383
Daniel G Welch, *President*
John C Hodgman, *CFO*
Jonathan A Leff, *Exec VP*
Sean P Nolan, *Exec VP*
Andrew Powell, *Exec VP*
EMP: 215
SQ FT: 56,000
SALES: 70.3MM
SALES (corp-wide): 53.9B **Privately Held**
WEB: www.intermune.com
SIC: 2834 8731 Pharmaceutical preparations; medical research, commercial

(P-8226)
INTERNATIONAL STEM CELL CORP (PA)
5950 Priestly Dr, Carlsbad (92008-8849)
PHONE.................................760 940-6383
Andrey Semechkin, *Ch of Bd*
Donald A Wright, *Ch of Bd*
Mahnaz Ebrahimi, *CFO*
Russell Kern, *Exec VP*
Sofya Bakalova, *Vice Pres*
EMP: 38
SQ FT: 9,848
SALES: 7.4MM **Publicly Held**
WEB: www.intlstemcell.com
SIC: 2834 Pharmaceutical preparations

(P-8227)
INTERNATIONAL VITAMIN CORP
Also Called: Adam Nutrition, A Division Ivc
11010 Hopkins St Ste B, Mira Loma (91752-3279)
PHONE.................................951 361-1120
Iliu Elisara, *Branch Mgr*
Alfredo Ferradas, *Safety Mgr*
EMP: 125 **Privately Held**
SIC: 2834 Vitamin, nutrient & hematinic preparations for human use
PA: International Vitamin Corp
    1 Park Plz Ste 800
    Irvine CA 92614

(P-8228)
INTERNATIONAL VITAMIN CORP (PA)
Also Called: I V C
1 Park Plz Ste 800, Irvine (92614-5998)
PHONE.................................949 664-5500
Steven Dai, *President*
Glenn Davis, *COO*
Eva Pinto, *Treasurer*
Jeff Moran, *Vice Pres*
Stephen Rosenman, *Vice Pres*
▲ EMP: 400
SQ FT: 166,000
SALES (est): 544.4MM **Privately Held**
SIC: 2834 5149 8099 Vitamin preparations; organic & diet foods; nutrition services

(P-8229)
INTERNTNAL HMEOPATHIC MFG DIST
7108 De Soto Ave Ste 105, Canoga Park (91303-3230)
PHONE.................................818 884-8040
James Rojas, *President*
EMP: 18
SQ FT: 4,000
SALES: 1.4MM **Privately Held**
SIC: 2834 Vitamin preparations

(P-8230)
INTERNTNAL MDCTION SYSTEMS LTD
Also Called: IMS
1886 Santa Anita Ave, South El Monte (91733-3414)
PHONE.................................626 442-6757
Jack Zhang, *President*
HI Lou, *President*
Mary Luo Zhang, *COO*
Pete Langosh, *Vice Pres*
Bernard Chu, *CIO*
▲ EMP: 720
SALES (est): 228.8MM
SALES (corp-wide): 240.1MM **Publicly Held**
WEB: www.ims-limited.com
SIC: 2834 2833 3841 Drugs acting on the central nervous system & sense organs; anesthetics, in bulk form; surgical & medical instruments
PA: Amphastar Pharmaceuticals Inc
    11570 6th St
    Rancho Cucamonga CA 91730
    909 980-9484

(P-8231)
IONIS PHARMACEUTICALS INC
2282 Faraday Ave, Carlsbad (92008-7208)
PHONE.................................760 603-3567
Stanley Crooke, *Branch Mgr*
Frederick T Muto, *Bd of Directors*
Jessie Daly, *Vice Pres*
Lori Cooper, *Executive*
Kym Bradley, *Associate Dir*
EMP: 22
SALES (corp-wide): 507.6MM **Publicly Held**
SIC: 2834 Pharmaceutical preparations
PA: Ionis Pharmaceuticals, Inc.
    2855 Gazelle Ct
    Carlsbad CA 92010
    760 931-9200

(P-8232)
IONIS PHARMACEUTICALS INC (PA)
2855 Gazelle Ct, Carlsbad (92010-6670)
PHONE.................................760 931-9200
Stanley T Crooke, *Ch of Bd*
B Lynne Parshall, *COO*
Elizabeth L Hougen, *CFO*
Sarah Boyce, *Officer*
C Frank Bennett, *Senior VP*
EMP: 277
SALES: 507.6MM **Publicly Held**
WEB: www.isispharm.com
SIC: 2834 8731 3845 Pharmaceutical preparations; medical research, commercial; electromedical equipment

(P-8233)
IOVANCE BIOTHERAPEUTICS INC (PA)
999 Skyway Rd Ste 150, San Carlos (94070-2724)
PHONE.................................650 260-7120
Maria Fardis, *President*
Wayne P Rothbaum, *Ch of Bd*
Gregory T Schiffman, *CFO*
Steven A Fischkoff, *Chief Mktg Ofcr*
Michael T Lotze, *Officer*
EMP: 23
SALES (est): 10.3MM **Publicly Held**
SIC: 2834 Pharmaceutical preparations

(P-8234)
IRISYS LLC
6828 Nncy Rdge Dr Ste 100, San Diego (92121)
PHONE.................................858 623-1520
Gerald Yakatan, *Mng Member*
Robert Gianini,
Jean Wang,
EMP: 49
SQ FT: 24,100
SALES (est): 8.8MM **Privately Held**
SIC: 2834 Druggists' preparations (pharmaceuticals)
PA: Irisys, Inc.
    6828 Nncy Rdge Dr Ste 100
    San Diego CA 92121

(P-8235)
ISIS PHARMACEUTICALS
1767 Avenida Segovia, Oceanside (92056-6230)
PHONE.................................760 603-2631
Gregory Hardee, *Vice Pres*
Joel Ekstrom, *Vice Pres*
Kristin Balogh, *Associate Dir*
Alex Bell, *Associate Dir*
Jill Hsiao, *Research*
EMP: 16
SALES (est): 2.1MM **Privately Held**
SIC: 2834 Pharmaceutical preparations

(P-8236)
JAGUAR HEALTH INC (PA)
Also Called: JAGUAR ANIMAL HEALTH
201 Mission St Ste 2375, San Francisco
(94105-1839)
PHONE....................415 371-8300
Lisa A Conte, *President*
James J Bochnowski, *Ch of Bd*
Karen S Wright, *CFO*
ARI Azhir, *Bd of Directors*
John Micek, *Bd of Directors*
EMP: 23
SQ FT: 6,008
SALES: 4.3MM **Publicly Held**
SIC: 2834 0752 Veterinary pharmaceutical
   preparations; animal specialty services

(P-8237)
JAMES STEWART
Also Called: Diagnostic Reagents
8931 S Vermont Ave, Los Angeles
(90044-4833)
PHONE....................323 778-1687
James Stewart, *Owner*
EMP: 22
SQ FT: 4,200
SALES (est): 2.1MM **Privately Held**
SIC: 2834

(P-8238)
**JANSSEN RESEARCH & DEV
LLC**
3210 Merryfield Row, San Diego
(92121-1126)
PHONE....................858 450-2000
Steve Schuetzle, *Manager*
EMP: 228
SALES (corp-wide): 76.4B **Publicly Held**
WEB: www.jnjpharmarnd.com
SIC: 2834 Pharmaceutical preparations
HQ: Janssen Research & Development, Llc
   920 Us Highway 202
   Raritan NJ 08869
   908 704-4000

(P-8239)
JARROW INDUSTRIES INC
12246 Hawkins St, Santa Fe Springs
(90670-3365)
PHONE....................562 906-1919
Jarrow Rogovin, *Ch of Bd*
Mohammed Khalid, *President*
David Chen, *CFO*
Ben Khowong, *Treasurer*
▲ EMP: 140
SQ FT: 125,000
SALES (est): 46.7MM **Privately Held**
WEB: www.jiimfg.com
SIC: 2834 Vitamin preparations

(P-8240)
**JAZZ PHARMACEUTICALS INC
(HQ)**
3170 Porter Dr, Palo Alto (94304-1212)
PHONE....................650 496-3777
Bruce C Cozadd, *Ch of Bd*
▲ EMP: 148
SALES: 1.6B **Privately Held**
SIC: 2834 Drugs acting on the central
   nervous system & sense organs

(P-8241)
K & K LABORATORIES INC
2160 Warmlands Ave, Vista (92084-3338)
PHONE....................760 758-2352
Alex Kononchuk Jr, *President*
Linda Kononchuk, *Admin Sec*
EMP: 35
SQ FT: 20,000
SALES (est): 4.2MM **Privately Held**
SIC: 2834 Vitamin, nutrient & hematinic
   preparations for human use

(P-8242)
KALYPSYS INC
333 S Grand Ave Ste 4070, Los Angeles
(90071-1544)
P.O. Box 1390, Solana Beach (92075-
7390)
PHONE....................858 552-0674
August Watanabe, *Ch of Bd*
John McKearn, *CEO*
David C Tiemeier, *COO*
EMP: 110
SQ FT: 42,000
SALES (est): 16.6MM **Privately Held**
WEB: www.kalypsys.com
SIC: 2834 Pharmaceutical preparations

(P-8243)
**KANAMAX INTERNATIONAL INC
(PA)**
10618 Rush St, South El Monte
(91733-3432)
PHONE....................213 399-3398
Kelvin Ng, *President*
▲ EMP: 15
SQ FT: 3,000
SALES (est): 1.9MM **Privately Held**
SIC: 2834 Liniments

(P-8244)
**KATE SOMERVILLE SKINCARE
LLC (DH)**
144 S Beverly Dr Ste 500, Beverly Hills
(90212-3023)
PHONE....................323 655-7546
Kate Somerville, *Mng Member*
Jeff Hansen,
Laura Shaff,
Michelle Taylor,
▲ EMP: 51
SALES (est): 13.6MM
SALES (corp-wide): 63B **Privately Held**
SIC: 2834 5122 Pharmaceutical prepara-
   tions; toiletries; cosmetics; perfumes
HQ: Kate Somerville Holdings, Llc
   144 S Beverly Dr Ste 500
   Beverly Hills CA 90212
   323 655-4170

(P-8245)
KAVI SKIN SOLUTIONS INC (PA)
700 Larkspur Landing Cir, Larkspur
(94939-1715)
PHONE....................415 839-5156
Kaveh Alizadeh, *President*
▲ EMP: 38
SQ FT: 2,400
SALES (est): 2.5MM **Privately Held**
SIC: 2834 Pharmaceutical preparations

(P-8246)
KC PHARMACEUTICALS INC
3220 Producer Way, Pomona
(91768-3915)
PHONE....................909 598-9499
Paul Kartiko, *Manager*
EMP: 50
SALES (est): 7.5MM
SALES (corp-wide): 20.6MM **Privately
Held**
SIC: 2834 Solutions, pharmaceutical
PA: Kc Pharmaceuticals Inc.
   3201 Producer Way
   Pomona CA 91768
   909 598-9499

(P-8247)
KEZAR LIFE SCIENCES INC
4000 Shoreline Ct Ste 300, South San
Francisco (94080-2005)
PHONE....................650 822-5600
John Fowler, *CEO*
Jean-Pierre Sommadossi, *Ch of Bd*
Christopher Kirk, *President*
Marc L Belsky, *CFO*
Niti Goel, *Chief Mktg Ofcr*
EMP: 20
SQ FT: 24,357
SALES (est): 5MM **Privately Held**
SIC: 2834 Pharmaceutical preparations

(P-8248)
**KINDRED BIOSCIENCES INC
(PA)**
1555 Bayshore Hwy Ste 200, Burlingame
(94010-1617)
PHONE....................650 701-7901
Richard Chin, *CEO*
Denise M Bevers, *President*
Denise Bevers, *COO*
Wendy Wee, *CFO*
Raymond Townsend, *Bd of Directors*
EMP: 41 EST: 2012
SALES (est): 13.8MM **Publicly Held**
SIC: 2834 Veterinary pharmaceutical
   preparations

(P-8249)
**KOSAN BIOSCIENCES
INCORPORATED**
3832 Bay Center Pl, Hayward
(94545-3619)
P.O. Box 4000, Princeton NJ (08543-4000)
PHONE....................650 995-7356
Helen S Kim, *President*
Peter Davis PHD, *Ch of Bd*
Gary S Titus, *CFO*
Peter J Licari PHD, *Senior VP*
Jonathan K Wright, *Senior VP*
EMP: 91
SALES (est): 10MM
SALES (corp-wide): 20.7B **Publicly Held**
WEB: www.kosan.com
SIC: 2834 8731 Pharmaceutical prepara-
   tions; commercial research laboratory
PA: Bristol-Myers Squibb Company
   430 E 29th St Fl 14
   New York NY 10016
   212 546-4000

(P-8250)
**KYOWA HAKKO KIRIN CAL INC
(DH)**
9420 Athena Cir, La Jolla (92037-1387)
PHONE....................858 952-7000
Kinya Ohgami, *President*
Hiroshi Makino, *Director*
▲ EMP: 41
SQ FT: 3,000
SALES (est): 15MM
SALES (corp-wide): 16.6B **Privately Held**
SIC: 2834 Pharmaceutical preparations
HQ: Kyowa Hakko Kirin Co., Ltd.
   1-9-2, Otemachi
   Chiyoda-Ku TKY 100-0
   352 057-200

(P-8251)
**KYTHERA
BIOPHARMACEUTICALS INC**
30930 Russell Ranch Rd # 300, Westlake
Village (91362-7378)
PHONE....................818 587-4500
A R D Bailey, *President*
A Robert D Bailey, *President*
John W Smither, *CFO*
Elisabeth A Sandoval, *Ch Credit Ofcr*
Frederick Beddingfield III, *Chief Mktg Ofcr*
EMP: 106
SQ FT: 33,198
SALES (est): 17MM **Privately Held**
SIC: 2834 Dermatologicals
PA: Allergan Public Limited Company
   Euro House
   Cork
   -

(P-8252)
L-NUTRA INC
8240 Zitola Ter, Playa Del Rey
(90293-7834)
PHONE....................310 245-1724
Fabrizio Schirano, *CEO*
EMP: 16 **Privately Held**
SIC: 2834 Pharmaceutical preparations
PA: L-Nutra Inc.
   8322 Beverly Blvd Ste 202
   Los Angeles CA 90048

(P-8253)
LABORATORIOS CAMACHO INC
9349 Melvin Ave Ste 1, Northridge
(91324-2480)
P.O. Box 2363, Los Angeles (90078-2363)
PHONE....................818 764-2748
Jorge Camacho, *President*
Gioconda Camacho, *Vice Pres*
EMP: 10
SQ FT: 3,500
SALES (est): 1.8MM **Privately Held**
WEB: www.laboratorioscamacho.com
SIC: 2834 Adrenal pharmaceutical prepa-
   rations

(P-8254)
LEADING BIOSCIENCES INC
5800 Armada Dr Ste 210, Carlsbad
(92008-4611)
PHONE....................858 395-6099
Greg Doyle, *CEO*
JD Finley, *CFO*

Clark Straw, *Chairman*
EMP: 10
SALES (est): 1.3MM **Privately Held**
SIC: 2834 Pharmaceutical preparations

(P-8255)
**LEINER HEALTH PRODUCTS
INC (DH)**
901 E 233rd St, Carson (90745-6204)
PHONE....................631 200-2000
Jeffrey A Nagel, *CEO*
Robert J La Ferriere, *President*
Crystal Wright, *President*
Michael Collins, *CFO*
Harvey Kamil, *Vice Ch Bd*
▼ EMP: 693
SQ FT: 488,000
SALES (est): 141.5MM **Publicly Held**
WEB: www.leiner.com
SIC: 2834 5122 Vitamin, nutrient & hema-
   tinic preparations for human use; vitamins
   & minerals
HQ: The Nature's Bounty Co
   2100 Smithtown Ave
   Ronkonkoma NY 11779
   631 200-2000

(P-8256)
**LEINER HEALTH PRODUCTS
INC**
7366 Orangewood Ave, Garden Grove
(92841-1412)
PHONE....................714 898-9936
James Smith, *Manager*
EMP: 315 **Publicly Held**
WEB: www.leiner.com
SIC: 2834 2844 2833 5122 Vitamin, nu-
   trient & hematinic preparations for human
   use; toilet preparations; medicinals &
   botanicals; vitamins & minerals
HQ: Leiner Health Products, Inc.
   901 E 233rd St
   Carson CA 90745
   631 200-2000

(P-8257)
LEINER HEALTH PRODUCTS INC
27655b Avenue Hopkins, Valencia
(91355-3493)
PHONE....................661 775-1422
Bob Taketani, *Manager*
EMP: 100 **Publicly Held**
WEB: www.leiner.com
SIC: 2834
HQ: Leiner Health Products, Inc.
   901 E 233rd St
   Carson CA 90745
   631 200-2000

(P-8258)
LEITERS ENTERPRISES INC
Also Called: Leiter's Compounding
17 Great Oaks Blvd, San Jose
(95119-1359)
PHONE....................800 292-6772
Bob Zollars, *Ch of Bd*
Jim Cunniff, *CEO*
Charles Leiter, *Vice Pres*
Rosa Bonillas, *Purchasing*
Christopher Long, *QC Mgr*
EMP: 84 EST: 2013
SALES (est): 22.3MM **Privately Held**
SIC: 2834 Druggists' preparations (phar-
   maceuticals)

(P-8259)
LIFEBLOOM CORPORATION
Also Called: B&A Health Products Co
925 W Lambert Rd Ste B, Brea
(92821-2943)
PHONE....................562 944-6800
Sam Ahn, *CEO*
Chong Ahn, *Vice Pres*
David Kim, *Purchasing*
▲ EMP: 20
SALES (est): 6MM **Privately Held**
SIC: 2834 Vitamin preparations

(P-8260)
**LIGAND PHARMACEUTICALS
INC**
10275 Science Center Dr, San Diego
(92121-1117)
PHONE....................858 550-7500
Matt Witte, *President*

EMP: 21
SALES (est): 3.6MM **Privately Held**
SIC: 2834 Pharmaceutical preparations

(P-8261)
LIGAND PHARMACEUTICALS INC (PA)
3911 Sorrento Valley Blvd # 110, San Diego (92121-1457)
PHONE...................858 550-7500
John L Higgins, *CEO*
John W Kozarich, *Ch of Bd*
Matthew W Foehr, *President*
Matthew Korenberg, *CFO*
Jason Aryeh, *Bd of Directors*
EMP: 21
SQ FT: 16,500
SALES: 141.1MM **Publicly Held**
WEB: www.ligand.com
SIC: 2834 Pharmaceutical preparations

(P-8262)
LILLY BIOTECHNOLOGY CENTER
10290 Campus Point Dr, San Diego (92121-1522)
PHONE...................858 597-4990
EMP: 14
SALES (est): 5.8MM **Privately Held**
SIC: 2834 Pharmaceutical preparations

(P-8263)
LIQUID BIOSCIENCE INC
26895 Aliso Creek Rd B800, Aliso Viejo (92656-5301)
PHONE...................949 432-9559
Matthew Nunez, *CEO*
EMP: 10
SALES (est): 409.5K **Privately Held**
SIC: 2834 Medicines, capsuled or ampuled

(P-8264)
LOBOB LABORATORIES INC
1440 Atteberry Ln, San Jose (95131-1410)
PHONE...................408 324-0381
Robert M Lohr, *President*
EMP: 35
SQ FT: 20,000
SALES (est): 5.1MM **Privately Held**
WEB: www.loboblabs.com
SIC: 2834 3851 2841 Solutions, pharmaceutical; ophthalmic goods; soap & other detergents

(P-8265)
M & L PHARMACEUTICALS INC
629 S Allen St, San Bernardino (92408-2250)
PHONE...................909 890-0078
Jorge Molina Jr, *President*
Guadalupe Molina, *Corp Secy*
EMP: 15
SQ FT: 6,000
SALES (est): 3.2MM **Privately Held**
WEB: www.mlpharmaceutical.com
SIC: 2834 Vitamin preparations

(P-8266)
MABVAX THRPEUTICS HOLDINGS INC (PA)
11535 Sorrento Valley Rd, San Diego (92121-1309)
PHONE...................858 259-9405
J David Hansen, *Ch of Bd*
Gregory P Hanson, *CFO*
Paul W Maffuid, *Exec VP*
Paul Resnick, *Vice Pres*
Philip O Livingston, *Security Dir*
EMP: 11
SQ FT: 14,971
SALES (est): 1.6MM **Publicly Held**
WEB: www.telik.com
SIC: 2834 Pharmaceutical preparations

(P-8267)
MACROGENICS WEST INC
3280 Byshore Blvd Ste 200, Brisbane (94005)
PHONE...................650 624-2600
Scott Koenig, *President*
Ezio Bonvini, *President*
EMP: 16
SALES (est): 3.6MM **Privately Held**
SIC: 2834 Druggists' preparations (pharmaceuticals)

(P-8268)
MCGUFF PHARMACEUTICALS INC
2921 W Macarthur Blvd # 142, Santa Ana (92704-6909)
PHONE...................714 918-7277
Ronald M McGuff, *President*
Damon Jones, *Vice Pres*
▲ **EMP:** 24
SQ FT: 12,000
SALES (est): 4.9MM
SALES (corp-wide): 27.5MM **Privately Held**
WEB: www.mcguffpharmaceuticals.com
SIC: 2834 Pharmaceutical preparations
PA: Mcguff Company, Inc.
3524 W Lake Center Dr
Santa Ana CA 92704
714 545-2491

(P-8269)
MCKENNA LABS INC (PA)
1601 E Orangethorpe Ave, Fullerton (92831-5230)
PHONE...................714 687-6888
Dennis Alexander Owen, *President*
Drew Naef, *COO*
James Sun, *Vice Pres*
Raquel Carey, *Purch Dir*
Natividad Vazquez, *Opers Mgr*
▲ **EMP:** 40
SQ FT: 62,000
SALES (est): 10.8MM **Privately Held**
WEB: www.mckennalabs.com
SIC: 2834 2844 Pharmaceutical preparations; toilet preparations

(P-8270)
MED-PHARMEX INC
2727 Thompson Creek Rd, Pomona (91767-1861)
PHONE...................909 593-7875
Avinash Ghanekar, *President*
Gerald Macedo, *CEO*
▲ **EMP:** 12
SQ FT: 18,000
SALES (est): 4.9MM **Privately Held**
SIC: 2834 Pharmaceutical preparations

(P-8271)
MEDICINES360
Also Called: M360
353 Sacramento St Ste 300, San Francisco (94111-3688)
PHONE...................415 951-8700
Jessica Grossman, *CEO*
Pamela Weir, *COO*
Mark Busch, *Vice Pres*
Sally Stephens, *VP Bus Dvlpt*
Bob Starr, *Associate Dir*
EMP: 14
SQ FT: 65,000
SALES: 7.6MM **Privately Held**
SIC: 2834 Pharmaceutical preparations

(P-8272)
MEDICINOVA INC (PA)
4275 Executive Sq Ste 300, La Jolla (92037-8408)
PHONE...................858 373-1500
Yuichi Iwaki, *President*
Jeff Himawan, *Ch of Bd*
Ryan Selhorn, *CFO*
Yoshio Ishizaka, *Bd of Directors*
Yutaka Kobayashi, *Bd of Directors*
EMP: 10
SQ FT: 5,219
SALES (est): 2.2MM **Publicly Held**
WEB: www.medicinova.com
SIC: 2834 8731 Pharmaceutical preparations; biotechical research, commercial

(P-8273)
MEDIMMUNE LLC
Also Called: Medimmune Vaccines
297 Bernardo Ave, Mountain View (94043-5205)
PHONE...................650 603-2000
David Mott, *CEO*
Christopher Rhodes, *Vice Pres*
David Andrews, *Associate Dir*
Ashley Hall, *Associate Dir*
Rafael Valdes-Camin, *Associate Dir*
EMP: 275
SALES (corp-wide): 22.4B **Privately Held**
WEB: www.medimmune.com
SIC: 2834 Pharmaceutical preparations
HQ: Medimmune, Llc
1 Medimmune Way
Gaithersburg MD 20878
301 398-0000

(P-8274)
MEDIMMUNE LLC
319 Bernardo Ave, Mountain View (94043-5225)
PHONE...................650 603-2000
Daniel McCabe, *Administration*
Ian Grant, *Technician*
David Tabor, *Research*
Sharon Urbano, *Research*
April Lopez, *Engineer*
EMP: 100
SALES (corp-wide): 22.4B **Privately Held**
WEB: www.medimmune.com
SIC: 2834 Pharmaceutical preparations
HQ: Medimmune, Llc
1 Medimmune Way
Gaithersburg MD 20878
301 398-0000

(P-8275)
MEDIVATION INC (HQ)
Also Called: Xtandi
525 Market St Ste 3600, San Francisco (94105-2747)
PHONE...................415 543-3470
David T Hung, *President*
Marion McCourt, *COO*
Jennifer Jarrett, *CFO*
Mohammad Hirmand, *Chief Mktg Ofcr*
Joseph Lobacki, *Officer*
EMP: 201
SQ FT: 143,000
SALES: 943.2MM
SALES (corp-wide): 52.5B **Publicly Held**
WEB: www.medivation.net
SIC: 2834 Adrenal pharmaceutical preparations
PA: Pfizer Inc.
235 E 42nd St
New York NY 10017
212 733-2323

(P-8276)
MEI PHARMA INC
3611 Vly Cntre Dr Ste 500, San Diego (92130)
PHONE...................858 369-7100
Daniel P Gold, *President*
Christine A White, *Ch of Bd*
David M Urso, *COO*
Brian G Drazba, *CFO*
Robert D Mass, *Chief Mktg Ofcr*
EMP: 25
SQ FT: 13,700
SALES: 23.2MM **Privately Held**
SIC: 2834 Pharmaceutical preparations

(P-8277)
MENLO THERAPEUTICS INC
200 Cardinal Way Fl 2, Redwood City (94063-4756)
PHONE...................650 486-1416
Steven Basta, *President*
Kristine Ball, *CFO*
Ted Ebel, *Bd of Directors*
Scott Whitcup, *Bd of Directors*
Paul Kwon, *Chief Mktg Ofcr*
EMP: 32 EST: 2011
SALES (est): 4.5MM **Privately Held**
SIC: 2834 Pharmaceutical preparations

(P-8278)
MERCK & CO INC
901 California Ave, Palo Alto (94304-1104)
PHONE...................650 496-6400
John T Curnutte, *President*
Jeanne Baker, *Research*
Wendy Blumenschein, *Research*
Danling Gu, *Research*
Barbara Joyceshaikh, *Research*
EMP: 100
SALES (corp-wide): 40.1B **Publicly Held**
SIC: 2834 Pharmaceutical preparations
PA: Merck & Co., Inc.
2000 Galloping Hill Rd
Kenilworth NJ 07033
908 740-4000

(P-8279)
MERCK SHARP & DOHME CORP
8355 Aero Dr, San Diego (92123-1718)
P.O. Box 23576 (92193-3576)
PHONE...................619 292-4900
Peter Kovacs, *President*
Cathy Hardalo, *Officer*
Robert Durgan, *Human Res Mgr*
EMP: 100
SALES (corp-wide): 40.1B **Publicly Held**
SIC: 2834 Pharmaceutical preparations
HQ: Merck Sharp & Dohme Corp.
2000 Galloping Hill Rd
Kenilworth NJ 07033
908 740-4000

(P-8280)
MERIAL LIMITED
1640 Lead Hill Blvd, Roseville (95661-3091)
PHONE...................916 780-9292
Colleen Curran, *Administration*
EMP: 14 EST: 2010
SALES (est): 1.4MM **Privately Held**
SIC: 2834 Pharmaceutical preparations

(P-8281)
METABASIS THERAPEUTICS INC
11085 N Torrey Pines Rd # 300, La Jolla (92037-1015)
PHONE...................858 550-7500
John L Higgins, *President*
Constance C Bienfait, *Vice Pres*
R Wayne Frost, *Vice Pres*
Molly A Holman, *Vice Pres*
Julie C Cunningham, *Commissioner*
EMP: 18 EST: 1997
SQ FT: 82,000
SALES (est): 2.9MM
SALES (corp-wide): 141.1MM **Publicly Held**
WEB: www.mbasis.com
SIC: 2834 Pharmaceutical preparations
PA: Ligand Pharmaceuticals Incorporated
3911 Sorrento Valley Blvd # 110
San Diego CA 92121
858 550-7500

(P-8282)
MGFSO LLC
Also Called: Medigreens
7372 Siena Dr, Huntington Beach (92648-6825)
PHONE...................949 500-7645
Mark Nashed,
John Paboojian,
Kelly Rossow-Soto,
EMP: 10
SQ FT: 5,227,200
SALES: 500K **Privately Held**
SIC: 2834 Pharmaceutical preparations

(P-8283)
MICROGENICS CORPORATION (HQ)
46500 Kato Rd, Fremont (94538-7310)
PHONE...................510 979-9147
Seth H Hoogasian, *CEO*
David Rubinfien, *President*
▲ **EMP:** 230
SQ FT: 108,000
SALES: 498.8MM
SALES (corp-wide): 20.9B **Publicly Held**
WEB: www.microgenics.com
SIC: 2834 Proprietary drug products
PA: Thermo Fisher Scientific Inc.
168 3rd Ave
Waltham MA 02451
781 622-1000

(P-8284)
MIRATI THERAPEUTICS INC
9393 Towne Centre Dr # 200, San Diego (92121-3070)
PHONE...................858 332-3410
Charles M Baum, *President*
Rodney W Lappe, *Ch of Bd*
Jamie A Donadio, *CFO*
Henry Fuchs, *Bd of Directors*
Craig Johnson, *Bd of Directors*
EMP: 52
SQ FT: 18,000

▲ = Import ▼=Export
◆ =Import/Export

SALES (est): 13.4MM **Privately Held**
SIC: **2834** 8731 Pharmaceutical preparations; biotechnical research, commercial

(P-8285)
MOM ENTERPRISES INC
1003 W Cutting Blvd # 110, Richmond (94804-2092)
PHONE..................................415 526-2710
Roshan Kaderali, *CEO*
Shiraz Kaderali, *President*
Yasmin Kaderali, *CEO*
Saritha Peruri, *Marketing Staff*
EMP: 10
SQ FT: 3,000
SALES: 11.6MM **Privately Held**
SIC: **2834** Antacids; extracts of botanicals: powdered, pilular, solid or fluid

(P-8286)
MURAD LLC (HQ)
2121 Park Pl Fl 1, El Segundo (90245)
PHONE..................................310 726-0600
Howard Murad MD, *President*
Elizabeth Ashmun, *Chief Mktg Ofcr*
▲ EMP: 160
SQ FT: 8,000
SALES (est): 55MM
SALES (corp-wide): 63B **Privately Held**
SIC: **2834** 5122 Vitamin, nutrient & hematinic preparations for human use; vitamin preparations; pharmaceuticals; proprietary (patent) medicines
PA: Unilever Plc
Unilever House
London EC4Y
207 822-5252

(P-8287)
MYA INTERNATIONAL INC
10030 Marconi Dr Ste 1, San Diego (92154-7292)
PHONE..................................619 429-6012
Ana Martins, *CEO*
Michael Martins, *President*
▲ EMP: 13
SQ FT: 8,000
SALES (est): 2.8MM **Privately Held**
SIC: **2834** Vitamin, nutrient & hematinic preparations for human use

(P-8288)
MYOGENIX INCORPORATED
2309 A St, Santa Maria (93455-1072)
PHONE..................................800 950-0348
Adam G Nielson, *President*
▲ EMP: 12
SALES (est): 2.2MM **Privately Held**
WEB: www.myogenix.com
SIC: **2834** Pharmaceutical preparations

(P-8289)
MYOKARDIA INC
333 Allerton Ave, South San Francisco (94080-4816)
PHONE..................................650 741-0900
T Anastasios Glanakakos, *CEO*
June Lee, *COO*
Taylor C Harris, *CFO*
Sunil Agarwal, *Bd of Directors*
Mary Cranston, *Bd of Directors*
EMP: 74
SALES: 22.5MM **Privately Held**
SIC: **2834** Drugs acting on the cardiovascular system, except diagnostic

(P-8290)
NADIN COMPANY
1815 Flower St, Glendale (91201-2024)
PHONE..................................818 500-8908
EMP: 25
SQ FT: 35,000
SALES (est): 2.2MM **Privately Held**
SIC: **2834**

(P-8291)
NATROL LLC (DH)
21411 Prairie St, Chatsworth (91311-5829)
PHONE..................................818 739-6000
Tom Zimmerman, *CEO*
Ivan Milenkovic, *Administration*
Edgar Rodriguez, *Comp Lab Dir*
Mirrella Jolicoeur, *Info Tech Dir*
Michael Berinde, *Info Tech Mgr*
◆ EMP: 179 EST: 2015

SALES (est): 105.3MM
SALES (corp-wide): 1.5B **Privately Held**
SIC: **2834** Pharmaceutical preparations
HQ: Aurobindo Pharma U.S.A., Inc.
279 Prnctn Hightstown Rd
East Windsor NJ 08520
732 839-9400

(P-8292)
NATURA-GENICS INC
6952 Buckeye St, Chino (91710-8248)
PHONE..................................909 597-6676
Renzo Bustamante, *President*
Renzo J Bustamante, *Principal*
▲ EMP: 10
SALES (est): 2.2MM **Privately Held**
SIC: **2834** Vitamin preparations

(P-8293)
NATURESTAR BIO TECH INC
1175 S Grove Ave Ste 101, Ontario (91761-3470)
PHONE..................................909 930-1878
Liqiong Fei, *President*
EMP: 15
SALES (est): 2MM **Privately Held**
WEB: www.naturestarusa.com
SIC: **2834** Vitamin, nutrient & hematinic preparations for human use

(P-8294)
NBTY MANUFACTURING LLC
Also Called: Nature's Bounty
5115 E La Palma Ave, Anaheim (92807-2018)
PHONE..................................714 765-8323
Steve Cahillane, *CEO*
Lily Mu, *Training Dir*
Jan Gaydon, *Purchasing*
Sunil Ratnayake, *QC Mgr*
Hans Lindgren,
▼ EMP: 224
SALES (est): 36.4MM **Publicly Held**
WEB: www.nbtymfg.com
SIC: **2834** Vitamin preparations
HQ: The Nature's Bounty Co
2100 Smithtown Ave
Ronkonkoma NY 11779
631 200-2000

(P-8295)
NEILMED PHARMACEUTICALS INC
601 Aviation Blvd, Santa Rosa (95403-1025)
PHONE..................................707 525-3784
Kaetan Mehta MD, *CEO*
Nina K Mehta, *President*
Ken Di, *CFO*
Manjunatha Prabhu, *Research*
Daniel Barba, *Graphic Designe*
▲ EMP: 300
SALES (est): 105.3MM **Privately Held**
WEB: www.nasalrinse.com
SIC: **2834** Pharmaceutical preparations

(P-8296)
NEKTAR THERAPEUTICS
150 Industrial Rd, San Carlos (94070-6256)
PHONE..................................650 622-1790
Dorian Rinella, *Senior VP*
Sunny Xie, *Vice Pres*
Kerry Ellis, *Executive Asst*
Swapnil Marghade, *Research*
Krishna Teja, *Technical Staff*
EMP: 37
SALES (est): 4.9MM **Privately Held**
SIC: **2834** Pharmaceutical preparations

(P-8297)
NEKTAR THERAPEUTICS (PA)
455 Mission Bay Blvd S, San Francisco (94158-2158)
PHONE..................................415 482-5300
Howard W Robin, *President*
Robert B Chess, *Ch of Bd*
John Nicholson, *COO*
Gil M Labrucherie, *CFO*
Joseph Krivulka, *Bd of Directors*
EMP: 280
SQ FT: 126,285
SALES: 307.7MM **Publicly Held**
SIC: **2834** Pharmaceutical preparations

(P-8298)
NERVEDA INC
3888 Quarter Mile Dr, San Diego (92130-1291)
PHONE..................................858 705-2365
CAM Gallagher, *Principal*
EMP: 72
SALES (est): 5.7MM **Privately Held**
SIC: **2834** Pharmaceutical preparations

(P-8299)
NEUROCRINE BIOSCIENCES INC (PA)
12780 El Camino Real # 100, San Diego (92130-2042)
PHONE..................................858 617-7600
William H Rastetter, *Ch of Bd*
David-Alexandre Gros, *President*
Kevin C Gorman, *CEO*
Matt Abernethy, *CFO*
Gary Lyons, *Bd of Directors*
EMP: 120
SQ FT: 140,000
SALES: 161.6MM **Publicly Held**
WEB: www.neurocrine.com
SIC: **2834** 2833 Pituitary gland pharmaceutical preparations; drugs acting on the central nervous system & sense organs; endocrine products

(P-8300)
NEXGEN PHARMA INC (PA)
46 Corporate Park Ste 100, Irvine (92606-3121)
P.O. Box 19516 (92623-9516)
PHONE..................................949 863-0340
Steven Brown, *CEO*
Gary P Korngold, *President*
Mark Nishi, *CFO*
Gene Nakagawa, *Exec VP*
Dr Deepak Thassu, *Vice Pres*
EMP: 190
SQ FT: 50,000
SALES (est): 57MM **Privately Held**
WEB: www.vitamer.com
SIC: **2834** Pharmaceutical preparations

(P-8301)
NEXGEN PHARMA INC
17802 Gillette Ave, Irvine (92614-6502)
PHONE..................................949 260-3702
Ian Gibson, *Vice Pres*
EMP: 45
SALES (corp-wide): 57MM **Privately Held**
WEB: www.vitamer.com
SIC: **2834** Vitamin, nutrient & hematinic preparations for human use
PA: Nexgen Pharma, Inc.
46 Corporate Park Ste 100
Irvine CA 92606
949 863-0340

(P-8302)
NEXGEN PHARMA INC
17802 Gillette Ave, Irvine (92614-6502)
PHONE..................................949 863-0340
Steve Brown, *President*
EMP: 15
SQ FT: 26,152
SALES (corp-wide): 57MM **Privately Held**
WEB: www.vitamer.com
SIC: **2834** Vitamin, nutrient & hematinic preparations for human use
PA: Nexgen Pharma, Inc.
46 Corporate Park Ste 100
Irvine CA 92606
949 863-0340

(P-8303)
NEXT PHARMACEUTICALS INC
360 Espinosa Rd, Salinas (93907-8895)
PHONE..................................831 621-8712
Charles Kosmont, *President*
Robert Garrison, *Chairman*
EMP: 50
SALES (est): 5.5MM **Privately Held**
WEB: www.nextpharmaceuticals.com
SIC: **2834** Vitamin, nutrient & hematinic preparations for human use; vitamin preparations

(P-8304)
NEXTPHARMA TECH USA INC
Also Called: Bioserv
5340 Eastgate Mall, San Diego (92121-2804)
PHONE..................................858 450-3123
Franck Latrille, *CEO*
Matthew Wilder, *Vice Pres*
Michel Blanc, *VP Bus Dvlpt*
Francois Ribeaux, *Business Dir*
Martin Sellers, *General Mgr*
EMP: 27
SQ FT: 38,000
SALES (est): 6.5MM **Privately Held**
WEB: www.bioservcorp.com
SIC: **2834** 2835 Pharmaceutical preparations; microbiology & virology diagnostic products
HQ: Nextpharma Technologies Holding Limited
1 Tannery House
Woking
148 347-9120

(P-8305)
NHK LABORATORIES (PA)
12230 Florence Ave, Santa Fe Springs (90670-3806)
PHONE..................................562 903-5835
M Amirul Karim, *CEO*
Shafiel Ahmed, *CFO*
Shafiel Karim, *CFO*
Nasima A Karim, *Vice Pres*
Rolando Sabilia, *Controller*
▲ EMP: 95
SQ FT: 90,000
SALES (est): 20.7MM **Privately Held**
WEB: www.nhklabs.com
SIC: **2834** 5122 Vitamin preparations; vitamins & minerals

(P-8306)
NITTO AVECIA PHARMA SVCS INC
4 Chrysler, Irvine (92618-2008)
PHONE..................................949 462-0814
Adam Fox, *Exec VP*
EMP: 42
SALES (corp-wide): 37.8MM **Privately Held**
SIC: **2834** Druggists' preparations (pharmaceuticals)
PA: Nitto Avecia Pharma Services Inc
10 Vanderbilt
Irvine CA 92618
949 951-4425

(P-8307)
NOVABAY PHARMACEUTICALS INC
2000 Powell St Ste 1150, Emeryville (94608-1866)
PHONE..................................510 899-8800
Jack McGovern, *CEO*
Mark M Sieczkarek, *Ch of Bd*
Thomas J Paulson, *CFO*
Gail Maderis, *Bd of Directors*
Mijia Wu, *Bd of Directors*
EMP: 26
SQ FT: 16,465
SALES: 18.2MM **Privately Held**
SIC: **2834** Drugs acting on the central nervous system & sense organs

(P-8308)
NOVARTIS CORPORATION
3115 Merryfield Row, San Diego (92121-1125)
PHONE..................................858 812-1741
Joerg Reinhardt, *Chairman*
EMP: 56
SALES (corp-wide): 49.1B **Privately Held**
SIC: **2834** Pharmaceutical preparations
HQ: Novartis Corporation
1 S Ridgedale Ave
East Hanover NJ 07936
212 307-1122

(P-8309)
NOVARTIS CORPORATION
150 Industrial Rd, San Carlos (94070-6256)
PHONE..................................650 631-3100
G Fukumitsu, *Principal*
Romain Taniere, *Program Mgr*

PRODUCTS & SVCS

Michael Schillaci, *Research*
Anne Berkley, *Engineer*
Chuck Kreider, *Director*
EMP: 56
SALES (corp-wide): 49.1B **Privately Held**
WEB: www.novartis.com
SIC: 2834 Veterinary pharmaceutical preparations
HQ: Novartis Corporation
    1 S Ridgedale Ave
    East Hanover NJ 07936
    212 307-1122

(P-8310)
NOVUS THERAPEUTICS INC
19900 Macarthur Blvd # 550, Irvine (92612-8426)
PHONE..................617 225-4305
Jodie P Morrison, *President*
Seth L Harrison, *Ch of Bd*
John S McBride, *COO*
Gerald E Quirk, *Exec VP*
EMP: 14
SQ FT: 15,981
SALES (est): 2MM **Privately Held**
SIC: 2834 Pharmaceutical preparations

(P-8311)
NUTRAWISE HEALTH & BEAUTY CORP (PA)
Also Called: Nutrawise Corporation
9600 Toledo Way, Irvine (92618-1808)
PHONE..................949 900-2400
Darren Rude, *CEO*
Patty Terzo-Rude, *President*
Theresa Rude, *Treasurer*
Heidi Kaufman, *Planning*
Marco Banda, *Info Tech Dir*
EMP: 62 EST: 2009
SQ FT: 130,000
SALES: 48MM **Privately Held**
SIC: 2834 Vitamin, nutrient & hematinic preparations for human use

(P-8312)
NUTRITION RESOURCE INC (PA)
Also Called: Nutribiotic
865 Parallel Dr, Lakeport (95453-5707)
P.O. Box 238 (95453-0238)
PHONE..................707 263-0411
Richard Perry, *President*
Lori Peters, *Production*
Kenny Ridgeway, *Marketing Staff*
◆ **EMP:** 16
SQ FT: 20,000
SALES (est): 4.3MM **Privately Held**
WEB: www.nutribiotic.com
SIC: 2834 2844 2841 2023 Vitamin preparations; ointments; toothpastes or powders, dentifrices; soap: granulated, liquid, cake, flaked or chip; dietary supplements, dairy & non-dairy based

(P-8313)
NUTRITIONAL ENGINEERING INC
1208 Avenida Chelsea, Vista (92081-8315)
PHONE..................760 599-5200
Ted Laoudis, *CEO*
Pamela Deshazo, *Purchasing*
EMP: 12
SQ FT: 12,000
SALES (est): 3.4MM **Privately Held**
WEB: www.herbalman.com
SIC: 2834 Vitamin preparations

(P-8314)
OBAGI COSMECEUTICALS LLC (PA)
Also Called: Obagi Medical
3760 Kilroy Airport Way, Long Beach (90806-2443)
PHONE..................800 636-7546
Jamie Castle, *President*
Mark T Taylor, *Senior VP*
Lisa Errecart, *Vice Pres*
Genevieve Wohland, *Senior Mgr*
EMP: 55
SQ FT: 30,884
SALES (est): 40.2MM **Privately Held**
SIC: 2834 Pharmaceutical preparations

(P-8315)
OCUNEXUS THERAPEUTICS INC
12481 High Bluff Dr D, San Diego (92130-3585)
PHONE..................858 480-2403
Bradford J Duft, *President*
David Paul, *CFO*
David E Eisenbud, *Officer*
James C Blair, *Director*
Anthony Phillips, *Director*
EMP: 14
SALES (est): 2.2MM **Privately Held**
SIC: 2834 Pharmaceutical preparations

(P-8316)
ODONATE THERAPEUTICS INC
4747 Executive Dr Ste 510, San Diego (92121-3100)
PHONE..................858 731-8180
Kevin C Tang, *Ch of Bd*
Robert D Millham, *COO*
John G Lemkey, *CFO*
Jeff L Vacirca, *Vice Ch Bd*
George Tidmarsh, *Bd of Directors*
EMP: 50
SALES (est): 662.5K **Privately Held**
SIC: 2834 Pharmaceutical preparations

(P-8317)
ONCOMED PHARMACEUTICALS INC
800 Chesapeake Dr, Redwood City (94063-4748)
PHONE..................650 995-8200
John Lewicki, *President*
Perry A Karsen, *Ch of Bd*
John A Lewicki, *President*
Elisha Gould, *Bd of Directors*
Laurence Lasky, *Bd of Directors*
EMP: 56
SQ FT: 45,690
SALES (est): 38.1MM **Privately Held**
WEB: www.oncomed.com
SIC: 2834 8071 Pharmaceutical preparations; medical laboratories; biological laboratory

(P-8318)
ONYX PHARMACEUTICALS INC
1 Amgen Center Dr, Newbury Park (91320-1730)
PHONE..................650 266-0000
Pablo Cagnoni, *President*
Helen Torley, *COO*
Matthew K Fust, *CFO*
Juergen Lasowski PHD, *Exec VP*
Suzanne M Shema Jdl, *Exec VP*
EMP: 741
SQ FT: 297,111
SALES (est): 228.8MM
SALES (corp-wide): 22.8B **Publicly Held**
WEB: www.onyx-pharm.com
SIC: 2834 8049 Drugs affecting parasitic & infective diseases; occupational therapist
PA: Amgen Inc.
    1 Amgen Center Dr
    Thousand Oaks CA 91320
    805 447-1000

(P-8319)
OPIANT PHARMACEUTICALS INC
201 Santa Monica Blvd B, Santa Monica (90401-2214)
PHONE..................301 598-5410
Roger Crystal, *President*
Michael Sinclair, *Ch of Bd*
David D O'Toole, *CFO*
Sam Martin, *Managing Dir*
EMP: 14
SALES: 11.7MM **Privately Held**
SIC: 2834 Pharmaceutical preparations

(P-8320)
OREXIGEN THERAPEUTICS INC (HQ)
3344 N Torrey Pines Ct # 200, La Jolla (92037-1024)
PHONE..................858 875-8600
Michael A Narachi, *President*
Thomas Cannell, *President*
Tom Cannell, *Officer*
Heather Ace, *Exec VP*
Preston Klassen, *Exec VP*

EMP: 67
SQ FT: 29,935
SALES (est): 33.7MM **Publicly Held**
WEB: www.robinson-pilaw.com
SIC: 2834 Pharmaceutical preparations
PA: Nalpropion Pharmaceuticals, Inc.
    3344 N Torrey Pines Ct # 200
    La Jolla CA 92037
    858 875-8600

(P-8321)
ORIC PHARMACEUTICALS INC
240 E Grand Ave, South San Francisco (94080-4811)
PHONE..................650 918-8818
Jacob Chacko, *CEO*
Rich Heyman, *Ch of Bd*
Pratik Multani, *Chief Mktg Ofcr*
Leonard Reyno, *Chief Mktg Ofcr*
Darcy Mootz, *Officer*
EMP: 31
SALES (est): 7.7MM **Privately Held**
SIC: 2834 Pharmaceutical preparations

(P-8322)
OTONOMY INC
4796 Executive Dr, San Diego (92121-3090)
PHONE..................619 323-2200
David A Weber, *President*
Jay Lichter, *Ch of Bd*
Paul E Cayer, *CFO*
Kathie Bishop, *Security Dir*
Robert Michael Savel II, *CTO*
EMP: 53
SQ FT: 62,000
SALES: 1.2MM **Privately Held**
SIC: 2834 8731 Pharmaceutical preparations; biological research

(P-8323)
P & L DEVELOPMENT LLC
Also Called: Pl Development
11840 Alameda St, Lynwood (90262-4019)
PHONE..................310 763-1377
James L Medford, *President*
EMP: 30 **Privately Held**
SIC: 2834 Pharmaceutical preparations
PA: P & L Development, Llc
    200 Hicks St
    Westbury NY 11590

(P-8324)
PACIFIC PHARMASCIENCE INC
23052 Alcalde Dr Ste A, Laguna Hills (92653-1327)
PHONE..................949 916-6955
Robert L Orr, *President*
EMP: 10
SALES (est): 1.3MM **Privately Held**
SIC: 2834 8748 Pharmaceutical preparations; testing services

(P-8325)
PACIFIC SHORE HOLDINGS INC
Also Called: Nature-Cide
8236 Remmet Ave, Canoga Park (91304-4156)
PHONE..................818 998-0996
Matthew Mills, *President*
Ronald J Tchorzewski, *CFO*
David E Toomey, *Exec VP*
Jennifer Mills, *Admin Sec*
▲ **EMP:** 12
SQ FT: 13,000
SALES (est): 2.6MM **Privately Held**
SIC: 2834 2879 Pharmaceutical preparations; pesticides, agricultural or household
PA: Med-X, Inc.
    8236 Remmet Ave
    Canoga Park CA 91304
    818 349-2870

(P-8326)
PACIRA PHARMACEUTICALS INC
10450 Science Center Dr, San Diego (92121-1119)
PHONE..................858 678-3950
Dave Stack, *President*
Senn Paul, *President*
James S Scibetta, *CFO*
Taunia Markvicka, *Senior VP*
Gordon Schooley, *Senior VP*
▲ **EMP:** 80

SQ FT: 82,000
SALES (est): 27.4MM **Publicly Held**
SIC: 2834 Pharmaceutical preparations
PA: Pacira Pharmaceuticals, Inc.
    5 Sylvan Way Ste 300
    Parsippany NJ 07054

(P-8327)
PEGASUS MED SERVICES/RENALAB
3570 Sibley Ln, Templeton (93465-9472)
PHONE..................805 226-8350
Gil McGuff, *President*
EMP: 15
SALES (est): 1.2MM **Privately Held**
SIC: 2834 Pharmaceutical preparations

(P-8328)
PENINSULA PHARMACEUTICALS
1751 Harbor Bay Pkwy, Alameda (94502-3001)
PHONE..................510 337-1060
Matthew A Wikler, *Chairman*
Stan E Abel, *CFO*
Debra Odink, *Vice Pres*
EMP: 21
SQ FT: 12,000
SALES: 2MM
SALES (corp-wide): 76.4B **Publicly Held**
WEB: www.cerexa.com
SIC: 2834 Pharmaceutical preparations; drugs acting on the gastrointestinal or genitourinary system
HQ: Ortho-Mcneil Pharmaceutical, Llc
    1000 Rte 202
    Raritan NJ 08869
    908 203-4090

(P-8329)
PEREZ DISTRIBUTING FRESNO INC (PA)
103 S Academy Ave, Sanger (93657-2428)
P.O. Box 579 (93657-0579)
PHONE..................800 638-3512
Emeterio P Perez, *President*
Alma Perez, *Vice Pres*
▲ **EMP:** 27
SQ FT: 16,000
SALES (est): 4.9MM **Privately Held**
WEB: www.perezdistfresno.com
SIC: 2834 Druggists' preparations (pharmaceuticals)

(P-8330)
PFENEX INC
10790 Roselle St, San Diego (92121-1508)
PHONE..................858 352-4400
Jason Grenfell-Gardner, *Ch of Bd*
Evert B Schimmelpennink, *President*
Shawn A Scranton, *COO*
Susan A Knudson, *CFO*
Patricia Lady,
EMP: 67
SQ FT: 46,959
SALES: 28.7MM **Privately Held**
SIC: 2834 Pharmaceutical preparations

(P-8331)
PFIZER HEALTH SOLUTIONS INC
2400 Broadway Ste 500, Santa Monica (90404-3072)
PHONE..................310 586-2550
Alan Lang, *Branch Mgr*
Levente Orosz, *Manager*
EMP: 10
SALES (corp-wide): 52.5B **Publicly Held**
SIC: 2834 Pharmaceutical preparations
HQ: Pfizer Health Solutions Inc
    150 E 42nd St Bsmt 2
    New York NY 10017
    314 274-1360

(P-8332)
PFIZER INC
11095 Torreyana Rd, San Diego (92121-1104)
PHONE..................858 622-7325
Cheryl Garner, *Manager*
Rick Bailey, *VP Human Res*
Jessica Escoto, *Recruiter*
Keith Wilner, *Director*
EMP: 148

▲ = Import ▼=Export
◆ =Import/Export

SALES (corp-wide): 52.5B **Publicly Held**
SIC: 2834 Pharmaceutical preparations
PA: Pfizer Inc.
235 E 42nd St
New York NY 10017
212 733-2323

(P-8333)
PFIZER INC
10646 Science Center Dr, San Diego
(92121-1150)
PHONE..................................858 622-3001
Mary Mateja, *Manager*
Tanya Russell, *Vice Pres*
Vik Kapoor, *Info Tech Dir*
Melissa Reynolds, *Info Tech Dir*
Jim Condelles, *Project Mgr*
EMP: 2000
SALES (corp-wide): 52.5B **Publicly Held**
WEB: www.pfizer.com
SIC: 2834 Pharmaceutical preparations
PA: Pfizer Inc.
235 E 42nd St
New York NY 10017
212 733-2323

(P-8334)
PH LABS ADVANCED NUTRITION
9760 Via De La Amistad, San Diego
(92154-7210)
PHONE..................................619 240-3263
EMP: 11 EST: 2014
SALES (est): 1.8MM **Privately Held**
SIC: 2834 Druggists' preparations (pharmaceuticals)

(P-8335)
PHARMACEUTIC LITHO LABEL INC
3990 Royal Ave, Simi Valley (93063-3380)
PHONE..................................805 285-5162
Timothy Laurence, *President*
Tom Moore, *President*
Merrill Jackson, *CFO*
Rick Machale, *Vice Pres*
Diana Fonseca, *Asst Controller*
▲ EMP: 85
SQ FT: 32,000
SALES (est): 35MM **Privately Held**
WEB: www.pharmaceuticlitho.com
SIC: 2834 Pharmaceutical preparations

(P-8336)
PHARMACYCLICS LLC (HQ)
995 E Arques Ave, Sunnyvale
(94085-4521)
PHONE..................................408 215-3000
Wulff-Erik Von Borcke, *President*
Betty Chang, *Vice Pres*
Gregory Hemmi, *Vice Pres*
Dana Lee, *Vice Pres*
Laurie Krekemeyer, *Executive*
EMP: 178
SALES (est): 440.3MM
SALES (corp-wide): 28.2B **Publicly Held**
SIC: 2834 Pharmaceutical preparations
PA: Abbvie Inc.
1 N Waukegan Rd
North Chicago IL 60064
847 932-7900

(P-8337)
PHOENIX PHARMACEUTICALS INC
330 Beach Rd, Burlingame (94010-2004)
PHONE..................................650 558-8898
Jaw-Kang Chang, *President*
Chang Jaw, *Info Tech Dir*
Laurent Ginestet-Araki, *Technical Staff*
Chentao Wang, *Marketing Mgr*
Crystal Chang, *Sales Mgr*
EMP: 20
SQ FT: 5,000
SALES (est): 7MM **Privately Held**
WEB: www.phoenixpeptide.com
SIC: 2834 8731 Pharmaceutical preparations; commercial physical research

(P-8338)
PHYTO TECH CORP
Also Called: Blue California Company
30111 Tomas, Rcho STA Marg
(92688-2125)
PHONE..................................949 635-1990

Steven Chen, *President*
▲ EMP: 25
SQ FT: 50,000
SALES (est): 6.1MM **Privately Held**
SIC: 2834 Vitamin, nutrient & hematinic preparations for human use

(P-8339)
PLEXXIKON INC
91 Bolivar Dr, Berkeley (94710-2210)
PHONE..................................510 647-4000
Gideon Bollag, *CEO*
Paul Lin, *COO*
Joseph Young, *Treasurer*
Keith B Nolop MD, *Chief Mktg Ofcr*
Prabha Ibrahim, *Senior VP*
EMP: 44
SQ FT: 10,000
SALES (est): 15.7MM
SALES (corp-wide): 9B **Privately Held**
WEB: www.plexxicon.com
SIC: 2834 Tablets, pharmaceutical
PA: Daiichi Sankyo Company, Limited
3-5-1, Nihonbashihoncho
Chuo-Ku TKY 103-0
362 251-111

(P-8340)
POLARIS PHARMACEUTICALS INC
9373 Towne Centre Dr # 150, San Diego
(92121-3027)
PHONE..................................858 452-6688
Bor Wen Wu, *CEO*
John Bomalaski, *Vice Pres*
Wen-Chin Tsai, *Exec Dir*
Robert E Hoffman, *CIO*
Heather Ho, *Accountant*
EMP: 28
SALES (est): 6MM **Privately Held**
SIC: 2834 Pharmaceutical preparations

(P-8341)
PORTOLA PHARMACEUTICALS INC (PA)
270 E Grand Ave, South San Francisco
(94080-4811)
PHONE..................................650 246-7000
William Lis, *CEO*
Hollings C Renton, *Ch of Bd*
Mardi C Dier, *CFO*
Laura Brege, *Bd of Directors*
David Stump, *Bd of Directors*
EMP: 163
SQ FT: 74,000
SALES (est): 22.5MM **Publicly Held**
SIC: 2834 Pharmaceutical preparations

(P-8342)
PREFERRED PHARMACEUTICALS INC
1250 N Lakeview Ave Ste O, Anaheim
(92807-1801)
PHONE..................................714 777-3729
Robert Kent, *President*
Mike Kent, *Vice Pres*
EMP: 10
SALES (est): 2.3MM **Privately Held**
SIC: 2834 Pharmaceutical preparations

(P-8343)
PRESIDIO PHARMACEUTICALS INC
1700 Owens St Ste 585, San Francisco
(94158-0008)
PHONE..................................415 655-7560
Leo Redmond, *President*
H Daniel Perez, *President*
EMP: 19
SQ FT: 8,000
SALES (est): 3.4MM **Privately Held**
WEB: www.presidiopharma.com
SIC: 2834 Pharmaceutical preparations

(P-8344)
PRIMAPHARMA INC
3443 Tripp Ct, San Diego (92121-1032)
PHONE..................................858 259-0969
Mark Livingston, *President*
Larry Braga, *Vice Pres*
Tony Dziabo, *Vice Pres*
Sarah Dziabo, *Associate Dir*
Nayaz Ahmed, *Engineer*
EMP: 35
SQ FT: 24,000

SALES: 5.2MM **Privately Held**
SIC: 2834 Pharmaceutical preparations

(P-8345)
PRINCIPIA BIOPHARMA INC
400 E Jamie Ct Ste 302, South San Francisco (94080-6230)
PHONE..................................650 416-7700
Martin Babler, *CEO*
Alan B Colowick, *Ch of Bd*
Christopher Y Chai, *CFO*
Steve Gourlay, *Chief Mktg Ofcr*
Dolca Thomas, *Chief Mktg Ofcr*
EMP: 53 EST: 2011
SQ FT: 30,000
SALES: 5.2MM **Privately Held**
SIC: 2834 Pharmaceutical preparations

(P-8346)
PROJECT MUSTANG DEV LLC
10115 Jefferson Blvd, Culver City
(90232-3519)
PHONE..................................323 275-4098
Adam Bierman, *Director*
EMP: 130
SQ FT: 45,000
SALES: 200K **Privately Held**
SIC: 2834 Pharmaceutical preparations

(P-8347)
PROMETHEUS LABORATORIES INC
9410 Carroll Park Dr, San Diego
(92121-5201)
PHONE..................................858 824-0895
Warren Cresswell, *CEO*
Peter Westlake, *CFO*
Jenny Alonso, *Vice Pres*
Robert Carlson, *Vice Pres*
Larry Mimms PHD, *Vice Pres*
EMP: 405
SQ FT: 99,000
SALES (est): 135.7MM
SALES (corp-wide): 90.8B **Privately Held**
WEB: www.prometheuslabs.com
SIC: 2834 8011 Pharmaceutical preparations; offices & clinics of medical doctors
HQ: Nestle Health Science Sa
Batiment 4
Epalinges VD 1066
216 326-100

(P-8348)
PROTAB LABORATORIES
25902 Towne Centre Dr, Foothill Ranch
(92610-3436)
PHONE..................................949 635-1930
Min W Chen, *CEO*
Xiao Zhou, *Co-Owner*
Shafiqul Islam, *Vice Pres*
Randy L Pollan, *Vice Pres*
Joanne Hsu, *Administration*
▲ EMP: 60
SQ FT: 100,000
SALES (est): 17.4MM **Privately Held**
SIC: 2834 Vitamin preparations

(P-8349)
PROTAGONIST THERAPEUTICS INC
7707 Gateway Blvd Ste 140, Newark
(94560-1160)
PHONE..................................510 474-0170
Dinesh V Patel, *President*
Harold E Selick, *Ch of Bd*
Thomas P O'Neil, *CFO*
Chaitan Khosla, *Bd of Directors*
Sarah Noonberg, *Bd of Directors*
EMP: 35
SQ FT: 42,877
SALES: 20MM **Privately Held**
SIC: 2834 8731 Pharmaceutical preparations; commercial physical research

(P-8350)
PUMA BIOTECHNOLOGY INC (PA)
10880 Wilshire Blvd # 2150, Los Angeles
(90024-4106)
P.O. Box 64945, Saint Paul MN (55164-0945)
PHONE..................................424 248-6500
Alan H Auerbach, *Ch of Bd*
Charles R Eyler, *Treasurer*
Steven Lo, *Ch Credit Ofcr*

Richard P Bryce, *Chief Mktg Ofcr*
Douglas Hunt, *Senior VP*
EMP: 70
SQ FT: 25,700
SALES: 27.6MM **Publicly Held**
SIC: 2834 Pharmaceutical preparations

(P-8351)
PURETEK CORPORATION
7900 Nelson Rd Unit A, Panorama City
(91402-6828)
PHONE..................................818 361-3949
Jeff Pressman, *Branch Mgr*
EMP: 130
SALES (est): 20.4MM **Privately Held**
SIC: 2834 2844 Pharmaceutical preparations; cosmetic preparations
PA: Puretek Corporation
7900 Nelson Rd
Panorama City CA 91402

(P-8352)
PURETEK CORPORATION (PA)
7900 Nelson Rd, Panorama City
(91402-6827)
PHONE..................................818 361-3316
Barry Pressman, *CEO*
Jeff Pressman, *Info Tech Mgr*
Nikki Chew, *Research*
Ann Huang, *Research*
Steve Goldstein, *Controller*
◆ EMP: 50
SQ FT: 114,000
SALES: 30MM **Privately Held**
WEB: www.pharmapure.net
SIC: 2834 Pharmaceutical preparations

(P-8353)
QUARK PHARMACEUTICALS INC (DH)
7999 Gateway Blvd Ste 310, Newark
(94560-1188)
PHONE..................................510 402-4020
Daniel Zurr, *President*
Philip B Simon, *Ch of Bd*
Rami Skaliter, *COO*
Joseph Rubinfeld, *Vice Ch Bd*
Elena Feinstein, *Officer*
EMP: 25
SALES (est): 6.8MM
SALES (corp-wide): 3.1B **Privately Held**
WEB: www.qbi.co.il
SIC: 2834 Pharmaceutical preparations
HQ: Sbi Biotech Co., Ltd.
1-6-1, Roppongi
Minato-Ku TKY
362 290-787

(P-8354)
QUOREX PHARM INC (PA)
2232 Rutherford Rd, Carlsbad
(92008-8814)
PHONE..................................760 602-1910
Robert Robb, *President*
Gary JG Atkinson, *CFO*
Krzysztof Appelt, *Exec VP*
Jeffrey Stein, *Exec VP*
Donald Mc Carthy, *Controller*
EMP: 42
SQ FT: 23,500
SALES (est): 2.8MM **Privately Held**
SIC: 2834 Pharmaceutical preparations

(P-8355)
RAFFAELLO RESEARCH LABS
120 The Village Unit 109, Redondo Beach
(90277-2561)
PHONE..................................310 618-8754
Rafael Akyuz, *President*
Linda Akyuz, *Treasurer*
EMP: 15
SQ FT: 12,500
SALES (est): 1.8MM **Privately Held**
SIC: 2834 Pharmaceutical preparations

(P-8356)
RANDAL OPTIMAL NUTRIENTS LLC
Also Called: Vimco
1595 Hampton Way, Santa Rosa
(95407-6844)
P.O. Box 7328 (95407-0328)
PHONE..................................707 528-1800
William A Robotham, *President*
Lynn J Brinker, *Corp Secy*

(PA)=Parent Co (HQ)=Headquarters (DH)=Div Headquarters
✿ = New Business established in last 2 years

2019 California
Manufacturers Register

345

PRODUCTS & SVCS

Donna Coats, *Vice Pres*
EMP: 32
SQ FT: 22,500
SALES (est): 8.3MM **Privately Held**
WEB: www.randalnutritional.com
SIC: 2834 5122 Vitamin preparations;
drugs, proprietaries & sundries

(P-8357)
RAPTOR PHARMACEUTICALS INC
7 Hamilton Landing # 100, Novato
(94949-8209)
PHONE..........................415 408-6200
Julie Anne Smith, *CEO*
EMP: 28 **EST:** 2005
SALES (est): 57.1K **Privately Held**
SIC: 2834 Pharmaceutical preparations
HQ: Horizon Pharmaceutical Llc
7 Hamilton Landing # 100
Novato CA 94949
-

(P-8358)
REDWOOD SCIENTIFIC TECH INC
820 N Mountain Ave # 100, Upland
(91786-4163)
PHONE..........................310 693-5401
Jason E Cardiff, *President*
Jacques Poujade, *Treasurer*
M Salah Zaki, *Chief Mktg Ofcr*
Eunjung Cardiff, *Admin Sec*
Rhonda Pearlman, *General Counsel*
EMP: 24 **EST:** 2014
SQ FT: 5,800
SALES (est): 606.5K **Privately Held**
SIC: 2834 Druggists' preparations (pharmaceuticals)

(P-8359)
RELYPSA INC
100 Cardinal Way, Redwood City
(94063-4755)
PHONE..........................650 421-9500
John A Orwin, *CEO*
Patrick Treanor, *President*
Kristine M Ball, *CFO*
Lance Berman, *Officer*
Stephen D Harrison, *Officer*
EMP: 406
SQ FT: 93,904
SALES: 18.5MM
SALES (corp-wide): 1.3B **Privately Held**
WEB: www.relypsa.com
SIC: 2834 Pharmaceutical preparations
PA: Vifor Pharma Ag
Rechenstrasse 37
St. Gallen SG 9014
588 528-111

(P-8360)
REMPEX PHARMACEUTICALS INC
3013 Science Park Rd Fl 1, San Diego
(92121-1101)
PHONE..........................858 875-2840
Stuart Kingsley, *President*
William Oconner, *CFO*
Olga Lomovskaya PHD, *Vice Pres*
EMP: 40
SQ FT: 60
SALES (est): 8.9MM
SALES (corp-wide): 44.7MM **Publicly Held**
SIC: 2834 Pharmaceutical preparations
PA: The Medicines Company
8 Sylvan Way
Parsippany NJ 07054
973 290-6000

(P-8361)
RESEARCH WAY LL LLC
Also Called: Research Way Partners
1900 Main St Ste 375, Irvine (92614-7332)
PHONE..........................608 830-6300
Justin Komppa, *Senior Partner*
EMP: 14
SALES (est): 682K **Privately Held**
SIC: 2834 Tablets, pharmaceutical

(P-8362)
RETROPHIN INC (PA)
3721 Vly Cntre Dr Ste 200, San Diego
(92130)
PHONE..........................760 260-8600
Stephen Aselage, *President*
Neil F McFarlane, *COO*
Neil McFarlane, *COO*
Laura M Clague, *CFO*
Noah L Rosenberg, *Officer*
EMP: 87
SQ FT: 23,107
SALES: 154.9MM **Publicly Held**
SIC: 2834 8731 Pharmaceutical preparations; biotechnical research, commercial

(P-8363)
REVANCE THERAPEUTICS INC
7555 Gateway Blvd, Newark (94560-1152)
PHONE..........................510 742-3400
Angus C Russell, *Ch of Bd*
L Daniel Browne, *President*
Abhay Joshi, *COO*
Robert Byrnes, *Bd of Directors*
Ronald Eastman, *Bd of Directors*
EMP: 106
SQ FT: 90,000
SALES: 262K **Privately Held**
WEB: www.revance.com
SIC: 2834 Pharmaceutical preparations

(P-8364)
RIGEL PHARMACEUTICALS INC (PA)
1180 Veterans Blvd, South San Francisco
(94080-1985)
PHONE..........................650 624-1100
Raul R Rodriguez, *President*
Gary A Lyons, *Ch of Bd*
Ryan D Maynard, *CFO*
Dean Schorno, *CFO*
Eldon C Mayer III, *Ch Credit Ofcr*
EMP: 126
SQ FT: 147,000
SALES: 4.4MM **Publicly Held**
WEB: www.rigel.com
SIC: 2834 8733 Pharmaceutical preparations; medical research

(P-8365)
RINAT NEUROSCIENCE CORP
230 E Grand Ave, South San Francisco
(94080-4811)
PHONE..........................650 615-7300
Patrick Lynn, *President*
Arnon Rosenthal, *CTO*
C Fletcher Payne, *Finance*
EMP: 16
SALES (est): 3.3MM
SALES (corp-wide): 52.5B **Publicly Held**
WEB: www.rinatneuro.com
SIC: 2834 Druggists' preparations (pharmaceuticals)
PA: Pfizer Inc.
235 E 42nd St
New York NY 10017
212 733-2323

(P-8366)
ROBINSON PHARMA INC (PA)
3330 S Harbor Blvd, Santa Ana
(92704-6831)
PHONE..........................714 241-0235
Tam H Nguyen, *CEO*
Tuong Nguyen, *President*
Van Nguye, *Officer*
Zue Delaney, *Vice Pres*
Thu Vu, *Vice Pres*
▲ **EMP:** 310
SQ FT: 124,000
SALES (est): 155.8MM **Privately Held**
WEB: www.robinsonpharma.com
SIC: 2834 Vitamin preparations

(P-8367)
ROBINSON PHARMA INC
2811 S Harbor Blvd, Santa Ana
(92704-5805)
PHONE..........................714 241-0235
Tam Nguyen, *President*
EMP: 186 **Privately Held**
SIC: 2834 Pharmaceutical preparations
PA: Robinson Pharma, Inc.
3330 S Harbor Blvd
Santa Ana CA 92704

(P-8368)
ROCHE PHARMACEUTICALS
4300 Hacienda Dr, Pleasanton
(94588-2722)
PHONE..........................908 635-5692
Fidel Fampo, *Principal*
Christine Reinauer, *Administration*
Amy Daugherty, *IT/INT Sup*
Damion Engelbart, *Engineer*
Misha Bringuier, *Recruiter*
EMP: 37 **EST:** 2017
SALES (est): 4.5MM **Privately Held**
SIC: 2834 Pharmaceutical preparations

(P-8369)
ROSE CHEM INTL - USA CORP
25 Rainbow Fls, Irvine (92603-3439)
PHONE..........................678 510-8864
Minh Nguyen Thi Thanh, *CEO*
Son Ngoc Ha, *CFO*
Lich Thi Thanh Nguyen, *Admin Sec*
EMP: 30 **EST:** 2015
SALES (est): 1.3MM **Privately Held**
SIC: 2834 Pharmaceutical preparations

(P-8370)
S K LABORATORIES INC
Also Called: S K Labs
5420 E La Palma Ave, Anaheim
(92807-2023)
PHONE..........................714 695-9800
Bansi Patel, *President*
Ramila B Patel, *Admin Sec*
▲ **EMP:** 35
SQ FT: 20,000
SALES (est): 15MM **Privately Held**
WEB: www.sklabs.com
SIC: 2834 Vitamin preparations

(P-8371)
SAMSON PHARMACEUTICALS INC
2027 Leo Ave, Commerce (90040-1626)
PHONE..........................323 722-3066
Jay Kassir, *President*
Tara Ward, *General Mgr*
Ziad Kassir, *Info Tech Mgr*
Kakeena Pina, *Research*
Jennifer Chan, *Marketing Staff*
▲ **EMP:** 40
SALES (est): 9.3MM **Privately Held**
SIC: 2834 Pharmaceutical preparations

(P-8372)
SANOFI US SERVICES INC
185 Berry St, San Francisco (94107-5705)
PHONE..........................415 856-5000
EMP: 136
SALES (corp-wide): 609.6MM **Privately Held**
SIC: 2834
HQ: Sanofi Us Services Inc.
55 Corporate Dr
Bridgewater NJ 08807
336 407-4994

(P-8373)
SANTARUS INC
3611 Vly Cntre Dr Ste 400, San Diego
(92130)
PHONE..........................858 314-5700
Blake Boland, *Principal*
EMP: 20
SALES (est): 2.7MM **Privately Held**
SIC: 2834 5122 Pharmaceutical preparations; pharmaceuticals

(P-8374)
SCICLONE PHARMACEUTICALS INC (HQ)
950 Tower Ln Ste 900, Foster City
(94404-2125)
PHONE..........................650 358-3456
Friedhelm Blobel, *President*
Wilson W Cheung, *CFO*
Carey Chern, *Ch Credit Ofcr*
Raymond A Low, *Controller*
Ivy Fan, *Manager*
EMP: 40
SQ FT: 11,900
SALES: 160.1MM **Privately Held**
WEB: www.scln.com
SIC: 2834 Druggists' preparations (pharmaceuticals)

(P-8375)
SEMNUR PHARMACEUTICALS
301 N Whisman Rd, Mountain View
(94043-3969)
PHONE..........................650 516-4310
Brent Ahrens, *Partner*
Beth Stannard, *Director*
EMP: 14 **EST:** 2016
SALES (est): 5MM **Privately Held**
SIC: 2834 Pharmaceutical preparations

(P-8376)
SENJU USA INC
21700 Oxnard St Ste 1070, Woodland Hills
(91367-8103)
PHONE..........................818 719-7190
AG Katayama, *President*
EMP: 15
SALES (est): 2.6MM
SALES (corp-wide): 333.6MM **Privately Held**
SIC: 2834 Druggists' preparations (pharmaceuticals)
PA: Senju Pharmaceutical Co.,Ltd.
3-1-9, Kawaramachi, Chuo-Ku
Osaka OSK 541-0
662 012-512

(P-8377)
SENSORY NEUROSTIMULATION INC
Also Called: Relaxis
1235 Puerta Del Sol # 600, San Clemente
(92673-6309)
PHONE..........................949 492-0550
Fred Burbank, *CEO*
Michael Jones, *COO*
Carl Swindle, *Vice Pres*
EMP: 11
SQ FT: 4,000
SALES: 60K **Privately Held**
SIC: 2834 5122 Druggists' preparations (pharmaceuticals); drugs & drug proprietaries

(P-8378)
SENTYNL THERAPEUTICS INC
420 Stevens Ave Ste 200, Solana Beach
(92075-2078)
PHONE..........................888 227-8725
Matt Heck, *CEO*
Daniel Stokely, *CFO*
Paul Maccini, *Officer*
Shawn Scranton, *Officer*
Michael Hercz, *Vice Pres*
EMP: 30 **EST:** 2011
SALES: 50MM
SALES (corp-wide): 865MM **Privately Held**
SIC: 2834 Pharmaceutical preparations
PA: Cadila Healthcare Limited
Zydus Tower, Satellite Cross Road,
Ahmedabad GJ 38001
792 686-8100

(P-8379)
SEYCHELLE WATER FILTRATION
32963 Calle Perfecto, San Juan Capistrano
(92675-4705)
P.O. Box 7003, Capistrano Beach (92624-7003)
PHONE..........................949 234-1999
Carl Palmer, *President*
Jim Allise, *COO*
Jim Place, *CFO*
EMP: 30
SALES: 6MM **Privately Held**
SIC: 2834 Chlorination tablets & kits (water purification)

(P-8380)
SHIRE RGENERATIVE MEDICINE INC
10933 N Torrey Pines Rd # 200, La Jolla
(92037-1054)
PHONE..........................858 202-0673
Jennifer Cassidy, *Branch Mgr*
Chuck Bankert, *Program Mgr*
Rick Allen, *Sales Executive*
EMP: 20
SALES (corp-wide): 15.1B **Privately Held**
SIC: 2834 Pharmaceutical preparations

▲ = Import ▼=Export
◆ =Import/Export

HQ: Shire Regenerative Medicine, Inc.
36 Church Ln
Westport CT 06880
877 422-4463

(P-8381)
SHIRE RGENERATIVE MEDICINE INC
Also Called: Advanced Biohealing.com
10933 N Torrey Pines Rd # 200, La Jolla
(92037-1054)
PHONE..................................858 754-5396
Kathy McGee, *Branch Mgr*
Dean Tozer, *Senior VP*
Theresa Dixon, *Vice Pres*
Dana Sacks, *Sales Staff*
Donald Ayers, *Manager*
EMP: 90
SALES (corp-wide): 15.1B **Privately Held**
WEB: www.advancedtissue.com
SIC: 2834 Pharmaceutical preparations
HQ: Shire Regenerative Medicine, Inc.
36 Church Ln
Westport CT 06880
877 422-4463

(P-8382)
SIMPSON INDUSTRIES INC
Also Called: Simpsonsimpson Industries
1093 E Bedmar St, Carson (90746-3601)
PHONE..................................310 605-1224
Rick Simpson, *CEO*
Robert Simpson, *COO*
Lovie Ebro-Cassiero, *Purchasing*
EMP: 50
SALES (est): 5.7MM **Privately Held**
SIC: 2834 Proprietary drug products

(P-8383)
SIRNA THERAPEUTICS INC
1700 Owens St, San Francisco
(94158-0004)
PHONE..................................415 512-7200
Howard W Robin, *President*
Gregory L Weaver, *CFO*
Roberto Guerciolini, *Chief Mktg Ofcr*
Barry Polisky, *Senior VP*
J Michael French, *Development*
EMP: 68
SALES (est): 5.9MM
SALES (corp-wide): 89.9MM **Publicly Held**
WEB: www.sirna.com
SIC: 2834 Pharmaceutical preparations
PA: Alnylam Pharmaceuticals, Inc.
300 3rd St Ste 3
Cambridge MA 02142
617 551-8200

(P-8384)
SKYEPHARMA INC
10450 Science Center Dr, San Diego
(92121-1119)
PHONE..................................858 678-3950
Steve Thornton, *President*
Geraldine Venthoye, *Vice Pres*
Garrett Mc Leish, *Admin Sec*
EMP: 14
SALES (est): 2.2MM **Privately Held**
SIC: 2834 Pharmaceutical preparations

(P-8385)
SOFT GEL TECHNOLOGIES INC (HQ)
6982 Bandini Blvd, Commerce
(90040-3326)
PHONE..................................323 726-0700
Steve Holtby, *CEO*
Ronald Udell, *President*
Hiroshi Kishimoto, *Treasurer*
Joann Falgado, *Office Mgr*
Charles Yoon, *Info Tech Dir*
▲ EMP: 100
SQ FT: 21,000
SALES (est): 25.9MM
SALES (corp-wide): 153.9MM **Privately Held**
WEB: www.soft-gel.com
SIC: 2834 Medicines, capsuled or ampuled
PA: Kenko Corporation
3-1-2, Iwamotocho
Chiyoda-Ku TKY 101-0
368 218-061

(P-8386)
SOLENO THERAPEUTICS INC (PA)
1235 Radio Rd Ste 110, Redwood City
(94065-1315)
PHONE..................................650 213-8444
Anish Bhatnagar, *Officer*
Ernest Mario, *Ch of Bd*
Jonathan R Wolter, *CFO*
Steinar Engelsen, *Bd of Directors*
EMP: 12 EST: 1999
SQ FT: 8,171
SALES (est): 1.9MM **Publicly Held**
WEB: www.capnia.com
SIC: 2834 Pharmaceutical preparations

(P-8387)
SONOMA PHARMACEUTICALS INC (PA)
1129 N Mcdowell Blvd, Petaluma
(94954-1110)
PHONE..................................707 283-0550
Jim Schutz, *President*
Marc Umscheid, *COO*
Robert E Miller, *CFO*
Jay E Birnbaum, *Bd of Directors*
Russell Harrison, *Bd of Directors*
EMP: 79
SALES: 16.6MM **Publicly Held**
WEB: www.oculusis.com
SIC: 2834 Dermatologicals

(P-8388)
SOVA PHARMACEUTICALS INC
11099 N Torrey Pines Rd, La Jolla
(92037-1029)
PHONE..................................858 750-4700
Jay Lichter, *CEO*
EMP: 10
SALES (est): 1.3MM **Privately Held**
SIC: 2834 Pharmaceutical preparations

(P-8389)
SPIRIT SCIENCES USA INC (PA)
6733 S Sepulveda Blvd # 108, Los Angeles
(90045-1525)
PHONE..................................310 568-1030
Donna Kasseinova, *CEO*
▲ EMP: 11
SQ FT: 2,400
SALES (est): 956.6K **Privately Held**
WEB: www.ru21.com
SIC: 2834 Pharmaceutical preparations

(P-8390)
SQUAREBAR INC
1035 22nd Ave Unit 8, Oakland
(94606-5271)
PHONE..................................530 412-0209
Alamedans Sarah, *Principal*
Andrew Gordon, *Principal*
EMP: 10
SALES (est): 1.7MM **Privately Held**
SIC: 2834 Vitamin, nutrient & hematinic preparations for human use

(P-8391)
ST JUDE MEDICAL LLC
Also Called: Sjm Facility
2375 Morse Ave, Irvine (92614-6233)
PHONE..................................949 769-5000
Minh Nguyen, *Info Tech Mgr*
Craig Takata, *Technician*
Abdi Darvish, *Research*
Sebastian Teodoru, *Research*
Patrick Senarith, *Engineer*
EMP: 25
SALES (corp-wide): 27.3B **Publicly Held**
SIC: 2834 Pharmaceutical preparations
HQ: St. Jude Medical, Llc
1 Saint Jude Medical Dr
Saint Paul MN 55117
651 756-2000

(P-8392)
STA PHARMACEUTICAL US LLC
6114 Nancy Ridge Dr, San Diego
(92121-3223)
PHONE..................................609 606-6499
Chen Hui, *CFO*
Stephen Shaw, *Director*
EMP: 40
SALES (est): 1.1MM **Privately Held**
SIC: 2834 Pharmaceutical preparations

(P-8393)
STANDARD HOMEOPATHIC CO (PA)
Also Called: Hyland's Homeopathic
204 W 131st St, Los Angeles (90061-1676)
P.O. Box 61067 (90061-0067)
PHONE..................................310 768-0700
John Pborneman, *CEO*
John P Borneman III, *Ch of Bd*
Dan Krombach, *CFO*
Margot Moore,
John Patten, *Manager*
▲ EMP: 100
SQ FT: 21,000
SALES (est): 27.6MM **Privately Held**
WEB: www.hylands.com
SIC: 2834 5912 Pharmaceutical preparations; drug stores

(P-8394)
STANDARD HOMEOPATHIC CO
Also Called: Hyland Homeopathic
108 W Walnut St Fl 1, Gardena
(90248-3107)
PHONE..................................424 224-4127
Janet Okubo, *Principal*
EMP: 22
SALES (corp-wide): 27.6MM **Privately Held**
SIC: 2834 Pharmaceutical preparations
PA: Standard Homeopathic Co.
204 W 131st St
Los Angeles CA 90061
310 768-0700

(P-8395)
STASON PHARMACEUTICALS INC (PA)
Also Called: IMT-Stason Laboratories
11 Morgan, Irvine (92618-2005)
PHONE..................................949 380-0752
Harry Fan, *CEO*
Karl Weinrich, *Officer*
Rudy Campos, *Human Res Mgr*
Steven Cheng, *Prdtn Mgr*
Dale Wallingford, *Facilities Mgr*
▲ EMP: 48
SQ FT: 37,149
SALES (est): 13.4MM **Privately Held**
SIC: 2834 Pharmaceutical preparations

(P-8396)
STEADYMED THERAPEUTICS INC
2603 Camino Ramon Ste 350, San Ramon
(94583-9127)
PHONE..................................925 361-7111
Jonathan Rigby, *President*
Peter Noymer, *Exec VP*
EMP: 15
SALES (est): 2.6MM **Privately Held**
SIC: 2834 Tranquilizers or mental drug preparations

(P-8397)
STELLAR BIOTECHNOLOGIES INC
332 E Scott St, Port Hueneme
(93041-2939)
PHONE..................................805 488-2147
Frank Oakes, *Ch of Bd*
Catherine Brisson, *COO*
Kathi Niffenegger, *CFO*
Dorothy Oakes, *Treasurer*
Daniel E Morse, *Bd of Directors*
EMP: 12
SALES: 228.2K **Privately Held**
WEB: www.stellarbiotech.com
SIC: 2834 Adrenal pharmaceutical preparations

(P-8398)
STERISYN INC
11969 Challenger Ct, Moorpark
(93021-7119)
PHONE..................................805 991-9694
Julie Anne, *Administration*
Timothy Henry, *CEO*
EMP: 30
SALES (est): 2MM **Privately Held**
SIC: 2834 Pharmaceutical preparations

(P-8399)
SUNESIS PHARMACEUTICALS INC (PA)
395 Oyster Point Blvd # 400, South San
Francisco (94080-1928)
PHONE..................................650 266-3500
Dayton Misfeldt, *CEO*
James W Young, *Ch of Bd*
Steve Carchedi, *Bd of Directors*
Steven Ketchum, *Bd of Directors*
Homer Pearce, *Bd of Directors*
EMP: 34
SQ FT: 15,378
SALES: 669K **Publicly Held**
WEB: www.sunesis.com
SIC: 2834 Pharmaceutical preparations

(P-8400)
SUPERIOR LABS INC
9921 Carmel Mountain Rd # 297, San
Diego (92129-2813)
PHONE..................................888 708-5227
EMP: 10
SALES (est): 457.2K **Privately Held**
SIC: 2834 8099 Vitamin, nutrient & hematinic preparations for human use; nutrition services

(P-8401)
SUPERNUTRITION
Also Called: Forever Young
1925 Brush St, Oakland (94612-1023)
PHONE..................................510 446-7980
Cathy Mooney, *Owner*
EMP: 30
SALES (est): 3.8MM **Privately Held**
WEB: www.supernutritionusa.com
SIC: 2834 Vitamin preparations

(P-8402)
SUSAN BIEGEL MD
1113 Alta Ave Ste 220, Upland
(91786-2803)
PHONE..................................909 985-1908
Susan Biegel, *Owner*
EMP: 16
SQ FT: 24,794
SALES (est): 3.7MM **Privately Held**
SIC: 2834 Medicines, capsuled or ampuled

(P-8403)
SUTRO BIOPHARMA INC (PA)
310 Utah Ave Ste 150, South San Francisco (94080-6803)
PHONE..................................650 392-8412
William J Newell, *CEO*
Daniel Janney, *Ch of Bd*
Edward Albini, *CFO*
Arturo Molina, *Chief Mktg Ofcr*
Shabbir T Anik, *Officer*
EMP: 128
SALES: 51.7MM **Publicly Held**
WEB: www.f-a-b-inc.com
SIC: 2834 Pharmaceutical preparations

(P-8404)
TALON THERAPEUTICS INC
157 Technology Dr, Irvine (92618-2402)
PHONE..................................949 788-6700
Joseph W Turgeon, *CEO*
EMP: 241
SQ FT: 50,000
SALES: 186MM **Publicly Held**
WEB: www.hanabiosciences.com
SIC: 2834 8731 Pharmaceutical preparations; commercial physical research
PA: Spectrum Pharmaceuticals, Inc.
11500 S Estrn Ave Ste 240
Henderson NV 89052

(P-8405)
TANOX INC (DH)
1 Dna Way, South San Francisco
(94080-4918)
PHONE..................................650 851-1607
Stephen G Juelsgaard, *President*
Zhengbin Yao, *Vice Pres*
Robert C Bast,
▲ EMP: 124
SQ FT: 111,000
SALES (est): 18.3MM
SALES (corp-wide): 53.9B **Publicly Held**
SIC: 2834 Pharmaceutical preparations

HQ: Genentech, Inc.
1 Dna Way
South San Francisco CA 94080
650 225-1000

(P-8406)
TANVEX BIOLOGICS INC
10421 Pacific Center Ct, San Diego
(92121-4339)
PHONE..................858 210-4100
Hardy Chan, *Manager*
EMP: 38 EST: 2012
SALES (est): 370.2K **Privately Held**
SIC: 2834 Pharmaceutical preparations
PA: Tanvex Biologics, Inc.
2030 Main St Ste 1050
Irvine CA 92614

(P-8407)
TARGETED MEDICAL PHARMA INC (PA)
Also Called: Tmp
2980 N Beverly Glen Cir # 1, Los Angeles
(90077-1726)
PHONE..................310 474-9809
Kim Giffoni, *CEO*
Kerry N Weems, *Ch of Bd*
William Horne, *CFO*
David S Silver, *Chief Mktg Ofcr*
William E Shell, *Med Doctor*
EMP: 24
SQ FT: 3,200
SALES: 5.2MM **Publicly Held**
WEB: www.ptlcentral.com
SIC: 2834 Pharmaceutical preparations

(P-8408)
TARSAL PHARMACEUTICALS INC
3909 Oceanic Dr Ste 401, Oceanside
(92056-5853)
PHONE..................818 919-9723
Ashak Fakous Botros, *CEO*
EMP: 20
SQ FT: 6,005
SALES (est): 846.9K **Privately Held**
SIC: 2834 Pharmaceutical preparations

(P-8409)
TEIKOKU PHARMA USA INC (HQ)
1718 Ringwood Ave, San Jose
(95131-1711)
PHONE..................408 501-1800
Masahisa Kitagawa, *President*
Ichiro Mori, *COO*
Atsumu Matsushita, *CFO*
Tetsuo Nagata, *Exec VP*
Larry Caldwell, *Vice Pres*
▲ EMP: 60
SALES (est): 16.2MM
SALES (corp-wide): 251.7MM **Privately Held**
WEB: www.teikokuusa.com
SIC: 2834 Pharmaceutical preparations
PA: Teikoku Seiyaku Co.,Ltd.
567, Sambommatsu
Higashikagawa KGA 769-2
879 252-221

(P-8410)
TESORX PHARMA LLC (PA)
3670 W Temple Ave, Pomona
(91768-2588)
PHONE..................909 595-0500
Ramachandran Thirucote, *CEO*
Willem A Robberts, *President*
Guru Betageri PHD, *Founder*
EMP: 13
SALES (est): 5.6MM **Privately Held**
SIC: 2834 Pharmaceutical preparations

(P-8411)
TEVA PARENTERAL MEDICINES INC
19 Hughes, Irvine (92618-1902)
P.O. Box 57049 (92619-7049)
PHONE..................949 455-4700
Phillip Frost, *Ch of Bd*
Karin Shanahan, *CEO*
Amir Elstein, *Vice Ch Bd*
Nir Baron, *Senior VP*
Iris Beck-Codner, *Vice Pres*
▲ EMP: 830

SQ FT: 148,000
SALES (est): 209.9MM
SALES (corp-wide): 22.3B **Privately Held**
WEB: www.lemmon.com
SIC: 2834 Pills, pharmaceutical
HQ: Teva Pharmaceuticals Usa, Inc.
1090 Horsham Rd
North Wales PA 19454
215 591-3000

(P-8412)
TEVA PHARMACEUTICALS USA INC
19 Hughes, Irvine (92618-1902)
PHONE..................949 457-2828
Binky Evidente, *General Mgr*
Mary Bazensky, *Executive Asst*
Cheng-Hsien Wang, *Engineer*
Bernard Shamsai, *Director*
Alejandra Haro, *Manager*
EMP: 39
SALES (corp-wide): 22.3B **Privately Held**
SIC: 2834 2833 Pharmaceutical preparations; medicinals & botanicals; penicillin: bulk, uncompounded; antibiotics
HQ: Teva Pharmaceuticals Usa, Inc.
1090 Horsham Rd
North Wales PA 19454
215 591-3000

(P-8413)
TFX INTERNATIONAL
Also Called: Platt Medical Center
72785 Frank Sinatra Dr, Rancho Mirage
(92270-3205)
PHONE..................760 836-3232
Michael Platt, *Owner*
EMP: 12
SALES (est): 2MM **Privately Held**
WEB: www.drplatt.com
SIC: 2834 8011 7299 Hormone preparations; specialized medical practitioners, except internal; personal appearance services

(P-8414)
THERAVANCE BIOPHARMA US INC
901 Gateway Blvd, South San Francisco
(94080-7024)
PHONE..................650 808-6000
Rick Winningham, *CEO*
Frank Pasqualone, *Senior VP*
Stuart Knight, *Vice Pres*
Paul Fatheree, *Associate Dir*
Lynne Gordon, *Associate Dir*
EMP: 244
SALES (est): 88.6MM **Privately Held**
SIC: 2834 Pharmaceutical preparations
PA: Theravance Biopharma Inc
C/O Maples Corporate Services Ltd
George Town GR CAYMAN

(P-8415)
THERAVNCE BPHRMA ANTBOTICS INC
901 Gateway Blvd, South San Francisco
(94080-7024)
PHONE..................877 275-6930
Rick Winningham, *CEO*
EMP: 200
SALES (est): 11.3MM **Privately Held**
SIC: 2834 Pharmaceutical preparations
PA: Theravance Biopharma Inc
C/O Maples Corporate Services Ltd
George Town GR CAYMAN

(P-8416)
THORX LABORATORIES INC
30831 Huntwood Ave, Hayward
(94544-7003)
PHONE..................510 240-6000
Frederick Wilkinson, *Principal*
EMP: 15
SALES (est): 214.3K
SALES (corp-wide): 1B **Publicly Held**
SIC: 2834 Pharmaceutical preparations
HQ: Impax Laboratories, Llc
30831 Huntwood Ave
Hayward CA 94544
510 240-6000

(P-8417)
TITAN MEDICAL ENTERPRISES INC
Also Called: US Apothecary Crown Labs
11100 Greenstone Ave, Santa Fe Springs
(90670-4640)
PHONE..................562 903-7236
James L McDaniel, *President*
James McDaniel, *President*
EMP: 15
SQ FT: 12,000
SALES (est): 3.9MM **Privately Held**
SIC: 2834 Vitamin preparations

(P-8418)
TITAN PHARMACEUTICALS INC (PA)
400 Oyster Point Blvd # 505, South San
Francisco (94080-1958)
PHONE..................650 244-4990
Sunil Bhonsle, *President*
Marc Rubin, *Ch of Bd*
Joseph Akers, *Bd of Directors*
Dane D Hallberg, *Officer*
EMP: 18
SQ FT: 9,255
SALES: 215K **Publicly Held**
WEB: www.titanpharm.com
SIC: 2834 Drugs acting on the central nervous system & sense organs

(P-8419)
TOCAGEN INC
4242 Campus Point Ct # 500, San Diego
(92121-1513)
PHONE..................858 412-8400
Martin J Duvall, *CEO*
Faheem Hasnain, *Ch of Bd*
Mark Foletta, *CFO*
Franklin Berger, *Bd of Directors*
Lori Kunkel, *Bd of Directors*
EMP: 67
SQ FT: 19,000
SALES: 41K **Privately Held**
SIC: 2834 Pharmaceutical preparations

(P-8420)
TRAGARA PHARMACEUTICALS INC
12481 High Bluff Dr # 150, San Diego
(92130-3585)
PHONE..................760 208-6900
Thomas Estok, *President*
Dennis Bilski, *Vice Pres*
Chris Lemasters, *Principal*
EMP: 18
SALES (est): 3MM **Privately Held**
SIC: 2834 Pharmaceutical preparations

(P-8421)
TRICIDA INC
7000 Shoreline Ct Ste 201, South San
Francisco (94080-7603)
PHONE..................415 429-7800
Gerrit Klaerner, *President*
Klaus Veitinger, *Ch of Bd*
Geoffrey M Parker, *CFO*
Claire Lockey, *Officer*
Jeroen Van Beek, *Officer*
EMP: 61
SQ FT: 26,897
SALES (est): 5.1MM **Privately Held**
SIC: 2834 Pharmaceutical preparations

(P-8422)
TRIUS THERAPEUTICS LLC
4747 Executive Dr # 1100, San Diego
(92121-3114)
PHONE..................858 452-0370
Jeffrey Stein, *President*
David S Kabakoff, *Ch of Bd*
John P Schmid, *CFO*
Kenneth Bartizal, *Officer*
John Finn, *Officer*
EMP: 90
SQ FT: 39,000
SALES (est): 14.2MM
SALES (corp-wide): 40.1B **Publicly Held**
WEB: www.triusrx.com
SIC: 2834 Antibiotics, packaged
HQ: Cubist Pharmaceuticals Llc
2000 Galloping Hill Rd
Kenilworth NJ 07033

(P-8423)
UBIOME INC
360 Langton St Ste 301, San Francisco
(94103-6236)
PHONE..................415 275-2461
Jessica Richman, *CEO*
Sharon Donovan, *President*
Farris Galyon, *Opers Mgr*
Jennifer Gerstenberger, *Manager*
EMP: 19
SALES (est): 3.9MM **Privately Held**
SIC: 2834 Pharmaceutical preparations

(P-8424)
UCSF SCHOOL OF PHARMACY
Also Called: Drug Product Services Lab
3333 California St, San Francisco
(94118-1981)
PHONE..................415 476-1444
Marcus Ferrone, *Director*
EMP: 10
SALES (est): 1MM **Privately Held**
SIC: 2834 Pharmaceutical preparations

(P-8425)
ULTRAGENYX PHARMACEUTICAL INC (PA)
60 Leveroni Ct, Novato (94949-5746)
PHONE..................415 483-8800
Emil D Kakkis, *President*
Daniel G Welch, *Ch of Bd*
Wladimir Hogenhuis, *COO*
Shalini Sharp, *CFO*
Camille L Bedrosian, *Chief Mktg Ofcr*
EMP: 178
SQ FT: 129,500
SALES: 2.6MM **Publicly Held**
SIC: 2834 Pharmaceutical preparations

(P-8426)
UNIVERSITY SOUTHERN CALIFORNIA
Also Called: Usc Molecular Imaging Center
2250 Alcazar St Ste B7, Los Angeles
(90089-0107)
PHONE..................323 442-3858
Peter Conti, *Director*
EMP: 18
SALES (corp-wide): 2.6B **Privately Held**
SIC: 2834 Pharmaceutical preparations
PA: University Of Southern California
3720 S Flower St Fl 3
Los Angeles CA 90089
213 740-7762

(P-8427)
UROVANT SCIENCES INC (PA)
5151 California Ave # 250, Irvine
(92617-3205)
PHONE..................949 226-6029
Keith Katkin, *President*
Christine Ocampo, *Senior VP*
EMP: 40
SQ FT: 8,000
SALES (est): 5MM **Publicly Held**
SIC: 2834 Pharmaceutical preparations

(P-8428)
US WHOLESALE DRUG CORP
2611 N San Fernando Rd, Los Angeles
(90065-1316)
PHONE..................323 227-4258
Virginia Farha, *President*
EMP: 12
SALES (est): 1.4MM **Privately Held**
SIC: 2834 Pharmaceutical preparations

(P-8429)
VALEANT PHARMACEUTICALS INTL
50 Technology Dr, Irvine (92618-2301)
PHONE..................800 548-5100
EMP: 15
SALES (corp-wide): 8.7B **Privately Held**
SIC: 2834 Pharmaceutical preparations
HQ: Valeant Pharmaceuticals International
400 Somerset Corp Blvd
Bridgewater NJ 08807
908 927-1400

(P-8430)
VAXART INC (PA)
290 Utah Ave Ste 200, South San Francisco (94080-6801)
PHONE..................650 550-3500

Wouter W Latour, *President*
John M Harland, *CFO*
Sean N Tucker, *Security Dir*
EMP: 16
SALES (est): 8.9MM **Publicly Held**
WEB: www.nabi.com
SIC: 2834 2836 Pharmaceutical preparations; drugs affecting parasitic & infective diseases; vaccines & other immunizing products

(P-8431)
VERSEON CORPORATION (PA)
48820 Kato Rd Ste 100b, Fremont (94538-7323)
PHONE..................510 668-1622
Adityo Prakash, *President*
Eniko Fodor, *COO*
David Kita, *Vice Pres*
Kevin Short, *Director*
David Williams, *Director*
EMP: 35
SQ FT: 8,000
SALES (est): 10.1MM **Privately Held**
WEB: www.verseon.com
SIC: 2834 Druggists' preparations (pharmaceuticals)

(P-8432)
VERUS PHARMACEUTICALS INC
11455 El Camino Real # 460, San Diego (92130-2088)
PHONE..................858 436-1600
Robert W Keith, *President*
CAM Garner, *Ch of Bd*
Richard Vincent, *CFO*
Ahmet S Tutuncu, *Vice Pres*
Adam Simpson, *General Counsel*
EMP: 16
SQ FT: 13,000
SALES (est): 3.1MM **Privately Held**
WEB: www.veruspharm.com
SIC: 2834 Pharmaceutical preparations

(P-8433)
VIBRANT CARE PHARMACY INC
7400 Macarthur Blvd Ste B, Oakland (94605-2939)
PHONE..................510 638-9851
Kalpesh Patel, *CEO*
EMP: 15 **EST:** 2015
SALES (est): 975.5K **Privately Held**
SIC: 2834 5912 Chlorination tablets & kits (water purification); drug stores

(P-8434)
VIKING THERAPEUTICS INC
12340 El Camino Real # 250, San Diego (92130-3093)
PHONE..................858 704-4660
Brian Lian, *President*
Lawson Macartney, *Ch of Bd*
Michael Morneau, *CFO*
Matthew Foehr, *Bd of Directors*
Stephen Webster, *Bd of Directors*
EMP: 12
SQ FT: 7,049
SALES (est): 2.8MM **Privately Held**
SIC: 2834 Pharmaceutical preparations

(P-8435)
VISTAGEN THERAPEUTICS INC
343 Allerton Ave, South San Francisco (94080-4816)
PHONE..................650 577-3600
Shawn Singh, *CEO*
H Ralph Snodgrass, *President*
Jerrold Dotson, *CFO*
Jerry Gin, *Bd of Directors*
Ralph Snodgrass, *Officer*
EMP: 11
SALES (est): 2MM **Privately Held**
WEB: www.vistagen-inc.com
SIC: 2834 Pharmaceutical preparations

(P-8436)
VITABEST NUTRITION INC
Also Called: Vit Best
2802 Dow Ave, Tustin (92780-7212)
PHONE..................714 832-9700
Gale Bensussen, *President*
Toni Clubb, *CFO*
Bing Jiang, *Admin Sec*
EMP: 275
SQ FT: 200,000

SALES (est): 76.4MM
SALES (corp-wide): 314.6MM **Privately Held**
SIC: 2834 Vitamin preparations
PA: Xiamen Kingdomway Group Company
No. 299 Yangguang West Road
Xiamen 36102
592 520-0446

(P-8437)
VITAL THERAPIES INC
15222 Avenue Of Science B, San Diego (92128-3422)
PHONE..................858 673-6840
Robert A Ashley, *COO*
EMP: 11
SALES (est): 1.9MM **Privately Held**
SIC: 2834 Pharmaceutical preparations

(P-8438)
VITAL THERAPIES INC
15010 Avenue Of Science, San Diego (92128-3420)
PHONE..................858 673-6840
Terence E Winters, *Ch of Bd*
Faheem Hasnain, *Ch of Bd*
Duane Nash, *President*
Michael V Swanson, *CFO*
Aron P Stern, *Officer*
EMP: 87
SQ FT: 19,000
SALES (est): 23.5MM **Privately Held**
WEB: www.vitaltherapies.com
SIC: 2834 Pharmaceutical preparations

(P-8439)
VIVUS INC (PA)
900 E Hamilton Ave # 550, Campbell (95008-0643)
PHONE..................650 934-5200
John Amos, *CEO*
David Y Norton, *Ch of Bd*
Ken Suh, *President*
Thomas B King, *CEO*
Scott Oehrlein, *COO*
EMP: 49
SQ FT: 45,240
SALES: 65.3MM **Publicly Held**
WEB: www.vivus.com
SIC: 2834 Druggists' preparations (pharmaceuticals); proprietary drug products

(P-8440)
VM DISCOVERY INC
45535 Northport Loop E, Fremont (94538-6461)
PHONE..................510 818-1018
Jay Wu, *President*
Chunmei Wang, *Project Mgr*
Ling Wang, *Manager*
Sandy Wong, *Manager*
EMP: 10
SALES (est): 1.5MM **Privately Held**
WEB: www.vmdiscovery.com
SIC: 2834 Druggists' preparations (pharmaceuticals)

(P-8441)
WEST COAST CLINICAL RES LLC
5525 Etiwanda Ave Ste 202, Tarzana (91356-6116)
PHONE..................818 776-0820
Eugene Dula, *Med Doctor*
Harley Wishner, *Med Doctor*
EMP: 10
SALES (est): 880K **Privately Held**
WEB: www.wccresearch.com
SIC: 2834 8011 Pharmaceutical preparations; offices & clinics of medical doctors

(P-8442)
WEST COAST LABORATORIES INC
156 E 162nd St, Gardena (90248-2802)
PHONE..................310 527-6163
Maurice Ovadia, *Manager*
EMP: 35
SQ FT: 4,000
SALES (corp-wide): 7.3MM **Privately Held**
WEB: www.westcoastlabsinc.com
SIC: 2834 Vitamin preparations

PA: West Coast Laboratories, Inc.
116 E Alondra Blvd
Gardena CA 90248
323 321-4774

(P-8443)
WEST COAST LABORATORIES INC (PA)
116 E Alondra Blvd, Gardena (90248-2806)
PHONE..................323 321-4774
Maurice Ovadia, *President*
Jamil Shad, *Treasurer*
Naim Abdullah, *Vice Pres*
Larry Bridwell, *Vice Pres*
Anwar Abdullah, *Admin Sec*
EMP: 15
SQ FT: 4,000
SALES (est): 7.3MM **Privately Held**
WEB: www.westcoastlabsinc.com
SIC: 2834 Vitamin preparations

(P-8444)
WILLPOWER LABS INC
Also Called: Mealenders
3318 California St Apt 4, San Francisco (94118-1996)
PHONE..................415 805-1518
Mark Bernstein, *CEO*
EMP: 10
SALES: 1.2MM **Privately Held**
SIC: 2834 Lozenges, pharmaceutical

(P-8445)
WRIGHT PHARMA INC
700 Kiernan Ave Ste A, Modesto (95356-9329)
PHONE..................209 549-9771
Eric Fogleman, *Branch Mgr*
EMP: 20
SALES (corp-wide): 4.5MM **Privately Held**
SIC: 2834 2023 Pharmaceutical preparations; dietary supplements, dairy & non-dairy based
PA: Wright Pharma, Inc.
201 Energy Pkwy Ste 400
Lafayette LA 70508
337 783-3096

(P-8446)
XENCOR INC
111 W Lemon Ave, Monrovia (91016-2809)
PHONE..................626 305-5900
Bassil I Dahiyat, *President*
Paul Foster, *Chief Mktg Ofcr*
John R Desjarlais, *Senior VP*
John J Kuch, *VP Finance*
EMP: 114
SQ FT: 48,000
SALES: 35.7MM **Privately Held**
SIC: 2834 Pharmaceutical preparations

(P-8447)
XOMA CORPORATION (PA)
2200 Powell St Ste 310, Emeryville (94608-2792)
PHONE..................510 204-7200
James R Neal, *CEO*
W Denman Van Ness, *Ch of Bd*
Thomas Burns, *CFO*
EMP: 12
SALES: 52.6MM **Publicly Held**
WEB: www.xoma.com
SIC: 2834 Pharmaceutical preparations

(P-8448)
YOUCARE PHARMA (USA) INC
132 Business Center Dr, Corona (92880-1724)
P.O. Box 668 (92878-0668)
PHONE..................951 258-3114
Weishi Yu, *CEO*
Maria Gastelum, *Buyer*
EMP: 60 **EST:** 2015
SQ FT: 160,000
SALES (est): 8.1MM **Privately Held**
SIC: 2834 Pharmaceutical preparations
HQ: Youcare Pharmaceutical Group Co., Ltd.
No.6, Hongda Middle Road, Economic & Technology Development Zone
Beijing 10017
106 786-5666

(P-8449)
ZACHARON PHARMACEUTICALS INC
105 Digital Dr, Novato (94949-8703)
PHONE..................415 506-6700
George Eric Davis, *CEO*
Douglas Downs, *CFO*
Charles Glass, *Senior VP*
Brett E Crawford, *Vice Pres*
Shripad Bhagwat, *Security Dir*
EMP: 10
SQ FT: 5,000
SALES (est): 1.1MM
SALES (corp-wide): 1.3B **Publicly Held**
SIC: 2834 Pharmaceutical preparations
PA: Biomarin Pharmaceutical Inc.
770 Lindaro St
San Rafael CA 94901
415 506-6700

(P-8450)
ZELZAH PHARMACY INC
Also Called: Good Neighbor Pharmacy
17911 Ventura Blvd, Encino (91316-3618)
PHONE..................818 609-0692
Pejman Javaheri, *Principal*
EMP: 11
SALES (est): 1.9MM **Privately Held**
SIC: 2834 5912 Druggists' preparations (pharmaceuticals); drug stores

(P-8451)
ZOGENIX INC (PA)
5858 Horton St Ste 455, Emeryville (94608-2072)
PHONE..................510 550-8300
Stephen J Farr, *President*
CAM L Garner, *Ch of Bd*
Ann D Rhoads, *CFO*
Louis Bock, *Bd of Directors*
James Breitmeyer, *Bd of Directors*
EMP: 62
SQ FT: 22,000
SALES: 9.8MM **Publicly Held**
SIC: 2834 Drugs acting on the central nervous system & sense organs

(P-8452)
ZOSANO PHARMA CORPORATION (PA)
34790 Ardentech Ct, Fremont (94555-3657)
PHONE..................510 745-1200
John P Walker, *President*
Georgia L Erbez, *CFO*
Greg Kitchener, *CFO*
Joseph Hagan, *Bd of Directors*
Troy Wilson, *Bd of Directors*
EMP: 39
SALES (est): 11.3MM **Publicly Held**
SIC: 2834 Pharmaceutical preparations

(P-8453)
ZS PHARMA INC
1100 Park Pl Fl 3, San Mateo (94403-1599)
PHONE..................650 753-1823
EMP: 14 **EST:** 2017
SALES (est): 4.1MM **Privately Held**
SIC: 2834 Pharmaceutical preparations

2835 Diagnostic Substances

(P-8454)
ABBOTT DIABETES CARE INC (HQ)
Also Called: Medisense
1360 S Loop Rd, Alameda (94502-7000)
PHONE..................510 749-5400
Lawrence W Huffman, *Vice Pres*
Mark C Tatro, *Vice Pres*
Robert D Brownell, *Principal*
Adam Heller, *Principal*
Charles T Liamos, *Principal*
▲ **EMP:** 250
SQ FT: 54,500
SALES (est): 128.7MM
SALES (corp-wide): 27.3B **Publicly Held**
WEB: www.abbottdiabetescare.com
SIC: 2835 3845 3823 In vitro diagnostics; electromedical equipment; industrial instrmnts msrmnt display/control process variable

P R O D U C T S & S V C S

PA: Abbott Laboratories
100 Abbott Park Rd
Abbott Park IL 60064
224 667-6100

(P-8455)
ACROMETRIX CORPORATION
46500 Kato Rd, Fremont (94538-7310)
PHONE................707 746-8888
David Hoffmeister, *CEO*
Michael Eck, *President*
EMP: 45
SQ FT: 26,000
SALES (est): 11.4MM **Privately Held**
WEB: www.acrometrix.com
SIC: 2835 In vitro & in vivo diagnostic substances

(P-8456)
ADEZA BIOMEDICAL CORPORATION
1240 Elko Dr, Sunnyvale (94089-2212)
PHONE................408 745-6491
Emory V Anderson, *President*
Andrew E Senyei, *Ch of Bd*
Mark D Fischer Colbrie, *CFO*
Durlin E Hickok, *Vice Pres*
Robert O Hussa, *Vice Pres*
EMP: 103
SQ FT: 22,600
SALES (est): 12.3MM
SALES (corp-wide): 3B **Publicly Held**
WEB: www.cytyc.com
SIC: 2835 Pregnancy test kits
HQ: Cytyc Corporation
250 Campus Dr
Marlborough MA 01752
508 263-2900

(P-8457)
ALERE INC
Also Called: Cholestech
6465 National Dr, Livermore (94550-8808)
PHONE................510 732-7200
Gregory Bennett, *Branch Mgr*
Julia Phelps, *Marketing Staff*
EMP: 375
SALES (corp-wide): 27.3B **Publicly Held**
SIC: 2835 Pregnancy test kits
HQ: Alere Inc.
51 Sawyer Rd Ste 200
Waltham MA 02453
781 647-3900

(P-8458)
ALERE SAN DIEGO INC
9975 Summers Ridge Rd, San Diego (92121-2997)
PHONE................858 455-4808
John Yonkin, *President*
Gary A King, *Vice Pres*
Mark Gladwell, *Principal*
S Elaine Walton, *QA Dir*
Heidi Langbein Allen, *Opers Mgr*
▲ **EMP:** 1003
SQ FT: 350,000
SALES (est): 228.8MM
SALES (corp-wide): 27.3B **Publicly Held**
WEB: www.biosite.com
SIC: 2835 In vitro & in vivo diagnostic substances
HQ: Alere Inc.
51 Sawyer Rd Ste 200
Waltham MA 02453
781 647-3900

(P-8459)
ALFA SCIENTIFIC DESIGNS INC
13200 Gregg St, Poway (92064-7121)
PHONE................858 513-3888
Chai Bunyagidj, *President*
Naishu Wang, *Ch of Bd*
Claudia Shen, *Treasurer*
Angela Shen, *Vice Pres*
Vivian Cao, *Buyer*
▲ **EMP:** 88
SQ FT: 39,000
SALES (est): 13MM **Privately Held**
WEB: www.alfascientific.com
SIC: 2835 In vitro & in vivo diagnostic substances

(P-8460)
ANTIBODIES INCORPORATED
25242 County Road 95, Davis (95616-9405)
P.O. Box 1560 (95617-1560)
PHONE................530 758-4400
Richard Krogsrud, *President*
Janice Stafford, *Officer*
Merritt Clark, *General Mgr*
Will Fry, *Manager*
Ricardo Rodarte, *Manager*
EMP: 18
SQ FT: 23,000
SALES (est): 4.2MM **Privately Held**
WEB: www.antibodiesinc.com
SIC: 2835 2836 In vitro & in vivo diagnostic substances; serums

(P-8461)
B D PHARMINGEN INC (HQ)
10975 Torreyana Rd, San Diego (92121-1106)
PHONE................858 812-8800
William Kozy, *President*
Andrew Lasp, *General Mgr*
Janis Wellberg, *Accounts Mgr*
EMP: 12
SQ FT: 80,000
SALES (est): 45.2MM
SALES (corp-wide): 12B **Publicly Held**
WEB: www.pharmingen.com
SIC: 2835 In vitro & in vivo diagnostic substances
PA: Becton, Dickinson And Company
1 Becton Dr
Franklin Lakes NJ 07417
201 847-6800

(P-8462)
BECKMAN INSTRUMENTS INC
2500 N Harbor Blvd, Fullerton (92835-2600)
PHONE................714 871-4848
John Collette, *President*
Steve Blanc, *District Mgr*
EMP: 23
SALES (est): 359.7K **Privately Held**
SIC: 2835 In vitro & in vivo diagnostic substances

(P-8463)
BIOSERV CORPORATION
Also Called: Bioserve
5340 Eastgate Mall, San Diego (92121-2804)
PHONE................917 817-1326
Henry Ji, *President*
Kevin Herde, *Vice Pres*
Rhonda Nichols, *QA Dir*
Jose Villar, *Engineer*
Keith Holmgren, *Director*
EMP: 27
SALES (est): 6.9MM
SALES (corp-wide): 151.8MM **Publicly Held**
SIC: 2835 2834 In vitro & in vivo diagnostic substances; pharmaceutical preparations
PA: Sorrento Therapeutics, Inc.
4955 Directors Pl
San Diego CA 92121
858 203-4100

(P-8464)
BIOSOURCE INTERNATIONAL INC
5791 Van Allen Way, Carlsbad (92008-7321)
PHONE................805 659-5759
Terrance J Bieker, *President*
Jean-Pierre L Conte, *Ch of Bd*
Alan Edrick, *CFO*
Kevin J Reagan PHD, *Exec VP*
Jozef Vangenechten, *Exec VP*
EMP: 167
SQ FT: 51,821
SALES (est): 44.3MM **Privately Held**
WEB: www.biofluids.com
SIC: 2835 In vitro & in vivo diagnostic substances

(P-8465)
BIOSPACIFIC INC (DH)
5980 Horton St Ste 360, Emeryville (94608-2058)
PHONE................510 652-6155
Sandy Koshkin, *President*
EMP: 10
SQ FT: 2,800
SALES (est): 987.8K
SALES (corp-wide): 642.9MM **Publicly Held**
WEB: www.biospacific.com
SIC: 2835 In vitro diagnostics
HQ: Research And Diagnostic Systems, Inc.
614 Mckinley Pl Ne
Minneapolis MN 55413
612 379-2956

(P-8466)
CANCER GENETICS INC
1640 Marengo St Ste 7, Los Angeles (90033-1057)
PHONE................323 224-3900
EMP: 113
SALES (corp-wide): 29.1MM **Publicly Held**
SIC: 2835 In vivo diagnostics
PA: Cancer Genetics, Inc.
201 Route 17 Fl 2
Rutherford NJ 07070
201 528-9200

(P-8467)
CELL MARQUE CORPORATION
6600 Sierra College Blvd, Rocklin (95677-4306)
PHONE................916 746-8900
Nora Lacey, *President*
David Zembo, *CFO*
Paul Ardi, *Vice Pres*
Anh Ngo, *Vice Pres*
Veronica Runyan, *Vice Pres*
EMP: 42
SALES (est): 10.6MM
SALES (corp-wide): 11.2MM **Privately Held**
WEB: www.cellmarque.com
SIC: 2835 In vitro & in vivo diagnostic substances
PA: Sigma-Aldrich Co. Llc
3050 Spruce St
Saint Louis MO 63103
877 856-5586

(P-8468)
CELLESTA INC
10554 Caminito Alvarez, San Diego (92126-5785)
PHONE................858 552-0888
Jia Xu, *President*
EMP: 15
SALES (est): 931.8K **Privately Held**
SIC: 2835 In vitro & in vivo diagnostic substances

(P-8469)
CELLESTIS INC
27220 Turnberry Ln # 200, Valencia (91355-1019)
PHONE................661 775-7480
Peer M Schatz, *CEO*
Anthony Radford, *President*
Roland Sackers, *CFO*
Nisha Gaulke, *Chief Mktg Ofcr*
Mark Boyle, *Senior VP*
▲ **EMP:** 12
SALES (est): 2.3MM
SALES (corp-wide): 1.4B **Privately Held**
SIC: 2835 Blood derivative diagnostic agents
HQ: Qiagen Gaithersburg, Inc.
19300 Germantown Rd
Germantown MD 20874
301 944-7000

(P-8470)
CLEARLIGHT DIAGNOSTICS LLC
428 Oakmead Pkwy, Sunnyvale (94085-4708)
PHONE................928 525-4290
Laurie Goodman, *Officer*
EMP: 10 EST: 2015
SALES (est): 725.4K **Privately Held**
SIC: 2835 Cytology & histology diagnostic agents

(P-8471)
CUE HEALTH INC
11175 Flintkote Ave, San Diego (92121-1209)
PHONE................256 651-1656
Ayub Khattak, *CEO*
Brad Younggren, *Chief Mktg Ofcr*
Clint Sever,
Robin Farias-Eisner, *Surgeon*
Dino Di Carlo, *Advisor*
EMP: 50
SQ FT: 7,557
SALES (est): 3MM **Privately Held**
SIC: 2835 In vitro diagnostics

(P-8472)
DANISCO US INC (DH)
Also Called: Genencor International
925 Page Mill Rd, Palo Alto (94304-1013)
PHONE................650 846-7500
James C Collins, *CEO*
Michael Blow, *President*
Joseph Millica, *Bd of Directors*
Soren Nielsen, *Exec VP*
Michael Arbige, *Senior VP*
◆ **EMP:** 200
SQ FT: 128,000
SALES (est): 280.3MM
SALES (corp-wide): 62.4B **Publicly Held**
SIC: 2835 8731 2899 2869 In vitro & in vivo diagnostic substances; commercial physical research; chemical preparations; industrial organic chemicals
HQ: E. I. Du Pont De Nemours And Company
974 Centre Rd
Wilmington DE 19805
302 774-1000

(P-8473)
DIAGNOSTICS FOR REAL WORLD LTD (PA)
845 Embedded Way, San Jose (95138-1030)
PHONE................408 773-1511
Helen H Lee, *President*
Vivian Laitila, *Director*
EMP: 13
SALES (est): 1.7MM **Privately Held**
WEB: www.drw-ltd.com
SIC: 2835 In vitro & in vivo diagnostic substances

(P-8474)
DIASORIN MOLECULAR LLC
11331 Valley View St, Cypress (90630-5300)
PHONE................562 240-6500
Carlo Rosa, *CEO*
EMP: 200
SALES: 90MM
SALES (corp-wide): 391.7MM **Privately Held**
SIC: 2835 5047 In vitro diagnostics; diagnostic equipment, medical
HQ: Diasorin Inc.
1951 Northwestern Ave S
Stillwater MN 55082
651 439-9710

(P-8475)
EPICUREN DISCOVERY
26081 Merit Cir Ste 116, Laguna Hills (92653-7017)
PHONE................949 588-5807
Colleen Lohrman, *President*
Glenn Davidson, *CFO*
Janae Muzzy, *Vice Pres*
Brett Hickman, *Graphic Designe*
Ann Andrews, *Training Spec*
▲ **EMP:** 65
SQ FT: 20,000
SALES (est): 17.1MM **Privately Held**
SIC: 2835 Enzyme & isoenzyme diagnostic agents

(P-8476)
FUJIFILM WAKO DIAGNOSTICS US
Also Called: Wako Life Sciences, Inc.
1025 Terra Bella Ave A, Mountain View (94043-1829)
PHONE................650 210-9153
Shinji Satomura, *CEO*
Kimiko Arimoto, *Marketing Staff*

EMP: 40
SALES (est): 8.2MM
SALES (corp-wide): 22.8B Privately Held
SIC: 2835 5047 In vitro & in vivo diagnostic substances; diagnostic equipment, medical
HQ: Fujifilm Wako Holdings U.S.A. Corporation
1600 Bellwood Rd
North Chesterfield VA 23237

(P-8477)
FULLER LABORATORIES
1312 E Valencia Dr, Fullerton (92831-4758)
PHONE..................................714 525-7660
Lee Fuller, *President*
Lynn Fuller, *Treasurer*
▼ EMP: 19
SQ FT: 12,500
SALES (est): 7.3MM Privately Held
WEB: www.fullerlabs.com
SIC: 2835 Microbiology & virology diagnostic products

(P-8478)
GEN-PROBE INCORPORATED
10210 Genetic Center Dr, San Diego (92121-4394)
PHONE..................................858 410-8000
Gene Walther, *Principal*
Brad Blake, *Vice Pres*
Vladislav Nodelman, *Associate Dir*
Jeff Burns, *Program Mgr*
Daniel Corrales, *General Mgr*
EMP: 74
SALES (corp-wide): 696.8MM Privately Held
SIC: 2835 In vitro diagnostics; microbiology & virology diagnostic products
HQ: Gen-Probe Incorporated
250 Campus Dr
Marlborough MA 01752
508 263-8937

(P-8479)
GIT AMERICA INC
230 Commerce Ste 190, Irvine (92602-1336)
PHONE..................................714 433-2180
Simon Park, *President*
▲ EMP: 10
SALES: 16.1MM Privately Held
WEB: www.gitauto.com
SIC: 2835 7371 In vitro & in vivo diagnostic substances; computer software development

(P-8480)
GNOSIS INTERNATIONAL LLC
8008 Westbury Ave, San Diego (92126-2134)
PHONE..................................858 254-6369
Chinh Vu, *CFO*
EMP: 20
SALES (est): 2.5MM Privately Held
SIC: 2835 In vitro & in vivo diagnostic substances

(P-8481)
HELICA BIOSYSTEMS INC
3310 W Macarthur Blvd, Santa Ana (92704-6804)
PHONE..................................714 578-7830
Wondu Wolde Mariam, *President*
Wondu Wolde-Mariam, *Executive*
Jess Hinton, *Technician*
Thu Huynh, *Research*
Sheila Ray, *Opers Mgr*
EMP: 17
SQ FT: 7,500
SALES (est): 2MM Privately Held
WEB: www.helica.com
SIC: 2835 2836 In vitro diagnostics; biological products, except diagnostic

(P-8482)
HYGIENA LLC (PA)
941 Avenida Acaso, Camarillo (93012-8755)
PHONE..................................805 388-2383
Steven Nason, *CEO*
Susan Nason, *Vice Pres*
Paul Meighan, *Research*
Shareef Ahmad, *Business Mgr*
Lewis Irina, *Opers Mgr*

EMP: 127
SQ FT: 30,000
SALES (est): 101.3MM Privately Held
WEB: www.hygiena.com
SIC: 2835 3812 8731 Microbiology & virology diagnostic products; search & detection systems & instruments; biological research

(P-8483)
IMMUNOSCIENCE LLC
6780 Sierra Ct Ste M, Dublin (94568-2630)
PHONE..................................925 400-6055
Robert J Nagy, *Branch Mgr*
EMP: 19
SALES (corp-wide): 4.4MM Privately Held
SIC: 2835 Microbiology & virology diagnostic products
PA: Immunoscience Llc
6780 Sierra Ct Ste M
Dublin CA 94568
925 460-8111

(P-8484)
INDI MOLECULAR INC
6160 Bristol Pkwy, Culver City (90230-6694)
PHONE..................................310 417-4999
Al Luderer, *CEO*
Heather Agnew, *Vice Pres*
EMP: 11 EST: 2013
SALES (est): 348.8K Privately Held
SIC: 2835 In vitro diagnostics
PA: Biodesix Inc.
2970 Wilderness Pl # 120
Boulder CO 80301

(P-8485)
INNOMINATA
Also Called: Genbio
15222 Avenue Of Science A, San Diego (92128-3422)
PHONE..................................858 592-9300
Fred Adler, *Partner*
David Lynette, *Partner*
Karen Saylor, *QA Dir*
▲ EMP: 18
SALES (est): 3.7MM Privately Held
WEB: www.genbio.com
SIC: 2835 In vitro diagnostics

(P-8486)
INNOVACON INC
9975 Summers Ridge Rd, San Diego (92121-2997)
PHONE..................................858 805-8900
John Bridgen, *CEO*
Jixun Lin, *President*
▲ EMP: 70
SALES (est): 12MM
SALES (corp-wide): 27.3B Publicly Held
SIC: 2835 In vitro & in vivo diagnostic substances
HQ: Alere Inc.
51 Sawyer Rd Ste 200
Waltham MA 02453
781 647-3900

(P-8487)
INTERNATIONAL IMMUNOLOGY CORP
25549 Adams Ave, Murrieta (92562-9747)
PHONE..................................951 677-5629
Shunsaku Shibota, *President*
▲ EMP: 42
SQ FT: 20,000
SALES (est): 8.7MM Privately Held
WEB: www.iicsera.com
SIC: 2835 2836 In vitro & in vivo diagnostic substances; biological products, except diagnostic

(P-8488)
LEHMAN MILLET INCORPORATED
Also Called: Leham Millet West
3 Macarthur Pl Ste 700, Santa Ana (92707-6078)
PHONE..................................714 850-7900
Bruce Lehman, *CEO*
EMP: 11

SALES (corp-wide): 68.4MM Privately Held
SIC: 2835 In vitro & in vivo diagnostic substances
HQ: Lehman Millet Incorporated
101 Tremont St Ste 205
Boston MA 02108
617 722-0019

(P-8489)
LIFE TECHNOLOGIES CORPORATION (HQ)
5781 Van Allen Way, Carlsbad (92008-7321)
P.O. Box 1039 (92018-1039)
PHONE..................................760 603-7200
Seth Hoogasian, *CEO*
Mark P Stevenson, *President*
Seth H Hoogasian, *CEO*
John A Cottingham, *Officer*
Peggy Lio, *Admin Sec*
▲ EMP: 140
SALES (est): 3.7B
SALES (corp-wide): 20.9B Publicly Held
WEB: www.lifetechnologies.com
SIC: 2835 2836 In vitro & in vivo diagnostic substances; biological products, except diagnostic
PA: Thermo Fisher Scientific Inc.
168 3rd Ave
Waltham MA 02451
781 622-1000

(P-8490)
LIFEOME BIOLABS INC
10054 Mesa Ridge Ct, San Diego (92121-2945)
PHONE..................................619 302-0129
Zheng Chaojun, *President*
EMP: 19
SALES (est): 1.6MM Privately Held
SIC: 2835 8731 Microbiology & virology diagnostic products; biological research; biotechnical research, commercial
PA: Lifeome Biolabs Inc.
1895 Avenida Del Oro # 6554
Oceanside CA 92056
619 302-0129

(P-8491)
LIFESCAN INC
901 Wrigley Way, Milpitas (95035-5407)
PHONE..................................408 263-9789
Peter Luther, *President*
EMP: 10
SALES (corp-wide): 343.2MM Privately Held
WEB: www.lifescan.com
SIC: 2835 3841 3845 Blood derivative diagnostic agents; medical instruments & equipment, blood & bone work; electromedical equipment
PA: Lifescan, Inc.
965 Chesterbrook Blvd
Chesterbrook PA 19087
800 227-8862

(P-8492)
LIFESCAN INC
542 Gibraltar Dr, Milpitas (95035-6315)
PHONE..................................408 263-9789
John Lipman, *Manager*
Phil Sharp, *Human Res Dir*
EMP: 10
SALES (corp-wide): 343.2MM Privately Held
WEB: www.lifescan.com
SIC: 2835 3841 In vitro & in vivo diagnostic substances; surgical & medical instruments
PA: Lifescan, Inc.
965 Chesterbrook Blvd
Chesterbrook PA 19087
800 227-8862

(P-8493)
LIFESCAN INC
1051 S Milpitas Blvd # 2, Milpitas (95035-6331)
PHONE..................................408 263-9789
Robert Coradini, *CEO*
EMP: 10

SALES (corp-wide): 343.2MM Privately Held
WEB: www.lifescan.com
SIC: 2835 In vitro & in vivo diagnostic substances
PA: Lifescan, Inc.
965 Chesterbrook Blvd
Chesterbrook PA 19087
800 227-8862

(P-8494)
MEDICAL ANALYSIS SYSTEMS INC (DH)
46360 Fremont Blvd, Fremont (94538-6406)
PHONE..................................510 979-5000
Steve Kondor, *President*
Eric Scheinerman, *CFO*
Darwin Richardson, *Vice Pres*
Flo Hockin, *Manager*
EMP: 150
SQ FT: 180,000
SALES (est): 7.5MM
SALES (corp-wide): 20.9B Publicly Held
WEB: www.mas-inc.com
SIC: 2835 Blood derivative diagnostic agents
HQ: Fisher Scientific International Llc
81 Wyman St
Waltham MA 02451
781 622-1000

(P-8495)
METRA BIOSYSTEMS INC (HQ)
2981 Copper Rd, Santa Clara (95051-0716)
PHONE..................................408 616-4300
John Tamerius, *Manager*
Bill Sommer, *Asst Controller*
EMP: 50
SQ FT: 24,000
SALES (est): 11.9MM
SALES (corp-wide): 277.7MM Publicly Held
SIC: 2835 In vitro & in vivo diagnostic substances
PA: Quidel Corporation
12544 High Bluff Dr # 200
San Diego CA 92130
858 552-1100

(P-8496)
MICROPOINT BIOSCIENCE INC
3521 Leonard Ct, Santa Clara (95054-2043)
PHONE..................................408 588-1682
Nan Zhang, *CEO*
▲ EMP: 30
SALES (est): 6.7MM
SALES (corp-wide): 17.3MM Privately Held
SIC: 2835 In vitro & in vivo diagnostic substances
PA: Micropoint Biotechnologies Co., Ltd.
6/F,Tianping Health Building,Gongye 5th Rd.,Shekou
Shenzhen 51806
755 866-7390

(P-8497)
MILLPLEDGE NORTH AMERICA INC
5310 Derry Ave Ste S&T, Agoura Hills (91301-4509)
PHONE..................................310 215-0400
Graham Cheslyn-Curtis, *CEO*
Nathan Smith, *Vice Pres*
▲ EMP: 11
SALES (est): 1.9MM
SALES (corp-wide): 2.6MM Privately Held
SIC: 2835 8734 5122 Veterinary diagnostic substances; veterinary testing; pharmaceuticals
HQ: Millpledge Limited
Whinleys Estate
Retford NOTTS DN22

(P-8498)
MONOGRAM BIOSCIENCES INC
345 Oyster Point Blvd, South San Francisco (94080-1913)
PHONE..................................650 635-1100
Floyd S Eberts III, *CEO*
Alfred G Merriweather, *CFO*

Michael J Dunn, *Officer*
Sarah Irwin, *Assoc VP*
Chuck Walworth, *Assoc VP*
EMP: 382
SQ FT: 41,000
SALES (est): 63.5MM **Publicly Held**
WEB: www.monogrambio.com
SIC: 2835 In vitro & in vivo diagnostic substances
PA: Laboratory Corporation Of America Holdings
358 S Main St
Burlington NC 27215

(P-8499)
NOVA-ONE DIAGNOSTICS LLC
Also Called: Nod
22287 Mulholland Hwy, Calabasas (91302-5157)
PHONE......................818 348-1543
Jonathan Gilchrist, *President*
Roseanne Gilchrist,
EMP: 70
SALES (est): 6.6MM **Privately Held**
SIC: 2835 In vitro & in vivo diagnostic substances

(P-8500)
NOVARTIS PHARMACEUTICALS CORP
Also Called: Novartis Biophrmctcl Ops-Vcvll
2010 Cessna Dr, Vacaville (95688-8712)
PHONE......................707 452-8081
Chris Busstioneau, *Manager*
Justin Stone, *Analyst*
EMP: 50
SALES (corp-wide): 49.1B **Privately Held**
WEB: www.chiron.com
SIC: 2835 2834 In vitro & in vivo diagnostic substances; pharmaceutical preparations
HQ: Novartis Pharmaceuticals Corporation
1 Health Plz
East Hanover NJ 07936
862 778-8300

(P-8501)
ORTHO-CLINICAL DIAGNOSTICS INC
1401 Red Hawk Cir E307, Fremont (94538-4747)
PHONE......................908 704-5910
EMP: 33
SALES (corp-wide): 696.9MM **Privately Held**
SIC: 2835 Blood derivative diagnostic agents
PA: Ortho-Clinical Diagnostics, Inc.
1001 Us Highway 202
Raritan NJ 08869
908 218-8000

(P-8502)
ORTHO-CLINICAL DIAGNOSTICS INC
612 W Katella Ave Ste B, Orange (92867-4608)
PHONE......................714 639-2323
Robert Black, *Branch Mgr*
EMP: 20
SQ FT: 2,200
SALES (corp-wide): 696.9MM **Privately Held**
WEB: www.orthoclinical.com
SIC: 2835 Blood derivative diagnostic agents
PA: Ortho-Clinical Diagnostics, Inc.
1001 Us Highway 202
Raritan NJ 08869
908 218-8000

(P-8503)
PACIFIC BIOTECH INC
10165 Mckellar Ct, San Diego (92121-4201)
PHONE......................858 552-1100
Wayne Kay, *President*
EMP: 220
SQ FT: 70,000
SALES (est): 11.7MM
SALES (corp-wide): 277.7MM **Publicly Held**
WEB: www.quidel.com
SIC: 2835 Pregnancy test kits

PA: Quidel Corporation
12544 High Bluff Dr # 200
San Diego CA 92130
858 552-1100

(P-8504)
PLASMA BIOLIFE SERVICES L P
15903 Strathern St, Van Nuys (91406-1313)
PHONE......................818 947-5600
Jeff Miller, *Branch Mgr*
EMP: 80
SALES (corp-wide): 15.1B **Privately Held**
SIC: 2835 Blood derivative diagnostic agents
HQ: Biolife Plasma Services L.P.
1435 Lake Cook Rd
Philadelphia PA 19182
847 940-5559

(P-8505)
PROZYME INC
3832 Bay Center Pl, Hayward (94545-3619)
PHONE......................510 638-6900
Sergey Vlasenko, *President*
Ted Haxo, *Vice Pres*
C Richard Hutchinson, *VP Info Sys*
Fiel Limjap, *Research*
Bopha Sun, *Research*
EMP: 47
SQ FT: 20,000
SALES (est): 11.3MM
SALES (corp-wide): 4.4B **Publicly Held**
WEB: www.prozyme.com
SIC: 2835 Blood derivative diagnostic agents
PA: Agilent Technologies, Inc.
5301 Stevens Creek Blvd
Santa Clara CA 95051
408 345-8886

(P-8506)
QUANTIMETRIX CORPORATION
2005 Manhattan Beach Blvd, Redondo Beach (90278-1205)
PHONE......................310 536-0006
Monty Ban, *President*
Edward Cleek, *CEO*
Abdee Akhavan, *CFO*
EMP: 70
SQ FT: 86,400
SALES (est): 18.3MM **Privately Held**
WEB: www.4qc.com
SIC: 2835 In vitro & in vivo diagnostic substances

(P-8507)
QUIDEL CORPORATION (PA)
12544 High Bluff Dr # 200, San Diego (92130-3050)
PHONE......................858 552-1100
Douglas C Bryant, *President*
Kenneth F Buechler, *Ch of Bd*
Randall J Steward, *CFO*
Michael D Abney Jr, *Senior VP*
Robert J Bujarski, *Senior VP*
EMP: 277 **EST:** 1979
SQ FT: 30,000
SALES: 277.7MM **Publicly Held**
WEB: www.quidel.com
SIC: 2835 Pregnancy test kits

(P-8508)
QUIDEL CORPORATION
10165 Mckellar Ct, San Diego (92121-4299)
PHONE......................858 552-1100
EMP: 11
SALES (corp-wide): 277.7MM **Publicly Held**
SIC: 2835 In vitro & in vivo diagnostic substances
PA: Quidel Corporation
12544 High Bluff Dr # 200
San Diego CA 92130
858 552-1100

(P-8509)
SCANTIBODIES LABORATORY INC (PA)
9336 Abraham Way, Santee (92071-2861)
PHONE......................619 258-9300
Thomas L Cantor, *CEO*
John Van Duzer, *COO*
Cheryl Cantor, *Vice Pres*

Gerardo Magana, *Business Dir*
Andrei Torres, *Administration*
▲ **EMP:** 240
SQ FT: 60,500
SALES (est): 97.2MM **Privately Held**
WEB: www.scantibodies.com
SIC: 2835 Pregnancy test kits

(P-8510)
SEKISUI AMERICA CORPORATION
Genzyme Diagnostics
6659 Top Gun St, San Diego (92121-4113)
PHONE......................858 452-3198
Brian Danieli, *Branch Mgr*
Irma Gonzales, *Human Resources*
Theresa Narciso, *Manager*
Lisa Williams, *Manager*
EMP: 21
SALES (corp-wide): 10.3B **Privately Held**
WEB: www.genzyme.com
SIC: 2835 In vitro & in vivo diagnostic substances
HQ: Sekisui America Corporation
333 Meadowlands Pkwy
Secaucus NJ 07094
201 423-7960

(P-8511)
SEQUENTA LLC
329 Oyster Point Blvd, South San Francisco (94080-1913)
PHONE......................650 243-3900
Tom Willis, *CEO*
Malek Faham, *Security Dir*
EMP: 60
SALES (est): 11.4MM **Privately Held**
SIC: 2835 2836 In vitro & in vivo diagnostic substances; biological products, except diagnostic
PA: Adaptive Biotechnologies Corporation
1551 Eastlake Ave E # 200
Seattle WA 98102

(P-8512)
SERADYN INC
46360 Fremont Blvd, Fremont (94538-6406)
PHONE......................317 610-3800
Mark Roberts, *President*
EMP: 90
SQ FT: 40,000
SALES (est): 7.9MM
SALES (corp-wide): 20.9B **Publicly Held**
WEB: www.seradyn.com
SIC: 2835 Microbiology & virology diagnostic products
HQ: Fisher Scientific International Llc
81 Wyman St
Waltham MA 02451
781 622-1000

(P-8513)
SIEMENS HLTHCARE DGNOSTICS INC
Also Called: Siemens Medical Solutions
5210 Pacific Concourse Dr, Los Angeles (90045-6900)
PHONE......................310 645-8200
Anthony Bihl, *Branch Mgr*
Howard Wilson, *Purchasing*
EMP: 55
SALES (corp-wide): 97.7B **Privately Held**
WEB: www.dpcweb.com
SIC: 2835 Veterinary diagnostic substances
HQ: Siemens Healthcare Diagnostics Inc.
511 Benedict Ave
Tarrytown NY 10591
914 631-8000

(P-8514)
SIEMENS HLTHCARE DGNOSTICS INC
2040 Enterprise Blvd, West Sacramento (95691-5045)
PHONE......................916 372-1900
Rick Lee, *Manager*
Jeff Jacobs, *Engineer*
EMP: 25
SALES (corp-wide): 97.7B **Privately Held**
WEB: www.dpcweb.com
SIC: 2835 In vitro & in vivo diagnostic substances

HQ: Siemens Healthcare Diagnostics Inc.
511 Benedict Ave
Tarrytown NY 10591
914 631-8000

(P-8515)
SINGULAR BIO INC
455 Mission Bay Blvd S # 145, San Francisco (94158-2159)
PHONE......................415 553-8773
Hywel Jones, *CEO*
EMP: 12
SALES (est): 308.2K **Privately Held**
SIC: 2835 In vitro diagnostics

(P-8516)
SOFIE BIOSCIENCES INC (PA)
6162 Bristol Pkwy, Culver City (90230-6604)
PHONE......................310 215-3159
Patrick W Phelps, *CEO*
Michael Phelps, *Ch of Bd*
Johannes Czernin, *Managing Dir*
Ruben Guzman, *Engineer*
Philipp Czernin, *Finance Dir*
EMP: 26
SQ FT: 3,500
SALES (est): 171.6MM **Privately Held**
SIC: 2835 In vitro diagnostics

(P-8517)
SOURCE BIO INC
43379 Bus Pk Dr Ste 100, Temecula (92590-3687)
PHONE......................951 676-1000
Duane Pinkerton, *President*
Theresa Pinkerton, *Exec VP*
◆ **EMP:** 10
SALES (est): 1.2MM **Privately Held**
WEB: www.sourcebioinc.com
SIC: 2835 Blood derivative diagnostic agents

(P-8518)
SYNBIOTICS LLC
16420 Via Esprillo, San Diego (92127-1702)
PHONE......................858 451-3771
Keith A Butler, *Branch Mgr*
Michael Woodard, *Exec Dir*
EMP: 20
SALES (corp-wide): 5.3B **Publicly Held**
SIC: 2835 Veterinary diagnostic substances
HQ: Synbiotics Llc
12200 Nw Ambassador
Kansas City MO 64163
816 464-3500

(P-8519)
SYNTRON BIORESEARCH INC
2774 Loker Ave W, Carlsbad (92010-6610)
PHONE......................760 930-2200
Charles Yu, *President*
Phan Khan, *Human Res Mgr*
Jennifer Lee, *Opers Staff*
Luke Shyu, *Production*
▲ **EMP:** 278
SALES (est): 44.5MM **Privately Held**
WEB: www.syntron.net
SIC: 2835 5122 In vitro & in vivo diagnostic substances; biologicals & allied products

(P-8520)
TECO DIAGNOSTICS
1268 N Lakeview Ave, Anaheim (92807-1831)
PHONE......................714 693-7788
K C Chen, *President*
Dhaval Waghela, *Research*
Winson Wong, *Research*
Nour Qasqas, *QC Mgr*
◆ **EMP:** 70
SQ FT: 40,000
SALES (est): 16.8MM **Privately Held**
WEB: www.tecodiag.com
SIC: 2835 5049 In vitro & in vivo diagnostic substances; laboratory equipment, except medical or dental

(P-8521)
TROVAGENE INC
11055 Flintkote Ave Ste A, San Diego (92121-1220)
PHONE......................858 952-7570

William J Welch, *CEO*
Thomas H Adams, *Ch of Bd*
Mark Erlander, *Officer*
Elizabeth Anderson, *Vice Pres*
Nicholas Nelson, *Vice Pres*
EMP: 72
SQ FT: 22,600
SALES: 505.4K **Privately Held**
SIC: 2835 2836 In vitro & in vivo diagnostic substances; biological products, except diagnostic

2836 Biological Prdts, Exc Diagnostic Substances

(P-8522)
10X GENOMICS INC (PA)
7068 Koll Center Pkwy # 401, Pleasanton (94566-3111)
PHONE..........................925 401-7300
Serge Saxonov, *CEO*
Benjamin Hindson, *President*
Bradford J Crutchfield, *Ch Credit Ofcr*
Jean Philibert,
Brad Crutchfield, *Officer*
EMP: 14
SALES (est): 5.4MM **Privately Held**
SIC: 2836 Biological products, except diagnostic

(P-8523)
ADVERUM BIOTECHNOLOGIES INC
1035 Obrien Dr Ste A, Menlo Park (94025-1408)
PHONE..........................650 272-6269
Leone Patterson, *President*
Paul B Cleveland, *Ch of Bd*
Linda Neuman, *Chief Mktg Ofcr*
Mehdi Gasmi, *Officer*
Jennifer Cheng, *Vice Pres*
EMP: 78
SQ FT: 36,000
SALES: 1.8MM **Privately Held**
SIC: 2836 8731 Biological products, except diagnostic; biotechnical research, commercial

(P-8524)
ALLIANCE ANALYTICAL INC
355 Fairview Way, Milpitas (95035-3024)
PHONE..........................800 916-5600
John H Muliken III, *President*
EMP: 25
SALES (est): 5.6MM **Privately Held**
SIC: 2836 5049 Biological products, except diagnostic; laboratory equipment, except medical or dental

(P-8525)
ALTA ADVANCED TECHNOLOGIES INC
760 E Sunkist St, Ontario (91761-1861)
PHONE..........................909 983-2973
Steven G Boland Jr, *President*
▲ **EMP:** 45
SQ FT: 12,723
SALES: 6MM **Privately Held**
SIC: 2836 2851 3827 Biological products, except diagnostic; coating, air curing; lens coating equipment

(P-8526)
AMGEN INC (PA)
1 Amgen Center Dr, Thousand Oaks (91320-1799)
PHONE..........................805 447-1000
Robert A Bradway, *Ch of Bd*
David W Meline, *CFO*
Cynthia M Patton, *Ch Credit Ofcr*
Murdo Gordon, *Exec VP*
David M Reese, *Exec VP*
◆ **EMP:** 2577
SALES: 22.8B **Publicly Held**
WEB: www.amgen.com
SIC: 2836 Biological products, except diagnostic

(P-8527)
AMGEN USA INC
1 Amgen Center Dr, Thousand Oaks (91320-1799)
PHONE..........................805 447-1000
Kevin W Sharer, *CEO*
EMP: 99
SALES (est): 1.3MM
SALES (corp-wide): 22.8B **Publicly Held**
SIC: 2836 Biological products, except diagnostic
PA: Amgen Inc.
1 Amgen Center Dr
Thousand Oaks CA 91320
805 447-1000

(P-8528)
AMPLIPHI BIOSCIENCES CORP (PA)
3579 Valley Centre Dr # 100, San Diego (92130-3316)
PHONE..........................858 829-0829
Paul C Grint, *CEO*
Jeremy Curnock Cook, *Ch of Bd*
Igor P Bilinsky, *COO*
Wendy S Johnson, *COO*
Steve R Martin, *CFO*
EMP: 32
SQ FT: 1,000
SALES: 115K **Publicly Held**
WEB: www.targen.com
SIC: 2836 Biological products, except diagnostic

(P-8529)
AUDENTES THERAPEUTICS INC
600 California St Fl 17, San Francisco (94108-2725)
PHONE..........................415 818-1001
Jonathan Silverstein, *Ch of Bd*
Matthew Patterson, *Ch of Bd*
Natalie Holles, *President*
Thomas Soloway, *CFO*
Louis Lange, *Bd of Directors*
EMP: 75 **EST:** 2012
SALES (est): 34MM **Privately Held**
SIC: 2836 Biological products, except diagnostic

(P-8530)
AZURE BIOSYSTEMS INC
6747 Sierra Ct Ste A, Dublin (94568-2651)
PHONE..........................925 307-7127
Alnoor Mohamedali Shivji, *CEO*
Brian Donnelly, *Engineer*
Connie Chan, *Opers Mgr*
Lisa Isailovic, *Marketing Staff*
▲ **EMP:** 40
SALES (est): 8.2MM **Privately Held**
SIC: 2836 Biological products, except diagnostic

(P-8531)
B-BRIDGE INTERNATIONAL INC
3350 Scott Blvd Bldg 29, Santa Clara (95054-3105)
PHONE..........................408 252-6200
Hiroyuki Masumoto, *CEO*
▲ **EMP:** 30
SALES (est): 6.5MM **Privately Held**
WEB: www.b-bridge.com
SIC: 2836 Biological products, except diagnostic

(P-8532)
BACHEM AMERICAS INC (DH)
Also Called: Bachem California
3132 Kashiwa St, Torrance (90505-4087)
PHONE..........................310 784-4440
Brian Gregg, *CEO*
Monica Mendoza, *Partner*
Michael Brenk, *CFO*
Peter Hutchings, *Vice Pres*
Fariba Jashnian, *Vice Pres*
▲ **EMP:** 194
SQ FT: 70,000
SALES (est): 67.1MM **Privately Held**
SIC: 2836 2834 Biological products, except diagnostic; pharmaceutical preparations
HQ: Bachem Holding Ag
Hauptstrasse 144
Bubendorf BL 4416
619 352-333

(P-8533)
BACHEM BIOSCIENCE INC
3132 Kashiwa St, Torrance (90505-4087)
PHONE..........................310 784-7322
Peter Grogg, *Ch of Bd*
Michael Pennington, *President*
Rolf Nyfeler, *CEO*
Epstein Ralph, *Vice Pres*
Loubna Kerkeb, *General Mgr*
▲ **EMP:** 37
SALES (est): 5.9MM **Privately Held**
SIC: 2836 2899 Biological products, except diagnostic; chemical preparations
HQ: Bachem Holding Ag
Hauptstrasse 144
Bubendorf BL 4416
619 352-333

(P-8534)
BIOCLIN THERAPEUTICS INC
1040 Davis St Ste 202, San Leandro (94577-1519)
PHONE..........................925 413-6140
Scott D Myers, *Ch of Bd*
Graeme Currie, *COO*
Julie Eastland, *CFO*
Esteban Abella, *Chief Mktg Ofcr*
Stephen Lau, *Executive*
EMP: 10
SALES (est): 1.3MM **Privately Held**
SIC: 2836 Biological products, except diagnostic

(P-8535)
BIOLEGEND INC (PA)
9727 Pacific Heights Blvd, San Diego (92121-3719)
PHONE..........................858 455-9588
Gene Lay, *President*
Bill Kullback, *CFO*
Kim Clark, *Vice Pres*
Kent Johnson, *Vice Pres*
Arnie Kana, *Associate Dir*
◆ **EMP:** 207
SQ FT: 75,000
SALES (est): 116.8MM **Privately Held**
WEB: www.biolegend.com
SIC: 2836 Biological products, except diagnostic

(P-8536)
BIOMER TECHNOLOGY LLC
1233 Quarry Ln 135, Pleasanton (94566-8452)
PHONE..........................925 426-0787
Cheng Chou,
Steve Lee,
EMP: 10
SQ FT: 3,000
SALES (est): 1.5MM **Privately Held**
WEB: www.biomertech.com
SIC: 2836 8731 Biological products, except diagnostic; biotechnical research, commercial

(P-8537)
BIOSEARCH TECHNOLOGIES INC (DH)
2199 S Mcdowell Blvd Ext, Petaluma (94954-6904)
PHONE..........................415 883-8400
Ronald M Cook, *President*
Daren Dick, *General Mgr*
Dia Jenkins, *Administration*
Ebin Koenig, *Network Enginr*
Danielle Washington, *Technician*
EMP: 120
SQ FT: 121,000
SALES (est): 26.5MM **Privately Held**
WEB: www.btidna.com
SIC: 2836 2899 2835 2869 Biological products, except diagnostic; chemical preparations; in vitro diagnostics; industrial organic chemicals
HQ: Lgc Science Group Limited
Queens Road
Teddington MIDDX
208 943-7000

(P-8538)
BIOTIME INC (PA)
1010 Atlantic Ave Ste 102, Alameda (94501-1147)
PHONE..........................510 521-3390
Brian Culley, *CEO*
Alfred D Kingsley, *Ch of Bd*

Russell Skibsted, *CFO*
Russell L Skibsted, *CFO*
Neal Bradsher, *Bd of Directors*
EMP: 55
SQ FT: 19,000
SALES: 3.4MM **Publicly Held**
WEB: www.biotimeinc.com
SIC: 2836 8731 Biological products, except diagnostic; biotechnical research, commercial

(P-8539)
CELLULAR BIOMEDICINE GROUP INC
19925 Stevens Creek Blvd # 100, Cupertino (95014-2384)
PHONE..........................408 973-7884
WEI Cao, *CEO*
Wen Tao Liu, *Ch of Bd*
Richard L Wang, *CFO*
Chun Kwok Au, *Bd of Directors*
Gang Ji, *Bd of Directors*
EMP: 77
SALES: 336.8K **Privately Held**
SIC: 2836 8731 Biological products, except diagnostic; biological research

(P-8540)
CENTERLINE PRECISION INC
2265 Calle Del Mundo, Santa Clara (95054-1006)
PHONE..........................408 988-4380
Ricardo Rengifo, *CEO*
EMP: 13
SQ FT: 5,000
SALES (est): 1.3MM **Privately Held**
WEB: www.centerlinep.com
SIC: 2836 Biological products, except diagnostic

(P-8541)
CHECKERSPOT INC
740 Heinz Ave, Berkeley (94710-2748)
PHONE..........................510 239-7921
Charles Dimmler, *CEO*
EMP: 10
SQ FT: 1,000
SALES (est): 119.8K **Privately Held**
SIC: 2836 Biological products, except diagnostic

(P-8542)
CIDARA THERAPEUTICS INC (PA)
6310 Nncy Rdge Dr Ste 101, San Diego (92121)
PHONE..........................858 752-6170
Jeffrey L Stein, *President*
Scott M Rocklage, *Ch of Bd*
Paul Daruwala, *COO*
Taylor Sandison, *Chief Mktg Ofcr*
Brady Johnson,
EMP: 49 **EST:** 2012
SQ FT: 29,638
SALES (est): 13.2MM **Publicly Held**
SIC: 2836 8731 Biological products, except diagnostic; biotechnical research, commercial

(P-8543)
CLINIQA CORPORATION (HQ)
495 Enterprise St, San Marcos (92078-4364)
PHONE..........................760 744-1900
Kevin Gould, *President*
C Granger Haugh, *CEO*
Dean Harriman, *CFO*
Larry Beaty, *Vice Pres*
Shing Kwan, *Vice Pres*
▼ **EMP:** 76
SQ FT: 25,000
SALES (est): 18.5MM
SALES (corp-wide): 563MM **Publicly Held**
WEB: www.cliniqa.com
SIC: 2836 Biological products, except diagnostic
PA: Bio-Techne Corporation
614 Mckinley Pl Ne
Minneapolis MN 55413
612 379-8854

PRODUCTS & SVCS

(P-8544)
CYTRX CORPORATION (PA)
11726 San Vicente Blvd # 650, Los Angeles
(90049-5079)
PHONE..................310 826-5648
Steven A Kriegsman, *Ch of Bd*
Eric L Curtis, *President*
John Y Caloz, *CFO*
Felix Kratz, *Vice Pres*
EMP: 20
SQ FT: 5,739
SALES: 100K **Publicly Held**
SIC: 2836 Biological products, except diagnostic

(P-8545)
DENALI THERAPEUTICS INC
151 Oyster Point Blvd # 2, South San Francisco (94080-1840)
PHONE..................650 866-8548
Ryan J Watts, *President*
Vicki Sato, *Ch of Bd*
Alexander O Schuth, *COO*
Steve E Krognes, *CFO*
Jay Flatley, *Bd of Directors*
EMP: 125
SALES (est): 54.9MM **Privately Held**
SIC: 2836 2834 Biological products, except diagnostic; pharmaceutical preparations

(P-8546)
DNA TWOPOINTO INC
Also Called: Dna2.0
37950 Central Ct Ste C, Newark
(94560-3464)
PHONE..................650 853-8347
Jeremy Minshull, *CEO*
Sridhar Govindarajan, *Vice Pres*
Claes Gustafsson, *Vice Pres*
Jon Ness, *Vice Pres*
Colleen V Ende, *Admin Asst*
▼ **EMP:** 68
SQ FT: 40,000
SALES (est): 16MM **Privately Held**
WEB: www.dna20.com
SIC: 2836 Biological products, except diagnostic

(P-8547)
DYNAVAX TECHNOLOGIES CORP (PA)
2929 7th St Ste 100, Berkeley
(94710-2753)
PHONE..................510 848-5100
Eddie Gray, *CEO*
Arnold L Oronsky, *Ch of Bd*
Michael S Ostrach, *CFO*
Laura Brege, *Bd of Directors*
Natale Ricciardi, *Bd of Directors*
EMP: 133
SQ FT: 55,200
SALES: 327K **Publicly Held**
WEB: www.dynavax.com
SIC: 2836 8731 Biological products, except diagnostic; biological research; commercial physical research

(P-8548)
EIGER BIOPHARMACEUTICALS INC (PA)
2155 Park Blvd, Palo Alto (94306-1543)
PHONE..................650 272-6138
David Cory, *President*
David Apelian, *COO*
James Welch, *CFO*
Gregg Alton, *Bd of Directors*
Jeffrey Glenn, *Bd of Directors*
EMP: 10
SQ FT: 1,570
SALES (est): 2.4MM **Publicly Held**
WEB: www.celladon.net
SIC: 2836 3845 Biological products, except diagnostic; cardiographs

(P-8549)
EVOLVA INC
101 Larkspur Landing Cir # 222, Larkspur
(94939-1750)
PHONE..................415 448-5451
Murali P Muthuwamy, *President*
Eric Peters, *QA Dir*
Philippe Prochasson, *Project Mgr*
Ros Abigail, *Research*
Mary Bosserman, *Research*
EMP: 15
SQ FT: 11,000
SALES: 5.8MM
SALES (corp-wide): 6.9MM **Privately Held**
SIC: 2836 Biological products, except diagnostic
HQ: Evolva Ag
Duggingerstrasse 23
Reinach BL 4153
614 852-000

(P-8550)
EXPRESSION SYSTEMS LLC (PA)
2537 2nd St, Davis (95618-5475)
PHONE..................877 877-7421
David Hedin,
EMP: 27
SQ FT: 27,000
SALES: 2MM **Privately Held**
WEB: www.expressionsystems.com
SIC: 2836 Culture media

(P-8551)
FATE THERAPEUTICS INC
3535 General Atomics Ct, San Diego
(92121-1140)
PHONE..................858 875-1800
William H Rastetter, *Ch of Bd*
J Scott Wolchko, *President*
John D Mendlein, *Vice Ch Bd*
Wen Bo Wang, *Senior VP*
Daniel D Shoemaker, *Security Dir*
EMP: 11 **EST:** 2007
SQ FT: 48,000
SALES: 4.1MM **Privately Held**
SIC: 2836 8731 Biological products, except diagnostic; biotechnical research, commercial

(P-8552)
FLASH BACK USA
1535 Templeton Rd, Templeton
(93465-9694)
PHONE..................805 434-0321
Andrew McArthur, *President*
EMP: 16
SALES (est): 1.5MM **Privately Held**
SIC: 2836 Veterinary biological products

(P-8553)
FUSION 360 INC
677 E Olive Ave, Turlock (95380-4013)
P.O. Box 1004 (95381-1004)
PHONE..................209 632-0139
Thomas Yamashita PHD, *President*
EMP: 12
SALES (est): 1.1MM **Privately Held**
SIC: 2836 Biological products, except diagnostic

(P-8554)
GENENTECH INC
1 Antibody Way, Oceanside (92056-5701)
PHONE..................760 231-2440
Ashraf Hanna, *Branch Mgr*
EMP: 300
SALES (corp-wide): 53.9B **Publicly Held**
SIC: 2836 Biological products, except diagnostic
HQ: Genentech, Inc.
1 Dna Way
South San Francisco CA 94080
650 225-1000

(P-8555)
GRIFOLS BIOLOGICALS LLC (DH)
2410 Lillyvale Ave, Los Angeles
(90032-3514)
PHONE..................323 225-2221
Greg Rich, *CEO*
Max Debrouwer, *CFO*
David Bell, *Vice Pres*
Lorraine Peddada, *Associate Dir*
Juan Garcia, *VP Mfg*
▲ **EMP:** 277 **EST:** 2003
SALES (est): 169.2MM
SALES (corp-wide): 696.8MM **Privately Held**
WEB: www.alphather.com
SIC: 2836 2834 Plasmas; pharmaceutical preparations

HQ: Grifols Shared Services North America, Inc.
2410 Lillyvale Ave
Los Angeles CA 90032
323 225-2221

(P-8556)
GRITSTONE ONCOLOGY INC (PA)
5858 Horton St Ste 210, Emeryville
(94608-2006)
PHONE..................510 871-6100
Andrew Allen, *President*
Jean-Marc Bellemin, *CFO*
Raphael Rousseau, *Chief Mktg Ofcr*
Jayant Aphale, *Exec VP*
Matthew Hawryluk, *Exec VP*
EMP: 71
SQ FT: 13,100
SALES (est): 26.6MM **Publicly Held**
SIC: 2836 Biological products, except diagnostic

(P-8557)
HALOZYME THERAPEUTICS INC (PA)
11388 Sorrento Valley Rd # 200, San Diego
(92121-1345)
PHONE..................858 794-8889
Helen I Torley, *President*
Connie L Matsui, *Ch of Bd*
Laurie D Stelzer, *CFO*
Harry J Leonhardt, *Ch Credit Ofcr*
Albert Kildani, *Vice Pres*
EMP: 84 **EST:** 1998
SQ FT: 76,000
SALES: 316.6MM **Publicly Held**
WEB: www.halozyme.com
SIC: 2836 2834 Biological products, except diagnostic; pharmaceutical preparations

(P-8558)
HEMOSTAT LABORATORIES INC (PA)
515 Industrial Way, Dixon (95620-9779)
P.O. Box 790 (95620-0790)
PHONE..................707 678-9594
Jim Mc Elligott, *President*
Gordon Murphy, *Vice Pres*
Kris Pfau, *Opers Mgr*
EMP: 20
SQ FT: 9,500
SALES (est): 3.1MM **Privately Held**
WEB: www.hemostat.com
SIC: 2836 2673 Blood derivatives; plastic & pliofilm bags

(P-8559)
HYGIEIA BIOLOGICAL LABS (PA)
1785 E Main St Ste 4, Woodland
(95776-6206)
P.O. Box 8300 (95776-8300)
PHONE..................530 661-1442
James L Wallis, *President*
Sarah Jamison, *Branch Mgr*
Dale M Wallis,
EMP: 20
SQ FT: 4,000
SALES (est): 3.2MM **Privately Held**
WEB: www.hygieialabs.com
SIC: 2836 5047 Veterinary biological products; veterinarians' equipment & supplies

(P-8560)
INFRATAB
4347 Raytheon Rd Unit 6, Oxnard
(93033-8225)
PHONE..................805 986-8880
Therese E Myers, *Principal*
Stanton Kaye, *Principal*
Jackie Goodman, *Marketing Staff*
EMP: 25
SQ FT: 15,000
SALES (est): 3.5MM **Privately Held**
WEB: www.infratab.com
SIC: 2836 Biological products, except diagnostic

(P-8561)
INOVIO PHARMACEUTICALS INC
10480 Wateridge Cir, San Diego
(92121-5773)
PHONE..................267 440-4200
Peter Kies, *CFO*
Paul Stead, *President*
Jennifer Lata, *Associate Dir*
Trevor Smith, *Associate Dir*
Tamburro Luigi, *Engineer*
EMP: 25 **Publicly Held**
SIC: 2836 Vaccines & other immunizing products
PA: Inovio Pharmaceuticals, Inc.
660 W Germantown Pike
Plymouth Meeting PA 19462

(P-8562)
INTEGRATED DNA TECH INC
6828 Nncy Rdge Dr Ste 400, San Diego
(92121)
PHONE..................858 410-6677
Jack Jacobs, *Vice Pres*
Dean E Daggett, *Agent*
Jeff Wolking, *Agent*
EMP: 17
SALES (corp-wide): 18.3B **Publicly Held**
SIC: 2836 Biological products, except diagnostic
HQ: Integrated Dna Technologies, Inc.
8180 Mccormick Blvd
Skokie IL 60076
847 745-1700

(P-8563)
IRVINE SCIENTIFIC SALES CO INC (DH)
1830 E Warner Ave, Santa Ana
(92705-5505)
PHONE..................949 261-7800
Yutaka Yamaguchi, *CEO*
Akiko Ohno, *President*
Ryo Iguchi, *CFO*
Toru Naganuma, *Officer*
Brian Gehring, *Area Mgr*
▲ **EMP:** 44
SQ FT: 20,000
SALES: 31.9MM
SALES (corp-wide): 22.8B **Privately Held**
WEB: www.irvinesci.com
SIC: 2836 5047 Blood derivatives; culture media; medical laboratory equipment
HQ: Fujifilm Holdings America Corporation
200 Summit Lake Dr Fl 2
Valhalla NY 10595
914 789-8100

(P-8564)
KODIAK SCIENCES INC (PA)
2631 Hanover St, Palo Alto (94304-1118)
PHONE..................650 281-0850
Victor Perlroth, *Ch of Bd*
John A Borgeson, *CFO*
Jason Ehrlich, *Chief Mktg Ofcr*
Hong Liang, *Senior VP*
EMP: 28
SQ FT: 11,000
SALES (est): 2.7MM **Publicly Held**
SIC: 2836 Biological products, except diagnostic

(P-8565)
LIFE TECHNOLOGIES CORPORATION
Also Called: Supplier Diversity Program
5791 Van Allen Way, Carlsbad
(92008-7321)
PHONE..................760 918-4259
Darshini Mehta, *Technical Staff*
Steven Hutt, *Sales Staff*
John Quinn, *Director*
Derek Levine, *Supervisor*
EMP: 100
SALES (corp-wide): 20.9B **Publicly Held**
SIC: 2836 Biological products, except diagnostic
HQ: Life Technologies Corporation
5781 Van Allen Way
Carlsbad CA 92008
760 603-7200

▲ = Import ▼=Export
◆ =Import/Export

(P-8566)
LIST BIOLOGICAL LABS INC
Also Called: List Labs
540 Division St, Campbell (95008-6906)
PHONE..............................408 866-6363
Karen Crawford, *President*
Debra Booth, *Vice Pres*
Debra Dye, *Vice Pres*
Linda Eaton, *Vice Pres*
Kent Davis, *Engineer*
▼ EMP: 25
SQ FT: 11,000
SALES (est): 8.3MM **Privately Held**
WEB: www.listlabs.com
SIC: 2836 Biological products, except diagnostic

(P-8567)
NANTKWEST INC (HQ)
3530 John Hopkins Ct, San Diego
(92121-1121)
PHONE..............................805 633-0300
Patrick Soon-Shiong, *Ch of Bd*
Barry J Simon, *President*
Steve Gorlin, *Vice Ch Bd*
Michael Blaszyk, *Bd of Directors*
Frederick Driscoll, *Bd of Directors*
EMP: 31
SQ FT: 44,681
SALES: 45K
SALES (corp-wide): 1.3MM **Publicly Held**
SIC: 2836 Biological products, except diagnostic
PA: Cambridge Equities, Lp
9922 Jefferson Blvd
Culver City CA 90232
858 350-2300

(P-8568)
NITTOBO AMERICA INC
25549 Adams Ave, Murrieta (92562-9747)
PHONE..............................951 677-5629
Tatsuo Sakae, *President*
◆ EMP: 97
SQ FT: 3,049,200
SALES: 18.8MM
SALES (corp-wide): 793.3MM **Privately Held**
SIC: 2836 Biological products, except diagnostic
PA: Nitto Boseki Co., Ltd.
2-4-1, Kojimachi
Chiyoda-Ku TKY 102-0
345 825-111

(P-8569)
ORGANOVO INC
6275 Nncy Rdge Dr Ste 110, San Diego
(92121)
PHONE..............................858 224-1000
Taylor Crouch, *CEO*
Craig Kussman, *CFO*
Sharon Presnell, *Officer*
Eric Davis, *Exec VP*
Susan Daugherty, *Senior VP*
EMP: 111
SALES (est): 1.5MM
SALES (corp-wide): 4.6MM **Publicly Held**
SIC: 2836 Biological products, except diagnostic
PA: Organovo Holdings, Inc.
6275 Nncy Rdge Dr Ste 110
San Diego CA 92121
858 224-1000

(P-8570)
PACIFICGMP
8810 Rehco Rd Ste E, San Diego
(92121-3262)
PHONE..............................858 550-4094
John Burton, *CEO*
Gary Pierce, *President*
Leigh N Pierce, *CTO*
Mike Faughnan, *Director*
EMP: 12
SQ FT: 7,245
SALES (est): 3.3MM
SALES (corp-wide): 30.7MM **Privately Held**
WEB: www.pacificgmp.com
SIC: 2836 Biological products, except diagnostic
PA: Abzena Limited
Babraham Hall
Cambridge CAMBS CB22
122 390-3498

(P-8571)
PAXVAX INC
4122 Sorrento Valley Blvd, San Diego
(92121-1431)
PHONE..............................858 450-9595
EMP: 10
SALES (corp-wide): 560.8MM **Publicly Held**
SIC: 2836 Vaccines
HQ: Paxvax, Inc.
555 Twin Dolphin Dr # 360
Redwood City CA 94065
-

(P-8572)
PDL BIOPHARMA INC
1500 Seaport Blvd, Redwood City
(94063-5540)
PHONE..............................650 454-1000
Daniel Levitt, *Branch Mgr*
EMP: 40
SALES (corp-wide): 320MM **Publicly Held**
WEB: www.pdl.com
SIC: 2836 Biological products, except diagnostic
PA: Pdl Biopharma, Inc.
932 Southwood Blvd
Incline Village NV 89451
775 832-8500

(P-8573)
PHL ASSOCIATES INC
24711 County Road 100a, Davis
(95616-9410)
PHONE..............................530 753-5881
Jeff Wichmann, *President*
Mary Holmes, *Admin Sec*
Gene Huh, *Technician*
Dr Howard Gray, *Director*
EMP: 10 EST: 1960
SQ FT: 7,000
SALES (est): 1.6MM **Privately Held**
WEB: www.phlassociates.com
SIC: 2836 Vaccines; veterinary biological products

(P-8574)
PLASVACC USA INC
1535 Templeton Rd, Templeton
(93465-9694)
PHONE..............................805 434-0321
Andrew McArthur, *President*
Heather Alspach, *Business Mgr*
Amanda Burgess, *Manager*
EMP: 15
SALES (est): 1MM **Privately Held**
WEB: www.plasvaccusa.com
SIC: 2836 Biological products, except diagnostic

(P-8575)
PROLACTA BIOSCIENCE INC (PA)
757 Baldwin Park Blvd, City of Industry
(91746-1504)
PHONE..............................626 599-9260
Scott A Elster, *CEO*
Tami D Ciranna, *CFO*
Victoria Niklas, *Chief Mktg Ofcr*
Joseph Fournell, *Vice Pres*
Alan Kofsky, *Vice Pres*
▼ EMP: 103
SQ FT: 65,000
SALES (est): 41.2MM **Privately Held**
WEB: www.prolacta.com
SIC: 2836 Biological products, except diagnostic

(P-8576)
PROTEUS DIGITAL HEALTH INC
3956 Point Eden Way, Hayward
(94545-3719)
PHONE..............................650 632-4031
Andrew Thompson, *Principal*
Richard Huang, *Research*
EMP: 168
SALES (corp-wide): 185.2MM **Privately Held**
SIC: 2836 Biological products, except diagnostic
PA: Proteus Digital Health, Inc.
2600 Bridge Pkwy
Redwood City CA 94065
650 632-4031

(P-8577)
PROTEUS DIGITAL HEALTH INC (PA)
2600 Bridge Pkwy, Redwood City
(94065-6136)
PHONE..............................650 632-4031
Andrew Thompson, *CEO*
Jonathan Symonds, *Ch of Bd*
Steven Fieler, *CFO*
Uneek Mehra, *CFO*
Molly O'Neill, *Officer*
▲ EMP: 250
SALES (est): 185.2MM **Privately Held**
WEB: www.proteusbiomedical.com
SIC: 2836 Biological products, except diagnostic

(P-8578)
SAGE (PA)
1410 Monument Blvd, Concord
(94520-4368)
PHONE..............................925 288-4827
Marc Weinstein, *COO*
EMP: 27
SALES (est): 9.6MM **Privately Held**
SIC: 2836 Veterinary biological products

(P-8579)
SANGUINE BIOSCIENCES INC
5000 Van Nuys Blvd # 205, Sherman Oaks
(91403-1717)
PHONE..............................818 926-5196
Brian Neman, *President*
Jake Loewenheim, *Vice Pres*
Arnaldo Salazar, *Marketing Staff*
Nicole Greenshpun, *Research Analys*
Kendra Hughes, *Manager*
▼ EMP: 70
SALES (est): 1MM **Privately Held**
WEB: www.sanguinebio.com
SIC: 2836 Biological products, except diagnostic

(P-8580)
SANTA CRUZ BIOTECHNOLOGY INC
2145 Delaware Ave, Santa Cruz
(95060-5706)
PHONE..............................831 457-3800
Matt Mullin, *Branch Mgr*
Brenda Stephenson, *COO*
Chris App, *CTO*
Kevin Tran, *Info Tech Mgr*
Cara Maraviglia, *Technical Mgr*
EMP: 44 **Privately Held**
SIC: 2836 Biological products, except diagnostic
PA: Santa Cruz Biotechnology, Inc.
10410 Finnell St
Dallas TX 75220
-

(P-8581)
SCRIPPS LABORATORIES INC
6838 Flanders Dr, San Diego (92121-2904)
PHONE..............................858 546-5800
Simon C Khoury, *President*
William Adams, *Sales Dir*
EMP: 20 EST: 1984
SQ FT: 32,000
SALES: 3.6MM
SALES (corp-wide): 2.9B **Privately Held**
WEB: www.scrippslabs.com
SIC: 2836 2835 Biological products, except diagnostic; in vitro & in vivo diagnostic substances
PA: Scripps Health
10140 Campus Point Dr Ax415
San Diego CA 92121
800 727-4777

(P-8582)
SHIRE RGENERATIVE MEDICINE INC
10933 N Torrey Pines Rd # 200, La Jolla
(92037-1054)
PHONE..............................858 754-3700
EMP: 100
SALES (corp-wide): 15.1B **Privately Held**
SIC: 2836 Biological products, except diagnostic
HQ: Shire Regenerative Medicine, Inc.
36 Church Ln
Westport CT 06880
877 422-4463

(P-8583)
SINUSYS CORPORATION
4030 Fabian Way, Palo Alto (94303-4607)
PHONE..............................650 213-9988
R Hoxie, *Officer*
Robert Hoxie, *Officer*
Lloyd Griese, *Vice Pres*
Christopher Schneider, *Technology*
Jason Fox, *Director*
EMP: 13
SALES (est): 2.5MM **Privately Held**
SIC: 2836 Biological products, except diagnostic

(P-8584)
TWIST BIOSCIENCE CORPORATION
455 Mission Bay Blvd S, San Francisco
(94158-2158)
PHONE..............................800 719-0671
Emily M Leproust, *Ch of Bd*
William Banyai, *COO*
James M Thorburn, *CFO*
Patrick Weiss, *Vice Pres*
Mark Daniels, *Admin Sec*
EMP: 221
SQ FT: 13,000
SALES: 10.7MM **Privately Held**
SIC: 2836 Biological products, except diagnostic

(P-8585)
VECTOR LABORATORIES INC (PA)
30 Ingold Rd, Burlingame (94010-2206)
PHONE..............................650 697-3600
James S Whitehead, *President*
William Cahalan, *Vice Pres*
Larry McIntyre, *Director*
◆ EMP: 52
SQ FT: 65,000
SALES (est): 12.7MM **Privately Held**
SIC: 2836 2899 Biological products, except diagnostic; chemical preparations

(P-8586)
VICAL INCORPORATED (PA)
10390 Pacific Center Ct, San Diego
(92121-4340)
PHONE..............................858 646-1100
Vijay B Samant, *President*
R Gordon Douglas, *Ch of Bd*
Richard Beleson, *Bd of Directors*
Gary A Lyons, *Bd of Directors*
Robert Merton, *Bd of Directors*
▼ EMP: 69
SQ FT: 68,400
SALES: 13.8MM **Publicly Held**
WEB: www.vical.com
SIC: 2836 8731 Biological products, except diagnostic; biological research

2841 Soap & Detergents

(P-8587)
ADVANCED BIOCATALYTICS CORP
18010 Sky Park Cir # 130, Irvine
(92614-6456)
PHONE..............................949 442-0880
Chris Harano, *President*
Guillermo Torres, *COO*
Carl Podella, *Exec VP*
Karen Frawley, *Accountant*
Andrew Malec, *Director*
EMP: 12 EST: 1996
SALES (est): 1.9MM **Privately Held**
WEB: www.abiocat.com
SIC: 2841 Detergents, synthetic organic or inorganic alkaline

(P-8588)
ALL ONE GOD FAITH INC (PA)
Also Called: Dr. Bronners Magic Soaps
1335 Park Center Dr, Vista (92081-8357)
P.O. Box 1958 (92085-1958)
PHONE..............................844 937-2551
David Bronner, *CEO*
Michael Bronner, *President*
Trudy Bronner, *CFO*
Marc De Rosa, *Sales Associate*
▲ EMP: 200
SQ FT: 126,000

SALES (est): 78.6MM **Privately Held**
SIC: **2841** 2834 2844 Soap: granulated,
liquid, cake, flaked or chip; lip balms; lotions, shaving; face creams or lotions;
suntan lotions & oils

(P-8589)
AMERICAS FINEST PRODUCTS
1639 9th St, Santa Monica (90404-3703)
PHONE..................................310 450-6555
Frank Kagarakis, *President*
Gilberto Barragan, *Vice Pres*
EMP: 20
SQ FT: 5,600
SALES (est): 3.8MM **Privately Held**
SIC: **2841** 2899 Soap & other detergents;
chemical preparations

(P-8590)
CUSTOM BLENDERS CORPORATION
39 California Ave Ste 108, Pleasanton
(94566-6279)
PHONE..................................510 635-4352
Debra Westlund, *President*
Stanley Westlund, *Chairman*
Gary Westlund, *Vice Pres*
EMP: 11
SQ FT: 26,000
SALES: 210K **Privately Held**
WEB: www.lehmanmfg.com
SIC: **2841** 2842 2899 Soap: granulated,
liquid, cake, flaked or chip; cleaning or
polishing preparations; water treating
compounds

(P-8591)
ECOLAB INC
18383 Railroad St, City of Industry
(91748-1218)
PHONE..................................626 935-1212
Mike Travis, *Branch Mgr*
Erika Nelson, *Manager*
Enrique Ponce, *Manager*
EMP: 10
SQ FT: 50,000
SALES (corp-wide): 13.8B **Publicly Held**
WEB: www.ecolab.com
SIC: **2841** Detergents, synthetic organic or
inorganic alkaline
PA: Ecolab Inc.
    1 Ecolab Pl
    Saint Paul MN 55102
    800 232-6522

(P-8592)
ECOLAB INC
3160 Crow Canyon Pl # 200, San Ramon
(94583-1100)
PHONE..................................925 215-8008
Sharon Haley, *Branch Mgr*
EMP: 61
SALES (corp-wide): 13.8B **Publicly Held**
SIC: **2841** Soap & other detergents
PA: Ecolab Inc.
    1 Ecolab Pl
    Saint Paul MN 55102
    800 232-6522

(P-8593)
FOLEX CO
2505 Folex Way, Spring Valley
(91978-2038)
P.O. Box 789, Tualatin OR (97062-0789)
PHONE..................................619 670-5588
Barrett Lash, *President*
Patty Lash, *Treasurer*
EMP: 11
SQ FT: 21,000
SALES (est): 2.2MM **Privately Held**
WEB: www.folexeast.com
SIC: **2841** Textile soap

(P-8594)
GREEN SOAP INC (PA)
450 E Grant Line Rd 1, Tracy (95376-2811)
PHONE..................................925 240-5546
Theresa Anne Ennis, *CEO*
EMP: 11 EST: 2010
SQ FT: 20,000
SALES (est): 3MM **Privately Held**
SIC: **2841** 5999 Soap & other detergents;
toiletries, cosmetics & perfumes

(P-8595)
KINGMAN INDUSTRIES INC
26370 Beckman Ct Ste A, Murrieta
(92562-1005)
PHONE..................................951 698-1812
Barbara Mandel, *CEO*
Paul Mandel Jr, *President*
Mitch Mayer, *President*
Barb Mandel, *Treasurer*
▲ EMP: 20
SQ FT: 23,000
SALES: 4MM **Privately Held**
WEB: www.kingmanindustries.com
SIC: **2841** 2869 5169 5122 Soap & other
detergents; industrial organic chemicals;
detergents & soaps, except specialty
cleaning; cosmetics

(P-8596)
LIFEKIND PRODUCTS INC
1415 Whispering Pines Ln # 100, Grass
Valley (95945-5976)
P.O. Box 1774 (95945-1774)
PHONE..................................530 477-5395
Walter Bader, *President*
EMP: 21
SALES (est): 3.9MM **Privately Held**
WEB: www.lifekind.com
SIC: **2841** 2515 Detergents, synthetic or-
ganic or inorganic alkaline; mattresses &
bedsprings

(P-8597)
MISSION KLEENSWEEP PROD INC
Also Called: Mission Laboratories
13644 Live Oak Ln, Baldwin Park
(91706-1317)
PHONE..................................323 223-1405
Toll Free:................................888   -
Helen Rosenbaum, *President*
EMP: 53
SQ FT: 75,000
SALES (est): 16.4MM **Privately Held**
WEB: www.missionlabs.net
SIC: **2841** 2842 Soap & other detergents;
specialty cleaning, polishes & sanitation
goods

(P-8598)
MY DIRTY JOBS LLC
1207 4th St Ph 1, Santa Monica
(90401-1340)
PHONE..................................310 393-5522
Glenn Michael, *Mng Member*
EMP: 12
SALES (est): 960K **Privately Held**
SIC: **2841** Soap & other detergents

(P-8599)
NEVER SCRUB
4225 Prado Rd Ste 103, Corona
(92880-7443)
PHONE..................................951 272-9922
Pauline Sim, *President*
EMP: 15 EST: 2014
SQ FT: 7,000
SALES (est): 1.7MM **Privately Held**
SIC: **2841** Soap & other detergents

(P-8600)
NORMAN FOX & CO
14970 Don Julian Rd, City of Industry
(91746-3111)
PHONE..................................626 581-5600
Donald R Holstine, *Principal*
EMP: 10
SALES (corp-wide): 6MM **Privately Held**
WEB: www.norfox.ws
SIC: **2841** Soap & other detergents
PA: Norman, Fox & Co.
    14970 Don Julian Rd
    City Of Industry CA 91746
    626 581-5600

(P-8601)
NUGENTEC OILFIELD CHEM LLC
1155 Park Ave, Emeryville (94608-3631)
PHONE..................................707 891-3012
Donato Polignone, *President*
▼ EMP: 34 EST: 2011

SALES (est): 2.9MM
SALES (corp-wide): 7.6MM **Privately
Held**
SIC: **2841** 2899 1389 Soap & other deter-
gents; chemical preparations; oil field
services
PA: Nugeneration Technologies, Llc
    1155 Park Ave
    Emeryville CA 94608
    707 820-4080

(P-8602)
P & L DEVELOPMENT LLC
Also Called: Pl Development
11865 Alameda St, Lynwood (90262-4022)
PHONE..................................323 567-2482
Jim Smith, *General Mgr*
EMP: 125 **Privately Held**
WEB: www.aaronindustriesinc.com
SIC: **2841** 2844 2834 Soap & other deter-
gents; toilet preparations; pharmaceutical
preparations
PA: P & L Development, Llc
    200 Hicks St
    Westbury NY 11590

(P-8603)
PANROSA ENTERPRISES INC
550 Monica Cir Ste 101, Corona
(92880-5496)
PHONE..................................951 339-5888
Peter Chengjian Pan, *President*
Jingwen Zhao, *CFO*
Chenyang Sun, *Admin Sec*
Shirley Zhang, *Accountant*
Julie Guest-Pinaroc, *Asst Mgr*
▲ EMP: 60
SALES (est): 1.7MM **Privately Held**
WEB: www.panrosa.com
SIC: **2841** Soap & other detergents

(P-8604)
PROCTER & GAMBLE MFG CO
8201 Fruitridge Rd, Sacramento
(95826-4716)
PHONE..................................916 383-3800
Bob Randall, *Branch Mgr*
Art Silva, *Engineer*
Kevin McKittrick, *Manager*
Karen Stevens, *Manager*
EMP: 130
SALES (corp-wide): 66.8B **Publicly Held**
SIC: **2841** Detergents, synthetic organic or
inorganic alkaline
HQ: The Procter & Gamble Manufacturing
    Company
    1 Procter And Gamble Plz
    Cincinnati OH 45202
    513 983-1100

(P-8605)
PROCTER & GAMBLE MFG CO
18125 Rowland St, City of Industry
(91748-1235)
PHONE..................................513 627-4678
Ashley Tucker, *Branch Mgr*
EMP: 371
SALES (corp-wide): 66.8B **Publicly Held**
SIC: **2841** 2079 2099 2844 Detergents,
synthetic organic or inorganic alkaline;
shortening & other solid edible fats;
peanut butter; toilet preparations; cake
mixes, prepared: from purchased flour
HQ: The Procter & Gamble Manufacturing
    Company
    1 Procter And Gamble Plz
    Cincinnati OH 45202
    513 983-1100

(P-8606)
PURE-CHEM PRODUCTS COMPANY INC
8371 Monroe Ave, Stanton (90680-2613)
PHONE..................................714 995-4141
Bruce Bereiter, *General Mgr*
William J Roe, *Exec VP*
EMP: 13 EST: 1973
SQ FT: 2,400
SALES (est): 3.3MM **Privately Held**
WEB: www.nalco.com
SIC: **2841** Soap & other detergents

(P-8607)
ROYAL CHEMICAL COMPANY LTD
2498 American Ave, Hayward
(94545-1810)
PHONE..................................510 782-8727
Harry Kohn, *Ch of Bd*
EMP: 15
SALES (corp-wide): 8.9MM **Privately
Held**
SIC: **2841** Soap: granulated, liquid, cake,
flaked or chip
HQ: Royal Chemical Company, Ltd.
    8679 Freeway Dr
    Macedonia OH 44056
    330 467-1300

(P-8608)
SHUGAR SOAPWORKS INC
5955 Rickenbacker Rd, Commerce
(90040-3029)
PHONE..................................323 234-2874
Dan Shugar, *President*
▲ EMP: 10
SQ FT: 10,000
SALES (est): 1.3MM **Privately Held**
WEB: www.shugarsoapworks.com
SIC: **2841**

(P-8609)
SOUTHERN CALIFORNIA SOAP CO
2700 Tanager Ave, Commerce
(90040-2721)
PHONE..................................323 888-1332
Robert Bergin, *President*
Linda Lafrenais, *Controller*
EMP: 10
SQ FT: 35,000
SALES (est): 1.3MM **Privately Held**
SIC: **2841** Soap & other detergents

(P-8610)
STAR PACIFIC INC
27462 Sunrise Farm Rd, Los Altos Hills
(94022-3221)
PHONE..................................510 471-6555
John Miller, *President*
Lee Price, *Treasurer*
Ed Kubiak, *Vice Pres*
EMP: 20
SQ FT: 57,000
SALES (est): 3.6MM **Privately Held**
SIC: **2841** Soap & other detergents

(P-8611)
TUULA INC
Also Called: Destiny Boutique
26019 Jefferson Ave Ste D, Murrieta
(92562-6986)
PHONE..................................858 761-6045
Tuula Hakkanen, *President*
Martin Hotte, *Vice Pres*
EMP: 12
SQ FT: 2,800
SALES: 5MM **Privately Held**
SIC: **2841** Detergents, synthetic organic or
inorganic alkaline

(P-8612)
UNIVERSAL SURFACE TECHLGY INC
Also Called: UST
13023 S Main St, Los Angeles
(90061-1605)
PHONE..................................310 352-6969
Fax: 310 352-6970
▲ EMP: 35
SQ FT: 30,000
SALES (est): 4.8MM **Privately Held**
SIC: **2841**

(P-8613)
VALUE PRODUCTS INC
Also Called: Pride Line Products
2128 Industrial Dr, Stockton (95206-4936)
PHONE..................................209 345-3817
Douglas Hall, *President*
Erica Hall, *Corp Secy*
June Guanzon, *Technician*
Ray Coronado, *Opers Mgr*
Silverio Fernandez, *Prdtn Mgr*
EMP: 25
SQ FT: 34,000

SALES (est): 4.8MM **Privately Held**
WEB: www.valueproductsinc.com
SIC: 2841 Detergents, synthetic organic or inorganic alkaline

---

2842 Spec Cleaning, Polishing & Sanitation Preparations

(P-8614)
2ND GEN PRODUCTIONS INC
Also Called: Mark V Products
400 El Sobrante Rd, Corona (92879-5755)
PHONE..................................800 877-6282
Mark Marchese, *CEO*
Dora Marchese, *President*
Frank Marchese, *Vice Pres*
Robert Marchese, *Admin Sec*
Winnie Sanchez, *Accounting Mgr*
EMP: 19
SALES (est): 1MM **Privately Held**
SIC: 2842 5013 Waxes for wood, leather & other materials; polishing preparations & related products; automotive supplies

(P-8615)
2ND GEN PRODUCTIONS INC
Also Called: Mark V Products
400 El Sobrante Rd, Corona (92879-5755)
PHONE..................................951 280-9799
Dennis Holloway, *CEO*
Jim Holloway, *Vice Pres*
EMP: 17
SQ FT: 25,000
SALES (est): 3.8MM **Privately Held**
WEB: www.mark-v.com
SIC: 2842 5013 Waxes for wood, leather & other materials; automotive supplies

(P-8616)
3-D INTERNATIONAL LLC
Also Called: 3d Detailing Products For The
20724 Centre Pointe Pkwy # 1, Santa Clarita (91350-2980)
PHONE..................................661 250-2020
Sefik T Goren,
Juan Derada, *General Mgr*
Javier Boxler, *Store Mgr*
Genaro Enaro, *Info Tech Mgr*
Ben Weinberg, *Data Proc Staff*
◆ **EMP:** 45
SQ FT: 30,000
SALES (est): 10.8MM **Privately Held**
WEB: www.3dproducts.com
SIC: 2842 Polishing preparations & related products

(P-8617)
3D/INTERNATIONAL INC
20724 Centre Pointe Pkwy # 1, Santa Clarita (91350-2980)
PHONE..................................661 250-2020
Tony Goren, *Manager*
EMP: 80
SALES (corp-wide): 3.1B **Privately Held**
SIC: 2842 Automobile polish
HQ: 3d/International, Inc.
2200 West Loop S Ste 200
Houston TX 77027
713 871-7000

(P-8618)
ALDRAN CHEMICAL INC
1313 N Carolan Ave, Burlingame (94010-2401)
PHONE..................................650 347-8242
Robert Mitch Drangle, *President*
EMP: 26
SQ FT: 19,000
SALES (est): 3.7MM **Privately Held**
WEB: www.aldranchemical.com
SIC: 2842 Cleaning or polishing preparations

(P-8619)
ALLBRITE CAR CARE PRODUCTS
1201 N Las Brisas St, Anaheim (92806-1823)
PHONE..................................714 666-8683
Jitu Jhaveri, *CEO*
Sarla Jhaveri, *Vice Pres*
EMP: 10

SQ FT: 8,110
SALES (est): 2.3MM **Privately Held**
SIC: 2842 5087 Specialty cleaning preparations; carwash equipment & supplies

(P-8620)
ANGELUS SHOE POLISH CO INC
Also Called: Angelus Formulations
12060 Florence Ave, Santa Fe Springs (90670-4406)
P.O. Box 3066, Cerritos (90703-3066)
PHONE..................................562 941-4242
Paul T Angelus, *President*
Linda Angelus, *Vice Pres*
Myrtle Angelus, *Vice Pres*
▲ **EMP:** 12 **EST:** 1907
SQ FT: 10,000
SALES (est): 3.5MM **Privately Held**
WEB: www.pacit4u.com
SIC: 2842 4783 Shoe polish or cleaner; packing & crating

(P-8621)
AQUA MIX INC
250 Benjamin Dr, Corona (92879-6508)
PHONE..................................951 256-3040
Rick Baldini, *President*
Manuel G Magallanes, *Ch of Bd*
Jill Magallanes, *Vice Pres*
William Tran, *Vice Pres*
EMP: 64
SQ FT: 74,000
SALES (est): 8.7MM **Privately Held**
WEB: www.aquamix.com
SIC: 2842 2891 Specialty cleaning preparations; sealants
HQ: Custom Building Products, Inc.
7711 Center Ave Ste 500
Huntington Beach CA 92647
800 272-8786

(P-8622)
AUTO-CHLOR SYSTEM WASH INC
16141 Hart St, Van Nuys (91406-3904)
PHONE..................................818 376-0940
Brian Gate, *Manager*
Mark Benz, *Manager*
EMP: 15
SALES (corp-wide): 55.8MM **Privately Held**
SIC: 2842 Laundry cleaning preparations
PA: Auto-Chlor System Of Washington, Inc.
450 Ferguson Dr
Mountain View CA 94043
650 967-3085

(P-8623)
AWESOME PRODUCTS INC (PA)
6370 Altura Blvd, Buena Park (90620-1001)
PHONE..................................714 562-8873
Loksarang D Hardas, *CEO*
Sanjay Sata, *VP Opers*
Tejas Shah, *Opers Mgr*
◆ **EMP:** 125
SQ FT: 250,000
SALES (est): 60.1MM **Privately Held**
WEB: www.awesomeproducts.com
SIC: 2842 Cleaning or polishing preparations

(P-8624)
BAF INDUSTRIES (PA)
Also Called: Pro Wax
1451 Edinger Ave Ste F, Tustin (92780-6250)
PHONE..................................714 258-8055
Michael P Bell, *CEO*
Otis F Bell, *President*
Michael Bell, *Director*
▲ **EMP:** 42 **EST:** 1935
SQ FT: 44,000
SALES (est): 9.1MM **Privately Held**
WEB: www.prowax.com
SIC: 2842 Cleaning or polishing preparations

(P-8625)
BEST SANITIZERS INC
310 Prvdnce Mine Rd # 120, Nevada City (95959-2981)
P.O. Box 1360, Penn Valley (95946-1360)
PHONE..................................530 265-1800
Hillard T Witt, *President*

Ed Hay, *Vice Pres*
Ryan Witt, *Vice Pres*
◆ **EMP:** 52
SQ FT: 10,000
SALES (est): 20MM **Privately Held**
WEB: www.bestsanitizers.com
SIC: 2842 Sanitation preparations

(P-8626)
BLUE CROSS LABORATORIES INC (PA)
20950 Centre Pointe Pkwy, Santa Clarita (91350-2975)
PHONE..................................661 255-0955
Darrell Mahler, *President*
Glenn Mahler, *Corp Secy*
◆ **EMP:** 160
SQ FT: 100,000
SALES (est): 38.7MM **Privately Held**
WEB: www.bc-labs.com
SIC: 2842 2844 Cleaning or polishing preparations; toilet preparations

(P-8627)
BRACTON SOSAFE INC
Also Called: Bracton Beer Line Cleaners
1061 N Shepard St Ste E, Anaheim (92806-2818)
PHONE..................................714 632-8499
Michael Hunter, *President*
EMP: 10
SALES (est): 907.3K **Privately Held**
SIC: 2842 Specialty cleaning, polishes & sanitation goods

(P-8628)
BUSHNELL INDUSTRIES INC
7449 Avenue 304, Visalia (93291-9466)
P.O. Box 1820, (93279-1820)
PHONE..................................559 651-9039
Robert Bushnell, *President*
EMP: 12
SQ FT: 11,000
SALES (est): 2.8MM **Privately Held**
WEB: www.bushii.com
SIC: 2842 7699 Specialty cleaning, polishes & sanitation goods; agricultural equipment repair services

(P-8629)
C & S PRODUCTS CA INC (PA)
Also Called: Coco Dry
1345 S Parkside Pl, Ontario (91761-4556)
PHONE..................................909 218-8971
James Stevens, *President*
Kevin Calvo, *Principal*
Lou Ferrero, *Principal*
Bill Habeger, *Principal*
Skip Hodgetts, *Principal*
EMP: 12
SQ FT: 14,000
SALES (est): 484K **Privately Held**
SIC: 2842 Sweeping compounds, oil or water absorbent, clay or sawdust

(P-8630)
CHEMCOR CHEMICAL CORPORATION
13770 Benson Ave, Chino (91710-7000)
PHONE..................................909 590-7234
Dave Tarquin, *CEO*
Frank Tarquin, *Vice Pres*
Brent Tarquin, *Purch Mgr*
▲ **EMP:** 10
SQ FT: 25,000
SALES (est): 3.1MM **Privately Held**
SIC: 2842 Specialty cleaning, polishes & sanitation goods

(P-8631)
CLEANLOGIC LLC
4051 S Broadway, Los Angeles (90037-1030)
PHONE..................................310 261-3001
Robert Smerling, *Mng Member*
EMP: 50
SALES (est): 1.8MM **Privately Held**
SIC: 2842 3582 3589 7699 Laundry cleaning preparations; drycleaning equipment & machinery, commercial; servicing machines, except dry cleaning; laundry: coin-oper.; machinery cleaning; biotechnical research, commercial

(P-8632)
CLOROX COMPANY (PA)
1221 Broadway Ste 1300, Oakland (94612-1871)
P.O. Box 24305 (94623-1305)
PHONE..................................510 271-7000
Benno Dorer, *Ch of Bd*
Dawn Willoughby, *COO*
Kevin B Jacobsen, *CFO*
Eric Reynolds, *Chief Mktg Ofcr*
Matthew Laszlo, *Officer*
▼ **EMP:** 277 **EST:** 1913
SALES: 6.1B **Publicly Held**
WEB: www.clorox.com
SIC: 2842 2673 2035 2844 Laundry cleaning preparations; polishing preparations & related products; food storage & frozen food bags, plastic; seasonings & sauces, except tomato & dry; dressings, salad: raw & cooked (except dry mixes); seasonings, meat sauces (except tomato & dry); cosmetic preparations; insecticides & pesticides

(P-8633)
CLOROX COMPANY
11940 S Harlan Rd, Lathrop (95330-8767)
PHONE..................................209 234-1094
EMP: 19
SALES (corp-wide): 6.1B **Publicly Held**
SIC: 2842 Specialty cleaning, polishes & sanitation goods
PA: The Clorox Company
1221 Broadway Ste 1300
Oakland CA 94612
510 271-7000

(P-8634)
CLOROX COMPANY
4900 Johnson Dr, Pleasanton (94588-3308)
PHONE..................................925 368-6000
Wayne L Delker, *President*
EMP: 19
SALES (corp-wide): 6.1B **Publicly Held**
SIC: 2842 Specialty cleaning, polishes & sanitation goods
PA: The Clorox Company
1221 Broadway Ste 1300
Oakland CA 94612
510 271-7000

(P-8635)
CLOROX PRODUCTS MFG CO
2600 Huntington Dr, Fairfield (94533-9736)
PHONE..................................707 437-1051
Scott Johnston, *Manager*
EMP: 55
SALES (corp-wide): 6.1B **Publicly Held**
SIC: 2842 Bleaches, household: dry or liquid
HQ: Clorox Products Manufacturing Company
1221 Broadway
Oakland CA 94612

(P-8636)
CLOROX PRODUCTS MFG CO
2300 W San Bernardino Ave, Redlands (92374-5000)
PHONE..................................909 307-2756
EMP: 85
SALES (corp-wide): 6.1B **Publicly Held**
SIC: 2842 Specialty cleaning, polishes & sanitation goods
HQ: Clorox Products Manufacturing Company
1221 Broadway
Oakland CA 94612

(P-8637)
CLOROX PRODUCTS MFG CO (HQ)
1221 Broadway, Oakland (94612-1837)
PHONE..................................510 271-7000
T E Bailey, *CEO*
Karen M Rose, *Treasurer*
Suzanne Thompson, *Vice Pres*
◆ **EMP:** 180
SALES (est): 338MM
SALES (corp-wide): 6.1B **Publicly Held**
SIC: 2842 Specialty cleaning, polishes & sanitation goods

PA: The Clorox Company
1221 Broadway Ste 1300
Oakland CA 94612
510 271-7000

(P-8638)
COCO PRODUCTS LLC
1345 S Parkside Pl, Ontario (91761-4556)
PHONE..........................909 218-8971
Steven Parker, *Mng Member*
EMP: 12
SQ FT: 14,000
SALES (est): 1.1MM **Privately Held**
SIC: 2842 Sweeping compounds, oil or
water absorbent, clay or sawdust

(P-8639)
EARTH LAB INC
5016 Maplewood Ave Unit B, Los Angeles
(90004-2504)
PHONE..........................310 310-9009
Jawon Suh, *CEO*
EMP: 10
SALES (est): 599.5K **Privately Held**
SIC: 2842 5169 Sanitation preparations,
disinfectants & deodorants; specialty
cleaning & sanitation preparations

(P-8640)
**ENVIRNMNTAL PDTS
APPLCTONS INC**
Also Called: Vermillion's Environmental
8-900 Ave 47 Ste 106, La Quinta (92253)
PHONE..........................760 779-1814
John Vermillion, *CEO*
Justin Vermillion, *Vice Pres*
EMP: 40
SALES (est): 3.3MM **Privately Held**
WEB: www.envirotac.com
SIC: 2842 Specialty cleaning, polishes &
sanitation goods

(P-8641)
FACTORY DIRECT DIST CORP
1001 B Ave Ste 100, San Diego
(92118-3422)
PHONE..........................619 435-3437
Edwin Michael Furey, *CEO*
Ed Furey, *Principal*
Michael Oconnor, *Principal*
John C Otten, *Principal*
EMP: 10
SALES (est): 2MM **Privately Held**
WEB: www.factorydirectcorp.com
SIC: 2842 2851 Specialty cleaning, pol-
ishes & sanitation goods; paints & allied
products

(P-8642)
GEA FARM TECHNOLOGIES INC
Also Called: W S West
2717 S 4th St, Fresno (93725-1938)
PHONE..........................559 497-5074
Warren Dorathy, *Manager*
EMP: 40
SALES (corp-wide): 5.4B **Privately Held**
WEB: www.westfaliasurge.com
SIC: 2842 Specialty cleaning, polishes &
sanitation goods
HQ: Gea Farm Technologies, Inc.
1880 Country Farm Dr
Naperville IL 60563
630 548-8200

(P-8643)
**GOODWIN AMMONIA COMPANY
(PA)**
12102 Industry St, Garden Grove
(92841-2814)
PHONE..........................714 894-0531
Tom Goodwin, *President*
Janice Fleet, *Corp Secy*
Gary Goodwin, *Vice Pres*
◆ **EMP:** 15 EST: 1922
SQ FT: 58,000
SALES (est): 31.9MM **Privately Held**
SIC: 2842 Automobile polish

(P-8644)
GRANITE GOLD INC
9170 Chesapeake Dr, San Diego
(92123-1003)
PHONE..........................858 499-8933
Leonard Sciarrino, *President*
Scott Martin, *COO*
Leonard Pellegrino, *Exec VP*

Mike Rose, *Vice Pres*
Dorothy Christensen, *Manager*
◆ **EMP:** 10
SQ FT: 5,000
SALES (est): 2.6MM **Privately Held**
SIC: 2842 Cleaning or polishing prepara-
tions

(P-8645)
GRANITIZE PRODUCTS INC
11022 Vulcan St, South Gate (90280-7621)
P.O. Box 2306 (90280-9306)
PHONE..........................562 923-5438
Tony Raymondo, *CEO*
Betty Raymondo, *Corp Secy*
Randy Bair, *General Mgr*
Joy Eastwood, *Office Mgr*
Rick Vargas, *Purch Mgr*
◆ **EMP:** 75
SQ FT: 30,000
SALES (est): 23.4MM **Privately Held**
WEB: www.granitize.com
SIC: 2842 Automobile polish; cleaning or
polishing preparations

(P-8646)
**HOCKING INTERNATIONAL
LABS INC (PA)**
980 Rancheros Dr, San Marcos
(92069-3029)
P.O. Box 462785, Escondido (92046-2785)
PHONE..........................760 432-5277
Bert E Hocking Jr, *President*
Sherry Hocking, *Treasurer*
Craig Robitaille, *Vice Pres*
Robert Munion, *Research*
▲ **EMP:** 21
SQ FT: 15,000
SALES (est): 11.6MM **Privately Held**
WEB: www.hockingintl.com
SIC: 2842 5087 Specialty cleaning prepa-
rations; service establishment equipment

(P-8647)
HOME & BODY COMPANY (PA)
Also Called: Direct Chemicals
18352 Enterprise Ln, Huntington Beach
(92648-1206)
PHONE..........................714 842-8000
Hazem H Haddad, *President*
Nadene Haddad, *Admin Sec*
▲ **EMP:** 34
SALES (est): 3.5MM **Privately Held**
WEB: www.directchemicals.com
SIC: 2842 2841 2899 2844 Bleaches,
household: dry or liquid; textile soap; es-
sential oils; face creams or lotions

(P-8648)
JASON MARKK INC
329 E 2nd St, Los Angeles (90012-4202)
PHONE..........................213 687-7060
Jason M Angsuvarn, *CEO*
▲ **EMP:** 34 EST: 2007
SALES (est): 805.8K **Privately Held**
SIC: 2842 Shoe polish or cleaner

(P-8649)
KIK-SOCAL INC
Also Called: K I K
9028 Dice Rd, Santa Fe Springs
(90670-2520)
PHONE..........................562 946-6427
Jeffrey M Nodland, *CEO*
Stratis Katsiris, *President*
William Smith, *President*
Ben W Kaak, *CFO*
Mark Luetger, *Maintence Staff*
EMP: 3000
SQ FT: 3,000,000 **Privately Held**
SIC: 2842 Bleaches, household: dry or liq-
uid; fabric softeners; ammonia, house-
hold; cleaning or polishing preparations
HQ: Kik International Houston Inc
2921 Corder St
Houston TX 77054
713 747-8710

(P-8650)
LAB-CLEAN LLC
3627 Briggeman Dr, Los Alamitos
(90720-2475)
PHONE..........................714 689-0063
Mark Cunningham, *Prgrmr*
Cathy Poe, *Administration*
Matthew Bays,

EMP: 25
SQ FT: 40,000
SALES (est): 4.9MM **Privately Held**
SIC: 2842 Cleaning or polishing prepara-
tions

(P-8651)
LMC ENTERPRISES (PA)
Also Called: Chemco Products Company
6401 Alondra Blvd, Paramount
(90723-3758)
PHONE..........................562 602-2116
Elaine S Cooper, *CEO*
Janis Utz, *President*
John D Grimes, *COO*
Shawn Carroll, *CFO*
David McCullough, *Exec VP*
EMP: 70 EST: 1962
SQ FT: 15,000
SALES (est): 25.3MM **Privately Held**
WEB: www.chemcoprod.com
SIC: 2842 Cleaning or polishing prepara-
tions; floor waxes

(P-8652)
LMC ENTERPRISES
Also Called: Flo-Kem
19402 S Susana Rd, Compton
(90221-5712)
PHONE..........................310 632-7124
Elaine Cooper, *CEO*
EMP: 50
SQ FT: 20,000
SALES (corp-wide): 25.3MM **Privately
Held**
SIC: 2842 Cleaning or polishing prepara-
tions; floor waxes
PA: Lmc Enterprises
6401 Alondra Blvd
Paramount CA 90723
562 602-2116

(P-8653)
M P M BUILDING SERVICES INC
Also Called: Mpm & Associates
7011 Hayvenhurst Ave F, Van Nuys
(91406-3822)
PHONE..........................818 708-9676
Paul Davis, *President*
Mike Danesh, *Vice Pres*
Pedro Lombera, *Supervisor*
EMP: 60
SQ FT: 35,000
SALES (est): 4.3MM **Privately Held**
WEB: www.mpmco.com
SIC: 2842 Specialty cleaning, polishes &
sanitation goods

(P-8654)
MAX-Q SYSTEMS INC
3449 Summerset Cir, Costa Mesa
(92626-1638)
PHONE..........................714 259-0181
Fred Mosher, *President*
Margaret Fix, *Corp Secy*
EMP: 12
SQ FT: 3,000
SALES (est): 2.1MM **Privately Held**
WEB: www.maxqsystems.com
SIC: 2842 8711 3679 Specialty cleaning
preparations; designing: ship, boat, ma-
chine & product; electronic circuits

(P-8655)
MEGUIARS INC (HQ)
Also Called: Brilliant Solutions
17991 Mitchell S, Irvine (92614-6015)
PHONE..........................949 752-8000
Barry J Meguiar, *President*
Michael W Meguiar, *Ch of Bd*
Catherine E Bayless, *Admin Sec*
Jamie Cruz, *Admin Asst*
◆ **EMP:** 50
SALES (est): 80.3MM
SALES (corp-wide): 31.6B **Publicly Held**
WEB: www.meguiars.com
SIC: 2842 Cleaning or polishing prepara-
tions; automobile polish; furniture polish
or wax
PA: 3m Company
3m Center
Saint Paul MN 55144
651 733-1110

(P-8656)
MORGAN GALLACHER INC
Also Called: Custom Chemical Formulators
8707 Millergrove Dr, Santa Fe Springs
(90670-2001)
PHONE..........................562 695-1232
Harriet Von Luft, *Ch of Bd*
David M Smith, *President*
Sufian Phoa, *Vice Pres*
▼ **EMP:** 46
SQ FT: 100,000
SALES (est): 10.7MM **Privately Held**
WEB: www.customchem.com
SIC: 2842 5169 Cleaning or polishing
preparations; industrial chemicals

(P-8657)
**MOTSENBOCKER ADVANCED
DEVELOPM (PA)**
Also Called: Lift Off
4901 Morena Blvd Ste 806, San Diego
(92117-7327)
P.O. Box 90947 (92169-2947)
PHONE..........................858 581-0222
Gregg Motsenbocker, *President*
Skip Motsenbocker, *COO*
Lori Motsenbocker, *Treasurer*
Patty Brooks, *Marketing Mgr*
EMP: 15
SQ FT: 8,600
SALES (est): 3.3MM **Privately Held**
WEB: www.liftoffinc.com
SIC: 2842 6794 Wax removers; patent
owners & lessors

(P-8658)
NEOGEN CORPORATION
1355 Paulson Rd, Turlock (95380-5541)
PHONE..........................800 995-1607
EMP: 28
SALES (corp-wide): 402.2MM **Publicly
Held**
SIC: 2842 Sanitation preparations; clean-
ing or polishing preparations
PA: Neogen Corporation
620 Lesher Pl
Lansing MI 48912
517 372-9200

(P-8659)
**OIL-DRI CORPORATION
AMERICA**
950 Petroleum Club Rd, Taft (93268-9748)
P.O. Box 1277 (93268-1277)
PHONE..........................661 765-7194
Rob Stillman, *Supervisor*
EMP: 10
SALES (corp-wide): 262.3MM **Publicly
Held**
SIC: 2842 Sweeping compounds, oil or
water absorbent, clay or sawdust
PA: Oil-Dri Corporation Of America
410 N Michigan Ave Fl 4
Chicago IL 60611
312 321-1515

(P-8660)
**OMEGA INDUSTRIAL SUPPLY
INC**
101 Grobric Ct, Fairfield (94534-1673)
PHONE..........................707 864-8164
Adam Brady, *CEO*
Lori Rehn, *President*
Dina Schindler, *Manager*
Niki Ryan, *Accounts Mgr*
EMP: 35
SQ FT: 10,000
SALES (est): 8.4MM **Privately Held**
WEB: www.onlyomega.com
SIC: 2842 5169 Sanitation preparations;
chemicals & allied products

(P-8661)
PACE INTERNATIONAL LLC
1104 N Nevada St, Visalia (93291)
PHONE..........................559 651-4877
Gorge Lobisser,
Michelle Smith, *Technical Mgr*
EMP: 29

▲ = Import ▼ =Export
◆ =Import/Export

SALES (corp-wide): 20.5B **Privately Held**
WEB: www.paceint.com
SIC: 2842 2879 2873 2899 Specialty
cleaning preparations; agricultural chemicals; plant foods, mixed: from plants making nitrog. fertilizers; water treating
compounds; emulsifiers, except food &
pharmaceutical; cutting oils, blending:
made from purchased materials
HQ: Pace International, Llc
5661 Branch Rd
Wapato WA 98951
800 936-6750

(P-8662)
PARADISE ROAD LLC
5872 Engineer Dr, Huntington Beach
(92649-1166)
PHONE.....................................714 894-1779
Lou Basenese, *President*
Tim Miller, *CEO*
▲ EMP: 25
SALES (est): 2.8MM **Privately Held**
SIC: 2842 Specialty cleaning, polishes &
sanitation goods

(P-8663)
PARK-RAND ENTERPRISES INC
Also Called: Meri Gol Products Limited
39630 Fairway Dr Apt 218, Palmdale
(93551-7570)
PHONE.....................................818 362-2565
Joseph N Gray, *President*
Robert C Swick, *Vice Pres*
EMP: 10
SALES (est): 820K **Privately Held**
SIC: 2842 Ammonia, household

(P-8664)
PATRIOT POLISHING COMPANY
47260 Wrangler Rd, Aguanga
(92536-9518)
PHONE.....................................310 903-7409
Raymond Esfandi, *CFO*
EMP: 15
SALES (est): 785.8K **Privately Held**
SIC: 2842 Metal polish

(P-8665)
**PEERLESS MATERIALS
COMPANY (PA)**
4442 E 26th St, Vernon (90058-4318)
P.O. Box 33228, Los Angeles (90033-0228)
PHONE.....................................323 266-0313
Louis J Buty, *President*
Estela Jauregui, *COO*
Peter H Pritchard, *Vice Pres*
▲ EMP: 36
SQ FT: 35,000
SALES (est): 4.7MM **Privately Held**
SIC: 2842 Sweeping compounds, oil or
water absorbent, clay or sawdust

(P-8666)
PLANET INC
Also Called: Planet Products
15791 Coleman Valley Rd, Occidental
(95465-9304)
P.O. Box 156 (95465-0156)
PHONE.....................................250 478-8171
Allen Stedman, *President*
Larry Brucia, *President*
Shandra Robson, *Prdtn Mgr*
EMP: 10
SQ FT: 1,500
SALES (est): 122K **Privately Held**
WEB: www.planetinc.com
SIC: 2842 Specialty cleaning, polishes &
sanitation goods

(P-8667)
**POWERPLUS CLEANING
SOLUTIONS**
1525 N Endeavor Ln Ste O, Anaheim
(92801-1156)
PHONE.....................................714 635-9264
Kevin Wang, *Owner*
EMP: 20
SALES (est): 2.8MM **Privately Held**
SIC: 2842 Specialty cleaning preparations

(P-8668)
**PRODUCTION CHEMICAL MFG
INC (PA)**
Also Called: Production Car Care Products
1000 E Channel St, Stockton (95205-4942)
P.O. Box 687, Alameda (94501-8687)
PHONE.....................................209 943-7337
Lewyn Boler, *President*
Blanche Boler, *Admin Sec*
EMP: 12 EST: 1979
SQ FT: 7,500
SALES (est): 6.6MM **Privately Held**
SIC: 2842 Cleaning or polishing prepara-
tions

(P-8669)
PURE BIOSCIENCE INC (PA)
1725 Gillespie Way, El Cajon (92020-1015)
PHONE.....................................619 596-8600
Henry R Lambert, *CEO*
Dave J Pfanzelter, *Ch of Bd*
Tom Myers, *COO*
Peter Wulff, *CFO*
Cliff Wechsler, *Exec VP*
EMP: 13
SQ FT: 7,400
SALES (est): 1.7MM **Publicly Held**
WEB: www.purebio.com
SIC: 2842 2879 Disinfectants, household
or industrial plant; agricultural chemicals

(P-8670)
PURICLE INC
11799 Jersey Blvd, Rancho Cucamonga
(91730-4936)
PHONE.....................................909 466-7125
Elisa Sim, *President*
EMP: 50
SQ FT: 37,000
SALES (est): 9.8MM **Privately Held**
WEB: www.puricle.com
SIC: 2842 Disinfectants, household or in-
dustrial plant

(P-8671)
QUANTUM GLOBAL TECH LLC
Also Called: Quantum Clean
1710 Ringwood Ave, San Jose
(95131-1711)
PHONE.....................................408 487-1770
Scott Nicholas, *CEO*
Susie Tognetti, *Administration*
EMP: 23
SALES (corp-wide): 924.3MM **Publicly
Held**
SIC: 2842 Specialty cleaning, polishes &
sanitation goods
HQ: Quantum Global Technologies, Llc
1900 Am Dr Ste 200
Quakertown PA 18951
215 892-9300

(P-8672)
QUANTUM GLOBAL TECH LLC
Also Called: Quantumclean
44010 Fremont Blvd, Fremont
(94538-6042)
PHONE.....................................510 687-8000
EMP: 49
SALES (corp-wide): 924.3MM **Publicly
Held**
SIC: 2842 Specialty cleaning, polishes &
sanitation goods
HQ: Quantum Global Technologies, Llc
1900 Am Dr Ste 200
Quakertown PA 18951
215 892-9300

(P-8673)
REFLECTECH INC
Also Called: Reflection Technology
5861 88th St Ste 100, Sacramento
(95828-1132)
PHONE.....................................916 388-7821
Dave Nugent, *President*
Ed Russell, *CFO*
Pete Hoffman, *Vice Pres*
EMP: 12
SQ FT: 12,000
SALES (est): 2.2MM **Privately Held**
SIC: 2842 Specialty cleaning preparations

(P-8674)
RENU CHEM INC
Also Called: Finish Renu Car Care
572 Malloy Ct, Corona (92880-2045)
PHONE.....................................951 736-8072
Jim Moreno, *CEO*
Nanette Moreno, *President*
EMP: 10 EST: 2008
SQ FT: 15,000
SALES: 1.4MM **Privately Held**
SIC: 2842 Automobile polish

(P-8675)
SANITEK PRODUCTS INC
3959 Goodwin Ave, Los Angeles
(90039-1187)
PHONE.....................................323 245-6781
Robert L Moseley, *President*
David Moseley, *Treasurer*
▲ EMP: 13 EST: 1941
SQ FT: 25,000
SALES (est): 3.2MM **Privately Held**
WEB: www.sanitek.com
SIC: 2842 2899 2992 2891 Sanitation
preparations, disinfectants & deodorants;
fire retardant chemicals; lubricating oils &
greases; adhesives & sealants; agricul-
tural chemicals; soap & other detergents

(P-8676)
SECONDWIND PRODUCTS INC
4301 Second Wind Way, Paso Robles
(93446-6304)
P.O. Box 2300 (93447-2300)
PHONE.....................................805 239-2555
Gus Blythe, *President*
Ken Fontes, *CFO*
EMP: 27
SQ FT: 24,250
SALES (est): 2.6MM **Privately Held**
WEB: www.2ndwind.com
SIC: 2842 3089 3131 3021 Stain re-
movers; shoe polish or cleaner; soling
strips, boot or shoe: plastic; footwear cut
stock; rubber & plastics footwear;
women's & misses' outerwear

(P-8677)
SOAPTRONIC LLC
20562 Crescent Bay Dr, Lake Forest
(92630-8845)
PHONE.....................................949 465-8955
Horst Binderbauer, *Mng Member*
Michael Schmitt, *Sales Dir*
◆ EMP: 25
SALES (est): 6.8MM **Privately Held**
WEB: www.soaptronic.com
SIC: 2842 2841 Sanitation preparations,
disinfectants & deodorants; soap & other
detergents

(P-8678)
SUNSHINE MAKERS INC (PA)
Also Called: Simple Green
15922 Pacific Coast Hwy, Huntington
Beach (92649-1894)
PHONE.....................................562 795-6000
Bruce P Fabrizio, *President*
Rose Concilia, *Vice Pres*
Jeffrey Hyder, *Vice Pres*
Patrick Sheehan, *Vice Pres*
Chris Wheeler, *Sales Staff*
▼ EMP: 51
SQ FT: 25,000
SALES (est): 9.2MM **Privately Held**
WEB: www.simplegreen.com
SIC: 2842 Cleaning or polishing prepara-
tions; degreasing solvent; specialty clean-
ing preparations

(P-8679)
SURF CITY GARAGE
5872 Engineer Dr, Huntington Beach
(92649-1166)
PHONE.....................................714 894-1707
Timothy D Miller, *President*
Matt Rigdon, *President*
▲ EMP: 33
SQ FT: 22,000
SALES (est): 6.9MM **Privately Held**
SIC: 2842 Cleaning or polishing prepara-
tions

(P-8680)
SURTEC INC
Also Called: Surtec System , The
1880 N Macarthur Dr, Tracy (95376-2841)
PHONE.....................................209 820-3700
William A Fields, *President*
Don C Fromm, *Treasurer*
Don Fromm, *Vice Pres*
Mark Granados, *Research*
Rick Cash, *Opers Staff*
◆ EMP: 50
SQ FT: 87,000
SALES (est): 17.2MM **Privately Held**
WEB: www.surtecsystem.com
SIC: 2842 5087 Specialty cleaning prepa-
rations; floor machinery, maintenance

(P-8681)
ULTRA CHEM LABS CORP
4581 Brickell Privado St, Ontario
(91761-7828)
PHONE.....................................909 605-1640
Christopher Shieh, *President*
Cesar Castro, *Admin Sec*
▲ EMP: 15
SQ FT: 19,000
SALES (est): 2.5MM **Privately Held**
SIC: 2842 Floor waxes

(P-8682)
**US CONTINENTAL MARKETING
INC (PA)**
310 Reed Cir, Corona (92879-1349)
PHONE.....................................951 808-8888
David Lee Williams, *President*
◆ EMP: 90
SQ FT: 40,000
SALES (est): 35.5MM **Privately Held**
WEB: www.uscontinental.com
SIC: 2842 Leather dressings & finishes;
shoe polish or cleaner

(P-8683)
WITT HILLARD
Also Called: Saraya Healthcare
310 Providence Mine Rd, Nevada City
(95959-2982)
PHONE.....................................530 510-0756
Hillard Witt, *Owner*
Cindi Linville, *Manager*
EMP: 35 EST: 2015
SQ FT: 55,000
SALES (est): 1.3MM **Privately Held**
SIC: 2842 Sanitation preparations, disin-
fectants & deodorants

2843 Surface Active &
Finishing Agents,
Sulfonated Oils

(P-8684)
ANTERRA GROUP INC
25255 Cabot Rd Ste 215, Laguna Hills
(92653-5508)
PHONE.....................................949 215-0658
Anthony J Terranova, *President*
Tracee H Terranova, *Vice Pres*
Natalie Rosin, *Marketing Staff*
Carlos Zatarain, *Consultant*
EMP: 10
SALES (est): 1.9MM **Privately Held**
SIC: 2843 Processing assistants

(P-8685)
CHEMEOR INC
727 Arrow Grand Cir, Covina (91722-2148)
PHONE.....................................626 966-3808
Yongchun Tang, *Ch of Bd*
Pat Mills, *CEO*
Patrick Shuler, *CFO*
Carl Aften, *Vice Pres*
Zayne Lu, *Vice Pres*
▲ EMP: 40
SQ FT: 16,000
SALES (est): 21.7MM **Privately Held**
SIC: 2843 1389 2911 Surface active
agents; chemically treating wells; aro-
matic chemical products

(P-8686)
HENKEL CORPORATION
20021 S Susana Rd, Compton
(90221-5721)
PHONE............................310 764-4600
Stacy Edwards, *Admin Asst*
Sarah Liao, *Info Tech Mgr*
Javier Gutierrez, *Technician*
Selene Hernandez, *Technician*
Jessica Hernandez, *Engineer*
EMP: 175
SALES (corp-wide): 23.6B **Privately Held**
SIC: 2843 Surface active agents
HQ: Henkel Us Operations Corporation
1 Henkel Way
Rocky Hill CT 06067
860 571-5100

(P-8687)
JUSTICE BROS DIST CO INC
Also Called: Justice Bros-J B Car Care Pdts
2734 Huntington Dr, Duarte (91010-2301)
PHONE............................626 359-9174
Edward R Justice Sr, *Ch of Bd*
Edward R Justice Jr, *President*
▲ EMP: 25
SQ FT: 33,000
SALES (est): 5.3MM **Privately Held**
WEB: www.justicebrothers.com
SIC: 2843 2899 Surface active agents;
chemical preparations

2844 Perfumes, Cosmetics & Toilet Preparations

(P-8688)
220 LABORATORIES INC
2321 3rd St, Riverside (92507-3306)
PHONE............................951 683-2912
Ian Sishman, *Manager*
EMP: 150 **Privately Held**
WEB: www.220labs.com
SIC: 2844 5122 5087 Cosmetic prepara-
tions; cosmetics, perfumes & hair prod-
ucts; beauty parlor equipment & supplies
PA: 220 Laboratories Inc.
2375 3rd St
Riverside CA 92507
-

(P-8689)
220 LABORATORIES INC (PA)
2375 3rd St, Riverside (92507-3306)
PHONE............................951 683-2912
Yoram Fishman, *CEO*
Ian Fishman, *President*
Mike Herzog, *Vice Pres*
George Allison, *Info Tech Mgr*
Heidi Guzman, *Human Res Mgr*
▲ EMP: 104
SQ FT: 130,000
SALES (est): 50.7MM **Privately Held**
WEB: www.220labs.com
SIC: 2844 Cosmetic preparations

(P-8690)
ADVANCED INST OF SKIN CARE
Also Called: Mineral Essence
7225 Fulton Ave, North Hollywood
(91605-4111)
PHONE............................818 765-2606
David Kohanbash, *President*
EMP: 10
SQ FT: 8,000
SALES (est): 1.1MM **Privately Held**
SIC: 2844 Cosmetic preparations

(P-8691)
ADVANCED SKIN & HAIR INC
Also Called: Revivogen
12121 Wilshire Blvd # 1012, Los Angeles
(90025-1176)
PHONE............................310 442-9700
Alex Khadavi, *CEO*
Alan Shargani, *President*
Sheri Carrie, *Office Mgr*
Jennifer Kay, *Accounts Mgr*
▲ EMP: 10
SALES (est): 1.7MM **Privately Held**
WEB: www.clearogen.com
SIC: 2844 Cosmetic preparations; hair
preparations, including shampoos

(P-8692)
ALLURE LABS INC
30901 Wiegman Ct, Hayward
(94544-7809)
PHONE............................510 489-8896
Sam Dhatt, *CEO*
Renu Dhatt, *Vice Pres*
Carlos Torres, *Manager*
▲ EMP: 30
SQ FT: 50,000
SALES (est): 9MM **Privately Held**
WEB: www.allurecosmetic.com
SIC: 2844 Cosmetic preparations

(P-8693)
AMERICAN INTERNATIONAL INDS
Also Called: Aii Beauty
2220 Gaspar Ave, Commerce
(90040-1516)
PHONE............................323 728-2999
Zvi Ryzman, *CEO*
◆ EMP: 1100
SQ FT: 224,000
SALES (est): 228.8MM **Privately Held**
SIC: 2844 Toilet preparations

(P-8694)
ANDALOU NATURALS
7250 Redwood Blvd Ste 208, Novato
(94945-3271)
PHONE............................415 446-9470
Stacey Kelly Egide, *CEO*
Mark A Egide, *President*
Erin Sellers, *Regl Sales Mgr*
Jonathan Cranford, *Sales Staff*
Ryan Eck, *Art Dir*
▲ EMP: 14
SQ FT: 2,500
SALES (est): 3.7MM **Privately Held**
SIC: 2844 Shampoos, rinses, conditioners:
hair; face creams or lotions

(P-8695)
ARBONNE INTERNATIONAL LLC (HQ)
9400 Jeronimo Rd, Irvine (92618-1907)
PHONE............................949 770-2610
Jean-David Schwartz, *CEO*
Alison Allen, *President*
Melody Allred, *President*
Carla Alvarado, *President*
Rebecca Banks, *President*
▲ EMP: 25
SQ FT: 37,000
SALES (est): 449.5MM **Privately Held**
WEB: www.arbonne.com
SIC: 2844 5961 5499 2834 Cosmetic
preparations; cosmetics & perfumes, mail
order; vitamin food stores; vitamin prepa-
rations
PA: Groupe Rocher Operations
Lecc Laboratoire Europeen De Cre-
ation
La Gacilly
299 297-474

(P-8696)
ARCHIPELAGO INC
Also Called: Archipelago Botanicals
2440 E 38th St, Vernon (90058-1708)
PHONE............................213 743-9200
David Klass, *CEO*
Gregory Corzine, *Admin Sec*
Robert Decrescenzo, *Accounting Mgr*
Kaleena Massaker, *Natl Sales Mgr*
Phuong Ha, *Assistant*
▲ EMP: 110
SALES (est): 29.6MM **Privately Held**
WEB: www.archipelago-usa.com
SIC: 2844 3999 Toilet preparations; can-
dles

(P-8697)
ARMINAK SOLUTIONS LLC
Also Called: Chrislie
1361 Mountain View Cir, Azusa
(91702-1649)
PHONE............................626 385-5858
Helga Arminak, *President*
Michele Cherpin, *Sales Staff*
EMP: 22
SQ FT: 55,000
SALES: 10MM **Privately Held**
SIC: 2844 Toilet preparations

(P-8698)
AWARE PRODUCTS INC
9250 Mason Ave, Chatsworth
(91311-6005)
PHONE............................818 206-6700
Joe Pender, *President*
EMP: 23
SALES (est): 7.9MM **Privately Held**
SIC: 2844 Toilet preparations

(P-8699)
AWARE PRODUCTS LLC
9250 Mason Ave, Chatsworth
(91311-6005)
PHONE............................818 206-6700
Chuck Greenberg, *CEO*
Lawrence Balingit, *CFO*
Penny L Hutchinson, *Vice Pres*
Michelle Jimenez, *Vice Pres*
Jeff Baum, *Info Tech Dir*
▲ EMP: 150
SQ FT: 60,000
SALES (est): 79.3MM
SALES (corp-wide): 24.9MM **Privately Held**
WEB: www.awareproducts.com
SIC: 2844 Hair preparations, including
shampoos
PA: Vpi Holding Company, Llc
676 N Michigan Ave
Chicago IL 60611
312 255-4800

(P-8700)
BATH PETALS INC
Also Called: Bath Promotions
15620 S Figueroa St, Gardena
(90248-2127)
PHONE............................310 532-4532
EMP: 10
SQ FT: 5,000
SALES (est): 395K **Privately Held**
WEB: www.bathpetals.com
SIC: 2844

(P-8701)
BELLAVUOS
417 N Azusa Ave, West Covina
(91791-1348)
PHONE............................626 653-0121
Etunaah Nguyen, *Owner*
EMP: 19
SALES (est): 1.2MM **Privately Held**
SIC: 2844 Manicure preparations

(P-8702)
BIO CREATIVE ENTERPRISES
Also Called: Bio Creative Labs
350 Kalmus Dr, Costa Mesa (92626-6013)
PHONE............................714 352-3600
Jason Freeman, *CEO*
▲ EMP: 15
SALES (est): 4MM **Privately Held**
WEB: www.source1enterprises.com
SIC: 2844 Toilet preparations

(P-8703)
BLACK PHOENIX INC
Also Called: Black Phoenix Alchemy Lab
12120 Sherman Way, North Hollywood
(91605-5501)
PHONE............................818 506-9404
Elizabeth Barrial, *CEO*
Brian Constantine, *President*
EMP: 10
SQ FT: 3,000
SALES (est): 1.7MM **Privately Held**
SIC: 2844 Toilet preparations

(P-8704)
BLUE CROSS BEAUTY PRODUCTS INC
557 Jessie St, San Fernando (91340-2542)
PHONE............................818 896-8681
Ray J Friedman, *Ch of Bd*
Mark Friedman, *President*
Lorraine Friedman, *Corp Secy*
▲ EMP: 35 EST: 1942
SQ FT: 12,000
SALES (est): 7.1MM **Privately Held**
SIC: 2844 Manicure preparations

(P-8705)
BLUEFIELD ASSOCIATES INC
1100 N Hellman Ave Ste B, Ontario
(91764-4506)
PHONE............................909 476-6027
Iheatu N Obioha, *CEO*
Chimere K Obioha, *Vice Pres*
Tembi Sukuta, *Vice Pres*
Sunil Ram, *QC Mgr*
Chimere Obioha, *Marketing Staff*
▲ EMP: 30
SQ FT: 30,000
SALES: 6.9MM **Privately Held**
WEB: www.bluefieldinc.com
SIC: 2844 7231 5122 Cosmetic prepara-
tions; beauty shops; cosmetics, perfumes
& hair products

(P-8706)
BOINCA INC
15000 S Avalon Blvd Ste F, Gardena
(90248-2035)
PHONE............................714 809-6313
Edward Bae, *CEO*
Andrew Kim, *Principal*
EMP: 14
SALES (est): 5.1MM **Privately Held**
SIC: 2844 Toilet preparations

(P-8707)
BOINCA INC
Also Called: Arctic Fox
1611 S Rancho Santa Fe Rd, San Marcos
(92078-5157)
PHONE............................619 398-7252
Edward Bae, *CEO*
EMP: 10
SALES (est): 409.5K **Privately Held**
SIC: 2844 Hair coloring preparations

(P-8708)
BOTANICALABS INC
21900 Plummer St, Chatsworth
(91311-4001)
PHONE............................818 466-5639
Kevin Wachs, *CEO*
Joseph Wachs, *Vice Pres*
Salvador Rodriguez, *Prdtn Mgr*
▲ EMP: 12
SALES (est): 3MM **Privately Held**
SIC: 2844 Shampoos, rinses, conditioners:
hair

(P-8709)
BOTANX
3357 E Miraloma Ave # 156, Anaheim
(92806-1937)
PHONE............................714 854-1601
James McGee, *Mng Member*
▲ EMP: 50
SALES (est): 9.6MM **Privately Held**
SIC: 2844 Cosmetic preparations

(P-8710)
BUDS COTTON INC
1240 N Fee Ana St, Anaheim (92807-1817)
P.O. Box 18073 (92817-8073)
PHONE............................714 223-7800
Dewitt Paul, *Ch of Bd*
Barry Williams, *President*
Carol Aarsleff, *Accountant*
Matt Paul, *VP Sales*
Cheryl Bowdish, *Manager*
▲ EMP: 30
SQ FT: 30,000
SALES (est): 6.9MM **Privately Held**
WEB: www.cottonbuds.com
SIC: 2844 Toilet preparations

(P-8711)
C A BOTANA INTERNATIONAL INC (PA)
9365 Waples St Ste A, San Diego
(92121-3904)
PHONE............................858 450-1717
Ursula Wagstaff Kuster, *CEO*
Dieter Kuster, *President*
Jim Lee, *CFO*
Laraine Poveromo, *Marketing Staff*
▲ EMP: 20
SALES (est): 4.8MM **Privately Held**
WEB: www.ca-botana.com
SIC: 2844 Face creams or lotions; cos-
metic preparations

(P-8712)
CALI CHEM INC
Also Called: Be Beauty
14271 Corp Dr Ste B, Garden Grove
(92843)
PHONE..............................714 265-3740
Tung Doan, *CEO*
Duc Doan, *President*
Brian Doan, *General Mgr*
Amy Doan, *Admin Sec*
▲ EMP: 25
SQ FT: 50,000
SALES (est): 6.2MM **Privately Held**
SIC: 2844 Face creams or lotions

(P-8713)
CALIFORNIA INTERFILL INC
8178 Mar Vista Ct, Riverside (92504-4324)
PHONE..............................951 351-2619
Thomas E Boyes, *President*
▲ EMP: 15
SQ FT: 20,000
SALES: 3.2MM **Privately Held**
SIC: 2844 Cosmetic preparations

(P-8714)
CARDINAL LABORATORIES INC
Also Called: Westwood Laboratories
710 S Ayon Ave, Azusa (91702-5123)
PHONE..............................626 610-1200
Tony Devos, *President*
Cheryl Kohorst, *CFO*
Deborah Pierce, *CFO*
Paul Schirmer, *Executive*
◆ EMP: 70 EST: 1971
SALES (est): 11.9MM **Privately Held**
WEB: www.cardinalpet.com
SIC: 2844 Face creams or lotions

(P-8715)
CLASSIC COSMETICS INC (PA)
9530 De Soto Ave, Chatsworth
(91311-5010)
PHONE..............................818 773-9042
Ida Csiszar, *CEO*
Frank Csiszar, *Corp Secy*
Steve Csiszar, *Vice Pres*
Israel Galindo, *Info Tech Mgr*
Robbie Dungey, *Manager*
▲ EMP: 150
SQ FT: 70,000
SALES (est): 46.3MM **Privately Held**
WEB: www.classiccosmetics.com
SIC: 2844 Cosmetic preparations

(P-8716)
COLLANA CLINICS
20427 Valley Blvd, Walnut (91789-2740)
PHONE..............................909 444-1515
George Eura, *President*
Dr Nebite Ergin, *Ch of Bd*
Dr George Euro, *President*
▲ EMP: 16
SQ FT: 10,335
SALES (est): 2.3MM **Privately Held**
SIC: 2844 5122 Face creams or lotions;
cosmetics

(P-8717)
COLONIAL ENTERPRISES INC
10620 Mulberry Ave, Fontana
(92337-7025)
PHONE..............................909 822-8700
Louis Navarro, *COO*
EMP: 40
SALES: 2.5MM **Privately Held**
SIC: 2844 2087 Shampoos, rinses, condi-
tioners: hair; powders, drink

(P-8718)
COLOR DESIGN LABORATORY
19151 Parthenia St Ste H, Northridge
(91324-5126)
PHONE..............................818 341-5100
Gilberto Amparo, *CEO*
Maria Amparo, *President*
Maria Gonzalez, *COO*
▲ EMP: 50
SQ FT: 9,000
SALES: 5MM **Privately Held**
SIC: 2844 Cosmetic preparations

(P-8719)
**COLORFUL PRODUCTS
CORPORATION**
996 Lawrence Dr Ste 301, Newbury Park
(91320-6020)
PHONE..............................805 498-2195
Cyril Faries, *President*
▲ EMP: 10
SQ FT: 18,000
SALES (est): 1.6MM **Privately Held**
SIC: 2844 Toilet preparations
PA: Inter Pacific Industries Inc
996 Lawrence Dr Ste 301
Newbury Park CA 91320
805 498-2195

(P-8720)
**COLUMBIA COSMETICS MFRS
INC (PA)**
1661 Timothy Dr, San Leandro
(94577-2311)
PHONE..............................510 562-5900
Rachel Rendel, *CEO*
Paul Northam, *Info Tech Mgr*
Ellen Aurandt, *Research*
Sayaka Matsumura, *Research*
Melissa Ramos, *Purch Agent*
▲ EMP: 80
SQ FT: 31,000
SALES (est): 21MM **Privately Held**
SIC: 2844 Cosmetic preparations

(P-8721)
CONOPCO INC
1400 Waterloo Rd, Stockton (95205-3743)
PHONE..............................209 466-9580
Max Nicholson, *Branch Mgr*
EMP: 150
SALES (corp-wide): 63B **Privately Held**
SIC: 2844 Toilet preparations
HQ: Conopco, Inc.
700 Sylvan Ave
Englewood Cliffs NJ 07632
201 894-2727

(P-8722)
COOLA LLC
Also Called: Coola Suncare
3200 Lionshead Ave, Carlsbad
(92010-4712)
PHONE..............................760 940-2125
Christopher J Birchby, *Manager*
EMP: 40
SALES (est): 602.6K **Privately Held**
SIC: 2844 5722 Suntan lotions & oils; sun-
tanning equipment & supplies

(P-8723)
CORE TECH PRODUCTS INC
1850 Sunnyside Ct, Bakersfield
(93308-6823)
PHONE..............................661 833-1572
James Boone, *CEO*
Brad Bierman, *President*
Cindy Hayef, *Treasurer*
EMP: 10
SQ FT: 5,000
SALES: 3MM **Privately Held**
SIC: 2844 Face creams or lotions

(P-8724)
CORETEX PRODUCTS INC (PA)
1850 Sunnyside Ct, Bakersfield
(93308-6823)
PHONE..............................661 834-6805
James Boone, *Chairman*
Brad Bierman, *President*
Richard B Bierman, *CEO*
Barbara Simpson, *Office Mgr*
Matt Brummett, *Prdtn Mgr*
▲ EMP: 14
SQ FT: 14,000
SALES (est): 3.1MM **Privately Held**
WEB: www.coretexproducts.com
SIC: 2844 Suntan lotions & oils

(P-8725)
COSMEDICA SKINCARE
2208 Srra Madows Dr Ste A, Rocklin
(95677)
PHONE..............................800 922-5280
Lucia Conway, *President*
Lucia Shin, *Principal*
EMP: 10
SQ FT: 2,000

SALES (est): 1.2MM **Privately Held**
SIC: 2844 5961 Face creams or lotions;
catalog & mail-order houses

(P-8726)
COSMETIC DESIGN GROUP LLC
Also Called: Perfekt Beauty
5673 Selmaraine Dr, Culver City
(90230-6119)
PHONE..............................310 397-9300
Alison Kohlenstein, *President*
EMP: 13
SALES (est): 2.4MM **Privately Held**
SIC: 2844 Cosmetic preparations

(P-8727)
COSMETIC ENTERPRISES LTD
12848 Pierce St, Pacoima (91331-2524)
PHONE..............................818 896-5355
Richard Saute, *President*
Arda Saute, *Treasurer*
Debbie Cadis, *Office Admin*
Paul Hwang, *Info Tech Mgr*
Laura Flores, *Human Res Dir*
▲ EMP: 19
SQ FT: 65,000
SALES (est): 6.5MM **Privately Held**
WEB: www.cosmeticent.com
SIC: 2844 Hair preparations, including
shampoos; cosmetic preparations

(P-8728)
COSMETIC GROUP USA INC
8430 Tujunga Ave, Sun Valley
(91352-3934)
PHONE..............................818 767-2889
Andrea Chuchvara, *CEO*
Steven Barrios, *Administration*
Ledian Dergrigorian, *Project Mgr*
Jade Halcon, *Project Mgr*
Nicole Mohammadi, *Project Mgr*
▲ EMP: 180
SQ FT: 80,000
SALES (est): 25MM **Privately Held**
WEB: www.colorfactoryla.com
SIC: 2844 Cosmetic preparations

(P-8729)
**COSMOBEAUTI LABS & MFG
INC**
Also Called: Cosmo Beauty Lab & Mfg
480 E Arrow Hwy, San Dimas
(91773-3340)
PHONE..............................909 971-9832
Barbara Choi, *President*
Allison Choi, *Sales Staff*
▲ EMP: 15
SQ FT: 10,000
SALES (est): 3.3MM **Privately Held**
SIC: 2844 Face creams or lotions

(P-8730)
COSWAY COMPANY INC
14805 S Maple Ave, Gardena
(90248-1994)
PHONE..............................310 527-9135
Jose Lozano, *Manager*
EMP: 50
SALES (corp-wide): 31.3MM **Privately
Held**
WEB: www.coswayco.com
SIC: 2844 5699 Face creams or lotions;
bathing suits
PA: Cosway Company, Inc.
20633 S Fordyce Ave
Carson CA 90810
310 900-4100

(P-8731)
COSWAY COMPANY INC (PA)
20633 S Fordyce Ave, Carson
(90810-1019)
PHONE..............................310 900-4100
Richard L Hough, *CEO*
Maggie Martinez, *Planning*
Lisa Miklavcic, *Planning*
Radesh Narine, *Engrg Dir*
Rosario Munayco, *Research*
▲ EMP: 20
SALES (est): 31.3MM **Privately Held**
WEB: www.coswayco.com
SIC: 2844 Face creams or lotions; cos-
metic preparations; shampoos, rinses,
conditioners: hair

(P-8732)
**CREATIVE IMAGE SYSTEMS
INC**
1921 E Acacia St, Ontario (91761-7921)
PHONE..............................909 947-8588
Steve Hong, *President*
◆ EMP: 12
SQ FT: 20,000
SALES (est): 2.3MM **Privately Held**
WEB: www.creativeimagesystems.com
SIC: 2844 Hair coloring preparations

(P-8733)
DAVID PIRROTTA DIST INC
7424 1/2 W Sunset Blvd # 5, Los Angeles
(90046-3446)
PHONE..............................323 645-7456
David Pirrotta, *CEO*
EMP: 12
SQ FT: 1,000
SALES (est): 980K **Privately Held**
SIC: 2844 Toilet preparations

(P-8734)
DAVIDS NATURAL TOOTHPASTE
40292 Rosewell Ct, Temecula
(92591-7599)
PHONE..............................949 933-1185
Eric Buss, *President*
EMP: 10 EST: 2015
SALES (est): 599.5K **Privately Held**
SIC: 2844 Toothpastes or powders, denti-
frices

(P-8735)
DEN-MAT CORPORATION (DH)
236 S Broadway St, Orcutt (93455)
PHONE..............................805 922-8491
Robert L Ibsen, *CEO*
Noreen Freitas, *Exec VP*
▲ EMP: 500
SQ FT: 2,500
SALES (est): 86.3MM
SALES (corp-wide): 168.8MM **Privately
Held**
WEB: www.denmat.com
SIC: 2844 3843 Toothpastes or powders,
dentifrices; dental materials

(P-8736)
DEN-MAT CORPORATION
21515 Vanowen St Ste 200, Canoga Park
(91303-2715)
PHONE..............................800 445-0345
Robert Brennis, *Manager*
EMP: 35
SALES (corp-wide): 168.8MM **Privately
Held**
WEB: www.denmat.com
SIC: 2844 Toothpastes or powders, denti-
frices
HQ: Den-Mat Corporation
236 S Broadway St
Orcutt CA 93455
805 922-8491

(P-8737)
**DERMACARE NEUROSCIENCE
INST**
2580 Corporate Pl F109, Monterey Park
(91754-7633)
PHONE..............................323 780-2981
EMP: 10
SALES (corp-wide): 782.3K **Privately
Held**
SIC: 2844
PA: Dermacare Neuroscience Institute
9595 Wilshire Blvd # 900
Beverly Hills CA 90212
310 271-7888

(P-8738)
DERMALOGICA LLC (HQ)
Also Called: Dermal Group, The
1535 Beachey Pl, Carson (90746-4005)
PHONE..............................310 900-4000
Aurelian Lis, *President*
Mathew Divaris, *Vice Pres*
Ram Reddy, *Vice Pres*
Thomas Curlin, *District Mgr*
David Goldstein, *General Mgr*
◆ EMP: 150
SQ FT: 52,000

PRODUCTS & SVCS

SALES (est): 129.6MM
SALES (corp-wide): 63B **Privately Held**
SIC: 2844 Cosmetic preparations
PA: Unilever Plc
　　Unilever House
　　London EC4Y
　　207 822-5252

(P-8739)
DERMANEW LLC (PA)
436 Smithwood Dr, Beverly Hills
(90212-4214)
PHONE......................626 442-2813
Dean Rhoades, *CEO*
Amby Longhoffer, *President*
▲ EMP: 11
SQ FT: 4,000
SALES (est): 907.2K **Privately Held**
WEB: www.dermanew.com
SIC: 2844 2834 Cosmetic preparations;
　　dermatologicals

(P-8740)
DIAMOND WIPES INTL INC (PA)
Also Called: D W I
4651 Schaefer Ave, Chino (91710-5542)
PHONE......................909 230-9888
Eve Yen, *CEO*
Jessica Lum, *President*
Angie Injian, *Senior VP*
Joseph Smith, *Senior VP*
Vivian Kul, *Vice Pres*
▲ EMP: 100
SALES (est): 29.5MM **Privately Held**
WEB: www.diamondwipes.com
SIC: 2844 Towelettes, premoistened

(P-8741)
EBA DESIGN INC
Also Called: Eba Performance Makeup
760 W 16th St Ste D, Costa Mesa
(92627-4319)
PHONE......................714 417-9222
Jarosian Turek, *President*
Lenka Urbanova, *Opers Staff*
▲ EMP: 12
SALES (est): 2.3MM **Privately Held**
SIC: 2844 Cosmetic preparations

(P-8742)
ECOLY INTERNATIONAL INC
Also Called: Sea Critters
5800 Bristol Pkwy Ste 700, Culver City
(90230-6993)
PHONE......................818 718-6982
Jim Morrison, *CEO*
EMP: 40
SQ FT: 2,200
SALES (est): 5.4MM **Privately Held**
SIC: 2844 5122 Hair preparations, includ-
　　ing shampoos; drugs, proprietaries & sun-
　　dries

(P-8743)
**EDDIES PERFUME & COSMTC
CO INC**
20929 Ventura Blvd, Woodland Hills
(91364-2334)
PHONE......................818 341-1717
Edmund Zafrani, *President*
Eli Zafrania, *Creative Dir*
Haim Zafrani, *Principal*
▲ EMP: 20
SQ FT: 15,000
SALES (est): 25MM **Privately Held**
WEB: www.eddiesperfume.com
SIC: 2844 5122 Perfumes, natural or syn-
　　thetic; drugs, proprietaries & sundries

(P-8744)
EDEN BEAUTY CONCEPTS INC
Also Called: Eufora
3215 Executive Rdg, Vista (92081-8527)
PHONE......................760 330-9941
Don Bewley, *Vice Pres*
John Cutrone, *Pharmacy Dir*
Laura Lima, *Executive Asst*
Sonia Gutierrez, *Admin Asst*
Carol Pacelli, *Admin Asst*
▲ EMP: 20
SQ FT: 10,000

SALES (est): 6MM **Privately Held**
WEB: www.eufora.net
SIC: 2844 5087 Shampoos, rinses, condi-
　　tioners: hair; face creams or lotions;
　　beauty salon & barber shop equipment &
　　supplies

(P-8745)
ELF BEAUTY INC (PA)
570 10th St, Oakland (94607-4038)
PHONE......................510 778-7787
Tarang P Amin, *Ch of Bd*
John P Bailey, *President*
Richard F Baruch Jr, *Ch Credit Ofcr*
Lauren Levitan, *Bd of Directors*
Kirk Perry, *Bd of Directors*
EMP: 29
SALES: 269.8MM **Publicly Held**
SIC: 2844 5122 5999 Cosmetic prepara-
　　tions; cosmetics; cosmetics

(P-8746)
ENORMAREL INC
9200 Mason Ave, Chatsworth
(91311-6005)
PHONE......................818 882-4666
Frank J Loffa, *President*
EMP: 10
SALES (est): 841.4K **Privately Held**
WEB: www.enormarel.com
SIC: 2844

(P-8747)
EXQUISITE CORPORATION
Also Called: Exquisite Mfg & Filling Serv
5000 Rivergrade Rd, Baldwin Park
(91706-1405)
PHONE......................626 856-0200
Lily Gozaly, *President*
▲ EMP: 30
SQ FT: 20,000
SALES (est): 5.6MM **Privately Held**
SIC: 2844 Toilet preparations

(P-8748)
FENCHEM INC (HQ)
15308 El Prado Rd, Chino (91710-7659)
PHONE......................909 597-8880
Shufeng Fan, *CEO*
Brian English, *Human Resources*
Jonathon Burch, *Manager*
Jason Betts, *Accounts Mgr*
◆ EMP: 10
SALES (est): 1.9MM **Privately Held**
SIC: 2844 Cosmetic preparations
PA: Fenchem Enterprises Ltd.
　　Room 1012, No.9, Baixia Road, Nan-
　　jing
　　Nantong
　　255 230-2162

(P-8749)
FMK LABS INC
1690 N Delilah St, Corona (92879-1866)
PHONE......................951 736-1212
Alex Minsung Kim, *CEO*
Dylan Kim, *Vice Pres*
Brittany Garay, *Admin Asst*
Esther Williams, *Planning*
Cecelia Kim, *Research*
▲ EMP: 35
SALES (est): 8.6MM **Privately Held**
SIC: 2844 Cosmetic preparations

(P-8750)
FNC MEDICAL CORPORATION
Also Called: Show Off Time
6000 Leland St, Ventura (93003-7605)
PHONE......................805 644-7576
Samuel S Pattillo, *President*
Samuel Pattillo, *President*
Synora Pattillo, *Vice Pres*
EMP: 20
SQ FT: 36,000
SALES (est): 4.7MM **Privately Held**
SIC: 2844 Cosmetic preparations

(P-8751)
FULL SPECTRUM OMEGA INC
12832 Nutwood St, Garden Grove
(92840-6312)
PHONE......................714 866-0039
Richard Brumfield, *CEO*
Guillermo Avina, *CFO*
EMP: 10

SALES (est): 211.6K **Privately Held**
SIC: 2844 7389 2834 Suntan lotions &
　　oils; ; tinctures, pharmaceutical

(P-8752)
GABELS COSMETICS INC
126 S Avenue 18, Los Angeles
(90031-1777)
PHONE......................323 221-2430
Sufian Phoa, *CEO*
EMP: 11
SQ FT: 20,000
SALES (est): 1MM **Privately Held**
SIC: 2844 Hair preparations, including
　　shampoos; cosmetic preparations

(P-8753)
GENERITECH CORPORATION
4967 E Lansing Way, Fresno (93727-7408)
PHONE......................559 346-0233
Gregory Banks, *President*
Norma Banks, *Vice Pres*
▲ EMP: 10
SQ FT: 5,000
SALES (est): 250K **Privately Held**
SIC: 2844 2834 Cosmetic preparations;
　　pharmaceutical preparations

(P-8754)
GIOVANNI COSMETICS INC
Also Called: Giovanni Hair Care & Cosmetics
2064 E University Dr, Rancho Dominguez
(90220-6419)
P.O. Box 6990, Beverly Hills (90212-6990)
PHONE......................310 952-9960
Giovanni J Guidotti, *CEO*
Arthur Guidotti, *Owner*
Peter Stathis, *President*
James Guidotti, *CFO*
Misty Velasco, *Admin Asst*
◆ EMP: 56
SALES (est): 13.5MM **Privately Held**
SIC: 2844 5122 5999 Cosmetic prepara-
　　tions; cosmetics, perfumes & hair prod-
　　ucts; cosmetics

(P-8755)
GLOBAL SALES INC
Also Called: Aniise Skin Care
1732 Westwood Blvd, Los Angeles
(90024-5608)
PHONE......................310 474-7700
Sheida Kimiabakhsh, *CEO*
Sharareh Kimiabakhsh, *Vice Pres*
Vafa Khoshbin, *Principal*
▲ EMP: 23 EST: 2011
SALES (est): 4.2MM **Privately Held**
SIC: 2844 5999 Hair preparations, includ-
　　ing shampoos; face creams or lotions; toi-
　　letries, cosmetics & perfumes

(P-8756)
GORDON LABORATORIES INC
751 E Artesia Blvd, Carson (90746-1202)
PHONE......................310 327-5240
Michael Pereira, *CFO*
Anthony Robertson, *COO*
Nina Varma, *Asst Controller*
Connie Rivas, *Human Resources*
Judy Hernandez, *Purchasing*
▲ EMP: 120 EST: 1967
SQ FT: 100,000
SALES: 32MM **Privately Held**
SIC: 2844 Cosmetic preparations

(P-8757)
**GRAHAM WEBB
INTERNATIONAL INC (DH)**
6109 De Soto Ave, Woodland Hills
(91367-3709)
PHONE......................760 918-3600
Rick Kornbluth, *President*
Thomas P Baumann, *Vice Pres*
EMP: 70
SQ FT: 30,000
SALES (est): 6.3MM **Publicly Held**
WEB: www.grahamwebb.com
SIC: 2844 Hair preparations, including
　　shampoos
HQ: Wella Corporation
　　6109 De Soto Ave
　　Woodland Hills CA 91367
　　818 999-5112

(P-8758)
GRATEFUL NATURALS CORP
213 Walter Ave, Newbury Park
(91320-4343)
PHONE......................323 379-4553
Monica Mayer, *Principal*
EMP: 17
SALES (est): 2.2MM **Privately Held**
SIC: 2844 Toilet preparations

(P-8759)
GS COSMECEUTICAL USA INC
131 Pullman St, Livermore (94551-5128)
PHONE......................925 371-5000
Gurpreet S Sangha, *CEO*
Gurkirpal Sandhu, *COO*
Varinder Sangha, *CFO*
Norman Poon, *Info Tech Mgr*
Laurie Herlich, *Buyer*
▲ EMP: 40
SQ FT: 60,000
SALES (est): 14.2MM **Privately Held**
SIC: 2844 Face creams or lotions; cos-
　　metic preparations

(P-8760)
GSCM VENTURES INC
Also Called: Pacific Naturals
12924 Pierce St, Pacoima (91331-2526)
PHONE......................818 303-2600
Gary McNelley, *President*
Gary Neeley, *President*
David Rivero, *Vice Pres*
▼ EMP: 30
SQ FT: 5,000
SALES (est): 9.3MM **Privately Held**
WEB: www.websupportcenter.com
SIC: 2844 Toilet preparations

(P-8761)
H2O PLUS LLC (PA)
111 Sutter St Fl 22, San Francisco
(94104-4540)
PHONE......................312 377-2132
Joy Chen, *President*
Robert Seidl, *CEO*
◆ EMP: 90
SQ FT: 82,000
SALES (est): 24MM **Privately Held**
SIC: 2844 5999 5122 Toilet preparations;
　　cosmetics; cosmetics

(P-8762)
HAIN CELESTIAL GROUP INC
2201 S Mcdowell Boulevard, Petaluma
(94954-7626)
PHONE......................707 347-1200
Esther Larson, *Branch Mgr*
Sandy McCormick, *Manager*
EMP: 56 **Publicly Held**
WEB: www.hain-celestial.com
SIC: 2844 Deodorants, personal
PA: The Hain Celestial Group Inc
　　1111 Marcus Ave Ste 100
　　New Hyde Park NY 11042

(P-8763)
HAND & NAIL HARMONY INC
Also Called: Hand and Nail Harmony
1545 Moonstone, Brea (92821-2876)
PHONE......................714 773-9758
Danny Haile, *CEO*
David Daniel, *President*
Kenneth Hewlett, *Vice Pres*
Gari-Dawn Tingler, *Vice Pres*
Merlie Martin, *Credit Mgr*
◆ EMP: 68
SALES (est): 23.6MM **Privately Held**
SIC: 2844 Cosmetic preparations

(P-8764)
**HARBER ALL NATURAL
PRODUCTS**
1440 3rd St, Riverside (92507-3481)
PHONE......................347 921-1004
Bruce Harrison, *President*
Eric Traughber, *Vice Pres*
EMP: 11
SQ FT: 25,000
SALES (est): 1MM
SALES (corp-wide): 2MM **Privately Held**
SIC: 2844 2079 Hair preparations, includ-
　　ing shampoos; suntan lotions & oils; face
　　creams or lotions; cooking oils, except
　　corn: vegetable refined

PA: Harber Foods Llc
1440 3rd St Ste 25
Riverside CA 92507
347 921-1004

(P-8765)
HARBER FOODS LLC (PA)
1440 3rd St Ste 25, Riverside
(92507-3462)
PHONE....................347 921-1004
Bruce Harrison, *President*
Eric Traughber, *Vice Pres*
EMP: 10
SQ FT: 25,000
SALES: 2MM **Privately Held**
SIC: 2844 4213 2035 2038 Hair preparations, including shampoos; face creams or lotions; suntan lotions & oils; refrigerated products transport; mayonnaise; breakfasts, frozen & packaged; dinners, frozen & packaged

(P-8766)
HONE & STROP INC
1617 Franklin St Apt 6, Santa Monica
(90404-4239)
PHONE....................424 262-4474
Rodney Bell, *CEO*
EMP: 12
SALES (est): 1MM **Privately Held**
SIC: 2844 5122 Depilatories (cosmetic); cosmetics

(P-8767)
HYDRABRUSH INC
701 S Andreasen Dr Ste C, Escondido
(92029-1950)
PHONE....................760 743-5160
Kenneth Hegemann, *President*
▲ **EMP:** 12
SQ FT: 10,000
SALES: 130.5K **Privately Held**
SIC: 2844 Oral preparations

(P-8768)
IBG HOLDINGS INC
24841 Avenue Tibbitts, Valencia
(91355-3405)
PHONE....................661 702-8680
Richard Mayne, *President*
Marissa Pomerantz, *Vice Pres*
▲ **EMP:** 20
SQ FT: 5,000
SALES (est): 3.3MM **Privately Held**
SIC: 2844 Cosmetic preparations

(P-8769)
INNOVATIVE BIOSCIENCES CORP
Also Called: Innovative Body Science
1849 Diamond St, San Marcos
(92078-5127)
PHONE....................760 603-0772
Michelle Barton, *President*
▲ **EMP:** 20
SQ FT: 16,000
SALES (est): 4.9MM **Privately Held**
WEB: www.innovativebodyscience.com
SIC: 2844 8742 Toilet preparations; management consulting services

(P-8770)
INNOVATIVE COSMETIC LABS INC
9740 Cozycroft Ave, Chatsworth
(91311-4401)
PHONE....................818 349-1121
David Stearn, *CEO*
Lynda Miles, *Vice Pres*
EMP: 15
SALES (est): 3.9MM **Privately Held**
SIC: 2844 Cosmetic preparations

(P-8771)
INTERNATIONAL ABRASIVE MFG CO
1221 N Lakeview Ave, Anaheim
(92807-1830)
PHONE....................714 779-9970
James George, *President*
▼ **EMP:** 35
SQ FT: 41,000

SALES: 670K **Privately Held**
WEB: www.inmnails.com
SIC: 2844 3423 3291 Manicure preparations; hand & edge tools; abrasive products

(P-8772)
INTERNATIONAL BEAUTY PDTS LLC (PA)
Also Called: Jerome Russell
8200 Remmet Ave, Canoga Park
(91304-4156)
PHONE....................818 999-1222
Jim Perry,
Jerome Russell, *Principal*
Tiffany Williams, *Accountant*
Sherry Hughes, *Manager*
EMP: 11
SQ FT: 1,000
SALES: 6MM **Privately Held**
WEB: www.jeromerussell.com
SIC: 2844 Toilet preparations

(P-8773)
IWEN NATURALS
4150 Mystic View Ct, Hayward
(94542-2166)
PHONE....................510 589-8019
I-Wen WEI, *Owner*
EMP: 10
SALES (est): 467.5K **Privately Held**
SIC: 2844 5999 Cosmetic preparations; cosmetics

(P-8774)
JAPONESQUE LLC
2420 Camino Ramon Ste 250, San Ramon
(94583-4319)
PHONE....................925 866-6670
Karen A McKay, *President*
▲ **EMP:** 16
SQ FT: 4,500
SALES (est): 3.9MM **Privately Held**
WEB: www.japonesque.com
SIC: 2844 5122 Cosmetic preparations; cosmetics

(P-8775)
JIVAGO INC (PA)
9454 Wilshire Blvd # 600, Beverly Hills
(90212-2931)
PHONE....................310 205-5535
Ilana V Jivago, *President*
◆ **EMP:** 15
SQ FT: 4,000
SALES (est): 3.8MM **Privately Held**
WEB: www.jivagoinc.com
SIC: 2844 Perfumes & colognes; face creams or lotions

(P-8776)
JOAR LABS INC
4115 San Fernando Rd, Glendale
(91204-2517)
PHONE....................818 243-0700
Arturo Martinez, *President*
▲ **EMP:** 40
SQ FT: 15,000
SALES (est): 5.6MM **Privately Held**
SIC: 2844 2833 Cosmetic preparations; vitamins, natural or synthetic: bulk, uncompounded

(P-8777)
JOHNSON & JOHNSON CONSUMER INC
Also Called: Neutrogena
5670 W 96th St, Los Angeles (90045)
PHONE....................310 642-1150
Byron Maidens, *Manager*
EMP: 46
SALES (corp-wide): 76.4B **Publicly Held**
WEB: www.neutrogena.com
SIC: 2844 Toilet preparations
HQ: Johnson & Johnson Consumer Inc.
199 Grandview Rd
Skillman NJ 08558
908 874-1000

(P-8778)
JOICO LABORATORIES INC
488 E Santa Clara St # 301, Arcadia
(91006-7229)
PHONE....................626 321-4100
Sara Jones, *President*
Akira Mochizuki, *Exec VP*

Takahiro Iwabuchi, *Director*
▲ **EMP:** 200 **EST:** 1976
SALES (est): 28.3MM **Privately Held**
WEB: www.joico.com
SIC: 2844 Hair preparations, including shampoos; cosmetic preparations

(P-8779)
JON DAVLER INC
9440 Gidley St, Temple City (91780-4211)
PHONE....................626 941-6558
David J Sheen, *President*
Christina Yang, *Vice Pres*
▲ **EMP:** 24
SQ FT: 12,000
SALES (est): 5.1MM **Privately Held**
SIC: 2844 Cosmetic preparations

(P-8780)
JOUER COSMETICS LLC
1929 Pontius Ave, Los Angeles
(90025-5611)
PHONE....................310 312-0500
Christina Zilber, *Mng Member*
Linh Bober, *CFO*
Laurie Cooper, *General Mgr*
Nicole Dintaman, *Admin Asst*
Megan Miyasaki, *Graphic Designe*
▲ **EMP:** 19
SALES (est): 3.6MM **Privately Held**
SIC: 2844 Cosmetic preparations

(P-8781)
KAMSUT INCORPORATED
Also Called: Kama Sutra
2151 Anchor Ct, Thousand Oaks
(91320-1604)
PHONE....................805 495-7479
Joseph Bolstad, *President*
Sarah Grant, *Accounts Mgr*
Christine Marsden, *Accounts Mgr*
▲ **EMP:** 20
SQ FT: 8,000
SALES (est): 4.4MM **Privately Held**
WEB: www.kamasutra.com
SIC: 2844 Cosmetic preparations

(P-8782)
KELLY TEEGARDEN ORGANICS LLC
Also Called: Kto
6524 Platt Ave Ste 224, West Hills
(91307-3218)
PHONE....................818 518-0707
Kelly Teegarden,
Amber Hunter, *General Mgr*
EMP: 12
SALES (est): 2.6MM **Privately Held**
SIC: 2844 Lipsticks

(P-8783)
KIM LAUBE & COMPANY INC
Also Called: Kelco
2221 Statham Blvd, Oxnard (93033-3913)
PHONE....................805 240-1300
Kim E Laube, *President*
◆ **EMP:** 40
SALES (est): 7.4MM **Privately Held**
WEB: www.kimlaubeco.com
SIC: 2844 3999 Hair preparations, including shampoos; shampoos, rinses, conditioners: hair; hair clippers for human use, hand & electric; pet supplies

(P-8784)
KUM KANG TRADING USAINC
Also Called: Black N Gold
6433 Alondra Blvd, Paramount
(90723-3758)
PHONE....................562 531-6111
Yoon OH, *President*
◆ **EMP:** 12
SQ FT: 20,000
SALES (est): 2.3MM **Privately Held**
SIC: 2844 Hair preparations, including shampoos

(P-8785)
KUSTOMER KINETICS INC
136 E Saint Joseph St A, Arcadia
(91006-7151)
PHONE....................626 445-6161
Jay Berger, *President*
William H Berger, *President*
EMP: 10

SALES (est): 1.4MM **Privately Held**
WEB: www.kustomerkinetics.com
SIC: 2844 Perfumes, natural or synthetic

(P-8786)
LANZA RESEARCH INTERNATIONAL
429 Santa Monica Blvd # 510, Santa Monica (90401-3401)
PHONE....................310 393-5227
Robert De Lanza, *President*
Jo-Ann Stamp, *Corp Secy*
Dana Story, *Exec VP*
EMP: 75
SQ FT: 40,000
SALES (est): 6.4MM **Privately Held**
WEB: www.davexlabs.com
SIC: 2844 5122 Shampoos, rinses, conditioners: hair; cosmetics

(P-8787)
LEE PHARMACEUTICALS
1434 Santa Anita Ave, South El Monte
(91733-3312)
PHONE....................626 442-3141
Ronald G Lee, *CEO*
Mike Agresti, *CFO*
▲ **EMP:** 82
SALES (est): 17.2MM **Privately Held**
WEB: www.leepharmaceuticals.com
SIC: 2844 2834 3843 Manicure preparations; depilatories (cosmetic); pharmaceutical preparations; enamels, dentists'; cement, dental

(P-8788)
LENUS HANDCRAFTED
3323 Thorn St, San Diego (92104-4747)
PHONE....................619 200-4266
Laura Lisauskas, *Principal*
EMP: 10
SALES: 80K **Privately Held**
SIC: 2844 7389 Face creams or lotions;

(P-8789)
LIBBY LABORATORIES INC
1700 6th St, Berkeley (94710-1806)
PHONE....................510 527-5400
Susan Libby, *President*
Gordon Libby, *Treasurer*
Charles Mendoza, *Info Tech Mgr*
James Pirie, *Plant Engr*
EMP: 23
SQ FT: 25,000
SALES (est): 2.3MM **Privately Held**
WEB: www.libbylabs.com
SIC: 2844 2834 2899 Cosmetic preparations; pharmaceutical preparations; solutions, pharmaceutical; chemical preparations

(P-8790)
LIQUID TECHNOLOGIES INC
14425 Yorba Ave, Chino (91710-5733)
PHONE....................909 393-9475
John Maruszewski, *CEO*
Marc Tomberlin, *CFO*
▲ **EMP:** 30
SALES (est): 8MM **Privately Held**
WEB: www.liquidtek.com
SIC: 2844 Hair preparations, including shampoos

(P-8791)
LYNEX COMPANY INC
375 Digital Dr, Morgan Hill (95037-2880)
PHONE....................408 778-7884
Lien Nguyen, *President*
Nicholas Dinh, *Vice Pres*
▲ **EMP:** 10
SQ FT: 1,500
SALES (est): 1.5MM **Privately Held**
WEB: www.lynex.com
SIC: 2844 Toilet preparations

(P-8792)
MARKWINS INTERNATIONAL CORP (PA)
22067 Ferrero, Walnut (91789-5214)
PHONE....................909 595-8898
Sung-Tsei Eric Chen, *President*
Jeff Rogers, *President*
Leslie H Hernandez, *CFO*
Lina Chen,
▲ **EMP:** 150
SQ FT: 320,000

PRODUCTS & SVCS

SALES (est): 240.1MM **Privately Held**
SIC: 2844 Cosmetic preparations

(P-8793)
MASTEY DE PARIS INC
25413 Rye Canyon Rd, Valencia
(91355-1269)
PHONE..................................661 257-4814
Stephen Mastey, *President*
Erick Calderon, *President*
Michael Ifergan, *Vice Pres*
Lesley Mastey, *Admin Sec*
EMP: 50
SQ FT: 63,000
SALES (est): 5.3MM **Privately Held**
SIC: 2844 Hair preparations, including
shampoos

(P-8794)
**MERESTONE MERCHANDISE
CORP**
Also Called: Jasmine La Belle
12823 Schabarum Ave, Irwindale
(91706-6808)
PHONE..................................626 337-6262
Dorothy Cao, *President*
Christy Chan, *CFO*
Joyce Chan, *Manager*
EMP: 12
SQ FT: 8,000
SALES (est): 1.6MM **Privately Held**
WEB: www.merestonegroup.com
SIC: 2844 5122 Cosmetic preparations;
cosmetics

(P-8795)
**MERLE NORMAN COSMETICS
INC (PA)**
9130 Bellanca Ave, Los Angeles
(90045-4772)
PHONE..................................310 641-3000
Jack B Nethercutt, *Ch of Bd*
Amy Hackbart, *COO*
Michael Cassidy, *CFO*
Helen Nethercutt, *Vice Ch Bd*
Carol Porta, *Vice Pres*
▲ EMP: 345 EST: 1974
SQ FT: 354,000
SALES (est): 64MM **Privately Held**
WEB: www.merlenorman.com
SIC: 2844 5999 Cosmetic preparations;
cosmetics

(P-8796)
MILESTONES PRODUCTS INC
Also Called: Q Perfumes
1965 S Tubeway Ave, Commerce
(90040-1611)
PHONE..................................323 728-3434
Edmond Sabet, *President*
▲ EMP: 10
SQ FT: 30,000
SALES (est): 3.1MM **Privately Held**
WEB: www.qperfumes.net
SIC: 2844 Perfumes & colognes

(P-8797)
MIXED CHICKS LLC
21208 Vanowen St, Canoga Park
(91303-2823)
PHONE..................................818 888-4008
Wendi Levy, *Mng Member*
Djata Grant, *Officer*
Kim Etheredge,
Brad Kaaya,
▲ EMP: 10
SQ FT: 2,500
SALES (est): 1.4MM **Privately Held**
SIC: 2844 5122 Hair preparations, includ-
ing shampoos; cosmetics

(P-8798)
MOSAIC DISTRIBUTORS LLC
Also Called: Chella
507 Calle San Pablo, Camarillo
(93012-8550)
PHONE..................................805 383-7711
Chris Kolodziejski, *CEO*
EMP: 10 EST: 2012
SALES (est): 1.3MM **Privately Held**
SIC: 2844 5122 Cosmetic preparations;
face creams or lotions; cosmetics

(P-8799)
**MOSAIC MARKETING
PARTNERS LLC**
Also Called: Chella Professional Skin Care
507 Calle San Pablo, Camarillo
(93012-8550)
PHONE..................................805 383-7711
Chris Kolodziejski,
▲ EMP: 10
SQ FT: 4,900
SALES (est): 644.2K **Privately Held**
SIC: 2844 Cosmetic preparations; face
creams or lotions

(P-8800)
MY WORLD STYLES LLC
Also Called: Players Circle Barbershop
16 Dutton Ave, San Leandro (94577-2839)
PHONE..................................800 355-4008
Allen Richard, *CEO*
EMP: 10
SQ FT: 2,000
SALES (est): 857.9K **Privately Held**
SIC: 2844 7241 Face creams or lotions;
barber college

(P-8801)
**NAKED PRINCESS WORLDWIDE
LLC (PA)**
11766 Wilshire Blvd Fl 9, Los Angeles
(90025-6548)
PHONE..................................310 271-1199
Jordana Woodland, *CEO*
▲ EMP: 15
SALES (est): 3.6MM **Privately Held**
SIC: 2844 Cosmetic preparations

(P-8802)
**NATURES BABY PRODUCTS
INC**
Also Called: Nature's Baby Organics
58 Dartmouth Dr, Rancho Mirage
(92270-3162)
PHONE..................................818 521-5054
Phil Wolvek, *CEO*
Adena Surabian, *President*
Beverly Wolvek, *Corp Secy*
▼ EMP: 10
SQ FT: 30,000
SALES (est): 1.4MM **Privately Held**
SIC: 2844 5137 Powder: baby, face, tal-
cum or toilet; baby goods

(P-8803)
NEUTRADERM INC
20660 Nordhoff St, Chatsworth
(91311-6114)
PHONE..................................818 534-3190
Samuel D Raoof, *CEO*
Toora J Raoof, *Principal*
Grace Barnes, *Admin Asst*
Bittu Ramani, *Admin Asst*
Sofia Bahram, *Accountant*
▲ EMP: 25
SALES (est): 10.2MM **Privately Held**
SIC: 2844 Cosmetic preparations

(P-8804)
**NEW FRAGRANCE
CONTINENTAL**
Also Called: La Natura
5033 Exposition Blvd, Los Angeles
(90016-3913)
PHONE..................................323 766-0060
Sabina Chazanas, *President*
Alejandro Chazanas, *Vice Pres*
EMP: 12
SQ FT: 5,000
SALES (est): 668.3K **Privately Held**
WEB: www.lanatura.com
SIC: 2844 Cosmetic preparations

(P-8805)
NUVORA INC
3350 Scott Blvd Ste 502, Santa Clara
(95054-3108)
PHONE..................................408 856-2200
Jerry Gin, *President*
Ben Ross, *Exec VP*
EMP: 20
SQ FT: 8,000
SALES (est): 3.5MM **Privately Held**
SIC: 2844 Oral preparations

(P-8806)
OLAPLEX LLC (PA)
1482 E Valley Rd Ste 701, Santa Barbara
(93108-1200)
PHONE..................................805 258-7680
Dean Christal,
Tyler Krebs, *Vice Pres*
EMP: 14
SALES (est): 2MM **Privately Held**
SIC: 2844 Hair preparations, including
shampoos

(P-8807)
ORAL ESSENTIALS INC
436 N Roxbury Dr, Beverly Hills
(90210-5026)
PHONE..................................888 773-5273
Kourosh Maddahi, *CEO*
Caroline Heerwagon, *COO*
Linda Kloeffer, *CFO*
Justin Maddahi, *Chief Mktg Ofcr*
Brent Burden, *VP Sales*
EMP: 13 EST: 2014
SALES (est): 162.9K **Privately Held**
SIC: 2844 Toothpastes or powders, denti-
frices

(P-8808)
ORLY INTERNATIONAL INC
Also Called: Sparitual
7710 Haskell Ave, Van Nuys (91406-1905)
PHONE..................................818 994-1001
Jeff Pink, *President*
Hana Hyman, *Assistant*
◆ EMP: 100 EST: 1977
SQ FT: 65,000
SALES (est): 36.8MM **Privately Held**
WEB: www.orlybeauty.com
SIC: 2844 Cosmetic preparations

(P-8809)
**PACIFIC WORLD CORPORATION
(PA)**
75 Enterprise Ste 300, Aliso Viejo
(92656-2626)
PHONE..................................949 598-2400
James Colleran, *CEO*
Joseph Fracassi, *President*
Joseph Jaeger, *COO*
Joel Carden, *Exec VP*
Craig Finney, *Exec VP*
▲ EMP: 151
SQ FT: 30,000
SALES (est): 70.9MM **Privately Held**
WEB: www.nailene.com
SIC: 2844 3421 3999 Cosmetic prepara-
tions; clippers, fingernail & toenail; finger-
nails, artificial

(P-8810)
PANCO MENS PRODUCTS INC
45605 Citrus Ave, Indio (92201-3451)
PHONE..................................760 342-4368
Gene Pantuso, *President*
EMP: 15 EST: 1964
SQ FT: 40,000
SALES (est): 2.6MM **Privately Held**
SIC: 2844 Toilet preparations; face creams
or lotions; lotions, shaving; shampoos,
rinses, conditioners: hair

(P-8811)
PBH MARKETING INC
Also Called: Paul Brown Hawaii
9960 Glenoaks Blvd Ste C, Sun Valley
(91352-1066)
PHONE..................................818 374-9000
Paul Brown, *President*
▲ EMP: 10
SALES (est): 1.2MM **Privately Held**
SIC: 2844 Hair preparations, including
shampoos

(P-8812)
PERSON & COVEY INC
616 Allen Ave, Glendale (91201-2014)
P.O. Box 25018 (91221-5018)
PHONE..................................818 937-5000
Lorne Person Jr, *CEO*
Lorne Person Sr, *Ch of Bd*
Sue Person, *Vice Pres*
Rayann Bates, *Executive*
William Marquardt, *MIS Dir*
EMP: 45 EST: 1941
SQ FT: 36,000

SALES (est): 9.4MM **Privately Held**
WEB: www.personandcovey.com
SIC: 2844 2834 Cosmetic preparations;
dermatologicals

(P-8813)
PETRA-1 LP
12386 Osborne Pl, Pacoima (91331-2013)
PHONE..................................866 334-3702
Benjamin Whitham, *Partner*
EMP: 15
SALES (est): 886.8K **Privately Held**
SIC: 2844 Toilet preparations

(P-8814)
**PHYSICANS FORMULA
HOLDINGS INC (HQ)**
22067 Ferrero, Walnut (91789-5214)
PHONE..................................626 334-3395
Ingrid Jackel, *CEO*
Jeffrey P Rogers, *President*
Leslie H Keegan, *Senior VP*
Jennifer Sharp, *Vice Pres*
Michelle Mosqueda, *Admin Asst*
▲ EMP: 33
SQ FT: 82,000
SALES (est): 28.3MM
SALES (corp-wide): 240.1MM **Privately
Held**
SIC: 2844 5122 Cosmetic preparations;
drugs, proprietaries & sundries
PA: Markwins International Corp
22067 Ferrero
Walnut CA 91789
909 595-8898

(P-8815)
**PHYSICIANS FORMULA INC
(DH)**
22067 Ferrero, City of Industry
(91789-5214)
PHONE..................................626 334-3395
Ingrid Jackel, *Ch of Bd*
Jeff Rogers, *President*
Joseph J Jaeger, *CFO*
Rick Kirchhoff, *Vice Pres*
Manuel Scates, *Purchasing*
▲ EMP: 57
SQ FT: 82,800
SALES (est): 28.3MM
SALES (corp-wide): 240.1MM **Privately
Held**
WEB: www.physiciansformula.com
SIC: 2844 Cosmetic preparations

(P-8816)
PHYSICIANS FORMULA INC
250 S 9th Ave, City of Industry
(91746-3309)
PHONE..................................626 334-3395
Jennifer Sharp, *Branch Mgr*
EMP: 100
SALES (corp-wide): 240.1MM **Privately
Held**
WEB: www.physiciansformula.com
SIC: 2844 Cosmetic preparations
HQ: Physicians Formula, Inc.
22067 Ferrero
City Of Industry CA 91789
626 334-3395

(P-8817)
PHYSICIANS FORMULA INC
753 Arrow Grand Cir, Covina (91722-2148)
PHONE..................................626 334-3395
Vivian Durra, *Branch Mgr*
EMP: 100
SALES (corp-wide): 240.1MM **Privately
Held**
WEB: www.physiciansformula.com
SIC: 2844 Cosmetic preparations
HQ: Physicians Formula, Inc.
22067 Ferrero
City Of Industry CA 91789
626 334-3395

(P-8818)
**PHYSICIANS FORMULA COSMT
INC**
22067 Ferrero, City of Industry
(91789-5214)
PHONE..................................626 334-3395
Jeffrey P Rogers, *President*
Joseph J Jaeger, *CFO*
EMP: 147

▲ = Import ▼=Export
◆ =Import/Export

SALES (est): 24.3K
SALES (corp-wide): 240.1MM **Privately Held**
SIC: 2844 Cosmetic preparations
HQ: Physicians Formula, Inc.
22067 Ferrero
City Of Industry CA 91789
626 334-3395

(P-8819)
PIXI INC
Also Called: Pixi Beauty
10351 Santa Monica Blvd # 410, Los Angeles (90025-6937)
PHONE...................................310 670-7767
Andrew Knox, *President*
Petra Strand Oppe, *Principal*
Dhruti Pabari, *Finance Mgr*
Mindy Chun, *Mktg Dir*
Sasha Imamori, *Marketing Staff*
▲ EMP: 19
SALES (est): 4.4MM **Privately Held**
SIC: 2844 Cosmetic preparations

(P-8820)
PLEROS LLC
Also Called: Neomen
2825 E Tahquitz Cyn W, Palm Springs (92262-6906)
PHONE...................................442 275-6764
Peter Zhu, *COO*
EMP: 10
SQ FT: 2,000
SALES: 2MM **Privately Held**
SIC: 2844 5999 Cosmetic preparations; cosmetics

(P-8821)
PRESTIGE COSMETICS INC
17780 Gothard St, Huntington Beach (92647-6216)
PHONE...................................714 375-0395
Sarjula Sanghvi, *President*
EMP: 11
SQ FT: 10,000
SALES (est): 1.9MM **Privately Held**
SIC: 2844 5122 Cosmetic preparations; cosmetics

(P-8822)
PRETIKA CORPORATION
16 Salermo, Laguna Niguel (92677-9032)
PHONE...................................949 481-8818
Thomas E Nichols, *President*
◆ EMP: 26
SQ FT: 22,500
SALES (est): 4.6MM **Privately Held**
WEB: www.pretika.com
SIC: 2844 Cosmetic preparations

(P-8823)
PRIMA FLEUR BOTANICALS INC
84 Galli Dr, Novato (94949-5706)
PHONE...................................415 455-0957
Marianne Griffeth, *President*
Ron Griffeth, *Treasurer*
Christina Mitaine, *Purch Mgr*
Donna Lenoue, *Mfg Staff*
Stacy Huang, *Sales Staff*
▲ EMP: 16
SQ FT: 5,000
SALES: 4MM **Privately Held**
WEB: www.primafleur.com
SIC: 2844 5169 Suntan lotions & oils; essential oils

(P-8824)
PRINCE DEVELOPMENT LLC
Also Called: Prince Reigns
23302 Oxnard St, Woodland Hills (91367-3123)
PHONE...................................866 774-6234
Edouard Joseph, *Mng Member*
Christine Joseph,
▼ EMP: 12
SQ FT: 3,800
SALES (est): 2MM **Privately Held**
SIC: 2844 Cosmetic preparations

(P-8825)
PRISHA COSMETICS INC
9260 Owensmouth Ave, Chatsworth (91311-5853)
PHONE...................................818 773-8784
Riken Shah, *President*
▲ EMP: 11

SQ FT: 6,800
SALES (est): 2.4MM **Privately Held**
SIC: 2844 Cosmetic preparations

(P-8826)
PROFESSIONAL SKIN CARE INC (PA)
Also Called: Only You Rx Skin Care
25028 Avenue Kearny, Valencia (91355-1253)
P.O. Box 753, Lafayette (94549-0753)
PHONE...................................661 257-7771
Dr James Paige, *President*
▲ EMP: 30
SQ FT: 25,000
SALES (est): 3.7MM **Privately Held**
SIC: 2844 5122 5087 Cosmetic preparations; drugs, proprietaries & sundries; cosmetics; beauty parlor equipment & supplies

(P-8827)
PURA NATURALS INC (HQ)
23101 Lake Center Dr # 100, Lake Forest (92630-2801)
PHONE...................................949 273-8100
Robert Doherty, *CEO*
Derek Duhame, *President*
Robert Switzer, *Admin Sec*
Jim Breech, *VP Sales*
EMP: 15
SQ FT: 4,000
SALES: 451.3K
SALES (corp-wide): 1.2MM **Privately Held**
SIC: 2844 Cosmetic preparations
PA: Advanced Innovative Recovery Technologies, Inc.
23101 Lake Center Dr # 100
Lake Forest CA 92630
949 273-8100

(P-8828)
REVLON INC
Creative Nail Design
1125 Joshua Way Ste 12, Vista (92081-7840)
PHONE...................................760 599-2900
Jim Northstrum, *Director*
John Gillespie, *MIS Dir*
EMP: 50 **Publicly Held**
WEB: www.revlon.com
SIC: 2844 Manicure preparations
PA: Revlon, Inc.
1 New York Plz
New York NY 10004

(P-8829)
RMF SALT HOLDINGS LLC
Also Called: San Francisco Bath Salt Co
30984 Santana St Hayward, Hayward (94544)
PHONE...................................510 477-9600
Lee J Williamson, *President*
▲ EMP: 16
SALES (est): 4.9MM
SALES (corp-wide): 36.3MM **Privately Held**
WEB: www.sfbsc.com
SIC: 2844 5149 Bath salts; salt, edible
PA: Red Monkey Foods, Inc.
6751 W Kings St
Springfield MO 65802
417 319-7300

(P-8830)
ROBANDA INTERNATIONAL INC
Also Called: World Amenities
8260 Cmino Santa Fe Ste A, San Diego (92121)
PHONE...................................619 276-7660
David Lieb, *President*
Gerald Leib, *Ch of Bd*
Helen Lieb, *CFO*
Anthony Lieb, *Vice Pres*
▲ EMP: 28
SQ FT: 20,000
SALES (est): 12MM **Privately Held**
WEB: www.robanda.com
SIC: 2844 Cosmetic preparations

(P-8831)
RUDOLPH INTERNATIONAL INC
1150 Beacon St, Brea (92821-2936)
P.O. Box 607 (92822-0607)
PHONE...................................714 529-5696
James Rudolph, *CEO*
Louise Rudolph, *President*
Eric Tran, *Vice Pres*
▲ EMP: 49
SQ FT: 25,000
SALES (est): 8.7MM **Privately Held**
WEB: www.rudolphinc.com
SIC: 2844 3842 3291 2899 Cosmetic preparations; applicators; cotton tipped; abrasive products; chemical preparations

(P-8832)
SAMUEL RAOOF
Also Called: Brandmd Skin Care
20660 Nordhoff St, Chatsworth (91311-6114)
PHONE...................................818 534-3180
Samuel Raoof, *Owner*
EMP: 20 EST: 2014
SALES (est): 1.4MM **Privately Held**
SIC: 2844 Deodorants, personal

(P-8833)
SANDRA SPARKS & ASSOCIATES
2510 Peninsula Rd, Oxnard (93035-2962)
PHONE...................................805 985-2057
Sandra Sparks, *Owner*
EMP: 13
SALES (est): 825K **Privately Held**
SIC: 2844 Cosmetic preparations

(P-8834)
SANITOR CORPORATION
8400 Cerritos Ave, Stanton (90680-2504)
PHONE...................................714 799-2722
John Robinson, *CEO*
▲ EMP: 14
SQ FT: 6,000
SALES (est): 3.1MM **Privately Held**
SIC: 2844 Cosmetic preparations

(P-8835)
SANTEE COSMETICS USA
13202 Estrella Ave, Gardena (90248-1520)
PHONE...................................310 329-2305
Jacklyn Kim, *Owner*
▲ EMP: 10 EST: 2008
SALES: 1MM **Privately Held**
SIC: 2844 Cosmetic preparations

(P-8836)
SAYDEL INC (PA)
Also Called: Nina Religion
2475 E Slauson Ave, Huntington Park (90255-2887)
PHONE...................................323 585-2800
Santo Gil Orta, *Owner*
Michael Orta, *Vice Pres*
EMP: 15
SQ FT: 11,000
SALES: 552.8K **Privately Held**
WEB: www.saydel.com
SIC: 2844 5049 5999 Perfumes, natural or synthetic; religious supplies; religious goods

(P-8837)
SCIENCE OF SKINCARE LLC
Also Called: Innovative Skin Care
3333 N San Fernando Blvd, Burbank (91504-2531)
PHONE...................................818 254-7961
C B Johns, *Mng Member*
Alec Call, *Vice Pres*
Jenny Cheng, *Business Mgr*
Carmela Mattox, *Business Mgr*
Katherine Medina, *Business Mgr*
▲ EMP: 76 EST: 2003
SQ FT: 36,000
SALES (est): 21.6MM **Privately Held**
WEB: www.innovativeskincare.com
SIC: 2844 Face creams or lotions

(P-8838)
SHADOW HOLDINGS LLC (PA)
Also Called: Bocchi Laboratories
26455 Ruether Ave, Santa Clarita (91350-2621)
PHONE...................................661 252-3807

Robert Bocchi,
Patrick Kelley,
Joe Pender,
Horacio Avila, *Manager*
Horacio Cabrera, *Manager*
EMP: 28
SQ FT: 88,500
SALES (est): 65.6MM **Privately Held**
SIC: 2844 Toilet preparations

(P-8839)
SHADOW HOLDINGS LLC
Also Called: Bocchi Laboratories
26421 Ruether Ave, Santa Clarita (91350-2621)
PHONE...................................661 252-3807
Robert J Bocchi, *Mng Member*
EMP: 472
SQ FT: 86,200
SALES (corp-wide): 65.6MM **Privately Held**
WEB: www.bocchilabs.com
SIC: 2844 Toilet preparations
PA: Shadow Holdings, Llc
26455 Ruether Ave
Santa Clarita CA 91350
661 252-3807

(P-8840)
SHEER DESIGN INC
6309 Esplanade, Playa Del Rey (90293-7581)
PHONE...................................310 306-2121
Mark Friedland, *President*
EMP: 60
SALES (est): 6.7MM **Privately Held**
SIC: 2844 Cosmetic preparations

(P-8841)
SHINE & PRETTY (USA) CORP
456 Constitution Ave, Camarillo (93012-8529)
PHONE...................................805 388-8581
Edward Sheu, *President*
▲ EMP: 10
SQ FT: 13,400
SALES (est): 1.3MM **Privately Held**
SIC: 2844 Cosmetic preparations

(P-8842)
SMALL WORLD TRADING CO
Also Called: Eo Products
90 Windward Way, San Rafael (94901-7200)
PHONE...................................415 945-1900
Susan Griffin-Black, *CEO*
Brad Black, *Principal*
EMP: 103
SQ FT: 40,000
SALES (est): 19.9MM **Privately Held**
WEB: www.eoproducts.com
SIC: 2844 Hair preparations, including shampoos; concentrates, perfume

(P-8843)
SMASHBOX BEAUTY COSMETICS INC
Also Called: Smashbox Cosmetics
8538 Warner Dr, Culver City (90232-2431)
PHONE...................................310 558-1490
Sara Moss, *CEO*
Jane Grosvenor, *Officer*
Simon James, *Vice Pres*
Paula Pontes, *Vice Pres*
Karen Quimby, *Vice Pres*
◆ EMP: 120 EST: 1996
SQ FT: 20,000
SALES (est): 25.7MM **Publicly Held**
WEB: www.smashbox.com
SIC: 2844 Toilet preparations
PA: The Estee Lauder Companies Inc
767 5th Ave Fl 1
New York NY 10153

(P-8844)
SMITH & VANDIVER CORPORATION
Also Called: Sinclair & Valentine
480 Airport Blvd, Watsonville (95076-2002)
PHONE...................................831 722-9526
Jeffrey K Slaboden, *CEO*
Corliss Deome, *Info Tech Mgr*
▲ EMP: 75
SQ FT: 55,000

(PA)=Parent Co (HQ)=Headquarters (DH)=Div Headquarters
✪ = New Business established in last 2 years

2019 California
Manufacturers Register

365

PRODUCTS & SVCS

SALES (est): 31.3MM **Privately Held**
WEB: www.smith-vandiver.com
SIC: 2844 Cosmetic preparations

(P-8845)
SOAP & WATER LLC
11450 Sheldon St, Sun Valley
(91352-1121)
PHONE.................................310 639-3990
Jill Belasco,
EMP: 20
SQ FT: 80,000
SALES (est): 1.6MM **Privately Held**
SIC: 2844 Face creams or lotions

(P-8846)
SPA GIRL CORPORATION
3100 W Warner Ave Ste 11, Santa Ana
(92704-5331)
PHONE.................................714 444-1040
Kerrie La Bianco, CEO
EMP: 20
SQ FT: 2,500
SALES: 5MM **Privately Held**
SIC: 2844 Cosmetic preparations

(P-8847)
SPATZ CORPORATION
Also Called: Spatz Laboratories
1600 Westar Dr, Oxnard (93033-2423)
PHONE.................................805 487-2122
Joel Lynn Nelson, CEO
John Nelson, COO
George Jefferson, CFO
Laura Nelson, Vice Pres
Maria Zendejas, Executive
▲ EMP: 145 EST: 1954
SQ FT: 62,000
SALES (est): 79.7MM **Privately Held**
WEB: www.spatzlabs.com
SIC: 2844 3089 Cosmetic preparations;
plastic containers, except foam

(P-8848)
STEARNS CORPORATION
Also Called: Derma E
2130 Ward Ave, Simi Valley (93065-1851)
PHONE.................................805 582-2710
Brenda Wu, President
Linda Miles, President
Michael Krmpotich, CFO
▲ EMP: 25
SALES (est): 5.5MM
SALES (corp-wide): 45MM **Privately Held**
SIC: 2844 Face creams or lotions
PA: Topix Pharmaceuticals Inc.
5200 New Horizons Blvd
Amityville NY 11701
631 226-7979

(P-8849)
SUMBODY UNION STREET LLC
118 N Main St, Sebastopol (95472-3447)
PHONE.................................707 823-4043
Kila Peterson,
Deborah Burnes,
EMP: 20
SALES (est): 2.1MM **Privately Held**
WEB: www.sumbody.com
SIC: 2844 5999 Toilet preparations; toi-
letries, cosmetics & perfumes

(P-8850)
SUN DEEP INC
Also Called: Sun Deep Cosmetics
31285 San Clemente St B, Hayward
(94544-7814)
P.O. Box 2814, Danville (94526-7814)
PHONE.................................510 441-2525
Jay Gill, CEO
Prabhleen S Gill, President
Ravi Gill, Corp Secy
Sundeep Gill, Vice Pres
▲ EMP: 40
SQ FT: 40,000
SALES (est): 8MM **Privately Held**
WEB: www.sundeepinc.com
SIC: 2844 5122 Cosmetic preparations;
toilet preparations; cosmetics, perfumes &
hair products

(P-8851)
SUNEVA MEDICAL INC (PA)
5870 Pacific Center Blvd, San Diego
(92121-4204)
PHONE.................................858 550-9999
Nicholas L Teti Jr, Ch of Bd
Preston Romm, President
Patricia Altavilla, COO
Joseph A Newcomb, CFO
Stewart M Brown, Vice Pres
EMP: 45 EST: 2009
SALES (est): 12.1MM **Privately Held**
SIC: 2844 3842 Cosmetic preparations;
cosmetic restorations

(P-8852)
TENDER LOVING THINGS INC
Also Called: Happy Company, The
26203 Prod Ave Ste 4, Hayward (94545)
PHONE.................................510 300-1260
Mark Juarez, CEO
Alan Widdoss, CFO
EMP: 20
SQ FT: 20,000
SALES (est): 3.8MM **Privately Held**
WEB: www.thehappycompany.com
SIC: 2844 2499 5122 Toilet preparations;
novelties, wood fiber; drugs, proprietaries
& sundries

(P-8853)
THIBIANT INTERNATIONAL INC
Also Called: Kdc-One
20320 Prairie St, Chatsworth (91311-6026)
PHONE.................................818 709-1345
Nicholas Whitley, CEO
Martin Tremblay, CPA
◆ EMP: 361
SQ FT: 350,000
SALES (est): 133.2MM
SALES (corp-wide): 603MM **Privately
Held**
WEB: www.thibiantspa.com
SIC: 2844 Cosmetic preparations
PA: Corporation Developpement Knowlton
Inc
255 Boul Roland-Therrien Bureau 100
Longueuil QC J4H 4
450 243-2000

(P-8854)
TRADEMARK COSMETIC INC
545 Columbia Ave, Riverside (92507-2183)
PHONE.................................951 683-2631
David Ryngler, CEO
Joy Boiani, CFO
Eko Handoko, Vice Pres
Julieta Vinluan, Research
▲ EMP: 38
SQ FT: 38,000
SALES (est): 11.5MM **Privately Held**
WEB: www.trademarkcosmetics.com
SIC: 2844 7231 5999 5122 Hair prepara-
tions, including shampoos; beauty shops;
cosmetics; cosmetics

(P-8855)
TRANS-INDIA PRODUCTS INC
Also Called: Shikai Products
3330 Coffey Ln Ste A&B, Santa Rosa
(95403-1917)
P.O. Box 2866 (95405-0866)
PHONE.................................707 544-0298
Dennis Sepp, President
Jason Sepp, CEO
Carol Sepp, Corp Secy
Vasant Telang, Vice Pres
▲ EMP: 25
SQ FT: 30,000
SALES (est): 6.4MM **Privately Held**
WEB: www.shikai.com
SIC: 2844 Face creams or lotions; cos-
metic preparations

(P-8856)
TU-K INDUSTRIES INC
5702 Firestone Pl, South Gate
(90280-3714)
PHONE.................................562 927-3365
Alpin K Kaler, President
Eleanor Kaler, Corp Secy
Rafael Esparza, Prdtn Mgr
Arman Cornell, Manager
▲ EMP: 30 EST: 1970
SQ FT: 40,000

SALES: 3.5MM **Privately Held**
WEB: www.2kindustries.com
SIC: 2844 Cosmetic preparations

(P-8857)
URBAN DECAL LLC (HQ)
Also Called: Urban Decay Cosmetics
833 W 16th St, Newport Beach
(92663-2801)
PHONE.................................949 574-9712
Adel Hamdan, Mng Member
Ella Tavara, President
John Ferrari, Treasurer
Jennifer Broadway, Assoc VP
Cole Martin, Assoc VP
▲ EMP: 35
SQ FT: 6,500
SALES (est): 6MM
SALES (corp-wide): 4.2B **Privately Held**
WEB: www.urbandecay.com
SIC: 2844 5122 Cosmetic preparations;
cosmetics, perfumes & hair products
PA: L'oreal
Kerastase Mizani L Oreal Profes-
sionne
Paris 75008
140 206-000

(P-8858)
US COTTON LLC
7100 W Sunnyview Ave, Visalia
(93291-9639)
PHONE.................................559 651-3015
Gary S Jordan, Principal
EMP: 293
SALES (corp-wide): 1.4B **Privately Held**
SIC: 2844 Toilet preparations
HQ: U.S. Cotton, Llc
531 Cotton Blossom Cir
Gastonia NC 28054
216 676-6400

(P-8859)
USP INC
Also Called: Enjoy Haircare
1818 Ord Way, Oceanside (92056-1502)
P.O. Box 5903 (92052-5903)
PHONE.................................760 842-7700
Patrick Dockry, Principal
Gordon Fletcher, Vice Pres
▲ EMP: 60
SQ FT: 60,000
SALES (est): 20MM **Privately Held**
SIC: 2844 Hair preparations, including
shampoos

(P-8860)
**V MANUFACTURING LOGISTICS
INC**
20501 Earlgate St, Walnut (91789-2909)
PHONE.................................909 869-6200
Florence Nacino, President
Beatriz Betancourt, Executive Asst
▲ EMP: 20
SALES: 2MM **Privately Held**
SIC: 2844 Cosmetic preparations

(P-8861)
VEGE - KURL INC
Also Called: Vege-Tech Company
412 W Cypress St, Glendale (91204-2402)
PHONE.................................818 956-5582
Eric W Huffman, President
Helen Huffman, Corp Secy
EMP: 60
SALES (est): 17.7MM **Privately Held**
WEB: www.vegekurl.com
SIC: 2844 2833 5122 Shampoos, rinses,
conditioners: hair; medicinals & botani-
cals; cosmetics, perfumes & hair products

(P-8862)
VERDE COSMETIC LABS LLC
19845 Nordhokk St, Northridge (91324)
PHONE.................................818 284-4080
John Mizialko, President
Linda Mile,
David Stearn,
EMP: 14
SQ FT: 13,000
SALES: 3.5MM **Privately Held**
SIC: 2844 Cosmetic preparations

(P-8863)
VIE PRODUCTS INC
9663 Santa Monica Blvd, Beverly Hills
(90210-4303)
PHONE.................................310 684-3566
Kevin Seib, President
EMP: 20
SALES (est): 2.2MM **Privately Held**
WEB: www.vieproducts.com
SIC: 2844 Cosmetic preparations

(P-8864)
VS VINCENZO LTD INC
34700 Pacific Coast Hwy, Capistrano
Beach (92624-1351)
PHONE.................................949 388-8791
Vincent Michael Spinnato, President
EMP: 10
SQ FT: 1,400
SALES (est): 1.1MM **Privately Held**
SIC: 2844 Toilet preparations

(P-8865)
**WESTRIDGE LABORATORIES
INC**
1671 E Saint Andrew Pl, Santa Ana
(92705-4932)
PHONE.................................714 259-9400
Gregg Richard Haskell, CEO
John Speelman, Vice Pres
John Spielman, Vice Pres
Stephanie Cazarin, Human Res Mgr
Veronica Amezcua, Purchasing
▲ EMP: 28
SALES (est): 8.1MM **Privately Held**
WEB: www.idlube.com
SIC: 2844 Cosmetic preparations

(P-8866)
**WESTWOOD LABORATORIES
INC (PA)**
710 S Ayon Ave, Azusa (91702-5123)
PHONE.................................626 969-3305
Tony De Vos, CEO
Cheryl Kohorst, CFO
▲ EMP: 42
SALES (est): 9.9MM **Privately Held**
SIC: 2844 Toilet preparations

(P-8867)
YES TO INC
Also Called: Yes To Carrots
177 E Colo Blvd Ste 110, Pasadena
(91105)
PHONE.................................626 365-1976
Ingrid Jackel, CEO
Lance Kalish, Shareholder
Ido Leffler, Shareholder
▲ EMP: 40
SQ FT: 3,000
SALES: 0 **Privately Held**
SIC: 2844 5122 Face creams or lotions;
cosmetic preparations; hair preparations,
including shampoos; cosmetics

(P-8868)
YOUNG NAILS INC
1149 N Patt St, Anaheim (92801-2568)
PHONE.................................714 525-2264
Habib Bishara Salo, CEO
Greg Salo, President
Young Salo, Vice Pres
▲ EMP: 18
SQ FT: 19,000
SALES (est): 6.2MM **Privately Held**
WEB: www.youngnails.com
SIC: 2844 Manicure preparations

(P-8869)
ZERRAN INTERNATIONAL CORP
Also Called: Www.zerran.com
12880 Pierce St, Pacoima (91331-2524)
PHONE.................................818 897-5494
Steven Saute, President
Richard Saute, Shareholder
Robert Saute, Shareholder
Cindy Van Steelandt, Mktg Dir
▲ EMP: 13
SALES (est): 2.4MM **Privately Held**
WEB: www.zerran.com
SIC: 2844 5122 Hair preparations, includ-
ing shampoos; hair preparations

▲ = Import ▼=Export
◆ =Import/Export

(P-8870)
ZION HEALTH INC
Also Called: Adama Minerals
430 E Grand Ave, South San Francisco
(94080-6207)
P.O. Box 282249, San Francisco (94128-2249)
PHONE..................650 520-4313
Haim Zion, *Principal*
EMP: 11
SALES (est): 622.7K **Privately Held**
SIC: 2844 Shampoos, rinses, conditioners: hair; lotions, shaving; deodorants, personal

(P-8871)
ZO SKIN HEALTH INC (PA)
5 Technology Dr, Irvine (92618-2302)
PHONE..................949 988-7524
Mark Williams, *CEO*
Kevin Cornett, *CFO*
Chris Kraneiss, *Vice Pres*
Rick Woodin, *Vice Pres*
Cindy Keyes, *Administration*
◆ EMP: 80
SQ FT: 12,000
SALES (est): 19.9MM **Privately Held**
SIC: 2844 Face creams or lotions

(P-8872)
ZOTOS INTERNATIONAL INC
Joico Laboratories Division
488 E Santa Clara St # 301, Arcadia
(91006-7229)
PHONE..................626 321-4100
Annie Hu, *Branch Mgr*
EMP: 30
SALES (corp-wide): 23.6B **Privately Held**
WEB: www.zotos.com
SIC: 2844 Hair preparations, including shampoos; cosmetic preparations
HQ: Zotos International, Inc.
100 Tokeneke Rd
Darien CT 06820
203 655-8911

2851 Paints, Varnishes, Lacquers, Enamels

(P-8873)
AEGIS INDUSTRIES INC
Also Called: Atlas Computer Centers
2360 Thompson Way Ste A, Santa Maria
(93455-1095)
P.O. Box 6558 (93456-6558)
PHONE..................805 922-2700
Robert Dickerson, *President*
EMP: 10
SALES (est): 1.1MM **Privately Held**
SIC: 2851 2891 5198 Paints, waterproof; sealants; paints

(P-8874)
ALLIED COATINGS INC
1125 Linda Vista Dr # 104, San Marcos
(92078-3819)
PHONE..................800 630-2375
Donald J Palazzo, *Principal*
EMP: 14
SALES (est): 2.3MM **Privately Held**
SIC: 2851 Vinyl coatings, strippable

(P-8875)
AMAZON ENVIRONMENTAL INC (PA)
Also Called: Amazon Paint
779 Palmyrita Ave, Riverside (92507-1811)
P.O. Box 9306, Whittier (90608-9306)
PHONE..................951 588-0206
Craig Elzinga, *President*
John P Segala, *Vice Pres*
John Segala, *Vice Pres*
Gloria Schoeppe, *Controller*
Frank Gonzales, *Plant Mgr*
EMP: 21
SQ FT: 12,000
SALES (est): 5MM **Privately Held**
WEB: www.amazonpaint.com
SIC: 2851 Paints & allied products

(P-8876)
AMERICA WOOD FINISHES INC
728 E 59th St, Los Angeles (90001-1004)
PHONE..................323 232-8256

Manuel Padilla, *President*
Elvira Padilla, *Admin Sec*
▲ EMP: 15
SALES (est): 2.4MM **Privately Held**
SIC: 2851 Paints, waterproof

(P-8877)
BEHR PROCESS CORPORATION
3001 S Yale St, Santa Ana (92704-6440)
PHONE..................714 545-7101
Jeffrey D Filley, *Branch Mgr*
EMP: 109
SQ FT: 63,755
SALES (corp-wide): 7.6B **Publicly Held**
WEB: www.behr.com
SIC: 2851 Paints & paint additives
HQ: Behr Process Corporation
1801 E Saint Andrew Pl
Santa Ana CA 92705

(P-8878)
BEHR PROCESS CORPORATION
1603 W Alton Ave, Santa Ana
(92704-7258)
PHONE..................714 545-7101
Jeffrey D Filley, *Branch Mgr*
EMP: 23
SQ FT: 54,819
SALES (corp-wide): 7.6B **Publicly Held**
WEB: www.behr.com
SIC: 2851 Paints & allied products
HQ: Behr Process Corporation
1801 E Saint Andrew Pl
Santa Ana CA 92705

(P-8879)
BEHR PROCESS CORPORATION (HQ)
1801 E Saint Andrew Pl, Santa Ana
(92705-5044)
PHONE..................714 545-7101
Jeffrey D Filley, *President*
Jonathan Sullivan, *Senior VP*
Lawrence F Leaman, *Vice Pres*
Richard Maus, *Vice Pres*
Jerry W Mollien, *Vice Pres*
▲ EMP: 700
SQ FT: 220,000
SALES: 1.5B
SALES (corp-wide): 7.6B **Publicly Held**
SIC: 2851 Paints & paint additives; stains: varnish, oil or wax; varnishes
PA: Masco Corporation
17450 College Pkwy
Livonia MI 48152
313 274-7400

(P-8880)
BEHR PROCESS CORPORATION
3400 W Garry Ave, Santa Ana
(92704-6421)
PHONE..................714 545-7101
Jeffrey D Filley, *Principal*
EMP: 91
SALES (corp-wide): 7.6B **Publicly Held**
SIC: 2851 Paints & paint additives
HQ: Behr Process Corporation
1801 E Saint Andrew Pl
Santa Ana CA 92705

(P-8881)
BEHR PROCESS CORPORATION
3130 S Harbor Blvd # 400, Santa Ana
(92704-6820)
PHONE..................714 545-7101
Jeffrey D Filley, *Branch Mgr*
EMP: 87
SALES (corp-wide): 7.6B **Publicly Held**
SIC: 2851 Paints & paint additives
HQ: Behr Process Corporation
1801 E Saint Andrew Pl
Santa Ana CA 92705

(P-8882)
BEHR PROCESS CORPORATION
3500 W Segerstrom Ave, Santa Ana
(92704-6406)
PHONE..................714 545-7101
Jeffrey D Filley, *Branch Mgr*
EMP: 18
SALES (corp-wide): 7.6B **Publicly Held**
SIC: 2851 Paints & paint additives

HQ: Behr Process Corporation
1801 E Saint Andrew Pl
Santa Ana CA 92705

(P-8883)
BEHR PROCESS CORPORATION
1995 S Standard Ave, Santa Ana
(92707-3004)
PHONE..................714 545-7101
Jeffrey D Filley, *Branch Mgr*
EMP: 65
SALES (corp-wide): 7.6B **Publicly Held**
SIC: 2851 Paints & paint additives
HQ: Behr Process Corporation
1801 E Saint Andrew Pl
Santa Ana CA 92705

(P-8884)
BEHR SALES INC (HQ)
Also Called: Behr Paint Corp.
3400 W Segerstrom Ave, Santa Ana
(92704-6405)
PHONE..................714 545-7101
Jeffrey D Filley, *CEO*
Jonathan M Sullivan, *CFO*
Anthony Demiro, *Senior VP*
EMP: 124 EST: 1948
SQ FT: 54,000
SALES (est): 472.3MM
SALES (corp-wide): 7.6B **Publicly Held**
SIC: 2851 Paints & paint additives; stains: varnish, oil or wax
PA: Masco Corporation
17450 College Pkwy
Livonia MI 48152
313 274-7400

(P-8885)
BENJAMIN MOORE & CO
3441 W Temple Ave, Pomona
(91768-3284)
PHONE..................909 444-0390
Ron Widner, *Manager*
Mike Branch, *Sales Executive*
EMP: 56
SALES (corp-wide): 242.1B **Publicly Held**
WEB: www.benjaminmoore.com
SIC: 2851 Paints: oil or alkyd vehicle or water thinned
HQ: Benjamin Moore & Co.
101 Paragon Dr
Montvale NJ 07645
201 573-9600

(P-8886)
CAL WEST SPCIALTY COATINGS INC
1058 W Evelyn Ave Ste 10, Sunnyvale
(94086-5794)
PHONE..................408 720-7440
Edward Woodhall, *President*
Brian Wong, *CFO*
Trusha Mair, *Administration*
Steve Holmlund, *Marketing Mgr*
Doug Badham, *Sales Staff*
▲ EMP: 10
SQ FT: 10,000
SALES (est): 1.6MM **Privately Held**
WEB: www.cal-west.net
SIC: 2851 2899 Lacquers, varnishes, enamels & other coatings; chemical preparations

(P-8887)
CARBOLINE COMPANY
5533 Brooks St, Montclair (91763-4547)
PHONE..................909 459-1090
Jose Fernandez, *Manager*
EMP: 20
SALES (corp-wide): 5.3B **Publicly Held**
SIC: 2851 Lacquers, varnishes, enamels & other coatings
HQ: Carboline Company
2150 Schuetz Rd Fl 1
Saint Louis MO 63146
314 644-1000

(P-8888)
CARBONYTE SYSTEMS INCORPORATED
3 Wayne Ct Ste A, Sacramento
(95829-1306)
PHONE..................916 387-0316

Gordon Rayner, *President*
William Coe, *Vice Pres*
Donna Coe, *Principal*
EMP: 10
SALES: 1.9MM **Privately Held**
WEB: www.carbonyte.com
SIC: 2851 Paints & paint additives

(P-8889)
CARDINAL INDUSTRIAL FINISHES (PA)
1329 Potrero Ave, South El Monte
(91733-3088)
P.O. Box 9296 (91733-0965)
PHONE..................626 444-9274
Lawrence C Felix, *CEO*
Laura Woods, *Managing Prtnr*
Pat Mathiesen, *CFO*
Keith Hocking, *Vice Pres*
Jason Nocero, *Creative Dir*
◆ EMP: 100 EST: 1952
SQ FT: 50,000
SALES (est): 85.1MM **Privately Held**
WEB: www.cardinalpaint.com
SIC: 2851 Lacquers, varnishes, enamels & other coatings

(P-8890)
CARDINAL INDUSTRIAL FINISHES
890 Commercial St, San Jose
(95112-1410)
PHONE..................408 452-8522
Tom Cross, *Manager*
Dave Lawson, *Regional Mgr*
EMP: 20
SALES (corp-wide): 85.1MM **Privately Held**
WEB: www.cardinalpaint.com
SIC: 2851 Paints & allied products
PA: Cardinal Industrial Finishes
1329 Potrero Ave
South El Monte CA 91733
626 444-9274

(P-8891)
CARDINAL PAINT AND POWDER INC
1329 Potrero Ave, South El Monte
(91733-3012)
PHONE..................626 444-9274
Lawrence C Felix, *President*
◆ EMP: 225
SQ FT: 50,000
SALES: 70MM **Privately Held**
SIC: 2851 Paints & allied products

(P-8892)
CARDINAL PAINT AND POWDER INC
15010 Don Julian Rd, City of Industry
(91746-3301)
PHONE..................626 937-6767
Stanley W Ekstrom, *Branch Mgr*
EMP: 45
SALES (corp-wide): 85.1MM **Privately Held**
SIC: 2851 Paints & allied products
PA: Cardinal Industrial Finishes
1329 Potrero Ave
South El Monte CA 91733
626 444-9274

(P-8893)
CATALINA INDUSTRIES INC
Also Called: Catalina Paint Stores
8814 Reseda Blvd, Northridge
(91324-4039)
PHONE..................818 772-8888
Bernard Cohn, *Owner*
EMP: 12
SQ FT: 3,050
SALES (corp-wide): 5.2MM **Privately Held**
WEB: www.catalinapaint.com
SIC: 2851 5198 Paints & allied products; paints
PA: Catalina Industries, Inc.
11919 Vose St
North Hollywood CA 91605
818 765-2629

(P-8894)
CDH PAINTING INC
802 Harris St, Eureka (95503-4542)
PHONE.............................707 443-4429
Duane Hagans, *President*
Jacquee Carlino, *Technology*
Clayton Hagans, *Director*
Gina Loya, *Manager*
EMP: 12
SALES: 650K **Privately Held**
SIC: 2851 Lacquers, varnishes, enamels &
other coatings

(P-8895)
CONDUCTIVE SCIENCE INC
11643 Rverside Dr Ste 115, Lakeside
(92040)
PHONE.............................858 699-1837
Tom Judish, *President*
▲ EMP: 10
SALES (est): 1.1MM **Privately Held**
SIC: 2851 Coating, air curing

(P-8896)
CONSOLIDATED COLOR
CORPORATION
12316 Carson St, Hawaiian Gardens
(90716-1604)
PHONE.............................562 420-7714
Michael J Muldown, *President*
Deborah Muldown, *Vice Pres*
Blessy Conde, *Technical Staff*
Lidia Cardenas, *Accounting Mgr*
Matthew Muldown, *Purchasing*
EMP: 25
SQ FT: 30,000
SALES (est): 5.2MM **Privately Held**
SIC: 2851 2865 Paints & paint additives;
cyclic crudes & intermediates

(P-8897)
CONTINENTAL COATINGS INC
10938 Beech Ave, Fontana (92337-7260)
PHONE.............................909 355-1200
Robert Wang, *President*
Jack Keenan, *Vice Pres*
Joe Seaton, *Vice Pres*
Stephanie Varela, *Mng Member*
Mathilde Mendez, *Director*
▲ EMP: 16 EST: 1976
SQ FT: 20,000
SALES (est): 4.9MM **Privately Held**
WEB: www.continentalcoatings.com
SIC: 2851 Paints & paint additives

(P-8898)
CONTRACT TRANSPORTATION
SYS CO
Also Called: Certified Distribution Svcs
12500 Slauson Ave Ste B2, Santa Fe
Springs (90670-8618)
PHONE.............................562 696-3262
Chuck Huff, *Branch Mgr*
EMP: 53
SALES (corp-wide): 14.9B **Publicly Held**
WEB: www.ctsoh.net
SIC: 2851 Paints & allied products
HQ: Contract Transportation System Co.
101 W Prospect Ave
Cleveland OH 44115
216 566-2000

(P-8899)
CRAWFORD PRODUCTS
COMPANY INC
409 N Park Ave, Montebello (90640-4137)
P.O. Box 4339, Whittier (90607-4339)
PHONE.............................323 721-6429
Deborah L Crawford, *President*
EMP: 12 EST: 1957
SALES (est): 2.4MM **Privately Held**
WEB: www.crawfords.com
SIC: 2851 Putty

(P-8900)
D J SIMPSON COMPANY (PA)
Also Called: Simpson Coatings Group, The
401 S Canal St A, South San Francisco
(94080-4606)
PHONE.............................650 225-9404
Timothy Simpson, *President*
EMP: 15
SQ FT: 35,000

SALES (est): 5MM **Privately Held**
WEB: www.djsimpson.com
SIC: 2851 Paints & allied products

(P-8901)
DUNCAN ENTERPRISES (HQ)
Also Called: Ilovetocreate A Duncan Entps
5673 E Shields Ave, Fresno (93727-7819)
PHONE.............................559 291-4444
Larry Duncan, *CEO*
Robert E Duncan, *Ch of Bd*
Larry Hermansen, *President*
Larry R Duncan, *CEO*
Valerie Marderosian, *Vice Pres*
◆ EMP: 170 EST: 1936
SQ FT: 260,000
SALES (est): 49.7MM **Privately Held**
WEB: www.duncancrafts.com
SIC: 2851 3299 3952 3944 Colors in oil,
except artists'; ceramic fiber; lead pencils
& art goods; games, toys & children's ve-
hicles
PA: Duncan Financial Corporation
5673 E Shields Ave
Fresno CA 93727
559 291-4444

(P-8902)
DURA TECHNOLOGIES INC
2720 S Willow Ave Ste A, Bloomington
(92316-3259)
P.O. Box 333 (92316-0333)
PHONE.............................909 877-8477
Douglas L Dennis, *President*
Gina L Dennis, *Vice Pres*
▲ EMP: 150
SQ FT: 14,000
SALES (est): 23.5MM **Privately Held**
SIC: 2851 Paints & allied products

(P-8903)
EAST BAY PAINT CENTER INC
990 San Pablo Ave, Albany (94706-2010)
PHONE.............................510 524-6582
Bob Langbein, *President*
Maria Langbein, *Vice Pres*
EMP: 15
SQ FT: 5,000
SALES (est): 5MM
SALES (corp-wide): 242.1B **Publicly**
Held
SIC: 2851 Enamels
HQ: Alachua Tung Oil Co Inc
51 Chestnut Ridge Rd
Montvale NJ 07645
201 573-9600

(P-8904)
ENGINEERED COATING TECH
INC
2838 E 54th St, Vernon (90058-3632)
PHONE.............................323 588-0260
Gloria Navarro, *President*
EMP: 12
SQ FT: 17,000
SALES (est): 1.6MM **Privately Held**
WEB: www.ecoatingtechnology.com
SIC: 2851

(P-8905)
ENGINERED PNT APPLICATIONS
LLC
1586 Franklin Ave, Redlands (92373-7102)
PHONE.............................626 737-7400
Ernest Mancilla,
Ernie Mancilla, *Project Mgr*
EMP: 12
SALES (est): 2MM **Privately Held**
WEB:
www.engineeredpaintapplications.com
SIC: 2851 3567 Paints & allied products;
industrial furnaces & ovens

(P-8906)
ENNIS-FLINT INC
200 2nd St, Bakersfield (93304-3200)
PHONE.............................661 328-0503
Richard Gonzalez, *Branch Mgr*
EMP: 20
SALES (corp-wide): 134.1MM **Privately**
Held
WEB: www.ennispaint.com
SIC: 2851 Paints & allied products

PA: Ennis-Flint, Inc.
4161 Piedmont Pkwy # 370
Greensboro NC 27410
800 331-8118

(P-8907)
EPMAR CORPORATION
13210 Barton Cir, Whittier (90605-3254)
PHONE.............................562 946-8781
Joe Matrange, *President*
Mary Pon, *Chief Mktg Ofcr*
Cathy Ramsey, *Office Mgr*
Christine Rivera, *Accountant*
◆ EMP: 38
SQ FT: 26,000
SALES (est): 14.2MM
SALES (corp-wide): 820MM **Publicly**
Held
WEB: www.epmar.com
SIC: 2851 2891 2821 3087 Epoxy coat-
ings; polyurethane coatings; adhesives &
sealants; plastics materials & resins; cus-
tom compound purchased resins
PA: Quaker Chemical Corporation
901 E Hector St
Conshohocken PA 19428
610 832-4000

(P-8908)
INTEGRATED OPTICAL SVCS
CORP
Also Called: Ios Optics
3150 Molinaro St, Santa Clara
(95054-2425)
PHONE.............................408 982-9510
Douglas Fitzpatrick, *President*
Elmer Valencia, *Treasurer*
Derek Fitzpatrick, *General Mgr*
Eduardo Taruc, *Office Mgr*
Rey Arellano, *VP Finance*
▲ EMP: 35
SQ FT: 19,000
SALES (est): 7.6MM **Privately Held**
WEB: www.ioscorp.net
SIC: 2851 3827 Paints & allied products;
prisms, optical

(P-8909)
JANCO CHEMICAL
CORPORATION
Also Called: Janco Airless Center
1235 5th St, Berkeley (94710-1395)
PHONE.............................510 527-9770
Glenn A Kjelstrom, *President*
Janice S Kjelstrom, *Vice Pres*
EMP: 13 EST: 1962
SQ FT: 12,000
SALES (est): 2.4MM **Privately Held**
SIC: 2851 5198 Wood stains; paint
brushes, rollers, sprayers

(P-8910)
KELLY-MOORE PAINT COMPANY
INC (PA)
Also Called: Kelly-Moore Paints
987 Commercial St, San Carlos
(94070-4018)
P.O. Box 3016 (94070-1316)
PHONE.............................650 592-8337
Steve De Voe, *Ch of Bd*
Roy George, *Exec VP*
Michael Black, *Vice Pres*
Todd Wirdzek, *Vice Pres*
Robert Stetson, *Risk Mgmt Dir*
◆ EMP: 250 EST: 1946
SQ FT: 350,000
SALES (est): 712MM **Privately Held**
WEB: www.kellymoore.com
SIC: 2851 Paints: oil or alkyd vehicle or
water thinned; lacquers, varnishes, enam-
els & other coatings; removers & cleaners

(P-8911)
KELLY-MOORE PAINT COMPANY
INC
Also Called: Kelly-Moore Paints
3954 Decoto Rd, Fremont (94555-3114)
PHONE.............................510 505-9834
EMP: 23
SALES (corp-wide): 712MM **Privately**
Held
SIC: 2851 Paints: oil or alkyd vehicle or
water thinned; lacquers, varnishes, enam-
els & other coatings; removers & cleaners

PA: Kelly-Moore Paint Company, Inc.
987 Commercial St
San Carlos CA 94070
650 592-8337

(P-8912)
KELLY-MOORE PAINT COMPANY
INC
Also Called: Kelly-Moore Paints
1075 Commercial St, San Carlos
(94070-4007)
PHONE.............................650 595-0333
Jasjit Valbiel, *Manager*
Joseph P Cristiano, *President*
EMP: 20
SALES (corp-wide): 712MM **Privately**
Held
WEB: www.kellymoore.com
SIC: 2851 5231 Vinyl coatings, strippable;
paints: oil or alkyd vehicle or water
thinned; lacquers, varnishes, enamels &
other coatings; removers & cleaners;
paint
PA: Kelly-Moore Paint Company, Inc.
987 Commercial St
San Carlos CA 94070
650 592-8337

(P-8913)
KOTT INC
27161 Burbank, El Toro (92610-2501)
PHONE.............................949 770-5055
John T Kott, *President*
Dorothy Kott, *Corp Secy*
EMP: 10
SALES (est): 557.4K
SALES (corp-wide): 5.1MM **Privately**
Held
WEB: www.kott.com
SIC: 2851 6794 Lacquers, varnishes,
enamels & other coatings; franchises,
selling or licensing
PA: Kott Koatings Inc
27161 Burbank
El Toro CA 92610
949 770-5055

(P-8914)
LAIRD COATINGS
CORPORATION
Also Called: Coatings Resource
15541 Commerce Ln, Huntington Beach
(92649-1601)
PHONE.............................714 894-5252
Edwin Laird, *CEO*
Jeff Laird, *President*
▲ EMP: 48
SQ FT: 17,500
SALES (est): 5.6MM **Privately Held**
WEB: www.coatingsresource.com
SIC: 2851 2865 Paints & paint additives;
dyes, synthetic organic

(P-8915)
LIFE PAINT COMPANY (PA)
12927 Sunshine Ave, Santa Fe Springs
(90670-4732)
P.O. Box 2488 (90670-0488)
PHONE.............................562 944-6391
Ronald Sibbrel, *President*
Fred Benson, *Corp Secy*
Mike De La Vega, *Vice Pres*
▲ EMP: 40
SQ FT: 30,000
SALES (est): 13.2MM **Privately Held**
WEB: www.lifepaint.com
SIC: 2851 2899 2821 Paints & allied
products; waterproofing compounds; ther-
mosetting materials

(P-8916)
MADDIEBRIT PRODUCTS LLC
Also Called: Grab Green
537 Constitution Ave B, Camarillo
(93012-8571)
PHONE.............................818 483-0096
Michael Edell,
Nicole Breitung, *Marketing Staff*
Drew Edell, *Mktg Coord*
Patricia Spencer,
Lindze Braff, *Accounts Mgr*
EMP: 10
SALES (est): 2.4MM **Privately Held**
SIC: 2851 Removers & cleaners

(P-8917)
MASTER POWDER COATING INC
13721 Bora Dr, Santa Fe Springs (90670-5007)
PHONE.................562 863-4135
Judith Flores, *CEO*
Juan Renteria, *Vice Pres*
Dalila Flores, *VP Opers*
EMP: 37 EST: 2006
SALES (est): 8.6MM Privately Held
SIC: 2851 Paints & allied products

(P-8918)
MIRACLE COVER (PA)
20721 Goshawk Ln, Huntington Beach (92646-5529)
P.O. Box 6081 (92615-6081)
PHONE.................714 842-8863
Paul D Jordan, *President*
Douglas Jordan, *Vice Pres*
Terri Jordan, *Vice Pres*
EMP: 11
SQ FT: 13,000
SALES: 800K Privately Held
SIC: 2851 5169 2891 Putty, wood fillers & sealers; chemicals, industrial & heavy; adhesives & sealants

(P-8919)
MONOPOLE INC
4661 Alger St, Los Angeles (90039-1127)
P.O. Box 250534, Glendale (91225-0534)
PHONE.................818 500-8585
Antoine Abikhalil, *President*
▲ EMP: 15
SQ FT: 40,000
SALES: 2MM Privately Held
WEB: www.monopoleinc.com
SIC: 2851 Paints & allied products

(P-8920)
MOTORSHIELD LLC
Also Called: Motoshieldpro
3364 Garfield Ave, Commerce (90040-3102)
PHONE.................323 396-9200
Rick Fung,
Maria Ortega, *General Mgr*
EMP: 15 EST: 2016
SALES (est): 1MM Privately Held
SIC: 2851 Undercoatings, paint

(P-8921)
MULTICOAT PRODUCTS INC
23331 Antonio Pkwy, Rcho STA Marg (92688-2664)
PHONE.................949 888-7100
Dave Maietta, *President*
John Dill, *Vice Pres*
Francisco Duran, *Executive*
Morrie Howard, *Manager*
EMP: 15 EST: 1995
SALES (est): 4.6MM Privately Held
SIC: 2851 2899 3299 3479 Paints & paint additives; waterproofing compounds; stucco; painting, coating & hot dipping

(P-8922)
PAINT-CHEM INC
Also Called: Transchem Coatings
1680 Miller Ave, Los Angeles (90063-1613)
P.O. Box 151014 (90015-8014)
PHONE.................213 747-7725
Amir Afshar, *President*
Eugene Golling, *Vice Pres*
Eddie Andrews, *Admin Sec*
EMP: 15
SQ FT: 8,000
SALES (est): 3MM Privately Held
SIC: 2851 5198 Coating, air curing; paints

(P-8923)
PERFORMANCE COATINGS INC
360 Lake Mendocino Dr, Ukiah (95482-9497)
P.O. Box 1569 (95482-1569)
PHONE.................707 462-3023
Barbara Newell, *Ch of Bd*
Gina Phillips, *Manager*
◆ EMP: 20
SQ FT: 4,300
SALES (est): 7.9MM Privately Held
WEB: www.penofin.com
SIC: 2851 Wood stains

(P-8924)
POLY-FIBER INC (PA)
Also Called: Consolidated Aircraft Coatings
4343 Fort Dr, Riverside (92509-6784)
P.O. Box 3129 (92519-3129)
PHONE.................951 684-4280
Jon Goldenbaum, *President*
Greg Albarin, *General Mgr*
Long Cao, *Research*
Greg Albarian, *Opers Staff*
Phyllis Goldenbaum, *Manager*
EMP: 20
SQ FT: 75,000
SALES: 2.1MM Privately Held
WEB: www.polyfiber.com
SIC: 2851 Undercoatings, paint

(P-8925)
PPG INDUSTRIES INC
5750 Imhoff Dr Ste A, Concord (94520-5330)
PHONE.................925 798-0539
Marlon Medina, *Principal*
EMP: 11
SALES (corp-wide): 14.2B Publicly Held
SIC: 2851 Paints & allied products
PA: Ppg Industries, Inc.
1 Ppg Pl
Pittsburgh PA 15272
412 434-3131

(P-8926)
PPG INDUSTRIES INC
10060 Mission Mill Rd, City of Industry (90601-1738)
PHONE.................562 692-4010
Gerald Roberts, *Manager*
EMP: 15
SALES (corp-wide): 14.7B Publicly Held
WEB: www.ppg.com
SIC: 2851 Paints & allied products
PA: Ppg Industries, Inc.
1 Ppg Pl
Pittsburgh PA 15272
412 434-3131

(P-8927)
PPG INDUSTRIES INC
Also Called: PPG 9726
1128 N Highland Ave, Los Angeles (90038-1205)
PHONE.................310 559-2335
Jim Dabbs, *Manager*
EMP: 24
SALES (corp-wide): 14.2B Publicly Held
WEB: www.ppg.com
SIC: 2851 Paints & allied products
PA: Ppg Industries, Inc.
1 Ppg Pl
Pittsburgh PA 15272
412 434-3131

(P-8928)
PPG INDUSTRIES INC
Also Called: PPG 9721
43639 10th St W, Lancaster (93534-4801)
PHONE.................661 945-7871
Jim Dabbs, *Branch Mgr*
EMP: 24
SALES (corp-wide): 14.2B Publicly Held
WEB: www.ppg.com
SIC: 2851 Paints & allied products
PA: Ppg Industries, Inc.
1 Ppg Pl
Pittsburgh PA 15272
412 434-3131

(P-8929)
PPG INDUSTRIES INC
Also Called: PPG 9722
74240 Highway 111, Palm Desert (92260-4138)
PHONE.................760 340-1762
David Warrez, *Branch Mgr*
EMP: 24
SALES (corp-wide): 14.2B Publicly Held
WEB: www.ppg.com
SIC: 2851 Paints & allied products
PA: Ppg Industries, Inc.
1 Ppg Pl
Pittsburgh PA 15272
412 434-3131

(P-8930)
PPG INDUSTRIES INC
Also Called: Industrial Coatings Division
15541 Commerce Ln, Huntington Beach (92649-1601)
PHONE.................714 894-5252
Jeff Laird, *Manager*
EMP: 30
SALES (corp-wide): 14.2B Publicly Held
WEB: www.ppg.com
SIC: 2851 Paints & allied products
PA: Ppg Industries, Inc.
1 Ppg Pl
Pittsburgh PA 15272
412 434-3131

(P-8931)
PPG INDUSTRIES INC
11601 United St, Mojave (93501-7048)
PHONE.................661 824-4532
Michelle Brown, *Purchasing*
Andrew Soehnlen, *Opers Mgr*
EMP: 24
SALES (corp-wide): 14.2B Publicly Held
WEB: www.ppg.com
SIC: 2851 Paints & allied products
PA: Ppg Industries, Inc.
1 Ppg Pl
Pittsburgh PA 15272
412 434-3131

(P-8932)
PRECISION COATINGS INC
1220 4th St, Berkeley (94710-1303)
PHONE.................510 525-3600
Michael Emmerich, *President*
EMP: 10
SALES (est): 815.6K Privately Held
SIC: 2851 Paints & allied products

(P-8933)
PRO LINE PAINT COMPANY
2646 Main St, San Diego (92113-3613)
PHONE.................619 232-8968
Anthony A Mitchell, *CEO*
▼ EMP: 48
SALES (est): 6.8MM Privately Held
SIC: 2851 5198 5231 Paints & allied products; paints; paint

(P-8934)
PRODUCTS/TECHNIQUES INC
Also Called: P T I
3271 S Riverside Ave, Bloomington (92316-3515)
P.O. Box 760 (92316-0760)
PHONE.................909 877-3951
Steven Andrews, *President*
Ryan Andrews, *Treasurer*
Barry Boden, *Vice Pres*
Sean Andrews, *Director*
Alice Phelps, *Manager*
EMP: 16 EST: 1947
SQ FT: 12,000
SALES (est): 4.7MM Privately Held
WEB: www.ptipaint.com
SIC: 2851 Coating, air curing

(P-8935)
PROWEST TECHNOLOGIES INC
Also Called: Procoat
2872 S Santa Fe Ave, San Marcos (92069-6046)
PHONE.................760 510-9003
Salim Khalfan, *President*
Debbie Walker, *Corp Secy*
EMP: 25
SQ FT: 3,500
SALES: 2.5MM Privately Held
WEB: www.daveblanchard.com
SIC: 2851 Paints & allied products

(P-8936)
R & S MANUFACTURING & SUP INC
16616 Garfield Ave, Paramount (90723-5305)
PHONE.................909 622-5881
Ronald Hoffman, *Principal*
Susan Hoffman, *Admin Sec*
Sheryl Hoffman-Knitz, *Sales Staff*
EMP: 18
SQ FT: 20,000
SALES (est): 3.8MM Privately Held
SIC: 2851 Colors in oil, except artists'

(P-8937)
R J MCGLENNON COMPANY INC (PA)
Also Called: Maclac Co
198 Utah St, San Francisco (94103-4826)
PHONE.................415 552-0311
Michael McGlennon, *President*
Michael Mc Glennon, *President*
EMP: 22
SQ FT: 30,000
SALES (est): 3.7MM Privately Held
WEB: www.maclac.com
SIC: 2851 Lacquer: bases, dopes, thinner; enamels

(P-8938)
RUPERT GIBBON & SPIDER INC
Also Called: Jacquard Products
1147 Healdsburg Ave, Healdsburg (95448-3405)
P.O. Box 425 (95448-0425)
PHONE.................800 442-0455
Asher Katz, *President*
Devon Scrivner, *Treasurer*
EMP: 35
SQ FT: 24,570
SALES (est): 7.3MM Privately Held
SIC: 2851 8742 5169 Paints & allied products; merchandising consultant; waxes, except petroleum

(P-8939)
SCOTCH PAINT CORPORATION
Also Called: Draw Tite
555 W 189th St, Gardena (90248-4293)
PHONE.................310 329-1259
Charles Mac Harg, *President*
Ching Macharg, *Finance Mgr*
EMP: 12
SQ FT: 12,000
SALES (est): 3.1MM Privately Held
WEB: www.scotchpaint.com
SIC: 2851 Paints & allied products

(P-8940)
SIERRACIN CORPORATION (HQ)
12780 San Fernando Rd, Sylmar (91342-3796)
PHONE.................818 741-1656
Barry N Gillespie, *CEO*
Michael H McGarry, *Exec VP*
Viktoras R Sekmakas, *Exec VP*
Frank S Sklarsky, *Exec VP*
David B Navikas, *Senior VP*
▲ EMP: 550 EST: 1952
SQ FT: 287,000
SALES (est): 94.9MM
SALES (corp-wide): 14.7B Publicly Held
WEB: www.sierracin.com
SIC: 2851 Paints & allied products
PA: Ppg Industries, Inc.
1 Ppg Pl
Pittsburgh PA 15272
412 434-3131

(P-8941)
SIMPSON COATINGS GROUP INC
401 S Canal St A, South San Francisco (94080-4606)
PHONE.................650 873-5990
Tim Simpson, *President*
Diane Simpson, *Admin Sec*
EMP: 25
SQ FT: 35,000
SALES (est): 5MM Privately Held
WEB: www.djsimpson.com
SIC: 2851 Paints & allied products
PA: D J Simpson Company
401 S Canal St A
South San Francisco CA 94080
650 225-9404

(P-8942)
SPECIALIZED MILLING CORP
Also Called: Specialty Finishes
10330 Elm Ave, Fontana (92337-7319)
PHONE.................909 357-7890
Jack Neems, *President*
Seymour S Neems, *Ch of Bd*
Adele Neems, *Treasurer*
EMP: 18
SQ FT: 11,000

SALES (est): 2.4MM **Privately Held**
SIC: 2851 Paints & allied products

(P-8943)
SPECIALTY COATINGS & CHEM INC
Also Called: Special-T
7360 Varna Ave, North Hollywood (91605-4008)
P.O. Box 32459, Los Angeles (90032-0459)
PHONE.............................818 983-0055
Alaistair Macdonald, *President*
W Daniel Ernt, *Vice Pres*
Larry Wick, *Admin Sec*
▲ EMP: 27 EST: 1964
SQ FT: 15,000
SALES (est): 5.4MM **Privately Held**
SIC: 2851 Plastics base paints & varnishes; enamels; lacquer: bases, dopes, thinner

(P-8944)
STILES PAINT MANUFACTURING INC
21595 Curtis St, Hayward (94545-1307)
PHONE.............................510 887-8868
Khosrow Sohrabi, *President*
Bruce Sohrabi, *Vice Pres*
EMP: 13
SQ FT: 19,000
SALES (est): 3.5MM **Privately Held**
SIC: 2851 Paints & paint additives

(P-8945)
SUPERIOR SNDBLST & COATING
8315 Beech Ave, Fontana (92335-3285)
PHONE.............................909 428-9994
Richard Weller, *President*
Ernesto Osuna, *Officer*
Kathleen A Weller, *Vice Pres*
EMP: 10
SQ FT: 10,900
SALES (est): 1.3MM **Privately Held**
SIC: 2851 5088

(P-8946)
TALYARPS CORPORATION
3465 S La Cienega Blvd, Los Angeles (90016-4409)
PHONE.............................310 559-2335
Fax: 310 836-6094
EMP: 25
SQ FT: 25,000
SALES (corp-wide): 33.6MM **Privately Held**
SIC: 2851
PA: Talyarps Corporation
143 Sparks Ave
Pelham NY 10803
914 699-3030

(P-8947)
TEXTURED COATINGS AMERICA INC
Also Called: Tex-Cote
5950 Avalon Blvd, Los Angeles (90003-1310)
P.O. Box 73109 (90003-0109)
PHONE.............................323 233-3111
Stuart M Haines, *Ch of Bd*
EMP: 20
SALES (corp-wide): 14.2MM **Privately Held**
WEB: www.texcoat.com
SIC: 2851 Paints & paint additives; lacquers, varnishes, enamels & other coatings
PA: Textured Coatings Of America Inc.
2422 E 15th St
Panama City FL 32405
800 454-0340

(P-8948)
TIBBETTS NEWPORT CORPORATION
2337 S Birch St, Santa Ana (92707-3402)
PHONE.............................714 546-6662
Shil Park, *President*
Minah Park, *Admin Sec*
EMP: 12
SQ FT: 25,000
SALES (est): 3.2MM **Privately Held**
SIC: 2851 Paints: oil or alkyd vehicle or water thinned

(P-8949)
TIGER CONSTRUCTION INC
6930 Rainbow Dr, San Jose (95129-3748)
PHONE.............................408 244-8124
Jin Choi, *President*
Bae Kim, *Vice Pres*
EMP: 18
SQ FT: 500
SALES (est): 3MM **Privately Held**
SIC: 2851 1752 Paints & allied products; carpet laying

(P-8950)
TRESCO PAINT CO
21595 Curtis St, Hayward (94545-1307)
PHONE.............................510 887-7254
Khosrow M Sohrabi, *President*
Behrooz Sohrabi, *Vice Pres*
EMP: 12
SQ FT: 18,000
SALES: 800K **Privately Held**
SIC: 2851 Paints & allied products

(P-8951)
TUFF KOTE SYSTEMS INC
7033 Orangethorpe Ave B, Buena Park (90621-3300)
PHONE.............................714 522-7341
William Ritt, *President*
EMP: 15
SQ FT: 2,000
SALES: 750K **Privately Held**
WEB: www.tuffkotesystemsintl.net
SIC: 2851 Paints & allied products

(P-8952)
US BIOSERVICES (PA)
5100 E Hunter Ave, Anaheim (92807-2049)
PHONE.............................800 801-1140
Mike Brunelle, *Principal*
Mike Hernandez, *Director*
EMP: 52
SALES (est): 7.1MM **Privately Held**
SIC: 2851 Paints & allied products

(P-8953)
VINYLVISIONS COMPANY LLC
Also Called: Trim Quick
1233 Enterprise Ct, Corona (92882-7126)
PHONE.............................800 321-8746
John P Halle, *Mng Member*
Helen Halle, *Mng Member*
EMP: 20
SQ FT: 40,000
SALES (est): 6.4MM **Privately Held**
SIC: 2851 Vinyl coatings, strippable

(P-8954)
WALTON INDUSTRIES INC
Also Called: General Coatings
1220 E North Ave, Fresno (93725-1930)
P.O. Box 11127 (93771-1127)
PHONE.............................559 233-6300
Lee Walton, *President*
EMP: 17
SQ FT: 40,000
SALES (est): 3.9MM **Privately Held**
WEB: www.generalcoatings.net
SIC: 2851 3086 Paints & allied products; insulation or cushioning material, foamed plastic

(P-8955)
WEATHERMAN PRODUCTS INC (PA)
Also Called: Rainguard International
21622 Surveyor Cir, Huntington Beach (92646-7068)
PHONE.............................949 515-8800
Claude Florent, *CEO*
Garrett Florent, *Manager*
▲ EMP: 15
SQ FT: 12,000
SALES: 2.8MM **Privately Held**
SIC: 2851 Paints & allied products

(P-8956)
WLS COATINGS INC
1680 Miller Ave, Los Angeles (90063-1613)
P.O. Box 151014 (90015-8014)
PHONE.............................310 538-2155
Walter Standridge, *President*
EMP: 10
SALES (est): 1.3MM **Privately Held**
SIC: 2851 Paints & allied products

(P-8957)
WONDER MARKETING INC
Also Called: Leather Cpr
11601 Wilshire Blvd # 2150, Los Angeles (90025-1757)
PHONE.............................310 235-1469
D Darren Zuzow, *President*
EMP: 40 EST: 1999
SQ FT: 14,000
SALES (est): 6.6MM **Privately Held**
WEB: www.leathercpr.com
SIC: 2851 Removers & cleaners

2861 Gum & Wood

(P-8958)
KINGSFORD PRODUCTS COMPANY LLC (HQ)
1221 Broadway Ste 1300, Oakland (94612-2072)
P.O. Box 24305 (94623-1305)
PHONE.............................510 271-7000
Richard T Conti, *President*
A W Biebl, *President*
Karen Rose, *CFO*
L L Hoover, *Treasurer*
B C Blewett, *Vice Pres*
▲ EMP: 75
SQ FT: 506,000
SALES (est): 115.5MM
SALES (corp-wide): 6.1B **Publicly Held**
WEB: www.kingsford.com
SIC: 2861 2099 2035 2033 Charcoal, except activated; dressings, salad: dry mixes; dressings, salad: raw & cooked (except dry mixes); barbecue sauce: packaged in cans, jars, etc.; insecticides, agricultural or household
PA: The Clorox Company
1221 Broadway Ste 1300
Oakland CA 94612
510 271-7000

2865 Cyclic-Crudes, Intermediates, Dyes & Org Pigments

(P-8959)
BIOTIUM INC
46117 Landing Pkwy, Fremont (94538-6407)
PHONE.............................510 265-1027
SEI Mao, *President*
Mikhail Guzaev, *Research*
Fei Mao, *Research*
Laurel Mason, *Opers Staff*
Candice Park, *Research Analys*
▼ EMP: 10
SALES (est): 2.6MM **Privately Held**
WEB: www.biotium.com
SIC: 2865 Dyes, synthetic organic

(P-8960)
CARETEX INC
4581 Firestone Blvd, South Gate (90280-3343)
PHONE.............................323 567-5074
Richard Kang, *President*
EMP: 65 EST: 1987
SQ FT: 30,000
SALES: 6MM **Privately Held**
SIC: 2865 2269 Dyes, synthetic organic; finishing plants

(P-8961)
COLOR SCIENCE INC
Also Called: C S I
1230 E Glenwood Pl, Santa Ana (92707-3000)
PHONE.............................714 434-1033
Jocelyn Eubank, *CEO*
Mark Hoffenberg, *President*
EMP: 15
SQ FT: 9,000
SALES (est): 5.7MM
SALES (corp-wide): 12.3MM **Privately Held**
WEB: www.modifiedplastics.com
SIC: 2865 Color pigments, organic

PA: Modified Plastics, Inc.
1240 E Glenwood Pl
Santa Ana CA 92707
714 546-4667

(P-8962)
DEALZER COM
9250 Reseda Blvd, Northridge (91324-3142)
PHONE.............................818 429-1155
Albert Frajian, *Owner*
EMP: 10 EST: 2008
SALES (est): 1.3MM **Privately Held**
SIC: 2865 Hydroquinones

(P-8963)
HAZTECH SYSTEMS INC
4996 Gold Leaf Dr, Mariposa (95338-8510)
P.O. Box 929 (95338-0929)
PHONE.............................209 966-8088
Thomas Archibald, *CEO*
Brenda Archibald, *Admin Sec*
Will Johnson, *Marketing Staff*
EMP: 20
SALES: 2MM **Privately Held**
WEB: www.hazcat.com
SIC: 2865 Chemical indicators

(P-8964)
PACIFIC VISTA FOODS LLC
2380 Back Nine St, Oceanside (92056-1701)
PHONE.............................760 908-9840
David Roberts, *President*
Jordan Scharg, *Treasurer*
Richard Navarro, *Vice Pres*
EMP: 48
SALES (est): 2.4MM **Privately Held**
SIC: 2865 5963 5142 5143 Acids, coal tar; direct selling establishments; dairy products, house-to-house; packaged frozen goods; ice cream & ices

(P-8965)
PERMALITE PLASTICS CORP
Also Called: Mks Color Composite
3121 E Ana St, Compton (90221-5606)
PHONE.............................310 669-9492
Frederic Van Bergh, *President*
Richard Van Bergh, *Vice Pres*
EMP: 30 EST: 1946
SQ FT: 16,000
SALES (est): 5.7MM **Privately Held**
WEB: www.permaliteplastics.com
SIC: 2865 2891 Color pigments, organic; adhesives

(P-8966)
US NIUTANG CHEMICAL INC
14266 Euclid Ave, Chino (91710-8803)
PHONE.............................909 631-2895
Jie Lin, *CEO*
Licheng Wang, *President*
▲ EMP: 20
SQ FT: 18,000
SALES: 10MM **Privately Held**
SIC: 2865 Cyclic organic intermediates

2869 Industrial Organic Chemicals, NEC

(P-8967)
ACULON INC
11839 Sorrento Valley Rd # 901, San Diego (92121-1040)
PHONE.............................858 350-9474
Eric L Bruner, *President*
Frank Archinaco, *Ch of Bd*
Gerald W Gruber, *CEO*
Christopher Harris, *COO*
Eric Hanson, *Vice Pres*
EMP: 10
SQ FT: 10,000
SALES (est): 1.5MM **Privately Held**
SIC: 2869 Industrial organic chemicals

(P-8968)
AEMETIS ADVNCED FELS KEYES INC
4209 Jessup Rd, Ceres (95307-9604)
P.O. Box 879, Keyes (95328-0879)
PHONE.............................209 632-4511
Eric McAfee, *CEO*
Andy Foster, *COO*

Todd Waltz, *CFO*
Lydia Beebe, *Bd of Directors*
Kelly Shaver, *Relations*
EMP: 47
SALES (est): 14.2MM
SALES (corp-wide): 150.1MM **Publicly Held**
SIC: 2869 Ethyl alcohol, ethanol
PA: Aemetis, Inc.
    20400 Stevens
    Cupertino CA 95014
    408 213-0940

(P-8969)
AEMETIS ADVNCED PDTS KEYES INC
20400 Stevens Creek Blvd, Cupertino (95014-2217)
PHONE..........................408 418-2415
Eric McAfee, *CEO*
Todd Waltz, *CFO*
EMP: 46 **EST:** 2016
SALES (est): 1.7MM **Privately Held**
SIC: 2869 Industrial organic chemicals

(P-8970)
AEROJET ROCKETDYNE DE INC (HQ)
8900 De Soto Ave, Canoga Park (91304-1967)
P.O. Box 7922 (91309-7922)
PHONE..........................818 586-1000
Eileen P Drake, *CEO*
Pete Gleszer, *Vice Pres*
Kristin Conner, *Comms Dir*
Waldemar Janowski, *Program Mgr*
Tyler Wade, *Program Mgr*
▲ **EMP:** 194
SALES (est): 700.9MM
SALES (corp-wide): 1.8B **Publicly Held**
SIC: 2869 3724 Rocket engine fuel, organic; aircraft engines & engine parts
PA: Aerojet Rocketdyne Holdings, Inc.
    222 N Pacific Coast Hwy
    El Segundo CA 90245
    310 252-8100

(P-8971)
AEROJET ROCKETDYNE DE INC
9001 Lurline Ave, Chatsworth (91311-6122)
PHONE..........................818 586-1000
Helen Lubin, *Branch Mgr*
EMP: 115
SALES (corp-wide): 1.8B **Publicly Held**
SIC: 2869 3724 Rocket engine fuel, organic; aircraft engines & engine parts
HQ: Inc Aerojet Rocketdyne Of De
    8900 De Soto Ave
    Canoga Park CA 91304
    818 586-1000

(P-8972)
AKZO NOBEL INC
Also Called: ICI Paints Store
1338 W 9th St 40a, Upland (91786-5720)
PHONE..........................909 981-6540
James Melgar, *Branch Mgr*
EMP: 34
SALES (corp-wide): 11.3B **Privately Held**
SIC: 2869 Industrial organic chemicals
HQ: Akzo Nobel Inc.
    525 W Van Buren St Fl 16
    Chicago IL 60607
    312 544-7000

(P-8973)
AKZO NOBEL INC
Also Called: ICI Paints Store
3010 Bristol St, Costa Mesa (92626-3036)
PHONE..........................714 966-0934
Art Peraza, *Branch Mgr*
EMP: 34
SALES (corp-wide): 11.3B **Privately Held**
SIC: 2869 Industrial organic chemicals
HQ: Akzo Nobel Inc.
    525 W Van Buren St Fl 16
    Chicago IL 60607
    312 544-7000

(P-8974)
AKZO NOBEL INC
Also Called: ICI Paints Store
735 N Escondido Blvd, Escondido (92025-1703)
PHONE..........................760 743-7374
Carlos Rios, *Branch Mgr*
EMP: 34
SALES (corp-wide): 11.3B **Privately Held**
SIC: 2869 Industrial organic chemicals
HQ: Akzo Nobel Inc.
    525 W Van Buren St Fl 16
    Chicago IL 60607
    312 544-7000

(P-8975)
ALLIANCE HOSE & EXTRUSIONS INC
533 W Collins Ave, Orange (92867-5509)
P.O. Box 1037, Gardena (90249-0037)
PHONE..........................714 202-8500
Scott H Franklin, *Vice Pres*
▲ **EMP:** 20
SQ FT: 15,000
SALES (est): 1.3MM
SALES (corp-wide): 5.3MM **Privately Held**
WEB: www.calgasket.com
SIC: 2869 Silicones
PA: California Gasket And Rubber Corporation
    533 W Collins Ave
    Orange CA 92867
    310 323-4250

(P-8976)
AMERICAN BIODIESEL INC
Also Called: Community Fuels
809 Snedeker Ave Ste C, Stockton (95203-4923)
PHONE..........................209 466-4823
Chris Young, *Principal*
Patrick Samson, *Plant Mgr*
EMP: 11
SALES (est): 1.6MM
SALES (corp-wide): 26.6MM **Privately Held**
SIC: 2869 Fuels
PA: American Biodiesel, Inc.
    809c Snedeker Ave
    Stockton CA 95203
    760 942-9306

(P-8977)
AMRICH ENERGY INC
1160 Marsh St Ste 105, San Luis Obispo (93401-3382)
PHONE..........................805 354-0830
Trent J Benedetti, *Principal*
EMP: 12
SALES (est): 2.4MM **Privately Held**
SIC: 2869 Hydraulic fluids, synthetic base

(P-8978)
AMYRIS INC (PA)
5885 Hollis St Ste 100, Emeryville (94608-2405)
PHONE..........................510 450-0761
John G Melo, *President*
Geoffrey Duyk, *Ch of Bd*
Joel Cherry, *President*
Eduardo Alvarez, *COO*
Kathleen Valiasek, *CFO*
EMP: 273
SQ FT: 136,000
SALES: 143.4MM **Publicly Held**
WEB: www.amyrisbiotech.com
SIC: 2869 Industrial organic chemicals

(P-8979)
APPLIED SILICONE CORPORATION
1050 Cindy Ln, Carpinteria (93013-2906)
PHONE..........................805 525-5657
Ralph Alastair Winn, *President*
Phil Galarnau, *Vice Pres*
▲ **EMP:** 70
SQ FT: 20,000
SALES (est): 14.5MM
SALES (corp-wide): 574.8MM **Privately Held**
SIC: 2869 Silicones

HQ: Nusil Technology Llc
    1050 Cindy Ln
    Carpinteria CA 93013
    805 684-8780

(P-8980)
BASF CATALYSTS LLC
46820 Fremont Blvd, Fremont (94538-6571)
PHONE..........................510 490-2150
Teresa Concreras, *Administration*
EMP: 12
SALES (corp-wide): 76B **Privately Held**
SIC: 2869 Industrial organic chemicals
HQ: Basf Catalysts Llc
    25 Middlesex Tpke
    Iselin NJ 08830
    732 205-5000

(P-8981)
BASF CORPORATION
138 E Meats Ave, Orange (92865-3310)
PHONE..........................714 921-1430
John Zomer, *Opers-Prdtn-Mfg*
EMP: 20
SQ FT: 10,000
SALES (corp-wide): 76B **Privately Held**
WEB: www.basf.com
SIC: 2869 2821 Industrial organic chemicals; plastics materials & resins
HQ: Basf Corporation
    100 Park Ave
    Florham Park NJ 07932
    973 245-6000

(P-8982)
BASF CORPORATION
38403 Cherry St, Newark (94560-4716)
PHONE..........................510 796-9911
Rich Hall, *Manager*
EMP: 12
SALES (corp-wide): 76B **Privately Held**
SIC: 2869 Industrial organic chemicals
HQ: Basf Corporation
    100 Park Ave
    Florham Park NJ 07932
    973 245-6000

(P-8983)
BASF ENZYMES LLC
3550 John Hopkins Ct, San Diego (92121-1121)
PHONE..........................858 431-8520
Matthew Lepore,
Robert Malone,
▲ **EMP:** 11
SALES (est): 264.2K
SALES (corp-wide): 76B **Privately Held**
SIC: 2869 Industrial organic chemicals
HQ: Basf Corporation
    100 Park Ave
    Florham Park NJ 07932
    973 245-6000

(P-8984)
BASF VENTURE CAPITAL AMER INC
46820 Fremont Blvd, Fremont (94538-6571)
PHONE..........................510 445-6140
Hans Ulrich Engel, *President*
EMP: 10
SALES (est): 1.1MM
SALES (corp-wide): 76B **Privately Held**
SIC: 2869 Industrial organic chemicals
HQ: Basfin Corporation
    100 Park Ave
    Florham Park NJ 07932
    973 245-6000

(P-8985)
BEARS FOR HUMANITY INC
Also Called: Futurama
841 Ocean View Ave, San Mateo (94401-3139)
PHONE..........................866 325-1668
Renju Prathap, *President*
EMP: 50
SQ FT: 10,000
SALES (est): 10MM **Privately Held**
SIC: 2869 Industrial organic chemicals

(P-8986)
BIODICO INC
Also Called: Biodiesel Industries
121 N Fir St Ste G, Ventura (93001-2093)
PHONE..........................805 689-9008
Russell T Teall, *President*
Christy Teall, *CFO*
Christine Teall, *Vice Pres*
Trey Teall, *VP Opers*
Michael Cassady, *Director*
EMP: 12
SALES (est): 40K **Privately Held**
SIC: 2869 Fuels

(P-8987)
BIODICO WESTSIDE LLC
426 Donze Ave, Santa Barbara (93101-1312)
PHONE..........................805 683-8103
Russell Teall,
EMP: 12 **EST:** 2014
SALES (est): 832.8K **Privately Held**
SIC: 2869 Industrial organic chemicals

(P-8988)
BIONEER INC
1301 Marina Village Pkwy # 110, Alameda (94501-1058)
PHONE..........................510 865-0330
Myeong Hee Kim, *CFO*
Hena Kie, *General Mgr*
Jennifer Horne, *Technology*
Nisha Sahay, *Mktg Dir*
Jen Scott, *Sales Mgr*
▲ **EMP:** 20
SQ FT: 22,000
SALES (est): 4.7MM
SALES (corp-wide): 20.8MM **Privately Held**
WEB: www.bioneer.com
SIC: 2869 Industrial organic chemicals
PA: Bioneer Corporation
    8-11 Munpyeongseo-Ro, Daedeok-Gu
    Daejeon 34302
    821 588-9788

(P-8989)
BIOTECH ENERGY OF AMERICA
30 Castro Ave, San Rafael (94901-4819)
PHONE..........................714 904-7844
Stig Westling, *CEO*
EMP: 10
SALES (est): 561.3K **Privately Held**
SIC: 2869 Industrial organic chemicals

(P-8990)
BIOTIX INC (HQ)
9880 Mesa Rim Rd, San Diego (92121-2979)
PHONE..........................858 875-7696
Paul Nowak, *CEO*
Ron Perkins, *COO*
Tony Altig, *CFO*
Mickie Henshall, *Vice Pres*
Celia Reyes, *Vice Pres*
◆ **EMP:** 30
SALES (est): 4.2MM **Privately Held**
SIC: 2869 Laboratory chemicals, organic

(P-8991)
CAL-INDIA FOODS INTERNATIONAL
Also Called: Specilty Enzymes Btechnologies
13591 Yorba Ave, Chino (91710-5071)
PHONE..........................909 613-1660
Vic Rathi, *President*
Prabha Rathi, *Managing Dir*
Jim Titus, *Marketing Staff*
▲ **EMP:** 20
SQ FT: 12,000
SALES (est): 6.2MM **Privately Held**
WEB: www.specialtyenzymes.com
SIC: 2869 Enzymes

(P-8992)
CALIFORNIA BIO-PRODUCTEX INC
13220 Crown Ave, Hanford (93230-9413)
PHONE..........................559 582-5308
Leo Wirzbicki, *President*
EMP: 25
SQ FT: 2,500
SALES (est): 4.6MM **Privately Held**
SIC: 2869 2099 Industrial organic chemicals; yeast

(P-8993)
CALYSTA INC (PA)
1140 Obrien Dr Ste B, Menlo Park
(94025-1411)
PHONE..................................650 492-6880
Alan Shaw, *CEO*
Ted Hull, *CFO*
Lynsey Wenger, *CFO*
Josh Silverman, *Officer*
Craig Barratt, *Vice Pres*
EMP: 22
SALES (est): 4.2MM **Privately Held**
SIC: 2869 Industrial organic chemicals

(P-8994)
CALZYME LABORATORIES INC (PA)
3443 Miguelito Ct, San Luis Obispo
(93401-7124)
PHONE..................................805 541-5754
Muzaffar Iqbal, *President*
Usman Iqbal, *CFO*
Umer Iqbal, *Vice Pres*
EMP: 14
SQ FT: 18,000
SALES: 3MM **Privately Held**
WEB: www.calzyme.com
SIC: 2869 Enzymes

(P-8995)
CARBON RECYCLING INCORPORATED
Also Called: Carbon Recycling Inernational
7938 Ivanhoe Ave Ste B, La Jolla
(92037-4569)
PHONE..................................619 491-9200
Kim-Chinh Tran, *President*
EMP: 15
SALES (est): 1MM **Privately Held**
SIC: 2869 Industrial organic chemicals

(P-8996)
CHEMSIL SILICONES INC
21900 Marilla St, Chatsworth (91311-4129)
PHONE..................................818 700-0302
James J Harrison, *CEO*
Patrick S Williams, *President*
Tom Martin, *Treasurer*
Ian Cleminson, *Vice Pres*
Bruce McDonald, *Vice Pres*
▲ EMP: 26
SQ FT: 32,789
SALES (est): 9.2MM
SALES (corp-wide): 1.3B **Publicly Held**
WEB: www.chemsil.com
SIC: 2869 Silicones
HQ: Innospec Active Chemicals Llc
510 W Grimes Ave
High Point NC 27260
336 882-3308

(P-8997)
CLARIANT CORPORATION
3350 W Bayshore Rd, Palo Alto
(94303-4238)
PHONE..................................650 494-1749
Kenneth Golder, *President*
EMP: 225
SALES (corp-wide): 665.7MM **Privately Held**
SIC: 2869 Industrial organic chemicals
HQ: Clariant Corporation
4000 Monroe Rd
Charlotte NC 28205
704 331-7000

(P-8998)
CLARIANT CORPORATION
801 W 14th St, Long Beach (90813-1403)
PHONE..................................661 763-5192
Devon Bench, *Manager*
EMP: 40
SALES (corp-wide): 665.7MM **Privately Held**
WEB: www.myclariant.com
SIC: 2869 Industrial organic chemicals
HQ: Clariant Corporation
4000 Monroe Rd
Charlotte NC 28205
704 331-7000

(P-8999)
CLARIANT PLAS COATINGS USA INC
14355 Ramona Ave, Chino (91710-5740)
PHONE..................................909 606-1325
Mike Urbano, *Branch Mgr*
EMP: 19
SALES (corp-wide): 665.7MM **Privately Held**
SIC: 2869 Industrial organic chemicals
HQ: Clariant Plastics & Coatings Usa Inc.
4000 Monroe Rd
Charlotte NC 28205
704 331-7000

(P-9000)
CODEXIS INC (PA)
200 Penobscot Dr, Redwood City
(94063-4718)
PHONE..................................650 421-8100
John J Nicols, *President*
Bernard J Kelley, *Ch of Bd*
Pam Cheng, *Bd of Directors*
Byron Dorgan, *Bd of Directors*
Kathleen Glaub, *Bd of Directors*
EMP: 108
SQ FT: 107,200
SALES: 50MM **Publicly Held**
WEB: www.codexis.com
SIC: 2869 8731 Industrial organic chemicals; commercial research laboratory

(P-9001)
CORONA PATHOLOGY
4444 W Riverside Dr # 308, Burbank
(91505-4073)
PHONE..................................818 566-1891
Conrad Gorospi, *Principal*
EMP: 13
SQ FT: 5,000
SALES (est): 350K **Privately Held**
SIC: 2869 Laboratory chemicals, organic

(P-9002)
COSKATA INC
Also Called: Coskata Energy
3945 Freedom Cir Ste 560, Santa Clara
(95054-1269)
PHONE..................................630 657-5800
William Roe, *President*
David Blair, *CFO*
Wesley J Bolsen, *Chief Mktg Ofcr*
Richard E Tobey, *Vice Pres*
John A Crum, *Principal*
EMP: 12
SALES (est): 4.9MM **Privately Held**
WEB: www.coskata.com
SIC: 2869 Ethyl alcohol, ethanol

(P-9003)
DNA HEALTH INSTITUTE LLC
Also Called: Dna Health Inst Cyrogenic Div
4562 Westinghouse St B, Ventura
(93003-5797)
PHONE..................................805 654-9363
Noel Aguilar,
Jessica Killion, *Marketing Staff*
EMP: 12 EST: 2001
SALES (est): 2.3MM **Privately Held**
WEB: www.dnaskin.com
SIC: 2869 Laboratory chemicals, organic

(P-9004)
EDENIQ INC
2505 N Shirk Rd, Visalia (93291-8605)
PHONE..................................559 302-1777
Brian Thome, *CEO*
Scott Janssen, *CFO*
CAM Cast, *Vice Pres*
Peter Kilner, *Vice Pres*
Dan Michalopoulos, *Vice Pres*
▲ EMP: 100
SQ FT: 35,000
SALES (est): 23.8MM **Privately Held**
WEB: www.edeniq.com
SIC: 2869 Fuels

(P-9005)
ETHANOL ENERGY SYSTEMS LLC
406 Delta Ave, Isleton (95641)
PHONE..................................916 777-5654
EMP: 10
SALES (est): 700.4K **Privately Held**
SIC: 2869

(P-9006)
FIRMENICH
424 S Atchison St, Anaheim (92805-4045)
PHONE..................................714 535-2871
Alejandra Camacho, *Vice Pres*
Chris Millington, *Vice Pres*
Adele Naidu, *Vice Pres*
Dana Rudin, *Executive*
Gonzalo Gonzalez, *Admin Sec*
EMP: 117
SALES (est): 18.9MM **Privately Held**
SIC: 2869 Industrial organic chemicals

(P-9007)
GFP ETHANOL LLC
Also Called: Calgren Renewable Fuels
11704 Road 120, Pixley (93256)
P.O. Box E (93256-1005)
PHONE..................................559 757-3850
Lyle Schlyer, *President*
Tim Morillo, *Plant Mgr*
Jerry Schroeder, *Plant Mgr*
Lanny Simpson, *Maintence Staff*
Jim Humphres, *Supervisor*
EMP: 34
SALES (est): 10.3MM **Privately Held**
SIC: 2869 2046 Ethyl alcohol, ethanol;
corn oil, crude
PA: Sjv Biodiesel, Llc
11704 Road 120
Pixley CA 93256
559 757-3850

(P-9008)
GLOBAL SILICONES INC
49 Industrial Way, Buellton (93427-9565)
PHONE..................................805 686-4500
Philip Galarneau, *President*
Erin Certs, *Manager*
EMP: 10
SALES (est): 1.9MM **Privately Held**
SIC: 2869 Industrial organic chemicals

(P-9009)
HEXION INC
Borden
625 The City Dr S Ste 300, Orange
(92868-4966)
PHONE..................................714 971-0180
Rick Steen, *Branch Mgr*
EMP: 14 **Privately Held**
SIC: 2869 Industrial organic chemicals
HQ: Hexion Inc.
180 E Broad St Fl 26
Columbus OH 43215
614 225-4000

(P-9010)
HOW 2 SAVE FUEL LLC
Also Called: How2savefuel.com
18017 Chtswrth St Ste 166, Granada Hills
(91344-5608)
PHONE..................................818 882-1189
Alex Rivera,
EMP: 10 EST: 2008
SALES (est): 1MM **Privately Held**
SIC: 2869

(P-9011)
INC AEROJET ROCKETDYNE OF DE
8495 Carla Ln, West Hills (91304-3201)
PHONE..................................818 586-9629
EMP: 115
SALES (corp-wide): 1.8B **Publicly Held**
SIC: 2869 3724 Rocket engine fuel, organic; aircraft engines & engine parts
HQ: Inc Aerojet Rocketdyne Of De
8900 De Soto Ave
Canoga Park CA 91304
818 586-1000

(P-9012)
INNOVATIVE ORGANICS INC
4905 E Hunter Ave, Anaheim (92807-2058)
PHONE..................................714 701-3900
Robert E Futrell Jr, *President*
Douglas E Ward, *Vice Pres*
EMP: 25
SQ FT: 30,000
SALES: 5.7MM **Privately Held**
SIC: 2869 2899 Industrial organic chemicals; chemical preparations

(P-9013)
INTERNATIONAL ACADEMY OF FIN (PA)
Also Called: Cordova Industries
13177 Foothill Blvd, Sylmar (91342-4830)
P.O. Box 922079 (91392-2079)
PHONE..................................818 361-7724
Sam Cordova, *President*
Steven M Cordova, *President*
Rodrick Cordova, *Exec VP*
Sam Scott Cordova, *Vice Pres*
Steven Schector, *Vice Pres*
EMP: 24
SQ FT: 6,000
SALES: 59MM **Privately Held**
SIC: 2869 3944 2879 Alcohols, industrial:
denatured (non-beverage); video game
machines, except coin-operated; insecticides, agricultural or household

(P-9014)
JAD CHEMICAL INC
Also Called: Custom Chemical Formulators
8707 Millergrove Dr, Santa Fe Springs
(90670-2001)
PHONE..................................310 833-7457
George Dixon, *President*
EMP: 15
SALES: 1,000K **Privately Held**
SIC: 2869 Industrial organic chemicals

(P-9015)
JDM PROPERTIES
410 S Golden State Blvd, Turlock
(95380-4959)
PHONE..................................209 632-0616
Joaquin Rose, *President*
EMP: 20
SQ FT: 4,410
SALES (est): 1.5MM **Privately Held**
SIC: 2869 5083 Hydraulic fluids, synthetic
base; farm implements

(P-9016)
JOHN B CAMPBELL MD A PROF CORP
9292 Chesapeake Dr # 100, San Diego
(92123-1060)
PHONE..................................858 576-9960
John B Campbell, *President*
EMP: 11
SALES (est): 1.2MM **Privately Held**
SIC: 2869 Laboratory chemicals, organic

(P-9017)
JSR MICRO INC (HQ)
Also Called: Materials Innovation
1280 N Mathilda Ave, Sunnyvale
(94089-1213)
PHONE..................................408 543-8800
Eric R Johnson, *President*
Hitoshi Inoue, *Treasurer*
Eiichi Kobayashi, *Senior VP*
Jim Mulready, *Vice Pres*
Maria Peterson, *Business Dir*
▲ EMP: 140
SQ FT: 12,125
SALES (est): 37MM
SALES (corp-wide): 3.9B **Privately Held**
WEB: www.jsrmicro.com
SIC: 2869 2899 Industrial organic chemicals; chemical preparations
PA: Jsr Corporation
1-9-2, Higashishimbashi
Minato-Ku TKY 105-0
362 183-500

(P-9018)
KORE INFRASTRUCTURE LLC
200 N Pacific Coast Hwy # 340, El Segundo (90245-4340)
PHONE..................................310 367-1003
EMP: 10
SALES (est): 1.6MM **Privately Held**
SIC: 2869 Fuels

(P-9019)
LA SUPPLY COMPANY LLC
13700 Rosecrans Ave, Santa Fe Springs
(90670-5027)
PHONE..................................562 404-1502
Song-Tak Chun, *Mng Member*
▲ EMP: 15
SQ FT: 24,000

▲ = Import ▼=Export
◆ =Import/Export

SALES (est): 4MM **Privately Held**
SIC: 2869 2865 Industrial organic chemicals; dyes & pigments

(P-9020)
LAMB FUELS INC
725 Main St Ste B, Chula Vista (91911-6168)
PHONE....................619 216-6940
Gregory Scott Lamb, *CEO*
Rochelle Lamb, *Admin Sec*
Kezin Parabia, *VP Opers*
▼ EMP: 21
SALES (est): 5.1MM **Privately Held**
WEB: www.lambfuels.com
SIC: 2869 Fuels

(P-9021)
LESLIES ORGANICS LLC
Also Called: Coconut Secret
298 Miller Ave, Mill Valley (94941-2829)
PHONE....................415 383-9800
Randy Stoler,
Mark Colbert, *General Mgr*
Steve Aronow, *Natl Sales Mgr*
Leslie Caren,
Dory Kwan, *Director*
▲ EMP: 14 EST: 2007
SALES (est): 2.8MM **Privately Held**
SIC: 2869 Sweeteners, synthetic

(P-9022)
MENLO ENERGY LLC
555 California St # 4600, San Francisco (94104-1503)
PHONE....................415 762-8200
Gaurav Shah, *Mng Member*
▲ EMP: 20
SQ FT: 34,000
SALES (est): 2.5MM **Privately Held**
SIC: 2869 2911 Glycerin; diesel fuels

(P-9023)
MOVEEL FUEL LLC
15000 S Avalon Blvd Ste K, Gardena (90248-2035)
P.O. Box 59118, Los Angeles (90059-0118)
PHONE....................213 748-1444
Serj Oganesyan, *Mng Member*
EMP: 10 EST: 2009
SALES (est): 2MM **Privately Held**
SIC: 2869 1311 Fuels; crude petroleum & natural gas production; crude petroleum production

(P-9024)
NEXSTEPPE SEEDS INC
400 E Jamie Ct Ste 202, South San Francisco (94080-6230)
PHONE....................650 887-5700
EMP: 35 EST: 2013
SALES (est): 3.4MM **Privately Held**
SIC: 2869

(P-9025)
NEXSUN CORP
3250 Wilshire Blvd # 1410, Los Angeles (90010-1604)
PHONE....................213 382-2220
Justin Lee, *Ch of Bd*
David Pyrce, *CEO*
EMP: 25
SALES (est): 3.3MM **Privately Held**
SIC: 2869 Industrial organic chemicals

(P-9026)
NORAC INC (PA)
405 S Motor Ave, Azusa (91702-3232)
PHONE....................626 334-2907
Wallace McCloskey, *President*
Frank Parrish, *Executive*
Olive J Mc Closkey, *Principal*
Lee Miller, *Principal*
Jim Scholler, *Principal*
▼ EMP: 258 EST: 1953
SQ FT: 10,000
SALES (est): 66.6MM **Privately Held**
WEB: www.norac.com
SIC: 2869 Industrial organic chemicals

(P-9027)
PACIFIC ETHANOL CENTRAL LLC (HQ)
400 Capitol Mall Ste 2060, Sacramento (95814-4436)
P.O. Box 10, Pekin IL (61555-0010)
PHONE....................916 403-2123
Neil M Koehler, *President*
EMP: 75
SALES (est): 180MM
SALES (corp-wide): 1.6B **Publicly Held**
SIC: 2869 Ethyl alcohol, ethanol
PA: Pacific Ethanol, Inc.
  400 Capitol Mall Ste 2060
  Sacramento CA 95814
  916 403-2123

(P-9028)
PACIFIC ETHANOL WEST LLC
400 Capitol Mall Ste 2060, Sacramento (95814-4436)
PHONE....................916 403-2123
Neil M Koehler,
EMP: 150
SALES (est): 16.1MM
SALES (corp-wide): 1.6B **Publicly Held**
SIC: 2869 Ethanolamines
PA: Pacific Ethanol, Inc.
  400 Capitol Mall Ste 2060
  Sacramento CA 95814
  916 403-2123

(P-9029)
PENTA BIOTECH INC
1100 Industrial Rd Ste 4, San Carlos (94070-4131)
PHONE....................650 598-9328
John Huang, *President*
EMP: 12
SQ FT: 11,000
SALES: 1MM **Privately Held**
WEB: www.pentabiotech.com
SIC: 2869 Industrial organic chemicals

(P-9030)
PRIMETECH SILICONES INC
6655 Doolittle Ave, Riverside (92503-1454)
PHONE....................951 509-6655
Salvador Avalos, *President*
Ophelia Avalos, *Vice Pres*
▲ EMP: 10
SQ FT: 12,000
SALES: 1.5MM **Privately Held**
SIC: 2869 Silicones

(P-9031)
PROPEL BIOFUELS INC (PA)
Also Called: Propel Fuels
1815 19th St, Sacramento (95811-6712)
PHONE....................800 871-0773
Robert R Elam, *President*
Koichi Kurisu, *COO*
Ken Jibiki, *Info Tech Dir*
Joanna Woessner, *Project Mgr*
Gordon Barnes, *Technology*
EMP: 10 EST: 2006
SQ FT: 3,200
SALES (est): 2.4MM **Privately Held**
SIC: 2869 Fuels

(P-9032)
PROTEMACH INC
Also Called: Golden Farms
7133 Remmet Ave, Canoga Park (91303-2016)
PHONE....................310 622-2693
Saed Moshaver, *CEO*
EMP: 11
SQ FT: 8,500
SALES: 1.8MM **Privately Held**
SIC: 2869 2099 Perfumes, flavorings & food additives; spices, including grinding

(P-9033)
PROVIVI INC
1701 Colorado Ave, Santa Monica (90404-3436)
PHONE....................310 828-2307
Pedro S L Coelho, *CEO*
Peter Meinhold, *Officer*
EMP: 25
SALES (est): 1.5MM **Privately Held**
SIC: 2869 Laboratory chemicals, organic

(P-9034)
PURE ONE ENVIRONMENTAL INC
Also Called: Pure One Business Svc Group
3400 W Warner Ave Ste A, Santa Ana (92704-5300)
PHONE....................714 641-1430
James Jordan, *President*
EMP: 10
SALES (est): 1.2MM **Privately Held**
SIC: 2869 8748 5169 Industrial organic chemicals; environmental consultant; organic chemicals, synthetic

(P-9035)
PUROSIL LLC
1660 Leeson Ln, Corona (92879-2061)
PHONE....................951 271-3900
EMP: 10
SALES (corp-wide): 126.4MM **Privately Held**
SIC: 2869 Silicones
HQ: Purosil Llc
  708 S Temescal St Ste 102
  Corona CA 92879
  -

(P-9036)
PUROSIL LLC (HQ)
708 S Temescal St Ste 102, Corona (92879-2096)
P.O. Box 2467 (92878-2467)
PHONE....................951 271-3900
Thomas M Garrett, *President*
▲ EMP: 54
SQ FT: 5,000
SALES: 25MM
SALES (corp-wide): 126.4MM **Privately Held**
SIC: 2869 Silicones
PA: Mcp Industries, Inc.
  708 S Temescal St Ste 101
  Corona CA 92879
  951 736-1881

(P-9037)
RENNOVIA INC
3040 Oakmead Village Dr, Santa Clara (95051-0808)
PHONE....................650 804-7400
Robert Wedinger, *CEO*
Thomas Boussie, *Vice Pres*
EMP: 15
SQ FT: 14,000
SALES (est): 4.9MM **Privately Held**
SIC: 2869 8731 Industrial organic chemicals; biotechnical research, commercial

(P-9038)
SAINT-GOBAIN CERAMICS PLAS INC
Innovative Organics Division
4905 E Hunter Ave, Anaheim (92807-2058)
PHONE....................714 701-3900
Robert E Futrell Jr, *Branch Mgr*
EMP: 30
SALES (corp-wide): 213.5MM **Privately Held**
WEB: www.sgceramics.com
SIC: 2869 2899 Industrial organic chemicals; chemical preparations
HQ: Saint-Gobain Ceramics & Plastics, Inc.
  750 E Swedesford Rd
  Valley Forge PA 19482

(P-9039)
SCIGEN INC
333 E Gardena Blvd, Gardena (90248-2815)
PHONE....................310 324-6576
Steve Wheeler, *President*
Tim Grant, *Officer*
Lori Wheeler, *Officer*
EMP: 10
SALES (est): 1.9MM **Privately Held**
SIC: 2869 2833 3089 5169 Laboratory chemicals, organic; medicinal chemicals; toilets, portable chemical; plastic; industrial chemicals; automatic chemical analyzers

(P-9040)
SEARLES VALLEY MINERALS INC
13200 Main St, Trona (93562-1915)
P.O. Box 96 (93592-0096)
PHONE....................760 372-2135
Avinash Puri, *President*
EMP: 24
SALES (corp-wide): 703.3MM **Privately Held**
WEB: www.svminerals.com
SIC: 2869 Industrial organic chemicals
HQ: Searles Valley Minerals Inc.
  9401 Indn Crk Pkwy # 1000
  Overland Park KS 66210
  913 344-9500

(P-9041)
SIERRA NATURAL SCIENCE INC
538 Brunken Ave Ste 2, Salinas (93901-4372)
PHONE....................831 757-1702
Kel Lemons, *President*
EMP: 18
SALES (est): 3MM **Privately Held**
SIC: 2869 Polyhydric alcohol esters, aminos, etc.

(P-9042)
SPECIALIZED PRODUCTS & DESIGN
1428 N Manzanita St, Orange (92867-3662)
PHONE....................714 289-1428
Dennis Bergdorf, *CFO*
Deborah Bergdorf, *Corp Secy*
EMP: 12
SQ FT: 6,000
SALES: 1.2MM **Privately Held**
SIC: 2869 3069 Silicones; tubing, rubber

(P-9043)
SPECILTY ENZYMES BTECHNOLOGIES
Also Called: Seb
13591 Yorba Ave, Chino (91710-5071)
PHONE....................909 613-1660
Vasant Rathi, *Principal*
Bhaskar Manolkar, *General Mgr*
Luis Giraldy, *Engrg Dir*
Rajendra Newase, *Prdtn Mgr*
EMP: 16
SALES (est): 3.3MM **Privately Held**
SIC: 2869 Enzymes

(P-9044)
SPOETY CUTS CORPORATION
6510 Wooster Ave, Los Angeles (90056-2132)
PHONE....................310 908-1512
Kinney D Marks, *President*
EMP: 10
SALES: 15K **Privately Held**
SIC: 2869 Industrial organic chemicals

(P-9045)
SWEET OVATIONS LLC
16911 S Normandie Ave, Gardena (90247-5437)
PHONE....................310 719-2600
David Daneshmayeh, *CEO*
Jack Miller, *Principal*
▲ EMP: 100
SALES: 19MM
SALES (corp-wide): 704.5MM **Privately Held**
SIC: 2869 2899 2099 2087 Industrial organic chemicals; chemical preparations; food preparations; flavoring extracts & syrups
PA: Zentis Gmbh & Co. Kg
  Julicher Str. 177
  Aachen 52070
  241 476-00

(P-9046)
USL PARALLEL PRODUCTS CAL
12281 Arrow Rte, Rancho Cucamonga (91739-9601)
PHONE....................909 980-1200
Gene Kiesel, *CEO*
Ken Reese, *President*
Tim Cusson, *Vice Pres*
Bob Pasma, *Vice Pres*
Jim Russell, *Vice Pres*

PRODUCTS & SVCS

▲ EMP: 35
SQ FT: 6,000
SALES (est): 8.3MM
SALES (corp-wide): 49.8MM Privately Held
SIC: 2869 Alcohols, industrial: denatured (non-beverage)
PA: Parallel Environmental Services Corporation
401 Industry Rd
Louisville KY 40208
502 471-2444

(P-9047)
UTAK LABORATORIES INC
25020 Avenue Tibbitts, Valencia (91355-3447)
PHONE..............................661 294-3935
James D Plutchak, CEO
EMP: 26
SQ FT: 12,000
SALES: 4MM Privately Held
WEB: www.utak.com
SIC: 2869 Industrial organic chemicals

(P-9048)
VALERO ENERGY CORPORATION
3400 E 2nd St, Benicia (94510-1005)
PHONE..............................707 745-7011
Don Wilson, Manager
Kathleen Fenton, Vice Pres
David Thackrey, Planning
Tom Rose, Project Mgr
Rebecca Sgambati, Technical Staff
EMP: 450
SALES (corp-wide): 93.9B Publicly Held
SIC: 2869 2911 Ethyl alcohol, ethanol; gasoline
PA: Valero Energy Corporation
1 Valero Way
San Antonio TX 78249
210 345-2000

(P-9049)
VERTIMASS LLC
2 Park Plz Ste 700, Irvine (92614-8517)
PHONE..............................949 417-1396
William Shopoff, Principal
Sandra Sciutto, CFO
Thomas Mullen, Principal
Charles Wyman, Principal
EMP: 11
SALES (est): 1MM Privately Held
SIC: 2869 Industrial organic chemicals

(P-9050)
VISCON CALIFORNIA LLC
3121 Standard St, Bakersfield (93308-6242)
PHONE..............................661 327-7061
Michael Porter,
Patrick Porter,
EMP: 10
SALES (est): 6MM Privately Held
WEB: www.visconusa.com
SIC: 2869 Fuels

(P-9051)
VISHAY SILICONIX LLC
2585 Junction Ave, San Jose (95134-1923)
PHONE..............................408 988-8000
Felix Zandman, Ch of Bd
David Valletta, Exec VP
Peter G Henrici, Senior VP
▲ EMP: 700
SALES (est): 100MM
SALES (corp-wide): 2.6B Publicly Held
SIC: 2869 Silicones
HQ: Siliconix Incorporated
2585 Junction Ave
San Jose CA 95134
408 988-8000

(P-9052)
WACKER CHEMICAL CORPORATION
Also Called: Precision Silicones
13910 Oaks Ave, Chino (91710-7010)
PHONE..............................909 590-8822
Sudipta Das, Branch Mgr
Ragin Amrutiya, Technical Mgr
Liz Bobo, Human Res Mgr
Barbara Hartford, Production
Maricela Sanchez, Manager
EMP: 44

SALES (corp-wide): 5.8B Privately Held
WEB: www.wackerchemicalcorporation.com
SIC: 2869 5169 Silicones; industrial chemicals
HQ: Wacker Chemical Corporation
3301 Sutton Rd
Adrian MI 49221
517 264-8500

(P-9053)
WINNER INDUSTRIAL CHEMICALS
154 W Foothill Blvd Ste A, Upland (91786-8702)
PHONE..............................909 887-6228
Detra Jones, President
Cornelius Wallace, CFO
Carol Redding, Vice Pres
EMP: 20
SALES (est): 2.2MM Privately Held
SIC: 2869 Industrial organic chemicals

(P-9054)
ZOLT INFORMATION SCIENCES INC
2401 N Glassell St, Orange (92865-2705)
P.O. Box 13500 (92857-8500)
PHONE..............................714 921-7489
William Shaw, President
EMP: 14
SALES (est): 2.2MM Privately Held
SIC: 2869 Industrial organic chemicals

2873 Nitrogenous Fertilizers

(P-9055)
1ST CHOICE FERTILIZER INC
1515 Aurora Dr, San Leandro (94577-3105)
PHONE..............................800 504-5699
Bright Omoruyi, Principal
EMP: 10
SALES: 500K Privately Held
SIC: 2873 Fertilizers: natural (organic), except compost

(P-9056)
AGRA TRADING LLC
60 Independence Cir # 203, Chico (95973-4921)
PHONE..............................530 894-1782
Jon Kim, Mng Member
EMP: 12
SQ FT: 1,800
SALES: 12MM Privately Held
WEB: www.agratrading.com
SIC: 2873 Fertilizers: natural (organic), except compost

(P-9057)
AIRGAS INC
15116 Canary Ave, La Mirada (90638-5218)
PHONE..............................714 521-4789
EMP: 10
SALES (corp-wide): 163.9MM Privately Held
SIC: 2873
HQ: Airgas, Inc.
259 N Radnor Chester Rd # 100
Radnor PA 19087
610 687-5253

(P-9058)
BOYER INC
105 Thompson Rd, Watsonville (95076)
PHONE..............................831 724-0123
Fred Willoughby, CEO
▲ EMP: 22
SALES (est): 4.7MM
SALES (corp-wide): 32.7MM Privately Held
SIC: 2873 2874 Nitrogenous fertilizers; phosphatic fertilizers
PA: Willoughby Farms, Inc.
261 Coward Rd
Watsonville CA
831 722-7763

(P-9059)
CVR NITROGEN LP (DH)
10877 Wilshire Blvd Fl 10, Los Angeles (90024-4251)
PHONE..............................310 571-9800
Keith B Forman, CEO
John H Diesch, President
Jeffrey R Spain, CFO
Wilfred Bahl Jr, Senior VP
Julie Dawoodjee Cafarella, Vice Pres
EMP: 10 EST: 2015
SALES: 340.7MM Publicly Held
SIC: 2873 Ammonium nitrate, ammonium sulfate

(P-9060)
DR EARTH INC
4021 Devon Ct, Vacaville (95688-8730)
P.O. Box 460, Winters (95694-0460)
PHONE..............................707 448-4676
Milad Shammas, President
Tyler Vinyard, Vice Pres
▲ EMP: 15
SQ FT: 958,320
SALES (est): 2MM Privately Held
SIC: 2873 5191 Fertilizers: natural (organic), except compost; fertilizer & fertilizer materials

(P-9061)
GRO-POWER INC
15065 Telephone Ave, Chino (91710-9614)
PHONE..............................909 393-3744
Brent Holden, President
Ana Gonzales, Office Mgr
David Diehl, Sales Staff
▼ EMP: 25
SALES (est): 5MM Privately Held
WEB: www.gropower.com
SIC: 2873 0782 0721 Fertilizers: natural (organic), except compost; lawn & garden services; crop planting & protection

(P-9062)
HYPONEX CORPORATION
Also Called: Scotts- Hyponex
15978 El Prado Rd, Chino (91708-9158)
PHONE..............................909 597-2811
Roclund White, Branch Mgr
Kay Scott, Office Mgr
EMP: 28
SQ FT: 10,000
SALES (corp-wide): 2.6B Publicly Held
SIC: 2873 Plant foods, mixed: from plants making nitrog. fertilizers
HQ: Hyponex Corporation
14111 Scottslawn Rd
Marysville OH 43040
937 644-0011

(P-9063)
HYPONEX CORPORATION
Also Called: Scotts- Hyponex
23390 E Flood Rd, Linden (95236-9488)
P.O. Box 479 (95236-0479)
PHONE..............................209 887-3845
Aaron Teach, Manager
EMP: 76
SALES (corp-wide): 2.6B Publicly Held
SIC: 2873 Plant foods, mixed: from plants making nitrog. fertilizers
HQ: Hyponex Corporation
14111 Scottslawn Rd
Marysville OH 43040
937 644-0011

(P-9064)
KELLOGG SUPPLY INC
Also Called: Kellogg Garden Product
12686 Locke Rd, Lockeford (95237-9701)
PHONE..............................209 727-3130
Clayton De Bie, Principal
EMP: 50
SALES (corp-wide): 80MM Privately Held
WEB: www.kellogggarden.com
SIC: 2873 5191 2875 Nitrogenous fertilizers; fertilizer & fertilizer materials; fertilizers, mixing only
PA: Kellogg Supply, Inc.
350 W Sepulveda Blvd
Carson CA 90745
310 830-2200

(P-9065)
MAR VISTA RESOURCES LLC
745 North Ave, Corcoran (93212-1906)
P.O. Box 218 (93212-0218)
PHONE..............................559 992-4535
Jay Irvine, President
Travis Cardoza, Info Tech Mgr
Rick Loya, Sales Staff
▲ EMP: 13
SALES (est): 20MM Privately Held
SIC: 2873 Plant foods, mixed: from plants making nitrog. fertilizers

(P-9066)
MINERAL KING MINERALS INC (PA)
7600 N Ingram Ave Ste 105, Fresno (93711-5824)
PHONE..............................559 582-9228
EMP: 18
SQ FT: 2,000
SALES (est): 1.5MM Privately Held
SIC: 2873

(P-9067)
NAC MFG INC
601 Kettering Dr, Ontario (91761-8153)
PHONE..............................909 472-3033
Stanley Hsiao, CEO
Jeff Zhang, Manager
EMP: 20
SQ FT: 106,000
SALES (est): 2.6MM Privately Held
SIC: 2873 Fertilizers: natural (organic), except compost

(P-9068)
NUTRIEN AG SOLUTIONS INC
2150 Eastman Ave, Oxnard (93030-5168)
P.O. Box 1307 (93032-1307)
PHONE..............................805 488-3646
Mike Dinsley, Manager
EMP: 16
SALES (corp-wide): 3.5K Privately Held
WEB: www.cropproductionservices.com
SIC: 2873 5261 Fertilizers: natural (organic), except compost; fertilizer
HQ: Nutrien Ag Solutions, Inc.
3005 Rocky Mountain Ave
Loveland CO 80538
970 685-3300

(P-9069)
NUTRIENT TECHNOLOGIES INC (PA)
1092 E Kamm Ave, Dinuba (93618-2842)
P.O. Box 903 (93618-0903)
PHONE..............................559 595-8090
Lester R Mc Nall, CEO
Jeff A Reimche, Vice Pres
Gerry Camp, Manager
Andrea Holeman, Manager
▲ EMP: 12
SQ FT: 45,000
SALES (est): 3.7MM Privately Held
SIC: 2873 Nitrogenous fertilizers

(P-9070)
RED STAR FERTILIZER CO
17132 Hellman Ave, Corona (92880-9724)
PHONE..............................909 597-4801
Donald C Mc Millan, Ch of Bd
Paul E Bernhard Jr, President
Michael Hughes, Corp Secy
EMP: 55
SQ FT: 52,100
SALES (est): 9.4MM Privately Held
SIC: 2873 2421 Fertilizers: natural (organic), except compost; sawmills & planing mills, general

(P-9071)
RENTECH NTRGN PASADENA SPA LLC
10877 Wilshire Blvd # 710, Los Angeles (90024-4341)
PHONE..............................310 571-9805
Colin H Campbell, Vice Pres
William Regan, Director
EMP: 18
SALES: 334.6MM Publicly Held
SIC: 2873 Nitrogenous fertilizers

HQ: Cvr Nitrogen, Lp
10877 Wilshire Blvd Fl 10
Los Angeles CA 90024
310 571-9800

(P-9072)
SCOTTS COMPANY LLC
742 Industrial Way, Shafter (93263-4018)
PHONE..............................661 387-9555
Aaron Leach, *Branch Mgr*
EMP: 17
SALES (corp-wide): 2.6B **Publicly Held**
WEB: www.scottscompany.com
SIC: 2873 Fertilizers: natural (organic), except compost
HQ: The Scotts Company Llc
14111 Scottslawn Rd
Marysville OH 43040
937 644-3729

(P-9073)
SMJ INC
Also Called: Lgm Company
2213 Chico Ave, El Monte (91733-1608)
PHONE..............................626 448-8042
Kenneth Walters, *President*
Matthew Walters, *Vice Pres*
Sandra Walters, *Admin Sec*
EMP: 10
SQ FT: 33,000
SALES (est): 1.2MM **Privately Held**
SIC: 2873 5191 Nitrogenous fertilizers; fertilizer & fertilizer materials

(P-9074)
SPAWN MATE INC
Also Called: Arroyo Grande Mushroom Farm
4000 Huasna Rd, Arroyo Grande (93420-6135)
P.O. Box 1551 (93421-1551)
PHONE..............................805 473-7250
Art Lopez, *General Mgr*
EMP: 38
SALES (corp-wide): 20.1MM **Privately Held**
WEB: www.spawnmate.com
SIC: 2873 0182 5148 Fertilizers: natural (organic), except compost; mushrooms grown under cover; vegetables
PA: Spawn Mate, Inc.
260 Westgate Dr
Watsonville CA 95076
831 763-5300

(P-9075)
TI INC
13802 Avenue 352, Visalia (93292-9543)
PHONE..............................559 972-1475
Bryce Iden, *Principal*
EMP: 12 EST: 1984
SALES (est): 729K **Privately Held**
SIC: 2873 Plant foods, mixed: from plants making nitrog. fertilizers

(P-9076)
ULTRA GRO LLC
1043 S Granada Dr, Madera (93637-4801)
PHONE..............................559 661-0977
Donald F Parreira,
Frank Casares, *Nutritionist*
Steven G Best,
Craig F Fourchy,
EMP: 25
SALES (est): 5.3MM **Privately Held**
SIC: 2873 Fertilizers: natural (organic), except compost

(P-9077)
WESTERN NUTRIENTS CORPORATION
245 Industrial St, Bakersfield (93307-2703)
PHONE..............................661 327-9604
Craig Waterman, *President*
Sandra Jaquez, *Office Mgr*
Mark Armstrong, *Sales Mgr*
Marie Fetalvero, *Manager*
Dawn Ryder, *Manager*
▲ EMP: 20
SQ FT: 6,000
SALES (est): 4.5MM **Privately Held**
WEB: www.westernnutrientscorp.com
SIC: 2873 Fertilizers: natural (organic), except compost; nitrogen solutions (fertilizer); plant foods, mixed: from plants making nitrog. fertilizers

(P-9078)
WESTERN ORGANICS INC
Gro-Well Brands
4343 Mckinley Ave, Stockton (95206-3906)
PHONE..............................209 982-4936
Jesus Redudlo, *Branch Mgr*
Jorge Vega, *Manager*
EMP: 40
SALES (corp-wide): 59.9MM **Privately Held**
WEB: www.sierraorganics.com
SIC: 2873 5199 Fertilizers: natural (organic), except compost; bark
PA: Western Organics, Inc.
420 E Southern Ave
Tempe AZ 85282
602 792-0275

(P-9079)
WHITTIER FERTILIZER COMPANY
9441 Kruse Rd, Pico Rivera (90660-1492)
PHONE..............................562 699-3461
Robert Osborn, *CEO*
Janet Osborn, *Corp Secy*
Jim Osborn, *General Mgr*
▲ EMP: 51
SQ FT: 20,000
SALES (est): 13.6MM **Privately Held**
SIC: 2873 5261 2875 Fertilizers: natural (organic), except compost; garden supplies & tools; fertilizers, mixing only

---
2874 Phosphatic Fertilizers

(P-9080)
JR SIMPLOT COMPANY
12688 S Colorado Ave, Helm (93627)
P.O. Box 128 (93627-0128)
PHONE..............................559 866-5681
Frank Gaufin, *Manager*
Keith Gaines, *Engineer*
Chris Ware, *Safety Mgr*
Matt Frank, *Prdtn Mgr*
EMP: 34
SQ FT: 2,000
SALES (corp-wide): 5.1B **Privately Held**
WEB: www.simplot.com
SIC: 2874 Phosphatic fertilizers
PA: J.R. Simplot Company
1099 W Front St
Boise ID 83702
208 780-3287

2875 Fertilizers, Mixing Only

(P-9081)
ACTAGRO LLC (PA)
677 W Palmdon Dr Ste 108, Fresno (93704-1094)
P.O. Box 309, Biola (93606-0309)
PHONE..............................559 369-2222
Monty Bayer, *CEO*
Greg Crawford, *COO*
Terri West, *CFO*
James Baker, *Planning*
Charlotte Botelho, *Human Resources*
▼ EMP: 23
SQ FT: 7,000
SALES (est): 42.4MM **Privately Held**
WEB: www.actagro.com
SIC: 2875 Fertilizers, mixing only

(P-9082)
BRANDT CONSOLIDATED INC
3654 S Willow Ave, Fresno (93725-9036)
PHONE..............................559 499-2100
Ricardo Aguirre, *Engineer*
Roseanne Bright, *Human Res Mgr*
EMP: 15
SALES (corp-wide): 166MM **Privately Held**
SIC: 2875 5191 Fertilizers, mixing only; farm supplies
PA: Brandt Consolidated, Inc.
2935 S Koke Mill Rd
Springfield IL 62711
217 547-5800

(P-9083)
COLD CREEK COMPOST INC
6000 Potter Valley Rd, Ukiah (95482-9260)
PHONE..............................707 485-5966
Martin Mileck, *President*
Mari Mileck, *Admin Sec*
Sam Todd, *Architect*
EMP: 11
SALES: 1.6MM **Privately Held**
SIC: 2875 5261 Compost; fertilizer

(P-9084)
JH BIOTECH INC (PA)
4951 Olivas Park Dr, Ventura (93003-7667)
P.O. Box 3538 (93006-3538)
PHONE..............................805 650-8933
Hsinhung John Hsu, *President*
◆ EMP: 23
SQ FT: 3,000
SALES (est): 15.5MM **Privately Held**
WEB: www.jhbiotech.com
SIC: 2875 Fertilizers, mixing only

(P-9085)
NUTRIEN AG SOLUTIONS INC
3348 Claus Rd, Modesto (95355-9725)
PHONE..............................209 551-1424
Dan Sardella, *Manager*
EMP: 35
SQ FT: 28,395
SALES (corp-wide): 3.5K **Privately Held**
WEB: www.cropproductionservices.com
SIC: 2875 5261 5191 5999 Fertilizers, mixing only; fertilizer; fertilizer & fertilizer materials; insecticides; insecticides
HQ: Nutrien Ag Solutions, Inc.
3005 Rocky Mountain Ave
Loveland CO 80538
970 685-3300

(P-9086)
TESSENDERIO KERLY INC
10724 Energy St, Hanford (93230-9518)
PHONE..............................559 582-9200
Amos Riley, *Office Mgr*
EMP: 21
SALES (est): 3.4MM **Privately Held**
SIC: 2875 Fertilizers, mixing only

(P-9087)
TRIAD ENERGY RESOURCES INC
Also Called: Triad Waste Management
204 Kerr Ave, Modesto (95354-3809)
PHONE..............................209 527-0607
Mike Daley, *President*
▲ EMP: 20
SALES (est): 3.3MM **Privately Held**
SIC: 2875 Fertilizers, mixing only

(P-9088)
TRUE ORGANIC PRODUCTS INC
20225 W Kamm Ave, Helm (93627)
PHONE..............................559 866-3001
Jake Evans, *Branch Mgr*
EMP: 15
SALES (corp-wide): 5.4MM **Privately Held**
SIC: 2875 Fertilizers, mixing only
PA: True Organic Products, Inc.
20225 W Kamm Ave
Helm CA 93627
559 866-3001

2879 Pesticides & Agricultural Chemicals, NEC

(P-9089)
AGRAQUEST INC (DH)
Also Called: Bayer Cropscience
890 Embarcadero Dr, West Sacramento (95605-1503)
PHONE..............................866 992-2937
James Blome, *CEO*
Michael Mille, *COO*
Joel R Jung, *CFO*
Jonathan Margolis, *Senior VP*
Ashish Malik, *Vice Pres*
▲ EMP: 53
SQ FT: 28,000

SALES (est): 27.9MM
SALES (corp-wide): 41.2B **Privately Held**
WEB: www.agraquest.com
SIC: 2879 Insecticides & pesticides
HQ: Bayer Cropscience Ag
Alfred-Nobel-Str. 50
Monheim Am Rhein 40789
217 338-0

(P-9090)
AMERICAN VANGUARD CORPORATION
2110 Davie Ave, Commerce (90040-1706)
PHONE..............................323 526-2372
Eric G Wintemute, *Ch of Bd*
EMP: 236
SALES (corp-wide): 355MM **Publicly Held**
SIC: 2879 Pesticides, agricultural or household
PA: American Vanguard Corporation
4695 Macarthur Ct
Newport Beach CA 92660
949 260-1200

(P-9091)
AMERICAN VANGUARD CORPORATION (PA)
Also Called: Avd
4695 Macarthur Ct, Newport Beach (92660-1882)
PHONE..............................949 260-1200
Eric G Wintemute, *Ch of Bd*
Ulrich G Trogele, *COO*
David T Johnson, *CFO*
Esmail Zirakparvar, *Bd of Directors*
Timothy J Donnelly, *Officer*
◆ EMP: 78
SQ FT: 19,953
SALES: 355MM **Publicly Held**
WEB: www.amvac-chemical.com
SIC: 2879 Pesticides, agricultural or household

(P-9092)
AMERICAN VANGUARD CORPORATION
Also Called: Amvac Chemical
4100 E Washington Blvd, Commerce (90023-4406)
PHONE..............................323 264-3910
Arun Malik, *Manager*
WEI Wan, *Software Dev*
EMP: 200
SALES (corp-wide): 355MM **Publicly Held**
WEB: www.amvac-chemical.com
SIC: 2879 5169 Chemicals & allied products; pesticides, agricultural or household
PA: American Vanguard Corporation
4695 Macarthur Ct
Newport Beach CA 92660
949 260-1200

(P-9093)
AMVAC CHEMICAL CORPORATION (HQ)
4695 Macarthur Ct # 1200, Newport Beach (92660-8859)
PHONE..............................323 264-3910
Eric C Wintemute, *President*
Timothy Donnelly, *President*
Bob Trogele, *COO*
David T Johnson, *CFO*
David Cassidy, *Exec VP*
◆ EMP: 36
SQ FT: 152,000
SALES (est): 47.1MM
SALES (corp-wide): 355MM **Publicly Held**
SIC: 2879 Pesticides, agricultural or household
PA: American Vanguard Corporation
4695 Macarthur Ct
Newport Beach CA 92660
949 260-1200

(P-9094)
AMVAC CHEMICAL CORPORATION
Also Called: American Vangaurd
4695 Macarthur Ct # 1200, Newport Beach (92660-8859)
PHONE..............................949 260-1212
Eric Wintemute, *President*

EMP: 18
SALES (corp-wide): 355MM **Publicly Held**
SIC: 2879 Insecticides & pesticides
HQ: Amvac Chemical Corporation
    4695 Macarthur Ct # 1200
    Newport Beach CA 92660
    323 264-3910

(P-9095)
CELLU-CON INC
19994 Meredith Dr, Strathmore (93267-9691)
P.O. Box 185 (93267-0185)
PHONE...............................559 568-0190
Duane Hilty, *President*
Carol Hilty, *Vice Pres*
John Yale, *Vice Pres*
EMP: 25
SQ FT: 15,000
SALES (est): 4.1MM **Privately Held**
WEB: www.cellucon.com
SIC: 2879 Soil conditioners

(P-9096)
CERTIS USA LLC
Also Called: Thermo Trilogy
720 5th St, Wasco (93280-1420)
PHONE...............................661 758-8471
Michael Hillberry, *Principal*
Bob Wilson, *Plant Engr*
EMP: 40
SALES (corp-wide): 45.9B **Privately Held**
WEB: www.certisusa.com
SIC: 2879 5191 Pesticides, agricultural or household; insecticides
HQ: Certis U.S.A. L.L.C.
    9145 Guilford Rd Ste 175
    Columbia MD 21046

(P-9097)
CLOROX INTERNATIONAL COMPANY (HQ)
1221 Broadway Fl 13, Oakland (94612-1837)
P.O. Box 24305 (94623-1305)
PHONE...............................510 271-7000
Benno Dorer, *Principal*
Warwick Every-Burns, *President*
Larry Peirof, *CEO*
William F Ausfahl, *Vice Pres*
Edward A Cutter, *Admin Sec*
◆ EMP: 75
SALES (est): 347.6MM
SALES (corp-wide): 6.1B **Publicly Held**
WEB: www.crispins.com
SIC: 2879 2842 Insecticides, agricultural or household; bleaches, household: dry or liquid
PA: The Clorox Company
    1221 Broadway Ste 1300
    Oakland CA 94612
    510 271-7000

(P-9098)
CMR MARKETING AND RES INC
3594 E Wawona Ave, Fresno (93725-9021)
P.O. Box 35000 (93745-5000)
PHONE...............................559 499-2100
John Salmonson, *President*
▲ EMP: 30
SQ FT: 70,000
SALES (est): 5.3MM
SALES (corp-wide): 166MM **Privately Held**
WEB: www.montereychemical.com
SIC: 2879 Agricultural chemicals
PA: Brandt Consolidated, Inc.
    2935 S Koke Mill Rd
    Springfield IL 62711
    217 547-5800

(P-9099)
CUSTOM AG FORMULATORS INC (PA)
3430 S Willow Ave, Fresno (93725-9004)
P.O. Box 26104 (93729-6104)
PHONE...............................559 435-1052
Gerald Steward, *CEO*
▼ EMP: 52
SALES (est): 17MM **Privately Held**
SIC: 2879 Agricultural chemicals

(P-9100)
DECCO US POST-HARVEST INC (HQ)
1713 S California Ave, Monrovia (91016-4623)
P.O. Box 120 (91017-0120)
PHONE...............................800 221-0925
Francois Girin, *President*
Tim Mowry, *Business Mgr*
Bill Eakle, *Opers Mgr*
◆ EMP: 50
SALES (est): 16.8MM
SALES (corp-wide): 1.1B **Privately Held**
SIC: 2879 Agricultural chemicals
PA: Upl Limited
    Cts No-610, Upl House,
    Mumbai MH 40005
    227 152-8000

(P-9101)
GARLIC RESEARCH LABS INC
Also Called: Garlic Valley Farm
624 Ruberta Ave, Glendale (91201-2335)
PHONE...............................800 424-7990
William Anderson, *CEO*
Bill Brock, *Shareholder*
Sonja Anderson, *Corp Secy*
▼ EMP: 10
SQ FT: 14,000
SALES (est): 1.4MM **Privately Held**
WEB: www.garlicbarrier.com
SIC: 2879 Insecticides & pesticides; insecticides, agricultural or household

(P-9102)
GROW MORE INC
15600 New Century Dr, Gardena (90248-2129)
PHONE...............................310 515-1700
John Atwill II, *CEO*
Phil Nash, *Managing Dir*
Anthony Sotak, *Safety Mgr*
◆ EMP: 62
SQ FT: 43,560
SALES (est): 17.7MM **Privately Held**
WEB: www.growmore.com
SIC: 2879 2899 2873 2869 Agricultural chemicals; chemical preparations; water treating compounds; nitrogenous fertilizers; industrial organic chemicals; cyclic crudes & intermediates

(P-9103)
HELENA AGRI-ENTERPRISES LLC
12218 11th Ave, Hanford (93230-9523)
P.O. Box 1263 (93232-1263)
PHONE...............................559 582-0291
Steve Dufur, *Manager*
EMP: 25
SALES (corp-wide): 70.7B **Privately Held**
WEB: www.helenachemical.com
SIC: 2879 5191 Agricultural chemicals; chemicals, agricultural
HQ: Helena Agri-Enterprises, Llc
    255 Schilling Blvd # 300
    Collierville TN 38017
    901 761-0050

(P-9104)
IMPERIAL COMPOST LLC
1698 Jones St Ste 5, Brawley (92227-1776)
PHONE...............................760 351-1900
Barbabra Laughrin, *Principal*
EMP: 15
SALES (est): 1.3MM **Privately Held**
SIC: 2879 Pesticides, agricultural or household

(P-9105)
MARRONE BIO INNOVATIONS INC
1540 Drew Ave, Davis (95618-6320)
PHONE...............................530 750-2800
Pamela G Marrone, *CEO*
Robert A Woods, *Ch of Bd*
James B Boyd, *President*
Michael Benoff, *Bd of Directors*
George Kerckhove, *Bd of Directors*
▲ EMP: 103
SQ FT: 27,300
SALES: 18.1MM **Privately Held**
WEB: www.marroneorganics.com
SIC: 2879 Agricultural chemicals

(P-9106)
MARY MATAVA
Also Called: Agri Service
3210 Oceanside Blvd, Oceanside (92056)
PHONE...............................760 439-9920
Mary Matava, *Owner*
EMP: 14
SALES (est): 1.3MM **Privately Held**
SIC: 2879 Soil conditioners

(P-9107)
MONSANTO COMPANY
500 Lucy Brown Rd, San Juan Bautista (95045-9713)
P.O. Box 183 (95045-0183)
PHONE...............................831 623-7016
EMP: 164
SALES (corp-wide): 41.2B **Privately Held**
SIC: 2879 Agricultural chemicals
HQ: Monsanto Company
    800 N Lindbergh Blvd
    Saint Louis MO 63167
    314 694-1000

(P-9108)
NATURAL PEST CONTROLS & FIREWD (PA)
Also Called: Npc Firewood
8864 Little Creek Dr, Orangevale (95662-2125)
PHONE...............................916 726-0855
Jeff Hadden, *Owner*
EMP: 15 EST: 1971
SQ FT: 60,000
SALES (est): 1.4MM **Privately Held**
WEB: www.natpestco.com
SIC: 2879 Insecticides & pesticides

(P-9109)
NOVARTIS CORPORATION
5300 Chiron Way, Emeryville (94608-2966)
PHONE...............................510 879-9500
EMP: 58
SALES (corp-wide): 49.1B **Privately Held**
SIC: 2879 0181 2032 2865 Agricultural chemicals; insecticides, agricultural or household; pesticides, agricultural or household; fungicides, herbicides; seeds, vegetable: growing of; baby foods, including meats: packaged in cans, jars, etc.; dyes & pigments; drugs acting on the cardiovascular system, except diagnostic
HQ: Novartis Corporation
    1 S Ridgedale Ave
    East Hanover NJ 07936
    212 307-1122

(P-9110)
PAULSEN WHITE OAK LP
3976 Garden Hwy, Nicolaus (95659-9711)
P.O. Box 151 (95659-0151)
PHONE...............................530 656-2201
Carol Thomsen, *General Ptnr*
Lee Ann Hanna, *Partner*
EMP: 12
SQ FT: 1,200
SALES (est): 2MM **Privately Held**
SIC: 2879 Pesticides, agricultural or household

(P-9111)
SEMPERVIRENS GROUP
Also Called: Orion Group, The
820 Coventry Rd, Kensington (94707-1411)
P.O. Box 8104, Berkeley (94707-8104)
PHONE...............................510 847-0801
Christopher Hall, *Owner*
EMP: 11 EST: 1983
SALES (est): 725.2K **Privately Held**
SIC: 2879 Agricultural chemicals

(P-9112)
SOUTHERN VALLEY CHEMICAL CO
S Derby & Sycamore Rd, Arvin (93203)
P.O. Box 181 (93203-0181)
PHONE...............................661 366-3308
Christopher C Carlson, *CEO*
Russel Carlson, *Corp Secy*
EMP: 11
SQ FT: 13,400
SALES (est): 4.5MM **Privately Held**
SIC: 2879 Insecticides & pesticides

(P-9113)
TECHNISOIL GLOBAL INC
5660 Westside Rd, Redding (96001-4450)
PHONE...............................530 605-4881
Sean Weaver,
James Abner, *Vice Pres*
Coree Ellis, *Opers Mgr*
Angela Logue, *Sales Staff*
EMP: 10
SQ FT: 2,000
SALES (est): 2.2MM **Privately Held**
SIC: 2879 Soil conditioners

(P-9114)
TERMINIX INTL CO LTD PARTNR
950 Riverside Pkwy Ste 40, West Sacramento (95605-1501)
PHONE...............................916 376-8770
Thomas Graston, *Principal*
Jeremy Fisher, *Manager*
EMP: 18
SALES (corp-wide): 2.9B **Publicly Held**
SIC: 2879 7342 Agricultural chemicals; disinfecting & pest control services
HQ: The Terminix International Company Limited Partnership
    150 Peabody Pl
    Memphis TN 38103
    901 766-1400

(P-9115)
TRICAL INC
28679 Rd 68, Visalia (93277)
PHONE...............................559 651-0736
Dean Storkan, *President*
EMP: 16
SALES (corp-wide): 29.7MM **Privately Held**
WEB: www.trical.com
SIC: 2879 Agricultural chemicals
PA: Trical, Inc.
    8100 Arroyo Cir
    Gilroy CA 95020
    831 637-0195

(P-9116)
TRICAL INC (PA)
8100 Arroyo Cir, Gilroy (95020-7305)
P.O. Box 1327, Hollister (95024-1327)
PHONE...............................831 637-0195
Dean Storkan, *CEO*
Hank Maze, *CFO*
Joanne Vargas, *Corp Secy*
▲ EMP: 30
SQ FT: 6,000
SALES (est): 29.7MM **Privately Held**
WEB: www.trical.com
SIC: 2879 Agricultural chemicals

(P-9117)
TRICAL INC
8770 Hwy 25, Hollister (95023)
PHONE...............................831 637-0195
Dean Storkan, *CEO*
EMP: 100
SALES (corp-wide): 29.7MM **Privately Held**
SIC: 2879 Agricultural chemicals
PA: Trical, Inc.
    8100 Arroyo Cir
    Gilroy CA 95020
    831 637-0195

(P-9118)
TRICAL INC
1029 Railroad St, Corona (92882-2416)
PHONE...............................951 737-6960
Joanne Vargas, *Manager*
EMP: 15
SALES (corp-wide): 29.7MM **Privately Held**
WEB: www.trical.com
SIC: 2879 Agricultural chemicals
PA: Trical, Inc.
    8100 Arroyo Cir
    Gilroy CA 95020
    831 637-0195

(P-9119)
TRICAL INC
1667 Purdy Rd, Mojave (93501-7403)
PHONE...............................661 824-2494
Neil Adkins, *Branch Mgr*
EMP: 20

SALES (corp-wide): 29.7MM **Privately Held**
SIC: 2879 Agricultural chemicals
PA: Trical, Inc.
   8100 Arroyo Cir
   Gilroy CA 95020
   831 637-0195

(P-9120)
VALENT USA LLC
Also Called: Valent Dublin Laboratories
6560 Trinity Ct, Dublin (94568-2627)
PHONE..................................925 256-2700
Glen Fujie, *Manager*
Joel Maurer, *Associate*
EMP: 20
SQ FT: 43,000
SALES (corp-wide): 20.5B **Privately Held**
WEB: www.valent.com
SIC: 2879 Agricultural chemicals
HQ: Valent U.S.A. Llc
   1600 Riviera Ave Ste 200
   Walnut Creek CA 94596
   925 256-2700

(P-9121)
WESTBRIDGE AGRICULTURAL PDTS
1260 Avenida Chelsea, Vista (92081-8315)
PHONE..................................760 599-8855
Christine Koenemann, *CEO*
Tina Koenemann, *President*
Richard Forsyth, *CFO*
Larry Parker, *Vice Pres*
Nicole Friend, *Office Mgr*
▲ EMP: 15
SQ FT: 8,000
SALES (est): 4.1MM
SALES (corp-wide): 6.5MM **Privately Held**
WEB: www.westbridge.com
SIC: 2879 Agricultural chemicals
PA: Westbridge Research Group
   1260 Avenida Chelsea
   Vista CA 92081
   760 599-8855

(P-9122)
WESTBRIDGE RESEARCH GROUP (PA)
1260 Avenida Chelsea, Vista (92081-8315)
PHONE..................................760 599-8855
William Fruehling, *Ch of Bd*
Christine Koenemann, *President*
Tina Koenemann, *CEO*
Richard Forsyth, *CFO*
Andy Hudson, *Director*
EMP: 12
SQ FT: 19,504
SALES (est): 6.5MM **Privately Held**
SIC: 2879 2873 Agricultural chemicals;
   fertilizers: natural (organic), except com-
   post

(P-9123)
YARA NORTH AMERICA INC
3961 Channel Dr, West Sacramento
(95691-3431)
PHONE..................................916 375-1109
David Johnson, *Manager*
EMP: 35
SQ FT: 2,000
SALES (corp-wide): 11.3B **Privately Held**
SIC: 2879 Agricultural chemicals
HQ: Yara North America, Inc
   100 N Tampa St Ste 3200
   Tampa FL 33602
   -

2891 Adhesives & Sealants

(P-9124)
3M COMPANY
7341 Anaconda Ave, Garden Grove
(92841-2921)
PHONE..................................714 373-2837
Allan Cole, *Principal*
EMP: 13
SALES (corp-wide): 31.6B **Publicly Held**
SIC: 2891 Sealants
PA: 3m Company
   3m Center
   Saint Paul MN 55144
   651 733-1110

(P-9125)
ABL AERO INC
Also Called: Able Aerospace Adhesives
25032 Anza Dr, Valencia (91355-3917)
PHONE..................................661 257-2500
Alicia Hed-Ram, *President*
Lata Wadhwani, *Office Mgr*
Kiran Singh, *Purch Agent*
Donna Gonsalves, *Representative*
EMP: 20
SQ FT: 10,000
SALES (est): 5MM **Privately Held**
WEB: www.ablaero.com
SIC: 2891 Adhesives & sealants

(P-9126)
AC PRODUCTS INC
Also Called: Quaker
9930 Painter Ave, Whittier (90605-2759)
PHONE..................................714 630-7311
Joseph Matrange, *President*
Hugh H Muller, *Exec VP*
Sheldon I Weinstein, *Vice Pres*
Ward Thompson, *Finance Mgr*
◆ EMP: 35
SQ FT: 28,000
SALES (est): 11.9MM
SALES (corp-wide): 820MM **Publicly Held**
WEB: www.quakerchem.com
SIC: 2891 2952 8731 Adhesives &
   sealants; coating compounds, tar; chemi-
   cal laboratory, except testing
PA: Quaker Chemical Corporation
   901 E Hector St
   Conshohocken PA 19428
   610 832-4000

(P-9127)
ADVANCED CHEMISTRY & TECH INC (HQ)
Also Called: AC Tech
7341 Anaconda Ave, Garden Grove
(92841-2921)
PHONE..................................714 373-8118
Joseph A Muklevicz, *President*
Dean Willard, *CEO*
▲ EMP: 23
SALES (est): 5.8MM
SALES (corp-wide): 31.6B **Publicly Held**
WEB: www.actechaero.com
SIC: 2891 Sealants
PA: 3m Company
   3m Center
   Saint Paul MN 55144
   651 733-1110

(P-9128)
ADVANTAGE ADHESIVES INC
8345 White Oak Ave, Rancho Cucamonga
(91730-3896)
PHONE..................................909 204-4990
Greg Lane, *President*
Jason Rowley, *Technical Staff*
Erika Machado, *Receptionist*
▲ EMP: 26 EST: 1998
SQ FT: 25,620
SALES (est): 4.9MM **Privately Held**
SIC: 2891 Adhesives

(P-9129)
AXIOM MATERIALS INC
2320 Pullman St, Santa Ana (92705-5507)
PHONE..................................949 623-4400
John D Lincoln, *CEO*
James Samuel Miele, *CFO*
Raj Dhawan, *VP Bus Dvlpt*
Legrand Lewis, *Admin Sec*
Justin Kast, *Controller*
▲ EMP: 35
SQ FT: 15,000
SALES (est): 18.6MM **Privately Held**
SIC: 2891 2295 Epoxy adhesives; resin or
   plastic coated fabrics

(P-9130)
BLAIR ADHESIVE PRODUCTS
11034 Lockport Pl, Santa Fe Springs
(90670-4635)
PHONE..................................562 946-6004
Scott Heger, *President*
Benny Garcia, *Purch Mgr*
EMP: 12
SQ FT: 15,000

SALES (est): 3.8MM **Privately Held**
SIC: 2891 Adhesives, paste; adhesives,
   plastic; glue; laminating compounds

(P-9131)
BONDLINE ELCTRNIC ADHSIVE CORP
777 N Pastoria Ave, Sunnyvale
(94085-2918)
PHONE..................................408 830-9200
Neal Olson, *CEO*
Erik V Olson, *President*
EMP: 25
SQ FT: 12,000
SALES (est): 3.6MM **Privately Held**
WEB: www.bondfilm.com
SIC: 2891 Adhesives

(P-9132)
BOSTIK INC
27460 Bostik Ct, Temecula (92590-3698)
PHONE..................................951 296-6425
Ed Lui, *Mng Officer*
Earl Totty, *Opers Mgr*
EMP: 60
SALES (corp-wide): 77.8MM **Privately Held**
WEB: www.bostik-us.com
SIC: 2891 2899 Adhesives; chemical
   preparations
HQ: Bostik, Inc.
   11320 W Wtertown Plank Rd
   Wauwatosa WI 53226
   414 774-2250

(P-9133)
BOYD CORPORATION (DH)
5960 Inglewood Dr Ste 115, Pleasanton
(94588-8611)
PHONE..................................209 236-1111
Mitchell Aiello, *President*
EMP: 19
SALES (est): 822MM
SALES (corp-wide): 874.5MM **Privately Held**
SIC: 2891 Adhesives & sealants
HQ: Lti Holdings, Inc.
   600 S Mcclure Rd
   Modesto CA 95357
   209 236-1111

(P-9134)
BOYD CORPORATION
600 S Mcclure Rd, Modesto (95357-0520)
PHONE..................................888 244-6931
EMP: 235
SALES (corp-wide): 874.5MM **Privately Held**
SIC: 2891 Adhesives & sealants
HQ: Boyd Corporation
   5960 Inglewood Dr Ste 115
   Pleasanton CA 94588
   209 236-1111

(P-9135)
BRADLEY TCHNOLOGIES-CALIFORNIA
447 E Rosecrans Ave, Gardena
(90248-2022)
PHONE..................................310 538-0714
Lawrence Stefan, *President*
Rhonda Rocca, *Admin Sec*
EMP: 20
SALES (est): 2.5MM **Privately Held**
SIC: 2891 Adhesives

(P-9136)
CTS CEMENT MANUFACTURING CORP (PA)
12442 Knott St, Garden Grove
(92841-2832)
PHONE..................................714 379-8260
Walter J Hoyle, *CEO*
Stephen Younger, *COO*
Sean Casey, *Regional Mgr*
Tom Fasano, *Regional Mgr*
Louis Priego, *Regional Mgr*
▲ EMP: 45
SQ FT: 14,000
SALES (est): 43MM **Privately Held**
SIC: 2891 Cement, except linoleum & tile

(P-9137)
CTS CEMENT MANUFACTURING CORP
2077 Linda Flora Dr, Los Angeles
(90077-1406)
PHONE..................................310 472-4004
Edward K Rice, *Branch Mgr*
EMP: 17
SALES (corp-wide): 43MM **Privately Held**
SIC: 2891 Cement, except linoleum & tile
PA: Cts Cement Manufacturing Corporation
   12442 Knott St
   Garden Grove CA 92841
   714 379-8260

(P-9138)
CUSTOM BUILDING PRODUCTS INC (DH)
Also Called: C-Cure
7711 Center Ave Ste 500, Huntington
Beach (92647-3076)
PHONE..................................800 272-8786
Don Devine, *CEO*
Brian Ellis, *President*
Thomas R Peck Jr, *President*
Scott Hanson, *Vice Pres*
Marc Powell, *Vice Pres*
◆ EMP: 65
SQ FT: 15,000
SALES (est): 443.6MM **Privately Held**
WEB: www.custombuildingproducts.com
SIC: 2891 Adhesives & sealants
HQ: The Quikrete Companies Llc
   5 Concourse Pkwy Ste 1900
   Atlanta GA 30328
   404 634-9100

(P-9139)
CUSTOM BUILDING PRODUCTS INC
6511 Salt Lake Ave, Bell (90201-2126)
PHONE..................................323 582-0846
Tom Milan, *Plant Mgr*
Fred Gomez, *Mfg Staff*
John Hueth, *Production*
Art Castillo, *Director*
Mario Hernandez, *Manager*
EMP: 75 **Privately Held**
WEB: www.custombuildingproducts.com
SIC: 2891 3273 2899 5032 Adhesives &
   sealants; ready-mixed concrete; chemical
   preparations; ceramic wall & floor tile
HQ: Custom Building Products, Inc.
   7711 Center Ave Ste 500
   Huntington Beach CA 92647
   800 272-8786

(P-9140)
DAVCO ENTERPRISES INC
Also Called: Design Polymerics
3301 W Segerstrom Ave, Santa Ana
(92704-6402)
PHONE..................................714 432-0600
Lyle R Davis, *President*
Matt Marowitz, *CFO*
Scott Witherow, *Vice Pres*
Jason Vandriel, *Controller*
Brandon Alderman, *Regl Sales Mgr*
▲ EMP: 13
SQ FT: 15,000
SALES (est): 4.1MM **Privately Held**
WEB: www.designpoly.com
SIC: 2891 Adhesives & sealants

(P-9141)
ELLSWORTH CORPORATION
Also Called: Ellsworth Adhesive Systems
25 Hubble, Irvine (92618-4209)
PHONE..................................949 341-9329
Jim Fisher, *Manager*
Michael McCourt, *Owner*
EMP: 12
SALES (corp-wide): 231.2MM **Privately Held**
WEB: www.ellsworth.com
SIC: 2891 Adhesives
PA: Ellsworth Corporation
   W129n10825 Washington Dr
   Germantown WI 53022
   262 253-8600

PRODUCTS & SVCS

(P-9142)
EVK INC
5235 Bandera St, Montclair (91763-4419)
PHONE.....................................617 335-3180
Ronald Izen, *President*
EMP: 50 EST: 2014
SQ FT: 30,000
SALES: 5MM Privately Held
SIC: 2891 Adhesives, plastic

(P-9143)
GENERAL SEALANTS INC
300 Turnbull Canyon Rd, City of Industry
(91745-1009)
P.O. Box 3855 (91744-0855)
PHONE.....................................626 961-0211
Bradley Boyle, *President*
Patricia Boyle, *Owner*
Patrick Boyle, *CFO*
▲ EMP: 120 EST: 1964
SQ FT: 96,000
SALES (est): 35.6MM Privately Held
WEB: www.generalsealants.com
SIC: 2891 Adhesives

(P-9144)
GLUESMITH INDUSTRIES
Also Called: Gluesmith, The
801 S Raymond Ave Ste 39, Alhambra
(91803-1545)
PHONE.....................................626 282-9390
Gustavo Portillo, *Owner*
EMP: 10
SQ FT: 4,000
SALES (est): 681.9K Privately Held
SIC: 2891 5169 Adhesives; adhesives &
sealants

(P-9145)
HB FULLER COMPANY
Also Called: Adhesves Sealants Coatings Div
10500 Industrial Ave, Roseville
(95678-6212)
PHONE.....................................916 787-6000
Frank Strasser, *Manager*
EMP: 60
SQ FT: 5,760
SALES (corp-wide): 2.3B Publicly Held
WEB: www.hbfuller.com
SIC: 2891 2851 2821 Adhesives; paints &
allied products; plastics materials & resins
PA: H.B. Fuller Company
1200 Willow Lake Blvd
Saint Paul MN 55110
651 236-5900

(P-9146)
**HENKEL ELECTRONIC MTLS
LLC**
14000 Jamboree Rd, Irvine (92606-1730)
PHONE.....................................888 943-6535
Benoit Pouliquen, *Vice Pres*
Paul R Berry, *President*
Alan P Syzdek, *President*
Jinu Choi, *Executive*
Stephen Ruatta, *Engineer*
EMP: 170
SQ FT: 75,000
SALES (est): 1MM
SALES (corp-wide): 23.6B Privately Held
SIC: 2891 Adhesives
PA: Henkel Ag & Co. Kgaa
Henkelstr. 67
Dusseldorf 40589
211 797-0

(P-9147)
HENKEL US OPERATIONS CORP
Dexter Electronics Mtls Div
15051 Don Julian Rd, City of Industry
(91746-3302)
P.O. Box 1282, La Puente (91749-1282)
PHONE.....................................626 968-6511
Jim Dehart, *Manager*
Lorretta Atkinson, *Business Anlyst*
EMP: 40
SALES (corp-wide): 23.6B Privately Held
SIC: 2891 Adhesives
HQ: Henkel Us Operations Corporation
1 Henkel Way
Rocky Hill CT 06067
860 571-5100

(P-9148)
HERNANDEZ ZEFERINO
Also Called: International Seals
1924 E Mcfadden Ave, Santa Ana
(92705-4705)
PHONE.....................................714 953-4010
Zeferino Hernandez, *Owner*
EMP: 19
SALES (est): 3.6MM Privately Held
WEB: www.international-seals.com
SIC: 2891 Sealants

(P-9149)
INSTANT ASPHALT INC
Also Called: Metacrylics
365 Obata Ct, Gilroy (95020-7036)
PHONE.....................................408 280-7733
Mark C Anthenien, *CEO*
Dale Anthenien, *Vice Pres*
Rick Berhorst, *Sales Staff*
EMP: 12
SQ FT: 116,305
SALES (est): 6.1MM Privately Held
WEB: www.metacrylics.com
SIC: 2891 2952 Adhesives & sealants; as-
phalt felts & coatings; roofing materials;
mastic roofing composition; roofing felts,
cements or coatings

(P-9150)
INTEGRAL PRODUCTS INC
24030 Frampton Ave, Harbor City
(90710-2102)
PHONE.....................................310 326-8889
John Lane, *Branch Mgr*
EMP: 40 Privately Held
SIC: 2891 Adhesives & sealants
PA: Integral Products, Inc.
24030 Frampton Ave
Harbor City CA 90710

(P-9151)
**INTEGRATED POLYMER INDS
INC**
9741 Irvine Center Dr, Irvine (92618-4324)
PHONE.....................................949 788-1050
Ergun Kirlikovali, *President*
Juliana Kirlikovali, *Vice Pres*
EMP: 50
SALES (est): 6.7MM Privately Held
SIC: 2891 Adhesives & sealants

(P-9152)
**INTERNATIONAL COATINGS CO
INC (PA)**
13929 166th St, Cerritos (90703-2431)
PHONE.....................................562 926-1010
Stephen W Kahane, *CEO*
Herbert A Wells, *Ch of Bd*
Janet Wells, *Corp Secy*
Sonja Pulliam, *Purch Agent*
Darrin Locke, *Prdtn Mgr*
▲ EMP: 40
SQ FT: 50,000
SALES (est): 10.3MM Privately Held
WEB: www.iccink.com
SIC: 2891 2899 3555 2893 Adhesives;
ink or writing fluids; printing trades ma-
chinery; printing ink; paints & allied prod-
ucts; plastics materials & resins

(P-9153)
IPS CORPORATION (HQ)
Also Called: Weld-On Adhesives
455 W Victoria St, Compton (90220-6064)
PHONE.....................................310 898-3300
Tracy Bilbrough, *CEO*
Greg Paquin, *President*
Will Barton, *CFO*
Gary Rosenfield, *Chief Mktg Ofcr*
Maria Kellison, *Senior Buyer*
◆ EMP: 180 EST: 1953
SQ FT: 22,000
SALES (est): 187.4MM
SALES (corp-wide): 28.1MM Privately
Held
SIC: 2891 Adhesives, plastic; cement, ex-
cept linoleum & tile

(P-9154)
IPS CORPORATION
Also Called: Weldon Company
17110 S Main St, Gardena (90248-3128)
PHONE.....................................310 516-7013

Eduardo Hernandez, *Branch Mgr*
EMP: 55
SALES (corp-wide): 28.1MM Privately
Held
SIC: 2891 Adhesives
HQ: Ips Corporation
455 W Victoria St
Compton CA 90220
310 898-3300

(P-9155)
MASK-OFF COMPANY INC
345 W Maple Ave, Monrovia (91016-3331)
PHONE.....................................626 303-8015
Steven B Sites, *President*
Dimitrianne Wood, *Admin Sec*
Jim Sites, *Director*
▲ EMP: 18 EST: 1950
SQ FT: 28,160
SALES (est): 4.8MM Privately Held
WEB: www.maskoff.com
SIC: 2891 Adhesives

(P-9156)
**MITSUBISHI CHEMICAL CRBN
FBR**
1822 Reynolds Ave, Irvine (92614-5714)
PHONE.....................................800 929-5471
Takashi Sasaki, *Vice Pres*
EMP: 110
SALES (corp-wide): 34.9B Privately Held
SIC: 2891 5169 Adhesives; chemical addi-
tives
HQ: Mitsubishi Chemical Carbon Fiber And
Composites, Inc.
5900 88th St
Sacramento CA 95828

(P-9157)
**NATIONAL CASEIN OF
CALIFORNIA**
3435 W Macarthur Blvd, Santa Ana
(92704-6805)
PHONE.....................................714 979-8400
Don White, *Manager*
Normon Evans, *Treasurer*
Charles Cook, *MIS Dir*
Robert Havens, *Engineer*
Edward McHugh, *Marketing Staff*
EMP: 11
SQ FT: 10,207
SALES (corp-wide): 6MM Privately Held
SIC: 2891 Adhesives
PA: National Casein Co
601 W 80th St
Chicago IL 60620
773 846-7300

(P-9158)
OATEY CO
6600 Smith Ave, Newark (94560-4220)
PHONE.....................................800 321-9532
David Smith, *Branch Mgr*
Tom O'Flaherty, *Vice Pres*
Andriy Androshchuk, *Purch Mgr*
Mason Oatey, *Regl Sales Mgr*
EMP: 24
SALES (corp-wide): 470MM Privately
Held
SIC: 2891 Cement, except linoleum & tile
PA: Oatey Co.
20600 Emerald Pkwy
Cleveland OH 44135
800 203-1155

(P-9159)
PACER TECHNOLOGY
11201 Jersey Blvd, Rancho Cucamonga
(91730-5133)
PHONE.....................................909 987-0550
Dale Drymon, *Manager*
EMP: 59
SALES (corp-wide): 19.3MM Privately
Held
SIC: 2891 Adhesives & sealants
HQ: Super Glue Corporation
3281 E Guasti Rd Ste 260
Ontario CA 91761
909 987-0550

(P-9160)
PACKAGING SYSTEMS INC
26435 Summit Cir, Santa Clarita
(91350-2991)
PHONE.....................................661 253-5700

Raymond J Gray, *CEO*
Steve Gray, *President*
Patricia Gray, *Exec VP*
▼ EMP: 42 EST: 1976
SQ FT: 25,700
SALES (est): 24.1MM Privately Held
WEB: www.pkgsys.net
SIC: 2891 Adhesives & sealants

(P-9161)
PLAS-TECH SEALING TECH LLC
252 Mariah Cir Fl 2, Corona (92879-1751)
PHONE.....................................951 737-2228
Chad Miller, *Mng Member*
Charlotte Miller,
Craig Miller Sr,
Eve Miller,
▲ EMP: 35
SQ FT: 16,000
SALES (est): 4.9MM Privately Held
WEB: www.plastechsealing.com
SIC: 2891 Sealants

(P-9162)
**PRC - DESOTO INTERNATIONAL
INC (HQ)**
Also Called: PPG Aerospace
24811 Ave Rockefeller, Valencia
(91355-3468)
PHONE.....................................661 678-4209
Michael H McGarry, *President*
Barry Gillespie, *CEO*
Ralph Dyba, *CFO*
Viktoras R Sekmakas, *Exec VP*
Frank S Sklarsky, *Exec VP*
▲ EMP: 320 EST: 1945
SQ FT: 200,000
SALES (est): 176.2MM
SALES (corp-wide): 14.7B Publicly Held
SIC: 2891 3089 Sealing compounds, syn-
thetic rubber or plastic; adhesives; plastic
containers, except foam
PA: Ppg Industries, Inc.
1 Ppg Pl
Pittsburgh PA 15272
412 434-3131

(P-9163)
**PRC - DESOTO INTERNATIONAL
INC**
Also Called: PPG Aerospace
11601 United St, Mojave (93501-7048)
PHONE.....................................949 474-0400
Michael H McGarry, *President*
EMP: 13
SALES (corp-wide): 14.7B Publicly Held
SIC: 2891 3089 Sealing compounds, syn-
thetic rubber or plastic; adhesives; plastic
containers, except foam
HQ: Prc - Desoto International, Inc.
24811 Ave Rockefeller
Valencia CA 91355
661 678-4209

(P-9164)
**PRC - DESOTO INTERNATIONAL
INC**
Also Called: PPG Aerospace
11601 United St, Mojave (93501-7048)
PHONE.....................................661 824-4532
Dave Richardson, *Branch Mgr*
EMP: 130
SALES (corp-wide): 14.2B Publicly Held
SIC: 2891 Sealing compounds, synthetic
rubber or plastic; adhesives
HQ: Prc - Desoto International, Inc.
24811 Ave Rockefeller
Valencia CA 91355
661 678-4209

(P-9165)
QSPAC INDUSTRIES INC (PA)
Also Called: Quality Service Pac Industry
15020 Marquardt Ave, Santa Fe Springs
(90670-5704)
PHONE.....................................562 407-3868
Jow-Lin Tang, *President*
Wu-Hsiung Chung, *CFO*
Vic Lee, *Vice Pres*
Ryan Martinez, *Graphic Designe*
Gloria Chang, *Accountant*
▲ EMP: 52
SQ FT: 96,000
SALES: 42MM Privately Held
SIC: 2891 Adhesives

(P-9166)
RAYNGUARD PROTECTIVE MTLS INC
8280 14th Ave, Sacramento (95826-4719)
PHONE..................................916 454-2560
Gordon Rayner, *President*
Richard Rayner, *Vice Pres*
Jeff Palmer, *Office Mgr*
Dave Hartman, *Manager*
EMP: 13
SQ FT: 1,200
SALES: 8.5MM **Privately Held**
WEB: www.raynguard.com
SIC: 2891 Adhesives & sealants

(P-9167)
RELIABLE PACKAGING SYSTEMS INC
Also Called: Astro Packaging
3845 E Miraloma Ave Ste A, Anaheim (92806-2111)
PHONE..................................714 572-1094
Debra Lynn Dillon, *President*
Debra Dillon, *President*
Ryan Dillon, *Info Tech Mgr*
Jesus Hernandez, *Engineer*
Chana Langer, *Purch Mgr*
EMP: 17
SQ FT: 5,500
SALES (est): 5.8MM **Privately Held**
WEB: www.astropackaging.com
SIC: 2891 3565 5084 5169 Adhesives & sealants; packaging machinery; packaging machinery & equipment; adhesives & sealants; consulting engineer

(P-9168)
RIVERSIDE LAMINATION CORP
3016 Kansas Ave Bldg 6, Riverside (92507-3456)
PHONE..................................951 682-0100
Theresa Santoro, *CEO*
Jerry Mahr, *General Mgr*
Steve Hobbs, *Sales Mgr*
EMP: 14 EST: 2008
SALES (est): 5.1MM **Privately Held**
SIC: 2891 Laminating compounds

(P-9169)
ROYAL ADHESIVES & SEALANTS LLC
Also Called: Bacon Adhesives
16731 Hale Ave, Irvine (92606-5006)
PHONE..................................949 863-1499
Jeff Swindells, *Branch Mgr*
EMP: 12
SALES (corp-wide): 2.3B **Publicly Held**
SIC: 2891 2821 Adhesives, plastic; plasticizer/additive based plastic materials
HQ: Royal Adhesives And Sealants Llc
2001 W Washington St
South Bend IN 46628
574 246-5000

(P-9170)
SIGNATURE FLEXIBLE PACKG INC
5519 Jillson St, Commerce (90040-1420)
PHONE..................................323 887-1997
Adrian Backer, *President*
Jeff Sewel, *Vice Pres*
Kelly Redding, *Admin Sec*
Armando Lira, *Technical Mgr*
Dio Brenes, *Technology*
▲ EMP: 82
SQ FT: 30,000
SALES (est): 18.9MM **Privately Held**
WEB: www.signatureflexible.com
SIC: 2891 2673 Adhesives & sealants; bags: plastic, laminated & coated

(P-9171)
SPECIALTY POLYMERS & SVCS INC
Also Called: SP&s
27822 Fremont Ct, Valencia (91355-1130)
PHONE..................................661 294-1790
Luciano Pilato, *President*
Christopher Meyer, *Vice Pres*
▲ EMP: 18
SQ FT: 27,000
SALES (est): 6MM **Privately Held**
WEB: www.spolymers.com
SIC: 2891 Adhesives

(P-9172)
STIC-ADHESIVE PRODUCTS CO INC
3950 Medford St, Los Angeles (90063-1675)
PHONE..................................323 268-2956
Junho Suh, *President*
Robert Suh, *General Mgr*
Bong Suh, *Info Tech Mgr*
Christy Sandoval, *Manager*
EMP: 150
SQ FT: 75,000
SALES (est): 29.2MM **Privately Held**
WEB: www.sticadhesive.com
SIC: 2891 2851 Adhesives; paints & allied products

(P-9173)
SUPER GLUE CORPORATION (HQ)
Also Called: Pacer Technology
3281 E Guasti Rd Ste 260, Ontario (91761-7642)
PHONE..................................909 987-0550
E T Gravette, *CEO*
Ron Gravette, *President*
Kristine Wright, *CFO*
Steve Burger, *Vice Pres*
James Gallagher, *Vice Pres*
◆ EMP: 113
SQ FT: 47,700
SALES (est): 29.5MM
SALES (corp-wide): 19.3MM **Privately Held**
WEB: www.supergluecorp.com
SIC: 2891 3089 3085 Adhesives & sealants; plastic containers, except foam; plastics bottles
PA: Cyan Holding Corporation
9420 Santa Anita Ave
Rancho Cucamonga CA 91730
909 987-0550

(P-9174)
SUPER GLUE CORPORATION
4970 Vanderbilt St, Ontario (91761-2202)
PHONE..................................909 987-0550
Richard Kay, *President*
Linda Worthy, *Sales Mgr*
EMP: 10
SALES (corp-wide): 19.3MM **Privately Held**
SIC: 2891 3089 Adhesives & sealants; laminating of plastic
HQ: Super Glue Corporation
3281 E Guasti Rd Ste 260
Ontario CA 91761
909 987-0550

(P-9175)
TCK USA CORPORATION
2580 Corp Pl Ste F101, Monterey Park (91754)
P.O. Box 1190, Alhambra (91802-1190)
PHONE..................................323 269-2969
Wendy Chen, *President*
Frank Chen, *Vice Pres*
▲ EMP: 14
SQ FT: 5,000
SALES (est): 1.7MM **Privately Held**
WEB: www.tckgroup.com
SIC: 2891 Sealing compounds, synthetic rubber or plastic

(P-9176)
TECHNICOTE INC
1141 California Ave, Corona (92881-7233)
PHONE..................................951 372-0627
George Parker, *Plant Mgr*
EMP: 50
SQ FT: 2,000
SALES (corp-wide): 78.2MM **Privately Held**
WEB: www.technicote.com
SIC: 2891 2675 Adhesives; die-cut paper & board
PA: Technicote, Inc.
222 Mound Ave
Miamisburg OH 45342
800 358-4448

(P-9177)
TECHPRO SALES & SERVICE INC
3429 Cerritos Ave, Los Alamitos (90720-2107)
P.O. Box 1411 (90720-1411)
PHONE..................................562 594-7878
John D Distefano, *CEO*
EMP: 10 EST: 1999
SALES (est): 778K **Privately Held**
SIC: 2891 Sealing compounds, synthetic rubber or plastic

(P-9178)
V HIMARK (USA) INC
Also Called: Cactus Tape
16019 E Foothill Blvd, Irwindale (91702-2813)
PHONE..................................626 305-5766
Charlie Huang, *President*
◆ EMP: 10
SQ FT: 12,000
SALES (est): 2.1MM **Privately Held**
WEB: www.vhimarkusa.com
SIC: 2891 Adhesives

(P-9179)
VARNI-LITE COATINGS ASSOCIATES
Also Called: Varni Lite
21595 Curtis St, Hayward (94545-1307)
PHONE..................................510 887-8997
Khosrow Sohrabi, *President*
Behrooz Sohrabi, *Vice Pres*
EMP: 10 EST: 1952
SQ FT: 24,000
SALES: 1.2MM **Privately Held**
SIC: 2891 Adhesives

(P-9180)
W R GRACE & CO - CONN
9541 Bus Ctr Dr Ste B, Rancho Cucamonga (91730)
PHONE..................................909 466-4610
Kenneth Lea, *Branch Mgr*
EMP: 14
SALES (corp-wide): 1.7B **Publicly Held**
WEB: www.grace.com
SIC: 2891 Adhesives & sealants
HQ: W. R. Grace & Co.-Conn.
7500 Grace Dr
Columbia MD 21044
410 531-4000

2892 Explosives

(P-9181)
ALPHA DYNO NOBEL
Also Called: Alpha Explosives
1682 Sabovich St 30a, Mojave (93501-1600)
P.O. Box 920 (93502-0920)
PHONE..................................661 824-1356
Richard Cross, *Manager*
Danniell Edwards, *Administration*
EMP: 17
SALES (corp-wide): 34MM **Privately Held**
WEB: www.alphaexplosives.com
SIC: 2892 5169 Explosives; explosives
PA: Alpha Dyno Nobel
3400 Nader Rd
Lincoln CA 95648
916 645-3377

(P-9182)
ENERGETIX SOLUTIONS INC
2601 Cherry Ln, Walnut Creek (94597-2108)
PHONE..................................925 926-6412
Alan Broca, *CEO*
Conrad K Wu, *Principal*
EMP: 12
SQ FT: 3,000
SALES (est): 1.8MM **Privately Held**
SIC: 2892 3629 Explosives; blasting machines, electrical

(P-9183)
MP ASSOCIATES INC
Also Called: M P A
6555 Jackson Valley Rd, Ione (95640-9630)
P.O. Box 546 (95640-0546)
PHONE..................................209 274-4715
Thaine Morris, *President*
David Pier, *Treasurer*
▲ EMP: 170
SQ FT: 3,112
SALES (est): 32.7MM **Privately Held**
WEB: www.mpassociates.com
SIC: 2892 2899 Explosives; pyrotechnic ammunition: flares, signals, rockets, etc.

(P-9184)
OWEN OIL TOOLS INC
5001 Standard St, Bakersfield (93308-4500)
PHONE..................................661 637-1380
Frank Isbell, *Manager*
EMP: 34
SALES (corp-wide): 659.8MM **Privately Held**
SIC: 2892 Explosives
HQ: Owen Oil Tools Lp
12001 County Road 1000
Godley TX 76044
817 551-0540

(P-9185)
TELEDYNE RISI INC (HQ)
32727 W Corral Hollow Rd, Tracy (95376)
P.O. Box 359 (95378-0359)
PHONE..................................925 456-9700
Dr Robert Mehrabian, *President*
EMP: 37
SQ FT: 5,000
SALES: 2MM
SALES (corp-wide): 2.6B **Publicly Held**
WEB: www.teledynereynolds.com
SIC: 2892 Explosives
PA: Teledyne Technologies Inc
1049 Camino Dos Rios
Thousand Oaks CA 91360
805 373-4545

(P-9186)
W A MURPHY INC
26550 National Trails Hwy, Helendale (92342-9605)
PHONE..................................760 245-8711
Sid Perry, *Manager*
EMP: 14
SQ FT: 2,000
SALES (corp-wide): 5.9MM **Privately Held**
WEB: www.murphypowder.com
SIC: 2892 Black powder (explosive)
PA: W. A. Murphy, Inc.
4144 Arden Dr
El Monte CA 91731
626 444-9271

2893 Printing Ink

(P-9187)
ALBATROSS USA INC
5439 W San Fernando Rd, Los Angeles (90039-1014)
PHONE..................................818 543-5850
▲ EMP: 15 EST: 2015
SALES (est): 1.4MM **Privately Held**
SIC: 2893 Printing ink

(P-9188)
AN ENVIRONMENTAL INKS
Also Called: Environmental Inks & Coatings
1920 S Quaker Ridge Pl, Ontario (91761-8041)
PHONE..................................909 930-9656
Paul Holmes, *Regional Mgr*
EMP: 10
SALES (corp-wide): 940.5K **Privately Held**
SIC: 2893 2899 Printing ink; ink or writing fluids
HQ: Environmental Inks And Coatings Canada Ltd.
1 Quality Products Rd
Morganton NC 28655
828 433-1922

P R O D U C T S & S V C S

(P-9189)
BOMARK INC
601 S 6th Ave, La Puente (91746-3026)
PHONE.............................626 968-1666
Herman R Schowe Jr, *Ch of Bd*
H Mark Schowe, *COO*
Kathie Virgil, *CFO*
EMP: 25
SQ FT: 21,000
SALES (est): 5.8MM **Privately Held**
WEB: www.bomarkinks.com
SIC: 2893 Printing ink

(P-9190)
DIVERSFIED NANO SOLUTIONS CORP
10531 4s Commons Dr, San Diego
(92127-3517)
PHONE.............................858 924-1017
Srinivasa Deshiikan, *President*
EMP: 50
SQ FT: 1,000
SALES (est): 2MM **Privately Held**
SIC: 2893 Printing ink

(P-9191)
EXPERT WORLDWIDE LLC
5439 W San Fernando Rd, Los Angeles
(90039-1014)
PHONE.............................818 543-5850
Larry D Lamb,
EMP: 15 EST: 1999
SQ FT: 24,500
SALES (est): 1.5MM **Privately Held**
SIC: 2893 2261 5169 2262 Printing ink;
chemical coating or treating of cotton
broadwoven fabrics; chemicals, industrial
& heavy; chemical coating or treating:
manmade broadwoven fabrics

(P-9192)
FARBOTECH COLOR INC
Also Called: K & E Printing Ink
1630 Yeager Ave, La Verne (91750-5853)
PHONE.............................909 596-9330
Edd Butch, *President*
Fiona Cummings, *Vice Pres*
▲ EMP: 15
SQ FT: 15,000
SALES (est): 2.5MM **Privately Held**
SIC: 2893 Printing ink

(P-9193)
FLEXO-TECHNOLOGIES INC
145 Flowerfield Ln, La Habra Heights
(90631-8446)
PHONE.............................626 444-2595
Helnut Eric Braun, *President*
EMP: 20 EST: 2001
SQ FT: 50,000
SALES: 7MM **Privately Held**
SIC: 2893 8742 Printing ink; management
consulting services

(P-9194)
FLINT GROUP US LLC
Also Called: Flint Ink North America Div
13055 Temple Ave, La Puente
(91746-1418)
PHONE.............................626 369-6900
Tom Stokes, *Manager*
Rosa Grijalva, *Buyer*
Nathan Perry, *Buyer*
EMP: 45
SQ FT: 52,835
SALES (corp-wide): 3.5B **Privately Held**
WEB: www.flintink.com
SIC: 2893 5085 2899 Printing ink; ink,
printers'; ink or writing fluids
PA: Flint Group Us Llc
14909 N Beck Rd
Plymouth MI 48170
734 781-4600

(P-9195)
FLINT GROUP US LLC
14930 Marquardt Ave, Santa Fe Springs
(90670-5129)
P.O. Box 2606 (90670-0606)
PHONE.............................562 903-7976
Larry Shanks, *Branch Mgr*
EMP: 19
SALES (corp-wide): 3.5B **Privately Held**
WEB: www.flintink.com
SIC: 2893 Printing ink

PA: Flint Group Us Llc
14909 N Beck Rd
Plymouth MI 48170
734 781-4600

(P-9196)
GANS INK AND SUPPLY CO INC (PA)
1441 Boyd St, Los Angeles (90033-3790)
P.O. Box 33806 (90033-0806)
PHONE.............................323 264-2200
Jeffrey Koppelman, *President*
Rita Kearsley, *Office Mgr*
Liz Koppelman, *Admin Sec*
Aaron Sures, *Technology*
Stuart Keck, *Purchasing*
▲ EMP: 50
SQ FT: 28,000
SALES (est): 22.5MM **Privately Held**
WEB: www.gansink.com
SIC: 2893 Printing ink

(P-9197)
GANS INK AND SUPPLY CO INC
1441 Boyd St, Los Angeles (90033-3790)
PHONE.............................770 529-7766
John Aylor, *Manager*
EMP: 11
SALES (corp-wide): 22.5MM **Privately
Held**
WEB: www.gansink.com
SIC: 2893 5085 5084 Printing ink; ink,
printers'; printing trades machinery, equip-
ment & supplies
PA: Gans Ink And Supply Co., Inc.
1441 Boyd St
Los Angeles CA 90033
323 264-2200

(P-9198)
GRAPHIC SCIENCES INC
4663 E Guasti Rd Ste B, Ontario
(91761-8196)
PHONE.............................909 947-3366
Daniel Ramos, *Branch Mgr*
EMP: 15
SALES (corp-wide): 7.8MM **Privately
Held**
SIC: 2893 Printing ink
PA: Graphic Sciences, Inc.
7515 Ne Ambassador Pl L
Portland OR 97220

(P-9199)
HADDADS FINE ARTS INC
3855 E Miraloma Ave, Anaheim
(92806-2124)
PHONE.............................714 996-2100
Paula Haddad, *President*
Leslie Cripps, *Officer*
EMP: 15
SQ FT: 17,000
SALES (est): 2.6MM **Privately Held**
WEB: www.haddadsfinearts.com
SIC: 2893 Lithographic ink

(P-9200)
INK 2000 CORP
19875 Nordhoff St, Northridge
(91324-3331)
PHONE.............................818 882-0168
Sheefang Yu, *President*
Kelvin Yu, *Director*
▲ EMP: 10
SQ FT: 5,000
SALES (est): 1.2MM **Privately Held**
WEB: www.ink2000.com
SIC: 2893 Printing ink

(P-9201)
INK MAKERS INC
2121 Yates Ave, Commerce (90040-1911)
PHONE.............................323 728-7500
Kendrick Mills III, *CEO*
Jean Mills, *Treasurer*
Stephen L Miller, *Vice Pres*
EMP: 15
SQ FT: 15,000
SALES: 1.7MM **Privately Held**
SIC: 2893

(P-9202)
INKJETMADNESSCOM INC
Also Called: Inkgrabber.com
2205 1st St Ste 103, Simi Valley
(93065-1981)
PHONE.............................805 583-7755
Keith Ramirez, *President*
Nick Paolucci, *Vice Pres*
Josh Needtoget, *Buyer*
Brandon Timar, *Manager*
▲ EMP: 16
SALES (est): 3.4MM **Privately Held**
WEB: www.inkjetmadness.com
SIC: 2893 Printing ink

(P-9203)
INX INTERNATIONAL INK CO
Also Called: INX Digital Intl
2125 Williams St, San Leandro
(94577-3224)
PHONE.............................510 895-8001
Micol Kranz, *Sales/Mktg Mgr*
EMP: 17
SALES (corp-wide): 1.4B **Privately Held**
SIC: 2893 Printing ink
HQ: Inx International Ink Co.
150 N Martingale Rd # 700
Schaumburg IL 60173
630 382-1800

(P-9204)
INX INTERNATIONAL INK CO
13821 Marquardt Ave, Santa Fe Springs
(90670-5016)
PHONE.............................562 404-5664
Elvis Tran, *Manager*
EMP: 12
SALES (corp-wide): 1.4B **Privately Held**
SIC: 2893 2899 Gravure ink; ink or writing
fluids
HQ: Inx International Ink Co.
150 N Martingale Rd # 700
Schaumburg IL 60173
630 382-1800

(P-9205)
INX INTERNATIONAL INK CO
1000 Business Park Dr, Dixon
(95620-4310)
PHONE.............................707 693-2990
EMP: 12
SALES (corp-wide): 1.4B **Privately Held**
SIC: 2893 Printing ink
HQ: Inx International Ink Co.
150 N Martingale Rd # 700
Schaumburg IL 60173
630 382-1800

(P-9206)
MERIT PRINTING INK COMPANY
1451 S Lorena St, Los Angeles
(90023-3718)
PHONE.............................323 268-1807
Donald W Pettijohn, *President*
Nancy B Pettijohn, *Vice Pres*
EMP: 12 EST: 1962
SQ FT: 8,000
SALES (est): 1.5MM **Privately Held**
SIC: 2893 Printing ink

(P-9207)
PRO COLORFLEX INK CORP
3588 Arden Rd, Hayward (94545-3921)
PHONE.............................510 293-3033
Rick Duarte, *President*
Jack Donelly, *President*
EMP: 12
SALES (est): 2.5MM **Privately Held**
WEB: www.procolorflex.com
SIC: 2893 Printing ink

(P-9208)
SELECT OFFICE SYSTEMS INC
1811 W Magnolia Blvd, Burbank
(91506-1725)
P.O. Box 11777 (91510-1777)
PHONE.............................818 861-8320
Andrew Hunter Rouse, *CEO*
EMP: 17
SALES (est): 2.8MM **Privately Held**
SIC: 2893 Printing ink

(P-9209)
SIEGWERK USA INC
871 Cotting Ct Ste H, Vacaville
(95688-9399)
PHONE.............................707 469-7648
Jason Wood, *Manager*
Albert Genzen, *Sr Consultant*
EMP: 29
SALES (corp-wide): 940.5K **Privately
Held**
WEB: www.sipana.com
SIC: 2893 Printing ink
HQ: Siegwerk Usa Inc.
3535 Sw 56th St
Des Moines IA 50321
515 471-2100

(P-9210)
SUN CHEMICAL CORPORATION
G P I
120 Mason Cir, Concord (94520-1214)
PHONE.............................925 695-2601
Ted Clinton, *Manager*
Warren Urton, *Branch Mgr*
EMP: 10
SALES (corp-wide): 7B **Privately Held**
WEB: www.sunchemical.com
SIC: 2893 Printing ink
HQ: Sun Chemical Corporation
35 Waterview Blvd Ste 100
Parsippany NJ 07054
973 404-6000

(P-9211)
SUN CHEMICAL CORPORATION
General Printing Ink Division
12963 Park St, Santa Fe Springs
(90670-4083)
PHONE.............................562 946-2327
Paul Stack, *Manager*
Mike Mena, *Plant Mgr*
EMP: 40
SALES (corp-wide): 7B **Privately Held**
WEB: www.sunchemical.com
SIC: 2893 5084 Printing ink; printing
trades machinery, equipment & supplies
HQ: Sun Chemical Corporation
35 Waterview Blvd Ste 100
Parsippany NJ 07054
973 404-6000

(P-9212)
SUN CHEMICAL CORPORATION
1599 Factor Ave, San Leandro
(94577-5615)
PHONE.............................510 618-1302
Tom Philis, *Branch Mgr*
Brian Zylka, *Human Resources*
EMP: 25
SALES (corp-wide): 7B **Privately Held**
WEB: www.sunchemical.com
SIC: 2893 Printing ink
HQ: Sun Chemical Corporation
35 Waterview Blvd Ste 100
Parsippany NJ 07054
973 404-6000

(P-9213)
TOYO INK INTERNATIONAL CORP
Also Called: Toyo Ink North America
11190 Valley View St, Cypress
(90630-5231)
PHONE.............................714 899-2377
Horacio Acosta, *Branch Mgr*
Bill Bonney, *CFO*
Whittney Roberts, *Manager*
EMP: 23
SALES (corp-wide): 2.1B **Privately Held**
WEB: www.toyoink.com
SIC: 2893 5085 2899 Printing ink; indus-
trial supplies; chemical preparations
HQ: Toyo Ink International Corp
1225 N Michael Dr
Wood Dale IL 60191

(P-9214)
UVEXS INCORPORATED
1287 Hammerwood Ave, Sunnyvale
(94089-2231)
P.O. Box 64310 (94088-4313)
PHONE.............................408 734-4402
Brent Puder, *President*
Dorthy Puder, *Shareholder*
Ben Funsten, *Design Engr*

▲ = Import ▼=Export
◆ =Import/Export

Lonnie Tillett, *Engineer*
Carol Toman, *CPA*
EMP: 14
SQ FT: 13,500
SALES (est): 2.8MM **Privately Held**
WEB: www.uvexs.com
SIC: 2893 5084 Letterpress or offset ink;
lithographic ink; screen process ink; print-
ing trades machinery, equipment & sup-
plies

(P-9215)
WESTCOAST INKSOLUTIONS LLC
5928 Garfield Ave, Commerce
(90040-3607)
PHONE.................................323 726-8100
John P Jilek Jr, *Opers Mgr*
Dan Delegge,
EMP: 15
SQ FT: 42,000
SALES: 3.5MM
SALES (corp-wide): 6MM **Privately Held**
WEB: www.inksolutions.com
SIC: 2893 2851 Printing ink; paints & al-
lied products
PA: Ink Solutions, Llc
800 Estes Ave
Elk Grove Village IL 60007
847 593-5200

(P-9216)
WIKOFF COLOR CORPORATION
1329 N Market Blvd # 160, Sacramento
(95834-2960)
PHONE.................................916 928-6965
Geoffrey Peters, *Branch Mgr*
EMP: 10
SALES (corp-wide): 150MM **Privately Held**
SIC: 2893 Printing ink
PA: Wikoff Color Corporation
1886 Merritt Rd
Fort Mill SC 29715
803 548-2210

(P-9217)
X TRI INC
8787 Plata Ln Ste 7, Atascadero
(93422-5395)
PHONE.................................805 286-4544
Anthony Foley, *Principal*
Laura Lynn Foley, *Principal*
EMP: 11
SALES (est): 1.7MM **Privately Held**
SIC: 2893 Printing ink

2895 Carbon Black

(P-9218)
ALDILA MATERIALS TECHNOLOGY (DH)
13450 Stowe Dr, Poway (92064-6860)
PHONE.................................858 513-1801
Pete Matthewson, *President*
▼ **EMP:** 33 **EST:** 1997
SALES (est): 21.4MM
SALES (corp-wide): 34.9B **Privately Held**
WEB: www.aldila.com
SIC: 2895 Carbon black
HQ: Aldila, Inc.
1945 Kellogg Ave
Carlsbad CA 92008
858 513-1801

2899 Chemical Preparations, NEC

(P-9219)
AMERICAN CONSUMER PRODUCTS LLC
23000 Avalon Blvd, Carson (90745-5017)
PHONE.................................310 443-3330
David Molayen, *President*
Kam Jahanbigloo, *Vice Pres*
Daryoosh Molayem, *Managing Dir*
▲ **EMP:** 22

SALES: 10.3MM
SALES (corp-wide): 39.5MM **Privately Held**
WEB: www.acillc.com
SIC: 2899 2844 2834 Chemical prepara-
tions; cosmetic preparations; pharmaceu-
tical preparations
PA: Tabletops Unlimited, Inc.
23000 Avalon Blvd
Carson CA 90745
310 549-6000

(P-9220)
AMERICAN PACIFIC MORTGAGE CORP
615 1st St, Benicia (94510-3211)
PHONE.................................707 746-4920
EMP: 14 **Privately Held**
SIC: 2899 Oxidizers, inorganic
PA: American Pacific Mortgage Corporation
3000 Lava Ridge Ct # 200
Roseville CA 95661

(P-9221)
AMERICAN QUALEX INTERNATIONAL
920a Calle Negocio Ste A, San Clemente
(92673-6201)
PHONE.................................949 492-8298
Dan Moothart, *President*
EMP: 10
SALES (est): 770K **Privately Held**
SIC: 2899 Chemical preparations

(P-9222)
AVALON CHEMICAL INC
1230 E Saint Gertrude Pl, Santa Ana
(92707-3030)
PHONE.................................714 540-3874
Alfred E Gallade, *President*
Richard A Gallade, *Vice Pres*
EMP: 45 **EST:** 1956
SALES (est): 4.3MM **Privately Held**
SIC: 2899 Chemical preparations

(P-9223)
AVISTA TECHNOLOGIES INC
140 Bosstick Blvd, San Marcos
(92069-5930)
PHONE.................................760 744-0536
David Walker, *President*
Karen Lindsey, *CFO*
Dan Comstock, *Vice Pres*
▼ **EMP:** 19 **EST:** 1999
SQ FT: 15,500
SALES (est): 5.5MM
SALES (corp-wide): 1.9MM **Privately Held**
WEB: www.avistatech.com
SIC: 2899 Chemical supplies for foundries;
water treating compounds
PA: Avista Technologies (Uk) Ltd.
13 Nasmyth Square
Livingston EH54
131 449-6677

(P-9224)
BASF CONSTRUCTION CHEM LLC
Degussa Construction
9060 Haven Ave, Rancho Cucamonga
(91730-5405)
PHONE.................................909 987-1758
Dave Lougheed, *Manager*
EMP: 21
SALES (corp-wide): 76B **Privately Held**
WEB: www.basf-admixtures.com
SIC: 2899 Concrete curing & hardening
compounds
HQ: Master Builders, Llc
23700 Chagrin Blvd
Beachwood OH 44122
216 831-5500

(P-9225)
CADE CORPORATION
100 Lewis St, San Jose (95112-5853)
PHONE.................................408 292-3435
Norman R Angell, *CEO*
Rozann Stenshoel, *President*
Ken Keeth, *Technical Staff*
Tony Dominguez, *Controller*
Natalie Sanchez, *Purch Agent*
EMP: 11

SQ FT: 25,000
SALES (est): 2.7MM **Privately Held**
WEB: www.cadeco.com
SIC: 2899 Waterproofing compounds

(P-9226)
CALIFORNIA RESPIRATORY CARE
16055 Ventura Blvd # 715, Encino
(91436-2601)
PHONE.................................818 379-9999
Efy Lavaei, *President*
EMP: 55
SALES (est): 4.1MM **Privately Held**
SIC: 2899 5047 5169 Chemical prepara-
tions; medical & hospital equipment; oxy-
gen

(P-9227)
CHEMDIV INC
Also Called: Chemical Diversity Labs
12760 High Bluff Dr # 370, San Diego
(92130-2017)
PHONE.................................858 794-4860
Nikolay P Savchuk, *CEO*
A Ivachtchenko, *Chairman*
Vadim Bichko, *Vice Pres*
Oleg Korzinov, *Vice Pres*
Sergey Bugrov, *Exec Dir*
EMP: 50 **EST:** 1995
SQ FT: 19,000
SALES (est): 16.7MM **Privately Held**
WEB: www.chemdiv.com
SIC: 2899 Chemical preparations

(P-9228)
CHEMICALS INCORPORATED
13560 Colombard Ct, Fontana
(92337-7702)
PHONE.................................951 681-9697
Earl Harper, *CEO*
Herbert N Long, *President*
Anthony Carter, *Vice Pres*
George Burke, *Manager*
▲ **EMP:** 15
SQ FT: 64,000
SALES (est): 3.9MM **Privately Held**
WEB: www.cheminc.com
SIC: 2899 Water treating compounds
PA: Harpure Enterprises, Inc.
13560 Colombard Ct
Fontana CA 92337

(P-9229)
CHEMTREAT INC
Also Called: Trident Technologies
8885 Rehco Rd, San Diego (92121-3261)
PHONE.................................804 935-2000
EMP: 23
SALES (corp-wide): 18.3B **Publicly Held**
SIC: 2899 Water treating compounds
HQ: Chemtreat, Inc.
5640 Cox Rd Ste 300
Glen Allen VA 23060
804 935-2000

(P-9230)
CHEVRON ORONITE COMPANY LLC (DH)
6001 Bollinger Canyon Rd, San Ramon
(94583-5737)
PHONE.................................713 432-2500
Desmond King, *President*
Rich Conway, *CFO*
Andrew Busby, *Design Engr*
Marshall Mahoney, *Engrg Dir*
Frank Oliveri, *Project Mgr*
◆ **EMP:** 50
SALES (est): 377.8MM
SALES (corp-wide): 141.7B **Publicly Held**
SIC: 2899 2869 1311 2821 Chemical
preparations; industrial organic chemi-
cals; crude petroleum & natural gas; poly-
styrene resins
HQ: Chevron U.S.A. Inc.
6001 Bollinger Canyon Rd D1248
San Ramon CA 94583
925 842-1000

(P-9231)
CHOSEN FOODS LLC (PA)
1747 Hancock St Ste A, San Diego
(92101-1130)
PHONE.................................877 674-2244

Gabriel Perez-Krieb, *Ch of Bd*
Peter Choi, *Accountant*
Ana Macias, *Controller*
Kylie Maraj, *Marketing Staff*
Cory Baran, *Sales Staff*
◆ **EMP:** 15
SQ FT: 8,000
SALES (est): 5.4MM **Privately Held**
SIC: 2899 Essential oils

(P-9232)
CONTRABAND CONTROL SPECIALISTS
Also Called: Zee Consulting
26 H St, Bakersfield (93304-2908)
P.O. Box 2365 (93303-2365)
PHONE.................................661 322-3363
Gary Zvirblis, *President*
EMP: 15
SALES (est): 2.2MM **Privately Held**
WEB: www.contrabandcontrol.com
SIC: 2899

(P-9233)
COPPER HARBOR COMPANY INC
2300 Davis St, San Leandro (94577-2206)
PHONE.................................510 639-4670
Daniel Walters, *President*
EMP: 16 **EST:** 1997
SQ FT: 18,000
SALES: 2MM **Privately Held**
WEB: www.copperharbor.com
SIC: 2899 2865 2911 Chemical supplies
for foundries; solvent naphtha; solvents

(P-9234)
COVAL MOLECULAR COATINGS INC
5341 Old Redwood Hwy, Petaluma
(94954-7126)
PHONE.................................707 242-6900
Richard Stenberg, *CEO*
Larry Hebert, *President*
EMP: 10
SALES (est): 1.2MM **Privately Held**
SIC: 2899 Chemical preparations

(P-9235)
CP KELCO US INC
2025 Harbor Dr, San Diego (92113-2214)
PHONE.................................858 467-6542
Andrew Currie, *Manager*
EMP: 30
SALES (corp-wide): 886.9MM **Privately Held**
WEB: www.cpkelco.com
SIC: 2899 Sizes
HQ: Cp Kelco U.S., Inc.
3100 Cumberland Blvd Se # 600
Atlanta GA 30339
678 247-7300

(P-9236)
CP KELCO US INC
8355 Aero Dr, San Diego (92123-1718)
P.O. Box 23576 (92123)
PHONE.................................858 292-4900
Greg Courney, *Manager*
Mary Ross, *Manager*
EMP: 20
SALES (corp-wide): 886.9MM **Privately Held**
WEB: www.cpkelco.com
SIC: 2899 Sizes
HQ: Cp Kelco U.S., Inc.
3100 Cumberland Blvd Se # 600
Atlanta GA 30339
678 247-7300

(P-9237)
CP KELCO US INC
8225 Aero Dr, San Diego (92123-1716)
PHONE.................................858 292-4900
Brenda Leitzow, *Administration*
Yamini Patel, *Research*
Laura Laslo, *Technical Staff*
Marcos Olivas, *Engineer*
Peter Hefti, *Accountant*
EMP: 12 **EST:** 2016
SALES (est): 946.4K **Privately Held**
SIC: 2899 Chemical preparations

PRODUCTS & SVCS

(P-9238)
CUTWATER SPIRITS LLC
9750 Distribution Ave, San Diego
(92121-2310)
PHONE..............................858 672-3848
EMP: 38
SALES (est): 10.4MM Privately Held
SIC: 2899 Distilled water

(P-9239)
CYANTEK CORPORATION
3055 Osgood Ct, Fremont (94539-5612)
P.O. Box 1209, Morgan Hill (95038-1209)
PHONE..............................510 651-3341
Christopher Vidoli, CEO
▲ EMP: 23
SQ FT: 16,000
SALES (est): 3.7MM
SALES (corp-wide): 465.5MM Publicly
Held
WEB: www.cyantek.com
SIC: 2899
PA: Kmg Chemicals, Inc.
300 Throckmorton St # 1900
Fort Worth TX 76102
817 761-6100

(P-9240)
DANNIER CHEMICAL INC
2302 Martin Ste 450, Irvine (92612-7401)
PHONE..............................949 221-8660
Daniel Shen, President
▲ EMP: 25 EST: 1992
SALES (est): 3.7MM Privately Held
WEB: www.dannier.com
SIC: 2899 2869 2833 Chemical prepara-
tions; antioxidants, rubber processing:
cyclic or acyclic; high purity grade chemi-
cals, organic; laboratory chemicals, or-
ganic; organic medicinal chemicals: bulk,
uncompounded

(P-9241)
DIAMON FUSION INTL INC
9361 Irvine Blvd, Irvine (92618-1669)
PHONE..............................949 388-8000
Adam Zax, President
Denise Robinson, CFO
Carl Christ, Vice Pres
Russell Slaybaugh, Vice Pres
Jeff Woolsey, Prdtn Mgr
EMP: 16
SQ FT: 4,500
SALES (est): 4.3MM Privately Held
WEB: www.diamonfusion.com
SIC: 2899 6794 Chemical preparations;
patent owners & lessors

(P-9242)
DRYVIT SYSTEMS INC
354 S Acacia St, Woodlake (93286-1644)
PHONE..............................559 564-3591
Dan Smith, Manager
EMP: 25
SQ FT: 20,000
SALES (corp-wide): 5.3B Publicly Held
WEB: www.dryvitcompanystore.com
SIC: 2899 Chemical preparations
HQ: Dryvit Systems, Inc.
1 Energy Way
West Warwick RI 02893
401 822-4100

(P-9243)
DURA-CHEM INC
18327 Pasadena St, Lake Elsinore
(92530-2766)
PHONE..............................951 245-7778
John Hassell, President
Allen Bass, Vice Pres
Kay Hassell, Vice Pres
William Fruscella, Manager
EMP: 10 EST: 1977
SQ FT: 6,000
SALES (est): 1.7MM Privately Held
WEB: www.thermobond3.com
SIC: 2899 2992 Chemical preparations;
lubricating oils

(P-9244)
E W SMITH CHEMICAL CO
4738 Murrieta St, Chino (91710-5182)
PHONE..............................909 590-9717
Robert D Cartwright, President
Gayle Lewis, Admin Sec
EMP: 12

SQ FT: 12,528
SALES (est): 2.2MM Privately Held
SIC: 2899 2842 Water treating compounds; specialty cleaning, polishes &
sanitation goods

(P-9245)
EKC TECHNOLOGY INC (DH)
Also Called: E K C Technology/Burmar Chem
2520 Barrington Ct, Hayward (94545-1163)
PHONE..............................510 784-9105
Ellen Kullman, CEO
Seng Wui Lim, President
John Odom, President
Thomas M Connelly Jr, Exec VP
David G Bills, Senior VP
◆ EMP: 115 EST: 1963
SQ FT: 65,000
SALES (est): 37.4MM
SALES (corp-wide): 62.4B Publicly Held
WEB: www.ekctech.com
SIC: 2899 Chemical preparations
HQ: E. I. Du Pont De Nemours And Com-
pany
974 Centre Rd
Wilmington DE 19805
302 774-1000

(P-9246)
ENOVA SOLUTIONS INC
3553 Landco Dr Ste B, Bakersfield
(93308-6169)
P.O. Box 21988 (93390-1988)
PHONE..............................661 327-2405
Richard Dyer, President
Jesse Holman, Treasurer
Michael Ripley, Admin Sec
EMP: 13
SALES (est): 2.7MM Privately Held
SIC: 2899 Oil treating compounds

(P-9247)
EUREKA CHEMICAL COMPANY
(PA)
234 Lawrence Ave, South San Francisco
(94080-6863)
P.O. Box 2205 (94083-2205)
PHONE..............................650 873-5374
Genevieve E Hess, CEO
D Tom Stanton, President
Amy Bruno, Info Tech Mgr
Marie Oxoby, Accountant
◆ EMP: 10
SQ FT: 16,000
SALES (est): 1.4MM Privately Held
WEB: www.eurekafluidfilm.com
SIC: 2899 Corrosion preventive lubricant

(P-9248)
EVERSPRING CHEMICAL INC
11577 W Olympic Blvd, Los Angeles
(90064-1522)
PHONE..............................310 707-1600
Marvin Lai, CEO
▲ EMP: 75
SQ FT: 2,000
SALES (est): 9.3MM Privately Held
SIC: 2899 Chemical preparations

(P-9249)
EVONIK CORPORATION
Also Called: Air Products
3305 E 26th St, Vernon (90058-4101)
PHONE..............................323 264-0311
William Ayacha, Branch Mgr
EMP: 40
SALES (corp-wide): 2.4B Privately Held
WEB: www.airproducts.com
SIC: 2899 2891 2821 Chemical prepara-
tions; adhesives & sealants; plastics ma-
terials & resins
HQ: Evonik Corporation
299 Jefferson Rd
Parsippany NJ 07054
973 929-8000

(P-9250)
EXCELLENT COATINGS INC
2780 La Mirada Dr Ste E, Vista
(92081-8404)
PHONE..............................760 598-1234
Gil Lackritz, President
Gwynn Stegen, COO
EMP: 15

SALES (est): 2MM Privately Held
WEB: www.excellentcoatings.com
SIC: 2899 Waterproofing compounds

(P-9251)
FLAMEMASTER CORPORATION
Also Called: Chemsil
13576 Desmond St, Pacoima
(91331-2315)
P.O. Box 4510 (91333-4500)
PHONE..............................818 890-1401
Joseph Mazin, CEO
Mary Kay Eason, Corp Secy
▲ EMP: 28
SALES (est): 4.3MM Privately Held
WEB: www.flamemaster.com
SIC: 2899 2819 1799 2891 Fire retardant
chemicals; industrial inorganic chemicals;
coating of metal structures at construction
site; sealing compounds, synthetic rubber
or plastic

(P-9252)
FUJIFILM ULTRA PURE SLTONS
INC (DH)
11225 Commercial Pkwy, Castroville
(95012-3205)
PHONE..............................831 632-2120
Christopher Fitzjohn, President
Mike Doi, Corp Secy
Bill Robb, Vice Pres
Sherman Stever, Vice Pres
Curtis Williams, VP Opers
▲ EMP: 20
SALES (est): 30MM
SALES (corp-wide): 22.8B Privately Held
WEB: www.ultrapuresolutions.net
SIC: 2899 Chemical preparations
HQ: Fujifilm Electronic Materials U.S.A.,
Inc.
80 Circuit Dr
North Kingstown RI 02852
401 522-9499

(P-9253)
GARRATT-CALLAHAN
COMPANY (PA)
50 Ingold Rd, Burlingame (94010-2206)
PHONE..............................650 697-5811
Jeffrey L Garratt, CEO
Matthew Colvin, CFO
Matthew R Garratt, Exec VP
Reema Rios, Human Res Mgr
EMP: 40 EST: 1904
SQ FT: 60,000
SALES (est): 69.4MM Privately Held
WEB: www.g-c.com
SIC: 2899 2911 Water treating com-
pounds; oils, lubricating

(P-9254)
GENERAL GRAPHIC
CHEMICALS CO
2525 Mandela Pkwy Ste 2, Oakland
(94607-1722)
P.O. Box 24472 (94623-1472)
PHONE..............................510 832-4404
Andrew Greenberg, President
Bruce Greenberg, President
▲ EMP: 17
SQ FT: 14,000
SALES (est): 2.5MM Privately Held
WEB: www.generalgraphic.com
SIC: 2899 Chemical preparations

(P-9255)
GGTW LLC
Also Called: South Bay Salt Works
1470 Bay Blvd, Chula Vista (91911-3942)
PHONE..............................619 423-3388
Glenn Warner, Owner
Tracy Strahl, Principal
▼ EMP: 20
SALES (est): 3.9MM Privately Held
SIC: 2899 Salt

(P-9256)
HAIR SYNDICUT
565 N Central Ave, Upland (91786-4241)
PHONE..............................909 946-3200
Cindy Allen, Owner
EMP: 15
SALES (est): 1MM Privately Held
WEB: www.hairsyndicut.com
SIC: 2899 Chemical preparations

(P-9257)
HEMOSURE INC
5358 Irwindale Ave, Baldwin Park
(91706-2086)
PHONE..............................888 436-6787
Dr John Wan, President
Sherry Wang, Human Res Mgr
EMP: 40
SALES (est): 14.8MM Privately Held
WEB: www.whpm.com
SIC: 2899 3841 Chemical preparations;
surgical & medical instruments
PA: W.H.P.M. Inc.
5358 Irwindale Ave
Irwindale CA 91706
626 443-8480

(P-9258)
HK ENTERPRISE GROUP INC
Also Called: Hawaii Kai
6540 Lusk Blvd Ste C270, San Diego
(92121-2783)
PHONE..............................858 652-4400
George Joseph, CEO
EMP: 10
SALES (est): 675.9K Privately Held
SIC: 2899 Salt

(P-9259)
HYDRANAUTICS (DH)
401 Jones Rd, Oceanside (92058-1216)
PHONE..............................760 901-2597
Brett Andrews, CEO
Upen Bharwada, COO
Ellen Class, Vice Pres
Michael Concannon, Vice Pres
Norio Ikeyama, Vice Pres
◆ EMP: 400
SQ FT: 150,000
SALES (est): 133.5MM
SALES (corp-wide): 8B Privately Held
WEB: www.hydranautics.com
SIC: 2899 3589 Chemical preparations;
water treatment equipment, industrial
HQ: Nitto Americas, Inc.
48500 Fremont Blvd
Fremont CA 94538
510 445-5400

(P-9260)
IL HELTH BUTY NATURAL OILS
INC
Also Called: Hbno
322 N Aviador St, Camarillo (93010-8302)
PHONE..............................805 384-0473
Josef Demangeat, CEO
EMP: 50
SALES (est): 1.8MM Privately Held
SIC: 2899 2836 Essential oils; extracts

(P-9261)
INDEPENDENT INK INC
13700 S Gramac Pl, Gardena (90249)
PHONE..............................310 523-4657
Ramesh Sudbraram, Manager
EMP: 24
SALES (corp-wide): 7.9MM Privately
Held
WEB: www.independentink.com
SIC: 2899 Ink or writing fluids
PA: Independent Ink, Inc.
13700 Gramercy Pl
Gardena CA 90249
310 523-4657

(P-9262)
INDIO PRODUCTS INC
Cultural Heritage Candle Co
5331 E Slauson Ave, Commerce
(90040-2916)
PHONE..............................323 720-9117
Marty Mayer, Owner
EMP: 33
SALES (corp-wide): 101.8MM Privately
Held
WEB: www.indioproducts.com
SIC: 2899 3999 5199 5049 Incense; can-
dles; candles; religious supplies
PA: Indio Products, Inc.
12910 Mulberry Dr Unit A
Whittier CA 90602
323 720-1188

▲ = Import ▼=Export
◆ =Import/Export

(P-9263)
INSULTECH LLC (PA)
3530 W Garry Ave, Santa Ana
(92704-6423)
PHONE..................714 384-0506
Lisa Romero, *Mng Member*
Michael Markantonis, *Vice Pres*
Rafael Castro, *Design Engr*
Alex Martinez, *Design Engr*
David Baccini, *Engineer*
▲ EMP: 75
SQ FT: 30,000
SALES (est): 17.3MM **Privately Held**
SIC: 2899 Insulating compounds

(P-9264)
INTEGRITY SUPPORT SERVICES INC
Also Called: Employment Screening Resources
7110 Redwood Blvd Ste C, Novato
(94945-4141)
PHONE..................415 898-0044
Lester S Rosen, *President*
Dawn Standerwick, *Vice Pres*
Pat Murphy, *Risk Mgmt Dir*
Bruce Guerra, *Opers Staff*
Shannon Durst, *Sales Executive*
EMP: 10
SALES (est): 2.2MM **Privately Held**
WEB: www.esrcheck.com
SIC: 2899 7323 7375 8742 ; credit reporting services; information retrieval services; human resource consulting services

(P-9265)
K2 PURE SOLUTIONS NOCAL LP
950 Loveridge Rd, Pittsburg (94565-2808)
PHONE..................647 776-0273
Chris McLean, *Partner*
Rosemary Aldrich, *Partner*
Rochelle Aquino, *Partner*
EMP: 21
SALES: 4.8MM **Privately Held**
SIC: 2899 Chemical preparations

(P-9266)
KELCO BIO POLYMERS
Also Called: CP Kelco
2025 Harbor Dr, San Diego (92113-2214)
PHONE..................619 595-5000
Diane E Salisbury, *Principal*
Tony Brentnall, *COO*
Mike Hughes, *Info Tech Mgr*
Melinda Robinson, *Business Anlyst*
George Hagedon, *Project Mgr*
EMP: 21
SALES (est): 3.6MM **Privately Held**
SIC: 2899 Chemical preparations

(P-9267)
KEMIRA WATER SOLUTIONS INC
14000 San Bernardino Ave, Fontana
(92335-5258)
PHONE..................909 429-4001
Keith Heasley, *Manager*
George Macgregor, *Technical Staff*
Dennis Ventimiglia, *Terminal Mgr*
EMP: 15
SALES (corp-wide): 2.9B **Privately Held**
WEB: www.kemiron.com
SIC: 2899 Water treating compounds
HQ: Kemira Water Solutions, Inc.
1000 Parkwood Cir Se # 500
Atlanta GA 30339
770 436-1542

(P-9268)
KEMIRA WATER SOLUTIONS INC
Also Called: Kemiron Pacific
14000 San Bernardino Ave, Fontana
(92335-5258)
PHONE..................909 350-5678
Hailu Mequira, *Manager*
EMP: 23
SALES (corp-wide): 2.9B **Privately Held**
WEB: www.kemiron.com
SIC: 2899 Water treating compounds

HQ: Kemira Water Solutions, Inc.
1000 Parkwood Cir Se # 500
Atlanta GA 30339
770 436-1542

(P-9269)
KIK POOL ADDITIVES INC
5160 E Airport Dr, Ontario (91761-7824)
PHONE..................909 390-9912
John A Christensen, *President*
Brian Patterson, *CFO*
David M Christensen, *Vice Pres*
Debra Schonk, *Vice Pres*
Chet Yoakum, *Vice Pres*
▲ EMP: 140 EST: 1958
SALES (est): 58.1MM **Privately Held**
WEB: www.kem-tek.com
SIC: 2899 3089 7389 5169 Chemical preparations; plastic hardware & building products; packaging & labeling services; swimming pool & spa chemicals

(P-9270)
KMG CHEMICALS INC
2340 Bert Dr, Hollister (95023-2510)
PHONE..................800 956-7467
Keith Hussinger, *Manager*
EMP: 40
SALES (corp-wide): 465.5MM **Publicly Held**
SIC: 2899 Chemical preparations
PA: Kmg Chemicals, Inc.
300 Throckmorton St # 1900
Fort Worth TX 76102
817 761-6100

(P-9271)
LAGUNA COUNTY SANATATION DIST
3500 Black Rd, Santa Maria (93455-5927)
PHONE..................805 934-6282
Mark Moya, *Principal*
EMP: 11
SALES (est): 1.1MM **Privately Held**
SIC: 2899 Water treating compounds

(P-9272)
LG NANOH2O INC
21250 Hawthorne Blvd # 330, Torrance
(90503-5541)
PHONE..................424 218-4000
Jeff Green, *CEO*
Doug Barnes, *COO*
John Markovich, *CFO*
Michael Demartino, *Vice Pres*
Nicholas Dyner, *Vice Pres*
▼ EMP: 35
SQ FT: 2,000
SALES (est): 7.3MM
SALES (corp-wide): 19.1B **Privately Held**
SIC: 2899 Distilled water
PA: Lg Chem, Ltd.
128 Yeoui-Daero, Yeongdeungpo-Gu
Seoul 07336
822 377-3111

(P-9273)
LM SCOFIELD COMPANY (DH)
12767 Imperial Hwy, Santa Fe Springs
(90670-4711)
PHONE..................323 720-3000
Phillip J Arnold, *President*
Bob Torres, *Regional Mgr*
Jesse Gulledge, *Technical Staff*
Sally Miller, *Credit Mgr*
Kristi Alexander, *Purchasing*
◆ EMP: 50
SQ FT: 36,000
SALES (est): 25.2MM
SALES (corp-wide): 213.5MM **Privately Held**
SIC: 2899 Concrete curing & hardening compounds
HQ: Sika Corporation
201 Polito Ave
Lyndhurst NJ 07071
201 933-8800

(P-9274)
LUBRIZOL ADVANCED MTLS INC
Also Called: LUBRIZOL ADVANCED MATERIALS, INC.
3115 Propeller Dr, Paso Robles
(93446-8524)
PHONE..................805 239-1550

Daniel McCornack, *Principal*
EMP: 68
SALES (corp-wide): 242.1B **Publicly Held**
WEB: www.pharma.noveoninc.com
SIC: 2899 Chemical preparations
HQ: Lubrizol Global Management, Inc
9911 Brecksville Rd
Brecksville OH 44141
216 447-5000

(P-9275)
LUBRIZOL CORPORATION
30211 Ave D Las Bandras, Rancho Santa
Margari (92688)
PHONE..................949 212-1863
EMP: 19
SALES (corp-wide): 182.1B **Publicly Held**
SIC: 2899
HQ: The Lubrizol Corporation
29400 Lakeland Blvd
Wickliffe OH 44092
440 943-4200

(P-9276)
MATSUI INTERNATIONAL CO INC
Also Called: Unimark
1501 W 178th St, Gardena (90248-3203)
PHONE..................310 767-7812
Masa Matsui, *President*
Akiko Matsui, *General Mgr*
Henry WEI, *Controller*
Sayaka Taira, *Human Resources*
Yoshiaki Kojima, *Export Mgr*
◆ EMP: 180
SQ FT: 30,000
SALES (est): 39.1MM
SALES (corp-wide): 25.7MM **Privately Held**
WEB: www.matsui-color.com
SIC: 2899 Ink or writing fluids
PA: Matsui Shikiso Chemical Co.,Ltd.
64, Sakuradani, Kamikazan, Ya-mashina-Ku
Kyoto KYO 607-8
755 945-613

(P-9277)
MC PRODUCTS INC
23331 Antonio Pkwy, Rcho STA Marg
(92688-2664)
PHONE..................949 888-7100
Dave Maietta, *President*
EMP: 17
SQ FT: 36,000
SALES (est): 6.2MM **Privately Held**
SIC: 2899 Waterproofing compounds

(P-9278)
MCGRAYEL COMPANY INC
Also Called: Eascare Products USA
5361 S Villa Ave, Fresno (93725-8903)
P.O. Box 12362 (93777-2362)
PHONE..................559 299-7660
Marvin J Rezac Jr, *CEO*
Evangelina Serrano, *President*
Todd Wilson, *Treasurer*
Tiffany Rolofson, *General Mgr*
Joseph Mendez, *Mfg Mgr*
EMP: 25
SQ FT: 10,000
SALES (est): 3.7MM **Privately Held**
WEB: www.mcgrayel.com
SIC: 2899 Water treating compounds

(P-9279)
MEDICAL CHEMICAL CORPORATION
Also Called: M C C
19430 Van Ness Ave, Torrance
(90501-1104)
P.O. Box 6217 (90504-0217)
PHONE..................310 787-6800
Emmanuel Didier, *President*
Patrick Braden, *Senior VP*
Kris Kontis, *Vice Pres*
Andy Rocha, *Vice Pres*
Pat Braden, *Lab Dir*
◆ EMP: 45
SQ FT: 35,000
SALES (est): 11.6MM **Privately Held**
WEB: www.med-chem.com
SIC: 2899 2841 Chemical preparations; soap & other detergents

(P-9280)
MICRO-TRACERS INC
1370 Van Dyke Ave, San Francisco
(94124-3313)
PHONE..................415 822-1100
David Eisenberg, *President*
Ngaly Frank, *CFO*
Cyrus Frank, *Admin Sec*
Todd Frank, *Mfg Dir*
Daria Gorohova, *Marketing Mgr*
▲ EMP: 10
SQ FT: 11,000
SALES (est): 2.1MM **Privately Held**
WEB: www.microtracers.com
SIC: 2899 Chemical preparations

(P-9281)
MIRACLE SEALANTS COMPANY LLC
12318 Lower Azusa Rd, Arcadia
(91006-5872)
PHONE..................626 443-6433
Joseph Salvo, *Co-CEO*
Bruce Palmore, *CFO*
Albert P Salvo, *Co-CEO*
Michelle Horvat, *Controller*
◆ EMP: 26
SQ FT: 24,000
SALES: 26.8MM
SALES (corp-wide): 5.3B **Publicly Held**
WEB: www.teamsalvo.com
SIC: 2899 2891 Chemical preparations; adhesives & sealants
HQ: Rust-Oleum Corporation
11 E Hawthorn Pkwy
Vernon Hills IL 60061
847 367-7700

(P-9282)
MISSION VALLEY REGIONAL OCCU
5019 Stevenson Blvd, Fremont
(94538-2449)
PHONE..................510 657-1865
Charles Brown, *Principal*
Gordon Sanford, *Principal*
EMP: 45
SALES (est): 2.2MM **Privately Held**
SIC: 2899 Chemical preparations

(P-9283)
MITANN INC (HQ)
Also Called: Zip-Chem Products
400 Jarvis Dr Ste A, Morgan Hill
(95037-8106)
PHONE..................408 782-2500
Dennis Wagner, *President*
Charles Portier, *Vice Pres*
▲ EMP: 24
SQ FT: 50,000
SALES (est): 10.5MM
SALES (corp-wide): 12MM **Privately Held**
WEB: www.zipchem.com
SIC: 2899 5169 2813 Chemical preparations; chemicals & allied products; industrial gases
PA: Andpak, Inc.
400 Jarvis Dr Ste A
Morgan Hill CA 95037
408 776-1072

(P-9284)
MOC PRODUCTS COMPANY INC (PA)
Also Called: Auto Edge Solutions
12306 Montague St, Pacoima
(91331-2279)
PHONE..................818 794-3500
Mark Waco, *CEO*
Dave Waco, *Vice Pres*
Alan Hope, *Info Tech Dir*
Dean Puett, *Design Engr*
Eric Berg, *VP Finance*
▲ EMP: 75
SQ FT: 100,000
SALES (est): 64.6MM **Privately Held**
WEB: www.mocproducts.com
SIC: 2899 7549 5169 Corrosion preventive lubricant; automotive maintenance services; chemicals & allied products

(PA)=Parent Co (HQ)=Headquarters (DH)=Div Headquarters
✪ = New Business established in last 2 years

2019 California
Manufacturers Register

383

PRODUCTS & SVCS

(P-9285)
NALCO COMPANY LLC
4900 California Ave 420b, Bakersfield
(93309-7024)
PHONE..................................661 864-7955
Danny Moreno, *Branch Mgr*
EMP: 17
SALES (corp-wide): 13.8B **Publicly Held**
SIC: 2899 Water treating compounds
HQ: Nalco Company Llc
1601 W Diehl Rd
Naperville IL 77478
630 305-1000

(P-9286)
NALCO COMPANY LLC
1000 Burnett Ave Ste 430, Concord
(94520-2091)
PHONE..................................800 798-2247
EMP: 12
SALES (corp-wide): 13.8B **Publicly Held**
WEB: www.nalco.com
SIC: 2899 Corrosion preventive lubricant
HQ: Nalco Company Llc
11177 S Stadium Dr
Sugar Land TX 77478
281 632-6500

(P-9287)
NALCO COMPANY LLC
980 Enchanted Way Ste 203, Simi Valley
(93065-0913)
PHONE..................................805 584-9950
Susan Ciciarelli, *Manager*
Cody Moore, *Sales Staff*
David Cuculic, *Manager*
Jeff Alvari, *Accounts Mgr*
Fred Rivers, *Accounts Mgr*
EMP: 12
SALES (corp-wide): 13.8B **Publicly Held**
WEB: www.nalco.com
SIC: 2899 Corrosion preventive lubricant
HQ: Nalco Company Llc
11177 S Stadium Dr
Sugar Land TX 77478
281 632-6500

(P-9288)
NANOSCALE COMBINATORIAL
Also Called: Nanosyn
3100 Central Expy, Santa Clara
(95051-0801)
PHONE..................................408 987-2000
Nikolai Sepetov, *President*
Olga Isskova, *Vice Pres*
Darren Liu, *Info Tech Mgr*
EMP: 35
SQ FT: 30,000
SALES (est): 7.5MM **Privately Held**
SIC: 2899 Chemical preparations

(P-9289)
NATIONAL SWEETWATER INC
Also Called: Sweetwater Technologies
43394 Calle De Velardo, Temecula
(92592-2625)
PHONE..................................951 303-0999
Debbie CHI-Man Lee, *President*
John W Cornell, *Vice Pres*
▲ EMP: 13
SQ FT: 2,400
SALES (est): 2.1MM **Privately Held**
SIC: 2899 8748 Water treating compounds; business consulting

(P-9290)
NEO TECH AQUA SOLUTIONS INC
3853 Calle Fortunada, San Diego
(92123-1824)
PHONE..................................858 571-6590
Stephen Dunham, *President*
George Diefenthal, *COO*
Rocky Springstead, *CFO*
EMP: 15
SQ FT: 6,000
SALES (est): 3.9MM **Privately Held**
WEB: www.uvsciences.com
SIC: 2899 Water treating compounds

(P-9291)
NORTH AMERICAN PETROLEUM
Also Called: Napro
11072 Via El Mercado, Los Alamitos
(90720-2812)
P.O. Box 2486 (90720-7486)
PHONE..................................562 598-6671
Melvin Kirschner, *President*
Marilyn K Kirschner, *Treasurer*
Seiichi Okazaki, *Vice Pres*
EMP: 20
SQ FT: 10,000
SALES (est): 2.8MM **Privately Held**
WEB: www.napro.com
SIC: 2899 8661 Oil treating compounds; religious organizations

(P-9292)
NUGENERATION TECHNOLOGIES LLC (PA)
Also Called: Nugentec
1155 Park Ave, Emeryville (94608-3631)
P.O. Box 30428, Stockton (95213-0428)
PHONE..................................707 820-4080
Donato Polignone,
Zephyr Mendez, *President*
Frank James, *Technology*
Shoeb Moiyadi, *Business Mgr*
Ashley Mrva, *Opers Mgr*
◆ EMP: 17 EST: 1997
SQ FT: 11,000
SALES: 7.6MM **Privately Held**
WEB: www.nugentec.com
SIC: 2899 2841 1389 Chemical preparations; soap & other detergents; lease tanks, oil field: erecting, cleaning & repairing; chemically treating wells; oil field services; servicing oil & gas wells

(P-9293)
OCEANS FLAVOR FOODS LLC
4492 Camino De La Plz, San Ysidro
(92173-3071)
PHONE..................................619 793-5269
Justin Fisher,
Alan Fisher, *CEO*
EMP: 10
SQ FT: 10,000
SALES: 8MM **Privately Held**
SIC: 2899 Salt

(P-9294)
OUDIMENTARY LLC
43170 Osgood Rd, Fremont (94539-5608)
PHONE..................................510 501-5057
Micah Anderson,
EMP: 11
SALES (est): 1.2MM **Privately Held**
SIC: 2899 Essential oils

(P-9295)
PACIFIC SCIENTIFIC ENERGETIC (HQ)
3601 Union Rd, Hollister (95023-9635)
PHONE..................................831 637-3731
Gregory Scaven, *President*
John Collins, *CFO*
John Davis, *Vice Pres*
Neal Kerr, *Business Dir*
Will Hunter, *Program Mgr*
EMP: 300
SQ FT: 65,000
SALES: 200MM
SALES (corp-wide): 6.6B **Publicly Held**
WEB: www.psemc.com
SIC: 2899 3489 3483 3699 Igniter grains, boron potassium nitrate; projectors: depth charge, grenade, rocket, etc.; arming & fusing devices for missiles; high-energy particle physics equipment; aircraft armament, except guns; fuses, safety
PA: Fortive Corporation
6920 Seaway Blvd
Everett WA 98203
425 446-5000

(P-9296)
PACIFIC WTRPRFING RSTRTION INC
2845 Pomona Blvd, Pomona (91768-3242)
PHONE..................................909 444-3052
Ronald Bithell, *CEO*
Anthony Bithell, *Vice Pres*
Tony Bithell, *VP Opers*
Brian Rhode, *Manager*
EMP: 32
SALES (est): 6.5MM **Privately Held**
SIC: 2899 7641 Waterproofing compounds; antique furniture repair & restoration

(P-9297)
PHIBRO ANIMAL HEALTH CORP
Phibro-Tech
8851 Dice Rd, Santa Fe Springs
(90670-2515)
PHONE..................................562 698-8036
Mark Alling, *Manager*
EMP: 50
SALES (corp-wide): 764.2MM **Publicly Held**
SIC: 2899 2819 Chemical preparations; industrial inorganic chemicals
HQ: Phibro Animal Health Corporation
300 Frank W Burr Blvd
Teaneck NJ 07666
201 329-7300

(P-9298)
PRESTONE PRODUCTS CORPORATION
Also Called: Kik Custom Products
19500 Mariner Ave, Torrance (90503-1644)
PHONE..................................424 271-4836
Raymond Yu, *Plant Mgr*
EMP: 30 **Privately Held**
WEB: www.honeywell.com
SIC: 2899 5531 5169 Antifreeze compounds; automotive parts; anti-freeze compounds
HQ: Prestone Products Corporation
1900 W Field Ct
Lake Forest IL 60045

(P-9299)
PRODUCTS USA LLC
2933 Bunker Hill Ln # 200, Santa Clara
(95054-1124)
PHONE..................................770 960-1120
Anthony Nash, *Owner*
Vanessa Williams, *Vice Pres*
Priscilla Franklin, *Director*
EMP: 15
SQ FT: 20,000
SALES (est): 1.7MM **Privately Held**
SIC: 2899 5169 2841 Chemical preparations; detergents; soap & other detergents

(P-9300)
RADIATOR SPECIALTY COMPANY
Also Called: Highway Safety Control
935 Enterprise Way, NAPA (94558-6209)
PHONE..................................707 252-0122
David Brock, *Manager*
EMP: 30
SALES (corp-wide): 81.9MM **Privately Held**
WEB: www.radiatorspecialty.com
SIC: 2899 3993 3561 3669 Antifreeze compounds; signs & advertising specialties; pumps & pumping equipment; transportation signaling devices
PA: Radiator Specialty Company Inc
600 Radiator Rd
Indian Trail NC 28079
704 688-2302

(P-9301)
RELTON CORPORATION
317 Rolyn Pl, Arcadia (91007-2838)
P.O. Box 60019 (91066-6019)
PHONE..................................800 423-1505
William Kinard, *Chairman*
Craig Kinard, *President*
Wm Craig Kinard, *CEO*
Kevin Kinard, *Treasurer*
Darcey Arena, *Vice Pres*
EMP: 65 EST: 1946
SQ FT: 20,000
SALES (est): 13.5MM **Privately Held**
WEB: www.relton.com
SIC: 2899 3423 3546 2992 Chemical preparations; masons' hand tools; power-driven handtools; lubricating oils & greases

(P-9302)
RICHARD K GOULD INC
Also Called: Sierra Chemical Company
788 Northport Dr, West Sacramento
(95691-2145)
PHONE..................................916 371-5943
Robert Gould, *CEO*
Steve Gould, *President*
Karen Silva, *Treasurer*
EMP: 20
SQ FT: 18,500
SALES (est): 5.2MM **Privately Held**
WEB: www.sierrachemicalcompany.com
SIC: 2899 5999 Oils & essential oils; cleaning equipment & supplies

(P-9303)
RONATEC C2C INC
5651 Palmer Way Ste H, Carlsbad
(92010-7244)
P.O. Box 1976, Fallbrook (92088-1976)
PHONE..................................760 476-1890
Shawn J Wetherald, *CEO*
James Wetherald, *Vice Pres*
▼ EMP: 12
SQ FT: 4,500
SALES: 7MM **Privately Held**
SIC: 2899 Chemical preparations

(P-9304)
SIGMA-ALDRICH CORPORATION
Also Called: Safc Pharma
6211 El Camino Real, Carlsbad
(92009-1604)
PHONE..................................760 710-6213
Tim Quinn, *Manager*
David Backer, *Business Dir*
Pocheng Liu, *Research*
EMP: 50
SALES (corp-wide): 18B **Privately Held**
WEB: www.sigmaaldrich.com
SIC: 2899 Chemical preparations
HQ: Sigma-Aldrich Corporation
3050 Spruce St
Saint Louis MO 63103
314 771-5765

(P-9305)
SIKA CORPORATION
12767 Imperial Hwy, Santa Fe Springs
(90670-4711)
PHONE..................................562 941-0231
Jerry Monarch, *Branch Mgr*
EMP: 17
SQ FT: 26,186
SALES (corp-wide): 213.5MM **Privately Held**
WEB: www.sikacorp.com
SIC: 2899 Concrete curing & hardening compounds
HQ: Sika Corporation
201 Polito Ave
Lyndhurst NJ 07071
201 933-8800

(P-9306)
SKASOL INCORPORATED
1696 W Grand Ave, Oakland (94607-1607)
PHONE..................................510 839-1000
David L Marchman, *President*
Ehsan Esmat, *Purchasing*
Matt Beauregard, *Manager*
Alexander Lechner, *Accounts Mgr*
EMP: 10
SQ FT: 23,000
SALES (est): 1.8MM **Privately Held**
WEB: www.skasol.com
SIC: 2899 Water treating compounds

(P-9307)
SNF HOLDING COMPANY
Also Called: Polypure
4690 Worth St, Los Angeles (90063-1630)
PHONE..................................323 266-4435
Alex Bravo, *General Mgr*
EMP: 13
SQ FT: 15,044 **Privately Held**
WEB: www.snfinc.com
SIC: 2899 Water treating compounds
HQ: Snf Holding Company
1 Chemical Plant Rd
Riceboro GA 31323

▲ = Import ▼=Export
◆ =Import/Export

(P-9308)
SOUTH ORANGE COUNTY WW AUTH
34156 Del Obispo St, Dana Point (92629-2916)
PHONE.................949 234-5400
Brian Peck, *Principal*
EMP: 17
SALES (est): 4.1MM **Privately Held**
SIC: 2899 Water treating compounds

(P-9309)
SUEZ WTS USA INC
Also Called: GE Water & Process Tech
3050 Pegasus Dr, Bakersfield (93308-6817)
PHONE.................661 393-3035
Anthony Rowe, *Branch Mgr*
EMP: 20
SALES (corp-wide): 51.4MM **Privately Held**
SIC: 2899 Water treating compounds
HQ: Suez Wts Usa, Inc.
4636 Somerton Rd
Trevose PA 19053
215 355-3300

(P-9310)
TCK MEMBRANE AMERICA INC
3390 E Miraloma Ave, Anaheim (92806-1911)
PHONE.................714 678-8832
Kenneth Yoon, *President*
▲ EMP: 10
SALES (est): 1.3MM **Privately Held**
SIC: 2899 Vegetable oils, vulcanized or sulfurized

(P-9311)
TEH-PARI INTERNATIONAL
Also Called: Auric Blends
334 Ohair Ct Ste B, Santa Rosa (95407-5706)
PHONE.................707 829-9116
Randy Graves, *President*
Wendy Nicholson, *Admin Sec*
▲ EMP: 20
SQ FT: 12,000
SALES (est): 2.5MM **Privately Held**
WEB: www.auricblends.com
SIC: 2899 Incense; essential oils

(P-9312)
TORAY MEMBRANE USA INC (DH)
13435 Danielson St, Poway (92064-6825)
PHONE.................858 218-2360
Steve Cappos, *CEO*
Tak Wakisaka, *Treasurer*
Tom Wolfe, *VP Bus Dvlpt*
◆ EMP: 90
SQ FT: 90,000
SALES (est): 20.3MM
SALES (corp-wide): 20.6B **Privately Held**
WEB: www.torayusa.com
SIC: 2899 Water treating compounds
HQ: Toray Holding (U.S.A.), Inc.
461 5th Ave Fl 9
New York NY 10017
212 697-8150

(P-9313)
TRI SERVICE CO INC
2465 Loma Ave, South El Monte (91733-1415)
P.O. Box 3513 (91733-0513)
PHONE.................626 442-3270
Jeff Rein, *CEO*
Elinore Rein, *Corp Secy*
EMP: 11
SQ FT: 8,300
SALES (est): 2.3MM **Privately Held**
SIC: 2899 7699 5084 Water treating compounds; boiler repair shop; industrial machinery & equipment

(P-9314)
UNITED PHARMA LLC
2317 Moore Ave, Fullerton (92833-2510)
PHONE.................714 738-8999
Bill Wang, *President*
Sue Lampley, *Purch Dir*
George Koo, *Prdtn Mgr*
▲ EMP: 130
SQ FT: 53,000

SALES (est): 45.4MM **Privately Held**
SIC: 2899 Gelatin: edible, technical, photographic or pharmaceutical

(P-9315)
URETHANE POLYMER INTERNATIONAL
Also Called: U P I
10880 Poplar Ave, Fontana (92337-7336)
PHONE.................909 357-7200
David Sokol, *CEO*
James Bolotin, *Vice Pres*
Tonia Lanier, *Admin Asst*
EMP: 20
SQ FT: 72,000
SALES (est): 6.5MM **Privately Held**
WEB: www.urethanepolymers.com
SIC: 2899 2851 2821 Waterproofing compounds; paints & allied products; plastics materials & resins
PA: O S L, Inc
1308 E Wakeham Ave
Santa Ana CA 92705
714 505-4923

(P-9316)
US ENVIRONMENTAL
Also Called: Kinetico Quality Water Systems
7085 Jurupa Ave Ste 1, Riverside (92504-1044)
PHONE.................951 359-9002
Donald Nalian, *Owner*
Tony Dezember, *Partner*
EMP: 10
SQ FT: 2,975
SALES: 750K **Privately Held**
SIC: 2899 5999 Water treating compounds; water purification equipment

(P-9317)
VULPINE INC
Also Called: Shape Products
1127 57th Ave, Oakland (94621-4427)
PHONE.................510 534-1186
Dan Daniel, *President*
Tony Weiler, *Vice Pres*
▲ EMP: 14 EST: 1979
SQ FT: 22,000
SALES (est): 5.6MM **Privately Held**
WEB: www.shapeproduct.com
SIC: 2899 5169 Chemical preparations; chemicals & allied products

(P-9318)
ZENON ENVIRONMENTAL CORP
Also Called: GE Water & Process Tech
760 Shadowridge Dr, Vista (92083-7986)
PHONE.................760 598-1800
Don Gruenigen, *Branch Mgr*
EMP: 36
SALES (corp-wide): 86.1MM **Privately Held**
SIC: 2899 3826 5084 3823 Water treating compounds; water testing apparatus; pumps & pumping equipment; industrial instrmnts msrmnt display/control process variable
HQ: Zenon Environmental Corp.
760 Shadowridge Dr
Vista CA 92083

2911 Petroleum Refining

(P-9319)
ACCU-BLEND CORPORATION
1500 W Mckinley St, Azusa (91702-3218)
PHONE.................626 334-7744
Xia Wang, *CEO*
Kenny Wang, *President*
▲ EMP: 17
SALES (est): 3.8MM **Privately Held**
WEB: www.accu-blend.com
SIC: 2911 Paraffin wax

(P-9320)
ASBURY GRAPHITE INC CALIFORNIA
2855 Franklin Canyon Rd, Rodeo (94572-2116)
PHONE.................510 799-3636
Stephen Riddle, *CEO*
Noah Nicoleson, *President*
Sue Rish, *CFO*

◆ EMP: 14 EST: 1986
SQ FT: 33,000
SALES (est): 37.6MM
SALES (corp-wide): 126.7MM **Privately Held**
SIC: 2911 3295 2899 Coke, petroleum; graphite, natural: ground, pulverized, refined or blended; fluxes: brazing, soldering, galvanizing & welding
PA: Asbury Carbons, Inc.
405 Old Main St
Asbury NJ 08802
908 537-2155

(P-9321)
ASTRA ENERGY HOLDINGS INC
301 Main St Ste 201, Huntington Beach (92648-5171)
PHONE.................714 969-6569
Clifford Winget III, *President*
▼ EMP: 165
SALES (est): 14.5MM **Privately Held**
WEB: www.astraenergy.net
SIC: 2911 5172 Petroleum refining; petroleum products
HQ: Astra Transcor Energy N.V.
Veerkade 5
Rotterdam
102 183-703

(P-9322)
B C SONG INTERNATIONAL INC
Also Called: Bcs International
2509 Technology Dr, Hayward (94545-4869)
PHONE.................510 785-8383
Ben C Song, *President*
EMP: 60
SQ FT: 10,000
SALES (est): 6.7MM **Privately Held**
WEB: www.bcsinternational.com
SIC: 2911 2834 Fuel additives; pharmaceutical preparations

(P-9323)
CALIFRNIA RSRCES ELK HILLS LLC
11109 River Run Blvd, Bakersfield (93311-8957)
P.O. Box 1001, Tupman (93276-1001)
PHONE.................661 412-5000
Karen Plotts,
Michael L Preston,
Marshall D Smith,
EMP: 400 EST: 1997
SQ FT: 8,000
SALES (est): 139.6MM
SALES (corp-wide): 2B **Publicly Held**
WEB: www.oxy.com
SIC: 2911 Oils, fuel
PA: California Resources Corporation
9200 Oakdale Ave Ste 900
Chatsworth CA 91311
888 848-4754

(P-9324)
CASTAIC TRUCK STOP INC
31611 Castaic Rd, Castaic (91384-3939)
PHONE.................661 295-1374
Sarkis Khrimian, *President*
Refe Dimmuck, *Opers Mgr*
EMP: 26
SQ FT: 2,000
SALES (est): 3.9MM **Privately Held**
SIC: 2911 7389 5812 Diesel fuels; flea market; American restaurant

(P-9325)
CHEVRON CAPTAIN COMPANY LLC (HQ)
Also Called: Chevron Products Company
6001 Bollinger Canyon Rd, San Ramon (94583-5737)
PHONE.................925 842-1000
John S Watson, *Ch of Bd*
Lydia Beebe, *Admin Sec*
Brad Busby, *Planning*
Mike Farrar, *Planning*
Dave Strait, *Info Tech Mgr*
◆ EMP: 200
SALES (est): 1B
SALES (corp-wide): 141.7B **Publicly Held**
SIC: 2911 Petroleum refining

PA: Chevron Corporation
6001 Bollinger Canyon Rd
San Ramon CA 94583
925 842-1000

(P-9326)
CHEVRON CORPORATION (PA)
6001 Bollinger Canyon Rd, San Ramon (94583-5737)
PHONE.................925 842-1000
Michael K Wirth, *Ch of Bd*
Patricia E Yarrington, *CFO*
John Caw, *Exec VP*
Joseph C Geagea, *Exec VP*
James W Johnson, *Exec VP*
EMP: 1329 EST: 1926
SALES: 141.7B **Publicly Held**
WEB: www.chevrontexaco.com
SIC: 2911 1311 1382 1321 Petroleum refining; crude petroleum production; oil & gas exploration services; natural gas liquids; filling stations, gasoline;

(P-9327)
CHEVRON CORPORATION
324 W El Segundo Blvd, El Segundo (90245-3635)
PHONE.................310 615-5000
William Simok, *Exec Dir*
Henry Kusch, *General Mgr*
Kevin Campbell, *Admin Sec*
Maria E Bonifacio, *Admin Asst*
Ryan Glennan, *Info Tech Mgr*
EMP: 812
SALES (corp-wide): 141.7B **Publicly Held**
SIC: 2911 1311 1382 1321 Petroleum refining; crude petroleum production; oil & gas exploration services; natural gas liquids; filling stations, gasoline
PA: Chevron Corporation
6001 Bollinger Canyon Rd
San Ramon CA 94583
925 842-1000

(P-9328)
CHEVRON CORPORATION
Unocal
13707 S Broadway, Los Angeles (90061-1011)
PHONE.................310 538-7600
Mike Caldwell, *Branch Mgr*
EMP: 250
SALES (corp-wide): 141.7B **Publicly Held**
WEB: www.chevrontexaco.com
SIC: 2911 4213 4212 Petroleum refining; trucking, except local; local trucking, without storage
PA: Chevron Corporation
6001 Bollinger Canyon Rd
San Ramon CA 94583
925 842-1000

(P-9329)
CHEVRON GLOBAL ENERGY INC (HQ)
Also Called: Chevron Global Lubricants
6001 Bollinger Canyon Rd, San Ramon (94583-5737)
P.O. Box 6046 (94583-0746)
PHONE.................925 842-1000
Jock D McKenzie, *Ch of Bd*
John S Watson, *Ch of Bd*
Glenn Johnson, *COO*
Richard J Guiltinan, *CFO*
Malcolm J McAuley, *Treasurer*
EMP: 100 EST: 1936
SQ FT: 200,000
SALES (est): 1.1B
SALES (corp-wide): 141.7B **Publicly Held**
SIC: 2911 4731 5172 Petroleum refining; freight transportation arrangement; petroleum products
PA: Chevron Corporation
6001 Bollinger Canyon Rd
San Ramon CA 94583
925 842-1000

(P-9330)
CLEAIRE ADVANCED EMISSION (PA)
1001 42nd St, Emeryville (94608-3620)
PHONE.................510 347-6103
Michael J Doherty,

EMP: 14
SALES (est): 2.3MM **Privately Held**
SIC: 2911 Diesel fuels

(P-9331)
D-1280-X INC
Also Called: Omstar Environmental Products
126 N Marine Ave, Wilmington
(90744-5723)
P.O. Box 6293, San Pedro (90734-6293)
PHONE.................................310 835-6909
Roberta L Skaggs, *CEO*
Richard J Skaggs, *President*
Howard Sargent, *Exec VP*
EMP: 12
SQ FT: 7,500
SALES (est): 1MM **Privately Held**
SIC: 2911 5169 Fuel additives; chemical
additives

(P-9332)
DE MENNO-KERDOON TRADING CO (HQ)
2000 N Alameda St, Compton
(90222-2702)
PHONE.................................310 537-7100
Jim Ennis, *COO*
Jay Demel, *Vice Pres*
Roger Graves, *Safety Dir*
Jim Tice, *Mktg Dir*
N Bonnie Booth, *Manager*
EMP: 149
SQ FT: 60,000
SALES (est): 29.4MM
SALES (corp-wide): 198.5MM **Privately Held**
SIC: 2911 Oils, fuel
PA: World Oil Marketing Company
9302 Garfield Ave
South Gate CA 90280
562 928-0100

(P-9333)
GLENCORE LTD
Chemoil
2020 Walnut Ave, Long Beach (90806)
PHONE.................................562 427-6611
Ted Christenson, *Manager*
Michael Kocinski, *Accounting Mgr*
EMP: 30
SALES (corp-wide): 205.4B **Privately Held**
WEB: www.aimalumni.com
SIC: 2911 Petroleum refining
HQ: Glencore Ltd.
330 Madison Ave
New York NY 10017
646 949-2500

(P-9334)
GOLDEN WEST REFINING COMPANY
13116 Imperial Hwy, Santa Fe Springs
(90670-4817)
P.O. Box 2128 (90670-0138)
PHONE.................................562 921-3581
Ted Orden, *President*
Moshe Sassover, *Senior VP*
EMP: 49
SQ FT: 22,000
SALES (est): 7MM
SALES (corp-wide): 7.3MM **Privately Held**
SIC: 2911 Gasoline
PA: Thrifty Oil Co.
13116 Imperial Hwy
Santa Fe Springs CA 90670
562 921-3581

(P-9335)
INTERNATIONAL GROUP INC
102 Cutting Blvd, Richmond (94804-2126)
PHONE.................................510 232-8704
EMP: 11 **Privately Held**
SIC: 2911 Paraffin wax
HQ: The International Group Inc
1007 E Spring St
Titusville PA 16354
814 827-4900

(P-9336)
INTERNATIONAL GROUP INC
102 Cutting Blvd, Richmond (94804-2126)
PHONE.................................510 232-8704
Ian King, *Branch Mgr*
EMP: 75 **Privately Held**

SIC: 2911 Paraffin wax; petrolatums, non-medicinal
HQ: International Group, Inc, The
50 Salome Dr
Scarborough ON M1S 2
416 293-4151

(P-9337)
LION TANK LINE INC
5801 Randolph St, Commerce
(90040-3415)
PHONE.................................323 726-1966
Levon Termandjyan, *President*
EMP: 28
SQ FT: 6,000
SALES (est): 4MM **Privately Held**
SIC: 2911 4213 Diesel fuels; liquid petroleum transport, non-local

(P-9338)
LOS ANGELES REFINING CO
2101 E Pacific Coast Hwy, Wilmington
(90744-2914)
PHONE.................................310 522-6000
EMP: 15
SALES (est): 2.3MM **Privately Held**
SIC: 2911 Petroleum refining

(P-9339)
M ARGESO & CO INC
2628 River Ave, Rosemead (91770-3302)
PHONE.................................626 573-3000
G Douglas Orr, *President*
Jim Mallory, *General Mgr*
EMP: 14
SALES (est): 2.9MM **Privately Held**
SIC: 2911 Paraffin wax

(P-9340)
MOLECULUM
3128 Red Hill Ave, Costa Mesa
(92626-4525)
PHONE.................................714 619-5139
Ivan Krylov, *Regional Mgr*
EMP: 18 EST: 2015
SALES (est): 805.6K **Privately Held**
SIC: 2911 Aromatic chemical products

(P-9341)
NOVVI LLC
5885 Hollis St Ste 100, Emeryville
(94608-2405)
PHONE.................................281 488-0833
EMP: 22
SALES (est): 5.4MM **Privately Held**
SIC: 2911 Oils, lubricating

(P-9342)
OBERON FUELS INC (PA)
2159 India St Ste 200, San Diego
(92101-1766)
PHONE.................................619 255-9361
Ruben S Martin III, *CEO*
Rebecca Boudreaux, *President*
Elliot Hicks, *COO*
Anna Levy, *Project Engr*
Dan Goodwin, *Director*
EMP: 10
SALES (est): 1.2MM **Privately Held**
SIC: 2911 Diesel fuels

(P-9343)
ORGANIC INFUSIONS INC (PA)
2390 Las Posas Rd, Camarillo
(93010-3479)
PHONE.................................805 419-4118
Rose Heart, *President*
▲ **EMP:** 10
SALES (est): 5.6MM **Privately Held**
SIC: 2911 2899 Aromatic chemical products; essential oils

(P-9344)
PARAMOUNT PETROLEUM CORP
8835 Somerset Blvd, Paramount
(90723-4658)
PHONE.................................562 633-4332
Wes Owens, *Branch Mgr*
EMP: 14
SALES (corp-wide): 7.2B **Publicly Held**
SIC: 2911 Petroleum refining
HQ: Paramount Petroleum Corporation
14700 Downey Ave
Paramount CA 90723
562 531-2060

(P-9345)
PARAMOUNT PETROLEUM CORP (DH)
Also Called: Paramount Asphalt
14700 Downey Ave, Paramount
(90723-4526)
P.O. Box 1418 (90723-1418)
PHONE.................................562 531-2060
W S Lovejoy, *CEO*
Steve S Farkas, *President*
Glenn Clausen, *Vice Pres*
Kathryn Gleeson, *Vice Pres*
Steve Leroy, *Vice Pres*
◆ **EMP:** 155
SQ FT: 6,000
SALES (est): 223.2MM
SALES (corp-wide): 7.2B **Publicly Held**
SIC: 2911 Petroleum refining

(P-9346)
PARAMOUNT PETROLEUM CORP
Also Called: Bakersfield Refinery
6451 Rosedale Hwy, Bakersfield
(93308-5902)
PHONE.................................661 326-4200
Jeff F Utley, *Manager*
EMP: 20
SALES (corp-wide): 7.2B **Publicly Held**
SIC: 2911 Gasoline
HQ: Paramount Petroleum Corporation
14700 Downey Ave
Paramount CA 90723
562 531-2060

(P-9347)
PARAMOUNT PETROLEUM CORP
1201 China Grade Loop, Bakersfield
(93308-9688)
P.O. Box 5655 (93388-5655)
PHONE.................................661 392-3630
Ron Clark, *Branch Mgr*
EMP: 14
SALES (corp-wide): 7.2B **Publicly Held**
SIC: 2911 Petroleum refining
HQ: Paramount Petroleum Corporation
14700 Downey Ave
Paramount CA 90723
562 531-2060

(P-9348)
PBF ENERGY INC
Also Called: Torrance Refinery
3700 W 190th St, Torrance (90504-5733)
PHONE.................................310 212-2800
Pete Trelenberg, *Manager*
EMP: 15
SALES (corp-wide): 21.7B **Publicly Held**
SIC: 2911 5541 Petroleum refining; gasoline service stations
PA: Pbf Energy Inc.
1 Sylvan Way Ste 2
Parsippany NJ 07054
973 455-7500

(P-9349)
PBF ENERGY WESTERN REGION LLC (DH)
111 W Ocean Blvd Ste 1500, Long Beach
(90802-7907)
PHONE.................................973 455-7500
Thomas J Nimbley, *CEO*
EMP: 354
SALES (est): 47.5MM
SALES (corp-wide): 21.7B **Publicly Held**
SIC: 2911 2992 Petroleum refining; lubricating oils

(P-9350)
PETROIL AMERICAS LIMITED
5651 W Pico Blvd Ste 102, Los Angeles
(90019-3874)
P.O. Box 399, Manhattan Beach (90267-0399)
PHONE.................................323 931-3720
Thorn Weathersby Jr, *President*
Oscar Weathersby, *Treasurer*
Belinda Weathersby, *Admin Sec*
EMP: 10
SALES: 3.2MM **Privately Held**
SIC: 2911 Oils, fuel; greases, lubricating; fuel additives

(P-9351)
PHILLIPS 66
Also Called: Los Angeles Refinery
1520 E Sepulveda Blvd, Carson
(90745-6140)
PHONE.................................310 522-9300
Chris Dennis, *Branch Mgr*
Robert Stanton, *Buyer*
EMP: 100
SALES (corp-wide): 104.6B **Publicly Held**
WEB: www.phillips66.com
SIC: 2911 5541 Oils, fuel; gasoline service stations
PA: Phillips 66
2331 City West Blvd
Houston TX 77042
281 293-6600

(P-9352)
REED & GRAHAM INC (PA)
690 Sunol St, San Jose (95126-3751)
P.O. Box 5940 (95150-5940)
PHONE.................................408 287-1400
Gerald R Graham Jr, *President*
Gerald R Graham Sr, *Ch of Bd*
Birtola Damon, *CFO*
Steven Reed Graham, *Senior VP*
David H Pinkham, *General Mgr*
▲ **EMP:** 50
SQ FT: 8,000
SALES (est): 30.9MM **Privately Held**
WEB: www.rginc.com
SIC: 2911 2952 8731 5032 Asphalt or asphaltic materials, made in refineries; road oils; coating compounds, tar; commercial research laboratory; brick, stone & related material

(P-9353)
REED & GRAHAM INC
26 Light Sky Ct, Sacramento (95828-1016)
PHONE.................................916 381-9900
Bruce Adams, *Manager*
Aldo Branch, *Admin Asst*
Audrea Jimenez, *Admin Asst*
Johnny Perez, *Plant Mgr*
Carl Springer, *Sales Staff*
EMP: 11
SALES (corp-wide): 30.9MM **Privately Held**
WEB: www.rginc.com
SIC: 2911 2952 Asphalt or asphaltic materials, made in refineries; road oils; coating compounds, tar
PA: Reed & Graham, Inc.
690 Sunol St
San Jose CA 95126
408 287-1400

(P-9354)
RHS GAS INC
520 W Pacific Coast Hwy, Long Beach
(90806-5237)
PHONE.................................310 710-2331
Nathan Sparer, *Principal*
EMP: 10
SALES (est): 450.6K **Privately Held**
SIC: 2911 Solvents

(P-9355)
ROCK ENGINEERED MCHY CO INC
Also Called: Remco
263 S Vasco Rd, Livermore (94551-9203)
PHONE.................................925 447-0805
Kevin Cadwalader, *President*
Michelle Martinez, *Admin Asst*
Michael Starnes, *Technical Staff*
Rich Lustig, *Finance Mgr*
Michael Sumaquial, *Analyst*
▼ **EMP:** 19
SQ FT: 30,000
SALES (est): 6.6MM **Privately Held**
WEB: www.remcovsi.com
SIC: 2911 5084 Heavy distillates; crushing machinery & equipment

(P-9356)
SAN JOAQUIN REFINING CO INC
3500 Shell St, Bakersfield (93308-5215)
P.O. Box 5576 (93388-5576)
PHONE.................................661 327-4257
Kenneth E Fait, *Ch of Bd*

▲ = Import ▼=Export
◆ =Import/Export

Majid Mojibi, *President*
Dorothy A Gribben, *Admin Sec*
David Pinkston, *IT/INT Sup*
Margie Duran, *Finance Dir*
EMP: 130
SQ FT: 15,000
SALES (est): 31MM **Privately Held**
WEB: www.sjr.com
SIC: 2911 Oils, fuel

(P-9357)
SHELL MARTINEZ REFINING CO
Also Called: Shell Martinez Refinery
3485 Pacheco Blvd, Martinez
(94553-2120)
P.O. Box 711 (94553-0071)
PHONE...............................925 313-3000
Alicia Igarraraz, *General Mgr*
▲ **EMP:** 900
SALES (est): 154.1MM
SALES (corp-wide): 305.1B **Privately Held**
SIC: 2911 Petroleum refining
HQ: Shell Oil Company
150 N Dairy Ashford Rd A
Houston TX 77079
713 241-6161

(P-9358)
SINCLAIR COMPANIES
7760 Crescent Ave, Buena Park
(90620-3953)
PHONE...............................714 826-5886
EMP: 107
SALES (corp-wide): 3.9B **Privately Held**
SIC: 2911 Petroleum refining
PA: The Sinclair Companies
550 E South Temple
Salt Lake City UT 84102
801 524-2700

(P-9359)
SINCLAIR COMPANIES
5792 N Palm Ave, Fresno (93704-1844)
PHONE...............................559 997-3617
EMP: 71
SALES (corp-wide): 3.9B **Privately Held**
SIC: 2911 Petroleum refining
PA: The Sinclair Companies
550 E South Temple
Salt Lake City UT 84102
801 524-2700

(P-9360)
SINCLAIR COMPANIES
1703 W Olive Ave, Fresno (93728-2617)
PHONE...............................559 351-1916
EMP: 71
SALES (corp-wide): 3.9B **Privately Held**
SIC: 2911 Petroleum refining
PA: The Sinclair Companies
550 E South Temple
Salt Lake City UT 84102
801 524-2700

(P-9361)
SOUTHERN CALIFORNIA BIODIESEL
Also Called: So California Biodiesel
18760 6th St Ste C, Bloomington
(92316-3725)
P.O. Box 1642, Pomona (91769-1642)
PHONE...............................951 377-4007
Kenneth Grubaugh, *President*
Daniel Grubaugh, *Vice Pres*
Matthew Grubaugh, *Vice Pres*
Joanne Grubaugh, *Admin Sec*
EMP: 11
SALES (est): 1MM **Privately Held**
SIC: 2911 8748 Diesel fuels; business consulting

(P-9362)
SUN COMPANY SAN BERNARDINO CAL
Also Called: Sun, The
290 N D St Ste 100, San Bernardino
(92401-1711)
PHONE...............................909 889-9666
Bob Balzer, *Manager*
Lupe Carrillo, *Clerk*
EMP: 200
SALES (corp-wide): 42MM **Privately Held**
SIC: 2911 2752 Petroleum refining; commercial printing, lithographic

---

PA: Sun Company Of San Bernardino, California
4030 Georgia Blvd
San Bernardino CA 92407
909 889-9666

(P-9363)
TESORO REFINING & MKTG CO LLC
150 Solano Way, Pacheco (94553-1465)
PHONE...............................925 372-3100
Jim Cleary, *Manager*
EMP: 700 **Publicly Held**
SIC: 2911 Petroleum refining
HQ: Tesoro Refining & Marketing Company Llc
19100 Ridgewood Pkwy
San Antonio TX 78259
210 828-8484

(P-9364)
TESORO REFINING & MKTG CO LLC
5905 N Paramount Blvd, Long Beach
(90805-3709)
PHONE...............................562 728-2215
EMP: 377 **Publicly Held**
SIC: 2911 5541 Petroleum refining; gasoline service stations
HQ: Tesoro Refining & Marketing Company Llc
19100 Ridgewood Pkwy
San Antonio TX 78259
210 828-8484

(P-9365)
TORCO INTERNATIONAL CORP
1720 S Carlos Ave, Ontario (91761-7920)
PHONE...............................909 980-1495
Ned Tanson, *President*
▼ **EMP:** 12
SQ FT: 30,000
SALES (est): 2.9MM **Privately Held**
WEB: www.torcousa.com
SIC: 2911 Oils, illuminating

(P-9366)
TORRANCE REFINING COMPANY LLC
3700 W 190th St, Torrance (90504-5733)
PHONE...............................310 483-6900
Thomas J Nimbley, *CEO*
EMP: 600
SALES (est): 25.1MM
SALES (corp-wide): 21.7B **Publicly Held**
SIC: 2911 2992 Petroleum refining; lubricating oils
HQ: Pbf Energy Western Region Llc
111 W Ocean Blvd Ste 1500
Long Beach CA 90802
973 455-7500

(P-9367)
TRICOR REFINING LLC
1134 Manor St, Bakersfield (93308-3553)
P.O. Box 5877 (93388-5877)
PHONE...............................661 393-7110
Majid Mojibi, *Mng Member*
Merle Menghini, *Executive*
Don Brookes, *Mng Member*
Kenneth E Fait, *Mng Member*
Ed Stratton, *Manager*
EMP: 28
SALES (est): 10.8MM **Privately Held**
WEB: www.tricorrefining.com
SIC: 2911 Oils, fuel

(P-9368)
UBI ENERGY CORPORATION
9465 Wilshire Blvd # 300, Beverly Hills
(90212-2612)
PHONE...............................310 283-6978
Salma Okonkwo, *Principal*
EMP: 200
SALES: 120MM **Privately Held**
SIC: 2911

(P-9369)
ULTRAMAR INC
Also Called: Frost Beacon
2233 Esplanade, Chico (95926-2203)
PHONE...............................530 345-7901
EMP: 12
SALES (corp-wide): 93.9B **Publicly Held**
SIC: 2911

HQ: Ultramar Inc.
1 Valero Way
San Antonio TX 78249
210 345-2000

(P-9370)
ULTRAMAR INC
Also Called: Village Center Ultramar
9508 E Palmdale Blvd, Palmdale
(93591-2202)
PHONE...............................661 944-2496
Ken Berglund, *Manager*
EMP: 12
SALES (corp-wide): 93.9B **Publicly Held**
WEB: www.divi.com
SIC: 2911 Petroleum refining
HQ: Ultramar Inc.
1 Valero Way
San Antonio TX 78249
210 345-2000

(P-9371)
VALERO ENERGY CORPORATION
Also Called: Depot 6, The
17928 Us Highway 18, Apple Valley
(92307-2103)
PHONE...............................760 946-3322
Kuldip Randhawa, *Branch Mgr*
EMP: 30
SALES (corp-wide): 93.9B **Publicly Held**
SIC: 2911 Petroleum refining
PA: Valero Energy Corporation
1 Valero Way
San Antonio TX 78249
210 345-2000

(P-9372)
VALERO REF COMPANY-CALIFORNIA
3400 E 2nd St, Benicia (94510-1005)
PHONE...............................707 745-7011
Dough Comeau, *Branch Mgr*
Greg Aton, *Administration*
Rick Hudson, *Administration*
John Quigley, *Technical Staff*
Elizabeth Crowley, *Engineer*
EMP: 500
SALES (corp-wide): 93.9B **Publicly Held**
SIC: 2911 Petroleum refining
HQ: Valero Refining Company-California
1 Valero Way
San Antonio TX 78249
210 345-2000

(P-9373)
VALERO REF COMPANY-CALIFORNIA
2401 E Anaheim St, Wilmington
(90744-4009)
PHONE...............................562 491-6754
Mark Thair, *Manager*
EMP: 500
SALES (corp-wide): 93.9B **Publicly Held**
SIC: 2911 Petroleum refining
HQ: Valero Refining Company-California
1 Valero Way
San Antonio TX 78249
210 345-2000

(P-9374)
VENOCO INC
7979 Hollister Ave, Goleta (93117-2421)
PHONE...............................805 961-2305
EMP: 40
SALES (corp-wide): 224.2MM **Privately Held**
SIC: 2911 5172
HQ: Venoco, Inc.
370 17th St Ste 3900
Denver CO 80202
303 626-8300

(P-9375)
WD-40 COMPANY
Also Called: Hdp Holdings
9715 Businesspark Ave, San Diego
(92131-1642)
PHONE...............................619 275-1400
Garry Ridge, *President*
Ernest Bernarducci PHD, *Vice Pres*
Robert Busacca, *Vice Pres*
Pete Dumiak, *Vice Pres*
Patricia Olsem, *Vice Pres*
EMP: 233

SALES (corp-wide): 408.5MM **Publicly Held**
WEB: www.wd40.com
SIC: 2911 Oils, lubricating
PA: Wd-40 Company
9715 Businesspark Ave
San Diego CA 92131
619 275-1400

(P-9376)
WORLD OIL MARKETING COMPANY (PA)
9302 Garfield Ave, South Gate
(90280-3805)
P.O. Box 1966 (90280-1966)
PHONE...............................562 928-0100
Robert S Roth, *President*
Florence Roth, *Vice Pres*
Richard Roth, *Vice Pres*
Steven Roth, *Vice Pres*
EMP: 20
SQ FT: 60,000
SALES (est): 198.5MM **Privately Held**
SIC: 2911 4953 2951 5541 Recycling, waste materials; paving mixtures; gasoline service stations; liquid petroleum transport, non-local; petroleum haulage, local; asphalt or asphaltic materials, made in refineries

---

2951 Paving Mixtures & Blocks

(P-9377)
AJW CONSTRUCTION
966 81st Ave, Oakland (94621-2512)
PHONE...............................510 568-2300
Ed Webster, *Principal*
Alfonso Quintor, *Principal*
Juan Quintor, *Principal*
EMP: 42
SALES (est): 9MM **Privately Held**
SIC: 2951 Asphalt paving mixtures & blocks

(P-9378)
CALIFORNIA COMMERCIAL ASP CORP (PA)
4211 Ponderosa Ave Ste C, San Diego
(92123-1525)
P.O. Box 23420 (92193-3420)
PHONE...............................858 513-0611
Donald Daley Jr, *President*
John Daley, *Principal*
David Hummel, *Principal*
EMP: 10
SALES (est): 4.2MM **Privately Held**
SIC: 2951 Asphalt & asphaltic paving mixtures (not from refineries)

(P-9379)
CALMAT CO (DH)
Also Called: Vulcan Materials
500 N Brand Blvd Ste 500 # 500, Glendale
(91203-3319)
P.O. Box 2950, Los Angeles (90051-0950)
PHONE...............................818 553-8821
Tom Hill, *CEO*
James W Smack, *President*
Danny R Shepherd, *COO*
Daniel F Sansone, *CFO*
Barbara Goodrich-Welk, *Vice Pres*
EMP: 150
SQ FT: 40,000
SALES (est): 514.5MM **Publicly Held**
SIC: 2951 1442 1429 3273 Asphalt & asphaltic paving mixtures (not from refineries); construction sand & gravel; igneous rock, crushed & broken-quarrying; ready-mixed concrete; commercial & industrial building operation; land subdividers & developers, residential
HQ: Legacy Vulcan, Llc
1200 Urban Center Dr
Vestavia AL 35242
205 298-3000

(P-9380)
CEMEX CNSTR MTLS PCF LLC
Also Called: Aggregate - Cache Creek S&G
30288 Highway 16, Madison (95653)
PHONE...............................530 666-2137
Anthony Russo, *President*
EMP: 22 **Privately Held**

PRODUCTS & SVCS

WEB: www.rinkermaterials.com
SIC: 2951 Asphalt & asphaltic paving mixtures (not from refineries)
HQ: Cemex Construction Materials Pacific, Llc
　1501 Belvedere Rd
　West Palm Beach FL 33406
　561 833-5555

(P-9381)
DELTA TRADING LP
Also Called: Crimson Resource Management
17731 Millux Rd, Bakersfield (93311-9714)
PHONE..............................661 834-5560
Mike Purdy, *Partner*
Rob McElroy, *General Mgr*
Paige Johnston, *Office Admin*
Gaby Diaz, *Technician*
Larry Hooker, *Manager*
EMP: 20
SALES (est): 6.8MM **Privately Held**
WEB: www.deltatradinglp.com
SIC: 2951 Asphalt paving mixtures & blocks

(P-9382)
DESERT BLOCK CO INC
11374 Tuxford St, Sun Valley (91352-2636)
PHONE..............................661 824-2624
Bill Fenzel, *President*
William Gapastione, *Vice Pres*
EMP: 12
SALES (est): 2.6MM **Privately Held**
SIC: 2951 3272 Concrete, asphaltic (not from refineries); concrete products, pre-cast

(P-9383)
EDGINGTON OIL COMPANY LLC
2400 E Artesia Blvd, Long Beach (90805-1786)
PHONE..............................562 423-1465
Wasyl Kurinij, *President*
T A Novelly, *CEO*
John Hank, *Vice Pres*
Christine Hughes, *Asst Treas*
EMP: 65
SALES (est): 48.3MM
SALES (corp-wide): 7.2B **Publicly Held**
WEB: www.edgoil.com
SIC: 2951 Asphalt paving mixtures & blocks
HQ: Alon Usa Energy, Inc.
　12700 Park Central Dr # 1600
　Dallas TX 75251

(P-9384)
ESCONDIDO SAND & GRAVEL LLC
500 N Tulip St, Escondido (92025-2533)
P.O. Box 462590 (92046-2590)
PHONE..............................760 432-4690
George Weir, *CEO*
Mark Weir, *Vice Pres*
EMP: 11
SALES (est): 4.4MM **Privately Held**
SIC: 2951 Asphalt paving mixtures & blocks

(P-9385)
GRANITE ROCK CO
365 Blomquist St, Redwood City (94063-2701)
PHONE..............................650 482-3800
Rich Sacher, *Manager*
EMP: 25
SQ FT: 2,500
SALES (corp-wide): 1.1B **Privately Held**
WEB: www.graniterock.com
SIC: 2951 2992 5032 Asphalt & asphaltic paving mixtures (not from refineries); lubricating oils & greases; brick, stone & related material
PA: Granite Rock Co.
　350 Technology Dr
　Watsonville CA 95076
　831 768-2000

(P-9386)
HANSON AGGREGATES LLC
Also Called: Lehigh Hanson
12560 Highway 67, Lakeside (92040-1159)
PHONE..............................858 715-5600
Terry Tyson, *Regional Mgr*
EMP: 15

SALES (corp-wide): 20.3B **Privately Held**
WEB: www.hansonind.com
SIC: 2951 Asphalt paving mixtures & blocks
HQ: Hanson Aggregates Llc
　8505 Freport Pkwy Ste 500
　Irving TX 75063
　469 417-1200

(P-9387)
HUNTMIX INC
Also Called: Calmut Industrial Asphalt
500 N Brand Blvd Ste 500, Glendale (91203-3319)
PHONE..............................818 548-5200
Fax: 323 254-1191
EMP: 165
SQ FT: 70,000
SALES (est): 12MM
SALES (corp-wide): 2.9B **Publicly Held**
SIC: 2951
HQ: Calmut Co.
　500 N Brand Blvd Ste 500
　Glendale CA 91203
　818 553-8821

(P-9388)
LEGACY VULCAN LLC
16001 1/2 E Foothill Blvd, Irwindale (91702)
PHONE..............................626 633-4258
John Sprein, *Branch Mgr*
EMP: 37 **Publicly Held**
WEB: www.vulcanmaterials.com
SIC: 2951 Asphalt paving mixtures & blocks
HQ: Legacy Vulcan, Llc
　1200 Urban Center Dr
　Vestavia AL 35242
　205 298-3000

(P-9389)
LEWIS BARRICADE INC
4000 Westerly Pl Ste 100, Newport Beach (92660-2347)
PHONE..............................661 363-0912
John R Lewis, *President*
Teresa Lewis, *Corp Secy*
EMP: 26 EST: 1998
SQ FT: 20,000
SALES (est): 4.2MM **Privately Held**
WEB: www.flashcoinc.com
SIC: 2951 7353 Concrete, asphaltic (not from refineries); heavy construction equipment rental

(P-9390)
NPG INC (PA)
Also Called: Goldstar Asphalt Products
1354 Jet Way, Perris (92571-7466)
P.O. Box 1515 (92572-1515)
PHONE..............................951 940-0200
Jeff Nelson, *President*
Sharon Nelson, *Officer*
Troy King, *Project Mgr*
EMP: 56
SQ FT: 6,900
SALES (est): 15.2MM **Privately Held**
WEB: www.goldstarasphalt.com
SIC: 2951 1799 1771 Asphalt & asphaltic paving mixtures (not from refineries); parking lot maintenance; driveway, parking lot & blacktop contractors

(P-9391)
OLDCASTLE APG WEST INC
4202 Gibralter Ct, Stockton (95206-3976)
PHONE..............................209 983-1609
Michelle Tompson, *Manager*
Cy Thomson, *Engineer*
EMP: 12
SALES (corp-wide): 29.7B **Privately Held**
WEB: www.oldcastlestockton.com
SIC: 2951 Asphalt paving mixtures & blocks
HQ: Oldcastle Apg West, Inc.
　4720 E Cotton Gin Loop L
　Phoenix AZ 85040
　602 302-9600

(P-9392)
PARAMOUNT PETROLEUM CORP
10090 Waterman Rd, Elk Grove (95624-4010)
PHONE..............................916 685-9253

John Adams, *General Mgr*
Neal Lyon, *Director*
EMP: 14
SQ FT: 3,000
SALES (corp-wide): 7.2B **Publicly Held**
SIC: 2951 Asphalt paving mixtures & blocks
HQ: Paramount Petroleum Corporation
　14700 Downey Ave
　Paramount CA 90723
　562 531-2060

(P-9393)
PAVEMENT RECYCLING SYSTEMS INC
Also Called: West Coast Milling
46205 Division St, Lancaster (93535-5908)
PHONE..............................661 948-5599
Steve Ward, *Manager*
EMP: 12
SQ FT: 1,000
SALES (est): 1.6MM
SALES (corp-wide): 126.7MM **Privately Held**
SIC: 2951 1611 Asphalt paving mixtures & blocks; surfacing & paving
PA: Pavement Recycling Systems, Inc.
　10240 San Sevaine Way
　Jurupa Valley CA 91752
　951 682-1091

(P-9394)
PETROCHEM MARKETING
3033 E Washington Blvd, Los Angeles (90023-4219)
PHONE..............................323 526-4084
Mike Burris, *Owner*
EMP: 12
SALES (est): 590K **Privately Held**
SIC: 2951 Asphalt paving mixtures & blocks

(P-9395)
RECYCLED AGGREGATE MTLS CO INC (PA)
Also Called: Ramco
2655 1st St 210, Simi Valley (93065-1547)
PHONE..............................805 522-1646
Dennis L Newman, *President*
EMP: 24
SALES (est): 3.4MM **Privately Held**
SIC: 2951 Concrete, asphaltic (not from refineries)

(P-9396)
REED & GRAHAM INC
26 Light Sky Ct, Sacramento (95828-1016)
PHONE..............................888 381-0800
Bruce Adams, *Branch Mgr*
EMP: 35
SALES (corp-wide): 30.9MM **Privately Held**
WEB: www.rginc.com
SIC: 2951 Paving mixtures
PA: Reed & Graham, Inc.
　690 Sunol St
　San Jose CA 95126
　408 287-1400

(P-9397)
SAN RAFAEL ROCK QUARRY INC
Also Called: Dutra Materials
961 Western Dr, Richmond (94801-3756)
PHONE..............................510 970-7700
Erin Johnson, *Manager*
EMP: 20
SALES (corp-wide): 145.1MM **Privately Held**
SIC: 2951 Asphalt paving mixtures & blocks
HQ: San Rafael Rock Quarry, Inc.
　1000 Point San Pedro Rd
　San Rafael CA 94901

(P-9398)
SOUTH WESTERN PAVING COMPANY
2250 E Orangethorpe Ave, Fullerton (92831-5329)
PHONE..............................714 577-5750
Kenneth L Nelson, *President*
EMP: 11
SQ FT: 1,800

SALES: 2.3MM **Privately Held**
SIC: 2951 Asphalt paving mixtures & blocks

(P-9399)
VSS EMULTECH INC (HQ)
Also Called: Valley Sleurry Seal Co
7200 Pit Rd, Redding (96001-5352)
PHONE..............................530 243-0111
Wendall Reed, *President*
Mike Heath, *Principal*
Jeff Nowlin, *Manager*
EMP: 15 EST: 1945
SQ FT: 1,000
SALES (est): 8.2MM
SALES (corp-wide): 197.8MM **Privately Held**
WEB: www.emultech.com
SIC: 2951 Asphalt & asphaltic paving mixtures (not from refineries)
PA: Basic Resources Inc
　928 12th St Ste 700
　Modesto CA 95354
　209 521-9771

(P-9400)
VSS EMULTECH INC
3785 Channel Dr, West Sacramento (95691-3421)
P.O. Box 981150 (95798-1150)
PHONE..............................916 371-8480
Doug Stach, *Manager*
EMP: 10
SALES (corp-wide): 197.8MM **Privately Held**
WEB: www.emultech.com
SIC: 2951 Asphalt & asphaltic paving mixtures (not from refineries)
HQ: Vss Emultech Inc
　7200 Pit Rd
　Redding CA 96001
　530 243-0111

2952 Asphalt Felts & Coatings

(P-9401)
ASPHALT PRODUCTS OIL CORP (HQ)
Also Called: Apoc
5903 N Paramount Blvd, Long Beach (90805-3709)
P.O. Box 5248 (90805-0248)
PHONE..............................562 423-6471
Raymond T Hyer Jr, *Ch of Bd*
Rudy Berumen, *Regional Mgr*
Frank Glasscock, *District Mgr*
Robert Hyer, *VP Sls/Mktg*
John Athanasion, *Sales Mgr*
EMP: 14
SQ FT: 30,000
SALES (est): 2MM
SALES (corp-wide): 266.8MM **Privately Held**
SIC: 2952 Asphalt felts & coatings
PA: Gardner-Gibson, Incorporated
　4161 E 7th Ave
　Tampa FL 33605
　813 248-2101

(P-9402)
BURKE INDUSTRIES INC
Burkeline Roofing
2250 S 10th St, San Jose (95112-4197)
PHONE..............................408 297-3500
John Hurley, *Principal*
EMP: 150
SALES (corp-wide): 775.9MM **Privately Held**
WEB: www.burkeind.com
SIC: 2952 3061 Roofing materials; mechanical rubber goods
HQ: Burke Industries, Inc.
　2250 S 10th St
　San Jose CA 95112
　408 297-3500

(P-9403)
CERTAINTEED CORPORATION
6400 Stevenson Blvd, Fremont (94538-2468)
PHONE..............................510 490-0890
Ed Foster, *Manager*
EMP: 65

SQ FT: 20,000
SALES (corp-wide): 213.5MM **Privately Held**
WEB: www.certainteed.net
SIC: 2952 2951 Asphalt felts & coatings; asphalt paving mixtures & blocks
HQ: Certainteed Corporation
20 Moores Rd
Malvern PA 19355
610 893-5000

(P-9404)
FONTANA PAPER MILLS INC
13733 Valley Blvd, Fontana (92335-5268)
P.O. Box 339 (92334-0339)
PHONE..............................909 823-4100
George Thagard III, *President*
Jeff Thagard, *Executive*
Ray G Thagard Jr, *Admin Sec*
Casey Tzeng, *Opers Staff*
Larry Huntoon, *Manager*
EMP: 56
SQ FT: 28,000
SALES (est): 18.8MM **Privately Held**
WEB: www.fontanaroof.com
SIC: 2952 2621 Roofing materials; felts, building

(P-9405)
GRANITE CONSTRUCTION INC
999 Mission Rock Rd, Santa Paula (93060-9730)
PHONE..............................805 879-0033
Scott McArthur, *Branch Mgr*
EMP: 67
SALES (corp-wide): 2.9B **Publicly Held**
WEB: www.graniteconstruction.com
SIC: 2952 Asphalt felts & coatings
PA: Granite Construction Incorporated
585 W Beach St
Watsonville CA 95076
831 724-1011

(P-9406)
HCO HOLDING I CORPORATION
Also Called: Henry Company
2270 S Castle Harbour Pl, Ontario (91761-5704)
PHONE..............................310 684-5320
Dave Distler, *Branch Mgr*
EMP: 10
SALES (corp-wide): 254.1MM **Privately Held**
SIC: 2952 Roof cement: asphalt, fibrous or plastic
HQ: Hco Holding I Corporation
999 N Pacific Coast Hwy
El Segundo CA 90245
323 583-5000

(P-9407)
HCO HOLDING II CORPORATION
999 N Sepulveda Blvd, El Segundo (90245-2714)
PHONE..............................310 955-9200
Brian C Strauss, *President*
EMP: 90
SALES (est): 46.2MM
SALES (corp-wide): 254.1MM **Privately Held**
SIC: 2952 2821 2891 Roof cement: asphalt, fibrous or plastic; polyurethane resins; sealants
HQ: Hco Holding I Corporation
999 N Pacific Coast Hwy
El Segundo CA 90245
323 583-5000

(P-9408)
HENRY COMPANY LLC (HQ)
999 N Pacific Coast Hwy, El Segundo (90245-2714)
PHONE..............................310 955-9200
Frank Ready, *President*
Jason Peel, *CFO*
Kurt Leibel, *Senior VP*
Mark Longfellow, *Vice Pres*
Ryan Mills, *Vice Pres*
◆ EMP: 100
SALES (est): 193MM **Publicly Held**
SIC: 2952 2821 2891 Roof cement: asphalt, fibrous or plastic; polyurethane resins; sealants

(P-9409)
HNC PARENT INC (PA)
999 N Pacific Coast Hwy, El Segundo (90245-2714)
PHONE..............................310 955-9200
Rob Newbold, *Principal*
EMP: 100 EST: 2012
SALES (est): 254.1MM **Privately Held**
SIC: 2952 2821 2891 Roof cement: asphalt, fibrous or plastic; polyurethane resins; sealants

(P-9410)
IN-O-VATE INC
Also Called: Inovate Roofing Products
9301 Garfield Ave, South Gate (90280-3804)
PHONE..............................562 806-7515
Bennie Freiborg, *Ch of Bd*
Mark Freiborg, *President*
EMP: 10
SQ FT: 75,160
SALES (est): 2.2MM **Privately Held**
WEB: www.in-o-vate-inc.com
SIC: 2952 Roofing materials

(P-9411)
JAMES HARDIE TRADING CO INC
26300 La Alameda Ste 400, Mission Viejo (92691-8372)
PHONE..............................949 582-2378
Bryon G Borgardt, *President*
Lance Sharpe, *Real Est Agnt*
EMP: 160
SALES (est): 28.9MM **Privately Held**
SIC: 2952 Siding materials
HQ: James Hardie Transition Co., Inc.
26300 La Alameda Ste 400
Mission Viejo CA 92691
949 348-1800

(P-9412)
LUNDAY-THAGARD COMPANY
9301 Garfield Ave, South Gate (90280-3804)
P.O. Box 1519 (90280-1519)
PHONE..............................562 928-6990
John Todorovich, *Vice Pres*
EMP: 50
SALES (corp-wide): 198.5MM **Privately Held**
SIC: 2952 2951 Roofing materials; asphalt paving mixtures & blocks
HQ: Lunday-Thagard Company
9302 Garfield Ave
South Gate CA 90280
562 928-7000

(P-9413)
MBTECHNOLOGY
188 S Teilman Ave, Fresno (93706-1334)
PHONE..............................559 233-2181
Bahman Behbehani, *President*
Rostam Felfeli, *Vice Pres*
Khogasteh Behbehani, *Admin Sec*
Steve Tejeda, *Controller*
Charlotte Behbehani, *Human Res Mgr*
▲ EMP: 31 EST: 1981
SQ FT: 54,000
SALES (est): 10.8MM **Privately Held**
WEB: www.mbtechnology.com
SIC: 2952 Roofing materials

(P-9414)
METROTILE MANUFACTURING LLC
Also Called: Metro Roof Products
3093 Industry St Ste A, Oceanside (92054-4895)
PHONE..............................760 435-9842
Patrick Tavaran, *CEO*
◆ EMP: 45
SQ FT: 47,000
SALES (est): 6.9MM **Privately Held**
WEB: www.smartroofs.com
SIC: 2952 Roofing materials
HQ: Headwaters Incorporated
10701 S River Front Pkwy # 300
South Jordan UT 84095

(P-9415)
MIDWESTERN PIPELINE SVCS INC (PA)
160 Klamath Ct, American Canyon (94503-9700)
PHONE..............................707 557-6633
T Michael Harrison, *President*
John L Poyas, *Senior VP*
Stan Brady, *Vice Pres*
Chris M Harrison, *Vice Pres*
Michael T Wilhite, *Vice Pres*
EMP: 17 EST: 1940
SQ FT: 20,000
SALES (est): 1.9MM **Privately Held**
WEB: www.midwesternpipelineservices.com
SIC: 2952 1799 Asphalt felts & coatings; welding on site

(P-9416)
OWENS CORNING SALES LLC
1501 N Tamarind Ave, Compton (90222-4130)
P.O. Box 5665 (90224-5665)
PHONE..............................310 631-1062
David Randalph, *Branch Mgr*
EMP: 175 **Publicly Held**
WEB: www.owenscorning.com
SIC: 2952 2951 1761 Roofing felts, cements or coatings; asphalt paving mixtures & blocks; roofing, siding & sheet metal work
HQ: Owens Corning Sales, Llc
1 Owens Corning Pkwy
Toledo OH 43659
419 248-8000

(P-9417)
REP-KOTE PRODUCTS INC
10938 Beech Ave, Fontana (92337-7260)
PHONE..............................909 355-1288
Robert Wang, *President*
EMP: 35
SQ FT: 20,000
SALES (est): 3.4MM **Privately Held**
WEB: www.continentalcoatings.us
SIC: 2952 5084 Asphalt felts & coatings; water pumps (industrial)

(P-9418)
RGM PRODUCTS INC
Also Called: Ridgeline
3301 Navone Rd, Stockton (95215-9312)
PHONE..............................559 499-2222
Clay Crum, *President*
Gus Freshwater, *Exec VP*
▲ EMP: 400
SALES (est): 49.6MM
SALES (corp-wide): 2.7B **Privately Held**
SIC: 2952 Asphalt felts & coatings
HQ: Elk Premium Building Products, Inc
14911 Quorum Dr Ste 600
Dallas TX 75254
972 851-0400

(P-9419)
TREMCO INCORPORATED
3060 E 44th St, Vernon (90058-2428)
PHONE..............................323 587-3014
Javier Hernandez, *Manager*
Nancy Ortez, *Marketing Staff*
EMP: 15
SALES (corp-wide): 5.3B **Publicly Held**
WEB: www.tremcoinc.com
SIC: 2952 Roofing felts, cements or coatings
HQ: Tremco Incorporated
3735 Green Rd
Beachwood OH 44122
216 292-5000

(P-9420)
TROPICAL ASPHALT LLC (PA)
Also Called: Tropical Roofing Products CA
14435 Macaw St, La Mirada (90638-5210)
PHONE..............................714 739-1408
Richard Zegelbone,
EMP: 15
SQ FT: 27,000
SALES (est): 12MM **Privately Held**
SIC: 2952 Asphalt felts & coatings

2992 Lubricating Oils & Greases

(P-9421)
ADELAIDE MARINE SERVICES LLC
100 W 35th St Unit Lm, National City (91950-7925)
PHONE..............................619 852-8722
Angela Putrino, *Mng Member*
EMP: 11
SQ FT: 4,600
SALES: 10MM **Privately Held**
SIC: 2992 Lubricating oils

(P-9422)
AMTECOL INC
Also Called: American Hi-Tech Petro & Chem
810 Wright Ave, Richmond (94804-3640)
PHONE..............................510 235-7979
Susan Wynn, *CEO*
Hoa K Dang, *President*
Truc Huynh, *Vice Pres*
Peter Nguyen, *Vice Pres*
Jack Wynn, *Marketing Mgr*
◆ EMP: 30
SALES (est): 15.4MM **Privately Held**
WEB: www.amtecol.com
SIC: 2992 Lubricating oils

(P-9423)
ARCTIC SILVER INCORPORATED
9826 W Legacy Ave, Visalia (93291-9544)
PHONE..............................559 740-0912
Nevin House, *President*
Rochelle Overstreet, *Corp Secy*
Gregg Malm, *Vice Pres*
Terri McCluskey, *Human Res Mgr*
▲ EMP: 12
SQ FT: 3,200
SALES (est): 1.8MM **Privately Held**
WEB: www.arcticsilver.com
SIC: 2992 Lubricating oils & greases

(P-9424)
ARMITE LABORATORIES INC
1560 Superior Ave Ste A4, Costa Mesa (92627-3676)
PHONE..............................949 646-9035
Josh Walker, *President*
Anders Folkedal, *Treasurer*
▲ EMP: 10 EST: 1923
SQ FT: 7,500
SALES: 2MM **Privately Held**
WEB: www.armitelabs.com
SIC: 2992 2843 2891 5172 Lubricating oils; penetrants; sealants; petroleum products; lubricating oils & greases

(P-9425)
BP LUBRICANTS USA INC
Also Called: BP Castrol
801 Wharf St, Richmond (94804-3557)
PHONE..............................510 236-6312
William Walter, *Branch Mgr*
Willie Leggett, *Site Mgr*
EMP: 40
SQ FT: 17,680
SALES (corp-wide): 240.2B **Privately Held**
WEB: www.castrolna.com
SIC: 2992 Cutting oils, blending: made from purchased materials
HQ: Bp Lubricants Usa Inc.
1500 Valley Rd
Wayne NJ 07470
973 633-2200

(P-9426)
CHAMPIONS CHOICE INC
1910 E Via Bur'on, Anaheim (92806-1228)
PHONE..............................714 635-4491
Adam W Huber, *Ch of Bd*
Al Baudoin, *President*
Melodie Reguero, *Treasurer*
Patrick Huber, *Vice Pres*
Candace Baudoin, *Admin Sec*
EMP: 13
SQ FT: 20,000
SALES (est): 1.6MM **Privately Held**
WEB: www.championschoice.com
SIC: 2992 Lubricating oils

(P-9427)
CHEM ARROW CORP
13643 Live Oak Ln, Irwindale
(91706-1317)
P.O. Box 2366, Baldwin Park (91706-1198)
PHONE..................................626 358-2255
Alphonse Spalding, *Ch of Bd*
Hemith Mitchello, *President*
▲ **EMP:** 25
SQ FT: 36,000
SALES (est): 9.5MM **Privately Held**
WEB: www.chemarrow.com
SIC: 2992 2899 Lubricating oils; rust ar-
resting compounds, animal or vegetable
oil base; fuel tank or engine cleaning
chemicals; metal treating compounds;
rust resisting compounds

(P-9428)
CHEMTOOL INCORPORATED
1300 Goodrick Dr, Tehachapi (93561-1508)
PHONE..................................661 823-7190
Bill Hart, *Manager*
EMP: 30
SALES (corp-wide): 242.1B **Publicly
Held**
WEB: www.chemtool.com
SIC: 2992 2899 5172 Oils & greases,
blending & compounding; chemical
preparations; lubricating oils & greases
HQ: Chemtool Incorporated
801 W Rockton Rd
Rockton IL 61072
815 957-4140

(P-9429)
CHERRY PIT
812 E Monte Vista Ave, Vacaville
(95688-2922)
PHONE..................................707 449-8378
Mike Cherry, *Principal*
EMP: 12
SALES (est): 1.3MM **Privately Held**
SIC: 2992 Lubricating oils & greases

(P-9430)
DEMENNO/KERDOON HOLDINGS
Also Called: D K Environmental
3650 E 26th St, Vernon (90058-4104)
PHONE..................................323 268-3387
Rodney Ananda, *Manager*
EMP: 53
SALES (corp-wide): 198.5MM **Privately
Held**
SIC: 2992 4953 Oils & greases, blending
& compounding; re-refining lubricating oils
& greases; transmission fluid: made from
purchased materials; refuse systems
HQ: Demenno/Kerdoon Holdings
9302 Garfield Ave
South Gate CA 90280
562 231-1550

(P-9431)
DEMENNO/KERDOON HOLDINGS (DH)
Also Called: Demenno-Kerdoon
9302 Garfield Ave, South Gate
(90280-3805)
PHONE..................................562 231-1550
Robert Roth, *Ch of Bd*
Bruce Demenno, *CEO*
Steve Kerdoon, *COO*
Mark Snell, *Principal*
EMP: 67 **EST:** 1971
SQ FT: 21,000
SALES (est): 25.9MM
SALES (corp-wide): 198.5MM **Privately
Held**
SIC: 2992 2911 Oils & greases, blending
& compounding; re-refining lubricating oils
& greases; transmission fluid: made from
purchased materials; petroleum refining

(P-9432)
EVERGREEN HOLDINGS INC (PA)
18952 Macarthur Blvd # 410, Irvine
(92612-1402)
PHONE..................................949 757-7770
Jacob Voogd, *Ch of Bd*
Gary Colbert, *President*
Jesus Romero, *CFO*
Atam Gossain, *Admin Sec*

▲ **EMP:** 20
SQ FT: 6,200
SALES (est): 20.6MM **Privately Held**
WEB: www.evergreenoil.com
SIC: 2992 4953 Re-refining lubricating oils
& greases; liquid waste, collection & dis-
posal

(P-9433)
EVERGREEN OIL INC (HQ)
Also Called: Evergreen Environmental Svcs
18025 S Broadway, Gardena (90248-3539)
PHONE..................................949 757-7770
Jake Voogd, *CEO*
Jesus Romero, *CFO*
George Lamont, *Exec VP*
Obert Gwaltney, *VP Opers*
EMP: 23
SALES (est): 48.2MM
SALES (corp-wide): 2.9B **Publicly Held**
WEB: www.evergreenoil.com
SIC: 2992 2911 4953 Lubricating oils &
greases; petroleum refining; refuse sys-
tems
PA: Clean Harbors, Inc.
42 Longwater Dr
Norwell MA 02061
781 792-5000

(P-9434)
EZ LUBE LLC
532 W Florida Ave, Hemet (92543-4007)
PHONE..................................951 766-1996
Richie Berling, *Manager*
EMP: 638
SALES (corp-wide): 22.5MM **Privately
Held**
SIC: 2992 Lubricating oils
PA: Ez Lube, Llc
3540 Howard Way Ste 200
Costa Mesa CA 92626
714 556-1312

(P-9435)
FLUID LUBRICATION & CHEM CO
18400 S Broadway, Gardena (90248-4633)
PHONE..................................800 826-2415
Christopher L Luther, *CEO*
EMP: 10
SALES (est): 1MM **Privately Held**
SIC: 2992 Lubricating oils

(P-9436)
HUSK-ITT DISTRIBUTORS CORP
Also Called: Huskey Specially Lubricants
1580 Industrial Ave, Norco (92860-2946)
PHONE..................................951 340-4000
Shelby R Huskey, *CEO*
Berlynda Bevacqua, *CFO*
Michael Montgomery, *Vice Pres*
Judy Wilde, *Finance*
EMP: 18
SQ FT: 30,000
SALES (est): 5.9MM **Privately Held**
WEB: www.huskey.com
SIC: 2992 Oils & greases, blending & com-
pounding

(P-9437)
ILLINOIS TOOL WORKS INC
1050 W 5th St, Azusa (91702-3308)
PHONE..................................847 724-7500
Gerald Miles, *General Mgr*
EMP: 130
SALES (corp-wide): 14.3B **Publicly Held**
SIC: 2992 2899 Lubricating oils; chemical
preparations
PA: Illinois Tool Works Inc.
155 Harlem Ave
Glenview IL 60025
847 724-7500

(P-9438)
INTERNATIONAL PETROLEUM PRODUC
Also Called: Ipac
7600 Dublin Blvd Ste 240, Dublin
(94568-2908)
PHONE..................................925 556-5530
Brian Cereghino, *CEO*
Jeff Crow, *President*
Alan Krock, *CFO*
Neil Olsen, *Project Mgr*
▲ **EMP:** 10
SQ FT: 7,500

SALES (est): 3.3MM **Privately Held**
WEB: www.ipac-inc.com
SIC: 2992 5172 Lubricating oils &
greases; petroleum products

(P-9439)
IPAC INC
7600 Dublin Blvd Ste 240, Dublin
(94568-2908)
PHONE..................................925 556-5530
Brian Cereghino, *President*
Carol Dsouza, *Purchasing*
Tammy Tinder, *Natl Sales Mgr*
Jeff Melendez, *Sales Staff*
EMP: 18
SALES (est): 4.4MM **Privately Held**
SIC: 2992 Lubricating oils & greases

(P-9440)
JONELL OIL CORPORATION
13649 Live Oak Ln, Irwindale
(91706-1317)
PHONE..................................626 303-4691
John Tarazi, *CEO*
Helen Tarazi, *President*
EMP: 10
SQ FT: 10,000
SALES: 2MM **Privately Held**
SIC: 2992 Re-refining lubricating oils &
greases

(P-9441)
LUBECO INC
6859 Downey Ave, Long Beach
(90805-1967)
PHONE..................................562 602-1791
Steven Rossi, *President*
EMP: 45
SQ FT: 20,000
SALES (est): 7.9MM **Privately Held**
SIC: 2992 2851 Lubricating oils &
greases; paints & allied products

(P-9442)
LUBRICATING SPECIALTIES CO (PA)
Also Called: Technolube Products
8015 Paramount Blvd, Pico Rivera
(90660-4811)
PHONE..................................562 776-4000
Stephen Milam, *President*
Robert L Cook, *Vice Pres*
Robert Kress, *Vice Pres*
Stephen Miller, *Vice Pres*
Richard Scott, *Business Mgr*
◆ **EMP:** 120
SQ FT: 70,000
SALES (est): 78.7MM **Privately Held**
WEB: www.lsc-online.com
SIC: 2992 Lubricating oils

(P-9443)
LUBRICATING SPECIALTIES CO
Also Called: Technolube Products
3365 E Slauson Ave, Vernon (90058-3914)
PHONE..................................562 776-4000
Stephen Milam, *CEO*
Sharon Alvarenga, *Purch Mgr*
Ken Allison, *Regl Sales Mgr*
Bernadette Cortez, *Supervisor*
EMP: 30
SALES (corp-wide): 78.7MM **Privately
Held**
WEB: www.lsc-online.com
SIC: 2992 Lubricating oils & greases
PA: Lubricating Specialties Company
8015 Paramount Blvd
Pico Rivera CA 90660
562 776-4000

(P-9444)
LUCAS OIL PRODUCTS INC (PA)
302 N Sheridan St, Corona (92880-2067)
PHONE..................................951 270-0154
Forrest Lucas, *CEO*
Kevin Asbell, *Vice Pres*
Charlotte Lucas, *Vice Pres*
Jolie McGarth, *Executive*
Jeff Carles, *General Mgr*
◆ **EMP:** 150
SQ FT: 80,000
SALES: 100MM **Privately Held**
WEB: www.lucasoil.com
SIC: 2992 5169 Lubricating oils &
greases; oil additives

(P-9445)
MACH OIL CORP
17835 Ventura Blvd # 301, Encino
(91316-3634)
P.O. Box 261414 (91426-1414)
PHONE..................................818 783-3567
Vahab Aghai, *President*
Amir Sabetin, *CFO*
EMP: 12
SALES (est): 935.7K **Privately Held**
SIC: 2992 Lubricating oils & greases

(P-9446)
PENNZOIL-QUAKER STATE COMPANY
2015 Grand St, Alameda (94501-1296)
PHONE..................................510 748-1331
Blake Fernandez, *Manager*
EMP: 11
SALES (corp-wide): 305.1B **Privately
Held**
WEB: www.pzl.com
SIC: 2992 Lubricating oils & greases
HQ: Pennzoil-Quaker State Company
150 N Dairy Ashford Rd
Houston TX 77079
713 245-4800

(P-9447)
PHILLIPS 66 SPECTRUM CORP
Also Called: Red Line Synthetic Oil
6100 Egret Ct, Benicia (94510-1269)
PHONE..................................707 745-6100
Ann M Oglesby, *Principal*
Marcie Johnson, *Office Mgr*
Timothy Decesaro, *Sales Staff*
Cameron Evans, *Sales Staff*
Michael Andrew, *Director*
EMP: 17
SALES (corp-wide): 28.8MM **Privately
Held**
SIC: 2992 Lubricating oils; brake fluid (hy-
draulic): made from purchased materials;
transmission fluid: made from purchased
materials
PA: Phillips 66 Spectrum Corporation
3010 Briarpark Dr
Houston TX 77042
281 293-6600

(P-9448)
ROSEMEAD OIL PRODUCTS INC
12402 Los Nietos Rd, Santa Fe Springs
(90670-2914)
P.O. Box 2645 (90670-0645)
PHONE..................................562 941-3261
Richard Schoensiegel Jr, *President*
▲ **EMP:** 11
SQ FT: 25,000
SALES (est): 2.6MM
SALES (corp-wide): 2.9B **Publicly Held**
WEB: www.rosemeadoil.com
SIC: 2992 5172 Oils & greases, blending
& compounding; lubricating oils & greases
PA: Clean Harbors, Inc.
42 Longwater Dr
Norwell MA 02061
781 792-5000

(P-9449)
SALCO DYNAMIC SOLUTIONS INC (PA)
Also Called: Salco Oil
6248 Surfpoint Cir, Huntington Beach
(92648-5590)
PHONE..................................714 374-7500
Lucy George, *CEO*
Scott George, *CFO*
EMP: 31
SALES: 713K **Privately Held**
SIC: 2992 5172 5085 5084 Oils &
greases, blending & compounding; petroleum products; industrial supplies; industrial machinery & equipment; machine
tools, metal cutting type; machine tool accessories

(P-9450)
SOUTH WEST LUBRICANTS INC
Also Called: Maxima Racing Oils
9266 Abraham Way, Santee (92071-5611)
PHONE..................................619 449-5000
Daniel J Massie, *CEO*
◆ **EMP:** 11

▲ = Import ▼=Export
◆ =Import/Export

SQ FT: 50,000
SALES (est): 4.4MM Privately Held
WEB: www.maximusa.com
SIC: 2992 Lubricating oils

(P-9451)
SOUTHERN COUNTIES OIL CO
2075 Alum Rock Ave, San Jose
(95116-2006)
PHONE..................408 251-0811
Kathy Demarco, Manager
EMP: 50
SALES (corp-wide): 1.2B Privately Held
WEB: www.coastoil.com
SIC: 2992 Lubricating oils
PA: Southern Counties Oil Co.
    1800 W Katella Ave # 400
    Orange CA 92867
    714 744-7140

(P-9452)
US LUBRICANTS INC
10735 Kadota Ave, Montclair (91763-6005)
PHONE..................909 469-1860
Harry J Barkett, President
William F Barkett, Corp Secy
▼ EMP: 20 EST: 1967
SQ FT: 35,000
SALES (est): 2.8MM Privately Held
SIC: 2992 Re-refining lubricating oils &
greases

(P-9453)
VAST ENTERPRISES
Also Called: Liquid Packaging
7739 Monroe St, Paramount (90723-5020)
PHONE..................562 633-3224
Joe Mouren-Laurens, CEO
Dean Mouren-Laurens, Vice Pres
EMP: 13
SQ FT: 18,000
SALES (est): 3.7MM Privately Held
WEB: www.liquidpackagingcompany.com
SIC: 2992 Transmission fluid: made from
purchased materials

(P-9454)
W S DODGE OIL CO INC
3710 Fruitland Ave, Maywood
(90270-2196)
PHONE..................323 583-3478
Tom Downs, President
David Downs, Corp Secy
Annemarie Downs, Vice Pres
▲ EMP: 17
SQ FT: 12,000
SALES (est): 6MM Privately Held
WEB: www.wsdodgeoil.com
SIC: 2992 Cutting oils, blending: made
from purchased materials

(P-9455)
WD-40 COMPANY (PA)
9715 Businesspark Ave, San Diego
(92131-1642)
PHONE..................619 275-1400
Garry O Ridge, President
Linda A Lang, Ch of Bd
Jay W Rembolt, CFO
Steven A Brass, Division Pres
Richard T Clampitt, Vice Pres
EMP: 277 EST: 1953
SALES: 408.5MM Publicly Held
WEB: www.wd40.com
SIC: 2992 2851 Lubricating oils; removers
& cleaners

2999 Products Of Petroleum & Coal, NEC

(P-9456)
LUNDAY-THAGARD COMPANY (HQ)
Also Called: Ltr
9302 Garfield Ave, South Gate
(90280-3805)
P.O. Box 1519 (90280-1519)
PHONE..................562 928-7000
Bernard B Roth, Ch of Bd
Robert Roth, President
Austin Miller, COO
Larry Mori, Vice Pres
Steve Roth, Vice Pres
EMP: 106

SQ FT: 16,000
SALES (est): 90.7MM
SALES (corp-wide): 198.5MM Privately
Held
SIC: 2999 2951 2911 Coke; paving
blocks; gases & liquefied petroleum
gases
PA: World Oil Marketing Company
    9302 Garfield Ave
    South Gate CA 90280
    562 928-0100

(P-9457)
RENTECH INC (PA)
10880 Wilshire Blvd # 1101, Los Angeles
(90024-4112)
PHONE..................310 571-9800
Keith Forman, President
Halbert S Washburn, Ch of Bd
Keith B Forman, President
Paul M Summers, CFO
Joseph V Herold, Senior VP
EMP: 85
SQ FT: 600
SALES: 150.7MM Privately Held
SIC: 2999 2873 6794 Waxes, petroleum:
not produced in petroleum refineries; ni-
trogenous fertilizers; patent buying, li-
censing, leasing

(P-9458)
WAX RESEARCH INC
Also Called: Globe Rider Distribution
1212 Distribution Way, Vista (92081-8816)
PHONE..................760 607-0850
John A Dahl, President
Cris Dahl, CFO
▲ EMP: 12
SQ FT: 22,000
SALES: 2MM Privately Held
WEB: www.stickybumps.com
SIC: 2999 Waxes, petroleum: not produced
in petroleum refineries

3011 Tires & Inner Tubes

(P-9459)
AMERICAN GENERAL TOOL GROUP
929 Poinsettia Ave # 101, Vista
(92081-8459)
PHONE..................760 745-7993
Nasreen Godil, President
EMP: 40
SALES (est): 6.4MM Privately Held
SIC: 3011 3492 3535 3822 Pneumatic
tires, all types; control valves, aircraft: hydraulic & pneumatic; control valves, fluid
power: hydraulic & pneumatic; pneumatic
tube conveyor systems; switches, pneumatic positioning remote

(P-9460)
BAS RECYCLING INC
14050 Day St, Moreno Valley (92553-9106)
PHONE..................951 214-6590
Ohannes Beudjekian, Ch of Bd
Sarkis Beudjeaian, CEO
▲ EMP: 40
SQ FT: 80,000
SALES (est): 14.7MM Privately Held
WEB: www.basrecycling.com
SIC: 3011 Tires, cushion or solid rubber

(P-9461)
BGM INSTALLATION INC
528 E D St, Wilmington (90744-6002)
PHONE..................310 830-3113
John Battaglia, Principal
EMP: 14
SALES (est): 2.3MM Privately Held
SIC: 3011 5211 Tires & inner tubes; lum-
ber & other building materials

(P-9462)
CARLSTAR GROUP LLC
1990 S Vintage Ave, Ontario (91761-2819)
PHONE..................310 816-1015
David Chavez, Branch Mgr
Alicia Campbell, Administration
Katrina Anderson, Opers Spvr
Ron Murrenus, Production
EMP: 142

SALES (corp-wide): 1B Privately Held
SIC: 3011 Industrial tires, pneumatic
PA: The Carlstar Group Llc
    725 Cool Springs Blvd
    Franklin TN 37067
    615 503-0220

(P-9463)
CONTINENTAL INTELLIGENT TRANSP
3901 N 1st St, San Jose (95134-1506)
PHONE..................408 391-9008
Seval Oza, Mng Member
Eileen Riorden, Executive Asst
Tammer Zein-El-Abedein, Administration
Tejas Desai,
Seval Oz, Mng Member
EMP: 20
SALES (est): 624.1K Privately Held
SIC: 3011 Tires & inner tubes

(P-9464)
COOPER TIRE & RUBBER COMPANY
9363 Lucas Ranch Rd, Rancho Cuca-
monga (91730-7938)
PHONE..................909 481-6437
William Tonaway, Manager
Mike Hundly, Manager
EMP: 12
SALES (corp-wide): 2.8B Publicly Held
WEB: www.coopertire.com
SIC: 3011 Tires & inner tubes
PA: Cooper Tire & Rubber Company Inc
    701 Lima Ave
    Findlay OH 45840
    419 423-1321

(P-9465)
ITW GLOBAL TIRE REPAIR INC
Also Called: Access Marketing
125 Venture Dr Ste 210, San Luis Obispo
(93401-9105)
PHONE..................805 489-0490
Juan Valls, CEO
Joe Bowman, Mktg Dir
◆ EMP: 71
SQ FT: 20,000
SALES (est): 18.3MM
SALES (corp-wide): 14.3B Publicly Held
WEB: www.slime.com
SIC: 3011 2891 Tire & inner tube materials
& related products; adhesives & sealants
PA: Illinois Tool Works Inc.
    155 Harlem Ave
    Glenview IL 60025
    847 724-7500

(P-9466)
MCLAREN INDUSTRIES INC (PA)
12440 Carson St, Hawaiian Gardens
(90716-1649)
PHONE..................310 212-1333
Richardson Doyle, CEO
George Valev, CFO
◆ EMP: 20
SQ FT: 17,500
SALES (est): 5.4MM Privately Held
WEB: www.mclarenusa.com
SIC: 3011 Automobile tires, pneumatic

(P-9467)
SKAT-TRAK INC
654 Avenue K, Calimesa (92320-1115)
P.O. Box 518 (92320-0518)
PHONE..................909 795-2505
Ken Stuart, President
Diane Stuart, Corp Secy
EMP: 115
SQ FT: 3,000
SALES (est): 15.9MM Privately Held
WEB: www.skat-trak.com
SIC: 3011 3599 3366 Tires & inner tubes;
propellers, ship & boat: machined; copper
foundries

(P-9468)
TOYO TIRE HLDINGS AMERICAS INC (HQ)
5900 Katella Ave Ste 200a, Cypress
(90630-5019)
PHONE..................562 431-6502
Tomoshige Mizutani, CEO
▲ EMP: 20

SALES (est): 284.7MM
SALES (corp-wide): 3.6B Privately Held
SIC: 3011 Automobile inner tubes
PA: Toyo Tire & Rubber Co.,Ltd.
    2-2-13, Fujinoki
    Itami HYO 664-0
    727 899-100

3021 Rubber & Plastic Footwear

(P-9469)
CROCS INC
2800 N Main St Unit 724, Santa Ana
(92705-6613)
PHONE..................714 568-0340
Betra Moore, Branch Mgr
EMP: 14
SALES (corp-wide): 1B Publicly Held
SIC: 3021 Shoes, rubber or rubber soled
fabric uppers
PA: Crocs, Inc.
    7477 Dry Creek Pkwy
    Niwot CO 80503
    303 848-7000

(P-9470)
DECKERS OUTDOOR CORPORATION
3175 Mission Oaks Blvd, Camarillo
(93012-5140)
PHONE..................805 437-2300
EMP: 12
SALES (corp-wide): 1.9B Publicly Held
SIC: 3021 Rubber & plastics footwear
PA: Deckers Outdoor Corporation
    250 Coromar Dr
    Goleta CA 93117
    805 967-7611

(P-9471)
FOUR STAR DISTRIBUTION
206 Calle Conchita, San Clemente
(92672-5404)
PHONE..................949 369-4420
Markus Bohi, CEO
Raul Ries, President
Brian Abraham, Info Tech Dir
Peter Shemonsky, Director
▲ EMP: 65
SALES (est): 8MM Privately Held
SIC: 3021 Shoes, plastic soles molded to
fabric uppers

(P-9472)
JEVIN ENTERPRISES INC
Also Called: Coast Dance Shoes
11548 Apulia Ct, Porter Ranch
(91326-4400)
P.O. Box 3876, Granada Hills (91394-
0876)
PHONE..................818 408-0488
Roxane Agopian, President
Harout Agopian, Treasurer
▲ EMP: 30
SALES (est): 3.5MM Privately Held
SIC: 3021 Arctics, rubber or rubber soled
fabric

(P-9473)
JOE MONTANA FOOTWEAR
228 Manhattan Beach Blvd, Manhattan
Beach (90266-5347)
PHONE..................310 318-3100
Robert Greenberg, CEO
EMP: 99
SALES (est): 4.4MM Privately Held
SIC: 3021 Rubber & plastics footwear

(P-9474)
K-SWISS INC (HQ)
523 W 6th St Ste 534, Los Angeles
(90014-1225)
PHONE..................323 675-2700
Philip Jeong, Ch of Bd
Mark Miller, President
Barney Waters, Chief Mktg Ofcr
Michael Heidenreich, Comms Mgr
Ivette Ramos, Accountant
▲ EMP: 142
SALES (est): 491.4MM
SALES (corp-wide): 1.3B Privately Held
WEB: www.kswiss.com
SIC: 3021 Rubber & plastics footwear

PRODUCTS & SVCS

PA: E Land World Co., Ltd.
36 Gasan Digital 1-Ro, Geumcheon-Gu
Seoul 08506
822 865-1083

(P-9475)
K-SWISS SALES CORP
31248 Oak Crest Dr # 150, Westlake Village (91361-4692)
PHONE..........818 706-5100
Cheryl Kuchinka, *President*
EMP: 242
SALES: 484MM
SALES (corp-wide): 1.3B **Privately Held**
WEB: www.kswiss.com
SIC: 3021 Rubber & plastics footwear
HQ: K-Swiss Inc.
523 W 6th St Ste 534
Los Angeles CA 90014
323 675-2700

(P-9476)
NIKE INC
222 E Redondo Beach Blvd C, Gardena (90248-2302)
PHONE..........310 670-6770
Ana Madrid, *Manager*
EMP: 38
SALES (corp-wide): 36.4B **Publicly Held**
WEB: www.nike.com
SIC: 3021 Rubber & plastics footwear
PA: Nike, Inc.
1 Sw Bowerman Dr
Beaverton OR 97005
503 671-6453

(P-9477)
PLS DIABETIC SHOE COMPANY INC
21500 Osborne St, Canoga Park (91304-1522)
PHONE..........818 734-7080
Ambartsum Kumuryan, *President*
Konstandin Kumuryan, *COO*
▲ **EMP:** 32
SQ FT: 24,031
SALES (est): 4.6MM **Privately Held**
SIC: 3021 Shoes, rubber or plastic molded to fabric

(P-9478)
PRINCIPLE PLASTICS
1136 W 135th St, Gardena (90247-1919)
P.O. Box 2408 (90247-0408)
PHONE..........310 532-3411
David Hoyt, *President*
Robert Hoyt, *CFO*
Russell Hokama,
▲ **EMP:** 27 **EST:** 1948
SQ FT: 28,000
SALES (est): 7.6MM **Privately Held**
WEB: www.sloggers.com
SIC: 3021 3949 2519 Galoshes, plastic; golf equipment; lawn & garden furniture, except wood & metal

(P-9479)
RECON 1 INC
Also Called: Emergency Preparedness Pdts
4045 Via Pescador, Camarillo (93012-6830)
PHONE..........805 388-3911
Toll Free:..........888 -
Gary Kalaydjian, *President*
Pete Kalaydjian, *CFO*
◆ **EMP:** 12
SQ FT: 7,000
SALES (est): 2.1MM **Privately Held**
SIC: 3021 5941 Rubber & plastics footwear; camping equipment

(P-9480)
SKECHERS COLLECTION LLC (HQ)
Also Called: Sketchers
228 Manhattan Beach Blvd, Manhattan Beach (90266-5347)
PHONE..........310 318-3100
Robert Greenberg, *Mng Member*
Jason Kartalis, *Director*
◆ **EMP:** 20
SALES (est): 1.7MM **Publicly Held**
WEB: www.skechers.com
SIC: 3021 5661 Shoes, rubber or plastic molded to fabric; shoe stores

(P-9481)
SKECHERS DIRECT
Also Called: Skechers USA
228 Manhattan Beach Blvd, Manhattan Beach (90266-5347)
PHONE..........310 318-3100
Robert Greenberg, *CEO*
Ted Weitzman,
EMP: 99
SQ FT: 25,000
SALES (est): 2.6MM **Privately Held**
SIC: 3021 Rubber & plastics footwear

(P-9482)
SKECHERS USA INC
Also Called: Skechers Factory Outlet 198
2796 Tanger Way, Barstow (92311-9414)
PHONE..........760 253-3707
EMP: 18 **Publicly Held**
SIC: 3021 Rubber & plastics footwear
PA: Skechers U.S.A., Inc.
228 Manhattan Beach Blvd # 200
Manhattan Beach CA 90266
-

(P-9483)
SKECHERS USA INC
Also Called: Skechers Factory Outlet 346
3320 Livermore Outlets Dr, Livermore (94551-4211)
PHONE..........925 447-2622
EMP: 18 **Publicly Held**
SIC: 3021 Rubber & plastics footwear
PA: Skechers U.S.A., Inc.
228 Manhattan Beach Blvd # 200
Manhattan Beach CA 90266

(P-9484)
SKECHERS USA INC
330 S Sepulveda Blvd, Manhattan Beach (90266-6828)
PHONE..........310 318-3100
Jeffrey Greenberg, *Vice Pres*
Ally Barron, *Manager*
Mandy Dimiero, *Manager*
Mark Henning, *Manager*
EMP: 25 **Publicly Held**
SIC: 3021 3149 5661 Shoes, rubber or plastic molded to fabric; athletic shoes, except rubber or plastic; shoe stores
PA: Skechers U.S.A., Inc.
228 Manhattan Beach Blvd # 200
Manhattan Beach CA 90266

(P-9485)
SKECHERS USA INC II (HQ)
225 S Sepulveda Blvd, Manhattan Beach (90266-6825)
PHONE..........310 318-3100
Robert Greenburg, *CEO*
Ed Jones, *Business Mgr*
Scott Dado, *Manager*
Maria Hernandez, *Manager*
◆ **EMP:** 95
SALES (est): 23.9MM **Publicly Held**
SIC: 3021 5661 Shoes, rubber or plastic molded to fabric; shoe stores

(P-9486)
SONICSENSORY INC (PA)
1161 Logan St, Los Angeles (90026-3210)
P.O. Box 24, Lake Peekskill NY (10537-0024)
PHONE..........818 256-7900
Susan Paley, *CEO*
Eddie Borjas, *CTO*
EMP: 15
SQ FT: 2,000
SALES (est): 2.6MM **Privately Held**
SIC: 3021 Shoes, rubber or rubber soled fabric uppers

(P-9487)
SUMMER RIO CORP (PA)
17501 Rowland St, City of Industry (91748-1115)
PHONE..........626 854-1498
Qing LI, *President*
Henry Liao, *Vice Pres*
Irene Lee, *Office Mgr*
Lauren Schneider, *Accounts Mgr*
◆ **EMP:** 20

SALES (est): 3.4MM **Privately Held**
WEB: www.summerrio.net
SIC: 3021 Canvas shoes, rubber soled; shoes, plastic soles molded to fabric uppers; shoes, rubber or plastic molded to fabric; shoes, rubber or rubber soled fabric uppers

(P-9488)
TOUCHSPORT FOOTWEAR LLC
2969 E Pcf Commerce Dr, E Rncho Dmngz (90221-5729)
PHONE..........310 763-0208
Peter Liow,
Simon Liow, *Software Dev*
▲ **EMP:** 10
SALES (est): 4.5MM **Privately Held**
SIC: 3021 Sandals, rubber

(P-9489)
VANS INC
6000 Sepulveda Blvd # 2155, Culver City (90230-6429)
PHONE..........310 390-7548
EMP: 10
SALES (corp-wide): 11.8B **Publicly Held**
SIC: 3021 Rubber & plastics footwear
HQ: Vans, Inc.
1588 S Coast Dr
Costa Mesa CA 92626
855 909-8267

(P-9490)
VANS INC
14006 Riverside Dr, Sherman Oaks (91423-1945)
PHONE..........818 990-1098
Rene Altervain, *Branch Mgr*
EMP: 10
SALES (corp-wide): 11.8B **Publicly Held**
SIC: 3021 Canvas shoes, rubber soled
HQ: Vans, Inc.
1588 S Coast Dr
Costa Mesa CA 92626
855 909-8267

(P-9491)
VANS INC
1354 Burlingame Ave, Burlingame (94010-4109)
PHONE..........650 401-3542
Nicole Clough, *Branch Mgr*
EMP: 11
SALES (corp-wide): 11.8B **Publicly Held**
SIC: 3021 5137 2326 Canvas shoes, rubber soled; women's & children's clothing; men's & boys' work clothing
HQ: Vans, Inc.
1588 S Coast Dr
Costa Mesa CA 92626
855 909-8267

(P-9492)
VANS INC
5232 E 2nd St, Long Beach (90803-5329)
PHONE..........562 856-1695
Jerry Rodriguez, *General Mgr*
EMP: 10
SALES (corp-wide): 11.8B **Publicly Held**
SIC: 3021 Canvas shoes, rubber soled
HQ: Vans, Inc.
1588 S Coast Dr
Costa Mesa CA 92626
855 909-8267

(P-9493)
VANS INC
3251 20th Ave Ste 237, San Francisco (94132-1974)
PHONE..........415 566-3762
Nikki Aclaro, *Branch Mgr*
EMP: 17
SALES (corp-wide): 11.8B **Publicly Held**
SIC: 3021 Canvas shoes, rubber soled
HQ: Vans, Inc.
1588 S Coast Dr
Costa Mesa CA 92626
855 909-8267

(P-9494)
VANS INC
13920 Cy Ctr Dr Ste 4035, Chino Hills (91709)
PHONE..........909 517-3141
Tyler Tritipo, *Branch Mgr*
Daniele Rodriguez, *Site Mgr*

EMP: 10
SALES (corp-wide): 11.8B **Publicly Held**
SIC: 3021 Canvas shoes, rubber soled
HQ: Vans, Inc.
1588 S Coast Dr
Costa Mesa CA 92626
855 909-8267

(P-9495)
VANS INC (DH)
Also Called: Vans Shoes
1588 S Coast Dr, Costa Mesa (92626-1533)
PHONE..........855 909-8267
Arthur I Carver, *Senior VP*
Scott J Blechman, *CFO*
Robert L Nagel, *Senior VP*
Sarah Crockett, *Vice Pres*
Craig E Gosselin, *Vice Pres*
▲ **EMP:** 277
SQ FT: 185,000
SALES (est): 751.5MM
SALES (corp-wide): 11.8B **Publicly Held**
SIC: 3021 2321 2329 2325 Canvas shoes, rubber soled; protective footwear, rubber or plastic; boots, rubber or rubber soled fabric; men's & boys' sports & polo shirts; polo shirts, men's & boys': made from purchased materials; men's & boys' sportswear & athletic clothing; jackets (suede, leatherette, etc.), sport: men's & boys'; slacks, dress: men's, youths' & boys'; shorts (outerwear): men's, youths' & boys'; hats, caps & millinery; canvas bags
HQ: Vf Outdoor, Llc
2701 Harbor Bay Pkwy
Alameda CA 94502
510 618-3500

(P-9496)
VANS INC
5800 Northgate Dr Ste 44, San Rafael (94903-6833)
PHONE..........415 479-1284
George Gray, *Branch Mgr*
EMP: 10
SALES (corp-wide): 11.8B **Publicly Held**
SIC: 3021 Canvas shoes, rubber soled
HQ: Vans, Inc.
1588 S Coast Dr
Costa Mesa CA 92626
855 909-8267

(P-9497)
VP FOOTWEAR INC
2536 Loma Ave, South El Monte (91733-1418)
PHONE..........626 443-2186
Peter Che, *President*
▲ **EMP:** 10
SQ FT: 10,000
SALES (est): 1.2MM **Privately Held**
WEB: www.vpfootwear.com
SIC: 3021 5139 Rubber & plastics footwear; shoes

3052 Rubber & Plastic Hose & Belting

(P-9498)
BERG-NELSON COMPANY INC
1633 W 17th St, Long Beach (90813-1285)
PHONE..........562 432-3491
Craig Nelson, *President*
Ray Dunn, *Vice Pres*
EMP: 12
SQ FT: 10,000
SALES (est): 1.3MM **Privately Held**
SIC: 3052 3492 Rubber & plastics hose & beltings; fluid power valves & hose fittings

(P-9499)
GANN PRODUCTS COMPANY INC
9540 Stewart And Gray Rd, Downey (90241-5590)
PHONE..........562 862-2337
Larry Gann, *President*
Lila Gann, *Corp Secy*
▲ **EMP:** 10 **EST:** 1954
SQ FT: 7,000

SALES (est): 2MM **Privately Held**
WEB: www.gannproducts.com
SIC: **3052** 3714 Automobile hose, rubber; motor vehicle body components & frame

(P-9500)
LEWIS-GOETZ AND COMPANY INC
Also Called: Valley Rubber & Gasket
4848c Frontier Way, Stockton
(95215-9670)
PHONE..................................209 944-0791
Brian Rowland, *Manager*
EMP: 11 **Privately Held**
SIC: **3052** 3053 5084 Rubber & plastics hose & beltings; gaskets, packing & sealing devices; industrial machinery & equipment
HQ: Eriks North America, Inc.
650 Washington Rd Ste 500
Pittsburgh PA 15228
800 937-9070

(P-9501)
NAT ARONSON & ASSOCIATES INC
Also Called: Aronson Manufacturing
7640 Gloria Ave Ste J, Van Nuys
(91406-1800)
P.O. Box 7795 (91409-7795)
PHONE..................................818 787-5160
Nathan Aronson, *CEO*
EMP: 16
SQ FT: 9,200
SALES (est): 2.7MM **Privately Held**
SIC: **3052** Rubber hose

(P-9502)
NORTH AMERICAN FIRE HOSE CORP
Also Called: Nafhc
910 Noble Way, Santa Maria (93454-1506)
P.O. Box 1968 (93456-1968)
PHONE..................................805 922-7076
Michael S Aubuchon, *CEO*
Virginia Aubuchon, *Admin Sec*
▲ EMP: 55
SQ FT: 43,000
SALES (est): 13.6MM **Privately Held**
WEB: www.nafhc.com
SIC: **3052** Fire hose, rubber

(P-9503)
OMEGA FIRE INC
441 W Allen Ave Ste 109, San Dimas
(91773-4702)
PHONE..................................818 404-6212
McKenzie Kordabadi, *Principal*
EMP: 10
SALES (est): 641.7K **Privately Held**
SIC: **3052** 3669 1711 2899 Fire hose, rubber; fire detection systems, electric; fire sprinkler system installation; fire extinguisher charges

(P-9504)
PARKER-HANNIFIN CORPORATION
Also Called: Parker Service Center
8460 Kass Dr, Buena Park (90621-3808)
PHONE..................................714 522-8840
Chris Wright, *Branch Mgr*
Rodney Craven, *Manager*
EMP: 21
SALES (corp-wide): 14.3B **Publicly Held**
WEB: www.parker.com
SIC: **3052** 3429 Rubber & plastics hose & beltings; manufactured hardware (general)
PA: Parker-Hannifin Corporation
6035 Parkland Blvd
Cleveland OH 44124
216 896-3000

(P-9505)
PRICE RUBBER COMPANY INC
17760 Ideal Pkwy, Manteca (95336-8992)
P.O. Box 100, French Camp (95231-0100)
PHONE..................................209 239-7478
Donna J Sprouse, *President*
Shurene Rehmke, *Vice Pres*
Christen A Lewis-Griffin, *Admin Sec*
EMP: 19
SQ FT: 15,000

SALES (est): 3.4MM **Privately Held**
SIC: **3052** 3053 Rubber & plastics hose & beltings; gaskets, packing & sealing devices

(P-9506)
RALPH L FLORIMONTE
517 Alondra Dr, Huntington Beach
(92648-3768)
PHONE..................................714 960-4470
Ralph Florimonte, *CEO*
EMP: 18 EST: 2001
SALES (est): 1MM **Privately Held**
SIC: **3052** Vacuum cleaner hose, plastic

(P-9507)
SANI-TECH WEST INC (PA)
1020 Flynn Rd, Camarillo (93012-8705)
PHONE..................................805 389-0400
Richard J Shor, *President*
Sherry Maxson, *Vice Pres*
Fredrick Melin, *CTO*
EMP: 80
SQ FT: 27,000
SALES (est): 16.6MM **Privately Held**
WEB: www.sani-techwest.com
SIC: **3052** 3053 Rubber hose; plastic hose; gasket materials

(P-9508)
TE CONNECTIVITY CORPORATION
Also Called: Raychem
305 Constitution Dr, Menlo Park
(94025-1110)
PHONE..................................650 361-3333
John McGraw, *Branch Mgr*
EMP: 350
SALES (corp-wide): 13.1B **Privately Held**
WEB: www.raychem.com
SIC: **3052** Plastic hose
HQ: Te Connectivity Corporation
1050 Westlakes Dr
Berwyn PA 19312
610 893-9800

(P-9509)
TECHNICAL HEATERS INC
Also Called: Thermolab
10959 Tuxford St, Sun Valley (91352-2626)
PHONE..................................818 361-7185
Bruce W Jones, *President*
EMP: 18
SQ FT: 35,000
SALES (est): 2.7MM **Privately Held**
WEB: www.techheat.com
SIC: **3052** Plastic hose; heater hose, rubber

(P-9510)
TK PAX INC
Also Called: P A X Industries
1561 Macarthur Blvd, Costa Mesa
(92626-1407)
PHONE..................................714 850-1330
Tom Kawaguchi, *President*
Randy Tamura, *Vice Pres*
Armando Martinez, *General Mgr*
▲ EMP: 30
SQ FT: 30,000
SALES (est): 5.9MM **Privately Held**
WEB: www.paxindustries.com
SIC: **3052** 3053 Rubber hose; plastic hose; gaskets, all materials

(P-9511)
TTI FLOOR CARE NORTH AMER INC
13055 Valley Blvd, Fontana (92335-2603)
PHONE..................................440 996-2802
Ross Verrocchi, *Manager*
EMP: 450
SALES (corp-wide): 6B **Privately Held**
SIC: **3052** 5722 Vacuum cleaner hose, plastic; vacuum cleaners
HQ: Tti Floor Care North America, Inc.
7005 Cochran Rd
Solon OH 44139

(P-9512)
WESTFLEX INC (PA)
Also Called: Western Hose & Gasket
325 W 30th St, National City (91950-7205)
PHONE..................................619 474-7400
Dixon G Legros, *President*

Paula Legros, *CFO*
Sarah Preciado, *Office Admin*
Landon Etchings, *Sales Staff*
▲ EMP: 30
SQ FT: 56,000
SALES (est): 6.7MM **Privately Held**
WEB: www.westflex.com
SIC: **3052** 3053 5085 Rubber & plastics hose & beltings; gaskets, packing & sealing devices; gaskets & sealing devices; gasket materials; gaskets, all materials; hose, belting & packing

---

3053 Gaskets, Packing & Sealing Devices

(P-9513)
A & D RUBBER PRODUCTS CO INC (PA)
1438 Bourbon St, Stockton (95204-2404)
PHONE..................................209 941-0100
Dale W Wolford, *President*
Ann Wolford, *Treasurer*
Bernie Aronofsky, *Opers Mgr*
Katherine Turner, *Receptionist*
▲ EMP: 28
SQ FT: 20,000
SALES (est): 4.2MM **Privately Held**
WEB: www.adrubber.com
SIC: **3053** 5085 2822 5169 Gaskets, packing & sealing devices; industrial supplies; synthetic rubber; synthetic resins, rubber & plastic materials

(P-9514)
A F C HYDRAULIC SEALS
4926 S Boyle Ave, Vernon (90058-3017)
PHONE..................................323 585-9110
Armando Cervantes, *President*
Felipe Cervantes, *Vice Pres*
EMP: 10
SQ FT: 7,000
SALES (est): 1.5MM **Privately Held**
SIC: **3053** 5199 Gaskets, all materials; rubber, crude

(P-9515)
ABLE INDUSTRIAL PRODUCTS INC (PA)
2006 S Baker Ave, Ontario (91761-7709)
PHONE..................................909 930-1585
Gilbert J Martinez, *CEO*
Gloria Martinez, *CFO*
Debbie Viramontes, *Admin Sec*
Tracy Rivas, *Purchasing*
Tyrone Dizon, *Sales Engr*
▲ EMP: 30 EST: 1974
SQ FT: 21,120
SALES (est): 9.7MM **Privately Held**
WEB: www.able123.com
SIC: **3053** 3069 5085 Gaskets, all materials; weather strip, sponge rubber; industrial supplies; hose, belting & packing; adhesives, tape & plasters; abrasives

(P-9516)
ADVANCED SEALING (DH)
15500 Blackburn Ave, Norwalk
(90650-6845)
PHONE..................................562 802-7782
Don Evans, *President*
Bill Clouse, *President*
Alan Stubblefield, *CFO*
Jeff Clouse, *Vice Pres*
Ann Cullen, *Controller*
▲ EMP: 64
SQ FT: 35,000
SALES: 19MM **Privately Held**
WEB: www.advseal.com
SIC: **3053** 3965 3052 2992 Gaskets, all materials; packing materials; fasteners; heater hose, rubber; lubricating oils; sealing compounds for pipe threads or joints; industrial valves; automatic regulating & control valves; pressure valves & regulators, industrial; steam traps
HQ: Eriks North America, Inc.
650 Washington Rd Ste 500
Pittsburgh PA 15228
800 937-9070

(P-9517)
AEROSPACE SEALS & GASKETS
1478 Davril Cir Ste A, Corona
(92880-6957)
PHONE..................................951 256-8380
Amparo Munoz, *Principal*
EMP: 30
SALES (est): 950K **Privately Held**
SIC: **3053** Gaskets, packing & sealing devices

(P-9518)
AIRSPACE SEAL AND GASKET CORP
1476 Davril Cir, Corona (92880)
PHONE..................................951 256-8380
Herb Menold, *President*
EMP: 26
SALES (est): 1.8MM **Privately Held**
SIC: **3053** Gaskets, packing & sealing devices

(P-9519)
AMERICAN GASKET & DIE COMPANY
2275 Paragon Dr, San Jose (95131-1307)
PHONE..................................408 441-6200
Kenneth J Cesena, *President*
EMP: 10 EST: 1976
SQ FT: 10,000
SALES (est): 1.5MM **Privately Held**
SIC: **3053** 3554 Gaskets, all materials; die cutting & stamping machinery, paper converting

(P-9520)
BRYANT RUBBER CORP (PA)
1112 Lomita Blvd, Harbor City
(90710-2205)
PHONE..................................310 530-2530
Steven Bryant, *Principal*
William J Bryant, *Shareholder*
Michael Arayata, *CFO*
Tracy Hunter, *Vice Pres*
Gloria Bryant, *Admin Sec*
EMP: 37
SQ FT: 60,000
SALES (est): 23.2MM **Privately Held**
WEB: www.bryantrubber.com
SIC: **3053** Gaskets, packing & sealing devices

(P-9521)
BRYANT RUBBER CORP
Also Called: Ingla Rubber Products
1083 W 251st St, Bellflower (90706)
PHONE..................................310 530-2530
Jack Klimek, *Branch Mgr*
EMP: 70
SALES (corp-wide): 23.2MM **Privately Held**
WEB: www.bryantrubber.com
SIC: **3053** 3061 Gaskets, packing & sealing devices; mechanical rubber goods
PA: Bryant Rubber Corp.
1112 Lomita Blvd
Harbor City CA 90710
310 530-2530

(P-9522)
CANNON GASKET INC
7784 Edison Ave, Fontana (92336-3635)
PHONE..................................909 355-1547
Billy Jr P Cannon, *President*
Candy Houle, *Admin Sec*
Travis Cannon, *Manager*
▲ EMP: 15
SQ FT: 10,000
SALES (est): 3.3MM **Privately Held**
WEB: www.cannongasket.com
SIC: **3053** Gaskets, all materials

(P-9523)
CHAVERS GASKET CORPORATION
23325 Del Lago Dr, Laguna Hills
(92653-1309)
PHONE..................................949 472-8118
Lloyd Chavers, *President*
Gino Roncelli, *Admin Sec*
EMP: 25
SQ FT: 13,000

PRODUCTS & SVCS

SALES (est): 4.8MM **Privately Held**
SIC: **3053** Gasket materials; gaskets, all
materials

(P-9524)
CIASONS INDUSTRIAL INC
1615 Boyd St, Santa Ana (92705-5103)
PHONE..................................714 259-0838
Paul Hsieh, *President*
Samuel Hsieh, *CFO*
Grace S P Hsieh, *Admin Sec*
▲ EMP: 30
SQ FT: 25,000
SALES (est): 4.7MM **Privately Held**
WEB: www.ciasons.com
SIC: **3053** 3563 Packing: steam engines,
pipe joints, air compressors, etc.; air &
gas compressors

(P-9525)
DAN-LOC GROUP LLC
Also Called: Dan-Loc Bolt & Gasket
20444 Tillman Ave, Carson (90746-3516)
PHONE..................................310 538-2822
Rudy Estrada, *Branch Mgr*
EMP: 100
SALES (corp-wide): 57.8MM **Privately
Held**
WEB: www.danloc.com
SIC: **3053** 3452 Gaskets & sealing de-
vices; bolts, nuts, rivets & washers
PA: Dan-Loc Group, Llc
725 N Drennan St
Houston TX 77003
713 356-3500

(P-9526)
DAR-KEN INC
Also Called: K & S Enterprises
10515 Rancho Rd, Adelanto (92301-3414)
PHONE..................................760 246-4010
Ken Mc Gilp, *Partner*
Darla Mc Gilp, *Partner*
Carl Kessler, *General Mgr*
Raquel Gonzales, *Office Mgr*
EMP: 32
SQ FT: 10,000
SALES (est): 4.2MM **Privately Held**
SIC: **3053** 3728 Gaskets, packing & seal-
ing devices; aircraft parts & equipment

(P-9527)
**ELASTOMER TECHNOLOGIES
INC**
Also Called: Roltec Gasket Manufacturing
255 Glider Cir, Corona (92880-2534)
PHONE..................................951 272-5820
Richard O Lester, *CEO*
Randall Lester, *President*
Joan R Lester, *Treasurer*
Randy Lester, *Executive*
EMP: 10
SQ FT: 7,000
SALES (est): 1.3MM **Privately Held**
SIC: **3053** Gasket materials

(P-9528)
**FERROTEC (USA)
CORPORATION**
Also Called: Ferrotec Temescal
4569 Las Positas Rd Ste C, Livermore
(94551-8865)
PHONE..................................925 371-4170
Michael Grivette, *Branch Mgr*
EMP: 50
SALES (corp-wide): 850.3MM **Privately
Held**
SIC: **3053** Gaskets & sealing devices
HQ: Ferrotec (Usa) Corporation
33 Constitution Dr
Bedford NH 03110
603 472-6800

(P-9529)
**FREUDENBERG-NOK GENERAL
PARTNR**
Also Called: International Seal Company
2041 E Wilshire Ave, Santa Ana
(92705-4726)
PHONE..................................714 834-0602
John Hudspeth, *Manager*
Sharon Jones, *Controller*
Edgar Torres, *Director*
EMP: 150
SQ FT: 28,928

SALES (corp-wide): 8.3B **Privately Held**
WEB: www.freudenberg-nok.com
SIC: **3053** Gaskets & sealing devices
HQ: Freudenberg-Nok General Partnership
47774 W Anchor Ct
Plymouth MI 48170
734 451-0020

(P-9530)
G F COLE CORPORATION (PA)
21735 S Western Ave, Torrance
(90501-3718)
PHONE..................................310 320-0601
Fritz Cole, *President*
Cathy Cole, *Vice Pres*
Elida Rodriguez, *Accountant*
▲ EMP: 19 EST: 1982
SQ FT: 26,000
SALES (est): 3.6MM **Privately Held**
WEB: www.gfcole.com
SIC: **3053** 3069 Gaskets, all materials;
hard rubber & molded rubber products

(P-9531)
GASKET MANUFACTURING CO
18001 S Main St, Gardena (90248-3530)
PHONE..................................310 217-5600
Maureen E Labor, *CEO*
Dewain R Butler, *Ch of Bd*
Vince Labor, *Vice Pres*
EMP: 33
SQ FT: 66,000
SALES (est): 7.1MM **Privately Held**
WEB: www.gasketmfg.com
SIC: **3053** Gaskets, all materials
PA: Gasket Associates Lp
18001 S Main St
Gardena CA 90248
-

(P-9532)
GASKET SPECIALTIES INC
Also Called: Rancho Cucamonga Division
8654 Helms Ave, Rancho Cucamonga
(91730-4520)
PHONE..................................909 987-4724
Louis Barbee, *Manager*
EMP: 10
SALES (corp-wide): 7.8MM **Privately
Held**
WEB: www.gsimfg.com
SIC: **3053** 5085 3452 Gaskets, all materi-
als; industrial supplies; bolts, nuts, rivets
& washers
PA: Gasket Specialties, Inc.
6200 Hollis St
Emeryville CA 94608
510 547-7955

(P-9533)
HAB ENTERPRISES INC
Also Called: Packaging Resource Group
15233 Ventura Blvd # 100, Sherman Oaks
(91403-2200)
PHONE..................................310 628-9000
Howard E Mallen, *President*
Chelly Ziegeler, *Vice Pres*
Cheresa Mallen, *Admin Sec*
EMP: 10
SQ FT: 3,000
SALES: 7.1MM **Privately Held**
SIC: **3053** 7336 Packing materials; pack-
age design

(P-9534)
HARBOR SEAL INCORPORATED
909 S Myrtle Ave, Monrovia (91016-3426)
PHONE..................................626 305-5754
Kunibert Gerhardt, *President*
Karen Edmonds, *Treasurer*
Marie Gerhardt, *Vice Pres*
EMP: 19
SQ FT: 10,000
SALES: 2MM **Privately Held**
WEB: www.harborsealinc.com
SIC: **3053** Gaskets, packing & sealing de-
vices

(P-9535)
**HUTCHINSON SEAL
CORPORATION (DH)**
Also Called: National O Rings
11634 Patton Rd, Downey (90241)
PHONE..................................248 375-4190
Christian Groche, *President*
Traci Lowe, *Cust Mgr*

Carol McDonald, *Manager*
▲ EMP: 430
SQ FT: 125,000
SALES (est): 64MM
SALES (corp-wide): 8.3B **Publicly Held**
SIC: **3053** Gaskets & sealing devices
HQ: Hutchinson Corporation
460 Fuller Ave Ne
Grand Rapids MI 49503
616 459-4541

(P-9536)
**INDUSTRIAL GASKET AND SUP
CO**
Also Called: Gasketfab Division
23018 Normandie Ave, Torrance
(90502-2691)
P.O. Box 4138 (90510-4138)
PHONE..................................310 530-1771
William P Hynes, *President*
Theresa Holmes, *Corp Secy*
Kevin P Treacy, *Vice Pres*
EMP: 23
SQ FT: 11,000
SALES (est): 4.4MM **Privately Held**
SIC: **3053** 5085 Gaskets & sealing de-
vices; gaskets; seals, industrial

(P-9537)
INERTECH SUPPLY INC
641 Monterey Pass Rd, Monterey Park
(91754-2418)
PHONE..................................626 282-2000
James Huang, *President*
Charlie C Miskell, *Vice Pres*
Bruce Wang, *Vice Pres*
Walter Lee, *Admin Sec*
Jean Okita, *Human Res Mgr*
▲ EMP: 75
SQ FT: 14,000
SALES (est): 10.8MM **Privately Held**
WEB: www.inertech.com
SIC: **3053** 2891 Gasket materials;
gaskets & sealing devices; gaskets; adhe-
sives & sealants

(P-9538)
J MILLER CO INC
Also Called: Miller Gasket Co
11537 Bradley Ave, San Fernando
(91340-2519)
PHONE..................................818 837-0181
Dennis D Miller, *President*
Elaine Miller, *Corp Secy*
Richard Miller, *General Mgr*
Ryan Young, *Manager*
▲ EMP: 35
SQ FT: 20,000
SALES (est): 6.2MM **Privately Held**
WEB: www.jmillerco.com
SIC: **3053** Gaskets, all materials

(P-9539)
KIRKHILL INC
300 E Cypress St, Brea (92821-4007)
PHONE..................................714 529-4901
Kevin McHenry, *Manager*
EMP: 700
SALES (corp-wide): 3.5B **Publicly Held**
SIC: **3053** 3728 2822 Gaskets, packing &
sealing devices; aircraft parts & equip-
ment; synthetic rubber
HQ: Kirkhill Inc.
300 E Cypress St
Brea CA 92821
714 529-4901

(P-9540)
KIRKHILL INC
Also Called: Haskon, Div of
300 E Cypress St, Brea (92821-4007)
PHONE..................................714 529-4901
Michael Harden, *Branch Mgr*
EMP: 700
SALES (corp-wide): 3.5B **Publicly Held**
WEB: www.kirkhill.com
SIC: **3053** 3728 2822 Gaskets, packing &
sealing devices; aircraft parts & equip-
ment; synthetic rubber
HQ: Kirkhill Inc.
300 E Cypress St
Brea CA 92821
714 529-4901

(P-9541)
LAMONS GASKET COMPANY
20009 S Rancho Way, Compton
(90220-6318)
PHONE..................................310 886-1133
Joe Medina, *Branch Mgr*
EMP: 18
SALES (corp-wide): 817.7MM **Publicly
Held**
SIC: **3053** 5085 Gaskets, all materials;
gaskets
HQ: Lamons Gasket Company
7300 Airport Blvd
Houston TX 77061
713 547-9527

(P-9542)
M G INDUSTRIES INC
Also Called: M G Industries Inc Gaskts
1427 W 16th St, Long Beach (90813-1399)
PHONE..................................562 436-9095
Barry Ferency, *President*
EMP: 19
SQ FT: 10,000
SALES (est): 2.3MM **Privately Held**
SIC: **3053** 3469 Gasket materials; metal
stampings

(P-9543)
MCMILLAN - HENDRYX INC
Also Called: American Seals West
3924 Starlite Dr Ste B, Ceres (95307-9766)
P.O. Box 1104 (95307-1104)
PHONE..................................209 538-2300
Gary Hendryx, *President*
EMP: 19
SQ FT: 10,000
SALES (est): 2.9MM **Privately Held**
WEB: www.americansealswest.com
SIC: **3053** Gaskets & sealing devices

(P-9544)
**MORGAN POLYMER SEALS LLC
(PA)**
2475 A Paseo De Las, San Diego (92154)
PHONE..................................858 679-4946
Kevin Morgan, *President*
Ed Ditz, *Controller*
Mark Conlee, *Sales Mgr*
▲ EMP: 22
SQ FT: 33,500
SALES: 23.5MM **Privately Held**
SIC: **3053** Gaskets & sealing devices

(P-9545)
PACIFIC DIE CUT INDUSTRIES
3399 Arden Rd, Hayward (94545-3924)
PHONE..................................510 732-8103
Mohammed M Behnam, *CEO*
▲ EMP: 73
SQ FT: 30,000
SALES (est): 16.4MM **Privately Held**
WEB: www.pacificdiecut.com
SIC: **3053** Gaskets & sealing devices

(P-9546)
**PACIFIC STATES FELT MFG CO
INC**
23850 Clawiter Rd Ste 20, Hayward
(94545-1723)
P.O. Box 5024 (94540-5024)
PHONE..................................510 783-2357
Walter L Perscheid Jr, *CEO*
Kristin Gudjohnsen, *General Mgr*
Robert Perscheid, *General Mgr*
EMP: 16
SQ FT: 23,000
SALES (est): 3.2MM **Privately Held**
WEB: www.pacificstatesfelt.com
SIC: **3053** 5085 Gaskets & sealing de-
vices; industrial supplies

(P-9547)
PARCO INC (PA)
1801 S Archibald Ave, Ontario
(91761-7677)
PHONE..................................909 947-2200
Adam Morrison Burgener, *President*
Louis W Burgener, *Ch of Bd*
Angela L Garcia, *Vice Pres*
W Carl Horn, *Vice Pres*
▲ EMP: 127
SQ FT: 154,000

▲ = Import ▼=Export
◆ =Import/Export

SALES (est): 34MM **Privately Held**
WEB: www.parcoinc.com
SIC: 3053 Gaskets, all materials

(P-9548)
PERFORMANCE SEALING INC
Also Called: PSI
1821 Langley Ave, Irvine (92614-5623)
PHONE..........................714 662-5918
Greg Pritchett, *President*
John Schroeder, *Engineer*
Johann Vanbel, *Engineer*
Lauren Pritchett, *Human Resources*
Larry Hicks, *Prdtn Mgr*
EMP: 12
SQ FT: 4,000
SALES (est): 4MM **Privately Held**
WEB: www.psiseal.com
SIC: 3053 Gaskets & sealing devices

(P-9549)
POLYMER CONCEPTS TECHNOLOGIES
13522 Manhasset Rd, Apple Valley
(92308-5790)
P.O. Box 2738 (92307-0052)
PHONE..........................760 240-4999
Rob Girman, *President*
Dean Anderson, *CEO*
Juli Hunzeker, *Info Tech Mgr*
EMP: 15
SQ FT: 3,000
SALES (est): 1.8MM **Privately Held**
WEB: www.polymerconcepts.com
SIC: 3053 Gaskets & sealing devices

(P-9550)
REAL SEAL CO INC
Also Called: Real Seal
1971 Don Lee Pl, Escondido (92029-1141)
PHONE..........................760 743-7263
Patrick Thomas Tobin, *CEO*
Rose Ann Tobin, *Corp Secy*
▲ EMP: 25
SQ FT: 22,000
SALES (est): 4.9MM **Privately Held**
WEB: www.real-seal.com
SIC: 3053 5085 Oil seals, rubber; industrial supplies

(P-9551)
ROETTELE INDUSTRIES
15485 Dupont Ave, Chino (91710-7605)
PHONE..........................909 606-8252
Mark Roettele, *President*
Maurice Roettele, *Ch of Bd*
Randal Roettele, *Treasurer*
Lon Roettele, *Vice Pres*
▲ EMP: 19
SQ FT: 15,000
SALES (est): 3.9MM **Privately Held**
WEB: www.roetteleindustries.com
SIC: 3053 5085 Gaskets, packing & sealing devices; industrial supplies

(P-9552)
ROMAN GLOBAL RESOURCES INC
1027 Calle Trepadora # 2, San Clemente
(92673-6290)
PHONE..........................949 276-4100
Val Roman, *President*
Adriana Roman, *Marketing Staff*
▲ EMP: 10
SQ FT: 3,500
SALES (est): 2.5MM **Privately Held**
WEB: www.romanseals.com
SIC: 3053 Gaskets, all materials

(P-9553)
RPM PRODUCTS INC (PA)
Also Called: Rubber Plastic & Metal Pdts
23272 Arroyo Vis, Rcho STA Marg
(92688-2610)
PHONE..........................949 888-8543
Mark Paolella, *President*
Suzanne Paolella, *Corp Secy*
▲ EMP: 35
SQ FT: 30,000
SALES (est): 22.5MM **Privately Held**
WEB: www.rpmproducts.com
SIC: 3053 3089 5085 Gaskets & sealing devices; injection molding of plastics; molding primary plastic; gaskets & seals

(P-9554)
SCE GASKETS INC
24927 Avenue Tibbitts F, Valencia
(91355-1284)
PHONE..........................661 728-9200
Ryan Hunter, *President*
Aaron Hunter, *Vice Pres*
Caleb Hunter, *Vice Pres*
▼ EMP: 10
SQ FT: 6,000
SALES (est): 1.7MM **Privately Held**
WEB: www.scegaskets.com
SIC: 3053 Gaskets & sealing devices

(P-9555)
SCOT GASKET COMPANY INC
Also Called: So Calif Oil Tool Co
8220 Atlantic Ave, Cudahy (90201-5806)
P.O. Box 30, Bell (90201-0030)
PHONE..........................323 560-6600
William Bill Hynes, *President*
EMP: 11 EST: 1936
SQ FT: 9,000
SALES (est): 1.4MM **Privately Held**
SIC: 3053 Gaskets, all materials

(P-9556)
SEAL SCIENCE INC (PA)
Also Called: S S I
17131 Daimler St, Irvine (92614-5508)
PHONE..........................949 253-3130
Frederick E Tuliper, *CEO*
Patricia Tuliper, *CFO*
▲ EMP: 68 EST: 1985
SQ FT: 25,000
SALES (est): 10.8MM **Privately Held**
WEB: www.sealscience.com
SIC: 3053 3089 3061 Gaskets & sealing devices; injection molding of plastics; mechanical rubber goods

(P-9557)
SEALING CORPORATION
7353 Greenbush Ave B, North Hollywood
(91605-4004)
PHONE..........................818 765-7327
John Patterson, *President*
Adrian Patterson, *Corp Secy*
Barry Lew, *Office Mgr*
▲ EMP: 15
SQ FT: 2,600
SALES (est): 2.5MM **Privately Held**
WEB: www.selcoseal.com
SIC: 3053 Gaskets & sealing devices

(P-9558)
SEWING COLLECTION INC
3113 E 26th St, Vernon (90058-8006)
PHONE..........................323 264-2223
Touraj Tour, *President*
Houshang Tour, *Vice Pres*
▲ EMP: 100
SQ FT: 135,000
SALES (est): 4.2MM **Privately Held**
SIC: 3053 5199 4953 Packing materials; packaging materials; recycling, waste materials

(P-9559)
SPIRA MANUFACTURING CORP
650 Jessie St, San Fernando (91340-2233)
PHONE..........................818 764-8222
George M Kunkel, *President*
Michael Kunkel, *General Mgr*
Bonnie Paul, *Admin Sec*
Wendy Kunkel, *Director*
EMP: 30
SQ FT: 15,000
SALES (est): 6.4MM **Privately Held**
WEB: www.spira-emi.com
SIC: 3053 Gaskets, all materials

(P-9560)
SWABPLUS INC
9669 Hermosa Ave, Rancho Cucamonga
(91730-5813)
PHONE..........................909 987-7898
Tom Y Lee, *CEO*
Garry Tsaur, *President*
Eddy C Wan, *COO*
▲ EMP: 41
SALES (est): 7MM **Privately Held**
WEB: www.swabplus.com
SIC: 3053 Packing materials

(P-9561)
TILLEY MANUFACTURING CO INC (PA)
Also Called: Precision Graphics
2734 Spring St, Redwood City
(94063-3524)
P.O. Box 5766 (94063-0766)
PHONE..........................650 365-3598
Owen Conley, *President*
Judy Meer, *VP Finance*
Al Chandler, *Manager*
▲ EMP: 26
SQ FT: 35,000
SALES (est): 7.5MM **Privately Held**
WEB: www.tilleymfg.com
SIC: 3053 3411 3634 3312 Gaskets, all materials; food containers, metal; beverage cans, metal: except beer; urns, electric: household; tool & die steel & alloys; metal stampings; pressed & blown glass

(P-9562)
TRELLEBORG SEALING SOLUTIONS E
Also Called: TSS El Segundo
2051 E Maple Ave, El Segundo
(90245-5009)
PHONE..........................310 322-8030
Kerry Ott, *Controller*
Linda Muroski, *President*
Tom Potosky, *Vice Pres*
Robert White, *Admin Sec*
EMP: 88 EST: 2017
SALES (est): 2.9MM
SALES (corp-wide): 3.7B **Privately Held**
SIC: 3053 Gaskets & sealing devices
HQ: Trelleborg Sealing Solutions Us, Inc.
2531 Bremer Rd
Fort Wayne IN 46803
260 749-9631

(P-9563)
WEST COAST GASKET CO
300 Ranger Ave, Brea (92821-6217)
PHONE..........................714 869-0123
Louis Russell, *Principal*
Jean Grey, *CEO*
Angela Steele, *Executive*
Christine Geraghty, *Human Res Mgr*
Charlene Assistant, *Purch Mgr*
EMP: 75
SQ FT: 50,000
SALES (est): 16.1MM **Privately Held**
SIC: 3053 3061 3469 5085 Gaskets, all materials; mechanical rubber goods; metal stampings; industrial supplies

---

3061 Molded, Extruded & Lathe-Cut Rubber Mechanical Goods

(P-9564)
CIANNA MEDICAL INC
6 Journey Ste 125, Aliso Viejo
(92656-5319)
PHONE..........................949 360-0059
Jill Anderson, *President*
Christopher F Serocke, *COO*
Gordon Busenbark, *CFO*
Sheri McCormick, *Business Mgr*
EMP: 68
SALES (est): 16.3MM **Privately Held**
SIC: 3061 Medical & surgical rubber tubing (extruded & lathe-cut)

(P-9565)
CRM CO LLC (PA)
Also Called: C R M
1301 Dove St Ste 940, Newport Beach
(92660-2483)
PHONE..........................949 263-9100
H Barry Takallou, *CEO*
Shepard Ansley,
Dr Hamid Malakooti,
Bob Jull, *Mng Member*
▲ EMP: 44
SALES (est): 11MM **Privately Held**
SIC: 3061 Mechanical rubber goods

(P-9566)
DYNATECT RO-LAB INC
8830 W Linne Rd, Tracy (95304-9109)
P.O. Box 450 (95378-0450)
PHONE..........................262 786-1500
Henry Wright, *General Mgr*
Marina Wright, *Corp Secy*
John Dodge, *Vice Pres*
▲ EMP: 50 EST: 1971
SQ FT: 65,000
SALES (est): 10.1MM
SALES (corp-wide): 1.8B **Privately Held**
WEB: www.rolabamerican.com
SIC: 3061 3052 3069 3089 Mechanical rubber goods; rubber & plastics hose & beltings; hard rubber & molded rubber products; plastic hardware & building products
HQ: Dynatect Manufacturing, Inc.
2300 S Calhoun Rd
New Berlin WI 53151
262 786-1500

(P-9567)
ICAD INC
345 Potrero Ave, Sunnyvale (94085-4115)
PHONE..........................408 419-2300
Deryl Banks, *Branch Mgr*
EMP: 69
SALES (corp-wide): 28.1MM **Publicly Held**
SIC: 3061 Medical & surgical rubber tubing (extruded & lathe-cut)
PA: Icad, Inc.
98 Spit Brook Rd Ste 100
Nashua NH 03062
603 882-5200

(P-9568)
J FLYING MANUFACTURING
11000 Brimhall Rd Ste E, Bakersfield
(93312-3022)
PHONE..........................805 839-9229
Dennis Walrath, *President*
Sindy Walrath, *Vice Pres*
EMP: 20
SALES (est): 300K **Privately Held**
SIC: 3061 3599 Mechanical rubber goods; amusement park equipment

(P-9569)
MIKRON PRODUCTS INC
2600 Homestead Pl, Compton
(90220-5610)
PHONE..........................323 245-1251
Nicholas Carone, *President*
Palma Carone, *Corp Secy*
Ed Duran, *Principal*
EMP: 100
SQ FT: 20,000
SALES (est): 10MM **Privately Held**
WEB: www.mikronproducts.com
SIC: 3061 Mechanical rubber goods

(P-9570)
PAC-WEST RUBBER PRODUCTS LLC
120 Venture St, San Marcos (92078-4353)
P.O. Box 2733 (92079-2733)
PHONE..........................760 891-0911
Nickolas R Duvall,
Kim P Duvall,
EMP: 12
SQ FT: 6,700
SALES (est): 1.7MM **Privately Held**
SIC: 3061 Mechanical rubber goods

(P-9571)
PERFORMANCE POLYMER TECH LLC
8801 Washington Blvd # 109, Roseville
(95678-6200)
PHONE..........................916 677-1414
Lonnie Wimberly, *President*
Ian Macauley, *Vice Pres*
Martha Wimberly, *Vice Pres*
Paul Parenti, *Controller*
Gary Wimberly, *Purch Mgr*
EMP: 35
SQ FT: 37,000
SALES (est): 7.2MM **Privately Held**
WEB: www.pptech.com
SIC: 3061 3069 Mechanical rubber goods; molded rubber products

PRODUCTS & SVCS

(P-9572)
R & R RUBBER MOLDING INC
2444 Loma Ave, South El Monte
(91733-1416)
P.O. Box 3533 (91733-0533)
PHONE..................................626 575-8105
S Castillo III, *Vice Pres*
Richard Patrick Norman, *President*
Sixto Castillo III, *Vice Pres*
Ken Hanke, *QC Mgr*
Lupe Frausto-Perez,
EMP: 35
SQ FT: 6,100
SALES (est): 2.4MM **Privately Held**
WEB: www.rrrubber.com
SIC: 3061 Mechanical rubber goods

(P-9573)
R D RUBBER TECHNOLOGY CORP
12870 Florence Ave, Santa Fe Springs
(90670-4540)
PHONE..................................562 941-4800
Walter V Hopkins Jr, *President*
Rosanne Dukowitz, *Exec VP*
Waler Hopkins, *CTO*
Britta Schesnack, *Clerk*
EMP: 27
SQ FT: 15,600
SALES (est): 5MM **Privately Held**
SIC: 3061 Mechanical rubber goods

(P-9574)
RUBBERCRAFT CORP CAL LTD (DH)
Also Called: Rubber Teck Division
3701 E Conant St, Long Beach
(90808-1783)
PHONE..................................562 354-2800
Marc Sanders, *CEO*
Eric Sanders, *CEO*
EMP: 238
SQ FT: 40,000
SALES (est): 31.5MM
SALES (corp-wide): 182.4MM **Privately Held**
WEB: www.rubbercraft.com
SIC: 3061 Appliance rubber goods (mechanical)
HQ: Sanders Industries
3701 E Conant St
Long Beach CA 90808
562 354-2920

(P-9575)
SANDEE PLASTIC EXTRUSIONS
14932 Gwenchris Ct, Paramount
(90723-3423)
PHONE..................................323 979-4020
Thomas Kunkel, *President*
EMP: 22
SQ FT: 14,000
SALES (est): 6.5MM
SALES (corp-wide): 15.8MM **Privately Held**
SIC: 3061 Medical & surgical rubber tubing (extruded & lathe-cut)
PA: Sandee Manufacturing Co.
10520 Waveland Ave
Franklin Park IL 60131
847 671-1335

(P-9576)
WESTLAND TECHNOLOGIES INC
107 S Riverside Dr, Modesto (95354-4004)
PHONE..................................800 877-7734
John Grizzard, *President*
Jan Hesser, *Executive*
Tegan Moncrief, *General Mgr*
Jennifer Stanford, *General Mgr*
Whitney Wells, *Info Tech Mgr*
EMP: 60
SQ FT: 117,000
SALES (est): 26.8MM
SALES (corp-wide): 685.7MM **Publicly Held**
WEB: www.westlandtech.com
SIC: 3061 3069 Mechanical rubber goods; flooring, rubber: tile or sheet
PA: Esco Technologies Inc.
9900 Clayton Rd Ste A
Saint Louis MO 63124
314 213-7200

3069 Fabricated Rubber Prdts, NEC

(P-9577)
3-D POLYMERS
13026 S Normandie Ave, Gardena
(90249-2126)
PHONE..................................310 324-7694
David Johnson, *President*
Kathleen Johnson, *Corp Secy*
EMP: 15
SQ FT: 11,000
SALES: 850K **Privately Held**
WEB: www.3-dpolymers.com
SIC: 3069 3089 3061 Hard rubber & molded rubber products; plastic processing; mechanical rubber goods

(P-9578)
3M COMPANY
1601 S Shamrock Ave, Monrovia
(91016-4248)
PHONE..................................626 358-0136
Bob Palmer, *Plant Mgr*
EMP: 21
SALES (corp-wide): 31.6B **Publicly Held**
WEB: www.mmm.com
SIC: 3069 Rubber coated fabrics & clothing
PA: 3m Company
3m Center
Saint Paul MN 55144
651 733-1110

(P-9579)
A B BOYD CO (PA)
Also Called: Boyd Corporation
600 S Mcclure Rd, Modesto (95357-0520)
PHONE..................................209 236-1111
Mitchell Aiello, *President*
Eric Struik, *CFO*
▲ **EMP:** 23
SQ FT: 100,000
SALES (est): 234.6MM **Privately Held**
WEB: www.boydcorp.com
SIC: 3069 2822 Hard rubber & molded rubber products; rubber automotive products; synthetic rubber

(P-9580)
ABBA ROLLER LLC (DH)
1351 E Philadelphia St, Ontario
(91761-5719)
PHONE..................................909 947-1244
Jeffrey Garvens,
▲ **EMP:** 20
SQ FT: 4,000
SALES (est): 2.4MM
SALES (corp-wide): 11.1MM **Privately Held**
SIC: 3069 Roll coverings, rubber
HQ: Electro-Coatings, Inc.
216 Baywood St
Houston TX 77011
713 923-5935

(P-9581)
ABBA RUBBER INTERNATIONAL INC
1351 E Philadelphia St, Ontario
(91761-5719)
P.O. Box 4030 (91761-1014)
PHONE..................................909 947-1244
Robert Mc Donald, *CEO*
EMP: 55 **EST:** 1958
SQ FT: 39,000
SALES (est): 513.3K **Privately Held**
WEB: www.abbarubber.com
SIC: 3069 Rolls, solid or covered rubber; molded rubber products

(P-9582)
ACE CALENDERING ENTERPRISES (PA)
Also Called: Midwest Rubber
1311 S Wanamaker Ave, Ontario
(91761-2237)
PHONE..................................909 937-1901
Gary Holcomb, *CEO*
Fred Rodriguez, *President*
Bob Rich, *Vice Pres*
EMP: 16

SALES (est): 1.8MM **Privately Held**
WEB: www.acecalender.com
SIC: 3069 Sheets, hard rubber

(P-9583)
ACUTEK ADHESIVE SPECIALTIES
540 N Oak St, Inglewood (90302-2985)
PHONE..................................310 419-0190
Jerry Muchin, *President*
Karen Kline, *Vice Pres*
EMP: 45
SQ FT: 25,000
SALES (est): 5.9MM **Privately Held**
WEB: www.acutek.com
SIC: 3069 Medical sundries, rubber

(P-9584)
ADVANCED PAPER FORMING LLC
541 W Rincon St, Corona (92880-2000)
P.O. Box 2679 (92878-2679)
PHONE..................................714 738-0300
EMP: 14
SQ FT: 16,000
SALES (est): 1.3MM **Privately Held**
SIC: 3069

(P-9585)
ALASCO RUBBER & PLASTICS CORP
1250 Enos Ave, Sebastopol (95472-4454)
PHONE..................................707 823-5270
EMP: 17
SALES (est): 982.2K
SALES (corp-wide): 1.8MM **Privately Held**
SIC: 3069
PA: Alasco Rubber & Plastic Corp
3432 Roberto Ct
San Luis Obispo CA 93401
805 543-3008

(P-9586)
AMES RUBBER MFG CO INC
Also Called: Ames Industrial
4516 Brazil St, Los Angeles (90039-1002)
PHONE..................................818 240-9313
Timothy L Brown, *CEO*
Pat Brown, *Corp Secy*
Susie Sandoval, *Lab Dir*
Maria Lepe, *Finance Mgr*
Chris Dittes, *Opers Mgr*
▲ **EMP:** 30
SQ FT: 20,000
SALES (est): 5.7MM **Privately Held**
WEB: www.armcocatalog.com
SIC: 3069 Medical & laboratory rubber sundries & related products; mechanical rubber goods

(P-9587)
APNEA SCIENCES CORPORATION
17 Brownsbury Rd, Laguna Niguel
(92677-9382)
PHONE..................................949 226-4421
James Fallon, *President*
EMP: 17
SALES (est): 1.4MM **Privately Held**
SIC: 3069 Medical & laboratory rubber sundries & related products

(P-9588)
ARROYO SECO RACQUET CLUB
920 Lohman Ln, South Pasadena
(91030-2906)
PHONE..................................323 258-4178
Chandler Thomas, *Manager*
EMP: 10
SALES (est): 721.5K **Privately Held**
SIC: 3069 7999 Balls, rubber; tennis courts, outdoor/indoor: non-membership

(P-9589)
ATLAS SPONGE RUBBER COMPANY
114 E Pomona Ave, Monrovia
(91016-4638)
PHONE..................................626 359-5391
Tom Johnston, *President*
Greg Johnston, *General Mgr*
EMP: 19
SQ FT: 30,000

SALES: 1.5MM **Privately Held**
SIC: 3069 Sponge rubber & sponge rubber products; molded rubber products

(P-9590)
ATM PLUS INC
Also Called: Fast Undercar
2232 Verus St Ste F, San Diego
(92154-4706)
PHONE..................................619 575-3278
Wally Hussannali, *President*
EMP: 14
SALES (est): 2.3MM **Privately Held**
SIC: 3069 Brake linings, rubber

(P-9591)
AVALCO INC
Also Called: Avalco Valves Inc.
2029 Verdugo Blvd Ste 710, Montrose
(91020-1626)
PHONE..................................310 676-3057
Alexander Armond, *CEO*
▲ **EMP:** 12
SQ FT: 10,000
SALES (est): 561.7K **Privately Held**
SIC: 3069 Industrial valves

(P-9592)
B CUMMING COMPANY A CORP
9990 Glenoaks Blvd Ste B, Sun Valley
(91352-1081)
PHONE..................................818 504-2571
David B Mazer, *President*
Neftali Martinez, *Vice Pres*
EMP: 10
SQ FT: 6,500
SALES: 1MM **Privately Held**
SIC: 3069 Toys, rubber

(P-9593)
BAND-IT RUBBER COMPANY INC
1711 N Delilah St, Corona (92879-1865)
PHONE..................................951 735-5072
Bernard Spangler, *President*
▲ **EMP:** 10
SQ FT: 20,000
SALES (est): 1.4MM **Privately Held**
SIC: 3069 Rubber bands

(P-9594)
BANDAG LICENSING CORPORATION
2500 E Thompson St, Long Beach
(90805-1836)
P.O. Box 140990, Nashville TN (37214-0990)
PHONE..................................562 531-3880
Martin G Carver, *CEO*
EMP: 57
SQ FT: 310,000
SALES (est): 5.8MM
SALES (corp-wide): 32.5B **Privately Held**
SIC: 3069 Reclaimed rubber & specialty rubber compounds
HQ: Bridgestone Bandag, Llc
2000 Bandag Dr
Muscatine IA 52761
563 262-2511

(P-9595)
BARGER & ASSOCIATES
Also Called: Advance Fabrication
140b Mast St, Morgan Hill (95037-5113)
PHONE..................................408 779-5424
Michael Barger, *President*
Mary S Barger, *Corp Secy*
Maria Plascencia, *Prdtn Mgr*
EMP: 33
SQ FT: 11,000
SALES (est): 5.9MM **Privately Held**
WEB: www.advancefabrication.com
SIC: 3069 3842 Orthopedic sundries, molded rubber; braces, orthopedic; trusses, orthopedic & surgical

(P-9596)
BURKE INDUSTRIES INC (HQ)
2250 S 10th St, San Jose (95112-4197)
PHONE..................................408 297-3500
Robert Pitman, *President*
Edward Reginelli, *CFO*
Lucy Ulrich, *Officer*
Paul Titcomb, *Planning Mgr*
Matthew Okashima, *Planning*
◆ **EMP:** 203 **EST:** 1945

▲ = Import ▼=Export
◆ =Import/Export

SQ FT: 115,930
SALES (est): 206MM
SALES (corp-wide): 775.9MM **Privately Held**
WEB: www.burkeind.com
SIC: **3069** 2822 2821 3061 Flooring, rubber: tile or sheet; molded rubber products; polyethylene, chlorosulfonated (hypalon); silicone rubbers; plastics materials & resins; silicone resins; mechanical rubber goods
PA: Mannington Mills Inc.
75 Mannington Mills Rd
Salem NJ 08079
856 935-3000

(P-9597)
CA-WA CORP
1360 W 1st St, Pomona (91766-1305)
PHONE..................................909 868-0630
Jim Sicilia, *CEO*
▲ EMP: 30
SQ FT: 10,000
SALES: 1.5MM **Privately Held**
SIC: **3069** Medical & laboratory rubber sundries & related products

(P-9598)
CALIFOAM PRODUCTS INC
10775 Silicon Ave, Montclair (91763-6022)
PHONE..................................909 364-1600
Javier Juarez, *CEO*
▲ EMP: 12
SQ FT: 24,000
SALES (est): 2.1MM **Privately Held**
WEB: www.califoamproducts.com
SIC: **3069** 5199 Foam rubber; packaging materials

(P-9599)
CALIFORNIA GASKET AND RBR CORP (PA)
533 W Collins Ave, Orange (92867-5509)
PHONE..................................310 323-4250
Scott H Franklin, *Vice Pres*
EMP: 40 EST: 1942
SQ FT: 51,000
SALES (est): 5.3MM **Privately Held**
WEB: www.calgasket.com
SIC: **3069** 3053 3469 3061 Molded rubber products; rubber automotive products; gaskets, packing & sealing devices; metal stampings; appliance rubber goods (mechanical)

(P-9600)
CENTURY RUBBER COMPANY INC
719 Rooster Dr, Bakersfield (93307-9807)
PHONE..................................661 366-7009
Steve Cozzetto, *President*
EMP: 13
SQ FT: 7,500
SALES (est): 2.3MM **Privately Held**
WEB: www.centuryrubber.com
SIC: **3069** Molded rubber products

(P-9601)
CONTINENTAL AMERICAN CORP
Also Called: Pioneer Balloon Co
1333 S Hillward Ave, West Covina (91791-3936)
PHONE..................................626 964-0164
Darlene Todorovich, *Principal*
EMP: 75
SALES (corp-wide): 228.7MM **Privately Held**
WEB: www.qualatex.com
SIC: **3069** 2759 5092 Balloons, advertising & toy: rubber; commercial printing; balloons, novelty
PA: Continental American Corporation
5000 E 29th St N
Wichita KS 67220
316 685-2266

(P-9602)
COOPER CROUSE-HINDS LLC
Also Called: Garry Electronics
705 W Ventura Blvd, Camarillo (93010)
PHONE..................................805 484-0543
Alexander M Cutler, *CEO*
EMP: 135 **Privately Held**

SIC: **3069** 3678 Hard rubber & molded rubber products; electronic connectors
HQ: Cooper Crouse-Hinds, Llc
1201 Wolf St
Syracuse NY 13208
315 477-7000

(P-9603)
COOPER CROUSE-HINDS LLC
Also Called: Wpi Salem Division
750 W Ventura Blvd, Camarillo (93010-8382)
PHONE..................................805 484-0543
Alexander M Cutler, *Ch of Bd*
EMP: 140 **Privately Held**
SIC: **3069** 3679 Hard rubber & molded rubber products; electronic circuits
HQ: Cooper Crouse-Hinds, Llc
1201 Wolf St
Syracuse NY 13208
315 477-7000

(P-9604)
CRICKET COMPANY LLC
68 Leveroni Ct Ste 200, Novato (94949-5769)
PHONE..................................415 475-4150
Wayne Clark, *Mng Member*
Mark Sawyer, *CFO*
Leticia Chavez, *Office Mgr*
▲ EMP: 25
SALES (est): 4.2MM **Privately Held**
WEB: www.cricketco.com
SIC: **3069** Capes, vulcanized rubber or rubberized fabric; brushes, rubber

(P-9605)
CYPRESS SPONGE RUBBER PRODUCTS
Also Called: Rubberite Cypress Sponge Rubbe
301 Goetz Ave, Santa Ana (92707-3707)
PHONE..................................714 546-6464
Barbara Ballou, *President*
Terry Brooks, *Vice Pres*
Dona Brooks, *Office Mgr*
Line Hennes, *Administration*
Ed Dewberry, *Sales Associate*
▲ EMP: 12
SQ FT: 25,000
SALES (est): 920K **Privately Held**
WEB: www.cypresssponge.com
SIC: **3069** Sheeting, rubber or rubberized fabric; sponge rubber & sponge rubber products

(P-9606)
DA/PRO RUBBER INC
28635 Braxton Ave, Valencia (91355-4112)
PHONE..................................661 775-6290
Harold Sosner, *Manager*
EMP: 100
SQ FT: 31,845
SALES (corp-wide): 69.2MM **Privately Held**
WEB: www.daprorubber.com
SIC: **3069** 3061 Molded rubber products; mechanical rubber goods
PA: Da/Pro Rubber, Inc.
601 N Poplar Ave
Broken Arrow OK 74012
918 258-9386

(P-9607)
DEVOLL RUBBER MFG GROUP INC
Also Called: Devoll Rubber Mfg Group
18626 Phantom St, Victorville (92394-7929)
PHONE..................................760 246-0142
John De Voll, *CEO*
Amanda De Voll, *Office Mgr*
EMP: 14
SQ FT: 8,000
SALES (est): 2.6MM **Privately Held**
WEB: www.devollrubber.com
SIC: **3069** Medical & laboratory rubber sundries & related products

(P-9608)
DURO FLEX RUBBER PRODUCTS INC
13215 Lakeland Rd, Santa Fe Springs (90670-4522)
PHONE..................................562 946-5533

John A Lozano, *President*
EMP: 11
SQ FT: 6,000
SALES (est): 1.8MM **Privately Held**
WEB: www.duroflexrubber.com
SIC: **3069** Molded rubber products

(P-9609)
DURO ROLLER COMPANY INC
Also Called: Cal State Rubber
13006 Park St, Santa Fe Springs (90670-4098)
PHONE..................................562 944-8856
Maureen Wayda, *President*
Julie Wayda, *Vice Pres*
▲ EMP: 16 EST: 1973
SQ FT: 8,100
SALES (est): 3MM **Privately Held**
WEB: www.duroroller.com
SIC: **3069** 3599 Molded rubber products; rubber rolls & roll coverings; machine & other job shop work

(P-9610)
ENVIRNMNTAL MLDING CNCEPTS LLC
Also Called: E M C
14050 Day St, Moreno Valley (92553-9106)
PHONE..................................951 214-6596
Sarkis Beudjekian, *Mng Member*
Anne Beudjikian,
◆ EMP: 15
SQ FT: 15,000
SALES (est): 2.9MM **Privately Held**
WEB: www.emcmolding.com
SIC: **3069** Reclaimed rubber & specialty rubber compounds

(P-9611)
ESTCO ENTERPRISES INC
1549 Simpson Way, Escondido (92029-1203)
PHONE..................................760 489-8745
Joshua Taylor, *President*
Judith Taylor, *Corp Secy*
Monica Ohlandt, *Admin Asst*
Steve Lothspeich, *Sales Staff*
EMP: 10
SQ FT: 10,000
SALES (est): 1.8MM **Privately Held**
WEB: www.estcoenterprises.com
SIC: **3069** Bags, rubber or rubberized fabric

(P-9612)
EVANTEC CORPORATION
Also Called: Evantec Scientific
4007 W Segerstrom Ave, Santa Ana (92704-6326)
PHONE..................................949 632-2811
Ann Nelson, *President*
Evelyn Bogner, *Corp Secy*
Paul Bogner, *Vice Pres*
EMP: 10
SQ FT: 18,000
SALES (est): 1.8MM **Privately Held**
WEB: www.evantec.com
SIC: **3069** 8742 Linings, vulcanizable rubber; business consultant; new business start-up consultant

(P-9613)
EZ INFLATABLES INC
1410 Vineland Ave, Baldwin Park (91706-5813)
PHONE..................................626 480-9100
Edgar Abraamyan, *President*
Eddie Abraamyan, *General Mgr*
Art Arakelyan, *Manager*
▲ EMP: 30 EST: 2007
SQ FT: 12,000
SALES: 1MM **Privately Held**
SIC: **3069** Balloons, advertising & toy: rubber

(P-9614)
FALCON WATERFREE TECH LLC (HQ)
2255 Barry Ave, Los Angeles (90064-1401)
PHONE..................................310 209-7250
James Krug,
Paul Liang, *Vice Pres*
Jake Jaskolski, *Sales Mgr*
Andrea Chase, *Marketing Staff*
Mariana Hodges, *Marketing Staff*
▼ EMP: 20 EST: 2000

SALES (est): 1.6MM
SALES (corp-wide): 12.1MM **Privately Held**
WEB: www.falconwaterfree.com
SIC: **3069** Pump sleeves, rubber
PA: Management Kingsley Llc Mapleton
9952 Santa Monica Blvd
Beverly Hills CA 90212
310 282-0780

(P-9615)
GAGNE-MULFORD ENTERPRISES
2490 Almond Ave, Concord (94520)
PHONE..................................925 671-7434
John W Mulford, *CEO*
EMP: 19 EST: 2013
SALES (est): 2.3MM **Privately Held**
SIC: **3069** Plumbers' rubber goods

(P-9616)
GIBBS PLASTIC & RUBBER CO
Also Called: Mint Grips
3959 Teal Ct, Benicia (94510-1212)
PHONE..................................707 746-7300
Lee Michels, *Partner*
Waunell Betker, *Technology*
Terrisa Whihengeon, *Manager*
EMP: 15
SQ FT: 14,000
SALES (est): 1.2MM **Privately Held**
WEB: www.gibbsrubber.com
SIC: **3069** 3061 Molded rubber products; mechanical rubber goods

(P-9617)
GOOD-WEST RUBBER CORP (PA)
Also Called: Goodyear Rbr Co Southern Cal
9615 Feron Blvd, Rancho Cucamonga (91730-4503)
PHONE..................................909 987-1774
Christian Groche, *President*
Fred Ledesma, *Vice Pres*
Harold W Sears, *Vice Pres*
Patrick Sears, *Vice Pres*
Frank Ramos, *Plant Mgr*
▲ EMP: 97
SQ FT: 56,000
SALES (est): 21.8MM **Privately Held**
SIC: **3069** 3061 5531 Molded rubber products; liner strips, rubber; mechanical rubber goods; automotive tires

(P-9618)
GOODWEST RUBBER LININGS INC
Also Called: Goodwest Linings & Coatings
8814 Industrial Ln, Rancho Cucamonga (91730-4528)
PHONE..................................888 499-0085
Ryan Sears, *President*
Larry Sears, *Corp Secy*
Fred Ledesma, *Vice Pres*
Patrick Sears, *Vice Pres*
Cleiber Martin, *Prdtn Mgr*
EMP: 20
SQ FT: 300,000
SALES (est): 4.9MM **Privately Held**
WEB: www.goodwestlining.com
SIC: **3069** Linings, vulcanizable rubber

(P-9619)
HARBOR PRODUCTS INC
15001 Lakewood Blvd, Paramount (90723-4513)
PHONE..................................562 633-8184
Bill Deal, *President*
Rudy Santana, *Vice Pres*
Edwin Aceituno, *Mktg Dir*
Beverly Elba, *Sales Mgr*
▲ EMP: 10 EST: 1975
SQ FT: 10,000
SALES: 750K **Privately Held**
SIC: **3069** Custom compounding of rubber materials

(P-9620)
HEXPOL COMPOUNDING CA INC
Also Called: Mrp Holdings Corp.
491 Wilson Way, City of Industry (91744-3935)
PHONE..................................626 961-0311
Tracy Garrison, *President*
Ernie Ulmer, *CFO*

David Schlothauer, *Managing Dir*
EMP: 97 **EST:** 2011
SALES (est): 11.8MM
SALES (corp-wide): 1.4B **Privately Held**
SIC: 3069 Custom compounding of rubber
　materials
HQ: Hexpol Holding Ab
　　Skeppsbron 3
　　Malmo
　　-

(P-9621)
HEXPOL COMPOUNDING LLC
Also Called: Hexpol Compounding California
8227 Sorensen Ave, Santa Fe Springs
(90670-2123)
PHONE.................................562 464-4480
Andrew Wallace, *Branch Mgr*
Deanna Andy, *Director*
Susan Guzman, *Director*
EMP: 50
SALES (corp-wide): 1.4B **Privately Held**
SIC: 3069 Molded rubber products
HQ: Hexpol Compounding Llc
　　14330 Kinsman Rd
　　Burton OH 44021
　　440 834-4644

(P-9622)
HEXPOL COMPOUNDING LLC
11841 Wakeman St, Santa Fe Springs
(90670-2130)
PHONE.................................562 464-4482
Andrew Wallace, *Manager*
EMP: 25
SALES (corp-wide): 1.4B **Privately Held**
SIC: 3069 Molded rubber products
HQ: Hexpol Compounding Llc
　　14330 Kinsman Rd
　　Burton OH 44021
　　440 834-4644

(P-9623)
HITT COMPANIES
Also Called: Hitt Marking Devices I D Tech
3231 W Macarthur Blvd, Santa Ana
(92704-6801)
PHONE.................................714 979-1405
Harold G Hitt, *President*
Ken Hitt, *Vice Pres*
Harold Hitt, *General Mgr*
Heidi Hitt, *Admin Sec*
Tue Truong, *Manager*
▲ **EMP:** 24
SQ FT: 10,000
SALES (est): 4.7MM **Privately Held**
WEB: www.hittmarking.com
SIC: 3069 3993 5199 Stationers' rubber
　sundries; signs & advertising specialties;
　badges

(P-9624)
HOLZ RUBBER COMPANY INC
Also Called: Hr
1129 S Sacramento St, Lodi (95240-5701)
PHONE.................................209 368-7171
James R Dryburgh, *President*
David Smith, *President*
Ben Tannler, *Vice Pres*
Stephen McBurnett, *Design Engr*
Ted Cooper, *Engineer*
▲ **EMP:** 120
SQ FT: 144,000
SALES (est): 18MM **Privately Held**
WEB: www.holzrubber.com
SIC: 3069 3441 3061 Molded rubber
　products; fabricated structural metal; me-
　chanical rubber goods

(P-9625)
HOUSTON RUBBER CO INC
12623 Foothill Blvd, Sylmar (91342-5312)
PHONE.................................818 899-1108
Thane Neely, *President*
EMP: 10
SQ FT: 6,000
SALES: 860K **Privately Held**
SIC: 3069 Molded rubber products

(P-9626)
HUTCHINSON AROSPC & INDUST INC
Also Called: Barry Controls Aerospace
4510 W Vanowen St, Burbank
(91505-1135)
P.O. Box 7710 (91510-7710)
PHONE.................................818 843-1000
Grant Hintze, *CEO*
Arnaud Vaz, *President*
Max Maggi, *Vice Pres*
L Garcia, *Admin Asst*
David Sio, *Info Tech Dir*
EMP: 156
SALES (corp-wide): 8.3B **Publicly Held**
WEB: www.barrycontrols.com
SIC: 3069 Molded rubber products
HQ: Hutchinson Aerospace & Industry, Inc.
　　82 South St
　　Hopkinton MA 01748
　　508 417-7000

(P-9627)
INFLATABLE ENTERPRISES INC
1418 Vineland Ave, Baldwin Park
(91706-5813)
PHONE.................................818 482-6509
Levon Abraamyan, *CEO*
▲ **EMP:** 11 **EST:** 2016
SQ FT: 10,000
SALES: 700K **Privately Held**
SIC: 3069 Rubberized fabrics

(P-9628)
INNOCOR WEST LLC
300-310 S Tippecanoe Ave, San
Bernardino (92408)
PHONE.................................909 307-3737
Carol S Eicher, *CEO*
Doug Vaughan, *CFO*
Kelly Marquez, *Administration*
▲ **EMP:** 21
SQ FT: 150,000
SALES (est): 2.7MM
SALES (corp-wide): 209.9MM **Privately
Held**
WEB: www.advancedinnovations.net
SIC: 3069 5021 Pillows, sponge rubber;
　mattresses
HQ: Innocor, Inc.
　　200 Schulz Dr Ste 2
　　Red Bank NJ 07701

(P-9629)
INTERNATIONAL RUBBER PDTS INC (PA)
Also Called: Irp
1035 Calle Amanecer, San Clemente
(92673-6260)
PHONE.................................909 947-1244
Rod Trujillo, *CEO*
Casper Zublin Jr, *President*
Rod Trujillo, *CEO*
Susan Perkins, *CFO*
Trey Atkins, *Exec VP*
▲ **EMP:** 97
SQ FT: 45,000
SALES (est): 26.2MM **Privately Held**
WEB: www.wagnerrubber.com
SIC: 3069 Medical & laboratory rubber
　sundries & related products

(P-9630)
IOMIC INC
10 Hughes Ste 103, Irvine (92618-1962)
PHONE.................................714 564-1600
Toshihiko Hachiro, *President*
CHI Wu, *Manager*
▲ **EMP:** 12
SALES (est): 1.6MM **Privately Held**
SIC: 3069 Grips or handles, rubber

(P-9631)
KIRKHILL INC
12023 Woodruff Ave, Downey
(90241-5603)
P.O. Box 7012 (90242-7012)
PHONE.................................562 803-1117
Robert L Harold, *Chairman*
Bruce Mekjian, *President*
Mike Brickner, *Vice Pres*
Gary Riopelle, *Principal*
Arlene Hite, *Admin Sec*
EMP: 95

SQ FT: 173,000
SALES (est): 15MM **Privately Held**
SIC: 3069 Acid bottles, rubber

(P-9632)
LEONARDS MOLDED PRODUCTS INC
25031 Anza Dr, Valencia (91355-3414)
PHONE.................................661 253-2227
Randy Smith, *President*
Frank Smith, *Vice Pres*
Marty Kudlac, *General Mgr*
Sherry Wampler, *Cust Mgr*
EMP: 25
SQ FT: 5,000
SALES (est): 4.2MM **Privately Held**
SIC: 3069 Molded rubber products

(P-9633)
LINE ONE LABORATORIES INC USA
9600 Lurline Ave, Chatsworth
(91311-5107)
PHONE.................................818 886-2288
Budiman Lee, *President*
Robert Gruber, *Vice Pres*
▲ **EMP:** 26
SQ FT: 22,000
SALES (est): 4.2MM **Privately Held**
SIC: 3069 5122 Medical & laboratory rub-
　ber sundries & related products; medical
　rubber goods

(P-9634)
MATZ RUBBER CO INC
1209 Chestnut St, Burbank (91506-1626)
PHONE.................................323 849-5170
Phillip Jensen, *President*
Jan Jensen, *Treasurer*
Janet Jensen, *Treasurer*
Chris Sayer, *Engineer*
Kara Sandiego, *Finance*
EMP: 25
SQ FT: 12,000
SALES (est): 3.6MM **Privately Held**
WEB: www.matzrubber.com
SIC: 3069 3541 3291 Rubber covered
　motor mounting rings (rubber bonded);
　machine tools, metal cutting type; abra-
　sive products

(P-9635)
MCP INDUSTRIES INC (PA)
Also Called: Mission Rubber Co
708 S Temescal St Ste 101, Corona
(92879-2096)
P.O. Box 1839 (92878-1839)
PHONE.................................951 736-1881
Walter N Garrett, *CEO*
Charlotte Garrett, *Corp Secy*
Owen Garrett, *Vice Pres*
Jay Clark, *Plant Mgr*
▲ **EMP:** 15
SQ FT: 100,000
SALES (est): 126.4MM **Privately Held**
WEB: www.missionrubber.com
SIC: 3069 3259 3089 Molded rubber
　products; sewer pipe or fittings, clay; in-
　jection molding of plastics

(P-9636)
MEDCONX INC
2901 Tasman Dr Ste 211, Santa Clara
(95054-1138)
PHONE.................................408 330-0003
Hal Kent, *President*
William Deihl, *CFO*
EMP: 22
SALES (est): 5MM **Privately Held**
SIC: 3069 Medical & laboratory rubber
　sundries & related products
PA: Atl Technology, Llc
　　1335 W 1650 N
　　Springville UT 84663

(P-9637)
MITCHELL PROCESSING LLC
2778 Pomona Blvd, Pomona (91768-3222)
PHONE.................................909 519-5759
Mark Mitchell,
EMP: 20
SQ FT: 100,000
SALES (est): 774.3K **Privately Held**
SIC: 3069 Custom compounding of rubber
　materials

(P-9638)
MITCHELL RUBBER PRODUCTS LLC (PA)
10220 San Sevaine Way, Mira Loma
(91752-1100)
PHONE.................................951 681-5655
Theodore C Ballou, *CEO*
Mark Mitchell, *Admin Sec*
▲ **EMP:** 235
SQ FT: 76,000
SALES (est): 84.4MM **Privately Held**
WEB: www.mitchellrubber.com
SIC: 3069 2891 2822 Mats or matting,
　rubber; floor coverings, rubber; rubber au-
　tomotive products; custom compounding
　of rubber materials; adhesives & sealants;
　synthetic rubber

(P-9639)
MITCHELL RUBBER PRODUCTS LLC
Valley Processing
10220 San Sevaine Way, Mira Loma
(91752-1100)
PHONE.................................951 681-5655
Jeff Mitchell, *Branch Mgr*
EMP: 100
SALES (corp-wide): 84.4MM **Privately
Held**
WEB: www.mitchellrubber.com
SIC: 3069 8721 3061 Rubber floor cover-
　ings, mats & wallcoverings; accounting,
　auditing & bookkeeping; mechanical rub-
　ber goods
PA: Mitchell Rubber Products Llc
　　10220 San Sevaine Way
　　Mira Loma CA 91752
　　951 681-5655

(P-9640)
MIZU INC (PA)
2225 Faraday Ave Ste E, Carlsbad
(92008-7212)
PHONE.................................307 690-3219
Tim Pogue, *CEO*
Mike Kenney, *Opers Mgr*
Rainey Pogue, *Mktg Coord*
Curtis Marcikic, *Associate*
▲ **EMP:** 16
SALES (est): 6.5MM **Privately Held**
SIC: 3069 Water bottles, rubber

(P-9641)
MODUS ADVANCED INC
1575 Greenville Rd, Livermore
(94550-9713)
PHONE.................................925 960-8700
Rick Mackirdy, *CEO*
Don E Ulery, *Chairman*
Dave Elliott, *QA Dir*
▲ **EMP:** 35
SQ FT: 25,000
SALES: 12MM **Privately Held**
WEB: www.westernrubber.com
SIC: 3069 Molded rubber products

(P-9642)
MOMENTUM MANAGEMENT LLC
Also Called: Bushman Products
1206 W Jon St, Torrance (90502-1208)
PHONE.................................310 329-2599
Justin Ross,
Keith Caggiano, *Principal*
Aumann Conde, *Principal*
Jeff Swenson, *Graphic Designe*
Conde Aumann, *Accounts Exec*
▲ **EMP:** 15
SALES (est): 2.6MM **Privately Held**
SIC: 3069 Toys, rubber

(P-9643)
MORTAN INDUSTRIES INC
880 Columbia Ave Ste 2, Riverside
(92507-2159)
PHONE.................................951 682-2215
John A Mortan, *President*
Frieda Mortan, *Vice Pres*
EMP: 27 **EST:** 1981
SQ FT: 22,000
SALES (est): 3.6MM **Privately Held**
WEB: www.mortanindustries.com
SIC: 3069 Hard rubber & molded rubber
　products

▲ = Import ▼=Export
◆ =Import/Export

(P-9644)
NEBIA INC
375 Alabama St Ste 200, San Francisco (94110-1966)
PHONE...................................203 570-6222
Philip Winter, CEO
EMP: 12
SQ FT: 3,700
SALES: 100K Privately Held
SIC: 3069 Bath sprays, rubber

(P-9645)
NEW WORLD MANUFACTURING INC
27627 Dutcher Creek Rd, Cloverdale (95425-9753)
P.O. Box 248 (95425-0248)
PHONE...................................707 894-5257
Gerald E Moore, President
Rebecca S Moore, Treasurer
G James Moore, Vice Pres
EMP: 12 EST: 1971
SQ FT: 7,500
SALES: 745.7K Privately Held
WEB: www.newworldmfg.com
SIC: 3069 2394 2515 Linings, vulcanizable rubber; liners & covers, fabric: made from purchased materials; air cushions & mattresses, canvas; mattresses, waterbed flotation

(P-9646)
NEWBY RUBBER INC
320 Industrial St, Bakersfield (93307-2706)
PHONE...................................661 327-5137
Kelly Newby, President
Lori Newby, Admin Sec
▼ EMP: 25
SQ FT: 80,000
SALES (est): 5.3MM Privately Held
WEB: www.newbyrubber.com
SIC: 3069 Molded rubber products; hard rubber & molded rubber products

(P-9647)
NEWLINE RUBBER COMPANY
13165 Monterey Hwy # 100, San Martin (95046-9204)
PHONE...................................408 214-0359
Cherie Newland, President
Joseph E Newland, CFO
John Newland, Vice Pres
EMP: 12
SQ FT: 8,000
SALES (est): 1.4MM Privately Held
WEB: www.newlinerubber.com
SIC: 3069 Molded rubber products

(P-9648)
NUSIL TECHNOLOGY LLC
2343 Pegasus Dr, Bakersfield (93308-6804)
PHONE...................................661 391-4750
Scott Mraz,
Timothy Steckler, Info Tech Mgr
Sherry Velasquez, Info Tech Mgr
Terry Payton, Engineer
Amanda Chandler, Production
EMP: 75
SALES (corp-wide): 574.8MM Privately Held
WEB: www.nusil.com
SIC: 3069 2821 Rubber coated fabrics & clothing; plastics materials & resins
HQ: Nusil Technology Llc
1050 Cindy Ln
Carpinteria CA 93013
805 684-8780

(P-9649)
NUSIL TECHNOLOGY LLC
1150 Mark Ave, Carpinteria (93013-2918)
PHONE...................................805 684-8780
Tom Baningan,
Dan Proctor, Engineer
EMP: 95
SALES (corp-wide): 574.8MM Privately Held
WEB: www.nusil.com
SIC: 3069 Bags, rubber or rubberized fabric
HQ: Nusil Technology Llc
1050 Cindy Ln
Carpinteria CA 93013
805 684-8780

(P-9650)
ONEILL WETSUITS LLC (PA)
1071 41st Ave, Santa Cruz (95062-4400)
P.O. Box 6300 (95063-6300)
PHONE...................................831 475-7500
Pat O'Neill, Mng Member
Jack O'Neill, Ch of Bd
John Pope, COO
Patrice Riley, Executive Asst
Bridget O'Neill, Admin Sec
◆ EMP: 70
SQ FT: 14,000
SALES (est): 24.3MM Privately Held
WEB: www.oneill.com
SIC: 3069 5091 Wet suits, rubber; watersports equipment & supplies

(P-9651)
P & E RUBBER PROCESSING INC
15380 Lyons Valley Rd, Jamul (91935-3509)
PHONE...................................760 241-2643
Edmundo Bolanos, President
EMP: 20
SQ FT: 10,000
SALES (est): 2.4MM Privately Held
SIC: 3069 Rubber hardware

(P-9652)
PACIFIC EAGLE USA INC
9707 El Poche St Ste H, South El Monte (91733-3001)
PHONE...................................626 455-0033
Arthur Shih, President
▲ EMP: 40
SALES (est): 3.4MM Privately Held
SIC: 3069 7389 Wet suits, rubber; barter exchange

(P-9653)
PACIFICTECH MOLDED PDTS INC
22805 Savi Ranch Pkwy F, Yorba Linda (92887-4634)
PHONE...................................714 279-9928
Jane Xu, President
Mike Lou, Project Mgr
Fred Valenzuela, Sales Mgr
▲ EMP: 18
SALES (est): 2.7MM Privately Held
SIC: 3069 Rubber automotive products

(P-9654)
PECA CORPORATION
9707 El Poche St Ste H, El Monte (91733-3001)
PHONE...................................626 452-8873
Arthur T S Shih, President
▲ EMP: 38
SQ FT: 6,200
SALES (est): 3.9MM Privately Held
SIC: 3069 5941 5091 3949 Wet suits, rubber; fishing equipment; fishing tackle; sporting & athletic goods

(P-9655)
PHOENIX DEVENTURES INC
18655 Madrone Pkwy # 180, Morgan Hill (95037-8101)
PHONE...................................408 782-6240
Jeffrey Christian, President
Justin Lance, Project Mgr
Clint Solomon, Research
Scott Arnett, Project Engr
Stephen Bower, Project Engr
EMP: 47
SQ FT: 30,000
SALES (est): 10MM Privately Held
SIC: 3069 Medical & laboratory rubber sundries & related products

(P-9656)
PIERCAN USA INC
160 Bosstick Blvd, San Marcos (92069-5930)
PHONE...................................760 599-4543
Vincent Lucas, President
Gean-Christopher Lucas, Treasurer
Stan Diniz, General Mgr
Antoine Dobrowolski, General Mgr
Philippe Bourdon, VP Opers
▲ EMP: 19
SQ FT: 16,000

SALES (est): 4.2MM Privately Held
WEB: www.latextechnology.com
SIC: 3069 2259 Rug backing compounds, latex; work gloves, knit

(P-9657)
PMR PRECISION MFG & RBR CO INC
1330 Etiwanda Ave, Ontario (91761-8605)
PHONE...................................909 605-7525
Samuel Surh, President
George Y Surh, Executive
George Surh, General Mgr
EMP: 30
SQ FT: 36,800
SALES (est): 5.1MM Privately Held
SIC: 3069 2295 Rubberized fabrics; coated fabrics, not rubberized

(P-9658)
POLY-SEAL INDUSTRIES
725 Channing Way, Berkeley (94710-2494)
PHONE...................................510 843-9722
Daniel K Baker, President
▼ EMP: 15
SQ FT: 6,250
SALES (est): 2.1MM Privately Held
SIC: 3069 Molded rubber products

(P-9659)
POLYMERIC TECHNOLOGY INC
1900 Marina Blvd, San Leandro (94577-3207)
PHONE...................................510 895-6001
Patrick Tool, CEO
Roger Castillo, Mfg Staff
▲ EMP: 50
SQ FT: 90,000
SALES (est): 10.1MM Privately Held
WEB: www.poly-tek.com
SIC: 3069 2821 8731 3061 Molded rubber products; plastics materials & resins; commercial physical research; mechanical rubber goods

(P-9660)
POLYPLEX PLASTICS OF N AMER
Also Called: Reflection Shoes
8511 Lankershim Blvd, Sun Valley (91352-3127)
PHONE...................................818 768-8866
Nichan Frouriam, President
EMP: 25
SQ FT: 10,000
SALES (est): 3.5MM Privately Held
SIC: 3069 3021 3144 Soles, boot or shoe: rubber, composition or fiber; shoes, rubber or rubber soled fabric uppers; women's footwear, except athletic

(P-9661)
PRO-TECH MATS INDUSTRIES INC
72370 Quarry Trl Ste A, Thousand Palms (92276-6647)
PHONE...................................760 343-3667
Randy Ernst, President
EMP: 14
SQ FT: 5,650
SALES (est): 3MM Privately Held
SIC: 3069 Medical & laboratory rubber sundries & related products

(P-9662)
PROCO PRODUCTS INC (PA)
2431 Wigwam Dr, Stockton (95205-2430)
P.O. Box 590 (95201-0590)
PHONE...................................209 943-6088
Edward Marchese, President
Robert Coffee, Vice Pres
Scott Wallace, Vice Pres
Michael Lassas, VP Admin
Jerry Oprondek, Admin Sec
▲ EMP: 28
SQ FT: 22,000
SALES (est): 6.2MM Privately Held
WEB: www.procoproducts.com
SIC: 3069 2821 3443 3441 Molded rubber products; polytetrafluoroethylene resins (teflon); pipe, standpipe & culverts; fabricated structural metal

(P-9663)
PROLAB ORTHOTICS INC
575 Airpark Rd, NAPA (94558-7514)
PHONE...................................707 257-4400
Paul Scherer, CEO
Aaron Meltzer, President
Larry Huppin, Director
EMP: 42
SQ FT: 8,200
SALES (est): 6.7MM Privately Held
WEB: www.prolab-usa.com
SIC: 3069 3842 Medical & laboratory rubber sundries & related products; surgical appliances & supplies

(P-9664)
PROMOTONAL DESIGN CONCEPTS INC
Also Called: Creative Inflatables
9872 Rush St, South El Monte (91733-2635)
PHONE...................................626 579-4454
Adam Melendez, CEO
Rick Villalpando, Project Mgr
Jason Ornelas, Sales Staff
George Mancina, Accounts Exec
◆ EMP: 71
SALES (est): 11.7MM Privately Held
WEB: www.creatableinflatables.com
SIC: 3069 7389 5092 2394 Balloons, advertising & toy: rubber; balloons, novelty & toy; toy novelties & amusements; canvas & related products; canvas awnings & canopies; shades, canvas: made from purchased materials

(P-9665)
PROTECTIVE INDUSTRIES INC
Also Called: Caplugs
18704 S Ferris Pl, Rancho Dominguez (90220-6400)
PHONE...................................310 537-2300
Fred Karam, Branch Mgr
Rob Cavallari, Accounting Mgr
Gono Loera, Purch Agent
Melanie Casey, Marketing Staff
EMP: 60
SALES (corp-wide): 2.9B Privately Held
WEB: www.mokon.com
SIC: 3069 Molded rubber products
HQ: Protective Industries, Inc.
2150 Elmwood Ave
Buffalo NY 14207
716 876-9951

(P-9666)
R & R SERVICES CORPORATION
Also Called: Geolabs Westlake Village
31119 Via Colinas Ste 502, Westlake Village (91362-3941)
PHONE...................................818 889-2562
Ronald Z Shmerling, President
Tim Casey, Vice Pres
Larry Stark, Project Engr
EMP: 25 EST: 1983
SALES (est): 3.7MM Privately Held
WEB: www.geolabswv.com
SIC: 3069 8999 8711 Laboratory sundries: cases, covers, funnels, cups, etc.; geological consultant; engineering services

(P-9667)
R & S PROCESSING CO INC
15712 Illinois Ave, Paramount (90723-4113)
P.O. Box 2037 (90723-8037)
PHONE...................................562 531-0738
Karen A Kelly, President
Anthony J Inga, Corp Secy
Linda M Inga, Vice Pres
Karen Kelly, Executive
Darlene Rodriguez, Info Tech Mgr
EMP: 73 EST: 1959
SQ FT: 53,000
SALES (est): 13.4MM Privately Held
WEB: www.rsprocessing.com
SIC: 3069 Reclaimed rubber (reworked by manufacturing processes)

(P-9668)
RELIABLE RUBBER PRODUCTS INC
2600 Yosemite Blvd Ste B, Modesto (95354-4041)
PHONE..............................209 525-9750
Marc Wilkins, *President*
William R Green, *Officer*
▲ EMP: 12
SQ FT: 13,000
SALES (est): 1.3MM **Privately Held**
SIC: 3069 Rubber hardware

(P-9669)
RENEE RIVERA HAIR ACCESSORIES
2295 Chestnut St Ste 2, San Francisco (94123-2654)
PHONE..............................415 776-6613
Renee Rivera, *Owner*
EMP: 10
SQ FT: 1,000
SALES (est): 901.5K **Privately Held**
SIC: 3069 Rubber hair accessories

(P-9670)
ROBERT CROWDER & CO INC
901 S Greenwood Ave Ste L, Montebello (90640-5835)
PHONE..............................323 248-7737
Oscar Cardenas, *President*
EMP: 12
SALES (est): 1.4MM **Privately Held**
SIC: 3069 5198 Wallcoverings, rubber; wallcoverings

(P-9671)
ROGERS CORPORATION
Also Called: Diversified Silicone
13937 Rosecrans Ave, Santa Fe Springs (90670-5209)
PHONE..............................562 404-8942
Brian Lindey, *General Mgr*
Bruce Brundy, *Vice Pres*
Brian Lindey, *Sales Mgr*
Diana Mendoza, *Director*
EMP: 60
SALES (corp-wide): 821MM **Publicly Held**
SIC: 3069 Bags, rubber or rubberized fabric
PA: Rogers Corporation
2225 W Chandler Blvd
Chandler AZ 85224
480 917-6000

(P-9672)
RUBBERITE CORP (PA)
Also Called: Rubberite Cypress Sponge Rubbe
301 Goetz Ave, Santa Ana (92707-3707)
PHONE..............................714 546-6464
Greg Brooks, *President*
Barbara Ballou, *Corp Secy*
Terry Brooks, *Vice Pres*
Aaron Brooks, *Plant Mgr*
Dave Chaney, *Plant Mgr*
▲ EMP: 15
SQ FT: 52,000
SALES (est): 2.1MM **Privately Held**
SIC: 3069 Molded rubber products

(P-9673)
S AND H RUBBER COMPANY INC
1141 E Elm Ave, Fullerton (92831-5023)
PHONE..............................714 526-2583
Mike Haney, *President*
Stephen Haney, *President*
EMP: 28
SQ FT: 5,406
SALES: 185.7K **Privately Held**
WEB: www.shrubber.com
SIC: 3069 3061 Washers, rubber; mechanical rubber goods

(P-9674)
SANTA FE RUBBER PRODUCTS INC
12306 Washington Blvd, Whittier (90606-2597)
PHONE..............................562 693-2776
William Krames, *President*
Michael Peterman, *Vice Pres*
Mike Peterman, *Vice Pres*

EMP: 50
SQ FT: 30,000
SALES (est): 8MM **Privately Held**
WEB: www.santaferubber.com
SIC: 3069 Molded rubber products

(P-9675)
SATORI SEAL CORPORATION
8455 Utica Ave, Rancho Cucamonga (91730-3809)
PHONE..............................909 987-8234
Anne Acebo, *President*
Dale McGrosky, *Vice Pres*
▲ EMP: 10
SQ FT: 10,000
SALES (est): 1.7MM **Privately Held**
WEB: www.satoriseal.com
SIC: 3069 5085 Molded rubber products; rubber goods, mechanical

(P-9676)
SEAL INNOVATIONS INC
820 S Palm Ave Ste 15, Alhambra (91803-1544)
PHONE..............................626 282-7325
Myrna Galvan, *President*
▲ EMP: 10
SALES (est): 1.2MM **Privately Held**
SIC: 3069 Fabricated rubber products

(P-9677)
SGT BOARDRIDERS INC
Also Called: Aleeda Wetsuits
7403 Slater Ave, Huntington Beach (92647-6228)
PHONE..............................714 274-8000
Steve Terry, *President*
EMP: 19
SQ FT: 6,000
SALES: 1.4MM **Privately Held**
SIC: 3069 Wet suits, rubber

(P-9678)
SHERCON INC
18704 S Ferris Pl, Rancho Dominguez (90220-6400)
PHONE..............................800 228-3218
Keith Ennis, *CEO*
EMP: 44
SQ FT: 50,000
SALES (est): 3.9MM
SALES (corp-wide): 2.9B **Privately Held**
WEB: www.shercon.com
SIC: 3069 3089 2672 Tape, pressure sensitive: rubber; injection molded finished plastic products; coated & laminated paper
HQ: Protective Industries, Inc.
2150 Elmwood Ave
Buffalo NY 14207
716 876-9951

(P-9679)
SOUTH BAY CORPORATION
Also Called: Windy Balloon Company
1335 W 134th St, Gardena (90247-1904)
PHONE..............................310 532-5353
Ashhad S Khan, *CEO*
Wendy L Khan, *Vice Pres*
▲ EMP: 14
SQ FT: 12,000
SALES (est): 1.4MM **Privately Held**
SIC: 3069 Balloons, advertising & toy: rubber

(P-9680)
STOCKTON RUBBER MFGCOINC
Also Called: SRC
5023 N Flood Rd, Linden (95236-9455)
P.O. Box 639 (95236-0639)
PHONE..............................209 887-1172
Earl D Wilson, *CEO*
Ursula Wilson, *Treasurer*
David V Teslaar, *Finance Mgr*
Sham Lee, *Bookkeeper*
Mayra Ledesma, *Purch Agent*
EMP: 28
SQ FT: 7,500
SALES (est): 5.7MM **Privately Held**
SIC: 3069 Medical & laboratory rubber sundries & related products

(P-9681)
SUMITOMO ELECTRIC INTERCONN (DH)
915 Armorlite Dr, San Marcos (92069-1440)
PHONE..............................760 761-0600
Nobuyoshi Fujinama, *President*
Yuri Muto, *Treasurer*
Dave Johnson, *General Mgr*
Caesar Camp, *Technology*
Michelle Tran, *Human Res Mgr*
▲ EMP: 60
SQ FT: 55,000
SALES (est): 7.2MM
SALES (corp-wide): 28.9B **Privately Held**
WEB: www.seipusa.com
SIC: 3069 Tubing, rubber
HQ: Sumitomo Electric Fine Polymer, Inc.
1-950, Asashironishi, Kumatoricho
Sennan-Gun OSK 590-0
724 521-301

(P-9682)
TA AEROSPACE CO (HQ)
28065 Franklin Pkwy, Valencia (91355-4117)
PHONE..............................661 775-1100
Carol Marinello, *President*
Alan Young, *General Mgr*
Harry Hong, *Info Tech Mgr*
Andrew Gonzalez, *Design Engr*
Tommy Sobol, *VP Engrg*
▲ EMP: 250
SQ FT: 100,000
SALES (est): 291.1MM
SALES (corp-wide): 2B **Publicly Held**
WEB: www.kirkhill.com
SIC: 3069 Reclaimed rubber & specialty rubber compounds
PA: Esterline Technologies Corp
500 108th Ave Ne Ste 1500
Bellevue WA 98004
425 453-9400

(P-9683)
TALCO FOAM INC (PA)
Also Called: Talco Foam Products
1631 Entp Blvd Ste 30, West Sacramento (95691)
PHONE..............................916 492-8840
Dave Talbot, *Principal*
▲ EMP: 15
SQ FT: 30,000
SALES (est): 3.2MM **Privately Held**
SIC: 3069 Foam rubber

(P-9684)
TAPE SERVICE LTD
4510 Carter Ct, Chino (91710-5060)
PHONE..............................909 627-8811
Edward Lewis Sr, *President*
Marleen Lewis, *Vice Pres*
EMP: 12
SQ FT: 25,000
SALES (est): 1.7MM **Privately Held**
WEB: www.tapeservice.com
SIC: 3069 7389 5113 Tape, pressure sensitive: rubber; packaging & labeling services; pressure sensitive tape

(P-9685)
TIMEMED LABELING SYSTEMS INC (DH)
27770 N Entrmt Dr Ste 200, Valencia (91355)
PHONE..............................818 897-1111
Cecil Kost, *CEO*
Patrick Singer, *President*
Tracey Carpentier, *COO*
Mark Segal, *CFO*
EMP: 100
SQ FT: 75,000
SALES (est): 11.9MM
SALES (corp-wide): 1.1B **Publicly Held**
SIC: 3069 Tape, pressure sensitive: rubber
HQ: Precision Dynamics Corporation
27770 N Entmt Dr Ste 200
Valencia CA 91355
818 897-1111

(P-9686)
TINYINKLINGCOM LLC
Also Called: Matsmatsmats.com
6303 Owensmouth Ave Fl 10, Woodland Hills (91367-2262)
PHONE..............................877 777-6287
Mark Carmer,
Gil Romano, *General Mgr*
▼ EMP: 12 EST: 2000
SALES (est): 2.4MM **Privately Held**
WEB: www.tinyinkling.com
SIC: 3069 5199 Rubber floor coverings, mats & wallcoverings; general merchandise, non-durable

(P-9687)
TRAFFIX DEVICES INC
12128 Yucca Rd, Adelanto (92301-2708)
PHONE..............................760 246-7171
Dennis Fortner, *Manager*
EMP: 35
SALES (corp-wide): 13MM **Privately Held**
WEB: www.traffixdevices.com
SIC: 3069 Medical & laboratory rubber sundries & related products
PA: Traffix Devices, Inc.
160 Avenida La Pata
San Clemente CA 92673
949 361-5663

(P-9688)
UROCARE PRODUCTS INC
2735 Melbourne Ave, Pomona (91767-1931)
PHONE..............................909 621-6013
Friedhelm Franke, *CEO*
Raymond Halsey-Franke, *President*
Sylvia Bender, *CFO*
Raymond Franke, *Vice Pres*
Glenn Franke, *Admin Sec*
▲ EMP: 11
SQ FT: 30,000
SALES (est): 2.4MM **Privately Held**
WEB: www.urocare.com
SIC: 3069 3089 Medical & laboratory rubber sundries & related products; injection molded finished plastic products

(P-9689)
VAL PAK PRODUCTS
20731 Centre Pointe Pkwy, Santa Clarita (91350-2967)
PHONE..............................661 252-0115
Ben Solakian, *Owner*
Ed Navickas, *Sales Mgr*
John Mihranian, *Accounts Exec*
EMP: 14
SQ FT: 33,700
SALES (est): 1.1MM **Privately Held**
SIC: 3069 Chlorinated rubbers, natural

(P-9690)
VIKING RUBBER PRODUCTS INC
2600 Homestead Pl, Compton (90220-5610)
PHONE..............................310 868-5200
Rod Trujillo, *CEO*
Leigh Munsell, *President*
Ricardo Ordonez, *CFO*
EMP: 80
SALES (est): 6.3MM
SALES (corp-wide): 26.2MM **Privately Held**
WEB: www.vikingrubber.com
SIC: 3069 3061 Custom compounding of rubber materials; mechanical rubber goods
PA: International Rubber Products, Inc.
1035 Calle Amanecer
San Clemente CA 92673
909 947-1244

(P-9691)
VIP RUBBER COMPANY INC (PA)
540 S Cypress St, La Habra (90631-6127)
PHONE..............................714 774-7635
Howard Vipperman, *President*
Kathy Leclair, *CFO*
Bernardyne Vipperman, *Corp Secy*
Dean Gillespie, *Vice Pres*
Thomas Leclair, *Vice Pres*
▲ EMP: 120

SQ FT: 58,000
SALES (est): 29.7MM Privately Held
WEB: www.plastic-rubber.com
SIC: 3069 3089 3061 Rubber hardware; sponge rubber & sponge rubber products; plastic hardware & building products; mechanical rubber goods

(P-9692)
WEST AMERICAN RUBBER CO LLC (PA)
Also Called: Warco
1337 W Braden Ct, Orange (92868-1123)
P.O. Box 6146 (92863-6146)
PHONE..................................714 532-3355
Steven Hemstreet, *Mng Member*
Timothy Hemstreet, *Vice Pres*
Renan Mendez, *Vice Pres*
Mark Johnson, *Technology*
Juan Lopez, *Engineer*
▲ EMP: 342
SQ FT: 12,500
SALES (est): 92.3MM Privately Held
WEB: www.warco.com
SIC: 3069 3061 3053 Sheets, hard rubber; mechanical rubber goods; gaskets, all materials

(P-9693)
WEST AMERICAN RUBBER CO LLC
Also Called: Warco
750 N Main St, Orange (92868-1106)
P.O. Box 6146 (92863-6146)
PHONE..................................714 406-5860
Renan Mendez, *Vice Pres*
Kelvin Baker, *CFO*
Dorothy David, *Executive*
EMP: 165
SALES (est): 27.9MM
SALES (corp-wide): 82.8MM Privately Held
WEB: www.warco.com
SIC: 3069 Sheets, hard rubber
PA: West American Rubber Company Llc
    1337 W Braden Ct
    Orange CA 92868
    714 406-5860

(P-9694)
Y & D RUBBER CORPORATION
1451 S Carlos Ave, Ontario (91761-7676)
PHONE..................................909 517-1683
Trinidad Yepez, *President*
Alma Torres, *Purchasing*
EMP: 12
SQ FT: 15,000
SALES (est): 2.1MM Privately Held
SIC: 3069 Custom compounding of rubber materials

```
┌─────────────────────────────┐
│  3081 Plastic Unsupported   │
│       Sheet & Film          │
└─────────────────────────────┘
```

(P-9695)
ADVANCED MATERIALS ANALYSIS
740 Sierra Vista Ave D, Mountain View (94043-2576)
PHONE..................................650 391-4190
GE Lou, *Principal*
EMP: 10
SALES (est): 1MM Privately Held
SIC: 3081 Photographic & X-ray film & sheet

(P-9696)
ARLON GRAPHICS LLC
200 Boysenberry Ln, Placentia (92870-6413)
PHONE..................................714 985-6300
Andrew McNeill, *President*
Andrew Huddlestone, *President*
Rich Trombino, *Vice Pres*
Chad Russell, *VP Sales*
◆ EMP: 150
SALES (est): 56.1MM
SALES (corp-wide): 331.1MM Privately Held
SIC: 3081 Vinyl film & sheet
PA: Flexcon Company, Inc.
    1 Flexcon Industrial Park
    Spencer MA 01562
    508 885-8200

(P-9697)
ARVINYL LAMINATES LP
233 N Sherman Ave, Corona (92882-1844)
PHONE..................................951 371-7800
Andy Peters, *Partner*
Linda Foster, *Sales Mgr*
EMP: 33
SALES (est): 11.5MM Privately Held
SIC: 3081 Vinyl film & sheet

(P-9698)
AVIATION AND INDUS DEV CORP
Also Called: Crystal Vision Packg Systems
23870 Hawthorne Blvd, Torrance (90505-5908)
PHONE..................................310 373-6057
Donald A Hilmer, *CEO*
Patricia Hilmer, *Corp Secy*
Meshia Barton, *Sales Mgr*
Karl Behrens, *Marketing Staff*
Oscar Castaneda, *Accounts Exec*
▲ EMP: 10
SQ FT: 8,650
SALES (est): 1.6MM Privately Held
WEB: www.crystalvisionpkg.com
SIC: 3081 5162 Packing materials, plastic sheet; plastics film

(P-9699)
BARNES PLASTICS INC
18903 Anelo Ave, Gardena (90248-4598)
PHONE..................................310 329-6301
Charles Walker, *CEO*
Scott Piepmeyer, *Vice Pres*
Kathy Choi, *Accounting Mgr*
▲ EMP: 30
SQ FT: 30,000
SALES (est): 5.2MM Privately Held
WEB: www.barnesplastics.com
SIC: 3081 Unsupported plastics film & sheet

(P-9700)
C & R EXTRUSIONS INC
2618 River Ave, Rosemead (91770-3302)
PHONE..................................626 642-0244
Luis Michel, *President*
EMP: 12
SALES (est): 1.5MM Privately Held
SIC: 3081 Plastic film & sheet

(P-9701)
C P FILMS INC
21019 Osborne St, Canoga Park (91304-1744)
PHONE..................................818 678-1450
Jose Luis Elizondo, *Plant Mgr*
◆ EMP: 45
SQ FT: 45,000
SALES (est): 5MM Publicly Held
SIC: 3081 Plastic film & sheet
PA: Eastman Chemical Company
    200 S Wilcox Dr
    Kingsport TN 37660

(P-9702)
COMMEX CORPORATION
20408 Corsair Blvd, Hayward (94545-1004)
PHONE..................................510 887-4000
Yau CHI Wai, *CEO*
Edward Yau, *President*
▲ EMP: 19
SQ FT: 50,000
SALES (est): 5.3MM
SALES (corp-wide): 3MM Privately Held
SIC: 3081 Plastic film & sheet
PA: Yau's International Holding, Inc
    20408 Corsair Blvd
    Hayward CA 94545
    510 887-4000

(P-9703)
CREATIVE IMPRESSIONS INC (PA)
7697 9th St, Buena Park (90621-2898)
PHONE..................................714 521-4441
Marc D Abbott, *President*
▲ EMP: 45
SQ FT: 8,000
SALES (est): 5.6MM Privately Held
SIC: 3081 Plastic film & sheet

(P-9704)
DELSTAR TECHNOLOGIES INC
9225 Isaac St, Santee (92071-5615)
PHONE..................................619 258-1503
Scott Anglin, *Owner*
Donna V Van Ligten, *Info Tech Mgr*
▲ EMP: 26 EST: 2013
SALES (est): 5.6MM Privately Held
SIC: 3081 Polypropylene film & sheet

(P-9705)
DELSTAR TECHNOLOGIES INC
Also Called: Swm
1306 Fayette St, El Cajon (92020-1513)
PHONE..................................619 258-1503
Mark Laughlin, *Manager*
EMP: 50 Publicly Held
SIC: 3081 Polypropylene film & sheet
HQ: Delstar Technologies, Inc.
    601 Industrial Rd
    Middletown DE 19709
    302 378-8888

(P-9706)
DIAL ACT CORPORATION
Also Called: Dialex
45979 Warm Springs Blvd # 3, Fremont (94539-6765)
PHONE..................................510 659-8099
Alex Yam, *CEO*
Alex Vainer, *President*
EMP: 13
SQ FT: 8,000
SALES: 1.5MM Privately Held
WEB: www.dialact.com
SIC: 3081 Unsupported plastics film & sheet

(P-9707)
DINSMORE & ASSOCIATES INC
1681 Kettering, Irvine (92614-5613)
PHONE..................................714 641-7111
Jason Dinsmore, *CEO*
Erin Dinsmore, *General Mgr*
James Ward, *Sls & Mktg Exec*
David Nord, *Marketing Staff*
Nick Dario, *Accounts Mgr*
▲ EMP: 15
SALES (est): 3.4MM Privately Held
WEB: www.dinsmoreinc.com
SIC: 3081 8711 Film base, cellulose acetate or nitrocellulose plastic; machine tool design

(P-9708)
FLEXCON COMPANY INC
12840 Reservoir St, Chino (91710-2944)
PHONE..................................909 465-0408
David R Trujillo, *Manager*
EMP: 35
SALES (corp-wide): 331.1MM Privately Held
WEB: www.flexcon.com
SIC: 3081 2679 Plastic film & sheet; labels, paper: made from purchased material
PA: Flexcon Company, Inc.
    1 Flexcon Industrial Park
    Spencer MA 01562
    508 885-8200

(P-9709)
GLAD PRODUCTS COMPANY (HQ)
1221 Broadway Ste A, Oakland (94612-1837)
PHONE..................................510 271-7000
William V Stephenson, *Ch of Bd*
Thomas H Rowland, *CFO*
Donald A De Santis, *CFO*
Joseph B Furey, *Vice Pres*
▲ EMP: 150
SQ FT: 40,000
SALES (est): 803.2MM
SALES (corp-wide): 6.1B Publicly Held
WEB: www.gladproducts.com
SIC: 3081 2673 2842 3295 Plastic film & sheet; plastic bags: made from purchased materials; automobile polish; waxes for wood, leather & other materials; cat box litter
PA: The Clorox Company
    1221 Broadway Ste 1300
    Oakland CA 94612
    510 271-7000

(P-9710)
IMPAK CORPORATION
Also Called: Impak Worldwide
13700 S Broadway, Los Angeles (90061-1012)
PHONE..................................323 277-4700
Kevin Cullen, *President*
Edber Aguirre, *General Mgr*
Raymond Torres, *General Mgr*
Lorraine Rincon, *Info Tech Mgr*
Phil Virga, *Sales Mgr*
◆ EMP: 15
SQ FT: 12,000
SALES (est): 4.2MM Privately Held
WEB: www.sorbentsystems.com
SIC: 3081 Packing materials, plastic sheet

(P-9711)
IRONWOOD PACKAGING LLC
8975 Cottage Ave, Rancho Cucamonga (91730-5235)
PHONE..................................909 581-0077
Bill O'Melveny, *CEO*
Ricardo Gutierrez, *Engineer*
Dan Matlock, *Plant Supt*
Lisa Marie Platz, *
William O'Melveny, *Mng Member*
▲ EMP: 21
SQ FT: 35,000
SALES (est): 4MM Privately Held
WEB: www.ironwoodpackaging.com
SIC: 3081 Unsupported plastics film & sheet

(P-9712)
KW PLASTICS RECYCLING DIVISION
1861 Sunnyside Ct, Bakersfield (93308-6848)
P.O. Box 80418 (93380-0418)
PHONE..................................661 392-0500
John Putman, *General Mgr*
Andy Johnson, *Materials Mgr*
EMP: 60
SALES (corp-wide): 70.7MM Privately Held
WEB: www.kwplastics.com
SIC: 3081 3089 3354 3082 Polypropylene film & sheet; plastic processing; aluminum extruded products; unsupported plastics profile shapes
PA: Kw Plastics
    279 Pike County Lake Rd
    Troy AL 36079
    334 566-1563

(P-9713)
LIFOAM INDUSTRIES LLC
Also Called: Lifoam Mfg
2340 E 52nd St, Vernon (90058-3444)
PHONE..................................323 587-1934
Dennis Bevans, *Branch Mgr*
EMP: 45
SQ FT: 40,000
SALES (corp-wide): 14.7B Publicly Held
WEB: www.lifoam.com
SIC: 3081 3086 Packing materials, plastic sheet; plastics foam products
HQ: Lifoam Industries, Llc
    9999 E 121st
    Belcamp MD 21017
    866 770-3626

(P-9714)
MERCURY PLASTICS INC
Poly Pak Packaging Div
2939 E Washington Blvd, Los Angeles (90023-4218)
PHONE..................................323 264-2400
Benjamin Deutsch, *Branch Mgr*
EMP: 95
SALES (corp-wide): 135.7MM Privately Held
SIC: 3081 2677 Polyethylene film; envelopes
PA: Mercury Plastics, Inc.
    14825 Salt Lake Ave
    City Of Industry CA 91746
    626 961-0165

(P-9715)
MERRILLS PACKAGING INC
Also Called: Merrill's Packaging Supply
1529 Rollins Rd, Burlingame (94010-2305)
PHONE..................................650 259-5959
Kenneth V Merrill, *CEO*

(PA)=Parent Co (HQ)=Headquarters (DH)=Div Headquarters
✿ = New Business established in last 2 years

2019 California
Manufacturers Register

401

PRODUCTS & SVCS

Bridget Esquivel, *Human Resources*
Gabriel King, *Prdtn Mgr*
Andy D Cpp, *Accounts Exec*
▲ **EMP:** 80
SQ FT: 60,000
SALES (est): 24.7MM **Privately Held**
WEB: www.merrills.com
SIC: 3081 Packing materials, plastic sheet

(P-9716)
METRO WORLD PLASTICS INC
344348 Shell St, San Francisco (94102)
PHONE..................................415 255-8515
Rip Ridley, *President*
EMP: 10
SQ FT: 2,000
SALES (est): 925.3K **Privately Held**
SIC: 3081 Polyethylene film

(P-9717)
MODERN WALL GRAPHICS LLC
2191 W Esplanade Ave, San Jacinto
(92582-3723)
PHONE..................................760 787-0346
Christa Demartini,
EMP: 25
SQ FT: 4,000
SALES (est): 3.2MM **Privately Held**
WEB: www.wallslicks.com
SIC: 3081 Floor or wall covering, unsup-
ported plastic

(P-9718)
MONTEBELLO PLASTICS LLC
601 W Olympic Blvd, Montebello
(90640-5229)
P.O. Box 789 (90640-0789)
PHONE..................................323 728-6814
Timothy F Guth,
EMP: 50
SQ FT: 25,000
SALES (est): 9.3MM **Privately Held**
SIC: 3081 2673 3089 Packing materials,
plastic sheet; trash bags (plastic film):
made from purchased materials; extruded
finished plastic products

(P-9719)
NATIONWIDE PLASTIC PRODUCTS
16809 Gramercy Pl, Gardena
(90247-5205)
PHONE..................................310 366-7585
Daniel Tai, *President*
John McGee, *CEO*
EMP: 30
SQ FT: 10,000
SALES (est): 2MM **Privately Held**
SIC: 3081 5093 Plastic film & sheet; plas-
tics scrap

(P-9720)
NCD ACQUISITION INC (PA)
Also Called: Light Impressions
10425 Slusher Dr, Santa Fe Springs
(90670-3750)
PHONE..................................203 565-8707
Steve Robinson, *President*
Ike Kent, *Vice Pres*
Sara Croft, *Director*
Kevin Duong, *Accounts Mgr*
EMP: 45
SQ FT: 110,000
SALES (est): 7.4MM **Privately Held**
SIC: 3081 2782 5112 Plastic film & sheet;
albums; looseleaf binders & devices; sta-
tionery & office supplies

(P-9721)
NEXUS CALIFORNIA INC
4551 Brickell Privado St, Ontario
(91761-7828)
PHONE..................................909 937-1000
Kariman Sholakh, *President*
▲ **EMP:** 15
SQ FT: 23,512
SALES (est): 3MM **Privately Held**
WEB: www.nexuscalifornia.com
SIC: 3081 2673 Plastic film & sheet; plas-
tic bags: made from purchased materials

(P-9722)
OCEANIA INC
14209 Gannet St, La Mirada (90638-5220)
PHONE..................................562 926-8886
Tai Leong, *CEO*

Angela Leung, *Vice Pres*
▲ **EMP:** 30
SALES (est): 5.4MM **Privately Held**
SIC: 3081 Plastic film & sheet

(P-9723)
PROVIDIEN THERMOFORMING INC (HQ)
Also Called: Specialty Manufacturing, Inc.
6740 Nancy Ridge Dr, San Diego
(92121-2230)
PHONE..................................858 850-1591
Jeffrey S Goble, *CEO*
Jenny Ames, *President*
Frank Ames Jr, *Admin Sec*
Paul Jazwin, *Manager*
▲ **EMP:** 48
SQ FT: 25,500
SALES (est): 7.4MM **Privately Held**
SIC: 3081 Unsupported plastics film &
sheet

(P-9724)
RIDOUT PLASTICS COMPANY
Also Called: Eplastics
5535 Ruffin Rd, San Diego (92123-1397)
PHONE..................................858 560-1551
Elliot Rabin, *President*
▼ **EMP:** 35
SQ FT: 32,000
SALES (est): 12.8MM **Privately Held**
WEB: www.ridoutplastics.com
SIC: 3081 3082 5162 2541 Unsupported
plastics film & sheet; unsupported plastics
profile shapes; plastics materials & basic
shapes; wood partitions & fixtures

(P-9725)
SAINT-GOBAIN SOLAR GARD LLC (DH)
4540 Viewridge Ave, San Diego
(92123-1637)
PHONE..................................866 300-2674
Steven Messmer, *Mng Member*
Kiku Connelly, *Materials Mgr*
Gary Phillips, *VP Sls/Mktg*
M Shawn Puccio,
◆ **EMP:** 88
SQ FT: 65,000
SALES (est): 67.7MM
SALES (corp-wide): 213.5MM **Privately Held**
SIC: 3081 5162 3479 Plastic film & sheet;
plastics film; coating of metals & formed
products
HQ: Saint-Gobain Performance Plastics
Corporation
31500 Solon Rd
Solon OH 44139
440 836-6900

(P-9726)
SCIENTIFIC SPECIALTIES INC
Also Called: Ssi
1310 Thurman St, Lodi (95240-3145)
PHONE..................................209 333-2120
Kenneth Hovatter, *Principal*
Gene Platter, *Vice Pres*
Bill Schmierer, *Controller*
Beverly Hutchinson, *Purch Mgr*
Karen Ware, *Marketing Staff*
◆ **EMP:** 100
SALES (est): 23.3MM **Privately Held**
WEB: www.scientificspecialties.com
SIC: 3081 Unsupported plastics film &
sheet

(P-9727)
SIMPLEX STRIP DOORS LLC (DH)
Also Called: Simplex Isolation Systems
14500 Miller Ave, Fontana (92336-1696)
PHONE..................................800 854-7951
▲ **EMP:** 30
SQ FT: 28,000
SALES (est): 4.8MM
SALES (corp-wide): 5.6B **Privately Held**
WEB: www.simplexstripdoors.com
SIC: 3081 Vinyl film & sheet

(P-9728)
SOUTHWALL TECHNOLOGIES INC (DH)
3788 Fabian Way, Palo Alto (94303-4601)
PHONE..................................650 798-1285

B Travis Smith, *CEO*
Mallorie Burak,
Michael Vargas, *VP Admin*
◆ **EMP:** 48
SQ FT: 30,174
SALES (est): 16.7MM **Publicly Held**
WEB: www.southwall.com
SIC: 3081 Polyethylene film
HQ: Solutia Inc.
575 Maryville Centre Dr
Saint Louis MO 63141
423 229-2000

(P-9729)
STOP-LOOK SIGN CO INTL INC
Also Called: Stop Look Plastics Inc
401 Commercial Way, La Habra
(90631-6168)
PHONE..................................562 690-7576
Larry Dobkin, *President*
Mike Dougherty, *Treasurer*
Christine Dougherty, *Vice Pres*
Janet Dobkin, *Admin Sec*
EMP: 15 **EST:** 1960
SQ FT: 8,000
SALES (est): 4MM **Privately Held**
WEB: www.stoplooksign.com
SIC: 3081 Plastic film & sheet

(P-9730)
STOROPACK INC
2210 Junction Ave, San Jose (95131-1210)
PHONE..................................408 435-1095
Lester Whisnant, *Manager*
EMP: 25
SALES (corp-wide): 443.7MM **Privately Held**
WEB: www.storopack.com
SIC: 3081 3086
HQ: Storopack, Inc.
4758 Devitt Dr
West Chester OH 45246
513 874-0314

(P-9731)
TRAFFIC WORKS INC
5720 Soto St, Huntington Park
(90255-2631)
PHONE..................................323 582-0616
Steve Josephson, *Owner*
▲ **EMP:** 20
SQ FT: 20,000
SALES (est): 3.6MM **Privately Held**
WEB: www.trafficworks.us
SIC: 3081 2678 Packing materials, plastic
sheet; stationery: made from purchased
materials

(P-9732)
TRANSCENDIA INC
9000 9th St Ste 140, Rancho Cucamonga
(91730-4499)
PHONE..................................909 944-9981
John Balderama, *Manager*
Paul Sweeney, *Accounts Mgr*
EMP: 15
SALES (corp-wide): 404.4MM **Privately Held**
WEB: www.interfilm-usa.com
SIC: 3081 Unsupported plastics film &
sheet
PA: Transcendia, Inc.
9201 Belmont Ave
Franklin Park IL 60131
847 678-1800

(P-9733)
TRM MANUFACTURING INC
375 Trm Cir, Corona (92879-1758)
P.O. Box 77520 (92877-0117)
PHONE..................................951 256-8550
Ted Moore, *President*
Anaisa Moore, *Vice Pres*
▲ **EMP:** 200
SQ FT: 200,000
SALES: 2.2MM **Privately Held**
WEB: www.trmmfg.com
SIC: 3081 Polyethylene film

(P-9734)
W PLASTICS INC
Also Called: Western Plastics Temecula
2543 41573 Dendy Pkwy, Temecula
(92590)
PHONE..................................800 442-9727
Michael T F Cunningham, *President*

Thomas C Cunningham, *Treasurer*
Patrick Cunningham, *Vice Pres*
Pamela Long, *Office Mgr*
Henri Lim, *Opers Staff*
◆ **EMP:** 35
SQ FT: 65,000
SALES (est): 9.2MM **Privately Held**
SIC: 3081 1799 Plastic film & sheet; food
service equipment installation

(P-9735)
WESTERN SUMMIT MFG CORP
Also Called: Southern International Packg
30200 Cartier Dr, Rancho Palos Verdes
(90275-5722)
PHONE..................................626 333-3333
Donald K Clark, *President*
EMP: 60
SQ FT: 55,000
SALES (est): 7.3MM **Privately Held**
SIC: 3081 2759 2673 Unsupported plas-
tics film & sheet; commercial printing;
bags: plastic, laminated & coated

3082 Plastic Unsupported Profile Shapes

(P-9736)
ALL WEST PLASTICS INC
5451 Argosy Ave, Huntington Beach
(92649-1038)
PHONE..................................714 894-9922
L Scott Leishman, *President*
EMP: 27
SQ FT: 35,000
SALES (est): 4.4MM **Privately Held**
WEB: www.allwestplastics.com
SIC: 3082 Unsupported plastics profile
shapes

(P-9737)
B GONE BIRD INC
15375 Barranca Pkwy Ste D, Irvine
(92618-2206)
PHONE..................................949 387-5662
Bruce Alan Donoho, *CEO*
Julianne Donoho, *President*
◆ **EMP:** 18
SQ FT: 7,100
SALES (est): 4.9MM **Privately Held**
WEB: www.birdbgone.com
SIC: 3082 Unsupported plastics profile
shapes

(P-9738)
C & M MANUFACTURING COMPANY
9640 Mission Gorge Rd B, Santee
(92071-3854)
PHONE..................................619 449-7200
Curt A Moore, *Principal*
EMP: 27
SALES (corp-wide): 541.5K **Privately Held**
SIC: 3082 Rods, unsupported plastic
PA: C & M Manufacturing Company, Inc
9640 Mission Gorge Rd B
Santee CA 92071
619 449-7200

(P-9739)
JSN PACKAGING PRODUCTS INC
9700 Jeronimo Rd, Irvine (92618-2019)
PHONE..................................949 458-0050
Jim Nagel, *President*
James H Nagel Jr, *CEO*
Sandra Nagel, *Treasurer*
EMP: 65
SALES (est): 10.1MM **Privately Held**
SIC: 3082 3089 Tubes, unsupported plas-
tic; caps, plastic

(P-9740)
KELCOURT PLASTICS INC (HQ)
Also Called: Kelpac Medical
1000 Calle Recodo, San Clemente
(92673-6225)
PHONE..................................949 361-0774
Patrick C Mickle, *President*
Robert Roper, *Treasurer*
▲ **EMP:** 53
SQ FT: 20,000

▲ = Import ▼=Export
◆ =Import/Export

SALES (est): 15MM
SALES (corp-wide): 41.7MM **Privately Held**
WEB: www.kelcourt.com
SIC: 3082 Tubes, unsupported plastic
PA: Ppc Industries Inc.
10101 78th Ave
Pleasant Prairie WI 53158
262 947-0900

(P-9741)
KELPAC MEDICAL
2189 Britannia Blvd, San Diego (92154-8307)
PHONE................................619 710-2550
EMP: 58
SALES (corp-wide): 41.7MM **Privately Held**
SIC: 3082 Tubes, unsupported plastic
HQ: Kelcourt Plastics, Inc.
1000 Calle Recodo
San Clemente CA 92673
949 361-0774

(P-9742)
MEDICAL EXTRUSION TECH INC (PA)
Also Called: M E T
26608 Pierce Cir Ste A, Murrieta (92562-1008)
PHONE................................951 698-4346
Tom E Bauer, *CEO*
I Rikki Bauer, *Vice Pres*
EMP: 42
SQ FT: 16,645
SALES (est): 9.8MM **Privately Held**
WEB: www.medicalextrusion.com
SIC: 3082 Tubes, unsupported plastic

(P-9743)
POLYMEREX MEDICAL CORP
7358 Trade St, San Diego (92121-2422)
PHONE................................858 695-0765
Yan-Ho Shu, *President*
Eileen Hsieh, *Admin Sec*
EMP: 15
SQ FT: 5,200
SALES (est): 2.7MM **Privately Held**
WEB: www.polymerex.com
SIC: 3082 3083 Tubes, unsupported plastic; laminated plastics plate & sheet

(P-9744)
REEVES EXTRUDED PRODUCTS INC
1032 Stockton Ave, Arvin (93203-2330)
P.O. Box 457 (93203-0457)
PHONE................................661 854-5970
Grady Reeves, *CEO*
Sandy Shelton, *Treasurer*
Beverly Palmer, *Admin Sec*
Steve Reeves, *Admin Sec*
EMP: 75
SQ FT: 45,000
SALES (est): 12.1MM **Privately Held**
WEB: www.reeves-extruded.com
SIC: 3082 Unsupported plastics profile shapes

3083 Plastic Laminated Plate & Sheet

(P-9745)
A B C PLASTICS INC
Also Called: A B C Plastic Fabrication,
9132 De Soto Ave, Chatsworth (91311-4907)
PHONE................................818 775-0065
Mark Walters, *President*
Ivan Jackovich, *Vice Pres*
Antonio Guerrero, *Prdtn Mgr*
James Miller, *Manager*
▲ EMP: 15
SQ FT: 8,000
SALES: 8MM **Privately Held**
WEB: www.abcplastics.com
SIC: 3083 7319 5046 3089 Plastic finished products, laminated; display advertising service; store fixtures; plastic processing

(P-9746)
ACRYLICORE INC
15902 S Broadway, Gardena (90248-2406)
PHONE................................310 515-4846
Shane Nia, *President*
Parisa Shahrooz-Art, *Sales Staff*
EMP: 13
SQ FT: 7,500
SALES (est): 2.6MM **Privately Held**
WEB: www.acrylicore.com
SIC: 3083 Plastic finished products, laminated

(P-9747)
ARMORED MOBILITY INC
5610 Scotts Valley Dr B332, Scotts Valley (95066-3476)
PHONE................................831 430-9899
Tony Pollace, *CEO*
Mike Berritto, *President*
Joel Bahu, *Vice Pres*
William Gazza, *Marketing Staff*
EMP: 34
SALES: 40.7K **Privately Held**
SIC: 3083 Plastic finished products, laminated

(P-9748)
ENDURAL LLC
1685 Scenic Ave Ste A, Costa Mesa (92626-1409)
PHONE................................714 434-6533
James P Burra,
Susan Williams,
EMP: 15 EST: 1961
SQ FT: 26,500
SALES: 7.5MM **Privately Held**
WEB: www.endural.com
SIC: 3083 Plastic finished products, laminated

(P-9749)
HERITAGE PRODUCTS LLC
20932c Currier Rd Unit C, Walnut (91789-3019)
PHONE................................909 839-1866
Ron Bollig, *Mng Member*
Jason Bollig, *Sales Staff*
Dana Bollig, *Mng Member*
EMP: 10
SALES (est): 1.2MM **Privately Held**
SIC: 3083 Plastic finished products, laminated

(P-9750)
INNOVATIVE PLASTICS INC
5502 Buckingham Dr, Huntington Beach (92649-5701)
PHONE................................714 891-8800
Gary Elmer, *President*
EMP: 12
SQ FT: 10,500
SALES (est): 1.5MM **Privately Held**
WEB: www.e-surfshop.com
SIC: 3083 5947 3089 Plastic finished products, laminated; gift, novelty & souvenir shop; plastic processing

(P-9751)
JOHNSON LAMINATING COATING INC
20701 Annalee Ave, Carson (90746-3503)
PHONE................................310 635-4929
Scott Davidson, *President*
Cristina Kovar, *Research*
Beverly Hadley, *Accountant*
Kathy Truver, *Controller*
Dory Lam, *Purchasing*
◆ EMP: 75
SQ FT: 50,000
SALES (est): 31.1MM **Privately Held**
WEB: www.johnsonwindowfilms.com
SIC: 3083 3081 2891 1541 Laminated plastic sheets; window sheeting, plastic; unsupported plastics film & sheet; adhesives & sealants; food products manufacturing or packing plant construction; silicones

(P-9752)
LINDSEY DOORS INC
Also Called: Lindsey Mfg
81101 Indio Blvd Ste D16, Indio (92201-1920)
PHONE................................760 775-1959
Pierre Letellier, *President*
Jacqueline Andrade, *Office Mgr*
Katherine Letellier, *Admin Sec*
Steve Gutierrez, *Purchasing*
EMP: 22
SALES (est): 4.2MM **Privately Held**
WEB: www.lindseydoors.com
SIC: 3083 1521 Thermoplastic laminates: rods, tubes, plates & sheet; single-family housing construction

(P-9753)
LITE EXTRUSIONS MANUFACTURING
15025 S Main St, Gardena (90248-1922)
PHONE................................323 770-4298
Paul Puga, *President*
William Puga, *Corp Secy*
Barbara Puga, *Vice Pres*
EMP: 30
SQ FT: 23,500
SALES (est): 5MM **Privately Held**
WEB: www.liteextrusions.com
SIC: 3083 Thermoplastic laminates: rods, tubes, plates & sheet

(P-9754)
NELCO PRODUCTS INC (HQ)
1100 E Kimberly Ave, Anaheim (92801-1101)
PHONE................................714 879-4293
Margaret M Kendrick, *CEO*
Emily Groehl, *Bd of Directors*
Sarah Dalrymple, *Accounts Exec*
▲ EMP: 105
SQ FT: 71,862
SALES (est): 24.6MM
SALES (corp-wide): 111.2MM **Publicly Held**
WEB: www.nelcoproducts.com
SIC: 3083 Laminated plastics plate & sheet
PA: Park Electrochemical Corp.
48 S Service Rd Ste 300
Melville NY 11747
631 465-3600

(P-9755)
PACIFIC PLASTIC TECHNOLOGY INC
Also Called: P P T
9555 Hyssop Dr, Rancho Cucamonga (91730-6124)
PHONE................................909 987-4200
Robert Sawyer Sr, *CEO*
James P Sawyer, *Exec VP*
Robert Sawyer Jr, *Vice Pres*
▲ EMP: 50
SALES (est): 11.7MM **Privately Held**
WEB: www.plastictech.com
SIC: 3083 8711 3544 Plastic finished products, laminated; engineering services; special dies, tools, jigs & fixtures

(P-9756)
PARAMOUNT LAMINATES INC
Also Called: Paramount Laminates & Cabinets
15527 Vermont Ave, Paramount (90723-4295)
PHONE................................562 531-7580
Dan Neeley, *President*
Wayne De Puy, *President*
Brian Depuy, *CEO*
Sheila De Puy, *Corp Secy*
EMP: 18
SQ FT: 5,000
SALES (est): 1.5MM **Privately Held**
WEB: www.paramountlaminate.com
SIC: 3083 Laminated plastics plate & sheet

(P-9757)
PHILLIPS BROS PLASTICS INC
17831 S Western Ave, Gardena (90248-3681)
PHONE................................310 532-8020
James Phillips, *President*
David Phillips, *General Mgr*
Alan Phillips, *VP Prdtn*
EMP: 20 EST: 1956
SQ FT: 28,000
SALES (est): 1.2MM **Privately Held**
SIC: 3083 3089 Plastic finished products, laminated; injection molding of plastics

(P-9758)
PLASTIC INNOVATIONS INC
10513 San Sevaine Way, Mira Loma (91752-3286)
PHONE................................951 361-0251
Vipulkumar Mandani, *CEO*
EMP: 17
SALES (est): 2.8MM **Privately Held**
SIC: 3083 Plastic finished products, laminated

(P-9759)
PLASTICS RESEARCH CORPORATION
Also Called: PRC
1400 S Campus Ave, Ontario (91761-4330)
PHONE................................909 391-9050
Gene Gregory, *CEO*
Robert Black, *President*
Michael Maedel, *Exec VP*
▲ EMP: 100
SQ FT: 105,000
SALES (est): 27.5MM **Privately Held**
SIC: 3083 Laminated plastics plate & sheet

(P-9760)
PLASTIFAB INC
Also Called: Plastifab/Leed Plastics
1425 Palomares St, La Verne (91750-5294)
PHONE................................909 596-1927
Rick Donnelly, *President*
Jerri Kelly, *Financial Exec*
EMP: 30
SQ FT: 15,000
SALES (est): 4.8MM **Privately Held**
WEB: www.pflv.biz
SIC: 3083 5162 3089 Laminated plastic sheets; plastics sheets & rods; plastic processing

(P-9761)
PLASTIFAB SAN DIEGO
12145 Paine St, Poway (92064-7124)
PHONE................................858 679-6600
Philip Staub, *Partner*
Richard E Donnelly, *Partner*
Robert M Lincoln, *Partner*
Mark Weinrich, *Partner*
EMP: 18
SQ FT: 15,000
SALES (est): 3.3MM **Privately Held**
WEB: www.plastifabsd.com
SIC: 3083 5162 3089 Laminated plastic sheets; plastics sheets & rods; plastic processing

(P-9762)
PTM & W INDUSTRIES INC
10640 Painter Ave, Santa Fe Springs (90670-4092)
PHONE................................562 946-4511
Charles E Owen, *CEO*
William Ryan, *Vice Pres*
Doug Mayer, *District Mgr*
John Peralta, *District Mgr*
Stacey Nickel, *Administration*
▲ EMP: 25
SQ FT: 25,000
SALES (est): 6.6MM **Privately Held**
WEB: www.ptm-w.com
SIC: 3083 2992 2891 2851 Plastic finished products, laminated; lubricating oils & greases; adhesives & sealants; paints & allied products; plastics materials & resins

(P-9763)
REPET INC
14207 Monte Vista Ave, Chino (91710-5724)
PHONE................................909 594-5333
Shubin Zhao, *President*
George Dadiani, *Vice Pres*
Nan Zhao, *Engineer*
Tony Kang, *Sales Staff*
Franscisco Hernandez, *Manager*
▲ EMP: 145
SALES (est): 36.5MM **Privately Held**
WEB: www.repetusa.com
SIC: 3083 Plastic finished products, laminated

(P-9764)
ROCK WEST COMPOSITES INC (PA)
1602 Precision Park Ln, San Diego (92173-1346)
PHONE.................................801 566-3402
James P Gormican, *CEO*
EMP: 20
SALES (est): 8.9MM **Privately Held**
WEB: www.rockwestcomposites.com
SIC: 3083 Laminated plastics plate & sheet

(P-9765)
SCHAFFER LABORATORIES INC
Also Called: Western Plastic Products
8441 Monroe Ave, Stanton (90680-2615)
PHONE.................................714 202-1594
▲ EMP: 13
SQ FT: 9,000
SALES: 750K **Privately Held**
SIC: 3083 3089

(P-9766)
SPARTECH LLC
14263 Gannet St, La Mirada (90638-5220)
PHONE.................................714 523-2260
Julie A McAlindon, *Manager*
EMP: 13
SALES (corp-wide): 1.4B **Privately Held**
SIC: 3083 Thermoplastic laminates: rods, tubes, plates & sheet
PA: Spartech Llc
   11650 Lkeside Crossing Ct
   Saint Louis MO 63105
   314 569-7400

(P-9767)
SWISS PRODUCTIONS INC
2801 Golf Course Dr, Ventura (93003-7610)
PHONE.................................805 654-8379
Kenneth Ray Putman, *CEO*
Joyce Snyder, *CFO*
Joyce C Snyder, *CFO*
Michelle Rogers, *Officer*
Richard G Petrash, *Senior VP*
▲ EMP: 46
SQ FT: 25,000
SALES (est): 5.8MM **Privately Held**
WEB: www.swissproductions.com
SIC: 3083 3469 Plastic finished products, laminated; metal stampings

(P-9768)
TURRET PUNCH CO INC
7780 Edison Ave, Fontana (92336-3635)
PHONE.................................909 587-1820
Carol Lang, *CEO*
Steve Lang, *President*
EMP: 10 EST: 1972
SQ FT: 33,500
SALES (est): 2.3MM **Privately Held**
WEB: www.goturethane.com
SIC: 3083 5169 3082 Plastic finished products, laminated; polyurethane products; unsupported plastics profile shapes

(P-9769)
VANDERVEER INDUSTRIAL PLAS LLC (PA)
515 S Melrose St, Placentia (92870-6337)
PHONE.................................714 579-7700
Greg Geiss, *CEO*
EMP: 40
SQ FT: 29,000
SALES: 10MM **Privately Held**
WEB: www.vanderveerplastics.com
SIC: 3083 Laminated plastics plate & sheet

(P-9770)
VCLAD LAMINATES INC
2103 Seaman Ave, South El Monte (91733-2628)
PHONE.................................626 442-2100
David Thomson, *President*
Anthony Cruz, *Manager*
▲ EMP: 20
SALES (est): 3.3MM **Privately Held**
WEB: www.vclad.com
SIC: 3083 2434 Laminated plastic sheets; wood kitchen cabinets

(P-9771)
VILLANUEVA PLASTIC COMPANY INC
372 W Tullock St, Rialto (92376-7702)
PHONE.................................909 581-3870
Jose C Villanueva, *President*
EMP: 11
SALES (est): 1.5MM **Privately Held**
SIC: 3083 Plastic finished products, laminated

(P-9772)
WORLD MANUFACTURING INC (PA)
350 Fischer Ave Ste B, Costa Mesa (92626-4508)
PHONE.................................714 662-3539
Michael Robinson, *President*
Alan Katz, *Vice Pres*
◆ EMP: 10
SQ FT: 22,000
SALES (est): 1.7MM **Privately Held**
WEB: www.worldmanufacturing.com
SIC: 3083 3081 3993 Plastic finished products, laminated; packing materials, plastic sheet; neon signs

---

3084 Plastic Pipe

(P-9773)
ADVANCED DRAINAGE SYSTEMS INC
1025 Commerce Dr, Madera (93637-5201)
P.O. Box 1117 (93639-1117)
PHONE.................................559 674-4989
Richard Tartaglia, *Branch Mgr*
EMP: 20
SQ FT: 16,000
SALES (corp-wide): 1.3B **Publicly Held**
WEB: www.ads-pipe.com
SIC: 3084 Plastics pipe
PA: Advanced Drainage Systems, Inc.
   4640 Trueman Blvd
   Hilliard OH 43026
   614 658-0050

(P-9774)
ALLWIRE INC
16395 Avenue 24 1/2, Chowchilla (93610-9564)
PHONE.................................559 665-4893
Allen Hopkins, *President*
EMP: 50
SALES (corp-wide): 20MM **Privately Held**
SIC: 3084 Plastics pipe
PA: Allwire, Inc.
   16395 Avenue 24 1/2
   Chowchilla CA 93610
   559 665-4893

(P-9775)
ASSISVIS INC
10780 Mulberry Ave, Fontana (92337-7062)
PHONE.................................909 628-2031
Ken Lam, *President*
EMP: 22
SALES (est): 4.9MM **Privately Held**
SIC: 3084 3089 Plastics pipe; plastic processing

(P-9776)
BEAR INDUSTRIAL HOLDINGS INC
Also Called: Bear Industrial Supply & Mfg
9971 Muirlands Blvd, Irvine (92618-2508)
PHONE.................................562 926-3000
Kevin E Wheeler, *CEO*
EMP: 21
SALES (est): 3.9MM **Privately Held**
WEB: www.bearism.com
SIC: 3084 Plastics pipe

(P-9777)
CHEVRON PHILLIPS CHEM CO LP
Also Called: Performance Pipe Div
6001 Bollinger Canyon Rd, San Ramon (94583-5737)
PHONE.................................909 420-5500
Phil Foley, *Branch Mgr*
Rita Rose, *Human Resources*
EMP: 80
SALES (corp-wide): 9.6B **Privately Held**
WEB: www.cpchem.com
SIC: 3084 Plastics pipe
HQ: Chevron Phillips Chemical Company Lp
   10001 Six Pines Dr
   The Woodlands TX 77380
   832 813-4100

(P-9778)
GEORG FISCHER HARVEL LLC
7001 Schirra Ct, Bakersfield (93313-2165)
PHONE.................................661 396-0653
EMP: 86
SALES (corp-wide): 4.2B **Privately Held**
SIC: 3084 Plastics pipe
HQ: Georg Fischer Harvel Llc
   300 Kuebler Rd
   Easton PA 18040
   610 252-7355

(P-9779)
HANCOR INC
140 Vineland Rd, Bakersfield (93307-9515)
PHONE.................................661 366-1520
James Tingle, *Manager*
EMP: 60
SALES (corp-wide): 1.3B **Publicly Held**
SIC: 3084 5051 Plastics pipe; pipe & tubing, steel
HQ: Hancor, Inc.
   4640 Trueman Blvd
   Hilliard OH 43026
   614 658-0050

(P-9780)
HUNTER INDUSTRIES INCORPORATED (PA)
1940 Diamond St, San Marcos (92078-5190)
PHONE.................................760 744-5240
Gregory Hunter, *President*
Kari Pelters, *Treasurer*
Olivia Almaraz, *Supervisor*
◆ EMP: 277
SQ FT: 450,000
SALES (est): 328.9MM **Privately Held**
WEB: www.hunterindustries.com
SIC: 3084 5087 Plastics pipe; sprinkler systems

(P-9781)
IPEX USA LLC
Valor Div of Naco Ind
2395 Maggio Cir, Lodi (95240-8814)
PHONE.................................209 368-7131
Daniel Gruber, *Branch Mgr*
EMP: 11
SQ FT: 8,500 **Privately Held**
WEB: www.nacopvc.com
SIC: 3084 Plastics pipe
HQ: Ipex Usa Llc
   10100 Rodney St
   Pineville NC 28134
   704 889-2431

(P-9782)
J-M MANUFACTURING COMPANY INC (PA)
Also Called: JM Eagle
5200 W Century Blvd, Los Angeles (90045-5928)
PHONE.................................800 621-4404
Walter Wang, *CEO*
John MAI, *CFO*
David Merritt, *Vice Pres*
Dan O'Connor, *Vice Pres*
Daniel Oconnor, *Vice Pres*
◆ EMP: 150
SQ FT: 24,000
SALES (est): 1B **Privately Held**
SIC: 3084 2821 3491 Plastics pipe; polyvinyl chloride resins (PVC); water works valves

(P-9783)
KAKUICHI AMERICA INC
23540 Telo Ave, Torrance (90505-4013)
PHONE.................................310 539-1590
Yasuo Ogami, *CEO*
Kenichi Tanaka, *Principal*
▲ EMP: 100
SQ FT: 110,000
SALES (est): 29.1MM
SALES (corp-wide): 2.4MM **Privately Held**
SIC: 3084 Plastics pipe
HQ: Kakuichi Co., Ltd.
   1415, Midoricho, Tsuruga
   Nagano NAG 380-0
   262 346-111

(P-9784)
PACIFIC PLASTICS INC
111 S Berry St, Brea (92821-4827)
PHONE.................................714 990-9050
Anayat Raminfar, *President*
Rahim Arian, *Treasurer*
Farhad Bahremand, *Vice Pres*
Rahim Kashanian, *Vice Pres*
Aman Ramin, *Vice Pres*
▲ EMP: 71
SQ FT: 32,000
SALES (est): 36.1MM **Privately Held**
SIC: 3084 Plastics pipe

(P-9785)
PRINSCO INC
2839 S Cherry Ave, Fresno (93706-5406)
PHONE.................................559 485-5542
John Hoff, *Executive*
Scott Shurston, *Cust Mgr*
EMP: 30
SALES (corp-wide): 89.7MM **Privately Held**
WEB: www.prinsco.com
SIC: 3084 Plastics pipe
PA: Prinsco, Inc.
   1717 16th St Ne Fl 3
   Willmar MN 56201
   320 978-4116

(P-9786)
PW EAGLE INC
Also Called: JM Eagle
5200 W Century Blvd Fl 10, Los Angeles (90045-5971)
PHONE.................................800 621-4404
EMP: 267
SALES (corp-wide): 978.3MM **Privately Held**
SIC: 3084
HQ: Pw Eagle, Inc.
   5200 W Century Blvd
   Los Angeles CA 90045
   800 621-4404

(P-9787)
PW EAGLE INC
Also Called: P W Pipe
23711 Rider St, Perris (92570-7114)
PHONE.................................951 657-7400
EMP: 267
SALES (corp-wide): 978.3MM **Privately Held**
SIC: 3084 3644
HQ: Pw Eagle, Inc.
   5200 W Century Blvd
   Los Angeles CA 90045
   800 621-4404

(P-9788)
PW EAGLE INC
Also Called: P W Pipe
3500 Robin Ln, Shingle Springs (95682)
P.O. Box 386 (95682-0386)
PHONE.................................530 677-2286
Fax: 530 677-3642
EMP: 100
SALES (corp-wide): 978.3MM **Privately Held**
SIC: 3084
HQ: Pw Eagle, Inc.
   5200 W Century Blvd
   Los Angeles CA 90045
   800 621-4404

(P-9789)
REHAU INCORPORATED
Also Called: Rehau Constructions
1250 Corona Pointe Ct # 301, Corona (92879-1780)
PHONE.................................951 549-9017
Joe Lepire, *Manager*
Omar Gonzalez, *Accounts Mgr*
EMP: 10 **Privately Held**
WEB: www.rehauna.com
SIC: 3084 3089 Plastics pipe; extruded finished plastic products

▲ = Import ▼=Export
◆ =Import/Export

PA: Rehau Incorporated
1501 Edwards Ferry Rd Ne
Leesburg VA 20176

(P-9790)
US PIPE FABRICATION LLC
Also Called: Water Works Manufacturing
3387 Plumas Arboga Rd, Marysville
(95901)
P.O. Box 2480 (95901-0089)
PHONE.....................530 742-5171
Tom Nascimento, *Vice Pres*
EMP: 35
SALES (corp-wide): 1.5B Publicly Held
SIC: 3084 3088 3494 Plastics pipe; plastics plumbing fixtures; valves & pipe fittings
HQ: Us Pipe Fabrication, Llc
2 Chase Corporate Dr # 200
Hoover AL 35244

(P-9791)
VALENCIA PIPE COMPANY
Also Called: Home-Flex
28839 Industry Dr, Valencia (91355-5419)
PHONE.....................661 257-3923
Andrew Dervin, *CEO*
Curt Meyer, *CFO*
Peter Dervin, *Vice Pres*
Uriel Sandoval, *Vice Pres*
Jon Eggly, *Info Tech Dir*
▲ EMP: 40 EST: 2007
SQ FT: 60,000
SALES: 40.7MM Privately Held
SIC: 3084 5074 3479 3312 Plastics pipe; pipes & fittings, plastic; coating or wrapping steel pipe; iron & steel: galvanized, pipes, plates, sheets, etc.

3085 Plastic Bottles

(P-9792)
AMCOR RIGID PLASTICS USA LLC
Also Called: Ball Plastic Container
14270 Ramona Ave, Chino (91710-5738)
PHONE.....................909 517-2700
Curt Crogan, *Branch Mgr*
EMP: 175
SALES (corp-wide): 9.1B Privately Held
WEB: www.ball.com
SIC: 3085 3411 Plastics bottles; metal cans
HQ: Amcor Rigid Plastics Usa, Llc
935 Technology Dr Ste 100
Ann Arbor MI 48108

(P-9793)
CHI FUNG PLASTICS INC
1000 54th Ave, Oakland (94601-5646)
PHONE.....................510 532-4835
Eric Wu, *President*
EMP: 13
SQ FT: 40,000
SALES: 2.2MM Privately Held
SIC: 3085 Plastics bottles

(P-9794)
CLASSIC CONTAINERS INC
1700 S Hellman Ave, Ontario (91761-7638)
PHONE.....................909 930-3610
Manny G Hernandez Sr, *CEO*
Manny Hernandez Jr, *Treasurer*
Ernie Hernandez, *Vice Pres*
Maria Hernandez, *Admin Sec*
Kevin Tippitt, *Sales Staff*
EMP: 280
SQ FT: 60,000
SALES (est): 68.1MM Privately Held
WEB: www.classiccontainers.com
SIC: 3085 5085 3089 Plastics bottles; industrial supplies; plastic containers, except foam

(P-9795)
CONSOLIDATED CONT HOLDINGS LLC
Also Called: California Plastics
12165 Madera Way, Riverside (92503-4849)
PHONE.....................951 340-9390

Steve Thompson, *Manager*
EMP: 32
SALES (corp-wide): 13.7B Publicly Held
SIC: 3085 Plastics bottles
HQ: Consolidated Container Holdings Llc
2500 Windy Ridge Pkwy Se
Atlanta GA 30339
678 742-4600

(P-9796)
CONSOLIDATED CONTAINER CO LLC
Mayfair Plastics
1500 E 223rd St, Carson (90745-4316)
PHONE.....................310 952-8736
Larry Lindsey, *Manager*
David Beard, *Sales Dir*
EMP: 80
SALES (corp-wide): 13.7B Publicly Held
WEB: www.cccllc.com
SIC: 3085 2656 Plastics bottles; sanitary food containers
HQ: Consolidated Container Company, Llc
3101 Towercreek Pkwy Se
Atlanta GA 30339
678 742-4600

(P-9797)
CONSOLIDATED CONTAINER CO LLC
Also Called: Reid Plastics
5772 Jurupa St Ste B, Ontario (91761-3643)
PHONE.....................909 390-6637
Steve Thompson, *Manager*
EMP: 15
SALES (corp-wide): 13.7B Publicly Held
WEB: www.cccllc.com
SIC: 3085 3556 Plastics bottles; beverage machinery; juice extractors, fruit & vegetable: commercial type
HQ: Consolidated Container Company, Llc
2500 Windy Ridge Pkwy Se
Atlanta GA 30339
678 742-4600

(P-9798)
CONSOLIDATED CONTAINER CO LLC
1620 Gobel Way, Modesto (95358-5745)
PHONE.....................209 531-9180
Michael Foley, *Principal*
EMP: 87
SALES (corp-wide): 13.7B Publicly Held
WEB: www.cccllc.com
SIC: 3085 2821 3089 Plastics bottles; polycarbonate resins; plastic containers, except foam
HQ: Consolidated Container Company, Llc
3101 Towercreek Pkwy Se
Atlanta GA 30339
678 742-4600

(P-9799)
GRAHAM PACKAGING CO EUROPE LLC
11555 Arrow Rte, Rancho Cucamonga (91730-4944)
PHONE.....................909 989-5367
EMP: 147 Privately Held
SIC: 3085
HQ: Graham Packaging Company Europe Llc
2401 Pleasant Valley Rd # 2
York PA 17402
717 849-8500

(P-9800)
LIQUI-BOX CORPORATION
Liqui-Box Division
5772 Jurupa St Ste C, Ontario (91761-3643)
PHONE.....................909 390-4646
Lou Pershin, *Principal*
EMP: 40
SALES (corp-wide): 412MM Privately Held
WEB: www.liquibox.com
SIC: 3085 3089 2656 Plastics bottles; plastic processing; sanitary food containers
PA: Liqui-Box Corporation
901 E Byrd St Ste 1105
Richmond VA 23219
804 325-1400

(P-9801)
MUNCHKIN INC (PA)
7835 Gloria Ave, Van Nuys (91406-1822)
PHONE.....................818 893-5000
Steven B Dunn, *CEO*
Andrew Keimach, *President*
Tom Emrey, *COO*
Jeff Hale, *COO*
Gary Rolfes, *CFO*
▲ EMP: 123
SQ FT: 63,000
SALES (est): 40.7MM Privately Held
WEB: www.munchkininc.com
SIC: 3085 3069 5999 Plastics bottles; teething rings, rubber; bibs, vulcanized rubber or rubberized fabric; infant furnishings & equipment

(P-9802)
NARAYAN CORPORATION
Also Called: Plastic Processing Co
13432 Estrella Ave, Gardena (90248-1513)
PHONE.....................310 719-7330
Harshad Desai, *President*
▲ EMP: 37
SALES (est): 6.1MM Privately Held
SIC: 3085 3089 Plastics bottles; bottle caps, molded plastic

(P-9803)
PLASCOR INC
972 Columbia Ave, Riverside (92507-2140)
PHONE.....................951 328-1010
David Harrigan, *President*
▼ EMP: 135
SQ FT: 50,000
SALES (est): 39.3MM Privately Held
SIC: 3085 Plastics bottles

(P-9804)
PLAXICON HOLDING CORPORATION
Also Called: Plaxicon Co
10660 Acacia St, Rancho Cucamonga (91730-5409)
PHONE.....................909 944-6868
Bill Williams, *CEO*
EMP: 130
SQ FT: 150,000
SALES (est): 13.2MM Privately Held
WEB: www.liquidcontainer.com
SIC: 3085 3089 Plastics bottles; plastic containers, except foam
HQ: Graham Packaging Company Europe Llc
2401 Pleasant Valley Rd # 2
York PA 17402

(P-9805)
POLY-TAINER INC (PA)
Also Called: Custom Molded Devices
450 W Los Angeles Ave, Simi Valley (93065-1646)
PHONE.....................805 526-3424
Paul G Strong, *President*
Julie Williams, *CEO*
Stephanie Strong, *Vice Pres*
Karrie Brooks, *Controller*
Dave Logan, *QC Mgr*
▲ EMP: 290 EST: 1970
SQ FT: 95,000
SALES (est): 80MM Privately Held
WEB: www.polytainer.com
SIC: 3085 Plastics bottles

(P-9806)
PRETIUM PACKAGING LLC
Also Called: Custom Blow Molding
946 S Andreasen Dr, Escondido (92029-1914)
PHONE.....................760 737-7995
EMP: 170
SALES (corp-wide): 141MM Privately Held
SIC: 3085 2671 Plastics bottles; plastic film, coated or laminated for packaging
HQ: Pretium Packaging, L.L.C.
15450 S Outer Forty Dr St
Chesterfield MO 63017
314 727-8200

(P-9807)
RING CONTAINER TECH LLC
3643 Finch Rd, Modesto (95357-4143)
PHONE.....................209 238-3426

Joel McDonald, *Manager*
Tom Sponder, *Plant Mgr*
Michael Reeves, *QC Mgr*
EMP: 23
SALES (corp-wide): 295MM Privately Held
WEB: www.ringcontainer.com
SIC: 3085 3411 Plastics bottles; food containers, metal
PA: Ring Container Technologies, Llc.
1 Industrial Park
Oakland TN 38060
800 280-7464

(P-9808)
RING CONTAINER TECH LLC
8275 Almeria Ave, Fontana (92335-3280)
PHONE.....................909 350-8416
Fred Miller, *Branch Mgr*
Brian Didlake, *Opers Mgr*
Kevin Devries, *Plant Mgr*
Maurice Klemish, *Mfg Staff*
EMP: 40
SQ FT: 60,800
SALES (corp-wide): 295MM Privately Held
WEB: www.ringcontainer.com
SIC: 3085 3411 3089 Plastics bottles; food containers, metal; blow molded finished plastic products
PA: Ring Container Technologies, Llc.
1 Industrial Park
Oakland TN 38060
800 280-7464

(P-9809)
TRIPLE DOT CORP
3302 S Susan St, Santa Ana (92704-6841)
PHONE.....................714 241-0888
Tony T Tsai, *President*
Elaine Chang, *Corp Secy*
Jason Tsai, *Vice Pres*
Michael Lin, *Administration*
▲ EMP: 36
SQ FT: 35,000
SALES (est): 6.3MM Privately Held
WEB: www.triple-dot.com
SIC: 3085 5085 3089 Plastics bottles; glass bottles; plastic containers, except foam

(P-9810)
US PLASTIC INC
1561 Estridge Ave Ste 102, Riverside (92507)
PHONE.....................951 300-9360
Kyeong Hee Lee, *President*
▲ EMP: 20
SALES (est): 4.6MM Privately Held
SIC: 3085 Plastics bottles

3086 Plastic Foam Prdts

(P-9811)
ADVANCED FOAM INC
1745 W 134th St, Gardena (90249-2015)
PHONE.....................310 515-0728
James Conley, *President*
Susan L Conley, *Admin Sec*
EMP: 38
SQ FT: 17,500
SALES (est): 7.1MM Privately Held
WEB: www.advancedfoam.net
SIC: 3086 3299 Packaging & shipping materials, foamed plastic; ornamental & architectural plaster work

(P-9812)
ADVANCED MATERIALS INC (HQ)
20211 S Susana Rd, Compton (90221-5725)
PHONE.....................310 537-5444
Fax: 310 763-6869
▲ EMP: 19
SQ FT: 56,000
SALES (est): 2.5MM
SALES (corp-wide): 138.8MM Publicly Held
WEB: www.ami4.com
SIC: 3086

PA: Ufp Technologies, Inc.
100 Hale St
Newburyport MA 01950
978 352-2200

(P-9813)
AGRI CEL INC
401 Road 192, Delano (93215-9598)
PHONE....................................661 792-2107
Louis Pandol, *President*
Jack Pandol, *Vice Pres*
Steve Pandol, *Vice Pres*
▲ EMP: 90
SQ FT: 30,000
SALES (est): 9.2MM **Privately Held**
WEB: www.agri-cel.com
SIC: 3086 Packaging & shipping materials,
foamed plastic

(P-9814)
ALLMAN PRODUCTS INC
21251 Deering Ct, Canoga Park
(91304-5016)
P.O. Box 10625 (91309-1625)
PHONE....................................818 715-0093
Allan Allman, *President*
▲ EMP: 20
SQ FT: 8,000
SALES (est): 3MM **Privately Held**
SIC: 3086 Plastics foam products

(P-9815)
ALLPAKFOAM & PACKAGING
20302 Clark St, Woodland Hills
(91367-5506)
PHONE....................................818 917-5660
Orlando Ayala Jr, *President*
▲ EMP: 10
SQ FT: 35,000
SALES (est): 496.5K **Privately Held**
SIC: 3086 Packaging & shipping materials,
foamed plastic

(P-9816)
AMERICAN POLY-FOAM COMPANY INC
1455 Crocker Ave, Hayward (94544-7032)
P.O. Box 3307 (94540-3307)
PHONE....................................510 786-3626
Steven T Alexakos, *President*
Doug Merkel, *General Mgr*
Theresa Andrade, *Human Res Mgr*
Matt Ballock, *Accounts Mgr*
Kevin Finerty, *Accounts Mgr*
▲ EMP: 25
SALES (est): 5.3MM **Privately Held**
SIC: 3086 Packaging & shipping materials,
foamed plastic

(P-9817)
ARCHITECTURAL FOAM PRODUCTS
3237 Santa Rosa Ave, Santa Rosa
(95407-7951)
PHONE....................................707 544-2779
Jose Gaitan, *Owner*
▼ EMP: 12
SALES (est): 953.1K **Privately Held**
SIC: 3086 Insulation or cushioning mate-
rial, foamed plastic

(P-9818)
ARTISTIC COVERINGS INC
14135 Artesia Blvd, Cerritos (90703-7025)
PHONE....................................562 404-9343
Troy Robinson, *President*
Michelle Robinson, *Vice Pres*
▲ EMP: 30
SQ FT: 24,000
SALES (est): 5.9MM **Privately Held**
WEB: www.artisticcoverings.com
SIC: 3086 3949 2759 Padding, foamed
plastic; track & field athletic equipment;
commercial printing

(P-9819)
ATLAS FOAM PRODUCTS
12836 Arroyo St, Sylmar (91342-5304)
PHONE....................................818 837-3626
Jeff Naples, *President*
Sandra Naples, *Admin Sec*
Pamela Lindlief, *Purch Agent*
EMP: 18
SQ FT: 28,000

SALES (est): 3.4MM **Privately Held**
WEB: www.atlasfoam.com
SIC: 3086 Packaging & shipping materials,
foamed plastic

(P-9820)
BACK SUPPORT SYSTEMS INC
67688 San Andreas St, Desert Hot Springs
(92240-6804)
P.O. Box 961 (92240-0907)
PHONE....................................760 329-1472
Jeffrey A Kalatsky, *President*
Jeff Kalatsky, *Info Tech Mgr*
▲ EMP: 17
SQ FT: 9,800
SALES (est): 1.6MM **Privately Held**
WEB: www.backsupportsystems.com
SIC: 3086 5047 Plastics foam products;
therapy equipment

(P-9821)
BOWERS & KELLY PRODUCTS INC
4572 E Eisenhower Cir, Anaheim
(92807-1823)
PHONE....................................714 630-1285
EMP: 26
SALES (est): 3.3MM **Privately Held**
SIC: 3086

(P-9822)
BUD WIL INC
Also Called: B W I
1170 N Red Gum St, Anaheim
(92806-2539)
PHONE....................................714 630-1242
M Charles Williams, *President*
EMP: 30
SQ FT: 22,000
SALES (est): 5MM **Privately Held**
SIC: 3086 Plastics foam products

(P-9823)
CALIFORNIA PERFORMANCE PACKG
Also Called: Pacific Tech Products Ontario
33200 Lewis St, Union City (94587-2202)
PHONE....................................909 390-4422
Randall Lake, *President*
EMP: 400
SALES (est): 34.2MM
SALES (corp-wide): 4MM **Privately Held**
SIC: 3086 Packaging & shipping materials,
foamed plastic
HQ: Great American Industries Inc
300 Plaza Dr
Vestal NY 13850
607 729-9331

(P-9824)
CAPPAC PLASTIC PRODUCTS
5835 S Malt Ave, Commerce (90040-3589)
PHONE....................................323 721-7542
Stephen Peterson, *Owner*
EMP: 20 EST: 1961
SQ FT: 27,000
SALES: 1.7MM **Privately Held**
SIC: 3086 2671 Packaging & shipping ma-
terials, foamed plastic; packaging paper &
plastics film, coated & laminated

(P-9825)
CARPENTER CO
Also Called: Carpenter E R Co
7809 Lincoln Ave, Riverside (92504-4442)
P.O. Box 7788 (92513-7788)
PHONE....................................951 354-7550
Jim Nanfeldt, *Manager*
EMP: 480
SALES (corp-wide): 2.1B **Privately Held**
WEB: www.carpenter.com
SIC: 3086 2821 7389 5033 Insulation or
cushioning material, foamed plastic; plas-
tics materials & resins; furniture finishing;
insulation materials
PA: Carpenter Co.
5016 Monument Ave
Richmond VA 23230
804 359-0800

(P-9826)
CLEAN CUT TECHNOLOGIES LLC
1145 N Ocean Cir, Anaheim (92806-1939)
PHONE....................................714 864-3500

Tim Bell,
Ken Munich, *Controller*
Dustin Kelekoma, *QC Mgr*
Matt Fullerton, *Sales Staff*
Larry Bonzoumet,
EMP: 100 EST: 2000
SALES (est): 11.8MM **Privately Held**
WEB: www.cleancuttek.com
SIC: 3086 Packaging & shipping materials,
foamed plastic

(P-9827)
CMD PRODUCTS
Also Called: C M D Products
1410 Flightline Dr Ste D, Lincoln
(95648-9494)
PHONE....................................916 434-0228
David Harris, *President*
▲ EMP: 15
SQ FT: 1,000
SALES (est): 2.8MM **Privately Held**
WEB: www.cmdproducts.com
SIC: 3086 Plastics foam products

(P-9828)
COLD PACK SYSTEM INC
9020 Activity Rd Ste A, San Diego
(92126-4454)
PHONE....................................858 586-0800
David McKinney, *CEO*
Alice Duong, *Principal*
▲ EMP: 15
SQ FT: 20,000
SALES: 3.5MM
SALES (corp-wide): 133.6K **Privately
Held**
WEB: www.coldpacksystem.com
SIC: 3086 2037 Packaging & shipping ma-
terials, foamed plastic; fruits, quick frozen
& cold pack (frozen)
PA: Coldpack
Cold Pack Cold Pack System
Alfortville
622 141-340

(P-9829)
CONSOLIDATED CONTAINER CO LP
Also Called: A Division Continental Can Co
1217 E Saint Gertrude Pl, Santa Ana
(92707-3029)
PHONE....................................714 241-6640
Cesare Calabrese, *Branch Mgr*
Milton Moore, *Engineer*
Veronica Banuelos, *Purch Mgr*
Armando Enriquez, *Maint Spvr*
EMP: 100
SALES (corp-wide): 13.7B **Publicly Held**
SIC: 3086 3085 Plastics foam products;
plastics bottles
HQ: Consolidated Container Company Lp
2500 Windy Ridge Pkwy Se # 1400
Atlanta GA 30339
678 742-4600

(P-9830)
CORRUGATED AND PACKAGING LLC
9651 Airway Rd Ste F, San Diego
(92154-7914)
PHONE....................................619 559-1564
David Ortiz,
Santiago Fernandez,
Ruben Villegas,
EMP: 205
SQ FT: 5,000
SALES: 7MM **Privately Held**
SIC: 3086 2653 Packaging & shipping ma-
terials, foamed plastic; corrugated & solid
fiber boxes

(P-9831)
CPD INDUSTRIES
Also Called: Custom Packaging Design
4665 State St, Montclair (91763-6130)
PHONE....................................909 465-5596
Carlos Hurtado, *President*
Sergio Briceno, *CFO*
Jeff Lenhardt, *Accounts Mgr*
EMP: 29
SQ FT: 22,000
SALES (est): 5.2MM **Privately Held**
WEB: www.casefoam.com
SIC: 3086 Packaging & shipping materials,
foamed plastic

(P-9832)
CUSTOM CONVERTING INC
2625 Temple Heights Dr C, Oceanside
(92056-3590)
PHONE....................................760 724-0664
Dan Kloos, *President*
Tresa Gliponeo, *Vice Pres*
Tolu Peters, *General Mgr*
Roma Kogan, *Purchasing*
▲ EMP: 15
SQ FT: 21,000
SALES (est): 3.5MM **Privately Held**
WEB: www.customconverting.com
SIC: 3086 Packaging & shipping materials,
foamed plastic

(P-9833)
DART CONTAINER CORP CALIFORNIA (PA)
150 S Maple Ctr, Corona (92880)
PHONE....................................951 735-8115
Robert C Dart, *CEO*
Kevin Fox, *Treasurer*
▲ EMP: 300
SQ FT: 50,000
SALES (est): 89.3MM **Privately Held**
SIC: 3086 Cups & plates, foamed plastic

(P-9834)
DART CONTAINER CORP CALIFORNIA
Also Called: Dart Container Corp Calif
1400 E Victor Rd, Lodi (95240-0833)
PHONE....................................209 333-8088
John Brice, *Manager*
Connie Castillo, *QC Dir*
Ron Crookham, *Plant Mgr*
Robert Vargas, *Maintence Staff*
EMP: 170
SALES (corp-wide): 89.3MM **Privately
Held**
SIC: 3086 Cups & plates, foamed plastic
PA: Dart Container Corporation Of Califor-
nia
150 S Maple Ctr
Corona CA 92880
951 735-8115

(P-9835)
DEPENDABLE PLAS & PATTERN INC
4900 Fulton Dr, Fairfield (94534-1641)
PHONE....................................707 863-4900
Harry Marquez, *President*
Emil Eger, *Vice Pres*
EMP: 50
SQ FT: 50,000
SALES (est): 8.4MM **Privately Held**
SIC: 3086 Plastics foam products

(P-9836)
DIVERSIFIED PACKAGING INC
2221 S Anne St, Santa Ana (92704-4410)
PHONE....................................714 850-9316
David A Hoyt, *President*
Kathleen Hoyt, *Treasurer*
Donald Hoyt, *Vice Pres*
EMP: 46
SALES (est): 5.2MM **Privately Held**
SIC: 3086 7389 Packaging & shipping ma-
terials, foamed plastic; packaging & label-
ing services

(P-9837)
DYNAMIKOS INC (PA)
Also Called: Media Products
720 Charcot Ave, San Jose (95131-2207)
PHONE....................................408 432-1711
William Patsuris, *President*
EMP: 10
SQ FT: 8,000
SALES (est): 1.6MM **Privately Held**
WEB: www.mediaproducts.com
SIC: 3086 Packaging & shipping materials,
foamed plastic

(P-9838)
EDM INTERNATIONAL LOGISTICS
2225 W Commwl Ave Ste 110, Alhambra
(91803)
PHONE....................................626 588-2299
Yijie Wan, *Principal*
▲ EMP: 13

SALES (est): 2.2MM **Privately Held**
SIC: **3086** Packaging & shipping materials, foamed plastic

(P-9839)
EPE INDUSTRIES USA INC
Also Called: Epe Industries USA Dallas
17654 Newhope St Ste A, Fountain Valley (92708-4294)
PHONE..................................800 315-0336
Robbie Seagroves, *Branch Mgr*
EMP: 15
SALES (corp-wide): 44.5MM **Privately Held**
SIC: **3086** Carpet & rug cushions, foamed plastic
HQ: Epe Industries Usa, Inc.
17654 Newhope St Ste A
Fountain Valley CA 92708

(P-9840)
EPE INDUSTRIES USA INC
Also Called: Epe USA
1500 Whipple Rd, Union City (94587-2046)
PHONE..................................800 315-0336
Alfonso Arzola, *Branch Mgr*
EMP: 10
SALES (corp-wide): 44.5MM **Privately Held**
SIC: **3086** Packaging & shipping materials, foamed plastic
HQ: Epe Industries Usa, Inc.
17654 Newhope St Ste A
Fountain Valley CA 92708

(P-9841)
EPE INDUSTRIES USA INC (HQ)
Also Called: Epe USA
17654 Newhope St Ste A, Fountain Valley (92708-4294)
PHONE..................................800 315-0336
Troy Merrell, *CEO*
Toshio Yanagi, *CFO*
Brittney Barela, *Admin Asst*
Sylvia Chavira, *Admin Asst*
Armida Tucker, *Accounting Mgr*
EMP: 18
SALES (est): 55.9MM
SALES (corp-wide): 44.5MM **Privately Held**
SIC: **3086** Ice chests or coolers (portable), foamed plastic; packaging & shipping materials, foamed plastic; padding, foamed plastic
PA: Epe Corporation
2-57-5, Nishinippori
Arakawa-Ku TKY 116-0
338 051-111

(P-9842)
FIVE STAR FOOD CONTAINERS INC
250 Eastgate Rd, Barstow (92311-3224)
PHONE..................................626 437-6219
Larry Luc, *President*
▲ EMP: 60
SALES: 30MM **Privately Held**
SIC: **3086** Plastics foam products

(P-9843)
FLORACRAFT CORPORATION
1315 E 3rd St, Pomona (91766-2212)
P.O. Box 420 (91769-0420)
PHONE..................................909 620-4410
Judy Thomski, *Manager*
EMP: 18
SALES (corp-wide): 50MM **Privately Held**
WEB: www.floracraft.com
SIC: **3086** Plastics foam products
PA: Floracraft Corporation
1 W Longfellow Pl
Ludington MI 49431
231 845-5127

(P-9844)
FOAM CONCEPTS INC
4729 E Wesley Dr, Anaheim (92807-1941)
PHONE..................................714 693-1037
Stephen C Ross, *Owner*
▲ EMP: 20
SQ FT: 9,000

SALES (est): 4.4MM **Privately Held**
WEB: www.styro-loc.com
SIC: **3086** Packaging & shipping materials, foamed plastic

(P-9845)
FOAM FABRICATORS INC
301 9th St Ste B, Modesto (95351-4055)
PHONE..................................209 523-7002
Daniel Schloss, *Manager*
EMP: 17 **Publicly Held**
WEB: www.foamfabricators.com
SIC: **3086** Packaging & shipping materials, foamed plastic
HQ: Foam Fabricators, Inc.
8722 E San Alberto Dr # 200
Scottsdale AZ 85258
480 607-7330

(P-9846)
FOAM FACTORY INC
17515 S Santa Fe Ave, Compton (90221-5400)
PHONE..................................310 603-9808
Felipe Alcazar, *President*
▼ EMP: 45
SQ FT: 40,000
SALES (est): 8.5MM **Privately Held**
WEB: www.foambymail.com
SIC: **3086** 3069 5199 5087 Insulation or cushioning material, foamed plastic; foam rubber; foams & rubber; upholsterers' equipment & supplies

(P-9847)
FOAM MOLDERS AND SPECIALTIES (PA)
Also Called: Foam Specialties
11110 Business Cir, Cerritos (90703-5523)
PHONE..................................562 924-7757
Daniel M Doke, *President*
Dan Doke, *President*
Norman Himel, *CFO*
Rory Strammer, *Vice Pres*
Pat Zaremba, *Vice Pres*
▲ EMP: 100
SQ FT: 35,600
SALES (est): 16MM **Privately Held**
WEB: www.foammolders.com
SIC: **3086** 3089 Plastics foam products; thermoformed finished plastic products

(P-9848)
FOAM MOLDERS AND SPECIALTIES
20004 State Rd, Cerritos (90703-6495)
PHONE..................................562 924-7757
EMP: 50
SALES (corp-wide): 16MM **Privately Held**
SIC: **3086** Plastics foam products
PA: Foam Molders And Specialties
11110 Business Cir
Cerritos CA 90703
562 924-7757

(P-9849)
FOAM PLASTICS & RBR PDTS CORP
Also Called: Case Club
4765 E Bryson St, Anaheim (92807-1901)
PHONE..................................714 779-0990
Kirk Plehn, *President*
Brent Plehn, *General Mgr*
Darren Plehn, *Sales Staff*
EMP: 15
SQ FT: 10,000
SALES (est): 2.8MM **Privately Held**
SIC: **3086** 5099 Plastics foam products; cases, carrying

(P-9850)
FOAM-CRAFT INC
2441 Cypress Way, Fullerton (92831-5103)
PHONE..................................714 459-9971
Bruce Schneider, *President*
Michael Blatt, *Admin Sec*
▲ EMP: 165
SQ FT: 110,000
SALES (est): 27.8MM
SALES (corp-wide): 459.1MM **Privately Held**
SIC: **3086** Plastics foam products

PA: Future Foam, Inc.
1610 Avenue N
Council Bluffs IA 51501
712 323-9122

(P-9851)
FOAMATION INC
11852 Glenoaks Blvd, San Fernando (91340-1804)
PHONE..................................818 837-6613
Joshua Cobb, *President*
Ariana Cobb, *COO*
EMP: 10 EST: 1999
SALES (est): 1.2MM **Privately Held**
WEB: www.foamation.com
SIC: **3086** Plastics foam products

(P-9852)
FOAMEX LP
1400 E Victoria Ave, San Bernardino (92408-2924)
PHONE..................................909 824-8981
Ron Paez, *Manager*
EMP: 47
SALES (corp-wide): 385.3MM **Privately Held**
SIC: **3086** Carpet & rug cushions, foamed plastic
PA: Foamex L.P.
1400 N Providence Rd # 2000
Media PA 19063
610 565-2374

(P-9853)
FREE-FLOW PACKAGING INTL INC (DH)
Also Called: FP International
34175 Ardenwood Blvd, Fremont (94555-3653)
PHONE..................................650 261-5300
Arthur Graham Emeritus, *CEO*
Joseph Nezwek, *President*
James Taylor, *COO*
James Blood, *Admin Sec*
Jeremy Culp, *Sales Staff*
▲ EMP: 25
SQ FT: 19,500
SALES (est): 113.3MM
SALES (corp-wide): 4.7B **Privately Held**
WEB: www.fpintl.com
SIC: **3086** Insulation or cushioning material, foamed plastic
HQ: Pregis Llc
1650 Lake Cook Rd Ste 400
Deerfield IL 60015
847 597-2200

(P-9854)
FREE-FLOW PACKAGING INTL INC
Also Called: FP International
34175 Ardenwood Blvd, Fremont (94555-3653)
PHONE..................................323 722-5112
Brian Auxren, *Enginr/R&D Mgr*
EMP: 30
SALES (corp-wide): 4.7B **Privately Held**
WEB: www.fpintl.com
SIC: **3086** Packaging & shipping materials, foamed plastic
HQ: Free-Flow Packaging International, Inc.
34175 Ardenwood Blvd
Fremont CA 94555
650 261-5300

(P-9855)
FUTURE FOAM INC
2451 Cypress Way, Fullerton (92831-5103)
PHONE..................................714 871-2344
Randall Lake, *Manager*
Jeanne Schmaus, *Office Mgr*
EMP: 30
SALES (corp-wide): 459.1MM **Privately Held**
SIC: **3086** Insulation or cushioning material, foamed plastic
PA: Future Foam, Inc.
1610 Avenue N
Council Bluffs IA 51501
712 323-9122

(P-9856)
FUTURE FOAM INC
1000 E Grant Line Rd # 100, Tracy (95304-2836)
PHONE..................................209 832-1886
Michael Walsh, *Branch Mgr*
EMP: 42
SALES (corp-wide): 459.1MM **Privately Held**
SIC: **3086** Carpet & rug cushions, foamed plastic; ice chests or coolers (portable), foamed plastic; insulation or cushioning material, foamed plastic
PA: Future Foam, Inc.
1610 Avenue N
Council Bluffs IA 51501
712 323-9122

(P-9857)
FUTURE FOAM INC
2441 Cypress Way, Fullerton (92831-5103)
PHONE..................................714 459-9971
EMP: 165
SALES (corp-wide): 459.1MM **Privately Held**
SIC: **3086** Plastics foam products
PA: Future Foam, Inc.
1610 Avenue N
Council Bluffs IA 51501
712 323-9122

(P-9858)
FUTURE FOAM INC
Also Called: Formcraft
2441 Cypress Way, Fullerton (92831-5103)
PHONE..................................714 459-9971
Frank Deleon, *Branch Mgr*
Athena Nicolaou, *General Mgr*
EMP: 42
SALES (corp-wide): 459.1MM **Privately Held**
SIC: **3086** 2515 Carpet & rug cushions, foamed plastic; mattresses, containing felt, foam rubber, urethane, etc.
PA: Future Foam, Inc.
1610 Avenue N
Council Bluffs IA 51501
712 323-9122

(P-9859)
FXI INC
Also Called: Foamex
2451 Polvorosa Ave, San Leandro (94577-2237)
P.O. Box 1735 (94577-0809)
PHONE..................................510 357-2600
Bud Silvey, *Manager*
EMP: 100 **Privately Held**
SIC: **3086** Packaging & shipping materials, foamed plastic
HQ: Fxi, Inc.
1400 N Providence Rd # 2000
Media PA 19063

(P-9860)
FXI INC
Also Called: Foamex
2060 N Batavia St, Orange (92865-3102)
PHONE..................................714 637-0110
Mark Stuart, *Branch Mgr*
EMP: 200 **Privately Held**
SIC: **3086** Padding, foamed plastic
HQ: Fxi, Inc.
1400 N Providence Rd # 2000
Media PA 19063

(P-9861)
GLORIANN FARMS INC
11104 W Tracy Blvd, Tracy (95304-9434)
PHONE..................................209 221-7121
Mark Bacchetti, *Branch Mgr*
EMP: 230
SALES (corp-wide): 33.1MM **Privately Held**
WEB: www.pbproduce.com
SIC: **3086** Plastics foam products
PA: Gloriann Farms, Inc.
4598 S Tracy Blvd Ste 160
Tracy CA 95377
209 834-0010

(P-9862)
GOLD VENTURE INC
Also Called: North American Foam & Packg
1050 S State College Blvd, Fullerton
(92831-5335)
PHONE..................................909 623-1810
Fax: 909 865-6880
▲ EMP: 150
SQ FT: 95,000
SALES (est): 19.6MM
SALES (corp-wide): 459.1MM Privately
Held
WEB: www.goldventure.com
SIC: 3086
PA: Future Foam, Inc.
1610 Avenue N
Council Bluffs IA 51501
712 323-9122

(P-9863)
HAPPY2EZ INC
14191 Beach Blvd Ste B, Westminster
(92683-4863)
PHONE..................................714 897-6100
Katherine Vu, CEO
Thanh Vo, Principal
▲ EMP: 14
SALES (est): 1.6MM Privately Held
SIC: 3086 5999 Plastics foam products;
foam & foam products

(P-9864)
HD CARRY INC
81 Columbia Ste 150, Aliso Viejo
(92656-4113)
P.O. Box 218, Lake Forest (92609-0218)
PHONE..................................949 831-6022
Gary W Lantz, President
Carol Lantz, Corp Secy
EMP: 15
SQ FT: 6,000
SALES (est): 2.2MM Privately Held
WEB: www.hdcarry.com
SIC: 3086 Packaging & shipping materials,
foamed plastic

(P-9865)
HUHTAMAKI INC
4209 Noakes St, Commerce (90023-4024)
PHONE..................................323 269-0151
Mark Pettigrew, Branch Mgr
Sandra Martinez, Plant Engr
Albert Victorero, Manager
EMP: 450
SALES (corp-wide): 35.2B Privately Held
SIC: 3086 3089 2657 2656 Cups &
plates, foamed plastic; plastic containers,
except foam; folding paperboard boxes;
sanitary food containers; disposable
plates, cups, napkins & eating utensils;
paperboard mills
HQ: Huhtamaki, Inc.
9201 Packaging Dr
De Soto KS 66018
913 583-3025

(P-9866)
INTER PACKING INC
Also Called: Flexy Foam
12315 Colony Ave, Chino (91710-2092)
PHONE..................................909 465-5555
Alfonso Cardenas, President
EMP: 20
SQ FT: 10,000
SALES (est): 2.4MM Privately Held
WEB: www.flexyfoam.com
SIC: 3086 2653 Padding, foamed plastic;
corrugated boxes, partitions, display
items, sheets & pad

(P-9867)
K & B FOAM INC
9335 Airway Rd Ste 100, San Diego
(92154-7930)
PHONE..................................619 661-1870
Kenji Kasahara, Ch of Bd
Yo Kojima, President
Masahiro Ieyoshi, Exec VP
▲ EMP: 150
SALES (est): 16.7MM Privately Held
WEB: www.kbfoam.com
SIC: 3086 Packaging & shipping materials,
foamed plastic

(P-9868)
**KIVA CONTAINER
CORPORATION**
Also Called: CP Products
2700 E Regal Park Dr, Anaheim
(92806-2417)
PHONE..................................714 630-3850
Claudia England, CEO
Norman England, Treasurer
Ken England, Vice Pres
Tina England, Admin Sec
EMP: 12
SQ FT: 14,800
SALES (est): 2.7MM Privately Held
WEB: www.cpproducts.net
SIC: 3086 Packaging & shipping materials,
foamed plastic

(P-9869)
MARKO PRODUCTS INC (PA)
Also Called: Marko Foam Products
2500 White Rd Ste A, Irvine (92614-6276)
PHONE..................................800 862-7561
Donald J Peterson, Ch of Bd
Tyson Peterson, President
Robert Mallon, Vice Pres
Ilir Bordoniqi, Engineer
▲ EMP: 98 EST: 1962
SQ FT: 114,000
SALES (est): 18.8MM Privately Held
WEB: www.markofoam.com
SIC: 3086 5999 Packaging & shipping ma-
terials, foamed plastic; packaging materi-
als: boxes, padding, etc.

(P-9870)
**MULTI-LINK INTERNATIONAL
CORP**
12235 Los Nietos Rd, Santa Fe Springs
(90670-2909)
PHONE..................................562 941-5380
SAI Hung Chan, President
Spencer Chan, COO
Maria Villagomez, Purch Agent
Michael Jenkins, Sales Staff
▼ EMP: 20
SQ FT: 45,000
SALES (est): 3.5MM Privately Held
WEB: www.multilinkintl.com
SIC: 3086 Plastics foam products

(P-9871)
**NEW IMAGE FOAM PRODUCTS
LLC**
6835 Power Inn Rd, Sacramento
(95828-2401)
P.O. Box 245509 (95824-5509)
PHONE..................................916 388-0741
Dave McDonald,
Wendy King, Office Mgr
Christian Kambel, Sales Staff
Arnold C Morairty,
EMP: 23
SQ FT: 47,000
SALES (est): 2.8MM Privately Held
SIC: 3086 Insulation or cushioning mate-
rial, foamed plastic

(P-9872)
OCEAN BLUE INC
Also Called: Teamwork Packaging
494 Commercial Rd, San Bernardino
(92408-3706)
PHONE..................................909 478-9910
Mehdi Abbas, President
▲ EMP: 20
SALES (est): 6.1MM Privately Held
SIC: 3086 Packaging & shipping materials,
foamed plastic

(P-9873)
PEDNAR PRODUCTS INC
1823 Enterprise Way, Monrovia
(91016-4272)
PHONE..................................626 960-9883
Art Narevsky, President
Sue Narevsky, Admin Sec
Mike Laban, Project Mgr
Ryan Sweeney, Products
Nick Narevsky, Sales Staff
◆ EMP: 10
SQ FT: 5,389
SALES (est): 1.3MM Privately Held
WEB: www.pednar.net
SIC: 3086 Plastics foam products

(P-9874)
PMC GLOBAL INC (PA)
12243 Branford St, Sun Valley
(91352-1010)
P.O. Box 1367 (91353-1367)
PHONE..................................818 896-1101
Philip E Kamins, CEO
Gary E Kamins, President
Thian C Cheong, CFO
Janette Whitt, CFO
◆ EMP: 3800
SALES (est): 2.5B Privately Held
WEB: www.pmcglobalinc.com
SIC: 3086 3674 2865 2816 Plastics foam
products; semiconductors & related de-
vices; food dyes or colors, synthetic; color
pigments; fiberglass insulation; industrial
inorganic chemicals

(P-9875)
**PMC LEADERS IN CHEMICALS
INC (HQ)**
12243 Branford St, Sun Valley
(91352-1010)
PHONE..................................818 896-1101
Gary Kamins, President
EMP: 200
SQ FT: 180,000
SALES: 300MM
SALES (corp-wide): 2.5B Privately Held
SIC: 3086 5169 Plastics foam products;
chemicals & allied products
PA: Pmc Global, Inc.
12243 Branford St
Sun Valley CA 91352
818 896-1101

(P-9876)
POMONA QUALITY FOAM LLC
1279 Philadelphia St, Pomona
(91766-5536)
PHONE..................................909 628-7844
Michael Clark,
Theodore Clark,
EMP: 67
SQ FT: 70,000
SALES (est): 3MM Privately Held
SIC: 3086 Plastics foam products

(P-9877)
PREGIS
159 N San Antonio Ave, Pomona
(91767-5635)
PHONE..................................909 469-8100
Don Crites, Manager
▲ EMP: 23
SALES (est): 4.2MM
SALES (corp-wide): 2.6B Privately Held
SIC: 3086 Packaging & shipping materials,
foamed plastic
PA: Aea Investors Lp
666 5th Ave Fl 36
New York NY 10103
212 644-5900

(P-9878)
**QUALITY FOAM PACKAGING
INC**
31855 Corydon St, Lake Elsinore
(92530-8501)
PHONE..................................951 245-4429
Noel A Castellon, President
Ruth Castellon, Corp Secy
James Barrett, Vice Pres
Jose Granda, General Mgr
Noel Castellon Jr, Plant Mgr
▲ EMP: 25
SQ FT: 56,000
SALES: 9.7MM Privately Held
WEB: www.qualitycase.com
SIC: 3086 Packaging & shipping materials,
foamed plastic

(P-9879)
QYCELL CORPORATION
600 Etiwanda Ave, Ontario (91761-8635)
PHONE..................................909 390-6644
Grant Kesler, CEO
▲ EMP: 25
SQ FT: 45,000
SALES: 14MM Privately Held
SIC: 3086 Plastics foam products

(P-9880)
RINCO INTERNATIONAL INC
31056 Genstar Rd, Hayward (94544-7830)
PHONE..................................510 785-1633
Rollin Yi, President
▲ EMP: 14 EST: 2006
SALES (est): 3.2MM Privately Held
SIC: 3086 Packaging & shipping materials,
foamed plastic

(P-9881)
**SABRED INTERNATIONAL
PACKG INC**
3740 Prospect Ave, Yorba Linda
(92886-1742)
P.O. Box 566 (92885-0566)
PHONE..................................714 996-2800
Sabrina Sierra, President
Edward A Sierra, Vice Pres
EMP: 22
SQ FT: 15,000
SALES (est): 3MM Privately Held
WEB: www.sabred.com
SIC: 3086 5199 5113 5087 Plastics foam
products; packaging materials; corrugated
& solid fiber boxes; janitors' supplies

(P-9882)
SEALED AIR CORPORATION
Packaging Products Div
19440 Arenth Ave, City of Industry
(91748-1424)
PHONE..................................909 594-1791
Rich Scheevel, Regional Mgr
Jamie Hall, Admin Sec
Kevin Conway, Safety Mgr
Sal Ybarra, Mfg Spvr
EMP: 75
SALES (corp-wide): 4.4B Publicly Held
WEB: www.sealedair.com
SIC: 3086 Packaging & shipping materials,
foamed plastic
PA: Sealed Air Corporation
2415 Cascade Pointe Blvd
Charlotte NC 28208
980 221-3235

(P-9883)
SEALED AIR CORPORATION
1835 W Almond Ave, Madera (93637-5209)
PHONE..................................559 675-0152
John Thezieo, Manager
EMP: 110
SALES (corp-wide): 4.4B Publicly Held
WEB: www.sealedair.com
SIC: 3086 Packaging & shipping materials,
foamed plastic
PA: Sealed Air Corporation
2415 Cascade Pointe Blvd
Charlotte NC 28208
980 221-3235

(P-9884)
SPECIALTY ENTERPRISES CO
Also Called: Seco Industries
6858 E Acco St, Commerce (90040-1902)
PHONE..................................323 726-9721
Charles De Heras, President
Carmen Avila, Human Res Dir
▲ EMP: 100
SQ FT: 60,000
SALES (est): 20.4MM Privately Held
WEB: www.seco-ind.com
SIC: 3086 3565 Plastics foam products;
packaging machinery

(P-9885)
STYROTEK INC
345 Road 176, Delano (93215-9471)
P.O. Box 1180 (93216-1180)
PHONE..................................661 725-4957
Martin Caratan, President
Dale Arthur, Corp Secy
Sanford L Campbell, Opers Mgr
▲ EMP: 110
SQ FT: 18,500
SALES (est): 26.6MM Privately Held
WEB: www.styrotek.com
SIC: 3086 Packaging & shipping materials,
foamed plastic

(P-9886)
TEMPLOCK ENTERPRISES LLC
1 N Calle Cesar Chavez # 170, Santa Barbara (93103-5621)
PHONE..................................805 962-3100

408   2019 California
Manufacturers Register   ▲ = Import ▼=Export
◆ =Import/Export

Brian Scarminach,
David Campbell, *Representative*
▲ EMP: 12
SQ FT: 5,000
SALES (est): 1.5MM **Privately Held**
WEB: www.templock.com
SIC: 3086 Packaging & shipping materials,
foamed plastic

(P-9887)
TEMPO PLASTIC CO
1227 N Miller Park Ct, Visalia
(93291-9343)
P.O. Box 44, Morro Bay (93443-0044)
PHONE......................559 651-7711
Douglas B Rogers, *President*
Doug Rogers, *Sales Staff*
▲ EMP: 15
SQ FT: 26,000
SALES (est): 1.1MM **Privately Held**
WEB: www.tempo-foam.com
SIC: 3086 Packaging & shipping materials,
foamed plastic; cups & plates, foamed
plastic; ice chests or coolers (portable),
foamed plastic

(P-9888)
TOPPER PLASTICS INC
Also Called: Tpi
461 E Front St, Covina (91723-1299)
PHONE......................626 331-0561
Patricia Beery, *CEO*
Lewis Beery, *CFO*
Susan Beery, *Admin Sec*
EMP: 15
SQ FT: 20,000
SALES (est): 2.2MM **Privately Held**
SIC: 3086 Packaging & shipping materials,
foamed plastic

(P-9889)
UFP TECHNOLOGIES INC
20211 S Susana Rd, Compton
(90221-5725)
PHONE......................714 662-0277
Richard Tunila, *Branch Mgr*
EMP: 50
SALES (corp-wide): 147.8MM **Publicly
Held**
SIC: 3086 Packaging & shipping materials,
foamed plastic
PA: Ufp Technologies, Inc.
100 Hale St
Newburyport MA 01950
978 352-2200

(P-9890)
VEFO INC
3202 Factory Dr, Pomona (91768-3903)
PHONE......................909 598-3856
Roger Voss, *President*
Pat Voss, *Admin Sec*
Bud Maloney, *Marketing Staff*
EMP: 20
SQ FT: 11,000
SALES (est): 4.1MM **Privately Held**
WEB: www.vefo-foamshapes.com
SIC: 3086 Plastics foam products

(P-9891)
W R GRACE & CO - CONN
Also Called: W R Grace Construction Pdts
2502 S Garnsey St, Santa Ana
(92707-3337)
PHONE......................714 979-4682
John Kozarovich, *Branch Mgr*
EMP: 29
SQ FT: 20,669
SALES (corp-wide): 1.7B **Publicly Held**
WEB: www.grace.com
SIC: 3086 Plastics foam products
HQ: W. R. Grace & Co.-Conn.
7500 Grace Dr
Columbia MD 21044
410 531-4000

(P-9892)
WALTER N COFFMAN INC
5180 Naranja St, San Diego (92114-3515)
PHONE......................619 266-2642
Walter N Coffman, *CEO*
Sherry Williams, *Manager*
EMP: 70
SALES (est): 10.4MM **Privately Held**
SIC: 3086 Cups & plates, foamed plastic

(P-9893)
WARDLEY INDUSTRIAL INC
907 Stokes Ave, Stockton (95215-4027)
P.O. Box 55323 (95205-8823)
PHONE......................209 932-1088
Jackey Wong, *President*
Ambrose Tam, *Treasurer*
Margaret Wong, *Admin Sec*
▲ EMP: 43
SQ FT: 165,000
SALES (est): 9.4MM **Privately Held**
WEB: www.wardleyfilm.com
SIC: 3086 5084 Packaging & shipping ma-
terials, foamed plastic; industrial machin-
ery & equipment

**3087 Custom Compounding
Of Purchased Plastic Resins**

(P-9894)
AUBIN INDUSTRIES INC
23833 S Chrisman Rd, Tracy (95304-8003)
PHONE......................800 324-0051
Philip Aubin, *President*
Linda Aubin, *Corp Secy*
EMP: 15
SQ FT: 13,000
SALES: 1.3MM **Privately Held**
WEB: www.aubinindustries.com
SIC: 3087 Custom compound purchased
resins

**3088 Plastic Plumbing
Fixtures**

(P-9895)
AQUATIC CO
Lasco Bathware
8101 E Kaiser Blvd # 200, Anaheim
(92808-2287)
PHONE......................714 993-1220
Scott Hartman, *Manager*
Mike Seymour, *President*
Paul Van Slyke, *Finance*
Dante San Miguel, *Manager*
EMP: 110
SQ FT: 5,000 **Privately Held**
SIC: 3088 1711 5211 Shower stalls, fiber-
glass & plastic; plumbing, heating, air-
conditioning contractors; bathroom
fixtures, equipment & supplies
PA: Aquatic Co.
1700 N Delilah St
Corona CA 92879

(P-9896)
AQUATIC CO (PA)
1700 N Delilah St, Corona (92879-1893)
PHONE......................714 993-1220
Gary Anderson, *CEO*
Ivy Dominguez, *Manager*
▲ EMP: 65
SALES (est): 305.3MM **Privately Held**
SIC: 3088 Shower stalls, fiberglass & plas-
tic

(P-9897)
AQUATIC INDUSTRIES INC
8101 E Kaiser Blvd # 200, Anaheim
(92808-2287)
PHONE......................800 877-2005
Anthony Reading, *CEO*
Margaret Voskamp, *Vice Pres*
EMP: 160
SQ FT: 78,004
SALES (est): 23.9MM **Privately Held**
SIC: 3088 5999 3949 Plastics plumbing
fixtures; hot tub & spa chemicals, equip-
ment & supplies; sporting & athletic goods

(P-9898)
**CREATIVE SHOWER DOOR
CORP**
43652 S Grimmer Blvd, Fremont
(94538-6381)
PHONE......................510 623-9000
John Patrick Olmstead, *Owner*
EMP: 12

SALES (est): 1.9MM **Privately Held**
SIC: 3088 Shower stalls, fiberglass & plastic

(P-9899)
ELMCO & ASSOC (PA)
11225 Trade Center Dr # 100, Rancho Cor-
dova (95742-6267)
PHONE......................916 383-0110
Kirk Kleinen, *Vice Pres*
Bruce Jenkins, *General Mgr*
Glen Swett, *Opers Mgr*
Diana Morales, *Sales Associate*
Leroy Biggers, *Sales Staff*
EMP: 11
SALES (est): 1.7MM **Privately Held**
SIC: 3088 Plastics plumbing fixtures

(P-9900)
EUROTECH SHOWERS INC
Also Called: E-Tech
23552 Commerce Center Dr B, Laguna
Hills (92653-1570)
PHONE......................949 716-4099
James Simmons, *President*
EMP: 25
SQ FT: 2,800
SALES (est): 575.1K **Privately Held**
SIC: 3088 5023 Shower stalls, fiberglass
& plastic; home furnishings

(P-9901)
FIBER CARE BATHS INC
9832 Yucca Rd Ste A, Adelanto
(92301-2471)
PHONE......................760 246-0019
Harry R Kilpatrick, *CEO*
Kaye Allen, *Controller*
EMP: 275
SQ FT: 6,000
SALES (est): 46.9MM **Privately Held**
WEB: www.fibercarebaths.com
SIC: 3088 Shower stalls, fiberglass & plas-
tic; tubs (bath, shower & laundry), plastic

(P-9902)
**FLORESTONE PRODUCTS CO
(PA)**
2851 Falcon Dr, Madera (93637-9287)
PHONE......................559 661-4171
Ronald R Flores, *CEO*
Carol Deaver, *Corp Secy*
Marcos Robles, *Purch Mgr*
Doug Brown, *Natl Sales Mgr*
▲ EMP: 47
SQ FT: 190,000
SALES (est): 7MM **Privately Held**
WEB: www.florestone.com
SIC: 3088 Shower stalls, fiberglass & plas-
tic; tubs (bath, shower & laundry), plastic

(P-9903)
JACUZZI INC
13925 City Center Dr # 200, Chino Hills
(91709-5438)
PHONE......................909 606-1416
Thomas Koos, *President*
EMP: 23
SALES (est): 3.5MM **Privately Held**
SIC: 3088 Tubs (bath, shower & laundry),
plastic

(P-9904)
JACUZZI PRODUCTS CO (DH)
13925 City Center Dr # 200, Chino Hills
(91709-5438)
PHONE......................909 606-1416
Thomas D Koos, *CEO*
Philip Weeks, *President*
▲ EMP: 120
SALES (est): 114.9MM **Privately Held**
SALES (corp-wide): 1.6B **Privately Held**
WEB: www.jacuzzico.net
SIC: 3088 Tubs (bath, shower & laundry),
plastic; hot tubs, plastic or fiberglass
HQ: Jacuzzi Inc.
14525 Monte Vista Ave
Chino CA 91710
909 606-7733

(P-9905)
JACUZZI WHIRLPOOL BATH INC
14525 Monte Vista Ave, Chino
(91710-5721)
PHONE......................909 548-7732
Jim Barry, *Manager*

EMP: 500
SALES (corp-wide): 1.6B **Privately Held**
WEB: www.jacuzzico.net
SIC: 3088 5091 Tubs (bath, shower &
laundry), plastic; fitness equipment & sup-
plies
HQ: Jacuzzi Products Co.
13925 City Center Dr # 200
Chino Hills CA 91709
909 606-1416

(P-9906)
LE ELEGANT BATH INC
Also Called: American Bath Factory
13405 Estelle St, Corona (92879-1877)
PHONE......................951 734-0238
Richard Wheeler, *President*
Debbie Wheeler, *Admin Sec*
◆ EMP: 120
SQ FT: 18,000
SALES (est): 23.1MM **Privately Held**
WEB: www.americanbathfactory.com
SIC: 3088 Tubs (bath, shower & laundry),
plastic

(P-9907)
MITRANI USA CORP
7451 Westcliff Dr, West Hills (91307-5210)
PHONE......................818 888-9994
Meir Levy, *Vice Pres*
Danny Mitrani, *Sales Dir*
▲ EMP: 10
SALES (est): 1.1MM **Privately Held**
WEB: www.mitrani-usa.com
SIC: 3088

(P-9908)
OUTSOL INC
Also Called: Rinsekit
5910 Sea Lion Pl Ste 120, Carlsbad
(92010-6656)
PHONE......................760 415-8060
Chris Crawford, *President*
EMP: 12
SALES (est): 484.2K **Privately Held**
SIC: 3088 Plastics plumbing fixtures

(P-9909)
PAINTED RHINO INC
14310 Veterans Way, Moreno Valley
(92553-9058)
PHONE......................951 656-5524
Ryan Franklin, *President*
▲ EMP: 35 EST: 2007
SQ FT: 25,000
SALES (est): 5.7MM **Privately Held**
SIC: 3088 Shower stalls, fiberglass & plas-
tic

(P-9910)
PEGGY S LANE INC
Also Called: C M P
2701 Merced St, San Leandro
(94577-5601)
PHONE......................510 483-1202
Matt Clementz, *President*
EMP: 100 EST: 1979
SQ FT: 35,000
SALES (est): 21.7MM **Privately Held**
SIC: 3088 3281 1752 1743 Tubs (bath,
shower & laundry), plastic; bathroom fix-
tures, plastic; cut stone & stone products;
floor laying & floor work; terrazzo, tile,
marble, mosaic work

(P-9911)
**SMITHS ACTION PLASTIC INC
(PA)**
Also Called: Action Plastics
645 S Santa Fe St, Santa Ana
(92705-4143)
PHONE......................714 836-4141
James A Smith, *President*
EMP: 15
SQ FT: 5,000
SALES (est): 9MM **Privately Held**
SIC: 3088 5063 3089 Plastics plumbing
fixtures; electrical fittings & construction
materials; plastic processing

(P-9912)
THERAPY TUBS
27973 Diaz Rd, Temecula (92590-3484)
P.O. Box 850 (92593-0850)
PHONE......................951 553-7001
Chet Millerd, *CEO*

Jack Gasper, *Vice Pres*
Frances Millerd, *Vice Pres*
Harris Millerd, *Admin Sec*
EMP: 10
SQ FT: 150,000
SALES (est): 1.8MM **Privately Held**
SIC: 3088 Hot tubs, plastic or fiberglass

(P-9913)
VORTEX WHIRLPOOL SYSTEMS INC
Also Called: Catalina Spas
26035 Jefferson Ave, Murrieta
(92562-6983)
PHONE....................................951 940-4556
Boyd Cargill, *President*
▲ **EMP:** 60
SQ FT: 100,000
SALES (est): 14.6MM **Privately Held**
WEB: www.catalinaspas.com
SIC: 3088 Hot tubs, plastic or fiberglass

(P-9914)
WATKINS MANUFACTURING CORP
1325 Hot Springs Way, Vista (92081-8360)
PHONE....................................760 598-6464
EMP: 11
SALES (corp-wide): 7.6B **Publicly Held**
SIC: 3088 Hot tubs, plastic or fiberglass
HQ: Watkins Manufacturing Corporation
1280 Park Center Dr
Vista CA 92081
760 598-6464

3089 Plastic Prdts

(P-9915)
A & S MOLD & DIE CORP
9705 Eton Ave, Chatsworth (91311-4306)
PHONE....................................818 341-5393
Arno Adlhoch, *CEO*
Karen Adlhoch, *Corp Secy*
Rina Caoyonan, *Accountant*
▲ **EMP:** 90
SQ FT: 35,000
SALES (est): 8MM **Privately Held**
WEB: www.aandsmold.com
SIC: 3089 3544 Injection molding of plastics; special dies, tools, jigs & fixtures

(P-9916)
A&A GLOBAL IMPORTS INC
3359 E 50th St, Vernon (90058-3003)
PHONE....................................323 767-5990
David Aryan, *President*
Brian Anav, *COO*
James Bunting, *CFO*
Adam Wolf, *Vice Pres*
▲ **EMP:** 26
SALES: 27.1MM **Privately Held**
SIC: 3089 Injection molded finished plastic products

(P-9917)
A-I-M PLASTICS INC
9326 Abraham Way, Santee (92071-2861)
PHONE....................................619 562-1164
Brian P Selby, *President*
Carol Selby, *CFO*
Chad Fox, *Vice Pres*
Gaetano Aprea, *Marketing Mgr*
EMP: 14
SQ FT: 11,497
SALES (est): 1.3MM **Privately Held**
SIC: 3089 Injection molded finished plastic products; injection molding of plastics

(P-9918)
ACCENT PLASTICS INC
1925 Elise Cir, Corona (92879-1882)
PHONE....................................951 273-7777
Thomas A Pridonoff, *CEO*
Bonnie Pridonoff, *Admin Sec*
Josue Cordon, *Administration*
Russell Tull, *Project Engr*
Vicki Coles, *Controller*
▲ **EMP:** 98
SQ FT: 56,000
SALES (est): 25.9MM **Privately Held**
WEB: www.accentplastics.com
SIC: 3089 Injection molding of plastics

(P-9919)
ACCO BRANDS USA LLC
14430 Best Ave, Garden Grove (92841)
PHONE....................................562 941-0505
Dennis L Chandler,
EMP: 35
SALES (corp-wide): 1.9B **Publicly Held**
WEB: www.gbc.com
SIC: 3089 2761 3496 2675 Injection molding of plastics; manifold business forms; clips & fasteners, made from purchased wire; folders, filing, die-cut: made from purchased materials
HQ: Acco Brands Usa Llc
4 Corporate Dr
Lake Zurich IL 60047
800 222-6462

(P-9920)
ACE COMPOSITES INC
1394 Sky Harbor Dr, Olivehurst
(95961-7416)
P.O. Box 59 (95961-0059)
PHONE....................................530 743-1885
Todd Hambrook, *President*
Noe Lopez, *Vice Pres*
John Pimentel, *Vice Pres*
Mark Phelps, *Admin Sec*
EMP: 55
SQ FT: 40,000
SALES (est): 8.5MM **Privately Held**
WEB: www.acecomposites.com
SIC: 3089 Plastic & fiberglass tanks

(P-9921)
ACE PRECISION MOLD CO INC
14701 Carmenita Rd, Norwalk
(90650-5230)
PHONE....................................562 921-8999
Mark S Hyon, *CEO*
Steve Chae, *Vice Pres*
EMP: 10
SQ FT: 2,100
SALES (est): 920K **Privately Held**
SIC: 3089 7699 Injection molding of plastics; industrial tool grinding

(P-9922)
ACORN-GENCON PLASTICS LLC
13818 Oaks Ave, Chino (91710-7008)
PHONE....................................909 591-8461
Donald E Morris, *Mng Member*
Jacqueline Morovati, *General Mgr*
Gabby Soria, *Office Mgr*
John Perrault, *Purchasing*
▲ **EMP:** 68
SQ FT: 94,000
SALES (est): 12.8MM **Privately Held**
WEB: www.acorn-gencon.com
SIC: 3089 3088 3821 3082 Injection molded finished plastic products; plastics plumbing fixtures; laboratory apparatus & furniture; unsupported plastics profile shapes

(P-9923)
ACRYLIC DESIGNS INC
1221 N Barsten Way, Anaheim
(92806-1822)
PHONE....................................714 630-1370
Mitchell Dedic, *President*
Vickie Dedic, *Vice Pres*
EMP: 10
SQ FT: 8,000
SALES (est): 1.5MM **Privately Held**
WEB: www.acrylicdesigns.com
SIC: 3089 7336 Molding primary plastic; commercial art & graphic design

(P-9924)
ACTION ENTERPRISES INC
Also Called: Actionmold
1911 S Betmor Ln, Anaheim (92805-6703)
PHONE....................................714 978-0333
Bill Hall, *CEO*
Steve Burd, *CFO*
EMP: 12
SALES (est): 1.4MM **Privately Held**
SIC: 3089 Injection molding of plastics

(P-9925)
ACTION INNOVATIONS INC
Also Called: Action Mold and Tool Co
1911 S Betmor Ln, Anaheim (92805-6703)
PHONE....................................714 978-0333

Bill Hall, *CEO*
Stephen Burd, *President*
EMP: 30
SQ FT: 15,000
SALES (est): 4.8MM **Privately Held**
WEB: www.actionmold.com
SIC: 3089 Injection molding of plastics

(P-9926)
ADVANCED CMPSITE PDTS TECH INC
Also Called: Acpt
15602 Chemical Ln, Huntington Beach
(92649-1507)
PHONE....................................714 895-5544
James C Leslie II, *President*
Theada Burgess, *Controller*
Ryan Clampitt, *Marketing Staff*
EMP: 45
SQ FT: 25,300
SALES (est): 9.9MM **Privately Held**
WEB: www.acpt.com
SIC: 3089 8748 Hardware, plastic; business consulting

(P-9927)
ADVANCED COMPOSITES ENGRG LLC
Also Called: Advanced Composites Engrg
42245 Sarah Way, Temecula (92590-3463)
PHONE....................................951 694-3055
Joe Albertellie,
Meredith Albertellie,
EMP: 10
SQ FT: 8,000
SALES (est): 1MM **Privately Held**
WEB: www.advancedcompositeseng.com
SIC: 3089 2221 Reinforcing mesh, plastic; flat panels, plastic; hardware, plastic; fiberglass fabrics

(P-9928)
ADVANCED ENGRG MLDING TECH INC
6510 Box Springs Blvd B, Riverside
(92507-0740)
P.O. Box 5620 (92517-5620)
PHONE....................................951 656-6607
Donald Furness, *President*
Helen Furness, *Vice Pres*
Bob Zielinski, *Engineer*
Onar Isip, *QC Mgr*
▲ **EMP:** 20
SQ FT: 12,000
SALES (est): 4.6MM **Privately Held**
WEB: www.aemt.com
SIC: 3089 Molding primary plastic; injection molding of plastics

(P-9929)
ADVANCED POLYMER TECH LLC
3837 Imperial Way, Stockton (95215-9691)
PHONE....................................209 464-2701
Steven Kessler, *Mng Member*
Scott Thompson, *Buyer*
Sue Canada, *Manager*
◆ **EMP:** 22
SQ FT: 40,000
SALES (est): 11MM **Privately Held**
WEB: www.aptllc.net
SIC: 3089 Injection molding of plastics

(P-9930)
ADVANCED THRMLFORMING ENTP INC
Also Called: A T E
3750 Oceanic Way, Oceanside
(92056-2650)
PHONE....................................760 722-4400
Hai Parson, *President*
Anh Doan, *Shareholder*
David Cox, *Vice Pres*
EMP: 13
SALES (est): 1.8MM **Privately Held**
SIC: 3089 Thermoformed finished plastic products

(P-9931)
AIR LOGISTICS CORPORATION (PA)
Also Called: Field Applied Cmposite Systems
146 Railroad Ave, Monrovia (91016-4642)
PHONE....................................626 633-0294
George H Schirtzinger, *CEO*

David Buckley, *Vice Pres*
Franz Worth, *Program Mgr*
George Schirtzinger, *CIO*
Scott Dorgan, *Accounting Mgr*
◆ **EMP:** 12
SALES (est): 4MM **Privately Held**
WEB: www.airlog.com
SIC: 3089 3728 Reinforcing mesh, plastic; aircraft parts & equipment

(P-9932)
AJAX - UNTD PTTRNS & MOLDS INC
Also Called: Ajax Custom Manufacturing
34585 7th St, Union City (94587-3673)
PHONE....................................510 476-8000
Dana Waldman, *CEO*
Mark REA, *Engineer*
Diana Alvarez, *Human Res Mgr*
Daryoosh Pazdel, *Opers Mgr*
Ramnik Nijjar, *Production*
EMP: 140
SQ FT: 85,000
SALES (est): 1.3MM
SALES (corp-wide): 655.8MM **Publicly Held**
WEB: www.ajaxmfg.com
SIC: 3089 3599 3543 Plastic processing; machine shop, jobbing & repair; foundry patternmaking
PA: Ichor Holdings, Ltd.
3185 Laurelview Ct
Fremont CA 94538
510 897-5200

(P-9933)
AKRA PLASTIC PRODUCTS INC
1504 E Cedar St, Ontario (91761-5761)
PHONE....................................909 930-1999
R Wayne Callaway, *President*
Bentley Callaway, *Vice Pres*
Alex Semeczko, *Vice Pres*
Brian Fuerbach, *Research*
EMP: 37 **EST:** 1972
SQ FT: 36,000
SALES (est): 6.6MM **Privately Held**
WEB: www.akraplastics.com
SIC: 3089 Injection molding of plastics; plastic processing

(P-9934)
ALLEN MOLD INC
1100 W Katella Ave Ste N, Orange
(92867-3515)
PHONE....................................714 538-6517
Clayton Allen, *President*
Mike Sillett, *Design Engr*
EMP: 18
SQ FT: 5,800
SALES (est): 3.5MM **Privately Held**
WEB: www.allenmold.com
SIC: 3089 Blow molded finished plastic products

(P-9935)
ALLTEC INTEGRATED MFG INC
Also Called: New Age Enclosures
2240 S Thornburg St, Santa Maria
(93455-1248)
PHONE....................................805 595-3500
Randall Dennis, *CEO*
Tonya Delgado, *Office Mgr*
Maria Martin, *Administration*
Moe Wilson, *Project Mgr*
Travis Gorter, *QC Mgr*
▲ **EMP:** 40
SQ FT: 13,500
SALES (est): 9.4MM **Privately Held**
WEB: www.alltecmfg.com
SIC: 3089 2821 Injection molding of plastics; plastics materials & resins

(P-9936)
ALPHENA TECHNOLOGIES
414 Cloverleaf Dr Ste B, Baldwin Park
(91706-6507)
PHONE....................................626 961-6098
Shirley Chung, *President*
▲ **EMP:** 10
SALES (est): 1.3MM **Privately Held**
SIC: 3089 Plastics products

(P-9937)
AMA PLASTICS (PA)
1100 Citrus St, Riverside (92507-1731)
PHONE....................................951 734-5600

▲ = Import ▼=Export
◆ =Import/Export

Mark Atchinson, *CEO*
Laura Raney, *President*
Ed Buehler, *Engineer*
Chris McMillon, *Engineer*
Don Jensen, *VP Finance*
◆ **EMP:** 393
SQ FT: 92,000
SALES (est): 149.5MM **Privately Held**
WEB: www.amaplastics.com
SIC: 3089 3544 Molding primary plastic;
forms (molds), for foundry & plastics
working machinery

(P-9938)
AMCOR RIGID PLASTICS USA
LLC
14270 Ramona Ave, Chino (91710-5738)
PHONE..................................520 746-0737
Dan Meyer, *Branch Mgr*
EMP: 16
SALES (corp-wide): 9.1B **Privately Held**
WEB: www.slpcamericas.com
SIC: 3089 Plastic containers, except foam
HQ: Amcor Rigid Plastics Usa, Llc
935 Technology Dr Ste 100
Ann Arbor MI 48108

(P-9939)
AMERICAN APPAREL ACC INC
(PA)
10160 Olney St, El Monte (91731-2312)
PHONE..................................626 350-3828
Lily Chang, *President*
Steve Bernstein, *Vice Pres*
▲ **EMP:** 21
SQ FT: 5,000
SALES: 2MM **Privately Held**
WEB: www.aaahangers.com
SIC: 3089 Injection molding of plastics

(P-9940)
AMERICAN DESIGN INC
1672 Industrial Blvd, Chula Vista
(91911-3922)
PHONE..................................619 429-1995
Bruce R Jamieson, *President*
Catherine Jamieson, *Corp Secy*
EMP: 16
SQ FT: 20,000
SALES: 2.8MM **Privately Held**
SIC: 3089 Plastic processing

(P-9941)
AMERICAN INNOTEK INC (PA)
Also Called: Brief Relief
2655 Vsta Pcf Drv Ocnside Oceanside,
Oceanside (92056)
PHONE..................................760 741-6600
Clarence A Cassidy, *Ch of Bd*
Niki Kopenhaver, *President*
Rafael Ignacio, *COO*
Terry H Cassidy, *Vice Pres*
Jeff Griffin, *QA Dir*
◆ **EMP:** 57
SQ FT: 54,000
SALES (est): 13.4MM **Privately Held**
WEB: www.restop.com
SIC: 3089 3431 3088 Plastic containers,
except foam; metal sanitary ware; plastics
plumbing fixtures

(P-9942)
AMERICAN INTERNATIONAL
RACING
1132 W Kirkwall Rd, Azusa (91702-5128)
PHONE..................................626 969-7733
Harold Hannemann, *President*
John Brewer, *Manager*
▲ **EMP:** 12
SALES (est): 935.4K **Privately Held**
WEB:
www.americaninternationalracing.com
SIC: 3089 Automotive parts, plastic

(P-9943)
AMERICAN PLASTIC CARD CO
21550 Oxnard St Ste 300, Woodland Hills
(91367-7109)
PHONE..................................818 784-4224
Jim Akbar, *President*
James Alexander, *Vice Pres*
Peggy Peterson, *Vice Pres*
EMP: 120
SQ FT: 50,000

SALES (est): 14MM **Privately Held**
WEB: www.apcci.com
SIC: 3089 2759 Identification cards, plas-
tic; commercial printing

(P-9944)
AMERICAN TECHNICAL
MOLDING INC
2052 W 11th St, Upland (91786-3509)
PHONE..................................909 982-1025
Brian King, *CEO*
▲ **EMP:** 120
SQ FT: 50,000
SALES (est): 26.9MM
SALES (corp-wide): 228.9MM **Privately**
Held
WEB: www.deepdraw.com
SIC: 3089 Injection molding of plastics
HQ: Bandera Acquisition, Llc
2 Hampshire St
Foxborough MA 02035
480 553-6400

(P-9945)
AMERIMADE TECHNOLOGY INC
449 Mountain Vista Pkwy, Livermore
(94551-8212)
PHONE..................................925 243-9090
Todd Thomas, *President*
Stephanie Castro, *Purch Mgr*
Lyn Duong,
EMP: 50
SQ FT: 65,000
SALES (est): 9.7MM **Privately Held**
WEB: www.amerimade.com
SIC: 3089 3674 Injection molding of plas-
tics; semiconductors & related devices

(P-9946)
AMFLEX PLASTICS
INCORPORATED
4039 Calle Platino Ste G, Oceanside
(92056-5827)
PHONE..................................760 643-1756
Raul A Castro, *President*
Ana Maria Castro, *CFO*
Mary Guzman, *Admin Asst*
EMP: 21
SQ FT: 18,000
SALES: 3.5MM **Privately Held**
WEB: www.amflex.com
SIC: 3089 Injection molded finished plastic
products

(P-9947)
ANAHEIM CUSTOM EXTRUDERS
INC
Also Called: Ace
4640 E La Palma Ave, Anaheim
(92807-1910)
PHONE..................................714 693-8508
William A Czapar, *Ch of Bd*
Chrintina Smith, *Exec VP*
EMP: 48
SQ FT: 26,000
SALES (est): 9.2MM **Privately Held**
WEB: www.acextrusions.com
SIC: 3089 3082 Extruded finished plastic
products; unsupported plastics profile
shapes

(P-9948)
ANDERSON MOULDS
INCORPORATED
3131 E Anita St, Stockton (95205-3904)
PHONE..................................209 943-1145
Garry W Anderson, *President*
Victoria Anderson, *Corp Secy*
▲ **EMP:** 15 **EST:** 1975
SQ FT: 48,000
SALES (est): 2.4MM **Privately Held**
WEB: www.andersonmoulds.com
SIC: 3089 Injection molding of plastics

(P-9949)
ANNMAR INDUSTRIES INC
990 S Jay Cir, Anaheim (92808-2105)
PHONE..................................714 630-5443
Mark Thornberg, *President*
Julie Thornberg, *Corp Secy*
EMP: 10
SQ FT: 9,160

SALES (est): 1.4MM **Privately Held**
WEB: www.annmarindustries.com
SIC: 3089 3471 3088 Plastic hardware &
building products; plating & polishing;
plastics plumbing fixtures

(P-9950)
ANURA PLASTIC ENGINEERIGN
5050 Rivergrade Rd, Baldwin Park
(91706-1405)
PHONE..................................626 814-9684
Wolfgang Buehler, *CEO*
Anura Welikala, *President*
EMP: 100
SQ FT: 35,000
SALES (est): 8.4MM **Privately Held**
WEB: www.apec-plastics.com
SIC: 3089 Injection molding of plastics

(P-9951)
AP PLASTICS
4025 Garner Rd, Riverside (92501-1043)
PHONE..................................951 782-0705
Gary A Bennett, *Principal*
EMP: 11
SALES (est): 1.6MM **Privately Held**
SIC: 3089 Air mattresses, plastic

(P-9952)
ARC PLASTICS INC
14010 Shoemaker Ave, Norwalk
(90650-4536)
PHONE..................................562 802-3299
Richard Renaudo, *President*
Olga Peralta, *Vice Pres*
EMP: 20
SQ FT: 1,600
SALES (est): 3.4MM **Privately Held**
SIC: 3089 Injection molded finished plastic
products; injection molding of plastics

(P-9953)
ARCHITECTURAL PLASTICS
INC
1299 N Mcdowell Blvd, Petaluma
(94954-1133)
PHONE..................................707 765-9898
Pierre Miremont, *President*
Mark Lindlow, *Exec VP*
Blake Miremont, *Mktg Dir*
Keith Kwitchoff, *Supervisor*
▼ **EMP:** 32
SQ FT: 16,000
SALES (est): 6.8MM **Privately Held**
WEB: www.archplastics.com
SIC: 3089 Injection molding of plastics

(P-9954)
ARGEE MFG CO SAN DIEGO INC
9550 Pathway St, Santee (92071-4169)
P.O. Box 710222 (92072-0222)
PHONE..................................619 449-5050
Robert Goldman, *President*
Ruth Goldman, *Treasurer*
Efi Mizrahi, *General Mgr*
Ali Bafandeh, *Controller*
▲ **EMP:** 75
SQ FT: 65,000
SALES (est): 16.4MM **Privately Held**
WEB: www.argeecorp.com
SIC: 3089 Plastic hardware & building
products

(P-9955)
ARLON LLC
Arlon Adhesives-Films Division
2811 S Harbor Blvd, Santa Ana
(92704-5805)
PHONE..................................714 540-2811
Elmer Pruim, *President*
Jim Freeland, *Mfg Mgr*
EMP: 150
SQ FT: 124,478
SALES (corp-wide): 821MM **Publicly**
Held
WEB: www.arlon.com
SIC: 3089 3081 2672 Plastic hardware &
building products; unsupported plastics
film & sheet; coated & laminated paper
HQ: Arlon Llc
1100 Governor Lea Rd
Bear DE 19701
302 834-2100

(P-9956)
ARMORCAST PRODUCTS
COMPANY
500 S Dupont Ave, Ontario (91761-1508)
PHONE..................................909 390-1365
Paul Boghossian, *Branch Mgr*
EMP: 40
SALES (corp-wide): 95.6MM **Privately**
Held
SIC: 3089 5092 Plastic processing; toys
PA: Armorcast Products Company, Inc.
13230 Saticoy St
North Hollywood CA 91605
818 982-3600

(P-9957)
ART SERVICES MELROSE
626 N Almont Dr, West Hollywood
(90069-5608)
PHONE..................................310 247-1452
Jeff Roberts, *President*
Russ Roberts, *Master*
EMP: 14
SALES (est): 1.2MM **Privately Held**
WEB: www.artservicesmelrose.com
SIC: 3089 Plastic processing

(P-9958)
ARTHURMADE PLASTICS INC
Also Called: Kirk Containers
2131 Garfield Ave, Commerce
(90040-1805)
PHONE..................................323 721-7325
Kirk Marounian, *President*
Arthur Marounian, *Vice Pres*
Silva Marounian, *Vice Pres*
EMP: 75
SQ FT: 20,000
SALES (est): 29.2MM **Privately Held**
WEB: www.apikirkcontainers.com
SIC: 3089 Injection molding of plastics

(P-9959)
ARTISTIC PLASTICS INC
725 E Harrison St, Corona (92879-1350)
PHONE..................................951 808-9700
Diane Mixson, *President*
EMP: 10 **EST:** 2011
SALES (est): 1.2MM **Privately Held**
SIC: 3089 Air mattresses, plastic

(P-9960)
ASTROFOAM MOLDING
COMPANY INC
4117 Calle Tesoro, Camarillo (93012-8760)
PHONE..................................805 482-7276
Anthony Bevan, *Ch of Bd*
Steven Bevan, *President*
Pamela R Bevan, *Corp Secy*
Christopher Bevan, *Vice Pres*
▲ **EMP:** 18
SQ FT: 21,000
SALES (est): 2.4MM **Privately Held**
WEB: www.astrofoam.com
SIC: 3089 Thermoformed finished plastic
products

(P-9961)
ATS PRODUCTS INC (PA)
2785 Goodrick Ave, Richmond
(94801-1109)
PHONE..................................510 234-3173
J Jeffrey Shea, *President*
Doug Williams, *Sales Staff*
Kathleen Passalacqua,
▲ **EMP:** 50
SQ FT: 35,000
SALES (est): 15.6MM **Privately Held**
WEB: www.atsduct.com
SIC: 3089 Plastic hardware & building
products

(P-9962)
AVERY PLASTICS INC
4070 Goldfinch St Ste A, San Diego
(92103-1865)
P.O. Box 180486, Coronado (92178-0486)
PHONE..................................619 696-1230
Martin Avery, *President*
Pauline Avery, *CEO*
Pauline A Avery, *Manager*
EMP: 95
SQ FT: 50,000
SALES (est): 11.6MM **Privately Held**
SIC: 3089 Injection molding of plastics

(P-9963)
AXIUM PLASTICS LLC
5701 Clark St, Ontario (91761-3640)
PHONE.................................909 969-0766
Kulwinder Singh, *Manager*
EMP: 58 **Privately Held**
SIC: 3089 Plastic containers, except foam
PA: Axium Plastics, Llc
9005 Smiths Mill Rd
New Albany OH 43054

(P-9964)
AXYGEN INC (HQ)
Also Called: Axygen Scientific
33210 Central Ave, Union City
(94587-2010)
PHONE.................................510 494-8900
Hemant Gupta, *President*
Amit Bansal, *CFO*
Todd C Gilmore, *Accounts Mgr*
◆ **EMP:** 50
SQ FT: 33,000
SALES (est): 21.9MM
SALES (corp-wide): 10.1B **Publicly Held**
WEB: www.axygen.com
SIC: 3089 Injection molding of plastics
PA: Corning Incorporated
1 Riverfront Plz
Corning NY 14831
607 974-9000

(P-9965)
B & S PLASTICS INC
Also Called: Waterway Plastics
2200 Sturgis Rd, Oxnard (93030-8978)
PHONE.................................805 981-0262
Bill Spears, *CEO*
Sandy Spears, *Corp Secy*
▲ **EMP:** 700
SQ FT: 240,000
SALES (est): 228.8MM **Privately Held**
WEB: www.waterwayplastics.com
SIC: 3089 Injection molding of plastics

(P-9966)
B AND P PLASTICS INC
Also Called: Advance Plastics
225 W 30th St, National City (91950-7203)
PHONE.................................619 477-1893
Bruce Browne, *President*
Patricia Browne, *General Mgr*
▲ **EMP:** 35
SQ FT: 10,000
SALES (est): 11.5MM **Privately Held**
WEB: www.advanceplastics.com
SIC: 3089 3061 Molding primary plastic;
mechanical rubber goods

(P-9967)
BACE MANUFACTURING INC
(HQ)
Also Called: Spm
3125 E Coronado St, Anaheim
(92806-1915)
PHONE.................................714 630-6002
Richard R Harris, *President*
Shannon White, *Vice Pres*
EMP: 700
SQ FT: 200,000
SALES (est): 80.5MM
SALES (corp-wide): 455.5MM **Privately Held**
WEB: www.spmfremont.com
SIC: 3089 Injection molding of plastics;
molding primary plastic
PA: Medplast Group, Inc.
7865 Northcourt Rd # 100
Houston TX 77040
480 553-6400

(P-9968)
BACE MANUFACTURING INC
Spm/Fremont, CA
45581 Northport Loop W, Fremont
(94538-6462)
PHONE.................................510 657-5800
James W Collins, *Manager*
EMP: 100
SALES (corp-wide): 455.5MM **Privately Held**
SIC: 3089 3544 Molding primary plastic;
special dies, tools, jigs & fixtures

HQ: Bace Manufacturing, Inc.
3125 E Coronado St
Anaheim CA 92806
714 630-6002

(P-9969)
BALDA C BREWER INC (DH)
Also Called: C Brewer Company
4501 E Wall St, Ontario (91761-8143)
PHONE.................................714 630-6810
Christoph Klaus, *CEO*
Steve Holland, *President*
Harold Hee, *Vice Pres*
Holly Alex, *Office Mgr*
Sal Tinajero, *Info Tech Mgr*
▲ **EMP:** 161 **EST:** 1968
SQ FT: 60,000
SALES (est): 47.3MM
SALES (corp-wide): 562.9K **Privately Held**
SIC: 3089 3544 Molding primary plastic;
special dies, tools, jigs & fixtures
HQ: Clere Ag
Schluterstr. 45
Berlin 10707
302 130-0430

(P-9970)
BALDA C BREWER INC
4501 E Wall St, Ontario (91761-8143)
PHONE.................................714 630-6810
EMP: 13
SALES (corp-wide): 562.9K **Privately Held**
SIC: 3089 Molding primary plastic
HQ: Balda C. Brewer, Inc.
4501 E Wall St
Ontario CA 91761
714 630-6810

(P-9971)
BARBER-WEBB COMPANY INC
(PA)
3833 Medford St, Los Angeles
(90063-1997)
PHONE.................................541 488-4821
Donald B Barber Jr, *President*
James Barber, *Exec VP*
Wr Greenbecker, *Senior VP*
Brian Barber, *Admin Sec*
Gaby Mendez, *Technology*
▼ **EMP:** 30
SQ FT: 106,000
SALES (est): 10.6MM **Privately Held**
WEB: www.barber-webb.com
SIC: 3089 Plastic processing

(P-9972)
BAYVIEW PLASTIC SOLUTIONS
INC
43651 S Grimmer Blvd, Fremont
(94538-6347)
PHONE.................................510 360-0001
Martin Hernandez, *President*
Terri Hernandez, *General Mgr*
Katie Loux, *Office Mgr*
Catherine Cardenas, *Admin Asst*
Nathan Martinez, *Prdtn Mgr*
EMP: 26
SALES (est): 5.5MM **Privately Held**
SIC: 3089 Plastic processing

(P-9973)
BEEMAK PLASTICS LLC
Also Called: Beemak-Idl Display Products
16711 Knott Ave, La Mirada (90638-6013)
PHONE.................................310 886-5880
Howard Topping, *President*
Chris Braun, *President*
Felix Salvador, *Design Engr*
Brett Sharp, *Engineer*
Alejandro Quintero, *Purchasing*
▲ **EMP:** 100
SQ FT: 110,000
SALES (est): 23.9MM
SALES (corp-wide): 581.8MM **Privately Held**
WEB: www.beemak.com
SIC: 3089 Injection molding of plastics;
plastic processing
HQ: Deflecto, Llc
7035 E 86th St
Indianapolis IN 46250
317 849-9555

(P-9974)
BENT MANUFACTURING CO
BDAA INC
15442 Chemical Ln, Huntington Beach
(92649-1220)
PHONE.................................714 842-0600
Bruce Christopher Bent, *CEO*
EMP: 10
SALES (est): 1.4MM **Privately Held**
SIC: 3089 3499 5093 Blow molded fin-
ished plastic products; barricades, metal;
barrels & drums

(P-9975)
BERICAP LLC
1671 Champagne Ave Ste B, Ontario
(91761-3650)
PHONE.................................909 390-5518
Steve Buckley, *President*
David Andison, *President*
Hany Shash, *Sr Corp Ofcr*
Ozgur Akin, *General Mgr*
Tarek Sultan, *General Mgr*
▲ **EMP:** 67
SALES (est): 19.9MM **Privately Held**
WEB: www.bericap.com
SIC: 3089 Injection molded finished plastic
products
HQ: Bericap Holding Gmbh
Kirchstr. 5
Budenheim 55257
613 929-020

(P-9976)
BERRY GLOBAL INC
3030 S Susan St, Santa Ana (92704-6435)
PHONE.................................714 751-2920
Martha Harmon, *Manager*
EMP: 14 **Publicly Held**
WEB: www.6sens.com
SIC: 3089 Bottle caps, molded plastic
HQ: Berry Global, Inc.
101 Oakley St
Evansville IN 47710
812 424-2904

(P-9977)
BERRY GLOBAL INC
4875 E Hunter Ave, Anaheim (92807-2005)
PHONE.................................714 777-5200
Don Parodi, *Manager*
Aaron Hill, *Technical Mgr*
Ken Clark, *Engineer*
James Green, *Engineer*
Suzanne Winkler, *Sales Staff*
EMP: 15 **Publicly Held**
SIC: 3089 3081 Bottle caps, molded plas-
tic; unsupported plastics film & sheet
HQ: Berry Global, Inc.
101 Oakley St
Evansville IN 47710
812 424-2904

(P-9978)
BERRY GLOBAL INC
14000 Monte Vista Ave, Chino
(91710-5537)
PHONE.................................909 465-9055
Salama Elsayed, *Branch Mgr*
EMP: 200 **Publicly Held**
SIC: 3089 3081 Bottle caps, molded plas-
tic; unsupported plastics film & sheet
HQ: Berry Global, Inc.
101 Oakley St
Evansville IN 47710
812 424-2904

(P-9979)
BERRY GLOBAL INC
13335 Orden Dr, Santa Fe Springs
(90670-6334)
PHONE.................................800 462-3843
Laura Reta, *Branch Mgr*
EMP: 25 **Publicly Held**
WEB: www.6sens.com
SIC: 3089 Plastic containers, except foam
HQ: Berry Global, Inc.
101 Oakley St
Evansville IN 47710
812 424-2904

(P-9980)
BERRY GLOBAL INC
4875 E Hunter Ave, Anaheim (92807-2005)
PHONE.................................714 777-5200
EMP: 127 **Publicly Held**

SIC: 3089 Bottle caps, molded plastic
HQ: Berry Global, Inc.
101 Oakley St
Evansville IN 47710
812 424-2904

(P-9981)
BETTER WORLD
MANUFACTURING INC (PA)
Also Called: A Better Trap
3535 N Sabre Dr, Fresno (93727-7817)
PHONE.................................559 291-4276
Richard Alvarado, *President*
Rich Alvarado, *President*
Janie Alvarado, *Vice Pres*
▲ **EMP:** 10
SQ FT: 25,000
SALES (est): 1.6MM **Privately Held**
WEB: www.jeffry.com
SIC: 3089 Injection molding of plastics

(P-9982)
BH-TECH INC
7841 Balboa Ave Ste 208, San Diego
(92111-2313)
PHONE.................................858 694-0900
Seung Hoon Han, *CEO*
Woo Hyuk Choi, *CFO*
EMP: 700
SQ FT: 500
SALES (est): 50MM **Privately Held**
SIC: 3089 Injection molding of plastics

(P-9983)
BLISTERPAK INC
3020 Supply Ave, Commerce (90040-2710)
PHONE.................................323 728-5555
Steven C Mattis, *CEO*
▲ **EMP:** 20 **EST:** 1974
SQ FT: 15,000
SALES (est): 4.6MM **Privately Held**
SIC: 3089 Thermoformed finished plastic
products

(P-9984)
BLOSS INC
1840 Enterprise Way, Monrovia
(91016-4271)
P.O. Box 417 (91017-0417)
PHONE.................................626 599-9944
Eileen Baumgartner, *President*
Ross Tiamson, *Corp Secy*
Glenn Giffin, *Vice Pres*
EMP: 36
SQ FT: 10,500
SALES (est): 5.7MM
SALES (corp-wide): 6.1MM **Privately Held**
WEB: www.bloss.com
SIC: 3089 7336 3081 3993 Engraving of
plastic; silk screen design; unsupported
plastics film & sheet; signs & advertising
specialties; automotive & apparel trim-
mings
PA: P K & Associates, Inc
214 N 1st Ave
Arcadia CA

(P-9985)
BLOW MOLDED PRODUCTS INC
Also Called: Bmp
4720 Felspar St, Riverside (92509-3068)
PHONE.................................951 360-6055
Larry Harden, *CEO*
Mike Bynum, *Director*
EMP: 40
SQ FT: 25,000
SALES (est): 9.7MM **Privately Held**
WEB: www.blowmoldedproducts.com
SIC: 3089 Blow molded finished plastic
products; injection molding of plastics

(P-9986)
BOLERO INDS INC A CAL CORP
Also Called: Bolero Plastics
11850 Burke St, Santa Fe Springs
(90670-2536)
PHONE.................................562 693-3000
Daniel Imasdounian, *CEO*
Vasken Imasdounian, *Vice Pres*
Annie Imasdounian, *Admin Sec*
Nova Imasdounian, *Safety Mgr*
EMP: 25 **EST:** 1975
SQ FT: 19,500

▲ = Import ▼ =Export
◆ =Import/Export

SALES (est): 4.2MM **Privately Held**
WEB: www.boleroplastics.com
SIC: **3089** Plastic processing

(P-9987)
BOMATIC INC (HQ)
Also Called: Bmi
43225 Business Park Dr, Temecula
(92590-3648)
P.O. Box 580 (92593-0580)
PHONE...............................909 947-3900
Kjeld R Hestehave, *President*
Borge Hestehave, *Ch of Bd*
Mary Ann, *CEO*
Kirk Franks, *CFO*
Kresten Hestehave, *Vice Pres*
▲ EMP: 40
SQ FT: 35,000
SALES (est): 23.6MM **Privately Held**
WEB: www.bomatic.com
SIC: **3089** Blow molded finished plastic
products; injection molding of plastics
PA: Universal Packaging West, Inc.
43225 Business Park Dr
Temecula CA 92590
909 947-3900

(P-9988)
BOMATIC INC
2181 E Francis St, Ontario (91761-7723)
PHONE...............................909 947-3900
Back Melon, *Manager*
EMP: 50
SALES (corp-wide): 23.6MM **Privately
Held**
WEB: www.bomatic.com
SIC: **3089** Plastic containers, except foam
HQ: Bomatic Inc.
43225 Business Park Dr
Temecula CA 92590
909 947-3900

(P-9989)
BOTTLEMATE INC
2095 Leo Ave, Commerce (90040-1626)
PHONE...............................323 887-9009
Kai-Win Chuang, *CEO*
Anderson Chuang, *Vice Pres*
MEI-LI Chang, *Admin Sec*
Katherine Chen, *Accounts Exec*
▲ EMP: 25
SQ FT: 25,000
SALES (est): 5MM **Privately Held**
WEB: www.bottlemate.com
SIC: **3089** 5162 Blow molded finished
plastic products; plastics products

(P-9990)
BRADLEY MANUFACTURING CO INC
Also Called: Bradley's Plastic Bag Co
9130 Firestone Blvd, Downey
(90241-5319)
PHONE...............................562 923-5556
Keith Smith, *President*
Richard Lane, *Corp Secy*
Robert Schneider, *Plant Mgr*
EMP: 28
SQ FT: 30,000
SALES (est): 4.9MM **Privately Held**
WEB: www.bradleybag.com
SIC: **3089** 3069 3083 2673 Plastic pro-
cessing; tubing, rubber; sheets, hard rub-
ber; laminated plastics plate & sheet;
bags: plastic, laminated & coated

(P-9991)
BRAIFORM ENTERPRISES INC
Plaza Plastic
576 N Gilbert St, Fullerton (92833-2549)
PHONE...............................714 526-0257
John Bontiorno, *Manager*
EMP: 100
SQ FT: 54,000 **Privately Held**
SIC: **3089** Clothes hangers, plastic; plastic
kitchenware, tableware & houseware
HQ: Braiform Enterprises Incorporated
12 Gerber Rd Ste B
Asheville NC 28803
828 277-6420

(P-9992)
BREWER IRVINE INC
Also Called: Brevet Industries
16661 Jamboree Rd, Irvine (92606-5118)
PHONE...............................949 474-7000

Charles Brewer, *President*
EMP: 65
SQ FT: 59,000
SALES (est): 9.6MM **Privately Held**
WEB: www.brevetind.com
SIC: **3089** Injection molded finished plastic
products

(P-9993)
BUILDING COMPONENTS
3148 Abington Dr, Beverly Hills
(90210-1101)
PHONE...............................310 274-6516
Clyde Berkus, *Owner*
EMP: 10
SALES (est): 1MM **Privately Held**
SIC: **3089** Plastic hardware & building
products

(P-9994)
BUMBLE BEE PLASTICS INC
10140 Shoemaker Ave, Santa Fe Springs
(90670-3404)
PHONE...............................562 903-0833
EMP: 15
SALES (corp-wide): 1.8MM **Privately
Held**
SIC: **3089** Injection molding of plastics
PA: Bee Bumble Plastics Inc
3553 Atlantic Ave 328
Long Beach CA 90807
310 749-1655

(P-9995)
BUMJIN AMERICA INC (PA)
2177 Britannia Blvd # 204, San Diego
(92154-8307)
PHONE...............................619 671-0386
Yong Jin Lee, *President*
Jason Park, *CFO*
Jeong Jae Park, *CFO*
Jeong Park, *CFO*
Cheol Park, *Purch Mgr*
▲ EMP: 14
SQ FT: 200,000
SALES (est): 3.9MM **Privately Held**
WEB: www.ssdplastics.com
SIC: **3089** Air mattresses, plastic; injection
molding of plastics

(P-9996)
C & G PLASTICS
Also Called: C & G Mercury Plastics
12729 Foothill Blvd, Sylmar (91342-5314)
PHONE...............................818 837-3773
Greg Leighton, *President*
▲ EMP: 25
SQ FT: 6,000
SALES (est): 1.5MM **Privately Held**
WEB: www.cgplastics.com
SIC: **3089** Injection molding of plastics

(P-9997)
C & R MOLDS INC
2737 Palma Dr, Ventura (93003-7651)
P.O. Box 5644 (93005-0644)
PHONE...............................805 658-7098
Randall Ohnemus, *President*
Marla Ohnemus, *Treasurer*
Steve Ohnemus, *Director*
Tom Alspaugh, *Manager*
▲ EMP: 24
SQ FT: 12,000
SALES (est): 4.7MM **Privately Held**
SIC: **3089** 3544 Injection molding of plas-
tics; plastic hardware & building products;
special dies, tools, jigs & fixtures

(P-9998)
C & S PLASTICS
12621 Foothill Blvd, Sylmar (91342-5312)
PHONE...............................818 896-2489
Charles E Spears, *President*
Karen Spears, *Admin Sec*
EMP: 15
SQ FT: 6,000
SALES (est): 2.5MM **Privately Held**
WEB: www.candsplastics.com
SIC: **3089** Injection molding of plastics

(P-9999)
C-PAK INDUSTRIES INC
4925 Hallmark Pkwy, San Bernardino
(92407-1870)
PHONE...............................909 880-6017
Arch Young, *President*

EMP: 28
SQ FT: 25,000
SALES: 2.5MM **Privately Held**
WEB: www.c-pak.net
SIC: **3089** Molding primary plastic

(P-10000)
CAL-MIL PLASTIC PRODUCTS INC (PA)
4079 Calle Platino, Oceanside
(92056-5805)
PHONE...............................800 321-9069
Johnny Callahan, *CEO*
Barney Callahan, *Vice Pres*
Mark Vollmar, *Opers Mgr*
Noel Flather, *Sales Mgr*
Dustin Smith,
◆ EMP: 30
SQ FT: 60,000
SALES (est): 9.5MM **Privately Held**
WEB: www.calmil.com
SIC: **3089** Plastic containers, except foam

(P-10001)
CAL-MOLD INCORPORATED
Also Called: Pierco
3900 Hamner Ave, Eastvale (91752-1017)
PHONE...............................951 361-6400
Erik Fleming, *President*
Edward T Fleming, *Chairman*
EMP: 220 EST: 1966
SQ FT: 170,000
SALES (est): 26.7MM **Privately Held**
WEB: www.mail.tstonramp.com
SIC: **3089** Injection molding of plastics

(P-10002)
CAL-TRON CORPORATION
2290 Dixon Ln, Bishop (93514-8094)
PHONE...............................760 873-8491
Dan J Pool, *President*
Colleen Pool, *Corp Secy*
EMP: 22
SQ FT: 24,000
SALES (est): 2MM **Privately Held**
WEB: www.caltroncorp.com
SIC: **3089** Injection molded finished plastic
products; injection molding of plastics

(P-10003)
CALIFORNIA FLEX CORPORATION (PA)
Also Called: Cal Flex
1318 1st St, San Fernando (91340-2804)
PHONE...............................818 361-1169
Clifford A Schroeder, *President*
Jani Schroeder, *Corp Secy*
Bill Griffith, *Vice Pres*
EMP: 16
SQ FT: 18,500
SALES (est): 4.7MM **Privately Held**
SIC: **3089** Ducting, plastic

(P-10004)
CALIFORNIA PLASTIC CNTRS INC
2210 E Artesia Blvd, Long Beach
(90805-1739)
PHONE...............................562 423-3900
Jeff Vice, *President*
Steve Rockenbach, *CFO*
Gottfried Schmidt, *Admin Sec*
EMP: 15
SQ FT: 20,000
SALES (est): 4.4MM **Privately Held**
SIC: **3089** Plastic containers, except foam

(P-10005)
CALIFORNIA PLASTICS INC
1611 S Rose Ave, Oxnard (93033-2470)
PHONE...............................805 483-8188
Rene Ribbers, *President*
Rebecca Ribbers, *CFO*
EMP: 12
SALES (est): 1.7MM **Privately Held**
SIC: **3089** Molding primary plastic

(P-10006)
CALIFORNIA QUALITY PLAS INC
Also Called: Bel-Air Cases
2104 S Cucamonga Ave, Ontario
(91761-5609)
PHONE...............................909 930-5667
Erik Calcott, *Branch Mgr*
EMP: 20

SALES (corp-wide): 12.7MM **Privately
Held**
SIC: **3089** Plastic containers, except foam;
boxes, plastic; flat panels, plastic; thermoformed finished plastic products
PA: California Quality Plastics, Inc.
2226 S Castle Harbour Pl
Ontario CA 91761
909 930-5535

(P-10007)
CAMBRO MANUFACTURING COMPANY (PA)
5801 Skylab Rd, Huntington Beach
(92647-2051)
P.O. Box 2000 (92647-2000)
PHONE...............................714 848-1555
Argyle Campbell, *CEO*
Ed Berecz, *Executive*
Jeff Sohn, *Regional Mgr*
Irma Aguilera, *Area Spvr*
Alice Saragosa, *Admin Asst*
◆ EMP: 500 EST: 1951
SQ FT: 300,000
SALES (est): 308.4MM **Privately Held**
WEB: www.cambro.com
SIC: **3089** Trays, plastic; plastic containers,
except foam

(P-10008)
CAMBRO MANUFACTURING COMPANY
7601 Clay Ave, Huntington Beach
(92648-2219)
PHONE...............................714 848-1555
David Capestro, *Manager*
Hector Gutierrez, *CTO*
Catherine Vu, *Marketing Mgr*
Ben Haro, *Manager*
EMP: 273
SALES (corp-wide): 308.4MM **Privately
Held**
SIC: **3089** Plastic containers, except foam
PA: Cambro Manufacturing Company Inc
5801 Skylab Rd
Huntington Beach CA 92647
714 848-1555

(P-10009)
CAMBRO MANUFACTURING COMPANY
5801 Skylab Rd, Huntington Beach
(92647-2051)
PHONE...............................714 848-1555
Argyle Campbell, *President*
EMP: 500
SALES (corp-wide): 308.4MM **Privately
Held**
SIC: **3089** Trays, plastic
PA: Cambro Manufacturing Company Inc
5801 Skylab Rd
Huntington Beach CA 92647
714 848-1555

(P-10010)
CANYON PLASTICS INC
28455 Livingston Ave, Valencia
(91355-4173)
PHONE...............................661 257-4293
Karshan A Gajera, *CEO*
Narashiman Vaidianatha, *Engineer*
Steven Cruz, *VP Sales*
▲ EMP: 78
SQ FT: 110,950
SALES (est): 13.2MM **Privately Held**
WEB: www.canyonplastics.com
SIC: **3089** 3544 Plastic containers, except
foam; injection molding of plastics; forms
(molds), for foundry & plastics working
machinery

(P-10011)
CAPCO/PSA
Also Called: California Art Products Co
11125 Vanowen St, North Hollywood
(91605-6316)
PHONE...............................818 762-4276
Zaven P Berberian, *President*
Andre Adidge, *Purchasing*
EMP: 26 EST: 1967
SQ FT: 18,000
SALES (est): 4.4MM **Privately Held**
SIC: **3089** 2821 Planters, plastic; plastic
containers, except foam; plastics materi-
als & resins

(P-10012)
CAPTIVE PLASTICS INC
601 Nestle Way Ste A, Lathrop
(95330-8759)
PHONE..................................209 858-9188
Jim Campbell, *Branch Mgr*
Bill Ventresca, *Engineer*
EMP: 100 **Publicly Held**
WEB: www.captiveplastics.com
SIC: 3089 Plastic containers, except foam
HQ: Captive Plastics, Inc.
101 Oakley St
Evansville IN 47710
812 424-2904

(P-10013)
CARAVAN MANUFACTURING CO INC
10814 Los Vaqueros Cir, Los Alamitos
(90720-2516)
PHONE..................................714 220-9722
Geoffrey Bennett, *President*
Geraldine Bennett, *Treasurer*
Tim Bennett, *Vice Pres*
EMP: 10
SQ FT: 12,500
SALES (est): 750K **Privately Held**
WEB: www.caravanmfg.com
SIC: 3089 Injection molded finished plastic products

(P-10014)
CARPOD INC
12132 Gothic Ave, Granada Hills
(91344-2819)
PHONE..................................818 395-8676
Martin Aghajanian, *President*
▲ **EMP:** 10
SQ FT: 1,000
SALES (est): 100K **Privately Held**
SIC: 3089 Automotive parts, plastic

(P-10015)
CCI INDUSTRIES INC (PA)
Also Called: Cool Curtain CCI
350 Fischer Ave Ste A, Costa Mesa
(92626-4508)
PHONE..................................714 662-3879
Michael Robinson, *President*
▲ **EMP:** 30
SQ FT: 15,000
SALES (est): 5.1MM **Privately Held**
WEB: www.coolcurtain.com
SIC: 3089 3564 3496 Doors, folding: plastic or plastic coated fabric; aircurtains (blower); grilles & grillework, woven wire

(P-10016)
CCL TUBE INC (HQ)
2250 E 220th St, Carson (90810-1638)
PHONE..................................310 635-4444
Andreas Iseli, *CEO*
Carlos Chavez, *Controller*
Chris Kellen, *Production*
Susan Early, *Marketing Mgr*
Jack Belt, *Manager*
▲ **EMP:** 200
SQ FT: 300,000
SALES (est): 44.6MM
SALES (corp-wide): 3.7B **Privately Held**
WEB: www.ccltubes.com
SIC: 3089 Injection molded finished plastic products
PA: Ccl Industries Inc
111 Gordon Baker Rd Suite 801
Toronto ON M2H 3
416 756-8500

(P-10017)
CECO ENVIRONMENTAL CORP
Also Called: Hee
4222 E La Palma Ave, Anaheim
(92807-1816)
PHONE..................................760 530-1409
Jamie Warren, *Branch Mgr*
EMP: 38
SALES (corp-wide): 345MM **Publicly Held**
SIC: 3089 Plastic & fiberglass tanks
PA: Ceco Environmental Corp.
14651 Dallas Pkwy
Dallas TX 75254
513 458-2600

(P-10018)
CENTRAL CALIFORNIA CONT MFG
Also Called: Synder California Container
800 Commerce Dr, Chowchilla
(93610-9395)
P.O. Box 848 (93610-0848)
PHONE..................................559 665-7611
Tom O'Connell, *CEO*
Shelli Humphries, *Controller*
EMP: 20
SQ FT: 2,500
SALES (est): 2.5MM **Privately Held**
SIC: 3089 Plastic containers, except foam

(P-10019)
CERTAINTEED CORONA INC
235 Radio Rd, Corona (92879-1725)
PHONE..................................951 272-1300
Marshall J Stuart, *Ch of Bd*
Kathryn Stuart, *Corp Secy*
EMP: 200
SQ FT: 128,000
SALES (est): 20.9MM
SALES (corp-wide): 213.5MM **Privately Held**
WEB: www.certainteed.net
SIC: 3089 3442 Doors, folding: plastic or plastic coated fabric; windows, plastic; metal doors, sash & trim
HQ: Certainteed Corporation
20 Moores Rd
Malvern PA 19355
610 893-5000

(P-10020)
CERTIFIED THERMOPLASTICS LLC
Also Called: Certified Thermoplastics Inc
26381 Ferry Ct, Santa Clarita
(91350-2998)
PHONE..................................661 222-3006
Robert Duncan, *President*
Sarah Pincus, *Office Mgr*
Joel Wilcox, *Sales Mgr*
Vanja Vujica, *Manager*
▲ **EMP:** 35
SQ FT: 30,000
SALES (est): 7.2MM
SALES (corp-wide): 558.1MM **Publicly Held**
WEB: www.ctplastics.com
SIC: 3089 Injection molding of plastics
HQ: Ducommun Labarge Technologies, Inc.
1601 E Broadway Rd
Phoenix AZ 85040
480 998-0733

(P-10021)
CG MOTOR SPORTS INC
5150 Eucalyptus Ave Ste A, Chino
(91710-9218)
PHONE..................................909 628-1440
Debbie Law, *President*
▲ **EMP:** 16
SALES (est): 2.5MM **Privately Held**
SIC: 3089 Automotive parts, plastic

(P-10022)
CHAUHAN INDUSTRIES INC
32 Wood Rd Ste A, Camarillo
(93010-8399)
PHONE..................................805 484-1616
Raj Chauhan, *President*
EMP: 16
SQ FT: 6,000
SALES: 1.5MM **Privately Held**
SIC: 3089 Windows, plastic

(P-10023)
CHAWK TECHNOLOGY INTL INC (PA)
1256 San Luis Obispo St, Hayward
(94544-7916)
PHONE..................................510 330-5299
Jonathan Chang, *CEO*
▲ **EMP:** 64
SALES: 29.3MM **Privately Held**
SIC: 3089 Injection molding of plastics

(P-10024)
CHEM-TAINER INDUSTRIES INC
Also Called: Chemtainer Industries
135 E Stanley St, Compton (90220-5604)
PHONE..................................310 635-5400
George Karathanas, *Opers-Prdtn-Mfg*
EMP: 30
SALES (corp-wide): 46.5MM **Privately Held**
WEB: www.chemtainer.com
SIC: 3089 2821 Plastic containers, except foam; plastics materials & resins
PA: Chem-Tainer Industries Inc.
361 Neptune Ave
West Babylon NY 11704
631 422-8300

(P-10025)
CHINA CUSTOM MANUFACTURING LTD
44843 Fremont Blvd, Fremont
(94538-6318)
PHONE..................................510 979-1920
George Huang, *President*
Robin Lee, *Vice Pres*
▲ **EMP:** 860
SALES (est): 71.7MM **Privately Held**
WEB: www.ccmfg.com
SIC: 3089 Injection molded finished plastic products; injection molding of plastics

(P-10026)
CHUBBY GORILLA INC
10425 Slusher Dr, Santa Fe Springs
(90670-3750)
PHONE..................................844 365-5218
Ibraheim Hamsa Aboabdo, *CEO*
Eyad Aboabdo, *Vice Pres*
EMP: 30
SALES (est): 302.9K **Privately Held**
SIC: 3089 Closures, plastic

(P-10027)
CLEAR-AD INC
Also Called: Brochure Holders 4u
2410 W 3rd St, Santa Ana (92703-3519)
PHONE..................................877 899-1002
Juan Diaz, *CEO*
Bruce Kelly, *Vice Pres*
Barbara Snow, *Purch Mgr*
EMP: 30
SQ FT: 17,006
SALES (est): 6MM **Privately Held**
WEB: www.clearad.com
SIC: 3089 3544 3993 3061 Injection molded finished plastic products; forms (molds), for foundry & plastics working machinery; displays & cutouts, window & lobby; medical & surgical rubber tubing (extruded & lathe-cut); advertising specialties

(P-10028)
CMP DISPLAY SYSTEMS INC
23301 Wilmington Ave, Carson
(90745-6209)
PHONE..................................805 499-3642
William M Hooker, *CEO*
Ken Collin, *President*
Bruce Miller, *Vice Pres*
EMP: 75
SALES: 10MM
SALES (corp-wide): 558.1MM **Publicly Held**
WEB: www.cmp-displays.com
SIC: 3089 3823 3812 Plastic processing; industrial instrmnts msrmnt display/control process variable; search & navigation equipment
HQ: Ducommun Labarge Technologies, Inc.
23301 Wilmington Ave
Carson CA 90745
310 513-7200

(P-10029)
COAST TO COAST MFG LLC
Also Called: Fire Windows and Doors
430 Nevada St, Redlands (92373-4244)
PHONE..................................909 798-5024
John Seymour, *Mng Member*
EMP: 11
SALES (est): 2.9MM **Privately Held**
WEB: www.coasttocoastmfg.com
SIC: 3089 Windows, plastic

(P-10030)
CODAN US CORPORATION
3511 W Sunflower Ave, Santa Ana
(92704-6926)
PHONE..................................714 430-1300
Peter Schwarz, *Ch of Bd*
Jeff Nielsen, *President*
Bernd J Larsen, *CEO*
Deon Miller, *Vice Pres*
Richard Warden, *Finance Mgr*
▲ **EMP:** 145
SQ FT: 180,000
SALES (est): 26.5MM
SALES (corp-wide): 177MM **Privately Held**
WEB: www.codanus.com
SIC: 3089 Molding primary plastic
HQ: Codan Medizinische Gerate Gmbh & Co Kg
Stig Husted-Andersen Str. 11
Lensahn 23738
436 351-11

(P-10031)
COLVIN-FRIEDMAN LLC
1311 Commerce St, Petaluma
(94954-1426)
PHONE..................................707 769-4488
Mitchell Friedman, *President*
Madelyn Helper, *Cust Mgr*
EMP: 25 **EST:** 1949
SQ FT: 10,000
SALES (est): 4.6MM **Privately Held**
WEB: www.colvin-friedman.com
SIC: 3089 5162 3544 Plastic processing; injection molding of plastics; plastics materials; dies, plastics forming

(P-10032)
COMAR LLC
Also Called: Paradigm Packaging West
9177 Center Ave, Rancho Cucamonga
(91730-5312)
PHONE..................................909 985-2750
Steve Costecki, *Manager*
EMP: 125
SALES (corp-wide): 12.9MM **Privately Held**
WEB: www.paradigmpackaging.com
SIC: 3089 Plastic containers, except foam; caps, plastic
HQ: Paradigm Packaging East Llc
141 5th St
Saddle Brook NJ 07663
201 909-3400

(P-10033)
COMMERCIAL PATTERNS INC
3162 Baumberg Ave Ste H, Hayward
(94545-4434)
PHONE..................................510 784-1014
Donald Loobey Sr, *President*
Mildred Loobey, *Treasurer*
Don Loobey Jr, *Vice Pres*
Mark Loobey, *Vice Pres*
EMP: 16
SQ FT: 8,000
SALES (est): 2MM **Privately Held**
WEB: www.commpattern.com
SIC: 3089 2821 Molding primary plastic; polyurethane resins

(P-10034)
CONROY & KNOWLTON INC
320 S Montebello Blvd, Montebello
(90640-5112)
PHONE..................................323 665-5288
William A Conroy, *President*
Michelle Conroy, *Manager*
EMP: 18 **EST:** 1946
SQ FT: 17,000
SALES: 2MM **Privately Held**
SIC: 3089 Plastic hardware & building products; injection molding of plastics

(P-10035)
CONSOLIDATED CONT HOLDINGS LLC
17851 Railroad St, City of Industry
(91748-1118)
PHONE..................................626 964-9657
Ric Ibarra, *Manager*
EMP: 50
SALES (corp-wide): 13.7B **Publicly Held**
SIC: 3089 Plastic containers, except foam
HQ: Consolidated Container Holdings Llc
2500 Windy Ridge Pkwy Se
Atlanta GA 30339
678 742-4600

▲ = Import ▼=Export
◆ =Import/Export

(P-10036)
CONSOLIDATED CONTAINER CO LLC
Also Called: Reid Plastics Customer Svcs
1070 Samuelson St, City of Industry
(91748-1219)
PHONE..............................888 425-7343
Fred Braham, *Principal*
Wayne Eldredge, *Mfg Staff*
EMP: 44
SALES (corp-wide): 13.7B **Publicly Held**
WEB: www.ccccllc.com
SIC: **3089** 3085 Plastic containers, except
foam; plastics bottles
HQ: Consolidated Container Company, Llc
2500 Windy Ridge Pkwy Se
Atlanta GA 30339
678 742-4600

(P-10037)
CONSOLIDATED CONTAINER CO LLC
4516 Azusa Canyon Rd, Irwindale
(91706-2742)
PHONE..............................626 856-2100
EMP: 60
SALES (corp-wide): 13.7B **Publicly Held**
SIC: **3089** Plastic containers, except foam
HQ: Consolidated Container Company, Llc
2500 Windy Ridge Pkwy Se
Atlanta GA 30339
678 742-4600

(P-10038)
CONSOLIDATED CONTAINER CO LLC
Also Called: Stewart/Walker Company
75 W Valpico Rd, Tracy (95376-9129)
PHONE..............................209 820-1700
Fred Branham, *Opers-Prdtn-Mfg*
EMP: 104
SALES (corp-wide): 13.7B **Publicly Held**
WEB: www.ccccllc.com
SIC: **3089** 3085 Pallets, plastic; plastics
bottles
HQ: Consolidated Container Company, Llc
2500 Windy Ridge Pkwy Se
Atlanta GA 30339
678 742-4600

(P-10039)
CONSOLIDATED CONTAINER CO LP
Envision Plastics
14312 Central Ave, Chino (91710-5752)
PHONE..............................909 590-7334
EMP: 50
SALES (corp-wide): 13.7B **Publicly Held**
SIC: **3089** Plastic containers, except foam
HQ: Consolidated Container Company Lp
2500 Windy Ridge Pkwy Se # 1400
Atlanta GA 30339
678 742-4600

(P-10040)
CONTAINER OPTIONS INC
1493 E San Bernardino Ave, San
Bernardino (92408-2927)
PHONE..............................909 478-0045
Patricia Shockey, *CEO*
Charles Shockley, *Office Mgr*
EMP: 18
SQ FT: 43,000
SALES: 5MM **Privately Held**
SIC: **3089** Plastic containers, except foam

(P-10041)
CONTAINER TECHNOLOGY INC (PA)
5454 San Patricio Dr, Santa Barbara
(93111-1455)
P.O. Box 60508 (93160-0508)
PHONE..............................805 683-5825
Gary Clancy, *President*
EMP: 20
SALES (est): 3.2MM **Privately Held**
WEB: www.containertechnology.com
SIC: **3089** 3443 5113 Plastic containers,
except foam; tubs, plastic (containers); in-
dustrial vessels, tanks & containers;
boxes & containers

(P-10042)
COOL-PAK LLC
401 N Rice Ave, Oxnard (93030-7936)
PHONE..............................805 981-2434
Niall Kelly,
Alicia Aldis, *Purchasing*
Victor Garcia, *Opers Mgr*
Ruben Trevino, *Plant Mgr*
Jim Scattini, *Sales Mgr*
▲ EMP: 85
SQ FT: 124,000
SALES (est): 23MM
SALES (corp-wide): 11.3B **Privately Held**
WEB: www.cool-pak.com
SIC: **3089** Plastic containers, except foam
HQ: Bunzl Distribution Usa, Llc
1 Cityplace Dr Ste 200
Saint Louis MO 63141
314 997-5959

(P-10043)
CORD INDUSTRIES INC
541 Industrial Way Ste 2, Fallbrook
(92028-2257)
PHONE..............................760 728-4590
Donald Conibear, *President*
EMP: 10 EST: 1976
SQ FT: 7,500
SALES (est): 1MM **Privately Held**
SIC: **3089** Injection molding of plastics

(P-10044)
CORNUCOPIA TOOL & PLASTICS INC
448 Sherwood Rd, Paso Robles
(93446-3554)
P.O. Box 1915 (93447-1915)
PHONE..............................805 238-7660
Larry Horn, *President*
Art Horn, *Vice Pres*
EMP: 47
SQ FT: 20,000
SALES (est): 9.8MM **Privately Held**
WEB: www.cornucopiaplastics.com
SIC: **3089** 3544 Injection molding of plas-
tics; industrial molds

(P-10045)
COSMETIC SPECIALTIES INTL LLC
550 E 3rd St, Oxnard (93030-6020)
PHONE..............................805 487-6698
Michael J Musso, *President*
Mark Hauptman, *President*
Bruce Bellerose, *COO*
David Paneiko, *CFO*
Chris Gedwed, *Exec VP*
▲ EMP: 102
SALES (est): 27.3MM
SALES (corp-wide): 4.6MM **Privately
Held**
SIC: **3089** Injection molded finished plastic
products; injection molding of plastics
PA: Asparron Capital, Llc
1701 W Northwest Hwy # 100
Grapevine TX 76051
817 865-6573

(P-10046)
COUNTRY PLASTICS INC
32501 Road 228, Woodlake (93286-9705)
PHONE..............................559 597-2556
Jay D Ayres, *President*
Jenny Ayres, *Corp Secy*
▲ EMP: 17
SQ FT: 3,000
SALES (est): 4.4MM **Privately Held**
WEB: www.countryplastics.net
SIC: **3089** Injection molded finished plastic
products; injection molding of plastics

(P-10047)
CPC GROUP INC
Also Called: New Paradise
11223 Rush St Ste I, South El Monte
(91733-3566)
PHONE..............................626 350-8848
Harry Pan, *President*
▲ EMP: 10
SQ FT: 5,000
SALES (est): 1.3MM **Privately Held**
SIC: **3089** Tableware, plastic; novelties,
plastic

(P-10048)
CRAFTECH EDM CORPORATION
Also Called: Crafttech
2941 E La Jolla St, Anaheim (92806-1306)
PHONE..............................714 630-8117
John Butler, *President*
Peggy Thomas, *CFO*
Alfredo Bonetto, *Senior VP*
John Ayers, *Vice Pres*
Douglas Barker, *Vice Pres*
▲ EMP: 220
SQ FT: 35,000
SALES (est): 68.1MM **Privately Held**
WEB: www.craftechcorp.com
SIC: **3089** 3559 Injection molding of plas-
tics; plastics working machinery

(P-10049)
CREATIVE COMPUTER PRODUCTS
Also Called: Creative Plastic Printing
6369 Nncy Rdge Dr Ste 200, San Diego
(92121)
PHONE..............................858 458-1965
Gerald McDevitt, *President*
Jeff Fleming, *Advisor*
EMP: 15
SQ FT: 3,000
SALES (est): 2.1MM **Privately Held**
WEB: www.creativeplastic.com
SIC: **3089** 3577

(P-10050)
CRESCENT PLASTICS INC
Also Called: Servtech Plastics
1711 S California Ave, Monrovia
(91016-4623)
PHONE..............................626 359-9248
Maqbool Zafar, *CEO*
Ralph Melton, *President*
▲ EMP: 12 EST: 2001
SALES (est): 2.2MM **Privately Held**
WEB: www.servtechplastics.com
SIC: **3089** Injection molding of plastics

(P-10051)
CROWN MFG CO INC
37625 Sycamore St, Newark (94560-3946)
PHONE..............................510 742-8800
Aziz Shariat, *CEO*
John Coffman, *Vice Pres*
Diosa Tenorio, *Office Mgr*
Salman Shariat, *Director*
▲ EMP: 40
SQ FT: 60,000
SALES (est): 8.2MM **Privately Held**
WEB: www.crown-plastics.com
SIC: **3089** Injection molding of plastics

(P-10052)
CURBELL PLASTICS INC
1670 Brandywine Ave Ste B, Chula Vista
(91911-6071)
PHONE..............................619 575-4633
Drew Singer, *Manager*
EMP: 20
SALES (corp-wide): 200.6MM **Privately
Held**
SIC: **3089** Doors, folding: plastic or plastic
coated fabric
HQ: Curbell Plastics, Inc.
7 Cobham Dr
Orchard Park NY 14127

(P-10053)
CUSTOM ENGINEERING PLASTICS LP
8558 Miramar Pl, San Diego (92121-2530)
PHONE..............................858 452-0961
Sylvia Hammond, *Managing Prtnr*
Jack Hammond, *Partner*
Jenn Quinn, *Office Mgr*
Michael Getgen, *QC Mgr*
Warren Werkmeister, *Manager*
▲ EMP: 18
SQ FT: 11,400
SALES (est): 3.1MM **Privately Held**
WEB: www.cepi.com
SIC: **3089** 3544 Injection molding of plas-
tics; forms (molds), for foundry & plastics
working machinery

(P-10054)
CUSTOM PLASTICS LLC (PA)
1305 Brooks St, Ontario (91762-3612)
PHONE..............................909 984-0200
Ammar Alshash, *Mng Member*
Linn W Derickson, *Principal*
Mary Sue Derickson, *Principal*
▲ EMP: 12
SALES (est): 3MM **Privately Held**
WEB: www.spinwelding.com
SIC: **3089** 5812 Injection molding of plas-
tics; eating places

(P-10055)
CYPRESS MANUFACTURING LLC
Also Called: Hitech Plastics and Molds
25620 Rye Canyon Rd Ste B, Valencia
(91355-1140)
PHONE..............................818 772-6592
Robert Loranger, *Manager*
Chris Loranger, *Administration*
Kevin Yang,
EMP: 10
SQ FT: 30,000
SALES (est): 4.4MM **Privately Held**
SIC: **3089** 3432 Injection molding of plas-
tics; plastic plumbing fixture fittings, as-
sembly

(P-10056)
CYTYDEL PLASTICS INC
17813 S Main St Ste 117, Gardena
(90248-3542)
PHONE..............................310 523-2884
Aeran Lee, *President*
Chang Lee, *Treasurer*
▲ EMP: 20
SQ FT: 10,200
SALES (est): 2.5MM **Privately Held**
WEB: www.cytydel.net
SIC: **3089** Plastic processing

(P-10057)
D & D PLASTICS INCORPORATED
Also Called: Rti
1632 W 139th St, Gardena (90249-3003)
PHONE..............................310 515-1934
Donald A Dettman, *President*
David Dettman, *Treasurer*
Dave Dettman, *Purchasing*
EMP: 15
SQ FT: 15,000
SALES (est): 2.5MM **Privately Held**
WEB: www.d-dplastics.com
SIC: **3089** Injection molding of plastics

(P-10058)
D W MACK CO INC
900 W 8th St, Azusa (91702-2216)
P.O. Box 1247, Monrovia (91017-1247)
PHONE..............................626 969-1817
Danny J Mack, *President*
Joseph Demarco, *Vice Pres*
Dennis S Mack, *Admin Sec*
Danny Mack, *Site Mgr*
Danny J Mack, *Plant Mgr*
▲ EMP: 40 EST: 1979
SALES (est): 7.6MM **Privately Held**
WEB: www.dwmack.com
SIC: **3089** Kits, plastic

(P-10059)
D&W FINE PACK LLC
Also Called: C&M Fine Pack
4162 Georgia Blvd, San Bernardino
(92407-1852)
PHONE..............................206 767-7777
EMP: 160
SALES (corp-wide): 614.5MM **Privately
Held**
SIC: **3089** Plastic containers, except foam
HQ: D&W Fine Pack Llc
777 Mark St Ste 101
Wood Dale IL 60191

(P-10060)
DCO ENVIRONMENTAL & RECYCL LLC
300 Montgomery St Ste 421, San Francisco
(94104-1903)
PHONE..............................573 204-3844
Claudine Osipow, *Mng Member*

PRODUCTS & SVCS

◆ EMP: 16
SALES (est): 3.8MM **Privately Held**
SIC: 3089 Plastic processing
PA: Dco International Trading Inc.
    300 Montgomery St Ste 421
    San Francisco CA 94104

(P-10061)
DECO PLASTICS INC
160 Denny Way, El Cajon (92020-1222)
PHONE..................................619 448-6843
William H Peck, *President*
Robert Peck, *Vice Pres*
EMP: 19
SQ FT: 8,500
SALES: 1MM **Privately Held**
SIC: 3089 Trays, plastic

(P-10062)
DELAMO MANUFACTURING INC
7171 Telegraph Rd, Montebello
(90640-6511)
PHONE..................................323 936-3566
Fred Morad, *CEO*
EMP: 80 EST: 2008
SQ FT: 120,000
SALES: 2MM **Privately Held**
SIC: 3089 Plastic kitchenware, tableware &
houseware

(P-10063)
DELFIN DESIGN & MFG INC
23301 Antonio Pkwy, Rcho STA Marg
(92688-2664)
PHONE..................................949 888-4644
John M Rief, *President*
Rita Williams, *Corp Secy*
Paul Iverson, *Exec VP*
▲ EMP: 28
SQ FT: 24,000
SALES (est): 6MM **Privately Held**
SIC: 3089 3083 Thermoformed finished
plastic products; plastic finished products,
laminated

(P-10064)
DELPHON INDUSTRIES LLC (PA)
Also Called: Touchmark
31398 Huntwood Ave, Hayward
(94544-7818)
PHONE..................................510 576-2220
Jeanne Beacham, *Mng Member*
Diana Morgan, *CFO*
Raj Varma, *CTO*
Tom Olen, *Technical Staff*
Emily Bloom, *Engineer*
▲ EMP: 123
SQ FT: 40,000
SALES (est): 25.8MM **Privately Held**
WEB: www.delphon.com
SIC: 3089 Plastic processing

(P-10065)
DELTA YIMIN TECHNOLOGIES INC
33170 Central Ave, Union City
(94587-2042)
PHONE..................................510 487-4411
Fred Betke, *President*
Richard Ellis, *Vice Pres*
▲ EMP: 48
SQ FT: 34,000
SALES (est): 15.1MM **Privately Held**
WEB: www.deltapacificinc.com
SIC: 3089 Injection molded finished plastic
products; injection molding of plastics

(P-10066)
DEMTECH SERVICES INC
6414 Capitol Ave, Diamond Springs
(95619-9393)
PHONE..................................530 621-3200
Dave McLaury, *President*
Gus Fauci, *Opers Mgr*
Tyler Harrison, *Manager*
▲ EMP: 24
SQ FT: 8,000
SALES (est): 5MM **Privately Held**
WEB: www.demtech.com
SIC: 3089 Thermoformed finished plastic
products

(P-10067)
DESIGN OCTAVES
2701 Research Park Dr, Soquel
(95073-2090)
PHONE..................................831 464-8500
Norman Weiss, *CEO*
Dan McCabe, *Vice Pres*
Nancie Newby, *Office Admin*
Julie Hottel, *Technology*
Eliseo Valencia, *Technology*
EMP: 30 EST: 1979
SQ FT: 21,000
SALES (est): 4.8MM **Privately Held**
WEB: www.designoctaves.com
SIC: 3089 3469 Cases, plastic; metal
stampings

(P-10068)
DESIGN WEST TECHNOLOGIES INC
2701 Dow Ave, Tustin (92780-7209)
PHONE..................................714 731-0201
Ryan Hur, *President*
Dustin Hur, *General Mgr*
Patrick Acuna, *Info Tech Mgr*
Kristofer Nicolas, *Project Engr*
Meryl Rosario, *Project Engr*
▲ EMP: 65
SQ FT: 60,000
SALES (est): 17MM **Privately Held**
SIC: 3089 8711 Injection molded finished
plastic products; electrical or electronic
engineering

(P-10069)
DESIGNER SASH AND DOOR SYS INC
Also Called: Designer Fashion Door
45899 Via Tornado, Temecula
(92590-3359)
PHONE..................................951 657-4179
Ross Eberhart, *President*
Kenneth McBride, *Treasurer*
EMP: 91
SQ FT: 20,000
SALES (est): 15.1MM **Privately Held**
SIC: 3089 2431 5211 Windows, plastic;
window frames & sash, plastic; doors,
folding: plastic or plastic coated fabric;
doors, wood; door & window products

(P-10070)
DIMENSIONAL PLASTICS CORP
6565 Crescent Park W # 111, Playa Vista
(90094-2284)
PHONE..................................305 691-5961
Sir Ronald Barnette, *President*
Allen Barnette, *Vice Pres*
◆ EMP: 20
SQ FT: 30,000
SALES (est): 3.5MM **Privately Held**
WEB: www.krinklglas.com
SIC: 3089 Molding primary plastic; casting
of plastic; laminating of plastic; synthetic
resin finished products

(P-10071)
DISPENSING DYNAMICS INTL INC (PA)
Also Called: Perrin Craft
1020 Bixby Dr, City of Industry
(91745-1703)
PHONE..................................626 961-3691
Dean Debuhr, *CEO*
Art Brake, *President*
Larry Maccormack, *President*
Chris Sigmon, *President*
Scott Strachan, *COO*
◆ EMP: 99
SQ FT: 57,000
SALES (est): 51.9MM **Privately Held**
WEB: www.perrin.com
SIC: 3089 3993 Injection molding of plas-
tics; signs & advertising specialties

(P-10072)
DISTINCTIVE PLASTICS INC
1385 Decision St, Vista (92081-8523)
PHONE..................................760 599-9100
Timothy Curnutt, *President*
Violeta Curnutt, *Vice Pres*
Tina Corson, *Materials Mgr*
▲ EMP: 62
SQ FT: 44,500

SALES (est): 13.6MM **Privately Held**
WEB: www.distinctiveplastics.com
SIC: 3089 3312 Injection molding of plas-
tics; tool & die steel

(P-10073)
DIVERSE OPTICS INC
10310 Regis Ct, Rancho Cucamonga
(91730-3055)
PHONE..................................909 593-9330
Erik Fleming, *President*
Letty Dela Cruz, *Sales Engr*
Deborah De Melo, *Director*
EMP: 20 EST: 1987
SQ FT: 20,000
SALES (est): 4.6MM **Privately Held**
WEB: www.diverseoptics.com
SIC: 3089 3827 Injection molding of plas-
tics; lenses, optical: all types except oph-
thalmic

(P-10074)
DODGE - WASMUND MFG INC
4510 Manning Rd, Pico Rivera
(90660-2191)
PHONE..................................562 692-8104
Gloria Schulz, *President*
Dennis Schulz, *Vice Pres*
▲ EMP: 12
SQ FT: 30,000
SALES (est): 1.9MM **Privately Held**
WEB: www.ladylynn.com
SIC: 3089 Plastic hardware & building
products; injection molding of plastics

(P-10075)
DOMINO PLASTICS MFG INC
601 Gateway Ct, Bakersfield (93307-6827)
PHONE..................................661 396-3744
W Thomas Bathe III, *CEO*
Neil Conway, *President*
EMP: 21
SQ FT: 16,000
SALES (est): 5.8MM **Privately Held**
WEB: www.dominoplastics.com
SIC: 3089 Billfold inserts, plastic

(P-10076)
DON CONIBEAR
541 Industrial Way Ste 2, Fallbrook
(92028-2257)
PHONE..................................760 728-4590
Don Conibear, *Owner*
EMP: 10
SALES: 1MM **Privately Held**
SIC: 3089 Plastic processing

(P-10077)
DOREL JUVENILE GROUP INC
9950 Calabash Ave, Fontana (92335-5210)
PHONE..................................909 428-0295
Carrisa John, *Principal*
EMP: 111
SALES (corp-wide): 2.5B **Privately Held**
WEB: www.coscoproducts.com
SIC: 3089 Plastic kitchenware, tableware &
houseware
HQ: Dorel Juvenile Group, Inc.
    2525 State St
    Columbus IN 47201
    800 457-5276

(P-10078)
DOREL JUVENILE GROUP INC
Also Called: Cosco Home & Office Products
5400 Shea Center Dr, Ontario
(91761-7892)
PHONE..................................909 390-5705
Rick Mc Cook, *Manager*
EMP: 111
SALES (corp-wide): 2.5B **Privately Held**
WEB: www.coscoproducts.com
SIC: 3089 Plastic kitchenware, tableware &
houseware
HQ: Dorel Juvenile Group, Inc.
    2525 State St
    Columbus IN 47201
    800 457-5276

(P-10079)
DUCLOS LENSES
20222 Bahama St, Chatsworth
(91311-6203)
PHONE..................................818 773-0600
Lenses Duclos, *Principal*
Matthew Duclos, *COO*

Evelyn Frederick, *Admin Asst*
Justin Rhoads, *Info Tech Mgr*
Aubrey Canfield, *Sales Associate*
EMP: 18
SALES (est): 3.3MM **Privately Held**
SIC: 3089 Lenses, except optical: plastic

(P-10080)
DURA PLASTIC PRODUCTS INC (PA)
533 E Third St, Beaumont (92223-2715)
P.O. Box 2097 (92223-0997)
PHONE..................................951 845-3161
Kevin L Rost, *CEO*
Ursula Rost, *Shareholder*
Willi K Rost, *Shareholder*
Hardy Rost, *President*
Monica Rost, *CFO*
◆ EMP: 100
SQ FT: 150,000
SALES (est): 33.8MM **Privately Held**
WEB: www.duraplastics.com
SIC: 3089 Fittings for pipe, plastic

(P-10081)
EAGLE MOLD TECHNOLOGIES INC
12330 Crosthwaite Cir, Poway
(92064-6823)
PHONE..................................858 530-0888
Ulrich Bark, *President*
Rosemary Bark, *Treasurer*
David Bark, *Vice Pres*
Gregory Bark, *Vice Pres*
Ronald Bark, *Vice Pres*
EMP: 20
SQ FT: 10,500
SALES (est): 4.3MM **Privately Held**
WEB: www.eaglemold.com
SIC: 3089 3544 Injection molded finished
plastic products; injection molding of plas-
tics; special dies, tools, jigs & fixtures

(P-10082)
EAGLE PRODUCTS - PLAST INDUST
10811 Fremont Ave, Ontario (91762-3912)
PHONE..................................909 465-1548
Henry Ngo, *President*
Thu Nguyen, *Corp Secy*
EMP: 20
SQ FT: 6,100
SALES (est): 2.2MM **Privately Held**
WEB: www.eagleproducts-inc.com
SIC: 3089 Plastic processing

(P-10083)
EAST LA LAMINATION INC
616 N Hazard Ave, Los Angeles
(90063-3338)
PHONE..................................323 881-9838
Videl Napoles, *President*
EMP: 10 EST: 2001
SALES: 100K **Privately Held**
SIC: 3089 Laminating of plastic

(P-10084)
ECOPLAST CORPORATION INC
13414 Slover Ave, Fontana (92337-6977)
PHONE..................................909 346-0450
Jose Perez, *President*
EMP: 59
SQ FT: 40,000
SALES (est): 13.2MM **Privately Held**
WEB: www.primelinepolymers.com
SIC: 3089 Plastic containers, except foam

(P-10085)
EDCO PLASTICS INC
2110 E Winston Rd, Anaheim
(92806-5534)
PHONE..................................714 772-1986
Edward A Contreras, *President*
Maria Contreras, *Vice Pres*
▲ EMP: 49
SQ FT: 25,000
SALES (est): 8.9MM **Privately Held**
SIC: 3089 Molding primary plastic; injec-
tion molding of plastics

▲ = Import ▼=Export
◆ =Import/Export

(P-10086)
EDGE PLASTICS INC (PA)
Also Called: O D I
3016 Kansas Ave Bldg 3, Riverside
(92507-3442)
PHONE.............................951 786-4750
Earl David Grimes, *President*
Holly Grimes, *Admin Sec*
Kathy Mascorro, *Accountant*
Ralph Vasquez, *Controller*
Eric Anderson, *Plant Mgr*
▲ EMP: 35
SQ FT: 23,000
SALES (est): 6.1MM **Privately Held**
WEB: www.edgeplastics.com
SIC: 3080 5199 5091 Injection molding of
plastics; advertising specialties; bicycle
parts & accessories

(P-10087)
EDRIS PLASTICS MFG INC
4560 Pacific Blvd, Vernon (90058-2208)
PHONE.............................323 581-7000
Hovanes Hovik Issagholian, *CEO*
▲ EMP: 26
SQ FT: 27,000
SALES (est): 5.7MM **Privately Held**
WEB: www.edrisplastics.com
SIC: 3089 Kitchenware, plastic

(P-10088)
**EE PAULEY PLASTIC
EXTRUSION**
17177 Navajo Rd, Apple Valley
(92307-1046)
PHONE.............................760 240-3737
EMP: 11 EST: 2010
SALES (est): 1.6MM **Privately Held**
SIC: 3089 Extruded finished plastic products

(P-10089)
EEP HOLDINGS LLC (PA)
4626 Eucalyptus Ave, Chino (91710-9215)
PHONE.............................909 597-7861
Earl E Payton, *CEO*
EMP: 12
SALES (est): 164.5MM **Privately Held**
SIC: 3089 3544 Molding primary plastic;
special dies, tools, jigs & fixtures

(P-10090)
EMPIRE WEST INC
Also Called: Empire West Plastics
9270 Graton Rd, Graton (95444-9375)
P.O. Box 511 (95444-0511)
PHONE.............................707 823-1190
Richard F Yonash, *CEO*
Edward J Davis, *President*
Donna Yonash, *Vice Pres*
Liz Faolain, *Project Mgr*
Ritch Foster, *Technology*
EMP: 28
SQ FT: 30,000
SALES (est): 4.9MM **Privately Held**
WEB: www.empirewest.com
SIC: 3089 Thermoformed finished plastic
products

(P-10091)
ENDUREQUEST CORPORATION
1813 Thunderbolt Dr, Porterville
(93257-9300)
PHONE.............................559 783-9220
Kenneth Dewing, *President*
Russell Sarno, *Vice Pres*
▲ EMP: 25
SQ FT: 10,000
SALES (est): 4.4MM **Privately Held**
SIC: 3089 Plastic hardware & building
products; injection molding of plastics

(P-10092)
**ENGINEERING MODEL
ASSOCIATES (PA)**
Also Called: Ema
1020 Wallace Way, City of Industry
(91748-1027)
PHONE.............................626 912-7011
John Jay Wanderman, *President*
Leon Katz, *Admin Sec*
EMP: 25
SQ FT: 28,000

SALES (est): 11.8MM **Privately Held**
SIC: 3089 5162 Plastic processing; plastics products

(P-10093)
ENTEGRIS INC
10070 Willow Creek Rd, San Diego
(92131-1623)
PHONE.............................858 452-0124
Jeff Spiegelman, *Branch Mgr*
EMP: 63
SALES (corp-wide): 1.3B **Publicly Held**
SIC: 3089 Plastic processing
PA: Entegris, Inc.
129 Concord Rd
Billerica MA 01821
978 436-6500

(P-10094)
**ENVIRONMENTAL SAMPLING
SUP INC**
640 143rd Ave, San Leandro (94578-3304)
PHONE.............................510 465-4988
William Levey, *Branch Mgr*
EMP: 11
SALES (corp-wide): 983.9MM **Privately
Held**
SIC: 3089 3231 Plastic containers, except
foam; products of purchased glass
HQ: Environmental Sampling Supply, Inc.
4101 Shuffel St Nw
North Canton OH 44720
330 497-9396

(P-10095)
**EXPRESS SYSTEMS & ENGRG
INC**
41357 Date St, Murrieta (92562-7030)
PHONE.............................951 461-1500
Mike Arndt, *President*
▲ EMP: 25
SQ FT: 14,000
SALES (est): 2.5MM **Privately Held**
WEB: www.exp-sys.com
SIC: 3089 Injection molding of plastics

(P-10096)
EXTRUMED INC (DH)
Also Called: Vesta
547 Trm Cir, Corona (92879-1768)
PHONE.............................951 547-7400
Phil Estes, *President*
Eric R Schnur, *CEO*
Chris Guglielmi, *CFO*
EMP: 47
SQ FT: 53,000
SALES (est): 18MM
SALES (corp-wide): 242.1B **Publicly
Held**
WEB: www.extrumed.com
SIC: 3089 Injection molding of plastics
HQ: Vesta Intermediate Funding, Inc.
9900 S 57th St
Franklin WI 53132
414 423-0550

(P-10097)
**FABRICATED EXTRUSION CO
LLC (PA)**
2331 Hoover Ave, Modesto (95354-3907)
PHONE.............................209 529-9200
Jeffrey S Aichele, *Mng Member*
Tom Peot, *Vice Pres*
Donald Travis, *Finance Mgr*
Phaedra Zamora, *Persnl Mgr*
Brett Genereux, *Plant Mgr*
EMP: 43
SQ FT: 36,000
SALES (est): 15.5MM **Privately Held**
WEB: www.fabexco.com
SIC: 3089 Extruded finished plastic products

(P-10098)
FABRICMATE SYSTEMS INC
2781 Golf Course Dr A, Ventura
(93003-7941)
PHONE.............................805 642-7470
Craig S Lanuza, *President*
▲ EMP: 18
SQ FT: 16,116
SALES (est): 4.1MM **Privately Held**
WEB: www.fabricmate.com
SIC: 3089 Extruded finished plastic products

(P-10099)
**FIELD MANUFACTURING CORP
(PA)**
1751 Torrance Blvd Ste H, Torrance
(90501-1726)
PHONE.............................310 781-9292
Patrick Field, *President*
▲ EMP: 100 EST: 1955
SQ FT: 20,000
SALES (est): 12.6MM **Privately Held**
WEB: www.fieldmfg.com
SIC: 3089 Injection molding of plastics

(P-10100)
**FISCHER MOLD
INCORPORATED**
393 Meyer Cir, Corona (92879-1078)
PHONE.............................951 279-1140
Robert Fischer, *President*
Eleanor Fischer, *Admin Sec*
▲ EMP: 60
SQ FT: 32,000
SALES (est): 14.2MM **Privately Held**
WEB: www.fischermoldinc.com
SIC: 3089 3544 Injection molding of plastics; special dies, tools, jigs & fixtures

(P-10101)
FIT-LINE INC
Also Called: Flarelink
2901 Tech Ctr, Santa Ana (92705-5657)
PHONE.............................714 549-9091
Ronni Levinson, *CEO*
Frank Hayesc, *Principal*
David Van Hooton, *Principal*
George Alvarado, *Opers Mgr*
▼ EMP: 20
SQ FT: 4,500
SALES (est): 4.1MM **Privately Held**
WEB: www.fit-line.net
SIC: 3089 Fittings for pipe, plastic

(P-10102)
FM PLASTICS
Also Called: FM Industries
9950 Marconi Dr Ste 106, San Diego
(92154-7272)
P.O. Box 431498, San Ysidro (92143-1498)
PHONE.............................619 661-5929
Frank Real, *President*
EMP: 38
SQ FT: 5,000
SALES (est): 3.9MM **Privately Held**
SIC: 3089 Trays, plastic

(P-10103)
FOAM FABRICATORS INC
1810 S Santa Fe Ave, Compton
(90221-5319)
PHONE.............................310 537-5760
Ted I Florkiewicz, *Opers-Prdtn-Mfg*
EMP: 17 **Publicly Held**
WEB: www.foamfabricators.com
SIC: 3089 3086 Molding primary plastic;
plastics foam products
HQ: Foam Fabricators, Inc.
8722 E San Alberto Dr # 200
Scottsdale AZ 85258
480 607-7330

(P-10104)
FOAM INJECTION PLASTICS
2548 Grant Ave, San Lorenzo
(94580-1810)
PHONE.............................510 317-0218
John Zolkos, *President*
EMP: 10
SALES (est): 1.2MM **Privately Held**
SIC: 3089 Injection molding of plastics

(P-10105)
FORMULA PLASTICS INC
451 Tecate Rd Ste 2b, Tecate (91980)
PHONE.............................866 307-1362
Alexander Mora, *CEO*
Elias Mora, *President*
Joe Mora, *Vice Pres*
Monica Mora, *Vice Pres*
▲ EMP: 500
SQ FT: 20,000
SALES (est): 42.8MM **Privately Held**
WEB: www.formulaplastics.com
SIC: 3089 Injection molding of plastics

(P-10106)
**FORTUNE BRANDS WINDOWS
INC**
Also Called: Simonton Windows
2019 E Monte Vista Ave, Vacaville
(95688-3100)
PHONE.............................707 446-7600
Tom Riseili, *General Mgr*
EMP: 101
SALES (corp-wide): 218.4MM **Privately
Held**
WEB: www.simonton.com
SIC: 3089 3442 Window frames & sash,
plastic; sash, door or window: metal
HQ: Fortune Brands Windows, Inc
3948 Townsfair Way # 200
Columbus OH 43219
614 532-3500

(P-10107)
FRESCO PLASTICS INC
5680 Carmel Valley Rd, Carmel
(93923-9506)
PHONE.............................831 625-9877
Jonathan C Drake,
EMP: 25
SALES (est): 1.9MM **Privately Held**
SIC: 3089 Plastic processing

(P-10108)
**FRESNO PRECISION PLASTICS
INC (PA)**
998 N Temperance Ave, Clovis
(93611-8606)
PHONE.............................559 323-9595
Henry Mata, *President*
John Flores III, *Vice Pres*
David Freriks, *Vice Pres*
Ken Russell, *Sales Mgr*
EMP: 10
SQ FT: 20,000
SALES (est): 12.3MM **Privately Held**
WEB: www.precisionplastics.ws
SIC: 3089 5162 3993 2821 Thermo-
formed finished plastic products; plastics
sheets & rods; signs & advertising spe-
cialties; plastics materials & resins; auto-
motive & apparel trimmings

(P-10109)
**FRESNO PRECISION PLASTICS
INC**
8456 Carbide Ct, Sacramento
(95828-5609)
PHONE.............................916 689-5284
David Frericks, *Manager*
EMP: 15
SALES (est): 1.4MM
SALES (corp-wide): 12.3MM **Privately
Held**
WEB: www.precisionplastics.ws
SIC: 3089 Injection molding of plastics
PA: Fresno Precision Plastics, Inc.
998 N Temperance Ave
Clovis CA 93611
559 323-9595

(P-10110)
G & D INDUSTRIES INC
1202 E Edna Pl, Covina (91724-2509)
PHONE.............................626 331-1250
Gary Adkins, *President*
Vicki Horton, *Treasurer*
Gregory L Adkins, *Vice Pres*
Cindy Taylor, *Admin Sec*
Greg Adkins, *Manager*
EMP: 12
SQ FT: 4,000
SALES (est): 1.9MM **Privately Held**
WEB: www.gdindustries.com
SIC: 3089 Injection molding of plastics;
plastic processing

(P-10111)
G B REMANUFACTURING INC
2040 E Cherry Indus Cir, Long Beach
(90805-4410)
PHONE.............................562 272-7333
Michael J Kitching, *President*
F William Kitching, *Chairman*
Patricia Kitching, *Treasurer*
Joe Evert, *Engineer*
Lisa Kitching, *Human Resources*
▲ EMP: 70
SQ FT: 26,400

SALES (est): 14.1MM **Privately Held**
WEB: www.gbreman.com
SIC: **3089** Injection molded finished plastic products

(P-10112)
GADIA POLYTHYLENE SUPPLIES INC
21141 Itasca St, Chatsworth (91311-4928)
PHONE..................................818 775-0096
Willy Gadia, *President*
Zinna Gadia, *President*
EMP: 14
SALES (est): 1.9MM **Privately Held**
SIC: **3089** 3086 Plastic containers, except foam; plastics foam products

(P-10113)
GARY MANUFACTURING INC
2626 Southport Way Ste E, National City (91950-8754)
PHONE..................................619 429-4479
Brian Smith, *President*
Helen Smith, *Vice Pres*
▲ EMP: 30 EST: 1958
SQ FT: 10,000
SALES (est): 5.8MM **Privately Held**
WEB: www.garymanufacturing.com
SIC: **3089** 2392 5162 2673 Plastic containers, except foam; napkins, fabric & nonwoven: made from purchased materials; tablecloths: made from purchased materials; plastics materials & basic shapes; bags: plastic, laminated & coated; textile bags; curtains & draperies

(P-10114)
GEIGER PLASTICS INC
16150 S Maple Ave A, Gardena (90248-2837)
PHONE..................................310 327-9926
Charlotte May, *President*
Vangie Ramirez, *Corp Secy*
Michael Kamau, *Prdtn Mgr*
Kent May, *Manager*
EMP: 20 EST: 1964
SQ FT: 10,000
SALES (est): 4.3MM **Privately Held**
WEB: www.geigerplastics.com
SIC: **3089** 3559 Injection molding of plastics; plastics working machinery

(P-10115)
GEMINI FILM & BAG INC (PA)
Also Called: Gemini Plastics
3574 Fruitland Ave, Maywood (90270-2008)
P.O. Box 806, Atwood (92811-0806)
PHONE..................................323 582-0901
James Fruth, *President*
Brian Kunisch, *CFO*
EMP: 25
SQ FT: 12,000
SALES (est): 3.5MM **Privately Held**
WEB: www.geminiplastics.com
SIC: **3089** 8742 Extruded finished plastic products; manufacturing management consultant

(P-10116)
GEO PLASTICS
2200 E 52nd St, Vernon (90058-3446)
PHONE..................................323 277-8106
Michael Abraham Morris, *CEO*
Justin Hunt, *Vice Pres*
Robert Burch, *Sales Mgr*
Rita Adams, *Manager*
▲ EMP: 27
SALES (est): 8.6MM **Privately Held**
WEB: www.geoplastics.com
SIC: **3089** Extruded finished plastic products

(P-10117)
GIBRALTAR PLASTIC PDTS CORP
12885 Foothill Blvd, Sylmar (91342-5317)
PHONE..................................818 365-9318
Harvey J Jacobs, *President*
Hilary Gauthier, *General Mgr*
Adam Libarkin, *General Mgr*
Keith Jacobs, *VP Mfg*
EMP: 25
SQ FT: 30,000

SALES (est): 6.1MM **Privately Held**
WEB: www.gibraltarplastic.com
SIC: **3089** Injection molded finished plastic products; cases, plastic

(P-10118)
GILL CORPORATION (PA)
4056 Easy St, El Monte (91731-1054)
PHONE..................................626 443-6094
Stephen E Gill, *President*
William Heinze, *CFO*
Irv Freund, *Vice Pres*
Bill Heinze, *Vice Pres*
Don Clark, *Admin Sec*
◆ EMP: 236
SQ FT: 390,000
SALES: 250.9MM **Privately Held**
WEB: www.mcgillcorp.com
SIC: **3089** 3469 3272 2448 Laminating of plastic; panels, building: plastic; honey-combed metal; panels & sections, prefabricated concrete; cargo containers, wood & metal combination; aircraft

(P-10119)
GKM INTERNATIONAL LLC
1725 Burbury Way, San Marcos (92078-0928)
PHONE..................................310 791-7092
Karen Murrey,
EMP: 99
SALES: 500K **Privately Held**
SIC: **3089**

(P-10120)
GKN AEROSPACE TRANSPARENCY SYS (DH)
12122 Western Ave, Garden Grove (92841-2915)
PHONE..................................714 893-7531
Hans Buthker, *CEO*
Joakim Anderson, *CEO*
Mike McCann, *CEO*
Will Hoy, *CFO*
Remy Behra, *Senior VP*
▲ EMP: 197
SQ FT: 324,000
SALES (est): 69.1MM
SALES (corp-wide): 12.7B **Privately Held**
WEB: www.gkntransparencysystems.com
SIC: **3089** 3231 3827 3728 Windows, plastic; windshields, plastic; mirrors, truck & automobile: made from purchased glass; optical instruments & lenses; aircraft parts & equipment; unsupported plastics film & sheet; plastics materials & resins
HQ: Gkn America Corp.
2715 Davey Rd Ste 300
Woodridge IL 60517
630 972-9300

(P-10121)
GLOBE PLASTICS INC
13477 12th St, Chino (91710-5206)
PHONE..................................909 464-1520
Nywood Wu, *President*
Clifton Chang, *Vice Pres*
▲ EMP: 20 EST: 1958
SQ FT: 12,000
SALES (est): 4.5MM **Privately Held**
WEB: www.globecomposites.com
SIC: **3089** 3544 Injection molding of plastics; special dies, tools, jigs & fixtures

(P-10122)
GLOVEFIT INTERNATIONAL CORP
4705 N Sonora Ave Ste 108, Fresno (93722-3947)
PHONE..................................559 243-1110
Bill Burgess, *Vice Pres*
▲ EMP: 15
SQ FT: 10,000
SALES (est): 1.7MM **Privately Held**
WEB: www.glovefit.com
SIC: **3089** Work gloves, plastic

(P-10123)
GOLDEN PLASTICS CORPORATION
8465 Baldwin St, Oakland (94621-1924)
PHONE..................................510 569-6465
Ron Pardee, *President*
Stewart Pardee, *President*

Ruth Pardee, *Corp Secy*
Daniel K Pardee, *Vice Pres*
Ronald S Pardee, *Vice Pres*
▲ EMP: 17
SQ FT: 9,500
SALES (est): 2.3MM **Privately Held**
WEB: www.goldenplasticscorp.com
SIC: **3089** Plastic hardware & building products; ducting, plastic; plastic processing

(P-10124)
GOLDMAN GLOBAL GREENFIELD INC
2025 E 48th St, Vernon (90058-2021)
PHONE..................................323 589-3444
Michelle Choi, *President*
▲ EMP: 19
SQ FT: 17,000
SALES (est): 2.2MM **Privately Held**
SIC: **3089** Plastic processing

(P-10125)
GRAHAM PACKAGING COMPANY LP
3300 W Segerstrom Ave, Santa Ana (92704-6403)
PHONE..................................714 979-1835
Paul Wu, *Manager*
Debbi Goyette, *Vice Pres*
Dave Fallat, *Purchasing*
Jack Pisarek, *Manager*
EMP: 60
SQ FT: 127,516 **Privately Held**
WEB: www.grahampackaging.com
SIC: **3089** Plastic containers, except foam
HQ: Graham Packaging Company, L.P.
700 Indian Springs Dr # 100
Lancaster PA 17601
717 849-8500

(P-10126)
GRAHAM PACKAGING COMPANY LP
9041 Pittsburgh Ave, Rancho Cucamonga (91730-5551)
P.O. Box 1568 (91729-1568)
PHONE..................................909 484-2900
George Plummer, *Manager*
EMP: 35 **Privately Held**
WEB: www.grahampackaging.com
SIC: **3089** Plastic containers, except foam
HQ: Graham Packaging Company, L.P.
700 Indian Springs Dr # 100
Lancaster PA 17601
717 849-8500

(P-10127)
GRAHAM PACKAGING COMPANY LP
Modesto Plant
513 S Mcclure Rd, Modesto (95357-0520)
PHONE..................................209 578-1112
Kevin Beveris, *Branch Mgr*
Mustafa Al Rawi, *QC Mgr*
Steve Enos, *Manager*
EMP: 80 **Privately Held**
WEB: www.grahampackaging.com
SIC: **3089** Plastic containers, except foam
HQ: Graham Packaging Company, L.P.
700 Indian Springs Dr # 100
Lancaster PA 17601
717 849-8500

(P-10128)
GRAND FUSION HOUSEWARES INC (PA)
12 Partridge, Irvine (92604-4519)
PHONE..................................888 614-7263
Hilton Blieden, *President*
EMP: 12
SQ FT: 1,000
SALES: 850.2K **Privately Held**
SIC: **3089** 3083 2869 Kitchenware, plastic; laminated plastic sheets; silicones

(P-10129)
GRAND PACKAGING PET TECH
513 S Mcclure Rd, Modesto (95357-0520)
PHONE..................................209 578-1112
Steve Enos, *Manager*
EMP: 55
SALES (est): 5.2MM **Privately Held**
SIC: **3089** Plastics products

(P-10130)
GRIFF INDUSTRIES INC
4515 Runway Dr, Lancaster (93536-8530)
PHONE..................................661 728-0111
Michael Griffin, *President*
◆ EMP: 19 EST: 1999
SQ FT: 8,400
SALES (est): 3.8MM **Privately Held**
WEB: www.griffindustries.com
SIC: **3089** Injection molding of plastics

(P-10131)
H N LOCKWOOD INC
880 Sweeney Ave, Redwood City (94063-3024)
P.O. Box 309, McArthur (96056-0309)
PHONE..................................650 366-9557
Daniel A Lockwood, *President*
Raoul Jeanneret, *Office Mgr*
Maggie Moreno, *Office Mgr*
EMP: 30
SQ FT: 1,030
SALES (est): 4.1MM **Privately Held**
WEB: www.hnlockwood.com
SIC: **3089** 2759 Plastic processing; commercial printing

(P-10132)
HAMMERHEAD INDUSTRIES INC
5720 Nicolle St, Ventura (93003-7612)
PHONE..................................805 658-9922
Kenneth S Collin Jr, *President*
John Salentine, *Vice Pres*
▲ EMP: 12
SQ FT: 8,000
SALES (est): 2.1MM **Privately Held**
WEB: www.gearkeeper.com
SIC: **3089** Injection molding of plastics

(P-10133)
HENRY PLASTIC MOLDING INC
Also Called: Hpmi
41703 Albrae St, Fremont (94538-3120)
PHONE..................................510 490-7993
Edwin Henry, *CEO*
Edwin L Henry Sr, *Shareholder*
Helen Henry, *Corp Secy*
Linda Henry, *Vice Pres*
Brian McCarthy, *Accountant*
▲ EMP: 165
SQ FT: 45,000
SALES (est): 32.9MM **Privately Held**
WEB: www.henryplastic.com
SIC: **3089** Injection molding of plastics

(P-10134)
HERMAN ENGINEERING & MFG INC
4501 E Airport Dr Ste B, Ontario (91761-7877)
PHONE..................................909 483-1631
Donald B Donisthorpe, *President*
Tiffany Herrmann, *Manager*
▲ EMP: 15
SQ FT: 30,000
SALES (est): 2.6MM **Privately Held**
SIC: **3089** Plastic containers, except foam

(P-10135)
HI-REL PLASTICS & MOLDING CORP
7575 Jurupa Ave, Riverside (92504-1012)
PHONE..................................951 354-0258
Rakesh Bajaria, *CEO*
Dennis Sovalia, *President*
Harry Thummer, *CFO*
Rick Bajria, *Vice Pres*
▲ EMP: 50
SQ FT: 15,000
SALES (est): 8MM **Privately Held**
SIC: **3089** 3549 3599 Injection molded finished plastic products; assembly machines, including robotic; machine shop, jobbing & repair

(P-10136)
HIGHLAND PLASTICS INC
Also Called: Hi-Plas
3650 Dulles Dr, Mira Loma (91752-3260)
PHONE..................................951 360-9587
James L Nelson, *Principal*
William B Warren, *CFO*
Yvette Warren, *Technology*
Viginia Warren, *Human Res Dir*

Barry Adams, *Plant Engr*
◆ EMP: 130 EST: 1974
SQ FT: 150,000
SALES (est): 30.9MM **Privately Held**
WEB: www.hiplas.com
SIC: 3089 Injection molding of plastics

(P-10137)
HONOR PLASTICS & MOLDING INC
730 E Francis St, Ontario (91761-5513)
PHONE....................................909 923-9710
Dinesh Savalia, *CEO*
EMP: 17 EST: 2016
SALES (est): 800.7K **Privately Held**
SIC: 3089 Injection molding of plastics

(P-10138)
HOOD MANUFACTURING INC
Also Called: Thermobile
2621 S Birch St, Santa Ana (92707-3410)
PHONE....................................714 979-7681
Michael Hood, *President*
Patrica Hood, *Admin Sec*
Michele Rauschenbach, *CIO*
EMP: 60
SQ FT: 24,000
SALES: 5MM **Privately Held**
WEB: www.goodserver.com
SIC: 3089 3585 Injection molded finished
plastic products; refrigeration & heating
equipment

(P-10139)
HOOSIER PLSTIC FABRICATION INC
1152 California Ave, Corona (92881-3324)
P.O. Box 78926 (92877-0164)
PHONE....................................951 272-3070
Robert G Simms, *CEO*
Shannon Sims, *Executive*
Shanna Garcia, *General Mgr*
Josh Sprague, *General Mgr*
Willie Abundez, *Info Tech Mgr*
EMP: 145
SQ FT: 45,000
SALES (est): 39MM **Privately Held**
WEB: www.hoosierplastic.com
SIC: 3089 Plastic processing

(P-10140)
HOPE PLASTIC CO INC
5353 Strohm Ave, North Hollywood
(91601-3526)
PHONE....................................818 769-5560
Steven Borden, *President*
Bill Borden, *Treasurer*
Hope Borden, *Admin Sec*
▲ EMP: 20 EST: 1964
SQ FT: 17,000
SALES (est): 3.9MM **Privately Held**
SIC: 3089 Injection molding of plastics

(P-10141)
HOUSEWARES INTERNATIONAL INC (PA)
Also Called: American Household Company
6015 Randolph St, Commerce
(90040-3417)
PHONE....................................323 581-3000
Kamyar Solouki, *CEO*
Sean Solouki, *Vice Pres*
Anthony Fernandez, *Info Tech Mgr*
Paula Love, *Accounting Mgr*
Glenda Seale, *Marketing Staff*
◆ EMP: 35
SQ FT: 80,000
SALES (est): 8.4MM **Privately Held**
WEB: www.housewaresintl.com
SIC: 3089 5023 Kitchenware, plastic;
kitchenware

(P-10142)
HULLS NORCAL WINDOW & DOOR
104 Stoney Hill Dr, Folsom (95630-4610)
PHONE....................................916 983-5792
Tom Nelson, *Branch Mgr*
EMP: 10 **Privately Held**
SIC: 3089 5031 Windows, plastic; doors &
windows; window frames, all materials
PA: Hull's Norcal Window & Door Inc
3140 Thorntree Dr
Chico CA 95973

(P-10143)
HUMANGEAR INC
636 Shrader St, San Francisco
(94117-2716)
PHONE....................................415 580-7553
Chris Miksovsky, *President*
Jordan Hurder, *Opers Staff*
▲ EMP: 19
SALES (est): 2.3MM **Privately Held**
SIC: 3089 Tubs, plastic (containers)

(P-10144)
HUSKY INJECTION MOLDING
3505 Cadillac Ave Ste N4, Costa Mesa
(92626-1433)
PHONE....................................714 545-8200
Michael Smith, *Manager*
EMP: 14
SQ FT: 6,501 **Privately Held**
SIC: 3089 Injection molding of plastics
HQ: Husky Injection Molding Systems, Inc.
288 North Rd
Milton VT 05468
802 859-8000

(P-10145)
ICHOR SYSTEMS INC
Also Called: Ajax
34585 7th St, Union City (94587-3673)
PHONE....................................510 476-8000
Tom Rohrs, *Manager*
EMP: 140
SALES (corp-wide): 655.8MM **Publicly Held**
SIC: 3089 3599 3543 Plastic processing;
machine shop, jobbing & repair; foundry
patternmaking
HQ: Ichor Systems, Inc.
3185 Laurelview Ct
Fremont CA 94538
-

(P-10146)
ICORE INTERNATIONAL INC
3780 Flightline Dr, Santa Rosa
(95403-1054)
PHONE....................................707 535-2750
Ted Perdue, *CEO*
Arnold Nixon, *CFO*
Mark McGrath, *Vice Pres*
Katherine Arcoleo, *Engineer*
Ludovic Pasquereau, *Business Mgr*
EMP: 205
SQ FT: 49,000
SALES (est): 77.1MM
SALES (corp-wide): 650.9MM **Privately Held**
WEB: www.icoreintl.com
SIC: 3089 Molding primary plastic
HQ: Zodiac Aerospace
Cs20001
Plaisir 78370
161 342-323

(P-10147)
IDEMIA AMERICA CORP
3150 E Ana St, Compton (90221-5607)
PHONE....................................310 884-7900
Eric Daniele, *Director*
Jf Arzel, *Vice Pres*
Antoine Kelman, *Vice Pres*
Didier Labat, *Administration*
Vronique De Moura, *Project Mgr*
EMP: 161
SALES (corp-wide): 4.5B **Privately Held**
WEB: www.oberthurcs.com
SIC: 3089 3083 Identification cards, plas-
tic; plastic finished products, laminated
HQ: Idemia America Corp.
296 Concord Rd Ste 300
Billerica MA 01821
978 215-2400

(P-10148)
IKEGAMI MOLD CORP AMERICA
3570 Camino Del Rio N # 106, San Diego
(92108-1747)
PHONE....................................619 858-6855
Masatomo Ikegami, *President*
Yoshiyuki Koga, *Vice Pres*
▼ EMP: 18
SALES (est): 2.6MM
SALES (corp-wide): 27.9MM **Privately Held**
SIC: 3089 Injection molding of plastics

PA: Ikegami Mold Engineering Co.,Ltd.
2-664-8, Toyonodai
Kazo STM 349-1
480 448-686

(P-10149)
INCA PLASTICS MOLDING CO INC
948 E Belmont St, Ontario (91761-4549)
PHONE....................................909 923-3235
Howard L Haigh, *President*
Jeff Clark, *Manager*
▲ EMP: 53
SQ FT: 33,000
SALES (est): 10.7MM **Privately Held**
WEB: www.incaplastics.com
SIC: 3089 3714 3544 3443 Injection
molding of plastics; motor vehicle parts &
accessories; special dies, tools, jigs & fix-
tures; fabricated plate work (boiler shop)

(P-10150)
INFINITI PLASTIC TECHNOLOGIES
11150 Santa Monica Blvd # 1280, Los An-
geles (90025-3380)
PHONE....................................310 618-8288
Saeed Yousefian, *CEO*
Catherine Wu, *Vice Pres*
▲ EMP: 19
SQ FT: 100,000
SALES (est): 2.7MM
SALES (corp-wide): 2.7MM **Privately Held**
SIC: 3089 Cases, plastic
PA: Infiniti Media, Inc.
11150 Santa Monica Blvd # 1280
Los Angeles CA 90025
310 618-8288

(P-10151)
INLINE PLASTICS INC
1950 S Baker Ave, Ontario (91761-7755)
PHONE....................................909 923-1033
Kelly Orr, *CEO*
Alfredo Perez, *Vice Pres*
Charlene Woodard, *Manager*
EMP: 25
SQ FT: 21,000
SALES (est): 7MM **Privately Held**
WEB: www.inlineplasticsinc.com
SIC: 3089 Extruded finished plastic prod-
ucts

(P-10152)
INNOVATIVE MOLDING (HQ)
1200 Valley House Dr # 100, Rohnert Park
(94928-4902)
PHONE....................................707 238-9250
Grahame W Reid, *CEO*
Lynn Brooks, *CEO*
Alan Williams, *CFO*
Robert T Stenson, *Corp Secy*
Rodger Moody, *Vice Pres*
EMP: 75
SQ FT: 27,000
SALES (est): 20.3MM
SALES (corp-wide): 817.7MM **Publicly Held**
WEB: www.innovativemolding.com
SIC: 3089 Bottle caps, molded plastic; in-
jection molding of plastics
PA: Trimas Corporation
38505 Woodward Ave # 200
Bloomfield Hills MI 48304
248 631-5450

(P-10153)
INNOVTIVE RTTIONAL MOLDING INC
Also Called: IRM
2300 W Pecan Ave, Madera (93637-5056)
PHONE....................................559 673-4764
Daniel Humphries, *President*
Shellie Humphries, *Vice Pres*
EMP: 12
SALES (est): 2.7MM **Privately Held**
SIC: 3089 Molding primary plastic

(P-10154)
INTERNATIONAL LAST MFG CO
Also Called: Salpy
5060 Densmore Ave, Encino (91436-1554)
PHONE....................................818 767-2045
Kevork Kalaidjian, *President*

Salpy Kalaidjian, *Vice Pres*
EMP: 20
SALES: 1MM **Privately Held**
SIC: 3089 3111 3131 5139 Soles, boot or
shoe: plastic; sole leather; inner soles,
leather; heels, shoe & boot: leather or
wood; shoes

(P-10155)
IPARTS INC
Also Called: Ipart Automotive
14975 Hilton Dr, Fontana (92336-2082)
PHONE....................................909 587-6059
Andy Banh, *Office Mgr*
EMP: 10 EST: 2013
SALES (est): 688.7K **Privately Held**
SIC: 3089 Automotive parts, plastic

(P-10156)
IPS INDUSTRIES INC
Also Called: Spectrum Bags
12641 166th St, Cerritos (90703-2101)
PHONE....................................562 623-2555
Frank Su, *CEO*
Peter Hii, *CFO*
David Silva, *Exec VP*
Ben Tran, *Exec VP*
Tricia Fu, *Executive*
◆ EMP: 80
SQ FT: 150,000
SALES (est): 33.7MM **Privately Held**
SIC: 3089 3629 Battery cases, plastic or
plastic combination; battery chargers, rec-
tifying or nonrotating

(P-10157)
ITOUCHLESS HOUSEWARES PDTS INC
777 Mariners Island Blvd # 125, San Mateo
(94404-5008)
PHONE....................................650 578-0578
Fong Chan, *President*
Shek Michael, *Marketing Staff*
Michael Shek, *Marketing Staff*
Karen Kuk, *Manager*
▲ EMP: 50
SALES (est): 6.8MM **Privately Held**
WEB: www.itouchless.com
SIC: 3089 Plastic kitchenware, tableware &
houseware

(P-10158)
J & L CSTM PLSTIC EXTRSONS INC
1532 Santa Anita Ave, South El Monte
(91733-3314)
PHONE....................................626 442-0711
Louis Salmon, *President*
Jaime Lizarraga, *Vice Pres*
EMP: 30
SALES (est): 5.1MM **Privately Held**
WEB: www.jlplastic.com
SIC: 3089 Plastic hardware & building
products; plastic processing

(P-10159)
J A ENGLISH II INC
Also Called: Pacific Plstcs-Njction Molding
1333 Keystone Way, Vista (92081-8311)
PHONE....................................760 598-5333
J A English II, *CEO*
▲ EMP: 25 EST: 1980
SQ FT: 22,000
SALES (est): 5.7MM **Privately Held**
WEB: www.pacificplastic.com
SIC: 3089 3544 Injection molding of plas-
tics; industrial molds

(P-10160)
J P SPECIALTIES INC
25811 Jefferson Ave, Murrieta
(92562-6961)
P.O. Box 1507, Lake Elsinore (92531-
1507)
PHONE....................................951 763-7077
David R Poole, *President*
Shannon Poole, *Corp Secy*
Stacy Guzman, *Administration*
◆ EMP: 10
SQ FT: 6,850

PRODUCTS & SVCS

SALES (est): 1.8MM **Privately Held**
WEB: www.jpspecialties.com
SIC: 3089 3548 5162 5082 Plastic hardware & building products; bands, plastic; closures, plastic; welding & cutting apparatus & accessories; plastics materials & basic shapes; construction & mining machinery

(P-10161)
JACOBSON PLASTICS INC
1401 Freeman Ave, Long Beach (90804-2518)
PHONE..........................562 433-4911
Jeff Jacobson, *President*
▲ EMP: 75 EST: 1962
SQ FT: 25,000
SALES (est): 13.4MM **Privately Held**
WEB: www.jacobsonplastics.com
SIC: 3089 3544 Injection molding of plastics; special dies, tools, jigs & fixtures

(P-10162)
JAKE STEHELIN ETIENNE
Also Called: Pope
8551 Canoga Ave, Canoga Park (91304-2609)
PHONE..........................818 998-4250
Etienne Stehelin, *Owner*
Jake Stehelin, *CTO*
EMP: 60
SQ FT: 9,700
SALES (est): 5MM **Privately Held**
SIC: 3089 3599 6519 3544 Injection molding of plastics; thermoformed finished plastic products; machine shop, jobbing & repair; real property lessors; special dies, tools, jigs & fixtures

(P-10163)
JARDEN CORPORATION
Also Called: Leslie-Locke
23610 Banning Blvd, Carson (90745-6220)
PHONE..........................800 755-9520
Frank Rodriquez, *Branch Mgr*
EMP: 98
SALES (corp-wide): 14.7B **Publicly Held**
SIC: 3089 2499 3634 Plastic containers, except foam; plastic kitchenware, tableware & houseware; toothpicks, wood; electric housewares & fans; electric household cooking appliances; electric household cooking utensils; personal electrical appliances
HQ: Jarden Corporation
221 River St
Hoboken NJ 07030

(P-10164)
JASON TOOL & ENGINEERING INC
7101 Honold Cir, Garden Grove (92841-1424)
PHONE..........................714 895-5067
Jack Winterswyk, *President*
Curtis H Thompson, *Corp Secy*
Roy Guerra, *Manager*
Aaron Winterswyk, *Manager*
▲ EMP: 30 EST: 1979
SQ FT: 30,000
SALES (est): 5.7MM **Privately Held**
WEB: www.jasontool.com
SIC: 3089 3544 Injection molding of plastics; dies, plastics forming

(P-10165)
JB PLASTICS INC
1921 E Edinger Ave, Santa Ana (92705-4720)
PHONE..........................714 541-8500
Joseph N Chiodo, *President*
Bruce Donoho, *Vice Pres*
EMP: 45
SQ FT: 30,000
SALES (est): 13.5MM **Privately Held**
WEB: www.jb-plastics.com
SIC: 3089 Injection molding of plastics

(P-10166)
JDR ENGINEERING CONS INC
3122 Maple St, Santa Ana (92707-4408)
PHONE..........................714 751-7084
Dionisio Rodriguez, *President*
Janet Rodriguez, *Vice Pres*
▲ EMP: 110

SQ FT: 25,000
SALES (est): 10MM **Privately Held**
SIC: 3089 Injection molding of plastics

(P-10167)
JEM-HD CO INC
10030 Via De La Amistad F, San Diego (92154-7299)
PHONE..........................619 710-1443
Jae Man Lee, *CEO*
EMP: 70
SALES (est): 4.5MM **Privately Held**
SIC: 3089 Injection molding of plastics

(P-10168)
JESS HOWARD
Also Called: Plastic Molding Shop, The
2800 Richter Ave, Oroville (95966-5939)
PHONE..........................530 533-3888
Jess Howard, *Owner*
▲ EMP: 12
SALES (est): 1.3MM **Privately Held**
SIC: 3089 Injection molding of plastics

(P-10169)
JET PLASTICS (PA)
941 N Eastern Ave, Los Angeles (90063-1307)
PHONE..........................323 268-6706
Lee R Johnson, *President*
Lee Johnson, *President*
Lon Johnson, *Vice Pres*
Lowell Johnson, *Vice Pres*
Lowel Johnson, *Admin Sec*
◆ EMP: 80
SQ FT: 30,000
SALES (est): 19.2MM **Privately Held**
WEB: www.jetplastics.com
SIC: 3089 Injection molded finished plastic products; injection molding of plastics

(P-10170)
JG PLASTICS GROUP LLC
335 Fischer Ave, Costa Mesa (92626-4522)
PHONE..........................714 751-4266
Dale Balough,
◆ EMP: 50
SQ FT: 32,000
SALES (est): 10.4MM **Privately Held**
WEB: www.jgplastics.com
SIC: 3089 3544 Injection molding of plastics; special dies, tools, jigs & fixtures

(P-10171)
JOHN L PERRY STUDIO INC
3000 Paseo Mercado # 102, Oxnard (93036-7960)
PHONE..........................805 981-9665
John L Perry, *President*
▲ EMP: 35
SALES (est): 3.7MM **Privately Held**
WEB: www.johnperry.com
SIC: 3089 Plastic processing

(P-10172)
JOHNSON DOC ENTERPRISES
11933 Vose St, North Hollywood (91605-5786)
PHONE..........................818 764-1543
Ronald Braverman, *President*
Chad Braverman, *COO*
Scott Watkins, *Vice Pres*
James Jackson, *Human Res Mgr*
Wendie Murphy, *Purch Mgr*
▲ EMP: 22 EST: 2014
SALES (est): 4.9MM **Privately Held**
SIC: 3089 Novelties, plastic

(P-10173)
JSN INDUSTRIES INC
9700 Jeronimo Rd, Irvine (92618-2019)
PHONE..........................949 458-0050
James H Nagel Jr, *CEO*
Sandra Nagel, *Vice Pres*
EMP: 70
SQ FT: 65,000
SALES (est): 16.8MM **Privately Held**
WEB: www.jsn.com
SIC: 3089 Injection molded finished plastic products

(P-10174)
JUNOPACIFIC INC
2840 Res Pk Dr Ste 160, Soquel (95073)
PHONE..........................831 462-1141

Jeff Wollerman, *Manager*
EMP: 150
SALES (corp-wide): 348.6MM **Privately Held**
SIC: 3089 Injection molding of plastics
HQ: Junopacific, Inc.
1040 Lund Blvd
Anoka MN 55303
763 703-5000

(P-10175)
KEEPCUP LTD
431 Colyton St, Los Angeles (90013-2210)
PHONE..........................310 957-2070
Gregory Lambert, *Administration*
▲ EMP: 10
SALES (est): 1.6MM **Privately Held**
SIC: 3089 Tumblers, plastic

(P-10176)
KENNERLEY-SPRATLING INC (PA)
2116 Farallon Dr, San Leandro (94577-6604)
PHONE..........................510 351-8230
Richard Spratling, *CEO*
Bill Roure, *CFO*
Paul Hoefler, *Principal*
Scott Krogh, *Analyst*
Ronnie Fong, *Senior Buyer*
▲ EMP: 250
SQ FT: 60,000
SALES (est): 135.2MM **Privately Held**
WEB: www.ksplastic.com
SIC: 3089 3082 Injection molding of plastics; unsupported plastics profile shapes

(P-10177)
KENNERLEY-SPRATLING INC
Also Called: M O S Plastics
2308 Zanker Rd, San Jose (95131-1115)
PHONE..........................408 944-9407
Douglas Cullum, *Principal*
EMP: 134
SALES (corp-wide): 135.2MM **Privately Held**
WEB: www.ksplastic.com
SIC: 3089 Injection molding of plastics
PA: Kennerley-Spratling, Inc.
2116 Farallon Dr
San Leandro CA 94577
510 351-8230

(P-10178)
KEPNER PLAS FABRICATORS INC
3131 Lomita Blvd, Torrance (90505-5158)
PHONE..........................310 325-3162
Frank Meyers, *CEO*
Meryl Lee, *General Mgr*
Meryl Bayley, *Admin Sec*
Jeff Zelin, *Purch Mgr*
Ben Cowart, *Sales Associate*
▲ EMP: 26
SQ FT: 50,000
SALES (est): 5.2MM **Privately Held**
WEB: www.kepnerplastics.com
SIC: 3089 Molding primary plastic; plastic processing

(P-10179)
KERR GROUP LLC
3301 Sturgis Rd, Oxnard (93030-7972)
PHONE..........................805 278-9155
Tim Guhl, *Branch Mgr*
EMP: 160 **Publicly Held**
WEB: www.kerrgroup.com
SIC: 3089 Closures, plastic; jars, plastic; tubs, plastic (containers); plastic containers, except foam
HQ: Kerr Group, Llc
1846 Charter Ln Ste 209
Lancaster PA 17601
812 424-2904

(P-10180)
KING PLASTICS INC
840 N Elm St, Orange (92867-7908)
P.O. Box 6229 (92863-6229)
PHONE..........................714 997-7540
Larry E Lathrum, *CEO*
Robert King, *Vice Pres*
Matt Chedister, *VP Opers*
Jacque Thas, *Manager*
▼ EMP: 96
SQ FT: 100,000

SALES: 16MM **Privately Held**
WEB: www.kingplastics.com
SIC: 3089 Plastic kitchenware, tableware & houseware; injection molded finished plastic products

(P-10181)
KIRK API CONTAINERS
2131 Garfield Ave, Commerce (90040-1805)
PHONE..........................323 278-5400
Arthur Marounian, *Vice Pres*
Vahe Joulhaian, *Plant Mgr*
Jerair Hovsepyan, *Warehouse Mgr*
Michael Mercado, *Manager*
▼ EMP: 32
SALES (est): 8.1MM **Privately Held**
SIC: 3089 Plastic containers, except foam

(P-10182)
KNIGHTSBRIDGE PLASTICS INC
Also Called: K P I
3075 Osgood Ct, Fremont (94539-5612)
PHONE..........................510 249-9722
Jean Nagra, *CEO*
Dave Platt, *President*
Dave Terry, *Treasurer*
Sean Tregear, *Vice Pres*
Kamal Saini, *Production*
▲ EMP: 58
SQ FT: 19,000
SALES (est): 16.4MM **Privately Held**
WEB: www.kpi.net
SIC: 3089 3423 Injection molding of plastics; hand & edge tools

(P-10183)
KOTONICA INC
3226 N Frederic St, Burbank (91504-1722)
PHONE..........................818 898-0978
Viken Kotoyan, *President*
▲ EMP: 15
SQ FT: 10,920
SALES (est): 1.6MM **Privately Held**
SIC: 3089 Plastic processing

(P-10184)
KRATOS UNMANNED AERIAL SYSTEMS
Also Called: Composite Engineering, Inc.
5381 Raley Blvd, Sacramento (95838-1701)
PHONE..........................916 431-7977
Eric M Demarco, *CEO*
Amy Fournier, *President*
Louis Grana, *Senior VP*
Michel M Fournier, *Vice Pres*
Jeff Herro, *Vice Pres*
▲ EMP: 350
SQ FT: 60,000
SALES (est): 115MM **Publicly Held**
WEB: www.cei.to
SIC: 3089 Pallets, plastic
PA: Kratos Defense & Security Solutions, Inc.
10680 Treena St Ste 600
San Diego CA 92131

(P-10185)
KURTZ FAMILY CORPORATION
Also Called: Milwright
1450 Industrial Ave, Sebastopol (95472-4848)
PHONE..........................707 823-1213
Stephen E Kurtz, *President*
EMP: 10
SQ FT: 9,000
SALES (est): 1.7MM **Privately Held**
WEB: www.milwright.net
SIC: 3089 Injection molding of plastics

(P-10186)
L & H MOLD & ENGINEERING INC (PA)
Also Called: L & H Molds
2239 1st St, La Verne (91750-5530)
PHONE..........................909 930-1547
Stan Hillary, *CEO*
Steve Hillary, *President*
Brenda Bishop, *Admin Sec*
EMP: 29 EST: 1974
SQ FT: 6,000

SALES: 3.1MM **Privately Held**
SIC: 3089 Injection molding of plastics

(P-10187)
LABCON NORTH AMERICA
3700 Lakeville Hwy # 200, Petaluma
(94954-7611)
PHONE.............................707 766-2100
James A Happ, *President*
Connie Hansen, *CFO*
Mike Ford, *General Mgr*
Ken Haas, *Admin Asst*
Lily Remennik, *Administration*
◆ EMP: 200
SQ FT: 120,000
SALES (est): 60.9MM
SALES (corp-wide): 226.4MM **Privately
Held**
WEB: www.labcon.com
SIC: 3089 Injection molding of plastics
PA: Helena Laboratories Corporation
1530 Lindbergh Dr
Beaumont TX 77707
409 842-3714

(P-10188)
LANTIC INC
Also Called: Molded Interconnect Industries
27081 Burbank, Foothill Ranch
(92610-2505)
PHONE.............................949 830-9951
Hung Vinh, *President*
Lien Pham, *Shareholder*
Hoi Vinh, *Shareholder*
Huy Vinh, *Shareholder*
Xuan L Cong, *Admin Sec*
▲ EMP: 15 EST: 1994
SQ FT: 10,700
SALES (est): 1.5MM **Privately Held**
WEB: www.lantic.com
SIC: 3089 Injection molding of plastics

(P-10189)
LEHRER BRLLNPRFKTION
WERKS INC (PA)
Also Called: Lbi - USA
20801 Nordhoff St, Chatsworth
(91311-5925)
P.O. Box 3519 (91313-3519)
PHONE.............................818 407-1890
Keith Lehrer, *President*
Julie Walker, *CFO*
Chett Lehrer, *Corp Secy*
Brian Friesz, *CTO*
Leo Yang, *Info Tech Mgr*
▲ EMP: 23
SQ FT: 38,000
SALES (est): 8.4MM **Privately Held**
SIC: 3089 Cases, plastic

(P-10190)
LEVEL TREK CORP
5670 Schaefer Ave Ste N, Chino
(91710-9021)
P.O. Box 8416, Rowland Heights (91748-
0416)
PHONE.............................626 689-4829
Anne Shaw, *Principal*
▲ EMP: 11
SALES (est): 1.1MM **Privately Held**
SIC: 3089 Plastics products

(P-10191)
LIDO INDUSTRIES INC
Also Called: Fiberglass Fabricators
456 S Montgomery Way, Orange
(92868-4015)
PHONE.............................714 633-3731
Lisa Burnam, *President*
Cliff E Ryan, *President*
Margaret L Ryan, *Vice Pres*
EMP: 10
SQ FT: 18,000
SALES (est): 1MM **Privately Held**
SIC: 3089 5199 Planters, plastic; pet sup-
plies

(P-10192)
LINER TECHNOLOGIES INC
Also Called: Flexi-Liner
4821 Chino Ave, Chino (91710-5132)
PHONE.............................909 594-6610
Tait Eyre, *President*
Randy Miller, *CFO*
Angela Eyre, *Admin Sec*
Saul Jauregui, *Mktg Dir*

Gunnar Ulander, *Manager*
▼ EMP: 20
SQ FT: 20,000
SALES (est): 4.3MM **Privately Held**
WEB: www.flexi-liner.com
SIC: 3089 Plastic containers, except foam

(P-10193)
LIQUI-BOX CORPORATION
Northern CA Operations
5000 Warehouse Way, Sacramento
(95826-4914)
PHONE.............................916 381-7052
Scott Falwell, *Opers-Prdtn-Mfg*
EMP: 100
SALES (corp-wide): 412MM **Privately
Held**
WEB: www.liquibox.com
SIC: 3089 2671 Plastic processing; pack-
aging paper & plastics film, coated & lami-
nated
PA: Liqui-Box Corporation
901 E Byrd St Ste 1105
Richmond VA 23219
804 325-1400

(P-10194)
LORITZ & ASSOCIATES INC
Also Called: L & A Plastics
24895 La Palma Ave, Yorba Linda
(92887-5531)
PHONE.............................714 694-0200
Edward F Loritz, *CEO*
Ken Loritz, *President*
Anita Court, *Vice Pres*
Anita Loritz, *General Mgr*
▲ EMP: 30
SQ FT: 6,000
SALES (est): 7.5MM **Privately Held**
SIC: 3089 Plastic containers, except foam

(P-10195)
LORMAC PLASTICS INC (PA)
2225 Meyers Ave, Escondido (92029-1005)
PHONE.............................760 745-9115
Wayne Browning, *CEO*
Ronald Klopf, *President*
Adrienne Klopf, *Vice Pres*
Steve Klopf, *Admin Sec*
Tonya Robins, *Administration*
▼ EMP: 13
SQ FT: 10,000
SALES (est): 1.4MM **Privately Held**
WEB: www.lormac.com
SIC: 3089 Thermoformed finished plastic
products

(P-10196)
M & A PLASTICS INC
11735 Sheldon St, Sun Valley
(91352-1580)
PHONE.............................818 768-0479
Guillermo S Morales, *President*
Nancy M Morales, *Treasurer*
EMP: 35
SQ FT: 20,000
SALES (est): 6MM **Privately Held**
WEB: www.maplastics.com
SIC: 3089 Injection molding of plastics

(P-10197)
MACRO PLASTICS INC (DH)
2250 Huntington Dr, Fairfield (94533-9732)
PHONE.............................707 437-1200
Warren Macdonald, *CEO*
Steve Moya, *CFO*
▲ EMP: 40
SQ FT: 28,000
SALES (est): 39.6MM **Privately Held**
SIC: 3089 Injection molding of plastics
HQ: Ipl Inc
140 Rue Commerciale
Saint-Damien-De-Buckland QC G0R 2
418 789-2880

(P-10198)
MAGIC PLASTICS INC
25215 Avenue Stanford, Santa Clarita
(91355-3923)
PHONE.............................800 369-0303
John Sarno, *CEO*
Patrick Madormo, *CFO*
Tony Madormo, *Vice Pres*
Nan Sarno, *Admin Sec*
Dawn Malla, *Admin Asst*
▲ EMP: 55

SQ FT: 75,000
SALES: 10.4MM **Privately Held**
WEB: www.magicplastics.com
SIC: 3089 Injection molding of plastics

(P-10199)
MANHATTAN COMPONENTS INC
5920 Lakeshore Dr, Cypress (90630-3371)
PHONE.............................714 761-7249
David Hattan, *President*
Dorothy Hattan, *Treasurer*
▲ EMP: 10
SQ FT: 10,987
SALES (est): 1.1MM **Privately Held**
SIC: 3089 Injection molding of plastics

(P-10200)
MASTER PLASTICS
INCORPORATED
820 Eubanks Dr Ste I, Vacaville
(95688-8837)
PHONE.............................707 451-3168
Ravi Mirchandani, *Principal*
▲ EMP: 25
SQ FT: 35,000
SALES (est): 7.2MM **Privately Held**
SIC: 3089 Injection molding of plastics

(P-10201)
MCNEAL ENTERPRISES INC
2031 Ringwood Ave, San Jose
(95131-1703)
PHONE.............................408 922-7290
De Anna McNeal-Mirzadegan, *CEO*
Deanna Godfrey, *Vice Pres*
De Anna Mirzadegan, *Vice Pres*
Robert McNeal, *Admin Sec*
Tommy Allison, *Marketing Staff*
EMP: 100
SQ FT: 62,000
SALES (est): 16.2MM **Privately Held**
WEB: www.mcneal.com
SIC: 3089 3498 3559 Injection molding of
plastics; laminating of plastic; thermo-
formed finished plastic products; closures,
plastic; tube fabricating (contract bending
& shaping); semiconductor manufacturing
machinery

(P-10202)
MDI EAST INC (HQ)
Also Called: Molded Devices
6918 Ed Perkic St, Riverside (92504-1001)
PHONE.............................951 509-6918
Brian P Anderson, *President*
Jason Fairfield, *CFO*
Chuck Brider, *Technology*
Lilian Gaithe, *Human Res Dir*
Edward Dayag, *Opers Mgr*
EMP: 39 EST: 2009
SALES (est): 9.4MM
SALES (corp-wide): 17.3MM **Privately
Held**
SIC: 3089 Molding primary plastic
PA: Molded Devices, Inc.
6918 Ed Perkic St
Riverside CA 92504
480 785-9100

(P-10203)
MEDEGEN LLC (DH)
4501 E Wall St, Ontario (91761-8143)
P.O. Box 515111, Los Angeles (90051-
5111)
PHONE.............................909 390-9080
Charles Stroupe, *CEO*
W Mark Dorris,
Paul M Ellis,
Jeffrey S Goble,
Michael E Stanley,
▲ EMP: 50
SQ FT: 3,000
SALES (est): 150.2MM
SALES (corp-wide): 12B **Publicly Held**
WEB: www.medegen.com
SIC: 3089 Injection molded finished plastic
products

(P-10204)
MEDPLAST GROUP INC
Also Called: South Plastic Molds
3125 E Coronado St, Anaheim
(92806-1915)
PHONE.............................951 273-1700
Jit Jagait, *General Mgr*
EMP: 100

SALES (corp-wide): 455.5MM **Privately
Held**
WEB: www.unitedplasticsgroup.com
SIC: 3089 Injection molded finished plastic
products
PA: Medplast Group, Inc.
7865 Northcourt Rd # 100
Houston TX 77040
480 553-6400

(P-10205)
MEDPLAST GROUP INC
45581 Northport Loop W, Fremont
(94538-6462)
PHONE.............................510 657-5800
Linda Amaral, *Branch Mgr*
EMP: 225
SALES (corp-wide): 455.5MM **Privately
Held**
WEB: www.unitedplasticsgroup.com
SIC: 3089 Injection molded finished plastic
products
PA: Medplast Group, Inc.
7865 Northcourt Rd # 100
Houston TX 77040
480 553-6400

(P-10206)
MEDWAY PLASTICS
CORPORATION
2250 E Cherry Indus Cir, Long Beach
(90805-4414)
PHONE.............................562 630-1175
Thomas Hutchinson Jr, *CEO*
Mary Hutchinson, *CFO*
Gerry Hutchinson, *Vice Pres*
Rick Hutchinson, *Vice Pres*
Sheryl McDaniel, *Vice Pres*
◆ EMP: 196
SALES (est): 55.5MM **Privately Held**
WEB: www.medwayplastics.com
SIC: 3089 Injection molded finished plastic
products; injection molding of plastics

(P-10207)
MEESE INC
Also Called: Meese Obitron Dunn Co
16404 Knott Ave, La Mirada (90638-5760)
PHONE.............................714 739-4005
Toll Free:.............................888 -
Mark McClung, *Manager*
Silvia Cardona, *Sales Staff*
EMP: 30
SQ FT: 54,792
SALES (corp-wide): 119.6MM **Privately
Held**
WEB: www.modroto.com
SIC: 3089 Molding primary plastic
HQ: Meese, Inc.
535 N Midland Ave
Saddle Brook NJ 07663
201 796-4490

(P-10208)
MERLIN-ALLTEC MOLD MAKING
INC
15543 Minnesota Ave, Paramount
(90723-4118)
PHONE.............................562 529-5050
Ranjiv Goonetilleke, *President*
▲ EMP: 10
SALES (est): 1.6MM **Privately Held**
WEB: www.plasticbus.com
SIC: 3089 3544 Injection molding of plas-
tics; special dies, tools, jigs & fixtures

(P-10209)
MERRICK ENGINEERING INC
(PA)
1275 Quarry St, Corona (92879-1707)
PHONE.............................951 737-6040
Abraham M Abui, *President*
Katina Brown, *CFO*
Katrina Brown, *Officer*
Roy Jorgensen, *Vice Pres*
Shannon Daugherty, *Branch Mgr*
◆ EMP: 250
SQ FT: 150,000
SALES: 88.8MM **Privately Held**
WEB: www.merrickengineering.com
SIC: 3089 Injection molding of plastics

(P-10210)
MICRODYNE PLASTICS INC
1901 E Cooley Dr, Colton (92324-6322)
PHONE..................................909 503-4010
Judy Lopez, *CEO*
Dustin Burleson, *Engineer*
Claudia Lopez AP, *Accountant*
Rhonda Torres, *Manager*
▲ EMP: 100
SQ FT: 33,000
SALES (est): 21.8MM **Privately Held**
WEB: www.microdyneplastics.com
SIC: 3089 Blow molded finished plastic
products; injection molding of plastics

(P-10211)
MICROMOLD INC
2100 Iowa Ave, Riverside (92507-2413)
P.O. Box 51118 (92517-2118)
PHONE..................................951 684-7130
Robert Aust, *President*
Ron Peterson, *Vice Pres*
Steve Wilbur, *Plant Mgr*
Bill Tischler, *QC Mgr*
Dave Dunn, *Mktg Dir*
EMP: 15
SQ FT: 11,000
SALES (est): 3.8MM **Privately Held**
WEB: www.micromoldinc.com
SIC: 3089 Molding primary plastic; injec-
tion molding of plastics

(P-10212)
MILGARD MANUFACTURING INC
Also Called: Milgard Windows
26879 Diaz Rd, Temecula (92590-3470)
PHONE..................................480 763-6000
Cory Hall, *Branch Mgr*
EMP: 14
SALES (corp-wide): 7.6B **Publicly Held**
WEB: www.milgard.com
SIC: 3089 3442 5211 3231 Windows,
plastic; sash, door or window: metal; door
& window products; products of pur-
chased glass; glass & glazing work; car-
pentry work
HQ: Milgard Manufacturing Incorporated
1010 54th Ave E
Fife WA 98424
253 922-6030

(P-10213)
MINA PRODUCT DEVELOPMENT INC
3020 Red Hill Ave, Costa Mesa
(92626-4524)
PHONE..................................714 966-2150
Babek Khamenian, *President*
▲ EMP: 10
SQ FT: 12,000
SALES (est): 1.2MM **Privately Held**
SIC: 3089 Molding primary plastic

(P-10214)
MISSION CUSTOM EXTRUSION INC
10904 Beech Ave, Fontana (92337-7260)
P.O. Box 310302 (92331-0302)
PHONE..................................909 822-1581
Moses Tersaud, *President*
EMP: 42
SQ FT: 23,400
SALES (est): 3.3MM **Privately Held**
SIC: 3089 Awnings, fiberglass & plastic
combination

(P-10215)
MISSION PLASTICS INC
1930 S Parco Ave, Ontario (91761-8312)
PHONE..................................909 947-7287
Patrick Dauphinee, *CEO*
Charles Montes, *Corp Secy*
▲ EMP: 120
SQ FT: 20,000
SALES (est): 36.7MM **Privately Held**
WEB: www.missionplastics.com
SIC: 3089 Injection molding of plastics

(P-10216)
MODERN CONCEPTS INC
3121 E Ana St, E Rncho Dmngz
(90221-5606)
PHONE..................................310 637-0013
Richard J Warpack, *President*
▲ EMP: 60

SQ FT: 42,000
SALES: 10MM **Privately Held**
SIC: 3089 3087 Coloring & finishing of
plastic products; custom compound purchased resins

(P-10217)
MODIFIED PLASTICS INC (PA)
1240 E Glenwood Pl, Santa Ana
(92707-3000)
PHONE..................................714 546-4667
Robert Estep, *CEO*
Jocelyn Eubank, *Corp Secy*
Troy Eubank, *Manager*
▲ EMP: 27
SQ FT: 18,000
SALES (est): 12.3MM **Privately Held**
WEB: www.modifiedplastics.com
SIC: 3089 Injection molding of plastics;
plastic processing

(P-10218)
MOHAMMAD KHAN
Also Called: M N Enterprises
2606 Imperial Ave, San Diego
(92102-4002)
PHONE..................................619 231-1664
Mohammad Khan, *Owner*
EMP: 12
SALES (est): 1MM **Privately Held**
SIC: 3089 5046 Kitchenware, plastic;
restaurant equipment & supplies

(P-10219)
MOLDED DEVICES INC (PA)
Also Called: Mdi
6918 Ed Perkic St, Riverside (92504-1001)
PHONE..................................480 785-9100
Brian Anderson, *President*
Charles Brider, *COO*
Jason Fairfield, *CFO*
Wayne Wilson, *Technology*
Brandy Blake,
▲ EMP: 30 EST: 1963
SQ FT: 26,000
SALES (est): 17.3MM **Privately Held**
WEB: www.moldeddevices.com
SIC: 3089 Injection molding of plastics

(P-10220)
MOLDED FIBER GL COMPANIES - W
Also Called: M F G West
9400 Holly Rd, Adelanto (92301-3900)
P.O. Box 370 (92301-0370)
PHONE..................................760 246-4042
Richard Morrison, *CEO*
Dave Denny, *Exec VP*
Jim Sommer, *Vice Pres*
Jackie Thomas, *Executive*
James Enslow, *Engineer*
▲ EMP: 100
SQ FT: 66,000
SALES (est): 22.8MM
SALES (corp-wide): 589.3MM **Privately
Held**
WEB: www.moldedfiberglass.com
SIC: 3089 Air mattresses, plastic
PA: Molded Fiber Glass Companies
2925 Mfg Pl
Ashtabula OH 44004
440 997-5851

(P-10221)
MOLDING CORPORATION AMERICA
10349 Norris Ave, Pacoima (91331-2220)
PHONE..................................818 890-7877
Mark Hurley, *CEO*
Sandra Rinder, *Vice Pres*
Dave Crowther, *General Mgr*
Lilia Gonzalez,
Elias Gonzalez, *Supervisor*
▲ EMP: 50
SQ FT: 59,000
SALES (est): 9.2MM **Privately Held**
WEB: www.moldingcorp.com
SIC: 3089 Injection molding of plastics

(P-10222)
MOLDING INTL & ENGRG INC
Also Called: M I E
42136 Avenida Alvarado, Temecula
(92590-3400)
PHONE..................................951 296-5010
Bradway B Adams, *CEO*

EMP: 80
SQ FT: 27,000
SALES (est): 8.5MM **Privately Held**
WEB: www.mie.com
SIC: 3089 3544 2821 Injection molded
finished plastic products; industrial molds;
plastics materials & resins

(P-10223)
MOLDING SOLUTIONS INC (PA)
3225 Regional Pkwy, Santa Rosa
(95403-8214)
PHONE..................................707 575-1218
Barbara F Roberts, *President*
EMP: 61
SQ FT: 22,000
SALES (est): 5.5MM **Privately Held**
SIC: 3089 Plastic hardware & building
products

(P-10224)
MONCO PRODUCTS INC
7562 Acacia Ave, Garden Grove
(92841-4057)
PHONE..................................714 891-2788
Tom Monson, *President*
Jerry Monson, *Vice Pres*
▲ EMP: 50 EST: 1979
SQ FT: 15,000
SALES (est): 6.4MM **Privately Held**
SIC: 3089 Injection molding of plastics

(P-10225)
MORGAN HILL PLASTICS INC
8118 Arroyo Cir, Gilroy (95020-7305)
PHONE..................................408 779-2118
Chet Hudson, *President*
EMP: 20 EST: 1972
SQ FT: 26,000
SALES (est): 2.7MM **Privately Held**
SIC: 3089 Injection molding of plastics;
plastic processing

(P-10226)
MORRIS ENTERPRISES INC
16799 Schoenborn St, North Hills
(91343-6107)
PHONE..................................818 894-9103
Morris Weinberg, *President*
Benjamin Weinberg, *Vice Pres*
EMP: 20 EST: 1959
SQ FT: 5,000
SALES (est): 1.6MM **Privately Held**
SIC: 3089 3676 3674 3577 Blow molded
finished plastic products; molding primary
plastic; electronic resistors; semiconduc-
tors & related devices; computer periph-
eral equipment

(P-10227)
MOSPLASTICS INC
2308 Zanker Rd, San Jose (95131-1115)
PHONE..................................408 944-9407
Douglas Cullum, *CEO*
Dan Flamen, *Shareholder*
Tom Howard, *Shareholder*
Werner Schultz, *President*
EMP: 134 EST: 1977
SQ FT: 60,000
SALES (est): 17.2MM
SALES (corp-wide): 135.2MM **Privately
Held**
WEB: www.mosinc.com
SIC: 3089 Injection molding of plastics
PA: Kennerley-Spratling, Inc.
2116 Farallon Dr
San Leandro CA 94577
510 351-8230

(P-10228)
MOTHER LODE PLAS MOLDING INC
Also Called: Central Plastics and Mfg
1905 N Macarthur Dr # 100, Tracy
(95376-2845)
PHONE..................................209 532-5146
Chand Shyani, *President*
Hiren Patel, *Vice Pres*
▲ EMP: 27
SQ FT: 30,000
SALES (est): 3.5MM **Privately Held**
WEB: www.mlplastics.com
SIC: 3089 2671 Injection molding of plas-
tics; thermoplastic coated paper for pack-
aging

(P-10229)
NANKAI ENVIRO-TECH CORPORATION
2320 Paseo De Las America, San Diego
(92154-7281)
PHONE..................................619 754-2250
Kan Kaneko, *CEO*
Takayoshi Hirayama, *President*
Hitoshi Nakamura, *Vice Pres*
Minoru Watanaba, *Admin Sec*
▲ EMP: 168
SALES (est): 48.5MM
SALES (corp-wide): 28.1K **Privately Held**
SIC: 3089 Molding primary plastic
HQ: Kuroda Electric Co., Ltd.
5-17-9, Minamioi
Shinagawa-Ku TKY 140-0
357 645-500

(P-10230)
NATIONAL DIVERSIFIED SALES INC (HQ)
Also Called: Nds
21300 Victory Blvd # 215, Woodland Hills
(91367-2525)
P.O. Box 339, Lindsay (93247-0339)
PHONE..................................559 562-9888
Michael Gummeson, *President*
Randall Stott, *CFO*
Mark Peterson, *Officer*
Sharon Vessels, *Vice Pres*
Consuelo Alarcon, *Admin Asst*
▲ EMP: 200
SQ FT: 5,000
SALES (est): 219.6MM
SALES (corp-wide): 1.2B **Privately Held**
SIC: 3089 Plastic hardware & building
products; fittings for pipe, plastic
PA: Norma Group Se
Edisonstr. 4
Maintal 63477
618 140-30

(P-10231)
NATIONAL MEDICAL PRODUCTS INC
57 Parker Unit A, Irvine (92618-1605)
PHONE..................................949 768-1147
Dahyabhai Patel, *President*
Kaushik Patel, *CFO*
Jack Kay, *Research*
EMP: 16
SQ FT: 28,630
SALES (est): 2.4MM **Privately Held**
WEB: www.jtip.com
SIC: 3089 Injection molded finished plastic
products

(P-10232)
NATIONAL SCIENTIFIC SUP CO INC
260 York Pl, Claremont (91711-4883)
PHONE..................................909 621-4585
EMP: 15
SALES (corp-wide): 5.4MM **Privately
Held**
SIC: 3089 Plastic processing
PA: National Scientific Supply Company,
Inc.
240 York Pl
Claremont CA
909 621-4585

(P-10233)
NEO PACIFIC HOLDINGS INC
Also Called: Pro-Action Products
14940 Calvert St, Van Nuys (91411-2603)
PHONE..................................818 786-2900
Steve Chan, *President*
▲ EMP: 48
SQ FT: 24,000
SALES (est): 9.5MM **Privately Held**
WEB: www.proactionpd.com
SIC: 3089 Injection molding of plastics

(P-10234)
NEOPLAST INC
1350 Citrus St, Riverside (92507-1625)
PHONE..................................951 300-9300
Richard S Risch, *President*
EMP: 19
SALES (est): 1.9MM **Privately Held**
SIC: 3089 Plastic processing

▲ = Import ▼=Export
◆ =Import/Export

(P-10235)
NEWELL BRANDS INC
17182 Nevada St, Victorville (92394-7806)
PHONE...................................760 246-2700
Cristi Mulvehill, *Manager*
EMP: 18
SALES (corp-wide): 14.7B **Publicly Held**
SIC: 3089 Plastic kitchenware, tableware &
houseware
PA: Newell Brands Inc.
221 River St Ste 13
Hoboken NJ 07030
201 610-6600

(P-10236)
**NEWLIGHT TECHNOLOGIES
INC**
14382 Astronautics Ln, Huntington Beach
(92647-2081)
PHONE...................................714 556-4500
Mark Herrema, *CEO*
Evan Creelman, *COO*
Kenton Kimmel, *CTO*
Dave Henton, *Development*
Wes Coleman, *Human Resources*
EMP: 29
SALES (est): 7.5MM **Privately Held**
SIC: 3089 Plastic processing

(P-10237)
NEWPORT LAMINATES INC
3121 W Central Ave, Santa Ana
(92704-5302)
PHONE...................................714 545-8335
Brad A Bollman, *President*
Wendy Bollman, *Vice Pres*
EMP: 40
SQ FT: 24,000
SALES (est): 3.8MM **Privately Held**
SIC: 3089 Fiber, vulcanized

(P-10238)
NEWPORT PLASTIC INC
Also Called: Country Weave
1525 E Edinger Ave, Santa Ana
(92705-4907)
PHONE...................................714 549-1955
Kay Hale, *President*
Mike Williams, *COO*
EMP: 20
SALES (est): 2.7MM
SALES (corp-wide): 9.3MM **Privately
Held**
SIC: 3089 Injection molding of plastics
PA: Newport Plastics, Llc
1525 E Edinger Ave
Santa Ana CA 92705
800 854-8402

(P-10239)
NEWPORT PLASTICS LLC (PA)
1525 E Edinger Ave, Santa Ana
(92705-4907)
PHONE...................................800 854-8402
Shirley Carlisle, *Principal*
Peter Bonin,
Kathleen Steck,
EMP: 25
SQ FT: 8,000
SALES (est): 9.3MM **Privately Held**
SIC: 3089 Injection molding of plastics

(P-10240)
NEWPORT THIN FILM LAB INC
13824 Magnolia Ave, Chino (91710-7027)
PHONE...................................909 591-0276
Scott Powers, *President*
Carrie Powers, *Corp Secy*
Brianne Mitchell, *Executive*
Anthony Arriaga, *Prdtn Mgr*
Ever Mata, *Sales Mgr*
EMP: 17
SQ FT: 11,118
SALES (est): 3.4MM **Privately Held**
WEB: www.newportlab.com
SIC: 3089 3827 Lenses, except optical:
plastic; optical instruments & lenses

(P-10241)
**NISHIBA INDUSTRIES
CORPORATION**
2360 Marconi Ct, San Diego (92154-7241)
PHONE...................................619 661-8866
Yoshiaki Nishiba, *President*
Claudia Gutierrez, *Technology*

▲ EMP: 650
SQ FT: 2,500
SALES (est): 108.8MM
SALES (corp-wide): 11.7MM **Privately
Held**
WEB: www.nishiba.com
SIC: 3089 5162 Plastic hardware &
building products; special dies, tools, jigs
& fixtures; plastics materials & basic
shapes
PA: Nishiba Industry Co., Ltd.
5-Ko, Hirosawacho
Kiryu GNM 376-0
277 541-196

(P-10242)
**NORCO INJECTION MOLDING
INC**
Also Called: Norco Plastics
14325 Monte Vista Ave, Chino
(91710-5726)
P.O. Box 2528 (91708-2528)
PHONE...................................909 393-4000
Jack Williams, *President*
John Williams, *General Mgr*
Candy Perez, *Human Resources*
Shellie Binchi, *Cust Mgr*
Letty Babcock, *Director*
▲ EMP: 100
SQ FT: 45,000
SALES (est): 15.1MM **Privately Held**
WEB: www.niminc.com
SIC: 3089 3544 Injection molding of plas-
tics; special dies, tools, jigs & fixtures

(P-10243)
NORCO PLASTICS INC
14325 Monte Vista Ave, Chino
(91710-5726)
P.O. Box 2528 (91708-2528)
PHONE...................................909 393-4000
John Williams, *CEO*
Robert Morck, *Opers Mgr*
▲ EMP: 90
SALES (est): 19.8MM **Privately Held**
SIC: 3089 Plastic containers, except foam;
injection molding of plastics

(P-10244)
NORTON PACKAGING INC (PA)
Also Called: Norpak
20670 Corsair Blvd, Hayward
(94545-1008)
PHONE...................................510 786-1922
Scott Norton, *Co-President*
Greg Norton, *Co-President*
Mark Norton, *Vice Pres*
Daphne Lam, *Controller*
Consuelo Flores, *HR Admin*
◆ EMP: 188
SQ FT: 7,200
SALES (est): 69.3MM **Privately Held**
WEB: www.nortonpackaging.com
SIC: 3089 Food casings, plastic; plastic
containers, except foam

(P-10245)
NORTON PACKAGING INC
5800 S Boyle Ave, Vernon (90058-3927)
PHONE...................................323 588-6167
Joe Schrick, *Branch Mgr*
David Hood, *Prdtn Mgr*
Ed Arzola, *QC Mgr*
EMP: 60
SALES (corp-wide): 69.3MM **Privately
Held**
WEB: www.nortonpackaging.com
SIC: 3089 5162 Plastic containers, except
foam; resins
PA: Norton Packaging, Inc.
20670 Corsair Blvd
Hayward CA 94545
510 786-1922

(P-10246)
NORWESCO INC
13241 11th Ave, Hanford (93230-9591)
PHONE...................................559 585-1668
Tom Smith, *Branch Mgr*
Rosa Garcia, *Human Resources*
EMP: 14
SALES (corp-wide): 44.1MM **Privately
Held**
WEB: www.ncmmolding.com
SIC: 3089 Septic tanks, plastic

PA: Norwesco, Inc.
4365 Steiner St
Saint Bonifacius MN 55375
952 446-1945

(P-10247)
NUBS PLASTICS INC
991 Park Center Dr, Vista (92081-8312)
PHONE...................................760 598-2525
Niyogi Ramolia, *President*
▼ EMP: 30
SQ FT: 13,000
SALES (est): 5.9MM **Privately Held**
WEB: www.progressivemolding.com
SIC: 3089 Injection molding of plastics

(P-10248)
NUCONIC PACKAGING LLC
4889 Loma Vista Ave, Vernon
(90058-3216)
PHONE...................................323 588-9033
Alan Franz, *CEO*
Francisco Diaz, *Opers Staff*
Skip Farber,
Camplastic Packaging,
Christopher Winkler,
▲ EMP: 31
SQ FT: 30,000
SALES (est): 10.2MM **Privately Held**
SIC: 3089 4783 Plastic containers, except
foam; packing & crating
PA: Carlin Capital Partners, Llc
15760 Ventura Blvd # 700
Encino CA 91436

(P-10249)
NURSERY SUPPLIES INC
534 W Struck Ave, Orange (92867-5522)
PHONE...................................714 538-0251
Dom Lovell, *Manager*
Tanya Reese, *Human Resources*
Rob Barnett, *Maintence Staff*
Elvia Tapias, *Manager*
EMP: 40
SALES (corp-wide): 173.2MM **Privately
Held**
WEB: www.nurserysupplies.com
SIC: 3089 Flower pots, plastic
PA: Nursery Supplies, Inc.
1415 Orchard Dr
Chambersburg PA 17201
717 263-7780

(P-10250)
NYPRO INC
Also Called: Nypro Healthcare Baja
505 Main St Rm 107, Chula Vista
(91911-6059)
PHONE...................................619 498-9250
Gregg Lambert, *General Mgr*
Jorge Mendez, *IT/INT Sup*
Michael Butkus, *Technology*
EMP: 75
SALES (corp-wide): 22.1B **Publicly Held**
WEB: www.nypro.com
SIC: 3089 3559 Injection molding of plas-
tics; robots, molding & forming plastics
HQ: Nypro Inc.
101 Union St
Clinton MA 01510
978 365-8100

(P-10251)
NYPRO SAN DIEGO INC
505 Main St, Chula Vista (91911-6075)
PHONE...................................619 482-7033
Gordon Lankton, *CEO*
Ernie Rice, *President*
Oscar Paredes, *Technology*
▼ EMP: 80
SQ FT: 66,000
SALES (est): 23MM
SALES (corp-wide): 22.1B **Publicly Held**
WEB: www.nypro.com
SIC: 3089 Injection molding of plastics
HQ: Nypro Inc.
101 Union St
Clinton MA 01510
978 365-8100

(P-10252)
**O K COLOR AMERICA
CORPORATION**
578 Amapola Ave, Torrance (90501-1472)
PHONE...................................310 320-9343

Osamu Hanatani, *Ch of Bd*
Tadashi Hanatani, *CEO*
Osamu Sakai, *Exec VP*
Shuichiro Wakimoto, *Admin Sec*
▲ EMP: 10
SQ FT: 10,102
SALES (est): 2.1MM
SALES (corp-wide): 40.6MM **Privately
Held**
WEB: www.calsakcolorants.com
SIC: 3089 5169 Injection molded finished
plastic products; synthetic resins, rubber
& plastic materials
PA: Ok-Kasei Co.,Ltd.
3-4-35, Torikaihonmachi
Settsu OSK 566-0
726 548-484

(P-10253)
OCEAN DIVERS USA LLC
Also Called: Odusa
975 Park Center Dr, Vista (92081-8312)
PHONE...................................760 599-6898
Don Weston, *Mng Member*
David Domshteyn, *COO*
Jim Pang Ching,
◆ EMP: 10
SQ FT: 9,000
SALES: 1MM **Privately Held**
WEB: www.odusa.net
SIC: 3089 Plastic processing

(P-10254)
**OFFSHORE PROMOTION INC
(PA)**
Also Called: Opi
3065 Beyer Blvd Ste 103, San Diego
(92154-3499)
PHONE...................................619 690-2622
Carlos Bustamante Sr, *President*
Carlos Bustamante Jr, *Admin Sec*
Lisa Niebla, *Admin Sec*
▼ EMP: 10
SALES (est): 950.8K **Privately Held**
SIC: 3089 Injection molded finished plastic
products

(P-10255)
OPTICOLOR INC
15281 Graham St, Huntington Beach
(92649-1108)
PHONE...................................714 893-8839
Daniel Neufeld, *President*
Jennifer Bryan, *Manager*
▲ EMP: 11
SQ FT: 10,000
SALES (est): 5.1MM **Privately Held**
WEB: www.opticolorinc.com
SIC: 3089 Extruded finished plastic prod-
ucts; plastic processing

(P-10256)
P S C MANUFACTURING INC
Also Called: Plastic Service Center
3424 De La Cruz Blvd, Santa Clara
(95054-2610)
PHONE...................................408 988-5115
Howard Roetken, *President*
Dreena Roetken, *Vice Pres*
EMP: 35
SQ FT: 26,000
SALES (est): 4.9MM **Privately Held**
SIC: 3089 Plastic processing

(P-10257)
PACIFIC MOLDING INC
1390 Dodson Way, Riverside (92507-2003)
P.O. Box 56251 (92517-1151)
PHONE...................................951 683-2100
EMP: 10 EST: 2011
SALES (est): 1.3MM **Privately Held**
SIC: 3089

(P-10258)
PACIFIC PLASTICS DESIGN INC
15570 Roxford St, Sylmar (91342-1263)
PHONE...................................818 364-6677
Don Asenbauer, *President*
Gayle Asenbauer, *Corp Secy*
EMP: 20
SQ FT: 25,000
SALES (est): 4.6MM **Privately Held**
WEB: www.pacificplasticsdesign.com
SIC: 3089 Plastic processing

P R O D U C T S   &   S V C S

(P-10259)
PACO PLASTICS & ENGRG INC
8540 Dice Rd, Santa Fe Springs
(90670-2592)
PHONE..................................562 698-0916
Greg K Dowden, *President*
Diana Dowden, *Vice Pres*
Dave Lowry, *General Mgr*
Alisha Attella, *Office Mgr*
Gina Aparicio, *Technical Staff*
EMP: 12
SQ FT: 12,000
SALES (est): 2.2MM **Privately Held**
WEB: www.pacoplastics.com
SIC: 3089 3429 Injection molding of plastics; aircraft hardware

(P-10260)
PACON INC
4249 Puente Ave, Baldwin Park
(91706-3420)
PHONE..................................626 814-4654
Robert M Austin, *CEO*
Michael Austin, *Vice Pres*
Michael A Austin, *Vice Pres*
Jeff Protzo, *Sales Staff*
▲ EMP: 103
SQ FT: 44,000
SALES (est): 22.9MM **Privately Held**
WEB: www.paconinc.com
SIC: 3089 Extruded finished plastic products

(P-10261)
PACTIV LLC
2024 Norris Rd, Bakersfield (93308-2238)
PHONE..................................661 392-4000
Steve Stewart, *Plant Mgr*
Wayne Schneider, *Admin Asst*
Cynthia Cole, *Purch Agent*
Doug Collins, *Opers Mgr*
Carlo Moreno, *Manager*
EMP: 300 **Privately Held**
WEB: www.pactiv.com
SIC: 3089 3086 Kitchenware, plastic; plastics foam products
HQ: Pactiv Llc
1900 W Field Ct
Lake Forest IL 60045
847 482-2000

(P-10262)
PACTIV LLC
12500 Slauson Ave Ste H1, Santa Fe
Springs (90670-8639)
PHONE..................................562 693-1451
Craig Snedden, *Manager*
Harry Sheets, *Research*
Viviana Guzman, *Controller*
Gus Gonzalez, *Human Res Dir*
Daniel Beltran, *Purch Mgr*
EMP: 94 **Privately Held**
WEB: www.pactiv.com
SIC: 3089 Plastic containers, except foam
HQ: Pactiv Llc
1900 W Field Ct
Lake Forest IL 60045
847 482-2000

(P-10263)
PACTIV LLC
Also Called: Pactiv Corp
8201 W Elowin Ct, Visalia (93291-9262)
PHONE..................................909 622-1151
Tim Tyler, *Manager*
EMP: 150 **Privately Held**
WEB: www.pactiv.com
SIC: 3089 Thermoformed finished plastic products
HQ: Pactiv Llc
1900 W Field Ct
Lake Forest IL 60045
847 482-2000

(P-10264)
PAN PACIFIC PLASTICS MFG INC
26551 Danti Ct, Hayward (94545-3917)
PHONE..................................510 785-6888
Ying Wang, *President*
Robert Lin, *CFO*
Mike Tan, *Vice Pres*
Maurice Wang, *Vice Pres*
Mark Shih, *Purch Mgr*
▲ EMP: 32 EST: 1974
SQ FT: 46,080

SALES (est): 6.1MM **Privately Held**
WEB: www.pppmi.com
SIC: 3089 2673 Plastic processing; bags: plastic, laminated & coated

(P-10265)
PANOB CORP
1531 E Cedar St, Ontario (91761-5762)
PHONE..................................909 947-8008
Arthur Graner Thorne, *President*
John Graner Thorne, *Treasurer*
Barbara Thorne, *Admin Sec*
EMP: 50
SQ FT: 12,000
SALES (est): 4.2MM
SALES (corp-wide): 6.8MM **Privately Held**
WEB: www.paramountpanels.com
SIC: 3089 3728 3613 Plastic processing; aircraft parts & equipment; switchgear & switchboard apparatus
PA: Paramount Panels, Inc.
1531 E Cedar St
Ontario CA 91761
909 947-8008

(P-10266)
PARAMOUNT PANELS INC (PA)
Also Called: California Plasteck
1531 E Cedar St, Ontario (91761-5762)
PHONE..................................909 947-8008
Arthur G Thorne, *President*
John Thorn, *Vice Pres*
John G Thorne, *Vice Pres*
Jorge Ramirez, *Engineer*
Sharol Bleicher, *Human Res Mgr*
EMP: 32 EST: 1962
SQ FT: 12,000
SALES (est): 6.8MM **Privately Held**
SIC: 3089 3812 3728 Plastic processing; search & navigation equipment; aircraft parts & equipment

(P-10267)
PARAMUNT PLSTIC FBRICATORS INC
Also Called: Paramount Fabricators
11251 Jersey Blvd, Rancho Cucamonga
(91730-5147)
PHONE..................................909 987-4757
Peter M Smits, *President*
Rose I Smits, *Vice Pres*
Jim Grace, *Sales Mgr*
EMP: 17
SQ FT: 60,000
SALES (est): 3.7MM **Privately Held**
WEB: www.paramountfabricators.com
SIC: 3089 Plastic containers, except foam

(P-10268)
PARKER PLASTICS INC
12762 Highway 29, Lower Lake
(95457-9872)
P.O. Box 459 (95457-0459)
PHONE..................................707 994-6363
George K Parker, *President*
Jack Parker, *Treasurer*
▲ EMP: 25
SQ FT: 3,200
SALES (est): 4.1MM **Privately Held**
SIC: 3089 Injection molding of plastics; thermoformed finished plastic products

(P-10269)
PBY PLASTICS INC
2571 Lindsey Privado Dr, Ontario
(91761-3452)
PHONE..................................909 930-6700
Joe Ilmberger, *President*
Janis K Ilmberger, *Treasurer*
Terry Baker, *Vice Pres*
Sam Powers, *Vice Pres*
EMP: 10
SQ FT: 5,000
SALES: 3.5MM **Privately Held**
SIC: 3089 Injection molding of plastics; plastic processing

(P-10270)
PEERLESS INJECTION MOLDING LLC
Also Called: Proplas Technologies
14321 Corp Dr, Garden Grove (92843)
PHONE..................................714 689-1920
Scott Taylor, *President*
▲ EMP: 50

SQ FT: 51,112
SALES (est): 12.7MM
SALES (corp-wide): 77.9MM **Privately Held**
WEB: www.peerlessmold.com
SIC: 3089 Injection molding of plastics
PA: Comar, Inc.
201 Laurel Rd Fl 2
Voorhees NJ 08043
856 692-6100

(P-10271)
PENINSULA PACKAGING LLC
2401 Bert Dr Ste A, Hollister (95023-2563)
PHONE..................................831 634-0940
Joe Nash, *Manager*
EMP: 180
SALES (corp-wide): 5B **Publicly Held**
SIC: 3089 7389 Plastic containers, except foam; packaging & labeling services
HQ: Peninsula Packaging, Llc
1030 N Anderson Rd
Exeter CA 93221
559 594-6813

(P-10272)
PERFORMNCE ENGINEERED PDTS INC
Also Called: P.E.P.
3270 Pomona Blvd, Pomona (91768-3282)
PHONE..................................909 594-7487
Patricia Dispenziere, *CEO*
Carl Dispenziere, *President*
Ann Campbell, *CFO*
▲ EMP: 70 EST: 1979
SQ FT: 47,000
SALES (est): 18.1MM **Privately Held**
SIC: 3089 3544 3441 Injection molding of plastics; special dies, tools, jigs & fixtures; fabricated structural metal

(P-10273)
PIGS TAIL USA LLC
925 W Lambert Rd, Brea (92821-2943)
PHONE..................................714 566-0011
Scott Bartlett, *CEO*
Andrew Mitchell, *VP Sales*
▲ EMP: 12
SALES (est): 3MM **Privately Held**
SIC: 3089 Hardware, plastic

(P-10274)
PIONETICS CORPORATION
151 Old County Rd Ste H, San Carlos
(94070-6247)
PHONE..................................650 551-0250
Gordon Mitchard, *President*
Martin Jessen, *Vice Pres*
▲ EMP: 12
SALES: 1MM **Privately Held**
WEB: www.pionetics.com
SIC: 3089 Extruded finished plastic products

(P-10275)
PITBULL GYM INCORPORATED
Also Called: Art Plates
10782 Edison Ct, Rancho Cucamonga
(91730-4845)
PHONE..................................909 980-7960
Gary John Vandenlangenberg, *President*
▲ EMP: 15
SQ FT: 10,120
SALES: 1.5MM **Privately Held**
WEB: www.fitness-wear-direct.com
SIC: 3089 5072 Bottle caps, molded plastic; hardware

(P-10276)
PITTMAN PRODUCTS INTERNATIONAL
Also Called: Pittman Outdoors
15330 Valley View Ave # 2, La Mirada
(90638-5238)
PHONE..................................562 926-6660
James Pittman, *CEO*
▲ EMP: 15
SQ FT: 900
SALES (est): 1.7MM **Privately Held**
SIC: 3089 Air mattresses, plastic

(P-10277)
PLA-COR INCORPORATED
10207 Buena Vista Ave D, Santee
(92071-4482)
P.O. Box 522, Campo (91906-0522)
PHONE..................................619 478-2139
Lewis Hein, *CEO*
Derrell J Weldy, *President*
Michael D Weldy, *Vice Pres*
EMP: 17
SQ FT: 6,000
SALES (est): 1.8MM **Privately Held**
WEB: www.pla-cor.com
SIC: 3089 Plastic hardware & building products

(P-10278)
PLANET PLEXI CORP
23282 Verdugo Dr, Laguna Hills
(92653-1335)
PHONE..................................949 206-1183
Bahram Bakhtiar, *Principal*
Padra Pazoki, *Administration*
EMP: 12
SALES (est): 1.8MM **Privately Held**
SIC: 3089 Injection molding of plastics; plastic processing

(P-10279)
PLASCENE INC
1600 Pacific Ave, Oxnard (93033-2746)
PHONE..................................562 695-0240
Hy Duy Tran, *CEO*
▲ EMP: 15
SALES (est): 1.2MM
SALES (corp-wide): 1.1MM **Privately Held**
SIC: 3089 5162 Air mattresses, plastic; plastics materials & basic shapes; plastics resins
HQ: Duy Tan Plastics Manufacturing Corporation
298 Ho Hoc Lam Street,
Ho Chi Minh
283 876-2222

(P-10280)
PLASIDYNE ENGINEERING & MFG
3230 E 59th St, Long Beach (90805-4502)
P.O. Box 5578 (90805-0578)
PHONE..................................562 531-0510
Dean C Sutherland, *President*
EMP: 22
SQ FT: 15,000
SALES: 2.3MM **Privately Held**
WEB: www.plasidyne.com
SIC: 3089 Plastic hardware & building products

(P-10281)
PLASMETEX INDUSTRIES
1425 Linda Vista Dr, San Marcos
(92078-3806)
PHONE..................................760 744-8300
Adolph Saupe, *President*
▲ EMP: 13 EST: 1963
SQ FT: 1,000
SALES (est): 1.3MM **Privately Held**
WEB: www.plasmetex.com
SIC: 3089 Molding primary plastic

(P-10282)
PLASTECH MOULDING & FABG
Also Called: Plastech Molding & Fabricating
16717 Spruce St, Hesperia (92345-6013)
PHONE..................................760 244-8078
William Sterling, *President*
Katherine O'Neill, *Vice Pres*
EMP: 31 EST: 1998
SQ FT: 14,000
SALES: 2.4MM **Privately Held**
WEB: www.plastch.com
SIC: 3089 Plastic hardware & building products; extruded finished plastic products

(P-10283)
PLASTHEC MOLDING INC
1945 S Grove Ave, Ontario (91761-5616)
PHONE..................................909 947-4267
Hector Carrion, *President*
James Downey, *Vice Pres*
EMP: 84 EST: 1978
SQ FT: 34,000

SALES (est): 14.8MM **Privately Held**
WEB: www.plasthec.com
SIC: 3089 Injection molding of plastics

(P-10284)
PLASTIC AND METAL CENTER INC
23162 La Cadena Dr, Laguna Hills (92653-1405)
PHONE.....................949 770-0610
Faramarz Khaladj, *President*
Fred Carr, *Vice Pres*
Denise Khaladj, *Admin Sec*
Nina Khaladj, *Sls & Mktg Exec*
Chris Jenkins, *Sales Mgr*
EMP: 25
SQ FT: 20,000
SALES (est): 5.1MM **Privately Held**
WEB: www.plastic-metal.com
SIC: 3089 Injection molding of plastics; thermoformed finished plastic products

(P-10285)
PLASTIC DRESS-UP COMPANY
11077 Rush St, South El Monte (91733-3546)
P.O. Box 3897, El Monte (91733-0897)
PHONE.....................626 442-7711
Myron H Funk, *President*
▲ EMP: 84
SQ FT: 130,000
SALES (est): 10.4MM **Privately Held**
WEB: www.pdu.com
SIC: 3089 Novelties, plastic

(P-10286)
PLASTIC FABRICATION TECH LLC
2320 E Cherry Indus Cir, Long Beach (90805-4417)
PHONE.....................773 509-1700
Jay Magness Jr, *President*
Mary Hutchinson, *CFO*
EMP: 100
SQ FT: 20,000
SALES (est): 6.4MM **Privately Held**
SIC: 3089 Plastic processing

(P-10287)
PLASTIC PACKAGE LLC (PA)
Also Called: Revere Packaging
4600 Beloit Dr, Sacramento (95838-2426)
PHONE.....................916 921-3399
Mike Miller, *CEO*
Steve Van Waardenberg, *COO*
Rich Brandani, *CFO*
EMP: 85
SQ FT: 50,000
SALES (est): 21MM **Privately Held**
SIC: 3089 Plastic containers, except foam

(P-10288)
PLASTIC PROCESSING CORP
13432 Estrella Ave, Gardena (90248-1513)
PHONE.....................310 719-7330
Dagmer Schulte-Derne, *Ch of Bd*
Steve Rockenbach, *CFO*
▲ EMP: 50
SQ FT: 20,000
SALES (est): 4.9MM **Privately Held**
SIC: 3089 Blow molded finished plastic products

(P-10289)
PLASTICS DEVELOPMENT CORP
960 Calle Negocio, San Clemente (92673-6201)
PHONE.....................949 492-0217
Inder Jain, *President*
Vijay Jain, *Corp Secy*
Sanie Jain, *Vice Pres*
▲ EMP: 23
SQ FT: 7,000
SALES (est): 4.9MM **Privately Held**
WEB: www.plasticsdev.com
SIC: 3089 Injection molding of plastics

(P-10290)
PLASTICS PLUS TECHNOLOGY INC
1495 Research Dr, Redlands (92374-4584)
PHONE.....................909 747-0555
Kathy Bodor, *President*
Barbara Saber, *Manager*

EMP: 33
SQ FT: 35,000
SALES (est): 8.8MM **Privately Held**
WEB: www.plasticsplus.com
SIC: 3089 3544 Injection molding of plastics; forms (molds), for foundry & plastics working machinery

(P-10291)
PLASTIJECT LLC
14811 Spring Ave, Santa Fe Springs (90670-5109)
PHONE.....................562 926-6705
EMP: 13 EST: 1997
SALES (est): 1.5MM **Privately Held**
SIC: 3089

(P-10292)
PLASTIQUE UNIQUE INC
3383 Livonia Ave, Los Angeles (90034-3127)
PHONE.....................310 839-3968
Christine Galonska, *President*
Lionel Funes, *Vice Pres*
Silvia Totado, *Director*
EMP: 27
SQ FT: 5,000
SALES (est): 3.8MM **Privately Held**
WEB: www.plastiqueuniqueinc.com
SIC: 3089 Injection molding of plastics

(P-10293)
PLASTO TECH INTERNATIONAL INC
4 Autry, Irvine (92618-2708)
PHONE.....................949 458-1880
Ben Khalaj, *President*
Jacqueline Khalaj, *CEO*
Benedicto Garcia, *Mfg Mgr*
▲ EMP: 20
SQ FT: 16,530
SALES (est): 4.2MM **Privately Held**
WEB: www.plastotech.com
SIC: 3089 5084 8711 7389 Injection molding of plastics; industrial machinery & equipment; consulting engineer; design, commercial & industrial; plastics sheets & rods

(P-10294)
PLASTPRO 2000 INC (PA)
Also Called: Plastpro Doors
5200 W Century Blvd Fl 9, Los Angeles (90045-5900)
PHONE.....................310 693-8600
Franco An, *CEO*
Shirley Wang, *President*
Johnny MAI, *CFO*
Walter Wang, *Chairman*
Benny Hugo, *Programmer Anys*
◆ EMP: 132
SALES (est): 20.7MM **Privately Held**
WEB: www.plastproinc.com
SIC: 3089 Fiberglass doors

(P-10295)
PLASTRUCT INC
1020 Wallace Way, City of Industry (91748-1027)
PHONE.....................626 912-7017
John J Wanderman, *President*
EMP: 57
SQ FT: 28,000
SALES (est): 7.5MM
SALES (corp-wide): 11.8MM **Privately Held**
WEB: www.plastruct.com
SIC: 3089 5945 3952 Plastic processing; hobby, toy & game shops; lead pencils & art goods
PA: Engineering Model Associates Inc
1020 Wallace Way
City Of Industry CA 91748
626 912-7011

(P-10296)
POLY MASTERS INDUSTRIES INC
2821 Century Blvd, South Gate (90280-5503)
PHONE.....................323 564-7824
Raffi A Aposhian, *President*
Karnig Oughourlian, *Treasurer*
▲ EMP: 20
SQ FT: 14,000

SALES (est): 2.7MM **Privately Held**
SIC: 3089 3144 3143 Molding primary plastic; women's footwear, except athletic; men's footwear, except athletic

(P-10297)
POLYMER LOGISTICS INC
1725 Sierra Ridge Dr, Riverside (92507-7133)
PHONE.....................951 567-2900
Albert Terrazas, *Branch Mgr*
EMP: 14 **Privately Held**
SIC: 3089 5085 5162 Pallets, plastic; boxes, crates, etc., other than paper; plastics materials & basic shapes
PA: Polymer Logistics, Inc.
4630 Woodland Corp Blvd
Tampa FL 33614

(P-10298)
POLYTECH COLOR & COMPOUNDING
847 S Wanamaker Ave, Ontario (91761-8152)
PHONE.....................909 923-7008
Brian Cockren, *President*
EMP: 13
SALES (est): 1.1MM **Privately Held**
SIC: 3089 5169 Coloring & finishing of plastic products; synthetic resins, rubber & plastic materials

(P-10299)
POP PLASTICS ACRYLIC DISP INC
8211 Orangethorpe Ave, Buena Park (90621-3811)
PHONE.....................714 523-8500
Jeff Dougherty, *President*
David A Lewis, *COO*
Steven K North, *CFO*
▲ EMP: 20
SQ FT: 15,000
SALES (est): 3.1MM **Privately Held**
SIC: 3089 Plates, plastic

(P-10300)
PPP LLC
601 W Olympic Blvd, Montebello (90640-5229)
P.O. Box 789 (90640-0789)
PHONE.....................323 832-9627
Evelyn Garcia, *Mng Member*
Martin Stoeckle, *Managing Dir*
Ute Carstens, *Opers Staff*
EMP: 50 EST: 2001
SALES (est): 7.2MM **Privately Held**
WEB: www.ppp.net
SIC: 3089 Blow molded finished plastic products

(P-10301)
PRE/PLASTICS INC
Also Called: Preplastics
12600 Locksley Ln Ste 100, Auburn (95602-2070)
PHONE.....................530 823-1820
Richard L Miller, *CEO*
Linda Miller, *Corp Secy*
Brian Miller, *Director*
EMP: 30
SQ FT: 20,000
SALES (est): 9.1MM **Privately Held**
WEB: www.preplastics.com
SIC: 3089 Injection molding of plastics

(P-10302)
PRECISE AEROSPACE MFG INC
Also Called: Precise Plastic Products
224 Glider Cir, Corona (92880-2533)
PHONE.....................951 898-0500
Ronnie E Harwood, *CEO*
Roxanne Abdi, *President*
Sandy Armas, *Manager*
▲ EMP: 42
SQ FT: 39,000
SALES (est): 13.7MM **Privately Held**
WEB: www.preciseplastic.com
SIC: 3089 3544 Molding primary plastic; industrial molds

(P-10303)
PRECISION INJECTION MOLDING CO
Also Called: Pimco
206 Lewis Ct, Corona (92882-1812)
PHONE.....................951 272-8028
Michael Murphy, *President*
Steve Crawford, *Corp Secy*
Masako Walsh, *Manager*
▲ EMP: 12
SALES (est): 2.2MM **Privately Held**
WEB: www.pimcoplastics.com
SIC: 3089 Injection molding of plastics

(P-10304)
PRECISION MOLDED PLASTICS INC
880 W 9th St, Upland (91786-4540)
PHONE.....................909 981-9662
David S Vanvoorhis, *CEO*
Ash Brown, *General Mgr*
EMP: 11
SQ FT: 8,000
SALES (est): 3.1MM **Privately Held**
WEB: www.precisionmoldedplastics.com
SIC: 3089 Injection molding of plastics

(P-10305)
PRECISION PLASTIC LLC
555 Twin Dolphin Dr, Redwood City (94065-2129)
PHONE.....................510 324-8676
Eric Appelblom,
EMP: 175
SALES (est): 9.4MM **Privately Held**
WEB: www.precision-plastics.net
SIC: 3089 Plastic processing

(P-10306)
PREDATOR MOTORSPORTS INC
1250 Distribution Way, Vista (92081-8816)
PHONE.....................760 734-1749
Ryan Wilson, *President*
Dan Wilson, *Vice Pres*
Nyela Wilson, *Controller*
Autumn Conquest, *Human Resources*
Garrett Robbins, *Sales Mgr*
▲ EMP: 15
SQ FT: 15,000
SALES (est): 3.1MM **Privately Held**
WEB: www.predatormotorsports.com
SIC: 3089 3465 Automotive parts, plastic; body parts, automobile: stamped metal

(P-10307)
PREMIUM PLASTICS MACHINE INC
15956 Downey Ave, Paramount (90723-5190)
PHONE.....................323 979-3889
David Pennington, *President*
Michael Robert Pennington, *Exec VP*
Suzanne Pennington, *Vice Pres*
▲ EMP: 16 EST: 1976
SQ FT: 6,241
SALES (est): 2.3MM **Privately Held**
SIC: 3089 Molding primary plastic; injection molding of plastics

(P-10308)
PREPRODUCTION PLASTICS INC
Also Called: P P I
210 Teller St, Corona (92879-1886)
PHONE.....................951 340-9680
Koby Loosen, *President*
Barbara Loosen, *Corp Secy*
Ron Loosen, *Principal*
Paul Rice, *Engineer*
Bert Bruch, *Buyer*
▲ EMP: 50
SQ FT: 45,000
SALES (est): 19.2MM **Privately Held**
WEB: www.ppiplastics.com
SIC: 3089 3544 Molding primary plastic; forms (molds), for foundry & plastics working machinery

(P-10309)
PRINCE LIONHEART INC (PA)
2421 Westgate Rd, Santa Maria (93455-1075)
PHONE.....................805 922-2250

Kelly Griffiths, *CEO*
Debbie Di Nardi, *Vice Pres*
Thomas McConnell, *Vice Pres*
Richard Siegel, *Opers Staff*
Martha Bowser, *Manager*
▲ **EMP:** 40
SQ FT: 80,000
SALES (est): 9.7MM **Privately Held**
WEB: www.princelionheart.com
SIC: 3089 Injection molding of plastics

(P-10310)
PRINCETON CASE WEST INC
1444 W Mccoy Ln, Santa Maria
(93455-1005)
PHONE...................805 928-8840
Douglas Laggrenm, *President*
Jim Laggren, *Vice Pres*
EMP: 20
SQ FT: 22,000
SALES (est): 3.5MM **Privately Held**
WEB: www.pcwest.net
SIC: 3089 3161 Cases, plastic; luggage

(P-10311)
PRO DESIGN GROUP INC
438 E Alondra Blvd, Gardena
(90248-2902)
PHONE...................310 767-1032
Chris Raab, *President*
Christopher Allen Raab, *President*
Maria Chanlder, *Vice Pres*
▼ **EMP:** 35
SQ FT: 50,000
SALES (est): 8.9MM **Privately Held**
WEB: www.conceptdisplay.com
SIC: 3089 Plastic kitchenware, tableware &
houseware; plastic processing

(P-10312)
**PRODUCT DESIGN
DEVELOPMENTS**
15611 Container Ln, Huntington Beach
(92649-1532)
PHONE...................714 898-6895
Steven F Doke, *President*
EMP: 35
SQ FT: 25,000
SALES (est): 5.3MM **Privately Held**
SIC: 3089 4724 Plastic containers, except
foam; travel agencies

(P-10313)
**PRODUCTIVITY CALIFORNIA
INC**
Also Called: Pro Cal
10533 Sessler St, South Gate
(90280-7251)
PHONE...................562 923-3100
Gary Vollers, *President*
Don Uchiyama, *Admin Sec*
EMP: 70
SQ FT: 100,000
SALES (est): 20.1MM
SALES (corp-wide): 547MM **Publicly
Held**
WEB: www.myersind.com
SIC: 3089 Plastic containers, except foam
PA: Myers Industries, Inc.
1293 S Main St
Akron OH 44301
330 253-5592

(P-10314)
**PROMEX INTERNATIONAL PLAS
INC**
12860 San Fernando Rd D, Sylmar
(91342-3783)
PHONE...................818 367-5352
Gilbert Anguiano, *President*
EMP: 42
SQ FT: 30,000
SALES (est): 6.9MM **Privately Held**
SIC: 3089 Injection molding of plastics

(P-10315)
PROULX MANUFACTURING INC
Also Called: Universal Products
11433 6th St, Rancho Cucamonga
(91730-6024)
PHONE...................909 980-0662
Richard Proulx, *President*
Raymond E Proulx, *CFO*
Lorraine Proulx, *Admin Sec*
◆ **EMP:** 45

SALES (est): 9.1MM **Privately Held**
WEB: www.universalproducts.com
SIC: 3089 Plastic hardware & building
products

(P-10316)
**PROVIDIEN INJCTION MOLDING
INC**
Also Called: Pedi
2731 Loker Ave W, Carlsbad (92010-6601)
PHONE...................760 931-1844
Jeffrey S Goble, *CEO*
Richard D Witchey Jr, *President*
Jim Yee, *Vice Pres*
Louise Witchey, *Admin Sec*
Casey Ayala, *Business Mgr*
◆ **EMP:** 74
SQ FT: 50,000
SALES (est): 24.3MM **Privately Held**
WEB: www.pediplastics.com
SIC: 3089 Injection molded finished plastic
products; injection molding of plastics
HQ: Witco Industries, Inc
2731 Loker Ave W
Carlsbad CA

(P-10317)
QUALI-TECH MOLD
5939 Sycamore Ct, Chino (91710-9139)
PHONE...................909 464-8124
Martin Lane, *Owner*
EMP: 10
SQ FT: 6,600
SALES (est): 850K **Privately Held**
SIC: 3089 Injection molding of plastics

(P-10318)
**QUASHNICK TOOL
CORPORATION**
225 N Guild Ave, Lodi (95240-0844)
PHONE...................209 334-5283
Robert Hampton, *CEO*
Terry Quashnick, *President*
Duane Saville, *Exec VP*
Jinnet Quashnick, *Admin Sec*
EMP: 45
SQ FT: 15,000
SALES (est): 6.8MM **Privately Held**
WEB: www.quashnick.com
SIC: 3089 3544 Injection molding of plas-
tics; industrial molds

(P-10319)
QUIET RIDE SOLUTIONS LLC
1122 S Wilson Way Ste 1, Stockton
(95205-7048)
PHONE...................209 942-4777
Timothy Cox, *President*
Melissa Elliott, *Sales Staff*
Jackie Cox,
Jacquelyn Cox,
▲ **EMP:** 12
SQ FT: 6,600
SALES (est): 1.6MM **Privately Held**
WEB: www.quietride.com
SIC: 3089 Automotive parts, plastic

(P-10320)
**R C WESTBURG ENGINEERING
INC**
23302 Vista Grande Dr, Laguna Hills
(92653-1410)
PHONE...................949 859-4648
Ronald C Westburg, *President*
Eileen Westburg, *Vice Pres*
▲ **EMP:** 12
SQ FT: 13,000
SALES: 750K **Privately Held**
SIC: 3089 3851 Injection molding of plas-
tics; protective eyeware

(P-10321)
**RADIUS PRODUCT
DEVELOPMENT INC**
6375 San Ignacio Ave, San Jose
(95119-1200)
PHONE...................408 361-6000
John Van Akkeren, *President*
EMP: 800

SALES (est): 25.7MM
SALES (corp-wide): 22.1B **Publicly Held**
SIC: 3089 3559 8711 7389 Injection
molding of plastics; robots, molding &
forming plastics; engineering services;
design, commercial & industrial
HQ: Nypro Inc.
101 Union St
Clinton MA 01510
978 365-8100

(P-10322)
RAKAR INCORPORATED
1700 Emerson Ave, Oxnard (93033-1847)
P.O. Box 2767 (93034-2767)
PHONE...................805 487-2721
Theresa Padilla, *CEO*
Janet Pittman, *Treasurer*
Barbara Mahaney, *Human Res Mgr*
Dan Pittman, *Plant Mgr*
Brent Melekian, *QC Mgr*
EMP: 48
SQ FT: 28,000
SALES (est): 9.9MM **Privately Held**
SIC: 3089 3544 Injection molding of plas-
tics; forms (molds), for foundry & plastics
working machinery

(P-10323)
RAMKO INJECTION INC
3500 Tanya Ave, Hemet (92545-9410)
PHONE...................951 652-3510
Robert G Andrei, *President*
EMP: 100
SALES: 16MM **Privately Held**
SIC: 3089 3364 Blow molded finished
plastic products; nonferrous die-castings
except aluminum

(P-10324)
RAMTEC ASSOCIATES INC
Also Called: Con-Tech Plastics
3200 E Birch St Ste B, Brea (92821-6287)
PHONE...................714 996-7477
Ralph Riehl, *President*
Vernon Meurer, *Vice Pres*
Vern Meurer, *Mktg Dir*
▲ **EMP:** 28
SQ FT: 35,000
SALES (est): 6.7MM **Privately Held**
WEB: www.contechplastics.com
SIC: 3089 Molding primary plastic; injec-
tion molding of plastics

(P-10325)
RAPID ACCU-FORM INC
3825 Sprig Dr, Benicia (94510-1248)
P.O. Box 699 (94510-0699)
PHONE...................707 745-1879
George L Brown, *President*
Linda Brown, *Vice Pres*
EMP: 15 **EST:** 1976
SQ FT: 29,000
SALES (est): 3.1MM **Privately Held**
WEB: www.rapidaccuform.com
SIC: 3089 3545 Plastic processing; tools
& accessories for machine tools

(P-10326)
RAPIDWERKS INCORPORATED
1257 Quarry Ln Ste 140, Pleasanton
(94566-8483)
PHONE...................925 417-0124
Scott Herbert, *President*
EMP: 25
SQ FT: 15,000
SALES: 5MM **Privately Held**
WEB: www.rapidwerks.com
SIC: 3089 Injection molding of plastics

(P-10327)
**RATERMANN MANUFACTURING
INC (PA)**
Also Called: Rmi
601 Pinnacle Pl, Livermore (94550-9705)
PHONE...................800 264-7793
George Ratermann, *President*
Brent Lockhart, *Vice Pres*
Melissa Adams, *Accounting Mgr*
Shane Page, *Purch Mgr*
Craig Pagano, *Natl Sales Mgr*
◆ **EMP:** 40
SQ FT: 20,000

SALES (est): 20MM **Privately Held**
SIC: 3089 3081 3679 Plastic processing;
packing materials, plastic sheet; cryogenic cooling devices for infrared detectors, masers

(P-10328)
REHRIG PACIFIC COMPANY (HQ)
4010 E 26th St, Vernon (90058-4477)
PHONE...................800 421-6244
William J Rehrig, *CEO*
Michael J Doka, *President*
James L Drew, *CFO*
Blair Chastain, *Vice Pres*
Jeff Hentges, *Vice Pres*
◆ **EMP:** 150
SQ FT: 200,000
SALES (est): 453.3MM **Privately Held**
SIC: 3089 2821 Cases, plastic; garbage
containers, plastic; molding primary plas-
tic; plasticizer/additive based plastic ma-
terials

(P-10329)
**REHRIG PACIFIC HOLDINGS
INC (PA)**
4010 E 26th St, Vernon (90058-4477)
PHONE...................323 262-5145
William J Rehrig, *CEO*
Michael J Doka, *President*
James L Drew, *CFO*
William Widmann, *Vice Pres*
Muriel Kiser, *Admin Sec*
EMP: 13
SALES (est): 462.7MM **Privately Held**
SIC: 3089 2821 Cases, plastic; garbage
containers, plastic; molding primary plas-
tic; plasticizer/additive based plastic ma-
terials

(P-10330)
**REINHOLD INDUSTRIES INC
(DH)**
12827 Imperial Hwy, Santa Fe Springs
(90670-4761)
PHONE...................562 944-3281
Clarence Hightower, *CEO*
Carl Walker, *CFO*
▲ **EMP:** 145
SQ FT: 130,000
SALES (est): 36.8MM **Publicly Held**
WEB: www.reinhold-ind.com
SIC: 3089 3764 2531 Molding primary
plastic; guided missile & space vehicle
propulsion unit parts; seats, aircraft

(P-10331)
RENY & CO INC
Also Called: Renymed
4505 Littlejohn St, Baldwin Park
(91706-2239)
PHONE...................626 962-3078
Steve Raiken, *CEO*
Renee Fernandez, *Office Mgr*
Renee Hamm, *Office Mgr*
Grigoriy Gorelik, *Project Engr*
Cassaundra Young-Puig, *Engineer*
EMP: 18 **EST:** 1985
SQ FT: 7,000
SALES (est): 6.2MM **Privately Held**
WEB: www.renyco.com
SIC: 3089 Plastic hardware & building
products; injection molding of plastics

(P-10332)
REPSCO INC
5300 Claus Rd Ste 3, Modesto
(95357-1665)
P.O. Box 2809, Parker CO (80134-1424)
PHONE...................303 294-0364
Paul Bennett Jr, *President*
John Shedd, *Shareholder*
Bob Flynn, *Vice Pres*
Shawn Byrne, *Sales Mgr*
Steve Faries, *Marketing Staff*
◆ **EMP:** 25
SALES (est): 7.8MM **Privately Held**
WEB: www.repsco.com
SIC: 3089 Plastic processing

(P-10333)
RESINART CORPORATION
Also Called: Resinart Plastics
1621 Placentia Ave, Costa Mesa
(92627-4311)
PHONE...................949 642-3665

▲ = Import ▼=Export
◆ =Import/Export

Gary Uecker, *President*
Frank Uecker, *Treasurer*
Gene Chandler, *Vice Pres*
EMP: 40
SQ FT: 15,000
SALES (est): 5.5MM **Privately Held**
WEB: www.resinart.com
SIC: 3089 Molding primary plastic; panels, building; plastic

(P-10334)
REYRICH PLASTICS INC
1734 S Vineyard Ave, Ontario (91761-7746)
PHONE..................................909 484-8444
Sandy Reyes, *President*
Tina Richter, *CFO*
EMP: 11
SQ FT: 1,000
SALES (est): 1.2MM **Privately Held**
SIC: 3089 Injection molding of plastics

(P-10335)
RIMNETICS INC
Also Called: R I M
3445 De La Cruz Blvd, Santa Clara (95054-2110)
PHONE..................................650 969-6590
David L Chew, *President*
Gary Quigley, *Principal*
Marjorie Chew, *Admin Sec*
Daniel Chew, *Marketing Mgr*
EMP: 46
SQ FT: 20,000
SALES (est): 9.2MM
SALES (corp-wide): 22.9MM **Privately Held**
WEB: www.rimnetics.com
SIC: 3089 Injection molding of plastics
PA: Minimatics, Inc.
3445 De La Cruz Blvd
Santa Clara CA 95054
650 969-5630

(P-10336)
RLS ENTERPRISES
Also Called: Del Craft Plastics
25072 Wilkes Pl, Laguna Hills (92653-4926)
PHONE..................................714 493-1735
Steve Hjelmstrom, *President*
Lora Crafton-Stogner, *CFO*
EMP: 20
SQ FT: 7,500
SALES: 1MM **Privately Held**
WEB: www.rlsenterprises.com
SIC: 3089 6531 Laminating of plastic; appraiser, real estate

(P-10337)
ROBBINS AUTO TOP LLC
321 Todd Ct, Oxnard (93030-5192)
P.O. Box 5567 (93031-5567)
PHONE..................................805 278-8249
Martin Brown, *President*
John Bath, *Plant Mgr*
Harry H Lynch, *Mng Member*
▲ **EMP:** 65
SQ FT: 53,000
SALES (est): 12.4MM **Privately Held**
WEB: www.robbinsautotopco.com
SIC: 3089 Automotive parts, plastic

(P-10338)
RODAK PLASTICS CO INC
31721 Knapp St, Hayward (94544-7827)
PHONE..................................510 471-0898
Charles Romero, *President*
Catherine Helms, *Corp Secy*
Paul Helms, *Vice Pres*
EMP: 12
SQ FT: 13,000
SALES (est): 1.6MM **Privately Held**
WEB: www.islamicdigest.net
SIC: 3089 Injection molding of plastics; plastic processing

(P-10339)
ROLENN MANUFACTURING INC (PA)
2065 Roberta St, Riverside (92507-2644)
PHONE..................................951 682-1185
Thomas J Accatino, *President*
Christie Accatino, *Corp Secy*
Larry Morrison, *Mfg Spvr*
EMP: 20 **EST:** 1965

SQ FT: 9,000
SALES (est): 6MM **Privately Held**
WEB: www.rolenn.com
SIC: 3089 3599 Injection molding of plastics; molding primary plastic; machine & other job shop work

(P-10340)
RONCO PLASTICS INCORPORATED
15022 Parkway Loop Ste B, Tustin (92780-6529)
PHONE..................................714 259-1385
Ronald L Pearson, *President*
EMP: 24
SQ FT: 28,000
SALES: 4.1MM **Privately Held**
SIC: 3089 Plastic containers, except foam; septic tanks, plastic

(P-10341)
RONFORD PRODUCTS INC
1116 E 2nd St, Pomona (91766-2114)
PHONE..................................909 622-7446
Carl Higgins, *Manager*
EMP: 28
SALES (corp-wide): 2.1MM **Privately Held**
WEB: www.ronfordproducts.com
SIC: 3089 5093 Plastic processing; plastics scrap
PA: Ronford Products, Inc.
16616 Garfield Ave
Paramount CA 90723
562 408-1081

(P-10342)
ROPAK CORPORATION (DH)
Also Called: Ropak Packaging
10540 Talbert Ave 200w, Fountain Valley (92708-6027)
PHONE..................................714 845-2845
Greg A Toft, *CEO*
◆ **EMP:** 35
SQ FT: 12,000
SALES (est): 308.8MM
SALES (corp-wide): 1.1B **Privately Held**
WEB: www.ropakcorp.com
SIC: 3089 Plastic containers, except foam

(P-10343)
ROTATIONAL MOLDING INC
Also Called: R M I
17038 S Figueroa St, Gardena (90248-3089)
PHONE..................................310 327-5401
Mario Poma, *CEO*
Douglas Russell, *CFO*
Sherri Poma, *Human Res Mgr*
Peter Ramos, *Sales Staff*
EMP: 65
SALES (est): 11.6MM **Privately Held**
SIC: 3089 Plastic containers, except foam; garbage containers, plastic

(P-10344)
ROTO LITE INC
2161 Maple Privado, Ontario (91761-7603)
PHONE..................................909 923-4353
Sandy Canzone, *President*
Dan Hammond, *Vice Pres*
John Hammond, *Admin Sec*
EMP: 22
SALES (est): 1MM **Privately Held**
WEB: www.rotolite.com
SIC: 3089 0781 Plastic containers, except foam; landscape services

(P-10345)
ROTO POWER INC
191 Granite St Ste A, Corona (92879-1286)
PHONE..................................951 751-9850
David Howey, *COO*
EMP: 16
SALES (est): 815.4K **Privately Held**
SIC: 3089 Injection molding of plastics

(P-10346)
ROTO WEST ENTERPRISES INC
15651 Container Ln, Huntington Beach (92649-1532)
PHONE..................................714 899-2030
EMP: 15
SALES (est): 1.1MM **Privately Held**
SIC: 3089

(P-10347)
ROYAL INTERPACK MIDWEST INC
475 Palmyrita Ave, Riverside (92507-1812)
PHONE..................................626 675-0637
EMP: 10 **EST:** 2015
SALES (est): 631.7K **Privately Held**
SIC: 3089

(P-10348)
ROYAL INTERPACK NORTH AMER INC
475 Palmyrita Ave, Riverside (92507-1812)
PHONE..................................951 787-6925
Radhika Shah, *CEO*
Tee Komsan, *President*
Visnau Chawla, *Principal*
Abu Hossain, *Administration*
Kunal Sidhpura, *Director*
▲ **EMP:** 45
SALES (est): 12.1MM **Privately Held**
SIC: 3089 Thermoformed finished plastic products

(P-10349)
RPM PLASTIC MOLDING INC
2821 E Miraloma Ave, Anaheim (92806-1804)
PHONE..................................714 630-9300
Michael Ferik, *CEO*
Phil Hothan, *Admin Sec*
▲ **EMP:** 25
SALES (est): 4.7MM **Privately Held**
SIC: 3089 Injection molding of plastics

(P-10350)
RSK TOOL INCORPORATED
410 W Carob St, Compton (90220-5213)
PHONE..................................310 537-3302
Ronald Kohagura, *President*
Mark Kohagura, *President*
Virginia Kohagura, *Vice Pres*
Laura Benedid, *Office Mgr*
EMP: 35
SQ FT: 27,000
SALES (est): 4.7MM **Privately Held**
WEB: www.rsktool.com
SIC: 3089 Injection molding of plastics

(P-10351)
RUSSELL-STANLEY
Also Called: Russell-Stanley West
9449 Santa Anita Ave, Rancho Cucamonga (91730-6118)
PHONE..................................909 980-7114
Robert Singleton, *President*
Daniel Miller, *President*
▼ **EMP:** 60
SQ FT: 75,000
SALES (est): 6.4MM
SALES (corp-wide): 1.1B **Privately Held**
WEB: www.mausergroup.com
SIC: 3089 Plastic containers, except foam
HQ: Mauser Usa, Llc
2 Tower Center Blvd 20-1
East Brunswick NJ 08816
732 353-7100

(P-10352)
RW WILSON INC
Also Called: High Sierra Plastics
375 Joe Smith Rd, Bishop (93514-8800)
PHONE..................................760 873-5600
Robert W Wilson, *CEO*
▲ **EMP:** 35
SQ FT: 23,000
SALES (est): 5.6MM **Privately Held**
WEB: www.highsierraplastics.com
SIC: 3089 3544 Blow molded finished plastic products; injection molding of plastics; thermoformed finished plastic products; industrial molds

(P-10353)
RYKO PLASTIC PRODUCTS INC
701 E Francis St, Ontario (91761-5514)
PHONE..................................909 773-0050
Melvin Victor Morrow, *President*
EMP: 10
SQ FT: 42,000
SALES (est): 1.6MM **Privately Held**
SIC: 3089 Plastic processing

(P-10354)
S C R MOLDING INC
2340 Pomona Rd, Corona (92880-6929)
PHONE..................................951 736-5490
Carl E Thompson, *President*
Richard H McCray, *Vice Pres*
Karen Thompson, *Admin Sec*
EMP: 18
SQ FT: 21,000
SALES (est): 2.5MM **Privately Held**
WEB: www.scrmolding.com
SIC: 3089 Injection molding of plastics

(P-10355)
S&B INDUSTRY INC
Also Called: Fxp Technologies
105 S Puente St, Brea (92821-3844)
PHONE..................................909 569-4155
Paul H Shiung, *President*
EMP: 60
SALES (corp-wide): 60.3B **Privately Held**
SIC: 3089 Injection molded finished plastic products
HQ: S&B Industry, Inc.
13301 Park Vista Blvd # 100
Fort Worth TX 76177

(P-10356)
SABERT CORPORATION
860 Palmyrita Ave, Riverside (92507-1810)
PHONE..................................951 342-0240
Steve Butler, *Manager*
EMP: 10
SALES (corp-wide): 161.6MM **Privately Held**
WEB: www.sabert.com
SIC: 3089 Dishes, plastic, except foam
PA: Sabert Corporation
2288 Main St
Sayreville NJ 08872
800 722-3781

(P-10357)
SAN DIEGO ACE INC
8490 Mathis Pl, San Diego (92127-6122)
P.O. Box 486, Tecate (91980-0486)
PHONE..................................619 252-3148
Young Moo Kwon, *President*
Ben Kwon, *General Mgr*
▲ **EMP:** 200 **EST:** 1992
SQ FT: 2,000
SALES: 9.2MM **Privately Held**
WEB: www.sandiegoace.com
SIC: 3089 Molding primary plastic

(P-10358)
SANDIA PLASTICS INC
Also Called: Ultimate Solutions
15571 Container Ln, Huntington Beach (92649-1530)
PHONE..................................714 901-8400
William Allan, *CEO*
Bisson Monty, *President*
▲ **EMP:** 31
SQ FT: 2,500
SALES (est): 7MM **Privately Held**
WEB: www.sandiaplastics.com
SIC: 3089 Injection molded finished plastic products

(P-10359)
SANTA CLARITA PLASTIC MOLDING
24735 Avenue Rockefeller, Valencia (91355-3466)
PHONE..................................661 294-2257
Walter Schrey, *President*
Thomas Schrey, *Principal*
EMP: 15 **EST:** 1998
SALES (est): 1.2MM **Privately Held**
WEB: www.santaclaritaplasticsurgeon.com
SIC: 3089 Plastic processing

(P-10360)
SANTA FE EXTRUDERS INC
15315 Marquardt Ave, Santa Fe Springs (90670-5709)
P.O. Box 524, Olney IL (62450-0524)
PHONE..................................562 921-8991
Brick Pinckney, *President*
Jeanne Pinckney, *Corp Secy*
EMP: 62 **EST:** 1981
SQ FT: 30,000

PRODUCTS & SVCS

SALES (est): 10.6MM **Privately Held**
WEB: www.sfext.com
SIC: 3089 3083 3081 2673 Extruded finished plastic products; laminated plastics plate & sheet; unsupported plastics film & sheet; bags: plastic, laminated & coated

(P-10361)
SANTA MONICA PLASTICS LLC
1631 Stanford St, Santa Monica
(90404-4113)
PHONE.....................310 403-2849
Eric Warren, *Mng Member*
EMP: 11 EST: 2011
SALES (est): 1.2MM **Privately Held**
SIC: 3089 Injection molded finished plastic products; plastic processing

(P-10362)
SCHAEFER SYSTEMS INTL INC
1250 Thurman St, Lodi (95240-3134)
PHONE.....................209 365-6030
Mark Phillips, *Branch Mgr*
Shannon Ramirez, *Office Admin*
EMP: 30
SALES (corp-wide): 1.6B **Privately Held**
WEB: www.ssimail.com
SIC: 3089 Injection molding of plastics
HQ: Schaefer Systems International, Inc.
    10021 Westlake Dr
    Charlotte NC 28273
    704 944-4500

(P-10363)
SCHOLLE IPN CORPORATION
2500 Cooper Ave, Merced (95348-4312)
PHONE.....................209 384-3100
Marcia Mickle, *Manager*
Mabel Acosta, *Manager*
EMP: 400
SQ FT: 80,000
SALES (corp-wide): 295.3MM **Privately Held**
WEB: www.scholle.com
SIC: 3089 2671 Plastic containers, except foam; packaging paper & plastics film, coated & laminated
PA: Scholle Ipn Corporation
    200 W North Ave
    Northlake IL 60164
    708 562-7290

(P-10364)
SCHOLLE IPN PACKAGING INC
2500 Cooper Ave, Merced (95348-4312)
PHONE.....................209 384-3100
Chris Bunggay, *Engineer*
Esmeralda Gutierrez, *Human Res Mgr*
Toin Kuijpers, *Sales Executive*
Tony Miranda, *Director*
EMP: 280
SALES (corp-wide): 295.3MM **Privately Held**
SIC: 3089 Plastic processing
HQ: Scholle Ipn Packaging, Inc.
    200 W North Ave
    Northlake IL 60164

(P-10365)
SCIENTIFIC MOLDING CORP LTD
3250 Brickway Blvd, Santa Rosa
(95403-8235)
PHONE.....................707 303-3041
EMP: 72
SALES (corp-wide): 601.9MM **Privately Held**
SIC: 3089
PA: Scientific Molding Corporation, Ltd.
    330 Smc Dr
    Somerset WI 54025
    715 247-3500

(P-10366)
SCOTLAND ENTRY SYSTEMS INC
16116 Leadwell St, Van Nuys
(91406-3424)
PHONE.....................818 376-0777
Bejan Souferian, *President*
CHI Bui, *Executive Asst*
EMP: 10

SALES (est): 1.6MM **Privately Held**
WEB: www.scotlandentry.com
SIC: 3089 1731 Fences, gates & accessories: plastic; safety & security specialization

(P-10367)
SCRIBNER ENGINEERING INC
11455 Hydraulics Dr, Rancho Cordova
(95742-6870)
PHONE.....................916 638-1515
Richard L Scribner, *President*
Janet Scribner, *Corp Secy*
Linda Beisner, *General Mgr*
EMP: 25
SQ FT: 30,000
SALES (est): 3.9MM **Privately Held**
SIC: 3089 Plastic processing

(P-10368)
SCRIBNER PLASTICS
11455 Hydraulics Dr, Rancho Cordova
(95742-6870)
PHONE.....................916 638-1515
Rick Scribner, *Owner*
Linda Beisner, *General Mgr*
EMP: 15 EST: 2001
SALES (est): 1.8MM **Privately Held**
WEB: www.scribnerplastics.com
SIC: 3089 Molding primary plastic; injection molding of plastics

(P-10369)
SCULPTOR BODY MOLDING (PA)
10817 W Stallion Ranch Rd, Sunland
(91040-3702)
PHONE.....................818 761-3767
Monica Canon Ferguson, *Principal*
Steve Ferguson, *Vice Pres*
EMP: 11
SALES (est): 1.4MM **Privately Held**
SIC: 3089 Molding primary plastic

(P-10370)
SENTINEL PLASTICS LLC
4492 Camino Dela Plz 23, San Ysidro
(92173)
P.O. Box 122157, Chula Vista (91912-6857)
PHONE.....................619 734-0213
Robert L Berwick, *Mng Member*
EMP: 40
SQ FT: 20,000
SALES: 20K **Privately Held**
SIC: 3089 Injection molding of plastics

(P-10371)
SERCO MOLD INC (PA)
Also Called: Serpac Electronic Enclosures
2009 Wright Ave, La Verne (91750-5812)
PHONE.....................626 331-0517
Patricia Ann Serio, *CEO*
Don Serio Jr, *Vice Pres*
Valencia Flavio, *Design Engr*
Van Hoang, *Engineer*
Lori Clark, *Manager*
▲ EMP: 45 EST: 1978
SQ FT: 85,000
SALES (est): 4.9MM **Privately Held**
WEB: www.serpac.com
SIC: 3089 3544 5999 Injection molding of plastics; injection molded finished plastic products; industrial molds; electronic parts & equipment

(P-10372)
SETCO LLC
4875 E Hunter Ave, Anaheim (92807-2005)
PHONE.....................812 424-2904
Patty Harper, *Branch Mgr*
Richard Hofmann,
EMP: 15 **Publicly Held**
SIC: 3089 Plastic containers, except foam
HQ: Setco, Llc
    101 Oakley St
    Evansville IN 47710
    812 424-2904

(P-10373)
SETON SCIENTIFIC CO
15789 Adams Rdg, Los Gatos
(95033-8037)
P.O. Box 750003, Petaluma (94975-0003)
PHONE.....................707 782-0900
Steven Nielsen, *Owner*

EMP: 11
SALES (est): 640K **Privately Held**
WEB: www.setonscientific.com
SIC: 3089 3085 Plastic containers, except foam; plastics bottles

(P-10374)
SF GLOBAL LLC
250 Frank H Ogawa Plz, Oakland
(94612-2010)
PHONE.....................888 536-5593
Raul Hinojosa,
EMP: 10
SALES (est): 1.1MM **Privately Held**
SIC: 3089 Identification cards, plastic

(P-10375)
SIERRACIN/SYLMAR CORPORATION
Also Called: PPG Aerospace
12780 San Fernando Rd, Sylmar
(91342-3728)
PHONE.....................818 362-6711
Barry Gillespie, *CEO*
▲ EMP: 600
SQ FT: 300,000
SALES (est): 150MM
SALES (corp-wide): 14.7B **Publicly Held**
WEB: www.sierracin.com
SIC: 3089 3812 3621 3231 Windshields, plastic; search & navigation equipment; motors & generators; products of purchased glass
PA: Ppg Industries, Inc.
    1 Ppg Pl
    Pittsburgh PA 15272
    412 434-3131

(P-10376)
SISTEMA US INC (PA)
775 Southpoint Blvd, Petaluma
(94954-1495)
P.O. Box 5068, Novato (94948-5068)
PHONE.....................707 773-2200
Simon Kirby, *President*
Peter Carter, *CFO*
▲ EMP: 30
SQ FT: 42,500
SALES (est): 4.2MM **Privately Held**
WEB: www.typhoonhousewares.com
SIC: 3089 Plastic kitchenware, tableware & houseware

(P-10377)
SKB CORPORATION (PA)
434 W Levers Pl, Orange (92867-3605)
PHONE.....................714 637-1252
Steven A Kottman, *CEO*
David Sanderson, *Vice Pres*
Don Weber, *VP Mfg*
◆ EMP: 350
SALES (est): 76.7MM **Privately Held**
WEB: www.skbcases.com
SIC: 3089 3161 Cases, plastic; luggage

(P-10378)
SMART INC
Also Called: Smart Wax
14108 S Western Ave, Gardena
(90249-3010)
PHONE.....................310 674-8135
David Knotek, *CEO*
Sergio Galindo, *Vice Pres*
Paul Schneider, *Vice Pres*
Braxton Matthews, *Accountant*
Alex Torres, *Human Res Mgr*
▲ EMP: 40
SALES (est): 13.6MM **Privately Held**
WEB: www.smartwax.com
SIC: 3089 5013 Automotive parts, plastic; automotive supplies & parts

(P-10379)
SMITHCO PLASTICS INC (PA)
3330 W Harvard St, Santa Ana
(92704-3920)
PHONE.....................714 545-9107
Stanley L Smith, *President*
Nancy Smith, *Treasurer*
Dan Smith, *Vice Pres*
EMP: 14
SQ FT: 8,500
SALES (est): 1.5MM **Privately Held**
SIC: 3089 Injection molding of plastics; plastic processing

(P-10380)
SNAPWARE CORPORATION
Also Called: Corningware Corelle & More
3900 Hamner Ave, Eastvale (91752-1017)
PHONE.....................951 361-3100
Kris Malkoski, *CEO*
Ken Tran, *COO*
Grant Hartman, *Vice Pres*
Alex Yuan, *Technology*
Susan R Mercado, *Controller*
◆ EMP: 180
SQ FT: 168,345
SALES (est): 48.7MM **Privately Held**
WEB: www.snapware.com
SIC: 3089 Plastic kitchenware, tableware & houseware
HQ: Corelle Brands Llc
    9525 Bryn Mawr Ave
    Rosemont IL 60018
    847 233-8600

(P-10381)
SNYDER INDUSTRIES INC
800 Commerce Dr, Chowchilla
(93610-9395)
PHONE.....................559 665-7612
Reyes Morales, *CEO*
EMP: 65
SALES (corp-wide): 3.7B **Privately Held**
SIC: 3089 Pallets, plastic
HQ: Snyder Industries, Inc.
    6940 O St Ste 100
    Lincoln NE 68510
    402 465-1206

(P-10382)
SOUTH BAY CSTM PLSTIC EXTRDRS
2554 Commercial St, San Diego
(92113-1132)
P.O. Box 131195 (92170-1195)
PHONE.....................619 544-0808
Abraham Rafiee, *President*
Hassan Rafiee, *Vice Pres*
EMP: 20
SQ FT: 14,000
SALES (est): 3MM **Privately Held**
WEB: www.southbayplastic.com
SIC: 3089 Plastic containers, except foam

(P-10383)
SPEC FORMLINERS INC
1038 E 4th St, Santa Ana (92701-4751)
PHONE.....................714 429-9500
Stephen A Deering, *CEO*
Anthony Zaha, *Vice Pres*
EMP: 26 EST: 1996
SQ FT: 23,000
SALES (est): 8.2MM **Privately Held**
WEB: www.specformliners.com
SIC: 3089 Plastic hardware & building products

(P-10384)
SPIN PRODUCTS INC
13878 Yorba Ave, Chino (91710-5518)
PHONE.....................909 590-7000
Paul Burlingham, *President*
William Burlingham, *Vice Pres*
Andrea Gutierrez, *Accounting Mgr*
Gonzalo Banuelos, *Prdtn Mgr*
▲ EMP: 24
SQ FT: 96,000
SALES (est): 5.8MM **Privately Held**
WEB: www.spinproducts.com
SIC: 3089 Plastic containers, except foam

(P-10385)
SPIRIT FOODSERVICE INC
Also Called: Spiritbrands
5951 Rickenbacker Rd, Commerce
(90040-3029)
PHONE.....................323 724-0503
Peter Maki, *Manager*
EMP: 70 **Privately Held**
SIC: 3089 Novelties, plastic
HQ: Spirit Foodservice, Llc
    200 Brickstone Sq Ste G05
    Andover MA 01810
    978 964-1551

(P-10386)
SR PLASTICS COMPANY LLC (PA)
640 Parkridge Ave, Norco (92860-3124)
PHONE..................951 520-9486
Larry Kaford, *Principal*
Larry Novak,
EMP: 15
SALES (est): 5.2MM **Privately Held**
SIC: 3089 Injection molding of plastics

(P-10387)
SR PLASTICS COMPANY LLC
692 Parkridge Ave, Norco (92860-3124)
PHONE..................951 479-5394
EMP: 30
SALES (corp-wide): 5.2MM **Privately Held**
SIC: 3089 Injection molding of plastics
PA: Sr Plastics Company, Llc
640 Parkridge Ave
Norco CA 92860
951 520-9486

(P-10388)
STACK PLASTICS INC
3525 Haven Ave, Menlo Park (94025-1009)
PHONE..................650 361-8600
Mark Rackley, *President*
Michael Mendonca, *Vice Pres*
David Diaz, *Engineer*
Carlos Hinojosa, *Maintence Staff*
▲ EMP: 30
SQ FT: 9,000
SALES (est): 6.9MM **Privately Held**
WEB: www.wcsplastics.com
SIC: 3089 Injection molding of plastics

(P-10389)
STAR PLASTIC DESIGN
25914 President Ave, Harbor City (90710-3333)
PHONE..................310 530-7119
Dana Maltun, *President*
Maria Martinez, *Prdtn Mgr*
▲ EMP: 60
SQ FT: 25,000
SALES (est): 9.2MM **Privately Held**
WEB: www.starplastic.com
SIC: 3089 Injection molding of plastics

(P-10390)
STAR SANITATION SERVICES
4 Harris Rd, Salinas (93908-8608)
PHONE..................831 754-6794
Bartley Walker, *Mng Member*
Sheryl Smith,
Raul Osorio, *Supervisor*
EMP: 10
SALES (est): 1.8MM **Privately Held**
SIC: 3089 1799 Toilets, portable chemical: plastic; fence construction

(P-10391)
STAR SHIELD SOLUTIONS LLC
4315 Santa Ana St, Ontario (91761-7872)
PHONE..................866 662-4477
Gil Stanfill, *Mng Member*
Jim Kwon, *Marketing Staff*
EMP: 60
SALES (est): 1.8MM **Privately Held**
SIC: 3089 7389 Automotive parts, plastic; financial services

(P-10392)
STEVE LESHNER CLEAR SYSTEMS
13438 Wyandotte St, North Hollywood (91605-4012)
PHONE..................818 764-9223
Steve Leshner, *Owner*
EMP: 11
SQ FT: 5,000
SALES: 658K **Privately Held**
SIC: 3089 5211 Injection molding of plastics; closets, interiors & accessories

(P-10393)
STRAND ART COMPANY INC
4700 E Hunter Ave, Anaheim (92807-1919)
PHONE..................714 777-0444
Kevin Strand, *President*
Vicky Strand, *Admin Sec*
▲ EMP: 50
SQ FT: 10,480

SALES (est): 7.9MM **Privately Held**
WEB: www.strandart.com
SIC: 3089 Injection molded finished plastic products

(P-10394)
STRATASYS DIRECT INC (DH)
Also Called: Stratasys Direct Manufacturing
28309 Avenue Crocker, Valencia (91355-1251)
PHONE..................661 295-4400
Joseph Allison, *CEO*
Peter Keller, *CFO*
Tom Smolders, *CFO*
Tom Vorgitch, *Vice Pres*
Lucy Hernandez, *Administration*
▲ EMP: 190
SQ FT: 24,000
SALES (est): 96.3MM
SALES (corp-wide): 2.9B **Privately Held**
WEB: www.solidconcepts.com
SIC: 3089 Plastic processing; casting of plastic
HQ: Stratasys Ltd
1 Holzman Haim
Rehovot 76704
893 143-14

(P-10395)
STUDER CREATIVE PACKAGING INC
5652 Mountain View Ave, Yorba Linda (92886-5528)
PHONE..................818 344-1665
James R Studer, *President*
Chris Studer, *Vice Pres*
Mike Studer, *Vice Pres*
Yvonne E Studer, *Admin Sec*
EMP: 14
SQ FT: 23,000
SALES (est): 1.1MM **Privately Held**
SIC: 3089 Thermoformed finished plastic products

(P-10396)
SUPERIOR MOLD CO INC
1927 E Francis St, Ontario (91761-7719)
PHONE..................909 947-7028
Anthony Codet, *CEO*
Eleanor Yates, *QC Mgr*
EMP: 21
SALES (est): 4.5MM **Privately Held**
SIC: 3089 Injection molding of plastics

(P-10397)
SYNTECH DEVELOPMENT & MFG INC
Also Called: S D M
13948 Mountain Ave, Chino (91710-9018)
PHONE..................909 465-5554
Harry N Herbert, *CEO*
Bob Hobbs, *President*
Eddie Montelongo, *President*
EMP: 25 EST: 1998
SQ FT: 11,000
SALES (est): 4.9MM **Privately Held**
WEB: www.sdmplastics.com
SIC: 3089 Injection molding of plastics

(P-10398)
TALCO PLASTICS INC
3270 E 70th St, Long Beach (90805-1821)
PHONE..................562 630-1224
Ajit Ferera, *Manager*
John Schmidt, *Plant Mgr*
EMP: 34
SALES (corp-wide): 90.5MM **Privately Held**
WEB: www.talcoplastics.com
SIC: 3089 4953 Extruded finished plastic products; recycling, waste materials
PA: Talco Plastics, Inc.
1000 W Rincon St
Corona CA 92880
951 531-2000

(P-10399)
TAMSHELL CORP
237 Glider Cir, Corona (92880-2534)
PHONE..................951 272-9395
John Hernandez, *President*
Art Pierce, *Vice Pres*
Adam Bolt, *General Mgr*
Chuck Sheridan, *Technical Staff*
Maricela Giles, *Controller*
EMP: 95

SQ FT: 20,000
SALES (est): 25.3MM **Privately Held**
WEB: www.tamshell.com
SIC: 3089 Caps, plastic; plastic hardware & building products; hardware, plastic; bearings, plastic

(P-10400)
TEKSUN INC
1549 N Poinsettia Pl # 1, Los Angeles (90046-3662)
PHONE..................310 479-0794
David Meyer, *President*
EMP: 15 EST: 1938
SQ FT: 6,800
SALES (est): 2.9MM **Privately Held**
WEB: www.teksun.com
SIC: 3089 Plastic processing; injection molded finished plastic products

(P-10401)
TGS MOLDING LLC
Also Called: Tgs Plastic
425 E Parkcenter Cir S, San Bernardino (92408-2872)
PHONE..................909 890-1707
Antoine Semaan, *Mng Member*
Lewis Allen,
Rima Semaan,
EMP: 11
SQ FT: 2,000
SALES (est): 800K **Privately Held**
SIC: 3089 Molding primary plastic

(P-10402)
THERMODYNE INTERNATIONAL LTD
1841 S Business Pkwy, Ontario (91761-8537)
PHONE..................909 923-9945
Gary S Ackerman, *Ch of Bd*
Scott Ackerman, *CFO*
Josh Ackerman, *Administration*
William Morgan, *Sales Staff*
◆ EMP: 110 EST: 1967
SQ FT: 57,500
SALES (est): 21MM **Privately Held**
WEB: www.shokstop.com
SIC: 3089 3694 Plastic containers, except foam; engine electrical equipment

(P-10403)
THREE-D PLASTICS INC
Also Called: Three-D Traffic Works
424 N Varney St, Burbank (91502-1732)
PHONE..................323 849-1316
Joe Dvoracek, *President*
Joan Robinson, *Controller*
EMP: 15
SALES (est): 1.7MM
SALES (corp-wide): 9.9MM **Privately Held**
WEB: www.trafficwks.com
SIC: 3089 Injection molded finished plastic products; injection molding of plastics
PA: Three-D Plastics, Inc.
430 N Varney St
Burbank CA 91502
323 849-1316

(P-10404)
THREE-D PLASTICS INC (PA)
Also Called: Three-D Traffics Works
430 N Varney St, Burbank (91502-1732)
PHONE..................323 849-1316
Frank J Dvoracek, *CEO*
Kathleen D Trumbo, *Corp Secy*
Joseph Dvoracek, *Vice Pres*
Jo Dvoracek, *Manager*
EMP: 37
SQ FT: 40,000
SALES (est): 9.9MM **Privately Held**
WEB: www.trafficwks.com
SIC: 3089 Injection molding of plastics

(P-10405)
TIGERS PLASTICS INC
14721 Lull St, Van Nuys (91405-1211)
PHONE..................818 901-9393
Set Ayrapetyan, *President*
EMP: 10
SALES (est): 1.5MM **Privately Held**
WEB: www.tigersinc.com
SIC: 3089 Boxes, plastic

(P-10406)
TNT PLASTIC MOLDING INC (PA)
725 E Harrison St, Corona (92879-1350)
PHONE..................951 808-9700
Diane Mixson, *President*
John Chadwick, *CFO*
Doug Chadwick, *Vice Pres*
Lynn Chadwick, *Vice Pres*
R J Jamaica, *Human Res Dir*
▲ EMP: 118
SQ FT: 30,000
SALES (est): 38.5MM **Privately Held**
WEB: www.artisticplastics.com
SIC: 3089 Injection molding of plastics

(P-10407)
TOM YORK ENTERPRISES INC
Also Called: Kal Plastics
2050 E 48th St, Vernon (90058-2022)
PHONE..................323 581-6194
Tom York, *CEO*
EMP: 25
SQ FT: 45,000
SALES (est): 4.1MM **Privately Held**
WEB: www.kal-plastics.com
SIC: 3089 3993 Boxes, plastic; tubs, plastic (containers); thermoformed finished plastic products; signs & advertising specialties

(P-10408)
TOTEX MANUFACTURING INC
3050 Lomita Blvd, Torrance (90505-5103)
PHONE..................310 326-2028
Tommy Tong, *President*
Helena Hui, *Controller*
Jim Sides, *Director*
Wayne WEI, *Accounts Mgr*
▲ EMP: 70
SALES (est): 31.5MM **Privately Held**
WEB: www.totexusa.com
SIC: 3089 5063 Battery cases, plastic or plastic combination; batteries, dry cell

(P-10409)
TRANPAK INC
2860 S East Ave, Fresno (93725-1909)
PHONE..................800 827-2474
Martin Ueland, *President*
Donna Ueland, *Treasurer*
Christian Ueland, *General Mgr*
Kim Wright, *Sales Staff*
◆ EMP: 21
SQ FT: 80,000
SALES: 9.3MM **Privately Held**
WEB: www.tranpak.com
SIC: 3089 Air mattresses, plastic

(P-10410)
TRIAD TOOL & ENGINEERING INC
Also Called: Engineered Plastic Division
1750 Rogers Ave, San Jose (95112-1109)
PHONE..................408 436-8411
William Bartlett, *President*
David C Bartlett, *Vice Pres*
James S Bartlett, *Vice Pres*
Mildred Carvelho, *Admin Sec*
Mark Santos, *Prdtn Mgr*
EMP: 35 EST: 1978
SQ FT: 39,960
SALES (est): 5.5MM **Privately Held**
SIC: 3089 3599 3364 3363 Injection molded finished plastic products; machine shop, jobbing & repair; zinc & zinc-base alloy die-castings; aluminum die-castings

(P-10411)
TRIDENT PRODUCTS INC
1370 W San Marcos Blvd # 120, San Marcos (92078-1601)
PHONE..................760 510-1160
David Brandt, *President*
Frank Stephan, *CFO*
EMP: 60
SQ FT: 48,000
SALES (est): 5.1MM **Privately Held**
SIC: 3089 Plastic hardware & building products; plastic processing

PRODUCTS & SVCS

(P-10412)
TRIM-LOK INC
6855 Hermosa Cir, Buena Park
(90620-1151)
P.O. Box 6180 (90622-6180)
PHONE.............................714 562-0500
Gary Whitener, *President*
◆ **EMP:** 180
SQ FT: 57,000
SALES: 36.2MM **Privately Held**
WEB: www.trimlok.com
SIC: 3089 Molding primary plastic

(P-10413)
TRU-FORM PLASTICS INC
14600 Hoover St, Westminster
(92683-5346)
PHONE.............................310 327-9444
Douglas W Sahm Sr, *CEO*
John D Evans, *COO*
Clauve Hurwicz, *CFO*
Anita Lorber, *Vice Pres*
Carlos Avalos, *Technology*
▲ **EMP:** 35
SQ FT: 1,000
SALES (est): 7.5MM **Privately Held**
WEB: www.truform.com
SIC: 3089 Pallets, plastic; plastic processing

(P-10414)
TST MOLDING LLC
Also Called: All Ameri Injec Moldi Servi
42322 Avenida Alvarado, Temecula
(92590-3445)
PHONE.............................951 296-6200
Terry Voss, *Mng Member*
Tammy Richer, *Accounting Mgr*
Dave Hawley,
EMP: 27
SALES: 4MM **Privately Held**
SIC: 3089 Molding primary plastic

(P-10415)
TTL HOLDINGS LLC (HQ)
4626 Eucalyptus Ave, Chino (91710-9215)
PHONE.............................909 597-7861
Earl E Payton, *Mng Member*
Liz Smith,
EMP: 11
SALES (est): 130.8MM
SALES (corp-wide): 171.5MM **Privately Held**
WEB: www.trendtechnologies.com
SIC: 3089 3544 Molding primary plastic; special dies, tools, jigs & fixtures
PA: Eep Holdings, Llc
4626 Eucalyptus Ave
Chino CA 91710
909 597-7861

(P-10416)
UDECOR INC (PA)
Also Called: Proceilingtiles
8302 Espresso Dr Ste 130, Bakersfield
(93312-5688)
PHONE.............................877 550-0600
James Welch, *President*
Robert Welch, *CEO*
Scott Fischer, *Vice Pres*
Stephen Stahl, *Opers Staff*
EMP: 10 EST: 2012
SQ FT: 6,000
SALES: 7.4MM **Privately Held**
SIC: 3089 5961 Injection molding of plastics;

(P-10417)
UFO DESIGNS (PA)
5812 Machine Dr, Huntington Beach
(92649-1101)
PHONE.............................714 892-4420
Jitendra Patel, *President*
Alfie Patel, *Vice Pres*
EMP: 16
SQ FT: 35,000
SALES (est): 3.8MM **Privately Held**
WEB: www.ufodesign.com
SIC: 3089 Injection molding of plastics

(P-10418)
UFO INC
2110 Belgrave Ave, Huntington Park
(90255-2713)
P.O. Box 58192, Los Angeles (90058-0192)
PHONE.............................323 588-5450

Efi Youavian, *President*
Efraim Youavian, *CEO*
◆ **EMP:** 50
SQ FT: 65,000
SALES (est): 14.8MM **Privately Held**
SIC: 3089 2842 5199 Sponges, plastic; specialty cleaning, polishes & sanitation goods; foams & rubber

(P-10419)
UNCKS UNIQUE PLASTICS INC
1215 Brooks St, Ontario (91762-3609)
PHONE.............................909 983-5181
Fax: 909 984-6376
EMP: 16
SALES (est): 1MM **Privately Held**
SIC: 3089 3544

(P-10420)
UPLAND FAB INC
1445 Brooks St Ste L, Ontario
(91762-3665)
PHONE.............................909 933-9185
Patsy Sapra, *CEO*
Jackson Sapra, *Shareholder*
Paul Sapra, *CEO*
Steven Sapra, *CFO*
Danial Herrera, *Plant Mgr*
EMP: 24 EST: 1970
SQ FT: 12,000
SALES (est): 5.4MM **Privately Held**
WEB: www.uplandfab.com
SIC: 3089 Plastic & fiberglass tanks; plastic processing

(P-10421)
URETHANE PRODUCTS CORPORATION
Also Called: U P C
17842 Sampson Ln, Huntington Beach
(92647-7147)
PHONE.............................800 913-0062
Kelly Goulis, *CEO*
Elizabeth Thermos, *President*
▲ **EMP:** 12
SQ FT: 13,000
SALES (est): 2.3MM **Privately Held**
WEB: www.urethaneproducts.com
SIC: 3089 Plastic processing

(P-10422)
URETHANE SCIENCE INC
8357 Standustrial St, Stanton
(90680-2617)
PHONE.............................714 828-3210
Roger Evans, *President*
Paula Evans, *Vice Pres*
EMP: 10 EST: 1981
SQ FT: 4,500
SALES (est): 580.8K **Privately Held**
WEB: www.hdmolding.com
SIC: 3089 3086 Injection molding of plastics; plastics foam products

(P-10423)
US POLYMERS INC (PA)
Also Called: Duramax Building Products
1057 S Vail Ave, Montebello (90640-6019)
PHONE.............................323 728-3023
Viken Ohanesian, *CEO*
Vram Ohanesian, *CFO*
Haigan Ohanesian, *Treasurer*
Jacques Ohanesian, *Vice Pres*
Svetlana Denisova, *Mktg Dir*
◆ **EMP:** 100
SQ FT: 70,000
SALES (est): 40.3MM **Privately Held**
WEB: www.uspolymersinc.com
SIC: 3089 3084 Shutters, plastic; plastics pipe

(P-10424)
USA EXTRUDED PLASTICS INC
965 E Discovery Ln, Anaheim
(92801-1147)
PHONE.............................714 991-6061
Joseph Florimonte, *President*
Vida Aiona, *Vice Pres*
Linda Florimonte, *Admin Sec*
EMP: 16
SQ FT: 11,000
SALES: 2.5MM **Privately Held**
WEB: www.usaextrudedplastics.com
SIC: 3089 Extruded finished plastic products

(P-10425)
V & P SCIENTIFIC INC
9823 Pacific Heights Blvd, San Diego
(92121-4704)
PHONE.............................858 455-0643
Patrick H Cleveland, *President*
John Chavez, *COO*
Victoria L Cleveland, *Corp Secy*
John Herich, *Technical Staff*
Theodore Cecilio, *Project Engr*
▲ **EMP:** 11
SQ FT: 7,000
SALES (est): 2.5MM **Privately Held**
WEB: www.vp-scientific.com
SIC: 3089 Novelties, plastic

(P-10426)
V-T INDUSTRIES INC
16222 Phoebe Ave, La Mirada
(90638-5610)
PHONE.............................714 521-2008
EMP: 16
SALES (corp-wide): 197.8MM **Privately Held**
SIC: 3089 3083 4213 2435 Plastic hardware & building products; doors, folding: plastic or plastic coated fabric; plastic finished products, laminated; trucking, except local; hardwood veneer & plywood; wood kitchen cabinets; millwork
PA: V-T Industries Inc.
1000 Industrial Park
Holstein IA 51025
712 368-4381

(P-10427)
VALLEY DECORATING COMPANY
2829 E Hamilton Ave, Fresno
(93721-3208)
PHONE.............................559 495-1100
James Offen, *President*
Rebecca Karmann, *Production*
▼ **EMP:** 20
SQ FT: 25,000
SALES (est): 4.1MM **Privately Held**
WEB: www.valleydecorating.com
SIC: 3089 Novelties, plastic

(P-10428)
VAN GRACE QUALITY INJECTION
Also Called: Crystal Tex Shoehorn
9164 Appleby St, Downey (90240-2915)
PHONE.............................323 931-5255
Dave Van Selow, *President*
EMP: 15
SQ FT: 2,000
SALES (est): 2.2MM **Privately Held**
SIC: 3089

(P-10429)
VANTAGE ASSOCIATES INC
12333 Los Nietos Rd, Santa Fe Springs
(90670-2911)
PHONE.............................562 968-1400
Paul Roy, *CEO*
Eric Clack, *President*
Andrea Alpinieri Glover, *CFO*
EMP: 65
SQ FT: 20,000
SALES (corp-wide): 63.6MM **Privately Held**
SIC: 3089 2499 5085 3621 Plastic processing; spools, reels & pulleys: wood; industrial supplies; motors & generators; aircraft parts & equipment; search & navigation equipment
PA: Vantage Associates Inc.
900 Civic Center Dr
National City CA 91950
619 477-6940

(P-10430)
VIANT MEDICAL LLC
45581 Northpoint Loop W, Fremont
(94538-6462)
PHONE.............................510 657-5800
Bill Tarajos, *Branch Mgr*
Gaynell Mays, *Human Res Mgr*
EMP: 11
SALES (corp-wide): 228.9MM **Privately Held**
SIC: 3089 Injection molding of plastics

HQ: Viant Medical, Llc
2 Hampshire St
Foxborough MA 02035
-

(P-10431)
VOLANT COOL AIR INTAKES INC
10285 Indiana Ct, Rancho Cucamonga
(91730-5332)
PHONE.............................909 476-7225
Anthony Quezada, *President*
EMP: 15
SQ FT: 12,000
SALES (est): 1.4MM **Privately Held**
SIC: 3089 Molding primary plastic

(P-10432)
VOLEX INC (HQ)
Also Called: Powercords
3110 Coronado Dr, Santa Clara
(95054-3205)
PHONE.............................669 444-1740
Christoph Eisenhardt, *CEO*
James Stuart, *President*
Nick Parker, *CFO*
Veronica Corral, *Buyer*
▲ **EMP:** 30 EST: 1979
SQ FT: 10,000
SALES: 403.6MM
SALES (corp-wide): 322.3MM **Privately Held**
WEB: www.volex.com
SIC: 3089 Injection molded finished plastic products
PA: Volex Plc
Holbrook House
Richmond TW10
203 370-8830

(P-10433)
VOLEX INC
511 E San Ysidro Blvd, San Ysidro
(92173-3150)
PHONE.............................619 205-4900
EMP: 28
SALES (corp-wide): 319.5MM **Privately Held**
SIC: 3089 Injection molded finished plastic products
HQ: Volex Inc.
3110 Coronado Dr
Santa Clara CA 95054
669 444-1740

(P-10434)
WADDINGTON NORTH AMERICA INC
Also Called: Wna City of Industry
1135 Samuelson St, City of Industry
(91748-1222)
PHONE.............................626 913-4022
Mike Evans, *President*
Matthew Ha, *Accountant*
EMP: 182
SALES (corp-wide): 2.9B **Privately Held**
SIC: 3089 Plastic kitchenware, tableware & houseware
HQ: Waddington North America, Inc.
50 E Rivercenter Blvd # 650
Covington KY 41011

(P-10435)
WATERDOG PRODUCTS INC
1148 Pioneer Way, El Cajon (92020-1925)
PHONE.............................619 441-9688
John Harriman, *President*
Klint Dingley, *Vice Pres*
Jayne Harriman, *Vice Pres*
Todd Widegren, *Vice Pres*
▲ **EMP:** 14
SQ FT: 12,400
SALES (est): 2.1MM **Privately Held**
WEB: www.waterdogproducts.com
SIC: 3089 Plastic & fiberglass tanks

(P-10436)
WCP INC
Also Called: West Coast Vinyl Windows
17730 Crusader Ave, Cerritos
(90703-2629)
PHONE.............................562 860-9040
Charles Neubauer, *President*
▲ **EMP:** 95
SQ FT: 50,000

▲ = Import ▼=Export
◆ =Import/Export

SALES (est): 21.7MM **Privately Held**
SIC: 3089 3211 Windows, plastic; insulating glass, sealed units

(P-10437)
WESCO ENTERPRISES INC
12681 Corral Pl, Santa Fe Springs
(90670-4748)
PHONE......................562 944-3100
John Song, *President*
▲ **EMP:** 16
SQ FT: 21,000
SALES (est): 3.4MM **Privately Held**
WEB: www.kingseal.com
SIC: 3089 3842 2499 Work gloves, plastic; gloves, safety; skewers, wood; toothpicks, wood

(P-10438)
WEST COAST PLASTICS INC
10025 Shoemaker Ave, Santa Fe Springs
(90670-3401)
PHONE......................562 777-8024
Javier Franco, *President*
Judith Garcia, *Vice Pres*
Bob Ibanez, *Admin Sec*
EMP: 11
SQ FT: 30,000
SALES (est): 2.4MM **Privately Held**
WEB: www.wcpi.net
SIC: 3089 Blow molded finished plastic products

(P-10439)
WEST COAST WINDOWS & DOORS
2170 Commerce Ave Ste C, Concord
(94520-4930)
PHONE......................925 681-1776
Richard Beil, *Owner*
EMP: 12
SALES (est): 1.4MM **Privately Held**
SIC: 3089 5031 5211 7299 Windows, plastic; doors & windows; windows, storm: wood or metal; home improvement & renovation contractor agency

(P-10440)
WEST-BAG INC
1161 Monterey Pass Rd, Monterey Park
(91754-3614)
PHONE......................323 264-0750
Luis Michel, *President*
Sixto Michel, *Vice Pres*
Lupe Nevada, *Manager*
EMP: 30
SQ FT: 12,000
SALES (est): 4.9MM **Privately Held**
SIC: 3089 5149 Food casings, plastic; sausage casings

(P-10441)
WESTERN CASE INCORPORATED
6400 Sycamore Canyon Blvd B, Riverside
(92507-0708)
P.O. Box 1456, Moreno Valley (92556-1456)
PHONE......................714 838-8460
Steven Santos, *Branch Mgr*
EMP: 10
SALES (corp-wide): 8MM **Privately Held**
SIC: 3089 Cases, plastic
PA: Western Case, Incorporated
6400 Sycam Canyo Blvd Ste
Riverside CA 92507
951 214-6380

(P-10442)
WESTERN CASE INCORPORATED (PA)
6400 Sycam Canyo Blvd Ste, Riverside
(92507)
PHONE......................951 214-6380
Toll Free:......................877 -
Paul F Queyrel, *CEO*
Steve Santos, *General Mgr*
▲ **EMP:** 50
SQ FT: 19,000
SALES (est): 8MM **Privately Held**
WEB: www.westerncase.com
SIC: 3089 3544 3444 Cases, plastic; special dies, tools, jigs & fixtures; sheet metalwork

(P-10443)
WESTLAKE ENGRG ROTO FORM
Also Called: Jaz Products
1041 E Santa Barbara St, Santa Paula
(93060-2820)
P.O. Box 3504, Westlake Village (91359-0504)
PHONE......................805 525-8800
Wade Zimmerman, *President*
Pat Zimmerman, *Corp Secy*
▲ **EMP:** 24
SQ FT: 75,000
SALES (est): 3.4MM **Privately Held**
WEB: www.jazproducts.com
SIC: 3089 Planters, plastic; cases, plastic; buoys & floats, plastic

(P-10444)
WILLIAM KREYSLER & ASSOC INC
501 Green Island Rd, American Canyon
(94503-9649)
PHONE......................707 552-3500
William Bartley Kreysler, *CEO*
Pat Sorensen, *Purch Agent*
Tim Oliver, *Opers Staff*
Jacque Giuffre, *Art Dir*
Joshua Zabel, *Director*
▼ **EMP:** 26
SALES (est): 5.4MM **Privately Held**
WEB: www.kreysler.com
SIC: 3089 Panels, building: plastic

(P-10445)
WINDOW HARDWARE SUPPLY
1717 Kirkham St, Oakland (94607-2214)
PHONE......................510 463-0301
Kevin Kemble, *Principal*
▲ **EMP:** 12
SALES (est): 1.7MM **Privately Held**
SIC: 3089 Window frames & sash, plastic

(P-10446)
WING INFLATABLES INC (HQ)
1220 5th St, Arcata (95521-6155)
P.O. Box 279 (95518-0279)
PHONE......................707 826-2887
Andrew Branagh, *CEO*
Mark French, *CFO*
Ken Carlson, *Vice Pres*
Jake Heimbuch, *Vice Pres*
Mark Lougheed, *Vice Pres*
▲ **EMP:** 115
SQ FT: 80,000
SALES (est): 23.3MM
SALES (corp-wide): 26.8MM **Privately Held**
WEB: www.wing.com
SIC: 3089 Plastic boats & other marine equipment; life rafts, nonrigid: plastic

(P-10447)
WIREWRIGHT INC
3563 Old Conejo Rd, Newbury Park
(91320-2122)
PHONE......................805 499-9194
Hubert Wright, *President*
EMP: 10
SALES (est): 1MM **Privately Held**
SIC: 3089 Hardware, plastic

(P-10448)
WNA COMET WEST INC
Also Called: Wna City of Industry
1135 Samuelson St, City of Industry
(91748-1222)
PHONE......................626 913-0724
Mike Evans, *President*
Gabriella Flores, *Principal*
Rodney Harano, *Principal*
Janet Parga, *Principal*
▲ **EMP:** 230
SALES (est): 28.5MM
SALES (corp-wide): 14.7B **Publicly Held**
SIC: 3089 Plastic kitchenware, tableware & houseware
PA: Newell Brands Inc.
221 River St Ste 13
Hoboken NJ 07030
201 610-6600

(P-10449)
WOMBAT PRODUCTS INC
Also Called: Portapaint
1384 Callens Rd Ste B, Ventura
(93003-5808)
PHONE......................805 794-1767
John Lockwood, *CEO*
Alexander Auerbach, *COO*
▲ **EMP:** 22
SQ FT: 5,000
SALES: 5K **Privately Held**
SIC: 3089 Pails, plastic; air mattresses, plastic

(P-10450)
WONDER GRIP USA INC
3070 Bristol St Ste 440, Costa Mesa
(92626-3066)
PHONE......................404 290-2015
Chris Weber, *Office Mgr*
EMP: 15 **Privately Held**
SIC: 3089 Work gloves, plastic

(P-10451)
WORLD INDUSTRIES INTERNATIONAL
Also Called: Pool Doctor
655 N Central Ave Fl 1700, Glendale
(91203-1439)
PHONE......................818 649-7858
Sam Nazaryan, *President*
Harold Urbak Sr, *Vice Pres*
Ida Nazaryan, *Admin Sec*
EMP: 12
SQ FT: 65,000
SALES (est): 5MM **Privately Held**
WEB: www.discountpoolshop.com
SIC: 3089 5091 3949 Injection molded finished plastic products; swimming pools, equipment & supplies; sporting & athletic goods

(P-10452)
WREX PRODUCTS INC CHICO
25 Wrex Ct, Chico (95928-7176)
PHONE......................530 895-3838
Wrex A Howard, *Ch of Bd*
Jim Barnett, *President*
James Barnett, *CEO*
Dennis Rupp, *Engineer*
Victor Morales, *Controller*
▲ **EMP:** 66
SQ FT: 70,000
SALES (est): 17.5MM **Privately Held**
WEB: www.wrexproducts.com
SIC: 3089 3363 3544 3599 Injection molding of plastics; aluminum die-castings; special dies, tools, jigs & fixtures; machine & other job shop work; sandblasting equipment

(P-10453)
WUNDER-MOLD INC
790 Eubanks Dr, Vacaville (95688-9470)
PHONE......................707 448-2349
Richard A Martindale, *CEO*
William Martindale, *Principal*
Calvin Swesey, *General Mgr*
▲ **EMP:** 22
SQ FT: 56,000
SALES (est): 4.2MM **Privately Held**
SIC: 3089 Injection molding of plastics; injection molded finished plastic products; plastic processing

(P-10454)
XTIME INC
1400 Bridge Pkwy Ste 200, Redwood City
(94065-6130)
PHONE......................650 508-4300
Neal East, *President*
Jim Doehrman, *CFO*
Adam Galper, *CTO*
EMP: 32 **EST:** 1999
SQ FT: 6,000
SALES (est): 9.4MM
SALES (corp-wide): 32.8B **Privately Held**
WEB: www.xtime.com
SIC: 3089 Automotive parts, plastic
HQ: Cox Automotive, Inc.
6205-A Pchtree Dnwoody Rd
Atlanta GA 30328
404 843-5000

(P-10455)
YOGI INVESTMENTS INC
Also Called: Creative Extruded Products
419 Capron Ave, West Covina
(91792-2828)
PHONE......................909 984-5703
Lanraman Patel, *Manager*
Arvind Patel, *Shareholder*
Bhavana Patel, *President*
Ketan Patel, *Treasurer*
Pankaj Patel, *Admin Sec*
EMP: 16
SQ FT: 8,000
SALES: 1MM **Privately Held**
SIC: 3089 Extruded finished plastic products

(P-10456)
ZEPCO
440 N Moss St Ste B, Burbank
(91502-1726)
PHONE......................818 848-0880
James Froelich, *Managing Prtnr*
Michael Froelich, *Partner*
EMP: 11
SQ FT: 2,000
SALES (est): 1.3MM **Privately Held**
WEB: www.bottlehangers.com
SIC: 3089 Injection molding of plastics

3111 Leather Tanning & Finishing

(P-10457)
ANDREW ALEXANDER INC
Also Called: Falltech
1306 S Alameda St, Compton
(90221-4803)
PHONE......................323 752-0066
Michael Dancyger, *President*
Jeff Crosson, *CFO*
▲ **EMP:** 100
SQ FT: 100,000
SALES (est): 29MM **Privately Held**
WEB: www.falltech.com
SIC: 3111 Harness leather

(P-10458)
DALE CHAVEZ COMPANY INC
35165 La Bonita Donna, Temecula (92592)
P.O. Box 468 (92593-0468)
PHONE......................951 303-0592
Dale Chavez, *President*
Patricia Chavez, *Vice Pres*
EMP: 10 **EST:** 1968
SALES (est): 1.3MM **Privately Held**
WEB: www.dalechavezsaddles.com
SIC: 3111 5199 Saddlery leather; leather, leather goods & furs

(P-10459)
HERITAGE LEATHER COMPANY INC
4011 E 52nd St, Maywood (90270-2205)
PHONE......................323 983-0420
Jose C Munoz, *CEO*
Gustavo Gonzalez, *President*
▲ **EMP:** 30
SQ FT: 5,000
SALES (est): 4.5MM **Privately Held**
WEB: www.heritageleatherco.com
SIC: 3111 Belting leather

(P-10460)
JISONCASE (USA) LIMITED
9674 Telstar Ave Ste A, El Monte
(91731-3022)
PHONE......................888 233-8880
Hong Chu Deng, *CEO*
EMP: 12 **EST:** 2012
SALES (est): 1.5MM **Privately Held**
SIC: 3111 Case leather

(P-10461)
LA LA LAND PRODUCTION & DESIGN
2155 E 7th St Ste 300, Los Angeles
(90023-1034)
PHONE......................323 267-8485
Alexander M Zar, *CEO*
Pedram Golparian, *Opers Mgr*
EMP: 35
SQ FT: 30,000

SALES: 4MM **Privately Held**
SIC: 3111 Accessory products, leather

(P-10462)
LEATHEROCK INTERNATIONAL INC
5285 Lovelock St, San Diego (92110-4012)
PHONE..................................619 299-7625
Laurence A Bloch, *CEO*
Rahleen Bloch, *Vice Pres*
▲ EMP: 27
SQ FT: 9,600
SALES (est): 4.2MM **Privately Held**
WEB: www.leatherock.com
SIC: 3111 2387 Bag leather; apparel belts

(P-10463)
LINEA PELLE INC (PA)
7107 Valjean Ave, Van Nuys (91406-3917)
PHONE..................................310 231-9950
Wynn Katz, *President*
Mira Katz, *Vice Pres*
Maria Salcedo, *Finance*
Ferdinand Santos, *Finance*
Kelley Paratore, *Sales Staff*
▲ EMP: 17
SQ FT: 5,000
SALES (est): 2.7MM **Privately Held**
WEB: www.lineapelleinc.com
SIC: 3111 5621 Accessory products, leather; dress shops

(P-10464)
LOTUSSE LLC
10700 Jersey Blvd Ste 610, Rancho Cucamonga (91730-5123)
PHONE..................................909 218-7757
Owen Loftus, *Principal*
EMP: 25
SALES (est): 1.9MM **Privately Held**
SIC: 3111 Shoe leather

(P-10465)
STITCH AND HIDE LLC
4 Bowie Rd, Rolling Hills (90274-5220)
PHONE..................................310 377-6912
Ross James Smith,
EMP: 10
SALES: 3MM **Privately Held**
SIC: 3111 3199 3171 3172 Accessory products, leather; belt laces, leather; handbags, women's; handbags, regardless of material: men's

(P-10466)
SU MANO INC
536 Milton Dr, San Gabriel (91775-2204)
PHONE..................................562 529-8835
Jeffrey Scott Kenney, *CEO*
EMP: 12
SALES (est): 1.1MM **Privately Held**
SIC: 3111 Bookbinders' leather

(P-10467)
T N T AUTO INC
535 Patrice Pl, Gardena (90248-4232)
PHONE..................................310 715-1117
Peter Shum, *President*
EMP: 75 EST: 1995
SALES (est): 5.5MM **Privately Held**
WEB: www.tntauto.com
SIC: 3111 Upholstery leather

(P-10468)
WILDLIFE FUR DRESSING INC
3415 Harold St, Ceres (95307-3614)
PHONE..................................209 538-2901
Armando Navas, *President*
▲ EMP: 17
SQ FT: 10,000
SALES (est): 1.6MM **Privately Held**
WEB: www.wildlifefur.com
SIC: 3111 Leather tanning & finishing

3131 Boot & Shoe Cut Stock & Findings

(P-10469)
CALIFORNIA STAY CO INC
2600 Overland Ave Apt 219, Los Angeles (90064-3252)
PHONE..................................310 839-7236
Louis Saltsman, *President*
Sidney Saltsman, *Treasurer*

Jeffrey Saltsman, *Vice Pres*
Richard Saltsmans, *Vice Pres*
Helen Saltsman, *Admin Sec*
EMP: 10
SQ FT: 10,000
SALES (est): 1MM **Privately Held**
WEB: www.calriv800.com
SIC: 3131 Stays, shoe

(P-10470)
CI MANAGEMENT LLC
2039 Seabrook Ct, Redwood City (94065-8478)
PHONE..................................650 654-8900
Peter E Katz, *Principal*
EMP: 10
SALES (est): 1.2MM **Privately Held**
SIC: 3131 Counters

(P-10471)
COUNTER
21209 Hawthorne Blvd B, Torrance (90503-5535)
PHONE..................................310 406-3300
Danielle Gumbs, *Principal*
EMP: 30 EST: 2010
SALES (est): 2.9MM **Privately Held**
SIC: 3131 Counters

(P-10472)
CYDWOQ INC
2102 Kenmere Ave, Burbank (91504-3413)
PHONE..................................818 848-8307
Rafi Balouzian, *President*
Richard Delamarter, *Shareholder*
◆ EMP: 28
SQ FT: 15,000
SALES (est): 4.5MM **Privately Held**
WEB: www.cydwoq.com
SIC: 3131 3199 Laces, shoe & boot: leather; leather belting & strapping

(P-10473)
INGRERSOLL RAND INDUS REFRIG
13770 Ramona Ave, Chino (91710-5423)
PHONE..................................909 477-2037
Michael Nobile, *Sales Mgr*
EMP: 13 EST: 2011
SALES (est): 1.6MM **Privately Held**
SIC: 3131 Rands

(P-10474)
PROSOUND COMMUNICATIONS INC
Also Called: Xotic Guitars & Effects
233 N Maclay Ave Ste 403, San Fernando (91340-2908)
PHONE..................................818 367-9593
Toshio Horiba, *CEO*
EMP: 10
SALES (est): 1.3MM **Privately Held**
WEB: www.prosoundcommunications.com
SIC: 3131 7389 Footwear cut stock;

(P-10475)
SIMPLE ORTHOTIC SOLUTIONS LLC
9960 Indiana Ave Ste 15, Riverside (92503-5457)
PHONE..................................951 353-8127
Gerardo Espinoza, *Mng Member*
EMP: 11
SQ FT: 4,800
SALES (est): 954.3K **Privately Held**
SIC: 3131 Inner soles, leather

(P-10476)
SOLE SOCIETY GROUP INC
8511 Steller Dr, Culver City (90232-2426)
PHONE..................................310 220-0808
Andy Solomon, *Mng Member*
Talitha Peters,
▲ EMP: 200
SALES (est): 11.1MM
SALES (corp-wide): 287.1MM **Privately Held**
SIC: 3131 5661 5621 Boot & shoe accessories; men's boots; women's boots; ready-to-wear apparel, women's
PA: Vcs Group Llc
411 W Putnam Ave Ste 210
Greenwich CT 06830
203 413-6500

(P-10477)
SUNSPORTS LP
7 Holland, Irvine (92618-2506)
PHONE..................................949 273-6202
Jamey Draper, *Partner*
▲ EMP: 200
SQ FT: 85,000
SALES (est): 20.5MM **Privately Held**
WEB: www.sunsportsusa.com
SIC: 3131 2395 Footwear cut stock; embroidery products, except schiffli machine

3142 House Slippers

(P-10478)
BONJOUR FLEURETTE INC
112 Mitchell Blvd Ste A, San Rafael (94903-2021)
PHONE..................................415 382-1603
Judith Flowers, *President*
Gerald A Seltzer, *CEO*
Carmel Barell, *Vice Pres*
Greta Longmire, *Vice Pres*
EMP: 14
SQ FT: 7,300
SALES (est): 1.1MM **Privately Held**
SIC: 3142 House slippers

(P-10479)
FREDI & SONS INC
58 Calle Cabrillo, Foothill Ranch (92610-1746)
PHONE..................................818 881-1170
Farrokh Torkzadeh, *President*
Korosh Torkzadeh, *Marketing Staff*
▲ EMP: 10
SALES (est): 1.1MM **Privately Held**
WEB: www.frediandsons.com
SIC: 3142 2253 House slippers; lounging robes, knit

3143 Men's Footwear, Exc Athletic

(P-10480)
BRAND X HURARCHES
Also Called: Bucate Plata Importing Co
4228 Telegraph Ave, Oakland (94609-2408)
PHONE..................................510 658-9006
Ronn Simpson, *Owner*
EMP: 49
SALES (est): 1.6MM **Privately Held**
WEB: www.brandxhuaraches.com
SIC: 3143 3144 6512 Boots, dress or casual: men's; women's footwear, except athletic; commercial & industrial building operation

(P-10481)
LANE INTERNATIONAL TRADING INC (PA)
33155 Transit Ave, Union City (94587-2091)
P.O. Box 2223 (94587-7223)
PHONE..................................510 489-7364
Lane Shay, *President*
▲ EMP: 100
SQ FT: 2,500
SALES (est): 7MM **Privately Held**
WEB: www.toolboxdesign.com
SIC: 3143 3144 Men's footwear, except athletic; women's footwear, except athletic

(P-10482)
PHOENIX FOOTWEAR GROUP INC (PA)
5937 Darwin Ct Ste 109, Carlsbad (92008-7363)
PHONE..................................760 602-9688
James R Riedman, *President*
James Clopton, *President*
Dennis Nelson, *CFO*
Larry Stuart Torchin, *Vice Pres*
Erin Adams, *Sales Mgr*
◆ EMP: 50
SQ FT: 21,700

SALES (est): 9.2MM **Publicly Held**
WEB: www.danielgreenco.com
SIC: 3143 3144 2329 2339 Men's footwear, except athletic; women's footwear, except athletic; men's & boys' sportswear & athletic clothing; sportswear, women's

(P-10483)
SHOES FOR CREWS INTL INC
760 Baldwin Park Blvd, City of Industry (91746-1503)
PHONE..................................561 683-5090
EMP: 25
SALES (corp-wide): 19.9MM **Privately Held**
SIC: 3143 3144 Work shoes, men's; women's footwear, except athletic
PA: Shoes For Crews International, Inc.
250 S Australian Ave # 1700
West Palm Beach FL 33401
561 683-5090

(P-10484)
STEVEN MADDEN LTD
938 N Fairfax Ave, West Hollywood (90046-7204)
PHONE..................................323 656-0012
Steve Madden, *Branch Mgr*
EMP: 75 **Publicly Held**
SIC: 3143 Men's footwear, except athletic
PA: Steven Madden, Ltd.
5216 Barnett Ave
Long Island City NY 11104

(P-10485)
STEVEN MADDEN LTD
6600 Topanga Canyon Blvd # 98, Canoga Park (91303-2609)
PHONE..................................818 713-9681
Vincent Madden, *Branch Mgr*
EMP: 75 **Publicly Held**
SIC: 3143 Men's footwear, except athletic
PA: Steven Madden, Ltd.
5216 Barnett Ave
Long Island City NY 11104

(P-10486)
STEVEN MADDEN LTD
24201 Valencia Blvd # 3506, Santa Clarita (91355-1861)
PHONE..................................661 753-9510
EMP: 75 **Publicly Held**
SIC: 3143 Men's footwear, except athletic
PA: Steven Madden, Ltd.
5216 Barnett Ave
Long Island City NY 11104

(P-10487)
STEVEN MADDEN LTD
4345 Camino De La Plz, San Diego (92173-3058)
PHONE..................................619 690-9761
EMP: 84 **Publicly Held**
SIC: 3143 Men's footwear, except athletic
PA: Steven Madden, Ltd.
5216 Barnett Ave
Long Island City NY 11104

(P-10488)
STEVEN MADDEN LTD
14006 Riverside Dr, Sherman Oaks (91423-1945)
PHONE..................................818 205-9563
EMP: 75 **Publicly Held**
SIC: 3143 Men's footwear, except athletic
PA: Steven Madden, Ltd.
5216 Barnett Ave
Long Island City NY 11104

(P-10489)
STEVEN MADDEN LTD
100 Citadel Dr, Commerce (90040-1580)
PHONE..................................323 346-0205
EMP: 79 **Publicly Held**
SIC: 3143 Men's footwear, except athletic
PA: Steven Madden, Ltd.
5216 Barnett Ave
Long Island City NY 11104

▲ = Import ▼ =Export
◆ =Import/Export

(P-10490)
STEVEN MADDEN LTD
6725 Kimball Ave, Chino (91708-9177)
PHONE...................................909 393-7575
Reyn Williams, *Branch Mgr*
EMP: 75 **Publicly Held**
WEB: www.mypinecastle.com
SIC: 3143 3144 3149 5661 Men's
footwear, except athletic; women's
footwear, except athletic; children's
footwear, except athletic; shoe stores;
women's shoes; men's boots; children's
shoes
PA: Steven Madden, Ltd.
521b Barnett Ave
Long Island City NY 11104

(P-10491)
STRATEGIC PARTNERS INC (PA)
Also Called: Cherokee Uniform
9800 De Soto Ave, Chatsworth
(91311-4411)
PHONE...................................818 671-2100
Michael Singer, *CEO*
Robert Pierpoint, *CFO*
Joy Panichi, *Accounts Mgr*
◆ EMP: 203
SQ FT: 140,000
SALES (est): 170.2MM **Privately Held**
WEB: www.strategicpartners.net
SIC: 3143 3144 5139 2339 Men's
footwear, except athletic; women's
footwear, except athletic; shoes; women's
& misses' outerwear; uniforms & vest-
ments; sweaters & sweater jackets: men's
& boys'

(P-10492)
VIONIC GROUP LLC
Also Called: Orthaheel
4040 Civic Center Dr # 430, San Rafael
(94903-4150)
PHONE...................................415 526-6932
Chris Gallagher, *CEO*
Connie X Rishwain, *President*
Bruce Campbell, *COO*
Steve Furtado, *CFO*
Lisa Bazinet, *Exec VP*
▲ EMP: 84
SQ FT: 16,000
SALES (est): 19.5MM
SALES (corp-wide): 2.7B **Publicly Held**
SIC: 3143 3144 Orthopedic shoes,
men's; orthopedic shoes, women's; ortho-
pedic shoes, children's
PA: Caleres, Inc.
8300 Maryland Ave
Saint Louis MO 63105
314 854-4000

(P-10493)
WOLVERINE WORLD WIDE INC
Also Called: Beaumont DC 52
1020 Prosperity Way, Beaumont
(92223-2624)
PHONE...................................800 253-2184
EMP: 15
SALES (corp-wide): 2.3B **Publicly Held**
SIC: 3143 Men's footwear, except athletic
PA: Wolverine World Wide, Inc.
9341 Courtland Dr Ne
Rockford MI 49351
616 866-5500

3144 Women's Footwear, Exc Athletic

(P-10494)
CALLEEN CORDERO DESIGNS INC
Also Called: Calleen Cordero Retail
7384 Beverly Blvd, Los Angeles
(90036-2501)
PHONE...................................818 764-0715
Calleen Cordero, *President*
Brigitte Guerra, *Prdtn Mgr*
Racheal Loberman, *Sales Staff*
▲ EMP: 15
SQ FT: 5,000

SALES (est): 2.5MM **Privately Held**
WEB: www.calleencordero.com
SIC: 3144 Women's footwear, except ath-
letic

(P-10495)
DAVIS SHOE THERAPEUTICS
3921 Judah St, San Francisco
(94122-1120)
PHONE...................................415 661-8705
Arnold Davis, *Owner*
EMP: 11
SQ FT: 3,000
SALES (est): 1MM **Privately Held**
SIC: 3144 3143 Orthopedic shoes,
women's; orthopedic shoes, men's

(P-10496)
EVOLUTION DESIGN LAB INC
150 S Los Robles Ave # 100, Pasadena
(91101-2441)
PHONE...................................626 960-8388
Jennet Chow, *CEO*
Pauline Cheng, *Purch Mgr*
Joanna Hughes, *Marketing Staff*
▲ EMP: 25
SALES (est): 3.7MM **Privately Held**
SIC: 3144 5139 Women's footwear, ex-
cept athletic; shoes

(P-10497)
IMPO INTERNATIONAL LLC
Also Called: Chili's
3510 Black Rd, Santa Maria (93455-5927)
P.O. Box 639 (93456-0639)
PHONE...................................805 922-7753
Laura Ann Hopkins, *Mng Member*
Laura Hopkins, *Vice Pres*
Julie Foster, *Cust Mgr*
Lori Thompson, *Supervisor*
▲ EMP: 24
SQ FT: 30,000
SALES (est): 4.4MM **Privately Held**
WEB: www.impo.com
SIC: 3144 Boots, canvas or leather:
women's; dress shoes, women's; san-
dals, women's

(P-10498)
J & A SHOE COMPANY INC
Also Called: Callisto Shoes Rolling Hills
960 Knox St Bldg A, Torrance
(90502-1086)
PHONE...................................310 324-0139
Leah Bizoumis, *President*
Valerie Kats, *Admin Sec*
▲ EMP: 108
SQ FT: 14,500
SALES (est): 17.9MM **Privately Held**
SIC: 3144 Women's footwear, except ath-
letic

(P-10499)
MECO-NAG CORPORATION
Also Called: Dezario Shoe Company
7306 Laurel Canyon Blvd, North Hollywood
(91605-3710)
P.O. Box 16565 (91615-6565)
PHONE...................................818 764-2020
Krikor Astourian, *President*
Vicki Astourian, *Vice Pres*
Cruz Martinez, *Admin Sec*
◆ EMP: 60
SQ FT: 10,000
SALES (est): 7.2MM **Privately Held**
SIC: 3144 Women's footwear, except ath-
letic

(P-10500)
MILLENNIAL BRANDS LLC
126 W 9th St, Los Angeles (90015-1500)
PHONE...................................925 230-0617
Catalin Gaitanaru, *Principal*
EMP: 18 **Privately Held**
SIC: 3144 Women's footwear, except ath-
letic
PA: Millennial Brands Llc
2000 Crow Canyon Pl # 300
San Ramon CA 94583

(P-10501)
ONNIK SHOE COMPANY INC
Also Called: Sergio Shoes
11443 Chandler Blvd, North Hollywood
(91601-2617)
PHONE...................................818 506-5353
Vartan Vartanian, *President*
▲ EMP: 30
SQ FT: 20,000
SALES (est): 7MM **Privately Held**
WEB: www.sergioshoes.com
SIC: 3144 Women's footwear, except ath-
letic

(P-10502)
OPPO ORIGINAL CORP
108 Brea Canyon Rd 118, Walnut
(91789-3086)
P.O. Box 4025, Diamond Bar (91765-0025)
PHONE...................................909 444-3000
Olive Wang, *Chairman*
Jim Wang, *Exec VP*
◆ EMP: 13
SQ FT: 12,000
SALES (est): 2.2MM **Privately Held**
SIC: 3144 Dress shoes, women's

(P-10503)
SURGEON WORLDWIDE INC
4000 Broadway Pl, Los Angeles
(90037-1010)
PHONE...................................707 501-7962
Mariko Chambrone, *Vice Pres*
EMP: 27
SALES (est): 904.1K **Privately Held**
SIC: 3144 3143 Women's footwear, ex-
cept athletic; men's footwear, except ath-
letic

(P-10504)
TATIOSSIAN BROS INC
Also Called: Tate Shoes
11144 Penrose St Ste 11, Sun Valley
(91352-5601)
PHONE...................................818 768-3200
John Tatiossian, *President*
Avo Tatiossian, *Treasurer*
Zoohrab Tatiossian, *Vice Pres*
David Tatiossian, *Admin Sec*
▲ EMP: 60
SQ FT: 15,000
SALES (est): 7.8MM **Privately Held**
WEB: www.tateshoes.com
SIC: 3144 Women's footwear, except ath-
letic

3149 Footwear, NEC

(P-10505)
FOOT LOCKER RETAIL INC
Also Called: Champs Sports
2059 Newpark Mall Fl 2, Newark
(94560-5249)
PHONE...................................510 797-5750
Arthur Cervantes, *Manager*
EMP: 19
SALES (corp-wide): 7.7B **Publicly Held**
WEB: www.venatorgroup.com
SIC: 3149 5661 Athletic shoes, except
rubber or plastic; footwear, athletic
HQ: Foot Locker Retail, Inc.
330 W 34th St
New York NY 10001

(P-10506)
KIA INCORPORATED (PA)
Also Called: Kia Group
16516 Via Esprillo # 100, San Diego
(92127-1728)
PHONE...................................858 824-2999
Reza Mohseni, *President*
Tannaz Mohseni, *CFO*
Bano Mohseni, *Vice Pres*
▲ EMP: 30
SQ FT: 25,000
SALES (est): 12.7MM **Privately Held**
SIC: 3149 Athletic shoes, except rubber or
plastic

(P-10507)
NELSON SPORTS INC
10528 Pioneer Blvd, Santa Fe Springs
(90670-3704)
PHONE...................................562 944-8081
Young Chu, *President*
Sook Hee Chu, *Admin Sec*
▲ EMP: 45
SQ FT: 10,000
SALES (est): 6.4MM **Privately Held**
WEB: www.nelsonsports.com
SIC: 3149 3021 Athletic shoes, except
rubber or plastic; rubber & plastics
footwear

(P-10508)
SANTA FE FOOTWEAR CORPORATION
9988 Santa Fe Springs Rd, Santa Fe
Springs (90670-2946)
PHONE...................................562 941-9689
Joel Tan, *President*
Joel O Tan, *President*
Debby Tio, *CFO*
▲ EMP: 15
SQ FT: 30,000
SALES (est): 2.4MM **Privately Held**
SIC: 3149 3144 5139 Children's footwear,
except athletic; women's footwear, except
athletic; footwear

(P-10509)
SKECHERS USA INC (PA)
228 Manhattan Beach Blvd # 200, Manhat-
tan Beach (90266-5356)
PHONE...................................310 318-3100
Robert Greenberg, *Ch of Bd*
Michael Greenberg, *President*
David Weinberg, *COO*
John Vandemore, *CFO*
Mark Nason, *Exec VP*
EMP: 80
SQ FT: 181,000
SALES: 4.1B **Publicly Held**
WEB: www.skechers.com
SIC: 3149 3021 Athletic shoes, except
rubber or plastic; shoes, rubber or plastic
molded to fabric

(P-10510)
SOLE TECHNOLOGY INC (PA)
Also Called: Etnies
26921 Fuerte, Lake Forest (92630-8149)
PHONE...................................949 460-2020
Pierre Senizergues, *President*
Paul Migaki, *COO*
Liza Ly, *CTO*
Mike Manzoori, *CTO*
Nick Thomas, *Technology*
▲ EMP: 131
SALES (est): 44.7MM **Privately Held**
WEB: www.soletechnology.com
SIC: 3149 5139 Athletic shoes, except
rubber or plastic; footwear

(P-10511)
SOLE TECHNOLOGY INC
17300 Slover Ave, Fontana (92337-8000)
PHONE...................................949 460-2020
George Almanza, *Manager*
EMP: 11 **Privately Held**
SIC: 3149 Athletic shoes, except rubber or
plastic
PA: Sole Technology, Inc.
26921 Fuerte
Lake Forest CA 92630

3161 Luggage

(P-10512)
ACE PRODUCTS ENTERPRISES INC
Also Called: Ace Products Group
3920 Cypress Dr Ste B, Petaluma
(94954-7603)
PHONE...................................707 765-1500
Allen R Poster, *President*
Charles Kieser, *CFO*
Will Burner, *Admin Asst*
Michelle Konrad, *Accountant*
Jesse Grossmann, *Sales Mgr*
▲ EMP: 21

SALES (est): 3.7MM **Privately Held**
WEB: www.aceproducts.com
SIC: 3161 3931 Musical instrument cases;
drums, parts & accessories (musical instruments)

(P-10513)
AMERICAN PRIDE INC
12285 Colony Ave, Chino (91710-2096)
PHONE..................................909 591-7688
Steve Liang, *President*
▲ EMP: 25
SQ FT: 9,966
SALES (est): 1.9MM **Privately Held**
SIC: 3161 Luggage

(P-10514)
ANVIL CASES INC
15730 Salt Lake Ave, City of Industry
(91745-1115)
PHONE..................................626 968-4100
Joseph Calzone, *President*
Vincent Calzone, *Vice Pres*
Richard Johnson, *District Mgr*
▲ EMP: 125
SQ FT: 60,000
SALES (est): 19.5MM **Privately Held**
WEB: www.anvilcase.com
SIC: 3161 Musical instrument cases;
cases, carrying
PA: Calzone, Ltd.
    225 Black Rock Ave
    Bridgeport CT 06605
    203 367-5766

(P-10515)
AR SQUARE
Also Called: Colorado's Bag Manufacture
8757 Lanyard Ct Ste 150, Rancho Cucamonga (91730-0810)
PHONE..................................909 985-5995
Eduardo Ramirez, *CEO*
EMP: 10
SQ FT: 5,100
SALES (est): 1.3MM **Privately Held**
SIC: 3161 Attache cases; briefcases;
cases, carrying

(P-10516)
BEATO INC
Also Called: Beato Musical Products
1050 E Dominguez St, Carson
(90746-7209)
PHONE..................................310 637-1180
Fred Beato, *President*
Eva Zamarriba, *Treasurer*
Steve Zamarriba, *Vice Pres*
Kitti Beato, *Admin Sec*
▲ EMP: 13 EST: 1979
SALES (est): 1.2MM **Privately Held**
WEB: www.beatobags.com
SIC: 3161 3931 Musical instrument cases;
percussion instruments & parts

(P-10517)
BRIDGEPORT PRODUCTS INC
26895 Aliso Creek Rd B, Aliso Viejo
(92656-5301)
PHONE..................................949 348-8800
Brent Foster, *President*
Jeffery Hahn, *Treasurer*
Timothy Byk, *Vice Pres*
David Scott, *Admin Sec*
◆ EMP: 76
SQ FT: 10,000
SALES (est): 11.1MM **Privately Held**
WEB: www.bridgeport-products.com
SIC: 3161 Traveling bags; cases, carrying

(P-10518)
CHUNMA USA INC
Also Called: Chunma America
2000 E 25th St, Vernon (90058-1128)
PHONE..................................323 846-0077
Jae Jung, *President*
◆ EMP: 10
SALES (est): 1.4MM
SALES (corp-wide): 4.3MM **Privately Held**
SIC: 3161 Luggage
PA: Chunma Corporation
    53 Hallimmal-Gil, Seongdong-Gu
    Seoul 04735
    222 989-0715

(P-10519)
DONY CORP
Also Called: Dony Trading Los Angeles
1065 S Vail Ave, Montebello (90640-6019)
PHONE..................................323 725-7697
Ming Yong LI, *President*
Guofan Jiang, *Shareholder*
Lawrence Lee, *Executive*
▲ EMP: 10
SALES (est): 1.6MM **Privately Held**
SIC: 3161 3171 4731 Luggage; women's
handbags & purses; freight transportation
arrangement

(P-10520)
EAGLE CREEK INC (DH)
Also Called: Eagle Creek Travel Gear
5935 Darwin Ct, Carlsbad (92008-7302)
PHONE..................................760 431-6400
Steve Barker, *President*
Bert Fenenga, *CFO*
Dale Penk, *Senior VP*
Ricky Schlesinger, *Senior VP*
◆ EMP: 98
SQ FT: 93,000
SALES (est): 46.7MM
SALES (corp-wide): 11.8B **Publicly Held**
WEB: www.eaglecreek.com
SIC: 3161 Traveling bags
HQ: Vf Outdoor, Llc
    2701 Harbor Bay Pkwy
    Alameda CA 94502
    510 618-3500

(P-10521)
ENCORE CASES INC
8818 Lankershim Blvd, Sun Valley
(91352-2516)
PHONE..................................818 768-8803
Gary A Peterson, *President*
Randy Romero, *Design Engr*
▲ EMP: 27
SQ FT: 20,000
SALES (est): 5.1MM **Privately Held**
WEB: www.encorecases.com
SIC: 3161 Cases, carrying

(P-10522)
G & G QUALITY CASE CO INC
2025 E 25th St, Vernon (90058-1127)
P.O. Box 58541, Los Angeles (90058-0541)
PHONE..................................323 233-2482
Efren Guzman, *President*
Ben Germain, *Treasurer*
Brandon Germain, *Software Dev*
▲ EMP: 70 EST: 1978
SQ FT: 13,500
SALES (est): 10.3MM **Privately Held**
WEB: www.ggqualitycase.com
SIC: 3161 Musical instrument cases

(P-10523)
HAMMITT INC
2101 Pacific Coast Hwy A, Hermosa Beach
(90254-2796)
PHONE..................................310 293-3787
Anthony J Drockton, *CEO*
Casie Lopez, *Opers Mgr*
Justin Buck, *Sales Staff*
▲ EMP: 15
SALES (est): 1.8MM **Privately Held**
SIC: 3161 3171 Traveling bags; women's
handbags & purses

(P-10524)
HSIAO & MONTANO INC
Also Called: Odyssey Innovative Designs
809 W Santa Anita Ave, San Gabriel
(91776-1016)
PHONE..................................626 588-2528
Mario Montano, *CEO*
John Hsiao, *Vice Pres*
Horng Ou, *Webmaster*
Alice Jen, *Controller*
Dave Lopez, *Sales Mgr*
▲ EMP: 50
SALES (est): 9.2MM **Privately Held**
WEB: www.odysseygear.com
SIC: 3161 3648 5084 1751 Musical instrument cases; lighting equipment;
woodworking machinery; cabinet & finish
carpentry

(P-10525)
JAN-AL INNERPRIZES INC
Also Called: Jan-Al Cases
3339 Union Pacific Ave, Los Angeles
(90023-3812)
P.O. Box 23337 (90023-0337)
PHONE..................................323 260-7212
Miriam Alejandro, *President*
Jan Michael Alejandro, *Vice Pres*
Dianne Parker, *Financial Exec*
EMP: 30
SQ FT: 16,000
SALES (est): 2.4MM **Privately Held**
WEB: www.janalcase.com
SIC: 3161 Luggage

(P-10526)
LOGISTERRA INC
6190 Fairmount Ave Ste K, San Diego
(92120-3428)
PHONE..................................619 280-9992
Tan V Nguyen, *President*
Ann Long, *Vice Pres*
EMP: 45
SQ FT: 14,000
SALES (est): 2.2MM **Privately Held**
WEB: www.rhodiana.com
SIC: 3161 5948 Cases, carrying; luggage
& leather goods stores

(P-10527)
M GROUP INC
Also Called: Bamboosa
9808 Venice Blvd Ste 706, Culver City
(90232-6827)
PHONE..................................843 221-7830
Michael Moore, *President*
Mindy Johnson, *Admin Sec*
EMP: 24
SQ FT: 10,000
SALES (est): 2.8MM **Privately Held**
SIC: 3161 5651 5136 5137 Clothing &
apparel carrying cases; family clothing
stores; men's & boys' clothing; women's &
children's clothing

(P-10528)
OGIO INTERNATIONAL INC
2180 Rutherford Rd, Carlsbad
(92008-7328)
PHONE..................................801 619-4100
Anthony Palma, *CEO*
Michael Pratt, *President*
▲ EMP: 100
SQ FT: 70,000
SALES (est): 19.3MM
SALES (corp-wide): 1B **Publicly Held**
SIC: 3161 2393 Traveling bags; textile
bags; canvas bags; duffle bags, canvas:
made from purchased materials
PA: Callaway Golf Company
    2180 Rutherford Rd
    Carlsbad CA 92008
    760 931-1771

(P-10529)
ONEIL KG BAGS
Also Called: K G Bags
124 Belvedere St Ste 12, San Rafael
(94901-4704)
PHONE..................................415 460-0111
Rob O'Neil, *Owner*
Jamie O"neil, *Vice Pres*
Ryan A Neil, *Manager*
EMP: 12
SALES (est): 1.4MM **Privately Held**
WEB: www.kgbags.com
SIC: 3161 Luggage

(P-10530)
PK INDUSTRIES INC
Also Called: International Apparel
1533 Olivella Way, San Diego
(92154-7716)
PHONE..................................619 428-6382
▲ EMP: 11
SALES (est): 870K **Privately Held**
SIC: 3161

(P-10531)
PMP PRODUCTS INC
1210 W Jon St, Torrance (90502-1208)
PHONE..................................310 549-5122
Mariah Qian, *President*
EMP: 15

SALES (est): 931.1K **Privately Held**
SIC: 3161 2231 Clothing & apparel carrying cases; apparel & outerwear broadwoven fabrics

(P-10532)
RJ SINGER INTERNATIONAL INC
Also Called: Ruben and Sharam
4801 W Jefferson Blvd, Los Angeles
(90016-3920)
PHONE..................................323 735-1717
Reouben Melamed, *President*
Farshad Melamed, *Vice Pres*
▲ EMP: 85
SQ FT: 20,000
SALES (est): 8.3MM **Privately Held**
WEB: www.rjsinger.com
SIC: 3161 2335 2393 2353 Cases, carrying; women's, juniors' & misses' dresses;
textile bags; hats & caps; T-shirts & tops,
women's: made from purchased materials

(P-10533)
SAFCOR INC
Also Called: Landmark Luggage & Gifts
13455 Ventura Blvd 237a, Sherman Oaks
(91423-3830)
PHONE..................................818 392-8437
EMP: 10 EST: 2011
SALES (est): 750K **Privately Held**
SIC: 3161

(P-10534)
SCOTT WELSHER
Also Called: To Die For
2031 S Lynx Ave, Ontario (91761-8011)
P.O. Box 5323, Orange (92863-5323)
PHONE..................................949 574-4000
Scott Welsher, *Owner*
Jason Welsher, *Co-Owner*
EMP: 10 EST: 1999
SQ FT: 1,900
SALES (est): 840.4K **Privately Held**
SIC: 3161 Clothing & apparel carrying
cases

(P-10535)
SIERRA AVIATION
3400 E Tahquitz Canyon Wa, Palm Springs
(92262-6920)
PHONE..................................760 778-2845
Jimmy Witt, *Manager*
EMP: 36
SALES (est): 2.6MM **Privately Held**
SIC: 3161 Luggage

(P-10536)
SIMON OF CALIFORNIA (PA)
9545 Sawyer St, Los Angeles
(90035-4105)
PHONE..................................310 559-4871
Simon Frank, *Owner*
Simon Blumberg, *President*
▲ EMP: 12
SQ FT: 10,000
SALES (est): 1.6MM **Privately Held**
SIC: 3161 3172 Luggage; personal leather
goods; wallets

(P-10537)
SKB CORPORATION
1633 N Leslie Way, Orange (92867-3633)
PHONE..................................714 637-1572
Steven Kottman, *Owner*
EMP: 300
SALES (corp-wide): 76.7MM **Privately Held**
WEB: www.skbcases.com
SIC: 3161 Cases, carrying
PA: S.K.B. Corporation
    434 W Levers Pl
    Orange CA 92867
    714 637-1252

(P-10538)
SPECULATIVE PRODUCT DESIGN LLC
303 Bryant St, Mountain View
(94041-1552)
PHONE..................................650 462-9086
EMP: 10 **Privately Held**
SIC: 3161
HQ: Speculative Product Design, Llc
    177 Bovet Rd Ste 200
    San Mateo CA 94402
    650 462-2040

▲ = Import ▼=Export
◆ =Import/Export

(P-10539)
SPECULATIVE PRODUCT DESIGN LLC (DH)
Also Called: Speck Products
177 Bovet Rd Ste 200, San Mateo (94402-3118)
PHONE.....................650 462-2040
Irene Baran, *CEO*
David Law, *President*
Mark Lemma, *CFO*
Rusty Everett, *Exec VP*
Bill De Dufour, *Director*
▲ EMP: 63
SQ FT: 5,000
SALES (est): 17.1MM **Privately Held**
WEB: www.speckdesign.com
SIC: 3161 Cases, carrying
HQ: Samsonite Llc
575 West St Ste 110
Mansfield MA 02048
508 851-1400

(P-10540)
TRAVELERS CHOICE TRAVELWARE
Also Called: Golden Pacific
2805 S Reservoir St, Pomona (91766-6526)
PHONE.....................909 529-7688
Roger Yang, *CEO*
▲ EMP: 72
SQ FT: 12,000
SALES (est): 12.4MM **Privately Held**
WEB: www.travelerchoice.com
SIC: 3161 Luggage

(P-10541)
WALKER/DUNHAM CORP
Also Called: Walker Bags
445 Barneveld Ave, San Francisco (94124-1501)
PHONE.....................415 821-3070
Eveline Dunham, *President*
Emily Hughes, *Vice Pres*
Marion Dunham, *Asst Sec*
EMP: 15
SQ FT: 10,000
SALES (est): 1.2MM **Privately Held**
SIC: 3161 Cases, carrying

(P-10542)
ZUCA INC
320 S Milpitas Blvd, Milpitas (95035-5421)
PHONE.....................408 377-9822
Bruce Kinnee, *President*
Meraf Gedlu, *Accounting Mgr*
◆ EMP: 20
SALES (est): 3.3MM **Privately Held**
WEB: www.zuca.com
SIC: 3161 5099 Luggage; luggage

3171 Handbags & Purses

(P-10543)
BRIGHTON COLLECTIBLES LLC
180 El Camino Real, Millbrae (94030-2606)
PHONE.....................650 838-0086
Jerry Kohl, *Branch Mgr*
EMP: 10
SALES (corp-wide): 375.3MM **Privately Held**
SIC: 3171 Women's handbags & purses
PA: Brighton Collectibles, Llc
14022 Nelson Ave
City Of Industry CA 91746
626 961-9381

(P-10544)
COACH INC
3333 Bristol St Ste 2883, Costa Mesa (92626-1821)
PHONE.....................949 365-0771
EMP: 15
SALES (corp-wide): 4.1B **Publicly Held**
SIC: 3171
PA: Coach, Inc.
516 W 34th St Bsmt 5
New York NY 10001
212 594-1850

(P-10545)
COACH INC
434 W Hillcrest Dr, Thousand Oaks (91360-4222)
PHONE.....................805 496-9933
EMP: 15
SALES (corp-wide): 4.1B **Publicly Held**
SIC: 3171
PA: Coach, Inc.
516 W 34th St Bsmt 5
New York NY 10001
212 594-1850

(P-10546)
DREAM PRODUCTS INCORPORATED
9754 Deering Ave, Chatsworth (91311-4301)
PHONE.....................818 773-4233
Richard Goldman, *CEO*
Christine Kneser, *Creative Dir*
Eneida Sanchez-Aguilar, *Buyer*
Brent Goldman, *Art Dir*
Stacy Decker, *Manager*
EMP: 22
SALES (est): 3.8MM **Privately Held**
SIC: 3171 3172 Women's handbags & purses; personal leather goods

(P-10547)
FRANCES MARY ACCESSORIES INC
3732 Mt Diablo Blvd # 260, Lafayette (94549-3643)
PHONE.....................925 962-2111
Mary Frances Shaffer, *President*
Carolyn Miller, *Office Mgr*
Amanda Savage, *Graphic Designe*
EMP: 1020
SALES (est): 4MM **Privately Held**
SIC: 3171 Handbags, women's

(P-10548)
GLASER DESIGNS INC
1469 Pacific Ave, San Francisco (94109-2640)
PHONE.....................415 552-3188
Myron Glaser, *President*
Kari Glaser, *Vice Pres*
EMP: 10
SQ FT: 10,000
SALES (est): 1.8MM **Privately Held**
SIC: 3171 3172 3161 Handbags, women's; personal leather goods; handbags, regardless of material: men's; clothing & apparel carrying cases

(P-10549)
GLOBAL UNLIMITED EXPORT LLC
3407 W 6th St Ste 802, Los Angeles (90020-2582)
PHONE.....................213 365-7051
Joshua Son, *President*
EMP: 11
SALES (est): 448.3K **Privately Held**
SIC: 3171 3999 Women's handbags & purses; handles, handbag & luggage

(P-10550)
ISABELLE HANDBAGS INC
3155 Bandini Blvd Unit A, Vernon (90058-4134)
PHONE.....................323 277-9888
Roye Xu, *President*
James LI, *Vice Pres*
Jessica Wellisch, *Creative Dir*
▲ EMP: 35
SQ FT: 2,000
SALES (est): 2.9MM **Privately Held**
SIC: 3171 5632 Handbags, women's; handbags

(P-10551)
PROJECT 1920 INC ✪
251 Post St Ste 412, San Francisco (94108-5019)
PHONE.....................415 990-9788
Wendy Wen, *Owner*
EMP: 20 EST: 2018
SALES (est): 970.1K **Privately Held**
SIC: 3171 Women's handbags & purses

(P-10552)
SVEN DESIGN INC
Also Called: Sven Design Handbag Outlet
2301 4th St, Berkeley (94710-2401)
PHONE.....................510 848-7836
Sven Stalman, *President*
Susan Stalman, *Vice Pres*
▲ EMP: 18
SQ FT: 3,500
SALES (est): 2.2MM **Privately Held**
SIC: 3171 3149 5948 5661 Women's handbags & purses; children's footwear, except athletic; luggage & leather goods stores; children's shoes; personal leather goods

(P-10553)
TAPESTRY INC
Also Called: Coach
100 Citadel Dr Ste 709, Commerce (90040-1641)
PHONE.....................323 725-6792
EMP: 15
SALES (corp-wide): 5.8B **Publicly Held**
SIC: 3171 Women's handbags & purses
PA: Tapestry, Inc.
10 Hudson Yards
New York NY 10001
212 594-1850

(P-10554)
TAPESTRY INC
28200 Highway 189, Lake Arrowhead (92352-9700)
PHONE.....................909 337-5207
EMP: 15
SALES (corp-wide): 5.8B **Publicly Held**
SIC: 3171 Handbags, women's
PA: Tapestry, Inc.
10 Hudson Yards
New York NY 10001
212 594-1850

(P-10555)
URBAN EXPRESSIONS INC
5500 Union Pacific Ave, Commerce (90022-5139)
PHONE.....................310 593-4574
Arash Vojdani, *President*
Farbod Shakouri, *Vice Pres*
▲ EMP: 20
SALES (est): 3.4MM **Privately Held**
SIC: 3171 5137 Handbags, women's; handbags

3172 Personal Leather Goods

(P-10556)
ALLEGRO MFG
Also Called: Allegro Creative
500 N Nash St, El Segundo (90245-2817)
PHONE.....................323 724-0101
EMP: 14
SALES (est): 3MM **Privately Held**
SIC: 3172 5199 Cosmetic bags; hairbrushes

(P-10557)
ALLEGRO PACIFIC CORPORATION
7250 Oxford Way, Commerce (90040-3643)
PHONE.....................323 724-0101
▲ EMP: 16
SALES (est): 2MM **Privately Held**
SIC: 3172

(P-10558)
CASE WORLD CO
301 S Doubleday Ave, Ontario (91761-1514)
PHONE.....................626 330-1000
Fax: 909 390-5222
EMP: 17
SALES (est): 1.6MM **Privately Held**
WEB: www.caseworld.tv
SIC: 3172

(P-10559)
DEUX LUX INC (PA)
11609 Vanowen St Ste B, North Hollywood (91605-6170)
PHONE.....................213 746-7040
Sara Naghedi, *President*
Joseph Bautista, *Accountant*
Kelly Cameron, *Production*
Fernanda Sienra, *Manager*
Geneva Barr, *Accounts Mgr*
▲ EMP: 15
SALES (est): 2.1MM **Privately Held**
SIC: 3172 Handbags, regardless of material: men's

(P-10560)
DIMO GEAR LLC
1160 Vienna Dr Ste A, Lodi (95242-9694)
PHONE.....................916 684-1051
James J Dimataris, *Mng Member*
▲ EMP: 25
SALES: 500K **Privately Held**
SIC: 3172 7389 Wallets;

(P-10561)
GARYS LEATHER CREATIONS INC
Also Called: Gary's of California
12644 Bradford Pl, Granada Hills (91344-1510)
PHONE.....................818 831-9977
Steven Matzdorff, *President*
Jeff Matzdorff, *Admin Sec*
EMP: 98
SQ FT: 45,000
SALES (est): 6.6MM **Privately Held**
SIC: 3172 Wallets; coin purses; key cases; card cases

(P-10562)
KATZKIN LEATHER INTERIORS INC
6868 W Acco St, Montebello (90640-5441)
PHONE.....................323 725-1243
Brooks Mayberry, *President*
▲ EMP: 15
SALES (est): 2MM **Privately Held**
SIC: 3172 Personal leather goods

(P-10563)
KOLTOV INC (PA)
300 S Lewis Rd Ste A, Camarillo (93012-6620)
PHONE.....................805 764-0280
Joe Covrigaru, *CEO*
Brett Stone, *President*
Phillip Shieh, *Principal*
▲ EMP: 20
SALES (est): 10MM **Privately Held**
SIC: 3172 5199 Personal leather goods; leather, leather goods & furs

(P-10564)
LEATHER PRO INC
Also Called: Turtleback Case
12900 Bradley Ave, Sylmar (91342-3829)
PHONE.....................818 833-8822
Brian Eremita, *President*
Al Eremita, *Admin Sec*
▲ EMP: 20
SQ FT: 13,000
SALES (est): 3.7MM **Privately Held**
WEB: www.leatherproinc.com
SIC: 3172 Personal leather goods

(P-10565)
LITE LINE FRAME BAGS
535 N Puente St, Brea (92821-2805)
PHONE.....................562 905-3150
Jim Porterfield, *President*
EMP: 20 EST: 2011
SALES (est): 1.3MM **Privately Held**
SIC: 3172 Cases, jewelry

(P-10566)
LOUIS VUITTON US MFG INC
Also Called: Lvusm
321 W Covina Blvd, San Dimas (91773-2907)
PHONE.....................909 599-2411
Jean Claude Calverone, *Director*
▲ EMP: 10
SQ FT: 100,000

SALES (est): 2.8MM
SALES (corp-wide): 315.2MM **Privately Held**
WEB: www.lvhm.com
SIC: 3172 3161 Handbags, regardless of material: men's; wallets; luggage
HQ: Louis Vuitton North America, Inc.
1 E 57th St
New York NY 10022
212 758-8877

(P-10567)
MASCORRO LEATHER INC
1303 S Gerhart Ave, Commerce (90022-4256)
PHONE..............................323 724-6759
Antonio Mascorro, *President*
Yolanda Mascorro, *Admin Sec*
▲ EMP: 100 EST: 1977
SQ FT: 20,000
SALES (est): 10.6MM **Privately Held**
SIC: 3172 Wallets

(P-10568)
MESKIN KHOSROW KAY
Also Called: Graffeo Leather Collection
661 Laurel St, San Carlos (94070-3111)
PHONE..............................650 595-3090
Khosrow Meskin, *Partner*
EMP: 48
SALES (est): 3.8MM **Privately Held**
SIC: 3172 5199 5948 3151 Personal leather goods; leather, leather goods & furs; leather goods, except luggage & shoes; leather gloves & mittens; apparel belts; leather & sheep-lined clothing

(P-10569)
RAIKA INC
13150 Saticoy St, North Hollywood (91605-3402)
PHONE..............................818 503-5911
Raika Alberts, *President*
Roxanne Nemati, *COO*
Wayne Alberts, *Executive*
▲ EMP: 38
SQ FT: 10,000
SALES (est): 4.7MM **Privately Held**
WEB: www.raikausa.com
SIC: 3172 5199 Personal leather goods; leather, leather goods & furs

(P-10570)
RUIZ INDUSTRIES INC
13027 Telfair Ave, Sylmar (91342-3548)
PHONE..............................818 582-6882
Maria Ruiz, *President*
Moises Ruiz, *President*
Maria E Ruiz, *Admin Sec*
EMP: 15 EST: 1976
SQ FT: 5,000
SALES (est): 1.8MM **Privately Held**
SIC: 3172 2821 Personal leather goods; vinyl resins

3199 Leather Goods, NEC

(P-10571)
AKER INTERNATIONAL INC
Also Called: Aker Leather Products
2248 Main St Ste 4, Chula Vista (91911-3932)
PHONE..............................619 423-5182
Kamuran Aker, *CEO*
Laurie Aker, *President*
Levent Aker, *COO*
▲ EMP: 30
SQ FT: 10,000
SALES (est): 3MM **Privately Held**
SIC: 3199 Holsters, leather; leather belting & strapping

(P-10572)
ARIAT INTERNATIONAL INC (PA)
3242 Whipple Rd, Union City (94587-1217)
PHONE..............................510 477-7000
Elizabeth Cross, *CEO*
Pankaj Gupta, *CFO*
Liz Bradley, *Vice Pres*
Rial Chew, *Vice Pres*
Megan Iwersen, *Vice Pres*
▲ EMP: 400

SALES (est): 275.5MM **Privately Held**
WEB: www.ariat.com
SIC: 3199 5139 5137 5136 Equestrian related leather articles; boots, horse; leather garments; footwear; women's & children's clothing; men's & boys' clothing

(P-10573)
CUSTOM LEATHERCRAFT MFG LLC (PA)
Also Called: CLC Work Gear
10240 Alameda St, South Gate (90280-5551)
PHONE..............................323 752-2221
Ron Pickens, *CEO*
Harry Karapetian, *Vice Pres*
Jim Fleming, *Regional Mgr*
Stefanie Leary, *Accounting Mgr*
Craig Anderson, *Controller*
◆ EMP: 50
SQ FT: 150,000
SALES (est): 60MM **Privately Held**
SIC: 3199 2394 Leather belting & strapping; aprons: welders', blacksmiths', etc.: leather; novelties, leather; canvas & related products

(P-10574)
ELEANOR RIGBY LEATHER CO
4660 La Jolla Village Dr # 100, San Diego (92122-4604)
PHONE..............................619 356-5590
Peter Robinson, *CEO*
▲ EMP: 30 EST: 2011
SQ FT: 2,000
SALES (est): 900K **Privately Held**
SIC: 3199 Leather garments

(P-10575)
M & L HAIGHT LLC
Also Called: Camp Bow Wow Temecula
42192 Sarah Way, Temecula (92590-3401)
PHONE..............................951 587-2267
Michael Haight, *Mng Member*
Lisa Haight, *Mng Member*
EMP: 22 EST: 2011
SQ FT: 150
SALES (est): 818K **Privately Held**
SIC: 3199 0752 Dog furnishings: collars, leashes, muzzles, etc.: leather; animal boarding services; boarding services, kennels

(P-10576)
OCCIDENTAL MANUFACTURING INC
4200 Ross Rd, Sebastopol (95472-2220)
PHONE..............................707 824-2560
Darryl G Thurner, *Owner*
Gerardo Becerra, *Principal*
Jeff Holmes, *Principal*
Michael Malley, *Manager*
EMP: 48 EST: 1980
SQ FT: 18,000
SALES (est): 16.7MM **Privately Held**
WEB: www.occidentalleather.com
SIC: 3199 Leather garments

(P-10577)
OFF LEAD INC
9751 N Highway 99, Stockton (95212-1603)
PHONE..............................209 931-6909
John C Weber, *President*
EMP: 11 EST: 2001
SALES (est): 1.2MM **Privately Held**
WEB: www.offlead.com
SIC: 3199 Dog furnishings: collars, leashes, muzzles, etc.: leather

(P-10578)
R & J LEATHERCRAFT
12155 Magnolia Ave Ste 8d, Riverside (92503-4903)
PHONE..............................951 688-1685
Ray Hazelwood, *Owner*
EMP: 10
SQ FT: 7,000
SALES (est): 530K **Privately Held**
SIC: 3199 Leather garments

(P-10579)
SAFARILAND LLC
3120 E Mission Blvd, Ontario (91761-2900)
P.O. Box 51478 (91761-0078)
PHONE..............................909 923-7300

Warren B Kanders, *Branch Mgr*
Robyn Sloan, *Executive Asst*
Lia Taubert, *Admin Asst*
Diane Dore, *Human Resources*
Tom Bailey, *Buyer*
EMP: 354
SALES (corp-wide): 875.1MM **Privately Held**
WEB: www.protecharmored.com
SIC: 3199 3842 Holsters, leather; bullet-proof vests
HQ: Safariland, Llc
13386 International Pkwy
Jacksonville FL 32218
904 741-5400

(P-10580)
SARAHS LEATHER MFG
3926 Hammel St, Los Angeles (90063-3514)
PHONE..............................323 262-2594
Juan Ramblaz, *Owner*
EMP: 29
SALES (est): 1.4MM **Privately Held**
SIC: 3199 Leather goods

(P-10581)
STIRWORKS INC
2010 Lincoln Ave, Pasadena (91103-1323)
PHONE..............................800 657-2427
Jean-Paul Labrosse, *CEO*
Rick Nessly, *Business Dir*
Lisa Karlin, *Opers Staff*
Martin Kozaczek, *Director*
EMP: 23
SALES (est): 4.2MM **Privately Held**
SIC: 3199 Stirrups, wood or metal

(P-10582)
SUNSET LEATHER GROUP
8527 Melrose Ave, West Hollywood (90069-5114)
PHONE..............................310 388-4898
Olivier Slama, *Principal*
EMP: 30
SALES (est): 2.1MM **Privately Held**
SIC: 3199 Leather garments

(P-10583)
TREND CHASERS LLC
2311 S Santa Fe Ave, Vernon (90058-1154)
PHONE..............................213 749-2661
Alon Zeltzer,
EMP: 50
SALES (est): 5.4MM **Privately Held**
SIC: 3199 Leather garments

(P-10584)
WHEELSKINS INC
2821 10th St, Berkeley (94710-2710)
PHONE..............................510 841-2128
James Valley, *President*
EMP: 17 EST: 1977
SQ FT: 15,000
SALES (est): 2.2MM **Privately Held**
WEB: www.wheelskins.com
SIC: 3199 3172 5199 5136 Novelties, leather; personal leather goods; chamois leather; gloves, men's & boys'; gloves, women's & children's

(P-10585)
YATES GEAR INC
2608 Hartnell Ave Ste 6, Redding (96002-2347)
PHONE..............................530 222-4606
John Yates, *President*
Karen Yates, *Vice Pres*
Brad Colombero, *Sales Staff*
▲ EMP: 55
SALES (est): 9.4MM **Privately Held**
WEB: www.yatesgear.com
SIC: 3199 3842 Safety belts, leather; personal safety equipment

3211 Flat Glass

(P-10586)
ABRISA INDUSTRIAL GLASS INC (HQ)
Also Called: Abrisa Glass & Coating
200 Hallock Dr, Santa Paula (93060-9646)
P.O. Box 85055, Chicago IL (60680-0851)
PHONE..............................805 525-4902
Blake Fennell, *CEO*
Holly Boschee, *CFO*
David Kwan, *Info Tech Dir*
Heather Swartz, *Credit Mgr*
Nathan Chambers, *Sales Associate*
▲ EMP: 90
SQ FT: 93,000
SALES (est): 23.9MM
SALES (corp-wide): 251.3MM **Privately Held**
WEB: www.abrisa.com
SIC: 3211 Strengthened or reinforced glass; tempered glass
PA: Graham Partners, Inc.
3811 West Chester Pike # 200
Newtown Square PA 19073
610 408-0500

(P-10587)
BUDGET ENTERPRISES INC
Also Called: Solar Art
9301 Research Dr, Irvine (92618-4288)
PHONE..............................949 697-9544
Matthew Darienzo, *CEO*
Jody Johnson, *Administration*
EMP: 25
SALES (est): 3.4MM **Privately Held**
SIC: 3211 Construction glass

(P-10588)
CARDINAL GLASS INDUSTRIES INC
Also Called: Cardinal C G
24100 Cardinal Ave, Moreno Valley (92551-9545)
PHONE..............................951 485-9007
Scott Paisley, *Branch Mgr*
Irene Orona, *COO*
Tracy Cashmer, *Executive*
Jennifer Gregg, *Purch Agent*
EMP: 75
SALES (corp-wide): 1B **Privately Held**
WEB: www.cardinalcorp.com
SIC: 3211 5039 3229 Flat glass; glass construction materials; pressed & blown glass
PA: Cardinal Glass Industries Inc
775 Pririe Ctr Dr Ste 200
Eden Prairie MN 55344
952 229-2600

(P-10589)
CARDINAL GLASS INDUSTRIES INC
Also Called: Cardinal Cg Company
680 Industrial Dr, Galt (95632-1598)
PHONE..............................209 744-8940
Michael Potter, *Manager*
Henry Montijo, *QA Dir*
James Sease, *Info Tech Mgr*
Allan Anasco, *Technology*
Dan Brechbill, *Engineer*
EMP: 150
SALES (corp-wide): 1B **Privately Held**
WEB: www.cardinalcorp.com
SIC: 3211 Construction glass
PA: Cardinal Glass Industries Inc
775 Pririe Ctr Dr Ste 200
Eden Prairie MN 55344
952 229-2600

(P-10590)
CATALINA TEMPERING INC
1125 E Lanzit Ave, Los Angeles (90059-1559)
PHONE..............................323 319-0070
Mike Balderrama, *General Mgr*
EMP: 30
SALES (corp-wide): 10.9MM **Privately Held**
SIC: 3211 Tempered glass
PA: Catalina Tempering, Inc.
1125 E Lanzit Ave
Los Angeles CA 90059
323 789-7800

▲ = Import ▼=Export
◆ =Import/Export

(P-10591)
CEVIANS LLC
3128 Red Hill Ave, Costa Mesa
(92626-4525)
PHONE..............................714 619-5135
Eric Lemay, *President*
EMP: 55
SALES (est): 16.1MM **Privately Held**
SIC: 3211 Flat glass

(P-10592)
CHAD EMPEY
Also Called: Glass Shop of The North Bay
1329 Scott St Ste G, Petaluma
(94954-6557)
PHONE..............................707 762-1900
Chad Empey, *Owner*
EMP: 15
SQ FT: 25,000
SALES: 1.1MM **Privately Held**
SIC: 3211 3231 Construction glass; mirrored glass

(P-10593)
GLASSWERKS LA INC
Glasswerks SD Division
42005 Zevo Dr, Temecula (92590-3780)
PHONE..............................800 729-1324
Rancy Stiecert, *Branch Mgr*
EMP: 20 **Privately Held**
SIC: 3211 Flat glass
HQ: Glasswerks La, Inc.
8600 Rheem Ave
South Gate CA 90280
323 789-7800

(P-10594)
GREENWOOD PRODUCTS INC
Also Called: Basin Medical
805 Barrington Ave, Ontario (91764-5118)
PHONE..............................909 548-4828
Frank Liu, *President*
▲ **EMP:** 15
SALES (est): 1MM **Privately Held**
SIC: 3211 Picture glass

(P-10595)
GUARDIAN INDUSTRIES LLC
11535 E Mountain View Ave, Kingsburg
(93631-9233)
PHONE..............................559 891-8867
Jeffery Booey, *Manager*
Jay Jayakrishnan, *Maintence Staff*
EMP: 275
SQ FT: 486,000
SALES (corp-wide): 42.9B **Privately Held**
WEB: www.guardian.com
SIC: 3211 3231 Sheet glass; tempered glass; products of purchased glass
HQ: Guardian Industries, Llc
2300 Harmon Rd
Auburn Hills MI 48326
248 340-1800

(P-10596)
GUARDIAN INDUSTRIES CORP
11535 E Mountain View Ave, Kingsburg
(93631-9233)
PHONE..............................559 891-8867
Fax: 714 525-3529
EMP: 60
SALES (corp-wide): 27.6B **Privately Held**
SIC: 3211 5231
HQ: Guardian Industries Corp.
2300 Harmon Rd
Auburn Hills MI 48326
248 340-1800

(P-10597)
GUARDIAN INDUSTRIES CORP
11535 E Mountain View Ave, Kingsburg
(93631-9233)
PHONE..............................559 638-3588
EMP: 90
SALES (corp-wide): 27.6B **Privately Held**
SIC: 3211 3231
HQ: Guardian Industries Corp.
2300 Harmon Rd
Auburn Hills MI 48326
248 340-1800

(P-10598)
GWLA ACQUISITION CORP (PA)
8600 Rheem Ave, South Gate
(90280-3333)
PHONE..............................323 789-7800

Randy Steinberg, *President*
Michael Torres, *CFO*
▲ **EMP:** 11
SALES (est): 74.4MM **Privately Held**
SIC: 3211 3231 6719 Tempered glass; mirrored glass; investment holding companies, except banks

(P-10599)
IGS INC
Also Called: Industrial Glass Service
916 E California Ave, Sunnyvale
(94085-4505)
PHONE..............................408 733-4621
John R Gracia, *President*
Rachelle McCray, *Exec VP*
Joe Crownover, *Regional Mgr*
▲ **EMP:** 15
SQ FT: 15,000
SALES (est): 1.9MM **Privately Held**
SIC: 3211 Optical glass, flat

(P-10600)
LINOLEUM SALES CO INC (PA)
Also Called: Anderson's Carpet & Linoleum
1000 W Grand Ave, Oakland (94607-2933)
PHONE..............................661 327-4053
Don Christophe, *CEO*
Tom Christophe, *President*
Bob Mullarkey, *CFO*
Vince Lopez, *Vice Pres*
Andrei Wallace, *Vice Pres*
EMP: 89 EST: 1954
SQ FT: 3,500
SALES (est): 24.6MM **Privately Held**
WEB: www.andersoncls.com
SIC: 3211 5713 Flat glass; floor covering stores

(P-10601)
MADERA GLASS
1825 Howard Rd, Madera (93637-5166)
PHONE..............................559 673-3583
Mike Cappelluti, *President*
EMP: 12
SQ FT: 5,490
SALES (est): 1.6MM **Privately Held**
SIC: 3211 Window glass, clear & colored

(P-10602)
MEDILAND CORPORATION
Also Called: Premium Windows
7027 Motz St, Paramount (90723-4842)
PHONE..............................562 630-9696
Carlos Landazuri, *CEO*
Jose Medina, *Admin Sec*
Kevin Vargas, *Technology*
Jessica M Oneal, *Controller*
Julio Varela, *Controller*
▲ **EMP:** 79
SALES (est): 9.1MM **Privately Held**
SIC: 3211 3645 Window glass, clear & colored; garden, patio, walkway & yard lighting fixtures: electric

(P-10603)
PILKINGTON NORTH AMERICA INC
Also Called: Pilkington Glass Co
500 E Louise Ave, Lathrop (95330-9352)
PHONE..............................209 858-6249
Todd Hoffman, *Manager*
Chris Miller, *Executive*
EMP: 435
SQ FT: 85,000
SALES (corp-wide): 5.6B **Privately Held**
WEB: www.low-eglass.com
SIC: 3211 3231 Flat glass; products of purchased glass
HQ: Pilkington North America, Inc.
811 Madison Ave Fl 3
Toledo OH 43604
614 802-7027

(P-10604)
PITTSBURGH GLASS WORKS LLC
815 Professor Ln, Sacramento
(95834-1193)
PHONE..............................916 419-1853
Scott Greys, *President*
EMP: 145 **Privately Held**
SIC: 3211 Flat glass

HQ: Pittsburgh Glass Works, Llc
30 Isabella St Ste 500
Pittsburgh PA 15212
-

(P-10605)
POMA GL SPECIALTY WINDOWS INC
Also Called: Afg Insulating Riverside Plant
813 Palmyrita Ave, Riverside (92507-1805)
PHONE..............................951 321-0116
Larry Goins, *Principal*
EMP: 60
SALES (corp-wide): 13B **Privately Held**
SIC: 3211 Insulating glass, sealed units
HQ: Poma Glass & Specialty Windows Inc.
11175 Cicero Dr Ste 400
Alpharetta GA 30022
404 446-4200

(P-10606)
SKYCO SKYLIGHTS INC
2995 Airway Ave Unit B, Costa Mesa
(92626-6021)
PHONE..............................949 629-4090
Ryan Marshall, *CEO*
Robert Marshall, *President*
Gary Ritchie, *Vice Pres*
EMP: 35
SQ FT: 25,000
SALES (est): 4.3MM **Privately Held**
SIC: 3211 Skylight glass

(P-10607)
SUN VALLEY SKYLIGHTS INC
Also Called: Sun Vlly Skylghts Plus Windws
12884 Pierce St, Pacoima (91331-2524)
PHONE..............................818 686-0032
David Witty, *President*
Abby Witty, *Vice Pres*
Larry Davis, *VP Opers*
Brian Friedmann, *Opers Mgr*
EMP: 11
SQ FT: 8,350
SALES (est): 1.2MM **Privately Held**
WEB: www.sunvalleyskylights.com
SIC: 3211 1761 Skylight glass; skylight installation

(P-10608)
SUNDOWN LIQUIDATING CORP (PA)
Also Called: Bristolite
401 Goetz Ave, Santa Ana (92707-3709)
PHONE..............................714 540-8950
Randolph Heartfield, *CEO*
Rick Beets, *President*
Jeff Rutledge, *General Mgr*
Darryl Liyama, *Admin Asst*
Darryl liyama, *Info Tech Mgr*
▼ **EMP:** 156 EST: 1970
SQ FT: 100,000
SALES: 32MM **Privately Held**
WEB: www.bristolite.com
SIC: 3211 Skylight glass

(P-10609)
TRANSIT CARE iNC (PA)
7900 Nelson Rd, Panorama City
(91402-6827)
PHONE..............................818 267-3002
William Baldwin, *President*
David Chaimowitz, *CFO*
EMP: 10
SQ FT: 20,000
SALES: 5.2MM **Privately Held**
WEB: www.transitcare.com
SIC: 3211 Strengthened or reinforced glass

(P-10610)
US HORIZON MANUFACTURING INC
Also Called: U.S. Horizon Mfg
28539 Industry Dr, Valencia (91355-5424)
PHONE..............................661 775-1675
Donald E Friest, *CEO*
Garrett A Russell, *President*
▲ **EMP:** 39 EST: 1998
SQ FT: 44,000
SALES (est): 4.3MM
SALES (corp-wide): 29.7B **Privately Held**
SIC: 3211 3429 Plate & sheet glass; manufactured hardware (general)

HQ: C.R. Laurence Co., Inc.
2503 E Vernon Ave
Vernon CA 90058
323 588-1281

(P-10611)
VITRO FLAT GLASS LLC
Also Called: Fresno Glass Plant
3333 S Peach Ave, Fresno (93725-9220)
P.O. Box 2748 (93745-2748)
PHONE..............................559 485-4660
Henry Good, *Manager*
EMP: 140
SALES (corp-wide): 132.7MM **Privately Held**
WEB: www.ppg.com
SIC: 3211 Window glass, clear & colored
PA: Vitro Flat Glass Llc
400 Guys Run Rd
Cheswick PA 15024
412 820-8500

(P-10612)
VITRO FLAT GLASS LLC
3333 S Peach Ave, Fresno (93725-9220)
PHONE..............................559 485-4660
Javier Gutierrez, *Manager*
EMP: 140
SALES (corp-wide): 132.7MM **Privately Held**
SIC: 3211 Float glass
PA: Vitro Flat Glass Llc
400 Guys Run Rd
Cheswick PA 15024
412 820-8500

(P-10613)
WSGLASS HOLDINGS INC (HQ)
Also Called: Western States Glass
3241 Darby Cmn, Fremont (94539-5601)
P.O. Box 6058 (94538-0658)
PHONE..............................510 623-5000
Michael A Smith, *President*
Michael S Foss, *Vice Pres*
Donald E Post, *Vice Pres*
Jonathan M Witkin, *Vice Pres*
▲ **EMP:** 33
SQ FT: 107,000
SALES (est): 22.9MM **Privately Held**
WEB: www.westernstatesglass.com
SIC: 3211 3231 Transparent optical glass, except lenses; insulating glass, sealed units; mirrored glass

3221 Glass Containers

(P-10614)
ACME VIAL & GLASS CO
1601 Commerce Way, Paso Robles
(93446-3626)
PHONE..............................805 239-2666
Debra C Knowles, *President*
Kay Anderson, *Vice Pres*
Corey Knowles, *General Mgr*
Angel Chairez, *Opers Mgr*
▲ **EMP:** 25
SALES (est): 3.8MM **Privately Held**
WEB: www.acmevial.com
SIC: 3221 3231 5113 Vials, glass; products of purchased glass; industrial & personal service paper

(P-10615)
ARDAGH GLASS INC
24441 Avenue 12, Madera (93637-9384)
PHONE..............................559 675-4700
Jaime Navaro, *Manager*
Joseph Vonmoos, *Engineer*
EMP: 34 **Privately Held**
WEB: www.sgcontainers.com
SIC: 3221 5719 Glass containers; glassware
HQ: Ardagh Glass Inc.
10194 Crosspoint Blvd
Indianapolis IN 46256
-

(P-10616)
ASEPTIC INNOVATIONS INC
4940 E Landon Dr, Anaheim (92807-1971)
PHONE..............................714 584-2110
Noel Calma, *CFO*
EMP: 20 EST: 2016
SQ FT: 37,771

PRODUCTS & SVCS

SALES (est): 634.1K **Privately Held**
SIC: 3221 Glass containers

(P-10617)
ASEPTIC TECHNOLOGY LLC
24855 Corbit Pl, Yorba Linda (92887-5543)
PHONE.................................714 694-0168
Joshua Cua,
Julie Hodson, *President*
Noel Calma, *CFO*
EMP: 64 EST: 2013
SQ FT: 59,300
SALES: 7.5MM **Privately Held**
SIC: 3221 Bottles for packing, bottling & canning: glass

(P-10618)
CCDA WATERS LLC
2121 E Winston Rd, Anaheim (92806-5535)
PHONE.................................714 991-7031
Jim Peterson,
EMP: 90
SALES (est): 6.7MM **Privately Held**
WEB: www.la.ko.com
SIC: 3221 Water bottles, glass

(P-10619)
CUSTOM PACK INC
11621 Cardinal Cir, Garden Grove (92843-3814)
PHONE.................................714 534-2201
Edward De Casas, *Branch Mgr*
EMP: 16
SALES (est): 659.1K
SALES (corp-wide): 1MM **Privately Held**
SIC: 3221 7389
PA: Custom Pack, Inc.
11661 Cardinal Cir
Garden Grove CA 92843
714 534-5353

(P-10620)
GALLO GLASS COMPANY (HQ)
605 S Santa Cruz Ave, Modesto (95354-4299)
P.O. Box 1230 (95353-1230)
PHONE.................................209 341-3710
Robert J Gallo, *President*
Thomas Clark, *Engineer*
MO Mashinchi, *Engineer*
Daniel Nelson, *Engineer*
Gordon Stewart, *Engineer*
▲ EMP: 1000 EST: 1957
SALES (est): 223.5MM
SALES (corp-wide): 2.6B **Privately Held**
SIC: 3221 Glass containers
PA: E. & J. Gallo Winery
600 Yosemite Blvd
Modesto CA 95354
209 341-3111

(P-10621)
LIFEFACTORY INC
3 Harbor Dr Ste 200, Sausalito (94965-1491)
PHONE.................................415 729-9820
Josh Brown, *Interim Pres*
Gina Del Vecchio, *VP Opers*
▲ EMP: 30
SQ FT: 6,000
SALES (est): 5.2MM
SALES (corp-wide): 34.9B **Privately Held**
SIC: 3221 Bottles for packing, bottling & canning: glass
HQ: Thermos L.L.C.
475 N Martingale Rd # 1100
Schaumburg IL 60173
847 439-7821

(P-10622)
MYERS WINE CNTRY KITCHENS LLC
511 Alexis Ct, NAPA (94558-7526)
PHONE.................................707 252-9463
Daren Cannels, *President*
Jill Sheehan, *VP Mktg*
Lance Jensen, *VP Sales*
▲ EMP: 20
SQ FT: 17,000
SALES (est): 3.4MM **Privately Held**
WEB: www.winecountrykitchens.com
SIC: 3221 Bottles for packing, bottling & canning: glass

(P-10623)
OWENS-BROCKWAY GLASS CONT INC
3600 Alameda Ave, Oakland (94601-3329)
PHONE.................................510 436-2000
Rod Detmear, *Manager*
EMP: 100
SALES (corp-wide): 6.8B **Publicly Held**
SIC: 3221 Glass containers
HQ: Owens-Brockway Glass Container Inc.
1 Michael Owens Way
Perrysburg OH 43551
567 336-8449

(P-10624)
PACIFIC VIAL MFG INC
2738 Supply Ave, Commerce (90040-2704)
PHONE.................................323 721-7004
Steven OH, *Principal*
▲ EMP: 40
SQ FT: 30,000
SALES: 100MM **Privately Held**
WEB: www.pacificvial.com
SIC: 3221 Vials, glass

(P-10625)
SAINT GOBAIN CONTAINERS INC
2600 Stanford Ct, Fairfield (94533-2767)
PHONE.................................707 437-8700
Phil Ringhome, *Principal*
EMP: 10
SALES (est): 1.2MM
SALES (corp-wide): 213.5MM **Privately Held**
WEB: www.saint-gobain.fr
SIC: 3221 Glass containers
PA: Compagnie De Saint-Gobain
La Defense 3 Tour Les Miroirs
Courbevoie 92400
147 623-000

(P-10626)
SAINT-GOBAIN PRFMCE PLAS CORP
7301 Orangewood Ave, Garden Grove (92841-1411)
PHONE.................................714 688-2612
EMP: 300
SALES (corp-wide): 213.5MM **Privately Held**
SIC: 3221 Glass containers
HQ: Saint-Gobain Performance Plastics Corporation
31500 Solon Rd
Solon OH 44139
440 836-6900

(P-10627)
SAXCO INTERNATIONAL LLC (PA)
1855 Gateway Blvd Ste 400, Concord (94520-3289)
PHONE.................................844 766-7819
Matthew Malenfant, *CEO*
Herbert L Sachs, *President*
Glenn Hartenbaum, *CFO*
Robin Willis, *Cust Mgr*
Keith Sachs, *Director*
◆ EMP: 12
SQ FT: 5,000
SALES (est): 50.3MM **Privately Held**
WEB: www.saxcointl.com
SIC: 3221 Bottles for packing, bottling & canning: glass

(P-10628)
WORLD WINE BOTTLES LLC
Also Called: World Wine Bottles & Packaging
1370 Trancas St Ste 411, NAPA (94558-2912)
PHONE.................................707 339-2102
Niel Sodell, *President*
Martin Foigelman,
▲ EMP: 50 EST: 2010
SQ FT: 50,000
SALES: 50MM **Privately Held**
SIC: 3221 5182 Bottles for packing, bottling & canning: glass; wine

---

3229 Pressed & Blown Glassware, NEC

(P-10629)
ADVANCED FIBERGLASS INC
Also Called: D G Motorsports
3225 Production Ave Ste A, Oceanside (92058-1338)
P.O. Box 568, Burlington WA (98233-0568)
PHONE.................................760 433-8731
David Green, *President*
Karen Green, *Vice Pres*
EMP: 10
SALES (est): 1.2MM **Privately Held**
WEB: www.dgmotorsports.com
SIC: 3229 2221 Glass fiber products; fiberglass fabrics

(P-10630)
ALAMILLO RADOLFO
Also Called: Pacific Light Blown Glass
4901 Patata St Ste 404, Cudahy (90201-5945)
PHONE.................................323 773-9614
Radolfo Alamillo, *Owner*
EMP: 12
SQ FT: 4,800
SALES: 1.1MM **Privately Held**
WEB: www.pacificlite.com
SIC: 3229 5023 Glassware, art or decorative; lamps: floor, boudoir, desk

(P-10631)
ALLIANCE FIBER OPTIC PDTS INC (HQ)
275 Gibraltar Dr, Sunnyvale (94089-1312)
PHONE.................................408 736-6900
Peter C Chang, *Ch of Bd*
Anita K Ho, *CFO*
David A Hubbard, *Exec VP*
▲ EMP: 68
SQ FT: 18,088
SALES: 81.1MM
SALES (corp-wide): 10.1B **Publicly Held**
WEB: www.afop.com
SIC: 3229 3661 Fiber optics strands; fiber optics communications equipment
PA: Corning Incorporated
1 Riverfront Plz
Corning NY 14831
607 974-9000

(P-10632)
AMERICAN QUALEX INC
920 Calle Negocio Ste A, San Clemente (92673-6207)
PHONE.................................949 492-8298
Dan Moothart, *President*
Charles Moothart, *Corp Secy*
Tun Khin, *Safety Mgr*
EMP: 10
SQ FT: 6,000
SALES (est): 1.1MM **Privately Held**
SIC: 3229 Scientific glassware

(P-10633)
ANNIEGLASS INC (PA)
310 Harvest Dr, Watsonville (95076-5103)
PHONE.................................831 761-2041
Annie Morhauser, *President*
EMP: 25
SQ FT: 16,000
SALES (est): 3.4MM **Privately Held**
WEB: www.annieglass.com
SIC: 3229 Tableware, glass or glass ceramic

(P-10634)
ANRITSU INSTRUMENTS COMPANY
490 Jarvis Dr, Morgan Hill (95037-2834)
PHONE.................................315 797-4449
Takanori Sumi, *President*
Frank Tiernan, *Vice Pres*
Robert Hendersen, *Admin Sec*
EMP: 50
SQ FT: 60,000
SALES (est): 4.7MM
SALES (corp-wide): 806.8MM **Privately Held**
WEB: www.nettest.com
SIC: 3229 Fiber optics strands

HQ: Anritsu U.S. Holding, Inc.
490 Jarvis Dr
Morgan Hill CA 95037
408 778-2000

(P-10635)
BAYSPEC INC
1101 Mckay Dr, San Jose (95131-1706)
PHONE.................................408 512-5928
William Yang, *President*
Eric Bergles, *Vice Pres*
EMP: 35
SQ FT: 48,000
SALES (est): 6.3MM **Privately Held**
WEB: www.bayspec.com
SIC: 3229 Fiber optics strands

(P-10636)
CALIFORNIA GLASS BENDING CORP
Also Called: CGB
2100 W 139th St, Gardena (90249-2412)
PHONE.................................310 549-5255
Robert N Green, *CEO*
Kelly Green, *Owner*
Oscar Ramirez, *Plant Mgr*
EMP: 30
SQ FT: 30,000
SALES (est): 3.9MM **Privately Held**
WEB: www.calglassbending.com
SIC: 3229 Pressed & blown glass

(P-10637)
CARLEY INC (PA)
1502 W 228th St, Torrance (90501-5105)
PHONE.................................310 325-8474
James A Carley, *President*
Margaret Tsang, *CFO*
Suzy Bush, *Manager*
▲ EMP: 300
SQ FT: 14,000
SALES (est): 30MM **Privately Held**
WEB: www.carleylamps.com
SIC: 3229 3646 3641 Lamp parts & shades, glass; commercial indusl & institutional electric lighting fixtures; electric lamps

(P-10638)
CDEQ
9421 Telfair Ave, Sun Valley (91352-1332)
PHONE.................................818 767-5143
Chaim Dekel, *President*
EMP: 30 EST: 1995
SQ FT: 10,000
SALES: 2.8MM **Privately Held**
SIC: 3229 Glassware, art or decorative

(P-10639)
CONNECTIVE SOLUTIONS LLC
14252 Culver Dr Ste A343, Irvine (92604-0317)
PHONE.................................800 241-2792
John Haney, *Mng Member*
Jeff Haney,
EMP: 10
SQ FT: 500
SALES: 100K **Privately Held**
WEB: www.connectivesol.com
SIC: 3229 Fiber optics strands

(P-10640)
DESAIS DESIGN CRAFT
408 S Gladys Ave, San Gabriel (91776-1923)
PHONE.................................626 285-3189
Navnit Desai, *President*
Dharmishta Desai, *Admin Sec*
EMP: 10
SQ FT: 9,500
SALES (est): 951.9K **Privately Held**
SIC: 3229 Lamp parts & shades, glass

(P-10641)
DONOCO INDUSTRIES INC
Also Called: Encore Plastics
5642 Research Dr Ste B, Huntington Beach (92649-1634)
P.O. Box 3208 (92605-3208)
PHONE.................................714 893-7889
Richard Harvey, *CEO*
Donald Okada, *CFO*
George West, *Treasurer*
EMP: 25
SQ FT: 12,000

SALES (est): 3MM Privately Held
WEB: www.encoreplastics.com
SIC: 3229 Tableware, glass or glass ceramic

(P-10642)
FARLOWS SCNTFIC GLSSBLWING INC
Also Called: Farlows Scentific Glassblowing
962 Golden Gate Ter Ste B, Grass Valley
(95945-5972)
PHONE..................................530 477-5513
Gary Farlow, *President*
Charolette Farlow, *Vice Pres*
Carol Conley, *Sales Mgr*
Jennifer Salzano, *Manager*
EMP: 25
SQ FT: 5,250
SALES (est): 2.3MM Privately Held
WEB: www.farlowsci.com
SIC: 3229 Scientific glassware

(P-10643)
GLAS WERK INC
29710 Ave De Las Bndra, Rcho STA Marg
(92688-2614)
PHONE..................................949 766-1296
Maik Bollhorn, *President*
▲ EMP: 26
SQ FT: 6,000
SALES: 2MM Privately Held
WEB: www.glaswerk.com
SIC: 3229 Scientific glassware

(P-10644)
GW PARTNERS INTERNATIONAL
Also Called: Gw Crystal
8351 Elm Ave Ste 106, Rancho Cucamonga (91730-7639)
P.O. Box 1995 (91729-1995)
PHONE..................................909 980-1010
Scott Erickson, *President*
▲ EMP: 11
SQ FT: 4,200
SALES (est): 1.8MM Privately Held
SIC: 3229 Novelty glassware

(P-10645)
H I S C INC
1009 Calle Recodo, San Clemente
(92673-6237)
P.O. Box 457 (92674-0457)
PHONE..................................949 492-8968
Robert Depalma, *President*
Joe Reese, *Partner*
Roxanne Depalma, *Shareholder*
◆ EMP: 10
SQ FT: 6,000
SALES (est): 1.2MM Privately Held
WEB: www.floralarranger.com
SIC: 3229 2381 3432 5193 Vases, glass; gloves, work: woven or knit, made from purchased materials; lawn hose nozzles & sprinklers; planters & flower pots; garden tools, hand

(P-10646)
HAUSENWARE KOYO LLC
2111 Laughlin Rd, Windsor (95492-8212)
PHONE..................................412 897-3064
Ulrich Honighausen,
Kelley Clayton,
▲ EMP: 10 EST: 2012
SQ FT: 18,000
SALES (est): 637.1K Privately Held
SIC: 3229 Tableware, glass or glass ceramic

(P-10647)
IFIBER OPTIX INC
14450 Chambers Rd, Tustin (92780-6914)
PHONE..................................714 665-9796
Sanjeev Jaiswal, *President*
▲ EMP: 25
SQ FT: 5,731
SALES (est): 4.5MM Privately Held
WEB: www.ifiberoptix.com
SIC: 3229 Fiber optics strands

(P-10648)
IMPERIAL ENTERPRISES INC
9666 Owensmouth Ave Ste A, Chatsworth
(91311-8044)
PHONE..................................818 886-5028
Galina Zingerman, *CEO*
Boris Zingerman, *Vice Pres*

Steven Zingerman, *Exec Dir*
▲ EMP: 40
SQ FT: 13,000
SALES (est): 3.7MM Privately Held
SIC: 3229 5023 Glassware, art or decorative; home furnishings

(P-10649)
INTEX FORMS INC
1333 Old County Rd, Belmont
(94002-3922)
PHONE..................................650 654-7855
Tom Olson, *Ch of Bd*
EMP: 32
SALES (est): 3.2MM Privately Held
SIC: 3229 Glass fiber products

(P-10650)
KIMDURLA INC
Also Called: Edwards Industries
9983 Glenoaks Blvd, Sun Valley
(91352-1023)
PHONE..................................818 504-4041
Milton Friedman, *President*
Norma Friedman, *Vice Pres*
EMP: 28
SALES: 3MM Privately Held
SIC: 3229 2299 Glassware, art or decorative; yarn, metallic, ceramic or paper fibers

(P-10651)
LARSON ELECTRONIC GLASS INC
2840 Bay Rd, Redwood City (94063-3503)
P.O. Box 371 (94064-0371)
PHONE..................................650 369-6734
Charles Kraft, *President*
Jill Kraft, *CFO*
▼ EMP: 10 EST: 1954
SQ FT: 10,000
SALES (est): 1.3MM Privately Held
SIC: 3229 Glassware, industrial

(P-10652)
LEGACY US LLC
Also Called: Legacy Glass Studios
1800 El Camino Real Ste D, Menlo Park
(94027-4103)
PHONE..................................650 714-9750
Kim Reeves,
Jeff Dalton,
EMP: 10
SQ FT: 3,500
SALES (est): 852.1K Privately Held
SIC: 3229 Glassware, industrial

(P-10653)
LEWIS JOHN GLASS STUDIO
10229 Pearmain St, Oakland (94603-3023)
PHONE..................................510 635-4607
John C Lewis, *Owner*
Lynn Zboyovsky, *Executive Asst*
EMP: 12
SQ FT: 17,000
SALES (est): 1.4MM Privately Held
WEB: www.johnlewisglass.com
SIC: 3229 5947 Pressed & blown glass; gift, novelty & souvenir shop

(P-10654)
LIFI LABS INC (PA)
Also Called: Lifx
350 Townsend St Ste 830, San Francisco
(94107-0009)
PHONE..................................650 739-5563
Jake Lawton, *Principal*
Tim Peters, *COO*
John Cameron, *Vice Pres*
EMP: 13
SALES (est): 13.5MM Privately Held
SIC: 3229 Bulbs for electric lights

(P-10655)
LIGHTSTREAMS INC
1111 Comstock St, Santa Clara
(95054-3407)
PHONE..................................408 492-1689
David Knox, *President*
▼ EMP: 10
SALES (est): 1.3MM Privately Held
SIC: 3229 Glass fibers, textile

(P-10656)
MEMORY GLASS LLC
325 Rutherford St Ste E, Goleta
(93117-3728)
PHONE..................................805 682-6469
Nicholas Savage,
Kim Price, *VP Sales*
Lena Savage,
Michael Savage,
▲ EMP: 10
SALES (est): 1MM Privately Held
SIC: 3229 Art, decorative & novelty glassware

(P-10657)
MODERN CERAMICS MFG INC
2240 Lundy Ave, San Jose (95131-1816)
PHONE..................................408 383-0554
Christina Hoang, *CEO*
Tuan Le, *Purch Agent*
Frank Kramer, *Opers Mgr*
Tim Nishimura, *QC Mgr*
Charisse Gilmore, *Clerk*
▲ EMP: 20 EST: 1999
SQ FT: 3,087
SALES (est): 6.7MM Privately Held
WEB: www.modernceramics.com
SIC: 3229 Tableware, glass or glass ceramic

(P-10658)
MODETEK INC
Also Called: Mode Tek
1720 San Pasqual St, Pasadena
(91106-3550)
PHONE..................................760 431-4190
Siamak Forouhar, *President*
EMP: 25 EST: 2000
SQ FT: 24,000
SALES (est): 1.1MM Privately Held
WEB: www.modetek.com
SIC: 3229 Fiber optics strands

(P-10659)
NEPTEC OPTICAL SOLUTIONS INC
48603 Warm Springs Blvd, Fremont
(94539-7782)
PHONE..................................510 687-1101
David Cheng, *President*
Eugene Lin, *Vice Pres*
Jianxun Fang, *CTO*
Sylvia Bustamante, *Purch Mgr*
Sharon Lu, *Purch Mgr*
▲ EMP: 25
SALES: 950K Privately Held
SIC: 3229 Pressed & blown glass

(P-10660)
NEXFON CORPORATION
7172 Regional St, Dublin (94568-2324)
PHONE..................................925 200-2233
Yi Qin, *President*
Dr Charles Qian, *Project Mgr*
▲ EMP: 12
SALES (est): 658.7K Privately Held
WEB: www.nexfon.com
SIC: 3229 Fiber optics strands

(P-10661)
OPTIWORKS INC (PA)
47211 Bayside Pkwy, Fremont
(94538-6517)
PHONE..................................510 438-4560
Roger Liang, *CEO*
Annie Kuo, *Vice Pres*
Steve Kuo, *Vice Pres*
Maggie Huang, *Human Resources*
Yanyan MA, *Senior Mgr*
EMP: 65
SALES (est): 16.9MM Privately Held
WEB: www.optiworks.com
SIC: 3229 Fiber optics strands

(P-10662)
ORBITS LIGHTWAVE INC
41 S Chester Ave, Pasadena (91106-3104)
PHONE..................................626 795-0667
Yaakov Shevy, *CEO*
EMP: 17 EST: 1999
SQ FT: 9,700
SALES (est): 1.9MM Privately Held
WEB: www.orbitslightwave.com
SIC: 3229

(P-10663)
ORIENT & FLUME ART GLASS CO
2161 Park Ave, Chico (95928-6702)
P.O. Box 3298 (95927-3298)
PHONE..................................530 893-0373
Douglas Boyd, *President*
John A Powell, *CFO*
EMP: 30
SQ FT: 20,000
SALES (est): 2.9MM Privately Held
WEB: www.orientandflume.com
SIC: 3229 8412 Glassware, art or decorative; museums & art galleries

(P-10664)
PERFORMANCE COMPOSITES INC
1418 S Alameda St, Compton
(90221-4802)
PHONE..................................310 328-6661
Francis Hu, *President*
Peter McNicol, *General Mgr*
Eddie Mejia, *Admin Asst*
Susan Tashiro, *Controller*
Elizabeth Bolanos, *Hum Res Coord*
EMP: 75
SQ FT: 46,000
SALES: 8.5MM Privately Held
WEB: www.performancecomposites.com
SIC: 3229 3624 3544 Glass fiber products; carbon & graphite products; special dies, tools, jigs & fixtures

(P-10665)
PRECISION GLASS BEVELLING INC
Also Called: Rbs Glass Designs
15201 Keswick St Ste A, Van Nuys
(91405-1014)
PHONE..................................818 989-2727
Richard Sloan, *President*
Mike Latzer, *Vice Pres*
▲ EMP: 20
SQ FT: 7,000
SALES (est): 2.1MM Privately Held
SIC: 3229 5231 Pressed & blown glass; glass, leaded or stained

(P-10666)
RANDOM TECHNOLOGIES LLC
2325 3rd St Ste 404, San Francisco
(94107-4304)
PHONE..................................415 255-1267
Amos Gottlieb, *Mng Member*
EMP: 10
SQ FT: 3,600
SALES (est): 1.4MM Privately Held
WEB: www.randomtechnologies.com
SIC: 3229 2821 Fiber optics strands; polytetrafluoroethylene resins (teflon)

(P-10667)
SHAMIR INSIGHT INC
9938 Via Pasar, San Diego (92126-4559)
PHONE..................................858 514-8330
Raanan Naftalovich, *CEO*
Joyce Hornaday, *VP Human Res*
Richard Dailey, *VP Sales*
▲ EMP: 77 EST: 1997
SALES (est): 14.5MM Privately Held
WEB: www.shamirlens.com
SIC: 3229 Optical glass
HQ: Shamir Optical Industry Ltd
Kibbutz
Shamir
469 018-86

(P-10668)
SPOTLITE AMERICA CORPORATION (PA)
9937 Jefferson Blvd # 110, Culver City
(90232-3505)
PHONE..................................310 829-0200
Halston Mikail, *CEO*
▲ EMP: 20 EST: 2014
SQ FT: 17,000
SALES (est): 27.5MM Privately Held
SIC: 3229 3699 Bulbs for electric lights; electrical equipment & supplies

P
R
O
D
U
C
T
S

&

S
V
C
S

(P-10669)
VITRICO CORP
Also Called: Firelight Glass
2181 Williams St, San Leandro
(94577-3224)
PHONE..................................510 652-6731
Karen Boss, *CEO*
James Maslach, *President*
EMP: 12
SQ FT: 20,000
SALES (est): 1.7MM **Privately Held**
SIC: 3229 Glassware, art or decorative;
glassware, industrial

(P-10670)
**WEST COAST QUARTZ
CORPORATION (HQ)**
Also Called: W C Q
1000 Corporate Way, Fremont
(94539-6105)
PHONE..................................510 249-2160
Johng S Bae, *CEO*
Dave Lopes, *President*
Howard Cho, *COO*
Tim Mattson, *Info Tech Mgr*
Jake Lee, *Finance Mgr*
▲ **EMP:** 97 **EST:** 1981
SQ FT: 60,000
SALES (est): 23.6MM
SALES (corp-wide): 59.5MM **Privately
Held**
WEB: www.wcq.com
SIC: 3229 3679 3674 5065 Glassware,
industrial; quartz crystals, for electronic
application; semiconductors & related de-
vices; semiconductor devices
PA: Worldex Co., Ltd.
Rm 22-1b 2l Gupo-Dong
Gumi 39422
254 456-9980

(P-10671)
WOLFRAM INC
1309 Doker Dr Ste B, Modesto
(95351-1603)
PHONE..................................209 238-9610
Steven Alexander, *President*
▲ **EMP:** 10
SQ FT: 5,000
SALES (est): 1MM **Privately Held**
WEB: www.wolfram.com
SIC: 3229 Lamp parts & shades, glass

(P-10672)
ZEONS INC
291 S Cienega Blvd 102, Beverly Hills
(90211)
PHONE..................................323 302-8299
Naved Jafry, *President*
EMP: 312
SQ FT: 3,500
SALES: 13MM **Privately Held**
SIC: 3229 1629 6211 Insulators, electri-
cal: glass; power plant construction; in-
vestment certificate sales; oil & gas lease
brokers

(P-10673)
ZX VECOR
2833 Leonis Blvd Ste 111, Vernon
(90058-3030)
PHONE..................................323 587-7100
Moses Ahtoot, *Owner*
EMP: 13
SALES (est): 506.1K **Privately Held**
SIC: 3229 Vases, glass

**3231 Glass Prdts Made Of
Purchased Glass**

(P-10674)
ALAN LEM & CO INC
Also Called: Advance Aqua Tanks
515 W 130th St, Los Angeles (90061-1180)
PHONE..................................310 538-4282
Alan Y Lem, *President*
EMP: 21
SQ FT: 11,000
SALES (est): 2.9MM **Privately Held**
WEB: www.advanceaquatanks.com
SIC: 3231 Aquariums & reflectors, glass

(P-10675)
ANTHONY DOORS INC
Also Called: Anthony International
12812 Arroyo St, Sylmar (91342-5301)
PHONE..................................818 365-9451
Jeff Clark, *Branch Mgr*
EMP: 425
SALES (corp-wide): 7.8B **Publicly Held**
WEB: www.kramerusa.net
SIC: 3231 5078 3585 Doors, glass: made
from purchased glass; tempered glass:
made from purchased glass; glass sheet,
bent: made from purchased glass; display
cases, refrigerated; evaporative con-
densers, heat transfer equipment
HQ: Anthony Doors, Inc.
12391 Montero Ave
Sylmar CA 91342
818 365-9451

(P-10676)
**ATLAS SPECIALTIES
CORPORATION (PA)**
Also Called: Atlas Shower Door Co
4337 Astoria St, Sacramento (95838-3001)
PHONE..................................503 636-8182
Edwin A Lindquist, *President*
Fred Ferri, *CFO*
Roger Lindquist, *Vice Pres*
EMP: 28 **EST:** 1955
SQ FT: 5,000
SALES (est): 3MM **Privately Held**
SIC: 3231 5039 Doors, glass: made from
purchased glass; glass construction ma-
terials

(P-10677)
**AVALON GLASS & MIRROR
COMPANY**
642 Alondra Blvd, Carson (90746-1049)
PHONE..................................323 321-8806
Salvador G Gomez, *President*
Randy Seeinberg, *President*
Ed Rosengrant, *Vice Pres*
Ruben Huerta, *Admin Sec*
▲ **EMP:** 100
SQ FT: 100,000
SALES (est): 15.3MM **Privately Held**
WEB: www.avalonmirrorglass.com
SIC: 3231 5023 5231 3211 Mirrored
glass; furniture tops, glass: cut, beveled
or polished; glassware; mirrors & pictures,
framed & unframed; glass; flat glass
PA: Gwla Acquisition Corp.
8600 Rheem Ave
South Gate CA 90280
-

(P-10678)
**BANANAFISH PRODUCTIONS
INC**
1536 W Embassy St, Anaheim
(92802-1016)
PHONE..................................714 956-2129
Dan Iman, *President*
Jerry Smith, *Principal*
EMP: 11
SQ FT: 4,500
SALES: 300K **Privately Held**
WEB: www.bananafishproductions.com
SIC: 3231 Ornamental glass: cut, en-
graved or otherwise decorated

(P-10679)
**BERGIN GLASS IMPRESSIONS
INC**
938 Kaiser Rd, NAPA (94558-6206)
PHONE..................................707 224-0111
Michael Bergin, *Owner*
EMP: 20
SALES (corp-wide): 3.5MM **Privately
Held**
WEB: www.berginglass.com
SIC: 3231 Ornamental glass: cut, en-
graved or otherwise decorated
PA: Bergin Glass Impressions, Inc.
2511 Napa Vly Ste
Napa CA 94558
707 224-0111

(P-10680)
BEVELED EDGE INC
Also Called: Original Glass Design
1740 Junction Ave Ste D, San Jose
(95112-1035)
PHONE..................................408 467-9900
Mark Idzal, *President*
▲ **EMP:** 16
SQ FT: 8,500
SALES (est): 1.7MM **Privately Held**
WEB: www.thebeveledge.com
SIC: 3231 Products of purchased glass

(P-10681)
**BLOMBERG WINDOWS
SYSTEMS**
Also Called: Blomberg Glass
1453 Blair Ave, Sacramento (95822-3410)
P.O. Box 22485 (95822-0485)
PHONE..................................916 428-8060
J Philip Collier, *Ch of Bd*
Ralph S Blomberg, *Vice Pres*
EMP: 135
SALES (est): 6.7MM **Privately Held**
SIC: 3231 Doors, glass: made from pur-
chased glass

(P-10682)
**CAMBRIDGE LASER
LABORATORIES**
853 Brown Rd, Fremont (94539-7090)
PHONE..................................510 651-0110
Brian L Bohan, *President*
Kimberley Darrah, *Admin Sec*
EMP: 10
SQ FT: 8,000
SALES (est): 1.3MM **Privately Held**
WEB: www.cambridgelasers.com
SIC: 3231 Medical & laboratory glassware:
made from purchased glass; scientific &
technical glassware: from purchased
glass

(P-10683)
**CARDINAL GLASS INDUSTRIES
INC**
Also Called: Cardinal Cg Company
1125 E Lanzit Ave, Los Angeles
(90059-1559)
PHONE..................................323 319-0070
EMP: 36
SALES (corp-wide): 1B **Privately Held**
SIC: 3231 Products of purchased glass
PA: Cardinal Glass Industries Inc
775 Pririe Ctr Dr Ste 200
Eden Prairie MN 55344
952 229-2600

(P-10684)
CARLOS SHOWER DOORS INC
300 Kentucky St, Bakersfield (93305-4230)
P.O. Box 6009 (93386-6009)
PHONE..................................661 327-5594
Phillip Calvillo, *President*
Loni Amado, *President*
Edward Amado, *Vice Pres*
Steven Amado, *Vice Pres*
Phillip C Calvillo, *Admin Sec*
EMP: 11
SQ FT: 10,000
SALES (est): 907.5K **Privately Held**
WEB: www.carlosshowerdoors.com
SIC: 3231 Doors, glass: made from pur-
chased glass; insulating glass: made from
purchased glass

(P-10685)
**CENTURY SHOWER DOOR CO
INC (PA)**
20100 Normandie Ave, Torrance
(90502-1211)
PHONE..................................310 327-8060
Toll Free:..................................866 -
Burton Slutske, *CEO*
I Siegel, *Treasurer*
Lois Sherman, *Vice Pres*
Lois Smolin, *Admin Sec*
▲ **EMP:** 49 **EST:** 1946
SQ FT: 30,000
SALES (est): 19.1MM **Privately Held**
WEB: www.centuryshower.com
SIC: 3231 Products of purchased glass

(P-10686)
CORAL REEF AQUARIUM
515 W 130th St, Los Angeles (90061-1180)
PHONE..................................310 538-4282
Alan Y Lem, *Owner*
EMP: 21
SALES (est): 1MM **Privately Held**
SIC: 3231 Ornamental glass: cut, en-
graved or otherwise decorated

(P-10687)
CUSTOM INDUSTRIES INC
1371 N Miller St, Anaheim (92806-1412)
PHONE..................................714 779-9101
Thomas McAfee, *President*
▲ **EMP:** 21
SALES (est): 3.8MM **Privately Held**
SIC: 3231 Doors, glass: made from pur-
chased glass

(P-10688)
**CV WNDOWS DORS RIVERSIDE
INC**
Also Called: Cv of Riverside
6676 Lance Dr, Riverside (92507-0769)
P.O. Box 802813, Santa Clarita (91380-
2813)
PHONE..................................951 784-8766
Kevin Grossman, *CEO*
EMP: 25
SALES (est): 4.5MM **Privately Held**
SIC: 3231 3211 3442 2431 Doors, glass:
made from purchased glass; window
glass, clear & colored; window & door
frames; windows & window parts & trim,
wood

(P-10689)
D G U TRADING CORPORATION
Also Called: Door & Glass Unique
1999 W Holt Ave, Pomona (91768-3352)
PHONE..................................909 469-1288
Linda Chuang, *President*
▲ **EMP:** 40
SQ FT: 5,000
SALES (est): 3.9MM **Privately Held**
WEB: www.adgu.com
SIC: 3231 5031 5211 Stained glass:
made from purchased glass; doors;
doors, wood or metal, except storm

(P-10690)
DA-LY GLASS CORP
Also Called: Western Glass Co
1193 W 2nd St, Pomona (91766-1308)
PHONE..................................323 589-5461
William J Dake, *President*
EMP: 30
SQ FT: 25,000
SALES (est): 3MM **Privately Held**
WEB: www.westernglassco.com
SIC: 3231 3281 3211 1411 Laminated
glass: made from purchased glass; deco-
rated glassware: chipped, engraved,
etched, etc.; cut stone & stone products;
flat glass; dimension stone

(P-10691)
**DECOR SHOWER DOOR AND
GLASS CO**
Also Called: Decor Shower Enclosures
1819 Tanen St Ste A, NAPA (94559-1392)
PHONE..................................707 253-0622
Brad Taylor, *President*
EMP: 10
SQ FT: 2,500
SALES: 600K **Privately Held**
SIC: 3231 Doors, glass: made from pur-
chased glass

(P-10692)
DIANE MARKIN INC
112 Penn St, El Segundo (90245-3907)
PHONE..................................310 322-0200
Diane Markin, *President*
▲ **EMP:** 12
SQ FT: 9,000
SALES: 1MM **Privately Held**
WEB: www.dianemarkin.com
SIC: 3231 3861 Art glass: made from pur-
chased glass; printing frames, photo-
graphic

▲ = Import ▼=Export
◆ =Import/Export

(P-10693)
DUO PANE INDUSTRIES
2444 Trevino Way, Fairfield (94534-7524)
PHONE.................................707 426-9696
Dave Crompton, *Owner*
EMP: 15
SQ FT: 15,000
SALES (est): 987.3K **Privately Held**
SIC: 3231 Insulating glass: made from purchased glass

(P-10694)
E & R GLASS CONTRACTORS INC
5369 Brooks St, Montclair (91763-4539)
PHONE.................................909 624-1763
Eric Dryden, *President*
Russ Dryden, *Vice Pres*
EMP: 22
SQ FT: 800
SALES (est): 3.2MM **Privately Held**
WEB: www.eandrglass.com
SIC: 3231 Products of purchased glass

(P-10695)
EMPIRE SHOWER DOORS INC
1217 N Mcdowell Blvd, Petaluma (94954-1112)
PHONE.................................707 773-2898
Roy German, *President*
Marylou German, *Admin Sec*
EMP: 15
SQ FT: 5,000
SALES (est): 2MM **Privately Held**
WEB: www.empireshowerdoors.com
SIC: 3231 5031 1793 Doors, glass: made from purchased glass; doors; glass & glazing work

(P-10696)
FABRICATED GLASS SPC INC
2350 S Watney Way Ste E, Fairfield (94533-6738)
PHONE.................................707 429-6160
Harvey Holtz, *President*
EMP: 17
SALES (corp-wide): 33.9MM **Privately Held**
WEB: www.fabglass.com
SIC: 3231 Mirrored glass
PA: Fabricated Glass Specialties, Inc.
101 E Rapp Rd
Talent OR 97540
541 535-1582

(P-10697)
FIRE AND LIGHT ORIGINALS LP
100 Ericson Ct Ste 100 # 100, Arcata (95521-8932)
PHONE.................................707 825-7500
John McClurg, *Partner*
Gaea Resources, *Partner*
Michelle Pontoni, *Information Mgr*
EMP: 18
SALES (est): 2.2MM **Privately Held**
WEB: www.fireandlight.com
SIC: 3231 Products of purchased glass

(P-10698)
FLYLEAF WINDOWS INC
11040 Bollinger Canyon Rd, San Ramon (94582-4969)
PHONE.................................925 344-1181
Billy Alcantara, *President*
EMP: 40
SALES: 500K **Privately Held**
SIC: 3231 3211 Doors, glass: made from purchased glass; window glass, clear & colored

(P-10699)
GAFFOGLIO FMLY MTLCRAFTERS INC (PA)
Also Called: Camera Ready Cars
11161 Slater Ave, Fountain Valley (92708-4921)
PHONE.................................714 444-2000
George Gaffoglio, *CEO*
Ruben Gaffoglio, *President*
Mike Alexander, *COO*
Catherine Merola, *Business Mgr*
EMP: 109
SQ FT: 94,000

SALES (est): 22.3MM **Privately Held**
WEB: www.metalcrafters.com
SIC: 3231 3711 3365 Mirrors, truck & automobile: made from purchased glass; automobile assembly, including specialty automobiles; aerospace castings, aluminum

(P-10700)
GLASSPLAX
26605 Madison Ave, Murrieta (92562-8909)
PHONE.................................951 677-4800
Steve Tortomasi, *President*
▲ EMP: 20
SALES (est): 2.2MM **Privately Held**
WEB: www.glassplax.com
SIC: 3231 5094 Ornamental glass: cut, engraved or otherwise decorated; trophies

(P-10701)
GLASSWERKS LA INC (HQ)
Also Called: Glasswerks Group
8600 Rheem Ave, South Gate (90280-3333)
PHONE.................................323 789-7800
Randy Steinberg, *President*
Edwin Rosengrant, *Vice Pres*
Ruben Huerta, *Admin Sec*
▲ EMP: 280 EST: 1949
SQ FT: 100,000
SALES (est): 59.1MM **Privately Held**
SIC: 3231 3211 Mirrored glass; tempered glass: made from purchased glass; furniture tops, glass: cut, beveled or polished; flat glass

(P-10702)
GOLDEN WEST GLASS
18153 Highway 12, Sonoma (95476-3639)
PHONE.................................707 939-9604
Robert Olson, *President*
EMP: 10
SALES (est): 1.2MM **Privately Held**
WEB: www.goldenwestglass.com
SIC: 3231 Products of purchased glass

(P-10703)
GP MERGER SUB INC
Also Called: Glaspro
9401 Ann St, Santa Fe Springs (90670-2613)
PHONE.................................562 946-7722
Joseph Green, *President*
John Griffin, *General Mgr*
Jason Hillman, *Info Tech Dir*
Rafaella Carreno, *Controller*
McNeill Bishop, *Mktg Dir*
▲ EMP: 85
SQ FT: 75,000
SALES (est): 17.8MM **Privately Held**
WEB: www.gftc.net
SIC: 3231 Laminated glass: made from purchased glass

(P-10704)
INDUSTRIAL GLASS PRODUCTS INC
4229 Union Pacific Ave, Los Angeles (90023-4016)
PHONE.................................323 526-7125
Esther Ramirez, *President*
▲ EMP: 15
SQ FT: 10,000
SALES: 900K **Privately Held**
WEB: www.industrialglassproducts.com
SIC: 3231 5039 Products of purchased glass; glass construction materials

(P-10705)
INNOVATIVE STRUCTURAL GL INC
Also Called: I S G
40220 Pierce Dr, Three Rivers (93271-9332)
P.O. Box 775 (93271-0775)
PHONE.................................559 561-7000
Manuel Marinos, *CEO*
Cynthia Marinos, *CFO*
Julie Gray, *Accounting Mgr*
Lisa Taviano, *Purchasing*
Peter Kulwitzky, *Opers Staff*
▲ EMP: 20
SQ FT: 100,000

SALES (est): 2.6MM **Privately Held**
WEB: www.structuralglass.com
SIC: 3231 Products of purchased glass

(P-10706)
INVENIOS LLC
320 N Nopal St, Santa Barbara (93103-3225)
PHONE.................................805 962-3333
Paul Then, *President*
EMP: 83
SALES (est): 2MM **Privately Held**
SIC: 3231 Products of purchased glass

(P-10707)
J & B MANUFACTURING CORP
Also Called: San Diego Mirror and Window
2780 La Mirada Dr Ste C, Vista (92081-8404)
PHONE.................................760 846-6316
Toll Free:.................................877 -
Daniel Jaoudi, *President*
EMP: 160
SQ FT: 40,000
SALES (est): 16.6MM **Privately Held**
WEB: www.sdmw.com
SIC: 3231 5231 5211 Doors, glass: made from purchased glass; glass; door & window products

(P-10708)
JANEL GLASS COMPANY INC
2960 Marsh St, Los Angeles (90039-2911)
P.O. Box 39849 (90039-0849)
PHONE.................................323 661-8621
Fax: 323 661-8738
EMP: 50
SQ FT: 27,000
SALES (est): 5.4MM **Privately Held**
SIC: 3231

(P-10709)
JS GLASS WHOLESALE
2035 E 37th St, Vernon (90058-1414)
PHONE.................................213 746-5577
Yong Yi, *Owner*
Ashley Hong, *Manager*
EMP: 12
SQ FT: 6,450
SALES (est): 749.2K **Privately Held**
SIC: 3231 Products of purchased glass

(P-10710)
JUDSON STUDIOS INC
200 S Avenue 66, Los Angeles (90042-3632)
PHONE.................................323 255-0131
David Judson, *President*
Joy Sola, *Administration*
Karen Judson, *Sales Staff*
EMP: 15 EST: 1897
SQ FT: 10,000
SALES (est): 1.5MM **Privately Held**
WEB: www.judsonstudios.com
SIC: 3231 Stained glass: made from purchased glass

(P-10711)
KINESTRAL TECHNOLOGIES INC (PA)
3955 Trust Way, Hayward (94545-3723)
PHONE.................................650 416-5200
Suk Bae Cha, *CEO*
Sam Bergh, *COO*
Geoffrey Richardson, *CFO*
Paul Nagel, *Senior VP*
Gregg Higashi, *Vice Pres*
▲ EMP: 105
SALES (est): 27.1MM **Privately Held**
SIC: 3231 Products of purchased glass

(P-10712)
LARRY MTHVIN INSTALLATIONS INC (HQ)
Also Called: L M I
501 Kettering Dr, Ontario (91761-8150)
PHONE.................................909 563-1700
Larry Methvin, *CEO*
Arnie Fielding, *CIO*
Richard Harvey, *Info Tech Mgr*
Leti Antuna, *Accountant*
Hal Perry, *Sales Staff*
▲ EMP: 200
SQ FT: 28,000

SALES (est): 58.7MM
SALES (corp-wide): 1.6B **Publicly Held**
SIC: 3231 3431 1751 Doors, glass: made from purchased glass; shower stalls, metal; carpentry work; window & door (prefabricated) installation
PA: Patrick Industries, Inc.
107 W Franklin St
Elkhart IN 46516
574 294-7511

(P-10713)
LARRY MTHVIN INSTALLATIONS INC
Also Called: LMI
128 N Cluff Ave, Lodi (95240-3104)
PHONE.................................209 368-2105
Christy Puerta, *Vice Pres*
EMP: 50
SALES (corp-wide): 1.6B **Publicly Held**
SIC: 3231 3088 Framed mirrors; shower stalls, fiberglass & plastic
HQ: Larry Methvin Installations, Inc.
501 Kettering Dr
Ontario CA 91761
909 563-1700

(P-10714)
LIPPERT COMPONENTS MFG INC
Hehr Glass Co
1021 Walnut Ave, Pomona (91766-6528)
PHONE.................................909 628-5557
Pete Adams, *Manager*
EMP: 50
SALES (corp-wide): 2.1B **Publicly Held**
WEB: www.hehrintl.com
SIC: 3231 5231 Doors, glass: made from purchased glass; glass
HQ: Lippert Components Manufacturing, Inc.
3501 County Road 6 E
Elkhart IN 46514
574 535-1125

(P-10715)
LUNDBERG STUDIOS INC
131 Old Coast Rd, Davenport (95017-4007)
PHONE.................................831 423-2532
Rebecca Lundberg, *President*
Donya Scharping, *Office Mgr*
EMP: 20 EST: 1970
SQ FT: 6,000
SALES: 2MM **Privately Held**
SIC: 3231 Art glass: made from purchased glass

(P-10716)
M AND W GLASS
10745 Vernon Ave, Ontario (91762-4040)
PHONE.................................909 517-3585
Florencio Sanchez, *Owner*
EMP: 22
SQ FT: 15,000
SALES (est): 1.8MM **Privately Held**
WEB: www.mandwglass.com
SIC: 3231 Cut & engraved glassware: made from purchased glass

(P-10717)
MAC THIN FILMS INC
2721 Giffen Ave, Santa Rosa (95407-5063)
PHONE.................................707 791-1650
Mark Madigan, *CEO*
Julie Leonhard, *CFO*
▲ EMP: 50
SALES: 3.5MM **Privately Held**
SIC: 3231 Products of purchased glass

(P-10718)
MADRONE HOSPICE INC
217 W Miner St, Yreka (96097-2919)
PHONE.................................530 842-2547
Judith Mc Quoid, *Branch Mgr*
EMP: 20 **Privately Held**
SIC: 3231 Novelties, glass: fruit, foliage, flowers, animals, etc.
PA: Madrone Hospice Inc
255 Collier Cir
Yreka CA 96097

(P-10719)
MANUFACTURERS/HYLAND LTD
650 Reed St, Santa Clara (95050-3010)
PHONE..................................408 748-1806
James P Hyland, *President*
Mary Jo Hyland, *Admin Sec*
EMP: 12
SQ FT: 3,000
SALES (est): 1MM **Privately Held**
WEB: www.jphc.com
SIC: 3231 3915 8322 4813 Art glass: made from purchased glass; jewelers' materials & lapidary work; individual & family services; telephone communication, except radio;

(P-10720)
MASTERPIECE LEADED WINDOWS
11651 Rverside Dr Ste 143, Lakeside (92040)
P.O. Box 710461, Santee (92072-0461)
PHONE..................................858 391-3344
Joel Debus, *President*
Joy J Debus, *Shareholder*
James Debus, *Senior VP*
Jim Debus, *Vice Pres*
Ellen Grant, *Accounts Mgr*
▲ EMP: 25
SQ FT: 2,000
SALES (est): 1.7MM **Privately Held**
WEB: www.mpglass.com
SIC: 3231 5023 Leaded glass; window furnishings

(P-10721)
MILGARD MANUFACTURING INC
Also Called: Milgard-Simi Valley
355 E Easy St, Simi Valley (93065-1801)
PHONE..................................805 581-6325
Wayne Ramay, *Branch Mgr*
Cal Mc Clure, *Maintenance Staff*
Calvin Mc Clure, *Maintence Staff*
EMP: 232
SALES (corp-wide): 7.6B **Publicly Held**
WEB: www.milgard.com
SIC: 3231 5031 3442 Products of purchased glass; metal doors, sash & trim; metal doors, sash & trim
HQ: Milgard Manufacturing Incorporated
1010 54th Ave E
Fife WA 98424
253 922-6030

(P-10722)
NEWPORT INDUSTRIAL GLASS INC
Also Called: Glass Fabrication and Dist
8610 Central Ave, Stanton (90680-2720)
P.O. Box 127 (90680-0127)
PHONE..................................714 484-7500
Ray Larsen, *Director*
Pilin Chung, *Shareholder*
EMP: 20
SALES (est): 2.7MM **Privately Held**
SIC: 3231 3827 3851 5039 Products of purchased glass; mirrors, optical; lens grinding, except prescription: ophthalmic; protective eyeware; exterior flat glass: plate or window

(P-10723)
OLDCASTLE BUILDINGENVELOPE INC
6850 Stevenson Blvd, Fremont (94538-2484)
PHONE..................................510 651-2292
Barry Adams, *Branch Mgr*
EMP: 63
SALES (corp-wide): 29.7B **Privately Held**
WEB: www.oldcastleglass.com
SIC: 3231 5231 Tempered glass: made from purchased glass; insulating glass: made from purchased glass; glass
HQ: Oldcastle Buildingenvelope, Inc.
5005 Lndn B Jnsn Fwy 10
Dallas TX 75244
214 273-3400

(P-10724)
OLDCASTLE BUILDINGENVELOPE INC
5631 Ferguson Dr, Commerce (90022-5132)
P.O. Box 22243, Los Angeles (90022-0243)
PHONE..................................323 722-2007
Luis Soto, *Principal*
Kristin Tharp, *President*
Lena Ingalls, *Human Res Dir*
EMP: 51
SQ FT: 200,000
SALES (corp-wide): 29.7B **Privately Held**
WEB: www.oldcastleglass.com
SIC: 3231 5231 Tempered glass: made from purchased glass; insulating glass: made from purchased glass; glass
HQ: Oldcastle Buildingenvelope, Inc.
5005 Lndn B Jnsn Fwy 10
Dallas TX 75244
214 273-3400

(P-10725)
PACIFIC ARTGLASS CORPORATION
Also Called: Pacific Glass
125 W 157th St, Gardena (90248-2225)
PHONE..................................310 516-7828
John Williams, *President*
▲ EMP: 23
SQ FT: 18,000
SALES (est): 3.1MM **Privately Held**
WEB: www.pacificartglass.com
SIC: 3231 Stained glass: made from purchased glass

(P-10726)
PAI GP INC
Also Called: Pai Enterprises
5914 Crenshaw Blvd, Los Angeles (90043-3030)
PHONE..................................323 549-5355
Robert Johnson, *President*
Michael Woodman, *CFO*
▲ EMP: 77
SQ FT: 4,000
SALES (est): 7.6MM **Privately Held**
WEB: www.paigp.com
SIC: 3231 Products of purchased glass

(P-10727)
PAUL CRIST STUDIOS INC
8317 Secura Way, Santa Fe Springs (90670-2213)
PHONE..................................562 696-9992
Paul Crist, *President*
EMP: 14
SALES (est): 1.2MM **Privately Held**
WEB: www.mosaicshades.com
SIC: 3231 Art glass: made from purchased glass; stained glass: made from purchased glass

(P-10728)
RAYOTEK SCIENTIFIC INC
Also Called: Rayotek Sight Windows
11499 Sorrento Valley Rd, San Diego (92121-1305)
PHONE..................................858 558-3671
William Raggio, *President*
Jessica Yadley, *CFO*
Denise Cunningham, *Executive Asst*
James Heimerl, *Engineer*
Matthew Raggio, *Production*
EMP: 51
SQ FT: 30,000
SALES (est): 6MM **Privately Held**
WEB: www.rayotek.com
SIC: 3231 8748 Products of purchased glass; business consulting

(P-10729)
RESEARCH & DEV GL PDTS & EQP
Also Called: Research & Dev GL Pdts &
1808 Harmon St, Berkeley (94703-2416)
PHONE..................................510 547-6464
Doug Dobson, *President*
EMP: 12
SQ FT: 10,000

SALES: 800K **Privately Held**
WEB: www.go.to
SIC: 3231 3229 Scientific & technical glassware: from purchased glass; ornamental glass: cut, engraved or otherwise decorated; pressed & blown glass

(P-10730)
SCI-TECH GLASSBLOWING INC
5555 Tech Cir, Moorpark (93021-1795)
PHONE..................................805 523-9790
Glenn Gaydick, *Shareholder*
Craig Gaydick, *Shareholder*
EMP: 12
SQ FT: 4,600
SALES (est): 1.1MM **Privately Held**
SIC: 3231 Scientific & technical glassware: from purchased glass

(P-10731)
SHOWERTEK INC
2775 Napa Valley Corp Dr, NAPA (94558)
PHONE..................................707 224-1480
Thomas Christianson, *CEO*
Alison T Christianson, *Vice Pres*
Douglas Hansel, *Creative Dir*
▲ EMP: 12
SQ FT: 7,050
SALES (est): 1.5MM **Privately Held**
WEB: www.showertek.com
SIC: 3231 3651 5063 Mirrored glass; household audio equipment; flashlights

(P-10732)
SREAM INC
12869 Temescal Canyon Rd A, Corona (92883-4021)
PHONE..................................951 245-6999
Jarir Farraj, *CEO*
Steve Rodriguez, *COO*
EMP: 34 EST: 2013
SALES (est): 2.8MM **Privately Held**
SIC: 3231 5231 Products of purchased glass; glass

(P-10733)
THERMALSUN GLASS PRODUCTS INC
3950 Brickway Blvd, Santa Rosa (95403-1070)
PHONE..................................707 579-9534
Jeffrey Paul Kloes, *CEO*
Amy Kloes, *Vice Pres*
▲ EMP: 34
SQ FT: 70,000
SALES (est): 6.4MM **Privately Held**
WEB: www.thermalsun.com
SIC: 3231 Insulating glass: made from purchased glass

(P-10734)
TRILOGY GLASS AND PACKG INC
975 Corporate Cntr Pkwy # 120, Santa Rosa (95407-5465)
PHONE..................................707 521-1300
Greg Windisch, *President*
Rick Miron, *CFO*
▲ EMP: 31
SQ FT: 24,000
SALES (est): 2.4MM
SALES (corp-wide): 548MM **Privately Held**
SIC: 3231 Products of purchased glass
HQ: Tricorbraun Inc.
6 Cityplace Dr Ste 1000
Saint Louis MO 63141
314 569-3633

(P-10735)
TRIVIEW GLASS INDUSTRIES LLC
711 S Stimson Ave, City of Industry (91745-1627)
PHONE..................................626 363-7980
Alexander A Kastaniuk, *CEO*
Joe Carlos, *Sales Dir*
Gabriela Bencomo, *Sales Staff*
Jorge Galvan, *Maintence Staff*
Miguel Barrientos, *Manager*
▲ EMP: 99
SALES (est): 20.8MM **Privately Held**
SIC: 3231 Products of purchased glass

(P-10736)
TWED-DELLS INC
Also Called: California Glass & Mirror Div
1900 S Susan St, Santa Ana (92704-3924)
PHONE..................................714 754-6900
Corey M Myer Jr, *President*
Gayle Myer, *Admin Sec*
▲ EMP: 38 EST: 1980
SQ FT: 45,000
SALES (est): 6.2MM **Privately Held**
WEB: www.tbmglass.com
SIC: 3231 Mirrored glass

(P-10737)
TWIN GLASS INDUSTRIES INC
16880 Joleen Way Ste 2, Morgan Hill (95037-4650)
PHONE..................................408 779-8801
Richard P Lopes, *CEO*
EMP: 10
SQ FT: 7,000
SALES (est): 1.2MM **Privately Held**
WEB: www.twinglass.com
SIC: 3231 Furniture tops, glass: cut, beveled or polished

(P-10738)
ULTRA GLASS
4001 Vista Park Ct Ste 1, Sacramento (95834-2975)
PHONE..................................916 338-3911
Kurtis Ryder, *President*
EMP: 15
SQ FT: 10,000
SALES (est): 4MM **Privately Held**
WEB: www.ultraglass.com
SIC: 3231 Doors, glass: made from purchased glass; insulating glass: made from purchased glass

(P-10739)
USA FIRE GLASS
Also Called: Oc Glass
6789 Quail Hill Pkwy # 613, Irvine (92603-4233)
PHONE..................................949 302-7728
Richard Newman, *CEO*
EMP: 16
SQ FT: 2,800
SALES (est): 820.5K **Privately Held**
WEB: www.usafireglass.com
SIC: 3231 Aquariums & reflectors, glass

(P-10740)
VIEW INC (PA)
Also Called: Soladigm
195 S Milpitas Blvd, Milpitas (95035-5425)
PHONE..................................408 263-9200
RAO Mulpuri, *CEO*
Brian Harrison, *COO*
Walt Lifsey, *COO*
Mike Armsby, *CFO*
James Fay, *CFO*
▲ EMP: 87
SALES (est): 45.1MM **Privately Held**
SIC: 3231 Products of purchased glass

(P-10741)
WARDROBE SPECIALTIES LTD
607 Glass Ln, Modesto (95356-9665)
PHONE..................................209 523-2094
Barbara Lee Stanton, *Partner*
EMP: 15
SQ FT: 5,400
SALES (est): 1.1MM **Privately Held**
SIC: 3231 Doors, glass: made from purchased glass

(P-10742)
ZADRO PRODUCTS INC
14462 Astronautics Ln # 101, Huntington Beach (92647-2077)
PHONE..................................714 892-9200
Zlatko Zadro, *President*
Becky Zadro, *Vice Pres*
◆ EMP: 35
SQ FT: 22,000
SALES (est): 5.5MM **Privately Held**
WEB: www.zadroinc.com
SIC: 3231 3089 3161 3641 Mirrored glass; organizers for closets, drawers, etc.: plastic; shoe kits; electric lamps; metal sanitary ware

▲ = Import ▼=Export
◆ =Import/Export

3241 Cement, Hydraulic

(P-10743)
CALPORTLAND COMPANY
Also Called: San Luis Obispo Rdymx Plant
219 Tank Farm Rd, San Luis Obispo
(93401-7509)
PHONE..................................805 345-3400
Dan Sampson, *Branch Mgr*
Keith Ybaben, *QA Dir*
EMP: 68
SALES (corp-wide): 8.1B **Privately Held**
SIC: 3241 Cement, hydraulic
HQ: Calportland Company
2025 E Financial Way
Glendora CA 91741
626 852-6200

(P-10744)
CALPORTLAND COMPANY
Also Called: California Portland Cement
9350 Oak Creek Rd, Mojave (93501-7738)
PHONE..................................661 824-2401
Bruce Shaffer, *Branch Mgr*
Brian Sleeper, *Human Res Mgr*
Brian Males, *Manager*
EMP: 130
SALES (corp-wide): 8.1B **Privately Held**
WEB: www.calportland.com
SIC: 3241 5032 5211 Masonry cement;
brick, stone & related material; cement
HQ: Calportland Company
2025 E Financial Way
Glendora CA 91741
626 852-6200

(P-10745)
CALPORTLAND COMPANY
695 S Rancho Ave, Colton (92324-3242)
P.O. Box 947 (92324-0947)
PHONE..................................909 825-4260
Mike Robertson, *Branch Mgr*
EMP: 36
SALES (corp-wide): 8.1B **Privately Held**
WEB: www.calportland.com
SIC: 3241 5211 Masonry cement; cement
HQ: Calportland Company
2025 E Financial Way
Glendora CA 91741
626 852-6200

(P-10746)
CALPORTLAND COMPANY
19409 National Trails Hwy, Oro Grande
(92368-9705)
PHONE..................................760 245-5321
EMP: 17
SALES (corp-wide): 8.1B **Privately Held**
SIC: 3241 3273 5032 Portland cement;
ready-mixed concrete; brick, stone & re-
lated material
HQ: Calportland Company
2025 E Financial Way
Glendora CA 91741
626 852-6200

(P-10747)
CALPORTLAND COMPANY
2201 W Washington St # 6, Stockton
(95203-2942)
PHONE..................................209 469-0109
Warren Burchett, *Manager*
EMP: 15
SALES (corp-wide): 8.1B **Privately Held**
WEB: www.calportland.com
SIC: 3241 3273 Portland cement; ready-
mixed concrete
HQ: Calportland Company
2025 E Financial Way
Glendora CA 91741
626 852-6200

(P-10748)
CALPORTLAND COMPANY (DH)
Also Called: Arizona Portland Cement
2025 E Financial Way, Glendora
(91741-4692)
P.O. Box 5025 (91740-0885)
PHONE..................................626 852-6200
Michio Kimura, *Ch of Bd*
James A Repman, *President*
Allen Hamblen, *CEO*
James A Wendoll, *CFO*
James Kim, *Treasurer*

▲ EMP: 77
SQ FT: 28,000
SALES (est): 171.5MM
SALES (corp-wide): 8.1B **Privately Held**
WEB: www.calportland.com
SIC: 3241 3273 5032 Portland cement;
ready-mixed concrete; brick, stone & re-
lated material
HQ: Taiheiyo Cement U.S.A., Inc.
2025 E Fincl Way Ste 200
Glendora CA 91741
626 852-6200

(P-10749)
CALPORTLAND COMPANY
Also Called: Catalina Pacific Concrete
8981 Bradley Ave, Sun Valley
(91352-2602)
PHONE..................................818 767-0508
Kenny Smart, *Branch Mgr*
EMP: 31
SALES (corp-wide): 8.1B **Privately Held**
WEB: www.calportland.com
SIC: 3241 3273 Cement, hydraulic; ready-
mixed concrete
HQ: Calportland Company
2025 E Financial Way
Glendora CA 91741
626 852-6200

(P-10750)
CALPORTLAND COMPANY
590 Live Oak Ave, Irwindale (91706-1315)
PHONE..................................626 691-2596
Wes May, *Branch Mgr*
Jennifer Bachman, *Administration*
Brian Reep, *Network Analyst*
Bill Leonard, *Technology*
Zuhair Hasan, *Engineer*
EMP: 68
SALES (corp-wide): 8.1B **Privately Held**
SIC: 3241 Portland cement
HQ: Calportland Company
2025 E Financial Way
Glendora CA 91741
626 852-6200

(P-10751)
CEMEX CNSTR MTLS PCF LLC
Also Called: Aggregate -Sunol Quarry
6527 Calaveras Rd, Sunol (94586-9530)
P.O. Box 546 (94586-0546)
PHONE..................................925 862-2201
Rich Biers, *Branch Mgr*
EMP: 12 **Privately Held**
SIC: 3241 Cement, hydraulic
HQ: Cemex Construction Materials Pacific,
Llc
1501 Belvedere Rd
West Palm Beach FL 33406
561 833-5555

(P-10752)
HANSON AGGREGATES LLC
3555 E Vineyard Ave, Oxnard (93036)
PHONE..................................805 485-3101
EMP: 65
SALES (corp-wide): 20.3B **Privately Held**
WEB: www.hansonind.com
SIC: 3241 Cement, hydraulic
HQ: Hanson Aggregates Llc
8505 Freport Pkwy Ste 500
Irving TX 75063
469 417-1200

(P-10753)
HANSON AGGREGATES LLC
5785 Mission Center Rd, San Diego
(92108-4387)
P.O. Box 639069 (92163-9069)
PHONE..................................619 299-8640
EMP: 25
SALES (corp-wide): 15.6B **Privately Held**
SIC: 3241
HQ: Hanson Aggregates Llc
8505 Freport Pkwy Ste 500
Irving TX 75063
469 417-1200

(P-10754)
HANSON AGGREGATES LLC
9255 Camino Santa Fe, San Diego
(92121-6209)
P.O. Box 639069 (92163-9069)
PHONE..................................858 577-2727
Kevin Everly, *Manager*

Ralph Reagan, *Office Mgr*
Matt Woods, *Transptn Dir*
Mike Charest, *Manager*
EMP: 15
SALES (corp-wide): 20.3B **Privately Held**
WEB: www.hansonind.com
SIC: 3241 Cement, hydraulic
HQ: Hanson Aggregates Llc
8505 Freport Pkwy Ste 500
Irving TX 75063
469 417-1200

(P-10755)
HANSON AGGREGATES LLC
19494 River Rock Rd, Corona
(92881-5094)
P.O. Box 1115 (92878-1115)
PHONE..................................951 371-7625
Rick Sanford, *Manager*
EMP: 30
SALES (corp-wide): 20.3B **Privately Held**
WEB: www.hansonind.com
SIC: 3241 1442 Cement, hydraulic; con-
struction sand & gravel
HQ: Hanson Aggregates Llc
8505 Freport Pkwy Ste 500
Irving TX 75063
469 417-1200

(P-10756)
HANSON LEHIGH INC
12667 Alcosta Blvd # 400, San Ramon
(94583-4427)
PHONE..................................925 244-6500
Dan Herrington, *CEO*
EMP: 40
SALES (est): 4.1MM **Privately Held**
SIC: 3241 Cement, hydraulic

(P-10757)
**HEADWATERS CONSTRUCTION
INC**
Also Called: Louis W Osborn Co.
16005 Phoebe Ave, La Mirada
(90638-5607)
PHONE..................................714 523-1530
Rudy Valverde, *General Mgr*
EMP: 30
SQ FT: 18,000
SALES (est): 3.8MM **Privately Held**
SIC: 3241 Cement, hydraulic

(P-10758)
JETSET CALIFORNIA INC
Also Called: Jet Set California
2150 Edison Ave, San Leandro
(94577-1131)
PHONE..................................510 632-7800
Greg Willener, *President*
EMP: 10
SQ FT: 8,000
SALES (est): 1.1MM **Privately Held**
WEB: www.jetsetcement.com
SIC: 3241 Masonry cement

(P-10759)
**LATICRETE INTERNATIONAL
INC**
22740 Temescal Canyon Rd, Corona
(92883-4107)
PHONE..................................951 277-1776
Todd Belanger, *General Mgr*
Karl Besescheck, *Planning*
Colby Fradette, *Planning*
Mitch Hawkins, *Technical Mgr*
Kevin Coronas, *Technical Staff*
EMP: 10
SALES (corp-wide): 158.7MM **Privately
Held**
WEB: www.laticrete.com
SIC: 3241 Cement, hydraulic
PA: Laticrete International, Inc.
1 Laticrete Park N
Bethany CT 06524
203 393-0010

(P-10760)
**LEHIGH SOUTHWEST CEMENT
CO**
13573 E Tehachapi Blvd, Tehachapi
(93561-8155)
PHONE..................................661 822-4445
Axel Conrads, *General Mgr*
Ron Hibdon, *President*
Michael Rohmaller, *Engineer*

Jaromir Vojtech, *Engineer*
Brian Bigley, *Safety Mgr*
EMP: 130
SALES (corp-wide): 20.3B **Privately Held**
SIC: 3241 3273 2951 1442 Portland ce-
ment; ready-mixed concrete; asphalt
paving mixtures & blocks; construction
sand & gravel
HQ: Lehigh Southwest Cement Company
2300 Clayton Rd Ste 300
Concord CA 94520
972 653-5500

(P-10761)
**LEHIGH SOUTHWEST CEMENT
CO**
24001 Stevens Creek Blvd, Cupertino
(95014-5659)
PHONE..................................408 996-4271
W Lee, *Branch Mgr*
Dave Peavey, *Materials Mgr*
EMP: 15
SALES (corp-wide): 20.3B **Privately Held**
SIC: 3241 2891 5032 5211 Portland ce-
ment; cement, except linoleum & tile; ce-
ment; cement
HQ: Lehigh Southwest Cement Company
2300 Clayton Rd Ste 300
Concord CA 94520
972 653-5500

(P-10762)
**LEHIGH SOUTHWEST CEMENT
CO (DH)**
2300 Clayton Rd Ste 300, Concord
(94520-2175)
PHONE..................................972 653-5500
Dan Harrington, *CEO*
Mark Esolen, *Opers Mgr*
Bill Boughton, *VP Sales*
Logan Rowe, *Sales Staff*
▲ EMP: 15
SQ FT: 10,000
SALES (est): 149.1MM
SALES (corp-wide): 20.3B **Privately Held**
SIC: 3241 2891 5032 5211 Portland ce-
ment; masonry cement; pozzolana ce-
ment; cement, except linoleum & tile;
cement; cement

(P-10763)
**LEHIGH SOUTHWEST CEMENT
CO**
2201 W Washington St, Stockton
(95203-2942)
PHONE..................................209 465-2624
Steve Olivas, *Manager*
Abel Martir, *Manager*
EMP: 15
SALES (corp-wide): 20.3B **Privately Held**
SIC: 3241 Masonry cement
HQ: Lehigh Southwest Cement Company
2300 Clayton Rd Ste 300
Concord CA 94520
972 653-5500

(P-10764)
**MITSUBISHI CEMENT
CORPORATION**
5808 State Highway 18, Lucerne Valley
(92356-8179)
PHONE..................................760 248-7373
Jim Russell, *Branch Mgr*
David Rader, *Safety Mgr*
Eric Jen, *Terminal Mgr*
EMP: 175
SALES (corp-wide): 15B **Privately Held**
WEB: www.mitsubishicement.com
SIC: 3241 Portland cement
HQ: Mitsubishi Cement Corporation
151 Cassia Way
Henderson NV 89014
702 932-3900

(P-10765)
**MOSS LANDING CEMENT CO
LLC**
7697 Highway 1, Moss Landing
(95039-9697)
PHONE..................................831 731-6000
Brent Constantz,
▲ EMP: 17
SALES (est): 2.6MM **Privately Held**
SIC: 3241 Masonry cement

(P-10766)
NATIONAL CEMENT COMPANY INC (HQ)
15821 Ventura Blvd # 475, Encino (91436-2935)
PHONE................................818 728-5200
James E Rotch, *Ch of Bd*
Denise Taylor, *Finance*
Michael Hoo, *Accountant*
Pragati Kapoor, *Controller*
David Ollis, *Traffic Mgr*
▲ EMP: 38 EST: 1920
SQ FT: 11,446
SALES (est): 339.8MM
SALES (corp-wide): 479.6MM **Privately Held**
SIC: 3241 3273 Portland cement; ready-mixed concrete
PA: Vicat
    Tour Manhattan
    Courbevoie 92400
    158 868-686

(P-10767)
NORTH AMERICA PWR & INFRA
19112 Gridley Rd 2001, Cerritos (90703-6613)
PHONE................................562 403-4337
Daniel Lu, *President*
Jacob Singh, *Principal*
EMP: 50
SALES (est): 1.3MM **Privately Held**
SIC: 3241 1611 Natural cement; general contractor, highway & street construction

(P-10768)
OLDCASTLE APG WEST INC
10714 Poplar Ave, Fontana (92337-7333)
PHONE................................909 355-6422
EMP: 40
SALES (corp-wide): 29.7B **Privately Held**
WEB: www.sierrapavers.com
SIC: 3241 Masonry cement
HQ: Oldcastle Apg West, Inc.
    4720 E Cotton Gin Loop L
    Phoenix AZ 85040
    602 302-9600

(P-10769)
RMC PACIFIC MATERIALS INC
30350 S Tracy Blvd, Tracy (95377-8121)
PHONE................................209 835-1454
Gordon Brown, *Manager*
EMP: 24 **Privately Held**
SIC: 3241 3273 1442 Cement, hydraulic; ready-mixed concrete; construction sand & gravel
HQ: Rmc Pacific Materials, Inc.
    6601 Koll Center Pkwy
    Pleasanton CA 94566
    925 426-8787

(P-10770)
RMC PACIFIC MATERIALS INC
700 Highway 1, Davenport (95017-9702)
P.O. Box 300 (95017-0300)
PHONE................................831 429-7200
Scott Renfrow, *Branch Mgr*
EMP: 150 **Privately Held**
SIC: 3241 Cement, hydraulic
HQ: Rmc Pacific Materials, Inc.
    6601 Koll Center Pkwy
    Pleasanton CA 94566
    925 426-8787

(P-10771)
RMC PACIFIC MATERIALS INC (DH)
6601 Koll Center Pkwy, Pleasanton (94566-3112)
PHONE................................925 426-8787
Eric F Woodhouse, *President*
Rodrigo Trevia O, *CFO*
▲ EMP: 200 EST: 1906
SQ FT: 30,000
SALES (est): 82MM **Privately Held**
SIC: 3241 3273 3531 1442 Cement, hydraulic; ready-mixed concrete; asphalt plant, including gravel-mix type; sand mining; gravel & pebble mining; abrasive products
HQ: Rmc Usa, Inc
    920 Memorial City Way
    Houston TX 77024
    713 650-6200

3251 Brick & Structural Clay Tile

(P-10772)
ARTO BRICK VENEER MFGCO
Also Called: Arto Brick & Tile
15209 S Broadway, Gardena (90248-1823)
PHONE................................310 768-8500
Arto Alajian, *Owner*
Patrick Blake, *Vice Pres*
Mike Oleson, *General Mgr*
Stephanie Morgan, *Sales Mgr*
EMP: 40
SQ FT: 18,000
SALES (est): 2.6MM **Privately Held**
WEB: www.artobrick.com
SIC: 3251 Brick & structural clay tile

(P-10773)
CALSTAR PRODUCTS INC
3945 Freedom Cir Ste 560, Santa Clara (95054-1269)
PHONE................................262 752-9131
Joel Rood, *CEO*
Mike Lemberg, *CFO*
EMP: 60
SALES (est): 13.4MM **Privately Held**
WEB: www.calstarcement.com
SIC: 3251 Paving brick, clay

(P-10774)
CASTAIC CLAY PRODUCTS LLC
32201 Castaic Lake Dr, Castaic (91384-4134)
PHONE................................661 259-3066
Dan Navarro,
Norma Gardner, *Accounting Mgr*
Doug Pearson, *Purch Agent*
EMP: 95
SALES (est): 6.8MM **Privately Held**
WEB: www.castaicbrick.com
SIC: 3251 Brick & structural clay tile

(P-10775)
CLAY CASTAIC MANUFACTURING CO
Also Called: Castaic Brick
32201 Castaic Lake Dr, Castaic (91384-4134)
PHONE................................661 259-3066
Mike Mallow, *CEO*
Annette Mallow, *Treasurer*
Dan Navarro, *Controller*
Susan Graves, *Personnel Exec*
Al Pinto, *Director*
EMP: 95
SQ FT: 10,000
SALES (est): 11.4MM **Privately Held**
SIC: 3251 Brick clay: common face, glazed, vitrified or hollow

(P-10776)
PABCO CLAY PRODUCTS LLC
Also Called: Gladding McBean
601 7th St, Lincoln (95648-1828)
PHONE................................916 645-3341
Bill Padavona, *Branch Mgr*
Jessica Ouwerkerk, *Project Mgr*
Joe Parker, *Natl Sales Mgr*
Veronica Alvarez, *Sales Engr*
Jamie Farnham, *Marketing Staff*
EMP: 250
SALES (corp-wide): 1.7B **Privately Held**
SIC: 3251 3253 3259 3269 Ceramic glazed brick, clay; ceramic wall & floor tile; clay sewer & drainage pipe & tile; roofing tile, clay; vases, pottery
HQ: Pabco Clay Products, Llc
    605 Industrial Way
    Dixon CA 95620

(P-10777)
PABCO CLAY PRODUCTS LLC
Also Called: H C Muddox
4875 Bradshaw Rd, Sacramento (95827-9727)
PHONE................................916 859-6320
Greg Morrison, *Branch Mgr*
Rocky Turner, *Safety Mgr*
Ed Alvis, *Maintence Staff*
EMP: 70
SALES (corp-wide): 1.7B **Privately Held**
SIC: 3251 Brick & structural clay tile

HQ: Pabco Clay Products, Llc
    605 Industrial Way
    Dixon CA 95620

3253 Ceramic Tile

(P-10778)
CALIFORNIA POTTERIES INC
Also Called: California Pot & Tile Works
859 E 60th St, Los Angeles (90001-1014)
PHONE................................323 235-4151
John McLean, *President*
EMP: 20
SALES (est): 2.4MM **Privately Held**
SIC: 3253 5032 Ceramic wall & floor tile; ceramic wall & floor tile

(P-10779)
CONCEPT STUDIO INC
3195 Red Hill Ave Ste G, Costa Mesa (92626-3430)
PHONE................................949 759-0606
Richard Goddard, *President*
Karen Bishop, *Vice Pres*
Carolyn Schneider, *Manager*
▲ EMP: 14
SQ FT: 5,000
SALES (est): 1.8MM **Privately Held**
WEB: www.conceptstudioinc.com
SIC: 3253 Ceramic wall & floor tile

(P-10780)
DURAMAR FLOOR INC
Also Called: Duramar Interior Surfaces
2500 White Rd Ste B, Irvine (92614-6276)
PHONE................................949 724-8800
Farhad Abdollahi, *President*
Tom Belcher, *Principal*
Nicholas Ounanian, *Principal*
▲ EMP: 19
SQ FT: 64,000
SALES (est): 2.9MM **Privately Held**
WEB: www.duramar.com
SIC: 3253 Floor tile, ceramic

(P-10781)
ELYSIUM MOSAICS INC
Also Called: Elysium Ceramics
1180 N Anaheim Blvd, Anaheim (92801-2502)
PHONE................................714 991-7885
Yue Zhou, *CEO*
▲ EMP: 17
SALES (est): 3.2MM **Privately Held**
SIC: 3253 Mosaic tile, glazed & unglazed: ceramic

(P-10782)
FIRE & EARTH CERAMICS
418 Santander Dr, San Ramon (94583-2143)
PHONE................................303 442-0245
Jeff Gaines, *Owner*
Clarence Harrison, *CIO*
EMP: 10
SALES: 500K **Privately Held**
SIC: 3253 Mosaic tile, glazed & unglazed: ceramic

(P-10783)
GBM MANUFACTURING INC
1188 S Airport Way, Stockton (95205-6933)
PHONE................................888 862-8397
Wen Jie Chen, *President*
Tony Shi, *Marketing Staff*
▲ EMP: 12
SQ FT: 30,000
SALES: 2MM **Privately Held**
SIC: 3253 Ceramic wall & floor tile

(P-10784)
JEFFREY COURT INC
620 Parkridge Ave, Norco (92860-3124)
PHONE................................951 340-3383
James Lawson, *President*
Janice Lawson, *CFO*
Frank Toms, *CFO*
Joann Leyva, *Technology*
Cindy Ramirez, *Human Resources*
▲ EMP: 75
SQ FT: 60,000
SALES (est): 12.3MM **Privately Held**
SIC: 3253 Ceramic wall & floor tile

(P-10785)
KEN MASON TILE INC
14600 S Western Ave, Gardena (90249-3306)
PHONE................................562 432-7574
Ken Paul, *President*
Glenn Paul, *Vice Pres*
EMP: 30
SQ FT: 7,500
SALES (est): 3.1MM **Privately Held**
WEB: www.kenmasontile.com
SIC: 3253 1743 3272 Mosaic tile, glazed & unglazed: ceramic; tile installation, ceramic; concrete products

(P-10786)
MALIBU CERAMIC WORKS
903 Fairbanks Ave, Long Beach (90813-2861)
P.O. Box 1406, Topanga (90290-1406)
PHONE................................310 455-2485
Robert Harris, *President*
Matthew Harris, *Opers Staff*
EMP: 20
SALES (est): 2.3MM **Privately Held**
SIC: 3253 Floor tile, ceramic

(P-10787)
OCEANSIDE GLASSTILE COMPANY (PA)
Also Called: Mandala
5858 Edison Pl, Carlsbad (92008-6519)
PHONE................................760 929-4000
Sean Gildea, *CEO*
Sean M Gildea, *CEO*
Greg Lehr, *COO*
Miles Bradley, *CFO*
John Marckx, *Exec VP*
▲ EMP: 375
SQ FT: 48,000
SALES (est): 97.7MM **Privately Held**
WEB: www.glasstile.com
SIC: 3253 5032 Mosaic tile, glazed & unglazed: ceramic; tile, clay or other ceramic, excluding refractory

(P-10788)
ORTECH INC
Also Called: Ortech Advanced Ceramics
6720 Folsom Blvd Ste 219, Sacramento (95819-4631)
PHONE................................916 549-9696
Oded Morgenshtern, *President*
▲ EMP: 20
SALES (est): 2.4MM **Privately Held**
SIC: 3253 Ceramic wall & floor tile

(P-10789)
PROGRESSIVE TECHNOLOGY INC
4130 Citrus Ave Ste 17, Rocklin (95677-4006)
PHONE................................916 632-6715
Shannon Rogers, *President*
Carol Rogers, *Vice Pres*
EMP: 30
SQ FT: 23,000
SALES (est): 4.8MM **Privately Held**
WEB: www.prgtech.com
SIC: 3253 Ceramic wall & floor tile

(P-10790)
SMD ENTERPRISES INC
Also Called: California Pot & Tile Works
859 E 60th St, Los Angeles (90001-1014)
PHONE................................323 235-4151
John R McLean, *President*
EMP: 35
SALES (est): 3.1MM **Privately Held**
SIC: 3253 3269 Floor tile, ceramic; ceramic wall & floor tile; art & ornamental ware, pottery

(P-10791)
SONOMA TILEMAKERS INC (DH)
7750 Bell Rd, Windsor (95492-8518)
PHONE................................707 837-8177
Jon Gray, *Partner*
Theresa Coey, *Managing Prtnr*
Kenneth E Wiedemann, *CEO*
Katherine Oliver, *Executive Asst*
Dana Higgins, *Human Res Dir*
▲ EMP: 59
SQ FT: 22,000

▲ = Import ▼=Export
◆ =Import/Export

SALES (est): 10.6MM
SALES (corp-wide): 42.4MM **Privately Held**
WEB: www.sonomatilemakers.com
SIC: 3253 Ceramic & floor tile
HQ: United Tile Corp.
750 S Michigan St
Seattle WA 98108
425 251-5290

(P-10792)
STRATAMET ADVANCED MTLS CORP
2718 Prune Ave, Fremont (94539-6780)
PHONE..................................510 440-1697
Mark Capalongan, *President*
EMP: 16
SALES (est): 1.7MM **Privately Held**
SIC: 3253

(P-10793)
SURFACES TILE CRAFT INC
7900 Andasol Ave, Northridge
(91325-4429)
PHONE..................................818 609-0719
Ricardo Gomez, *CEO*
Yesenia Reynoso, *Admin Sec*
EMP: 15
SALES (est): 1.4MM **Privately Held**
SIC: 3253 Mosaic tile, glazed & unglazed: ceramic

(P-10794)
SWISSTRAX LLC
82579 Fleming Way Ste A, Indio
(92201-2395)
PHONE..................................760 347-3330
Randy A Nelson, *CEO*
Jim Miller, *Vice Pres*
◆ EMP: 17
SALES (est): 3.8MM **Privately Held**
SIC: 3253 Ceramic wall & floor tile

(P-10795)
TILE ARTISANS INC
4288 State Highway 70, Oroville
(95965-8340)
PHONE..................................800 601-4199
Dale Marsh, *President*
▲ EMP: 10
SQ FT: 16,000
SALES (est): 855.6K **Privately Held**
WEB: www.tileartisans.com
SIC: 3253 Ceramic wall & floor tile

(P-10796)
TILE GUILD INC
2424 E 55th St, Vernon (90058-3506)
PHONE..................................323 581-3770
Dennis Caffrey, *President*
EMP: 15
SQ FT: 18,000
SALES (est): 1MM **Privately Held**
WEB: www.tileguildinc.com
SIC: 3253 Ceramic wall & floor tile

(P-10797)
WIZARD ENTERPRISE
12605 Daphne Ave, Hawthorne
(90250-3309)
PHONE..................................323 756-8430
Thomas Meagher, *Partner*
Michael Meagher, *Partner*
Charles Clark, *Maintence Staff*
EMP: 10
SALES (est): 1.3MM **Privately Held**
SIC: 3253 5092 5032 Ceramic wall & floor tile; arts & crafts equipment & supplies; ceramic wall & floor tile

3255 Clay Refractories

(P-10798)
B & B REFRACTORIES INC
12121 Los Nietos Rd, Santa Fe Springs
(90670-2907)
PHONE..................................562 946-4535
John Svet, *President*
Jeanette Svet, *Vice Pres*
▲ EMP: 18 EST: 1965
SQ FT: 50,000
SALES (est): 2.2MM **Privately Held**
WEB: www.bbrefractories.com
SIC: 3255 Clay refractories

(P-10799)
HANDCRAFT TILE INC
786 View Dr, Pleasanton (94566-9791)
PHONE..................................408 262-1140
EMP: 11 EST: 1953
SQ FT: 13,000
SALES (est): 1.3MM **Privately Held**
WEB: www.handcrafttile.com
SIC: 3255

(P-10800)
PROTECH MINERALS INC
17092 S D St, Victorville (92395-3304)
PHONE..................................760 245-3441
Chul Lim Choe, *President*
Chong Choe, *Vice Pres*
EMP: 10
SQ FT: 3,757
SALES (est): 1.4MM **Privately Held**
SIC: 3255 Tile, clay refractory

3259 Structural Clay Prdts, NEC

(P-10801)
EAGLE ROOFING PRODUCTS FLA LLC (PA)
3546 N Riverside Ave, Rialto (92377-3802)
PHONE..................................909 822-6000
Robert C Burlingame, *Mng Member*
Efrain Amaya, *Sales Staff*
Joe H Anderson Jr,
M D Anderson,
Kevin C Burlingame,
EMP: 34
SALES (est): 48.6MM **Privately Held**
SIC: 3259 Roofing tile, clay

(P-10802)
MARUHACHI CERAMICS AMERICA INC
1985 Sampson Ave, Corona (92879-6006)
PHONE..................................800 736-6221
Yoshihiro Suzuki, *President*
Linda Hanson, *CFO*
Sharon Suzuki, *Executive*
Yoshi Suzuki, *General Mgr*
Thelma Svoboda, *Mktg Dir*
▲ EMP: 22
SQ FT: 83,250
SALES (est): 5.3MM **Privately Held**
WEB: www.mca-tile.com
SIC: 3259 Roofing tile, clay

(P-10803)
PABCO BUILDING PRODUCTS LLC
Also Called: Gladding McBean
601 7th St, Lincoln (95648-1828)
PHONE..................................916 645-3341
Erik Absalon, *General Mgr*
EMP: 100
SQ FT: 952
SALES (corp-wide): 1.7B **Privately Held**
SIC: 3259 Architectural terra cotta; clay sewer & drainage pipe & tile
HQ: Pabco Building Products, Llc
10600 White Rock Rd # 100
Rancho Cordova CA 95670
510 792-1577

3261 China Plumbing Fixtures & Fittings

(P-10804)
BBK SPECIALTIES INC
24147 Del Monte Dr # 297, Valencia
(91355-3855)
PHONE..................................661 255-2857
EMP: 15
SALES (est): 1.6MM **Privately Held**
SIC: 3261 3431

(P-10805)
HCP INDUSTRIES INC
415 Otterson Dr Ste 10, Chico
(95928-8239)
P.O. Box 6747 (95927-6747)
PHONE..................................530 899-5591
Norman Hueckel, *President*
Dixie Hueckel, *Corp Secy*

EMP: 13
SQ FT: 22,800
SALES (est): 1.4MM **Privately Held**
WEB: www.hcpindustries.com
SIC: 3261 Soap dishes, vitreous china

(P-10806)
LOTUS HYGIENE SYSTEMS INC
1621 E Saint Andrew Pl, Santa Ana
(92705-4932)
PHONE..................................714 259-8805
Xiang Liu, *President*
▲ EMP: 20
SQ FT: 10,000
SALES (est): 1.5MM **Privately Held**
WEB: www.lotusseats.com
SIC: 3261 Vitreous plumbing fixtures

(P-10807)
STAFFORD SOAP CANDLE CO
S Pmb 130-31805, Temecula (92592)
PHONE..................................951 302-3476
Lauren Stafford, *Owner*
EMP: 10 EST: 1996
SALES (est): 468.2K **Privately Held**
SIC: 3261 Bathroom accessories/fittings, vitreous china or earthenware

(P-10808)
TUBULAR SPECIALTIES MFG INC
Also Called: T S M
13011 S Spring St, Los Angeles
(90061-1685)
PHONE..................................310 515-4801
Marcia Lynn Hemphill, *CEO*
L C Huntley, *Ch of Bd*
Arif Mansuri, *Treasurer*
Patricia Watts, *Vice Pres*
Mansuri Arif, *Director*
▲ EMP: 62 EST: 1966
SQ FT: 38,000
SALES (est): 8.8MM **Privately Held**
WEB: www.calltsm.com
SIC: 3261 2656 3446 Bathroom accessories/fittings, vitreous china or earthenware; sanitary food containers; railings, prefabricated metal

(P-10809)
WESTINGHOUSE A BRAKE TECH CORP
Microphor
452 E Hill Rd, Willits (95490-9721)
PHONE..................................707 459-5563
EMP: 35
SALES (corp-wide): 3.8B **Publicly Held**
SIC: 3261 3589 Toilet fixtures, vitreous china; sewage treatment equipment
PA: Westinghouse Air Brake Technologies Corporation
1001 Airbrake Ave
Wilmerding PA 15148
412 825-1000

3262 China, Table & Kitchen Articles

(P-10810)
SKY ONE INC
Also Called: Vertex China
1793 W 2nd St, Pomona (91766-1253)
PHONE..................................909 622-3333
Hoi Shum, *President*
Gary Dallas, *Vice Pres*
Ken Joyce, *Vice Pres*
▲ EMP: 19
SQ FT: 14,000
SALES (est): 3.1MM **Privately Held**
SIC: 3262 Dishes, commercial or household: vitreous china

3263 Earthenware, Whiteware, Table & Kitchen Articles

(P-10811)
BROMWELL COMPANY (PA)
8605 Santa Monica Blvd, Los Angeles
(90069-4109)
PHONE..................................800 683-2626
Sean Bandawat, *President*
EMP: 10
SALES (est): 2.1MM **Privately Held**
SIC: 3263 Semivitreous table & kitchenware

(P-10812)
BSH HOME APPLIANCES CORP
1901 Main St Ste 600, Irvine (92614-0521)
PHONE..................................949 440-7100
Gary Thyer, *Manager*
EMP: 35
SALES (corp-wide): 261.7MM **Privately Held**
SIC: 3263 Semivitreous table & kitchenware
HQ: Bsh Home Appliances Corporation
1901 Main St Ste 600
Irvine CA 92614

(P-10813)
MASTERS IN METAL INC
131 Lombard St, Oxnard (93030-5161)
PHONE..................................805 988-1992
Wayne R Haddox, *President*
Dennis Haddox, *Vice Pres*
Jeannette Worthy, *Office Mgr*
Jonathan Huerta, *Executive Asst*
Pat Behabe, *Mktg Dir*
▲ EMP: 50
SQ FT: 11,000
SALES (est): 7.1MM **Privately Held**
WEB: www.mastersinmetal.com
SIC: 3263 3952 Commercial tableware or kitchen articles, fine earthenware; sizes, gold & bronze: artists'

(P-10814)
WRENCHWARE INC
2751 Reche Canyon Rd # 104, Colton
(92324-9570)
PHONE..................................951 784-2717
Edwin A Jonas Jr, *President*
◆ EMP: 10
SALES (est): 855.2K **Privately Held**
SIC: 3263 Tableware, household & commercial: semivitreous

3264 Porcelain Electrical Splys

(P-10815)
ALTA PROPERTIES INC
Channel Industries
839 Ward Dr, Santa Barbara (93111-2920)
PHONE..................................805 967-0171
EMP: 475
SALES (corp-wide): 197.5MM **Privately Held**
SIC: 3264 Porcelain electrical supplies
PA: Alta Properties, Inc.
879 Ward Dr
Santa Barbara CA 93111
805 967-0171

(P-10816)
ALTA PROPERTIES INC (PA)
Also Called: Ctg
879 Ward Dr, Santa Barbara (93111-2920)
P.O. Box 90326 (93190-0326)
PHONE..................................805 967-0171
Robert F Carlson, *CEO*
Paul J Downey, *CFO*
Randy Copperman, *Vice Pres*
Gary Douville, *Vice Pres*
Mark Shaw, *Vice Pres*
▲ EMP: 167
SQ FT: 21,000

P R O D U C T S
& S V C S

SALES (est): 197.5MM **Privately Held**
WEB: www.channeltech.com
SIC: 3264 3699 3823 3679 Porcelain electrical supplies; underwater sound equipment; infrared instruments, industrial process type; transducers, electrical

(P-10817)
COUNTIS INDUSTRIES INC
Also Called: Orbit Industries
12295 Charles Dr, Grass Valley (95945-9371)
PHONE..................................530 272-8334
EMP: 20 EST: 1956
SQ FT: 10,000
SALES: 10MM **Privately Held**
WEB: www.countis.com
SIC: 3264 3423

(P-10818)
KOMAG INCORPORATED
1710 Automation Pkwy, San Jose (95131-1873)
PHONE..................................408 576-2150
Tim Starkey, *Principal*
Frank Cunanan, *Research*
Kiet Lam, *Engineer*
EMP: 19
SALES (est): 1.8MM **Privately Held**
SIC: 3264 Magnets, permanent: ceramic or ferrite

(P-10819)
LEON ASSEMBLY SOLUTIONS INC
Also Called: Imesa
10650 Scripps Ranch Blvd # 123, San Diego (92131-2471)
PHONE..................................858 397-2826
Alejandro A Leon, *CEO*
Rachel Padden, *Admin Asst*
EMP: 100
SQ FT: 120
SALES: 4.7MM **Privately Held**
SIC: 3264 7389 Porcelain electrical supplies;

(P-10820)
MAGNET SALES & MFG CO INC (HQ)
Also Called: Integrated Magnetics
11248 Playa Ct, Culver City (90230-6100)
PHONE..................................310 391-7213
Anil Nanji, *President*
Gary Hooper, *CFO*
Will Effertz, *IT Executive*
Oscar Rios, *Info Tech Dir*
Ben Pendleton, *Info Tech Mgr*
▲ EMP: 75 EST: 1930
SQ FT: 45,000
SALES (est): 39.9MM
SALES (corp-wide): 47.2MM **Privately Held**
WEB: www.magnetsales.com
SIC: 3264 3621 Porcelain electrical supplies; servomotors, electric; coils, for electric motors or generators; torque motors, electric
PA: Integrated Technologies Group, Inc.
11250 Playa Ct
Culver City CA 90230
310 391-7213

(P-10821)
PACIFIC CERAMICS INC
824 San Aleso Ave, Sunnyvale (94085-1411)
PHONE..................................408 747-4600
Dennis J Fleming, *President*
EMP: 39
SALES (est): 5.4MM **Privately Held**
WEB: www.pceramics.com
SIC: 3264 Magnets, permanent: ceramic or ferrite

(P-10822)
PRECISION FRRITES CERAMICS INC
5432 Production Dr, Huntington Beach (92649-1525)
PHONE..................................714 901-7622
Myung Sook Hong, *CEO*
Sung MO Hong, *President*
Frank Hong, *Vice Pres*
Ji SOO Lee, *Vice Pres*

EMP: 90
SQ FT: 23,811
SALES (est): 14.4MM **Privately Held**
WEB: www.semiceramic.com
SIC: 3264 3674 3599 Porcelain electrical supplies; semiconductors & related devices; machine shop, jobbing & repair

(P-10823)
SAN JOSE DELTA ASSOCIATES INC
482 Sapena Ct, Santa Clara (95054-2442)
PHONE..................................408 727-1448
Scott J Budde, *CEO*
EMP: 50
SQ FT: 12,500
SALES (est): 6.3MM **Privately Held**
WEB: www.sanjosedelta.com
SIC: 3264 Magnets, permanent: ceramic or ferrite; porcelain parts for electrical devices, molded

(P-10824)
SHIP SUPPLY INTERNATIONAL INC
Also Called: Universal Maritime
1215 255th St, Harbor City (90710-2914)
PHONE..................................310 325-3188
Mike Konstantas, *CEO*
EMP: 10
SALES (est): 1.7MM
SALES (corp-wide): 27.4MM **Privately Held**
SIC: 3264 3699 5063 2297 Porcelain electrical supplies; electrical equipment & supplies; electrical apparatus & equipment; bonded-fiber fabrics, except felt; ship furniture
PA: Ship Supply Of Florida, Inc.
10800 Nw 103rd St Ste 1
Miami FL 33178
305 681-7447

(P-10825)
TOP GREENER INC
1701 E Edinger Ave Ste A1, Santa Ana (92705-5000)
PHONE..................................626 254-3367
Xiaodan Zheng, *CEO*
EMP: 13
SQ FT: 5,015
SALES (est): 487K **Privately Held**
SIC: 3264 Porcelain electrical supplies

3269 Pottery Prdts, NEC

(P-10826)
AGRI-TECH INDUSTRIES LLC
119 Stony Knoll Rd, El Cajon (92019-2024)
PHONE..................................619 205-9509
David Martinez, *CEO*
Javier Haro, *CFO*
EMP: 20 EST: 2009
SQ FT: 17,000
SALES (est): 1.8MM **Privately Held**
SIC: 3269 3281 2431 Vases, pottery; statuary, marble; trellises, wood

(P-10827)
ASDAK INTERNATIONAL
Also Called: Oggi
1809 1/2 N Orngethorpe Pa, Anaheim (92801-1141)
PHONE..................................714 449-0733
Ajit Das, *President*
Barbara Das, *CFO*
Paul Williamson, *Vice Pres*
Stephen Curtis, *Natl Sales Mgr*
▲ EMP: 12
SQ FT: 29,000
SALES (est): 2MM **Privately Held**
SIC: 3269 Pottery cooking & kitchen articles

(P-10828)
BERNEY-KARP INC
3350 E 26th St, Vernon (90058-4145)
PHONE..................................323 260-7122
Morry Karp, *President*
Anna Ramos, *Vice Pres*
Vicky Salaises, *Sales Staff*
▲ EMP: 74 EST: 1970
SQ FT: 80,000

SALES (est): 8.2MM **Privately Held**
WEB: www.ceramic-source.com
SIC: 3269 Pottery cooking & kitchen articles

(P-10829)
CLAY DESIGNS INC
519 W 15th St, Long Beach (90813-1505)
PHONE..................................562 432-3991
James L Camm, *President*
Cathy Camm, *CFO*
Silvia Valle, *Director*
▲ EMP: 43
SQ FT: 15,000
SALES (est): 5MM **Privately Held**
WEB: www.claydesign.com
SIC: 3269 Figures: pottery, china, earthenware & stoneware; stoneware pottery products

(P-10830)
DEERS MERCHANDISE INC
347 Enterprise Pl, Pomona (91768-3245)
P.O. Box 624, Azusa (91702-0624)
PHONE..................................909 869-8619
Edmond Tong, *President*
▼ EMP: 16
SQ FT: 86,000
SALES: 11MM
SALES (corp-wide): 6.4MM **Privately Held**
SIC: 3269 Textile guides, porcelain
PA: Desiree Company Limited
Rm 74 G/F Peninsula Ctr
Tsim Sha Tsui East KLN
276 442-21

(P-10831)
GAINEY CERAMICS INC
1200 Arrow Hwy, La Verne (91750-5217)
PHONE..................................909 596-4464
Steve Gainey, *CEO*
▲ EMP: 150
SQ FT: 75,500
SALES (est): 13.5MM **Privately Held**
WEB: www.gaineyceramics.com
SIC: 3269 Flower pots, red earthenware

(P-10832)
HAGEN-RENAKER INC (PA)
914 W Cienega Ave, San Dimas (91773-2415)
PHONE..................................909 599-2341
Susan Renaker Nikas, *President*
Mary Lou Salas, *Treasurer*
EMP: 178
SQ FT: 88,964
SALES (est): 14.4MM **Privately Held**
WEB: www.hagenrenaker.com
SIC: 3269 0181 Figures: pottery, china, earthenware & stoneware; nursery stock, growing of

(P-10833)
JAY GEE SALES
Also Called: We-Cel Creations
703 Arroyo St, San Fernando (91340-2248)
PHONE..................................818 365-1311
Gary S Gelzer, *Owner*
Jerry Gelzer, *Owner*
EMP: 11
SQ FT: 1,200
SALES (est): 662.6K **Privately Held**
SIC: 3269 5945 Vases, pottery; ceramics supplies

(P-10834)
POTTERY BY LEVINE ACQUISITION
Also Called: Levine Gifts
1185 Campbell Ave, San Jose (95126-1068)
PHONE..................................408 773-0418
Marc Sobil, *President*
▲ EMP: 25
SQ FT: 12,000
SALES (est): 2.5MM **Privately Held**
WEB: www.electricartwarmers.com
SIC: 3269 Pottery household articles, except kitchen articles

(P-10835)
SANTA BARBARA DESIGN STUDIO (PA)
1600 Pacific Ave, Oxnard (93033-2746)
P.O. Box 6087, Santa Barbara (93160-6087)
PHONE..................................805 966-3883
Raymond Markow, *CEO*
▲ EMP: 53
SQ FT: 2,400
SALES (est): 8.3MM **Privately Held**
WEB: www.santabarbaraceramicdesign.com
SIC: 3269 5719 Art & ornamental ware, pottery; pottery

(P-10836)
STEVEN RHOADES CERAMIC DESIGNS
17595 Harvard Ave Ste C, Irvine (92614-8522)
PHONE..................................949 250-1076
Steven Rhoades, *Owner*
▲ EMP: 12
SALES (est): 771.5K **Privately Held**
SIC: 3269 5023 Art & ornamental ware, pottery; pottery

(P-10837)
STONEWARE DESIGN CO
5332 Polis Dr, La Palma (90623-1787)
PHONE..................................562 432-8145
Mung Huot Taing, *Owner*
EMP: 15
SQ FT: 30,000
SALES: 450K **Privately Held**
SIC: 3269 Stoneware pottery products

(P-10838)
WEST COAST PORCELAIN INC
133 N Sherman Ave, Corona (92882-1842)
PHONE..................................951 278-8680
Jim Hatfield, *President*
Dean Reade, *Vice Pres*
EMP: 20
SQ FT: 30,000
SALES (est): 2.2MM **Privately Held**
SIC: 3269 Chemical porcelain

(P-10839)
WORLD TRADITIONS INC
332 Camino De La Luna, Perris (92571-2992)
PHONE..................................951 990-6346
Mariela Molina, *CEO*
EMP: 30
SALES (est): 1.5MM **Privately Held**
SIC: 3269 Pottery products

(P-10840)
YF MANUFACTURE INC
2455 Maple Ave, Pomona (91767-2232)
PHONE..................................626 768-0029
Peihua Ninci, *President*
EMP: 15
SALES (est): 453.5K **Privately Held**
SIC: 3269 Pottery products

3271 Concrete Block & Brick

(P-10841)
AIR-VOL BLOCK INC
1 Suburban Rd, San Luis Obispo (93401-7523)
P.O. Box 931 (93406-0931)
PHONE..................................805 543-1314
Robert J Miller, *President*
Richard Ayres, *Vice Pres*
Steve Henderson, *Sales Staff*
Brian Avila, *Facilities Mgr*
Steve Arnett, *Manager*
EMP: 40
SQ FT: 1,400
SALES (est): 8.3MM **Privately Held**
WEB: www.airvolblock.com
SIC: 3271 Blocks, concrete or cinder: standard

(P-10842)
ANGELUS BLOCK CO INC
4575 E Vineyard Ave, Oxnard
(93036-1009)
PHONE...................805 485-1137
Sonny Foster, *Manager*
EMP: 45
SALES (corp-wide): 21.6MM **Privately Held**
WEB: www.angelusblock.com
SIC: 3271 5211 Blocks, concrete or cinder: standard; masonry materials & supplies
PA: Angelus Block Co., Inc.
11374 Tuxford St
Sun Valley CA 91352
714 637-8594

(P-10843)
ANGELUS BLOCK CO INC
1705 N Main St, Orange (92865-4116)
PHONE...................714 637-8594
John Suratt, *Manager*
Laurie McDougall, *Plant Mgr*
Laurie Kenney, *Manager*
EMP: 51
SQ FT: 21,528
SALES (corp-wide): 21.6MM **Privately Held**
WEB: www.angelusblock.com
SIC: 3271 Blocks, concrete or cinder: standard
PA: Angelus Block Co., Inc.
11374 Tuxford St
Sun Valley CA 91352
714 637-8594

(P-10844)
APPLIED LIQUID POLYMER
17213 Roseton Ave, Artesia (90701-2645)
PHONE...................562 402-6300
Jon Paul Zentgraf Sr, *Principal*
EMP: 11 EST: 2007
SALES (est): 550K **Privately Held**
SIC: 3271 Brick, concrete

(P-10845)
BASALITE BUILDING PRODUCTS LLC
Also Called: Basalite-Tracy
11888 W Linne Rd, Tracy (95377-8102)
PHONE...................209 833-3670
Bryan Langland, *Executive*
Keith Brady, *Plant Mgr*
EMP: 150
SQ FT: 20,000
SALES (corp-wide): 1.7B **Privately Held**
WEB: www.basalite.com
SIC: 3271 1741 Blocks, concrete or cinder: standard; masonry & other stonework
HQ: Basalite Building Products, Llc
2150 Douglas Blvd Ste 260
Roseville CA 95661
707 678-1901

(P-10846)
CALSTONE COMPANY
13755 Llagas Ave, San Martin (95046-9563)
PHONE...................408 686-9627
Joe Young, *Manager*
EMP: 15
SQ FT: 23,262
SALES (corp-wide): 15.3MM **Privately Held**
WEB: www.calstone.com
SIC: 3271 Blocks, concrete or cinder: standard
PA: Calstone Company
1155 Aster Ave
Sunnyvale CA 94086
408 984-8800

(P-10847)
CALSTONE COMPANY
421 Crystal Way, Galt (95632-8418)
PHONE...................209 745-2981
Ted Schimdt, *Manager*
EMP: 50
SALES (corp-wide): 15.3MM **Privately Held**
WEB: www.calstone.com
SIC: 3271 3272 Blocks, concrete or cinder: standard; concrete products

(P-10848)
CASTLELITE BLOCK LLC (PA)
8615 Robben Rd, Dixon (95620-9608)
PHONE...................707 678-3465
John Espinoza,
EMP: 22
SALES (est): 4.8MM **Privately Held**
WEB: www.castleliteblock.com
SIC: 3271 Blocks, concrete or cinder: standard

(P-10849)
CEMEX CNSTR MTLS PCF LLC
Also Called: Readymix - Fairfield R/M
1601 Cement Hill Rd, Fairfield (94533-2659)
PHONE...................707 422-2520
Vince Bush, *Vice Pres*
EMP: 50 **Privately Held**
WEB: www.rinkermaterials.com
SIC: 3271 Blocks, concrete or cinder: standard
HQ: Cemex Construction Materials Pacific, Llc
1501 Belvedere Rd
West Palm Beach FL 33406
561 833-5555

(P-10850)
CEMEX CNSTR MTLS PCF LLC
Also Called: Readymix - Tremont R/M
7059 Tremont Rd, Dixon (95620-9609)
PHONE...................707 580-3138
Ed Ozbun, *Manager*
EMP: 12 **Privately Held**
WEB: www.rinkermaterials.com
SIC: 3271 Blocks, concrete or cinder: standard
HQ: Cemex Construction Materials Pacific, Llc
1501 Belvedere Rd
West Palm Beach FL 33406
561 833-5555

(P-10851)
EARTHPRO INC
2010 El Camino Real, Santa Clara (95050-4051)
PHONE...................408 294-1920
EMP: 28
SALES (est): 1.8MM **Privately Held**
SIC: 3271

(P-10852)
GLASSPOOLE MASONRY INC
6645 Albatross St, Ventura (93003-6218)
PHONE...................805 368-0129
Brian Glasspoole, *President*
Ron Glasspoole, *Vice Pres*
EMP: 17
SALES: 950K **Privately Held**
SIC: 3271 Concrete block & brick

(P-10853)
GREENSCAPE SOLUTIONS INC
7051 27th St, Riverside (92509-1538)
PHONE...................909 714-8333
Claudia Lanuza, *President*
EMP: 26
SALES (est): 2.2MM **Privately Held**
SIC: 3271 Blocks, concrete: landscape or retaining wall

(P-10854)
L P MCNEAR BRICK CO INC
Also Called: McNear Brick & Block
1 Mcnear Brickyard Rd, San Rafael (94901-8310)
P.O. Box 151380 (94915-1380)
PHONE...................415 453-7702
John E McNear, *CEO*
Jeffrey McNear, *President*
Dan Mc Near, *CFO*
Daniel McNear, *CFO*
Daniel M Near, *Treasurer*
◆ EMP: 70
SALES (est): 13MM **Privately Held**
WEB: www.mcnear.com
SIC: 3271 3251 Brick, concrete; brick clay: common face, glazed, vitrified or hollow

(P-10855)
ORCO BLOCK & HARDSCAPE (PA)
11100 Beach Blvd, Stanton (90680-3219)
PHONE...................714 527-2239
Richard J Muth, *CEO*
Eldon La Bossiere, *Office Mgr*
Mary M Muth, *Admin Sec*
Tom Coyne, *Sales Staff*
Felix Negrete, *Cust Mgr*
EMP: 60
SQ FT: 5,000
SALES (est): 33.4MM **Privately Held**
WEB: www.orco-block.com
SIC: 3271 Architectural concrete: block, split, fluted, screen, etc.; blocks, concrete or cinder: standard

(P-10856)
ORCO BLOCK & HARDSCAPE
3501 Oceanside Blvd, Oceanside (92056-2602)
PHONE...................760 757-1780
EMP: 35
SALES (corp-wide): 33.4MM **Privately Held**
WEB: www.orco-block.com
SIC: 3271 3272 2951 Concrete block & brick; concrete products, precast; asphalt paving mixtures & blocks
PA: Orco Block & Hardscape
11100 Beach Blvd
Stanton CA 90680
714 527-2239

(P-10857)
ORCO BLOCK & HARDSCAPE
26380 Palomar Rd, Romoland (92585-9811)
PHONE...................951 928-3619
Fax: 951 928-3153
EMP: 28
SALES (corp-wide): 33.6MM **Privately Held**
SIC: 3271 3272
PA: Orco Block & Hardscape
11100 Beach Blvd
Stanton CA 90680
714 527-2239

(P-10858)
QUINN DEVELOPMENT CO
Also Called: Mission Concrete Products
5787 Obata Way, Gilroy (95020-7018)
PHONE...................408 842-9320
Charles Quinn Jr, *CEO*
Patrick Quinn, *President*
Dawn Quinn, *Treasurer*
EMP: 12
SQ FT: 36,000
SALES (est): 2.4MM **Privately Held**
SIC: 3271 Blocks, concrete: landscape or retaining wall

(P-10859)
RCP BLOCK & BRICK INC (PA)
8240 Broadway, Lemon Grove (91945-2004)
P.O. Box 579 (91946-0579)
PHONE...................619 460-9101
Michael Finch, *CEO*
Eugene M Chubb, *Corp Secy*
Charles T Finch, *Vice Pres*
EMP: 57
SQ FT: 4,000
SALES (est): 48.2MM **Privately Held**
WEB: www.rcpblock.com
SIC: 3271 5211 5032 Blocks, concrete or cinder: standard; masonry materials & supplies; concrete building products

(P-10860)
RCP BLOCK & BRICK INC
8755 N Magnolia Ave, Santee (92071-4594)
PHONE...................619 448-2240
Randy Scott, *Branch Mgr*
EMP: 20
SALES (corp-wide): 48.2MM **Privately Held**
WEB: www.rcpblock.com
SIC: 3271 5032 5211 Blocks, concrete or cinder: standard; concrete & cinder block; lumber & other building materials

(P-10861)
RCP BLOCK & BRICK INC
75 N 4th Ave, Chula Vista (91910-1007)
PHONE...................619 474-1516
Tim Ostrom, *Manager*
EMP: 24
SALES (corp-wide): 48.2MM **Privately Held**
WEB: www.rcpblock.com
SIC: 3271 5032 5211 Blocks, concrete or cinder: standard; concrete & cinder block; concrete & cinder block
PA: Rcp Block & Brick, Inc.
8240 Broadway
Lemon Grove CA 91945
619 460-9101

(P-10862)
RCP BLOCK & BRICK INC
577 N Vulcan Ave, Encinitas (92024-2120)
PHONE...................760 753-1164
Chico Savage, *Manager*
EMP: 20
SALES (corp-wide): 48.2MM **Privately Held**
WEB: www.rcpblock.com
SIC: 3271 5211 Blocks, concrete or cinder: standard; lumber & other building materials
PA: Rcp Block & Brick, Inc.
8240 Broadway
Lemon Grove CA 91945
619 460-9101

(P-10863)
SOIL RETENTION PRODUCTS INC (PA)
2501 State St, Carlsbad (92008-1624)
PHONE...................951 928-8477
Jan Jansson, *President*
Jan Erik Jansson, *President*
Julia Schmid Janson, *Manager*
◆ EMP: 13
SQ FT: 25,000
SALES (est): 4.1MM **Privately Held**
SIC: 3271 Blocks, concrete: landscape or retaining wall

(P-10864)
SOIL RETENTION PRODUCTS INC
1765 Watson Rd, Romoland (92585)
PHONE...................951 928-8477
Richard Aydlette, *Manager*
Niklas Jansson, *Engineer*
Barbara Oneil, *Engineer*
Don Wedeking, *Sales Staff*
EMP: 13
SALES (corp-wide): 4.1MM **Privately Held**
SIC: 3271 Blocks, concrete: landscape or retaining wall
PA: Soil Retention Products, Inc.
2501 State St
Carlsbad CA 92008
951 928-8477

(P-10865)
SUMMIT SERVICES INC
Also Called: PCA Summit Service
1430 Valle Grande, Escondido (92025-7637)
P.O. Box 270392, San Diego (92198-2392)
PHONE...................760 737-7630
Peter Atkins, *President*
▲ EMP: 12
SALES (est): 1.3MM **Privately Held**
WEB: www.summit-services.com
SIC: 3271 Blocks, concrete: landscape or retaining wall

(P-10866)
UV LANDSCAPING LLC
Also Called: Landscape Contractor
477 Old Natividad Rd, Salinas (93906-1407)
P.O. Box 4022 (93912-4022)
PHONE...................831 275-5296
EMP: 18
SALES (est): 1MM **Privately Held**
SIC: 3271 0782 4971

PRODUCTS & SVCS

(P-10867)
VALLEY ROCK LNDSCPE MATERIAL (PA)
4018 Taylor Rd, Loomis (95650-9004)
PHONE..................916 652-7209
Kurtis D Nixon, *President*
Don Clark, *CFO*
Kelly Nixon, *Vice Pres*
EMP: 13
SQ FT: 300
SALES: 4.1MM Privately Held
SIC: 3271 5261 Blocks, concrete: landscape or retaining wall; nurseries & garden centers

(P-10868)
VIGILANT BALLISTICS INC
1055 W 7th St Ph 33, Los Angeles (90017-2528)
PHONE..................213 212-3232
Paul Tremaine, *President*
EMP: 15
SALES (est): 646.6K Privately Held
SIC: 3271 Blocks, concrete or cinder: standard; blocks, concrete: heat absorbing; architectural concrete: block, split, fluted, screen, etc.

(P-10869)
WESTERN STATES WHOLESALE INC (PA)
Also Called: C-Cure
1420 S Bon View Ave, Ontario (91761-4405)
P.O. Box 3340 (91761-0934)
PHONE..................909 947-0028
Randall Humphreys, *CEO*
Donna Humphreys, *Corp Secy*
Robert Humphreys, *Vice Pres*
James Goette, *Human Resources*
Kelli Clavel, *Purchasing*
▲ EMP: 215
SQ FT: 60,000
SALES (est): 73.1MM Privately Held
WEB: www.wswcorp.com
SIC: 3271 5072 5032 5211 Concrete block & brick; bolts; nuts (hardware); screws; drywall materials; lumber products

3272 Concrete Prdts

(P-10870)
ACKER STONE INDUSTRIES INC (HQ)
13296 Temescal Canyon Rd, Corona (92883-5299)
PHONE..................951 674-0047
Giora Ackerstein, *Ch of Bd*
Anita May, *Asst Controller*
Veronica Trinkle, *Production*
Mike Millard, *Sales Mgr*
Matthew Watters, *Sales Associate*
▲ EMP: 50
SQ FT: 14,000
SALES (est): 13.8MM Privately Held
WEB: www.ackerstone.com
SIC: 3272 3271 Concrete products, precast; paving blocks, concrete; blocks, concrete: landscape or retaining wall
PA: Ackerstein Zvi Ltd.
103 Medinat Hayehudim
Herzliya
995 966-66

(P-10871)
AMERICAN ORNAMENTAL STUDIO
1 Fairview Pl, Millbrae (94030-1114)
PHONE..................650 589-0561
Lara Giambastiani, *President*
EMP: 12
SQ FT: 7,500
SALES (est): 790K Privately Held
SIC: 3272 Precast terrazo or concrete products

(P-10872)
AMERON INTERNATIONAL CORP
1020 B St, Fillmore (93015-1024)
PHONE..................425 258-2616
William Miner, *Branch Mgr*

EMP: 115
SALES (corp-wide): 7.3B Publicly Held
SIC: 3272 Cylinder pipe, prestressed or pretensioned concrete
HQ: Ameron International Corporation
7909 Parkwood Circle Dr
Houston TX 77036
713 375-3700

(P-10873)
AMERON INTERNATIONAL CORP
Ameron Concrete & Steel Pipe
10681 Fthill Blvd Ste 450, Rancho Cucamonga (91730)
PHONE..................909 944-4100
Larry Williams, *Principal*
Debra Perez, *Human Res Mgr*
Debra Stramaglia, *Purchasing*
EMP: 34
SQ FT: 43,240
SALES (corp-wide): 7.3B Publicly Held
WEB: www.ameron.com
SIC: 3272 Concrete products, precast
HQ: Ameron International Corporation
7909 Parkwood Circle Dr
Houston TX 77036
713 375-3700

(P-10874)
AMERON INTERNATIONAL CORP
Ameron Pole Products & Systems
1020 B St, Fillmore (93015-1024)
PHONE..................805 524-0223
West Allison, *Manager*
EMP: 100
SALES (corp-wide): 7.3B Publicly Held
WEB: www.ameron.com
SIC: 3272 3648 3646 3441 Concrete products, precast; lighting equipment; commercial indusl & institutional electric lighting fixtures; fabricated structural metal; steel pipe & tubes
HQ: Ameron International Corporation
7909 Parkwood Circle Dr
Houston TX 77036
713 375-3700

(P-10875)
AMERON INTERNATIONAL CORP
Ameron Concrete & Steel Pipe
10681 Fthill Blvd Ste 450, Rancho Cucamonga (91730)
PHONE..................909 944-4100
David Tantalean, *Sales Staff*
Manuel Ramirez, *Engineer*
EMP: 67
SALES (corp-wide): 7.3B Publicly Held
WEB: www.ameron.com
SIC: 3272 3312 5051 Pipe, concrete or lined with concrete; blast furnaces & steel mills; pipe & tubing, steel
HQ: Ameron International Corporation
7909 Parkwood Circle Dr
Houston TX 77036
713 375-3700

(P-10876)
AMERON INTERNATIONAL CORP
Ameron Water Transm Group
10681 Fthill Blvd Ste 450, Rancho Cucamonga (91730)
PHONE..................909 944-4100
William M Smith, *President*
EMP: 40
SALES (corp-wide): 7.3B Publicly Held
WEB: www.ameron.com
SIC: 3272 3317 Concrete products; steel pipe & tubes
HQ: Ameron International Corporation
7909 Parkwood Circle Dr
Houston TX 77036
713 375-3700

(P-10877)
ANOZIRA INCORPORATED
2415 San Ramon Vly Blvd, San Ramon (94583-5381)
PHONE..................925 771-8400
Brian Haber, *President*
EMP: 15

SALES (est): 1.1MM Privately Held
SIC: 3272 1611 7389 Paving materials, prefabricated concrete; highway & street construction;

(P-10878)
ARCHITCTURAL FACADES UNLIMITED
600 E Luchessa Ave, Gilroy (95020-7068)
PHONE..................408 846-5350
Mary Alice Kinzler Bracken, *CEO*
Francis X Bracken, *Vice Pres*
Francis Bracken, *Vice Pres*
Robert Bianco, *Sales Staff*
Richelda Domondon, *Sr Project Mgr*
EMP: 75
SQ FT: 35,000
SALES (est): 16.5MM Privately Held
WEB: www.architecturalfacades.com
SIC: 3272 Concrete products, precast

(P-10879)
AUBURN TILE INC
545 W Main St, Ontario (91762-3718)
P.O. Box 10 (91762-8010)
PHONE..................909 984-2841
Udo Helferich, *President*
Steve Helferich, *Vice Pres*
EMP: 17
SQ FT: 6,000
SALES (est): 1.5MM Privately Held
WEB: www.auburntile.com
SIC: 3272 Roofing tile & slabs, concrete

(P-10880)
AVILAS GARDEN ART (PA)
14608 Merrill Ave, Fontana (92335-4219)
PHONE..................909 350-4546
Ralph G Avila, *Owner*
EMP: 60
SQ FT: 7,000
SALES (est): 9.1MM Privately Held
SIC: 3272 5261 5211 5199 Precast terrazo or concrete products; lawn ornaments; masonry materials & supplies; statuary

(P-10881)
BASALITE BUILDING PRODUCTS LLC (HQ)
2150 Douglas Blvd Ste 260, Roseville (95661-3873)
PHONE..................707 678-1901
Scott Weber, *President*
Dallas Barrett, *CFO*
Richard Blickensderfer, *Bd of Directors*
Alfred Mueller, *Bd of Directors*
Fredrick Nelson, *Bd of Directors*
◆ EMP: 37
SALES (est): 199.3MM
SALES (corp-wide): 1.7B Privately Held
WEB: www.basalite.com
SIC: 3272 Concrete products, precast
PA: Pacific Coast Building Products, Inc.
10600 White Rock Rd # 100
Rancho Cordova CA 95670
916 631-6500

(P-10882)
BASALITE BUILDING PRODUCTS LLC
Also Called: Epic Plastics
104 E Turner Rd, Lodi (95240-0673)
PHONE..................209 333-6161
Dallas Barrett Jr, *CFO*
Lupe Salazar, *Opers Mgr*
Rob Navarre, *Director*
EMP: 25
SALES (corp-wide): 1.7B Privately Held
SIC: 3272 Concrete products
HQ: Basalite Building Products, Llc
2150 Douglas Blvd Ste 260
Roseville CA 95661
707 678-1901

(P-10883)
BENNETT & BENNETT INC
955 S Commerce Way, Lemoore (93245-9001)
PHONE..................559 896-0200
Bill Sharp, *Manager*
EMP: 15

SALES (est): 2.4MM
SALES (corp-wide): 18.9MM Privately Held
WEB: www.bennettbennett.com
SIC: 3272 5211 Pipe, concrete or lined with concrete; masonry materials & supplies
PA: Bennett & Bennett, Inc.
955 S Commerce Way
Lemoore CA 93245
559 582-9336

(P-10884)
BESCAL INC
Also Called: Bes Concrete Products
10304 W Linne Rd, Tracy (95377-9128)
PHONE..................209 836-3492
Mark Jurich, *President*
EMP: 48
SALES (est): 6.7MM Privately Held
WEB: www.bescal.com
SIC: 3272

(P-10885)
BLACKS IRRIGATIONS SYSTEMS
Also Called: Black's Irrigation Systems
144 N Chowchilla Blvd, Chowchilla (93610)
PHONE..................559 665-4891
James Black, *President*
Cheryl Black, *Corp Secy*
EMP: 12
SQ FT: 1,500
SALES (est): 1.7MM Privately Held
SIC: 3272 Irrigation pipe, concrete

(P-10886)
BOND MANUFACTURING CO INC (PA)
1700 W 4th St, Antioch (94509-1008)
PHONE..................925 252-1135
Daryl Merritt, *CEO*
Ronald Merritt, *Ch of Bd*
Cameron Jenkins, *Principal*
Catherine Sulprizio, *Controller*
◆ EMP: 220
SQ FT: 250,000
SALES (est): 103MM Privately Held
WEB: www.bondmfg.com
SIC: 3272 5083 Fireplaces, concrete; lawn & garden machinery & equipment; garden machinery & equipment

(P-10887)
BONSAL AMERICAN INC
16005 Phoebe Ave, La Mirada (90638-5607)
PHONE..................714 523-1530
Frank Maggio, *Branch Mgr*
EMP: 34
SALES (corp-wide): 29.7B Privately Held
WEB: www.bonsalamerican.com
SIC: 3272 1442 3253 2899 Dry mixture concrete; construction sand & gravel; ceramic wall & floor tile; chemical preparations
HQ: Bonsal American, Inc.
625 Griffith Rd Ste 100
Charlotte NC 28217
704 525-1621

(P-10888)
BORAL ROOFING LLC
1990 Riverview Dr, San Bernardino (92408-3044)
PHONE..................909 796-8324
Kevin Oneil, *Superintendent*
EMP: 45
SALES (corp-wide): 3.1B Privately Held
WEB: www.monierlifetile.com
SIC: 3272 3259 Roofing tile & slabs, concrete; roofing tile, clay
HQ: Boral Roofing Llc
7575 Irvine Center Dr # 100
Irvine CA 92618
949 756-1605

(P-10889)
BORAL ROOFING LLC
Also Called: Monier Lifetile
3511 N Riverside Ave, Rialto (92377-3803)
PHONE..................909 822-4407
Kevin O Neil, *Manager*
EMP: 80 Privately Held
WEB: www.monierlifetile.com

▲ = Import ▼=Export
◆ =Import/Export

SIC: **3272 3251 5032 2952** Roofing tile & slabs, concrete; brick clay: common face, glazed, vitrified or hollow; cinders; asphalt felts & coatings
HQ: Boral Roofing Llc
7575 Irvine Center Dr # 100
Irvine CA 92618
949 756-1605

(P-10890)
BORDER PRECAST INC
615 Us Highway 111, Brawley (92227-2903)
PHONE..................................760 351-1233
EMP: 10
SALES (est): 710K **Privately Held**
SIC: **3272**

(P-10891)
BRIGHT LITE STRUCTURES LLC
90 S Park St, San Francisco (94107-1807)
PHONE..................................636 575-7559
Rick Holman, *Med Doctor*
EMP: 10
SALES (est): 20.8K **Privately Held**
SIC: **3272** Concrete stuctural support & building material

(P-10892)
BUILDMAT PLUS INVESTMENTS INC
Also Called: Metroll
15435 Arrow Blvd Bldg A, Fontana (92335-1222)
P.O. Box 305, Rancho Cucamonga (91739-0305)
PHONE..................................909 823-7663
Shamsher Kanji, *CEO*
EMP: 12 **EST:** 2011
SQ FT: 17,000
SALES (est): 3.4MM **Privately Held**
SIC: **3272** Concrete stuctural support & building material

(P-10893)
CALAVERAS MATERIALS INC
1100 Lowe Rd, Hughson (95326-9178)
PHONE..................................209 883-0448
George Lefler, *Manager*
EMP: 11
SALES (corp-wide): 20.3B **Privately Held**
SIC: **3272** Concrete products
HQ: Calaveras Materials Inc.
1100 Lowe Rd
Hughson CA 95326
209 883-0448

(P-10894)
CALERA CORPORATION
Also Called: Chemetry
7697 Highway 1, Moss Landing (95039-9697)
PHONE..................................831 731-6000
Ryan Gilliam, *CEO*
Jill Aufricht, *CFO*
Bob Snyder, *Security Dir*
Randy Seeker, *CTO*
Tom Albrecht, *Research*
EMP: 40 **EST:** 1985
SALES (est): 15.2MM **Privately Held**
SIC: **3272 2869** Concrete products; industrial organic chemicals

(P-10895)
CALIFORNIA CONCRETE PIPE CORP
2960 S Highway 99, Stockton (95215-8047)
PHONE..................................209 466-4212
James B Schack, *Ch of Bd*
Cy Thomson III, *Vice Pres*
Michael Lynch, *Admin Sec*
Robert Quinn, *Asst Sec*
EMP: 19 **EST:** 1980
SQ FT: 2,440
SALES (est): 1.9MM
SALES (corp-wide): 29.7B **Privately Held**
SIC: **3272** Sewer pipe, concrete
HQ: Oldcastle Precast, Inc.
1002 15th St Sw Ste 110
Auburn WA 98001
253 833-2777

(P-10896)
CALIFORNIA PRECAST STONE MFG
1796 Karen Ct, Hemet (92545-1644)
P.O. Box 40 (92546-0040)
PHONE..................................951 657-7913
Quint Mumford, *President*
John Mumford, *Vice Pres*
EMP: 16
SQ FT: 7,700
SALES: 1.2MM **Privately Held**
WEB: www.californiaprecast.com
SIC: **3272** Concrete products, precast

(P-10897)
CEMEX CNSTR MTLS PCF LLC
Also Called: Readymix - Old River Rm
11638 Old River Rd, Bakersfield (93311-9798)
PHONE..................................661 396-0510
Keith Stogeell, *General Mgr*
EMP: 30 **Privately Held**
SIC: **3272** Concrete products
HQ: Cemex Construction Materials Pacific, Llc
1501 Belvedere Rd
West Palm Beach FL 33406
561 833-5555

(P-10898)
CENTINELA CONCRETE VAULT CO
Also Called: Enderle Vault Co
720 E Florence Ave, Inglewood (90301-1406)
PHONE..................................310 674-2115
Walter Birch, *President*
EMP: 16 **EST:** 1963
SQ FT: 14,000
SALES (est): 1.3MM **Privately Held**
WEB: www.enderlevault.com
SIC: **3272** Burial vaults, concrete or precast terrazzo

(P-10899)
CENTRAL PRECAST CONCRETE INC
Also Called: Western Concrete Products
3500 Boulder St, Pleasanton (94566-4700)
P.O. Box 727 (94566-0868)
PHONE..................................925 417-6854
Don Hmphreys, *President*
Vince Bormolini, *Corp Secy*
Charles Bormolini, *Vice Pres*
EMP: 30
SQ FT: 3,000
SALES (est): 2.6MM
SALES (corp-wide): 1.3B **Publicly Held**
WEB: www.westernconcreteproducts.com
SIC: **3272 1442** Manhole covers or frames, concrete; culvert pipe, concrete; sewer pipe, concrete; construction sand & gravel
PA: U.S. Concrete, Inc.
331 N Main St
Euless TX 76039
817 835-4105

(P-10900)
CHANNEL SYSTEMS INC
74 98th Ave, Oakland (94603-1002)
PHONE..................................510 568-7170
Lauren Bockmiller, *President*
Douglas Bockmiller, *Treasurer*
▲ EMP: 45
SQ FT: 20,000
SALES (est): 4.6MM **Privately Held**
WEB: www.channelsystems.com
SIC: **3272 5031 1542 1541** Building materials, except block or brick: concrete; building materials, interior; nonresidential construction; industrial buildings & warehouses

(P-10901)
CHRISTY VAULT COMPANY (PA)
1000 Collins Ave, Colma (94014-3299)
PHONE..................................650 994-1378
Robert B Christensen, *Ch of Bd*
Gregg Christensen, *Vice Pres*
EMP: 30
SQ FT: 16,500
SALES (est): 5.3MM **Privately Held**
SIC: **3272** Burial vaults, concrete or precast terrazzo; concrete products, precast

(P-10902)
CLARK - PACIFIC CORPORATION (PA)
Also Called: Clark Pacific
1980 S River Rd, West Sacramento (95691-2817)
PHONE..................................916 371-0305
Robert Clark, *President*
Don Clark, *President*
Jim Clark, *Social Dir*
Bob Clark, *Principal*
Robert E Clark, *Principal*
▲ EMP: 300
SQ FT: 20,000
SALES (est): 156.6MM **Privately Held**
WEB: www.clarkpacific.com
SIC: **3272 5032** Concrete products, precast; brick, stone & related material

(P-10903)
CLARK - PACIFIC CORPORATION
131 Los Angeles St, Irwindale (91706)
PHONE..................................626 962-8751
Ed Wopschall, *Branch Mgr*
EMP: 75
SALES (est): 9.1MM
SALES (corp-wide): 156.6MM **Privately Held**
SIC: **3272** Concrete products, precast
PA: Clark - Pacific Corporation
1980 S River Rd
West Sacramento CA 95691
916 371-0305

(P-10904)
CLARK - PACIFIC CORPORATION
13592 Slover Ave, Fontana (92337-6978)
PHONE..................................909 823-1433
Donald Clark, *Owner*
EMP: 120
SALES (corp-wide): 156.6MM **Privately Held**
WEB: www.clarkpacific.com
SIC: **3272 5211** Concrete products, precast; masonry materials & supplies
PA: Clark - Pacific Corporation
1980 S River Rd
West Sacramento CA 95691
916 371-0305

(P-10905)
CLARK - PACIFIC CORPORATION
3478 Buskirk Ave Ste 1039, Pleasant Hill (94523-4344)
PHONE..................................925 746-7176
Wayne Edwards, *Branch Mgr*
EMP: 63
SALES (corp-wide): 156.6MM **Privately Held**
SIC: **3272** Concrete products
PA: Clark - Pacific Corporation
1980 S River Rd
West Sacramento CA 95691
916 371-0305

(P-10906)
CON-FAB CALIFORNIA CORPORATION (PA)
Also Called: Confab
1910 Lathrop Rd, Lathrop (95330-9708)
PHONE..................................209 249-4700
Philip French, *President*
Miaja French, *Shareholder*
Emily Porter, *HR Admin*
Alan Leatham, *Manager*
EMP: 20
SQ FT: 2,400
SALES (est): 4.8MM **Privately Held**
WEB: www.confabca.com
SIC: **3272** Concrete products, precast

(P-10907)
CONCRETEWORKS STUDIO INC
1137 57th Ave, Oakland (94621-4427)
PHONE..................................510 534-7141
Mark Rogero, *CEO*
Sohan Mutucumarana, *Pharmacy Dir*
Ll Saunders, *Accounting Mgr*
Sophia Pennella, *Opers Mgr*
James Macko, *Prdtn Mgr*
EMP: 15
SQ FT: 6,000

SALES: 3.5MM **Privately Held**
WEB: www.concreteworks.com
SIC: **3272** Precast terrazo or concrete products

(P-10908)
COOK CONCRETE PRODUCTS INC
5461 Eastside Rd, Redding (96001-4533)
P.O. Box 720280 (96099-7280)
PHONE..................................530 243-2562
L Edward Shaw, *President*
EMP: 35
SQ FT: 1,000
SALES (est): 6MM **Privately Held**
WEB: www.cookconcreteproducts.com
SIC: **3272** Concrete products, precast

(P-10909)
CORDEIRO VAULT CO (PA)
281 5th St, Vallejo (94590-7209)
P.O. Box 1724 (94590-0172)
PHONE..................................707 552-1045
Robert A Cordeiro, *President*
Gloria Cordeiro, *Treasurer*
Danny Cordeiro, *Admin Sec*
EMP: 24
SQ FT: 9,000
SALES (est): 3.3MM **Privately Held**
SIC: **3272** Burial vaults, concrete or precast terrazzo; grave markers, concrete

(P-10910)
CORESLAB STRUCTURES LA INC
150 W Placentia Ave, Perris (92571-3200)
PHONE..................................951 943-9119
Mario Franciosa, *CEO*
Lou Franciosa, *President*
Jorgen Clausen, *Vice Pres*
Robert H Konoske, *Vice Pres*
Bob Konoske, *General Mgr*
EMP: 200
SQ FT: 25,000
SALES (est): 38.7MM **Privately Held**
SIC: **3272** Concrete products, precast
HQ: Coreslab Holdings U S Inc
332 Jones Rd Suite 1
Stoney Creek ON L8E 5
905 643-0220

(P-10911)
CREATIVE STONE MFG INC (PA)
Also Called: Coronado Stone Products
11191 Calabash Ave, Fontana (92337-7018)
PHONE..................................909 357-8295
Melton Bacon, *President*
Scott Ebersole, *Vice Pres*
Amy Toledo, *Comptroller*
Bob Ratkovic, *Production*
Coy Green, *Sales Staff*
▲ EMP: 180
SQ FT: 10,000
SALES (est): 57.7MM **Privately Held**
WEB: www.arroyo.net
SIC: **3272** Siding, precast stone

(P-10912)
CULTURED STONE CORPORATION (DH)
Hwy 29 & Tower Rd, NAPA (94559)
PHONE..................................707 255-1727
Stephen Nowak, *CEO*
EMP: 739
SQ FT: 17,000
SALES (est): 34MM **Publicly Held**
WEB: www.culturedstone.com
SIC: **3272 3281** Cast stone, concrete; cut stone & stone products
HQ: Owens Corning Sales, Llc
1 Owens Corning Pkwy
Toledo OH 43659
419 248-8000

(P-10913)
DCC GENERAL ENGRG CONTRS INC
2180 Meyers Ave, Escondido (92029-1001)
PHONE..................................760 480-7400
Frank D'Agostini, *President*
Scott Woods, *Vice Pres*
EMP: 75
SQ FT: 2,100

SALES (est): 12.6MM **Privately Held**
SIC: 3272 1771 3531 Concrete products;
curb & sidewalk contractors; asphalt
plant, including gravel-mix type

(P-10914)
DESIGN INDUSTRIES INC
17918 Brook Dr W, Madera (93638-9624)
P.O. Box 26386, Fresno (93729-6386)
PHONE....................559 675-3535
Robert Cisco, *President*
James Cisco, *Vice Pres*
EMP: 15
SQ FT: 8,283
SALES: 1.7MM **Privately Held**
SIC: 3272 1791 Concrete stuctural sup-
port & building material; concrete rein-
forcement, placing of

(P-10915)
DIVERSITECH CORPORATION
9252 Cassia Rd, Adelanto (92301-3936)
PHONE....................760 246-4200
Nelson Janapha, *Manager*
EMP: 10
SQ FT: 60,000
SALES (corp-wide): 69.9MM **Privately
Held**
SIC: 3272 Concrete products
HQ: Diversitech Corporation
6650 Sugarloaf Pkwy # 100
Duluth GA 30097
678 542-3600

(P-10916)
DIXIETRUSS INC
Also Called: Mission Truss
12538 Vigilante Rd, Lakeside (92040-1112)
PHONE....................619 873-0440
Francisco Hernandez, *CEO*
Erica Chadbourne, *Finance Mgr*
EMP: 10
SALES (est): 1.6MM **Privately Held**
SIC: 3272 Roofing tile & slabs, concrete

(P-10917)
DO IT RIGHT PRODUCTS LLC
44321 62nd St W, Lancaster (93536-7533)
PHONE....................661 722-9664
Elana K Sherve, *Principal*
EMP: 12 EST: 2008
SALES (est): 1.8MM **Privately Held**
SIC: 3272 Concrete products

(P-10918)
DYNAMIC PRE-CAST CO INC
5300 Sebastopol Rd, Santa Rosa
(95407-6423)
PHONE....................707 573-1110
Guenter Meiburg, *President*
Elaine Meiburg, *Vice Pres*
Sharon Elder, *Finance Mgr*
EMP: 15
SQ FT: 2,500
SALES (est): 3.8MM **Privately Held**
WEB: www.dynamicprecast.com
SIC: 3272 1771 Concrete products, pre-
cast; concrete work

(P-10919)
EDESSA INC
Also Called: Thompson Building Materials
11027 Cherry Ave, Fontana (92337-7118)
PHONE....................909 823-1377
Fax: 909 823-8409
▲ EMP: 23
SALES (est): 4.2MM **Privately Held**
SIC: 3272 5032

(P-10920)
EISEL ENTERPRISES INC
714 Fee Ana St, Placentia (92870-6705)
PHONE....................714 993-1706
Lyle Eisel, *President*
Janis Eisel, *Corp Secy*
April Davis, *Vice Pres*
Kim Webster, *Vice Pres*
Eric Webster, *General Mgr*
EMP: 35
SQ FT: 4,000
SALES (est): 6.1MM **Privately Held**
SIC: 3272 Meter boxes, concrete

(P-10921)
ELK CORPORATION OF TEXAS
6200 S Zerker Rd, Shafter (93263-9612)
PHONE....................661 391-3900
Gus Freshwater, *Vice Pres*
EMP: 150
SALES (corp-wide): 2.7B **Privately Held**
SIC: 3272 2952 Precast terrazo or con-
crete products; asphalt felts & coatings
HQ: Elk Corporation Of Texas
14911 Quorum Dr Ste 600
Dallas TX 75254

(P-10922)
EMPIRE PRE CAST
19473 Grand Ave, Lake Elsinore
(92530-6341)
PHONE....................951 609-1590
Carol Stahl, *Owner*
EMP: 25 EST: 2000
SALES: 2MM **Privately Held**
SIC: 3272 Precast terrazo or concrete
products

(P-10923)
FARLEY PAVING STONE CO INC
Also Called: Farley Interlocking Pav Stones
75135 Sheryl Ave Ste A, Palm Desert
(92211-5114)
P.O. Box 10946 (92255-0946)
PHONE....................760 773-3960
Shon Farley, *Vice Pres*
Charissa Farley, *President*
Hector Gonzalez, *Vice Pres*
EMP: 70
SQ FT: 900
SALES (est): 8.9MM **Privately Held**
SIC: 3272 3531 3281 Paving materials,
prefabricated concrete; pavers; curbing,
paving & walkway stone; paving blocks,
cut stone

(P-10924)
FAST ACCESS INC
Also Called: Elements Archtectural Surfaces
1765 Howard Pl, Redlands (92373-8090)
PHONE....................909 748-1245
Michael Menendez, *CEO*
EMP: 16
SALES (est): 1.3MM **Privately Held**
SIC: 3272 Concrete products

(P-10925)
FIOLAS DEVELOPMENT LLC
Also Called: Fiola Development
5362 Bolsa Ave Ste H, Huntington Beach
(92649-1055)
PHONE....................714 893-7559
John C Fiola, *Mng Member*
Magiee Fiola, *Vice Pres*
EMP: 10
SALES (est): 1MM **Privately Held**
SIC: 3272 Building materials, except block
or brick: concrete

(P-10926)
FIORE STONE INC
19930 Jolora Ave, Corona (92881-4615)
PHONE....................909 424-0221
Bruce Raabe, *President*
EMP: 45
SQ FT: 160,000
SALES (est): 7MM **Privately Held**
SIC: 3272 Concrete products, precast

(P-10927)
FLORENCE & NEW ITLN ART CO
INC
27735 Industrial Blvd, Hayward
(94545-4045)
PHONE....................510 785-9674
Mariano Fontana, *CEO*
Gerard Fontana, *CFO*
Marc Fontana, *Vice Pres*
Rick M Moore, *Sales Mgr*
▲ EMP: 40
SQ FT: 30,000
SALES (est): 6.6MM **Privately Held**
WEB: www.florenceartcompany.com
SIC: 3272 Concrete products

(P-10928)
FOAMTEC LLC
4420 Commodity Way Ste A, Shingle
Springs (95682-7250)
PHONE....................916 851-8621
Jeffrey Lemon, *Executive*
◆ EMP: 12
SQ FT: 9,000
SALES: 1.2MM **Privately Held**
SIC: 3272 Building materials, except block
or brick: concrete

(P-10929)
FOLSOM READY MIX INC (PA)
3401 Fitzgerald Rd, Rancho Cordova
(95742-6815)
PHONE....................916 851-8300
Scott Silva, *President*
Randy Barnes, *Vice Pres*
Rick Masciovecchio, *Vice Pres*
Lynne Walker, *Accounting Mgr*
Jesse Diaz, *Mfg Staff*
EMP: 30
SALES (est): 9.5MM **Privately Held**
WEB: www.folsomreadymix.com
SIC: 3272 3273 Concrete stuctural sup-
port & building material; ready-mixed con-
crete

(P-10930)
FORTERRA PIPE & PRECAST
LLC
7020 Tokay Ave, Sacramento
(95828-2418)
PHONE....................916 379-9695
Drew Black, *Manager*
EMP: 60
SALES (corp-wide): 1.5B **Publicly Held**
SIC: 3272 Pipe, concrete or lined with con-
crete
HQ: Forterra Pipe & Precast, Llc
511 E John Carpenter Fwy
Irving TX 75062
469 458-7973

(P-10931)
FORTERRA PIPE & PRECAST
LLC
Also Called: South Coast Materials Co
9229 Harris Plant Rd, San Diego
(92145-0001)
P.O. Box 639069 (92163-9069)
PHONE....................858 715-5600
Carol Hartwig, *Branch Mgr*
Ron Thompson, *Plant Mgr*
Ian Firth, *Plant Supt*
EMP: 15
SALES (corp-wide): 1.5B **Publicly Held**
WEB: www.hansonplc.com
SIC: 3272 Concrete products
HQ: Forterra Pipe & Precast, Llc
511 E John Carpenter Fwy
Irving TX 75062
469 458-7973

(P-10932)
GEORGE L THROOP CO
Also Called: Do It Best
444 N Fair Oaks Ave, Pasadena
(91103-3619)
P.O. Box 92405 (91109-2405)
PHONE....................626 796-0285
Jeffrey Throop, *President*
Ann T Comey, *Corp Secy*
George L Throop III, *Vice Pres*
▲ EMP: 32
SQ FT: 10,500
SALES (est): 9.1MM **Privately Held**
SIC: 3272 5211 5251 Concrete products;
millwork & lumber; cement; hardware

(P-10933)
GEORGETOWN PRECAST INC
2420 Georgia Slide Rd, Georgetown
(95634-2201)
P.O. Box 65 (95634-0065)
PHONE....................530 333-4404
Ronny R Beam, *President*
EMP: 12 EST: 1974
SQ FT: 2,600
SALES (est): 1.5MM **Privately Held**
SIC: 3272 3273 5039 Septic tanks, con-
crete; tanks, concrete; manhole covers or
frames, concrete; ready-mixed concrete;
septic tanks

(P-10934)
GIANNINI GARDEN ORNAMENTS
INC
225 Shaw Rd, South San Francisco
(94080-6605)
PHONE....................650 873-4493
Piera Giannini, *President*
Alessandro Giannini, *Sales Staff*
Joan Chiorato, *Manager*
▲ EMP: 30
SALES (est): 6.2MM **Privately Held**
WEB: www.gianninigarden.com
SIC: 3272 Concrete products

(P-10935)
HEADWATERS INCORPORATED
1345 Philadelphia St, Pomona
(91766-5564)
PHONE....................909 627-9066
Jim Johnson, *Manager*
EMP: 15
SALES (corp-wide): 3.1B **Privately Held**
SIC: 3272 Concrete products
HQ: Headwaters Incorporated
10701 S River Front Pkwy # 300
South Jordan UT 84095

(P-10936)
HEITMAN BROOKS II LLC (PA)
Also Called: Brooks Products
1850 S Parco Ave, Ontario (91761-8302)
PHONE....................909 947-7470
Micheal Heitman, *Mng Member*
Frederick C Heitman,
EMP: 14
SQ FT: 25,000
SALES: 3.7MM **Privately Held**
WEB: www.brooksproducts.net
SIC: 3272 Concrete products, precast

(P-10937)
HILFIKER PIPE CO
Also Called: Hilfiker Retaining Walls
1902 Hilfiker Ln, Eureka (95503-5711)
PHONE....................707 443-5091
Harold Hilfiker, *President*
Brenda Peterson, *Treasurer*
Bill Hilfiker, *Vice Pres*
William K Hilfiker, *Vice Pres*
Brian Stringer, *Vice Pres*
EMP: 30 EST: 1900
SQ FT: 14,400
SALES (est): 5.3MM **Privately Held**
WEB: www.hilfiker.com
SIC: 3272 3315 5051 5074 Concrete
products, precast; wall & ceiling squares,
concrete; welded steel wire fabric; pipe &
tubing, steel; pipes & fittings, plastic

(P-10938)
HILLHOLDER BLOCKS BY
MODERN
3239 Bancroft Dr, Spring Valley
(91977-2613)
PHONE....................619 463-6344
Jack Spencer, *President*
Deborah Fehlberg, *Vice Pres*
EMP: 13
SQ FT: 3,890
SALES (est): 1MM **Privately Held**
SIC: 3272 Concrete products, precast

(P-10939)
HYDRO CONDUIT OF TEXAS LP
Also Called: Colton Facilities
1205 S Rancho Ave, Colton (92324-3342)
PHONE....................909 825-1500
Rob Courney, *Branch Mgr*
EMP: 18 **Privately Held**
WEB: www.prestressservices.com
SIC: 3272 5051 3599 Pipe, concrete or
lined with concrete; pipe & tubing, steel;
machine shop, jobbing & repair
HQ: Hydro Conduit Of Texas, Lp
6560 Langfield Rd 3-H
Houston TX 77092

(P-10940)
INDEPNDENT FLR TSTG INSPTN
INC
2300 Clayton Rd Ste 1240, Concord
(94520-2121)
PHONE....................925 676-7682

▲ = Import ▼=Export
◆ =Import/Export

Lee Eliseian, *President*
EMP: 16
SALES (est): 381.1K **Privately Held**
SIC: 3272 8611 Floor slabs & tiles, precast concrete; business associations

(P-10941)
J & R CONCRETE PRODUCTS INC
440 W Markham St, Perris (92571-8138)
PHONE..................................951 943-5855
Raul Ramirez, *President*
EMP: 42
SQ FT: 40,000
SALES (est): 7.5MM **Privately Held**
SIC: 3272 Meter boxes, concrete

(P-10942)
JENSEN ENTERPRISES INC
7210 State Highway 32, Orland (95963-9790)
PHONE..................................530 865-4277
Don Jensen, *Branch Mgr*
EMP: 15
SALES (corp-wide): 154.1MM **Privately Held**
WEB: www.jensenprecast.net
SIC: 3272 5039 Concrete products, precast; septic tanks
PA: Jensen Enterprises, Inc.
825 Steneri Way
Sparks NV 89431
775 352-2700

(P-10943)
JENSEN ENTERPRISES INC
Also Called: Jensen Precast
14221 San Bernardino Ave, Fontana (92335-5232)
PHONE..................................909 357-7264
Carol Kohanle, *Manager*
Terry Velarde, *Human Res Mgr*
Ray Cuevas, *Manager*
Evelyn Ponce, *Clerk*
EMP: 300
SALES (corp-wide): 154.1MM **Privately Held**
SIC: 3272 7699 5211 5039 Concrete products, precast; waste cleaning services; masonry materials & supplies; septic tanks; concrete forms, sheet metal
PA: Jensen Enterprises, Inc.
825 Steneri Way
Sparks NV 89431
775 352-2700

(P-10944)
KRI STAR ENTERPRISES INC (PA)
360 Sutton Pl, Santa Rosa (95407-8121)
PHONE..................................800 579-8819
Douglas Allard, *President*
▲ EMP: 36
SALES (est): 3.6MM **Privately Held**
WEB: www.kristar.com
SIC: 3272 Liquid catch basins, tanks & covers: concrete

(P-10945)
KRISTICH-MONTEREY PIPE CO INC
225 Salinas Rd Ste B, Royal Oaks (95076-5253)
P.O. Box 606, Watsonville (95077-0606)
PHONE..................................831 724-4186
Chris Kristich, *President*
EMP: 12
SQ FT: 2,000
SALES (est): 2.1MM **Privately Held**
SIC: 3272 Pipe, concrete or lined with concrete

(P-10946)
KTI INCORPORATED
Also Called: Rialto Concrete Products
3009 N Laurel Ave, Rialto (92377-3725)
PHONE..................................909 434-1888
Kenneth D Thompson, *CEO*
Daniel J Deming, *President*
Jerry Cowden, *Vice Pres*
EMP: 100
SQ FT: 400
SALES (est): 32.3MM **Privately Held**
SIC: 3272 Concrete products, precast

(P-10947)
L K LEHMAN TRUCKING
Also Called: A & L Ready-Mix
19333 Industrial Dr, Sonora (95370-9232)
P.O. Box 9 (95370-0009)
PHONE..................................209 532-5586
Vince Estosipo, *Manager*
EMP: 26
SALES (corp-wide): 3.2MM **Privately Held**
SIC: 3272 3429 3273 3271 Concrete products, precast; manufactured hardware (general); ready-mixed concrete; concrete block & brick; construction sand & gravel
PA: L. K. Lehman Trucking
19333 Industrial Dr
Sonora CA 95370
209 532-5586

(P-10948)
LEBATA INC
Also Called: A & A Ready Mix Concrete
4621 Teller Ave Ste 130, Newport Beach (92660-2165)
PHONE..................................949 253-2800
Kurt Caillier, *President*
John Gaeta, *CFO*
Ray Sansom, *Sales Staff*
EMP: 30
SALES (est): 4.6MM **Privately Held**
SIC: 3272 Dry mixture concrete

(P-10949)
LEGACY VULCAN LLC
3195 Andreasen Dr, Lafayette (94549-4801)
P.O. Box 2472, Richmond (94802)
PHONE..................................925 284-4686
Larry P Boland, *President*
Tom Gay, *Managing Prtnr*
Tabitha Jones, *Human Resources*
Larry Clemons, *Purchasing*
Stacy Pickett, *Manager*
EMP: 15 **Publicly Held**
WEB: www.vulcanmaterials.com
SIC: 3272 Concrete products
HQ: Legacy Vulcan, Llc
1200 Urban Center Dr
Vestavia AL 35242
205 298-3000

(P-10950)
LEGACY VULCAN LLC
Also Called: Sales Office
16013 E Foothill Blvd, Irwindale (91702-2813)
PHONE..................................626 856-6148
Bill Watts, *Ltd Ptnr*
EMP: 15 **Publicly Held**
WEB: www.vulcanmaterials.com
SIC: 3272 Concrete products
HQ: Legacy Vulcan, Llc
1200 Urban Center Dr
Vestavia AL 35242
205 298-3000

(P-10951)
LEGACY VULCAN LLC
Also Called: San Emidio Quarry
Hwy W 166 Of Old Rver Rd, Bakersfield (93313)
PHONE..................................661 858-2673
Dan Bectel, *General Mgr*
EMP: 30 **Publicly Held**
WEB: www.vulcanmaterials.com
SIC: 3272 Concrete products
HQ: Legacy Vulcan, Llc
1200 Urban Center Dr
Vestavia AL 35242
205 298-3000

(P-10952)
LEGACY VULCAN LLC
Also Called: Gustine Ready Mix
28525 Bambouer Rd, Gustine (95322-9570)
PHONE..................................209 854-3088
EMP: 16
SALES (corp-wide): 3.5B **Publicly Held**
SIC: 3272
HQ: Legacy Vulcan, Llc
1200 Urban Center Dr
Vestavia AL 35242
205 298-3000

(P-10953)
LEGACY VULCAN LLC
Also Called: Oceanside Ready Mix
2925 Industry St, Oceanside (92054-4813)
PHONE..................................760 439-0624
Al Thrower, *Manager*
EMP: 14 **Publicly Held**
WEB: www.vulcanmaterials.com
SIC: 3272 Concrete products
HQ: Legacy Vulcan, Llc
1200 Urban Center Dr
Vestavia AL 35242
205 298-3000

(P-10954)
LINDSAY TRNSP SOLUTIONS INC (HQ)
Also Called: Barrier Systems Sales & Svc
180 River Rd, Rio Vista (94571-1208)
PHONE..................................707 374-6800
Richard W Parod, *CEO*
David B Downing, *President*
Chris Sanders, *COO*
Mark A Roth, *Treasurer*
James Raabe, *Vice Pres*
▲ EMP: 85
SQ FT: 45,000
SALES (est): 62.3MM
SALES (corp-wide): 547.7MM **Publicly Held**
WEB: www.barriersystemsinc.com
SIC: 3272 3559 Concrete products, precast; concrete products machinery
PA: Lindsay Corporation
2222 N 111th St
Omaha NE 68164
402 829-6800

(P-10955)
LITE STONE CONCRETE LLC
12650 Highway 67 Ste B, Lakeside (92040-1132)
PHONE..................................619 596-9151
John B Ward, *Manager*
Van Hunt, *Plant Mgr*
Edward Van Hunt, *Manager*
EMP: 14
SALES (est): 1.7MM **Privately Held**
WEB: www.litestoneconcrete.com
SIC: 3272 Concrete products

(P-10956)
MERLOS PRECAST PRODUCTS
13115 S Broadway, Los Angeles (90061-1121)
PHONE..................................310 323-0234
Totito Merlos, *Owner*
Andie Merlos, *Manager*
EMP: 15
SALES (est): 1.2MM **Privately Held**
SIC: 3272 Stone, cast concrete

(P-10957)
MID-STATE CONCRETE PRODUCTS
1625 E Donovan Rd Ste C, Santa Maria (93454-2519)
P.O. Box 219 (93456-0219)
PHONE..................................805 928-2855
Ralph Vander Veen, *President*
Pat Vander Veen, *Vice Pres*
Anneke Vander Veen, *General Mgr*
Pat V Derveen, *Admin Sec*
Terri Rogers, *Controller*
EMP: 23
SQ FT: 2,000
SALES (est): 4.8MM **Privately Held**
WEB: www.midstateconcrete.com
SIC: 3272 Concrete products, precast; covers, catch basin: concrete; manhole covers or frames, concrete; septic tanks, concrete

(P-10958)
MODERN STAIRWAYS INC
3239 Bancroft Dr, Spring Valley (91977-2698)
PHONE..................................619 466-1484
Jack Spencer, *President*
Deborah Spencer, *Vice Pres*
EMP: 12 EST: 1962
SQ FT: 1,000

SALES (est): 1.2MM **Privately Held**
WEB: www.modernstairways.com
SIC: 3272 Burial vaults, concrete or precast terrazzo; grave markers, concrete; steps, prefabricated concrete

(P-10959)
N V CAST STONE LLC
Also Called: NAPA Valley Cast Stone
1111 Green Island Rd, Vallejo (94503-9639)
PHONE..................................707 261-6615
Mark Akey, *Mng Member*
Tom Brown,
Jeff Latreille,
Bill Tough,
EMP: 100
SQ FT: 50,000
SALES (est): 32.9MM **Privately Held**
WEB: www.nvcssystems.com
SIC: 3272 3281 Concrete products, precast; cut stone & stone products

(P-10960)
NEWBASIS WEST LLC
2626 Kansas Ave, Riverside (92507-2600)
PHONE..................................951 787-0600
Karl Stockbridge, *CEO*
Jennifer Ewing, *CFO*
Kim Ruiz, *Controller*
Kimberly Ruiz, *Controller*
Angela Walker, *Human Res Mgr*
◆ EMP: 115
SALES (est): 44.3MM **Privately Held**
SIC: 3272 Manhole covers or frames, concrete; tanks, concrete; meter boxes, concrete; concrete products, precast
PA: Echo Rock Ventures, Inc.
370 Hammond Dr
Auburn CA 95603
530 823-9600

(P-10961)
NEWMAN AND SONS INC (PA)
2655 1st St 210, Simi Valley (93065-1547)
PHONE..................................805 522-1646
Dennis L Newman, *President*
EMP: 41 EST: 1938
SQ FT: 12,500
SALES (est): 3.6MM **Privately Held**
SIC: 3272 Paving materials, prefabricated concrete

(P-10962)
NUCAST INDUSTRIES INC
Also Called: Robbins Precast
23220 Park Canyon Dr, Corona (92883-6006)
PHONE..................................951 277-8888
David Minasian, *Principal*
Anthony Minasian, *Principal*
EMP: 14
SQ FT: 5,000
SALES (est): 2.8MM **Privately Held**
SIC: 3272 5211 Concrete products, precast; masonry materials & supplies

(P-10963)
OLDCAST PRECAST (DH)
Also Called: Riverside Foundary
2434 Rubidoux Blvd, Riverside (92509-2144)
PHONE..................................951 788-9720
Thomas D Lynch, *Ch of Bd*
John R Waren, *President*
EMP: 35
SQ FT: 7,000
SALES (est): 4.6MM
SALES (corp-wide): 29.7B **Privately Held**
SIC: 3272 3271 Concrete products, precast; concrete block & brick
HQ: Oldcastle Precast, Inc.
1002 15th St Sw Ste 110
Auburn WA 98001
253 833-2777

(P-10964)
OLDCASTLE PRECAST INC
Also Called: Utility Vault
10650 Hemlock Ave, Fontana (92337-7296)
P.O. Box 310039 (92331-0039)
PHONE..................................909 428-3700
Glenn Scheaffer, *Manager*
Adriana Ramirez, *Safety Mgr*
EMP: 162

(PA)=Parent Co (HQ)=Headquarters (DH)=Div Headquarters
✿ = New Business established in last 2 years

2019 California
Manufacturers Register

451

PRODUCTS & SVCS

SALES (corp-wide): 29.7B **Privately Held**
WEB: www.oldcastle-precast.com
SIC: **3272** Concrete products, precast
HQ: Oldcastle Precast, Inc.
   1002 15th St Sw Ste 110
   Auburn WA 98001
   253 833-2777

(P-10965)
OLDCASTLE PRECAST INC
10441 Vine St, Lakeside (92040-2415)
PHONE.................................619 390-2251
EMP: 49
SALES (corp-wide): 29.7B **Privately Held**
SIC: **3272** Concrete products
HQ: Oldcastle Precast, Inc.
   1002 15th St Sw Ste 110
   Auburn WA 98001
   253 833-2777

(P-10966)
OLDCASTLE PRECAST INC
2960 S Highway 99, Stockton
(95215-8047)
P.O. Box 30610 (95213-0610)
PHONE.................................209 235-1173
Cy Thomson, *Manager*
EMP: 50
SALES (corp-wide): 29.7B **Privately Held**
WEB: www.oldcastle-precast.com
SIC: **3272** Pipe, concrete or lined with con-
   crete
HQ: Oldcastle Precast, Inc.
   1002 15th St Sw Ste 110
   Auburn WA 98001
   253 833-2777

(P-10967)
OLDCASTLE PRECAST INC
Also Called: Old Castle Inclosure Solution
801 S Pine St, Madera (93637-5219)
PHONE.................................559 675-1813
Greg Barner, *Manager*
EMP: 11
SALES (corp-wide): 29.7B **Privately Held**
SIC: **3272** Concrete products
HQ: Oldcastle Precast, Inc.
   1002 15th St Sw Ste 110
   Auburn WA 98001
   253 833-2777

(P-10968)
OLDCASTLE PRECAST INC
5236 Arboga Rd, Marysville (95901)
PHONE.................................530 742-8368
Sherman Wren, *Manager*
EMP: 35
SALES (corp-wide): 29.7B **Privately Held**
WEB: www.oldcastle-precast.com
SIC: **3272 3644** Concrete products; non-
   current-carrying wiring services
HQ: Oldcastle Precast, Inc.
   1002 15th St Sw Ste 110
   Auburn WA 98001
   253 833-2777

(P-10969)
OLDCASTLE PRECAST INC
Also Called: Utility Vault
2434 Rubidoux Blvd, Riverside
(92509-2144)
PHONE.................................951 683-8200
John Scott, *Manager*
Jodi Norberg, *Office Mgr*
Bob Vildibill, *Regl Sales Mgr*
EMP: 50
SALES (corp-wide): 29.7B **Privately Held**
WEB: www.oldcastle-precast.com
SIC: **3272 3446** Concrete products, pre-
   cast; pipe, concrete or lined with con-
   crete; open flooring & grating for
   construction
HQ: Oldcastle Precast, Inc.
   1002 15th St Sw Ste 110
   Auburn WA 98001
   253 833-2777

(P-10970)
OUTDOOR CREATIONS INC
2270 Barney Rd, Anderson (96007-4305)
P.O. Box 50, Round Mountain (96084-
0050)
PHONE.................................530 365-6106
Albert E Puhlman Jr, *President*
EMP: 10
SQ FT: 10,000

SALES (est): 1.9MM **Privately Held**
SIC: **3272** Concrete products, precast

(P-10971)
OVER & OVER READY MIX INC
Also Called: Borges Rock Product
8216 Tujunga Ave, Sun Valley
(91352-3932)
P.O. Box 309, Moorpark (93020-0309)
PHONE.................................818 983-1588
Ed Borges, *President*
EMP: 80
SALES (est): 13.4MM **Privately Held**
SIC: **3272 3273** Concrete products; ready-
   mixed concrete

(P-10972)
**PACIFIC INTRLOCK
PVNGSTONE INC (PA)**
1895 San Felipe Rd, Hollister
(95023-2541)
PHONE.................................831 637-9163
Dean Richardt Tonder, *CEO*
John Tonder, *Principal*
Tim Donovan, *Mktg Dir*
EMP: 18
SALES (est): 2.5MM **Privately Held**
SIC: **3272** Concrete products, precast

(P-10973)
PACIFIC STONE DESIGN INC
1201 E Wakeham Ave, Santa Ana
(92705-4145)
PHONE.................................714 836-5757
Scott Sterling, *President*
Kathy Sterling, *CFO*
EMP: 45 EST: 1996
SQ FT: 40,000
SALES (est): 7.6MM **Privately Held**
WEB: www.pacificstone.net
SIC: **3272** Concrete products, precast

(P-10974)
**PARAGON BUILDING
PRODUCTS INC (PA)**
2191 5th St Ste 111, Norco (92860-1966)
P.O. Box 99 (92860-0099)
PHONE.................................951 549-1155
Jeffrey M Goodman, *President*
Jack Goodman, *CEO*
Richard Goodman, *Corp Secy*
▲ EMP: 25
SQ FT: 16,500
SALES (est): 29.3MM **Privately Held**
WEB: www.paragonbp.us
SIC: **3272 3271 5032** Dry mixture con-
   crete; concrete block & brick; brick, con-
   crete; paving blocks, concrete; brick,
   stone & related material

(P-10975)
PIRANHA PIPE & PRECAST INC
16000 Avenue 25, Chowchilla
(93610-9353)
P.O. Box 670 (93610-0670)
PHONE.................................559 665-7473
Anita Simpson, *President*
▲ EMP: 28
SALES (est): 5.6MM **Privately Held**
SIC: **3272** Precast terrazo or concrete
   products

(P-10976)
POLE DANZER
3777 Paseo De Olivos, Fallbrook
(92028-8601)
PHONE.................................760 419-9514
Robert Trent, *Owner*
EMP: 10
SALES (est): 727.7K **Privately Held**
SIC: **3272** Poles & posts, concrete

(P-10977)
**PORTERVILLE CONCRETE PIPE
INC**
474 S Main St, Porterville (93257-5324)
P.O. Box 408 (93258-0408)
PHONE.................................559 784-6187
Vincent Jurkovich, *President*
Steve Jurkovich, *Corp Secy*
Nick Jurkovich, *Executive*
EMP: 16
SQ FT: 1,500

SALES (est): 1.9MM **Privately Held**
SIC: **3272** Pipe, concrete or lined with concrete

(P-10978)
**PRECAST CON TECH
UNLIMITED LLC**
Also Called: Ctu Precast
1260 Furneaux Rd, Olivehurst
(95961-7415)
PHONE.................................530 749-6501
Rez Moulla,
Robert Roesner, *Officer*
Todd Whitney, *Officer*
Kiran Pandhare, *Design Engr*
Kevin Steinkraus, *Opers Mgr*
EMP: 45
SQ FT: 50,000
SALES (est): 13.1MM **Privately Held**
SIC: **3272** Concrete products, precast

(P-10979)
PRECAST INNOVATIONS INC
1670 N Main St, Orange (92867-3405)
PHONE.................................714 921-4060
Chester Valdovinos, *President*
EMP: 28
SQ FT: 20,000
SALES (est): 4.1MM **Privately Held**
SIC: **3272 1791** Concrete products, pre-
   cast; precast concrete structural framing
   or panels, placing of

(P-10980)
PRECAST REPAIR
Also Called: Cano Architecture
5494 Morgan St, Ontario (91762-4631)
PHONE.................................909 627-5477
Delfie Cano, *Owner*
Ray Conel, *Co-Owner*
EMP: 20 EST: 1989
SALES (est): 1.8MM **Privately Held**
WEB: www.precastrepair.com
SIC: **3272** Precast terrazo or concrete
   products

(P-10981)
PRECISION TILE CO
Also Called: Penrose Coping Company
11140 Penrose St, Sun Valley
(91352-2785)
PHONE.................................818 767-7673
Brad Rose, *President*
Patricia Rose, *Treasurer*
Wallace Rose, *Vice Pres*
EMP: 12
SQ FT: 4,000
SALES (est): 890K **Privately Held**
SIC: **3272 1743** Copings, concrete; tile in-
   stallation, ceramic

(P-10982)
**PRIME BUILDING MATERIAL
INC**
Also Called: Eldorado Stone
7811 Lankershim Blvd, North Hollywood
(91605-2523)
PHONE.................................818 503-4242
Alfredo Martinez, *Manager*
EMP: 10 **Privately Held**
SIC: **3272** Concrete products, precast
PA: Prime Building Material, Inc.
   6900 Lankershim Blvd
   North Hollywood CA 91605

(P-10983)
**PRIME FORMING & CNSTR
SUPS**
Also Called: Fitzgerald Formliners
1500a E Chestnut Ave, Santa Ana
(92701-6321)
PHONE.................................714 547-6710
Edward Fitzgerald, *President*
Brian Sheehan, *General Mgr*
John Beutz, *Project Mgr*
Charisma Toledo, *Accounting Mgr*
Eric Lundberg, *Natl Sales Mgr*
EMP: 46
SQ FT: 30,000
SALES (est): 9.7MM **Privately Held**
WEB: www.formliners.com
SIC: **3272** Concrete products

SALES (est): 1.9MM **Privately Held**
SIC: **3272** Concrete products, precast

(P-10984)
QUIKRETE CALIFORNIA LLC
Also Called: Quickrete
3940 Temescal Canyon Rd, Corona
(92883-5618)
PHONE.................................951 277-3155
John O Winshester, *Mng Member*
Steve Bell, *Manager*
EMP: 130
SALES (est): 23.9MM **Privately Held**
SIC: **3272** Concrete products
HQ: The Quikrete Companies Llc
   5 Concourse Pkwy Ste 1900
   Atlanta GA 30328
   404 634-9100

(P-10985)
QUIKRETE COMPANIES INC
Also Called: Quikrete Northern California
14200 Road 284, Porterville (93257-9374)
PHONE.................................559 781-1949
Ron Santiago, *General Mgr*
Alejandro Saldana, *Manager*
EMP: 16 **Privately Held**
WEB: www.quikrete.com
SIC: **3272** Concrete products
HQ: The Quikrete Companies Llc
   5 Concourse Pkwy Ste 1900
   Atlanta GA 30328
   404 634-9100

(P-10986)
QUIKRETE COMPANIES LLC
7705 Wilbur Way, Sacramento
(95828-4929)
PHONE.................................510 490-4670
Dennis McGovern, *Branch Mgr*
EMP: 46 **Privately Held**
SIC: **3272** Dry mixture concrete
HQ: The Quikrete Companies Llc
   5 Concourse Pkwy Ste 1900
   Atlanta GA 30328
   404 634-9100

(P-10987)
QUIKRETE COMPANIES LLC
9265 Camino Santa Fe, San Diego
(92121-2201)
PHONE.................................858 549-2371
Pete Samone, *Branch Mgr*
EMP: 39 **Privately Held**
SIC: **3272** Concrete products
HQ: The Quikrete Companies Llc
   5 Concourse Pkwy Ste 1900
   Atlanta GA 30328
   404 634-9100

(P-10988)
QUIKRETE COMPANIES LLC
Also Called: Quikrete of Atlanta
6950 Stevenson Blvd, Fremont
(94538-2400)
PHONE.................................510 490-4670
Vicky Harper, *Human Res Dir*
Dennis McGovern, *Maintence Staff*
Steven B Rafael, *Manager*
EMP: 100 **Privately Held**
WEB: www.quikrete.com
SIC: **3272 5032** Concrete products, pre-
   cast; cement
HQ: The Quikrete Companies Llc
   5 Concourse Pkwy Ste 1900
   Atlanta GA 30328
   404 634-9100

(P-10989)
QUIKRETE COMPANIES LLC
Also Called: True Cast Concrete Products
11145 Tuxford St, Sun Valley (91352-2632)
PHONE.................................323 875-1367
Greg Gibhel, *Principal*
EMP: 75 **Privately Held**
WEB: www.quikrete.com
SIC: **3272 3271 5211** Steps, prefabricated
   concrete; concrete block & brick; masonry
   materials & supplies
HQ: The Quikrete Companies Llc
   5 Concourse Pkwy Ste 1900
   Atlanta GA 30328
   404 634-9100

(P-10990)
QUIKRETE COMPANIES LLC
7705 Wilbur Way, Sacramento
(95828-4929)
PHONE.................................916 689-8840

Norman Wong, *Manager*
Robert Hernandez, *Sales Mgr*
EMP: 39 **Privately Held**
WEB: www.quikrete.com
SIC: 3272 Concrete products
HQ: The Quikrete Companies Llc
5 Concourse Pkwy Ste 1900
Atlanta GA 30328
404 634-9100

(P-10991)
REDWOOD VALLEY GRAVEL PRODUCTS
11200 East Rd, Redwood Valley
(95470-6108)
PHONE..................707 485-8585
David Ford, *President*
Melvin Ford, *Vice Pres*
EMP: 13
SQ FT: 1,280
SALES (est): 1.3MM **Privately Held**
WEB: www.redwoodvalleygravel.com
SIC: 3272 Septic tanks, concrete

(P-10992)
RIVER VALLEY PRECAST INC
14796 Washington Dr, Fontana
(92335-6263)
PHONE..................928 764-3839
Darryl Kerr, *President*
EMP: 20
SALES (est): 2.1MM **Privately Held**
SIC: 3272 Precast terrazo or concrete products

(P-10993)
RMR PRODUCTS INC (PA)
11011 Glenoaks Blvd Ste 1, Pacoima
(91331-1634)
PHONE..................818 890-0896
David McKendrick, *CEO*
Jim McKendrick, *President*
EMP: 25
SQ FT: 3,200
SALES (est): 3.2MM **Privately Held**
SIC: 3272 Chimney caps, concrete

(P-10994)
ROCK SOLID STONE LLC
308 Industrial Way Ste B, Fallbrook
(92028-2356)
PHONE..................760 731-6191
Scott Morel,
Elidio Escobedo, *Partner*
EMP: 15
SALES (est): 2.3MM **Privately Held**
SIC: 3272 Stone, cast concrete

(P-10995)
ROMA FABRICATING CORPORATION
Also Called: Roma Marble & Tile
2638 S Santa Fe Ave, San Marcos
(92069-5926)
P.O. Box 1231 (92079-1231)
PHONE..................760 727-8040
Pietro Deangelis, *President*
Leo Deangelis, *CFO*
Marco Deangelis, *Vice Pres*
Bruno Deangelis, *Admin Sec*
EMP: 20
SQ FT: 3,500
SALES (est): 1.6MM **Privately Held**
SIC: 3272 1743 Precast terrazo or concrete products; marble installation, interior

(P-10996)
SAN BENITO SUPPLY (PA)
2984 Monterey Hwy, San Jose
(95111-3155)
PHONE..................831 637-5526
Mark Schipper, *President*
Ted Schipper, *Admin Sec*
EMP: 129
SQ FT: 1,870
SALES (est): 24.1MM **Privately Held**
WEB: www.sanbenitosupply.com
SIC: 3272 5032 Concrete products; brick, stone & related material

(P-10997)
SAN DIEGO PRECAST CONCRETE INC (HQ)
Also Called: US Concrete Precast
2735 Cactus Rd, San Diego (92154-8024)
PHONE..................619 240-8000
Douglas McLaughlin, *President*
EMP: 32 EST: 1999
SQ FT: 1,600
SALES (est): 9.5MM
SALES (corp-wide): 1.3B **Publicly Held**
SIC: 3272 3281 Meter boxes, concrete; prestressed concrete products; urns, cut stone
PA: U.S. Concrete, Inc.
331 N Main St
Euless TX 76039
817 835-4105

(P-10998)
SANDMAN INC (PA)
Also Called: Star Concrete
1404 S 7th St, San Jose (95112-5927)
PHONE..................408 947-0669
Gerald Ray Blatt, *CEO*
Nicole Candelaria, *CFO*
EMP: 42
SQ FT: 14,000
SALES (est): 17.6MM **Privately Held**
SIC: 3272 3273 Dry mixture concrete; ready-mixed concrete

(P-10999)
SANDMAN INC
1510 S 7th St, San Jose (95112-5929)
PHONE..................408 947-0159
EMP: 48
SALES (corp-wide): 17.6MM **Privately Held**
SIC: 3272 Building materials, except block or brick: concrete
PA: Sandman, Inc.
1404 S 7th St
San Jose CA 95112
408 947-0669

(P-11000)
SANDSTONE DESIGNS INC
14828 Calvert St, Van Nuys (91411-2707)
PHONE..................818 787-5005
Mesrop Badalyan, *President*
Jiro J Badalyan, *General Mgr*
▲ **EMP:** 20
SQ FT: 20,000
SALES (est): 1.1MM **Privately Held**
SIC: 3272 Concrete products, precast

(P-11001)
SELVAGE CONCRETE PRODUCTS
3309 Sebastopol Rd, Santa Rosa
(95407-6740)
PHONE..................707 542-2762
Bill C Banthrall, *President*
Linda J Banthrall, *Vice Pres*
William Kelley, *General Mgr*
EMP: 12 EST: 1952
SQ FT: 1,112
SALES: 1.3MM **Privately Held**
WEB: www.selvageconcrete.com
SIC: 3272 Septic tanks, concrete

(P-11002)
SIERRA PRECAST INC
Also Called: U.S. Concrete Precast Group
1 Live Oak Ave, Morgan Hill (95037-9245)
PHONE..................408 779-1000
Eric Scholz, *President*
EMP: 62 EST: 1974
SQ FT: 4,000
SALES (est): 6.8MM
SALES (corp-wide): 1.3B **Publicly Held**
WEB: www.sierraprecast.com
SIC: 3272 1771 Panels & sections, prefabricated concrete; columns, concrete; concrete work
PA: U.S. Concrete, Inc.
331 N Main St
Euless TX 76039
817 835-4105

(P-11003)
SISSELL BROS
4322 E 3rd St, Los Angeles (90022-1501)
PHONE..................323 261-0106

John F Foote, *President*
Joan M Foote, *Treasurer*
Dorothy Sissell, *Vice Pres*
EMP: 13
SQ FT: 7,000
SALES (est): 1MM **Privately Held**
SIC: 3272 Burial vaults, concrete or precast terrazzo

(P-11004)
SONOMA CAST STONE CORPORATION
133 Copeland St Ste A, Petaluma
(94952-3145)
PHONE..................877 283-2400
James Herwatt, *CEO*
Stephen Rosenblatt, *President*
David Jensen, *Treasurer*
Kris Adriano, *Bookkeeper*
◆ **EMP:** 25 EST: 1997
SQ FT: 42,000
SALES (est): 4.5MM **Privately Held**
WEB: www.sonomastone.com
SIC: 3272 Concrete products

(P-11005)
SOUTHER CAST STONE INC
235 Via Del Monte, Oceanside
(92058-1223)
PHONE..................760 754-9697
Phillip Souther, *President*
EMP: 20
SQ FT: 7,000
SALES (est): 4.1MM **Privately Held**
SIC: 3272 Concrete products

(P-11006)
STEPSTONE INC (PA)
17025 S Main St, Gardena (90248-3125)
PHONE..................310 327-7474
Gordon S McWilliams, *CEO*
Paul Mitchell, *President*
EMP: 50
SQ FT: 15,000
SALES (est): 10.2MM **Privately Held**
WEB: www.stepstoneinc.com
SIC: 3272 Concrete products, precast; burial vaults, concrete or precast terrazzo

(P-11007)
STEPSTONE INC
13238 S Figueroa St, Los Angeles
(90061-1140)
PHONE..................310 327-7474
Kelsy Carrington, *Branch Mgr*
EMP: 40
SALES (corp-wide): 10.2MM **Privately Held**
WEB: www.stepstoneinc.com
SIC: 3272 Concrete products, precast
PA: Stepstone, Inc.
17025 S Main St
Gardena CA 90248
310 327-7474

(P-11008)
STREUTER TECHNOLOGIES
208 Avenida Fabricante # 200, San Clemente (92672-7536)
PHONE..................949 369-7630
Bart S Streuter, *President*
Brad Streuter, *Vice Pres*
▲ **EMP:** 50
SQ FT: 13,000
SALES (est): 7.4MM **Privately Held**
WEB: www.streuter.com
SIC: 3272 3089 5051 Concrete window & door components, sills & frames; windows, plastic; ferrous metals

(P-11009)
STRUCTURECAST
8261 Mccutchen Rd, Bakersfield
(93311-9407)
PHONE..................661 833-4490
Brent Dezember, *President*
Rick Treatch, *CFO*
Ann Dzember, *Corp Secy*
Anna Dezember, *General Mgr*
Glenn McMillan, *Project Mgr*
EMP: 100
SQ FT: 10,000

SALES (est): 14.7MM **Privately Held**
WEB: www.structurecast.com
SIC: 3272 1791 Precast terrazo or concrete products; precast concrete structural framing or panels, placing of

(P-11010)
SWEET SEPTIC SYSTEMS INC (PA)
Also Called: Sweet Air
7121 Green Valley Rd, Placerville
(95667-9356)
PHONE..................530 622-8768
Charles Sweet, *President*
Sheila Sweet, *Corp Secy*
Annette Fly, *Vice Pres*
EMP: 12
SQ FT: 1,200
SALES (est): 2.6MM **Privately Held**
SIC: 3272 7699 5046 Septic tanks, concrete; culvert pipe, concrete; septic tank cleaning service; restaurant equipment & supplies

(P-11011)
TULARE COUNTY SEPTIC TANK INC
19412 Road 96, Tulare (93274-9156)
P.O. Box 726 (93275-0726)
PHONE..................559 686-8531
Betty Harper, *President*
Glenda Allen, *Corp Secy*
Gary Harper, *Vice Pres*
EMP: 15
SALES: 671.7K **Privately Held**
SIC: 3272 1711 Septic tanks, concrete; plumbing, heating, air-conditioning contractors

(P-11012)
UNITED MEMORIAL PRODUCTS INC
Also Called: United Memorial/Matthews Intl
4845 Pioneer Blvd, Whittier (90601-1842)
P.O. Box 721 (90608-0721)
PHONE..................562 699-3578
Joseph Bartolacci, *Owner*
Mac Sharrock, *General Mgr*
▲ **EMP:** 65
SALES (est): 7MM
SALES (corp-wide): 1.5B **Publicly Held**
SIC: 3272 3281 Concrete stuctural support & building material; cut stone & stone products
PA: Matthews International Corporation
2 N Shore Ctr Ste 200
Pittsburgh PA 15212
412 442-8200

(P-11013)
UNIVERSAL PRECAST CONCRETE INC
16538 Clear Creek Rd, Redding
(96001-5111)
PHONE..................530 243-6477
Paul D'Amico, *CEO*
Gary McCall, *Admin Sec*
◆ **EMP:** 14
SQ FT: 15,000
SALES (est): 3.5MM **Privately Held**
SIC: 3272 Concrete products, precast

(P-11014)
US CONCRETE INC
Also Called: American Concrete Products
1 Live Oak Ave, Morgan Hill (95037-9245)
PHONE..................408 779-1000
Eric Scholz, *Manager*
EMP: 28
SALES (corp-wide): 1.3B **Publicly Held**
SIC: 3272 Concrete products, precast
PA: U.S. Concrete, Inc.
331 N Main St
Euless TX 76039
817 835-4105

(P-11015)
UTILITY COMPOSITE SOLUTIONS IN (PA)
4600 Pavlov Ave Unit 221, San Diego
(92122-3869)
PHONE..................858 442-3187
Lyle Dunbar, *President*
Denis Rediker, *COO*
Scott Homes, *Senior VP*

Walt Losch, *Vice Pres*
EMP: 10
SQ FT: 10,000
SALES: 700K **Privately Held**
SIC: 3272 8711 Poles & posts, concrete; engineering services

(P-11016)
W R MEADOWS INC
Also Called: W. R. Meadows Southern Cal
2300 Valley Blvd, Pomona (91768-1168)
P.O. Box 667, Walnut (91788-0667)
PHONE..................................909 469-2606
Michael Knapp, *Branch Mgr*
EMP: 30
SALES (corp-wide): 120.1MM **Privately Held**
WEB: www.wrmeadows.com
SIC: 3272 3444 2899 2891 Concrete products; concrete forms, sheet metal; chemical preparations; adhesives & sealants
PA: W. R. Meadows, Inc.
   300 Industrial Dr
   Hampshire IL 60140
   847 214-2100

(P-11017)
WALTERS & WOLF GLASS COMPANY
41450 Cowbell Rd, Fremont (94538)
PHONE..................................510 226-9800
Jody Vegas, *Branch Mgr*
EMP: 68
SALES (corp-wide): 104.1MM **Privately Held**
SIC: 3272 Precast terrazo or concrete products
PA: Walters & Wolf Glass Company
   41450 Boscell Rd
   Fremont CA 94538
   510 490-1115

(P-11018)
WALTERS & WOLF PRECAST
41450 Boscell Rd, Fremont (94538-3103)
PHONE..................................510 226-9800
Randy A Wolf, *President*
Jeff B Belzer, *CFO*
Doug Frost, *Vice Pres*
Ed Knowles, *Vice Pres*
Juliusz Knuzynkski, *Vice Pres*
▲ **EMP:** 160
SALES (est): 21.7MM **Privately Held**
SIC: 3272 Concrete products, precast

(P-11019)
WATERGUSH INC
440 N Wolfe Rd Ste E252, Sunnyvale (94085-3869)
PHONE..................................408 524-3074
EMP: 44
SALES (est): 2.9MM **Privately Held**
SIC: 3272 Fountains, concrete

(P-11020)
WE HALL COMPANY INC
Also Called: Pacific Corrugated Pipe Co
5999 Power Inn Rd, Sacramento (95824-2318)
PHONE..................................916 383-4891
Rob Roles, *Manager*
EMP: 14
SALES (corp-wide): 24MM **Privately Held**
SIC: 3272 Culvert pipe, concrete
PA: W.E. Hall Company, Inc.
   471 Old Newport Blvd # 205
   Newport Beach CA 92663
   949 650-4555

(P-11021)
WILLIS CONSTRUCTION CO INC
2261 San Juan Hwy, San Juan Bautista (95045-9565)
PHONE..................................831 623-2900
Lawrence M Willis, *CEO*
Mark Hildebrand, *President*
Tom Yezek, *CFO*
Roger Ely, *Vice Pres*
Saul Rocha, *Systs Prg Mgr*
◆ **EMP:** 120 **EST:** 1976
SQ FT: 4,000

SALES: 30.6MM **Privately Held**
WEB: www.pre-cast.org
SIC: 3272 1791 Concrete products, pre-cast; precast concrete structural framing or panels, placing of

---

3273 Ready-Mixed Concrete

(P-11022)
A & A READY MIXED CONCRETE INC
10250 W Linne Rd, Tracy (95377-9128)
PHONE..................................209 830-5070
Jessey Diaz, *Branch Mgr*
EMP: 18
SALES (corp-wide): 57.6MM **Privately Held**
WEB: www.aareadymix.com
SIC: 3273 Ready-mixed concrete
PA: A & A Ready Mixed Concrete, Inc.
   4621 Teller Ave Ste 130
   Newport Beach CA 92660
   949 253-2800

(P-11023)
A & A READY MIXED CONCRETE INC
Also Called: Associated Ready Mixed Con
134 W Redondo Beach Blvd, Gardena (90248-2290)
PHONE..................................310 515-0933
Ray Kemp, *Manager*
Danny Kane, *Executive*
EMP: 30
SALES (corp-wide): 57.6MM **Privately Held**
WEB: www.aareadymix.com
SIC: 3273 Ready-mixed concrete
PA: A & A Ready Mixed Concrete, Inc.
   4621 Teller Ave Ste 130
   Newport Beach CA 92660
   949 253-2800

(P-11024)
A & A READY MIXED CONCRETE INC (PA)
4621 Teller Ave Ste 130, Newport Beach (92660-2165)
PHONE..................................949 253-2800
Kurt Caillier, *President*
Randy Caillier, *Corp Secy*
Mike Hagemeister, *Vice Pres*
Michael Krussman, *Vice Pres*
Heidi Bright, *Admin Asst*
▲ **EMP:** 45
SQ FT: 8,000
SALES (est): 57.6MM **Privately Held**
WEB: www.aareadymix.com
SIC: 3273 Ready-mixed concrete

(P-11025)
A & A READY MIXED CONCRETE INC
Also Called: A&A Concrete Supply
1201 Market St, Yuba City (95991-3414)
PHONE..................................530 671-1220
Harry Johnston, *Manager*
EMP: 10
SALES (corp-wide): 57.6MM **Privately Held**
WEB: www.aareadymix.com
SIC: 3273 Ready-mixed concrete
PA: A & A Ready Mixed Concrete, Inc.
   4621 Teller Ave Ste 130
   Newport Beach CA 92660
   949 253-2800

(P-11026)
A & A READY MIXED CONCRETE INC
Also Called: A & A Concrete Supply
3578 Esplanade A, Chico (95973-0209)
PHONE..................................530 342-5989
Tim Hostettler, *Manager*
EMP: 20
SQ FT: 20,000
SALES (corp-wide): 57.6MM **Privately Held**
WEB: www.aareadymix.com
SIC: 3273 8611 Ready-mixed concrete; business associations

PA: A & A Ready Mixed Concrete, Inc.
   4621 Teller Ave Ste 130
   Newport Beach CA 92660
   949 253-2800

(P-11027)
A & A READY MIXED CONCRETE INC
3809 Bithell Ln, Suisun City (94585-9644)
PHONE..................................707 399-0682
Bob Perrine, *Branch Mgr*
EMP: 24
SALES (corp-wide): 57.6MM **Privately Held**
SIC: 3273 Ready-mixed concrete
PA: A & A Ready Mixed Concrete, Inc.
   4621 Teller Ave Ste 130
   Newport Beach CA 92660
   949 253-2800

(P-11028)
A & A READY MIXED CONCRETE INC
Also Called: A&A Concrete Supply
4035 E Mariposa Rd, Stockton (95215-8142)
PHONE..................................209 546-1950
Matt Murphy, *General Mgr*
EMP: 25
SALES (corp-wide): 57.6MM **Privately Held**
WEB: www.aareadymix.com
SIC: 3273 Ready-mixed concrete
PA: A & A Ready Mixed Concrete, Inc.
   4621 Teller Ave Ste 130
   Newport Beach CA 92660
   949 253-2800

(P-11029)
A & A READY MIXED CONCRETE INC
Also Called: A&A Concrete Supply
8272 Berry Ave, Sacramento (95828-1602)
PHONE..................................916 383-3756
Ron Boburn, *Branch Mgr*
Ron Coburn, *Regional Mgr*
EMP: 35
SALES (corp-wide): 57.6MM **Privately Held**
WEB: www.aareadymix.com
SIC: 3273 Ready-mixed concrete
PA: A & A Ready Mixed Concrete, Inc.
   4621 Teller Ave Ste 130
   Newport Beach CA 92660
   949 253-2800

(P-11030)
A TEICHERT & SON INC
Also Called: Teichert Readymix
7466 Pacific Ave, Pleasant Grove (95668-9708)
PHONE..................................916 991-8170
Dave Bearden, *Division Mgr*
EMP: 40
SALES (corp-wide): 784MM **Privately Held**
SIC: 3273 Ready-mixed concrete
HQ: A. Teichert & Son, Inc.
   3500 American River Dr
   Sacramento CA 95864

(P-11031)
A TEICHERT & SON INC
Also Called: Teichert Readymix
8609 Jackson Rd, Sacramento (95826-9731)
PHONE..................................916 386-6920
Dave Bearden, *Division Mgr*
EMP: 40
SALES (corp-wide): 784MM **Privately Held**
SIC: 3273 Ready-mixed concrete
HQ: A. Teichert & Son, Inc.
   3500 American River Dr
   Sacramento CA 95864

(P-11032)
A TEICHERT & SON INC
Also Called: Teichert Readymix
535 Levy Rd, Folsom (95630-6921)
PHONE..................................916 985-0207
Dave Bearden, *Division Mgr*
EMP: 40

SALES (corp-wide): 784MM **Privately Held**
SIC: 3273 Ready-mixed concrete
HQ: A. Teichert & Son, Inc.
   3500 American River Dr
   Sacramento CA 95864

(P-11033)
A TEICHERT & SON INC
Also Called: Teichert Readymix
721 Berry St, Roseville (95678-1307)
PHONE..................................916 783-7132
Dave Bearden, *Division Mgr*
EMP: 40
SALES (corp-wide): 784MM **Privately Held**
SIC: 3273 Ready-mixed concrete
HQ: A. Teichert & Son, Inc.
   3500 American River Dr
   Sacramento CA 95864

(P-11034)
ALLIANCE READY MIX INC
310 James Way Ste 210, Pismo Beach (93449-2877)
P.O. Box 1163, Arroyo Grande (93421-1163)
PHONE..................................805 556-3015
Brandt Robertson, *President*
EMP: 10
SALES (est): 1.7MM **Privately Held**
SIC: 3273 Ready-mixed concrete

(P-11035)
ALLIANCE READY MIX INC
915 Sheridan Rd, Arroyo Grande (93420-5834)
P.O. Box 1163 (93421-1163)
PHONE..................................805 343-0360
Brandt Robertson, *President*
EMP: 15
SALES (est): 2.8MM **Privately Held**
SIC: 3273 Ready-mixed concrete

(P-11036)
ALLIED CONCRETE & SUPPLY CO
440 Mitchell Rd Ste B, Modesto (95354-3915)
P.O. Box 1022 (95353-1022)
PHONE..................................209 524-3177
Michael G Ruddy Sr, *President*
Martin J Ruddy III, *Treasurer*
James M Ruddy, *Vice Pres*
Martin Ruddy Jr, *Vice Pres*
Sally Ruddy, *Vice Pres*
EMP: 20
SQ FT: 3,500
SALES: 800K **Privately Held**
WEB: www.allied-concrete-supply.com
SIC: 3273 Ready-mixed concrete

(P-11037)
ALLIED CONCRETE RDYMX SVCS LLC
450 Amador St, San Francisco (94124-1248)
P.O. Box 2104, Alameda (94501-0208)
PHONE..................................415 282-8117
Randy Burgo,
Brad Burgo,
Gary Burgo,
EMP: 11
SALES (est): 3.2MM **Privately Held**
SIC: 3273 Ready-mixed concrete

(P-11038)
ALPHA MATERIALS INC
6170 20th St, Riverside (92509-2031)
PHONE..................................951 788-5150
Brian Oaks, *President*
EMP: 36
SQ FT: 1,200
SALES (est): 6.4MM **Privately Held**
SIC: 3273 Ready-mixed concrete

(P-11039)
AMADOR TRANSIT MIX INC
Also Called: Knife River
12480 Ridge Rd, Sutter Creek (95685-9673)
P.O. Box 1265, Jackson (95642-1265)
PHONE..................................209 223-0406
Brian Drake, *President*

▲ = Import ▼=Export
◆ =Import/Export

Brian E Drake, *Vice Pres*
EMP: 35
SALES (est): 4.2MM
SALES (corp-wide): 4.4B **Publicly Held**
WEB: www.fullercontracting.com
SIC: 3273 1611 Ready-mixed concrete;
grading
HQ: Knife River Corporation
1150 W Century Ave
Bismarck ND 58503
701 530-1400

(P-11040)
AMERICAN READY MIX INC
1141 W Graaf Ave, Ridgecrest
(93555-2307)
P.O. Box 1138 (93556-1138)
PHONE...................................760 446-4556
Leroy Ladd, *President*
Donna Ladd, *Vice Pres*
EMP: 15
SQ FT: 500
SALES (est): 1.6MM **Privately Held**
WEB: www.americanreadymix.net
SIC: 3273 Ready-mixed concrete

(P-11041)
**ANTHONYS RDYMX & BLDG
SUPS INC (PA)**
4500 Manhattan Beach Blvd, Lawndale
(90260-2040)
PHONE...................................310 542-9400
Anthony Pagnini, *President*
Rudy Monteza, *CIO*
Tracy Bricker, *Info Tech Mgr*
Sammy Briones, *Sales Mgr*
EMP: 15
SQ FT: 4,000
SALES (est): 1.8MM **Privately Held**
WEB: www.anthonysreadymix.com
SIC: 3273 Ready-mixed concrete

(P-11042)
**ANTIOCH BUILDING MATERIALS
CO**
Also Called: Brentwood Readymix
6823 Brentwood Blvd, Brentwood
(94513-2121)
P.O. Box 870, Antioch (94509-0086)
PHONE...................................925 634-3541
Neil Larson, *Manager*
EMP: 20
SQ FT: 8,538
SALES (corp-wide): 15.2MM **Privately
Held**
SIC: 3273 Ready-mixed concrete
PA: Antioch Building Materials, Co.
1375 California Ave
Pittsburg CA 94565
925 432-0171

(P-11043)
ARROW TRANSIT MIX
507 E Avenue L12, Lancaster
(93535-5417)
PHONE...................................661 945-7600
H D Follendore, *President*
Christine Follendore, *Admin Sec*
Charla Anderson, *Bookkeeper*
EMP: 35
SQ FT: 7,200
SALES (est): 7.6MM **Privately Held**
SIC: 3273 Ready-mixed concrete

(P-11044)
**ASSOC READY MIXED
CONCRETE**
9645 Washburn Rd, Downey (90241-5614)
PHONE...................................562 923-7281
Jim Lytle, *Manager*
EMP: 15 **Privately Held**
SIC: 3273 Ready-mixed concrete
PA: Assoc Ready Mixed Concrete Inc
6851 E Avenue T
Littlerock CA

(P-11045)
**ASSOC READY MIXED
CONCRETE**
25901 Towne Centre Dr, El Toro
(92610-2462)
PHONE...................................949 580-1844
Steve Fausneaucht, *Branch Mgr*
Ron Huff, *Director*

EMP: 15 **Privately Held**
SIC: 3273 Ready-mixed concrete
PA: Assoc Ready Mixed Concrete Inc
6851 E Avenue T
Littlerock CA

(P-11046)
**ASSOCIATED READY MIX CON
INC (PA)**
4621 Teller Ave Ste 130, Newport Beach
(92660-2165)
PHONE...................................949 253-2800
Kurt Caillier, *President*
Randy Caillier, *Corp Secy*
Chris Pizano, *Vice Pres*
Jacque Harvey, *Executive*
Jaret Ramirez, *Info Tech Mgr*
EMP: 40
SALES (est): 17.5MM **Privately Held**
SIC: 3273 Ready-mixed concrete

(P-11047)
**ASSOCIATED READY MIX
CONCRETE**
8946 Bradley Ave, Sun Valley
(91352-2601)
PHONE...................................818 504-3100
Tim Sullivan, *Manager*
EMP: 40 **Privately Held**
SIC: 3273 Ready-mixed concrete
PA: Associated Ready Mix Concrete, Inc.
4621 Teller Ave Ste 130
Newport Beach CA 92660

(P-11048)
AZUSA ROCK INC
Also Called: Los Banos Rock and Ready Mix
22101 Sunset Dr, Los Banos (93635)
P.O. Box 1111 (93635-1111)
PHONE...................................209 826-5066
Wayne Stoughton, *Manager*
EMP: 30 **Publicly Held**
SIC: 3273 Ready-mixed concrete
HQ: Azusa Rock, Inc.
3901 Fish Canyon Rd
Azusa CA 91702
858 530-9444

(P-11049)
B & B RED-I-MIX CONCRETE INC
Also Called: B & B Services
590 Live Oak Ave, Baldwin Park
(91706-1315)
PHONE...................................626 359-8371
Mike Gatherer, *President*
EMP: 31
SQ FT: 4,400
SALES (est): 2.9MM **Privately Held**
SIC: 3273 Ready-mixed concrete

(P-11050)
BEACON CONCRETE INC
Also Called: Lighthouse Trucking
1597 S Bluff Rd, Montebello (90640-6601)
PHONE...................................323 889-7775
Lou Earlabaugh, *President*
Suzanne Earlabaugh, *Vice Pres*
EMP: 27
SALES (est): 3.4MM **Privately Held**
SIC: 3273 Ready-mixed concrete

(P-11051)
BODE CONCRETE LLC
755 Stockton Ave, San Jose (95126-1839)
PHONE...................................415 920-7100
Danvers Boardman, *Mng Member*
Douglas Boardman,
Kathy Boardman,
Randolph Boardman,
EMP: 67
SQ FT: 5,000
SALES (est): 4.8MM
SALES (corp-wide): 1.3B **Publicly Held**
SIC: 3273 Ready-mixed concrete
HQ: Central Concrete Supply Co.Inc.
755 Stockton Ave
San Jose CA 95126
408 293-6272

(P-11052)
BUILDERS CONCRETE INC (DH)
3664 W Ashlan Ave, Fresno (93722-4499)
P.O. Box 9129 (93790-9129)
PHONE...................................559 225-3667

Charlie Wensley, *President*
Don Unmacht, *President*
Dominique Bidet, *Corp Secy*
Mark Mitzel, *Vice Pres*
Rod Gonzales, *Credit Mgr*
EMP: 50
SQ FT: 2,500
SALES (est): 7.8MM
SALES (corp-wide): 479.6MM **Privately
Held**
WEB: www.buildersconcrete.com
SIC: 3273 Ready-mixed concrete
HQ: National Cement Company Of Califor-
nia, Inc.
15821 Ventura Blvd # 475
Encino CA 91436
818 728-5200

(P-11053)
**C B CONCRETE
CONSTRUCTION**
641 University Ave, Los Gatos
(95032-4415)
PHONE...................................408 354-3484
Christopher Bearden, *Principal*
EMP: 10 **EST:** 2008
SALES (est): 1.2MM **Privately Held**
SIC: 3273 1771 1741 Ready-mixed con-
crete; driveway contractor; masonry &
other stonework

(P-11054)
CAL PORTLAND CEMENT CO
Also Called: Calportland
695 S Rancho Ave, Colton (92324-3242)
PHONE...................................909 423-0436
Allen Hamblen, *CEO*
Kirk McDonald, *Vice Pres*
Deanne Powers, *Accounting Mgr*
Stacie Reynolds, *Purch Agent*
Mark Rock, *Safety Mgr*
EMP: 23
SALES (est): 3.3MM **Privately Held**
SIC: 3273 Ready-mixed concrete

(P-11055)
**CALAVERAS MATERIALS INC
(DH)**
Also Called: CMI
1100 Lowe Rd, Hughson (95326-9178)
P.O. Box 26240, Fresno (93729-6240)
PHONE...................................209 883-0448
David Vickers, *President*
EMP: 20
SQ FT: 8,000
SALES (est): 23.2MM
SALES (corp-wide): 20.3B **Privately Held**
SIC: 3273 5032 3272 2951 Ready-mixed
concrete; sand, construction; gravel; con-
crete products; asphalt paving mixtures &
blocks; construction sand & gravel

(P-11056)
CALPORTLAND COMPANY
Also Called: Catalina Pacific Concrete
1030 W Gladstone St, Azusa (91702-4207)
PHONE...................................626 334-3226
Bill Klawatter, *Manager*
April Avila, *Technology*
EMP: 15
SALES (corp-wide): 8.1B **Privately Held**
WEB: www.calportland.com
SIC: 3273 Ready-mixed concrete
HQ: Calportland Company
2025 E Financial Way
Glendora CA 91741
626 852-6200

(P-11057)
CATALINA PACIFIC CONCRETE
19030 Normandie Ave, Torrance
(90502-1009)
PHONE...................................310 532-4600
Patrick E Greene, *President*
EMP: 23
SQ FT: 1,500
SALES (est): 2.8MM **Privately Held**
SIC: 3273 Ready-mixed concrete

(P-11058)
CEMEX (PA)
5180 Gldn Fthl Pkwy # 200, El Dorado Hills
(95762-9347)
PHONE...................................916 941-2800
Paul Brittain, *Owner*
EMP: 26

SALES (est): 4.5MM **Privately Held**
SIC: 3273 Ready-mixed concrete

(P-11059)
CEMEX INC
3990 Concours Ste 200, Ontario
(91764-7971)
PHONE...................................909 974-5500
Gilberto Perez, *President*
Bryan Forgey, *General Mgr*
Gary Clay, *Manager*
EMP: 30 **Privately Held**
SIC: 3273 Ready-mixed concrete
HQ: Cemex, Inc.
10100 Katy Fwy Ste 300
Houston TX 77043
713 650-6200

(P-11060)
CEMEX CEMENT INC
9035 Happy Camp Rd, Moorpark
(93021-9726)
P.O. Box 1030 (93020-1030)
PHONE...................................805 529-1355
Tom Powell, *Branch Mgr*
EMP: 50 **Privately Held**
SIC: 3273 1442 Ready-mixed concrete;
construction sand & gravel
HQ: Cemex Cement, Inc.
10100 Katy Fwy Ste 300
Houston TX 77043
713 650-6200

(P-11061)
CEMEX CNSTR MTLS PCF LLC
3221 N Riverside Ave, Rialto (92377-3823)
PHONE...................................951 377-9657
EMP: 10 **Privately Held**
SIC: 3273 Ready-mixed concrete
HQ: Cemex Construction Materials Pacific,
Llc
1501 Belvedere Rd
West Palm Beach FL 33406
561 833-5555

(P-11062)
CEMEX CNSTR MTLS PCF LLC
Also Called: Aggregate -Eliot Quarry
1544 Stanley Blvd, Pleasanton
(94566-6308)
P.O. Box 697 (94566-0866)
PHONE...................................925 846-2824
Gordon Brown, *Branch Mgr*
EMP: 45 **Privately Held**
SIC: 3273 Ready-mixed concrete
HQ: Cemex Construction Materials Pacific,
Llc
1501 Belvedere Rd
West Palm Beach FL 33406
561 833-5555

(P-11063)
CEMEX CNSTR MTLS PCF LLC
Also Called: Sierra Rm / Bm
5481 Davidson Rd, El Dorado (95623)
PHONE...................................530 626-3590
Susanne Combellack, *Branch Mgr*
EMP: 38 **Privately Held**
SIC: 3273 Ready-mixed concrete
HQ: Cemex Construction Materials Pacific,
Llc
1501 Belvedere Rd
West Palm Beach FL 33406
561 833-5555

(P-11064)
CEMEX CNSTR MTLS PCF LLC
Also Called: Readymix -Tracy Rm Dual
30350 S Tracy Blvd, Tracy (95377-8121)
PHONE...................................209 835-1454
Jerry Larson, *Branch Mgr*
EMP: 23 **Privately Held**
SIC: 3273 Ready-mixed concrete
HQ: Cemex Construction Materials Pacific,
Llc
1501 Belvedere Rd
West Palm Beach FL 33406
561 833-5555

(P-11065)
CEMEX CNSTR MTLS PCF LLC
Also Called: Shop -Ncal Rmx Fixed Maint
Sho
1601 Cement Hill Rd, Fairfield
(94533-2659)
PHONE...................................707 422-2520

Graham Dubois, *Principal*
EMP: 33 **Privately Held**
SIC: 3273 Ready-mixed concrete
HQ: Cemex Construction Materials Pacific,
Llc
1501 Belvedere Rd
West Palm Beach FL 33406
561 833-5555

(P-11066)
CEMEX CNSTR MTLS PCF LLC
Also Called: Aggregate -Patterson Quarry
8705 Camp Far West Rd, Sheridan
(95681-9757)
PHONE..................................916 645-1949
EMP: 38 **Privately Held**
SIC: 3273 Ready-mixed concrete
HQ: Cemex Construction Materials Pacific,
Llc
1501 Belvedere Rd
West Palm Beach FL 33406
561 833-5555

(P-11067)
CEMEX CNSTR MTLS PCF LLC
Also Called: Readymix -Orange Rm Dual
1730 N Main St, Orange (92865-4117)
P.O. Box 54423, Los Angeles (90054-0423)
PHONE..................................714 637-9470
James Nelli, *Manager*
EMP: 15 **Privately Held**
SIC: 3273 Ready-mixed concrete
HQ: Cemex Construction Materials Pacific,
Llc
1501 Belvedere Rd
West Palm Beach FL 33406
561 833-5555

(P-11068)
CEMEX CNSTR MTLS PCF LLC
Also Called: Shop -Bradshaw Maintenance
Sho
9751 Kiefer Blvd, Sacramento
(95827-3828)
PHONE..................................916 364-2470
Ed Ozbun, *Branch Mgr*
EMP: 23 **Privately Held**
SIC: 3273 Ready-mixed concrete
HQ: Cemex Construction Materials Pacific,
Llc
1501 Belvedere Rd
West Palm Beach FL 33406
561 833-5555

(P-11069)
CEMEX CNSTR MTLS PCF LLC
Also Called: Readymix -Oakland Rm
333 23rd Ave, Oakland (94606-5303)
PHONE..................................925 858-4344
Ray L Groue, *Branch Mgr*
EMP: 38 **Privately Held**
SIC: 3273 Ready-mixed concrete
HQ: Cemex Construction Materials Pacific,
Llc
1501 Belvedere Rd
West Palm Beach FL 33406
561 833-5555

(P-11070)
CEMEX CNSTR MTLS PCF LLC
Also Called: Readymix -Concord Rm Dual
3951 Laura Alice Way, Concord
(94520-8544)
PHONE..................................925 688-1025
Jack Shade, *Manager*
EMP: 20
SQ FT: 2,000 **Privately Held**
SIC: 3273 Ready-mixed concrete
HQ: Cemex Construction Materials Pacific,
Llc
1501 Belvedere Rd
West Palm Beach FL 33406
561 833-5555

(P-11071)
CEMEX CNSTR MTLS PCF LLC
Also Called: Cem - Sacramento Terminal
8251 Power Ridge Rd, Sacramento
(95826-4723)
PHONE..................................916 383-0526
EMP: 19 **Privately Held**
SIC: 3273 Ready-mixed concrete

HQ: Cemex Construction Materials Pacific,
Llc
1501 Belvedere Rd
West Palm Beach FL 33406
561 833-5555

(P-11072)
CEMEX CNSTR MTLS PCF LLC
Also Called: Readymix - Delano Rm
1100 Garzoli Ave, Delano (93215-9303)
PHONE..................................661 725-1819
Keith Stogle, *Branch Mgr*
EMP: 23 **Privately Held**
SIC: 3273 Ready-mixed concrete
HQ: Cemex Construction Materials Pacific,
Llc
1501 Belvedere Rd
West Palm Beach FL 33406
561 833-5555

(P-11073)
CEMEX CNSTR MTLS PCF LLC
Also Called: Readymix -Redlands Rm Dual
8203 Alabama Ave, Highland (92346-4255)
PHONE..................................909 335-3105
Erick Garcia, *Branch Mgr*
EMP: 17 **Privately Held**
SIC: 3273 Ready-mixed concrete
HQ: Cemex Construction Materials Pacific,
Llc
1501 Belvedere Rd
West Palm Beach FL 33406
561 833-5555

(P-11074)
CEMEX CNSTR MTLS PCF LLC
Also Called: Admin - Shafter Admin Office
131 Vultee Ave, Shafter (93263-4049)
PHONE..................................661 746-3423
Scott Ely, *Branch Mgr*
EMP: 23 **Privately Held**
SIC: 3273 Ready-mixed concrete
HQ: Cemex Construction Materials Pacific,
Llc
1501 Belvedere Rd
West Palm Beach FL 33406
561 833-5555

(P-11075)
CEMEX CNSTR MTLS PCF LLC
Also Called: Readymix -Newman Rm
3407 W Stuhr Rd, Newman (95360-9774)
PHONE..................................209 862-0182
EMP: 23
SALES (corp-wide): 15.4B **Privately Held**
SIC: 3273
HQ: Cemex Construction Materials Pacific,
Llc
1501 Belvedere Rd
West Palm Beach FL 33406
561 833-5555

(P-11076)
CEMEX CNSTR MTLS PCF LLC
Also Called: Readymix -Walnut Rm
20903 Currier Rd, Walnut (91789-3020)
PHONE..................................909 594-0105
Gary Garcia, *Branch Mgr*
EMP: 20 **Privately Held**
SIC: 3273 Ready-mixed concrete
HQ: Cemex Construction Materials Pacific,
Llc
1501 Belvedere Rd
West Palm Beach FL 33406
561 833-5555

(P-11077)
CEMEX CNSTR MTLS PCF LLC
Also Called: Readymix -Fontana Rm
13200 Santa Ana Ave, Fontana
(92337-8215)
PHONE..................................909 355-8754
Scott Mullins, *Branch Mgr*
EMP: 15 **Privately Held**
SIC: 3273 Ready-mixed concrete
HQ: Cemex Construction Materials Pacific,
Llc
1501 Belvedere Rd
West Palm Beach FL 33406
561 833-5555

(P-11078)
CEMEX CNSTR MTLS PCF LLC
Also Called: Readymix -Modesto Rm
318 Beard Ave, Modesto (95354-4025)
PHONE..................................209 524-6322

Jerry Larsen, *Branch Mgr*
EMP: 23 **Privately Held**
SIC: 3273 Ready-mixed concrete
HQ: Cemex Construction Materials Pacific,
Llc
1501 Belvedere Rd
West Palm Beach FL 33406
561 833-5555

(P-11079)
CEMEX CNSTR MTLS PCF LLC
Also Called: Readymix -Compton Rm
2722 N Alameda St, Compton
(90222-2302)
P.O. Box 57002, Irvine (92619-7002)
PHONE..................................310 603-9122
Pete Pacheco, *Vice Pres*
EMP: 16 **Privately Held**
SIC: 3273 Ready-mixed concrete
HQ: Cemex Construction Materials Pacific,
Llc
1501 Belvedere Rd
West Palm Beach FL 33406
561 833-5555

(P-11080)
CEMEX CNSTR MTLS PCF LLC
Also Called: Readymix -Los Angeles Rm Dual
625 Lamar St, Los Angeles (90031-2512)
PHONE..................................323 221-1828
David Martinez, *Manager*
EMP: 23 **Privately Held**
SIC: 3273 Ready-mixed concrete
HQ: Cemex Construction Materials Pacific,
Llc
1501 Belvedere Rd
West Palm Beach FL 33406
561 833-5555

(P-11081)
CEMEX CNSTR MTLS PCF LLC
Also Called: Readymix -Hollywood Rm Dual
1000 N La Brea Ave, West Hollywood
(90038-2324)
PHONE..................................323 466-4928
Jim Henderson, *Branch Mgr*
EMP: 34 **Privately Held**
SIC: 3273 Ready-mixed concrete
HQ: Cemex Construction Materials Pacific,
Llc
1501 Belvedere Rd
West Palm Beach FL 33406
561 833-5555

(P-11082)
CEMEX MATERIALS LLC
7059 Tremont Rd, Dixon (95620-9609)
PHONE..................................707 678-4311
Ed Ozbun, *Branch Mgr*
EMP: 27 **Privately Held**
SIC: 3273 Ready-mixed concrete
HQ: Cemex Materials, Llc
1501 Belvedere Rd
West Palm Beach FL 33406
561 833-5555

(P-11083)
CEMEX MATERIALS LLC
401 Wright Ave, Richmond (94804-3508)
PHONE..................................510 234-3616
Karl H Watson Jr, *Branch Mgr*
EMP: 38 **Privately Held**
SIC: 3273 Ready-mixed concrete
HQ: Cemex Materials, Llc
1501 Belvedere Rd
West Palm Beach FL 33406
561 833-5555

(P-11084)
CEMEX MATERIALS LLC
1601 Cement Hill Rd, Fairfield
(94533-2659)
PHONE..................................707 448-7121
Marc Mammola, *Manager*
EMP: 10 **Privately Held**
WEB: www.rinkermaterials.com
SIC: 3273 Ready-mixed concrete
HQ: Cemex Materials, Llc
1501 Belvedere Rd
West Palm Beach FL 33406
561 833-5555

(P-11085)
CEMEX MATERIALS LLC
385 Tower Rd, NAPA (94558)
P.O. Box 3508 (94558-0553)
PHONE..................................707 255-3035
George Kerr, *Manager*
EMP: 25
SQ FT: 30,000 **Privately Held**
WEB: www.prestressservices.com
SIC: 3273 Ready-mixed concrete
HQ: Cemex Materials, Llc
1501 Belvedere Rd
West Palm Beach FL 33406
561 833-5555

(P-11086)
CEMEX MATERIALS LLC
4150 N Brawley Ave, Fresno (93722-3914)
PHONE..................................559 275-2241
EMP: 27 **Privately Held**
WEB: www.rinkermaterials.com
SIC: 3273 Ready-mixed concrete
HQ: Cemex Materials, Llc
1501 Belvedere Rd
West Palm Beach FL 33406
561 833-5555

(P-11087)
CEMEX MATERIALS LLC
1205 S Rancho Ave, Colton (92324-3342)
PHONE..................................909 825-1500
Lindsey Hank, *Manager*
EMP: 22 **Privately Held**
WEB: www.rinkermaterials.com
SIC: 3273 Ready-mixed concrete
HQ: Cemex Materials, Llc
1501 Belvedere Rd
West Palm Beach FL 33406
561 833-5555

(P-11088)
CEMEX USA INC
8731 Orange St, Redlands (92374-1779)
PHONE..................................909 798-1144
EMP: 120
SALES (corp-wide): 15.4B **Privately Held**
SIC: 3273
HQ: Cemex U.S.A., Inc.
929 Gessner Rd Ste 1900
Houston TX 77024
713 650-6200

(P-11089)
CEMEX USA INC
3990 Concours Ste 200, Ontario
(91764-7971)
PHONE..................................909 974-5500
Mike Bauder, *Principal*
EMP: 11
SALES (est): 1.8MM **Privately Held**
SIC: 3273 Ready-mixed concrete

(P-11090)
**CENTRAL CONCRETE SUPPLY
COINC (HQ)**
Also Called: Westside Building Materials
755 Stockton Ave, San Jose (95126-1839)
PHONE..................................408 293-6272
William T Albanese, *CEO*
Scott Perrine, *President*
Laurie Cerrito, *Vice Pres*
Jeff Davis, *Vice Pres*
David Perry, *Vice Pres*
EMP: 80
SQ FT: 2,000
SALES (est): 83.1MM
SALES (corp-wide): 1.3B **Publicly Held**
SIC: 3273 Ready-mixed concrete
PA: U.S. Concrete, Inc.
331 N Main St
Euless TX 76039
817 835-4105

(P-11091)
**CENTRAL CONCRETE SUPPLY
COINC**
755 Stockton Ave, San Jose (95126-1839)
PHONE..................................408 404-1000
William Albany, *Vice Pres*
EMP: 45
SALES (corp-wide): 1.3B **Publicly Held**
SIC: 3273 Ready-mixed concrete

▲ = Import ▼=Export
◆ =Import/Export

HQ: Central Concrete Supply Co.Inc.
755 Stockton Ave
San Jose CA 95126
408 293-6272

(P-11092)
CHAPARRAL CONCRETE
COMPANY (DH)
590 Live Oak Ave, Baldwin Park
(91706-1315)
PHONE.....................626 359-8371
Hisayuki Uchikoba, *CFO*
EMP: 10
SALES (est): 1.4MM
SALES (corp-wide): 8.1B **Privately Held**
SIC: 3273 Ready-mixed concrete
HQ: Calportland Company
2025 E Financial Way
Glendora CA 91741
626 852-6200

(P-11093)
CLAY MIX LLC
1003 N Abby St, Fresno (93701-1007)
PHONE.....................559 485-0065
Ritsuko Miyazaki, *Principal*
EMP: 12
SALES (est): 1.7MM **Privately Held**
SIC: 3273 Ready-mixed concrete

(P-11094)
CLEARLAKE LAVA INC
Also Called: Point Lakeview Rock & Redi-Mix
13329 Point Lakeview Rd, Lower Lake
(95457-9728)
PHONE.....................707 995-1515
Don Vantelt, *President*
EMP: 15
SALES (corp-wide): 8MM **Privately Held**
SIC: 3273 5211 Ready-mixed concrete;
cement
PA: Clearlake Lava Inc
14572 E Highway 20
Clearlake Oaks CA 95423
707 998-1115

(P-11095)
CONCRETE INC
749 S Stanislaus St, Stockton
(95206-1570)
P.O. Box 66001 (95206-0901)
PHONE.....................209 830-1962
David Varney, *Branch Mgr*
EMP: 30
SALES (corp-wide): 4.4B **Publicly Held**
SIC: 3273 Ready-mixed concrete
HQ: Concrete, Inc.
400 S Lincoln St
Stockton CA 95203
209 933-6999

(P-11096)
CONCRETE INC
10260 Waterman Rd, Elk Grove
(95624-9403)
PHONE.....................209 933-6999
Terry Hildestad, *Branch Mgr*
EMP: 10
SALES (corp-wide): 4.4B **Publicly Held**
SIC: 3273 Ready-mixed concrete
HQ: Concrete, Inc.
400 S Lincoln St
Stockton CA 95203
209 933-6999

(P-11097)
CONCRETE INC (DH)
400 S Lincoln St, Stockton (95203-3312)
P.O. Box 66001 (95206-0901)
PHONE.....................209 933-6999
David C Barney, *CEO*
Terry D Hildestad, *CEO*
Larry Hansen, *CFO*
Mary Ann Johnson, *Vice Pres*
Terri Ozment, *Executive*
EMP: 55
SALES (est): 14.4MM
SALES (corp-wide): 4.4B **Publicly Held**
SIC: 3273 5032 Ready-mixed concrete;
brick, stone & related material
HQ: Knife River Corporation
1150 W Century Ave
Bismarck ND 58503
701 530-1400

(P-11098)
CONCRETE READY MIX INC
33 Hillsdale Ave, San Jose (95136-1308)
P.O. Box 50006 (95150-0006)
PHONE.....................408 224-2452
Ron Minnis, *President*
EMP: 35
SALES (est): 5.5MM **Privately Held**
WEB: www.concretecrm.com
SIC: 3273 Ready-mixed concrete

(P-11099)
CORONET CONCRETE
PRODUCTS
Also Called: Desert Redi Mix
83801 Avenue 45, Indio (92201-3311)
PHONE.....................760 398-2441
James Richert, *CEO*
EMP: 24
SQ FT: 2,000
SALES (est): 5.5MM **Privately Held**
SIC: 3273 3272 Ready-mixed concrete;
concrete products; manhole covers or
frames, concrete

(P-11100)
CROOKSHANKS SALES CO INC
Also Called: CSC Ranch
2375 Dairy Ave, Corcoran (93212-3503)
P.O. Box 338 (93212-0338)
PHONE.....................559 992-5077
Jason Proctor, *President*
Donna Proctor, *President*
Morris Proctor, *Treasurer*
Alex Cook, *Vice Pres*
Dorothy Crookshanks, *Vice Pres*
EMP: 50
SQ FT: 2,500
SALES (est): 6.4MM **Privately Held**
SIC: 3273 0191 3275 Ready-mixed con-
crete; general farms, primarily crop; agri-
cultural gypsum

(P-11101)
DENNIE MANNING CONCRETE
INC
Also Called: D & K Concrete Co
15815 Arrow Blvd, Fontana (92335-3245)
PHONE.....................909 823-7521
Steve Mogan, *President*
Denise Manning, *Corp Secy*
L G Manning, *Vice Pres*
EMP: 13 EST: 1923
SQ FT: 1,000
SALES (est): 3MM **Privately Held**
SIC: 3273 Ready-mixed concrete

(P-11102)
DIVERSIFIED MINERALS INC
Also Called: Dmi Ready Mix
1100 Mountain View Ave F, Oxnard
(93030-7213)
PHONE.....................805 247-1069
James W Price, *President*
Sharron Price, *Corp Secy*
▲ EMP: 44
SQ FT: 44,482
SALES (est): 16MM **Privately Held**
SIC: 3273 4013 3531 3241 Ready-mixed
concrete; railroad terminals; bituminous,
cement & concrete related products &
equipment; batching plants, for aggregate
concrete & bulk cement; pozzolana ce-
ment

(P-11103)
E-Z HAUL READY MIX INC
Also Called: Star Building Products
1538 N Blackstone Ave, Fresno
(93703-3612)
PHONE.....................559 233-6603
Calvin Coley, *President*
Pat Coley, *Treasurer*
Donald Crawford, *Vice Pres*
EMP: 30
SQ FT: 1,500
SALES (est): 5.2MM **Privately Held**
SIC: 3273 5211 Ready-mixed concrete;
cement

(P-11104)
ELITE READY-MIX LLC
550 Greenville Rd, Livermore
(94550-9297)
PHONE.....................916 366-4627

Dominic Sposeto, *Mng Member*
Braxton Edwards, *Opers Mgr*
Greg Franklin, *Sales Mgr*
Larry Elseberry, *Sales Staff*
Billie Sposeto
EMP: 35
SALES (est): 7.4MM **Privately Held**
SIC: 3273 Ready-mixed concrete

(P-11105)
FAR WEST EQUIPMENT
RENTALS
649 7th St, Lincoln (95648-1828)
PHONE.....................916 645-2929
Jeff Drennor, *President*
EMP: 15
SALES (est): 1.1MM **Privately Held**
SIC: 3273 Ready-mixed concrete

(P-11106)
FEATHER RIVER CONCRETE
PRODUCT
675 State Box Rd, Oroville (95965-5885)
PHONE.....................530 532-7915
EMP: 10
SALES (corp-wide): 4.6MM **Privately**
Held
SIC: 3273
PA: Feather River Concrete Product
1295 State Highway 99
Gridley CA 95948
530 846-5842

(P-11107)
FOLSOM READY MIX INC
19291 Latona Rd, Anderson (96007-9405)
PHONE.....................530 365-0191
Brian Phillippen, *Vice Pres*
EMP: 17
SALES (corp-wide): 9.5MM **Privately**
Held
SIC: 3273 Ready-mixed concrete
PA: Folsom Ready Mix, Inc.
3401 Fitzgerald Rd
Rancho Cordova CA 95742
916 851-8300

(P-11108)
FOOTHILL READY MIX INC
11415 State Highway 99w, Red Bluff
(96080-7716)
PHONE.....................530 527-2565
Kevin Brunnemer, *President*
Cathy Brunnemer, *Admin Sec*
EMP: 20 EST: 1979
SQ FT: 1,000
SALES (est): 3.3MM **Privately Held**
SIC: 3273 Ready-mixed concrete

(P-11109)
FRONTIER CONCRETE INC
717 Mercantile St, Vista (92083-5919)
P.O. Box 3800 (92085-3800)
PHONE.....................760 724-4483
Mike Williams, *President*
EMP: 10
SALES (est): 1.7MM **Privately Held**
SIC: 3273 Ready-mixed concrete

(P-11110)
GARY BALE REDI-MIX CON INC
16131 Construction Cir W, Irvine
(92606-4410)
PHONE.....................949 786-9441
Kyle Goerlitz, *CEO*
Carol Beck, *Controller*
Rod Giacomini, *Sales Staff*
EMP: 80
SALES (est): 26.7MM **Privately Held**
SIC: 3273 Ready-mixed concrete

(P-11111)
GIBBEL BROS INC
Also Called: True Cast Concrete Products
11145 Tuxford St, Sun Valley (91352-2632)
PHONE.....................323 875-1367
Gregory Gibbel, *President*
EMP: 50 EST: 1965
SQ FT: 1,500
SALES (est): 5.5MM **Privately Held**
SIC: 3273 3271 Ready-mixed concrete;
blocks, concrete or cinder: standard

(P-11112)
GIBSON AND SCHAEFER INC
(PA)
1126 Rock Wood Rd, Heber (92249)
PHONE.....................619 352-3535
Don Gibson, *President*
Maria Schaefer, *Treasurer*
P M Schaefer, *Vice Pres*
Rhoberta Gibson, *Admin Sec*
EMP: 50
SQ FT: 1.440
SALES: 8MM **Privately Held**
SIC: 3273 5032 Ready-mixed concrete;
gravel

(P-11113)
GOLDEN EMPIRE CONCRETE
CO
8211 Gosford Rd, Bakersfield
(93313-9663)
PHONE.....................661 325-6990
Charlie Wensley, *President*
EMP: 40
SQ FT: 1,200
SALES (est): 3.9MM
SALES (corp-wide): 479.6MM **Privately**
Held
SIC: 3273 5211 Ready-mixed concrete;
cement
HQ: National Cement Company Of Califor-
nia, Inc.
15821 Ventura Blvd # 475
Encino CA 91436
818 728-5200

(P-11114)
GRANITE ROCK CO
Also Called: Pavex Construction Co
1755 Del Monte Blvd, Seaside
(93955-3603)
PHONE.....................831 392-3700
Mike Chernetsky, *Manager*
EMP: 35
SALES (corp-wide): 1.1B **Privately Held**
WEB: www.graniterock.com
SIC: 3273 5032 Ready-mixed concrete;
brick, stone & related material; sand, con-
struction; stone, crushed or broken
PA: Granite Rock Co.
350 Technology Dr
Watsonville CA 95076
831 768-2000

(P-11115)
HANFORD READY-MIX INC
9800 Kent St, Elk Grove (95624-9483)
PHONE.....................916 405-1918
Preston Hanford Jr, *CEO*
Diane Hanford-Butz, *Vice Pres*
EMP: 22
SQ FT: 3,500
SALES (est): 4.4MM **Privately Held**
SIC: 3273 Ready-mixed concrete

(P-11116)
HANFORD SAND & GRAVEL INC
9800 Kent St, Elk Grove (95624-9483)
PHONE.....................916 782-9150
Preston Hanford III, *President*
Diane Hanford-Butz, *Corp Secy*
Jacqueline Hanford, *Vice Pres*
EMP: 11
SALES (est): 1.9MM **Privately Held**
SIC: 3273 Ready-mixed concrete

(P-11117)
HANSON AGGREGATES LLC
13550 Live Oak Ln, Irwindale
(91706-1318)
PHONE.....................626 358-1811
Carol Smith, *Principal*
EMP: 30
SALES (corp-wide): 20.3B **Privately Held**
WEB: www.hansonind.com
SIC: 3273 5032 Ready-mixed concrete;
stone, crushed or broken; sand, construc-
tion; gravel
HQ: Hanson Aggregates Llc
8505 Freport Pkwy Ste 500
Irving TX 75063
469 417-1200

PRODUCTS & SVCS

(P-11118)
HANSON AGGRGTES MD-PACIFIC INC
Also Called: Lehigh Hanson
180 Atascadero Rd, Morro Bay
(93442-1515)
P.O. Box 71, San Luis Obispo (93406-0071)
PHONE..................................805 928-3764
John Newhaul, *Manager*
EMP: 11
SALES (corp-wide): 20.3B **Privately Held**
SIC: 3273 1442 Ready-mixed concrete; construction sand & gravel
HQ: Hanson Aggregates Mid-Pacific, Inc.
12667 Alcosta Blvd # 400
San Ramon CA
-

(P-11119)
HI-GRADE MATERIALS CO
6500 E Avenue T, Littlerock (93543-1722)
P.O. Box 1050 (93543-1050)
PHONE..................................661 533-3100
Rod Elderton, *Manager*
EMP: 32
SALES (corp-wide): 53.1MM **Privately Held**
SIC: 3273 Ready-mixed concrete
HQ: Hi-Grade Materials Co.
17671 Bear Valley Rd
Hesperia CA
760 244-9325

(P-11120)
HOLLIDAY ROCK TRUCKING INC (PA)
1401 N Benson Ave, Upland (91786-2166)
PHONE..................................909 982-1553
Frederick N Holliday, *President*
Penny Holliday, *President*
Ronald Chambers, *Vice Pres*
John Holliday, *Vice Pres*
EMP: 60
SQ FT: 2,000
SALES (est): 7.9MM **Privately Held**
SIC: 3273 4212 Ready-mixed concrete; local trucking, without storage

(P-11121)
HOLLISTER LANDSCAPE SUPPLY INC (HQ)
520 Crazy Horse Canyon Rd A, Salinas (93907-9224)
PHONE..................................831 443-8644
Barbara A Chapin, *President*
Sharon Holmes, *Admin Sec*
EMP: 10 **EST:** 2000
SQ FT: 1,500
SALES (est): 6.6MM **Privately Held**
SIC: 3273 5032 Ready-mixed concrete; aggregate

(P-11122)
J F SHEA CO INC (PA)
655 Brea Canyon Rd, Walnut (91789-3078)
P.O. Box 494519, Redding (96049-4519)
PHONE..................................909 594-9500
Peter O Shea Jr, *CEO*
John Francis Shea, *President*
James Shontere, *CFO*
Robert R O'Dell, *Treasurer*
Andy Roundtree, *Vice Pres*
▲ **EMP:** 35 **EST:** 1881
SALES (est): 2.2B **Privately Held**
SIC: 3273 Bridge, tunnel & elevated highway; highway & street construction; water, sewer & utility lines

(P-11123)
J F SHEA CO INC
Also Called: Shasta Ready Mix
17400 Clear Creek Rd, Redding (96001-5113)
PHONE..................................530 246-2200
Jim McCowen, *Principal*
EMP: 35
SALES (corp-wide): 2.2B **Privately Held**
SIC: 3273 Ready-mixed concrete
PA: J. F. Shea Co., Inc.
655 Brea Canyon Rd
Walnut CA 91789
909 594-9500

(P-11124)
KEN ANDERSON
Also Called: Cen Cal Rock & Ready Mix
904 Frontage Rd, Ripon (95366)
PHONE..................................209 604-8579
Ken Anderson, *Owner*
EMP: 25
SALES (est): 1.5MM **Privately Held**
SIC: 3273 5191 Ready-mixed concrete; farm supplies

(P-11125)
KYLES ROCK & REDI-MIX INC
1221 San Simeon Dr, Roseville (95661-5364)
PHONE..................................916 681-4848
Kyle Rosburg, *CEO*
Patti Rosburg, *CFO*
EMP: 40
SQ FT: 1,700
SALES (est): 5.3MM **Privately Held**
SIC: 3273 Ready-mixed concrete

(P-11126)
LEES CONCRETE MATERIALS INC
200 S Pine St, Madera (93637-5206)
P.O. Box 509 (93639-0509)
PHONE..................................559 486-2440
Tom Da Silva, *President*
Deidre Da Silva, *Treasurer*
EMP: 19
SQ FT: 7,000
SALES (est): 4.8MM **Privately Held**
SIC: 3273 Ready-mixed concrete

(P-11127)
LEGACY VULCAN LLC
Also Called: Western Division
655 W Tehachapi Blvd, Tehachapi (93561-1685)
PHONE..................................661 822-4158
Gunner Hildebrandt, *Manager*
EMP: 26 **Publicly Held**
WEB: www.vulcanmaterials.com
SIC: 3273 Ready-mixed concrete
HQ: Legacy Vulcan, Llc
1200 Urban Center Dr
Vestavia AL 35242
205 298-3000

(P-11128)
LEGACY VULCAN LLC
Also Called: Saticoy Rock Asphalt and Rdymx
6029 E Vineyard Ave, Oxnard (93036-1042)
PHONE..................................805 647-1161
Robert Dryden, *Branch Mgr*
EMP: 26 **Publicly Held**
WEB: www.vulcanmaterials.com
SIC: 3273 Ready-mixed concrete
HQ: Legacy Vulcan, Llc
1200 Urban Center Dr
Vestavia AL 35242
205 298-3000

(P-11129)
LEGACY VULCAN LLC
Also Called: Bakersfield Yard Asp & Rdymx
8517 E Panama Ln, Bakersfield (93307-9400)
P.O. Box 22800 (93390-2800)
PHONE..................................661 835-4800
Gene Weslo, *Manager*
Tony Smith, *Sales Staff*
EMP: 75 **Publicly Held**
WEB: www.vulcanmaterials.com
SIC: 3273 2951 Ready-mixed concrete; asphalt paving mixtures & blocks
HQ: Legacy Vulcan, Llc
1200 Urban Center Dr
Vestavia AL 35242
205 298-3000

(P-11130)
LEGACY VULCAN LLC
Also Called: Rock & Sand Plant
7220 Trade St Ste 200, San Diego (92121-2326)
P.O. Box 3098 (92163-3098)
PHONE..................................858 566-2730
Dave Becker, *Branch Mgr*
EMP: 20 **Publicly Held**
WEB: www.vulcanmaterials.com
SIC: 3273 Ready-mixed concrete

HQ: Legacy Vulcan, Llc
1200 Urban Center Dr
Vestavia AL 35242
205 298-3000

(P-11131)
LEGACY VULCAN LLC
Also Called: Triangle Rock Products
11501 Florin Rd, Sacramento (95830-9499)
PHONE..................................916 682-0850
Robert Fine, *Manager*
EMP: 18 **Publicly Held**
WEB: www.vulcanmaterials.com
SIC: 3273 Ready-mixed concrete
HQ: Legacy Vulcan, Llc
1200 Urban Center Dr
Vestavia AL 35242
205 298-3000

(P-11132)
LEGACY VULCAN LLC
7107 E Avenue T, Littlerock (93543-1703)
PHONE..................................661 533-2125
Lorene Harrigan, *Manager*
EMP: 26 **Publicly Held**
WEB: www.vulcanmaterials.com
SIC: 3273 Ready-mixed concrete
HQ: Legacy Vulcan, Llc
1200 Urban Center Dr
Vestavia AL 35242
205 298-3000

(P-11133)
LEGACY VULCAN LLC
Also Called: Sun Valley Rock and Asphalt
11401 Tuxford St, Sun Valley (91352-2639)
PHONE..................................818 983-0146
Jim Dean, *Branch Mgr*
EMP: 26
SQ FT: 16,945 **Publicly Held**
WEB: www.vulcanmaterials.com
SIC: 3273 Ready-mixed concrete
HQ: Legacy Vulcan, Llc
1200 Urban Center Dr
Vestavia AL 35242
205 298-3000

(P-11134)
LEHIGH SOUTHWEST CEMENT CO
15390 Wonderland Blvd, Redding (96003-8526)
PHONE..................................530 275-1581
James Ellison, *Opers-Prdtn-Mfg*
Joe Baudizzon, *Project Engr*
EMP: 115
SALES (corp-wide): 20.3B **Privately Held**
SIC: 3273 3241 Ready-mixed concrete; cement, hydraulic
HQ: Lehigh Southwest Cement Company
2300 Clayton Rd Ste 300
Concord CA 94520
972 653-5500

(P-11135)
LIVINGSTONS CONCRETE SVC INC (PA)
5416 Roseville Rd, North Highlands (95660-5097)
PHONE..................................916 334-4313
Patricia Henley, *President*
Edith Livingston, *Corp Secy*
Ted Henley, *Vice Pres*
Shannon Russi, *Vice Pres*
Larry Livingston, *Principal*
EMP: 85
SALES (est): 14.5MM **Privately Held**
WEB: www.livingstonsconcrete.com
SIC: 3273 Ready-mixed concrete

(P-11136)
LIVINGSTONS CONCRETE SVC INC
Also Called: Plant 1
5416 Roseville Rd, North Highlands (95660-5097)
PHONE..................................916 334-4313
Terry Regan, *Branch Mgr*
EMP: 27
SALES (est): 1.3MM
SALES (corp-wide): 14.5MM **Privately Held**
WEB: www.livingstonsconcrete.com
SIC: 3273 Ready-mixed concrete

PA: Livingston's Concrete Service, Inc.
5416 Roseville Rd
North Highlands CA 95660
916 334-4313

(P-11137)
LIVINGSTONS CONCRETE SVC INC
Also Called: Plant 3
2915 Lesvos Ct, Lincoln (95648-9341)
PHONE..................................916 334-4313
Bill Redden, *Branch Mgr*
EMP: 24
SALES (corp-wide): 14.5MM **Privately Held**
WEB: www.livingstonsconcrete.com
SIC: 3273 Ready-mixed concrete
PA: Livingston's Concrete Service, Inc.
5416 Roseville Rd
North Highlands CA 95660
916 334-4313

(P-11138)
LYNCH READY MIX CONCRETE CO
Also Called: Mission Ready Mix
11011 Azahar St Ste 4, Ventura (93004-1944)
PHONE..................................805 647-2817
Robert A Lynch, *President*
Laverne Lynch, *Vice Pres*
EMP: 12
SQ FT: 1,700
SALES (est): 2.4MM **Privately Held**
WEB: www.missionreadymix.com
SIC: 3273 Ready-mixed concrete

(P-11139)
M B I READY-MIX L L C
44 Central St, Colfax (95713-9006)
PHONE..................................530 346-2432
Paul Manuel, *Principal*
Kellye Manuel,
Matthew Melugin,
James Milhous,
Gary Smith,
EMP: 20
SALES (est): 1.7MM **Privately Held**
SIC: 3273 Ready-mixed concrete

(P-11140)
MATHEWS READY MIX LLC
Also Called: Mathews Readymix
249 Lamon St, Yuba City (95991-4200)
P.O. Box 749, Marysville (95901-0020)
PHONE..................................530 671-2400
Lee Cooper, *Manager*
EMP: 20
SALES (corp-wide): 1.3B **Publicly Held**
WEB: www.eaglematerials.com
SIC: 3273 Ready-mixed concrete
HQ: Mathews Ready Mix Llc
4711 Hammonton Rd
Marysville CA 95901
530 749-6525

(P-11141)
MATHEWS READYMIX INC
1619 Skyway, Chico (95928)
PHONE..................................530 893-8856
Chad Christee, *Branch Mgr*
EMP: 12
SQ FT: 4,780
SALES (est): 1MM **Privately Held**
SIC: 3273 Ready-mixed concrete

(P-11142)
METRO READY MIX
1635 James Rd, Bakersfield (93308-9749)
P.O. Box 80487 (93380-0487)
PHONE..................................661 829-7851
Corky Graviss, *Owner*
EMP: 11
SALES (est): 1.4MM **Privately Held**
SIC: 3273 Ready-mixed concrete

(P-11143)
MIX GARDEN INC
1083 Vine St, Healdsburg (95448-4830)
PHONE..................................707 433-4327
Michael J Kopetsky, *Principal*
EMP: 10
SALES (est): 1MM **Privately Held**
SIC: 3273 Ready-mixed concrete

▲ = Import ▼=Export
◆ =Import/Export

(P-11144)
MS CAST STONE INC
Also Called: Souther Archtctural Cast Stone
235 Via Del Monte, Oceanside
(92058-1223)
PHONE................................760 754-9697
Marco Souther, *President*
Angela Souther, *Admin Sec*
EMP: 30 EST: 2016
SALES (est): 1.9MM **Privately Held**
SIC: 3273 Ready-mixed concrete

(P-11145)
NATIONAL CEMENT CO CAL INC
Also Called: Lebec - Ncc CA Cement Company
5 Miles East Of I 5 Ofc H, Lebec (93243)
PHONE................................661 248-6733
Gerardo Valds, *Branch Mgr*
EMP: 1▲
SALES (corp-wide): 479.6MM **Privately Held**
SIC: 3273 Ready-mixed concrete
HQ: National Cement Company Of California, Inc.
15821 Ventura Blvd # 475
Encino CA 91436
818 728-5200

(P-11146)
NATIONAL CEMENT CO CAL INC (DH)
15821 Ventura Blvd # 475, Encino
(91436-2935)
PHONE................................818 728-5200
Steven Weiss, *President*
Pragati Kapoor, *CFO*
Dominique Bidet, *Treasurer*
▲ EMP: 31
SQ FT: 12,000
SALES (est): 68MM
SALES (corp-wide): 479.6MM **Privately Held**
SIC: 3273 Ready-mixed concrete
HQ: National Cement Company, Inc.
15821 Ventura Blvd # 475
Encino CA 91436
818 728-5200

(P-11147)
NATIONAL READY MIXED CON CO
4549 Brazil St, Los Angeles (90039-1001)
PHONE................................323 245-5539
Bob McFarlane, *Branch Mgr*
EMP: 11
SALES (corp-wide): 479.6MM **Privately Held**
SIC: 3273 Ready-mixed concrete
HQ: National Ready Mixed Concrete Co
15821 Ventura Blvd # 475
Encino CA 91436
818 728-5200

(P-11148)
NATIONAL READY MIXED CON CO
6969 Deering Ave, Canoga Park
(91303-2171)
PHONE................................818 884-0893
Mike Randolph, *Manager*
EMP: 11
SALES (corp-wide): 479.6MM **Privately Held**
SIC: 3273 Ready-mixed concrete
HQ: National Ready Mixed Concrete Co
15821 Ventura Blvd # 475
Encino CA 91436
818 728-5200

(P-11149)
NATIONAL READY MIXED CON CO (DH)
15821 Ventura Blvd # 475, Encino
(91436-4778)
PHONE................................818 728-5200
Tim Toland, *CEO*
Don Unmacht, *Vice Pres*
Jim Banes, *Opers Mgr*
Helen Giampietro, *Transportation*
▲ EMP: 20
SQ FT: 40,000

SALES (est): 32.4MM
SALES (corp-wide): 479.6MM **Privately Held**
SIC: 3273 Ready-mixed concrete
HQ: National Cement Company Of California, Inc.
15821 Ventura Blvd # 475
Encino CA 91436
818 728-5200

(P-11150)
NATIONAL READY MIXED CON CO
11725 Artesia Blvd, Artesia (90701-3850)
PHONE................................562 865-6211
Sher Cowan, *Branch Mgr*
Sam Hild, *General Mgr*
EMP: 11
SALES (corp-wide): 479.6MM **Privately Held**
SIC: 3273 Ready-mixed concrete
HQ: National Ready Mixed Concrete Co
15821 Ventura Blvd # 475
Encino CA 91436
818 728-5200

(P-11151)
NAVAJO CONCRETE INC
Also Called: Navajo Rock & Block
2484 Ramada Dr, Paso Robles
(93446-3949)
P.O. Box 117, Templeton (93465-0117)
PHONE................................805 238-0955
Fax: 805 238-0140
EMP: 15
SQ FT: 144
SALES (est): 1.8MM **Privately Held**
SIC: 3273

(P-11152)
NORCAL RECYCLED ROCK AGGREGATE (PA)
291a Shell Ln, Willits (95490-4520)
P.O. Box 2088, Ukiah (95482-2088)
PHONE................................707 459-9636
Frank Dutra, *President*
EMP: 11
SALES (est): 1.7MM **Privately Held**
SIC: 3273 Ready-mixed concrete

(P-11153)
OUTBACK INC
4201 W Shaw Ave Ste 106, Fresno
(93722-6216)
PHONE................................559 369-7261
EMP: 12
SALES (corp-wide): 30.1MM **Privately Held**
SIC: 3273 Ready-mixed concrete
PA: Outback Inc.
4201 W Shaw Ave Ste 106
Fresno CA 93722
559 293-3880

(P-11154)
P & L CONCRETE PRODUCTS INC
1900 Roosevelt Ave, Escalon
(95320-1763)
PHONE................................209 838-1448
Jeff Francis, *President*
Arlene Francis, *Vice Pres*
EMP: 22
SQ FT: 1,500
SALES (est): 4.3MM **Privately Held**
WEB: www.plconcrete.net
SIC: 3273 Ready-mixed concrete

(P-11155)
PACIFIC AGGREGATES INC
28251 Lake St, Lake Elsinore
(92530-1635)
PHONE................................951 245-2460
Bary Culli, *CEO*
Edward Rutherford, *CEO*
Kai Chin, *Vice Pres*
Dale Kline, *Vice Pres*
Kim Chan, *Controller*
▲ EMP: 90
SQ FT: 1,000
SALES (est): 12.1MM
SALES (corp-wide): 911.7MM **Privately Held**
WEB: www.castlecooke.net
SIC: 3273 Ready-mixed concrete

PA: Castle & Cooke, Inc.
1 Dole Dr
Westlake Village CA 91362
310 374-3952

(P-11156)
PARAMOUNT READY MIX CON INC
13949 Stage Rd, Santa Fe Springs
(90670-5215)
P.O. Box 2823 (90670-0823)
PHONE................................562 404-4125
Toll Free:................................888 -
Charles J Oliver, *President*
Janielle Bousema, *Vice Pres*
EMP: 38
SALES: 9MM **Privately Held**
WEB: www.paramountreadymix.com
SIC: 3273 Ready-mixed concrete

(P-11157)
PLEASANTON READY MIX CONCRETE
Also Called: Pleasanton Readymix Concrete
3400 Boulder St, Pleasanton (94566-4769)
P.O. Box 879 (94566-0874)
PHONE................................925 846-3226
Albert Riebli, *President*
John Santos, *Treasurer*
EMP: 15
SQ FT: 1,000
SALES (est): 4MM **Privately Held**
SIC: 3273 Ready-mixed concrete

(P-11158)
PUENTE READY MIX INC (PA)
209 N California Ave, City of Industry
(91744-4324)
P.O. Box 3345 (91744-0345)
PHONE................................626 968-0711
Mark Keuning, *Ch of Bd*
Ronald A Biang, *President*
Kevin Keuning, *Vice Pres*
Marcia Biang, *Admin Sec*
EMP: 23 EST: 1949
SQ FT: 5,000
SALES (est): 4.3MM **Privately Held**
SIC: 3273 Ready-mixed concrete

(P-11159)
RANCHO READY MIX (PA)
28251 Lake St, Lake Elsinore
(92530-1635)
PHONE................................951 674-0488
William Summers, *President*
Mal Gatherer, *Corp Secy*
EMP: 50
SQ FT: 1,000
SALES (est): 12MM **Privately Held**
SIC: 3273 Ready-mixed concrete

(P-11160)
RC READYMIX CO INC
1227 Greenville Rd, Livermore
(94550-9299)
PHONE................................925 449-7785
Rob Costa, *President*
Rob C0sta, *President*
EMP: 24 EST: 1998
SALES (est): 4.9MM **Privately Held**
SIC: 3273 Ready-mixed concrete

(P-11161)
RIGHT AWAY CONCRETE PMPG INC
401 Kennedy St, Oakland (94606-5321)
PHONE................................510 536-1900
David Filipek, *Manager*
Jose Chacon, *Supervisor*
EMP: 30
SQ FT: 3,328
SALES (corp-wide): 1.3B **Publicly Held**
SIC: 3273 1771 Ready-mixed concrete; concrete pumping
HQ: Right Away Concrete Pumping, Inc.
725 Julie Ann Way
Oakland CA 94621

(P-11162)
RMC PACIFIC MATERIALS INC
1544 Stanley Blvd, Pleasanton
(94566-6308)
P.O. Box 249 (94566-0836)
PHONE................................925 846-2824

Rich Bier, *Plant Mgr*
Steve Powers, *Branch Mgr*
EMP: 42 **Privately Held**
SIC: 3273 3241 Ready-mixed concrete; cement, hydraulic; construction sand & gravel
HQ: Rmc Pacific Materials, Inc.
6601 Koll Center Pkwy
Pleasanton CA 94566
925 426-8787

(P-11163)
ROBAR ENTERPRISES INC (PA)
17671 Bear Valley Rd, Hesperia
(92345-4902)
PHONE................................760 244-5456
Jonathan D Hove, *CEO*
Al Calvanico, *CFO*
Robert E Hove, *Chairman*
Sean McGill, *Branch Mgr*
Linda Long, *MIS Dir*
EMP: 150 EST: 1981
SQ FT: 26,000
SALES (est): 53.1MM **Privately Held**
WEB: www.robarenterprises.com
SIC: 3273 5051 3441 Ready-mixed concrete; steel; building components, structural steel

(P-11164)
ROBERTSONS DISTRIBUTORS INC
1990 N Hargrave St, Banning
(92220-7000)
PHONE................................951 849-4766
Bill Lambert, *Manager*
EMP: 12
SALES (corp-wide): 3.7MM **Privately Held**
WEB: www.robertsonshomedecor.com
SIC: 3273 Ready-mixed concrete
PA: Robertsons Distributors, Inc
18217 Parthenia St
Northridge CA 91325
818 701-0168

(P-11165)
ROBERTSONS RDY MIX LTD A CAL
2975 Hwy 18, Lake Arrowhead (92352)
P.O. Box 3600, Corona (92878-3600)
PHONE................................909 337-7577
Carl Moore, *Manager*
EMP: 10
SALES (corp-wide): 15B **Privately Held**
WEB: www.rrmca.com
SIC: 3273 Ready-mixed concrete
HQ: Robertson's Ready Mix, Ltd., A California Limited Partnership
200 S Main St Ste 200 # 200
Corona CA 92882
951 493-6500

(P-11166)
ROBERTSONS RDY MIX LTD A CAL
12203 Violet Rd, Adelanto (92301-2714)
PHONE................................760 246-4000
Jim Konoske, *Manager*
EMP: 10
SALES (corp-wide): 15B **Privately Held**
WEB: www.rrmca.com
SIC: 3273 5211 1771 Ready-mixed concrete; cement; concrete pumping
HQ: Robertson's Ready Mix, Ltd., A California Limited Partnership
200 S Main St Ste 200 # 200
Corona CA 92882
951 493-6500

(P-11167)
ROBERTSONS READY MIX LTD (HQ)
200 S Main St Ste 200 # 200, Corona
(92882-2212)
P.O. Box 3600 (92878-3600)
PHONE................................951 493-6500
Jon Troesh, *Partner*
Don Rubidoux, *General Mgr*
Todd Dragna, *QA Dir*
Anthony Lunetta, *Software Dev*
Steven Walthers, *Controller*
▲ EMP: 85
SQ FT: 22,008

P
R
O
D
U
C
T
S

&

S
V
C
S

SALES (est): 627MM
SALES (corp-wide): 15B Privately Held
WEB: www.rrmca.com
SIC: 3273 3531 5032 2951 Ready-mixed concrete; bituminous, cement & concrete related products & equipment; asphalt plant, including gravel-mix type; concrete plants; asphalt mixture; paving mixtures; concrete mixtures; asphalt paving mixtures & blocks; construction sand & gravel
PA: Mitsubishi Materials Corporation
1-3-2, Otemachi
Chiyoda-Ku TKY 100-0
352 525-200

(P-11168)
ROBERTSONS READY MIX LTD
2470 Pomona Blvd, Pomona (91768-3276)
PHONE................................909 623-9185
Dan Hawley, Area Spvr
EMP: 30
SALES (corp-wide): 15B Privately Held
WEB: www.rrmca.com
SIC: 3273 Ready-mixed concrete
HQ: Robertson's Ready Mix, Ltd., A California Limited Partnership
200 S Main St Ste 200 # 200
Corona CA 92882
951 493-6500

(P-11169)
ROBERTSONS READY MIX LTD
200 S Main St Ste 200 # 200, Corona (92882-2212)
PHONE................................800 834-7557
Robert Burmeister, President
EMP: 20
SALES (corp-wide): 15B Privately Held
SIC: 3273 Ready-mixed concrete
HQ: Robertson's Ready Mix, Ltd., A California Limited Partnership
200 S Main St Ste 200 # 200
Corona CA 92882
951 493-6500

(P-11170)
ROBERTSONS READY MIX LTD
27401 3rd St, Highland (92346-4242)
PHONE................................909 425-2930
Dennis Troesh, President
EMP: 28
SALES (corp-wide): 15B Privately Held
SIC: 3273 Ready-mixed concrete
HQ: Robertson's Ready Mix, Ltd., A California Limited Partnership
200 S Main St Ste 200 # 200
Corona CA 92882
951 493-6500

(P-11171)
SERVICE ROCK PRODUCTS CORP
2820 E Main St, Barstow (92311-5882)
PHONE................................760 252-1615
Vince Bommarito, Manager
EMP: 35
SALES (corp-wide): 15B Privately Held
WEB: www.servicerock.com
SIC: 3273 Ready-mixed concrete
HQ: Service Rock Products Corporation
151 Cassia Way
Henderson NV 89014
702 798-0568

(P-11172)
SERVICE ROCK PRODUCTS CORP
7900 Moss Ave, California City (93505-4311)
P.O. Box 3600, Corona (92878-3600)
PHONE................................760 373-9140
Clark Monier, Branch Mgr
EMP: 30
SALES (corp-wide): 15B Privately Held
WEB: www.servicerock.com
SIC: 3273 Ready-mixed concrete
HQ: Service Rock Products Corporation
151 Cassia Way
Henderson NV 89014
702 798-0568

(P-11173)
SERVICE ROCK PRODUCTS CORP
200 S Main St Ste 200 # 200, Corona (92882-2212)
PHONE................................760 245-7997
Alex Delgado, Branch Mgr
EMP: 12
SALES (corp-wide): 15B Privately Held
WEB: www.servicerock.com
SIC: 3273 Ready-mixed concrete
HQ: Service Rock Products Corporation
151 Cassia Way
Henderson NV 89014
702 798-0568

(P-11174)
SERVICE ROCK PRODUCTS CORP
2157 W Inyokern Rd, Ridgecrest (93555-8538)
PHONE................................760 446-2606
George Vernaci, Manager
EMP: 51
SALES (corp-wide): 15B Privately Held
WEB: www.servicerock.com
SIC: 3273 Ready-mixed concrete
HQ: Service Rock Products Corporation
151 Cassia Way
Henderson NV 89014
702 798-0568

(P-11175)
SERVICE ROCK PRODUCTS CORP
37790 75th St E, Palmdale (93552-4200)
PHONE................................661 533-3443
Ron Pinion, Manager
EMP: 30
SALES (corp-wide): 15B Privately Held
WEB: www.servicerock.com
SIC: 3273 5032 1442 Ready-mixed concrete; stone, crushed or broken; construction sand & gravel
HQ: Service Rock Products Corporation
151 Cassia Way
Henderson NV 89014
702 798-0568

(P-11176)
SHAMROCK MATERIALS INC (PA)
181 Lynch Creek Way # 201, Petaluma (94954-2388)
P.O. Box 751300 (94975-1300)
PHONE................................707 781-9000
Eugene B Ceccotti, CEO
Robert Bowen, CFO
Jeff Nehmens, Vice Pres
Tom Hunt, Opers Mgr
Greg Gehring, Marketing Staff
▲ EMP: 25 EST: 1945
SQ FT: 5,000
SALES (est): 30.3MM Privately Held
WEB: www.shamrockmat.com
SIC: 3273 5211 Ready-mixed concrete; lumber & other building materials

(P-11177)
SHAMROCK MATERIALS INC
Also Called: Shamrock Materials of Cotati
8150 Gravenstein Hwy, Cotati (94931-4127)
PHONE................................707 792-4695
Jorge Barjas, Manager
Robert Fidelman, Info Tech Dir
EMP: 15
SALES (corp-wide): 30.3MM Privately Held
WEB: www.shamrockmat.com
SIC: 3273 Ready-mixed concrete
PA: Shamrock Materials, Inc.
181 Lynch Creek Way # 201
Petaluma CA 94954
707 781-9000

(P-11178)
SHAMROCK MATERIALS INC
Also Called: Shamrock Fireplace
548 Du Bois St, San Rafael (94901-3964)
P.O. Box 751300, Petaluma (94975-1300)
PHONE................................415 455-1575
Mike Isetta, Manager
EMP: 29

SALES (corp-wide): 30.3MM Privately Held
WEB: www.shamrockmat.com
SIC: 3273 Ready-mixed concrete
PA: Shamrock Materials, Inc.
181 Lynch Creek Way # 201
Petaluma CA 94954
707 781-9000

(P-11179)
SHAMROCK MATERIALS OF NOVATO
7552 Redwood Blvd, Novato (94945-2425)
P.O. Box 808044, Petaluma (94975-8044)
PHONE................................415 892-1571
Eugene B Ceccotti, CEO
EMP: 15
SALES (est): 1.6MM
SALES (corp-wide): 30.3MM Privately Held
WEB: www.shamrockmat.com
SIC: 3273 Ready-mixed concrete
PA: Shamrock Materials, Inc.
181 Lynch Creek Way # 201
Petaluma CA 94954
707 781-9000

(P-11180)
SIERRA-TAHOE READY MIX INC
1526 Emerald Bay Rd, South Lake Tahoe (96150-6112)
PHONE................................530 541-1877
Donald Wallace, President
William Santos, Treasurer
EMP: 22
SQ FT: 2,000
SALES (est): 18.8MM Privately Held
SIC: 3273 Ready-mixed concrete

(P-11181)
SOUSA READY MIX LLC
Also Called: Siskiyou County Family Plng R
100 Upton Rd, Mount Shasta (96067-9169)
P.O. Box 157 (96067-0157)
PHONE................................530 926-4485
Gregory Juell, Mng Member
EMP: 15 EST: 1976
SQ FT: 1,200
SALES: 1.7MM Privately Held
SIC: 3273 Ready-mixed concrete

(P-11182)
SOUTH VALLEY MATERIALS INC (DH)
7673 N Ingram Ave Ste 101, Fresno (93711-5854)
P.O. Box 26240 (93729-6240)
PHONE................................559 277-7060
James G Brown, President
EMP: 60
SQ FT: 6,000
SALES (est): 9MM
SALES (corp-wide): 20.3B Privately Held
SIC: 3273 Ready-mixed concrete

(P-11183)
SOUTH VALLEY MATERIALS INC
7761 Hanford Armona Rd, Hanford (93230-9343)
P.O. Box 26240, Fresno (93729-6240)
PHONE................................559 582-0532
David Vickers, Branch Mgr
Steve Tarantino, Vice Pres
EMP: 36
SALES (corp-wide): 20.3B Privately Held
SIC: 3273 Ready-mixed concrete
HQ: South Valley Materials, Inc.
7673 N Ingram Ave Ste 101
Fresno CA 93711
559 277-7060

(P-11184)
SPRAGUES ROCK AND SAND COMPANY (PA)
Also Called: Spragues Ready Mix
230 Longden Ave, Irwindale (91706-1328)
PHONE................................626 445-2125
Carole Cotter, Ch of Bd
Michael Toland, President
Gerald Anctil, Treasurer
Juli Paez, Corp Secy
Steven Toland, Vice Pres
EMP: 22
SQ FT: 2,100

SALES (est): 7.2MM Privately Held
SIC: 3273 Ready-mixed concrete

(P-11185)
SPRAGUES ROCK AND SAND COMPANY
Also Called: Spragues Ready Mix Concrete
5400 Bennett Rd, Simi Valley (93063-5135)
PHONE................................805 522-7010
Michael Toland, Manager
EMP: 15
SALES (est): 1.6MM
SALES (corp-wide): 7.2MM Privately Held
SIC: 3273 Ready-mixed concrete
PA: Spragues' Rock And Sand Company
230 Longden Ave
Irwindale CA 91706
626 445-2125

(P-11186)
STANDARD CONCRETE PRODUCTS (HQ)
Also Called: Associated Ready Mix Concrete
13550 Live Oak Ln, Baldwin Park (91706-1318)
P.O. Box 15326, Santa Ana (92735-0326)
PHONE................................310 829-4537
David Hummel, President
Brian Serra, Vice Pres
EMP: 20
SQ FT: 2,400
SALES (est): 13.1MM
SALES (corp-wide): 57.6MM Privately Held
WEB: www.standard-concrete.com
SIC: 3273 Ready-mixed concrete
PA: A & A Ready Mixed Concrete, Inc.
4621 Teller Ave Ste 130
Newport Beach CA 92660
949 253-2800

(P-11187)
STATE READY MIX INC
3127 Los Angeles Ave, Oxnard (93036-1010)
PHONE................................805 647-2817
Robert Lynch, President
EMP: 30
SALES (corp-wide): 5.8MM Privately Held
WEB: www.statereadymix.com
SIC: 3273 Ready-mixed concrete
PA: State Ready Mix, Inc.
1011 Azahar St Ste 1
Ventura CA 93004
805 647-2817

(P-11188)
STATE READY MIX INC (PA)
1011 Azahar St Ste 1, Ventura (93004)
PHONE................................805 647-2817
Russell Cochran, CEO
Robert A Lynch, President
EMP: 40
SALES (est): 5.8MM Privately Held
WEB: www.statereadymix.com
SIC: 3273 Ready-mixed concrete

(P-11189)
STEVE ROCK & READY MIX
5044 Osgood Way, Fair Oaks (95628-5272)
P.O. Box 1764 (95628-1764)
PHONE................................916 966-1600
Steve Boblitt, Owner
EMP: 10
SALES: 950K Privately Held
SIC: 3273 4212 5211 Ready-mixed concrete; local trucking, without storage; concrete & cinder block

(P-11190)
SUPERIOR READY MIX CONCRETE LP
Also Called: Srm Contracting & Paving
7192 Mission Gorge Rd, San Diego (92120-1131)
PHONE................................619 265-0955
Brent Cooper, Branch Mgr
EMP: 50
SALES (corp-wide): 232MM Privately Held
WEB: www.superiorrm.com
SIC: 3273 Ready-mixed concrete

PA: Superior Ready Mix Concrete L.P.
1508 Mission Rd
Escondido CA 92029
760 745-0556

(P-11191)
SUPERIOR READY MIX CONCRETE LP
Also Called: Canyon Rock & Asphalt
7500 Mission Gorge Rd, San Diego (92120-1304)
PHONE..................619 265-0296
Tracy Mall, *Manager*
EMP: 45
SALES (corp-wide): 232MM **Privately Held**
WEB: www.superiorrm.com
SIC: 3273 Ready-mixed concrete
PA: Superior Ready Mix Concrete L.P.
1508 Mission Rd
Escondido CA 92029
760 745-0556

(P-11192)
SUPERIOR READY MIX CONCRETE LP
802 E Main St, El Centro (92243-9474)
P.O. Box 400 (92244-0400)
PHONE..................760 352-4341
Donald Lee, *Branch Mgr*
EMP: 30
SALES (corp-wide): 232MM **Privately Held**
SIC: 3273 Ready-mixed concrete
PA: Superior Ready Mix Concrete L.P.
1508 Mission Rd
Escondido CA 92029
760 745-0556

(P-11193)
SUPERIOR READY MIX CONCRETE LP
Also Called: American Ready Mix
1508 W Mission St, Escondido (92029)
PHONE..................760 728-1128
Greg Sage, *Manager*
EMP: 15
SALES (corp-wide): 232MM **Privately Held**
WEB: www.superiorrm.com
SIC: 3273 1442 Ready-mixed concrete; construction sand & gravel
PA: Superior Ready Mix Concrete L.P.
1508 Mission Rd
Escondido CA 92029
760 745-0556

(P-11194)
SUPERIOR READY MIX CONCRETE LP
24635 Temescal Canyon Rd, Corona (92883-5422)
PHONE..................951 277-3553
Justine Moss, *Branch Mgr*
EMP: 45
SALES (corp-wide): 232MM **Privately Held**
WEB: www.superiorrm.com
SIC: 3273 Ready-mixed concrete
PA: Superior Ready Mix Concrete L.P.
1508 Mission Rd
Escondido CA 92029
760 745-0556

(P-11195)
SUPERIOR READY MIX CONCRETE LP (PA)
Also Called: Southland Ready Mix Concrete
1508 Mission Rd, Escondido (92029-1194)
PHONE..................760 745-0556
Donald Lee, *Partner*
EMP: 50
SQ FT: 3,000
SALES (est): 232MM **Privately Held**
WEB: www.superiorrm.com
SIC: 3273 1611 5032 Ready-mixed concrete; surfacing & paving; gravel; sand; construction

(P-11196)
SUPERIOR READY MIX CONCRETE LP
Also Called: Hemet Ready Mix
1130 N State St, Hemet (92543-1510)
PHONE..................951 658-9225

Wayne Heckerman, *Principal*
EMP: 40
SALES (corp-wide): 232MM **Privately Held**
WEB: www.superiorrm.com
SIC: 3273 5211 Ready-mixed concrete; masonry materials & supplies
PA: Superior Ready Mix Concrete L.P.
1508 Mission Rd
Escondido CA 92029
760 745-0556

(P-11197)
SUPERIOR READY MIX CONCRETE LP
Also Called: TTT Concrete
12494 Highway 67, Lakeside (92040-1133)
PHONE..................619 443-7510
Jerry Anderson, *Manager*
EMP: 40
SQ FT: 3,200
SALES (corp-wide): 232MM **Privately Held**
WEB: www.superiorrm.com
SIC: 3273 Ready-mixed concrete
PA: Superior Ready Mix Concrete L.P.
1508 Mission Rd
Escondido CA 92029
760 745-0556

(P-11198)
SUPERIOR READY MIX CONCRETE LP
72270 Varner Rd, Thousand Palms (92276-3341)
PHONE..................760 343-3418
Mark Higgins, *Manager*
EMP: 30
SALES (corp-wide): 232MM **Privately Held**
WEB: www.superiorrm.com
SIC: 3273 Ready-mixed concrete
PA: Superior Ready Mix Concrete L.P.
1508 Mission Rd
Escondido CA 92029
760 745-0556

(P-11199)
TEICHERT INC (PA)
3500 American River Dr, Sacramento (95864-5802)
P.O. Box 15002 (95851-0002)
PHONE..................916 484-3011
Judson T Riggs, *President*
Louis V Riggs, *Ch of Bd*
Narendra M Pathipati, *CFO*
Bob Deruiter, *Vice Pres*
Clark Hulbert, *Vice Pres*
▲ EMP: 179 EST: 1887
SALES (est): 784MM **Privately Held**
WEB: www.teichert.com
SIC: 3273 5032 1611 1442 Ready-mixed concrete; brick, stone & related material; highway & street construction; construction sand & gravel; single-family housing construction; air ducts, sheet metal

(P-11200)
TROESH READYMIX INC
2280 Hutton Rd, Nipomo (93444-9448)
PHONE..................805 928-3764
Steve Troesh, *President*
Renee Troesh, *Vice Pres*
EMP: 70
SALES (est): 8.7MM **Privately Held**
SIC: 3273 Ready-mixed concrete

(P-11201)
US CONCRETE INC
Also Called: Westside Concrete Materials
755 Stockton Ave, San Jose (95126-1839)
PHONE..................408 947-8606
Dave Perry, *Branch Mgr*
EMP: 13
SALES (corp-wide): 1.3B **Publicly Held**
SIC: 3273 Ready-mixed concrete
PA: U.S. Concrete, Inc.
331 N Main St
Euless TX 76039
817 835-4105

(P-11202)
VIKING READY MIX CO INC
Also Called: Glendale Ready-Mixed Concrete
4549 Brazil St, Los Angeles (90039-1001)
PHONE..................818 243-4243

Joe Perez, *Branch Mgr*
EMP: 24
SALES (corp-wide): 479.6MM **Privately Held**
SIC: 3273 Ready-mixed concrete
HQ: Viking Ready Mix Co., Inc.
3664 W Ashlan Ave
Fresno CA 93722
559 225-3667

(P-11203)
VIKING READY MIX CO INC
4988 Firestone Blvd, South Gate (90280-3544)
PHONE..................323 564-1866
Gary Hill, *Manager*
EMP: 21
SALES (corp-wide): 479.6MM **Privately Held**
SIC: 3273 Ready-mixed concrete
HQ: Viking Ready Mix Co., Inc.
3664 W Ashlan Ave
Fresno CA 93722
559 225-3667

(P-11204)
VIKING READY MIX CO INC
1641 Tollhouse, Clovis (93611)
P.O. Box 9129, Fresno (93790-9129)
PHONE..................559 225-3667
Charlie Wensley, *Manager*
EMP: 21
SQ FT: 5,984
SALES (corp-wide): 479.6MM **Privately Held**
SIC: 3273 Ready-mixed concrete
HQ: Viking Ready Mix Co., Inc.
3664 W Ashlan Ave
Fresno CA 93722
559 225-3667

(P-11205)
VIKING READY MIX CO INC
12100 11th Ave, Hanford (93230-9523)
PHONE..................559 344-7931
Don Unmacht, *Manager*
EMP: 15
SALES (corp-wide): 479.6MM **Privately Held**
SIC: 3273 Ready-mixed concrete
HQ: Viking Ready Mix Co., Inc.
3664 W Ashlan Ave
Fresno CA 93722
559 225-3667

(P-11206)
VIKING READY MIX CO INC
11725 Artesia Blvd, Artesia (90701-3850)
PHONE..................562 865-6211
Sher Cowan, *Manager*
EMP: 20
SQ FT: 2,151
SALES (corp-wide): 479.6MM **Privately Held**
SIC: 3273 Ready-mixed concrete
HQ: Viking Ready Mix Co., Inc.
3664 W Ashlan Ave
Fresno CA 93722
559 225-3667

(P-11207)
VIKING READY MIX CO INC
15203 Oxnard St, Van Nuys (91411-2617)
PHONE..................818 786-2210
Richard Vowman, *Manager*
EMP: 20
SALES (corp-wide): 479.6MM **Privately Held**
SIC: 3273 Ready-mixed concrete
HQ: Viking Ready Mix Co., Inc.
3664 W Ashlan Ave
Fresno CA 93722
559 225-3667

(P-11208)
VIKING READY MIX CO INC
Also Called: Skyline Concrete
9010 Norris Ave, Sun Valley (91352-2617)
PHONE..................818 768-0050
Michael Randauf, *Manager*
EMP: 30
SALES (corp-wide): 479.6MM **Privately Held**
SIC: 3273 Ready-mixed concrete

HQ: Viking Ready Mix Co., Inc.
3664 W Ashlan Ave
Fresno CA 93722
559 225-3667

(P-11209)
VIKING READY MIX CO INC
Also Called: National Ready Mix
2620 Buena Vista St, Duarte (91010-3338)
PHONE..................626 303-7755
Sergio Dalenduela, *Manager*
EMP: 32
SALES (corp-wide): 479.6MM **Privately Held**
SIC: 3273 5211 Ready-mixed concrete; cement
HQ: Viking Ready Mix Co., Inc.
3664 W Ashlan Ave
Fresno CA 93722
559 225-3667

(P-11210)
VIKING READY MIX CO INC
Also Called: Skyline Concrete
6969 Deering Ave, Canoga Park (91303-2171)
PHONE..................818 884-0893
Mike Randolph, *Manager*
EMP: 20
SALES (corp-wide): 479.6MM **Privately Held**
SIC: 3273 Ready-mixed concrete
HQ: Viking Ready Mix Co., Inc.
3664 W Ashlan Ave
Fresno CA 93722
559 225-3667

(P-11211)
VULCAN MATERIALS CO
849 W Washington Ave, Escondido (92025-1634)
P.O. Box 461179 (92046-1179)
PHONE..................760 737-3486
A F Gerstell, *President*
Brian Foster, *Office Mgr*
Roland Gonzales, *Safety Dir*
EMP: 50
SALES (est): 5MM **Publicly Held**
WEB: www.calmat.com
SIC: 3273 Ready-mixed concrete
HQ: Calmat Co.
500 N Brand Blvd Ste 500 # 500
Glendale CA 91203
818 553-8821

(P-11212)
WERNER CORPORATION
Also Called: Foster Sand & Gravel
25050 Maitri Rd, Corona (92883-5105)
PHONE..................951 277-4586
Mark Miller, *Manager*
EMP: 15
SALES (corp-wide): 8.6MM **Privately Held**
SIC: 3273 Ready-mixed concrete
PA: Werner Corporation
25555 Maitri Rd
Corona CA 92883
951 277-3900

(P-11213)
WESTERN READY MIX CONCRETE CO (PA)
Gyle Rd, Willows (95988)
PHONE..................530 934-2185
James B Hill, *President*
EMP: 10
SQ FT: 1,000
SALES (est): 2.8MM **Privately Held**
SIC: 3273 5211 Ready-mixed concrete; sand & gravel

(P-11214)
YREKA TRANSIT MIX CONCRETE
126 Schantz Rd, Yreka (96097-9556)
PHONE..................530 842-4351
Darren Rose, *President*
EMP: 12
SQ FT: 2,300
SALES: 1MM **Privately Held**
SIC: 3273 Ready-mixed concrete

PRODUCTS & SVCS

3274 Lime

(P-11215)
LHOIST NORTH AMERICA ARIZ INC
Also Called: Industry Terminal Us31
14931 Salt Lake Ave, City of Industry
(91746-3115)
PHONE.....................................626 336-4578
Emilio Asence, *Terminal Mgr*
David R Puryear, *Vice Pres*
Antoine Riguelle, *Vice Pres*
Laurent Yvon, *Vice Pres*
Didier Lesueur, *Research*
EMP: 10
SQ FT: 80,529 **Privately Held**
SIC: 3274 5032 Lime; lime building products
HQ: Lhoist North America Of Arizona, Inc.
5600 Clearfork Main St
Fort Worth TX 76109
817 732-8164

3275 Gypsum Prdts

(P-11216)
BESTWALL LLC
Also Called: Georgia-Pacific
1401 W Pier D St, Long Beach
(90802-1025)
P.O. Box 337350, North Las Vegas NV
(89033-7350)
PHONE.....................................562 435-7094
Scott Mc Donald, *Sales Mgr*
Jimmie Kingston, *Principal*
John Simpson, *Controller*
Robert Cyphers, *Plant Mgr*
EMP: 20
SALES (corp-wide): 42.9B **Privately Held**
WEB: www.gp.com
SIC: 3275 Wallboard, gypsum
HQ: Georgia-Pacific Llc
133 Peachtree St Nw
Atlanta GA 30303
404 652-4000

(P-11217)
FLANNERY INC (PA)
300 Parkside Dr, San Fernando
(91340-3035)
PHONE.....................................818 837-7585
Barry A Rutherford, *President*
EMP: 10
SQ FT: 21,000
SALES (est): 2.1MM **Privately Held**
WEB: www.flannerytrim.com
SIC: 3275 5072 Plaster & plasterboard, gypsum; miscellaneous fasteners

(P-11218)
GEORGIA-PACIFIC LLC
801 Minaker Dr, Antioch (94509-2134)
P.O. Box 460 (94509-0511)
PHONE.....................................925 757-2870
Kurt Betty, *Opers-Prdtn-Mfg*
EMP: 105
SALES (corp-wide): 42.9B **Privately Held**
WEB: www.gp.com
SIC: 3275 Wallboard, gypsum
HQ: Georgia-Pacific Llc
133 Peachtree St Nw
Atlanta GA 30303
404 652-4000

(P-11219)
HACKER INDUSTRIES INC (PA)
1600 Newport Dr 275, Newport Beach
(92660)
P.O. Box 5918 (92662-5918)
PHONE.....................................949 729-3101
Wesley D Hacker, *President*
Kerry V Hacker, *Vice Pres*
Julie Akers, *Accountant*
Kurt Whittington, *Marketing Mgr*
Christina Eater, *Marketing Staff*
▲ **EMP:** 11
SALES (est): 2.9MM **Privately Held**
WEB: www.hackerindustries.com
SIC: 3275 Cement, keene's

(P-11220)
NEW NGC INC
1850 Pier B St, Long Beach (90813-2604)
P.O. Box 1888 (90801-1888)
PHONE.....................................562 435-4465
Tim Fout, *Manager*
EMP: 120
SALES (corp-wide): 685.8MM **Privately Held**
WEB: www.natgyp.com
SIC: 3275 Gypsum products
HQ: New Ngc, Inc.
2001 Rexford Rd
Charlotte NC 28211

(P-11221)
PABCO BUILDING PRODUCTS LLC
Also Called: Pabco Gypsum
37851 Cherry St, Newark (94560-4348)
PHONE.....................................510 792-9555
Charlie Coleman, *Manager*
Philip Kohl, *VP Sls/Mktg*
Cheri Cabral, *Cust Mgr*
EMP: 90
SALES (corp-wide): 1.7B **Privately Held**
SIC: 3275 Gypsum products
HQ: Pabco Building Products, Llc
10600 White Rock Rd # 100
Rancho Cordova CA 95670
510 792-1577

(P-11222)
PABCO BUILDING PRODUCTS LLC
37849 Cherry St, Newark (94560-4348)
PHONE.....................................510 792-1577
Ryan Lucchetti, *President*
EMP: 20
SALES (corp-wide): 1.7B **Privately Held**
SIC: 3275 3251 3259 Gypsum products; brick clay: common face, glazed, vitrified or hollow; architectural terra cotta
HQ: Pabco Building Products, Llc
10600 White Rock Rd # 100
Rancho Cordova CA 95670
510 792-1577

(P-11223)
PABCO BUILDING PRODUCTS LLC (HQ)
10600 White Rock Rd # 100, Rancho Cordova (95670-6293)
PHONE.....................................510 792-1577
Ryan Lucchetti, *President*
Brian Hobdy, *CFO*
Jack Haarlander, *Bd of Directors*
Alfred Mueller, *Bd of Directors*
Larry Solari, *Bd of Directors*
▲ **EMP:** 20
SALES (est): 232.6MM
SALES (corp-wide): 1.7B **Privately Held**
SIC: 3275 3251 3259 Gypsum products; brick clay: common face, glazed, vitrified or hollow; architectural terra cotta
PA: Pacific Coast Building Products, Inc.
10600 White Rock Rd # 100
Rancho Cordova CA 95670
916 631-6500

(P-11224)
PABCO BUILDING PRODUCTS LLC
Also Called: Pabco Paper
4460 Pacific Blvd, Vernon (90058-2206)
PHONE.....................................323 581-6113
Mike Willoughby, *Branch Mgr*
Kristin Martin, *Associate*
EMP: 75
SALES (corp-wide): 1.7B **Privately Held**
SIC: 3275 Gypsum products
HQ: Pabco Building Products, Llc
10600 White Rock Rd # 100
Rancho Cordova CA 95670
510 792-1577

(P-11225)
PACIFIC COAST SUPPLY LLC
Also Called: Pacific Supply
30158 Road 68, Visalia (93291-9586)
P.O. Box 1429 (93279-1429)
PHONE.....................................559 651-2185
Kevin Viera, *Branch Mgr*
EMP: 25

SALES (corp-wide): 1.7B **Privately Held**
SIC: 3275 3272 2952 5211 Wallboard, gypsum; concrete products; asphalt felts & coatings; lumber & other building materials
HQ: Pacific Coast Supply, Llc
4290 Roseville Rd
North Highlands CA 95660
916 971-2301

(P-11226)
UNITED STATES GYPSUM COMPANY
3810 Evan Hewes Hwy, Imperial
(92251-9529)
PHONE.....................................760 358-3200
George Keelan, *Finance*
EMP: 300
SALES (corp-wide): 3.2B **Publicly Held**
WEB: www.usg.com
SIC: 3275 Gypsum products
HQ: United States Gypsum Company
550 W Adams St Ste 1300
Chicago IL 60661
312 606-4000

3281 Cut Stone Prdts

(P-11227)
AGORA NATURAL SURFACES INC
339 W 168th St, Gardena (90248-2732)
PHONE.....................................310 715-1088
Halil Turkkan, *President*
▲ **EMP:** 14
SALES (est): 1.9MM **Privately Held**
SIC: 3281 3253 Table tops, marble; ceramic wall & floor tile; mosaic tile, glazed & unglazed: ceramic

(P-11228)
ALPINE MARBLE
917 E Katella Ave, Anaheim (92805-6616)
P.O. Box 1076, Orange (92856-0076)
PHONE.....................................714 704-9030
Gary Milewski, *Owner*
▲ **EMP:** 16
SALES (est): 1.5MM **Privately Held**
SIC: 3281 Cut stone & stone products

(P-11229)
AMERICAN MARBLE & GRANITE CO (PA)
4084 Whittier Blvd, Los Angeles
(90023-2527)
P.O. Box 23156 (90023-0156)
PHONE.....................................323 268-7979
John Vega, *President*
EMP: 14 **EST:** 1894
SQ FT: 600
SALES (est): 2.1MM **Privately Held**
SIC: 3281 5999 Tombstones, cut stone (not finishing or lettering only); tombstones

(P-11230)
AMERICAN MARBLE & ONYX CO INC
10321 S La Cienega Blvd, Los Angeles
(90045-6109)
PHONE.....................................323 776-0900
Frederick Gherardi, *President*
Susan Gibbs, *Treasurer*
Steve Gherardi, *Vice Pres*
▲ **EMP:** 20
SQ FT: 30,000
SALES (est): 2.3MM **Privately Held**
WEB: www.amocmarble.com
SIC: 3281 1743 Marble, building: cut & shaped; marble installation, interior

(P-11231)
ANDREA ZEE CORPORATION
Also Called: Marble Palace
711 S San Joaquin St, Stockton
(95203-3727)
PHONE.....................................209 462-1700
Ravi K Sharma, *President*
Christine George, *Vice Pres*
EMP: 16
SALES (est): 980K **Privately Held**
SIC: 3281 5023 Marble, building: cut & shaped; floor coverings

(P-11232)
ART CRAFT STATUARY INC
10441 Edes Ave, Oakland (94603-3015)
PHONE.....................................510 633-1411
Alipio Fabbri, *President*
Ivana Fabbri, *Vice Pres*
EMP: 40
SQ FT: 43,000
SALES: 2MM **Privately Held**
WEB: www.artcraftstatuary.com
SIC: 3281 3272 Cut stone & stone products; concrete products

(P-11233)
AZ COUNTERTOPS INC
1445 S Hudson Ave, Ontario (91761)
PHONE.....................................909 983-5386
Jay Shah, *President*
Ray Shah, *Vice Pres*
▲ **EMP:** 50
SALES (est): 8.7MM **Privately Held**
SIC: 3281 Marble, building: cut & shaped

(P-11234)
BARRYS CULTURED MARBLE INC
866 Teal Dr, Benicia (94510-1249)
PHONE.....................................707 745-3444
Barry Martin, *President*
Carole Martin, *Vice Pres*
EMP: 11
SALES (est): 1MM **Privately Held**
SIC: 3281 5211 1799 Cut stone & stone products; bathroom fixtures, equipment & supplies; counter top installation

(P-11235)
BEST CHEER STONE INC (PA)
3190 E Miraloma Ave, Anaheim
(92806-1906)
PHONE.....................................714 399-1588
Chung Lun Ko, *CEO*
Yanlin K Xu, *CFO*
Kathy Xu, *Controller*
Kaiser Tang, *Director*
Judy Chang, *Manager*
▲ **EMP:** 22
SALES: 25MM **Privately Held**
SIC: 3281 5032 Stone, quarrying & processing of own stone products; building stone

(P-11236)
BEST MARBLE CO
2446 Teagarden St, San Leandro
(94577-4336)
PHONE.....................................510 614-0155
Dwight Hammack, *Owner*
EMP: 25
SALES (est): 2.4MM **Privately Held**
SIC: 3281 2821 Marble, building: cut & shaped; granite, cut & shaped; plastics materials & resins

(P-11237)
BEST-WAY MARBLE & TILE CO INC
Also Called: Best Way Marble
5037 Telegraph Rd, Los Angeles
(90022-4922)
PHONE.....................................323 266-6794
Shelley Herrera, *President*
Eddie Escarrega, *Project Mgr*
Carlos Vidaurri, *Supervisor*
◆ **EMP:** 28
SQ FT: 16,000
SALES (est): 3.2MM **Privately Held**
WEB: www.bestwaymarble.com
SIC: 3281 1743 Table tops, marble; marble installation, interior

(P-11238)
BETTY STILLWELL
Also Called: Baja Onyx & Marble Intl
524 W Calle Primera # 1004, San Ysidro
(92173-2836)
PHONE.....................................619 428-2001
Bettye Stilwell, *Owner*
EMP: 55 **EST:** 1968
SQ FT: 700
SALES (est): 3.3MM **Privately Held**
SIC: 3281 1743 Furniture, cut stone; building stone products; terrazzo, tile, marble, mosaic work

▲ = Import ▼=Export
◆ =Import/Export

(P-11239)
CARNEVALE & LOHR INC
6521 Clara St, Bell Gardens (90201-5634)
PHONE.................................562 927-8311
Louie Carnevale, *CEO*
David Carnevale, *Principal*
Michael Carnevale, *Principal*
Edmund B Lohr IV, *Principal*
James Christensen, *Project Mgr*
▲ EMP: 26
SALES (est): 3.6MM **Privately Held**
SIC: 3281 1741 Cut stone & stone products; marble masonry, exterior construction

(P-11240)
CENTRAL MARBLE SUPPLY INC
Also Called: Marble Works of San Diego
3754 Main St Ste B, San Diego
(92113-3834)
PHONE.................................619 595-1800
Charlene Butler, *President*
Michael Butler, *President*
EMP: 15
SQ FT: 5,000
SALES: 1MM **Privately Held**
WEB: www.marbleworkssandiego.com
SIC: 3281 1743 Marble, building: cut & shaped; marble installation, interior

(P-11241)
COAST FLAGSTONE CO
1810 Colorado Ave, Santa Monica
(90404-3412)
PHONE.................................310 829-4010
Timothy Jevne, *Owner*
EMP: 70 EST: 2010
SALES (est): 4MM **Privately Held**
SIC: 3281 Flagstones

(P-11242)
COLD SPRING GRANITE COMPANY
Raymond Granite Div
36772 Road 606, Raymond (93653-9703)
PHONE.................................559 689-3257
John Mansfield, *President*
EMP: 40
SQ FT: 4,000
SALES (corp-wide): 308.8MM **Privately Held**
WEB:
www.granitemountainstonedesign.com
SIC: 3281 1411 5032 Granite, cut & shaped; granite, dimension-quarrying; brick, stone & related material
PA: Cold Spring Granite Company Inc
17482 Granite West Rd
Cold Spring MN 56320
320 685-3621

(P-11243)
COLD SPRING GRANITE COMPANY
802 W Pinedale Ave # 102, Fresno
(93711-5771)
PHONE.................................559 438-2100
Julio Orozco, *Branch Mgr*
EMP: 22
SALES (corp-wide): 308.8MM **Privately Held**
SIC: 3281 Dimension stone for buildings
PA: Cold Spring Granite Company Inc
17482 Granite West Rd
Cold Spring MN 56320
320 685-3621

(P-11244)
COLOR SKY INC
14439 Joanbridge St, Baldwin Park
(91706-1747)
PHONE.................................626 338-8565
Yuehua Zhao, *CEO*
Kuanghao Tseng,
EMP: 11
SALES: 452K **Privately Held**
SIC: 3281 Cut stone & stone products

(P-11245)
CORTIMA CO
83778 Avenue 45, Indio (92201-3310)
PHONE.................................760 347-5535
Franz P Jevne III, *President*
Cynthia Jevne, *Treasurer*
EMP: 20

SQ FT: 23,000
SALES (est): 2.3MM **Privately Held**
WEB: www.cortima.com
SIC: 3281 Marble, building: cut & shaped; granite, cut & shaped

(P-11246)
COUNTER FIT
6925 Roseville Rd, Sacramento
(95842-1660)
PHONE.................................916 569-8570
Sasha Nahpatel, *President*
EMP: 10
SALES (est): 1.1MM **Privately Held**
SIC: 3281 Granite, cut & shaped

(P-11247)
DAVIS STONE INC
519 Venture St, Escondido (92029-1213)
PHONE.................................760 745-7881
Ken Davis, *President*
Denise Davis, *CFO*
▲ EMP: 26
SQ FT: 9,000
SALES: 2.6MM **Privately Held**
WEB: www.davisstone.com
SIC: 3281 Table tops, marble

(P-11248)
DEJAGERS INC
45846 Flower St, Indio (92201-4606)
PHONE.................................760 775-4755
Gordon Dejager, *President*
Darryl Williams, *Vice Pres*
EMP: 25
SALES (est): 2.2MM **Privately Held**
SIC: 3281 Granite, cut & shaped

(P-11249)
DEMILLE MARBLE & GRANITE INC
72091 Woburn Ct Ste D, Thousand Palms
(92276-2317)
PHONE.................................760 341-7525
Mark Demille, *President*
EMP: 30
SALES (est): 3.6MM **Privately Held**
WEB: www.demillemarble.com
SIC: 3281 1741 Marble, building: cut & shaped; marble masonry, exterior construction

(P-11250)
EMPORIUM DI SANARREY CORP
Also Called: Pietri Bersage Store Design
631 S East St, Anaheim (92805-4842)
P.O. Box 6219, Fullerton (92834-6219)
PHONE.................................714 780-5474
Helenee Cruz, *Principal*
Clemente Cruz, *President*
EMP: 10
SALES: 526K **Privately Held**
SIC: 3281 Cut stone & stone products

(P-11251)
FOREMOST INTERIORS INC
2318 Gold River Rd, Rancho Cordova
(95670-4413)
PHONE.................................916 635-1423
Randall Mertes, *President*
Rose Mertes, *Admin Sec*
EMP: 30
SQ FT: 10,000
SALES (est): 4MM **Privately Held**
WEB: www.foremostinteriors.com
SIC: 3281 2434 1751 Marble, building: cut & shaped; wood kitchen cabinets; carpentry work

(P-11252)
GGF MARBLE & SUPPLY INC
1375 Franquette Ave Ste F, Concord
(94520-7932)
PHONE.................................925 676-8385
Gaspare Giorgio Fundaro, *President*
Gregory Markeil,
Vince Rizzuto,
◆ EMP: 15
SQ FT: 2,500
SALES (est): 1MM **Privately Held**
SIC: 3281 Furniture, cut stone

(P-11253)
GREEK MARBLE INC
1600 N San Fernando Rd, Los Angeles
(90065-1262)
PHONE.................................323 221-6624
Levon Gorlekian, *President*
▲ EMP: 10
SQ FT: 9,000
SALES: 900K **Privately Held**
SIC: 3281 Marble, building: cut & shaped; granite, cut & shaped

(P-11254)
HALABI INC (PA)
Also Called: Duracite
2100 Huntington Dr, Fairfield (94533-9731)
PHONE.................................707 402-1600
Fadi M Halabi, *CEO*
George Marino, *CFO*
EMP: 137
SQ FT: 66,000
SALES (est): 109MM **Privately Held**
WEB: www.duracite.com
SIC: 3281 1799 Cut stone & stone products; counter top installation

(P-11255)
HALABI INC
1009 Martin Ave, Santa Clara
(95050-2608)
PHONE.................................800 660-4167
EMP: 12
SALES (corp-wide): 109MM **Privately Held**
WEB: www.duracite.com
SIC: 3281 1799 Cut stone & stone products; counter top installation
PA: Halabi, Inc.
2100 Huntington Dr
Fairfield CA 94533
707 402-1600

(P-11256)
HANSON AGGRGTES MD-PACIFIC INC
Pine Hollow To Kaiser Rd, Clayton (94517)
PHONE.................................925 672-4955
Dave Autsen, *Manager*
EMP: 10
SALES (corp-wide): 20.3B **Privately Held**
SIC: 3281 3531 Cut stone & stone products; aggregate spreaders
HQ: Hanson Aggregates Mid-Pacific, Inc.
12667 Alcosta Blvd # 400
San Ramon CA

(P-11257)
J M BOONE & SONS
Also Called: Boone Memorials
22039 Sawmill Flat Rd, Sonora
(95370-8509)
PHONE.................................209 532-2506
Gordon Boone, *Partner*
Jerry Boone, *Partner*
EMP: 10
SALES (est): 680K **Privately Held**
SIC: 3281 Monuments, cut stone (not finishing or lettering only)

(P-11258)
KAMMERER ENTERPRISES INC
Also Called: American Marble
1280 N Melrose Dr, Vista (92083-3469)
PHONE.................................760 560-0550
William S Kammerer, *CEO*
Bill Kammerer, *President*
Karl Miethke, *Vice Pres*
▲ EMP: 100
SALES (est): 16.2MM **Privately Held**
WEB: www.amarble.com
SIC: 3281 Curbing, granite or stone

(P-11259)
L&S STONE LLC (DH)
Also Called: L & S Stone and Fireplace Shop
1370 Grand Ave Ste B, San Marcos
(92078-2404)
PHONE.................................760 736-3232
Chuck Baer, *President*
◆ EMP: 50
SQ FT: 35,000
SALES (est): 7.8MM
SALES (corp-wide): 3.1B **Privately Held**
WEB: www.lsfireplace.com
SIC: 3281 Cut stone & stone products

HQ: Eldorado Stone Llc
1370 Grand Ave Bldg B
San Marcos CA 92078
800 925-1491

(P-11260)
LEGACY VULCAN LLC
11099 Old Friant Rd, Fresno (93730-0808)
PHONE.................................559 434-1202
Frank Costa, *Manager*
Bart Mayer, *Plant Mgr*
Jeff Guinn, *Sales Mgr*
EMP: 60 **Publicly Held**
WEB: www.vulcanmaterials.com
SIC: 3281 Cut stone & stone products
HQ: Legacy Vulcan, Llc
1200 Urban Center Dr
Vestavia AL 35242
205 298-3000

(P-11261)
MARBLE CITY COMPANY INC
611 Taylor Way Ste 6, San Carlos
(94070-6305)
PHONE.................................650 802-8189
Andrei Gourji, *President*
Sarah Vilotti, *Business Dir*
▲ EMP: 12
SQ FT: 8,000
SALES: 1.6MM **Privately Held**
WEB: www.marblecityca.com
SIC: 3281 Table tops, marble

(P-11262)
MARBLE SHOP INC (PA)
180 Bliss Ave, Pittsburg (94565-4977)
PHONE.................................925 439-6910
Barbara Gutridge, *President*
EMP: 25
SQ FT: 7,800
SALES (est): 3.2MM **Privately Held**
SIC: 3281 Marble, building: cut & shaped; granite, cut & shaped

(P-11263)
MONTGOMERY MARBLE CO
8711 Younger Creek Dr, Sacramento
(95828-1030)
PHONE.................................916 383-1563
James M Montgomery, *President*
Kay Montgomery, *Admin Sec*
▲ EMP: 13
SQ FT: 12,000
SALES (est): 1.3MM **Privately Held**
WEB: www.montgomerymarble.com
SIC: 3281 Marble, building: cut & shaped; stone, quarrying & processing of own stone products

(P-11264)
MOVA STONE INC
4361 Pell Dr Ste 100, Sacramento
(95838-2581)
PHONE.................................916 922-2080
Vasily Moskalets, *President*
EMP: 24
SQ FT: 11,000
SALES (est): 2.2MM **Privately Held**
SIC: 3281 Curbing, granite or stone

(P-11265)
MULHERIN MONUMENTAL INC
1000 S 2nd St, El Centro (92243-3448)
PHONE.................................760 353-7717
Joe Mulherin, *President*
Yolanda Mulherin, *Corp Secy*
EMP: 12
SALES: 1MM **Privately Held**
SIC: 3281 Monument or burial stone, cut & shaped

(P-11266)
NIDI TEC INC
3936 E Coronado St, Anaheim
(92807-1609)
PHONE.................................714 777-9323
Nilesh M Shah, *President*
EMP: 11
SALES (corp-wide): 4.6MM **Privately Held**
SIC: 3281 Granite, cut & shaped
PA: Nidi Tec, Inc
1285 N Fairbury Ln
Anaheim CA 92807
714 630-8080

PRODUCTS & SVCS

(P-11267)
PAUL MERRILL COMPANY INC
912 Bonnie Way, Brea (92821-2011)
PHONE..................................562 691-1871
Paul Merrill, *President*
Marlene Merrill, *Admin Sec*
EMP: 14
SALES (est): 1.1MM **Privately Held**
SIC: 3281 Granite, cut & shaped

(P-11268)
PAVESTONE LLC
27600 County Road 90, Winters
(95694-9003)
PHONE..................................530 795-4400
Wes May, *Manager*
Jeannie Del Toro, *Transptn Dir*
EMP: 50 **Privately Held**
WEB: www.pavestone.com
SIC: 3281 Paving blocks, cut stone
HQ: Pavestone, Llc
    5 Concourse Pkwy Ste 1900
    Atlanta GA 30328
    404 926-3167

(P-11269)
PERMECO
1970 Walker St, La Verne (91750-5144)
P.O. Box 337 (91750-0337)
PHONE..................................909 599-9600
Mark Carson, *President*
Linn Childress, *Vice Pres*
▲ EMP: 12
SQ FT: 15,600
SALES (est): 2MM **Privately Held**
SIC: 3281 Granite, cut & shaped; marble,
building: cut & shaped

(P-11270)
PRECISION GRANITE USA INC
Also Called: Precision Granite Company
174 N Aspan Ave, Azusa (91702-4224)
P.O. Box 427, Whittier (90608-0427)
PHONE..................................562 696-8328
John De Leon, *President*
▲ EMP: 24
SQ FT: 11,904
SALES: 400K **Privately Held**
SIC: 3281 Granite, cut & shaped

(P-11271)
PRIME SURFACES INC
25111 Normandie Ave, Harbor City
(90710-2407)
P.O. Box 821 (90710-0821)
PHONE..................................310 448-2292
Chad M Benner, *President*
EMP: 10
SQ FT: 9,600
SALES (est): 1.1MM **Privately Held**
SIC: 3281 5211 Cut stone & stone prod-
ucts; counter tops

(P-11272)
PROVENCE STONE
1040 Varian St, San Carlos (94070-5315)
PHONE..................................650 631-5600
Motaz Elias, *President*
▲ EMP: 11
SALES (est): 2MM **Privately Held**
WEB: www.provencestone.com
SIC: 3281 Marble, building: cut & shaped

(P-11273)
PYRAMID GRANITE & METALS INC
660 Superior St, Escondido (92029-1330)
PHONE..................................760 745-6309
Philip M Hoadley, *President*
Linda Forrest, *Vice Pres*
EMP: 24
SQ FT: 5,000
SALES: 2MM **Privately Held**
WEB: www.pyramidgranite.com
SIC: 3281 Granite, cut & shaped

(P-11274)
QORTSTONE INC
Also Called: Qrtstone
7733 Lemona Ave, Van Nuys (91405-1137)
PHONE..................................877 899-7678
Ani Vartabetian, *CEO*
Mina Marvavi, *Office Mgr*
▲ EMP: 11

SALES (est): 72.6K **Privately Held**
SIC: 3281 Cut stone & stone products

(P-11275)
RCS CUSTOM STONEWORKS
3280 Vine St Ste 201, Riverside
(92507-2610)
PHONE..................................714 309-0620
Anthony Beber, *Owner*
EMP: 12
SALES: 800K **Privately Held**
SIC: 3281 Granite, cut & shaped; marble,
building: cut & shaped

(P-11276)
REGAL CULTURED MARBLE INC
1239 E Franklin Ave, Pomona
(91766-5450)
P.O. Box 780534, Maspeth NY (11378-
0534)
PHONE..................................909 802-2388
Phillip K Black, *President*
David Sklar, *Vice Pres*
EMP: 50 EST: 1968
SQ FT: 12,000
SALES (est): 3.6MM **Privately Held**
SIC: 3281 2821 Bathroom fixtures, cut
stone; plastics materials & resins

(P-11277)
RUGGERI MARBLE AND GRANITE INC
16001 S San Pedro St C, Gardena
(90248-2543)
PHONE..................................310 513-2155
Andre Ruggeri, *President*
Robert Ruggeri, *Treasurer*
Giovanna F MWC, *Office Mgr*
Veronica Espinoza, *Admin Sec*
▲ EMP: 80
SQ FT: 6,650
SALES (est): 11.2MM **Privately Held**
WEB: www.ruggerimarble.com
SIC: 3281 5032 Marble, building: cut &
shaped; granite, cut & shaped; ceramic
wall & floor tile

(P-11278)
SHARCAR ENTERPRISES INC
Also Called: Custom Marble & Onyx
201 Winmoore Way, Modesto
(95358-5743)
P.O. Box 581710 (95358-0030)
PHONE..................................209 531-2200
Carl Schenewark, *President*
Daryl Schenewark, *Treasurer*
Sharon Schenewark, *Admin Sec*
EMP: 70
SQ FT: 10,000
SALES (est): 9MM **Privately Held**
SIC: 3281 1799 Bathroom fixtures, cut
stone; counter top installation

(P-11279)
SINOSOURCE INTL CO INC
230 Adrian Rd, Millbrae (94030-3103)
PHONE..................................650 697-6668
Ken Jiang, *President*
▲ EMP: 15
SALES (est): 2MM **Privately Held**
SIC: 3281 Urns, cut stone

(P-11280)
SOUTH BAY MARBLE INC (PA)
15745 E Alta Vista Way, San Jose
(95127-1736)
PHONE..................................650 594-4251
Bob Sutton, *President*
▲ EMP: 19 EST: 1978
SALES (est): 2.7MM **Privately Held**
SIC: 3281 Marble, building: cut & shaped;
building stone products; granite, cut &
shaped

(P-11281)
STANDRIDGE GRANITE CORPORATION
9437 Santa Fe Springs Rd, Santa Fe
Springs (90670-2684)
PHONE..................................562 946-6334
Deborah Deleon, *President*
Steven Piel, *Plant Mgr*
EMP: 30
SQ FT: 24,000

SALES (est): 3.9MM **Privately Held**
WEB: www.standridgegranite.com
SIC: 3281 1411 Granite, cut & shaped; di-
mension stone

(P-11282)
STONE MERCHANTS LLC
889 Linda Flora Dr, Los Angeles
(90049-1628)
PHONE..................................310 471-1815
Yogesh Anand, *CEO*
▲ EMP: 60 EST: 2008
SALES (est): 3.3MM **Privately Held**
SIC: 3281 Cut stone & stone products

(P-11283)
SUN MARBLE INC
Also Called: Sun Marble/Home Express
1300 Norman Ave, Santa Clara
(95054-2056)
PHONE..................................510 783-9900
Gloria You, *CEO*
Wen Lin Sheu, *President*
▲ EMP: 24
SQ FT: 7,000
SALES (est): 3.1MM **Privately Held**
SIC: 3281 Granite, cut & shaped; house-
hold articles, except furniture: cut stone

(P-11284)
SUPERIOR STONE PRODUCTS INC
923 E Arlee Pl, Anaheim (92805-5645)
PHONE..................................714 635-7775
Costandi Awadalla, *President*
EMP: 15 EST: 2014
SALES (est): 1.4MM **Privately Held**
SIC: 3281 Cut stone & stone products

(P-11285)
VENTURA GL INC
12595 Foothill Blvd, Sylmar (91342-5310)
PHONE..................................818 890-1886
John Ventura, *President*
EMP: 15
SQ FT: 8,000
SALES (est): 2MM **Privately Held**
SIC: 3281 5032 Marble, building: cut &
shaped; marble building stone

(P-11286)
VETERANS EMPLOYMENT AGENCY INC
3906 Ginko Way, Sacramento
(95834-3833)
PHONE..................................650 245-0599
Irvin Goodwin, *CEO*
EMP: 12
SALES (est): 796.1K **Privately Held**
SIC: 3281 Cut stone & stone products

3291 Abrasive Prdts

(P-11287)
ABRASIVE WHEELS INC
17841 E Valley Blvd, City of Industry
(91744-5733)
PHONE..................................626 935-8800
Isidro Topete, *President*
EMP: 10
SQ FT: 10,000
SALES (est): 1.1MM **Privately Held**
WEB: www.abrasivewheels.com
SIC: 3291 5085 Wheels, abrasive; abra-
sives

(P-11288)
ARROW ABRASIVE COMPANY INC
12033 1/2 Regentview Ave, Downey
(90241-5517)
PHONE..................................562 869-2282
Alan Bates, *President*
Linda Bates, *Corp Secy*
Michael Bates, *Vice Pres*
EMP: 11
SQ FT: 5,000
SALES: 700K **Privately Held**
SIC: 3291 Wheels, grinding: artificial

(P-11289)
BUFF AND SHINE MFG INC
2139 E Del Amo Blvd, Rancho Dominguez
(90220-6301)
PHONE..................................310 886-5111
Richard Umbrell, *President*
Elizabeth Umbrell, *Vice Pres*
▲ EMP: 40
SQ FT: 25,792
SALES (est): 9.6MM **Privately Held**
WEB: www.buffandshine.com
SIC: 3291 Buffing or polishing wheels,
abrasive or nonabrasive

(P-11290)
CAPITOL STEEL PRODUCTS
Also Called: Ruben Ortiz
6331 Power Inn Rd Ste B, Sacramento
(95824-2353)
PHONE..................................916 383-3368
Ruben Ortiz, *General Mgr*
Bud Lindau, *Owner*
EMP: 11
SALES (est): 1.3MM **Privately Held**
SIC: 3291 Abrasive metal & steel products

(P-11291)
CARBIDE PRODUCTS CO INC
22711 S Western Ave, Torrance
(90501-4994)
PHONE..................................310 320-7910
Arthur E Johnson, *President*
Irene W Johnson, *Corp Secy*
Gary Johnson, *Vice Pres*
Scott Morrison, *Manager*
EMP: 10 EST: 1954
SQ FT: 4,000
SALES (est): 940K **Privately Held**
SIC: 3291 Tungsten carbide abrasive

(P-11292)
COLUMBIA STONE PRODUCTS
663 S Rancho Santa Fe Rd, San Marcos
(92078-3973)
PHONE..................................760 737-3215
Faruk Delener, *Principal*
▲ EMP: 12
SALES (est): 1.2MM **Privately Held**
SIC: 3291 Silicon carbide abrasive

(P-11293)
FALCON ABRASIVE MANUFACTURING
5490 Brooks St, Montclair (91763-4520)
P.O. Box 713, Walnut (91788-0713)
PHONE..................................909 598-3078
Steve De La Torre, *President*
Rosemarie De Latorre, *Corp Secy*
▼ EMP: 17
SQ FT: 6,900
SALES (est): 2.2MM **Privately Held**
WEB: www.falconabrasive.com
SIC: 3291 5085 Wheels, abrasive; indus-
trial supplies

(P-11294)
INDUSTRIAL MINERAL COMPANY USA
100 Oceangate Ste 600, Long Beach
(90802-4366)
PHONE..................................562 553-5203
Praem Thanabalsingam, *CEO*
EMP: 10
SALES (est): 1.3MM **Privately Held**
SIC: 3291 Abrasive products

(P-11295)
JASON INCORPORATED
Jackson Lea Division
13006 Philadelphia St # 305, Whittier
(90601-4210)
PHONE..................................562 921-9821
Ron Locher, *Vice Pres*
EMP: 33
SQ FT: 30,000
SALES (corp-wide): 648.6MM **Publicly
Held**
WEB: www.jasoninc.com
SIC: 3291 2273 3599 Buffing or polishing
wheels, abrasive or nonabrasive; automo-
bile floor coverings, except rubber or plas-
tic; custom machinery

HQ: Jason Incorporated
833 E Michigan St Ste 900
Milwaukee WI 53202
414 277-9300

(P-11296)
JET ABRASIVES INC
Also Called: Jet & Western Abrasives
1891 E Miraloma Ave, Placentia
(92870-6707)
PHONE...................................323 588-1245
Barry Rothstein, *President*
Joy Demain, *Shareholder*
EMP: 33
SQ FT: 36,000
SALES (est): 3MM **Privately Held**
WEB: www.gritbiz.com
SIC: 3291 Abrasive products

(P-11297)
MAGNUM ABRASIVES INC
758 S Allen St, San Bernardino
(92408-2210)
PHONE...................................909 890-1100
Manuel Acuna, *President*
Richard Frenkel, *Vice Pres*
▲ EMP: 20
SQ FT: 13,400
SALES (est): 2.6MM **Privately Held**
WEB: www.magnumabrasives.com
SIC: 3291 5085 Abrasive products; abrasives

(P-11298)
MAVERICK ABRASIVES CORPORATION
4340 E Miraloma Ave, Anaheim
(92807-1886)
PHONE...................................714 854-9531
Rami Aryan, *President*
Junior Lucatero, *Sales Mgr*
▲ EMP: 27
SQ FT: 15,000
SALES (est): 6MM **Privately Held**
WEB: www.maverickabrasives.com
SIC: 3291 Abrasive products

(P-11299)
MK TOOL AND ABRASIVE INC
4710 S Eastern Ave, Los Angeles
(90040-2913)
PHONE...................................562 776-8818
Olinda Kapila, *President*
Rajiv Kapila, *Vice Pres*
Rashmi Kapila, *Manager*
▲ EMP: 14
SQ FT: 15,000
SALES (est): 1.8MM **Privately Held**
SIC: 3291 3541 5251 Synthetic abrasives; abrasive buffs, bricks, cloth, paper, stones, etc.; machine tools, metal cutting type; builders' hardware

(P-11300)
PAC-COM INTERNATIONAL
11217 Shoemaker Ave, Santa Fe Springs
(90670-4644)
PHONE...................................562 903-3900
Sang Park, *President*
▲ EMP: 13
SALES (est): 1.4MM **Privately Held**
SIC: 3291 Abrasive products

(P-11301)
PEARLMAN ENTERPRISES INC (DH)
6210 Garfield Ave, Commerce
(90040-3613)
PHONE...................................800 969-5561
Daniel Davidenko, *CEO*
Eric Aguirre, *CFO*
John Waterworth, *CFO*
EMP: 215
SALES (est): 65.7MM
SALES (corp-wide): 12.8MM **Privately Held**
SIC: 3291 3843 3991 3421 Wheels, abrasive; abrasive points, wheels & disks, dental; brushes, household or industrial; razor blades & razors; fabricated structural metal
HQ: Pearlman Holdings, Inc.
3950 Steve Reynolds Blvd
Norcross GA 30093
800 458-6222

(P-11302)
PW BRANDS LLC
Also Called: Safeguard Covers
32565 Golden Lantern St B, Dana Point
(92629-3261)
PHONE...................................949 916-0600
Tricia Pilkerton,
▲ EMP: 14 EST: 2010
SALES (est): 1.3MM **Privately Held**
SIC: 3291 Metallic abrasive

(P-11303)
SIMPSON MANUFACTURING CO INC
5151 S Airport Way, Stockton
(95206-3991)
PHONE...................................209 234-7775
David McDonald, *Manager*
EMP: 350
SALES (corp-wide): 977MM **Publicly Held**
SIC: 3291 Metallic abrasive
PA: Simpson Manufacturing Co., Inc.
5956 W Las Positas Blvd
Pleasanton CA 94588
925 560-9000

(P-11304)
SUPREME ABRASIVES
Also Called: Continental Machine Tool Co
1021 Fuller St, Santa Ana (92701-4212)
PHONE...................................949 250-8644
William W Taylor, *CEO*
Robert Longman, *Vice Pres*
▲ EMP: 19 EST: 1958
SQ FT: 20,000
SALES (est): 2.3MM **Privately Held**
SIC: 3291 Wheels, abrasive

(P-11305)
TECHNIFEX PRODUCTS LLC
25261 Rye Canyon Rd, Valencia
(91355-1203)
PHONE...................................661 294-3800
Montgomery C Lunde, *CEO*
Rockne J Hall, *Chairman*
Joe Ortiz, *Vice Pres*
Jim Sharits, *Vice Pres*
Sherry Ferguson, *Controller*
◆ EMP: 25
SALES (est): 4.7MM **Privately Held**
WEB: www.sensorytheatersystems.com
SIC: 3291 Steel wool

(P-11306)
TYFLONG INTERNATIONAL INC
606 Pena Dr, Davis (95618-7720)
P.O. Box 4208 (95617-4208)
PHONE...................................530 746-3001
Manyu LI, *President*
Sarah Liu, *CFO*
David Knapp, *Vice Pres*
Martin Arata, *Sales Mgr*
Kelly Wade, *Manager*
▲ EMP: 10
SQ FT: 8,000
SALES (est): 757.7K **Privately Held**
WEB: www.tyflong.com
SIC: 3291 Abrasive products

(P-11307)
VIBRA FINISH CO (PA)
Also Called: Vibrahone
2220 Shasta Way, Simi Valley
(93065-1831)
PHONE...................................805 578-0033
Haskel Hall, *President*
Jerry Rindal, *Vice Pres*
◆ EMP: 20 EST: 1924
SQ FT: 41,000
SALES (est): 4MM **Privately Held**
WEB: www.vibrafinish.com
SIC: 3291 Abrasive products

(P-11308)
WESTERN ABRASIVES INC
4383 Fruitland Ave, Vernon (90058-3119)
PHONE...................................323 588-1245
Martin Rothstein, *President*
Yvonne Medkiff, *Treasurer*
Barry Rothstein, *Vice Pres*
EMP: 16
SQ FT: 36,000
SALES (est): 2MM **Privately Held**
SIC: 3291

(P-11309)
YEAGER ENTERPRISES CORP
Also Called: Pasco
7100 Village Dr, Buena Park (90621-2261)
PHONE...................................714 994-2040
Joseph O'Mera, *CEO*
David M Yeager, *President*
Joan F Yeager, *Vice Pres*
▲ EMP: 81
SQ FT: 55,000
SALES (est): 11.5MM **Privately Held**
SIC: 3291 Abrasive products

3292 Asbestos products

(P-11310)
FRANCO AMERICAN CORPORATION
Also Called: Franco American Textile
1051 Monterey Pass Rd, Monterey Park
(91734-3612)
PHONE...................................323 268-2345
Roland Jones, *President*
▲ EMP: 18
SALES (est): 2.6MM **Privately Held**
SIC: 3292 Asbestos textiles, except insulating material

(P-11311)
H2 ENVIRONMENTAL
13122 6th St, Chino (91710-4105)
PHONE...................................909 628-0369
Amy Disantiago, *Owner*
EMP: 14
SALES (est): 2.2MM **Privately Held**
SIC: 3292 1799 Asbestos products; asbestos removal & encapsulation

(P-11312)
LAMART CORPORATION
Also Called: Orcon Aerospace
2600 Central Ave Ste E, Union City
(94587-3187)
P.O. Box 2936, Douglas GA (31534-2936)
PHONE...................................510 489-8100
EMP: 110
SALES (corp-wide): 103.6MM **Privately Held**
SIC: 3292 3559 Blankets, insulating for aircraft asbestos; bag seaming & closing machines (sewing machinery)
PA: Lamart Corporation
16 Richmond St
Clifton NJ 07011
973 772-6262

(P-11313)
THERMOSTATIC INDUSTRIES INC
Also Called: T M O
9654 Hermosa Ave, Rancho Cucamonga
(91730-5812)
PHONE...................................323 277-0900
Alan M Goldman, *CEO*
Sanford Lathrop Jr, *President*
▲ EMP: 30
SQ FT: 1,500
SALES (est): 4.9MM **Privately Held**
WEB: www.thermostatic.com
SIC: 3292 Pipe covering (heat insulating material), except felt; asbestos textiles, except insulating material

---

3295 Minerals & Earths: Ground Or Treated

(P-11314)
3M COMPANY
18750 Minnesota Rd, Corona
(92881-4313)
PHONE...................................951 737-3441
Flees Peter, *Branch Mgr*
Vance Coffman, *Bd of Directors*
Carolyn Bates, *Executive*
Linda Thomas, *Info Tech Mgr*
Grant Miller, *Project Engr*
EMP: 150
SALES (corp-wide): 31.6B **Publicly Held**
WEB: www.mmm.com
SIC: 3295 2952 Roofing granules; asphalt felts & coatings

PA: 3m Company
3m Center
Saint Paul MN 55144
651 733-1110

(P-11315)
A&M PRODUCTS MANUFACTURING CO (HQ)
1221 Broadway Ste 51, Oakland
(94612-1837)
PHONE...................................510 271-7000
Lawrence Peiros, *Principal*
▲ EMP: 37
SALES (est): 11.7MM
SALES (corp-wide): 6.1B **Publicly Held**
SIC: 3295 Minerals, ground or treated
PA: The Clorox Company
1221 Broadway Ste 1300
Oakland CA 94612
510 271-7000

(P-11316)
ALGER ALTERNATIVE ENERGY LLC
1536 Jones St, Brawley (92227-1700)
PHONE...................................317 493-5289
Harold Leonard Alger II, *President*
EMP: 11
SALES (corp-wide): 1.3MM **Privately Held**
SIC: 3295 Minerals, ground or treated
PA: Alger Alternative Energy Llc
7362 Remcon Cir
El Paso TX 79912
915 317-8447

(P-11317)
AZTEC PERLITE COMPANY INC
1518 Simpson Way, Escondido
(92029-1205)
PHONE...................................760 741-1733
Domenic Di Nardo, *President*
Anna Di Nardo, *Owner*
EMP: 15
SQ FT: 5,000
SALES (est): 2.2MM **Privately Held**
SIC: 3295 Perlite, aggregate or expanded

(P-11318)
CLAY LAGUNA CO (HQ)
14400 Lomitas Ave, City of Industry
(91746-3018)
PHONE...................................626 330-0631
Jonathan W Brooks, *Principal*
Laurie Brooks, *Corp Secy*
Jon Pacini, *Manager*
◆ EMP: 127
SQ FT: 110,000
SALES (est): 20.6MM
SALES (corp-wide): 9.5MM **Privately Held**
SIC: 3295 5032 Clay, ground or otherwise treated; tile & clay products
PA: Jon Brooks, Inc.
14400 Lomitas Ave
City Of Industry CA 91746
626 330-0631

(P-11319)
DESICCARE INC
3400 Pomona Blvd, Pomona (91768-3236)
PHONE...................................909 444-8272
Shaneen Aros, *CFO*
Ted McIntyre, *President*
Kevin Faust, *Info Tech Mgr*
David Wells, *QC Mgr*
Michael McClure, *Sales Staff*
EMP: 20 **Privately Held**
SIC: 3295 Desiccants, clay: activated
PA: Desiccare, Inc.
985 Damonte Ranch Pkwy
Reno NV 89521

(P-11320)
GEO DRILLING FLUIDS INC
Also Called: Imco
7268 Frasinetti Rd, Sacramento
(95828-3717)
PHONE...................................916 383-2811
Eric Sruck, *Systems Mgr*
EMP: 21
SQ FT: 5,000

SALES (corp-wide): 66.3MM **Privately Held**
WEB: www.clayimco.com
SIC: 3295 5945 Clay for petroleum refining, chemically processed; barite, ground or otherwise treated; ceramics supplies
PA: Geo Drilling Fluids, Inc.
1431 Union Ave
Bakersfield CA 93305
661 325-5919

(P-11321)
ISP GRANULE PRODUCTS INC
1900 Hwy 104, Ione (95640)
PHONE.........................209 274-2930
Sunil Kumar, *President*
EMP: 100
SALES (est): 8.6MM
SALES (corp-wide): 86.2MM **Privately Held**
SIC: 3295 Roofing granules
HQ: Isp Minerals Llc
34 Charles St
Hagerstown MD 21740

(P-11322)
JOHN CRANE INC
Also Called: Crane, John
12760 Florence Ave, Santa Fe Springs (90670-3906)
PHONE.........................562 802-2555
Dave Bretfch, *General Mgr*
Gary Cannon, *Mfg Staff*
EMP: 35
SALES (corp-wide): 4.1B **Privately Held**
WEB: www.johncrane.com
SIC: 3295 3541 3053 Minerals, ground or treated; lapping machines; gaskets, packing & sealing devices
HQ: John Crane Inc.
227 W Monroe St Ste 1800
Chicago IL 60606
312 605-7800

(P-11323)
JON BROOKS INC (PA)
Also Called: Laguna Clay Company
14400 Lomitas Ave, City of Industry (91746-3018)
PHONE.........................626 330-0631
Jon Brooks, *President*
Laurie Brooks, *Corp Secy*
◆ EMP: 103
SQ FT: 117,000
SALES (est): 9.5MM **Privately Held**
SIC: 3295 5085 Clay, ground or otherwise treated; refractory material

(P-11324)
PARATECH INC
15940 Minnesota Ave, Paramount (90723-4914)
P.O. Box 718 (90723-0718)
PHONE.........................562 633-2045
Steven F Park, *President*
EMP: 20
SQ FT: 17,300
SALES (est): 2.3MM **Privately Held**
WEB: www.paratech.com
SIC: 3295 Steatite, ground or otherwise treated

(P-11325)
RDM MULTI-ENTERPRISES INC
20428 Belshire Ave, Lakewood (90715-1604)
PHONE.........................562 924-1820
Evelyn Difrancesco, *CEO*
Ronald Difrancesco, *Vice Pres*
Lori Cook, *Office Mgr*
EMP: 12
SALES (est): 962K **Privately Held**
SIC: 3295 3291 Roofing granules; metallic abrasive

(P-11326)
SGL TECHNIC INC (DH)
Also Called: Inc Polycarbon
28176 Avenue Stanford, Valencia (91355-1119)
PHONE.........................661 257-0500
Scott Carlton, *President*
Brian Green, *Vice Pres*
Sandy Chase, *Executive*
Michael Dehaven, *CTO*

Rick Bell, *Manager*
▲ EMP: 56
SQ FT: 130,000
SALES (est): 16.9MM
SALES (corp-wide): 1B **Privately Held**
WEB: www.polycarbon.com
SIC: 3295 3624 Graphite, natural: ground, pulverized, refined or blended; carbon & graphite products
HQ: Sgl Carbon, Llc
10715 David Taylor Dr # 460
Charlotte NC 28262
704 593-5100

(P-11327)
SPECIALTY GRANULES LLC
1900 State Hwy 104, Ione (95640)
P.O. Box 400 (95640-0400)
PHONE.........................209 274-5323
George Dias, *Plant Mgr*
Steve Contreras, *Maintence Staff*
EMP: 50
SALES (corp-wide): 86.2MM **Privately Held**
SIC: 3295 Roofing granules
PA: Specialty Granules Llc
13424 Pa Ave Ste 303
Hagerstown MD 21742
301 733-4000

3296 Mineral Wool

(P-11328)
ACOUSTICAL INTERIORS INC (PA)
123 Princeton Ave, El Granada (94018)
PHONE.........................650 728-9441
Janet McLurg, *Exec VP*
Josh Murphy, *Manager*
EMP: 10
SALES (est): 1.6MM **Privately Held**
WEB: www.acousticalinteriors.com
SIC: 3296 1742 Acoustical board & tile, mineral wool; acoustical & ceiling work

(P-11329)
C A SCHROEDER INC (PA)
Also Called: Casco Mfg
1318 1st St, San Fernando (91340-2804)
PHONE.........................818 365-9561
Susan A Knudsen, *CEO*
Clifford A Schroeder, *President*
William Griffith, *Vice Pres*
Bill Griffith, *General Mgr*
Frank Adams, *Information Mgr*
EMP: 42
SQ FT: 18,500
SALES (est): 7.1MM **Privately Held**
WEB: www.cal-flex.com
SIC: 3296 3585 3444 3433 Fiberglass insulation; refrigeration & heating equipment; sheet metalwork; heating equipment, except electric

(P-11330)
CERTAINTEED CORPORATION
17775 Avenue 23 1/2, Chowchilla (93610-9758)
PHONE.........................559 665-4831
James Vicary, *Manager*
Glenn Abraham, *Opers-Prdtn-Mfg*
EMP: 400
SALES (corp-wide): 213.5MM **Privately Held**
WEB: www.certainteed.net
SIC: 3296 5033 Fiberglass insulation; insulation materials
HQ: Certainteed Corporation
20 Moores Rd
Malvern PA 19355
610 893-5000

(P-11331)
CONSOLIDATED FIBRGLS PDTS CO
Also Called: Conglas
3801 Standard St, Bakersfield (93308-5230)
PHONE.........................661 323-6026
Daron J Thomas, *CEO*
Jack Pfeffer, *Vice Ch Bd*
Douglas Legron, *Purch Agent*
Mike Lewis, *Opers Staff*
EMP: 60

SQ FT: 20,000
SALES (est): 9.2MM **Privately Held**
WEB: www.conglas.com
SIC: 3296 Fiberglass insulation

(P-11332)
INSULFAB INC
4725 Calle Alto, Camarillo (93012-8538)
PHONE.........................805 482-2751
Sieg Borck, *President*
William Brown, *Corp Secy*
Ernest Sieger, *Vice Pres*
Candice Simpkins, *Manager*
EMP: 58
SQ FT: 23,000
SALES (est): 4.2MM **Privately Held**
SIC: 3296 Insulation: rock wool, slag & silica minerals

(P-11333)
JOHNS MANVILLE CORPORATION
5916 County Road 49, Willows (95988-9703)
PHONE.........................530 934-6243
Tom Lowe, *Branch Mgr*
Daniel Mercado, *Safety Mgr*
Felix Chavez, *Production*
Robert Young, *Maintence Staff*
Marianne Krantz, *Manager*
EMP: 340
SALES (corp-wide): 242.1B **Publicly Held**
WEB: www.jm.com
SIC: 3296 Fiberglass insulation
HQ: Johns Manville Corporation
717 17th St Ste 800
Denver CO 80202
303 978-2000

(P-11334)
JOHNS MANVILLE CORPORATION
4301 Firestone Blvd, South Gate (90280-3318)
PHONE.........................323 568-2220
Rudi Bianchi, *Manager*
Rafael Cabral, *Safety Mgr*
David Gilmartin, *Plant Mgr*
Marlon Hernandez, *Assistant*
EMP: 60
SALES (corp-wide): 242.1B **Publicly Held**
WEB: www.jm.com
SIC: 3296 Mineral wool
HQ: Johns Manville Corporation
717 17th St Ste 800
Denver CO 80202
303 978-2000

(P-11335)
KNAUF INSULATION INC
3100 Ashby Rd, Shasta Lake (96019-9136)
PHONE.........................530 275-9665
Bill Taylor, *Branch Mgr*
Scott Skipton, *Engineer*
John Sabol, *Opers Dir*
Randy Turner, *Plant Engr*
Brady Adkins, *Sales Staff*
EMP: 150
SALES (corp-wide): 6.8B **Privately Held**
WEB: www.knaufusa.com
SIC: 3296 Mineral wool
HQ: Knauf Insulation, Inc.
1 Knauf Dr
Shelbyville IN 46176
317 398-4434

(P-11336)
LAMART CALIFORNIA INC
33428 Alvarado Niles Rd, Union City (94587-3110)
P.O. Box 1648, Clifton NJ (07015-1648)
PHONE.........................973 772-6262
Steven Hirsh, *President*
Graeme Silbert, *CFO*
EMP: 20 EST: 2016
SALES (est): 767.3K
SALES (corp-wide): 103.6MM **Privately Held**
SIC: 3296 Fiberglass insulation
PA: Lamart Corporation
16 Richmond St
Clifton NJ 07011
973 772-6262

(P-11337)
LAMVIN INC
4675 North Ave, Oceanside (92056-3511)
PHONE.........................760 806-6400
Robin Gray, *President*
EMP: 30 EST: 1965
SQ FT: 30,000
SALES (est): 4.7MM **Privately Held**
WEB: www.lamvin.com
SIC: 3296 3275 Acoustical board & tile, mineral wool; gypsum products

(P-11338)
UNITED STATES MINERAL PDTS CO
Also Called: Isolatek International
4062 Georgia Blvd, San Bernardino (92407-1847)
PHONE.........................909 473-6993
Adrienne Bowen, *Branch Mgr*
Stanley Warenda, *Manager*
EMP: 70
SALES (corp-wide): 48.6MM **Privately Held**
SIC: 3296 Mineral wool insulation products
PA: United States Mineral Products Company Inc
41 Furnace St
Stanhope NJ 07874
973 347-1200

(P-11339)
UPF CORPORATION
3747 Standard St, Bakersfield (93308-5228)
PHONE.........................661 323-8227
Jack Pfeffer, *President*
Mike Rushing, *Supervisor*
▼ EMP: 35
SALES (est): 5.9MM **Privately Held**
WEB: www.upf-usa.com
SIC: 3296 Fiberglass insulation

3297 Nonclay Refractories

(P-11340)
COORSTEK VISTA INC
2065 Thibodo Rd, Vista (92081-7988)
PHONE.........................760 542-7065
John K Coors, *CEO*
Richard Palicka, *President*
▲ EMP: 101
SQ FT: 106,000
SALES (est): 11.7MM
SALES (corp-wide): 909.3MM **Privately Held**
WEB: www.coorstek.com
SIC: 3297 Nonclay refractories
HQ: Coorstek, Inc.
14143 Denver West Pkwy # 400
Lakewood CO 80401
303 271-7000

(P-11341)
HEATSHIELD PRODUCTS INC
938 S Anderson Dr Ste Cd, Valley Center (92082)
P.O. Box 462500, Escondido (92046-2500)
PHONE.........................760 751-0441
Bruce Heye, *Partner*
Stephen J Heye, *Partner*
EMP: 20
SQ FT: 500
SALES: 2.5MM **Privately Held**
SIC: 3297 High temperature mortar, nonclay

(P-11342)
SIMONS BRICK CORPORATION
4301 Firestone Blvd, South Gate (90280-3318)
PHONE.........................951 279-1000
John Williams, *President*
EMP: 20
SQ FT: 24,000
SALES (est): 2MM
SALES (corp-wide): 1.7B **Privately Held**
WEB: www.simonsbrick.com
SIC: 3297 5211 Brick refractories; brick
HQ: Basalite Building Products, Llc
2150 Douglas Blvd Ste 260
Roseville CA 95661
707 678-1901

▲ = Import ▼=Export
◆ =Import/Export

3299 Nonmetallic Mineral Prdts, NEC

(P-11343)
A S BATLE COMPANY
Also Called: Www.asbworkshop.com
224 Mississippi St, San Francisco
(94107-2529)
PHONE.............................415 864-3300
Delia Batle, *Partner*
Agelio Batle, *Partner*
▲ EMP: 10
SALES: 400K **Privately Held**
WEB: www.asbworkshop.com
SIC: 3299 5712 Architectural sculptures: gypsum, clay, papier mache, etc.; custom made furniture, except cabinets

(P-11344)
ALS GARDEN ART INC (PA)
311 W Citrus St, Colton (92324-1412)
P.O. Box 70 (92324-0070)
PHONE.............................909 424-0221
Donald Bracci, *President*
EMP: 290 EST: 1949
SQ FT: 305,000
SALES (est): 18.1MM **Privately Held**
WEB: www.alsgardenart.com
SIC: 3299 3272 Statuary: gypsum, clay, papier mache, metal, etc.; concrete products

(P-11345)
APPROVED NETWORKS INC (PA)
Also Called: Approved Optics
6 Orchard Ste 150, Lake Forest
(92630-8352)
PHONE.............................800 590-9535
Thomas Horton, *Managing Dir*
Kurt Dumteman, *COO*
Ron Beale, *CFO*
Angela Lunt, *Info Tech Mgr*
Denise Ryan, *Opers Staff*
EMP: 54 EST: 2010
SQ FT: 9,500
SALES: 123MM **Privately Held**
SIC: 3299 Art goods: plaster of paris, papier mache & scagliola

(P-11346)
ATTLAS BYSHORE ART STUDIO LLC
2207 Quesada Ave, San Francisco
(94124-1921)
PHONE.............................415 282-2815
Attila Tivadar, *Mng Member*
▲ EMP: 11
SQ FT: 4,058
SALES: 1MM **Privately Held**
WEB: www.attilastudio.com
SIC: 3299 Statuary: gypsum, clay, papier mache, metal, etc.

(P-11347)
BLUE EAGLE STUCCO PRODUCTS
1407 N Clark St, Fresno (93703-3615)
PHONE.............................559 485-4100
Tom Graves, *Owner*
EMP: 12
SALES (est): 1.1MM **Privately Held**
SIC: 3299 Stucco

(P-11348)
BMI PRODUCTS NORTHERN CAL INC
990 Ames Ave, Milpitas (95035-6303)
PHONE.............................408 293-4008
Arnold Germann, *CEO*
▲ EMP: 11
SQ FT: 22,000
SALES (est): 2.7MM
SALES (corp-wide): 213.5MM **Privately Held**
WEB: www.bmi-products.com
SIC: 3299 5091 Stucco; watersports equipment & supplies; golf & skiing equipment & supplies
HQ: Schenker-Winkler Holding Ag
Bannabni 16
Baar ZG 3018

(P-11349)
BRANDELLI ARTS INC
12362 9th St, Garden Grove (92840-3537)
PHONE.............................714 537-0969
Robert Brandelli, *President*
Aurora Brandelli, *Vice Pres*
EMP: 46
SALES (est): 3.2MM **Privately Held**
WEB: www.brandelliarts.com
SIC: 3299 3272 Statuary: gypsum, clay, papier mache, metal, etc.; concrete products

(P-11350)
BURLINGAME INDUSTRIES INC
Also Called: Eagle Roofing Products Co
2352 N Locust Ave, Rialto (92377-5000)
PHONE.............................909 355-7000
Robert Burlingame, *President*
Brandi Lessner, *Marketing Staff*
Hawk Kinney, *Sales Staff*
Elven Whitchurch, *Cust Mgr*
EMP: 200
SQ FT: 76,704
SALES (corp-wide): 81.5MM **Privately Held**
SIC: 3299 3272 2952 Tile, sand lime; concrete products; asphalt felts & coatings
PA: Burlingame Industries, Incorporated
3546 N Riverside Ave
Rialto CA 92377
909 355-7000

(P-11351)
CAL COAST STUCCO
10932 Tuxford St, Sun Valley (91352-2625)
PHONE.............................818 767-0115
Michael D Masino, *Principal*
Roger Gackenbach, *Vice Pres*
Debi Negrete, *Controller*
Dale Sweitzer, *Superintendent*
▲ EMP: 13
SALES (est): 2MM **Privately Held**
SIC: 3299 Stucco

(P-11352)
CERADYNE INC (HQ)
1922 Barranca Pkwy, Irvine (92606-4826)
PHONE.............................949 862-9600
Joel P Moskowitz, *CEO*
Mike Lipscombe, *President*
Jerrold J Pellizzon, *CFO*
Thomas A Cole, *Vice Pres*
Peter Hartl, *Vice Pres*
◆ EMP: 277
SQ FT: 99,000
SALES (est): 574.4MM
SALES (corp-wide): 31.6B **Publicly Held**
WEB: www.ceradyne.com
SIC: 3299 3671 Ceramic fiber; cathode ray tubes, including rebuilt
PA: 3m Company
3m Center
Saint Paul MN 55144
651 733-1110

(P-11353)
CERADYNE INC
17466 Daimler St, Irvine (92614-5514)
PHONE.............................949 756-0642
Joel Moskowitz, *Branch Mgr*
EMP: 11
SQ FT: 33,965
SALES (corp-wide): 31.6B **Publicly Held**
WEB: www.ceradyne.com
SIC: 3299 3264 Ceramic fiber; porcelain electrical supplies
HQ: Ceradyne, Inc.
1922 Barranca Pkwy
Irvine CA 92606
714 549-0421

(P-11354)
CHINA MASTER USA ENTRMT CO
17890 Castleton St # 230, City of Industry
(91748-1756)
PHONE.............................626 810-9372
Richard Wang, *Mng Member*
EMP: 12
SALES (est): 689.8K **Privately Held**
WEB: www.chinamasterusa.com
SIC: 3299 Ceramic fiber

(P-11355)
DOUGLAS & STURGESS INC
1023 Factory St, Richmond (94801-2161)
PHONE.............................510 235-8411
Arthur Cordisco, *Manager*
EMP: 10
SQ FT: 10,250
SALES (corp-wide): 1.1MM **Privately Held**
WEB: www.artstuf.com
SIC: 3299 Art goods: plaster of paris, papier mache & scagliola
PA: Douglas & Sturgess, Inc
730 Bryant St
San Francisco CA 94107
415 896-6283

(P-11356)
FOUNDRY SERVICE & SUPPLIES INC
2029 S Parco Ave, Ontario (91761-5700)
PHONE.............................909 284-5000
Curt Parnell, *CEO*
Joel Leathers, *Vice Pres*
▲ EMP: 24
SQ FT: 40,000
SALES (est): 4.5MM **Privately Held**
WEB: www.foundryservice.com
SIC: 3299 Art goods: plaster of paris, papier mache & scagliola

(P-11357)
J P WEAVER & COMPANY INC
941 Air Way, Glendale (91201-3001)
PHONE.............................818 500-1740
Lenna Tyler Kast, *President*
Joshua Kast, *Technical Mgr*
Adam Kast, *Director*
EMP: 15
SQ FT: 10,000
SALES (est): 1.2MM **Privately Held**
WEB: www.jpweaver.com
SIC: 3299 2431 Moldings, architectural: plaster of paris; millwork

(P-11358)
LOMELIS STATUARY INC (PA)
Also Called: Lomeli's Gardens
11921 E Brandt Rd, Lockeford
(95237-9708)
P.O. Box 1356 (95237-1356)
PHONE.............................209 367-1131
Doris Lomeli, *President*
Adriana Lomeli, *Treasurer*
Carlos Lomeli, *Admin Sec*
Elsa Lomeli, *Admin Sec*
EMP: 25
SQ FT: 28,000
SALES (est): 2.2MM **Privately Held**
WEB: www.lomelis-statuary.com
SIC: 3299 5021 5261 Statuary: gypsum, clay, papier mache, metal, etc.; outdoor & lawn furniture; nurseries & garden centers

(P-11359)
MAXFORD TECHNOLOGY LLC
2225 Calle De Luna, Santa Clara
(95054-1002)
PHONE.............................408 855-8288
Jonathan Chan,
Stella Lau, *Manager*
▲ EMP: 16
SQ FT: 22,000
SALES (est): 14.5MM **Privately Held**
WEB: www.maxfordtech.com
SIC: 3299 Non-metallic mineral statuary & other decorative products

(P-11360)
MERLEX STUCCO INC
Also Called: Merlex Stucco Mfg
2911 N Orange Olive Rd, Orange
(92865-1699)
PHONE.............................877 547-8822
Steve Combs, *President*
▲ EMP: 35 EST: 1963
SQ FT: 30,000
SALES (est): 7.6MM **Privately Held**
WEB: www.merlex.com
SIC: 3299 Stucco

(P-11361)
MONTEREY FOAM COMPANY INC
1716 Stone Ave Ste A, San Jose
(95125-1308)
P.O. Box 28365 (95159-8365)
PHONE.............................408 279-6756
Mitchell Dougherty, *President*
David Anderson, *Admin Sec*
EMP: 10
SALES (est): 860K **Privately Held**
SIC: 3299 Ornamental & architectural plaster work

(P-11362)
MORGAN TECHNICAL CERAMICS INC
2425 Whipple Rd, Hayward (94544-7807)
PHONE.............................510 491-1100
Mark Robertshaw, *CEO*
Andrew Hosty, *COO*
Kevin Dangerfield, *CFO*
Andrew Shilston, *Chairman*
Eva Yeh, *Human Res Mgr*
EMP: 18 EST: 1991
SALES (est): 2.7MM **Privately Held**
SIC: 3299 Ceramic fiber

(P-11363)
MOTOART LLC
21809 S Western Ave, Torrance
(90501-3724)
PHONE.............................310 375-4531
David Hall,
Charlotte Hoover, *Bookkeeper*
Piedra Stone, *Sales Executive*
Ramona Cox, *Marketing Staff*
Donovan Fell,
EMP: 10
SQ FT: 1,400
SALES: 1.7MM **Privately Held**
WEB: www.motoart.com
SIC: 3299 Architectural sculptures: gypsum, clay, papier mache, etc.

(P-11364)
OMEGA PRODUCTS CORP (HQ)
Also Called: Omega Products International
8111 Fruitridge Rd, Sacramento
(95826-4759)
P.O. Box 77220, Corona (92877-0107)
PHONE.............................916 635-3335
Kenneth R Thompson, *President*
Lutz Lamparter, *COO*
Todd Martin, *Vice Pres*
Debi Mosqueda, *Executive Asst*
Alejandra Becerra, *Human Res Dir*
▲ EMP: 60
SQ FT: 11,000
SALES (est): 34MM
SALES (corp-wide): 77.9MM **Privately Held**
WEB: www.omega-products.com
SIC: 3299 2899 Stucco; chemical preparations
PA: Opal Service, Inc.
282 S Anita Dr
Orange CA 92868
714 935-0900

(P-11365)
OMEGA PRODUCTS CORP
282 S Anita Dr Fl 3, Orange (92868-3308)
P.O. Box 1149 (92856-0149)
PHONE.............................714 935-0900
Todd Martin, *Manager*
EMP: 32
SALES (corp-wide): 77.9MM **Privately Held**
WEB: www.omega-products.com
SIC: 3299 Stucco
HQ: Omega Products Corp.
8111 Fruitridge Rd
Sacramento CA 95826
916 635-3335

(P-11366)
OPAL SERVICE INC (PA)
282 S Anita Dr, Orange (92868-3308)
P.O. Box 1149 (92856-0149)
PHONE.............................714 935-0900
Kenneth R Thompson, *CEO*
▲ EMP: 30
SQ FT: 1,200

PRODUCTS & SVCS

SALES (est): 77.9MM **Privately Held**
SIC: **3299** 5031 5211 Stucco; doors & windows; lumber & other building materials

(P-11367)
PAREX USA INC (DH)
4125 E La Palma Ave # 250, Anaheim (92807-1869)
PHONE..................................714 778-2266
Rodrigo Lacerda, *President*
Esther Ramirez, *Human Resources*
Sergio Flores, *Sales Staff*
▲ EMP: 30 EST: 1926
SALES (est): 139.8MM **Privately Held**
WEB: www.parexlahabra.com
SIC: **3299** 5031 Stucco; building materials, interior

(P-11368)
PAREX USA INC
11290 Vallejo Ct, French Camp (95231-9771)
PHONE..................................209 983-8002
Steve Horn, *Manager*
EMP: 20 **Privately Held**
WEB: www.parexlahabra.com
SIC: **3299** 2851 Stucco; paints & allied products
HQ: Parex Usa, Inc.
   4125 E La Palma Ave # 250
   Anaheim CA 92807
   714 778-2266

(P-11369)
RICHARD MACDONALD STUDIOS INC (PA)
Also Called: Mac Donald, Richard Galleries
16 Lower Ragsdale Dr, Monterey (93940-5728)
PHONE..................................831 655-0424
Richard Mac Donald Jr, *President*
Hedy Woodrow, *Exec VP*
Edrees Rohina, *Technology*
▲ EMP: 14
SALES (est): 3MM **Privately Held**
WEB: www.dawsoncolefineart.com
SIC: **3299** Architectural sculptures: gypsum, clay, papier mache, etc.

(P-11370)
SMALL PRECISION TOOLS INC
Also Called: Wire Bonding Tools
1330 Clegg St, Petaluma (94954-1127)
PHONE..................................707 765-4545
Peter Glutz, *President*
Joe Gracia, *CFO*
Yanling Geng, *Vice Pres*
Mary Ong, *Vice Pres*
Julie Carr, *Administration*
▲ EMP: 94
SQ FT: 25,000
SALES (est): 14.4MM
SALES (corp-wide): 27.3MM **Privately Held**
WEB: www.smallprecisiontools.com
SIC: **3299** Ceramic fiber
PA: Spt Roth Ag
   Werkstrasse 28
   Lyss BE 3250
   323 878-080

(P-11371)
SPECIALTY CELLULAR PRODUCTS CO
Also Called: Ultracor
2763 Boeing Way, Stockton (95206-3983)
PHONE..................................925 454-3010
Mike Fellman, *President*
Gail Fellman, *Admin Mgr*
Bill Madru, *Admin Sec*
EMP: 14
SQ FT: 10,000
SALES (est): 2MM **Privately Held**
WEB: www.ultracorinc.com
SIC: **3299** Ceramic fiber

(P-11372)
STATUE FACTORY LLC
10 Industrial Way, Brisbane (94005-1097)
PHONE..................................415 468-4870
Dino Belluomini, *Partner*
Marc Belluomini, *Partner*
◆ EMP: 35 EST: 1977
SQ FT: 14,000

SALES (est): 3MM **Privately Held**
SIC: **3299** Statuary: gypsum, clay, papier mache, metal, etc.

(P-11373)
VANDORN PLASTERING
657 Lincoln Rd Ste D, Yuba City (95991-6671)
PHONE..................................530 671-2748
Darryll Vandorn, *Owner*
EMP: 10 EST: 2007
SALES (est): 823.7K **Privately Held**
SIC: **3299** 1771 1742

(P-11374)
VASARI PLASTER AND STUCCO LLC
1725 N Ventura Ave, Ventura (93001-1573)
PHONE..................................805 845-2497
Lara G Romeo, *Principal*
EMP: 13
SALES (est): 1.3MM **Privately Held**
SIC: **3299**

(P-11375)
YLA INC
Also Called: CCS Composites
2450 Cordelia Rd, Fairfield (94534-1651)
PHONE..................................707 359-3400
Paul Draghi, *CEO*
Scott Unger, *President*
Berman Ng, *Controller*
EMP: 87
SQ FT: 42,000
SALES (est): 11.4MM
SALES (corp-wide): 1.4B **Privately Held**
WEB: www.tencate.com
SIC: **3299** Ceramic fiber
HQ: Tencate Advanced Composites Usa, Inc.
   18410 Butterfield Blvd
   Morgan Hill CA 95037
   408 776-0700

3312 Blast Furnaces, Coke Ovens, Steel & Rolling Mills

(P-11376)
ALLEGHENY LUDLUM LLC
Also Called: ATI Allegheny Ludlum
8570 Mercury Ln, Pico Rivera (90660-3796)
PHONE..................................562 654-3900
W D Lieser, *Branch Mgr*
WEI Xu, *Engineer*
EMP: 16 **Publicly Held**
WEB: www.alleghenyludlum.com
SIC: **3312** Sheet or strip, steel, cold-rolled: own hot-rolled; stainless steel
HQ: Allegheny Ludlum, Llc
   1000 Six Ppg Pl
   Pittsburgh PA 15222
   412 394-2800

(P-11377)
AMERICAN BLAST SYSTEMS INC
Also Called: Blast Structures
16182 Gothard St Ste H, Huntington Beach (92647-3642)
PHONE..................................949 244-6859
Kassie Stratton, *Manager*
EMP: 25
SALES (corp-wide): 4.7MM **Privately Held**
SIC: **3312** Blast furnace & related products
PA: American Blast Systems, Inc.
   3101 Villa Way
   Newport Beach CA 92663
   949 244-6859

(P-11378)
AMERICAN PLANT SERVICES INC (PA)
6242 N Paramount Blvd, Long Beach (90805-3714)
P.O. Box 727 (90801-0727)
PHONE..................................562 630-1773
George M Bragg, *President*
Mary-Ann Pool, *Treasurer*
EMP: 51

SALES (est): 8.9MM **Privately Held**
SIC: **3312** Blast furnaces & steel mills

(P-11379)
ARTSONS MANUFACTURING COMPANY
4915 Cecilia St, Cudahy (90201-5995)
PHONE..................................323 773-3469
Jeffery A Winders, *CEO*
Jeffrey A Winders, *CEO*
Steve Winders, *CFO*
Art L Winders, *Vice Pres*
Steve Wedell, *Marketing Staff*
▲ EMP: 28
SALES (est): 6.7MM **Privately Held**
SIC: **3312** Wire products, steel or iron

(P-11380)
BAMBACIGNO STEEL COMPANY
4930 Mchenry Ave, Modesto (95356-9669)
PHONE..................................209 524-9681
Mary Bambacigno, *CEO*
Bill Boughton, *Vice Pres*
Sheila Arnold, *Admin Sec*
Nicole Kochman, *Accountant*
EMP: 48
SQ FT: 51,440
SALES (est): 10.9MM **Privately Held**
WEB: www.bambacigno.com
SIC: **3312** Structural shapes & pilings, steel

(P-11381)
BROWN-PACIFIC INC
Also Called: B P W
13639 Bora Dr, Santa Fe Springs (90670-5010)
PHONE..................................562 921-3471
Ron R Nagele, *CEO*
Emmanuel Pak, *Exec VP*
Claudia Nagele, *Vice Pres*
Kenneth Brown, *Principal*
Lois Weech, *Sales Staff*
EMP: 32
SQ FT: 35,000
SALES (est): 12.4MM **Privately Held**
WEB: www.brownpacific.com
SIC: **3312** 3355 3357 3356 Bar, rod & wire products; wire, aluminum: made in rolling mills; bars, rolled, aluminum; nonferrous wiredrawing & insulating; nonferrous rolling & drawing; cold finishing of steel shapes; steel wire & related products

(P-11382)
CALIFORNIA AMFORGE CORPORATION
750 N Vernon Ave, Azusa (91702-2231)
PHONE..................................626 334-4931
William Taylor, *Branch Mgr*
EMP: 100
SQ FT: 20,000
SALES (corp-wide): 21.2MM **Privately Held**
WEB: www.cal-amforge.com
SIC: **3312** 3462 Forgings, iron & steel; iron & steel forgings
PA: California Amforge Corporation
   750 N Vernon Ave
   Azusa CA 91702
   626 334-4931

(P-11383)
CALIFORNIA STEEL INDS INC (HQ)
Also Called: Si
14000 San Bernardino Ave, Fontana (92335-5259)
P.O. Box 5080 (92334-5080)
PHONE..................................909 350-6300
Marcelo Botelho, *President*
Hiroshi Adachi, *Ch of Bd*
Tadaaki Yamaguchi, *Ch of Bd*
Ricardo Bernardes, *Exec VP*
Brett Guge, *Exec VP*
▲ EMP: 277
SALES (est): 247.4MM **Privately Held**
WEB: www.californiasteel.com
SIC: **3312** 3317 Slabs, steel; plate, sheet & strip, except coated products; pipes, wrought: welded, lock joint or heavy riveted

(P-11384)
CALIFORNIA STEEL INDS INC
1 California Steel Way, Fontana (92335)
PHONE..................................909 350-6300
Kyle Schulty, *Branch Mgr*
Eryka Crossley, *Manager*
EMP: 23 **Privately Held**
SIC: **3312** 3317 Slabs, steel; plate, sheet & strip, except coated products; pipes, wrought: welded, lock joint or heavy riveted
HQ: California Steel Industries, Inc.
   14000 San Bernardino Ave
   Fontana CA 92335
   909 350-6300

(P-11385)
CALIFORNIA STL STAIR RAIL MFR
587 Carnegie St, Manteca (95337-6102)
PHONE..................................209 824-1785
Richard G Lee, *President*
Dave Geserick, *CFO*
EMP: 30 EST: 1997
SQ FT: 30,000
SALES (est): 6.9MM **Privately Held**
WEB: www.calstair.com
SIC: **3312** Rails, steel or iron; structural shapes & pilings, steel

(P-11386)
CARPENTER TECHNOLOGY CORP
Also Called: Carpenter Specialty Alloys
8250 Milliken Ave, Rancho Cucamonga (91730-3927)
PHONE..................................909 476-4000
Sean Bell, *Manager*
EMP: 33
SALES (corp-wide): 2.1B **Publicly Held**
SIC: **3312** Stainless steel
PA: Carpenter Technology Corporation
   1735 Market St Fl 15
   Philadelphia PA 19103
   610 208-2000

(P-11387)
CARTER HOLT HARVEY HOLDINGS
1230 Railroad St, Corona (92882-1837)
PHONE..................................951 272-8180
John Miller, *President*
EMP: 53
SQ FT: 60,000
SALES (est): 4.3MM **Privately Held**
WEB: www.chh.com
SIC: **3312** Blast furnaces & steel mills
HQ: Carter Holt Harvey Limited
   173 Captain Springs Road
   Auckland
   -

(P-11388)
CHAPALA IRON & MANUFACTURING
1301 Callens Rd, Ventura (93003-5602)
PHONE..................................805 654-9803
Patrick Davis, *Owner*
EMP: 15
SQ FT: 3,600
SALES (est): 2MM **Privately Held**
SIC: **3312** 3446 Blast furnaces & steel mills; architectural metalwork

(P-11389)
CITY INDUSTRIAL TOOL & DIE (PA)
25524 Frampton Ave, Harbor City (90710-2907)
PHONE..................................310 530-1234
Steve Kuljis, *President*
Eileen Kuljis, *Admin Sec*
EMP: 12
SQ FT: 5,000
SALES (est): 895.2K **Privately Held**
SIC: **3312** 3469 3444 3544 Tool & die steel & alloys; metal stampings; sheet metalwork; special dies, tools, jigs & fixtures

(P-11390)
COAST CUTTERS CO INC
2500 Royale Pl, Fullerton (92833-1526)
PHONE..................................626 444-2965

▲ = Import ▼=Export
◆ =Import/Export

Bill Dunlap, *President*
Bonnie Dunlap, *Corp Secy*
Steve Dunlap, *Vice Pres*
John Merritt, *Vice Pres*
EMP: 10
SQ FT: 6,500
SALES: 700K **Publicly Held**
SIC: 3312 5072 Tool & die steel; power tools & accessories

(P-11391)
COMMERCIAL METALS COMPANY
12451 Arrow Rte, Etiwanda (91739-9601)
PHONE..................909 899-9993
Chris Lloyd, *Branch Mgr*
EMP: 10
SALES (corp-wide): 4.6B **Publicly Held**
SIC: 3312 Blast furnaces & steel mills
PA: Commercial Metals Company
6565 N Mcarthr Blvd # 800
Irving TX 75039
214 689-4300

(P-11392)
DESIGN SHAPES IN STEEL INC
10315 Rush St, South El Monte (91733-3341)
PHONE..................626 579-2032
Peter Costruba II, *President*
EMP: 20
SQ FT: 10,000
SALES: 2MM **Privately Held**
SIC: 3312 3446 3444 Primary finished or semifinished shapes; architectural metalwork; sheet metalwork

(P-11393)
EASYFLEX INC
Also Called: Easy Flex
7423 Doig Dr, Garden Grove (92841-1807)
PHONE..................888 577-8999
Sunmin Kim OH, *President*
Hun Kim, *General Mgr*
◆ **EMP:** 25
SQ FT: 30,000
SALES (est): 8.7MM **Privately Held**
SIC: 3312 Stainless steel

(P-11394)
FLOW DYNAMICS INC
1215 E Acacia St Ste 104, Ontario (91761-4003)
PHONE..................909 930-5522
John McCarthy, *President*
Philip Espinoza, *Vice Pres*
EMP: 16
SQ FT: 2,222
SALES (est): 4.4MM **Privately Held**
SIC: 3312 Stainless steel

(P-11395)
GOLDEN STATE ASSEMBLY INC
47823 Westinghouse Dr, Fremont (94539-7437)
P.O. Box 611913, San Jose (95161-1913)
PHONE..................510 226-8155
Yesenia Castillo, *President*
Nancy Martinez, *Accounting Mgr*
Cesar Madrueno, *Materials Mgr*
Vicente Madrueno, *Production*
EMP: 300
SALES (est): 17.3MM **Privately Held**
SIC: 3312 3357 3355 3679 Wire products, steel or iron; aluminum wire & cable; aluminum wire & cable; harness assemblies for electronic use: wire or cable; assembly machines, non-metalworking

(P-11396)
GONDOLA SKATE MVG SYSTEMS INC (PA)
9941 Prospect Ave, Santee (92071-4318)
PHONE..................619 222-6487
Frank C Cozza, *CEO*
Sharmin Self, *Administration*
EMP: 13
SQ FT: 2,000
SALES: 4MM **Privately Held**
WEB: www.gondolaskate.com
SIC: 3312 Locomotive wheels, rolled

(P-11397)
GRAND METALS INC
Also Called: Select Fabrications
325 N Cota St, Corona (92880-2014)
PHONE..................310 327-5554
Kevin Malloy, *President*
Thomas Malloy, *Ch of Bd*
EMP: 11
SQ FT: 18,000
SALES (est): 2.1MM **Privately Held**
SIC: 3312 Structural shapes & pilings, steel

(P-11398)
HERRICK CORPORATION
Stockton Steel
3003 E Hammer Ln, Stockton (95212-2801)
P.O. Box 8429 (95208-0429)
PHONE..................209 956-4751
Tom Juano, *Manager*
Annette Borba, *Manager*
EMP: 186
SALES (corp-wide): 244.7MM **Privately Held**
SIC: 3312 3441 Structural shapes & pilings, steel; fabricated structural metal
PA: The Herrick Corporation
3003 E Hammer Ln
Stockton CA 95212
209 956-4751

(P-11399)
HOLT TOOL & MACHINE INC
2909 Middlefield Rd, Redwood City (94063-3328)
PHONE..................650 364-2547
Leo Hoenighausen, *President*
Ulrich Hoenighausen, *CFO*
Remus Regneala, *Vice Pres*
Karen Garcia, *Technology*
EMP: 21
SQ FT: 12,000
SALES (est): 5.7MM **Privately Held**
SIC: 3312 3469 7692 3544 Tool & die steel & alloys; metal stampings; welding repair; special dies, tools, jigs & fixtures

(P-11400)
INTERNATIONAL MFG TECH INC (DH)
Also Called: Nassco
2798 Harbor Dr, San Diego (92113-3650)
PHONE..................619 544-7741
Willam J Cuddy, *CEO*
James C Scott, *President*
William J Cuddy, *Manager*
Jaime De Chico, *Assistant*
▲ **EMP:** 24
SALES (est): 24.8MM
SALES (corp-wide): 30.9B **Publicly Held**
SIC: 3312 3731 Structural & rail mill products; shipbuilding & repairing
HQ: Nassco Holdings Incorporated
2798 Harbor Dr
San Diego CA 92113
619 544-3400

(P-11401)
INTERSTATE REBAR INC
2457 N Ventura Ave Ste L, Ventura (93001-0345)
P.O. Box 670, Oak View (93022-0670)
PHONE..................805 643-6892
Ronald Moore, *President*
Annette Hall, *Manager*
EMP: 10
SALES (est): 1.7MM **Privately Held**
SIC: 3312 Plate, sheet & strip, except coated products; tool & die steel & alloys

(P-11402)
KEN-WOR CORP
Also Called: Parcor
13962 Enterprise Dr, Garden Grove (92843-4021)
PHONE..................714 554-6210
Steve Worrell, *President*
Ken Upton, *Treasurer*
EMP: 38
SQ FT: 10,000
SALES (est): 3MM **Privately Held**
SIC: 3312 3444 Stainless steel; sheet metalwork

(P-11403)
KVA INC
Also Called: Kva Stainless
2802 Luciernaga St, Carlsbad (92009-5926)
PHONE..................760 489-1500
Joe Mc Crink, *Vice Pres*
Douglas Gore, *Principal*
Danny Codd, *Engineer*
EMP: 15
SALES (est): 2.6MM **Privately Held**
SIC: 3312 Stainless steel

(P-11404)
LAMAR TOOL AND DIE CASTING INC
4230 Technology Dr, Modesto (95356-9484)
PHONE..................209 545-5525
Larry Snoreen, *President*
Margie Snoreen, *Treasurer*
Brian Kolsters, *Vice Pres*
Carol Lemmons, *Human Resources*
Craig Feaga, *Safety Mgr*
▲ **EMP:** 41
SQ FT: 20,000
SALES (est): 5.5MM **Privately Held**
WEB: www.lamartoolanddie.com
SIC: 3312 3463 3364 Tool & die steel & alloys; nonferrous forgings; nonferrous die-castings except aluminum

(P-11405)
LINCOLN IRON WORKS
507 7th St, Santa Monica (90402-2707)
PHONE..................310 684-2543
EMP: 22 EST: 2012
SALES (est): 2.1MM **Privately Held**
SIC: 3312

(P-11406)
MAC PRODUCTS INC
Also Called: Mac Performance Exhaust
43214 Black Deer Loop # 113, Temecula (92590-3428)
PHONE..................951 296-3077
Mack Jones Sr, *President*
Mack Jones Jr, *Corp Secy*
▲ **EMP:** 52
SQ FT: 56,000
SALES (est): 10.2MM **Privately Held**
WEB: www.macperformance.com
SIC: 3312 3751 3714 Tubes, steel & iron; motorcycles, bicycles & parts; motor vehicle parts & accessories

(P-11407)
MIKES METAL WORKS INC
3552 Fowler Canyon Rd, Jamul (91935-1602)
PHONE..................619 440-8804
Mike Hancock, *President*
JD Hudson, *Manager*
EMP: 18
SQ FT: 6,000
SALES (est): 4.1MM **Privately Held**
WEB: www.mikesmetalworksinc.com
SIC: 3312 Stainless steel

(P-11408)
NORTHLAND PROCESS PIPING INC
400 E St, Lemoore (93245-2616)
PHONE..................559 925-9724
Cal Bredek, *Supervisor*
EMP: 100
SALES (corp-wide): 30.2MM **Privately Held**
SIC: 3312 Stainless steel
PA: Northland Process Piping, Inc.
1662 320th Ave
Isle MN 56342
320 679-2119

(P-11409)
PACIFIC TOLL PROCESSING INC
Also Called: P T P
24724 Wilmington Ave, Carson (90745-6127)
PHONE..................310 952-4992
Anthony J Camasta, *CEO*
Mark Proner, *Exec VP*
Conni Fields, *General Mgr*
EMP: 40

SQ FT: 101,000
SALES (est): 11.6MM **Privately Held**
WEB: www.pacifictoll.com
SIC: 3312 4785 Structural & rail mill products; toll road operation

(P-11410)
PRECISION WIRE PRODUCTS INC
Also Called: Lcl Pacific
11215 Wilmington Ave, Los Angeles (90059-1299)
PHONE..................323 569-8165
Frank Vega, *Branch Mgr*
Elliot Garcia, *Asst Director*
EMP: 25
SALES (corp-wide): 42.4MM **Privately Held**
WEB: www.precisionwireproducts.com
SIC: 3312 Wire products, steel or iron
PA: Precision Wire Products, Inc.
6150 Sheila St
Commerce CA 90040
323 890-9100

(P-11411)
PRICE INDUSTRIES INC
Also Called: International Iron Products
10883 Thornmint Rd, San Diego (92127-2403)
PHONE..................858 673-4451
Kenneth Alan Price, *President*
Barbara Price, *Admin Sec*
Manuel Velazquez, *Technician*
Matthew Mastenbrook, *Purch Mgr*
Miguel Varela, *Purchasing*
EMP: 75
SQ FT: 4,000
SALES (est): 17.8MM **Privately Held**
WEB: www.intliron.com
SIC: 3312 3441 1791 5072 Structural & rail mill products; fabricated structural metal; structural steel erection; bolts, nuts & screws

(P-11412)
QUALITY CRAFT MOLD INC
6424 Woodward Dr, Magalia (95954-8709)
PHONE..................530 873-7790
Chris Moritz, *President*
EMP: 10
SQ FT: 4,200
SALES (est): 1.3MM **Privately Held**
WEB: www.qualitycraftinc.com
SIC: 3312 Tool & die steel & alloys

(P-11413)
R S R STEEL FABRICATION INC
11040 I Ave, Hesperia (92345-5214)
PHONE..................760 244-2210
Hector Grijalva, *President*
Ruth Grijalva, *Vice Pres*
EMP: 28
SQ FT: 12,000
SALES (est): 6.1MM **Privately Held**
SIC: 3312 Structural shapes & pilings, steel

(P-11414)
REDLINE PRCISION MACHINING INC
907 E Francis St, Ontario (91761-5631)
PHONE..................909 483-1273
Jon Bouch, *CEO*
Cheryl Bouch, *Admin Sec*
EMP: 15 EST: 1997
SQ FT: 10,000
SALES: 2MM **Privately Held**
SIC: 3312 Tool & die steel & alloys

(P-11415)
RELIABLE MILL SUPPLY CO
1550 Millview Rd, Ukiah (95482-3341)
P.O. Box 269 (95482-0269)
PHONE..................707 462-1458
Norman E Johnson Jr, *President*
Harold Johnson, *Vice Pres*
Bow Johnson, *Admin Sec*
EMP: 10
SQ FT: 27,000
SALES (est): 2.3MM **Privately Held**
SIC: 3312 5051 5085 Blast furnaces & steel mills; metals service centers & offices; mill supplies

(P-11416)
RHINO MANUFACTURING GROUP INC
14440 Meadowrun St, San Diego (92129-3328)
PHONE..................858 869-4010
Heather Mordhorst, *CEO*
Aimee Gaede, *COO*
▲ EMP: 12
SALES (est): 1.1MM **Privately Held**
WEB: www.rhinomfg.net
SIC: 3312 1771 5051 5085 Stainless steel; concrete work; steel; rubber goods, mechanical; foams & rubber; rubber, crude

(P-11417)
RTM PRODUCTS INC
13120 Arctic Cir, Santa Fe Springs (90670-5508)
PHONE..................562 926-2400
Robert M Thierjung, *Principal*
EMP: 23
SALES (est): 4.6MM **Privately Held**
SIC: 3312 Tool & die steel & alloys; tool & die steel

(P-11418)
SAEMIE CORPORATION
Also Called: Zinik Wheels
3199 E La Palma Ave Ste A, Anaheim (92806-2800)
PHONE..................714 632-0530
Gun Woo Kim, *President*
Heekwon Kim, *Vice Pres*
◆ EMP: 10
SQ FT: 15,000
SALES (est): 6.5MM **Privately Held**
SIC: 3312 5013 Wheels; wheels, motor vehicle

(P-11419)
SEARING INDUSTRIES INC
8901 Arrow Rte, Rancho Cucamonga (91730-4410)
P.O. Box 3059 (91729-3059)
PHONE..................909 948-3030
Lee Searing, *President*
Steve Abbey, *Exec VP*
Richard Searing, *Exec VP*
Mmargaret Cantu, *Vice Pres*
Annie Wood, *Office Mgr*
◆ EMP: 120
SQ FT: 265,000
SALES (est): 46.6MM **Privately Held**
WEB: www.searingindustries.com
SIC: 3312 3317 Tubes, steel & iron; hot-rolled iron & steel products; steel pipe & tubes

(P-11420)
SIMSOLVE
310 Elizabeth Ln, Corona (92880-2504)
PHONE..................951 898-6880
Dennis Anderson, *President*
EMP: 10
SALES (est): 897.6K **Privately Held**
SIC: 3312 Rails, steel or iron

(P-11421)
SMITH BROS STRL STL PDTS INC
Also Called: Smith Bros Cstm Met Fbrication
1535 Potrero Ave, South El Monte (91733-3016)
PHONE..................626 350-1872
Christopher Smith, *President*
Chris Smith, *President*
Reginald Smith, *Vice Pres*
EMP: 15 EST: 1976
SQ FT: 30,000
SALES (est): 2.4MM **Privately Held**
SIC: 3312 Structural shapes & pilings, steel

(P-11422)
SOUTHERN CAL GOLD PDTS INC
2350 Santiago Ct, Oxnard (93030-7932)
P.O. Box 1933, Camarillo (93011-1933)
PHONE..................805 988-0777
Glenn Harris, *CEO*
Gina Harris, *Treasurer*
EMP: 10

SALES (est): 2.2MM **Privately Held**
SIC: 3312 Armor plate

(P-11423)
STAR STAINLESS SCREW CO
30150 Ahern Ave, Union City (94587-1202)
PHONE..................510 489-6569
Tim Roberto, *Manager*
EMP: 15
SALES (corp-wide): 106.9MM **Privately Held**
SIC: 3312 5072 Stainless steel; hardware
PA: Star Stainless Screw Co
30 W End Rd
Totowa NJ 07512
973 256-2300

(P-11424)
STRADA WHEELS INC
560 S Magnolia Ave, Ontario (91762-4011)
PHONE..................626 336-1634
Enrico Aiello, *President*
Joyce Aiello, *Vice Pres*
Maria Yneguez, *General Mgr*
Tommy Gun, *Sales Staff*
▲ EMP: 14
SALES (est): 2.4MM **Privately Held**
SIC: 3312 5014 Wheels; tires & tubes

(P-11425)
STRESSTEEL INC
Also Called: Sas Stressteel
47375 Fremont Blvd, Fremont (94538-6521)
PHONE..................888 284-8752
Michael A Pagano, *CEO*
Dion Gray, *CFO*
Frank Gummich, *General Mgr*
Claudio Hunger, *Engineer*
Tom Pavlovic, *Engineer*
▲ EMP: 11
SALES (est): 2.2MM **Privately Held**
SIC: 3312 8711 Bar, rod & wire products; engineering services

(P-11426)
USS-PSCO INDS A CAL JINT VENTR (PA)
900 Loveridge Rd, Pittsburg (94565-2808)
P.O. Box 471 (94565-0471)
PHONE..................800 877-7672
Michael Piekut, *Manager*
United States Steel Corporatio, *Partner*
Chris Beltran, *Vice Chairman*
Sungwon Shin, *Vice Pres*
Tim Lear, *Associate Dir*
▲ EMP: 759
SQ FT: 100,000
SALES (est): 648.9MM **Privately Held**
WEB: www.ussposco.com
SIC: 3312 Sheet or strip, steel, cold-rolled: own hot-rolled; tinplate; iron & steel: galvanized, pipes, plates, sheets, etc.

(P-11427)
WAYNE TOOL & DIE CO
15853 Olden St, Sylmar (91342-1249)
PHONE..................818 364-1611
Kenneth E Ruggles, *President*
EMP: 50
SQ FT: 1,200
SALES (est): 4.4MM **Privately Held**
SIC: 3312 Tool & die steel

(P-11428)
WEISER IRON INC
10700 Jersey Blvd Ste 680, Rancho Cucamonga (91730-5122)
PHONE..................909 429-4600
David Metoyer, *President*
Carmela Metoyer, *Corp Secy*
EMP: 47
SQ FT: 20,000
SALES (est): 10.6MM **Privately Held**
WEB: www.weiseriron.com
SIC: 3312 Structural shapes & pilings, steel

(P-11429)
WHEEL AND TIRE CLUB INC
Also Called: Discounted Wheel Warehouse
1301 Burton St, Fullerton (92831-5212)
PHONE..................714 422-3505
Naeem Niamat, *President*
◆ EMP: 35 EST: 2013
SQ FT: 42,000

SALES: 18MM **Privately Held**
SIC: 3312 Locomotive wheels, rolled

3313 Electrometallurgical Prdts

(P-11430)
R D MATHIS COMPANY
2840 Gundry Ave, Signal Hill (90755-1813)
P.O. Box 92916, Long Beach (90809-2916)
PHONE..................562 426-7049
Robert Lumley, *President*
Barbara Bennett, *Treasurer*
Kirk Bennett, *Vice Pres*
EMP: 25 EST: 1963
SQ FT: 10,000
SALES (est): 5.4MM **Privately Held**
WEB: www.rdmathis.com
SIC: 3313 8711 3567 3443 Molybdenum silicon, not made in blast furnaces; engineering services; industrial furnaces & ovens; fabricated plate work (boiler shop); fabricated structural metal

(P-11431)
TUNGSTEN HEAVY POWDER INC (PA)
Also Called: Tungsten Heavy Powder & Parts
6170 Cornerstone Ct E # 310, San Diego (92121-3767)
PHONE..................858 693-6100
Joseph Sery, *CEO*
Oscar Cruz, *COO*
Chris Witt, *CFO*
Russel Lewis, *Vice Pres*
Rosemarie Naputi, *Office Mgr*
▲ EMP: 60
SQ FT: 10,000
SALES: 39.2MM **Privately Held**
WEB: www.tungstenheavypowder.com
SIC: 3313 Tungsten carbide powder

3315 Steel Wire Drawing & Nails & Spikes

(P-11432)
BULLZEYE MFG
13625 Clements Rd, Lodi (95240-9754)
P.O. Box 187, Linden (95236-0187)
PHONE..................209 482-5626
Brian Gideon, *Mng Member*
EMP: 15 EST: 2010
SALES (est): 936.9K **Privately Held**
SIC: 3315 Steel wire & related products

(P-11433)
CARLISLE INTERCONNECT TECH INC
Thermax
4200 Garner Rd, Riverside (92501-1003)
PHONE..................951 788-0252
Kevin Dyer, *Production*
Jessica Lund, *Production*
EMP: 20
SALES (corp-wide): 4B **Publicly Held**
SIC: 3315 2241 3496 Steel wire & related products; narrow fabric mills; miscellaneous fabricated wire products
HQ: Carlisle Interconnect Technologies, Inc.
100 Tensolite Dr
Saint Augustine FL 32092

(P-11434)
D & D TECHNOLOGIES USA INC
17531 Metzler Ln, Huntington Beach (92647-6242)
PHONE..................949 852-5140
David Calabria, *CEO*
Myrna Sanchez, *Manager*
▼ EMP: 29
SALES: 12MM **Privately Held**
SIC: 3315
HQ: D & D Technologies Pty. Limited
U6 4 Aquatic Dr
Frenchs Forest NSW 2086

(P-11435)
DAVIS WIRE CORPORATION (HQ)
5555 Irwindale Ave, Irwindale (91706-2046)
PHONE..................626 969-7651
Jim Baske, *President*
Emily Heisley, *Ch of Bd*
Hak Kim, *CFO*
▲ EMP: 150
SQ FT: 265,000
SALES (est): 86.7MM **Privately Held**
WEB: www.daviswire.com
SIC: 3315 Wire, ferrous/iron; wire products, ferrous/iron: made in wiredrawing plants

(P-11436)
DAYTON SUPERIOR CORPORATION
6001 20th St, Riverside (92509-2030)
PHONE..................951 782-9517
Jeffrey Bokn, *Branch Mgr*
EMP: 65 **Publicly Held**
SIC: 3315 Steel wire & related products
HQ: Dayton Superior Corporation
1125 Byers Rd
Miamisburg OH 45342
937 866-0711

(P-11437)
DAYTON SUPERIOR CORPORATION
562 W Santa Ana Ave, Bloomington (92316-2914)
PHONE..................909 820-0112
John Ciccerelli, *President*
EMP: 40 **Publicly Held**
SIC: 3315 Steel wire & related products
HQ: Dayton Superior Corporation
1125 Byers Rd
Miamisburg OH 45342
937 866-0711

(P-11438)
DHL WIRE PRODUCTS
Also Called: Chandler Wire Products
2325 1st St, La Verne (91750-5532)
PHONE..................909 596-2909
Debra Oehmke, *Principal*
EMP: 10
SALES (est): 631.8K **Privately Held**
SIC: 3315 Steel wire & related products

(P-11439)
DOOR SERVICE COMPANY
Also Called: Patton Door and Gate
680 S Williams Rd, Palm Springs (92264-1549)
PHONE..................760 320-0788
Fax: 760 323-9553
EMP: 15 EST: 2007
SALES (est): 1.2MM **Privately Held**
SIC: 3315 1751

(P-11440)
FENCER ENTERPRISES LLC
Also Called: Wireman Fence Products
3644 Recycle Rd, Rancho Cordova (95742-7330)
PHONE..................916 635-1700
Lisa Leonard Hilbers, *Mng Member*
EMP: 12
SQ FT: 10,000
SALES (est): 2.8MM **Privately Held**
WEB: www.wiremanfence.com
SIC: 3315 Chain link fencing; fence gates posts & fittings: steel

(P-11441)
GEHR GROUP INC (PA)
7400 E Slauson Ave, Commerce (90040-3308)
PHONE..................323 728-5558
David Lifschitz, *CEO*
Mark Goldman, *COO*
EMP: 22
SALES (est): 92.6MM **Privately Held**
SIC: 3315 5063 6531 Wire & fabricated wire products; wire & cable; real estate agent, commercial; real estate agent, residential

(P-11442)
HALSTEEL INC (DH)
4190 Santa Ana St Ste A, Ontario
(91761-1527)
P.O. Box 90100, San Bernardino (92427-1100)
PHONE..............................909 937-1001
Rebecca Kalis, *President*
Donald Halstead, *Treasurer*
Ed Halstead, *Vice Pres*
EMP: 20
SQ FT: 100,000
SALES (est): 5.4MM
SALES (corp-wide): 183.8MM **Privately Held**
WEB: www.halsteel.com
SIC: 3315 5051 Nails, steel: wire or cut; staples, steel: wire or cut; nails
HQ: Tree Island Industries Ltd
    3933 Boundary Rd
    Richmond BC V6V 1
    604 524-3744

(P-11443)
HAMROCK INC
12521 Los Nietos Rd, Santa Fe Springs
(90670-2915)
PHONE..............................562 944-0255
Stephen R Hamrock, *Principal*
Vena Peterson, *Controller*
Martin Hamrock, *Manager*
▲ EMP: 250
SQ FT: 169,000
SALES (est): 49MM **Privately Held**
WEB: www.hamrock.com
SIC: 3315 2542 3496 3317 Wire & fabricated wire products; racks, merchandise display or storage: except wood; miscellaneous fabricated wire products; steel pipe & tubes

(P-11444)
HANGERS RANDY WEST COAST CTR
Also Called: Manetti Group
5350 Zambrano St, Commerce
(90040-3036)
PHONE..............................323 728-2253
Gabrino Bonuelos, *Manager*
Mario Sebastrano, *Manager*
Claudia Gutierrez, *Accounts Mgr*
▲ EMP: 18
SALES (est): 2.8MM **Privately Held**
SIC: 3315 Hangers (garment), wire

(P-11445)
HOGAN CO INC
2741 S Lilac Ave, Bloomington
(92316-3213)
PHONE..............................909 421-0245
Kraig B Hogan, *President*
◆ EMP: 20
SQ FT: 9,150
SALES (est): 5.3MM **Privately Held**
SIC: 3315 3531 Spikes, steel: wire or cut; bituminous, cement & concrete related products & equipment

(P-11446)
INWESCO INCORPORATED (PA)
746 N Coney Ave, Azusa (91702-2239)
PHONE..............................626 334-7115
David L Morris, *CEO*
EMP: 65
SQ FT: 30,000
SALES (est): 25MM **Privately Held**
WEB: www.inwesco.com
SIC: 3315 Steel wire & related products

(P-11447)
IZURIETA FENCE COMPANY INC
3000 Gilroy St, Los Angeles (90039-2819)
PHONE..............................323 661-4759
Peter Izurieta, *Owner*
EMP: 10
SALES (est): 1.5MM **Privately Held**
SIC: 3315 1799 Chain link fencing; fence construction

(P-11448)
MASTER-HALCO INC
8008 Church Ave, Highland (92346-4318)
PHONE..............................909 350-4740
Paul Stites, *Branch Mgr*
EMP: 50

SALES (corp-wide): 51.7B **Privately Held**
WEB: www.fenceonline.com
SIC: 3315 4226 7692 3496 Fence gates posts & fittings: steel; special warehousing & storage; welding repair; miscellaneous fabricated wire products; metal stampings
HQ: Master-Halco, Inc.
    3010 Lbj Fwy Ste 800
    Dallas TX 75234
    972 714-7300

(P-11449)
MERCHANTS METALS LLC
6466 Mission Blvd, Riverside (92509-4128)
PHONE..............................951 686-1888
Rob Sisco, *Manager*
EMP: 12
SQ FT: 8,750
SALES (corp-wide): 2.3B **Privately Held**
SIC: 3315 3496 Fence gates posts & fittings: steel; miscellaneous fabricated wire products
HQ: Merchants Metals Llc
    211 Perimeter Center Pkwy
    Atlanta GA 30346
    770 741-0300

(P-11450)
MK MAGNETICS INC
17030 Muskrat Ave, Adelanto
(92301-2258)
PHONE..............................760 246-6373
Magne Stangenes, *President*
John Stangenes, *Vice Pres*
Jay Runge, *Admin Sec*
Bryce E Kelchner, *Info Tech Dir*
Susan Knowlton, *Human Res Mgr*
▲ EMP: 53
SQ FT: 45,000
SALES (est): 11.1MM
SALES (corp-wide): 19.3MM **Privately Held**
WEB: www.mkmagnetics.com
SIC: 3315 Steel wire & related products
PA: Stangenes Industries, Inc.
    1052 E Meadow Cir
    Palo Alto CA 94303
    650 855-9926

(P-11451)
NEW PRODUCT INTEGRATION SOLUTN
Also Called: Npi Solutions
685 Jarvis Dr Ste A, Morgan Hill
(95037-2813)
PHONE..............................408 944-9178
Kevin R Andersen, *President*
Dawn Casterson, *CFO*
Scott Ngo, *Project Engr*
Cindy E Chambers, *Controller*
▲ EMP: 65
SQ FT: 15,000
SALES (est): 25.9MM **Privately Held**
WEB: www.npisolutions.com
SIC: 3315 Cable, steel: insulated or armored

(P-11452)
PRO DETENTION INC
Also Called: Viking Products
2238 N Glassell St Ste K, Orange
(92865-2742)
PHONE..............................714 881-3680
Mike Peterson, *CEO*
▲ EMP: 70
SQ FT: 120,000
SALES (est): 8MM **Privately Held**
SIC: 3315 Wire & fabricated wire products

(P-11453)
ROBERT P MARTIN COMPANY
Also Called: Bob Martin Co
2209 Seaman Ave, South El Monte
(91733-2630)
PHONE..............................323 686-2220
Robert P Martin Jr, *CEO*
Naomi Martin, *President*
Sandra Aldana, *General Mgr*
EMP: 14
SQ FT: 14,000
SALES (est): 1.7MM **Privately Held**
SIC: 3315 3357 Wire & fabricated wire products; nonferrous wiredrawing & insulating

(P-11454)
SAC VALLEY ORNAMENTAL IR OUTL
8540 Thys Ct, Sacramento (95828-1007)
P.O. Box 277127 (95827-7127)
PHONE..............................916 383-6340
Mark Eveleth, *President*
EMP: 10
SALES (est): 689K **Privately Held**
SIC: 3315 1791 Fence gates posts & fittings: steel; structural steel erection

(P-11455)
SAFELAND INDUSTRIAL SUPPLY INC (PA)
10278 Birtcher Dr, Jurupa Valley
(91752-1827)
PHONE..............................909 786-1967
Lijun Zhang, *President*
▲ EMP: 16
SALES (est): 2.3MM **Privately Held**
SIC: 3315 3312 Steel wire & related products; stainless steel

(P-11456)
SILICON VALLEY MFG INC
6520 Central Ave, Newark (94560-3933)
PHONE..............................510 791-9450
Mark Serpa, *Principal*
EMP: 24 EST: 2007
SALES (est): 5MM **Privately Held**
SIC: 3315 Steel wire & related products

(P-11457)
SOFT FLEX CO
22678 Broadway, Sonoma (95476-8217)
P.O. Box 80 (95476-0080)
PHONE..............................707 938-3539
Scott Clark, *Partner*
Mike Sherman, *Partner*
EMP: 20
SQ FT: 2,500
SALES (est): 3.8MM **Privately Held**
WEB: www.softflextm.com
SIC: 3315 3915 Steel wire & related products; jewelry parts, unassembled

(P-11458)
SUMIDEN WIRE PRODUCTS CORP (HQ)
1412 El Pinal Dr, Stockton (95205-2642)
PHONE..............................209 466-8924
Brian Burr, *CEO*
Matt Matsubara, *Treasurer*
Gail Gleason, *Accountant*
Dianna Russel, *Controller*
Phil Johnson, *Safety Mgr*
◆ EMP: 32 EST: 1979
SQ FT: 109,000
SALES (est): 32.4MM
SALES (corp-wide): 28.9B **Privately Held**
WEB: www.sumidenwire.com
SIC: 3315 Wire products, ferrous/iron: made in wiredrawing plants
PA: Sumitomo Electric Industries, Ltd.
    4-5-33, Kitahama, Chuo-Ku
    Osaka OSK 541-0
    662 204-141

(P-11459)
SUN POWER SECURITY GATES INC
438 Tyler Rd, Merced (95341-8807)
P.O. Box 2044 (95344-0044)
PHONE..............................209 722-3990
Robert Osborn, *President*
Gene Felling, *Vice Pres*
Dusty Major, *General Mgr*
EMP: 17
SQ FT: 3,500
SALES (est): 2MM **Privately Held**
WEB: www.sun-power.com
SIC: 3315 3677 Fence gates posts & fittings: steel; transformers power supply, electronic type

(P-11460)
TREE ISLAND WIRE (USA) INC (DH)
Also Called: TI Wire
3880 Valley Blvd, Walnut (91789-1515)
P.O. Box 90100, San Bernardino (92427-1100)
PHONE..............................909 594-7511

Amar S Doman, *Ch of Bd*
Dale R Maclean, *CEO*
Nancy Davies, *CFO*
Stephen Ogden, *Vice Pres*
Monet Martin, *Sales Staff*
▲ EMP: 250
SALES (est): 139.3MM
SALES (corp-wide): 183.8MM **Privately Held**
SIC: 3315 Wire, steel: insulated or armored
HQ: Tree Island Industries Ltd
    3933 Boundary Rd
    Richmond BC V6V 1
    604 524-3744

(P-11461)
TREE ISLAND WIRE (USA) INC
Industrial Alloys
13470 Philadelphia Ave, Fontana
(92337-7700)
PHONE..............................909 594-7511
Rebecca Kalis, *Branch Mgr*
EMP: 90
SALES (corp-wide): 183.8MM **Privately Held**
SIC: 3315 Wire, steel: insulated or armored
HQ: Tree Island Wire (Usa), Inc.
    3880 Valley Blvd
    Walnut CA 91789

(P-11462)
TREE ISLAND WIRE (USA) INC
K-Lath
3880 W Valley Blvd, Pomona (91769)
PHONE..............................909 595-6617
Ken Stufford, *Manager*
EMP: 256
SALES (corp-wide): 183.8MM **Privately Held**
SIC: 3315 Wire, steel: insulated or armored
HQ: Tree Island Wire (Usa), Inc.
    3880 Valley Blvd
    Walnut CA 91789

(P-11463)
TREE ISLAND WIRE (USA) INC
12459 Arrow Rte, Rancho Cucamonga
(91739-9807)
PHONE..............................800 255-6974
Krish Singh, *Branch Mgr*
EMP: 75 **Privately Held**
SIC: 3315 Wire & fabricated wire products

(P-11464)
US HANGER COMPANY LLC
17501 S Denver Ave, Gardena
(90248-3410)
PHONE..............................310 323-8030
Gene Livshin, *Mng Member*
▲ EMP: 47
SALES (est): 7.2MM **Privately Held**
SIC: 3315 5199 Hangers (garment), wire; clothes hangers

(P-11465)
WAVENET INC
707 E Sepulveda Blvd, Carson
(90745-6032)
PHONE..............................310 885-4200
Ylhong Jang, *President*
Kevin Chang, *COO*
▲ EMP: 20
SQ FT: 29,000
SALES (est): 18.2MM **Privately Held**
SIC: 3315 Wire & fabricated wire products

(P-11466)
WIRETECH INC (PA)
6440 Canning St, Commerce (90040-3122)
PHONE..............................323 722-4933
William Hillpot, *President*
▲ EMP: 87
SALES (est): 41.2MM **Privately Held**
WEB: www.wiretech.com
SIC: 3315 Steel wire & related products

3316 Cold Rolled Steel Sheet, Strip & Bars

(P-11467)
ARROW STEEL PRODUCTS INC
13171 Santa Ana Ave, Fontana
(92337-6949)
PHONE...................................909 349-1032
Gerald Baldanado, *President*
Jessica Cully, *Director*
EMP: 10
SQ FT: 22,000
SALES (est): 1MM **Privately Held**
SIC: 3316 Cold-rolled strip or wire

(P-11468)
CALSTRIP INDUSTRIES INC (PA)
3030 Dulles Dr, Mira Loma (91752-3240)
PHONE...................................323 726-1345
Thomas B Nelis, *Chairman*
Jon Nelis, *CEO*
Paul Garcia, *Manager*
EMP: 40 **EST:** 1939
SQ FT: 135,000
SALES (est): 160MM **Privately Held**
WEB: www.calstripsteel.com
SIC: 3316 Strip steel, cold-rolled: from purchased hot-rolled; sheet, steel, cold-rolled: from purchased hot-rolled

(P-11469)
DIETRICH INDUSTRIES INC
2525 S Airport Way, Stockton
(95206-3521)
PHONE...................................209 547-9066
Randy Rose, *Manager*
EMP: 56
SALES (corp-wide): 3.5B **Publicly Held**
WEB: www.dietrichmetalframing.com
SIC: 3316 Cold finishing of steel shapes
HQ: Dietrich Industries, Inc.
200 W Old Wilson Bridge Rd
Worthington OH 43085
800 873-2604

(P-11470)
KIP STEEL INC
1650 Valley Ln, Fullerton (92833-1718)
PHONE...................................714 461-1051
EMP: 23
SALES (corp-wide): 2.1MM **Privately Held**
SIC: 3316 Cold finishing of steel shapes
PA: Kip Steel, Inc.
21314 Twisted Willow Ln
Katy TX 77450
714 461-1051

(P-11471)
REMINGTON ROLL FORMING INC
2445 Chico Ave, El Monte (91733-1612)
P.O. Box 9325 (91733-0979)
PHONE...................................626 350-5196
Thomas Henry, *President*
EMP: 15
SQ FT: 25,000
SALES (est): 2.3MM **Privately Held**
SIC: 3316 Cold finishing of steel shapes

(P-11472)
WE HALL COMPANY INC (PA)
Also Called: Pacific Corrugated Pipe Co
471 Old Newport Blvd # 205, Newport Beach (92663-4243)
P.O. Box 15010 (92659-5010)
PHONE...................................949 650-4555
J K Leason, *CEO*
Jim Andre, *President*
EMP: 90
SQ FT: 3,000
SALES (est): 24MM **Privately Held**
WEB: www.pcpipe.com
SIC: 3316 Cold finishing of steel shapes

3317 Steel Pipe & Tubes

(P-11473)
AMERON INTERNATIONAL CORP
Ameron Steel Fabrication
10681 Fthill Blvd Ste 450, Rancho Cucamonga (91730)
PHONE...................................909 944-4100
Richard Kaatz, *Manager*
EMP: 150
SALES (corp-wide): 7.3B **Publicly Held**
WEB: www.ameron.com
SIC: 3317 Steel pipe & tubes
HQ: Ameron International Corporation
7909 Parkwood Circle Dr
Houston TX 77036
713 375-3700

(P-11474)
CALIFORNIA STEEL AND TUBE LLC
16049 Stephens St, City of Industry
(91745-1717)
PHONE...................................626 968-5511
Rick Hirsch, *President*
Ron Prichard, *Vice Pres*
Steve Snodgrass, *Plant Mgr*
EMP: 108 **EST:** 1952
SQ FT: 108,000
SALES (est): 28.4MM
SALES (corp-wide): 7.4B **Privately Held**
WEB: www.californiasteelandtube.com
SIC: 3317 Welded pipe & tubes
HQ: Kloeckner Metals Corporation
500 Colonial Center Pkwy # 500
Roswell GA 30076

(P-11475)
CHARMAN MANUFACTURING INC
5681 S Downey Rd, Vernon (90058-3719)
PHONE...................................213 489-7000
Shahab Namvar, *President*
Shawn Namvar, *President*
Ezra Namvar, *Principal*
David Namvar, *Purchasing*
Don Pascaran, *Marketing Staff*
▲ **EMP:** 23
SALES (est): 4.8MM **Privately Held**
SIC: 3317 Steel pipe & tubes

(P-11476)
COLTRIN INC
4466 Worth St, Los Angeles (90063-2538)
PHONE...................................323 266-6872
Carlos Vega, *President*
Luis Vega, *Manager*
EMP: 10
SALES (est): 1.6MM **Privately Held**
SIC: 3317 Steel pipe & tubes

(P-11477)
CONTECH ENGNERED SOLUTIONS INC
950 S Coast Dr Ste 145, Costa Mesa
(92626-7833)
PHONE...................................714 281-7883
EMP: 1289
SALES (corp-wide): 119.2MM **Privately Held**
SIC: 3317 Steel pipe & tubes
PA: Contech Engineered Solutions Inc.
9025 Ctr Pinte Dr Ste 400
West Chester OH 45069
513 645-7000

(P-11478)
CRITERION AUTOMATION INC
1722 Production Cir, Riverside
(92509-1717)
PHONE...................................951 683-2400
Chris Carda, *President*
Brad Laeger, *Vice Pres*
Christopher J Carda, *Marketing Staff*
EMP: 13
SALES (est): 3.2MM **Privately Held**
WEB: www.criterionautomation.com
SIC: 3317 5719 Steel pipe & tubes; metalware

(P-11479)
HANNIBAL INDUSTRIES INC (PA)
3851 S Santa Fe Ave, Vernon
(90058-1712)
PHONE...................................323 513-1200
Blanton Bartlett, *President*
Heidy Moon, *CFO*
Steve Rogers, *Vice Pres*
David Thang, *Administration*
Mohammad Farooq, *Info Tech Dir*
◆ **EMP:** 214
SQ FT: 285,000
SALES (est): 62.9MM **Privately Held**
WEB: www.hannibalindustries.com
SIC: 3317 Tubes, seamless steel

(P-11480)
IMPERIAL PIPE SERVICES LLC
Also Called: Kelly Pipe Company
12375 Brown Ave, Riverside (92509-1868)
PHONE...................................951 682-3307
Leonard Shapiro,
Bob Raber,
Steve Teller,
EMP: 21
SALES (est): 742.8K
SALES (corp-wide): 72.3MM **Privately Held**
WEB: www.sandhillmgmt.com
SIC: 3317 Steel pipe & tubes
PA: Shapco Inc.
1666 20th St Ste 100
Santa Monica CA 90404
310 264-1666

(P-11481)
K-TUBE CORPORATION
Also Called: K Tube Technologies
13400 Kirkham Way Frnt, Poway
(92064-7167)
PHONE...................................858 513-9229
Greg May, *CEO*
Laurie Montanez, *Admin Asst*
Carl Lindberg, *Info Tech Mgr*
Houman Esmaeilpour, *Technician*
Robert Rubic, *Engineer*
EMP: 100
SQ FT: 75,000
SALES (est): 29.5MM
SALES (corp-wide): 981.1MM **Privately Held**
WEB: www.ktube.com
SIC: 3317 Tubing, mechanical or hypodermic sizes: cold drawn stainless
PA: Cook Group Incorporated
750 N Daniels Way
Bloomington IN 47404
812 339-2235

(P-11482)
MARUICHI AMERICAN CORPORATION
11529 Greenstone Ave, Santa Fe Springs
(90670-4622)
PHONE...................................562 903-8600
Wataru Cho Morita, *President*
Teruo Horikawa, *Ch of Bd*
Yasunori Yoshimura, *CEO*
Mike Ishikawa, *Exec VP*
Makoto Ishikawa, *Vice Pres*
▲ **EMP:** 85
SQ FT: 240,000
SALES (est): 63MM
SALES (corp-wide): 1.4B **Privately Held**
WEB: www.macsfs.com
SIC: 3317 Pipes, seamless steel; tubes, seamless steel
PA: Maruichi Steel Tube Ltd.
5-1-60, Namba, Chuo-Ku
Osaka OSK 542-0
666 438-101

(P-11483)
MASKELL PIPE & SUPPLY INC (PA)
Also Called: Maskell Fusion Tech Services
560 W Rincon St, Corona (92880-2018)
PHONE...................................909 574-8662
Salma Bushala, *CEO*
Ali Boulger, *Principal*
Emily Kouri, *Principal*
▼ **EMP:** 15
SQ FT: 21,000
SALES (est): 5MM **Privately Held**
SIC: 3317 3498 4941 4952 Steel pipe & tubes; fabricated pipe & fittings; pipe fittings, fabricated from purchased pipe; water supply; sewerage systems; heavy construction equipment rental; excavation & grading, building construction

(P-11484)
NORTHWEST PIPE COMPANY
12351 Rancho Rd, Adelanto (92301-2711)
PHONE...................................760 246-3191
Charles Koenig, *Vice Pres*
EMP: 300
SALES (corp-wide): 132.7MM **Publicly Held**
WEB: www.nwpipe.com
SIC: 3317 3321 Pipes, wrought: welded, lock joint or heavy riveted; gray & ductile iron foundries
PA: Northwest Pipe Company
201 Ne Park Plaza Dr # 100
Vancouver WA 98684
360 397-6250

(P-11485)
ROSCOE MOSS MANUFACTURING CO (PA)
Also Called: Roscoe Moss Company
4360 Worth St, Los Angeles (90063-2536)
P.O. Box 31064 (90031-0064)
PHONE...................................323 261-4185
Roscoe Moss Jr, *Ch of Bd*
Robert A Vanvaler, *President*
Tony Creque, *CFO*
George E Moss, *Vice Ch Bd*
Kevin McGillicuddy, *General Mgr*
▼ **EMP:** 90 **EST:** 1913
SQ FT: 20,000
SALES (est): 23.2MM **Privately Held**
WEB: www.roscoemoss.com
SIC: 3317 Well casing, wrought: welded, lock joint or heavy riveted; tubes, wrought: welded or lock joint

(P-11486)
ROSCOE MOSS MANUFACTURING CO
4360 Worth St, Los Angeles (90063-2536)
P.O. Box 31064 (90031-0064)
PHONE...................................323 263-4111
Roscoe Moss Jr, *Ch of Bd*
Robert V Valer, *President*
George E Moss, *Vice Ch Bd*
EMP: 80
SQ FT: 20,000
SALES (est): 4.5MM
SALES (corp-wide): 23.2MM **Privately Held**
WEB: www.roscoemoss.com
SIC: 3317 Steel pipe & tubes
PA: Roscoe Moss Manufacturing Company
4360 Worth St
Los Angeles CA 90063
323 261-4185

(P-11487)
SUPERIOR TECH INC
Also Called: Superior Technologies
13850 Benson Ave, Chino (91710-7005)
PHONE...................................909 364-2300
Peter Chifo, *Principal*
Allen Roe, *Opers Staff*
EMP: 16
SALES (est): 2.9MM **Privately Held**
WEB: www.superior-tech.net
SIC: 3317 Tubes, wrought: welded or lock joint

(P-11488)
TUBE ONE INDUSTRIES INC
4055 Garner Rd, Riverside (92501-1043)
PHONE...................................951 300-2998
Kimber Liu, *CEO*
Susan Liu, *Vice Pres*
Richard Liu, *Regl Sales Mgr*
Patrick Liu, *Manager*
▲ **EMP:** 15
SQ FT: 46,000
SALES (est): 3.4MM **Privately Held**
SIC: 3317 Steel pipe & tubes

▲ = Import ▼=Export
◆ =Import/Export

(P-11489)
VALLEY METALS LLC
Also Called: Leggett & Platt 0768
13125 Gregg St, Poway (92064-7122)
P.O. Box 85402, San Diego (92186-5402)
PHONE....................................858 513-1300
Kirk Nelson, *Mng Member*
EMP: 40 EST: 1946
SQ FT: 47,700
SALES (est): 11.4MM
SALES (corp-wide): 3.9B **Publicly Held**
WEB: www.valleymetals.com
SIC: 3317 Tubes, wrought: welded or lock
joint
HQ: Western Pneumatic Tube Company,
Llc
835 6th St S
Kirkland WA 98033
425 822-8271

(P-11490)
VEST INC
6023 Alcoa Ave, Vernon (90058-3954)
P.O. Box 58827, Los Angeles (90058-0827)
PHONE....................................800 421-6370
Kenji Morita, *CEO*
Iwaki Sugimoto, *President*
Hide Yamada, *President*
Sam Fukazawa, *CFO*
▲ EMP: 77
SQ FT: 312,000
SALES (est): 828.9K
SALES (corp-wide): 34.5B **Privately Held**
WEB: www.vestinc.com
SIC: 3317 3547 Tubes, wrought: welded
or lock joint; rolling mill machinery
HQ: Shoji Jfe Trade America Inc
301 E Ocean Blvd Ste 1750
Long Beach CA 90802
562 637-3500

3321 Gray Iron Foundries

(P-11491)
**ALHAMBRA FOUNDRY
COMPANY LTD**
Also Called: Afco
1147 S Meridian Ave, Alhambra
(91803-1218)
P.O. Box 469 (91802-0469)
PHONE....................................626 289-4294
Arzhang Baghkhanian, *CEO*
James Wright, *Vice Pres*
Mike Smalski, *General Mgr*
▲ EMP: 46
SQ FT: 48,370
SALES: 8MM **Privately Held**
WEB: www.alhambrafoundry.com
SIC: 3321 3312 5051 Gray iron castings;
structural shapes & pilings, steel; iron &
steel (ferrous) products; cast iron pipe;
steel

(P-11492)
EJ USA INC
2020 W 14th St, Long Beach (90813-1042)
PHONE....................................562 528-0258
Aess Illes, *Branch Mgr*
EMP: 12 **Privately Held**
SIC: 3321 Manhole covers, metal
HQ: Ej Usa, Inc.
301 Spring St
East Jordan MI 49727
800 874-4100

(P-11493)
FOX HILLS INDUSTRIES
5831 Research Dr, Huntington Beach
(92649-1385)
PHONE....................................714 893-1940
John Burk, *President*
Doug Reichard, *President*
Raj Mittal, *Vice Pres*
Frank Reilly, *Vice Pres*
Raj Mintill, *Administration*
▲ EMP: 25
SQ FT: 20,000
SALES (est): 6.1MM **Privately Held**
SIC: 3321 3366 3365 3322 Ductile iron
castings; castings (except die): brass; alu-
minum foundries; malleable iron foundries

(P-11494)
**GLOBE IRON FOUNDRY INC
(PA)**
5649 Randolph St, Commerce
(90040-3489)
PHONE....................................323 723-8983
John M Pratto, *President*
Othon Garcia, *CFO*
John Pratto Jr, *Vice Pres*
Jeff Pratto, *VP Sales*
Mike Gaston, *Maintence Staff*
EMP: 64
SQ FT: 58,000
SALES (est): 13.3MM **Privately Held**
WEB: www.globeiron.com
SIC: 3321 3543 3369 Gray iron castings;
ductile iron castings; industrial patterns;
nonferrous foundries

(P-11495)
JDH PACIFIC INC (PA)
14821 Artesia Blvd, La Mirada
(90638-6006)
PHONE....................................562 926-8088
Donald Hu, *President*
▲ EMP: 30
SQ FT: 103,000
SALES (est): 33.4MM **Privately Held**
SIC: 3321 3324 3599 3462 Gray iron
castings; commercial investment cast-
ings, ferrous; crankshafts & camshafts,
machining; iron & steel forgings; machin-
ery forgings, ferrous

(P-11496)
LODI IRON WORKS INC (PA)
Also Called: Galt Steel Foundry
820 S Sacramento St, Lodi (95240-4710)
P.O. Box 1150 (95241-1150)
PHONE....................................209 368-5395
Kevin Van Steenberge, *President*
Michael Van Steenberge, *Vice Pres*
Michael Vansteenberg, *Purch Mgr*
Mike Van Steenberge, *VP Mfg*
Gwen Krenecki, *Director*
EMP: 46 EST: 1943
SQ FT: 11,000
SALES (est): 13.4MM **Privately Held**
WEB: www.lodiiron.com
SIC: 3321 3312 Gray iron castings; stain-
less steel

(P-11497)
LODI IRON WORKS INC
Also Called: Galt Steel Foundry
609 W Amador St, Galt (95632)
PHONE....................................209 368-5395
Ken Degrammont, *Manager*
Kevin Van Steenberge, *President*
EMP: 10
SALES (corp-wide): 13.4MM **Privately
Held**
WEB: www.lodiiron.com
SIC: 3321 3312 Gray & ductile iron
foundries; stainless steel
PA: Lodi Iron Works, Inc.
820 S Sacramento St
Lodi CA 95240
209 368-5395

(P-11498)
MCWANE INC (PA)
Also Called: AB & I Foundry
7825 San Leandro St, Oakland
(94621-2515)
PHONE....................................510 632-3467
Allan Boscacci, *President*
Clifford Wixson, *Ch of Bd*
John Callagy, *CFO*
Kevin McCullough, *Vice Pres*
Patricia Boscacci, *Admin Sec*
▲ EMP: 195 EST: 1906
SQ FT: 150,000
SALES (est): 38.2MM **Privately Held**
WEB: www.abifoundry.com
SIC: 3321 3494 Soil pipe & fittings: cast
iron; gray iron castings; valves & pipe fit-
tings

(P-11499)
MESA CASTINGS INC (PA)
Also Called: Mesa Machining
22401 Harwich Ln, Huntington Beach
(92646-8449)
P.O. Box 530900, San Diego (92153-0900)
PHONE....................................714 962-1064

Gary Harrison, *CEO*
Ramiro Valenzuela, *Administration*
EMP: 124
SQ FT: 35,000
SALES (est): 14.5MM **Privately Held**
WEB: www.mesacastings.com
SIC: 3321 Gray & ductile iron foundries

(P-11500)
RIDGE FOUNDRY INC
Also Called: Ridge Cast Metals
1554 Doolittle Dr, San Leandro
(94577-2271)
PHONE....................................510 352-0551
Norman Stamm, *President*
Zaffar Khan, *Comptroller*
EMP: 20 EST: 1956
SQ FT: 25,000
SALES (est): 3.6MM **Privately Held**
SIC: 3321 3325 3369 3365 Gray iron
castings; ductile iron castings; steel
foundries; nonferrous foundries; alu-
minum foundries; malleable iron foundries

(P-11501)
THOMPSON GUNDRILLING INC
13840 Saticoy St, Van Nuys (91402-6582)
PHONE....................................323 873-4045
Michael Thompson, *President*
Virginia Ramsey, *CFO*
Pablo Gonlaez, *Engineer*
Robert Thompson, *Director*
EMP: 39
SQ FT: 32,000
SALES (est): 3.4MM **Privately Held**
WEB: www.thompsongundrilling.com
SIC: 3321 Gray & ductile iron foundries

(P-11502)
ULTRACAST LLC
3701 E Conant St, Long Beach
(90808-1783)
PHONE....................................860 253-5015
Jay Horrocks,
Rick Ginsburg,
EMP: 26
SALES (est): 4.1MM **Privately Held**
WEB: www.ultracast.com
SIC: 3321 Cast iron pipe & fittings

3322 Malleable Iron Foundries

(P-11503)
COVERT IRON WORKS
7821 Otis S Ave, Huntington Park (90255)
PHONE....................................323 560-2792
Fax: 323 560-8351
EMP: 19 EST: 1923
SQ FT: 20,000
SALES (est): 2.2MM **Privately Held**
WEB: www.covertironworks.com
SIC: 3322 3321

(P-11504)
**STEVEN HANDELMAN STUDIOS
(PA)**
Also Called: Handelman, Steven Studios
716 N Milpas St, Santa Barbara
(93103-3029)
PHONE....................................805 884-9070
Steven Handelman, *Owner*
EMP: 50 EST: 1973
SALES (est): 8.7MM **Privately Held**
WEB: www.stevenhandelmanstudios.com
SIC: 3322 Malleable iron foundries

3324 Steel Investment Foundries

(P-11505)
**ACCURATE PRFMCE
MACHINING INC**
2255 S Grand Ave, Santa Ana
(92705-5206)
PHONE....................................714 434-7811
Robert Keith Fischer, *CEO*
Karen Fischer, *Treasurer*
Larry Taylor, *Vice Pres*
Chris Straub, *Sales Staff*
EMP: 21 EST: 1996
SQ FT: 3,200

SALES (est): 4.7MM **Privately Held**
SIC: 3324 Aerospace investment castings,
ferrous

(P-11506)
**ALIGN AEROSPACE HOLDING
INC (DH)**
21123 Nordhoff St, Chatsworth
(91311-5816)
PHONE....................................818 727-7800
Jerome De Truchis, *President*
You Lei, *COO*
Pan Linwu, *CFO*
Chen Hongliang, *Exec VP*
EMP: 11
SALES (est): 114.7MM **Privately Held**
SIC: 3324 Aerospace investment castings,
ferrous
HQ: Avic International Zhuhai Co., Ltd.
Inside Of Airchina Area, Jiuzhou
Boulevard
Zhuhai 51901
756 323-3222

(P-11507)
**ARCONIC GLOBAL FAS & RINGS
INC**
Arconic Fstening Systems Rings
800 S State College Blvd, Fullerton
(92831-5334)
PHONE....................................714 871-1550
Craig Brown, *Manager*
EMP: 100
SALES (corp-wide): 12.9B **Publicly Held**
SIC: 3324 3365 Aerospace investment
castings, ferrous; aerospace castings,
aluminum
HQ: Arconic Global Fasteners & Rings, Inc.
3990a Heritage Oak Ct
Simi Valley CA 93063
805 527-3600

(P-11508)
CAST PARTS INC (DH)
Also Called: Cpp-Pomona
4200 Valley Blvd, Walnut (91789-1408)
PHONE....................................909 595-2252
Steve Clodfelter, *President*
Ali Ghavami, *COO*
EMP: 185
SQ FT: 300,000
SALES (est): 59.5MM
SALES (corp-wide): 6.3B **Privately Held**
WEB: www.castparts.com
SIC: 3324 3365 Steel investment
foundries; aluminum foundries
HQ: Consolidated Precision Products Corp.
1621 Euclid Ave Ste 1850
Cleveland OH 44115
216 453-4800

(P-11509)
CAST PARTS INC
Also Called: Cpp-City of Industry
16800 Chestnut St, City of Industry
(91748-1017)
PHONE....................................626 937-3444
David Atwood, *Branch Mgr*
Gloria Arballo, *Purchasing*
Karen Beck-Ashley, *QC Mgr*
EMP: 160
SALES (corp-wide): 6.3B **Privately Held**
SIC: 3324 Aerospace investment castings,
ferrous
HQ: Cast Parts, Inc.
4200 Valley Blvd
Walnut CA 91789
909 595-2252

(P-11510)
**CIRCOR AEROSPACE PDTS
GROUP**
2301 Wardlow Cir, Corona (92880-2801)
PHONE....................................951 270-6200
Scott Buckhout, *President*
Pritesh Patel, *Info Tech Dir*
EMP: 300
SALES (est): 17.8MM
SALES (corp-wide): 661.7MM **Publicly
Held**
SIC: 3324 Aerospace investment castings,
ferrous
PA: Circor International, Inc.
30 Corporate Dr Ste 200
Burlington MA 01803
781 270-1200

PRODUCTS & SVCS

(P-11511)
CONSOLIDATED FOUNDRIES INC
Also Called: C P P
4200 W Valley Blvd, Pomona (91769)
PHONE..................................909 595-2252
Steve Clodfelter, *President*
Benjamin Mahr, *Vice Pres*
Hoang Nguyen, *Info Tech Mgr*
Robert Abban, *Engineer*
Patrick Knudson, *Engineer*
▲ EMP: 44
SALES (est): 13.6MM **Privately Held**
SIC: 3324 Aerospace investment castings, ferrous

(P-11512)
IMAGE CASTING INC
131 Lombard St, Oxnard (93030-5161)
PHONE..................................805 986-1106
Steve Bowles, *President*
Francisco Marroquin, *Vice Pres*
Pat Bhave, *VP Sales*
EMP: 45
SQ FT: 12,000
SALES (est): 6.1MM **Privately Held**
WEB: www.imagecastings.com
SIC: 3324 Steel investment foundries

(P-11513)
KRALLCAST INC
16205 Ward Way, City of Industry (91745-1715)
PHONE..................................626 333-0678
Anthony Krallman, *President*
EMP: 12
SQ FT: 12,000
SALES (est): 1.2MM **Privately Held**
WEB: www.krallcast.com
SIC: 3324 Commercial investment castings, ferrous

(P-11514)
MCDANIEL INC
10807 Monte Vista Ave, Montclair (91763-6113)
PHONE..................................909 591-8353
Timothy McDaniel, *President*
Shelly McDaniel, *Vice Pres*
Dave Davidson, *Supervisor*
EMP: 16
SALES (est): 4.6MM **Privately Held**
SIC: 3324 Steel investment foundries

(P-11515)
MILLER CASTINGS INC (PA)
2503 Pacific Park Dr, Whittier (90601-1680)
PHONE..................................562 695-0461
Ralph Miller, *President*
Hadi Khandehroo, *CEO*
Adrian Zuniga, *Admin Asst*
Bahman Khandehroo, *Engineer*
▲ EMP: 97
SQ FT: 40,000
SALES (est): 75.4MM **Privately Held**
WEB: www.millercastings.com
SIC: 3324 Steel investment foundries

(P-11516)
MILLER CASTINGS INC
12251 Coast Dr, Whittier (90601-1608)
PHONE..................................562 695-0461
EMP: 10
SALES (corp-wide): 75.4MM **Privately Held**
SIC: 3324 Steel investment foundries
PA: Miller Castings, Inc.
  2503 Pacific Park Dr
  Whittier CA 90601
  562 695-0461

(P-11517)
MODERN PATTERN & FNDRY CO INC
5610 Alcoa Ave, Vernon (90058-3793)
PHONE..................................323 583-4921
Roland B Meckel, *President*
Carol Meckel, *Corp Secy*
Christina Haidet, *Executive Asst*
EMP: 46
SQ FT: 42,000

SALES (est): 8.4MM **Privately Held**
SIC: 3324 3369 Steel investment foundries; castings, except die-castings, precision

(P-11518)
NET SHAPES INC
1336 E Francis St Ste B, Ontario (91761-5723)
PHONE..................................909 947-3231
Joseph S Cannone, *President*
Cordy Champan, *QA Dir*
Jaime Venturina, *Purch Dir*
Sonja Norvaez, *Sales Executive*
EMP: 120
SQ FT: 43,500
SALES (est): 25.6MM **Privately Held**
WEB: www.netshapes.com
SIC: 3324 Steel investment foundries

(P-11519)
PAC-RANCHO INC (DH)
11000 Jersey Blvd, Rancho Cucamonga (91730-5103)
PHONE..................................909 987-4721
Steve Clodfelter, *President*
Ali Ghavami, *Vice Pres*
Jodi Miller, *Info Tech Mgr*
Andy Bose, *Manager*
EMP: 180
SQ FT: 55,000
SALES (est): 20.3MM
SALES (corp-wide): 6.3B **Privately Held**
SIC: 3324 3354 3369 Commercial investment castings, ferrous; aluminum extruded products; nonferrous foundries
HQ: Consolidated Precision Products Corp.
  1621 Euclid Ave Ste 1850
  Cleveland OH 44115
  216 453-4800

(P-11520)
PACIFIC COMPOSITES INC
221 Calle Pintoresco, San Clemente (92672-7505)
PHONE..................................949 498-8600
EMP: 12
SQ FT: 12,000
SALES: 1.5MM **Privately Held**
SIC: 3324

(P-11521)
REED MANUFACTURING INC
Also Called: American Casting Co
51 Fallon Rd, Hollister (95023-9401)
PHONE..................................831 637-5641
John Reed, *President*
Simeon Bauer, *Vice Pres*
Chris St John, *Vice Pres*
Jeff Ferrara, *Engineer*
EMP: 35
SQ FT: 7,200
SALES (est): 8.6MM **Privately Held**
WEB: www.americancastingco.com
SIC: 3324 Commercial investment castings, ferrous

(P-11522)
SIERRA TECHNICAL SERVICES INC
Also Called: STS
101 Commercial Way Apt D, Tehachapi (93561-1427)
PHONE..................................661 823-1092
Roger Hayes, *President*
Debra Hayes, *Vice Pres*
EMP: 15
SQ FT: 7,000
SALES: 1.8MM **Privately Held**
SIC: 3324 8711 Aerospace investment castings, ferrous; engineering services

3325 Steel Foundries, NEC

(P-11523)
CALIFORNIA ELECTRIC STEEL
250 Monte Verda, Angels Camp (95222)
PHONE..................................209 736-0465
Norman Stamm, *President*
Lorne Whittle, *President*
Joanne Whittle, *Corp Secy*
Donna Stamm, *Vice Pres*
EMP: 24 EST: 1854
SQ FT: 10,000

SALES (est): 5.5MM **Privately Held**
SIC: 3325 Alloy steel castings, except investment

(P-11524)
DAMERON ALLOY FOUNDRIES (PA)
6330 Gateway Dr Ste B, Cypress (90630-4836)
PHONE..................................310 631-5165
John W Dameron, *President*
Augustin Huerta, *Exec VP*
Joseph De Julio, *Vice Pres*
▲ EMP: 100 EST: 1946
SQ FT: 5,000
SALES (est): 22.1MM **Privately Held**
WEB: www.dameron.net
SIC: 3325 3324 Steel foundries; commercial investment castings, ferrous

(P-11525)
LIQUIDMETAL TECHNOLOGIES INC (PA)
20321 Valencia Cir, Lake Forest (92630-8159)
PHONE..................................949 635-2100
Lugee LI, *Ch of Bd*
Bruce Bromage, *COO*
Abdi Mahamedi, *Vice Ch Bd*
Bryce Van, *VP Finance*
▲ EMP: 28
SQ FT: 41,000
SALES: 321K **Publicly Held**
SIC: 3325 Alloy steel castings, except investment

(P-11526)
METAL CAST INC
Also Called: Metalcast
2002 W Chestnut Ave, Santa Ana (92703-4341)
PHONE..................................714 285-9792
Rigoberto Urquiza, *President*
EMP: 20
SQ FT: 12,000
SALES (est): 3.7MM **Privately Held**
SIC: 3325 Alloy steel castings, except investment

(P-11527)
STRATEGIC MATERIALS CORP
8616 Otis St, South Gate (90280-3220)
P.O. Box 1606 (90280-1606)
PHONE..................................323 567-2195
Steven Livingston, *President*
Earl Deeble, *Admin Sec*
EMP: 38
SQ FT: 34,000
SALES (est): 8.1MM **Privately Held**
WEB: www.smccast.com
SIC: 3325 Steel foundries

(P-11528)
TUSCO CASTING CORPORATION
934 E Victor Rd, Lodi (95240-0722)
P.O. Box 537 (95241-0537)
PHONE..................................209 368-5137
Kevin Steiger, *President*
Tanen Steiger, *Vice Pres*
EMP: 20 EST: 1965
SQ FT: 20,000
SALES (est): 3.7MM **Privately Held**
SIC: 3325 3365 3322 Alloy steel castings, except investment; aluminum foundries; malleable iron foundries

(P-11529)
WEST COAST FOUNDRY LLC (HQ)
2450 E 53rd St, Huntington Park (90255)
PHONE..................................323 583-1421
Michael Bargani, *President*
John Heine, *CFO*
▲ EMP: 20
SQ FT: 18,000
SALES (est): 10.6MM
SALES (corp-wide): 112MM **Privately Held**
SIC: 3325 Alloy steel castings, except investment
PA: Speyside Equity Fund I Lp
  430 E 86th St
  New York NY 10028
  212 994-0308

(P-11530)
WEST COAST STEEL & PROC LLC (PA)
Also Called: Steelco USA
3534 Philadelphia St, Chino (91710-2088)
PHONE..................................909 393-8405
Erik Gamm,
EMP: 75
SALES (est): 20.5MM **Privately Held**
SIC: 3325 Steel foundries

3331 Primary Smelting & Refining Of Copper

(P-11531)
CORRPRO COMPANIES INC
10260 Matern Pl, Santa Fe Springs (90670-3248)
PHONE..................................562 944-1636
Randy Galinski, *Principal*
Elena Vanroggen, *Engineer*
EMP: 21
SALES (corp-wide): 1.3B **Publicly Held**
WEB: www.corrpro.com
SIC: 3331 1799 Cathodes (primary), copper; corrosion control installation
HQ: Corrpro Companies, Inc.
  1055 W Smith Rd
  Medina OH 44256
  330 723-5082

3334 Primary Production Of Aluminum

(P-11532)
ADVANCED PATTERN & MOLD
1720 S Balboa Ave, Ontario (91761-7773)
PHONE..................................909 930-3444
Dan Hilger, *Partner*
Chris Vanderhagen, *Partner*
EMP: 15
SQ FT: 10,400
SALES (est): 2.3MM **Privately Held**
WEB: www.advancedpattern.com
SIC: 3334 Primary aluminum

(P-11533)
ALCOA INC
1300 Rancho Conejo Blvd, Newbury Park (91320-1405)
PHONE..................................805 498-4594
Jacob Dwood, *Branch Mgr*
EMP: 427
SALES (corp-wide): 12.9B **Publicly Held**
SIC: 3334 Primary aluminum
PA: Arconic Inc.
  390 Park Ave Fl 12
  New York NY 10022
  212 836-2758

(P-11534)
ARCONIC INC
Also Called: Alcoa
1300 Rancho Conejo Blvd, Newbury Park (91320-1405)
PHONE..................................805 262-4230
EMP: 427
SALES (corp-wide): 12.9B **Publicly Held**
SIC: 3334 Primary aluminum
PA: Arconic Inc.
  390 Park Ave Fl 12
  New York NY 10022
  212 836-2758

(P-11535)
ARCONIC INC
Also Called: Alcoa
800 S State College Blvd, Fullerton (92831-5334)
PHONE..................................714 871-1550
Ui Choi, *Branch Mgr*
Phillip Lee, *Technology*
Richard Kohli, *Engineer*
Genevieve Retamosa, *Engineer*
Bernie Rios, *Engineer*
EMP: 427
SALES (corp-wide): 12.9B **Publicly Held**
SIC: 3334 Primary aluminum
PA: Arconic Inc.
  390 Park Ave Fl 12
  New York NY 10022
  212 836-2758

(P-11536)
ARCONIC INC
Also Called: Alcoa
801 S Placentia Ave, Fullerton
(92831-5153)
PHONE.............................714 278-8981
Anne Brown, *Director*
EMP: 427
SALES (corp-wide): 12.9B **Publicly Held**
SIC: 3334 Primary aluminum
PA: Arconic Inc.
390 Park Ave Fl 12
New York NY 10022
212 836-2758

(P-11537)
ARCONIC INC
Also Called: Alcoa
3016 Lomita Blvd, Torrance (90505-5103)
PHONE.............................212 836-2674
Quan Tran, *Manager*
EMP: 427
SALES (corp-wide): 12.9B **Publicly Held**
SIC: 3334 Primary aluminum
PA: Arconic Inc.
390 Park Ave Fl 12
New York NY 10022
212 836-2758

(P-11538)
ARCONIC INC
Also Called: Alcoa
12975 Bradley Ave, Sylmar (91342-3830)
PHONE.............................818 367-2261
James Costello, *President*
Natanael Orellana, *Engineer*
EMP: 427
SALES (corp-wide): 12.9B **Publicly Held**
SIC: 3334 Primary aluminum
PA: Arconic Inc.
390 Park Ave Fl 12
New York NY 10022
212 836-2758

(P-11539)
KAISER ALUMINUM
CORPORATION (PA)
27422 Portola Pkwy # 350, Foothill Ranch
(92610-2837)
PHONE.............................949 614-1740
Jack A Hockema, *Ch of Bd*
Keith A Harvey, *President*
Daniel J Rinkenberger, *CFO*
Melinda C Ellsworth, *Treasurer*
Courtney RB Lynn, *Treasurer*
▼ EMP: 60
SQ FT: 36,000
SALES: 1.4B **Publicly Held**
WEB: www.kaiseral.com
SIC: 3334 3353 3354 3355 Primary alu-
minum; aluminum sheet, plate & foil; alu-
minum rod & bar; bars, extruded,
aluminum; rods, extruded, aluminum;
wire, aluminum: made in rolling mills;
cable, aluminum: made in rolling mills

(P-11540)
MAURICE & MAURICE ENGRG
INC
17579 Mesa St Ste B4, Hesperia
(92345-8308)
P.O. Box 403682 (92340-3682)
PHONE.............................760 949-5151
Jennifer Thomas, *CEO*
Aron Maurice, *Treasurer*
Jennifer Maurice, *Admin Sec*
EMP: 27 EST: 1973
SQ FT: 22,000
SALES: 2MM **Privately Held**
WEB: www.mauricemawer.com
SIC: 3334 Primary aluminum

(P-11541)
PRL ALUMINUM INC
14760 Don Julian Rd, City of Industry
(91746-3107)
PHONE.............................626 968-7507
Roberto Landeros, *CEO*
Aamer Javaid, *Info Tech Dir*
Monica Borges, *Sales Staff*
David Olague, *Sales Staff*
EMP: 100

SALES (est): 24.3MM
SALES (corp-wide): 71.8MM **Privately Held**
SIC: 3334 Primary aluminum
PA: Prl Glass Systems, Inc.
13644 Nelson Ave
City Of Industry CA 91746
626 961-5890

┌─────────────────────────────┐
│ **3339 Primary Nonferrous** │
│   **Metals, NEC**   │
└─────────────────────────────┘

(P-11542)
A D S GOLD INC
3843 E Eagle Dr, Anaheim (92807-1705)
PHONE.............................714 632-1888
Patrick Joe Lopez, *CEO*
Nancy Lopez, *Office Mgr*
EMP: 14
SQ FT: 8,600
SALES (est): 3.3MM **Privately Held**
WEB: www.adsgold.com
SIC: 3339 Precious metals

(P-11543)
ARGEN CORPORATION (PA)
Also Called: Jelenko
5855 Oberlin Dr, San Diego (92121-3706)
PHONE.............................858 455-7900
Anton Woolf, *CEO*
Lou Azzara, *President*
Jackie Woolf, *President*
Jay Lowy, *COO*
Neil Wainstein, *CFO*
▲ EMP: 203
SQ FT: 39,609
SALES (est): 57.6MM **Privately Held**
WEB: www.argen.com
SIC: 3339 3843 Precious metals; dental
equipment & supplies

(P-11544)
COMMODITY RESOURCE
ENVMTL INC
Also Called: Commodity Rsource Enviromen-
tal
11847 United St, Mojave (93501-7047)
PHONE.............................661 824-2416
Mike Kelsey, *Manager*
EMP: 44
SALES (est): 6MM
SALES (corp-wide): 13.7MM **Privately Held**
SIC: 3339 3341 Precious metals; second-
ary nonferrous metals
PA: Commodity Resource & Environmental,
Inc.
116 E Prospect Ave
Burbank CA 91502
818 843-2811

(P-11545)
FOREM MANUFACTURING INC
Also Called: Forem Metal
844 66th Ave, Oakland (94621-3716)
PHONE.............................510 577-9500
Roland Maynard, *President*
EMP: 12
SALES (est): 1.1MM **Privately Held**
SIC: 3339

(P-11546)
IRA GOLD GROUP LLC
9107 Wilshire Blvd # 450, Beverly Hills
(90210-5531)
PHONE.............................800 984-6008
Robert Smith, *Partner*
EMP: 10
SALES: 15MM **Privately Held**
SIC: 3339 Precious metals

(P-11547)
J & B REFINING INC
Also Called: J & B Enterprises
1650 Russell Ave, Santa Clara
(95054-2031)
PHONE.............................408 988-7900
Ken Epsman, *President*
Javier Espinosa, *Accounts Mgr*
EMP: 10 EST: 1973
SQ FT: 22,000
SALES (est): 1.7MM **Privately Held**
WEB: www.jandb.com
SIC: 3339 Precious metals

(P-11548)
NL INDUSTRIES INC
Also Called: Axel Johnson Metals
403 Ryder St, Vallejo (94590-7269)
PHONE.............................707 552-4850
Howard Harcker, *Vice Pres*
EMP: 40
SALES (corp-wide): 112MM **Publicly Held**
SIC: 3339 3341 Titanium metal, sponge &
granules; secondary nonferrous metals
PA: N L Industries, Inc.
5430 Lbj Fwy Ste 1700
Dallas TX 75240
972 233-1700

(P-11549)
PCC ROLLMET INC
1822 Deere Ave, Irvine (92606-4817)
PHONE.............................949 221-5333
Ken Buck, *President*
Mark Donegan, *Ch of Bd*
Shawn Hagel, *CFO*
EMI Donis, *Vice Pres*
EMP: 70
SALES (est): 21.4MM
SALES (corp-wide): 242.1B **Publicly Held**
SIC: 3339 Nickel refining (primary)
HQ: Precision Castparts Corp.
4650 Sw Mcdam Ave Ste 300
Portland OR 97239
503 946-4800

(P-11550)
SUPERIOR QUARTZ INC
Also Called: Silica Engineering Group
3370 Edward Ave, Santa Clara
(95054-2309)
PHONE.............................408 844-9663
Nermin Aganbegovic, *President*
Mirela Aganbegovic, *Business Dir*
EMP: 15
SQ FT: 13,000
SALES: 6.4MM **Privately Held**
WEB: www.silicaeng.com
SIC: 3339 3679 3264 Silicon, pure; quartz
crystals, for electronic application; mag-
nets, permanent: ceramic or ferrite

(P-11551)
WESTERN MESQUITE MINES
INC
6502 E Us Highway 78, Brawley
(92227-9306)
PHONE.............................928 341-4653
Randall Oliphant, *Chairman*
Cory Atiyeh, *President*
Robert Gallagher, *CEO*
W Hanson P Geo, *Vice Pres*
Penny Brian, *Admin Sec*
EMP: 20
SALES (est): 14MM
SALES (corp-wide): 604.4MM **Privately Held**
SIC: 3339 Gold refining (primary)
PA: New Gold Inc
181 Bay St Suite 3510
Toronto ON M5J 2
416 324-6000

┌─────────────────────────────┐
│ **3341 Secondary Smelting &** │
│   **Refining Of Nonferrous** │
│   **Metals**   │
└─────────────────────────────┘

(P-11552)
ALL METALS INC (PA)
Also Called: Ecs Refining
705 Reed St, Santa Clara (95050-3942)
PHONE.............................408 200-7000
James L Taggart, *President*
Kenneth Taggart, *Vice Pres*
Thomas Hogye, *Business Dir*
▲ EMP: 20 EST: 1980
SQ FT: 24,000
SALES (est): 11.6MM **Privately Held**
WEB: www.allmetals.com
SIC: 3341 4953 3339 Secondary precious
metals; tin smelting & refining (sec-
ondary); lead smelting & refining (sec-
ondary); silver recovery from used
photographic film; refuse systems; pri-
mary nonferrous metals

(P-11553)
AQUA METALS INC (PA)
1010 Atlantic Ave, Alameda (94501-1147)
PHONE.............................510 479-7635
Stephen Cotton, *President*
S Shariq Yosufzai, *Ch of Bd*
Selwyn Mould, *COO*
Judd Merrill, *CFO*
EMP: 69
SQ FT: 21,697
SALES: 2MM **Publicly Held**
SIC: 3341 Lead smelting & refining (sec-
ondary)

(P-11554)
CUSTOM ALLOY SALES INC
(PA)
Also Called: Custom Alloy Light Metals
13191 Crssrds Pkwy N 37, City of Industry
(91746)
PHONE.............................626 369-3641
Brandon J Cox, *CEO*
Kenneth J Cox, *President*
Tim Chisum, *CFO*
Nicholas Drakos, *Vice Pres*
Maria Marquez, *Human Res Dir*
◆ EMP: 80
SALES: 150MM **Privately Held**
WEB: www.customingot.com
SIC: 3341 5051 Aluminum smelting & re-
fining (secondary); zinc

(P-11555)
DAVID H FELL & CO INC (PA)
6009 Bandini Blvd, Los Angeles
(90040-2967)
PHONE.............................323 722-9992
Larry Fell, *CEO*
Lawrence Fell, *President*
Sondra Fell, *Treasurer*
▼ EMP: 24
SQ FT: 18,000
SALES (est): 4.5MM **Privately Held**
WEB: www.dhfco.com
SIC: 3341 5094 Secondary precious met-
als; bullion, precious metals

(P-11556)
ESPERER HOLDINGS INC (PA)
3820 State St, Santa Barbara
(93105-3182)
PHONE.............................805 880-4220
D Stephen Sorensen, *CEO*
Julie Danley, *Director*
EMP: 20 EST: 2011
SALES (est): 3.8MM **Privately Held**
SIC: 3341 3911 Secondary precious met-
als; jewelry, precious metal; medals, pre-
cious or semiprecious metal

(P-11557)
GEMINI INDUSTRIES INC
2311 Pullman St, Santa Ana (92705-5585)
PHONE.............................949 250-4011
M Elguindy, *CEO*
Melinda Munoz, *CFO*
Melissa Jones, *Executive*
Diana Keiffer, *Admin Sec*
John Estrada, *Manager*
▲ EMP: 75
SQ FT: 150,000
SALES (est): 17.9MM **Privately Held**
SIC: 3341 Secondary precious metals;
platinum group metals, smelting & refining
(secondary)

(P-11558)
GPS METALS LAB INC
12396 World Trade Dr, San Diego
(92128-3786)
PHONE.............................858 433-6125
Christian Galvis, *Principal*
Miguel Palomino, *President*
EMP: 30
SALES (est): 1.5MM **Privately Held**
SIC: 3341 5051 5093 3339 Secondary
precious metals; recovery & refining of
nonferrous metals; nonferrous metal
sheets, bars, rods, etc.; nonferrous met-
als scrap; precious metals

(P-11559)
HERAEUS PRCOUS MTLS N AMER LLC (DH)
15524 Carmenita Rd, Santa Fe Springs (90670-5610)
PHONE..................562 921-7464
Roland Gerner, *Mng Member*
Harriet Bachman, *Administration*
Marlon Mendoza, *Research*
Nicole Taylor, *Research*
Fernando Aurea Jr, *Engineer*
▲ EMP: 200
SQ FT: 71,000
SALES (est): 70.1MM **Privately Held**
WEB: www.heraeusca.com
SIC: 3341 2899 Gold smelting & refining (secondary); silver smelting & refining (secondary); platinum group metals, smelting & refining (secondary); chemical preparations; salt
HQ: Heraeus Holding Gesellschaft Mit Beschrankter Haftung
Heraeusstr. 12-14
Hanau 63450
618 135-0

(P-11560)
MATTHEY JOHNSON INC
Also Called: Noble Metals
12205 World Trade Dr, San Diego (92128-3766)
P.O. Box Orld Trade (92128)
PHONE..................858 716-2400
Steve Hill, *Branch Mgr*
Chris Craft, *Info Tech Dir*
Zane Wyatt, *Engineer*
Bernie Caseja, *Purch Agent*
Dan Faupel, *Manager*
EMP: 139
SALES (corp-wide): 19.7B **Privately Held**
SIC: 3341 Secondary nonferrous metals
HQ: Matthey Johnson Inc
435 Devon Park Dr Ste 600
Wayne PA 19087
610 971-3000

(P-11561)
MATTHEY JOHNSON INC
12205 World Trade Dr, San Diego (92128-3766)
PHONE..................858 716-2400
Brian Woodward, *Manager*
EMP: 111
SALES (corp-wide): 15B **Privately Held**
SIC: 3341 5047 Secondary nonferrous metals; medical equipment & supplies
HQ: Matthey Johnson Inc
435 Devon Park Dr Ste 600
Wayne PA 19087
610 971-3000

(P-11562)
METECH RECYCLING INC
6200 Engle Way, Gilroy (95020-7012)
PHONE..................408 848-3050
Tom Richards, *Branch Mgr*
EMP: 30
SQ FT: 40,000
SALES (corp-wide): 29.6MM **Privately Held**
SIC: 3341 3339 Secondary nonferrous metals; primary nonferrous metals
HQ: Metech Recycling, Inc.
111 Adams Rd Ste 3
Clinton MA 01510
508 795-1950

(P-11563)
ON-GARD METALS INC
8638 Cleta St, Downey (90241-5201)
PHONE..................562 622-9057
Dick Gard, *President*
EMP: 12
SQ FT: 6,000
SALES (est): 1.1MM **Privately Held**
SIC: 3341 Aluminum smelting & refining (secondary)

(P-11564)
PROCESS MATERIALS INC
5625 Brisa St Ste B, Livermore (94550-2526)
PHONE..................925 245-9626
Barry Nudelman, *President*
Lori Nudelman, *CFO*
Adam Nudelman, *Manager*
▲ EMP: 13
SQ FT: 18,000
SALES (est): 2.4MM **Privately Held**
WEB: www.processmaterials.com
SIC: 3341 Secondary nonferrous metals

(P-11565)
QUEMETCO INC
720 S 7th Ave, City of Industry (91746-3124)
PHONE..................626 937-3239
Bob Finn, *Branch Mgr*
EMP: 150
SQ FT: 10,000
SALES (corp-wide): 320.9MM **Privately Held**
SIC: 3341 2899 4953 3312 Lead smelting & refining (secondary); chemical preparations; refuse systems; blast furnaces & steel mills
HQ: Quemetco, Inc.
2777 N Stemmons Fwy # 1800
Dallas TX 75207
317 247-1303

(P-11566)
QUEMETCO WEST LLC
720 S 7th Ave, City of Industry (91746-3124)
PHONE..................626 330-2294
Robert E Finn,
George Cummins,
Peter King,
▲ EMP: 20
SALES (est): 2MM
SALES (corp-wide): 6.3MM **Privately Held**
SIC: 3341 Lead smelting & refining (secondary)
HQ: Eco-Bat America Llc
2777 N Stemmons Fwy # 1800
Dallas TX 75207
214 688-4000

(P-11567)
SIMS RECYCLING SOLUTIONS INC
8855 Washington Blvd, Roseville (95678-5935)
PHONE..................916 772-5600
Carl Yue, *Engineer*
EMP: 45 **Privately Held**
SIC: 3341 Secondary precious metals
HQ: Sims Recycling Solutions, Inc.
1600 Harvester Rd
West Chicago IL 60185
630 231-6060

(P-11568)
TEXAS TST INC
13428 Benson Ave, Chino (91710-5258)
PHONE..................951 685-2155
Andrew G Stein, *CEO*
Robert Stein, *President*
Tony Rocha, *Manager*
◆ EMP: 50
SALES (est): 9.5MM
SALES (corp-wide): 67.6MM **Privately Held**
SIC: 3341 Aluminum smelting & refining (secondary)
PA: Tst, Inc.
13428 Benson Ave
Chino CA 91710
951 685-2155

(P-11569)
THOROCK METALS INC
1213 S Pacific Coast Hwy, Redondo Beach (90277-4905)
PHONE..................310 537-1597
Holly Kadota, *President*
Holly M Kadota, *President*
Craig Mock, *CFO*
Jeff Mock, *Exec VP*
EMP: 25 EST: 1968
SQ FT: 50,000
SALES (est): 4.7MM **Privately Held**
WEB: www.thorockmetals.com
SIC: 3341 Aluminum smelting & refining (secondary)

(P-11570)
TST INC
Alpase
13428 Benson Ave, Chino (91710-5258)
PHONE..................951 727-3169
Andrew G Stein, *CEO*
EMP: 40
SALES (corp-wide): 67.6MM **Privately Held**
SIC: 3341 Aluminum smelting & refining (secondary)
PA: Tst, Inc.
13428 Benson Ave
Chino CA 91710
951 685-2155

(P-11571)
TST INC (PA)
Also Called: Timco Aluminum Alloys
13428 Benson Ave, Chino (91710-5258)
PHONE..................951 685-2155
Andrew G Stein, *CEO*
Robert A Stein, *Ch of Bd*
Greg Levine, *Vice Pres*
◆ EMP: 260
SQ FT: 123,000
SALES (est): 67.6MM **Privately Held**
WEB: www.tst-inc.com
SIC: 3341 5093 Aluminum smelting & refining (secondary); metal scrap & waste materials

3351 Rolling, Drawing & Extruding Of Copper

(P-11572)
C F W RESEARCH & DEV CO
Also Called: Cfw Precision Metal Components
338 S 4th St, Grover Beach (93433-1999)
P.O. Box 446 (93483-0446)
PHONE..................805 489-8750
Michael A Greenelsh, *President*
Kathryn Greenelsh, *Corp Secy*
Harlan Silva, *Vice Pres*
Dan Wickstrom, *Prdtn Mgr*
EMP: 16
SQ FT: 10,000
SALES (est): 4.3MM
SALES (corp-wide): 10MM **Privately Held**
WEB: www.cfwpmc.com
SIC: 3351 Wire, copper & copper alloy
PA: California Fine Wire Co.
338 S 4th St
Grover Beach CA 93433
805 489-5144

(P-11573)
CTS FABRICATION USA INC
11220 Pyrites Way Ste 300, Gold River (95670-6334)
PHONE..................916 852-6303
Gary Stanley, *President*
Terry Stanley, *Shareholder*
Mary Stanley, *Admin Sec*
▲ EMP: 10
SALES (est): 1.7MM **Privately Held**
WEB: www.ctsflange.com
SIC: 3351 Copper pipe

3353 Aluminum Sheet, Plate & Foil

(P-11574)
AMERICAN ALUPACK INDS LLC
1201 N Rice Ave, Oxnard (93030-7964)
PHONE..................805 485-1500
Manny Thakkar, *CEO*
Mita Thakkar, *President*
Neal Thakkar, *Vice Pres*
Irma H Thakkar, *Director*
◆ EMP: 35
SQ FT: 60,000
SALES: 17MM **Privately Held**
SIC: 3353 Foil, aluminum

(P-11575)
EURAMAX HOLDINGS INC
Also Called: Amerimax
1411 N Daly St, Anaheim (92806-1503)
PHONE..................714 563-8260
Steve Bringers, *Manager*
EMP: 12
SALES (corp-wide): 861.3MM **Privately Held**
SIC: 3353 5051 Coils, sheet aluminum; aluminum bars, rods, ingots, sheets, pipes, plates, etc.
PA: Omnimax Holdings, Inc.
303 Research Dr Ste 400
Norcross GA 30092
770 449-7066

(P-11576)
ITW SEMISYSTEMS INC
625 Wool Creek Dr Ste G, San Jose (95112-2622)
PHONE..................408 350-0244
EMP: 30
SALES (est): 3.7MM
SALES (corp-wide): 41MM **Privately Held**
WEB: www.mdc-vacuum.com
SIC: 3353
PA: Mdc Vacuum Products, Llc
30962 Santana St
Hayward CA 94544
510 265-3500

(P-11577)
KAISER ALUMINUM FAB PDTS LLC (HQ)
Also Called: Kafp
27422 Portola Pkwy # 200, Foothill Ranch (92610-2831)
PHONE..................949 614-1740
Jack A Hockema, *President*
Joseph P Bellino, *CFO*
John M Donnan, *Vice Pres*
Rebecca Harris, *Planning*
Chris Daniels, *Engineer*
◆ EMP: 2200
SALES (est): 788MM
SALES (corp-wide): 1.4B **Publicly Held**
WEB: www.kaisertwd.com
SIC: 3353 3334 3354 3355 Aluminum sheet, plate & foil; primary aluminum; aluminum rod & bar; wire, aluminum: made in rolling mills
PA: Kaiser Aluminum Corporation
27422 Portola Pkwy # 350
Foothill Ranch CA 92610
949 614-1740

(P-11578)
KAISER ALUMINUM INVESTMENTS CO (HQ)
Also Called: Kaic
27422 Portola Pkwy # 350, Foothill Ranch (92610-2837)
PHONE..................949 614-1740
Jack A Hockema, *President*
Joseph P Bellino, *CFO*
Daniel J Rinkenberger, *Treasurer*
John M Donnan, *Vice Pres*
EMP: 200
SALES (est): 209.2MM
SALES (corp-wide): 1.4B **Publicly Held**
SIC: 3353 3334 3354 3355 Aluminum sheet, plate & foil; primary aluminum; aluminum rod & bar; wire, aluminum: made in rolling mills
PA: Kaiser Aluminum Corporation
27422 Portola Pkwy # 350
Foothill Ranch CA 92610
949 614-1740

(P-11579)
MAVERICK ENTERPRISES INC
751 E Gobbi St, Ukiah (95482-6205)
PHONE..................707 463-5591
Steve Otterbeck, *President*
Mike Benetti, *COO*
Jay Frysinger, *Treasurer*
Jon Henderson, *Chief Mktg Ofcr*
Kevin Forster, *Vice Pres*
▲ EMP: 105
SQ FT: 30,000
SALES (est): 31.4MM **Privately Held**
WEB: www.maverickcaps.com
SIC: 3353 Foil, aluminum
PA: Pcm Companies, Llc
2150 Dodd Rd
Mendota Heights MN 55120

▲ = Import ▼=Export
◆ =Import/Export

(P-11580)
SOUTHWIRE INC (HQ)
Also Called: Electrical Products Division
11695 Pacific Ave, Fontana (92337-8225)
PHONE..............................310 884-8500
Mark Kaminski, *COO*
John Wasz, *President*
EMP: 15
SQ FT: 210,000
SALES (est): 83.2MM
SALES (corp-wide): 2.4B **Privately Held**
WEB: www.alflex.com
SIC: 3353 3644 3315 Coils, sheet aluminum; electric conduits & fittings; cable, steel: insulated or armored
PA: Southwire Company, Llc
    1 Southwire Dr
    Carrollton GA 30119
    770 832-4242

(P-11581)
TCI TEXARKANA INC
5855 Obispo Ave, Long Beach
(90805-3715)
PHONE..............................562 808-8000
Johnny Hsieh, *CEO*
James Chang, *Vice Pres*
Andrew Chang, *Controller*
EMP: 15
SALES (est): 547K
SALES (corp-wide): 2.1B **Privately Held**
SIC: 3353 Coils, sheet aluminum
HQ: Ta Chen International, Inc.
    5855 Obispo Ave
    Long Beach CA 90805
    562 808-8000

(P-11582)
TECHNICAL ANODIZE
1142 Price Ave, Pomona (91767-5838)
PHONE..............................909 865-9034
Fernando Salazar, *Partner*
Emilio Mendez, *Partner*
EMP: 13
SALES (est): 1.9MM **Privately Held**
SIC: 3353 3471 2796 Plates, aluminum; sand blasting of metal parts; electrotype plates

---
3354 Aluminum Extruded Prdts

(P-11583)
BUILDIT ENGINEERING CO INC
3074 N Lima St, Burbank (91504-2012)
PHONE..............................818 244-6666
Barry Alberts, *President*
Pat Alberts, *Treasurer*
Scott Alberts, *Vice Pres*
▲ **EMP:** 12
SQ FT: 8,000
SALES (est): 1.8MM **Privately Held**
WEB: www.builditengineering.com
SIC: 3354 3312 8711 Aluminum extruded products; stainless steel; engineering services

(P-11584)
CASELLA ALUMINUM EXTRUSIONS
Also Called: C A E
824 N Todd Ave, Azusa (91702-2228)
PHONE..............................714 961-8322
Mauro Casella, *President*
Edward Capper, *Admin Sec*
EMP: 12
SQ FT: 8,000
SALES (est): 1.5MM **Privately Held**
SIC: 3354

(P-11585)
COLUMBIA ALUMINUM PRODUCTS LLC
2565 Sampson Ave, Corona (92879-7109)
PHONE..............................323 728-7361
Drew D Mumford, *Owner*
Grant Palenske, *Vice Pres*
Tito Laureola, *Software Dev*
▲ **EMP:** 70
SQ FT: 60,000

SALES (est): 22.5MM **Privately Held**
WEB:
www.columbiaaluminumproductsllc.com
SIC: 3354 Aluminum extruded products

(P-11586)
FRY REGLET CORPORATION (PA)
12342 Hawkins St, Santa Fe Springs
(90670-3367)
P.O. Box 2546 (90670-0546)
PHONE..............................562 903-9500
Stephen Reed, *CEO*
Avon M Hall, *President*
James Tuttle, *CFO*
EMP: 200 EST: 1945
SQ FT: 20,000
SALES (est): 94.8MM **Privately Held**
WEB: www.fryreglet.com
SIC: 3354 Aluminum extruded products

(P-11587)
GEMINI ALUMINUM CORPORATION
3255 Pomona Blvd, Pomona (91768-3291)
P.O. Box 1462, Sandpoint ID (83864-0866)
PHONE..............................909 595-7403
Alan J Hardy, *President*
Healani Hardy, *Admin Sec*
EMP: 30 EST: 1976
SQ FT: 10,000
SALES (est): 9.6MM **Privately Held**
SIC: 3354 Aluminum rod & bar

(P-11588)
GLOBAL TRUSS AMERICA LLC
4295 Charter St, Vernon (90058-2520)
PHONE..............................323 415-6225
Charles Davies, *Mng Member*
Kenneth Kahn, *General Mgr*
◆ **EMP:** 55
SQ FT: 60,000
SALES (est): 16MM **Privately Held**
WEB: www.globaltruss.com
SIC: 3354 Aluminum extruded products

(P-11589)
HASTINGS IRRIGATION PIPE CO
17619 Road 24, Madera (93638-9645)
PHONE..............................559 675-1200
Geryanne Hansen, *Manager*
EMP: 14
SQ FT: 22,000
SALES (corp-wide): 35MM **Privately Held**
WEB: www.hipco-ne.com
SIC: 3354 Pipe, extruded, aluminum
PA: Hastings Irrigation Pipe Co.
    1801 E South St
    Hastings NE 68901
    402 463-6633

(P-11590)
HYDRO EXTRUDER LLC
18111 Railroad St, City of Industry
(91748-1216)
PHONE..............................626 964-3411
Matt Zundel, *Sales Dir*
Leslie Estrada, *Hum Res Coord*
EMP: 300
SALES (corp-wide): 13.8B **Privately Held**
SIC: 3354 Aluminum extruded products
HQ: Hydro Extruder, Llc
    Airport Offc Park
    Moon Township PA 15108

(P-11591)
KAISER ALUMINUM CORPORATION
6250 Bandini Blvd, Commerce
(90040-3168)
PHONE..............................323 726-8011
D F Smith, *Principal*
John Soullier, *Project Mgr*
Rob Matuska, *Research*
Chojnicki Ed, *Engineer*
Pam Reding, *Accountant*
EMP: 21
SALES (corp-wide): 1.4B **Publicly Held**
SIC: 3354 Aluminum extruded products
PA: Kaiser Aluminum Corporation
    27422 Portola Pkwy # 350
    Foothill Ranch CA 92610
    949 614-1740

(P-11592)
KAISER ALUMINUM FAB PDTS LLC
6250 Bandini Blvd, Commerce
(90040-3168)
PHONE..............................323 722-7151
D F Smith, *Branch Mgr*
EMP: 150
SALES (corp-wide): 1.4B **Publicly Held**
WEB: www.kaisertwd.com
SIC: 3354 Aluminum extruded products
HQ: Kaiser Aluminum Fabricated Products, Llc
    27422 Portola Pkwy # 200
    Foothill Ranch CA 92610
    -

(P-11593)
LUXFER INC
1995 3rd St, Riverside (92507-3483)
PHONE..............................951 684-5110
Brian McGuire, *Manager*
EMP: 178
SALES (corp-wide): 441.3MM **Privately Held**
WEB: www.luxfer-ecare.com
SIC: 3354 3728 Aluminum extruded products; aircraft parts & equipment
HQ: Luxfer Inc.
    3016 Kansas Ave Bldg 1
    Riverside CA 92507
    336 578-4515

(P-11594)
MAGELLAN INTERNATIONAL CORP
Also Called: Magerack
4453 Enterprise St, Fremont (94538-6306)
PHONE..............................510 656-6661
Jason Xie, *President*
▲ **EMP:** 10
SQ FT: 3,000
SALES (est): 5MM **Privately Held**
WEB: www.magellancorp.com
SIC: 3354 7389 Shapes, extruded aluminum; translation services

(P-11595)
MERIT ALUMINUM INC (PA)
2480 Railroad St, Corona (92880-5418)
PHONE..............................951 735-1770
Michael Rapport, *President*
Evan Rapport, *Vice Pres*
Vincent Lee, *Human Res Mgr*
▲ **EMP:** 100
SQ FT: 58,000
SALES (est): 42.9MM **Privately Held**
WEB: www.frontier-aluminum.com
SIC: 3354 Aluminum extruded products

(P-11596)
MICRO TRIM INC
3613 W Macarthur Blvd # 605, Santa Ana
(92704-6846)
PHONE..............................714 241-7046
Robert Catena, *President*
Jodi Catena, *Treasurer*
Stefanie Catena, *Vice Pres*
Lori Peterson, *Marketing Mgr*
EMP: 12
SQ FT: 4,500
SALES (est): 1.3MM **Privately Held**
WEB: www.microtrim.com
SIC: 3354 Aluminum extruded products

(P-11597)
MOBILE DESIGNS INC
4650 Caterpillar Rd, Redding (96003-1416)
PHONE..............................530 244-1050
William Marsh, *President*
▼ **EMP:** 13
SALES (est): 2.2MM **Privately Held**
WEB: www.mobiledesigns.com
SIC: 3354 Aluminum extruded products

(P-11598)
NEAL FEAY COMPANY
Also Called: Troy Metal Products
133 S La Patera Ln, Goleta (93117-3291)
PHONE..............................805 967-4521
Neal C Rasmussen, *CEO*
N J Rasmussen, *Corp Secy*
Alex Rasmussen, *Vice Pres*
Alan Owens, *Executive*
Bret Vanderhyden, *Design Engr*

EMP: 60 EST: 1944
SQ FT: 50,000
SALES (est): 13.3MM **Privately Held**
WEB: www.nealfeay.com
SIC: 3354 3469 Tube, extruded or drawn, aluminum; electronic enclosures, stamped or pressed metal

(P-11599)
PARAMOUNT EXTRUSIONS COMPANY (PA)
6833 Rosecrans Ave, Paramount
(90723-3152)
P.O. Box 847 (90723-0847)
PHONE..............................562 634-3291
Charles E Munson, *CEO*
Leslie C Munson, *President*
Frank Fry, *Vice Pres*
Gary Munson, *Admin Sec*
▲ **EMP:** 30
SQ FT: 2,000
SALES (est): 6MM **Privately Held**
WEB: www.paramountextrusions.com
SIC: 3354 3312 Aluminum extruded products; blast furnaces & steel mills

(P-11600)
PARAMOUNT EXTRUSIONS COMPANY
6833 Rosecrans Ave Ste A, Paramount
(90723-3152)
P.O. Box 847 (90723-0847)
PHONE..............................562 634-3291
Les Munson, *President*
EMP: 24
SALES (est): 2.9MM
SALES (corp-wide): 6MM **Privately Held**
WEB: www.paramountextrusions.com
SIC: 3354 Aluminum extruded products
PA: Paramount Extrusions Company
    6833 Rosecrans Ave
    Paramount CA 90723
    562 634-3291

(P-11601)
QUALITY ALUMINUM FORGE LLC
793 N Cypress St, Orange (92867-6605)
PHONE..............................714 633-1195
Trish Caracio, *Principal*
EMP: 11
SALES (corp-wide): 121.4MM **Publicly Held**
SIC: 3354 Aluminum extruded products
HQ: Quality Aluminum Forge, Llc
    794 N Cypress St
    Orange CA 92867
    714 639-8191

(P-11602)
SAPA EXTRUSIONS INC
2821 E Philadelphia St A, Ontario
(91761-8522)
PHONE..............................909 947-7682
EMP: 166
SALES (corp-wide): 80MM **Privately Held**
SIC: 3354
HQ: Sapa Extrusions, Inc.
    9600 Bryn Mawr Ave # 250
    Rosemont IL 60018
    412 299-2286

(P-11603)
SIERRA ALUMINUM COMPANY (HQ)
2345 Fleetwood Dr, Riverside
(92509-2426)
PHONE..............................951 781-7800
Edward A Harris, *CEO*
Rod Hunt, *Vice Pres*
Tim Lara, *Vice Pres*
Shayne Seever, *Vice Pres*
Scott Ciley, *Executive*
▲ **EMP:** 24
SQ FT: 62,000
SALES (est): 10.1MM **Privately Held**
WEB: www.sierraaluminum.com
SIC: 3354 Aluminum extruded products
PA: Samuel, Son & Co., Limited
    2360 Dixie Rd
    Mississauga ON L4Y 1
    905 279-5460

P
R
O
D
U
C
T
S
&
S
V
C
S

(P-11604)
SUN VALLEY PRODUCTS INC
Also Called: Sun Valley Extrusion
4640 Sperry St, Los Angeles (90039-1018)
PHONE...............................818 247-8350
Kerry Dodge, *Branch Mgr*
EMP: 35
SALES (corp-wide): 5.8MM **Privately Held**
WEB: www.sunvalleyextrusion.com
SIC: 3354 Aluminum extruded products
HQ: Sun Valley Products, Inc.
4626 Sperry St
Los Angeles CA 90039
818 247-8350

(P-11605)
SUN VALLEY PRODUCTS INC (HQ)
4626 Sperry St, Los Angeles (90039-1018)
PHONE...............................818 247-8350
Jennifer K Hillman, *President*
Rosanne M Kusar, *Ch of Bd*
Angelica K Clark, *Treasurer*
EMP: 60 EST: 1960
SQ FT: 64,980
SALES (est): 9MM
SALES (corp-wide): 5.8MM **Privately Held**
WEB: www.sunvalleyextrusion.com
SIC: 3354 Aluminum extruded products
PA: Darfield Industries Inc
4626 Sperry St
Los Angeles CA 90039
818 247-8350

(P-11606)
SUPERIOR METAL SHAPES INC
4730 Eucalyptus Ave, Chino (91710-9255)
PHONE...............................909 947-3455
David A Stockton, *President*
Yasushi Shimabukuro, *Consultant*
EMP: 40
SQ FT: 64,000
SALES: 7MM **Privately Held**
SIC: 3354 Shapes, extruded aluminum

(P-11607)
TRULITE GL ALUM SOLUTIONS LLC
19430 San Jose Ave, City of Industry (91748-1421)
PHONE...............................800 877-8439
Elizabeth Hemsing, *Manager*
Bertha Sanchez, *Human Res Dir*
Manny Marrujo, *Cust Mgr*
Hector Sarinana, *Manager*
EMP: 16 **Privately Held**
SIC: 3354 Aluminum extruded products
PA: Trulite Glass & Aluminum Solutions, Llc
403 Westpark Ct Ste 201
Peachtree City GA 30269

(P-11608)
UNIVERSAL ALLOY CORPORATION
Also Called: Alu Menziken
2871 E John Ball Way, Anaheim (92806-2497)
PHONE...............................714 630-7200
Nancy Newmeyr, *Branch Mgr*
EMP: 300
SALES (corp-wide): 117.5MM **Privately Held**
WEB: www.menzaero.com
SIC: 3354 Shapes, extruded aluminum
HQ: Universal Alloy Corporation
180 Lamar Haley Pkwy
Canton GA 30114
888 479-7230

(P-11609)
UNIVERSAL MLDING EXTRUSION INC (DH)
Also Called: Umex
9151 Imperial Hwy, Downey (90242-2808)
PHONE...............................562 401-1015
Dominick L Baione, *CEO*
Dominic Baione, *Executive*
Ashley Peterson, *Sales Associate*
Sonia Prines, *Sales Staff*
▼ EMP: 45

SALES (est): 49.1MM **Privately Held**
WEB: www.umextrude.com
SIC: 3354 Aluminum extruded products
HQ: Universal Molding Company
9151 Imperial Hwy
Downey CA 90242
310 886-1750

(P-11610)
US POLYMERS INC
5910 Bandini Blvd, Commerce (90040-2963)
PHONE...............................323 727-6888
Vram Ohanesiam, *Manager*
EMP: 37
SALES (corp-wide): 40.3MM **Privately Held**
WEB: www.uspolymersinc.com
SIC: 3354 5719 Aluminum extruded products; window furnishings
PA: U.S. Polymers, Inc.
1057 S Vail Ave
Montebello CA 90640
323 728-3023

(P-11611)
VISION SYSTEMS INC
11322 Woodside Ave N, Santee (92071-4728)
PHONE...............................619 258-7300
Fred W Witte, *President*
James Schlereth, *Vice Pres*
Steve Lehman, *Project Mgr*
Whitey Rishel, *Purch Mgr*
Jorge Carter, *Buyer*
▲ EMP: 60
SQ FT: 32,000
SALES (est): 34.1MM **Privately Held**
WEB: www.visionsystems.org
SIC: 3354 3442 Aluminum extruded products; window & door frames

(P-11612)
VISTA METALS CORP (PA)
13425 Whittram Ave, Fontana (92335-2999)
PHONE...............................909 823-4278
Andrew Primack, *CEO*
Raymond Alpert, *Corp Secy*
Steve Chevlin, *Exec VP*
Robert Praefke, *Exec VP*
Mark Sprecher, *Vice Pres*
◆ EMP: 197 EST: 1961
SQ FT: 17,000
SALES (est): 70.9MM **Privately Held**
SIC: 3354 3341 Aluminum extruded products; aluminum smelting & refining (secondary)

3355 Aluminum Rolling & Drawing, NEC

(P-11613)
ARCADIA INC
2324 Del Monte St, West Sacramento (95691-3807)
PHONE...............................916 375-1478
Eddy Sala, *Branch Mgr*
EMP: 20
SALES (corp-wide): 128.3MM **Privately Held**
WEB: www.arcadiaincorporated.com
SIC: 3355 Extrusion ingot, aluminum: made in rolling mills
PA: Arcadia, Inc.
2301 E Vernon Ave
Vernon CA 90058
323 269-7300

(P-11614)
ARCADIA INC (PA)
Also Called: Arcadia Norcal
2301 E Vernon Ave, Vernon (90058-8052)
PHONE...............................323 269-7300
James Schladen, *CEO*
Khan Chow, *CFO*
Pat Homkaew, *CFO*
Henry Nguyen, *Executive*
Dan Spielberger, *General Mgr*
▲ EMP: 250
SQ FT: 50,000

SALES (est): 128.3MM **Privately Held**
WEB: www.arcadiaincorporated.com
SIC: 3355 Extrusion ingot, aluminum: made in rolling mills

(P-11615)
CST POWER AND CONSTRUCTION INC (HQ)
879 W 190th St Ste 1100, Gardena (90248-4205)
PHONE...............................310 523-2322
Walter G Mitchell, *Ch of Bd*
Charles E Miller, *President*
Joseph Schmidt, *CEO*
◆ EMP: 70 EST: 1964
SALES: 19MM
SALES (corp-wide): 346.5MM **Privately Held**
SIC: 3355 3569 3448 3444 Structural shapes, rolled, aluminum; filter elements, fluid, hydraulic line; prefabricated metal buildings; sheet metalwork; fabricated structural metal

(P-11616)
DURALUM PRODUCTS INC (PA)
8269 Alpine Ave, Sacramento (95826-4708)
P.O. Box 1061, Fair Oaks (95628-1061)
PHONE...............................916 452-7021
William Anson, *CEO*
Bill Anson, *President*
Cheryl L Anson, *Corp Secy*
EMP: 14 EST: 1962
SQ FT: 40,000
SALES (est): 8.3MM **Privately Held**
WEB: www.duralum.com
SIC: 3355 Aluminum rolling & drawing

(P-11617)
DURALUM PRODUCTS INC
2485 Railroad St, Corona (92880-5419)
PHONE...............................951 736-4500
Ron Cull, *Manager*
EMP: 15
SALES (corp-wide): 8.3MM **Privately Held**
WEB: www.duralum.com
SIC: 3355 Aluminum rolling & drawing
PA: Duralum Products, Inc.
8269 Alpine Ave
Sacramento CA 95826
916 452-7021

(P-11618)
INTERSTATE STEEL CENTER CO
7001 S Alameda St, Los Angeles (90001-2204)
P.O. Box 58364 (90058-0364)
PHONE...............................323 583-0855
Leon Banks, *President*
William Korth, *Admin Sec*
EMP: 50
SQ FT: 53,000
SALES (est): 5.3MM **Privately Held**
SIC: 3355 3312 Coils, wire aluminum: made in rolling mills; blast furnaces & steel mills

(P-11619)
JAYCO HAWAII CALIFORNIA
1468 66th St, Emeryville (94608-1014)
PHONE...............................510 601-9916
John Delay, *President*
EMP: 10
SALES (est): 1.3MM **Privately Held**
SIC: 3355 Rails, rolled & drawn, aluminum

(P-11620)
METALS USA BUILDING PDTS LP (DH)
955 Columbia St, Brea (92821-2923)
P.O. Box 12639, Houston TX (77217-2639)
PHONE...............................713 946-9000
Charles Canning, *Partner*
Robert McPherson, *Partner*
▲ EMP: 700
SQ FT: 60,000
SALES (est): 319.5MM
SALES (corp-wide): 9.7B **Publicly Held**
WEB: www.gerardusa.com
SIC: 3355 5031 1542 Structural shapes, rolled, aluminum; building materials, exterior; commercial & office buildings, renovation & repair

HQ: Metals Usa, Inc.
4901 Nw 17th Way Ste 405
Fort Lauderdale FL 33309
954 202-4000

(P-11621)
METALS USA BUILDING PDTS LP
1951 S Parco Ave Ste C, Ontario (91761-8315)
PHONE...............................800 325-1305
Steve Brang, *Manager*
EMP: 45
SALES (corp-wide): 9.7B **Publicly Held**
WEB: www.gerardusa.com
SIC: 3355 Structural shapes, rolled, aluminum
HQ: Metals Usa Building Products Lp
955 Columbia St
Brea CA 92821
713 946-9000

(P-11622)
METALS USA BUILDING PDTS LP
11340 White Rock Rd Ste B, Rancho Cordova (95742-6606)
PHONE...............................916 635-2245
EMP: 25
SALES (corp-wide): 9.2B **Publicly Held**
SIC: 3355
HQ: Metals Usa Building Products Lp
2440 Albright Dr
Houston TX 92821
713 946-9000

(P-11623)
METALS USA BUILDING PDTS LP
955 Columbia St, Brea (92821-2923)
PHONE...............................714 529-0407
Fred Seal, *General Mgr*
EMP: 30
SALES (corp-wide): 9.7B **Publicly Held**
WEB: www.gerardusa.com
SIC: 3355 Structural shapes, rolled, aluminum
HQ: Metals Usa Building Products Lp
955 Columbia St
Brea CA 92821
713 946-9000

(P-11624)
SKYREACH L S EXTRSONS USA CORP
9281 Pittsburgh Ave Ste A, Rancho Cucamonga (91730-5510)
PHONE...............................909 204-3550
Gavin Taylor, *General Mgr*
Ming Lu, *Purchasing*
▲ EMP: 10
SALES (est): 1.5MM **Privately Held**
SIC: 3355 3229 Extrusion ingot, aluminum: made in rolling mills; glass fiber products

(P-11625)
SOUTHERN ALUM FINSHG CO INC
Also Called: Saf West
4356 Caterpillar Rd, Redding (96003-1422)
PHONE...............................530 244-7518
Sam Heier, *Branch Mgr*
EMP: 90
SALES (corp-wide): 50.2MM **Privately Held**
SIC: 3355 Structural shapes, rolled, aluminum
PA: Southern Aluminum Finishing Company, Inc.
1581 Huber St Nw
Atlanta GA 30318
404 355-1560

(P-11626)
WERNER SYSTEMS INC
Also Called: Woodbridge Glass
14321 Myford Rd, Tustin (92780-7022)
PHONE...............................714 838-4444
Virgina Siciliani, *CEO*
Vito Siciliani, *Director*
▲ EMP: 20
SQ FT: 58,000

SALES (est): 6.1MM **Privately Held**
WEB: www.wernerengineering.com
SIC: **3355** Aluminum rolling & drawing

3356 Rolling, Drawing-Extruding Of Nonferrous Metals

(P-11627)
DYNAMET INCORPORATED
16052 Beach Blvd Ste 221, Huntington Beach (92647-3855)
PHONE.....................714 375-3150
Tom Proteau, *Manager*
EMP: 25
SALES (corp-wide): 2.1B **Publicly Held**
WEB: www.dynamet.com
SIC: **3356** Titanium & titanium alloy bars, sheets, strip, etc.
HQ: Dynamet Incorporated
195 Museum Rd
Washington PA 15301
724 228-1000

(P-11628)
FLASHCO MANUFACTURING INC (PA)
150 Todd Rd Ste 400, Santa Rosa (95407-8101)
PHONE.....................707 824-4448
Gregory J Morrow, *CEO*
▲ EMP: 30
SQ FT: 7,500
SALES (est): 6.7MM **Privately Held**
WEB: www.flashcomfg.com
SIC: **3356** Lead & lead alloy bars, pipe, plates, shapes, etc.

(P-11629)
GRANDIS METALS INTL CORP
Also Called: Grandis Titanium
29752 Ave De Las Bndra, Rcho STA Marg (92688-2615)
PHONE.....................949 459-2621
Vasily T Semeniuta, *President*
Igor Krjenitski, *Vice Pres*
Theodore Semeniuta, *Vice Pres*
◆ EMP: 12
SALES (est): 1.6MM **Privately Held**
SIC: **3356** Titanium

(P-11630)
HI TECH SOLDER
700 Monroe Way, Placentia (92870-6308)
PHONE.....................714 572-1200
Jose Salas, *Partner*
Hector Salas, *Partner*
EMP: 10
SALES (est): 870K **Privately Held**
SIC: **3356** Solder: wire, bar, acid core, & rosin core

(P-11631)
INTERSPACE BATTERY INC (PA)
2009 W San Bernardino Rd, West Covina (91790-1006)
PHONE.....................626 813-1234
Paul Godber, *Ch of Bd*
Donald W Godber, *President*
Richard Murrietta, *Manager*
EMP: 12
SQ FT: 36,000
SALES (est): 3.4MM **Privately Held**
SIC: **3356** 3691 Battery metal; storage batteries

(P-11632)
JOAOS A TIN FISH BAR & EATERY
2750 Dewey Rd, San Diego (92106-6142)
PHONE.....................619 794-2192
Mike Alves, *Owner*
EMP: 30
SALES (est): 2.7MM **Privately Held**
SIC: **3356** Tin

(P-11633)
MS2 TECHNOLOGIES LLC
2448 E 25th St, Vernon (90058-1209)
PHONE.....................310 277-4110
Larry Kay,
Cindy Flame,

EMP: 10
SALES: 2.5MM **Privately Held**
SIC: **3356** Nonferrous rolling & drawing

(P-11634)
NEW CNTURY MTALS SOUTHEAST INC
Also Called: Rti Los Angeles
15723 Shoemaker Ave, Norwalk (90650-6863)
PHONE.....................562 356-6804
Marie T Batz, *Admin Sec*
EMP: 14
SALES (est): 2.6MM
SALES (corp-wide): 12.9B **Publicly Held**
SIC: **3356** Titanium; titanium & titanium alloy bars, sheets, strip, etc.; titanium & titanium alloy: rolling, drawing or extruding
HQ: Rti International Metals, Inc.
1000 Warren Ave
Niles OH 44446

(P-11635)
OCEANIA INTERNATIONAL LLC
Also Called: Stanford Advanced Materials
23661 Birtcher Dr, Lake Forest (92630-1770)
PHONE.....................949 407-8904
Alexander Chen, *Mng Member*
Ken Gai, *Sales Engr*
Kristopher Lin, *Sales Engr*
Colin Zarnegar, *Sales Engr*
Alex Chen,
▲ EMP: 40 EST: 2012
SALES (est): 10.6MM **Privately Held**
SIC: **3356** 3313 Titanium & titanium alloy bars, sheets, strip, etc.; zirconium & zirconium alloy bars, sheets, strip, etc.; ferromolybdenum; ferrosilicon, not made in blast furnaces; ferrotungsten

(P-11636)
P KAY METAL INC (PA)
Also Called: P K Metal
2448 E 25th St, Los Angeles (90058-1209)
PHONE.....................323 585-5058
Larry Kay, *President*
Sharon Kay, *Treasurer*
Cindy Flame, *Admin Sec*
Luis A Guerra, *Plant Mgr*
▲ EMP: 45
SQ FT: 25,000
SALES: 58.5MM **Privately Held**
WEB: www.pkaymetal.com
SIC: **3356** Lead & lead alloy bars, pipe, plates, shapes, etc.

(P-11637)
TITANIUM METALS CORPORATION
Also Called: Timet
403 Ryder St, Vallejo (94590-7269)
PHONE.....................707 552-4850
David Madsen, *Principal*
Alun Davies, *Plant Mgr*
EMP: 98
SALES (corp-wide): 242.1B **Publicly Held**
SIC: **3356** 3366 3313 Titanium; titanium & titanium alloy bars, sheets, strip, etc.; castings (except die); electrometallurgical products
HQ: Titanium Metals Corporation
224 Valley Creek Blvd # 200
Exton PA 44128
610 968-1300

(P-11638)
UMC ACQUISITION CORP (PA)
Also Called: Universal Molding Company
9151 Imperial Hwy, Downey (90242-2808)
PHONE.....................562 940-0300
Dominick L Baione, *Ch of Bd*
Edward L Koch III, *President*
EMP: 50
SQ FT: 62,000
SALES (est): 57MM **Privately Held**
SIC: **3356** 3354 3471 3479 Nonferrous rolling & drawing; aluminum extruded products; anodizing (plating) of metals or formed products; aluminum coating of metal products

(P-11639)
UNIVERSAL MOLDING COMPANY (HQ)
9151 Imperial Hwy, Downey (90242-2808)
PHONE.....................310 886-1750
Dominick L Baione, *Ch of Bd*
Carol Hansen, *Exec VP*
Tom Webster, *Executive*
Emily Gonzales, *Office Mgr*
Julius Sarosi, *Engineer*
EMP: 160
SQ FT: 62,000
SALES (est): 55.8MM **Privately Held**
WEB: www.universalmold.com
SIC: **3356** 3354 3448 3471 Nonferrous rolling & drawing; aluminum extruded products; screen enclosures; anodizing (plating) of metals or formed products; aluminum coating of metal products; sheet metalwork

(P-11640)
VSMPO TIRUS US
2850 E Cedar St, Ontario (91761-8514)
PHONE.....................909 230-9020
Dave Richardson, *Owner*
◆ EMP: 45
SALES (est): 6.3MM
SALES (corp-wide): 50.2K **Privately Held**
SIC: **3356** Titanium
HQ: Vsmpo-Tirus, U.S., Inc.
1745 Shea Center Dr # 330
Highlands Ranch CO 80129
720 746-1023

(P-11641)
VSMPO-TIRUS US INC
Also Called: West Coast Service Center
2850 E Cedar St, Ontario (91761-8514)
PHONE.....................909 230-9020
Dave Richardson, *Manager*
EMP: 20
SALES (corp-wide): 50.2K **Privately Held**
WEB: www.vsmpo-tirus.com
SIC: **3356** Titanium
HQ: Vsmpo-Tirus, U.S., Inc.
1745 Shea Center Dr # 330
Highlands Ranch CO 80129
720 746-1023

3357 Nonferrous Wire Drawing

(P-11642)
ALPHA WIRE CORPORATION
Also Called: Coast Custom Cable
1048 E Burgrove St, Carson (90746-3514)
PHONE.....................310 639-9473
Michael Dugar, *Branch Mgr*
EMP: 750
SALES (corp-wide): 225.8MM **Privately Held**
SIC: **3357** 3699 Coaxial cable, nonferrous; electrical equipment & supplies
PA: Alpha Wire Corporation
711 Lidgerwood Ave
Elizabeth NJ 07202
908 925-8000

(P-11643)
ARIA TECHNOLOGIES INC
102 Wright Brothers Ave, Livermore (94551-9240)
PHONE.....................925 292-1616
Paula McGuinness, *CEO*
Joe McGuinness, *President*
Dave Dickens, *Vice Pres*
▲ EMP: 20
SQ FT: 15,000
SALES (est): 5.6MM **Privately Held**
WEB: www.ariatech.com
SIC: **3357** Communication wire

(P-11644)
BEE WIRE & CABLE INC
2850 E Spruce St, Ontario (91761-8550)
PHONE.....................909 923-5800
Arjan Bera, *President*
Kiran Kaneria, *Treasurer*
Nalin Kaneria, *Admin Sec*
▲ EMP: 26
SQ FT: 34,400

SALES (est): 6.3MM **Privately Held**
WEB: www.beeflex.com
SIC: **3357** Building wire & cable, nonferrous

(P-11645)
BELDEN INC
47823 Westinghouse Dr, Fremont (94539-7437)
PHONE.....................510 438-9071
Dhrupad Trevidi, *President*
Keith Bodwin, *Administration*
EMP: 10
SALES (est): 2.3B **Publicly Held**
SIC: **3357** Nonferrous wiredrawing & insulating
PA: Belden Inc.
1 N Brentwood Blvd Fl 15
Saint Louis MO 63105
314 854-8000

(P-11646)
BLAKE WIRE & CABLE CORP
16134 Runnymede St, Van Nuys (91406-2912)
PHONE.....................818 781-8300
Robert Weiner, *President*
Victor Weiner, *Vice Pres*
EMP: 12
SQ FT: 5,500
SALES (est): 3.3MM **Privately Held**
WEB: www.blakewire.com
SIC: **3357** 5051 Nonferrous wiredrawing & insulating; wire

(P-11647)
BRIDGEWAVE COMMUNICATIONS INC
17034 Camino San Bernardo, San Diego (92127-5708)
PHONE.....................408 567-6900
Amir Makleff, *President*
John Keating, *CFO*
Eli Pasternak, *CTO*
Thu Nguyen, *QC Mgr*
Jim Norton, *Sales Staff*
▲ EMP: 25
SALES (est): 6.4MM **Privately Held**
WEB: www.bridgewave.com
SIC: **3357** 3229 Communication wire; pressed & blown glass

(P-11648)
BROADATA COMMUNICATIONS INC
2545 W 237th St Ste K, Torrance (90505-5229)
PHONE.....................310 530-1416
Freddie Lin, *President*
Patty Shaw, *CFO*
Gary Fong, *Design Engr*
Christopher Kim, *Engineer*
Duke Tran, *Engineer*
▲ EMP: 19 EST: 2000
SQ FT: 10,000
SALES: 13.2MM **Privately Held**
WEB: www.bcifiber.com
SIC: **3357** 3663 Fiber optic cable (insulated); television broadcasting & communications equipment

(P-11649)
CALIFORNIA INSULATED WIRE &
3050 N California St, Burbank (91504-2004)
PHONE.....................818 569-4930
Bill Boyd, *President*
Lois Boyd, *Corp Secy*
Bruce Boyd, *Vice Pres*
Micheal Boyd, *Vice Pres*
EMP: 60
SQ FT: 26,000
SALES (est): 16.2MM **Privately Held**
SIC: **3357** Communication wire; fiber optic cable (insulated)

(P-11650)
CALMONT ENGINEERING & ELEC (PA)
Also Called: Calmont Wire & Cable
420 E Alton Ave, Santa Ana (92707-4278)
PHONE.....................714 549-0336
Barbara Monteleone, *President*
Blanche F Chilcote, *Treasurer*

P R O D U C T S & S V C S

Heather Priest, *Admin Asst*
Dan Dawson, *Engineer*
Hung Tran, *Engineer*
EMP: 37 **EST:** 1958
SQ FT: 24,000
SALES: 4.5MM **Privately Held**
WEB: www.calmont.com
SIC: 3357 3061 Nonferrous wiredrawing & insulating; medical & surgical rubber tubing (extruded & lathe-cut)

(P-11651)
CARMEN ABATO ENTERPRISES
11258 Monarch St Ste G, Garden Grove
(92841-1436)
PHONE...................714 895-1887
David Abato, *President*
Jolin Abato, *Treasurer*
EMP: 11
SQ FT: 6,500
SALES: 1MM **Privately Held**
SIC: 3357 7629 5065 Communication wire; electrical measuring instrument repair & calibration; electronic parts

(P-11652)
CENTURUM INFORMATION TECH INC
4250 Pacific Hwy Ste 105, San Diego
(92110-3219)
PHONE...................619 224-1100
Brad Geiger, *Manager*
EMP: 50
SALES (corp-wide): 57.1MM **Privately Held**
SIC: 3357 Shipboard cable, nonferrous
HQ: Centurum Information Technology, Inc.
651 Route 73 N Ste 107
Marlton NJ 08053
856 751-1111

(P-11653)
CENTURY WIRE & CABLE INC
7400 E Slauson Ave, Commerce
(90040-3300)
PHONE...................213 236-8879
David Lifschitz, *CEO*
Galen Ho'o, *President*
Saleem Baakza, *Vice Pres*
Anthony Batista, *Vice Pres*
Carl Tom, *VP Mktg*
EMP: 100
SALES (est): 12.2MM
SALES (corp-wide): 92.6MM **Privately Held**
WEB: www.centurywire.com
SIC: 3357 5063 Nonferrous wiredrawing & insulating; electrical apparatus & equipment
HQ: Gehr Industries, Inc.
7400 E Slauson Ave
Commerce CA 90040
323 728-5558

(P-11654)
CFKBA INC (PA)
150 Jefferson Dr, Menlo Park (94025-1115)
PHONE...................650 847-3900
Richard Johns, *Ch of Bd*
Laurent Mayer, *Vice Pres*
Wendell Jesseman, *Admin Sec*
◆ **EMP:** 63
SQ FT: 43,000
SALES (est): 5.9MM **Privately Held**
WEB: www.baycable.com
SIC: 3357 5063 Nonferrous wiredrawing & insulating; wire & cable

(P-11655)
CICOIL LLC
24960 Avenue Tibbitts, Valencia
(91355-3426)
PHONE...................661 295-1295
Howard Lind, *CEO*
Giulie Styles, *Office Mgr*
EMP: 80
SQ FT: 16,000
SALES: 12.2MM **Privately Held**
WEB: www.cicoil.com
SIC: 3357 Aircraft wire & cable, nonferrous

(P-11656)
COAST 2 COAST CABLES LLC
3162 E La Palma Ave Ste D, Anaheim
(92806-2810)
PHONE...................714 666-1062

Lynn Swearingen, *Mng Member*
Ronald Benadom,
EMP: 17
SQ FT: 14,040
SALES: 2.3MM **Privately Held**
SIC: 3357 Nonferrous wiredrawing & insulating

(P-11657)
DACON SYSTEMS INC
1891 N Delilah St, Corona (92879-1800)
PHONE...................951 735-2100
Drexel Daniels, *President*
Mark Daniels, *CEO*
▲ **EMP:** 10
SQ FT: 14,000
SALES (est): 1.7MM **Privately Held**
WEB: www.daconsys.com
SIC: 3357 Communication wire; automotive wire & cable, except ignition sets; nonferrous; building wire & cable, nonferrous

(P-11658)
DACON SYSTEMS INC
Also Called: Victor Wire & Cable
12915 S Spring St, Los Angeles
(90061-1631)
PHONE...................310 842-9933
Robert Smith, *General Mgr*
Mark Daniels, *President*
EMP: 10
SALES (est): 594.7K **Privately Held**
SIC: 3357 5051 Nonferrous wiredrawing & insulating; metals service centers & offices

(P-11659)
DICAR INC
1285 Alma Ct, San Jose (95112-5943)
PHONE...................408 295-1106
Edward Garcia, *CEO*
Ed Garcia, *President*
Diana M Garcia, *CFO*
Carol Garcia, *Vice Pres*
EMP: 26
SQ FT: 9,900
SALES (est): 8MM **Privately Held**
WEB: www.dicarinc.com
SIC: 3357 3599 3089 3679 Coaxial cable, nonferrous; communication wire; machine & other job shop work; blow molded finished plastic products; harness assemblies for electronic use: wire or cable

(P-11660)
FALMAT INC
Also Called: C B S
1873 Diamond St, San Marcos
(92078-5128)
PHONE...................800 848-4257
Lewis Brian Falk, *CEO*
Shannon Baroni, *Corp Secy*
Donald Falk, *Vice Pres*
▲ **EMP:** 175
SQ FT: 40,000
SALES (est): 57.3MM **Privately Held**
WEB: www.falmat.com
SIC: 3357 5063 Nonferrous wiredrawing & insulating; wire & cable

(P-11661)
FIBEROPTIC SYSTEMS INC
60 Moreland Rd Ste A, Simi Valley
(93065-1643)
PHONE...................805 579-6600
Sanford S Stark, *President*
Kathy Hanau, *CFO*
EMP: 29
SQ FT: 14,000
SALES (est): 6.6MM **Privately Held**
WEB: www.fiberopticsystems.com
SIC: 3357 3229 Fiber optic cable (insulated); fiber optics strands

(P-11662)
FORWARD INTEGRATION TECHNOLOGY
444 Nelo St, Santa Clara (95054-2144)
PHONE...................408 988-3330
Mitra Vakili, *President*
Ray Vakili, *General Mgr*
EMP: 15
SQ FT: 5,000

SALES: 500K **Privately Held**
SIC: 3357 7373 Nonferrous wiredrawing & insulating; systems integration services

(P-11663)
GEHR INDUSTRIES INC (HQ)
7400 E Slauson Ave, Commerce
(90040-3300)
PHONE...................323 728-5558
David Lifschitz, *CEO*
Galen Ho'o, *President*
Mark Goldman, *COO*
Saleem Baakza, *Vice Pres*
Eric Kang, *Vice Pres*
▲ **EMP:** 150 **EST:** 1965
SQ FT: 260,000
SALES (est): 77.5MM
SALES (corp-wide): 92.6MM **Privately Held**
SIC: 3357 5063 5072 5085 Nonferrous wiredrawing & insulating; electrical apparatus & equipment; hardware; industrial supplies
PA: The Gehr Group Inc
7400 E Slauson Ave
Commerce CA 90040
323 728-5558

(P-11664)
GLOBAL MFG SOLUTIONS LLC
2100 E Valencia Dr Ste D, Fullerton
(92831-4811)
PHONE...................562 356-3222
Mike Lin, *Mng Member*
Tom Liu, *General Mgr*
Maria Eugley, *Sales Executive*
Eugene Tsai,
▲ **EMP:** 20
SQ FT: 10,000
SALES (est): 3.4MM **Privately Held**
WEB: www.gocables.com
SIC: 3357 Communication wire

(P-11665)
JUDD WIRE INC
870 Los Vallecitos Blvd, San Marcos
(92069-1479)
PHONE...................760 744-7720
Hiro Sugiyama, *Branch Mgr*
Kenji Tamura, *Engineer*
Norma Canon, *Assistant VP*
EMP: 11
SQ FT: 105,000
SALES (corp-wide): 28.9B **Privately Held**
WEB: www.juddwire.com
SIC: 3357 3315 Communication wire; steel wire & related products
HQ: Judd Wire Inc.
124 Turnpike Rd
Turners Falls MA 01376
413 863-9402

(P-11666)
MX ELECTRONICS MFG INC
Also Called: Interconnect Solutions
1651 E Saint Andrew Pl, Santa Ana
(92705-4932)
PHONE...................714 258-0200
Lawrence Reusing, *President*
Mike Anderson, *CFO*
◆ **EMP:** 58
SQ FT: 40,000
SALES (est): 15.2MM **Privately Held**
WEB: www.isiconnect.com
SIC: 3357 Aluminum wire & cable
PA: Experts En Memoire Internationale Inc,
Les
2321 Rue Cohen
Saint-Laurent QC H4R 2
514 333-5010

(P-11667)
NEPTEC OS INC
Also Called: Neptec Optical Solutions
48603 Warm Springs Blvd, Fremont
(94539-7782)
PHONE...................510 687-1101
David Cheng, *President*
Chaoyu Yue, *Vice Pres*
EMP: 25 **EST:** 2008
SALES: 500K **Privately Held**
WEB: www.neptecos.com
SIC: 3357 Fiber optic cable (insulated)

(P-11668)
OKONITE COMPANY
2900 Skyway Dr, Santa Maria
(93455-1897)
PHONE...................805 922-6682
Rick Flory, *Branch Mgr*
Cameron Carranza, *Technology*
Keith Weaver, *Electrical Engi*
Bob Parsons, *Accountant*
Elbert Bustle, *Plant Engr*
EMP: 150
SQ FT: 10,000
SALES (corp-wide): 407MM **Privately Held**
WEB: www.okonite.com
SIC: 3357 Nonferrous wiredrawing & insulating
PA: The Okonite Company Inc
102 Hilltop Rd
Ramsey NJ 07446
201 825-0300

(P-11669)
OPTICOMM CORP
2015 Chestnut St, Alhambra (91803-1542)
PHONE...................626 293-3400
David Caidar, *President*
Allon Caider, *Vice Pres*
EMP: 23
SQ FT: 15,000
SALES (est): 2.8MM
SALES (corp-wide): 122.9MM **Publicly Held**
WEB: www.opticomm.com
SIC: 3357 8748 Fiber optic cable (insulated); telecommunications consultant
PA: Emcore Corporation
2015 Chestnut St
Alhambra CA 91803
626 293-3400

(P-11670)
PRECISION FIBER PRODUCTS INC
Also Called: Pfp
142 N Milpitas Blvd # 298, Milpitas
(95035-4401)
PHONE...................408 946-4040
Ray Pierce, *President*
Amanda Jensen, *Accounting Mgr*
◆ **EMP:** 10
SALES (est): 1.6MM **Privately Held**
WEB: www.precisionfiberproducts.com
SIC: 3357 Fiber optic cable (insulated)

(P-11671)
PRIME WIRE & CABLE INC (HQ)
280 Machlin Ct, Walnut (91789-3026)
PHONE...................888 445-9955
Juhng-Shyu Shieh, *CEO*
Joe Ferlauto, *President*
Jeff Millar-Sax, *Vice Pres*
Meng Loh, *Creative Dir*
Jerzy Marcinkowsky, *Engineer*
▲ **EMP:** 50
SQ FT: 150,000
SALES: 76.4MM
SALES (corp-wide): 392.6MM **Privately Held**
WEB: www.primewirecable.com
SIC: 3357 Building wire & cable, nonferrous
PA: Yfc-Boneagle Electric Co., Ltd.
No. 12-9, Ln. 130, Sec. 2, Zhongshan
E. Rd.,
Taoyuan City TAY 32741
347 788-46

(P-11672)
QPC FIBER OPTIC LLC
27612 El Lazo, Laguna Niguel
(92677-3913)
PHONE...................949 361-8855
Steven J Wilkes, *President*
David Olsen, *CFO*
Jason Hernandez, *Office Mgr*
Gary Flora, *Sales Staff*
EMP: 28
SQ FT: 1,400
SALES: 2.5MM **Privately Held**
WEB: www.qpcfiber.com
SIC: 3357 Fiber optic cable (insulated)

▲ = Import ▼=Export
◆ =Import/Export

(P-11673)
RF PRECISION CABLES INC
1600 S Anaheim Blvd Ste A, Anaheim
(92805-6231)
PHONE......................................714 772-7567
Sabry El Masry, *President*
David Rivers, *Vice Pres*
Sabry Masry, *Administration*
▲ EMP: 11
SQ FT: 1,700
SALES: ¹MM **Privately Held**
WEB: www.rfprecisioncables.com
SIC: 3357 3679 Coaxial cable, nonferrous;
  microwave components

(P-11674)
SOUTH BAY CABLE CORP (PA)
54125 Maranatha Dr, Idyllwild (92549)
P.O. Box 67 (92549-0067)
PHONE......................................951 659-2183
Gordon W Brown Sr, *CEO*
Joyce Brown, *Treasurer*
Oscar Lehuede, *Engineer*
Jennifer Feddema, *Manager*
Ann Erler, *Accounts Mgr*
EMP: 75
SQ FT: 80,000
SALES (est): 14.6MM **Privately Held**
WEB: www.southbaycable.com
SIC: 3357 Nonferrous wiredrawing & insu-
  lating

(P-11675)
SOUTH BAY CABLE CORP
42033 Rio Nedo, Temecula (92590-3705)
P.O. Box 67, Idyllwild (92549-0067)
PHONE......................................951 296-9900
Gordon Brown, *President*
Mark Collis, *Sales Staff*
EMP: 15
SALES (corp-wide): 14.6MM **Privately
Held**
WEB: www.southbaycable.com
SIC: 3357 Nonferrous wiredrawing & insu-
  lating
PA: South Bay Cable Corp.
  54125 Maranatha Dr
  Idyllwild CA 92549
  951 659-2183

(P-11676)
STANDARD WIRE & CABLE CO (PA)
Also Called: AMERICAN WIRE SALES
2050 E Vista Bella Way, Rancho
Dominguez (90220-6109)
P.O. Box 9054, Compton (90224-9054)
PHONE......................................310 609-1811
Russell J Skrable, *President*
Dick Hampikian, *Ch of Bd*
◆ EMP: 40
SQ FT: 45,000
SALES: 8.6MM **Privately Held**
WEB: www.standard-wire.com
SIC: 3357 5063 Coaxial cable, nonferrous;
  wire & cable; electronic wire & cable;
  power wire & cable

(P-11677)
SUPERIOR ESSEX INC
5250 Ontario Mills Pkwy # 300, Ontario
(91764-5131)
PHONE......................................909 481-4804
Victor Alegria, *Branch Mgr*
EMP: 10
SALES (corp-wide): 105.4MM **Privately
Held**
SIC: 3357 Nonferrous wiredrawing & insu-
  lating
HQ: Superior Essex Inc.
  6120 Powers Ferry Rd # 150
  Atlanta GA 30339
  770 657-6000

(P-11678)
TAG-CONNECT LLC
433 Airport Blvd Ste 425, Burlingame
(94010-2014)
PHONE......................................877 244-4156
Neil Sherman, *Principal*
Takako Sherman, *Office Mgr*
EMP: 12
SALES (est): 1.4MM **Privately Held**
SIC: 3357 Coaxial cable, nonferrous

(P-11679)
TE CONNECTIVITY CORPORATION
501 Oakside Ave Side, Redwood City
(94063-3800)
PHONE......................................650 361-3333
Batu Berkok, *Plant Mgr*
EMP: 10
SALES (corp-wide): 13.1B **Privately Held**
WEB: www.raychem.com
SIC: 3357 Automotive wire & cable, except
  ignition sets: nonferrous
HQ: Te Connectivity Corporation
  1050 Westlakes Dr
  Berwyn PA 19312
  610 893-9800

(P-11680)
TYCO INTERNATIONAL MGT CO LLC
300 Constitution Dr, Menlo Park
(94025-1140)
PHONE......................................650 361-3333
Don Wood, *Principal*
EMP: 300 **Privately Held**
SIC: 3357 Communication wire
HQ: Tyco International Management Com-
  pany, Llc
  9 Roszel Rd Ste 2
  Princeton NJ 08540
  609 720-4200

(P-11681)
VICTOR WIRE AND CABLE LLC
12915 S Spring St, Los Angeles
(90061-1631)
PHONE......................................310 842-9933
Robert Smith, *Sales Executive*
EMP: 11
SQ FT: 20,000
SALES (est): 2.1MM **Privately Held**
WEB: www.victorwire.com
SIC: 3357 Nonferrous wiredrawing & insu-
  lating

(P-11682)
WINTRONICS INTERNATIONAL INC
Also Called: Winstronics
3817 Spinnaker Ct, Fremont (94538-6537)
PHONE......................................510 226-7588
Ben Yueh, *President*
Molly Morrison, *Sales Staff*
Eileen Hsu, *Accounts Mgr*
▲ EMP: 25
SQ FT: 12,000
SALES (est): 9.5MM **Privately Held**
WEB: www.winsusa.com
SIC: 3357 Communication wire

(P-11683)
WIRE TECHNOLOGY CORPORATION
9527 Laurel St, Los Angeles (90002-2653)
P.O. Box 1608, South Gate (90280-1608)
PHONE......................................310 635-6935
Rachel Mendoza, *President*
Darlene Delange, *Vice Pres*
Robert Mendoza, *Principal*
EMP: 25 EST: 1970
SQ FT: 4,000
SALES (est): 5.5MM **Privately Held**
WEB: www.wiretechnology.com
SIC: 3357 Nonferrous wiredrawing & insu-
  lating

3363 Aluminum Die

(P-11684)
AEROTEC ALLOYS INC
10632 Alondra Blvd, Norwalk (90650-5301)
PHONE......................................562 809-1378
Robert W Franklin, *CEO*
Mitchell Frahm, *Vice Pres*
Shery Franklin, *Vice Pres*
Eddie Fabian, *Controller*
Karene Alexander, *Human Res Mgr*
EMP: 50
SQ FT: 18,000

SALES (est): 14.1MM **Privately Held**
WEB: www.aerotecalloys.com
SIC: 3363 3312 3365 3325 Aluminum
  die-castings; blast furnaces & steel mills;
  aluminum foundries; steel foundries

(P-11685)
ALLOY DIE CASTING CO
Also Called: Alloy De Casting Co
6550 Caballero Blvd, Buena Park
(90620-1130)
PHONE......................................714 521-9800
Eric Sanders, *President*
Mark McEachern, *Info Tech Mgr*
Steven Lopez, *Technology*
EMP: 350 EST: 1939
SQ FT: 55,000
SALES (est): 85.1MM
SALES (corp-wide): 182.4MM **Privately
Held**
WEB: www.alloydie.com
SIC: 3363 Aluminum die-castings
HQ: Sanders Industries
  3701 E Conant St
  Long Beach CA 90808
  562 354-2920

(P-11686)
ALPHACAST FOUNDRY INC
826 S Santa Fe Ave, Los Angeles
(90021-1725)
PHONE......................................213 624-7156
Luis Rangel, *President*
EMP: 10
SQ FT: 6,800
SALES (est): 1.7MM **Privately Held**
SIC: 3363 Aluminum die-castings

(P-11687)
ALUMINUM DIE CASTING CO INC
10775 San Sevaine Way, Mira Loma
(91752-1146)
PHONE......................................951 681-3900
Steve Bennett, *CEO*
James Bennett, *Shareholder*
Rudy Bennett, *Vice Pres*
Carolyn Hibbs,
EMP: 65 EST: 1950
SQ FT: 31,000
SALES (est): 16.6MM **Privately Held**
WEB: www.adc3900.com
SIC: 3363 3364 Aluminum die-castings;
  nonferrous die-castings except aluminum

(P-11688)
ARROW DIECASTING INC
4031 Goodwin Ave, Los Angeles
(90039-1197)
PHONE......................................323 245-8439
Kirk Harris, *President*
Lynn Harris, *Vice Pres*
EMP: 10 EST: 1955
SQ FT: 7,400
SALES: 1MM **Privately Held**
SIC: 3363 3364 Aluminum die-castings;
  zinc & zinc-base alloy die-castings

(P-11689)
BEALS CASTINGS INC
520 S Palmetto Ave, Ontario (91762-4121)
PHONE......................................909 986-3849
John Reed, *President*
EMP: 40
SQ FT: 1,248
SALES (est): 3.6MM **Privately Held**
SIC: 3363 3364 3369 3365 Aluminum
  die-castings; nonferrous die-castings ex-
  cept aluminum; nonferrous foundries; alu-
  minum foundries

(P-11690)
CALIDAD INC
1730 S Balboa Ave, Ontario (91761-7773)
PHONE......................................909 947-3937
Don Cornell, *President*
Nola Cornell, *Corp Secy*
Daniel Garcia, *Vice Pres*
Blake Orlando, *Engineer*
Danielle Antinora, *Bookkeeper*
EMP: 30
SQ FT: 10,000

SALES (est): 5.9MM **Privately Held**
WEB: www.calidadinc.com
SIC: 3363 3365 3324 Aluminum die-castings; aluminum foundries; steel investment foundries

(P-11691)
COOLING SOURCE INC
2021 Las Positas Ct # 101, Livermore
(94551-7311)
PHONE......................................925 292-1293
Michel Gelinas, *President*
Wayne Finger, *Regl Sales Mgr*
Jason Shrider, *Sales Staff*
George Fox, *Manager*
▲ EMP: 118 EST: 2009
SQ FT: 4,000
SALES (est): 23.4MM **Privately Held**
SIC: 3363 3354 3325 3469 Aluminum
  die-castings; shapes, extruded aluminum;
  alloy steel castings, except investment;
  metal stampings

(P-11692)
EAST BAY BRASS FOUNDRY INC
1200 Chesley Ave, Richmond
(94801-2144)
PHONE......................................510 233-7171
Milton G Stewart, *President*
Teresa K Stewart, *Admin Sec*
EMP: 20
SQ FT: 16,700
SALES (est): 1.8MM **Privately Held**
WEB: www.eastbaybrass.com
SIC: 3363 3364 3366 3369 Aluminum
  die-castings; brass & bronze die-castings;
  bronze foundry; nonferrous foundries; alu-
  minum foundries

(P-11693)
EDELBROCK FOUNDRY CORP
1320 S Buena Vista St, San Jacinto
(92583-4665)
PHONE......................................951 654-6677
Otis Victor Edelbrock, *President*
Nancy Edelbrock, *Treasurer*
Ronald L Webb, *Exec VP*
Aristedes Seles, *Vice Pres*
Samantha Alpirez, *Admin Sec*
EMP: 691
SQ FT: 75,000
SALES (est): 91.5MM **Privately Held**
WEB: www.edelbrock.com
SIC: 3363 3365 3325 Aluminum die-cast-
  ings; aluminum foundries; steel foundries
HQ: Edelbrock, Llc
  2700 California St
  Torrance CA 90503
  310 781-2222

(P-11694)
HYATT DIE CAST ENGRG CORP - S
12250 Industry St, Garden Grove
(92841-2816)
PHONE......................................714 622-2131
Mike Senter, *Branch Mgr*
EMP: 23
SALES (est): 2.3MM
SALES (corp-wide): 24.4MM **Privately
Held**
SIC: 3363 Aluminum die-castings
PA: Hyatt Die Cast And Engineering Corpo-
  ration - South
  4656 Lincoln Ave
  Cypress CA 90630
  714 826-7550

(P-11695)
HYATT DIE CAST ENGRG CORP - S
Also Called: Hyatt Die Casting
1250 Kifer Rd, Sunnyvale (94086-5304)
PHONE......................................408 523-7000
Kul Dhanota, *Branch Mgr*
EMP: 40
SALES (corp-wide): 24.4MM **Privately
Held**
WEB: www.hyattdiecast.com
SIC: 3363 Aluminum die-castings
PA: Hyatt Die Cast And Engineering Corpo-
  ration - South
  4656 Lincoln Ave
  Cypress CA 90630
  714 826-7550

(P-11696)
ICSN INC
521 Princeland Ct, Corona (92879-1383)
PHONE....................................951 687-2305
Kevin Ko, *Principal*
Michelle Macias, *Project Mgr*
Renee Lee, *Accounting Mgr*
Joon Lee, *Director*
▲ EMP: 13
SALES (est): 1.7MM **Privately Held**
SIC: 3363 Aluminum die-castings

(P-11697)
KEARNEYS ALUMINUM FOUNDRY INC (PA)
2660 S Dearing Ave, Fresno (93725-2104)
P.O. Box 2926 (93745-2926)
PHONE....................................559 233-2591
Victor T Kearney Sr, *CEO*
Gary A Kearney, *President*
Michael Kearney, *President*
William Kearney, *President*
Robert Kearney Jr, *Vice Pres*
▲ EMP: 20
SQ FT: 80,000
SALES (est): 3.4MM **Privately Held**
SIC: 3363 Aluminum die-castings

(P-11698)
KENWALT DIE CASTING CORP
8719 Bradley Ave, Sun Valley (91352-2799)
PHONE....................................818 768-5800
Ken Zaucha Sr, *President*
Rose Zaucha, *Shareholder*
Justin Robertson, *Sales Associate*
▼ EMP: 25
SQ FT: 20,000
SALES (est): 6.3MM **Privately Held**
WEB: www.kenwalt.com
SIC: 3363 Aluminum die-castings

(P-11699)
MAGNESIUM ALLOY PDTS CO INC
2420 N Alameda St, Compton (90222-2895)
P.O. Box 4668 (90224-4668)
PHONE....................................310 605-1440
J W Long, *President*
Maria Mendez, *General Mgr*
M B Long, *Admin Sec*
Neil Wenborne, *Info Tech Mgr*
EMP: 46 EST: 1945
SQ FT: 90,000
SALES (est): 9.7MM **Privately Held**
SIC: 3363 Aluminum die-castings

(P-11700)
MAGNESIUM ALLOY PRODUCTS CO LP
2420 N Alameda St, Compton (90222-2895)
PHONE....................................323 636-2276
Richard Killen, *Partner*
James Long, *Partner*
EMP: 50
SALES: 4.5MM **Privately Held**
SIC: 3363 Aluminum die-castings

(P-11701)
PACIFIC DIE CASTING CORP
6155 S Eastern Ave, Commerce (90040-3401)
PHONE....................................323 725-1308
Jeff Orlandini, *Vice Pres*
Sonny Yun, *Shareholder*
▲ EMP: 150
SQ FT: 8,000
SALES (est): 22.8MM **Privately Held**
SIC: 3363 Aluminum die-castings

(P-11702)
PENINSULA LIGHT METALS LLC (HQ)
875 W 8th St, Azusa (91702-2247)
PHONE....................................626 765-4856
Steve Frediani,
Anthony Bozzuto, *Vice Pres*
Jeremy Majewski, *Technology*
William Grady, *Director*
Edward Hanley, *Manager*
◆ EMP: 10
SQ FT: 5,000

SALES (est): 1.7MM **Privately Held**
WEB: www.peninsula-lm.com
SIC: 3363 Aluminum die-castings

(P-11703)
PERFORMANCE ALUMINUM PRODUCTS
520 S Palmetto Ave, Ontario (91762-4121)
PHONE....................................909 391-4131
John Reed, *President*
▲ EMP: 20
SALES (est): 3.1MM **Privately Held**
WEB: www.performancealuminum.com
SIC: 3363 Aluminum die-castings

(P-11704)
PIONEER DIECASTERS INC
4209 Chevy Chase Dr, Los Angeles (90039-1294)
PHONE....................................323 245-6561
Carl H Spahr, *President*
Gretchen Perry, *Admin Sec*
EMP: 17
SQ FT: 18,000
SALES: 1.8MM **Privately Held**
SIC: 3363 3364 5051 Aluminum die-castings; zinc & zinc-base alloy die-castings; aluminum bars, rods, ingots, sheets, pipes, plates, etc.

(P-11705)
SAN JOSE DIE CASTING CORP
2475 Autumnvale Dr, San Jose (95131-1802)
PHONE....................................408 262-6500
Everett Callaghan, *President*
Leonid Kirshon, *Vice Pres*
Mark Callaghan, *VP Mfg*
Laura Almazora, *Sales Mgr*
▲ EMP: 27
SQ FT: 23,000
SALES (est): 6.1MM **Privately Held**
WEB: www.sjdiecasting.com
SIC: 3363 3364 3599 3441 Aluminum die-castings; zinc & zinc-base alloy die-castings; machine shop, jobbing & repair; fabricated structural metal; nonferrous foundries

(P-11706)
SEA SHIELD MARINE PRODUCTS
Also Called: American Zinc Enterprises
20832 Currier Rd, Walnut (91789-3017)
PHONE....................................909 594-2507
Wendell Walter Godwin, *CEO*
Shelley Lopez, *CFO*
Alicia Vongoeben, *Administration*
▲ EMP: 45
SQ FT: 25,000
SALES: 5MM **Privately Held**
WEB: www.diecastofamerica.com
SIC: 3363 3364 Aluminum die-castings; magnesium & magnesium-base alloy die-castings; zinc & zinc-base alloy die-castings

(P-11707)
SKS DIE CAST & MACHINING INC (PA)
1849 Oak St, Alameda (94501-1412)
PHONE....................................510 523-2541
Sean Keating, *CEO*
Jerome W Keating, *President*
Menelos J Moore, *Treasurer*
Leonore Keating, *Admin Sec*
Jesusa Fusade, *Asst Treas*
▲ EMP: 44
SQ FT: 50,000
SALES (est): 9.1MM **Privately Held**
WEB: www.sksdiecasting.com
SIC: 3363 3845 Aluminum die-castings; electromedical equipment

(P-11708)
VENUS ALLOYS INC (PA)
1415 S Allec St, Anaheim (92805-6306)
PHONE....................................714 635-8800
E K Venugopal, *President*
Kousalya Venugopal, *Admin Sec*
EMP: 24
SQ FT: 20,000
SALES: 60K **Privately Held**
SIC: 3363 3364 Aluminum die-castings; brass & bronze die-castings

---

3364 Nonferrous Die Castings, Exc Aluminum

(P-11709)
AMERICAN DIE CASTING INC
14576 Fontlee Ln, Fontana (92335-2599)
PHONE....................................909 356-7768
Walter Mueller, *President*
Marjorie Mueller, *Treasurer*
Jeffrey Mueller, *Vice Pres*
EMP: 50
SQ FT: 20,000
SALES: 7MM **Privately Held**
SIC: 3364 3363 Zinc & zinc-base alloy die-castings; brass & bronze die-castings; lead & zinc die-castings; aluminum die-castings

(P-11710)
CALIFORNIA DIE CASTING INC
1820 S Grove Ave, Ontario (91761-5613)
PHONE....................................909 947-9947
Dan C Lane, *President*
Roy Herring, *Corp Secy*
Jerry C Holland, *Vice Pres*
Tom Thomas, *Vice Pres*
Cindy Ortega, *Manager*
EMP: 49
SQ FT: 3,000
SALES (est): 8.6MM **Privately Held**
WEB: www.caldiecast.com
SIC: 3364 3363 Nonferrous die-castings except aluminum; aluminum die-castings

(P-11711)
CUSTOM DESIGN IRON WORKS INC
9182 Kelvin Ave, Chatsworth (91311-5901)
PHONE....................................818 700-9182
Shaia Schuchmacher, *President*
Beverly Schuchmacher, *Vice Pres*
EMP: 13
SQ FT: 4,980
SALES (est): 2.4MM **Privately Held**
SIC: 3364 1799 Nonferrous die-castings except aluminum; ornamental metal work

(P-11712)
DEL MAR INDUSTRIES (PA)
Also Called: Del Mar Die Casting Co
12901 S Western Ave, Gardena (90249-1917)
P.O. Box 881, Venice (90294-0881)
PHONE....................................323 321-0600
D R Taylor, *CEO*
Susan Davis, *Shareholder*
Louis A Cuhrt, *CFO*
Judith Taylor, *Admin Sec*
EMP: 100 EST: 1968
SQ FT: 68,000
SALES (est): 14.9MM **Privately Held**
WEB: www.delmarindustries.com
SIC: 3364 Zinc & zinc-base alloy die-castings; magnesium & magnesium-base alloy die-castings

(P-11713)
DEL MAR INDUSTRIES
Gardena Plating Co
12901 S Western Ave, Gardena (90249-1917)
PHONE....................................310 327-2634
Fax: 310 327-2904
EMP: 25 **Privately Held**
SIC: 3364 3471
PA: Del Mar Industries
12901 S Western Ave
Gardena CA 90249
323 321-0600

(P-11714)
DYNACAST INC
25952 Commercentre Dr, Lake Forest (92630-8815)
PHONE....................................949 707-1211
John Hess, *Branch Mgr*
Van Mathony, *Engineer*
Michelle Coffelt, *Buyer*
Chris Mitchell, *Opers Mgr*
EMP: 140
SALES (corp-wide): 1.2B **Privately Held**
SIC: 3364 Nonferrous die-castings except aluminum

HQ: Dynacast Inc
14045 Ballantyne Ste
Charlotte NC 28277
704 927-2790

(P-11715)
FTG AEROSPACE INC (DH)
20740 Marilla St, Chatsworth (91311-4407)
PHONE....................................818 407-4024
Michael Labrador, *President*
▼ EMP: 42
SQ FT: 13,000
SALES: 21MM
SALES (corp-wide): 74.8MM **Privately Held**
SIC: 3364 Nonferrous die-castings except aluminum
HQ: Firan Technology Group (Usa) Corporation
20750 Marilla St
Chatsworth CA 91311
818 407-4024

(P-11716)
PRESSURE CAST PRODUCTS CORP
4210 E 12th St, Oakland (94601-4411)
PHONE....................................510 532-7310
Willis Mc Neil, *President*
Vikki Cantwell, *General Mgr*
Jean Mc Neil, *Admin Sec*
▲ EMP: 45
SQ FT: 30,000
SALES (est): 7.9MM **Privately Held**
WEB: www.pressurecastproducts.com
SIC: 3364 3363 Zinc & zinc-base alloy die-castings; aluminum die-castings

(P-11717)
PROTECH MATERIALS INC
20919 Cabot Blvd, Hayward (94545-1155)
PHONE....................................510 887-5870
MEI Zhang, *President*
Larry Liu, *Vice Pres*
▲ EMP: 16
SQ FT: 7,100
SALES (est): 3.6MM **Privately Held**
SIC: 3364 3443 Nonferrous die-castings except aluminum; high vacuum coaters, metal plate

(P-11718)
VERTECHS ENTERPRISES INC (PA)
1071 Industrial Pl, El Cajon (92020-3107)
PHONE....................................858 578-3900
Geosef Straza, *CEO*
George C Straza, *Admin Sec*
Glen Lawford, *Engineer*
Dick Warner, *Chief Engr*
Todd Elliott, *Opers Staff*
▲ EMP: 63
SALES (est): 16.3MM **Privately Held**
SIC: 3364 3724 3544 Copper & copper alloy die-castings; aircraft engines & engine parts; die sets for metal stamping (presses)

3365 Aluminum Foundries

(P-11719)
ADM WORKS LLC
1343 E Wilshire Ave, Santa Ana (92705-4420)
PHONE....................................714 245-0536
Jimmy Garcia, *Office Admin*
Eric Schwartz, *Chief Engr*
Javier Valbibieso,
EMP: 23
SALES (est): 5MM **Privately Held**
SIC: 3365 7389 8711 Aerospace castings, aluminum; design services; engineering services

(P-11720)
AEROL CO INC (PA)
19560 S Rancho Way, Rancho Dominguez (90220-6038)
PHONE....................................310 762-2660
Frederick M Seibert, *CEO*
Anthony Olivier, *President*
Ron Olivier, *Vice Pres*
Fe Lorma Rivera, *Controller*
Alan Escobar, *Purch Mgr*

▲ = Import ▼=Export
◆ =Import/Export

▲ EMP: 36
SQ FT: 45,000
SALES (est): 5.1MM Privately Held
SIC: 3365 2821 3714 3728 Aluminum
foundries; plastics materials & resins;
motor vehicle parts & accessories;
wheels, aircraft; manufactured hardware
(general); industrial trucks & tractors

(P-11721)
AIRCRAFT FOUNDRY CO INC
Also Called: Afco
5316 Pacific Blvd, Huntington Park
(90255-2596)
PHONE....................323 587-3171
Ronald Caliva, President
Don Caliva, Treasurer
Donald Caliva, Treasurer
Ken Caliva, Vice Pres
Glenn Caliva, Admin Sec
EMP: 18 EST: 1942
SQ FT: 16,000
SALES: 500K Privately Held
WEB: www.aircraftfoundry.com
SIC: 3365 Aluminum & aluminum-based
alloy castings

(P-11722)
ALCAST MFG INC
2910 Fisk Ln, Redondo Beach
(90278-5437)
PHONE....................310 542-3581
Kiwon Ban, CEO
SOO Ban, Treasurer
Angela Gonzalez, Admin Mgr
Angelica Oreta, Accounting Mgr
▲ EMP: 55
SQ FT: 28,000
SALES (est): 16MM Privately Held
WEB: www.alcast.com
SIC: 3365 3366 3544 3369 Aluminum
foundries; brass foundry; special dies,
tools, jigs & fixtures; nonferrous foundries;
nonferrous die-castings except aluminum;
fabricated structural metal

(P-11723)
ALUMISTAR INC
Also Called: Pacific Cast Products
12711 Imperial Hwy, Santa Fe Springs
(90670-4711)
PHONE....................562 633-6673
Peter Lake, President
▲ EMP: 26
SQ FT: 20,000
SALES (est): 4.5MM Privately Held
WEB: www.alumistar.com
SIC: 3365 Aluminum & aluminum-based
alloy castings

(P-11724)
AMERICAN INTERNATIONAL ENGINEE
860 Arroyo St, San Fernando
(91340-1832)
PHONE....................818 365-8000
Ward H White, President
EMP: 23
SQ FT: 12,000
SALES (est): 3.6MM Privately Held
WEB: www.aiem.com
SIC: 3365 Aluminum foundries

(P-11725)
ANGELUS ALUMINUM FOUNDRY CO
3479 E Pico Blvd, Los Angeles
(90023-3084)
PHONE....................323 268-0145
Edward E Vena, President
Henry L Vena, Vice Pres
Judy Vena, Admin Sec
EMP: 11 EST: 1953
SQ FT: 12,800
SALES (est): 1.4MM Privately Held
SIC: 3365 Aluminum & aluminum-based
alloy castings

(P-11726)
BUDDY BAR CASTING CORPORATION
10801 Sessler St, South Gate
(90280-7222)
PHONE....................562 861-9664
Edward W Barksdale Sr, Principal

Bill Fell, President
Ty Barksdale, Corp Secy
John Fell, Vice Pres
Mike McKeen, Vice Pres
▲ EMP: 80 EST: 1953
SQ FT: 25,000
SALES (est): 18.1MM Privately Held
WEB: www.buddybarcasting.com
SIC: 3365 Aluminum & aluminum-based
alloy castings

(P-11727)
CASTOR ENGINEERING INC
450 Commercial Way, La Habra
(90631-6167)
P.O. Box 3808 (90632-3808)
PHONE....................562 690-4036
Lawrence Bailey, President
Amber L Bailey, Vice Pres
Emily Deutsch, Internal Med
▼ EMP: 10
SQ FT: 6,500
SALES: 1MM Privately Held
SIC: 3365 Aerospace castings, aluminum

(P-11728)
CHOICE FOODSERVICES INC
Also Called: Children's Choice
569 San Ramon Valley Blvd, Danville
(94526-4024)
PHONE....................925 837-0104
Justin Gagnon, President
Ryan Mariopti, CFO
Keith Cosbey, Director
▲ EMP: 80
SALES (est): 23.1MM Privately Held
SIC: 3365 5049 Cooking/kitchen utensils,
cast aluminum; school supplies

(P-11729)
CONSOLDTED PRECISION PDTS CORP
Also Called: Cpp Cudahy
8333 Wilcox Ave, Cudahy (90201-5919)
P.O. Box 1099 (90201-7099)
PHONE....................323 773-2363
Steve Gallardo, Branch Mgr
EMP: 130
SALES (corp-wide): 6.3B Privately Held
SIC: 3365 3324 Aluminum foundries; steel
investment foundries
HQ: Consolidated Precision Products Corp.
1621 Euclid Ave Ste 1850
Cleveland OH 44115
216 453-4800

(P-11730)
CONSOLDTED PRECISION PDTS CORP
705 Industrial Way, Port Hueneme
(93041-3505)
PHONE....................805 488-6451
EMP: 190
SALES (corp-wide): 6.3B Privately Held
SIC: 3365 Aluminum foundries
HQ: Consolidated Precision Products Corp.
1621 Euclid Ave Ste 1850
Cleveland OH 44115
216 453-4800

(P-11731)
CRAFTECH METAL FORMING INC
24100 Water Ave Ste B, Perris
(92570-6738)
PHONE....................951 940-6444
Richard L Shaw, President
EMP: 50
SQ FT: 26,000
SALES (est): 10.8MM Privately Held
WEB: www.craftechmetal.com
SIC: 3365 Aerospace castings, aluminum

(P-11732)
CYGNET AEROSPACE CORP
1971 Fearn Ave, Los Osos (93402-2517)
P.O. Box 6603 (93412-6603)
PHONE....................805 528-2376
Christopher Szarek, President
Rose Garza, Bd of Directors
EMP: 10

SALES (est): 580K Privately Held
WEB: www.cygnet-aero.com
SIC: 3365 5088 Aerospace castings, aluminum; transportation equipment & supplies

(P-11733)
CYTEC ENGINEERED MATERIALS INC
1440 N Kraemer Blvd, Anaheim
(92806-1404)
PHONE....................714 632-1174
Ron Martin, Branch Mgr
Alain Theoret, General Mgr
Austin Liu, Technician
Paul Clark, Technology
Keith Hwang, Project Engr
EMP: 125
SQ FT: 135,055
SALES (corp-wide): 10MM Privately
Held
WEB: www.cytecengineeredmaterials.com
SIC: 3365 2891 2851 2823 Aerospace
castings, aluminum; adhesives &
sealants; paints & allied products; cellu-
losic manmade fibers
HQ: Cytec Engineered Materials Inc.
2085 E Tech Cir Ste 300
Tempe AZ 85284

(P-11734)
CYTEC ENGINEERED MATERIALS INC
1440 N Cramer Blvd, Anaheim (92806)
PHONE....................714 666-4302
EMP: 188
SALES (corp-wide): 10MM Privately
Held
SIC: 3365 Aerospace castings, aluminum
HQ: Cytec Engineered Materials Inc.
2085 E Tech Cir Ste 300
Tempe AZ 85284

(P-11735)
DC PARTNERS INC
Also Called: Soligen 2006
19329 Bryant St, Northridge (91324-4114)
PHONE....................818 285-0692
Amir Gnessin, Manager
EMP: 30
SALES (corp-wide): 8.3MM Privately
Held
WEB: www.soligen2006.com
SIC: 3365 Aluminum foundries
PA: Dc Partners, Inc.
19329 Bryant St
Northridge CA 91324
714 558-9444

(P-11736)
DC PARTNERS INC (PA)
Also Called: Soligen 2006
19329 Bryant St, Northridge (91324-4114)
PHONE....................714 558-9444
Yehoram Uziel, President
Alecia Wagner, Principal
EMP: 60
SALES (est): 8.3MM Privately Held
WEB: www.soligen2006.com
SIC: 3365 3599 Aluminum foundries; ma-
chine & other job shop work

(P-11737)
DC PARTNERS INC
Also Called: Soligen 2006
19408 Londelius St, Northridge
(91324-3511)
PHONE....................818 718-1221
Gary Kanegis, Principal
Chick Lewis, Opers Staff
David Hadley, Director
Patrick J Lavelle, Director
EMP: 25
SALES (est): 3.3MM
SALES (corp-wide): 8.3MM Privately
Held
WEB: www.soligen2006.com
SIC: 3365 Aluminum foundries
PA: Dc Partners, Inc.
19329 Bryant St
Northridge CA 91324
714 558-9444

(P-11738)
DOWELL ALUMINUM FOUNDRY INC
11342 Hartland St, North Hollywood
(91605-6387)
PHONE....................323 877-9645
Lynn F Dompe, President
EMP: 19 EST: 1954
SQ FT: 17,000
SALES (est): 3.7MM Privately Held
SIC: 3365 3369 Aluminum foundries; non-
ferrous foundries

(P-11739)
DWA ALMINUM COMPOSITES USA INC
21100 Superior St, Chatsworth
(91311-4308)
PHONE....................818 998-1504
Mark R Van Den Bergh, CEO
Gary Wolfe, COO
J J Shah, CFO
Neel Shah, Project Mgr
Cory Smith, QC Mgr
EMP: 20
SQ FT: 40,000
SALES (est): 5MM Privately Held
SIC: 3365 Aluminum & aluminum-based
alloy castings

(P-11740)
EMPLOYEE OWNED PACIFIC CAST PR
Also Called: Aluminum Casting Company
12711 Imperial Hwy, Santa Fe Springs
(90670-4711)
PHONE....................562 633-6673
Alex B Hall, President
EMP: 30
SQ FT: 18,000
SALES (est): 3.9MM Privately Held
SIC: 3365 Aluminum & aluminum-based
alloy castings

(P-11741)
FONTANA FOUNDRY CORPORATION
8306 Cherry Ave, Fontana (92335-3026)
PHONE....................909 822-6128
Jeffrey Ritz, President
Susan Ritz, CFO
EMP: 25
SQ FT: 11,500
SALES (est): 5MM Privately Held
WEB: www.fontanafoundry.com
SIC: 3365 Aluminum & aluminum-based
alloy castings

(P-11742)
GENERAL FOUNDRY SERVICE CORP
1390 Business Center Pl, San Leandro
(94577-2212)
PHONE....................510 297-5040
Edward J Ritelli Jr, CEO
Edward J Ritelli Sr, President
Joe Wilhelm, Administration
Steve Bybee, Manager
EMP: 70
SQ FT: 15,200
SALES (est): 14.6MM Privately Held
WEB: www.genfoundry.com
SIC: 3365 3543 3369 3324 Aluminum &
aluminum-based alloy castings; machin-
ery castings, aluminum; industrial pat-
terns; nonferrous foundries; steel
investment foundries

(P-11743)
INTERORBITAL SYSTEMS
1394 Barnes St Bldg 7, Mojave
(93501-1673)
P.O. Box 662 (93502-0662)
PHONE....................661 824-1662
Randa Milliron, CEO
Roderick Milliron, President
EMP: 12
SQ FT: 6,000
SALES (est): 150K Privately Held
WEB: www.interorbital.com
SIC: 3365 3764 Aerospace castings, alu-
minum; guided missile & space vehicle
propulsion unit parts; propulsion units for
guided missiles & space vehicles

PRODUCTS & SVCS

(P-11744)
KEARNEY PATTERN WORKS & FNDRY
40 S Montgomery St, San Jose (95110-2518)
PHONE..................................408 293-7414
James W Wagner, *President*
EMP: 30
SALES (est): 4.2MM **Privately Held**
SIC: 3365 3369 Aluminum & aluminum-based alloy castings; nonferrous foundries

(P-11745)
LYNWOOD PATTERN SERVICE INC
2528 E 127th St, Compton (90222-1514)
P.O. Box 536, Lynwood (90262-0536)
PHONE..................................310 631-2225
Jose Alvarez, *President*
Benjamen Alvarez, *Vice Pres*
Jason Alvarez, *Manager*
EMP: 15
SQ FT: 4,000
SALES (est): 2MM **Privately Held**
SIC: 3365 3543 Aluminum & aluminum-based alloy castings; foundry patternmaking

(P-11746)
MAGPARTS (DH)
Also Called: Cpp-Azusa
1545 W Roosevelt St, Azusa (91702-3281)
PHONE..................................626 334-7897
Richard H Emerson, *President*
L Scott Mac Donald, *Vice Pres*
Ellen E Skatvold, *Admin Sec*
Stephen A Mac Donald, *Site Mgr*
Jesus Diaz, *Safety Mgr*
EMP: 73
SQ FT: 100,000
SALES (est): 19.8MM
SALES (corp-wide): 6.3B **Privately Held**
WEB: www.magparts.com
SIC: 3365 3369 Aluminum & aluminum-based alloy castings; magnesium & magnes.-base alloy castings, exc. die-casting
HQ: Consolidated Precision Products Corp.
1621 Euclid Ave Ste 1850
Cleveland OH 44115
216 453-4800

(P-11747)
OASIS ALLOY WHEELS INC
Also Called: Oasis Metal Works
400 S Lemon St, Anaheim (92805-3816)
PHONE..................................714 533-3286
EMP: 13
SQ FT: 10,000
SALES: 2MM **Privately Held**
WEB: www.oasiswheels.com
SIC: 3365

(P-11748)
PAC FOUNDRIES INC
Also Called: Prime Alloy Steel Casting
705 Industrial Way, Port Hueneme (93041-3505)
PHONE..................................805 986-1308
Steve Clodfelter, *President*
Armando Ortiz, *Info Tech Dir*
EMP: 229
SALES (est): 37.2MM
SALES (corp-wide): 6.3B **Privately Held**
WEB: www.pacificalloy.com
SIC: 3365 Aerospace castings, aluminum
HQ: Consolidated Precision Products Corp.
1621 Euclid Ave Ste 1850
Cleveland OH 44115
216 453-4800

(P-11749)
RELATIVITY SPACE INC
8701 Aviation Blvd, Inglewood (90301-2003)
PHONE..................................972 978-8946
Tim Ellis, *CEO*
Alexander Kwan, *Vice Pres*
Jordan Noone, *CTO*
EMP: 10
SQ FT: 9,600
SALES: 500K **Privately Held**
SIC: 3365 Aerospace castings, aluminum

(P-11750)
TRILORE TECHNOLOGIES INC
3000 Danville Blvd 525f, Alamo (94507-1574)
PHONE..................................925 295-0734
John Collins, *CEO*
Pritam Dhaliwal, *CFO*
Jason Pearson, *Vice Pres*
EMP: 30
SQ FT: 24,000
SALES (est): 5.1MM **Privately Held**
WEB: www.trilore.com
SIC: 3365 Aluminum foundries

(P-11751)
VAN BRUNT FOUNDRY INC
5136 Chakemco St, South Gate (90280-6443)
PHONE..................................323 569-2832
Richard Ledesma, *President*
EMP: 12 EST: 1963
SQ FT: 10,000
SALES (est): 1.3MM **Privately Held**
SIC: 3365 Aluminum & aluminum-based alloy castings

3366 Copper Foundries

(P-11752)
ACME CASTINGS INC
6009 Santa Fe Ave, Huntington Park (90255-2723)
PHONE..................................323 583-3129
Lee Lewis, *President*
Ruth Lewis, *Corp Secy*
EMP: 40 EST: 1963
SQ FT: 25,000
SALES (est): 6.2MM **Privately Held**
WEB: www.acme-castings.com
SIC: 3366 3325 3365 3322 Copper foundries; alloy steel castings, except investment; aluminum foundries; malleable iron foundries

(P-11753)
AMERICAN FINE ARTS FOUNDRY LLC
2520 N Ontario St Ste A, Burbank (91504-4708)
PHONE..................................818 848-7593
Brett Barney,
Chris Delling, *Mktg Dir*
Angel Meza, *Sales Staff*
EMP: 25
SQ FT: 3,000
SALES (est): 4.1MM **Privately Held**
WEB: www.afafoundry.com
SIC: 3366 3544 Castings (except die): bronze; forms (molds), for foundry & plastics working machinery

(P-11754)
ART BRONZE INC
11275 San Fernando Rd, San Fernando (91340-3422)
PHONE..................................818 897-2222
Ian G Killips, *CEO*
EMP: 29
SQ FT: 11,400
SALES: 1.8MM **Privately Held**
SIC: 3366 3312 Bronze foundry; stainless steel

(P-11755)
ASI/SILICA MACHINERY LLC (PA)
6404 Independence Ave, Woodland Hills (91367-2607)
PHONE..................................818 920-1962
Ed Connor,
Steven Benson, *Technician*
Dr Frank Dabby,
Fred Golob,
EMP: 23 EST: 1997
SQ FT: 11,000
SALES (est): 5.4MM **Privately Held**
WEB: www.asisilica.com
SIC: 3366 Machinery castings: brass

(P-11756)
E R METALS INC
Also Called: Heritage Bronze
14407 Main St, Hesperia (92345-4617)
PHONE..................................760 948-2309

Robert Escoto Sr, *President*
Robert Escoto Jr, *Corp Secy*
EMP: 13
SALES (est): 1.5MM **Privately Held**
WEB: www.heritagebronze.com
SIC: 3366 3363 Copper foundries; aluminum die-castings

(P-11757)
FLEETWOOD CONTINENTAL INC
19451 S Susana Rd, Compton (90221-5713)
PHONE..................................310 609-1477
David J Forster, *President*
Rich Curry, *Executive*
David Forester, *Safety Mgr*
▲ EMP: 75
SQ FT: 5,000
SALES (est): 16.3MM **Privately Held**
WEB: www.fleetcon.com
SIC: 3366 3823 3561 3523 Castings (except die): bronze; turbine flow meters, industrial process type; pumps & pumping equipment; farm machinery & equipment

(P-11758)
FRESNO VALVES & CASTINGS INC (PA)
7736 E Springfield Ave, Selma (93662-9408)
P.O. Box 40 (93662-0040)
PHONE..................................559 834-2511
Jeffery T Showalter, *CEO*
John E Showalter, *President*
Jeffrey T Showalter, *CEO*
Kevin Follansbee, *CFO*
Rich Bonzo, *Engineer*
▲ EMP: 200
SALES (est): 56.2MM **Privately Held**
WEB: www.fresnovalves.com
SIC: 3366 3494 3523 3491 Brass foundry; pipe fittings; sprinkler systems, field; irrigation equipment, self-propelled; industrial valves

(P-11759)
GALAXY DIE & ENGINEERING INC
Also Called: Galaxy Bearing Company
24910 Avenue Tibbitts, Valencia (91355-3426)
PHONE..................................661 775-9301
Jawahar Saini, *President*
Hamid Baig, *Shareholder*
Sooltan Ali Bhoy, *Shareholder*
Malkiat Saini, *Shareholder*
Mohammed Shaikh, *Analyst*
EMP: 40
SQ FT: 30,000
SALES: 3.2MM **Privately Held**
WEB: www.galaxybearing.com
SIC: 3366 3575 Bushings & bearings; computer terminals

(P-11760)
GASSER-OLDS INC
2618 Fruitland Ave, Vernon (90058-2220)
PHONE..................................323 583-9031
Richard J Efurd, *Vice Pres*
John W Efurd III, *Vice Pres*
EMP: 25
SQ FT: 8,000
SALES (est): 4.7MM **Privately Held**
WEB: www.gasserolds.com
SIC: 3366 5099 3369 3365 Brass foundry; bronze foundry; castings (except die): brass; monuments & grave markers; nonferrous foundries; aluminum foundries

(P-11761)
MAJOR BRASS FOUNDRY INC (PA)
16206 S Main St, Gardena (90248-2890)
PHONE..................................310 324-0177
Don Wood, *President*
Scott Wood, *Vice Pres*
Jennifer Wood, *Admin Sec*
▲ EMP: 10 EST: 1959
SQ FT: 30,000
SALES (est): 2.7MM **Privately Held**
SIC: 3366 Brass foundry

(P-11762)
MARTIN BRASS FOUNDRY
22427 Bear Creek Dr N, Murrieta (92562-3088)
PHONE..................................951 698-7041
Roland L Martin, *President*
Glen Martin, *Vice Pres*
John W Martin, *Admin Sec*
EMP: 55
SQ FT: 20,000
SALES (est): 6.3MM **Privately Held**
WEB: www.martinbrass.com
SIC: 3366 Brass foundry; bronze foundry

(P-11763)
MATTHEWS INTERNATIONAL CORP
442 W Esplanade Ave 105, San Jacinto (92583-5006)
PHONE..................................951 537-6615
Rocky Thornton, *Manager*
EMP: 25
SALES (corp-wide): 1.5B **Publicly Held**
SIC: 3366 Copper foundries
PA: Matthews International Corporation
2 N Shore Ctr Ste 200
Pittsburgh PA 15212
412 442-8200

(P-11764)
MONTCLAIR BRONZE INC (PA)
5621 State St, Montclair (91763-6241)
P.O. Box 2009 (91763-0509)
PHONE..................................909 986-2664
Dan Griffiths, *CEO*
Wayne Freeberg, *President*
Dan Griffiths, *CEO*
Thomas Freeberg, *Admin Sec*
Magdi Abdellatif, *Sales Engr*
EMP: 30
SQ FT: 8,000
SALES (est): 4.5MM **Privately Held**
SIC: 3366 3599 Bronze foundry; machine shop, jobbing & repair

(P-11765)
POINTECH
Hunters Point Shpyd, San Francisco (94124)
P.O. Box 884234 (94188-4234)
PHONE..................................415 822-8704
Eric Swenson, *Owner*
EMP: 20
SALES (est): 3.9MM **Privately Held**
WEB: www.pointech.net
SIC: 3366 Copper foundries

(P-11766)
SIERRA SCULPTURE INC
Also Called: Van Howd Studios
13333 New Airport Rd, Auburn (95602-7419)
P.O. Box 7197 (95604-7197)
PHONE..................................530 887-1581
Douglas Van Howd, *President*
Nancy Van Howd, *Executive*
Holly Thomasson, *Sales Staff*
EMP: 11
SQ FT: 6,000
SALES (est): 1.3MM **Privately Held**
SIC: 3366 Bronze foundry

3369 Nonferrous Foundries: Castings, NEC

(P-11767)
AIRBOLT INDUSTRIES INC
25334 Stanford Ave Unit B, Valencia (91355)
PHONE..................................818 767-5600
Melissa Ramirez, *President*
Oscar Ramirez, *CEO*
EMP: 11 EST: 2015
SQ FT: 7,000
SALES (est): 1.5MM **Privately Held**
SIC: 3369 3365 Aerospace castings, nonferrous: except aluminum; aerospace castings, aluminum

▲ = Import ▼=Export
◆ =Import/Export

(P-11768)
ALLIEDSIGNAL AROSPC SVC CORP (HQ)
Also Called: Allied Signal Aerospace
2525 W 190th St, Torrance (90504-6002)
PHONE..............................310 323-9500
Bernd F Kessler, *President*
James V Gelly, *Treasurer*
Mary Beth Orson, *Vice Pres*
Lois H Fuchs, *Asst Treas*
David A Cohen, *Asst Sec*
EMP: 46
SALES (est): 21.3MM
SALES (corp-wide): 40.5B **Publicly Held**
SIC: 3369 3822 3812 3769 Nonferrous foundries; auto controls regulating residntl & coml environmt & applncs; search & navigation equipment; guided missile & space vehicle parts & auxiliary equipment; fabricated plate work (boiler shop)
PA: Honeywell International Inc.
115 Tabor Rd
Morris Plains NJ 07950
973 455-2000

(P-11769)
AURORA CASTING & ENGRG INC
1790 E Lemonwood Dr, Santa Paula (93060-9510)
PHONE..............................805 933-2761
John Carlos Penrose, *CEO*
Andrew Penrose, *General Mgr*
David Martinsson, *QA Dir*
John Handberry, *Engineer*
Eduardo Sumaran, *QC Mgr*
EMP: 65
SQ FT: 25,000
SALES (est): 14.1MM **Privately Held**
SIC: 3369 Nonferrous foundries

(P-11770)
B & G AEROSPACE METALS
1801 Railroad St, Corona (92880-2512)
P.O. Box 2767, Fallbrook (92088-2767)
PHONE..............................951 738-8133
John Bowling, *President*
Vince Bowling, *Vice Pres*
EMP: 25
SQ FT: 20,000
SALES (est): 2.1MM **Privately Held**
SIC: 3369 Nonferrous foundries

(P-11771)
CAST-RITE INTERNATIONAL INC (PA)
515 E Airline Way, Gardena (90248-2501)
PHONE..............................310 532-2080
Donald E Dehaan, *CEO*
Howard Watkins, *CFO*
Wynn Chapman, *Vice Pres*
▲ **EMP:** 90
SQ FT: 59,330
SALES (est): 27.4MM **Privately Held**
SIC: 3369 Zinc & zinc-base alloy castings, except die-castings

(P-11772)
CPP-PORT HUENEME
705 Industrial Way, Port Hueneme (93041-3505)
PHONE..............................805 488-6451
Steve Clodfelter, *Owner*
Kinjal Patel, *QC Mgr*
EMP: 230
SQ FT: 12,770
SALES (est): 24MM
SALES (corp-wide): 6.3B **Privately Held**
WEB: www.cfi-pac.com
SIC: 3369 Castings, except die-castings, precision
HQ: Consolidated Precision Products Corp.
1621 Euclid Ave Ste 1850
Cleveland OH 44115
216 453-4800

(P-11773)
CRESTOR INC
23 Rockview Dr, Santa Cruz (95062-5411)
PHONE..............................831 475-4435
H E Mueller, *Manager*
J A Annigoni, *Manager*
EMP: 12

SALES (est): 870K **Privately Held**
WEB: www.crestorinc.com
SIC: 3369 3479 Nonferrous foundries; etching on metals

(P-11774)
DECCO CASTINGS INC
1596 Pioneer Way, El Cajon (92020-1673)
PHONE..............................619 444-9437
Carl Decina, *President*
EMP: 45
SQ FT: 20,000
SALES (est): 15.4MM **Privately Held**
WEB: www.deccocastings.com
SIC: 3369 3365 3325 Nonferrous foundries; aluminum foundries; steel foundries

(P-11775)
DELT INDUSTRIES INC
90 W Easy St Ste 2, Simi Valley (93065-6206)
PHONE..............................805 579-0213
Estelle Lee, *President*
Jerry Martin, *Vice Pres*
Debra Schultz, *Admin Sec*
EMP: 18
SQ FT: 10,000
SALES (est): 3.8MM **Privately Held**
SIC: 3369 5088 Nonferrous foundries; transportation equipment & supplies

(P-11776)
EXCELITY
Also Called: Solara Engineering
11127 Dora St, Sun Valley (91352-3339)
PHONE..............................818 767-1000
Shaun Tan, *President*
Amit Garg, *Officer*
EMP: 50
SALES (est): 9.5MM **Privately Held**
SIC: 3369 3812 Aerospace castings, nonferrous: except aluminum; acceleration indicators & systems components, aerospace

(P-11777)
FENICO PRECISION CASTINGS INC
7805 Madison St, Paramount (90723-4220)
PHONE..............................562 634-5000
Don Tomeo, *President*
Sherry Tomeo, *CFO*
Sonny Tran, *Engineer*
Gary Gunning, *Prdtn Mgr*
Bruce Nesmith, *Manager*
▲ **EMP:** 75
SQ FT: 20,000
SALES (est): 14.8MM **Privately Held**
SIC: 3369 3366 3324 3322 Machinery castings, nonferrous: ex. alum., copper, die, etc.; copper foundries; steel investment foundries; malleable iron foundries

(P-11778)
FS - PRECISION TECH CO LLC
3025 E Victoria St, Compton (90221-5616)
PHONE..............................310 638-0595
Juan Molina, *VP Human Res*
Betty Ruffalo, *Info Tech Mgr*
Israel Sanchez, *Controller*
Gabriela Del Real,
Israel M Sanchez,
▲ **EMP:** 100
SALES (est): 23.9MM **Privately Held**
WEB: www.fs-precision.com
SIC: 3369 Titanium castings, except die-casting
PA: Fs-North America, Inc.
5710 Mellon Rd
Export PA 15632

(P-11779)
IMPRO INDUSTRIES USA INC (DH)
21660 Copley Dr Ste 100, Diamond Bar (91765-4174)
PHONE..............................909 396-6525
Hui INA Wang, *CEO*
Julia Chang, *Treasurer*
Anrı C Conder, *Purch Mgr*
James Chen, *Purchasing*
Miki Chiou, *Opers Mgr*
▲ **EMP:** 10

SALES (est): 4.4MM **Privately Held**
SIC: 3369 5051 Castings, except die-castings, precision; castings, rough: iron or steel
HQ: Impro (China) Limited
No.18, Furong Road 5, Xishan Economy Development Zone
Wuxi
510 851-6553

(P-11780)
PANKL AEROSPACE SYSTEMS
16615 Edwards Rd, Cerritos (90703-2437)
PHONE..............................562 207-6300
Horst Rieger, *CEO*
Harry Glieder, *President*
Pat Heim, *Buyer*
Christian Escudero, *Opers Staff*
Barry Calvert, *Director*
EMP: 75
SQ FT: 63,040
SALES (est): 21.2MM
SALES (corp-wide): 1.4B **Privately Held**
SIC: 3369 3724 Aerospace castings, nonferrous: except aluminum; aircraft engines & engine parts
HQ: Pankl Holdings, Inc.
1902 Mcgaw Ave
Irvine CA 92614

(P-11781)
PCC STRUCTURALS INC
Also Called: PCC Structurals-San Leandro
414 Hester St, San Leandro (94577-1024)
PHONE..............................510 568-6400
Craig Milton, *Branch Mgr*
Debbie Shenk, *Prgrmr*
David Pagan, *Engineer*
Aaron Jones, *Production*
Doug Delprete, *Sales Mgr*
EMP: 180
SALES (corp-wide): 242.1B **Publicly Held**
SIC: 3369 Nonferrous foundries
HQ: Pcc Structurals, Inc.
4600 Se Harney Dr
Portland OR 97206
503 777-3881

(P-11782)
PRIME ALLOY STEEL CASTINGS INC
717 Industrial Way, Port Hueneme (93041-3505)
PHONE..............................805 488-6451
Steve Clodfelter, *CEO*
Ali Ghavami, *COO*
Michael Dyar, *CFO*
William Fanner, *Vice Pres*
Bill Fanner, *Manager*
EMP: 140
SQ FT: 12,000
SALES (est): 14.4MM
SALES (corp-wide): 6.3B **Privately Held**
WEB: www.pacfoundries.com
SIC: 3369 Castings, except die-castings, precision
HQ: Consolidated Precision Products Corp.
1621 Euclid Ave Ste 1850
Cleveland OH 44115
216 453-4800

(P-11783)
RADIAN THERMAL PRODUCTS INC
Also Called: Radian Heat Sinks
2160 Walsh Ave, Santa Clara (95050-2512)
PHONE..............................408 988-6200
Gerald L McIntyre, *Chairman*
Mong Hu, *CEO*
Thierry Sin, *Exec VP*
Abhinav Sharma, *Engineer*
Phoebe LI, *Controller*
▲ **EMP:** 54
SQ FT: 26,500
SALES (est): 15.1MM **Privately Held**
SIC: 3369 Castings, except die-castings, precision

(P-11784)
SANTA ROSA LEAD PRODUCTS INC
33 S University St, Healdsburg (95448-4021)
PHONE..............................707 431-1477
Jeremy Winter, *General Mgr*
EMP: 27 **EST:** 1973
SQ FT: 6,100
SALES (est): 5.6MM
SALES (corp-wide): 476MM **Privately Held**
SIC: 3369 3444 Lead castings, except die-castings; sheet metalwork
PA: Metalico, Inc.
135 Dermody St
Cranford NJ 07016
908 497-9610

(P-11785)
SYNERTECH PM INC
11711 Monarch St, Garden Grove (92841-1830)
PHONE..............................714 898-9151
Charles Barre, *CEO*
Kristen Barre, *President*
Victor Samarov, *Vice Pres*
Catherine Crawford, *Admin Asst*
▲ **EMP:** 17
SQ FT: 20,000
SALES (est): 3.4MM **Privately Held**
WEB: www.synertechpm.com
SIC: 3369 Aerospace castings, nonferrous: except aluminum

(P-11786)
TECHNI-CAST CORP
11220 Garfield Ave, South Gate (90280-7586)
PHONE..............................562 923-4585
Bryn Jhan Van Hiel II, *President*
Donald Van Hiel, *Vice Pres*
Lynne Van Hiel, *Vice Pres*
Elaine M Kay, *Admin Sec*
▲ **EMP:** 80 **EST:** 1954
SQ FT: 60,000
SALES (est): 20.3MM **Privately Held**
WEB: www.techni-cast.com
SIC: 3369 3599 3364 3325 Lead, zinc & white metal; machinery castings, nonferrous: ex. alum., copper, die, etc.; machine shop, jobbing & repair; nonferrous die-castings except aluminum; steel foundries

(P-11787)
UNITED CASTINGS INC
5154 F St, Chino (91710-5161)
PHONE..............................909 627-7645
Albert Lewis, *President*
Doris Lewis, *Corp Secy*
Tina Moss, *Manager*
▲ **EMP:** 11
SQ FT: 6,000
SALES (est): 1.7MM
SALES (corp-wide): 9.5MM **Privately Held**
WEB: www.uncastings.com
SIC: 3369 Castings, except die-castings, precision
PA: Glass Incorporated International
14055 Laurelwood Pl
Covina CA 91724
909 628-4212

3398 Metal Heat Treating

(P-11788)
ABRASIVE FINISHING CO
Also Called: Afco
14920 S Main St, Gardena (90248-1921)
PHONE..............................310 323-7175
William Swanson, *President*
EMP: 32 **EST:** 1957
SQ FT: 2,600
SALES (est): 5MM **Privately Held**
WEB: www.abrasivefinishing.com
SIC: 3398 3471 Shot peening (treating steel to reduce fatigue); plating & polishing

(P-11789)
ACCURATE STEEL TREATING INC
10008 Miller Way, South Gate (90280-5496)
PHONE...................................562 927-6528
Ronald Loyns, *President*
Mike Bastin, *Vice Pres*
Tom Kreun, *QC Mgr*
EMP: 38
SQ FT: 10,000
SALES (est): 8.7MM **Privately Held**
WEB: www.accuratesteeltreating.com
SIC: 3398 Metal heat treating

(P-11790)
ADB INDUSTRIES
Also Called: Subsidy of Be Aerospace
1400 Manhattan Ave, Fullerton (92831-5222)
PHONE...................................310 679-9193
Brian Dietz, *President*
EMP: 90
SQ FT: 50,000
SALES (est): 10.3MM **Publicly Held**
WEB: www.adbco.com
SIC: 3398 8711 7692 3444 Brazing (hardening) of metal; engineering services; welding repair; sheet metalwork
HQ: Tsi Group, Inc.
94 Tide Mill Rd
Hampton NH 03842

(P-11791)
AEROCRAFT HEAT TREATING CO INC
15701 Minnesota Ave, Paramount (90723-4120)
PHONE...................................562 674-2400
David W Dickson, *CEO*
Robert Lyddon, *Vice Pres*
EMP: 57 **EST:** 1947
SQ FT: 18,000
SALES (est): 14.2MM
SALES (corp-wide): 242.1B **Publicly Held**
WEB: www.aerocraft-ht.com
SIC: 3398 Metal heat treating
HQ: Precision Castparts Corp.
4650 Sw Mcdam Ave Ste 300
Portland OR 97239
503 946-4800

(P-11792)
AL-MAG HEAT TREAT
9735 Alpaca St, South El Monte (91733-3028)
PHONE...................................626 442-8570
Don Dees, *President*
EMP: 13
SQ FT: 12,000
SALES (est): 1.1MM **Privately Held**
SIC: 3398 Metal heat treating

(P-11793)
AREMAC HEAT TREATING INC
330 S 9th Ave, City of Industry (91746-3311)
P.O. Box 90068 (91715-0068)
PHONE...................................626 333-3898
B E Kopaskie, *President*
Bernard E Kopaskie, *President*
D R Butler, *Vice Pres*
Jan Kopaskie, *Admin Sec*
Steve Allensworth, *Sales Mgr*
EMP: 38
SQ FT: 14,000
SALES (est): 10.8MM **Privately Held**
SIC: 3398 Metal heat treating

(P-11794)
ASTRO ALUMINUM TREATING CO INC
11040 Palmer Ave, South Gate (90280-7497)
PHONE...................................562 923-4344
Mark R Dickson, *President*
Victor Gonzalez, *Executive*
Miguel Nuevano, *MIS Staff*
Robert Hansen, *Project Mgr*
Mark Streiff, *Finance Mgr*
EMP: 90 **EST:** 1977
SQ FT: 4,800

SALES (est): 24.2MM **Privately Held**
WEB: www.astroaluminum.com
SIC: 3398 Metal heat treating

(P-11795)
BODYCOTE IMT INC
Also Called: Alum-A-Therm
7474 Garden Grove Blvd, Westminster (92683-2227)
PHONE...................................714 893-6561
Jeff Monty, *Branch Mgr*
Mark Estrada, *Technology*
EMP: 55
SALES (corp-wide): 911.9MM **Privately Held**
SIC: 3398 Metal heat treating
HQ: Bodycote Imt, Inc.
155 River St
Andover MA 01810
978 470-0876

(P-11796)
BODYCOTE THERMAL PROC INC
2900 S Sunol Dr, Vernon (90058-4315)
PHONE...................................323 264-0111
Chris Hall, *Branch Mgr*
EMP: 10
SALES (corp-wide): 911.9MM **Privately Held**
SIC: 3398 Metal heat treating
HQ: Bodycote Thermal Processing, Inc.
12700 Park Central Dr # 700
Dallas TX 75251
214 904-2420

(P-11797)
BODYCOTE THERMAL PROC INC
515 W Apra St Ste A, Compton (90220-5502)
PHONE...................................310 604-8000
Jose Catano, *Branch Mgr*
Tracy Glende, *President*
Helen Reynoso, *Director*
Bart Hall, *Accounts Mgr*
Jose Salcedo, *Supervisor*
EMP: 21
SALES (corp-wide): 911.9MM **Privately Held**
SIC: 3398 Metal heat treating
HQ: Bodycote Thermal Processing, Inc.
12700 Park Central Dr # 700
Dallas TX 75251
214 904-2420

(P-11798)
BODYCOTE THERMAL PROC INC
7474 Garden Grove Blvd, Westminster (92683-2227)
PHONE...................................714 893-6561
Manuel Granillo, *Branch Mgr*
EMP: 80
SQ FT: 7,369
SALES (corp-wide): 911.9MM **Privately Held**
SIC: 3398 Metal heat treating
HQ: Bodycote Thermal Processing, Inc.
12700 Park Central Dr # 700
Dallas TX 75251
214 904-2420

(P-11799)
BODYCOTE THERMAL PROC INC
11845 Burke St, Santa Fe Springs (90670-2537)
PHONE...................................562 693-3135
Paul Dymond, *Branch Mgr*
EMP: 26
SALES (corp-wide): 911.9MM **Privately Held**
SIC: 3398 Brazing (hardening) of metal
HQ: Bodycote Thermal Processing, Inc.
12700 Park Central Dr # 700
Dallas TX 75251
214 904-2420

(P-11800)
BODYCOTE THERMAL PROC INC
4240 Technology Dr, Fremont (94538-6337)
PHONE...................................510 492-4200

Paul Dymond, *Manager*
Al Luna, *Opers Mgr*
Dan Swan, *Manager*
EMP: 25
SALES (corp-wide): 911.9MM **Privately Held**
SIC: 3398 Metal heat treating
HQ: Bodycote Thermal Processing, Inc.
12700 Park Central Dr # 700
Dallas TX 75251
214 904-2420

(P-11801)
BODYCOTE THERMAL PROC INC
9921 Romandel Ave, Santa Fe Springs (90670-3441)
PHONE...................................562 946-1717
Manuel Granillo, *Principal*
Terri Galvan, *Human Res Mgr*
EMP: 31
SALES (corp-wide): 911.9MM **Privately Held**
SIC: 3398 Metal heat treating
HQ: Bodycote Thermal Processing, Inc.
12700 Park Central Dr # 700
Dallas TX 75251
214 904-2420

(P-11802)
BODYCOTE USA INC
2900 S Sunol Dr, Vernon (90058-4315)
PHONE...................................323 264-0111
Antoniely Cebreros, *Info Tech Mgr*
Oscar Ortiz, *Manager*
EMP: 10
SQ FT: 31,717
SALES (corp-wide): 911.9MM **Privately Held**
SIC: 3398 Metal heat treating
HQ: Bodycote Usa, Inc.
12700 Park Central Dr # 700
Dallas TX 75251
214 904-2420

(P-11803)
BURBANK STEEL TREATING INC
415 S Varney St, Burbank (91502-2194)
PHONE...................................818 842-0975
Mildred Bennett, *Ch of Bd*
Larry Bennett, *President*
Kenneth Bennett, *Vice Pres*
Oscar Osornio, *Planning*
EMP: 45
SQ FT: 16,000
SALES (est): 8.8MM **Privately Held**
WEB: www.burbanksteel.com
SIC: 3398 Metal heat treating

(P-11804)
BYINGTON STEEL TREATING INC (PA)
1225 Memorex Dr, Santa Clara (95050-2888)
PHONE...................................408 727-6630
Kathryn Byington, *CEO*
Clyde D Byington, *President*
Sean Byington, *COO*
Catherine A Byington, *Vice Pres*
Don Judson, *Vice Pres*
EMP: 22
SQ FT: 25,000
SALES (est): 3.6MM **Privately Held**
WEB: www.byingtonsteel.com
SIC: 3398 Tempering of metal

(P-11805)
CALSTRIP STEEL CORPORATION (HQ)
3030 Dulles Dr, Mira Loma (91752-3240)
PHONE...................................323 838-2097
Thomas B Nelis, *President*
Douglas Clark, *Vice Pres*
▲ **EMP:** 77
SQ FT: 190,000
SALES (est): 18.6MM
SALES (corp-wide): 160MM **Privately Held**
WEB: www.calstripsteel.com
SIC: 3398 3316 Metal heat treating; strip steel, cold-rolled: from purchased hot-rolled

PA: Calstrip Industries, Inc.
3030 Dulles Dr
Mira Loma CA 91752
323 726-1345

(P-11806)
CERTIFIED METAL CRAFT INC
877 Vernon Way, El Cajon (92020-1940)
PHONE...................................619 593-3636
John C Wiederkehr, *President*
Mark Wiederkehr, *Vice Pres*
Tim Wiederkehr, *General Mgr*
Jeff Wiederkehr, *Supervisor*
EMP: 30
SQ FT: 29,500
SALES (est): 7.8MM **Privately Held**
WEB: www.certifiedmetalcraft.com
SIC: 3398 Brazing (hardening) of metal; tempering of metal

(P-11807)
CITY STEEL HEAT TREATING INC
1221 W Struck Ave, Orange (92867-3531)
PHONE...................................562 789-7373
Samuel Boyer, *President*
EMP: 15
SALES (est): 1.8MM **Privately Held**
SIC: 3398 Metal heat treating

(P-11808)
COAST HEAT TREATING CO
1767 Industrial Way, Los Angeles (90023-4394)
PHONE...................................323 263-6944
Frank Garcia, *President*
EMP: 36
SQ FT: 10,000
SALES: 1.5MM **Privately Held**
SIC: 3398 Metal heat treating

(P-11809)
CONTINENTAL HEAT TREATING INC
10643 Norwalk Blvd, Santa Fe Springs (90670-3821)
PHONE...................................562 944-8808
James Stull, *President*
Dennis Hugie, *Principal*
Don Lowman, *Principal*
Ken Nelson, *Principal*
Shaun Radford, *General Mgr*
EMP: 62
SQ FT: 20,000
SALES (est): 16MM **Privately Held**
SIC: 3398 Metal heat treating

(P-11810)
COOK INDUCTION HEATING CO INC
4925 Slauson Ave, Maywood (90270-3094)
P.O. Box 430 (90270-0430)
PHONE...................................323 560-1327
Keith Doolittle, *CEO*
Richard Egkan, *Vice Pres*
EMP: 21
SQ FT: 24,500
SALES (est): 4.4MM **Privately Held**
SIC: 3398 3728 Metal heat treating; aircraft assemblies, subassemblies & parts

(P-11811)
DIVERSFIED MTLLRGICAL SVCS INC
Also Called: Varco Heat Treating
12101 Industry St, Garden Grove (92841-2813)
P.O. Box 5500 (92846-0500)
PHONE...................................714 895-7777
Don A Gay, *President*
Winston E Mote, *Vice Pres*
EMP: 35
SQ FT: 28,000
SALES (est): 8.2MM **Privately Held**
WEB: www.varcoheat.com
SIC: 3398 4924 3479 Metal heat treating; natural gas distribution; coating of metals & formed products

(P-11812)
GARNER HEAT TREAT INC
10001 Denny St, Oakland (94603-3090)
PHONE...................................510 568-0587
Alvenia Garner, *President*
EMP: 10

▲ = Import ▼=Export
◆ =Import/Export

SQ FT: 12,000
SALES (est): 1.5MM **Privately Held**
SIC: 3398 Metal heat treating

(P-11813)
H P APPLICATIONS
4727 E 49th St, Vernon (90058-2703)
PHONE..................................323 585-2894
Gustavo Perez, *President*
EMP: 12
SALES (est): 1MM **Privately Held**
SIC: 3398 Metal heat treating

(P-11814)
HI TECH HEAT TREATING INC
331 W 168th St, Gardena (90248-2732)
PHONE..................................310 532-3705
Alastair Oldfield, *President*
EMP: 16
SALES: 1.1MM **Privately Held**
SIC: 3398 Metal heat treating

(P-11815)
INTERNTONAL METALLURGICAL SVCS
Also Called: Scarrott Metallurgical Co
6371 Arizona Cir, Los Angeles
(90045-1201)
PHONE..................................310 645-7300
Dave Scarrott, *President*
Ralph Jones, *Vice Pres*
Jose Cartano, *General Mgr*
Jose Catano, *General Mgr*
Bob Fairbanks, *Data Proc Staff*
EMP: 19
SQ FT: 8,000
SALES (est): 4.5MM **Privately Held**
WEB: www.scarrott.com
SIC: 3398 Brazing (hardening) of metal

(P-11816)
KOPASKIE METALLURGICAL INC
330 S 9th Ave, City of Industry
(91746-3311)
P.O. Box 90068 (91715-0068)
PHONE..................................626 333-3898
Bernard E Kopaskie, *President*
Jan Kopaskie, *Treasurer*
D R Butler, *Vice Pres*
Rosemarie Camacho, *Controller*
EMP: 35
SQ FT: 12,000
SALES: 3MM **Privately Held**
SIC: 3398 8711 Metal heat treating; engineering services

(P-11817)
KPI SERVICES INC
Also Called: Kittyhawk Products
11651 Monarch St, Garden Grove
(92841-1816)
PHONE..................................714 895-5024
Charles Barre, *CEO*
Dennis Poor, *President*
Lois Barre, *Corp Secy*
Steve Belloise, *Vice Pres*
Dee Dee Poor, *Vice Pres*
▲ **EMP:** 35 **EST:** 1995
SQ FT: 12,500
SALES (est): 11.9MM **Privately Held**
WEB: www.kittyhawkinc.com
SIC: 3398 Metal heat treating

(P-11818)
METAL IMPROVEMENT COMPANY LLC
2588 Industry Way A, Lynwood
(90262-4015)
PHONE..................................323 585-2168
Amando Yanez, *Manager*
Marilu Romero, *Human Res Mgr*
EMP: 50
SQ FT: 28,260
SALES (corp-wide): 2.2B **Publicly Held**
WEB: www.mic-houston.com
SIC: 3398 Shot peening (treating steel to reduce fatigue)
HQ: Metal Improvement Company, Llc
80 E Rte 4 Ste 310
Paramus NJ 07652
201 843-7800

(P-11819)
METAL IMPROVEMENT COMPANY LLC
E/M Coatings Solutions
6940 Farmdale Ave, North Hollywood
(91605-6210)
PHONE..................................818 983-1952
Brent Taylor, *Branch Mgr*
Ernie Lucero, *Safety Mgr*
EMP: 85
SALES (corp-wide): 2.2B **Publicly Held**
WEB: www.curtisswright.com
SIC: 3398 Shot peening (treating steel to reduce fatigue)
HQ: Metal Improvement Company, Llc
80 E Rte 4 Ste 310
Paramus NJ 07652
201 843-7800

(P-11820)
METAL IMPROVEMENT COMPANY LLC
Also Called: Para Tech Coating
35 Argonaut Ste A1, Laguna Hills
(92656-4151)
PHONE..................................949 855-8010
Bill Gleason, *Manager*
Patricia Langraphi, *QA Dir*
Gustavo Arredondo, *Technical Mgr*
Jennifer Pyle, *Technology*
Matt Staniszewski, *Engineer*
EMP: 30
SALES (corp-wide): 2.2B **Publicly Held**
SIC: 3398 Shot peening (treating steel to reduce fatigue)
HQ: Metal Improvement Company, Llc
80 E Rte 4 Ste 310
Paramus NJ 07652
201 843-7800

(P-11821)
METAL IMPROVEMENT COMPANY LLC
E/M Coatings Services
20751 Superior St, Chatsworth
(91311-4416)
PHONE..................................818 407-6280
Brent Taylor, *Branch Mgr*
EMP: 96
SALES (corp-wide): 2.2B **Publicly Held**
SIC: 3398 Shot peening (treating steel to reduce fatigue)
HQ: Metal Improvement Company, Llc
80 E Rte 4 Ste 310
Paramus NJ 07652
201 843-7800

(P-11822)
METAL IMPROVEMENT COMPANY LLC
7655 Longard Rd Bldg A, Livermore
(94551-8208)
PHONE..................................925 960-1090
Jim McManus, *Manager*
Marissa Skog, *Manager*
EMP: 40
SALES (corp-wide): 2.2B **Publicly Held**
WEB: www.mic-houston.com
SIC: 3398 Shot peening (treating steel to reduce fatigue)
HQ: Metal Improvement Company, Llc
80 E Rte 4 Ste 310
Paramus NJ 07652
201 843-7800

(P-11823)
METAL IMPROVEMENT COMPANY LLC
2151 S Hathaway St, Santa Ana
(92705-5247)
PHONE..................................714 546-4160
Joe Wheaton, *Manager*
EMP: 18
SALES (corp-wide): 2.2B **Publicly Held**
WEB: www.mic-houston.com
SIC: 3398 Shot peening (treating steel to reduce fatigue)
HQ: Metal Improvement Company, Llc
80 E Rte 4 Ste 310
Paramus NJ 07652
201 843-7800

(P-11824)
METAL IMPROVEMENT COMPANY LLC
2588a Industry Way, Lynwood
(90262-4015)
PHONE..................................323 563-1533
Amando Yanez, *Manager*
EMP: 17
SALES (corp-wide): 2.2B **Publicly Held**
WEB: www.mic-houston.com
SIC: 3398 Shot peening (treating steel to reduce fatigue)
HQ: Metal Improvement Company, Llc
80 E Rte 4 Ste 310
Paramus NJ 07652
201 843-7800

(P-11825)
METAL PRODUCTS ENGINEERING
3050 Leonis Blvd, Vernon (90058-2914)
PHONE..................................323 581-8121
Luppe R Luppen, *Ch of Bd*
Paula Luppen, *Corp Secy*
EMP: 24 **EST:** 1997
SQ FT: 40,000
SALES (est): 1.8MM
SALES (corp-wide): 2.4MM **Privately Held**
WEB: www.metalproductseng.com
SIC: 3398 3469 3578 3596 Metal heat treating; metal stampings; change making machines; scales & balances, except laboratory
PA: Luppen Holdings, Inc.
3050 Leonis Blvd
Vernon CA 90058
323 581-8121

(P-11826)
NEWTON HEAT TREATING COMPANY
19235 E Walnut Dr N, City of Industry
(91748-1494)
P.O. Box 8010, Rowland Heights (91748-0010)
PHONE..................................626 964-6528
Greg Newton, *President*
Linda Malcor, *Admin Sec*
Miguel Zaragoza, *QC Mgr*
EMP: 71
SQ FT: 1,900
SALES: 4MM **Privately Held**
WEB: www.newtonheattreating.com
SIC: 3398 8734 3444 Metal heat treating; X-ray inspection service, industrial; sheet metalwork

(P-11827)
PEEN-RITE INC
11662 Sheldon St, Sun Valley
(91352-1597)
PHONE..................................818 767-3676
Bill Swanson, *President*
Richard Bluth, *Vice Pres*
Tillie Bluth, *Admin Sec*
EMP: 16 **EST:** 1965
SQ FT: 13,000
SALES (est): 3.2MM **Privately Held**
WEB: www.peenrite.com
SIC: 3398 Shot peening (treating steel to reduce fatigue)

(P-11828)
QUALITY HEAT TREATING INC
3305 Burton Ave, Burbank (91504-3199)
PHONE..................................818 840-8212
James G Stull, *President*
EMP: 34
SQ FT: 20,000
SALES (est): 6.9MM **Privately Held**
WEB: www.qualityht.com
SIC: 3398 3471 Metal heat treating; sand blasting of metal parts

(P-11829)
SOLAR ATMOSPHERES INC
8606 Live Oak Ave, Fontana (92335-3172)
PHONE..................................909 217-7400
Amy Blanes, *Branch Mgr*
EMP: 39
SALES (corp-wide): 30.5MM **Privately Held**
WEB: www.solaratm.com
SIC: 3398 Annealing of metal
PA: Solar Atmospheres, Inc.
1969 Clearview Rd
Souderton PA 18964
215 721-1502

(P-11830)
SUPERHEAT FGH SERVICES INC
1333 Willow Pass Rd, Concord
(94520-7930)
PHONE..................................925 808-6711
Brad Hennig, *Branch Mgr*
EMP: 18 **Privately Held**
SIC: 3398 Metal heat treating
HQ: Superheat Fgh Services, Inc.
313 Garnet Dr
New Lenox IL 60451
708 478-0205

(P-11831)
SUPREME STEEL TREATING INC
2466 Seaman Ave, El Monte (91733-1926)
PHONE..................................626 350-5865
Neal Begerow, *President*
EMP: 23
SQ FT: 5,400
SALES (est): 4.2MM **Privately Held**
WEB: www.supremesteeltreating.com
SIC: 3398 Metal heat treating

(P-11832)
TEAM INC
Also Called: Team Industrial Services
2580 W 237th St, Torrance (90505-5217)
PHONE..................................310 514-2312
Bill Pigeon, *Manager*
EMP: 60
SALES (corp-wide): 1.2B **Publicly Held**
SIC: 3398 3567 Metal heat treating; heating units & devices, industrial: electric; fuel-fired furnaces & ovens
HQ: Team, Inc.
5095 Paris St
Denver CO 80239

(P-11833)
THERMAL-VAC TECHNOLOGY INC
1221 W Struck Ave, Orange (92867-3531)
PHONE..................................714 997-2601
Steve Driscol, *CEO*
Aaron Anderson, *President*
Ely Enriquez, *Buyer*
EMP: 41
SQ FT: 26,800
SALES (est): 13.3MM **Privately Held**
WEB: www.thermal-vac.com
SIC: 3398 Brazing (hardening) of metal

(P-11834)
THERMO PRODUCTS INC
Also Called: Thermcore
13185 Nevada City Ave, Grass Valley
(95945-9568)
PHONE..................................909 888-2882
Larry Nameche, *President*
David Wade, *CEO*
Maria Wade, *Admin Sec*
▲ **EMP:** 55
SQ FT: 235,000
SALES (est): 6.9MM **Privately Held**
WEB: www.thermcore.com
SIC: 3398 Metal heat treating

(P-11835)
TRI-J METAL HEAT TREATING CO (PA)
327 E Commercial St, Pomona
(91767-5505)
PHONE..................................909 622-9999
Debra Cramer, *Admin Sec*
Albert W James Jr, *President*
Robert L James, *Vice Pres*
Lena James, *Admin Sec*
▲ **EMP:** 19 **EST:** 1976
SQ FT: 17,500
SALES (est): 3MM **Privately Held**
SIC: 3398 Annealing of metal

(P-11836)
TRI-J METAL HEAT TREATING CO
327 E Commercial St, Pomona (91767-5505)
PHONE..............................909 622-9999
Albert W James Jr, *President*
EMP: 10
SALES (corp-wide): 3MM **Privately Held**
SIC: 3398 Annealing of metal; brazing (hardening) of metal; metal burning
PA: Tri-J Metal Heat Treating Co.
   327 E Commercial St
   Pomona CA 91767
   909 622-9999

(P-11837)
TRIUMPH GROUP INC
2136 S Hathaway St, Santa Ana (92705-5248)
PHONE..............................714 546-9842
Jeffry D Frisby, *CEO*
Christyne Contreras, *Purch Agent*
Darin McCoy, *QC Mgr*
Mike Thomas, *Production*
Renato Torres, *Director*
EMP: 350 **Publicly Held**
SIC: 3398 3479 3471 8734 Shot peening (treating steel to reduce fatigue); coating of metals & formed products; electroplating & plating; metallurgical testing laboratory
PA: Triumph Group, Inc.
   899 Cassatt Rd Ste 210
   Berwyn PA 19312

(P-11838)
VALLEY METAL TREATING INC
355 S East End Ave, Pomona (91766-2312)
PHONE..............................909 623-6316
James G Stull, *President*
EMP: 38
SQ FT: 8,000
SALES (est): 7.5MM **Privately Held**
WEB: www.valleymt.net
SIC: 3398 Metal heat treating

3399 Primary Metal Prdts, NEC

(P-11839)
ALINABAL INC
Lamsco West
29101 The Old Rd, Valencia (91355-1014)
PHONE..............................661 877-9356
Glad Baldwin, *General Mgr*
Ralph Hernandez, *Production*
EMP: 25
SALES (corp-wide): 52.2MM **Privately Held**
WEB: www.dacoinstrument.com
SIC: 3399 3469 Laminating steel; stamping metal for the trade
HQ: Alinabal, Inc.
   28 Woodmont Rd
   Milford CT 06460
   203 877-3241

(P-11840)
HAI ADVNCED MTL SPCIALISTS INC
Also Called: H A I
1688 Sierra Madre Cir, Placentia (92870-6628)
PHONE..............................714 414-0575
Daren J Gansert, *President*
Debra Gansert, *Vice Pres*
▲ **EMP:** 15
SQ FT: 10,000
SALES (est): 3.7MM **Privately Held**
WEB: www.haiams.com
SIC: 3399 Powder, metal

(P-11841)
LEE FASTENERS INC
230 Clary Ave, San Gabriel (91776-1375)
PHONE..............................626 287-6848
Michael Hua, *President*
▲ **EMP:** 10
SQ FT: 20,000

SALES (est): 1.3MM **Privately Held**
WEB: www.leefasteners.com
SIC: 3399 Metal fasteners

(P-11842)
MELLING TOOL RUSH METALS LLC
Also Called: Melling Sintered Metals
16100 S Figueroa St, Gardena (90248-2617)
PHONE..............................580 725-3295
Mark Melling, *CEO*
▲ **EMP:** 65
SQ FT: 48,000
SALES: 8MM
SALES (corp-wide): 281.5MM **Privately Held**
WEB: www.cloyes.com
SIC: 3399 Powder, metal
PA: Melling Tool Co.
   2620 Saradan Dr
   Jackson MI 49202
   517 787-8172

(P-11843)
MICRO SURFACE ENGR INC (PA)
Also Called: Ball TEC
1550 E Slauson Ave, Los Angeles (90011-5099)
P.O. Box 58611 (90011)
PHONE..............................323 582-7348
Eugene A Gleason Jr, *President*
Eugene A Gleason III, *Corp Secy*
Helen Gleason, *Vice Pres*
Patricia Johnson, *Finance Dir*
Tony Velazquez, *Prdtn Mgr*
EMP: 35 **EST:** 1952
SQ FT: 46,000
SALES (est): 5.7MM **Privately Held**
WEB: www.precisionballs.com
SIC: 3399 Steel balls

(P-11844)
PARMATECH CORPORATION
2221 Pine View Way, Petaluma (94954-5688)
PHONE..............................707 778-2266
Peter Frost, *CEO*
Caryn E Mitchell, *Treasurer*
Tom Chagnon, *General Mgr*
Bryan Mc Bride, *General Mgr*
Timur Gasanov, *Engineer*
▲ **EMP:** 75
SQ FT: 22,000
SALES (est): 19.7MM
SALES (corp-wide): 86.7MM **Privately Held**
WEB: www.parmatech.com
SIC: 3399 Powder, metal
PA: Atw Companies, Inc.
   125 Metro Center Blvd # 3001
   Warwick RI 02886
   401 244-1002

(P-11845)
PERRY TOOL & RESEARCH INC
3415 Enterprise Ave, Hayward (94545-3284)
PHONE..............................510 782-9226
Kenneth Fasselman, *CEO*
EMP: 35
SQ FT: 13,000
SALES (est): 7.9MM **Privately Held**
WEB: www.perrytool.com
SIC: 3399 Powder, metal

(P-11846)
PRECISION PWDRED MET PARTS INC
145 Atlantic St, Pomona (91768-3286)
PHONE..............................909 595-5656
Maurice Bridgman, *President*
David Connelly, *Corp Secy*
Andy Pirkle, *CIO*
Carlos Maldini, *Engineer*
Quan Nguyen, *Chief Engr*
▲ **EMP:** 48
SQ FT: 25,000
SALES (est): 16.1MM **Privately Held**
WEB: www.precisionpm.com
SIC: 3399 Powder, metal

(P-11847)
SCAFCO CORPORATION
2443 Foundry Park Ave, Fresno (93706-4531)
PHONE..............................559 256-9911
Larry Stone, *President*
EMP: 20
SALES (corp-wide): 158MM **Privately Held**
SIC: 3399 Iron ore recovery from open hearth slag
PA: Scafco Corporation
   2800 E Main Ave
   Spokane WA 99202
   509 343-9000

(P-11848)
SENJU COMTEK CORP
1171 N 4th St Ste 80, San Jose (95112-4968)
PHONE..............................408 792-3830
Ryoichi Suzuki, *Branch Mgr*
Hiro Ota, *Info Tech Mgr*
EMP: 15
SALES (corp-wide): 556.7MM **Privately Held**
WEB: www.senjucomtek.com
SIC: 3399 Paste, metal
HQ: Senju Comtek Corp.
   2989 San Ysidro Way
   Santa Clara CA 95051

(P-11849)
SENJU COMTEK CORP (HQ)
2989 San Ysidro Way, Santa Clara (95051-0604)
PHONE..............................408 963-5300
Masato Shimamura, *CEO*
Derek Daily, *General Mgr*
◆ **EMP:** 11
SALES (est): 7.6MM
SALES (corp-wide): 556.7MM **Privately Held**
WEB: www.senjucomtek.com
SIC: 3399 Paste, metal
PA: Senju Metal Industry Co.,Ltd.
   23, Hashidocho, Senju
   Adachi-Ku TKY 120-0
   338 885-151

(P-11850)
SIMPSON MANUFACTURING CO INC (PA)
5956 W Las Positas Blvd, Pleasanton (94588-8540)
PHONE..............................925 560-9000
Karen Colonias, *CEO*
Peter N Louras Jr, *Ch of Bd*
Brian J Magstadt, *CFO*
Kevin Swartzendruber, *Senior VP*
EMP: 150
SALES: 977MM **Publicly Held**
WEB: www.simpsonmfg.com
SIC: 3399 3441 Metal fasteners; building components, structural steel

(P-11851)
UNITED METAL PRODUCTS INC
Also Called: Ump
234 N Sherman Ave, Corona (92882-1843)
PHONE..............................951 739-9535
Bernie Smokowski, *President*
Jacqueline Lowery, *Corp Secy*
Patricia Smokowski, *Vice Pres*
Jim Murphy, *General Mgr*
Bobby Merino, *Sales Associate*
EMP: 14
SALES (est): 2.5MM **Privately Held**
WEB: www.unitedmetalproducts.com
SIC: 3399 Metal fasteners

(P-11852)
VALIMET INC (PA)
431 Sperry Rd, Stockton (95206-3907)
P.O. Box 31690 (95213-1690)
PHONE..............................209 444-1600
Kurt F Leopold, *CEO*
George Campbell, *President*
Michaela Leopold, *Admin Sec*
Autumn Hatten, *Admin Asst*
Sifan Zhu, *Engineer*
EMP: 58
SQ FT: 200,000

SALES (est): 26.4MM **Privately Held**
WEB: www.valimet.com
SIC: 3399 Powder, metal

(P-11853)
VAST NATIONAL INC
Also Called: De Anza Muffler Service
4398 Market St, Riverside (92501-3518)
PHONE..............................951 788-7030
Fershteh Bavadi, *CEO*
EMP: 12
SQ FT: 10,000
SALES (est): 2MM **Privately Held**
SIC: 3399 Nails: aluminum, brass or other nonferrous metal or wire

3411 Metal Cans

(P-11854)
AMERICAN PRODUCTION CO INC
Also Called: Super Chef
2734 Spring St, Redwood City (94063-3524)
P.O. Box 5766 (94063-0766)
PHONE..............................650 368-5334
Owen Conley, *President*
EMP: 69
SQ FT: 35,000
SALES (est): 7.3MM
SALES (corp-wide): 7.5MM **Privately Held**
WEB: www.tilleymfg.com
SIC: 3411 2656 3412 Food & beverage containers; sanitary food containers; metal barrels, drums & pails
PA: Tilley Manufacturing Co, Inc
   2734 Spring St
   Redwood City CA 94063
   650 365-3598

(P-11855)
ARDAGH METAL PACKAGING USA INC
936 Barracuda St, San Pedro (90731-7353)
PHONE..............................310 519-2400
Mike Born, *Manager*
Mike Borne, *General Mgr*
Frank Cuebas, *Engrg Mgr*
Jim Barton, *Engineer*
Mick Leahy, *Opers Mgr*
EMP: 150 **Privately Held**
WEB: www.impresspkg.com
SIC: 3411 Metal cans
HQ: Ardagh Metal Packaging Usa Inc.
   600 N Bell Ave
   Carnegie PA 15106

(P-11856)
BALL CORPORATION
Also Called: Metal Fd Hhld Pdts Pckging Div
300 Greger St, Oakdale (95361-8613)
PHONE..............................209 848-6500
Michael Wright, *Branch Mgr*
Dave Miller, *President*
Sylvia Weinmeister, *Vice Pres*
Michael Hetzler, *Info Tech Mgr*
Kent Adams, *Project Mgr*
EMP: 260
SALES (corp-wide): 10.9B **Publicly Held**
WEB: www.ball.com
SIC: 3411 Metal cans
PA: Ball Corporation
   10 Longs Peak Dr
   Broomfield CO 80021
   303 469-3131

(P-11857)
BALL METAL BEVERAGE CONT CORP
Ball Metal Beverage Cont Div
2400 Huntington Dr, Fairfield (94533-9734)
PHONE..............................707 437-7516
David R Trujillo, *Branch Mgr*
Julian Almaraz, *Manager*
EMP: 172
SQ FT: 115,000
SALES (corp-wide): 10.9B **Publicly Held**
SIC: 3411 Metal cans

▲ = Import ▼=Export
◆ =Import/Export

HQ: Ball Metal Beverage Container Corp.
9300 W 108th Cir
Westminster CO 80021

(P-11858)
BWAY CORPORATION
11440 Pacific Ave, Fontana (92337-8226)
PHONE..............................951 361-4100
Mark Klug, *Manager*
EMP: 30
SALES (corp-wide): 1.1B **Privately Held**
WEB: www.bwaycorp.com
SIC: 3411 3499 Metal cans; ammunition boxes, metal
HQ: Bway Corporation
375 Northridge Rd Ste 600
Atlanta GA 30350

(P-11859)
JOSEPH COMPANY INTERNATIONAL
1711 Langley Ave, Irvine (92614-5679)
PHONE..............................949 474-2200
Mitchell J Joseph, *President*
▲ **EMP:** 20
SQ FT: 18,000
SALES (est): 3.8MM **Privately Held**
SIC: 3411 Food & beverage containers

(P-11860)
KLEAN KANTEEN INC
3960 Morrow Ln, Chico (95928-8912)
PHONE..............................530 592-4552
James Osgood, *CEO*
Darrell Cresswell, *President*
Jeff Cresswell, *COO*
Deanna Kemper, *Executive Asst*
Kevin Welch, *Info Tech Mgr*
▲ **EMP:** 40
SQ FT: 5,000
SALES (est): 10MM **Privately Held**
WEB: www.justjumpit.com
SIC: 3411 Food containers, metal

(P-11861)
MAT MAT
21029 Itasca St, Chatsworth (91311-4924)
PHONE..............................818 678-9392
Fernando Roblesgio, *President*
EMP: 10
SALES (est): 716K **Privately Held**
SIC: 3411 Can lids & ends, metal

(P-11862)
METAL CONTAINER CORPORATION
7155 Central Ave, Riverside (92504-1400)
PHONE..............................951 354-0444
Bob Parker, *Branch Mgr*
EMP: 200
SALES (corp-wide): 1.9B **Privately Held**
SIC: 3411 Can lids & ends, metal
HQ: Metal Container Corporation
3636 S Geyer Rd Ste 100
Saint Louis MO 63127
314 577-2000

(P-11863)
METAL CONTAINER CORPORATION
10980 Inland Ave, Mira Loma (91752-1127)
PHONE..............................951 360-4500
Otto Sosapavon, *Principal*
Todd Griffin, *Engineer*
Adriana Peguero, *Engineer*
Ana Scafidi, *Human Res Mgr*
Jon Carleton, *Buyer*
EMP: 171
SALES (corp-wide): 1.9B **Privately Held**
SIC: 3411 Aluminum cans
HQ: Metal Container Corporation
3636 S Geyer Rd Ste 100
Saint Louis MO 63127
314 577-2000

(P-11864)
PACIFIC BRIDGE PACKAGING INC
103 Exchange Pl, Pomona (91768-4307)
PHONE..............................909 598-1988
Peter Chang, *CEO*
William Hsu, *General Mgr*
▲ **EMP:** 10

SQ FT: 10,000
SALES (est): 121.8K **Privately Held**
SIC: 3411 3499 3221 3085 Metal cans; aerosol valves, metal; bottles for packing, bottling & canning; glass; plastics bottles

(P-11865)
PERINE LOWE INC
Also Called: Child To Cherish
400 N Berry St, Brea (92821-3104)
P.O. Box 533 (92822-0533)
PHONE..............................714 990-1590
Patrice Lowe, *President*
Gordon Lowe, *Vice Pres*
▲ **EMP:** 10
SQ FT: 21,750
SALES (est): 112.3K **Privately Held**
WEB: www.childtocherish.com
SIC: 3411 3944 Tin cans; games, toys & children's vehicles

(P-11866)
SILGAN CONTAINERS CORPORATION (DH)
21600 Oxnard St Ste 1600, Woodland Hills (91367-3609)
PHONE..............................818 348-3700
Anthony J Allott, *CEO*
Thomas J Snyder, *Ch of Bd*
James D Beam, *President*
R Phillip Silver, *Vice Ch Bd*
Frank W Hogan III, *Senior VP*
◆ **EMP:** 100
SALES (est): 511.7MM
SALES (corp-wide): 4B **Publicly Held**
SIC: 3411 Food containers, metal
HQ: Silgan Containers Llc
21600 Oxnard St Ste 1600
Woodland Hills CA 91367
818 710-3700

(P-11867)
SILGAN CONTAINERS LLC (HQ)
21600 Oxnard St Ste 1600, Woodland Hills (91367-5082)
PHONE..............................818 710-3700
Thomas Snyder, *Mng Member*
Ron Ford, *CFO*
Richard Brewer, *Senior VP*
Daniel Carson, *Senior VP*
Michael Beninato, *Vice Pres*
◆ **EMP:** 100
SALES (est): 2B
SALES (corp-wide): 4B **Publicly Held**
WEB: www.silgancontainers.com
SIC: 3411 Food containers, metal
PA: Silgan Holdings Inc.
4 Landmark Sq Ste 400
Stamford CT 06901
203 975-7110

(P-11868)
SILGAN CONTAINERS MFG CORP
4000 Yosemite Blvd, Modesto (95357-1580)
PHONE..............................209 521-6469
William Jennings, *Bd of Directors*
EMP: 82
SALES (corp-wide): 4B **Publicly Held**
SIC: 3411 Metal cans
HQ: Silgan Containers Manufacturing Corporation
21600 Oxnard St Ste 1600
Woodland Hills CA 91367

(P-11869)
SILGAN CONTAINERS MFG CORP
2200 Wilbur Ave, Antioch (94509-8506)
PHONE..............................925 778-8000
Arnold Naimark, *Branch Mgr*
EMP: 30
SALES (corp-wide): 4B **Publicly Held**
WEB: www.silgancontainers.com
SIC: 3411 Metal cans
HQ: Silgan Containers Manufacturing Corporation
21600 Oxnard St Ste 1600
Woodland Hills CA 91367

(P-11870)
SILGAN CONTAINERS MFG CORP
3250 Patterson Rd, Riverbank (95367-2938)
PHONE..............................209 869-3601
Gary Miller, *Branch Mgr*
EMP: 45
SQ FT: 200,000
SALES (corp-wide): 4B **Publicly Held**
WEB: www.silgancontainers.com
SIC: 3411 Metal cans
HQ: Silgan Containers Manufacturing Corporation
21600 Oxnard St Ste 1600
Woodland Hills CA 91367

(P-11871)
SILGAN CONTAINERS MFG CORP (DH)
21600 Oxnard St Ste 1600, Woodland Hills (91367-5082)
PHONE..............................818 710-3700
Thomas Snyder, *Principal*
EMP: 277
SALES (est): 358.4MM
SALES (corp-wide): 4B **Publicly Held**
SIC: 3411 Metal cans
HQ: Silgan Containers Llc
21600 Oxnard St Ste 1600
Woodland Hills CA 91367
818 710-3700

(P-11872)
THREE STONE HEARTH
1581 University Ave, Berkeley (94703-1422)
PHONE..............................510 981-1334
Larry Wisch, *Principal*
Otto Thorsen, *Facilities Mgr*
Mary Dee, *Cashier*
Linda Kallenberger, *Supervisor*
EMP: 16
SALES (est): 2.5MM **Privately Held**
SIC: 3411 Food & beverage containers

3412 Metal Barrels, Drums, Kegs & Pails

(P-11873)
B STEPHEN COOPERAGE INC
10746 Vernon Ave, Ontario (91762-4039)
P.O. Box 9537 (91762-9537)
PHONE..............................909 591-2929
Toll Free:..............................877 -
Mike Stephen, *CEO*
Ben Stephen, *President*
Morlene Fisher, *Sales Dir*
EMP: 15
SQ FT: 174,240
SALES (est): 1.2MM **Privately Held**
SIC: 3412 Metal barrels, drums & pails

(P-11874)
GREIF INC
8250 Almeria Ave, Fontana (92335-3279)
PHONE..............................909 350-2112
Andy Wade, *Manager*
Yohana Manzo, *Safety Mgr*
Kristi Kho, *Sales Executive*
Jim Boswell, *Maintence Staff*
Michael Dempsey, *Director*
EMP: 25
SQ FT: 73,320
SALES (corp-wide): 3.6B **Publicly Held**
WEB: www.greif.com
SIC: 3412 2674 2655 2449 Drums, shipping; metal; bags: uncoated paper & multiwall; fiber cans, drums & similar products; wood containers
PA: Greif, Inc.
425 Winter Rd
Delaware OH 43015
740 549-6000

(P-11875)
MYERS CONTAINER LLC
21508 Ferrero B, Walnut (91789-5216)
PHONE..............................800 406-9377
Manuel Vasquez,
EMP: 25

SALES (corp-wide): 30.5MM **Privately Held**
WEB: www.myerscontainer.com
SIC: 3412 Metal barrels, drums & pails
HQ: Myers Container, Llc
8435 Ne Killingsworth St
Portland OR 97220

3421 Cutlery

(P-11876)
ARCH FOODS INC
610 85th Ave, Oakland (94621-1223)
PHONE..............................510 868-6000
EMP: 30 **Privately Held**
SIC: 3421 5149 Cutlery; dried or canned foods
PA: Arch Foods Inc
25817 Clawiter Rd
Hayward CA 94545

(P-11877)
ARCH FOODS INC (PA)
25817 Clawiter Rd, Hayward (94545-3217)
P.O. Box 2355, Clovis (93613-2355)
PHONE..............................510 331-8352
Jeff Lim, *CEO*
Ida Maria, *Manager*
▼ **EMP:** 50
SQ FT: 2,000
SALES (est): 4MM **Privately Held**
WEB: www.archfoods.com
SIC: 3421 5149 Cutlery; dried or canned foods

(P-11878)
ASIAS FINEST
407 Camino Del Rio S, San Diego (92108-3502)
PHONE..............................619 297-0800
EMP: 14
SALES (est): 894.1K **Privately Held**
SIC: 3421 Table & food cutlery, including butchers'

(P-11879)
EDGEWELL PER CARE BRANDS LLC
599 S Barranca Ave, Covina (91723-2777)
PHONE..............................949 466-0131
EMP: 360
SALES (corp-wide): 2.3B **Publicly Held**
WEB: www.eveready.com
SIC: 3421 Razor blades & razors
HQ: Edgewell Personal Care Brands, Llc
6 Research Dr
Shelton CT 06484
203 944-5500

(P-11880)
GILLETTE COMPANY
19900 Macarthur Blvd, Irvine (92612-2445)
PHONE..............................949 851-2222
Charles Kiernan, *President*
EMP: 10
SALES (corp-wide): 66.8B **Publicly Held**
WEB: www.gillette.com
SIC: 3421 2844 3951 2899 Razor blades & razors; toilet preparations; pens & mechanical pencils; correction fluid
HQ: The Gillette Company
1 Gillette Park
Boston MA 02127
617 421-7000

(P-11881)
NEPTUNE TRADING INC
4021 Greystone Dr, Ontario (91761-3100)
PHONE..............................909 923-0236
Margaret Lu, *President*
Michael Lu, *Vice Pres*
Nicholas Sanchez, *Creative Dir*
▲ **EMP:** 11
SQ FT: 38,000
SALES (est): 3.6MM **Privately Held**
SIC: 3421 5092 5072 Knife blades & blanks; toy novelties & amusements; cutlery

PRODUCTS & SVCS

(P-11882)
PRESSED RIGHT LLC
23615 El Toro Rd, Lake Forest
(92630-4707)
PHONE.................................866 257-5774
Robert Szutz, *Director*
EMP: 16
SALES (est): 2.6MM **Privately Held**
SIC: 3421 Table & food cutlery, including
butchers'

(P-11883)
SIERRA FOODS INC
13352 Imperial Hwy, Santa Fe Springs
(90670-4819)
PHONE.................................562 802-3500
EMP: 10
SALES (corp-wide): 9.4MM **Privately
Held**
SIC: 3421 Table & food cutlery, including
butchers'
PA: Sierra Foods, Inc.
23300 Cinema Dr
Santa Clarita CA 91355
661 254-1025

(P-11884)
SOORAKSAN SOOJEBI
4003 Wilshire Blvd Ste I, Los Angeles
(90010-3431)
PHONE.................................213 389-2818
EMP: 11 EST: 2010
SALES: 600K **Privately Held**
SIC: 3421

3423 Hand & Edge Tools

(P-11885)
ADVANCED CUTTING TOOLS INC
17741 Metzler Ln, Huntington Beach
(92647-6246)
PHONE.................................714 842-9376
Stjepan Herceg, *President*
EMP: 30
SQ FT: 10,200
SALES (est): 4.3MM **Privately Held**
SIC: 3423 3545 5251 Hand & edge tools;
machine tool accessories; tools

(P-11886)
BRITISH AMERICAN TL & DIE LLC
2273 E Via Burton, Anaheim (92806-1222)
PHONE.................................714 776-8995
Graham Butler, *CEO*
EMP: 175
SALES: 21MM **Privately Held**
SIC: 3423 Cutting dies, except metal cutting

(P-11887)
CALIFORNIA FLEXRAKE CORP
9620 Gidley St, Temple City (91780-4215)
PHONE.................................626 443-4026
John P McGuire, *President*
Tom Perkins, *Natl Sales Mgr*
Richard McGuire, *Maintence Staff*
▲ EMP: 25
SALES (est): 6.3MM **Privately Held**
WEB: www.flexrake.com
SIC: 3423 Garden & farm tools, including
shovels

(P-11888)
CATALINA TEMPERING INC (PA)
1125 E Lanzit Ave, Los Angeles
(90059-1559)
PHONE.................................323 789-7800
Randy Steinberg, *President*
EMP: 31
SALES (est): 10.9MM **Privately Held**
WEB: www.catalinatempering.com
SIC: 3423 Cutters, glass

(P-11889)
CONSOLIDATED DEVICES INC (HQ)
Also Called: CDI Torque Products
19220 San Jose Ave, City of Industry
(91748-1417)
PHONE.................................626 965-0668
Michael King, *President*

Gary Keefe, *CEO*
Jim Godby, *VP Mktg*
▲ EMP: 25
SQ FT: 90,000
SALES: 18.8MM
SALES (corp-wide): 3.6B **Publicly Held**
WEB: www.cditorque.com
SIC: 3423 3679 3625 5072 Wrenches,
hand tools; transducers, electrical; control
equipment, electric; hardware
PA: Snap-On Incorporated
2801 80th St
Kenosha WI 53143
262 656-5200

(P-11890)
CRAFTSMAN CUTTING DIES INC (PA)
Also Called: Ccd
2273 E Via Burton, Anaheim (92806-1222)
PHONE.................................714 776-8995
Thomas Hughes, *President*
Cathy Ong-Chan, *Treasurer*
Ronald Ong, *Vice Pres*
▲ EMP: 25
SQ FT: 11,000
SALES (est): 2.8MM **Privately Held**
SIC: 3423 3544 Cutting dies, except metal
cutting; special dies, tools, jigs & fixtures

(P-11891)
CSS GLOBAL
13487 Ranchero Way, Grass Valley
(95949-8359)
PHONE.................................530 268-3324
David P Lampson, *President*
EMP: 10
SQ FT: 15,000
SALES: 250K **Privately Held**
WEB: www.cssglobalinc.com
SIC: 3423 Carpenters' hand tools, except
saws; levels, chisels, etc.

(P-11892)
DURSTON MANUFACTURING COMPANY
Also Called: Vim Tools
1395 Palomares St, La Verne
(91750-5241)
P.O. Box 340 (91750-0340)
PHONE.................................909 593-1506
Donovan Norton, *CEO*
James Maloney, *President*
Mary Dills, *Accounting Mgr*
▲ EMP: 18 EST: 1946
SQ FT: 29,000
SALES (est): 3.6MM **Privately Held**
WEB: www.vimtools.com
SIC: 3423 Mechanics' hand tools

(P-11893)
EQH LIMITED INC
5440 Mcconnell Ave, Los Angeles
(90066-7037)
PHONE.................................310 736-4130
Eric Golden, *President*
EMP: 27
SALES (est): 3.4MM **Privately Held**
WEB: www.equipoisinc.com
SIC: 3423 3523 Tools or equipment for
use with sporting arms; planting, haying,
harvesting & processing machinery

(P-11894)
FLEX-MATE INC
Also Called: D & G Manufacturing
1855 E 29th St Ste E, Signal Hill
(90755-1919)
PHONE.................................562 426-7169
Theresa Gleason, *President*
EMP: 12
SQ FT: 6,000
SALES (est): 1.8MM **Privately Held**
SIC: 3423 Hand & edge tools

(P-11895)
GARDEN PALS INC
1300 Valley Vista Dr # 209, Diamond Bar
(91765-3940)
PHONE.................................909 605-0200
WEI Chun Hsu, *CEO*
Robert Deal, *COO*
▲ EMP: 20

SALES (est): 487MM
SALES (corp-wide): 18.5MM **Privately
Held**
WEB: www.gardenpals.com
SIC: 3423 Garden & farm tools, including
shovels
PA: Formosa Tools Co., Ltd.
22, Yen Hai Rd., Sec. 2,
Fushing Hsiang CHA 50645
477 002-10

(P-11896)
HALEX CORPORATION (HQ)
4200 Santa Ana St Ste A, Ontario
(91761-1539)
PHONE.................................909 629-6219
Mark Chichak, *President*
▲ EMP: 43
SALES (est): 38.1MM
SALES (corp-wide): 1B **Publicly Held**
WEB: www.halexcorp.com
SIC: 3423 Carpet layers' hand tools
PA: Gcp Applied Technologies Inc.
62 Whittemore Ave
Cambridge MA 02140
617 876-1400

(P-11897)
IDL TOOLS INTERNATIONAL LLC
2438 Cades Way, Vista (92081-7830)
PHONE.................................760 598-8888
Sean M Quinn, *Mng Member*
Mike Donath, *CFO*
▲ EMP: 10
SALES: 2.7MM **Privately Held**
WEB: www.idltools.com
SIC: 3423 Screw drivers, pliers, chisels,
etc. (hand tools)

(P-11898)
KAL-CAMERON MANUFACTURING (HQ)
Also Called: Pro American Premium Tools
4265 Puente Ave, Baldwin Park
(91706-3420)
PHONE.................................626 338-7308
John Toshima, *Ch of Bd*
EMP: 100
SQ FT: 32,000
SALES (est): 11.7MM
SALES (corp-wide): 23MM **Privately
Held**
SIC: 3423 Mechanics' hand tools
PA: American Kal Enterprises, Inc.
4265 Puente Ave
Baldwin Park CA 91706
626 338-7308

(P-11899)
KEMPER ENTERPRISES INC
13595 12th St, Chino (91710-5208)
P.O. Box 696 (91708-0696)
PHONE.................................909 627-6191
Herbert H Stampfl, *President*
Librado Cortez, *Admin Sec*
Richard Harrison, *Info Tech Mgr*
Jun Cortez, *Finance*
Debbie Biessener, *Manager*
▲ EMP: 30
SQ FT: 30,000
SALES (est): 6.2MM **Privately Held**
WEB: www.kemperdolls.com
SIC: 3423 Hand & edge tools

(P-11900)
LARIN CORP
5651 Schaefer Ave, Chino (91710-9048)
PHONE.................................909 464-0605
Shouyun Zhang, *President*
▲ EMP: 20
SQ FT: 50,000
SALES (est): 4MM **Privately Held**
WEB: www.larincorp.com
SIC: 3423 Jacks: lifting, screw or ratchet
(hand tools)

(P-11901)
LEITCH & CO INC
Also Called: Intertool Innovative Tooling
1607 Abram Ct, San Leandro
(94577-3226)
PHONE.................................510 483-2323
Fax: 510 483-2391
▼ EMP: 10

SALES (est): 1.4MM **Privately Held**
WEB: www.leitchco.com
SIC: 3423 5085 5251

(P-11902)
MORGAN MANUFACTURING INC
521 2nd St, Petaluma (94952-5121)
P.O. Box 737 (94953-0737)
PHONE.................................707 763-6848
Carl T Palmgren, *President*
Lillian Raposo, *Vice Pres*
EMP: 15
SALES (est): 2.8MM **Privately Held**
WEB: www.morganmfg.com
SIC: 3423 3499 Hand & edge tools; stabi-
lizing bars (cargo), metal

(P-11903)
NUPLA CORPORATION
11912 Sheldon St, Sun Valley
(91352-1509)
PHONE.................................818 768-6800
Ronald Ortiz, *President*
Annette Vitale, *Human Resources*
Abel Aguilera, *Buyer*
▲ EMP: 120
SQ FT: 160,000
SALES (est): 20.7MM
SALES (corp-wide): 309.2MM **Publicly
Held**
WEB: www.nuplacorp.com
SIC: 3423 3089 Hand & edge tools; han-
dles, brush or tool: plastic
PA: Q.E.P. Co., Inc.
1001 Brkn Snd Pkwy Nw A
Boca Raton FL 33487
561 994-5550

(P-11904)
OMEGA TECHNOLOGIES INC
31125 Via Colinas Ste 905, Westlake Vil-
lage (91362-3972)
PHONE.................................818 264-7970
John Bland Schoolland, *President*
▲ EMP: 13
SQ FT: 3,800
SALES: 4.2MM **Privately Held**
WEB: www.omegatec.com
SIC: 3423 5072 5085 Hand & edge tools;
hand tools; industrial tools

(P-11905)
PACIFIC HANDY CUTTER INC
Also Called: PHC
17819 Gillette Ave, Irvine (92614-6501)
PHONE.................................714 662-1033
Mark Marinovich, *CEO*
Matt Paul, *Sr Exec VP*
▲ EMP: 35
SQ FT: 16,000
SALES (est): 8.7MM
SALES (corp-wide): 202.6MM **Privately
Held**
SIC: 3423 3421 Hand & edge tools; cut-
lery
HQ: Phc Sharp Holdings, Inc
17819 Gillette Ave
Irvine CA 92614
714 662-1033

(P-11906)
PRECISION JEWELRY TOOLS & SUPS
1555 Alum Rock Ave, San Jose
(95116-2426)
PHONE.................................408 251-7990
Robert Persekian, *President*
EMP: 20
SQ FT: 12,000
SALES: 2MM **Privately Held**
WEB: www.percisiondisplays.com
SIC: 3423 Jewelers' hand tools

(P-11907)
PRODUCTS ENGINEERING CORP (PA)
Also Called: PEC Tool
2645 Maricopa St, Torrance (90503-5144)
PHONE.................................310 787-4500
Richard A Luboviski, *CEO*
Bernard Brooks, *Treasurer*
Julie Hood, *Vice Pres*
Sandy Luboviski, *Vice Pres*
Gary Mitchell, *Admin Asst*
▲ EMP: 60 EST: 1960
SQ FT: 68,000

SALES: 4.5MM **Privately Held**
WEB: www.pectools.com
SIC: 3423 Hand & edge tools

(P-11908)
QUADRTECH CORPORATION
Also Called: Studex
521 W Rosecrans Ave, Gardena
(90248-1514)
PHONE..................................310 523-1697
Vladimir Reil, *President*
Christie Arana, *Admin Asst*
Ed Boerg, *Manager*
▲ EMP: 185
SALES (est): 24.9MM **Privately Held**
WEB: www.quadrtech.com
SIC: 3423 3915 Jewelers' materials & lapidary work; jewelers' hand tools

(P-11909)
SCHLEY PRODUCTS INC
5350 E Hunter Ave, Anaheim (92807-2053)
PHONE..................................714 693-7666
Paul Schley, *President*
Chad Schley, *Vice Pres*
Mark Schley, *Vice Pres*
Rich Lomanto, *General Mgr*
▲ EMP: 11
SQ FT: 10,000
SALES (est): 2.2MM **Privately Held**
WEB: www.sptool.com
SIC: 3423 Mechanics' hand tools

(P-11910)
SHARP PROFILES LLC
828 W Cienega Ave, San Dimas
(91773-2489)
PHONE..................................760 246-9446
Rick Rybkowski,
EMP: 15
SALES (est): 3.8MM **Privately Held**
SIC: 3423

(P-11911)
STANLEY ACCESS TECH LLC
4230 E Airport Dr Ste 107, Ontario
(91761-3702)
PHONE..................................909 628-9272
John Rapisarda, *Manager*
EMP: 225
SALES (corp-wide): 12.7B **Publicly Held**
WEB: www.stanleyworks.com
SIC: 3423 Hand & edge tools
HQ: Stanley Access Technologies Llc
65 Scott Swamp Rd
Farmington CT 06032

(P-11912)
SUPERCLOSET
Also Called: Kind Led Grow Lights
3555 Airway Dr, Santa Rosa (95403-1605)
P.O. Box 6105 (95406-0105)
PHONE..................................831 588-7829
Kip Lewis Andersen, *CEO*
Rory Kagan, *CEO*
Nicholas Schweitzer, *COO*
Stacey Martin, *Human Res Mgr*
Jeff James, *Purchasing*
▲ EMP: 20
SQ FT: 18,000
SALES (est): 3.3MM **Privately Held**
SIC: 3423 5261 Garden & farm tools, including shovels; lawn & garden equipment

(P-11913)
TRONEX TECHNOLOGY INCORPORATED
2860 Cordelia Rd Ste 230, Fairfield
(94534-1808)
PHONE..................................707 426-2550
Arne Salvesen, *President*
Karin Salvesen, *Vice Pres*
Nina Blaicher, *Manager*
EMP: 20
SQ FT: 4,000
SALES (est): 3.2MM **Privately Held**
WEB: www.tronextools.com
SIC: 3423 5049 Screw drivers, pliers, chisels, etc. (hand tools); precision tools

(P-11914)
UNDERGROUND AUTOWERKS INC (PA)
106 E 17th St, National City (91950-4512)
PHONE..................................619 336-9000
Andrew Castellanos, *Principal*
EMP: 11
SALES (est): 1.4MM **Privately Held**
SIC: 3423 Mechanics' hand tools

(P-11915)
WALLBOARD TOOL CO INC
1697 Seabright Ave, Long Beach
(90813-1146)
P.O. Box 20319 (90801-3319)
PHONE..................................562 437-0701
Jon Masterson, *CEO*
Jon A Masterson, *CEO*
Craig Glenn, *Vice Pres*
Richard Cross, *Sales Mgr*
▲ EMP: 240 EST: 1953
SALES (est): 47MM **Privately Held**
WEB: www.wallboardtoolco.com
SIC: 3423 Hand & edge tools

(P-11916)
WESTCO IRON WORKS INC (PA)
5828 S Naylor Rd, Livermore (94551-8308)
PHONE..................................925 961-9152
Mark Shoermsser, *President*
Scott Hofstede, *CFO*
Brad Thompson, *Vice Pres*
John Winger, *Vice Pres*
EMP: 70
SALES (est): 20MM **Privately Held**
WEB: www.westcoironworks.com
SIC: 3423 Ironworkers' hand tools

3425 Hand Saws & Saw Blades

(P-11917)
DIAMOND K2
23911 Garnier St Ste C, Torrance
(90505-7523)
P.O. Box 346 (90508-0346)
PHONE..................................310 539-6116
Les Kuzmick, *Ch of Bd*
Richard Kirby, *President*
EMP: 21
SQ FT: 7,600
SALES (est): 4MM **Privately Held**
SIC: 3425 3531 5082 Saw blades & handsaws; construction machinery; concrete processing equipment

(P-11918)
FANNO SAW WORKS
224 W 8th Ave, Chico (95926-3242)
P.O. Box 628 (95927-0628)
PHONE..................................530 895-1762
Robert A Fanno, *President*
▲ EMP: 10
SQ FT: 8,000
SALES (est): 1.6MM **Privately Held**
SIC: 3425 Saw blades & handsaws

(P-11919)
HI-LINE INDUSTRIAL SAW AND SUP
416 W Meats Ave, Orange (92865-2625)
PHONE..................................714 921-1600
William Johnston, *President*
Diane Y Johnston, *Vice Pres*
EMP: 11
SQ FT: 7,000
SALES: 3MM **Privately Held**
SIC: 3425 5072 Saw blades & handsaws; saw blades

(P-11920)
NORDIC SAW & TOOL MFRS
2114 Divanian Dr, Turlock (95382-9680)
P.O. Box 1128 (95381-1128)
PHONE..................................209 634-9015
Dewey Larson, *President*
EMP: 30
SQ FT: 11,000

SALES (est): 2.6MM **Privately Held**
WEB: www.nordicsaw.com
SIC: 3425 3421 3545 Saw blades & handsaws; knives: butchers', hunting, pocket, etc.; bits for use on lathes, planers, shapers, etc.

(P-11921)
SAWBIRD INC (PA)
Also Called: Cal Saw Canada
721 Brannan St, San Francisco
(94103-4927)
PHONE..................................415 861-0644
Warren M Bird, *President*
Benson L Joseph, *Vice Pres*
Hazel E Bird, *Admin Sec*
▲ EMP: 20
SQ FT: 17,500
SALES (est): 3.3MM **Privately Held**
WEB: www.calsaw.com
SIC: 3425 3423 7699 Saw blades for hand or power saws; knives, agricultural or industrial; knife, saw & tool sharpening & repair

(P-11922)
WESTERN SAW MANUFACTURERS INC
3200 Camino Del Sol, Oxnard
(93030-8998)
PHONE..................................805 981-0999
Kevin Baron, *CEO*
Kraig Baron, *President*
Frank Baron, *CEO*
Nancy Pounds, *Corp Secy*
Steve Williams, *Info Tech Dir*
▲ EMP: 50
SQ FT: 70,000
SALES: 11MM **Privately Held**
WEB: www.westernsaw.com
SIC: 3425 3546 Saw blades & handsaws; power-driven handtools

3429 Hardware, NEC

(P-11923)
ACCURIDE INTERNATIONAL INC (PA)
12311 Shoemaker Ave, Santa Fe Springs
(90670-4721)
PHONE..................................562 903-0200
Scott E Jordan, *CEO*
Chao Huang, *Vice Pres*
Sid Kalantar, *Vice Pres*
Jerome Barr, *Principal*
Steve Helms, *Info Tech Dir*
▲ EMP: 47
SALES (est): 508.1MM **Privately Held**
WEB: www.accuride.com
SIC: 3429 Manufactured hardware (general)

(P-11924)
ACTRON MANUFACTURING INC
1841 Railroad St, Corona (92880-2512)
PHONE..................................951 371-0885
Frank Rechberg, *CEO*
Dow Rechberg, *Corp Secy*
EMP: 93
SQ FT: 30,000
SALES (est): 20.1MM **Privately Held**
WEB: www.actronmfginc.com
SIC: 3429 Aircraft hardware

(P-11925)
ALARIN AIRCRAFT HINGE INC
Also Called: Commerce
6231 Randolph St, Commerce
(90040-3514)
PHONE..................................323 725-1666
Gregory A Sanders, *President*
Lloyd Wallis, *General Mgr*
Netty Chang, *Finance Mgr*
Joce Tonnu, *QC Dir*
EMP: 25
SQ FT: 11,000
SALES (est): 5MM **Privately Held**
WEB: www.alarin.com
SIC: 3429 3728 Aircraft hardware; aircraft parts & equipment

(P-11926)
ALVIN D TROYER AND ASSOCIATES
310 Shaw Rd Ste F, South San Francisco
(94080-6615)
PHONE..................................650 574-0167
Gary Troyer, *President*
Dan Troyer, *Vice Pres*
EMP: 11
SALES (est): 790K **Privately Held**
SIC: 3429 Door locks, bolts & checks

(P-11927)
AMERICAN EMPEROR INC
1900 E 12th St, Oakland (94606-4821)
PHONE..................................510 536-6868
Cheuk Kin Wong, *CEO*
EMP: 15
SALES (est): 4.9MM **Privately Held**
SIC: 3429 Furniture builders' & other household hardware

(P-11928)
ARCMATE MANUFACTURING CORP
911 S Andreasen Dr, Escondido
(92029-1934)
PHONE..................................760 489-1140
Bob Traber, *CEO*
Robert Traber, *President*
▲ EMP: 12
SQ FT: 6,650
SALES (est): 1.3MM **Privately Held**
WEB: www.arcmate.com
SIC: 3429 5072 5251 Manufactured hardware (general); hand tools; tools, hand

(P-11929)
ASCO SINTERING CO
2750 Garfield Ave, Commerce
(90040-2610)
P.O. Box 911157 (90091-1157)
PHONE..................................323 725-3550
Neil Moore, *CEO*
Bob Lebrun, *CFO*
Robert Lebrun, *CFO*
Samuel Moorman, *Engineer*
Ian Harris, *Plant Mgr*
▲ EMP: 33 EST: 1971
SQ FT: 69,000
SALES: 9MM **Privately Held**
WEB: www.ascosintering.com
SIC: 3429 3714 Manufactured hardware (general); motor vehicle parts & accessories

(P-11930)
ASSA ABLOY RSDENTIAL GROUP INC (HQ)
15250 Stafford St, City of Industry
(91744-4418)
PHONE..................................626 961-0413
Thomas Millar, *President*
Ping Tsai, *Engineer*
Birk Sorensen, *VP Mfg*
Erik Swenson, *VP Opers*
Rick Julian, *Pub Rel Dir*
◆ EMP: 200
SQ FT: 38,000
SALES (est): 100.5MM
SALES (corp-wide): 9B **Privately Held**
WEB: www.emtek.com
SIC: 3429 Manufactured hardware (general)
PA: Assa Abloy Ab
Klarabergsviadukten 90
Stockholm 111 6
850 648-500

(P-11931)
AUTOMOTIVE RACING PRODUCTS INC (PA)
Also Called: A R P
1863 Eastman Ave, Ventura (93003-8084)
PHONE..................................805 339-2200
Gary Holzapfel, *CEO*
Mike Holzapfel, *President*
Kelly Schau, *CFO*
Robert Florine, *Exec VP*
Robert Flourin, *Vice Pres*
▲ EMP: 65
SQ FT: 10,000

SALES (est): 29.6MM **Privately Held**
WEB: www.arp-bolts.com
SIC: **3429** 3714 3452 Manufactured hardware (general); motor vehicle parts & accessories; bolts, nuts, rivets & washers

(P-11932)
AUTOMOTIVE RACING PRODUCTS INC
Also Called: A R P
1760 E Lemonwood Dr, Santa Paula (93060-9510)
PHONE................................805 525-1497
Michael Holzapsel, *Branch Mgr*
Chris Raschke, *Sales Dir*
Art Venegas, *Sales Staff*
EMP: 60
SALES (est): 9MM
SALES (corp-wide): 29.6MM **Privately Held**
WEB: www.arp-bolts.com
SIC: **3429** Manufactured hardware (general)
PA: Automotive Racing Products, Inc.
1863 Eastman Ave
Ventura CA 93003
805 339-2200

(P-11933)
AVIBANK MFG INC
Avk Industrial Products
25323 Rye Canyon Rd, Valencia (91355-1205)
PHONE................................661 257-2329
James M Wolpert, *General Mgr*
EMP: 85
SQ FT: 23,000
SALES (corp-wide): 242.1B **Publicly Held**
SIC: **3429** 3541 3452 Manufactured hardware (general); machine tools, metal cutting type; bolts, nuts, rivets & washers
HQ: Avibank Mfg., Inc.
11500 Sherman Way
North Hollywood CA 91605
818 392-2100

(P-11934)
B & B SPECIALTIES INC (PA)
4321 E La Palma Ave, Anaheim (92807-1887)
PHONE................................714 985-3000
Bruce Borchardt, *President*
▲ EMP: 190
SQ FT: 40,000
SALES (est): 40.3MM **Privately Held**
WEB: www.bbspecialties.com
SIC: **3429** 3452 Metal fasteners; bolts, nuts, rivets & washers

(P-11935)
BAIER MARINE COMPANY INC
2920 Airway Ave, Costa Mesa (92626-6008)
PHONE................................800 455-3917
Mark Smith, *President*
Felice Lineberry, *Manager*
▼ EMP: 20
SALES: 1,000K **Privately Held**
WEB: www.baiermarine.com
SIC: **3429** Manufactured hardware (general)

(P-11936)
BALDWIN HARDWARE CORPORATION (DH)
Also Called: Baldwin Brass
19701 Da Vinci, Foothill Ranch (92610-2622)
PHONE................................949 672-4000
David R Lumley, *CEO*
▲ EMP: 816 EST: 1944
SQ FT: 300,000
SALES (est): 99.6MM
SALES (corp-wide): 5B **Publicly Held**
SIC: **3429** Builders' hardware; locks or lock sets; cabinet hardware
HQ: Spectrum Brands, Inc.
3001 Deming Way
Middleton WI 53562
608 275-3340

(P-11937)
BATON LOCK & HARDWARE CO INC
Also Called: Baton Security
14275 Commerce Dr, Garden Grove (92843-4944)
PHONE................................714 265-3636
Hwei Ying Chen, *President*
Fong Shiang Hsu, *President*
Sharron Hsu, *Vice Pres*
WEI Hsu, *Vice Pres*
◆ EMP: 24
SQ FT: 15,025
SALES (est): 3.1MM **Privately Held**
WEB: www.batonlockusa.com
SIC: **3429** Keys, locks & related hardware; locks or lock sets

(P-11938)
BAUER INDUSTRIES (PA)
Also Called: Sports Rack Vehicle Outfitters
708 Alhambra Blvd Ste 2, Sacramento (95816-3851)
PHONE................................916 648-9200
Greg Bauer, *President*
John Bauer, *Vice Pres*
Tom Mollerus, *Vice Pres*
▲ EMP: 11
SQ FT: 2,500
SALES (est): 15.5MM **Privately Held**
WEB: www.bauerworld.com
SIC: **3429** 5013 5531 5961 Motor vehicle hardware; automotive supplies & parts; automotive accessories; automotive supplies & equipment, mail order

(P-11939)
BULDOOR LLC
647 Camino De Los, San Clemente (92673)
PHONE................................877 388-1366
Luis Morales, *Mng Member*
▲ EMP: 10
SQ FT: 20,000
SALES: 4MM **Privately Held**
SIC: **3429** 5072 Manufactured hardware (general); hardware

(P-11940)
C-FAB
932 W 17th St, Costa Mesa (92627-4403)
P.O. Box 6177, Laguna Niguel (92607-6177)
PHONE................................949 646-2616
Steve Degroote, *Owner*
EMP: 25
SQ FT: 7,000
SALES: 1.2MM **Privately Held**
WEB: www.cfab.com
SIC: **3429** Marine hardware

(P-11941)
CAL-JUNE INC (PA)
Also Called: Jim-Buoy
5238 Vineland Ave, North Hollywood (91601-3221)
P.O. Box 9551 (91609-1551)
PHONE................................323 877-4164
James H Robertson, *President*
Jennifer D Jacobson, *President*
Andrea Robertson, *Vice Pres*
Melini Robertson, *Vice Pres*
▼ EMP: 48 EST: 1966
SQ FT: 3,000
SALES (est): 9.3MM **Privately Held**
WEB: www.jimbuoy.com
SIC: **3429** Marine hardware

(P-11942)
CALIFORNIA SCREW PRODUCTS CORP
14957 Gwenchris Ct, Paramount (90723-3423)
P.O. Box 228 (90723-0228)
PHONE................................562 633-6626
Larry Valeriano, *CEO*
Letitia Serrano, *Human Res Dir*
Vikki Errett, *Purchasing*
Sal Vazquez, *Plant Mgr*
Larry Baleriano, *Mktg Dir*
EMP: 108
SQ FT: 20,000

SALES (est): 14.7MM **Privately Held**
WEB: www.calscrew.net
SIC: **3429** 3452 Metal fasteners; bolts, nuts, rivets & washers

(P-11943)
CALMEX FIREPLACE EQUIPMENT MFG
Also Called: Calmex Fireplace Equip Mfg
13629 Talc St, Santa Fe Springs (90670-5113)
PHONE................................716 645-2901
Maria Hirshal, *President*
Rosa Franco, *Vice Pres*
EMP: 15
SQ FT: 15,000
SALES: 2MM **Privately Held**
WEB: www.calmexfireplaces.com
SIC: **3429** Fireplace equipment, hardware: andirons, grates, screens

(P-11944)
CIRCOR AEROSPACE INC
Also Called: Circor Aerospace Machining Ctr
2301 Wardlow Cir, Corona (92880-2801)
PHONE................................951 270-6200
Steve Alford, *Branch Mgr*
EMP: 91
SALES (corp-wide): 661.7MM **Publicly Held**
SIC: **3429** 3599 3451 3497 Manufactured hardware (general); machine & other job shop work; machine shop, jobbing & repair; screw machine products; metal foil & leaf; aircraft parts & equipment
HQ: Circor Aerospace, Inc.
2301 Wardlow Cir
Corona CA 92880

(P-11945)
CLAMP MANUFACTURING CO INC
Also Called: Kant-Twist
1503 Adelia Ave, South El Monte (91733-3093)
PHONE................................626 579-5379
Louise Saurenman, *President*
Stephen Saurenman, *Treasurer*
John Saurenman, *Admin Sec*
EMP: 12
SQ FT: 13,000
SALES (est): 2MM **Privately Held**
WEB: www.clampmfg.com
SIC: **3429** 3423 Clamps, metal; hand & edge tools

(P-11946)
CLEMES & CLEMES INC
650 San Pablo Ave, Pinole (94564-2600)
PHONE................................510 724-2036
Henry J Clemes, *President*
Peggy Clemes, *Corp Secy*
EMP: 14
SQ FT: 20,000
SALES (est): 1.7MM **Privately Held**
SIC: **3429** 5251 Art squares, textile fiber

(P-11947)
CRAIN CUTTER COMPANY INC
1155 Wrigley Way, Milpitas (95035-5426)
PHONE................................408 946-6100
Millard Crain Jr, *CEO*
Jennifer Crain, *Shareholder*
Lance Crain, *Shareholder*
Lou Pinon, *Asst Office Mgr*
▲ EMP: 87
SQ FT: 110,000
SALES (est): 20.8MM **Privately Held**
WEB: www.craintools.com
SIC: **3429** 3545 Manufactured hardware (general); machine tool accessories

(P-11948)
CRD MFG INC
1539 W Orange Grove Ave A, Orange (92868-1110)
PHONE................................714 871-3300
Timothy Carroll, *CEO*
EMP: 18
SALES (est): 3.5MM **Privately Held**
SIC: **3429** 3699 Motor vehicle hardware; welding machines & equipment, ultrasonic

(P-11949)
CREMAX U S A CORPORATION
Also Called: Icy Dock USA
11740 Clark St, Arcadia (91006-5805)
PHONE................................626 956-8800
Jeff Fung, *Branch Mgr*
Roy Lin, *Sales Staff*
EMP: 10 **Privately Held**
SIC: **3429** Manufactured hardware (general)
PA: Cremax Tech Co., Ltd.
2f, 18, Lane 609, Chung Hsin Rd., Sec. 5,
New Taipei City 24159
229 993-251

(P-11950)
CUSTOM HARDWARE MFG INC
2112 E 4th St Ste 228g, Santa Ana (92705-3840)
PHONE................................714 547-7440
▲ EMP: 45
SQ FT: 4,500
SALES: 3.4MM **Privately Held**
WEB: www.chmi.com
SIC: **3429**

(P-11951)
DARNELL CORPORATION
17915 Railroad St, City of Industry (91748-1113)
PHONE................................626 912-1688
Brent Bargar, *President*
EMP: 52
SALES (est): 8.5MM **Privately Held**
SIC: **3429** Manufactured hardware (general)

(P-11952)
DOVAL INDUSTRIES INC
Also Called: Doval Industries Co
3961 N Mission Rd, Los Angeles (90031-2931)
PHONE................................323 226-0335
Cruz Sandoval, *CEO*
▲ EMP: 65
SALES (est): 9.6MM **Privately Held**
SIC: **3429** 5072 2759 Keys, locks & related hardware; hardware; screen printing

(P-11953)
EDDIE MOTORSPORTS
11479 6th St, Rancho Cucamonga (91730-6024)
PHONE................................909 581-7398
Frank E Borges, *Owner*
John Henry, *Marketing Staff*
▲ EMP: 10
SQ FT: 26,000
SALES (est): 100K **Privately Held**
SIC: **3429** Aircraft & marine hardware, inc. pulleys & similar items

(P-11954)
EUROPEAN SERVICES GROUP
Also Called: Topslide International
5062 Caspian Cir, Huntington Beach (92649-1210)
PHONE................................714 898-0595
Gus P Frousiakis, *President*
John Frousiakis, *Vice Pres*
◆ EMP: 14
SALES (est): 1.6MM **Privately Held**
WEB: www.topslide.com
SIC: **3429** Furniture builders' & other household hardware

(P-11955)
FXC CORPORATION (PA)
3050 Red Hill Ave, Costa Mesa (92626-4524)
PHONE................................714 556-7400
Irene Chevrier, *CEO*
Kelly Densmore, *Technology*
Michael Urban, *Materials Mgr*
Rick Velazquez, *Marketing Staff*
EMP: 21
SQ FT: 26,000
SALES (est): 14.7MM **Privately Held**
WEB: www.fxcguardian.com
SIC: **3429** 2399 Parachute hardware; parachutes

(P-11956)
GARDNER FAMILY LTD PARTNERSHIP
Also Called: HMC Display
300 Commerce Dr, Madera (93637-5215)
PHONE..................559 675-8149
Curtis K Gardner,
▲ EMP: 25 EST: 1967
SQ FT: 45,000
SALES (est): 4.9MM Privately Held
SIC: 3429 Manufactured hardware (general)

(P-11957)
GARHAUER MARINE CORPORATION
1062 W 9th St, Upland (91786-5726)
PHONE..................909 985-9993
William Felgenhauer, President
Mary Felgenhauer, Admin Sec
EMP: 33
SQ FT: 10,000
SALES (est): 5MM Privately Held
WEB: www.garhauermarine.com
SIC: 3429 Marine hardware

(P-11958)
HARTWELL CORPORATION (DH)
Also Called: Hasco
900 Richfield Rd, Placentia (92870-6788)
PHONE..................714 993-4200
Joel Reiss, CEO
John Leary, President
Vicki Saugstad, CFO
Liz Rodriguez, Executive Asst
Kristina Arney, Project Leader
▲ EMP: 200
SQ FT: 134,000
SALES (est): 203.8MM
SALES (corp-wide): 3.5B Publicly Held
WEB: www.hartwellcorp.com
SIC: 3429 Aircraft hardware
HQ: Mckechnie Aerospace Investments, Inc.
20 Pacifica Ste 200
Irvine CA
859 887-6200

(P-11959)
HEARTHCO INC
5781 Pleasant Valley Rd, El Dorado (95623-4200)
PHONE..................530 622-3877
Dan Zacher, President
Laurene Zacher, CFO
Paul Amador, Sales Mgr
EMP: 25 EST: 2001
SALES (est): 4.3MM Privately Held
WEB: www.heartco.com
SIC: 3429 Fireplace equipment, hardware: andirons, grates, screens

(P-11960)
HI-SHEAR CORPORATION
2600 Skypark Dr, Torrance (90505-5373)
PHONE..................310 326-8110
Kurt Weideman, Manager
EMP: 25 Privately Held
WEB: www.hi-shear.com
SIC: 3429 3452 Manufactured hardware (general); bolts, nuts, rivets & washers
HQ: Hi-Shear Corporation
2600 Skypark Dr
Torrance CA 90505
310 784-4025

(P-11961)
HODGE PRODUCTS INC
Also Called: Www.masterlocks.com
7365 Mission Gorge Rd F, San Diego (92120-1274)
P.O. Box 1326, El Cajon (92022-1326)
PHONE..................619 444-3147
Anthony Hodge, President
Allan Hodge, Treasurer
▲ EMP: 25
SALES (est): 10MM Privately Held
WEB: www.hpionline.com
SIC: 3429 5099 Locks or lock sets; locks & lock sets

(P-11962)
HOLLYWOOD BED SPRING MFG INC
5959 Corvette St, Commerce (90040-1601)
PHONE..................323 887-9500
Larry Harrow, CEO
Jason Harrow, President
Andrea Harrow, Admin Sec
◆ EMP: 90
SQ FT: 55,000
SALES (est): 18.5MM Privately Held
WEB: www.hollywoodbed.com
SIC: 3429 2515 2511 2514 Manufactured hardware (general); mattresses & bedsprings; wood household furniture; frames for box springs or bedsprings: metal

(P-11963)
HOLLYWOOD ENGINEERING INC
Also Called: Hollywood Bike Racks
12812 S Spring St, Los Angeles (90061-1620)
PHONE..................310 516-8600
Neil Nusbaum, President
Andre Levy, Vice Pres
Evan Nusbaum, Sales Mgr
▲ EMP: 10 EST: 1973
SQ FT: 35,000
SALES (est): 4.5MM Privately Held
WEB: www.hollywoodracks.com
SIC: 3429 3496 Bicycle racks, automotive; miscellaneous fabricated wire products

(P-11964)
INTELLIGENT ENERGY INC
1731 Tech Dr Ste 755, San Jose (95110)
PHONE..................562 997-3600
Henri Winand, President
Larry Frost, Corp Secy
Hazen Burford, Vice Pres
Dennis Hayter, VP Bus Dvlpt
Julian Hughes, Director
EMP: 30
SQ FT: 9,600
SALES (est): 5.6MM
SALES (corp-wide): 4.4MM Privately Held
WEB: www.intelligent-energy.com
SIC: 3429 3694 Bicycle racks, automotive; alternators, automotive
PA: Intelligent Energy Limited
Charnwood Building
Loughborough LEICS LE11
150 927-1271

(P-11965)
JAMES P MCNAIR CO INC
Also Called: Valma Properties
2236 Irving St, San Francisco (94122-1619)
P.O. Box 22072 (94122-0072)
PHONE..................415 681-2200
Lydia McNair, President
Linda Idiart, Treasurer
Michael James Mc Nair, Vice Pres
Rhonda Bouyea, Admin Sec
EMP: 10
SQ FT: 2,200
SALES (est): 1.1MM Privately Held
SIC: 3429 6512 6514 Locks or lock sets; nonresidential building operators; dwelling operators, except apartments

(P-11966)
JONATHAN ENGNRED SLUTIONS CORP (PA)
250 Commerce Ste 100, Irvine (92602-1341)
PHONE..................714 665-4400
Paul Salazar, CEO
Michael Berneth, President
Eric Hersom, Officer
Wes Firisin, Regional Mgr
Les Van Kanten, Admin Sec
▲ EMP: 44
SQ FT: 120,000
SALES (est): 84.1MM Privately Held
WEB: www.jonathanengr.com
SIC: 3429 3562 Manufactured hardware (general); ball bearings & parts

(P-11967)
K & W MANUFACTURING CO INC
23107 Temescal Canyon Rd, Corona (92883-6001)
PHONE..................951 277-3300
Gerald W Keck, President
Denise Jure, Vice Pres
Carolyn Keck, Admin Sec
EMP: 16
SQ FT: 15,000
SALES: 400K Privately Held
WEB: www.k-and-w-mfg.com
SIC: 3429 3631 Fireplace equipment, hardware: andirons, grates, screens; barbecues, grills & braziers (outdoor cooking)

(P-11968)
KL-MEGLA AMERICA LLC
2221 Celsius Ave Ste A, Oxnard (93030-7258)
PHONE..................818 334-5311
Peter Reinecke, CEO
Julie Maddox, Office Mgr
Chun MI, Sales Staff
Lawrence Glasner, Mng Member
▲ EMP: 20 EST: 2008
SALES (est): 3MM Privately Held
SIC: 3429 Manufactured hardware (general)

(P-11969)
KLINKY MANUFACTURING CO
4000 W Magnolia Blvd D, Burbank (91505-2827)
PHONE..................818 766-6256
Dee Maser, President
▲ EMP: 10
SALES (est): 688.9K Privately Held
SIC: 3429 Keys, locks & related hardware

(P-11970)
LIGHT COMPOSITE CORPORATION
Also Called: Forespar
22322 Gilberto, Rcho STA Marg (92688-2102)
PHONE..................949 858-8820
Robert R Foresman, President
Marilyn Holst, Treasurer
Juin Foresman, Principal
Cordie Gary, Admin Sec
▲ EMP: 60
SALES (est): 5.8MM Privately Held
SIC: 3429 Marine hardware

(P-11971)
LOCK AMERICA INC
Also Called: Mr Lock
9168 Stellar Ct, Corona (92883-4923)
PHONE..................951 277-5180
Ming Shiao, President
Frank Minnella, CEO
Watson Visuwan, Vice Pres
Candice Smith, Technology
▲ EMP: 19
SQ FT: 11,500
SALES (est): 3.2MM Privately Held
WEB: www.laigroup.com
SIC: 3429 5099 Keys, locks & related hardware; locks & lock sets

(P-11972)
MAC ENGINEERING & COMPONENTS
5122 Calle Del Sol, Santa Clara (95054-1009)
PHONE..................408 286-3030
Chris Cardamon, Owner
EMP: 12
SALES (est): 1.7MM Privately Held
SIC: 3429 5085 Builders' hardware; fasteners, industrial: nuts, bolts, screws, etc.

(P-11973)
MARIN USA
265 Bel Marin Keys Blvd, Novato (94949-5724)
PHONE..................415 382-6000
Matt Vanenkevort, CEO
▲ EMP: 20
SALES (est): 1.7MM Privately Held
SIC: 3429 Bicycle racks, automotive

(P-11974)
MCDANIEL MANUFACTURING INC
6180 Enterprise Dr Ste D, Diamond Springs (95619-9471)
PHONE..................530 626-6336
John McDaniel, President
Nora McDaniel, Corp Secy
EMP: 15
SALES (est): 2.3MM Privately Held
WEB: www.mcdanielmfg.com
SIC: 3429 3443 3089 Manufactured hardware (general); stills, pressure: metal plate; hardware, plastic

(P-11975)
MCMAHON STEEL COMPANY INC
1880 Nirvana Ave, Chula Vista (91911-6118)
PHONE..................619 671-9700
Derek J McMahon, President
Kevin McMahon, Vice Pres
Suriano Ed, Info Tech Mgr
Cynthia Dealba, Human Res Dir
Steve Ridings,
EMP: 120
SQ FT: 14,300
SALES (est): 32.6MM Privately Held
WEB: www.mcmahonsteel.com
SIC: 3429 1791 3441 Manufactured hardware (general); structural steel erection; fabricated structural metal

(P-11976)
MOELLER MFG & SUP LLC
Also Called: Moeller Mfg & Sup Inc
805 E Cerritos Ave, Anaheim (92805-6328)
PHONE..................714 999-5551
Stevens Chevillotte, President
Peter George, CEO
Debbie Comstock, Director
EMP: 45 EST: 1978
SALES: 14MM
SALES (corp-wide): 167.6MM Privately Held
WEB: www.moellermfg.com
SIC: 3429 3452 Aircraft hardware; washers, metal
PA: Consolidated Aerospace Manufacturing, Llc
1425 S Acacia Ave
Fullerton CA 92831
714 989-2797

(P-11977)
MONADNOCK COMPANY
Also Called: Lisi Aerospace
16728 Gale Ave, City of Industry (91745-1803)
PHONE..................626 964-6581
Christian Darville, CEO
Michael Reyes, Vice Pres
Mike Reyes, General Mgr
Curtis Kerr, Planning
Paul Maddox, IT/INT Sup
▼ EMP: 190 EST: 1987
SQ FT: 90,000
SALES (est): 50MM Privately Held
WEB: www.monadnock.com
SIC: 3429 Aircraft hardware; metal fasteners
HQ: Hi-Shear Corporation
2600 Skypark Dr
Torrance CA 90505
310 784-4025

(P-11978)
MONOGRAM AEROSPACE FAS INC (HQ)
3423 Garfield Ave, Commerce (90040-3103)
PHONE..................323 722-4760
David Adler, President
▲ EMP: 135
SQ FT: 97,500
SALES (est): 50.8MM
SALES (corp-wide): 817.7MM Publicly Held
WEB: www.monogramaerospace.com
SIC: 3429 3452 Manufactured hardware (general); bolts, metal; rivets, metal; screws, metal

PRODUCTS & SVCS

PA: Trimas Corporation
38505 Woodward Ave # 200
Bloomfield Hills MI 48304
248 631-5450

(P-11979)
MOORE TOOL CO
16701 Chestnut St Ste 8, Hesperia
(92345-6114)
PHONE..................................760 949-4142
Cliff Moore, *Owner*
EMP: 21
SQ FT: 12,000
SALES (est): 2MM **Privately Held**
SIC: 3429 5072 Motor vehicle hardware;
miscellaneous fasteners

(P-11980)
NUSET INC
1364 Marion Ct, City of Industry
(91745-2418)
PHONE..................................626 246-1668
Caron Ng, *CEO*
EMP: 20
SALES (est): 745.5K **Privately Held**
SIC: 3429 Keys, locks & related hardware

(P-11981)
ORION ORNAMENTAL IRON INC
6918 Tujunga Ave, North Hollywood
(91605-6212)
PHONE..................................818 752-0688
Sunil Patel, *CEO*
Atul Patel, *President*
Tiffany Wardzinski, *Marketing Staff*
▲ **EMP:** 40
SQ FT: 30,000
SALES (est): 5.3MM **Privately Held**
WEB: www.ironartbyorion.com
SIC: 3429 Builders' hardware

(P-11982)
PACIFIC LOCK COMPANY (PA)
25605 Hercules St, Valencia (91355-5051)
PHONE..................................661 294-3707
Gregory B Waugh, *President*
Patty Yang, *CFO*
Joshua Fleagane, *Vice Pres*
Lori Peterson, *Marketing Staff*
Giovanna Chavez, *Accounts Mgr*
▲ **EMP:** 29
SQ FT: 18,000
SALES (est): 3.1MM **Privately Held**
WEB: www.paclock.com
SIC: 3429 3699 5099 Keys & key blanks;
security devices; locks & lock sets

(P-11983)
PAU HANA GROUP LLC
Also Called: Kjl Fasteners
94601 State Rte 70, Chilcoot (96105)
PHONE..................................530 993-6800
Kristine L J Lock, *Mng Member*
Raymond W Lock,
EMP: 12
SQ FT: 5,000
SALES (est): 2.5MM **Privately Held**
WEB: www.kjlfast.com
SIC: 3429 Manufactured hardware (general)

(P-11984)
PECOWOOD INC
7707 Alondra Blvd, Paramount
(90723-5003)
PHONE..................................562 633-2538
Danny Pezzino, *President*
EMP: 12
SQ FT: 8,000
SALES (est): 1.6MM **Privately Held**
SIC: 3429

(P-11985)
R C PRODUCTS CORP
22322 Gilberto, Rcho STA Marg
(92688-2102)
PHONE..................................949 858-8820
Robert R Foresman, *President*
Marilyn Holst, *Admin Sec*
EMP: 60
SQ FT: 40,000
SALES (est): 3.8MM
SALES (corp-wide): 9.2MM **Privately Held**
WEB: www.forespar.com
SIC: 3429 Marine hardware

PA: Forespar Products Corp.
22322 Gilberto
Rcho Sta Marg CA 92688
949 858-8820

(P-11986)
RAILMAKERS INC
864 W 18th St, Costa Mesa (92627-4411)
PHONE..................................949 642-6506
John Hawley, *President*
David C Hawley, *Corp Secy*
EMP: 12
SQ FT: 10,000
SALES (est): 1.7MM **Privately Held**
WEB: www.railmakers.com
SIC: 3429 Marine hardware

(P-11987)
REVERSICA DESIGN INC
1900 Commercial Way Ste A, Santa Cruz
(95065-1844)
PHONE..................................831 459-9033
EMP: 10
SALES (est): 580K **Privately Held**
SIC: 3429

(P-11988)
RPC LEGACY INC
Also Called: Terry Hinge & Hardware
14600 Arminta St, Van Nuys (91402-5902)
PHONE..................................818 787-9000
Authur William, *Branch Mgr*
EMP: 75
SALES (corp-wide): 16.1MM **Privately Held**
WEB: www.rockfordprocess.com
SIC: 3429 Manufactured hardware (general)
PA: Rpc Legacy, Inc.
2020 7th St
Rockford IL 61104
815 966-2000

(P-11989)
RYADON INC
25932 Wright, Foothill Ranch (92610-3502)
PHONE..................................949 768-8333
Jill K Walker, *President*
Kent Walker, *Vice Pres*
▲ **EMP:** 25
SALES (est): 5.6MM **Privately Held**
WEB: www.ryadon.com
SIC: 3429 Manufactured hardware (general)

(P-11990)
SATURN FASTENERS INC
425 S Varney St, Burbank (91502-2193)
PHONE..................................818 973-1807
Raymond D Barker Jr, *President*
Laura Elaine Barker, *Chairman*
Sal Saldivar, *Purchasing*
▲ **EMP:** 112
SQ FT: 38,000
SALES (est): 20MM **Privately Held**
WEB: www.saturnfasteners.com
SIC: 3429 5085 5072 3452 Metal fasteners; industrial supplies; bolts, nuts &
screws; bolts, nuts, rivets & washers
HQ: Acument Global Technologies, Inc.
6125 18 Mile Rd
Sterling Heights MI 48314
586 254-3900

(P-11991)
SCHLAGE LOCK COMPANY LLC
2297 Niels Bohr Ct # 209, San Diego
(92154-7928)
PHONE..................................619 671-0276
Rosa Cardenas, *Manager*
EMP: 20 **Privately Held**
SIC: 3429 Locks or lock sets
HQ: Schlage Lock Company Llc
11819 N Pennsylvania St
Carmel IN 46032
317 810-3700

(P-11992)
SECURITY DOOR CONTROLS (PA)
801 Avenida Acaso, Camarillo
(93012-8726)
P.O. Box 3670 (93011-3670)
PHONE..................................805 494-0622
David A Geringer, *President*
Arthur V Geringer, *Ch of Bd*

Gloria Marchand, *Corp Secy*
Richard Geringer, *Vice Pres*
Shane Geringer, *Vice Pres*
▲ **EMP:** 50
SQ FT: 19,000
SALES (est): 5.1MM **Privately Held**
WEB: www.sdcsecurity.com
SIC: 3429 Door locks, bolts & checks

(P-11993)
SOLID-SCOPE MACHINING CO INC
17925 Adria Maru Ln, Carson
(90746-1401)
PHONE..................................310 523-2366
Patsy Rhinehart, *President*
Robert Rhinehart, *Vice Pres*
EMP: 16
SQ FT: 6,000
SALES (est): 3.1MM **Privately Held**
WEB: www.solid-scope.com
SIC: 3429 3728 Aircraft hardware; aircraft parts & equipment

(P-11994)
SPEP ACQUISITION CORP (PA)
Also Called: Sierra Pacific Engrg & Pdts
4041 Via Oro Ave, Long Beach
(90810-1458)
P.O. Box 5246, Carson (90749-5246)
PHONE..................................310 608-0693
David Mochalski, *CEO*
Shaffiq Rahim, *CFO*
Larry Mirik, *Chairman*
◆ **EMP:** 85
SQ FT: 48,300
SALES (est): 24.2MM **Privately Held**
WEB: www.SPEP.com
SIC: 3429 8711 5072 Manufactured hardware (general); engineering services;
hardware

(P-11995)
STAR DIE CASTING INC
12209 Slauson Ave, Santa Fe Springs
(90670-2605)
PHONE..................................562 698-0627
Jer Ming Yu, *President*
MEI H Yu, *Treasurer*
Mark Chen, *QC Mgr*
▲ **EMP:** 80
SQ FT: 13,290
SALES (est): 9.4MM **Privately Held**
SIC: 3429 3364 3544 Builders' hardware;
nonferrous die-castings except aluminum;
special dies & tools

(P-11996)
STAR ONE INVESTMENTS LLC
1304 Buttercup Ct, Roseville (95661-5459)
PHONE..................................916 858-1178
Danny Walrath,
EMP: 15
SALES (est): 3MM **Privately Held**
SIC: 3429 Manufactured hardware (general)

(P-11997)
STORUS CORPORATION
3266 Buskirk Ave, Pleasant Hill
(94523-4315)
PHONE..................................925 322-8700
Scott Kaminski, *President*
David Kaminski, *Vice Pres*
▲ **EMP:** 10
SALES (est): 1.6MM **Privately Held**
WEB: www.storus.com
SIC: 3429 Builders' hardware

(P-11998)
SYNERGETIC TECH GROUP INC
1712 Earhart, La Verne (91750-5826)
PHONE..................................909 305-4711
Kevin E Jones, *CEO*
EMP: 10
SQ FT: 2,400
SALES (est): 2MM **Privately Held**
SIC: 3429 3821 5065 Aircraft hardware;
worktables, laboratory; electronic parts &
equipment

(P-11999)
T G SCHMEISER CO INC
Also Called: Schmeiser Farm Equipment
3160 E California Ave, Fresno
(93702-4108)
P.O. Box 1047 (93714-1047)
PHONE..................................559 486-4569
Andrew W Cummings, *CEO*
Andrew Wcummings, *CEO*
Shirley Cummings, *Corp Secy*
Olga Pirogova, *Engineer*
Dave Vleet, *Opers Mgr*
▼ **EMP:** 35
SQ FT: 36,000
SALES (est): 6MM **Privately Held**
WEB: www.tgschmeiser.com
SIC: 3429 3523 Manufactured hardware
(general); soil preparation machinery, except turf & grounds

(P-12000)
THERMAPAK TECHNOLOGIES INC
1210 E Green St Ste 102, Pasadena
(91106-5801)
PHONE..................................909 612-9380
WEI Xiong, *CEO*
Wayne Wang, *President*
▲ **EMP:** 15
SQ FT: 2,000
SALES (est): 1.7MM **Privately Held**
SIC: 3429 Manufactured hardware (general)

(P-12001)
TOMORROWS HEIRLOOMS INC
Also Called: Stone Manufacturing Company
1636 W 135th St, Gardena (90249-2506)
P.O. Box 1325 (90249-0325)
PHONE..................................310 323-6720
Amit V Patel, *President*
Sumi Patel, *Treasurer*
Kumar V Patel, *Vice Pres*
EMP: 26
SQ FT: 22,000
SALES (est): 4.3MM **Privately Held**
WEB: www.stonemfg.com
SIC: 3429 Fireplace equipment, hardware:
andirons, grates, screens

(P-12002)
TOP LINE MFG INC
7032 Alondra Blvd, Paramount
(90723-3926)
P.O. Box 739 (90723-0739)
PHONE..................................562 633-0605
Anne Graffy, *CEO*
Salim Khan, *Bookkeeper*
Tom Graffy, *Plant Mgr*
Wendy Medina, *Sales Associate*
▲ **EMP:** 29
SQ FT: 20,000
SALES (est): 5.9MM **Privately Held**
WEB: www.toplinemfg.com
SIC: 3429 Motor vehicle hardware; bicycle
racks, automotive; luggage racks, car top

(P-12003)
TRIANGLE BRASS MFG CO INC (PA)
Also Called: Trimco
1351 Rocky Point Dr, Oceanside
(92056-5864)
P.O. Box 23277, Los Angeles (90023-0277)
PHONE..................................323 262-4191
Martin Simon, *President*
Gloria Simon, *Vice Pres*
Tanisha St Onge, *Accountant*
▲ **EMP:** 70
SQ FT: 45,000
SALES (est): 12.5MM **Privately Held**
WEB: www.trimcobbw.com
SIC: 3429 Door opening & closing devices,
except electrical

(P-12004)
TUL INC
663 Brea Canyon Rd Ste 6, Walnut
(91789-3045)
PHONE..................................909 444-0577
Ted Chen, *President*
Richard Shen, *Marketing Staff*
▲ **EMP:** 100

SALES (est): 9MM **Privately Held**
SIC: 3429 Manufactured hardware (general)

(P-12005)
UMPCO INC
7100 Lampson Ave, Garden Grove
(92841-3914)
P.O. Box 5158 (92846-0158)
PHONE....................714 897-3531
Dan Miller, *CEO*
EMP: 75
SQ FT: 60,000
SALES (est): 18.7MM **Privately Held**
WEB: www.umpco.com
SIC: 3429 Clamps, metal

(P-12006)
US RACK INC
2850 Falcon Dr, Madera (93637-9287)
PHONE....................559 661-3050
Christopher Green, *President*
Stevie Green, *Mktg Dir*
Stephanie Green,
▲ EMP: 10 EST: 1999
SQ FT: 3,600
SALES (est): 629.2K **Privately Held**
WEB: www.usrack.com
SIC: 3429 Luggage racks, car top

(P-12007)
VIT PRODUCTS INC
2063 Wineridge Pl, Escondido
(92029-1931)
PHONE....................760 480-6702
Don Pagano, *President*
Arthur Arns, *Ch of Bd*
EMP: 36
SQ FT: 24,000
SALES (est): 6.9MM **Privately Held**
WEB: www.vitproducts.com
SIC: 3429 2295 Clamps, couplings, nozzles & other metal hose fittings; coated fabrics, not rubberized

(P-12008)
WEISER LOCK CORPORATION
19701 Da Vinci, Foothill Ranch
(92610-2622)
PHONE....................949 672-4000
David R Lumley, *CEO*
▲ EMP: 18
SALES (est): 3.4MM
SALES (corp-wide): 5B **Publicly Held**
WEB: www.blackanddecker.com
SIC: 3429
HQ: Spectrum Brands, Inc.
3001 Deming Way
Middleton WI 53562
608 275-3340

(P-12009)
WESTERN HARDWARE COMPANY
161 Commerce Way, Walnut (91789-2719)
PHONE....................909 595-6201
Gayle E Pacheco, *President*
▲ EMP: 12
SALES (est): 1.7MM **Privately Held**
SIC: 3429 Manufactured hardware (general)

(P-12010)
WINDLINE MARINE
14601 S Broadway, Gardena (90248-1811)
PHONE....................310 516-9812
Robert Barbour, *Ch of Bd*
Glenn Smith, *President*
Steven Jason Ruiz, *CFO*
Irma Limon, *Admin Sec*
Jason Ruiz, *Info Tech Dir*
EMP: 184
SQ FT: 50,000
SALES (est): 25.7MM **Privately Held**
SIC: 3429 Marine hardware

(P-12011)
YOUNG ENGINEERS INC
25841 Commercentre Dr, Lake Forest
(92630-8812)
P.O. Box 278 (92609-0278)
PHONE....................949 581-9411
Miki Young, *President*
Pat Wells, *President*
Terry Litwinski, *Sales Staff*
EMP: 65

SQ FT: 26,000
SALES (est): 14.5MM **Privately Held**
WEB: www.youngengineers.com
SIC: 3429 Aircraft hardware

(P-12012)
YOUNGDALE MANUFACTURING CORP
1216 Liberty Way Ste B, Vista
(92081-8369)
P.O. Box 3209 (92085-3209)
PHONE....................760 727-0644
Peter Youngdale, *Ch of Bd*
Joseph Carrick, *President*
Christine Carrick, *Vice Pres*
Susan Youngdale, *VP Finance*
Dan Day, *Manager*
▲ EMP: 20
SQ FT: 25,000
SALES (est): 4MM **Privately Held**
SIC: 3429 Cabinet hardware

3431 Enameled Iron & Metal Sanitary Ware

(P-12013)
ALTMANS PRODUCTS LLC
7136 Kittyhawk Ave Apt 4, Los Angeles
(90045-2137)
PHONE....................310 559-4093
Edgardo Flores, *CEO*
▲ EMP: 38
SQ FT: 1,300
SALES (est): 8.6MM **Privately Held**
WEB: www.altmansproducts.com
SIC: 3431 Sinks: enameled iron, cast iron or pressed metal
PA: Grupo Industrial Saltillo, S.A.B. De C.V.
Blvd. Isidro Lopez Zertuche No. 1495
Saltillo COAH. 25000

(P-12014)
HYDRO SYSTEMS INC (PA)
29132 Avenue Paine, Valencia
(91355-5402)
PHONE....................661 775-0686
Scott G Steinhardt, *President*
Larry Burroughs, *Vice Pres*
Dave Ortwein, *Vice Pres*
EMP: 96
SQ FT: 90,000
SALES (est): 17.8MM **Privately Held**
WEB: www.hydrosystem.com
SIC: 3431 3432 3088 Bathtubs: enameled iron, cast iron or pressed metal; plumbing fixture fittings & trim; plastics plumbing fixtures

(P-12015)
KOHLER CO
675 E Central Ave, San Bernardino
(92408-2403)
PHONE....................909 890-4291
Gary Mayfield, *Branch Mgr*
EMP: 48
SALES (corp-wide): 7.6B **Privately Held**
SIC: 3431 Plumbing fixtures: enameled iron cast iron or pressed metal
PA: Kohler Co.
444 Highland Dr
Kohler WI 53044
920 457-4441

(P-12016)
MAG AEROSPACE INDUSTRIES INC
Also Called: Monogram Systems
1500 Glenn Curtiss St, Carson
(90746-4012)
P.O. Box 11189 (90749-1189)
PHONE....................310 631-3800
Sebastien Weber, *President*
Mark Scott, *CFO*
Tim Birbeck, *Vice Pres*
Mike Nieves, *Vice Pres*
Gil Lenhard, *Executive*
◆ EMP: 350
SQ FT: 150,000

SALES (est): 163.4MM
SALES (corp-wide): 650.9MM **Privately Held**
SIC: 3431 3728 Plumbing fixtures: enameled iron cast iron or pressed metal; portable chemical toilets, metal; aircraft parts & equipment
HQ: Zodiac Aerospace
Cs20001
Plaisir 78370
161 342-323

(P-12017)
SEACHROME CORPORATION
1906 E Dominguez St, Long Beach
(90810-1002)
PHONE....................310 427-8010
Sam C Longo Jr, *CEO*
Sam C Longo Sr, *Corp Secy*
▲ EMP: 112
SQ FT: 50,000
SALES (est): 25.9MM **Privately Held**
WEB: www.seachrome.com
SIC: 3431 5072 3842 3429 Bathroom fixtures, including sinks; builders' hardware; surgical appliances & supplies; manufactured hardware (general)

3432 Plumbing Fixture Fittings & Trim, Brass

(P-12018)
A & C TRADE CONSULTANTS INC
Also Called: A & C Imports & Exports
1 Edwards Ct Ste 101, Burlingame
(94010-2428)
PHONE....................650 375-7000
Sharon H Hsu, *President*
Sharon Hsu, *President*
▲ EMP: 10
SQ FT: 20,000
SALES: 4MM **Privately Held**
WEB: www.actradesf.com
SIC: 3432 5734 Plumbing fixture fittings & trim; magnetic disks

(P-12019)
ACORNVAC INC
Also Called: Acorn Vac
13818 Oaks Ave, Chino (91710-7008)
PHONE....................909 902-1141
Donald E Morris, *CEO*
Tom Zinn, *Engineer*
Craig Johnson, *Natl Sales Mgr*
Ron Mims, *Manager*
Mark Sibayan, *Manager*
EMP: 20
SALES (est): 3.8MM
SALES (corp-wide): 85MM **Privately Held**
SIC: 3432 Plastic plumbing fixture fittings, assembly
PA: Acorn Engineering Company
15125 Proctor Ave
City Of Industry CA 91746
800 488-8999

(P-12020)
ALL-AMERICAN MFG CO
2201 E 51st St, Vernon (90058-2814)
PHONE....................323 581-6293
John F Norton, *President*
▲ EMP: 25
SQ FT: 20,000
SALES (est): 4.5MM **Privately Held**
WEB: www.aamfgco.com
SIC: 3432 3469 Plumbing fixture fittings & trim; stamping metal for the trade

(P-12021)
AMERICAN BRASS & ALUM FNDRY CO
2060 Garfield Ave, Commerce
(90040-1804)
P.O. Box 80304, Los Angeles (90040)
PHONE....................800 545-9988
Tony Orapallo Jr, *President*
Robert A Orapallo, *Vice Pres*
◆ EMP: 20
SQ FT: 15,000

SALES (est): 2.3MM **Privately Held**
WEB: www.abainc.net
SIC: 3432 Plumbers' brass goods: drain cocks, faucets, spigots, etc.; plastic plumbing fixture fittings, assembly

(P-12022)
AMERISINK INC (PA)
835 Fremont Ave, San Leandro
(94577-5713)
PHONE....................510 667-9998
Wilson Qi, *President*
◆ EMP: 15
SQ FT: 20,900
SALES (est): 2.1MM **Privately Held**
SIC: 3432 Plumbing fixture fittings & trim

(P-12023)
AQUEST INC
4120 Pine Meadows Way, Pebble Beach
(93953-3021)
PHONE....................831 622-9296
Bruce Oliver, *CEO*
Robert J Brecha, *President*
Neil Oliver, *President*
Betty Oliver, *Admin Sec*
▲ EMP: 25
SQ FT: 13,000
SALES (est): 3.2MM **Privately Held**
WEB: www.aquestinc.com
SIC: 3432 Faucets & spigots, metal & plastic

(P-12024)
ARROWHEAD BRASS & PLUMBING LLC
4900 Valley Blvd, Los Angeles
(90032-3317)
PHONE....................323 221-9137
Fred Schneider, *CEO*
▲ EMP: 80
SQ FT: 35,000
SALES (est): 18.9MM **Privately Held**
SIC: 3432 Faucets & spigots, metal & plastic

(P-12025)
BRADLEY CORP
5556 Ontario Mills Pkwy, Ontario
(91764-5117)
PHONE....................909 481-7255
Ron Schamb, *Branch Mgr*
EMP: 12
SALES (corp-wide): 175.9MM **Privately Held**
WEB: www.bradleycorp.com
SIC: 3432 Plumbing fixture fittings & trim
PA: Bradley Corporation
W142n9101 Fountain Blvd
Menomonee Falls WI 53051
262 251-6000

(P-12026)
BRASSTECH INC
Also Called: Newport Brass
2001 Carnegie Ave, Santa Ana
(92705-5531)
PHONE....................949 417-5207
John V Halso, *CEO*
John Crvarich, *Vice Pres*
◆ EMP: 340
SQ FT: 70,000
SALES (est): 80.3MM
SALES (corp-wide): 7.6B **Publicly Held**
WEB: www.newportbrass.com
SIC: 3432 Plumbing fixture fittings & trim
PA: Masco Corporation
17450 College Pkwy
Livonia MI 48152
313 274-7400

(P-12027)
CALIFORNIA FAUCETS INC
5231 Argosy Ave, Huntington Beach
(92649-1015)
PHONE....................657 400-1639
Blas Ramierez, *Branch Mgr*
EMP: 19
SALES (corp-wide): 17.7MM **Privately Held**
WEB: www.calfaucets.com
SIC: 3432 Faucets & spigots, metal & plastic

PRODUCTS & SVCS

PA: California Faucets, Inc.
5271 Argosy Ave
Huntington Beach CA 92649
714 890-0450

(P-12028)
CALIFORNIA FAUCETS INC (PA)
5271 Argosy Ave, Huntington Beach
(92649-1015)
PHONE..................714 890-0450
Jeff Silverstein, *CEO*
Sonia Silverstein, *Corp Secy*
John Wojtaszek, *Vice Pres*
Jamie Flores, *Admin Asst*
Bridget Ratzlaff, *Admin Asst*
▲ EMP: 75
SALES (est): 17.7MM **Privately Held**
WEB: www.calfaucets.com
SIC: 3432 Faucets & spigots, metal & plastic

(P-12029)
CENTRAL VLY ASSEMBLY PACKG INC
5515 E Lamona Ave 103, Fresno
(93727-2226)
PHONE..................559 486-4260
Nate Perry, *CEO*
John Perry, *COO*
EMP: 24
SALES (est): 3.5MM **Privately Held**
SIC: 3432 3565 3089 3824 Plastic plumbing fixture fittings, assembly; bag opening, filling & closing machines; vacuum packaging machinery; blister or bubble formed packaging, plastic; linear counters

(P-12030)
CHAMPION-ARROWHEAD LLC
5147 Alhambra Ave, Los Angeles
(90032-3413)
PHONE..................323 221-9137
Jim Shearer, *Mng Member*
▲ EMP: 99 EST: 1936
SQ FT: 4,000
SALES (est): 1.2MM **Privately Held**
WEB: www.arrowheadbrass.com
SIC: 3432 Plumbing fixture fittings & trim

(P-12031)
CISCOS SHOP
2911 E Miraloma Ave # 17, Anaheim
(92806-1838)
PHONE..................657 230-9158
Francisco Chavez, *Partner*
EMP: 10
SALES (est): 1.3MM **Privately Held**
SIC: 3432 Plumbing fixture fittings & trim

(P-12032)
COLLICUTT ENERGY SERVICES INC
12349 Hawkins St, Santa Fe Springs
(90670-3366)
PHONE..................562 944-4413
Toll Free:..................866
Tim Rahman, *Branch Mgr*
EMP: 25
SQ FT: 77,000
SALES (est): **Privately Held**
SIC: 3432 Plumbing fixture fittings & trim
HQ: Collicutt Energy Services Inc.
940 Riverside Pkwy Ste 80
West Sacramento CA 95605

(P-12033)
COLUMBIA SANITARY PRODUCTS
Also Called: Columbia Products Co
1622 Browning, Irvine (92606-4809)
PHONE..................949 474-0777
Dorothy Lazier, *CEO*
Paul Escalera, *President*
▲ EMP: 20
SQ FT: 20,000
SALES: 10MM **Privately Held**
WEB: www.columbiasinks.com
SIC: 3432 Plumbing fixture fittings & trim

(P-12034)
FISHER MANUFACTURING CO INC (PA)
1900 S O St, Tulare (93274-6850)
P.O. Box 60 (93275-0060)
PHONE..................559 685-5200
Ray Fisher Jr, *President*
Kay Fisher, *Shareholder*
Karen Lauterbach, *Shareholder*
Kathleen Sebahar, *Shareholder*
Steve Sebahar, *Vice Pres*
◆ EMP: 38
SQ FT: 50,000
SALES (est): 4MM **Privately Held**
WEB: www.fisher-mfg.com
SIC: 3432 Plumbers' brass goods: drain cocks, faucets, spigots, etc.

(P-12035)
FLUIDMASTER INC (PA)
30800 Rancho Viejo Rd, San Juan Capistrano (92675-1564)
PHONE..................949 728-2000
Robert Anderson Schoepe, *CEO*
Terry Bland, *CFO*
Kevin Buckner, *Officer*
Robert Connell, *Exec VP*
Bill Martin, *Vice Pres*
◆ EMP: 400
SALES (est): 230.8MM **Privately Held**
WEB: www.fluidmaster.com
SIC: 3432 3089 Plumbing fixture fittings & trim; injection molding of plastics

(P-12036)
G T WATER PRODUCTS INC
5239 N Commerce Ave, Moorpark
(93021-1763)
PHONE..................805 529-2900
George Tash, *President*
Russell Reasner, *Vice Pres*
Steve Schmitt, *Vice Pres*
Julie Shipley, *Vice Pres*
Debra Tash, *Vice Pres*
▲ EMP: 17
SQ FT: 20,000
SALES (est): 4.1MM **Privately Held**
WEB: www.gtwaterproducts.com
SIC: 3432 Plumbing fixture fittings & trim

(P-12037)
GMS LANDSCAPES INC
207 Camino Leon, Camarillo (93012-8635)
PHONE..................805 402-3925
Sarah Corbin, *President*
EMP: 85
SALES (est): 2.6MM **Privately Held**
SIC: 3432 0781 Plumbing fixture fittings & trim; landscape services

(P-12038)
HIRSCH PIPE & SUPPLY CO INC
31920 Del Obispo St # 275, San Juan
Capistrano (92675-3192)
PHONE..................949 487-7009
Bill Glockner, *Branch Mgr*
EMP: 24
SALES (corp-wide): 162.2MM **Privately Held**
SIC: 3432 5074 5251 Plumbing fixture fittings & trim; plumbing fittings & supplies; pumps & pumping equipment
PA: Hirsch Pipe & Supply Co., Inc.
15025 Oxnard St Ste 100
Van Nuys CA 91411
818 756-0900

(P-12039)
MASCO CORPORATION
19914 Via Baron Way, Rancho Dominguez
(90220)
PHONE..................313 274-7400
EMP: 94
SALES (corp-wide): 7.6B **Publicly Held**
SIC: 3432 2434 Faucets & spigots, metal & plastic; vanities, bathroom: wood
PA: Masco Corporation
17450 College Pkwy
Livonia MI 48152
313 274-7400

(P-12040)
MCP INDUSTRIES INC
Also Called: Mission Rubber
1660 Leeson Ln, Corona (92879-2061)
PHONE..................951 736-1313

Charlotte Garrett, *Admin Sec*
EMP: 50
SALES (corp-wide): 126.4MM **Privately Held**
WEB: www.missionrubber.com
SIC: 3432 Plumbing fixture fittings & trim
PA: Mcp Industries, Inc.
708 S Temescal St Ste 101
Corona CA 92879
951 736-1881

(P-12041)
MUIRSIS INC
2841 Saturn St Ste J, Brea (92821-6226)
PHONE..................714 579-1555
Allen Yeh, *President*
Ralph Bedolla, *Opers Staff*
Maria Block, *Manager*
▲ EMP: 10
SALES (est): 950.9K **Privately Held**
SIC: 3432 Plumbing fixture fittings & trim

(P-12042)
PIPE GUARD INC
10723 Sherman Way, Sun Valley
(91352-5155)
PHONE..................818 765-2424
Peter Zamkochyan, *President*
EMP: 20
SALES (est): 975.3K **Privately Held**
SIC: 3432 Plumbing fixture fittings & trim

(P-12043)
PLUMBEREX SPECIALTY PDTS INC
72170 Dunham Way Ste A, Thousand
Palms (92276-9702)
P.O. Box 1684, Palm Springs (92263-1684)
PHONE..................760 343-7363
Gabriel Lechuga Jr, *President*
Patricia Lechuga, *Vice Pres*
EMP: 30
SQ FT: 20,000
SALES (est): 3.8MM **Privately Held**
WEB: www.plumberex.com
SIC: 3432 Plumbing fixture fittings & trim

(P-12044)
PLUMBING PRODUCTS INC
Also Called: Trim To Trade
77551 El Duna Ct Ste I, Palm Desert
(92211-4147)
PHONE..................760 343-3306
Gary Yavitz, *President*
Jessie Yavitz, *Corp Secy*
▲ EMP: 15 EST: 1947
SQ FT: 36,000
SALES (est): 2.3MM **Privately Held**
WEB: www.plumbingproducts.com
SIC: 3432 3431 Plumbers' brass goods: drain cocks, faucets, spigots, etc.; bathroom fixtures, including sinks

(P-12045)
PRICE PFISTER INC
Also Called: Pfister Faucets
19701 Da Vinci, Foothill Ranch
(92610-2622)
PHONE..................949 672-4003
James M Loree, *President*
Craig A Douglas, *Treasurer*
Bruce Beatt, *Admin Sec*
EMP: 161
SALES (est): 9.2MM
SALES (corp-wide): 5B **Publicly Held**
SIC: 3432 Plumbing fixture fittings & trim
HQ: Spectrum Brands Legacy, Inc.
3001 Deming Way
Middleton WI 53562

(P-12046)
PRICE PFISTER INC (DH)
Also Called: Price Pfister Brass Mfg
19701 Da Vinci, Foothill Ranch
(92610-2622)
PHONE..................949 672-4000
Gregory John Gluchowski, *CEO*
▲ EMP: 800
SQ FT: 127,612
SALES (est): 115.3MM
SALES (corp-wide): 5B **Publicly Held**
SIC: 3432 Faucets & spigots, metal & plastic; plumbers' brass goods: drain cocks, faucets, spigots, etc.

HQ: Spectrum Brands, Inc.
3001 Deming Way
Middleton WI 53562
608 275-3340

(P-12047)
RAIN BIRD CORPORATION
Also Called: Rain Bird Golf Division
970 W Sierra Madre Ave, Azusa
(91702-1873)
PHONE..................626 812-3400
Matt Circle, *Manager*
Dave Evans, *Principal*
EMP: 30
SALES (corp-wide): 98.2MM **Privately Held**
WEB: www.rainbird.com
SIC: 3432 3494 3433 Plumbing fixture fittings & trim; valves & pipe fittings; heating equipment, except electric
PA: Rain Bird Corporation
970 W Sierra Madre Ave
Azusa CA 91702
626 812-3400

(P-12048)
RSS MANUFACTURING
1261 Logan Ave, Costa Mesa
(92626-4004)
PHONE..................714 361-4800
Geoffrey Escalette, *Owner*
Shane Strange, *Info Tech Dir*
▲ EMP: 14
SALES (est): 2.2MM **Privately Held**
SIC: 3432 Faucets & spigots, metal & plastic; plumbers' brass goods: drain cocks, faucets, spigots, etc.

(P-12049)
SANTEC INC
3501 Challenger St Fl 2, Torrance
(90503-1697)
PHONE..................310 542-0063
Nicolas Chen, *CEO*
James S Chen, *Principal*
▲ EMP: 50
SQ FT: 32,000
SALES (est): 9.5MM **Privately Held**
SIC: 3432 Faucets & spigots, metal & plastic

(P-12050)
STRUCTURES UNLIMITED
7671 Arlington Ave, Riverside
(92503-1407)
PHONE..................951 688-6300
Jim Bean, *President*
EMP: 10
SALES (est): 1MM **Privately Held**
SIC: 3432 Plumbing fixture fittings & trim

(P-12051)
SUNRISE SPECIALTY COMPANY
61 Skyway Ln, Oakland (94619-3627)
PHONE..................510 729-7277
Robert Weinstein, *CEO*
Malcolm Smith, *Ch of Bd*
◆ EMP: 13
SQ FT: 100,000
SALES (est): 2.8MM **Privately Held**
WEB: www.sunrisespecialty.com
SIC: 3432 Plumbers' brass goods: drain cocks, faucets, spigots, etc.

(P-12052)
TBS IRRIGATION PRODUCTS INC
1532 N Johnson Ave, El Cajon
(92020-1618)
PHONE..................619 579-0520
Michael J Folkman, *President*
Neil Faulkman, *Corp Secy*
William Butson, *Vice Pres*
EMP: 20
SQ FT: 25,000
SALES (est): 4.6MM **Privately Held**
SIC: 3432 3523 3088 Lawn hose nozzles & sprinklers; farm machinery & equipment; plastics plumbing fixtures

(P-12053)
TRIPOS INDUSTRIES INC
Also Called: Tripus Industries
2448 Glendower Ave, Los Angeles
(90027-1111)
PHONE..................323 669-0488

▲ = Import ▼=Export
◆ =Import/Export

SA Young Hong, *President*
EMP: 25
SQ FT: 6,500
SALES (est): 2.2MM **Privately Held**
SIC: 3432 Plumbing fixture fittings & trim

(P-12054)
VALADONS PLUMBING SERVICE INC
315 Coleshill St, Bakersfield (93312-7046)
P.O. Box 20748 (93390-0748)
PHONE..................................661 201-1460
EMP: 11
SALES (est): 2.3MM **Privately Held**
SIC: 3432

(P-12055)
WATERLESS CO INC
1050 Joshua Way, Vista (92081-7807)
PHONE..................................760 727-7723
Klaus Reichardt, *President*
Lisa Saenz Brown, *Vice Pres*
Niki Bradley, *Marketing Mgr*
▲ EMP: 10
SQ FT: 30,000
SALES (est): 1.6MM **Privately Held**
WEB: www.waterless.com
SIC: 3432 Plastic plumbing fixture fittings, assembly

(P-12056)
WATERSTONE LLC
Also Called: Waterstone Faucets
41180 Raintree Ct, Murrieta (92562-7020)
PHONE..................................951 304-0520
Christopher G Kuran, *Mng Member*
Steve Kliewer, *Vice Pres*
Julie Colio, *Human Res Dir*
Pam Donnelly, *Purchasing*
Joe Harnit, *Production*
▲ EMP: 210
SQ FT: 42,000
SALES: 13MM **Privately Held**
SIC: 3432 Faucets & spigots, metal & plastic

3433 Heating Eqpt

(P-12057)
ADVANCED CONSERVATION TECHNOLO
Also Called: Act Inc Dmand Kontrols Systems
3176 Pullman St Ste 119, Costa Mesa (92626-3317)
PHONE..................................714 668-1200
Larry Acker, *CEO*
Donna-Marie Acker, *President*
Kristine Parker, *Vice Pres*
Victor Ye, *Finance Mgr*
EMP: 16
SQ FT: 7,000
SALES (est): 3MM **Privately Held**
WEB: www.gothotwater.com
SIC: 3433 Boilers, low-pressure heating; steam or hot water

(P-12058)
BIOTHERM HYDRONIC INC
Also Called: True Leaf Technologies
476 Primero Ct, Cotati (94931-3014)
P.O. Box 750967, Petaluma (94975-0967)
PHONE..................................707 794-9660
Jim K Rearden, *CEO*
Michael G Muchow, *CFO*
Michael Muchow, *CFO*
John Irish, *Manager*
▲ EMP: 15
SQ FT: 10,000
SALES (est): 4.1MM **Privately Held**
WEB: www.trueleaf.net
SIC: 3433 Heating equipment, except electric

(P-12059)
BROAN-NUTONE LLC
622 Emery Rd, Tecate (91980)
P.O. Box 1910 (91980-1910)
PHONE..................................262 673-8795
Joel Fletcher, *Mng Member*
Almon C Hall,
EMP: 227 EST: 1999

SALES (est): 40.3MM
SALES (corp-wide): 2.7B **Privately Held**
SIC: 3433 3564 Solar heaters & collectors; ventilating fans; industrial or commercial
HQ: Nortek, Inc.
8000 Phoenix Pkwy
O Fallon MO 63368
636 561-7300

(P-12060)
CAPITAL COOKING EQUIPMENT
13211 Florence Ave, Santa Fe Springs (90670-4509)
PHONE..................................562 903-1168
Surjit Kalsi, *Co-COB*
Joey Kitabayashi, *President*
Roberto Bernal, *Co-COB*
Alejandro Bernal, *Exec VP*
Raul Chita, *Exec VP*
▲ EMP: 47
SQ FT: 7,000
SALES (est): 9.7MM **Privately Held**
WEB: www.capital-cooking.com
SIC: 3433 3631 Stoves, wood & coal burning: gas ranges, domestic

(P-12061)
COEN COMPANY INC (DH)
951 Mariners Island Blvd # 410, San Mateo (94404-1558)
PHONE..................................650 522-2100
Earl W Schnell, *President*
Samantha Jones, *Administration*
Mey Saephan, *Administration*
Todd Robertson, *Technician*
Sarah Edenfield, *Project Mgr*
◆ EMP: 40 EST: 1912
SALES (est): 17.1MM
SALES (corp-wide): 42.9B **Privately Held**
WEB: www.coen.com
SIC: 3433 3823 Burners, furnaces, boilers & stokers; combustion control instruments
HQ: Koch Chemical Technology Group, Llc
4111 E 37th St N
Wichita KS 67220
316 828-8515

(P-12062)
ENVISION SOLAR INTL INC
5660 Eastgate Dr, San Diego (92121-2816)
PHONE..................................858 799-4583
Desmond Wheatley, *President*
Chris Caulson, *CFO*
EMP: 22
SQ FT: 50,000
SALES: 3.7MM **Privately Held**
WEB: www.envisionsolar.com
SIC: 3433 Boilers, low-pressure heating: steam or hot water

(P-12063)
FAFCO INC (PA)
435 Otterson Dr, Chico (95928-8207)
PHONE..................................530 332-2100
Freeman A Ford, *Ch of Bd*
Robert C Leckinger, *CEO*
Nancy I Garvin, *CFO*
Jeff Monian, *Info Tech Mgr*
JD Tenuta, *Opers Mgr*
◆ EMP: 48
SQ FT: 57,500
SALES (est): 8.3MM **Privately Held**
WEB: www.fafco.com
SIC: 3433 Heaters, swimming pool: oil or gas

(P-12064)
FINART INC (PA)
201 W Dyer Rd Ste C, Santa Ana (92707-3426)
PHONE..................................714 957-1757
Tadeusz Kasperowicz, *President*
▲ EMP: 10
SQ FT: 10,000
SALES: 600K **Privately Held**
WEB: www.finart.com
SIC: 3433 Room & wall heaters, including radiators

(P-12065)
GC AERO INC (PA)
21143 Hawth Blvd Ste 136, Torrance (90503)
PHONE..................................310 539-7600

Jim Cowherd, *President*
▲ EMP: 15
SQ FT: 11,500
SALES (est): 1.5MM **Privately Held**
WEB: www.gcaero.com
SIC: 3433 3674 3822 3672 Heating equipment, except electric; integrated circuits, semiconductor networks, etc.; temperature controls, automatic; printed circuit boards

(P-12066)
GREENVOLTS INC
19200 Stevens Creek Blvd # 200, Cupertino (95014-2530)
PHONE..................................415 963-4030
David Gudmundson, *President*
Uday Bellary, *CFO*
Scott Shoults, *Vice Pres*
EMP: 90
SALES (est): 14.5MM **Privately Held**
WEB: www.greenvolts.com
SIC: 3433 Solar heaters & collectors

(P-12067)
HEATEFLEX CORPORATION
Also Called: Safna A Division of Heateflex
405 E Santa Clara St, Arcadia (91006-7227)
PHONE..................................626 599-8566
Jorge Ramirez, *President*
Cathy Zhou, *Controller*
EMP: 38
SALES (est): 10.2MM **Privately Held**
WEB: www.heateflex.com
SIC: 3433 3823 3559 3443 Heating equipment, except electric; industrial instrmnts msrmnt display/control process variable; ammunition & explosives, loading machinery; buoys, metal; assembly machines, non-metalworking

(P-12068)
IHP OPERATIONS LLC
Also Called: Innovative Hearth Products
2701 S Harbor Blvd, Santa Ana (92704-5838)
PHONE..................................714 549-7782
Mark Klein, *CEO*
Linda Pahl, *CFO*
Pilar Garcia, *Regional Mgr*
Leo T Litonjua, *Engineer*
John Phillips, *Engineer*
▲ EMP: 347
SQ FT: 146,000
SALES (est): 119.1MM
SALES (corp-wide): 45.3MM **Privately Held**
SIC: 3433 Heating equipment, except electric
PA: Innovative Hearth Holdings, Llc
2701 S Harbor Blvd
Santa Ana CA 92704
714 549-7782

(P-12069)
INDUSTRIAL MANUFACTURING INC
10110 Norwalk Blvd, Santa Fe Springs (90670-3326)
P.O. Box 3163 (90670-0163)
PHONE..................................562 941-5888
Eddie Cerda, *President*
EMP: 14
SQ FT: 15,700
SALES (est): 1MM **Privately Held**
SIC: 3433 Radiators, except electric

(P-12070)
INFRARED DYNAMICS INC
3830 Prospect Ave, Yorba Linda (92886-1742)
PHONE..................................714 572-4050
Robert Cowan, *President*
▲ EMP: 32 EST: 1959
SQ FT: 23,500
SALES (est): 6.4MM **Privately Held**
WEB: www.infradyne.com
SIC: 3433 5075 Heating equipment, except electric; warm air heating equipment & supplies

(P-12071)
INNOVATIVE COMBUSTION TECH (PA)
Also Called: S.T. Johnson Company
5160 Fulton Dr, Fairfield (94534-1639)
PHONE..................................510 652-6000
Antonio De La O, *President*
Todd Cole, *Vice Pres*
Barbara Florio, *Admin Sec*
Brett Barnes, *Sales Mgr*
Linda Macpherson, *Manager*
▼ EMP: 16 EST: 1903
SALES (est): 8.5MM **Privately Held**
WEB: www.stjohnson.com
SIC: 3433 Gas-oil burners, combination

(P-12072)
INNOVATIVE HEARTH HOLDINGS LLC (PA)
Also Called: Innovative Hearth Products IHP
2701 S Harbor Blvd, Santa Ana (92704-5838)
PHONE..................................714 549-7782
Mark Klein, *CEO*
Linda Pahl, *CFO*
EMP: 580 EST: 1971
SQ FT: 146,000
SALES (est): 45.3MM **Privately Held**
SIC: 3433 Wall heaters, except electric

(P-12073)
IRONRIDGE INC (PA)
28357 Industrial Blvd, Hayward (94545-4428)
PHONE..................................800 227-9523
William Kim, *Ch of Bd*
Eren Flood, *Partner*
Rich Tiu, *CEO*
Corey Geiger, *COO*
Jim Clark, *CFO*
▲ EMP: 70
SQ FT: 10,000
SALES (est): 30.1MM **Privately Held**
WEB: www.2seas.com
SIC: 3433 5074 Solar heaters & collectors; heating equipment & panels, solar

(P-12074)
MANTA SOLAR CORPORATION
5420 Fulton St, San Francisco (94121-3535)
PHONE..................................928 853-6216
Carlos Kronen, *CEO*
EMP: 10
SALES (est): 708.1K **Privately Held**
SIC: 3433 Solar heaters & collectors

(P-12075)
MANUFACTURERS COML FIN LLC
Also Called: Benchmark Thermal
13185 Nevada City Ave, Grass Valley (95945-9568)
PHONE..................................530 477-5011
Michael Kayman,
Roger Ruttenberg, *Vice Pres*
Eric Doan, *Accountant*
EMP: 40
SQ FT: 8,000
SALES (est): 1.3MM **Privately Held**
SIC: 3433 Room & wall heaters, including radiators

(P-12076)
PYRON SOLAR III LLC
1216 Liberty Way Ste A, Vista (92081-8369)
P.O. Box 5427, Bakersfield (93388-5427)
PHONE..................................760 599-5100
Stanley W Ellis, *CEO*
Stephanie Rosenthal, *President*
Duncan Earl, *CTO*
Joe Bentley, *Chief Engr*
EMP: 10
SQ FT: 8,000
SALES (est): 1MM **Privately Held**
SIC: 3433 Solar heaters & collectors
PA: Ellis Energy Investments, Inc.
1400 Norris Rd
Bakersfield CA 93308

(P-12077)
R E DILLARD 1 LLC
300 California St Fl 7, San Francisco
(94104-1415)
PHONE..............................415 675-1500
Greg Wilson, *Treasurer*
EMP: 99
SALES (est): 5.3MM **Privately Held**
SIC: 3433 Solar heaters & collectors

(P-12078)
RASMUSSEN IRON WORKS INC
12028 Philadelphia St, Whittier
(90601-3925)
PHONE..............................562 696-8718
Theodore Rasmussen, *President*
Rett Rasmussen, *Vice Pres*
T E Rasmussen, *Vice Pres*
Philippe Richard, *Vice Pres*
Ray Vazla, *Vice Pres*
▲ EMP: 50 EST: 1907
SQ FT: 40,000
SALES (est): 10.1MM **Privately Held**
WEB: www.bbqislands.com
SIC: 3433 Logs, gas fireplace

(P-12079)
RAYPAK INC (DH)
2151 Eastman Ave, Oxnard (93030-5194)
PHONE..............................805 278-5300
Kevin McDonald, *Vice Pres*
Bill Patterson, *CFO*
Rich Corcoran, *Vice Pres*
Michael Sentovich, *Vice Pres*
Bob Morgan, *General Mgr*
◆ EMP: 320
SQ FT: 250,000
SALES (est): 117.9MM
SALES (corp-wide): 394.3MM **Privately Held**
WEB: www.raypak.com
SIC: 3433 Heaters, swimming pool: oil or gas
HQ: Rheem Manufacturing Company Inc
1100 Abernathy Rd # 1700
Atlanta GA 30328
770 351-3000

(P-12080)
RE TRANQUILLITY 8 LLC
300 California St Fl 7, San Francisco
(94104-1415)
PHONE..............................415 675-1500
Yumin Liu, *President*
Helen Kang Shin, *Vice Pres*
EMP: 86
SALES (est): 3.4MM
SALES (corp-wide): 3.3B **Privately Held**
SIC: 3433 Solar heaters & collectors
HQ: Recurrent Energy Development Holdings, Llc
3000 Oak Rd Ste 300
Walnut Creek CA 94597
415 675-1500

(P-12081)
REAL GOODS SOLAR INC
41567 Cherry St, Murrieta (92562-9193)
PHONE..............................951 304-3301
John Shaeffer, *Branch Mgr*
EMP: 125 **Publicly Held**
SIC: 3433 Solar heaters & collectors
PA: Real Goods Solar, Inc.
110 16th St Ste 300
Denver CO 80202

(P-12082)
RETECH SYSTEMS LLC
100 Henry Station Rd, Ukiah (95482-2116)
PHONE..............................707 462-6522
Earl Good, *President*
Wojciech Modrzyk, *Vice Pres*
Brian Flinn, *Program Mgr*
Reuben Jacobsen, *Program Mgr*
Jared Paz, *Program Mgr*
◆ EMP: 120 EST: 2001
SALES (est): 51MM
SALES (corp-wide): 73.5MM **Privately Held**
WEB: www.retechsystemsllc.com
SIC: 3433 Burners, furnaces, boilers & stokers

PA: Seco Warwick S A
Ul. Sobieskiego 8
Swiebodzin 66-20
486 838-2050

(P-12083)
SCHEU MANUFACTURING CO (PA)
297 Stowell St, Upland (91786-6624)
P.O. Box 250 (91785-0250)
PHONE..............................909 982-8933
Leland C Scheu, *Ch of Bd*
Daniel N League Jr, *Shareholder*
Allyn Scheu, *President*
▲ EMP: 15
SQ FT: 7,000
SALES (est): 7.1MM **Privately Held**
SIC: 3433 Space heaters, except electric

(P-12084)
SILICON ENERGY LLC (PA)
9 Cushing Ste 200, Irvine (92618-4227)
PHONE..............................360 618-6500
Gary Shaver, *Mng Member*
▲ EMP: 18
SQ FT: 26,000
SALES (est): 2.6MM **Privately Held**
SIC: 3433 Solar heaters & collectors

(P-12085)
SMA AMERICA PRODUCTION LLC
6020 West Oaks Blvd # 300, Rocklin
(95765-5472)
PHONE..............................720 347-6000
Pierre Pascal Urbon,
John McCauley, *Sales Mgr*
Brice Warner, *Sales Engr*
Shannon Mahoney, *Senior Mgr*
◆ EMP: 200 EST: 2009
SQ FT: 150,000
SALES (est): 89.2MM
SALES (corp-wide): 1B **Privately Held**
SIC: 3433 Solar heaters & collectors
HQ: Sma Solar Technology America Llc
6020 West Oaks Blvd
Rocklin CA 95765
916 625-0870

(P-12086)
SOLAR ENRGY WORLD LTD LBLTY CO
1300 Park Newport Apt 209, Newport Beach (92660-5031)
PHONE..............................973 887-1082
George Dunning,
Al Gleeson,
Tope Lala,
Geff Mirken,
EMP: 25
SALES (est): 2.7MM **Privately Held**
SIC: 3433 Solar heaters & collectors

(P-12087)
SOLAR INDUSTRIES INC
731 N Market Blvd Ste J, Sacramento
(95834-1211)
PHONE..............................916 567-9650
Kerry Bradford, *Manager*
EMP: 26
SALES (corp-wide): 83.8MM **Privately Held**
SIC: 3433 Solar heaters & collectors
PA: Solar Industries, Inc.
4940 S Alvernon Way
Tucson AZ 85706
520 790-8989

(P-12088)
SOLARRESERVE LLC (PA)
520 Broadway Fl 6, Santa Monica
(90401-2420)
PHONE..............................310 315-2200
Kevin Smith, *CEO*
Tim Rosenzweig, *CFO*
Tom Georgis, *Senior VP*
Alistair Jessop, *Senior VP*
Stephen Mullennix, *Senior VP*
EMP: 20
SALES (est): 5.9MM **Privately Held**
SIC: 3433 1711 4911 Solar heaters & collectors; solar energy contractor; electric services

(P-12089)
SOLARROOFSCOM INC
5840 Gibbons Dr Ste H, Carmichael
(95608-6903)
PHONE..............................916 481-7200
Albert C Rich, *President*
Susan Rich, *CEO*
EMP: 11
SQ FT: 8,000
SALES: 576K **Privately Held**
WEB: www.solarroofs.com
SIC: 3433 Solar heaters & collectors

(P-12090)
ST JOHNSON COMPANY LLC
5160 Fulton Dr, Fairfield (94534-1639)
PHONE..............................510 652-6000
Antonio De La O, *President*
EMP: 40
SALES (est): 5.2MM
SALES (corp-wide): 8.5MM **Privately Held**
SIC: 3433 Heating equipment, except electric
PA: Innovative Combustion Technologies Inc
5160 Fulton Dr
Fairfield CA 94534
510 652-6000

(P-12091)
SUNEARTH INC
8425 Almeria Ave, Fontana (92335-3288)
PHONE..............................909 434-3100
Richard R Reed, *CEO*
Carol E Silva, *Admin Sec*
▲ EMP: 45
SQ FT: 17,000
SALES (est): 9.5MM
SALES (corp-wide): 15.3MM **Privately Held**
WEB: www.sunearthinc.com
SIC: 3433 Solar heaters & collectors
PA: The Solaray Corporation
761 Ahua St
Honolulu HI 96819
808 523-0711

(P-12092)
SUNTECH AMERICA INC (PA)
Also Called: Suntech Power
2721 Shattuck Ave, Berkeley (94705-1008)
PHONE..............................415 882-9922
Zhengrong Shi, *CEO*
John Lefebvre, *President*
David King, *CFO*
▲ EMP: 16
SALES (est): 2.8MM **Privately Held**
WEB: www.suntech-power.com
SIC: 3433 Solar heaters & collectors

(P-12093)
SUNWATER SOLAR INC
865 Marina Bay Pkwy # 39, Richmond
(94804-6426)
P.O. Box 688, Novato (94948-0688)
PHONE..............................650 739-5297
EMP: 12
SQ FT: 2,000
SALES (est): 1.7MM **Privately Held**
SIC: 3433

(P-12094)
WAX BOX FIRELOG CORPORATION
Also Called: Cleanflame
1791 State Highway 99, Gridley
(95948-2209)
PHONE..............................530 846-2200
Kory H Hamman, *CEO*
Howard Hamman, *CFO*
Brian Hamman, *Vice Pres*
▲ EMP: 42
SQ FT: 50,000
SALES: 3.5MM **Privately Held**
SIC: 3433 Logs, gas fireplace

3441 Fabricated Structural Steel

(P-12095)
101 VERTICAL FABRICATION INC
10255 Beech Ave, Fontana (92335-6356)
PHONE..............................909 428-6000
Dustin J Nabor, *President*
Fidel J Nabor, *Ch of Bd*
Paul Kwon, *CFO*
Richard Berg, *Vice Pres*
Jim O'Shea, *Comptroller*
EMP: 27
SQ FT: 48,000
SALES: 2.4MM
SALES (corp-wide): 17.9MM **Privately Held**
WEB: www.101pipe.com
SIC: 3441 Fabricated structural metal
PA: 101 Pipe & Casing, Inc.
30300 Agoura Rd Ste 240
Agoura Hills CA 91301
818 707-9101

(P-12096)
3 D STUDIOS
800 51st Ave, Oakland (94601-5627)
PHONE..............................510 535-1809
Fax: 510 535-1534
EMP: 14
SQ FT: 5,000
SALES (est): 1.2MM **Privately Held**
WEB: www.3dstudios.net
SIC: 3441

(P-12097)
A & A FABRICATION & POLSG CORP
12031 Philadelphia St, Whittier
(90601-3926)
PHONE..............................562 696-0441
Amanda Henderson, *President*
EMP: 16
SQ FT: 14,000
SALES: 1.8MM **Privately Held**
SIC: 3441 Fabricated structural metal

(P-12098)
A M T METAL FABRICATORS INC
211 Parr Blvd, Richmond (94801-1119)
PHONE..............................510 236-1414
Michael R Turpen, *President*
Cheryl Turpen, *CFO*
Charles McKinney, *General Mgr*
Will Fowler, *Manager*
EMP: 20
SQ FT: 12,000
SALES (est): 5.5MM **Privately Held**
WEB: www.amtmetals.com
SIC: 3441 Building components, structural steel

(P-12099)
ABRAHAM STEEL FABRICATION INC
2741 Mcmillan Ave Ste B, San Luis Obispo
(93401-6796)
PHONE..............................805 544-8610
David Rivas, *President*
EMP: 10
SQ FT: 7,200
SALES (est): 1.6MM **Privately Held**
WEB: www.abrahamsteel.com
SIC: 3441 3446 3713 Building components, structural steel; architectural metalwork; truck beds

(P-12100)
ABSOLUTE MACHINING
20622 Superior St Unit 4, Chatsworth
(91311-4432)
PHONE..............................818 709-7367
Tim Ohanlon, *Owner*
EMP: 15 EST: 1996
SALES (est): 502.5K **Privately Held**
SIC: 3441 Fabricated structural metal

(P-12101)
ACCELRTED MTAL FABRICATION LLC
2955 Farrar Ave, Modesto (95354-4118)
PHONE..............................209 846-7998

Bruce Elliott, *Partner*
Dave Raybourn, *Partner*
EMP: 10 EST: 2013
SALES (est): 1.6MM **Privately Held**
SIC: 3441 Fabricated structural metal

(P-12102)
ACCURATE METAL PRODUCTS INC
4276 Campbell St, Riverside (92509-2617)
PHONE 951 360-3594
Elanor Quintero, *President*
Tony Schmidt, *Admin Sec*
EMP: 15
SALES (est): 1.4MM **Privately Held**
SIC: 3441 Fabricated structural metal

(P-12103)
ADTEK INC
1460 Ellerd Dr, Turlock (95380-5749)
PHONE 209 634-0300
Bob Zinzenoul, *Principal*
Tom Ady, *Senior VP*
Amanda Coons, *Office Mgr*
Mike Spence, *Prgrmr*
Ken Spence, *Opers Mgr*
EMP: 30
SALES (est): 6.6MM **Privately Held**
SIC: 3441 Building components, structural steel

(P-12104)
ADVANCED LGS LLC
11905 Regentview Ave, Downey (90241-5515)
PHONE 818 652-4252
Alex Youssef,
EMP: 12 EST: 2015
SALES: 3MM **Privately Held**
SIC: 3441 Building components, structural steel

(P-12105)
ADVANCED METAL FORMING INC
2618 National Ave, San Diego (92113-3693)
P.O. Box 13530 (92170-3530)
PHONE 619 239-9437
Jacqueline Beavan, *President*
Charles Teahan, *Vice Pres*
EMP: 10 EST: 1966
SQ FT: 1,800
SALES (est): 1.2MM **Privately Held**
WEB: www.advancedmetalforming.com
SIC: 3441 Fabricated structural metal

(P-12106)
AEROFAB CORPORATION
4001 E Leaverton Ct, Anaheim (92807-1610)
PHONE 714 635-0902
Matthew Owen, *President*
George Robinson, *Vice Pres*
EMP: 17
SQ FT: 10,000
SALES (est): 3.5MM **Privately Held**
SIC: 3441 Fabricated structural metal

(P-12107)
AFAKORI INC
Also Called: AAF Steel Structural
29390 Hunco Way, Lake Elsinore (92530-2757)
PHONE 949 859-4277
Amir A Fakori, *President*
Luz Marina Agreda, *Admin Sec*
Luz Agreda, *Administration*
▲ **EMP:** 20
SQ FT: 15,000
SALES (est): 2.2MM **Privately Held**
WEB: www.afakoriwelding.com
SIC: 3441 Building components, structural steel

(P-12108)
AG MACHINING INC
609 Science Dr, Moorpark (93021-2005)
PHONE 805 531-9555
Angel Garcia, *President*
Bryan Garcia, *Vice Pres*
Eddie Garcia, *Vice Pres*
Tyler McCall, *Buyer*
▲ **EMP:** 85
SQ FT: 117,000

SALES: 15.4MM **Privately Held**
WEB: www.agmachininginc.com
SIC: 3441 3444 Fabricated structural metal; sheet metalwork; metal housings, enclosures, casings & other containers; pipe, sheet metal; restaurant sheet metalwork

(P-12109)
AHLBORN STRUCTURAL STEEL INC
1230 Century Ct, Santa Rosa (95403-1042)
PHONE 707 573-0742
Thomas Ahlborn, *CEO*
Lance Ballenger, *Vice Pres*
Cathy Ahlborn, *Admin Sec*
Katrina Parker, *Administration*
Nick Beebe, *Project Mgr*
EMP: 34
SALES (est): 7.9MM **Privately Held**
WEB: www.ahlbornstructural.com
SIC: 3441 Fabricated structural metal

(P-12110)
ALL WEST FABRICATORS INC
44875 Fremont Blvd, Fremont (94538-6318)
PHONE 510 623-1200
Gary J Lee, *President*
Keith Lee, *Vice Pres*
EMP: 40 EST: 1996
SALES (est): 4.5MM **Privately Held**
SIC: 3441 Fabricated structural metal for bridges

(P-12111)
AMAZING STEEL COMPANY
Also Called: Mitchellamazing
4564 Mission Blvd, Montclair (91763-6106)
PHONE 909 590-0393
Jim Mitchell, *President*
EMP: 20
SQ FT: 25,000
SALES (est): 2.5MM **Privately Held**
SIC: 3441 7692 7699 Fabricated structural metal; welding repair; hydraulic equipment repair

(P-12112)
AMERICAN STEEL MASTERS INC
15050 Proctor Ave, City of Industry (91746-3305)
PHONE 626 333-3375
Jose Luis Hernandez, *President*
EMP: 21
SALES (est): 4.5MM **Privately Held**
SIC: 3441 Fabricated structural metal

(P-12113)
ANVIL STEEL CORPORATION
Also Called: Anvil Iron
134 W 168th St, Gardena (90248-2729)
PHONE 310 329-5811
Gerry Bustrum, *CEO*
Paul Schifino, *President*
Gary Cannon, *CFO*
Mike Norton, *Vice Pres*
Mark Waldron, *Vice Pres*
▲ **EMP:** 90
SQ FT: 4,000
SALES (est): 28.8MM **Privately Held**
WEB: www.anvilsteel.com
SIC: 3441 Fabricated structural metal

(P-12114)
ASC PROFILES INC
Also Called: AEP Span
10905 Beech Ave, Fontana (92337-7295)
PHONE 909 823-0401
Steve Balding, *Manager*
EMP: 150
SQ FT: 71,842 **Privately Held**
WEB: www.ascpacific.com
SIC: 3441 3448 Fabricated structural metal; prefabricated metal buildings
HQ: Asc Profiles Llc
2110 Enterprise Blvd
West Sacramento CA 95691
916 372-6851

(P-12115)
AZTEC TECHNOLOGY CORPORATION (PA)
Also Called: Aztec Containers
2550 S Santa Fe Ave, Vista (92084-8098)
PHONE 760 727-2300
Brian Hyndman, *CEO*
Michael Hyndman, *Treasurer*
Catherine Hyndman, *Vice Pres*
Theresa Gualtieri, *General Mgr*
Steven Hyndman, *Admin Sec*
EMP: 20
SQ FT: 3,000
SALES: 9.5MM **Privately Held**
WEB: www.azteccontainer.com
SIC: 3441 Fabricated structural metal

(P-12116)
BAY CITY MARINE INC (PA)
1625 Cleveland Ave, National City (91950-4212)
PHONE 619 477-3991
Michelle Ralph, *President*
Paul Ralph, *COO*
Steve Johnston, *Vice Pres*
EMP: 25
SQ FT: 11,000
SALES (est): 4.8MM **Privately Held**
WEB: www.baycitymarine.com
SIC: 3441 3731 7699 Fabricated structural metal; military ships, building & repairing; boat repair

(P-12117)
BIG VALLEY METALS
620 Houston St Ste 1, West Sacramento (95691-2255)
P.O. Box 934 (95691-0934)
PHONE 916 372-2383
J Robert Vela, *Owner*
EMP: 13
SALES (est): 2.1MM **Privately Held**
SIC: 3441 Fabricated structural metal

(P-12118)
BILL WILLIAMS WELDING CO
1735 Santa Fe Ave, Long Beach (90813-1292)
PHONE 562 432-5421
Martha Williams-Hermon, *President*
EMP: 25 EST: 1945
SQ FT: 30,000
SALES (est): 2.1MM **Privately Held**
SIC: 3441 7692 Fabricated structural metal; automotive welding

(P-12119)
BOBS IRON INC
740 Kevin Ct, Oakland (94621-4040)
PHONE 510 567-8983
Robert Smith, *President*
EMP: 20
SQ FT: 9,500
SALES (est): 2MM **Privately Held**
SIC: 3441 Fabricated structural metal

(P-12120)
BOYD CORPORATION (PA)
Also Called: Boyd Construction
5832 Ohio St, Yorba Linda (92886-5323)
P.O. Box 6012, Anaheim (92816-0012)
PHONE 714 533-2375
Mitch Aiello, *President*
EMP: 12 EST: 1980
SALES (est): 12.2MM **Privately Held**
WEB: www.boydcompanies.com
SIC: 3441 2891 Fabricated structural metal; adhesives

(P-12121)
BRUNTON ENTERPRISES INC
Also Called: Plas-Tal Manufacturing Co
8815 Sorensen Ave, Santa Fe Springs (90670-2636)
PHONE 562 945-0013
Sean P Brunton, *CEO*
John W Brunton Jr, *President*
Doug Robson, *Treasurer*
Patrick Scott, *Network Mgr*
Dennis Donnatin, *Project Mgr*
EMP: 125 EST: 1947
SQ FT: 45,000
SALES (est): 37.7MM **Privately Held**
WEB: www.plas-tal.com
SIC: 3441 Fabricated structural metal

(P-12122)
C & R PIER MFG (PA)
Also Called: C & R Mfg
275 S Rancho Ave, Colton (92324-3236)
PHONE 909 872-6444
Donna Clifton, *President*
EMP: 38
SQ FT: 30,000
SALES (est): 2.1MM **Privately Held**
WEB: www.crpier.com
SIC: 3441 Fabricated structural metal

(P-12123)
C A BUCHEN CORP
9231 Glenoaks Blvd, Sun Valley (91352-2688)
PHONE 818 767-5408
John Oster, *CEO*
Ryan Chapman, *Vice Pres*
EMP: 25
SQ FT: 22,500
SALES (est): 4.5MM **Privately Held**
WEB: www.cabuchen.com
SIC: 3441 1791 3312 Fabricated structural metal; structural steel erection; iron & steel: galvanized, pipes, plates, sheets, etc.

(P-12124)
C AND R SALES INC
Also Called: Kretzschmar Steel
3750 S Riverside Ave, Colton (92324-3329)
PHONE 951 686-6864
Tim Kretzschmar, *President*
EMP: 19 EST: 1978
SQ FT: 1,800
SALES (est): 5.4MM **Privately Held**
SIC: 3441 Fabricated structural metal

(P-12125)
CAC FABRICATION INC
9710 Owensmouth Ave Ste C, Chatsworth (91311-8077)
PHONE 818 882-2626
David Agins, *President*
EMP: 12
SQ FT: 5,000
SALES (est): 1MM **Privately Held**
WEB: www.cacfab.com
SIC: 3441 Fabricated structural metal

(P-12126)
CALCON STEEL CONSTRUCTION
Also Called: Hamilton Iron Works
1226 W 196th St, Torrance (90502-1101)
PHONE 310 768-8094
Sung Nam, *President*
Hannah Nam, *Admin Sec*
EMP: 20
SQ FT: 50,000
SALES (est): 3.7MM **Privately Held**
SIC: 3441 Fabricated structural metal

(P-12127)
CALCRAFT CORPORATION
Also Called: Calcraft Company
1426 S Willow Ave, Rialto (92376-7720)
PHONE 909 879-2900
Daniel Steven Ensman, *President*
Dan Ensman, *Executive*
Gloria Ensman, *Admin Sec*
Mike Sentell, *Sales Executive*
John Sevo, *Mktg Dir*
EMP: 15
SQ FT: 30,000
SALES (est): 4.4MM **Privately Held**
SIC: 3441 Fabricated structural metal

(P-12128)
CAPITOL IRON WORKS INC
7009 Power Inn Rd, Sacramento (95828-2498)
PHONE 916 381-1554
Daniel D Howard, *President*
Steve Hartzell, *President*
Diana Howard, *Corp Secy*
Ruben Reyes, *Project Mgr*
EMP: 20
SQ FT: 3,000
SALES: 2.2MM **Privately Held**
WEB: www.capitolironworks.com
SIC: 3441 Fabricated structural metal

(P-12129)
CAPITOL STEEL FABRICATORS INC
3565 Greenwood Ave, Commerce (90040-3305)
PHONE..........................323 721-5460
James Moreland, *President*
Eric Jonkey, *Shareholder*
Janice Moreland, *Vice Pres*
EMP: 25
SQ FT: 10,000
SALES (est): 7MM **Privately Held**
WEB: www.capitolsteel.com
SIC: 3441 Fabricated structural metal

(P-12130)
CARLYLE GLASGOW WLDG SVCS INC
4747 E State St Ste A, Ontario (91762-3924)
P.O. Box 1194, Brea (92822-1194)
PHONE..........................909 902-1814
Carlyle F Glasgow, *President*
Katrina Glasgow, *Vice Pres*
EMP: 12
SALES (est): 1.8MM **Privately Held**
WEB: www.carlylegwelding.com
SIC: 3441 Fabricated structural metal

(P-12131)
CARROLL METAL WORKS INC
740 W 16th St, National City (91950-4205)
PHONE..........................619 477-9125
Pat Carroll, *President*
EMP: 95
SQ FT: 11,500
SALES (est): 18.7MM **Privately Held**
SIC: 3441 Fabricated structural metal

(P-12132)
CARTER GROUP (PA)
Also Called: Alling Iron Works
511 Houston St, West Sacramento (95691-2213)
PHONE..........................916 333-5070
Joe Neal Carter, *President*
Renee Mason, *Corp Secy*
EMP: 20
SQ FT: 22,000
SALES: 7MM **Privately Held**
WEB: www.farallonboats.com
SIC: 3441 Fabricated structural metal

(P-12133)
CENTRAL VALLEY MACHINING INC
5820 E Harvard Ave, Fresno (93727-1373)
PHONE..........................559 291-7749
Long MAI, *President*
Peter MAI, *Vice Pres*
EMP: 20
SQ FT: 5,000
SALES: 1.2MM **Privately Held**
SIC: 3441 Fabricated structural metal

(P-12134)
CH INDUSTRIAL TECHNOLOGY INC
3160 E California Ave, Fresno (93702-4108)
PHONE..........................559 485-8011
Cameron Williams, *President*
Jeremiah Burleson, *Admin Sec*
▲ EMP: 13
SQ FT: 17,000
SALES: 1.2MM **Privately Held**
SIC: 3441 Fabricated structural metal

(P-12135)
CHRIS FRENCH METAL INC
2500 Union St, Oakland (94607-2462)
PHONE..........................510 238-9339
Chris French, *President*
EMP: 10
SALES (est): 2.3MM **Privately Held**
SIC: 3441 Fabricated structural metal

(P-12136)
COAST AEROSPACE MFG INC
950 Richfield Rd, Placentia (92870-6732)
PHONE..........................714 893-8066
Louis Ponce, *President*
David Rodriguez, *President*
Steven Castillo, *Vice Pres*
Frank Fleck, *Vice Pres*

Emma Balibalos, *Office Mgr*
EMP: 43
SALES (est): 9.8MM **Privately Held**
WEB: www.coastaerospace.com
SIC: 3441 Fabricated structural metal; special dies & tools; semiconductor manufacturing machinery; wire & cable; machine tool design

(P-12137)
COLUMBIA STEEL INC
2175 N Linden Ave, Rialto (92377-4445)
PHONE..........................909 874-8840
Gustavo Waldemar Theisen, *CEO*
Charmaine Helenihi, *CFO*
William Young, *Chairman*
Luis Theisen, *Vice Pres*
Patrick Garrett, *Info Tech Mgr*
EMP: 75 EST: 1975
SQ FT: 63,384
SALES (est): 35.7MM **Privately Held**
WEB: www.columbiasteelinc.com
SIC: 3441 Building components, structural steel

(P-12138)
COMMERCIAL SHEET METAL WORKS
Also Called: CSM Metal Fabricating & Engrg
1800 S San Pedro St, Los Angeles (90015-3711)
PHONE..........................213 748-7321
Jack L Gardener, *President*
Wade Hilton, *Project Mgr*
▲ EMP: 27 EST: 1916
SQ FT: 22,000
SALES (est): 10.4MM **Privately Held**
WEB: www.csmworks.com
SIC: 3441 Fabricated structural metal

(P-12139)
COMPLETE METAL FABRICATION INC
596 E Main St, El Centro (92243-9471)
P.O. Box 1529 (92244-1529)
PHONE..........................760 353-0260
Jesse Ray Riddle, *CEO*
Arita Riddle, *Info Tech Mgr*
EMP: 19
SALES (est): 4.3MM **Privately Held**
SIC: 3441 Fabricated structural metal

(P-12140)
CONSTEEL INDUSTRIAL INC
15435 Woodcrest Dr, Whittier (90604-3236)
PHONE..........................562 806-4575
Luis Lagarica, *CEO*
Maria Torres, *CFO*
Russ Lambert, *Admin Sec*
Frankie Alamintos, *Director*
Robert Geronca, *Director*
EMP: 27
SALES: 8.2MM **Privately Held**
SIC: 3441 Fabricated structural metal

(P-12141)
CONXTECH INC
24493 Clawiter Rd, Hayward (94545-2219)
PHONE..........................510 264-9111
EMP: 110
SALES (corp-wide): 76.2MM **Privately Held**
SIC: 3441 Building components, structural steel
PA: Conxtech, Inc.
6701 Koll Center Pkwy
Pleasanton CA 94566
510 264-9111

(P-12142)
CONXTECH INC (PA)
6701 Koll Center Pkwy, Pleasanton (94566-8061)
PHONE..........................510 264-9111
Robert J Simmons, *President*
Howard Franklin, *CFO*
Jason Berry, *Vice Pres*
Raymond G Kitasoe, *Vice Pres*
Kelly Lutrell, *Vice Pres*
◆ EMP: 150
SQ FT: 100,000
SALES (est): 76.2MM **Privately Held**
WEB: www.conxtech.com
SIC: 3441 Building components, structural steel

(P-12143)
CORBELL PRODUCTS INC
14650 Hawthorne Ave, Fontana (92335-2509)
PHONE..........................909 574-9139
Frank Stavinski, *President*
Elaine Lucero, *Treasurer*
EMP: 46
SQ FT: 26,000
SALES (est): 5.2MM **Privately Held**
SIC: 3441 Fabricated structural metal

(P-12144)
CORCORAN SAWTELLE ROSPRIM INC
Also Called: Sawtelle & Rosprim Machine Sp
542 Otis Ave, Corcoran (93212-1823)
PHONE..........................559 992-2117
Terry Kwast, *President*
EMP: 30
SQ FT: 35,000
SALES (est): 6.8MM **Privately Held**
SIC: 3441 3599 Fabricated structural metal; machine shop, jobbing & repair

(P-12145)
COVINA WELDING & SHTMTL INC
473 E Front St, Covina (91723-1205)
P.O. Box 5039 (91723-5039)
PHONE..........................626 332-6293
Larry Evans, *President*
Miguel A Ayala, *Vice Pres*
EMP: 17 EST: 1944
SQ FT: 13,000
SALES (est): 2.7MM **Privately Held**
SIC: 3441 Fabricated structural metal

(P-12146)
CUSTOM SOURCE DESIGN INC
15642 Dupont Ave Ste A, Chino (91710-7616)
PHONE..........................909 597-5221
Christopher Montoya, *President*
▲ EMP: 12
SALES: 2MM **Privately Held**
SIC: 3441 Fabricated structural metal

(P-12147)
CUSTOM STEEL FABRICATION INC
Also Called: C & J Industries
11966 Rivera Rd, Santa Fe Springs (90670-2232)
PHONE..........................562 907-2777
John Toscano, *President*
Carole Toscano, *CEO*
EMP: 17
SQ FT: 3,400
SALES (est): 2.6MM **Privately Held**
SIC: 3441 Fabricated structural metal

(P-12148)
CW INDUSTRIES
1735 Santa Fe Ave, Long Beach (90813-1242)
PHONE..........................562 432-5421
Craig Wildvank, *Principal*
EMP: 12
SALES (est): 2MM **Privately Held**
SIC: 3441 3548 5084 Building components, structural steel; welding apparatus; oil refining machinery, equipment & supplies

(P-12149)
D D WIRE CO INC (PA)
4335 Temple City Blvd, Temple City (91780-4229)
PHONE..........................626 442-0459
Wes Berry, *President*
James Howe, *COO*
David Berry, *CFO*
Dorsey Wire, *Principal*
Elizabeth D Berry, *Admin Sec*
EMP: 22 EST: 1963
SQ FT: 24,000
SALES (est): 4.6MM **Privately Held**
WEB: www.ddwire.com
SIC: 3441 3469 Fabricated structural metal; stamping metal for the trade

(P-12150)
D D WIRE CO INC
4942 Encinita Ave, Temple City (91780-3705)
PHONE..........................626 285-0298
Wesley Berry, *Manager*
Dorsey Wire, *Owner*
EMP: 15
SALES (corp-wide): 4.6MM **Privately Held**
WEB: www.ddwire.com
SIC: 3441 3469 Fabricated structural metal; metal stampings
PA: D. D. Wire Co., Inc.
4335 Temple City Blvd
Temple City CA 91780
626 442-0459

(P-12151)
DAVISON IRON WORKS INC
8845 Elder Creek Rd Ste A, Sacramento (95828-1835)
PHONE..........................916 381-2121
Andrew Peszynski, *President*
Candy Holland, *Vice Pres*
EMP: 50
SQ FT: 3,500
SALES (est): 12.7MM **Privately Held**
WEB: www.davisoniron.com
SIC: 3441 Fabricated structural metal

(P-12152)
DELTA REBAR SERVICES INC
2410 Bates Ave, Concord (94520-1206)
PHONE..........................925 798-4220
Dan Yust, *President*
EMP: 12
SQ FT: 700
SALES (est): 2.3MM **Privately Held**
SIC: 3441 Fabricated structural metal

(P-12153)
DIVERSIFIED HANGAR COMPANY
5905 Monterey Rd, Paso Robles (93446-7670)
PHONE..........................805 239-8229
Bryan Watson, *Owner*
EMP: 10
SQ FT: 10,000
SALES (est): 640K **Privately Held**
SIC: 3441 Building components, structural steel

(P-12154)
DONALD H BINKLEY
Also Called: D & D Engineering
2901 Commerce Way, Turlock (95380-9471)
PHONE..........................209 664-9792
Donald H Binkley, *Owner*
EMP: 17
SALES (est): 2.3MM **Privately Held**
SIC: 3441 3599 Fabricated structural metal; machine shop, jobbing & repair

(P-12155)
EANDI METAL WORKS INC (PA)
976 23rd Ave, Oakland (94606-5011)
PHONE..........................510 532-8311
Joseph J Eandi, *CEO*
Lisa Eandi, *Shareholder*
Jeffrey Eandi, *Vice Pres*
Lewis Eandi, *Vice Pres*
Loretta Eandi, *Admin Sec*
EMP: 15 EST: 1928
SQ FT: 50,000
SALES (est): 1.4MM **Privately Held**
SIC: 3441 3446 Fabricated structural metal; architectural metalwork

(P-12156)
EW CORPRTION INDUS FABRICATORS (PA)
1002 E Main St, El Centro (92243)
P.O. Box 2189 (92244-2189)
PHONE..........................760 337-0020
Tiberio R Esparza, *President*
◆ EMP: 80 EST: 1973
SQ FT: 100,000
SALES (est): 12.3MM **Privately Held**
WEB: www.ewcorporation.com
SIC: 3441 Fabricated structural metal

▲ = Import ▼=Export
◆ =Import/Export

(P-12157)
EXCELSIOR METALS INC
2681 N Business Park Ave, Fresno
(93727-8639)
PHONE...................................559 294-9284
Raymond R Roush III, *President*
EMP: 27
SQ FT: 10,000
SALES (est): 7.6MM **Privately Held**
WEB: www.excelsiormetals.com
SIC: 3441 Fabricated structural metal

(P-12158)
FABCO STEEL FABRICATION INC
14688 San Bernardino Ave, Fontana
(92335-5319)
P.O. Box 8636, Alta Loma (91701-0636)
PHONE...................................909 350-1535
John E Schick, *President*
Rich Schick, *CFO*
EMP: 35 EST: 1979
SQ FT: 30,000
SALES (est): 11MM **Privately Held**
WEB: www.fabcosteel.com
SIC: 3441 Fabricated structural metal

(P-12159)
FABRICATION TECH INDS INC
2200 Haffley Ave, National City
(91950-6418)
P.O. Box 1447 (91951-1447)
PHONE...................................619 477-4141
Tom Houshar, *Ch of Bd*
Joey Houshar, *President*
Eduardo Elizarraras, *COO*
Tom Narey, *CFO*
Martha Houshar, *Admin Sec*
▲ EMP: 71
SQ FT: 35,000
SALES (est): 23.9MM **Privately Held**
WEB: www.ftisd.com
SIC: 3441 Fabricated structural metal

(P-12160)
FAT CUTS
15140 Bledsoe St Ste B, Sylmar
(91342-2709)
PHONE...................................818 367-1540
Juan Ochoa, *President*
EMP: 10
SALES (est): 1.2MM **Privately Held**
SIC: 3441 Fabricated structural metal

(P-12161)
FERROSAUR INC
Also Called: Industrial Welding
4821 Mountain Lakes Blvd, Redding
(96003-1454)
PHONE...................................530 246-7843
Thomas Largent, *Vice Pres*
Thomas R Largent, *CEO*
EMP: 13
SQ FT: 33,000
SALES (est): 3.1MM **Privately Held**
SIC: 3441 7692 2298 5932 Fabricated
structural metal; welding repair; rope, ex-
cept asbestos & wire; building materials,
secondhand

(P-12162)
FIFE METAL FABRICATING INC
4191 Eastside Rd, Redding (96001-3884)
PHONE...................................530 243-4696
Doyle Fife Jr, *President*
Joanne Fife, *Corp Secy*
EMP: 17 EST: 1965
SQ FT: 10,000
SALES (est): 3.7MM **Privately Held**
SIC: 3441 3446 Building components,
structural steel; architectural metalwork

(P-12163)
FLORIAN INDUSTRIES INC
151 Industrial Way, Brisbane (94005-1003)
PHONE...................................415 330-9000
Chuck Lutz, *President*
Jim Barreto, *Mfg Staff*
EMP: 15
SQ FT: 2,000
SALES: 2MM **Privately Held**
SIC: 3441 Fabricated structural metal

(P-12164)
FOSS MARITIME COMPANY
49 W Pier D St, Long Beach (90802)
PHONE...................................562 437-6098
Wendall Koi, *Principal*
EMP: 10
SALES (corp-wide): 2B **Privately Held**
SIC: 3441 Boat & barge sections, prefabri-
cated metal
HQ: Foss Maritime Company
450 Alaskan Way S
Seattle WA 98104
206 281-3800

(P-12165)
FREEBERG INDUS FBRICATION CORP
2874 Progress Pl, Escondido (92029-1516)
PHONE...................................760 737-7614
Marc Brown, *President*
James R St John, *CEO*
John Freeberg, *Controller*
EMP: 85
SQ FT: 128,000
SALES (est): 22.9MM **Privately Held**
WEB: www.freeberg.com
SIC: 3441 3444 Fabricated structural
metal; sheet metalwork

(P-12166)
FRESNO FAB-TECH INC
1035 K St, Sanger (93657-3383)
PHONE...................................559 875-9800
Chris Kisling, *President*
EMP: 40
SQ FT: 35,000
SALES (est): 10.7MM **Privately Held**
SIC: 3441 Fabricated structural metal

(P-12167)
GAMBOA INCORPORATED
Also Called: Metro Steel
1355 Presioca St, Spring Valley
(91977-4221)
PHONE...................................619 448-9995
Ken Gamboa, *CEO*
Jolly Gamboa, *Admin Sec*
EMP: 14
SALES (est): 3.6MM **Privately Held**
WEB: www.gamboa.com
SIC: 3441 1791 Fabricated structural
metal for bridges; structural steel erection

(P-12168)
GAMMELL INDUSTRIES INC
7535 Jackson St, Paramount (90723-4909)
PHONE...................................562 634-6653
James Ruffner, *President*
Roy Gammell, *Vice Pres*
EMP: 10
SQ FT: 13,000
SALES (est): 880K **Privately Held**
SIC: 3441 Fabricated structural metal

(P-12169)
GAYLE MANUFACTURING CO INC (PA)
1455 E Kentucky Ave, Woodland
(95776-6121)
P.O. Box 1365 (95776-1365)
PHONE...................................530 662-0284
Gary Glenn, *President*
James Deblasio, *CFO*
David Deblasio, *Vice Pres*
Christopher Mahler, *Vice Pres*
Nelson Vieira, *Vice Pres*
EMP: 142
SQ FT: 72,000
SALES (est): 91.9MM **Privately Held**
SIC: 3441 Fabricated structural metal

(P-12170)
GENERAL STEEL FABRICATORS INC
12179 Branford St Ste B, Sun Valley
(91352-5733)
PHONE...................................818 897-1300
Mehrad Maleki, *President*
EMP: 15
SALES (est): 504.6K **Privately Held**
SIC: 3441 Fabricated structural metal

(P-12171)
GERLINGER FNDRY MCH WORKS INC (PA)
1527 Sacramento St, Redding
(96001-1914)
P.O. Box 992195 (96099-2195)
PHONE...................................530 243-1053
Fred Gerlinger, *CEO*
Jo Gerlinger, *CFO*
Tim Gerlinger, *Vice Pres*
Scott Anthis, *Sales Mgr*
Rick Eagle, *Sales Staff*
EMP: 37
SQ FT: 45,000
SALES (est): 12.9MM **Privately Held**
WEB: www.gerlinger.com
SIC: 3441 3494 7692 5051 Fabricated
structural metal; valves & pipe fittings;
welding repair; steel

(P-12172)
GLAZIER STEEL INC
650 Sandoval Way, Hayward (94544-7129)
PHONE...................................510 471-5300
Craig Glazier, *CEO*
Harold Glazier, *President*
Scott Yackzan, *Project Mgr*
EMP: 75 EST: 1982
SQ FT: 26,897
SALES (est): 24.4MM **Privately Held**
SIC: 3441 Fabricated structural metal

(P-12173)
GOLDEN STATE STEEL & STAIR INC (PA)
479 Mason St, Vacaville (95688-4540)
P.O. Box 5203 (95696-5203)
PHONE...................................707 455-0400
Joan Baker, *President*
Fred Baker, *CFO*
EMP: 20
SQ FT: 3,500
SALES (est): 4.7MM **Privately Held**
WEB: www.gsssinc.com
SIC: 3441 Fabricated structural metal

(P-12174)
GRATING PACIFIC INC (PA)
3651 Sausalito St, Los Alamitos
(90720-2436)
PHONE...................................562 598-4314
Ronald S Robertson, *President*
Jeffrey Robertson, *Vice Pres*
Stacy Henry, *Office Mgr*
David Scheuerlein, *Sales Mgr*
◆ EMP: 20
SQ FT: 40,000
SALES (est): 21.1MM **Privately Held**
SIC: 3441 3446 Fabricated structural
metal; architectural metalwork

(P-12175)
HERRICK CORPORATION (PA)
Also Called: San Bernandina Steel
3003 E Hammer Ln, Stockton
(95212-2801)
P.O. Box 8429 (95208-0429)
PHONE...................................209 956-4751
David H Dornsife, *CEO*
Doug Griffin, *President*
Peter Abila, *CFO*
Robert Hazleton, *Vice Pres*
John Reitmeier, *Vice Pres*
▲ EMP: 50
SALES (est): 244.7MM **Privately Held**
SIC: 3441 Fabricated structural metal

(P-12176)
HITECH METAL FABRICATION CORP
Also Called: H M F
1705 S Claudina Way, Anaheim
(92805-6544)
PHONE...................................714 635-3505
Ba V Nguyen, *President*
Matthew Vu, *Vice Pres*
Lucia Coronel, *Admin Mgr*
Norman Pham, *Purch Agent*
EMP: 60
SQ FT: 42,850
SALES (est): 13.6MM **Privately Held**
SIC: 3441 Fabricated structural metal

(P-12177)
HOMESTEAD SHEET METAL
9031 Memory Ln, Spring Valley
(91977-2152)
PHONE...................................619 469-4373
George Tomlanovich, *President*
Chuck Highfill, *Corp Secy*
EMP: 20
SQ FT: 5,625
SALES (est): 4.8MM **Privately Held**
WEB: www.homesteadsheetmetal.com
SIC: 3441 Fabricated structural metal

(P-12178)
INDUSTRIAL MACHINE & MFG CO
Also Called: Immco
2626 Seaman Ave, El Monte (91733-1930)
PHONE...................................626 444-0181
Diane Teresa, *President*
Ron Teresa, *Corp Secy*
David Teresa, *Vice Pres*
Mark Teresa, *Vice Pres*
EMP: 15 EST: 1959
SQ FT: 5,500
SALES (est): 866.3K **Privately Held**
WEB: www.immcohandtrucks.com
SIC: 3441 3569 3537 Fabricated struc-
tural metal; assembly machines, non-met-
alworking; industrial trucks & tractors

(P-12179)
INNOVATION ALLEY LLC
5473 E Hedges Ave, Fresno (93727-2252)
PHONE...................................559 453-6974
Donald Ripley, *President*
EMP: 12
SALES: 1.5MM **Privately Held**
SIC: 3441 Fabricated structural metal

(P-12180)
INTEGRAL ENGRG FABRICATION INC
520 Hofgaarden St, City of Industry
(91744-5529)
PHONE...................................626 369-0958
John Zheng, *CEO*
Son T Nguyen, *Admin Sec*
EMP: 25
SQ FT: 20,000
SALES (est): 5.3MM **Privately Held**
WEB: www.integral-ef.com
SIC: 3441 Fabricated structural metal

(P-12181)
INTELLIGENT FIXTURE
3350 Gilman Rd, El Monte (91732-3201)
PHONE...................................626 279-1300
Pompeyo Ugalde, *Principal*
EMP: 53
SALES (est): 6.7MM **Privately Held**
SIC: 3441 Fabricated structural metal

(P-12182)
IRON DOG FABRICATION INC
3450 Regional Pkwy Ste E, Santa Rosa
(95403-8247)
PHONE...................................707 579-7831
Duncan Woods, *President*
Cynthia Woods, *Corp Secy*
EMP: 17
SQ FT: 18,000
SALES (est): 4.3MM **Privately Held**
SIC: 3441 7692 1791 Building compo-
nents, structural steel; welding repair;
structural steel erection

(P-12183)
JAANN INC
225 W 15th St, National City (91950-4407)
PHONE...................................619 336-0584
Jesus Lavin, *President*
EMP: 10
SALES (est): 1MM **Privately Held**
SIC: 3441 Fabricated structural metal

(P-12184)
JAMAC STEEL INC
533 E Belmont St, Ontario (91761-3352)
P.O. Box 3877 (91761-0983)
PHONE...................................909 983-7592
William J McKernan, *CEO*
Maggie Mc Kernan, *Vice Pres*
EMP: 24

SALES (est): 6.2MM **Privately Held**
SIC: 3441 Fabricated structural metal

(P-12185)
JC METAL SPECIALISTS INC (PA)
220 Michelle Ct, San Francisco (94124)
PHONE..................415 822-3878
Judy Chan, *President*
Jeffrey Chan, *CFO*
EMP: 38
SQ FT: 7,500
SALES (est): 7.6MM **Privately Held**
SIC: 3441 Building components, structural steel

(P-12186)
JCI METAL PRODUCTS (PA)
6540 Federal Blvd, Lemon Grove (91945-1311)
PHONE..................619 229-8206
Marcel Becker, *CEO*
Mark Withers, *President*
Don Cooke, *CFO*
Lorey Topham, *CFO*
Rich Bartlett, *Vice Pres*
EMP: 57
SQ FT: 21,000
SALES (est): 9.2MM **Privately Held**
SIC: 3441 1761 Fabricated structural metal for ships; architectural sheet metal work

(P-12187)
JL MALLARD INC
4747 Live Oak Canyon Rd, La Verne (91750-2319)
P.O. Box 23 (91750-0023)
PHONE..................909 593-3403
Scott W Skipper, *President*
EMP: 25 EST: 1952
SQ FT: 12,000
SALES (est): 3.9MM **Privately Held**
SIC: 3441 3443 Fabricated structural metal; fabricated plate work (boiler shop)

(P-12188)
JOHASEE REBAR INC
18059 Rosedale Hwy, Bakersfield (93314-8684)
PHONE..................661 589-0972
Mike Hill Sr, *CEO*
Michael Hill Jr, *COO*
Tamara L Chapman, *CFO*
Tami Chapman, *CFO*
Tara Carrasco, *Administration*
EMP: 47
SALES (est): 18.2MM **Privately Held**
WEB: www.johaseerebar.com
SIC: 3441 1791 Fabricated structural metal; concrete reinforcement, placing of
PA: Lms Holdings (Ab) Ltd
       7452 132 St
       Surrey BC V3W 4
       604 598-9930

(P-12189)
K SHORT INC
126 W Walnut Ave, Monrovia (91016-3444)
PHONE..................626 358-8511
Karl G Short, *President*
Margaret Short, *Vice Pres*
EMP: 10
SQ FT: 11,000
SALES (est): 1.5MM **Privately Held**
SIC: 3441 Fabricated structural metal

(P-12190)
KASCO FAB INC
4529 S Chestnut Ave Lowr, Fresno (93725-9244)
PHONE..................559 442-1018
Hidemi Kimura, *CEO*
Ken Kimura, *Vice Pres*
EMP: 75
SQ FT: 200,000
SALES (est): 14.5MM **Privately Held**
SIC: 3441 3449 Building components, structural steel; miscellaneous metalwork

(P-12191)
KC METAL PRODUCTS INC (PA)
Also Called: Kc Metals
1960 Hartog Dr, San Jose (95131-2212)
PHONE..................408 436-8754
Robert J Daugherty, *President*

Sandra Daugherty, *Admin Sec*
EMP: 72
SQ FT: 60,000
SALES (est): 11.9MM **Privately Held**
WEB: www.kcmetals.com
SIC: 3441 3429 Fabricated structural metal; manufactured hardware (general)

(P-12192)
KSU CORPORATION
3 Emmy Ln, Ladera Ranch (92694-1521)
PHONE..................951 409-7055
Luz Marina Agreda, *CEO*
EMP: 15
SALES (est): 688.2K **Privately Held**
SIC: 3441 Building components, structural steel

(P-12193)
LEES IMPERIAL WELDING INC
3300 Edison Way, Fremont (94538-6150)
PHONE..................510 657-4900
Gary Lee, *CEO*
Keith Lee, *Vice Pres*
EMP: 150
SQ FT: 59,000
SALES (est): 43MM **Privately Held**
SIC: 3441 Fabricated structural metal

(P-12194)
LEEWAY IRON WORKS INC
565 Estabrook St, San Leandro (94577-3511)
PHONE..................510 357-8637
John Louis, *President*
Audrey Louis, *Office Mgr*
EMP: 10 EST: 1963
SQ FT: 5,200
SALES (est): 798.6K **Privately Held**
SIC: 3441 1799 Fabricated structural metal; ornamental metal work

(P-12195)
LEHMANS MANUFACTURING CO INC
4960 E Jensen Ave, Fresno (93725-1897)
PHONE..................559 486-1700
Adam Lehman Jr, *Ch of Bd*
Kenneth Lehman, *President*
Joyce Lehman, *Corp Secy*
Sharon Ramirez, *Manager*
EMP: 15 EST: 1946
SQ FT: 36,000
SALES (est): 4.3MM **Privately Held**
WEB: www.lehmansmfg.com
SIC: 3441 Fabricated structural metal

(P-12196)
LIGHTCAP INDUSTRIES, INC.
Also Called: JC Supply & Manufacturing
1612 S Cucamonga Ave, Ontario (91761-4513)
PHONE..................909 930-3772
EMP: 50
SQ FT: 41,000
SALES (est): 1.1MM **Privately Held**
WEB: www.jcsupply.us
SIC: 3441 3479 Building components, structural steel; painting, coating & hot dipping

(P-12197)
LMI AEROSPACE INC
1377 Specialty Dr, Vista (92081-8521)
PHONE..................760 599-4477
Ed Campbell, *General Mgr*
EMP: 132
SALES (corp-wide): 1MM **Privately Held**
SIC: 3441 Fabricated structural metal
HQ: Lmi Aerospace, Inc.
       411 Fountain Lakes Blvd
       Saint Charles MO 63301
       636 946-6525

(P-12198)
M W REID WELDING INC
Also Called: SOUTH BAY WELDING
781 Oconner St, El Cajon (92020-1644)
PHONE..................619 401-5880
Bruce A Reid, *President*
Susan Reid, *Corp Secy*
Timothy Fair, *Vice Pres*
Timothy Hill, *Vice Pres*
Leona Jameson, *Office Mgr*
EMP: 78
SQ FT: 25,000

SALES: 17.9MM **Privately Held**
WEB: www.southbaywelding.com
SIC: 3441 Fabricated structural metal

(P-12199)
MADISON INDUSTRIES INC ARIZONA
18000 Studebaker Rd # 305, Cerritos (90703-2679)
PHONE..................602 252-3083
John S Frey, *President*
Barbara A Cruncleton, *Corp Secy*
Robert E Hanson, *Vice Pres*
EMP: 20 EST: 1947
SQ FT: 4,000
SALES (est): 4.5MM
SALES (corp-wide): 129.8MM **Privately Held**
SIC: 3441 3448 Building components, structural steel; prefabricated metal buildings
PA: John S. Frey Enterprises
       1900 E 64th St
       Los Angeles CA 90001
       323 583-4061

(P-12200)
MADRUGA IRON WORKS INC
305 Gandy Dancer Dr, Tracy (95377-9083)
PHONE..................209 832-7003
Joseph Raymond Madruga, *CEO*
Elizabeth Betsy Madruga, *President*
Raymond M Madruga, *President*
Mary E Weber, *Agent*
EMP: 45
SQ FT: 50,000
SALES (est): 18.8MM **Privately Held**
WEB: www.madrugaironworks.com
SIC: 3441 3599 Fabricated structural metal; machine shop, jobbing & repair

(P-12201)
MANCIAS STEEL COMPANY INC
519 Horning St, San Jose (95112-2913)
PHONE..................408 295-5096
Lupe Mancias Jr, *President*
Rick Mancias, *Vice Pres*
EMP: 12
SQ FT: 12,000
SALES (est): 2MM **Privately Held**
WEB: www.manciassteel.com
SIC: 3441 Fabricated structural metal

(P-12202)
MARIN MANUFACTURING INC
195 Mill St, San Rafael (94901-4020)
PHONE..................415 453-1825
Daniel G Seright, *President*
Richard A Simanek, *Corp Secy*
EMP: 12
SQ FT: 12,000
SALES (est): 199.9K **Privately Held**
SIC: 3441 3599 7692 Building components, structural steel; machine shop, jobbing & repair; welding repair

(P-12203)
MAYA STEELS FABRICATION INC
301 E Compton Blvd, Gardena (90248-2015)
PHONE..................310 532-8830
Meir Amsalam, *CEO*
Yechiel Yogev, *CEO*
Yogev Yechiel, *Treasurer*
Sara Haddad, *Vice Pres*
Angie Martires, *Office Mgr*
EMP: 64 EST: 1982
SQ FT: 65,000
SALES (est): 26.6MM **Privately Held**
WEB: www.mayasteel.com
SIC: 3441 Building components, structural steel

(P-12204)
MCCAIN MANUFACTURING INC
2633 Progress St, Vista (92081-8402)
PHONE..................760 295-9290
Jeffrey Lynn McCain, *CEO*
EMP: 61
SALES (est): 60.4K **Privately Held**
SIC: 3441 Fabricated structural metal

(P-12205)
MCM FABRICATORS INC
Also Called: Global Fabricators
720 Commerce Way, Shafter (93263-9530)
P.O. Box 80247, Bakersfield (93380-0247)
PHONE..................661 589-2774
Jim L Moses, *President*
Melissa Garza, *Officer*
Bill Chaney, *Vice Pres*
Gary E Moses, *Vice Pres*
Gary Moses, *Vice Pres*
EMP: 140 EST: 1982
SQ FT: 12,000
SALES (est): 40.8MM **Privately Held**
WEB: www.globalfab.com
SIC: 3441 Fabricated structural metal

(P-12206)
MCWHIRTER STEEL INC
42211 7th St E, Lancaster (93535-5400)
PHONE..................661 951-8998
David McWhirter, *President*
Angela McWhirter, *CFO*
Nathan McWhirter, *Director*
EMP: 15
SQ FT: 21,000
SALES (est): 4MM **Privately Held**
WEB: www.dandddweldinginc.com
SIC: 3441 1791 Fabricated structural metal; structural steel erection; iron work, structural

(P-12207)
METAL FABRICATION AND ART LLC
3499 E 15th St, Los Angeles (90023-3833)
PHONE..................323 980-9595
Landon Ryan, *President*
EMP: 10
SALES (est): 2.3MM **Privately Held**
SIC: 3441 Fabricated structural metal

(P-12208)
METAL SUPPLY LLC
11810 Center St, South Gate (90280-7832)
PHONE..................562 634-9940
Dion Genchi, *President*
Bruce E Hubert, *Owner*
Deann Jenki, *General Mgr*
Barbara Hubert, *Admin Sec*
Julio Alfaro, *Engineer*
▼ **EMP:** 63
SQ FT: 50,000
SALES (est): 8MM **Privately Held**
WEB: www.metalsupply.com
SIC: 3441 5051 Fabricated structural metal; iron & steel (ferrous) products; aluminum bars, rods, ingots, sheets, pipes, plates, etc.

(P-12209)
METALS USA BUILDING PDTS LP
6450a Caballero Blvd, Buena Park (90620-1128)
PHONE..................714 522-7852
Tom Bush, *Branch Mgr*
EMP: 70
SALES (corp-wide): 9.7B **Publicly Held**
WEB: www.gerardusa.com
SIC: 3441 3444 Fabricated structural metal; sheet metalwork
HQ: Metals Usa Building Products Lp
       955 Columbia St
       Brea CA 92821
       713 946-9000

(P-12210)
METALSET INC
1200 Hensley St, Richmond (94801-1900)
PHONE..................510 233-9998
Wesley Sillineri, *Principal*
Wes Sillineri, *President*
Shaun McMahon, *Project Mgr*
Ron Becker, *Controller*
Dave Alvarez, *Mfg Staff*
EMP: 22
SALES (est): 6.1MM **Privately Held**
SIC: 3441 Fabricated structural metal

(P-12211)
MILLERS FAB & WELD CORP
6100 Industrial Ave, Riverside (92504-1120)
PHONE..................951 359-3100

▲ = Import ▼=Export
◆ =Import/Export

James Miller, *President*
EMP: 21 EST: 1964
SQ FT: 2,100
SALES: 2.5MM **Privately Held**
SIC: 3441 Fabricated structural metal

(P-12212)
MITCHELL FABRICATION
Also Called: Amazing Steel
4564 Mission Blvd, Montclair (91763-6106)
PHONE...................................909 590-0393
Jim Mitchell, *President*
Steven Miks, *Mfg Staff*
▲ EMP: 30
SQ FT: 35,000
SALES (est): 7.1MM **Privately Held**
SIC: 3441 Fabricated structural metal

(P-12213)
MJM EXPERT PIPE FBRCATION WLDG
3404 Wrenwood St, Bakersfield (93309-9331)
PHONE...................................661 330-8698
Michael J Martin, *Owner*
EMP: 20
SALES: 500K **Privately Held**
SIC: 3441 Fabricated structural metal

(P-12214)
MONSTER ROUTE INC
3559 Haven Ave Ste A, Menlo Park (94025-1009)
PHONE...................................650 368-1628
SAI M Chiang, *President*
▲ EMP: 12
SQ FT: 2,500
SALES (est): 3.1MM **Privately Held**
SIC: 3441 Fabricated structural metal

(P-12215)
MONTEREY BAY REBAR INC (PA)
547 Airport Blvd, Watsonville (95076-2003)
PHONE...................................831 724-3013
Raoul Ortiz, *President*
Enrique Regalado, *Office Mgr*
EMP: 13
SALES: 2MM **Privately Held**
SIC: 3441 Fabricated structural metal

(P-12216)
MUHLHAUSER ENTERPRISES INC (PA)
Also Called: Muhlhauser Steel
2437 S Willow Ave, Bloomington (92316-2974)
PHONE...................................909 877-2792
William C Muhlhauser, *President*
Gisela Muhlhauser, *Corp Secy*
EMP: 30 EST: 1961
SALES (est): 4.6MM **Privately Held**
SIC: 3441 1791 Building components, structural steel; structural steel erection

(P-12217)
MUHLHAUSER STEEL INC
2437 S Willow Ave, Bloomington (92316-2974)
P.O. Box 159 (92316-0159)
PHONE...................................909 877-2792
William Muhlhauser, *President*
Zigfried Muhlhauser, *Senior VP*
EMP: 20
SQ FT: 80,000
SALES (est): 2.1MM
SALES (corp-wide): 4.6MM **Privately Held**
WEB: www.msisteel.com
SIC: 3441 1791 Building components, structural steel; structural steel erection
PA: Muhlhauser Enterprises, Inc.
2437 S Willow Ave
Bloomington CA 92316
909 877-2792

(P-12218)
MYWI FABRICATORS INC
2115-2119 Edwards Ave, South El Monte (91733)
PHONE...................................626 279-6994
Henry Yue, *President*
Jeanne Yue, *Admin Sec*
EMP: 18
SQ FT: 5,000

SALES (est): 4.1MM **Privately Held**
WEB: www.mywifabricators.com
SIC: 3441 Fabricated structural metal

(P-12219)
NATIONAL METAL FABRICATORS
28435 Century St, Hayward (94545-4862)
P.O. Box 56478 (94545-6478)
PHONE...................................510 887-6231
Steven L Kint, *CEO*
Gayle Kint, *Corp Secy*
Mark Nickles, *Vice Pres*
Mike Wieber, *Vice Pres*
Albert Wentzel, *Technology*
EMP: 25
SQ FT: 26,000
SALES (est): 5.5MM **Privately Held**
WEB: www.nationalmetalfabricators.com
SIC: 3441 Fabricated structural metal

(P-12220)
OC WATERJET
2280 N Batavia St, Orange (92865-3106)
PHONE...................................714 685-0851
David Gaulke, *Principal*
EMP: 10
SALES (est): 570K **Privately Held**
SIC: 3441 Boat & barge sections, prefabricated metal

(P-12221)
OLSON AND CO STEEL
3488 W Ashlan Ave, Fresno (93722-4443)
PHONE...................................559 224-7811
Del Stephens, *Branch Mgr*
Stacy Ciha, *Admin Asst*
Robert Moretti, *Chief Engr*
Billie O'Brien, *Accounting Mgr*
Steve Rivera, *Safety Mgr*
EMP: 100
SALES (est): 16.4MM
SALES (corp-wide): 68.4MM **Privately Held**
WEB: www.olsonsteel.com
SIC: 3441 3446 Building components, structural steel; architectural metalwork
PA: Olson And Co. Steel
1941 Davis St
San Leandro CA 94577
510 489-4680

(P-12222)
PACIFIC COAST FABRICATORS INC
14375 Telephone Ave, Chino (91710-5777)
PHONE...................................909 627-3833
Michael Scheck, *President*
Anthony Caruso, *Admin Sec*
EMP: 10
SALES (est): 744.5K **Privately Held**
SIC: 3441 Fabricated structural metal

(P-12223)
PACIFIC COAST IRONWORKS INC
8831 Miner St, Los Angeles (90002-1835)
PHONE...................................323 585-1320
Andrew Larkin, *President*
Ron David, *Treasurer*
Max Gonzalez, *Vice Pres*
Mike Larkin, *Vice Pres*
EMP: 15
SQ FT: 22,000
SALES (est): 3.3MM **Privately Held**
SIC: 3441 Fabricated structural metal

(P-12224)
PACIFIC MARITIME INDS CORP
Also Called: P M I
1790 Dornoch Ct, San Diego (92154-7206)
PHONE...................................619 575-8141
John Atkinson, *CEO*
Ana Rios, *Executive*
Phu Vu, *Engineer*
▲ EMP: 110 EST: 1995
SQ FT: 38,000
SALES (est): 37.9MM **Privately Held**
WEB: www.pacmaritime.com
SIC: 3441 Fabricated structural metal

(P-12225)
PACIFIC STEEL FABRICATORS INC
8275 San Leandro St, Oakland (94621-1901)
PHONE...................................209 464-9474
Andres Estrada, *President*
Alfonso Beas, *Vice Pres*
Miguel Beas, *Vice Pres*
Oscar Ortiz, *Vice Pres*
EMP: 36
SQ FT: 80,000
SALES: 4MM **Privately Held**
SIC: 3441 Building components, structural steel

(P-12226)
PARAMOUNT ROLL FORMING CO INC
12120 Florence Ave, Santa Fe Springs (90670-4434)
PHONE...................................562 944-6151
Kenneth Moscrip, *Ch of Bd*
Todd Carlson, *CFO*
Myrtle Moscrip, *Corp Secy*
Rommel Ocampo, *Manager*
▲ EMP: 23
SQ FT: 15,000
SALES (est): 5.4MM **Privately Held**
WEB: www.paramount-roll.com
SIC: 3441 Fabricated structural metal

(P-12227)
PARK STEEL CO INC
515 E Pine St, Compton (90222-2817)
P.O. Box 4787 (90224-4787)
PHONE...................................310 638-6101
Gregory M Park, *President*
Sally O Park, *Treasurer*
Randy Park, *Admin Sec*
EMP: 18
SQ FT: 70,000
SALES (est): 4.3MM **Privately Held**
SIC: 3441 1791 Bridge sections, prefabricated highway; concrete reinforcement, placing of

(P-12228)
PERPETUAL MOTION GROUP INC
11939 Sherman Rd, North Hollywood (91605-3717)
PHONE...................................818 982-4300
Joe Rando, *Principal*
EMP: 100
SQ FT: 55,000
SALES (est): 5.8MM **Privately Held**
SIC: 3441 Fabricated structural metal

(P-12229)
PLACER WATERWORKS INC
1325 Furneaux Rd, Plumas Lake (95961-7485)
PHONE...................................530 742-9675
Karl Kern, *President*
Sheila Kern, *Vice Pres*
EMP: 20
SQ FT: 10,500
SALES (est): 5.8MM **Privately Held**
WEB: www.placerwaterworks.com
SIC: 3441 Fabricated structural metal

(P-12230)
PRECISION METAL CRAFTS
16920 Gridley Pl, Cerritos (90703-1740)
PHONE...................................562 468-7080
Coleman Conard III, *Owner*
EMP: 18
SQ FT: 24,100
SALES (est): 3MM **Privately Held**
SIC: 3441 Fabricated structural metal

(P-12231)
PRECISION WELDING INC
241 Enterprise Pkwy, Lancaster (93534-7201)
PHONE...................................661 729-3436
David R Jones, *President*
David Jones, *President*
EMP: 23
SQ FT: 10,000
SALES (est): 5.7MM **Privately Held**
SIC: 3441 1799 Fabricated structural metal; welding on site

(P-12232)
PREMIER STEEL STRUCTURES INC
13345 Estelle St, Corona (92879-1881)
PHONE...................................951 356-6655
Armando Rodarte, *President*
EMP: 30 EST: 2016
SALES (est): 5.5MM **Privately Held**
SIC: 3441 Fabricated structural metal

(P-12233)
PROJECT STEEL COMPANY INC
6826 Cupeno Ave, Hesperia (92345-8726)
PHONE...................................760 947-0531
Robert Zambrano, *CEO*
Lorena Zambrano, *Treasurer*
EMP: 14
SQ FT: 3,000
SALES: 1.5MM **Privately Held**
SIC: 3441 Fabricated structural metal

(P-12234)
R I INDUSTRIES INC
2910 S Archibald Ave A, Ontario (91761-7358)
PHONE...................................909 923-7747
William Franklin Rowan Sr, *CEO*
Ardith Rowan, *Treasurer*
William Franklin Rowan Jr, *Vice Pres*
EMP: 40 EST: 1978
SQ FT: 12,000
SALES (est): 10.9MM **Privately Held**
WEB: www.rimetal.com
SIC: 3441 Building components, structural steel

(P-12235)
RAMP ENGINEERING INC
6850 Walthall Way, Paramount (90723-2028)
PHONE...................................562 531-8030
Mark Scott, *CEO*
Robert C Scott, *Ch of Bd*
Lisa Scott, *CFO*
Nathan Scott, *Software Dev*
EMP: 16
SQ FT: 12,000
SALES (est): 4.2MM **Privately Held**
WEB: www.rampengineering.com
SIC: 3441 Fabricated structural metal

(P-12236)
RICHARDSON STEEL INC
9102 Harness St Ste A, Spring Valley (91977-3924)
PHONE...................................619 697-5892
John Richardson, *President*
Lance Richardson, *COO*
Natalie N Lautner, *CFO*
Ken Lautner, *General Mgr*
EMP: 32
SQ FT: 5,000
SALES (est): 8.2MM **Privately Held**
SIC: 3441 Fabricated structural metal

(P-12237)
RND CONTRACTORS INC
14796 Jurupa Ave Ste A, Fontana (92337-7232)
PHONE...................................909 429-8500
Nancy Sauter, *President*
Russ Sauter, *Vice Pres*
EMP: 40
SALES (est): 12MM **Privately Held**
SIC: 3441 Fabricated structural metal

(P-12238)
ROBECKS WLDG & FABRICATION INC
1150 Mabury Rd Ste 1, San Jose (95133-1031)
PHONE...................................408 287-0202
Armon Robeck, *President*
Laurie Morado, *Corp Secy*
Ronald Robeck, *Vice Pres*
EMP: 22
SQ FT: 6,000
SALES (est): 4.7MM **Privately Held**
SIC: 3441 7692 Fabricated structural metal; welding repair

(P-12239)
ROSE METAL PRODUCTS INC
Also Called: R M P
1754 Tech Dr Ste 100, San Jose (95110)
P.O. Box 3238, Springfield MO (65808-3238)
PHONE....................................417 865-1676
Wiley P Buchanan, *President*
Richard Splitter, *COO*
Billy Pendleton, *Treasurer*
James Skinner, *Vice Pres*
Mark T Wickizer, *Vice Pres*
EMP: 62 EST: 1960
SQ FT: 88,675
SALES (est): 17.8MM **Privately Held**
WEB: www.rosemetalproducts.com
SIC: 3441 5051 Fabricated structural metal; sheets, metal

(P-12240)
SCHROEDER IRON CORPORATION
8417 Beech Ave, Fontana (92335-1200)
PHONE....................................909 428-6471
Linda Schroeder, *President*
Ezequiel Ruvalcaba, *Engineer*
Lydia Enciso, *Manager*
EMP: 30
SQ FT: 23,000
SALES (est): 9MM **Privately Held**
WEB: www.schroederiron.com
SIC: 3441 Building components, structural steel

(P-12241)
SCRAPE CERTIFIED WELDING INC
2525 Old Highway 395, Fallbrook (92028-8794)
PHONE....................................760 728-1308
Jeff D Scrape, *President*
EMP: 91
SALES: 14.7MM **Privately Held**
SIC: 3441 Fabricated structural metal

(P-12242)
SIERRA METAL FABRICATORS INC
Also Called: Sierra Metalk Fabricators
529 Searls Ave, Nevada City (95959-3003)
P.O. Box 1359 (95959-1359)
PHONE....................................530 265-4591
Jason White, *President*
EMP: 30 EST: 1974
SQ FT: 30,000
SALES (est): 6.6MM **Privately Held**
WEB: www.sierrametal.com
SIC: 3441 Fabricated structural metal

(P-12243)
SMB INDUSTRIES INC (PA)
Also Called: Metal Works Supply
550 Georgia Pacific Way, Oroville (95965-9638)
PHONE....................................530 534-6266
Sean Pierce, *President*
Mike Phulps, *Treasurer*
Tristan Hamblin, *Officer*
EMP: 68
SQ FT: 45,000
SALES: 216K **Privately Held**
SIC: 3441 Expansion joints (structural shapes), iron or steel

(P-12244)
SPARTAN INC
3030 M St, Bakersfield (93301-2137)
PHONE....................................661 327-1205
John Wood, *President*
Louis Stern, *CEO*
Tami Black, *CFO*
Greg Fry, *Treasurer*
Teresa Wood, *Treasurer*
▼ EMP: 65
SQ FT: 125,000
SALES (est): 14.8MM **Privately Held**
SIC: 3441 8711 Fabricated structural metal; engineering services

(P-12245)
SPEC IRON INC
7244 Varna Ave, North Hollywood (91605-4102)
PHONE....................................818 765-4070
Razmik Pouladian, *President*

EMP: 10
SQ FT: 4,000
SALES (est): 1.3MM **Privately Held**
SIC: 3441 Fabricated structural metal

(P-12246)
SS METAL FABRICATORS
1626 Ohms Way, Costa Mesa (92627-4329)
PHONE....................................949 631-4272
Kim Harding, *Owner*
EMP: 12
SALES (est): 1.8MM **Privately Held**
SIC: 3441 Fabricated structural metal

(P-12247)
STAINLESS PROCESS SYSTEMS INC
1650 Beacon Pl, Oxnard (93033-2433)
PHONE....................................805 483-7100
Mark Hayman, *President*
EMP: 14 EST: 2007
SQ FT: 27,126
SALES: 2.6MM **Privately Held**
SIC: 3441 Fabricated structural metal

(P-12248)
STL FABRICATION INC
10207 Elm Ave, Fontana (92335-6322)
PHONE....................................909 823-5033
Ruben Ramirez, *Principal*
EMP: 10
SALES (est): 2.4MM **Privately Held**
SIC: 3441 Building components, structural steel

(P-12249)
STO-KAR ENTERPRISES
1112 Arroyo St Ste 2, San Fernando (91340-1850)
PHONE....................................818 886-5600
Maureen Stone, *President*
EMP: 20
SQ FT: 5,000
SALES (est): 3.3MM **Privately Held**
SIC: 3441 Fabricated structural metal

(P-12250)
STRETCH-RUN INC
Also Called: Pleasanton Steel Supply
6621 Brisa St, Livermore (94550-2505)
PHONE....................................925 606-1599
Gil Badilla, *President*
EMP: 11
SQ FT: 5,500
SALES (est): 1.8MM **Privately Held**
SIC: 3441 5051 3799 2833 Building components, structural steel; steel; wheelbarrows; vitamins, natural or synthetic: bulk, uncompounded

(P-12251)
SUBURBAN STEEL INC (PA)
706 W California Ave, Fresno (93706-3599)
PHONE....................................559 268-6281
Stan J Cavalla, *President*
Ron Cavalla, *Vice Pres*
EMP: 40
SQ FT: 12,000
SALES (est): 9MM **Privately Held**
SIC: 3441 3446 Building components, structural steel; railings, bannisters, guards, etc.: made from metal pipe

(P-12252)
SUMMIT INDUSTRIES INC
Also Called: Jardine Performance Products
1280 Graphite Dr, Corona (92881-3308)
PHONE....................................951 739-5900
Rick May, *Manager*
EMP: 40
SALES (corp-wide): 15.2MM **Privately Held**
WEB: www.jardineproducts.com
SIC: 3441 Fabricated structural metal
PA: Summit Industries Inc.
    1220 Railroad St
    Corona CA
    951 371-1744

(P-12253)
SURI STEEL INC
5851 Towne Ave, Los Angeles (90003-1323)
PHONE....................................323 224-3166

Marco Cartin, *President*
EMP: 12
SALES: 500K **Privately Held**
SIC: 3441 Building components, structural steel

(P-12254)
SVM MACHINING INC
6520 Central Ave, Newark (94560-3933)
PHONE....................................510 791-9450
Mark Serpa, *President*
EMP: 30
SALES (est): 6.5MM **Privately Held**
WEB: www.svmfg.com
SIC: 3441 Building components, structural steel

(P-12255)
T M INDUSTRIES INCORPORATED
1085 Di Giulio Ave, Santa Clara (95050-2805)
PHONE....................................408 736-5202
Nicholas F Hayes, *President*
Dayle V Hayes, *Vice Pres*
▼ EMP: 12
SQ FT: 18,000
SALES (est): 1.9MM **Privately Held**
WEB: www.tmindustriesinc.com
SIC: 3441 Fabricated structural metal

(P-12256)
T&S MANUFACTURING TECH LLC
Also Called: Atech Manufacturing
1530 Oakland Rd Ste 120, San Jose (95112-1241)
PHONE....................................408 441-0285
Tony Tolani,
Shalini Tolani,
EMP: 20
SQ FT: 6,000
SALES (est): 5.5MM **Privately Held**
SIC: 3441 3999 Fabricated structural metal; atomizers, toiletry

(P-12257)
TAN SET CORPORATION
Also Called: Specialty Metal Fabrication
1 S Fairview Ave, Goleta (93117-3364)
PHONE....................................805 967-4567
Tanis M Hammond, *President*
Seth Hammond, *Vice Pres*
EMP: 12
SQ FT: 15,000
SALES (est): 1MM **Privately Held**
SIC: 3441 Fabricated structural metal

(P-12258)
TARDIF SHEET METAL & AC
412 N Santa Fe St, Santa Ana (92701-4907)
PHONE....................................714 547-7135
Michael J Tardif, *President*
Mercedes Tardif, *Vice Pres*
EMP: 10 EST: 1956
SQ FT: 15,000
SALES (est): 900K **Privately Held**
SIC: 3441 1761 1711 Fabricated structural metal; sheet metalwork; warm air heating & air conditioning contractor

(P-12259)
TERMINAL MANUFACTURING CO LLC
Also Called: T M C
707 Gilman St, Berkeley (94710-1312)
PHONE....................................510 526-3071
Steve Millinger, *Mng Member*
Jorge Carapia, *Project Mgr*
Kristen Hatch, *Technology*
Richard Robison,
EMP: 30
SQ FT: 30,000
SALES (est): 7.9MM **Privately Held**
SIC: 3441 Fabricated structural metal

(P-12260)
TITAN METAL FABRICATORS INC (PA)
352 Balboa Cir, Camarillo (93012-8644)
PHONE....................................805 487-5050
Steve Muscarella, *President*
Tom Muscarella, *Vice Pres*

▲ EMP: 69 EST: 1998
SQ FT: 15,000
SALES (est): 32.9MM **Privately Held**
WEB: www.titanmf.com
SIC: 3441 Fabricated structural metal

(P-12261)
TOBIN STEEL COMPANY INC
817 E Santa Ana Blvd, Santa Ana (92701-3909)
P.O. Box 717 (92702-0717)
PHONE....................................714 541-2268
Linda A Robin, *CEO*
Carl Tobin, *President*
Jim Tobin, *Vice Pres*
Steve Tobin, *Vice Pres*
Linda Tobin, *Controller*
EMP: 65
SQ FT: 20,000
SALES (est): 19.2MM **Privately Held**
WEB: www.tobinsteel.com
SIC: 3441 Building components, structural steel

(P-12262)
TOLAR MANUFACTURING CO INC
258 Mariah Cir, Corona (92879-1751)
PHONE....................................951 808-0081
Gary Tolar, *President*
Rhonda Tolar, *Vice Pres*
Rolando Andrade, *Design Engr*
Carlos Garcia, *Design Engr*
Eli Meza, *Engineer*
▲ EMP: 40
SQ FT: 22,000
SALES (est): 20MM **Privately Held**
WEB: www.tolarmfg.com
SIC: 3441 3599 3448 Fabricated structural metal; machine shop, jobbing & repair; prefabricated metal buildings

(P-12263)
TRANS BAY STEEL CORPORATION (PA)
536 Cleveland Ave, Berkeley (94710-1007)
PHONE....................................510 277-3756
William Kavicky, *President*
William H Kroplin, *Vice Pres*
EMP: 50
SQ FT: 150,000
SALES (est): 7.4MM **Privately Held**
SIC: 3441 Fabricated structural metal

(P-12264)
TRINITY STEEL CORPORATION
Also Called: Con Sol Enterprises
184 Rocklite Rd, Ventura (93001-1540)
PHONE....................................805 648-3486
Patrick Barrett, *President*
Craig Brown, *Vice Pres*
Matthew Brown, *Manager*
EMP: 10
SALES (est): 1.4MM **Privately Held**
SIC: 3441 Fabricated structural metal

(P-12265)
TRUSSWORKS INTERNATIONAL INC
2850 E Coronado St, Anaheim (92806-2503)
PHONE....................................714 630-2772
Michael Farrell, *President*
Ali Shantyaei, *Vice Pres*
Candice Morrow, *Human Res Mgr*
EMP: 60 EST: 2007
SQ FT: 60,000
SALES (est): 19.1MM **Privately Held**
SIC: 3441 3446 1791 Fabricated structural metal; architectural metalwork; stairs, fire escapes, balconies, railings & ladders; fences, gates, posts & flagpoles; stairs, staircases, stair treads: prefabricated metal; building front installation metal

(P-12266)
ULMER INDUSTRIES INC
15243 Valley Blvd, Fontana (92335-6358)
P.O. Box 2299, Glendora (91740-2299)
PHONE....................................909 823-7111
Herbert Ulmer, *President*
Dar Ulmer, *Corp Secy*
EMP: 22
SQ FT: 1,000

SALES (est): 5.3MM **Privately Held**
WEB: www.ulmerind.com
SIC: 3441 Fabricated structural metal

(P-12267)
UNISTRUT INTERNATIONAL CORP
1679 Atlantic St, Union City (94587-2048)
PHONE..................................510 476-1200
Tim Kipper, *Manager*
EMP: 10 **Publicly Held**
WEB: www.unistrutconstruction.com
SIC: 3441 Fabricated structural metal
HQ: Unistrut International Corporation
16100 Lathrop Ave
Harvey IL 60426
800 882-5543

(P-12268)
UNIVERSAL CELL SITE SVCS INC
2428 Research Dr, Livermore (94550-3850)
PHONE..................................925 447-4500
Jeremy L King, *President*
EMP: 40
SQ FT: 15,000
SALES: 4MM **Privately Held**
SIC: 3441 Tower sections, radio & television transmission

(P-12269)
UNIVERSAL STEEL SERVICES INC
5034 Heintz St, Baldwin Park (91706-1816)
P.O. Box 2428, Irwindale (91706-1232)
PHONE..................................626 960-1455
Ramon T Lopez, *CEO*
Meira Carrasco, *Manager*
EMP: 12
SALES (est): 2.5MM **Privately Held**
SIC: 3441 Building components, structural steel

(P-12270)
US TOWER CORP
1099 W Ropes Ave, Woodlake (93286-1806)
PHONE..................................559 564-6000
Everett Cook, *Manager*
Devin Aldridge, *Admin Asst*
Jan Wilson, *Planning*
Teng Yang, *Technology*
Remigio Fernandez, *Engineer*
EMP: 52
SALES (corp-wide): 19.1MM **Privately Held**
WEB: www.ustower.com
SIC: 3441 Tower sections, radio & television transmission
PA: Us Tower Corp.
702 E North St
Lincoln KS 67455
785 524-9966

(P-12271)
V & F FABRICATION COMPANY INC
13902 Seaboard Cir, Garden Grove (92843-3910)
PHONE..................................714 265-0630
Vinh Nguyen, *President*
Vinh Van Nguyen, *CEO*
Bao Truong, *General Mgr*
Kim Tinh, *Office Mgr*
Sen Truong, *Admin Sec*
▲ EMP: 35
SALES (est): 8.5MM **Privately Held**
SIC: 3441 3599 3769 3444 Fabricated structural metal; machine shop, jobbing & repair; guided missile & space vehicle parts & auxiliary equipment; sheet metalwork

(P-12272)
VALMONT INDUSTRIES INC
4116 Whiteside St, Los Angeles (90063-1619)
PHONE..................................323 264-6660
Sandy Valencia, *Branch Mgr*
Barry Ruffalo, *Exec VP*
Joshua Dixon, *Vice Pres*
Irma Taddi, *Office Mgr*
Aliscia Anderson, *Administration*

EMP: 69
SALES (corp-wide): 2.7B **Publicly Held**
SIC: 3441 Fabricated structural metal
PA: Valmont Industries, Inc.
1 Valmont Plz Ste 500
Omaha NE 68154
402 963-1000

(P-12273)
VALMONT INDUSTRIES INC
Also Called: Valmont Newmark
3970 Lenwood Rd, Barstow (92311-9408)
PHONE..................................760 253-3070
Glyde Reeves, *Manager*
Phillip Dyess, *Opers Mgr*
EMP: 10
SALES (corp-wide): 2.7B **Publicly Held**
WEB: www.valmont.com
SIC: 3441 Fabricated structural metal
PA: Valmont Industries, Inc.
1 Valmont Plz Ste 500
Omaha NE 68154
402 963-1000

(P-12274)
VIRGIL WALKER INC
Also Called: Auton Motorized Systems
24856 Avenue Rockefeller, Valencia (91355-3467)
PHONE..................................661 797-4101
Arthur Walker, *CEO*
EMP: 15
SALES (est): 1MM **Privately Held**
SIC: 3441 Fabricated structural metal

(P-12275)
VORTEX ENGINEERING LLC
9425 Wheatlands Ct, Santee (92071-2831)
PHONE..................................619 258-9660
Andrew Dumke, *Ch of Bd*
EMP: 12
SQ FT: 12,777
SALES (est): 1.6MM **Privately Held**
SIC: 3441 3443 3444 3449 Fabricated structural metal; fabricated plate work (boiler shop); sheet metalwork; miscellaneous metalwork

(P-12276)
VSC INCORPORATED (PA)
Also Called: VULCAN STEEL COMPANY
2038 S Sycamore Ave, Bloomington (92316-2463)
P.O. Box 386 (92316-0386)
PHONE..................................909 877-0975
Davis H Hopper, *CEO*
Connie Gonzales, *Manager*
EMP: 10 EST: 1963
SQ FT: 2,000
SALES: 5.3MM **Privately Held**
SIC: 3441 Building components, structural steel

(P-12277)
WADCO INDUSTRIES INC
Also Called: Wadco Steel Sales
2625 S Willow Ave, Bloomington (92316-3258)
PHONE..................................909 874-7800
David D Scheibel, *CEO*
Salvador Arratia, *President*
Scott Brown, *Treasurer*
Elaine Lucero, *Treasurer*
Anthony Salazar, *Vice Pres*
EMP: 47
SQ FT: 50,000
SALES (est): 9.5MM **Privately Held**
WEB: www.wadco.co
SIC: 3441 5051 Building components, structural steel; steel

(P-12278)
WADE METAL PRODUCTS
1818 Los Angeles St, Fresno (93721-3113)
PHONE..................................559 237-9233
Marian Esquibel, *CEO*
Curtis Esquibel, *CFO*
EMP: 15
SQ FT: 12,000
SALES (est): 4MM **Privately Held**
SIC: 3441 Fabricated structural metal

(P-12279)
WELDWAY INC
521 Hi Tech Pkwy, Oakdale (95361-9395)
PHONE..................................209 847-8083

Mike Sala, *President*
Steve Brooks, *Corp Secy*
EMP: 35
SQ FT: 4,500
SALES (est): 7.1MM **Privately Held**
WEB: www.weldwayinc.com
SIC: 3441 Fabricated structural metal

(P-12280)
WESTAR METAL FABRICATION INC
1926 Potrero Ave, South El Monte (91733-3025)
PHONE..................................626 350-0718
Uoqi Lee, *President*
▲ EMP: 10
SALES (est): 1.4MM **Privately Held**
WEB: www.westarmetal.com
SIC: 3441 Fabricated structural metal

(P-12281)
WESTECH METAL FABRICATION INC
3420 E St, San Diego (92102-3336)
PHONE..................................619 702-9353
Jeff Bjelland, *President*
Mike Bjelland, *Vice Pres*
EMP: 11
SQ FT: 18,000
SALES (est): 1.6MM **Privately Held**
WEB: www.westechmetalfab.com
SIC: 3441 7692 3446 Welding repair; stairs, fire escapes, balconies, railings & ladders; railings, bannisters, guards, etc.: made from metal pipe; ornamental metalwork; fabricated structural metal for ships

(P-12282)
WESTERN BAY SHEET METAL INC
1410 Hill St, El Cajon (92020-5749)
PHONE..................................619 233-1753
James Lozano, *President*
Helena Lopez, *Corp Secy*
Roy Lozano, *Vice Pres*
▲ EMP: 45 EST: 1981
SQ FT: 9,800
SALES (est): 16.1MM **Privately Held**
WEB: www.westernbay.net
SIC: 3441 3444 Fabricated structural metal; sheet metalwork

(P-12283)
WILKINS DESIGN AND MFG INC
Also Called: Wilschur Design and Mfg
2619 Oak St, Santa Ana (92707-3720)
PHONE..................................714 564-3351
Paul Wilkins, *President*
Rob Daniels, *Prdtn Mgr*
EMP: 30
SQ FT: 11,000
SALES (est): 4.6MM **Privately Held**
WEB: www.wilschur.com
SIC: 3441 Fabricated structural metal

(P-12284)
WOODLAND WELDING WORKS
1955 E Main St, Woodland (95776-6202)
P.O. Box 1194 (95776-1194)
PHONE..................................530 666-5531
Felix Franco, *President*
Sara Franco, *Admin Sec*
Maribel Santiago, *Accountant*
Ray Stemler, *Marketing Staff*
EMP: 12
SQ FT: 18,000
SALES (est): 2.6MM **Privately Held**
WEB: www.woodlandwelding.com
SIC: 3441 Fabricated structural metal

(P-12285)
YUBA CITY STEEL PRODUCTS CO
532 Crestmont Ave, Yuba City (95991-6209)
PHONE..................................530 673-4554
Clinton L West, *Ch of Bd*
Robert Zellner, *President*
▼ EMP: 30 EST: 1944
SQ FT: 81,000
SALES (est): 8.5MM **Privately Held**
WEB: www.ycsteel.com
SIC: 3441 Fabricated structural metal

3442 Metal Doors, Sash, Frames, Molding & Trim

(P-12286)
A & A CUSTOM SHUTTERS
10465 San Fernando Rd # 8, Pacoima (91331-2602)
PHONE..................................818 383-1819
Aaron Lopez, *President*
EMP: 10
SALES (est): 910K **Privately Held**
SIC: 3442 Shutters, door or window: metal

(P-12287)
ACCENT INDUSTRIES INC (PA)
Also Called: Accent Awnings
1600 E Saint Gertrude Pl, Santa Ana (92705-5312)
PHONE..................................714 708-1389
Karl Desmarais, *CEO*
▲ EMP: 30
SQ FT: 26,000
SALES (est): 3MM **Privately Held**
WEB: www.accentawnings.com
SIC: 3442 3444 2394 5999 Shutters, door or window: metal; awnings & canopies; canvas & related products; awnings

(P-12288)
ACTIVE WINDOW PRODUCTS
Also Called: Z Industries
5431 W San Fernando Rd, Los Angeles (90039-1088)
P.O. Box 39125 (90039-0125)
PHONE..................................323 245-5185
Michael Schoenfeld, *President*
Rosa Castro, *Treasurer*
▲ EMP: 53
SQ FT: 96,000
SALES (est): 10.4MM **Privately Held**
SIC: 3442 Storm doors or windows, metal

(P-12289)
ADVANCE OVERHEAD DOOR INC
15829 Stagg St, Van Nuys (91406-1969)
PHONE..................................818 781-5590
Leland S Groshong, *President*
Don Henderson, *Treasurer*
Marguerite Groshong, *Admin Sec*
EMP: 37 EST: 1956
SQ FT: 25,000
SALES (est): 4.7MM **Privately Held**
SIC: 3442 2431 Garage doors, overhead: metal; garage doors, overhead: wood

(P-12290)
ADVANCED ARCHITECTURAL FRAMES
Also Called: Advance Architectural
17102 Newhope St, Fountain Valley (92708-8223)
PHONE..................................424 209-6018
EMP: 33
SQ FT: 4,000
SALES: 6.4MM **Privately Held**
SIC: 3442 5211

(P-12291)
ALUMATHERM INCORPORATED
1717 Kirkham St, Oakland (94607-2214)
PHONE..................................510 832-2819
Kevin Smith, *President*
EMP: 10 EST: 1954
SQ FT: 22,000
SALES (est): 1.1MM **Privately Held**
SIC: 3442 Casements, aluminum; screens, window, metal

(P-12292)
ARCADIA INC
2323 Firestone Blvd, South Gate (90280-2684)
PHONE..................................310 665-0490
EMP: 40
SALES (corp-wide): 128.3MM **Privately Held**
SIC: 3442 Window & door frames
PA: Arcadia, Inc.
2301 E Vernon Ave
Vernon CA 90058
323 269-7300

PRODUCTS & SVCS

(P-12293)
ARCHITECTURAL BLOMBERG LLC
Also Called: Blomberg Window Systems
1453 Blair Ave, Sacramento (95822-3410)
PHONE.................................916 428-8060
Jeremy Drucker, *Mng Member*
EMP: 32
SALES: 84MM **Privately Held**
SIC: 3442 Window & door frames

(P-12294)
ATRIUM DOOR & WIN CO ARIZ INC
5455 E La Palma Ave Ste A, Anaheim (92807-2006)
PHONE.................................714 693-0601
Gregory T Faherty, *President*
Randall S Fojtasek, *President*
Jeff Hull, *CEO*
EMP: 300
SQ FT: 220,000
SALES (est): 40.8MM
SALES (corp-wide): 218.4MM **Privately Held**
SIC: 3442 Screen & storm doors & windows
HQ: Atrium Windows And Doors, Inc.
959 Profit Dr
Dallas TX 75247
214 583-1840

(P-12295)
B & B DOORS AND WINDOWS INC
11455 Ilex Ave, San Fernando (91340-3430)
PHONE.................................818 837-8480
Jeffrey C Brothers, *CEO*
Lori Brothers, *Treasurer*
EMP: 20
SQ FT: 7,200
SALES: 2.5MM **Privately Held**
SIC: 3442 5031 Window & door frames; doors & windows

(P-12296)
BAYFAB METALS INC
870 Doolittle Dr, San Leandro (94577-1079)
PHONE.................................510 568-8950
Susan Miranda, *President*
Paul Tavares, *Project Mgr*
EMP: 20
SQ FT: 21,000
SALES (est): 4.4MM **Privately Held**
WEB: www.bayfabmetals.com
SIC: 3442 3444 3446 3499 Metal doors, sash & trim; metal housings, enclosures, casings & other containers; louvers, ventilating; shims, metal; name plates: except engraved, etched, etc.: metal

(P-12297)
BAYSIDE SHUTTERS
Also Called: Southwest Shutter Shaque
1464 N Batavia St, Orange (92867-3505)
PHONE.................................714 628-9994
John Bussjaeger, *Owner*
▲ **EMP:** 10 **EST:** 1989
SQ FT: 5,000
SALES (est): 846.4K **Privately Held**
WEB: www.baysideshutters.com
SIC: 3442 Metal doors, sash & trim

(P-12298)
BELCO CABINETS INC
1109 Black Diamond Way, Lodi (95240-0746)
PHONE.................................209 334-5437
Roy Belanger, *President*
EMP: 15 **EST:** 1978
SQ FT: 21,000
SALES: 2.3MM **Privately Held**
SIC: 3442 2434 Metal doors; wood kitchen cabinets

(P-12299)
BEST ROLL-UP DOOR INC
13202 Arctic Cir, Santa Fe Springs (90670-5510)
PHONE.................................562 802-2233
Edward Choi, *President*
▲ **EMP:** 20
SQ FT: 15,000

SALES (est): 4MM **Privately Held**
SIC: 3442 Rolling doors for industrial buildings or warehouses, metal

(P-12300)
BLOMBERG BUILDING MATERIALS (PA)
Also Called: Blomberg Window Systems
1453 Blair Ave, Sacramento (95822-3410)
P.O. Box 22485 (95822-0485)
PHONE.................................916 428-8060
J Philip Collier, *CEO*
Jan Miller, *Sales Staff*
Steve Reynolds, *Manager*
EMP: 100
SALES (est): 13.1MM **Privately Held**
WEB: www.blombergwindowsystems.com
SIC: 3442 Metal doors, sash & trim

(P-12301)
BLUM CONSTRUCTION CO INC
Also Called: European Rolling Shutters
404 Umbarger Rd Ste A, San Jose (95111-2083)
PHONE.................................408 629-3740
Helmut Blum, *President*
Renate Blum, *Vice Pres*
▲ **EMP:** 15
SQ FT: 10,500
SALES (est): 2.8MM **Privately Held**
WEB: www.ers-shading.com
SIC: 3442 3444 1751 1799 Shutters, door or window: metal; awnings & canopies; window & door installation & erection; awning installation

(P-12302)
BONELLI ENTERPRISES
Also Called: Bonelli Windows and Doors
330 Corey Way, South San Francisco (94080-6709)
PHONE.................................650 873-3222
David J Bonelli, *President*
Mara Bonelli, *Admin Sec*
EMP: 25
SQ FT: 25,000
SALES (est): 5MM
SALES (corp-wide): 1.9B **Privately Held**
WEB: www.bonelli.com
SIC: 3442 1751 Window & door frames; screen & storm doors & windows; window & door (prefabricated) installation
PA: Pella Corporation
102 Main St
Pella IA 50219
641 621-1000

(P-12303)
CLEAR VIEW LLC
1650 Las Plumas Ave Ste A, San Jose (95133-1657)
PHONE.................................408 271-2734
Daniel Lezotte,
Andrew Lezotte, *Mng Member*
EMP: 15
SALES (est): 1.5MM **Privately Held**
SIC: 3442 5084 Screen doors, metal; industrial machinery & equipment

(P-12304)
COLUMBIA HOLDING CORP
14400 S San Pedro St, Gardena (90248-2027)
PHONE.................................310 327-4107
Daryl McCollend, *Ch of Bd*
Lawrence Goodman, *President*
▲ **EMP:** 300
SQ FT: 100,000
SALES (est): 23.8MM **Privately Held**
SIC: 3442 2431 2439 Metal doors, sash & trim; millwork; structural wood members

(P-12305)
CR LAURENCE CO INC
Columbia Manufacturing Corp
14400 S San Pedro St, Gardena (90248-2027)
PHONE.................................310 327-9300
EMP: 14
SALES (corp-wide): 29.7B **Privately Held**
SIC: 3442 Screen doors, metal
HQ: C.R. Laurence Co., Inc.
2503 E Vernon Ave
Vernon CA 90058
323 588-1281

(P-12306)
DC SHADES & SHUTTERS AWNINGS
2370 Thunderbird Dr, Thousand Oaks (91362-3236)
PHONE.................................818 597-9705
David Chadida, *Owner*
EMP: 10
SALES (est): 300K **Privately Held**
SIC: 3442 5719 Shutters, door or window: metal; window furnishings

(P-12307)
DECRATEK INC
2875 Executive Pl, Escondido (92029-1524)
PHONE.................................760 747-1706
Richard Smerud, *President*
EMP: 30
SQ FT: 25,000
SALES (est): 3.9MM **Privately Held**
WEB: www.decratek.com
SIC: 3442 Window & door frames

(P-12308)
DESIGNLINE WINDOWS & DOORS INC
5674 El Camino Real Ste K, Carlsbad (92008-7130)
PHONE.................................760 931-9422
Harry Norman McCurry, *President*
Norman McCurry, *President*
Dennis Alba, *Vice Pres*
Bob Ross, *Vice Pres*
EMP: 20
SALES (est): 2MM **Privately Held**
SIC: 3442 Window & door frames

(P-12309)
DIABLO MOLDING & TRIM COMPANY
5600 Sunol Blvd Ste C, Pleasanton (94566-8802)
P.O. Box 2190, Dublin (94568-0218)
PHONE.................................925 417-0663
Alex Blumin, *President*
EMP: 22
SALES (est): 3.4MM **Privately Held**
WEB: www.diablomolding.com
SIC: 3442 Molding, trim & stripping

(P-12310)
DOOR COMPONENTS INC
Also Called: DCI Hollow Metal On Demand
7980 Redwood Ave, Fontana (92336-1638)
PHONE.................................909 770-5700
Robert Briggs, *President*
Ronald Green, *Vice Pres*
Cindi Bowen, *Info Tech Mgr*
Steven Escalera, *Technology*
Aaron Schirmers, *Engineer*
EMP: 200
SQ FT: 45,000
SALES (est): 45.4MM **Privately Held**
WEB: www.doorcomponents.com
SIC: 3442 Metal doors; sash, door or window: metal

(P-12311)
EAST BAY GLASS COMPANY INC
Also Called: Jal-Vue Window Company
515 Independent Rd, Oakland (94621-3721)
PHONE.................................510 834-2535
Neda Ahmed, *President*
Adel M Ali, *Vice Pres*
Barbara Stewart, *Accounting Mgr*
Miguel Aviles, *Opers Mgr*
Miguel A Aviles, *Manager*
▲ **EMP:** 11
SQ FT: 18,000
SALES: 2.5MM **Privately Held**
SIC: 3442 1793 1542 Window & door frames; glass & glazing work; commercial & office building contractors

(P-12312)
EDEY MANUFACTURING CO INC
Also Called: Edey Door
2159 E 92nd St, Los Angeles (90002-2509)
PHONE.................................323 566-6151
Fax: 323 566-0262
EMP: 21
SQ FT: 54,000

SALES (est): 1.3MM **Privately Held**
WEB: www.edeydoors.com
SIC: 3442

(P-12313)
ELEGANCE ENTRIES INC
Also Called: Elegance Entries and Windows
1130 N Kraemer Blvd Ste G, Anaheim (92806-1918)
PHONE.................................714 632-3667
Fred W Polivka, *CEO*
Brian Polivka, *Treasurer*
Tracy Polivka, *Admin Sec*
EMP: 18
SQ FT: 5,300
SALES (est): 2.7MM **Privately Held**
WEB: www.eleganceentries.com
SIC: 3442 5211 Window & door frames; door & window products

(P-12314)
ELIZABETH SHUTTERS INC
525 S Rancho Ave, Colton (92324-3240)
PHONE.................................909 825-1531
Dean Frost, *CEO*
Maren Frost, *CFO*
Maggie Castaneda, *Accountant*
EMP: 45
SQ FT: 51,000
SALES (est): 6.7MM **Privately Held**
WEB: www.elizabethshutters.com
SIC: 3442 5023 5211 2431 Shutters, door or window: metal; window furnishings; door & window products; millwork

(P-12315)
EUROLINE STEEL WINDOWS
Also Called: Euroline Steel Windows & Doors
22600 Savi Ranch Pkwy E, Yorba Linda (92887-4616)
PHONE.................................877 590-2741
Elyas Balta, *CEO*
▲ **EMP:** 20
SALES (est): 3.7MM **Privately Held**
SIC: 3442 Window & door frames

(P-12316)
FANBOYS WINDOW FACTORY INC (PA)
10750 Saint Louis Dr, El Monte (91731-2028)
PHONE.................................626 280-8787
Lili Bell, *CEO*
Jeff Bell, *COO*
EMP: 21
SQ FT: 10,000
SALES: 2MM **Privately Held**
SIC: 3442 Window & door frames

(P-12317)
FORDERER CORNICE WORKS
3364 Arden Rd, Hayward (94545-3923)
PHONE.................................415 431-4100
Fax: 510 783-6646
EMP: 10 **EST:** 1875
SQ FT: 1,000
SALES (est): 2MM **Privately Held**
SIC: 3442 5031 3429 2431

(P-12318)
GILWIN COMPANY
2354 Lapham Dr, Modesto (95354-3912)
PHONE.................................209 522-9775
Donald P Miller, *President*
EMP: 23
SQ FT: 27,000
SALES (est): 2.6MM **Privately Held**
SIC: 3442 Window & door frames; casements, aluminum

(P-12319)
GRANDESIGN DECOR INC
1727 N 1st St, San Jose (95112-4510)
PHONE.................................408 436-9969
Gail Hung, *President*
EMP: 25
SALES (est): 3.1MM **Privately Held**
WEB: www.gdecor.com
SIC: 3442 Window & door frames

(P-12320)
HRH DOOR CORP
Also Called: Wayne - Dalton Sacramento
830 Prosessor Ln, Sacramento (95834)
PHONE.................................916 928-0600
Jim Lawrence, *Principal*

▲ = Import ▼=Export
◆ =Import/Export

EMP: 30
SALES (corp-wide): 619.8MM **Privately Held**
WEB: www.waynedalton.com
SIC: 3442 2431 Metal doors, sash & trim; millwork
PA: Hrh Door Corp.
1 Door Dr
Mount Hope OH 44660
850 208-3400

(P-12321)
J T WALKER INDUSTRIES INC
Also Called: Rite Screen
9322 Hyssop Dr, Rancho Cucamonga (91730-6103)
PHONE...............................909 481-1909
Dan Harvey, *President*
EMP: 50
SQ FT: 36,929
SALES (corp-wide): 1.1B **Privately Held**
SIC: 3442 Screen & storm doors & windows
PA: J. T. Walker Industries, Inc.
1310 N Hercules Ave Ste A
Clearwater FL 33765
727 461-0501

(P-12322)
JANUS INTERNATIONAL GROUP LLC
2535 W La Palma Ave, Anaheim (92801-2612)
PHONE...............................714 503-6120
David Curtis, *Principal*
EMP: 30
SALES (corp-wide): 293.9MM **Privately Held**
SIC: 3442 Metal doors
PA: Janus International Group, Llc
135 Janus Intl Blvd
Temple GA 30179
770 562-2850

(P-12323)
JOANKA INC
Also Called: M & A Custom Doors
25510 Frampton Ave, Harbor City (90710-2907)
PHONE...............................310 326-8940
Manuel A Valenzuela, *President*
EMP: 13
SQ FT: 4,640
SALES (est): 1.2MM **Privately Held**
SIC: 3442 Window & door frames

(P-12324)
K K MOLDS INC
926 Western Ave Ste D, Glendale (91201-2390)
PHONE...............................818 548-8988
Frank Kan, *President*
Man Yee Kan, *Admin Sec*
▲ **EMP:** 10
SALES: 1.3MM **Privately Held**
SIC: 3442 Moldings & trim, except automobile: metal

(P-12325)
L & L LOUVERS INC
12355 Doherty St, Riverside (92503-4842)
PHONE...............................951 735-9300
Terry Green, *President*
Robert Hammond, *Vice Pres*
EMP: 24
SQ FT: 11,000
SALES (est): 3.6MM **Privately Held**
WEB: www.louver1.com
SIC: 3442 Louvers, shutters, jalousies & similar items

(P-12326)
LAWRENCE ROLL UP DOORS INC (PA)
4525 Littlejohn St, Baldwin Park (91706-2239)
PHONE...............................626 962-4163
Paul Weston Freberg, *CEO*
▲ **EMP:** 35 **EST:** 1925
SQ FT: 35,000
SALES (est): 17.9MM **Privately Held**
WEB: www.lawrencedoors.com
SIC: 3442 3446 Rolling doors for industrial buildings or warehouses, metal; architectural metalwork

(P-12327)
LAWRENCE ROLL UP DOORS INC
11035 Stranwood Ave, Mission Hills (91345-1416)
PHONE...............................818 837-1963
Paul Lawrence, *President*
EMP: 10
SALES (corp-wide): 17.9MM **Privately Held**
WEB: www.lawrencedoors.com
SIC: 3442 Rolling doors for industrial buildings or warehouses, metal
PA: Lawrence Roll Up Doors, Inc.
4525 Littlejohn St
Baldwin Park CA 91706
626 962-4163

(P-12328)
LAWRENCE ROLL UP DOORS INC
1406 Virginia Ave Ste 10, Baldwin Park (91706-5805)
PHONE...............................626 338-6041
Robert Lee, *Manager*
EMP: 10
SALES (corp-wide): 17.9MM **Privately Held**
WEB: www.lawrencedoors.com
SIC: 3442 Rolling doors for industrial buildings or warehouses, metal
PA: Lawrence Roll Up Doors, Inc.
4525 Littlejohn St
Baldwin Park CA 91706
626 962-4163

(P-12329)
M N M MANUFACTURING INC
3019 E Harcourt St, Compton (90221-5503)
PHONE...............................310 898-1099
Matt Klein, *President*
Elizabeth Klein, *Vice Pres*
Suzanne Figueroa, *Executive*
Marlene Klein, *Admin Sec*
EMP: 60
SQ FT: 24,000
SALES (est): 8MM **Privately Held**
WEB: www.mnmmfg.com
SIC: 3442 Sash, door or window: metal

(P-12330)
MAKO OVERHEAD DOOR INC
5618 E La Palma Ave, Anaheim (92807-2110)
PHONE...............................714 998-0122
Mike McCall, *Owner*
EMP: 12
SALES: 2MM **Privately Held**
SIC: 3442 Garage doors, overhead: metal; jalousies, metal

(P-12331)
METAL MANUFACTURING CO INC
2240 Evergreen St, Sacramento (95815-3281)
PHONE...............................916 922-3484
Jerry Guest, *President*
Troy Smith, *Treasurer*
Henry Baum, *Admin Sec*
EMP: 20
SQ FT: 19,000
SALES: 2MM **Privately Held**
SIC: 3442 Metal doors; window & door frames

(P-12332)
METAL TITE PRODUCTS (PA)
Also Called: Krieger Speciality Products
4880 Gregg Rd, Pico Rivera (90660-2107)
PHONE...............................562 695-0645
Robert J McCluney, *President*
Charles Mc Cluney, *Shareholder*
James Mc Cluney, *Shareholder*
A W Mc Cluney, *Ch of Bd*
Susan Hayden, *Executive*
EMP: 58
SQ FT: 39,000
SALES (est): 10.2MM **Privately Held**
WEB: www.kriegersteel.com
SIC: 3442 1751 Metal doors; window & door frames; window & door (prefabricated) installation

(P-12333)
MILGARD MANUFACTURING INC
2451 Bert Dr, Hollister (95023-2563)
PHONE...............................831 636-0114
Eric Yaryarbrough, *Branch Mgr*
EMP: 160
SALES (corp-wide): 7.6B **Publicly Held**
WEB: www.milgard.com
SIC: 3442 2431 Metal doors; sash, door or window: metal; millwork
HQ: Milgard Manufacturing Incorporated
1010 54th Ave E
Fife WA 98424
253 922-6030

(P-12334)
MILGARD MANUFACTURING INC
Also Called: Milgard Windows
6050 88th St, Sacramento (95828-1119)
PHONE...............................916 387-0700
Bert Dimauro, *Branch Mgr*
EMP: 186
SALES (corp-wide): 7.6B **Publicly Held**
SIC: 3442 Window & door frames
HQ: Milgard Manufacturing Incorporated
1010 54th Ave E
Fife WA 98424
253 922-6030

(P-12335)
MILLWORKS ETC INC (PA)
Also Called: Steel Works Etc
2586 Calcite Cir, Newbury Park (91320-1203)
PHONE...............................805 499-3400
Robin W Shattuck, *CEO*
Beverly Buswell, *Controller*
Danette Linder, *Purch Mgr*
Christine Bohannan, *Manager*
Mike Starkey, *Manager*
◆ **EMP:** 25
SALES (est): 4.5MM **Privately Held**
SIC: 3442 Window & door frames

(P-12336)
MODULEX INC
2392 Bateman Ave, Duarte (91010-3312)
PHONE...............................626 256-9508
Arden L Boren, *President*
Robin Landy, *Vice Pres*
EMP: 35
SQ FT: 33,000
SALES (est): 3.7MM **Privately Held**
WEB: www.modulex.com
SIC: 3442 3354 Window & door frames; shapes, extruded aluminum

(P-12337)
MULTIQUIP INDUSTRIES CORP
22605 La Palma Ave # 507, Yorba Linda (92887-6713)
PHONE...............................888 996-7267
Daniel Burgess, *President*
EMP: 17 **EST:** 2012
SALES (est): 2.9MM **Privately Held**
SIC: 3442 3537 Rolling doors for industrial buildings or warehouses, metal; loading docks: portable, adjustable & hydraulic

(P-12338)
OMNIMAX INTERNATIONAL INC
Also Called: Alumax Building Products
28921 Us Highway 74, Sun City (92585-9675)
PHONE...............................951 928-1000
Mitchell B Lewis, *CEO*
EMP: 106
SALES (corp-wide): 861.3MM **Privately Held**
WEB: www.amerimaxbp.com
SIC: 3442 3444 5999 Casements, aluminum; sheet metalwork; awnings
HQ: Omnimax International, Inc.
30 Technology Pkwy S # 400
Peachtree Corners GA 30092

(P-12339)
R & S AUTOMATION INC
283 W Bonita Ave, Pomona (91767-1848)
PHONE...............................800 962-3111
Jerry Bradfield, *Manager*
Brad Goepner, *Manager*
EMP: 12

SALES (corp-wide): 3MM **Privately Held**
WEB: www.doorsbyrns.com
SIC: 3442 3446 5031 5063 Metal doors; grillwork, ornamental metal; doors; door frames, all materials; motor controls, starters & relays: electric; door & window repair
PA: R & S Automation, Inc.
2041 W Avenue 140th
San Leandro CA 94577
510 357-4110

(P-12340)
R & S ERECTION INCORPORATED (PA)
2057 W Avenue 140th, San Leandro (94577-5623)
PHONE...............................510 483-3710
Ray Ellias Zarodney, *CEO*
Dennis Hansen, *Project Mgr*
Kevin Smith, *Agent*
EMP: 10
SALES (est): 11MM **Privately Held**
SIC: 3442 Rolling doors for industrial buildings or warehouses, metal; louvers, shutters, jalousies & similar items

(P-12341)
R & S MANUFACTURING INC (HQ)
Also Called: R & S Rolling Door Products
33955 7th St, Union City (94587-3521)
P.O. Box 2737 (94587-7737)
PHONE...............................510 429-1788
Gordon J Ong, *President*
James Greaves, *Treasurer*
Ray Zarodney, *4dmin Sec*
Robert R Smith, *Director*
▲ **EMP:** 25
SQ FT: 36,136
SALES: 5.4MM
SALES (corp-wide): 11MM **Privately Held**
SIC: 3442 3231 Rolling doors for industrial buildings or warehouses, metal; louvers, shutters, jalousies & similar items; products of purchased glass
PA: R & S Erection, Incorporated
2057 W Avenue 140th
San Leandro CA 94577
510 483-3710

(P-12342)
R & S MFG SOUTHERN CAL INC
Also Called: R & S Mfg
283 W Bonita Ave, Pomona (91767-1848)
PHONE...............................909 596-2090
Ray Rodney, *CEO*
EMP: 14
SQ FT: 15,000
SALES (est): 3MM
SALES (corp-wide): 11MM **Privately Held**
SIC: 3442 5031 Rolling doors for industrial buildings or warehouses, metal; doors & windows
HQ: R & S Manufacturing, Inc.
33955 7th St
Union City CA 94587
510 429-1788

(P-12343)
R & S OVERHEAD DOOR OF SO CAL
Also Called: Door Doctor
1617 N Orangethorpe Way, Anaheim (92801-1228)
PHONE...............................714 680-0600
David Fowler, *President*
EMP: 25
SALES (est): 3.2MM **Privately Held**
SIC: 3442 7699 1731 3446 Rolling doors for industrial buildings or warehouses, metal; door & window repair; access control systems specialization; gates, ornamental metal

(P-12344)
R LANG COMPANY
Also Called: Truframe
8240 W Doe Ave, Visalia (93291-9263)
P.O. Box 7960 (93290-7960)
PHONE...............................559 651-0701
Richard A Lang, *President*
Judith D Lang, *Corp Secy*
◆ **EMP:** 75

(PA)=Parent Co (HQ)=Headquarters (DH)=Div Headquarters
✿ = New Business established in last 2 years

2019 California
Manufacturers Register

507

PRODUCTS & SVCS

SALES (est): 14.6MM **Privately Held**
WEB: www.rollaway.com
SIC: **3442** 3444 3211 5031 Screen
doors, metal; window & door frames; skylights, sheet metal; flat glass; windows

(P-12345)
SAN JOAQUIN WINDOW INC (PA)
Also Called: ATI Windows
1455 Columbia Ave, Riverside
(92507-2013)
PHONE............................909 946-3697
Stephen Schwartz, *CEO*
Daniel Schwartz, *President*
EMP: 61
SQ FT: 190,000
SALES: 14.2MM **Privately Held**
SIC: **3442** 5211 Metal doors, sash & trim;
door & window products

(P-12346)
SCREEN SHOP INC
601 Hamline St, San Jose (95110-1192)
PHONE............................408 295-7384
John V Salamida, *President*
Sue Green, *Vice Pres*
Sue Greene, *Admin Asst*
EMP: 10
SQ FT: 2,200
SALES: 2MM **Privately Held**
WEB: www.thescreenshop.com
SIC: **3442** 2431 5211 Screen & storm
doors & windows; screens, window,
metal; screen doors, metal; window
screens, wood frame; doors, wood; door
& window products; doors, storm: wood or
metal; windows, storm: wood or metal

(P-12347)
SECURITY METAL PRODUCTS CORP (DH)
5678 Concours, Ontario (91764-5394)
PHONE............................310 641-6690
Chris Holloway, *CEO*
EMP: 29
SALES (est): 5.3MM
SALES (corp-wide): 9B **Privately Held**
SIC: **3442** Metal doors
HQ: Assa Abloy Inc.
110 Sargent Dr
New Haven CT 06511
203 624-5225

(P-12348)
SOLATUBE INTERNATIONAL INC (PA)
2210 Oak Ridge Way, Vista (92081-8341)
PHONE............................888 765-2882
David W Rillie, *CEO*
Kathy Cittel, *Admin Asst*
Dana Carlson, *Manager*
Kerri Taylor, *Manager*
▲ EMP: 100
SQ FT: 105,000
SALES (est): 24.3MM **Privately Held**
WEB: www.solatube.com
SIC: **3442** Metal doors, sash & trim

(P-12349)
STILES CUSTOM METAL INC
1885 Kinser Rd, Ceres (95307-4606)
PHONE............................209 538-3667
David Stiles, *President*
Jim Ludlow, *Corp Secy*
Clark Ludlow, *Officer*
Steve Stiles, *Vice Pres*
Lisa Stancliff, *Project Mgr*
EMP: 87
SQ FT: 56,000
SALES (est): 17.4MM **Privately Held**
WEB: www.stilesdoor.com
SIC: **3442** Metal doors; window & door
frames

(P-12350)
SUPERIOR BUILDING PRODUCTS
27040 San Bernardino Ave, Redlands
(92374-5023)
PHONE............................909 930-1802
Richard H Crowther II, *President*
▲ EMP: 20

SALES (est): 6.1MM
SALES (corp-wide): 221.8MM **Privately Held**
SIC: **3442** Window & door frames; screen
& storm doors & windows; metal doors
PA: Prime-Line Products Company
26950 San Bernardino Ave
Redlands CA 92374
909 887-8118

(P-12351)
TJE COMPANY
Also Called: Onyx Shutters
18343 Gale Ave, City of Industry
(91748-1201)
PHONE............................909 869-7777
Sylvia Lee, *CEO*
Philip Kim, *Vice Pres*
◆ EMP: 18 EST: 2007
SALES (est): 3.3MM **Privately Held**
SIC: **3442** Shutters, door or window: metal

(P-12352)
TMP LLC
Also Called: Titan Metal Products
3011 Academy Way, Sacramento
(95815-1540)
PHONE............................916 920-2555
Glen Harelson, *President*
Flora Harelson, *Treasurer*
EMP: 23 EST: 1977
SQ FT: 18,000
SALES (est): 5.7MM **Privately Held**
WEB: www.titanmetalproducts.com
SIC: **3442** Metal doors; window & door
frames; sash, door or window: metal;
moldings & trim, except automobile: metal

(P-12353)
TORRANCE STEEL WINDOW CO INC
1819 Abalone Ave, Torrance (90501-3704)
PHONE............................310 328-9181
Dong K Lim, *President*
Michael Hahn, *Financial Exec*
▲ EMP: 45
SQ FT: 32,000
SALES (est): 8.6MM **Privately Held**
WEB: www.torrancesteelwindow.com
SIC: **3442** Window & door frames

(P-12354)
UNIQUE GARAGE DOOR INC (PA)
6259 Descanso Ave, Buena Park
(90620-1012)
PHONE............................714 223-1493
Robert Kelley, *CEO*
Arnulfo Valenzuela, *Vice Pres*
▼ EMP: 48
SQ FT: 30,000
SALES: 20MM **Privately Held**
SIC: **3442** Garage doors, overhead: metal

(P-12355)
WINDOW ENTERPRISES INC
Also Called: Torrence Aluminum Window
430 Nevada St, Redlands (92373-4244)
PHONE............................951 943-4894
Grant Murphy, *CEO*
Mike Bean, *Admin Sec*
Ed Van Hoy, *Director*
▲ EMP: 30
SQ FT: 45,000
SALES (est): 6.9MM **Privately Held**
SIC: **3442** Storm doors or windows, metal

(P-12356)
WONDER METALS CORPORATION
4351 Caterpillar Rd, Redding (96003-1494)
P.O. Box 994427 (96099-4427)
PHONE............................530 241-3251
Viki Cubbage, *President*
Brandon Long, *Opers Mgr*
EMP: 14
SQ FT: 38,000
SALES (est): 2.6MM **Privately Held**
WEB: www.wondermetals.com
SIC: **3442** Louvers, shutters, jalousies &
similar items

3443 Fabricated Plate Work

(P-12357)
ACD LLC
Also Called: A C D
2321 Pullman St, Santa Ana (92705-5512)
PHONE............................949 261-7533
James Estes, *Managing Dir*
Richard S Young, *Executive*
Leo Arreola, *General Mgr*
Mike Coco, *General Mgr*
Cherylan Hobbs, *Admin Asst*
◆ EMP: 117
SQ FT: 52,000
SALES: 39.6MM
SALES (corp-wide): 1.2B **Privately Held**
WEB: www.acdcom.com
SIC: **3443** 3559 Cryogenic tanks, for liq-
uids & gases; cryogenic machinery, in-
dustrial
HQ: Cryogenic Industries Holdings, Inc.
5910 Pcf Ctr Blvd Ste 110
San Diego CA

(P-12358)
AERO-CLAS HEAT TRAN PROD INC
1677 Curtiss Ct, La Verne (91750-5848)
PHONE............................909 596-1630
Paul Saurenman, *CEO*
EMP: 15
SALES (est): 3.2MM **Privately Held**
SIC: **3443** Heat exchangers: coolers (after,
inter), condensers, etc.

(P-12359)
APPLIED SYSTEMS LLC
15342 Valencia Ave, Fontana
(92335-3284)
P.O. Box 366 (92334-0366)
PHONE............................909 854-3200
Chris Phillips,
EMP: 10
SALES (est): 375.5K **Privately Held**
SIC: **3443** Industrial vessels, tanks & con-
tainers

(P-12360)
ATK SPACE SYSTEMS INC (DH)
Also Called: Space Components
6033 Bandini Blvd, Commerce
(90040-2968)
PHONE............................323 722-0222
Daniel J Murphy, *CEO*
Ronald D Dittemore, *Senior VP*
James Armor, *Vice Pres*
Thomas R Wilson, *Vice Pres*
◆ EMP: 50
SQ FT: 104,000
SALES (est): 173.9MM **Publicly Held**
WEB: www.psi-pci.com
SIC: **3443** Fabricated plate work (boiler
shop)
HQ: Northrop Grumman Innovation Sys-
tems, Inc.
45101 Warp Dr
Dulles VA 20166
703 406-5000

(P-12361)
B H TANK WORKS INC
1919 N San Fernando Rd, Los Angeles
(90065-1228)
PHONE............................323 221-1579
Fax: 323 221-6559
EMP: 17
SALES (est): 1.9MM **Privately Held**
WEB: www.bhtank.com
SIC: **3443**

(P-12362)
BA HOLDINGS (DH)
3016 Kansas Ave Bldg 1, Riverside
(92507-3445)
PHONE............................951 684-5110
John S Rhodes, *CEO*
Michael Meier, *Controller*
EMP: 30
SALES (est): 139.1MM
SALES (corp-wide): 441.3MM **Privately Held**
SIC: **3443** 3728 Cylinders, pressure: metal
plate; aircraft parts & equipment

(P-12363)
BASIC INDUSTRIES INTL INC
Also Called: Pacific Metal Products
10850 Wilshire Blvd, Los Angeles
(90024-4305)
PHONE............................951 226-1500
John Wallace, *President*
Steven W Burge, *Director*
EMP: 200
SALES (est): 57K **Privately Held**
SIC: **3443** 3446 Fabricated plate work
(boiler shop); architectural metalwork

(P-12364)
BENICIA FABRICATION & MCH INC
101 E Channel Rd, Benicia (94510-1155)
PHONE............................707 745-8111
Thomas D Cepernich, *CEO*
Dennis Michael Rose, *President*
Steven Rose, *Exec VP*
Mike Spangler, *Safety Mgr*
Jerry Core, *QC Mgr*
EMP: 150
SQ FT: 80,000
SALES (est): 40.7MM **Privately Held**
WEB: www.beniciafab.com
SIC: **3443** 3599 Fabricated plate work
(boiler shop); machine shop, jobbing & re-
pair

(P-12365)
BLACOH FLUID CONTROLS INC (PA)
601 Columbia Ave Ste D, Riverside
(92507-2149)
PHONE............................951 342-3100
Andrew Yeghnazar, *President*
Gary Cornell, *President*
Vise Diana, *COO*
Frank Smith, *Exec VP*
Dianna Vise, *Vice Pres*
EMP: 12 EST: 1977
SQ FT: 11,000
SALES (est): 2.4MM **Privately Held**
WEB: www.blacoh.com
SIC: **3443** Fabricated plate work (boiler
shop)

(P-12366)
BREEZAIRE PRODUCTS CO
8610 Production Ave Ste A, San Diego
(92121-2278)
PHONE............................858 566-7465
Ronald Brown, *President*
▼ EMP: 10
SQ FT: 1,200
SALES (est): 1.7MM **Privately Held**
WEB: www.breezaire.com
SIC: **3443** 3585 Economizers (boilers);
beer dispensing equipment

(P-12367)
CALIENTE SYSTEMS INC
6821 Central Ave, Newark (94560-3938)
PHONE............................510 790-0300
Rajan Barma, *CEO*
John Hughes, *Treasurer*
EMP: 91
SQ FT: 10,000
SALES (est): 7.9MM **Privately Held**
WEB: www.calientesystems.net
SIC: **3443** 3567 3433 Heat exchangers,
plate type; industrial furnaces & ovens;
heating equipment, except electric

(P-12368)
CATALINA CYLINDERS INC (PA)
7300 Anaconda Ave, Garden Grove
(92841-2930)
PHONE............................714 890-0999
Gregory Keeler, *CEO*
Roark Keeler, *CFO*
Richard Hill, *Vice Pres*
Tom Newell, *General Mgr*
Bob Brockar, *Manager*
EMP: 29
SALES (est): 22.9MM **Privately Held**
SIC: **3443** 3491 Fabricated plate work
(boiler shop); compressed gas cylinder
valves

(P-12369)
CENTRAL COAST STAINLESS
825 26th St, Paso Robles (93446-1242)
P.O. Box 3229 (93447-3229)
PHONE..................................805 238-0888
Tim Selby, *Mng Member*
Frank Visker, *Controller*
EMP: 25
SALES (est): 3.3MM **Privately Held**
SIC: 3443 Fuel tanks (oil, gas, etc.): metal
plate

(P-12370)
CENTRAL VALLEY TANK OF CAL
4752 E Carmen Ave, Fresno (93703-4501)
PHONE..................................559 456-3500
Kathy Tackett, *President*
EMP: 16
SALES (est): 3.9MM **Privately Held**
SIC: 3443 Boiler shop products: boilers,
smokestacks, steel tanks

(P-12371)
CERTIFIED STAINLESS SVC INC
Also Called: Westmark
441 Business Park Way, Atwater
(95301-9499)
PHONE..................................209 356-3300
Chris Portmann, *Branch Mgr*
EMP: 15
SALES (corp-wide): 58.7MM **Privately Held**
SIC: 3443 3569. Tanks for tank trucks,
metal plate; firefighting apparatus & related equipment
PA: Certified Stainless Service Inc.
2704 Railroad Ave
Ceres CA 95307
209 537-4747

(P-12372)
CERTIFIED STAINLESS SVC INC (PA)
Also Called: West-Mark
2704 Railroad Ave, Ceres (95307-4600)
P.O. Box 100 (95307-0100)
PHONE..................................209 537-4747
Grant Smith, *President*
Jack Smith, *Shareholder*
William Doughty, *CFO*
Scott Vincent, *Corp Secy*
Todd Vincent, *Vice Pres*
▲ EMP: 180
SQ FT: 64,000
SALES (est): 58.7MM **Privately Held**
WEB: www.west-mark.com
SIC: 3443 3715 7538 Tanks for tank
trucks, metal plate; truck trailers; general
truck repair

(P-12373)
CERTIFIED STAINLESS SVC INC
Also Called: Digital Factory
581 Industry Way, Atwater (95301-9457)
P.O. Box 100, Ceres (95307-0100)
PHONE..................................209 537-4747
Grant Smith, *Manager*
EMP: 50
SALES (corp-wide): 58.7MM **Privately Held**
WEB: www.west-mark.com
SIC: 3443 3569 Tanks for tank trucks,
metal plate; firefighting apparatus & related equipment
PA: Certified Stainless Service Inc.
2704 Railroad Ave
Ceres CA 95307
209 537-4747

(P-12374)
CHART INC
46441 Landing Pkwy, Fremont
(94538-6496)
PHONE..................................408 371-3303
Daniel Sullivan, *Branch Mgr*
EMP: 21 **Publicly Held**
SIC: 3443 Fabricated plate work (boiler shop)
HQ: Chart Inc.
407 7th St Nw
New Prague MN 56071
952 758-4484

(P-12375)
CJI PROCESS SYSTEMS INC
Also Called: Lee Ray Sandblasting
12000 Clark St, Santa Fe Springs
(90670-3709)
PHONE..................................562 777-0614
Archie Cholakian, *President*
John Cholakian, *Vice Pres*
▼ EMP: 70
SQ FT: 35,000
SALES (est): 25.5MM **Privately Held**
WEB: www.cjiprocesssystems.com
SIC: 3443 3441 3444 Tanks, lined: metal
plate; fabricated structural metal; sheet
metalwork

(P-12376)
CMT SHEET METAL
22732 Granite Way Ste C, Laguna Hills
(92653-1263)
PHONE..................................949 679-9868
Wes Hinze, *CEO*
Wes Hinze Jr, *President*
Gayle Hinze, *Admin Sec*
EMP: 15
SALES (est): 3.4MM **Privately Held**
SIC: 3443 Boiler & boiler shop work

(P-12377)
COMPUTRUS INC
250 Klug Cir, Corona (92880-5409)
PHONE..................................951 245-9103
William Turnbull, *President*
Scott R Carroll, *Vice Pres*
EMP: 40
SALES (est): 6.5MM
SALES (corp-wide): 242.1B **Publicly Held**
WEB: www.computrus.com
SIC: 3443 Truss plates, metal
HQ: Mitek Industries, Inc.
16023 Swinly Rdg
Chesterfield MO 63017
314 434-1200

(P-12378)
CONSOLIDATED FABRICATORS CORP (PA)
Also Called: CF
14620 Arminta St, Van Nuys (91402-5902)
PHONE..................................818 901-1005
Michael J Melideo, *CEO*
Jeff Lombardi, *President*
Kerry Holmes, *Vice Pres*
Brian A Atwater, *Managing Dir*
Brandon Jones, *General Mgr*
▲ EMP: 110 EST: 1974
SQ FT: 150,000
SALES: 106MM **Privately Held**
WEB: www.con-fab.com
SIC: 3443 5051 3444 Dumpsters,
garbage; steel; studs & joists, sheet metal

(P-12379)
CONTAINMENT CONSULTANTS INC
Also Called: Ideal Envmtl Pdts & Svcs
110 Old Gilroy St, Gilroy (95020-6948)
P.O. Box 307 (95021-0307)
PHONE..................................408 848-6998
Anne Anderson, *President*
Kristeen Snyder, *Project Mgr*
EMP: 16
SQ FT: 14,000
SALES (est): 3.5MM **Privately Held**
WEB: www.chem-stor.com
SIC: 3443 8748 Tanks, standard or custom fabricated: metal plate; environmental
consultant

(P-12380)
CONTAINMENT SOLUTIONS INC
2600 Pegasus Dr, Bakersfield
(93308-6809)
PHONE..................................661 399-9556
Joe Wiegand, *Manager*
Valerie Austin, *Human Res Mgr*
Tom Wright, *Sales Executive*
Dorrie Melville, *Manager*
EMP: 100 **Privately Held**
WEB: www.containmentsolutions.com
SIC: 3443 Industrial vessels, tanks & containers

HQ: Containment Solutions, Inc.
333 N Rivershire Dr # 190
Conroe TX 77304

(P-12381)
CONTECH ENGNERED SOLUTIONS LLC
2245 Canyon Creek Rd, Redding
(96001-3727)
PHONE..................................530 243-1207
Jerry Burton, *Manager*
EMP: 20 **Privately Held**
SIC: 3443 3444 Fabricated plate work
(boiler shop); sheet metalwork
HQ: Contech Engineered Solutions Llc
9025 Centre Pointe Dr # 400
West Chester OH 45069
513 645-7000

(P-12382)
CONTINENTAL SECOND SHIFT LLC
3008 S Croddy Way, Santa Ana
(92704-6305)
PHONE..................................619 985-6038
James Gilbreath,
EMP: 19
SQ FT: 1,500
SALES: 350K **Privately Held**
SIC: 3443 Fabricated plate work (boiler
shop)

(P-12383)
COOK AND COOK INCORPORATED
Also Called: Royal Welding & Fabricating
1000 E Elm Ave, Fullerton (92831-5022)
PHONE..................................714 680-6669
Wallace F Cook, *President*
Patricia Cook, *Vice Pres*
Veronica Covarrubias, *Human Resources*
Merritt Read, *Safety Mgr*
EMP: 30
SQ FT: 30,000
SALES (est): 6.8MM **Privately Held**
WEB: www.royalwelding.com
SIC: 3443 3599 3444 Industrial vessels,
tanks & containers; amusement park
equipment; sheet metalwork

(P-12384)
DAVIS GREGG ENTERPRISES INC
8525 Roland Acres Dr, Santee
(92071-4453)
PHONE..................................619 449-4250
Davis Gregg, *President*
Mary Gregg, *Vice Pres*
Maryann Gregg, *Sales Executive*
▲ EMP: 14
SQ FT: 4,800
SALES (est): 1.2MM **Privately Held**
SIC: 3443 Tanks, standard or custom fabricated: metal plate

(P-12385)
DESIGN FORM INC
8250 Electric Ave, Stanton (90680-2640)
PHONE..................................714 952-3700
Glenn Baldwin, *CEO*
EMP: 11
SQ FT: 7,000
SALES: 1.2MM **Privately Held**
WEB: www.designform.com
SIC: 3443 Tanks, standard or custom fabricated: metal plate

(P-12386)
DUNWEIZER MACHINE INC
Also Called: Dunweizer Mch & Fabrication
8338 Allport Ave, Santa Fe Springs
(90670-2108)
PHONE..................................562 698-7787
Dennis Schweizer, *President*
Jim Van Eperen, *Marketing Staff*
EMP: 19
SQ FT: 20,000
SALES (est): 3.7MM **Privately Held**
SIC: 3443 3599 Fabricated plate work
(boiler shop); machine shop, jobbing & repair

(P-12387)
EDGE ELECTRONICS CORPORATION
Also Called: Mc Intyre Coil
14670 Wicks Blvd, San Leandro
(94577-6716)
PHONE..................................510 614-7988
Dennis T Wong, *President*
William Schwartz, *Vice Pres*
EMP: 25
SQ FT: 20,300
SALES (est): 4.3MM **Privately Held**
SIC: 3443 Heat exchangers, plate type

(P-12388)
HARSCO CORPORATION
Also Called: Harsco Distribution Center
5580 Cherry Ave, Long Beach
(90805-5504)
PHONE..................................909 444-2527
Ron Eickelman, *Branch Mgr*
EMP: 15
SALES (corp-wide): 1.6B **Publicly Held**
WEB: www.harsco.com
SIC: 3443 Fabricated plate work (boiler
shop)
PA: Harsco Corporation
350 Poplar Church Rd
Camp Hill PA 17011
717 763-7064

(P-12389)
HAYDEN PRODUCTS LLC
Also Called: Hayden Industrial Products
1393 E San Bernardino Ave, San
Bernardino (92408-2964)
PHONE..................................951 736-2600
Harold Lehon, *Mng Member*
Peter Camenzind, *Co-Owner*
James Neitz, *President*
Sam George, *Business Dir*
Loper Greg, *Info Tech Mgr*
▲ EMP: 80
SQ FT: 55,000
SALES (est): 29.4MM **Privately Held**
WEB: www.haydenindustrial.com
SIC: 3443 Heat exchangers, condensers &
components

(P-12390)
HYUNDAI TRANSLEAD (HQ)
8880 Rio San Diego Dr # 600, San Diego
(92108-1634)
PHONE..................................619 574-1500
Bong Jae Lee, *CEO*
Moon S Chung, *COO*
Glen Harney, *COO*
Steve Choi, *CFO*
Sb Yoon, *CFO*
◆ EMP: 87
SALES (est): 907.4MM
SALES (corp-wide): 38B **Privately Held**
WEB: www.translead.com
SIC: 3443 3715 3412 Industrial vessels,
tanks & containers; semitrailers for truck
tractors; metal barrels, drums & pails
PA: Hyundai Motor Company
12 Heolleung-Ro, Seocho-Gu
Seoul 06797
822 346-4111

(P-12391)
ITW BLDING CMPONENTS GROUP INC
Also Called: ITW Alpine
8351 Rovana Cir, Sacramento
(95828-2522)
PHONE..................................916 387-0116
Sally Thomas, *Sales/Mktg Mgr*
John Matthews, *Prdtn Mgr*
EMP: 30
SALES (corp-wide): 14.3B **Publicly Held**
WEB: www.alpineengineeredproducts.com
SIC: 3443 3469 Truss plates, metal;
stamping metal for the trade
HQ: Itw Building Components Group, Inc.
13389 Lakefront Dr
Earth City MO 63045
314 344-9121

(P-12392)
JOHANSING IRON WORKS INC
849 Jackson St, Benicia (94510-2907)
P.O. Box 847 (94510-0847)
PHONE..................................707 361-8190

Thomas Johansing, *President*
Bruce Sherman, *Admin Sec*
EMP: 10
SQ FT: 20,000
SALES (est): 1.4MM **Privately Held**
WEB: www.johansing.com
SIC: 3443 Heat exchangers, plate type; vessels, process or storage (from boiler shops): metal plate

(P-12393)
KEESEE TANK COMPANY
Also Called: Advance Pacific Tank
721 S Melrose St, Placentia (92870-6307)
PHONE..................714 528-1814
Kenneth Keesee, *Owner*
EMP: 10
SQ FT: 60,000
SALES (est): 1.7MM **Privately Held**
SIC: 3443 Fabricated plate work (boiler shop)

(P-12394)
KSM VACUUM PRODUCTS INC
1959 Concourse Dr, San Jose (95131-1708)
PHONE..................408 514-2400
Yun Ho Kim, *CEO*
Robert Snowden, *Principal*
Denny Laines, *Engineer*
▲ **EMP:** 14
SALES (est): 2.8MM **Privately Held**
SIC: 3443 High vacuum coaters, metal plate

(P-12395)
LA VILLETA DE SONOMA
23000 Arnold Dr, Sonoma (95476-9208)
PHONE..................707 939-9392
Leon Mardo, *Principal*
▲ **EMP:** 22
SALES (est): 1.8MM **Privately Held**
WEB: www.lavilleta.com
SIC: 3443 Annealing boxes, pots, or covers

(P-12396)
LUXFER-GTM TECHNOLOGIES LLC (PA)
1619 Shattuck Ave, Berkeley (94709-1611)
PHONE..................415 856-0570
Michael Koonce, *President*
Dan Jones, *Mfg Dir*
Tim Tiger, *Sales Staff*
EMP: 20 **EST:** 2012
SQ FT: 1,700
SALES: 3.6MM **Privately Held**
SIC: 3443 Tanks for tank trucks, metal plate

(P-12397)
M-5 STEEL MFG INC (PA)
1450 Mirasol St, Los Angeles (90023-3148)
PHONE..................323 263-9383
Douglas A Linkon, *CEO*
Henry Casas, *Info Tech Mgr*
▲ **EMP:** 50
SQ FT: 100,000
SALES (est): 7.2MM **Privately Held**
SIC: 3443 3444 Fabricated plate work (boiler shop); gutters, sheet metal

(P-12398)
MCKENNA BOILER WORKS INC
1510 N Spring St, Los Angeles (90012-1925)
PHONE..................323 221-1171
Richard R Smith, *President*
James F Smith, *Treasurer*
EMP: 15
SQ FT: 14,000
SALES (est): 3.5MM **Privately Held**
SIC: 3443 7699 Boilers: industrial, power, or marine; boiler repair shop

(P-12399)
MELCO STEEL INC
1100 W Foothill Blvd, Azusa (91702-2818)
PHONE..................626 334-7875
Michel Kashou, *President*
Joann Reese, *Corp Secy*
Mazin Kashou, *Vice Pres*
Tom Rockecharlie, *Vice Pres*
EMP: 30
SQ FT: 25,500

SALES (est): 7.6MM **Privately Held**
SIC: 3443 Vessels, process or storage (from boiler shops): metal plate; autoclaves, industrial

(P-12400)
MODERN CUSTOM FABRICATION
2421 E California Ave, Fresno (93721-3301)
P.O. Box 11925 (93775-1925)
PHONE..................559 264-4741
James E Jones, *CEO*
James W Gray, *Vice Pres*
John W Jones, *Principal*
Barbara Nix, *Human Res Mgr*
Jim Gray, *Director*
EMP: 35 **EST:** 2001
SALES (est): 10.3MM
SALES (corp-wide): 126.3MM **Privately Held**
WEB: www.modweldco.com
SIC: 3443 Fabricated plate work (boiler shop)
PA: Modern Welding Company, Inc.
2880 New Hartford Rd
Owensboro KY 42303
270 685-4400

(P-12401)
MOSIER BROS
19580 Avenue 344, Woodlake (93286)
PHONE..................559 564-3304
Mark Taylor, *President*
C Joanne Taylor, *Admin Sec*
Byron Taylor, *Director*
EMP: 10 **EST:** 1963
SQ FT: 5,000
SALES (est): 1.8MM **Privately Held**
SIC: 3443 Tanks, lined: metal plate

(P-12402)
NATIONWIDE BOILER INCORPORATED (PA)
42400 Christy St, Fremont (94538-3141)
PHONE..................510 490-7100
Larry Day, *President*
Ken Bliss, *Shareholder*
James Hermerding, *Vice Pres*
Michele Tomas, *Vice Pres*
William Testa, *Director*
◆ **EMP:** 51
SQ FT: 35,000
SALES: 29.2MM **Privately Held**
WEB: www.nationwideboiler.com
SIC: 3443 Fabricated plate work (boiler shop)

(P-12403)
P-W WESTERN INC
9415 Kruse Rd, Pico Rivera (90660-1430)
PHONE..................562 463-9055
Timothy Place, *CEO*
Emilia Gonzales, *Finance*
EMP: 65
SQ FT: 60,000
SALES: 10MM
SALES (corp-wide): 20.7MM **Privately Held**
WEB: www.pwtray.com
SIC: 3443 Cable trays, metal plate
HQ: P-W Industries Inc
9415 Kruse Rd
Pico Rivera CA 90660
562 463-9055

(P-12404)
PACIFIC STEAM EQUIPMENT INC
Also Called: P S E Boilers
11748 Slauson Ave, Santa Fe Springs (90670-2227)
PHONE..................562 906-9292
William S Shanahan MD, *President*
Shin Duk Kang, *Vice Pres*
Santiago A Kuan, *Sales Mgr*
▲ **EMP:** 25 **EST:** 1954
SQ FT: 22,500
SALES (est): 5MM **Privately Held**
WEB: www.pacificsteam.com
SIC: 3443 5074 3582 2841 Tanks, standard or custom fabricated: metal plate; boilers: industrial, power, or marine; plumbing & hydronic heating supplies; steam fittings; commercial laundry equipment; soap & other detergents

(P-12405)
PACIFIC TANK LTD
17177 Muskrat Ave, Adelanto (92301-2260)
PHONE..................760 246-6136
Norvald Farestveit, *President*
Robert A Clanton, *Corp Secy*
EMP: 12
SQ FT: 10,000
SALES (est): 2.2MM **Privately Held**
WEB: www.pacifictank.com
SIC: 3443 Tanks, standard or custom fabricated: metal plate

(P-12406)
PALMDALE HEAT TREATING INC
38834 17th St E, Palmdale (93550-3915)
PHONE..................661 274-8604
Jon Fishel, *President*
Janette Gorman, *Treasurer*
Catherine Battaglia, *Corp Secy*
James Rodgers, *Vice Pres*
EMP: 15
SQ FT: 5,000
SALES (est): 2MM **Privately Held**
SIC: 3443 Fabricated plate work (boiler shop)

(P-12407)
PARKER-HANNIFIN CORPORATION
Hydraulic Accumulator Division
14087 Borate St, Santa Fe Springs (90670-5336)
PHONE..................562 404-1938
Mark Gagnon, *Branch Mgr*
EMP: 20
SALES (corp-wide): 12B **Publicly Held**
WEB: www.parker.com
SIC: 3443 3052 2822 Fabricated plate work (boiler shop); rubber & plastics hose & beltings; synthetic rubber
PA: Parker-Hannifin Corporation
6035 Parkland Blvd
Cleveland OH 44124
216 896-3000

(P-12408)
PERRIS SKYVENTURE
Also Called: Perris Wind Tunnel
2093 Goetz Rd, Perris (92570-9315)
PHONE..................951 940-4290
Ben Conatser, *President*
Diane Conatser, *Vice Pres*
Susan Jones, *Info Tech Mgr*
Pat Conatser, *Manager*
EMP: 15
SQ FT: 1,788
SALES (est): 2.1MM **Privately Held**
WEB: www.perrisskyventure.com
SIC: 3443 Wind tunnels

(P-12409)
POLARGY INC
1148 Sonora Ct, Sunnyvale (94086-5308)
PHONE..................408 752-0186
Cary Frame, *President*
EMP: 30
SALES (est): 6.5MM **Privately Held**
SIC: 3443 3585 Reactor containment vessels, metal plate; parts for heating, cooling & refrigerating equipment

(P-12410)
PREMIERE RECYCLE CO
348 Phelan Ave, San Jose (95112-4103)
PHONE..................408 297-7910
Robert Hill, *President*
EMP: 50
SALES (est): 6.2MM **Privately Held**
WEB: www.premierrecycle.com
SIC: 3443 4953 4212 Dumpsters, garbage; garbage: collecting, destroying & processing; local trucking, without storage

(P-12411)
PROTEC ARISAWA AMERICA INC
2455 Ash St, Vista (92081-8424)
PHONE..................760 599-4800
Shinichi Miura, *President*
Tim Schag, *COO*
◆ **EMP:** 50

SALES (est): 15.7MM **Privately Held**
SIC: 3443 Process vessels, industrial: metal plate

(P-12412)
QUALITY VESSEL ENGINEERING INC
8515 Chetle Ave, Santa Fe Springs (90670-2205)
PHONE..................562 696-2100
John Gill, *President*
Jeff Cribbs, *Manager*
EMP: 15
SALES (est): 2.8MM **Privately Held**
WEB: www.howardfab.com
SIC: 3443 Cylinders, pressure: metal plate

(P-12413)
RECON SERVICES INC
2255 Via Cerro, Jurupa Valley (92509-2412)
P.O. Box 60816, Irvine (92602-6027)
PHONE..................951 682-1400
William Mitchell, *President*
Katheryn Siroonian, *Vice Pres*
EMP: 15
SQ FT: 15,000
SALES (est): 3MM **Privately Held**
SIC: 3443 Industrial vessels, tanks & containers

(P-12414)
RICHFIELD ENGINEERING INC
Also Called: L W Lefort
1135 Fee Ana St, Placentia (92870-6761)
PHONE..................714 524-3741
Don Robinson, *President*
Mike Grant, *Manager*
EMP: 40
SQ FT: 40,000
SALES (est): 4MM
SALES (corp-wide): 6.7MM **Privately Held**
WEB: www.robinsonmfginc.com
SIC: 3443 Metal parts
PA: Robinson Manufacturing, Inc.
1136 Richfield Rd
Placentia CA 92870
714 524-7395

(P-12415)
RILEYS TANKS/D&J SERVICE
3261 S Elm Ave, Fresno (93706-5622)
PHONE..................559 237-1403
Joseph V Riley, *Co-Owner*
Ramona J Riley, *Co-Owner*
EMP: 12
SQ FT: 10,000
SALES (est): 1.3MM **Privately Held**
WEB: www.rileystanks.com
SIC: 3443 Gas holders, metal plate; water tanks, metal plate

(P-12416)
ROY E HANSON JR MFG (PA)
Also Called: Hanson Tank
1600 E Washington Blvd, Los Angeles (90021-3123)
PHONE..................213 747-7514
Jonathan Goss, *CEO*
Roy E Hanson Jr, *Shareholder*
Johnathan Goss, *CEO*
Thys Dorenbosch, *Treasurer*
Cliff Jones, *Vice Pres*
▼ **EMP:** 90
SQ FT: 55,000
SALES (est): 13.1MM **Privately Held**
WEB: www.hansontank.com
SIC: 3443 Fuel tanks (oil, gas, etc.): metal plate

(P-12417)
S & H WELDING INC
8604 Elder Creek Rd, Sacramento (95828-1803)
PHONE..................916 386-8921
John Jones, *President*
EMP: 15
SQ FT: 10,000
SALES (est): 3.3MM **Privately Held**
WEB: www.calottery.com
SIC: 3443 Fabricated plate work (boiler shop)

▲ = Import ▼=Export
◆ =Import/Export

(P-12418)
S BRAVO SYSTEMS INC
Also Called: Bravo Support
2929 Vail Ave, Commerce (90040-2615)
PHONE...................................323 888-4133
Paola Bravo Recendez, *CEO*
Jonathan Smith, *Technology*
Matthew Beck, *Graphic Designe*
Gracie Kurt, *Safety Dir*
Keith Pearson, *Opers Mgr*
▲ EMP: 26
SQ FT: 40,000
SALES (est): 9.4MM **Privately Held**
WEB: www.sbravo.com
SIC: 3443 Containers, shipping (bombs, etc.): metal plate

(P-12419)
SAN-I-PAK PACIFIC INC
23535 S Bird Rd, Tracy (95304-9339)
P.O. Box 1183 (95378-1183)
PHONE...................................209 836-2310
John L Hall, *CEO*
Wilburn Hall, *Vice Pres*
EMP: 50
SQ FT: 25,000
SALES (est): 9.9MM **Privately Held**
WEB: www.sanipak.com
SIC: 3443 Sterilizing chambers, metal plate

(P-12420)
SID E PARKER BOILER MFG CO INC
Also Called: Parker Boiler Co
5930 Bandini Blvd, Commerce (90040-2903)
PHONE...................................323 727-9800
Sid D Danenhauer, *Ch of Bd*
Ed Marchak, *CFO*
Greg G Danenhauer, *Vice Pres*
Greg Danenhauer, *Vice Pres*
Mike McDonald, *Engineer*
▲ EMP: 66
SQ FT: 80,000
SALES: 15MM **Privately Held**
WEB: www.parkerboiler.com
SIC: 3443 3433 Boilers: industrial, power, or marine; heating equipment, except electric

(P-12421)
SMS INDUSTRIAL INC
Also Called: Winery Services Group
1628 N Main St, Salinas (93906-5102)
PHONE...................................831 337-4271
Orlando T Michelon, *Principal*
Corinne White, *President*
Lonny White, *General Mgr*
EMP: 13
SQ FT: 2,100
SALES (est): 3.1MM **Privately Held**
WEB: www.summitmechanicalsystems.com
SIC: 3443 Tanks, standard or custom fabricated: metal plate

(P-12422)
SOUTH GATE ENGINEERING LLC
13477 Yorba Ave, Chino (91710-5055)
PHONE...................................909 628-2779
Peter Morin,
William Paolino, *Mng Member*
EMP: 115 EST: 1947
SALES (est): 32.7MM **Privately Held**
WEB: www.southgateengineering.com
SIC: 3443 Vessels, process or storage (from boiler shops): metal plate; heat exchangers: coolers (after, inter), condensers, etc.

(P-12423)
SPX COOLING TECHNOLOGIES INC
Recold Division
550 Mercury Ln, Brea (92821-4830)
PHONE...................................714 529-6080
Doug Vickers, *Manager*
EMP: 40
SALES (corp-wide): 1.4B **Publicly Held**
WEB: www.cts.spx.com
SIC: 3443 Fabricated plate work (boiler shop)

HQ: Spx Cooling Technologies, Inc.
7401 W 129th St
Overland Park KS 66213
913 664-7400

(P-12424)
SPX CORPORATION
17815 Newhope St Ste M, Fountain Valley (92708-5426)
PHONE...................................714 434-2576
John Blystone, *Branch Mgr*
EMP: 99
SALES (corp-wide): 1.4B **Publicly Held**
WEB: www.spx.com
SIC: 3443
PA: Spx Corporation
13320a Balntyn Corp Pl
Charlotte NC 28277
980 474-3700

(P-12425)
SPX CORPORATION
1515 S Harris Ct, Anaheim (92806-5932)
PHONE...................................714 634-3855
EMP: 12
SALES (corp-wide): 1.4B **Publicly Held**
SIC: 3443
PA: Spx Corporation
13320a Balntyn Corp Pl
Charlotte NC 28277
980 474-3700

(P-12426)
SPX CORPORATION
1531 7th St, Riverside (92507-4454)
PHONE...................................951 781-4484
William Mc Weeleny, *Principal*
EMP: 97
SALES (corp-wide): 1.4B **Publicly Held**
WEB: www.spx.com
SIC: 3443 Cooling towers, metal plate
PA: Spx Corporation
13320a Balntyn Corp Pl
Charlotte NC 28277
980 474-3700

(P-12427)
STEEL STRUCTURES INC
28777 Avenue 15 1/2, Madera (93638-2316)
PHONE...................................559 673-8021
Daniel Riley, *President*
Tracy Riley, *Vice Pres*
EMP: 22
SQ FT: 44,000
SALES: 5MM **Privately Held**
WEB: www.steelstructuresinc.com
SIC: 3443 Tanks, standard or custom fabricated: metal plate; process vessels, industrial: metal plate

(P-12428)
STEEL UNLIMITED INC (PA)
Also Called: Sui Companies
3200 Myers St, Riverside (92503-5530)
PHONE...................................909 873-1222
Mike Frabotta, *President*
David Sunde, *Vice Pres*
Eric C Carpenter, *Data Proc Staff*
Annamarie Velarde, *Personnel Assit*
Vic Carlino, *Sales Staff*
▲ EMP: 75 EST: 1996
SQ FT: 142,000
SALES (est): 18.7MM **Privately Held**
WEB: www.steelunlimited.com
SIC: 3443 Plate work for the metalworking trade

(P-12429)
STRUCTURAL COMPOSITES INDS LLC (DH)
Also Called: SCI
336 Enterprise Pl, Pomona (91768-3244)
PHONE...................................909 594-7777
Ken Miller, *Mng Member*
Bruce Riser, *Finance*
◆ EMP: 40
SALES (est): 21.6MM
SALES (corp-wide): 3.5B **Publicly Held**
WEB: www.scicomposites.com
SIC: 3443 Tanks, lined: metal plate
HQ: Worthington Cylinder Corporation
200 W Wlson Bridge Rd
Worthington OH 43085
614 840-3210

(P-12430)
SUPERIOR STORAGE TANK INC
14700 Industry Cir, La Mirada (90638-5817)
PHONE...................................714 226-1914
Griff Williams, *CEO*
Rob Henderson, *COO*
EMP: 15
SALES (est): 3.4MM **Privately Held**
SIC: 3443 7692 Fuel tanks (oil, gas, etc.): metal plate; welding repair

(P-12431)
SUPERIOR TANK CO INC (PA)
Also Called: Stci
9500 Lucas Ranch Rd, Rancho Cucamonga (91730-5724)
PHONE...................................909 912-0580
Jesus Eric Marquez, *President*
Lewis A Marquez, *Treasurer*
Denise Rocha, *Office Mgr*
George Marquez, *Admin Sec*
Marc Hayes, *Project Mgr*
◆ EMP: 50
SQ FT: 53,392
SALES: 32.7MM **Privately Held**
SIC: 3443 3494 1791 1794 Fuel tanks (oil, gas, etc.): metal plate; water tanks, metal plate; valves & pipe fittings; structural steel erection; excavation work

(P-12432)
TAIT & ASSOCIATES INC
2131 S Dupont Dr, Anaheim (92806-6102)
PHONE...................................714 560-8222
Jim Streipz, *Branch Mgr*
Richard Tait, *Vice Pres*
Andy Tait, *Regional Mgr*
EMP: 100
SALES (corp-wide): 37.2MM **Privately Held**
SIC: 3443 Fuel tanks (oil, gas, etc.): metal plate
PA: Tait & Associates, Inc.
701 Parkcenter Dr
Santa Ana CA 92705
866 584-0283

(P-12433)
THERMAL ENGRG INTL USA INC (HQ)
18000 Studebaker Rd # 400, Cerritos (90703-2679)
PHONE...................................323 726-0641
Thomas Richardson, *President*
Brian Antonini, *President*
William Farris, *President*
Andrew Finizio, *President*
Abraham L Yarden, *President*
◆ EMP: 225 EST: 1919
SQ FT: 18,000
SALES: 75.8MM
SALES (corp-wide): 509MM **Privately Held**
WEB: www.thermalengint.com
SIC: 3443 8711 Air coolers, metal plate; condensers, steam; heat exchangers: coolers (after, inter), etc.; economizers (boilers); professional engineer
PA: Babcock Power Inc.
6 Kimball Ln Ste 210
Lynnfield MA 01940
978 646-3300

(P-12434)
THERMAL EQUIPMENT CORPORATION
Also Called: TEC
2030 E University Dr, Compton (90220-6410)
PHONE...................................310 328-6600
Nancy Huffman, *President*
Osvaldo Lopez, *Engineer*
Martin Holguin, *Buyer*
Chris Montgomery, *Safety Mgr*
▼ EMP: 45
SQ FT: 45,000
SALES (est): 13MM **Privately Held**
WEB: www.thermalequipment.com
SIC: 3443 3821 2842 Autoclaves, industrial; process vessels, industrial: metal plate; vessels, process or storage (from boiler shops): metal plate; laboratory apparatus & furniture; specialty cleaning, polishes & sanitation goods

PA: Km3 Holdings Company Inc
2030 E University Dr
Rancho Dominguez CA
310 328-6600

(P-12435)
THERMALLY ENGINEERED MANUFACTU
Also Called: T E M P
543 W 135th St, Gardena (90248-1505)
PHONE...................................310 523-9934
Robert Greenwood, *President*
Binh Vinh, *Vice Pres*
▲ EMP: 27
SQ FT: 50,000
SALES: 4.4MM **Privately Held**
WEB: www.temp.com
SIC: 3443 Heat exchangers, condensers & components

(P-12436)
THOMPSON TANK INC
8029 Phlox St, Downey (90241-4816)
P.O. Box 790, Lakewood (90714-0790)
PHONE...................................562 869-7711
David B Thompson, *President*
Robert I Grue, *Treasurer*
EMP: 19
SQ FT: 225,000
SALES (est): 4.7MM **Privately Held**
WEB: www.thompsontank.com
SIC: 3443 7699 3715 3713 Tanks, standard or custom fabricated: metal plate; tank repair & cleaning services; truck trailers; truck & bus bodies

(P-12437)
UNIVERSAL DEFENSE
412 Cucamonga Ave, Claremont (91711-5019)
P.O. Box 1372 (91711-1372)
PHONE...................................909 626-4178
Christine A Sayegh, *Principal*
EMP: 20
SALES (est): 1.7MM **Privately Held**
SIC: 3443 Fabricated plate work (boiler shop)

(P-12438)
VENDING SECURITY PRODUCTS
770 Newton Way, Costa Mesa (92627-4277)
PHONE...................................949 646-1474
Bruce Jenks, *President*
Jason Luke, *Office Mgr*
▲ EMP: 10
SQ FT: 3,000
SALES (est): 1.5MM **Privately Held**
SIC: 3443 Metal parts

(P-12439)
WAGNER PLATE WORKS WEST INC (PA)
Also Called: P V T Supply
14015 Garfield Ave, Paramount (90723-2137)
PHONE...................................562 531-6050
Jack Brian Purtell, *President*
EMP: 25
SQ FT: 60,000
SALES (est): 5.7MM **Privately Held**
WEB: www.pvtpvt.com
SIC: 3443 5051 Tanks, lined: metal plate; pipe & tubing, steel

(P-12440)
WATERCREST INC
4850 E Airport Dr, Ontario (91761-7818)
PHONE...................................909 390-3944
Jeremiah B Robins, *CEO*
Gary F Johnson, *President*
▲ EMP: 51
SQ FT: 29,000
SALES (est): 7MM **Privately Held**
SIC: 3443 Heat exchangers, condensers & components

(P-12441)
WELLS STRUTHERS CORPORATION
Also Called: Tei Struthers Wells
10375 Slusher Dr, Santa Fe Springs (90670-3748)
PHONE...................................814 726-1000
John C Wallace, *President*

PRODUCTS & SVCS

Joe Nitzken, *COO*
John M Carey, *Vice Pres*
Jan Contreras, *Vice Pres*
Burton M Abrams, *Admin Sec*
EMP: 30
SQ FT: 30,000
SALES (est): 4.3MM **Privately Held**
SIC: 3443 Heat exchangers, plate type; heat exchangers: coolers (after, inter), condensers, etc.; pressurizers or auxiliary equipment, nuclear: metal plate

(P-12442)
WESTERN COMBUSTION ENGRG INC
640 E Realty St, Carson (90745-6016)
P.O. Box 5331, San Pedro (90733-5331)
PHONE...................................310 834-9389
Marcia L Paul, *CEO*
Christian R Paul, *President*
EMP: 12 **EST:** 1977
SQ FT: 10,000
SALES (est): 2.7MM **Privately Held**
WEB: www.westerncombustion.com
SIC: 3443 7699 3567 Heat exchangers: coolers (after, inter), condensers, etc.; boiler & heating repair services; industrial furnaces & ovens

(P-12443)
WORTHINGTON CYLINDER CORP
336 Enterprise Pl, Pomona (91768-3244)
PHONE...................................909 594-7777
EMP: 191
SALES (corp-wide): 3.5B **Publicly Held**
SIC: 3443 Cylinders, pressure: metal plate
HQ: Worthington Cylinder Corporation
200 W Wlson Bridge Rd
Worthington OH 43085
614 840-3210

(P-12444)
XCHANGER MANUFACTURING CORP
Also Called: Wiegmann & Rose
9131 San Leandro St # 220, Oakland (94603-1208)
P.O. Box 4187 (94614-4187)
PHONE...................................510 632-8828
Scott E Logan, *President*
Jack E Logan, *President*
Suzette Logan, *Administration*
EMP: 21
SQ FT: 80,000
SALES (est): 4.5MM **Privately Held**
WEB: www.wiegmannandrose.com
SIC: 3443 Heat exchangers: coolers (after, inter), condensers, etc.

(P-12445)
XTREME MANUFACTURING LLC
1775 Park St Ste 82, Selma (93662-3659)
PHONE...................................559 891-2978
Jose Vallejo, *Branch Mgr*
EMP: 21
SALES (corp-wide): 61.4MM **Privately Held**
SIC: 3443 Metal parts
PA: Xtreme Manufacturing, Llc
1401 Mineral Ave
Las Vegas NV 89106
702 851-3701

3444 Sheet Metal Work

(P-12446)
101 ROOFING & SHEET METAL CO
1390 Wallace Ave, San Francisco (94124-3316)
PHONE...................................415 695-0101
Christie Chung, *Owner*
EMP: 11
SALES (est): 620K **Privately Held**
SIC: 3444 1761 Sheet metalwork; roofing contractor

(P-12447)
253 INC
245 E Harris Ave, South San Francisco (94080-6807)
PHONE...................................650 737-5670

Michael Calleja, *CEO*
EMP: 10
SALES: 950K **Privately Held**
SIC: 3444 Sheet metalwork

(P-12448)
5H SHEET METAL FABRICATION INC
1826 W Business Center Dr, Orange (92867-7904)
PHONE...................................714 633-7544
Hoa Nguyen, *CEO*
Helena Nguyen, *CFO*
Hoa Thi Nguyen, *Admin Sec*
EMP: 15
SQ FT: 10,000
SALES (est): 2.3MM **Privately Held**
SIC: 3444 Sheet metalwork

(P-12449)
A & G INDUSTRIES INC
341 Enterprise St, San Marcos (92078-4339)
PHONE...................................760 891-0323
Roger B Souders, *CEO*
Nate Souders, *Buyer*
EMP: 13
SQ FT: 6,000
SALES (est): 2.4MM **Privately Held**
SIC: 3444 Sheet metal specialties, not stamped

(P-12450)
A & J PRECISION SHEETMETAL INC
1161 N 4th St, San Jose (95112-4945)
PHONE...................................408 885-9134
Amrik Atwal, *CEO*
Jagtar Atwal, *President*
Suki Atwal, *Vice Pres*
Zenelia Aguilar, *Manager*
▲ **EMP:** 52
SQ FT: 1,600
SALES (est): 10.6MM **Privately Held**
WEB: www.ajsheetmetal.com
SIC: 3444 Sheet metalwork

(P-12451)
A & M SCULPTURED METALS LLC
Also Called: A & M Sculpture Lighting
1781 N Indiana St, Los Angeles (90063-2523)
PHONE...................................323 263-2221
Jerry Orlandini,
EMP: 30
SQ FT: 10,000
SALES (est): 5MM **Privately Held**
SIC: 3444 Sheet metalwork

(P-12452)
A H K ELECTRONIC SHTMTL INC
875 Jarvis Dr Ste 120, Morgan Hill (95037-2887)
PHONE...................................408 778-3901
Vinai Kumar, *President*
Farid Ghantous, *COO*
Malisha Maupin, *Vice Pres*
Paul Pace, *Accounts Exec*
EMP: 20
SQ FT: 30,000
SALES (est): 3.9MM **Privately Held**
WEB: www.ahksheetmetal.com
SIC: 3444 Sheet metal specialties, not stamped

(P-12453)
A R S MECHANICAL
1205 N 5th St Frnt Frnt, San Jose (95112-4443)
PHONE...................................408 288-8822
Henry Lee, *President*
Connie Wong, *President*
EMP: 12
SALES: 1MM **Privately Held**
SIC: 3444 1711 Metal ventilating equipment; hoods, range: sheet metal; plumbing, heating, air-conditioning contractors

(P-12454)
A-1 METAL PRODUCTS INC
2707 Supply Ave, Commerce (90040-2703)
PHONE...................................323 721-3334
Jerry Calsbeek, *President*
Patricia Calsbeek, *Corp Secy*

EMP: 24 **EST:** 1952
SQ FT: 40,000
SALES (est): 5MM **Privately Held**
WEB: www.a1metalproducts.com
SIC: 3444 Sheet metal specialties, not stamped

(P-12455)
ABC MECHANICAL INC
Also Called: El Cajon Sheet Metal Mfg
10521 Ironwood Ave, Santee (92071-1202)
PHONE...................................619 520-4643
Bonnie Brandt, *President*
EMP: 30
SQ FT: 18,000
SALES (est): 2.8MM **Privately Held**
SIC: 3444 Sheet metalwork

(P-12456)
ABLE SHEET METAL INC (PA)
614 N Ford Blvd, Los Angeles (90022-1195)
PHONE...................................323 269-2181
Dmitri Triphon, *CEO*
Gurgen Tovmasyan, *Vice Pres*
Marina Kalinin, *Office Mgr*
Sharon Cohn, *Technology*
Sharon Cofsky Cohn, *Manager*
▲ **EMP:** 40
SQ FT: 25,000
SALES: 6MM **Privately Held**
SIC: 3444 Sheet metal specialties, not stamped

(P-12457)
ACCURATE HEATING & COOLING INC
Also Called: Tru-Fit Manufacturing
3515 Yosemite Ave, Lathrop (95330-9748)
PHONE...................................209 858-4125
Joan Kauffman, *President*
Melvin Kauffman, *Shareholder*
Jill Brandenburg, *Corp Secy*
Janet Murray, *Manager*
EMP: 23
SQ FT: 30,000
SALES (est): 5MM **Privately Held**
WEB: www.deltaac.com
SIC: 3444 Ducts, sheet metal

(P-12458)
ADAMS-CAMPBELL COMPANY LTD
15323 Proctor Ave, City of Industry (91745-1022)
P.O. Box 3867 (91744-0867)
PHONE...................................626 330-3425
Bob Ludlam, *General Mgr*
EMP: 25
SALES (corp-wide): 12MM **Privately Held**
WEB: www.adamscampbell.com
SIC: 3444 Sheet metalwork
PA: Adams-Campbell Company Ltd
15343 Proctor Ave
City Of Industry CA 91745
626 330-3425

(P-12459)
ADVANCED METAL MFG INC
49 Strathearn Pl, Simi Valley (93065-1653)
PHONE...................................805 322-4161
Scott Stewart, *CEO*
Gina Stewart, *Controller*
▲ **EMP:** 23
SALES (est): 4.4MM **Privately Held**
SIC: 3444 Sheet metalwork

(P-12460)
ADVANCED METAL WORKS INC
1560 H St, Fresno (93721-1616)
PHONE...................................559 237-2332
Preston Cross, *President*
Graydon William Cross, *Manager*
EMP: 11
SALES (est): 1.6MM **Privately Held**
WEB: www.fourcsmetal.com
SIC: 3444 Awnings & canopies

(P-12461)
ADVANCED MFG & DEV INC
Also Called: Metalfx
200 N Lenore Ave, Willits (95490-3209)
PHONE...................................707 459-9451
Gordon Short, *President*
▲ **EMP:** 122

SQ FT: 65,000
SALES: 19.6MM
SALES (corp-wide): 1.4B **Publicly Held**
WEB: www.metalfx.com
SIC: 3444 2541 3469 3567 Housings for business machines, sheet metal; cabinets, except refrigerated: show, display, etc.: wood; metal stampings; industrial furnaces & ovens; coin-operated amusement machines; boxes, wood
PA: Avista Corporation
1411 E Mission Ave
Spokane WA 99202
509 489-0500

(P-12462)
AERO BENDING COMPANY
560 Auto Center Dr Ste A, Palmdale (93551-4485)
PHONE...................................661 948-2363
Robert Burns, *President*
EMP: 30
SQ FT: 26,000
SALES (est): 8.4MM **Privately Held**
WEB: www.aerobendingco.com
SIC: 3444 5088 Sheet metalwork; aircraft engines & engine parts

(P-12463)
AERO PRECISION ENGINEERING INC
11300 Hindry Ave, Los Angeles (90045-6228)
PHONE...................................310 642-9747
Sherry L Martinez, *President*
John Segotta, *Prgrmr*
Tom Segotta, *Exec Sec*
EMP: 45
SQ FT: 55,000
SALES (est): 8.1MM **Privately Held**
WEB: www.aeroprecisioneng.com
SIC: 3444 3599 Sheet metal specialties, not stamped; machine shop, jobbing & repair

(P-12464)
AF GOMES INC
901 Commercial St Ste 140, San Jose (95112-1441)
PHONE...................................408 453-7300
Albert Gomes, *President*
Fern Gomes, *COO*
Ashley Taylor, *Opers Staff*
EMP: 25
SQ FT: 1,100
SALES (est): 4.1MM **Privately Held**
SIC: 3444 Sheet metalwork

(P-12465)
AIR TRANSPORT MANUFACTURING
2629 Foothill Blvd, La Crescenta (91214-3511)
PHONE...................................818 504-3300
Kirn Kessen, *President*
John Callahan, *Vice Pres*
Richard Norris, *Admin Sec*
EMP: 10
SQ FT: 18,000
SALES (est): 750K **Privately Held**
SIC: 3444 Sheet metalwork

(P-12466)
AIRCRAFT STAMPING COMPANY INC
1285 Paseo Alicia, San Dimas (91773-4407)
PHONE...................................323 283-1239
Michael Nolan, *President*
Linda Nolan, *Shareholder*
EMP: 30
SQ FT: 17,900
SALES (est): 3.9MM **Privately Held**
WEB: www.aircraftstamping.com
SIC: 3444 3469 Sheet metalwork; metal stampings

(P-12467)
AIRTRONICS METAL PRODUCTS INC (PA)
140 San Pedro Ave, Morgan Hill (95037-5123)
PHONE...................................408 977-7800
Jeff Burke, *CEO*
John Richardson, *Ch of Bd*

James Ellis, *Vice Pres*
Fermin Rodriguez, *Vice Pres*
▲ **EMP:** 139
SQ FT: 55,000
SALES (est): 37.4MM **Privately Held**
WEB: www.airtronics.com
SIC: 3444 3479 Sheet metalwork; painting, coating & hot dipping

(P-12468)
AKAS MANUFACTURING CORPORATION
Also Called: Labtronix
3200 Investment Blvd, Hayward (94545-3807)
PHONE...................510 786-3200
Santosh Sud, *President*
Artie Sud, *Vice Pres*
EMP: 25
SQ FT: 60,000
SALES (est): 3.2MM **Privately Held**
WEB: www.labtronix.com
SIC: 3444 3441 Sheet metalwork; fabricated structural metal

(P-12469)
ALCO ENGRG & TOOLING CORP
Also Called: Alco Metal Fab
3001 Oak St, Santa Ana (92707-4235)
PHONE...................714 556-6060
Frank Vallefuoco, *President*
Angelo D'Eramo, *Corp Secy*
Tom Hare, *Vice Pres*
Arnold Casado, *Purchasing*
EMP: 40 EST: 1944
SQ FT: 32,000
SALES (est): 8.6MM **Privately Held**
SIC: 3444 Sheet metalwork

(P-12470)
ALL METAL FABRICATION
617 S Raymond Ave, Pasadena (91105-3219)
PHONE...................626 449-6191
Rick Meone, *Owner*
EMP: 10
SQ FT: 1,500
SALES (est): 879.4K **Privately Held**
SIC: 3444 Sheet metalwork

(P-12471)
ALL SPEC SHEET METAL INC
547 Bliss Ave, Pittsburg (94565-5001)
PHONE...................925 427-4900
Dwayne Jones, *President*
Dennis Jones, *Vice Pres*
Tim Sharkey, *General Mgr*
EMP: 12
SALES (est): 1.5MM **Privately Held**
SIC: 3444 1761 Sheet metalwork; sheet metalwork

(P-12472)
ALL-WAYS METAL INC
401 E Alondra Blvd, Gardena (90248-2901)
PHONE...................310 217-1177
Shirley Pickens, *President*
Scott Pickens, *Vice Pres*
Jesse Gutierrez, *General Mgr*
Rachelle Pickens, *Info Tech Mgr*
EMP: 30
SQ FT: 29,000
SALES (est): 7.1MM **Privately Held**
WEB: www.allwaysmetal.com
SIC: 3444 Sheet metal specialties, not stamped

(P-12473)
ALLIANCE METAL PRODUCTS INC
20844 Plummer St, Chatsworth (91311-5004)
PHONE...................818 709-1204
Dan L Rowlett Jr, *CEO*
EMP: 212
SQ FT: 2,000
SALES (est): 726K **Privately Held**
SIC: 3444 Sheet metal specialties, not stamped

(P-12474)
ALPHA PRODUCTIONS INCORPORATED
5830 W Jefferson Blvd, Los Angeles (90016-3109)
PHONE...................310 559-1364
Missak Azirian, *President*
John Forker, *Controller*
▲ **EMP:** 25
SQ FT: 25,000
SALES (est): 3.8MM **Privately Held**
WEB: www.alphaawning.com
SIC: 3444 Awnings, sheet metal

(P-12475)
AMD INTERNATIONAL TECH LLC
Also Called: International Rite-Way Pdts
1725 S Campus Ave, Ontario (91761-4346)
PHONE...................909 985-8300
Ravinder Joshi,
EMP: 25
SQ FT: 17,000
SALES (est): 2.6MM **Privately Held**
SIC: 3444 1761 Sheet metal specialties, not stamped; sheet metalwork

(P-12476)
AMERICAN AEROSPACE PDTS INC
1720 S Santa Fe St, Santa Ana (92705-4813)
PHONE...................714 662-7620
Syed Ahsun, *President*
EMP: 15
SQ FT: 10,000
SALES (est): 725.9K **Privately Held**
SIC: 3444 3728 5072 Sheet metalwork; aircraft parts & equipment; hardware

(P-12477)
AMERICAN AIRCRAFT PRODUCTS INC
Also Called: A A P
15411 S Broadway, Gardena (90248-2207)
PHONE...................310 532-7434
Gerald R Tupper, *President*
EMP: 67
SQ FT: 54,000
SALES (est): 16.7MM **Privately Held**
WEB: www.americanaircraft.com
SIC: 3444 3599 Sheet metalwork; machine shop, jobbing & repair

(P-12478)
AMERICAN COFFEE URN MFG CO INC
Also Called: A C U Precision Sheet Metal
5178 Western Way, Perris (92571-7422)
PHONE...................951 943-1495
Jeff Johs, *President*
Andy Johs, *Vice Pres*
EMP: 13
SQ FT: 9,280
SALES (est): 2MM **Privately Held**
SIC: 3444 Sheet metalwork

(P-12479)
AMERICAN METAL PROCESSING
390 Front St, El Cajon (92020-4206)
PHONE...................619 444-6171
Daniel Cummings, *President*
EMP: 30
SQ FT: 15,000
SALES (est): 4MM **Privately Held**
SIC: 3444

(P-12480)
AMERICAN RANGE CORPORATION
13592 Desmond St, Pacoima (91331-2315)
PHONE...................818 897-0808
Shane Demirjian, *President*
Mourad Demirjian, *Vice Pres*
Jose Guevara, *General Mgr*
Nairi Lakhouian, *Engineer*
Albert M Too, *Engineer*
◆ **EMP:** 120
SQ FT: 125,000
SALES (est): 26.9MM **Privately Held**
WEB: www.americanrange.com
SIC: 3444 3631 Hoods, range: sheet metal; household cooking equipment

(P-12481)
AMERICAN SHEET METAL INC
1430 N Daly St, Anaheim (92806-1502)
PHONE...................714 780-0155
Eli Choueiry, *President*
EMP: 11
SQ FT: 5,588
SALES (est): 2.1MM **Privately Held**
SIC: 3444 Sheet metal specialties, not stamped

(P-12482)
ANDRUS SHEET METAL INC
Also Called: Seaport Stainless
5021 Seaport Ave, Richmond (94804-4638)
PHONE...................510 232-8687
Ray Doving, *President*
Linda Doving, *Vice Pres*
Ryan Doving, *Vice Pres*
Larry Camilleri, *Plant Mgr*
EMP: 30 EST: 1977
SQ FT: 14,000
SALES (est): 6.9MM **Privately Held**
WEB: www.seaportstainless.com
SIC: 3444 Restaurant sheet metalwork

(P-12483)
ANGELS SHEET METAL INC
Also Called: Distinctive Metals By Angel S
320 N Main St, Angels Camp (95222-9206)
PHONE...................209 736-0911
Jerri Mills, *President*
EMP: 10
SALES (corp-wide): 4.9MM **Privately Held**
SIC: 3444 Sheet metalwork
PA: Angel's Sheet Metal, Inc.
2502 Gun Club Rd
Angels Camp CA 95222
209 736-0911

(P-12484)
ANGELUS SHEET METAL MFG CO
Also Called: Angelus Sheet Metal & Plbg Sup
4800 Valley Blvd, Los Angeles (90032-3315)
PHONE...................323 221-4191
Ronald S Coutin, *President*
Leonard Coutin, *Manager*
EMP: 13
SQ FT: 24,000
SALES (est): 1.1MM **Privately Held**
SIC: 3444 Sheet metalwork

(P-12485)
ANOROC PRECISION SHTMTL INC
19122 S Santa Fe Ave, Compton (90221-5910)
PHONE...................310 515-6015
Roxanne Zavala, *CEO*
Pete Corona, *Vice Pres*
James Roberts, *Engineer*
EMP: 25 EST: 1978
SQ FT: 15,000
SALES (est): 4.5MM **Privately Held**
WEB: www.anoroc.com
SIC: 3444 Sheet metal specialties, not stamped

(P-12486)
AP PRECISION METALS INC
1215 30th St, San Diego (92154-3477)
PHONE...................619 628-0003
Lane A Litke, *CEO*
Susan D Miller, *Treasurer*
Victor B Miller, *Vice Pres*
Dustin Campbell, *General Mgr*
Logan Litke, *General Mgr*
EMP: 11
SALES (est): 2MM **Privately Held**
WEB: www.apprecision.com
SIC: 3444 Sheet metalwork

(P-12487)
ARRK PRODUCT DEV GROUP USA INC
4747 Executive Dr Ste 550, San Diego (92121-3118)
PHONE...................858 552-1587
Carlos Herrera, *President*
Koji Tsujino, *CEO*
Takuya Kasai, *CFO*

▲ **EMP:** 145
SQ FT: 37,764
SALES (est): 27.6MM
SALES (corp-wide): 12.4B **Privately Held**
SIC: 3444 Sheet metalwork
HQ: Arrk Corporation
2-2-9, Minamihommachi, Chuo-Ku
Osaka OSK 541-0
662 601-801

(P-12488)
ARTHUR P LAMARRE & SONS INC
1918 Paulson Rd Ste 101, Turlock (95380-8738)
P.O. Box 2704 (95381-2704)
PHONE...................209 667-6557
Arthur Lamarre Jr, *President*
Steven Lamarre, *CFO*
Kevin Lamarre, *Vice Pres*
David Lamarre, *Admin Sec*
EMP: 10
SQ FT: 7,500
SALES (est): 1MM **Privately Held**
SIC: 3444 Ducts, sheet metal

(P-12489)
ARTISTIC WELDING INC
Also Called: Precision Sheet Metal
505 E Gardena Blvd, Gardena (90248-2915)
PHONE...................310 515-4922
George R Sandoval, *President*
Mary Sandoval, *Admin Sec*
EMP: 65 EST: 1974
SQ FT: 85,000
SALES (est): 11.2MM **Privately Held**
WEB: www.artistic-welding.com
SIC: 3444 Sheet metalwork

(P-12490)
ASCENT TECHNOLOGY INC
838 Jury Ct, San Jose (95112-2815)
PHONE...................408 213-1080
Mark S Fanelli, *President*
Frank Tseng, *CEO*
Joy Kan, *Human Res Mgr*
Jeff Cherenoff, *VP Sales*
▲ **EMP:** 35
SALES (est): 4.5MM **Privately Held**
WEB: www.ascenttech.com
SIC: 3444 3364 Sheet metalwork; nonferrous die-castings except aluminum

(P-12491)
ASM CONSTRUCTION INC
Also Called: American Sheet Metal
1947 John Towers Ave, El Cajon (92020-1117)
PHONE...................619 449-1966
Robert Burner, *President*
Ron Burner Jr, *CFO*
EMP: 41
SQ FT: 9,000
SALES (est): 9.2MM **Privately Held**
WEB: www.americansm.com
SIC: 3444 Sheet metalwork

(P-12492)
ASM PRECISION INC
613 Martin Ave Ste 106, Rohnert Park (94928-2000)
PHONE...................707 584-7950
Mario R Felciano, *President*
Jay Sandoval, *Vice Pres*
EMP: 15 EST: 2007
SQ FT: 9,000
SALES (est): 4MM **Privately Held**
SIC: 3444 Sheet metal specialties, not stamped

(P-12493)
ATLAS SHEET METAL INC
19 Musick, Irvine (92618-1638)
PHONE...................949 600-8787
James M Odlum, *President*
EMP: 17
SQ FT: 5,500
SALES (est): 3.5MM **Privately Held**
WEB: www.atlassheetmetal.net
SIC: 3444 Sheet metalwork

PRODUCTS & SVCS

(P-12494)
AWNING MATRIX
Also Called: Biagel One
4319 Santa Ana St Ste B, Ontario
(91761-7852)
PHONE...................................909 447-5100
Mark Burg, *Owner*
Roana Burg, *Owner*
EMP: 11
SQ FT: 12,000
SALES (est): 674.8K **Privately Held**
SIC: 3444 Awnings & canopies

(P-12495)
AXIAL INDUSTRIES INC
1991 Senter Rd, San Jose (95112-2631)
PHONE...................................408 977-7800
Buddy G Rogers Jr, *CEO*
Michael Nevin, *Principal*
EMP: 145
SQ FT: 42,000
SALES (est): 13.6MM
SALES (corp-wide): 37.4MM **Privately Held**
WEB: www.axialind.com
SIC: 3444 Sheet metal specialties, not stamped
PA: Airtronics Metal Products, Inc.
140 San Pedro Ave
Morgan Hill CA 95037
408 977-7800

(P-12496)
AYMAR ENGINEERING
9434 Abraham Way, Santee (92071-5835)
PHONE...................................619 562-1121
Wayne Aymar, *Owner*
EMP: 14
SQ FT: 13,000
SALES (est): 2.2MM **Privately Held**
WEB: www.aymarengineering.com
SIC: 3444 3469 Sheet metal specialties, not stamped; metal stampings

(P-12497)
AZACHOROK CONTRACT SVCS LLC
320 Grand Cypress Ave # 502, Palmdale
(93551-3622)
PHONE...................................661 951-6566
Loren Peterson,
EMP: 14
SQ FT: 12,000
SALES (est): 2.5MM **Privately Held**
WEB: www.accuratemachineco.com
SIC: 3444 3663 Sheet metalwork; airborne radio communications equipment; carrier equipment, radio communications

(P-12498)
B & CAWNINGS INC
Also Called: B & C Industries
3082 E Miraloma Ave, Anaheim
(92806-1810)
PHONE...................................714 632-3303
CHI Le, *Chairman*
Buu Pham, *President*
Jeff Pham, *Vice Pres*
Chris Walker, *Vice Pres*
Matthew Walker, *Vice Pres*
▲ **EMP:** 30
SQ FT: 7,000
SALES (est): 4.2MM **Privately Held**
WEB: www.bcawnings.com
SIC: 3444 Awnings, sheet metal

(P-12499)
B & G METAL INC
9408 Gidley St, Temple City (91780-4211)
PHONE...................................626 444-8566
Bob Ellingsworth, *President*
EMP: 12
SALES (est): 935.9K **Privately Held**
WEB: www.bgsminc.com
SIC: 3444 Sheet metalwork

(P-12500)
B METAL FABRICATION INC
318 S Maple Ave, South San Francisco
(94080-6306)
PHONE...................................650 615-7705
Robert Steinebel, *CEO*
Berthold Steinebel, *President*
Brigitte Steinebel, *CFO*
Barbara Blundell, *Vice Pres*
Bob Foster, *Vice Pres*
EMP: 30
SQ FT: 14,000
SALES (est): 6MM **Privately Held**
WEB: www.bmetalfabrication.com
SIC: 3444 Sheet metal specialties, not stamped

(P-12501)
BARZILLAI MANUFACTURING CO
1410 S Cucamonga Ave, Ontario
(91761-4509)
PHONE...................................909 947-4200
Ray Richmond, *President*
Garrett Zopf, *Treasurer*
EMP: 17
SQ FT: 5,200
SALES (est): 2.2MM **Privately Held**
SIC: 3444 Sheet metalwork

(P-12502)
BASMAT INC (PA)
Also Called: McStarlite
1531 240th St, Harbor City (90710-1308)
PHONE...................................310 325-2063
John W Basso, *CEO*
John Allen Basso, *President*
Sharon Stelter, *Admin Sec*
Yevgeny Korolyov, *Administration*
Mark Ryan, *Administration*
▲ **EMP:** 100
SQ FT: 42,000
SALES (est): 20.7MM **Privately Held**
WEB: www.mcstarlite.com
SIC: 3444 Sheet metalwork

(P-12503)
BAY CITIES TIN SHOP INC
Also Called: Bay Cities Metal Products
301 E Alondra Blvd, Gardena
(90248-2809)
PHONE...................................310 660-0351
Henry Kamberg, *CEO*
Gary Mugford, *President*
Debra Childress, *Vice Pres*
EMP: 43
SALES (est): 9.1MM **Privately Held**
WEB: www.baycitiesmetalproducts.com
SIC: 3444 Sheet metal specialties, not stamped

(P-12504)
BELLAMA CSTM MET FBRCATORS INC
Also Called: B C M
3129 Main St, Chula Vista (91911-5705)
PHONE...................................619 585-3351
Michael Bellama, *President*
Randy Bellama, *Treasurer*
Don Bellama, *Vice Pres*
Robert Page, *Vice Pres*
Jo Ann Bellama, *Admin Sec*
EMP: 10
SQ FT: 10,000
SALES (est): 1.4MM **Privately Held**
SIC: 3444 Sheet metalwork

(P-12505)
BEND-TEK INC
3431 W Maywood Ave, Santa Ana
(92704-4423)
PHONE...................................714 210-8966
Mac Le, *President*
Mactin Le, *President*
EMP: 45
SQ FT: 7,000
SALES (est): 9.1MM **Privately Held**
WEB: www.bendtekinc.com
SIC: 3444 Pipe, sheet metal

(P-12506)
BMB METAL PRODUCTS CORPORATION
Also Called: B M B
11460 Elks Cir, Rancho Cordova
(95742-7332)
PHONE...................................916 631-9120
Jerry Mc Donald, *President*
Jerry Donald, *Vice Pres*
Jolene Harlos,
Jim Lopey, *Manager*
EMP: 24 **EST:** 1966
SQ FT: 23,000

SALES (est): 6.3MM **Privately Held**
WEB: www.bmbcorp.com
SIC: 3444 Sheet metalwork

(P-12507)
BOOZAK INC
Also Called: K Squared Metals
508 Chaney St Ste A, Lake Elsinore
(92530-2797)
PHONE...................................951 245-6045
Kevin Kluzak, *President*
Kevin Booth, *Vice Pres*
EMP: 45
SALES (est): 5.8MM **Privately Held**
WEB: www.boozak.com
SIC: 3444 Sheet metalwork

(P-12508)
BORGA STL BLDNGS CMPONENTS INC
300 W Peach St, Fowler (93625-2530)
P.O. Box 35 (93625-0035)
PHONE...................................559 834-5375
Ronald Heskett, *CEO*
Pete Garza, *Opers Mgr*
EMP: 35
SQ FT: 90,000
SALES (est): 10MM **Privately Held**
SIC: 3444 3448 3446 Metal housings, enclosures, casings & other containers; buildings, portable: prefabricated metal; railings, prefabricated metal

(P-12509)
BOTNER MANUFACTURING INC
900 Aladdin Ave, San Leandro
(94577-4308)
PHONE...................................510 569-2943
Donn Botner, *President*
Shelly Botner, *Sales Mgr*
▲ **EMP:** 10
SQ FT: 45,000
SALES (est): 3.6MM **Privately Held**
SIC: 3444 3441 Sheet metalwork; fabricated structural metal

(P-12510)
BRADY SHEET METAL INC
320 N Victory Blvd, Burbank (91502-1840)
PHONE...................................818 846-4043
Steve Drugan, *President*
Craig Brady, *Vice Pres*
EMP: 10 **EST:** 1933
SQ FT: 5,000
SALES (est): 1.5MM **Privately Held**
SIC: 3444 Sheet metalwork

(P-12511)
BROADWAY AC HTG & SHTMTL
Also Called: Broadway Sheet Metal
7855 Burnet Ave, Santa Monica (90404)
PHONE...................................310 829-3416
Alexander Merzel, *President*
Anna Merzel, *CFO*
Vince Lombardo, *Admin Sec*
EMP: 35
SQ FT: 7,000
SALES (est): 4MM **Privately Held**
SIC: 3444 Sheet metalwork

(P-12512)
BT SHEET METAL INC
1031 Calle Trepadora D, San Clemente
(92673-6289)
PHONE...................................949 481-5715
Brad Tetherton, *President*
EMP: 12
SQ FT: 5,000
SALES: 1.3MM **Privately Held**
SIC: 3444 Sheet metalwork

(P-12513)
BURLINGAME HTG VENTILATION INC
821 Malcolm Rd, Burlingame (94010-1406)
PHONE...................................650 697-9142
Douglass Ulrich, *CEO*
Fred Ulrich, *President*
Patricia Ann Ulrich, *Corp Secy*
EMP: 15
SQ FT: 3,000
SALES (est): 2.6MM **Privately Held**
SIC: 3444 1711 Sheet metalwork; heating & air conditioning contractors

(P-12514)
C & J METAL PRODUCTS INC
6323 Alondra Blvd, Paramount
(90723-3750)
P.O. Box 130, Bellflower (90707-0130)
PHONE...................................562 634-3101
Roy L Chapman, *President*
Isabelle Chapman, *Corp Secy*
▲ **EMP:** 40 **EST:** 1946
SQ FT: 37,000
SALES (est): 6.3MM **Privately Held**
WEB: www.cjmetals.com
SIC: 3444 Ventilators, sheet metal

(P-12515)
C&J FAB CENTER INC
Also Called: Gardena Sheet Metal
1415 W 135th St, Gardena (90249-2232)
PHONE...................................310 323-0970
Charlie Rim, *President*
EMP: 10
SQ FT: 12,000
SALES (est): 1.3MM **Privately Held**
SIC: 3444 Sheet metalwork

(P-12516)
C&O MANUFACTURING COMPANY INC
9640 Beverly Rd, Pico Rivera
(90660-2137)
PHONE...................................562 692-7525
Cesar Gonzalez, *President*
Luz Rivera, *Officer*
Oscar Valdez, *Vice Pres*
EMP: 67
SQ FT: 22,000
SALES (est): 13.1MM **Privately Held**
WEB: www.cnomfg.com
SIC: 3444 Sheet metal specialties, not stamped

(P-12517)
CAD WORKS INC
16366 E Valley Blvd, La Puente
(91744-5546)
PHONE...................................626 336-5491
David Paquini, *President*
Cecilia Chavez, *CFO*
Avrahan Garcia, *Vice Pres*
Abraham Garcia, *Mktg Dir*
EMP: 20
SQ FT: 10,000
SALES: 100K **Privately Held**
WEB: www.cadworks.us
SIC: 3444 Sheet metalwork

(P-12518)
CAL PAC SHEET METAL INC
2720 S Main St Ste B, Santa Ana
(92707-3404)
PHONE...................................714 979-2733
Marushkah Kurtz, *CEO*
Collin Cumbee, *CFO*
Bob Catalano, *Vice Pres*
Carolyn Miller, *Principal*
Craig Faucher, *Project Mgr*
EMP: 40
SQ FT: 5,000
SALES (est): 8MM **Privately Held**
WEB: www.calpacsheetmetal.com
SIC: 3444 Sheet metal specialties, not stamped

(P-12519)
CALIFORNIA EXPANDED MET PDTS (PA)
Also Called: Cemco
13191 Crosrds Pkwy N 32, City of Industry
(91746)
PHONE...................................626 369-3564
Raymond E Poliquin, *CEO*
Richard Poliquin, *President*
Tom Porter, *Exec VP*
◆ **EMP:** 68 **EST:** 1982
SQ FT: 40,000
SALES (est): 73.8MM **Privately Held**
SIC: 3444 Sheet metalwork

(P-12520)
CALIFORNIA HYDROFORMING CO INC
850 Lawson St, City of Industry
(91748-1103)
PHONE...................................626 912-0036
David Bonafede, *President*

David Wickey, *Vice Pres*
EMP: 15 **EST:** 1956
SQ FT: 17,500
SALES (est): 3.3MM **Privately Held**
WEB: www.cal-hydro.com
SIC: 3444 3469 Sheet metalwork; stamping metal for the trade

(P-12521)
CALIFORNIA METAL GROUP INC
Also Called: B C Lighting
1205 S Alameda St, Compton
(90220-4803)
PHONE....................310 609-1400
Benjamin Castellanos, *President*
EMP: 12
SQ FT: 7,200
SALES: 1MM **Privately Held**
SIC: 3444 3441 Sheet metalwork; fabricated structural metal

(P-12522)
CALIFORNIA PANEL SYSTEMS LLP
1020 N Marshall Ave, El Cajon
(92020-1829)
PHONE....................619 562-7010
Joe Isom, *President*
Karl J Isom, *Partner*
EMP: 20
SALES (est): 1.1MM **Privately Held**
SIC: 3444 Sheet metalwork

(P-12523)
CALIFORNIA PRECISION PDTS INC
Also Called: Cppi
6790 Flanders Dr, San Diego (92121-2902)
PHONE....................858 638-7300
Joe Bean, *CEO*
Stacy Bean, *Administration*
EMP: 80
SQ FT: 50,000
SALES (est): 17.2MM **Privately Held**
WEB: www.calprec.com
SIC: 3444 Sheet metal specialties, not stamped

(P-12524)
CAMPBELL & LOFTIN INC
Also Called: Superior Sheet Metal
1560 N Missile Way, Anaheim
(92801-1223)
PHONE....................714 871-1950
Sue Loftin, *President*
Sue Loften, *President*
Casey Crowder, *Vice Pres*
EMP: 10
SQ FT: 15,000
SALES (est): 2MM **Privately Held**
SIC: 3444 Elbows, for air ducts, stovepipes, etc.: sheet metal

(P-12525)
CAPTIVE-AIRE SYSTEMS INC
2510 Cloudcrest Way, Riverside
(92507-3027)
PHONE....................951 231-5102
EMP: 13
SALES (corp-wide): 292.4MM **Privately Held**
SIC: 3444 Restaurant sheet metalwork
PA: Captive-Aire Systems, Inc.
4641 Paragon Park Rd # 104
Raleigh NC 27616
919 882-2410

(P-12526)
CAPTIVE-AIRE SYSTEMS INC
6856 Lockheed Dr, Redding (96002-9769)
PHONE....................530 351-7150
Csaba Sikur, *Branch Mgr*
EMP: 140
SALES (corp-wide): 292.4MM **Privately Held**
WEB: www.captiveaire.com
SIC: 3444 Metal ventilating equipment
PA: Captive-Aire Systems, Inc.
4641 Paragon Park Rd # 104
Raleigh NC 27616
919 882-2410

(P-12527)
CARDINAL SHEET METAL INC
3184 Durahart St, Riverside (92507-3449)
PHONE....................951 788-8800

Penny Seyler, *President*
Bruce Seyler, *Vice Pres*
Johny Riteveld, *Admin Sec*
EMP: 10
SQ FT: 9,000
SALES (est): 1.5MM **Privately Held**
SIC: 3444 Roof deck, sheet metal; siding, sheet metal

(P-12528)
CARSON VALLEY INC
13215 Barton Cir, Whittier (90605-3255)
PHONE....................562 906-0062
Mark Priestley, *President*
Carmen Priestley, *Vice Pres*
Gary Lemay, *Foreman/Supr*
EMP: 11
SQ FT: 6,500
SALES (est): 1.1MM **Privately Held**
WEB: www.carsonvalley.com
SIC: 3444 Pipe, sheet metal

(P-12529)
CARTEL INDUSTRIES LLC
17152 Armstrong Ave, Irvine (92614-5718)
PHONE....................949 474-3200
William Penick,
Vickie Chukiat, *Controller*
Kirby Unfried, *QC Mgr*
Andy Van Der Roest, *Sales Staff*
Gant Penick,
▲ **EMP:** 49
SQ FT: 30,000
SALES (est): 13.3MM **Privately Held**
WEB: www.cartelind.com
SIC: 3444 Sheet metal specialties, not stamped

(P-12530)
CG MANUFACTURING INC
Also Called: K-Bros
21021 Osborne St, Canoga Park
(91304-1744)
PHONE....................818 886-1191
George Thomas, *President*
Bill Kim, *Vice Pres*
EMP: 11
SQ FT: 15,000
SALES (est): 195.1K **Privately Held**
WEB: www.k-bros.com
SIC: 3444 Sheet metalwork

(P-12531)
CIRCLEMASTER INC
7777 Alvarado Rd Ste 320, La Mesa
(91942-8247)
PHONE....................858 578-3900
Neville T Henkel Jr, *President*
EMP: 10
SQ FT: 4,000
SALES (est): 920K **Privately Held**
WEB: www.circlemaster.net
SIC: 3444 Sheet metalwork

(P-12532)
CLARKWESTERN DIETRICH BUILDING
Also Called: Clarkdietrich Building Systems
6510 General Rd, Riverside (92509-0103)
PHONE....................951 360-3500
Clark Dietrich, *Owner*
Reymundo Rangel, *Programmer Anys*
EMP: 14
SALES (corp-wide): 20.2B **Privately Held**
SIC: 3444 8711 3081 Studs & joists, sheet metal; engineering services; vinyl film & sheet
HQ: Clarkwestern Dietrich Building Systems Llc
9050 Centre Pointe Dr
West Chester OH 45069

(P-12533)
COAST SHEET METAL INC
990 W 17th St, Costa Mesa (92627-4403)
PHONE....................949 645-2224
Wayne Chambers, *President*
Marna Chambers, *Vice Pres*
EMP: 35 **EST:** 1960
SQ FT: 3,800
SALES (est): 5.8MM **Privately Held**
WEB: www.coastsheetmetal.com
SIC: 3444 Sheet metal specialties, not stamped

(P-12534)
COMCO SHEET METAL COMPANY
237 Southbrook Pl, Clayton (94517-1035)
PHONE....................510 832-6433
Armand Butticci III, *President*
Maria Butticci, *Corp Secy*
EMP: 12 **EST:** 1945
SQ FT: 13,000
SALES (est): 1.6MM **Privately Held**
SIC: 3444 Restaurant sheet metalwork

(P-12535)
COMPUMERIC ENGINEERING INC
Also Called: Bearsaver
1390 S Milliken Ave, Ontario (91761-1585)
PHONE....................909 605-1697
Jeannie Hankins, *CEO*
David Moore, *COO*
EMP: 45
SQ FT: 30,000
SALES (est): 9.6MM **Privately Held**
WEB: www.compumeric.com
SIC: 3444 Sheet metalwork

(P-12536)
COMPUTER METAL PRODUCTS CORP
Also Called: Vline Industries
370 E Easy St, Simi Valley (93065-1802)
PHONE....................805 520-6966
Jim Visage, *President*
Angel Angeles, *COO*
Karen Bender, *CFO*
Keith Murphy, *Prdtn Mgr*
Chris Visage, *Sales Mgr*
EMP: 90
SQ FT: 25,000
SALES (est): 18MM **Privately Held**
WEB: www.computermetal.com
SIC: 3444 Sheet metalwork

(P-12537)
CONCISE FABRICATORS INC
7550 Panasonic Way, San Diego
(92154-8207)
PHONE....................520 746-3226
James Dean Johnson, *President*
Bill Maples, *CFO*
Todd Krause, *Director*
Andy Platt, *Manager*
▼ **EMP:** 50
SQ FT: 120,000
SALES (est): 14.4MM **Privately Held**
SIC: 3444 Sheet metalwork
PA: Blackbird Management Group, Llc
240 E Illinois St # 2004
Chicago IL 60611
-

(P-12538)
CONTRACT METAL PRODUCTS INC
45535 Northport Loop W Fl Flr 1, Fremont
(94538)
PHONE....................510 979-4811
John Young, *President*
EMP: 30 **EST:** 1974
SQ FT: 80,000
SALES (est): 6.2MM **Privately Held**
WEB: www.contractmetals.com
SIC: 3444 3599 7692 Sheet metal specialties, not stamped; machine shop, jobbing & repair; welding repair

(P-12539)
COPP INDUSTRIAL MFG INC
2837 Metropolitan Pl, Pomona
(91767-1897)
PHONE....................909 593-7448
Larry R Marvin, *CEO*
Brian Hershman, *President*
EMP: 21
SQ FT: 15,000
SALES (est): 4.5MM **Privately Held**
WEB: www.coppmfg.com
SIC: 3444 Sheet metalwork

(P-12540)
CORTEC PRECISION SHTMTL INC (PA)
2231 Will Wool Dr, San Jose (95112-2628)
PHONE....................408 278-8540

Mike Corrales, *Vice Pres*
John Corrales, *President*
Richard Corrales, *Vice Pres*
Armando Miranda, *Technology*
Chris Chambers, *Engineer*
EMP: 153
SQ FT: 78,000
SALES: 21.5MM **Privately Held**
SIC: 3444 Sheet metal specialties, not stamped

(P-12541)
COY INDUSTRIES INC
Also Called: E R C Company
2970 E Maria St, E Rncho Dmngz
(90221-5802)
PHONE....................310 603-2970
Michael Coy, *President*
James Patrick Coy, *Corp Secy*
Pat Coy, *Project Leader*
Ramiro Espitia, *Engineer*
Edna Lockwood, *Human Res Dir*
EMP: 95 **EST:** 1972
SQ FT: 50,000
SALES: 5.8MM **Privately Held**
WEB: www.errcco.com
SIC: 3444 3469 Sheet metal specialties, not stamped; metal stampings

(P-12542)
CPC FABRICATION INC
2904 Oak St, Santa Ana (92707-3723)
PHONE....................714 549-2426
Thomas Baker, *CEO*
Stacey Sarver, *Office Mgr*
Lyn Baker, *Admin Sec*
Jonathan Edwards, *Director*
EMP: 31
SQ FT: 15,000
SALES (est): 6.4MM **Privately Held**
WEB: www.cpcfab.com
SIC: 3444 Sheet metal specialties, not stamped

(P-12543)
CREATIVE MFG SOLUTIONS
18400 Sutter Blvd, Morgan Hill
(95037-2819)
PHONE....................408 327-0600
Tim Patrick Herlihy, *President*
Tammy Herlihy, *CFO*
Jorge Magana, *Prgrmr*
Mike Provencio, *Engineer*
Gilbert Ruiz, *QC Mgr*
EMP: 22
SQ FT: 12,000
SALES (est): 5.9MM **Privately Held**
SIC: 3444 Sheet metal specialties, not stamped

(P-12544)
CROWN PRODUCTS INC
Also Called: Crown Steel
177 Newport Dr Ste A, San Marcos
(92069-1470)
PHONE....................760 471-1188
David J Carr, *President*
Carol Doherty, *Financial Exec*
EMP: 22 **EST:** 1969
SQ FT: 20,000
SALES (est): 4.6MM **Privately Held**
SIC: 3444 3589 Sheet metalwork; commercial cooking & foodwarming equipment

(P-12545)
CRUNCH METALS CO INC
15645 Commerce Ln, Huntington Beach
(92649-1603)
PHONE....................714 897-0552
James Hamilton, *CEO*
EMP: 11
SQ FT: 7,500
SALES (est): 1.4MM **Privately Held**
SIC: 3444 Sheet metalwork

(P-12546)
CUSTOM FABRICATED METALS LLC
14580 Manzanita Dr, Fontana
(92335-5377)
PHONE....................909 822-8828
Dan Vartan, *Mng Member*
Dave Macias,
EMP: 10 **EST:** 1997
SQ FT: 15,000

SALES (est): 2.2MM **Privately Held**
WEB: www.cfm2000.com
SIC: 3444 Sheet metalwork

(P-12547)
D & B PRECISION SHTMTL INC
693 Hi Tech Pkwy, Oakdale (95361-9372)
PHONE....................................209 848-3030
Loretta Ballard, *President*
Wes Ballard, *Vice Pres*
Rosa Hernandez, *Office Mgr*
Regi Mendoza, *Regl Sales Mgr*
Jorge Ayala, *Manager*
EMP: 12
SQ FT: 10,000
SALES (est): 3.1MM **Privately Held**
SIC: 3444 Sheet metalwork

(P-12548)
DAAZE INC
Also Called: C & H Metal Products
1714 S Grove Ave Ste B, Ontario
(91761-4550)
PHONE....................................626 442-4961
Octavio Hurtado, *Principal*
Jeanet Alvarez, *CFO*
Octavio Hurtado III, *Admin Sec*
EMP: 15 EST: 1982
SQ FT: 28,000
SALES (est): 2.4MM **Privately Held**
WEB: www.chmetals.com
SIC: 3444 Sheet metalwork

(P-12549)
DALE BRISCO INC
2132 S Temperance Ave, Fowler
(93625-9760)
PHONE....................................559 834-5926
Jamie Brisco, *President*
Blake Brisco, *Sales Staff*
EMP: 17
SQ FT: 50,000
SALES: 1MM **Privately Held**
WEB: www.dalebriscoinc.com
SIC: 3444 Pipe, sheet metal; ducts, sheet
metal; flues & pipes, stove or furnace:
sheet metal; pile shells, sheet metal

(P-12550)
DANRICH WELDING COINC
7001 Jackson St, Paramount (90723-4834)
PHONE....................................562 634-4811
Richard Schenk, *President*
Jacob Emeneger, *General Mgr*
EMP: 12 EST: 1970
SQ FT: 10,800
SALES (est): 1.8MM **Privately Held**
WEB: www.danrichwelding.com
SIC: 3444 7692 Sheet metalwork; welding
repair

(P-12551)
DAVE ANNALA
Also Called: Weld Design
1628 E Wilshire Ave, Santa Ana
(92705-4505)
PHONE....................................714 541-8383
Dave Annala, *Owner*
EMP: 10
SQ FT: 6,000
SALES: 899K **Privately Held**
SIC: 3444 7692 Sheet metalwork; welding
repair

(P-12552)
DAVE WHIPPLE SHEET METAL INC
1077 N Cuyamaca St, El Cajon
(92020-1803)
PHONE....................................619 562-6962
Dave Whipple Sr, *President*
Carol Whipple, *Treasurer*
Jillian Olshewski, *Executive Asst*
Stacy Riggs, *Admin Asst*
EMP: 34
SQ FT: 9,000
SALES (est): 7.2MM **Privately Held**
WEB: www.whipplesm.com
SIC: 3444 Sheet metalwork

(P-12553)
DECK WEST INC
1900 Sanguinetti Ln, Stockton
(95205-3403)
PHONE....................................209 939-9700
Patty Shipman, *CEO*

Cliff Heard, *Project Mgr*
EMP: 11
SQ FT: 26,000
SALES (est): 1.5MM **Privately Held**
WEB: www.deckwest.com
SIC: 3444 Metal roofing & roof drainage
equipment; metal flooring & siding

(P-12554)
DECRA ROOFING SYSTEMS INC (DH)
1230 Railroad St, Corona (92882-1837)
PHONE....................................951 272-8180
Willard C Hudson Jr, *President*
Chad Colton, *Vice Pres*
Tom Batterberry, *Executive*
Matt Albrecht, *Regional Mgr*
Jeff Bennett, *Regional Mgr*
▲ EMP: 70
SQ FT: 60,000
SALES (est): 29.6MM **Privately Held**
SIC: 3444 Metal roofing & roof drainage
equipment
HQ: Fletcher Building Holdings Usa, Inc.
1230 Railroad St
Corona CA 92882
951 272-8180

(P-12555)
DELAFOIL HOLDINGS INC (PA)
18500 Von Karman Ave # 450, Irvine
(92612-0504)
PHONE....................................949 752-4580
Drew Adams, *Managing Dir*
EMP: 310
SALES (est): 17.1MM **Privately Held**
WEB: www.stonecreekcapital.com
SIC: 3444 Radiator shields or enclosures,
sheet metal

(P-12556)
DELANEY MANUFACTURING INC
6810 Downing Ave, Bakersfield
(93308-5810)
PHONE....................................661 587-6681
Bill McBride, *Principal*
Mike Combs, *Opers Mgr*
EMP: 14 EST: 2008
SQ FT: 50,000
SALES: 2.5MM **Privately Held**
SIC: 3444 Sheet metalwork

(P-12557)
DELTA FABRICATION INC
9600 De Soto Ave, Chatsworth
(91311-5012)
PHONE....................................818 407-4000
Chava Ostrowsky, *CEO*
Joe Ostrowsky, *President*
Zvi Allweil, *Sls & Mktg Exec*
EMP: 90
SQ FT: 20,000
SALES (est): 17.1MM **Privately Held**
SIC: 3444 Sheet metalwork

(P-12558)
DEPENDABLE PRECISION MFG INC
1111 S Stockton St Ste A, Lodi
(95240-5933)
PHONE....................................209 369-1055
Clifford L McBride, *President*
EMP: 17 EST: 1978
SQ FT: 30,000
SALES: 2.3MM **Privately Held**
SIC: 3444 Sheet metal specialties, not
stamped

(P-12559)
DEROSA ENTERPRISES INC
Also Called: PSI
15935 Spring Oaks Rd # 1, El Cajon
(92021-2648)
PHONE....................................760 743-5500
Gabriel De Rosa, *President*
Matt De Rosa, *General Mgr*
Watt De Rosa, *General Mgr*
EMP: 40
SQ FT: 13,000
SALES (est): 6.6MM **Privately Held**
WEB: www.psimfg.com
SIC: 3444 Sheet metal specialties, not
stamped

(P-12560)
DEVINCENZI METAL PRODUCTS INC
1809 Castenada Dr, Burlingame
(94010-5716)
PHONE....................................650 692-5800
Robert C Devincenzi, *CEO*
Janice Samuelson, *Corp Secy*
Steven Devincenzi, *Vice Pres*
Albert Sevilla, *Supervisor*
▲ EMP: 75 EST: 1978
SQ FT: 90,000
SALES (est): 18.1MM **Privately Held**
WEB: www.devmetal.com
SIC: 3444 Sheet metal specialties, not
stamped

(P-12561)
DIMIC STEEL TECH INC
145 N 8th Ave, Upland (91786-5402)
PHONE....................................909 946-6767
Miles Dimic, *President*
Anna Dimic, *CFO*
▲ EMP: 24
SQ FT: 45,000
SALES (est): 6.8MM **Privately Held**
WEB: www.dimicsheetmetal.com
SIC: 3444 Sheet metal specialties, not
stamped

(P-12562)
DIRECT SURPLUS SALES INC
Also Called: Surplus Ctys Fbrction Mfg Wldg
4801 Feather River Blvd # 3, Oroville
(95965-9690)
PHONE....................................530 533-9999
Walter Seidenglanz, *Manager*
EMP: 10
SALES (corp-wide): 3.7MM **Privately
Held**
WEB: www.hwy70.net
SIC: 3444 Metal housings, enclosures,
casings & other containers
PA: Direct Surplus Sales Inc
4514 Pacific Heights Rd
Oroville CA 95965
530 534-9956

(P-12563)
DOKA USA LTD
Also Called: Conesco Industries
6901 Central Ave, Riverside (92504-1407)
PHONE....................................951 509-0023
Peter Franceschina, *Principal*
Pietro Da Sacco, *Engineer*
Sharon Abbott, *Opers Mgr*
EMP: 13
SALES (corp-wide): 1.7B **Privately Held**
SIC: 3444 Concrete forms, sheet metal
HQ: Doka Usa Ltd.
214 Gates Rd
Little Ferry NJ 07643
201 641-6500

(P-12564)
DUR-RED PRODUCTS
4900 Cecilia St, Cudahy (90201-5993)
PHONE....................................323 771-9000
Russell Smith, *President*
Linda Harrison, *Corp Secy*
EMP: 50
SQ FT: 135,000
SALES (est): 8.5MM **Privately Held**
WEB: www.dur-red.com
SIC: 3444 3446 Sheet metalwork; archi-
tectural metalwork

(P-12565)
E & S PRECISION SHEETMETAL MFG
19298 Mclane St, North Palm Springs
(92258)
P.O. Box 581136 (92258-1136)
PHONE....................................760 329-1607
Steve Egresits, *President*
Margit R Egresits, *Corp Secy*
EMP: 18
SQ FT: 10,000
SALES (est): 2.8MM **Privately Held**
SIC: 3444 Sheet metal specialties, not
stamped

(P-12566)
E-M MANUFACTURING INC
1290 Dupont Ct, Manteca (95336-6003)
P.O. Box 397, Half Moon Bay (94019-0397)
PHONE....................................209 825-1800
Jody Elliot, *President*
Mike Elliot, *Corp Secy*
Scott Hicken, *Manager*
EMP: 19
SQ FT: 15,500
SALES (est): 36.7K **Privately Held**
SIC: 3444 Sheet metal specialties, not
stamped; metal housings, enclosures,
casings & other containers

(P-12567)
ECB CORP
Also Called: Omni Duct Systems
1650 Parkway Blvd, West Sacramento
(95691-5020)
PHONE....................................916 492-8900
Lou Yuhas, *Branch Mgr*
Steve Pedroza, *Sales Mgr*
EMP: 40
SALES (est): 3.9MM
SALES (corp-wide): 27.6MM **Privately
Held**
WEB: www.omniduct.com
SIC: 3444 Ducts, sheet metal
PA: Ecb Corp.
6400 Artesia Blvd
Buena Park CA 90620
714 385-8900

(P-12568)
ECLIPSE METAL FABRICATION INC
2901 Spring St, Redwood City
(94063-3935)
PHONE....................................650 298-8731
Joe Anaya, *President*
Eduardo Molina, *CFO*
Eduardo Melina, *Treasurer*
Al Cuevas, *Financial Exec*
EMP: 50
SQ FT: 15,000
SALES (est): 12.4MM **Privately Held**
WEB: www.eclipsemf.com
SIC: 3444 Sheet metalwork

(P-12569)
EDWARDS SHEET METAL SUPPLY INC
7810 Burnet Ave, Van Nuys (91405-1009)
PHONE....................................818 785-8600
Edward Der-Mesropian, *President*
Jacqueline Der-Mesropian, *Corp Secy*
EMP: 25
SQ FT: 20,000
SALES (est): 4.3MM **Privately Held**
SIC: 3444 Booths, spray: prefabricated
sheet metal

(P-12570)
ELITE E/M INC
340 Martin Ave, Santa Clara (95050-3112)
PHONE....................................408 988-3505
Igor Brovarny, *President*
EMP: 32
SQ FT: 12,300
SALES: 5.1MM **Privately Held**
WEB: www.eliteem.com
SIC: 3444 3559 3599 3542 Forming ma-
chine work, sheet metal; semiconductor
manufacturing machinery; machine &
other job shop work; presses: forming,
stamping, punching, sizing (machine
tools); design, commercial & industrial;
mechanical engineering

(P-12571)
EMPIRE SHEET METAL INC
1215 S Bon View Ave, Ontario
(91761-4402)
PHONE....................................909 923-2927
Martin Layman, *President*
EMP: 14
SALES (est): 2.7MM **Privately Held**
SIC: 3444 Sheet metalwork

(P-12572)
EMTEC ENGINEERING
16840 Joleen Way Ste F1, Morgan Hill
(95037-4606)
PHONE....................................408 779-5800

▲ = Import ▼=Export
◆ =Import/Export

Edward R Ruminski, *President*
Cathy Britton, *Manager*
EMP: 19
SQ FT: 16,000
SALES (est): 4.2MM **Privately Held**
SIC: 3444 3599 3469 Sheet metalwork; machine shop, jobbing & repair; metal stampings

(P-12573)
ENCORE INDUSTRIES
597 Brennan St, San Jose (95131-1202)
PHONE................408 416-0501
Gary Vogel, *CEO*
Tom Fitzgerald, *Treasurer*
Gordon Tigue, *Vice Pres*
▲ **EMP:** 50
SALES (est): 11.8MM **Privately Held**
SIC: 3444 3441 Sheet metalwork; fabricated structural metal

(P-12574)
EQUIPMENT DESIGN & MFG INC
119 Explorer St, Pomona (91768-3278)
PHONE................909 594-2229
Rick Clewett, *CEO*
Steve Clewett, *Vice Pres*
Ryan Clewett, *Admin Sec*
Jack Cave, *Engineer*
EMP: 55
SQ FT: 27,400
SALES (est): 6.5MM **Privately Held**
WEB: www.equipmentdesign.net
SIC: 3444 Sheet metalwork

(P-12575)
ESM AEROSPACE INC
1203 W Isabel St, Burbank (91506-1407)
PHONE................818 841-3653
Jerome Flament, *President*
Rina Flament, *Admin Sec*
EMP: 25
SQ FT: 8,900
SALES: 2.9MM **Privately Held**
SIC: 3444 Casings, sheet metal

(P-12576)
ESPANA METAL CRAFT INC
7600 Ventura Canyon Ave, Van Nuys (91402-6372)
PHONE................818 988-4988
Salvador J Espana, *President*
Catalina Espana, *Owner*
EMP: 18
SQ FT: 7,300
SALES (est): 3.3MM **Privately Held**
WEB: www.espanametal.com
SIC: 3444 Sheet metalwork

(P-12577)
EVERT HANCOCK INCORPORATED
Also Called: Amfab
1809 N National St, Anaheim (92801-1016)
PHONE................714 870-0376
Greg Evert, *President*
Scott Evert, *General Mgr*
EMP: 10
SQ FT: 10,000
SALES: 90K **Privately Held**
SIC: 3444 Sheet metal specialties, not stamped

(P-12578)
EXCEL SHEET METAL INC (PA)
Also Called: Excel Bridge Manufacturing Co.
12001 Shoemaker Ave, Santa Fe Springs (90670-4718)
PHONE................562 944-0701
Craig E Vasquez, *CEO*
Jeffrey Vasquez, *Vice Pres*
▼ **EMP:** 60
SQ FT: 16,000
SALES (est): 9.6MM **Privately Held**
WEB: www.excelbridge.com
SIC: 3444 1622 Sheet metalwork; bridge construction

(P-12579)
EXECUTIVE TOOL INC
1220 N Richfield Rd, Anaheim (92807-1812)
PHONE................714 996-1276
Vahan Bandoian, *President*
Doris Bandoian, *Corp Secy*
Charles R Cook, *Vice Pres*

EMP: 28 **EST:** 1971
SQ FT: 20,000
SALES (est): 4.5MM **Privately Held**
SIC: 3444 3599 Sheet metalwork; machine shop, jobbing & repair

(P-12580)
EXHAUST CENTER INC
Also Called: Eci Fuel Systems
1794 W 11th St, Upland (91786-3504)
PHONE................951 685-8602
Greg S Mitchell, *CEO*
Robert Mitchell, *CFO*
EMP: 15
SQ FT: 15,000
SALES (est): 3.7MM **Privately Held**
WEB: www.ecifuelsystems.com
SIC: 3444 Sheet metalwork

(P-12581)
EXPRESS SHEET METAL PRODUCT
10131 Flora Vista St, Bellflower (90706-4804)
PHONE................562 925-9340
Ramon Castaneda, *Vice Pres*
EMP: 16
SQ FT: 6,000
SALES (est): 2.3MM **Privately Held**
SIC: 3444 Sheet metalwork

(P-12582)
F T B & SON INC
11551 Markon Dr, Garden Grove (92841-1808)
PHONE................714 891-8003
Frank Taylor Brown, *CEO*
Kathy M Ayers, *CFO*
EMP: 23 **EST:** 1972
SQ FT: 37,000
SALES (est): 4.6MM **Privately Held**
WEB: www.ftbson.com
SIC: 3444 Ducts, sheet metal

(P-12583)
FAB TRON
1358 N Jefferson St, Anaheim (92807-1614)
PHONE................714 996-4270
William Hayes, *Partner*
Robert Hayes, *Partner*
Chris Walker, *Administration*
EMP: 10
SQ FT: 17,000
SALES (est): 1.6MM **Privately Held**
WEB: www.fabtron.com
SIC: 3444 3441 Sheet metalwork; fabricated structural metal

(P-12584)
FABRICATION NETWORK INC
Also Called: Fabnet
5410 E La Palma Ave, Anaheim (92807-2023)
PHONE................714 393-5282
Robert F Denham, *President*
Donald V Eide, *CFO*
EMP: 75
SQ FT: 45,000
SALES (est): 7.5MM **Privately Held**
WEB: www.fabnetonline.com
SIC: 3444 3599 Metal housings, enclosures, casings & other containers; forming machine work, sheet metal; machine shop, jobbing & repair

(P-12585)
FABRITEC PRECISION INC (PA)
1060 Reno Ave, Modesto (95351-1233)
P.O. Box 32370, San Jose (95152-2370)
PHONE................209 529-8504
Jack Taek Bong Kim, *President*
Hester Lou-Kim, *Corp Secy*
EMP: 15 **EST:** 1997
SQ FT: 16,800
SALES (est): 1.9MM **Privately Held**
WEB: www.fabpi.com
SIC: 3444 Sheet metalwork

(P-12586)
FABTRONIC INC
5026 Calmview Ave, Baldwin Park (91706-1899)
PHONE................626 962-3293
Carlos Duarte, *President*
David Thompson, *Vice Pres*

▼ **EMP:** 20
SQ FT: 26,000
SALES (est): 2MM **Privately Held**
SIC: 3444 3829 Sheet metal specialties, not stamped; fare registers for street cars, buses, etc.

(P-12587)
FLETCHER BLDG HOLDINGS USA INC (DH)
1230 Railroad St, Corona (92882-1837)
PHONE................951 272-8180
Willard Hudson, *President*
Steve Jones, *CFO*
John Miller, *Vice Pres*
◆ **EMP:** 70
SQ FT: 60,000
SALES (est): 29.8MM **Privately Held**
SIC: 3444 Metal roofing & roof drainage equipment
HQ: Fletcher Building (Australia) Pty Ltd
L 4 68 Waterloo Rd
Macquarie Park NSW 2113
289 860-900

(P-12588)
FLEXTRONICS INTL PA INC
677 Gibraltar Dr, Milpitas (95035-6335)
PHONE................408 577-2489
Mukul Penmatcha, *Engineer*
Christopher Wiegel, *Engineer*
Tim Griffin, *Director*
Bob Stabler, *Director*
EMP: 11
SALES (corp-wide): 23.8B **Privately Held**
SIC: 3444 Sheet metalwork
HQ: Flextronics International Pa, Inc.
847 Gibraltar Dr
Milpitas CA 95035
408 576-7000

(P-12589)
FORCE FABRICATION INC
2233 Statham Blvd, Oxnard (93033-3913)
PHONE................805 754-2235
Justin Gamble, *Vice Pres*
Isabella Gamble, *President*
Anne Davis, *CFO*
EMP: 10
SALES: 500K **Privately Held**
SIC: 3444 Pipe, sheet metal

(P-12590)
FORTERRA PIPE & PRECAST LLC
30781 San Diego St, Shafter (93263-9764)
PHONE................661 746-3527
Deloras Thornberg, *Principal*
EMP: 15
SALES (corp-wide): 1.5B **Publicly Held**
SIC: 3444 3531 Sheet metalwork; asphalt plant, including gravel-mix type
HQ: Forterra Pipe & Precast, Llc
511 E John Carpenter Fwy
Irving TX 75062
469 458-7973

(P-12591)
FOUR SEASONS RESTAURANT EQP
412 Jenks Cir, Corona (92880-2506)
PHONE................951 278-9100
Larry Kaye, *President*
EMP: 29
SQ FT: 19,000
SALES (est): 4.5MM **Privately Held**
SIC: 3444 Restaurant sheet metalwork

(P-12592)
FUNKTION USA
3465 Ann Dr, Carlsbad (92008-2002)
PHONE................760 473-4171
John Bandimere, *Owner*
EMP: 10
SALES (est): 899.9K **Privately Held**
WEB: www.functionusa.com
SIC: 3444 7319 Sheet metalwork; display advertising service

(P-12593)
GAINES MANUFACTURING INC
12200 Kirkham Rd, Poway (92064-6806)
PHONE................858 486-7100
Ted Gaines, *Owner*
EMP: 40

SQ FT: 23,000
SALES (est): 6.5MM **Privately Held**
WEB: www.gainesmfg.com
SIC: 3444 Mail (post office) collection or storage boxes, sheet metal

(P-12594)
GARD INC
Also Called: Reliable Sheet Metal Works
524 E Walnut Ave, Fullerton (92832-2540)
PHONE................714 738-5891
Arthur Schade, *President*
Dan Schade, *Corp Secy*
Arthur Schade Jr, *Vice Pres*
EMP: 20 **EST:** 1956
SQ FT: 12,000
SALES (est): 3.9MM **Privately Held**
SIC: 3444 Sheet metal specialties, not stamped

(P-12595)
GCM MEDICAL & OEM DIVISION INC
Also Called: Global Contract Manufacturing
1350 Atlantic St, Union City (94587-2004)
PHONE................510 475-0404
Seanus Meaghr, *President*
Maria Martinez, *Purch Agent*
Walt Webster, *Opers Mgr*
Peter Peng, *Sales Executive*
Steve Kirby, *Facilities Mgr*
▲ **EMP:** 78 **EST:** 1983
SQ FT: 80,000
SALES (est): 30.5MM **Privately Held**
WEB:
www.globalcontractmanufacturing.com
SIC: 3444 3541 Sheet metalwork; machine tools, metal cutting type
PA: Hi-Tech Manufacturing, Llc
9815 Leland Ave
Schiller Park IL 60176

(P-12596)
GENERAL FORMING CORPORATION
2413 Moreton St, Torrance (90505-5395)
PHONE................310 326-0624
Charles E Vegher, *CEO*
Joanne Vegher, *Vice Pres*
Richard Rudshagen, *General Mgr*
Efrain Partida, *Prgrmr*
Tim Wall, *Purch Mgr*
EMP: 47
SQ FT: 18,000
SALES (est): 9.3MM **Privately Held**
SIC: 3444 3812 3769 Sheet metal specialties, not stamped; search & navigation equipment; guided missile & space vehicle parts & auxiliary equipment

(P-12597)
GEORGE HOOD INC
890 Faulstich Ct, San Jose (95112-1361)
PHONE................408 295-6507
Charles Crow, *Controller*
Katy Laubach, *President*
EMP: 34 **EST:** 2014
SALES (est): 1.8MM **Privately Held**
SIC: 3444 Roof deck, sheet metal

(P-12598)
GERARD ROOF PRODUCTS LLC (DH)
Also Called: Gerard Roofing Technologies
721 Monroe Way, Placentia (92870-6309)
PHONE................714 529-0407
Donald P Newman, *Mng Member*
EMP: 30
SALES (est): 4.6MM **Privately Held**
SIC: 3444 Sheet metalwork

(P-12599)
GKN AEROSPACE CAMARILLO INC
4680 Calle Carga, Camarillo (93012-8559)
PHONE................805 383-6684
Richard Oldfield, *CEO*
David Lind, *President*
Bernd Hermann, *CFO*
▲ **EMP:** 19
SQ FT: 25,000

SALES (est): 7.3MM
SALES (corp-wide): 12.7B **Privately Held**
WEB: www.sheetsmfg.com
SIC: 3444 Sheet metalwork
PA: Gkn Limited
　　Po Box 55
　　Redditch WORCS B98 0
　　152 751-7715

(P-12600)
GRAYD-A PRCSION MET FBRICATORS
13233 Florence Ave, Santa Fe Springs
(90670-4509)
PHONE............................562 944-8951
William Gray Jr, *President*
Jo Dell Gray, *Corp Secy*
William Gray III, *Vice Pres*
EMP: 20
SQ FT: 17,500
SALES (est): 4.2MM **Privately Held**
WEB: www.grayd-a.com
SIC: 3444 Sheet metal specialties, not stamped

(P-12601)
GRAYSIX COMPANY
2427 4th St, Berkeley (94710-2488)
PHONE............................510 845-5936
Robert Gray, *President*
Matthew D Gray, *Sales Staff*
EMP: 24 EST: 1946
SQ FT: 16,000
SALES (est): 3.8MM **Privately Held**
SIC: 3444 3469 Housings for business machines, sheet metal; metal stampings

(P-12602)
GROUP MANUFACTURING SERVICES (PA)
1928 Hartog Dr, San Jose (95131-2212)
PHONE............................408 436-1040
Curtis Molyneaux, *President*
Patti Thatcher, *CFO*
Dennis Mimolis, *Safety Mgr*
David Guerra, *Marketing Staff*
Dave Molyneaux, *Sales Staff*
EMP: 80
SQ FT: 30,000
SALES (est): 17.7MM **Privately Held**
WEB: www.groupmanufacturing.com
SIC: 3444 Ducts, sheet metal

(P-12603)
GROUP MANUFACTURING SERVICES
2751 Merc Dr Ste 900, Rancho Cordova (95742)
PHONE............................916 858-3270
Jerry Myrick, *Manager*
EMP: 13
SALES (corp-wide): 17.7MM **Privately Held**
WEB: www.groupmanufacturing.com
SIC: 3444 Sheet metal specialties, not stamped
PA: Group Manufacturing Services Inc
　　1928 Hartog Dr
　　San Jose CA 95131
　　408 436-1040

(P-12604)
GUTTERGLOVE INC
8860 Industrial Ave # 140, Roseville (95678-6204)
PHONE............................916 624-5000
Matt Smith, *CEO*
Catherine Austin, *Executive*
Robert Lenney, *Director*
▲ EMP: 60
SQ FT: 43,000
SALES: 11MM **Privately Held**
SIC: 3444 Gutters, sheet metal

(P-12605)
HAIMETAL DUCT INC
625 Arroyo St, San Fernando (91340-2219)
PHONE............................818 768-2315
Rouben Hovsepian, *President*
EMP: 16
SQ FT: 10,000
SALES: 2.2MM **Privately Held**
SIC: 3444 Ducts, sheet metal; ventilators, sheet metal

(P-12606)
HALLMARK METALS INC
600 W Foothill Blvd, Glendora (91741-2403)
PHONE............................626 335-1263
Joseph Allen Zerucha, *CEO*
Scott Schoenick, *President*
Marina Carmona, *Treasurer*
David Peifer, *Vice Pres*
Candice Schoenick, *Vice Pres*
EMP: 28 EST: 1959
SQ FT: 23,000
SALES (est): 6.5MM **Privately Held**
WEB: www.hallmarkmetals.com
SIC: 3444 3469 Sheet metalwork; machine parts, stamped or pressed metal

(P-12607)
HAMILTON METALCRAFT INC
848 N Fair Oaks Ave, Pasadena (91103-3046)
PHONE............................626 795-4811
Sandra Stahler, *President*
EMP: 25 EST: 1966
SQ FT: 10,000
SALES (est): 4.4MM **Privately Held**
WEB: www.hamiltonmetal.com
SIC: 3444 Casings, sheet metal

(P-12608)
HARDCRAFT INDUSTRIES INC
Also Called: Peninsula Metal Fabrication
2221 Ringwood Ave, San Jose (95131-1736)
PHONE............................408 432-8340
Andrew Brandt Kwiram, *President*
Bill Carrozza, *Purch Agent*
Mike Dometrovich, *Sales Executive*
Don Davis, *Sales Staff*
EMP: 52
SALES (est): 2.6MM **Privately Held**
SIC: 3444 Forming machine work, sheet metal

(P-12609)
HARO INDUSTRIES INC
Also Called: Hh Industries
9635 Heinrich Hertz Dr # 4, San Diego (92154-7918)
PHONE............................619 407-0500
Javier Haro, *Presidentt*
Katia Lopez, *Office Admin*
▲ EMP: 160 EST: 2009
SQ FT: 5,000
SALES: 1MM **Privately Held**
SIC: 3444 Sheet metalwork

(P-12610)
HARRIS PRECISION
Also Called: Harris Precision Sheet Metal
161 Lost Lake Ln, Campbell (95008-6615)
PHONE............................408 866-4160
Barry B Harris, *Owner*
EMP: 13
SQ FT: 2,000
SALES (est): 1.1MM **Privately Held**
SIC: 3444 Sheet metal specialties, not stamped

(P-12611)
HENRY LI
Also Called: Central Machine & Sheet Metal
1020 Rock Ave, San Jose (95131-1610)
PHONE............................408 944-9100
Henry LI, *Owner*
EMP: 10
SALES (est): 1.2MM **Privately Held**
SIC: 3444 Sheet metalwork

(P-12612)
HI-CRAFT METAL PRODUCTS
606 W 184th St, Gardena (90248-4282)
PHONE............................310 323-6949
Bill Gerich, *CEO*
Jennifer Gerich, *Shareholder*
Ted Gerich, *Shareholder*
Liz Gallagher, *Corp Secy*
Edward P Gerich, *Vice Pres*
EMP: 20 EST: 1948
SQ FT: 11,000
SALES (est): 4.4MM **Privately Held**
WEB: www.hicraftmetal.com
SIC: 3444 3469 Sheet metal specialties, not stamped; metal stampings

(P-12613)
HILL MANUFACTURING COMPANY LLC
3363 Edward Ave, Santa Clara (95054-2334)
PHONE............................408 988-4744
J Douglas Wickham,
Barbara A Wickham, *CFO*
Anthony Knezevich, *Managing Dir*
EMP: 46
SQ FT: 24,500
SALES (est): 9.2MM **Privately Held**
WEB: www.hill-mfg.com
SIC: 3444 Sheet metal specialties, not stamped

(P-12614)
HOLZINGER INDUS SHTMTL INC
12440 Mccann Dr, Santa Fe Springs (90670-3335)
PHONE............................562 944-6337
Frank Alverez, *President*
EMP: 12
SQ FT: 9,000
SALES: 1MM **Privately Held**
SIC: 3444 Sheet metalwork

(P-12615)
HP PRECISION INC
548 S Pacific St Ste B100, San Marcos (92078-4071)
PHONE............................760 752-9377
Bradley S Hayes, *President*
Tho Phan, *COO*
EMP: 21
SALES (est): 5MM **Privately Held**
WEB: www.hppmf.com
SIC: 3444 Sheet metalwork

(P-12616)
HSI MECHANICAL INC
1013 N Emerald Ave, Modesto (95351-2851)
PHONE............................209 408-0183
Tim Scott, *Principal*
Preston Stephens, *President*
Brent Holloway, *Vice Pres*
EMP: 21
SQ FT: 4,000
SALES (est): 1.2MM **Privately Held**
SIC: 3444 Sheet metalwork

(P-12617)
HUB CONSTRUCTION SPC INC
Also Called: Hub Construction Speciality
5310 San Fernando Rd, Glendale (91203-2407)
PHONE............................909 379-2100
Dean Oveton, *Branch Mgr*
EMP: 100
SALES (corp-wide): 48.1MM **Privately Held**
SIC: 3444 Concrete forms, sheet metal
PA: Hub Construction Specialties, Inc.
　　379 S I St
　　San Bernardino CA 92410
　　909 889-0161

(P-12618)
I & A INC
Also Called: Peninsula Metal Fabrication
2221 Ringwood Ave, San Jose (95131-1736)
PHONE............................408 432-8340
Anthony Davis, *President*
Heather Jevens, *CFO*
Ishbel Davis, *Vice Pres*
Ian Davis, *Principal*
Mike Dometrovich, *Sales Executive*
EMP: 41
SQ FT: 48,000
SALES (est): 7.4MM **Privately Held**
WEB: www.pmf.com
SIC: 3444 Sheet metal specialties, not stamped

(P-12619)
IMPAKT HOLDINGS LLC
490 Gianni St, Santa Clara (95054-2413)
PHONE............................650 692-5800
Dan Rubin, *CEO*
Daniel Yang, *COO*
Kirk Johnson, *CFO*
EMP: 14
SALES (est): 2.8MM **Privately Held**
SIC: 3444 Sheet metalwork

(P-12620)
INFINITY KITCHEN PRODUCTS INC
Also Called: Infinity Stainless Products
7750 Scout Ave, Bell Gardens (90201-4942)
PHONE............................562 806-5771
Serafin Valdez, *President*
Rachel Haasis, *Sales Staff*
Victor Valdez, *Director*
EMP: 15
SQ FT: 25,000
SALES (est): 3.1MM **Privately Held**
WEB: www.infinitystainless.com
SIC: 3444 Restaurant sheet metalwork

(P-12621)
INNOVATIVE DESIGN AND SHEET ME
Also Called: Innovative Emergency Equipment
616 Mrlbrugh Ave Unit S-1, Riverside (92507)
PHONE............................951 222-2270
EMP: 16 EST: 2015
SALES (est): 99.4K **Privately Held**
SIC: 3444 3699 3647 3641 Forming machine work, sheet metal; skylights, sheet metal; trouble lights; dome lights, automotive; flasher lights, automotive; pilot lights, radio

(P-12622)
INTEGRITY SHEET METAL INC
319 Mcarthur Way Ste 1, Upland (91786-5669)
PHONE............................909 608-0449
William Hicks, *President*
EMP: 10
SALES (est): 1.7MM **Privately Held**
SIC: 3444 Sheet metalwork

(P-12623)
INTERLOCK INDUSTRIES INC
Also Called: Middle Sales
1326 Paddock Pl, Woodland (95776-5919)
PHONE............................530 668-5690
Dwight Isaac, *Manager*
EMP: 56
SALES (corp-wide): 390.6MM **Privately Held**
WEB: www.metalsales.us.com
SIC: 3444 Roof deck, sheet metal
PA: Interlock Industries, Inc.
　　545 S 3rd St Ste 310
　　Louisville KY 40202
　　502 569-2007

(P-12624)
INTERNATIONAL ASSOCIATION OF S
Also Called: Local 162
2840 El Centro Rd Ste 110, Sacramento (95833-9700)
PHONE............................916 922-1133
Dennis Canevail, *President*
Tony Scavone, *Director*
EMP: 10
SALES (corp-wide): 253.8K **Privately Held**
WEB: www.smw7.org
SIC: 3444 Sheet metalwork
PA: International Association Of Sheet Metal, Air, Rail And Transportation Workers
　　1750 New York Ave Nw # 600
　　Washington DC 20006
　　202 783-5880

(P-12625)
INTERNATIONAL WEST INC
Also Called: Continental Industries
1025 N Armando St, Anaheim (92806-2606)
PHONE............................714 632-9190
Jeffery Aaron Hayden, *President*
Tami Hayden, *CFO*
Paul Leiter, *VP Opers*
Chris Pruno, *Mktg Dir*
Michelle Hayden, *Manager*
EMP: 56
SQ FT: 8,500
SALES (est): 12.5MM **Privately Held**
WEB: www.continental-ind.net
SIC: 3444 Sheet metalwork

▲ = Import ▼=Export
◆ =Import/Export

(P-12626)
INVENTIVE RESOURCES INC
Also Called: Iri
5038 Salida Blvd, Salida (95368-9403)
P.O. Box 1316 (95368-1316)
PHONE......................................209 545-1663
John A Paoluccio, CEO
John J Paoluccio, President
Dorene Paoluccio, CFO
EMP: 10
SQ FT: 3,313
SALES (est): 597.2K Privately Held
WEB: www.biocoal.net
SIC: 3444 8731 3826 Ducts, sheet metal;
commercial research laboratory; environ-
mental testing equipment

(P-12627)
J & L METAL PRODUCTS
1121 Railroad St Ste 103, Corona
(92882-8219)
PHONE......................................951 278-0100
James C Ciarletta, President
Jay Ciarletta, Treasurer
EMP: 19
SALES (est): 3.8MM Privately Held
SIC: 3444 Sheet metal specialties, not
stamped

(P-12628)
JAUBIN SALES & MFG CORP
Also Called: J Sheet Metal
2006 E Gladwick St, Compton
(90220-6202)
PHONE......................................310 631-8647
Marie Jaubin, President
EMP: 12
SQ FT: 10,000
SALES (est): 990K Privately Held
WEB: www.jsheetmetal.com
SIC: 3444 Sheet metal specialties, not
stamped

(P-12629)
JBW PRECISION INC
2650 Lavery Ct, Newbury Park
(91320-1581)
PHONE......................................805 499-1973
David Ogden, President
Dawn Spalding, Corp Secy
Jack Ogden, Vice Pres
Rhonda Ogden, Marketing Mgr
EMP: 23 EST: 1969
SQ FT: 2,500
SALES (est): 4.9MM Privately Held
WEB: www.jbwprecision.com
SIC: 3444 Forming machine work, sheet
metal

(P-12630)
JEFFREY FABRICATION LLC
Also Called: C & J Metal Prducts
6323 Alondra Blvd, Paramount
(90723-3750)
PHONE......................................562 634-3101
Lilly Chang, Mng Member
EMP: 50
SALES (est): 7MM Privately Held
SIC: 3444 Sheet metalwork

(P-12631)
JIM JAMES ENTERPRISES INC
9148 Jordan Ave, Chatsworth
(91311-5707)
PHONE......................................818 772-8595
Irene Hagle, President
Chris H Hagle, Purch Mgr
EMP: 10 EST: 1974
SQ FT: 10,000
SALES (est): 1MM Privately Held
SIC: 3444 Sheet metal specialties, not
stamped

(P-12632)
JOHNSON INDUSTRIAL SHEET METAL
2131 Barstow St, Sacramento
(95815-3628)
P.O. Box 15859 (95852-0859)
PHONE......................................916 927-8244
Curtis Johnson, President
Donna Johnson, Vice Pres
EMP: 10
SQ FT: 8,000

SALES (est): 1.7MM Privately Held
WEB: www.johnson-ind.com
SIC: 3444 Sheet metal specialties, not
stamped

(P-12633)
JRI INC
Also Called: John Russo Industrial Metal
38021 Cherry St, Newark (94560-4524)
PHONE......................................510 494-5300
Ralph Colet, President
EMP: 24
SQ FT: 170,000
SALES (est): 4.1MM Privately Held
SIC: 3444 Sheet metalwork

(P-12634)
K & E MANUFACTURING INC
1966 Freeman Ave, Signal Hill
(90755-1241)
PHONE......................................562 494-7570
Ernesto Sandoval, President
Yolanda Gallegos, Manager
EMP: 16
SQ FT: 15,000
SALES (est): 1.3MM Privately Held
SIC: 3444 Sheet metalwork

(P-12635)
K C SHEETMETAL INC
943 Berryessa Rd Ste B3, San Jose
(95133-1007)
PHONE......................................408 441-6620
Phil Casey, Owner
EMP: 10
SQ FT: 7,700
SALES (est): 590K Privately Held
SIC: 3444 Sheet metalwork

(P-12636)
KARGO MASTER INC
11261 Trade Center Dr, Rancho Cordova
(95742-6223)
PHONE......................................916 638-8703
John Hancock, President
David Lewis, Vice Pres
Nick Wendell, Engineer
Terri Aquino, Accountant
Marscelles Ramirez, Sales Staff
EMP: 40
SALES (est): 9MM Privately Held
WEB: www.kargomaster.com
SIC: 3444 Sheet metalwork

(P-12637)
KARL M SMITH INC
1204 Dairy Ave, Corcoran (93212-2500)
P.O. Box 817 (93212-0817)
PHONE......................................559 992-4109
Pauline Smith, President
Karl M Smith, Vice Pres
EMP: 25
SQ FT: 11,000
SALES (est): 4.2MM Privately Held
SIC: 3444 Sheet metalwork

(P-12638)
KB SHEETMETAL FABRICATION INC
17371 Mount Wynne Cir B, Fountain Valley
(92708-4107)
PHONE......................................714 979-1780
Cong Nguyen, President
Tung Vo, Vice Pres
Dawne Connell, QA Dir
Trinh Huynh, Sales Staff
Joyce Lorenz, Sales Staff
EMP: 25
SQ FT: 12,000
SALES (est): 4.3MM Privately Held
SIC: 3444 3441 Sheet metalwork; fabri-
cated structural metal

(P-12639)
KEITH E ARCHAMBEAU SR INC
Also Called: American Precision Sheet Metal
20615 Plummer St, Chatsworth
(91311-5112)
PHONE......................................818 718-6110
Keith Archambeau Jr, President
John Wetlson, Vice Pres
EMP: 20
SQ FT: 10,000
SALES (est): 4.1MM Privately Held
SIC: 3444 Sheet metal specialties, not
stamped

(P-12640)
L & T PRECISION CORPORATION
12105 Kirkham Rd, Poway (92064-6870)
PHONE......................................858 513-7874
Loc Nguyen, President
Tho Nguyen, Vice Pres
Tien D Nguyen, Principal
Tien Nguyen, Admin Sec
Kent Griffin, Opers Mgr
EMP: 110
SQ FT: 48,000
SALES (est): 32.1MM Privately Held
WEB: www.ltprecision.com
SIC: 3444 3599 Sheet metal specialties,
not stamped; machine & other job shop
work

(P-12641)
LAPTALO ENTERPRISES INC
Also Called: J L Precision Sheet Metal
2360 Zanker Rd, San Jose (95131-1115)
PHONE......................................408 727-6633
Jakov Laptalo, CEO
Michael Laptalo, President
Tony Grizelj, Vice Pres
Todd Morey, Vice Pres
Slavko Laptalo, Admin Sec
EMP: 100
SQ FT: 60,000
SALES (est): 38.4MM Privately Held
SIC: 3444 Sheet metal specialties, not
stamped

(P-12642)
LOR-VAN MANUFACTURING LLC
3307 Edward Ave, Santa Clara
(95054-2341)
PHONE......................................408 980-1045
Christopher Girardot,
Ismelda Lopez, Engineer
Ed Simmonds, Sales Staff
Lorena Lopez,
EMP: 28
SQ FT: 6,400
SALES (est): 5.8MM Privately Held
WEB: www.lor-vanmfg.com
SIC: 3444 3699 Sheet metal specialties,
not stamped; laser welding, drilling & cut-
ting equipment

(P-12643)
LUNAS SHEET METAL INC
3125 Molinaro St Ste 102, Santa Clara
(95054-2433)
PHONE......................................408 492-1260
Antonio Luna, President
Maria Luna, CFO
EMP: 15
SQ FT: 10,000
SALES (est): 2.9MM Privately Held
SIC: 3444 Sheet metalwork

(P-12644)
LYNAM INDUSTRIES INC
13050 Santa Ana Ave, Fontana
(92337-6948)
PHONE......................................951 360-1919
Troy Lindstrom, President
Eugene Martin, Engineer
Brian Nguyen, Engineer
Luis Muro, Opers Mgr
Aniceto Jimenez, Opers Staff
▲ EMP: 85
SQ FT: 39,000
SALES (est): 25MM Privately Held
WEB: www.lynamindustries.com
SIC: 3444 Sheet metal specialties, not
stamped

(P-12645)
LYNX ENTERPRISES INC
724 E Grant Line Rd Ste B, Tracy
(95304-2800)
PHONE......................................209 833-3400
Vance R Anderson, President
Keith J Anderson, CFO
Carlos Aldona, Admin Sec
Rosalinda Orta, Purchasing
Mary Tomatis-Costa, Clerk
▲ EMP: 60
SQ FT: 52,000

SALES: 13.5MM Privately Held
WEB: www.fleetwoodrv.com
SIC: 3444 3446 3443 3441 Sheet metalwork; architectural metalwork; fabricated
plate work (boiler shop); fabricated structural metal

(P-12646)
M C I MANUFACTURING INC (PA)
1020 Rock Ave, San Jose (95131-1610)
PHONE......................................408 456-2700
Henry LI, President
EMP: 45
SQ FT: 22,000
SALES: 5MM Privately Held
WEB: www.mcimfg.com
SIC: 3444 Metal housings, enclosures,
casings & other containers

(P-12647)
M&G DURAVENT INC (DH)
877 Cotting Ct, Vacaville (95688-9354)
PHONE......................................707 446-1786
Brooks Sherman, President
Victor Lambert, Vice Pres
▲ EMP: 350
SALES (est): 104.6MM Privately Held
SIC: 3444 Metal ventilating equipment
HQ: M & G Group Europe B.V.
Dr. A.F. Philipsweg 39
Assen
503 139-944

(P-12648)
M&L METALS INC
25362 Cypress Ave, Hayward
(94544-2208)
PHONE......................................510 732-1745
Mike Lowe, President
Stephanie Reese, Manager
EMP: 11
SQ FT: 6,000
SALES: 1.1MM Privately Held
SIC: 3444 Sheet metalwork

(P-12649)
M-T METAL FABRICATIONS INC
536 Lewelling Blvd Ste A, San Leandro
(94579-1845)
PHONE......................................510 357-5262
Ross Bigler, President
Justin Bigler, Vice Pres
EMP: 14
SQ FT: 12,900
SALES: 2MM Privately Held
SIC: 3444 Sheet metal specialties, not
stamped

(P-12650)
MAC CAL COMPANY
Also Called: Mac Cal Manufacturing
1737 Junction Ave, San Jose (95112-1010)
PHONE......................................408 441-1435
Michael Hall, President
Renee Hall, CEO
Cathy McDonald, CFO
Marlene Kamiya, Executive
Bob Duncan, General Mgr
EMP: 80
SALES (est): 18.9MM Privately Held
WEB: www.maccal.com
SIC: 3444 3479 7336 Sheet metal spe-
cialties, not stamped; housings for busi-
ness machines, sheet metal; name
plates: engraved, etched, etc.; silk screen
design

(P-12651)
MAG HIGH TECH
14718 Arminta St, Panorama City
(91402-5904)
PHONE......................................818 786-8366
Jerry Rothlisberger, Owner
EMP: 12
SALES (est): 1MM Privately Held
SIC: 3444 Forming machine work, sheet
metal

(P-12652)
MARINE & REST FABRICATORS INC
3768 Dalbergia St, San Diego
(92113-3815)
PHONE......................................619 232-7267
Carlos Velazquez, President

EMP: 44
SQ FT: 7,600
SALES (est): 8.4MM Privately Held
SIC: 3444 3731 Restaurant sheet metal-work; military ships, building & repairing

(P-12653)
MASS PRECISION INC
46555 Landing Pkwy, Fremont (94538-6421)
PHONE................................408 954-0200
Greg Kraus, Manager
EMP: 125
SALES (corp-wide): 69.3MM Privately Held
SIC: 3444 3599 Sheet metalwork; machine shop, jobbing & repair
PA: Mass Precision, Inc.
   2110 Oakland Rd
   San Jose CA 95131
   408 954-0200

(P-12654)
MASS PRECISION INC (PA)
Also Called: Machining and Frame Division
2110 Oakland Rd, San Jose (95131-1565)
PHONE................................408 954-0200
Al Stucky Jr, President
W Ray Allen, CFO
▲ EMP: 200
SQ FT: 200,000
SALES: 69.3MM Privately Held
WEB: www.massprecision.com
SIC: 3444 3599 Sheet metal specialties, not stamped; machine shop, jobbing & repair

(P-12655)
MASTER ENTERPRISES INC
Also Called: A B C Restaurant Equipment Co
2025 Lee Ave, South El Monte (91733-2505)
PHONE................................626 442-1821
Brian Kim Lien, CEO
Wen Lin, Treasurer
Thanh Quach, Admin Sec
EMP: 20
SQ FT: 20,000
SALES (est): 3.5MM Privately Held
WEB: www.masel.net
SIC: 3444 5087 Restaurant sheet metal-work; restaurant supplies

(P-12656)
MASTER FAB INC
9210 Stellar Ct, Corona (92883-4906)
PHONE................................951 277-4772
Kenneth Scheel, President
Troy Jackson, Admin Sec
EMP: 16 EST: 1980
SQ FT: 11,000
SALES (est): 3.6MM Privately Held
SIC: 3444 Sheet metalwork

(P-12657)
MASTER METAL PRODUCTS COMPANY
495 Emory St, San Jose (95110-1999)
PHONE................................408 275-1210
Lee A Henderson, President
Jason Quick, Auditing Mgr
Aaron Alcones, Opers Mgr
EMP: 12 EST: 1942
SQ FT: 18,000
SALES (est): 2.3MM Privately Held
SIC: 3444 Sheet metal specialties, not stamped

(P-12658)
MATERIAL SUPPLY INC (PA)
Also Called: MSI Hvac
11700 Industry Ave, Fontana (92337-6934)
PHONE................................951 801-5004
Dion Quinn, CEO
Bob Billiu, Vice Pres
Jon Dautrich, Vice Pres
Robert Hascall, Vice Pres
Johnson Uy, Administration
EMP: 170
SQ FT: 80,000

SALES (est): 95.7MM Privately Held
WEB: www.msihvac.com
SIC: 3444 5075 7623 1711 Metal ventilating equipment; warm air heating & air conditioning; air filters; ventilating equipment & supplies; air conditioning repair; heating & air conditioning contractors

(P-12659)
MATTHEWS MANUFACTURING INC
3301 E 14th St, Los Angeles (90023-3801)
PHONE................................323 980-4373
Benyamin Mikhael-Ford, President
Fiyodor Mikhael-Ford, Corp Secy
Fred Mikhael-Ford, Vice Pres
EMP: 27
SQ FT: 20,000
SALES (est): 34K Privately Held
SIC: 3444 3599 Sheet metalwork; machine shop, jobbing & repair

(P-12660)
MAXIMUM QUALITY METAL PDTS INC
Also Called: Max Q
1017 E Acacia St, Ontario (91761-4554)
PHONE................................909 902-5018
John Kim, President
Paul Kim, Admin Sec
EMP: 20
SQ FT: 10,000
SALES: 4.9MM Privately Held
SIC: 3444 Sheet metalwork

(P-12661)
MAYONI ENTERPRISES
10320 Glenoaks Blvd, Pacoima (91331-1699)
PHONE................................818 896-0026
Isaac Benyehuda, CEO
Isaac Glazer, Vice Pres
EMP: 60
SQ FT: 17,000
SALES: 3MM Privately Held
SIC: 3444 3581 Sheet metal specialties, not stamped; automatic vending machines

(P-12662)
MCMILLIN MFG CORP
Also Called: McMillin Wire Products
40 E Verdugo Ave, Burbank (91502-1931)
PHONE................................323 981-8585
Bruce Goodman, President
EMP: 57
SQ FT: 42,000
SALES (est): 6.8MM Privately Held
SIC: 3444 3496 3441 3315 Sheet metal-work; miscellaneous fabricated wire products; fabricated structural metal; steel wire & related products

(P-12663)
MEADOWS SHEET METAL AND AC INC
Also Called: Meadows Mechanical
333 Crown Vista Dr, Gardena (90248-1705)
PHONE................................310 615-1125
Madonna Rose, CEO
Dennis Johnson, CFO
Thomas Nolan, Exec VP
Brett Nayudu, Project Mgr
Yazmin Rubio, Project Engr
EMP: 50 EST: 1949
SQ FT: 5,000
SALES (est): 21.7MM Privately Held
SIC: 3444 1711 Sheet metalwork; heating & air conditioning contractors

(P-12664)
MELROSE METAL PRODUCTS INC
44533 S Grimmer Blvd, Fremont (94538-6309)
PHONE................................510 657-8771
Mitchell A Hoppe, CEO
Harry Hoppe, Shareholder
Shirley Hoppe, Vice Pres
EMP: 20
SQ FT: 40,000

SALES (est): 6.8MM Privately Held
WEB: www.gomelrose.com
SIC: 3444 Sheet metal specialties, not stamped; ventilators, sheet metal; booths, spray: prefabricated sheet metal; cowls or scoops, air (ship ventilators): sheet metal

(P-12665)
MERIT ENDS INC
Also Called: Merit USA
620 Clark Ave, Pittsburg (94565-5000)
PHONE................................925 427-2500
Peter A Ryner, CEO
EMP: 25
SQ FT: 200,000
SALES (est): 7.3MM Privately Held
SIC: 3444 Sheet metalwork
PA: Viking Processing Corporation
   620 Clark Ave
   Pittsburg CA 94565

(P-12666)
METAL ENGINEERING & MFG
1031b W Kirkwall Rd, Azusa (91702-5127)
PHONE................................626 334-5271
Petra Markoski, Owner
EMP: 12
SALES (est): 1.1MM Privately Held
WEB: www.metaleng.com
SIC: 3444 Sheet metalwork

(P-12667)
METAL FINISHING SOLUTIONS INC
870 Comstock St, Santa Clara (95054-3404)
PHONE................................408 988-8642
Tony Grizeli, Principal
Joe Kulic, General Mgr
EMP: 10
SALES (est): 1.4MM Privately Held
SIC: 3444 Sheet metalwork

(P-12668)
METAL MASTER INC
4611 Overland Ave, San Diego (92123-1233)
PHONE................................858 292-8880
Benito Garrido, President
Dianne Yeaman, CFO
Donald Wagner, Vice Pres
Ray Chan, Executive
Ricky Ruiz, Purchasing
EMP: 41
SQ FT: 30,000
SALES (est): 9.7MM Privately Held
WEB: www.metalmasterinc.com
SIC: 3444 3541 Sheet metalwork; metal housings, enclosures, casings & other containers; milling machines

(P-12669)
METAL SALES MANUFACTURING CORP
14213 Whittram Ave, Fontana (92335-3045)
P.O. Box 8922, Rancho Cucamonga (91701-0922)
PHONE................................909 829-8618
Kevin Fitzgerald, Manager
EMP: 10
SALES (corp-wide): 390.6MM Privately Held
SIC: 3444 1761 Metal roofing & roof drainage equipment; roofing contractor
HQ: Metal Sales Manufacturing Corporation
   545 S 3rd St Ste 200
   Louisville KY 40202
   502 855-4300

(P-12670)
METAL-FAB SERVICES INDUSTRIES
2500 E Miraloma Way, Anaheim (92806-1608)
PHONE................................714 630-7771
Carlos Mondragon, CEO
▲ EMP: 49
SQ FT: 28,000
SALES (est): 10.4MM Privately Held
SIC: 3444 Sheet metal specialties, not stamped

(P-12671)
METALPRO INDUSTRIES INC
28064 Avenue Stanford H, Santa Clarita (91355-1158)
PHONE................................661 294-0764
Robert Theberge, President
Edmundo Gomez, Treasurer
Mark Theberge, Vice Pres
Mary Badberg, Office Mgr
Arlan Sams, Admin Sec
EMP: 40
SQ FT: 13,000
SALES (est): 6.5MM Privately Held
WEB: www.metalproindustries.net
SIC: 3444 Sheet metal specialties, not stamped

(P-12672)
METALS DIRECT INC
6771 Eastside Rd, Redding (96001-5059)
PHONE................................530 605-1931
Dale Williams, President
Terry Williams, Vice Pres
EMP: 29
SALES: 3.1MM Privately Held
SIC: 3444 5082 1761 5039 Siding, sheet metal; contractors' materials; roofing, siding & sheet metal work; metal buildings; agricultural building contractors

(P-12673)
MEYERS SHEET METAL BOX INC
138 W Harris Ave, South San Francisco (94080-6009)
PHONE................................650 873-8889
James H C Liang, President
Chung Lai Liang, Corp Secy
EMP: 12
SQ FT: 7,500
SALES (est): 1.7MM Privately Held
SIC: 3444 Sheet metalwork

(P-12674)
MICROFAB MANUFACTURING INC
Also Called: Microfab Mfg Shtmtl Pdts
220 Distribution St, San Marcos (92078-4358)
PHONE................................760 744-7240
Scott Dillard, Owner
Nancy Dillard, Vice Pres
EMP: 16
SQ FT: 10,252
SALES (est): 1.1MM Privately Held
WEB: www.microfabmfg.com
SIC: 3444 Sheet metal specialties, not stamped

(P-12675)
MICROFORM PRECISION LLC
4244 S Market Ct Ste A, Sacramento (95834-1243)
PHONE................................916 419-0580
Timothy E Rice, Mng Member
▲ EMP: 55 EST: 1981
SQ FT: 42,000
SALES (est): 13.8MM Privately Held
WEB: www.mform.com
SIC: 3444 Sheet metal specialties, not stamped

(P-12676)
MIDDLE ATLANTIC PRODUCTS INC
11150 Inland Ave Ste A, Mira Loma (91752-1164)
PHONE................................800 266-7225
Keith Blackwell, Branch Mgr
EMP: 15
SALES (corp-wide): 20.7MM Privately Held
WEB: www.middleatlantic.com
SIC: 3444 Sheet metalwork
HQ: Middle Atlantic Products, Inc.
   300 Fairfield Rd
   Fairfield NJ 07004
   973 839-1011

(P-12677)
MIKES SHEET METAL PRODUCTS
Also Called: Uniproducts
3315 Elkhorn Blvd, North Highlands (95660-3112)
PHONE..................................916 348-3800
Michael R Meredith, *President*
Ginny Meredith, *Vice Pres*
EMP: 25
SQ FT: 10,000
SALES (est): 4.4MM **Privately Held**
SIC: 3444 Ducts, sheet metal

(P-12678)
MILLENNIUM METALCRAFT INC
3201 Osgood Cmn, Fremont (94539-5029)
PHONE..................................510 657-4700
Kenneth Watson, *President*
Gwendolyn Watson, *CFO*
EMP: 30
SQ FT: 8,100
SALES: 4MM **Privately Held**
SIC: 3444 Sheet metal specialties, not stamped

(P-12679)
MILLS ACQUISITION CORPORATION
Also Called: Advanced Components Technology
1035 22nd Ave, Oakland (94606-5253)
PHONE..................................650 365-2801
Ron Mills, *President*
Marita Mills, *Corp Secy*
▲ EMP: 20
SQ FT: 12,500
SALES: 1.6MM **Privately Held**
SIC: 3444 Sheet metalwork

(P-12680)
MINTIE CORPORATION
1114 N San Fernando Rd, Los Angeles (90065-1126)
PHONE..................................510 351-5868
Bill Kelly, *Branch Mgr*
EMP: 15
SALES (corp-wide): 15.3MM **Privately Held**
WEB: www.mintie.com
SIC: 3444 Ducts, sheet metal
PA: Mintie Corporation
1114 N San Fernando Rd
Los Angeles CA 90065
323 225-4111

(P-12681)
MMIX TECHNOLOGIES
Also Called: Countywide Metal
1348 Pioneer Way, El Cajon (92020-1626)
P.O. Box 12794 (92022-2794)
PHONE..................................619 631-6644
Emmaneul J Carlos, *CEO*
Emmanuel J Carlos, *President*
EMP: 10
SALES (est): 1.5MM **Privately Held**
SIC: 3444 Forming machine work, sheet metal

(P-12682)
MMP SHEET METAL INC
501 Commercial Way, La Habra (90631-6170)
PHONE..................................562 691-1055
Frank Varanelli, *President*
EMP: 30 EST: 1977
SQ FT: 8,500
SALES (est): 5.1MM **Privately Held**
SIC: 3444 Sheet metal specialties, not stamped

(P-12683)
MODERN-AIRE VENTILATING INC
Also Called: Modern Aire Ventilating
7319 Lankershim Blvd, North Hollywood (91605-3895)
PHONE..................................818 765-9870
Steven Herman, *President*
Jennifer Cifelli, *Office Mgr*
Robert Delmazo, *VP Sales*
Patrick Hartman, *Manager*
EMP: 20 EST: 1956
SQ FT: 20,000

SALES (est): 3.3MM **Privately Held**
WEB: www.modernaire.com
SIC: 3444 3645 Hoods, range: sheet metal; residential lighting fixtures

(P-12684)
MODULAR METAL FABRICATORS INC
24600 Nandina Ave, Moreno Valley (92551-9537)
PHONE..................................951 242-3154
E E Gearing, *CEO*
Don Gearing, *President*
John Wingate, *Treasurer*
Mike Beam, *Exec VP*
Pat Geary, *Director*
▲ EMP: 130
SQ FT: 200,000
SALES (est): 25.2MM **Privately Held**
SIC: 3444 Pipe, sheet metal; ducts, sheet metal

(P-12685)
MONACO SHEET METAL
Also Called: Sun Sheet Metal
5131 Santa Fe St Ste A, San Diego (92109-1612)
PHONE..................................858 272-0297
Troy Monaco, *President*
EMP: 10
SQ FT: 12,048
SALES (est): 1MM **Privately Held**
SIC: 3444 Sheet metalwork

(P-12686)
MONTEREY MECHANICAL CO
Also Called: Contra Costa Metal Fabricators
1126 Landini Ln, Concord (94520-3704)
PHONE..................................925 689-6670
Todd Monday, *Manager*
EMP: 10
SALES (corp-wide): 73.4MM **Privately Held**
WEB: www.montmech.com
SIC: 3444 1761 Sheet metalwork; sheet metalwork
PA: Monterey Mechanical Co.
8275 San Leandro St
Oakland CA 94621
510 632-3173

(P-12687)
MORTENSON PRECISION
Also Called: Mortensen Precision Shtmtl
1943 Hartog Dr, San Jose (95131-2213)
PHONE..................................408 441-7380
Bill Mortenson, *Owner*
EMP: 20
SALES (est): 2.2MM **Privately Held**
SIC: 3444 Sheet metal specialties, not stamped

(P-12688)
MORTS CUSTOM SHEETMETAL
18121 Clear Creek Rd, Redding (96001-5233)
PHONE..................................530 241-7013
David Cox, *Owner*
Jeannine Cox, *Co-Owner*
EMP: 10
SQ FT: 2,000
SALES: 900K **Privately Held**
SIC: 3444 Sheet metalwork

(P-12689)
MS INDUSTRIAL SHTMTL INC
Also Called: Baghouse and Indus Shtmtl Svcs
1731 Pomona Rd, Corona (92880-6963)
PHONE..................................951 272-6610
Nancy Nicola, *Ch of Bd*
Tammy Surratt, *Officer*
Dan Suffel, *Vice Pres*
Warren Lampkin, *Principal*
Jessica Salas, *Manager*
EMP: 130
SQ FT: 35,000
SALES (est): 37.3MM **Privately Held**
SIC: 3444 Sheet metalwork

(P-12690)
NEW CAL METALS INC
3495 Swetzer Rd, Granite Bay (95746)
P.O. Box 1126, Loomis (95650-1126)
PHONE..................................916 652-7424
Larry Dumm, *President*
Slate Bryer, *Shareholder*

Chris Tataschiore, *Vice Pres*
▲ EMP: 15 EST: 2008
SQ FT: 15,000
SALES (est): 2.4MM **Privately Held**
SIC: 3444 Metal ventilating equipment

(P-12691)
NEW GREENSCREEN INCORPORATED
Impac International
11445 Pacific Ave, Fontana (92337-8227)
PHONE..................................951 685-9660
Kory Lavoy, *Division Mgr*
EMP: 50
SIC: 3444 3315 Housings for business machines, sheet metal; steel wire & related products
PA: New Greenscreen, Incorporated
5500 Jurupa St
Ontario CA 91761

(P-12692)
NOLL/NORWESCO LLC
1320 Performance Dr, Stockton (95206-4925)
PHONE..................................209 234-1600
Gary Henry, *Mng Member*
Alex MAI, *Officer*
Rick Johnson, *General Mgr*
EMP: 130
SALES (est): 21.7MM
SALES (corp-wide): 986.9MM **Publicly Held**
SIC: 3444 Sheet metalwork
PA: Gibraltar Industries, Inc.
3556 Lake Shore Rd # 100
Buffalo NY 14219
716 826-6500

(P-12693)
NOR-CAL METAL FABRICATORS
1121 3rd St, Oakland (94607-2509)
PHONE..................................510 350-0121
Robert C Hall, *Ch of Bd*
Michael Tran, *President*
Rick Turner, *Info Tech Mgr*
Chau Truong, *Accountant*
Craig Macdonald, *Director*
▲ EMP: 51 EST: 1960
SQ FT: 100,000
SALES (est): 14MM **Privately Held**
SIC: 3444 3661 Sheet metal specialties, not stamped; telephone & telegraph apparatus

(P-12694)
NORTH VALLEY RAIN GUTTERS
27 Freight Ln Ste C, Chico (95973-8962)
PHONE..................................530 894-3347
Michael Gaston, *Owner*
EMP: 12
SQ FT: 3,000
SALES (est): 1.1MM **Privately Held**
SIC: 3444 1761 Gutters, sheet metal; downspouts, sheet metal; gutter & downspout contractor

(P-12695)
OC METALS INC
2720 S Main St Ste B, Santa Ana (92707-3404)
PHONE..................................714 668-0783
Marushkah Kurtz, *CEO*
Mari Kurtz, *President*
EMP: 20
SQ FT: 23,000
SALES (est): 5.2MM **Privately Held**
SIC: 3444 Sheet metalwork

(P-12696)
ONETO MANUFACTURING COMPANY
146 S Maple Ave, South San Francisco (94080-6302)
PHONE..................................650 875-1710
Jack Liberator, *President*
Barbara L Liberatore, *Vice Pres*
Robert Liberatore, *Admin Sec*
EMP: 16
SQ FT: 20,000
SALES (est): 2.5MM **Privately Held**
SIC: 3444 Sheet metal specialties, not stamped

(P-12697)
ORTRONICS INC
Also Called: Electrorack
1443 S Sunkist St, Anaheim (92806-5626)
PHONE..................................714 776-5420
Mark Panico, *President*
James Laperriere, *Treasurer*
Robert Julian, *Vice Pres*
Valerie Alsante, *Admin Sec*
James Telles, *Technical Staff*
▲ EMP: 120
SQ FT: 50,000
SALES (est): 25.8MM
SALES (corp-wide): 20.7MM **Privately Held**
WEB: www.electrorack.com
SIC: 3444 3679 Sheet metalwork; power supplies, all types: static
HQ: Legrand Holding, Inc.
60 Woodlawn St
West Hartford CT 06110
860 233-6251

(P-12698)
OXNARD PRCSION FABRICATION INC
Also Called: O P F
2200 Teal Club Rd, Oxnard (93030-8640)
PHONE..................................805 985-0447
David Garza, *President*
Robert Valles, *Vice Pres*
EMP: 30
SQ FT: 107,000
SALES (est): 6.2MM **Privately Held**
WEB: www.opfinc.com
SIC: 3444 3469 3443 Sheet metal specialties, not stamped; metal stampings; fabricated plate work (boiler shop)

(P-12699)
P A S U INC
1891 Nirvana Ave, Chula Vista (91911-6117)
PHONE..................................619 421-1151
Donald R Palumbo, *President*
▲ EMP: 115 EST: 1979
SQ FT: 100,000
SALES (est): 17.1MM **Privately Held**
WEB: www.gceindustries.com
SIC: 3444 3825 Sheet metalwork; test equipment for electronic & electrical circuits

(P-12700)
P T INDUSTRIES INC
3220 Industry Dr, Signal Hill (90755-4014)
PHONE..................................562 961-3431
Kim Nguyen, *President*
Thuy Nguyen, *Admin Sec*
Johnny Nguyen, *Director*
EMP: 19
SQ FT: 19,000
SALES (est): 3.9MM **Privately Held**
SIC: 3444 Sheet metalwork

(P-12701)
PACIFIC AWARD METALS INC (HQ)
1450 Virginia Ave, Baldwin Park (91706-5819)
P.O. Box 7865 (91706-7865)
PHONE..................................626 814-4410
Brian J Lipke, *CEO*
W Brent Taylor, *President*
Lorraine Rivas, *Human Res Mgr*
Frank Fulford, *VP Sales*
EMP: 100
SQ FT: 110,000
SALES (est): 73.9MM
SALES (corp-wide): 986.9MM **Publicly Held**
WEB: www.awardmetals.com
SIC: 3444 3312 Sheet metalwork; blast furnaces & steel mills
PA: Gibraltar Industries, Inc.
3556 Lake Shore Rd # 100
Buffalo NY 14219
716 826-6500

(P-12702)
PACIFIC AWARD METALS INC
13169 Slover Ave, Fontana (92337-6923)
PHONE..................................626 814-4410
EMP: 50

P R O D U C T S & S V C S

SALES (corp-wide): 986.9MM **Publicly Held**
SIC: **3444** 3312 Sheet metalwork; blast furnaces & steel mills
HQ: Pacific Award Metals, Inc.
  1450 Virginia Ave
  Baldwin Park CA 91706
  626 814-4410

(P-12703)
PACIFIC AWARD METALS INC
1450 Virginia Ave, Baldwin Park (91706-5819)
PHONE..................626 814-4410
Robert Smith, *Branch Mgr*
EMP: 60
SQ FT: 17,000
SALES (corp-wide): 986.9MM **Publicly Held**
WEB: www.awardmetals.com
SIC: **3444** 3564 Sheet metalwork; blowers & fans
HQ: Pacific Award Metals, Inc.
  1450 Virginia Ave
  Baldwin Park CA 91706
  626 814-4410

(P-12704)
PACIFIC DUCT INC
5499 Brooks St, Montclair (91763-4563)
PHONE..................909 635-1335
Riad M Wahid, *President*
Brad Smead, *Opers Mgr*
Rob Lepore, *Sales Staff*
George Bobo, *Supervisor*
▲ EMP: 30
SQ FT: 15,000
SALES (est): 6.4MM **Privately Held**
WEB: www.pacificduct.com
SIC: **3444** 5075 5039 Metal ventilating equipment; warm air heating & air conditioning; air ducts, sheet metal

(P-12705)
PACIFIC MARINE SHTMTL CORP
Also Called: Southwest Manufacturing Svcs
2650 Jamacha Rd, El Cajon (92019-6316)
PHONE..................858 869-8900
H Allen Weckerly, *Chairman*
Daren S Weckerly, *CEO*
Karl Lepiane, *CFO*
Jose Luis Gutierrez, *Vice Pres*
Danielle Wilkerson, *Business Dir*
▲ EMP: 200
SQ FT: 110,000
SALES: 31MM **Privately Held**
WEB: www.swfab.com
SIC: **3444** Sheet metalwork

(P-12706)
PACIFIC METALS GROUP LLC
Also Called: Pacmet Aerospace
787 S Wanamaker Ave, Ontario (91761-8116)
PHONE..................909 218-8889
David A Janes Jr, *President*
Marco Vissuet, *Consultant*
▲ EMP: 50
SQ FT: 45,000
SALES (est): 10.5MM **Privately Held**
WEB: www.cmemetalstamping.com
SIC: **3444** Sheet metalwork

(P-12707)
PACIFIC MODERN HOMES INC
9723 Railroad St, Elk Grove (95624-2456)
P.O. Box 670 (95759-0670)
PHONE..................916 685-9514
Anthony Colbert, *President*
Anthony B Colbert, *President*
Chris J Fellersen, *Senior VP*
Kenneth S Rader, *Vice Pres*
Ken Rader, *Marketing Staff*
▼ EMP: 20
SQ FT: 3,800
SALES (est): 3.1MM **Privately Held**
WEB: www.pmhi.com
SIC: **3444** 5031 Metal roofing & roof drainage equipment; building materials, exterior; building materials, interior

(P-12708)
PACIFIC SHEET METAL INC
Also Called: Pacific Metal Fab & Design
497 S Pine St, Madera (93637-5213)
PHONE..................559 661-4044

Michael Hayes, *President*
EMP: 10
SQ FT: 8,000
SALES (est): 1.7MM **Privately Held**
SIC: **3444** Sheet metal specialties, not stamped

(P-12709)
PALEX METALS INC
3601 Thomas Rd, Santa Clara (95054-2040)
PHONE..................408 496-6111
Donald J Russo, *President*
John Jameson, *CFO*
Mary Magda Russo, *Vice Pres*
EMP: 45 EST: 1973
SALES (est): 7MM **Privately Held**
WEB: www.palexmetals.com
SIC: **3444** Sheet metal specialties, not stamped

(P-12710)
PCI INDUSTRIES INC
6501 Potello St, Commerce (90040)
PHONE..................323 728-0004
Greg Skilley, *Vice Pres*
EMP: 100
SALES (corp-wide): 48.2MM **Privately Held**
SIC: **3444** 3564 Metal ventilating equipment; filters, air: furnaces, air conditioning equipment, etc.
PA: Pci Industries, Inc.
  5101 Blue Mound Rd
  Fort Worth TX 76106
  817 509-2300

(P-12711)
PEGA PRECISION INC
18800 Adams Ct, Morgan Hill (95037-2816)
PHONE..................408 776-3700
Lewis H Fast, *President*
Aaron Fast, *Vice Pres*
EMP: 20
SQ FT: 30,000
SALES (est): 4.2MM **Privately Held**
WEB: www.precisionpega.com
SIC: **3444** 3599 Housings for business machines, sheet metal; machine shop, jobbing & repair

(P-12712)
PENFIELD PRODUCTS INC
Also Called: Custom Home Accessories
11300 Trade Center Dr A, Rancho Cordova (95742-6329)
PHONE..................916 635-0231
Jeffrey Feldman, *CEO*
EMP: 22
SQ FT: 18,000
SALES: 5MM **Privately Held**
SIC: **3444** 5999 Mail (post office) collection or storage boxes, sheet metal; trophies & plaques

(P-12713)
PERI FORMWORK SYSTEMS INC
15369 Valencia Ave, Fontana (92335-3268)
PHONE..................909 356-5797
Gustavo Berringer, *Systems Staff*
Andrea Casas, *Manager*
EMP: 24
SALES (corp-wide): 59.7MM **Privately Held**
WEB: www.peri-usa.com
SIC: **3444** Concrete forms, sheet metal
HQ: Peri Formwork Systems, Inc.
  7135 Dorsey Run Rd
  Elkridge MD 21075
  410 712-7225

(P-12714)
PETERSON SHEET METAL INC
Also Called: Peterson Sheetmetal
12925 Alcosta Blvd Ste 2, San Ramon (94583-1341)
PHONE..................925 830-1766
Carl Peterson, *President*
Darlene Peterson, *Vice Pres*
EMP: 13
SQ FT: 3,200
SALES (est): 1.6MM **Privately Held**
SIC: **3444** Sheet metalwork

(P-12715)
PINNACLE MANUFACTURING CORP
17680 Butterfield Blvd # 100, Morgan Hill (95037-3173)
PHONE..................408 778-6100
Philip Stolzman, *President*
Kristin Mullen, *Manager*
▲ EMP: 35
SALES (est): 8.9MM **Privately Held**
SIC: **3444** Sheet metalwork

(P-12716)
PINNACLE PRECISION SHTMTL CORP (PA)
5410 E La Palma Ave, Anaheim (92807-2023)
PHONE..................714 777-3129
David Oddo, *President*
Paul Oddo, *Shareholder*
Brian McLaughlin, *Vice Pres*
Barbara Holmes, *Admin Sec*
Angela Carlson, *Human Resources*
EMP: 185 EST: 1973
SALES (est): 37MM **Privately Held**
SIC: **3444** Sheet metalwork

(P-12717)
PINNACLE PRECISION SHTMTL CORP
Fabnet
5410 E La Palma Ave, Anaheim (92807-2023)
PHONE..................714 777-3129
Robert F Denham, *Branch Mgr*
EMP: 75
SALES (corp-wide): 37MM **Privately Held**
SIC: **3444** 3599 Metal housings, enclosures, casings & other containers; forming machine work, sheet metal; machine shop, jobbing & repair
PA: Pinnacle Precision Sheet Metal Corporation
  5410 E La Palma Ave
  Anaheim CA 92807
  714 777-3129

(P-12718)
PNA CONSTRUCTION TECH INC
301 Espee St Ste E, Bakersfield (93301-2659)
PHONE..................661 326-1700
Matt Wilen, *Principal*
EMP: 35
SALES (corp-wide): 11MM **Privately Held**
SIC: **3444** Concrete forms, sheet metal
PA: P.N.A. Construction Technologies, Inc.
  1349 W Bryn Mawr Ave
  Itasca IL 60143
  770 668-9500

(P-12719)
PRECISE INDUSTRIES INC
610 Neptune Ave, Brea (92821-2909)
PHONE..................714 482-2333
Terry D Wells, *President*
Jose Quintana, *Program Mgr*
Robert L Wells, *Admin Sec*
Dave Trubey, *Info Tech Dir*
Jan Van Der Kolk, *Prgrmr*
▲ EMP: 120
SQ FT: 78,000
SALES (est): 29.5MM **Privately Held**
WEB: www.preciseind.com
SIC: **3444** 3679 3599 Sheet metalwork; electronic circuits; machine & other job shop work

(P-12720)
PRECISION MTAL FABRICATION INC
1942 Sunny Side Pl, Santa Fe Springs (90670)
PHONE..................562 941-2169
Justo Parga, *President*
EMP: 16
SQ FT: 16,000
SALES (est): 1.9MM **Privately Held**
SIC: **3444** Sheet metalwork

(P-12721)
PRECISION STEEL PRODUCTS INC
Also Called: Steel Products International
13124 Avalon Blvd, Los Angeles (90061-2738)
PHONE..................310 523-2002
Raul De Latorre, *President*
Deborah De Latorre, *Admin Sec*
EMP: 22
SQ FT: 24,000
SALES (est): 3.4MM **Privately Held**
WEB: www.steelproducts.biz
SIC: **3444** 3441 Sheet metalwork; fabricated structural metal

(P-12722)
PRISM AEROSPACE
3087 12th St, Riverside (92507-4904)
PHONE..................951 582-2850
Eng Tan, *CEO*
Peng Tan, *President*
Robert Perez, *Vice Pres*
Joe Mahfet, *Program Mgr*
EMP: 50
SQ FT: 100,000
SALES: 11.9MM **Privately Held**
SIC: **3444** 3812 Forming machine work, sheet metal; aircraft/aerospace flight instruments & guidance systems; acceleration indicators & systems components, aerospace

(P-12723)
PRO METAL PRODUCTS
25559 Jesmond Dene Rd, Escondido (92026-8602)
PHONE..................760 480-0212
Fred West, *Owner*
EMP: 14
SQ FT: 12,000
SALES (est): 1.5MM **Privately Held**
SIC: **3444** Sheet metalwork

(P-12724)
PRO-TEK MANUFACTURING INC
4849 Southfront Rd, Livermore (94551-9482)
PHONE..................925 454-8100
Steven M Krider, *President*
Sargon Alkurge, *Vice Pres*
Daniel McKenzie, *Vice Pres*
Ron Biela, *Sales Dir*
▲ EMP: 49
SQ FT: 35,240
SALES (est): 11.5MM **Privately Held**
WEB: www.protekmfg.com
SIC: **3444** 3449 Sheet metalwork; miscellaneous metalwork

(P-12725)
PROMPT PRECISION METALS INC
1649 E Whitmore Ave, Ceres (95307-7203)
PHONE..................209 531-1210
Don Widdifield, *President*
Ken Eddleman, *COO*
Joan Widdifield, *Admin Sec*
EMP: 65
SQ FT: 70,000
SALES (est): 11.8MM **Privately Held**
WEB: www.promptprecision.com
SIC: **3444** Sheet metal specialties, not stamped

(P-12726)
PWP MANUFACTURING LLC
1325 Norman Ave, Santa Clara (95054-2027)
PHONE..................408 748-0120
Kimberly Reed,
Birge Clark, *Sales Staff*
Michael Reed,
EMP: 25
SQ FT: 18,000
SALES (est): 4.7MM **Privately Held**
SIC: **3444** 3315 Sheet metal specialties, not stamped; wire products, ferrous/iron; made in wiredrawing plants

(P-12727)
QUALITY FABRICATION
9631 Irondale Ave, Chatsworth
(91311-5009)
PHONE..................................818 407-5015
Pradeep Kumar, *CEO*
▲ EMP: 100
SALES (est): 26.3MM **Privately Held**
WEB: www.quality-fab.com
SIC: 3444 Sheet metal specialties, not
    stamped

(P-12728)
QUALITY METAL FABRICATION LLC
2350 Wilbur Way, Auburn (95602-9500)
PHONE..................................530 887-7388
Thomas Neithercutt, *Mng Member*
EMP: 27
SQ FT: 12,000
SALES (est): 4.8MM **Privately Held**
WEB: www.qualitymetalfabrication.com
SIC: 3444 1799 Sheet metalwork; welding
    on site

(P-12729)
R & R DUCTWORK LLC
12820 Lakeland Rd, Santa Fe Springs
(90670-4515)
PHONE..................................562 944-9660
Brian Klebowski, *Mng Member*
EMP: 18
SQ FT: 14,000
SALES: 1.5MM **Privately Held**
SIC: 3444 Ducts, sheet metal

(P-12730)
R & V SHEET METAL INC
3197 Grapevine St, Mira Loma
(91752-3501)
PHONE..................................951 361-9455
Ricardo Rico, *President*
EMP: 12
SALES (est): 1.3MM **Privately Held**
SIC: 3444 Sheet metalwork

(P-12731)
RADIATION PROTECTION & SPC INC
1531 W Orangewood Ave, Orange
(92868-2006)
PHONE..................................714 771-7702
John Jory, *President*
EMP: 15
SALES (est): 3MM **Privately Held**
SIC: 3444 Radiator shields or enclosures,
    sheet metal

(P-12732)
RAMDA METAL SPECIALTIES INC
13012 Crenshaw Blvd, Gardena
(90249-1544)
PHONE..................................310 538-2136
Daniel Guevara, *CEO*
EMP: 25
SQ FT: 25,000
SALES: 2.5MM **Privately Held**
WEB: www.ramda.com
SIC: 3444 Metal housings, enclosures,
    casings & other containers

(P-12733)
RAYCO BURIAL PRODUCTS INC
Also Called: Rayco B Products
1601 Raymond Ave, Monrovia
(91016-4690)
PHONE..................................626 357-1996
Geza Dala, *President*
Valerie Dala, *Treasurer*
Ilene Sakamoto, *Vice Pres*
Martin Dala, *Admin Sec*
EMP: 30 EST: 1961
SQ FT: 20,000
SALES (est): 4.7MM **Privately Held**
SIC: 3444 Sheet metal specialties, not
    stamped

(P-12734)
RDFABRICATORS INC
11880 Western Ave, Stanton (90680-3438)
PHONE..................................714 634-2078
Raymond D Foye, *President*
Mark Sybirski, *Marketing Staff*
EMP: 18 EST: 1979
SQ FT: 12,000
SALES (est): 1.2MM **Privately Held**
WEB: www.rdfabricators.com
SIC: 3444 Sheet metal specialties, not
    stamped

(P-12735)
RECOATING-WEST INC (PA)
Also Called: Rwi
4170 Douglas Blvd Ste 120, Granite Bay
(95746-9703)
PHONE..................................916 652-8290
Brian Hope, *President*
Ian Cameron, *CFO*
Cheryl Poderzay, *Office Mgr*
Glenn Shafto, *Analyst*
Kent McClain, *Sales Mgr*
▲ EMP: 35
SQ FT: 41,000
SALES (est): 5.9MM **Privately Held**
WEB: www.recoatingwest.com
SIC: 3444 Sheet metalwork

(P-12736)
REDDING METAL CRAFTERS INC
3871 Rancho Rd, Redding (96002-9328)
PHONE..................................530 222-4400
Robert Robinson III, *President*
Barbara Robinson, *Corp Secy*
Gregory Robinson, *Vice Pres*
EMP: 11
SQ FT: 10,000
SALES (est): 1.3MM **Privately Held**
SIC: 3444 Restaurant sheet metalwork

(P-12737)
RIGOS EQUIPMENT MFG LLC
Also Called: Rigos Sheet Metal
14501 Joanbridge St, Baldwin Park
(91706-1749)
PHONE..................................626 813-6621
Yury Anguiano,
Yury I Anguiano, *Sales Executive*
EMP: 23
SQ FT: 3,600
SALES (est): 4MM **Privately Held**
SIC: 3444 Sheet metalwork

(P-12738)
ROBERT F CHAPMAN INC
43100 Exchange Pl, Lancaster
(93535-4524)
PHONE..................................661 940-9482
Tim Mitchell, *CEO*
John H Mitchell, *President*
Paulette Mitchell, *Admin Sec*
Mario Lua, *Business Mgr*
Roy Pitchlynn, *Prdtn Mgr*
EMP: 53
SQ FT: 62,000
SALES (est): 13MM **Privately Held**
WEB: www.robertfchapman.com
SIC: 3444 3549 Sheet metalwork; metal-
    working machinery

(P-12739)
ROMLA CO
Also Called: Romla Ventilator Co
9668 Heinrich Hertz Dr D, San Diego
(92154-7919)
PHONE..................................619 946-1224
Ronald W Haneline, *CEO*
Bob Haneline, *Vice Pres*
Robert Haneline, *Vice Pres*
Jesse Soto, *Purchasing*
Vicky Gadea, *Buyer*
▲ EMP: 33 EST: 1945
SQ FT: 18,000
SALES (est): 8.2MM **Privately Held**
WEB: www.romla.com
SIC: 3444 Metal ventilating equipment

(P-12740)
RON NUNES ENTERPRISES LLC
7703 Las Positas Rd, Livermore
(94551-8205)
PHONE..................................925 371-0220
Ron Nunes, *President*
Mark Timm, *Marketing Staff*
EMP: 15
SQ FT: 28,000
SALES (est): 2.7MM **Privately Held**
WEB: www.ronnunes.com
SIC: 3444 7692 3443 3441 Sheet metal
    specialties, not stamped; welding repair;
    fabricated plate work (boiler shop); fabri-
    cated structural metal

(P-12741)
RONALD F OGLETREE INC
Also Called: Ogletree's
935 Vintage Ave, Saint Helena
(94574-1400)
PHONE..................................707 963-3537
Ronald Ogletree, *President*
Matthew CIA, *Vice Pres*
EMP: 45 EST: 1946
SQ FT: 22,500
SALES (est): 8.5MM **Privately Held**
WEB: www.ogletreecorp.com
SIC: 3444 3441 1791 Sheet metal spe-
    cialties, not stamped; fabricated structural
    metal; structural steel erection

(P-12742)
ROYAL MANUFACTURING INDS INC
600 W Warner Ave, Santa Ana
(92707-3347)
PHONE..................................714 668-9199
Robert Rieck, *President*
EMP: 14
SQ FT: 9,000
SALES (est): 2.2MM **Privately Held**
WEB: www.royalmfgind.com
SIC: 3444 Sheet metalwork

(P-12743)
ROYALITE MFG INC
1055 Terminal Way, San Carlos
(94070-3226)
PHONE..................................650 637-1440
Robert Amarillas, *President*
Dez Farnady, *General Mgr*
Jan Prins, *Sales Mgr*
Percy Landa, *Sales Staff*
▼ EMP: 14
SALES (est): 2.3MM **Privately Held**
WEB: www.royalite-mfg.com
SIC: 3444 3446 Skylights, sheet metal;
    ladders, for permanent installation: metal

(P-12744)
RSR METAL SPINNING INC
850 E Edna Pl, Covina (91723-1410)
PHONE..................................626 814-2339
Russell Spencer, *President*
Jenny Spencer, *Admin Sec*
Stacey Gutierrez, *Controller*
EMP: 15
SQ FT: 6,800
SALES (est): 2.3MM **Privately Held**
WEB: www.rsrmetalspinning.com
SIC: 3444 Sheet metalwork

(P-12745)
RUSS INTERNATIONAL INC
1658 W 132nd St, Gardena (90249-2006)
PHONE..................................310 329-7121
Randy Carter, *CEO*
Edmond Russ, *Chairman*
Joshua Bettencourt, *Technology*
Louise Moore, *Manager*
▲ EMP: 22
SQ FT: 20,000
SALES (est): 4.2MM **Privately Held**
WEB: www.russ-international.com
SIC: 3444 Sheet metal specialties, not
    stamped

(P-12746)
S & L CONTRACTING
900 W Kern Ave Ste 900 # 900, Mc Farland
(93250-1815)
PHONE..................................661 371-6379
Sergio Tindeo, *President*
EMP: 50
SALES (est): 2.6MM **Privately Held**
SIC: 3444 Sheet metalwork

(P-12747)
SA SERVING LINES INC
Also Called: G A Systems
226 W Carleton Ave, Orange (92867-3608)
PHONE..................................714 848-7529
Steve Aderson, *CEO*
Pat Devalle, *CFO*

Virginia Anderson, *Corp Secy*
EMP: 19
SALES (est): 3MM **Privately Held**
SIC: 3444 Metal housings, enclosures,
    casings & other containers

(P-12748)
SABRIN CORPORATION
Also Called: Astronics Company
2836 E Walnut St, Pasadena (91107-3755)
PHONE..................................626 792-3813
Josef Wrablicz, *President*
Millie Wrablicz, *Corp Secy*
Boyd Gaebel, *Buyer*
▲ EMP: 19 EST: 1961
SQ FT: 8,000
SALES (est): 3.8MM **Privately Held**
SIC: 3444 Forming machine work, sheet
    metal

(P-12749)
SAE ENGINEERING INC
365 Reed St, Santa Clara (95050-3107)
PHONE..................................408 492-1784
Benjamin Yates, *Chairman*
Alan Pats, *President*
James Millich, *Vice Pres*
Joanna Yates, *Vice Pres*
▲ EMP: 40
SQ FT: 30,000
SALES: 8.1MM
SALES (corp-wide): 48.6MM **Privately
Held**
SIC: 3444 3599 Sheet metalwork; ma-
    chine shop, jobbing & repair
PA: Hilby-Yates, Inc.
    282 Brokaw Rd
    Santa Clara CA 95050
    408 988-0700

(P-12750)
SAL J ACSTA SHEETMETAL MFG INC
Also Called: Acosta Sheet Metal Mfg Co
930 Remillard Ct, San Jose (95122-2625)
PHONE..................................408 275-6370
Sal J Acosta, *CEO*
Anthony Morales, *CFO*
Randy Acosta, *Treasurer*
Sandi Acosta, *Vice Pres*
Michelle Acosta, *Admin Sec*
▲ EMP: 65
SQ FT: 118,000
SALES (est): 16.2MM **Privately Held**
WEB: www.acostallc.com
SIC: 3444 Sheet metal specialties, not
    stamped

(P-12751)
SAN DEGO PRCSION MACHINING INC
9375 Ruffin Ct, San Diego (92123-5304)
PHONE..................................858 499-0379
William Matteson, *CEO*
Cavett Miller, *Administration*
Jim Fox, *Sales Mgr*
EMP: 50 EST: 1971
SQ FT: 23,000
SALES (est): 10.2MM **Privately Held**
WEB: www.sdpm.com
SIC: 3444 3599 3312 Sheet metalwork;
    machine shop, jobbing & repair; stainless
    steel

(P-12752)
SAXTON INDUSTRIAL INC
1736 Standard Ave, Glendale
(91201-2010)
PHONE..................................818 265-0702
Ben Abadian, *President*
Marjan Abadian, *Vice Pres*
▲ EMP: 18
SQ FT: 33,000
SALES: 2MM **Privately Held**
WEB: www.saxtonindustrial.com
SIC: 3444 3499 3724 Sheet metalwork;
    trophies, metal, except silver; aircraft en-
    gines & engine parts

(P-12753)
SCREEN TECH INC
4754 Bennett Dr, Livermore (94551-4800)
PHONE..................................408 885-9750
Stevan S Robertson, *Principal*
Marsha Robertson, *Vice Pres*
Matt Larson, *Opers Mgr*

Joshua Robertson, *Plant Mgr*
Jason Bortoli, *VP Sales*
▲ **EMP:** 60
SQ FT: 52,000
SALES (est): 13.4MM **Privately Held**
WEB: www.screentechinc.com
SIC: 3444 Sheet metal specialties, not
  stamped

(P-12754)
SE-GI PRODUCTS INC
20521 Teresita Way, Lake Forest
(92630-8142)
PHONE....................................951 737-8320
◆ **EMP:** 21
SALES (est): 4MM **Privately Held**
SIC: 3444

(P-12755)
SEGUNDO METAL PRODUCTS INC
Also Called: Advantage Metal Products
7855 Southfront Rd, Livermore
(94551-8230)
PHONE....................................925 667-2009
Mike Segundo, *President*
Phil Segundo, *Executive*
▲ **EMP:** 80
SQ FT: 60,000
SALES (est): 16.2MM **Privately Held**
WEB: www.advantagemetal.com
SIC: 3444 Sheet metalwork

(P-12756)
SHAFER METAL STAKE (PA)
25176 Avenue 5 1/2, Madera (93637-9586)
PHONE....................................559 674-9487
Merwyn E Shafer, *Owner*
EMP: 14 **EST:** 1979
SQ FT: 1,300
SALES (est): 2MM **Privately Held**
SIC: 3444 Sheet metalwork

(P-12757)
SHEET METAL PROTOTYPE INC
19420 Londelius St, Northridge
(91324-3511)
PHONE....................................818 772-2715
Jane E Lamborn, *President*
EMP: 11
SQ FT: 7,500
SALES (est): 1.5MM **Privately Held**
SIC: 3444 Sheet metal specialties, not
  stamped

(P-12758)
SHEET METAL SERVICE
2310 E Orangethorpe Ave, Anaheim
(92806-1231)
PHONE....................................714 446-0196
Miguel Nunez, *President*
EMP: 18
SQ FT: 10,000
SALES (est): 4.1MM **Privately Held**
SIC: 3444 Sheet metalwork

(P-12759)
SHEET METAL SPECIALIST LLC
11698 Warm Springs Rd, Riverside
(92505-5862)
PHONE....................................951 351-6828
Michael Uranga,
Sandy Sligar,
EMP: 38
SQ FT: 18,000
SALES (est): 6.2MM **Privately Held**
SIC: 3444 Sheet metal specialties, not
  stamped

(P-12760)
SHEET MTAL FABRICATION SUP INC
2020 Railroad Dr, Sacramento
(95815-3515)
PHONE....................................916 641-6884
Cipriano Espinor, *President*
John Espinor, *Vice Pres*
Cheree Batchelor, *Office Admin*
Rick Espinor, *Manager*
EMP: 80
SQ FT: 14,000
SALES (est): 12.6MM **Privately Held**
SIC: 3444 Ducts, sheet metal

(P-12761)
SHEETMETAL ENGINEERING
1780 Voyager Ave, Simi Valley
(93063-3301)
PHONE....................................805 306-0390
Kenneth Chamberlain, *President*
Kathy Chou, *CFO*
David Reed, *Vice Pres*
Dave L Reed, *Technology*
Tony Zapata, *Manager*
EMP: 25
SQ FT: 21,000
SALES (est): 4.2MM **Privately Held**
WEB: www.sheetmetaleng.com
SIC: 3444 1799 Sheet metal specialties,
  not stamped; welding on site

(P-12762)
SHOWERDOORDIRECT LLC
20100 Normandie Ave, Torrance
(90502-1211)
PHONE....................................310 327-8060
Adam Slutske,
▲ **EMP:** 51
SALES (est): 5.2MM
SALES (corp-wide): 19.1MM **Privately Held**
SIC: 3444 Bins, prefabricated sheet metal;
  radiator shields or enclosures, sheet
  metal
PA: Century Shower Door Co., Inc.
  20100 Normandie Ave
  Torrance CA 90502
  310 327-8060

(P-12763)
SMS FABRICATIONS INC
11698 Warm Springs Rd, Riverside
(92505-5862)
PHONE....................................951 351-6828
Michael A Uranga, *CEO*
Sandy Sligar, *President*
Scott Sligar, *Vice Pres*
EMP: 36
SALES (est): 7.4MM **Privately Held**
SIC: 3444 Sheet metalwork

(P-12764)
SOMAR CORPORATION
13006 Halldale Ave, Gardena
(90249-2118)
PHONE....................................310 329-1446
Martin Torres, *President*
Ramona Torres, *Office Mgr*
EMP: 16
SQ FT: 32,000
SALES (est): 2.7MM **Privately Held**
SIC: 3444 3353 Sheet metalwork; alu-
  minum sheet, plate & foil

(P-12765)
SOUTH BAY DIVERSFD SYSTEMS INC
Also Called: U S Fabrications
1841 National Ave, Hayward (94545-1707)
PHONE....................................510 784-3094
Thomas S Waller, *President*
▲ **EMP:** 15
SALES (est): 3.7MM **Privately Held**
WEB: www.usfabrications.com
SIC: 3444 Sheet metalwork

(P-12766)
SPACESONICS INCORPORATED
Also Called: Paysonic
30300 Union City Blvd, Union City
(94587-1514)
PHONE....................................650 610-0999
Ignacio C Palomarez, *President*
Elizabeth Palomarez, *Treasurer*
Hortencia Villanuedo, *Admin Sec*
Carlos Palomarez, *Info Tech Dir*
Diane Palomarez, *Info Tech Mgr*
▲ **EMP:** 90
SQ FT: 55,000
SALES (est): 23.9MM **Privately Held**
WEB: www.spacesonic.com
SIC: 3444 Metal housings, enclosures,
  casings & other containers

(P-12767)
SPAN-O-MATIC INC
825 Columbia St, Brea (92821-2917)
PHONE....................................714 256-4700
Wolfgang Arnold, *President*
Erik A Arnold, *CEO*

Carl Arnold, *Vice Pres*
Lynda Arnold, *Vice Pres*
Frank Mann, *Engineer*
EMP: 40 **EST:** 1972
SQ FT: 50,000
SALES (est): 8.4MM **Privately Held**
WEB: www.spanomatic.com
SIC: 3444 Sheet metalwork

(P-12768)
SPEC-BUILT SYSTEMS INC
2150 Michael Faraday Dr, San Diego
(92154-7903)
PHONE....................................619 661-8100
Randy Eifler, *President*
EMP: 75
SQ FT: 25,000
SALES (est): 22.4MM **Privately Held**
WEB: www.specbuilt.com
SIC: 3444 Sheet metalwork

(P-12769)
SPECIALTY FABRICATIONS INC
2674 Westhills Ct, Simi Valley
(93065-6234)
PHONE....................................805 579-9730
Mark Zimmerman, *President*
Randy Zimmerman, *Corp Secy*
EMP: 49 **EST:** 1978
SQ FT: 80,000
SALES (est): 11.8MM **Privately Held**
WEB: www.specfabinc.com
SIC: 3444 3599 Sheet metalwork; ma-
  chine & other job shop work

(P-12770)
SPRAY ENCLOSURE TECHNOLOGIES
Also Called: Spray Tech
1427 N Linden Ave, Rialto (92376-8601)
PHONE....................................909 419-7011
Tyler Rand, *President*
▲ **EMP:** 30
SQ FT: 59,000
SALES (est): 7.4MM **Privately Held**
WEB: www.mercuryairmakeup.com
SIC: 3444 Booths, spray: prefabricated
  sheet metal

(P-12771)
STEELDYNE INDUSTRIES
Also Called: ABC Sheet Metal
2871 E La Cresta Ave, Anaheim
(92806-1817)
PHONE....................................714 630-6200
Jeff Duveneck, *President*
Richard Duveneck, *Vice Pres*
Art Benner, *Controller*
EMP: 40
SQ FT: 20,000
SALES (est): 11.8MM **Privately Held**
WEB: www.abcsheetmetal.com
SIC: 3444 Sheet metalwork

(P-12772)
STEELER INC
2901 Orange Grove Ave, North Highlands
(95660-5703)
PHONE....................................916 483-3600
Kirk Bache, *Manager*
EMP: 10
SALES (corp-wide): 41.7MM **Privately Held**
WEB: www.steeler.com
SIC: 3444 5072 Studs & joists, sheet
  metal; builders' hardware; miscellaneous
  fasteners
PA: Steeler, Inc.
  10023 Martin Luther King
  Seattle WA 98178
  206 725-8500

(P-12773)
STEIN INDUSTRIES INC (PA)
4005 Artesia Ave, Fullerton (92833-2519)
PHONE....................................714 522-4560
Rudi Steinhilber, *CEO*
Theodore Steinhilber, *President*
Dave Spivy, *CFO*
EMP: 37 **EST:** 1982
SQ FT: 30,800
SALES (est): 4.6MM **Privately Held**
WEB: www..steinindustries.com
SIC: 3444 2599 Sheet metalwork; work
  benches, factory

(P-12774)
STOLL METALCRAFT INC
24808 Anza Dr, Valencia (91355-1258)
PHONE....................................661 295-0401
Gunter Stoll, *President*
Angelica Alonzo, *Manager*
EMP: 105
SQ FT: 45,000
SALES (est): 24.8MM **Privately Held**
WEB: www.stoll-metalcraft.com
SIC: 3444 Sheet metal specialties, not
  stamped

(P-12775)
STRETCH FORMING CORPORATION
Also Called: Sfc
804 S Redlands Ave, Perris (92570-2478)
PHONE....................................951 443-0911
Brian D Geary, *CEO*
Jim Lowther, *General Mgr*
Jose Corvorubbias, *Info Tech Mgr*
Joseph Nunez, *Engineer*
Linda Baghbanmanesh, *Accounting Mgr*
▲ **EMP:** 105
SQ FT: 97,000
SALES (est): 14.2MM **Privately Held**
SIC: 3444 Sheet metalwork

(P-12776)
SUN SHEETMETAL SOLUTIONS INC
3565 Charter Park Dr, San Jose
(95136-1346)
P.O. Box 731244 (95173-1244)
PHONE....................................408 445-8047
Chau Nguyen, *President*
Rebecca Trinhle, *CFO*
Tom Nguyen, *Vice Pres*
Kevin Trinhle, *Accounts Mgr*
EMP: 20 **EST:** 2000
SQ FT: 10,000
SALES (est): 4.6MM **Privately Held**
WEB: www.sunsheetmetals.com
SIC: 3444 3552 Sheet metal specialties,
  not stamped; fabric forming machinery &
  equipment

(P-12777)
SUPERIOR DUCT FABRICATION INC
1683 Mount Vernon Ave, Pomona
(91768-3300)
PHONE....................................909 620-8565
Mike Hilgert, *CEO*
Kerry Bootke, *Vice Pres*
◆ **EMP:** 107
SQ FT: 3,900
SALES (est): 33.5MM **Privately Held**
WEB: www.sdfab.com
SIC: 3444 Ducts, sheet metal

(P-12778)
SUPERIOR METAL FABRICATORS
4768 Felspar St, Riverside (92509-3038)
PHONE....................................951 360-2474
Ron Didonanto, *President*
Dave Anderson, *Vice Pres*
EMP: 12
SQ FT: 10,000
SALES (est): 1.3MM **Privately Held**
SIC: 3444 Sheet metalwork

(P-12779)
SUPERIOR METALS INC
838 Jury Ct Ste B, San Jose (95112-2815)
PHONE....................................408 938-3488
Hugo Navarez, *President*
EMP: 15
SQ FT: 7,000
SALES (est): 1.9MM **Privately Held**
SIC: 3444 Sheet metalwork

(P-12780)
SWEET DONALDSON MET SPINNING
3535 Union Pacific Ave, Los Angeles
(90023-3921)
P.O. Box 2993, La Habra (90632-2993)
PHONE....................................323 268-8730
Jim Dimaria, *President*
EMP: 10
SQ FT: 6,000

SALES (est): 1.3MM **Privately Held**
SIC: 3444 Forming machine work, sheet
metal

(P-12781)
SWIFT FAB
515 E Alondra Blvd, Gardena
(90248-2903)
PHONE.................................310 366-7295
Robert Senter, *Owner*
Carla Senter, *General Mgr*
EMP: 17
SQ FT: 6,000
SALES (est): 2.1MM **Privately Held**
WEB: www.swiftfab.com
SIC: 3444 Sheet metal specialties, not
stamped

(P-12782)
SWIFT-COR PRECISION INC
344 W 157th St, Gardena (90248-2135)
PHONE.................................310 354-1207
Sam Longo Jr, *President*
Tony Serge, *CFO*
EMP: 62
SQ FT: 100,000
SALES (est): 8.8MM **Privately Held**
WEB: www.swiftcor.com
SIC: 3444 Sheet metalwork

(P-12783)
TALINS COMPANY
17800 S Main St Ste 121, Gardena
(90248-3511)
PHONE.................................310 378-3715
George Talbott, *Owner*
EMP: 15 EST: 1977
SQ FT: 3,200
SALES (est): 1.6MM **Privately Held**
SIC: 3444 Sheet metalwork

(P-12784)
TAYLOR WINGS INC
3720 Omec Cir, Rancho Cordova
(95742-7303)
PHONE.................................916 851-9464
Terry Taylor, *President*
Samantha Sanderson, *Admin Asst*
Chris Roberts, *Production*
EMP: 25
SQ FT: 11,700
SALES (est): 5.3MM **Privately Held**
WEB: www.taylorwings.com
SIC: 3444 Sheet metalwork

(P-12785)
TED RIECK ENTERPRISES INC
Also Called: Royal Metal
1228 S Wright St, Santa Ana (92705-4507)
PHONE.................................714 542-4763
Ted Rieck, *President*
Penny Rieck, *Vice Pres*
EMP: 14
SQ FT: 9,000
SALES: 1.5MM **Privately Held**
SIC: 3444 Sheet metalwork

(P-12786)
TEE -N -JAY MANUFACTURING INC
9145 Glenoaks Blvd, Sun Valley
(91352-2612)
PHONE.................................818 504-2961
Jeff Berns, *President*
Tamara Berns, *Corp Secy*
Sandra Hollingsworth, *Office Mgr*
Jessica Berns-Hall, *Purch Mgr*
Jessica Berns, *Opers Staff*
EMP: 20
SQ FT: 10,187
SALES (est): 3MM **Privately Held**
WEB: www.tee-n-jay.com
SIC: 3444 Sheet metalwork

(P-12787)
TEOHC CALIFORNIA INC
1320 Performance Dr, Stockton
(95206-4925)
PHONE.................................209 234-1600
Nicholas L Saakvitne, *CEO*
Gary Henry, *President*
Jim Willis, *CFO*
Alex MAI, *Officer*
Mark J Comfort, *Vice Pres*
EMP: 350 EST: 1943
SQ FT: 350,000

SALES (est): 31.7MM
SALES (corp-wide): 986.9MM **Publicly Held**
WEB: www.gibraltar1.com
SIC: 3444 3479 Furnace casings, sheet
metal; gutters, sheet metal; galvanizing of
iron, steel or end-formed products
PA: Gibraltar Industries, Inc.
3556 Lake Shore Rd # 100
Buffalo NY 14219
716 826-6500

(P-12788)
TFC MANUFACTURING INC
4001 Watson Plaza Dr, Lakewood
(90712-4034)
PHONE.................................562 426-9559
Majid Shahbazi, *President*
Hamid Sharifat, *Vice Pres*
Baldo Marquez, *Purchasing*
EMP: 81
SQ FT: 28,500
SALES (est): 21.7MM **Privately Held**
WEB: www.tfcmfg.com
SIC: 3444 Sheet metalwork

(P-12789)
THERMA LLC
1601 Las Plumas Ave, San Jose
(95133-1613)
PHONE.................................408 347-3400
Joseph Parisi, *CEO*
Nicki Parisi, *CFO*
Mat Hayashi, *Project Mgr*
Jon Litle, *Project Mgr*
Kerry Coltun, *Project Engr*
▲ EMP: 1200
SALES (est): 228.8MM
SALES (corp-wide): 26.9MM **Privately Held**
WEB: www.therma.com
SIC: 3444 3448 Sheet metalwork; prefab-
ricated metal components
PA: Therma Holdings Llc
17 Bridge Sq
Westport CT

(P-12790)
THOMAS E DAVIS INC
Also Called: Tedco
6736 Preston Ave Ste A, Livermore
(94551-8521)
P.O. Box 2376 (94551-2376)
PHONE.................................925 373-1373
Cynthia Davis, *President*
Michael Davis, *President*
Jennifer J Hunt, *CFO*
EMP: 10
SQ FT: 12,000
SALES (est): 1.2MM **Privately Held**
WEB: www.tedcosheetmetal.com
SIC: 3444 Sheet metal specialties, not
stamped

(P-12791)
TN SHEET METAL INC
18385 Bandilier Cir, Fountain Valley
(92708-7001)
PHONE.................................714 593-0100
Thony Quang Nguyen, *CEO*
▲ EMP: 19 EST: 2001
SQ FT: 12,035
SALES (est): 4.3MM **Privately Held**
SIC: 3444 Ducts, sheet metal

(P-12792)
TREND TECHNOLOGIES LLC (DH)
4626 Eucalyptus Ave, Chino (91710-9215)
P.O. Box 515001, Los Angeles (90051-5001)
PHONE.................................909 597-8961
Earl Payton, *Mng Member*
Jeffrey Stump, *Vice Pres*
Barb Raftree, *Admin Asst*
Margarita Betancourt, *Controller*
Scott Talbot, *QC Mgr*
▲ EMP: 200
SQ FT: 125,000

SALES (est): 130.8MM
SALES (corp-wide): 164.5MM **Privately Held**
SIC: 3444 3469 3499 3089 Metal housings, enclosures, casings & other containers; electronic enclosures, stamped or
pressed metal; aquarium accessories,
metal; injection molding of plastics
HQ: Ttl Holdings, Llc
4626 Eucalyptus Ave
Chino CA 91710
909 597-7861

(P-12793)
TRI FAB ASSOCIATES INC
48351 Lakeview Blvd, Fremont
(94538-6533)
PHONE.................................510 651-7628
Ronald A Brochu, *President*
Joseph R Santosuosso, *CEO*
Judy Archer, *Controller*
Richard Petrarca, *Controller*
Michael Taft, *QC Mgr*
EMP: 90
SQ FT: 35,000
SALES (est): 18.5MM **Privately Held**
WEB: www.trifab.com
SIC: 3444 Sheet metal specialties, not
stamped

(P-12794)
TRI PRECISION SHEETMETAL INC
845 N Elm St, Orange (92867-7909)
PHONE.................................714 632-8838
Ross Morrow, *President*
Rob Morrow, *CFO*
EMP: 40
SALES (est): 8.8MM **Privately Held**
WEB: www.triprecision.com
SIC: 3444 Housings for business ma-
chines, sheet metal; sheet metal special-
ties, not stamped

(P-12795)
TRI-M CO
528 E Mission Rd, San Marcos
(92069-1825)
PHONE.................................760 744-5115
Richard Martin, *Partner*
Jackie Martin, *Partner*
EMP: 47
SQ FT: 100,000
SALES (est): 9MM **Privately Held**
WEB: www.tri-m-co.com
SIC: 3444 Sheet metal specialties, not
stamped

(P-12796)
TRIO METAL STAMPING INC
15318 Proctor Ave, City of Industry
(91745-1023)
PHONE.................................626 336-1228
Damian Rickard, *CEO*
Rudy Hernandez, *COO*
Georgia Boris, *Corp Secy*
EMP: 53
SQ FT: 75,000
SALES (est): 8MM **Privately Held**
WEB: www.triometalstamping.com
SIC: 3444 3469 Sheet metalwork; stamp-
ing metal for the trade

(P-12797)
TRU-DUCT INC
2500 Swetwater Sprng Blvd, Spring Valley
(91978-2007)
PHONE.................................619 660-3858
Drew E Miles, *CEO*
EMP: 45
SQ FT: 14,400
SALES (est): 11.3MM **Privately Held**
SIC: 3444 Ducts, sheet metal

(P-12798)
UNITED DURALUME PRODUCTS INC
350 S Raymond Ave, Fullerton
(92831-4689)
PHONE.................................714 773-4011
Mike Winston Adams, *CEO*
EMP: 15
SQ FT: 128,600
SALES (est): 3.2MM **Privately Held**
SIC: 3444 1521 Awnings & canopies; patio
& deck construction & repair

(P-12799)
UNITED FABRICATION INC
1250 Avenida Acaso Ste C, Camarillo
(93012-8729)
PHONE.................................805 482-2354
John Osgood, *President*
Philip Amanta, *President*
EMP: 15
SQ FT: 11,000
SALES: 2MM **Privately Held**
SIC: 3444 2514 Metal ventilating equip-
ment; cabinets; radio & television: metal

(P-12800)
UNITED MECH MET FBRICATORS INC
Also Called: Umec
548 Claire St, Hayward (94541-6412)
PHONE.................................510 537-4744
Gina Wang, *CEO*
Barry Brescia, *President*
Albert Sevilla, *Manager*
EMP: 50
SQ FT: 18,000
SALES (est): 13.1MM **Privately Held**
WEB: www.umec.net
SIC: 3444 3443 3556 Sheet metalwork;
fabricated plate work (boiler shop); food
products machinery

(P-12801)
UNITED SHEETMETAL INC
44153 S Grimmer Blvd, Fremont
(94538-6350)
PHONE.................................510 257-1858
Chung Yuan Tsai, *CEO*
Peggy Loo, *CFO*
▲ EMP: 11
SALES (est): 2.2MM
SALES (corp-wide): 54.9MM **Privately Held**
WEB: www.unitedsheetmetal.com
SIC: 3444 Sheet metal specialties, not
stamped
PA: Cheng Fwa Industrial Co., Ltd.
5f, 252, Sec. 2, New Taipei Blvd.,
New Taipei City 24158
229 951-439

(P-12802)
US PRECISION SHEET METAL INC
Also Called: U S Precision Manufacturing
4020 Garner Rd, Riverside (92501-1006)
PHONE.................................951 276-2611
Amanda Hawkins, *CEO*
Ray Mayo, *President*
Sal Giulano, *Vice Pres*
EMP: 68 EST: 1981
SQ FT: 25,000
SALES (est): 13.3MM **Privately Held**
WEB: www.usprecision.net
SIC: 3444 Sheet metal specialties, not
stamped

(P-12803)
USK MANUFACTURING INC
720 Zwissig Way, Union City (94587-3602)
PHONE.................................510 471-7555
Moon Do Kim, *CEO*
Jina Kim, *Vice Pres*
Cindy Fong, *Principal*
Frences Hsu, *Controller*
▲ EMP: 45
SQ FT: 85,000
SALES: 5MM **Privately Held**
WEB: www.uskmfg.com
SIC: 3444 Sheet metalwork

(P-12804)
VALLEY PRECISION METAL PRODUCT
Also Called: Valley Engravers
27771 Avenue Hopkins, Santa Clarita
(91355-1223)
PHONE.................................661 607-0100
Toll Free:...888 -
Howard R Vermillion Jr, *President*
EMP: 30
SQ FT: 15,000

(PA)=Parent Co (HQ)=Headquarters (DH)=Div Headquarters
✪ = New Business established in last 2 years

SALES (est): 4.8MM
SALES (corp-wide): 6.5MM **Privately Held**
WEB: www.valleyprecisionmetal.com
SIC: **3444** 3599 Sheet metalwork; machine shop, jobbing & repair
PA: Valley Precision Metal Products, Inc.
27771 Avenue Hopkins
Valencia CA 91355
661 607-0100

(P-12805)
VANGUARD FABRICATION CORP
14578 Hawthorne Ave, Fontana (92335-2507)
PHONE..................................909 355-0832
Bill Tully, *President*
EMP: 12
SQ FT: 7,000
SALES (est): 2MM **Privately Held**
SIC: **3444** Sheet metalwork

(P-12806)
VERCO DECKING INC
8333 Lime Ave, Fontana (92335)
P.O. Box 3487 (92334-3487)
PHONE..................................909 822-8079
Mike Decasas, *Opers-Prdtn-Mfg*
EMP: 15
SALES (corp-wide): 20.2B **Publicly Held**
SIC: **3444** Siding, sheet metal
HQ: Verco Decking, Inc.
4340 N 42nd Ave
Phoenix AZ 85019
602 272-1347

(P-12807)
VERCO DECKING INC
607 Wilbur Ave, Antioch (94509-7502)
P.O. Box 1259 (94509-0125)
PHONE..................................925 778-2102
Tim Ferrier, *Manager*
EMP: 15
SQ FT: 49,914
SALES (corp-wide): 20.2B **Publicly Held**
SIC: **3444** 3441 Roof deck, sheet metal; fabricated structural metal
HQ: Verco Decking, Inc.
4340 N 42nd Ave
Phoenix AZ 85019
602 272-1347

(P-12808)
VERSAFAB CORP (PA)
15919 S Broadway, Gardena (90248-2489)
PHONE..................................800 421-1822
Edward Penfold Jr, *Ch of Bd*
Joe Flynn, *President*
Sylvia Franco, *QC Mgr*
EMP: 43 EST: 1982
SQ FT: 35,000
SALES: 8.3MM **Privately Held**
WEB: www.versafabcorp.com
SIC: **3444** 3465 3496 3469 Sheet metalwork; moldings or trim, automobile: stamped metal; miscellaneous fabricated wire products; metal stampings

(P-12809)
VERSAFORM CORPORATION
1377 Specialty Dr, Vista (92081-8521)
PHONE..................................760 599-0961
Ronals S Saks, *President*
EMP: 73
SQ FT: 24,000
SALES (est): 11.4MM
SALES (corp-wide): 1MM **Privately Held**
WEB: www.lmiaerospace.com
SIC: **3444** 3549 3398 Forming machine work, sheet metal; sheet metal specialties, not stamped; metalworking machinery; metal heat treating
HQ: Lmi Aerospace, Inc.
411 Fountain Lakes Blvd
Saint Charles MO 63301
636 946-6525

(P-12810)
VIVER CO INC
Also Called: Viver Sheet Metal
1934 W 144th St, Gardena (90249-2928)
PHONE..................................310 327-4578
Victor Loya, *Owner*
EMP: 10
SQ FT: 5,000

SALES (est): 1MM **Privately Held**
SIC: **3444** Ducts, sheet metal

(P-12811)
VIVID INC
1250 Memorex Dr, Santa Clara (95050-2812)
P.O. Box 700125, San Jose (95170-0125)
PHONE..................................408 982-9101
John Comeau, *President*
Walt Pena, *Vice Pres*
Albert Comeau, *Project Mgr*
Keith Lough, *Project Mgr*
Thomas Nguyen, *Project Mgr*
▲ EMP: 53
SQ FT: 38,800
SALES (est): 10.3MM **Privately Held**
WEB: www.vividinc.com
SIC: **3444** Sheet metalwork

(P-12812)
VTS SHEETMETAL SPECIALIST CO
1041 N Grove St, Anaheim (92806-2015)
PHONE..................................714 237-1420
Tom Bonnett, *President*
SA H Vo, *Admin Sec*
EMP: 31
SQ FT: 21,300
SALES (est): 3.4MM **Privately Held**
WEB: www.vtsfab.com
SIC: **3444** Metal housings, enclosures, casings & other containers

(P-12813)
W A CALL MANUFACTURING CO INC
1710 Rogers Ave, San Jose (95112-1189)
PHONE..................................408 436-1450
W A Pat Call Jr, *President*
Justin Pourroy, *Vice Pres*
EMP: 15 EST: 1950
SQ FT: 36,250
SALES (est): 2.9MM **Privately Held**
SIC: **3444** 5075 Metal ventilating equipment; warm air heating & air conditioning

(P-12814)
W E HALL CO
Also Called: Pacific Corrugated Pipe
13680 Slover Ave, Fontana (92337-6951)
PHONE..................................909 829-4235
Sandee Knuckey, *Manager*
EMP: 12
SALES (corp-wide): 24MM **Privately Held**
SIC: **3444** 3449 5051 3312 Culverts, sheet metal; miscellaneous metalwork; pipe & tubing, steel; blast furnaces & steel mills
PA: W.E. Hall Company, Inc.
471 Old Newport Blvd # 205
Newport Beach CA 92663
949 650-4555

(P-12815)
WENCON DEVELOPMENT INC
Also Called: Quick Mount Pv
2700 Mitchell Dr 2, Walnut Creek (94598-1602)
PHONE..................................925 687-6686
Stuart Wentworth, *Principal*
Jeff Spies, *President*
Claudia Wentworth, *President*
Mark Ammerman, *Vice Pres*
Sam Cast, *Vice Pres*
▲ EMP: 88
SQ FT: 1,700
SALES (est): 15.6MM **Privately Held**
SIC: **3444** Awnings & canopies

(P-12816)
WEST COAST CUSTOM SHEET METAL
9045 Glenoaks Blvd, Sun Valley (91352-2040)
PHONE..................................818 252-7500
George Vartan, *President*
EMP: 19
SQ FT: 8,500
SALES (est): 2.7MM **Privately Held**
SIC: **3444** Sheet metalwork

(P-12817)
WEST COAST FAB INC
700 S 32nd St, Richmond (94804-4106)
PHONE..................................510 529-0177
Thomas Nelson, *President*
Diane Burnett, *Controller*
Scott Shelby, *QC Mgr*
EMP: 15
SQ FT: 18,000
SALES (est): 3.7MM **Privately Held**
WEB: www.westcoastfabinc.com
SIC: **3444** Sheet metal specialties, not stamped

(P-12818)
WESTFAB MANUFACTURING INC
3370 Keller St, Santa Clara (95054-2612)
PHONE..................................408 727-0550
Akbar Soleimanieh, *President*
Homeira Lotfi, *CFO*
EMP: 45
SQ FT: 22,000
SALES (est): 5MM **Privately Held**
WEB: www.westfab.com
SIC: **3444** Sheet metalwork

(P-12819)
WILL-MANN INC
225 E Santa Fe Ave, Fullerton (92832-1917)
P.O. Box 976 (92836-0976)
PHONE..................................714 870-0350
Manfred Frischmuth, *President*
Sabina Andrassy, *Treasurer*
Lore Frischmuth, *Vice Pres*
Tracy Herget, *Manager*
EMP: 40
SQ FT: 30,000
SALES (est): 8.2MM **Privately Held**
WEB: www.will-mann.com
SIC: **3444** 7692 3471 Sheet metal specialties, not stamped; welding repair; plating & polishing

(P-12820)
WINBO USA INC
2120 California Ave Ste 2, Corona (92881-3301)
PHONE..................................951 738-9978
Eddie Cheung, *President*
▲ EMP: 40
SALES (est): 592.6K **Privately Held**
SIC: **3444** Machine guards, sheet metal

3446 Architectural & Ornamental Metal Work

(P-12821)
A AND M ORNAMENTAL IRON & WLDG
1611 Railroad St, Corona (92880-2503)
PHONE..................................951 734-6730
Michael J Tallick, *Owner*
EMP: 14
SQ FT: 4,000
SALES (est): 2MM **Privately Held**
SIC: **3446** Architectural metalwork

(P-12822)
A/C FOLDING GATES
1374 E 9th St, Pomona (91766-3831)
PHONE..................................909 629-3026
Clifton G Adams, *Owner*
EMP: 13
SQ FT: 16,000
SALES (est): 970K **Privately Held**
SIC: **3446** 1799 Gates, ornamental metal; fence construction

(P-12823)
ABLE IRON WORKS
222 Hershey St, Pomona (91767-5810)
PHONE..................................909 397-5300
Stephen Holmes, *CEO*
Darcy Schultz, *Office Mgr*
Bob Pittinger, *Project Mgr*
Oscar Tapia, *Director*
EMP: 20
SQ FT: 12,000
SALES: 10MM **Privately Held**
WEB: www.ableironwork.com
SIC: **3446** Architectural metalwork

(P-12824)
ABS MANUFACTURERS INC
519 Horning St, San Jose (95112-2913)
PHONE..................................408 295-5984
Rick Mancias, *President*
Lupe Mancias Jr, *Vice Pres*
EMP: 17
SQ FT: 4,000
SALES (est): 2.6MM **Privately Held**
WEB: www.classof72.com
SIC: **3446** Ornamental metalwork

(P-12825)
ACCESS PROFESSIONAL INC
Also Called: Access Professional Systems
1955 Cordell Ct Ste 104, El Cajon (92020-0901)
PHONE..................................858 571-4444
Russell Scheppmann, *President*
EMP: 18
SALES (est): 4.7MM **Privately Held**
SIC: **3446** 7521 1731 Fences, gates, posts & flagpoles; automobile parking; voice, data & video wiring contractor

(P-12826)
ACE IRON INC
929 Howard St, Marina Del Rey (90292-5518)
PHONE..................................510 324-3300
Aejaz Sareshwala, *President*
EMP: 145
SQ FT: 60,000
SALES (est): 16.5MM **Privately Held**
WEB: www.aceiron.com
SIC: **3446** 3441 1791 Fences or posts, ornamental iron or steel; building components, structural steel; structural steel erection

(P-12827)
ACTIANCE INC
1400 Seaport Blvd, Redwood City (94063-5594)
PHONE..................................650 631-6300
EMP: 42
SALES (est): 10.3MM **Privately Held**
SIC: **3446**

(P-12828)
ACTION IRONWORKS
1215 K St Fl 17, Sacramento (95814-3954)
PHONE..................................916 503-2270
Brad Jones, *Owner*
EMP: 12
SQ FT: 10,000
SALES: 700K **Privately Held**
SIC: **3446** Architectural metalwork

(P-12829)
ADF INCORPORATED
Also Called: Able Design and Fabrication
1550 W Mahalo Pl, Rancho Dominguez (90220-5422)
PHONE..................................310 669-9700
Lou Mannick, *President*
Duc Luu, *Info Tech Dir*
Brian Webster, *Engineer*
Mercedes Chavez, *Human Res Mgr*
Paul Ash, *Sales Dir*
EMP: 30
SQ FT: 23,000
SALES (est): 7.5MM **Privately Held**
WEB: www.able-design.com
SIC: **3446** Partitions & supports/studs, including accoustical systems

(P-12830)
ALABAMA METAL INDUSTRIES CORP
Also Called: Amico Fontana
11093 Beech Ave, Fontana (92337-7268)
P.O. Box 310353 (92331-0353)
PHONE..................................909 350-9280
Lilly Mc Donalds, *Branch Mgr*
Susan Esquibel, *Office Mgr*
EMP: 45
SALES (corp-wide): 986.9MM **Publicly Held**
WEB: www.amico-online.com
SIC: **3446** Open flooring & grating for construction
HQ: Alabama Metal Industries Corporation
3245 Fayette Ave
Birmingham AL 35208
205 787-2611

▲ = Import ▼=Export
◆ =Import/Export

(P-12831)
AMERICAN STEEL & STAIRWAYS INC
8525 Forest St Ste A, Gilroy (95020-3797)
PHONE......................408 848-2992
Martin Vollrath, *President*
Margit Vollrath, *Treasurer*
Thomas Vollrath, *Vice Pres*
Nancy Vollrath, *General Mgr*
EMP: 33
SQ FT: 18,000
SALES (est): 8.3MM **Privately Held**
WEB:
www.americansteelandstairways.com
SIC: 3446 3441 Ornamental metalwork;
fabricated structural metal

(P-12832)
ARBOR FENCE INC
22725 8th St E Ste C, Sonoma
(95476-2829)
PHONE......................707 938-3133
Ronald Wooden, *President*
EMP: 22
SALES (est): 4MM **Privately Held**
WEB: www.arborfence.com
SIC: 3446 3315 2499 5211 Fences,
gates, posts & flagpoles; chain link fenc-
ing; fencing; wood; fencing; security de-
vices

(P-12833)
ARCHITECTURAL ENTERPRISES INC
Also Called: Hi-Tech Iron Works
5821 Randolph St, Commerce
(90040-3415)
PHONE......................323 268-4000
Tom Lee, *President*
John S Lee, *Treasurer*
Alma Gutierrez, *Admin Sec*
EMP: 40
SQ FT: 20,000
SALES (est): 3.3MM **Privately Held**
SIC: 3446 Fences or posts, ornamental
iron or steel; gates, ornamental metal

(P-12834)
ATR TECHNOLOGIES INCORPORATED
Also Called: Aluminum Tube Railings
805 Towne Center Dr, Pomona
(91767-5901)
PHONE......................909 399-9724
Donald Terry, *President*
Debbie Terry, *Partner*
Dave C Terry, *Treasurer*
Debra L Terry, *Admin Sec*
Bert Roark, *Sales Mgr*
▼ EMP: 15
SQ FT: 15,800
SALES (est): 1.5MM **Privately Held**
WEB: www.atrtechnologies.com
SIC: 3446 Architectural metalwork

(P-12835)
AZTECA ORNAMENTAL METALS
Also Called: Azteca Ornamental Iron Works
2738 Stingle Ave, Rosemead (91770-3329)
PHONE......................626 280-2822
Ricardo Gomez, *Owner*
Magdaleno Gomez Sr,
EMP: 12 EST: 1966
SALES (est): 1.1MM **Privately Held**
SIC: 3446 Fences or posts, ornamental
iron or steel

(P-12836)
BAY ORNAMENTAL IRON INC
757 Newton Way, Costa Mesa
(92627-4277)
PHONE......................949 548-1015
Fax: 949 423-0084
EMP: 24
SQ FT: 4,000
SALES (est): 3.5MM **Privately Held**
WEB: www.bayornamentaliron.com
SIC: 3446

(P-12837)
BLACKLION ENTERPRISES INC (PA)
1731 Bonita Vista Dr, San Bernardino
(92404-2107)
PHONE......................951 328-0400

Bryan Decarvalho, *CEO*
EMP: 12
SQ FT: 18,000
SALES: 1.1MM **Privately Held**
SIC: 3446 Architectural metalwork

(P-12838)
BRADFIELD MANUFACTURING INC
2633 E Mardi Gras Ave, Anaheim
(92806-3243)
PHONE......................714 543-8348
Gerry L Bradfield, *President*
Nola Read, *Treasurer*
Roderick S Bradfield, *Vice Pres*
EMP: 18
SQ FT: 12,000
SALES: 1.5MM **Privately Held**
WEB: www.bradfieldstairs.com
SIC: 3446 Stairs, staircases, stair treads:
prefabricated metal

(P-12839)
BRODHEAD GRATING PRODUCTS LLC
3651 Sausalito St, Los Alamitos
(90720-2436)
PHONE......................562 598-4314
Ronald Robertson,
EMP: 12
SQ FT: 20,000
SALES (est): 1.2MM **Privately Held**
SIC: 3446 Open flooring & grating for con-
struction

(P-12840)
BRODHEAD STEEL PRODUCTS CO (PA)
7550 Alpine Rd, La Honda (94020-9785)
PHONE......................650 871-8251
David R Brodhead, *President*
Joy Asdoorian, *Corp Secy*
EMP: 30 EST: 1945
SQ FT: 2,500
SALES (est): 3.5MM **Privately Held**
SIC: 3446 1791 Open flooring & grating
for construction; concrete reinforcement,
placing of

(P-12841)
CANTERBURY DESIGNS INC
Also Called: Canterbury International
5632 W Washington Blvd, Los Angeles
(90016-1986)
PHONE......................323 936-7111
Larry Snyder, *President*
Laura Snyder, *Vice Pres*
John Flanton, *Manager*
▲ EMP: 20 EST: 1964
SQ FT: 13,000
SALES (est): 3.9MM **Privately Held**
WEB: www.compvillage.com
SIC: 3446 3873 Architectural metalwork;
clocks, assembly of

(P-12842)
CHALLENGER ORNAMENTAL IR WORKS
437 W Palmer Ave, Glendale (91204-2407)
PHONE......................818 507-7030
Nerses Espanosian, *President*
EMP: 14
SQ FT: 6,500
SALES (est): 1MM **Privately Held**
SIC: 3446 Architectural metalwork; gates,
ornamental metal; railings, prefabricated
metal; grillwork, ornamental metal

(P-12843)
CLARK STEEL FABRICATORS INC
12610 Vigilante Rd, Lakeside (92040-1113)
P.O. Box 1370 (92040-0910)
PHONE......................619 390-1502
Kimberley L Clark, *President*
Kevin B Clark, *Vice Pres*
Kevin Clark, *General Mgr*
Mark Mendoza, *General Mgr*
Tarah Miinch, *Office Admin*
EMP: 45 EST: 1977
SQ FT: 12,500
SALES (est): 11.8MM **Privately Held**
WEB: www.clarksteelfab.com
SIC: 3446 3441 Architectural metalwork;
fabricated structural metal

(P-12844)
COLUMBIA FABRICATING CO INC
5079 Gloria Ave, Encino (91436-1553)
PHONE......................818 247-4220
Joseph Goldberg, *CEO*
Dalia Goldberg, *CFO*
EMP: 50
SQ FT: 19,000
SALES (est): 9.6MM **Privately Held**
SIC: 3446 Architectural metalwork

(P-12845)
CRABTREE GLASS COMPANY INC
13203 Sherman Way, North Hollywood
(91605-4649)
PHONE......................818 765-1840
Jerry Otworth, *CEO*
Stephanie Otworth, *Manager*
EMP: 10
SQ FT: 1,553
SALES (est): 1.7MM **Privately Held**
WEB: www.crabtreeglass.com
SIC: 3446 1793 Architectural metalwork;
glass & glazing work

(P-12846)
CRANEVEYOR CORP
13730 Central Ave, Chino (91710-5503)
PHONE......................909 627-6801
Mike Williams, *Branch Mgr*
EMP: 20
SALES (est): 2.6MM
SALES (corp-wide): 33.2MM **Privately
Held**
SIC: 3446 3536 Railings, bannisters,
guards, etc.: made from metal pipe;
hoists, cranes & monorails
PA: Craneveyor Corp.
1524 Potrero Ave
El Monte CA 91733
626 442-1524

(P-12847)
CURRAN ENGINEERING COMPANY INC
28727 Industry Dr, Valencia (91355-5414)
P.O. Box 26, Castaic (91310-0026)
PHONE......................800 643-6353
Douglas M Curran, *CEO*
Patrick Curran, *President*
EMP: 20 EST: 1947
SQ FT: 20,000
SALES (est): 3.7MM **Privately Held**
WEB: www.curranengineering.com
SIC: 3446 5399 Architectural metalwork;
Army-Navy goods

(P-12848)
CUSTOM METAL WORKS
2233 W 2nd St, Santa Ana (92703-3511)
PHONE......................714 953-5481
Fax: 714 953-5494
EMP: 10
SQ FT: 4,000
SALES: 400K **Privately Held**
SIC: 3446

(P-12849)
DENNISON INC
Also Called: Maxxon Company
17901 Railroad St, City of Industry
(91748-1113)
PHONE......................626 965-8917
Dennis MA, *President*
▲ EMP: 47
SQ FT: 26,000
SALES: 16MM **Privately Held**
WEB: www.maxxonusa.com
SIC: 3446 Architectural metalwork

(P-12850)
DEVINCNZI ARCHTCTURAL PDTS INC
1717 Adrian Rd, Burlingame (94010-2104)
PHONE......................650 692-5800
Robert Devincenzi, *President*
Janice Devincenzi-Samuelson, *Treasurer*
William Galvin, *Vice Pres*
Steven Devincenzi, *Admin Sec*
EMP: 14 EST: 1982
SQ FT: 11,000
SALES (est): 3MM **Privately Held**
SIC: 3446 Architectural metalwork

(P-12851)
EAGLE IRON FABRICATION INC
Also Called: Eagle Iron Works
100 Medburn St Ste A, Concord
(94520-1123)
PHONE......................925 686-9510
Vic Griffith, *Partner*
Jim Pola, *Vice Pres*
EMP: 10
SQ FT: 5,500
SALES (est): 1.2MM **Privately Held**
WEB: www.eagleironworks.net
SIC: 3446 Fences or posts, ornamental
iron or steel

(P-12852)
ECLIPSE DESIGN INC
427 Corona Rd, Petaluma (94954-1406)
P.O. Box 750727 (94975-0727)
PHONE......................707 763-3104
Russ Williams, *President*
EMP: 10
SALES (est): 1.4MM **Privately Held**
WEB: www.eclipsedesignp.com
SIC: 3446 Ornamental metalwork

(P-12853)
EUROCRAFT ARCHTECTURAL MET INC
5619 Watcher St, Bell Gardens
(90201-1632)
PHONE......................323 771-1323
John Fechter, *President*
David Sawez, *General Mgr*
Kris Debruyne, *Prdtn Mgr*
EMP: 30
SQ FT: 30,000
SALES (est): 5.4MM **Privately Held**
WEB: www.eurocraftmetal.com
SIC: 3446 Architectural metalwork

(P-12854)
FABLE INC
595 Quarry Rd, San Carlos (94070-6222)
PHONE......................650 598-9616
James Guaspari, *President*
A J Guaspari, *Vice Pres*
EMP: 10
SQ FT: 21,000
SALES (est): 1.3MM **Privately Held**
WEB: www.fableinc.com
SIC: 3446 Ornamental metalwork

(P-12855)
FABRICOR PRODUCTS INC
Also Called: Fabricor Stamping
22512 Curtis Pl, California City
(93505-6009)
PHONE......................760 373-8292
Roy S Waisman, *President*
EMP: 10
SQ FT: 10,000
SALES (est): 732K **Privately Held**
WEB: www.fabricorproducts.com
SIC: 3446 3469 Lamp posts, metal; metal
stampings

(P-12856)
FENCE FACTORY
Perimeter Security Systems
1482 Callens Rd, Ventura (93003-5605)
PHONE......................805 644-5482
Phillip Mumma, *Sales/Mktg Mgr*
EMP: 10
SALES (corp-wide): 29.9MM **Privately
Held**
WEB: www.fencefactory.com
SIC: 3446 Gates, ornamental metal
HQ: Fence Factory
2419 Palma Dr
Ventura CA 93003
805 644-7207

(P-12857)
GLENDALE IRON
Also Called: Glendale Stl & Orna Ironworks
4208 Chevy Chase Dr, Los Angeles
(90039-1225)
PHONE......................818 247-1098
Henry Ostray, *Owner*
EMP: 10
SALES: 630K **Privately Held**
SIC: 3446 Architectural metalwork

(P-12858)
GOLD COAST IRONWORKS
531 Montgomery Ave, Oxnard
(93036-1066)
P.O. Box 1453, Oak View (93022-1453)
PHONE..........................805 485-6921
Richard Gill McFerron, *CEO*
Joanne McFerron, *Treasurer*
Adam Bennett, *Project Engr*
EMP: 15
SQ FT: 3,200
SALES: 2.5MM **Privately Held**
WEB: www.gcironworks.com
SIC: 3446 Architectural metalwork

(P-12859)
GREGORY PATTERSON
Also Called: Ccoi Gate & Fence
1741 Shelton Dr, Hollister (95023-9245)
P.O. Box 669, Aromas (95004-0669)
PHONE..........................831 636-1015
Gregory Patterson, *Owner*
Kate Deegan, *Sales Staff*
EMP: 20
SQ FT: 3,000
SALES (est): 3.1MM **Privately Held**
SIC: 3446 Fences or posts, ornamental
iron or steel; gates, ornamental metal

(P-12860)
HART & COOLEY INC
1121 Annadale Ave, Sanger (93657-3247)
P.O. Box 127 (93657-0127)
PHONE..........................559 875-1212
David Daniels, *Manager*
EMP: 50 **Privately Held**
SIC: 3446 Grillwork, ornamental metal
HQ: Hart & Cooley, Inc.
5030 Corp Exch Blvd Se
Grand Rapids MI 49512
616 656-8200

(P-12861)
INFINITY ACCESS PLUS INC
12945 Sherman Way Ste 8, North Holly-
wood (91605-7308)
PHONE..........................818 270-8172
Kirby Gray, *President*
EMP: 10
SALES (est): 1MM **Privately Held**
SIC: 3446 Fences, gates, posts & flag-
poles

(P-12862)
IRON MASTER
759 Arroyo St Ste D, San Fernando
(91340-2277)
P.O. Box 260, North Hollywood (91603-
0260)
PHONE..........................818 361-4060
Sandor Czene, *Owner*
Scott Bush, *Sales Engr*
EMP: 15 EST: 1978
SQ FT: 12,650
SALES: 1MM **Privately Held**
SIC: 3446 3441 Architectural metalwork;
fabricated structural metal

(P-12863)
IRON SHIELD INC
5926 Agnes Ave, Temple City
(91780-2217)
PHONE..........................626 287-4568
J Chou, *President*
EMP: 10 EST: 1990
SALES: 120K **Privately Held**
SIC: 3446 Gates, ornamental metal

(P-12864)
J TALLEY CORPORATION (PA)
Also Called: Talley Metal Fabrication
989 W 7th St, San Jacinto (92582-3813)
P.O. Box 850 (92581-0850)
PHONE..........................951 654-2123
Joe Brown Talley, *CEO*
Eloy Ochoa, *Foreman/Supr*
Rick Hammond, *Manager*
EMP: 40 EST: 1963
SQ FT: 13,400
SALES (est): 8.2MM **Privately Held**
WEB: www.talleymetal.com
SIC: 3446 3444 Railings, prefabricated
metal; sheet metalwork

(P-12865)
JAGUARS WROGHT IRON
Also Called: Jaguar Mfg Cstm Wrought Ir
300 Union Ave, Bakersfield (93307-1555)
PHONE..........................661 323-5015
Josh Hubble, *Owner*
EMP: 21
SQ FT: 5,000
SALES (est): 2.6MM **Privately Held**
SIC: 3446 Architectural metalwork

(P-12866)
**JANSEN ORNAMENTAL SUPPLY
CO**
10926 Schmidt Rd, El Monte (91733-2708)
PHONE..........................626 442-0271
Mike Jansen, *CEO*
Harry Jansen, *President*
John Jansen, *Admin Sec*
▲ EMP: 30 EST: 1960
SQ FT: 22,000
SALES (est): 6.7MM **Privately Held**
WEB: www.jansensupply.com
SIC: 3446 Architectural metalwork

(P-12867)
JMI STEEL INC
8983 San Fernando Rd, Sun Valley
(91352-1410)
PHONE..........................818 768-3955
Martin J Blaha, *President*
EMP: 21
SQ FT: 11,000
SALES (est): 4.3MM **Privately Held**
SIC: 3446 Fences or posts, ornamental
iron or steel

(P-12868)
JONES IRON WORKS
2658 Griffith Park Blvd, Los Angeles
(90039-2520)
PHONE..........................323 386-2368
EMP: 15 EST: 2013
SQ FT: 5,000
SALES (est): 890K **Privately Held**
SIC: 3446

(P-12869)
K & J WIRE PRODUCTS CORP
1220 N Lance Ln, Anaheim (92806-1812)
PHONE..........................714 816-0360
Klaus Borutzki, *President*
Barbara Borutzki, *Corp Secy*
Johan Borutzki, *Manager*
EMP: 28
SQ FT: 21,000
SALES (est): 2.8MM **Privately Held**
WEB: www.kajwire.com
SIC: 3446 3496 5046 3315 Architectural
metalwork; miscellaneous fabricated wire
products; store fixtures & display equip-
ment; wire & fabricated wire products

(P-12870)
KAWNEER COMPANY INC
Also Called: Brite Vue Div
7200 W Doe Ave, Visalia (93291-9296)
PHONE..........................559 651-4000
Norris McElroy, *Branch Mgr*
Teresa Martin, *Purch Agent*
EMP: 250
SQ FT: 200,000
SALES (corp-wide): 12.9B **Publicly Held**
WEB: www.kawneer.com
SIC: 3446 Architectural metalwork
HQ: Kawneer Company, Inc.
555 Guthridge Ct
Norcross GA 30092
770 449-5555

(P-12871)
KESCLO FINANCIAL INC
Also Called: Air Distribution Products
150 W 6th St Ste 205, San Pedro
(90731-3300)
PHONE..........................800 322-8676
Charles Close, *President*
Mike Kessler, *Vice Pres*
▲ EMP: 36
SALES (est): 2.3MM **Privately Held**
SIC: 3446 Registers (air), metal

(P-12872)
L & H IRON INC
Also Called: Lartech
1049 Felipe Ave, San Jose (95122-2602)
PHONE..........................408 287-8797
Kirk Larson, *President*
EMP: 11
SALES (est): 810K **Privately Held**
SIC: 3446 3441 Fabricated structural
metal; stairs, staircases, stair treads: pre-
fabricated metal

(P-12873)
LAVI INDUSTRIES (PA)
27810 Avenue Hopkins, Valencia
(91355-3409)
PHONE..........................877 275-5284
Gavriel Lavi, *President*
Yariv Blumkine, *COO*
Susan Lavi, *Vice Pres*
Julia Fakhouri, *Accounting Mgr*
Kristin Legeiter, *Purchasing*
▲ EMP: 80
SQ FT: 80,000
SALES (est): 17MM **Privately Held**
SIC: 3446 Architectural metalwork

(P-12874)
LINDBLADE METALWORKS INC
Also Called: Lindblade Metal Works
14355 Macaw St, La Mirada (90638-5208)
PHONE..........................714 670-7172
Vernon Lindblade, *CEO*
Marilyn Lindblade, *Vice Pres*
Tim Hostetler, *Sales Associate*
EMP: 20
SQ FT: 16,250
SALES (est): 5.3MM **Privately Held**
WEB: www.lindblademetalworks.com
SIC: 3446 Architectural metalwork

(P-12875)
**LNI CUSTOM MANUFACTURING
INC**
12536 Chadron Ave, Hawthorne
(90250-4808)
PHONE..........................310 978-2000
Scott Blakely, *CEO*
EMP: 50
SQ FT: 25,000
SALES (est): 12.2MM **Privately Held**
WEB: www.lnisigns.com
SIC: 3446 5046 Architectural metalwork;
neon signs

(P-12876)
LUR INC
Also Called: Lumar Metals
599 S East End Ave, Pomona
(91766-2302)
PHONE..........................909 623-4999
Marlene Racca, *President*
Cindy Rowland, *Office Mgr*
EMP: 15
SQ FT: 10,000
SALES (est): 3.2MM **Privately Held**
WEB: www.lumarmetals.com
SIC: 3446 Architectural metalwork

(P-12877)
M C METAL INC
1347 Donner Ave, San Francisco
(94124-3612)
PHONE..........................415 822-2288
Jeffrey Mark, *President*
EMP: 17
SALES (est): 3.8MM **Privately Held**
SIC: 3446 Architectural metalwork

(P-12878)
**MAGNUM FENCE AND
SECURITY INC**
1070 N Ventura Ave, Ventura (93001-1704)
PHONE..........................805 641-3656
Ralph Coolman, *President*
Ericka Coolman, *Vice Pres*
EMP: 12
SQ FT: 1,760
SALES (est): 2.3MM **Privately Held**
WEB: www.magnumfence.com
SIC: 3446 Fences, gates, posts & flag-
poles

(P-12879)
MAS METALS INC
600 Montague St, San Leandro
(94577-4324)
PHONE..........................510 259-1426
Mitzon Altana, *President*
EMP: 12
SALES (est): 2.7MM **Privately Held**
SIC: 3446 Architectural metalwork

(P-12880)
MASTER METAL WORKS INC
Also Called: Mmw Operation
1805 Potrero Ave, South El Monte
(91733-3022)
P.O. Box 3585, La Puente (91744-0585)
PHONE..........................626 444-8818
Susan Barnard, *President*
Brian Elliott, *Vice Pres*
EMP: 27
SQ FT: 18,000
SALES (est): 7.2MM **Privately Held**
WEB: www.mastermetalworks.com
SIC: 3446 3444 Architectural metalwork;
sheet metal specialties, not stamped

(P-12881)
METAL X DIRECT INC
1304 Logan Ave Ste A, Costa Mesa
(92626-4021)
PHONE..........................949 336-0055
Sean Lancona, *President*
EMP: 14
SQ FT: 2,000
SALES: 1MM **Privately Held**
SIC: 3446 3441 Architectural metalwork;
building components, structural steel

(P-12882)
**MODERN METAL
INSTALLATIONS**
4400 Shady Oak Way, Fair Oaks
(95628-5727)
PHONE..........................916 316-0997
Richard Sharon, *Owner*
EMP: 10
SALES: 750K **Privately Held**
SIC: 3446 Architectural metalwork

(P-12883)
MOZ DESIGNS INC
711 Kevin Ct, Oakland (94621-4039)
PHONE..........................510 632-0853
Murry Sandford, *CEO*
Alexander Noliwe, *CFO*
Herbert M Sandford III, *Vice Pres*
Tripp Sanford, *Vice Pres*
Juan Alatorre, *Project Mgr*
◆ EMP: 25
SQ FT: 10,000
SALES: 4.8MM **Privately Held**
WEB: www.mozdesigns.com
SIC: 3446 Architectural metalwork

(P-12884)
OLSON AND CO STEEL (PA)
1941 Davis St, San Leandro (94577-1262)
PHONE..........................510 489-4680
David Olson, *CEO*
Dylan Olson, *President*
Thomas Fluehr, *COO*
Kevin Cullen, *CFO*
Yolanda Coria, *Administration*
▲ EMP: 225
SQ FT: 130,000
SALES (est): 68.4MM **Privately Held**
WEB: www.olsonsteel.com
SIC: 3446 3441 Architectural metalwork;
fabricated structural metal

(P-12885)
RAMI DESIGNS INC
24 Hammond Ste E, Irvine (92618-1680)
PHONE..........................949 588-8288
Ron Taybi, *President*
EMP: 19
SQ FT: 6,000
SALES: 6MM **Privately Held**
SIC: 3446 3299 3229 Architectural metal-
work; architectural sculptures: gypsum,
clay, papier mache, etc.; glass furnishings
& accessories

(P-12886)
ROYAL STALL
1865 Industrial Way, Sanger (93657-9501)
P.O. Box 568 (93657-0568)
PHONE..................................559 875-8100
Richard Funston, *Owner*
Kay Funston, *Co-Owner*
EMP: 11
SQ FT: 8,000
SALES: 1MM **Privately Held**
WEB: www.royalstall.com
SIC: 3446 3448 Fences, gates, posts &
   flagpoles; farm & utility buildings

(P-12887)
SALOMON DOMINGUEZ
Also Called: Delta Ironworks
15420 Meridian Rd, Salinas (93907-8788)
P.O. Box 10580 (93912-7580)
PHONE..................................831 663-1190
Salomon Dominguez, *Owner*
EMP: 15
SQ FT: 9,000
SALES (est): 2.7MM **Privately Held**
SIC: 3446 3441 Architectural metalwork;
   fabricated structural metal

(P-12888)
**SANIE MANUFACTURING
COMPANY**
2600 S Yale St, Santa Ana (92704-5228)
PHONE..................................714 751-7700
Mendi Haidarali, *President*
Mohammad Haidari, *Vice Pres*
EMP: 18 **EST:** 1981
SQ FT: 8,900
SALES (est): 5.2MM **Privately Held**
WEB: www.saniemfg.com
SIC: 3446 Fences or posts, ornamental
   iron or steel

(P-12889)
**SAPPHIRE MANUFACTURING
INC**
505 Porter Way, Placentia (92870-6454)
PHONE..................................714 401-3117
Hector Garibay, *CEO*
EMP: 20
SQ FT: 25,000
SALES: 3MM **Privately Held**
SIC: 3446 7371 Fences or posts, orna-
   mental iron or steel; computer software
   development & applications

(P-12890)
**SECURITY CONTRACTOR SVCS
INC**
Also Called: S C S
5311 Jackson St, North Highlands
(95660-5004)
PHONE..................................916 338-4800
Basil Lobaugh, *Manager*
Larry Marshall, *Asst Controller*
Alena Sowdon, *Marketing Staff*
EMP: 26
SALES (corp-wide): 37.6MM **Privately
Held**
WEB: www.scsfence.com
SIC: 3446 5211 Fences or posts, orna-
   mental iron or steel; lumber & other build-
   ing materials
PA: Security Contractor Services, Inc.
   5339 Jackson St
   North Highlands CA 95660
   916 338-4200

(P-12891)
SECURUS INC
Also Called: Holdrite
14284 Danielson St, Poway (92064-8885)
PHONE..................................858 391-0414
Timothy McConnell, *President*
Marc Coffer, *Treasurer*
Michelle M Hubbard, *Admin Sec*
◆ **EMP:** 50
SQ FT: 46,000
SALES (est): 19.7MM **Privately Held**
WEB: www.holdrite.com
SIC: 3446 3351 3431 5162 Acoustical
   suspension systems, metal; tubing, cop-
   per & copper alloy; plumbing fixtures;
   enameled iron cast iron or pressed metal;
   plastics materials & basic shapes

PA: Reliance Worldwide Corporation Limited
   28 Chapman Pl
   Eagle Farm QLD 4009

(P-12892)
**SONOMA ACCESS CTRL
SYSTEMS INC**
21600 8th St E, Sonoma (95476-2821)
PHONE..................................707 935-3458
David Nisenson, *President*
Paula Nisenson, *Vice Pres*
EMP: 25
SQ FT: 8,000
SALES (est): 3.8MM **Privately Held**
WEB: www.access-control-systems.net
SIC: 3446 1799 Gates, ornamental metal;
   fence construction

(P-12893)
**SPECIAL IRON SECURITY
SYSTEMS**
2030 Rosemead Blvd, El Monte
(91733-1518)
PHONE..................................626 443-7877
Ricky McKeyne, *President*
EMP: 10
SQ FT: 15,000
SALES (est): 1MM **Privately Held**
SIC: 3446 1799 Fences, gates, posts &
   flagpoles; fence construction

(P-12894)
STEVE ZAPPETINI & SON INC
885 Penny Royal Ln, San Rafael
(94903-4303)
PHONE..................................415 454-2511
David J Zappetini, *President*
Russell Zappetini, *President*
David Zappetini, *Corp Secy*
EMP: 28
SQ FT: 10,000
SALES (est): 4.1MM **Privately Held**
SIC: 3446 3713 7692 Railings, bannis-
   ters, guards, etc.: made from metal pipe;
   stairs, staircases, stair treads: prefabri-
   cated metal; grillwork, ornamental metal;
   truck bodies (motor vehicles); welding re-
   pair

(P-12895)
SURCO PRODUCTS INC
14001 S Main St, Los Angeles
(90061-2196)
PHONE..................................310 323-2520
Ludwig Surkin, *President*
Uri Surkin, *Vice Pres*
Amir Surkin, *Cust Mgr*
▲ **EMP:** 15 **EST:** 1971
SQ FT: 20,000
SALES (est): 2.5MM **Privately Held**
SIC: 3446 3429 Ladders, for permanent
   installation: metal; luggage racks, car top

(P-12896)
TAJIMA USA DISSOLVING CORP
Also Called: Tajima /Crl
   2503 E Vernon Ave, Vernon (90058-1826)
   P.O. Box 58923, Los Angeles (90058-0923)
PHONE..................................323 588-1281
Bernard P Harris, *Ch of Bd*
EMP: 12
SALES (est): 1.2MM
SALES (corp-wide): 29.7B **Privately Held**
WEB: www.tajimacorpusa.com
SIC: 3446 Architectural metalwork
HQ: C.R. Laurence Co., Inc.
   2503 E Vernon Ave
   Vernon CA 90058
   323 588-1281

(P-12897)
TECHNIBUILDERS IRON INC
1049 Felipe Ave, San Jose (95122-2602)
PHONE..................................408 287-8797
Roy S Larson, *President*
EMP: 34
SQ FT: 7,200
SALES (est): 5.5MM **Privately Held**
SIC: 3446 Ornamental metalwork

(P-12898)
**THORNTON STEEL & IR WORKS
INC**
1323 S State College Pkwy, Anaheim
(92806-5242)
PHONE..................................714 491-8800
Ken Thornton, *CEO*
Steven Braseny, *President*
Richard Salcedo, *Vice Pres*
EMP: 20
SQ FT: 12,200
SALES (est): 3.3MM **Privately Held**
WEB: www.thorntonsteelironworks.com
SIC: 3446 Architectural metalwork

(P-12899)
**TJS METAL MANUFACTURING
INC**
10847 Drury Ln, Lynwood (90262-1833)
PHONE..................................310 604-1545
Jose Antonio Gallegos, *CEO*
EMP: 26 **EST:** 1999
SQ FT: 30,000
SALES (est): 8.4MM **Privately Held**
SIC: 3446 Architectural metalwork

(P-12900)
TRI-STATE STAIRWAY CORP
706 W California Ave, Fresno
(93706-3502)
PHONE..................................559 268-0875
Ron Cavella, *President*
Sharry Cavella, *Corp Secy*
Stan Cavella, *Vice Pres*
EMP: 40
SQ FT: 1,000
SALES: 5.1MM
SALES (corp-wide): 9MM **Privately Held**
WEB: www.travcorps.com
SIC: 3446 3272 Railings, bannisters,
   guards, etc.: made from metal pipe; con-
   crete products, precast
PA: Suburban Steel, Inc.
   706 W California Ave
   Fresno CA 93706
   559 268-6281

(P-12901)
**UNION PACIFIC RAILROAD
COMPANY**
Also Called: Union Pacific Lines
2401 E Sepulveda Blvd, Long Beach
(90810-1945)
PHONE..................................562 490-7000
Herman Madden, *Superintendent*
EMP: 300
SALES (corp-wide): 21.2B **Publicly Held**
WEB: www.uprr.com
SIC: 3446 Stairs, staircases, stair treads:
   prefabricated metal
HQ: Union Pacific Railroad Company Inc
   1400 Douglas St
   Omaha NE 68179
   402 544-5000

(P-12902)
V I P IRONWORKS INC
8319 Hindry Ave, Los Angeles
(90045-3205)
PHONE..................................310 216-2890
Hector Guiterrez, *President*
EMP: 10
SQ FT: 5,109
SALES (est): 1.7MM **Privately Held**
SIC: 3446 5051 Architectural metalwork;
   iron & steel (ferrous) products

(P-12903)
VALLEY STAIRWAY INC
5684 E Shields Ave, Fresno (93727-7818)
P.O. Box 245, Clovis (93613-0245)
PHONE..................................559 299-0151
Jerry De George, *President*
Anthony De George Jr, *Corp Secy*
EMP: 16 **EST:** 1957
SQ FT: 29,464
SALES (est): 2.9MM **Privately Held**
WEB: www.valleystairwayinc.com
SIC: 3446 Stairs, staircases, stair treads:
   prefabricated metal

(P-12904)
**WASHINGTON ORNA IR WORKS
INC**
Production Steel
17913 S Main St, Gardena (90248-3520)
PHONE..................................310 327-8660
Luke Welsh, *Manager*
Eric Welsh, *Project Mgr*
EMP: 20
SALES (corp-wide): 24.6MM **Privately
Held**
WEB: www.washingtoniron.com
SIC: 3446 1542 Architectural metalwork;
   nonresidential construction
PA: Washington Ornamental Iron Works
   Inc.
   17926 S Broadway
   Gardena CA 90248
   310 327-8660

(P-12905)
WEIS/ROBART PARTITIONS INC
Also Called: Michigan Metal Partitions
3501 E La Palma Ave, Anaheim
(92806-2117)
PHONE..................................714 666-0822
John R Penner, *President*
Eleanor Penner, *Treasurer*
Beverly Booms, *Vice Pres*
Sarah Michener, *Vice Pres*
Donald Harms, *Admin Sec*
EMP: 15
SQ FT: 8,000
SALES: 2MM **Privately Held**
WEB: www.weisrobart.com
SIC: 3446 Partitions, ornamental metal

(P-12906)
**WEST CAST ARCHITECTURAL
SHTMTL**
Also Called: West Coast Asm
2215 Oakland Rd, San Jose (95131-1416)
PHONE..................................408 776-2700
Mark Yeager, *CEO*
Paul Deharo, *Shareholder*
Randi Stefani, *Office Mgr*
Lynn Murphy, *Executive Asst*
Jason Boyd, *Project Mgr*
EMP: 10 **EST:** 2012
SALES (est): 2.7MM **Privately Held**
SIC: 3446 Architectural metalwork

(P-12907)
**WESTERN SQUARE
INDUSTRIES INC**
1621 N Brdwy, Stockton (95205)
PHONE..................................209 944-0921
Trygue Mikkelsen, *President*
▲ **EMP:** 40
SQ FT: 44,000
SALES (est): 10.5MM **Privately Held**
SIC: 3446 2542 2514 3441 Fences or
   posts, ornamental iron or steel; gates, or-
   namental metal; racks, merchandise dis-
   play or storage: except wood; tables,
   household: metal; fabricated structural
   metal

(P-12908)
**WROUGHT IRON FENCING &
SUPPLY**
1370 La Mirada Dr, San Marcos
(92078-2443)
PHONE..................................760 591-3110
Thomas W Barrett, *President*
Tom Barrett, *President*
EMP: 35
SALES (est): 4.7MM **Privately Held**
WEB:
www.wroughtironfencingandsupply.com
SIC: 3446 Fences, gates, posts & flag-
   poles

3448 Prefabricated Metal Buildings & Cmpnts

(P-12909)
ACORN ENGINEERING COMPANY (PA)
Also Called: Morris Group International
15125 Proctor Ave, City of Industry (91746-3327)
P.O. Box 3527 (91744-0527)
PHONE...................800 488-8999
Donald E Morris, *President*
John Plowman, *CFO*
Charles C Fredricks, *Treasurer*
Keith Marshall, *Exec VP*
Vince Conti, *Vice Pres*
▲ **EMP:** 702 **EST:** 1955
SQ FT: 120,000
SALES: 85MM **Privately Held**
WEB: www.whitehallmfg.com
SIC: 3448 3431 3442 Buildings, portable: prefabricated metal; plumbing fixtures: enameled iron cast iron or pressed metal; metal doors

(P-12910)
ADAPTIVE MODULAR SOLUTIONS INC
3025 E Dominguez St, Carson (90810-1437)
PHONE...................310 299-7680
Natasaha Deski, *Vice Pres*
EMP: 84
SALES (est): 2.6MM **Privately Held**
SIC: 3448 Prefabricated metal buildings

(P-12911)
AFC FINISHING SYSTEMS
250 Airport Pkwy, Oroville (95965-9249)
PHONE...................530 533-8907
Carl Lee Hagan, *President*
Nicky Trevino, *Vice Pres*
James Barton, *Plant Mgr*
Chris Funk, *Sales Mgr*
Kimberly Nickerson, *Marketing Staff*
EMP: 35
SQ FT: 56,000
SALES (est): 9.8MM **Privately Held**
WEB: www.afc-ca.com
SIC: 3448 3444 3441 Prefabricated metal buildings; sheet metalwork; fabricated structural metal

(P-12912)
AGRA TECH INC
2131 Piedmont Way, Pittsburg (94565-5071)
PHONE...................925 432-3342
Eloise Pound, *Manager*
EMP: 16
SALES (corp-wide): 2.9MM **Privately Held**
WEB: www.agra-tech.com
SIC: 3448 Greenhouses: prefabricated metal
PA: Agra Tech, Inc.
2131 Piedmont Way
Pittsburg CA 94565
925 432-3399

(P-12913)
ALLIED CONTAINER SYSTEMS INC
Also Called: ACS
511 Wilbur Ave Ste B4, Antioch (94509-7563)
PHONE...................925 944-7600
Brian Horsfall, *Ch of Bd*
Robbin Kilgore, *Officer*
Susan Horsfall, *Vice Pres*
Quinton Miller, *General Mgr*
Tanwir Rahman, *Controller*
▼ **EMP:** 140
SQ FT: 20,000
SALES (est): 28.4MM **Privately Held**
WEB: www.alliedcontainer.com
SIC: 3448 8748 3559 Prefabricated metal buildings; environmental consultant; chemical machinery & equipment

(P-12914)
ALLIED MDULAR BLDG SYSTEMS INC (PA)
642 W Nicolas Ave, Orange (92868-1316)
PHONE...................714 516-1188
Fred Ketcho, *CEO*
Kevin Peithman, *President*
Richard Navarro, *Treasurer*
Raj Singh, *Vice Pres*
Cathy Peithman, *Admin Sec*
EMP: 38
SQ FT: 35,000
SALES (est): 9.1MM **Privately Held**
WEB: www.alliedmodular.com
SIC: 3448 Prefabricated metal buildings

(P-12915)
ALUMAWALL INC
1701 S 7th St Ste 9, San Jose (95112-6000)
PHONE...................408 275-7165
David M Warda, *President*
Lori Warda, *Vice Pres*
Steven Aguilar, *Technology*
Dagmar Fleet, *Controller*
Joe Alvarez, *Manager*
EMP: 65
SQ FT: 50,000
SALES (est): 17.1MM **Privately Held**
WEB: www.alumawall.com
SIC: 3448 Prefabricated metal components

(P-12916)
AMERICAN CARPORTS INC (PA)
1415 Clay St, Colusa (95932-2064)
PHONE...................866 730-9865
Primo Castillo, *President*
Milton Castillo, *President*
Venani Torres, *Corp Secy*
EMP: 11
SQ FT: 500,000
SALES (est): 3.7MM **Privately Held**
SIC: 3448 Garages, portable: prefabricated metal; carports: prefabricated metal

(P-12917)
AMERICORE INC
19705 August Ave, Hilmar (95324-9302)
P.O. Box 1353 (95324-1353)
PHONE...................209 632-5679
Ryan Marques Cunha, *President*
EMP: 47 **EST:** 2007
SALES (est): 13.2MM **Privately Held**
SIC: 3448 3699 3841 Prefabricated metal buildings; electrical welding equipment; diagnostic apparatus, medical

(P-12918)
ASC PROFILES LLC
5001 Bailey Loop, McClellan (95652-2530)
PHONE...................916 376-2899
Richard Stewart, *Branch Mgr*
EMP: 33 **Privately Held**
SIC: 3448 Prefabricated metal buildings
HQ: Asc Profiles Llc
2110 Enterprise Blvd
West Sacramento CA 95691
916 372-6851

(P-12919)
BARNS AND BUILDINGS INC
23100 Baxter Rd, Wildomar (92595-9699)
P.O. Box 1555 (92595-1555)
PHONE...................951 678-4571
Russell Greer, *CEO*
Barret Hilzer, *COO*
EMP: 80
SQ FT: 40,000
SALES (est): 7.6MM **Privately Held**
SIC: 3448 1541 5083 Prefabricated metal components; steel building construction; livestock equipment

(P-12920)
BARNS BY HARRAHS
3489 S 99w, Corning (96021-9736)
PHONE...................530 824-4611
Toll Free:...................888 -
Dave Harrah, *Partner*
Dennis Harrah, *Partner*
EMP: 12
SALES (est): 1.5MM **Privately Held**
WEB: www.barnsbyharrahs.com
SIC: 3448 Farm & utility buildings

(P-12921)
BLUESCOPE BUILDINGS N AMER INC
Also Called: Butler Manufacturing
7440 W Doe Ave, Visalia (93291-9296)
P.O. Box 1590 (93279-1590)
PHONE...................559 651-5300
Scott Wilson, *Branch Mgr*
EMP: 200 **Privately Held**
SIC: 3448 Prefabricated metal buildings
HQ: Bluescope Buildings North America, Inc.
1540 Genessee St
Kansas City MO 64102

(P-12922)
BLUESCOPE BUILDINGS N AMER INC
530 S Tegner Rd, Turlock (95380-9406)
PHONE...................209 667-4951
Dan Mueller, *Manager*
EMP: 250
SQ FT: 6,400 **Privately Held**
SIC: 3448 Prefabricated metal buildings
HQ: Bluescope Buildings North America, Inc.
1540 Genessee St
Kansas City MO 64102

(P-12923)
CA-TE LP
Also Called: California Technology
33230 La Colina Dr, Springville (93265-9617)
PHONE...................559 539-1530
Guy Minter, *Partner*
EMP: 10
SALES (est): 1.2MM **Privately Held**
SIC: 3448 Prefabricated metal components

(P-12924)
CALIFORNIA EXPANDED MET PDTS
Also Called: Cemco
1001a Pittsburg Antoch Hwy, Pittsburg (94565-4199)
PHONE...................925 473-9340
Ned Martin, *Manager*
EMP: 40
SALES (corp-wide): 73.8MM **Privately Held**
SIC: 3448 3449 3444 3441 Prefabricated metal buildings; miscellaneous metalwork; sheet metalwork; fabricated structural metal
PA: California Expanded Metal Products Company
13191 Crosrds Pkwy N 32
City Of Industry CA 91746
626 369-3564

(P-12925)
CALIFORNIA RAMP WORKS INC
273 N Benson Ave, Upland (91786-5614)
PHONE...................909 949-1601
Brian Moore, *President*
Joseph M Ciaglia Jr, *Director*
EMP: 25
SALES (est): 4.7MM **Privately Held**
SIC: 3448 Ramps: prefabricated metal

(P-12926)
CBC STEEL BUILDINGS LLC
1700 E Louise Ave, Lathrop (95330-9795)
P.O. Box 1009 (95330-1009)
PHONE...................209 858-2425
Steve Campbell, *President*
Steve Darley, *District Mgr*
Faron Moyers, *District Mgr*
Bill Roberson, *District Mgr*
David McKay, *Info Tech Mgr*
EMP: 120
SQ FT: 105,000
SALES (est): 36.7MM
SALES (corp-wide): 20.2B **Publicly Held**
WEB: www.cbcsteelbuildings.com
SIC: 3448 Prefabricated metal buildings
PA: Nucor Corporation
1915 Rexford Rd Ste 400
Charlotte NC 28211
704 366-7000

(P-12927)
CLAMSHELL STRUCTURES INC
Also Called: Clamshell Buildings
1101 Maulhardt Ave, Oxnard (93030-7995)
PHONE...................805 988-1340
Gregory J Mangan, *CEO*
Michael R Kane, *Vice Pres*
Dean Daddario, *Analyst*
Jose Trujillo, *Buyer*
Jennie Westling, *Manager*
EMP: 15
SQ FT: 46,000
SALES (est): 5.2MM
SALES (corp-wide): 1MM **Privately Held**
WEB: www.clamshell.com
SIC: 3448 Prefabricated metal buildings
PA: Clamshell Holdings, Inc.
1101 Maulhardt Ave
Oxnard CA 93030
805 988-1340

(P-12928)
DURACOLD REFRIGERATION MFG LLC
1551 S Primrose Ave, Monrovia (91016-4542)
PHONE...................626 358-1710
Harold Monsher, *General Ptnr*
Ben Monsher, *Partner*
EMP: 22
SQ FT: 25,000
SALES (est): 4.2MM **Privately Held**
SIC: 3448 3585 Prefabricated metal components; refrigeration & heating equipment

(P-12929)
EMERALD KINGDOM GREENHOUSE LLC
104 Masonic Ln, Weaverville (96093)
PHONE...................530 215-5670
Kate Brown,
▲ **EMP:** 30
SALES (est): 5.5MM **Privately Held**
SIC: 3448 5191 Greenhouses: prefabricated metal; greenhouse equipment & supplies

(P-12930)
ENVIROPLEX INC
4777 Carpenter Rd, Stockton (95215-8106)
PHONE...................209 466-8000
Glenn Owens, *President*
EMP: 60
SQ FT: 102,000
SALES (est): 10.6MM
SALES (corp-wide): 462MM **Publicly Held**
WEB: www.enviroplexinc.com
SIC: 3448 Buildings, portable: prefabricated metal
PA: Mcgrath Rentcorp
5700 Las Positas Rd
Livermore CA 94551
925 606-9200

(P-12931)
FCP INC
23100 Baxter Rd, Wildomar (92595-9699)
P.O. Box 1555 (92595-1555)
PHONE...................951 678-4571
Russell J Greer, *CEO*
Barret Hilzer, *COO*
Mike Regan, *Division Mgr*
Stuart Wilson, *Opers Mgr*
Melanie Fennell, *Assistant*
EMP: 100
SQ FT: 200,000
SALES: 15MM **Privately Held**
SIC: 3448 1541 Prefabricated metal components; steel building construction

(P-12932)
FONTANA INTERNATIONAL INC
14978 Ceres Ave Ste B, Fontana (92335-4285)
PHONE...................909 854-4532
Pat Orozco, *Chairman*
◆ **EMP:** 10
SALES: 1MM **Privately Held**
SIC: 3448 Prefabricated metal components

(P-12933)
GRO-TECH SYSTEMS INC
17282 Cattle Dr, Rough and Ready
(95975-9761)
PHONE..................................530 432-7012
Scott Patrick Stephan, *CEO*
EMP: 14
SALES (est): 4.4MM **Privately Held**
SIC: 3448 Greenhouses: prefabricated
metal

(P-12934)
H ROBERTS CONSTRUCTION
2165 W Gaylord St, Long Beach
(90813-1033)
PHONE..................................562 590-4825
Kathleen F Roberts, *President*
EMP: 51 **EST:** 1988
SQ FT: 1,100
SALES: 8.2MM **Privately Held**
SIC: 3448 Buildings, portable: prefabri-
cated metal

(P-12935)
INTERSTATE CARPORTS CORP
1280 S Buena Vista St A, San Jacinto
(92583-4603)
PHONE..................................951 654-1750
Robert Aguilar, *President*
EMP: 11
SQ FT: 4,800
SALES: 2.5MM **Privately Held**
SIC: 3448 Buildings, portable: prefabri-
cated metal

(P-12936)
JOHN L CONLEY INC
Also Called: Conley's Mfg & Sales
4344 Mission Blvd, Montclair (91763-6017)
PHONE..................................909 627-0981
John L Conley, *CEO*
Tom Conley, *President*
Dean Conley, *Vice Pres*
Howard Davis, *Vice Pres*
▲ **EMP:** 75 **EST:** 1946
SALES (est): 18.5MM **Privately Held**
WEB: www.conleys.com
SIC: 3448 3441 Greenhouses: prefabri-
cated metal; buildings, portable: prefabri-
cated metal; fabricated structural metal

(P-12937)
JTS MODULAR INC
7001 Mcdivitt Dr Ste B, Bakersfield
(93313-2030)
P.O. Box 41765 (93384-1765)
PHONE..................................661 835-9270
Dene Hurlbert, *President*
Phillip Engler, *Vice Pres*
Lee Hawkins, *Vice Pres*
John Hurlbert, *Vice Pres*
EMP: 50
SQ FT: 4,000
SALES (est): 14.2MM **Privately Held**
SIC: 3448 Prefabricated metal buildings

(P-12938)
KINGSPAN INSULATED PANELS INC
Kingspan API
2000 Morgan Rd, Modesto (95358-9407)
PHONE..................................209 531-9091
Russell Shiels, *President*
David Tyndall, *General Mgr*
Andrew Hamer, *Office Mgr*
Eric Jurus, *Regl Sales Mgr*
Derek Payne, *Regl Sales Mgr*
EMP: 90 **Privately Held**
SIC: 3448 Prefabricated metal buildings
HQ: Kingspan Insulated Panels Inc.
726 Summerhill Dr
Deland FL 32724
386 626-6789

(P-12939)
KRAEMER & CO MFG INC
3778 County Road 99w, Orland
(95963-9785)
PHONE..................................530 865-7982
Ben Kraemer, *President*
Nancy Kraemer, *Treasurer*
Gerald Kraemer, *Admin Sec*
EMP: 15
SQ FT: 6,900

SALES (est): 3.5MM **Privately Held**
WEB: www.kcomfg.com
SIC: 3448 3523 3441 3412 Farm & utility
buildings; farm machinery & equipment;
elevators, farm; fabricated structural
metal; metal barrels, drums & pails

(P-12940)
M & K BUILDERS INC
3212 Bixby Way, Stockton (95209-1590)
P.O. Box 690727 (95269-0727)
PHONE..................................209 478-7531
Jerry Kaufman, *President*
Kevin Kaufman, *Admin Sec*
Matt Kaufman, *Admin Sec*
EMP: 13
SALES: 500K **Privately Held**
SIC: 3448 Buildings, portable: prefabri-
cated metal

(P-12941)
MADERA CARPORTS INC
17462 Baldwin St, Madera (93638-9418)
PHONE..................................559 662-1815
Jose L Madera, *President*
Daisy Kraus, *Manager*
EMP: 12
SQ FT: 625
SALES (est): 2.4MM **Privately Held**
SIC: 3448 Carports: prefabricated metal

(P-12942)
MADISON INDUSTRIES (HQ)
18000 Studebaker Rd # 305, Cerritos
(90703-2681)
PHONE..................................323 583-4061
John Frey Jr, *President*
John Samuel Frey, *President*
Grace Lee, *Controller*
Kathy Martin, *Controller*
Mike Eyestone, *Purchasing*
EMP: 35
SQ FT: 24,000
SALES (est): 11MM
SALES (corp-wide): 129.8MM **Privately Held**
SIC: 3448 3441 1542 Prefabricated metal
buildings; fabricated structural metal; non-
residential construction
PA: John S. Frey Enterprises
1900 E 64th St
Los Angeles CA 90001
323 583-4061

(P-12943)
MCELROY METAL MILL INC
17031 Koala Rd, Adelanto (92301-2246)
PHONE..................................760 246-5545
Pete Nadler, *Business Mgr*
Joe Corban, *Manager*
EMP: 35
SQ FT: 37,700
SALES (corp-wide): 373.4MM **Privately Held**
WEB: www.mcelroymetal.com
SIC: 3448 Prefabricated metal components
PA: Mcelroy Metal Mill, Inc.
1500 Hamilton Rd
Bossier City LA 71111
318 747-8000

(P-12944)
MCGRATH RENTCORP
Also Called: Mobile Management
11450 Mission Blvd, Mira Loma
(91752-1015)
PHONE..................................951 360-6600
Thomas Sanders, *Manager*
Brett Turley, *General Mgr*
Dawn Harrison, *Opers Mgr*
Lily Bechtel, *Opers Staff*
EMP: 110
SALES (corp-wide): 462MM **Publicly Held**
SIC: 3448 7519 Prefabricated metal build-
ings; trailer rental
PA: Mcgrath Rentcorp
5700 Las Positas Rd
Livermore CA 94551
925 606-9200

(P-12945)
MOBILE MINI INC
44580 Old Warm Sprng Blvd, Fremont
(94538-6152)
PHONE..................................510 252-9326

Andrew Lemen, *Manager*
EMP: 10
SALES (corp-wide): 533.5MM **Publicly Held**
SIC: 3448 3441 3412 7359 Buildings,
portable: prefabricated metal; fabricated
structural metal; metal barrels, drums &
pails; equipment rental & leasing
PA: Mobile Mini, Inc.
4646 E Van Buren St # 400
Phoenix AZ 85008
480 894-6311

(P-12946)
MOBILE MINI INC
3902 Esplanade, Chico (95973-0200)
PHONE..................................530 345-7645
Dave Stevens, *Branch Mgr*
EMP: 20
SALES (corp-wide): 533.5MM **Publicly Held**
WEB: www.mobilemini.com
SIC: 3448 Buildings, portable: prefabri-
cated metal
PA: Mobile Mini, Inc.
4646 E Van Buren St # 400
Phoenix AZ 85008
480 894-6311

(P-12947)
MOBILE MINI INC
8160 Junipero St, Sacramento
(95828-1604)
PHONE..................................916 381-1351
Caleb Pagan, *Branch Mgr*
EMP: 20
SALES (corp-wide): 533.5MM **Publicly Held**
WEB: www.mobilemini.com
SIC: 3448 Buildings, portable: prefabri-
cated metal
PA: Mobile Mini, Inc.
4646 E Van Buren St # 400
Phoenix AZ 85008
480 894-6311

(P-12948)
MOBILE MINI INC
16351 Mckinley Ave, Lathrop (95330-8702)
PHONE..................................209 858-9300
Lora Kirsten, *Branch Mgr*
EMP: 40
SALES (corp-wide): 533.5MM **Publicly Held**
WEB: www.mobilemini.com
SIC: 3448 Buildings, portable: prefabri-
cated metal
PA: Mobile Mini, Inc.
4646 E Van Buren St # 400
Phoenix AZ 85008
480 894-6311

(P-12949)
MOBILE MINI INC
42207 3rd St E, Lancaster (93535-5314)
P.O. Box 1538, Rialto (92377-1538)
PHONE..................................909 356-1690
Craig Nelson, *General Mgr*
Robin Pace, *Human Res Mgr*
EMP: 150
SALES (corp-wide): 533.5MM **Publicly Held**
WEB: www.mobilemini.com
SIC: 3448 Buildings, portable: prefabri-
cated metal
PA: Mobile Mini, Inc.
4646 E Van Buren St # 400
Phoenix AZ 85008
480 894-6311

(P-12950)
MOBILE MINI INC
Also Called: Mobile Mini Storage
12345 Crosthwaite Cir, Poway
(92064-6817)
PHONE..................................858 578-9222
Dennis D'Assis, *Branch Mgr*
EMP: 25
SALES (corp-wide): 533.5MM **Publicly Held**
WEB: www.mobilemini.com
SIC: 3448 3441 3412 7359 Buildings,
portable: prefabricated metal; fabricated
structural metal; drums, shipping: metal;
shipping container leasing

PA: Mobile Mini, Inc.
4646 E Van Buren St # 400
Phoenix AZ 85008
480 894-6311

(P-12951)
MORIN CORP
Also Called: Morin West
10707 Commerce Way, Fontana
(92337-8216)
PHONE..................................909 428-3747
Ilhan Eser, *Vice Pres*
Steve Crocker, *Social Dir*
EMP: 30 **Privately Held**
SIC: 3448 Prefabricated metal buildings
HQ: Morin Corp
685 Middle St
Bristol CT 06010
860 584-0900

(P-12952)
MORRIS GROUP INTERNATIONAL (PA)
15125 Proctor Ave, City of Industry
(91746-3327)
PHONE..................................626 336-4561
Donald E Morris, *President*
Mike Polis, *Vice Pres*
Charles White, *Vice Pres*
EMP: 17
SALES (est): 10.6MM **Privately Held**
SIC: 3448 3431 3842 3442 Buildings,
portable: prefabricated metal; plumbing
fixtures: enameled iron cast iron or
pressed metal; grafts, artificial: for sur-
gery; metal doors

(P-12953)
NCI GROUP INC
Also Called: Metal Coaters
9123 Center Ave, Rancho Cucamonga
(91730-5312)
PHONE..................................909 987-4681
Colin Lally, *Branch Mgr*
Darrell Bancroft, *Office Mgr*
Kathy Delaney, *Human Res Dir*
Ray Rodriguez, *Marketing Staff*
EMP: 75
SALES (corp-wide): 1.7B **Publicly Held**
SIC: 3448 3446 Prefabricated metal build-
ings; prefabricated metal components; ar-
chitectural metalwork
HQ: Nci Group, Inc.
10943 N Sam Huston Pkwy W
Houston TX 77064
281 897-7788

(P-12954)
NCI GROUP INC
Also Called: Metal Building Components Mbci
550 Industry Way, Atwater (95301-9457)
P.O. Box 793 (95301-0793)
PHONE..................................209 357-1000
Bill Jones, *Manager*
Danny Saldana, *Plant Supt*
EMP: 125
SALES (corp-wide): 1.7B **Publicly Held**
SIC: 3448 Prefabricated metal buildings;
prefabricated metal components
HQ: Nci Group, Inc.
10943 N Sam Huston Pkwy W
Houston TX 77064
281 897-7788

(P-12955)
ORANGE COUNTY ERECTORS INC
517 E La Palma Ave, Anaheim
(92801-2536)
PHONE..................................714 502-8455
Richard Lewis, *CEO*
Sandra Lewis, *Senior VP*
Joe Pennachio, *Safety Dir*
Tiffany Pennachio, *Cust Mgr*
EMP: 50 **EST:** 1975
SQ FT: 80,000
SALES (est): 17.2MM **Privately Held**
WEB: www.ocerectors.com
SIC: 3448 3441 1791 Buildings, portable:
prefabricated metal; fabricated structural
metal; structural steel erection

(PA)=Parent Co (HQ)=Headquarters (DH)=Div Headquarters
✪ = New Business established in last 2 years

2019 California
Manufacturers Register

PRODUCTS & SVCS

531

(P-12956)
PRE-INSULATED METAL TECH INC (HQ)
Also Called: All Weather Insulated Panels
929 Aldridge Rd, Vacaville (95688-9282)
PHONE....................707 359-2280
William H Lowery, *President*
Michael T Lowery, *Vice Pres*
Gary Robinson, *General Mgr*
Danielle Bates, *Admin Asst*
Nathan Gates, *Project Mgr*
▲ EMP: 50
SQ FT: 96,000
SALES (est): 27MM **Privately Held**
SIC: 3448 Panels for prefabricated metal buildings

(P-12957)
PROGRESSIVE MARKETING PDTS INC
2620 Palisades Dr, Corona (92882-0631)
PHONE....................714 888-1700
Leonard Dozier, *CEO*
Kathy Bent, *CFO*
Richard Pierro, *Co-CEO*
Tiffany Dozier, *Exec VP*
Sam Malik, *Exec VP*
▲ EMP: 80
SQ FT: 47,000
SALES (est): 21.3MM **Privately Held**
WEB: www.premiermounts.com
SIC: 3448 Prefabricated metal buildings

(P-12958)
QUICK DECK INC
15390 Byron Hwy, Byron (94514)
P.O. Box 537 (94514-0537)
PHONE....................925 516-0603
Fred A Wagner III, *President*
Graham L Scott, *Vice Pres*
Kathy Freer, *Office Mgr*
EMP: 10
SQ FT: 2,500
SALES (est): 1MM **Privately Held**
SIC: 3448 3537 7352 Ramps: prefabricated metal; platforms, cargo; medical equipment rental

(P-12959)
ROBERTSON-CECO II CORPORATION
Also Called: Star Building Systems
12101 E Brandt Rd, Lockeford (95237-9550)
PHONE....................209 727-5504
Greg Lewis, *Manager*
EMP: 120
SQ FT: 7,000
SALES (corp-wide): 1.7B **Publicly Held**
WEB: www.robertsonceco.com
SIC: 3448 Buildings, portable: prefabricated metal
HQ: Robertson-Ceco Ii Corporation
10943 N Sam Huston Pkwy W
Houston TX 77064

(P-12960)
SARAMARK INC
15660 Mckinley Ave, Lathrop (95330-8525)
P.O. Box 82 (95330-0082)
PHONE....................408 971-3881
Mark A Collishaw, *CEO*
Markus Deleeuw, *Sales Mgr*
EMP: 50
SALES (est): 9.9MM **Privately Held**
WEB: www.saramark.com
SIC: 3448 Prefabricated metal buildings

(P-12961)
SOLO STEEL ERECTORS INC
762 Portal Dr, Chico (95973-1230)
PHONE....................530 893-2293
Shawn M Bentley, *President*
Shawn Bentley, *President*
Jason Baldridge, *Treasurer*
Nikolas Radtke, *Corp Secy*
EMP: 12
SALES: 1.9MM **Privately Held**
SIC: 3448 1521 Prefabricated metal buildings; single-family housing construction

(P-12962)
STELL INDUSTRIES INC
Also Called: C-Thru Sunrooms
1477 Davril Cir, Corona (92880-6957)
PHONE....................951 369-8777
Gary P Stell Jr, *CEO*
Jason S Albany, *President*
Mike Leigh, *President*
EMP: 50 EST: 1947
SQ FT: 5,000
SALES (est): 11.3MM **Privately Held**
WEB: www.c-thru.com
SIC: 3448 Sunrooms, prefabricated metal

(P-12963)
T M P SERVICES INC (PA)
2929 Kansas Ave, Riverside (92507-2639)
PHONE....................951 213-3900
Prentiss Tarver Jr, *Shareholder*
Shari Taylor, *President*
Pete Tarver, *Treasurer*
Doug Peacock, *Sales Mgr*
Cecilia Villarreal, *Director*
EMP: 25
SQ FT: 32,000
SALES: 6MM **Privately Held**
WEB: www.tmpservices.com
SIC: 3448 Ramps: prefabricated metal

(P-12964)
TIFFANY STRUCTURES
13162 Hwy 8 Bus Spc 205, El Cajon (92021)
PHONE....................619 905-9684
Raymond Tiffany, *Owner*
Julia Tiffany, *Co-Owner*
EMP: 25
SQ FT: 1,100
SALES (est): 2.5MM **Privately Held**
SIC: 3448 Prefabricated metal components

(P-12965)
TOLCO INCORPORATED
Also Called: Viking Fabrication
6480 Box Springs Blvd, Riverside (92507-0744)
PHONE....................951 656-3111
Patrick Shaughnessy, *Principal*
EMP: 30
SALES (est): 3.7MM **Privately Held**
SIC: 3448 Prefabricated metal buildings

(P-12966)
TONY BORGES
Also Called: Component Hsing Systems U S A
8685 Bowers Ave, South Gate (90280-3317)
PHONE....................310 962-8700
Tony Borges, *Owner*
EMP: 22
SQ FT: 40,000
SALES: 5MM **Privately Held**
SIC: 3448 Buildings, portable: prefabricated metal

(P-12967)
UNITED CARPORTS LLC
7280 Sycamore Canyon Blvd # 1, Riverside (92508-2316)
PHONE....................800 757-6742
Ryan Spates, *CEO*
Garrett Spates, *Vice Pres*
EMP: 18
SQ FT: 5,000
SALES (est): 3.3MM **Privately Held**
SIC: 3448 Prefabricated metal buildings

(P-12968)
US COVER LLC
1309 S Eastern Ave, Commerce (90040-5610)
P.O. Box 22268, Los Angeles (90022-0268)
PHONE....................323 838-2700
Gregory Naiman,
G D Neumann, *Principal*
EMP: 15
SALES: 1.8MM **Privately Held**
WEB: www.uscover.com
SIC: 3448 Prefabricated metal buildings

(P-12969)
WESTERN METAL SUPPLY CO INC
2115 E Valley Pkwy Ste B, Escondido (92027-2703)
PHONE....................760 233-7800
Abel Caballero, *President*
Scott Tanner, *Admin Sec*
EMP: 15
SALES: 3.2MM **Privately Held**
SIC: 3448 Prefabricated metal buildings

3449 Misc Structural Metal Work

(P-12970)
ACME SCREW PRODUCTS INC
7950 S Alameda St, Huntington Park (90255-6697)
PHONE....................323 581-8611
Richard Matthews, *President*
Cynthia Matthews, *Admin Sec*
EMP: 25 EST: 1942
SQ FT: 13,500
SALES (est): 4.5MM **Privately Held**
SIC: 3449 Miscellaneous metalwork

(P-12971)
AMC MACHINING INC
1540 Commerce Way, Paso Robles (93446-3524)
P.O. Box 665 (93447-0665)
PHONE....................805 238-5452
Alex Camp, *President*
EMP: 21
SQ FT: 10,000
SALES: 4MM **Privately Held**
SIC: 3449 Miscellaneous metalwork

(P-12972)
BACKSTAGE EQUIPMENT INC
Also Called: Backstage Studio Equip
8052 Lankershim Blvd, North Hollywood (91605-1609)
PHONE....................818 504-6026
Cary Griffith, *President*
EMP: 13
SQ FT: 9,801
SALES (est): 2.6MM **Privately Held**
WEB: www.backstageweb.com
SIC: 3449 3646 Miscellaneous metalwork; commercial indusl & institutional electric lighting fixtures

(P-12973)
BONNER METAL PROCESSING LLC
6052 Industrial Way Ste A, Livermore (94551-9711)
PHONE....................925 455-3833
Robert Bonner,
Renato Garofani,
Long Hoang,
EMP: 34
SQ FT: 15,000
SALES (est): 5.2MM **Privately Held**
SIC: 3449 Miscellaneous metalwork

(P-12974)
CALIFORNIA STEEL PRODUCTS
10851 Drury Ln, Lynwood (90262-1833)
PHONE....................310 603-5645
Enrique Garcia, *President*
Ricardo Moctezuma, *Vice Pres*
EMP: 12
SALES (est): 2.1MM **Privately Held**
SIC: 3449 3452 3312 Miscellaneous metalwork; bolts, metal; rods, iron & steel: made in steel mills

(P-12975)
CANYON STEEL FABRICATORS INC
1751 Spruce St, Riverside (92507-2351)
PHONE....................951 683-2352
Thomas J Baggett, *President*
Ray Magnon, *Vice Pres*
Doug Magnon, *Admin Sec*
Heather Johnston, *Manager*
EMP: 22
SQ FT: 9,000

SALES (est): 4.5MM **Privately Held**
SIC: 3449 Bars, concrete reinforcing: fabricated steel

(P-12976)
CROSNO CONSTRUCTION INC
819 Sheridan Rd, Arroyo Grande (93420-5833)
PHONE....................805 343-7437
Wade Crosno, *President*
Jaime Crosno, *CFO*
Mike Whitney, *Vice Pres*
Brian Terberg, *Engineer*
Allen Stanfield, *Buyer*
EMP: 48
SQ FT: 5,000
SALES (est): 18.1MM **Privately Held**
SIC: 3449 Bars, concrete reinforcing: fabricated steel

(P-12977)
DB BUILDING FASTENERS INC (PA)
Also Called: Db Building Fasteners
5555 E Gibralter, Ontario (91764-5121)
P.O. Box 4407, Rancho Cucamonga (91729-4407)
PHONE....................909 581-6740
Brent Dooley, *President*
Andrew Cohn, *Treasurer*
John Dooley III, *Vice Pres*
Marco Ramos, *Sales Staff*
Danny Cintron, *Warehouse Mgr*
▲ EMP: 20
SALES (est): 5.5MM **Privately Held**
WEB: www.selfdrillers.com
SIC: 3449 Miscellaneous metalwork

(P-12978)
FYFE CO LLC (HQ)
4995 Murphy Canyon Rd # 110, San Diego (92123-4365)
PHONE....................858 444-2970
Edward Fyfe,
Victor Reyes, *Regional Mgr*
Reymundo Ortiz, *Engineer*
Tommy Jimenez, *Business Mgr*
Dana Davis, *Asst Controller*
EMP: 17
SQ FT: 6,000
SALES (est): 4.4MM
SALES (corp-wide): 1.3B **Publicly Held**
WEB: www.fyfeco.com
SIC: 3449 Bars, concrete reinforcing: fabricated steel
PA: Aegion Corporation
17988 Edison Ave
Chesterfield MO 63005
636 530-8000

(P-12979)
H WAYNE LEWIS INC
Also Called: Amber Steel Co.
312 S Willow Ave, Rialto (92376-6313)
P.O. Box 900 (92377-0900)
PHONE....................909 874-2213
H Wayne Lewis, *CEO*
Kriss Lewis, *COO*
Janet Lewis, *Treasurer*
Dan Bergen, *Vice Pres*
Shannon Gonzalez, *Financial Exec*
EMP: 40
SQ FT: 8,100
SALES: 14.7MM **Privately Held**
WEB: www.ambersteel.net
SIC: 3449 Bars, concrete reinforcing: fabricated steel

(P-12980)
INNOVATIVE METAL INDS INC
Also Called: Southwest Data Products
1330 Riverview Dr, San Bernardino (92408-2944)
PHONE....................909 796-6200
Kelly Brodhagan, *Principal*
Jesse Brodhagen, *Exec VP*
▲ EMP: 100
SQ FT: 150,000
SALES (est): 20.5MM **Privately Held**
SIC: 3449 Curtain wall, metal

(P-12981)
JOHASEE REBAR LP (PA)
18059 Rosedale Hwy, Bakersfield (93314-8684)
PHONE....................604 598-9930

▲ = Import ▼=Export
◆ =Import/Export

Norm Streu, *President*
Janice Comeau, *CFO*
Mike Schutz, *Vice Pres*
EMP: 15
SALES: 15MM **Privately Held**
SIC: 3449 Bars, concrete reinforcing: fabricated steel

(P-12982)
JR DANIELS COMMERCIAL BLDRS
Also Called: Innovative Steel Structures
907 Maze Blvd, Modesto (95351-1851)
PHONE..................209 545-6040
James R Daniels, *President*
EMP: 60
SQ FT: 1,900
SALES (est): 8.3MM **Privately Held**
SIC: 3449 Bars, concrete reinforcing: fabricated steel

(P-12983)
KING WIRE PARTITIONS INC
Also Called: A A A Partitions
6044 N Figueroa St, Los Angeles (90042-4232)
P.O. Box 42220 (90042-0220)
PHONE..................323 256-4846
Max Behshid, *President*
Farid Behshid, *Vice Pres*
Millie Behshid, *Vice Pres*
▲ **EMP:** 30
SQ FT: 24,000
SALES: 3MM **Privately Held**
WEB: www.kingwireusa.com
SIC: 3449 5046 3496 Miscellaneous metalwork; partitions; miscellaneous fabricated wire products

(P-12984)
LUSTRE-CAL NAMEPLATE CORP
715 S Guild Ave, Lodi (95240-3153)
P.O. Box 439 (95241-0439)
PHONE..................209 370-1600
Clydene Hohenrieder, *CEO*
Joseph Hohenrieder, *President*
Heather Chartrand, *COO*
▲ **EMP:** 65
SQ FT: 50,000
SALES (est): 14.5MM **Privately Held**
WEB: www.lustrecal.com
SIC: 3449 Miscellaneous metalwork

(P-12985)
NI INDUSTRIES INC
7300 E Slauson Ave, Commerce (90040-3627)
PHONE..................309 283-3355
David Adler, *President*
Brian McGuire, *President*
Anil Shanehg, *Vice Pres*
▲ **EMP:** 25
SQ FT: 30,000
SALES (est): 3.4MM
SALES (corp-wide): 817.7MM **Publicly Held**
WEB: www.niindustries.com
SIC: 3449 Miscellaneous metalwork
PA: Trimas Corporation
38505 Woodward Ave # 200
Bloomfield Hills MI 48304
248 631-5450

(P-12986)
PACIFIC INTERNATIONAL STL CORP
2889 Navone Rd, Stockton (95215-9324)
PHONE..................209 931-0900
James H Lewis, *President*
Carol Lewis, *Corp Secy*
EMP: 25
SQ FT: 3,500
SALES (est): 3.7MM **Privately Held**
WEB: www.pacificinternational.com
SIC: 3449 5051 Miscellaneous metalwork; steel

(P-12987)
PACIFIC STEEL GROUP (PA)
Also Called: Psg
4805 Murphy Canyon Rd, San Diego (92123-4324)
PHONE..................858 251-1100
Eric Benson, *Principal*

John Scurlock, *President*
Monica Kamoss, *CFO*
EMP: 79
SQ FT: 26,000
SALES (est): 129.1MM **Privately Held**
SIC: 3449 Bars, concrete reinforcing: fabricated steel

(P-12988)
PACIFIC STEEL GROUP
2301 Napa Vallejo Hwy, NAPA (94558-6242)
PHONE..................707 669-3136
Alfredo Gonzalez, *Branch Mgr*
EMP: 21
SALES (corp-wide): 129.1MM **Privately Held**
SIC: 3449 Bars, concrete reinforcing: fabricated steel
PA: Pacific Steel Group
4805 Murphy Canyon Rd
San Diego CA 92123
858 251-1100

(P-12989)
PACIFIC WEST FOREST PRODUCTS
13434 Browns Valley Dr, Chico (95973-9322)
P.O. Box 2082 (95927-2082)
PHONE..................530 899-7313
Keith Iindquist, *President*
Kevin Linquist, *Vice Pres*
▲ **EMP:** 16
SQ FT: 37,000
SALES (est): 3.2MM **Privately Held**
SIC: 3449 5031 Custom roll formed products; lumber: rough, dressed & finished

(P-12990)
PSCMB REPAIRS INC
Also Called: Quality Industry Repair
12145 Slauson Ave, Santa Fe Springs (90670-2603)
PHONE..................626 448-7778
Stephany Castellanos, *CEO*
EMP: 40
SALES (est): 6.3MM **Privately Held**
SIC: 3449 Miscellaneous metalwork

(P-12991)
QUALITY STEEL FABRICATORS INC
13275 Gregg St, Poway (92064-7120)
PHONE..................858 748-8400
Bryan J Miller, *President*
Cheryl Wolf, *Controller*
EMP: 20
SALES (est): 4.3MM **Privately Held**
SIC: 3449 Bars, concrete reinforcing: fabricated steel

(P-12992)
SHIRLEE INDUSTRIES INC
13985 Sycamore Way, Chino (91710-7017)
PHONE..................909 590-4120
Tom Shaw, *CFO*
Jeff Shaw, *Vice Pres*
EMP: 12
SQ FT: 35,000
SALES (est): 2.2MM **Privately Held**
WEB: www.shirleeindustries.com
SIC: 3449 3444 Miscellaneous metalwork; sheet metalwork

(P-12993)
SIMPSON STRONG-TIE COMPANY INC (HQ)
5956 W Las Positas Blvd, Pleasanton (94588-8540)
P.O. Box 10789 (94588-0789)
PHONE..................925 560-9000
Karen Colonias, *CEO*
Phillip Kingsfather, *President*
Terry Kingsfather, *President*
Michael Herbert, *Vice Pres*
▲ **EMP:** 150
SQ FT: 89,000
SALES (est): 479.1MM
SALES (corp-wide): 977MM **Publicly Held**
SIC: 3449 2891 Joists, fabricated bar; adhesives

PA: Simpson Manufacturing Co., Inc.
5956 W Las Positas Blvd
Pleasanton CA 94588
925 560-9000

(P-12994)
SIMPSON STRONG-TIE COMPANY INC
5151 S Airport Way, Stockton (95206-3991)
PHONE..................209 234-7775
Bruce Lewis, *Branch Mgr*
EMP: 100
SALES (corp-wide): 977MM **Publicly Held**
SIC: 3449 3444 3441 Joists, fabricated bar; sheet metalwork; fabricated structural metal
HQ: Simpson Strong-Tie Company Inc.
5956 W Las Positas Blvd
Pleasanton CA 94588
925 560-9000

(P-12995)
SIMPSON STRONG-TIE COMPANY INC
12246 Holly St, Riverside (92509-2314)
PHONE..................714 871-8373
Dave Simpson, *Principal*
EMP: 58
SALES (corp-wide): 977MM **Publicly Held**
SIC: 3449 Joists, fabricated bar
HQ: Simpson Strong-Tie Company Inc.
5956 W Las Positas Blvd
Pleasanton CA 94588
925 560-9000

(P-12996)
SIMPSON STRONG-TIE INTL INC (DH)
5956 W Las Positas Blvd, Pleasanton (94588-8540)
P.O. Box 10789 (94588-0789)
PHONE..................925 560-9000
Karen Colonias, *CEO*
▲ **EMP:** 100
SQ FT: 89,000
SALES (est): 22.9MM
SALES (corp-wide): 977MM **Publicly Held**
SIC: 3449 Joists, fabricated bar
HQ: Simpson Strong-Tie Company Inc.
5956 W Las Positas Blvd
Pleasanton CA 94588
925 560-9000

(P-12997)
SOLHER IRON
1555 Galvez Ave Ste 400, San Francisco (94124-1707)
PHONE..................415 822-9900
Martin Solorzano, *Owner*
Francisco Rangel, *Project Mgr*
EMP: 12
SALES (est): 2.5MM **Privately Held**
WEB: www.solheriron.com
SIC: 3449 Bars, concrete reinforcing: fabricated steel

(P-12998)
SRSS LLC
1400 Airport Blvd, Santa Rosa (95403-1023)
PHONE..................707 544-7777
Mark Ferronato, *Manager*
Rodney Ferronato, *Manager*
EMP: 14
SALES (est): 2.4MM **Privately Held**
SIC: 3449 Bars, concrete reinforcing: fabricated steel

(P-12999)
STEEL TOE ENTERPRISES
Also Called: Anderson
967 W Hyde Park Blvd, Inglewood (90302-3307)
PHONE..................310 828-9677
Thomas Manzella, *President*
▲ **EMP:** 12 **EST:** 1998
SQ FT: 8,000
SALES (est): 1.1MM **Privately Held**
SIC: 3449 Bars, concrete reinforcing: fabricated steel

(P-13000)
TAMCO INC (DH)
Also Called: Tamco Steel
12459 Arrow Rte, Rancho Cucamonga (91739-9807)
P.O. Box 325 (91739-0325)
PHONE..................909 899-0660
Jack D Stutz, *President*
Carl Krepper, *Vice Pres*
A Brad Wilkins, *Vice Pres*
◆ **EMP:** 63
SQ FT: 150,000
SALES (est): 49.7MM **Privately Held**
WEB: www.tamcosteel.com
SIC: 3449 Blast furnaces & steel mills
HQ: Gerdau Ameristeel Us Inc.
4221 W Boy Scout Blvd # 600
Tampa FL 33607
813 286-8383

(P-13001)
TRI STAR METALS INC
8749 Pedrick Rd, Dixon (95620-9604)
PHONE..................707 678-1140
Robert Clouse, *President*
Barbara Delaney, *Vice Pres*
Andrew Delaney, *Director*
Aaron Moynihan, *Director*
EMP: 10
SQ FT: 11,200
SALES (est): 1.6MM **Privately Held**
WEB: www.dixonymachine.com
SIC: 3449 Miscellaneous metalwork

(P-13002)
UNITED MISC & ORNA STL INC
Also Called: Umo Steel
4700 Horner St, Union City (94587-2531)
PHONE..................510 429-8755
Juan M Romero, *President*
Jose Barrera, *Vice Pres*
Jose G Romero, *Principal*
EMP: 48
SALES (est): 2.7MM **Privately Held**
WEB: www.umosteelinc.com
SIC: 3449 Bars, concrete reinforcing: fabricated steel

(P-13003)
VISTA STEEL CO INC (PA)
6100 Francis Botello Rd C, Goleta (93117-3259)
PHONE..................805 964-4732
Maria Di Maggio, *President*
EMP: 50 **EST:** 1969
SQ FT: 600
SALES (est): 7.9MM **Privately Held**
SIC: 3449 Bars, concrete reinforcing: fabricated steel

(P-13004)
WESTCO INDUSTRIES INC
Also Called: Corbell Products
2625 S Willow Ave, Bloomington (92316-3258)
PHONE..................909 874-8700
David Schibel, *President*
Erick Maravilla, *Info Tech Mgr*
▲ **EMP:** 25
SQ FT: 25,000
SALES (est): 5.2MM **Privately Held**
SIC: 3449 Bars, concrete reinforcing: fabricated steel

3451 Screw Machine Prdts

(P-13005)
A & A MACHINE & DEV CO INC
16625 Gramercy Pl, Gardena (90247-5201)
PHONE..................310 532-7706
Arlene Hymovitz, *President*
Eric Hymovitz, *Vice Pres*
EMP: 18
SQ FT: 12,000
SALES (est): 4MM **Privately Held**
WEB: www.aamach.com
SIC: 3451 Screw machine products

(P-13006)
ABEL AUTOMATICS INC
Also Called: Abel Reels
165 N Aviador St, Camarillo (93010-8484)
PHONE..................805 484-8789

David C Dragoo, *CEO*
▲ EMP: 30
SQ FT: 16,000
SALES: 3MM **Privately Held**
SIC: 3451 3949 Screw machine products;
reels, fishing

(P-13007)
ACCU-SWISS INC (PA)
544 Armstrong Way, Oakdale
(95361-9367)
PHONE...................................209 847-1016
Sohel Sareshwala, *President*
Asfiya Sareshwala, *Corp Secy*
Ali Gabajiwala, *Engineer*
EMP: 19
SQ FT: 10,000
SALES (est): 4MM **Privately Held**
WEB: www.accuswissinc.com
SIC: 3451 8711 Screw machine products;
engineering services

(P-13008)
AD-DE-PRO INC
8276 Phlox St, Downey (90241-4883)
P.O. Box 807 (90241-0807)
PHONE...................................562 862-1915
Tom Burdett, *President*
Beverly Mathis, *Treasurer*
EMP: 16 EST: 1965
SQ FT: 5,000
SALES (est): 1.3MM **Privately Held**
SIC: 3451 Screw machine products

(P-13009)
ALGER PRECISION MACHINING LLC
724 S Bon View Ave, Ontario (91761-1913)
PHONE...................................909 986-4591
Duane Femrite, *Principal*
▲ EMP: 160
SQ FT: 35,000
SALES (est): 44MM **Privately Held**
WEB: www.alger1.com
SIC: 3451 Screw machine products

(P-13010)
ALPHA OMEGA SWISS INC
23305 La Palma Ave, Yorba Linda
(92887-4773)
PHONE...................................714 692-8009
Dale La Rock, *President*
Randy L Jones, *Vice Pres*
Robert Palmer, *General Mgr*
EMP: 30
SQ FT: 15,500
SALES (est): 3.3MM **Privately Held**
WEB: www.alphaomegaswiss.com
SIC: 3451 3599 Screw machine products;
machine shop, jobbing & repair

(P-13011)
ALVA MANUFACTURING INC
236 E Orangethorpe Ave, Placentia
(92870-6442)
PHONE...................................714 237-0925
Tam V Nguyen, *Principal*
Chris Robledo, *Program Mgr*
Sarah Naguib, *Admin Asst*
Pat Moag, *QC Mgr*
EMP: 24
SQ FT: 15,000
SALES (est): 1.5MM **Privately Held**
SIC: 3451 3452 3728 3599 Screw ma-
chine products; bolts, nuts, rivets & wash-
ers; aircraft parts & equipment; machine
& other job shop work; machine shop,
jobbing & repair

(P-13012)
ANWRIGHT CORPORATION
10225 Glenoaks Blvd, Pacoima
(91331-1605)
P.O. Box 330940 (91333-0940)
PHONE...................................818 896-2465
Lloyd Anderson, *President*
David Richardson, *Vice Pres*
Elva Guadiana, *Bookkeeper*
Harry A Olivar, *Agent*
EMP: 48
SQ FT: 15,000
SALES: 2.4MM **Privately Held**
WEB: www.anwright.com
SIC: 3451 3599 Screw machine products;
machine shop, jobbing & repair

(P-13013)
ASSOCIATED SCREW MACHINE PDTS
Also Called: A S M P
23978 Connecticut St A, Hayward
(94545-1637)
PHONE...................................510 783-3831
Mike Schenkhuizen, *President*
EMP: 25
SQ FT: 12,000
SALES (est): 4.6MM **Privately Held**
SIC: 3451 Screw machine products

(P-13014)
ATHANOR GROUP INC
921 E California St, Ontario (91761-1918)
PHONE...................................909 467-1205
Duane L Femrite, *President*
Richard Krause, *Vice Pres*
EMP: 165 EST: 1958
SQ FT: 35,600
SALES (est): 11.3MM **Privately Held**
SIC: 3451 Screw machine products

(P-13015)
ATLAS SCREW MACHINE PDTS CO
560 Natoma St, San Francisco
(94103-2885)
PHONE...................................415 621-6737
John Stadlberger, *President*
Mike Boitano, *Vice Pres*
EMP: 10
SQ FT: 2,500
SALES (est): 1.3MM **Privately Held**
WEB: www.atlasscrew.com
SIC: 3451 Screw machine products

(P-13016)
BALDA HK PLASTICS INC
Also Called: H K Prcision Turning Machining
3229 Roymar Rd, Oceanside (92058-1311)
PHONE...................................760 757-1100
Dan Wannigen, *Manager*
Juan Rosa, *Engineer*
EMP: 60
SQ FT: 9,808
SALES (corp-wide): 562.9K **Privately
Held**
WEB: www.hkplasticseng.com
SIC: 3451 3544 3089 Screw machine
products; special dies & tools; injection
molded finished plastic products
HQ: Balda Hk Plastics Inc.
1825 Corporate Ctr
Oceanside CA 92056
760 757-1200

(P-13017)
BTM-BEARTECH MANUFACTURING
Also Called: Btm-Beartech Manufacturing
LLC
910 S Placentia Ave Ste A, Placentia
(92870-8001)
P.O. Box 10422, Santa Ana (92711-0422)
PHONE...................................714 550-1700
Rick E Fobear, *President*
James Thomas, *Mng Member*
EMP: 10
SQ FT: 7,000
SALES: 684.5K
SALES (corp-wide): 8.4MM **Privately
Held**
WEB: www.beartechmfg.com
SIC: 3451 3452 3599 Screw machine
products; bolts, nuts, rivets & washers;
machine & other job shop work; machine
shop, jobbing & repair
PA: Beartech Alloys, Inc.
910 S Placentia Ave Ste A
Placentia CA 92870
714 550-1700

(P-13018)
COLUMBIA SCREW PRODUCTS INC
2901 Halladay St, Santa Ana (92705-5622)
PHONE...................................714 549-1171
William E Gorham, *President*
Dolores Gorham, *Treasurer*
Candy Agajanian, *Finance Mgr*
Candy Gorham, *Manager*
EMP: 15
SQ FT: 4,000

SALES: 800K **Privately Held**
WEB: www.columbiascrew.com
SIC: 3451 Screw machine products

(P-13019)
CRELLIN MACHINE COMPANY
Also Called: BT Screw Products
114 W Elmyra St, Los Angeles
(90012-1819)
P.O. Box 60099, Pasadena (91116-6099)
PHONE...................................323 225-8101
Richard Kirkendall, *President*
EMP: 45
SQ FT: 22,000
SALES (est): 6.5MM **Privately Held**
WEB: www.btcrellin.com
SIC: 3451 3541 Screw machine products;
machine tools, metal cutting type

(P-13020)
CUTTING EDGE MACHINING INC (PA)
100 San Lucar Ct, Sunnyvale
(94086-5213)
PHONE...................................408 738-8677
Jack Corey, *CEO*
Gloria J Corey, *Corp Secy*
EMP: 25
SQ FT: 50,000
SALES (est): 7MM **Privately Held**
WEB: www.cemnv.com
SIC: 3451 Screw machine products

(P-13021)
DESIGNED METAL CONNECTIONS INC (DH)
Also Called: Permaswage USA
14800 S Figueroa St, Gardena
(90248-1719)
PHONE...................................310 323-6200
Thomas McDonnell, *Vice Pres*
▲ EMP: 500
SQ FT: 175,000
SALES (est): 194MM
SALES (corp-wide): 242.1B **Publicly
Held**
SIC: 3451 Screw machine products
HQ: Precision Castparts Corp.
4650 Sw Mcdam Ave Ste 300
Portland OR 97239
503 946-4800

(P-13022)
EDWARD KOEHN CO INC
820 Folger Ave, Berkeley (94710-2817)
PHONE...................................510 843-0821
Paul Koehn, *President*
Beatrice Koehn, *Treasurer*
EMP: 10 EST: 1942
SQ FT: 4,500
SALES (est): 1.1MM **Privately Held**
SIC: 3451 Screw machine products

(P-13023)
FASTENER INNOVATION TECH INC
Also Called: F I T
19300 S Susana Rd, Compton
(90221-5711)
PHONE...................................310 538-1111
Larry Valeriano, *CEO*
Jorge Molina, *Vice Pres*
Irma Preston, *Purch Agent*
Gary Legaspi, *Sales Staff*
EMP: 100
SQ FT: 65,000
SALES: 20.6MM **Privately Held**
WEB: www.fitfastener.com
SIC: 3451 3728 3452 3429 Screw ma-
chine products; aircraft parts & equip-
ment; bolts, nuts, rivets & washers;
manufactured hardware (general)

(P-13024)
GLENCO MANUFACTURING COMPANY
707 S Hope Ave, Ontario (91761-1826)
PHONE...................................909 984-3348
Fax: 909 988-5970
EMP: 50
SQ FT: 15,027
SALES (est): 8.8MM **Privately Held**
WEB: www.glencomfg.com
SIC: 3451

(P-13025)
GT PRECISION INC
Also Called: Alard Machine Products
1629 W 132nd St, Gardena (90249-2005)
PHONE...................................310 323-4374
Gregg Thompson, *CEO*
Andrew Lozano, *Planning*
Jose Zaragoza, *Info Tech Mgr*
Carlos Ferrer, *Controller*
Greg Granja, *Controller*
▲ EMP: 107
SQ FT: 11,700
SALES (est): 20.9MM **Privately Held**
WEB: www.alardmachine.com
SIC: 3451 Screw machine products

(P-13026)
H&M PRECISION MACHINING
Also Called: H & M Precision Machining
504 Robert Ave, Santa Clara (95050-2955)
PHONE...................................408 982-9184
Jane Harvey, *President*
Dick Ussery, *General Mgr*
EMP: 11
SQ FT: 8,000
SALES (est): 1.7MM **Privately Held**
SIC: 3451 3469 Screw machine products;
machine parts, stamped or pressed metal

(P-13027)
HTS-ENGINEERING INC
4079 Oceanside Blvd Ste J, Oceanside
(92056-5810)
PHONE...................................760 631-2070
Chris Dubreuil, *CEO*
Angela Robertson, *Manager*
EMP: 15
SQ FT: 7,700
SALES (est): 2.2MM **Privately Held**
WEB: www.hts-engineering.com
SIC: 3451 Screw machine products

(P-13028)
IRL-MEX MANUFACTURING COMPANY
Also Called: Union Swiss Manufacturing Co
1436 Flower St, Glendale (91201-2422)
PHONE...................................818 246-7211
Mathew Graham, *President*
Victor Paquini, *Vice Pres*
EMP: 10
SQ FT: 3,500
SALES (est): 1.9MM **Privately Held**
WEB: www.unionswiss.com
SIC: 3451 Screw machine products

(P-13029)
JUNE PRECISION MFG INC
Also Called: Tri-State Manufacturing
22276 Chestnut Ln, Lake Forest
(92630-4303)
PHONE...................................949 855-9121
David Oldfield, *President*
EMP: 10
SALES: 950K **Privately Held**
SIC: 3451 Screw machine products

(P-13030)
L & S MACHINE INC
Also Called: L&S Machine Enterprises
711 W 17th St Ste H2, Costa Mesa
(92627-4347)
PHONE...................................562 924-9007
Keith Longerot, *President*
EMP: 15
SQ FT: 12,500
SALES (est): 1MM **Privately Held**
WEB: www.lsmachine.com
SIC: 3451 Screw machine products

(P-13031)
MARS ENGINEERING COMPANY INC
Also Called: Vin-Max
699 Montague St, San Leandro
(94577-4323)
PHONE...................................510 483-0541
Manny Ambrosio, *President*
Christy Ambrosio, *Corp Secy*
EMP: 35
SQ FT: 15,000
SALES (est): 6.9MM **Privately Held**
WEB: www.marseng.com
SIC: 3451 Screw machine products

(P-13032)
MERCED SCREW PRODUCTS INC
1861 Grogan Ave, Merced (95341-6432)
PHONE....................................209 723-7706
Steve Centivich, *President*
EMP: 40
SQ FT: 17,000
SALES (est): 7.4MM **Privately Held**
SIC: 3451 Screw machine products

(P-13033)
NORSCO INC
1816 Ackley Cir, Oakdale (95361-9446)
PHONE....................................209 845-2327
Greg Siekierski, *President*
EMP: 10
SALES (est): 1.1MM **Privately Held**
WEB: www.norscoinc.com
SIC: 3451 Screw machine products

(P-13034)
ONYX INDUSTRIES INC (PA)
Also Called: Quad R Tech
1227 254th St, Harbor City (90710-2912)
PHONE....................................310 539-8830
Vladimir Reil, *CEO*
▲ **EMP:** 100
SQ FT: 30,000
SALES (est): 21MM **Privately Held**
SIC: 3451 Screw machine products

(P-13035)
ONYX INDUSTRIES INC
521 W Rosecrans Ave, Gardena
(90248-1514)
PHONE....................................310 851-6161
Siamak Maghoul, *Branch Mgr*
Ed Oberg, *Officer*
Babamet Sharma, *Info Tech Mgr*
EMP: 20
SALES (corp-wide): 21MM **Privately Held**
SIC: 3451 Screw machine products
PA: Onyx Industries Inc
1227 254th St
Harbor City CA 90710
310 539-8830

(P-13036)
PACIFIC SCREW PRODUCTS INC
Also Called: Rollin J. Lobaugh
1331c Old County Rd, Belmont
(94002-3922)
PHONE....................................650 583-9682
Jack Corey, *President*
Gloria Corey, *Corp Secy*
EMP: 52
SQ FT: 24,000
SALES (est): 10.2MM **Privately Held**
WEB: www.rjlobaugh.com
SIC: 3451 Screw machine products

(P-13037)
PENCOM ACCURACY INC
Also Called: Accuracy Screw Machine Pdts
1300 Industrial Rd Ste 21, San Carlos
(94070-4141)
PHONE....................................510 785-5022
Bill Gardiner, *President*
Deborah Gardiner, *Treasurer*
EMP: 52
SQ FT: 8,000
SALES (est): 6.7MM
SALES (corp-wide): 148.3MM **Privately Held**
WEB: www.pencomsf.com
SIC: 3451 Screw machine products
PA: Peninsula Components, Inc.
1300 Industrial Rd Ste 21
San Carlos CA 94070
650 593-3288

(P-13038)
PRECISION TECHNOLOGY AND MFG
3147 Durahart St, Riverside (92507-3463)
PHONE....................................951 788-0252
Jose Pompa, *President*
Lorraine Pagones, *Corp Secy*
Juan Pompa, *Vice Pres*
EMP: 43
SQ FT: 9,000

SALES (est): 5.8MM **Privately Held**
WEB: www.pretechm.com
SIC: 3451 3643 Screw machine products;
contacts, electrical

(P-13039)
PRICE MANUFACTURING CO INC
372 N Smith Ave, Corona (92880-6971)
PHONE....................................951 371-5660
Robert P Schiffmacher, *CEO*
Ively Schiffmacher, *Corp Secy*
EMP: 32
SQ FT: 15,600
SALES (est): 6.9MM **Privately Held**
WEB: www.pricemfg.com
SIC: 3451 Screw machine products

(P-13040)
R & R MACHINE PRODUCTS INC
760 W Mill St, San Bernardino
(92410-3348)
PHONE....................................909 885-7500
Eric Reiser, *President*
Belinda Reiser, *Corp Secy*
Karl Reiser, *Vice Pres*
EMP: 13
SQ FT: 5,000
SALES (est): 1MM **Privately Held**
WEB: www.grscrew.com
SIC: 3451 3643 Screw machine products;
electric connectors; contacts, electrical

(P-13041)
SIERRA SWISS & MACHINE INC
12854 Earhart Ave Ste 103, Auburn
(95602-9015)
P.O. Box 2797, Grass Valley (95945-2797)
PHONE....................................530 346-1110
David Gerken, *President*
Ann Gerken, *Corp Secy*
EMP: 13
SQ FT: 3,000
SALES (est): 1.6MM **Privately Held**
SIC: 3451

(P-13042)
SORENSON ENGINEERING INC (PA)
32032 Dunlap Blvd, Yucaipa (92399-1767)
PHONE....................................909 795-2434
David L Sorenson, *President*
Paul Sewell, *Principal*
Steve Sorenson, *Exec Dir*
Robert Lunderville, *Research*
Grant Feenstra, *Engineer*
▲ **EMP:** 170 **EST:** 1956
SQ FT: 61,000
SALES (est): 36.2MM **Privately Held**
WEB: www.sorensoneng.com
SIC: 3451 Screw machine products

(P-13043)
SWISS-MICRON INC
22361 Gilberto Ste A, Rcho STA Marg
(92688-2103)
PHONE....................................949 589-0430
Kurt Sollberger, *CEO*
Beverley Sollberger, *Vice Pres*
Daniel Porter, *Engineer*
Casey Colliflower, *Purch Mgr*
Alan McManus, *Prdtn Mgr*
EMP: 53
SQ FT: 16,000
SALES: 7MM **Privately Held**
WEB: www.swissmicron.com
SIC: 3451 Screw machine products

(P-13044)
SWISS-TECH MACHINING LLC
10564 Industrial Ave # 130, Roseville
(95678-6223)
PHONE....................................916 797-6010
Pete Kummli,
EMP: 25
SQ FT: 20,000
SALES (est): 3.7MM **Privately Held**
WEB: www.stmachining.com
SIC: 3451 Screw machine products

(P-13045)
T L MACHINE INC
14272 Commerce Dr, Garden Grove
(92843-4942)
PHONE....................................714 554-4154
Thanh X Ly, *President*

Thanh Ly, *President*
Quynh Nguyen, *Executive*
Tuyen Ly, *Admin Sec*
Kathleen Pratt, *Benefits Mgr*
▲ **EMP:** 90
SQ FT: 39,126
SALES (est): 21.8MM **Privately Held**
WEB: www.tlmachine.com
SIC: 3451 3561 3593 3728 Screw ma-
chine products; pumps & pumping equip-
ment; fluid power cylinders & actuators;
aircraft parts & equipment; aircraft; guided
missiles & space vehicles

(P-13046)
THOMAS T BERNSTEIN
1160 Daveric Dr, Pasadena (91107-1740)
PHONE....................................626 351-0570
Thomas T Bernstein, *Owner*
EMP: 40
SALES (est): 1.5MM **Privately Held**
SIC: 3451 Screw machine products

(P-13047)
TRIUMPH PRECISION PRODUCTS
Also Called: TP Products
13636 Vaughn St Ste A, San Fernando
(91340-3052)
PHONE....................................818 897-4700
Victor Linares, *President*
Javier Cervantes, *Vice Pres*
Jesus Cervantes, *Admin Sec*
EMP: 17
SQ FT: 19,500
SALES: 2.3MM **Privately Held**
WEB: www.tpproducts.com
SIC: 3451 Screw machine products

(P-13048)
UNIVERSAL SCREW PRODUCTS INC
20421 Earl St, Torrance (90503-2414)
P.O. Box 14241 (90503-8241)
PHONE....................................310 371-1170
Ken Shank, *President*
Michael Flannigan, *Admin Sec*
EMP: 20
SQ FT: 6,000
SALES (est): 3.7MM **Privately Held**
SIC: 3451 Screw machine products

(P-13049)
V M P INC
24830 Avenue Tibbitts, Valencia
(91355-3404)
PHONE....................................661 294-9934
Betty Schreiner, *President*
Steve Schreiner, *Treasurer*
Robert Schreiner Jr, *Vice Pres*
Suzanne St George, *Admin Sec*
▲ **EMP:** 16
SQ FT: 25,000
SALES (est): 3.1MM **Privately Held**
WEB: www.vmpinc.com
SIC: 3451 Screw machine products

(P-13050)
WARD AUTOMATIC MACHINE PDTS
1265 Goodrick Dr Ste E, Tehachapi
(93561-1562)
PHONE....................................661 822-7543
Ralph Ward, *President*
Bess Ward, *Treasurer*
Jeff Ward, *Opers Mgr*
EMP: 10
SQ FT: 7,500
SALES (est): 1MM **Privately Held**
WEB: www.wardautomatic.com
SIC: 3451 Screw machine products

(P-13051)
WESTERN GRINDING SERVICE INC
2375 De La Cruz Blvd, Santa Clara
(95050-2920)
PHONE....................................650 591-2635
David P Wilson, *Ch of Bd*
Ethan C Wilson, *President*
Rob Brindle, *VP Mfg*
Cathy Day, *Director*
EMP: 30
SQ FT: 28,000

SALES (est): 6.4MM **Privately Held**
WEB: www.westerngrinding.com
SIC: 3451 Screw machine products

(P-13052)
WESTERN SCREW PRODUCTS INC
11770 Slauson Ave, Santa Fe Springs
(90670-2269)
PHONE....................................562 698-5793
Lester P Kovats, *President*
William Doolittle, *Corp Secy*
Margaret K Doolittle, *Vice Pres*
Steve Kovats, *Vice Pres*
EMP: 50 **EST:** 1940
SQ FT: 30,000
SALES (est): 9MM **Privately Held**
WEB: www.westernscrew.com
SIC: 3451 Screw machine products

(P-13053)
WYATT PRECISION MACHINE INC
3301 E 59th St, Long Beach (90805-4503)
PHONE....................................562 634-0524
Dennis Allison, *President*
Allen Harmon, *Vice Pres*
Paul Layton, *Vice Pres*
EMP: 47
SQ FT: 14,000
SALES (est): 8.5MM **Privately Held**
WEB: www.wyattprecisionmachine.com
SIC: 3451 Screw machine products

(P-13054)
ZENITH SCREW PRODUCTS INC
10910 Painter Ave, Santa Fe Springs
(90670-4552)
P.O. Box 2747 (90670-0747)
PHONE....................................562 941-0281
Kenneth Miller, *President*
Donald S Miller, *Ch of Bd*
Connie Miller, *Treasurer*
Keith L Miller, *Vice Pres*
EMP: 20
SQ FT: 7,000
SALES (est): 1.3MM **Privately Held**
WEB: www.zspinc.com
SIC: 3451 Screw machine products

3452 Bolts, Nuts, Screws, Rivets & Washers

(P-13055)
3-V FASTENER CO INC
320 Reed Cir, Corona (92879-1349)
PHONE....................................951 734-4391
Dave Werner, *President*
Jordan Law, *Vice Pres*
EMP: 56
SQ FT: 18,500
SALES (est): 13.2MM
SALES (corp-wide): 167.6MM **Privately Held**
WEB: www.3vfasteners.com
SIC: 3452 Bolts, metal; nuts, metal;
screws, metal
PA: Consolidated Aerospace Manufactur-
ing, Llc
1425 S Acacia Ave
Fullerton CA 92831
714 989-2797

(P-13056)
A J FASTENERS INC
Also Called: Pacific Hardware Sales
2800 E Miraloma Ave, Anaheim
(92806-1803)
PHONE....................................714 630-1556
Lawrence Roa, *President*
▲ **EMP:** 20
SQ FT: 15,000
SALES (est): 3.2MM **Privately Held**
WEB: www.ajfasteners.com
SIC: 3452 5072 3469 Screws, metal;
screws; metal stampings

(P-13057)
ALLFAST FASTENING SYSTEMS LLC
15200 Don Julian Rd, City of Industry (91745-1098)
P.O. Box 3166 (91744-0166)
PHONE..............................626 968-9388
James H Randall,
Loretta Ceballos, *Purch Mgr*
Maria Mora, *Safety Mgr*
Mike Reyes, *Mfg Spvr*
◆ **EMP:** 58 **EST:** 1971
SALES (est): 40.9MM
SALES (corp-wide): 817.7MM **Publicly Held**
WEB: www.allfastinc.com
SIC: 3452 Bolts, nuts, rivets & washers
PA: Trimas Corporation
38505 Woodward Ave # 200
Bloomfield Hills MI 48304
248 631-5450

(P-13058)
ANILLO INDUSTRIES INC (PA)
2090 N Glassell St, Orange (92865-3306)
P.O. Box 5586 (92863-5586)
PHONE..............................714 637-7000
Kurt Hilton Koch, *President*
Mark Koch, *Vice Pres*
EMP: 28
SQ FT: 80,000
SALES (est): 5.6MM **Privately Held**
WEB: www.anilloinc.com
SIC: 3452 3325 3499 3429 Washers;
bushings, cast steel: except investment;
shims, metal; manufactured hardware
(general)

(P-13059)
B&B HARDWARE INC
Also Called: Sealtight Technology
5370 Hollister Ave Ste 2, Santa Barbara (93111-2399)
P.O. Box 60840 (93160-0840)
PHONE..............................805 683-6700
Larry Bogatz, *President*
Diana Bogatz, *Vice Pres*
Thomas Hussey, *Manager*
▲ **EMP:** 28
SQ FT: 4,000
SALES (est): 5MM **Privately Held**
WEB: www.sealtightfastener.com
SIC: 3452 5085 Bolts, nuts, rivets & washers; industrial supplies

(P-13060)
BLUE CIRCLE CORP
7520 Monroe St, Paramount (90723-4922)
PHONE..............................562 531-2711
Ronald E Anderson, *President*
Chris Anderson, *Vice Pres*
Jeffrey Anderson, *Vice Pres*
Walda Anderson, *Admin Sec*
EMP: 15
SQ FT: 13,000
SALES (est): 1.4MM **Privately Held**
SIC: 3452 3365 Bolts, metal; aluminum & aluminum-based alloy castings

(P-13061)
BRILES AEROSPACE INC
1559 W 135th St, Gardena (90249-2219)
PHONE..............................310 701-2087
Michael P Briles, *President*
EMP: 12
SQ FT: 22,000
SALES (est): 900K **Privately Held**
SIC: 3452 Bolts, nuts, rivets & washers

(P-13062)
BUTLER INC
1600 W 166th St, Gardena (90247-4704)
PHONE..............................310 323-3114
John Hollern, *President*
Cynthia Hollern, *Vice Pres*
Tod Polidori, *QC Mgr*
EMP: 14
SQ FT: 10,000
SALES (est): 2.6MM **Privately Held**
SIC: 3452 Bolts, metal

(P-13063)
C B S FASTENERS INC
1345 N Brasher St, Anaheim (92807-2046)
PHONE..............................714 779-6368
Gerald Bozarth, *President*

Rosa Velasco, *Info Tech Mgr*
EMP: 39
SQ FT: 10,400
SALES (est): 6.8MM **Privately Held**
WEB: www.cbsfasteners.com
SIC: 3452 Screws, metal

(P-13064)
CONCRETEACCESSORIESCOM
130 N Gilbert St, Fullerton (92833-2505)
PHONE..............................714 871-9434
Vasken Kassarjian, *President*
▲ **EMP:** 15
SALES: 3MM **Privately Held**
SIC: 3452 Bolts, nuts, rivets & washers

(P-13065)
CONKLIN & CONKLIN INCORPORATED
34201 7th St, Union City (94587-3655)
PHONE..............................510 489-5500
James Edward Conklin, *President*
Barbara Conklin, *Vice Pres*
▲ **EMP:** 30
SQ FT: 23,000
SALES (est): 4.5MM **Privately Held**
SIC: 3452 Bolts, nuts, rivets & washers

(P-13066)
DOUBLECO INCORPORATED
Also Called: R & D Fasteners
9444 9th St, Rancho Cucamonga (91730-4509)
P.O. Box 250, Upland (91785-0250)
PHONE..............................909 481-0799
Craig Scheu, *President*
Leland Scheu, *Sr Corp Ofcr*
Ryan McCaffrey, *General Mgr*
Allyn Scheu, *Admin Sec*
Nancy Casey, *Purch Mgr*
EMP: 100
SQ FT: 30,000
SALES (est): 28.4MM **Privately Held**
WEB: www.rdfast.com
SIC: 3452 5072 Bolts, metal; bolts

(P-13067)
DUPREE INC
Also Called: Stake Fastener
14395 Ramona Ave, Chino (91710-5740)
P.O. Box 1797 (91708-1797)
PHONE..............................909 597-4889
Jim Pon, *President*
James D Dupree, *Vice Pres*
▲ **EMP:** 31 **EST:** 1958
SQ FT: 60,000
SALES (est): 7.2MM **Privately Held**
WEB: www.dupreeinc.com
SIC: 3452 6512 Bolts, metal; gate hooks;
commercial & industrial building operation

(P-13068)
FASTENER DEPOT INC
6166 Enterprise Dr Ste A, Diamond Springs (95619-9440)
PHONE..............................530 621-3070
Mildred Navalance, *President*
Kellie Huntington, *Marketing Staff*
EMP: 10
SALES (est): 1.9MM **Privately Held**
SIC: 3452 Bolts, nuts, rivets & washers

(P-13069)
FEDERAL MANUFACTURING CORP
9825 De Soto Ave, Chatsworth (91311-4412)
PHONE..............................818 341-9825
Helen Rainey, *President*
Arthur Rainey, *President*
Paul Rainey, *Vice Pres*
Sharon Carlson, *Manager*
EMP: 42
SQ FT: 36,000
SALES (est): 8MM **Privately Held**
WEB: www.federalmanufacturing.com
SIC: 3452 3812 3462 3429 Bolts, metal;
search & navigation equipment; iron &
steel forgings; manufactured hardware
(general)

(P-13070)
GOLDEN BOLT LLC
9361 Canoga Ave, Chatsworth (91311-5879)
PHONE..............................818 626-8261

Crystal Crook,
EMP: 12
SALES (est): 2.4MM **Privately Held**
SIC: 3452 Bolts, metal

(P-13071)
HI-SHEAR CORPORATION (DH)
2600 Skypark Dr, Torrance (90505-5373)
PHONE..............................310 784-4025
Christian Darville, *CEO*
Edmond Balassanian, *Vice Pres*
Martin Wilson, *Buyer*
▲ **EMP:** 600 **EST:** 1943
SQ FT: 180,000
SALES (est): 245.8MM **Privately Held**
WEB: www.hi-shear.com
SIC: 3452 3429 Bolts, nuts, rivets & washers; aircraft hardware
HQ: Lisi Aerospace
42 A 52
Paris 75012
140 198-200

(P-13072)
HUCK INTERNATIONAL INC
Also Called: Arconic Fstening Systems Rings
900 E Watson Center Rd, Carson (90745-4201)
PHONE..............................310 830-8200
Jim Dawn, *Manager*
Hojat Boojani, *Engineer*
Hootsa Gladkikh, *Engineer*
Harold Jason, *Engineer*
Gustavo Lopez, *Engineer*
EMP: 203
SALES (corp-wide): 12.9B **Publicly Held**
WEB: www.huck.com
SIC: 3452 Nuts, metal
HQ: Huck International, Inc.
3724 E Columbia St
Tucson AZ 85714
520 519-7400

(P-13073)
IDEAL FASTENERS INC
3850 E Miraloma Ave, Anaheim (92806-2127)
PHONE..............................714 630-7840
George Hennes, *President*
Lawrence McBride, *Treasurer*
David Boehm, *Vice Pres*
Brain Vo, *Sales Staff*
EMP: 50 **EST:** 1969
SQ FT: 35,500
SALES (est): 9.9MM **Privately Held**
WEB: www.idealfasteners.com
SIC: 3452 Screws, metal

(P-13074)
INSTRUMENT BEARING FACTORY USA
19360 Rinaldi St, Northridge (91326-1607)
PHONE..............................818 989-5052
Dorothy Heller, *President*
EMP: 50
SQ FT: 30,000
SALES (est): 2.6MM **Privately Held**
SIC: 3452 5085 Bolts, metal; industrial supplies

(P-13075)
JW MANUFACTURING INC
Also Called: Arconic Fstening Systems Rings
12989 Bradley Ave, Sylmar (91342)
PHONE..............................805 498-4594
Jacob Wood, *President*
▲ **EMP:** 60
SQ FT: 40,000
SALES (est): 7.7MM **Privately Held**
SIC: 3452 5072 Nuts, metal; bolts, nuts & screws

(P-13076)
KINGFA GLOBAL INC
1910 S Archibald Ave D, Ontario (91761-8501)
PHONE..............................909 212-5413
Xiaojun Gao, *CEO*
EMP: 11
SALES (est): 1.4MM
SALES (corp-wide): 1MM **Privately Held**
SIC: 3452 5961 Bolts, nuts, rivets & washers; tools & hardware, mail order

PA: Wuxi Zhuocheng Mechanical Components Co., Ltd.
Building 6, Liando U-Valley 2, Beitang District
Wuxi 21410
510 823-5066

(P-13077)
MS AEROSPACE INC
13928 Balboa Blvd, Sylmar (91342-1086)
PHONE..............................818 833-9095
Michel Szostak, *CEO*
Jerome Taieb, *CFO*
Jim Cole, *Vice Pres*
Michelle Szostak, *VP Bus Dvlpt*
Nelson Ruiz, *Administration*
EMP: 302
SALES (est): 95.8MM **Privately Held**
WEB: www.msaerospace.com
SIC: 3452 3728 Bolts, nuts, rivets & washers; aircraft parts & equipment

(P-13078)
ND INDUSTRIES INC
Also Called: N D Industries
13929 Dinard Ave, Santa Fe Springs (90670-4920)
PHONE..............................562 926-3321
Tim Marzano, *Technology*
David Palmquist, *Assistant*
EMP: 40
SALES (corp-wide): 86.1MM **Privately Held**
WEB: www.ndindustries.com
SIC: 3452 2891 5072 Bolts, nuts, rivets & washers; adhesives & sealants; screws
PA: Nd Industries, Inc.
1000 N Crooks Rd
Clawson MI 48017
248 288-0000

(P-13079)
NYLOK LLC
Also Called: Nylok Western Fastener
313 N Euclid Way, Anaheim (92801-6738)
PHONE..............................714 635-3993
Scott Plantiga, *Manager*
EMP: 45
SALES (corp-wide): 18MM **Privately Held**
SIC: 3452 Bolts, nuts, rivets & washers
PA: Nylok, Llc
15260 Hallmark Ct
Macomb MI 48042
586 786-0100

(P-13080)
POWER FASTENERS INC
650 E 60th St, Los Angeles (90001-1012)
P.O. Box 512056 (90051-0056)
PHONE..............................323 232-4362
Patrick Harrington, *President*
▲ **EMP:** 30
SQ FT: 35,000
SALES (est): 5.1MM **Privately Held**
WEB: www.powerfasteners.com
SIC: 3452 3448 Bolts, nuts, rivets & washers; prefabricated metal components

(P-13081)
RISCO INC
390 Risco Cir, Beaumont (92223-2676)
PHONE..............................951 769-2899
Joseph A Frainee II, *CEO*
Cynthia R Frainee, *Vice Pres*
Carrie Ugapo, *Office Mgr*
Carlos Armijo, *Info Tech Dir*
Gisela Silvana, *Payroll Mgr*
EMP: 30 **EST:** 1964
SQ FT: 30,000
SALES: 3MM **Privately Held**
WEB: www.risco-fasteners.com
SIC: 3452 Bolts, metal; rivets, metal

(P-13082)
SCHRILLO COMPANY LLC
16750 Schoenborn St, North Hills (91343-6192)
PHONE..............................818 894-8241
Edward Schrillo, *Mng Member*
Donna Talamantez, *COO*
Anthony Schrillo, *Exec VP*
Jeri Nowlen, *Admin Sec*
Paul Matsushita, *Engineer*
▲ **EMP:** 40
SQ FT: 60,000

SALES (est): 9.3MM **Privately Held**
WEB: www.schrillo.com
SIC: 3452 Screws, metal

(P-13083)
SPS TECHNOLOGIES LLC
Also Called: Pb Fasteners
1700 W 132nd St, Gardena (90249-2008)
PHONE...................................310 323-6222
EMP: 260
SALES (corp-wide): 242.1B **Publicly Held**
SIC: 3452 Screws, metal
HQ: Sps Technologies, Llc
301 Highland Ave
Jenkintown PA 19046
215 572-3000

(P-13084)
SPS TECHNOLOGIES LLC
Air Industries
12570 Knott St, Garden Grove
(92841-3932)
PHONE...................................714 892-5571
Michael Wu, *Controller*
Bob Reece, *Bd of Directors*
Kevin Stein, *Exec VP*
James O'Connor, *Info Tech Dir*
Edward Park, *Director*
EMP: 50
SALES (corp-wide): 242.1B **Publicly Held**
WEB: www.spst.com
SIC: 3452 Bolts, metal
HQ: Sps Technologies, Llc
301 Highland Ave
Jenkintown PA 19046
215 572-3000

(P-13085)
STUD WELDING SYSTEMS INC
15306 Proctor Ave, City of Industry
(91745-1023)
PHONE...................................626 330-7434
Gary Edward, *CEO*
Ed Murphy, *Manager*
EMP: 20
SALES (est): 3.3MM **Privately Held**
WEB: www.sws4studs.com
SIC: 3452 3548 Rivets, metal; welding apparatus

(P-13086)
SUNLAND AEROSPACE FASTENERS
12920 Pierce St, Pacoima (91331-2526)
PHONE...................................818 485-8929
Jack Wilson, *CEO*
EMP: 14
SQ FT: 11,000
SALES (est): 1.1MM **Privately Held**
SIC: 3452 Bolts, nuts, rivets & washers

(P-13087)
TWIST TITE MFG INC
13344 Cambridge St, Santa Fe Springs
(90670-4904)
PHONE...................................562 229-0990
Spiro Aykias, *CEO*
Martha Leonard, *Admin Mgr*
EMP: 32
SQ FT: 18,200
SALES (est): 6.1MM **Privately Held**
WEB: www.twisttitemfg.com
SIC: 3452 Bolts, nuts, rivets & washers

(P-13088)
U-C COMPONENTS INC (PA)
18700 Adams Ct, Morgan Hill
(95037-2804)
P.O. Box 430 (95038-0430)
PHONE...................................408 782-1929
Nancy Anderson, *President*
Rick Anderson, *General Mgr*
EMP: 23
SQ FT: 16,000
SALES: 5MM **Privately Held**
WEB: www.uccomponents.com
SIC: 3452 Screws, metal; washers, metal

(P-13089)
VALLEY-TODECO INC (DH)
Also Called: Arconic Fstening Systems Rings
12975 Bradley Ave, Sylmar (91342-3852)
PHONE...................................800 992-4444
Jim Cotello, *President*

Beatriz Jimenez, *Engineer*
▲ EMP: 40
SQ FT: 105,000
SALES (est): 17.5MM
SALES (est): 12.9B **Publicly Held**
SIC: 3452 5085 Bolts, nuts, rivets & washers; fasteners, industrial: nuts, bolts, screws, etc.
HQ: Arconic Global Fasteners & Rings, Inc.
3990a Heritage Oak Ct
Simi Valley CA 93063
805 527-3600

3462 Iron & Steel Forgings

(P-13090)
A-1 ORNAMENTAL IRONWORKS INC
4637 E White Ave, Fresno (93702-1623)
PHONE...................................559 251-1447
Alfredo Arreguin, *President*
EMP: 10
SQ FT: 1,080
SALES (est): 748K **Privately Held**
SIC: 3462 3446 Ornamental metal forgings, ferrous; architectural metalwork

(P-13091)
AJAX FORGE COMPANY (PA)
1956 E 48th St, Vernon (90058-2006)
PHONE...................................323 582-6307
Fred Goble, *President*
Steve Mc Elrath, *Shareholder*
Carol Mc Neal, *Controller*
EMP: 20
SQ FT: 10,000
SALES (est): 3.3MM **Privately Held**
SIC: 3462 Iron & steel forgings

(P-13092)
AJAX FORGE COMPANY
1960 E 48th St, Vernon (90058-2006)
PHONE...................................323 582-6307
Fred Goble, *Manager*
EMP: 20
SQ FT: 22,443
SALES (corp-wide): 3.3MM **Privately Held**
SIC: 3462 Iron & steel forgings
PA: Ajax Forge Company
1956 E 48th St
Vernon CA 90058
323 582-6307

(P-13093)
ALLIED FITTING LP
11040 Inland Ave, Mira Loma (91752-1154)
PHONE...................................909 390-0101
Jamie Marshal, *Branch Mgr*
EMP: 12
SALES (corp-wide): 83.7MM **Privately Held**
WEB: www.alliedfit.com
SIC: 3462 Flange, valve & pipe fitting forgings, ferrous
PA: Allied Fitting, L.P.
7200 Mykawa Rd
Houston TX 77033
713 799-1100

(P-13094)
BAY EQUIPMENT CO INC
44221 S Grimmer Blvd, Fremont
(94538-6309)
PHONE...................................510 226-8800
Pat Pecoraro, *President*
Gerry Pecoraro, *Vice Pres*
EMP: 12
SQ FT: 18,000
SALES (est): 2.3MM **Privately Held**
WEB: www.bayequipmentco.com
SIC: 3462 5082 Construction or mining equipment forgings, ferrous; scaffolding

(P-13095)
BERKELEY FORGE & TOOL INC
1331 Eastshore Hwy, Berkeley
(94710-1320)
PHONE...................................510 525-5117
Peter Bierwith, *President*
Paul Bierwith, *Shareholder*
Robert Bierwith, *Corp Secy*
Ed Hinckley, *Vice Pres*
Crisologo Urizar, *Regional Mgr*

▲ EMP: 80
SQ FT: 50,000
SALES (est): 23.1MM **Privately Held**
WEB: www.berkforge.com
SIC: 3462 Construction or mining equipment forgings, ferrous

(P-13096)
COULTER FORGE TECHNOLOGY INC
Also Called: Coulter Steel and Forge
1494 67th St, Emeryville (94608-1016)
P.O. Box 8008 (94662-0901)
PHONE...................................510 420-3500
Peter Bierwith, *President*
Robert Bierwith, *Vice Pres*
Wayne Lehnert, *General Mgr*
Cola Chan, *Asst Controller*
John Martin, *QC Mgr*
▲ EMP: 18
SQ FT: 20,000
SALES (est): 4.1MM **Privately Held**
WEB: www.coulter-forge.com
SIC: 3462 Iron & steel forgings

(P-13097)
ESCO INDUSTRIES INC
1755 Iowa Ave Bldg A, Riverside
(92507-0525)
P.O. Box 52568 (92517-3568)
PHONE...................................951 782-2130
Chung LI Lin, *President*
▲ EMP: 15
SALES: 47.1MM **Privately Held**
SIC: 3462 Automotive & internal combustion engine forgings

(P-13098)
FANSTEEL INC
Also Called: Fansteel California Drop Forge
1033 Alhambra Ave, Los Angeles
(90012-2929)
PHONE...................................323 221-1134
Bill Wagner, *Branch Mgr*
Robert Giroux, *Opers Mgr*
EMP: 82
SALES (corp-wide): 153MM **Privately Held**
SIC: 3462 Iron & steel forgings
PA: Fansteel Inc.
1746 Commerce Rd
Creston IA 50801
641 782-8521

(P-13099)
FIRTH RIXSON INC
11711 Arrow Rte, Rancho Cucamonga
(91730-4902)
PHONE...................................909 483-2200
EMP: 21
SALES (corp-wide): 23.9B **Publicly Held**
SIC: 3462
HQ: Firth Rixson, Inc.
1616 Harvard Ave 53
Newburgh Heights OH 44105
860 760-1040

(P-13100)
FORGED METALS INC
Also Called: Arconic Fstening Systems Rings
10685 Beech Ave, Fontana (92337-7212)
PHONE...................................909 350-9260
Christopher Tong, *Design Engr*
Michael Hausman, *Manager*
▲ EMP: 200
SQ FT: 4,800
SALES (est): 109.1MM
SALES (corp-wide): 12.9B **Publicly Held**
SIC: 3462 Iron & steel forgings
PA: Arconic Inc.
390 Park Ave Fl 12
New York NY 10022
212 836-2758

(P-13101)
G & N RUBICON GEAR INC
225 Citation Cir, Corona (92880-2523)
PHONE...................................951 278-9860
Melvin Edwards, *Ch of Bd*
Ryan B Edwards, *President*
Frank Salazar, *Admin Sec*
EMP: 55
SQ FT: 25,000
SALES (est): 14.8MM **Privately Held**
SIC: 3462 Gears, forged steel

(P-13102)
JAZ DISTRIBUTION INC
8485 Artesia Blvd Ste B, Buena Park
(90621-4195)
PHONE...................................714 521-3888
Tavis Tan, *President*
Mark Uchinao, *Vice Pres*
▲ EMP: 16
SALES: 5.8MM **Privately Held**
WEB: www.jazalloy.com
SIC: 3462 5013 Railroad wheels, axles, frogs or other equipment: forged; automotive supplies & parts

(P-13103)
KIMS WELDING AND IRON WORKS
Also Called: Kim's Fence
2331 E Orangethorpe Ave, Fullerton
(92831-5330)
PHONE...................................714 680-7700
David S Kim, *President*
EMP: 20
SQ FT: 5,000
SALES (est): 2.2MM **Privately Held**
SIC: 3462 1799 Ornamental metal forgings, ferrous; welding on site

(P-13104)
LONG PROPERTIES LLC (PA)
4651 Quail Lakes Dr, Stockton
(95207-5258)
P.O. Box 77937 (95267-1237)
PHONE...................................209 948-4644
David Long, *President*
EMP: 13
SALES (est): 8.4MM **Privately Held**
SIC: 3462 Iron & steel forgings

(P-13105)
LUFKIN INDUSTRIES LLC
Also Called: Gear Division
31127 Coberly Rd, Shafter (93263-9702)
PHONE...................................661 746-0792
EMP: 12
SALES (corp-wide): 122B **Publicly Held**
SIC: 3462 Gears, forged steel
HQ: Lufkin Industries, Llc
601 S Raguet St
Lufkin TX 75904
936 634-2211

(P-13106)
MATTCO FORGE INC (PA)
16443 Minnesota Ave, Paramount
(90723-4985)
PHONE...................................562 634-8635
Denis B Brady, *CEO*
John Lindbeck, *President*
Daniel Fitzgerald, *Vice Pres*
▲ EMP: 53
SQ FT: 150,000
SALES (est): 13.9MM **Privately Held**
WEB: www.mattcoforge.com
SIC: 3462 Iron & steel forgings

(P-13107)
NEWMAN FLANGE & FITTING CO
1649 L St, Newman (95360-1048)
P.O. Box 905 (95360-0905)
PHONE...................................209 862-2977
Samuel Liebelt, *President*
Penny Mello, *Chairman*
Helmut Liebelt, *Treasurer*
Tom Leblanc, *General Mgr*
▲ EMP: 70 EST: 1974
SQ FT: 1,800
SALES: 14.6MM **Privately Held**
SIC: 3462 Flange, valve & pipe fitting forgings, ferrous

(P-13108)
PACIFIC FORGE INC
10641 Etiwanda Ave, Fontana
(92337-6991)
PHONE...................................909 390-0701
Leland Boren, *Chairman*
Ronald D Browne, *President*
Jacqueline Dyer, *Vice Pres*
EMP: 55 EST: 1955
SQ FT: 34,816

PRODUCTS & SVCS

SALES: 20MM
SALES (corp-wide): 319.4MM **Privately Held**
WEB: www.pacificforge.com
SIC: 3462 3463 Iron & steel forgings; non-ferrous forgings
PA: Avis Industrial Corporation
1909 S Main St
Upland IN 46989
765 998-8100

(P-13109)
PERFORMANCE FORGED PRODUCTS
7401 Telegraph Rd, Montebello (90640-6515)
PHONE.................................323 722-3460
James Gilliland, *President*
Frank Andrus, *Shareholder*
Lois Gilliland, *Treasurer*
Millie Orozco, *Office Mgr*
Christopher Ambrosini, *Manager*
EMP: 20
SQ FT: 20,000
SALES (est): 5.8MM **Privately Held**
SIC: 3462 Automotive & internal combustion engine forgings

(P-13110)
PRECISION METAL PRODUCTS INC (HQ)
850 W Bradley Ave, El Cajon (92020-1277)
PHONE.................................619 448-2711
Randy L Greely, *CEO*
Ross Worthington, *General Mgr*
▲ **EMP:** 138 **EST:** 1963
SQ FT: 92,000
SALES (est): 20.1MM
SALES (corp-wide): 223.8MM **Privately Held**
WEB: www.pmp-elcajon.com
SIC: 3462 Iron & steel forgings
PA: Hbd Industries Inc
5200 Upper Metro
Dublin OH 43017
614 526-7000

(P-13111)
PREMCO FORGE INC
5200 Tweedy Blvd, South Gate (90280-5397)
PHONE.................................323 564-6666
Brian James Patrick, *President*
Randall Roschnafsky, *Sales Mgr*
EMP: 10
SQ FT: 16,000
SALES (est): 2MM **Privately Held**
SIC: 3462 Iron & steel forgings

(P-13112)
PREMIER GEAR & MACHINING INC
2360 Pomona Rd, Corona (92880-6929)
P.O. Box 2799 (92878-2799)
PHONE.................................951 278-5505
Steve Golden, *President*
Huy Nguyen, *Treasurer*
Edward Florian, *Purchasing*
EMP: 25
SQ FT: 21,000
SALES (est): 5.8MM **Privately Held**
WEB: www.premiergearinc.com
SIC: 3462 3599 Iron & steel forgings; machine shop, jobbing & repair

(P-13113)
SCODAN SYSTEMS INC
12373 Barringer St, South El Monte (91733-4141)
PHONE.................................626 444-1020
Eric Yang, *President*
Hector Pinedo, *Vice Pres*
EMP: 13
SQ FT: 10,000
SALES (est): 2.5MM **Privately Held**
SIC: 3462 Automotive & internal combustion engine forgings

(P-13114)
TIMKEN GEARS & SERVICES INC
Also Called: Philadelphia Gear
12935 Imperial Hwy, Santa Fe Springs (90670-4715)
PHONE.................................310 605-2600
Tony Tartaglio, *Branch Mgr*
Richard Brossia, *Manager*
EMP: 26
SALES (corp-wide): 3B **Publicly Held**
WEB: www.philagear.com
SIC: 3462 Gear & chain forgings; gears, forged steel; anchors, forged
HQ: Timken Gears & Services Inc.
901 E 8th Ave Ste 100
King Of Prussia PA 19406

(P-13115)
TURBO INTERNATIONAL
2151 Las Palmas Dr Ste E, Carlsbad (92011-1575)
PHONE.................................760 476-1444
Seth Carks, *CEO*
Alex Jimenez, *Accounts Mgr*
▲ **EMP:** 17
SALES (est): 3.1MM **Privately Held**
SIC: 3462 Automotive forgings, ferrous: crankshaft, engine, axle, etc.

(P-13116)
VALLEY FORGE ACQUISITION CORP
444 S Motor Ave, Azusa (91702-3231)
PHONE.................................626 969-8701
Michael K Holmes, *President*
Michael Holmes, *President*
EMP: 15
SQ FT: 37,000
SALES (est): 2.9MM
SALES (corp-wide): 68.2MM **Privately Held**
SIC: 3462 Iron & steel forgings
PA: Tuffli Company Incorporated
2780 Skypark Dr Ste 460
Torrance CA 90505
310 326-5500

(P-13117)
VI-STAR GEAR CO INC
7312 Jefferson St, Paramount (90723-4094)
PHONE.................................323 774-3750
Thomas R Redfield, *President*
Chris Redfield, *Vice Pres*
EMP: 30
SQ FT: 12,000
SALES (est): 4.8MM **Privately Held**
SIC: 3462 3728 Iron & steel forgings; gears, aircraft power transmission

(P-13118)
VOSSLOH SIGNALING USA INC
Also Called: J Manufacturing
12799 Loma Rica Dr, Grass Valley (95945-9552)
P.O. Box 600 (95945-0600)
PHONE.................................530 272-8194
Normand Frenette, *CEO*
Lisa Goddard, *Controller*
▲ **EMP:** 24
SQ FT: 20,000
SALES (est): 5.7MM
SALES (corp-wide): 1B **Privately Held**
WEB: www.jmirail.com
SIC: 3462 Railroad wheels, axles, frogs or other equipment: forged
HQ: Vossloh Track Material, Inc.
5662a Leesport Ave
Reading PA 19605
610 926-5400

3463 Nonferrous Forgings

(P-13119)
ALUM-ALLOY CO INC
603 S Hope Ave, Ontario (91761-1824)
PHONE.................................909 986-0410
David Howell, *CEO*
Clark Howell, *President*
Marilyn Howell, *Corp Secy*
Armando Olague, *Supervisor*
EMP: 40
SQ FT: 20,000
SALES (est): 5.6MM **Privately Held**
SIC: 3463 3365 Aluminum forgings; aluminum foundries

(P-13120)
ALUMINUM PRECISION PDTS INC
1001 Mcwane Blvd, Oxnard (93033-9016)
PHONE.................................805 488-4401
Richard Hayes, *Branch Mgr*
Jennifer Meyers, *General Mgr*
Bennett Straker, *Engineer*
Wally Kieffer, *Safety Dir*
Dave Bishop, *Sales Staff*
EMP: 125
SQ FT: 15,000
SALES (corp-wide): 213.4MM **Privately Held**
SIC: 3463 Aluminum forgings
PA: Aluminum Precision Products, Inc.
3333 W Warner Ave
Santa Ana CA 92704
714 546-8125

(P-13121)
ALUMINUM PRECISION PDTS INC
Also Called: Jigmasters Tool & Gauge
502 E Alton Ave, Santa Ana (92707-4244)
PHONE.................................714 549-4075
William Peacock, *Manager*
EMP: 100
SALES (corp-wide): 213.4MM **Privately Held**
WEB: www.aluminumprecision.com
SIC: 3463 7389 3599 Aluminum forgings; grinding, precision: commercial or industrial; machine shop, jobbing & repair
PA: Aluminum Precision Products, Inc.
3333 W Warner Ave
Santa Ana CA 92704
714 546-8125

(P-13122)
CONTINENTAL FORGE COMPANY (PA)
412 E El Segundo Blvd, Compton (90222-2317)
PHONE.................................310 603-1014
Margaret A Haueisen, *President*
EMP: 85 **EST:** 1969
SQ FT: 27,000
SALES (est): 18.5MM **Privately Held**
WEB: www.cforge.com
SIC: 3463 Aluminum forgings

(P-13123)
EARTHQUAKE PROTECTION SYSTEMS
Also Called: E P S
451 Azuar Ave Bldg 759, Vallejo (94592-1148)
PHONE.................................707 644-5993
Victor Zayas, *President*
Julie Robinson, *CFO*
Stanley Low, *Vice Pres*
Anoop Mokha, *Vice Pres*
◆ **EMP:** 80
SQ FT: 310,000
SALES: 40MM **Privately Held**
WEB: www.earthquakeprotection.com
SIC: 3463 Bearing & bearing race forgings, nonferrous

(P-13124)
INDEPENDENT FORGE COMPANY
692 N Batavia St, Orange (92868-1221)
PHONE.................................714 997-7337
Rosemary Ruiz, *President*
Gloria Lopez, *COO*
Joe Ramirez, *Vice Pres*
▲ **EMP:** 40
SQ FT: 11,900
SALES (est): 7.2MM **Privately Held**
WEB: www.independentforge.com
SIC: 3463 Aluminum forgings

(P-13125)
LINDSEY MANUFACTURING CO
Also Called: Lindsey International Co.
760 N Georgia Ave, Azusa (91702-2249)
P.O. Box 877 (91702-0877)
PHONE.................................626 969-3471
Keith E Lindsey, *President*
Frederick Findley, *CFO*
Saul Silva, *CFO*
Lela Lindsey, *Admin Sec*
Sergio Cortez, *Project Engr*

(P-13126)
LUXFER INC
Superform USA
6825 Jurupa Ave, Riverside (92504-1039)
PHONE.................................951 351-4100
Michael Reynolds, *Vice Pres*
Mark Chivers, *General Mgr*
Karen Rice, *Info Tech Mgr*
EMP: 38
SALES (corp-wide): 441.3MM **Privately Held**
WEB: www.luxfer-ecare.com
SIC: 3463 Aluminum forgings
HQ: Luxfer Inc.
3016 Kansas Ave Bldg 1
Riverside CA 92507
336 578-4515

(P-13127)
PRESS FORGE COMPANY
7700 Jackson St, Paramount (90723-5073)
P.O. Box 1432 (90723-1432)
PHONE.................................562 531-4962
Jeffrey M Carlton, *CEO*
Michael Buxton, *President*
Mike Buxton, *President*
▲ **EMP:** 80
SQ FT: 32,726
SALES (est): 23.3MM
SALES (corp-wide): 242.1B **Publicly Held**
SIC: 3463 Aircraft forgings, nonferrous
HQ: Precision Castparts Corp.
4650 Sw Mcdam Ave Ste 300
Portland OR 97239
503 946-4800

(P-13128)
QUALITY ALUMINUM FORGE LLC (HQ)
794 N Cypress St, Orange (92867-6606)
PHONE.................................714 639-8191
Michael S Lipscomb, *CEO*
James P Woidke, *President*
Jeffrey P Gotschall, *Chairman*
Francisco Garcia, *Vice Pres*
Greg Genco, *General Mgr*
EMP: 59 **EST:** 2011
SALES (est): 46.6MM
SALES (corp-wide): 121.4MM **Publicly Held**
SIC: 3463 Aluminum forgings
PA: Sifco Industries, Inc.
970 E 64th St
Cleveland OH 44103
216 881-8600

(P-13129)
SIERRA ALLOYS COMPANY
5467 Ayon Ave, Irwindale (91706-2044)
PHONE.................................626 969-6711
Craig Culaciati, *CEO*
Jeff Augustyn, *Exec VP*
Ed Brennan, *Vice Pres*
▲ **EMP:** 52 **EST:** 1974
SQ FT: 75,000
SALES (est): 14.7MM **Privately Held**
WEB: www.sierraalloys.com
SIC: 3463 3494 3312 Nonferrous forgings; valves & pipe fittings; blast furnaces & steel mills

(P-13130)
SUPERFORM USA INCORPORATED
6825 Jurupa Ave, Riverside (92504-1039)
P.O. Box 5375 (92517-5375)
PHONE.................................951 351-4100
Michael Reynolds, *Vice Pres*
Phil Taylor, *Business Mgr*
▼ **EMP:** 29
SQ FT: 25,000
SALES (est): 205.3K
SALES (corp-wide): 441.3MM **Privately Held**
SIC: 3463 Aluminum forgings

▲ = Import ▼=Export
◆ =Import/Export

HQ: Luxfer Inc.
3016 Kansas Ave Bldg 1
Riverside CA 92507
336 578-4515

(P-13131)
TURBINE ENG CMPNENTS TECH CORP
Also Called: Tech Powers
8839 Pioneer Blvd, Santa Fe Springs
(90670-2007)
P.O. Box 2966 (90670-0966)
PHONE................................562 908-0200
Ronald L Patlian, *Branch Mgr*
Andi Ly, *Human Res Mgr*
Melissa Roberts, *Materials Mgr*
James McDowell, *Marketing Mgr*
George Florez, *Marketing Staff*
EMP: 105 **Privately Held**
WEB: www.tectcorp.com
SIC: 3463 3599 Engine or turbine forgings, nonferrous; machine shop, jobbing & repair
HQ: Turbine Engine Components Technologies Corporation
1211 Old Albany Rd
Thomasville GA 31792
229 228-2600

(P-13132)
WEBER METALS INC
16706 Garfield Ave, Paramount
(90723-5315)
PHONE................................562 602-0260
John R Creed, *President*
Paul Dennis, *CFO*
Leon Kranz, *CTO*
Jamison Hart, *Financial Analy*
Steve Enke, *Purch Mgr*
◆ **EMP:** 500 **EST:** 1949
SQ FT: 270,000
SALES (est): 200MM
SALES (corp-wide): 3.1B **Privately Held**
WEB: www.webermetals.com
SIC: 3463 Aluminum forgings
PA: Otto Fuchs - Kg -
Derschlager Str. 26
Meinerzhagen 58540
235 473-0

(P-13133)
WJB BEARINGS INC
535 Brea Canyon Rd, City of Industry
(91789-3001)
PHONE................................909 598-6238
John Jun Jiang, *CEO*
▲ **EMP:** 25
SQ FT: 30,000
SALES (est): 5.5MM **Privately Held**
SIC: 3463 5085 Bearing & bearing race forgings, nonferrous; bearings

3465 Automotive Stampings

(P-13134)
3M COMPANY
8981 Us Highway 395, Oak Hills
(92344-9220)
PHONE................................760 949-4204
Beth Larock, *Branch Mgr*
Kevin Bilbee, *Technology*
EMP: 80
SALES (corp-wide): 31.6B **Publicly Held**
SIC: 3465 Automotive stampings
PA: 3m Company
3m Center
Saint Paul MN 55144
651 733-1110

(P-13135)
AC AIR TECHNOLOGY INC
13832 Magnolia Ave, Chino (91710-7027)
PHONE................................855 884-7222
Anthony Yu Chan, *CEO*
EMP: 11 **EST:** 2012
SALES (est): 85.8K **Privately Held**
SIC: 3465 Body parts, automobile: stamped metal

(P-13136)
APOLLO METAL SPINNING CO INC
15315 Illinois Ave, Paramount
(90723-4108)
PHONE................................562 634-5141
George Di Matteo, *President*
Josephine Di Matteo, *Corp Secy*
EMP: 15
SQ FT: 4,650
SALES: 1.2MM **Privately Held**
SIC: 3465 3469 5015 Hub caps, automobile: stamped metal; spinning metal for the trade; automotive parts & supplies, used

(P-13137)
BECS PACIFIC LTD
600 Enterprise Way, Bakersfield
(93307-6821)
PHONE................................661 397-9400
Kris A Wolfenstein, *Branch Mgr*
EMP: 10
SALES (corp-wide): 17.4MM **Privately Held**
SIC: 3465 Body parts, automobile: stamped metal
PA: Becs Pacific Ltd
2825 Pellissier Pl
City Of Industry CA 90601
562 908-6890

(P-13138)
C W MOSS AUTO PARTS INC
402 W Chapman Ave, Orange
(92866-1308)
PHONE................................714 639-3083
Derek Looney, *President*
EMP: 10
SQ FT: 15,108
SALES (est): 1.5MM **Privately Held**
WEB: www.cwmoss.com
SIC: 3465 5531 Body parts, automobile: stamped metal; automotive parts

(P-13139)
CARR PATTERN CO INC
27447 Bostik Ct, Temecula (92590-3698)
PHONE................................951 719-1068
Jeff Carr, *CEO*
Jeff A Carr, *CEO*
EMP: 10 **EST:** 1945
SQ FT: 23,000
SALES (est): 197.6K **Privately Held**
WEB: www.carr.com
SIC: 3465 5051 Body parts, automobile: stamped metal; metals service centers & offices

(P-13140)
KYOHO MANUFACTURING CALIFORNIA
Also Called: Khmca
809 Walker Ave, Oakland (94610-2018)
PHONE................................209 941-6200
Shigenori Hamada, *President*
Bill Borten, *Vice Pres*
▲ **EMP:** 168
SALES (est): 17.5MM
SALES (corp-wide): 275.7B **Privately Held**
SIC: 3465 Automotive stampings
HQ: Kyoho Machine Works,Ltd.
6, Toyotacho
Toyota AIC 471-0
565 281-881

(P-13141)
MARINE FENDERS INTL INC
909 Mahar Ave, Wilmington (90744-3828)
PHONE................................310 834-7037
Gerald Thermos, *President*
◆ **EMP:** 25
SQ FT: 22,000
SALES (est): 7.3MM **Privately Held**
WEB: www.marinefendersintl.com
SIC: 3465 Fenders, automobile: stamped or pressed metal

(P-13142)
ROOTLIEB INC
815 S Soderquist Rd, Turlock
(95380-5723)
P.O. Box 1810 (95381-1810)
PHONE................................209 632-2203
Thomas H Rootlieb, *President*
EMP: 13
SQ FT: 25,000
SALES (est): 1.6MM **Privately Held**
WEB: www.rootlieb.com
SIC: 3465 Fenders, automobile: stamped or pressed metal; body parts, automobile: stamped metal

(P-13143)
SALEEN AUTOMOTIVE INC (PA)
2735 Wardlow Rd, Corona (92882-2869)
PHONE................................800 888-8945
Steve Saleen, *Ch of Bd*
Amy Boylan, *President*
David Fiene, *CFO*
EMP: 22
SALES (est): 3.8MM **Publicly Held**
SIC: 3465 3711 Body parts, automobile: stamped metal; automobile assembly, including specialty automobiles; automobile bodies, passenger car, not including engine, etc.

(P-13144)
SEYMOUR LEVINGER & CO
Also Called: Spectre Performance
1455 Citrus St, Riverside (92507-1603)
PHONE................................909 673-9800
Amir Rosenbaum, *CEO*
▲ **EMP:** 40
SQ FT: 16,000
SALES (est): 5.8MM **Privately Held**
WEB: www.spectreperformance.com
SIC: 3465 Body parts, automobile: stamped metal

(P-13145)
T-REX TRUCK PRODUCTS INC
Also Called: T-Rex Grilles
2365 Railroad St, Corona (92880-5411)
PHONE................................800 287-5900
Behrouz Mizban, *President*
Tom Ameduri, *Sales Staff*
Juan Crespo, *Supervisor*
▼ **EMP:** 55
SQ FT: 45,000
SALES (est): 12.1MM **Privately Held**
SIC: 3465 Automotive stampings

(P-13146)
TROY SHEET METAL WORKS INC
Also Called: Troy Products
1024 S Vail Ave, Montebello (90640-6020)
PHONE................................323 720-4100
Carl Moses Kahalewai, *CEO*
Paul Alvarado, *Shareholder*
Marci Norkin, *Shareholder*
Carol Stewart, *Shareholder*
Rigo Guadiana, *CFO*
EMP: 33
SQ FT: 16,000
SALES (est): 9.4MM **Privately Held**
WEB: www.troyproducts.com
SIC: 3465 3444 3714 3564 Automotive stampings; sheet metalwork; motor vehicle parts & accessories; blowers & fans

(P-13147)
WRIGHTSPEED INC
650 W Tower Ave, Alameda (94501-5047)
PHONE................................866 960-9482
Ian Wright, *CEO*
David Wagenseller, *CFO*
Ian Welch, *Business Dir*
Elliot Brand, *Technology*
Bram Bonsen, *Engineer*
▲ **EMP:** 76
SALES (est): 16.1MM **Privately Held**
SIC: 3465 Differentials & parts, motor vehicle

3466 Crowns & Closures

(P-13148)
RIEKE CORPORATION
1200 Valley House Dr # 100, Rohnert Park
(94928-4902)
PHONE................................707 238-9250
Rohnert Park, *Branch Mgr*
EMP: 180
SALES (corp-wide): 817.7MM **Publicly Held**
SIC: 3466 Closures, stamped metal
HQ: Rieke Corporation
500 W 7th St
Auburn IN 46706
260 925-3700

3469 Metal Stampings, NEC

(P-13149)
20TH CENTURY SPRING MFG
Also Called: Twentieth Century Spring Mfg
1282 Lorelei Ct, Campbell (95008-1716)
PHONE................................408 727-9100
Roy Pavloff, *President*
EMP: 20
SQ FT: 10,000
SALES (est): 2.2MM **Privately Held**
SIC: 3469 3496 3493 Stamping metal for the trade; wire winding; steel springs, except wire

(P-13150)
4X DEVELOPMENT INC
2650 E 28th St, Signal Hill (90755-2202)
PHONE................................562 424-2225
Alex Horeczko, *President*
Scott Dudek, *Vice Pres*
EMP: 10
SQ FT: 11,000
SALES: 3MM **Privately Held**
WEB: www.extremesupply.com
SIC: 3469 Helmets, steel

(P-13151)
5TH AXIS INC
7140 Engineer Rd, San Diego
(92111-1422)
PHONE................................858 505-0432
Michelle Grangetto, *President*
Steve Grangetto, *COO*
Christopher Taylor, *Vice Pres*
▲ **EMP:** 61
SQ FT: 21,000
SALES: 6.8MM **Privately Held**
SIC: 3469 Machine parts, stamped or pressed metal

(P-13152)
A & F METAL PRODUCTS
520 Farnel Rd Ste L, Santa Maria
(93458-4993)
PHONE................................805 346-2040
Art Andrade, *Owner*
EMP: 10
SALES: 850K **Privately Held**
SIC: 3469 Metal stampings

(P-13153)
A & J MANUFACTURING COMPANY
70 Icon, Foothill Ranch (92610-3000)
PHONE................................714 544-9570
Ada Gentry, *Ch of Bd*
Pam Woodward, *Treasurer*
Janice Lyerly, *Vice Pres*
Ian Amstedter, *Info Tech Dir*
EMP: 32
SQ FT: 40,000
SALES (est): 7.3MM **Privately Held**
WEB: www.aj-racks.com
SIC: 3469 Electronic enclosures, stamped or pressed metal

(P-13154)
A-W ENGINEERING COMPANY INC
8528 Dice Rd, Santa Fe Springs
(90670-2590)
PHONE................................562 945-1041
Guy Hansen, *President*
Anthony Giangrande, *Treasurer*
EMP: 36 **EST:** 1965
SQ FT: 38,000
SALES (est): 8.9MM **Privately Held**
WEB: www.aw-eng.com
SIC: 3469 3544 Stamping metal for the trade; special dies & tools

PRODUCTS & SVCS

(P-13155)
A-Z MFG INC
Also Called: AZ Manufacturing
3101 W Segerstrom Ave, Santa Ana
(92704-5811)
PHONE....................714 444-4446
Ann Lukas, *Principal*
Glenn Shanks, *General Mgr*
Gary Lukas, *Admin Sec*
Anne Lukas, *Sales Executive*
EMP: 40
SQ FT: 16,096
SALES: 6.5MM **Privately Held**
WEB: www.azmfginc.com
SIC: 3469 Metal stampings

(P-13156)
AAA STAMPING INC
1630 Shearwater St, Ontario (91761-5710)
P.O. Box 4027 (91761-1001)
PHONE....................909 947-4151
Tom Hendrickson, *President*
Sal Chico, *Vice Pres*
EMP: 20 **EST:** 1974
SQ FT: 15,100
SALES (est): 4.1MM **Privately Held**
SIC: 3469 Machine parts, stamped or pressed metal

(P-13157)
AARON DUTT ENTERPRISES INC
Also Called: Bowers Machining
1140 N Kraemer Blvd Ste M, Anaheim
(92806-1919)
PHONE....................714 632-7035
Ajaya Kumar Dutt, *President*
Jiwan Dutt, *Vice Pres*
EMP: 10
SQ FT: 4,000
SALES: 730K **Privately Held**
SIC: 3469 8711 Machine parts, stamped or pressed metal; engineering services

(P-13158)
ACRONTOS MANUFACTURING INC
Also Called: Al Industries
1641 E Saint Gertrude Pl, Santa Ana
(92705-5311)
PHONE....................714 850-9133
Ngoc V Hoang, *President*
EMP: 30
SQ FT: 22,000
SALES (est): 6.1MM **Privately Held**
WEB: www.alindustries.com
SIC: 3469 3599 3441 Metal stampings; machine & other job shop work; fabricated structural metal

(P-13159)
ACTION STAMPING INC
517 S Glendora Ave, Glendora
(91741-6212)
P.O. Box 778 (91740-0778)
PHONE....................626 914-7466
Henry Reynolds, *CEO*
Terry Reynolds, *President*
Mike Chavez, *Opers Mgr*
▲ **EMP:** 42
SQ FT: 55,000
SALES (est): 7.6MM **Privately Held**
SIC: 3469 Stamping metal for the trade

(P-13160)
ADVANCED HONEYCOMB TECH
1015 Linda Vista Dr Ste C, San Marcos
(92078-2609)
PHONE....................760 744-3200
Richard Greven, *President*
Rick Greven, *Vice Pres*
Money Greven, *Admin Sec*
Susan Betz, *Sls & Mktg Exec*
EMP: 25
SQ FT: 10,000
SALES: 3.5MM **Privately Held**
WEB: www.ahtinc.com
SIC: 3469 2679 Honeycombed metal; honeycomb core & board: made from purchased material

(P-13161)
ALCO TECH INC
Also Called: Crome Gallery
12750 Raymer St Unit 2, North Hollywood
(91605-4227)
PHONE....................818 503-9209
Ben Tavakkoli, *President*
EMP: 11
SALES (est): 133.1K **Privately Held**
SIC: 3469 3479 7692 4581 Metal stampings; painting, coating & hot dipping; welding repair; aircraft maintenance & repair services

(P-13162)
ALL NEW STAMPING CO
10801 Lower Azusa Rd, El Monte
(91731-1307)
P.O. Box 5948 (91734-1948)
PHONE....................626 443-8813
Donald Schuil, *President*
Robert Larson, *Corp Secy*
EMP: 150 **EST:** 1962
SQ FT: 40,000
SALES: 9.9MM **Privately Held**
WEB: www.allnewstamping.com
SIC: 3469 3441 3444 Stamping metal for the trade; fabricated structural metal; sheet metal specialties, not stamped

(P-13163)
ALPINE INDUSTRIES
5820 Serrano Dr, Mount Shasta
(96067-9127)
P.O. Box 277 (96067-0277)
PHONE....................530 926-2460
David Webb, *Owner*
EMP: 13
SALES (est): 803.5K **Privately Held**
SIC: 3469 Metal stampings

(P-13164)
AMITY WASHER & STAMPING CO
10926 Painter Ave, Santa Fe Springs
(90670-4529)
PHONE....................562 941-1259
James M Mc Ginley, *President*
Nancy Wilson, *Admin Sec*
EMP: 25
SQ FT: 15,000
SALES (est): 2.6MM **Privately Held**
WEB: www.amity.com
SIC: 3469 3544 Metal stampings; special dies, tools, jigs & fixtures

(P-13165)
APT METAL FABRICATORS INC
11164 Bradley Ave, Pacoima (91331-2405)
PHONE....................818 896-7478
Dennis M Vigo, *President*
Susan Vigo, *Corp Secy*
Paul Alfaro, *Admin Sec*
Monica Gutierrez, *Site Mgr*
Tom Cekalovich, *Plant Mgr*
▼ **EMP:** 26
SQ FT: 18,000
SALES (est): 6.4MM **Privately Held**
WEB: www.aptmetal.com
SIC: 3469 Stamping metal for the trade

(P-13166)
ASCENT MANUFACTURING LLC
2545 W Via Palma, Anaheim (92801-2624)
PHONE....................714 540-6414
Travis Mullen, *CEO*
David Kramer, *VP Sales*
EMP: 34
SQ FT: 17,000
SALES (est): 3.9MM **Privately Held**
WEB: www.ascentmfg.com
SIC: 3469 1796 Machine parts, stamped or pressed metal; machinery installation

(P-13167)
B-J MACHINE INC
1763 N Batavia St, Orange (92865-4103)
PHONE....................714 685-0712
Larry T Vu, *President*
EMP: 10 **EST:** 1998
SQ FT: 6,000
SALES (est): 1.2MM **Privately Held**
SIC: 3469 Machine parts, stamped or pressed metal

(P-13168)
BANDEL MFG INC
4459 Alger St, Los Angeles (90039-1292)
PHONE....................818 246-7493
Ed Finley, *President*
Chester Carlson, *Exec VP*
Esteban Rivera, *Manager*
EMP: 23 **EST:** 1947
SQ FT: 15,000
SALES (est): 5.4MM **Privately Held**
WEB: www.bandel.com
SIC: 3469 Stamping metal for the trade

(P-13169)
BERTOLIN ENGINEERING CORP
485 Robert Ave, Santa Clara (95050-2918)
PHONE....................408 988-0166
Frank Bertolin, *President*
EMP: 13
SQ FT: 5,000
SALES (est): 1.6MM **Privately Held**
SIC: 3469 8711 Automobile license tags, stamped metal; mechanical engineering

(P-13170)
BINDER METAL PRODUCTS INC
14909 S Broadway, Gardena (90248-1817)
P.O. Box 2306 (90247-0306)
PHONE....................323 321-4835
Steve Binder, *President*
Ana Weber, *CFO*
Jerry Shain, *Vice Pres*
Olivia Gutierrez, *Human Res Mgr*
Melissa Loera, *Human Res Mgr*
▲ **EMP:** 75 **EST:** 1925
SQ FT: 35,000
SALES (est): 19.5MM **Privately Held**
WEB: www.bindermetal.com
SIC: 3469 Metal stampings

(P-13171)
BLOOMERS METAL STAMPINGS INC
28615 Braxton Ave, Valencia (91355-4112)
PHONE....................661 257-2955
Matt Holland, *CEO*
Perry Bloomer, *President*
Ella H Bloomer, *CFO*
EMP: 30
SQ FT: 25,000
SALES (est): 5.6MM **Privately Held**
WEB: www.bloomersmetal.com
SIC: 3469 Stamping metal for the trade

(P-13172)
BOX MASTER
17000 Sierra Hwy, Canyon Country
(91351-1615)
PHONE....................661 298-2666
Linda Neville, *Owner*
EMP: 25
SALES (est): 1.6MM **Privately Held**
WEB: www.boxmaster.com
SIC: 3469 Boxes: tool, lunch, mail, etc.: stamped metal

(P-13173)
BRICE TOOL & STAMPING
1170 N Van Horne Way, Anaheim
(92806-2506)
PHONE....................714 630-6400
Russel Brice, *President*
Linda Brice, *Manager*
EMP: 15 **EST:** 1956
SQ FT: 10,000
SALES (est): 2.2MM **Privately Held**
WEB: www.bricetool.com
SIC: 3469 3544 Stamping metal for the trade; dies, steel rule

(P-13174)
C&C METAL FORM & TOOLING INC
Also Called: Promag
10654 Garfield Ave, South Gate
(90280-7334)
PHONE....................562 861-9554
Chris Chiang, *President*
Mike Ballard, *General Mgr*
Mike Kurvink, *General Mgr*
Kristy Kessler, *Sales Dir*
Drew Kelley, *Marketing Staff*
EMP: 25

SALES (est): 3.2MM **Privately Held**
WEB: www.promagindustries.com
SIC: 3469 5941 3482 7389 Stamping metal for the trade; sporting goods & bicycle shops; small arms ammunition; design services

(P-13175)
CABRAC INC
13250 Paxton St, Pacoima (91331-2356)
PHONE....................818 834-0177
Hans Kaufmann, *President*
EMP: 20 **EST:** 1973
SQ FT: 20,000
SALES (est): 3.4MM **Privately Held**
WEB: www.cabrac.com
SIC: 3469 Electronic enclosures, stamped or pressed metal

(P-13176)
CALFABCO (PA)
Also Called: Mr Washerman
1432 Chico Ave, South El Monte
(91733-2936)
PHONE....................323 265-1205
Boris Elbaum, *President*
Jerry Garcia, *Asst Mgr*
EMP: 15
SQ FT: 6,000
SALES (est): 2.6MM **Privately Held**
SIC: 3469 Stamping metal for the trade

(P-13177)
CAMISASCA AUTOMOTIVE MFG INC
20341 Hermana Cir, Lake Forest
(92630-8701)
PHONE....................949 452-0195
Henry Camisasca, *CEO*
EMP: 20
SALES (corp-wide): 5.2MM **Privately Held**
SIC: 3469 Automobile license tags, stamped metal
PA: Camisasca Automotive Manufacturing, Inc.
20352 Hermana Cir
Lake Forest CA 92630
949 452-0195

(P-13178)
CAMISASCA AUTOMOTIVE MFG INC (PA)
20352 Hermana Cir, Lake Forest
(92630-8701)
PHONE....................949 452-0195
Henry Camisasca, *CEO*
Georgann Camisasca, *CFO*
John Van, *Creative Dir*
John Nowland, *Prdtn Mgr*
David Kha, *Manager*
▲ **EMP:** 20
SQ FT: 16,000
SALES (est): 5.2MM **Privately Held**
WEB: www.camincusa.com
SIC: 3469 Automobile license tags, stamped metal

(P-13179)
CARAN PRECISION ENGRG MFG CORP
Spiveco
2830 Orbiter St, Brea (92821-6224)
PHONE....................714 447-5400
Raymond Sheeks, *President*
EMP: 90
SALES (corp-wide): 22.7MM **Privately Held**
WEB: www.caranprecision.com
SIC: 3469 3599 Metal stampings; machine & other job shop work
PA: Caran Precision Engineering & Manufacturing Corp.
2830 Orbiter St
Brea CA 92821
714 447-5400

(P-13180)
CARSONS INC
Also Called: Carson's Coatings
550 Industrial Dr Ste 200, Galt
(95632-1647)
PHONE....................209 745-2387
Duane Carson, *President*
Terry Carson, *Vice Pres*

▲ **EMP:** 20
SQ FT: 53,000
SALES (est): 3MM **Privately Held**
WEB: www.carsonscoatings.com
SIC: 3469 Architectural panels or parts, porcelain enameled

(P-13181)
CHEEK ENGINEERING & STAMPING
1732 Mcgaw Ave, Irvine (92614-5732)
PHONE..............................714 832-9480
Chris Huff, *President*
Julia Huff, *Vice Pres*
EMP: 10
SQ FT: 25,000
SALES: 1.3MM **Privately Held**
WEB: www.cheekengineering.com
SIC: 3469 Stamping metal for the trade

(P-13182)
CIMRMAAN IVO
Also Called: Deft Precision Machining
7550 Trade St, San Diego (92121-2412)
PHONE..............................858 693-1536
Ivo Cimrmaan, *Owner*
EMP: 11
SQ FT: 4,000
SALES (est): 1.2MM **Privately Held**
SIC: 3469 Machine parts, stamped or pressed metal

(P-13183)
CKD INDUSTRIES INC
501 E Jamie Ave, La Habra (90631-6842)
PHONE..............................714 871-5600
Rolf Hess, *President*
Rose Hess, *Vice Pres*
EMP: 12
SQ FT: 15,000
SALES: 1MM **Privately Held**
SIC: 3469 8711 3544 Metal stampings; designing; ship, boat, machine & product; special dies & tools

(P-13184)
CNC MACHINING SERVICE INC
1130 E Acequia Ave, Visalia (93292-6557)
PHONE..............................559 732-5599
Greg Montgomery, *President*
EMP: 12
SQ FT: 8,000
SALES (est): 1.7MM **Privately Held**
SIC: 3469 Machine parts, stamped or pressed metal

(P-13185)
COMMERCIAL METAL FORMING INC
341 W Collins Ave, Orange (92867-5505)
PHONE..............................714 532-6321
Mark Davidson, *Manager*
EMP: 55 **Privately Held**
WEB: www.cmforming.com
SIC: 3469 Metal stampings
PA: Commercial Metal Forming, Inc.
    341 W Collins Ave
    Orange CA 92867

(P-13186)
COMMERCIAL METAL FORMING INC (PA)
341 W Collins Ave, Orange (92867-5505)
PHONE..............................714 532-6321
William Kowal, *President*
Donald E Washdewicz, *Vice Pres*
Phil Smith, *Engineer*
Marie Votino, *Buyer*
Kymberli Wagner, *Buyer*
▲ **EMP:** 25
SALES (est): 11.9MM **Privately Held**
SIC: 3469 Metal stampings

(P-13187)
CONSOLIDATED FABRICATORS CORP
901 Simmerhorn Rd, Galt (95632-8501)
PHONE..............................209 745-4604
Laurance Beralino, *Manager*
Renee Fernandez, *Associate*
EMP: 80

SALES (corp-wide): 106MM **Privately Held**
WEB: www.con-fab.com
SIC: 3469 Metal stampings
PA: Consolidated Fabricators Corporation
    14620 Arminta St
    Van Nuys CA 91402
    818 901-1005

(P-13188)
CONTEXT ENGINEERING CO
Also Called: Sidco Labelling Systems
1043 Di Giulio Ave, Santa Clara (95050-2805)
PHONE..............................408 748-9112
David Clemson, *President*
Martin Clemson, *Vice Pres*
Lucy Del Real, *General Mgr*
Maral Panossian, *General Mgr*
Mary Clemson, *Admin Sec*
▲ **EMP:** 25
SQ FT: 4,500
SALES (est): 3.2MM **Privately Held**
WEB: www.contextengineering.com
SIC: 3469 5131 5084 Electronic enclosures, stamped or pressed metal; labels; industrial machinery & equipment

(P-13189)
CRENSHAW DIE AND MFG CORP
7432 Prince Dr, Huntington Beach (92647-4553)
PHONE..............................949 475-5505
James V Ireland, *CEO*
Dale Congelliere, *President*
Sharon Piers, *CFO*
AMR Gendy, *Opers Mgr*
EMP: 55
SQ FT: 38,000
SALES (est): 12.2MM **Privately Held**
WEB: www.crenshawdiemfg.com
SIC: 3469 Stamping metal for the trade

(P-13190)
CYGNET STAMPNG & FABRICTNG INC
916 Western Ave, Glendale (91201)
PHONE..............................818 240-7574
Ron Ernst, *Manager*
Johnathan Swan, *Vice Pres*
EMP: 10
SALES (corp-wide): 4.6MM **Privately Held**
SIC: 3469 Stamping metal for the trade
PA: Cygnet Stamping And Fabricating, Inc., A Swan Technologies Corporation
    613 Justin Ave
    Glendale CA 91201
    818 240-7574

(P-13191)
CYGNET STAMPNG & FABRICTNG INC (PA)
613 Justin Ave, Glendale (91201-2326)
PHONE..............................818 240-7574
Marko Swan, *President*
E Michael Swan, *Vice Pres*
John Swan, *Vice Pres*
EMP: 30
SQ FT: 28,000
SALES (est): 4.6MM **Privately Held**
SIC: 3469 Stamping metal for the trade

(P-13192)
DECCO GRAPHICS INC
24411 Frampton Ave, Harbor City (90710-2107)
PHONE..............................310 534-2861
Harry B Line, *President*
Alex Pitones,
Phil Kielty, *Cust Mgr*
EMP: 43
SQ FT: 5,000
SALES (est): 8.2MM **Privately Held**
SIC: 3469 2759 Stamping metal for the trade; commercial printing

(P-13193)
DETERMAN INDUSTRIES INC
4246 Roseville Rd, North Highlands (95660-5710)
PHONE..............................916 974-1977
Greg Determan, *President*
Candy Determan, *Vice Pres*
Shirley Doran, *Admin Sec*
EMP: 10

SQ FT: 5,000
SALES (est): 1.1MM **Privately Held**
SIC: 3469 Kitchen fixtures & equipment: metal, except cast aluminum

(P-13194)
DIAMOND PERFORATED METALS INC
Also Called: Amico - Diamond Perforated
7300 W Sunnyview Ave, Visalia (93291-9605)
PHONE..............................559 651-1889
Brian Lipke, *CEO*
Guy Anderson, *Vice Pres*
Joe Smith, *Vice Pres*
Steve Seitz, *Sales Staff*
EMP: 78
SQ FT: 80,000
SALES (est): 27.1MM
SALES (corp-wide): 986.9MM **Publicly Held**
WEB: www.diamondperf.com
SIC: 3469 Perforated metal, stamped
PA: Gibraltar Industries, Inc.
    3556 Lake Shore Rd # 100
    Buffalo NY 14219
    716 826-6500

(P-13195)
DIE-NAMIC FABRICATION INC
378 E Orange Show Rd, San Bernardino (92408-2414)
PHONE..............................909 350-2870
C Anthony Esposito, *CEO*
Louise A Uphus, *Corp Secy*
Genelle J Esposito, *Vice Pres*
Louise Uphus, *Executive*
Jessica Valle, *Manager*
EMP: 10
SQ FT: 20,000
SALES (est): 1.9MM **Privately Held**
WEB: www.die-namicfab.com
SIC: 3469 3441 Metal stampings; fabricated structural metal

(P-13196)
DIVERSIFIED TOOL & DIE
2585 Birch St, Vista (92081-8433)
PHONE..............................760 598-9100
Ernst Wilms, *CEO*
Rosa Wilms, *Partner*
Ron Cook, *Prdtn Mgr*
EMP: 30
SQ FT: 33,000
SALES (est): 4.6MM **Privately Held**
WEB: www.stamping.com
SIC: 3469 3544 Stamping metal for the trade; special dies & tools

(P-13197)
E2E MFG LLC
7139 Koll Center Pkwy, Pleasanton (94566-3120)
PHONE..............................925 862-2057
Igonni Fajardo,
Humera Nawaz, *Program Mgr*
Christine Luna, *Office Mgr*
Oscar Salazar, *Info Tech Mgr*
Dennis Custodio, *Engineer*
▲ **EMP:** 46
SQ FT: 11,238
SALES (est): 9.3MM **Privately Held**
WEB: www.fourte.com
SIC: 3469 Metal stampings

(P-13198)
EAGLEWARE MANUFACTURING CO INC
12683 Corral Pl, Santa Fe Springs (90670-4748)
PHONE..............................562 320-3100
Brett L Gross, *President*
Eric Gross, *Vice Pres*
▲ **EMP:** 32
SQ FT: 130,000
SALES (est): 5.6MM **Privately Held**
SIC: 3469 3421 Stamping metal for the trade; household cooking & kitchen utensils, metal; cooking ware, except porcelain enamelled; cutlery

(P-13199)
EBSCO PRODUCTIONS INC
1040 N Las Palmas Ave 1, Los Angeles (90038-2409)
PHONE..............................323 960-2599

Scott A Stone, *President*
EMP: 50
SALES (est): 3.9MM **Privately Held**
SIC: 3469 Radio or television chassis, stamped metal

(P-13200)
ELIXIR INDUSTRIES
24800 Chrisanta Dr # 100, Mission Viejo (92691-4833)
PHONE..............................949 860-5000
EMP: 10
SQ FT: 57,707
SALES (corp-wide): 28.3MM **Privately Held**
SIC: 3469 3714 3441
PA: Elixir Industries
    24800 Chrisanta Dr # 210
    Mission Viejo CA 92691
    949 860-5000

(P-13201)
ERC CONCEPTS CO INC
1255 Birchwood Dr, Sunnyvale (94089-2206)
P.O. Box 62019 (94088-2019)
PHONE..............................408 734-5345
Felix Oramas, *President*
Reina Oramas, *Vice Pres*
EMP: 35
SQ FT: 17,000
SALES (est): 7.4MM **Privately Held**
WEB: www.erc-concepts.com
SIC: 3469 Machine parts, stamped or pressed metal

(P-13202)
EUGENIOS SHEET METAL INC
2151 Maple Privado, Ontario (91761-7603)
PHONE..............................909 923-2002
Eugenio M Lozano, *President*
EMP: 18
SQ FT: 10,000
SALES (est): 3.9MM **Privately Held**
WEB: www.eugeniossheetmetal.com
SIC: 3469 Machine parts, stamped or pressed metal

(P-13203)
EXACT CNC INDUSTRIES INC
20640 Bahama St, Chatsworth (91311)
PHONE..............................818 527-1908
Harout H Neksalyan, *CEO*
EMP: 10
SALES (est): 1.1MM **Privately Held**
SIC: 3469 Machine parts, stamped or pressed metal

(P-13204)
EXCEL INDUSTRIES INC
Also Called: Accu-Tek
1601 Fremont Ct, Ontario (91761-8309)
PHONE..............................909 947-4867
William Kohout, *President*
EMP: 21
SALES (est): 3.6MM **Privately Held**
WEB: www.accu-tekfirearms.com
SIC: 3469 3484 3542 3496 Metal stampings; small arms; machine tools, metal forming type; miscellaneous fabricated wire products

(P-13205)
FALLBROOK INDUSTRIES INC
Also Called: Standish Precision Products
323 Industrial Way Ste 1, Fallbrook (92028-2357)
PHONE..............................760 728-7229
Michael Standish, *President*
Dennis Standish, *Vice Pres*
Emily Standish, *Opers Mgr*
William Howard, *Prdtn Mgr*
▲ **EMP:** 20
SQ FT: 15,000
SALES (est): 3.7MM **Privately Held**
WEB: www.standishproducts.com
SIC: 3469 Machine parts, stamped or pressed metal

(P-13206)
FORM & FUSION MFG INC
11251 Trade Center Dr, Rancho Cordova (95742-6223)
PHONE..............................916 638-8576
Greg Bryant, *Manager*
EMP: 10

SALES (corp-wide): 4.4MM **Privately Held**
SIC: 3469 Metal stampings
PA: Form & Fusion Mfg., Inc.
11261 Trade Center Dr
Rancho Cordova CA 95742
916 638-8576

(P-13207)
FORM & FUSION MFG INC (PA)
Also Called: Urgent Upfits
11261 Trade Center Dr, Rancho Cordova (95742-6223)
PHONE..................916 638-8576
John Hancock, *President*
Dave Lewis, *Shareholder*
EMP: 27
SQ FT: 40,000
SALES: 4.4MM **Privately Held**
SIC: 3469 3465 Metal stampings; automotive stampings

(P-13208)
GALAXY MANUFACTURING INC
3200 Bassett St, Santa Clara (95054-2701)
P.O. Box 1153 (95052-1153)
PHONE..................408 654-4583
EMP: 11
SQ FT: 5,000
SALES (est): 1.7MM **Privately Held**
WEB: www.galaxymfg.net
SIC: 3469

(P-13209)
GERGAY AND ASSOCIATES
78 Delmar St, San Francisco (94114-4006)
PHONE..................415 431-4163
George Gergay, *Partner*
Andrea Gergay, *Partner*
Nicole Gergay, *Partner*
Peter Gergay, *Partner*
EMP: 49
SALES: 5MM **Privately Held**
SIC: 3469 Porcelain enameled products & utensils

(P-13210)
GLOBAL PCCI (GPC) (PA)
2465 Campus Dr Ste 100, Irvine (92612-1502)
PHONE..................757 637-9000
Sherri Bovino, *Partner*
Robert W Urban,
EMP: 120
SQ FT: 10,000
SALES (est): 21.2MM **Privately Held**
SIC: 3469 4499 Metal stampings; salvaging, distressed vessels & cargoes

(P-13211)
GRASS MANUFACTURING CO INC
2850 Bay Rd, Redwood City (94063-3503)
PHONE..................650 366-2556
Eric Grass, *President*
Bonnie Grass, *Admin Sec*
Jennifer Grass, *Bookkeeper*
EMP: 10
SQ FT: 8,000
SALES (est): 1.1MM **Privately Held**
WEB: www.grassmfg.com
SIC: 3469 Stamping metal for the trade

(P-13212)
GRIMCO INC
13454 Imperial Hwy, Santa Fe Springs (90670-4820)
PHONE..................562 449-4964
Marty Meisner, *Branch Mgr*
EMP: 24
SALES (corp-wide): 97.1MM **Privately Held**
SIC: 3469 2759 3429 Patterns on metal; screen printing; manufactured hardware (general)
PA: Grimco, Inc.
1585 Fencorp Dr
Fenton MO 63026
636 305-0088

(P-13213)
HANMAR LLC (PA)
Also Called: Metalite Manufacturing
11441 Bradley Ave, Pacoima (91331-2304)
PHONE..................818 240-0170
Hannes Michael Schachtner, *CEO*

Jan Schacatner, *CFO*
Joe Sauceda, *Program Mgr*
Tony Mayer, *Office Mgr*
Leonard Alvidez, *Sales Mgr*
EMP: 42 **EST:** 1969
SQ FT: 25,000
SALES (est): 8.9MM **Privately Held**
SIC: 3469 Spinning metal for the trade; stamping metal for the trade

(P-13214)
HARTWELL CORPORATION
9810 6th St, Rancho Cucamonga (91730-5795)
PHONE..................909 987-4616
Finmon Elliot, *Branch Mgr*
Paul Huh, *Prgrmr*
Tim Owen, *Business Mgr*
Valerie Porter, *Buyer*
Cheryl Vogt, *Safety Mgr*
EMP: 62
SQ FT: 101,495
SALES (corp-wide): 3.5B **Publicly Held**
WEB: www.hartwellcorp.com
SIC: 3469 3429 Metal stampings; manufactured hardware (general)
HQ: Hartwell Corporation
900 Richfield Rd
Placentia CA 92870
714 993-4200

(P-13215)
HEADED REINFORCEMENT CORP
Also Called: H R C
11200 Condor Ave, Fountain Valley (92708-6106)
PHONE..................714 557-1455
Kjell L Dahl, *CEO*
Christian Dahl, *Vice Pres*
Jennifer Schmid, *Admin Asst*
◆ **EMP:** 15
SQ FT: 23,000
SALES (est): 3.9MM **Privately Held**
WEB: www.hrc-usa.com
SIC: 3469 Machine parts, stamped or pressed metal

(P-13216)
HESTAN SMART COOKING INC
1 Meyer Plz, Vallejo (94590-5925)
PHONE..................773 710-1538
Stanley Cheng, *CEO*
EMP: 10
SALES (est): 400.4K **Privately Held**
SIC: 3469 5046 Cooking ware, except porcelain enamelled; cooking equipment, commercial
PA: Meyer International Holdings Limited C/O: Vistra (Bvi) Limited Road Town

(P-13217)
HI TECH HONEYCOMB INC
9355 Ruffin Ct, San Diego (92123-5304)
PHONE..................858 974-1600
Joao J Costa, *CEO*
Selma Costa, *President*
John J Costa, *CEO*
Michael Corbosiero, *Officer*
John Costa, *Vice Pres*
EMP: 136
SQ FT: 20,000
SALES (est): 33.8MM **Privately Held**
WEB: www.hthoneycomb.com
SIC: 3469 Honeycombed metal

(P-13218)
HI-TEMP INSULATION INC
4700 Calle Alto, Camarillo (93012-8489)
PHONE..................805 484-2774
Sieg Borck, *CEO*
Neal Prosser, *Engineer*
Susan Shearer, *Train & Dev Mgr*
Angie Parras, *Purch Agent*
Jay Wood, *Prdtn Mgr*
▲ **EMP:** 310
SQ FT: 100,000
SALES: 74.7MM **Privately Held**
WEB: www.hi-tempinsulation.com
SIC: 3469 3296 Spinning metal for the trade; fiberglass insulation

(P-13219)
HOME PARADISE LLC
Also Called: Cabinet Home
7000 E Slauson Ave, Commerce (90040-3621)
PHONE..................626 284-9999
Jian Q Chen, *President*
▲ **EMP:** 13
SQ FT: 6,000
SALES (est): 2.7MM **Privately Held**
SIC: 3469 1799 Kitchen fixtures & equipment, porcelain enameled; kitchen fixtures & equipment: metal, except cast aluminum; kitchen & bathroom remodeling

(P-13220)
HOUSTON BAZZ CO
Also Called: Bazz Houston Co
12700 Western Ave, Garden Grove (92841-4017)
PHONE..................714 898-2666
Javier Castro, *President*
Chester O Houston, *Corp Secy*
Manuel Lopez, *Info Tech Mgr*
Karen Burley, *Technical Staff*
Cecilia Rodriguez, *Technical Staff*
▲ **EMP:** 85
SQ FT: 50,000
SALES (est): 21.3MM **Privately Held**
WEB: www.bazz-houston.com
SIC: 3469 3495 3493 Machine parts, stamped or pressed metal; mechanical springs, precision; steel springs, except wire

(P-13221)
HSG MANUFACTURING INC
13346 Monte Vista Ave, Chino (91710-5147)
PHONE..................909 902-5915
Gill Singh, *President*
Hadasen Singh, *Principal*
▲ **EMP:** 12
SQ FT: 8,000
SALES (est): 7MM **Privately Held**
WEB: www.hsgmanufacturing.com
SIC: 3469 Machine parts, stamped or pressed metal

(P-13222)
HUGIN COMPONENTS INC
Also Called: H C I
4231 Pacific St Ste 23, Rocklin (95677-2135)
PHONE..................916 652-1070
Steve Katonis, *President*
Sharon Katonis, *Vice Pres*
EMP: 15
SQ FT: 18,000
SALES (est): 2.4MM **Privately Held**
WEB: www.hugincomponents.com
SIC: 3469 Electronic enclosures, stamped or pressed metal

(P-13223)
IMPERIAL CAL PRODUCTS INC
425 Apollo St, Brea (92821-3110)
PHONE..................714 990-9100
Shari Bittel, *President*
Kathy Flentye, *Vice Pres*
Mary Fallon, *Marketing Staff*
Janet Dirisio, *Manager*
▲ **EMP:** 35
SQ FT: 35,000
SALES (est): 3.8MM **Privately Held**
WEB: www.imperialhoods.com
SIC: 3469 Kitchen fixtures & equipment: metal, except cast aluminum

(P-13224)
INFINITY STAMPS INC
Also Called: Branding Irons Unlimited
8577 Canoga Ave, Canoga Park (91304-2609)
PHONE..................818 576-1188
Billie Eglich, *President*
Oren Eglich, *General Mgr*
Dan Post, *Info Tech Mgr*
Dennis Eglich, *Opers Mgr*
EMP: 10
SQ FT: 4,500
SALES (est): 1.8MM **Privately Held**
WEB: www.infinitystamps.com
SIC: 3469 Stamping metal for the trade

(P-13225)
INNOVATIVE STAMPING INC
Also Called: Innovative Systems
2068 E Gladwick St, Compton (90220-6202)
P.O. Box 5327 (90224-5327)
PHONE..................310 537-6996
Gerald L Czaban, *President*
Kim Stevenson, *Vice Pres*
▼ **EMP:** 32
SQ FT: 128,000
SALES (est): 5MM **Privately Held**
WEB: www.innovative-sys.com
SIC: 3469 Metal stampings

(P-13226)
INTERPLEX NASCAL INC (DH)
15777 Gateway Cir, Tustin (92780-6470)
PHONE..................714 505-2900
Jim Martellotti, *President*
John Fili, *General Mgr*
Brittany Garcia, *Engineer*
▲ **EMP:** 65 **EST:** 1969
SQ FT: 33,000
SALES (est): 11.5MM
SALES (corp-wide): 223.2MM **Privately Held**
WEB: www.interplexchina.com
SIC: 3469 Stamping metal for the trade
HQ: Interplex Industries, Inc.
231 Ferris Ave
Rumford RI 02916
718 961-6212

(P-13227)
INTRI-PLEX TECHNOLOGIES INC (HQ)
751 S Kellogg Ave, Goleta (93117-3832)
PHONE..................805 683-3414
Lawney J Falloon, *CEO*
David Janes, *Ch of Bd*
Lawrence Ellis, *CFO*
John Sullivan, *Vice Pres*
▲ **EMP:** 134
SQ FT: 46,000
SALES (est): 28.1MM
SALES (corp-wide): 24.4MM **Privately Held**
SIC: 3469 Stamping metal for the trade
PA: Ipt Holding Inc
751 S Kellogg Ave
Goleta CA 93117
805 683-3414

(P-13228)
J & D FABRICATING & REPAIR INC
2360 Westgate Rd, Santa Maria (93455-1046)
P.O. Box 5487 (93456-5487)
PHONE..................805 928-9674
Joe Trevino, *President*
David Cox, *Treasurer*
EMP: 17
SQ FT: 12,500
SALES: 3.5MM **Privately Held**
SIC: 3469 Structural steel erection; building front installation metal; iron work, structural

(P-13229)
J-MARK MANUFACTURING INC
Also Called: J-Mark Company
2480 Coral St, Vista (92081-8430)
PHONE..................760 727-6956
Mark Baker, *President*
Debbie Baker, *Treasurer*
Dale Jackson, *Vice Pres*
Carol Jackson, *Admin Sec*
Steve Tugwell, *Prdtn Mgr*
EMP: 22
SQ FT: 24,000
SALES: 3.5MM **Privately Held**
SIC: 3469 3599 Electronic enclosures, stamped or pressed metal; machine shop, jobbing & repair

(P-13230)
JAY MANUFACTURING CORP
Also Called: Jay Mfg
7425 Fulton Ave, North Hollywood (91605-4116)
PHONE..................818 255-0500
Michael Jordan, *President*
Marna Jordan, *Treasurer*

Katheryn Jordan, *Admin Sec*
Mark Jordan, *Production*
EMP: 10 **EST:** 1944
SQ FT: 16,000
SALES (est): 1.7MM **Privately Held**
WEB: www.jaymfg.com
SIC: 3469 Stamping metal for the trade

(P-13231)
JB INDUSTRIES CORP
Also Called: J B I
451 Commercial Way, La Habra
(90631-6168)
P.O. Box 17365, Anaheim (92817-7365)
PHONE....................562 691-2105
Jaime Borja, *President*
Jim Borja Jr, *CFO*
Mercedes Borja, *Vice Pres*
EMP: 12
SQ FT: 10,000
SALES (est): 2.6MM **Privately Held**
SIC: 3469 3599 Machine parts, stamped
or pressed metal; machine shop, jobbing
& repair

(P-13232)
KAGA (USA) INC
2620 S Susan St, Santa Ana (92704-5816)
PHONE....................714 540-2697
Masaaki Nozaki, *President*
Fumio Shiina, *Treasurer*
Takashi Nozaki, *Vice Pres*
Nobuharu Nozaki, *Admin Sec*
Asami Fujioka, *Accountant*
▲ **EMP:** 30
SQ FT: 38,400
SALES: 6.3MM
SALES (corp-wide): 49.6MM **Privately
Held**
WEB: www.kagainc.com
SIC: 3469 Electronic enclosures, stamped
or pressed metal
PA: Kaga,Inc.
140, Ni, Ota, Tsubatamachi
Kahoku-Gun ISH 929-0
762 893-131

(P-13233)
KATLAN INDUSTRIES INC
Also Called: Leejay Industries
3202 Blume Dr, Los Alamitos (90720-4813)
PHONE....................562 618-0940
Lance Schumacher, *President*
Rebecca Schumacher, *Vice Pres*
EMP: 10
SQ FT: 12,000
SALES: 600K **Privately Held**
SIC: 3469 3429 Machine parts, stamped
or pressed metal; cabinet hardware

(P-13234)
KB DELTA INC
Also Called: KB Delta Comprsr Valve Parts
3340 Fujita St, Torrance (90505-4017)
PHONE....................310 530-1539
Boris Giourof, *CEO*
Katarina Giourof, *Vice Pres*
Daniel Cedeno, *Manager*
Mauricio Rodriguez, *Manager*
▼ **EMP:** 37
SQ FT: 5,500
SALES (est): 7MM **Privately Held**
WEB: www.kbdelta.com
SIC: 3469 5085 7699 Machine parts,
stamped or pressed metal; industrial sup-
plies; compressor repair

(P-13235)
KELLY TOOL & MFGCOINC
433 S Palm Ave, Alhambra (91803-1422)
PHONE....................626 289-7962
Labron H Burdette, *President*
EMP: 10 **EST:** 1957
SQ FT: 12,000
SALES (est): 1.4MM **Privately Held**
SIC: 3469 3541 Stamping metal for the
trade; machine tools, metal cutting type;
machine tool replacement & repair parts,
metal cutting types

(P-13236)
KING PRECISION INC
111 Harrison Ct, Santa Cruz (95062-1125)
PHONE....................831 426-2704
Dallas King, *President*
Richard King, *Senior VP*

EMP: 27
SQ FT: 8,000
SALES (est): 4MM **Privately Held**
WEB: www.kingprecision.com
SIC: 3469 7692 3829 3827 Machine
parts, stamped or pressed metal; welding
repair; measuring & controlling devices;
optical instruments & lenses; guided missile & space vehicle parts & auxiliary
equipment

(P-13237)
KINGS CRATING INC
Also Called: Reyes Machining
1364 Pioneer Way, El Cajon (92020-1626)
PHONE....................619 590-2631
Manuel Reyes, *CEO*
Shelia Reyes, *CFO*
Lynn Mason, *Admin Sec*
EMP: 30
SQ FT: 30,000
SALES (est): 1.9MM **Privately Held**
WEB: www.reyesmfg.com
SIC: 3469
PA: King's Crating, Inc.
1364 Pioneer Way
El Cajon CA 92020
-

(P-13238)
KITCHEN EQUIPMENT MFG CO INC
Also Called: Kemco
2102 Maple Privado, Ontario (91761-7602)
PHONE....................909 923-3153
David Rodriguez, *President*
EMP: 40
SQ FT: 15,000
SALES (est): 7.7MM **Privately Held**
SIC: 3469 3431 Kitchen fixtures & equip-
ment, porcelain enameled; metal sanitary
ware

(P-13239)
KITCOR CORPORATION
9959 Glenoaks Blvd, Sun Valley
(91352-1085)
PHONE....................323 875-2820
Kent Kitchen, *Principal*
Alice Kitchen, *Treasurer*
Bob Kitchen, *Vice Pres*
Jim Kitchen, *Vice Pres*
Kimberly Schulman, *Office Mgr*
EMP: 35 **EST:** 1943
SQ FT: 42,000
SALES (est): 10.6MM **Privately Held**
WEB: www.kitcor.com
SIC: 3469 Kitchen fixtures & equipment:
metal, except cast aluminum

(P-13240)
KOPYKAKE ENTERPRISES INC (PA)
Also Called: Mayer Baking Co
3699 W 240th St, Torrance (90505-6002)
PHONE....................310 373-8906
Gerald G Mayer, *President*
Greg Mayer, *CFO*
Rick Mayer, *Vice Pres*
David Good, *Buyer*
Gary A Newland, *Plant Mgr*
◆ **EMP:** 19 **EST:** 1970
SQ FT: 22,000
SALES (est): 6.5MM **Privately Held**
WEB: www.kopykake.com
SIC: 3469 2051 Kitchen fixtures & equip-
ment: metal, except cast aluminum; bak-
ery: wholesale or wholesale/retail
combined

(P-13241)
LARRY SPUN PRODUCTS INC
1533 S Downey Rd, Los Angeles
(90023-4042)
PHONE....................323 881-6300
Hilario F Hurtado, *CEO*
EMP: 49
SQ FT: 6,000
SALES (est): 8.3MM **Privately Held**
SIC: 3469 Spinning metal for the trade

(P-13242)
LOCK-RIDGE TOOL COMPANY INC
2000 Pomona Blvd, Pomona (91768-3323)
PHONE....................909 865-8309
Keith Clark, *President*
Penney Clark, *Corp Secy*
Ashford Clark, *Vice Pres*
▲ **EMP:** 52
SQ FT: 21,000
SALES (est): 9.4MM **Privately Held**
WEB: www.lockridgetool.com
SIC: 3469 Stamping metal for the trade

(P-13243)
LUPPEN HOLDINGS INC (PA)
Also Called: Metal Products Engineering
3050 Leonis Blvd, Vernon (90058-2914)
PHONE....................323 581-8121
Luppe R Luppen, *Ch of Bd*
Paula Luppen, *Treasurer*
Ray Woodmansee, *Vice Pres*
▲ **EMP:** 24 **EST:** 1940
SQ FT: 40,000
SALES (est): 2.4MM **Privately Held**
WEB: www.metalproductseng.com
SIC: 3469 3578 3596 Stamping metal for
the trade; change making machines;
scales & balances, except laboratory

(P-13244)
M L Z INC
Also Called: Spun Products
1800 W 9th St, Long Beach (90813-2614)
PHONE....................562 436-3540
Larry Weber, *President*
Linda Weber, *Admin Sec*
Ana Pena, *Admin Asst*
EMP: 10
SQ FT: 4,000
SALES: 1.1MM **Privately Held**
WEB: www.spunproducts.com
SIC: 3469 Spinning metal for the trade

(P-13245)
MC WILLIAM & SON INC
Also Called: California Tool & Die
421 S Irwindale Ave, Azusa (91702-3217)
PHONE....................626 969-1821
Dan McWilliam, *President*
Shilo Ammons, *COO*
Dana Matejka, *Corp Secy*
EMP: 19
SQ FT: 26,000
SALES (est): 4.2MM **Privately Held**
WEB: www.californiatool-die.com
SIC: 3469 3544 Stamping metal for the
trade; special dies, tools, jigs & fixtures

(P-13246)
MCINTIRE TOOL DIE & MACHINE (PA)
Also Called: Omega Tool Die & Machine
308 S Mountain View Ave, San Bernardino
(92408-1415)
PHONE....................909 888-0440
Barbara McIntire, *President*
Chester L McIntire, *Shareholder*
Jane Kingsley, *Treasurer*
EMP: 12
SQ FT: 13,500
SALES (est): 2.3MM **Privately Held**
WEB: www.omegatool-usa.com
SIC: 3469 Metal stampings

(P-13247)
METALITE MANUFACTURING COMPANY
Also Called: Metalite Mfg Companys
11441 Bradley Ave, Pacoima (91331-2304)
PHONE....................818 890-2802
Hanness Schachtner, *CEO*
Jan Schacatner, *CFO*
Bud Van Netta, *Marketing Staff*
Gracy Alan, *Manager*
EMP: 39 **EST:** 1923
SQ FT: 58,000
SALES (est): 8.9MM **Privately Held**
SIC: 3469 Stamping metal for the trade
PA: Hanmar, Llc
11441 Bradley Ave
Pacoima CA 91331
818 240-0170

(P-13248)
METCO MANUFACTURING INC
Also Called: Metco Fourslide Manufacturing
17540 S Denver Ave, Gardena
(90248-3411)
PHONE....................310 516-6547
Jack Bishop, *President*
Dana Beisel, *Vice Pres*
Darryl Scholl, *Vice Pres*
Shirley Bishop, *Admin Sec*
EMP: 29
SQ FT: 11,200
SALES (est): 6.1MM **Privately Held**
WEB: www.metcofourslide.com
SIC: 3469 Stamping metal for the trade

(P-13249)
MEYER COOKWARE INDUSTRIES INC
1 Meyer Plz, Vallejo (94590-5925)
PHONE....................707 551-2800
Stanley Cheng, *Ch of Bd*
EMP: 50
SALES (est): 13.6MM **Privately Held**
WEB: www.meyer.com
SIC: 3469 Cooking ware, except porcelain
enamelled
HQ: Meyer Corporation, U.S.
1 Meyer Plz
Vallejo CA 94590
707 551-2800

(P-13250)
MEYER CORPORATION US (HQ)
Also Called: Meyer Wines
1 Meyer Plz, Vallejo (94590-5925)
PHONE....................707 551-2800
Stanley Kin Sui Cheng, *CEO*
Ed Blackman, *COO*
Barry Minehart, *Branch Mgr*
▲ **EMP:** 80
SQ FT: 180,000
SALES (est): 90.1MM **Privately Held**
WEB: www.meyer.com
SIC: 3469 3631 5023 Cooking ware, ex-
cept porcelain enamelled; household
cooking equipment; kitchenware

(P-13251)
MICRO MATRIX SYSTEMS (PA)
Also Called: M M S
4651 Brooks St, Montclair (91763-4796)
PHONE....................909 626-8544
Grant P Zarbock, *CEO*
Kerry Zarbock, *Vice Pres*
▲ **EMP:** 25
SQ FT: 22,500
SALES (est): 3MM **Privately Held**
WEB: www.mmsys.biz
SIC: 3469 Stamping metal for the trade

(P-13252)
NANOPRECISION PRODUCTS INC
802 Calle Plano, Camarillo (93012-8557)
PHONE....................310 597-4991
Michael K Barnoski, *CEO*
Ryan Vallance, *CTO*
Shawn Matsuda, *Technical Staff*
Connie Yao, *Technical Staff*
Ren Yang, *Engineer*
EMP: 25
SALES (est): 7.7MM **Privately Held**
SIC: 3469 3721 Stamping metal for the
trade; research & development on aircraft
by the manufacturer

(P-13253)
NATIONAL METAL STAMPINGS INC
42110 8th St E, Lancaster (93535-5444)
PHONE....................661 945-1157
William T Bloomer, *President*
Madeleine J Bloomer, *Corp Secy*
Bill Bloomer, *General Mgr*
John Doyle, *General Mgr*
Joe Gedang, *Info Tech Mgr*
▲ **EMP:** 70
SQ FT: 20,000
SALES (est): 13.2MM **Privately Held**
WEB: www.nationalmetal.com
SIC: 3469 Stamping metal for the trade

(P-13254)
NEW GORDON INDUSTRIES LLC
13750 Rosecrans Ave, Santa Fe Springs (90670-5027)
PHONE..................................562 483-7378
Steven Lazar, *President*
Daniel Laskaris, *General Mgr*
Michelle Scott, *Accountant*
Lisa Wheeler, *QC Mgr*
EMP: 22
SQ FT: 22,000
SALES (est): 4.9MM **Privately Held**
WEB: www.ngica.com
SIC: 3469 Stamping metal for the trade

(P-13255)
ORANGE METAL SPINNING AND STAM
2601 Orange Ave, Santa Ana (92707-3724)
P.O. Box 80070, Rcho STA Marg (92688-0070)
PHONE..................................714 754-0770
Mario Haber, *President*
Enrique Haber, *Vice Pres*
Elsa Haber, *Admin Sec*
EMP: 13
SQ FT: 10,000
SALES (est): 1.2MM **Privately Held**
SIC: 3469 Spinning metal for the trade

(P-13256)
P P MFG CO INC
13130 Arctic Cir, Santa Fe Springs (90670-5508)
PHONE..................................562 921-3640
Ronald Burr, *President*
Glenn Burr, *Treasurer*
EMP: 14
SQ FT: 10,000
SALES (est): 1.4MM **Privately Held**
SIC: 3469 3544 Stamping metal for the trade; special dies & tools

(P-13257)
PACIFIC METAL STAMPINGS INC
28415 Witherspoon Pkwy, Valencia (91355-4174)
PHONE..................................661 257-7656
Donald Schlotfelt, *CEO*
Brian Schlotfelt, *Vice Pres*
▲ **EMP:** 30
SQ FT: 21,000
SALES (est): 6.5MM **Privately Held**
WEB: www.pacificmetalstampings.com
SIC: 3469 Stamping metal for the trade

(P-13258)
PACIFIC PRECISION METALS INC
Also Called: Tubing Seal Cap Co
1100 E Orangethorpe Ave, Anaheim (92801-1161)
PHONE..................................951 226-1500
Ajay N Thakkar, *President*
Kent Davidson, *VP Sales*
EMP: 130
SQ FT: 2,063
SALES (est): 30.6MM **Privately Held**
SIC: 3469 3429 2599 8711 Stamping metal for the trade; door locks, bolts & checks; locks or lock sets; cabinets, factory; machine tool design; metal household furniture
PA: Triyar Sv, Llc
10850 Wilshire Blvd
Los Angeles CA 90024

(P-13259)
PERRINS REGISTRATION OFFICE
17727 Chatsworth St, Granada Hills (91344-5604)
PHONE..................................818 832-1332
Cynthia Perrin, *Principal*
EMP: 10
SALES (est): 854.1K **Privately Held**
SIC: 3469 Automobile license tags, stamped metal

(P-13260)
PLATESCAN INC
20101 Sw Birch St Ste 250, Newport Beach (92660-1770)
PHONE..................................949 851-1600
Robert Pinzler, *Vice Pres*
EMP: 23
SALES: 950K **Privately Held**
SIC: 3469 Automobile license tags, stamped metal

(P-13261)
POL-TECH PRECISION INC
Also Called: Pol Tech Precision Co
4447 Enterprise St, Fremont (94538-6306)
PHONE..................................510 656-6832
Mark Nowicki, *President*
EMP: 10
SQ FT: 900
SALES (est): 153.9K **Privately Held**
WEB: www.pol-tech.com
SIC: 3469 Machine parts, stamped or pressed metal

(P-13262)
PRECISION RESOURCE INC
Also Called: Precision Resource Cal Div
5803 Engineer Dr, Huntington Beach (92649-1127)
PHONE..................................714 891-4439
Robert Fitzgerald, *Principal*
EMP: 275
SQ FT: 27,000
SALES (corp-wide): 215MM **Privately Held**
WEB: www.precisionresource.com
SIC: 3469 3544 Stamping metal for the trade; special dies, tools, jigs & fixtures
PA: Precision Resource, Inc.
25 Forest Pkwy
Shelton CT 06484
203 925-0012

(P-13263)
PRICE-LEHO CO INC
3841 Mission Oaks Blvd, Camarillo (93012-5099)
PHONE..................................805 482-8967
Theresa Leho, *Chairman*
Robert Leho, *President*
EMP: 10
SQ FT: 12,800
SALES: 250K **Privately Held**
SIC: 3469 3544 Metal stampings; special dies & tools

(P-13264)
PROFESSIONAL FINISHING SYSTEMS
Also Called: Pfs
12341 Gladstone Ave, Sylmar (91342-5319)
PHONE..................................818 365-8888
Vern Coley, *CEO*
Pat Ramnarine, *Vice Pres*
EMP: 17
SQ FT: 14,000
SALES (est): 3.1MM **Privately Held**
WEB: www.profinishing.com
SIC: 3469 5084 3471 Machine parts, stamped or pressed metal; machine tools & metalworking machinery; plating & polishing

(P-13265)
PROFORMANCE MANUFACTURING INC
1922 Elise Cir, Corona (92879-1882)
PHONE..................................951 279-1230
Robert Morales, *President*
EMP: 20
SQ FT: 21,000
SALES (est): 3.9MM **Privately Held**
WEB: www.proformancemfg.com
SIC: 3469 3599 3451 3312 Machine parts, stamped or pressed metal; machine & other job shop work; screw machine products; blast furnaces & steel mills; special dies, tools, jigs & fixtures

(P-13266)
PROTO LAMINATIONS INC
13666 Bora Dr, Santa Fe Springs (90670-5006)
PHONE..................................562 926-4777

Mark R Rippy, *President*
Tina L Rippy, *Corp Secy*
EMP: 12
SQ FT: 11,000
SALES (est): 1.9MM **Privately Held**
WEB: www.protolam.com
SIC: 3469 Machine parts, stamped or pressed metal

(P-13267)
PROTOTYPE & SHORT-RUN SVCS INC
Also Called: Pass
1310 W Collins Ave, Orange (92867-5415)
PHONE..................................714 449-9661
Jack Mc Devitt, *President*
Lorene Schmdt, *Office Mgr*
Moises Navarro, *Engineer*
Florence Lulu Montoya, *Manager*
EMP: 25
SQ FT: 6,700
SALES: 8MM **Privately Held**
WEB: www.prototype-shortrun.com
SIC: 3469 Stamping metal for the trade

(P-13268)
QUALITY METAL SPINNING AND
4047 Transport St, Palo Alto (94303-4914)
PHONE..................................650 858-2491
Joseph Czisch Jr, *President*
Xenia Czisch, *Vice Pres*
EMP: 30
SQ FT: 34,000
SALES (est): 6.8MM **Privately Held**
WEB: www.qmsshields.com
SIC: 3469 3599 Stamping metal for the trade; machine shop, jobbing & repair

(P-13269)
R & R STAMPING FOUR SLIDE CORP
2440 Railroad St, Corona (92880-5418)
PHONE..................................909 595-6444
David A Janes Jr, *President*
EMP: 60 EST: 1988
SQ FT: 65,000
SALES (est): 5.2MM **Privately Held**
WEB: www.cmemetal.com
SIC: 3469 3444 Stamping metal for the trade; sheet metalwork

(P-13270)
R ZAMORA INC
Also Called: Tecxel
2826 La Mirada Dr Ste D, Vista (92081-8445)
PHONE..................................760 597-1130
Reggie Zamora, *President*
EMP: 21
SQ FT: 10,000
SALES: 2.5MM **Privately Held**
WEB: www.tecxel.com
SIC: 3469 Machine parts, stamped or pressed metal

(P-13271)
RAGO & SON INC
1029 51st Ave, Oakland (94601-5653)
P.O. Box 7309 (94601-0309)
PHONE..................................510 536-5700
Dominic Anthony Rago, *CEO*
Dominic Rago, *President*
Deborah Rago, *Corp Secy*
Gerald Accardo Jr, *Vice Pres*
Gerald Accardo Sr, *Vice Pres*
EMP: 80 EST: 1969
SQ FT: 38,000
SALES (est): 20.2MM **Privately Held**
WEB: www.rago-son.com
SIC: 3469 Stamping metal for the trade

(P-13272)
SCHUBERTH NORTH AMERICA LLC
33 Journey Ste 200, Aliso Viejo (92656-5345)
PHONE..................................949 215-0893
Randy Northrup,
Doreena Daniel, *Controller*
EMP: 15
SQ FT: 2,000
SALES (est): 6.3MM
SALES (corp-wide): 775.7K **Privately Held**
SIC: 3469 Helmets, steel

HQ: Schuberth Gmbh
Stegelitzer Str. 12
Magdeburg 39126
391 810-60

(P-13273)
SERRA MANUFACTURING CORP (PA)
3039 E Las Hermanas St, Compton (90221-5575)
P.O. Box 5684 (90224-5684)
PHONE..................................310 537-4560
Kris Hernandez, *CEO*
John Hernandez, *President*
Roy Cerda, *Vice Pres*
Steve Fitzpatrick, *Vice Pres*
Kim Cerda, *Administration*
EMP: 48
SQ FT: 28,000
SALES: 7MM **Privately Held**
WEB: www.serramfg.com
SIC: 3469 Stamping metal for the trade

(P-13274)
SESSA MANUFACTURING & WELDING
2932 Golf Course Dr, Ventura (93003-7689)
PHONE..................................805 644-2284
Michael J Sessa, *CEO*
Lea Sessa, *Shareholder*
EMP: 40 EST: 1980
SQ FT: 15,500
SALES (est): 7MM **Privately Held**
WEB: www.sessamfg.com
SIC: 3469 Stamping metal for the trade

(P-13275)
SHAWVER METAL TECH INC
881 Moffat Blvd, Manteca (95336-5820)
PHONE..................................209 239-9896
J C Shawver, *President*
Triny Shawver, *CFO*
EMP: 14
SALES (est): 2.3MM **Privately Held**
SIC: 3469 Stamping metal for the trade

(P-13276)
SKM INDUSTRIES INC
Also Called: Job Shop Managers
28966 Hancock Pkwy, Valencia (91355-1069)
PHONE..................................661 294-8373
Sanjeev Kapoor, *President*
Ana Heman, *Technology*
▼ **EMP:** 14
SQ FT: 4,300
SALES (est): 3.1MM **Privately Held**
WEB: www.skmproducts.com
SIC: 3469 Machine parts, stamped or pressed metal

(P-13277)
SLIDE SYSTEMS INC
1448 240th St, Harbor City (90710-1307)
PHONE..................................310 539-3416
Myra Beisel, *President*
Minnie Mook, *Vice Pres*
Marla Smith, *Vice Pres*
EMP: 19
SQ FT: 10,000
SALES: 3MM **Privately Held**
SIC: 3469 Stamping metal for the trade

(P-13278)
SOUTHWEST GREENE INTL INC
Also Called: Greene Group
4055 Calle Platino # 200, Oceanside (92056-5861)
PHONE..................................760 639-4960
Alexis Willingham, *President*
Steve James, *Engineer*
Curtis McCabe, *Engineer*
Tim Peterson, *Manager*
▲ **EMP:** 105
SQ FT: 80,000
SALES (est): 20.8MM **Privately Held**
SIC: 3469 Metal stampings

(P-13279)
SPECIALTY FINANCE INC
Also Called: David Engineering & Mfg
1230 Quarry St, Corona (92879-1708)
PHONE..................................951 735-5200
Mike David, *CEO*
Michael David, *President*

▲ = Import ▼=Export
◆ =Import/Export

Sarah Caoile, *Technology*
EMP: 30
SALES: 5MM **Privately Held**
SIC: 3469 3544 Metal stampings; special dies & tools

(P-13280)
SPECIALTY INTERNATIONAL INC
11144 Penrose St Ste 11, Sun Valley (91352-5601)
PHONE..................................818 768-8810
Anthony J Magnone, *President*
Jack McConnell, *Vice Pres*
▲ **EMP:** 100
SALES (est): 15.7MM **Privately Held**
WEB: www.specialtyinternational.com
SIC: 3469 Metal stampings

(P-13281)
STEICO INDUSTRIES INC
1814 Ord Way, Oceanside (92056-1502)
PHONE..................................760 438-8015
Troy Steiner, *CEO*
▲ **EMP:** 230
SQ FT: 52,000
SALES: 36.8MM
SALES (corp-wide): 1.3B **Privately Held**
WEB: www.steicoindustries.com
SIC: 3469 5051 Metal stampings; metals service centers & offices
HQ: Senior Operations Llc
300 E Devon Ave
Bartlett IL 60103
630 837-1811

(P-13282)
STRATUS COML COOKING EQP INC
1760 W 1st St, Irwindale (91702-3259)
PHONE..................................626 969-7041
Robert Spenuzza, *CEO*
EMP: 11
SALES (est): 1.4MM **Privately Held**
SIC: 3469 Kitchen fixtures & equipment: metal, except cast aluminum

(P-13283)
SUNSTONE COMPONENTS GROUP INC (HQ)
Also Called: Sun Stone Sales
42136 Avenida Alvarado, Temecula (92590-3400)
PHONE..................................951 296-5010
Bradway B Adams, *CEO*
David Bernard, *CFO*
EMP: 60
SALES (est): 11.2MM
SALES (corp-wide): 42.4MM **Privately Held**
WEB: www.sss-i.com
SIC: 3469 Metal stampings
PA: Pancon Corporation
350 Revolutionary Dr
East Taunton MA 02718
781 297-6000

(P-13284)
TEAM MANUFACTURING INC
2625 Homestead Pl, Rancho Dominguez (90220-5610)
PHONE..................................310 639-0251
Ed Ellis, *CEO*
James Cheatham, *Vice Pres*
Luis Almanza, *Manager*
▲ **EMP:** 50
SQ FT: 34,000
SALES: 6.8MM **Privately Held**
WEB: www.teammfg.com
SIC: 3469 3544 Stamping metal for the trade; die sets for metal stamping (presses)

(P-13285)
TECHNLOGY KNWLDGABLE MACHINING
Also Called: Tekma
1920 Kona Dr, Compton (90220-5417)
PHONE..................................310 608-7756
Phong Ly, *President*
Hoa Ly, *Treasurer*
EMP: 10
SQ FT: 10,000

SALES: 650K **Privately Held**
SIC: 3469 Machine parts, stamped or pressed metal

(P-13286)
TOOLANDER ENGINEERING INC
1110 Via Callejon, San Clemente (92673-6230)
PHONE..................................949 498-8339
Fred Kutzmarski, *President*
Harry F Kutzmarski, *Shareholder*
Steve Kutzmarski, *Vice Pres*
EMP: 10
SQ FT: 10,000
SALES (est): 950K **Privately Held**
SIC: 3469 3544 Stamping metal for the trade; special dies & tools

(P-13287)
TOP NOTCH MANUFACTURING INC
1488 Pioneer Way Ste 17, El Cajon (92020-1633)
PHONE..................................619 588-2033
Peter Vickonoff, *President*
Patricia Santore, *CFO*
Jason Janik, *General Mgr*
EMP: 11
SQ FT: 6,000
SALES (est): 880K **Privately Held**
SIC: 3469 3444 Machine parts, stamped or pressed metal; sheet metalwork

(P-13288)
TRAVIS MIKE INC
Also Called: Mt
2420 Celsius Ave Ste D, Oxnard (93030-5160)
PHONE..................................805 201-3363
Travis Frazier, *CEO*
Mike Brabante, *Principal*
▲ **EMP:** 10
SALES: 2MM **Privately Held**
SIC: 3469 Machine parts, stamped or pressed metal

(P-13289)
TRU-FORM INDUSTRIES INC (PA)
Also Called: Tru Form Industries
14511 Anson Ave, Santa Fe Springs (90670-5393)
PHONE..................................562 802-2041
Vernon M Hildebrandt, *CEO*
Vern Hildebrandt, *MIS Mgr*
Cindy Suer, *Human Res Mgr*
Josie Carillo, *Purch Mgr*
Mark Tiedeman, *Sales Executive*
▲ **EMP:** 70
SQ FT: 50,000
SALES (est): 13.8MM **Privately Held**
WEB: www.tru-form.com
SIC: 3469 3496 3429 Metal stampings; clips & fasteners, made from purchased wire; manufactured hardware (general)

(P-13290)
TUNG TAI GROUP
1726 Rogers Ave, San Jose (95112-1109)
PHONE..................................408 573-8681
Toll Free:..................................877 -
Joseph Chen, *President*
Rebecca Vera, *Office Mgr*
Patrick Wong, *Manager*
◆ **EMP:** 12
SALES (est): 2.4MM **Privately Held**
SIC: 3469 5093 Metal stampings; metal scrap & waste materials

(P-13291)
VALLEY STAMPING INC
24304 Creekside Dr, Newhall (91321-3900)
PHONE..................................661 259-4562
John W Lee, *President*
Merrilyn Lee, *Vice Pres*
EMP: 10
SQ FT: 5,500
SALES: 760K **Privately Held**
SIC: 3469 Stamping metal for the trade

(P-13292)
VANGUARD TOOL & MFG CO INC
Also Called: Vanguard Tool & Manufacturing
8388 Utica Ave, Rancho Cucamonga (91730-3849)
PHONE..................................909 980-9392
Robert A Scudder, *President*
Connie Scudder, *Vice Pres*
EMP: 49
SQ FT: 47,000
SALES (est): 9.5MM **Privately Held**
SIC: 3469 Stamping metal for the trade

(P-13293)
VERDUGO TOOL & ENGRG CO INC
20600 Superior St, Chatsworth (91311-4414)
PHONE..................................818 998-1101
Kevin Gresiak, *President*
Johny Abarca, *Manager*
Arminda Aguayo, *Manager*
EMP: 17
SQ FT: 15,000
SALES (est): 3.8MM **Privately Held**
WEB: www.verdugotool.com
SIC: 3469 3544 Metal stampings; special dies & tools

(P-13294)
WALKER SPRING & STAMPING CORP
1555 S Vintage Ave, Ontario (91761-3655)
PHONE..................................909 390-4300
Lang Walker, *Ch of Bd*
Bruce Walker, *President*
Carmen Prieto, *CFO*
Randy Walker, *Vice Pres*
Marianne Sichi, *Principal*
▲ **EMP:** 110 **EST:** 1954
SQ FT: 108,000
SALES (est): 31.1MM **Privately Held**
WEB: www.walkercorp.com
SIC: 3469 3495 Stamping metal for the trade; precision springs

(P-13295)
WEST COAST MANUFACTURING INC
1822 Western Ave, Stanton (90680)
PHONE..................................714 897-4221
Patrick Hundley, *President*
Minerva Hundley, *Vice Pres*
Ann Marie Lind, *Manager*
▲ **EMP:** 26
SQ FT: 8,000
SALES (est): 5.6MM **Privately Held**
WEB: www.westcoastmfg.com
SIC: 3469 Machine parts, stamped or pressed metal

(P-13296)
WEST COAST METAL STAMPING INC
550 W Crowther Ave, Placentia (92870-6312)
PHONE..................................714 792-0322
Jerome R Reinhart, *President*
Dan A Totoiu, *Vice Pres*
EMP: 32
SQ FT: 58,000
SALES: 5MM **Privately Held**
WEB: www.bjtooldie.com
SIC: 3469 Metal stampings

(P-13297)
WESTERN METAL SPINNING & MFG
Also Called: Western Metal Spinning Farming
5055 Western Way, Perris (92571-7420)
PHONE..................................951 657-0711
David Domanske, *President*
EMP: 10 **EST:** 1945
SQ FT: 20,000
SALES (est): 1.9MM **Privately Held**
WEB: www.kissaviation.com
SIC: 3469 3411 Spinning metal for the trade; metal cans

(P-13298)
WILLIAMS METAL BLANKING DIES
16222 Minnesota Ave, Paramount (90723-4916)
PHONE..................................562 634-4592
Verle Williams, *President*
Fred Harmon, *Vice Pres*
EMP: 12
SQ FT: 10,000
SALES: 810.2K **Privately Held**
SIC: 3469 3544 Stamping metal for the trade; special dies & tools

---

3471 Electroplating, Plating, Polishing, Anodizing & Coloring

---

(P-13299)
A & D PLATING INC
2265 Micro Pl Ste A, Escondido (92029-1011)
PHONE..................................760 480-4580
Antonio Medina, *President*
EMP: 11
SQ FT: 2,400
SALES: 550K **Privately Held**
SIC: 3471 Electroplating of metals or formed products; plating of metals or formed products

(P-13300)
A & E ANODIZING INC
652 Charles St Ste A, San Jose (95112-1433)
PHONE..................................408 297-5910
Edwardo Ibanez, *President*
Angelica Ibanez, *CFO*
EMP: 15
SALES (est): 1.6MM **Privately Held**
SIC: 3471 Anodizing (plating) of metals or formed products

(P-13301)
A&A METAL FINISHING ENTPS LLC
8290 Alpine Ave, Sacramento (95826-4748)
PHONE..................................916 442-1063
Anthony R Nole, *Vice Pres*
Nancy M Casale, *Admin Sec*
EMP: 20
SALES (est): 1.9MM **Privately Held**
SIC: 3471 Electroplating of metals or formed products; finishing, metals or formed products

(P-13302)
A-H PLATING INC
28079 Avenue Stanford, Valencia (91355-1104)
PHONE..................................818 845-6243
John Waschack, *President*
EMP: 65
SALES (est): 5.2MM
SALES (corp-wide): 30MM **Privately Held**
WEB: www.sunvairoverhaul.com
SIC: 3471 Plating of metals or formed products
HQ: Sunvair, Inc.
29145 The Old Rd
Valencia CA 91355
661 294-3777

(P-13303)
AAA PLATING & INSPECTION INC
424 E Dixon St, Compton (90222-1420)
PHONE..................................323 979-8930
Gerald Wahlin, *CEO*
Charles Schwan, *Corp Secy*
Sunny Chandler, *Lab Dir*
Hugo Munos, *Electrical Engi*
Marie Reed, *Human Res Mgr*
EMP: 95
SQ FT: 50,000
SALES (est): 15.1MM **Privately Held**
WEB: www.aaaplating.com
SIC: 3471 8734 Anodizing (plating) of metals or formed products; metallurgical testing laboratory

PRODUCTS & SVCS

(P-13304)
ABLE METAL PLATING INC
932 86th Ave, Oakland (94621-1642)
P.O. Box 43480 (94624-0480)
PHONE...................510 569-6539
Jose Vasquez, *President*
Rafael De La Paz, *Vice Pres*
Elizabeth Vasquez, *Vice Pres*
EMP: 20
SQ FT: 7,500
SALES: 1MM **Privately Held**
SIC: 3471 Electroplating of metals or
formed products

(P-13305)
ACCUCROME PLATING CO INC
115 W 154th St, Gardena (90248-2201)
PHONE...................310 327-8268
Armen Maghtessian, *President*
EMP: 10
SQ FT: 1,800
SALES (est): 896.8K **Privately Held**
SIC: 3471 Chromium plating of metals or
formed products; cleaning, polishing & fin-
ishing

(P-13306)
ACCURATE ANODIZING INC
1801 W El Segundo Blvd, Compton
(90222-1026)
P.O. Box 5207 (90224-5207)
PHONE...................310 637-0349
Thomas P Oakes, *President*
John Oakes, *Corp Secy*
Laura Oakes, *Exec VP*
EMP: 10
SQ FT: 8,000
SALES (est): 1.1MM **Privately Held**
SIC: 3471 Anodizing (plating) of metals or
formed products; plating of metals or
formed products

(P-13307)
ACCURATE PLATING COMPANY
2811 Alcazar St, Los Angeles (90033-1108)
P.O. Box 33348 (90033-0348)
PHONE...................323 268-8567
Dennis Orr, *President*
Rigo Rodriguez, *Vice Pres*
EMP: 30 EST: 1949
SQ FT: 18,000
SALES (est): 3.6MM **Privately Held**
WEB: www.accurateplating.com
SIC: 3471 Electroplating of metals or
formed products

(P-13308)
ACTIVE PLATING INC
1411 E Pomona St, Santa Ana
(92705-4802)
PHONE...................714 547-0356
Keith Korta, *President*
EMP: 25
SQ FT: 6,000
SALES (est): 3.3MM **Privately Held**
SIC: 3471 Electroplating of metals or
formed products; plating of metals or
formed products

(P-13309)
**ADVANCED SURFACE
FINISHING INC**
1181 N 4th St Ste 50, San Jose
(95112-4962)
PHONE...................408 275-9718
Salah Hamed, *President*
Jose Diaz, *Vice Pres*
EMP: 10
SQ FT: 17,000
SALES: 1.5MM **Privately Held**
SIC: 3471 Plating of metals or formed
products

(P-13310)
ADVANCED TECH PLATING
1061 N Grove St, Anaheim (92806-2015)
PHONE...................714 630-7093
Meliton Gomez, *President*
Danny Gomez, *Sales Associate*
EMP: 30
SQ FT: 9,706
SALES (est): 2.6MM **Privately Held**
SIC: 3471 Plating of metals or formed
products

(P-13311)
**AERO MANUFACTURING &
PLTG CO**
Also Called: Automation Plating
927 Thompson Ave, Glendale
(91201-2011)
PHONE...................818 241-2844
William Wiggins, *Chairman*
Peter Wiggins, *Chairman*
EMP: 50 EST: 1958
SQ FT: 65,000
SALES (est): 4.4MM **Privately Held**
WEB: www.apczinc.com
SIC: 3471 Plating & polishing

(P-13312)
AERODYNAMIC PLATING CO
13620 S Saint Andrews Pl, Gardena
(90249-2480)
PHONE...................310 329-7959
Joe Reynoso Jr, *President*
Joe Reynoso Sr, *Treasurer*
EMP: 60 EST: 1967
SQ FT: 5,500
SALES (est): 5.7MM **Privately Held**
SIC: 3471 Anodizing (plating) of metals or
formed products; electroplating of metals
or formed products

(P-13313)
AGUILAR WILLIAMS INC
Also Called: Tool & Jig Plating Co
7635 Baldwin Pl, Whittier (90602-1024)
PHONE...................562 693-2736
Jesus Aguilar, *President*
Michael Williams, *Treasurer*
Leonor Oropeza, *Admin Sec*
EMP: 13
SALES (est): 720K **Privately Held**
SIC: 3471 Chromium plating of metals or
formed products

(P-13314)
AI INDUSTRIES LLC (PA)
1725 E Byshore Rd Ste 101, Redwood City
(94063)
PHONE...................650 366-4099
Shannon Lew,
Bob Mosko, *Human Res Mgr*
EMP: 79
SQ FT: 27,000
SALES (est): 19.4MM **Privately Held**
WEB: www.aiindustries.com
SIC: 3471 3479 Anodizing (plating) of met-
als or formed products; coating of metals
& formed products

(P-13315)
ALCO PLATING CORP (PA)
Also Called: Modern Plating
1400 Long Beach Ave, Los Angeles
(90021-2794)
PHONE...................213 749-7561
E Edward Manzetti, *President*
Emil Edward Manzetti, *President*
David Manzetti, *Vice Pres*
▲ EMP: 110
SQ FT: 65,000
SALES (est): 10.5MM **Privately Held**
SIC: 3471 Electroplating of metals or
formed products

(P-13316)
ALERT PLATING COMPANY
9939 Glenoaks Blvd, Sun Valley
(91352-1023)
PHONE...................818 771-9304
David La Liberte, *President*
Maurice La Liberte, *Ch of Bd*
Ed Lee, *Treasurer*
Shirley La Liberte, *Admin Sec*
EMP: 45
SQ FT: 22,000
SALES (est): 6.8MM **Privately Held**
SIC: 3471 Finishing, metals or formed
products; plating of metals or formed
products

(P-13317)
**ALL METALS PROC SAN DIEGO
INC**
Also Called: AMC
8401 Standustrial St, Stanton
(90680-2688)
PHONE...................714 828-8238

Kevin Fairfax, *Vice Pres*
EMP: 120
SQ FT: 27,000
SALES (est): 16.2MM **Privately Held**
WEB: www.drilube.com
SIC: 3471 3479 8734 Electroplating of
metals or formed products; enameling, including porcelain, of metal products;
painting of metal products; X-ray inspection service, industrial; metallurgical testing laboratory

(P-13318)
ALLBLACK CO INC
13090 Park St, Santa Fe Springs
(90670-4032)
PHONE...................562 946-2955
Juan F Guerrero, *President*
Lorena Guerrero, *Corp Secy*
▲ EMP: 39
SQ FT: 12,000
SALES (est): 3MM **Privately Held**
SIC: 3471 Finishing, metals or formed
products

(P-13319)
ALLEN INDUSTRIAL INC
960 S Hathaway St, Banning (92220-6302)
P.O. Box 776 (92220-0006)
PHONE...................951 849-4966
David Dohoda, *Owner*
EMP: 10
SALES (est): 1MM **Privately Held**
SIC: 3471 7699 Plating of metals or
formed products; industrial machinery &
equipment repair

(P-13320)
**ALLOY TECH
ELECTROPOLISHING**
2220 S Huron Dr, Santa Ana (92704-4947)
PHONE...................714 434-6604
Ursula Zagner, *CEO*
George Zagner, *Vice Pres*
EMP: 10
SQ FT: 10,000
SALES (est): 1.2MM **Privately Held**
WEB: www.atep.com
SIC: 3471 Cleaning, polishing & finishing

(P-13321)
ALM CHROME
654 Young St, Santa Ana (92705-5633)
PHONE...................714 545-3540
Lanberto Morales, *Owner*
Cindy Ramos, *Manager*
EMP: 50
SALES (est): 3.2MM **Privately Held**
SIC: 3471 Electroplating of metals or
formed products

(P-13322)
**ALPHA POLISHING
CORPORATION (PA)**
Also Called: General Plating
1313 Mirasol St, Los Angeles
(90023-3108)
PHONE...................323 263-7593
Alan Olick, *President*
Trinidad Gonzales, *Vice Pres*
Luis Casillas, *Manager*
EMP: 60
SQ FT: 7,500
SALES (est): 10.5MM **Privately Held**
WEB: www.generalplating.com
SIC: 3471 3911 Plating of metals or
formed products; polishing, metals or
formed products; pins (jewelry), precious
metal

(P-13323)
ALPHACOAT FINISHING LLC
9350 Cabot Dr, San Diego (92126-4311)
PHONE...................949 748-7796
Ravinder Joshi,
Vaishali Joshi,
EMP: 28 EST: 2017
SALES (est): 1.7MM **Privately Held**
SIC: 3471 Plating of metals or formed
products

(P-13324)
ALUMFLAM NORTH AMERICA
16604 Edwards Rd, Cerritos (90703-2438)
PHONE...................562 926-9520
Carl Lorentzen, *Principal*

EMP: 20
SALES (est): 1.4MM **Privately Held**
SIC: 3471 Coloring & finishing of aluminum
or formed products

(P-13325)
ALUMIN-ART PLATING CO INC
803 W State St, Ontario (91762-4130)
PHONE...................909 983-1866
David Rudy, *President*
Barbara Newman, *Treasurer*
Joyce Clements, *Vice Pres*
Isaac Rudy, *Safety Mgr*
Jerry Newman, *Manager*
EMP: 30 EST: 1961
SQ FT: 6,500
SALES: 1.5MM **Privately Held**
SIC: 3471 Electroplating of metals or
formed products

(P-13326)
ALUMINUM COATING TECH INC
Also Called: A.C.T.
8290 Alpine Ave, Sacramento
(95826-4748)
PHONE...................916 442-1063
Steven S Hickey, *CEO*
EMP: 20
SALES (est): 1.6MM **Privately Held**
SIC: 3471 Plating of metals or formed
products

(P-13327)
**AMEX PLATING
INCORPORATED**
3333 Woodward Ave, Santa Clara
(95054-2628)
PHONE...................408 986-8222
Jose Rodriguez, *President*
Sylvia D Rodriguez, *CEO*
Rebeca Rodriguez, *Vice Pres*
Nhan Lu, *General Mgr*
EMP: 30
SQ FT: 10,850
SALES (est): 3.6MM **Privately Held**
SIC: 3471 Finishing, metals or formed
products; anodizing (plating) of metals or
formed products

(P-13328)
ANADITE CAL RESTORATION TR
Also Called: Metal Finishing Division
10647 Garfield Ave, South Gate
(90280-7391)
P.O. Box 1399 (90280-1399)
PHONE...................562 861-2205
Margie Gutierrez, *Branch Mgr*
EMP: 46
SALES (corp-wide): 4.2MM **Privately
Held**
WEB: www.anadite.com
SIC: 3471 Finishing, metals or formed
products
PA: Anadite California Restoration Trust
711 W Hurst Blvd
Hurst TX 76053
817 282-9171

(P-13329)
ANAPLEX CORPORATION
15547 Garfield Ave, Paramount
(90723-4033)
PHONE...................714 522-4481
Carmen Campbell, *CEO*
Bernie Kerper, *President*
EMP: 48 EST: 1962
SQ FT: 38,000
SALES (est): 5.9MM **Privately Held**
SIC: 3471 Plating of metals or formed
products; finishing, metals or formed
products

(P-13330)
ANOCOTE
7550 Trade St, San Diego (92121-2412)
PHONE...................858 566-1015
Romy Cimarmann, *President*
EMP: 12
SQ FT: 1,100
SALES (est): 994K **Privately Held**
SIC: 3471 Coloring & finishing of aluminum
or formed products

▲ = Import ▼=Export
◆ =Import/Export

(P-13331)
ANODIZING INDUSTRIES INC
5222 Alhambra Ave, Los Angeles
(90032-3403)
P.O. Box 32459 (90032-0459)
PHONE..................................323 227-4916
Eugene J Golling, *President*
Amir Afshar, *Vice Pres*
Arvin Mellat, *Production*
George Dominguez, *Manager*
▲ EMP: 30
SQ FT: 8,000
SALES (est): 4.6MM Privately Held
WEB: www.anodizingindustries.com
SIC: 3471 3479 2396 Anodizing (plating)
  of metals or formed products; cleaning,
  polishing & finishing; painting of metal
  products; automotive & apparel trimmings

(P-13332)
ANODYNE INC
2230 S Susan St, Santa Ana (92704-4493)
PHONE..................................714 549-3321
Ralph Adams, *President*
Patti Kientz, *Vice Pres*
Gary Fox, *Director*
Sue Grace, *Accounts Mgr*
EMP: 49 EST: 1960
SQ FT: 30,000
SALES (est): 7.5MM Privately Held
SIC: 3471 8734 Anodizing (plating) of met-
  als or formed products; testing laborato-
  ries

(P-13333)
APPLIED ANODIZE INC
622 Charcot Ave Ste D, San Jose
(95131-2205)
PHONE..................................408 435-9191
Jose Muguerza, *President*
EMP: 55 EST: 1978
SQ FT: 14,000
SALES (est): 5MM Privately Held
SIC: 3471 Coloring & finishing of aluminum
  or formed products; finishing, metals or
  formed products; plating of metals or
  formed products

(P-13334)
AQUARIAN COATINGS CORP
1140 N Tustin Ave, Anaheim (92807-1778)
PHONE..................................714 632-0230
Ronald Marquez, *President*
Rose Marquez, *Vice Pres*
Roy Burns, *Marketing Staff*
EMP: 37 EST: 1974
SQ FT: 20,000
SALES (est): 3.3MM Privately Held
SIC: 3471 Electroplating of metals or
  formed products

(P-13335)
ARA TECHNOLOGY
1286 Anvilwood Ave, Sunnyvale
(94089-2203)
PHONE..................................408 734-8131
Mardig Chakalian, *President*
Haig Chakalian, *Vice Pres*
EMP: 20 EST: 1977
SQ FT: 10,000
SALES (est): 1.9MM Privately Held
SIC: 3471 Plating of metals or formed
  products

(P-13336)
ARTISTIC PLTG & MET FINSHG INC
2801 E Miraloma Ave, Anaheim
(92806-1804)
PHONE..................................619 661-1691
Kipton Kahler, *President*
EMP: 100
SQ FT: 44,573
SALES (est): 10.2MM Privately Held
SIC: 3471 Chromium plating of metals or
  formed products

(P-13337)
ARTURO CAMPOS
Also Called: A&A Plating
796 Palmyrita Ave Ste B, Riverside
(92507-1824)
PHONE..................................951 300-2111
Arturo Campos, *Owner*
▼ EMP: 12 EST: 2007
SQ FT: 3,680

SALES (est): 882.5K Privately Held
SIC: 3471 Plating of metals or formed
  products

(P-13338)
ASSOCIATED PLATING COMPANY
Also Called: A P C
9636 Ann St, Santa Fe Springs
(90670-2902)
PHONE..................................562 946-5525
Michael Evans, *President*
Jon Shulkin, *Shareholder*
Diane Crane, *Vice Pres*
Randy Roth, *Plant Engr*
Theresa Flores,
▲ EMP: 42 EST: 1952
SQ FT: 18,000
SALES (est): 4.8MM Privately Held
WEB: www.associatedplating.com
SIC: 3471 Finishing, metals or formed
  products; electroplating of metals or
  formed products

(P-13339)
ASTRO CHROME AND POLSG CORP
8136 Lankershim Blvd, North Hollywood
(91605-1611)
PHONE..................................818 781-1463
Jesse Gonzalez, *President*
Eazi Tamen, *General Mgr*
EMP: 23
SQ FT: 3,000
SALES (est): 1.7MM Privately Held
SIC: 3471 Plating of metals or formed
  products

(P-13340)
ATMF INC
Also Called: Ano-Tech Metal Finishing
807 Lincoln Ave, Clovis (93612-2245)
PHONE..................................559 299-6836
Carol Downs, *CEO*
Kelly S Downs, *President*
Gregory Ott, *Vice Pres*
Ken Ruiz, *Opers Mgr*
EMP: 30
SQ FT: 8,000
SALES (est): 5.1MM Privately Held
WEB: www.atmf.com
SIC: 3471 Anodizing (plating) of metals or
  formed products; coloring & finishing of
  aluminum or formed products

(P-13341)
AUTOMATION PLATING CORPORATION
927 Thompson Ave, Glendale
(91201-2011)
PHONE..................................323 245-4951
William D Wiggins, *Co-COB*
Peter K Wiggins, *CEO*
Pat Kinzy, *COO*
Marcia Mitchell, *CFO*
Edward Lee, *Admin Sec*
EMP: 40
SQ FT: 65,000
SALES (est): 6.1MM Privately Held
SIC: 3471 Plating of metals or formed
  products

(P-13342)
B & C PLATING CO
1507 S Sunol Dr, Los Angeles
(90023-4031)
PHONE..................................323 263-6757
Dick Patel, *President*
Suresh Sheth, *Admin Sec*
EMP: 22
SQ FT: 10,000
SALES (est): 2.3MM Privately Held
WEB: www.bandcplating.com
SIC: 3471 2899 Plating of metals or
  formed products; chemical preparations

(P-13343)
B D AND G SANDBLASTING CO
2428 E 54th St, Vernon (90058-3504)
PHONE..................................323 583-1741
Edward W Lynch, *President*
Judy Lynch, *Treasurer*
EMP: 19
SQ FT: 3,000

SALES (est): 2MM Privately Held
SIC: 3471 Sand blasting of metal parts

(P-13344)
BARRY AVENUE PLATING CO INC
2210 Barry Ave, Los Angeles (90064-1488)
PHONE..................................310 478-0078
Chuck Kearsley, *President*
Charles B Kearsley IV, *President*
Kenneth F Kearsley, *Vice Pres*
Cruz Maldonado, *General Mgr*
Timothy Dearn, *Opers Mgr*
▼ EMP: 88 EST: 1951
SQ FT: 26,000
SALES: 15.1MM Privately Held
SIC: 3471 Plating of metals or formed
  products

(P-13345)
BHC INDUSTRIES INC
239 E Greenleaf Blvd, Compton
(90220-4913)
PHONE..................................310 632-2000
Gary Barken, *President*
EMP: 25 EST: 2000
SQ FT: 20,000
SALES (est): 3.8MM Privately Held
SIC: 3471 Chromium plating of metals or
  formed products

(P-13346)
BLACK OXIDE INDUSTRIES INC
1745 N Orangethorpe Park, Anaheim
(92801-1139)
PHONE..................................714 870-9610
Pete Mata, *President*
Evelyn Mata, *Corp Secy*
Edward Mata, *Vice Pres*
EMP: 35 EST: 1974
SALES (est): 5MM Privately Held
WEB: www.blackoxideindustries.com
SIC: 3471 3479 Electroplating & plating;
  coating of metals & formed products

(P-13347)
BLACK OXIDE SERVICE INC
Also Called: Bos
1070 Linda Vista Dr Ste A, San Marcos
(92078-2653)
PHONE..................................760 744-8692
Leopold Slivnik, *President*
EMP: 10
SQ FT: 1,250
SALES (est): 1.1MM Privately Held
WEB: www.blackoxideservice.com
SIC: 3471 5169 Plating of metals or
  formed products; chemicals & allied prod-
  ucts

(P-13348)
BLAIRS METAL POLSG PLTG CO INC
17760 Crusader Ave, Cerritos
(90703-2629)
PHONE..................................562 860-7106
Keith W Blair, *CEO*
Keith Blair, *Vice Pres*
EMP: 13
SQ FT: 10,000
SALES: 1MM Privately Held
SIC: 3471 Plating of metals or formed
  products

(P-13349)
BOBBYS METAL FINISHING
12423 Gladstone Ave # 25, Sylmar
(91342-5341)
PHONE..................................818 837-1928
Roberto Montenegro, *Principal*
EMP: 10
SALES (est): 734.3K Privately Held
SIC: 3471 Cleaning, polishing & finishing

(P-13350)
BODYCOTE THERMAL PROC INC
3370 Benedict Way, Huntington Park
(90255-4517)
PHONE..................................323 583-1231
Chris Hall, *Branch Mgr*
EMP: 87
SQ FT: 16,694

SALES (corp-wide): 911.9MM Privately
Held
SIC: 3471 3398 Plating & polishing; metal
  heat treating
HQ: Bodycote Thermal Processing, Inc.
  12700 Park Central Dr # 700
  Dallas TX 75251
  214 904-2420

(P-13351)
BONNER PROCESSING INC
6052 Industrial Way Ste A, Livermore
(94551-9711)
PHONE..................................925 455-3833
Robert Bonner, *President*
EMP: 40
SQ FT: 19,500
SALES (est): 3.8MM Privately Held
SIC: 3471 Tumbling (cleaning & polishing)
  of machine parts

(P-13352)
BOWMAN PLATING CO INC
2631 E 126th St, Compton (90222-1599)
P.O. Box 5205 (90224-5205)
PHONE..................................310 639-4343
Mac Esfandi, *President*
John Esfandi, *Shareholder*
Cyrus Gipoor, *Shareholder*
Massoud Akhavi, *Officer*
Rashel Esfandi, *Admin Sec*
EMP: 150 EST: 1952
SALES (est): 21.7MM Privately Held
WEB: www.bowmanplating.com
SIC: 3471 Plating of metals or formed
  products

(P-13353)
BRITE PLATING CO INC
1313 Mirasol St, Los Angeles
(90023-3108)
PHONE..................................323 263-7593
Alan Olick, *CEO*
Kashiam Patel, *Vice Pres*
EMP: 71
SQ FT: 60,000
SALES (est): 7.5MM Privately Held
SIC: 3471 Plating of metals or formed
  products

(P-13354)
BRONZE-WAY PLATING CORPORATION (PA)
3301 E 14th St, Los Angeles (90023-3893)
PHONE..................................323 266-6933
Sarkis Mikhael-Fard, *President*
Benjamin Mikhael-Fard, *Vice Pres*
Fiyodor Mikhael-Fard, *Vice Pres*
Fred Mikhael-Fard, *Vice Pres*
EMP: 44 EST: 1956
SQ FT: 27,000
SALES (est): 3.2MM Privately Held
SIC: 3471 Electroplating of metals or
  formed products

(P-13355)
BUDS POLISHING & METAL FINSHG
1156 N Kraemer Pl, Anaheim (92806-1922)
PHONE..................................714 632-0121
Forrest Graybill, *President*
EMP: 15
SALES (est): 1.7MM Privately Held
SIC: 3471 Polishing, metals or formed
  products

(P-13356)
BURBANK PLATING SERVICE CORP
13561 Desmond St, Pacoima
(91331-2394)
PHONE..................................818 899-1157
Robert Scheer, *President*
Andy Scheer, *Vice Pres*
▲ EMP: 15
SQ FT: 20,000
SALES (est): 1.2MM Privately Held
SIC: 3471 Plating of metals or formed
  products

(P-13357)
BURLINGTON ENGINEERING INC
220 W Grove Ave, Orange (92865-3204)
PHONE..................................714 921-4045

P
R
O
D
U
C
T
S

&

S
V
C
S

Karen Corbell, *President*
David Corbell, *Vice Pres*
EMP: 21
SQ FT: 18,000
SALES (est): 2.2MM **Privately Held**
WEB: www.burlingtoneng.com
SIC: 3471 3398 Plating & polishing; metal
heat treating

(P-13358)
BUSH POLISHING & CHROME
2236 W 2nd St, Santa Ana (92703-3511)
PHONE..................714 537-7440
David L Bush Sr, *Owner*
Chris Hefferon, *Opers Dir*
EMP: 12
SALES: 1MM **Privately Held**
WEB: www.bushpolishingandchrome.com
SIC: 3471 Finishing, metals or formed
products

(P-13359)
C C M D INC
Also Called: Hytech Processing
700 Centinela Ave, Inglewood
(90302-2414)
PHONE..................310 673-5532
Michael S Graves, *President*
Odette Graves, *CFO*
EMP: 15
SQ FT: 7,000
SALES: 850K **Privately Held**
WEB: www.hytechprocessing.com
SIC: 3471 Finishing, metals or formed
products

(P-13360)
C P AUTO PRODUCTS INC
3901 Medford St, Los Angeles
(90063-1608)
PHONE..................323 266-3850
Tom Longo, *President*
▲ **EMP:** 50
SQ FT: 100,000
SALES (est): 5MM **Privately Held**
WEB: www.derale.com
SIC: 3471 3714 3564 Plating of metals or
formed products; motor vehicle parts &
accessories; blowers & fans

(P-13361)
CADILLAC PLATING INC
1147 W Struck Ave, Orange (92867-3529)
PHONE..................714 639-0342
Adan Ibarra, *President*
Lupe Ibarra, *Treasurer*
Alfred Ibarra, *Assistant VP*
EMP: 18 **EST:** 1972
SQ FT: 6,000
SALES (est): 2.2MM **Privately Held**
SIC: 3471 Plating of metals or formed
products; electroplating of metals or
formed products

(P-13362)
CAL-AURUM INDUSTRIES
15632 Container Ln, Huntington Beach
(92649-1533)
PHONE..................714 898-0996
Paul A Ginder, *President*
Chuck Tygard, *Vice Pres*
Allen Witbeck, *Vice Pres*
Denise Penn, *Human Res Mgr*
Jason Nations, *Purch Mgr*
EMP: 35 **EST:** 1971
SQ FT: 25,000
SALES (est): 5.9MM **Privately Held**
WEB: www.cal-aurum.com
SIC: 3471 Plating of metals or formed
products

(P-13363)
CAL-TRON PLATING INC
11919 Rivera Rd, Santa Fe Springs
(90670-2209)
PHONE..................562 945-1181
Carl Troncale Jr, *CEO*
Carl Troncale Sr, *Ch of Bd*
EMP: 45 **EST:** 1961
SQ FT: 15,000
SALES (est): 3.5MM **Privately Held**
SIC: 3471 Electroplating of metals or
formed products; polishing, metals or
formed products

(P-13364)
**CALIFORNIA METAL
PROCESSING CO**
1518 W Slauson Ave # 1530, Los Angeles
(90047-1230)
PHONE..................323 753-2247
Terry Andersen, *Partner*
Merry Anderson, *Ltd Ptnr*
Robert Gates, *Ltd Ptnr*
Thelma Gates, *Ltd Ptnr*
EMP: 21
SQ FT: 10,800
SALES: 1.8MM **Privately Held**
SIC: 3471 8734 Plating of metals or
formed products; testing laboratories

(P-13365)
**CALIFORNIA TECHNICAL PLTG
CORP**
11533 Bradley Ave, San Fernando
(91340-2519)
PHONE..................818 365-8205
David Anzures Sr, *President*
Sandra Anzures, *Corp Secy*
Brett Lpio, *General Mgr*
EMP: 45
SQ FT: 26,000
SALES (est): 5.1MM **Privately Held**
WEB: www.caltechplating.com
SIC: 3471 Plating of metals or formed
products; cleaning & descaling metal
products; chromium plating of metals or
formed products

(P-13366)
CARTER PLATING INC
1842 N Keystone St, Burbank
(91504-3417)
PHONE..................818 842-1325
Val T Romney Sr, *President*
Earlene Romney, *Vice Pres*
EMP: 11 **EST:** 1953
SQ FT: 2,400
SALES (est): 1.1MM **Privately Held**
SIC: 3471 Plating of metals or formed
products

(P-13367)
CEMCOAT INC
4928 W Jefferson Blvd, Los Angeles
(90016-3923)
PHONE..................323 733-0125
Farzaneh Aalam, *President*
Mike Aalam, *Vice Pres*
Valentino Aquino, *Plant Mgr*
EMP: 20
SQ FT: 14,500
SALES (est): 2.3MM **Privately Held**
SIC: 3471 Plating of metals or formed
products

(P-13368)
**CERTIFIED STEEL TREATING
CORP**
2454 E 58th St, Vernon (90058-3592)
PHONE..................323 583-8711
Janice Davis, *President*
Pauline Nicolls, *Shareholder*
Dante Germano, *CFO*
Jeff Davis, *General Mgr*
Chuck Groves, *General Mgr*
EMP: 42
SQ FT: 30,000
SALES (est): 9.2MM **Privately Held**
WEB: www.certifiedsteeltreat.com
SIC: 3471 3398 Sand blasting of metal
parts; annealing of metal

(P-13369)
CHICO METAL FINISHING INC
3151 Richter Ave, Oroville (95966-5918)
PHONE..................530 534-7308
Tom Cosf, *President*
Jim Marry, *General Mgr*
EMP: 10
SQ FT: 7,500
SALES (est): 936.5K **Privately Held**
SIC: 3471 Plating of metals or formed
products

(P-13370)
CHROMAL PLATING COMPANY
Also Called: Chromal Plating & Grinding
1748 Workman St, Los Angeles
(90031-3395)
PHONE..................323 222-0119
Ethel Bokelman, *President*
Robin Ospoin, *CFO*
Robin Bokelman, *Corp Secy*
Ray F Bokelman Jr, *Vice Pres*
Diane L Remilinger, *Vice Pres*
EMP: 28
SQ FT: 20,625
SALES (est): 4.2MM **Privately Held**
WEB: www.chromal.com
SIC: 3471 3999 Electroplating of metals or
formed products; custom pulverizing &
grinding of plastic materials

(P-13371)
CHROME DEPOSIT CORP
Also Called: Roll Technology West
900 Loveridge Rd, Pittsburg (94565-2808)
P.O. Box 472 (94565-0047)
PHONE..................925 432-4507
Jim Goehring, *General Mgr*
EMP: 91
SALES (est): 7.9MM **Privately Held**
SIC: 3471 Chromium plating of metals or
formed products

(P-13372)
**CLASSIC COMPONENTS INC
(PA)**
Also Called: South Bay Chrome
3420 W Fordham Ave, Santa Ana
(92704-4422)
PHONE..................714 619-5690
Bernard R Glass, *President*
Gary Glass, *Admin Sec*
EMP: 10
SQ FT: 17,000
SALES (est): 2.9MM **Privately Held**
WEB: www.chromeplating.com
SIC: 3471 Chromium plating of metals or
formed products

(P-13373)
CLEAN SCIENCES INC
301 Whitney Pl, Fremont (94539-7665)
PHONE..................510 440-8660
Jonathan Kaye, *President*
Raquel Villaroman, *Executive Asst*
Snehal Patel, *Technician*
Dave Mortenson, *QC Mgr*
EMP: 12
SALES (est): 1.8MM **Privately Held**
WEB: www.cleansciences.com
SIC: 3471 Cleaning & descaling metal
products

(P-13374)
**COAST TO COAST MET FINSHG
CORP**
401 S Raymond Ave, Alhambra
(91803-1532)
PHONE..................626 282-2122
Gildardo Bernal, *President*
David Bernal, *Admin Sec*
EMP: 25
SQ FT: 20,000
SALES (est): 3.7MM **Privately Held**
SIC: 3471 3646 3645 Finishing, metals or
formed products; commercial indusl & in-
stitutional electric lighting fixtures; resi-
dential lighting fixtures

(P-13375)
**COASTLINE METAL FINISHING
CORP**
7061 Patterson Dr, Garden Grove
(92841-1414)
PHONE..................714 895-9099
Tracy Glende, *CEO*
Jamie Mitchell, *CFO*
Matthew Alty, *Vice Pres*
Juan Cadenas, *General Mgr*
Allan Fowler, *Manager*
EMP: 83
SQ FT: 18,600
SALES (est): 9.3MM **Privately Held**
WEB: www.coastlinemetalfinishing.com
SIC: 3471 Finishing, metals or formed
products; electroplating & plating; anodiz-
ing (plating) of metals or formed products

(P-13376)
COLORCARDS 960
6224 Via Regla, San Diego (92122-3921)
PHONE..................858 535-9311
Robert Munroe, *Partner*
Duane R Churchwell, *Partner*
EMP: 46
SALES (est): 1.7MM **Privately Held**
SIC: 3471 3999 Coloring & finishing of
aluminum or formed products; manufac-
turing industries

(P-13377)
**COMMERCIAL SAND BLAST
COMPANY**
Also Called: Gcm Coating
2678 E 26th St, Vernon (90058-1218)
P.O. Box 58184, Los Angeles (90058-0184)
PHONE..................323 581-8672
Fax: 323 589-2121
EMP: 11
SQ FT: 5,200
SALES (est): 1.4MM **Privately Held**
WEB: www.commercialsandblast.com
SIC: 3471 3479

(P-13378)
COMPONENT SURFACES INC
11880 Cmnty Rd Ste 380, Poway (92064)
PHONE..................858 513-3656
David Sheilds, *President*
EMP: 15
SQ FT: 1,000
SALES: 350K **Privately Held**
SIC: 3471 Plating of metals or formed
products

(P-13379)
CONNECTOR PLATING CORP
327 W 132nd St, Los Angeles
(90061-1105)
PHONE..................310 323-1622
Dale S Chung, *President*
EMP: 10
SQ FT: 12,000
SALES (est): 1.3MM **Privately Held**
SIC: 3471 Plating of metals or formed
products

(P-13380)
CONNELL PROCESSING INC
3094 N Avon St, Burbank (91504-2003)
PHONE..................818 845-7661
Stephen Lee, *President*
David Augustine, *Vice Pres*
EMP: 27
SQ FT: 25,000
SALES: 3.5MM **Privately Held**
WEB: www.connellprocessing.com
SIC: 3471 Finishing, metals or formed
products; electroplating of metals or
formed products

(P-13381)
**CONTINUOUS COATING CORP
(PA)**
Also Called: Clinch-On Cornerbead Company
520 W Grove Ave, Orange (92865-3210)
PHONE..................714 637-4642
Ralph M Scott, *President*
Kenneth N Harel, *Corp Secy*
Kenneth Harel, *Manager*
EMP: 85
SQ FT: 84,000
SALES (est): 15MM **Privately Held**
WEB: www.clinchon.com
SIC: 3471 3444 7389 Electroplating of
metals or formed products; sheet metal
specialties, not stamped; metal slitting &
shearing

(P-13382)
CRISOL METAL FINISHING
444 E Gardena Blvd C, Gardena
(90248-2914)
PHONE..................310 516-1165
Sebastian Carlo, *Owner*
EMP: 12
SALES (est): 1.4MM **Privately Held**
SIC: 3471 Plating of metals or formed
products

▲ = Import ▼=Export
◆ =Import/Export

(P-13383)
CSL OPERATING LLC
Also Called: C S L
529 Aldo Ave, Santa Clara (95054-2263)
PHONE..................................408 727-0893
Mahesh Naik, *President*
Tim Mickael, *Manager*
Mark Weber, *Manager*
▲ **EMP:** 55
SQ FT: 16,000
SALES (est): 7.5MM **Privately Held**
SIC: 3471 Anodizing (plating) of metals or
formed products; cleaning & descaling
metal products; electroplating of metals or
formed products; cleaning, polishing & fin-
ishing

(P-13384)
DANCO ANODIZING INC (PA)
Also Called: Danco Metal Surfacing
44 La Porte St, Arcadia (91006-2827)
P.O. Box 660727 (91066-0727)
PHONE..................................626 445-3303
Sherri Vivian Scherer, *President*
David Tatge, *Treasurer*
EMP: 40 **EST:** 1971
SQ FT: 10,000
SALES: 13.3MM **Privately Held**
WEB: www.danco.net
SIC: 3471 Anodizing (plating) of metals or
formed products

(P-13385)
DANCO ANODIZING INC
1750 E Monticello Ct, Ontario
(91761-7740)
PHONE..................................909 923-0562
Joe Galvan, *Manager*
Krista Panneton, *Office Mgr*
Tony Defries, *Info Tech Dir*
EMP: 20
SALES (corp-wide): 13.3MM **Privately
Held**
WEB: www.danco.net
SIC: 3471 Anodizing (plating) of metals or
formed products
PA: Danco Anodizing, Inc.
44 La Porte St
Arcadia CA 91006
626 445-3303

(P-13386)
DECORE PLATING COMPANY INC
434 W 164th St, Gardena (90248-2727)
PHONE..................................310 324-6755
Don Argo, *President*
Diana Argo, *Vice Pres*
EMP: 10 **EST:** 1962
SQ FT: 7,128
SALES (est): 1MM **Privately Held**
SIC: 3471 Plating & polishing

(P-13387)
DILLON AIRCRAFT DEBURRING
11771 Sheldon St, Sun Valley
(91352-1506)
PHONE..................................818 768-0801
Pedro Dillon, *President*
Consuelo Dillon, *Treasurer*
Alejandra Dillon, *Vice Pres*
EMP: 20
SQ FT: 4,000
SALES (est): 1.7MM **Privately Held**
SIC: 3471 Cleaning, polishing & finishing

(P-13388)
DIMAD ENTERPRISES INC (PA)
Also Called: Dimad Metal Finishing
44 La Porte St, Arcadia (91006-2827)
P.O. Box 660727 (91066-0727)
PHONE..................................626 445-3303
Bruce P Merwin, *President*
David Tatge, *Treasurer*
EMP: 14 **EST:** 1974
SQ FT: 2,000
SALES (est): 1.5MM **Privately Held**
SIC: 3471 Plating & polishing

(P-13389)
DU-ALL ANODIZING CORPORATION
730 Chestnut St, San Jose (95110-1803)
PHONE..................................408 275-6694
Edward Marchand, *President*

Greg Marchand, *President*
Tony Evins, *Vice Pres*
EMP: 18
SALES (est): 1.1MM **Privately Held**
SIC: 3471 Anodizing (plating) of metals or
formed products

(P-13390)
DU-ALL ANODIZING INC
730 Chestnut St, San Jose (95110-1803)
PHONE..................................408 275-6694
Gregrey Marchand, *President*
Tony Athens, *Vice Pres*
EMP: 20
SQ FT: 10,000
SALES (est): 1.7MM **Privately Held**
WEB: www.duallanodizing.com
SIC: 3471 6531 Anodizing (plating) of met-
als or formed products; finishing, metals
or formed products; real estate agents &
managers

(P-13391)
DUNHAM METAL PROCESSING CO
936 N Parker St, Orange (92867-5580)
P.O. Box 3736 (92857-0736)
PHONE..................................714 532-5551
Charles H Dunham, *Owner*
EMP: 40
SALES (est): 3.1MM **Privately Held**
SIC: 3471 2396 3341 Anodizing (plating)
of metals or formed products; plating of
metals or formed products; automotive &
apparel trimmings; secondary nonferrous
metals

(P-13392)
E F T FAST QUALITY SERVICE
2328 S Susan St, Santa Ana (92704-4421)
PHONE..................................714 751-1487
Michael Carnarius, *President*
Francis Ang, *President*
Ernesto Melecia, *Vice Pres*
Eiko Senaca, *Principal*
EMP: 10
SALES (est): 1.4MM **Privately Held**
SIC: 3471 Plating & polishing

(P-13393)
E M E INC
Also Called: Electro Machine & Engrg Co
500 E Pine St, Compton (90222-2818)
P.O. Box 4998 (90224-4998)
PHONE..................................310 639-1621
Wesley Turnbow, *CEO*
Steven Turnbow, *President*
Randy Turnbow, *Chairman*
Eloy Sandoval, *Admin Asst*
Margret Hammonds, *Human Res Mgr*
EMP: 125
SQ FT: 65,000
SALES: 8.8MM **Privately Held**
WEB: www.emeplating.com
SIC: 3471 2899 Anodizing (plating) of met-
als or formed products; chemical prepara-
tions

(P-13394)
EL MONTE PLATING COMPANY
11409 Stewart St, El Monte (91731-2748)
PHONE..................................626 448-3607
Darrel Jensen, *Owner*
EMP: 16
SQ FT: 5,000
SALES (est): 870K **Privately Held**
SIC: 3471 Plating of metals or formed
products; polishing, metals or formed
products

(P-13395)
ELECTRO PLATING SPECIALTIES
2436 American Ave, Hayward
(94545-1810)
PHONE..................................510 786-1881
Mary L Hall, *President*
Debbie McPeek, *Executive*
EMP: 32
SQ FT: 10,000
SALES (est): 3.7MM **Privately Held**
WEB: www.eps-plating.com
SIC: 3471 Electroplating of metals or
formed products

(P-13396)
ELECTROCHEM SOLUTIONS INC
32500 Central Ave, Union City
(94587-2032)
PHONE..................................510 476-1840
David Rossiter, *CEO*
Carol Walsh, *Human Res Mgr*
EMP: 14
SALES (est): 1.3MM **Privately Held**
SIC: 3471 Electroplating of metals or
formed products

(P-13397)
ELECTROCHEM SOLUTIONS LLC
32500 Central Ave, Union City
(94587-2032)
PHONE..................................510 476-1840
David Rossiter, *President*
Martin Delfino, *Controller*
EMP: 62
SQ FT: 21,315
SALES (est): 6.1MM **Privately Held**
SIC: 3471 Electroplating of metals or
formed products

(P-13398)
ELECTRODE TECHNOLOGIES INC
Also Called: Reid Metal Finishing
3110 W Harvard St Ste 14, Santa Ana
(92704-3940)
PHONE..................................714 549-3771
Tim A Grandcolas, *President*
Ivan Padron, *Admin Sec*
▲ **EMP:** 40
SQ FT: 10,000
SALES (est): 5.7MM **Privately Held**
SIC: 3471 Finishing, metals or formed
products

(P-13399)
ELECTROLIZING INC
1947 Hooper Ave, Los Angeles
(90011-1354)
P.O. Box 11900 (90011-0900)
PHONE..................................213 749-7876
Susan B Grant, *President*
Jack Morgan, *Vice Pres*
Janet James, *Sales Mgr*
EMP: 26 **EST:** 1947
SQ FT: 10,000
SALES (est): 3.5MM **Privately Held**
SIC: 3471 Electroplating of metals or
formed products

(P-13400)
ELECTROLURGY INC (PA)
1121 Duryea Ave, Irvine (92614-5519)
PHONE..................................949 250-4494
Eron G Eklund, *President*
June Eklund, *Ch of Bd*
Sean Eklund, *Vice Pres*
EMP: 48
SQ FT: 25,000
SALES (est): 14.1MM **Privately Held**
WEB: www.electrolurgy.com
SIC: 3471 3429 Electroplating of metals or
formed products; anodizing (plating) of
metals or formed products; polishing,
metals or formed products; marine hard-
ware

(P-13401)
ELECTROMATIC INC
7351 Radford Ave, North Hollywood
(91605-3715)
PHONE..................................818 765-3236
Norman Francis, *Branch Mgr*
EMP: 10
SQ FT: 7,351
SALES (corp-wide): 3.1MM **Privately
Held**
WEB: www.electromatic.com
SIC: 3471 Polishing, metals or formed
products
PA: Electromatic Inc
789 S Kellogg Ave
Goleta CA 93117
805 964-9880

(P-13402)
ELECTROMATIC INC (PA)
789 S Kellogg Ave, Goleta (93117-3884)
PHONE..................................805 964-9880
Mary F Wilk, *President*
Wyman Winn, *Vice Pres*
Terry Gamino, *Office Mgr*
Diana Wilk, *Admin Sec*
EMP: 10
SQ FT: 18,000
SALES (est): 3.1MM **Privately Held**
WEB: www.electromatic.com
SIC: 3471 Polishing, metals or formed
products

(P-13403)
ELECTROMATIC INC
14025 Stage Rd, Santa Fe Springs
(90670-5225)
PHONE..................................562 623-9993
Diego Alvizo, *Manager*
EMP: 15
SALES (corp-wide): 3.1MM **Privately
Held**
WEB: www.electromatic.com
SIC: 3471 Polishing, metals or formed
products
PA: Electromatic Inc
789 S Kellogg Ave
Goleta CA 93117
805 964-9880

(P-13404)
ELECTRON PLATING III INC
13932 Enterprise Dr, Garden Grove
(92843-4021)
PHONE..................................714 554-2210
Jose Luis Padilla Sr, *President*
Luis Padilla Sr, *President*
EMP: 32
SQ FT: 10,000
SALES (est): 3.8MM **Privately Held**
SIC: 3471 Electroplating of metals or
formed products; plating of metals or
formed products

(P-13405)
ELECTRONIC CHROME GRINDING CO
9128 Dice Rd, Santa Fe Springs
(90670-2545)
PHONE..................................562 946-6671
Philip Reed, *President*
Jeannette Goble, *Corp Secy*
Dale Reed, *Vice Pres*
Mike Reed, *Vice Pres*
EMP: 22
SQ FT: 55,000
SALES (est): 3.2MM **Privately Held**
SIC: 3471 3599 Electroplating of metals or
formed products; machine shop, jobbing
& repair

(P-13406)
ELECTRONIC PRECISION SPC INC
545 Mercury Ln, Brea (92821-4831)
PHONE..................................714 256-8950
Henry Brown, *President*
Ashley Rodriguez, *Office Mgr*
Jeff Powell, *Planning*
Magdeline Marunez, *Sales Staff*
Eddie Sabala,
EMP: 34
SQ FT: 4,000
SALES (est): 5.4MM **Privately Held**
WEB: www.elecprec.com
SIC: 3471 Electroplating of metals or
formed products

(P-13407)
ELITE METAL FINISHING LLC
540 Spectrum Cir, Oxnard (93030-8988)
PHONE..................................805 983-4320
Joe Hansen, *President*
George Hansen,
EMP: 135
SQ FT: 55,000
SALES: 3.3MM **Privately Held**
WEB: www.elitemetalfinishing.com
SIC: 3471 8734 Plating of metals or
formed products; testing laboratories;
metallurgical testing laboratory

PRODUCTS & SVCS

(P-13408)
ETCHED MEDIA CORPORATION
101 Gilman Ave, Campbell (95008-3005)
PHONE..........................408 374-6895
Elias Antoun, *President*
Farid Ghantous, *Vice Pres*
Jane Strang, *Buyer*
David Bui, *Production*
Kenny Vo, *Production*
▲ EMP: 32 EST: 1980
SQ FT: 15,000
SALES (est): 5.1MM **Privately Held**
WEB: www.etchedmedia.com
SIC: 3471 3479 3993 2396 Decorative plating & finishing of formed products; name plates: engraved, etched, etc.; signs & advertising specialties; automotive & apparel trimmings

(P-13409)
F & H PLATING LLC
Also Called: F & H Plating Co
12023 Vose St Ste A, North Hollywood (91605-5775)
PHONE..........................818 765-1221
Ron Bernal,
Randy Bernal,
EMP: 15
SQ FT: 5,000
SALES: 700K **Privately Held**
SIC: 3471 Electroplating of metals or formed products

(P-13410)
FINE QUALITY METAL FINSHG INC
1640 Daisy Ave, Long Beach (90813-1525)
PHONE..........................562 983-7425
Edna Bolour, *President*
Cy Gipoor, *Shareholder*
Manoucher Esfandi, *Treasurer*
EMP: 15
SQ FT: 6,000
SALES (est): 1.9MM **Privately Held**
WEB: www.finequalitymetalfinishing.com
SIC: 3471 Plating of metals or formed products

(P-13411)
FLORENCE INTERNATIONAL COMPANY
Also Called: Dixon Hard Chrome
11645 Pendleton St, Sun Valley (91352-2502)
PHONE..........................818 767-9650
Ronald Dixon, *President*
Donald Dixon, *Vice Pres*
Lawrence Dixon, *Vice Pres*
Audrey Farber, *Info Tech Mgr*
EMP: 45
SQ FT: 15,000
SALES (est): 5MM **Privately Held**
SIC: 3471 8734 Plating of metals or formed products; chromium plating of metals or formed products; testing laboratories

(P-13412)
FOUR-D METAL FINISHING INC
1065 Memorex Dr, Santa Clara (95050-2809)
PHONE..........................408 730-5722
Peter Deguara, *President*
EMP: 30
SQ FT: 11,000
SALES (est): 3.7MM **Privately Held**
WEB: www.aanddstudios.com
SIC: 3471 Electroplating of metals or formed products

(P-13413)
GCG CORPORATION
Also Called: Gcg Precision Metal Finishing
608 Ruberta Ave, Glendale (91201-2335)
PHONE..........................818 247-8508
Eugene Cockran, *President*
Gene Cockran, *Vice Pres*
EMP: 12
SQ FT: 13,000
SALES (est): 1.3MM **Privately Held**
SIC: 3471 Plating of metals or formed products

(P-13414)
GEM ENTERPRISES LLC
300 N Andreasen Dr, Escondido (92029-1317)
PHONE..........................760 746-6616
Jason Guthrie,
Rick Guthrie,
Russ Guthrie,
EMP: 25
SQ FT: 5,300
SALES: 1MM **Privately Held**
SIC: 3471 Plating & polishing

(P-13415)
GENERAL GRINDING INC
Also Called: Stailess Polishing Co.
801 51st Ave, Oakland (94601-5694)
PHONE..........................510 261-5557
Michael Bardon, *President*
Daniel Bardon, *Corp Secy*
EMP: 34 EST: 1944
SQ FT: 22,500
SALES: 3.5MM **Privately Held**
SIC: 3471 Plating & polishing

(P-13416)
GEORGE INDUSTRIES
4116 Whiteside St, Los Angeles (90063-1619)
PHONE..........................323 264-6660
Jeff Briggs, *President*
EMP: 380
SQ FT: 38,200
SALES: 34.7MM
SALES (corp-wide): 2.7B **Publicly Held**
WEB: www.valmont.com
SIC: 3471 3479 Anodizing (plating) of metals or formed products; cleaning & descaling metal products; plating of metals or formed products; aluminum coating of metal products
PA: Valmont Industries, Inc.
   1 Valmont Plz Ste 500
   Omaha NE 68154
   402 963-1000

(P-13417)
GLOBAL PLATING INC
44620 S Grimmer Blvd, Fremont (94538-6386)
PHONE..........................510 659-8764
Douglas Brothers, *President*
EMP: 35
SQ FT: 23,000
SALES: 2.9MM **Privately Held**
SIC: 3471 Plating of metals or formed products; finishing, metals or formed products; electroplating of metals or formed products

(P-13418)
GRANATH & GRANATH INC
Also Called: Sonic Plating Company
1930 W Rosecrans Ave, Gardena (90249-2930)
P.O. Box 5387 (90249-5387)
PHONE..........................310 327-5740
Richard E Granath Jr, *President*
Richard E Granath Sr, *Vice Pres*
Tina Mc Vey, *Admin Sec*
EMP: 22 EST: 1964
SQ FT: 40,000
SALES (est): 2.5MM **Privately Held**
SIC: 3471 Anodizing (plating) of metals or formed products; plating of metals or formed products

(P-13419)
GRAYBILLS METAL POLISHING INC
1212 E Puente Ave, West Covina (91790-1358)
PHONE..........................626 967-5742
Steve Graybill, *President*
EMP: 10
SQ FT: 10,000
SALES: 467K **Privately Held**
SIC: 3471

(P-13420)
GSP ACQUISITION CORPORATION
Also Called: Gardena Specialized Processing
19745 Lassen St, Chatsworth (91311-5646)
PHONE..........................310 532-9430
Michael Palatas, *President*
EMP: 42
SQ FT: 10,000
SALES: 1.1MM **Privately Held**
SIC: 3471 Finishing, metals or formed products

(P-13421)
HAMMON PLATING CORPORATION
890 Commercial St, Palo Alto (94303-4905)
PHONE..........................650 494-2691
Tom Wooten, *President*
Glen Phinney, *Corp Secy*
Dil Jeer, *QC Mgr*
Phillip Kelman, *Opers Staff*
John Montoya, *Director*
EMP: 35
SQ FT: 5,000
SALES (est): 5.1MM **Privately Held**
WEB: www.hammonplating.com
SIC: 3471 Electroplating of metals or formed products; plating of metals or formed products

(P-13422)
HANE & HANE INC
Also Called: University Plating Co
650 University Ave, San Jose (95110-1828)
PHONE..........................408 292-2140
Carter Hane, *President*
EMP: 20 EST: 1958
SQ FT: 700
SALES (est): 2.1MM **Privately Held**
SIC: 3471 Electroplating of metals or formed products

(P-13423)
HAROS ANODIZING SPECIALIST
630 Walsh Ave, Santa Clara (95050-2600)
PHONE..........................408 980-0892
Espanisalo Haro, *Owner*
EMP: 10
SQ FT: 2,500
SALES (est): 1MM **Privately Held**
SIC: 3471 Anodizing (plating) of metals or formed products

(P-13424)
HENRYS METAL POLISHING WORKS
3445 Union Pacific Ave, Los Angeles (90023-3834)
PHONE..........................323 263-9701
Danny Reese, *President*
EMP: 13
SQ FT: 7,000
SALES (est): 1.5MM **Privately Held**
SIC: 3471 Polishing, metals or formed products

(P-13425)
HIGHTOWER PLATING & MFG CO
Also Called: Hightower Metals
2090 N Glassell St, Orange (92865-3306)
P.O. Box 5586 (92863-5586)
PHONE..........................714 637-9110
Kurt Koch, *President*
Mark Koch, *Vice Pres*
EMP: 50
SQ FT: 8,000
SALES (est): 5.6MM **Privately Held**
SIC: 3471 Plating of metals or formed products

(P-13426)
HIXSON METAL FINISHING
829 Production Pl, Newport Beach (92663-2809)
PHONE..........................800 900-9798
Carl Blazik, *Principal*
Douglas Greene, *President*
Gary Ragan, *Lab Dir*
Liz Cervantes, *Technician*
John Crowell, *Technician*
EMP: 85
SQ FT: 38,000
SALES (est): 15.7MM **Privately Held**
WEB: www.hixsonmetalfinishing.com
SIC: 3471 Finishing, metals or formed products

(P-13427)
HUDSON PLATING WORKS
11941 Hertz Ave, Moorpark (93021-7145)
PHONE..........................805 517-1222
David Hudson, *President*
Donna Hudson, *Vice Pres*
William Hudson, *Vice Pres*
EMP: 14
SALES (est): 1.2MM **Privately Held**
SIC: 3471 Plating of metals or formed products

(P-13428)
HUMBERTO MURILLO INC
Also Called: Data Electronic Services
410 Nantucket Pl, Santa Ana (92703-3545)
PHONE..........................714 541-2628
Humberto Murillo, *President*
EMP: 45
SALES: 4MM **Privately Held**
SIC: 3471 Electroplating of metals or formed products

(P-13429)
HY-TECH PLATING INC
1011 American St, San Carlos (94070-5303)
PHONE..........................650 593-4566
Wendell Wessbecher, *President*
Joel Osias, *Exec VP*
EMP: 22
SALES (est): 2.1MM **Privately Held**
SIC: 3471 Finishing, metals or formed products; plating of metals or formed products

(P-13430)
INDUSTRIAL METAL FINISHING
1941 Petra Ln, Placentia (92870-6749)
PHONE..........................714 628-8808
Robert E Hayden, *President*
EMP: 19
SQ FT: 12,000
SALES (est): 2.4MM **Privately Held**
WEB: www.indmetfin.com
SIC: 3471 3398 Finishing, metals or formed products; shot peening (treating steel to reduce fatigue)

(P-13431)
INDUSTRIAL ZINC PLATING CORP
Also Called: Industrial Plating Co
7217 San Luis St, Carlsbad (92011-4622)
P.O. Box 9518, Long Beach (90810-0518)
PHONE..........................760 918-6877
Raymond C Ball, *President*
Patricia Ball, *Vice Pres*
EMP: 25
SQ FT: 45,000
SALES: 2MM **Privately Held**
SIC: 3471

(P-13432)
INTA TECHNOLOGIES CORPORATION
2281 Calle De Luna, Santa Clara (95054-1023)
PHONE..........................408 748-9955
Mina Doshi, *President*
Elsa Mendoza, *Research*
Tony Gerillo, *Engineer*
Jerry Walias, *Engineer*
Nina Doshi, *Controller*
EMP: 23
SQ FT: 15,000
SALES (est): 3.9MM **Privately Held**
WEB: www.intatech.com
SIC: 3471 2891 Electroplating of metals or formed products; sealants

(P-13433)
INTEGRATED MFG TECH INC (DH)
Also Called: IMT International
1477 N Milpitas Blvd, Milpitas (95035-3160)
PHONE..........................408 934-5879
Andy Loung, *CEO*

Kay Tan, *CFO*
▲ EMP: 13 EST: 1980
SQ FT: 21,000
SALES: 10MM
SALES (corp-wide): 78.2MM **Privately Held**
SIC: 3471 3599 Polishing, metals or formed products; machine shop, jobbing & repair
HQ: Asl International Trading, Inc.
1477 N Milpitas Blvd
Milpitas CA 95035
510 659-9770

(P-13434)
INTERNTIONAL PHOTO PLATES CORP
Also Called: Nanofilm
2641 Townsgate Rd Ste 100, Westlake Village (91361-2724)
PHONE..................805 496-5031
Valdis Sneberg, *President*
Dale Burow, *Vice Pres*
Maria Flores, *Executive*
Melissa Partida, *General Mgr*
Dorothy Cesari, *Admin Sec*
▲ EMP: 37
SQ FT: 8,000
SALES (est): 5MM **Privately Held**
WEB: www.nanofilm.com
SIC: 3471 2796 Plating & polishing; platemaking services

(P-13435)
J P TURGEON & SONS INC
7758 Scout Ave, Bell (90201-4942)
PHONE..................323 773-3105
David E Turgeon, *President*
Robert L Turgeon, *Treasurer*
Joseph Phillip Turgeon Jr, *Vice Pres*
Charles D Turgeon, *Admin Sec*
▲ EMP: 25
SQ FT: 9,200
SALES (est): 1.8MM **Privately Held**
SIC: 3471 Polishing, metals or formed products; buffing for the trade

(P-13436)
JD PROCESSING INC
2220 Cape Cod Way, Santa Ana (92703-3563)
PHONE..................714 972-8161
Thomas Scimeca, *CEO*
Daniel Nguyen, *Manager*
EMP: 50
SALES (est): 276.4K **Privately Held**
SIC: 3471 3559 Anodizing (plating) of metals or formed products; anodizing equipment

(P-13437)
K & L ANODIZING CORPORATION
272 W Elm Ave, Burbank (91502)
P.O. Box 311 (91503-0311)
PHONE..................323 849-6815
Donald Leiker, *Branch Mgr*
EMP: 77
SALES (corp-wide): 9.5MM **Privately Held**
WEB: www.klanodizing.com
SIC: 3471 Anodizing (plating) of metals or formed products
PA: K & L Anodizing Corporation
1200 S Victory Blvd
Burbank CA 91502
323 849-6815

(P-13438)
KANETIC LTD LLC
Also Called: Kane Aerospace
7000 Merrill Ave, Chino (91710-9091)
PHONE..................505 228-5692
Jana Spruce, *President*
John Spruce, *CEO*
EMP: 10 EST: 2016
SALES (est): 373.2K **Privately Held**
SIC: 3471 3429 Plating & polishing; metal fasteners

(P-13439)
KEN HOFFMANN INC
Also Called: Palm Springs Plating
345 Del Sol Rd, Palm Springs (92262-1607)
P.O. Box 4488 (92263-4488)
PHONE..................760 325-6012
Ken Hoffmann, *President*
EMP: 20
SQ FT: 4,200
SALES (est): 3.1MM **Privately Held**
WEB: www.psplating.com
SIC: 3471 Electroplating of metals or formed products

(P-13440)
KRYLER CORP
Also Called: Pecific Grinding
1217 E Ash Ave, Fullerton (92831-5019)
PHONE..................714 871-9611
Chet Krygier Sr, *President*
Phyllis Krygier, *Admin Sec*
EMP: 30
SQ FT: 900
SALES (est): 3.8MM **Privately Held**
WEB: www.krylercorp.com
SIC: 3471 Chromium plating of metals or formed products

(P-13441)
L N L ANODIZING INC
9900 Glenoaks Blvd Ste 3, Sun Valley (91352-1061)
PHONE..................818 768-9224
George Larry Sentena, *President*
EMP: 21
SQ FT: 6,000
SALES (est): 1.5MM **Privately Held**
WEB: www.lnlanodizing.com
SIC: 3471 Anodizing (plating) of metals or formed products

(P-13442)
LA HABRA PLATING CO INC
900 S Cypress St, La Habra (90631-6887)
PHONE..................562 694-2704
Sylvester Roblea, *President*
EMP: 10 EST: 1972
SQ FT: 6,800
SALES: 740K **Privately Held**
WEB: www.lahabraplating.com
SIC: 3471 Plating of metals or formed products

(P-13443)
LAKIN INDUSTRIES INC (PA)
Also Called: A & G Electropolish
18330 Ward St, Fountain Valley (92708-6853)
PHONE..................714 968-6438
Gary Lakin, *CEO*
EMP: 12
SQ FT: 6,200
SALES (est): 2.4MM **Privately Held**
SIC: 3471 Electroplating & plating; polishing, metals or formed products

(P-13444)
LEOS METAL POLISHING
Also Called: Leos Metal Polishing Works
10980 Alameda St, Lynwood (90262-1722)
PHONE..................310 635-5257
Tranquelino Leos, *Owner*
Tranquilino Leos, *Owner*
EMP: 15
SQ FT: 1,250
SALES: 900K **Privately Held**
SIC: 3471 Polishing, metals or formed products

(P-13445)
LORTZ & SON MFG CO
Also Called: Lortz Manufacturing
4042 Patton Way, Bakersfield (93308-5030)
PHONE..................281 241-9418
Nathan C Lortz, *President*
Steven E Fisher, *Shareholder*
Karen Lortz, *Admin Sec*
Erin Lemay, *Associate*
EMP: 130 EST: 1939
SQ FT: 50,000

SALES (est): 14MM **Privately Held**
WEB: www.lortz.com
SIC: 3471 3443 7692 3441 Plating & polishing; fabricated plate work (boiler shop); welding repair; fabricated structural metal

(P-13446)
M & G CUSTOM POLISHING
8356 Standustrial St, Stanton (90680-2618)
PHONE..................714 995-0261
Martin Ayala, *Partner*
Gerardo Ayala, *Partner*
EMP: 13
SQ FT: 1,500
SALES (est): 1.1MM **Privately Held**
SIC: 3471 Polishing, metals or formed products

(P-13447)
M & R PLATING CORPORATION
12375 Montague St, Arleta (91331-2214)
PHONE..................818 896-2700
Andres Rauda, *CEO*
EMP: 17
SQ FT: 11,000
SALES (est): 2.7MM **Privately Held**
WEB: www.m-rplatingcorp.com
SIC: 3471 Plating of metals or formed products

(P-13448)
M P C INDUSTRIAL PRODUCTS INC
Also Called: M P C Industries
2150 Mcgaw Ave, Irvine (92614-0912)
PHONE..................949 863-0106
Paul F Queyrel, *Chairman*
John A Spencer, *CFO*
▲ EMP: 30 EST: 1952
SQ FT: 55,000
SALES (est): 4.8MM **Privately Held**
SIC: 3471 3541 Polishing, metals or formed products; grinding, polishing, buffing, lapping & honing machines

(P-13449)
MAIN STEEL LLC
3100 Jefferson St, Riverside (92504-4339)
PHONE..................951 789-3010
Mike Folley, *Branch Mgr*
EMP: 52 **Privately Held**
SIC: 3471 Polishing, metals or formed products; buffing for the trade
HQ: Main Steel, Llc
2200 Pratt Blvd
Elk Grove Village IL 60007
847 916-1220

(P-13450)
MAKPLATE LLC
5780 Obata Way, Gilroy (95020-7092)
PHONE..................408 842-7572
Naaim Ali Yahya,
Zain Yahya, *Vice Pres*
Yusuf Zhumkhawala PHD,
EMP: 12
SQ FT: 5,000
SALES (est): 1MM **Privately Held**
WEB: www.makplate.com
SIC: 3471 Gold plating

(P-13451)
MENCARINI & JARWIN INC
Also Called: Chrome Craft
5950 88th St, Sacramento (95828-1109)
PHONE..................916 383-1660
Philip B Jarwin, *Ch of Bd*
Lillian J Jarwin, *President*
Judith Marrs, *Admin Sec*
EMP: 16
SQ FT: 46,000
SALES: 2MM **Privately Held**
SIC: 3471 Chromium plating of metals or formed products

(P-13452)
METAL CHEM INC
21514 Nordhoff St, Chatsworth (91311-5822)
PHONE..................818 727-9951
Carlos Pongo, *President*
EMP: 30

SALES (est): 3.5MM **Privately Held**
SIC: 3471 3443 Plating of metals or formed products; fabricated plate work (boiler shop)

(P-13453)
METAL PREPARATIONS
1000 E Ocean Blvd # 416, Long Beach (90802-8510)
PHONE..................213 628-5176
Jeff Savage, *President*
Jason Savage, *Vice Pres*
EMP: 25
SQ FT: 32,000
SALES (est): 2.5MM **Privately Held**
WEB: www.metalpreparations.com
SIC: 3471 Cleaning & descaling metal products; polishing, metals or formed products

(P-13454)
METAL SURFACES INC
6060 Shull St, Bell Gardens (90201-6297)
P.O. Box 5001 (90202-5001)
PHONE..................562 927-1331
Charles K Bell, *CEO*
Sam Bell, *COO*
Allan Erlandson, *CFO*
Nel Wallace, *Human Res Mgr*
Theresa Bell, *Purchasing*
EMP: 150
SQ FT: 85,000
SALES (est): 22.3MM **Privately Held**
WEB: www.metalsurfaces.com
SIC: 3471 Electroplating of metals or formed products

(P-13455)
METALCO
1475 67th St, Emeryville (94608-1079)
P.O. Box 621, Newcastle (95658-0621)
PHONE..................510 652-7470
Fritz Wisbar, *President*
William Lentz, *Vice Pres*
Luay Jardaneh, *General Mgr*
Margaret Duffield, *Admin Sec*
EMP: 12 EST: 1946
SQ FT: 15,500
SALES (est): 1.4MM **Privately Held**
SIC: 3471 Anodizing (plating) of metals or formed products

(P-13456)
MILNERS ANODIZING
3330 Mcmaude Pl, Santa Rosa (95407-8120)
PHONE..................707 584-1188
Terry Burson, *Owner*
Claire Burson, *Co-Owner*
EMP: 15
SQ FT: 7,200
SALES: 891K **Privately Held**
WEB: www.milnersanodizing.com
SIC: 3471 Anodizing (plating) of metals or formed products

(P-13457)
MODESTO PLTG & POWDR COATING
436 Mitchell Rd Ste D, Modesto (95354-3932)
P.O. Box 576095 (95357-6095)
PHONE..................209 526-2696
Tom Sutter, *President*
Rex Sutter, *Vice Pres*
EMP: 10
SALES (est): 1.3MM **Privately Held**
WEB: www.modestoplating.com
SIC: 3471 5169 Chromium plating of metals or formed products; chemicals & allied products

(P-13458)
MONTOYA & JARAMILLO INC
Also Called: Swift Metal Finishing
1161 Richard Ave, Santa Clara (95050-2843)
PHONE..................408 727-5776
Robert Montoya Jr, *President*
Dyanne Castro, *Treasurer*
EMP: 19 EST: 1963
SQ FT: 6,000
SALES (est): 1.3MM **Privately Held**
SIC: 3471 Electroplating of metals or formed products

P R O D U C T S & S V C S

(P-13459)
MORRELLS ELECTRO PLATING INC
Also Called: Morrell's Metal Finishing
432 E Euclid Ave, Compton (90222-2899)
P.O. Box 3085 (90223-3085)
PHONE..............................310 639-1024
Cyrus Gipoor, *President*
EMP: 30 **EST:** 1948
SQ FT: 20,000
SALES (est): 5.1MM **Privately Held**
WEB: www.morrellsplating.com
SIC: 3471 Anodizing (plating) of metals or
formed products; chromium plating of
metals or formed products

(P-13460)
MULTICHROME COMPANY INC (PA)
Also Called: Microplate
1013 W Hillcrest Blvd, Inglewood
(90301-2019)
PHONE..............................310 216-1086
Steven A Peterman, *President*
EMP: 31 **EST:** 1962
SQ FT: 5,000
SALES (est): 3MM **Privately Held**
WEB: www.multiplate.com
SIC: 3471 Electroplating of metals or
formed products

(P-13461)
NASMYTH TMF INC
29102 Hancock Pkwy, Valencia
(91355-1066)
PHONE..............................818 954-9504
Peter Smith, *CEO*
EMP: 54
SQ FT: 10,000
SALES (est): 6.2MM
SALES (corp-wide): 92.3MM **Privately
Held**
SIC: 3471 3479 Anodizing (plating) of met-
als or formed products; coating of metals
& formed products
PA: Nasmyth Group Limited
Nasmyth House
Coventry W MIDLANDS CV7 9
247 636-1156

(P-13462)
NECLEC
5945 E Harvard Ave, Fresno (93727-8621)
PHONE..............................559 797-0103
Rod Bandy, *President*
EMP: 32
SQ FT: 9,955
SALES (est): 1.8MM **Privately Held**
SIC: 3471 Chromium plating of metals or
formed products

(P-13463)
NEUTRON PLATING INC
2993 E Blue Star St, Anaheim
(92806-2511)
PHONE..............................714 632-9241
Manuel Zavala, *President*
Glafira Zavala, *Treasurer*
Manuel Zavala Jr, *Vice Pres*
Sylvia Cassillas, *Admin Sec*
EMP: 70
SQ FT: 16,000
SALES (est): 5.8MM **Privately Held**
WEB: www.gepower.com
SIC: 3471 Electroplating of metals or
formed products; anodizing (plating) of
metals or formed products

(P-13464)
NEUTRONIC STAMPING & PLATING
10550 Lawson River Ave, Fountain Valley
(92708-6911)
PHONE..............................714 964-8900
Nicholas Ravlich, *CFO*
Ronald Naus, *Mfg Mgr*
Robert Soltero, *Opers Mgr*
Dennis Fox, *Marketing Staff*
EMP: 30
SQ FT: 27,000
SALES (est): 4.4MM **Privately Held**
WEB: www.neutronicstamping.com
SIC: 3471 3469 Plating & polishing; metal
stampings

(P-13465)
NEW AGE METAL FINISHING LLC
2169 N Pleasant Ave, Fresno
(93705-4730)
PHONE..............................559 498-8585
Michael Zelinski,
EMP: 26
SQ FT: 5,000
SALES (est): 3MM **Privately Held**
SIC: 3471 Electroplating of metals or
formed products

(P-13466)
NORMANDY REFINISHERS INC
355 S Rosemead Blvd, Pasadena
(91107-4955)
PHONE..............................626 792-9202
Gregory Sarkisian, *President*
Doris Sarkisian, *Vice Pres*
EMP: 22
SQ FT: 2,000
SALES (est): 1.7MM **Privately Held**
SIC: 3471 3431 Decorative plating & fin-
ishing of formed products; bathroom fix-
tures, including sinks

(P-13467)
NORTH COUNTY POLISHING
220 S Hale Ave Ste A, Escondido
(92029-1719)
PHONE..............................760 480-0847
Michael Meziere, *Partner*
David Meziere, *Partner*
Don Meziere, *Partner*
EMP: 28
SQ FT: 1,200
SALES: 140K **Privately Held**
SIC: 3471 Polishing, metals or formed
products

(P-13468)
OMNI METAL FINISHING INC (PA)
11665 Coley River Cir, Fountain Valley
(92708-4279)
PHONE..............................714 979-9414
Victor M Salazar, *President*
Ruben Angel, *Ch of Bd*
Filiberto Hernandez, *Treasurer*
Ramiro Salazar, *Admin Sec*
Nancy Geibe, *Telecom Exec*
EMP: 100
SQ FT: 34,000
SALES (est): 17.1MM **Privately Held**
WEB: www.omnimetal.com
SIC: 3471 Plating of metals or formed
products

(P-13469)
OPTI-FORMS INC
42310 Winchester Rd, Temecula
(92590-4810)
PHONE..............................951 296-1300
Ralph C Dawson, *CEO*
Clint Tinker, *Chairman*
Kevin Thompson, *Exec VP*
Robert Brunson, *Vice Pres*
EMP: 52
SQ FT: 61,000
SALES (est): 7.4MM **Privately Held**
WEB: www.optiforms.com
SIC: 3471 3827 Plating of metals or
formed products; optical instruments &
lenses

(P-13470)
ORANGE COUNTY PLATING CO INC
940 N Parker St 960, Orange
(92867-5581)
PHONE..............................714 532-4610
Lawrence J Honikel, *President*
Jeanne T Honikel, *Corp Secy*
Daniel L Honikel, *Vice Pres*
EMP: 50
SQ FT: 12,000
SALES (est): 5MM **Privately Held**
WEB: www.ocplating.com
SIC: 3471 Electroplating of metals or
formed products

(P-13471)
ORDWAY METAL POLISHING
1901 N San Fernando Rd, Los Angeles
(90065-1281)
PHONE..............................323 225-3373
Jim Pratt, *Owner*
EMP: 20
SQ FT: 4,000
SALES (est): 1MM **Privately Held**
SIC: 3471 Polishing, metals or formed
products

(P-13472)
P K SELECTIVE METAL PLTG INC
415 Mathew St, Santa Clara (95050-3105)
PHONE..............................408 988-1910
Peter Kellett, *President*
EMP: 16
SQ FT: 21,000
SALES (est): 1.5MM **Privately Held**
WEB: www.pkselective.com
SIC: 3471 Anodizing (plating) of metals or
formed products; plating of metals or
formed products

(P-13473)
PENTRATE METAL PROCESSING
3517 E Olympic Blvd, Los Angeles
(90023-3976)
PHONE..............................323 269-2121
John J Grana, *President*
Nick Grana, *Corp Secy*
Vincent Grana, *Vice Pres*
Frank Grana, *Purchasing*
EMP: 30 **EST:** 1945
SQ FT: 18,000
SALES (est): 4MM **Privately Held**
WEB: www.pentrate.com
SIC: 3471 Electroplating of metals or
formed products; plating of metals or
formed products

(P-13474)
PG IMTECH OF CALIFORNIA LLC
8424 Secura Way, Santa Fe Springs
(90670-2216)
PHONE..............................562 945-8943
Chuck Wolitski,
Fred Mose,
EMP: 11
SQ FT: 6,450
SALES (est): 333.9K **Privately Held**
SIC: 3471 Anodizing (plating) of metals or
formed products

(P-13475)
PLASMA RGGEDIZED SOLUTIONS INC
5452 Business Dr, Huntington Beach
(92649-1226)
PHONE..............................714 893-6063
Bob Marla, *Branch Mgr*
EMP: 25
SALES (corp-wide): 16.3MM **Privately
Held**
WEB: www.plasmasystems.com
SIC: 3471 3479 Electroplating & plating;
coating of metals & formed products
PA: Plasma Ruggedized Solutions, Inc.
2284 Ringwood Ave Ste A
San Jose CA 95131
408 954-8405

(P-13476)
PLATERONICS PROCESSING INC
9164 Independence Ave, Chatsworth
(91311-5902)
PHONE..............................818 341-2191
Joseph Roter, *President*
Lee F Roter, *Corp Secy*
Marvin Roter, *Vice Pres*
EMP: 35
SQ FT: 6,500
SALES: 3MM **Privately Held**
WEB: www.plateronics.com
SIC: 3471 5051 Finishing, metals or
formed products; metals service centers
& offices

(P-13477)
PRECIOUS METALS PLATING CO INC
2635 Orange Ave, Santa Ana (92707-3738)
PHONE..............................714 546-6271
Chad Wayne Bird, *President*
Betty Bird, *Admin Sec*
Elizaabeth Bird, *Sales Executive*
EMP: 15 **EST:** 1957
SQ FT: 6,500
SALES (est): 3.6MM **Privately Held**
WEB: www.pmplating.com
SIC: 3471 Electroplating of metals or
formed products

(P-13478)
PRECISION ANODIZING & PLTG INC
Also Called: P A P
1601 N Miller St, Anaheim (92806-1469)
PHONE..............................714 996-1601
Jose A Salazar, *CEO*
Tracy Betow, *Human Res Dir*
Jordan Salazar, *Purchasing*
Imelda Isidora, *Exec Sec*
Julie Gutierrez, *Manager*
EMP: 89
SQ FT: 44,000
SALES (est): 13.2MM **Privately Held**
WEB: www.anodizing-plating.com
SIC: 3471 Electroplating of metals or
formed products

(P-13479)
PREMIER METAL PROCESSING INC
971 Vernon Way, El Cajon (92020-1832)
PHONE..............................760 415-9027
Mohammed Shamsi, *President*
EMP: 10
SQ FT: 13,000
SALES (est): 630K **Privately Held**
SIC: 3471 Plating & polishing; electroplat-
ing & plating; anodizing (plating) of metals
or formed products; electroplating of met-
als or formed products

(P-13480)
PRIDE METAL POLISHING INC
10822 Saint Louis Dr, El Monte
(91731-2030)
PHONE..............................626 350-1326
Rod Lowell, *President*
EMP: 19
SQ FT: 15,000
SALES (est): 1.9MM **Privately Held**
WEB: www.pridepolishing.com
SIC: 3471 Polishing, metals or formed
products

(P-13481)
PRIME PLATING AEROSPACE INC
11321 Goss St, Sun Valley (91352-3206)
P.O. Box 1843 (91353-1843)
PHONE..............................818 768-9100
Fred Schmidt, *President*
EMP: 12 **EST:** 2012
SALES (est): 641.6K **Privately Held**
SIC: 3471 Electroplating of metals or
formed products; plating of metals or
formed products

(P-13482)
PROCESS STAINLESS LAB INC (PA)
Also Called: Advance Elctro Polishing
1280 Memorex Dr, Santa Clara
(95050-2812)
PHONE..............................408 980-0535
Clay Hudson, *Owner*
David Hays, *Co-Owner*
Hector I Valdez, *General Mgr*
Lou Moore, *Bookkeeper*
David Diller, *Accounts Mgr*
EMP: 27
SQ FT: 8,000
SALES: 3.2MM **Privately Held**
WEB: www.pslinc.com
SIC: 3471 Polishing, metals or formed
products

▲ = Import ▼=Export
◆ =Import/Export

(P-13483)
PRODIGY SURFACE TECH INC
Also Called: Arrhenius
807 Aldo Ave Ste 103, Santa Clara
(95054-2254)
PHONE..................408 492-9390
John Shaw, *President*
Mark Danitschek, *COO*
James Kikoshima, *Vice Pres*
Sheila Tosado, *Cust Mgr*
EMP: 38
SQ FT: 14,500
SALES (est): 4.8MM **Privately Held**
WEB: www.prodigysurfacetech.com
SIC: 3471 Electroplating of metals or
formed products; plating of metals or
formed products

(P-13484)
PROFESSIONAL FINISHING INC
770 Market Ave, Richmond (94801-1303)
PHONE..................510 233-7629
Ricardo E Gomez, *President*
David Buchholz, *General Mgr*
Ana Prado, *Office Mgr*
EMP: 60
SQ FT: 18,000
SALES (est): 7.6MM **Privately Held**
WEB: www.profinn.com
SIC: 3471 Plating & polishing

(P-13485)
QUAKER CITY PLATING
Also Called: Quaker City Plating & Silvrsm
11729 Washington Blvd, Whittier
(90606-2498)
P.O. Box 2406 (90610-2406)
PHONE..................562 945-3721
Michael Crain, *Managing Prtnr*
Angelo Dirado, *Managing Prtnr*
Lourdes Ortiz, *CIO*
Ena R Wiley, *Manager*
▲ EMP: 220
SQ FT: 48,000
SALES (est): 58.8MM **Privately Held**
WEB: www.quakercityplating.com
SIC: 3471 Plating of metals or formed
products

(P-13486)
QUALITY CONTROL PLATING INC
4425 E Airport Dr Ste 113, Ontario
(91761-7815)
PHONE..................909 605-0206
Jay J Singh, *Vice Pres*
Mona Singh, *President*
EMP: 22
SQ FT: 3,500
SALES (est): 2.1MM **Privately Held**
SIC: 3471 Plating of metals or formed
products

(P-13487)
R L ANODIZING
Also Called: R L Anodizing & Plating
11331 Penrose St, Sun Valley
(91352-3109)
PHONE..................818 252-3804
Raymond Lane, *Owner*
EMP: 15
SALES (est): 920K **Privately Held**
SIC: 3471 Anodizing (plating) of metals or
formed products

(P-13488)
RAPID INDUSTRIES
Also Called: Rapid Plating
1216 W Slauson Ave, Los Angeles
(90044-2822)
PHONE..................323 753-5255
Florence Fratello, *President*
EMP: 10
SQ FT: 3,200
SALES (est): 1.1MM **Privately Held**
SIC: 3471 Plating & polishing

(P-13489)
RD METAL POLISHING INC
244 Pioneer Pl, Pomona (91768-3275)
PHONE..................909 594-8393
Ron Delgado Jr, *President*
Ranulfo M Delgado Sr, *Vice Pres*
Louie Delgado, *Sales Executive*
EMP: 38
SQ FT: 11,000

SALES (est): 3MM **Privately Held**
SIC: 3471 Polishing, metals or formed
products

(P-13490)
REAL PLATING INC
1245 W 2nd St, Pomona (91766-1310)
PHONE..................909 623-2304
Juan Real, *CEO*
EMP: 25 EST: 2007
SQ FT: 5,264
SALES (est): 2MM **Privately Held**
SIC: 3471 Plating of metals or formed
products

(P-13491)
RON KEHL ENGINEERING
384 Umbarger Rd Ste B, San Jose
(95111-2079)
PHONE..................408 629-6632
Ron Kehl, *Owner*
▲ EMP: 12
SQ FT: 6,000
SALES (est): 877.2K **Privately Held**
SIC: 3471 3599 8711 Polishing, metals or
formed products; machine & other job
shop work; industrial engineers

(P-13492)
ROSE MANUFACTURING GROUP INC
Also Called: Elite Metal Finishing
2525 Jason Ct Ste 102, Oceanside
(92056-3000)
PHONE..................760 407-0232
Dan Rose, *President*
EMP: 14
SQ FT: 3,300
SALES (est): 1.8MM **Privately Held**
SIC: 3471 Plating of metals or formed
products; sand blasting of metal parts

(P-13493)
ROSENKRANZ ENTERPRISES INC
Also Called: A & B Sandblast Co
2447 E 54th St, Los Angeles (90058-3503)
PHONE..................323 583-9021
Lance Rosenkranz, *President*
EMP: 15
SQ FT: 40,000
SALES (est): 1.3MM **Privately Held**
SIC: 3471 Sand blasting of metal parts

(P-13494)
S & K PLATING INC
2727 N Compton Ave, Compton
(90222-1097)
PHONE..................310 632-7141
Mardig Tchakalian, *President*
Hagop Chakalian, *General Mgr*
EMP: 25
SQ FT: 7,500
SALES (est): 2.6MM **Privately Held**
SIC: 3471 Electroplating of metals or
formed products

(P-13495)
SAFE PLATING INC
18001 Railroad St, City of Industry
(91748-1215)
PHONE..................626 810-1872
Magdy Seif, *President*
Mario Gomez, *Executive*
Cielo Gamboa, *IT/INT Sup*
Cielo Paguio, *Manager*
EMP: 58
SQ FT: 35,000
SALES (est): 7.6MM **Privately Held**
WEB: www.safeplating.com
SIC: 3471 Gold plating; electroplating of
metals or formed products

(P-13496)
SAL RODRIGUEZ
Also Called: Quality Plating
1680 Almaden Expy Ste I, San Jose
(95125-1324)
PHONE..................408 993-8091
Sal Rodriguez, *Owner*
EMP: 10
SALES (est): 625.9K **Privately Held**
SIC: 3471 Plating of metals or formed
products

(P-13497)
SANFORD METAL PROCESSING CO
990 Obrien Dr, Menlo Park (94025-1407)
PHONE..................650 327-5172
Jose Sandoval, *President*
EMP: 10
SQ FT: 7,500
SALES (est): 750K **Privately Held**
SIC: 3471 Plating of metals or formed
products; anodizing (plating) of metals or
formed products

(P-13498)
SANTA ANA PLATING CORP (PA)
1726 E Rosslynn Ave, Fullerton
(92831-5111)
PHONE..................310 923-8305
Tony Kakuk, *President*
Michael F Gustin, *Owner*
EMP: 55
SQ FT: 17,100
SALES (est): 5.6MM **Privately Held**
SIC: 3471 Finishing, metals or formed
products; plating of metals or formed
products

(P-13499)
SANTA CLARA PLATING CO INC
1773 Grant St, Santa Clara (95050-3974)
PHONE..................408 727-9315
Thomas L Coss, *President*
Wendy Coss, *Shareholder*
Janet Bauerly, *Controller*
EMP: 85 EST: 1974
SQ FT: 13,000
SALES (est): 9.3MM **Privately Held**
WEB: www.scpci.com
SIC: 3471 Electroplating of metals or
formed products

(P-13500)
SANTOSHI CORPORATION
Also Called: Alum-A-Coat
2439 Seaman Ave, El Monte (91733-1936)
PHONE..................626 444-7118
Hershad Shah, *President*
Raksha Shah, *Vice Pres*
EMP: 33
SQ FT: 15,000
SALES (est): 6.2MM **Privately Held**
SIC: 3471 Coloring & finishing of aluminum
or formed products; electroplating of met-
als or formed products

(P-13501)
SCHMIDT INDUSTRIES INC
Also Called: Prime Plating
11321 Goss St, Sun Valley (91352-3206)
P.O. Box 1843 (91353-1843)
PHONE..................818 768-9100
Fred Schmidt, *President*
Jennifer Schmidt, *Admin Sec*
EMP: 90
SQ FT: 30,000
SALES (est): 11.2MM **Privately Held**
SIC: 3471 Anodizing (plating) of metals or
formed products

(P-13502)
SEMANO INC
31757 Knapp St, Hayward (94544-7827)
PHONE..................510 489-2360
Frank Largusa, *President*
Terry Dillon, *Corp Secy*
Hans Sellge, *Vice Pres*
Jose Dacorro, *Prdtn Mgr*
Harrison Pham, *QC Mgr*
▲ EMP: 35
SQ FT: 13,000
SALES (est): 5.7MM **Privately Held**
SIC: 3471 Electroplating of metals or
formed products

(P-13503)
SHEFFIELD PLATERS INC
9850 Waples St, San Diego (92121-2921)
PHONE..................858 546-8484
Dale Watkins Jr, *President*
Shelley Watkins, *Shareholder*
Mark Watkins, *Exec VP*
EMP: 45 EST: 1966
SQ FT: 20,000

SALES (est): 6.5MM **Privately Held**
WEB: www.sheffieldplaters.com
SIC: 3471 Plating of metals or formed
products

(P-13504)
SILICON VALLEY ELECTRO PLATING
Also Called: Sepco
44727 Aguila Ter, Fremont (94539-6293)
PHONE..................408 945-1444
Jatinder M Mahajan, *President*
EMP: 30
SQ FT: 17,000
SALES (est): 3.1MM **Privately Held**
SIC: 3471 Plating of metals or formed
products

(P-13505)
SIZE CONTROL PLATING CO
13349 Temple Ave, La Puente
(91746-1580)
PHONE..................626 369-3014
Ron Todden, *President*
EMP: 11 EST: 1958
SQ FT: 8,800
SALES: 700K **Privately Held**
WEB: www.sizecontrol.net
SIC: 3471 8734 Electroplating of metals or
formed products; product testing laborato-
ries

(P-13506)
SJ VALLEY PLATING INC
491 Perry Ct, Santa Clara (95054-2624)
PHONE..................408 988-5502
Jeff Adams, *President*
Michele Adams, *Admin Sec*
EMP: 12
SQ FT: 10,000
SALES (est): 1MM **Privately Held**
SIC: 3471 Chromium plating of metals or
formed products; plating of metals or
formed products

(P-13507)
SOUTHWEST PLATING CO INC
1344 W Slauson Ave, Los Angeles
(90044-2897)
PHONE..................323 753-3781
Gus Brigantino, *Owner*
EMP: 15
SALES (est): 1.7MM **Privately Held**
SIC: 3471 Plating of metals or formed
products

(P-13508)
SPECTRUM PLATING COMPANY INC
202 W 140th St, Los Angeles (90061-1006)
PHONE..................310 533-0748
Mary McMeans, *CEO*
Jesus Diaz, *Corp Secy*
Donna Martinez, *Vice Pres*
EMP: 25
SQ FT: 60,000
SALES (est): 4.2MM **Privately Held**
WEB: www.spectrumplating.com
SIC: 3471 Electroplating of metals or
formed products

(P-13509)
STABILE PLATING COMPANY INC
1150 E Edna Pl, Covina (91724-2592)
PHONE..................626 339-9091
David Crest, *President*
Eric Crest, *Vice Pres*
Steven Crest, *Vice Pres*
EMP: 22 EST: 1959
SQ FT: 6,000
SALES (est): 1.5MM **Privately Held**
WEB: www.stabileplating.com
SIC: 3471 3444 3353 Plating of metals or
formed products; sheet metalwork; alu-
minum sheet, plate & foil

(P-13510)
STAINLESS MICRO-POLISH INC
1286 N Grove St, Anaheim (92806-2113)
PHONE..................714 632-8903
Robert Maculsay, *President*
Elizabeth Maculsay, *Treasurer*
Michael Gierut, *General Mgr*
EMP: 15 EST: 1979

(PA)=Parent Co (HQ)=Headquarters (DH)=Div Headquarters
✿ = New Business established in last 2 years

2019 California
Manufacturers Register

553

PRODUCTS & SVCS

SQ FT: 10,000
SALES (est): 2MM **Privately Held**
WEB: www.stainlessmicropolish.com
SIC: 3471 Polishing, metals or formed
products

(P-13511)
STANDARD METAL PRODUCTS INC
1541 W 132nd St, Gardena (90249-2107)
P.O. Box 7636, Torrance (90504-9036)
PHONE.................................310 532-9861
Danny Corrales Jr, *CEO*
Dan Corrales Sr, *Corp Secy*
Jo Ann Stanley, *Bookkeeper*
EMP: 35 EST: 1972
SQ FT: 24,000
SALES (est): 3.9MM **Privately Held**
WEB: www.sheet-metal.com
SIC: 3471 3444 Cleaning, polishing & fin-
ishing; sheet metalwork

(P-13512)
STAR FINISHES INC
40429 Brickyard Dr, Madera (93636-9515)
PHONE.................................559 261-1076
Doug Hagen, *President*
EMP: 15
SQ FT: 7,760
SALES (est): 800K **Privately Held**
WEB: www.starfinishes.com
SIC: 3471 Finishing, metals or formed
products

(P-13513)
STUART-DEAN CO INC
14731 Franklin Ave Ste L, Tustin
(92780-7221)
PHONE.................................714 544-4460
Steven Materazzo, *Manager*
Bill Batz, *Manager*
EMP: 16
SALES (corp-wide): 65.4MM **Privately Held**
WEB: www.mail.stuartdean.com
SIC: 3471 Polishing, metals or formed
products
PA: Stuart-Dean Co. Inc.
450 Fashion Ave Ste 3800
New York NY 10123
212 273-6900

(P-13514)
SUPERIOR CONNECTOR PLATING INC
Also Called: Superior Plating
1901 E Cerritos Ave, Anaheim
(92805-6427)
PHONE.................................714 774-1174
Juan Martin, *President*
EMP: 22
SQ FT: 7,500
SALES (est): 1.6MM **Privately Held**
SIC: 3471 Electroplating of metals or
formed products

(P-13515)
SUPERIOR METAL FINISHING INC
1733 W 134th St, Gardena (90249-2015)
PHONE.................................310 464-8010
William Leffingwell Sr, *President*
Duane O'Reilly, *Corp Secy*
EMP: 14
SQ FT: 5,290
SALES (est): 1.4MM **Privately Held**
WEB: www.superiormetalfinishing.com
SIC: 3471 Finishing, metals or formed
products

(P-13516)
SUPERIOR PLATING INC
9001 Glenoaks Blvd, Sun Valley
(91352-2040)
PHONE.................................818 252-1088
Riad Hussein, *President*
EMP: 35
SALES (est): 2.7MM **Privately Held**
SIC: 3471

(P-13517)
SUPERIOR PROCESSING
1115 Las Brisas Pl, Placentia (92870-6644)
PHONE.................................714 524-8525
Michael P Mc Guire, *President*

EMP: 10
SQ FT: 7,500
SALES: 1MM **Privately Held**
WEB: www.superior-processing.com
SIC: 3471 Electroplating of metals or
formed products; gold plating

(P-13518)
SURFACING SOLUTIONS INC
27637 Commerce Center Dr, Temecula
(92590-2521)
PHONE.................................951 699-0035
Tiffany Halverson, *President*
Shawn Halverson, *Vice Pres*
Carrie Brown, *Accountant*
Kristin Weisz, *Manager*
EMP: 16
SQ FT: 5,000
SALES (est): 2.1MM **Privately Held**
SIC: 3471 Decorative plating & finishing of
formed products

(P-13519)
SYMCOAT METAL PROCESSING INC
7887 Dunbrook Rd Ste C, San Diego
(92126-4382)
PHONE.................................858 451-3313
Sylvia Twiggs, *President*
Michelle Kanganis, *Vice Pres*
EMP: 27
SQ FT: 12,000
SALES (est): 2.9MM **Privately Held**
WEB: www.symcoat.net
SIC: 3471 3341 Finishing, metals or
formed products; secondary nonferrous
metals

(P-13520)
TECHNIC INC
1170 N Hawk Cir, Anaheim (92807-1789)
PHONE.................................714 632-0200
Mike Chicos, *Opers-Prdtn-Mfg*
Jeff Cannis, *Technical Mgr*
Maria Coe, *Human Res Mgr*
EMP: 30
SALES (corp-wide): 140.9MM **Privately Held**
WEB: www.technic.com
SIC: 3471 2899 3678 3672 Plating of
metals or formed products; plating com-
pounds; electronic connectors; printed cir-
cuit boards; precious metals;
semiconductor devices
PA: Technic, Inc.
47 Molter St
Cranston RI 02910
401 781-6100

(P-13521)
TLI ENTERPRISES INC
Also Called: Thermionics Metal Processing
3118 Depot Rd, Hayward (94545-2708)
PHONE.................................510 786-0680
Al Nielsen, *Manager*
EMP: 75
SQ FT: 1,300
SALES (corp-wide): 12MM **Privately Held**
WEB: www.thermionicscorp.com
SIC: 3471 8711 7342 Cleaning & descal-
ing metal products; engineering services;
disinfecting & pest control services
PA: Tli Enterprises, Inc.
23950 Clawiter Rd
Hayward CA 94545
510 538-3304

(P-13522)
TMW CORPORATION
Also Called: Aero Chrome Plating
14647 Arminta St, Panorama City
(91402-5901)
PHONE.................................818 374-1074
Moheb Mansour, *Vice Pres*
Mourad Yousef, *Vice Pres*
Michael R Tawadros, *Opers Mgr*
EMP: 42
SALES (est): 5.4MM
SALES (corp-wide): 10.5MM **Privately Held**
SIC: 3471 Electroplating of metals or
formed products

PA: T.M.W. Corporation
15148 Bledsoe St
Sylmar CA 91342
818 362-5665

(P-13523)
TRIDENT PLATING INC
10046 Romandel Ave, Santa Fe Springs
(90670-3424)
PHONE.................................562 906-2556
Maty Rodriguez, *President*
Ian Holmber, *Corp Secy*
Juan Carlos Rodriguez, *Vice Pres*
EMP: 28 EST: 1981
SQ FT: 18,197
SALES: 2MM **Privately Held**
SIC: 3471 Gold plating; electroplating of
metals or formed products

(P-13524)
TRIUMPH PROCESSING INC
2605 Industry Way, Lynwood (90262-4007)
PHONE.................................323 563-1338
Peter Labarbera, *CEO*
Richard C III, *CEO*
Steven Campeggi, *Finance*
Eric Purinton, *Safety Mgr*
Ashok Advani, *Opers Staff*
EMP: 103 EST: 1968
SQ FT: 140,000
SALES (est): 16.4MM
SALES (corp-wide): 103MM **Privately Held**
WEB: www.dvindustries.com
SIC: 3471 3398 3356 Anodizing (plating)
of metals or formed products; finishing,
metals or formed products; polishing,
metals or formed products; metal heat
treating; nonferrous rolling & drawing
PA: Valence Surface Technologies Llc
1790 Hughes Landing Blvd
The Woodlands TX 77380
888 540-0878

(P-13525)
U M S INC
Also Called: A C Plating
317 Mount Vernon Ave, Bakersfield
(93307-2743)
PHONE.................................661 324-5454
Robert D McBride, *President*
EMP: 22 EST: 1968
SQ FT: 15,000
SALES (est): 2.4MM **Privately Held**
WEB: www.acplating.com
SIC: 3471 Plating of metals or formed
products

(P-13526)
U S CHROME CORP CALIFORNIA
1480 Canal Ave, Long Beach (90813-1244)
PHONE.................................562 437-2825
Nick R Stahenoli, *Manager*
EMP: 17
SQ FT: 4,800
SALES (corp-wide): 28.5MM **Privately Held**
WEB: www.uschromeofca.com
SIC: 3471 Chromium plating of metals or
formed products
HQ: U S Chrome Corporation Of California
175 Garfield Ave
Stratford CT
203 378-9622

(P-13527)
ULTRA-PURE METAL FINISHING
1764 N Case St, Orange (92865-4212)
PHONE.................................714 637-3150
David Juarez, *President*
Nina Juarez, *Vice Pres*
EMP: 17
SQ FT: 11,160
SALES (est): 1.9MM **Privately Held**
SIC: 3471 Electroplating of metals or
formed products

(P-13528)
ULTRAMET
12173 Montague St, Pacoima
(91331-2210)
PHONE.................................818 899-0236
Andrew Duffy, *CEO*
James Kaplan, *Shareholder*
Richard B Kaplan, *Shareholder*

John Benander, *Program Mgr*
Walter Abrams, *Admin Sec*
▲ EMP: 79
SQ FT: 43,000
SALES (est): 16.2MM **Privately Held**
WEB: www.ultramet.com
SIC: 3471 8731 Electroplating & plating;
commercial physical research

(P-13529)
UNIVERSAL METAL PLATING
704 S Taylor Ave, Montebello (90640-5562)
PHONE.................................626 969-7932
Guadalupe Martinez, *Partner*
EMP: 15
SALES (corp-wide): 1.8MM **Privately Held**
SIC: 3471 Chromium plating of metals or
formed products
PA: Universal Metal Plating
1526 W 1st St
Irwindale CA 91702
626 969-7931

(P-13530)
V & M PLATING CO
14024 Avalon Blvd, Los Angeles
(90061-2692)
PHONE.................................310 532-5633
Anthony Babiak, *President*
Timothy Babiak, *Vice Pres*
Jeff Babiak, *General Mgr*
▲ EMP: 19
SQ FT: 7,500
SALES (est): 1.4MM **Privately Held**
WEB: www.vmplating.com
SIC: 3471 Chromium plating of metals or
formed products; electroplating of metals
or formed products

(P-13531)
VALLEY CHROME PLATING INC
Also Called: Wing Master
1028 Hoblitt Ave, Clovis (93612-2805)
P.O. Box 189 (93613-0189)
PHONE.................................559 298-8094
Thomas A Lucas, *CEO*
Ray Lucas, *President*
Catherine L Booey, *Corp Secy*
Greg Lucas, *Vice Pres*
Matthew Lucas, *Vice Pres*
▲ EMP: 70
SQ FT: 30,000
SALES (est): 13.8MM **Privately Held**
WEB: www.valleychrome.com
SIC: 3471 3714 Plating of metals or
formed products; bumpers &
bumperettes, motor vehicle

(P-13532)
VIRGIL M STUTZMAN INC
Also Called: Stutzman Plating
5045 Exposition Blvd, Los Angeles
(90016-3913)
PHONE.................................323 732-9146
Virgil M Stutzman, *President*
Joseph C Stutzman, *Corp Secy*
James D Stutzman, *Vice Pres*
EMP: 50
SQ FT: 4,000
SALES (est): 5.2MM **Privately Held**
WEB: www.stutzmanplating.com
SIC: 3471 5051 3369 3364 Electroplating
of metals or formed products; metals
service centers & offices; nonferrous
foundries; nonferrous die-castings except
aluminum

(P-13533)
WE FIVE-R CORPORATION
Also Called: Bank C Plating Co
1507 S Sunol Dr, Los Angeles
(90023-4031)
PHONE.................................323 263-6757
Dick Patel, *President*
◆ EMP: 18 EST: 1950
SQ FT: 8,000
SALES (est): 1.2MM **Privately Held**
SIC: 3471 Plating of metals or formed
products

(P-13534)
WEST VALLEY PLATING INC
21061 Superior St Ste A, Chatsworth
(91311-4330)
PHONE.................................818 709-1684

▲ = Import ▼=Export
◆ =Import/Export

Josephina Campos, *President*
EMP: 15
SALES (est): 2.1MM **Privately Held**
SIC: 3471 Plating of metals or formed products; electroplating of metals or formed products

(P-13535)
WHITING ENTERPRISES
Also Called: Hi-Tech Metal Polishing
10140 Romandel Ave, Santa Fe Springs (90670-3434)
PHONE.....................562 946-5100
William S Whiting, *President*
Antoinette L Whiting, *Vice Pres*
EMP: 40
SQ FT: 16,000
SALES (est): 5.1MM **Privately Held**
WEB: www.globalmortgagecorp.net
SIC: 3471 Polishing, metals or formed products

3479 Coating & Engraving, NEC

(P-13536)
A & R POWDER COATING INC
1198 N Grove St Ste B, Anaheim (92806-2136)
PHONE.....................714 630-0709
Jack Rainwater, *President*
Everett Ryan, *President*
EMP: 12
SQ FT: 5,500
SALES: 900K **Privately Held**
SIC: 3479 Coating of metals & formed products

(P-13537)
A-1 ENGRAVING CO INC
8225 Phlox St, Downey (90241-4880)
PHONE.....................562 861-2216
Jack E Young, *President*
Grace Young, *Corp Secy*
Don Schram, *Vice Pres*
EMP: 12
SQ FT: 22,900
SALES (est): 1.2MM **Privately Held**
SIC: 3479 Engraving jewelry silverware, or metal; etching & engraving

(P-13538)
ABACUS POWDER COATING
1829 Tyler Ave, South El Monte (91733-3617)
PHONE.....................626 443-7556
Esther Davidoff, *President*
EMP: 25
SALES (est): 3MM **Privately Held**
WEB: www.abacuspowder.com
SIC: 3479 Coating of metals & formed products

(P-13539)
ACCURATE DIAL & NAMEPLATE INC (PA)
329 Mira Loma Ave, Glendale (91204-2912)
PHONE.....................323 245-9181
Jerry D Childs, *President*
David V Howarth, *CEO*
Erin Dyer, *Vice Pres*
Barb Menzel, *Marketing Mgr*
EMP: 12
SALES (est): 3.5MM **Privately Held**
SIC: 3479 3613 2759 1721 Name plates: engraved, etched, etc.; control panels, electric; commercial printing; painting & paper hanging; signs & advertising specialties

(P-13540)
ADFA INCORPORATED
Also Called: A&A Jewelry Supply
319 W 6th St, Los Angeles (90014-1703)
PHONE.....................213 627-8004
Robert Adem, *President*
Naim Farah, *Vice Pres*
Danny Farah, *General Mgr*
▲ **EMP:** 45 **EST:** 1986
SALES (est): 3.4MM **Privately Held**
SIC: 3479 3548 3172 Engraving jewelry silverware, or metal; electric welding equipment; cases, jewelry

(P-13541)
ADVANCE FINISHING
11645 S Broadway, Los Angeles (90061-1834)
PHONE.....................323 754-2889
Ramon Verdin, *Owner*
EMP: 18 **EST:** 1981
SQ FT: 10,000
SALES: 1MM **Privately Held**
SIC: 3479 Painting of metal products

(P-13542)
ADVANCED INDUS COATINGS INC
950 Industrial Dr, Stockton (95206-3927)
PHONE.....................209 234-2700
Toll Free:.....................877 -
Ronald Cymanski, *President*
David Arney, *COO*
Marianne Arney, *Corp Secy*
Steve Hockett, *Vice Pres*
EMP: 53
SQ FT: 48,000
SALES (est): 6.9MM **Privately Held**
WEB: www.aic-coatings.com
SIC: 3479 Coating of metals & formed products

(P-13543)
ADVANCED METAL COATINGS INC
4901 E 12th St, Oakland (94601-5109)
PHONE.....................510 535-0185
Clyde Delp, *President*
Brent Delp, *Vice Pres*
EMP: 12
SQ FT: 23,000
SALES (est): 1MM **Privately Held**
SIC: 3479 Painting, coating & hot dipping

(P-13544)
AERO POWDER COATING INC
710 Monterey Pass Rd, Monterey Park (91754-3607)
PHONE.....................323 264-6405
Phillip Kontos, *President*
EMP: 39
SQ FT: 27,000
SALES (est): 3.3MM **Privately Held**
SIC: 3479 Coating of metals & formed products

(P-13545)
AIRCOAT INC
13405 S Broadway, Los Angeles (90061-1127)
PHONE.....................310 527-2258
Francisco Ramirez, *President*
EMP: 15
SQ FT: 20,000
SALES: 900K **Privately Held**
SIC: 3479 Painting of metal products; painting, coating & hot dipping

(P-13546)
ALL SOURCE COATINGS INC
10625 Scripps Ranch Blvd D, San Diego (92131-1012)
PHONE.....................858 586-0903
Jerry Zumbro, *President*
Emily Pinkston, *Office Mgr*
Sarah Kindt, *Admin Asst*
EMP: 21
SQ FT: 2,000
SALES: 980K **Privately Held**
SIC: 3479 1721 Aluminum coating of metal products; painting & paper hanging; commercial painting

(P-13547)
ALLIANCE CHEMICAL & ENVMTL
Also Called: Alliance Finishing and Mfg
1721 Ives Ave, Oxnard (93033-1866)
PHONE.....................805 385-3330
Mark Hyman, *President*
Heather Hyman, *Vice Pres*
Bill Morgan, *QC Mgr*
EMP: 16
SQ FT: 15,600
SALES (est): 2.4MM **Privately Held**
WEB: www.starkart.com
SIC: 3479 Coating of metals & formed products

(P-13548)
AMERICAN ETCHING & MFG
13730 Desmond St, Pacoima (91331-2706)
PHONE.....................323 875-3910
Gary Kipka, *President*
Frances De Torre, *Officer*
EMP: 45
SQ FT: 20,000
SALES (est): 5.7MM **Privately Held**
WEB: www.aemetch.com
SIC: 3479 Etching on metals

(P-13549)
AMERICAN PWDR COATING PNTG INC
9445 Washburn Rd, Downey (90242-2912)
PHONE.....................562 861-6348
Scott Tellkamp, *President*
Lauren Warfield, *General Mgr*
EMP: 35
SALES (est): 2.9MM **Privately Held**
WEB: www.korsar.com
SIC: 3479 Coating of metals & formed products; painting, coating & hot dipping

(P-13550)
AMERICAN SAFETY TECHNOLOGIES
679 Anita St Ste A, Chula Vista (91911-4662)
PHONE.....................619 575-0590
C Heard, *Principal*
EMP: 25
SALES (corp-wide): 3.1MM **Privately Held**
WEB: www.americansafetytech.com
SIC: 3479 Coating of metals & formed products
PA: American Safety Technologies, Inc
130 Commerce Dr
Montgomeryville PA 18936
215 855-8450

(P-13551)
ANDREWS POWDER COATING INC
10138 Canoga Ave, Chatsworth (91311-3005)
PHONE.....................818 700-1030
Scott Andrews, *President*
EMP: 28 **EST:** 1991
SALES (est): 3.6MM **Privately Held**
SIC: 3479 Coating of metals & formed products

(P-13552)
APPLIED COATINGS & LININGS
3224 Rosemead Blvd, El Monte (91731-2807)
PHONE.....................626 280-6354
James Horton, *President*
Ed Horton, *Corp Secy*
EMP: 24
SQ FT: 150,000
SALES (est): 2.7MM **Privately Held**
WEB: www.appliedcoatings.com
SIC: 3479 3471 Coating of metals & formed products; coating or wrapping steel pipe; plating & polishing

(P-13553)
APPLIED POWDERCOAT INC (PA)
3101 Camino Del Sol, Oxnard (93030-8999)
PHONE.....................805 981-1991
Victor Anselmo, *President*
J Michael Hagan, *Ch of Bd*
George Grippo, *Plant Mgr*
Deborah Anselmo, *Manager*
Denise Tellez, *Receptionist*
EMP: 32
SQ FT: 30,000
SALES (est): 5.2MM **Privately Held**
WEB: www.appliedpowder.com
SIC: 3479 Coating of metals & formed products

(P-13554)
ATLAS GALVANIZING LLC
2639 Leonis Blvd, Vernon (90058-2203)
PHONE.....................323 587-6247
Victor Bruno Jr,
Patricia New,

EMP: 36 **EST:** 1936
SQ FT: 20,000
SALES (est): 5.2MM **Privately Held**
WEB: www.atlasgalvanizing.com
SIC: 3479 Galvanizing of iron, steel or end-formed products

(P-13555)
B & B ENAMELING INC
17591 Sampson Ln, Huntington Beach (92647-7722)
PHONE.....................714 848-0044
Jay V Bogert, *President*
EMP: 10
SQ FT: 7,000
SALES (est): 1.2MM **Privately Held**
SIC: 3479 Enameling, including porcelain, of metal products; coating of metals & formed products

(P-13556)
B & C PAINTING SOLUTIONS INC
107 Val Dervin Pkwy, Stockton (95206-4001)
PHONE.....................209 982-0422
Gary Maggard, *CEO*
Gloria Parker, *Manager*
EMP: 28
SQ FT: 40,000
SALES (est): 3.8MM **Privately Held**
WEB: www.bcpaintingsolutions.com
SIC: 3479 Coating of metals & formed products

(P-13557)
B R & F SPRAY INC (PA)
3380 De La Cruz Blvd, Santa Clara (95054-2608)
PHONE.....................408 988-7582
Ronald Grainger, *President*
Florence Grainger, *Corp Secy*
EMP: 10
SQ FT: 14,000
SALES (est): 1.2MM **Privately Held**
WEB: www.brf-spray.com
SIC: 3479 3471 Painting of metal products; plating & polishing

(P-13558)
BELL POWDER COATING INC
4747 Mcgrath St, Ventura (93003-6495)
P.O. Box 7117 (93006-7117)
PHONE.....................805 658-2233
Carl Bell, *President*
Judith Bell, *Vice Pres*
EMP: 15
SQ FT: 16,500
SALES (est): 1.5MM **Privately Held**
SIC: 3479 Aluminum coating of metal products; coating of metals & formed products

(P-13559)
BEX ENGRAVING COMPANY INC
1101 E Ash Ave Ste C, Fullerton (92831-5030)
PHONE.....................714 879-6593
Andrea Beck, *President*
EMP: 12
SQ FT: 1,800
SALES (est): 1.2MM **Privately Held**
WEB: www.bexengraving.com
SIC: 3479 Engraving jewelry silverware, or metal

(P-13560)
BJS&T ENTERPRISES INC
Also Called: San Diego Powder Coating
1702 N Magnolia Ave # 101, El Cajon (92020-1287)
PHONE.....................619 448-7795
Bob Johnson, *President*
Stephen Johnson, *Vice Pres*
Philip Johnson, *General Mgr*
Michelle Simmons, *General Mgr*
Teri Howe, *Accounting Mgr*
EMP: 15
SQ FT: 7,000
SALES (est): 2.3MM **Privately Held**
SIC: 3479 Coating of metals & formed products

(P-13561)
BRIGHT SHARK POWDER COATING
4530 Schaefer Ave, Chino (91710-5539)
PHONE......................................909 591-1385
Rosalva Garcia, *Partner*
EMP: 14
SQ FT: 9,600
SALES (est): 2.1MM **Privately Held**
SIC: 3479 Coating of metals & formed products

(P-13562)
CAL NOR POWDER COATING INC
265 E Clay St, Ukiah (95482-4915)
PHONE......................................707 462-0217
Robert Loucks, *CEO*
EMP: 10
SQ FT: 30,000
SALES: 740K **Privately Held**
SIC: 3479 Painting of metal products; coating of metals & formed products

(P-13563)
CALIFORNIA ETCHING INC
840 Jackson St, NAPA (94559-1322)
PHONE......................................707 224-9966
Tim L Arnold, *President*
EMP: 10
SQ FT: 3,200
SALES (est): 1.3MM **Privately Held**
WEB: www.californiaetching.com
SIC: 3479 Etching & engraving

(P-13564)
CALIFORNIA SPECIALTY PAINTING
9310 Norwalk Blvd, Santa Fe Springs (90670-2926)
PHONE......................................562 622-7800
George Gilbert, *President*
EMP: 13
SALES (est): 1.6MM **Privately Held**
WEB: www.calpaint.com
SIC: 3479 Painting, coating & hot dipping

(P-13565)
CALSPRAY INC
1905 Bay Rd, East Palo Alto (94303-1394)
PHONE......................................650 325-0096
John Garcia, *President*
EMP: 14 EST: 1966
SQ FT: 10,000
SALES (est): 1MM **Privately Held**
SIC: 3479 Painting of metal products

(P-13566)
CALWEST GALVANIZING CORP
2226 E Dominguez St, Long Beach (90810-1086)
PHONE......................................310 549-2200
Toll Free:.......................................888
Corey Wraguen, *General Mgr*
Isaac Maldonado, *Asst Mgr*
▲ **EMP:** 70
SQ FT: 20,000
SALES (est): 8.4MM
SALES (corp-wide): 2.7B **Publicly Held**
WEB: www.calwestgalvanizing.com
SIC: 3479 3317 3523 Galvanizing of iron, steel or end-formed products; steel pipe & tubes; fertilizing, spraying, dusting & irrigation machinery
PA: Valmont Industries, Inc.
   1 Valmont Plz Ste 500
   Omaha NE 68154
   402 963-1000

(P-13567)
CERTIFIED ENAMELING INC
3342 Emery St, Los Angeles (90023-3810)
PHONE......................................323 264-4403
Glenn Ziegel, *President*
Adrian Quijano, *General Mgr*
Maria Tinajero, *Info Tech Mgr*
Rocio Tinajero, *Prdtn Mgr*
EMP: 95 EST: 1953
SQ FT: 50,000
SALES (est): 14.1MM **Privately Held**
WEB: www.certifiedenameling.com
SIC: 3479 Coating of metals & formed products

(P-13568)
CLASS A POWDERCOAT INC
8538 Tiogawoods Dr, Sacramento (95828-5000)
PHONE......................................916 681-7474
Klay Stubbs, *President*
Kirk Stubbs, *Vice Pres*
EMP: 25
SQ FT: 25,000
SALES (est): 3.3MM **Privately Held**
SIC: 3479 3471 Painting of metal products; sand blasting of metal parts

(P-13569)
COATING SERVICES GROUP LLC
Also Called: Csg
11649 Rverside Dr Ste 139, Lakeside (92040)
PHONE......................................619 596-7444
Hans Sleeuwenhoek, *CEO*
Jeff Grant, *President*
EMP: 10
SQ FT: 5,500
SALES: 1MM **Privately Held**
SIC: 3479 Etching & engraving

(P-13570)
COATINGS BY SANDBERG INC
856 N Commerce St, Orange (92867-7900)
PHONE......................................714 538-0888
Nona Sandberg, *President*
Gerald Sandberg, *Admin Sec*
James Dunham, *Purch Mgr*
EMP: 14 EST: 1997
SQ FT: 12,000
SALES (est): 1.6MM **Privately Held**
WEB: www.cbs-dichroic.com
SIC: 3479 Coating of metals & formed products

(P-13571)
COLOR TEC INDUSTRIAL FINISHING
11231 Ilex Ave, Pacoima (91331-2725)
PHONE......................................818 897-2669
Michael Cabral, *Owner*
EMP: 20
SQ FT: 6,000
SALES (est): 1.7MM **Privately Held**
SIC: 3479 Coating of metals & formed products

(P-13572)
CREST COATING INC
1361 S Allec St, Anaheim (92805-6304)
PHONE......................................714 635-7090
Michael D Erickson, *CEO*
Bonnie George, *Vice Pres*
Mike Frasz, *Info Tech Mgr*
Louie Munet, *Buyer*
Jeff Erickson, *Sales Mgr*
▲ **EMP:** 60 EST: 1968
SQ FT: 55,000
SALES (est): 9.4MM **Privately Held**
WEB: www.crestcoating.com
SIC: 3479 Coating of metals & formed products

(P-13573)
CUSTOM ENAMELERS INC
18340 Mount Baldy Cir, Fountain Valley (92708-6181)
PHONE......................................714 540-7884
Ronald Folmer, *President*
Janet Folmer, *Treasurer*
Daryl Folmer, *Vice Pres*
EMP: 30
SQ FT: 27,000
SALES (est): 3.5MM **Privately Held**
SIC: 3479 Enameling, including porcelain, of metal products; coating of metals & formed products

(P-13574)
DENMAC INDUSTRIES INC
7616 Rosecrans Ave, Paramount (90723-2508)
P.O. Box 2144 (90723-8144)
PHONE......................................562 634-2714
Mark Plechot, *President*
Maurice Plechot, *CFO*
James Campagna, *Vice Pres*
Briana Plechot, *Representative*
▲ **EMP:** 40
SQ FT: 20,000
SALES (est): 5.9MM **Privately Held**
WEB: www.denmac-ind.com
SIC: 3479 Coating of metals with plastic or resins

(P-13575)
DOUG TRIM SUB CONTRACTOR
32010 Alaga Ave, Pearblossom (93553-3465)
PHONE......................................661 944-2884
Doug Trim, *Principal*
EMP: 12
SALES (est): 560K **Privately Held**
SIC: 3479 1721 Painting, coating & hot dipping; painting & paper hanging

(P-13576)
DRYWIRED DEFENSE LLC
9606 Santa Monica Blvd # 4, Beverly Hills (90210-4427)
PHONE......................................310 684-3891
Alex Nesic, *Vice Pres*
Kailey Bradt, *Engineer*
EMP: 20 EST: 2012
SQ FT: 4,000
SALES (est): 1.9MM **Privately Held**
SIC: 3479 3672 Coating electrodes; coating, rust preventive; printed circuit boards

(P-13577)
DURA COAT PRODUCTS INC (PA)
5361 Via Ricardo, Riverside (92509-2414)
PHONE......................................951 341-6500
Myung K Hong, *CEO*
Suzanne Faust, *CFO*
Lorrie Y Hong, *Admin Sec*
Sue Javier, *Accountant*
Raul Muytoy, *Human Resources*
▲ **EMP:** 64
SQ FT: 29,000
SALES (est): 81MM **Privately Held**
SIC: 3479 2851 Aluminum coating of metal products; coating of metals & formed products; paints & allied products

(P-13578)
E-FAB INC
1075 Richard Ave, Santa Clara (95050-2815)
P.O. Box 239 (95052-0239)
PHONE......................................408 727-5218
James W Scales, *President*
Carol Spicker, *CFO*
Jerry Banks, *Vice Pres*
Ed Hinson, *General Mgr*
Lou Madamba, *General Mgr*
EMP: 22
SQ FT: 4,000
SALES (est): 2MM **Privately Held**
WEB: www.e-fab.com
SIC: 3479 Etching & engraving

(P-13579)
ECP POWDER COATING
Also Called: El Cajon Plating
1835 John Towers Ave A, El Cajon (92020-1145)
PHONE......................................619 448-3932
Scott Rasmussen, *President*
Diane Rasmussen, *Admin Sec*
EMP: 11
SQ FT: 7,400
SALES (est): 1.4MM **Privately Held**
SIC: 3479 Coating of metals & formed products; painting, coating & hot dipping

(P-13580)
EEMUS MANUFACTURING CORP
11111 Rush St, South El Monte (91733-3548)
PHONE......................................626 443-8841
Gitte Simionian, *President*
Richard Mitchell, *Vice Pres*
Art Arteaga, *Principal*
EMP: 14
SQ FT: 20,000
SALES (est): 1.5MM **Privately Held**
SIC: 3479 Etching on metals

(P-13581)
ELECTRO METAL FINISHING CORP (PA)
1194 N Grove St, Anaheim (92806-2109)
PHONE......................................714 630-8940
Tony Vargas, *President*
Melissa Vargas, *Controller*
EMP: 17
SQ FT: 11,900
SALES: 1.6MM **Privately Held**
WEB: www.electrometalfinish.com
SIC: 3479 Painting of metal products

(P-13582)
ELECTRO STAR INDUS COATING INC
Also Called: Electro Star Powder Coatings
1945 Airport Blvd, Red Bluff (96080-4518)
PHONE......................................530 527-5400
Baron A Pierce, *President*
Susan Pierce, *CFO*
EMP: 15 EST: 1979
SQ FT: 4,000
SALES (est): 1.4MM **Privately Held**
WEB: www.electrostar.net
SIC: 3479 Coating of metals & formed products

(P-13583)
ELECTRO TECH COATINGS INC
836 Rancheros Dr Ste A, San Marcos (92069-7035)
PHONE......................................760 746-0292
Adam P Mitchell, *President*
Linda Mitchell, *CFO*
Allen L Mitchell, *Vice Pres*
Rebecca Flowers, *Office Mgr*
Denise Mitchell, *Admin Sec*
EMP: 20
SQ FT: 13,000
SALES: 1MM **Privately Held**
WEB: www.electrotechcoatings.com
SIC: 3479 3471 Painting, coating & hot dipping; sand blasting of metal parts

(P-13584)
ENGINEERED APPLICATION LLC
4727 E 49th St, Vernon (90058-2703)
PHONE......................................323 585-2894
Gil Hestmark,
EMP: 16
SALES (est): 2.2MM **Privately Held**
WEB: www.engineeredapps.com
SIC: 3479 Coating of metals & formed products

(P-13585)
ETS EXPRESS INC (PA)
420 Lombard St, Oxnard (93030-5100)
PHONE......................................805 278-7771
Sharon Eyal, *President*
Ely Eastman, *Engineer*
Shlomo Cohen, *Regl Sales Mgr*
Calvin Dixon, *Sales Staff*
Adam Kovar, *Sales Staff*
▲ **EMP:** 35
SQ FT: 40,000
SALES (est): 14.1MM **Privately Held**
WEB: www.etsexpress.com
SIC: 3479 3231 Etching & engraving; cut & engraved glassware; made from purchased glass

(P-13586)
EXCLUSIVE POWDER COATINGS INC
24922 Anza Dr Ste C, Valencia (91355-1230)
P.O. Box 803307, Santa Clarita (91380-3307)
PHONE......................................661 294-9812
Mark Kier, *CEO*
▲ **EMP:** 11
SQ FT: 8,500
SALES (est): 1.7MM **Privately Held**
SIC: 3479 Coating of metals & formed products

(P-13587)
EXPERT COATINGS & GRAPHICS LLC
1570 S Lewis St, Anaheim (92805-6423)
PHONE......................................714 476-2086
Sandra Day, *CEO*
EMP: 12

▲ = Import ▼ =Export
◆ =Import/Export

SALES (est): 1.8MM **Privately Held**
SIC: **3479** Painting, coating & hot dipping

(P-13588)
FLAME-SPRAY INC
4674 Alvarado Canyon Rd, San Diego
(92120-4304)
PHONE.................................619 283-2007
Larry Suhl, *President*
Pam Scalzo, *Shareholder*
Darrel Suhl, *Vice Pres*
Roxy Suhl, *Office Mgr*
▲ EMP: 20
SQ FT: 20,000
SALES (est): 3.3MM **Privately Held**
WEB: www.flamesprayinc.com
SIC: **3479** Coating of metals & formed
products

(P-13589)
FLETCHER COATING CO
426 W Fletcher Ave, Orange (92865-2612)
PHONE.................................714 637-4763
Kurtis Breeding, *CEO*
John Bejarano, *Plant Mgr*
Melinda Mauzy, *Cust Mgr*
▲ EMP: 50
SQ FT: 37,500
SALES (est): 5.5MM **Privately Held**
WEB: www.fletcherkote.com
SIC: **3479** Coating of metals & formed
products

(P-13590)
FOREMOST ENAMELING CO INC
Also Called: Foremost Enmling Powdr Coating
1608 W 139th St, Gardena (90249-3003)
PHONE.................................323 321-3941
William Claypool, *President*
Donald Claypool, *Vice Pres*
Dorothy Claypool, *Admin Sec*
EMP: 11
SQ FT: 13,500
SALES (est): 1.1MM **Privately Held**
WEB: www.foremostcoating.com
SIC: **3479** Coating of metals & formed
products

(P-13591)
FRONT EDGE TECHNOLOGY INC
13455 Brooks Dr Ste A, Baldwin Park
(91706-2254)
PHONE.................................626 856-8979
Simon Nieh, *President*
Roger Lin, *CFO*
EMP: 26
SQ FT: 18,000
SALES (est): 2.3MM **Privately Held**
WEB: www.frontedgetechnology.com
SIC: **3479** Coating of metals & formed
products

(P-13592)
FUSION COATINGS INC
6589 Las Positas Rd, Livermore
(94551-5157)
PHONE.................................925 443-8083
Paul Fleury, *President*
Julie Fleury, *Co-Owner*
EMP: 15
SQ FT: 7,000
SALES: 1MM **Privately Held**
WEB: www.fusioncoatings.com
SIC: **3479** Coating of metals & formed
products

(P-13593)
FVO SOLUTIONS INC
Also Called: FOOTHILL VOCATIONAL OP-
PORTUNIT
789 N Fair Oaks Ave, Pasadena
(91103-3045)
PHONE.................................626 449-0218
William C Murphy, *CEO*
Gretchen Reed, *Chairman*
▲ EMP: 75
SQ FT: 24,000
SALES: 1.7MM **Privately Held**
WEB: www.foothillvoc.org
SIC: **3479 3999** Coating of metals &
formed products; gold stamping, except
books

(P-13594)
GB INDUSTRIAL SPRAY INC
1140 Bessemer Ave Ste 1, Manteca
(95337-6108)
PHONE.................................209 825-7176
Gary L Beauchamp, *CEO*
EMP: 16
SALES (est): 1.5MM **Privately Held**
SIC: **3479** Painting of metal products

(P-13595)
GEBE ELECTRONIC SERVICES INC
4112 W Jefferson Blvd, Los Angeles
(90016-4125)
PHONE.................................323 731-2439
R O Fergus Sr, *President*
R O Fergus Jr, *Treasurer*
Gregory Fergus, *Vice Pres*
EMP: 25
SQ FT: 10,500
SALES: 1MM **Privately Held**
SIC: **3479** Bonderizing of metal or metal
products; coating of metals & formed
products

(P-13596)
GEMTECH INDS GOOD EARTH MFG
Also Called: Gemtech International
2737 S Garnsey St, Santa Ana
(92707-3340)
PHONE.................................714 848-2517
Shig Shiwota, *President*
Maya Shiwota, *Vice Pres*
David Shiwota, *Managing Dir*
▲ EMP: 24
SQ FT: 10,500
SALES (est): 3.4MM **Privately Held**
WEB: www.gemtechpowder.com
SIC: **3479** Painting of metal products

(P-13597)
GILBERT SPRAY COAT INC
300 Laurelwood Rd, Santa Clara
(95054-2311)
PHONE.................................408 988-0747
Todd McLean, *President*
Lisa McLean, *Vice Pres*
EMP: 20 EST: 1939
SQ FT: 5,000
SALES (est): 2MM **Privately Held**
WEB: www.gilbertspray.com
SIC: **3479** Painting of metal products;
painting, coating & hot dipping

(P-13598)
GRAND-WAY FABRI-GRAPHIC INC
22550 Lamplight Pl, Santa Clarita
(91350-5729)
PHONE.................................818 206-8560
Marlene Kane, *President*
EMP: 20
SQ FT: 10,500
SALES (est): 2MM **Privately Held**
SIC: **3479** Etching & engraving; painting of
metal products

(P-13599)
GUERNSEY COATING LABORATORY
1788 Goodyear Ave, Ventura (93003-8080)
PHONE.................................805 642-1508
Peter Guernsey, *Owner*
Robert Mendenhall, *Sales Staff*
EMP: 12
SQ FT: 9,000
SALES (est): 1.2MM **Privately Held**
WEB: www.gclinc.com
SIC: **3479** Coating of metals & formed
products

(P-13600)
HALEY INDUS CTINGS LININGS INC
4185 Charter St, Vernon (90058-2503)
PHONE.................................323 588-8086
Yvonne P Haley, *President*
EMP: 21
SQ FT: 14,000
SALES (est): 3.5MM **Privately Held**
SIC: **3479 1771** Coating of metals &
formed products; flooring contractor

(P-13601)
HIGH-TECH COATINGS INC
1724 S Santa Fe St, Santa Ana
(92705-4813)
PHONE.................................714 547-2122
Dan C Hilton, *Owner*
Sharon Hilton, *Human Res Mgr*
EMP: 15
SQ FT: 8,500
SALES (est): 1.5MM **Privately Held**
SIC: **3479** Coating of metals & formed
products

(P-13602)
HUES METAL FINISHING INC
977 Linda Vista Dr, San Marcos
(92078-2611)
PHONE.................................760 744-5566
Dolour S Smith-Wormald, *CEO*
Gregg L Wormald, *President*
EMP: 17
SQ FT: 11,000
SALES: 700K **Privately Held**
WEB: www.huesinc.com
SIC: **3479** Painting of metal products

(P-13603)
INLAND POWDER COATING CORP
Also Called: Prs Industries
1656 S Bon View Ave Ste F, Ontario
(91761-4419)
P.O. Box 3427 (91761-0943)
PHONE.................................909 947-1122
David Paul Flatten, *President*
Debbie Flatten, *Corp Secy*
EMP: 104
SQ FT: 83,000
SALES (est): 15.1MM **Privately Held**
WEB: www.inlandpowder.com
SIC: **3479 3471** Painting, coating & hot
dipping; sand blasting of metal parts

(P-13604)
INNOVATIVE TECHNOLOGY INC
Also Called: Inovati
1501 Cook Pl, Santa Barbara (93117-3123)
P.O. Box 60007 (93160-0007)
PHONE.................................805 571-8384
Howard Gabel, *President*
Ralph Tapphorn, *Vice Pres*
Miho Hirata, *Manager*
EMP: 10
SQ FT: 4,000
SALES (est): 1.3MM **Privately Held**
WEB: www.inovati.com
SIC: **3479 3399** Coating of metals &
formed products; powder, metal

(P-13605)
ISLAND POWDER COATING
1830 Tyler Ave, South El Monte
(91733-3618)
PHONE.................................626 279-2460
Joe Graham, *Owner*
EMP: 30
SALES (est): 5.3MM **Privately Held**
SIC: **3479** Coating of metals & formed
products

(P-13606)
ITALIX COMPANY INC
120 Mast St Ste A, Morgan Hill
(95037-5154)
PHONE.................................408 988-2487
Robert L Armanasco, *President*
Frank Fantino, *CEO*
Trisha Coyoca, *Info Tech Mgr*
Jeff Zweers, *QC Mgr*
Tony Atella, *Sales Executive*
EMP: 19
SQ FT: 8,000
SALES (est): 2.9MM **Privately Held**
WEB: www.italix.com
SIC: **3479 3471** Etching, photochemical;
finishing, metals or formed products

(P-13607)
KENNEDY NAME PLATE CO INC
4501 Pacific Blvd, Vernon (90058-2207)
PHONE.................................323 585-0121
William J Kennedy Jr, *President*
Mike Kennedy, *Vice Pres*
EMP: 25
SQ FT: 36,000

SALES: 3MM **Privately Held**
WEB: www.knpco.com
SIC: **3479 7336 3993 3444** Name plates:
engraved, etched, etc.; silk screen design; signs & advertising specialties;
sheet metalwork; coated & laminated
paper; packaging paper & plastics film,
coated & laminated

(P-13608)
KENS SPRAY EQUIPMENT INC (DH)
Also Called: Alloy Processing
1900 W Walnut St, Compton (90220-5019)
PHONE.................................310 635-9995
Joseph I Snowden, *Principal*
Brian Leibl, *President*
Sandra Jeglum, *Corp Secy*
Vanessa Avila, *Vice Pres*
Uriel Navarro, *Cust Mgr*
EMP: 59
SQ FT: 37,000
SALES (est): 27.5MM
SALES (corp-wide): 242.1B **Publicly Held**
WEB: www.alloyprocessing.com
SIC: **3479** Painting, coating & hot dipping
HQ: Precision Castparts Corp.
4650 Sw Mcdam Ave Ste 300
Portland OR 97239
503 946-4800

(P-13609)
KION TECHNOLOGY INC
2190 Oakland Rd, San Jose (95131-1571)
PHONE.................................408 435-3008
Moto Hayashi, *President*
Shirley Chau, *Admin Sec*
EMP: 15
SQ FT: 8,000
SALES (est): 1.7MM **Privately Held**
WEB: www.kiontechnology.com
SIC: **3479** Coating of metals & formed
products

(P-13610)
LEONS POWDER COATING
834 49th Ave, Oakland (94601-5136)
PHONE.................................510 437-9224
Jose Pelayo, *Owner*
EMP: 13
SALES (est): 1.3MM **Privately Held**
SIC: **3479** Coating of metals with plastic or
resins; painting, coating & hot dipping

(P-13611)
LICENSE FRAME INC
Also Called: Baron & Baron
15462 Electronic Ln, Huntington Beach
(92649-1334)
PHONE.................................714 903-7550
Catherine Baron, *President*
Peter Baron, *Vice Pres*
▲ EMP: 25
SALES (est): 2.1MM **Privately Held**
WEB: www.licenseframe.com
SIC: **3479** Engraving jewelry silverware, or
metal

(P-13612)
LINABOND INC
1161 Avenida Acaso, Camarillo
(93012-8720)
PHONE.................................805 484-7373
Richard Bertram, *President*
German Gilli, *Vice Pres*
Georgia Dreifus, *Admin Sec*
▲ EMP: 12
SQ FT: 23,000
SALES (est): 1.6MM **Privately Held**
WEB: www.linabond.com
SIC: **3479** Coating of metals with plastic or
resins

(P-13613)
LOS ANGELES GALVANIZING CO
2518 E 53rd St, Huntington Park
(90255-2505)
PHONE.................................323 583-2263
Lance Michael Rosenkranz, *CEO*
Jamie Rosenkranz, *Vice Pres*
Lance Rosenkranz, *Vice Pres*
Tim Rosenkranz, *Vice Pres*
EMP: 58 EST: 1932
SQ FT: 26,000

SALES (est): 8.7MM **Privately Held**
WEB: www.lagalvanizing.com
SIC: 3479 Galvanizing of iron, steel or end-formed products

(P-13614)
LUSTER COTE INC
10841 Business Dr, Fontana (92337-8235)
PHONE..................................909 355-9995
Jan Niblett, *President*
EMP: 14
SQ FT: 29,000
SALES: 1.1MM **Privately Held**
SIC: 3479 3444 Coating of metals & formed products; awnings, sheet metal

(P-13615)
MABEL BAAS INC
Also Called: Royal Coatings
3960 Royal Ave, Simi Valley (93063-3380)
PHONE..................................805 520-8075
Marilyn Teperson, *President*
Irene Espinoza, *Vice Pres*
EMP: 50
SALES (est): 7.1MM **Privately Held**
WEB: www.royalcoatings.com
SIC: 3479 Coating of metals & formed products; painting, coating & hot dipping

(P-13616)
MELROSE NAMEPLATE AND LABEL CO (PA)
26575 Corporate Ave, Hayward (94545-3920)
PHONE..................................510 732-3100
Chris Somers, *President*
Kathy Brenner, *Admin Sec*
▲ EMP: 40
SQ FT: 33,000
SALES (est): 6.6MM **Privately Held**
WEB: www.melrose-nl.com
SIC: 3479 3993 3643 3355 Name plates: engraved, etched, etc.; signs & advertising specialties; current-carrying wiring devices; aluminum rolling & drawing; laminated plastics plate & sheet; coated & laminated paper

(P-13617)
MERCURY METAL DIE & LETTER CO (PA)
Also Called: Hts Division
600 3rd St Ste A, Lake Elsinore (92530-2748)
P.O. Box 86 (92531-0086)
PHONE..................................951 674-8717
Hugh Mosbacher, *President*
John McGarry, *Sales Mgr*
▲ EMP: 15
SQ FT: 10,000
SALES (est): 1.8MM **Privately Held**
WEB: www.mercurymarking.com
SIC: 3479 3953 Engraving jewelry silverware, or metal; marking devices

(P-13618)
METAL COATERS CALIFORNIA INC
Also Called: Metal Coaters System
9123 Center Ave, Rancho Cucamonga (91730-5312)
PHONE..................................909 987-4681
Norman C Chambers, *CEO*
Dick Klein, *President*
EMP: 75
SALES (est): 11.5MM
SALES (corp-wide): 1.7B **Publicly Held**
SIC: 3479 Painting of metal products
PA: Nci Building Systems, Inc.
10943 N Sam Huston Pkwy W
Houston TX 77064
281 897-7788

(P-13619)
MOORE QUALITY GALVANIZING INC
3001 Falcon Dr, Madera (93637-8601)
P.O. Box 420 (93639-0420)
PHONE..................................559 673-2822
Thomas E Moore, *President*
Kellie Moore, *Corp Secy*
Marie Moore, *Vice Pres*
Craig Bridges, *Manager*
EMP: 30
SQ FT: 11,000

SALES (est): 4.6MM **Privately Held**
WEB: www.mooregalvanizing.com
SIC: 3479 Galvanizing of iron, steel or end-formed products

(P-13620)
MOORE QUALITY GALVANIZING LP
3001 Falcon Dr, Madera (93637-8601)
P.O. Box 420 (93639-0420)
PHONE..................................559 673-2822
Marie Moore, *General Ptnr*
Kellie Moore, *Partner*
EMP: 28
SQ FT: 18,000
SALES: 6MM **Privately Held**
SIC: 3479 Galvanizing of iron, steel or end-formed products

(P-13621)
NEWPORT METAL FINISHING INC
Also Called: Brass Tech
3230 S Standard Ave, Santa Ana (92705-5630)
PHONE..................................714 556-8411
Ron Foy, *President*
EMP: 70
SQ FT: 10,000
SALES (est): 6.1MM **Privately Held**
SIC: 3479 3471 Painting, coating & hot dipping; plating & polishing

(P-13622)
NORM HARBOLDT
Also Called: Primo Sandblasting
17592 Gothard St, Huntington Beach (92647-6214)
PHONE..................................714 596-4242
Norm Harboldt, *President*
EMP: 20
SQ FT: 10,000
SALES: 900K **Privately Held**
SIC: 3479 Coating of metals & formed products

(P-13623)
NU TEC POWDERCOATING
2990 E Blue Star St, Anaheim (92806-2511)
PHONE..................................714 632-5045
Joseph Kent, *Owner*
EMP: 11
SQ FT: 6,500
SALES (est): 861.4K **Privately Held**
SIC: 3479 Painting of metal products; coating of metals & formed products

(P-13624)
OLYMPIC COATINGS
2200 Micro Pl, Escondido (92029-1010)
PHONE..................................760 745-3322
Joel Johnson, *Owner*
EMP: 25
SQ FT: 4,500
SALES (est): 2.4MM **Privately Held**
WEB: www.olycoatings.com
SIC: 3479 Coating of metals & formed products

(P-13625)
OPTICAL COATING LABORATORY LLC (HQ)
Also Called: Ocli
2789 Northpoint Pkwy, Santa Rosa (95407-7397)
PHONE..................................707 545-6440
Fred Van Milligen, *President*
Shawn Cullen, *General Mgr*
Margot Brewer, *Analyst*
EMP: 400 EST: 1963
SQ FT: 490,000
SALES (est): 131MM
SALES (corp-wide): 880.4MM **Publicly Held**
WEB: www.ocli.com
SIC: 3479 3577 3827 Coating of metals & formed products; computer peripheral equipment; optical instruments & lenses
PA: Viavi Solutions Inc.
6001 America Center Dr # 6
San Jose CA 95002
408 404-3600

(P-13626)
OUR POWDER COATING INC
Also Called: Stretch Film Center
10103 Freeman Ave, Santa Fe Springs (90670-3407)
P.O. Box 3007, Whittier (90605-0007)
PHONE..................................562 946-0525
Mehdi Kohnechi, *President*
EMP: 10
SQ FT: 30,000
SALES (est): 1.2MM **Privately Held**
WEB: www.ourpowdercoating.com
SIC: 3479 Coating of metals & formed products

(P-13627)
PAC POWDER INC
Also Called: Pacific Powder Coating
148 S G St Ste 9, Arcata (95521-6690)
PHONE..................................707 826-1630
Ken Stevenson, *President*
Patti Lohr, *Admin Sec*
EMP: 10
SQ FT: 55,000
SALES (est): 1.2MM **Privately Held**
SIC: 3479 3441 Coating of metals & formed products; fabricated structural metal

(P-13628)
PACIFIC GALVANIZING INC
715 46th Ave, Oakland (94601-5096)
PHONE..................................510 261-7331
William Branagh, *President*
EMP: 25
SQ FT: 16,000
SALES: 3.7MM
SALES (corp-wide): 16.5MM **Privately Held**
WEB: www.branagh.com
SIC: 3479 Galvanizing of iron, steel or end-formed products
PA: Branagh Inc.
750 Kevin Ct
Oakland CA 94621
510 638-6455

(P-13629)
PACIFIC METAL FINISHING INC
440 Sherwood Rd, Paso Robles (93446-3554)
PHONE..................................805 237-8886
Riaz Mohammad, *President*
EMP: 10
SQ FT: 12,000
SALES (est): 1.2MM **Privately Held**
SIC: 3479 Coating of metals & formed products

(P-13630)
PACIFIC POWDER COATING INC
8637 23rd Ave, Sacramento (95826-4903)
PHONE..................................916 381-1154
Jeffrey M Rochester, *President*
▲ EMP: 30
SQ FT: 40,000
SALES: 6.3MM **Privately Held**
WEB: www.pacpowder.com
SIC: 3479 3449 Coating of metals & formed products; miscellaneous metalwork

(P-13631)
PAINT SPECIALISTS INC
8629 Bradley Ave, Sun Valley (91352-3303)
P.O. Box 1124 (91353-1124)
PHONE..................................818 771-0552
Mike Kim, *President*
EMP: 25
SQ FT: 15,000
SALES (est): 2.3MM **Privately Held**
SIC: 3479 Coating of metals & formed products; painting of metal products

(P-13632)
PEARSON ENGINEERING CORP
Also Called: Vaga Industries
2505 Loma Ave, South El Monte (91733-1417)
PHONE..................................626 442-7436
Colleen Trost, *President*
EMP: 15
SQ FT: 10,000

SALES (est): 2.2MM **Privately Held**
WEB: www.vaga.com
SIC: 3479 Etching, photochemical

(P-13633)
PERFORMANCE POWDER INC
2940 E La Jolla St Ste A, Anaheim (92806-1349)
PHONE..................................714 632-0600
Kevin Aaberg, *President*
Robert Goldberg, *Vice Pres*
EMP: 29
SALES (est): 3.6MM **Privately Held**
WEB: www.powdercoatz.com
SIC: 3479 Coating of metals & formed products; painting of metal products

(P-13634)
PGM METAL FINISHING
409 W Blueridge Ave, Orange (92865-4203)
PHONE..................................714 282-9193
David Hill, *President*
EMP: 15
SQ FT: 4,800
SALES (est): 1.2MM **Privately Held**
SIC: 3479 Painting of metal products

(P-13635)
PLASMA RGGEDIZED SOLUTIONS INC (PA)
2284 Ringwood Ave Ste A, San Jose (95131-1722)
PHONE..................................408 954-8405
Jim Stameson, *CEO*
Evan Persky, *CFO*
Hoang Nguyen, *Opers Mgr*
EMP: 68
SALES (est): 16.3MM **Privately Held**
WEB: www.plasmasystems.com
SIC: 3479 Coating of metals & formed products

(P-13636)
PLASMA TECHNOLOGY INCORPORATED (PA)
Also Called: P T I
1754 Crenshaw Blvd, Torrance (90501-3384)
PHONE..................................310 320-3373
Robert Donald Dowell, *CEO*
Andy D'Amato, *Vice Pres*
Satish Dixit, *Vice Pres*
Diane Parkhurst, *Admin Asst*
Rich Peterson, *Info Tech Dir*
▲ EMP: 73 EST: 1984
SQ FT: 40,000
SALES (est): 17.4MM **Privately Held**
SIC: 3479 Coating of metals & formed products

(P-13637)
PORTER POWDER COATING INC
510 S Rose St, Anaheim (92805-4751)
PHONE..................................714 956-2010
Jerry D Porter, *President*
Eugene Gonzalez, *Vice Pres*
EMP: 10 EST: 1996
SQ FT: 12,497
SALES (est): 1MM **Privately Held**
WEB: www.porterpowder.com
SIC: 3479 Coating of metals & formed products

(P-13638)
POWDER COATING USA INC
440 Sherwood Rd, Paso Robles (93446-3554)
PHONE..................................805 237-8886
John C Wright Jr, *President*
EMP: 11
SALES (est): 1.3MM **Privately Held**
SIC: 3479 Coating of metals & formed products

(P-13639)
POWDERCOAT SERVICES LLC
Also Called: Powdercoat Services, Inc.
1747 W Lincoln Ave Ste K, Anaheim (92801-6770)
PHONE..................................714 533-2251
Ravi RAO, *President*
Annalee Binswanger, *Office Mgr*
Alan Doughouz, *Info Tech Mgr*

▲ **EMP:** 38
SQ FT: 75,000
SALES (est): 9.5MM **Privately Held**
WEB: www.powdercoatservices.com
SIC: 3479 7211 Coating of metals &
formed products; power laundries, family
& commercial
PA: Meridian General Capital Fund Ii, L.P.
46 Peninsula Ctr
Rllng Hls Est CA

(P-13640)
PREMIER COATINGS INC
Also Called: Premier Finishing
7910 Longe St, Stockton (95206-3933)
PHONE.....................................209 982-5585
Craig M Walters, *President*
Thom Foulks, *Vice Pres*
Wendy Foulks, *Admin Sec*
EMP: 75
SQ FT: 30,000
SALES (est): 11.4MM **Privately Held**
SIC: 3479 Hot dip coating of metals or
formed products

(P-13641)
PRIMO POWDER COATING & SNDBLST
17592 Gothard St, Huntington Beach
(92647-6214)
PHONE.....................................714 596-4242
Daniel Regan, *Owner*
EMP: 10
SALES (est): 882.9K **Privately Held**
SIC: 3479 Coating of metals & formed
products

(P-13642)
PRO FAB TECH LLC
970 W Foothill Blvd, Azusa (91702-2842)
PHONE.....................................626 804-7200
James M Probst,
Sandy Probst, *Manager*
EMP: 10
SQ FT: 20,000
SALES (est): 1.7MM **Privately Held**
SIC: 3479 Aluminum coating of metal prod-
ucts

(P-13643)
PVD COATINGS II LLC
5271 Argosy Ave, Huntington Beach
(92649-1015)
PHONE.....................................714 899-4892
Red Silversterstein, *Mng Member*
EMP: 18
SALES (est): 364.3K **Privately Held**
WEB: www.pvdcoatings.net
SIC: 3479 Coating of metals & formed
products

(P-13644)
PYRAMID POWDER COATING INC
12251 Montague St, Pacoima
(91331-2212)
PHONE.....................................818 768-5898
Quasim Riaz, *President*
EMP: 25
SQ FT: 9,000
SALES (est): 2.4MM **Privately Held**
WEB: www.ppcoating.com
SIC: 3479 Painting, coating & hot dipping

(P-13645)
QUALITY PAINTING CO
19136 San Jose Ave, Rowland Heights
(91748-1415)
PHONE.....................................626 964-2529
Louise J Merkel, *President*
Ronald Merkel, *Treasurer*
James H Merkel, *Vice Pres*
EMP: 21
SQ FT: 15,000
SALES (est): 600K **Privately Held**
SIC: 3479 Coating of metals with plastic or
resins; painting of metal products; var-
nishing of metal products

(P-13646)
QUALITY POWDER COATING LLC
Also Called: Quality Coating
7373 Atoll Ave Ste B, North Hollywood
(91605-4108)
PHONE.....................................818 982-8322
Nazim Khan,
Hasmukh Bhakta,
Shivie Dillon,
EMP: 16
SQ FT: 20,000
SALES (est): 1.7MM **Privately Held**
WEB: www.qualitycoating.com
SIC: 3479 Coating of metals & formed
products; painting, coating & hot dipping

(P-13647)
RELIABLE POWDER COATINGS LLC
1577 Factor Ave, San Leandro
(94577-5615)
PHONE.....................................510 895-5551
Shawn Taylor,
EMP: 14
SQ FT: 32,000
SALES (est): 1.8MM **Privately Held**
SIC: 3479 Coating of metals & formed
products

(P-13648)
RGF ENTERPRISES INC
220 Citation Cir, Corona (92880-2522)
PHONE.....................................951 734-6922
Rodney G Fisher, *President*
EMP: 26 **EST:** 1976
SQ FT: 15,000
SALES (est): 3.2MM **Privately Held**
SIC: 3479 Coating of metals & formed
products

(P-13649)
RICHMOND METAL PAINTING
1143 Marina Way S, Richmond
(94804-3742)
PHONE.....................................510 232-7541
Enrique Ron, *Owner*
EMP: 10
SQ FT: 10,400
SALES: 700K **Privately Held**
SIC: 3479 Painting, coating & hot dipping

(P-13650)
RTS POWDER COATING INC (PA)
15121 Sierra Bonita Ln, Chino
(91710-8904)
PHONE.....................................909 393-5404
Donald D Reed Sr, *President*
EMP: 20
SQ FT: 8,100
SALES: 1.1MM **Privately Held**
WEB: www.ddrjrii.com
SIC: 3479 Coating of metals & formed
products

(P-13651)
S B I F INC
Also Called: Santa Barbara Indus Finshg
873 S Kellogg Ave, Goleta (93117-3805)
PHONE.....................................805 683-1711
Shelby See Jr, *President*
Rochelle See, *Corp Secy*
EMP: 15 **EST:** 1971
SQ FT: 6,750
SALES (est): 1.7MM **Privately Held**
WEB: www.sbifin.com
SIC: 3479 7336 Painting of metal prod-
ucts; silk screen design

(P-13652)
S C COATINGS CORPORATION
41745 Elm St Ste 101, Murrieta
(92562-1405)
PHONE.....................................951 461-9777
Michael Podratz, *Vice Pres*
Audrey Podratz, *Vice Pres*
Victor Lopez, *General Mgr*
Amanda Mitchell, *Manager*
EMP: 20
SALES: 1.5MM **Privately Held**
SIC: 3479 Coating of metals with silicon

(P-13653)
SAN DEGO PRTECTIVE COATING INC
9344 Wheatlands Rd Ste A, Santee
(92071-5643)
P.O. Box 713130 (92072-3130)
PHONE.....................................619 448-7795
Robert Johnson, *President*
Steve Johnson, *Vice Pres*
Theresa Johnson, *Admin Sec*
EMP: 17
SALES: 1MM **Privately Held**
WEB: www.sandiegopowdercoating.com
SIC: 3479 Coating of metals & formed
products

(P-13654)
SCIENTIFIC METAL FINISHING
3180 Molinaro St, Santa Clara
(95054-2425)
PHONE.....................................408 970-9011
Theodore G Otto III, *President*
Kathleen Otto, *CFO*
Desi Lopez, *Prdtn Mgr*
EMP: 40
SQ FT: 18,000
SALES (est): 5.1MM **Privately Held**
WEB: www.scientificmetal.com
SIC: 3479 2851 Coating of metals &
formed products; paints & allied products

(P-13655)
SCIENTIFIC SPRAY FINISHES INC
315 S Richman Ave, Fullerton
(92832-2195)
PHONE.....................................714 871-5541
Carlos A Lopez, *President*
Sharon Lopez, *Corp Secy*
EMP: 35 **EST:** 1964
SQ FT: 15,000
SALES (est): 1.5MM **Privately Held**
SIC: 3479 3399 Coating of metals &
formed products; powder, metal

(P-13656)
SDC TECHNOLOGIES INC (DH)
45 Parker Ste 100, Irvine (92618-1658)
PHONE.....................................714 939-8300
Antonios Grigoriou, *CEO*
Yutaka Yamamoto, *CFO*
Sapna Blackburn, *Vice Pres*
Richard Chang, *Vice Pres*
Tim Huntley, *Administration*
▲ **EMP:** 25
SQ FT: 16,800
SALES (est): 14.5MM
SALES (corp-wide): 12.4B **Privately Held**
SIC: 3479 2851 Coating of metals with
plastic or resins; paints & allied products
HQ: Mitsui Chemicals America, Inc.
800 Westchester Ave N607
Rye Brook NY 10573
914 253-0777

(P-13657)
SHAWCOR PIPE PROTECTION LLC
14000 San Bernardino Ave, Fontana
(92335-5258)
P.O. Box 1317 (92334-1317)
PHONE.....................................909 357-9002
Heath Legg, *Manager*
EMP: 10
SALES (corp-wide): 1.2B **Privately Held**
WEB: www.bredero-shaw.com
SIC: 3479 2891 Coating or wrapping steel
pipe; adhesives & sealants
HQ: Shawcor Pipe Protection Llc
3838 N Sam Houston Pkwy E # 300
Houston TX 77032

(P-13658)
SHMAZE INDUSTRIES INC
Also Called: Shmaze Custom Coatings
20792 Canada Rd, Lake Forest
(92630-6732)
PHONE.....................................949 583-1448
Michael Shamassian, *President*
Joanne Shamassian, *Treasurer*
Craig Rysavy, *Opers Staff*
EMP: 50
SQ FT: 21,500

SALES (est): 6.3MM **Privately Held**
WEB: www.shmaze.com
SIC: 3479 Coating of metals with plastic or
resins

(P-13659)
SLICKOTE
Also Called: Paint Chem
730 University Ave, Burbank (91504-3925)
PHONE.....................................818 749-3066
Eddie Andrews, *General Mgr*
EMP: 15
SALES (est): 1.1MM **Privately Held**
WEB: www.slickote.com
SIC: 3479 Coating of metals & formed
products

(P-13660)
SOCCO PLASTIC COATING COMPANY
11251 Jersey Blvd, Rancho Cucamonga
(91730-5147)
PHONE.....................................909 987-4753
Peter M Smits Jr, *President*
Rose Smits, *Vice Pres*
Tom Smits, *CPA*
Ryan Grace, *Bookkeeper*
EMP: 25
SQ FT: 60,000
SALES (est): 3.3MM **Privately Held**
WEB: www.soccoplastics.com
SIC: 3479 3444 3088 2851 Coating of
metals with plastic or resins; sheet metal-
work; plastics plumbing fixtures; paints &
allied products

(P-13661)
SPECIALTY COATING SYSTEMS INC
4435 E Airport Dr Ste 100, Ontario
(91761-7816)
PHONE.....................................909 390-8818
Steven Frease, *Branch Mgr*
EMP: 30 **Privately Held**
SIC: 3479 Painting, coating & hot dipping
HQ: Specialty Coating Systems, Inc.
7645 Woodland Dr
Indianapolis IN 46278

(P-13662)
SPECILIZED CRMIC POWDR COATING
Also Called: Specialized Coating
5862 Research Dr, Huntington Beach
(92649-1348)
PHONE.....................................714 901-2628
Lee Crecelius, *President*
EMP: 12
SALES: 1.1MM **Privately Held**
WEB: www.specializedcoating.com
SIC: 3479 Chasing on metals

(P-13663)
SPRAYLINE ENTERPRISES INC
10774 Grand Ave, Ontario (91762-4007)
PHONE.....................................909 627-8411
Phil Merenda, *President*
Russ Guthrie, *Treasurer*
Candy Merenda, *Vice Pres*
Darlene Guthrie, *Principal*
EMP: 20
SQ FT: 9,000
SALES: 500K **Privately Held**
SIC: 3479 Painting of metal products

(P-13664)
SPRAYTRONICS INC
6001 Butler Ln Ste 204, Scotts Valley
(95066-3548)
PHONE.....................................408 988-3636
Steven G Perez, *President*
Gene Freiley, *Vice Pres*
EMP: 20
SQ FT: 30,000
SALES (est): 1.9MM **Privately Held**
WEB: www.spraytronics.com
SIC: 3479

(P-13665)
ST PIERRE GONZALEZ ENTERPRISES
419 E La Palma Ave, Anaheim
(92801-2534)
PHONE.....................................714 491-2191

(PA)=Parent Co (HQ)=Headquarters (DH)=Div Headquarters
✿ = New Business established in last 2 years

Jose Gonzalez, *President*
EMP: 30
SALES (est): 1.7MM **Privately Held**
SIC: 3479 Painting, coating & hot dipping

(P-13666)
STA-BRITE-ANO
Also Called: STA-Brite Anodizing
8602 Orwell Ave, Westminster
(92683-7631)
PHONE..................................323 581-1432
Gary Newton, *Partner*
Robert Sherman, *Partner*
EMP: 14
SQ FT: 5,000
SALES (est): 1.1MM **Privately Held**
SIC: 3479 Aluminum coating of metal products

(P-13667)
STEELSCAPE INC
11200 Arrow Rte, Rancho Cucamonga
(91730-4805)
PHONE..................................909 987-4711
Ron Hurst, *Branch Mgr*
Hector Quezada, *Engineer*
Steven Gomez, *Manager*
EMP: 17
SALES (corp-wide): 191.2MM **Privately Held**
WEB: www.steelscape.com
SIC: 3479 Coating of metals & formed products
PA: Steelscape, Llc
   222 W Kalama River Rd
   Kalama WA 98625
   360 673-8200

(P-13668)
SUB-ONE TECHNOLOGY INC
161 S Vasco Rd Ste L, Livermore
(94551-5130)
PHONE..................................925 924-1020
Dore Rosenblum, *President*
▼ **EMP:** 12
SQ FT: 19,315
SALES (est): 2.5MM
SALES (corp-wide): 20.1B **Publicly Held**
WEB: www.sub-one.com
SIC: 3479 Coating or wrapping steel pipe
PA: Aecom
   1999 Avenue Of The Stars # 2600
   Los Angeles CA 90067
   213 593-8000

(P-13669)
SUNDIAL INDUSTRIES INC
Also Called: Powder Painting By Sundial
8421 Telfair Ave, Sun Valley (91352-3926)
PHONE..................................818 767-4477
Toll Free:..................................866 -
Hasu Bhakta, *President*
Naseen Khan, *Corp Secy*
Gurtreet Riaz, *Vice Pres*
▲ **EMP:** 30
SQ FT: 13,000
SALES (est): 5.2MM **Privately Held**
SIC: 3479 Coating of metals & formed products

(P-13670)
SUNDIAL POWDER COATINGS INC
Also Called: Bottle Coatings
8421 Telfair Ave, Sun Valley (91352-3926)
PHONE..................................818 767-4477
Hasu Bhakta, *CEO*
EMP: 25 **EST:** 1995
SALES (est): 3.4MM **Privately Held**
WEB: www.sundialpowdercoatings.com
SIC: 3479 Coating of metals with plastic or resins; coating of metals & formed products

(P-13671)
SURFACE MDFICATION SYSTEMS INC
12917 Park St, Santa Fe Springs
(90670-4045)
PHONE..................................562 946-7472
Rajan Bamola, *President*
Larry V Gilpin, *Vice Pres*
Thomas Ewell, *Engineer*
Karla Cano, *Director*
EMP: 10
SQ FT: 12,000

SALES (est): 1.3MM **Privately Held**
WEB:
www.surfacemodificationsystems.com
SIC: 3479 Coating of metals & formed products

(P-13672)
THERM-O-NAMEL INC
2780 M L King Jr Blvd, Lynwood (90262)
PHONE..................................310 631-7866
Grant Kinsman, *President*
Colleen Kinsman, *Corp Secy*
Byron Kinsman, *Vice Pres*
Sylvia Kinsman, *Vice Pres*
EMP: 15 **EST:** 1950
SQ FT: 15,000
SALES (est): 1.8MM **Privately Held**
WEB: www.therm-o-namel.com
SIC: 3479 3555 2851 2759 Painting of metal products; coating of metals & formed products; printing trades machinery; paints & allied products; commercial printing; automotive & apparel trimmings

(P-13673)
TIODIZE CO INC (PA)
5858 Engineer Dr, Huntington Beach
(92649-1166)
PHONE..................................714 898-4377
Thomas R Adams, *CEO*
Siera Shrout, *Creative Dir*
Patty Enna, *Controller*
Lynnette Cubbin, *Purch Mgr*
Tom Moore, *Purchasing*
EMP: 65 **EST:** 1966
SQ FT: 26,000
SALES (est): 9.9MM **Privately Held**
SIC: 3479 Coating of metals & formed products

(P-13674)
TIODIZE CO INC
Tiodize Company
5858 Engineer Dr, Huntington Beach
(92649-1166)
PHONE..................................248 348-6050
Mark Miller, *General Mgr*
EMP: 10
SALES (corp-wide): 9.9MM **Privately Held**
WEB: www.tiodize.com
SIC: 3479 Coating of metals & formed products
PA: Tiodize Co., Inc.
   5858 Engineer Dr
   Huntington Beach CA 92649
   714 898-4377

(P-13675)
ULTIMATE METAL FINISHING CORP
6150 Sheila St, Commerce (90040-2407)
PHONE..................................323 890-9100
John Ondrasik, *President*
James M Sales, *General Mgr*
EMP: 12
SQ FT: 4,800
SALES (est): 943.4K
SALES (corp-wide): 42.4MM **Privately Held**
WEB: www.precisionwireproducts.com
SIC: 3479 Coating of metals & formed products
PA: Precision Wire Products, Inc.
   6150 Sheila St
   Commerce CA 90040
   323 890-9100

(P-13676)
UNITED WESTERN ENTERPRISES INC
Also Called: Uwe
850 Flynn Rd Ste 200, Camarillo
(93012-8783)
PHONE..................................805 389-1077
Gerald Williams, *President*
Mike Lynch, *Vice Pres*
Rigo Flores, *Prdtn Mgr*
Eric Martinez, *Prdtn Mgr*
EMP: 29
SQ FT: 21,000
SALES (est): 3.9MM **Privately Held**
WEB: www.uweinc.com
SIC: 3479 Etching, photochemical

(P-13677)
VACMET INC
8740 Hellman Ave, Rancho Cucamonga
(91730-4418)
P.O. Box 3526 (91729-3526)
PHONE..................................909 948-9344
Carl Grindle, *CEO*
Gladys Marroquin, *Treasurer*
EMP: 49
SALES (est): 3.5MM **Privately Held**
SIC: 3479 Coating of metals with plastic or resins

(P-13678)
VAIDER INC
Also Called: Vaider Manufacturing
553 Martin Ave Ste 1, Rohnert Park
(94928-2091)
PHONE..................................707 584-3655
John Follenvaider, *President*
Shane Follenvaider, *Vice Pres*
Janine Follenvaider, *Admin Sec*
EMP: 10
SQ FT: 9,000
SALES (est): 800K **Privately Held**
WEB: www.vaidermfg.com
SIC: 3479 Coating of metals & formed products

(P-13679)
VISTA COATINGS INC
Also Called: Vista Powder Coatings
1440 6th St, Manhattan Beach
(90266-6344)
PHONE..................................310 635-7697
Mike Acuna, *President*
EMP: 20
SQ FT: 10,000
SALES (est): 1MM **Privately Held**
SIC: 3479 Painting of metal products

(P-13680)
WESTERN EDGE INC
37957 Sierra Hwy, Palmdale (93550-5375)
PHONE..................................661 947-3900
Kris E Johnson, *Owner*
EMP: 13
SALES (est): 1.3MM **Privately Held**
SIC: 3479 Painting of metal products

(P-13681)
WILSENERGY LLC
42440 Winchester Rd, Temecula
(92590-2504)
P.O. Box 1085, Murrieta (92564-1085)
PHONE..................................951 676-7700
Shanyn Wilson,
Steve Wilson,
EMP: 10 **EST:** 2011
SQ FT: 5,700
SALES (est): 1MM **Privately Held**
SIC: 3479 5065 Painting of metal products; coils, electronic

(P-13682)
WM J MATSON COMPANY
213 N Olive St, Ventura (93001-2515)
PHONE..................................805 684-9410
William J Matson, *President*
Ann Matson, *Vice Pres*
EMP: 15
SQ FT: 5,000
SALES (est): 750K **Privately Held**
SIC: 3479 Coating of metals & formed products

3482 Small Arms

(P-13683)
H3 HIGH SECURITY SOLUTIONS LLC
434 1/2 Palos Verdes Blvd, Redondo Beach
(90277-6514)
PHONE..................................310 373-2319
Bazzel Baz, *Principal*
EMP: 25
SALES (est): 2MM **Privately Held**
SIC: 3482 Small arms ammunition

3483 Ammunition, Large

(P-13684)
REYNOLDS SYSTEMS INC
18649 State Highway 175, Middletown
(95461)
PHONE..................................707 928-5244
Richard Reynolds, *CEO*
Elizabeth Amendola, *Manager*
Rosa Leon, *Supervisor*
EMP: 10
SQ FT: 6,000
SALES (est): 2.3MM **Privately Held**
WEB: www.reynoldssystems.com
SIC: 3483 Ammunition, except for small arms

(P-13685)
URUHU HIGHLANDS LTD
14360 Valerio St Apt 311, Van Nuys
(91405-1463)
PHONE..................................424 213-9725
Nicholas Kasule, *Principal*
EMP: 10
SALES (est): 399.4K **Privately Held**
SIC: 3483 7389 Ammunition, except for small arms;

3484 Small Arms

(P-13686)
ALLIANT TCHSYSTEMS OPRTONS LLC
151 Martinvale Ln Ste 150, San Jose
(95119-1455)
PHONE..................................408 513-3271
EMP: 11 **Publicly Held**
SIC: 3484 Small arms
HQ: Alliant Techsystems Operations Llc
   4700 Nathan Ln N
   Plymouth MN 55442

(P-13687)
ENTREPRISE ARMS INC
Also Called: Enterprise Arms
15509 Arrow Hwy, Irwindale (91706-2002)
PHONE..................................626 962-4692
Walter Chow, *CEO*
Howard Chow, *President*
EMP: 30
SQ FT: 15,000
SALES (est): 4.4MM **Privately Held**
WEB: www.entreprise.com
SIC: 3484 3949 Small arms; sporting & athletic goods

(P-13688)
PHASE 5 WEAPON SYSTEMS INC
Also Called: Phase 5 Tactical
501 Giuseppe Ct Ste C, Roseville
(95678-6310)
PHONE..................................916 787-4273
Kenneth Montes, *Owner*
EMP: 12 **EST:** 2009
SALES (est): 1.6MM **Privately Held**
SIC: 3484 Guns (firearms) or gun parts, 30 mm. & below

(P-13689)
PHOENIX ARMS
4231 E Brickell St, Ontario (91761-1512)
PHONE..................................909 937-6900
Dave Brazeau, *Owner*
▲ **EMP:** 20
SALES (est): 2.5MM **Privately Held**
SIC: 3484 Guns (firearms) or gun parts, 30 mm. & below

(P-13690)
SAI INDUSTRIES
Also Called: Standard Armament
631 Allen Ave, Glendale (91201-2013)
PHONE..................................818 842-6144
Curtis Correll, *CEO*
Gary Correll, *President*
Marcene Correll, *Vice Pres*
Cathy Joens, *Admin Sec*
Jesse Correll, *Engineer*
◆ **EMP:** 40 **EST:** 1950
SQ FT: 24,000

▲ = Import ▼=Export
◆ =Import/Export

SALES: 5MM Privately Held
WEB: www.standardarmament.com
SIC: 3484 Guns (firearms) or gun parts, 30 mm. & below

(P-13691)
TACTICOMBAT INC
11640 Mcbean Dr, El Monte (91732-1105)
PHONE..............................626 315-4433
Daisy Chan, President
Tik Yan TSE, CEO
EMP: 11
SQ FT: 2,500
SALES: 1MM Privately Held
SIC: 3484 3949 Small arms; sporting & athletic goods

(P-13692)
WEATHERBY INC
1605 Commerce Way, Paso Robles (93446-3644)
P.O. Box 6630, Sheridan WY (82801-7102)
PHONE..............................307 675-7800
Roy E Weatherby Jr, CEO
Bruce W Dixon, CFO
Jason Evans, Vice Pres
Paul Shepard, Admin Sec
Mike Schwiebert, VP Mktg
◆ EMP: 50
SQ FT: 38,000
SALES (est): 36MM Privately Held
WEB: www.weatherby.com
SIC: 3484 5091 Rifles or rifle parts, 30 mm. & below; sporting & recreation goods

(P-13693)
ZEV TECHNOLOGIES INC (PA)
Also Called: Glockworx
1051 Yarnell Pl, Oxnard (93033-2453)
PHONE..............................805 486-5800
Matthew Ridenour, CEO
Alec Wolf, President
Roe Wolf, Admin Sec
Dave Roberts, VP Mktg
Andrew Harding, Sales Associate
EMP: 18
SALES (est): 4.8MM Privately Held
SIC: 3484 Guns (firearms) or gun parts, 30 mm. & below

3489 Ordnance & Access, NEC

(P-13694)
ARMTEC DEFENSE PRODUCTS CO (HQ)
85901 Avenue 53, Coachella (92236-2607)
PHONE..............................760 398-0143
Robert W Cremin, CEO
Neal Brune, Vice Pres
Victoria Lindsey, Vice Pres
Liinda Kieft, Info Tech Mgr
Eric Muscarella, Network Mgr
◆ EMP: 330
SQ FT: 108,000
SALES (est): 74MM
SALES (corp-wide): 2B Publicly Held
SIC: 3489 Artillery or artillery parts, over 30 mm.
PA: Esterline Technologies Corp
    500 108th Ave Ne Ste 1500
    Bellevue WA 98004
    425 453-9400

(P-13695)
NETWORKS ELECTRONIC CO LLC
9750 De Soto Ave, Chatsworth (91311-4409)
PHONE..............................818 341-0440
Tamara Marie Christen, Mng Member
Terry Soroor, Design Engr
Syed Khadri, Project Engr
Andrew Campany, Engineer
Lucy Lopez, Manager
▼ EMP: 26
SQ FT: 25,000
SALES (est): 6.2MM Privately Held
SIC: 3489 Ordnance & accessories

(P-13696)
ROBERTS RESEARCH LABORATORY
23150 Kashiwa Ct, Torrance (90505-4027)
PHONE..............................310 320-7310
David Roberts, President
A L Roberts, President
Kathryn Roberts, Corp Secy
David E Roberts, Vice Pres
EMP: 15 EST: 1964
SQ FT: 10,000
SALES (est): 2.4MM Privately Held
SIC: 3489 8731 Ordnance & accessories; commercial research laboratory

(P-13697)
VIRGIN ORBIT LLC
4022 E Conant St, Long Beach (90808-1777)
PHONE..............................562 384-4400
George Whitesides, CEO
Dan Hart, President
Jon Campagna, Vice Pres
Chris Madden, Controller
Jennifer Ogren, Manager
EMP: 300 EST: 2016
SQ FT: 150,000
SALES (est): 93.8K Privately Held
SIC: 3489 3761 Guided missiles & space vehicles

3491 Industrial Valves

(P-13698)
A & G INSTR SVC & CALIBRATION
1227 N Tustin Ave, Anaheim (92807-1616)
PHONE..............................714 630-7400
Bill Arnould, President
Humberto Mexia, Vice Pres
EMP: 17
SQ FT: 4,100
SALES (est): 3.1MM Privately Held
WEB: www.a-and-g.com
SIC: 3491 7699 Process control regulator valves; professional instrument repair services

(P-13699)
ACS INSTRUMENTATION VALVES INC
3065 Richmond Pkwy # 106, Richmond (94806-5719)
PHONE..............................510 262-1880
Elizabeth Niemczyk, CEO
EMP: 99
SALES (est): 3.2MM Privately Held
SIC: 3491 Automatic regulating & control valves

(P-13700)
ADVANCED PROCESS SERVICES INC
4350 E Washington Blvd, Commerce (90023-4410)
PHONE..............................323 278-6530
Somjit Burdi, CEO
Thomas Burdi, Vice Pres
EMP: 20
SALES (est): 4.9MM Privately Held
WEB: www.advprocserv.com
SIC: 3491 Process control regulator valves

(P-13701)
AQUASYN LLC
9525 Owensmouth Ave Ste E, Chatsworth (91311-8006)
PHONE..............................818 350-0423
Dean Richards, Branch Mgr
Vincent Mitchell, Business Mgr
Chris Bullock, Mfg Mgr
Chris Belieu, Sales Staff
Patricia Hall, Cust Mgr
EMP: 18
SALES (corp-wide): 15MM Privately Held
SIC: 3491 Industrial valves
PA: Aquasyn, Llc
    1771 South Sutro Ter
    Carson City NV 89706
    818 350-0423

(P-13702)
ASCO AUTOMATIC SWITCH
Also Called: Asco Automatic Switch Co
333 City Blvd W Ste 2140, Orange (92868-2966)
PHONE..............................714 937-0811
Sam Ladva, Manager
Mark Hallenbeck, Principal
Travis Walsh, Technical Staff
Scott Cameron, Manager
EMP: 10
SALES (est): 758.4K Privately Held
SIC: 3491 Industrial valves

(P-13703)
AUTOMATIC SWITCH COMPANY
120 S Chaparral Ct # 200, Anaheim (92808-2237)
PHONE..............................714 283-4000
Jeremy Lass, Manager
EMP: 13
SALES (corp-wide): 15.2B Publicly Held
WEB: www.ascoval.com
SIC: 3491 Solenoid valves
HQ: Automatic Switch Company
    50-60 Hanover Rd
    Florham Park NJ 07932
    973 966-2000

(P-13704)
AUTOMATION & ENTERTAINMENT INC (PA)
25870 Soquel San Jose Rd, Los Gatos (95033-9235)
PHONE..............................408 353-4223
Paul Wilkinson, CEO
EMP: 13 EST: 2011
SALES (est): 4.1MM Privately Held
SIC: 3491 Automatic regulating & control valves

(P-13705)
BAILEY VALVE INC
264 W Fallbrook Ave # 105, Fresno (93711-5807)
PHONE..............................559 434-2838
Eric Brewer, President
John Edward, Vice Pres
▲ EMP: 35
SQ FT: 3,500
SALES (est): 10.6MM Privately Held
WEB: www.baileyvalve.com
SIC: 3491 Industrial valves

(P-13706)
BARBEE VALVE & SUPPLY INC (HQ)
745 Main St, Anaheim (92805)
PHONE..............................619 585-8484
Timothy Wilkinson, CEO
EMP: 12
SALES (est): 2.1MM
SALES (corp-wide): 17MM Privately Held
WEB: www.selcoproducts.com
SIC: 3491 5085 Industrial valves; valves & fittings
PA: Sel Sales, Inc.
    8780 Technology Way
    Reno NV 89521
    775 674-5100

(P-13707)
BERMINGHAM CONTROLS INC A (PA)
11144 Business Cir, Cerritos (90703-5523)
PHONE..............................562 860-0463
Gregory Gass, President
Edwin Bonner, CFO
Kevin Mulholland, Vice Pres
Michelle Lindley, Sales Staff
EMP: 37
SQ FT: 20,000
SALES: 15MM Privately Held
WEB: www.bermingham.com
SIC: 3491 3823 5084 Industrial valves; industrial instrmnts msrmnt display/control process variable; industrial machinery & equipment

(P-13708)
BURKERT CONTROMATIC CORP (PA)
Also Called: Burkert Fluid Control Systems
2572 White Rd, Irvine (92614-6236)
PHONE..............................949 251-1224
Harm Stratman, President
EMP: 14
SQ FT: 12,000
SALES (est): 24.6MM Privately Held
WEB: www.burkert-usa.com
SIC: 3491 Industrial valves

(P-13709)
BURKERT CONTROMATIC CORP
Also Called: Burkert Fluid Control Systems
2572 White Rd, Irvine (92614-6236)
PHONE..............................949 223-3100
Harm Stratman, President
Bryan McLaughlin, Area Mgr
Doug Randall, Info Tech Mgr
Manny Moreno, Sales Associate
Robert Neal, Sales Associate
EMP: 104
SQ FT: 56,000
SALES (corp-wide): 24.6MM Privately Held
SIC: 3491 Industrial valves
PA: Burkert Contromatic Corp.
    2572 White Rd
    Irvine CA 92614
    949 251-1224

(P-13710)
CHLADNI & JARIWALA INC
Also Called: Baja Products
1120 E Locust St, Ontario (91761-4537)
PHONE..............................909 947-5227
Buck Jariwala, President
George Chladni, Vice Pres
▲ EMP: 25
SQ FT: 1,000
SALES (est): 3.8MM Privately Held
WEB: www.rkvalve.com
SIC: 3491 3053 3086 Industrial valves; gaskets, all materials; oil seals, rubber; insulation or cushioning material, foamed plastic

(P-13711)
CIRCOR AEROSPACE INC (HQ)
Also Called: Circle Seal Controls
2301 Wardlow Cir, Corona (92880-2801)
P.O. Box 2824, Spartanburg SC (29304-2824)
PHONE..............................951 270-6200
Scott Buckhout, CEO
Carl Nasca, President
Renuka Ayer, Vice Pres
Steve Cartolano, Vice Pres
Christopher Celtruda, Vice Pres
▲ EMP: 245
SQ FT: 100,000
SALES (est): 80.4MM
SALES (corp-wide): 661.7MM Publicly Held
WEB: www.circleseal.com
SIC: 3491 3494 3769 5085 Pressure valves & regulators, industrial; plumbing & heating valves; guided missile & space vehicle parts & auxiliary equipment; seals, industrial
PA: Circor International, Inc.
    30 Corporate Dr Ste 200
    Burlington MA 01803
    781 270-1200

(P-13712)
COMPONENTS FOR AUTOMATION INC (PA)
Also Called: Gc Valves
1737 Lee St, Simi Valley (93065-3652)
PHONE..............................805 582-0065
Victoria Janousek, President
James Janousek, Managing Dir
Sara Shunkwiler, Office Mgr
Paul Janousek, Manager
Chuck Stevens, Manager
▲ EMP: 10
SQ FT: 2,400
SALES (est): 3.3MM Privately Held
WEB: www.cfa-inc.com
SIC: 3491 5085 Solenoid valves; valves & fittings

(P-13713)
CONTROL COMPONENTS INC (DH)
Also Called: IMI CCI
22591 Avenida Empresa, Rcho STA Marg (92688-2012)
PHONE.....................949 858-1877
Charles Merrimon, *President*
Sukhjit Purcaval, *CFO*
Ralph Chiarella, *Credit Staff*
Mary Whetnight, *Senior Buyer*
Marcelo Jimenez, *Manager*
▲ EMP: 365
SQ FT: 75,000
SALES (est): 196MM
SALES (corp-wide): 2.3B **Privately Held**
WEB: www.ccivalve.com
SIC: 3491 Process control regulator valves
HQ: Imi Americas Inc.
    5400 S Delaware St
    Littleton CO 80120
    763 488-5400

(P-13714)
CURTISS-WRIGHT CORPORATION
Also Called: Defense Solutions
28965 Avenue Penn, Santa Clarita (91355-4185)
PHONE.....................661 257-4430
Val Zarov, *Program Mgr*
Brenin Steinhart, *Contract Mgr*
James Shields, *Manager*
EMP: 21
SALES (corp-wide): 2.2B **Publicly Held**
SIC: 3491 Industrial valves
PA: Curtiss-Wright Corporation
    130 Harbour Place Dr # 300
    Davidson NC 28036
    704 869-4600

(P-13715)
CURTISS-WRIGHT FLOW CONTROL
Also Called: Curtiss-Wrght Nuclear-Enertech
2950 E Birch St, Brea (92821-6246)
PHONE.....................714 528-2301
Stan Miller, *Branch Mgr*
Andrew Labate, *Info Tech Mgr*
Arlene Corkhill, *Director*
AVI Shelcoviz, *Director*
EMP: 85
SALES (corp-wide): 2.2B **Publicly Held**
WEB: www.curtisswright.com
SIC: 3491 Industrial valves
HQ: Curtiss-Wright Flow Control Service
    Corporation
    2950 E Birch St
    Brea CA 92821
    714 982-1898

(P-13716)
FCKINGSTON CO
Also Called: Storm Manufacturing
23201 Normandie Ave, Torrance (90501-5050)
PHONE.....................310 326-8287
Joe Taormina, *President*
Rick Ward, *Information Mgr*
Joe Bui, *Engineer*
▲ EMP: 70
SQ FT: 32,500
SALES (est): 10.1MM **Privately Held**
WEB: www.fckingston.com
SIC: 3491 3494 Industrial valves; plumbing & heating valves

(P-13717)
FLOW N CONTROL INC
4452 Ocean View Blvd # 201, Montrose (91020-1287)
PHONE.....................818 330-7425
Rick Jesmok, *Principal*
EMP: 11 EST: 2014
SALES (est): 1.4MM **Privately Held**
SIC: 3491 Industrial valves

(P-13718)
HUDSON VALVE CO INC
5630 District Blvd # 108, Bakersfield (93313-2109)
PHONE.....................661 831-6208
Philip Van Horn, *President*
Gerald Van Horn, *Treasurer*
Wayne Van Horn, *Admin Sec*
EMP: 20
SQ FT: 3,027
SALES (est): 1.9MM **Privately Held**
SIC: 3491

(P-13719)
HYDRO FITTING MFG CORP
733 E Edna Pl, Covina (91723-1409)
P.O. Box 1558 (91722-0558)
PHONE.....................626 967-5151
Seth Schwartz, *President*
Carol Lynn, *Human Resources*
Lorna Burnette, *Buyer*
EMP: 45 EST: 1962
SQ FT: 16,500
SALES (est): 9.3MM **Privately Held**
WEB: www.hydrofitting.com
SIC: 3491 Industrial valves

(P-13720)
INTERNTNAL PLYMR SOLUTIONS INC
Also Called: Ipolymer
5 Studebaker, Irvine (92618-2013)
PHONE.....................949 458-3731
Patrick P Lee, *CEO*
Michael Siino, *President*
Richard Ryan, *CFO*
Mark O'Donnell, *Treasurer*
Jiri Dlab, *Engineer*
EMP: 33
SQ FT: 18,000
SALES (est): 8.3MM **Privately Held**
WEB: www.becomfg.com
SIC: 3491 3674 Industrial valves; semiconductors & related devices

(P-13721)
JAMES JONES COMPANY
1470 S Vintage Ave, Ontario (91761-3646)
PHONE.....................909 418-2558
Jerry Schnelzer, *General Mgr*
Suzie Espiritu, *Sales Staff*
◆ EMP: 141
SQ FT: 68,000
SALES (est): 22.4MM
SALES (corp-wide): 826MM **Publicly Held**
WEB: www.jamesjones.com
SIC: 3491 3494 Fire hydrant valves; pipe fittings
HQ: Mueller Group, Llc
    1200 Abernathy Rd
    Atlanta GA 30328
    770 206-4200

(P-13722)
LEEMCO INC (PA)
360 S Mount Vernon Ave, Colton (92324-3912)
PHONE.....................909 422-0088
Ali Marandi, *President*
Allen Marandi, *Vice Pres*
Susan Hillpot, *Executive Asst*
Jaime Hernandize, *Prdtn Mgr*
Tony Garner, *Manager*
◆ EMP: 11 EST: 1969
SALES (est): 1.3MM **Privately Held**
WEB: www.leemco.com
SIC: 3491 Gas valves & parts, industrial

(P-13723)
LITTLE FIREFIGHTER CORPORATION
Also Called: Firefighter Gas Safety Pdts
204 S Center St, Santa Ana (92703-4302)
PHONE.....................714 834-0410
Tod Minato, *President*
Ezra Kent, *Prdtn Mgr*
EMP: 16
SQ FT: 8,000
SALES (est): 3.4MM **Privately Held**
WEB: www.littlefirefighter.com
SIC: 3491 Gas valves & parts, industrial

(P-13724)
LUBRICATION SCIENTIFICS INC
Also Called: All Technology Machine
17651 Armstrong Ave, Irvine (92614-5727)
PHONE.....................714 557-0664
Richard T Hanley, *President*
Adam Rinderer, *Opers Mgr*
EMP: 15
SQ FT: 6,000
SALES (est): 3.9MM **Privately Held**
WEB: www.lubesci.com
SIC: 3491 Industrial valves

(P-13725)
MDC VACUUM PRODUCTS LLC
23874b Cabot Blvd, Hayward (94545-1661)
PHONE.....................510 265-3500
Roger Cockroft, *Branch Mgr*
EMP: 61
SALES (corp-wide): 41MM **Privately Held**
SIC: 3491 Industrial valves
PA: Mdc Vacuum Products, Llc
    30962 Santana St
    Hayward CA 94544
    510 265-3500

(P-13726)
MEGGITT NORTH HOLLYWOOD INC (HQ)
Also Called: Meggitt Control Systems
12838 Saticoy St, North Hollywood (91605-3505)
PHONE.....................818 765-8160
Dennis Hutton, *CEO*
Jon Bonar, *General Mgr*
Eric G Lardiere, *Admin Sec*
Mary Rustia, *Info Tech Mgr*
Surendhar Nalla, *Engineer*
▲ EMP: 230
SQ FT: 10,000
SALES (est): 102.7MM
SALES (corp-wide): 2.6B **Privately Held**
WEB: www.whittakercontrols.com
SIC: 3491 Industrial valves
PA: Meggitt Plc
    Atlantic House, Aviation Park West
    Christchurch BH23
    120 259-7597

(P-13727)
METREX VALVE CORP
505 S Vermont Ave, Glendora (91741-6206)
PHONE.....................626 335-4027
Doug Jorgensen, *President*
Scott Burson, *President*
Walter E Jorgensen, *President*
Andrea Jorgensen, *Corp Secy*
Alfred Doug Jorgensen, *Vice Pres*
▲ EMP: 25
SQ FT: 25,000
SALES (est): 5.2MM **Privately Held**
WEB: www.metrexvalve.com
SIC: 3491 Industrial valves

(P-13728)
MICRO MATIC USA INC
19791 Bahama St, Northridge (91324-3350)
PHONE.....................818 882-8012
Peter J Muzzonigro, *President*
Jeff Smigiel, *Creative Dir*
Lara Sestito, *Regl Sales Mgr*
Mark Stirett, *Regl Sales Mgr*
Denise Albrecht, *Sales Mgr*
EMP: 21
SALES (corp-wide): 323.5MM **Privately Held**
SIC: 3491 5087 3585 Industrial valves; liquor dispensing equipment & systems; soda fountain & beverage dispensing equipment & parts
HQ: Micro Matic Usa, Inc.
    2386 Simon Ct
    Brooksville FL 34604
    352 544-1081

(P-13729)
PACIFIC SEISMIC PRODUCTS INC
233 E Avenue H8, Lancaster (93535-1821)
PHONE.....................661 942-4499
Etsuko Ikegaya, *President*
Shigeko I Aramaki, *Corp Secy*
Giovanny Martinez, *Mfg Mgr*
EMP: 24
SQ FT: 10,000
SALES: 2.6MM **Privately Held**
SIC: 3491 Industrial valves

(P-13730)
PACIFIC VALVES
Also Called: Crane Co
3201 Walnut Ave, Signal Hill (90755-5225)
PHONE.....................562 426-2531
Anthony Duncan, *Principal*
Mark Controls Corporation, *Owner*
▲ EMP: 78
SQ FT: 128,128
SALES (est): 933.3K **Privately Held**
SIC: 3491 Industrial valves

(P-13731)
QVE INC
7829 Industry Ave, Pico Rivera (90660-4305)
PHONE.....................626 961-0114
Harold Fortner, *President*
EMP: 21
SALES (est): 1.7MM **Privately Held**
SIC: 3491 3443 Industrial valves; space simulation chambers, metal plate

(P-13732)
RHINO VALVE USA INC
5833 Pembroke Ave, Bakersfield (93308-4020)
PHONE.....................661 587-0220
Mark D Norman, *President*
Deborah Lockhart, *CFO*
Andy Bush, *Vice Pres*
Lee Patterson, *General Mgr*
Shawn Underwood, *Manager*
▲ EMP: 10
SQ FT: 6,800
SALES (est): 2.1MM **Privately Held**
SIC: 3491 Industrial valves

(P-13733)
SIZTO TECH CORPORATION
892 Commercial St, Palo Alto (94303-4905)
PHONE.....................650 856-8833
Chung Sizto, *President*
EMP: 12 EST: 1975
SALES (est): 1.9MM **Privately Held**
SIC: 3491 Industrial valves

(P-13734)
STORM MANUFACTURING GROUP INC
23201 Normandie Ave, Torrance (90501-5050)
PHONE.....................310 326-8287
Dale Philippi, *CEO*
Russell Kneipp, *President*
Bob Straw, *Vice Pres*
Rick Ward, *Vice Pres*
Georgia S Claessens, *Admin Sec*
▲ EMP: 74
SQ FT: 41,936
SALES (est): 13.8MM
SALES (corp-wide): 76MM **Privately Held**
WEB: www.storm-manufacturing.com
SIC: 3491 3494 Industrial valves; sprinkler systems, field
PA: Storm Industries, Inc.
    23223 Normandie Ave
    Torrance CA 90501
    310 534-5232

(P-13735)
VAT INCORPORATED
655 River Oaks Pkwy, San Jose (95134-1907)
PHONE.....................408 813-2700
Tom Murphy, *Branch Mgr*
EMP: 20
SALES (corp-wide): 700.3MM **Privately Held**
SIC: 3491 Industrial valves
HQ: Vat Incorporated
    655 River Oaks Pkwy
    San Jose CA 95134
    781 935-1446

▲ = Import ▼=Export
◆ =Import/Export

3492 Fluid Power Valves & Hose Fittings

(P-13736)
ALTERNATIVE HOSE INC (PA)
1251 N Sunshine Way Ste B, Anaheim
(92806-1759)
PHONE.....................714 414-0904
John Fuller, *CEO*
EMP: 12
SALES (est): 2.3MM **Privately Held**
WEB: www.alternativehose.com
SIC: 3492 Hose & tube fittings & assemblies, hydraulic/pneumatic

(P-13737)
CONTROL ENTERPRISES INC
Also Called: C E I
40124 Highway 49, Oakhurst (93644-8826)
PHONE.....................559 683-2044
Deborah Hill-Gossett, *President*
Ken Gossett, *Vice Pres*
EMP: 10 EST: 1981
SQ FT: 5,800
SALES (est): 761.7K **Privately Held**
WEB: www.ceivalve.com
SIC: 3492 Fluid power valves & hose fittings

(P-13738)
CRANE CO
13105 Saticoy St, North Hollywood
(91605-3403)
PHONE.....................310 403-2820
EMP: 32
SALES (corp-wide): 2.7B **Publicly Held**
SIC: 3492 Control valves, fluid power: hydraulic & pneumatic
PA: Crane Co.
100 1st Stamford Pl # 300
Stamford CT 06902
203 363-7300

(P-13739)
DIAMOND-U PRODUCTS INC
Also Called: C P Products
515 W Cowles St, Long Beach
(90813-1567)
PHONE.....................562 436-8245
Dominic Picarelli, *CEO*
Claudia Marcogliese, *CFO*
Margarita Castellanos, *Manager*
Irma Mireles, *Manager*
▲ EMP: 10
SQ FT: 20,000
SALES (est): 2.1MM **Privately Held**
WEB: www.diamondu.com
SIC: 3492 Hose & tube fittings & assemblies, hydraulic/pneumatic

(P-13740)
ELECTROFILM MFG CO LLC
Also Called: Hartzell Aerospace
28150 Industry Dr, Valencia (91355-4100)
PHONE.....................661 257-2242
Daniel L Oconnell,
James W Brown III,
Joseph W Brown,
Matthew Jesch,
David Schmidt,
EMP: 80
SQ FT: 43,000
SALES (est): 21.7MM
SALES (corp-wide): 2.5B **Publicly Held**
WEB: www.ef-heaters.com
SIC: 3492 3728 3812 Control valves, aircraft: hydraulic & pneumatic; aircraft body & wing assemblies & parts; aircraft assemblies, subassemblies & parts; aircraft power transmission equipment; aircraft propellers & associated equipment; acceleration indicators & systems components, aerospace
HQ: Itt Aerospace Controls Llc
28150 Industry Dr
Valencia CA 91355
315 568-7258

(P-13741)
FABER ENTERPRISES INC
14800 S Figueroa St, Gardena
(90248-1719)
PHONE.....................310 323-6200
Kevin M Stein, *CEO*

Esther Faber, *Ch of Bd*
Ronald E Spencer, *President*
Marilyn Spencer, *Treasurer*
Loretta Appel, *Vice Pres*
EMP: 110
SALES (est): 27.9MM **Privately Held**
WEB: www.faberent.com
SIC: 3492 Control valves, aircraft: hydraulic & pneumatic

(P-13742)
FUJIKIN OF AMERICA INC (HQ)
454 Kato Ter, Fremont (94539-8332)
PHONE.....................408 980-8269
Hiroshi Ogawa, *CEO*
Masayuki Hida, *Managing Dir*
Masato Asai, *Engineer*
Jorge Paz, *Business Mgr*
Mohamed Saleem, *Controller*
▲ EMP: 22
SQ FT: 5,000
SALES (est): 13.3MM
SALES (corp-wide): 829MM **Privately Held**
SIC: 3492 Control valves, fluid power: hydraulic & pneumatic
PA: Fujikin Incorporated
1-4-8, Shibata, Kita-Ku
Osaka OSK 530-0
663 727-141

(P-13743)
INDUSTRIAL TUBE COMPANY LLC
28150 Industry Dr, Valencia (91355-4100)
PHONE.....................661 295-4000
Farrokh Batliwala,
Bronwyn Wilber, *Train & Dev Mgr*
Daniel L Oconnell,
Christophe Rouzot, *Manager*
EMP: 99
SQ FT: 28,000
SALES (est): 31.7MM
SALES (corp-wide): 2.5B **Publicly Held**
WEB: www.industrialtube.net
SIC: 3492 3728 3812 Control valves, aircraft: hydraulic & pneumatic; aircraft body & wing assemblies & parts; aircraft assemblies, subassemblies & parts; aircraft power transmission equipment; aircraft propellers & associated equipment; acceleration indicators & systems components, aerospace
HQ: Itt Aerospace Controls Llc
28150 Industry Dr
Valencia CA 91355
315 568-7258

(P-13744)
MARTIN AEROSPACE CORPORATION
Also Called: Martin Company, The
11150 Tennessee Ave 1b, Los Angeles
(90064-1814)
PHONE.....................310 231-0055
C B Martin, *President*
EMP: 10 EST: 1983
SQ FT: 5,060
SALES (est): 1.4MM **Privately Held**
SIC: 3492 Hose & tube fittings & assemblies, hydraulic/pneumatic

(P-13745)
S&H MELKES INC
9928 Hayward Way, South El Monte
(91733-3114)
PHONE.....................626 448-5062
David Fisher, *President*
Dao Ha, *Vice Pres*
EMP: 20
SALES (est): 2.3MM **Privately Held**
SIC: 3492 3728 Fluid power valves & hose fittings; aircraft parts & equipment

(P-13746)
WESTFIELD HYDRAULICS INC
13834 Del Sur St, San Fernando
(91340-3440)
PHONE.....................818 896-6414
Robert Schacht, *CEO*
Frank Davis, *Director*
Kenneth Starbird, *Director*
Jack Umbarger, *Director*
EMP: 15
SQ FT: 10,500

SALES: 1.8MM **Privately Held**
SIC: 3492 Control valves, fluid power: hydraulic & pneumatic

3493 Steel Springs, Except Wire

(P-13747)
AMERICAN SPRING INC
321 W 135th St, Los Angeles (90061-1001)
PHONE.....................310 324-2181
Ty Kehlenbec, *President*
▲ EMP: 16
SQ FT: 25,000
SALES (est): 3.5MM **Privately Held**
SIC: 3493 3446 Coiled flat springs; acoustical suspension systems, metal

(P-13748)
ARGO SPRING MFG CO INC
13930 Shoemaker Ave, Norwalk
(90650-4597)
PHONE.....................800 252-2740
Gene Fox, *President*
Kay Greathouse, *Corp Secy*
Michael Fox, *Vice Pres*
▲ EMP: 55 EST: 1966
SQ FT: 20,000
SALES (est): 11MM **Privately Held**
WEB: www.argospring.com
SIC: 3493 3495 3469 3599 Coiled flat springs; wire springs; stamping metal for the trade; custom machinery; springs; miscellaneous fabricated wire products

(P-13749)
EIBACH SPRINGS INC
264 Mariah Cir, Corona (92879-1751)
PHONE.....................951 256-8300
Greg Cooley, *President*
Sieglinde Eibach, *Corp Secy*
Gary Peek, *Vice Pres*
Stephanie Davison, *HR Admin*
Daniel Brockman, *Purchasing*
◆ EMP: 60
SQ FT: 52,000
SALES (est): 17.2MM
SALES (corp-wide): 549.8K **Privately Held**
SIC: 3493 Steel springs, except wire
HQ: Heinrich Eibach Gmbh
Am Lennedamm 1
Finnentrop 57413
272 151-10

(P-13750)
JUENGERMANN INC
Also Called: Spring Industries
1899 Palma Dr Ste A, Ventura
(93003-5739)
PHONE.....................805 644-7165
Peter Juengermann, *President*
Erich Juengermann, *Admin Sec*
EMP: 40 EST: 1974
SQ FT: 21,600
SALES (est): 8MM **Privately Held**
WEB: www.springind.com
SIC: 3493 3495 Steel springs, except wire; wire springs

(P-13751)
MATTHEW WARREN INC
Also Called: Helical Products
901 W Mccoy Ln, Santa Maria
(93455-1109)
PHONE.....................805 928-3851
Leroy McChesney, *Branch Mgr*
EMP: 30
SALES (corp-wide): 169MM **Privately Held**
SIC: 3493 Helical springs, hot wound: railroad equipment etc.; hot wound springs, except wire; cold formed springs; coiled flat springs
HQ: Matthew Warren, Inc.
9501 Tech Blvd Ste 401
Rosemont IL 60018
847 349-5760

(P-13752)
MATTHEW WARREN INC
Also Called: Century Spring
5959 Triumph St, Commerce (90040-1609)
PHONE.....................800 237-5225

Bill Cook, *Principal*
Crystal Wiemals, *Admin Asst*
Ayda Mashhadchi, *Engineer*
EMP: 75
SALES (corp-wide): 169MM **Privately Held**
SIC: 3493 Coiled flat springs; cold formed springs; helical springs, hot wound: railroad equipment etc.; hot wound springs, except wire
HQ: Matthew Warren, Inc.
9501 Tech Blvd Ste 401
Rosemont IL 60018
847 349-5760

(P-13753)
OHARA METAL PRODUCTS
4949 Fulton Dr Ste E, Fairfield
(94534-1648)
PHONE.....................707 863-9090
Tim Ives, *President*
Irene O'Hara, *CEO*
Kathleen O'Hara,
Sande Garcia, *Cust Mgr*
EMP: 30
SQ FT: 20,000
SALES (est): 5.4MM **Privately Held**
WEB: www.oharamfg.com
SIC: 3493 3721 5051 5085 Steel springs, except wire; helicopters; metals service centers & offices; industrial supplies

(P-13754)
SCHELLINGER SPRING INC
8477 Utica Ave, Rancho Cucamonga
(91730-3809)
PHONE.....................909 373-0799
Dean Schellinger, *President*
EMP: 18
SQ FT: 12,000
SALES (est): 3MM **Privately Held**
WEB: www.schellingerspring.com
SIC: 3493 Steel springs, except wire

(P-13755)
SPACE SPRING AND STAMPING CO
5341 Argosy Ave, Huntington Beach
(92649-1036)
PHONE.....................714 255-9800
Vance S Hale Sr, *President*
Linda Hamerski, *Corp Secy*
Vance S Hale Jr, *Vice Pres*
EMP: 15
SQ FT: 12,000
SALES: 1.1MM **Privately Held**
SIC: 3493 3469 Coiled flat springs; stamping metal for the trade

(P-13756)
SUPERSPRINGS INTERNATIONAL
505 Maple St, Carpinteria (93013-2070)
PHONE.....................805 745-5553
Mike Visser, *President*
Gerry Lamberti, *CEO*
Robbie Overby, *Mktg Dir*
Tj Miller, *Marketing Staff*
Pat Curry, *Manager*
EMP: 11
SALES (est): 1.6MM **Privately Held**
WEB: www.supersprings.com
SIC: 3493 Automobile springs

3494 Valves & Pipe Fittings, NEC

(P-13757)
ALLAN AIRCRAFT SUPPLY CO LLC
11643 Vanowen St, North Hollywood
(91605-6128)
PHONE.....................818 765-4992
Robert Kahmann, *Mng Member*
Kris Common, *Executive*
Bob Kahman, *General Mgr*
Robert N Kahmann, *General Mgr*
Rex Jackson, *Info Tech Mgr*
EMP: 45 EST: 1952
SQ FT: 30,000
SALES (est): 10MM **Privately Held**
WEB: www.allanaircraft.com
SIC: 3494 Pipe fittings

(P-13758)
AMERON INTERNATIONAL CORP
Ameron Concrete & Steel Pipe
10100 W Linne Rd, Tracy (95377-9128)
PHONE.....................................209 836-5050
Lynn Pindar, *Branch Mgr*
Denisse Vignon, *Safety Mgr*
Thomas Wormstall, *Production*
EMP: 102
SALES (corp-wide): 7.3B **Publicly Held**
WEB: www.ameron.com
SIC: 3494 3317 3272 Pipe fittings; steel pipe & tubes; concrete products
HQ: Ameron International Corporation
  7909 Parkwood Circle Dr
  Houston TX 77036
  713 375-3700

(P-13759)
ANCO INTERNATIONAL INC
19851 Cajon Blvd, San Bernardino (92407-1828)
PHONE.....................................909 887-2521
Marjorie A Nielsen, *President*
EMP: 36
SQ FT: 13,500
SALES (est): 7.6MM **Privately Held**
WEB: www.ancointernational.com
SIC: 3494 3599 3492 Valves & pipe fittings; machine shop, jobbing & repair; fluid power valves & hose fittings

(P-13760)
BACKFLOW APPARATUS & VALVE
Also Called: Bavco
20435 S Susana Rd, Long Beach (90810-1136)
PHONE.....................................310 639-5231
James C Purzycki, *CEO*
Bob Purzycki, *Vice Pres*
EMP: 25
SQ FT: 10,000
SALES: 6MM **Privately Held**
WEB: www.bavco.com
SIC: 3494 Plumbing & heating valves

(P-13761)
BERMAD INC (PA)
Also Called: Bermad Control Valves
3816 S Willow Ave Ste 101, Fresno (93725-9241)
PHONE.....................................877 577-4283
Nadav Yakir, *President*
Giora Cameron, *Marketing Staff*
Yiftah Enav, *Manager*
Eyal Geller, *Manager*
▲ EMP: 35
SQ FT: 10,000
SALES (est): 7.8MM **Privately Held**
SIC: 3494 Sprinkler systems, field

(P-13762)
BRASSCRAFT MANUFACTURING CO
Also Called: Brasscraft Corona
215 N Smith Ave, Corona (92880-1741)
PHONE.....................................951 735-4375
Val Perillo, *Branch Mgr*
EMP: 94
SALES (corp-wide): 7.6B **Publicly Held**
WEB: www.brasscraft.com
SIC: 3494 3432 5074 Valves & pipe fittings; plumbing fixture fittings & trim; plumbing fittings & supplies
HQ: Brasscraft Manufacturing Company
  39600 Orchard Hill Pl
  Novi MI 48375
  248 305-6000

(P-13763)
DIE CRAFT STAMPING INC
Also Called: Gorlitz Sewer and Drain
10132 Norwalk Blvd, Santa Fe Springs (90670-3326)
PHONE.....................................562 944-2395
Gerd Kruger, *President*
Edward A Dzwonkowski, *Agent*
▲ EMP: 28
SQ FT: 20,000
SALES (est): 3.2MM **Privately Held**
WEB:
SIC: 3494 Couplings, except pressure & soil pipe

(P-13764)
DRAGON VALVES INC (PA)
13457 Excelsior Dr, Norwalk (90650-5235)
PHONE.....................................562 921-6605
Christopher Bond, *President*
Daniel Rios, *Prdtn Mgr*
C Bond, *VP Sales*
Judy Kimura, *Sales Staff*
▲ EMP: 20
SALES: 5MM **Privately Held**
WEB: www.dragonvalves.com
SIC: 3494 Valves & pipe fittings

(P-13765)
FEDERAL INDUSTRIES INC
Also Called: FI
645 Hawaii St, El Segundo (90245-4814)
PHONE.....................................310 297-4040
AVI Wacht, *President*
Asher Bartov, *CEO*
Mark Overturf, *Engineer*
EMP: 15
SALES (est): 3.4MM **Privately Held**
SIC: 3494 3728 Valves & pipe fittings; aircraft parts & equipment

(P-13766)
G-G DISTRIBUTION & DEV CO INC
Also Called: G/G Industries
28545 Livingston Ave, Valencia (91355-4166)
PHONE.....................................661 257-5700
John Gedney, *President*
Richard Greenberg, *CFO*
Mary Ellen, *Admin Sec*
▲ EMP: 120
SQ FT: 175,000
SALES (est): 20.5MM **Privately Held**
WEB: www.ggind.com
SIC: 3494 3088 Plumbing & heating valves; plastics plumbing fixtures

(P-13767)
GALT PIPE COMPANY
Also Called: Pvc Pipe Fttngs Irrgation Pdts
321 Elm Ave, Galt (95632-1511)
PHONE.....................................209 745-2936
Anne Steenblock, *President*
Ann Steenblock, *President*
Dennis Swinney, *CFO*
Alberta Barquist, *Corp Secy*
EMP: 12
SQ FT: 9,000
SALES (est): 2MM **Privately Held**
WEB: www.galtpipe.com
SIC: 3494 Pipe fittings

(P-13768)
GRISWOLD CONTROLS LLC (PA)
2803 Barranca Pkwy, Irvine (92606-5177)
P.O. Box 19612 (92623-9612)
PHONE.....................................949 559-6000
Brooks Sherman, *CEO*
Jesse Teasley, *Info Tech Mgr*
Dacian Roman, *Research*
Stefan Tuineag, *Engineer*
Karen Longo, *Accountant*
▲ EMP: 130 EST: 1960
SQ FT: 60,000
SALES (est): 39.3MM **Privately Held**
SIC: 3494 3491 Valves & pipe fittings; industrial valves

(P-13769)
INSTRUMENT & VALVE SERVICES CO
6851 Walthall Way A, Paramount (90723-2028)
PHONE.....................................562 633-0179
Larry Baumber, *Manager*
EMP: 77
SALES (corp-wide): 15.2B **Publicly Held**
WEB: www.instrum3nt.com
SIC: 3494 Valves & pipe fittings
HQ: Instrument & Valve Services Company
  205 S Center St
  Marshalltown IA 50158

(P-13770)
MILLS IRON WORKS
14834 S Maple Ave, Gardena (90248-1936)
PHONE.....................................323 321-6520
Jeffrey Griffith, *CEO*
Kenneth E Berger, *President*
EMP: 75
SQ FT: 48,000
SALES (est): 18.2MM **Privately Held**
WEB: www.millsiron.com
SIC: 3494 Pipe fittings

(P-13771)
MISSION RUBBER COMPANY LLC (HQ)
1660 Leeson Ln, Corona (92879-2061)
P.O. Box 2349 (92878-2349)
PHONE.....................................951 736-1313
David Vansell,
Chris Vansell, *Vice Pres*
▲ EMP: 80
SQ FT: 100,000
SALES (est): 37.1MM
SALES (corp-wide): 126.4MM **Privately Held**
SIC: 3494 Couplings, except pressure & soil pipe
PA: Mcp Industries, Inc.
  708 S Temescal St Ste 101
  Corona CA 92879
  951 736-1881

(P-13772)
MORRILL INDUSTRIES INC
24754 E River Rd, Escalon (95320-8601)
PHONE.....................................209 838-2550
Ken Morrill, *President*
Wayne Morrill, *CFO*
Diane Cordray, *Admin Sec*
Bob Morrill, *Prdtn Mgr*
Ed Morrill, *Sales Staff*
▲ EMP: 55
SALES (est): 11.8MM **Privately Held**
WEB: www.morrill-industries.net
SIC: 3494 Sprinkler systems, field

(P-13773)
NOR-CAL PRODUCTS INC (DH)
1967 S Oregon St, Yreka (96097-3462)
P.O. Box 518 (96097-0518)
PHONE.....................................530 842-4457
Tom Deany, *President*
David Stone, *CFO*
Monica Coupens, *General Mgr*
Eric Edin, *Engineer*
Jeff Hadley, *Engineer*
▲ EMP: 140 EST: 1946
SQ FT: 57,000
SALES (est): 39.7MM
SALES (corp-wide): 505.7MM **Privately Held**
WEB: www.nor-calproducts.com
SIC: 3494 Valves & pipe fittings

(P-13774)
RAIN BIRD CORPORATION (PA)
970 W Sierra Madre Ave, Azusa (91702-1873)
PHONE.....................................626 812-3400
Anthony W La Fetra, *President*
Mike Donoghue, *Vice Pres*
Nickolas S Kaleyias, *Principal*
Heidi Hanson, *Admin Asst*
Lisa Grant, *Administration*
▲ EMP: 125 EST: 1946
SALES (est): 98.2MM **Privately Held**
WEB: www.rainbird.com
SIC: 3494 3432 3523 Sprinkler systems, field; lawn hose nozzles & sprinklers; farm machinery & equipment

(P-13775)
SPS TECHNOLOGIES LLC
Airdrome Precision Components
14800 S Figueroa St, Gardena (90248-1719)
PHONE.....................................562 426-9411
Ben Needleman, *Controller*
EMP: 65
SALES (corp-wide): 242.1B **Publicly Held**
SIC: 3494 Valves & pipe fittings

HQ: Sps Technologies, Llc
  301 Highland Ave
  Jenkintown PA 19046
  215 572-3000

(P-13776)
STRAIGHTLINE MECHANICAL INC
1051 E 6th St, Santa Ana (92701-4752)
PHONE.....................................714 204-0940
Jacob Flora, *President*
EMP: 10 EST: 2009
SALES (est): 660K **Privately Held**
SIC: 3494 Pipe fittings

(P-13777)
VACCO INDUSTRIES (DH)
10350 Vacco St, South El Monte (91733-3399)
PHONE.....................................626 443-7121
Antonio E Gonzalez, *CEO*
Wayne Stalnecker, *President*
Vince Greco, *Vice Pres*
Robert Mc Creadie, *Vice Pres*
Paul Rowan, *Executive*
EMP: 250
SALES (est): 50.3MM
SALES (corp-wide): 685.7MM **Publicly Held**
WEB: www.vacco.com
SIC: 3494 3492 3728 Valves & pipe fittings; fluid power valves & hose fittings; aircraft parts & equipment
HQ: Esco Technologies Holding Llc
  9900 Clayton Rd Ste A
  Saint Louis MO 63124
  314 213-7200

(P-13778)
VALLEY PIPE & SUPPLY INC
1801 Santa Clara St, Fresno (93721-2865)
P.O. Box 551 (93709-0551)
PHONE.....................................559 233-0321
Mitchell Long, *CEO*
Charles Long, *CFO*
Charles C Long, *Treasurer*
Stuart Smith, *Sales Mgr*
Gary Hanson, *Sales Staff*
▲ EMP: 32
SQ FT: 20,000
SALES (est): 7.8MM **Privately Held**
SIC: 3494 5051 5085 5074 Valves & pipe fittings; pipe & tubing, steel; valves & fittings; pipes & fittings, plastic; plumbing & heating valves; farm machinery & equipment

(P-13779)
VALTERRA PRODUCTS LLC (PA)
15230 San Fernando, Mission Hills (91345)
PHONE.....................................818 898-1671
Dennis Lunder, *Principal*
Bryan Fletcher, *Vice Pres*
George Grengs, *Principal*
▲ EMP: 20
SQ FT: 50,000
SALES (est): 51.8MM **Privately Held**
WEB: www.valterra.com
SIC: 3494 3088 3949 3432 Valves & pipe fittings; plastics plumbing fixtures; skateboards; plumbing fixture fittings & trim

(P-13780)
WILLIAMS MANUFACTURING COMPANY
12727 Foothill Blvd, Sylmar (91342-5314)
PHONE.....................................818 898-2272
Oscar Pineda, *President*
Tammy Delrais, *Director*
Paul Williams, *Manager*
EMP: 12 EST: 1974
SQ FT: 7,400
SALES: 500K **Privately Held**
SIC: 3494 Pipe fittings

▲ = Import ▼=Export
◆ =Import/Export

3495 Wire Springs

(P-13781)
AARD INDUSTRIES INC
Also Called: Aard Spring & Stamping
42075 Avenida Alvarado, Temecula
(92590-3486)
PHONE 951 296-0844
William Verstegen, *President*
EMP: 22
SQ FT: 5,000
SALES (est): 4.1MM **Privately Held**
WEB: www.aard.com
SIC: 3495 3469 Wire springs; metal
stampings

(P-13782)
ADVANCED PRECISION SPRING
1754 Junction Ave Ste A, San Jose
(95112-1037)
PHONE 408 436-6595
John Nguyen, *President*
Tom Nguyen, *Vice Pres*
EMP: 15
SQ FT: 6,000
SALES: 3MM **Privately Held**
WEB: www.apspring.com
SIC: 3495 3469 Precision springs; metal
stampings

(P-13783)
ADVANEX AMERICAS INC (HQ)
5780 Cerritos Ave, Cypress (90630-4741)
PHONE 714 995-4519
Kiyoshi Kato, *Ch of Bd*
Yuichi Kato, *President*
James F Grueser, *Exec VP*
Antonio Aguilar, *Project Engr*
Jake Iliopoulos, *Engineer*
▲ EMP: 92 EST: 1966
SQ FT: 52,000
SALES (est): 24.1MM
SALES (corp-wide): 190.4MM **Privately
Held**
WEB: www.katospring.com
SIC: 3495 Wire springs
PA: Advanex Inc.
6-1-1, Tabata
Kita-Ku TKY 114-0
338 225-860

(P-13784)
ALFONSO JARAMILLO
Also Called: Acxess Spring
2225 E Cooley Dr, Colton (92324-6324)
PHONE 951 276-2777
Alfonso Jaramillo, *Owner*
Ashley Hughes, *Site Mgr*
EMP: 12
SQ FT: 2,500
SALES: 400K **Privately Held**
WEB: www.acxesspring.com
SIC: 3495 Wire springs

(P-13785)
AMERICAN PRECISION SPRING
1513 Arbuckle Ct, Santa Clara
(95054-3401)
PHONE 408 986-1020
Kathleen Chu, *President*
Mike Remily, *Vice Pres*
EMP: 23 EST: 1979
SQ FT: 1,500
SALES (est): 4.5MM **Privately Held**
WEB: www.americanprecspring.com
SIC: 3495 Mechanical springs, precision

(P-13786)
ATLAS SPRING MFGCORP
10635 Santa Monica Blvd, Los Angeles
(90025-8300)
PHONE 310 532-6200
Melvin Bayer, *President*
Stan Grietzer, *Corp Secy*
Jeff Miller, *Vice Pres*
Mary Ann Lamascus, *General Mgr*
EMP: 140
SQ FT: 100,000
SALES (est): 12.9MM **Privately Held**
SIC: 3495 Upholstery springs, unassembled

(P-13787)
BAL SEAL ENGINEERING INC
(PA)
19650 Pauling, Foothill Ranch
(92610-2610)
PHONE 949 334-8500
Richard Dawson, *CEO*
Hugh Cook, *President*
Jeff Huber, *President*
Sean McCarthy, *CFO*
Peter J Balsells, *Chairman*
▲ EMP: 277 EST: 1959
SQ FT: 325,000
SALES (est): 125.9MM **Privately Held**
WEB: www.balseal.com
SIC: 3495 Wire springs

(P-13788)
BETTS COMPANY (PA)
Also Called: Betts Spring Manufacturing
2843 S Maple Ave, Fresno (93725-2217)
PHONE 559 498-3304
William M Betts IV, *Ch of Bd*
Bill Betts, *President*
Donald Devany, *Vice Pres*
Marcus Shiveley, *Vice Pres*
David Peterson, *Administration*
▲ EMP: 75
SQ FT: 7,500
SALES (est): 70.1MM **Privately Held**
WEB: www.bettspring.com
SIC: 3495 3493 Wire springs; instrument
springs, precision; mechanical springs,
precision; automobile springs

(P-13789)
BETTS COMPANY
Betts Spring Manufacturing
2843 S Maple Ave, Fresno (93725-2217)
PHONE 559 498-3304
Carlos Holguin, *Branch Mgr*
EMP: 32
SALES (corp-wide): 70.1MM **Privately
Held**
SIC: 3495 3493 Wire springs; instrument
springs, precision; mechanical springs,
precision; automobile springs
PA: Betts Company
2843 S Maple Ave
Fresno CA 93725
559 498-3304

(P-13790)
BETTS COMPANY
Also Called: Betts Truck Parts
10771 Almond Ave Ste B, Fontana
(92337-7165)
PHONE 909 427-9988
Dan Paul, *Manager*
EMP: 17
SALES (corp-wide): 70.1MM **Privately
Held**
WEB: www.bettspring.com
SIC: 3495 3493 Wire springs; instrument
springs, precision; mechanical springs,
precision; automobile springs
PA: Betts Company
2843 S Maple Ave
Fresno CA 93725
559 498-3304

(P-13791)
C & M SPRING & ENGINEERING
CO
5244 Las Flores Dr, Chino (91710-9610)
P.O. Box 2559 (91708-2559)
PHONE 909 597-2030
Paul Lockhart, *President*
EMP: 26
SQ FT: 15,000
SALES (est): 4.7MM **Privately Held**
WEB: www.cmspring.com
SIC: 3495 3496 Mechanical springs, precision; miscellaneous fabricated wire products

(P-13792)
CLIO INC
Also Called: B&B Spring Co
12981 166th St, Cerritos (90703-2104)
PHONE 562 926-3724
Jerome M Johnson, *President*
Reva J Johnson, *CEO*
Angela Christofferson, *Technology*
EMP: 28

SQ FT: 2,000
SALES (est): 4.8MM **Privately Held**
SIC: 3495 3679 Wire springs; transducers,
electrical

(P-13793)
DIVERSIFIED SPRING TECH
9233 Santa Fe Springs Rd, Santa Fe
Springs (90670-2617)
PHONE 562 944-4049
Leo Hernandez, *President*
Olga Hernandez, *Vice Pres*
Marilyn Hernandez, *Purchasing*
EMP: 11
SQ FT: 4,000
SALES: 350K **Privately Held**
WEB: www.diversifiedspring.com
SIC: 3495 3316 5085 Precision springs;
clock springs, precision; instrument
springs, precision; mechanical springs,
precision; cold-rolled strip or wire; springs

(P-13794)
FOREMOST SPRING COMPANY
INC
Also Called: Foremost Spring & Mfg
11876 Burke St, Santa Fe Springs
(90670-2536)
PHONE 562 923-0791
Forrest Gardner, *President*
Christine Brown, *Vice Pres*
Jesus Silva, *Admin Sec*
EMP: 15
SQ FT: 20,000
SALES (est): 1.6MM **Privately Held**
WEB: www.foremostspring.com
SIC: 3495 3469 3493 Mechanical springs,
precision; stamping metal for the trade;
steel springs, except wire

(P-13795)
J HOWARD SERVICE GROUP
INC
2755 Seaboard Ln, Long Beach
(90805-3751)
PHONE 562 602-0224
Jim Arakawa, *President*
EMP: 12
SQ FT: 20,000
SALES: 900K **Privately Held**
WEB: www.paramountspring.com
SIC: 3495 3469 Wire springs; metal
stampings

(P-13796)
NEWCOMB SPRING CORP
Also Called: Newcomb Spring of California
8380 Cerritos Ave, Stanton (90680-2514)
PHONE 714 995-5341
Robert Guard, *Manager*
Rick Guard, *Plant Mgr*
EMP: 30
SALES (corp-wide): 71.2MM **Privately
Held**
WEB: www.newcombspring.com
SIC: 3495 3469 5085 Wire springs;
stamping metal for the trade; springs
PA: Spring Newcomb Corp
5408 Panola Indus Blvd
Decatur GA 30035
770 981-2803

(P-13797)
ORLANDO SPRING CORP
5341 Argosy Ave, Huntington Beach
(92649-1036)
PHONE 562 594-8411
Frank Mauro, *President*
Zachary Fischer, *CEO*
Todd Crow, *Controller*
EMP: 40
SQ FT: 20,000
SALES (est): 8.5MM **Privately Held**
SIC: 3495 Wire springs

(P-13798)
PENINSULA SPRING
CORPORATION
6750 Silacci Way, Gilroy (95020-7035)
P.O. Box 1782 (95021-1782)
PHONE 408 848-3361
Joe Kilmer, *President*
Laura Hampel, *Officer*
Muriel Kilmer, *Vice Pres*
EMP: 18

SQ FT: 10,000
SALES: 1.3MM **Privately Held**
WEB: www.peninsulaspring.com
SIC: 3495 3444 3498 3496 Precision
springs; forming machine work, sheet
metal; fabricated pipe & fittings; miscellaneous fabricated wire products

(P-13799)
PERIDOT CORPORATION
1072 Serpentine Ln, Pleasanton
(94566-4731)
PHONE 925 461-8830
Patrick Pickerell, *President*
Debra Vansickle, *Vice Pres*
Diane Wardin, *Office Mgr*
EMP: 60
SQ FT: 30,000
SALES (est): 11.5MM **Privately Held**
WEB: www.peridotcorp.com
SIC: 3495 Wire springs

(P-13800)
PRECISION COIL SPRING
COMPANY
10107 Rose Ave, El Monte (91731-1898)
PHONE 626 448-9731
Albert H Goering, *CEO*
Bert Goering, *President*
Cheryl Hyland, *VP Accounting*
Don Adkins, *VP Sales*
Tony Brandlin, *Director*
EMP: 100
SQ FT: 45,000
SALES (est): 22.8MM **Privately Held**
WEB: www.pcspring.com
SIC: 3495 Wire springs

(P-13801)
REV CO SPRING
MFANUFACTURING
9915 Alburtis Ave, Santa Fe Springs
(90670-3209)
PHONE 562 949-1958
Evelyn Valles, *President*
Vicky Garcia, *Corp Secy*
Rudy Valles, *Vice Pres*
EMP: 12
SQ FT: 6,000
SALES (est): 750K **Privately Held**
SIC: 3495 Precision springs

(P-13802)
SPRING DELGAU INC
Also Called: Delgau Spring
322 N Garfield Ave, Corona (92882-1826)
PHONE 951 371-1000
Bernard Delgau, *President*
EMP: 10 EST: 1978
SQ FT: 7,800
SALES (est): 1.7MM **Privately Held**
WEB: www.delgauspring.com
SIC: 3495 Wire springs

(P-13803)
STECHER ENTERPRISES INC
Also Called: C&F Wire Products
8536 Central Ave, Stanton (90680-2718)
PHONE 714 484-6900
Fred Stecher, *Director*
Tammy Stecher, *President*
Carol Stecher, *Vice Pres*
EMP: 15
SQ FT: 10,000
SALES: 1.3MM **Privately Held**
WEB: www.cfwireproducts.com
SIC: 3495 Instrument springs, precision

(P-13804)
SUPERIOR SPRING COMPANY
1260 S Talt Ave, Anaheim (92806-5533)
PHONE 714 490-0881
Robert De Long Jr, *President*
Brad Delong, *Vice Pres*
Robert Long, *Technology*
EMP: 25
SQ FT: 17,000
SALES (est): 5.3MM **Privately Held**
WEB: www.superiorspring.com
SIC: 3495 Wire springs

PRODUCTS & SVCS

(P-13805)
TRICOSS INC
Also Called: Tri County Spring & Stamping
4450 Dupont Ct Ste A, Ventura
(93003-7790)
PHONE..................................805 644-4107
Karl Schlosser, *President*
Ingrid Boehm, *Admin Sec*
▼ EMP: 10
SQ FT: 7,800
SALES: 500K Privately Held
WEB: www.tricossinc.com
SIC: 3495 3469 3496 Wire springs; metal stampings; wire cloth & woven wire products

(P-13806)
UNITED PRECISION CORP
20810 Plummer St, Chatsworth
(91311-5004)
PHONE..................................818 576-9540
Robert Stanley Hawrylo, *CEO*
EMP: 11 EST: 2014
SQ FT: 7,500
SALES (est): 1.3MM Privately Held
SIC: 3495 Precision springs; instrument springs, precision

3496 Misc Fabricated Wire Prdts

(P-13807)
ACCURATE WIRE & DISPLAY INC
Also Called: Kersting Library Products
3600 Oak Cliff Dr, Fallbrook (92028-9413)
PHONE..................................310 532-7821
Craig Tannahill, *President*
▲ EMP: 50
SALES (est): 4.4MM Privately Held
SIC: 3496 2514 2517 7319

(P-13808)
AM&S MFG INC
Also Called: AM&s Design
498 Sapena Ct, Santa Clara (95054-2426)
PHONE..................................800 519-5709
Andrew Le, *CEO*
Tucker Harrison, *COO*
Vincent Rondas, *Vice Pres*
EMP: 12
SQ FT: 16,000
SALES: 750K Privately Held
SIC: 3496 3999 3599 Miscellaneous fabricated wire products; dock equipment & supplies, industrial; machine & other job shop work; machine shop, jobbing & repair; electrical discharge machining (EDM)

(P-13809)
AMERICAN WIRE INC
784 S Lugo Ave, San Bernardino
(92408-2236)
PHONE..................................909 884-9990
Bian Bie Liem, *CEO*
▲ EMP: 19
SQ FT: 12,000
SALES (est): 4MM Privately Held
WEB: www.americanwirecorp.com
SIC: 3496 Mesh, made from purchased wire

(P-13810)
ANAHEIM WIRE PRODUCTS INC (PA)
1009 E Vermont Ave, Anaheim
(92805-5618)
PHONE..................................714 563-8300
Michael Lewis, *President*
Mike Tweedle, *Vice Pres*
▲ EMP: 20
SQ FT: 14,000
SALES (est): 3.9MM Privately Held
WEB: www.anaheimwire.com
SIC: 3496 Miscellaneous fabricated wire products

(P-13811)
AUTOMOTIVE ELECTRONICS SVCS
Also Called: Aeswave.com
5465 E Hedges Ave, Fresno (93727-2279)
PHONE..................................559 292-7851
Jorge Menchu, *President*
Carlos Menchu, *General Mgr*
Mario Vejar, *Technical Staff*
▲ EMP: 13
SALES (est): 2.8MM Privately Held
WEB: www.aeswave.com
SIC: 3496 7373 Cable, uninsulated wire: made from purchased wire; systems software development services

(P-13812)
BILL WOOD LATHING
12188 Central Ave Pmb 621, Chino
(91710-2420)
PHONE..................................909 628-1733
William Wood, *Owner*
Deborah Long, *Manager*
EMP: 25
SALES (est): 1.8MM Privately Held
SIC: 3496 Lath, woven wire

(P-13813)
BLACKTALON INDUSTRIES INC
481 Technology Way, NAPA (94558-7571)
P.O. Box 300 (94559-0300)
PHONE..................................707 256-1812
Brent Morgan, *President*
EMP: 13
SALES (est): 1.6MM Privately Held
SIC: 3496 7382 Fencing, made from purchased wire; burglar alarm maintenance & monitoring

(P-13814)
CABLE MOORE INC (PA)
4700 Coliseum Way, Oakland
(94601-5008)
P.O. Box 4067 (94614-4067)
PHONE..................................510 436-8000
Sandra Moore, *CEO*
Gregory Moore, *Corp Secy*
Ron Garcia, *Sales Staff*
Roy Guzman, *Sales Staff*
Greg Moore, *Sales Staff*
◆ EMP: 40
SQ FT: 12,500
SALES (est): 11MM Privately Held
WEB: www.cablemoore.com
SIC: 3496 Wire chain

(P-13815)
CABLESTRAND CORP
Also Called: Cable Strand
2660 Signal Pkwy, Long Beach
(90755-2205)
PHONE..................................562 595-4527
Allan Weiss, *President*
Paul Weiss, *Chairman*
Karen Weiss, *Vice Pres*
▲ EMP: 10
SQ FT: 16,000
SALES (est): 1.6MM Privately Held
SIC: 3496 Cable, uninsulated wire: made from purchased wire

(P-13816)
CALIFORNIA WIRE PRODUCTS CORP
Also Called: Cal-Monarch
1316 Railroad St, Corona (92882-1840)
PHONE..................................951 371-7730
John G Frei, *CEO*
Samuel A Agajanian, *President*
Francis Estaris, *CFO*
Sam Agajanian, *Principal*
Kenny Kuhns, *Prdtn Mgr*
▲ EMP: 30
SQ FT: 34,000
SALES (est): 7.5MM Privately Held
WEB: www.cawire.com
SIC: 3496 2542 Screening, woven wire: made from purchased wire; partitions for floor attachment, prefabricated: except wood

(P-13817)
CARPENTER GROUP
112 Bgley St Crnr Of Rlro Corner Of Railro, Vallejo (94592)
PHONE..................................707 562-3543
Dane Oliver, *Branch Mgr*
EMP: 17
SALES (corp-wide): 27.8MM Privately Held
WEB: www.carpenterrigging.com
SIC: 3496 Miscellaneous fabricated wire products
PA: The Carpenter Group
222 Napoleon St
San Francisco CA 94124
415 285-1954

(P-13818)
CARPENTER GROUP
Also Called: Cableco
13100 Firestone Blvd, Santa Fe Springs
(90670-5517)
PHONE..................................562 942-8076
Ray Stys, *Branch Mgr*
Hugh Yoder, *Marketing Staff*
EMP: 10
SALES (corp-wide): 27.8MM Privately Held
WEB: www.carpenterrigging.com
SIC: 3496 2394 Cable, uninsulated wire: made from purchased wire; liners & covers, fabric: made from purchased materials
PA: The Carpenter Group
222 Napoleon St
San Francisco CA 94124
415 285-1954

(P-13819)
CLOSETMAID CORPORATION
5150 Edison Ave Ste C, Chino
(91710-5786)
PHONE..................................909 590-4444
Ken Graper, *Branch Mgr*
EMP: 15
SALES (corp-wide): 1.5B Publicly Held
WEB: www.closetmaidmail.com
SIC: 3496 Miscellaneous fabricated wire products
HQ: Closetmaid Llc
650 Sw 27th Ave
Ocala FL 34471
352 401-6000

(P-13820)
COVE FOUR-SLIDE STAMPING CORP (PA)
Also Called: Cove West Division
355 S Hale Ave, Fullerton (92831-4805)
P.O. Box 272, Freeport NY (11520-0272)
PHONE..................................516 379-4232
Barry Jaffe, *Principal*
Marjorie R Jaffee, *Admin Sec*
Jose Montoya, *Plant Mgr*
Augie Ruiz, *Agent*
▲ EMP: 75 EST: 1960
SQ FT: 50,000
SALES (est): 10.7MM Privately Held
SIC: 3496 3469 Miscellaneous fabricated wire products; metal stampings

(P-13821)
COVE FOUR-SLIDE STAMPING CORP
Cove West
335 S Hale Ave, Fullerton (92831-4805)
PHONE..................................714 525-2930
Augustine Ruiz, *Manager*
EMP: 40
SALES (corp-wide): 10.7MM Privately Held
SIC: 3496 3452 3315 Miscellaneous fabricated wire products; bolts, nuts, rivets & washers; wire & fabricated wire products
PA: Cove Four-Slide & Stamping Corp.
355 S Hale Ave
Fullerton CA 92831
516 379-4232

(P-13822)
CUSTOM WIRE PRODUCTS
7580 North Ave, Lemon Grove
(91945-1699)
PHONE..................................619 469-2328
Fax: 619 469-4809

EMP: 12
SQ FT: 9,000
SALES (est): 910K Privately Held
WEB: www.custom-wire.com
SIC: 3496

(P-13823)
DAHLHAUSER MANUFACTURING CO
1855 Russell Ave, Santa Clara
(95054-2035)
PHONE..................................408 988-3717
Dan Dahlhauser, *President*
EMP: 20 EST: 1966
SQ FT: 22,000
SALES: 2MM Privately Held
SIC: 3496 Wire fasteners

(P-13824)
DANIEL GERARD WORLDWIDE INC
13055 Jurupa Ave, Fontana (92337-6982)
PHONE..................................800 635-8296
EMP: 13
SALES (corp-wide): 91.8MM Privately Held
SIC: 3496 Miscellaneous fabricated wire products
PA: Daniel Gerard Worldwide Inc
34 Barnhart Dr
Hanover PA 17331
800 232-3332

(P-13825)
EJAY FILTRATION INC
3036 Durahart St, Riverside (92507-3446)
P.O. Box 5268 (92517-5268)
PHONE..................................951 683-0805
Jerry Green, *CEO*
Cheryl Young, *President*
Bob Rostig, *Vice Pres*
Jennifer Hall, *General Mgr*
Kavin McNabb, *QA Dir*
EMP: 33
SQ FT: 14,000
SALES (est): 4.8MM Privately Held
WEB: www.ejayfiltration.com
SIC: 3496 Mesh, made from purchased wire

(P-13826)
FEATHER FARM INC
1181 4th Ave, NAPA (94559-3617)
PHONE..................................707 255-8833
Jim Brown, *President*
Arlyta Brown, *Vice Pres*
▲ EMP: 14
SQ FT: 20,000
SALES (est): 2.1MM Privately Held
WEB: www.featherfarm.com
SIC: 3496 0752 Cages, wire; breeding services, pet & animal specialties (not horses)

(P-13827)
FEENEY INC
2603 Union St, Oakland (94607-2423)
PHONE..................................510 893-9473
Grissell Ralston, *CEO*
Katrina Ralston, *President*
Steven Imbrenda, *CFO*
Richard Ralston, *Principal*
Chad Baird, *Info Tech Mgr*
▼ EMP: 48 EST: 1948
SQ FT: 29,000
SALES (est): 11.9MM Privately Held
SIC: 3496 Miscellaneous fabricated wire products

(P-13828)
FENCE FACTORY
2650 El Camino Real, Atascadero
(93422-1915)
PHONE..................................805 462-1362
Jay Foster, *Manager*
EMP: 12
SALES (corp-wide): 29.9MM Privately Held
WEB: www.fencefactory.com
SIC: 3496 5039 3446 Fencing, made from purchased wire; wire fence, gates & accessories; architectural metalwork
HQ: Fence Factory
2419 Palma Dr
Ventura CA 93003
805 644-7207

▲ = Import ▼=Export
◆ =Import/Export

(P-13829)
FITTINGS THAT FIT INC
4628 Mission Blvd, Montclair (91763-6135)
PHONE..................................909 248-2808
Eric C Wang, *President*
▲ EMP: 15
SALES (est): 2.5MM **Privately Held**
WEB: www.ffi-ftf.com
SIC: 3496 Fencing, made from purchased wire

(P-13830)
FLYNN AND ENSLOW INC (PA)
3401 Enterprise Ave, Hayward (94545-3201)
P.O. Box 4433, Walnut Creek (94596-0433)
PHONE..................................415 863-5340
Jamie Yoder, *CEO*
▲ EMP: 24
SQ FT: 15,000
SALES (est): 5.3MM **Privately Held**
WEB: www.flynnenslow.com
SIC: 3496 5051 Screening, woven wire: made from purchased wire; wire cloth & woven wire products; hardware cloth, woven wire; mesh, made from purchased wire; wire screening; steel decking; metal wires, ties, cables & screening; reinforcement mesh, wire

(P-13831)
FREDS FENCING INC
10560 Kenney St, Santee (92071-4507)
PHONE..................................619 562-5331
Shadi Khouri, *CEO*
EMP: 12
SQ FT: 2,500
SALES (est): 1.4MM **Privately Held**
SIC: 3496 Miscellaneous fabricated wire products

(P-13832)
GROSSI FABRICATION INC
3200 Tully Rd, Hughson (95326-9816)
P.O. Box 937 (95326-0937)
PHONE..................................209 883-2817
Larry Grossi, *President*
Shanon Grossi, *Vice Pres*
EMP: 20
SALES (est): 4.4MM **Privately Held**
SIC: 3496 Netting, woven wire: made from purchased wire

(P-13833)
INNOVIVE LLC (PA)
10019 Waples Ct, San Diego (92121-2962)
PHONE..................................858 309-6620
Dee Conger, *CEO*
Claudia Lee, *Admin Asst*
Paul Jackson, *VP Engrg*
Samuel Lujan, *Project Engr*
Leroy Jenson, *Engineer*
▲ EMP: 40
SQ FT: 50,000
SALES (est): 11.3MM **Privately Held**
WEB: www.innoviveinc.com
SIC: 3496 Cages, wire

(P-13834)
INTAKE SCREENS INC
8417 River Rd, Sacramento (95832-9710)
PHONE..................................916 665-2727
Russell Berry IV, *President*
Russell M Berry III, *Vice Pres*
Judy McAvoy, *Office Mgr*
Ronaele Berry, *Admin Sec*
Jacob Chapin, *Design Engr*
EMP: 15
SQ FT: 3,300
SALES (est): 3.7MM **Privately Held**
WEB: www.intakescreensinc.com
SIC: 3496 Screening, woven wire: made from purchased wire

(P-13835)
INTERMETRO INDUSTRIES CORP
9420 Santa Anita Ave, Rancho Cucamonga (91730-6117)
PHONE..................................909 987-4731
John Skuchas, *Branch Mgr*
EMP: 28
SQ FT: 56,000 **Privately Held**
WEB: www.metro.com

SIC: 3496 2542 Miscellaneous fabricated wire products; partitions & fixtures, except wood
HQ: Intermetro Industries Corporation
651 N Washington St
Wilkes Barre PA 18705
570 825-2741

(P-13836)
K I O KABLES INC
Also Called: Kio Kables
2525 W 10th St, Antioch (94509-1374)
PHONE..................................925 778-7500
Bruce Scott, *President*
EMP: 18
SQ FT: 1,500
SALES (est): 2.6MM **Privately Held**
SIC: 3496 Cable, uninsulated wire: made from purchased wire

(P-13837)
K METAL PRODUCTS INC
Also Called: Benchmark Engineering Div of
11935 Baker Pl, Santa Fe Springs (90670-2551)
PHONE..................................562 693-5425
EMP: 200
SQ FT: 54,000
SALES (est): 12.5MM **Privately Held**
SIC: 3496 3444 2542 3498

(P-13838)
KEVIN WHALEY
Also Called: Whaley, Kevin Enterprises
9565 Pathway St, Santee (92071-4184)
PHONE..................................619 596-4000
Kevin M Whaley, *Owner*
▼ EMP: 25
SQ FT: 24,000
SALES (est): 3.4MM **Privately Held**
SIC: 3496 Cages, wire

(P-13839)
MERCHANTS METALS LLC
6829 Mccomber St, Sacramento (95828-2515)
PHONE..................................916 381-8243
Sara Uyeno, *Manager*
EMP: 10
SALES (corp-wide): 2.3B **Privately Held**
SIC: 3496 Miscellaneous fabricated wire products
HQ: Merchants Metals Llc
211 Perimeter Center Pkwy
Atlanta GA 30346
770 741-0300

(P-13840)
MERCHANTS METALS LLC
10401 Glenoaks Blvd, Pacoima (91331-1609)
PHONE..................................818 896-6111
Ryan Anartsdale, *Manager*
EMP: 10
SALES (corp-wide): 2.3B **Privately Held**
SIC: 3496 5211 Fencing, made from purchased wire; mesh, made from purchased wire; concrete reinforcing mesh & wire; fencing
HQ: Merchants Metals Llc
211 Perimeter Center Pkwy
Atlanta GA 30346
770 741-0300

(P-13841)
MIWA INC
5733 San Leandro St Ofc, Oakland (94621-4426)
PHONE..................................510 261-5999
Thomas Yan, *President*
Sandra Yan, *Vice Pres*
▲ EMP: 25
SQ FT: 45,000
SALES (est): 2.4MM **Privately Held**
WEB: www.miwafuton.com
SIC: 3496 2512 2511 7919 Mats & matting; couches, sofas & davenports: upholstered on wood frames; screens, privacy: wood; lighting, lamps & accessories

(P-13842)
PACIFIC WIRE PRODUCTS INC
10725 Vanowen St, North Hollywood (91605-6402)
PHONE..................................818 755-6400
Charles L Swick, *President*

EMP: 25
SQ FT: 28,000
SALES: 3MM **Privately Held**
WEB: www.pacificwire.com
SIC: 3496 Miscellaneous fabricated wire products

(P-13843)
PRECISION WIRE PRODUCTS INC (PA)
6150 Sheila St, Commerce (90040-2407)
PHONE..................................323 890-9100
Vladimir John Ondrasik Jr, *Principal*
V John Ondrasik, *President*
Crystal McLaughlin, *Safety Dir*
◆ EMP: 200
SQ FT: 200,000
SALES (est): 42.4MM **Privately Held**
WEB: www.precisionwireproducts.com
SIC: 3496 Grocery carts, made from purchased wire

(P-13844)
PREFERRED WIRE PRODUCTS INC
401 N Minnewawa Ave, Clovis (93611-9194)
PHONE..................................559 324-0140
Bradley Actis, *President*
Robert Actis, *Vice Pres*
▲ EMP: 10
SALES (est): 1.7MM **Privately Held**
SIC: 3496 Miscellaneous fabricated wire products

(P-13845)
PROCESS SPECIALTIES INC
1660 W Linne Rd Ste A, Tracy (95377-8025)
PHONE..................................209 832-1344
Edward Morris, *President*
Mark Hinkle, *Vice Pres*
Manny D Arroz, *Admin Sec*
Garry Jenkins, *Engineer*
Steve Hayashi, *Manager*
EMP: 23
SQ FT: 20,000
SALES: 8.2MM **Privately Held**
WEB: www.processspecialties.com
SIC: 3496 Miscellaneous fabricated wire products

(P-13846)
PS INTL INC
655 Vineland Ave, City of Industry (91746-1912)
PHONE..................................626 333-8168
▲ EMP: 10
SALES (est): 779.3K **Privately Held**
SIC: 3496 Cages, wire

(P-13847)
R & B WIRE PRODUCTS INC
2902 W Garry Ave, Santa Ana (92704-6510)
PHONE..................................714 549-3355
Richard G Rawlins, *President*
Frank Rowe, *Vice Pres*
Mike Keys, *General Mgr*
Pedro Contreras, *Technology*
Steve Votaw, *Purch Mgr*
◆ EMP: 35 EST: 1948
SQ FT: 20,000
SALES (est): 10.4MM **Privately Held**
WEB: www.rbwire.com
SIC: 3496 Miscellaneous fabricated wire products

(P-13848)
RAMPONE INDUSTRIES LLC
14235 Commerce Dr, Garden Grove (92843-4944)
PHONE..................................949 581-8701
Horacio Rampone,
▲ EMP: 30
SQ FT: 20,000
SALES (est): 6.3MM **Privately Held**
WEB: www.ramponewire.com
SIC: 3496 Miscellaneous fabricated wire products

(P-13849)
RAPID MANUFACTURING A (PA)
8080 E Crystal Dr, Anaheim (92807-2524)
PHONE..................................714 974-2432
Joseph Lang, *Partner*

Steven Chan, *Program Mgr*
Adriana Dominguez, *Program Mgr*
Jorge Sanchez, *Administration*
Rick Heng, *Info Tech Mgr*
EMP: 180
SQ FT: 19,500
SALES (est): 49.6MM **Privately Held**
WEB: www.rapidmfg.com
SIC: 3496 Miscellaneous fabricated wire products

(P-13850)
RFC WIRE FORMS INC
525 Brooks St, Ontario (91762-3702)
PHONE..................................909 467-0559
Donald C Kemby, *CEO*
Ryan Gonzales, *General Mgr*
Christine Kemby, *Admin Sec*
Amber Magana, *Admin Asst*
Angelica Ramirez, *Admin Asst*
◆ EMP: 70 EST: 1946
SQ FT: 29,000
SALES (est): 15MM **Privately Held**
WEB: www.rfcwireforms.com
SIC: 3496 Miscellaneous fabricated wire products

(P-13851)
ROCATEQ NORTH AMERICA
4155 Blackhwk Lasas Cir, Danville (94506)
PHONE..................................925 648-7794
Linda Downs, *Exec Dir*
▲ EMP: 15
SALES (est): 2.4MM **Privately Held**
SIC: 3496 Grocery carts, made from purchased wire

(P-13852)
RPS INC
20331 Corisco St, Chatsworth (91311)
PHONE..................................818 350-8088
Travis Miller, *President*
EMP: 25 EST: 2017
SQ FT: 1,000
SALES (est): 1MM **Privately Held**
SIC: 3496 7389 Miscellaneous fabricated wire products; design services

(P-13853)
SPECIALTY STEEL PRODUCTS INC
Also Called: California Cage Co
1202 Piper Ranch Rd, San Diego (92154-7714)
PHONE..................................664 637-6704
Gilberto Gallardo, *CEO*
EMP: 10
SALES (est): 2.3MM **Privately Held**
WEB: www.ssp-inc.net
SIC: 3496 Cages, wire

(P-13854)
SYNERGISTIC RESEARCH INC
1736 E Borchard Ave, Santa Ana (92705-4605)
PHONE..................................949 642-2800
Theodore Denney III, *President*
▲ EMP: 15
SALES (est): 2.5MM **Privately Held**
WEB: www.synergisticresearch.com
SIC: 3496 Cable, uninsulated wire: made from purchased wire

(P-13855)
SYSTEMS WIRE & CABLE LIMITED
1165 N Stanford Ave, Los Angeles (90059-3516)
PHONE..................................310 532-7870
Ueli Burkhardt, *CEO*
Robert Gaisford, *Vice Pres*
Jennifer Harman, *Office Mgr*
Pete Burkhardt, *Admin Sec*
EMP: 13
SQ FT: 15,000
SALES (est): 2.6MM **Privately Held**
WEB: www.systemswire.com
SIC: 3496 Cable, uninsulated wire: made from purchased wire

(P-13856)
T AND T INDUSTRIES INC (PA)
1835 Dawns Way Ste A, Fullerton (92831-5301)
PHONE..................................714 284-6555
John Vaughn, *President*

PRODUCTS & SVCS

John Mayberry, *Officer*
▲ **EMP:** 13 **EST:** 1943
SQ FT: 10,000
SALES (est): 9.2MM **Privately Held**
SIC: 3496 Clips & fasteners, made from
purchased wire

(P-13857)
TOP-SHELF FIXTURES LLC (PA)
5263 Schaefer Ave, Chino (91710-5554)
P.O. Box 2470 (91708-2470)
PHONE.............................909 627-7423
Alonso Munoz, *Mng Member*
Dennis Poudel, *Vice Pres*
Olivia Norris, *Executive Asst*
Matthew Beard, *Design Engr*
Juan Verduzco, *Project Mgr*
EMP: 59
SQ FT: 90,000
SALES (est): 18.5MM **Privately Held**
WEB: www.topshelffixtures.com
SIC: 3496 Miscellaneous fabricated wire
products

(P-13858)
**UNITED SNSHINE AMRCN INDS
CORP**
Also Called: USA Industries
2808 E Marywood Ln, Orange
(92867-1912)
PHONE.............................801 972-5124
James Pearsall, *President*
Bill Stratton, *Shareholder*
Micheal Yates, *Shareholder*
Kirk Williams, *Vice Pres*
EMP: 25
SQ FT: 25,000
SALES (est): 3.9MM **Privately Held**
SIC: 3496

(P-13859)
UNIVERSAL WIRE INC
1705 S Campus Ave, Ontario (91761-4346)
PHONE.............................626 285-2288
Mahesh Vaghasia, *President*
Himat Desai, *CFO*
Rashmikant Vaghasia, *Vice Pres*
Parshottam Lakhani, *Admin Sec*
▲ **EMP:** 14 **EST:** 1958
SQ FT: 15,000
SALES (est): 2.8MM **Privately Held**
WEB: www.universalwireinc.com
SIC: 3496 Miscellaneous fabricated wire
products

(P-13860)
US RIGGING SUPPLY CORP
1600 E Mcfadden Ave, Santa Ana
(92705-4310)
PHONE.............................714 545-7444
Richard T Walker, *CEO*
Andre Mendoza, *General Mgr*
Paul Ottone, *Opers Mgr*
Eddie Arias, *Sales Staff*
Doug Heim, *Sales Staff*
◆ **EMP:** 50
SQ FT: 20,000
SALES (est): 11MM **Privately Held**
WEB: www.usrigging.com
SIC: 3496 5051 Miscellaneous fabricated
wire products; rope, wire (not insulated)

(P-13861)
VOLK ENTERPRISES INC
618 S Kilroy Rd, Turlock (95380-9531)
PHONE.............................209 632-3826
Anthony Volks, *Manager*
EMP: 60 **Privately Held**
SIC: 3496 3089 Miscellaneous fabricated
wire products; plastic processing
PA: Volk Enterprises, Inc.
1335 Ridgeland Pkwy # 120
Alpharetta GA 30004

(P-13862)
WALKER CORPORATION
1555 S Vintage Ave, Ontario (91761-3655)
P.O. Box 2146, Bakersfield (93303-2146)
PHONE.............................909 390-4300
Randall Walker, *Vice Pres*
EMP: 32 **EST:** 2015
SALES (est): 7.2MM **Privately Held**
SIC: 3496 Miscellaneous fabricated wire
products

(P-13863)
WESTERN WIRE WORKS INC
7923 Cartilla Ave, Rancho Cucamonga
(91730-3069)
PHONE.............................909 483-1186
Zanley I Galton, *President*
EMP: 13
SALES (corp-wide): 33.6MM **Privately
Held**
SIC: 3496 Woven wire products
PA: Western Wire Works, Inc.
3950 Nw Saint Helens Rd
Portland OR 97210
503 445-0319

(P-13864)
**WHITMOR PLSTIC WIRE CABLE
CORP (PA)**
Also Called: Whitmor Wire and Cable
27737 Avenue Hopkins, Santa Clarita
(91355-1223)
PHONE.............................661 257-2400
Michael Weiss, *President*
Mark Lee, *Vice Pres*
Stella Reaza, *Principal*
Jeff Siebert, *VP Mfg*
Dwight Van Lake, *Director*
▼ **EMP:** 92 **EST:** 1959
SQ FT: 50,000
SALES (est): 32MM **Privately Held**
WEB: www.wireandcable.com
SIC: 3496 5063 3357 Cable, uninsulated
wire: made from purchased wire; electri-
cal apparatus & equipment; nonferrous
wiredrawing & insulating

(P-13865)
**WHITMOR PLSTIC WIRE CABLE
CORP**
Also Called: Whitmor Wirenetics
28420 Stanford Ave, Valencia (91355)
PHONE.............................661 257-2400
Jeff Siebert, *Vice Pres*
EMP: 40
SALES (est): 5MM
SALES (corp-wide): 32MM **Privately
Held**
SIC: 3496 5063 Cable, uninsulated wire:
made from purchased wire; electrical ap-
paratus & equipment
PA: Whitmor Plastic Wire And Cable Corp.
27737 Avenue Hopkins
Santa Clarita CA 91355
661 257-2400

(P-13866)
WYREFAB INC
15711 S Broadway, Gardena (90248-2401)
P.O. Box 3767 (90247-7467)
PHONE.............................310 523-2147
Charles Nick, *President*
John P Massey, *Corp Secy*
John Massey, *Production*
EMP: 42 **EST:** 1948
SQ FT: 55,000
SALES (est): 7.9MM **Privately Held**
WEB: www.wyrefab.com
SIC: 3496 Miscellaneous fabricated wire
products

(P-13867)
Z B WIRE WORKS INC
1139 Brooks St, Ontario (91762-3607)
PHONE.............................909 391-0995
Guadalupe Zamarripa, *President*
Carmen Zamarripa, *Shareholder*
Jose Zamarripa, *Shareholder*
Alvaro Zammaripa, *Shareholder*
Paul Zammarripa, *Shareholder*
EMP: 10
SQ FT: 10,000
SALES (est): 1.7MM **Privately Held**
WEB: www.zbwireworks.com
SIC: 3496 Miscellaneous fabricated wire
products

3497 Metal Foil & Leaf

(P-13868)
**AAMSTAMP MACHINE
COMPANY LLC**
38960 Trade Center Dr B, Palmdale
(93551-3715)
PHONE.............................661 272-0500
Gordon Starr, *Mng Member*
Ron Johnson, *Opers Mgr*
Ashley Baker, *Sales Dir*
Matthew Starr,
EMP: 10
SQ FT: 10,000
SALES (est): 1.2MM **Privately Held**
WEB: www.aamstamp.com
SIC: 3497 Metal foil & leaf

(P-13869)
FRM USA LLC
Also Called: Framing Fabrics International
6001 Santa Monica Blvd, Los Angeles
(90038-1807)
PHONE.............................323 469-9006
Chaim Neuberg, *CEO*
Larry Neuberg, *Principal*
EMP: 50 **EST:** 1999
SQ FT: 15,000
SALES (est): 4.3MM **Privately Held**
WEB: www.framingfabrics.com
SIC: 3497 Metal foil & leaf

(P-13870)
MATERION BRUSH INC
Also Called: Brush Wellman
44036 S Grimmer Blvd, Fremont
(94538-6346)
PHONE.............................510 623-1500
Edward Hefter, *Managing Dir*
Damon Harris, *Design Engr*
EMP: 40
SQ FT: 50,000
SALES (corp-wide): 1.1B **Publicly Held**
WEB: www.brushwellman.com
SIC: 3497 3442 3699 3444 Metal foil &
leaf; window & door frames; electrical
equipment & supplies; sheet metalwork;
engineering services
HQ: Materion Brush Inc.
6070 Parkland Blvd Ste 1
Mayfield Heights OH 44124
216 486-4200

(P-13871)
**NORTH PACIFIC
INTERNATIONAL**
5944 Sycamore Ct, Chino (91710-9138)
PHONE.............................909 628-2224
Tsugio Imai, *President*
▲ **EMP:** 10
SQ FT: 13,000
SALES (est): 3MM **Privately Held**
WEB: www.npcfoil.com
SIC: 3497 2396 Metal foil & leaf; fabric
printing & stamping

3498 Fabricated Pipe & Pipe Fittings

(P-13872)
ACCURATE TUBE BENDING INC
37770 Timber St, Newark (94560-4443)
P.O. Box 990, Fremont (94537-0990)
PHONE.............................510 790-6500
Jon Morrow, *President*
EMP: 33
SQ FT: 28,000
SALES (est): 6.2MM **Privately Held**
WEB: www.atbending.com
SIC: 3498 Tube fabricating (contract bend-
ing & shaping)

(P-13873)
AEROFIT LLC
1425 S Acacia Ave, Fullerton (92831-5317)
PHONE.............................714 521-5060
Jordan A Law, *Managing Prtnr*
David A Werner, *Partner*
Cecilia Donan, *Personnel Assit*
Martha Smith, *Manager*
▲ **EMP:** 150
SQ FT: 67,000

SALES (est): 46.2MM
SALES (corp-wide): 167.6MM **Privately
Held**
WEB: www.aerofit.net
SIC: 3498 Pipe fittings, fabricated from
purchased pipe
PA: Consolidated Aerospace Manufactur-
ing, Llc
1425 S Acacia Ave
Fullerton CA 92831
714 989-2797

(P-13874)
**AL & KRLA PIPE FABRICATORS
INC**
Also Called: Pipe Fabricators International
8047 Wing Ave, El Cajon (92020-1245)
PHONE.............................619 448-0060
Alvaro Mena, *President*
EMP: 12
SALES: 450K **Privately Held**
SIC: 3498 Fabricated pipe & fittings

(P-13875)
AMERIFLEX INC
2390 Railroad St, Corona (92880-5410)
PHONE.............................951 737-5557
John Bagnuolo, *CEO*
Chester Kwasniak, *CFO*
▲ **EMP:** 76
SQ FT: 32,000
SALES (est): 18.3MM
SALES (corp-wide): 169MM **Privately
Held**
WEB: www.ameriflex.net
SIC: 3498 3494 3674 Fabricated pipe &
fittings; valves & pipe fittings; semicon-
ductors & related devices
HQ: Mw Industries, Inc.
9501 Tech Blvd Ste 401
Rosemont IL 60018
847 349-5760

(P-13876)
ANVIL INTERNATIONAL LLC
551 N Loop Dr, Ontario (91761-8629)
PHONE.............................909 418-3233
Gwyn Lundy, *Credit Mgr*
EMP: 12
SALES (corp-wide): 2.3B **Privately Held**
WEB: www.anvilint.com
SIC: 3498 3321 3317 Fabricated pipe &
fittings; gray & ductile iron foundries; steel
pipe & tubes
HQ: Anvil International, Llc
2 Holland Way
Exeter NH 03833
603 418-2800

(P-13877)
B F MC GILLA INC
Also Called: Advance Pipe Bending & Fabg
Co
2020 E Slauson Ave, Huntington Park
(90255-2726)
PHONE.............................323 581-8288
Gary McCray, *President*
Peter Bowman, *Corp Secy*
Malcolm Field, *Vice Pres*
EMP: 20 **EST:** 1976
SQ FT: 4,100
SALES (est): 3.3MM **Privately Held**
WEB: www.advancepipebending.com
SIC: 3498 Tube fabricating (contract bend-
ing & shaping)

(P-13878)
**BAKER COUPLING COMPANY
INC**
2929 S Santa Fe Ave, Vernon
(90058-1425)
PHONE.............................323 583-3444
Ramendra Satyarthi, *President*
▲ **EMP:** 35
SQ FT: 65,000
SALES (est): 8.8MM **Privately Held**
WEB: www.bdssoftware.com
SIC: 3498 Couplings, pipe: fabricated from
purchased pipe; pipe fittings, fabricated
from purchased pipe

(P-13879)
BASSANI MANUFACTURING
Also Called: Bassani Exhaust
2900 E La Jolla St, Anaheim (92806-1305)
PHONE.............................714 630-1821

Darryl Bassani, *President*
Becky Bassani, *Corp Secy*
Gary Naito, *Adv Dir*
Kurt Gordon, *Manager*
▲ EMP: 46 EST: 1969
SQ FT: 20,791
SALES (est): 9.9MM **Privately Held**
WEB: www.bassani.com
SIC: 3498 3599 Fabricated pipe & fittings;
machine shop, jobbing & repair

(P-13880)
**CAL PIPE MANUFACTURING INC
(PA)**
Also Called: Calpipe Security Bollards
19440 S Dminguez Hills Dr, Compton
(90220-6417)
PHONE...................................562 803-4388
Dan Markus, *President*
Sheri Caine-Markus, *Vice Pres*
Mike Lang, *Sales Dir*
▲ EMP: 45
SQ FT: 125,000
SALES (est): 9.5MM **Privately Held**
WEB: www.calpipe.com
SIC: 3498 Tube fabricating (contract bend-
ing & shaping)

(P-13881)
**CALIFORNIA PIPE
FABRICATORS**
7277 Chevron Way, Dixon (95620-9772)
PHONE...................................707 678-3069
Dennis A Rinearson, *President*
Brenda Rinearson, *Vice Pres*
Jennifer Sarley, *Manager*
Julia Chandler, *Accounts Mgr*
EMP: 35
SQ FT: 4,800
SALES: 7MM **Privately Held**
SIC: 3498 Fabricated pipe & fittings

(P-13882)
COTT TECHNOLOGIES INC
14923 Proctor Ave, La Puente
(91746-3206)
PHONE...................................626 961-3399
Gilbert L Decardenas, *President*
George C Salmas, *Vice Pres*
EMP: 11
SALES (est): 1.4MM **Privately Held**
WEB: www.cotttechnologies.com
SIC: 3498 Piping systems for pulp paper &
chemical industries

(P-13883)
CRYOWORKS INC
3309 Grapevine St, Mira Loma
(91752-3503)
PHONE...................................951 360-0920
Timothy L Mast, *President*
Tamara Sipos, *CFO*
Donna J Mast, *Vice Pres*
EMP: 30
SALES: 5.9MM **Privately Held**
SIC: 3498 1711 Fabricated pipe & fittings;
plumbing contractors

(P-13884)
**CUSTOM PIPE & FABRICATION
INC (HQ)**
Also Called: Custom Pipe & Coupling Co Inc
10560 Fern Ave, Stanton (90680-2648)
P.O. Box 978 (90680-0978)
PHONE...................................800 553-3058
Danny Daniel, *CEO*
Leonard Shapiro, *Treasurer*
Erline Cardenas, *Human Res Mgr*
Tara Kirkland, *Marketing Staff*
Lupe Villa, *Sales Staff*
◆ EMP: 60
SQ FT: 8,000
SALES: 61.3MM
SALES (corp-wide): 72.3MM **Privately
Held**
WEB: www.custompipe.com
SIC: 3498 Tube fabricating (contract bend-
ing & shaping)
PA: Shapco Inc.
1666 20th St Ste 100
Santa Monica CA 90404
310 264-1666

(P-13885)
EDMUND A GRAY CO (PA)
2277 E 15th St, Los Angeles (90021-2852)
PHONE...................................213 625-0376
Lawrence Gray Jr, *CEO*
Patricia Gray, *Corp Secy*
Larry Gray, *Vice Pres*
Lawrence Gray III, *Vice Pres*
Anna Ramos, *Finance Mgr*
▲ EMP: 71
SQ FT: 50,000
SALES (est): 17.5MM **Privately Held**
WEB: www.eagray.com
SIC: 3498 Pipe fittings, fabricated from
purchased pipe

(P-13886)
ELECTROLURGY INC
Also Called: Electrolurgy Manufacturing
1217 E Normandy Pl, Santa Ana
(92705-4135)
PHONE...................................714 641-7488
Sean Eklund, *Owner*
Lisa Arangua, *Controller*
EMP: 35
SALES (corp-wide): 14.1MM **Privately
Held**
WEB: www.electrolurgy.com
SIC: 3498 Tube fabricating (contract bend-
ing & shaping)
PA: Electrolurgy, Inc.
1121 Duryea Ave
Irvine CA 92614
949 250-4494

(P-13887)
**EXPRESS PIPE & SUPPLY CO
LLC (DH)**
Also Called: Expressions Home Gallery
1666 20th St Ste 200a, Santa Monica
(90404-3828)
PHONE...................................310 204-7238
Greg Boiko, *President*
EMP: 35
SALES (est): 76.2MM **Privately Held**
SIC: 3498 5074 Pipe fittings, fabricated
from purchased pipe; plumbing & hy-
dronic heating supplies
HQ: Morsco Supply, Llc
100 E 15th St Ste 200
Fort Worth TX 76102
877 709-2227

(P-13888)
FLEXIBLE METAL INC (HQ)
Also Called: FMI
1685 Brandywine Ave, Chula Vista
(91911-6020)
PHONE...................................678 280-0127
Donald R Heye, *CEO*
▲ EMP: 70
SALES (est): 40.2MM
SALES (corp-wide): 96.5MM **Privately
Held**
WEB: www.flexiblemetal.com
SIC: 3498 Fabricated pipe & fittings
PA: Hyspan Precision Products, Inc.
1685 Brandywine Ave
Chula Vista CA 91911
619 421-1355

(P-13889)
FLO-MAC INC
1846 E 60th St, Los Angeles (90001-1420)
P.O. Box 1078, Huntington Park (90255-
1078)
PHONE...................................323 583-8751
Larry Smith, *President*
Mark Smith, *Treasurer*
Scott Crane, *Vice Pres*
EMP: 21 EST: 1974
SQ FT: 14,000
SALES (est): 4.7MM **Privately Held**
WEB: www.flo-mac.com
SIC: 3498 Pipe fittings, fabricated from
purchased pipe

(P-13890)
ILCO INDUSTRIES INC
1308 W Mahalo Pl, Compton (90220-5418)
PHONE...................................310 631-8655
Elias Awad, *President*
EMP: 35
SQ FT: 23,000

SALES (est): 7.1MM **Privately Held**
WEB: www.ilcoind.com
SIC: 3498 3492 Manifolds, pipe: fabricated from purchased pipe; pipe fittings,
fabricated from purchased pipe; pipe sections fabricated from purchased pipe;
tube fabricating (contract bending & shaping); hose & tube fittings & assemblies,
hydraulic/pneumatic

(P-13891)
JIFCO INC (PA)
Also Called: Jifco Fabaricated Piping
571 Exchange Ct, Livermore (94550-2400)
P.O. Box 589 (94551-0589)
PHONE...................................925 449-4665
Jay Forni Jr, *President*
John Nuche, *Project Mgr*
Kerry Thach, *Project Mgr*
Rick Pastor, *Opers Mgr*
Monica Spina Forni, *Director*
EMP: 60
SALES (est): 17.4MM **Privately Held**
WEB: www.jifco.com
SIC: 3498 Tube fabricating (contract bend-
ing & shaping)

(P-13892)
KAISER ENTERPRISES INC
Also Called: Insight Mfg Services
798 Murphys Creek Rd, Murphys
(95247-9562)
P.O. Box 2609 (95247-2609)
PHONE...................................209 728-2091
Loretta Dietz Kaiser, *President*
Herman Kaiser, *COO*
Jonelle Lewis, *Human Resources*
Laurie Fox,
EMP: 75
SQ FT: 6,900
SALES: 15MM **Privately Held**
SIC: 3498 Coils, pipe: fabricated from pur-
chased pipe

(P-13893)
LEVCO FAB INC
10757 Fremont Ave, Ontario (91762-3910)
PHONE...................................909 465-0840
Ben Levacy, *President*
Gail Levacy, *CFO*
EMP: 11
SQ FT: 6,000
SALES (est): 1.9MM **Privately Held**
SIC: 3498 Fabricated pipe & fittings

(P-13894)
**LINKTECH QUICK COUPLINGS
INC**
3000 Bunsen Ave Ste A, Ventura
(93003-7639)
PHONE...................................805 339-0055
Randall Rehder, *President*
EMP: 30
SALES (est): 4.1MM
SALES (corp-wide): 2B **Publicly Held**
SIC: 3498 3592 5085 Couplings, pipe:
fabricated from purchased pipe; valves;
valves & fittings
PA: Nordson Corporation
28601 Clemens Rd
Westlake OH 44145
440 892-1580

(P-13895)
**MARINE & INDUSTRIAL
SERVICES**
2391 W 10th St, Antioch (94509-1366)
PHONE...................................925 757-8791
Thomas M Hannaford, *President*
Janell Gruner, *Admin Asst*
Kyle Hannaford, *Manager*
EMP: 16
SQ FT: 21,000
SALES (est): 3.7MM **Privately Held**
SIC: 3498 Pipe fittings, fabricated from
purchased pipe

(P-13896)
**MARK IV METAL PRODUCTS
INC**
544 W 132nd St, Gardena (90248-1504)
PHONE...................................310 217-9700
David Viana, *President*
Andrew Segal, *Shareholder*
Melanie Viana, *Office Mgr*

Alejandro Viana, *Admin Sec*
EMP: 12
SQ FT: 20,000
SALES (est): 2MM **Privately Held**
WEB: www.markivmetal.com
SIC: 3498 Tube fabricating (contract bend-
ing & shaping)

(P-13897)
MD STAINLESS SERVICES
8241 Phlox St, Downey (90241-4841)
PHONE...................................562 904-7022
Marvin Davis, *President*
Sunshine Olsen, *Treasurer*
Ralph Gallardo, *General Mgr*
Clay Guinaldo, *Purch Mgr*
EMP: 20
SQ FT: 15,000
SALES (est): 6MM **Privately Held**
WEB: www.mdstainless.com
SIC: 3498 1711 Fabricated pipe & fittings;
process piping contractor

(P-13898)
ONE-WAY MANUFACTURING INC
1195 N Osprey Cir, Anaheim (92807-1709)
PHONE...................................714 630-8833
Sue Huang, *CEO*
Ike Huang, *COO*
EMP: 23
SQ FT: 19,400
SALES (est): 5.1MM **Privately Held**
WEB: www.onewaymfg.com
SIC: 3498 3599 1541 7692 Tube fabri-
cating (contract bending & shaping); ma-
chine & other job shop work; truck &
automobile assembly plant construction;
welding repair; mechanical engineering;
fluxes: brazing, soldering, galvanizing &
welding

(P-13899)
**PERFORMANCE TUBE BENDING
INC**
5462 Diaz St, Baldwin Park (91706-2026)
PHONE...................................626 939-9000
Jaime R Renella, *President*
▲ EMP: 17
SALES (est): 3.1MM **Privately Held**
SIC: 3498 Tube fabricating (contract bend-
ing & shaping)

(P-13900)
**PERNSTNER SONS
FABRICATION INC**
712 W Harding Rd, Turlock (95380-9743)
PHONE...................................209 345-2430
Jesse J Pernsteiner, *President*
EMP: 14
SALES: 120K **Privately Held**
SIC: 3498 Fabricated pipe & fittings

(P-13901)
**PIPE FABRICATING & SUPPLY
CO (PA)**
1235 N Kraemer Blvd, Anaheim
(92806-1921)
PHONE...................................714 630-5200
Fred E Simmons, *CEO*
John M Eagle, *Vice Pres*
▲ EMP: 100 EST: 1945
SQ FT: 90,000
SALES: 11.2MM **Privately Held**
WEB: www.pipefab.com
SIC: 3498 Tube fabricating (contract bend-
ing & shaping)

(P-13902)
RIGHT MANUFACTURING LLC
7949 Stromesa Ct Ste G, San Diego
(92126-6338)
PHONE...................................858 566-7002
Greg Lyon,
Lh Byrd, *Mfg Mgr*
▲ EMP: 30 EST: 1971
SQ FT: 15,000
SALES (est): 6.6MM **Privately Held**
SIC: 3498 3444 Tube fabricating (contract
bending & shaping); sheet metalwork

PRODUCTS & SVCS

(P-13903)
RUSSELL FABRICATION CORP
Also Called: American Fabrication
4940 Gilmore Ave, Bakersfield
(93308-6150)
PHONE............................661 861-8495
Kevin Russell, *President*
EMP: 45
SALES (est): 9.6MM **Privately Held**
SIC: 3498 3444 Fabricated pipe & fittings;
sheet metalwork

(P-13904)
SAN FRANCISCO PIPE &
Also Called: SF Tube
23099 Connecticut St, Hayward
(94545-1605)
PHONE............................510 785-9148
Rafael M Nunez, *CEO*
Ray Yamanaka, *General Mgr*
Khanh Tran, *Engineer*
Sandra Esparza,
Liz Nunez, *Manager*
EMP: 46
SALES (est): 10.1MM **Privately Held**
WEB: www.sfpipentube.com
SIC: 3498 Fabricated pipe & fittings

(P-13905)
**SUPERIOR PIPE FABRICATORS
INC**
10211 S Alameda St, Los Angeles
(90002-3837)
PHONE............................323 569-6500
Robert E Moehlman, *President*
EMP: 10
SQ FT: 64,000
SALES: 1MM **Privately Held**
WEB: www.superiorpipefab.com
SIC: 3498 Pipe fittings, fabricated from
purchased pipe

(P-13906)
**SUPERIOR TUBE PIPE BNDING
FBCO**
Also Called: Superior Tbeppe Bnding Fbrctn
2407 Industrial Pkwy W, Hayward
(94545-5007)
PHONE............................510 782-9311
Jon T Morrow Jr, *President*
EMP: 50
SQ FT: 22,000
SALES (est): 6.5MM **Privately Held**
SIC: 3498 Tube fabricating (contract bend-
ing & shaping); pipe sections fabricated
from purchased pipe

(P-13907)
**TRINITY PROCESS SOLUTIONS
INC**
4740 E Bryson St, Anaheim (92807-1901)
PHONE............................714 701-1112
Jack Brunner, *President*
Candace Brunner, *Vice Pres*
EMP: 20
SQ FT: 13,000
SALES: 3.9MM **Privately Held**
WEB: www.trinityprocesssolutions.com
SIC: 3498 3317 8711 Fabricated pipe &
fittings; welded pipe & tubes; engineering
services

(P-13908)
TRYMAX
5900 E Lerdo Hwy, Shafter (93263-4023)
PHONE............................661 391-1572
Jim Garner, *Owner*
▲ **EMP:** 11 **EST:** 2010
SALES (est): 1.3MM **Privately Held**
SIC: 3498 Fabricated pipe & fittings

(P-13909)
TUBE BENDING LLC
4747 Citrus Dr, Pico Rivera (90660-2034)
PHONE............................562 692-5829
Richard Alvarez,
Beatrice Alvarez,
EMP: 12 **EST:** 2004
SQ FT: 6,460
SALES (est): 1.3MM **Privately Held**
SIC: 3498 Tube fabricating (contract bend-
ing & shaping)

(P-13910)
U S WEATHERFORD L P
19468 Creek Rd, Bakersfield (93314-8451)
PHONE............................661 746-1391
Geary Colvin, *Branch Mgr*
EMP: 18 **Privately Held**
SIC: 3498 3533 Fabricated pipe & fittings;
oil field machinery & equipment
HQ: U S Weatherford L P
179 Weatherford Dr
Schriever LA 70395
985 493-6100

(P-13911)
**WEATHERFORD
INTERNATIONAL LLC**
201 Hallock Dr, Santa Paula (93060-9647)
PHONE............................805 933-0200
EMP: 51 **Privately Held**
SIC: 3498 3533 Fabricated pipe & fittings;
oil & gas field machinery
HQ: Weatherford International, Llc
2000 Saint James Pl
Houston TX 77056
713 693-4000

(P-13912)
WESSEX INDUSTRIES INC
8619 Red Oak St, Rancho Cucamonga
(91730-4820)
PHONE............................562 944-5760
Archie Castillo, *President*
Linne A Castillo, *CFO*
Edward Mojica, *Vice Pres*
EMP: 25
SQ FT: 30,000
SALES (est): 6.3MM **Privately Held**
WEB: www.wessexindustriesinc.com
SIC: 3498 8742 Pipe fittings, fabricated
from purchased pipe; pipe sections fabri-
cated from purchased pipe; management
consulting services

**3499 Fabricated Metal Prdts,
NEC**

(P-13913)
A-L-L MAGNETICS
Also Called: Magnet Source Tm, The
2831 E Via Martens, Anaheim
(92806-1751)
PHONE............................714 632-1754
John E Nellessen, *CEO*
Edith Johnson, *Sales Mgr*
▲ **EMP:** 11
SQ FT: 14,000
SALES (est): 2.4MM **Privately Held**
WEB: www.allmagnetics.com
SIC: 3499 5945 5943 5199 Magnets,
permanent: metallic; arts & crafts sup-
plies; school supplies; advertising special-
ties

(P-13914)
AG SPRAYING
5815 S Calaveras Ave, Tranquillity
(93668-9709)
P.O. Box 686 (93668-0686)
PHONE............................559 698-9507
Nino W Carvalho, *Owner*
EMP: 10
SALES: 250K **Privately Held**
SIC: 3499 Nozzles, spray: aerosol, paint or
insecticide

(P-13915)
ALPHA MAGNETICS INC
23453 Bernhardt St, Hayward
(94545-1622)
PHONE............................510 732-6698
Ken Wadsworth, *President*
▲ **EMP:** 10 **EST:** 1972
SQ FT: 20,000
SALES (est): 1.8MM **Privately Held**
WEB: www.alphamag.com
SIC: 3499 Magnets, permanent: metallic

(P-13916)
**AMERICAN SECURITY
PRODUCTS CO**
Also Called: Amsec
11925 Pacific Ave, Fontana (92337-8231)
PHONE............................951 685-9680
Dave Lazier, *CEO*
Tony Maniaci, *President*
Tom Cassutt, *CFO*
Thomas Cassutt, *Bd of Directors*
Robert Sallee, *Vice Pres*
◆ **EMP:** 220
SQ FT: 150,000
SALES (est): 64MM **Privately Held**
SIC: 3499 1731 Safes & vaults, metal;
safety & security specialization

(P-13917)
ANACROWN INC
Also Called: Lantor
25835 Narbonne Ave # 250, Lomita
(90717-3074)
PHONE............................310 530-1165
Victor A Jauch, *President*
Marjorie Mendoza, *Web Dvlpr*
Ke Xu, *Finance*
▲ **EMP:** 12
SQ FT: 18,000
SALES: 859.5K **Privately Held**
WEB: www.anacrown.com
SIC: 3499 5992 Novelties & giftware, in-
cluding trophies; florists

(P-13918)
**ANDERSON BROS ARTISTIC
IRON CO**
310 Elizabeth Ln, Corona (92880-2504)
PHONE............................951 898-6880
Dennis Anderson, *President*
Dale Anderson, *Vice Pres*
EMP: 10
SQ FT: 10,000
SALES (est): 1.4MM **Privately Held**
SIC: 3499 1791 Ironing boards, metal; iron
work, structural

(P-13919)
ARTISAN HOUSE INC
8238 Lankershim Blvd, North Hollywood
(91605-1613)
PHONE............................818 767-7476
Dennis Damore, *Branch Mgr*
EMP: 30
SALES (corp-wide): 2.7MM **Privately
Held**
SIC: 3499 Novelties & specialties, metal
PA: Artisan House, Inc.
3750 Cohasset St
Burbank CA 91505
818 565-5030

(P-13920)
ARVI MANUFACTURING INC
1256 Birchwood Dr Ste B, Sunnyvale
(94089-2205)
PHONE............................408 734-4776
Harold Kirksey, *CEO*
Rita Kirksey, *CFO*
▲ **EMP:** 11
SQ FT: 5,000
SALES: 1.4MM **Privately Held**
WEB: www.arvi.net
SIC: 3499 Machine bases, metal

(P-13921)
**AWI ACQUISITION COMPANY
(PA)**
Also Called: Allied International
13207 Bradley Ave, Sylmar (91342-1204)
PHONE............................818 364-2333
Timothy Florian, *Ch of Bd*
Melissa Berninger, *CFO*
Nina Da Costa, *Manager*
▲ **EMP:** 82
SQ FT: 106,000
SALES (est): 12.9MM **Privately Held**
WEB: www.alliedtools.com
SIC: 3499 5072 Stabilizing bars (cargo),
metal; hand tools

(P-13922)
**BARRICADE CO & TRAFFIC SUP
INC (PA)**
Also Called: T B C
3963 Santa Rosa Ave, Santa Rosa
(95407-8274)
PHONE............................707 523-2350
Jennifer R Pitts, *President*
Jonathan Beckwith, *Branch Mgr*
Robert F Pitts, *Admin Sec*
EMP: 17
SQ FT: 21,000
SALES (est): 5.4MM **Privately Held**
WEB: www.barri-cade.com
SIC: 3499 Barricades, metal

(P-13923)
BEY-BERK INTERNATIONAL (PA)
9145 Deering Ave, Chatsworth
(91311-5802)
PHONE............................818 773-7534
Kurken Y Berksanlar, *President*
Serop Beylerian, *Vice Pres*
◆ **EMP:** 24
SQ FT: 19,800
SALES (est): 3.9MM **Privately Held**
SIC: 3499 3873 Novelties & giftware, in-
cluding trophies; clocks, assembly of

(P-13924)
**BISHOP-WISECARVER
CORPORATION (PA)**
2104 Martin Way, Pittsburg (94565-5027)
PHONE............................925 439-8272
Pamela Kan, *CEO*
Ali Jabbari, *President*
Shelley Galvin, *Treasurer*
Timothy Silsbee, *Exec Dir*
Barbara Williams, *Executive Asst*
▲ **EMP:** 55
SQ FT: 80,000
SALES (est): 15.7MM **Privately Held**
WEB: www.bwc.com
SIC: 3499 5085 3823 Machine bases,
metal; bearings; industrial instrmnts
msrmnt display/control process variable

(P-13925)
BULLET GUARD CORPORATION
3963 Commerce Dr, West Sacramento
(95691-2168)
PHONE............................800 233-5632
Sharon Durst, *CEO*
Karlin Lynch, *President*
Marcia Lynch, *Corp Secy*
EMP: 14
SQ FT: 36,000
SALES (est): 4.1MM **Privately Held**
WEB: www.bulletguard.com
SIC: 3499 5099 1796 3316 Fire- or bur-
glary-resistive products; safety equipment
& supplies; installing building equipment;
cold finishing of steel shapes; blast fur-
naces & steel mills; products of pur-
chased glass

(P-13926)
CAL-WELD INC
4308 Solar Way, Fremont (94538-6335)
PHONE............................510 226-0100
Maurice Carson, *President*
EMP: 116
SALES (est): 49.1MM
SALES (corp-wide): 655.8MM **Publicly
Held**
SIC: 3499 Aerosol valves, metal
HQ: Ichor Holdings, Llc
9660 Sw Herman Rd
Tualatin OR 97062
503 625-2251

(P-13927)
**CALIFORNIA COMPACTOR SVC
INC**
17000 Sierra Hwy, Canyon Country
(91351-1615)
PHONE............................661 298-5556
Linda Nevill, *Principal*
EMP: 15 **EST:** 2014
SALES (est): 1.2MM **Privately Held**
SIC: 3499 Bank chests, metal

(P-13928)
CALRAM LLC
Also Called: MB Calram LLC
829 Via Alondra, Camarillo (93012-8046)
PHONE............................805 987-6205
Dwayne Perkar, *CEO*
EMP: 10
SQ FT: 25,000
SALES (est): 518.7K
SALES (corp-wide): 2.1B **Publicly Held**
WEB: www.calraminc.com
SIC: 3499 Novelties & specialties, metal

PA: Carpenter Technology Corporation
1735 Market St Fl 15
Philadelphia PA 19103
610 208-2000

(P-13929)
CHATSWORTH PRODUCTS INC (PA)
Also Called: C P I
29899 Agoura Rd Ste 120, Agoura Hills
(91301-2493)
PHONE.....................818 735-6100
Larry Renaud, *President*
Michael Custer, *President*
Tom Jorgenson, *CFO*
Larry Varblow, *Corp Secy*
Ted Behrens, *Exec VP*
◆ **EMP:** 460
SQ FT: 16,000
SALES (est): 175.8MM **Privately Held**
WEB: www.chatsworth.com
SIC: 3499 2542 Machine bases, metal;
partitions & fixtures, except wood

(P-13930)
CHATSWORTH PRODUCTS iNC
9353 Winnetka Ave, Chatsworth
(91311-6033)
PHONE.....................818 882-8595
Michael Custer, *Manager*
EMP: 177
SQ FT: 68,634
SALES (corp-wide): 175.8MM **Privately Held**
WEB: www.chatsworth.com
SIC: 3499 2542 Machine bases, metal;
partitions & fixtures, except wood
PA: Chatsworth Products, Inc.
29899 Agoura Rd Ste 120
Agoura Hills CA 91301
818 735-6100

(P-13931)
CORK POPS
7 Commercial Blvd Ste 3, Novato
(94949-6106)
PHONE.....................415 884-6000
William Federighi, *President*
Linda Bridges, *Vice Pres*
Susan Federighi, *Admin Sec*
Susan Poti, *Controller*
Lori Mahoney,
◆ **EMP:** 10
SQ FT: 17,000
SALES (est): 1.6MM **Privately Held**
WEB: www.corkpops.com
SIC: 3499 Novelties & specialties, metal

(P-13932)
CRAFTED METALS INC
9220 Birch St, Spring Valley (91977-4111)
PHONE.....................619 464-1090
John Wheeler, *President*
Vivian Wheeler, *Vice Pres*
EMP: 10
SQ FT: 10,000
SALES (est): 1.9MM **Privately Held**
WEB: www.craftedmetals.com
SIC: 3499 Metal ladders

(P-13933)
DEC FABRICATORS INC
16916 Gridley Pl, Cerritos (90703-1740)
PHONE.....................562 403-3626
William Befort, *President*
EMP: 18
SQ FT: 20,000
SALES (est): 3.3MM **Privately Held**
WEB: www.decfabricators.com
SIC: 3499 2434 Furniture parts, metal;
wood kitchen cabinets

(P-13934)
DIVERSE MCHNING FBRICATION LLC
Also Called: Component Finishing
3620 Cincinnati Ave Ste A, Rocklin
(95765-1203)
P.O. Box 348327, Sacramento (95834-8327)
PHONE.....................916 672-6591
Wade F Gadberry,
Wade Gadberry,
EMP: 13
SQ FT: 5,000

SALES: 398.4K **Privately Held**
WEB: www.componentfinishing.com
SIC: 3499 Ammunition boxes, metal

(P-13935)
DO IT AMERICAN MFG COMPANY LLC
137 Vander St, Corona (92880-1752)
PHONE.....................951 254-9204
Moises Vasquez, *Mng Member*
Jon Armstrong, *VP Opers*
Kathy Armstrong, *Marketing Mgr*
John Armstrong,
Alicia Macias,
EMP: 16
SQ FT: 20,000
SALES (est): 4.4MM **Privately Held**
SIC: 3499 3545 8711 Machine bases,
metal; machine tool accessories; engineering services

(P-13936)
DOT BLUE SAFES CORPORATION
2707 N Garey Ave, Pomona (91767-1809)
PHONE.....................909 445-8888
Berge Jalakian, *CEO*
Scott Bernal, *Controller*
Jason Esser, *Opers Staff*
Ben Lockhart, *Sales Dir*
▲ **EMP:** 42
SQ FT: 90,000
SALES (est): 15.4MM **Privately Held**
SIC: 3499 8741 Safes & vaults, metal;
management services

(P-13937)
DSTYLE INC
Also Called: Allan Copley Designs
3451 Main St Ste 108, Chula Vista
(91911-5894)
PHONE.....................619 662-0560
Roberto Besquin, *Manager*
Lonnie Nicholson, *Vice Pres*
▲ **EMP:** 10
SQ FT: 40,000
SALES (est): 2.2MM
SALES (corp-wide): 685.6MM **Publicly Held**
SIC: 3499 5021 Furniture parts, metal; furniture
PA: Kimball International, Inc.
1600 Royal St
Jasper IN 47549
812 482-1600

(P-13938)
ECOOLTHING CORP
Also Called: Cool Things
1321 E Saint Gertrude Pl A, Santa Ana
(92705-5241)
P.O. Box 6022, Irvine (92616-6022)
PHONE.....................714 368-4791
Connie Wang, *President*
Linda Wang, *Vice Pres*
▲ **EMP:** 50
SQ FT: 10,000
SALES: 12.8MM **Privately Held**
SIC: 3499 5199 Novelties & giftware, including trophies; gifts & novelties

(P-13939)
ENERGY ABSORPTION SYSTEMS INC
3617 Cincinnati Ave, Rocklin (95765-1202)
PHONE.....................916 645-8181
Barry Stephens, *Manager*
Pat Leonhardt, *Executive*
EMP: 150
SQ FT: 22,968
SALES (corp-wide): 3.6B **Publicly Held**
WEB: www.energyabsorption.com
SIC: 3499 3842 3669 3823 Barricades,
metal; surgical appliances & supplies;
transportation signaling devices; absorption analyzers: infrared, X-ray, etc.: industrial
HQ: Energy Absorption Systems, Inc.
70 W Madison St Ste 2350
Chicago IL 60602
312 467-6750

(P-13940)
EVANS INDUSTRIES INC
Darnell-Rose Div
17915 Railroad St, City of Industry
(91748-1113)
PHONE.....................626 912-1688
Bob Batistic, *Manager*
Rick Chichester, *Chief Mktg Ofcr*
Brent Bargar, *Vice Pres*
Kelly Grimshaw, *Office Mgr*
David Blaine, *Art Dir*
EMP: 120
SALES (corp-wide): 30MM **Privately Held**
WEB: www.eiihq.com
SIC: 3499 5072 Wheels: wheelbarrow,
stroller, etc.: disc, stamped metal; casters
& glides
HQ: Evans Industries, Inc.
249 Boston St
Detroit MI 48243
313 259-2266

(P-13941)
EXECUTIVE SAFE AND SEC CORP (PA)
Also Called: Amphion
10722 Edison Ct, Rancho Cucamonga
(91730-4845)
PHONE.....................909 947-7020
Scott C Denton, *President*
Robyn Denton, *COO*
George Chenarides, *Vice Pres*
Jason Velez, *Project Mgr*
Michael Vaughn, *Director*
◆ **EMP:** 30
SQ FT: 11,000
SALES (est): 4.8MM **Privately Held**
WEB: www.amphion.biz
SIC: 3499 5072 7382 5099 Safes &
vaults, metal; security devices, locks; confinement surveillance systems maintenance & monitoring; locks & lock sets

(P-13942)
G2 METAL FAB
6954 Preston Ave, Livermore (94551-9545)
PHONE.....................925 443-7903
Orlando Gutierrez, *President*
Nohora Gutierrez, *Vice Pres*
Kyle Inman, *Manager*
EMP: 27 **EST:** 2007
SALES (est): 9.6MM **Privately Held**
SIC: 3499 Wheels: wheelbarrow, stroller,
etc.: disc, stamped metal

(P-13943)
GEORGE SEGOVIA
9612 Beverly Rd, Pico Rivera
(90660-2137)
PHONE.....................562 699-8554
George Segovia, *Owner*
Taylor Gagne, *Exec VP*
◆ **EMP:** 15
SQ FT: 5,000
SALES: 1MM **Privately Held**
WEB: www.homelandsafes.com
SIC: 3499 Safes & vaults, metal

(P-13944)
GIFTS INTERNATIONAL INC
799 Palmyrita Ave, Riverside (92507-1811)
PHONE.....................909 854-3977
Mingsong Yao, *President*
▲ **EMP:** 18
SQ FT: 130,000
SALES (est): 2.8MM **Privately Held**
SIC: 3499 Novelties & giftware, including
trophies

(P-13945)
HAMMOND ENTERPRISES INC
549 Garcia Ave Ste C, Pittsburg
(94565-7402)
PHONE.....................925 432-3537
Alan B Hammond, *CEO*
▲ **EMP:** 20
SQ FT: 12,500
SALES (est): 4.2MM **Privately Held**
SIC: 3499 Fire- or burglary-resistive products

(P-13946)
HY JO MFG IMPORTS CORP
7615 Siempre Viva Rd B, San Diego
(92154-6217)
PHONE.....................619 671-1018
John Benator, *CEO*
EMP: 25
SALES (est): 2.6MM **Privately Held**
SIC: 3499 Picture frames, metal

(P-13947)
HYSPAN PRECISION PRODUCTS INC
1683 Brandywine Ave, Chula Vista (91911)
PHONE.....................619 421-1355
Bertha Mercado, *Controller*
EMP: 99
SQ FT: 60,000
SALES (est): 3.9MM **Privately Held**
SIC: 3499 Reels, cable: metal

(P-13948)
INLAND MARINE INDUSTRIES INC
Also Called: Inland Metal Technologies
3245 Depot Rd, Hayward (94545-2709)
PHONE.....................510 785-8555
Jennifer Sutton, *President*
◆ **EMP:** 180
SALES (est): 41MM **Privately Held**
WEB: www.inlandmetal.com
SIC: 3499 Shims, metal

(P-13949)
INNOVATIVE METAL PRODUCTS INC
2443 Cades Way Ste 200, Vista
(92081-7885)
PHONE.....................760 734-1010
Scott Whitney, *CEO*
EMP: 24 **EST:** 2006
SALES (est): 4.7MM **Privately Held**
SIC: 3499 Metal household articles

(P-13950)
J & J PRODUCTS INC
Also Called: J & J Co
9134 Independence Ave, Chatsworth
(91311-5902)
PHONE.....................818 998-4250
Peter Hauber, *President*
David Kline, *Controller*
Connie Dickinson, *Manager*
Gabi Girard, *Manager*
EMP: 16
SQ FT: 6,400
SALES (est): 2MM **Privately Held**
WEB: www.jandjproducts.com
SIC: 3499 5091 3089 Ammunition boxes,
metal; hunting equipment & supplies;
plastic processing

(P-13951)
JC METAL
238 Michelle Ct, South San Francisco
(94080-6201)
PHONE.....................650 827-1618
Jeffrey Chan, *Principal*
KY Kam, *General Mgr*
Lee Sudi, *Contractor*
EMP: 11
SALES (est): 169.3K **Privately Held**
SIC: 3499 Fabricated metal products

(P-13952)
JORGE SEGOVIA
Also Called: Home Land Safe Co
9612 Beverly Rd, Pico Rivera
(90660-2137)
PHONE.....................562 699-8554
George Segovia, *President*
EMP: 20
SALES (est): 1.2MM **Privately Held**
SIC: 3499 5999 Doors, safe & vault:
metal; vaults & safes

(P-13953)
LA PROPOINT INC
10870 La Tuna Canyon Rd, Sun Valley
(91352-2009)
PHONE.....................818 767-6800
Mark Riddlesperger, *President*
James Hartman, *Vice Pres*
Suzan Singh, *Executive Asst*
Brad Powers, *Technical Mgr*

PRODUCTS & SVCS

Mark Youngs, *Project Mgr*
▼ **EMP:** 30
SQ FT: 28,000
SALES: 4.2MM **Privately Held**
WEB: www.lapropoint.com
SIC: 3499 3449 Metal household articles; miscellaneous metalwork

(P-13954)
LINDSAY/BARNETT INCORPORATED
Also Called: Gallery
2194 Edison Ave Ste H, San Leandro (94577-1130)
PHONE.................510 483-6300
Christie B Jordan, *President*
EMP: 11
SQ FT: 25,000
SALES (est): 2.2MM **Privately Held**
WEB: www.galleryinc.com
SIC: 3499 3231 Novelties & giftware, including trophies; products of purchased glass

(P-13955)
LOBOSTAR INC
14601 S Broadway, Gardena (90248-1811)
PHONE.................310 516-9812
Steve Escarcega, *Manager*
EMP: 60
SALES (est): 11.6MM **Privately Held**
SIC: 3499 Fabricated metal products

(P-13956)
MAGNETIC COMPONENT ENGRG INC (PA)
Also Called: M C E
2830 Lomita Blvd, Torrance (90505-5101)
PHONE.................310 784-3100
Linda Montgomerie, *CEO*
Chris Nanji, *General Mgr*
Van Le, *Info Tech Mgr*
Kelvin Rebollo, *Engineer*
Brian Beeler, *Natl Sales Mgr*
▲ **EMP:** 93
SQ FT: 50,000
SALES (est): 13.3MM **Privately Held**
WEB: www.mceproducts.com
SIC: 3499 3677 Magnets, permanent: metallic; electronic coils, transformers & other inductors

(P-13957)
MATERIAL CONTROL INC
Also Called: Cotterman Company
6901a District Blvd, Bakersfield (93313-2013)
PHONE.................661 617-6033
Tony Ortiz, *Branch Mgr*
EMP: 32
SALES (est): 4.9MM
SALES (corp-wide): 69.9MM **Privately Held**
WEB: www.cotterman.com
SIC: 3499 Metal ladders
PA: Material Control Inc.
130 Seltzer Rd
Croswell MI 48422
630 892-4274

(P-13958)
MESA SAFE COMPANY INC
337 W Freedom Ave, Orange (92865-2647)
P.O. Box 52282, Irvine (92619-2282)
PHONE.................714 202-8000
George L Vicente, *President*
Chris Nakao, *Vice Pres*
Mary Croinin, *Admin Sec*
Devin Rohrbacker, *Sales Mgr*
◆ **EMP:** 40
SQ FT: 75,000
SALES (est): 5.8MM **Privately Held**
WEB: www.mesasafe.com
SIC: 3499 5044 Safes & vaults, metal; vaults & safes

(P-13959)
MICHAEL D WILSON INC
Also Called: Strathmore Ladder
19774 Orange Belt Dr, Strathmore (93267)
P.O. Box 307 (93267-0307)
PHONE.................559 568-1115
Michael D Wilson, *President*
Gary Wilson, *Treasurer*
Jeanie Wilson, *Vice Pres*

EMP: 12
SQ FT: 7,800
SALES (est): 2.3MM **Privately Held**
WEB: www.citrusladder.com
SIC: 3499 Ladders, portable: metal

(P-13960)
NIBCO INC
1375 Sampson Ave, Corona (92879-1748)
PHONE.................951 737-5599
Steve Malm, *Manager*
EMP: 212
SALES (corp-wide): 721.4MM **Privately Held**
WEB: www.nibco.com
SIC: 3499 Strapping, metal
PA: Nibco Inc.
1516 Middlebury St
Elkhart IN 46516
574 295-3000

(P-13961)
OLDCASTLE PRECAST INC
Also Called: Utility Vault
801 S Pine St, Madera (93637-5219)
PHONE.................559 674-8093
William Wood, *Manager*
EMP: 20
SQ FT: 8,000
SALES (corp-wide): 29.7B **Privately Held**
WEB: www.oldcastle-precast.com
SIC: 3499 1799 3443 3443 Safes & vaults, metal; welding on site; sheet metalwork; fabricated plate work (boiler shop)
HQ: Oldcastle Precast, Inc.
1002 15th St Sw Ste 110
Auburn WA 98001
253 833-2777

(P-13962)
PAPPALECCO
3650 5th Ave Ste 104, San Diego (92103-4243)
PHONE.................619 906-5566
Francesco Bucci, *Branch Mgr*
EMP: 19 **Privately Held**
SIC: 3499 Ice cream freezers, household, nonelectric: metal
PA: Pappalecco
1602 State St
San Diego CA 92101

(P-13963)
PEREZ SEVERINO
Also Called: Alannas Engineer Manufacturing
9710 Owensmouth Ave Lbby, Chatsworth (91311-8074)
PHONE.................818 701-1522
Severiano Perez, *Owner*
EMP: 15
SALES (est): 2.8MM **Privately Held**
SIC: 3499 8711 Machine bases, metal; engineering services

(P-13964)
PHIL WOOD & COMPANY
1125 N 7th St A, San Jose (95112-4428)
P.O. Box 90389 (95109-3389)
PHONE.................408 292-4137
Peter Enright, *President*
EMP: 15
SQ FT: 6,000
SALES (est): 1.6MM **Privately Held**
SIC: 3499 Wheels: wheelbarrow, stroller, etc.: disc, stamped metal

(P-13965)
PREMIER BARRICADES
28441 Felix Valdez Ave, Temecula (92590-1843)
PHONE.................877 345-9700
Conor J Loushin, *President*
EMP: 10
SALES (est): 1.7MM **Privately Held**
SIC: 3499 Barricades, metal
PA: Boston Barricade Company Inc.
1151 19th St
Vero Beach FL 32960

(P-13966)
PSM INDUSTRIES INC (PA)
14000 Avalon Blvd, Los Angeles (90061-2636)
PHONE.................888 663-8256

Craig Paullin, *CEO*
Mary Sherrill, *Treasurer*
Susan Paullin, *Admin Sec*
Greg Jones, *Engineer*
Justin Schmidt, *Mfg Staff*
▲ **EMP:** 89 **EST:** 1956
SALES (est): 22.9MM **Privately Held**
WEB: www.pacificsintered.com
SIC: 3499 Friction material, made from powdered metal

(P-13967)
QUADRANT SOLUTIONS INC
Also Called: Quadrant Technology
561 Monterey Rd, Morgan Hill (95037-9001)
PHONE.................408 463-9451
Chris Moore, *Principal*
Gary Hoyt, *Technology*
EMP: 10 **Privately Held**
SIC: 3499 Magnets, permanent: metallic
PA: Quadrant Solutions Incorporated
10606 Meeting St 101
Prospect KY 40059

(P-13968)
QUALITY MAGNETICS CORPORATION
18025 Adria Maru Ln, Carson (90746-1403)
P.O. Box 1238, Desert Hot Springs (92240-0947)
PHONE.................310 632-1941
William K Buckley, *CEO*
Chante Buckley, *CFO*
▲ **EMP:** 18
SQ FT: 27,000
SALES (est): 4.3MM **Privately Held**
WEB: www.qmcnet.com
SIC: 3499 3299 Magnets, permanent: metallic; ceramic fiber

(P-13969)
R & K INDUSTRIAL PRODUCTS CO
Also Called: R&K Industrial Wheels
1945 7th St, Richmond (94801-1639)
PHONE.................510 234-7212
Jorge Ramirez, *President*
EMP: 30
SQ FT: 48,000
SALES (est): 5.4MM **Privately Held**
WEB: www.rkwheels.com
SIC: 3499 Wheels: wheelbarrow, stroller, etc.: disc, stamped metal

(P-13970)
R & R METAL FABRICATORS
14846 Ramona Blvd, Baldwin Park (91706-3436)
PHONE.................626 960-6400
Martha Rodriguez, *Manager*
EMP: 11
SALES (est): 1.3MM **Privately Held**
SIC: 3499 Fire- or burglary-resistive products

(P-13971)
SCHOTT MAGNETICS
1401 Air Wing Rd, San Diego (92154-7705)
PHONE.................619 661-7510
Rob Rossi, *Owner*
▲ **EMP:** 16
SALES (est): 1.4MM **Privately Held**
SIC: 3499 Magnetic shields, metal

(P-13972)
SCHUMAN ENTERPRISES INC
Also Called: Js Manufacturing
1621 Ord Way, Oceanside (92056-3599)
PHONE.................760 940-1322
Joel J Schuman, *President*
Danielle Schuman, *Office Mgr*
Taylor Schuman, *HR Admin*
EMP: 10 **EST:** 2010
SALES (est): 1.9MM **Privately Held**
SIC: 3499 Novelties & specialties, metal

(P-13973)
SIERRA SAFETY COMPANY
215 Taylor Rd, Newcastle (95658-9601)
PHONE.................916 663-2026
Daniel L Robinson, *President*
EMP: 14 **EST:** 1977

SQ FT: 6,000
SALES (est): 4MM **Privately Held**
WEB: www.sierrasafetyco.com
SIC: 3499 Barricades, metal

(P-13974)
SPORTSMEN STEEL SAFE FABG CO (PA)
Also Called: Sportsman Steel Gun Safe
6311 N Paramount Blvd, Long Beach (90805-3301)
PHONE.................562 984-0244
Kevin Hand, *CEO*
Chris Cude, *CFO*
Ernie Vonepp, *Marketing Staff*
▲ **EMP:** 22
SQ FT: 30,000
SALES (est): 3.4MM **Privately Held**
SIC: 3499 5999 Safes & vaults, metal; safety supplies & equipment

(P-13975)
STOKES LADDERS INC
4545 Renfro Dr, Kelseyville (95451)
P.O. Box 445 (95451-0445)
PHONE.................707 279-4306
Jerry Hook, *President*
Karen Hook, *Vice Pres*
Cheryl Bryant, *Bookkeeper*
EMP: 10
SQ FT: 3,600
SALES (est): 1.1MM **Privately Held**
WEB: www.stokesladders.com
SIC: 3499 Ladders, portable: metal

(P-13976)
STRYKER ENTERPRISES INC
Also Called: Recognition Products Mfg
1358 E San Fernando St, San Jose (95116-2329)
PHONE.................408 295-6300
William J Stryker Jr, *President*
▲ **EMP:** 22 **EST:** 1948
SQ FT: 12,000
SALES (est): 3.9MM **Privately Held**
WEB: www.plaque.com
SIC: 3499 Trophies, metal, except silver

(P-13977)
STURDY GUN SAFE MANUFACTRUING
Also Called: Sturdy Safe
2030 S Sarah St, Fresno (93721-3316)
PHONE.................559 485-8361
Terry Pratt, *Owner*
▲ **EMP:** 11
SQ FT: 15,000
SALES: 400K **Privately Held**
SIC: 3499 Safes & vaults, metal

(P-13978)
TDA MAGNETICS LLC
1175 W Victoria St, Rancho Dominguez (90220-5813)
PHONE.................424 213-1585
Tracy Moon, *President*
Jeff Calvert, *Opers Mgr*
EMP: 13 **EST:** 2015
SALES (est): 996K **Privately Held**
SIC: 3499 Magnets, permanent: metallic

(P-13979)
TRIDUS INTERNATIONAL INC
Also Called: Tridus Magnetics and Assenblie
1145 W Victoria St, Compton (90220-5813)
PHONE.................310 884-3200
Bong Duk Lee, *Ch of Bd*
Hang Up Moon, *President*
Young Ha, *Admin Sec*
Alma Espinoza, *Purchasing*
Tracy Moon, *VP Sales*
▲ **EMP:** 10
SQ FT: 3,000
SALES (est): 1.9MM **Privately Held**
WEB: www.tridus.com
SIC: 3499 5084 Magnets, permanent: metallic; industrial machinery & equipment

(P-13980)
UNISORB INC
101 N Indian Hill Blvd C2-201, Claremont (91711-4670)
PHONE.................626 793-1000
Peter Moore, *Branch Mgr*
EMP: 14

▲ = Import ▼=Export
◆ =Import/Export

SALES (corp-wide): 5.4MM **Privately Held**
SIC: **3499** Machine bases, metal
HQ: Unisorb Inc.
 4117 Felters Rd Ste A
 Michigan Center MI 49254

(P-13981)
WATER STUDIO INC
5681 Selmaraine Dr, Culver City
(90230-6119)
PHONE..................................310 313-5553
Sean C So, *President*
Sean So, *Principal*
EMP: 12
SQ FT: 8,000
SALES (est): 2.8MM **Privately Held**
SIC: **3499** Fountains (except drinking),
 metal

(P-13982)
WATERFOUNTAINSCOM INC
13870 Riverside Dr, Apple Valley
(92307-5989)
PHONE..................................760 946-0525
Gary E Jackson, *President*
▲ EMP: 10
SALES (est): 1.1MM **Privately Held**
WEB: www.waterfountains.com
SIC: **3499** Fountains (except drinking),
 metal

(P-13983)
WERNER CO
1810 Grogan Ave, Merced (95341-6404)
PHONE..................................209 383-3989
Saied Djavadi, *Branch Mgr*
EMP: 10 **Privately Held**
SIC: **3499** Ladders, portable: metal
HQ: Werner Co
 93 Werner Rd
 Greenville PA 16125

(P-13984)
WESTERN FAB INC
Also Called: Western Fabricators
9823 E Ave, Hesperia (92345-6280)
PHONE..................................760 949-1441
Bryon Porter, *President*
Mandi Porter, *Corp Secy*
EMP: 15
SQ FT: 4,800
SALES (est): 3.3MM **Privately Held**
SIC: **3499** Welding tips, heat resistant:
 metal

(P-13985)
WOODSIDE INVESTMENT INC
Also Called: Michael and Company
12405 E Brandt Rd, Lockeford
(95237-9571)
P.O. Box 1100 (95237-1100)
PHONE..................................209 787-8040
Jung Kamburov, *Principal*
Dennis Wood, *President*
EMP: 70 EST: 1991
SQ FT: 50,000
SALES (est): 15.1MM **Privately Held**
WEB: www.michaelandcofabricators.com
SIC: **3499** Aerosol valves, metal

(P-13986)
Z MANUFACTURING INC
2679 Sierra Way, La Verne (91750-5642)
PHONE..................................909 593-2191
Steve Ziolkowski, *President*
Jeanette Ziolkowski, *Vice Pres*
Diego Vargas, *Manager*
EMP: 25
SQ FT: 30,000
SALES (est): 4.1MM **Privately Held**
WEB: www.zmanufacturinginc.com
SIC: **3499** 8711 3751 Reels, cable: metal;
 engineering services; motorcycles, bicy-
 cles & parts

3511 Steam, Gas & Hydraulic Turbines &

(P-13987)
ALTURDYNE POWER SYSTEMS INC
1405 N Johnson Ave, El Cajon
(92020-1615)
PHONE..................................619 343-3204
Frank Verbeke, *President*
Andy Park, *Manager*
EMP: 30
SQ FT: 3,000
SALES: 6.5MM **Privately Held**
SIC: **3511** 1731 Gas turbine generator set
 units, complete; electric power systems
 contractors

(P-13988)
ARCTURUS MARINE SYSTEMS
Also Called: American Bow Thruster
517a Martin Ave, Rohnert Park
(94928-2048)
PHONE..................................707 586-3155
D Milo Hallerberg, *CEO*
Ira Cushing, *Engineer*
Claus Endruhn, *Engineer*
Wayne Paugh, *Prdtn Mgr*
Greg Timm, *Facilities Mgr*
▲ EMP: 53
SQ FT: 12,000
SALES (est): 13.5MM **Privately Held**
SIC: **3511** Hydraulic turbines

(P-13989)
BABCOCK & WILCOX COMPANY
Also Called: Babcock and Wilcox
710 Airpark Rd, NAPA (94558-7518)
PHONE..................................707 259-1122
David Pavlik, *General Mgr*
Greg Mosko, *Partner*
Michael Morash, *Vice Pres*
Brennan Lee, *Prgrmr*
Steve Elefter, *Project Mgr*
EMP: 25
SALES (corp-wide): 1.5B **Publicly Held**
SIC: **3511** Turbines & turbine generator
 sets
HQ: The Babcock & Wilcox Company
 20 S Van Buren Ave
 Barberton OH 44203
 330 753-4511

(P-13990)
BAE SYSTEMS CONTROLS INC
5140 W Goldleaf Cir G100, Los Angeles
(90056-1666)
PHONE..................................323 642-5000
Doug Spring, *Manager*
James Foltyn, *Engineer*
Stephanie Carrera, *Accounting Dir*
EMP: 135
SALES (corp-wide): 24.2B **Privately Held**
WEB: www.baesystemscontrols.com
SIC: **3511** 3721 3812 3728 Turbines &
 turbine generator sets; aircraft; search &
 navigation equipment; aircraft parts &
 equipment
HQ: Bae Systems Controls Inc.
 1098 Clark St
 Endicott NY 13760
 607 770-2000

(P-13991)
CAPSTONE TURBINE CORPORATION (PA)
16640 Stagg St, Van Nuys (91406-1630)
PHONE..................................818 734-5300
Darren R Jamison, *President*
Holly A Van Deursen, *Ch of Bd*
Jayme L Brooks, *CFO*
Jayme Brooks, *CFO*
Paul Deweese, *Bd of Directors*
EMP: 151
SQ FT: 79,000
SALES: 82.8MM **Publicly Held**
WEB: www.capstoneturbine.com
SIC: **3511** Turbines & turbine generator
 sets

(P-13992)
CATERPILLAR PWR GNRTN SYS
2200 Pacific Hwy, San Diego (92101-1745)
PHONE..................................858 694-6629
Ennodio Ramos,
Gregory Gorin, *Vice Pres*
Henrik Scherer, *Business Dir*
Justin Waldron, *Admin Sec*
Doug Wagenbach, *Project Mgr*
EMP: 44
SALES (est): 1.1MM
SALES (corp-wide): 45.4B **Publicly Held**
SIC: **3511** Gas turbine generator set units,
 complete
PA: Caterpillar Inc.
 510 Lake Cook Rd Ste 100
 Deerfield IL 60015
 224 551-4000

(P-13993)
CLIPPER WINDPOWER PLC
6305 Carpinteria Ave # 300, Carpinteria
(93013-2901)
PHONE..................................805 690-3275
Mauricio Quintana,
Michael Keane,
EMP: 740
SALES (est): 77.2MM **Privately Held**
SIC: **3511** Turbines & turbine generator
 sets

(P-13994)
ENER-CORE POWER INC (HQ)
8965 Research Dr Ste 100, Irvine
(92618-4246)
PHONE..................................949 428-3300
Alain Castro, *CEO*
Boris Maslov, *President*
Douglas Demaret, *Vice Pres*
Douglas Hamrin, *Vice Pres*
Steve Lampe, *Vice Pres*
EMP: 15
SALES (est): 11.2MM **Publicly Held**
SIC: **3511** Turbines & turbine generator
 sets
PA: Ener-Core, Inc.
 8965 Research Dr Ste 100
 Irvine CA 92618
 949 616-3300

(P-13995)
ENERGENT CORPORATION
1831 Carnegie Ave, Santa Ana
(92705-5528)
PHONE..................................949 885-0365
Lance G Hays, *President*
Eufemio Guzman, *Engineer*
EMP: 13
SALES (est): 3.2MM **Privately Held**
SIC: **3511** Turbines & turbine generator
 sets

(P-13996)
GALAXY ENERGY SYSTEMS INC
362 N Palm Canyon Dr, Palm Springs
(92262-5668)
PHONE..................................760 778-4254
Hans Petermann, *President*
Bill Ost, *Treasurer*
EMP: 10
SALES: 5.5MM **Privately Held**
SIC: **3511** Gas turbines, mechanical drive

(P-13997)
GE WIND ENERGY LLC
13681 Chantico Rd, Tehachapi
(93561-8188)
PHONE..................................661 823-6423
Gerlad Turk, *Manager*
Ryan Timmerman, *Manager*
EMP: 238
SALES (corp-wide): 122B **Publicly Held**
SIC: **3511** Turbines & turbine generator
 sets
HQ: Ge Wind Energy, Llc
 13000 Jameson Rd
 Tehachapi CA 93561

(P-13998)
GENERAL ELECTRIC COMPANY
26226 Antelope Rd, Romoland
(92585-8739)
P.O. Box 1240 (92585-0240)
PHONE..................................951 928-2829
Jim McNaughton, *Branch Mgr*

EMP: 500
SALES (corp-wide): 122B **Publicly Held**
SIC: **3511** Turbines & turbine generator
 sets
PA: General Electric Company
 41 Farnsworth St
 Boston MA 02210
 617 443-3000

(P-13999)
J H P & ASSOCIATES INC
28005 Smyth Dr, Valencia (91355-4023)
PHONE..................................661 799-5888
John Zhang, *Vice Pres*
C Y Zou, *Chairman*
Leeann Lu, *Project Mgr*
▲ EMP: 20
SQ FT: 3,000
SALES (est): 2MM **Privately Held**
WEB: www.jhptech.com
SIC: **3511** 3823 3679 3498 Turbines &
 turbine generator set units, complete;
 pressure gauges, dial & digital; harness
 assemblies for electronic use: wire or
 cable; manifolds, pipe: fabricated from
 purchased pipe; thermometers & temper-
 ature sensors

(P-14000)
JLM ENERGY INC
Also Called: Honeywell Authorized Dealer
3735 Placer Corp Dr Ste A, Rocklin
(95765-1209)
PHONE..................................916 304-1603
Erin Clark, *CEO*
Kraig Clark, *President*
Mason Mullendore, *Software Dev*
Robert Mennell, *Software Engr*
Josh Beckwith, *Project Mgr*
◆ EMP: 45
SALES (est): 10.4MM **Privately Held**
SIC: **3511** Turbines & turbine generator
 sets

(P-14001)
LA TURBINE (PA)
28557 Industry Dr, Valencia (91355-5424)
PHONE..................................661 294-8290
John Maskaluk, *CEO*
Danny Mascari, *President*
Dominique Maskaluk, *CFO*
Julie Stalmans, *Executive Asst*
Mary Dobson, *Administration*
▼ EMP: 72
SQ FT: 90,000
SALES (est): 24.5MM **Privately Held**
WEB: www.laturbine.com
SIC: **3511** Turbines & turbine generator
 sets & parts

(P-14002)
MODULAR WIND ENERGY INC
1709 Apollo Ct, Seal Beach (90740-5617)
PHONE..................................562 304-6782
Gregor Gnadig, *CEO*
Richard Bjorkman, *CFO*
Dr Myles Baker, *CTO*
EMP: 53
SQ FT: 150,000
SALES (est): 9.5MM **Privately Held**
SIC: **3511** Turbines & turbine generator
 sets

(P-14003)
NATEL ENERGY INC
2401 Monarch St, Alameda (94501-7513)
PHONE..................................510 342-5269
Gia Schneider, *CEO*
Abe Schneider, *President*
Adam Atkinson-Lewis, *Vice Pres*
Peder Aune, *Engineer*
Rodrigo Linares, *Engineer*
EMP: 14
SALES (est): 3.5MM **Privately Held**
SIC: **3511** Hydraulic turbines

(P-14004)
SOLAR TURBINES INCORPORATED (HQ)
2200 Pacific Hwy, San Diego (92101-1773)
P.O. Box 85376 (92186-5376)
PHONE..................................619 544-5000
Thomas Pellette, *President*
C K Scott-Stanfel, *CFO*
Daniel Boylan, *Treasurer*
P F Browning, *Vice Pres*

D W Esbeck, *Vice Pres*
◆ **EMP:** 3890
SQ FT: 1,080,000
SALES (est): 2B
SALES (corp-wide): 45.4B **Publicly Held**
WEB: www.esolar.cat.com
SIC: 3511 Gas turbine generator set units, complete
PA: Caterpillar Inc.
510 Lake Cook Rd Ste 100
Deerfield IL 60015
224 551-4000

(P-14005)
SOLAR TURBINES INCORPORATED
9250a Sky Park Ct, San Diego (92123-4302)
PHONE..................858 715-2060
Ronald Miller, *Principal*
Adrian Garcia, *Design Engr*
Kevin Goon, *Design Engr*
Mojgan Komeylyan, *Design Engr*
Ruben Zosa, *Design Engr*
EMP: 175
SQ FT: 60,155
SALES (corp-wide): 45.4B **Publicly Held**
WEB: www.esolar.cat.com
SIC: 3511 Gas turbine generator set units, complete
HQ: Solar Turbines Incorporated
2200 Pacific Hwy
San Diego CA 92101
619 544-5000

(P-14006)
SOLAR TURBINES INCORPORATED
18 Morgan Ste 100, Irvine (92618-2074)
PHONE..................949 450-0870
Julie Martin, *Manager*
Gareth Jones, *Opers Staff*
Kris Sharpe, *Manager*
EMP: 10
SALES (corp-wide): 45.4B **Publicly Held**
WEB: www.esolar.cat.com
SIC: 3511 Gas turbine generator set units, complete
HQ: Solar Turbines Incorporated
2200 Pacific Hwy
San Diego CA 92101
619 544-5000

(P-14007)
SOLAR TURBINES INTL CO (DH)
Also Called: Stico
2200 Pacific Hwy, San Diego (92101-1773)
P.O. Box 85376 (92186-5376)
PHONE..................619 544-5000
Thomas Pellette, *CEO*
Steve Gosslin, *President*
Greg Barr, *Vice Pres*
D W Esbeck, *Vice Pres*
D M Lehmann, *Vice Pres*
EMP: 20 **EST:** 1977
SALES (est): 57.5MM
SALES (corp-wide): 45.4B **Publicly Held**
SIC: 3511 Gas turbine generator set units, complete
HQ: Solar Turbines Incorporated
2200 Pacific Hwy
San Diego CA 92101
619 544-5000

(P-14008)
SOLAR TURBINES INTL CO
9330 Sky Park Ct, San Diego (92123-4304)
PHONE..................858 694-1616
Steve Gosslin, *President*
Paul Cramer, *General Mgr*
Stinson McElhinney, *Info Tech Mgr*
Srinivas Samavedam, *Info Tech Mgr*
Sean Garceau, *Engng Exec*
EMP: 23
SALES (corp-wide): 45.4B **Publicly Held**
SIC: 3511 Gas turbine generator set units, complete
HQ: Solar Turbines International Co Inc
2200 Pacific Hwy
San Diego CA 92101
619 544-5000

(P-14009)
SOLTECH SOLAR INC
1836 Commercenter Cir, San Bernardino (92408-3430)
PHONE..................909 890-2282
EMP: 10
SALES (est): 690K **Privately Held**
SIC: 3511

(P-14010)
TERRAJOULE CORPORATION
1051 Fife Ave, Palo Alto (94301-3027)
PHONE..................650 269-0494
Stephen Bisset, *CEO*
Pat Rezza, *COO*
Andrew Murdoch, *Engineer*
Roop Karihaloo, *VP Mktg*
▲ **EMP:** 10
SQ FT: 5,700
SALES (est): 1.9MM **Privately Held**
SIC: 3511 Steam engines

(P-14011)
UNIVERSAL TURBO TECHNOLOGY
1120 E Elm Ave, Fullerton (92831-5024)
PHONE..................714 600-9585
Marius Paul, *Principal*
EMP: 86
SALES (est): 4.3MM **Privately Held**
SIC: 3511 Turbines & turbine generator sets

(P-14012)
WEPOWER LLC
32 Journey Ste 250, Aliso Viejo (92656-5329)
PHONE..................866 385-9463
Marvin Winkler, *Mng Member*
Howard Makler, *President*
Thomas Schiff,
Kevin B Donovan, *Director*
▲ **EMP:** 15
SALES (est): 1.8MM **Privately Held**
SIC: 3511 Turbines & turbine generator set units, complete

3519 Internal Combustion Engines, NEC

(P-14013)
AGILITY FUEL SYSTEMS LLC
3335 Susan St Ste 100, Costa Mesa (92626-1647)
PHONE..................256 831-6155
Tom Russell, *Branch Mgr*
EMP: 12
SALES (corp-wide): 175.1MM **Privately Held**
SIC: 3519 Diesel, semi-diesel or duel-fuel engines, including marine
HQ: Agility Fuel Systems, Llc
3335 Susan St Ste 100
Costa Mesa CA 92626

(P-14014)
BOOSTPOWER USA INC
2560 Calcite Cir, Newbury Park (91320-1203)
PHONE..................805 376-6077
Alexi Sahagian, *President*
EMP: 12
SALES (est): 2.4MM **Privately Held**
WEB: www.boostpower.com
SIC: 3519 7699 Marine engines; marine engine repair

(P-14015)
CUMMINS INC
14775 Wicks Blvd, San Leandro (94577-6717)
PHONE..................510 351-6101
Michael Doherty, *Manager*
EMP: 20
SALES (corp-wide): 20.4B **Publicly Held**
WEB: www.cummins.com
SIC: 3519 Internal combustion engines
PA: Cummins Inc.
500 Jackson St
Columbus IN 47201
812 377-5000

(P-14016)
CUMMINS PACIFIC LLC
5150 Boyd Rd, Arcata (95521-4449)
PHONE..................707 822-7392
April Farris, *Branch Mgr*
EMP: 13
SALES (corp-wide): 20.4B **Publicly Held**
WEB: www.cleaire.com
SIC: 3519 Internal combustion engines
HQ: Cummins Pacific, Llc
1939 Deere Ave
Irvine CA 92606

(P-14017)
CUMMINS PACIFIC LLC
5125 Caterpillar Rd, Redding (96003-2049)
PHONE..................530 244-6898
Mike Goodwin, *Branch Mgr*
Ed James, *Marketing Staff*
EMP: 13
SALES (corp-wide): 20.4B **Publicly Held**
WEB: www.cleaire.com
SIC: 3519 Internal combustion engines
HQ: Cummins Pacific, Llc
1939 Deere Ave
Irvine CA 92606

(P-14018)
CUMMINS PACIFIC LLC
875 Riverside Pkwy, West Sacramento (95605-1502)
PHONE..................916 371-0630
Mike Goodwin, *Branch Mgr*
John Ray, *Sales Staff*
EMP: 47
SALES (corp-wide): 20.4B **Publicly Held**
WEB: www.cleaire.com
SIC: 3519 5063 7629 Diesel engine rebuilding; generators; generator repair
HQ: Cummins Pacific, Llc
1939 Deere Ave
Irvine CA 92606

(P-14019)
CUMMINS PACIFIC LLC
9520 Stewart And Gray Rd, Downey (90241-5559)
PHONE..................866 934-4373
Susan Morales, *Principal*
EMP: 40
SALES (corp-wide): 20.4B **Publicly Held**
SIC: 3519 Internal combustion engines
HQ: Cummins Pacific, Llc
1939 Deere Ave
Irvine CA 92606

(P-14020)
CUMMINS PACIFIC LLC
3061 S Riverside Ave, Bloomington (92316-3527)
PHONE..................909 877-0433
Brandon Daste, *Principal*
EMP: 50
SALES (corp-wide): 20.4B **Publicly Held**
WEB: www.ccpionline.com
SIC: 3519 Internal combustion engines
HQ: Cummins Pacific, Llc
1939 Deere Ave
Irvine CA 92606

(P-14021)
CUMMINS PACIFIC LLC
5333 N Cornelia Ave, Fresno (93722-6403)
PHONE..................559 277-6760
Joseph Ayerza Suzanne, *Principal*
Virgil Antonio, *Parts Mgr*
EMP: 65
SALES (corp-wide): 20.4B **Publicly Held**
WEB: www.cleaire.com
SIC: 3519 Internal combustion engines
HQ: Cummins Pacific, Llc
1939 Deere Ave
Irvine CA 92606

(P-14022)
CUMMINS PACIFIC LLC
4601 E Brundage Ln, Bakersfield (93307-2311)
PHONE..................661 325-9404
Robert Bickie, *Branch Mgr*

EMP: 50
SALES (corp-wide): 20.4B **Publicly Held**
WEB: www.cleaire.com
SIC: 3519 Diesel engine rebuilding
HQ: Cummins Pacific, Llc
1939 Deere Ave
Irvine CA 92606

(P-14023)
CUMMINS PACIFIC LLC (HQ)
1939 Deere Ave, Irvine (92606-4818)
PHONE..................949 253-6000
Mark Yragui, *President*
Joe Nguyen, *Technology*
John Baker, *Engineer*
Suzie Arabian, *Opers Mgr*
Jonathan Evans, *VP Sales*
▲ **EMP:** 85
SALES (est): 89.3MM
SALES (corp-wide): 20.4B **Publicly Held**
WEB: www.ccpionline.com
SIC: 3519 5063 7538 Internal combustion engines; generators; general automotive repair shops
PA: Cummins Inc.
500 Jackson St
Columbus IN 47201
812 377-5000

(P-14024)
CUMMINS PACIFIC LLC
310 N Johnson Ave, El Cajon (92020-3114)
PHONE..................619 593-3093
Steve Gallant, *Branch Mgr*
Bunrath Seu, *Info Tech Mgr*
EMP: 25
SALES (corp-wide): 20.4B **Publicly Held**
WEB: www.ccpionline.com
SIC: 3519 Internal combustion engines
HQ: Cummins Pacific, Llc
1939 Deere Ave
Irvine CA 92606

(P-14025)
CUMMINS PACIFIC LLC
3958 Transport St, Ventura (93003-5128)
PHONE..................805 644-7281
Dan Elliott, *Manager*
EMP: 25
SALES (corp-wide): 20.4B **Publicly Held**
WEB: www.ccpionline.com
SIC: 3519 5063 Internal combustion engines; generators
HQ: Cummins Pacific, Llc
1939 Deere Ave
Irvine CA 92606

(P-14026)
DETROIT DIESEL CORPORATION
10645 Studebaker Rd Fl 2, Downey (90241-3173)
PHONE..................562 929-7016
Glen Nutting, *Vice Pres*
EMP: 15
SALES (corp-wide): 193.7B **Privately Held**
WEB: www.detroitdeisel.com
SIC: 3519 Engines, diesel & semi-diesel or dual-fuel
HQ: Detroit Diesel Corporation
13400 W Outer Dr
Detroit MI 48239
313 592-5000

(P-14027)
ECOLOGIC ENGINE TSTG LABS LLC
1370 S Acacia Ave, Fullerton (92831-5316)
PHONE..................714 774-3385
Donel Olson, *Mng Member*
Nick Barber, *Project Mgr*
Paula Sisler, *Project Mgr*
Michael Barnett, *Project Engr*
Mike Carter, *Engineer*
▲ **EMP:** 15
SALES (est): 345K **Privately Held**
WEB: www.extengine.com
SIC: 3519 Parts & accessories, internal combustion engines

(P-14028)
GALE BANKS ENGINEERING
Also Called: Banks Power Products
546 S Duggan Ave, Azusa (91702-5136)
PHONE..............................626 969-9600
Gale C Banks III, *President*
Vicki L Banks, *Vice Pres*
▲ EMP: 195
SQ FT: 121,000
SALES (est): 69.1MM **Privately Held**
WEB: www.getpower.com
SIC: 3519 3714 Parts & accessories, internal combustion engines; motor vehicle parts & accessories

(P-14029)
RACING BEAT INC
4789 E Wesley Dr, Anaheim (92807-1941)
PHONE..............................714 779-8677
James Mederer, *President*
▲ EMP: 20
SQ FT: 7,500
SALES (est): 3.3MM **Privately Held**
WEB: www.racingbeat.com
SIC: 3519 Parts & accessories, internal combustion engines

(P-14030)
SOUTHWEST PRODUCTS CORPORATION
2875 Cherry Ave, Signal Hill (90755-1908)
PHONE..............................360 887-7400
Jason Hair, *Branch Mgr*
EMP: 15
SALES (corp-wide): 18.1MM **Privately Held**
SIC: 3519 Diesel engine rebuilding
HQ: Southwest Products Corporation
11690 N 132nd Ave
Surprise AZ 85379
306 887-7400

(P-14031)
SOUTHWEST PRODUCTS CORPORATION
85 Enterprise Ct Ste B, Galt (95632-8162)
PHONE..............................209 745-6000
Patrick Cofild, *Branch Mgr*
EMP: 33
SALES (corp-wide): 18.1MM **Privately Held**
SIC: 3519 Diesel engine rebuilding
HQ: Southwest Products Corporation
11690 N 132nd Ave
Surprise AZ 85379
306 887-7400

(P-14032)
TRACY INDUSTRIES INC
Also Called: Genuine Parts Distributors
3200 E Guasti Rd Ste 100, Ontario (91761-8661)
P.O. Box 1260 (91762)
PHONE..............................562 692-9034
Timothy Engvall, *CEO*
Erma Jean Tracy, *Vice Pres*
David Rosenberger, *Admin Sec*
▲ EMP: 172
SALES (est): 142MM **Privately Held**
SIC: 3519 7538 Internal combustion engines; engine rebuilding: automotive

(P-14033)
TRANSONIC COMBUSTION INC
461 Calle San Pablo, Camarillo (93012-8506)
PHONE..............................805 465-5145
Wolfgang Bullmer, *President*
Timothy Noonan, *CFO*
Mike Cheiky, *CTO*
EMP: 40
SALES (est): 7.9MM **Privately Held**
WEB: www.tscombustion.com
SIC: 3519 Internal combustion engines

(P-14034)
UNITED STATES DEPT OF NAVY
Also Called: Vfa 122 Power Plants
Vfa 122 Hanger 5, Lemoore (93246-0001)
PHONE..............................559 998-2488
Patrick Cleary,
EMP: 600 **Publicly Held**
SIC: 3519 9711 Jet propulsion engines; Navy;

HQ: United States Department Of The Navy
1200 Navy Pentagon
Washington DC 20350
-

(P-14035)
VALLEY POWER SYSTEMS INC (PA)
Also Called: John Deere Authorized Dealer
425 S Hacienda Blvd, City of Industry (91745-1123)
PHONE..............................626 333-1243
Hampton Clark Lee, *Ch of Bd*
Michael Barnett, *President*
Robert K Humphryes, *CFO*
Richard Kickliter, *Vice Pres*
Bruce Noble, *Vice Pres*
▲ EMP: 100
SQ FT: 49,000
SALES (est): 181.2MM **Privately Held**
WEB: www.valleypowersystems.com
SIC: 3519 5082 Marine engines; construction & mining machinery

---
3523 Farm Machinery &

(P-14036)
AG RAY INC
Also Called: Injection Molding
20400 N Kennefick Rd, Acampo (95220-9708)
P.O. Box 1708, Woodbridge (95258-1708)
PHONE..............................209 334-1999
Rose Rogan, *President*
EMP: 12
SALES: 966K **Privately Held**
SIC: 3523 3089 Cabs, tractors & agricultural machinery; injection molded finished plastic products

(P-14037)
AGRIFIM IRRIGATION PDTS INC
Also Called: Nds
2855 S East Ave, Fresno (93725-1908)
PHONE..............................559 443-6680
Rael Sacks, *President*
▲ EMP: 15
SQ FT: 15,200
SALES (est): 2.9MM
SALES (corp-wide): 1.2B **Privately Held**
WEB: www.agrifimusa.com
SIC: 3523 Farm machinery & equipment
HQ: National Diversified Sales, Inc.
21300 Victory Blvd # 215
Woodland Hills CA 91367
559 562-9888

(P-14038)
AIR-O FAN PRODUCTS CORPORATION (PA)
Also Called: Air O Fan
507 E Dinuba Ave, Reedley (93654-3531)
PHONE..............................559 638-6546
Larry E Davis, *CEO*
Byre Davis, *President*
Ruby Davis, *Corp Secy*
David Lincoln, *Vice Pres*
Sean Gahan, *Info Tech Dir*
◆ EMP: 13 EST: 1945
SQ FT: 2,000
SALES (est): 8.1MM **Privately Held**
SIC: 3523 Fertilizing machinery, farm; dusters, mechanical: agricultural

(P-14039)
ALBERS MFG CO INC (PA)
Also Called: Albers Dairy Equipment. Inc
14323 Albers Way, Chino (91710-1134)
PHONE..............................909 597-5537
Teo Albers Jr, *President*
◆ EMP: 21
SQ FT: 10,000
SALES (est): 6.4MM **Privately Held**
WEB: www.albersdairyequipment.com
SIC: 3523 Barn stanchions & standards

(P-14040)
AMARILLO WIND MACHINE LLC
20513 Avenue 256, Exeter (93221-9656)
P.O. Box 96809, Chicago IL (60693-6809)
PHONE..............................559 592-4256
Steven Chaloupka, *President*
EMP: 18
SQ FT: 12,000

SALES: 8.3MM
SALES (corp-wide): 242.1B **Publicly Held**
WEB: www.amarillogear.com
SIC: 3523 7699 Farm machinery & equipment; agricultural equipment repair services
HQ: Amarillo Gear Company Llc
2401 W Sundown Ln
Amarillo TX 79118
806 622-1273

(P-14041)
AMERICAN INTERNATIONAL MFG CO
Also Called: Aim Mail Centers
1230 Fortna Ave, Woodland (95776-5905)
PHONE..............................530 666-2446
John Bridges, *CEO*
David Neilson, *President*
Chistophre Neilson, *Principal*
Shelley Marten, *Administration*
Michael Webster, *Engineer*
EMP: 29
SQ FT: 23,000
SALES (est): 8.6MM **Privately Held**
WEB: www.aimfab.com
SIC: 3523 3556 Farm machinery & equipment; food products machinery

(P-14042)
AQUANEERING INC
7960 Stromesa Ct, San Diego (92126-4329)
PHONE..............................858 578-2028
Mark Francis, *President*
Wendy Porter-Francis, *Vice Pres*
Bobbi Baur, *Mktg Dir*
Brendan C Delbos, *Sales Staff*
Tina Reneau, *Manager*
EMP: 30
SQ FT: 5,100
SALES (est): 8.7MM **Privately Held**
WEB: www.aquaneer.com
SIC: 3523 Farm machinery & equipment

(P-14043)
AWETA-AUTOLINE INC (PA)
4516 E Citron, Fresno (93725-9861)
PHONE..............................559 244-8340
Jeanluc Delcasse, *CEO*
Art Lopez, *President*
▲ EMP: 45
SQ FT: 20,000
SALES (est): 6.2MM **Privately Held**
WEB: www.autolinesorters.com
SIC: 3523 Grading, cleaning, sorting machines, fruit, grain, vegetable

(P-14044)
B W IMPLEMENT CO
288 W Front St, Buttonwillow (93206)
P.O. Box 758 (93206-0758)
PHONE..............................661 764-5254
John C Blair, *President*
Julien Parsons, *Treasurer*
Alene Parsons, *Admin Sec*
EMP: 22
SQ FT: 85,000
SALES (est): 4.3MM **Privately Held**
WEB: www.bwimp.com
SIC: 3523 5083 5999 Tractors, farm; farm implements; farm machinery

(P-14045)
BIANCHI ORCHARD SYSTEMS INC
Also Called: Orchard Equipment Mfg
1221 Independence Pl, Gridley (95948-9341)
P.O. Box 743, Palo Cedro (96073-0743)
PHONE..............................530 846-5625
Mahmood A Dean, *President*
Mahmood Dean, *President*
▲ EMP: 130
SALES (est): 22.5MM **Privately Held**
SIC: 3523

(P-14046)
BIG TEX TRAILER MFG INC
1425 E Sixth St, Beaumont (92223-2505)
PHONE..............................951 845-5344
John Armstrong, *General Mgr*
EMP: 15

SALES (corp-wide): 6.6B **Privately Held**
WEB: www.big-tex.com
SIC: 3523 5013 Farm machinery & equipment; motor vehicle supplies & new parts
HQ: Big Tex Trailer Manufacturing, Inc.
950 Interstate Hwy 30 E
Mount Pleasant TX 75455
903 575-0300

(P-14047)
BRAZEAU THCROUGHBRED FARMS LP
30500 State St, Hemet (92543-9258)
PHONE..............................951 925-8957
Nadine Anderson, *Manager*
Paul Brazeau, *Vice Pres*
EMP: 17
SALES (est): 1MM **Privately Held**
SIC: 3523 0291 0752 Harvesters, fruit, vegetable, tobacco, etc.; animal specialty farm, general; boarding services, horses: racing & non-racing

(P-14048)
BRITZ FERTILIZERS INC
12498 11th Ave, Hanford (93230-9523)
PHONE..............................559 582-0942
Keith Roberts, *Manager*
EMP: 30
SALES (corp-wide): 330.6MM **Privately Held**
WEB: www.britzinc.com
SIC: 3523 2873 Spreaders, fertilizer; nitrogenous fertilizers
HQ: Britz Fertilizers, Inc.
3265 W Figarden Dr
Fresno CA 93711
559 448-8000

(P-14049)
BROCKS TRAILERS INC
6901 E Brundage Ln, Bakersfield (93307-3057)
PHONE..............................661 363-5038
Matthew E Brock, *President*
Amanda Shannon, *Marketing Staff*
EMP: 35
SALES (est): 5.7MM **Privately Held**
WEB: www.brockstrailersinc.com
SIC: 3523 5013 7539 5511 Trailers & wagons, farm; trailer parts & accessories; trailer repair; trucks, tractors & trailers: new & used; utility trailers; welding on site

(P-14050)
CAGECO INC
16225 Beaver Rd, Adelanto (92301-3908)
PHONE..............................800 605-4859
Mike Alexander, *President*
EMP: 38
SALES (est): 8.5MM **Privately Held**
SIC: 3523 Barn, silo, poultry, dairy & livestock machinery

(P-14051)
CAL-COAST DAIRY SYSTEMS INC
424 S Tegner Rd, Turlock (95380-9406)
P.O. Box 737 (95381-0737)
PHONE..............................209 634-9026
Lon Baptista, *President*
Lori Baptista, *Vice Pres*
Stacy Souza, *Office Mgr*
Paul Borges, *Materials Mgr*
EMP: 30
SQ FT: 16,000
SALES (est): 6.8MM **Privately Held**
WEB: www.calcoastinc.com
SIC: 3523 1542 8711 5083 Dairy equipment (farm); agricultural building contractors; structural engineering; dairy machinery & equipment; residential construction; fabricated plate work (boiler shop)

(P-14052)
CALIFORNIA FARM EQUIPMENT MAG
17045 S Central Vly Hwy, Shafter (93263-2704)
P.O. Box 1597 (93263-1597)
PHONE..............................661 589-0435
Andrew Cummings, *President*
EMP: 14

P R O D U C T S & S V C S

SALES (est): 709.4K **Privately Held**
SIC: 3523 Balers, farm: hay, straw, cotton, etc.

(P-14053)
CHERRY VALLEY SHEET METAL
39638 Avenida Sonrisa, Cherry Valley (92223-4399)
PHONE....................................951 845-1578
Peter Schaeffer, *Partner*
Tony Schmidt, *Partner*
EMP: 10 EST: 1960
SQ FT: 10,000
SALES (est): 760K **Privately Held**
SIC: 3523 Poultry brooders, feeders & waterers

(P-14054)
COE ORCHARD EQUIPMENT INC
3453 Riviera Rd, Live Oak (95953-9713)
PHONE....................................530 695-5121
Lyman Coe, *CEO*
Lois A Coe, *CFO*
▲ EMP: 100
SQ FT: 45,000
SALES (est): 8.6MM **Privately Held**
WEB: www.coeshakers.com
SIC: 3523 Harvesters, fruit, vegetable, tobacco, etc.

(P-14055)
CUSTOM EQUIPMENT COINC
90 Rock Creek Rd Ste 9, Copperopolis (95228-9251)
PHONE....................................209 785-9891
Craig D Robinson, *President*
Christie Robinson, *Admin Sec*
EMP: 10
SQ FT: 20,000
SALES: 1.4MM **Privately Held**
SIC: 3523 7699 Farm machinery & equipment; farm machinery repair

(P-14056)
D & M MANUFACTURING
5400 S Villa Ave, Fresno (93725-9798)
PHONE....................................559 834-4668
Judy Tolentino, *Owner*
EMP: 18 EST: 1987
SQ FT: 10,000
SALES (est): 699.2K **Privately Held**
SIC: 3523 Fertilizing, spraying, dusting & irrigation machinery

(P-14057)
DALES WELDING INC
Also Called: Dale's Welding & Fabrication
1112 Abbott St A, Salinas (93901-4598)
PHONE....................................831 424-6583
Dale Scheff, *President*
Peggy Scheff, *Corp Secy*
Jeff Scheff, *General Mgr*
EMP: 13
SQ FT: 11,250
SALES: 1MM **Privately Held**
SIC: 3523 7692 Farm machinery & equipment; welding repair

(P-14058)
DCI DONOR SERVICES INC
Also Called: Golden State Donor Services
3940 Industrial Blvd # 100, West Sacramento (95691-6507)
PHONE....................................916 567-1600
Helen Nels, *Manager*
EMP: 29 **Privately Held**
WEB: www.gsds.org
SIC: 3523 Transplanters
PA: Dci Donor Services, Inc.
    1600 Hayes St Ste 300
    Nashville TN 37203

(P-14059)
DIG CORPORATION
1210 Activity Dr, Vista (92081-8510)
PHONE....................................760 727-0914
David Levy, *President*
Racquell Bibens, *Controller*
Duy Johnson, *Commissioner*
Greg Smith, *Manager*
▲ EMP: 84
SQ FT: 45,000

SALES (est): 24.2MM **Privately Held**
WEB: www.digcorp.com
SIC: 3523 Irrigation equipment, self-propelled

(P-14060)
DKP INC
275 N Marks Ave, Fresno (93706-1102)
PHONE....................................559 266-2695
Douglas R King, *President*
EMP: 45
SQ FT: 12,000
SALES (est): 5MM
SALES (corp-wide): 5.6MM **Privately Held**
SIC: 3523 Cotton pickers & strippers
PA: R. M. King Company
    315 N Marks Ave
    Fresno CA
    559 266-0258

(P-14061)
DOAN INC
2406 John St, Riverside (92503-6130)
P.O. Box 7398 (92513-7398)
PHONE....................................951 275-2432
Cevin Doan, *President*
Pauline Doan, *Treasurer*
EMP: 13
SALES: 1.7MM **Privately Held**
SIC: 3523 Farm machinery & equipment

(P-14062)
DOMRIES ENTERPRISES INC
12281 Road 29, Madera (93638-8332)
PHONE....................................559 485-4306
Candyce L Domries, *CEO*
Lorraine Domries, *Treasurer*
▲ EMP: 35 EST: 1924
SQ FT: 65,000
SALES (est): 8.6MM **Privately Held**
SIC: 3523 5084 Soil preparation machinery, except turf & grounds; fertilizing, spraying, dusting & irrigation machinery; industrial machinery & equipment

(P-14063)
DOUBLE K INDUSTRIES INC
9711 Mason Ave, Chatsworth (91311-5208)
PHONE....................................818 772-2887
Greg Crisp, *CEO*
Valerie Crisp, *General Mgr*
Cresencio Lomeli, *Prdtn Mgr*
Danita Adkins, *Manager*
▲ EMP: 24
SALES (est): 6.2MM **Privately Held**
SIC: 3523 Farm machinery & equipment

(P-14064)
DOWDYS SALES AND SERVICES
15185 Avenue 224, Tulare (93274-9305)
PHONE....................................559 688-6973
Brad Dowdy, *President*
Melinda Dowdy, *Corp Secy*
Chris Ince, *Parts Mgr*
EMP: 15
SALES (est): 3.4MM **Privately Held**
WEB: www.dowdys.com
SIC: 3523 Farm machinery & equipment

(P-14065)
DURAND-WAYLAND MACHINERY INC (PA)
1041 E Dinuba Ave, Reedley (93654-3578)
PHONE....................................559 591-6904
Fred A Durand III, *President*
Bill Leverett, *Treasurer*
John Seay, *Vice Pres*
EMP: 50
SQ FT: 70,000
SALES (est): 8.9MM **Privately Held**
SIC: 3523 5084 Sprayers & spraying machines, agricultural; industrial machinery & equipment

(P-14066)
EARTHOLOGYTECH LLC
928 F Ave, Coronado (92118-2510)
PHONE....................................619 435-5296
Christopher Giglio,
▲ EMP: 20
SQ FT: 1,200
SALES: 300K **Privately Held**
SIC: 3523 Turf & grounds equipment

(P-14067)
EXETER MERCANTILE COMPANY
258 E Pine St, Exeter (93221-1750)
P.O. Box 67 (93221-0067)
PHONE....................................559 592-2121
Robert G Schelling, *President*
Sidney Schelling Jr, *Corp Secy*
Brian Schelling, *Vice Pres*
EMP: 19
SQ FT: 22,000
SALES (est): 4.8MM **Privately Held**
WEB: www.exetermercantile.com
SIC: 3523 3537 5072 Tractors, farm; industrial trucks & tractors; hardware

(P-14068)
FLORY INDUSTRIES
4737 Toomes Rd, Salida (95368)
P.O. Box 908 (95368-0908)
PHONE....................................209 545-1167
Howard Flory, *CEO*
Rodney Flory, *Treasurer*
Marlin Flory, *Vice Pres*
Norman Flory, *Admin Sec*
EMP: 75 EST: 1904
SQ FT: 12,000
SALES (est): 36.1MM **Privately Held**
WEB: www.floryindustries.com
SIC: 3523 5083 5041 0173 Harvesters, fruit, vegetable, tobacco, etc.; farm equipment parts & supplies; fabricated structural metal; tree nuts

(P-14069)
GREENBROZ INC
955 Vernon Way, El Cajon (92020-1832)
PHONE....................................844 379-8746
Cullen Raichart, *CEO*
EMP: 16
SQ FT: 7,000
SALES (est): 3.1MM **Privately Held**
SIC: 3523 Farm machinery & equipment

(P-14070)
HYDROPOINT DATA SYSTEMS INC
1720 Corporate Cir, Petaluma (94954-6924)
PHONE....................................707 769-9696
Chris Spain, *CEO*
Paul Ciandrini, *President*
Adam Opoczynski, *President*
Mardi Diamond, *Vice Pres*
Chris Manchuck, *Vice Pres*
▲ EMP: 50
SQ FT: 18,000
SALES (est): 13.3MM **Privately Held**
WEB: www.hydropoint.com
SIC: 3523 Irrigation equipment, self-propelled

(P-14071)
INVELOP INC
Also Called: Double K Industries
9711 Mason Ave, Chatsworth (91311-5208)
PHONE....................................818 772-2887
Gregory S Crisp, *President*
Richard Ward, *Director*
◆ EMP: 40
SQ FT: 20,700
SALES (est): 6.5MM **Privately Held**
SIC: 3523 3999 3841 Clippers, for animal use: hand or electric; pet supplies; veterinarians' instruments & apparatus

(P-14072)
IRRITEC USA INC
1420 N Irritec Way, Fresno (93703-4432)
PHONE....................................559 275-8825
Daniel W Eisenberg, *Principal*
▲ EMP: 19
SALES (est): 6.6MM **Privately Held**
SIC: 3523 Irrigation equipment, self-propelled

(P-14073)
J & L IRRIGATION COMPANY INC
4264 W Jensen Ave, Fresno (93706-9049)
PHONE....................................559 237-2181
Lu Dwyer, *President*
EMP: 10
SQ FT: 10,000

SALES (est): 1.9MM **Privately Held**
SIC: 3523 Irrigation equipment, self-propelled

(P-14074)
JACKRABBIT (PA)
Also Called: Dakota AG Welding
471 Industrial Ave, Ripon (95366-2768)
PHONE....................................209 599-6118
Bill Kirkendall, *CEO*
▲ EMP: 82
SQ FT: 15,000
SALES (est): 34.6MM **Privately Held**
WEB: www.jackrabbit.bz
SIC: 3523 Harvesters, fruit, vegetable, tobacco, etc.

(P-14075)
JAIN IRRIGATION INC
2851 E Florence Ave, Fresno (93721-3407)
P.O. Box 71447, Salt Lake City UT (84171-0447)
PHONE....................................559 485-7171
Elizabeth Maxwell, *Branch Mgr*
Kris Nightengale, *Vice Pres*
Rick Restuccia, *Vice Pres*
Chawarn Khongsub, *Sales Mgr*
Brad Holliday, *Sales Staff*
EMP: 150
SALES (corp-wide): 64.8MM **Privately Held**
WEB: www.aquariusbrands.com
SIC: 3523 4971 3999 Irrigation equipment, self-propelled; irrigation systems; atomizers; toiletry
PA: Jain Irrigation, Inc.
    6975 S Union Park Ctr # 600
    Midvale UT 84047
    909 395-5200

(P-14076)
JOHNSON FARM MACHINERY CO INC
Also Called: Johnson Manufacturing
38574 Kentucky Ave, Woodland (95695-5835)
P.O. Box 1237 (95776-1237)
PHONE....................................530 662-1788
Kirk David Friedman, *CEO*
EMP: 10
SQ FT: 33,000
SALES (est): 3.2MM **Privately Held**
WEB: www.jfmco.com
SIC: 3523 Trailers & wagons, farm; planting machines, agricultural

(P-14077)
KAMPER FABRICATION INC
20107 N Ripon Rd, Ripon (95366-9758)
P.O. Box 177 (95366-0177)
PHONE....................................209 599-7137
Richard Kamper, *President*
Brenda Kamper, *Corp Secy*
EMP: 23
SQ FT: 24,800
SALES (est): 4.2MM **Privately Held**
SIC: 3523 Farm machinery & equipment

(P-14078)
KINGSBURG CULTIVATOR INC
40190 Road 36, Kingsburg (93631-9621)
PHONE....................................559 897-3662
Clint Erling, *President*
Allen Scheidt, *Vice Pres*
EMP: 17
SQ FT: 1,400
SALES (est): 3.9MM **Privately Held**
WEB: www.kci-mfg.com
SIC: 3523 Harvesters, fruit, vegetable, tobacco, etc.

(P-14079)
KIRBY MANUFACTURING INC (PA)
484 S St 59, Merced (95341-6541)
P.O. Box 989 (95341-0989)
PHONE....................................209 723-0778
Richard M Kirby, *President*
William T Kirby, *Treasurer*
Madeleine Kirby Davenport, *Vice Pres*
Kelly Sellers, *Admin Sec*
Jonthan Garcia, *Purch Mgr*
▼ EMP: 68
SQ FT: 45,000

SALES (est): 15.4MM **Privately Held**
WEB: www.kirbymfg.com
SIC: **3523** Cattle feeding, handling & watering equipment; haying machines: mowers, rakes, stackers, etc.

(P-14080)
KIRBY MANUFACTURING INC
Also Called: Kirby-Tulare Manufacturing
1478 N J St, Tulare (93274-1308)
PHONE....................559 686-1571
Tom Day, *Branch Mgr*
Brett Baker, *Sales Mgr*
EMP: 12
SALES (corp-wide): 15.4MM **Privately Held**
WEB: www.kirbymfg.com
SIC: **3523** Cattle feeding, handling & watering equipment
PA: Kirby Manufacturing, Inc.
484 S St 59
Merced CA 95341
209 723-0778

(P-14081)
KUBOTA TRACTOR CORPORATION
1175 S Guild Ave, Lodi (95240-3154)
PHONE....................209 334-9910
Rex Young, *Manager*
EMP: 19
SALES (corp-wide): 15.6B **Privately Held**
WEB: www.kubota.com
SIC: **3523** 5082 5083 Tractors, farm; construction & mining machinery; tractors, agricultural
HQ: Kubota Tractor Corporation
1000 Kubota Dr
Grapevine TX 76051
817 756-1171

(P-14082)
LAIRD MFG LLC (PA)
Also Called: Laird Manufacturing
531 S State Highway 59, Merced (95341-6925)
P.O. Box 1053 (95341-1053)
PHONE....................209 722-4145
Lee Cansler,
Manuel Rosa, *Sales Mgr*
Issac Isako,
◆ EMP: 40 EST: 1937
SQ FT: 15,000
SALES (est): 11MM **Privately Held**
WEB: www.lairdmfg.com
SIC: **3523** 7692 Cattle feeding, handling & watering equipment; welding repair

(P-14083)
LYON TECHNOLOGIES INC
1690 Brandywine Ave Ste A, Chula Vista (91911-6072)
PHONE....................619 216-3400
Scott Martin, *President*
Leon W Parma, *Ch of Bd*
Roy D Clark, *Vice Chairman*
Rebecca Trinh, *Purchasing*
Jennifer Castellanos, *Sales Mgr*
▲ EMP: 25 EST: 1915
SQ FT: 40,000
SALES (est): 6.4MM **Privately Held**
WEB: www.lyonelectric.com
SIC: **3523** 3444 3841 Farm machinery & equipment; sheet metalwork; veterinarians' instruments & apparatus

(P-14084)
MEDIFARM SO CAL INC
2040 Main St Ste 225, Irvine (92614-8219)
PHONE....................855 447-6967
Derek Peterson, *Ch of Bd*
Kenneth Vande Vrede, *COO*
Michael James, *CFO*
Michael A Nahass, *Corp Secy*
EMP: 41 EST: 2017
SALES (est): 1.4MM **Publicly Held**
SIC: **3523** Farm machinery & equipment
PA: Terra Tech Corp.
2040 Main St Ste 225
Irvine CA 92614

(P-14085)
MYTREX INC
4070 N Palm St Ste 707, Fullerton (92835-1036)
PHONE....................949 800-9725
Ashley Myung Hee Lee, *President*
Helen J Chuang, *CFO*
EMP: 12
SQ FT: 10,000
SALES: 100K **Privately Held**
SIC: **3523** Peanut combines, diggers, packers & threshers

(P-14086)
NIKKEL IRON WORKS CORPORATION
17045 S Central Vly Hwy, Shafter (93263-2704)
P.O. Box 1597 (93263-1597)
PHONE....................661 746-4904
Andrew Cummings, *President*
Shirley Cummings, *Corp Secy*
Karl Almquist, *General Mgr*
EMP: 17 EST: 1924
SQ FT: 26,000
SALES (est): 4MM **Privately Held**
WEB: www.nikkelironworks.com
SIC: **3523** Farm machinery & equipment

(P-14087)
NYX INDUSTRIES INC
Also Called: Salco Products
1930 S Rochester Ste 111, Ontario (91761-2346)
PHONE....................909 937-3923
Gabriel Hermida, *CEO*
Cindy Chavez, *President*
▲ EMP: 13
SQ FT: 8,000
SALES: 2.5MM **Privately Held**
SIC: **3523** Irrigation equipment, self-propelled

(P-14088)
OLSON IRRIGATION SYSTEMS
Also Called: Olson Industrial Systems
10910 Wheatlands Ave A, Santee (92071-2867)
P.O. Box 711570 (92072-1570)
PHONE....................619 562-3100
Donald Olson, *President*
Kathleen Baldwin, *Treasurer*
▲ EMP: 28
SQ FT: 17,000
SALES (est): 6.9MM
SALES (corp-wide): 1.1B **Publicly Held**
WEB: www.olsonirrigation.com
SIC: **3523** Sprayers & spraying machines, agricultural
HQ: Evoqua Water Technologies Llc
210 6th Ave Ste 3300
Pittsburgh PA 15222
724 772-0044

(P-14089)
ORCHARD MACHINERY CORPORATION (PA)
Also Called: Orchard Harvest
2700 Colusa Hwy, Yuba City (95993-8927)
PHONE....................530 673-2822
Don Mayo, *CEO*
Brian Anderson, *Vice Pres*
Greg Kriss, *Vice Pres*
Joe Martinez, *Vice Pres*
Tom Thomas, *Vice Pres*
▲ EMP: 60
SQ FT: 70,000
SALES (est): 20.2MM **Privately Held**
WEB: www.shakermaker.com
SIC: **3523** Shakers, tree: nuts, fruits, etc.

(P-14090)
OXBO INTERNATIONAL CORPORATION
10825 W Goshen Ave, Visalia (93291-8759)
PHONE....................559 897-7012
Rick Radon, *Branch Mgr*
EMP: 12
SALES (corp-wide): 98.9K **Privately Held**
WEB: www.oxbocorp.com
SIC: **3523** Farm machinery & equipment
HQ: Oxbo International Corporation
7275 Batavia Byron Rd
Byron NY 14422
585 548-2665

(P-14091)
PELLENC AMERICA INC (HQ)
3171 Guerneville Rd, Santa Rosa (95401-4028)
PHONE....................707 568-7286
Marc Paisnel, *President*
J L Guigues, *Director*
Roger Pellenc, *Director*
J P Pettavino, *Director*
Taylor Webb, *Parts Mgr*
▲ EMP: 48
SQ FT: 50,000
SALES (est): 5MM
SALES (corp-wide): 156MM **Privately Held**
SIC: **3523** Farm machinery & equipment
PA: Pellenc
Notre Dame
Pertuis 84120
490 094-700

(P-14092)
PERRYS CUSTOM CHOPPING
21365 Williams Ave, Hilmar (95324-9602)
PHONE....................209 667-8777
Jeff Perry, *Principal*
EMP: 15
SALES (est): 3MM **Privately Held**
SIC: **3523** Harvesters, fruit, vegetable, tobacco, etc.

(P-14093)
PINNACLE AGRICULTURE DIST INC
Also Called: Performance Agriculture
1100 S Madera Ave, Kerman (93630-9139)
PHONE....................559 842-4601
Raymond Maul, *Branch Mgr*
EMP: 18
SALES (corp-wide): 1.4B **Privately Held**
SIC: **3523** 5191 Sprayers & spraying machines, agricultural; fertilizer & fertilizer materials; feed
HQ: Pinnacle Agriculture Distribution, Inc.
1880 Fall Rver Dr Ste 100
Loveland CO 80538
970 800-4300

(P-14094)
PRODUCE AVAILABLE INC (PA)
Also Called: Valley Spuds of Oxnard
910 Commercial Ave, Oxnard (93030-7232)
PHONE....................805 483-5292
Helmut Brinkmann, *President*
Marlene C Kaiser, *Vice Pres*
Travis Dergan, *Comp Spec*
Kaitlin Gardiner, *Mktg Dir*
Regina Dergan, *Sales Mgr*
EMP: 57
SQ FT: 20,000
SALES (est): 13.2MM **Privately Held**
WEB: www.produceavailable.com
SIC: **3523** Potato diggers, harvesters & planters

(P-14095)
RAINDRIP INC
2250 Agate Ct, Simi Valley (93065-1842)
P.O. Box 339, Lindsay (93247-0339)
PHONE....................818 710-4023
Barry N Hanish, *President*
Jim Whittle, *CFO*
Ruth Mehra, *Admin Sec*
EMP: 50
SQ FT: 31,000
SALES (est): 5.4MM
SALES (corp-wide): 1.2B **Privately Held**
WEB: www.raindrip.com
SIC: **3523** Irrigation equipment, self-propelled
HQ: National Diversified Sales, Inc.
21300 Victory Blvd # 215
Woodland Hills CA 91367
559 562-9888

(P-14096)
RAMSAY HIGHLANDER INC
Also Called: Highlander Harvesting Aid
45 Gonzales River Rd, Gonzales (93926)
PHONE....................831 675-3453
Frank Maconachy, *President*
Michele Maconachy, *Corp Secy*
Chris Garnett, *Vice Pres*
David Offerdahl, *Vice Pres*
Manuel Tavena, *Project Mgr*
▲ EMP: 38
SQ FT: 34,000
SALES (est): 10.1MM **Privately Held**
WEB: www.harvestingaid.com
SIC: **3523** 5999 7692 7699 Farm machinery & equipment; farm machinery; welding repair; hydraulic equipment repair

(P-14097)
RANCH SYSTEMS LLC
37 Commercial Blvd # 101, Novato (94949-6112)
PHONE....................415 884-2770
Jacob Christfort,
Kelly McPeak, *Administration*
Terrence Jones, *Manager*
EMP: 10
SQ FT: 3,600
SALES (est): 2.4MM **Privately Held**
SIC: **3523** Irrigation equipment, self-propelled

(P-14098)
RANDELL EQUIPTMENT & MFG
Also Called: Randell Equipment & Mfg
15260 County Line Rd, Delano (93215-9427)
PHONE....................661 725-6380
Lee Brown, *Vice Pres*
▼ EMP: 28
SALES (est): 4.6MM **Privately Held**
WEB: www.randellequipment.com
SIC: **3523** Sprayers & spraying machines, agricultural

(P-14099)
REN CORPORATION
2201 Francisco Dr, El Dorado Hills (95762-3713)
PHONE....................916 739-2000
Andrew Furia, *CEO*
EMP: 10 EST: 2014
SQ FT: 10,000
SALES: 1MM **Privately Held**
SIC: **3523** Grading, cleaning, sorting machines, fruit, grain, vegetable

(P-14100)
RJ BOUDREAU INC
Also Called: Rjb
1641 Princeton Ave Ste 6, Modesto (95350-5759)
PHONE....................209 480-3172
Ron Boudreau, *President*
EMP: 12
SQ FT: 5,000
SALES: 1MM **Privately Held**
WEB: www.rjb-brand.com
SIC: **3523** 3561 Dairy equipment (farm); pumps & pumping equipment

(P-14101)
RUSSELL KC & SON
375 E Paige Ave, Tulare (93274-8902)
PHONE....................559 686-3236
Kirby Russell,
EMP: 20
SQ FT: 17,100
SALES (est): 3.1MM **Privately Held**
SIC: **3523** Dairy equipment (farm)

(P-14102)
SAN JOAQUIN EQUIPMENT LLC
2413 Crows Landing Rd, Modesto (95358-6109)
PHONE....................209 538-3831
Tim Stokes, *Manager*
EMP: 36
SALES (est): 2MM **Privately Held**
SIC: **3523** Farm machinery & equipment
PA: Belkorp Industries Inc
1508 Broadway W Suite 900
Vancouver BC V6J 1
604 688-8531

(P-14103)
SCAFCO CORPORATION
Also Called: Scafco Steel Stud Mfg
4301 Jetway Ct, North Highlands (95660-5701)
PHONE....................916 624-7700

Miguel Da Costa, *Branch Mgr*
Justo Fegurgur, *Branch Mgr*
EMP: 39
SALES (corp-wide): 158MM **Privately Held**
WEB: www.scafco.com
SIC: 3523 Farm machinery & equipment
PA: Scafco Corporation
2800 E Main Ave
Spokane WA 99202
509 343-9000

(P-14104)
SIGNATURE CONTROL SYSTEMS INC
16485 Laguna Canyon Rd # 130, Irvine (92618-3848)
PHONE..................949 580-3640
Brian Smith, *President*
Jane Smith, *Vice Pres*
Tim Troast, *General Mgr*
Don Clark, *Manager*
Hector Clemente, *Manager*
▼ **EMP:** 100 **EST:** 2000
SQ FT: 7,000
SALES (est): 22.9MM **Privately Held**
WEB: www.signaturecontrolsystems.com
SIC: 3523 Irrigation equipment, self-propelled

(P-14105)
SIMPLY COUNTRY INC
10110 Harvest Ln, Rough and Ready (95975-9783)
PHONE..................530 615-0565
EMP: 15 **EST:** 2011
SQ FT: 6,800
SALES (est): 1.2MM **Privately Held**
SIC: 3523

(P-14106)
SPECIALIZED DAIRY SERVICE INC
Also Called: S D S
1710 E Philadelphia St, Ontario (91761-7705)
PHONE..................909 923-3420
Joe T Trujillo, *CEO*
Joe Trujillo, *Vice Pres*
EMP: 22
SQ FT: 25,000
SALES (est): 6.8MM **Privately Held**
SIC: 3523 3556 5083 Dairy equipment (farm); dairy & milk machinery; dairy machinery & equipment

(P-14107)
STORM INDUSTRIES INC (PA)
23223 Normandie Ave, Torrance (90501-5050)
PHONE..................310 534-5232
Dale R Philippi, *CEO*
Guy E Marge, *Ch of Bd*
Georgia Claessens, *Corp Secy*
Elizabeth McGovern, *Vice Pres*
Jane Storm, *Vice Pres*
▲ **EMP:** 100
SALES (est): 76MM **Privately Held**
WEB: www.storemanagement.com
SIC: 3523 6552 Irrigation equipment, self-propelled; subdividers & developers

(P-14108)
TERRA TECH CORP (PA)
2040 Main St Ste 225, Irvine (92614-8219)
PHONE..................855 447-6967
Derek Peterson, *Ch of Bd*
Kenneth Vande Vrede, *COO*
Michael James, *CFO*
Michael A Nahass, *Treasurer*
EMP: 31
SALES: 35.8MM **Publicly Held**
SIC: 3523 Farm machinery & equipment

(P-14109)
TIGER CASED HOLE SERVICES INC
2828 Junipero Ave, Signal Hill (90755-2112)
PHONE..................562 426-4044
Joseph Baxter, *Principal*
Augustine Hernandez, *Vice Pres*
EMP: 13
SALES (est): 2.1MM **Privately Held**
SIC: 3523 Farm machinery & equipment

(P-14110)
TORO COMPANY
1588 N Marshall Ave, El Cajon (92020-1523)
PHONE..................619 562-2950
Timothy Young, *Manager*
Chris Stowell, *Executive*
Bud Vesta, *General Mgr*
Judy Ludwigson, *Executive Asst*
Patty Gagner, *Administration*
EMP: 91
SQ FT: 86,578
SALES (corp-wide): 2.5B **Publicly Held**
WEB: www.toro.com
SIC: 3523 Irrigation equipment, self-propelled
PA: The Toro Company
8111 Lyndale Ave S
Bloomington MN 55420
952 888-8801

(P-14111)
TORO COMPANY
5825 Jasmine St, Riverside (92504-1183)
P.O. Box 489 (92502-0489)
PHONE..................951 688-9221
Kendrick Melrose, *Manager*
Phil Burkart, *Vice Pres*
Amber Khan, *Sr Software Eng*
Jeff Meyer, *Software Engr*
Steve Kish, *Design Engr*
EMP: 74
SALES (corp-wide): 2.5B **Publicly Held**
WEB: www.toro.com
SIC: 3523 Irrigation equipment, self-propelled
PA: The Toro Company
8111 Lyndale Ave S
Bloomington MN 55420
952 888-8801

(P-14112)
TORO COMPANY
70221 Dinah Shore Dr, Rancho Mirage (92270-1314)
PHONE..................760 321-8396
Robert Wells, *Manager*
EMP: 100
SALES (corp-wide): 2.5B **Publicly Held**
WEB: www.toro.com
SIC: 3523 3524 Fertilizing, spraying, dusting & irrigation machinery; lawn & garden mowers & accessories
PA: The Toro Company
8111 Lyndale Ave S
Bloomington MN 55420
952 888-8801

(P-14113)
TURF STAR INC (PA)
2438 Radley Ct, Hayward (94545-1127)
PHONE..................800 585-8001
Gene Warne, *CEO*
Len Gregory, *President*
Marie Warne, *Admin Sec*
▲ **EMP:** 15 **EST:** 1963
SQ FT: 16,000
SALES (est): 60.3MM **Privately Held**
WEB: www.turfstar.com
SIC: 3523 4971 5083 Turf & grounds equipment; water distribution or supply systems for irrigation; lawn machinery & equipment

(P-14114)
VAL PLASTIC USA L L C
4570 Eucalyptus Ave Ste C, Chino (91710-9200)
PHONE..................909 390-9600
Dablu Kundu, *General Mgr*
▲ **EMP:** 15
SQ FT: 11,000
SALES (est): 2.8MM **Privately Held**
SIC: 3523 Fertilizing, spraying, dusting & irrigation machinery

(P-14115)
VALLEY FABRICATION INC
1056 Pellet Ave, Salinas (93901-4539)
P.O. Box 3618 (93912-3618)
PHONE..................831 757-5151
George Glen Heffington, *CEO*
Peter De Groot, *Vice Pres*
Jason Tracy, *Project Engr*
Tyler Brandt, *Purch Mgr*
Laurie Ferreira, *Manager*

▲ **EMP:** 60
SQ FT: 86,000
SALES (est): 14.4MM **Privately Held**
WEB: www.valleyfabricationinc.com
SIC: 3523 7699 5013 Farm machinery & equipment; farm machinery repair; truck parts & accessories

(P-14116)
VIERRA BROS FARMS LLC
Also Called: Vierra Bros Dairy
6960 Crane Rd, Oakdale (95361-8017)
PHONE..................209 247-3468
David Vierra,
Manuel J Vierra,
EMP: 10
SALES (est): 556.6K **Privately Held**
SIC: 3523 0191 Spreaders, fertilizer; general farms, primarily crop

(P-14117)
W THREE CO
1679 River Dr D, Brawley (92227-1747)
P.O. Box 1110 (92227-1110)
PHONE..................760 344-5841
Gary Williams, *Partner*
Jerry Williams, *Partner*
EMP: 20
SQ FT: 15,000
SALES (est): 2.6MM **Privately Held**
SIC: 3523 5083 Harvesters, fruit, vegetable, tobacco, etc.; agricultural machinery & equipment

(P-14118)
WARREN & BAERG MFG INC
39950 Road 108, Dinuba (93618-9518)
PHONE..................559 591-6790
Robert L Baerg, *Chairman*
Randy R Baerg, *President*
Bradley Carter, *Engineer*
Louis Garcia, *Engineer*
Mary Villarreal, *Mktg Coord*
▲ **EMP:** 20
SQ FT: 15,000
SALES (est): 6MM **Privately Held**
SIC: 3523 Planting, haying, harvesting & processing machinery

(P-14119)
WASCO HARDFACING CO
4585 E Citron, Fresno (93725)
PHONE..................559 485-5860
EMP: 20 **EST:** 2017
SALES (est): 2.6MM **Privately Held**
SIC: 3523 Farm machinery & equipment

(P-14120)
WASCO HARDFACING CO
2660 S East Ave, Fresno (93706-5408)
P.O. Box 2395 (93745-2395)
PHONE..................559 485-5860
Robin R Messick, *CEO*
▲ **EMP:** 60
SQ FT: 20,000
SALES (est): 13.6MM **Privately Held**
SIC: 3523 Farm machinery & equipment

(P-14121)
WASCO MANUFACTURING CO
2660 S East Ave, Fresno (93706-5408)
P.O. Box 2395 (93745-2395)
PHONE..................559 485-5860
Robin Messick, *President*
Gloria Zaragoza, *Administration*
Gilbert Villegas, *Opers Mgr*
EMP: 40
SQ FT: 23,100
SALES (est): 4.7MM **Privately Held**
WEB: www.ag1.net
SIC: 3523 Farm machinery & equipment

(P-14122)
WEATHER TEC CORP
5645 E Clinton Ave, Fresno (93727-1308)
PHONE..................559 291-5555
Nick Sterling Rogers, *CEO*
William H Rogers, *President*
Judith Rogers, *Treasurer*
▲ **EMP:** 12
SQ FT: 40,000
SALES (est): 3.2MM **Privately Held**
WEB: www.weathertec.com
SIC: 3523 3494 Farm machinery & equipment; sprinkler systems; field

(P-14123)
WEISS-MCNAIR LLC (DH)
100 Loren Ave, Chico (95928-7450)
PHONE..................530 891-6214
Larry Demmer, *President*
Glenn Stanley, *President*
Aaron Davidson, *Research*
Josh Gertsch, *Engineer*
Kelly Womack, *Engineer*
▲ **EMP:** 80
SQ FT: 32,000
SALES (est): 17.3MM
SALES (corp-wide): 4.9B **Privately Held**
WEB: www.weissram.com
SIC: 3523 Farm machinery & equipment
HQ: Gould Paper Corporation
99 Park Ave Fl 10
New York NY 10016
212 301-0000

(P-14124)
WELDCRAFT INDUSTRIES
18794 Avenue 96, Terra Bella (93270-9630)
P.O. Box 11104 (93270-1104)
PHONE..................559 784-4322
Gerald R Micke, *President*
Dixie L Micke, *Vice Pres*
EMP: 15
SALES (est): 3.6MM **Privately Held**
SIC: 3523 5191 Harvesters, fruit, vegetable, tobacco, etc.; farm supplies

(P-14125)
WILBUR-ELLIS COMPANY LLC
2903 S Cedar Ave, Fresno (93725-2324)
P.O. Box 1286 (93715-1286)
PHONE..................559 442-1220
Doug Hudson, *General Mgr*
EMP: 57
SALES (corp-wide): 3B **Privately Held**
WEB: www.wilbur-ellis.com
SIC: 3523 Farm machinery & equipment
HQ: Wilbur-Ellis Company Llc
345 California St Fl 27
San Francisco CA 94104
415 772-4000

(P-14126)
WILCOX BROTHERS INC
Also Called: Wilcox AG Products
14180 State Highway 160, Walnut Grove (95690-9741)
P.O. Box 70 (95690-0070)
PHONE..................916 776-1784
Alan Wilcox, *President*
Bruce Wilcox, *Vice Pres*
Jerry Valdovinos, *Prdtn Mgr*
▲ **EMP:** 57
SQ FT: 10,800
SALES (est): 16.7MM **Privately Held**
SIC: 3523 Farm machinery & equipment

3524 Garden, Lawn Tractors & Eqpt

(P-14127)
GRAND PACIFIC FIRE PROTECTION
13100 Red Corral Dr, Corona (92883-6312)
PHONE..................951 226-8304
Dave Boecking, *President*
EMP: 10
SALES (est): 654K **Privately Held**
SIC: 3524 Lawn & garden equipment

(P-14128)
MANUTECH MFG & DIST
2080 Sunset Dr, Pacific Grove (93950-3729)
P.O. Box 51295 (93950-6295)
PHONE..................831 655-8794
Angelo Villucci, *Owner*
Kevin Vilucci, *Co-Owner*
EMP: 11
SQ FT: 5,000
SALES (est): 1.3MM **Privately Held**
WEB: www.manutech.com
SIC: 3524 Blowers & vacuums, lawn

▲ = Import ▼=Export
◆ =Import/Export

(P-14129)
MC LANE MANUFACTURING INC
7110 Rosecrans Ave, Paramount (90723-2530)
PHONE..................................562 633-8158
Elmer E Malchow, *Ch of Bd*
Olivia Osorio, *Treasurer*
Ronald Mc Lane, *Vice Pres*
◆ **EMP:** 65 **EST:** 1942
SQ FT: 75,000
SALES (est): 13.1MM **Privately Held**
WEB: www.mclanemower.com
SIC: 3524 Lawnmowers, residential: hand or power; edgers, lawn

(P-14130)
POWER - TRIM CO
11150 Dana Cir, Cypress (90630-5132)
PHONE..................................714 523-8560
James O Dykes, *CEO*
Philip Shearer, *Vice Pres*
Barbara Dykes, *Admin Sec*
▼ **EMP:** 15
SQ FT: 28,000
SALES: 6.5MM **Privately Held**
WEB: www.powertrim.com
SIC: 3524 5083 Edgers, lawn; lawn & garden machinery & equipment

(P-14131)
R & R MAINTENANCE GROUP
1255 Treat Blvd Ste 300, Walnut Creek (94597-7965)
PHONE..................................707 863-0328
Ruben Maturin, *Principal*
EMP: 12
SALES: 180K **Privately Held**
SIC: 3524 Lawn & garden equipment

(P-14132)
ROTARY CORP
3359 E North Ave Ste 102, Fresno (93725-2641)
PHONE..................................559 445-1108
Ed Nelson, *President*
EMP: 10
SALES (est): 1.3MM **Privately Held**
SIC: 3524 Lawn & garden equipment

(P-14133)
SCOTTS TEMECULA OPERATIONS LLC (DH)
42375 Remington Ave, Temecula (92590-2512)
PHONE..................................951 719-1700
Jim Hagedorn, *CEO*
Barry Sanders, *President*
Thomas Kelly, *Bd of Directors*
Alex Hernandez, *Vice Pres*
Bob Bawcombe, *General Mgr*
▲ **EMP:** 25 **EST:** 1953
SQ FT: 400,000
SALES (est): 29.6MM
SALES (corp-wide): 2.6B **Publicly Held**
SIC: 3524 Lawn & garden equipment
HQ: The Scotts Company Llc
14111 Scottslawn Rd
Marysville OH 43040
937 644-3729

(P-14134)
SPRAYING DEVICES INC
Also Called: S D I
447 E Caldwell Ave, Visalia (93277-7609)
P.O. Box 3107 (93278-3107)
PHONE..................................559 734-5555
William S Bennet II, *President*
Denise Bennett, *Vice Pres*
EMP: 17 **EST:** 1982
SQ FT: 16,000
SALES (est): 4.3MM **Privately Held**
WEB: www.sprayingdevices.com
SIC: 3524 Lawn & garden equipment

(P-14135)
SPYDER MANUFACTURING INC
545 Porter Way, Placentia (92870-6454)
PHONE..................................714 528-8010
Gary J Monnig, *Principal*
Marc J Paquet, *Corp Secy*
Jules P Paquet, *Vice Pres*
Matthew Monnig, *Prdtn Mgr*
Alicia Parra, *Manager*
▲ **EMP:** 13

SQ FT: 11,000
SALES (est): 3MM **Privately Held**
WEB: www.spyder-mfg.com
SIC: 3524 Lawn & garden equipment

(P-14136)
TRU-CUT INC
141 E 157th St, Gardena (90248-2508)
PHONE..................................310 630-0422
Nabi Merchant, *CEO*
▲ **EMP:** 35
SQ FT: 28,620
SALES (est): 7.3MM **Privately Held**
SIC: 3524 5083 Lawn & garden mowers & accessories; lawnmowers, residential: hand or power; edgers, lawn; lawn & garden machinery & equipment; lawn machinery & equipment

(P-14137)
VERTICAL HYDRO GARDEN INC
1676 W Lincoln Ave, Anaheim (92801-5501)
PHONE..................................916 458-4987
John Taylor, *President*
▲ **EMP:** 15
SALES (est): 1MM **Privately Held**
SIC: 3524 5083 Lawn & garden equipment; garden machinery & equipment
PA: Greengro Technologies, Inc.
1676 W Lincoln Ave
Anaheim CA 92801

(P-14138)
WESTERN CACTUS GROWERS INC
1860 Monte Vista Dr, Vista (92084-7124)
P.O. Box 2018 (92085-2018)
PHONE..................................760 726-1710
Thomas Hans Britsch, *CEO*
Margaret Britsch, *Vice Pres*
▲ **EMP:** 25
SQ FT: 6,000
SALES (est): 4.1MM **Privately Held**
SIC: 3524 0181 Lawn & garden equipment; florists' greens & flowers

---
3531 Construction Machinery & Eqpt

(P-14139)
AGRICULTURAL MANUFACTURING
4106 S Cedar Ave, Fresno (93725-2703)
PHONE..................................559 485-1662
David Sprott, *President*
▲ **EMP:** 10
SQ FT: 6,000
SALES: 1.5MM **Privately Held**
WEB: www.agmanco.com
SIC: 3531 Aggregate spreaders

(P-14140)
ALTEC INDUSTRIES INC
325 Industrial Way, Dixon (95620-9763)
PHONE..................................707 678-0800
James Pitts, *Manager*
Debbie Muhl, *Executive*
Mark Clare, *Associate Dir*
James Pitts, *Office Mgr*
James C Pitts, *MIS Dir*
EMP: 60
SQ FT: 17,664
SALES (corp-wide): 766.2MM **Privately Held**
WEB: www.altec.com
SIC: 3531 3536 3713 3537 Derricks, except oil & gas field; aerial work platforms: hydraulic/elec. truck/carrier mounted; cranes, overhead traveling; truck bodies (motor vehicles); industrial trucks & tractors; conveyors & conveying equipment
HQ: Altec Industries, Inc.
210 Inverness Center Dr
Birmingham AL 35242
205 991-7733

(P-14141)
AMERICAN COMPACTION EQP INC
Also Called: Compaction American
29380 Hunco Way, Lake Elsinore (92530-2757)
PHONE..................................949 661-2921
Richard S Anderson, *CEO*
Monty Ihde, *President*
Kelly Ihde, *Corp Secy*
Darryl Kanell, *Vice Pres*
Mike Shoemaker, *Vice Pres*
▲ **EMP:** 24
SQ FT: 8,500
SALES: 9.2MM
SALES (corp-wide): 18.8B **Privately Held**
WEB: www.acewheels.com
SIC: 3531 7353 Soil compactors: vibratory; heavy construction equipment rental
HQ: Cascade Corporation
2201 Ne 201st Ave
Fairview OR 97024
503 669-6300

(P-14142)
AUTOBAHN CONSTRUCTION INC
933 N Batavia St Ste A, Orange (92867-5590)
PHONE..................................714 769-7025
Ali Solehjou, *President*
EMP: 11
SALES: 1.2MM **Privately Held**
WEB: www.autobahnconstruction.com
SIC: 3531 Road construction & maintenance machinery

(P-14143)
B C H MANUFACTURING CO INC
10012 Denny St, Oakland (94603-3004)
PHONE..................................510 569-6586
Barbara Barton, *President*
Lois Crowell, *Shareholder*
James E Crowell, *Corp Secy*
James M Barton, *Vice Pres*
James Barton, *VP Sls/Mktg*
EMP: 10
SQ FT: 10,000
SALES: 1.4MM **Privately Held**
SIC: 3531 1081 3444 Railroad related equipment; metal mining services; forming machine work, sheet metal

(P-14144)
BDM ENGINEERING INC
1031 S Linwood Ave, Santa Ana (92705-4323)
P.O. Box 3087, Tustin (92781-3087)
PHONE..................................714 558-6129
Barlowe D Moonilal, *President*
▼ **EMP:** 20
SQ FT: 20,000
SALES (est): 4.8MM **Privately Held**
WEB: www.bdm-engineering.com
SIC: 3531 Construction machinery

(P-14145)
BINDEL BROS GRADING &
1104 Madison Ln, Salinas (93907-1818)
PHONE..................................831 754-1490
William C Bindel, *President*
Bob Bindel, *Vice Pres*
EMP: 12
SQ FT: 2,000
SALES (est): 1.9MM **Privately Held**
SIC: 3531 1794 Buckets, excavating: clamshell, concrete, dragline, etc.; forestry related equipment; excavation & grading, building construction

(P-14146)
BLACK DIAMOND BLADE COMPANY (PA)
Also Called: Cutting Edge Supply
234 E O St, Colton (92324-3466)
PHONE..................................800 949-9014
John Brenner, *CEO*
Franklin J Brenner Sr, *President*
Hoby Brenner, *Treasurer*
Franklin Brennerc, *Admin Sec*
▲ **EMP:** 45 **EST:** 1950
SQ FT: 16,000

SALES (est): 35.1MM **Privately Held**
WEB: www.cuttingedgesupply.com
SIC: 3531 Blades for graders, scrapers, dozers & snow plows; road construction & maintenance machinery

(P-14147)
BLASTRAC NA
5220 Gaines St, San Diego (92110-2623)
PHONE..................................800 256-3440
Lenore Lipoufski, *Principal*
Rebecca Salvatierra, *Project Mgr*
▲ **EMP:** 11
SALES (est): 690K **Privately Held**
SIC: 3531 Construction machinery

(P-14148)
BRENT ENGINEERING INC
81 Shield, Irvine (92618-5212)
PHONE..................................949 679-5630
Ron Burek, *President*
EMP: 15
SALES (est): 3.7MM **Privately Held**
WEB: www.brentengineering.com
SIC: 3531 Road construction & maintenance machinery

(P-14149)
CAL VSTA EROSION CTRL PDTS LLC
459 Country Rd 99w 99 W, Arbuckle (95912)
P.O. Box 954 (95912-0954)
PHONE..................................530 476-0706
Renee Shadinger, *CEO*
Bryan Shadinger, *President*
John Shadinger, *CFO*
Maggie Shadinger, *Controller*
EMP: 35
SALES (est): 2.9MM **Privately Held**
WEB: www.calvistaerosion.com
SIC: 3531 Construction machinery

(P-14150)
CALIFORNIA MFG & ENGRG CO LLC
1401 S Madera Ave, Kerman (93630-9139)
PHONE..................................559 842-1500
Frank Shanahan,
Karen Emery,
Richard Spencer,
▲ **EMP:** 130
SALES (est): 13MM **Privately Held**
WEB: www.dfmfg.com
SIC: 3531 Construction machinery

(P-14151)
CALIFORNIA STONE COATING
37911 Von Euw Cmn, Fremont (94536-3963)
PHONE..................................510 284-2554
Kevin Farrer, *Owner*
EMP: 15
SALES (est): 2.1MM **Privately Held**
SIC: 3531 Roofing equipment

(P-14152)
CAMLEVER INC
954 S East End Ave, Pomona (91766-3837)
PHONE..................................909 629-9669
John Z Harris, *President*
Vanessa Rolden, *Admin Sec*
EMP: 12
SQ FT: 2,500
SALES (est): 2.5MM **Privately Held**
SIC: 3531 3799 3312 Construction machinery; wheelbarrows; blast furnaces & steel mills

(P-14153)
CARON COMPACTOR CO
1204 Ullrey Ave, Escalon (95320-8618)
PHONE..................................800 448-8236
James O Caron, *CEO*
Judith S Caron, *Vice Pres*
Mark Stapp, *Sales Mgr*
Joe Kelley, *Sales Staff*
▲ **EMP:** 25 **EST:** 1969
SQ FT: 18,000
SALES (est): 6.2MM **Privately Held**
WEB: www.caroncompactor.com
SIC: 3531 3441 Construction machinery attachments; fabricated structural metal

PRODUCTS & SVCS

(P-14154)
CASTLE & COOKE INC
Pacific Aggregates
28251 Lake St, Lake Elsinore
(92530-1635)
PHONE..................................951 245-2460
Mike Garcia, Manager
EMP: 80
SALES (corp-wide): 911.7MM **Privately Held**
SIC: 3531 Mixers, concrete
PA: Castle & Cooke, Inc.
1 Dole Dr
Westlake Village CA 91362
310 374-3952

(P-14155)
CATERPILLAR INC
17364 Hawthorne Blvd, Torrance
(90504-1033)
PHONE..................................310 921-9811
Jerry Meza, Branch Mgr
EMP: 16
SALES (corp-wide): 45.4B **Publicly Held**
SIC: 3531 Construction machinery
PA: Caterpillar Inc.
510 Lake Cook Rd Ste 100
Deerfield IL 60015
224 551-4000

(P-14156)
CATERPILLAR INC
5101 E Airport Dr, Ontario (91761-7825)
PHONE..................................909 390-9035
Jason Baumann, Branch Mgr
EMP: 385
SALES (corp-wide): 45.4B **Publicly Held**
SIC: 3531 3519 3511 Construction machinery; engines, diesel & semi-diesel or dual-fuel; gas turbine generator set units, complete
PA: Caterpillar Inc.
510 Lake Cook Rd Ste 100
Deerfield IL 60015
224 551-4000

(P-14157)
CAVOTEC INET US INC
5665 Corporate Ave, Cypress
(90630-4727)
PHONE..................................714 947-0005
Mike Larkin, President
Dorothy Chen, CFO
Sandra Torres, Info Tech Mgr
▼ EMP: 70
SALES: 24MM
SALES (corp-wide): 223.6MM **Privately Held**
WEB: www.inetas.com
SIC: 3531 Airport construction machinery
HQ: Cavotec Us Holdings, Inc.
5665 Corporate Ave
Cypress CA 90630
714 545-7900

(P-14158)
CLEASBY MANUFACTURING CO INC (PA)
1414 Bancroft Ave, San Francisco
(94124-3603)
P.O. Box 24132 (94124-0132)
PHONE..................................415 822-6565
Leslie John Cleasby, President
John Cleasby, President
Tony Griego, Plant Mgr
EMP: 20
SQ FT: 21,000
SALES: 5MM **Privately Held**
SIC: 3531 5033 Roofing equipment; roofing & siding materials

(P-14159)
COUNTY OF LOS ANGELES
Also Called: Public Works, Dept of
14959 Proctor Ave, La Puente
(91746-3206)
PHONE..................................626 968-3312
Mike Lee, Manager
EMP: 20 **Privately Held**
WEB: www.co.la.ca.us
SIC: 3531 9111 Road construction & maintenance machinery; bituminous batching plants; executive offices

PA: County Of Los Angeles
500 W Temple St Ste 437
Los Angeles CA 90012
213 974-1101

(P-14160)
COUNTY OF LOS ANGELES
Also Called: Public Works, Dept of
3637 Winter Canyon Rd, Malibu
(90265-4834)
PHONE..................................310 456-8014
Mark Sanchez, Manager
EMP: 16 **Privately Held**
WEB: www.co.la.ca.us
SIC: 3531 9621 Graders, road (construction machinery); regulation, administration of transportation
PA: County Of Los Angeles
500 W Temple St Ste 437
Los Angeles CA 90012
213 974-1101

(P-14161)
COUNTY OF SAN BERNARDINO
Also Called: Public Works Dept
825 E 3rd St, San Bernardino
(92415-1000)
PHONE..................................909 387-7942
Peter Wulfman, Manager
EMP: 560 **Privately Held**
SIC: 3531 9199 Road construction & maintenance machinery; bituminous batching plants; general government administration
PA: County Of San Bernardino
385 N Arrowhead Ave
San Bernardino CA 92415
909 387-3841

(P-14162)
CUSTOM BUILDING PRODUCTS INC
3525 Zephyr Ct, Stockton (95206-4210)
PHONE..................................209 983-8322
EMP: 40 **Privately Held**
WEB: www.custombuildingproducts.com
SIC: 3531 Concrete grouting equipment
HQ: Custom Building Products, Inc.
7711 Center Ave Ste 500
Huntington Beach CA 92647
800 272-8786

(P-14163)
DAVE HUMPHREY ENTERPRISES INC
Also Called: Noble Concrete Plants
145 Gandy Dancer Dr, Tracy (95377-8911)
PHONE..................................209 835-2222
Scott Humphrey, CEO
David G Humphrey, President
Heidi Herbert, Corp Secy
Bonnie Doyle, Accountant
▲ EMP: 13
SQ FT: 1,000
SALES (est): 3.9MM **Privately Held**
WEB: www.dhenoble.com
SIC: 3531 Batching plants, for aggregate concrete & bulk cement

(P-14164)
EAGLE ROCK INCORPORATED
40029 La Grange Rd, Junction City
(96048)
PHONE..................................530 623-4444
Larry E Yingling, President
David W Yingling, Vice Pres
EMP: 15 EST: 1980
SQ FT: 720
SALES (est): 2.9MM **Privately Held**
SIC: 3531 2951 1423 Rock crushing machinery, portable; capstans, ship; asphalt & asphaltic paving mixtures (not from refineries); crushed & broken granite

(P-14165)
ENDEAVOR HOMES INC
655 Cal Oak Rd, Oroville (95965-9621)
P.O. Box 1947 (95965-1947)
PHONE..................................530 534-0300
Del Fleener, President
Shonie Schufeldt, Treasurer
William Wicklas, Vice Pres
Bill Woods, Vice Pres
EMP: 20

SALES (est): 6.4MM **Privately Held**
WEB: www.endeavorhomes.com
SIC: 3531 2439 Construction machinery; trusses, wooden roof

(P-14166)
EVERPAC
1499 Palmyrita Ave, Riverside
(92507-1600)
PHONE..................................951 686-4560
William R Johnson, President
EMP: 30
SALES (est): 3.1MM **Privately Held**
WEB: www.everpac.com
SIC: 3531 Construction machinery

(P-14167)
GATOR MACHINERY COMPANY
11020 Cherry Ave, Fontana (92337-7119)
PHONE..................................909 823-1688
Charles Wu, President
Shirley Wu, Admin Sec
David Zhou, Engineer
Ernie Gallegos, Sales Mgr
◆ EMP: 11
SALES (est): 3.1MM **Privately Held**
WEB: www.gatormachinery.com
SIC: 3531 Rock crushing machinery, portable

(P-14168)
GC PRODUCTS INC
601 7th St, Lincoln (95648-1828)
PHONE..................................916 645-3870
John Coburn, President
Michael Coburn, Vice Pres
Keith Coburn, Sales Mgr
EMP: 43
SQ FT: 4,000
SALES (est): 8.4MM **Privately Held**
SIC: 3531 Construction machinery

(P-14169)
GLOBAL POLISHING SOLUTIONS LLC (HQ)
Also Called: Diamatic Management Services
5220 Gaines St, San Diego (92110-2623)
PHONE..................................619 295-5505
Stephen Klugherz, President
Brian McKinley, CEO
John Rittean, Vice Pres
Rebecca Salvatierra, Vice Pres
Jason Squires, Sales Staff
▲ EMP: 30
SALES: 25MM
SALES (corp-wide): 42.5MM **Privately Held**
SIC: 3531 5082 Surfacers, concrete grinding; concrete processing equipment
PA: Blastrac Global, Inc.
222 Greystone Rd
Evergreen CO 80439
405 478-3440

(P-14170)
GLOBAL PRECISION MANUFACTURING
38 Hollins Dr, Santa Cruz (95060-1815)
PHONE..................................831 239-9469
Edwin Taylor, Owner
Ed Taylor, Engineer
EMP: 10
SALES (est): 749.6K **Privately Held**
SIC: 3531 3444 Construction machinery; sheet metalwork

(P-14171)
GREENFORM LLC
12900 Prairie Ave, Hawthorne
(90250-5306)
PHONE..................................310 331-1665
Felix Schneider, Principal
▲ EMP: 10
SALES (est): 960.8K **Privately Held**
SIC: 3531 Bituminous, cement & concrete related products & equipment

(P-14172)
GROUND HOG INC
1470 Victoria Ct, San Bernardino
(92408-2831)
P.O. Box 290 (92402-0290)
PHONE..................................909 478-5700
Edward Carlson, President
Jack Carlson, Corp Secy
Allen Carlson, Natl Sales Mgr

▼ EMP: 25 EST: 1948
SQ FT: 52,000
SALES (est): 6.8MM **Privately Held**
WEB: www.groundhoginc.com
SIC: 3531 Posthole diggers, powered; entrenching machines

(P-14173)
GUNTERT ZMMERMAN CONST DIV INC
222 E 4th St, Ripon (95366-2761)
PHONE..................................209 599-0066
Ronald M Guntert Jr, CEO
Denise Guntert, Vice Pres
Mary Frampton, Executive Asst
Michael Boelens, Electrical Engi
Iovtcho Delev, Engineer
▲ EMP: 50 EST: 1942
SQ FT: 10,000
SALES (est): 23.1MM **Privately Held**
SIC: 3531 3599 Pavers; machine & other job shop work

(P-14174)
H & L TOOTH COMPANY (PA)
1540 S Greenwood Ave, Montebello
(90640-6536)
P.O. Box 48, Owasso OK (74055-0048)
PHONE..................................323 721-5146
Richard L Launder, Ch of Bd
Brian L Launder, Vice Pres
▲ EMP: 85 EST: 1931
SQ FT: 220,000
SALES (est): 13.2MM **Privately Held**
SIC: 3531 Bucket or scarifier teeth; construction machinery attachments

(P-14175)
HADAL INC
2107 Livingston St, Oakland (94606-5218)
PHONE..................................510 864-0600
EMP: 11 **Privately Held**
SIC: 3531 Marine related equipment
PA: Hadal, Inc.
1907 Dennison St
Oakland CA 94606
-

(P-14176)
HIROK INC
Also Called: Spitzlift
5644 Kearny Mesa Rd Ste H, San Diego
(92111-1311)
P.O. Box 3423, Ramona (92065-0959)
PHONE..................................619 713-5066
Michael Spitsbergen, CEO
Mark Spitsbergen, Vice Pres
EMP: 20
SQ FT: 2,500
SALES (est): 4.5MM **Privately Held**
WEB: www.hirok.com
SIC: 3531 Construction machinery

(P-14177)
JLG INDUSTRIES INC
Also Called: Jlg Serviceplus
7820 Lincoln Ave, Riverside (92504-4443)
PHONE..................................951 509-1227
Eric Golden, Manager
Lance Elbin, Sales Staff
EMP: 125
SALES (corp-wide): 6.8B **Publicly Held**
SIC: 3531 Cranes
HQ: Jlg Industries, Inc.
1 J L G Dr
Mc Connellsburg PA 17233
717 485-5161

(P-14178)
KENCO ENGINEERING INC
2155 Pfe Rd, Roseville (95747-9765)
P.O. Box 1467 (95678-8467)
PHONE..................................916 782-8494
David Lutz, President
Donald Lutz, Vice Pres
EMP: 30
SQ FT: 25,000
SALES (est): 7.7MM **Privately Held**
WEB: www.kencoengineering.com
SIC: 3531 5082 Construction machinery attachments; general construction machinery & equipment

▲ = Import ▼=Export
◆ =Import/Export

(P-14179)
KOMAX SYSTEMS INC
15301 Graham St, Huntington Beach
(92649-1110)
PHONE..............................310 830-4320
Robert S Smith, *President*
Robert Smith, *President*
Suzi Smith, *Engineer*
Frank Estrada, *Mfg Mgr*
Hayden Smith, *Production*
EMP: 25
SQ FT: 28,000
SALES (est): 7.6MM **Privately Held**
WEB: www.komax.com
SIC: 3531 Mixers: ore, plaster, slag, sand, mortar, etc.

(P-14180)
LAS ANIMAS CON & BLDG SUP INC
146 Encinal St, Santa Cruz (95060-2111)
P.O. Box 507 (95061-0507)
PHONE..............................831 425-4084
Scott French, *President*
EMP: 20
SALES (est): 6.6MM **Privately Held**
SIC: 3531 Cement silos (batch plant)

(P-14181)
MESA INDUSTRIES INC
Gunite Supplies & Equipment
1726 S Magnolia Ave, Monrovia
(91016-4511)
PHONE..............................626 359-9361
Kent Sexton, *Manager*
Sal Romero, *Opers Staff*
EMP: 20
SQ FT: 18,286
SALES (est): 4.7MM
SALES (corp-wide): 27.3MM **Privately Held**
SIC: 3531 Concrete gunning equipment
PA: Mesa Industries, Inc.
4027 Eastern Ave
Cincinnati OH 45226
513 321-2950

(P-14182)
MIXMOR INC
3131 Casitas Ave, Los Angeles
(90039-2499)
PHONE..............................323 664-1941
Michael K McNamara, *CEO*
Ann B Mc Namara, *Corp Secy*
David Ojeda, *Engineer*
William Preston, *Sales Mgr*
EMP: 19
SQ FT: 17,000
SALES (est): 6.6MM **Privately Held**
WEB: www.mixmor.com
SIC: 3531 Construction machinery

(P-14183)
PAUL A EVANS INC
1215 Audubon Rd, Mount Shasta
(96067-9006)
P.O. Box 940 (96067-0940)
PHONE..............................530 859-2505
Paul A Evans, *President*
EMP: 15 EST: 2005
SALES (est): 1.1MM **Privately Held**
SIC: 3531 Buckets, excavating: clamshell, concrete, dragline, etc.

(P-14184)
PETER PUGGER MANUFACTURING
3661 Christy Ln, Ukiah (95482-3088)
PHONE..............................707 463-1333
Randolph C Wood, *CEO*
▲ EMP: 11
SQ FT: 15,000
SALES (est): 3.3MM **Privately Held**
WEB: www.peterpugger.com
SIC: 3531 Mixers: ore, plaster, slag, sand, mortar, etc.

(P-14185)
QUIK MFG CO
Also Called: Q M C
18071 Mount Washington St, Fountain Valley (92708-6118)
PHONE..............................714 754-0337
Dannielle Schmidt, *Ch of Bd*
Steve Schmidt, *President*

Seth Schmidt, *General Mgr*
Mike Hunter, *Mfg Staff*
George Hunter, *Opers Staff*
▲ EMP: 28
SQ FT: 25,000
SALES: 1.2MM **Privately Held**
WEB: www.qmccranes.com
SIC: 3531 Cranes

(P-14186)
R E ATCKISON CO INC
1801 W Gladstone St, Azusa (91702-3206)
PHONE..............................626 334-0266
Edwards J Atckison, *President*
Roger Atckison, *Corp Secy*
EMP: 11
SQ FT: 2,000
SALES: 2.7MM **Privately Held**
SIC: 3531 Aerial work platforms: hydraulic/elec. truck/carrier mounted

(P-14187)
REGINA F BARAJAS
Also Called: C and R Pavers
629 Fern St, Escondido (92027-2105)
PHONE..............................760 500-0809
Regina F Barajas, *Owner*
EMP: 10 EST: 2010
SALES: 900K **Privately Held**
SIC: 3531 Pavers

(P-14188)
SANTA ROSA LEAD PRODUCTS LLC (PA)
33 S University St, Healdsburg
(95448-4021)
PHONE..............................800 916-5323
EMP: 17 EST: 2014
SALES (est): 3.5MM **Privately Held**
SIC: 3531 Roofing equipment

(P-14189)
SCHAMAS MFG CO INC
6356 N Irwindale Ave, Irwindale
(91702-3210)
PHONE..............................626 334-6870
William Schaeffler, *President*
Ralph Mason, *Vice Pres*
EMP: 15
SQ FT: 5,000
SALES (est): 2.4MM **Privately Held**
SIC: 3531 5084 Construction machinery; materials handling machinery

(P-14190)
SILO CITY INC
1401 S Union Ave, Bakersfield
(93307-4141)
PHONE..............................661 387-0179
Michael Clift, *CEO*
▲ EMP: 24
SQ FT: 174,240
SALES (est): 7.4MM **Privately Held**
SIC: 3531 Bituminous, cement & concrete related products & equipment

(P-14191)
SNL GROUP INC
9818 Holton Way, Redding (96003-9546)
PHONE..............................530 222-5048
Eric Stephens, *Vice Pres*
Tim Lewis, *Principal*
Cynthia Stephens, *Admin Sec*
EMP: 13
SQ FT: 5,000
SALES (est): 3.7MM **Privately Held**
SIC: 3531 Plows: construction, excavating & grading

(P-14192)
TANFIELD ENGRG SYSTEMS US INC
Also Called: Upright
2686 S Maple Ave, Fresno (93725-2108)
PHONE..............................559 443-6602
Roy Stanley, *President*
Charles Brooks, *CFO*
Doug King, *General Mgr*
David Sternweis, *Controller*
Darren Kell, *Director*
EMP: 15
SQ FT: 67,727

SALES (est): 3.8MM
SALES (corp-wide): 266.3K **Privately Held**
SIC: 3531 Aerial work platforms: hydraulic/elec. truck/carrier mounted
PA: Tanfield Group Plc
Sandgate House
Newcastle-Upon-Tyne

(P-14193)
TINK INC
2361 Durham Dayton Hwy, Durham
(95938-9604)
PHONE..............................530 895-0897
Robert J Du Bose, *CEO*
Dan M Du Bose, *Vice Pres*
Dan D Bose, *VP Finance*
Roy Farrell, *VP Sales*
Brian Greenwood, *Parts Mgr*
EMP: 40
SQ FT: 53,000
SALES (est): 12.7MM **Privately Held**
SIC: 3531 3444 Construction machinery; sheet metalwork

(P-14194)
TNT INDUSTRIAL CONTRACTORS INC (PA)
3800 Happy Ln, Sacramento (95827-9721)
PHONE..............................916 395-8400
Josh Twist, *CEO*
John Morrill, *Project Mgr*
Jannie Ridola, *Technology*
Dave Richter, *Sr Project Mgr*
EMP: 35
SQ FT: 4,000
SALES: 16.8MM **Privately Held**
WEB: www.tntindustrial.com
SIC: 3531 Construction machinery

(P-14195)
TRIO ENGINEERED PRODUCTS INC (HQ)
12823 Schabarum Ave, Irwindale
(91706-6808)
PHONE..............................626 851-3966
Michael Francis Burke, *CEO*
Eugene Xue, *Vice Pres*
▲ EMP: 29
SALES (est): 7.1MM
SALES (corp-wide): 3.1B **Privately Held**
WEB: www.trioproducts.com
SIC: 3531 Construction machinery attachments; aggregate spreaders
PA: Weir Group Plc(The)
1 West Regent Street
Glasgow G2 1R
141 637-7111

(P-14196)
TUSCANY PAVERS INC
241 S Twin Oaks Valley Rd, San Marcos
(92078-4330)
PHONE..............................866 596-4092
Daniel Winfield, *Principal*
EMP: 11
SALES (est): 1.8MM **Privately Held**
SIC: 3531 Pavers

(P-14197)
US SAWS INC (PA)
Also Called: U S Saw & Blades
3702 W Central Ave, Santa Ana
(92704-5832)
PHONE..............................860 668-2402
Bruce Root, *CEO*
C W Duncan, *President*
Bill Glynn, *Vice Pres*
Brandon Utesch, *Sales Mgr*
▲ EMP: 18
SQ FT: 4,000
SALES: 7MM **Privately Held**
WEB: www.ussaws.com
SIC: 3531 5082 Blades for graders, scrapers, dozers & snow plows; road construction & maintenance machinery

(P-14198)
VOLVO CONSTRUCTION EQP & SVCS
22099 Knabe Rd, Corona (92883-7111)
PHONE..............................951 277-7620
Mike Franks, *Principal*
EMP: 26

SALES (est): 31.1MM
SALES (corp-wide): 39.6B **Privately Held**
SIC: 3531 Construction machinery
HQ: Saba Holding Company, Llc
312 Volvo Way
Shippensburg PA 17257
717 532-9181

(P-14199)
WESTERN EQUIPMENT MFG INC
Also Called: Western Equipment Mfg
1160 Olympic Dr, Corona (92881-3390)
PHONE..............................951 284-2000
Kenneth R Thompson, *CEO*
William Weihl, *President*
▲ EMP: 19
SALES (est): 5.1MM **Privately Held**
SIC: 3531 Finishers & spreaders (construction equipment)

3532 Mining Machinery & Eqpt

(P-14200)
AUTOMATED PACKG SYSTEMS INC
10440 Ontiveros Pl Ste 1, Santa Fe Springs
(90670-7335)
PHONE..............................562 941-1476
Bernie Lerner, *President*
Sharon Spaeth, *Admin Asst*
Robert Ferrante, *Electrical Engi*
Chris Houin, *Engineer*
Chris Schantz, *Materials Mgr*
EMP: 12
SALES (corp-wide): 225.2MM **Privately Held**
WEB: www.autobag.com
SIC: 3532 5113 3565 2671 Mining machinery; industrial & personal service paper; packaging machinery; packaging paper & plastics film, coated & laminated; packaging materials
PA: Automated Packaging Systems Inc.
10175 Philipp Pkwy
Streetsboro OH 44241
330 528-2000

(P-14201)
POLYALLOYS
14000 Avalon Blvd, Los Angeles
(90061-2636)
PHONE..............................310 715-9800
Craig Paulin, *CEO*
Eden Ines, *Controller*
EMP: 75
SALES (est): 7.6MM
SALES (corp-wide): 22.9MM **Privately Held**
SIC: 3532 Amalgamators (metallurgical or mining machinery)
PA: Psm Industries, Inc.
14000 Avalon Blvd
Los Angeles CA 90061
888 663-8256

(P-14202)
REED INTERNATIONAL (HQ)
Also Called: Saunco Air Technologies
13024 Lake Rd, Hickman (95323-9667)
P.O. Box 178 (95323-0178)
PHONE..............................209 874-2357
Wendell Reed, *President*
John Birchall, *Sales Mgr*
▼ EMP: 20 EST: 1973
SALES (est): 3.5MM
SALES (corp-wide): 197.8MM **Privately Held**
WEB: www.saunco.com
SIC: 3532 5531 3564 3444 Mining machinery; automotive & home supply stores; blowers & fans; sheet metalwork
PA: Basic Resources Inc
928 12th St Ste 700
Modesto CA 95354
209 521-9771

(P-14203)
SPAULDING EQUIPMENT COMPANY (PA)
Also Called: Spaulding Crusher Parts
75 Paseo Adelanto, Perris (92570-9343)
P.O. Box 1807 (92572-1807)
PHONE..............................951 943-4531

PRODUCTS & SVCS

George E Spaulding, *Ch of Bd*
James Michael Spaulding, *President*
Fred Stemrich, *Treasurer*
Norman Vetter, *Vice Pres*
◆ **EMP:** 47
SALES (est): 10.2MM **Privately Held**
SIC: 3532 5082 7699 Mineral beneficia-
tion equipment; mineral beneficiation ma-
chinery; industrial machinery & equipment
repair

(P-14204)
WEBER DRILLING CO INC
401 Hindry Ave, Inglewood (90301-2015)
PHONE..................310 670-7708
Marlene Wood, *President*
Ronald Wood, *Vice Pres*
EMP: 25
SQ FT: 7,000
SALES (est): 4.6MM **Privately Held**
SIC: 3532 Drills & drilling equipment, min-
ing (except oil & gas)

3533 Oil Field Machinery & Eqpt

(P-14205)
AERA ENERGY LLC
29010 Shell Rd, Coalinga (93210-9235)
PHONE..................559 935-7418
Kevin Peck, *Branch Mgr*
EMP: 25
SALES (corp-wide): 305.1B **Privately Held**
WEB: www.aeraenergy.com
SIC: 3533 1311 Oil & gas drilling rigs &
equipment; crude petroleum & natural gas
production
HQ: Aera Energy Llc
10000 Ming Ave
Bakersfield CA 93311
661 665-5000

(P-14206)
AMR INDUSTRIES ENTERPRISES INC
2131 19th Ave Ste 203, San Francisco
(94116-1868)
PHONE..................415 860-5566
Kristo Regjo, *CEO*
EMP: 23
SALES (est): 5.1MM **Privately Held**
SIC: 3533 Oil & gas field machinery

(P-14207)
AQUEOS CORPORATION
2550 Eastman Ave, Ventura (93003-7714)
PHONE..................805 676-4330
Theodore Roche, *Branch Mgr*
Richard Campbell, *Project Mgr*
Dane Wilson, *Commercial*
William Kim, *Supervisor*
Jason Thach, *Supervisor*
EMP: 45
SALES (corp-wide): 44.3MM **Privately Held**
SIC: 3533 Oil & gas field machinery
PA: Aqueos Corporation
231 Highway 96
Broussard LA 70518
337 714-0033

(P-14208)
BAKER HGHES OLFLD OPRTIONS LLC
5421 Argosy Ave, Huntington Beach
(92649-1038)
PHONE..................714 893-8511
Dave Dillion, *Branch Mgr*
EMP: 55
SALES (corp-wide): 122B **Publicly Held**
WEB: www.bot.bhi-net.com
SIC: 3533 Oil field machinery & equipment
HQ: Baker Hughes Oilfield Operations Llc
17021 Aldine Westfield Rd
Houston TX 77073
713 879-1000

(P-14209)
BAKER HGHES OLFLD OPRTIONS LLC
9865 W Olympic Blvd, Beverly Hills
(90212-3760)
PHONE..................310 843-9632
EMP: 99
SALES (corp-wide): 122B **Publicly Held**
SIC: 3533 Oil & gas field machinery
HQ: Baker Hughes Oilfield Operations Llc
17021 Aldine Westfield Rd
Houston TX 77073
713 879-1000

(P-14210)
BAKER HUGHES A GE COMPANY LLC
5421 Argosy Ave, Huntington Beach
(92649-1038)
PHONE..................714 893-8511
David A Patti, *Manager*
EMP: 84
SALES (corp-wide): 122B **Publicly Held**
SIC: 3533 Oil & gas field machinery
HQ: Baker Hughes, A Ge Company, Llc
17021 Aldine Westfield Rd
Houston TX 77073
713 439-8600

(P-14211)
BAKER HUGHES A GE COMPANY LLC
5010 Lisa Marie Ct, Bakersfield
(93313-2700)
PHONE..................661 837-9601
Bob Kilby, *Manager*
EMP: 87
SALES (corp-wide): 122B **Publicly Held**
WEB: www.bakerhughes.com
SIC: 3533 Oil & gas field machinery
HQ: Baker Hughes, A Ge Company, Llc
17021 Aldine Westfield Rd
Houston TX 77073
713 439-8600

(P-14212)
BAKER HUGHES A GE COMPANY LLC
6117 Schirra Ct, Bakersfield (93313-2167)
PHONE..................661 834-9654
Joe Howard, *Branch Mgr*
Aaron Bowser, *Opers Staff*
EMP: 87
SALES (corp-wide): 122B **Publicly Held**
WEB: www.bakerhughes.com
SIC: 3533 Oil & gas field machinery
HQ: Baker Hughes, A Ge Company, Llc
17021 Aldine Westfield Rd
Houston TX 77073
713 439-8600

(P-14213)
CAMERON INTERNATIONAL CORP
4315 Yeager Way, Bakersfield
(93313-2018)
PHONE..................661 323-8183
Keith Smith, *District Mgr*
EMP: 10 **Publicly Held**
SIC: 3533 5084 Oil field machinery &
equipment; drilling equipment, excluding
bits
HQ: Cameron International Corporation
4646 W Sam Houston Pkwy N
Houston TX 77041

(P-14214)
CAMERON INTERNATIONAL CORP
535 Getty Ct Ste A, Benicia (94510-1179)
PHONE..................707 752-8800
EMP: 49 **Publicly Held**
SIC: 3533 Oil field machinery & equipment
HQ: Cameron International Corporation
4646 W Sam Houston Pkwy N
Houston TX 77041

(P-14215)
CAMERON INTERNATIONAL CORP
Also Called: Cooper Cameron Valves
562 River Park Dr, Redding (96003-5381)
PHONE..................530 242-6965
EMP: 56
SALES (corp-wide): 10.3B **Publicly Held**
SIC: 3533
PA: Cameron International Corporation
1333 West Loop S Ste 1700
Houston TX 77041
713 513-3300

(P-14216)
CAMERON INTERNATIONAL CORP
Also Called: Camserv
1282 Bayview Farm Rd, Pinole (94564)
PHONE..................510 928-1480
EMP: 56 **Publicly Held**
SIC: 3533 Oil & gas field machinery
HQ: Cameron International Corporation
4646 W Sam Houston Pkwy N
Houston TX 77041

(P-14217)
CAMERON WEST COAST (PA)
9452 Resenda Ave, Fontana (92335-2541)
PHONE..................909 355-8995
Charles Jerry Funderburk, *President*
Garry Stevens, *Vice Pres*
▲ **EMP:** 10
SQ FT: 14,000
SALES (est): 1.2MM **Privately Held**
WEB: www.elcoinc.com
SIC: 3533 7353 Oil field machinery &
equipment; oil field equipment, rental or
leasing

(P-14218)
CHANCELLOR OIL TOOLS INC
3521 Gulf St, Bakersfield (93308-5210)
PHONE..................661 324-2213
David Fleming, *CFO*
EMP: 40
SQ FT: 8,800
SALES (est): 6.7MM
SALES (corp-wide): 818.6MM **Publicly Held**
SIC: 3533 Drilling tools for gas, oil or water
wells
HQ: Team Oil Tools, L.P.
4310 N Sam Houston Pkwy E
Houston TX 77032
936 242-8825

(P-14219)
CONTROL SYSTEMS INTL INC
1 Sterling, Irvine (92618-2517)
PHONE..................949 238-4150
Rob Lewis, *General Mgr*
EMP: 34
SALES (corp-wide): 15B **Privately Held**
SIC: 3533 Oil & gas field machinery
HQ: Control Systems International, Inc.
8040 Nieman Rd
Shawnee Mission KS 66214
913 599-5010

(P-14220)
DAWSON ENTERPRISES (PA)
Also Called: Cavins Oil Well Tools
2853 Cherry Ave, Signal Hill (90755-1908)
P.O. Box 6039, Long Beach (90806-0039)
PHONE..................562 424-8564
James M Dawson, *CEO*
Harry Dawson, *President*
Jim Moore, *Executive*
Robert Phillips, *Purch Mgr*
Cheryl Reyes, *Buyer*
◆ **EMP:** 36
SQ FT: 19,000
SALES (est): 10.5MM **Privately Held**
WEB: www.cavins.com
SIC: 3533 7359 Bits, oil & gas field tools:
rock; garage facility & tool rental

(P-14221)
DOWNHOLE STABILIZATION INC
3515 Thomas Way, Bakersfield
(93308-6215)
P.O. Box 2467 (93303-2467)
PHONE..................661 631-1044
Jim Calanchini, *President*
Diane Calanchini, *Corp Secy*
Jacob Banducci, *Vice Pres*
Joe Calanchini, *Vice Pres*
Mike Jarboe, *Vice Pres*
▲ **EMP:** 38
SQ FT: 8,800
SALES (est): 11.8MM **Privately Held**
WEB: www.downholedrillingtools.com
SIC: 3533 5082 3599 1389 Drilling tools
for gas, oil or water wells; wellpoints
(drilling equipment); machine shop, job-
bing & repair; oil field services

(P-14222)
FARLEY MACHINE INC
1600 S Union Ave, Bakersfield
(93307-4146)
PHONE..................661 397-4987
Paul J Farley, *President*
Winney Farley, *Corp Secy*
J B Rogers, *Vice Pres*
EMP: 13
SQ FT: 1,400
SALES (est): 2.5MM **Privately Held**
WEB: www.farley.rwisp.com
SIC: 3533 Oil field machinery & equipment;
water well drilling equipment

(P-14223)
FIRSTAR INTERNATIONAL GROUP
160 W Fthill Pkwy Ste 105, Corona
(92882)
PHONE..................918 845-2402
Peggy Zuber, *Owner*
Muhsin Al-Hashimi, *CEO*
Ramsey Faraj, *Principal*
EMP: 10
SALES (est): 528.6K **Privately Held**
SIC: 3533 7389 Oil & gas drilling rigs &
equipment;

(P-14224)
FMC TECHNOLOGIES INC
621 Burning Tree Rd, Fullerton
(92833-1448)
PHONE..................714 872-5574
Rose Folli, *Principal*
EMP: 15
SALES (corp-wide): 15B **Privately Held**
SIC: 3533 Oil field machinery & equipment
HQ: Fmc Technologies, Inc.
11740 Katy Fwy Energy Tow
Houston TX 77079
281 591-4000

(P-14225)
FTT HOLDINGS INC
3020 Old Ranch Pkwy, Seal Beach
(90740-2765)
PHONE..................562 430-6262
Bryan Livingston, *President*
James Leonetti, *CFO*
David Haas, *Exec VP*
EMP: 12
SALES (est): 1.7MM **Privately Held**
SIC: 3533 Oil field machinery & equipment

(P-14226)
GLOBAL ELASTOMERIC PDTS INC
5551 District Blvd, Bakersfield
(93313-2126)
PHONE..................661 831-5380
Phil W Embury, *President*
Sandy Embury, *Vice Pres*
Tom Burnes, *Administration*
Jim Pickering, *Safety Mgr*
Zachary Ellis, *Sales Staff*
▲ **EMP:** 55
SQ FT: 20,000
SALES (est): 12.3MM **Privately Held**
WEB: www.globaleee.com
SIC: 3533 5084 Oil & gas field machinery;
oil refining machinery, equipment & sup-
plies; oil well machinery, equipment &
supplies

(P-14227)
HARBISON-FISCHER INC
200 Carver St, Shafter (93263-4008)
PHONE.................................661 399-0628
EMP: 31
SALES (corp-wide): 1.4B **Publicly Held**
SIC: 3533 Oil field machinery & equipment
HQ: Harbison-Fischer, Inc.
   901 N Crowley Rd
   Crowley TX 76036
   817 297-2211

(P-14228)
HYDRIL COMPANY
3237 Patton Way, Bakersfield
(93308-5717)
PHONE.................................661 588-9332
Ken Steinke, *Branch Mgr*
EMP: 343 **Privately Held**
SIC: 3533 Oil field machinery & equipment
HQ: Hydril Company
   302 Mccarty St
   Houston TX 77029

(P-14229)
HYDRIL USA DISTRIBUTION LLC
3237 Patton Way, Bakersfield
(93308-5717)
PHONE.................................661 588-9332
Baryy Park, *Manager*
EMP: 12
SALES (corp-wide): 122B **Publicly Held**
WEB: www.hydril.com
SIC: 3533 1389 Oil & gas field machinery;
   oil field services
HQ: Hydril Usa Distribution Llc
   3300 N Sam Houston Pkwy E
   Houston TX 77032
   281 449-2000

(P-14230)
KBA ENGINEERING LLC
2157 Mohawk St, Bakersfield
(93308-6020)
P.O. Box 1200 (93302-1200)
PHONE.................................661 323-0487
Richard C Jones, *Mng Member*
Sarah Sackewitz, *Human Res Mgr*
Chris Ryan, *Purch Mgr*
Martin Alonzo, *Safety Dir*
Ryan Fergon, *Safety Mgr*
EMP: 95
SQ FT: 45,000
SALES (est): 19.6MM **Privately Held**
WEB: www.kbaeng.com
SIC: 3533 3462 Oil & gas field machinery;
   gear & chain forgings

(P-14231)
KMT INTERNATIONAL INC
344 De Leon Ave, Fremont (94539-5705)
PHONE.................................510 713-1400
Boris Melamed, *President*
Eugene Kravets, *Vice Pres*
▼ EMP: 42
SQ FT: 10,000
SALES: 14MM **Privately Held**
SIC: 3533 Gas field machinery & equip-
   ment

(P-14232)
LASALLE INTL HLDINGS GROUP INC
9667 Owensmouth Ave, Chatsworth
(91311-4819)
P.O. Box 7396, Northridge (91327-7396)
PHONE.................................818 233-8000
Pierre Yenokian, *President*
Jan Papazian, *CFO*
◆ EMP: 40
SQ FT: 70,000
SALES (est): 5.2MM **Privately Held**
SIC: 3533 5047 1382 Oil & gas field ma-
   chinery; medical & hospital equipment; oil
   & gas exploration services; geological ex-
   ploration, oil & gas field

(P-14233)
NATIONAL OILWELL VARCO INC
Also Called: Nov
1701 W Sequoia Ave, Orange
(92868-1015)
PHONE.................................714 978-1900

Francisco Arellano, *Branch Mgr*
EMP: 24
SALES (corp-wide): 7.3B **Publicly Held**
SIC: 3533 Oil & gas drilling rigs & equip-
   ment
PA: National Oilwell Varco, Inc.
   7909 Parkwood Circle Dr
   Houston TX 77036
   713 346-7500

(P-14234)
NATIONAL OILWELL VARCO INC
759 N Eckhoff St, Orange (92868-1005)
P.O. Box 6626 (92863-6626)
PHONE.................................714 978-1900
Owen Unruh, *Principal*
Trung Nguyen, *Software Engr*
Michael Ballacchino, *Engineer*
William McClusky, *Engineer*
Joel Olivera, *Engineer*
EMP: 50
SALES (corp-wide): 7.3B **Publicly Held**
WEB: www.natoil.com
SIC: 3533 Oil field machinery & equipment
PA: National Oilwell Varco, Inc.
   7909 Parkwood Circle Dr
   Houston TX 77036
   713 346-7500

(P-14235)
NATIONAL OILWELL VARCO INC
743 N Eckhoff St, Orange (92868-1005)
PHONE.................................714 978-1900
Owan Unruh, *Manager*
Luke Schuessler, *Design Engr*
Stan Curlee, *Electrical Engi*
Laura Acocella, *Engineer*
Terry Coombs, *Engineer*
EMP: 23
SALES (corp-wide): 7.3B **Publicly Held**
SIC: 3533 Bits, oil & gas field tools: rock
PA: National Oilwell Varco, Inc.
   7909 Parkwood Circle Dr
   Houston TX 77036
   713 346-7500

(P-14236)
NATIONAL OILWELL VARCO INC
Also Called: Nov Orange Warehouse
752 N Poplar St, Orange (92868-1014)
PHONE.................................714 978-1900
Pete Miller, *President*
Stanley Stone, *Contractor*
EMP: 23
SALES (corp-wide): 7.3B **Publicly Held**
SIC: 3533 Oil field machinery & equipment
PA: National Oilwell Varco, Inc.
   7909 Parkwood Circle Dr
   Houston TX 77036
   713 346-7500

(P-14237)
OIL COUNTRY MANUFACTURING
300 W Stanley Ave, Ventura (93001-1395)
PHONE.................................805 643-1200
Ed Patterson III, *General Mgr*
Robert M Nelson, *Vice Pres*
◆ EMP: 130
SQ FT: 100,000
SALES (est): 24.1MM **Privately Held**
SIC: 3533 5084 Oil field machinery &
   equipment; industrial machinery & equip-
   ment

(P-14238)
SEABOARD INTERNATIONAL INC
Also Called: Weir Seaboard
3912 Gilmore Ave, Bakersfield
(93308-6214)
PHONE.................................661 325-5026
Rex Duhn, *Branch Mgr*
EMP: 97
SALES (corp-wide): 3.1B **Privately Held**
SIC: 3533 Oil & gas field machinery
HQ: Seaboard International Inc.
   13815 South Fwy
   Houston TX 77047
   713 644-3535

(P-14239)
TECHNIPFMC US HOLDINGS INC
5200 Northspur Ct, Bakersfield
(93308-6185)
PHONE.................................661 283-1069
Lee McHorse, *Branch Mgr*
EMP: 15
SALES (corp-wide): 15B **Privately Held**
SIC: 3533 Oil & gas field machinery
HQ: Fmc Technologies, Inc.
   11740 Katy Fwy Energy Tow
   Houston TX 77079
   281 591-4000

(P-14240)
TECHNIPFMC US HOLDINGS INC
810 Manley Dr, San Gabriel (91776-2327)
PHONE.................................310 328-1236
Russell Lew, *Branch Mgr*
EMP: 18
SALES (corp-wide): 15B **Privately Held**
SIC: 3533 Oil & gas field machinery
HQ: Fmc Technologies, Inc.
   11740 Katy Fwy Energy Tow
   Houston TX 77079
   281 591-4000

(P-14241)
TECHNIPFMC US HOLDINGS INC
260 Cousteau Pl, Davis (95618-5490)
PHONE.................................530 753-6718
John T Gremp, *Ch of Bd*
Clayton Kleppinger, *Engineer*
Matthew Brown, *Finance*
George Shirreffs, *Director*
Dave Langley, *Manager*
EMP: 28
SALES (corp-wide): 15B **Privately Held**
SIC: 3533 Oil & gas field machinery
HQ: Fmc Technologies, Inc.
   11740 Katy Fwy Energy Tow
   Houston TX 77079
   281 591-4000

(P-14242)
TEXAS BOOM COMPANY INC
2433 Sagebrush Ct, La Jolla (92037-7036)
PHONE.................................281 441-2002
Sourena Fakhimi, *President*
EMP: 10
SALES (est): 1.3MM **Privately Held**
WEB: www.texasboom.com
SIC: 3533 8748 Oil & gas field machinery;
   environmental consultant

(P-14243)
WEATHERFORD INTERNATIONAL LLC
3701 Enterprise St, Shafter (93263-2212)
PHONE.................................661 589-2146
Daniel Erbs, *Manager*
EMP: 40 **Privately Held**
SIC: 3533 Oil & gas field machinery
HQ: Weatherford International, Llc
   2000 Saint James Pl
   Houston TX 77056
   713 693-4000

(P-14244)
WEATHERFORD INTERNATIONAL INC
3356 Lime Ave, Long Beach (90755-4612)
PHONE.................................562 595-0931
Gary Kennedy, *Branch Mgr*
Tracie Breedlove, *Manager*
EMP: 16 **Privately Held**
WEB: www.weatherford.com
SIC: 3533 Oil & gas field machinery
HQ: Weatherford International, Llc
   2000 Saint James Pl
   Houston TX 77056
   713 693-4000

(P-14245)
WWT INTERNATIONAL INC
1150 N Tustin Ave, Anaheim (92807-1735)
PHONE.................................714 632-0810
Bruce Moore, *Director*
Philip Mock, *Engineer*
EMP: 13
SALES (corp-wide): 6MM **Privately Held**
SIC: 3533 1389 Oil & gas field machinery;
   oil field services

PA: Wwt International, Inc.
   9758 Whithorn Dr
   Houston TX 77095
   281 345-8019

3534 Elevators & Moving Stairways

(P-14246)
ELEVATOR EQUIPMENT CORPORATION (PA)
Also Called: Eeco
4035 Goodwin Ave, Los Angeles
(90039-1190)
P.O. Box 39714 (90039-0714)
PHONE.................................323 245-0147
Abe Salehpour, *CEO*
Robert Alterman, *CFO*
Abdul Mozayeni, *CFO*
Don Brown, *Engineer*
◆ EMP: 75
SQ FT: 20,000
SALES (est): 18.5MM **Privately Held**
WEB: www.eecovalves.com
SIC: 3534 Elevators & equipment

(P-14247)
ELEVATOR INDUSTRIES INC
110 Main Ave, Sacramento (95838-2015)
PHONE.................................916 921-1495
Guy Buckman, *President*
Jason Buckman, *Vice Pres*
▲ EMP: 16 EST: 2013
SQ FT: 1,500
SALES (est): 482.9K **Privately Held**
SIC: 3534 7699 Elevators & equipment;
   elevators: inspection, service & repair

(P-14248)
ELEVATOR RESEARCH & MFG CO
1417 Elwood St, Los Angeles
(90021-2812)
PHONE.................................213 746-1914
Frank Edward Park, *President*
Lynn Park, *Vice Pres*
Denny Marques, *Executive*
David Alvarez, *General Mgr*
Rogers Barnet, *General Mgr*
EMP: 96 EST: 1964
SQ FT: 5,000
SALES (est): 18.5MM
SALES (corp-wide): 67.8MM **Privately Held**
WEB: www.elevatorresearch.com
SIC: 3534 Elevators & equipment
PA: Dewhurst Plc
   Unit 9 Hampton Business Park Bolney
   Way
   Feltham MIDDX TW13
   208 744-8200

(P-14249)
GAL MANUFACTURING CO LLC
Also Called: Bore-Max
3380 Gilman Rd, El Monte (91732-3201)
PHONE.................................626 443-8616
Bret Sturm, *Branch Mgr*
EMP: 14
SALES (corp-wide): 2B **Privately Held**
SIC: 3534 Elevators & equipment
HQ: G.A.L. Manufacturing Company, Llc
   50 E 153rd St
   Bronx NY 10451
   718 292-9000

(P-14250)
GMS ELEVATOR SERVICES INC
401 Borrego Ct, San Dimas (91773-2971)
PHONE.................................909 599-3904
G Matthew Simpkins, *President*
Nate Simpkins, *General Mgr*
Pamela Simpkins, *Admin Sec*
Camille Albin, *Info Tech Mgr*
Shea Nolan, *Project Mgr*
EMP: 35
SQ FT: 4,000
SALES (est): 9.5MM **Privately Held**
SIC: 3534 1796 Elevators & equipment;
   elevator installation & conversion

(P-14251)
HKA ELEVATOR CONSULTING INC
23211 S Pointe Dr Ste 101, Laguna Hills (92653-1478)
PHONE..................................949 348-9711
Daryl Anderson, *President*
Alexandros Bletsos, *Manager*
EMP: 10
SQ FT: 3,500
SALES: 3MM **Privately Held**
WEB: www.hkaconsulting.com
SIC: 3534 Elevators & moving stairways

(P-14252)
INTERNACIONAL DE ELEVADORES SA
9475 Nicola Tesla Ct, San Diego (92154-7613)
PHONE..................................619 955-6180
EMP: 10 **Privately Held**
SIC: 3534

(P-14253)
NEXT LEVEL ELEVATOR INC
2199 N Batavia St Ste S, Orange (92865-3107)
PHONE..................................888 959-6010
Jevon Hadley, *President*
EMP: 11
SALES (est): 766K **Privately Held**
SIC: 3534 Elevators & equipment

(P-14254)
NIDEC MOTOR CORPORATION
Also Called: McE
11380 White Rock Rd, Rancho Cordova (95742-6522)
PHONE..................................916 638-4011
Mohamed Ezzeddine, *Vice Pres*
David Adcock, *Administration*
Daniel Jones, *Research*
Michael Poon, *Technical Staff*
Jeffrey Counts, *Engineer*
EMP: 400
SALES (corp-wide): 13.9B **Privately Held**
SIC: 3534 3613 Elevators & equipment; switchgear & switchboard apparatus
HQ: Nidec Motor Corporation
　　8050 West Florissant Ave
　　Saint Louis MO 63136

(P-14255)
POWERLIFT DUMBWAITERS INC
2444 Georgia Slide Rd, Georgetown (95634-2201)
P.O. Box 4390 (95634-4390)
PHONE..................................800 409-5438
John B Reite, *President*
◆ EMP: 26
SQ FT: 7,500
SALES (est): 5.7MM **Privately Held**
WEB: www.dumbwaiters.com
SIC: 3534 Dumbwaiters

(P-14256)
S & H ENTERPRISES INC
6200 Enterprise Dr, Diamond Springs (95619-9448)
PHONE..................................530 626-8043
Tom Garnley, *President*
Henry Bollinger, *Area Mgr*
EMP: 10
SALES (est): 1.1MM
SALES (corp-wide): 1.6MM **Privately Held**
SIC: 3534 Elevators & equipment; dumb-waiters
PA: S & H Enterprises, Inc.
　　11 Broad St
　　Glens Falls NY
　　518 798-0871

(P-14257)
SAN FRANCISCO ELEV SVCS INC
6517 Sierra Ln, Dublin (94568-2798)
PHONE..................................925 829-5400
Donovan McKeever, *President*
Brian McLemore, *Sales Mgr*
EMP: 50
SALES (est): 2.4MM **Privately Held**
SIC: 3534 Stair elevators, motor powered

(P-14258)
SCHINDLER ELEVATOR CORPORATION
555 Mccormick St, San Leandro (94577-1107)
PHONE..................................510 382-2075
Dennis Devos, *Manager*
Alex Capiato, *General Mgr*
David Stanley, *Manager*
EMP: 30
SALES (corp-wide): 10.3B **Privately Held**
WEB: www.us.schindler.com
SIC: 3534 1796 7699 Elevators & equipment; elevator installation & conversion; elevators: inspection, service & repair
HQ: Schindler Elevator Corporation
　　20 Whippany Rd
　　Morristown NJ 07960
　　973 397-6500

(P-14259)
SPECIALIZED ELEVATOR CORP
14320 Iseli Rd, Santa Fe Springs (90670-5204)
PHONE..................................562 407-1200
Don Webster, *President*
Barry Meacham, *Treasurer*
Karen Morris, *General Mgr*
Robert Baehr, *Admin Sec*
Garret Irelan, *Sales Mgr*
EMP: 60
SQ FT: 6,000
SALES: 11.7MM **Privately Held**
WEB: www.specializedelevator.com
SIC: 3534 Elevators & moving stairways

(P-14260)
TL SHIELD & ASSOCIATES INC (PA)
Also Called: Inclinator of California
1030 Arroyo St, San Fernando (91340-1822)
P.O. Box 6845, Thousand Oaks (91359-6845)
PHONE..................................818 509-8228
Thomas Louis Shield, *President*
Ron Woodward, *Administration*
Sophie Murray, *Manager*
EMP: 35
SQ FT: 2,000
SALES (est): 12.2MM **Privately Held**
WEB: www.tlshield.com
SIC: 3534 1796 Elevators & equipment; elevator installation & conversion

(P-14261)
WINTER & BAIN MANUFACTURING (PA)
1417 Elwood St, Los Angeles (90021-2812)
PHONE..................................213 749-3568
Henry Spencer, *Owner*
Henry W Spencer, *President*
Tom Oliver, *General Mgr*
Victoria Brennan, *Representative*
EMP: 16
SQ FT: 8,000
SALES (est): 2.4MM **Privately Held**
SIC: 3534 Elevators & moving stairways

(P-14262)
WINTER & BAIN MANUFACTURING
1410 Elwood St, Los Angeles (90021-2813)
PHONE..................................213 749-3561
Fax: 213 749-0208
EMP: 11
SQ FT: 9,000
SALES (est): 2.5MM **Privately Held**
SIC: 3534 5084

3535 Conveyors & Eqpt

(P-14263)
AIR TUBE TRANSFER SYSTEMS INC
Also Called: A T T
715 N Cypress St, Orange (92867-6605)
PHONE..................................714 363-0700
Rick Blodgett, *President*
Frankie Green, *Financial Analy*
EMP: 25

SQ FT: 10,000
SALES (est): 5.4MM **Privately Held**
WEB: www.attsystems.com
SIC: 3535 1796 7699 3494 Pneumatic tube conveyor systems; machinery installation; industrial equipment services; valves & pipe fittings

(P-14264)
AMERICAN ULTRAVIOLET WEST INC
Also Called: Lesco
23555 Telo Ave, Torrance (90505-4012)
PHONE..................................310 784-2930
Meredith C Stines, *President*
Michael Barton, *Engineer*
▲ EMP: 21
SQ FT: 22,775
SALES (est): 6.3MM **Privately Held**
WEB: www.lescouv.com
SIC: 3535 5065 Conveyors & conveying equipment; electronic parts

(P-14265)
APEX CONVEYOR CORP
41674 Corning Pl, Murrieta (92562-7023)
P.O. Box 812 (92564-0812)
PHONE..................................951 304-7808
Dave Hill,
Barbara Hill,
EMP: 25
SQ FT: 19,000
SALES (est): 5.5MM **Privately Held**
WEB: www.apexconveyor.com
SIC: 3535 Conveyors & conveying equipment

(P-14266)
APEX CONVEYOR SYSTEMS INC
41674 Corning Pl, Murrieta (92562-7023)
PHONE..................................951 304-7808
Greg King, *President*
Wenda King, *Admin Sec*
EMP: 14 EST: 2015
SQ FT: 15,000
SALES (est): 1.3MM **Privately Held**
SIC: 3535 Belt conveyor systems, general industrial use

(P-14267)
CAL-FAB SYSTEMS INC
16425 Beaver Rd, Adelanto (92301-3905)
PHONE..................................760 246-4454
Michael Burke, *President*
Eugene Xue, *CFO*
EMP: 27
SALES (est): 5.7MM **Privately Held**
WEB: www.westernengsystems.com
SIC: 3535 Conveyors & conveying equipment

(P-14268)
CASE AUTOMATION CORPORATION
208 Jason Ct, Corona (92879-6101)
PHONE..................................951 493-6666
Don Nielsen, *President*
EMP: 12
SQ FT: 15,000
SALES: 1.2MM **Privately Held**
WEB: www.caseautomation.com
SIC: 3535 5084 Conveyors & conveying equipment; industrial machinery & equipment

(P-14269)
CLOUDMINDS TECHNOLOGY INC
4500 Great America Pkwy # 2, Santa Clara (95054-1283)
PHONE..................................650 391-6817
Bill Huang, *CEO*
Robert Zhang, *President*
Karl Frederick Rauscher, *Chairman*
EMP: 10
SALES (est): 895.3K **Privately Held**
SIC: 3535 Robotic conveyors
PA: Beijing Cloudmind Technology Co., Ltd.
　　Room 601-602,4a
　　Block,Baiziwan,Chaoyang District.
　　Beijing
　　105 166-2353

(P-14270)
CONVEYOR MFG & SVC INC
771 Marylind Ave, Claremont (91711-3531)
PHONE..................................909 621-0406
Jesus Dehorta, *President*
Josefina Dehorta, *Treasurer*
EMP: 15
SQ FT: 30,000
SALES (est): 4.5MM **Privately Held**
WEB: www.conveyormfg.com
SIC: 3535 Conveyors & conveying equipment

(P-14271)
D & B SUPPLY CORP
Also Called: Air Link International
1189 N Grove St Ste A, Anaheim (92806-2138)
PHONE..................................714 632-3020
Frank Marchette, *CEO*
Cynthia Marchette, *Admin Sec*
▲ EMP: 13
SQ FT: 10,700
SALES (est): 4.1MM **Privately Held**
WEB: www.airlinkint.com
SIC: 3535 Pneumatic tube conveyor systems

(P-14272)
DAIRY CONVEYOR CORP
15212 Connector Ln, Huntington Beach (92649-1118)
PHONE..................................714 891-0883
Gary Frintenburge, *President*
EMP: 20
SALES (corp-wide): 29.4MM **Privately Held**
SIC: 3535 7699 5084 Conveyors & conveying equipment; industrial machinery & equipment repair; materials handling machinery
PA: Dairy Conveyor Corp.
　　38 Mount Ebo Rd S
　　Brewster NY 10509
　　845 278-7878

(P-14273)
DEAMCO CORPORATION
6520 E Washington Blvd, Commerce (90040-1822)
PHONE..................................323 890-1190
Armen Hovannesian, *President*
Nick Kanian, *Principal*
▲ EMP: 55
SQ FT: 55,000
SALES (est): 17.5MM **Privately Held**
WEB: www.deamco.com
SIC: 3535 Conveyors & conveying equipment

(P-14274)
FLO STOR ENGINEERING INC (PA)
Also Called: Flostor
21371 Cabot Blvd, Hayward (94545-1650)
PHONE..................................510 887-7179
Robert Weeks, *Owner*
Robin Arceneaux, *Admin Asst*
John Andrews, *Project Mgr*
Sam Weeks, *Project Mgr*
Keith Bawa, *Controller*
▼ EMP: 30
SALES (est): 4.9MM **Privately Held**
WEB: www.flostor.com
SIC: 3535 Conveyors & conveying equipment

(P-14275)
HECO PACIFIC MANUFACTURING
1510 Pacific St, Union City (94587-2099)
PHONE..................................510 487-1155
Malik A Alarab, *President*
Malik Alarab, *Executive*
Allan M Alarab, *Admin Sec*
Allan Alarab, *Sales Executive*
▼ EMP: 25
SQ FT: 34,000
SALES (est): 11.2MM **Privately Held**
WEB: www.hecopacific.com
SIC: 3535 3536 3531 Conveyors & conveying equipment; cranes, overhead traveling; construction machinery

(P-14276)
INGALLS CONVEYORS INC
1005 W Olympic Blvd, Montebello
(90640-5121)
PHONE...................................323 837-9900
Toll Free:...888 -
Maged Labib Nakla, *CEO*
Steve Ingalls, *President*
Colleen Ingalls, *Admin Sec*
EMP: 21
SQ FT: 174,000
SALES (est): 4.3MM **Privately Held**
WEB: www.ingallsconveyors.com
SIC: 3535 8711 Conveyors & conveying
equipment; consulting engineer

(P-14277)
INTELLIGRATED SYSTEMS INC
5903 Christie Ave, Emeryville
(94608-1925)
PHONE...................................510 263-2300
Susan Porter, *Manager*
EMP: 264
SALES (corp-wide): 40.5B **Publicly Held**
SIC: 3535 5084 7371 Conveyors & con-
veying equipment; industrial machinery &
equipment; computer software develop-
ment
HQ: Intelligrated Systems, Inc.
7901 Innovation Way
Mason OH 45040
866 936-7300

(P-14278)
INTELLIGRATED SYSTEMS INC
3721 Douglas Blvd Ste 345, Roseville
(95661-4254)
PHONE...................................916 772-6800
Susan Porter, *Manager*
EMP: 264
SALES (corp-wide): 40.5B **Publicly Held**
SIC: 3535 5084 7371 Conveyors & con-
veying equipment; industrial machinery &
equipment; computer software develop-
ment
HQ: Intelligrated Systems, Inc.
7901 Innovation Way
Mason OH 45040
866 936-7300

(P-14279)
NEXT LEVEL WAREHOUSE SOLUTIONS
555 Display Way, Sacramento
(95838-3371)
PHONE...................................916 922-7225
Jim Edmondson, *President*
Tom Weaver, *Sales Staff*
EMP: 10
SQ FT: 20,000
SALES (est): 1.9MM **Privately Held**
WEB: www.nextlevelwhse.com
SIC: 3535 3537 Conveyors & conveying
equipment; platforms, stands, tables, pal-
lets & similar equipment; lift trucks, indus-
trial: fork, platform, straddle, etc.

(P-14280)
OMRON ADEPT TECHNOLOGIES INC (DH)
Also Called: Adept Technology
4550 Norris Canyon Rd # 150, San Ramon
(94583-1369)
PHONE...................................925 245-3400
Rob Cain, *President*
Joachim Melis, *President*
Seth Halio, *CFO*
John Dixson, *General Mgr*
Deron Jackson, *CTO*
▲ **EMP:** 170
SQ FT: 57,000
SALES (est): 54.2MM
SALES (corp-wide): 8B **Privately Held**
WEB: www.adept.com
SIC: 3535 7372 Robotic conveyors;
prepackaged software; operating systems
computer software
HQ: Omron Management Center Of Amer-
ica, Inc.
2895 Greenspoint Pkwy # 100
Hoffman Estates IL 60169
224 520-7650

(P-14281)
PRIDE CONVEYANCE SYSTEMS INC
Also Called: P C S
1781 Shelton Dr, Hollister (95023-9404)
PHONE...................................831 637-1787
Shannon Pride, *President*
Pat Jordon, *Vice Pres*
Ruben Padilla, *Vice Pres*
Bill Stewart, *Vice Pres*
Mike Zgragen, *Vice Pres*
▲ **EMP:** 75
SQ FT: 36,000
SALES (est): 34.8MM **Privately Held**
WEB: www.prideconveyance.com
SIC: 3535 Conveyors & conveying equip-
ment

(P-14282)
RALPHS-PUGH CO INC
3931 Oregon St, Benicia (94510-1101)
PHONE...................................707 745-6222
William G Pugh, *CEO*
Deborah Pugh, *Corp Secy*
Tom Anderson, *Vice Pres*
Derrick Shelton, *Natl Sales Mgr*
Wendy Beltran, *Sales Mgr*
EMP: 65 EST: 1912
SQ FT: 36,000
SALES (est): 21.9MM **Privately Held**
WEB: www.ralphs-pugh.com
SIC: 3535 Conveyors & conveying equip-
ment

(P-14283)
RCI RACK CNVYOR INSTLLTION INC
346 S I St Ste 9, San Bernardino
(92410-2443)
PHONE...................................909 381-4818
Walt Thompson, *President*
Sheri Thompson, *CFO*
EMP: 23
SQ FT: 10,000
SALES (est): 2MM **Privately Held**
SIC: 3535 1796 Belt conveyor systems,
general industrial use; millwright

(P-14284)
SARDEE CORPORATION CALIFORNIA
2731 E Myrtle St, Stockton (95205-4793)
PHONE...................................209 466-1526
Steve Sarovich, *President*
Dolores Sarovich, *Corp Secy*
Alan Bassett, *Vice Pres*
Alex Graham, *Vice Pres*
EMP: 40
SQ FT: 20,000
SALES (est): 8.1MM **Privately Held**
SIC: 3535 Conveyors & conveying equip-
ment

(P-14285)
SCREW CONVEYOR PACIFIC CORP
7807 W Doe Ave, Visalia (93291-9275)
PHONE...................................559 651-2131
Randy Smith, *Principal*
EMP: 20
SALES (corp-wide): 20.5MM **Privately Held**
WEB: www.screwconveyor.com
SIC: 3535 Conveyors & conveying equip-
ment
PA: Screw Conveyor Pacific Corp
700 Hoffman St
Hammond IN 46327
219 931-1450

(P-14286)
SDI INDUSTRIES INC (PA)
13000 Pierce St, Pacoima (91331-2528)
PHONE...................................818 890-6002
Krish Nathan, *CEO*
Mark Conrad, *CFO*
Sheva Shalmani, *Engineer*
Parviz Jarrahzadeh, *Accounting Mgr*
Parviz Jarrah Zadeh, *Accounting Mgr*
▲ **EMP:** 150
SQ FT: 80,000

SALES (est): 40.6MM **Privately Held**
WEB: www.sdiindustries.com
SIC: 3535 3537 8748 8711 Conveyors &
conveying equipment; industrial trucks &
tractors; business consulting; engineering
services; machinery installation

(P-14287)
SMART MACHINES INC
46702 Bayside Pkwy, Fremont
(94538-6582)
PHONE...................................510 661-5000
K Charles Janac, *President*
Sharon Andres, *Controller*
EMP: 29
SQ FT: 15,258
SALES (est): 4.7MM
SALES (corp-wide): 692.8MM **Publicly Held**
SIC: 3535 Robotic conveyors
PA: Brooks Automation, Inc.
15 Elizabeth Dr
Chelmsford MA 01824
978 262-2400

(P-14288)
SMP ROBOTICS SYSTEMS CORP
851 Burlway Rd Ste 216, Burlingame
(94010-1709)
PHONE...................................415 572-2316
Leo Ryzhenko, *CEO*
EMP: 55 EST: 2014
SQ FT: 350
SALES (est): 4.4MM **Privately Held**
SIC: 3535 Robotic conveyors

(P-14289)
STOCKTON TRI-INDUSTRIES INC
2141 E Anderson St, Stockton
(95205-7010)
P.O. Box 6097 (95206-0097)
PHONE...................................209 948-9701
Fred Wells, *President*
Harrison Freddie Wells, *CEO*
Ray Smith, *Corp Secy*
Jeff Yon, *Accounts Mgr*
EMP: 65
SQ FT: 32,000
SALES (est): 22.3MM **Privately Held**
WEB: www.stocktontri.com
SIC: 3535 3599 Conveyors & conveying
equipment; machine shop; jobbing & re-
pair

(P-14290)
TERRA NOVA TECHNOLOGIES INC
10770 Rockville St Ste A, Santee
(92071-8505)
PHONE...................................619 596-7400
Ronald R Kelly, *President*
Grant Ling, *Treasurer*
George M Bernard, *Vice Pres*
Judy Zeigler, *Vice Pres*
Vivienne Schiffer, *Admin Sec*
◆ **EMP:** 80
SQ FT: 8,366
SALES (est): 27.9MM
SALES (corp-wide): 6.7B **Privately Held**
WEB: www.tntinc.com
SIC: 3535 8742 Conveyors & conveying
equipment; management consulting serv-
ices; industrial & labor consulting services
PA: Amec Foster Wheeler Limited
4th Floor Old Change House
London EC4V
207 429-7500

(P-14291)
TIG/M LLC
9160 Jordan Ave, Chatsworth
(91311-5707)
PHONE...................................818 709-8500
Alvaro Villa, *CEO*
Brad Read, *President*
David Hall, *CFO*
Polly Chellew, *Project Mgr*
Bradley Read,
EMP: 30
SQ FT: 2,000
SALES: 1.5MM **Privately Held**
SIC: 3535 Trolley conveyors

(P-14292)
WHEELER & REEDER INC
3334 Montrose Ave, La Crescenta
(91214-3341)
PHONE...................................323 268-4163
Chandler Young, *President*
EMP: 10 EST: 1943
SQ FT: 9,000
SALES (est): 1.1MM **Privately Held**
SIC: 3535 3444 5084 Conveyors & con-
veying equipment; sheet metalwork; con-
veyor systems

3536 Hoists, Cranes & Monorails

(P-14293)
AGE LOGISTICS CORPORATION
426 E Duarte Rd, Monrovia (91016-4603)
PHONE...................................626 243-5253
Yehuda Fishman, *CEO*
Roger N McMullin, *CEO*
James Sameth, *COO*
Jim Sameth, *COO*
Daniel Fishman, *Principal*
EMP: 10
SQ FT: 101,000
SALES (est): 2.1MM **Privately Held**
WEB: www.agelogistics.com
SIC: 3536 Hoists

(P-14294)
CARPENTER GROUP (PA)
Also Called: Cable-Cisco
222 Napoleon St, San Francisco
(94124-1017)
PHONE...................................415 285-1954
Bernard L Martin, *CEO*
Frank Joost, *Vice Pres*
Patty Oliverio, *Admin Sec*
Ralph Key, *Info Tech Dir*
▲ **EMP:** 33
SQ FT: 26,000
SALES (est): 27.8MM **Privately Held**
WEB: www.carpenterrigging.com
SIC: 3536 2394 5085 3496 Hoists; liners
& covers, fabric: made from purchased
materials; industrial supplies; cable, unin-
sulated wire: made from purchased wire

(P-14295)
CRANEVEYOR CORP (PA)
1524 Potrero Ave, El Monte (91733-3017)
P.O. Box 3727 (91733-0727)
PHONE...................................626 442-1524
Frank Gaetano Trimboli, *CEO*
Greg Bischoff, *President*
Thomas Saunders, *CFO*
Hector Valiente, *Treasurer*
Tim Chavez, *Vice Pres*
▲ **EMP:** 90
SQ FT: 47,320
SALES: 33.2MM **Privately Held**
SIC: 3536 3446 Cranes, overhead travel-
ing; monorail systems; railings, bannis-
ters, guards, etc.: made from metal pipe

(P-14296)
DEMAG CRANES & COMPONENTS CORP
Also Called: Material Handling Division
13290 Sabre Blvd, Victorville (92394-7943)
PHONE...................................909 880-8800
Michael Perera, *Manager*
EMP: 22
SALES (corp-wide): 3.7B **Privately Held**
WEB: www.demag-us.com
SIC: 3536 7389 5999 5084 Hoists;
cranes & monorail systems; crane & aer-
ial lift service; engine & motor equipment
& supplies; hoists; construction machin-
ery; installing building equipment
HQ: Demag Cranes & Components Corp.
6675 Parkland Blvd # 200
Solon OH 44139
440 248-2400

(P-14297)
HARRINGTON HOISTS INC
2341 Pomona Rincon Rd # 103, Corona
(92880-6937)
PHONE...................................717 665-2000
Bill Erkenbrak, *Branch Mgr*
EMP: 10

SALES (corp-wide): 449.9MM **Privately Held**
WEB: www.harringtonhoists.com
SIC: 3536 Hoists, cranes & monorails
HQ: Harrington Hoists, Inc.
    401 W End Ave
    Manheim PA 17545

(P-14298)
HYDROHOIST MARINE GROUP INC
1501 Discovery Bay Blvd, Discovery Bay (94505-9340)
PHONE.............................925 513-0507
Ron Martin, *Director*
EMP: 23
SALES (corp-wide): 29.3MM **Privately Held**
SIC: 3536 Boat lifts
PA: Hydrohoist Marine Group, Inc.
    915 W Blue Starr Dr
    Claremore OK 74017
    918 341-6811

(P-14299)
KONECRANES INC
2900 E Belle Ter Bldg A, Bakersfield (93307-6925)
PHONE.............................661 397-9700
EMP: 26
SALES (corp-wide): 3.7B **Privately Held**
SIC: 3536 Hoists, cranes & monorails
HQ: Konecranes, Inc.
    4401 Gateway Blvd
    Springfield OH 45502

(P-14300)
KONECRANES INC
Also Called: Crane Pro Services
5637 Blaribera St, Livermore (94550)
PHONE.............................925 273-0140
Christie Elder, *Manager*
EMP: 14
SALES (corp-wide): 3.7B **Privately Held**
SIC: 3536 Cranes, industrial plant
HQ: Konecranes, Inc.
    4401 Gateway Blvd
    Springfield OH 45502

(P-14301)
MOBILE EQUIPMENT COMPANY
Also Called: Mobile Equipment Appraisers
3610 Gilmore Ave, Bakersfield (93308-6208)
PHONE.............................661 327-8476
Evelyn Stanfill, *President*
Felecia Stanfill, *Corp Secy*
Paul J Faulconer, *Vice Pres*
Gary Stanfill, *General Mgr*
EMP: 20
SQ FT: 18,580
SALES (est): 4.6MM **Privately Held**
WEB: www.mobile-equipment.com
SIC: 3536 8748 3559 Cranes, overhead traveling; safety training service; automotive related machinery

(P-14302)
SHEEDY DRAYAGE CO
Also Called: Sheedy Hoist
34301 7th St, Union City (94587-3653)
PHONE.............................510 441-7300
James Butler, *Branch Mgr*
EMP: 10
SALES (corp-wide): 25MM **Privately Held**
WEB: www.sheedycrane.com
SIC: 3536 7389 5211 Hoists; crane & aerial lift service; lumber & other building materials
PA: Sheedy Drayage Co.
    1215 Michigan St
    San Francisco CA 94107
    415 648-7171

(P-14303)
TRADEMARK HOIST INC
Also Called: Trademark Hoist & Crane
1369 Ridgeway St, Pomona (91768-2701)
PHONE.............................909 455-0801
Mike Mendoza, *President*
Frank Carletello, *Vice Pres*
John Carletello, *Admin Sec*

Andrea Mercado, *Technology*
Isabel Mirabal, *Manager*
EMP: 20
SQ FT: 4,400
SALES (est): 6.2MM **Privately Held**
WEB: www.trademark-hoist.com
SIC: 3536 Hoists, cranes & monorails

(P-14304)
WESTMONT INDUSTRIES (PA)
10805 Painter Ave Uppr, Santa Fe Springs (90670-4541)
PHONE.............................562 944-6137
Diane Henderson, *President*
David Chetwood, *CFO*
Teodik Mirzaie, *General Mgr*
Angela Morey, *Project Engr*
Danny Gamez, *Sales Staff*
▼ EMP: 60
SALES (est): 23.6MM **Privately Held**
WEB: www.westmont.com
SIC: 3536 3533 Cranes, industrial plant; oil & gas field machinery

---

3537 Indl Trucks, Tractors, Trailers & Stackers

(P-14305)
ABOVE ALL CO FOREARM FORKLIFT
Also Called: A.A.C. Forearm Forklift
14832 Arrow Hwy, Baldwin Park (91706-1823)
PHONE.............................626 962-2990
Mark Lopreiato, *President*
David Correa, *Opers Mgr*
EMP: 30
SQ FT: 15,000
SALES: 4MM **Privately Held**
SIC: 3537 Lift trucks, industrial: fork, platform, straddle, etc.

(P-14306)
ACTIVE ID LLC
845 Embedded Way, San Jose (95138-1030)
PHONE.............................408 782-3900
George Khalil,
EMP: 10
SALES (est): 411.2K **Privately Held**
SIC: 3537 Platforms, cargo

(P-14307)
ANCRA INTERNATIONAL LLC (HQ)
875 W 8th St, Azusa (91702-2247)
PHONE.............................626 765-4800
Steve Frediani, *CEO*
Nelson Fong, *Vice Pres*
Jessie Pan, *Controller*
▲ EMP: 130
SALES (est): 60MM **Privately Held**
WEB: www.ancra-llc.com
SIC: 3537 Lift trucks, industrial: fork, platform, straddle, etc.; loading docks: portable, adjustable & hydraulic

(P-14308)
ANSONS TRANSPORTATION INC
438 E Shaw Ave Ste 434, Fresno (93710-7602)
PHONE.............................559 892-1867
Kimberly Rodriguez, *President*
EMP: 25
SALES: 2.6MM **Privately Held**
SIC: 3537 Trucks, tractors, loaders, carriers & similar equipment

(P-14309)
ANTHONY WELDED PRODUCTS INC (PA)
1447 S Lexington St, Delano (93215-9700)
P.O. Box 299, Simi Valley (93062-0299)
PHONE.............................661 721-7211
Frank S Salvucci Sr, *Chairman*
Elsie Salvucci, *President*
Fred Martinez, *Sales Executive*
EMP: 20
SQ FT: 25,000

SALES (est): 9.2MM **Privately Held**
WEB: www.anthonycarts.com
SIC: 3537 3444 3443 Dollies (hand or power trucks), industrial except mining; sheet metalwork; fabricated plate work (boiler shop)

(P-14310)
ARBON EQUIPMENT CORPORATION
Also Called: Right Height
22607 Old Canal Rd, Yorba Linda (92887-4601)
PHONE.............................414 355-2600
Jeff King, *Manager*
EMP: 10
SALES (corp-wide): 691.8MM **Privately Held**
WEB: www.arbonequipment.com
SIC: 3537 Loading docks: portable, adjustable & hydraulic
HQ: Arbon Equipment Corporation
    8900 N Arbon Dr
    Milwaukee WI 53223
    414 355-2600

(P-14311)
BEST INDUSTRIAL SUPPLY
9711 Rush St, South El Monte (91733-1730)
PHONE.............................626 279-5090
James Nickleson, *Partner*
Mike Burgi, *Partner*
EMP: 12
SALES (est): 2.5MM **Privately Held**
WEB: www.bestindustrialsupply.com
SIC: 3537 Forklift trucks

(P-14312)
BISHAMON INDUSTRIES CORP
5651 E Francis St, Ontario (91761-3601)
PHONE.............................909 390-0055
Wataru Sugiura, *President*
Robert Clark, *Vice Pres*
Robert Stone, *Vice Pres*
Steve Oconnell, *Purchasing*
Carl Campbell, *Opers Staff*
▲ EMP: 45 EST: 1986
SQ FT: 77,000
SALES: 10MM **Privately Held**
WEB: www.bishamon.com
SIC: 3537 Lift trucks, industrial: fork, platform, straddle, etc.

(P-14313)
CIMC REEFER TRAILER INC
22101 Alessandro Blvd, Moreno Valley (92553-8215)
PHONE.............................951 218-1414
▲ EMP: 13
SALES (est): 4MM **Privately Held**
SIC: 3537 Truck trailers, used in plants, docks, terminals, etc.

(P-14314)
CORONADO EQUIPMENT SALES
2275 La Crosse Ave # 210, Colton (92324-4464)
PHONE.............................877 830-7447
David B Coronado, *President*
Donna Coronado, *Vice Pres*
EMP: 11
SALES (est): 2.4MM **Privately Held**
SIC: 3537 3429 Forklift trucks; clamps, metal

(P-14315)
CRANEWORKS SOUTHWEST INC
1312 E Barham Dr, San Marcos (92078-4503)
PHONE.............................760 735-9793
Marise Williams, *Office Mgr*
EMP: 20
SALES (est): 4.9MM **Privately Held**
SIC: 3537 7353 Cranes, industrial truck; cranes & aerial lift equipment, rental or leasing

(P-14316)
CROWN EQUIPMENT CORPORATION
1355 E Fntana Ave Ste 102, Fresno (93725)
P.O. Box 641173, Cincinnati OH (45264-1173)
PHONE.............................559 585-8000
Keith Heinke, *General Mgr*
EMP: 24
SALES (corp-wide): 3.1B **Privately Held**
SIC: 3537 Forklift trucks
PA: Crown Equipment Corporation
    44 S Washington St
    New Bremen OH 45869
    419 629-2311

(P-14317)
CROWN EQUIPMENT CORPORATION
Also Called: Crown Lift Trucks
1300 Palomares St, La Verne (91750-5232)
PHONE.............................626 968-0556
Kevin McCarthy, *Manager*
EMP: 58
SQ FT: 28,000
SALES (corp-wide): 3.1B **Privately Held**
SIC: 3537 Lift trucks, industrial: fork, platform, straddle, etc.
PA: Crown Equipment Corporation
    44 S Washington St
    New Bremen OH 45869
    419 629-2311

(P-14318)
CROWN EQUIPMENT CORPORATION
Also Called: Crown Lift Trucks
4250 Greystone Dr, Ontario (91761-3104)
PHONE.............................909 923-8357
Mike Lammers, *Manager*
EMP: 139
SALES (corp-wide): 3.1B **Privately Held**
SIC: 3537 Lift trucks, industrial: fork, platform, straddle, etc.
PA: Crown Equipment Corporation
    44 S Washington St
    New Bremen OH 45869
    419 629-2311

(P-14319)
CROWN EQUIPMENT CORPORATION
Also Called: Crown Lift Trucks
1400 Crocker Ave, Hayward (94544-7031)
PHONE.............................510 471-7272
Scott Walter, *Manager*
EMP: 45
SALES (corp-wide): 3.1B **Privately Held**
SIC: 3537 Lift trucks, industrial: fork, platform, straddle, etc.
PA: Crown Equipment Corporation
    44 S Washington St
    New Bremen OH 45869
    419 629-2311

(P-14320)
CROWN EQUIPMENT CORPORATION
Also Called: Crown Lift Trucks
1420 Enterprise Blvd, West Sacramento (95691-3485)
PHONE.............................916 373-8980
Ron Bensman, *Manager*
EMP: 44
SALES (corp-wide): 3.1B **Privately Held**
SIC: 3537 Lift trucks, industrial: fork, platform, straddle, etc.
PA: Crown Equipment Corporation
    44 S Washington St
    New Bremen OH 45869
    419 629-2311

(P-14321)
CROWN EQUIPMENT CORPORATION
Also Called: Crown Lift Trucks
4061 Via Oro Ave, Long Beach (90810-1458)
PHONE.............................310 952-6600
Tom Labrador, *Branch Mgr*
EMP: 64

▲ = Import ▼ =Export
◆ =Import/Export

SALES (corp-wide): 3.1B **Privately Held**
SIC: **3537** Lift trucks, industrial: fork, platform, straddle, etc.
PA: Crown Equipment Corporation
44 S Washington St
New Bremen OH 45869
419 629-2311

(P-14322)
DARRELL ZBROWSKI
Also Called: Dz Tranz Group
8465 Vassar Ave, Canoga Park
(91304-2508)
PHONE................................818 324-5961
Darrell Zbrowski, *Owner*
EMP: 90 EST: 2013
SALES: 15.3MM **Privately Held**
SIC: **3537** Trucks: freight, baggage, etc.:
industrial, except mining

(P-14323)
**DAYTON SUPERIOR
CORPORATION**
Also Called: American Highway Technology
5300 Claus Rd Ste 7, Modesto
(95357-1665)
PHONE................................209 869-1201
Wesley Tilton, *Manager*
EMP: 25 **Publicly Held**
WEB: www.daytonsuperior.com
SIC: **3537** Loading docks: portable, ad-
justable & hydraulic
HQ: Dayton Superior Corporation
1125 Byers Rd
Miamisburg OH 45342
937 866-0711

(P-14324)
FREMONT PACKAGE EXPRESS
734 Still Breeze Way, Sacramento
(95831-5544)
PHONE................................916 541-1812
Terrence Wong, *Owner*
EMP: 15
SALES: 800K **Privately Held**
SIC: **3537** Trucks: freight, baggage, etc.:
industrial, except mining

(P-14325)
**GOLDEN GATE FREIGHTLINER
INC**
Also Called: Golden Gate Truck Center
2727 E Central Ave, Fresno (93725-2425)
P.O. Box 12346 (93777-2346)
PHONE................................559 486-4310
EMP: 150
SALES (est): 13.2MM
SALES (corp-wide): 161.5MM **Privately
Held**
WEB: www.goldengatetruckcenter.com
SIC: **3537** 5511 Trucks: freight, baggage,
etc.: industrial, except mining; new &
used car dealers
HQ: Golden Gate Freightliner, Inc.
8200 Baldwin St
Oakland CA 94621
559 486-4310

(P-14326)
**HI DESERT FORKLIFT
SERVICES**
15603 Tenth St, Victorville (92395-3342)
PHONE................................760 241-4575
Alejandro Franco, *President*
Alex Franco, *President*
EMP: 10
SALES (est): 1.2MM **Privately Held**
SIC: **3537** Forklift trucks

(P-14327)
HYDRAULIC SHOP INC
2753 S Vista Ave, Bloomington
(92316-3269)
PHONE................................909 875-9336
Christopher O Kirk, *President*
EMP: 20
SQ FT: 4,500
SALES (est): 4.8MM **Privately Held**
SIC: **3537** Industrial trucks & tractors

(P-14328)
**INDUSTRIAL DESIGN
PRODUCTS**
2700 Pomona Blvd, Pomona (91768-3222)
P.O. Box 7846, Norco (92860-8095)
PHONE................................909 468-0693
Richard Fleischhacker Jr, *President*
Jose Pizarro, *Exec VP*
EMP: 12
SQ FT: 14,000
SALES (est): 2.1MM **Privately Held**
WEB: www.idp-inc.com
SIC: **3537** 5084 2542 Platforms, stands,
tables, pallets & similar equipment; mate-
rials handling machinery; pallet racks: ex-
cept wood

(P-14329)
J&S GOODWIN INC (HQ)
5753 E Sta Ana Cyn G355, Anaheim
(92807-3230)
PHONE................................714 956-4040
Arthur J Goodwin, *CEO*
Scott Currie, *COO*
Mark McGregor, *CFO*
Adam Navarro, *General Mgr*
Sharon Goodwin, *Admin Sec*
◆ EMP: 73
SQ FT: 3,000
SALES (est): 45.1MM
SALES (corp-wide): 5.4B **Publicly Held**
SIC: **3537** 5088 5084 Trucks, tractors,
loaders, carriers & similar equipment; golf
carts; materials handling machinery
PA: Polaris Industries Inc.
2100 Highway 55
Medina MN 55340
763 542-0500

(P-14330)
JE THOMSON & COMPANY LLC
Also Called: Carousel USA
6370 N Irwindale Ave, Irwindale
(91702-3210)
PHONE................................626 334-7190
John Thomson,
▲ EMP: 15
SQ FT: 20,000
SALES (est): 5.3MM **Privately Held**
SIC: **3537** 3535 Tables, lift: hydraulic; trol-
ley conveyors; bulk handling conveyor
systems; robotic conveyors

(P-14331)
**KARRIOR ELECTRIC VEHICLES
INC**
Also Called: Karrior Indus Elc Vehicles
570 W 184th St, Gardena (90248-4202)
PHONE................................310 515-7600
George Kettel, *President*
EMP: 11
SQ FT: 12,000
SALES (est): 1.2MM **Privately Held**
SIC: **3537** 7629 Industrial trucks & trac-
tors; electrical equipment repair services

(P-14332)
KEY MATERIAL HANDLING INC
4790 Alamo St, Simi Valley (93063-1837)
PHONE................................805 520-6007
Richard Galbraith, *President*
Kimberly Galbraith, *Treasurer*
John Galbraith, *Vice Pres*
▲ EMP: 12
SQ FT: 2,000
SALES (est): 1.6MM **Privately Held**
WEB: www.keymaterial.com
SIC: **3537** 4953 5084 5021 Platforms,
stands, tables, pallets & similar equip-
ment; trucks, tractors, loaders, carriers &
similar equipment; hazardous waste col-
lection & disposal; conveyor systems;
shelving

(P-14333)
LATOURETTE LIFT SERVICES
4368 Bandini Blvd, Vernon (90058-4323)
P.O. Box 58163, Los Angeles (90058-0163)
PHONE................................323 262-9111
Edward Latourette, *Owner*
Scott Henningsen, *General Mgr*
EMP: 15
SALES (est): 1.4MM **Privately Held**
SIC: **3537** Lift trucks, industrial: fork, plat-
form, straddle, etc.

(P-14334)
MACS LIFT GATE INC
2715 Seaboard Ln, Long Beach
(90805-3751)
PHONE................................562 634-5962
Richard Mac Donald, *General Mgr*
EMP: 19
SALES (corp-wide): 3.1MM **Privately
Held**
SIC: **3537** 5531 3999 Lift trucks, indus-
trial: fork, platform, straddle, etc.; truck
equipment & parts; wheelchair lifts
PA: Mac's Lift Gate, Inc.
2801 E South St
Long Beach CA 90805
562 634-5962

(P-14335)
MARDIAN EQUIPMENT CO INC
10168 Channel Rd, Lakeside (92040-1704)
PHONE................................619 938-8071
George Wheeler, *Manager*
EMP: 25
SALES (corp-wide): 10MM **Privately
Held**
SIC: **3537** 7353 Cranes, industrial truck;
heavy construction equipment rental
PA: Mardian Equipment Co., Inc.
221 S 35th Ave
Phoenix AZ 85009
602 272-2671

(P-14336)
**MATERIAL HANDLING
SOLUTIONS**
12359 Meritage Ct, Rancho Cucamonga
(91739-8826)
PHONE................................909 908-9663
Nevins Howard, *Owner*
EMP: 11
SALES (est): 2.2MM **Privately Held**
SIC: **3537** Forklift trucks

(P-14337)
**MECHANIZED ENGINEERING
SYSTEMS**
Also Called: Mensi
737 E 223rd St, Carson (90745-4111)
P.O. Box 17278, Anaheim (92817-7278)
PHONE................................310 830-9763
Ernest J Stramotas, *President*
EMP: 10
SQ FT: 8,000
SALES: 2MM **Privately Held**
WEB: www.mensilift.com
SIC: **3537** 5049 Containers (metal), air
cargo; engineers' equipment & supplies

(P-14338)
NOR CAL TRUCK SALES & MFG
Also Called: Nor Car Truck Sales
200 Industrial Way, Benicia (94510-1191)
PHONE................................925 787-9735
David Jenkins, *Owner*
EMP: 15
SALES: 3.5MM **Privately Held**
SIC: **3537** 5511 Trucks, tractors, loaders,
carriers & similar equipment; trucks, trac-
tors & trailers: new & used

(P-14339)
OFF DOCK USA INC
22700 S Alameda St, Carson (90810-1909)
PHONE................................310 522-4400
Michael R Sullivan, *President*
John Burke, *Vice Pres*
EMP: 16
SALES (est): 4.2MM **Privately Held**
SIC: **3537** Containers (metal), air cargo

(P-14340)
PAPE MATERIAL HANDLING INC
2600 Peck Rd, City of Industry
(90601-1620)
P.O. Box 60007 (91716-0007)
PHONE................................562 692-9311
Steve Smith, *Manager*
Jordan Pape, *President*
Chris Wetle, *President*
William Mc Kinley, *Div Sub Head*
EMP: 100

SALES (corp-wide): 587.9MM **Privately
Held**
WEB: www.johnson-machinery.com
SIC: **3537** 5084 Forklift trucks; industrial
machinery & equipment
HQ: Pape' Material Handling, Inc.
355 Goodpasture Island Rd
Eugene OR 97401
541 683-5073

(P-14341)
POWER PT INC
Also Called: AAA Pallet
23120 Oleander Ave, Perris (92570-5662)
PHONE................................951 490-4149
Tyson Paulis, *CEO*
EMP: 20
SALES (est): 951.5K **Privately Held**
SIC: **3537** Platforms, stands, tables, pallets
& similar equipment

(P-14342)
PRECISION FORKLIFT
15389 Avenue 288, Visalia (93292-9670)
PHONE................................559 805-5487
Beth Flynt, *Principal*
EMP: 11
SALES (est): 1.5MM **Privately Held**
SIC: **3537** Forklift trucks

(P-14343)
PRODUCTBOARD INC
392 Staten Ave, Oakland (94610-3430)
PHONE................................844 472-6273
Noah Barr, *Vice Pres*
EMP: 10
SALES (est): 411.2K **Privately Held**
SIC: **3537** Platforms, cargo

(P-14344)
**QUALITY LIFT AND EQUIPMENT
INC**
10845 Norwalk Blvd, Santa Fe Springs
(90670-3825)
P.O. Box 2581 (90670-0581)
PHONE................................562 903-2131
John Andrews, *CEO*
◆ EMP: 10
SQ FT: 3,000
SALES: 1.2MM **Privately Held**
WEB: www.2ndshiftlift.com
SIC: **3537** 7699 Forklift trucks; industrial
truck repair

(P-14345)
REBAS INC
Also Called: Toyota-Lift of Los Angeles
12907 Imperial Hwy, Santa Fe Springs
(90670-4715)
PHONE................................562 941-4155
Shankar Basu, *Ch of Bd*
Simon Walker, *COO*
Andres Zamora, *Administration*
Bo Hansson Holmquist, *Technology*
Chris Myers, *VP Finance*
▲ EMP: 104
SQ FT: 103,000
SALES (est): 78.2MM **Privately Held**
WEB: www.toyota-lift.com
SIC: **3537** Forklift trucks

(P-14346)
SHRED-TECH USA LLC
1100 S Grove Ave, Ontario (91761-4572)
PHONE................................909 923-2783
Robert L Dibenedetto,
EMP: 50
SQ FT: 64,000
SALES (est): 5.1MM **Privately Held**
SIC: **3537** Industrial trucks & tractors

(P-14347)
**SOUTHERN CALIFORNIA MTL
HDLG**
168 E Freedom Ave, Anaheim
(92801-1004)
PHONE................................714 773-9630
Ron Walter, *Manager*
EMP: 35
SALES (corp-wide): 38.5B **Privately Held**
WEB: www.scmh.com
SIC: **3537** Forklift trucks

HQ: Southern California Material Handling
Inc
12393 Slauson Ave
Whittier CA 90606
562 949-1006

(P-14348)
STROPPINI ENTERPRISES
2546 Mercantile Dr Ste A, Rancho Cordova
(95742-8203)
PHONE..................................916 635-8181
Gilbert Stroppini, *Owner*
▲ **EMP:** 17
SQ FT: 12,000
SALES (est): 3.1MM **Privately Held**
SIC: 3537 Platforms, stands, tables, pallets
& similar equipment; tables, lift: hydraulic

(P-14349)
SUPERIOR TRAILER WORKS
13700 Slover Ave, Fontana (92337-7067)
PHONE..................................909 350-0185
Jack N Pocock, *CEO*
Jay Pocock, *Corp Secy*
Mike Espinosa, *Manager*
▲ **EMP:** 50
SQ FT: 4,000
SALES (est): 17.2MM **Privately Held**
WEB: www.superiortrailerworks.com
SIC: 3537 7539 Industrial trucks & trac-
tors; trailer repair

(P-14350)
TAYLOR-DUNN
MANUFACTURING CO (DH)
2114 W Ball Rd, Anaheim (92804-5498)
PHONE..................................714 956-4040
Keith Simon, *CEO*
Sandy Carlson, *Human Res Mgr*
Bill Manning, *Sales Mgr*
Brian Maclean, *Sales Staff*
Billy Hensley, *Manager*
◆ **EMP:** 100
SQ FT: 145,000
SALES (est): 49.8MM
SALES (corp-wide): 5.4B **Publicly Held**
WEB: www.taylor-dunn.com
SIC: 3537 Trucks, tractors, loaders, carri-
ers & similar equipment
HQ: Polaris Sales Inc.
2100 Highway 55
Hamel MN 55340
763 542-0500

(P-14351)
WALTCO LIFT CORP
227 E Compton Blvd, Gardena
(90248-1909)
PHONE..................................323 321-4131
Marshall Walker, *Branch Mgr*
EMP: 69
SALES (corp-wide): 3.8B **Privately Held**
SIC: 3537 3714 Industrial trucks & trac-
tors; motor vehicle parts & accessories
HQ: Waltco Lift Corp.
285 Northeast Ave
Tallmadge OH 44278
330 633-9191

(P-14352)
WIGGINS LIFT CO INC
2571 Cortez St, Oxnard (93036-1642)
P.O. Box 5187 (93031-5187)
PHONE..................................805 485-7821
Hattie Wiggins, *Ch of Bd*
Michael M Wiggins, *President*
Michelle Mc Dowell, *Treasurer*
Paul Hurbace, *Vice Pres*
Jack Mc Dowell, *Vice Pres*
◆ **EMP:** 50
SQ FT: 55,000
SALES (est): 31.2MM **Privately Held**
SIC: 3537 Forklift trucks

(P-14353)
WIN-HOLT EQUIPMENT CORP
2717 N Towne Ave, Pomona (91767-2263)
PHONE..................................909 625-2624
Michael O'Brien, *Manager*
EMP: 15
SQ FT: 36,000
SALES (corp-wide): 83.1MM **Privately
Held**
WEB: www.winholt.com
SIC: 3537 Industrial trucks & tractors

PA: Win-Holt Equipment Corp.
20 Crossways Park Dr N # 205
Woodbury NY 11797
516 222-0335

3541 Machine Tools: Cutting

(P-14354)
ACCEL MANUFACTURING INC
1709 Grant St, Santa Clara (95050-3939)
PHONE..................................408 727-5883
Loc Pham, *President*
EMP: 15
SALES (est): 3.6MM **Privately Held**
SIC: 3541 Machine tool replacement & re-
pair parts, metal cutting types

(P-14355)
ACS CO LTD
6341 San Ignacio Ave, San Jose
(95119-1202)
PHONE..................................408 981-7162
Jae Hoon Jung, *Managing Dir*
EMP: 125
SALES (est): 10MM **Privately Held**
SIC: 3541 Machine tools, metal cutting
type

(P-14356)
AEROSPACE AND COML
TOOLING INC
Also Called: A C T
1866 S Lake Pl, Ontario (91761-5788)
PHONE..................................909 930-5780
Oscar Borello, *President*
EMP: 16
SQ FT: 20,000
SALES (est): 3.5MM **Privately Held**
SIC: 3541 Machine tools, metal cutting
type

(P-14357)
AEROSPACE TOOL GRINDING
14020 Shoemaker Ave, Norwalk
(90650-4536)
P.O. Box 1536 (90651-1536)
PHONE..................................562 802-3339
Alonzo Burgos, *President*
Azzie Burgos, *Vice Pres*
EMP: 15
SALES (est): 1.1MM **Privately Held**
SIC: 3541 5251 Machine tools, metal cut-
ting type; tools

(P-14358)
AKIRA SEIKI U S A INC
255 Capitol St, Livermore (94551-5210)
PHONE..................................925 443-1200
Alan Kludjian, *President*
▲ **EMP:** 17
SALES (est): 2.6MM **Privately Held**
WEB: www.akira-seiki.com
SIC: 3541 Machine tools, metal cutting
type

(P-14359)
ALL STAR PRECISION
8739 Lion St, Rancho Cucamonga
(91730-4428)
PHONE..................................909 944-8373
Scott Jackson, *Owner*
Ron Jackson, *Partner*
EMP: 23
SALES (est): 332.7K **Privately Held**
WEB: www.allstarprecision.com
SIC: 3541 Machine tools, metal cutting
type

(P-14360)
ALTAMONT MANUFACTURING
INC
241 Rickenbacker Cir, Livermore
(94551-7216)
PHONE..................................925 371-5401
Robert Stivers, *President*
Richard Stivers, *Vice Pres*
EMP: 18
SALES: 3MM **Privately Held**
SIC: 3541 Machine tools, metal cutting
type

(P-14361)
ALVARADO MICRO PRECISION
INC
Also Called: Boring Thrading Bars Unlimited
2389 La Mirada Dr Ste 9, Vista
(92081-7863)
PHONE..................................760 598-0186
Jorge E Alvarado, *President*
EMP: 10 EST: 1997
SQ FT: 2,400
SALES (est): 1.6MM **Privately Held**
WEB: www.alvaradomicro.com
SIC: 3541 Screw & thread machines

(P-14362)
BERNHARDT & BERNHARDT
INC
Also Called: Protool Co
14771 Myford Rd Ste D, Tustin
(92780-7206)
PHONE..................................714 544-0708
Norbert Bernhardt, *President*
Mark Taylor, *QC Mgr*
Jeffrey Wichert, *Facilities Mgr*
EMP: 15 EST: 1974
SQ FT: 4,600
SALES: 1MM **Privately Held**
SIC: 3541 Numerically controlled metal
cutting machine tools

(P-14363)
BEST CARBIDE CUTTING
TOOLS INC
1401 W Walnut St, Rancho Dominguez
(90220-5012)
PHONE..................................310 464-8050
Salvador Nunez, *Chairman*
Mark Nunez, *President*
Robert Nunez, *Vice Pres*
Salvador Nunez Jr, *Principal*
Carmen Nunez, *Admin Sec*
▲ **EMP:** 85
SQ FT: 46,000
SALES (est): 18.9MM **Privately Held**
WEB: www.bestcarbide.com
SIC: 3541 Machine tools, metal cutting
type

(P-14364)
CREMACH TECH INC (PA)
Also Called: Creative Machine Technology
369 Meyer Cir, Corona (92879-1078)
PHONE..................................951 735-3194
Mike McNeeley, *CEO*
Jae Wan Choi, *Vice Pres*
Jae Choi, *Vice Pres*
Joseph Howard, *Program Mgr*
Stephen OH, *Technology*
EMP: 71
SQ FT: 34,000
SALES: 13MM **Privately Held**
WEB: www.cmtus.com
SIC: 3541 8711 Machine tools, metal cut-
ting type; designing: ship, boat, machine
& product

(P-14365)
CREMACH TECH INC
Also Called: Creative Machine Technology
400 E Parkridge Ave, Corona (92879-6618)
PHONE..................................951 735-3194
Mike McNeeley, *Branch Mgr*
EMP: 29 Privately Held
SIC: 3541 Machine tools, metal cutting
type
PA: Cremach Tech, Inc.
369 Meyer Cir
Corona CA 92879

(P-14366)
CTD MACHINES INC
2382 E 48th St, Vernon (90058-2026)
PHONE..................................213 689-4455
Kiwon Ban, *General Mgr*
Thomas Orlando, *President*
Ellen Orlando, *Corp Secy*
Seymour Lehrer, *Vice Pres*
Shirley Lehrer, *Vice Pres*
EMP: 18 EST: 1967
SQ FT: 33,000
SALES (est): 4.2MM **Privately Held**
WEB: www.ctdsaw.com
SIC: 3541 Cutoff machines (metalworking
machinery)

(P-14367)
D G INDUSTRIES
226 Viking Ave, Brea (92821-3818)
PHONE..................................714 990-3787
David Gillanders, *President*
▲ **EMP:** 13
SQ FT: 5,500
SALES (est): 2.2MM **Privately Held**
WEB: www.dgindustries.com
SIC: 3541 Screw machines, automatic

(P-14368)
DANAIR INC (PA)
1150 E Acequia Ave, Visalia (93292-6557)
P.O. Box 2577, Elko NV (89803-2577)
PHONE..................................559 734-1961
Mark Hayward, *President*
Dan Scilagyi, *Shareholder*
James Martin, *Corp Secy*
EMP: 10
SQ FT: 7,500
SALES: 3MM **Privately Held**
WEB: www.danairinc.com
SIC: 3541 Centering machines

(P-14369)
DELTA LATH & PLASTER INC
Also Called: Wash System and Dry Wall
Works
5451 Whse Way Ste 105, Sacramento
(95826)
PHONE..................................916 383-6756
Kevin Nelson, *President*
EMP: 20 EST: 2011
SALES (est): 2MM **Privately Held**
SIC: 3541 7299 Lathes; home improve-
ment & renovation contractor agency

(P-14370)
DEVELOPMENT ASSOC
CONTRLS
Also Called: D A C
6390 Rose Ln, Carpinteria (93013-2922)
PHONE..................................805 684-8307
Edward W Vernon, *President*
EMP: 43 EST: 1994
SALES (est): 5.3MM **Privately Held**
WEB: www.dacvision.com
SIC: 3541 Lathes, metal cutting & polishing
HQ: Dac Vision Incorporated
3630 W Miller Rd Ste 350
Garland TX 75041
972 677-2700

(P-14371)
DMG MORI MANUFACTURING
USA INC (HQ)
Also Called: DTL Research & Technical Ctr
3805 Faraday Ave, Davis (95618-7773)
PHONE..................................530 746-7400
Adam Hansel, *President*
Hiroshi Takami, *Treasurer*
Zach Piner, *Vice Pres*
Natsuo Okada, *Admin Sec*
▲ **EMP:** 29
SALES (est): 21.9MM
SALES (corp-wide): 3.9B **Privately Held**
SIC: 3541 Machine tools, metal cutting
type
PA: Dmg Mori Co., Ltd.
2-35-16, Meieki, Nakamura-Ku
Nagoya AIC 450-0
525 871-811

(P-14372)
DMG MORI USA INC
5740 Warland Dr, Cypress (90630-5030)
PHONE..................................562 430-3800
Shuji Yamashita, *Manager*
EMP: 12
SALES (corp-wide): 3.9B **Privately Held**
SIC: 3541 5084 Machine tools, metal cut-
ting type; machine tools & accessories
HQ: Dmg Mori Usa, Inc.
2400 Huntington Blvd
Hoffman Estates IL 60192
847 593-5400

(P-14373)
DOLLAR SHAVE CLUB INC (DH)
13335 Maxella Ave, Marina Del Rey
(90292-5619)
P.O. Box 5688, Santa Monica (90409-
5688)
PHONE..................................310 975-8528

Michael Dubin, *CEO*
Danny Miles, *Officer*
Alec Brownstein, *Vice Pres*
David Kujda, *Vice Pres*
Janet Song, *Vice Pres*
EMP: 48 **EST:** 2011
SALES (est): 32.7MM
SALES (corp-wide): 63B **Privately Held**
SIC: 3541 3991 2844 Shaving machines (metalworking); shaving brushes; shaving preparations
HQ: Unilever Manufacturing (Us), Inc.
2900 W Truman Blvd
Jefferson City MO 65109
800 298-5018

(P-14374)
DORINGER MANUFACTURING CO INC
13400 Estrella Ave, Gardena (90248-1513)
PHONE..............................310 366-7766
William Bailey, *President*
Lisa Pomeroy, *Treasurer*
EMP: 15
SQ FT: 50,000
SALES: 6MM **Privately Held**
WEB: www.doringer.com
SIC: 3541 Machine tools, metal cutting type
PA: Cold Saws Of America, Inc
13400 Estrella Ave
Gardena CA
310 366-7766

(P-14375)
DOWNEY GRINDING CO
12323 Bellflower Blvd, Downey (90242-2829)
P.O. Box 583 (90241-0583)
PHONE..............................562 803-5556
Larry Sequeira, *President*
Darla Sequeira, *Corp Secy*
Steve Shailer, *Info Tech Mgr*
Todd Prochnow, *Warehouse Mgr*
Keri Prochnow, *Manager*
▲ **EMP:** 50
SQ FT: 27,000
SALES (est): 7.9MM **Privately Held**
WEB: www.downeygrinding.com
SIC: 3541 3599 Machine tools, metal cutting type; machine shop, jobbing & repair

(P-14376)
DR DBURR INC
12943 S Budlong Ave, Gardena (90247-1511)
PHONE..............................310 323-6900
Arturo Alvarez, *Owner*
Jess Alvarez, *Manager*
EMP: 15
SQ FT: 3,500
SALES: 500K **Privately Held**
WEB: www.drdburr.com
SIC: 3541 3471 Deburring machines; cleaning, polishing & finishing

(P-14377)
DUCOMMUN AEROSTRUCTURES INC
4001 El Mirage Rd, Adelanto (92301-9489)
PHONE..............................760 246-4191
Art McFarlan, *Manager*
EMP: 34
SQ FT: 1,152
SALES (corp-wide): 558.1MM **Publicly Held**
SIC: 3541 Chemical milling machines
HQ: Ducommun Aerostructures, Inc.
268 E Gardena Blvd
Gardena CA 90248
310 380-5390

(P-14378)
DUNSTAN ENTERPRISES INC
Also Called: Green's Metal Cutoff
2825 Seaboard Ln, Long Beach (90805-3753)
PHONE..............................562 630-6292
Renee Dunstan, *President*
EMP: 16
SQ FT: 12,000
SALES (est): 3MM **Privately Held**
SIC: 3541 Machine tools, metal cutting type

(P-14379)
ENSIGN US DRLG CAL INC (HQ)
7001 Charity Ave, Bakersfield (93308-5824)
PHONE..............................661 589-0111
Selby Porter, *President*
EMP: 63
SALES (est): 15.8MM
SALES (corp-wide): 783.9MM **Privately Held**
SIC: 3541 Drilling & boring machines
PA: Ensign Energy Services Inc
400 5 Ave Sw Suite 1000
Calgary AB T2P 0
403 262-1361

(P-14380)
G & L TOOLING INC
14526 Carmenita Rd, Norwalk (90650)
PHONE..............................562 802-2857
EMP: 12 **EST:** 1978
SQ FT: 15,000
SALES: 1MM **Privately Held**
SIC: 3541

(P-14381)
GNB CORPORATION
Also Called: GNB Vacuum Excellence Defined
3200 Dwight Rd Ste 100, Elk Grove (95758-6461)
PHONE..............................916 233-3543
Kenneth W Harrison, *President*
Donald A Bendix, *Corp Secy*
Klaus Rindt, *Vice Pres*
▲ **EMP:** 60
SQ FT: 62,500
SALES (est): 20.7MM
SALES (corp-wide): 45.9B **Privately Held**
WEB: www.gnbvalves.com
SIC: 3541 3491 Machine tools, metal cutting type; industrial valves
HQ: Ellison Technologies, Inc.
9912 Pioneer Blvd
Santa Fe Springs CA 90670
562 949-8311

(P-14382)
GODDARD ROTARY TOOL CO INC
525 Opper St, Escondido (92029-1019)
PHONE..............................760 743-6717
Raymond J Goddard, *President*
Gary Goddard, *Vice Pres*
EMP: 11
SQ FT: 10,000
SALES: 478K **Privately Held**
SIC: 3541 Machine tools, metal cutting type

(P-14383)
I & I DEBURRING INC
14504 Carmenita Rd Ste A, Norwalk (90650-5290)
PHONE..............................562 802-0058
Gary Wollum, *President*
Gary Klema, *Principal*
EMP: 19
SQ FT: 4,300
SALES (est): 2.2MM **Privately Held**
WEB: www.i-i-deburring.com
SIC: 3541 Machine tools, metal cutting type

(P-14384)
JCR AIRCRAFT DEBURRING LLC
Also Called: Jcr Deburring
221 Foundation Ave, La Habra (90631-6812)
PHONE..............................714 870-4427
Juan Carlos Ruiz, *Mng Member*
Scott Ruiz, *Production*
Omar Ruiz, *Manager*
EMP: 38
SALES (est): 8.2MM **Privately Held**
SIC: 3541 3471 Deburring machines; plating & polishing

(P-14385)
JWC CARBIDE INC
33700 Calle Vis, Temecula (92592-9189)
PHONE..............................714 540-8870
Fax: 714 668-8600
EMP: 14

SQ FT: 5,900
SALES: 2.2MM **Privately Held**
WEB: www.jwccarbide.com
SIC: 3541

(P-14386)
K-V ENGINEERING INC
2411 W 1st St, Santa Ana (92703-3509)
PHONE..............................714 229-9977
Khanh G Vu, *President*
Christie Vu, *CFO*
Duong Vu, *Treasurer*
Timothy Iliff, *Accountant*
Linda Nou, *Buyer*
EMP: 30
SQ FT: 22,000
SALES (est): 7.4MM **Privately Held**
SIC: 3541 3542 Milling machines; machine tools, metal forming type; punching & shearing machines; press brakes; riveting machines

(P-14387)
KYOCERA PRECISION TOOLS INC
3565 Cadillac Ave, Costa Mesa (92626-1401)
PHONE..............................714 428-3600
James Good, *CEO*
EMP: 123
SALES (corp-wide): 14.8B **Publicly Held**
SIC: 3541 3845 3843 3841 Machine tools, metal cutting type; endoscopic equipment, electromedical; cutting instruments, dental; surgical & medical instruments; machine tool accessories
HQ: Kyocera Precision Tools, Inc
102 Industrial Park Rd
Hendersonville NC 28792
800 823-7284

(P-14388)
LEAN MANUFACTURING GROUP LLC
29170 Avenue Penn, Valencia (91355-5420)
PHONE..............................661 702-9400
Kimberly Prezioso, *Manager*
EMP: 10
SALES (est): 1.8MM **Privately Held**
SIC: 3541 Machine tools, metal cutting type

(P-14389)
LEITZ TOOLING SYSTEMS LP
1145 Orange Show Rd, San Bernardino (92408-2803)
PHONE..............................909 799-8494
Holger Nagel, *Manager*
EMP: 11
SALES (corp-wide): 3.3MM **Privately Held**
SIC: 3541 Machine tools, metal cutting type
PA: Leitz Tooling Systems Lp
4301 East Paris Ave Se
Grand Rapids MI 49512
800 253-6070

(P-14390)
LIBOON GROUP INC
Also Called: Velox Cnc
1746 W Katella Ave Ste 6, Orange (92867-3431)
PHONE..............................714 639-3639
Ronald Liboon, *Principal*
▲ **EMP:** 11 **EST:** 2011
SQ FT: 8,000
SALES (est): 385K **Privately Held**
SIC: 3541 7389 Milling machines; design, commercial & industrial

(P-14391)
LISI MEDICAL JEROPA INC (DH)
950 Borra Pl, Escondido (92029-2011)
PHONE..............................760 432-9785
Christian Darville, *CEO*
Richard Warren, *General Mgr*
Jacob Hirsch, *Engineer*
Keith Johnson, *Engineer*
Andrew Murphy, *Engineer*
▲ **EMP:** 70
SALES (est): 68.3MM **Privately Held**
WEB: www.jeropa.com
SIC: 3541 Machine tools, metal cutting type

HQ: Hi-Shear Corporation
2600 Skypark Dr
Torrance CA 90505
310 784-4025

(P-14392)
MELFRED BORZALL INC
2712 Airpark Dr, Santa Maria (93455-1418)
PHONE..............................805 614-4344
Dick Melsheimer, *Principal*
Eric Melsheimer, *Chief Engr*
▲ **EMP:** 40
SQ FT: 30,000
SALES (est): 8.9MM **Privately Held**
SIC: 3541 Drilling & boring machines

(P-14393)
METLSAW SYSTEMS INC
2950 Bay Vista Ct, Benicia (94510-1123)
PHONE..............................707 746-6200
Lisa Kvech, *CEO*
Kenneth Forman, *Information Mgr*
Tom Kvech, *Engineer*
Bruce Rowland, *Controller*
Scott Clark, *Purch Mgr*
▲ **EMP:** 21
SQ FT: 30,000
SALES (est): 6.7MM
SALES (corp-wide): 928.2MM **Privately Held**
WEB: www.metlsaw.com
SIC: 3541 Saws & sawing machines
HQ: Indel, Inc.
10 Indel Ave
Rancocas NJ 08073
609 267-9000

(P-14394)
METRIC MACHINING (PA)
Also Called: Master Machine Products
3263 Trade Center Dr, Riverside (92507-3432)
PHONE..............................909 947-9222
David Parker, *Principal*
Richard R Parker, *Shareholder*
Bill Stahlke, *Engineer*
Magdalena Lopez, *Controller*
▲ **EMP:** 50
SQ FT: 45,000
SALES: 7MM **Privately Held**
SIC: 3541 Machine tools, metal cutting type

(P-14395)
MONARCH PRECISION DEBURRING
1514 E Edinger Ave Ste C, Santa Ana (92705-4918)
PHONE..............................714 258-0342
Russ Little, *President*
EMP: 15
SQ FT: 6,100
SALES (est): 2.4MM **Privately Held**
SIC: 3541 Machine tools, metal cutting type

(P-14396)
NEW CENTURY MACHINE TOOLS INC
9641 Santa Fe Springs Rd, Santa Fe Springs (90670-2917)
PHONE..............................562 906-8455
David Duquette, *CEO*
EMP: 15
SQ FT: 35,000
SALES (est): 1.7MM **Privately Held**
SIC: 3541

(P-14397)
OPTIMA INDUSTRIES INC
22771 S Wstn Ave Ste 201b, Torrance (90501)
PHONE..............................310 533-8448
Joe Manalahta, *President*
William Marantette, *Vice Pres*
Joseph Smith, *Director*
EMP: 15
SQ FT: 5,000
SALES (est): 1.4MM **Privately Held**
SIC: 3541 3823 Machine tools, metal cutting type; controllers for process variables, all types

(P-14398)
PAPCO SCREW PRODUCTS INC
Also Called: Papco Parts
9410 De Soto Ave Ste A, Chatsworth
(91311-4993)
PHONE..............................818 341-2266
Norman J Grencius, *President*
EMP: 13
SQ FT: 6,000
SALES (est): 2.4MM **Privately Held**
WEB: www.papcoparts.com
SIC: 3541 3451 Screw machines, automatic; screw machine products

(P-14399)
PAUL DOSIER ASSOCIATES INC
913 Chicago Ave, Placentia (92870-1713)
PHONE..............................714 556-7075
David A Dosier, *President*
EMP: 13
SQ FT: 7,500
SALES: 730K **Privately Held**
SIC: 3541 3599 Machine tool replacement & repair parts, metal cutting types; machine & other job shop work

(P-14400)
PRECISION DEBURRING SERVICES
4440 Manning Rd, Pico Rivera
(90660-2164)
PHONE..............................562 944-4497
Darren Smith, *President*
▲ **EMP:** 80
SALES (est): 5.8MM **Privately Held**
SIC: 3541 Machine tools, metal cutting type

(P-14401)
PRECON INC
Also Called: Precon Gage
3131 E La Palma Ave, Anaheim
(92806-2895)
PHONE..............................714 630-7632
James Von Zabern, *President*
Audrey Von Zabern, *Treasurer*
EMP: 20
SQ FT: 10,500
SALES (est): 2.9MM **Privately Held**
WEB: www.precon-inc.com
SIC: 3541 3545 3823 3471 Deburring machines; saws & sawing machines; grinding machines, metalworking; gauges (machine tool accessories); industrial instrmnts msrmnt display/control process variable; plating & polishing

(P-14402)
PRODUCTION SAW
9790 Glenoaks Blvd Ste 8, Sun Valley
(91352-1055)
P.O. Box 1341 (91353-1341)
PHONE..............................818 765-6100
Oscar George, *Manager*
EMP: 10
SALES (est): 845.8K **Privately Held**
SIC: 3541 7812

(P-14403)
REPUBLIC MACHINERY CO INC (PA)
Also Called: Lagun Engineering Solutions
800 Sprucelake Dr, Harbor City
(90710-1607)
PHONE..............................310 518-1100
Vivian Bezic, *CEO*
Joseph Bezic, *President*
Nicole Bezic, *Controller*
Mike Cannon, *Regl Sales Mgr*
James Garvey, *Regl Sales Mgr*
▲ **EMP:** 30
SQ FT: 30,000
SALES (est): 6.9MM **Privately Held**
SIC: 3541 3542 3549 3545 Drilling & boring machines; arbor presses; extruding machines (machine tools); metal; metalworking machinery; machine knives, metalworking; drilling machine attachments & accessories

(P-14404)
RH STRASBAUGH (PA)
825 Buckley Rd, San Luis Obispo
(93401-8192)
PHONE..............................805 541-6424
Alan Strasbaugh, *President*
Allan Paterson, *President*
Eric Jacobson, *Vice Pres*
Bill Kalenian, *Vice Pres*
Brad Diaz, *VP Opers*
EMP: 82
SQ FT: 135,000
SALES (est): 12.7MM **Publicly Held**
SIC: 3541 3559 5065 Grinding, polishing, buffing, lapping & honing machines; grinding machines, metalworking; semiconductor manufacturing machinery; electronic parts & equipment

(P-14405)
ROBB-JACK CORPORATION (PA)
3300 Nicolaus Rd Ste 1, Lincoln
(95648-9574)
PHONE..............................916 645-6045
David Baker, *President*
Steve Handrop, *Exec VP*
EMP: 82
SQ FT: 42,000
SALES (est): 17MM **Privately Held**
WEB: www.robbjack.com
SIC: 3541 Machine tools, metal cutting type

(P-14406)
RYTAN INC
455 Maple Ave, Torrance (90503-3807)
PHONE..............................310 328-6553
Riley M Sopko, *President*
▲ **EMP:** 18
SQ FT: 20,400
SALES (est): 3.4MM **Privately Held**
WEB: www.rytan.com
SIC: 3541 Keysetting machines

(P-14407)
S L FUSCO INC (PA)
1966 E Via Arado, Rancho Dominguez
(90220-6100)
P.O. Box 5924, Compton (90224-5924)
PHONE..............................310 868-1010
Jerald C Rosin, *CEO*
Eric Rosin, *President*
Arlene Rosin, *Vice Pres*
Omar Sanchez, *Purch Agent*
Tom Burke, *Director*
▲ **EMP:** 45 **EST:** 1941
SQ FT: 40,000
SALES: 44.9MM **Privately Held**
WEB: www.slfusco.com
SIC: 3541 Machine tools, metal cutting type

(P-14408)
S S SCHAFFER CO INC
Also Called: Steel Services Co
5637 District Blvd, Vernon (90058-5518)
PHONE..............................323 560-1430
Steven Schaffer Jr, *President*
Marcia Schaffer, *Treasurer*
Caroline Sallenbach, *Vice Pres*
William Salenbach, *Admin Sec*
William Salenbach, *Engineer*
EMP: 15 **EST:** 1940
SQ FT: 30,000
SALES (est): 2.9MM **Privately Held**
SIC: 3541 Grinding machines, metalworking

(P-14409)
SAAVY INC
516 W Lincoln Ave, Montebello
(90640-3561)
PHONE..............................323 728-2137
Anie Piliguian, *President*
▲ **EMP:** 12
SALES (est): 1.7MM **Privately Held**
SIC: 3541 Buffing & polishing machines

(P-14410)
SAF-T-KUT LLC
2652 Dow Ave, Tustin (92780-7208)
PHONE..............................657 210-4426
Dan Tsujioka, *Mng Member*
Emmett Ebner,
EMP: 25
SQ FT: 1,000
SALES: 100K **Privately Held**
SIC: 3541 5072 Pipe cutting & threading machines; hardware

(P-14411)
SHERLINE PRODUCTS INCORPORATED
3235 Executive Rdg, Vista (92081-8527)
PHONE..............................760 727-5181
Joe Martin, *President*
Karl W Rohlin III, *CEO*
Charla Papp, *CFO*
Kat Powell, *Info Tech Dir*
▲ **EMP:** 30 **EST:** 1973
SQ FT: 65,000
SALES (est): 6.5MM **Privately Held**
WEB: www.sherline.com
SIC: 3541 3545 Lathes, metal cutting & polishing; machine tool accessories

(P-14412)
SHIELDS ENTERPRISES INC
Also Called: D and D Tools
8740 Avenida Costa Blanca, San Diego
(92154-6246)
PHONE..............................619 276-9100
Deann Dutro, *President*
Floyd Dutro, *Corp Secy*
EMP: 50 **EST:** 1995
SALES (est): 3.8MM **Privately Held**
SIC: 3541 Machine tools, metal cutting type

(P-14413)
SOUTHERN CALIFORNIA CARBIDE
12216 Thatcher Ct, Poway (92064-6876)
PHONE..............................858 513-7777
Harjeet Singh, *President*
Satanm Singh, *Vice Pres*
EMP: 20 **EST:** 1978
SQ FT: 10,000
SALES (est): 1.8MM **Privately Held**
SIC: 3541 3545 Machine tools, metal cutting type; machine tool accessories

(P-14414)
SOUTHWESTERN INDUSTRIES INC (PA)
2615 Homestead Pl, Rancho Dominguez
(90220-5610)
P.O. Box 9066, Compton (90224-9066)
PHONE..............................310 608-4422
Richard Leonhard, *CEO*
Stephen Pinto, *President*
Bruce Meredith, *Executive*
Michael McGarry, *Regional Mgr*
Brian Barnett, *General Mgr*
▲ **EMP:** 70 **EST:** 1953
SALES (est): 28.6MM **Privately Held**
SIC: 3541 Machine tools, metal cutting type

(P-14415)
SUPERTEC MACHINERY INC
Also Called: St Supertec
6435 Alondra Blvd, Paramount
(90723-3758)
PHONE..............................562 220-1675
Randy Oscar Chu, *CEO*
George Shih, *President*
Rafael Vasquez, *Regl Sales Mgr*
Don Staggenborg, *Sales Mgr*
▲ **EMP:** 15
SQ FT: 8,420
SALES (est): 3.1MM **Privately Held**
WEB: www.supertecusa.com
SIC: 3541 3542 7389 Grinding, polishing, buffing, lapping & honing machines; grinding machines, metalworking; machine tools, metal forming type; grinding, precision: commercial or industrial

(P-14416)
TESCO PRODUCTS
25601 Avenue Stanford, Santa Clarita
(91355-1103)
PHONE..............................661 257-0153
Mark Terry, *CEO*
EMP: 12
SQ FT: 2,500
SALES: 300K **Privately Held**
WEB: www.tescoproducts.com
SIC: 3541 5032 Grinding, polishing, buffing, lapping & honing machines; brick, stone & related material

(P-14417)
TJ AEROSPACE INC
12601 Monarch St, Garden Grove
(92841-3918)
PHONE..............................714 891-3564
Tien N Dang, *CEO*
EMP: 23
SQ FT: 6,000
SALES (est): 7MM **Privately Held**
SIC: 3541 Machine tools, metal cutting type

(P-14418)
TOOL MAKERS INTERNATIONAL INC
Also Called: T M I
3390 Woodward Ave, Santa Clara
(95054-2629)
P.O. Box 4840 (95056-4840)
PHONE..............................408 980-8888
Patrick Chronis, *President*
Mark Haight, *General Mgr*
Pat Chronis, *VP Mfg*
Connie Chronis, *Manager*
EMP: 13 **EST:** 1961
SQ FT: 22,000
SALES (est): 2.6MM **Privately Held**
WEB: www.toolmakersintl.com
SIC: 3541 Machine tools, metal cutting type

(P-14419)
TREAT ENTERPRISES
Also Called: Cameron Micro Drill Presses
19401 Rawhide Rd, Sonora (95370-9416)
PHONE..............................209 532-2220
Lonnie Leo Treat, *President*
Anita Treat, *Principal*
Bob Huish, *General Mgr*
▲ **EMP:** 14
SQ FT: 16,000
SALES (est): 2.9MM **Privately Held**
WEB: www.cameronmicrodrillpress.com
SIC: 3541 3559 3589 3545 Drill presses; glass making machinery: blowing, molding, forming, etc.; water filters & softeners, household type; machine tool accessories; machine tools, metal forming type

(P-14420)
TRUPART MANUFACTURING INC
Also Called: Trupart Mfg
4450 Dupont Ct Ste A, Ventura
(93003-7790)
PHONE..............................805 644-4107
Shane Prukop, *President*
Ingrid Boem, *CFO*
Jose Mendoza, *Engineer*
EMP: 10
SALES (est): 2MM **Privately Held**
SIC: 3541 Machine tools, metal cutting type

(P-14421)
US UNION TOOL INC (HQ)
1260 N Fee Ana St, Anaheim (92807-1817)
PHONE..............................714 521-6242
Hideo Hirano, *President*
Robert Smallwood, *President*
Sherry Smith, *Database Admin*
John McCandlish, *Manager*
▲ **EMP:** 45
SQ FT: 44,000
SALES (est): 121.5MM
SALES (corp-wide): 206.9MM **Privately Held**
WEB: www.usuniontool.com
SIC: 3541 Machine tools, metal cutting type
PA: Union Tool Co.
6-17-1, Minamioi
Shinagawa-Ku TKY 140-0
354 931-001

(P-14422)
VALLEY CUTTING SYSTEM INC
1455 N Belmont Rd, Exeter (93221-9669)
P.O. Box 607, Three Rivers (93271-0607)
PHONE..............................559 684-1229
▲ **EMP:** 35
SALES (est): 3.4MM **Privately Held**
SIC: 3541 Cutoff machines (metalworking machinery)

▲ = Import ▼=Export
◆ =Import/Export

(P-14423)
WESTERN FIBER CO INC
4234a Sandrini Rd, Arvin (93203-9200)
P.O. Box 22665, Bakersfield (93390-2665)
PHONE..............................661 854-5556
John Scarrone, *President*
▲ **EMP:** 40
SALES (est): 5.8MM **Privately Held**
SIC: 3541 Electrical discharge erosion machines

```
3542 Machine Tools:
     Forming
```

(P-14424)
3DEO INC
14000 Van Ness Ave Ste C, Gardena
(90249-2942)
PHONE..............................844 496-3825
Matthew Petros, *CEO*
Matthew Sand, *President*
EMP: 11
SQ FT: 13,000
SALES (est): 133.9K **Privately Held**
SIC: 3542 Robots for metal forming: pressing, extruding, etc.

(P-14425)
ADDITION MFG TECH CA INC
1391 Specialty Dr Ste A, Vista
(92081-8521)
PHONE..............................760 597-5220
Phillippe Jaubert, *President*
Francois Patanchon, *Vice Pres*
▲ **EMP:** 35
SQ FT: 23,432
SALES (est): 9.8MM **Privately Held**
WEB: www.eatonleonard.com
SIC: 3542 Bending machines
PA: Addition Manufacturing Technologies
Llc
1637 Kingsview Dr
Lebanon OH 45036
513 228-7000

(P-14426)
AIR FRAME FORMING INC
15717 Colorado Ave, Paramount
(90723-4210)
PHONE..............................562 663-1662
Carolina Abad, *President*
EMP: 10
SQ FT: 10,000
SALES (est): 900.8K **Privately Held**
SIC: 3542 Machine tools, metal forming type

(P-14427)
AMBRIT INDUSTRIES INC
432 Magnolia Ave, Glendale (91204-2406)
PHONE..............................818 243-1224
Paul Yaussi, *President*
Louis A Yaussi, *Corp Secy*
Michelle Taylor, *Manager*
EMP: 38 **EST:** 1946
SQ FT: 9,184
SALES (est): 5.6MM **Privately Held**
SIC: 3542 3363 Die casting machines;
aluminum die-castings

(P-14428)
AMERICAN PNEUMATIC TOOLS INC
Also Called: APT
1000 S Grand Ave, Santa Ana
(92705-4122)
PHONE..............................562 204-1555
Kim Eads, *President*
Dan O Brien, *CFO*
▲ **EMP:** 16
SQ FT: 15,000
SALES (est): 3.3MM **Privately Held**
WEB: www.apt-tools.com
SIC: 3542 3541 3546 3532 Machine
tools, metal forming type; machine tools,
metal cutting type; power-driven hand-
tools; mining machinery; hand & edge
tools

(P-14429)
AMERICAN PRECISION HYDRAULICS
5601 Research Dr, Huntington Beach
(92649-1620)
PHONE..............................714 903-8610
Susan Smith, *President*
Steve Smith, *Vice Pres*
Judith Spirtos, *QC Mgr*
EMP: 23
SQ FT: 6,500
SALES (est): 3.5MM **Privately Held**
SIC: 3542 Presses: hydraulic & pneumatic,
mechanical & manual

(P-14430)
AUTOMOTIVE ENGINEERED PDTS INC
7149 Mission Gorge Rd, San Diego
(92120-1100)
PHONE..............................619 229-7797
James J Bittle, *CFO*
Craig White, *Admin Sec*
John Eldridge, *Sales Mgr*
EMP: 57
SQ FT: 10,000
SALES (est): 7.5MM **Privately Held**
WEB: www.jbaracingengines.com
SIC: 3542 3714 Headers; motor vehicle
parts & accessories

(P-14431)
BORDEN MANUFACTURING
3314 Pacific Trl, Cottonwood (96022)
PHONE..............................530 347-6642
Ralph Borden, *Partner*
Karen Borden, *Partner*
EMP: 45
SQ FT: 7,200
SALES (est): 7.7MM **Privately Held**
SIC: 3542 Stretching machines

(P-14432)
BROTHERS MACHINE & TOOL INC
11095 Inland Ave, Jurupa Valley
(91752-1155)
PHONE..............................951 361-9454
Jose E Razo, *President*
EMP: 20
SALES (est): 2.8MM **Privately Held**
SIC: 3542 Machine tools, metal forming
type
PA: Brothers Machine & Tool, Inc.
11098 Inland Ave
Jurupa Valley CA 91752

(P-14433)
BROTHERS MACHINE & TOOL INC (PA)
11098 Inland Ave, Jurupa Valley
(91752-1154)
PHONE..............................951 361-2909
Jose E Razzo, *President*
Jose L Razzo, *Treasurer*
Jose F Razzo, *Vice Pres*
Ana Rios, *Admin Sec*
EMP: 15
SALES (est): 2MM **Privately Held**
SIC: 3542 Machine tools, metal forming
type

(P-14434)
CARANDO TECHNOLOGIES INC
345 N Harrison St, Stockton (95203-2801)
P.O. Box 1167 (95201-1167)
PHONE..............................209 948-6500
Sidney A Scheutz, *CEO*
Laura Keir, *CFO*
Elise Woods, *Purch Mgr*
▼ **EMP:** 25
SQ FT: 35,000
SALES (est): 6.2MM **Privately Held**
WEB: www.carando.net
SIC: 3542 3548 3599 Machine tools,
metal forming type; welding apparatus;
custom machinery; machine shop, job-
bing & repair

(P-14435)
CIRCLE INDUSTRIAL MFG CORP
Also Called: Cim
2727 N Slater Ave, Compton (90222)
PHONE..............................310 638-5101

Debra Cosio, *Branch Mgr*
EMP: 15
SALES (corp-wide): 5.1MM **Privately Held**
WEB: www.circleindustrial.com
SIC: 3542 Sheet metalworking machines
PA: Circle Industrial Mfg. Corporation
1613 W El Segundo Blvd
Compton CA 90222
310 638-5101

(P-14436)
COASTAL DIE CUTTING INC
4025 Pacific Hwy, San Diego (92110-2028)
PHONE..............................619 677-3180
Kevin Otsuka, *President*
Mary Jenkins, *CFO*
EMP: 17
SQ FT: 19,746
SALES (est): 2.1MM **Privately Held**
SIC: 3542 7389 3544 Die casting & ex-
truding machines; packaging & labeling
services; dies & die holders for metal cut-
ting, forming, die casting

(P-14437)
H & N TOOL & DIE CO INC
201 Jason Ct Ste B, Corona (92879-7100)
PHONE..............................951 372-9071
Tom Nassen, *President*
Rick Nassen, *Treasurer*
Jim Nassen, *Vice Pres*
▼ **EMP:** 10
SQ FT: 8,000
SALES (est): 1MM **Privately Held**
WEB: www.hnspringnstamping.com
SIC: 3542 3495 3469 Presses: forming,
stamping, punching, sizing (machine
tools); wire springs; machine parts,
stamped or pressed metal

(P-14438)
HORN MACHINE TOOLS INC (PA)
Also Called: H M T
40455 Brickyard Dr # 101, Madera
(93636-9516)
PHONE..............................559 431-4131
Kent Horn, *President*
▲ **EMP:** 32 **EST:** 1996
SALES (est): 7.6MM **Privately Held**
SIC: 3542 5084 Bending machines; indus-
trial machinery & equipment

(P-14439)
HYPRESS TECHNOLOGIES INC
340 Hearst Dr, Oxnard (93030-5174)
PHONE..............................805 485-4060
John W Keefer, *President*
EMP: 18
SQ FT: 9,100
SALES (est): 1.8MM **Privately Held**
SIC: 3542 Presses: hydraulic & pneumatic,
mechanical & manual

(P-14440)
INTERNATIONAL FORMING TECH INC
2331 Sturgis Rd, Oxnard (93030-8934)
PHONE..............................805 278-8060
Siggy Rivalta, *President*
EMP: 40
SALES (est): 5.5MM **Privately Held**
SIC: 3542 Machine tools, metal forming
type

(P-14441)
LIP HING METAL INC
738 Phillips, Rowland Heights
(91748-1146)
PHONE..............................714 871-9220
Ronald Chow, *Principal*
▲ **EMP:** 10
SALES (est): 1.3MM **Privately Held**
SIC: 3542 Arbor presses

(P-14442)
LOUIS LEVIN & SON INC
13550 Larwin Cir, Santa Fe Springs
(90670-5031)
PHONE..............................562 802-8066
Dale Waite, *President*
EMP: 11
SQ FT: 6,500

SALES (est): 1.8MM **Privately Held**
WEB: www.levinlathe.com
SIC: 3542 Machine tools, metal forming
type

(P-14443)
MAGNETIC METALS CORPORATION
2475 W La Palma Ave, Anaheim
(92801-2610)
PHONE..............................714 828-4625
Linda Cannon, *Branch Mgr*
EMP: 40
SQ FT: 50,400
SALES (corp-wide): 928.2MM **Privately Held**
WEB: www.magnet.com
SIC: 3542 Magnetic forming machines
HQ: Magnetic Metals Corporation
1900 Hayes Ave
Camden NJ 08105
856 964-7842

(P-14444)
MATHY MACHINE INC
9315 Wheatlands Rd, Santee
(92071-2860)
PHONE..............................619 448-0404
Jay Mathy, *President*
Paul Carpenter, *General Mgr*
Bryan Mathy, *Engineer*
EMP: 30
SQ FT: 14,000
SALES (est): 5.7MM **Privately Held**
WEB: www.mathymachine.com
SIC: 3542 Machine tools, metal forming
type

(P-14445)
MEDLIN MATERIAL HANDLING EQP
Also Called: Medlin Equipment
14903 Marquardt Ave, Santa Fe Springs
(90670-5128)
PHONE..............................562 229-1991
Mark Medlin, *Principal*
Pat Crowder, *General Mgr*
▲ **EMP:** 12
SQ FT: 10,000
SALES (est): 2.4MM **Privately Held**
SIC: 3542 5084 Machine tools, metal
forming type; materials handling machin-
ery

(P-14446)
MJC ENGINEERING AND TECH INC
15401 Assembly Ln, Huntington Beach
(92649-1329)
PHONE..............................714 890-0618
Carl Lorentzen, *President*
Bernd Hermann, *CFO*
Gro Jensen, *CFO*
Per Carlson, *Vice Pres*
Kristi Jensen, *Admin Sec*
▲ **EMP:** 18
SQ FT: 10,000
SALES (est): 7.2MM **Privately Held**
WEB: www.mjcengineering.com
SIC: 3542 Spinning machines, metal

(P-14447)
MORAN TOOLS
2515 Bella Vista Dr, Vista (92084-7841)
P.O. Box 1141 (92085-1141)
PHONE..............................760 801-3570
Max Moran, *Owner*
EMP: 20
SALES (est): 2.6MM **Privately Held**
SIC: 3542 Machine tools, metal forming
type

(P-14448)
NOLL INC
390 Buckley Rd Frnt, San Luis Obispo
(93401-8164)
PHONE..............................805 543-3602
John M Noll, *President*
Andy Levy, *Engineer*
EMP: 10 **EST:** 1958
SQ FT: 12,500
SALES (est): 1MM **Privately Held**
WEB: www.nollinc.com
SIC: 3542 3498 Thread rolling machines;
fabricated pipe & fittings

(P-14449)
NUGIER PRESS COMPANY INC
Also Called: Nugier Hydraulics
18031 La Salle Ave, Gardena
(90248-3606)
PHONE...................................310 515-6025
Gary Livick, *President*
EMP: 17 EST: 1994
SALES (est): 732K **Privately Held**
WEB: www.nugier.com
SIC: 3542 5084 Presses: hydraulic &
pneumatic, mechanical & manual; industrial machinery & equipment

(P-14450)
PHANTOM TOOL & DIE CO
23535 Us Highway 18, Apple Valley
(92307-4345)
PHONE...................................760 240-4249
Jack Probert, *Owner*
EMP: 10
SQ FT: 14,500
SALES: 150K **Privately Held**
SIC: 3542 Headers

(P-14451)
PHI
Also Called: PHI Hydraulics
14955 Salt Lake Ave E, City of Industry
(91746-3133)
PHONE...................................626 968-9680
Yuriy Rakhlin, *President*
Uyuriy Rakhlin, *Vice Pres*
Ruth Willis, *Technology*
David Morrow, *Purch Agent*
Terry Evraets, *Manager*
▼ EMP: 25
SQ FT: 25,930
SALES: 3.5MM **Privately Held**
WEB: www.tulipcorp.com
SIC: 3542 3549 Presses: hydraulic &
pneumatic, mechanical & manual; metalworking machinery

(P-14452)
**PRECISION FASTENER
TOOLING**
11530 Western Ave, Stanton (90680-3490)
PHONE...................................714 898-8558
Charles Boyles, *President*
James Azevedo, *Treasurer*
EMP: 19 EST: 1981
SQ FT: 10,000
SALES (est): 3.2MM **Privately Held**
SIC: 3542 3544 Bulldozers (metalworking
machinery); special dies, tools, jigs & fixtures

(P-14453)
**PRECISION FORMING GROUP
LLC**
511 Commercial Way, La Habra
(90631-6170)
PHONE...................................562 501-1985
Mario Diaz, *Mng Member*
EMP: 15
SALES (est): 1.1MM **Privately Held**
SIC: 3542 Metal deposit forming machines

(P-14454)
RAY CHINN CONSTRUCTION INC
424 24th St, Bakersfield (93301-4104)
PHONE...................................661 327-2731
Raymond Dean Chinn, *President*
EMP: 35
SALES (est): 5.3MM **Privately Held**
SIC: 3542 Mechanical (pneumatic or hydraulic) metal forming machines

(P-14455)
SEYI - AMERICA INC
17534 Von Karman Ave, Irvine
(92614-6208)
PHONE...................................909 839-1151
Clair Kuo, *CEO*
Sammy Lin, *Project Mgr*
Scott Braito, *Regl Sales Mgr*
David Hattabaugh, *Manager*
▲ EMP: 10
SALES (est): 2MM
SALES (corp-wide): 133.1MM **Privately
Held**
WEB: www.seyi-america.com
SIC: 3542 Presses: forming, stamping,
punching, sizing (machine tools)

PA: Shieh Yih Machinery Industry Co., Ltd.
446, Nan Shang Rd.,
Taoyuan City TAY 33392
335 254-66

(P-14456)
SHARP INDUSTRIES INC (PA)
3501 Challenger St Fl 2, Torrance
(90503-1697)
PHONE...................................310 370-5990
James Chen, *Ch of Bd*
Nicholas Chen, *CEO*
George Lee, *Senior VP*
Roger Lee, *Vice Pres*
▲ EMP: 25
SQ FT: 40,000
SALES (est): 6.2MM **Privately Held**
WEB: www.sharp-industries.com
SIC: 3542 Arbor presses

(P-14457)
SUTHERLAND PRESSES
22561 Carbon Mesa Rd, Malibu
(90265-5018)
PHONE...................................310 453-6981
Mark D Sutherland, *CEO*
Ray Fausz, *Sales Staff*
Sergio Sierra, *Sales Staff*
Lynie Ueda, *Associate*
▲ EMP: 12
SQ FT: 10,500
SALES (est): 2.5MM **Privately Held**
WEB: www.sutherlandpresses.com
SIC: 3542 Presses: forming, stamping,
punching, sizing (machine tools); presses:
hydraulic & pneumatic, mechanical &
manual

(P-14458)
TRI A MACHINE INC
7221 Garden Grove Blvd Ab, Garden Grove
(92841-4218)
PHONE...................................714 408-8907
Anthony Nguyen, *President*
Trisha Nguyen, *Treasurer*
Luan Nguyen, *Admin Sec*
EMP: 15
SALES (est): 700K **Privately Held**
SIC: 3542 3541 Spinning lathes; chemical
milling machines; electrochemical milling
machines; turret lathes

(P-14459)
UNIVERSAL PUNCH CORP
4001 W Macarthur Blvd, Santa Ana
(92704-6307)
P.O. Box 26879 (92799-6879)
PHONE...................................714 556-4488
Kenneth L Williams, *President*
Joan Williams, *CFO*
Kevin Williams, *Vice Pres*
▲ EMP: 55
SQ FT: 52,000
SALES (est): 12.8MM **Privately Held**
WEB: www.universalpunch.com
SIC: 3542 3545 3544 3452 Punching &
shearing machines; machine tool accessories; special dies, tools, jigs & fixtures;
bolts, nuts, rivets & washers

(P-14460)
US INDUSTRIAL TOOL & SUP CO
Also Called: Usit Co
14083 S Normandie Ave, Gardena
(90249-2614)
PHONE...................................310 464-8400
Keith Rowland, *CEO*
▲ EMP: 47 EST: 1955
SQ FT: 35,000
SALES (est): 8.9MM **Privately Held**
WEB: www.ustool.com
SIC: 3542 3546 Machine tools, metal
forming type; power-driven handtools

(P-14461)
WELDTEK INC
3431 W Maywood Ave, Santa Ana
(92704-4423)
PHONE...................................714 210-8966
Mactin Le, *President*
EMP: 80
SALES (est): 4.6MM **Privately Held**
SIC: 3542 7692 Bending machines; welding repair

(P-14462)
WEST COAST-ACCUDYNE INC
Also Called: Accudyne Engineering & Eqp
7180 Scout Ave, Bell (90201-3202)
P.O. Box 2159 (90202-2159)
PHONE...................................562 927-2546
George F Schofhauser, *President*
Jill Wigney, *Corp Secy*
Kurt Anderegg, *Vice Pres*
▲ EMP: 20 EST: 1954
SALES (est): 6.2MM **Privately Held**
WEB: www.accudyneeng.com
SIC: 3542 5084 Presses: forming, stamping, punching, sizing (machine tools); machine tools & accessories

(P-14463)
XY CORP INC
Also Called: E P S Products
1258 Montalvo Way Ste A, Palm Springs
(92262-5441)
PHONE...................................760 323-0333
Jerry Good, *President*
Greg Good, *Vice Pres*
Janice Freeman, *General Mgr*
Jerry Andre, *Engineer*
EMP: 15
SQ FT: 14,000
SALES (est): 3MM **Privately Held**
WEB: www.xydroid.com
SIC: 3542 3299 Presses: hydraulic &
pneumatic, mechanical & manual; ornamental & architectural plaster work

3543 Industrial Patterns

(P-14464)
CENTURY PATTERN CO INC
15925 Piuma Ave, Cerritos (90703-1526)
PHONE...................................562 402-1707
Min Ho Yang, *President*
EMP: 10 EST: 1976
SQ FT: 14,000
SALES: 800K **Privately Held**
SIC: 3543 Industrial patterns

(P-14465)
HP CORE CO INC
1843 E 58th Pl, Los Angeles (90001-1415)
PHONE...................................323 582-1688
Ken Catalfo, *President*
Charles Catalfo, *Vice Pres*
EMP: 18 EST: 1964
SQ FT: 12,000
SALES (est): 998.2K **Privately Held**
SIC: 3543 Foundry cores

(P-14466)
R H PATTERN
10700 Jersey Blvd Ste 590, Rancho Cucamonga (91730-5124)
PHONE...................................909 484-9141
Robert Hansen, *President*
EMP: 47
SALES (est): 6.1MM **Privately Held**
SIC: 3543 Industrial patterns

(P-14467)
SWISS PATTERN CORP
2611 S Yale St, Santa Ana (92704-5227)
PHONE...................................714 545-8040
Daniel Dick, *President*
EMP: 11
SQ FT: 8,000
SALES (est): 1.7MM **Privately Held**
SIC: 3543 Industrial patterns

(P-14468)
TECHSHOP SAN JOSE LLC
300 S 2nd St, San Jose (95113-2711)
PHONE...................................408 916-4144
Mark Hatch, *CEO*
Emily Elhoffer,
Addie Langford, *Manager*
EMP: 17
SALES (est): 1.6MM **Privately Held**
SIC: 3543 3599 Industrial patterns; machine & other job shop work

3544 Dies, Tools, Jigs, Fixtures & Indl Molds

(P-14469)
A B G INSTRUMENTS & ENGRG
604 30th St, Paso Robles (93446-1293)
PHONE...................................805 238-6262
William Andrasko, *Owner*
EMP: 10
SQ FT: 4,500
SALES (est): 829.2K **Privately Held**
SIC: 3544 Special dies & tools

(P-14470)
**ACE CLEARWATER
ENTERPRISES INC**
1614 Kona Dr, Compton (90220-5412)
PHONE...................................310 538-5380
James D Dodson, *Branch Mgr*
EMP: 12
SALES (corp-wide): 42.8MM **Privately
Held**
WEB: www.aceclearwater.com
SIC: 3544 3728 3769 Special dies, tools,
jigs & fixtures; aircraft parts & equipment;
guided missile & space vehicle parts &
auxiliary equipment
PA: Ace Clearwater Enterprises, Inc.
19815 Magellan Dr
Torrance CA 90502
310 323-2140

(P-14471)
ADVANCED ENVIROMENTAL
2420 W Carson St, Torrance (90501-3145)
PHONE...................................310 782-9400
Raymond Castro, *Owner*
EMP: 11
SALES (est): 652.8K **Privately Held**
SIC: 3544 5031 Industrial molds; molding,
all materials

(P-14472)
**ADVANCED MACHINING
TOOLING INC**
Also Called: C S C
13535 Danielson St, Poway (92064-6868)
PHONE...................................858 486-9050
Terry A Deane, *CEO*
Tony Cerda, *President*
Jodi Deane, *CFO*
EMP: 46
SQ FT: 31,000
SALES (est): 10.4MM **Privately Held**
WEB: www.amtmfg.com
SIC: 3544 3599 Special dies, tools, jigs &
fixtures; machine shop, jobbing & repair

(P-14473)
**ADVANCED MOLD
TECHNOLOGY INC**
1560 Moonstone, Brea (92821-2876)
PHONE...................................714 990-0144
Dana Mitchell, *President*
◆ EMP: 19
SQ FT: 8,800
SALES (est): 4.4MM **Privately Held**
WEB: www.advancedmold.com
SIC: 3544 Industrial molds

(P-14474)
ALCO MANUFACTURING INC
207 E Alton Ave, Santa Ana (92707-4416)
PHONE...................................714 549-5007
Frank Reuland, *President*
Ingrid Reuland, *Treasurer*
EMP: 15 EST: 1980
SQ FT: 11,000
SALES (est): 2.8MM **Privately Held**
WEB: www.alcomanufacturinginc.com
SIC: 3544 3469 3444 Special dies &
tools; stamping metal for the trade; sheet
metalwork

(P-14475)
**AMBRIT ENGINEERING
CORPORATION**
2640 Halladay St, Santa Ana (92705-5649)
PHONE...................................714 557-1074
Terrence Saul, *CEO*
John F Mattimoe, *President*
Thomas W Vickers, *Corp Secy*
Lisa Jane, *Executive Asst*

▲ = Import ▼=Export
◆ =Import/Export

Geoff Ennis, *Info Tech Mgr*
▲ EMP: 65
SQ FT: 32,000
SALES (est): 19.9MM **Privately Held**
WEB: www.ambritengineering.com
SIC: 3544 Forms (molds), for foundry &
   plastics working machinery

(P-14476)
AMERICAN DIE & ROLLFORMING
3495 Swetzer Rd, Loomis (95650-9581)
PHONE..............................916 652-7667
Christopher Tatasciore, *President*
Slate Bryer, *Vice Pres*
Larry Dumm, *Admin Sec*
▲ EMP: 10
SALES (est): 1.7MM **Privately Held**
SIC: 3544 Special dies & tools

(P-14477)
AMERICAN INDUSTRIAL CORP
Also Called: Universe Industries
1624 N Orangethorpe Way, Anaheim
(92801-1227)
PHONE..............................714 680-4763
Cirilo Nunez, *President*
Perle Nunez, *Ch of Bd*
EMP: 10
SQ FT: 7,000
SALES (est): 1.5MM **Privately Held**
SIC: 3544 3599 3469 3541 Special dies,
   tools, jigs & fixtures; machine & other job
   shop work; metal stampings; machine
   tools, metal cutting type; machine tool ac-
   cessories; ball & roller bearings

(P-14478)
AMERICAN PLASTIC PRODUCTS INC
9243 Glenoaks Blvd, Sun Valley
(91352-2614)
PHONE..............................818 504-1073
Roupen Yegavian, *President*
Varosh Petrosian, *Vice Pres*
▲ EMP: 75
SQ FT: 35,000
SALES (est): 9.3MM **Privately Held**
WEB: www.americanelectro.com
SIC: 3544 Industrial molds

(P-14479)
AMTEC HUMAN CAPITAL INC
21661 Audubon Way, El Toro (92630-5752)
PHONE..............................949 472-0396
Arvie Martin, *Branch Mgr*
EMP: 29
SALES (corp-wide): 5.3MM **Privately Held**
SIC: 3544 Industrial molds
PA: Amtec Human Capital, Inc.
   13920 City Center Dr # 250
   Chino Hills CA
   714 993-1900

(P-14480)
ART MOLD DIE CASTING INC
11872 Sheldon St, Sun Valley
(91352-1507)
PHONE..............................818 767-6464
Leo Benavides, *President*
Arman Sarkissian, *Vice Pres*
EMP: 25
SQ FT: 14,000
SALES (est): 3.7MM **Privately Held**
WEB: www.artmoldinc.com
SIC: 3544 3369 3363 Industrial molds;
   nonferrous foundries; aluminum die-cast-
   ings

(P-14481)
ATS TOOL INC
Also Called: Ats Workholding
30222 Esperanza, Rcho STA Marg
(92688-2121)
PHONE..............................949 888-1744
William Murphy, *President*
Sean Murphy, *Vice Pres*
Tim Schneider, *Vice Pres*
Hardig Mark, *Technical Staff*
Mike Harper, *Engineer*
▲ EMP: 20
SALES (est): 3.6MM **Privately Held**
SIC: 3544 Jigs & fixtures

(P-14482)
AVIS ROTO DIE CO
1560 N San Fernando Rd, Los Angeles
(90065-1225)
PHONE..............................323 255-7070
Avetis Iskanian, *CEO*
Hasmink Iskanian, *Administration*
Jack Iskanian, *Purch Mgr*
EMP: 30
SQ FT: 32,000
SALES (est): 5.7MM **Privately Held**
WEB: www.avisrd.com
SIC: 3544 Paper cutting dies

(P-14483)
B & R MOLD INC
4564 E Los Angeles Ave C, Simi Valley
(93063-3428)
PHONE..............................805 526-8665
Brent Robinson, *President*
Stephen Yamani, *Executive*
Lynette Armstrong, *Manager*
EMP: 12
SALES (est): 1.6MM **Privately Held**
WEB: www.brmold.com
SIC: 3544 Industrial molds

(P-14484)
BARROT CORPORATION
1881 Kaiser Ave, Irvine (92614-5707)
PHONE..............................949 852-1640
Jesus Barrot, *President*
Robert Barrot, *Treasurer*
Carlos Barrot, *Vice Pres*
James Barrot, *Admin Sec*
EMP: 22
SQ FT: 15,000
SALES (est): 4.2MM **Privately Held**
WEB: www.barrotcorp.com
SIC: 3544 3769 Special dies & tools;
   guided missile & space vehicle parts &
   auxiliary equipment

(P-14485)
BENDA TOOL & MODEL WORKS INC
Also Called: A & B Diecasting
900 Alfred Nobel Dr, Hercules
(94547-1814)
PHONE..............................510 741-3170
Robert Dathe, *President*
Stephen Dathe, *CEO*
Judy Newsome, *COO*
Ben Dathe, *Vice Pres*
Linda Perla, *Admin Mgr*
▲ EMP: 35 EST: 1946
SQ FT: 60,000
SALES (est): 8.9MM **Privately Held**
WEB: www.bendatool.com
SIC: 3544 Dies, steel rule; industrial molds

(P-14486)
BERNMAN MOLD AND ENGINEERING
1219 S Bon View Ave, Ontario
(91761-4402)
PHONE..............................909 930-3844
Manuel J Solario, *President*
EMP: 10
SQ FT: 2,600
SALES (est): 1MM **Privately Held**
SIC: 3544 Industrial molds

(P-14487)
BUCY DIE CASTING
633 S Glenwood Pl, Burbank (91506-2891)
PHONE..............................818 843-5044
Thomas L Bucy Jr, *President*
Ricardo Cruz, *CFO*
Thomas Bucy Sr, *Vice Pres*
Janell R Bucy, *Admin Sec*
EMP: 13
SQ FT: 6,000
SALES (est): 1.9MM **Privately Held**
WEB: www.bucycast.com
SIC: 3544 Dies & die holders for metal cut-
   ting, forming, die casting

(P-14488)
C & H MOLDING INCORPORATED
11160 Thurston Ln, Mira Loma
(91752-1426)
PHONE..............................951 361-5030
Hugh W Fitzell, *President*

Sarah Fitzell, *Corp Secy*
EMP: 20
SALES (est): 3MM **Privately Held**
SIC: 3544 Forms (molds), for foundry &
   plastics working machinery

(P-14489)
C & L TOOL AND DIE INC
8684 Avenida De La Fuente # 12, San
Diego (92154-6220)
PHONE..............................619 270-8385
Ernesto Islas, *President*
Esperanza Islas, *Corp Secy*
EMP: 10
SQ FT: 1,000
SALES (est): 1MM **Privately Held**
SIC: 3544 Special dies & tools

(P-14490)
CACO-PACIFIC CORPORATION (PA)
813 N Cummings Rd, Covina
(91724-2597)
PHONE..............................626 331-3361
Robert G Hoffmann, *President*
Manfred Hoffman, *Ch of Bd*
Thom Williams, *Admin Sec*
▲ EMP: 142
SQ FT: 45,000
SALES (est): 19.1MM **Privately Held**
SIC: 3544 Industrial molds

(P-14491)
CAL NOR DESIGN INC (PA)
14126 Washington Ave, San Leandro
(94578-3325)
P.O. Box 2756, Dublin (94568-0275)
PHONE..............................925 829-7722
William Simon, *President*
EMP: 19
SQ FT: 4,000
SALES (est): 1.9MM **Privately Held**
SIC: 3544 Paper cutting dies

(P-14492)
CAL WEST CONSTRUCTION INC
4670 N Wilson Ave, Fresno (93704-3037)
PHONE..............................559 217-3306
Kevin Deciglie, *President*
EMP: 10
SALES (est): 584K **Privately Held**
SIC: 3544 Industrial molds

(P-14493)
CAST-RITE CORPORATION
515 E Airline Way, Gardena (90248-2593)
PHONE..............................310 532-2080
Donald De Haan, *President*
Howard Watkins, *CFO*
Wynn Chapman, *Vice Pres*
Donald Dehaan, *General Mgr*
Shirley Martian, *Controller*
▲ EMP: 98
SQ FT: 74,712
SALES (est): 20.3MM
SALES (corp-wide): 27.4MM **Privately Held**
WEB: www.cast-rite.com
SIC: 3544 3471 3363 Special dies &
   tools; plating & polishing; aluminum die-
   castings
PA: Cast-Rite International, Inc.
   515 E Airline Way
   Gardena CA 90248
   310 532-2080

(P-14494)
CHARLES MEISNER INC
201 Sierra Pl Ste A, Upland (91786-5668)
PHONE..............................909 946-8216
Charles Meisner, *President*
Carol Meisner, *Corp Secy*
Tara Meisner, *Purchasing*
EMP: 25 EST: 1972
SQ FT: 19,000
SALES (est): 5.5MM **Privately Held**
SIC: 3544 3599 Special dies & tools; ma-
   chine shop, jobbing & repair

(P-14495)
CHIP-MAKERS TOOLING SUPPLY INC
7352 Whittier Ave, Whittier (90602-1131)
PHONE..............................562 698-5840
Stephen Smith, *CEO*
Paul Hartman, *President*

Patty Rivera, *Treasurer*
EMP: 17
SQ FT: 10,000
SALES (est): 3.2MM **Privately Held**
WEB: www.chip-makers.com
SIC: 3544 Special dies, tools, jigs & fix-
   tures

(P-14496)
CJ ENTERPRISES
Also Called: Precision Enterprises
11530 Western Ave, Stanton (90680-3435)
PHONE..............................714 898-8558
Chuck Boyles, *Partner*
EMP: 25
SALES (est): 2.4MM **Privately Held**
SIC: 3544 Special dies, tools, jigs & fix-
   tures

(P-14497)
CLAMA PRODUCTS INC
1993 Ritchey St, Santa Ana (92705-5100)
PHONE..............................714 258-8606
Hector Sandino, *President*
EMP: 17
SQ FT: 6,000
SALES: 1.2MM **Privately Held**
WEB: www.clamaproducts.com
SIC: 3544 3089 Industrial molds; injection
   molding of plastics

(P-14498)
COLBRIT MANUFACTURING CO INC
9666 Owensmouth Ave Ste G, Chatsworth
(91311-8050)
PHONE..............................818 709-3608
Gerardo Cruz, *President*
Marina Cruz, *Vice Pres*
▲ EMP: 30
SQ FT: 6,000
SALES (est): 5.2MM **Privately Held**
WEB: www.colbrit.com
SIC: 3544 Special dies & tools

(P-14499)
COMPUTED TOOL & ENGINEERING
2910 E Ricker Way, Anaheim (92806-2526)
PHONE..............................714 630-3911
Oscar Torres, *President*
Isabel Torres, *Admin Sec*
EMP: 16
SQ FT: 8,825
SALES (est): 3.2MM **Privately Held**
WEB: www.computedtool.com
SIC: 3544 Special dies & tools

(P-14500)
COMPUTER PLASTICS
1914 National Ave, Hayward (94545-1784)
PHONE..............................510 785-3600
Wayne L Harshbarger, *President*
EMP: 21 EST: 1969
SQ FT: 12,700
SALES (est): 3.4MM **Privately Held**
WEB: www.4cpi.com
SIC: 3544 3089 Special dies & tools;
   molding primary plastic

(P-14501)
CONCRETE MOLD CORPORATION
Also Called: Besser Company
2121 E Del Amo Blvd, Compton
(90220-6301)
PHONE..............................310 537-5171
Bradley Gardner, *President*
EMP: 35 EST: 1960
SQ FT: 30,000
SALES (est): 6.2MM
SALES (corp-wide): 244.1MM **Privately Held**
SIC: 3544 Industrial molds
PA: Besser Company
   801 Johnson St
   Alpena MI 49707
   989 354-4111

PRODUCTS & SVCS

(P-14502)
CUSTOM TOOLING & STAMPING OF O
Also Called: Custom Tooling & Automation
1182 N Knollwood Cir, Anaheim
(92801-1307)
PHONE...................714 979-6782
Robert Kaeton, *President*
EMP: 10
SALES (est): 1.3MM **Privately Held**
SIC: 3544 Special dies, tools, jigs & fixtures

(P-14503)
DAUNTLESS INDUSTRIES INC
Also Called: Dauntless Molds
806 N Grand Ave, Covina (91724-2418)
PHONE...................626 966-4494
George R Payton, *President*
Norm Holt, *General Mgr*
EMP: 25
SQ FT: 15,000
SALES (est): 5.6MM **Privately Held**
WEB: www.dauntlessmolds.com
SIC: 3544 Forms (molds), for foundry & plastics working machinery

(P-14504)
DECREVEL INCORPORATED
1836 Soscol Ave, NAPA (94559-1349)
PHONE...................707 258-8065
P James Decrevel Sr, *President*
Sara Decrevel, *CFO*
EMP: 11
SQ FT: 4,500
SALES (est): 1.5MM **Privately Held**
WEB: www.decrevel.com
SIC: 3544 2752 Special dies & tools; die sets for metal stamping (presses); commercial printing, lithographic

(P-14505)
DIAMOND INJECTION MOLDS INC
4365 E Lowell St Ste E, Ontario
(91761-2226)
PHONE...................909 390-2260
Mark Spangler, *President*
Geri Spangler, *Admin Sec*
▲ **EMP:** 14
SQ FT: 10,000
SALES (est): 2.3MM **Privately Held**
WEB: www.diamondmolds.com
SIC: 3544 Industrial molds

(P-14506)
DIE CRAFT ENGINEERING & MFG CO
Also Called: Diecraft
11975 Florence Ave, Santa Fe Springs
(90670-4404)
PHONE...................562 777-8809
Stepan Manoukian, *President*
EMP: 10
SQ FT: 12,000
SALES (est): 1.5MM **Privately Held**
WEB: www.diecraft.com
SIC: 3544 Special dies, tools, jigs & fixtures

(P-14507)
DIE SHOP
7302 Adams St, Paramount (90723-4008)
PHONE...................562 630-4400
Hector Ramirez, *Owner*
Hector J Ramirez, *Principal*
▲ **EMP:** 15
SQ FT: 4,000
SALES (est): 968K **Privately Held**
SIC: 3544 Special dies & tools

(P-14508)
DIVERSIFIED MFG TECH INC
Also Called: Dmt
931 S Via Rodeo, Placentia (92870-6780)
PHONE...................714 577-7000
Michael McMillian, *CEO*
EMP: 12 **EST:** 2011
SALES: 2MM **Privately Held**
SIC: 3544 3089 Industrial molds; injection molding of plastics

(P-14509)
DL TOOL AND MFG CO INC
11828 Glenoaks Blvd, San Fernando
(91340-1804)
PHONE...................818 837-3451
Don A Verity, *President*
Lynne Verity, *Vice Pres*
EMP: 10
SQ FT: 10,500
SALES (est): 1.4MM **Privately Held**
SIC: 3544 Die sets for metal stamping (presses)

(P-14510)
EDRO ENGINEERING INC (DH)
20500 Carrey Rd, Walnut (91789-2417)
PHONE...................909 594-5751
Eric Henn, *President*
Laurinda Diaz, *Shareholder*
Dave Delgato, *Officer*
Mike Guscott, *Vice Pres*
Daniel Previch, *Info Tech Dir*
◆ **EMP:** 85
SQ FT: 60,000
SALES (est): 22.3MM
SALES (corp-wide): 16B **Privately Held**
WEB: www.edro.com
SIC: 3544 3599 Special dies & tools; machine shop, jobbing & repair
HQ: Voestalpine High Performance Metals Corporation
2505 Millennium Dr
Elgin IL 60124
877 992-8764

(P-14511)
EDRO SPECIALTY STEELS INC
20500 Carrey Rd, Walnut (91789-2417)
PHONE...................800 368-3376
Terry Henn, *President*
▲ **EMP:** 11
SALES (est): 1.5MM **Privately Held**
SIC: 3544 Special dies & tools

(P-14512)
ENNIS INC
1600 S Claudina Way, Anaheim
(92805-6541)
PHONE...................714 765-0400
Perry Shokouhi, *Branch Mgr*
EMP: 250
SALES (corp-wide): 370.1MM **Publicly Held**
WEB: www.ennis.com
SIC: 3544 Special dies, tools, jigs & fixtures
PA: Ennis, Inc.
2441 Presidential Pkwy
Midlothian TX 76065
972 775-9801

(P-14513)
ENSTROM MOLD & ENGINEERING
235 Trade St, San Marcos (92078-4373)
PHONE...................760 744-1880
Fred Enstrom, *President*
Greg Metzger, *Vice Pres*
Janice Enstrom, *Admin Sec*
EMP: 17
SQ FT: 12,000
SALES (est): 3MM **Privately Held**
WEB: www.enstrommold.com
SIC: 3544 3089 Industrial molds; plastic processing

(P-14514)
FAIRWAY INJECTION MOLDS INC
20109 Paseo Del Prado, Walnut
(91789-2665)
PHONE...................909 595-2201
Brian Jones, *Managing Dir*
Perry Morgan, *CEO*
Ken Sowski, *Design Engr*
Enrique Barra, *Project Engr*
Mery Lim, *Accountant*
▲ **EMP:** 54
SQ FT: 31,147
SALES (est): 16MM **Privately Held**
WEB: www.fairwaymolds.com
SIC: 3544 Industrial molds

(P-14515)
FELIX TOOL & ENGINEERING
14535 Bessemer St, Van Nuys
(91411-2804)
P.O. Box 6902, Beverly Hills (90212-6902)
PHONE...................818 994-9401
John Felix, *President*
EMP: 23
SQ FT: 6,000
SALES (est): 2.8MM **Privately Held**
WEB: www.felixtool.com
SIC: 3544 3469 Special dies, tools, jigs & fixtures; metal stampings

(P-14516)
FLOTRON INC
2630 Progress St, Vista (92081-8412)
PHONE...................760 727-2700
Danny K Horrell, *President*
EMP: 24
SQ FT: 25,000
SALES: 3.5MM **Privately Held**
WEB: www.flotron.com
SIC: 3544 Special dies & tools

(P-14517)
FUSION PRODUCT MFG INC
440 Industrial Rd, Tecate (91980)
PHONE...................619 819-5521
Adalberto L Ramirez, *President*
Simon Ramirez, *Treasurer*
Jose Ramirez, *Admin Sec*
Arturo Mendez, *Project Mgr*
Xico Ramirez, *Opers Mgr*
▼ **EMP:** 72
SQ FT: 36,000
SALES (est): 2.9MM **Privately Held**
SIC: 3544 Forms (molds), for foundry & plastics working machinery

(P-14518)
FUTURE MOLDS INC
10349 Regis Ct, Rancho Cucamonga
(91730-3055)
PHONE...................909 989-7398
Tony R Parsons, *President*
Bruce Lutz, *Vice Pres*
EMP: 10
SQ FT: 11,000
SALES (est): 1.2MM **Privately Held**
SIC: 3544 Industrial molds

(P-14519)
G B MOLD & TOOL DESIGN
640 Giguere Ct, San Jose (95133-1737)
PHONE...................408 254-3871
George Bunea, *Owner*
EMP: 10
SQ FT: 1,400
SALES (est): 809.6K **Privately Held**
SIC: 3544 Industrial molds

(P-14520)
G E SHELL CORE CO
8346 Salt Lake Ave, Cudahy (90201-5817)
PHONE...................323 773-4242
Raul Rivera, *General Mgr*
EMP: 30
SALES (est): 2.5MM
SALES (corp-wide): 6.3B **Privately Held**
SIC: 3544 Industrial molds
HQ: Consolidated Precision Products Corp.
1621 Euclid Ave Ste 1850
Cleveland OH 44115
216 453-4800

(P-14521)
GEMINI MFG & ENGRG INC
1020 E Vermont Ave, Anaheim
(92805-5617)
PHONE...................714 999-0010
Sandra Lowry, *President*
David Lowry, *Vice Pres*
Mike Clavin, *Prdtn Mgr*
EMP: 20
SQ FT: 40,000
SALES (est): 8.4MM **Privately Held**
WEB: www.geminimfg.com
SIC: 3544 3599 Subpresses, metalworking; machine shop, jobbing & repair

(P-14522)
GMS MOLDS (PA)
729 E 223rd St, Carson (90745-4111)
PHONE...................310 684-1168
Bradley Gardner, *Owner*

EMP: 10
SALES (est): 2.4MM **Privately Held**
SIC: 3544 Industrial molds

(P-14523)
GRUBER SYSTEMS INC
29083 The Old Rd, Valencia (91355-1083)
PHONE...................661 257-0464
John Hoskinson, *Ch of Bd*
Katherine Pavard, *President*
Jim Thiessen, *President*
Diana Arima, *Treasurer*
Steve Miller, *Vice Pres*
◆ **EMP:** 45
SQ FT: 100,000
SALES (est): 13.5MM **Privately Held**
WEB: www.gruber-systems.com
SIC: 3544 3842 3531 3537 Industrial molds; whirlpool baths, hydrotherapy equipment; construction machinery; industrial trucks & tractors

(P-14524)
HAYES MANUFACTURING SVCS LLC
1178 Sonora Ct, Sunnyvale (94086-5308)
PHONE...................408 730-5035
Matthew Hayes, *President*
Dolores Valdez, *Accountant*
Maria Villanueva, *Purch Agent*
Dan Bunnell, *Manager*
Doloris V Longoria, *Manager*
EMP: 27
SQ FT: 22,000
SALES (est): 5.1MM
SALES (corp-wide): 6.2MM **Privately Held**
WEB: www.hayesms.com
SIC: 3544 3089 Industrial molds; plastic processing
PA: Core Industrial Partners, Llc
200 N La Salle St # 2360
Chicago IL 60601
312 566-4880

(P-14525)
HUGHES BROS AIRCRAFTERS INC
11010 Garfield Pl, South Gate
(90280-7512)
PHONE...................323 773-4541
Susan Hughes, *President*
James P Hughes, *Vice Pres*
Michael Hall, *General Mgr*
Francisco Morales, *Manager*
EMP: 43
SQ FT: 15,000
SALES (est): 9MM **Privately Held**
WEB: www.hbai.com
SIC: 3544 3449 3444 Die sets for metal stamping (presses); plastering accessories, metal; sheet metalwork

(P-14526)
IDEA TOOLING & ENGINEERING INC
20601 Annalee Ave, Carson (90746-3527)
PHONE...................310 608-7488
Peter Janner, *President*
Inga Janner, *Treasurer*
Monica Janner, *Vice Pres*
Moe Sumbulan, *Vice Pres*
▲ **EMP:** 56
SQ FT: 20,000
SALES (est): 9.8MM **Privately Held**
WEB: www.ite-plastics.com
SIC: 3544 3061 Special dies & tools; forms (molds), for foundry & plastics working machinery; mechanical rubber goods

(P-14527)
INDUSTRIAL TOOL AND DIE INC
1330 E Saint Gertrude Pl, Santa Ana
(92705-5222)
PHONE...................714 549-1686
Joseph W Adlesh, *President*
EMP: 10
SQ FT: 3,500
SALES: 1.3MM **Privately Held**
SIC: 3544 Special dies & tools

▲ = Import ▼=Export
◆ =Import/Export

(P-14528)

J D TOOL & MACHINE CO INC
12321 Sampson St Ste D, Riverside
(92503-4809)
P.O. Box 2349, Corona (92878-2349)
PHONE..................................951 371-6652
Donna Coulter, *President*
Deletha Gamar, *Admin Sec*
EMP: 10
SQ FT: 8,800
SALES (est): 815.6K **Privately Held**
SIC: 3544 3599 Industrial molds; machine shop, jobbing & repair

(P-14529)

JW MOLDING INC
2523 Calcite Cir, Newbury Park
(91320-1204)
PHONE..................................805 499-2682
Ralf Wolters, *President*
Bridgette Wolters, *Admin Sec*
EMP: 15
SQ FT: 16,000
SALES (est): 3.7MM **Privately Held**
WEB: www.jwmolding.com
SIC: 3544 3089 Forms (molds), for foundry & plastics working machinery; injection molding of plastics

(P-14530)

KAMASHIAN ENGINEERING INC
9128 Rose St, Bellflower (90706-6420)
PHONE..................................562 920-9692
Jerry A Kamashian, *President*
David Cox, *Shareholder*
Harut Avetisyan, *Engineer*
Kathy Neal, *Manager*
EMP: 10
SQ FT: 4,000
SALES (est): 1.6MM **Privately Held**
WEB: www.kamashian.com
SIC: 3544 Special dies & tools

(P-14531)

KECK & SCHMIDT TOOL & DIE INC
2610 Troy Ave, El Monte (91733-1492)
PHONE..................................626 579-3890
Dieter J Keck, *President*
Tisgisela Keck, *Treasurer*
Sandy Worssold, *Admin Sec*
EMP: 12
SQ FT: 10,500
SALES: 3MM **Privately Held**
WEB: www.keckandschmidt.com
SIC: 3544 3469 Special dies & tools; metal stampings

(P-14532)

KINGSON MOLD & MACHINE INC
1350 Titan Way, Brea (92821-3707)
PHONE..................................714 871-0221
Gregory S Rex, *CEO*
EMP: 36
SQ FT: 8,500
SALES (est): 3.7MM **Privately Held**
WEB: www.kingsonmold.com
SIC: 3544 5031 Industrial molds; molding, all materials

(P-14533)

KIPE MOLDS INC
340 E Crowther Ave, Placentia
(92870-6419)
PHONE..................................714 572-9576
George B Kipe Jr, *President*
Rebbeca L Kipe, *Treasurer*
George B Kipe Sr, *Admin Sec*
EMP: 15 **EST:** 1970
SQ FT: 15,000
SALES (est): 3.3MM **Privately Held**
WEB: www.kipemolds.com
SIC: 3544 Industrial molds

(P-14534)

LEE MACHINE PRODUCTS
Also Called: Pneumatic Tube Carrier
2030 Central Ave, Duarte (91010-2913)
PHONE..................................626 301-4105
Thomas Young, *President*
Steve Young, *General Mgr*
EMP: 14 **EST:** 1965
SQ FT: 7,100

SALES: 8.2MM **Privately Held**
WEB: www.leemachine.com
SIC: 3544 3535 3949 7699 Special dies, tools, jigs & fixtures; pneumatic tube conveyor systems; tennis equipment & supplies; industrial machinery & equipment repair

(P-14535)

LEO MOLDS
125 W Victoria St, Gardena (90248-3522)
PHONE..................................562 714-4807
Adhemar Paolini, *Owner*
EMP: 12
SQ FT: 6,000
SALES (est): 906.5K **Privately Held**
SIC: 3544 Industrial molds

(P-14536)

M I T INC
Also Called: Morin Industrial Technology
15202 Pipeline Ln, Huntington Beach
(92649-1136)
PHONE..................................714 899-6066
Rene Morin, *President*
EMP: 15
SQ FT: 12,000
SALES (est): 2.7MM **Privately Held**
WEB: www.m-i-s.com
SIC: 3544 Forms (molds), for foundry & plastics working machinery

(P-14537)

MACDONALD CARBIDE CO
4510 Littlejohn St, Baldwin Park
(91706-2298)
PHONE..................................626 960-4034
Amy Mac Donald, *President*
Amy S Macdonald, *Agent*
◆ **EMP:** 20
SQ FT: 11,140
SALES (est): 3.7MM **Privately Held**
WEB: www.macdonaldcarbide.com
SIC: 3544 3545 Special dies & tools; machine tool accessories

(P-14538)

MAGOR MOLD LLC
420 S Lone Hill Ave, San Dimas
(91773-4600)
PHONE..................................909 592-5729
Wolfgang Buhler, *President*
Bruce Rissinger, *Project Engr*
Martin Schottli, *Director*
Dan Agnew, *Manager*
Steve Iiams, *Manager*
▲ **EMP:** 68
SQ FT: 15,000
SALES (est): 11.9MM **Privately Held**
WEB: www.magormold.com
SIC: 3544 Industrial molds
HQ: Mould Technologies Holding Ag
Industrie Grossholz
Diessenhofen TG
526 462-244

(P-14539)

MASTER WASHER STAMPING SVC CO
80899 Camino San Lucas, Indio
(92203-7468)
PHONE..................................323 722-0969
William Scallon, *President*
Betty Reina, *Vice Pres*
EMP: 12
SALES: 3MM **Privately Held**
SIC: 3544 3469 Die sets for metal stamping (presses); metal stampings

(P-14540)

MECTEC MOLDS INC
1525 Howard Access Rd D, Upland
(91786-2574)
PHONE..................................909 981-3636
T J Wilder, *CEO*
Kristine Wilder, *Admin Sec*
EMP: 10
SQ FT: 4,800
SALES (est): 907.5K **Privately Held**
WEB: www.mectec-molds.com
SIC: 3544 Industrial molds

(P-14541)

METRIC DESIGN & MANUFACTURING
217 E Hacienda Ave, Campbell
(95008-6616)
PHONE..................................408 378-4544
Gunther Unruh, *President*
Nguyet Unruh, *Admin Sec*
EMP: 11
SQ FT: 10,000
SALES (est): 1.4MM **Privately Held**
SIC: 3544 7389 3599 Special dies & tools; grinding, precision: commercial or industrial; machine shop, jobbing & repair

(P-14542)

MJOLNIR INDUSTRIES LLC
Also Called: D & M Precision
5701 Perkins Rd, Oxnard (93033-9014)
PHONE..................................805 488-3550
Jeffrey Ballard, *Mng Member*
EMP: 12
SQ FT: 14,000
SALES (est): 1.3MM **Privately Held**
SIC: 3544 3599 Special dies, tools, jigs & fixtures; machine shop, jobbing & repair

(P-14543)

MOLD MASTERS INC
Also Called: Construction Masters
715 Ruberta Ave, Glendale (91201-2336)
PHONE..................................323 999-2599
Austin Reid, *President*
EMP: 10
SALES: 950K **Privately Held**
SIC: 3544 Industrial molds

(P-14544)

MOLD USA
322 Culver Blve Apt 6, Playa Del Rey
(90293)
PHONE..................................310 823-6653
Jaclyn Resnick, *Principal*
EMP: 10
SALES (est): 653.7K **Privately Held**
SIC: 3544 Industrial molds

(P-14545)

MOLD VISION INC
18351 Pasadena St, Lake Elsinore
(92530-2766)
PHONE..................................951 245-8020
Greg Yocum, *President*
Charles Premananthan, *Vice Pres*
EMP: 15
SALES (est): 1.9MM **Privately Held**
WEB: www.moldvision.net
SIC: 3544 Special dies & tools

(P-14546)

MOREAU WETZEL ENGINEERING CO
24424 Main St Ste 604, Carson
(90745-6394)
PHONE..................................310 830-5479
Fax: 310 830-5487
EMP: 10 **EST:** 1952
SQ FT: 9,000
SALES: 750K **Privately Held**
SIC: 3544 3599

(P-14547)

MR MOLD & ENGINEERING CORP
2700 E Imperial Hwy Ste C, Brea
(92821-6711)
PHONE..................................714 996-5511
Richard Finnie, *President*
Marilyn Finnie, *Vice Pres*
Ashley Cupp, *Office Mgr*
Sharon Valentine, *Office Mgr*
Mike Coleman, *Engineer*
EMP: 31
SQ FT: 14,000
SALES (est): 4.2MM **Privately Held**
WEB: www.mrmold.com
SIC: 3544 Special dies & tools; jigs & fixtures

(P-14548)

N S CERAMIC MOLDING CO
1336 E Francis St Unit 1, Ontario
(91761-5723)
PHONE..................................909 947-3231
James Cannone, *President*

Joanne Ashworth, *Vice Pres*
Jean Mary Zimman, *Vice Pres*
EMP: 45
SQ FT: 8,500
SALES (est): 4.8MM **Privately Held**
SIC: 3544 Industrial molds

(P-14549)

NEVILLE INDUSTRIES INC
Also Called: B & H Tool Company
285 Pawnee St Ste D, San Marcos
(92078-2458)
PHONE..................................760 471-8949
Peter Neville, *President*
EMP: 10
SQ FT: 5,000
SALES (est): 900K **Privately Held**
WEB: www.bhtool.com
SIC: 3544 Dies, plastics forming

(P-14550)

NIRON INC
20541 Earlgate St, Walnut (91789-2909)
PHONE..................................909 598-1526
Glen Nieberle, *President*
Cheryl Nieberle, *Admin Sec*
EMP: 40
SQ FT: 17,000
SALES (est): 5MM **Privately Held**
WEB: www.niron.com
SIC: 3544 3089 Industrial molds; injection molding of plastics

(P-14551)

NOATEX CORPORATION
2711 Plaza Del Amo # 511, Torrance
(90503-7344)
PHONE..................................310 783-0133
Osamu Nishiyama, *CEO*
▲ **EMP:** 10
SQ FT: 6,400
SALES (est): 1MM **Privately Held**
SIC: 3544 Special dies, tools, jigs & fixtures

(P-14552)

OCEANSIDE PLASTIC ENTERPRISES
3038 Industry St Ste 108, Oceanside
(92054-4871)
PHONE..................................760 433-0779
Axel Mnich Jr, *President*
EMP: 10
SALES (est): 1.1MM **Privately Held**
SIC: 3544 Industrial molds

(P-14553)

OLIPHANT TOOL COMPANY
15652 Chemical Ln, Huntington Beach
(92649-1507)
PHONE..................................714 903-6336
William Oliphant, *Owner*
EMP: 35
SQ FT: 12,000
SALES (est): 3MM **Privately Held**
SIC: 3544 7699 Special dies & tools; industrial tool grinding

(P-14554)

PACE PUNCHES INC
297 Goddard, Irvine (92618-4604)
PHONE..................................949 428-2750
Edward W Pepper, *President*
▲ **EMP:** 55
SQ FT: 30,000
SALES (est): 9.7MM **Privately Held**
WEB: www.pacepunches.com
SIC: 3544 Punches, forming & stamping

(P-14555)

PACIFIC DIE CAST INC
15980 Bloomfield Ave, Cerritos
(90703-2155)
PHONE..................................562 407-1390
J R Edens, *President*
▲ **EMP:** 12
SALES (est): 1.7MM **Privately Held**
SIC: 3544 Special dies & tools

(P-14556)

PACIFIC DIE SERVICES INC
7626 Baldwin Pl, Whittier (90602-1001)
PHONE..................................562 907-4463
Eric Syndinos, *President*
EMP: 12
SQ FT: 5,000

PRODUCTS & SVCS

SALES (est): 1.5MM **Privately Held**
SIC: 3544 Dies, steel rule

(P-14557)
PACIFIC SOUTHWEST MOLDS
12307 Woodruff Ave, Downey
(90241-5609)
PHONE....................................562 803-9811
Manuel Cabral, *Owner*
Emanuel Cabral, *Partner*
Terry Duerr, *Partner*
EMP: 12
SQ FT: 6,000
SALES: 400K **Privately Held**
WEB: www.pacificsouthwestmolds.com
SIC: 3544 Industrial molds

(P-14558)
PDC LLC
Also Called: Precision Diecut
4675 Vinita Ct, Chino (91710-5731)
PHONE....................................626 334-5000
Steve Gasparelli, *Mng Member*
Jane Gray, *Finance Mgr*
Patti L W McGlasson,
EMP: 20
SQ FT: 11,000
SALES (est): 5MM **Privately Held**
SIC: 3544 Special dies, tools, jigs & fixtures

(P-14559)
PLASTIKON INDUSTRIES INC (PA)
688 Sandoval Way, Hayward (94544-7129)
PHONE....................................510 400-1010
Fred Soofer, *President*
Fereydoon Soofer, *CEO*
Michele Shaw, *Officer*
Peter F Petri, *Vice Pres*
Eugene Udoh, *Business Dir*
▲ **EMP:** 252 **EST:** 2010
SQ FT: 90,000
SALES (est): 118.5MM **Privately Held**
WEB: www.plastikon.com
SIC: 3544 3089 Special dies, tools, jigs & fixtures; injection molded finished plastic products

(P-14560)
POPE PLASTICS INC
9134 Independence Ave, Chatsworth
(91311-5902)
PHONE....................................818 701-1850
EMP: 40
SQ FT: 30,000
SALES (est): 6.5MM **Privately Held**
SIC: 3544

(P-14561)
PRECISION FORGING DIES INC
10710 Sessler St, South Gate
(90280-7221)
PHONE....................................562 861-1878
Dan Kloss, *President*
Ed Kloss, *General Mgr*
EMP: 27
SALES (est): 5.4MM **Privately Held**
SIC: 3544 Special dies & tools

(P-14562)
PRESTIGE MOLD INCORPORATED
11040 Tacoma Dr, Rancho Cucamonga
(91730-4857)
PHONE....................................909 980-6600
Donna C Pursell, *CEO*
Robert Conner, *Vice Pres*
Lance Spangler, *Vice Pres*
Shawn Pecore, *CIO*
Dan Perkins, *Project Mgr*
▲ **EMP:** 60
SQ FT: 28,500
SALES (est): 13.2MM **Privately Held**
SIC: 3544 Industrial molds
PA: Pres-Tek Plastics, Inc.
11060 Tacoma Dr
Rancho Cucamonga CA
909 360-1600

(P-14563)
PRO MOLD INC
415 Grumman Dr, Riverside (92508-9453)
PHONE....................................951 776-0555
Ronald L Fields, *President*
Ed Bickel, *Vice Pres*

Randy Herr, *Vice Pres*
EMP: 11
SQ FT: 10,000
SALES (est): 1.3MM **Privately Held**
SIC: 3544 3089 Forms (molds), for foundry & plastics working machinery; injection molding of plastics

(P-14564)
PUNCH PRESS PRODUCTS INC
Also Called: Auto Trend Products
2035 E 51st St, Vernon (90058-2818)
PHONE....................................323 581-7151
Delmo Molinari, *Chairman*
CJ Matiszik, *President*
▲ **EMP:** 67
SQ FT: 150,000
SALES (est): 16.8MM **Privately Held**
WEB: www.punch-press.com
SIC: 3544 3469 3471 Special dies & tools; metal stampings; plating & polishing

(P-14565)
PYRAMID MOLD & TOOL
10155 Sharon Cir, Rancho Cucamonga
(91730-5300)
PHONE....................................909 476-2555
Stephen M Hoare, *President*
Brandan Heyes, *Admin Sec*
EMP: 42
SQ FT: 30,300
SALES (est): 6MM **Privately Held**
WEB: www.pyramidmold.com
SIC: 3544 Molding compounds, plastics

(P-14566)
ROTEX PUNCH COMPANY INC (PA)
Also Called: Valves & Cylinders
2350 Alvarado St, San Leandro
(94577-4314)
P.O. Box 2017 (94577-0308)
PHONE....................................510 357-3600
Ronald F Rose, *President*
Jeanne St Clair, *Admin Sec*
EMP: 10 **EST:** 1926
SQ FT: 27,000
SALES (est): 1.1MM **Privately Held**
WEB: www.rotexpunch.com
SIC: 3544 3491 3443 3565 Dies & die holders for metal cutting, forming, die casting; industrial valves; cylinders, pressure; metal plate; wrapping machines; presses: forming, stamping, punching, sizing (machine tools)

(P-14567)
ROTO-DIE COMPANY INC
Also Called: Rotometrics
712 N Valley St Ste B, Anaheim
(92801-3828)
PHONE....................................714 991-8701
Dick Townsend, *Manager*
EMP: 13
SALES (corp-wide): 195.5MM **Privately Held**
WEB: www.rotometrics.com
SIC: 3544 Special dies & tools
PA: Roto-Die Company, Inc.
800 Howerton Ln
Eureka MO 63025
636 587-3600

(P-14568)
S AND S CARBIDE TOOL INC
2830 Via Orange Way Ste D, Spring Valley
(91978-1743)
PHONE....................................619 670-5214
Dennis Strong, *President*
Gary Stewart, *Vice Pres*
Jean-Francois Giroux, *General Mgr*
Isabelle Perreault, *Info Tech Mgr*
EMP: 25
SQ FT: 6,000
SALES (est): 4.5MM **Privately Held**
SIC: 3544 Special dies, tools, jigs & fixtures

(P-14569)
SANTA FE ENTERPRISES INC
Also Called: SFE
11654 Pike St, Santa Fe Springs
(90670-2938)
PHONE....................................562 692-7596
David Warner, *President*
Bob Becker, *Vice Pres*

EMP: 27
SQ FT: 20,000
SALES (est): 5.8MM **Privately Held**
SIC: 3544 Special dies & tools

(P-14570)
SCHREY & SONS MOLD CO INC
24735 Avenue Rockefeller, Valencia
(91355-3466)
PHONE....................................661 294-2260
Walter Schrey, *President*
Gertrude Schrey, *Corp Secy*
Thomas Schrey, *Vice Pres*
William Schrey, *Vice Pres*
James Otec, *Design Engr*
EMP: 35
SQ FT: 53,000
SALES (est): 6.5MM **Privately Held**
WEB: www.schrey.com
SIC: 3544 Industrial molds; special dies & tools

(P-14571)
SOUTH COAST MOLD INC
1852 Mcgaw Ave, Irvine (92614-5734)
PHONE....................................949 253-2000
Paul Novak, *Principal*
Diane Novak, *Principal*
EMP: 10
SALES (est): 839.6K **Privately Held**
WEB: www.southcoastmold.com
SIC: 3544 Industrial molds

(P-14572)
STAINLESS INDUSTRIAL COMPANIES
11111 Santa Monica Blvd # 1120, Los Angeles (90025-3333)
PHONE....................................310 575-9400
Anthony Pritzker, *President*
▲ **EMP:** 100 **EST:** 1998
SALES: 32.3MM
SALES (corp-wide): 242.1B **Publicly Held**
SIC: 3544 Special dies & tools
HQ: The Marmon Group Llc
181 W Madison St Ste 2600
Chicago IL 60602

(P-14573)
SUPERIOR JIG INC
1540 N Orangethorpe Way, Anaheim
(92801-1289)
PHONE....................................714 525-4777
John Morrissey, *President*
Tracy Reed, *Corp Secy*
Susan Hunter, *Technology*
EMP: 22
SQ FT: 14,000
SALES (est): 5.1MM **Privately Held**
WEB: www.sji.net
SIC: 3544 3599 Special dies & tools; jigs & fixtures; machine shop, jobbing & repair

(P-14574)
T & S DIE CUTTING
13301 Alondra Blvd Ste A, Santa Fe Springs (90670-5563)
PHONE....................................562 802-1731
James Good, *Owner*
EMP: 12
SQ FT: 16,000
SALES: 1.7MM **Privately Held**
SIC: 3544 Dies, steel rule

(P-14575)
T I B INC
Also Called: B.T.i Tool Engineering
9525 Pathway St, Santee (92071-4170)
PHONE....................................619 562-3071
James W Jim Barnhill, *President*
Chris Barnhill, *Vice Pres*
James T Todd Barnhill, *Vice Pres*
EMP: 18
SQ FT: 1,000
SALES (est): 3.4MM **Privately Held**
WEB: www.bti-tool.com
SIC: 3544 Jigs & fixtures; die sets for metal stamping (presses)

(P-14576)
TARPIN CORPORATION
Also Called: Western Forge Die
5361 Business Dr, Huntington Beach
(92649-1223)
PHONE....................................714 891-6944
Harold Jermakian, *President*
EMP: 35
SALES (est): 5.2MM **Privately Held**
WEB: www.westernforgedie.com
SIC: 3544 Dies, steel rule; special dies & tools

(P-14577)
TASCO MOLDS INC
6260 Prescott Ct, Chino (91710-7111)
PHONE....................................909 613-1926
Paul S Faris, *President*
EMP: 13
SALES: 1MM **Privately Held**
SIC: 3544 Forms (molds), for foundry & plastics working machinery

(P-14578)
THUNDERBIRD INDUSTRIES INC
695 W Terrace Dr, San Dimas
(91773-2917)
PHONE....................................909 394-1633
Donald Serio, *President*
EMP: 25
SQ FT: 20,000
SALES (est): 3.3MM **Privately Held**
SIC: 3544 3089 Industrial molds; injection molding of plastics

(P-14579)
TMK MANUFACTURING
2110 Oakland Rd, San Jose (95131-1565)
PHONE....................................408 732-3200
EMP: 60
SQ FT: 15,700
SALES (est): 3.3MM **Privately Held**
SIC: 3544 3599 3469

(P-14580)
TOOLS & PRODUCTION INC
466 W Arrow Hwy Ste C, San Dimas
(91773-2940)
PHONE....................................626 286-0213
Michael Lamberti, *President*
▲ **EMP:** 20 **EST:** 1955
SQ FT: 10,000
SALES (est): 3.5MM **Privately Held**
WEB: www.toolsandproduction.com
SIC: 3544 Special dies & tools; punches, forming & stamping

(P-14581)
TOTALLY RADICAL ASSOCIATES INC
Also Called: Tra Medical
1025 Ortega Way Ste A, Placentia
(92870-7174)
PHONE....................................714 630-2740
James Pontillo, *President*
EMP: 15
SQ FT: 8,300
SALES (est): 1.6MM **Privately Held**
WEB: www.tra-medical.com
SIC: 3544 Industrial molds

(P-14582)
TRIO TOOL & DIE CO (PA)
3340 W El Segundo Blvd, Hawthorne
(90250-4892)
PHONE....................................310 644-4431
John Arroues, *President*
Dale Norton, *Office Mgr*
Dennis Armstrong, *Manager*
EMP: 18 **EST:** 1954
SQ FT: 9,200
SALES (est): 4.1MM **Privately Held**
WEB: www.triotoolanddie.com
SIC: 3544 Dies & die holders for metal cutting, forming, die casting; special dies & tools

(P-14583)
UNITED CALIFORNIA CORPORATION
12200 Woodruff Ave, Downey
(90241-5608)
P.O. Box 4250 (90241-1250)
PHONE....................................562 803-1521
Dale L Bethke, *President*

▲ = Import ▼=Export
◆ =Import/Export

Billie Huckins, *Admin Sec*
Erma Parrish, *Accounting Mgr*
Eric Cortez, *Purch Mgr*
EMP: 200
SQ FT: 85,000
SALES (est): 22.9MM **Privately Held**
SIC: 3544 Special dies & tools

(P-14584)
UPM INC
Also Called: Universal Plastic Mold
13245 Los Angeles St, Baldwin Park
(91706-2295)
PHONE..........................626 962-4001
Jason Dowling, *CEO*
Steve Dowling, *President*
Don Ashleigh, *Vice Pres*
Kelley Dowling, *Executive Asst*
Jeanette Garcia, *Human Res Dir*
▼ **EMP:** 290
SQ FT: 100,000
SALES (est): 72.4MM **Privately Held**
SIC: 3544 3089 Special dies, tools, jigs & fixtures; injection molding of plastics

(P-14585)
US DIES INC (PA)
1992 Rockefeller Dr # 300, Ceres
(95307-7274)
PHONE..........................209 664-1402
Thomas Mason, *President*
Diana L Mason, *Corp Secy*
Ken Thomas, *Vice Pres*
Karen Kusumi, *Office Mgr*
EMP: 23 **EST:** 1971
SQ FT: 21,000
SALES (est): 4.2MM **Privately Held**
WEB: www.pwcdies.com
SIC: 3544 Dies, steel rule

(P-14586)
US STEEL RULE DIES INC
Also Called: M D D
40 E Verdugo Ave, Burbank (91502-1931)
PHONE..........................562 921-0690
David Reynolds, *President*
John Washburn, *COO*
EMP: 35
SALES (est): 5MM **Privately Held**
SIC: 3544 Special dies & tools

(P-14587)
VALCO PLANER WORKS INC
Also Called: Valco Precision Works
6131 Maywood Ave, Huntington Park
(90255-3213)
PHONE..........................323 582-6355
Leonel F Valerio, *President*
Carlos Valerio, *Corp Secy*
Leonel G Valerio Jr, *Vice Pres*
Oscar Valerio, *General Mgr*
Austin Ebert, *Engineer*
▼ **EMP:** 25 **EST:** 1953
SQ FT: 10,000
SALES (est): 4.9MM **Privately Held**
WEB: www.valcoplaner.com
SIC: 3544 3545 Special dies, tools, jigs & fixtures; machine tool accessories

(P-14588)
VALLEY MFG & ENGRG INC
9105 De Garmo Ave, Sun Valley
(91352-2608)
PHONE..........................818 504-6085
Keith Gross, *President*
May Cahme, *Vice Pres*
EMP: 10
SQ FT: 35,000
SALES (est): 1.5MM **Privately Held**
SIC: 3544 3089 3083 Industrial molds; injection molded finished plastic products; laminated plastics plate & sheet

(P-14589)
VELCO TOOL & DIE INC
20431 Barents Sea Cir, Lake Forest
(92630-8807)
PHONE..........................949 855-6638
Jose M Velez, *President*
EMP: 10
SQ FT: 5,350
SALES (est): 2.2MM **Privately Held**
WEB: www.velco.net
SIC: 3544 Dies & die holders for metal cutting, forming, die casting

(P-14590)
WAGNER DIE SUPPLY (PA)
2041 Elm Ct, Ontario (91761-7619)
PHONE..........................909 947-3044
Ellsworth Knutson, *President*
John Knutson, *Treasurer*
Mike Knutson, *Vice Pres*
Tom Knutson, *Admin Sec*
▲ **EMP:** 36
SALES (est): 8MM **Privately Held**
SIC: 3544 Dies, steel rule; special dies & tools

(P-14591)
WEST RAPCO ENVIRONMENTAL SVCS
Also Called: Rapco-West Asbestos
23852 Pacific Coast Hwy # 941, Malibu
(90265-4876)
PHONE..........................310 450-3335
Steven Amici, *President*
EMP: 30
SQ FT: 2,500
SALES (est): 3.1MM **Privately Held**
SIC: 3544 Industrial molds

(P-14592)
WRIGHT ENGINEERED PLASTICS INC
3681 N Laughlin Rd, Santa Rosa
(95403-1027)
PHONE..........................707 575-1218
Barbara F Roberts, *CEO*
Karrie Bertsch, *Engineer*
Mike Nellis, *Plant Mgr*
Matt Calahan, *QC Mgr*
◆ **EMP:** 61
SQ FT: 25,000
SALES (est): 13.2MM
SALES (corp-wide): 5.5MM **Privately Held**
WEB: www.wepmolding.com
SIC: 3544 3089 Special dies, tools, jigs & fixtures; plastic hardware & building products
PA: Molding Solutions Inc
3225 Regional Pkwy
Santa Rosa CA 95403
707 575-1218

(P-14593)
YORK ENGINEERING
4405 Lincoln Ave, Los Angeles
(90041-3321)
PHONE..........................323 256-0439
Phillip Shin, *Owner*
EMP: 11
SQ FT: 3,000
SALES (est): 1.3MM **Privately Held**
WEB: www.yorkengineering.com
SIC: 3544 Special dies, tools, jigs & fixtures

3545 Machine Tool Access

(P-14594)
ABG ENGINEERING INC
42213 Sarah Way, Temecula (92590-3463)
PHONE..........................714 282-8204
Joyce Gledhill, *President*
EMP: 10 **EST:** 2011
SALES (est): 1.6MM **Privately Held**
SIC: 3545 Precision measuring tools

(P-14595)
ACCU-GRINDING INC
Also Called: Westcoast Tool Products
8516 San Fernando Rd, Sun Valley
(91352-3110)
PHONE..........................818 768-4497
Ruben Cortez, *President*
Rubin Cortez, *President*
Antonette Cortez, *Manager*
EMP: 19
SQ FT: 8,000
SALES (est): 1.5MM **Privately Held**
SIC: 3545 3599 Drill bushings (drilling jig); machine shop, jobbing & repair

(P-14596)
ADTECH TOOL ENGRG CORPORATIONS
13620 Cimarron Ave, Gardena
(90249-2459)
PHONE..........................310 515-1717
James Lee, *President*
EMP: 13
SQ FT: 11,024
SALES (est): 1.8MM **Privately Held**
SIC: 3545 Collets (machine tool accessories)

(P-14597)
ALTUS POSITIONING SYSTEMS INC
20725 S Wstn Ave Ste 100, Torrance
(90501)
PHONE..........................310 541-8139
Neil Vancans, *President*
MO Kapila, *Director*
Eric Albrecht, *Manager*
EMP: 12
SALES (est): 2MM **Privately Held**
WEB: www.altus-ps.com
SIC: 3545 Precision tools, machinists'

(P-14598)
AMERICAN QUALITY TOOLS INC
12650 Magnolia Ave Ste B, Riverside
(92503-4690)
PHONE..........................951 280-4700
Mukesh Aghi, *President*
Rakesh Aghi, *Vice Pres*
David Goodman, *General Mgr*
Bertha Najera, *Human Res Mgr*
Lorraine Valenzuela, *Manager*
▲ **EMP:** 45
SQ FT: 22,000
SALES (est): 8.6MM **Privately Held**
WEB: www.aqtools.com
SIC: 3545 Cutting tools for machine tools

(P-14599)
AMO CORPORATION
9580 Oak Avenue Pkwy # 9, Folsom
(95630-1888)
PHONE..........................916 791-2001
Alton Werner, *President*
EMP: 10
SALES (est): 984.5K **Privately Held**
SIC: 3545 Machine tool accessories
HQ: Amo Automatisierung MeBtechnik
Optik Gmbh
Nofing 4
St. Peter Am Hart 4963
772 265-8560

(P-14600)
AMP III LLC
Also Called: Advanced Machine Programming
465 Woodview Ave, Morgan Hill
(95037-2800)
PHONE..........................408 779-2927
Kent Rounds,
EMP: 65
SALES (est): 5.2MM **Privately Held**
SIC: 3545 Precision tools, machinists'

(P-14601)
AMPERTECH INC
636 S State College Blvd, Fullerton
(92831-5138)
PHONE..........................714 523-4068
Jenny Wang, *President*
Kirby Ku, *Vice Pres*
▲ **EMP:** 50 **EST:** 2000
SQ FT: 4,000
SALES (est): 4MM **Privately Held**
WEB: www.ampertech.com
SIC: 3545 3679 Machine tool accessories; electronic circuits

(P-14602)
ASI TOOLING LLC
1780 La Costa Meadows Dr # 103, San Marcos (92078-9101)
PHONE..........................760 744-2520
Melissa Theriault,
Richard Theriault, *Mng Member*
EMP: 12 **EST:** 2008
SALES (est): 1.9MM **Privately Held**
SIC: 3545 Cutting tools for machine tools

(P-14603)
ATS WORKHOLDING INC
Also Called: Ats Systems
30222 Esperanza, Rcho STA Marg
(92688-2121)
PHONE..........................800 321-1833
Charles A Goad, *CEO*
Wu Robert, *CFO*
Ken Erkenbrack, *Vice Pres*
Carlos Hernandez, *Principal*
Blake Daub, *Technology*
▲ **EMP:** 67
SQ FT: 22,840
SALES (est): 30MM **Privately Held**
WEB: www.atsworkholding.com
SIC: 3545 Milling machine attachments (machine tool accessories)

(P-14604)
AUTOCAL INC
1976 E Mcfadden Ave, Santa Ana
(92705-4706)
PHONE..........................714 550-7444
Hassan Kaeni, *President*
Nader Kaeni, *Vice Pres*
EMP: 14
SQ FT: 1,400
SALES (est): 134.2K **Privately Held**
WEB: www.autocal.net
SIC: 3545 Machine tool accessories

(P-14605)
BARKER-CANOGA INC
Also Called: J B Manufacturing Co
16528 Koala Rd Ste A, Adelanto
(92301-3966)
PHONE..........................760 246-4777
John Barker, *CEO*
Yvonne Barker, *President*
Mike Barker, *Treasurer*
EMP: 10 **EST:** 1965
SQ FT: 8,000
SALES (est): 880K **Privately Held**
SIC: 3545 Honing heads

(P-14606)
BARRANCA HOLDINGS LTD
Also Called: Barranca Diamond Products
22815 Frampton Ave, Torrance
(90501-5034)
PHONE..........................310 523-5867
Brian Delahaut, *President*
▲ **EMP:** 12 **EST:** 1998
SALES (est): 1.4MM
SALES (corp-wide): 47.1MM **Privately Held**
WEB: www.barrancadiamond.com
SIC: 3545 Diamond cutting tools for turning, boring, burnishing, etc.
PA: Diamond Mk Products Inc
1315 Storm Pkwy
Torrance CA 90501
310 539-5221

(P-14607)
BEAM DYNAMICS INC
5100 Patrick Henry Dr, Santa Clara
(95054-1112)
PHONE..........................408 764-4805
Mathew Bye, *President*
Jon Maroney, *Vice Pres*
Blaine Boloich, *Director*
EMP: 12
SQ FT: 4,200
SALES (est): 1.1MM
SALES (corp-wide): 1.7B **Publicly Held**
WEB: www.beamdynamics.com
SIC: 3545 Machine tool accessories
PA: Coherent, Inc.
5100 Patrick Henry Dr
Santa Clara CA 95054
408 764-4000

(P-14608)
BENEN MANUFACTURING LLC
1872 Hartog Dr, San Jose (95131-2203)
PHONE..........................408 573-7252
Giang T Tran,
EMP: 10 **EST:** 2011
SALES (est): 2MM **Privately Held**
SIC: 3545 Measuring tools & machines, machinists' metalworking type

PRODUCTS & SVCS

(P-14609)
BLAHA OLDRIH
Also Called: Quality Machining
114 10th St, Ramona (92065-2103)
PHONE......................................760 789-9791
Oldrih Blaha, *Partner*
Melita Blaha, *Partner*
EMP: 10
SQ FT: 3,100
SALES (est): 1.4MM **Privately Held**
SIC: 3545 3599 Machine tool accessories;
machine shop, jobbing & repair

(P-14610)
BROACH MASTERS INC
1605 Industrial Dr, Auburn (95603-9018)
PHONE......................................530 885-1939
Mark Vian, *President*
Elizabeth Vian, *Vice Pres*
EMP: 27
SALES (est): 5MM **Privately Held**
SIC: 3545 3599 Precision tools, machin-
ists'; machine shop, jobbing & repair

(P-14611)
C & GTOOL INC
910 Striker Ave Ste B, Sacramento
(95834-1163)
PHONE......................................916 614-9114
Daniel Crowninshield, *President*
EMP: 11
SQ FT: 8,000
SALES (est): 18MM **Privately Held**
SIC: 3545 Precision tools, machinists'

(P-14612)
**CALIFORNIA REAMER
COMPANY INC**
12747 Los Nietos Rd, Santa Fe Springs
(90670-3007)
PHONE......................................562 946-6377
David J Neptune, *President*
EMP: 11
SQ FT: 5,500
SALES (est): 1.3MM **Privately Held**
SIC: 3545 Reamers, machine tool

(P-14613)
CAMPBELL ENGINEERING INC
20412 Barents Sea Cir, Lake Forest
(92630-8807)
PHONE......................................949 859-3306
James Campbell, *President*
Carolyn Campbell, *Principal*
EMP: 24 EST: 1994
SQ FT: 3,800
SALES: 2MM **Privately Held**
SIC: 3545 3541 Precision measuring
tools; lathes, metal cutting & polishing

(P-14614)
CARBIDE COMPANY LLC
Also Called: Monster Tool Company
2470 Ash St Ste 1, Vista (92081-8461)
P.O. Box 1749, San Marcos (92079-1749)
PHONE......................................760 477-1000
Pamela Rae Brossman, *Mng Member*
Mark Dalhover, *Mfg Dir*
Pam Brossman,
Josh Lynberg,
Taylor Smale, *Accounts Mgr*
◆ EMP: 100
SQ FT: 30,000
SALES: 22MM **Privately Held**
SIC: 3545 Machine tool accessories

(P-14615)
CARBRO CORPORATION
15724 Condon Ave, Lawndale
(90260-2531)
P.O. Box 278 (90260-0278)
PHONE......................................310 643-8400
Ed Plano, *President*
Jay Rosenbluth, *Treasurer*
Anders Plano, *General Mgr*
Ingela Jussen, *Office Mgr*
Willie Jussen, *Purchasing*
EMP: 40
SQ FT: 14,500
SALES (est): 6MM **Privately Held**
SIC: 3545 End mills; files, machine tool;
reamers, machine tool

(P-14616)
**CONCEPT PART SOLUTIONS
INC**
2047 Zanker Rd, San Jose (95131-2107)
PHONE......................................408 748-1244
Richard L Diehl, *CEO*
Saori Japan, *Partner*
Bruce Dickson, *Managing Dir*
MO China, *General Mgr*
Ikuko Kato, *Sales Dir*
EMP: 44
SALES (est): 10.5MM **Privately Held**
SIC: 3545 Machine tool accessories

(P-14617)
COORSTEK INC
4544 Mcgrath St, Ventura (93003-6492)
PHONE......................................805 644-5583
EMP: 100
SALES (corp-wide): 829.3MM **Privately
Held**
SIC: 3545
HQ: Coorstek, Inc.
     14143 Denver Ste 400
     Golden CO 80401
     303 271-7000

(P-14618)
COORSTEK INC
Also Called: Coorstek Ventura Geiser Bondin
4544 Mcgrath St, Ventura (93003-6492)
PHONE......................................805 644-5583
Dan Luzi, *Manager*
Tedd Allen, *Info Tech Dir*
David Montoya, *Engineer*
EMP: 200
SALES (corp-wide): 909.3MM **Privately
Held**
SIC: 3545 Machine tool accessories
HQ: Coorstek, Inc.
     14143 Denver West Pkwy # 400
     Lakewood CO 80401
     303 271-7000

(P-14619)
COPLAN & COPLAN INC
Also Called: Speedpress Sign Supply
2270 Camino Vida Roble H, Carlsbad
(92011-1503)
PHONE......................................760 268-0583
Jacob Coplan, *CEO*
Noah Coplan, *Vice Pres*
Pamela D Tuck, *Executive*
Marita Coplan, *Mktg Dir*
◆ EMP: 20
SQ FT: 14,000
SALES (est): 3.9MM **Privately Held**
WEB: www.speedpress.com
SIC: 3545 Tools & accessories for machine
tools

(P-14620)
CRAIG TOOLS INC
142 Lomita St, El Segundo (90245-4113)
PHONE......................................310 322-0614
William B Cleveland, *President*
Don Tripler, *Exec VP*
Arnulfo Garcia, *Purch Agent*
D Jason Oaga, *Production*
▼ EMP: 37 EST: 1958
SQ FT: 13,000
SALES (est): 7.1MM **Privately Held**
WEB: www.craigtools.com
SIC: 3545 Precision tools, machinists'

(P-14621)
CRITERION MACHINE WORKS
765 W 16th St, Costa Mesa (92627-4302)
PHONE......................................949 631-5444
Gary Vanderpol, *CEO*
Bob Wahlstrom, *President*
Sandi Kallas, *Principal*
Frank McDougall, *Principal*
EMP: 40
SQ FT: 30,000
SALES (est): 4.5MM **Privately Held**
WEB: www.criterionmachineworks.com
SIC: 3545 Machine tool attachments & ac-
cessories; cutting tools for machine tools

(P-14622)
DAC INTERNATIONAL INC (PA)
Also Called: D A C
6390 Rose Ln, Carpinteria (93013-2998)
PHONE......................................805 684-8307
Kenneth R Payne, *President*

George Heavican, *VP Sales*
▲ EMP: 34
SQ FT: 17,500
SALES: 10MM **Privately Held**
WEB: www.dac-intl.com
SIC: 3545 Machine tool accessories

(P-14623)
DEWEYL TOOL CO INC
959 Transport Way, Petaluma
(94954-1474)
PHONE......................................707 765-5779
William Cline, *President*
Susan Blow, *Vice Pres*
Linda Cline, *Vice Pres*
EMP: 35
SQ FT: 20,000
SALES (est): 6MM **Privately Held**
WEB: www.deweyl.com
SIC: 3545 Machine tool attachments & ac-
cessories

(P-14624)
DIAMOTEC INC
3545 Lomita Blvd Ste C, Torrance
(90505-5022)
PHONE......................................310 539-4994
Varoujan Kundakjian, *President*
Alex Kundakjian, *Vice Pres*
Rod Shahinian, *Vice Pres*
Houry Abacyan, *Admin Sec*
EMP: 12
SQ FT: 5,000
SALES: 2.3MM **Privately Held**
WEB: www.diamotec.com
SIC: 3545 Tools & accessories for machine
tools

(P-14625)
**DIGITAL TECHNOLOGY LAB
CORP**
Also Called: DTL Mori Seiki
3805 Faraday Ave, Davis (95618-7773)
PHONE......................................530 746-7400
Zach Piner, *President*
Hiroshi Takami, *Treasurer*
Adam Hansel, *Vice Pres*
Natsuo Okada, *Admin Sec*
▲ EMP: 55
SALES (est): 9MM
SALES (corp-wide): 3.9B **Privately Held**
SIC: 3545 Machine tool accessories
HQ: Dmg Mori Usa, Inc.
     2400 Huntington Blvd
     Hoffman Estates IL 60192
     847 593-5400

(P-14626)
DNMC
21600 8th St E, Sonoma (95476-2821)
PHONE......................................707 935-0353
Scott Lewis, *President*
EMP: 30
SALES (est): 1.6MM **Privately Held**
WEB: www.dnmc.com
SIC: 3545 Chucks: drill, lathe or magnetic
(machine tool accessories)

(P-14627)
**DRILLING & TRENCHING SUP
INC (PA)**
Also Called: Drilling World
1458 Mariani Ct, Tracy (95376-2825)
PHONE......................................510 895-1650
David Wellington Moran, *CEO*
Erin B Moran, *Admin Sec*
Dianne Gonzales, *Manager*
◆ EMP: 17
SQ FT: 52,000
SALES (est): 9.2MM **Privately Held**
WEB: www.drillingworld.com
SIC: 3545 Drilling machine attachments &
accessories

(P-14628)
DYNATEX INTERNATIONAL
5577 Skylane Blvd, Santa Rosa
(95403-1048)
PHONE......................................707 542-4227
Kate Henry, *CEO*
John Tyler, *President*
Leanne Sarasy, *Vice Pres*
Dale Humphrey, *Engineer*
Melanie Jones-Carter, *Purchasing*
EMP: 21 EST: 1958
SQ FT: 15,000

SALES (est): 3.8MM **Privately Held**
SIC: 3545 Cutting tools for machine tools

(P-14629)
EDWARDS ENTERPRISES
4544 Mcgrath St, Ventura (93003-6492)
PHONE......................................805 644-5583
John Coors, *President*
Lance Morford, *Plant Mgr*
John Pritzkau, *Plant Mgr*
Richard Valueff, *Plant Supt*
Heidi Hansen, *Accounts Mgr*
EMP: 280 EST: 1957
SQ FT: 62,000
SALES (est): 498.1K
SALES (corp-wide): 909.3MM **Privately
Held**
SIC: 3545 Tools & accessories for machine
tools
HQ: Coorstek, Inc.
     14143 Denver West Pkwy # 400
     Lakewood CO 80401
     303 271-7000

(P-14630)
ELCON PRECISION LLC
1009 Timothy Dr, San Jose (95133-1043)
PHONE......................................408 292-7800
Dan Brumlik, *Chairman*
Pater Smith, *President*
Jamie Howton, *Mng Member*
EMP: 23
SALES (est): 5MM **Privately Held**
SIC: 3545 Precision tools, machinists'

(P-14631)
FARRS CUSTOM CARBIDE INC
1000 Ortega Way Ste B, Placentia
(92870-7162)
PHONE......................................800 684-0411
Richard J Farr, *Principal*
Jeff Miklaus, *General Mgr*
EMP: 11
SALES (est): 1.7MM **Privately Held**
SIC: 3545 Machine tool accessories

(P-14632)
**FAY AND QRTRMINE MCHINING
CORP**
Also Called: Fay & Quartermaine Machining
2745 Seaman Ave, El Monte (91733-1935)
PHONE......................................323 686-0224
David Cary, *President*
Yolanda Benitez, *Office Mgr*
EMP: 10
SQ FT: 8,000
SALES (est): 1.6MM **Privately Held**
SIC: 3545 Precision tools, machinists'

(P-14633)
FORCE FLOW
2430 Stanwell Dr Ste 110, Concord
(94520-4847)
PHONE......................................925 686-6700
Mark Nelson, *President*
David Nelson, *CFO*
EMP: 30
SALES (est): 5.3MM **Privately Held**
WEB: www.forceflow.com
SIC: 3545 Scales, measuring (machinists'
precision tools)

(P-14634)
**FOX THERMAL INSTRUMENTS
INC**
399 Reservation Rd, Marina (93933-3229)
PHONE......................................831 384-4300
William Roller, *CEO*
Bradley Philip Lesko, *President*
Ron Provost, *Vice Pres*
Al Arreola, *Regional Mgr*
Raj Pillay, *Admin Asst*
▲ EMP: 20 EST: 1993
SQ FT: 8,000
SALES (est): 4.2MM
SALES (corp-wide): 1.4B **Privately Held**
WEB: www.foxthermalinstruments.com
SIC: 3545 Gauges (machine tool acces-
sories)
HQ: Onicon Incorporated
     11451 Belcher Rd S
     Largo FL 33773
     727 447-6140

▲ = Import ▼=Export
◆ =Import/Export

(P-14635)
FREEFORM RESEARCH & DEV
Also Called: Sling-Light
1539 Monrovia Ave Ste 23, Newport Beach
(92663-2853)
PHONE..................................949 646-3217
Stephen B Wheeler, *President*
Nova Wheeler, *Vice Pres*
EMP: 10
SALES (est): 1MM **Privately Held**
WEB: www.slinglight.com
SIC: 3545 Drilling machine attachments &
accessories

(P-14636)
FRT OF AMERICA LLC
1101 S Winchester Blvd, San Jose
(95128-3901)
PHONE..................................408 261-2632
Thomas Fries,
EMP: 11
SALES (est): 1.2MM
SALES (corp-wide): 7.4MM **Privately
Held**
SIC: 3545 Measuring tools & machines,
machinists' metalworking type
PA: Fries Research & Technology Gmbh
Friedrich-Ebert-Str. 75
Bergisch Gladbach 51429
220 484-2430

(P-14637)
GAGE WAFCO CO INC
16625 Gramercy Pl, Gardena
(90247-5201)
PHONE..................................310 532-3106
Patricia Hymovitz, *President*
Arlene Hymovitz, *Vice Pres*
EMP: 12
SQ FT: 3,000
SALES (est): 1.5MM **Privately Held**
SIC: 3545

(P-14638)
**GANG YAN DIAMOND
PRODUCTS INC**
4620 Mission Blvd, Montclair (91763-6135)
PHONE..................................909 590-2255
Xianpu Shen, *President*
Paul Shen, *Vice Pres*
▲ EMP: 16
SALES (est): 2.9MM **Privately Held**
SIC: 3545 Diamond cutting tools for turn-
ing, boring, burnishing, etc.

(P-14639)
**GENIUS TOOLS AMERICAS
CORP (PA)**
1440 E Cedar St, Ontario (91761-8300)
PHONE..................................909 230-9588
Edward Chou, *President*
Andrew Hwang, *Vice Pres*
▲ EMP: 12
SALES (est): 2.4MM **Privately Held**
WEB: www.geniustoolsusa.com
SIC: 3545 Tools & accessories for machine
tools

(P-14640)
HEXAGON METROLOGY INC
7 Orchard Ste 102, Lake Forest
(92630-8334)
PHONE..................................949 916-4490
Thomas Weinert, *Principal*
EMP: 50
SALES (corp-wide): 18.8MM **Privately
Held**
SIC: 3545 3823 Precision measuring
tools; industrial instrmnts msrmnt dis-
play/control process variable
HQ: Hexagon Metrology, Inc.
250 Circuit Dr
North Kingstown RI 02852
401 886-2000

(P-14641)
HTE MANUFACTURING INC
Also Called: HI Tech Engineering
4610 Calle Quetzal, Camarillo
(93012-8558)
PHONE..................................805 987-5449
Michelle Schuckmann, *President*
Chris Schuckmann, *Vice Pres*
EMP: 18
SQ FT: 8,000

SALES (est): 2.6MM **Privately Held**
SIC: 3545 3541 Precision tools, machinists'; machine tools, metal cutting type

(P-14642)
JORDAN COMPANYS
2122 S El Camino Real E, San Clemente
(92672-4277)
P.O. Box 309 (92674-0309)
PHONE..................................949 492-0804
John Jordan, *Ch of Bd*
EMP: 36
SALES (est): 2.9MM **Privately Held**
SIC: 3545 8748 Machine tool accessories;
telecommunications consultant

(P-14643)
KEEN-KUT PRODUCTS INC
Also Called: N W D T
3190 Diablo Ave, Hayward (94545-2702)
PHONE..................................510 785-5168
Frank Lenner, *President*
Diana Lenner, *Vice Pres*
EMP: 10
SQ FT: 8,000
SALES (est): 1.5MM **Privately Held**
WEB: www.keenkut.com
SIC: 3545 Diamond cutting tools for turn-
ing, boring, burnishing, etc.

(P-14644)
**KEMPTON MACHINE WORKS
INC**
4070 E Leaverton Ct, Anaheim
(92807-1610)
PHONE..................................714 990-0596
Greg Kempton, *President*
EMP: 12
SQ FT: 14,000
SALES (est): 1.4MM **Privately Held**
SIC: 3545 3599 Tools & accessories for
machine tools; machine shop, jobbing &
repair

(P-14645)
LOCK-N-STITCH INC
1015 S Soderquist Rd, Turlock
(95380-5726)
PHONE..................................209 632-2345
Gary J Reed, *CEO*
Louise Reed, *President*
Brandi Rollins, *Corp Secy*
Arthur Reyes, *Human Res Mgr*
Arno Oja, *Mfg Mgr*
▲ EMP: 42
SQ FT: 33,000
SALES (est): 4.9MM **Privately Held**
WEB: www.locknstitch.com
SIC: 3545 Threading tools (machine tool
accessories)

(P-14646)
MACHNET INC
11835 W Olympic Blvd 1280e, Los Angeles
(90064-5811)
PHONE..................................310 909-2020
Gene Taubman, *CEO*
Rocky Lepez, *Sales Associate*
EMP: 12 EST: 2009
SALES (est): 1.8MM **Privately Held**
SIC: 3545 Tools & accessories for machine
tools

(P-14647)
MAKINO INC
17800 Newhope St Ste K, Fountain Valley
(92708-5429)
PHONE..................................714 444-4334
Jonathan Haye, *Branch Mgr*
EMP: 20
SALES (corp-wide): 1.7B **Privately Held**
SIC: 3545 Tools & accessories for machine
tools
HQ: Makino Inc.
7680 Innovation Way
Mason OH 45040
513 573-7200

(P-14648)
**MARSHALL GENUINE
PRODUCTS LLC**
Also Called: Mgp Caliper Covers
616 Marsat Ct, Chula Vista (91911-4646)
PHONE..................................619 754-4099
Michael Barland, *Mng Member*
Mike Barland, *Mng Member*

EMP: 18
SQ FT: 14,500
SALES: 2.5MM **Privately Held**
SIC: 3545 Calipers & dividers

(P-14649)
MECADAQ AEROSPACE LLC
Also Called: Meca Aerospace
2806 S Susan St, Santa Ana (92704-5821)
PHONE..................................714 442-9703
Julien Dubecq, *President*
▲ EMP: 10
SQ FT: 7,000
SALES: 1MM
SALES (corp-wide): 1.4MM **Privately
Held**
SIC: 3545 Precision tools, machinists'
HQ: Mecadaq Tarnos
Pole Technologique Jean Be
Tarnos 40220

(P-14650)
**MERCURY BROACH COMPANY
INC**
2546 Seaman Ave, El Monte (91733-1986)
PHONE..................................626 443-5904
Mark Eberlein, *President*
EMP: 14
SQ FT: 7,000
SALES (est): 2.2MM **Privately Held**
SIC: 3545 Broaches (machine tool acces-
sories)

(P-14651)
**MEYCO MACHINE AND TOOL
INC**
11579 Martens River Cir, Fountain Valley
(92708-4201)
P.O. Box 9659 (92728-9659)
PHONE..................................714 435-1546
Manuel Gomez, *CEO*
Victor Salazar, *Vice Pres*
Lorena Estrada, *Principal*
Max Gomez, *Principal*
Edith Martinez, *Principal*
EMP: 38 EST: 1996
SQ FT: 12,500
SALES: 4.2MM **Privately Held**
WEB: www.meycomachine.com
SIC: 3545 Tools & accessories for machine
tools

(P-14652)
**MICRO TOOL &
MANUFACTURING INC**
6494 Federal Blvd, Lemon Grove
(91945-1376)
PHONE..................................619 582-2884
Fae Galea, *President*
Michael H Galea, *Corp Secy*
Charles Galea, *Vice Pres*
John Galea, *Assistant VP*
Steve J Galea, *Assistant VP*
EMP: 22
SQ FT: 10,000
SALES: 5MM **Privately Held**
SIC: 3545 3544 Precision tools, machin-
ists'; jigs: inspection, gauging & checking;
die sets for metal stamping (presses)

(P-14653)
MIST INCORPORATED
9006 Fullbright Ave, Chatsworth
(91311-6125)
PHONE..................................818 678-5619
Ken Perlis, *Vice Pres*
Steve Miller, *President*
Scott Febles, *General Mgr*
Kenneth Perlis, *General Mgr*
▲ EMP: 20 EST: 2000
SQ FT: 14,000
SALES (est): 4MM **Privately Held**
WEB: www.mist-tools.com
SIC: 3545 5085 Cutting tools for machine
tools; tools

(P-14654)
MKKR INC
Also Called: Matko
430 E Parkcenter Cir N, San Bernardino
(92408-2869)
P.O. Box 8891, Redlands (92375-2091)
PHONE..................................909 890-5994
Matthew Curtis, *President*

Rowena Rivera-Curtis, *Vice Pres*
EMP: 11
SQ FT: 23,500
SALES (est): 1.5MM **Privately Held**
WEB: www.matko.com
SIC: 3545 Scales, measuring (machinists'
precision tools)

(P-14655)
**MOTORS & CONTROLS INTL INC
(PA)**
1440 N Burton Pl, Anaheim (92806-1204)
PHONE..................................714 956-0480
Lester Tjelmeland, *President*
Katherine Tjelmeland, *Corp Secy*
▲ EMP: 27
SQ FT: 35,000
SALES (est): 2.7MM **Privately Held**
WEB: www.mc-w.com
SIC: 3545 3621 Industrial machinery &
equipment repair

(P-14656)
MUELLER GAGES COMPANY
318 Agostino Rd, San Gabriel
(91776-2505)
P.O. Box 310 (91778-0310)
PHONE..................................626 287-2911
Rhett Mueller, *President*
Sandra Mueller, *Admin Sec*
EMP: 13 EST: 1949
SQ FT: 10,500
SALES: 1.3MM **Privately Held**
WEB: www.mueller-gages.com
SIC: 3545 Precision tools, machinists'

(P-14657)
NATIONAL DIAMOND LAB CAL
4650 Alger St, Los Angeles (90039-1192)
PHONE..................................818 240-5770
Jerry Howard, *CEO*
Mary Pettet, *Office Mgr*
◆ EMP: 11
SQ FT: 10,000
SALES: 1.8MM **Privately Held**
WEB: www.diamondtooling.com
SIC: 3545 Precision measuring tools

(P-14658)
O AND Y PRECISION INC
312 Piercy Rd, San Jose (95138-1401)
PHONE..................................408 362-1333
Majid Yahyaie, *CEO*
Robbie Oyar,
EMP: 12
SQ FT: 3,000
SALES (est): 1.3MM **Privately Held**
SIC: 3545 Machine tool accessories

(P-14659)
OMEGA DIAMOND INC
10125 Ophir Rd, Newcastle (95658-9504)
PHONE..................................916 652-8122
Samuel Devai, *President*
Roneily Devai, *Admin Sec*
▲ EMP: 17
SQ FT: 3,000
SALES (est): 3.3MM **Privately Held**
WEB: www.omegadiamond.com
SIC: 3545 Diamond cutting tools for turn-
ing, boring, burnishing, etc.

(P-14660)
**PELAGIC PRESSURE SYSTEMS
CORP**
2002 Davis St, San Leandro (94577-1211)
PHONE..................................510 569-3100
Michael Hollis, *CEO*
Mike Hollis, *COO*
Robert Hollis, *Vice Pres*
Nicole Romero, *Buyer*
Blake Bortner, *Opers Mgr*
▲ EMP: 75 EST: 1979
SQ FT: 74,000
SALES (est): 14.4MM
SALES (corp-wide): 65.5MM **Privately
Held**
WEB: www.pelagicnet.com
SIC: 3545 Gauges (machine tool acces-
sories)
PA: Aqua-Lung America, Inc.
2340 Cousteau Ct
Vista CA 92081
760 597-5000

(P-14661)
PENHALL DIAMOND PRODUCTS INC
Also Called: Norton Company
1345 S Acacia Ave, Fullerton (92831-5315)
PHONE.................................714 776-0937
Dave Dodd, *General Mgr*
▲ EMP: 76
SQ FT: 30,000
SALES: 7.6MM
SALES (corp-wide): 213.5MM Privately Held
WEB: www.sgabrasives.com
SIC: 3545 Diamond cutting tools for turning, boring, burnishing, etc.; diamond dressing & wheel crushing attachments
HQ: Saint-Gobain Abrasives, Inc.
1 New Bond St
Worcester MA 01606
508 795-5000

(P-14662)
PENNOYER-DODGE CO
6650 San Fernando Rd, Glendale (91201-1745)
PHONE.................................818 547-2100
Hazel Dodge, *President*
Karen Dodge, *Admin Sec*
EMP: 40
SALES: 4.5MM Privately Held
WEB: www.pdgage.com
SIC: 3545 8734 5084 3643 Gauges (machine tool accessories); precision tools, machinists'; calibration & certification; instruments & control equipment; current-carrying wiring devices; special dies, tools, jigs & fixtures

(P-14663)
PICO CRIMPING TOOLS CO
Also Called: Pico Corporation
444 Constitution Ave, Camarillo (93012-8504)
PHONE.................................805 388-5510
Shelley Green, *Ch of Bd*
Mark Green, *Vice Pres*
EMP: 10 EST: 1955
SQ FT: 10,000
SALES (est): 1.1MM Privately Held
WEB: www.picotools.com
SIC: 3545 Machine tool accessories

(P-14664)
PIONEER BROACH COMPANY (PA)
6434 Telegraph Rd, Commerce (90040-2593)
PHONE.................................323 728-1263
Gary M Ezor, *CEO*
Robert Ezor, *Vice Pres*
Karin Ezor, *Admin Sec*
▲ EMP: 50
SQ FT: 22,000
SALES (est): 9.6MM Privately Held
WEB: www.pioneerbroach.com
SIC: 3545 3599 3541 Broaches (machine tool accessories); machine shop, jobbing & repair; machine tools, metal cutting type

(P-14665)
PLANETARY MACHINE AND ENGRG
976 S Andreasen Dr Ste A, Escondido (92029-1949)
PHONE.................................760 489-5571
William Heath, *President*
Layne Oaks, *Vice Pres*
EMP: 11
SQ FT: 6,000
SALES (est): 1.8MM Privately Held
SIC: 3545 Precision tools, machinists'

(P-14666)
PRECISION AEROSPACE & TECH INC
2320 E Orangethorpe Ave A, Anaheim (92806-1223)
PHONE.................................714 543-2966
Barton Webb, *CEO*
Anthony Anish, *President*
Jitu Banker, *CFO*
Tony Anish, *Admin Sec*
EMP: 24
SQ FT: 50,000

SALES: 2.5MM
SALES (corp-wide): 8.7MM Publicly Held
WEB: www.eranengineering.com
SIC: 3545
PA: M Line Holdings, Inc.
2214 Avalon St
Costa Mesa CA 92627
714 630-6253

(P-14667)
PRECISION CUTTING TOOLS INC
13701 Excelsior Dr, Santa Fe Springs (90670-5104)
PHONE.................................562 921-7898
Audrey Sheth, *CEO*
▲ EMP: 30
SQ FT: 20,000
SALES (est): 5.4MM Privately Held
WEB: www.pctcutters.com
SIC: 3545 3541 Cutting tools for machine tools; drilling machine tools (metal cutting)

(P-14668)
PRO TOOL SERVICES INC
1704 Sunnyside Ct, Bakersfield (93308-6859)
P.O. Box 80235 (93380-0235)
PHONE.................................661 393-9222
Ron Jacobs, *President*
Mark Gardner, *Treasurer*
Mark Gardener, *Corp Secy*
EMP: 30
SQ FT: 4,000
SALES (est): 6.4MM Privately Held
SIC: 3545 Tools & accessories for machine tools

(P-14669)
PROGRESSIVE TOOL & DIE INC
17016 S Broadway, Gardena (90248-3114)
PHONE.................................310 327-0569
Peter Martin, *President*
Sandra Martin, *Admin Sec*
EMP: 10
SQ FT: 6,100
SALES (est): 1.7MM Privately Held
SIC: 3545 7389 Precision tools, machinists'; grinding, precision: commercial or industrial

(P-14670)
QUALITY GRINDING COMPANY INC
6800 Caballero Blvd, Buena Park (90620-1136)
P.O. Box 5968 (90622-5968)
PHONE.................................714 228-2100
Cornel Feceu, *President*
EMP: 16 EST: 1946
SQ FT: 29,000
SALES (est): 2.4MM Privately Held
WEB: www.qualitygrinding.net
SIC: 3545 3599 3541 Precision tools, machinists'; machine shop, jobbing & repair

(P-14671)
RAFCO-BRICKFORM LLC (PA)
Also Called: Rafco Products Brickform
11061 Jersey Blvd, Rancho Cucamonga (91730-5135)
PHONE.................................909 484-3399
Robert Freis, *Mng Member*
Harlan Baldridge, *Executive*
Matt Bissanti, *Mng Member*
Stanley Zawadzki, *Manager*
▲ EMP: 72 EST: 1973
SQ FT: 79,000
SALES (est): 17.7MM Privately Held
SIC: 3545 5169 Machine tool accessories; adhesives, chemical

(P-14672)
SBMC SOLUTIONS LLC
2960 Copper Rd, Santa Clara (95051-0722)
PHONE.................................408 732-3200
Robert Sick,
Mark Giles,
Robert D Judson Jr,
EMP: 70
SQ FT: 80,000

SALES: 10MM Privately Held
WEB: www.sbmcsolutions.com
SIC: 3545 3444 3443 Precision tools, machinists'; sheet metalwork; tanks, standard or custom fabricated: metal plate

(P-14673)
SCIENTIFIC CUTTING TOOLS INC
110 W Easy St, Simi Valley (93065-1689)
PHONE.................................805 584-9495
Dale Christopher, *President*
Jan Kaye, *Vice Pres*
Meghann Lackey, *Executive*
Jeff Kaye, *General Mgr*
Gary Christopher, *Admin Sec*
EMP: 37
SQ FT: 25,000
SALES (est): 6.8MM Privately Held
WEB: www.sct-usa.com
SIC: 3545 Machine tool accessories

(P-14674)
SEV-CAL TOOL INC
3231 Halladay St, Santa Ana (92705-5628)
PHONE.................................714 549-3347
James F Severance, *President*
William E Severance, *Corp Secy*
Naomi Severance, *Vice Pres*
EMP: 20
SQ FT: 8,000
SALES (est): 3.3MM Privately Held
SIC: 3545 3541 3423 Cutting tools for machine tools; machine tools, metal cutting type; hand & edge tools

(P-14675)
SHARP-RITE TOOL INC
8443 Whirlaway St, Alta Loma (91701-1324)
PHONE.................................909 948-1234
Gary Kropik, *President*
Raeann Kropik, *Vice Pres*
EMP: 15
SQ FT: 5,000
SALES: 2.5MM Privately Held
SIC: 3545 Cutting tools for machine tools

(P-14676)
SMTCL USA INC
17038 Gale Ave, City of Industry (91745-1807)
PHONE.................................626 667-1192
Jianming Zhao, *CEO*
Dan Barbera, *President*
Richard Ormrod, *President*
▲ EMP: 15 EST: 2009
SALES (est): 4.2MM
SALES (corp-wide): 45.4MM Privately Held
SIC: 3545 Machine tool attachments & accessories
PA: Shenyang Machine Tool Imp & Exp Co.,Ltd
No.1,17a ,Kaifa Road ,Shenyang Economic & Technological Developm
Shenyang 11014
242 519-1501

(P-14677)
SONNET TOOL
3348 W El Segundo Blvd, Hawthorne (90250-4845)
PHONE.................................310 219-7790
Morris Gross, *President*
EMP: 45
SALES (est): 4.3MM Privately Held
SIC: 3545 3541 Cutting tools for machine tools; machine tools, metal cutting type

(P-14678)
SOUTHLAND MANUFACTURING INC
Also Called: Southland Enterprises
210 Market Pl, Escondido (92029-1354)
PHONE.................................760 745-7913
Diana Young, *President*
Ruth E Young, *President*
Donald L Young, *Chairman*
Diana Guminsky, *Corp Secy*
Mike Guminski, *Manager*
EMP: 15
SQ FT: 4,000
SALES (est): 2.6MM Privately Held
WEB: www.southlandent.com
SIC: 3545 Tool holders

(P-14679)
SOUTHLAND TOOL MFG INC
1430 N Hundley St, Anaheim (92806-1322)
PHONE.................................714 632-8198
David Pryor, *President*
▲ EMP: 16
SALES (est): 3MM Privately Held
SIC: 3545 Machine tool accessories

(P-14680)
STADCO (PA)
Also Called: Standard Tool & Die Co
107 S Avenue 20, Los Angeles (90031-1709)
PHONE.................................323 227-8888
Doug Paletz, *President*
Bob Parsi, *COO*
Bret Matta, *Vice Pres*
Karen Abbott, *Accounts Mgr*
EMP: 146
SQ FT: 15,000
SALES (est): 32.2MM Privately Held
SIC: 3545 3599 Precision tools, machinists'; machine shop, jobbing & repair

(P-14681)
STEP TOOLS UNLIMITED INC
Also Called: Destiny Tool
3233 De La Cruz Blvd C, Santa Clara (95054-2604)
PHONE.................................408 988-8898
Guy Calamia, *President*
Nettie Calamia, *Corp Secy*
EMP: 15 EST: 1980
SQ FT: 6,000
SALES (est): 3.5MM Privately Held
WEB: www.destinytool.com
SIC: 3545 Cutting tools for machine tools

(P-14682)
STEWART TOOL COMPANY
3647 Omec Cir, Rancho Cordova (95742-7302)
PHONE.................................916 635-8321
Mark Richard Stewart, *CEO*
Craig Harrington, *Corp Secy*
Dave Hassemeyer, *Admin Sec*
EMP: 55
SQ FT: 22,000
SALES (est): 15.9MM Privately Held
WEB: www.stewarttool.com
SIC: 3545 3544 7692 Precision tools, machinists'; jigs & fixtures; special dies & tools; welding repair

(P-14683)
SYGMA INC
13168 Flores St, Santa Fe Springs (90670-4023)
PHONE.................................562 906-8880
Jimmy Fung, *CEO*
▼ EMP: 15
SQ FT: 10,000
SALES (est): 1.4MM Privately Held
SIC: 3545 Machine tool accessories

(P-14684)
TLC MACHINING INCORPORATED
Also Called: US Machining
2571 Chant Ct, San Jose (95122-1004)
PHONE.................................408 321-9002
Tom Lovato, *President*
Dolores Lovato, *Vice Pres*
EMP: 35
SQ FT: 5,000
SALES (est): 4.5MM Privately Held
SIC: 3545

(P-14685)
TMK MANUFACTURING INC
Also Called: Aaron Bennett
2233 Calle Del Mundo, Santa Clara (95054-1006)
PHONE.................................408 844-8289
Aaron Bennett, *President*
Israel Sanchez, *Vice Pres*
EMP: 20
SQ FT: 17,000
SALES: 2MM Privately Held
WEB: www.tmk-inc.com
SIC: 3545 Precision tools, machinists'

(P-14686)
TOOLSTER BELTS INC
3525a Del Mar Heights Rd, San Diego (92130)
PHONE..............................858 583-0681
Stuart Lyle, *President*
▲ EMP: 10
SALES (est): 820K **Privately Held**
SIC: 3545 Tool holders

(P-14687)
TOSCO - TOOL SPECIALTY COMPANY
1011 E Slauson Ave, Los Angeles (90011-5296)
P.O. Box 512157 (90051-0157)
PHONE..............................323 232-3561
Jerry Tetzlaff, *President*
Ted Tetzlaff, *Vice Pres*
Scott Smythe, *Manager*
▲ EMP: 25
SQ FT: 19,500
SALES: 3.3MM **Privately Held**
WEB: www.toolspecialty.com
SIC: 3545 Cutting tools for machine tools

(P-14688)
TT MACHINE CORP
11651 Anabel Ave, Garden Grove (92843-3708)
PHONE..............................714 534-5288
Al Tran, *Manager*
EMP: 20
SALES (est): 4.4MM **Privately Held**
SIC: 3545 Machine tool accessories

(P-14689)
TURNHAM CORPORATION (PA)
Also Called: Blake Manufacturing Co
15312 Proctor Ave, City of Industry (91745-1023)
PHONE..............................626 330-0415
John R Turnham, *President*
▲ EMP: 17
SQ FT: 7,500
SALES (est): 2.6MM **Privately Held**
WEB: www.blakemanufacturing.com
SIC: 3545 3599 Machine tool accessories; machine shop, jobbing & repair

(P-14690)
TURNHAM CORPORATION
Also Called: Blake Manufacturing
15310 Proctor Ave, City of Industry (91745-1023)
PHONE..............................626 968-6481
John Turnham, *Branch Mgr*
EMP: 10
SALES (corp-wide): 2.6MM **Privately Held**
WEB: www.blakemanufacturing.com
SIC: 3545 3728 3599 Machine tool accessories; aircraft assemblies, subassemblies & parts; machine shop, jobbing & repair
PA: Turnham Corporation
15312 Proctor Ave
City Of Industry CA 91745
626 330-0415

(P-14691)
UNITED DRILL BUSHING CORP
Also Called: United California
12200 Woodruff Ave, Downey (90241-5608)
P.O. Box 4250 (90241-1250)
PHONE..............................562 803-1521
Dale L Bethke, *President*
Billie Huckins, *Admin Sec*
Olivia Clauson, *Human Res Dir*
Fred Clauson, *QC Dir*
EMP: 150 EST: 1964
SQ FT: 80,000
SALES (est): 25.8MM **Privately Held**
WEB: www.ucc-udb.com
SIC: 3545 3544 Drill bushings (drilling jig); drilling machine attachments & accessories; tools & accessories for machine tools; special dies, tools, jigs & fixtures

(P-14692)
VERTEX DIAMOND TOOL COMPANY
940 W Cienega Ave, San Dimas (91773-2454)
PHONE..............................909 599-1129
Tony Pontone, *CEO*
Loretta Pontone Houchin, *President*
Kenneth Houchin, *Vice Pres*
EMP: 51
SQ FT: 13,000
SALES: 3MM **Privately Held**
WEB: www.vertexdiamondtool.com
SIC: 3545 Diamond cutting tools for turning, boring, burnishing, etc.

(P-14693)
VIKING PRODUCTS INC
20 Doppler, Irvine (92618-4306)
PHONE..............................949 379-5100
Marc Kaplan, *CEO*
Donna Raymond, *Manager*
EMP: 40
SQ FT: 12,000
SALES (est): 8.7MM **Privately Held**
SIC: 3545 Precision measuring tools

(P-14694)
WESTERN GAGE CORPORATION
3316 Maya Linda Ste A, Camarillo (93012-8776)
PHONE..............................805 445-1410
Donald E Moors, *President*
Nanette Moors, *Corp Secy*
Sharon Garcia, *Sls & Mktg Exec*
EMP: 24
SQ FT: 22,000
SALES (est): 5.8MM **Privately Held**
WEB: www.westerngage.com
SIC: 3545 Gauges (machine tool accessories)

(P-14695)
WETMORE TOOL AND ENGRG CO
Also Called: Wetmore Cutting Tools
5091 G St, Chino (91710-5141)
PHONE..............................909 364-1000
Phil Kurtz, *President*
Mike Gallegos, *CFO*
Keith Rowland, *Exec VP*
Rosie Ortiz, *Human Res Mgr*
Juan Chanax, *Director*
▲ EMP: 75
SQ FT: 32,000
SALES (est): 18MM **Privately Held**
WEB: www.hpwetmore.com
SIC: 3545 5084 3544 3541 Cutting tools for machine tools; industrial machinery & equipment; special dies, tools, jigs & fixtures; machine tools, metal cutting type; bolts, nuts, rivets & washers

(P-14696)
XCELIRON CORP
9540 Vassar Ave, Chatsworth (91311-4141)
PHONE..............................818 700-8404
Richard Diorio, *President*
Ric Diorio, *Vice Pres*
Randy Jones, *Vice Pres*
EMP: 10
SQ FT: 10,600
SALES: 1.3MM **Privately Held**
WEB: www.xceliron.com
SIC: 3545 3471 Cutting tools for machine tools; plating of metals or formed products

(P-14697)
YILLIK PRECISION INDUSTRIES
1621 S Cucamonga Ave, Ontario (91761-4514)
PHONE..............................909 947-2785
Ray Yillik, *President*
Doris Yillik, *Corp Secy*
Paul Filko, *Vice Pres*
EMP: 55
SQ FT: 14,000

SALES (est): 7.7MM
SALES (corp-wide): 22.9MM **Privately Held**
WEB: www.yillik.com
SIC: 3545 3568 3366 Drill bushings (drilling jig); power transmission equipment; copper foundries
PA: Psm Industries, Inc.
14000 Avalon Blvd
Los Angeles CA 90061
888 663-8256

3546 Power Hand Tools

(P-14698)
BLACK & DECKER (US) INC
Also Called: Dewalt Service Center 148
9020 Alondra Blvd, Bellflower (90706-4206)
PHONE..............................562 925-7551
Fax: 562 925-2561
EMP: 14
SALES (corp-wide): 11.4B **Publicly Held**
SIC: 3546
HQ: Black & Decker (U.S.) Inc.
1000 Stanley Dr
New Britain CT 06053
860 225-5111

(P-14699)
BLACK & DECKER CORPORATION
3949 E Guasti Rd Ste A, Ontario (91761-1549)
PHONE..............................909 390-5548
EMP: 15
SALES (corp-wide): 11B **Publicly Held**
SIC: 3546
HQ: The Black & Decker Corporation
701 E Joppa Rd
Towson MD 21286
410 716-3900

(P-14700)
BOLTTECH MANNINGS INC
16926 Keegan Ave, Carson (90746-1322)
PHONE..............................310 604-9500
Michael Zastera, *Manager*
EMP: 57
SALES (corp-wide): 460.4MM **Privately Held**
SIC: 3546 Power-driven handtools
HQ: Bolttech Mannings, Inc.
501 Mosside Blvd
North Versailles PA 15137
724 872-4873

(P-14701)
BOLTTECH MANNINGS INC
475 Industrial Way, Benicia (94510-1119)
PHONE..............................707 751-0157
Peter Smith, *Branch Mgr*
EMP: 57
SALES (corp-wide): 460.4MM **Privately Held**
SIC: 3546 Power-driven handtools
HQ: Bolttech Mannings, Inc.
501 Mosside Blvd
North Versailles PA 15137
724 872-4873

(P-14702)
CHURCHILL AEROSPACE LLC
5091 G St, Chino (91710-5141)
PHONE..............................909 266-3116
Keith Rowland,
EMP: 157
SALES: 22.2MM **Privately Held**
SIC: 3546 Power-driven handtools

(P-14703)
DIAMOND TECH INCORPORATED
4347 Pacific St, Rocklin (95677-2117)
P.O. Box 756 (95677-0756)
PHONE..............................916 624-1118
Sean Ward, *President*
Maureen Ward, *Admin Sec*
Ingo Pfeiffer, *Research*
Anne Gregory, *Agent*
▲ EMP: 10
SQ FT: 9,000

SALES (est): 1.6MM **Privately Held**
WEB: www.dtiinnovations.com
SIC: 3546 Drills & drilling tools; saws & sawing equipment

(P-14704)
GEORGE JUE MFG CO INC
Also Called: Paramont Metal & Supply Co
8140 Rosecrans Ave, Paramount (90723-2794)
PHONE..............................562 634-8181
Vincent Jue, *CEO*
George Jue, *President*
Elenor Sylva, *Admin Sec*
▲ EMP: 60 EST: 1946
SQ FT: 80,000
SALES (est): 15.8MM **Privately Held**
WEB: www.champion-equipment.com
SIC: 3546 Drills & drilling tools

(P-14705)
GRANBERG PUMP AND METER LTD
Also Called: Granberg International
1051 Los Medanos St, Pittsburg (94565-2561)
PHONE..............................707 562-2099
Erik Granberg, *President*
Sylvia Mahley, *Office Mgr*
Brian Mohr, *Project Mgr*
◆ EMP: 19
SQ FT: 9,000
SALES: 1.8MM **Privately Held**
WEB: www.granberg.com
SIC: 3546 Power-driven handtools

(P-14706)
HEAD FIRST PRODUCTIONS INC
Also Called: Headfirst Products
14848 Northam St, La Mirada (90638-5747)
PHONE..............................714 522-3311
Bill Thompson, *President*
▲ EMP: 15
SQ FT: 2,000
SALES (est): 1.9MM **Privately Held**
SIC: 3546 3496 5085 Power-driven handtools; miscellaneous fabricated wire products; fasteners, industrial: nuts, bolts, screws, etc.

(P-14707)
MEISEI CORPORATION
3350 Willow Ln, Thousand Oaks (91361-4935)
PHONE..............................805 497-2626
Akio Fukunaga, *President*
Fumio Fukunaga, *Vice Pres*
EMP: 11
SQ FT: 14,000
SALES (est): 2MM **Privately Held**
SIC: 3546 Power-driven handtools

(P-14708)
MK DIAMOND PRODUCTS INC (PA)
1315 Storm Pkwy, Torrance (90501-5041)
PHONE..............................310 539-5221
Robert J Delahaut, *President*
Brian Delahaut, *Vice Pres*
Steve Nichols, *Sales Staff*
◆ EMP: 200
SQ FT: 35,000
SALES (est): 47.1MM **Privately Held**
WEB: www.mkdiamond.com
SIC: 3546 3425 Saws & sawing equipment; saw blades & handsaws

(P-14709)
ROBERT BOSCH TOOL CORPORATION
302 E 3rd St 31-1812, Calexico (92231-2760)
P.O. Box 2837 (92232-2837)
PHONE..............................760 357-5603
Ian Morris, *Manager*
EMP: 186
SALES (corp-wide): 261.7MM **Privately Held**
WEB: www.vermontamerican.com
SIC: 3546 Power-driven handtools

PRODUCTS & SVCS

HQ: Robert Bosch Tool Corporation
1800 W Central Rd
Mount Prospect IL 60056

(P-14710)
SEESCAN INC (PA)
Also Called: Seektech
3855 Ruffin Rd, San Diego (92123-1813)
PHONE..................................858 244-3300
Mark Olsson, *President*
John Chew, *Vice Pres*
Kira Olsson, *Comms Mgr*
Erik Hawley, *Info Tech Dir*
Ryan Bulger, *Software Engr*
▲ EMP: 180
SQ FT: 63,641
SALES (est): 31.6MM **Privately Held**
WEB: www.seektechinc.com
SIC: 3546 Power-driven handtools

(P-14711)
SHG HOLDINGS CORP (PA)
Also Called: Zephyr Tool Group
201 Hindry Ave, Inglewood (90301-1519)
PHONE..................................310 410-4907
Bernard J Kersulis, *President*
EMP: 100
SQ FT: 53,000
SALES (est): 10.1MM **Privately Held**
SIC: 3546 Power-driven handtools

(P-14712)
THE BLACK & DECKER INC
19701 Da Vinci, El Toro (92610-2622)
PHONE..................................949 672-4000
Chris Metz, *Manager*
Michelle McMasters, *Admin Asst*
EMP: 450
SALES (corp-wide): 12.7B **Publicly Held**
WEB: www.blackanddecker.com
SIC: 3546 3553 Power-driven handtools;
woodworking machinery
HQ: The Black & Decker Corporation
701 E Joppa Rd
Towson MD 21286
410 716-3900

(P-14713)
ZEPHYR MANUFACTURING CO INC
Also Called: Zephyr Tool Group
201 Hindry Ave, Inglewood (90301-1519)
PHONE..................................310 410-4907
Ray Chin, *VP Finance*
Robert Szanter, *Finance*
Tom Houstan, *VP Mfg*
Tom Houstan, *VP Mfg*
Earl Houston, *VP Sales*
▲ EMP: 100
SQ FT: 60,000
SALES (est): 20.5MM **Privately Held**
SIC: 3546 3545 3423 Power-driven hand-
tools; machine tool accessories; hand &
edge tools
PA: Shg Holdings Corp
201 Hindry Ave
Inglewood CA 90301

(P-14714)
ZIRCON CORPORATION (PA)
1580 Dell Ave, Campbell (95008-6918)
PHONE..................................408 866-8600
John Stauss, *President*
Charles J Stauss, *Ch of Bd*
John R Stauss, *President*
Robert Wyler, *Admin Sec*
Steve Schwarzenbach, *Electrical Engi*
▲ EMP: 45
SQ FT: 6,000
SALES (est): 18.5MM **Privately Held**
WEB: www.zircon.com
SIC: 3546 Power-driven handtools

3547 Rolling Mill Machinery & Eqpt

(P-14715)
GEORGE L KOVACS
Also Called: Gerson's Machinery Co
1810 W Business Center Dr, Orange
(92867-7904)
PHONE..................................714 538-8026

George L Kovacs, *Owner*
EMP: 25
SQ FT: 12,000
SALES (est): 2.2MM **Privately Held**
WEB: www.gersons.com
SIC: 3547 3542 Rolling mill machinery;
machine tools, metal forming type

(P-14716)
JOHN LIST CORPORATION
Also Called: Protocast
9732 Cozycroft Ave, Chatsworth
(91311-4498)
PHONE..................................818 882-7848
John List, *President*
Susan List, *Vice Pres*
EMP: 47 EST: 1966
SQ FT: 16,000
SALES (est): 9MM **Privately Held**
WEB: www.protocastjlc.com
SIC: 3547 3365 3369 3366 Ferrous &
nonferrous mill equipment, auxiliary; alu-
minum & aluminum-based alloy castings;
nonferrous foundries; copper foundries

(P-14717)
OLD COUNTRY MILLWORK INC
Also Called: O C M
5855 Hooper Ave, Los Angeles
(90001-1280)
PHONE..................................323 234-2940
Gerard J Kilgallon, *CEO*
▲ EMP: 38
SQ FT: 36,000
SALES (est): 11.5MM **Privately Held**
WEB: www.e-ocm.com
SIC: 3547 3479 Rolling mill machinery;
painting, coating & hot dipping

(P-14718)
ROBINSON ENGINEERING CORP
3575 Grapevine St, Mira Loma
(91752-3505)
PHONE..................................951 361-8000
Peter Robinson, *President*
Zora Robinson, *Vice Pres*
EMP: 14
SQ FT: 20,000
SALES: 1.2MM **Privately Held**
SIC: 3547 Rolling mill machinery

3548 Welding Apparatus

(P-14719)
AMADA MIYACHI AMERICA INC (HQ)
1820 S Myrtle Ave, Monrovia (91016-4833)
PHONE..................................626 303-5676
David Fawcett, *President*
Kunio Minejima, *COO*
Barbara Kuntz, *Chief Mktg Ofcr*
David Cielinski, *Vice Pres*
James Malloy, *Vice Pres*
◆ EMP: 165
SQ FT: 70,000
SALES (est): 43.9MM
SALES (corp-wide): 2.8B **Privately Held**
WEB: www.miyachiunitek.com
SIC: 3548 3699 3829 Soldering equip-
ment, except hand soldering irons; laser
welding, drilling & cutting equipment;
measuring & controlling devices
PA: Amada Holdings Co., Ltd.
200, Ishida
Isehara KNG 259-1
463 961-111

(P-14720)
AMERICA MOUNTAIN WLDG INDS INC
1613 Chelsea Rd Ste 208, San Marino
(91108-2419)
PHONE..................................626 698-8066
Hong Kang, *CEO*
EMP: 10
SALES (est): 2MM **Privately Held**
SIC: 3548 Welding apparatus

(P-14721)
ARC MACHINES INC (HQ)
Also Called: A M I
14320 Arminta St, Panorama City
(91402-6869)
PHONE..................................818 896-9556

Douglas B Solomon, *Vice Pres*
John Porter, *Info Tech Mgr*
Ben Gollwitzer, *Electrical Engi*
Xavier Jauregui, *Engineer*
Richard Reivydas, *Purch Mgr*
▲ EMP: 100
SQ FT: 96,000
SALES (est): 52.4MM
SALES (corp-wide): 3.3B **Publicly Held**
WEB: www.arcmachines.com
SIC: 3548 3621 3566 Welding & cutting
apparatus & accessories; motors & gen-
erators; speed changers, drives & gears
PA: Colfax Corporation
420 Natl Bus Pkwy Ste 500
Annapolis Junction MD 20701
301 323-9000

(P-14722)
CL OLSON & ASSOCIATES INC
Also Called: Irvine Welding
508 Central Ave, Lake Elsinore
(92530-2734)
PHONE..................................951 245-6233
Clare Olson, *President*
EMP: 12
SQ FT: 9,800
SALES (est): 2.1MM **Privately Held**
SIC: 3548 7692 Welding apparatus; weld-
ing repair

(P-14723)
CREATIVE PATHWAYS INC
20815 Higgins Ct, Torrance (90501-1830)
PHONE..................................310 530-1965
Timothy Rohrberg, *President*
Patrica Rohrberg, *Admin Sec*
Patricia Rohrberg, *Opers Staff*
EMP: 35
SQ FT: 29,000
SALES (est): 4MM **Privately Held**
WEB: www.creativepathways.com
SIC: 3548 Welding & cutting apparatus &
accessories

(P-14724)
DIAMOND GROUND PRODUCTS INC
2651 Lavery Ct, Newbury Park
(91320-1502)
PHONE..................................805 498-3837
James C Elizarraz, *President*
▲ EMP: 30
SQ FT: 40,000
SALES (est): 6MM **Privately Held**
WEB: www.diamondground.com
SIC: 3548 Electrodes, electric welding;
welding & cutting apparatus & acces-
sories

(P-14725)
DIAMOND WELD INDUSTRIES INC
63 W North Ave, Fresno (93706-5516)
PHONE..................................559 268-9999
Nachhatar Dhaliwal, *President*
Jassy Dhaliwal, *CFO*
Gille Dhaliwal, *Vice Pres*
Balbir Dhaliwal, *Admin Sec*
▲ EMP: 10
SQ FT: 15,000
SALES (est): 1.6MM **Privately Held**
SIC: 3548 Welding apparatus

(P-14726)
INNOVATIVE MANUFACTURING INC
Also Called: Innovative Mounts
1366 N Hundley St, Anaheim (92806-1301)
PHONE..................................714 524-5246
Tim Hastings, *CEO*
Greg Hastings, *CFO*
EMP: 15
SQ FT: 5,000
SALES (est): 3.4MM **Privately Held**
WEB: www.innovativemounts.com
SIC: 3548 Welding & cutting apparatus &
accessories

(P-14727)
JANDA COMPANY INC
226 N Sherman Ave Ste A, Corona
(92882-7122)
PHONE..................................951 734-1935
Janet White, *CEO*

Sheryl Dreiling, *Executive*
EMP: 20
SQ FT: 299,000
SALES (est): 4.5MM **Privately Held**
WEB: www.jandawelders.com
SIC: 3548 Spot welding apparatus, electric

(P-14728)
KUTON WELDING INC
11380 Luddington St, Sun Valley
(91352-3106)
PHONE..................................818 771-0964
Minh That Ton, *President*
EMP: 14
SALES (est): 1.1MM **Privately Held**
SIC: 3548 1799 Welding & cutting appara-
tus & accessories; welding on site

(P-14729)
LODESTONE LLC
Also Called: Weldstone Portable Welders
4769 E Wesley Dr, Anaheim (92807-1941)
PHONE..................................714 970-0900
Richard H Barden, *President*
Patricia Walck,
EMP: 16
SALES: 950K **Privately Held**
WEB: www.weldstone.net
SIC: 3548 8742 Welding apparatus; man-
agement consulting services

(P-14730)
LONGEVITY GLOBAL INC
23591 Foley St, Hayward (94545-1676)
PHONE..................................877 566-4462
Simon Katz, *CEO*
Carlos Moreno, *Manager*
▲ EMP: 20
SQ FT: 7,000
SALES (est): 2.5MM **Privately Held**
SIC: 3548 3545 3541 3699 Welding ap-
paratus; machine tool accessories; ma-
chine tools, metal cutting type; welding
machines & equipment, ultrasonic; metal-
working machinery

(P-14731)
M K PRODUCTS INC
Also Called: Mk Manufacturing
16882 Armstrong Ave, Irvine (92606-4975)
PHONE..................................949 798-1425
Chris Westlake, *President*
Joe Lapaglia, *CFO*
Joseph J Lapaglia, *CFO*
Rick Dietz, *VP Admin*
Barbara Pierce, *Admin Sec*
▲ EMP: 81
SQ FT: 80,000
SALES (est): 20MM **Privately Held**
WEB: www.mkprod.com
SIC: 3548 Electric welding equipment

(P-14732)
MAITLEN & BENSON INC
Also Called: Wypo
1395 Obispo Ave, Long Beach
(90804-2509)
P.O. Box 4146 (90804-0146)
PHONE..................................562 597-2200
Kem Gallagher, *President*
Gary Ghio, *Shareholder*
Debbie Wilder, *Corp Secy*
EMP: 30
SQ FT: 5,000
SALES (est): 4MM **Privately Held**
WEB: www.wypo.com
SIC: 3548 3499 Welding & cutting appara-
tus & accessories; welding tips, heat re-
sistant; metal

(P-14733)
MILLER ELECTRIC MFG CO
2523 Ellington Ct, Simi Valley
(93063-5322)
PHONE..................................805 520-7494
C Breeden, *Branch Mgr*
EMP: 207
SALES (corp-wide): 14.3B **Publicly Held**
SIC: 3548 Welding apparatus
HQ: Miller Electric Mfg. Llc
1635 W Spencer St
Appleton WI 54914
920 734-9821

▲ = Import ▼=Export
◆ =Import/Export

(P-14734)
ONEX RF AUTOMATION INC
1824 Flower Ave, Duarte (91010-2931)
PHONE..................................626 358-6639
Onik Bogosyan, *President*
EMP: 12 EST: 1991
SALES (est): 3.1MM Privately Held
SIC: 3548 Welding apparatus

(P-14735)
OTTO ARC SYSTEMS INC
3921 Sandstone Dr Ste 1, El Dorado Hills
(95762-9343)
PHONE..................................916 939-3400
Alan S Avis Jr, *President*
▲ EMP: 10
SALES: 950K Privately Held
SIC: 3548 Welding apparatus

(P-14736)
PERKINS
Also Called: Perkins Family Restaurant
7312 Varna Ave Ste A, North Hollywood
(91605-4008)
PHONE..................................818 764-9293
William Perkins, *Owner*
EMP: 21
SALES (est): 1.4MM Privately Held
SIC: 3548

(P-14737)
PRAXAIR INC
1950 Loveridge Rd, Pittsburg (94565-4113)
PHONE..................................925 427-1950
John Bellicci, *Branch Mgr*
Rodrigo Rosas, *Plant Mgr*
EMP: 20
SALES (corp-wide): 11.4B Privately Held
SIC: 3548 2813 Welding apparatus; industrial gases
PA: Praxair, Inc.
10 Riverview Dr
Danbury CT 06810
203 837-2000

(P-14738)
SENSBEY INC (PA)
833 Mahler Rd Ste 3, Burlingame
(94010-1609)
PHONE..................................650 697-2032
Katsuhiro Enokawa, *President*
Hiro Ito, *Vice Pres*
EMP: 15
SQ FT: 22,000
SALES (est): 1.5MM Privately Held
WEB: www.sensbey.com
SIC: 3548 3634 3822 Soldering equipment, except hand soldering irons; heating units, for electric appliances; built-in thermostats, filled system & bimetal types

(P-14739)
SIKAMA INTERNATIONAL INC
118 E Gutierrez St, Santa Barbara
(93101-2314)
P.O. Box 40298 (93140-0298)
PHONE..................................805 962-1000
Sigurd R Wathne, *President*
Mariellen Wathne, *Treasurer*
Kail S Wathne, *Vice Pres*
Phillip Skeen, *Sales Mgr*
EMP: 13 EST: 1982
SQ FT: 9,300
SALES: 2MM Privately Held
WEB: www.sikama.com
SIC: 3548 Soldering equipment, except hand soldering irons

(P-14740)
SSCO MANUFACTURING INC
Also Called: ARC Products
1245 30th St, San Diego (92154-3477)
PHONE..................................619 628-1022
Victor B Miller, *President*
Susan D Miller, *Treasurer*
Lane A Litke, *Vice Pres*
EMP: 35
SQ FT: 21,000
SALES (est): 7.9MM
SALES (corp-wide): 2.6B Publicly Held
WEB: www.arc-products.com
SIC: 3548 5085 7629 7699 Electric welding equipment; welding supplies; circuit board repair; welding equipment repair

PA: Lincoln Electric Holdings, Inc.
22801 Saint Clair Ave
Cleveland OH 44117
216 481-8100

(P-14741)
SUPER WELDING SOUTHERN CAL INC
609 Anita St, Chula Vista (91911-4619)
PHONE..................................619 239-8003
Roberto Victoria, *President*
Manuel Victoria, *Officer*
Amelia Victoria, *Vice Pres*
EMP: 20
SQ FT: 54,577
SALES: 2MM Privately Held
SIC: 3548 1799 Arc welding generators, alternating current & direct current; welding on site

(P-14742)
TECHNICAL DEVICES COMPANY
560 Alaska Ave, Torrance (90503-3904)
PHONE..................................310 618-8437
Douglas N Winther, *CEO*
Rey Malazo, *CFO*
EMP: 48 EST: 1977
SQ FT: 35,000
SALES (est): 6.2MM
SALES (corp-wide): 9.2MM Privately Held
WEB: www.technicaldev.com
SIC: 3548 3471 3544 3423 Soldering equipment, except hand soldering irons; cleaning, polishing & finishing; special dies & tools; hand & edge tools
PA: Winther Technologies, Inc.
560 Alaska Ave
Torrance CA 90503
310 618-8437

(P-14743)
VERIDIAM INC (DH)
1717 N Cuyamaca St, El Cajon
(92020-1110)
P.O. Box 609036, San Diego (92160-9036)
PHONE..................................619 448-1000
Chuck Passarelli, *CEO*
Kevin S Beaver, *CFO*
Thomas Cresante, *Principal*
Marco Bruno, *General Mgr*
Josh Groff, *Technician*
▲ EMP: 142
SQ FT: 250,000
SALES (est): 88.7MM
SALES (corp-wide): 143.6MM Privately Held
WEB: www.veridiam.com
SIC: 3548 3545 3317 Welding apparatus; machine tool accessories; steel pipe & tubes
HQ: Whi Capital Partners
191 N Wacker Dr Ste 1500
Chicago IL 60606
312 621-0590

(P-14744)
WHITE INDUSTRIAL CORPORATION
Also Called: Pdr-America
3869 Dividend Dr Ste 1, Shingle Springs
(95682-7252)
PHONE..................................530 676-6262
Dave White, *President*
Sharon White, *Admin Sec*
▲ EMP: 11
SQ FT: 5,200
SALES (est): 2.2MM Privately Held
WEB: www.pdr-america.com
SIC: 3548 Welding apparatus

(P-14745)
WINTHER TECHNOLOGIES INC (PA)
Also Called: Technical Devices
560 Alaska Ave, Torrance (90503-3904)
PHONE..................................310 618-8437
Douglas N Winther, *President*
Roberto Garcia, *Technology*
Julie Fields, *Purch Mgr*
Julio Trinidad, *Plant Mgr*
▲ EMP: 46
SQ FT: 32,000

SALES (est): 9.2MM Privately Held
SIC: 3548 3544 3542 3471 Soldering equipment, except hand soldering irons; special dies & tools; machine tools, metal forming type; cleaning & descaling metal products

---

3549 Metalworking Machinery, NEC

(P-14746)
5-STARS ENGINEERING ASSOCIATES
3393 De La Cruz Blvd, Santa Clara
(95054-2633)
PHONE..................................408 380-4849
Efrain Ojeda, *CEO*
Luis Vargas, *Vice Pres*
EMP: 26
SALES: 4.5MM Privately Held
SIC: 3549 Assembly machines, including robotic

(P-14747)
ADAPT AUTOMATION INC
1661 Palm St Ste A, Santa Ana
(92701-5190)
PHONE..................................714 662-4454
Case Van Mechelen, *Principal*
Case V Mechelen, *CEO*
Tia V Mechelen, *Corp Secy*
Peter Smit, *Vice Pres*
EMP: 34
SQ FT: 50,000
SALES (est): 9.1MM Privately Held
SIC: 3549 Assembly machines, including robotic

(P-14748)
ASSEMBLY AUTOMATION INDUSTRIES
1849 Business Center Dr, Duarte
(91010-2902)
PHONE..................................626 303-2777
Francis E Frost, *CEO*
Elizabeth Frost, *Corp Secy*
EMP: 35
SQ FT: 10,000
SALES (est): 7.7MM Privately Held
WEB: www.assemblyauto.com
SIC: 3549 Metalworking machinery

(P-14749)
BMCI INC
Also Called: Bergandi Machinery Company
1689 S Parco Ave, Ontario (91761-8308)
P.O. Box 3790 (91761-0977)
PHONE..................................951 361-8000
Scott Barsotti, *President*
Gary Costanzo, *COO*
Jose Garcia, *Vice Pres*
▼ EMP: 45
SQ FT: 45,000
SALES (est): 10MM Privately Held
WEB: www.bergandi.com
SIC: 3549 3548 Wiredrawing & fabricating machinery & equipment, ex. die; welding apparatus

(P-14750)
EUBANKS ENGINEERING CO (PA)
3022 Inland Empire Blvd, Ontario
(91764-4803)
P.O. Box 8490, Rancho Cucamonga
(91701-0490)
PHONE..................................909 483-2456
David Eubanks, *Principal*
Maria Sanders, *General Mgr*
Armando Zacarias, *General Mgr*
EMP: 30
SQ FT: 34,000
SALES (est): 5.5MM Privately Held
WEB: www.eubanks.com
SIC: 3549 3825 Wiredrawing & fabricating machinery & equipment, ex. die; test equipment for electronic & electrical circuits

(P-14751)
GANESH INDUSTRIES LLC
20869 Plummer St, Chatsworth
(91311-5005)
PHONE..................................818 349-9166
Harvinder Singh, *President*
▲ EMP: 10
SQ FT: 20,000
SALES (est): 797.3K Privately Held
SIC: 3549 Metalworking machinery

(P-14752)
GOLDEN STATE ENGINEERING INC
15338 Garfield Ave, Paramount
(90723-4092)
PHONE..................................562 634-3125
Alexandra Rostovski, *CEO*
Eugenio Rostovski, *President*
Mary Saguini, *CEO*
Tom Scroggin, *Vice Pres*
EMP: 120
SQ FT: 65,000
SALES (est): 33.2MM Privately Held
WEB: www.goldenstateeng.com
SIC: 3549 3541 3451 8711 Metalworking machinery; grinding, polishing, buffing, lapping & honing machines; screw machine products; engineering services; bolts, nuts, rivets & washers

(P-14753)
GOLNEX INC
4259 Aplicella Ct, Manteca (95337-8480)
PHONE..................................510 490-6003
Michael Wang, *President*
◆ EMP: 20
SALES: 2MM Privately Held
WEB: www.golnex.com
SIC: 3549 5085 Screw driving machines; industrial supplies

(P-14754)
H P SOLUTIONS INC
Also Called: H F Johnston Mfg Co
2475 Ash St, Vista (92081-8424)
PHONE..................................760 727-2880
Bradley Hayes, *President*
EMP: 45
SQ FT: 40,327
SALES (est): 6.6MM
SALES (corp-wide): 2B Publicly Held
SIC: 3549 Metalworking machinery
PA: Nordson Corporation
28601 Clemens Rd
Westlake OH 44145
440 892-1580

(P-14755)
HAEGER INCORPORATED (DH)
811 Wakefield Dr, Oakdale (95361-7792)
PHONE..................................209 848-4000
Alan Phillips, *CEO*
Wouter Kleizen, *President*
Pat Mann, *Info Tech Mgr*
Sander Vanderbor, *Engineer*
Rick Costa, *Manager*
▲ EMP: 24
SQ FT: 36,000
SALES (est): 3.7MM Privately Held
WEB: www.haeger.com
SIC: 3549 Metalworking machinery
HQ: Phillips Corporation
7390 Coca Cola Dr Ste 200
Hanover MD 21076
800 878-4747

(P-14756)
LAVANG TECH PRCSION SHEET MTLS
14480 Hoover St, Westminster
(92683-5319)
PHONE..................................714 901-2782
Andy Fan, *Owner*
Andy Pham, *Vice Pres*
Kenny Tran, *General Mgr*
Andy Vu, *General Mgr*
EMP: 13
SQ FT: 10,700
SALES (est): 1.5MM Privately Held
WEB: www.lavang-tech.com
SIC: 3549 Metalworking machinery

P R O D U C T S & S V C S

(P-14757)
LIP HING METAL MFG AMER INC
738 Phillips, Rowland Heights
(91748-1146)
PHONE..............................626 810-8204
Ronald Chow, *President*
▲ EMP: 10
SQ FT: 15,000
SALES (est): 1.7MM **Privately Held**
SIC: 3549 Metalworking machinery

(P-14758)
LTD TECH INC
2630 Lavery Ct Ste B, Newbury Park
(91320-1534)
PHONE..............................805 480-1886
Lonny Deboisblanc, *President*
Bonnie D Boisblanc, *CFO*
Bonnie Deboisblanc, *CFO*
Eli Zegarra, *Manager*
▲ EMP: 16 EST: 2002
SQ FT: 5,000
SALES (est): 2.5MM **Privately Held**
WEB: www.ltdtechnology.com
SIC: 3549 Assembly machines, including
robotic

(P-14759)
LTI BOYD
600 S Mcclure Rd, Modesto (95357-0520)
PHONE..............................800 554-0200
Mitch Aiello, *President*
Kurt Wetzel, *CFO*
▲ EMP: 766
SALES (est): 84.4MM **Privately Held**
SIC: 3549 3053 8711 Metalworking ma-
chinery; gaskets, packing & sealing de-
vices; industrial engineers
PA: Sentinel Capital Partners Llc
330 Madison Ave Fl 27
New York NY 10017

(P-14760)
NEATO ROBOTICS INC (HQ)
8100 Jarvis Ave Ste 100, Newark
(94560-1192)
PHONE..............................510 795-1351
Giacomo Marini, *CEO*
Holly Anderson, *CFO*
Nancy Nunziati, *Vice Pres*
Aron Cooperman, *Program Mgr*
Brenda Chang, *Executive Asst*
▲ EMP: 56 EST: 2005
SQ FT: 13,000
SALES (est): 25.7MM
SALES (corp-wide): 3.4B **Privately Held**
SIC: 3549 3524 Assembly machines, in-
cluding robotic; blowers & vacuums, lawn
PA: Vorwerk & Co. Kg
Muhlenweg 17-37
Wuppertal 42275
202 564-0

(P-14761)
ONE SOURCE AUTOMATION INC
310 Trousdale Dr Ste B, Chula Vista
(91910-1078)
PHONE..............................619 422-4010
Joseph Calvillo, *CEO*
Lori Silva, *Manager*
EMP: 12
SQ FT: 3,600
SALES (est): 1.4MM **Privately Held**
WEB: www.osautomation.com
SIC: 3549 Metalworking machinery

(P-14762)
POSITRONICS INCORPORATED
173 Spring St Ste 120, Pleasanton
(94566-9401)
PHONE..............................925 931-0211
Howard Miles, *President*
Vincent Leung, *Vice Pres*
Radoslaw Szambelan, *Sr Software Eng*
Michel Theunissen, *Sr Software Eng*
John Thoits, *Software Engr*
EMP: 14
SQ FT: 2,200
SALES (est): 1.6MM **Privately Held**
WEB: www.posincorp.com
SIC: 3549 Assembly machines, including
robotic

(P-14763)
**PRODUCTION ASSMBLY
SYSTEMS INC**
12568 Kirkham Ct, Poway (92064-8899)
PHONE..............................858 748-6700
Charles D Ross, *President*
Andy Kaiser, *Controller*
EMP: 22
SQ FT: 12,000
SALES (est): 4.9MM **Privately Held**
WEB: www.production-systems.com
SIC: 3549 Assembly machines, including
robotic

(P-14764)
QUARTET MECHANICS INC
4055 Clipper Ct, Fremont (94538-6540)
PHONE..............................510 490-1886
Henry Walter, *Principal*
EMP: 12
SALES (est): 2MM **Privately Held**
SIC: 3549 Assembly machines, including
robotic

(P-14765)
ROYAL SYSTEMS GROUP
18301 Napa St, Northridge (91325-3617)
PHONE..............................818 717-5010
Royal E Bush, *President*
Joe Bush, *Mktg Dir*
EMP: 12
SALES (est): 2.4MM **Privately Held**
SIC: 3549 Metalworking machinery

(P-14766)
SAKE ROBOTICS
570 El Camino Real 150-3, Redwood City
(94063-1200)
PHONE..............................650 207-4021
Paul Ekas, *Principal*
EMP: 10
SALES (est): 769.1K **Privately Held**
SIC: 3549 Assembly machines, including
robotic

(P-14767)
**SUITABLE TECHNOLOGIES INC
(PA)**
921 E Charleston Rd, Palo Alto
(94303-4903)
PHONE..............................650 294-3170
Scott Wendell Hassan, *CEO*
David Lundmark, *COO*
Bo Preising, *Officer*
Milan Bhalala, *Vice Pres*
Jason Wilson, *Administration*
▲ EMP: 15
SALES (est): 4.3MM **Privately Held**
SIC: 3549 Assembly machines, including
robotic

(P-14768)
TELEDYNE INSTRUMENTS INC
Also Called: Teledyne Seabotix
9970 Carroll Canyon Rd B, San Diego
(92131-1106)
PHONE..............................619 239-5959
EMP: 68
SALES (corp-wide): 2.6B **Publicly Held**
SIC: 3549 Propeller straightening presses
HQ: Teledyne Instruments, Inc.
1049 Camino Dos Rios
Thousand Oaks CA 91360
805 373-4545

(P-14769)
**TEMECULA PRECISON
FABRICATION**
Also Called: Temecula Precision Mfg
42201 Sarah Way, Temecula (92590-3463)
PHONE..............................951 699-4066
Steve Leckband, *President*
Teri Leckband, *Vice Pres*
EMP: 13
SALES (est): 3MM **Privately Held**
SIC: 3549 Assembly machines, including
robotic

(P-14770)
TUBE FORM SOLUTIONS LLC
Also Called: Eaton Leonard Tooling
1398 Poinsettia Ave # 101, Vista
(92081-8504)
PHONE..............................760 599-5001
Jeff Jacobs,

EMP: 10
SALES (corp-wide): 18.4MM **Privately
Held**
SIC: 3549 3545 Metalworking machinery;
tools & accessories for machine tools
PA: Tube Form Solutions, Llc
435 Roske Dr
Elkhart IN 46516
574 295-5041

(P-14771)
UBTECH ROBOTICS CORP
767 S Alameda St, Los Angeles
(90021-1660)
PHONE..............................213 261-7153
John Rhee, *CEO*
EMP: 30
SALES: 10MM **Privately Held**
SIC: 3549 Assembly machines, including
robotic
PA: Ubtech Robotics Corp.
Floor 16?22, Building C1, Nanshan
Zhiyuan, No.1001, Xueyuan Boul
Shenzhen
755 834-7442

(P-14772)
WALLNER EXPAC INC (PA)
Also Called: W T E
1274 S Slater Cir, Ontario (91761-1522)
PHONE..............................909 481-8800
Sophia Wallner, *Ch of Bd*
Michael Wallner, *CEO*
Paul Wallner, *Vice Pres*
▲ EMP: 55
SALES (est): 23.3MM **Privately Held**
WEB: www.expac.com
SIC: 3549 3542 Metalworking machinery;
machine tools, metal forming type

3552 Textile Machinery

(P-14773)
**AARON CHANG PHOTO ACTIVE
WEAR**
Also Called: Aaron Chang Clothing
2611 S Coast Highway 101, Cardiff By The
Sea (92007-2100)
PHONE..............................760 635-0041
Erica Chang, *President*
Aaron Chang, *CEO*
EMP: 19
SALES: 4MM **Privately Held**
SIC: 3552 Dyeing, drying & finishing ma-
chinery & equipment

(P-14774)
AUTOMETRIX INC
12098 Charles Dr, Grass Valley
(95945-8418)
PHONE..............................530 477-5065
John Palmer, *President*
John Yates, *Vice Pres*
Jeanna Zangara, *Office Mgr*
Tyler Green, *Electrical Engi*
Terri Van Wagner, *Opers Mgr*
EMP: 18
SQ FT: 11,000
SALES (est): 5.3MM **Privately Held**
WEB: www.autometrix.com
SIC: 3552 Textile machinery

(P-14775)
DILCO INDUSTRIAL INC
205 E Bristol Ln, Orange (92865-2715)
PHONE..............................714 998-5266
Jay R Dille, *President*
Jay R Dille Jr, *Vice Pres*
Jay Dille, *Vice Pres*
Tina Dille, *Admin Sec*
Ren Dille, *Administration*
EMP: 15
SQ FT: 6,000
SALES (est): 3.4MM **Privately Held**
SIC: 3552 3993 Silk screens for textile in-
dustry; signs & advertising specialties

(P-14776)
EVERPAC
Also Called: Eveready Pacific Corp
1499 Palmyrita Ave, Riverside
(92507-1600)
PHONE..............................951 774-3274
William R Johnson Jr, *President*

EMP: 54
SALES (est): 3.9MM
SALES (corp-wide): 205.9MM **Privately
Held**
WEB: www.johnson-machinery.com
SIC: 3552 Textile machinery
PA: Johnson Machinery Co.
800 E La Cadena Dr
Riverside CA 92507
951 686-4560

(P-14777)
**P&Y T-SHRTS SILK SCREENING
INC**
Also Called: American Printworks
2126 E 52nd St, Vernon (90058-3448)
P.O. Box 58742, Los Angeles (90058-0742)
PHONE..............................323 585-4604
Yossi Zaga, *President*
Linda Bates, *VP Opers*
EMP: 100
SQ FT: 35,000
SALES (est): 15.8MM **Privately Held**
WEB: www.hraco.com
SIC: 3552 5136 Silk screens for textile in-
dustry; shirts, men's & boys'

(P-14778)
PALACE TEXTILE INC
Also Called: Palace Textiles
8453 Terradell St, Pico Rivera
(90660-5042)
PHONE..............................323 587-7756
▲ EMP: 52
SQ FT: 26,000
SALES (est): 3.5MM **Privately Held**
SIC: 3552 2391 2211

(P-14779)
**PORTABLE SPNDLE REPR
SPCIALIST**
Also Called: Al's Machine Shop
10803 Fremont Ave Ste A, Ontario
(91762-3901)
PHONE..............................909 591-7220
Mark Twogood, *President*
Miguel Ramirez, *Vice Pres*
EMP: 15
SALES (est): 1.8MM **Privately Held**
SIC: 3552 Spindles, textile

(P-14780)
**STITCH CITY INDUSTRIES INC
(PA)**
Also Called: Garmentprinter.com
11823 Slauson Ave Ste 31, Santa Fe
Springs (90670-6525)
PHONE..............................562 408-6144
Fernando Padilla, *CEO*
Arnold Gil, *Sales Staff*
Patti Thomson, *Sales Staff*
EMP: 10
SQ FT: 2,000
SALES (est): 1.8MM **Privately Held**
SIC: 3552 7219 2396 Embroidery ma-
chines; garment making, alteration & re-
pair; printing & embossing on plastics
fabric articles

(P-14781)
SURFACE ENGINEERING SPC
919 Hamlin Ct, Sunnyvale (94089-1402)
PHONE..............................408 734-8810
Richard Peattie, *President*
Jane Peattie, *Vice Pres*
Brett Courtney, *Engineer*
David Rich, *Engineer*
EMP: 20 EST: 1976
SQ FT: 18,000
SALES (est): 5.8MM **Privately Held**
WEB: www.surfeng.com
SIC: 3552 7389 Spindles, textile; grinding,
precision: commercial or industrial

(P-14782)
TAJIMA USA INC
19925 S Susana Rd, Compton
(90221-5726)
PHONE..............................310 604-8200
Ron Krasnitz, *President*
▲ EMP: 25
SQ FT: 25,000

SALES (est): 3MM
SALES (corp-wide): 112.9MM **Privately Held**
WEB: www.tajima.com
SIC: 3552 Embroidery machines
PA: Tajima Industries Ltd.
3-19-22, Shirakabe, Higashi-Ku
Nagoya AIC 461-0
529 323-811

(P-14783)
VERSICOLOR INC
Also Called: Versicolor Screenprinting
934 Calle Negocio Ste E, San Clemente
(92673-6210)
PHONE..........................949 361-9698
Mark Feiner, *President*
Sheila Feiner, *Admin Sec*
Cameron Cogan, *Prdtn Mgr*
EMP: 10
SQ FT: 10,000
SALES (est): 950K **Privately Held**
WEB: www.versicolorinc.com
SIC: 3552 2759 Silk screens for textile industry; screen printing

3553 Woodworking

(P-14784)
A-1 PLASTICS INCORPORATED
618 W Bradley Ave, El Cajon (92020-1214)
PHONE..........................619 444-9442
James Blakemore Jr, *CEO*
Mary R Blakemore, *Treasurer*
EMP: 12
SQ FT: 25,000
SALES: 2.1MM **Privately Held**
SIC: 3553 Cabinet makers' machinery

(P-14785)
KVAL INC
Also Called: Kval Machinery Co
825 Petaluma Blvd S, Petaluma
(94952-5134)
PHONE..........................707 762-4363
Gerald Kvalheim, *CEO*
Andrew M Kvalheim, *Treasurer*
Nate Kvalheim, *Officer*
Dave Kvalheim, *Vice Pres*
Mark Kvalheim, *Vice Pres*
▲ **EMP:** 125
SALES (est): 34.6MM **Privately Held**
WEB: www.kvalinc.com
SIC: 3553 5084 Woodworking machinery; industrial machinery & equipment

(P-14786)
PROFESSIONAL MCHY GROUP INC
1885 N Macarthur Dr, Tracy (95376-2820)
PHONE..........................209 832-0100
Kirk Gass, *President*
David Hegger, *Vice Pres*
EMP: 10
SQ FT: 18,000
SALES (est): 2.5MM **Privately Held**
WEB: www.professionalmachinery.com
SIC: 3553 Woodworking machinery

(P-14787)
VOORWOOD COMPANY
Also Called: Turbosand
2350 Barney Rd, Anderson (96007-4306)
PHONE..........................530 365-3311
Adam Britton, *CEO*
Larry Ackernecht, *Vice Pres*
Steve Shifflet, *Admin Sec*
Brian Evans, *CTO*
Jim Hawkins, *Engineer*
▼ **EMP:** 30
SQ FT: 60,000
SALES (est): 8.3MM **Privately Held**
WEB: www.turbosand.com
SIC: 3553 Woodworking machinery

(P-14788)
WANESHEAR TECHNOLOGIES LLC
3471 N State St, Ukiah (95482-3080)
PHONE..........................707 462-4761
Ron McGehee, *Partner*
Ron Mc Gehee, *Partner*
Clark McGehee, *Partner*
▼ **EMP:** 35

SALES (est): 2.5MM **Privately Held**
SIC: 3553

(P-14789)
WESTERN MOTOR WORKS INC
8332 Osage Ave, Los Angeles
(90045-4401)
PHONE..........................310 382-6896
Hamid Baher, *President*
Alfa Rodriguez, *Controller*
EMP: 14
SALES (est): 1.9MM **Privately Held**
SIC: 3553 Woodworking machinery

3554 Paper Inds Machinery

(P-14790)
ADVANCED LASER DIES INC
7647 Industry Ave Ste 200, Pico Rivera
(90660-4300)
PHONE..........................562 949-0081
Leo Denlea, *President*
Lisa Denlea, *Vice Pres*
Jerry Zinn, *Office Mgr*
EMP: 10
SQ FT: 5,200
SALES (est): 1.8MM **Privately Held**
WEB: www.advancedlaserdies.com
SIC: 3554 7373 Die cutting & stamping machinery, paper converting; computer-aided design (CAD) systems service

(P-14791)
CTRA INDUSTRIAL MACHINE
11817 Slauson Ave, Santa Fe Springs
(90670-2219)
PHONE..........................562 698-5188
Jeannine Aviles, *President*
EMP: 11
SQ FT: 8,142
SALES (est): 1.5MM **Privately Held**
SIC: 3554 Folding machines, paper

(P-14792)
ELLISON EDUCATIONAL EQP INC (PA)
Also Called: Sizzix
25862 Commercentre Dr, Lake Forest
(92630-8877)
PHONE..........................949 598-8822
Richard Birse, *CEO*
Kristin Highberg, *CEO*
Reed Feist, *CFO*
▲ **EMP:** 110
SQ FT: 132,000
SALES (est): 25.2MM **Privately Held**
WEB: www.ellison.com
SIC: 3554 Cutting machines, paper

(P-14793)
G G C INC (PA)
Also Called: Enterprise Company
2624 Rousselle St, Santa Ana
(92707-3729)
P.O. Box 15546 (92735-0546)
PHONE..........................714 835-6530
Daniel C Gould, *CEO*
Orval Gould, *President*
John Drissen, *Corp Secy*
John A Gould, *Vice Pres*
▼ **EMP:** 44
SQ FT: 18,000
SALES (est): 7.6MM **Privately Held**
WEB: www.enterpriseco.com
SIC: 3554 3535 3523 3421 Paper industries machinery; conveyors & conveying equipment; farm machinery & equipment; cutlery

(P-14794)
G G C INC
Also Called: Enterprise Co
2624 Rousselle St, Santa Ana
(92707-3729)
PHONE..........................714 835-0551
Orbal Gould, *Manager*
EMP: 47
SALES (corp-wide): 7.6MM **Privately Held**
WEB: www.enterpriseco.com
SIC: 3554 7699 Paper industries machinery; industrial equipment services

PA: G G C, Inc.
2624 Rousselle St
Santa Ana CA 92707
714 835-6530

(P-14795)
GEO M MARTIN COMPANY (PA)
1250 67th St, Emeryville (94608-1121)
P.O. Box 8464, Oakland (94662-0464)
PHONE..........................510 652-2200
Merrill D Martin, *CEO*
Robert A Morgan, *President*
Lillian Martin, *CFO*
George R Martin, *Exec VP*
Daniel J D'Angelo, *Vice Pres*
▲ **EMP:** 100
SQ FT: 50,000
SALES (est): 15.1MM **Privately Held**
WEB: www.geomartin.com
SIC: 3554 Corrugating machines, paper

(P-14796)
GEORGE M MARTIN CO
910 Folger Ave, Berkeley (94710-2820)
PHONE..........................510 652-2200
George Martin, *Principal*
EMP: 10
SALES (est): 1.6MM **Privately Held**
SIC: 3554 Paper industries machinery

(P-14797)
MOEN INDUSTRIES
10330 Pioneer Blvd # 235, Santa Fe
Springs (90670-6012)
PHONE..........................562 946-6381
Carl Moen, *President*
Lenard Moen, *Shareholder*
Bill Pounds, *Engineer*
Bob Storms, *Marketing Staff*
▲ **EMP:** 43
SQ FT: 38,400
SALES (est): 6.1MM
SALES (corp-wide): 53.9MM **Privately Held**
SIC: 3554 5084 3565 Box making machines, paper; industrial machinery & equipment; packaging machinery
PA: R. A. Pearson Company
8120 W Sunset Hwy
Spokane WA 99224
509 838-6226

(P-14798)
PREZANT COMPANY
Also Called: A A Prezant Discount Rbr Bands
940 S Amphlett Blvd, San Mateo
(94402-1801)
PHONE..........................650 342-7413
Shel M Prezant, *President*
Terri R Prezant, *Vice Pres*
EMP: 15 EST: 1953
SQ FT: 18,000
SALES (est): 1.8MM **Privately Held**
SIC: 3554 2674 2671 3069 Fourdrinier machines, paper manufacturing; paper bags: made from purchased materials; plastic film, coated or laminated for packaging; rubber bands; plastic bags: made from purchased materials

3555 Printing Trades Machinery & Eqpt

(P-14799)
AMERICAN THERMOFORM CORP (PA)
1758 Brackett St, La Verne (91750-5855)
PHONE..........................909 593-6711
Gary S Nunnelly, *President*
Ruth Haggen, *Vice Pres*
▲ **EMP:** 10 EST: 1961
SQ FT: 13,000
SALES (est): 1.9MM **Privately Held**
WEB: www.americanthermoform.com
SIC: 3555 Printing trades machinery

(P-14800)
ANAJET LLC
1100 Valencia Ave, Tustin (92780-6428)
PHONE..........................714 662-3200
Chase Roh, *President*
Marius Der Watt, *Manager*
▲ **EMP:** 20

SALES (est): 11.2MM **Privately Held**
SIC: 3555 Printing trades machinery

(P-14801)
APPLIED MANUFACTURING TECH INC
Also Called: Amtec
1464 N Hundley St Anaheim, Anaheim
(92806)
PHONE..........................714 630-9530
Hadi Lalani, *President*
▲ **EMP:** 11
SQ FT: 3,500
SALES (est): 3.1MM **Privately Held**
SIC: 3555 3542 3842 Printing trades machinery; marking machines; welders' hoods

(P-14802)
ASPE INC
42295 Avenida Alvarado # 5, Temecula
(92590-3471)
PHONE..........................951 296-2595
Alexander Szyszko, *CEO*
Thomas Szyszko, *Vice Pres*
Hanson Pulickal, *Business Mgr*
Mark Dito, *Sales Staff*
Matt Yeazel, *Sales Staff*
▲ **EMP:** 15 EST: 2011
SALES: 2MM **Privately Held**
SIC: 3555 Printing trades machinery

(P-14803)
BAY CLASSIFIEDS INC
Also Called: Classified Flea Market
433 Hegenberger Rd # 205, Oakland
(94621-1448)
PHONE..........................510 636-1867
Steve Marini, *President*
EMP: 25
SALES (est): 2.7MM **Privately Held**
WEB: www.bayclassifieds.com
SIC: 3555 2711 Mats, advertising & newspaper; newspapers

(P-14804)
CAL PLATE (PA)
17110 Jersey Ave, Artesia (90701-2694)
PHONE..........................562 403-3000
Richard Borelli, *President*
EMP: 52 EST: 1966
SQ FT: 33,000
SALES (est): 16.2MM **Privately Held**
WEB: www.calplate.com
SIC: 3555 3423 3544 Printing plates; cutting dies, except metal cutting; special dies, tools, jigs & fixtures

(P-14805)
CONTAINER GRAPHICS CORP
1137 Graphics Dr, Modesto (95351-1501)
PHONE..........................209 577-0181
Brian Bennett, *Manager*
EMP: 60
SALES (corp-wide): 3MM **Privately Held**
WEB: www.containergraphics.com
SIC: 3555 Printing trades machinery
PA: Container Graphics Corp.
114 Ednbrgh S Dr Ste 104
Cary NC 27511
919 481-4200

(P-14806)
EPIC PRINTING INK CORP
233 Pioneer Pl, Pomona (91768-3255)
PHONE..........................909 598-6771
Cliff Miller, *President*
Tim Bradley, *Vice Pres*
Jeremy Bradley, *Office Mgr*
EMP: 19
SQ FT: 7,300
SALES (est): 3.3MM **Privately Held**
SIC: 3555 Printing trades machinery

(P-14807)
EXECUTIVE BUS SOLUTIONS INC
21356 Nordhoff St Ste 108, Chatsworth
(91311-6917)
PHONE..........................805 499-3290
Mohamad K Nassar, *CEO*
Jamie Royland, *Manager*
EMP: 12
SALES (est): 1.8MM **Privately Held**
SIC: 3555 Copy holders, printers'

PRODUCTS & SVCS

(P-14808)
FISHER GRAPHIC INDS A CAL CORP
1137 Graphics Dr, Modesto (95351-1501)
PHONE..............................209 577-0181
Phillip Saunders, *President*
EMP: 400
SQ FT: 36,000
SALES (est): 2.7MM
SALES (corp-wide): 3MM **Privately Held**
WEB: www.containergraphics.com
SIC: 3555 2796 Printing plates; platemaking services
PA: Container Graphics Corp.
114 Ednbrgh S Dr Ste 104
Cary NC 27511
919 481-4200

(P-14809)
FOOT IMPRINT INC
15373 Proctor Ave, City of Industry (91745-1022)
PHONE..............................626 991-4430
CHI Du, *President*
EMP: 50
SALES: 2MM **Privately Held**
SIC: 3555 Printing presses

(P-14810)
HARRIS & BRUNO MACHINE CO INC (PA)
Also Called: Harris & Bruno International
8555 Washington Blvd, Roseville (95678-5901)
PHONE..............................916 781-7676
Nick Bruno, *CEO*
Donnie Pullins, *Vice Pres*
Whitnee Mezzanares, *Admin Asst*
Jim Brown, *Administration*
Joe Braun, *Project Mgr*
▲ EMP: 64 EST: 1944
SQ FT: 45,000
SALES (est): 26.2MM **Privately Held**
WEB: www.harris-bruno.com
SIC: 3555 Printing trades machinery

(P-14811)
HEIDELBERG INSTRUMENTS INC
2539 W 237th St Ste A, Torrance (90505-5239)
PHONE..............................310 212-5071
Christian Bach, *President*
Gisela La Bella, *Officer*
Niels Wijnaendts, *Sales Staff*
EMP: 10
SALES: 1.5MM
SALES (corp-wide): 2.4B **Privately Held**
WEB: www.heidelberg-instruments.com
SIC: 3555 5084 Printing trades machinery; instruments & control equipment
HQ: Heidelberg Instruments Mikrotechnik Gmbh
Tullastr. 2
Heidelberg 69126
622 134-300

(P-14812)
IKONG E-COMMERCE INC
385 S Lemon Ave Ste E429, Walnut (91789-2727)
PHONE..............................888 556-1522
EMP: 10
SALES (est): 421.5K **Privately Held**
SIC: 3555

(P-14813)
IMPERIAL RUBBER PRODUCTS INC
5691 Gates St, Chino (91710-7603)
PHONE..............................909 393-0528
Ronald Hill, *CEO*
Bob Schwartz, *President*
Steve Huff, *Vice Pres*
EMP: 35
SQ FT: 20,000
SALES (est): 9.6MM **Privately Held**
WEB: www.imprub.com
SIC: 3555 Printing trades machinery

(P-14814)
K C PHOTO ENGRAVING CO
2666 Nina St, Pasadena (91107)
PHONE..............................626 795-4127
Michael Curley, *President*

Dale Curley, *Treasurer*
Dan Curley, *Vice Pres*
EMP: 30
SQ FT: 23,000
SALES (est): 4.3MM **Privately Held**
WEB: www.kcpe.net
SIC: 3555 2796 2791 Plates, offset; photoengraving plates, linecuts or halftones; typesetting

(P-14815)
KERNING DATA SYSTEMS INC
9301 Jordan Ave Ste 102, Chatsworth (91311-5863)
PHONE..............................818 882-8712
Quentin Leef, *President*
EMP: 13
SALES (est): 2.4MM **Privately Held**
WEB: www.kerningdata.com
SIC: 3555 1731 Printing trades machinery; computer installation

(P-14816)
LITH-O-ROLL CORPORATION
9521 Telstar Ave, El Monte (91731-2994)
P.O. Box 5328 (91734-1328)
PHONE..............................626 579-0340
Rita Sepe, *President*
Jeff Espett, *Vice Pres*
Chris Murray, *Marketing Staff*
EMP: 50
SQ FT: 30,000
SALES (est): 10.3MM **Privately Held**
SIC: 3555 Printing trades machinery

(P-14817)
MACDERMID PRTG SOLUTIONS LLC
260 S Pacific St, San Marcos (92078-2461)
PHONE..............................760 510-6277
Lori Chapman, *Branch Mgr*
EMP: 76
SALES (corp-wide): 3.7B **Publicly Held**
SIC: 3555 Printing plates
HQ: Macdermid Graphics Solutions, Llc
5210 Phillip Lee Dr Sw
Atlanta GA 30336

(P-14818)
MATTHEWS INTERNATIONAL CORP
5555 Fresca Dr, La Palma (90623-1006)
PHONE..............................562 921-0994
Richard Wolff, *General Mgr*
EMP: 50
SALES (corp-wide): 1.5B **Publicly Held**
SIC: 3555 Printing plates
PA: Matthews International Corporation
2 N Shore Ctr Ste 200
Pittsburgh PA 15212
412 442-8200

(P-14819)
OCE DSPLAY GRPHICS SYSTEMS INC
2811 Orchard Pkwy, San Jose (95134-2013)
PHONE..............................773 714-8500
▼ EMP: 100
SALES (est): 34.5K
SALES (corp-wide): 30.7B **Privately Held**
SIC: 3555 3577
HQ: Oce Holding B.V.
Sint Urbanusweg 43
Venlo 5914
773 592-222

(P-14820)
ONE TOUCH SOLUTIONS INC
Also Called: ONE TOUCH OFFICE TECHNOLOGY
370 Amapola Ave Ste 106, Torrance (90501-7241)
PHONE..............................310 320-6868
William Rees, *CEO*
Jayson Beasley, *COO*
Mark Stratton, *CFO*
Ron Perez, *Director*
Rick Cottrell, *Manager*
EMP: 15
SQ FT: 5,182
SALES: 6.1MM **Privately Held**
SIC: 3555 Printing trades machinery

(P-14821)
PACIFIC BARCODE INC
27531 Enterprise Cir W 201c, Temecula (92590-4888)
PHONE..............................951 587-8717
Michael Meadors, *President*
Michelle Meadors, *Vice Pres*
Savannah Santiago, *General Mgr*
Sandy Kucera, *Technology*
Ross Buckley, *Opers Mgr*
EMP: 15 EST: 1999
SQ FT: 8,600
SALES (est): 4.4MM **Privately Held**
WEB: www.pacificbarcode.com
SIC: 3555 2759 3565 3577 Printing trades machinery; commercial printing; labeling machines, industrial; bar code (magnetic ink) printers

(P-14822)
PAMARCO GLOBAL GRAPHICS INC
Also Called: Pamarco Western
6907 Marlin Cir, La Palma (90623-1018)
PHONE..............................714 739-0700
Richard Shields, *Manager*
EMP: 29 **Privately Held**
SIC: 3555 Printing trades machinery
HQ: Pamarco Global Graphics, Inc.
235 E 11th Ave
Roselle NJ 07203
908 241-1200

(P-14823)
PARA PLATE & PLASTICS CO INC
15910 Shoemaker Ave, Cerritos (90703-2200)
PHONE..............................562 404-3434
Shane Pearson, *President*
Robert J Clapp, *President*
John Greenamyer, *Treasurer*
Steve Binnard, *Vice Pres*
Barbara Kishiyama, *Controller*
EMP: 27 EST: 1945
SQ FT: 17,000
SALES: 3MM **Privately Held**
SIC: 3555 7336 2796 Printing plates; commercial art & graphic design; platemaking services

(P-14824)
PHOTOSTONE LLC
Also Called: Stone Impressions
8495 Redwood Creek Ln, San Diego (92126-1068)
PHONE..............................858 274-3400
Gregory Smith,
Gregory T Smith,
Melinda Smith,
EMP: 10
SALES (est): 1.8MM **Privately Held**
WEB: www.photostone.com
SIC: 3555 Lithographic stones

(P-14825)
PIC MANUFACTURING INC
410 Sherwood Rd, Paso Robles (93446-3554)
P.O. Box 665 (93447-0665)
PHONE..............................805 238-5451
Michael D Camp, *President*
EMP: 16 EST: 1962
SQ FT: 9,000
SALES (est): 2.4MM **Privately Held**
SIC: 3555 Printing trade parts & attachments

(P-14826)
QUINTEL CORPORATION
685 Jarvis Dr Ste A, Morgan Hill (95037-2813)
PHONE..............................408 776-5190
Jeffrey C Lane, *President*
Howard Green, *Chief Mktg Ofcr*
Robert Borawski, *Admin Sec*
Keith Radousky, *CTO*
EMP: 20 EST: 1978
SQ FT: 12,500
SALES (est): 3.3MM **Privately Held**
WEB: www.quintelcorp.com
SIC: 3555 Printing trades machinery

(P-14827)
RIMA ENTERPRISES INC
Also Called: Rima-System
5340 Argosy Ave, Huntington Beach (92649-1037)
PHONE..............................714 893-4534
Horst K Steinhart, *CEO*
Luis Leal, *Technology*
Jeff Schwarz, *Engineer*
Thao Tran, *Human Res Dir*
Venu Sunkara, *Opers Staff*
▲ EMP: 62
SQ FT: 50,000
SALES (est): 12.2MM **Privately Held**
WEB: www.rimasystem.com
SIC: 3555 Bookbinding machinery

(P-14828)
THISTLE ROLLER CO INC
209 Van Norman Rd, Montebello (90640-5393)
PHONE..............................323 685-5322
Lizbeth Karpynec, *CEO*
Eric Karpynetz, *Vice Pres*
Luis Lopez, *Safety Mgr*
▲ EMP: 35
SQ FT: 45,000
SALES (est): 9.3MM **Privately Held**
SIC: 3555 3312 2796 Printing trades machinery; blast furnaces & steel mills; platemaking services

(P-14829)
US RUBBER ROLLER COMPANY INC
1516 7th St, Riverside (92507-4421)
PHONE..............................951 682-2221
Jose Uribe, *President*
Lebizia Uribe, *Vice Pres*
Ramie Uribe, *Admin Sec*
EMP: 18
SQ FT: 10,000
SALES: 1.5MM **Privately Held**
SIC: 3555 Printing trades machinery

(P-14830)
XEROX INTERNATIONAL PARTNERS (HQ)
Also Called: Fuji Xerox
3174 Porter Dr, Palo Alto (94304-1212)
PHONE..............................408 953-2700
Sunil Gupta, *Partner*
▲ EMP: 50
SALES (est): 15.1MM
SALES (corp-wide): 10.2B **Publicly Held**
WEB: www.xerox.com
SIC: 3555 Leads, printers'
PA: Xerox Corporation
201 Merritt 7
Norwalk CT 06851
203 968-3000

3556 Food Prdts Machinery

(P-14831)
ALUMINUM PROS INC
Also Called: Malco Manufacturing
13917 S Main St, Los Angeles (90061-2151)
PHONE..............................310 366-7696
Fax: 310 366-7694
EMP: 12 EST: 2011
SALES (est): 970K **Privately Held**
SIC: 3556

(P-14832)
APEX BREWING SUPPLY
3237 Rippey Rd Ste 600, Loomis (95650-7662)
PHONE..............................916 250-7950
Joseph Fredrickson, *President*
▲ EMP: 10
SQ FT: 15,000
SALES: 4MM **Privately Held**
SIC: 3556 Food products machinery

(P-14833)
ATLAS PACIFIC ENGINEERING CO
Also Called: Sinclair Systems
3115 S Willow Ave, Fresno (93725-9349)
PHONE..............................559 233-4500
Don Freeman, *Principal*

EMP: 60
SALES (corp-wide): 93.8MM **Privately Held**
WEB: www.atlaspacific.com
SIC: 3556 Food products machinery
HQ: Atlas Pacific Engineering Company
  1 Atlas Ave
  Pueblo CO 81001
  719 948-3040

(P-14834)
ATLAS PACIFIC ENGINEERING CO
4500 N Star Way, Modesto (95356-9534)
PHONE.....................................209 574-9884
Regina Webster, *Principal*
EMP: 44
SALES (corp-wide): 93.8MM **Privately Held**
WEB: www.atlaspacific.com
SIC: 3556 5046 Food products machinery; commercial equipment
HQ: Atlas Pacific Engineering Company
  1 Atlas Ave
  Pueblo CO 81001
  719 948-3040

(P-14835)
AVALON MFG CO INCOIRPORATED
509 Bateman Cir, Corona (92880-2012)
PHONE.....................................951 340-0280
Bill Enger, *President*
Troy Enger, *Vice Pres*
EMP: 14 EST: 1976
SQ FT: 19,277
SALES (est): 3.2MM **Privately Held**
WEB: www.enger.com
SIC: 3556 Bakery machinery
PA: Enger, Inc.
  509 Bateman Cir
  Corona CA 92880

(P-14836)
BHOGART LLC
1919 Monterey Hwy Ste 80, San Jose (95112-6147)
PHONE.....................................855 553-3887
Kimberly Schaefer, *Partner*
Kevin Dolan, *Partner*
Thomas Lynch, *CEO*
David Schaefer, *CTO*
EMP: 38
SALES (est): 7.7MM **Privately Held**
SIC: 3556 Smokers, food processing equipment

(P-14837)
BILLINGTON WELDING & MFG INC
Also Called: Bwm
  1442 N Emerald Ave, Modesto (95351-1115)
P.O. Box 4460 (95352-4460)
PHONE.....................................209 526-0846
Timothy Ryan Billington, *CEO*
Francis Billington, *President*
Dave Davis, *Safety Mgr*
EMP: 60
SQ FT: 26,000
SALES (est): 13.8MM **Privately Held**
WEB: www.hopkinsbwm.com
SIC: 3556 3535 Food products machinery; conveyors & conveying equipment

(P-14838)
BIOSYNTHETIC TECHNOLOGIES LLC (HQ)
Also Called: Lubrigreen
  2 Park Plz Ste 200, Irvine (92614-8569)
P.O. Box 856, Malta MT (59538-0856)
PHONE.....................................949 390-5910
Allen Barbieri,
Jakob Bredsguard, *Officer*
John Hopkins, *Manager*
EMP: 13
SQ FT: 4,800
SALES (est): 1.6MM
SALES (corp-wide): 3.7B **Publicly Held**
WEB: www.peaksandprairies.com
SIC: 3556 Oilseed crushing & extracting machinery

PA: Calumet Specialty Products Partners Lp
  2780 Waterfront Pkwy
  Indianapolis IN 46214
  317 328-5660

(P-14839)
BLENTECH CORPORATION
2899 Dowd Dr, Santa Rosa (95407-7897)
PHONE.....................................707 523-5949
Darrell Horn, *President*
Daniel Voit, *COO*
Joseph Yarnall, *Exec VP*
Kelly Hamilton, *Executive Asst*
Gina Solheim, *Executive Asst*
▲ EMP: 60
SQ FT: 27,000
SALES (est): 18.6MM **Privately Held**
WEB: www.blentech.com
SIC: 3556 Mixers, commercial, food; meat processing machinery; poultry processing machinery; pasta machinery

(P-14840)
CASA HERRERA INC (PA)
2655 Pine St, Pomona (91767-2115)
PHONE.....................................909 392-3930
Michael L Herrera, *CEO*
Alfred J Herrera, *President*
Ronald L Meade, *President*
Susan A Herrera, *Treasurer*
Frank J Herrera, *Exec VP*
◆ EMP: 136 EST: 1970
SQ FT: 100,000
SALES (est): 25.4MM **Privately Held**
WEB: www.casaherrera.com
SIC: 3556 Food products machinery

(P-14841)
CHOOLJIAN & SONS INC
Also Called: Del Ray Packaging
  Del Rey Ave, Del Rey (93616)
P.O. Box 160 (93616-0160)
PHONE.....................................559 888-2031
Gerald Chooljian, *Corp Secy*
EMP: 60
SQ FT: 1,152
SALES (corp-wide): 29.1MM **Privately Held**
SIC: 3556 Dehydrating equipment, food processing
PA: Chooljian & Sons, Inc.
  5287 S Del Rey Ave
  Del Rey CA 93616
  559 888-2031

(P-14842)
COMMERCIAL MANUFACTURING
2432 S Railroad Ave, Fresno (93706-5108)
P.O. Box 947 (93714-0947)
PHONE.....................................559 237-1855
Larry Hagopian, *President*
Charles Uju, *CIO*
Michael Tarver, *Engineer*
Armando Garza, *Manager*
EMP: 45
SQ FT: 45,000
SALES (est): 11.3MM **Privately Held**
WEB: www.commercialmfg.com
SIC: 3556 Food products machinery

(P-14843)
CRIVELLER CALIFORNIA CORP
185 Grant Ave, Healdsburg (95448-9539)
PHONE.....................................707 431-2211
Bruno Criveller, *President*
Mario Creveller, *Vice Pres*
Shane Curtis, *Executive*
Ann Magida, *Marketing Staff*
Lynn Dow, *Sales Staff*
◆ EMP: 15
SALES: 5MM **Privately Held**
SIC: 3556 Brewers' & maltsters' machinery

(P-14844)
DALE GROVE CORPORATION
Also Called: Gdc
  1501 Stone Creek Dr, San Jose (95132-1933)
PHONE.....................................408 251-7220
Stephanie Mattos, *CEO*
John R Mattos, *Vice Pres*
Ruth Howell, *Bookkeeper*
EMP: 36 EST: 1965
SQ FT: 28,000

SALES (est): 5.9MM **Privately Held**
WEB: www.grovedale.com
SIC: 3556 3535 3429 Food products machinery; conveyors & conveying equipment; manufactured hardware (general)

(P-14845)
EMILIOMITI LLC
2129 Harrison St, San Francisco (94110-1321)
PHONE.....................................415 621-1171
Emilio Mitidieri, *Mng Member*
Reama Barclay, *Manager*
▲ EMP: 13 EST: 1979
SQ FT: 5,000
SALES (est): 2MM **Privately Held**
SIC: 3556 Pasta machinery

(P-14846)
FOOD EQUIPMENT MFG CO
Also Called: Femco
  175 Mitchell Rd, Hollister (95023-9603)
P.O. Box 257 (95024-0257)
PHONE.....................................831 637-1624
Sal Felice, *President*
Elizabeth Felice, *Treasurer*
EMP: 12
SQ FT: 2,800
SALES (est): 2.3MM **Privately Held**
SIC: 3556 Food products machinery

(P-14847)
FOOD MAKERS BAKERY EQP INC
16019 Adelante St, Irwindale (91702-3255)
PHONE.....................................626 358-1343
Tom Fowler, *Principal*
Linda Fowler, *Admin Sec*
▲ EMP: 40
SQ FT: 51,000
SALES (est): 11MM **Privately Held**
WEB: www.foodmakersequipment.com
SIC: 3556 Bakery machinery

(P-14848)
FOODTOOLS INC (PA)
315 Laguna St, Santa Barbara (93101-1716)
PHONE.....................................805 962-8383
Martin Grano, *Ch of Bd*
Matt Browne, *Vice Pres*
Doug Petrovich, *Vice Pres*
Lindsay Getman, *Purch Mgr*
Lindsay Hayes, *Purch Mgr*
◆ EMP: 20
SQ FT: 8,500
SALES (est): 8.4MM **Privately Held**
WEB: www.foodtools.com
SIC: 3556 2679 Slicers, commercial, food; paper products, converted

(P-14849)
FOTIS AND SON IMPORTS INC
15451 Electronic Ln, Huntington Beach (92649-1333)
PHONE.....................................714 894-9022
Peter Georgatsos, *President*
Laura Georgatsos, *Corp Secy*
Russ Hillas, *Exec VP*
Eleni Hillas, *Principal*
▲ EMP: 50
SQ FT: 34,000
SALES (est): 14.9MM **Privately Held**
WEB: www.greekfoodandwine.com
SIC: 3556 Food products machinery

(P-14850)
FPEC CORPORATION A CAL CORP (PA)
Also Called: Food Processing Equipment Co
  13623 Pumice St, Santa Fe Springs (90670-5105)
PHONE.....................................562 802-3727
Alan Davison, *CEO*
Ethel Davison, *Corp Secy*
Doug Webster, *Engineer*
Margo Blunk, *Human Res Mgr*
EMP: 18
SQ FT: 18,000
SALES (est): 9.9MM **Privately Held**
WEB: www.fpec.com
SIC: 3556 Food products machinery

(P-14851)
G & I ISLAS INDUSTRIES INC (PA)
Also Called: G & I Industries
  12860 Schabarum Ave, Baldwin Park (91706-6801)
P.O. Box 1262 (91706-7262)
PHONE.....................................626 960-5020
Gonzalo R Islas, *CEO*
Sara Islas, *Vice Pres*
▲ EMP: 27
SQ FT: 12,500
SALES (est): 5.4MM **Privately Held**
SIC: 3556 5084 Bakery machinery; food industry machinery

(P-14852)
GARROUTTE INC (PA)
151 Kearney St, Watsonville (95076-4244)
PHONE.....................................831 722-2487
Eugene Teeter, *President*
Jean Teeter, *President*
EMP: 90
SQ FT: 37,500
SALES: 1MM **Privately Held**
WEB: www.garroutte.com
SIC: 3556 Food products machinery

(P-14853)
GENERIC MANUFACTURING CORP
27455 Bostik Ct, Temecula (92590-3698)
PHONE.....................................951 296-2838
Lonnie Belt, *President*
EMP: 10
SQ FT: 20,000
SALES (est): 2MM **Privately Held**
SIC: 3556 Food products machinery

(P-14854)
GERARD H TANZI INC
Also Called: Industrial Machining Co
  22555 Sawmill Flat Rd, Columbia (95310)
P.O. Box 1159 (95310-1159)
PHONE.....................................209 532-0855
Gerard H Tanzi, *President*
EMP: 10
SQ FT: 2,000
SALES (est): 1.4MM **Privately Held**
SIC: 3556 3724 Smokers, food processing equipment; aircraft engines & engine parts

(P-14855)
GOLDEN PACIFIC SEAFOODS INC
700 S Raymond Ave, Fullerton (92831-5233)
PHONE.....................................714 589-8888
Tony Zavala, *President*
EMP: 45
SALES: 10MM **Privately Held**
SIC: 3556 Meat, poultry & seafood processing machinery

(P-14856)
HACKETT INDUSTRIES INC
Also Called: West Star Industries
  4445 E Fremont St, Stockton (95215-4007)
PHONE.....................................209 955-8220
Michelle E Focke, *CEO*
Richard Hackett, *President*
Mark Lathrop, *CFO*
Joe Lebel, *General Mgr*
Carolyn Hackett, *Admin Sec*
EMP: 43
SQ FT: 90,000
SALES (est): 9.4MM **Privately Held**
SIC: 3556 3444 3431 Food products machinery; sheet metalwork; metal sanitary ware

(P-14857)
HAYWARD GORDON US INC
9351 Industrial Way, Adelanto (92301-3932)
PHONE.....................................760 246-3430
EMP: 42 **Privately Held**
SIC: 3556 Cutting, chopping, grinding, mixing & similar machinery; mixers, feed, except agricultural
HQ: Hayward Gordon Us, Inc.
  1541 S 92nd Pl
  Seattle WA 98108
  206 767-5660

PRODUCTS & SVCS

(P-14858)
HEPHAESTUS INNOVATIONS
2661 W Bch St Ste 3b Suit, Watsonville
(95076)
PHONE..............................831 254-8555
Jessica Garcia, *President*
EMP: 12
SALES (est): 649.1K **Privately Held**
SIC: 3556 Dehydrating equipment, food
processing

(P-14859)
ICE LINK LLC
954 N Batavia St, Orange (92867-5589)
PHONE..............................714 771-6580
Eric Berge, *Mng Member*
Mary Palomino, *Executive*
Willie Wiginton, *Marketing Staff*
EMP: 12
SALES (est): 1.5MM **Privately Held**
SIC: 3556 Food products machinery

(P-14860)
INTERSTATE MEAT CO INC
Also Called: Sterling Pacific Meat Co.
6114 Scott Way, Commerce (90040-3518)
PHONE..............................323 838-9400
James T Asher, *President*
Luis Munoz, *Vice Pres*
Tony Cuevas, *Director*
EMP: 16
SALES (est): 3.4MM **Privately Held**
SIC: 3556 Meat processing machinery

(P-14861)
J C FORD COMPANY
Also Called: JC Ford
901 S Leslie St, La Habra (90631-6841)
PHONE..............................714 871-7361
Scott D Ruhe, *CEO*
Chia Thao, *Project Mgr*
Orlando Hurtado, *Engineer*
Ares Polyzos, *Engineer*
Mike Minidis, *Materials Mgr*
◆ EMP: 95
SQ FT: 80,000
SALES (est): 41.5MM **Privately Held**
WEB: www.jcford.com
SIC: 3556 Food products machinery
PA: Ruhe Corporation
901 S Leslie St
La Habra CA 90631

(P-14862)
JOHN BEAN TECHNOLOGIES
CORP
Also Called: Jbt Food Tech Madera
2300 W Industrial Ave, Madera
(93637-5210)
PHONE..............................559 661-3200
Eric Madsen, *Branch Mgr*
Bill Kreamer, *Info Tech Mgr*
Jon Howden, *Design Engr*
Rick Ripley, *Design Engr*
Maria Milian, *Electrical Engi*
EMP: 165 **Publicly Held**
SIC: 3556 Food products machinery
PA: John Bean Technologies Corporation
70 W Madison St Ste 4400
Chicago IL 60602

(P-14863)
JOHN BEAN TECHNOLOGIES
CORP
1660 Iowa Ave Ste 100, Riverside
(92507-0501)
P.O. Box 5710 (92517-5710)
PHONE..............................951 222-2300
Thomas Brickweg, *Principal*
Christina Campos, *Vice Pres*
Margaret Wright, *Purchasing*
EMP: 50 **Publicly Held**
SIC: 3556 3542 3523 Dairy & milk ma-
chinery; nail heading machines; dairy
equipment (farm)
PA: John Bean Technologies Corporation
70 W Madison St Ste 4400
Chicago IL 60602

(P-14864)
JOHN BEAN TECHNOLOGIES
CORP
9829 W Legacy Ave, Visalia (93291-9544)
PHONE..............................559 651-8300
Billy Wofford, *Branch Mgr*
Dana Dillard, *Manager*
EMP: 108 **Publicly Held**
SIC: 3556 Food products machinery
PA: John Bean Technologies Corporation
70 W Madison St Ste 4400
Chicago IL 60602

(P-14865)
JUICEBOT & CO LLC
999 Corporate Dr Ste 100, Ladera Ranch
(92694-2149)
PHONE..............................651 270-8860
Kamal Mohammand, *Mng Member*
EMP: 10
SALES (est): 421.5K **Privately Held**
SIC: 3556 2037 Juice extractors, fruit &
vegetable: commercial type; fruit juices

(P-14866)
JUICY WHIP INC
1668 Curtiss Ct, La Verne (91750-5848)
PHONE..............................909 392-7500
Gus Stratton, *President*
▲ EMP: 28
SQ FT: 23,000
SALES (est): 7.2MM **Privately Held**
WEB: www.juicywhip.com
SIC: 3556 2033 Beverage machinery; fruit
juices: fresh; fruit juices: concentrated,
hot pack

(P-14867)
LAWRENCE EQUIPMENT INC
(PA)
2034 Peck Rd, El Monte (91733-3727)
PHONE..............................626 442-2894
John Lawrence, *CEO*
Jack Kirkpatrick, *Shareholder*
Linda Lawrence, *Vice Pres*
Glenn Shelton, *Vice Pres*
Karen Foster, *Info Tech Dir*
▲ EMP: 200
SQ FT: 50,000
SALES (est): 98.1MM **Privately Held**
WEB: www.lawrenceequipment.com
SIC: 3556 Flour mill machinery

(P-14868)
MACHINE BUILDING
SPECIALTIES
Also Called: Conveyor Concepts
1977 Blake Ave, Los Angeles (90039-3832)
PHONE..............................323 666-8289
Charles Conaway, *Ch of Bd*
Dennis James Conaway, *President*
Sharon Conaway, *Treasurer*
Sandra Conaway, *Admin Sec*
EMP: 25 EST: 1960
SQ FT: 17,000
SALES (est): 5.5MM **Privately Held**
SIC: 3556 3535 Bakery machinery; belt
conveyor systems, general industrial use

(P-14869)
MARTIN ENGINEERING CO INC
5454 2nd St, Irwindale (91706-2000)
PHONE..............................626 960-5153
Jonathan Martin, *President*
Joanne Hughes, *Manager*
EMP: 15
SQ FT: 10,000
SALES: 3MM **Privately Held**
SIC: 3556 Food products machinery

(P-14870)
MEAT PACKERS BUTCHERS
SUP INC
Also Called: Mpbs Industries
2820 E Washington Blvd, Los Angeles
(90023-4274)
PHONE..............................323 268-8514
Jimmy Jin, *CEO*
Shaofa Jin, *Ch of Bd*
Pat Ward, *Regl Sales Mgr*
▲ EMP: 17
SQ FT: 16,000

SALES (est): 4.1MM **Privately Held**
WEB: www.mpbs.com
SIC: 3556 Food products machinery

(P-14871)
MIGHTY SOY INC
1227 S Eastern Ave, Los Angeles
(90022-4809)
PHONE..............................323 266-6969
Maung Myint, *President*
Gin Yee Lee, *Vice Pres*
EMP: 14 EST: 1980
SQ FT: 8,000
SALES: 485.9K **Privately Held**
SIC: 3556 2099 2075 Smokers, food pro-
cessing equipment; food preparations;
soybean oil mills

(P-14872)
MONTEREY COAST BREWING
LLC
165 Main St, Salinas (93901-3403)
PHONE..............................831 758-2337
Charles Lloyd,
Lucy Lloyd,
EMP: 12
SALES (est): 1.5MM **Privately Held**
SIC: 3556 Brewers' & maltsters' machinery

(P-14873)
NATIONAL BAND SAW
COMPANY
1055 W Avenue L12, Lancaster
(93534-7045)
P.O. Box 800190, Santa Clarita (91380-
0190)
PHONE..............................661 294-9552
Harley Frank, *President*
Norman Frank, *Ch of Bd*
Chris Tuttle, *Vice Pres*
◆ EMP: 17
SQ FT: 12,000
SALES (est): 3.4MM **Privately Held**
WEB: www.nbsparts.com
SIC: 3556 Meat processing machinery

(P-14874)
O H I COMPANY
820 S Pershing Ave, Stockton
(95206-1176)
P.O. Box 622 (95201-0622)
PHONE..............................209 466-8921
Thomas W Hubbard, *CEO*
Ben Wallace, *Vice Pres*
▲ EMP: 26 EST: 1970
SQ FT: 40,000
SALES (est): 8.1MM **Privately Held**
WEB: www.ohicompany.com
SIC: 3556 3443 Food products machinery;
fabricated plate work (boiler shop)

(P-14875)
PACIFIC PACKAGING MCHY LLC
(HQ)
Also Called: Pack West Machinery
200 River Rd, Corona (92880-1435)
PHONE..............................949 369-2425
Gerald Carpino, *CEO*
Jerry Carpino, *President*
Suzanne Brown, *Bookkeeper*
Ann Tau, *Bookkeeper*
Tom Rawson, *Opers Mgr*
▲ EMP: 25 EST: 1962
SQ FT: 30,000
SALES (est): 4.4MM
SALES (corp-wide): 619.9MM **Privately**
Held
WEB: www.pacificpak.com
SIC: 3556 3565 Food products machinery;
packaging machinery
PA: Pro Mach, Inc.
50 E Rivercntr Blvd 180
Covington KY 41011
513 831-8778

(P-14876)
PACKERS MANUFACTURING
INC
4212 W Hemlock Ave, Visalia
(93277-6902)
PHONE..............................559 732-4886
Dwight Plumley, *President*
Teddy A Plumley, *Treasurer*
EMP: 24
SQ FT: 22,250

SALES (est): 3.8MM **Privately Held**
SIC: 3556 7699 Packing house machinery; industrial machinery & equipment repair

(P-14877)
PHANTOM CARRIAGE
BREWERY
18525 S Main St, Gardena (90248-4611)
PHONE..............................310 538-5834
Jack Wignot, *CEO*
Martin Seab, *General Mgr*
EMP: 25
SALES (est): 2.3MM **Privately Held**
SIC: 3556 Brewers' & maltsters' machinery

(P-14878)
POTENTIAL DESIGN INC
4185 E Jefferson Ave, Fresno
(93725-9707)
P.O. Box 69, Fowler (93625-0069)
PHONE..............................559 834-5361
William Tjerrild, *President*
Jim J Tjerrild, *CFO*
▼ EMP: 17
SQ FT: 20,000
SALES (est): 9.1MM **Privately Held**
WEB: www.lonesomegeorge.com
SIC: 3556 Packing house machinery

(P-14879)
PURATOS CORPORATION
Also Called: Puratos West Coast
18831 S Laurel Park Rd, Compton
(90220-6004)
PHONE..............................310 632-1361
Carlos Figuerido, *Manager*
EMP: 30 **Privately Held**
WEB: www.puratos.com
SIC: 3556 7699 5046 2041 Bakery ma-
chinery; restaurant equipment repair; bak-
ery equipment & supplies; flour & other
grain mill products
HQ: Puratos Corporation
1660 Suckle Hwy
Pennsauken NJ 08110

(P-14880)
RBM CONVEYOR SYSTEMS INC
1570 W Mission Blvd, Pomona
(91766-1247)
PHONE..............................909 620-1333
Roobik Kureghian, *President*
Armine Kureghian, *Treasurer*
Arin Azadkhanyan, *Engineer*
Emin Kureghian, *Purch Mgr*
▲ EMP: 20
SQ FT: 40,000
SALES (est): 6.7MM **Privately Held**
WEB: www.rbmcsi.com
SIC: 3556 8711 3537 3535 Food prod-
ucts machinery; engineering services; in-
dustrial trucks & tractors; conveyors &
conveying equipment

(P-14881)
REXNORD INDUSTRIES LLC
Also Called: Industrial Components Div
2175 Union Pl, Simi Valley (93065-1661)
PHONE..............................805 583-5514
Dave Kleinhaus, *Manager*
EMP: 152 **Publicly Held**
SIC: 3556 3568 Food products machinery;
couplings, shaft: rigid, flexible, universal
joint, etc.
HQ: Rexnord Industries, Llc
247 W Freshwater Way # 200
Milwaukee WI 53204
414 643-3000

(P-14882)
RIPON MFG CO
Also Called: RMC
652 S Stockton Ave, Ripon (95366-2798)
PHONE..............................209 599-2148
Glenn Navarro, *President*
Ursula Navarro, *Treasurer*
EMP: 20
SQ FT: 45,000
SALES (est): 5.7MM **Privately Held**
WEB: www.riponmfgco.com
SIC: 3556 3535 Food products machinery;
conveyors & conveying equipment

▲ = Import ▼=Export
◆ =Import/Export

(P-14883)
RMJV LP
Also Called: Fresh Creative Foods
3285 Corporate Vw, Vista (92081-8528)
PHONE....................................503 526-5752
Diana Robertson, *Partner*
Rff LLC, *General Ptnr*
Jorge Villalobos, *General Mgr*
Patricia Duenas, *Human Res Mgr*
Craig Dixon, *Manager*
EMP: 300
SQ FT: 35,000
SALES (est): 91.1MM
SALES (corp-wide): 1.7B **Privately Held**
SIC: 3556 Food products machinery
PA: Reser's Fine Foods, Inc.
15570 Sw Jenkins Rd
Beaverton OR 97006
503 643-6431

(P-14884)
SHAVER SPECIALTY CO INC
20608 Earl St, Torrance (90503-3009)
PHONE....................................310 370-6941
George Shaver, *President*
Ronald Shaver, *Vice Pres*
▲ EMP: 22 EST: 1937
SQ FT: 20,000
SALES (est): 3.6MM **Privately Held**
WEB: www.shaverengines.com
SIC: 3556 3599 Choppers, commercial,
food; machine shop, jobbing & repair

(P-14885)
SPX FLOW US LLC
26561 Rancho Pkwy S, Lake Forest
(92630-8301)
PHONE....................................949 455-8150
Brian Ahern, *Manager*
EMP: 67
SALES (corp-wide): 1.9B **Publicly Held**
SIC: 3556 Food products machinery
HQ: Spx Flow Us, Llc
135 Mount Read Blvd
Rochester NY 14611
585 436-5550

(P-14886)
STAINLESS WORKS MFG INC
225 Salinas Rd Bldg 5a, Royal Oaks
(95076-5253)
PHONE....................................831 728-5097
Jose Medina, *Owner*
EMP: 22 EST: 2002
SALES: 3MM **Privately Held**
WEB: www.stainlessworksmfg.com
SIC: 3556 Food products machinery

(P-14887)
STALFAB
131 Algen Ln, Watsonville (95076-8624)
P.O. Box 780 (95077-0780)
PHONE....................................831 786-1600
Eric Buksa, *Owner*
EMP: 12
SQ FT: 5,000
SALES (est): 1.6MM **Privately Held**
SIC: 3556 Food products machinery

(P-14888)
SUPERIOR FOOD MACHINERY INC
8311 Sorensen Ave, Santa Fe Springs
(90670-2125)
PHONE....................................562 949-0396
Danny Reyes, *President*
Polo Reyes, *President*
Marc Reyes, *Vice Pres*
Carlos Cruz, *General Mgr*
Apolonio Reyes, *Agent*
EMP: 23
SQ FT: 14,000
SALES (est): 6MM **Privately Held**
WEB: www.superiorinc.com
SIC: 3556 Food products machinery

(P-14889)
TOMRA SORTING INC (DH)
Also Called: Best USA
875 Embarcadero Dr, West Sacramento
(95605-1503)
PHONE....................................720 870-2240
Bert Van Der Auwera, *CEO*
Paul Berghmans, *President*
Eddy De Reyes, *Vice Pres*
Johan Peeters, *Vice Pres*

Marc Ryman, *Vice Pres*
▲ EMP: 91
SQ FT: 6,000
SALES (est): 22.4MM
SALES (corp-wide): 901.9MM **Privately Held**
WEB: www.bestusa.com
SIC: 3556 Food products machinery
HQ: Tomra Sorting Nv
Romeinse Straat 20
Leuven 3001
163 963-96

(P-14890)
TPI MARKETING LLC
Also Called: Twin Peaks Ingredients
14985 Hilton Dr, Fontana (92336-2082)
P.O. Box 1745, Rancho Cucamonga
(91729-1745)
PHONE....................................302 703-0283
Kyle Boen, *Mng Member*
Trevor Boen,
EMP: 10
SQ FT: 10,000
SALES: 2MM **Privately Held**
SIC: 3556 5499 5149 Food products ma-
chinery; vitamin food stores; health foods

(P-14891)
TRIPLE E MANUFACTURING INC
Also Called: Ernst Mfg
2121 S Union Ave, Bakersfield
(93307-4155)
P.O. Box 70155 (93387-0155)
PHONE....................................661 831-7553
Martin W Etcheverry, *President*
Rick Etcheverry, *Treasurer*
EMP: 25
SQ FT: 40,000
SALES (est): 4.2MM **Privately Held**
SIC: 3556 3565 Packing house machin-
ery; packaging machinery

(P-14892)
UNIMARK INTERNATIONAL INC
22601 Allview Ter, Laguna Beach
(92651-1547)
PHONE....................................949 497-1235
Richard Ness, *President*
EMP: 12
SQ FT: 5,000
SALES (est): 1.3MM **Privately Held**
SIC: 3556 5149 Food products machinery;
groceries & related products

(P-14893)
UNITED BAKERY EQUIPMENT CO INC
Also Called: Hartman Slices Division
19216 S Laurel Park Rd, Compton
(90220-6008)
PHONE....................................310 635-8121
Loren Schieler, *Manager*
Paul Bastasch, *Vice Pres*
Anita Nunez, *Office Mgr*
Michael Bastasch, *Engineer*
EMP: 40
SQ FT: 63,089
SALES (corp-wide): 37MM **Privately Held**
SIC: 3556 5046 Slicers, commercial, food;
bakery equipment & supplies
PA: United Bakery Equipment Company.
Inc.
19216 S Laurel Park Rd
Compton CA 90220
310 635-8121

(P-14894)
VALLEY PACKLINE SOLUTIONS
5259 Avenue 408, Reedley (93654-9131)
PHONE....................................559 638-7821
Jim Parra, *Principal*
EMP: 30
SALES (est): 8.7MM **Privately Held**
SIC: 3556 Dehydrating equipment, food
processing

(P-14895)
VERSACO MANUFACTURING INC
550 E Luchessa Ave, Gilroy (95020-7068)
PHONE....................................408 848-2880
Alan R Owens, *President*
John K Ishizuka, *Vice Pres*
Alan Owens, *Manager*

EMP: 15
SQ FT: 30,000
SALES (est): 3.2MM **Privately Held**
SIC: 3556 3661 3312 3537 Food products machinery; telephone & telegraph
apparatus; structural & rail mill products;
industrial trucks & tractors

(P-14896)
VISTAN CORPORATION
Ashlock Company
855 Montague St, San Leandro
(94577-4327)
P.O. Box 1676 (94577-0398)
PHONE....................................510 351-0560
Sheryl Sullivan, *Branch Mgr*
Ted Hubbard, *Engineer*
Sherrill Sullivan, *Engineer*
EMP: 13
SQ FT: 11,345
SALES (corp-wide): 21.8MM **Privately Held**
WEB: www.sloughcreek.com
SIC: 3556 7359 Food products machinery;
equipment rental & leasing
PA: Vistan Corporation
3870 Halfway Rd
The Plains VA 20198
540 253-5540

(P-14897)
WILLIAM BOUNDS LTD
23625 Madison St, Torrance (90505-6004)
P.O. Box 1547 (90505-0547)
PHONE....................................310 375-0505
Helen Bounds, *President*
Sharon Bounds, *Vice Pres*
Rick Fouse, *Manager*
▲ EMP: 30
SQ FT: 18,000
SALES (est): 6.1MM **Privately Held**
WEB: www.wmboundsltd.com
SIC: 3556 8733 Food products machinery;
noncommercial research organizations

(P-14898)
WILLIE BYLSMA
Also Called: W & J Dairy
10217 Atlas Ct, Oakdale (95361-7776)
PHONE....................................209 847-3362
Willie Bylsma, *Owner*
Jolene C Bylsma, *Principal*
EMP: 18
SALES: 500K **Privately Held**
SIC: 3556 Dairy & milk machinery

3559 Special Ind Machinery, NEC

(P-14899)
AC PHOTONICS INC
2701 Northwestern Pkwy, Santa Clara
(95051-0947)
PHONE....................................408 986-9838
Yongjian Wang, *President*
Zuhong Qu, *Vice Pres*
Sunny Chen, *Managing Dir*
▲ EMP: 24
SQ FT: 10,000
SALES (est): 20MM **Privately Held**
WEB: www.acphotonics.com
SIC: 3559 Fiber optics strand coating ma-
chinery

(P-14900)
ADCON LAB INC
6110 Running Springs Rd, San Jose
(95135-2209)
PHONE....................................408 531-9187
Raymond Jin, *President*
◆ EMP: 20
SALES: 2MM **Privately Held**
WEB: www.adconlab.com
SIC: 3559 Semiconductor manufacturing
machinery

(P-14901)
ADCOTECH CORPORATION
1980 Tarob Ct, Milpitas (95035-6824)
PHONE....................................408 943-9999
Ron B Stillman, *President*
EMP: 93

SALES (est): 4.3MM
SALES (corp-wide): 811.4MM **Publicly Held**
SIC: 3559 Electron tube making machinery
HQ: Jdsu Acterna Holdings Llc
1 Milestone Center Ct
Germantown MD 20876
240 404-1550

(P-14902)
ADVANCED INDUSTRIAL CERAMICS
2449 Zanker Rd, San Jose (95131-1116)
PHONE....................................408 955-9990
Chau Nguyen, *Owner*
EMP: 25
SQ FT: 7,500
SALES (est): 7MM **Privately Held**
SIC: 3559 3674 Semiconductor manufac-
turing machinery; stud bases or mounts
for semiconductor devices

(P-14903)
ADVANCED INTL TECH LLC
9909 Hibert St Ste A, San Diego
(92131-1069)
PHONE....................................858 566-2945
Margaret Yount, *President*
EMP: 10
SQ FT: 5,000
SALES (est): 750K **Privately Held**
WEB: www.aitechnology-usa.com
SIC: 3559 Electronic component making
machinery

(P-14904)
ADVENIRA ENTERPRISES INC
320 Soquel Way, Sunnyvale (94085-4101)
PHONE....................................408 732-3950
Elmira Ryabova, *CEO*
Christopher Mah, *Research*
Martin Mogaard, *Engineer*
Val Ryabov, *Engineer*
EMP: 16
SALES: 2.9MM **Privately Held**
SIC: 3559 Chemical machinery & equip-
ment

(P-14905)
ALTAIR TECHNOLOGIES INC
41970 Christy St, Fremont (94538-3160)
PHONE....................................650 508-8700
Chris Ferrari, *CEO*
Gary Atkins, *CFO*
Chris Wallace, *CFO*
Curtis Allen, *Facilities Mgr*
▼ EMP: 30
SALES (est): 8.2MM **Privately Held**
WEB: www.altairusa.com
SIC: 3559 7692 Electronic component
making machinery; brazing

(P-14906)
AMERGENCE TECHNOLOGY INC
295 Brea Canyon Rd, Walnut
(91789-3049)
PHONE....................................909 859-8400
Shavonne Tran, *President*
▲ EMP: 29
SQ FT: 40,000
SALES (est): 4MM **Privately Held**
SIC: 3559 Recycling machinery

(P-14907)
APPLIED MATERIALS INC
3320 Scott Blvd, Santa Clara (95054-3101)
PHONE....................................408 727-5555
Mary Ryan, *Branch Mgr*
Sean Herbert, *Software Engr*
Hyman Lam, *Engineer*
Allen Lau, *Engineer*
Juan Rocha, *Engineer*
EMP: 50
SALES (corp-wide): 14.5B **Publicly Held**
SIC: 3559 Semiconductor manufacturing
machinery
PA: Applied Materials, Inc.
3050 Bowers Ave
Santa Clara CA 95054
408 727-5555

PRODUCTS & SVCS

(P-14908)
APPLIED MATERIALS INC
4675 Macarthur Ct, Newport Beach
(92660-1875)
PHONE..................949 244-1600
EMP: 46
SALES (corp-wide): 14.5B **Publicly Held**
SIC: 3559 Semiconductor manufacturing
machinery
PA: Applied Materials, Inc.
      3050 Bowers Ave
      Santa Clara CA 95054
      408 727-5555

(P-14909)
APPLIED MATERIALS INC
380 Fairview Way, Milpitas (95035-3062)
PHONE..................408 727-5555
Stacey Brown, *Principal*
Kenneth Tran, *Engineer*
EMP: 48
SALES (corp-wide): 14.5B **Publicly Held**
SIC: 3559 Semiconductor manufacturing
machinery
PA: Applied Materials, Inc.
      3050 Bowers Ave
      Santa Clara CA 95054
      408 727-5555

(P-14910)
APPLIED MATERIALS INC (PA)
3050 Bowers Ave, Santa Clara
(95054-3298)
P.O. Box 58039 (95052-8039)
PHONE..................408 727-5555
Gary E Dickerson, *President*
Thomas J Iannotti, *Ch of Bd*
Daniel J Durn, *CFO*
Thomas F Larkins, *Senior VP*
Omkaram Nalamasu, *Senior VP*
EMP: 800
SALES: 14.5B **Publicly Held**
WEB: www.appliedmaterials.com
SIC: 3559 3674 Semiconductor manufac-
turing machinery; semiconductors & re-
lated devices

(P-14911)
APPLIED MATERIALS INC
3101 Scott Blvd, Santa Clara (95054-3318)
PHONE..................512 272-3692
Melinda Loveday, *Executive Asst*
Thuc Tran, *Technician*
Tim Melzer, *Project Engr*
John Miller, *Project Engr*
Jacob Andrews, *Engineer*
EMP: 11
SALES (corp-wide): 14.5B **Publicly Held**
SIC: 3559 Semiconductor manufacturing
machinery
PA: Applied Materials, Inc.
      3050 Bowers Ave
      Santa Clara CA 95054
      408 727-5555

(P-14912)
APPLIED MATERIALS INC
9000 Foothills Blvd, Roseville
(95747-4411)
PHONE..................916 786-3900
Scott Ribordy, *Principal*
EMP: 10
SALES (corp-wide): 14.5B **Publicly Held**
WEB: www.appliedmaterials.com
SIC: 3559 Semiconductor manufacturing
machinery
PA: Applied Materials, Inc.
      3050 Bowers Ave
      Santa Clara CA 95054
      408 727-5555

(P-14913)
APPLIED MATERIALS INC
3535 Garrett Dr Bldg 100, Santa Clara
(95054-2811)
P.O. Box 58039 (95052-8039)
PHONE..................408 727-5555
Darren Mattingly, *Manager*
Kathleen Ramp, *Program Mgr*
Jamini Samantaray, *Software Engr*
Eashpreet Bajwa, *Network Enginr*
Satish Baskaran, *IT/INT Sup*
EMP: 48
SALES (corp-wide): 14.5B **Publicly Held**
SIC: 3559 Semiconductor manufacturing
machinery

PA: Applied Materials, Inc.
      3050 Bowers Ave
      Santa Clara CA 95054
      408 727-5555

(P-14914)
APPLIED MATERIALS INC
974 E Arques Ave, Sunnyvale
(94085-4520)
PHONE..................408 727-5555
James Morgan, *Branch Mgr*
Pravin Narwankar, *Vice Pres*
Nir Merry, *Managing Dir*
Tri Nguyen, *Technician*
Zhiqiang Guo, *Design Engr*
EMP: 48
SALES (corp-wide): 14.5B **Publicly Held**
WEB: www.appliedmaterials.com
SIC: 3559 Semiconductor manufacturing
machinery
PA: Applied Materials, Inc.
      3050 Bowers Ave
      Santa Clara CA 95054
      408 727-5555

(P-14915)
ARSYS INC
Also Called: Ellexar
1428 S Grand Ave, Santa Ana
(92705-4400)
PHONE..................714 654-7681
Allan Emami, *President*
EMP: 10
SQ FT: 2,100
SALES: 350K **Privately Held**
SIC: 3559 Electronic component making
machinery

(P-14916)
AUTOTECHBIZCOM INC
23551 Commerce Center Dr I, Laguna Hills
(92653-1513)
PHONE..................949 245-7033
EMP: 13
SQ FT: 1,500
SALES: 2.2MM **Privately Held**
SIC: 3559 7359

(P-14917)
AVANZATO TECHNOLOGY CORP
5335 Mcconnell Ave, Los Angeles
(90066-7025)
PHONE..................312 509-0506
Carissa Davino, *CEO*
Jeremy Green, *Director*
EMP: 20
SALES (est): 821.2K **Privately Held**
SIC: 3559 5065 Electronic component
making machinery; electronic parts

(P-14918)
B & W ENVMTL SOLUTIONS LLC
2200 Sacramento St # 1106, San Francisco
(94115-2304)
PHONE..................415 931-3381
Larry Barnblatt, *Principal*
EMP: 10 **EST:** 1995
SALES (est): 890K **Privately Held**
SIC: 3559 Tire grooving machines; tire re-
treading machinery & equipment

(P-14919)
BARKENS HARDCHROME INC
239 E Greenleaf Blvd, Compton
(90220-4913)
PHONE..................310 632-2000
Gary Barken, *CEO*
Aiko Barken, *Vice Pres*
Carol Barken, *Vice Pres*
Ken Ames, *Manager*
EMP: 25
SQ FT: 60,000
SALES (est): 6.8MM **Privately Held**
WEB: www.barkenshardchrome.com
SIC: 3559 5082 Metal finishing equipment
for plating, etc.; oil field equipment

(P-14920)
BELOVAC LLC
435 E Lincoln St Ste A, Banning
(92220-6012)
PHONE..................951 427-4299
Jeff Bell, *Owner*
EMP: 18
SALES (est): 3.8MM **Privately Held**
SIC: 3559 Plastics working machinery

(P-14921)
BENDPAK INC
1645 E Lemonwood Dr, Santa Paula
(93060-9651)
PHONE..................805 933-9970
Donald Ray Henthorn, *President*
Jeffery Kritzer, *Senior VP*
Manuela Vega, *Export Mgr*
Ryan Delapp, *Sales Staff*
◆ **EMP:** 150
SQ FT: 30,000
SALES (est): 61.1MM **Privately Held**
WEB: www.bendpak.com
SIC: 3559 3537 Automotive related ma-
chinery; automotive maintenance equip-
ment; industrial trucks & tractors

(P-14922)
BIJAN RAD INC
Also Called: Park O Mate
16125 Cantlay St, Van Nuys (91406-3416)
PHONE..................818 902-1606
Bijan RAD, *CEO*
◆ **EMP:** 25
SQ FT: 9,000
SALES (est): 3.6MM **Privately Held**
SIC: 3559 1731 Parking facility equipment
& supplies; access control systems spe-
cialization

(P-14923)
BOOM INDUSTRIAL INC
167 University Pkwy, Pomona
(91768-4301)
PHONE..................909 495-3555
Huiwen Chen, *CEO*
EMP: 60
SALES (est): 2.5MM **Privately Held**
SIC: 3559 3069 Rubber working machin-
ery, including tires; rubber automotive
products; castings, rubber

(P-14924)
BREE ENGINEERING CORP
1275 Stone Dr Ste A, San Marcos
(92078-4097)
PHONE..................760 510-4950
Dan Bree, *President*
Jackie Bree, *CFO*
Laura Nellesen, *Purchasing*
Bree Dan, *Agent*
EMP: 30
SQ FT: 7,600
SALES (est): 2MM **Privately Held**
WEB: www.breeeng.com
SIC: 3559 Electronic component making
machinery

(P-14925)
BROOKS AUTOMATION INC
13915 Danielson St # 103, Poway
(92064-8884)
P.O. Box 231280, San Diego (92193-1280)
PHONE..................858 527-7000
Emil Erickson, *CFO*
Glenn Neal, *Software Engr*
EMP: 12
SALES (corp-wide): 692.8MM **Publicly
Held**
SIC: 3559 Semiconductor manufacturing
machinery
PA: Brooks Automation, Inc.
      15 Elizabeth Dr
      Chelmsford MA 01824
      978 262-2400

(P-14926)
CARL HERRMANN ASSOCIATES
Also Called: Cha Industries
4201 Business Center Dr, Fremont
(94538-6357)
PHONE..................510 683-8554
Richard R Herrmann, *Chairman*
Richard J Roth, *President*
Ahmad Azimi, *CFO*
Paul Metzler, *Vice Pres*
Gerry Wies, *Data Proc Staff*
▼ **EMP:** 45
SQ FT: 39,000
SALES (est): 11.4MM **Privately Held**
WEB: www.chaindustries.com
SIC: 3559 Semiconductor manufacturing
machinery

(P-14927)
**CHEMICAL SAFETY
TECHNOLOGY INC**
Also Called: C S T I
2461 Autumnvale Dr, San Jose
(95131-1802)
PHONE..................408 263-0984
Lincoln Bejan, *President*
Jackie Bejan, *Vice Pres*
Quan Nguyen, *Electrical Engi*
EMP: 26
SQ FT: 14,000
SALES (est): 6MM **Privately Held**
WEB: www.kemsafe.com
SIC: 3559 Refinery, chemical processing &
similar machinery

(P-14928)
CLEANPARTSET INC
Also Called: Tset, Inc.
3530 Bassett St, Santa Clara (95054-2704)
PHONE..................408 886-3300
Patrick Bogart, *CEO*
Joreg Hohnloser, *President*
Lisa Peddy, *CFO*
Ken Pelan, *CFO*
Bernard Adams, *Principal*
▲ **EMP:** 24
SQ FT: 35,000
SALES (est): 3.8MM
SALES (corp-wide): 12.7MM **Privately
Held**
WEB: www.tosohset.com
SIC: 3559 Semiconductor manufacturing
machinery
HQ: Cleanpart International, Inc
      631 International Pkwy
      Richardson TX 75081
      -

(P-14929)
COLD JET LLC
10281 Trademark St Ste A, Rancho Cuca-
monga (91730-5846)
PHONE..................513 831-3211
Steve Schick, *Manager*
EMP: 10
SALES (corp-wide): 65MM **Privately
Held**
WEB: www.coldjet.com
SIC: 3559 Cryogenic machinery, industrial
PA: Cold Jet, Llc
      455 Wards Corner Rd # 100
      Loveland OH 45140
      513 831-3211

(P-14930)
COSMODYNE LLC
3010 Old Ranch Pkwy # 300, Seal Beach
(90740-2750)
PHONE..................562 795-5990
Ross Brown,
Frank Andrews, *President*
Sean Jones, *Project Mgr*
Irina Dean, *Research*
Andrew Jennings, *Project Engr*
◆ **EMP:** 50
SQ FT: 125,000
SALES (est): 14.3MM
SALES (corp-wide): 1.2B **Privately Held**
SIC: 3559 Smelting & refining machinery &
equipment
HQ: Cryogenic Industries Holdings, Inc.
      5910 Pcf Ctr Blvd Ste 110
      San Diego CA

(P-14931)
CP MANUFACTURING INC (HQ)
6795 Calle De Linea, San Diego
(92154-8017)
PHONE..................619 477-3175
Robert M Davis, *President*
Ruth Davis, *Ch of Bd*
Michael W Howard, *COO*
Terry Schneider, *COO*
Theodora Davis Inman, *Vice Pres*
▲ **EMP:** 104 **EST:** 1977
SQ FT: 60,572
SALES (est): 27.4MM
SALES (corp-wide): 113.6MM **Privately
Held**
WEB: www.cpmfg.com
SIC: 3559 Recycling machinery

PA: Ims Recycling Services, Inc.
2697 Main St
San Diego CA 92113
619 231-2521

(P-14932)
CROSSING AUTOMATION INC (HQ)
46702 Bayside Pkwy, Fremont
(94538-6582)
PHONE..................510 661-5000
Robert B Macknight Kkk, *President*
Mark D Morelli, *President*
Stephen S Schwartz, *CEO*
Lindon G Robertson, *Exec VP*
David C Gray, *Senior VP*
▲ EMP: 38
SQ FT: 5,500
SALES (est): 65.7MM
SALES (corp-wide): 692.8MM **Publicly Held**
WEB: www.crossinginc.com
SIC: 3559 Semiconductor manufacturing machinery
PA: Brooks Automation, Inc.
15 Elizabeth Dr
Chelmsford MA 01824
978 262-2400

(P-14933)
CRYOGENIC MACHINERY CORP
7306 Greenbush Ave, North Hollywood
(91605-4096)
PHONE..................818 765-6688
Peter Fritz, *President*
Adrian Unger, *Treasurer*
EMP: 12
SQ FT: 10,000
SALES (est): 2.7MM **Privately Held**
WEB: www.cryomach.com
SIC: 3559 7699 Cryogenic machinery, industrial; industrial machinery & equipment repair

(P-14934)
CRYOPORT SYSTEMS INC (HQ)
17305 Daimler St, Irvine (92614-5510)
PHONE..................949 540-7204
Jerrell W Shelton, *President*
Robert S Stefanovich, *CFO*
Ramkumar Mandalam, *Bd of Directors*
Dee Kelly, *Vice Pres*
Gregory Stevens, *Exec Dir*
EMP: 14
SQ FT: 28,000
SALES (est): 2.5MM
SALES (corp-wide): 11.9MM **Publicly Held**
WEB: www.cryoport.com
SIC: 3559 Cryogenic machinery, industrial
PA: Cryoport Systems Inc
17305 Daimler St
Irvine CA 92614
949 470-2300

(P-14935)
CRYOQUIP LLC (HQ)
25720 Jefferson Ave, Murrieta
(92562-6929)
PHONE..................951 677-2060
Ross M Brown, *CEO*
William J Hallinan, *President*
Gary Steres, *CFO*
Rebecca Jerkins, *Administration*
Paige Deshler, *Engineer*
◆ EMP: 12
SQ FT: 110
SALES (est): 3.5MM
SALES (corp-wide): 1.2B **Privately Held**
WEB: www.cryoquip.com
SIC: 3559 8711 Cryogenic machinery, industrial; engineering services
PA: Nikkiso Co.,Ltd.
4-20-3, Ebisu
Shibuya-Ku TKY 150-0
334 433-711

(P-14936)
CRYST MARK INC A SWAN TECHNO C
Also Called: Crystal Mark
613 Justin Ave, Glendale (91201-2326)
PHONE..................818 240-7520
John Swan, *President*
E Michael Swan, *Vice Pres*
Marko S Swan, *Vice Pres*

Pauline Swan, *Asst Sec*
Diana Galvez, *Assistant*
EMP: 40
SQ FT: 18,000
SALES (est): 9.6MM **Privately Held**
WEB: www.crystalmarkinc.com
SIC: 3559 3471 Semiconductor manufacturing machinery; screening equipment, electric; sand blasting of metal parts

(P-14937)
CUSTOM METAL FINISHING CORP
17804 S Western Ave, Gardena
(90248-3620)
P.O. Box 368 (90248-0368)
PHONE..................310 532-5075
David Alverez, *President*
Larry Alvarez, *Shareholder*
Victor Alvarez, *Shareholder*
Kelly Alverez, *Treasurer*
Lilly Alvarez, *Vice Pres*
EMP: 40
SQ FT: 7,500
SALES (est): 5.6MM **Privately Held**
WEB: www.custommetalfinishing.com
SIC: 3559 3471 Metal finishing equipment for plating, etc.; plating & polishing

(P-14938)
CUSTOPHARM INC (PA)
Also Called: Leucadia Pharmaceuticals
2325 Camino Vida Roble A, Carlsbad
(92011-1567)
PHONE..................760 683-0901
William Larkins, *CEO*
Dave McCleary, *Vice Pres*
EMP: 17
SALES (est): 4.9MM **Privately Held**
SIC: 3559 8071 Chemical machinery & equipment; medical laboratories

(P-14939)
DATA PHYSICS CORPORATION
9031 Polsa Ct, Corona (92883)
PHONE..................408 216-8443
Kevin McIntosh, *Manager*
EMP: 25
SALES (corp-wide): 13.9MM **Privately Held**
SIC: 3559
PA: Data Physics Corporation
2480 N 1st St Ste 100
San Jose CA 95131
408 437-0100

(P-14940)
DURON INCORPORATED
4633 Camden Dr, Corona Del Mar
(92625-3104)
PHONE..................949 721-0900
Paul P Duron, *President*
EMP: 10
SALES (est): 954K **Privately Held**
SIC: 3559 8711 Cryogenic machinery, industrial; consulting engineer

(P-14941)
DYNALINEAR TECHNOLOGIES INC
51 E Campbell Ave 108b, Campbell
(95008-2988)
PHONE..................408 376-5090
GI Young Lee, *President*
EMP: 10
SALES (est): 1.2MM **Privately Held**
WEB: www.dynalinear.com
SIC: 3559 Semiconductor manufacturing machinery

(P-14942)
E P Z INC
2262 Calle Del Mundo, Santa Clara
(95054-1005)
PHONE..................408 735-1820
Guillermo Gutierrez, *President*
EMP: 10
SQ FT: 12,000
SALES (est): 1.6MM **Privately Held**
WEB: www.epz.net
SIC: 3559 Refinery, chemical processing & similar machinery

(P-14943)
EAGLE VALLEY GINNING LLC
27480 S Bennett Rd, Firebaugh
(93622-9405)
PHONE..................209 826-5002
Aaron Barcellos,
John F Bennett,
Timothy R Hall,
EMP: 26
SALES (est): 2.6MM **Privately Held**
SIC: 3559 Cotton ginning machinery

(P-14944)
EBS PRODUCTS
15134 Goldenwest Cir, Westminster
(92683-5235)
P.O. Box 11060 (92685-1060)
PHONE..................714 896-6700
Peter C Hollub, *President*
Janice Walters, *Office Mgr*
Manuel Rendon, *Opers Mgr*
EMP: 12
SALES (est): 1.7MM **Privately Held**
SIC: 3559 Automotive related machinery

(P-14945)
EKSO BIONICS INC (PA)
1414 Harbour Way S # 1201, Richmond
(94804-3628)
PHONE..................510 984-1761
Eythor Bender, *CEO*
Nathan Harding, *COO*
Max Scheder- Biesehin, *CFO*
Bianca Momand, *Vice Pres*
Jeffrey Stoll, *Project Mgr*
EMP: 74
SALES (est): 17.9MM **Privately Held**
WEB: www.berkeleyexoworks.com
SIC: 3559 Cryogenic machinery, industrial

(P-14946)
ELITE PROPERTY MAINTENANCE
3759 Pine Hollow Way, Antelope
(95843-5440)
PHONE..................916 275-3956
Roy Hill, *President*
EMP: 10
SALES (est): 421.5K **Privately Held**
SIC: 3559 Parking facility equipment & supplies

(P-14947)
ENERGY RECOVERY INC (PA)
1717 Doolittle Dr, San Leandro
(94577-2231)
PHONE..................510 483-7370
Chris Gannon, *President*
Hans Peter Michelet, *Ch of Bd*
Chris M Gannon, *President*
Josh Ballard, *CFO*
Alexander Buehler, *Bd of Directors*
▲ EMP: 114
SQ FT: 170,000
SALES: 58.1MM **Publicly Held**
SIC: 3559 Desalination equipment

(P-14948)
ENVIROKINETICS INC (PA)
101 S Milliken Ave, Ontario (91761-7836)
PHONE..................909 621-7599
Henry Seal, *President*
Long Le, *Vice Pres*
EMP: 15
SQ FT: 6,000
SALES (est): 5.8MM **Privately Held**
SIC: 3559 Petroleum refinery equipment

(P-14949)
EPOCH INTERNATIONAL ENTPS INC
10542 Calle Lee Ste 114, Los Alamitos
(90720-2550)
PHONE..................714 484-8015
Foad Ghalili, *President*
Yemi Kifle, *Comms Mgr*
Shawna Jia, *Department Mgr*
Ladon Ghalili, *General Mgr*
Mandy Shi, *Engineer*
EMP: 80
SQ FT: 2,000
SALES: 26.2MM **Privately Held**
WEB: www.epoch-int.com
SIC: 3559 Electronic component making machinery

(P-14950)
ESPACE ENTERPRISES TECH INC
Also Called: E Enterprise Tech
3010 N 1st St, San Jose (95134-2023)
PHONE..................408 844-8176
Esther Hutchinson, *President*
Phan Pham, *Founder*
Pham Phan, *Vice Pres*
EMP: 12
SQ FT: 7,000
SALES (est): 4MM **Privately Held**
WEB: www.e-enterprisetech.com
SIC: 3559 Semiconductor manufacturing machinery

(P-14951)
EXCELLON ACQUISITION LLC (HQ)
Also Called: Excellon Automation Co
20001 S Rancho Way, Compton
(90220-6318)
PHONE..................310 668-7700
Bailey Su,
EMP: 38
SQ FT: 35,000
SALES (est): 10.9MM
SALES (corp-wide): 1.8MM **Privately Held**
WEB: www.excellon.com
SIC: 3559 Semiconductor manufacturing machinery

(P-14952)
EXPERT SEMICONDUCTOR TECH INC
Also Called: Expertech
10 Victor Sq Ste 100, Scotts Valley
(95066-3562)
P.O. Box 66508 (95067-6508)
PHONE..................831 439-9300
Jonathan George, *CEO*
Mark Cooper, *Vice Pres*
Colin Wilson, *Manager*
EMP: 25
SQ FT: 40,000
SALES (est): 6.3MM **Privately Held**
WEB: www.exper-tech.com
SIC: 3559 Semiconductor manufacturing machinery

(P-14953)
FANUC AMERICA CORPORATION
Also Called: Fanuc Robotics West
25951 Commercentre Dr, Lake Forest
(92630-8805)
PHONE..................949 595-2700
Mike Hollingsworth, *Manager*
James Farmer, *District Mgr*
Peter Fitzgerald, *General Mgr*
Florin Stef, *Design Engr*
EMP: 30
SALES (corp-wide): 6.8B **Privately Held**
WEB: www.fanucrobotics.com
SIC: 3559 3548 3569 Metal finishing equipment for plating, etc.; electric welding equipment; robots, assembly line: industrial & commercial
HQ: Fanuc America Corporation
3900 W Hamlin Rd
Rochester Hills MI 48309
248 377-7000

(P-14954)
FC MANAGEMENT SERVICES
Also Called: PC Recycle
2580 Azurite Cir, Newbury Park
(91320-1201)
PHONE..................805 499-0050
Fulton Connor, *President*
Jill North, *Manager*
EMP: 21
SALES: 2.5MM **Privately Held**
SIC: 3559 Electronic component making machinery

(P-14955)
FLIGHT MICROWAVE CORPORATION
410 S Douglas St, El Segundo
(90245-4628)
PHONE..................310 607-9819
Rolf Kich, *President*
Mike Callas, *CFO*

PRODUCTS & SVCS

Mark Van Alstyne, *Vice Pres*
Richard Bennett, *Director*
EMP: 30
SQ FT: 8,000
SALES (est): 5.7MM **Privately Held**
WEB: www.flightmicrowave.com
SIC: 3559 Electronic component making
machinery

(P-14956)
FLIR MOTION CTRL SYSTEMS INC
6769 Hollister Ave, Goleta (93117-3001)
PHONE...................................650 692-3900
Philip Kahn, *President*
David Gaw, *Vice Pres*
▼ **EMP:** 26
SQ FT: 6,000
SALES (est): 2.8MM
SALES (corp-wide): 1.8B **Publicly Held**
WEB: www.dperception.com
SIC: 3559 3541 Semiconductor manufac-
turing machinery; robots for drilling, cut-
ting, grinding, polishing, etc.
PA: Flir Systems, Inc.
27700 Sw Parkway Ave
Wilsonville OR 97070
503 498-3547

(P-14957)
FUZETRON INC
Also Called: Creative Industries
2111 Paseo Grande, El Cajon
(92019-3854)
PHONE...................................619 244-5141
▲ **EMP:** 15
SQ FT: 8,000
SALES (est): 1.1MM **Privately Held**
WEB: www.creativewheels.com
SIC: 3559 8732

(P-14958)
GARAGE EQUIPMENT SUPPLY INC
646 Flinn Ave Ste A, Moorpark
(93021-1895)
PHONE...................................805 530-0027
Danette Henthorn, *CEO*
Gary Henthorn, *President*
Mike Oconnell, *Empl Benefits*
▲ **EMP:** 15
SQ FT: 25,000
SALES (est): 16MM **Privately Held**
WEB: www.gesusa.com
SIC: 3559 Automotive maintenance equip-
ment

(P-14959)
GEI INC
Also Called: GALAXY ENTERPRISES IN-
TERNATION
301 E Arrow Hwy Ste 108, San Dimas
(91773-3364)
PHONE...................................909 592-2234
Vincent Chung, *President*
Karen Kean, *Controller*
▲ **EMP:** 10
SQ FT: 5,000
SALES (est): 1.5MM **Privately Held**
WEB: www.gei-inc.com
SIC: 3559 Electronic component making
machinery

(P-14960)
GLASTAR CORPORATION
8425 Canoga Ave, Canoga Park
(91304-2607)
PHONE...................................818 341-0301
Lorie Mitchell, *President*
George Lopez, *Buyer*
EMP: 20
SQ FT: 14,000
SALES (est): 4.3MM **Privately Held**
WEB: www.glastar.com
SIC: 3559 3563 3231 Glass making ma-
chinery; blowing, molding, forming, etc.;
spraying & dusting equipment; products
of purchased glass

(P-14961)
GLOBALFOUNDRIES US INC (HQ)
Also Called: Global Foundries
2600 Great America Way, Santa Clara
(95054-1169)
PHONE...................................408 462-3900
Thomas Caulfield, *CEO*
Dr John Goldsberry, *CFO*
Louis Lupin, *Officer*
Daniel Durn, *Exec VP*
Michael Noonen, *Exec VP*
▲ **EMP:** 277
SALES (est): 1.2B
SALES (corp-wide): 8.5B **Privately Held**
SIC: 3559 3825 5065 Semiconductor
manufacturing machinery; semiconductor
test equipment; semiconductor devices
PA: Mubadala Development Company Pjsc
Near Muroor 4th Road Mamoura A
Buildings, Mohammed Bin Khalifa 1
Abu Dhabi
241 358-45

(P-14962)
GOLDEN BY-PODUCTS INC
Also Called: Scrap Tire Company
13000 Newport Rd, Ballico (95303-9704)
P.O. Box 1 (95303-0001)
PHONE...................................209 668-4855
Brett Barstow, *CEO*
Jana Nairn, *President*
Karen Barstow, *CFO*
Amber Barstow, *Corp Secy*
EMP: 70
SQ FT: 3,000
SALES (est): 14MM **Privately Held**
WEB: www.goldenscraptire.com
SIC: 3559 0173 Tire grooving machines;
tire retreading machinery & equipment;
tire shredding machinery; almond grove

(P-14963)
GREENVITY COMMUNICATIONS INC (PA)
2150 Trade Zone Blvd, San Jose
(95131-1730)
PHONE...................................408 935-9358
Hung Nguyen, *CEO*
John Tero, *President*
Edward Inyoung Cho, *Vice Pres*
Jayesh Desai, *Vice Pres*
Edward Cho, *VP Sls/Mktg*
EMP: 21 EST: 2010
SQ FT: 10,000
SALES: 20MM **Privately Held**
SIC: 3559 3674 Semiconductor manufac-
turing machinery; semiconductors & re-
lated devices

(P-14964)
HANTRONIX INC
10080 Bubb Rd, Cupertino (95014-4132)
PHONE...................................408 252-1100
Wayne Choi, *CEO*
Wendy Lee, *Accountant*
Shirley Chan, *Sales Staff*
Richard Kim, *Sales Staff*
Jaime Lim, *Sales Staff*
▲ **EMP:** 22
SQ FT: 10,000
SALES: 22.3MM **Privately Held**
WEB: www.hantronix.com
SIC: 3559 5065 3577 Electronic compo-
nent making machinery; electronic parts &
equipment; computer peripheral equip-
ment

(P-14965)
HEXCO INTERNATIONAL (PA)
Also Called: Cryogenic Industries
25720 Jefferson Ave, Murrieta
(92562-6929)
PHONE...................................951 677-2081
Ross M Brown, *CEO*
William Hallinan, *President*
Chris Chlebek, *Controller*
Peter Sniezynski, *Manager*
Brent West, *Manager*
◆ **EMP:** 50
SQ FT: 5,000
SALES (est): 36MM **Privately Held**
SIC: 3559 3561 3443 Cryogenic machin-
ery, industrial; pumps & pumping equip-
ment; fabricated plate work (boiler shop)

(P-14966)
HORNEDO INC
Also Called: Pacific Collision Equipment
2424 Brayton Ave, Signal Hill (90755-3508)
PHONE...................................562 490-2120
Robert Hornedo, *President*
Norma Martinez, *Office Mgr*
Shawn Alarcon, *Sales Mgr*
Tom Balliet, *Manager*
▲ **EMP:** 13
SQ FT: 6,000
SALES (est): 2.8MM **Privately Held**
WEB: www.crashtools.com
SIC: 3559 Automotive related machinery

(P-14967)
I3 NANOTEC LLC
Also Called: Ctg
1295 67th St, Emeryville (94608-1120)
PHONE...................................510 594-2299
Jim Wile, *President*
John Bluhm, *Vice Pres*
Steven McCormick, *Vice Pres*
Manish Goel,
EMP: 10
SQ FT: 8,000
SALES (est): 1.4MM **Privately Held**
SIC: 3559 Recycling machinery

(P-14968)
IMTEC ACCULINE LLC
Also Called: Intelligent Quartz Solutions
49036 Milmont Dr, Fremont (94538-7301)
PHONE...................................510 770-1800
Paul V Mendes, *Mng Member*
Derek Mendes, *Administration*
Ken Struven, *Engineer*
Emily Xiang, *Senior Buyer*
Maria Gonzalez, *Opers Staff*
▲ **EMP:** 24
SQ FT: 27,000
SALES (est): 6MM **Privately Held**
WEB: www.imtecacculine.com
SIC: 3559 Semiconductor manufacturing
machinery

(P-14969)
INDUSTRIAL DYNAMICS CO LTD (PA)
Also Called: Filtec
3100 Fujita St, Torrance (90505-4007)
P.O. Box 2945 (90509-2945)
PHONE...................................310 325-5633
David Storey, *President*
Leon Coetzee, *Vice Pres*
Angie Herrera, *Executive*
Steve M Calhoun, *Principal*
Jackson Chad, *General Mgr*
▲ **EMP:** 216 EST: 1960
SQ FT: 155,000
SALES (est): 38.4MM **Privately Held**
WEB: www.pcbdriller.com
SIC: 3559 3829 Screening equipment,
electric; measuring & controlling devices

(P-14970)
INDUSTRIAL TOOLS INC
1111 S Rose Ave, Oxnard (93033-2499)
PHONE...................................805 483-1111
Donald O Murphy, *President*
John E Anderson, *Ch of Bd*
Kay Nolan, *CFO*
Adam Roof, *Info Tech Dir*
Michael Moffatt, *Technology*
EMP: 50 EST: 1961
SQ FT: 65,000
SALES (est): 11.4MM **Privately Held**
WEB: www.indtools.com
SIC: 3559 3545 3544 3541 Semiconduc-
tor manufacturing machinery; machine
tool accessories; special dies, tools, jigs &
fixtures; machine tools, metal cutting type

(P-14971)
INTEGRTED SILICON SOLUTION INC
Also Called: Issi
1623 Buckeye Dr, Milpitas (95035-7423)
PHONE...................................408 969-6600
Peter Sullivan, *CEO*
Paul Jei-Zensong, *Senior VP*
Sanjiv Asthana, *Vice Pres*
Alan Zhuang, *Info Tech Mgr*
Amy Guiriba, *Human Res Dir*
EMP: 22

SALES (est): 4.3MM **Privately Held**
SIC: 3559 Automotive related machinery

(P-14972)
INTEVAC INC (PA)
3560 Bassett St, Santa Clara (95054-2704)
PHONE...................................408 986-9888
David S Dury, *Ch of Bd*
Wendell T Blonigan, *President*
Richard Lavine, *President*
James Moniz, *CFO*
Matthew Drapkin, *Bd of Directors*
▲ **EMP:** 92
SQ FT: 169,583
SALES: 112.8MM **Publicly Held**
SIC: 3559 Semiconductor manufacturing
machinery

(P-14973)
INTEVAC INC
Intevac Fabrication Center
3560 Bassett St, Santa Clara (95054-2704)
PHONE...................................408 986-9888
Don Cordoni, *Manager*
EMP: 20
SALES (corp-wide): 112.8MM **Publicly
Held**
SIC: 3559 3674 Semiconductor manufac-
turing machinery; semiconductors & re-
lated devices
PA: Intevac, Inc.
3560 Bassett St
Santa Clara CA 95054
408 986-9888

(P-14974)
JACKS TECHNOLOGIES & INDS INC
Also Called: J T I
225 N Palomares St, Pomona
(91767-5549)
PHONE...................................909 865-2595
David Jacks, *President*
Randy Walston, *Vice Pres*
▲ **EMP:** 10
SQ FT: 4,000
SALES (est): 2MM **Privately Held**
WEB: www.zeph.com
SIC: 3559 Electronic component making
machinery

(P-14975)
JASPER DISPLAY CORP
2952 Bunker Hill Ln # 110, Santa Clara
(95054-1103)
PHONE...................................408 831-5788
Kenneth Tai, *CEO*
Mike Stover, *Vice Pres*
Kaushik Sheth, *General Mgr*
Robert Lo, *Software Engr*
Robert Savage, *Software Engr*
EMP: 20 EST: 2009
SALES (est): 860.9K **Privately Held**
SIC: 3559 Electronic component making
machinery
PA: Jasper Display Corp.
7f-16, 81, Shui Li Rd,
Hsinchu City 30059
357 527-68

(P-14976)
JGM AUTOMOTIVE TOOLING INC
Also Called: Motec USA
5355 Industrial Dr, Huntington Beach
(92649-1516)
PHONE...................................714 895-7001
James Munn, *CEO*
EMP: 24
SQ FT: 8,000
SALES (est): 4.7MM **Privately Held**
SIC: 3559 5531 Automotive maintenance
equipment; automobile & truck equipment
& parts

(P-14977)
JOHNSON MARBLE MACHINERY INC
7325 Varna Ave, North Hollywood
(91605-4009)
PHONE...................................818 764-6186
Mark Brandtner, *Regional Mgr*
Ted Johnson, *President*
Jean May Johnson, *Vice Pres*
▲ **EMP:** 10

▲ = Import ▼=Export
◆ =Import/Export

SQ FT: 20,000
SALES (est): 4MM **Privately Held**
SIC: **3559** 5084 5032 Stone working machinery; industrial machinery & equipment; marble building stone

(P-14978)
K V R INVESTMENT GROUP INC
Also Called: Pacific Plating
12113 Branford St, Sun Valley (91352-5710)
PHONE................................818 896-1102
Rakesh Bajaria, *President*
Benny Kadhrota, *Treasurer*
Ken Pansuria, *Vice Pres*
Harry Thummar, *Vice Pres*
EMP: 60 EST: 1997
SALES (est): 9.2MM **Privately Held**
SIC: **3559** 3471 Metal finishing equipment for plating, etc.; plating & polishing

(P-14979)
KEYSSA SYSTEMS INC
655 Campbell Technology P, Campbell (95008-5060)
PHONE................................408 637-2300
Eric Almgren, *CEO*
John McAdoo, *CFO*
Mariel Van Tatenhove, *Vice Pres*
EMP: 10
SALES (est): 271.4K **Privately Held**
SIC: **3559** 5065 Semiconductor manufacturing machinery; semiconductor devices

(P-14980)
LAM RESEARCH CORPORATION
3724 Dawn Cir, Union City (94587-2626)
PHONE................................510 572-2186
Stephen Truong, *Principal*
EMP: 72
SALES (corp-wide): 11B **Publicly Held**
SIC: **3559** Semiconductor manufacturing machinery
PA: Lam Research Corporation
4650 Cushing Pkwy
Fremont CA 94538
510 572-0200

(P-14981)
LAM RESEARCH CORPORATION
46555 Landing Pkwy, Fremont (94538-6421)
PHONE................................510 572-3200
James Bagley, *Branch Mgr*
Thad Nicholson, *Engineer*
EMP: 86
SALES (corp-wide): 11B **Publicly Held**
WEB: www.lamrc.com
SIC: **3559** Semiconductor manufacturing machinery
PA: Lam Research Corporation
4650 Cushing Pkwy
Fremont CA 94538
510 572-0200

(P-14982)
LAM RESEARCH INTL HOLDG CO (HQ)
4650 Cushing Pkwy, Fremont (94538-6401)
PHONE................................510 572-0200
Martin Anstice, *CEO*
Douglas Bettinger, *CFO*
EMP: 11
SALES (est): 6.4MM
SALES (corp-wide): 11B **Publicly Held**
SIC: **3559** Semiconductor manufacturing machinery
PA: Lam Research Corporation
4650 Cushing Pkwy
Fremont CA 94538
510 572-0200

(P-14983)
LEGACY SYSTEMS INCORPORATED
4160 Technology Dr Ste E, Fremont (94538-6360)
PHONE................................510 651-2312
Robert Matthews, *President*
Dipak Dutta, *Vice Pres*
EMP: 10
SALES (est): 1.6MM **Privately Held**
SIC: **3559** Chemical machinery & equipment

(P-14984)
LILY POND PRODUCTS
Also Called: Campbell Pump Co
351 W Cromwell Ave # 105, Fresno (93711-6115)
P.O. Box 939, Sanger (93657-0939)
PHONE................................559 431-5203
Fred Campbell, *Owner*
EMP: 10
SQ FT: 2,000
SALES (est): 701.9K **Privately Held**
WEB: www.lilypond.com
SIC: **3559** 3561 Clay working & tempering machines; pumps & pumping equipment

(P-14985)
LYTEN INC
933 Kifer Rd Ste B, Sunnyvale (94086-5208)
PHONE................................650 400-5635
Daniel Cook, *CEO*
Scott Mobley, *COO*
William Wraith, *Chairman*
Dean Witter, *Principal*
EMP: 10
SALES (est): 1.5MM **Privately Held**
SIC: **3559** Chemical machinery & equipment

(P-14986)
MARKETING BUS ADVANTAGE INC
1940 Olivera Rd Ste E, Concord (94520-5484)
PHONE................................925 933-3637
Rachel A Browne, *CEO*
Merrick Browne, *Vice Pres*
EMP: 10
SQ FT: 10,000
SALES (est): 670K **Privately Held**
SIC: **3559** Automotive maintenance equipment

(P-14987)
MATTSON TECHNOLOGY INC (HQ)
47131 Bayside Pkwy, Fremont (94538-6517)
PHONE................................510 657-5900
Fusen Chen, *President*
J Michael Dodson, *COO*
Tung Nguyen, *Vice Pres*
Johannes Keppler, *General Mgr*
James C Oswalt, *Project Mgr*
▲ EMP: 186
SQ FT: 101,000
SALES: 172.5MM
SALES (corp-wide): 3.5MM **Privately Held**
SIC: **3559** Semiconductor manufacturing machinery
PA: Beijing E-Town International Investment & Development Co., Ltd.
Building 61, Bda International Business Avenue, No.2, Jingyuan (
Beijing 10017
108 716-2565

(P-14988)
MEEDER EQUIPMENT COMPANY (PA)
Also Called: Ransome Manufacturing
3495 S Maple Ave, Fresno (93725-2494)
P.O. Box 12446 (93777-2446)
PHONE................................559 485-0979
Jeffrey D Vertz, *President*
Jeffrey Vertz, *President*
James Moe, *Corp Secy*
Wane Morgan, *Vice Pres*
Jenny Shelby, *Executive*
▲ EMP: 45
SQ FT: 13,000
SALES: 24MM **Privately Held**
WEB: www.ransomemfg.com
SIC: **3559** 5084 3714 8711 Refinery, chemical processing & similar machinery; industrial machinery & equipment; propane conversion equipment; propane conversion equipment, motor vehicle; building construction consultant

(P-14989)
MEGA MACHINERY INC
6688 Doolittle Ave, Riverside (92503-1432)
PHONE................................951 300-9300

Richard Risch, *President*
Roger Blaney, *Vice Pres*
EMP: 15
SQ FT: 20,000
SALES (est): 3.8MM **Privately Held**
WEB: www.mega.biz
SIC: **3559** Plastics working machinery

(P-14990)
MICROBAR INC
45473 Warm Springs Blvd, Fremont (94539-6104)
PHONE................................510 659-9770
Michael Lund, *President*
EMP: 295
SQ FT: 50,000
SALES (est): 29.8MM **Privately Held**
SIC: **3559**

(P-14991)
MMR TECHNOLOGIES INC (PA)
41 Daggett Dr, San Jose (95134-2109)
PHONE................................650 962-9620
William Little, *CEO*
Maria Reeves, *Admin Asst*
Jessica Jordan, *Administration*
EMP: 16
SQ FT: 6,700
SALES (est): 2.5MM **Privately Held**
SIC: **3559** Cryogenic machinery, industrial

(P-14992)
MOORE EPITAXIAL INC
Also Called: Moore Technologies
1422 Harding Ave, Tracy (95376-3319)
PHONE................................209 833-0100
Gary Moore, *President*
Tim Brown, *Vice Pres*
▲ EMP: 30
SQ FT: 22,000
SALES (est): 5.9MM **Privately Held**
WEB: www.mooretech.com
SIC: **3559** 3674 Semiconductor manufacturing machinery; wafers (semiconductor devices)

(P-14993)
MOREHOUSE-COWLES LLC
Also Called: Epworth Morehouse Cowles
13930 Magnolia Ave, Chino (91710-7029)
PHONE................................909 627-7222
Michael E Pfau, *President*
EMP: 25
SALES (est): 5.9MM
SALES (corp-wide): 574.8MM **Privately Held**
WEB: www.morehousecowles.com
SIC: **3559** Chemical machinery & equipment
HQ: Nusil Technology Llc
1050 Cindy Ln
Carpinteria CA 93013
805 684-8780

(P-14994)
MPJ RECYCLING LLC
2100 21st St Ste B, Sacramento (95818-1762)
PHONE................................916 761-5740
Maryann Hodgson, *CEO*
John Hodgson,
EMP: 10
SQ FT: 100
SALES (est): 1.1MM **Privately Held**
WEB: www.mpjrecycling.com
SIC: **3559** Recycling machinery

(P-14995)
MT SYSTEMS INC
Also Called: Micro Tech Systems
49040 Milmont Dr, Fremont (94538-7301)
PHONE................................510 651-5277
Thomas Mike Vukosav, *President*
▼ EMP: 17
SQ FT: 16,000
SALES (est): 6MM **Privately Held**
WEB: www.macrotron2.com
SIC: **3559** Semiconductor manufacturing machinery

(P-14996)
MULTIBEAM CORPORATION
3951 Burton Dr, Santa Clara (95054-1583)
PHONE................................408 980-1800
Dr David K Lam, *Ch of Bd*
Lynn Barringer, *President*

Ted Prescop, *Principal*
Peter Tran, *Engineer*
EMP: 35
SALES (est): 5.9MM **Privately Held**
SIC: **3559** Semiconductor manufacturing machinery

(P-14997)
N-TEK INC
Also Called: Ntek
823 Kifer Rd, Sunnyvale (94086-5204)
P.O. Box 71001 (94086-0976)
PHONE................................408 735-8442
Zoltron Albert, *President*
Zoltan Albert, *Owner*
EMP: 30
SALES (est): 1.7MM **Privately Held**
SIC: **3559** 3674 Semiconductor manufacturing machinery; semiconductors & related devices

(P-14998)
NANOMETRICS INCORPORATED (PA)
1550 Buckeye Dr, Milpitas (95035-7418)
PHONE................................408 545-6000
Bruce C Rhine, *Ch of Bd*
Timothy J Stultz, *President*
Jeff Andreson, *CFO*
Jeffrey Andreson, *CFO*
S Mark Borowicz, *Exec VP*
EMP: 270
SQ FT: 135,692
SALES: 258.6MM **Publicly Held**
WEB: www.nanometrics.com
SIC: **3559** 3829 Semiconductor manufacturing machinery; geophysical or meteorological electronic equipment

(P-14999)
NEODORA LLC
Also Called: Espe Machine Work / Ver Mfg
1545 Berger Dr, San Jose (95112-2704)
PHONE................................650 283-3319
Madhumathi Rupakukla,
EMP: 20 EST: 2014
SQ FT: 12,000
SALES (est): 1.5MM **Privately Held**
SIC: **3559** Sewing machines & hat & zipper making machinery

(P-15000)
NEW LOGIC RESEARCH INC
5040 Commercial Cir Ste A, Concord (94520-1250)
PHONE................................510 655-7305
Gregory Johnson, *CEO*
Dr J Brad Culkin, *President*
Julie Vukuvojac, *CFO*
Monty Burns, *Chief Mktg Ofcr*
Suzanne Meade, *Office Mgr*
▲ EMP: 90
SQ FT: 44,000
SALES (est): 19.6MM **Privately Held**
WEB: www.newlogicresearch.com
SIC: **3559** Chemical machinery & equipment

(P-15001)
NORCHEM CORPORATION (PA)
5649 Alhambra Ave, Los Angeles (90032-3107)
PHONE................................323 221-0221
Gevork Minissian, *CEO*
▲ EMP: 55
SQ FT: 50,000
SALES (est): 11.8MM **Privately Held**
SIC: **3559** 2842 2841 Chemical machinery & equipment; laundry cleaning preparations; soap & other detergents

---

3559 Special Ind Machinery, NEC

(P-15002)
OMEGA ENGINEERING INC
Also Called: Newport Electronics
2229 S Yale St, Santa Ana (92704-4426)
PHONE................................714 540-4914
Bill Keating, *General Mgr*
Tyrent Young, *MIS Mgr*
Martick Noravian, *Manager*

P R O D U C T S   &   S V C S

EMP: 70
SALES (corp-wide): 2B **Privately Held**
SIC: 3559 3829 3822 3825 Electronic component making machinery; temperature sensors, except industrial process & aircraft; temperature controls, automatic; measuring instruments & meters, electric; switchgear & switchboard apparatus; pumps & pumping equipment
HQ: Omega Engineering, Inc.
    800 Connecticut Ave 5n01
    Norwalk CT 06854
    203 359-1660

(P-15003)
P & L SPECIALTIES
1650 Almar Pkwy, Santa Rosa (95403-8253)
PHONE......................707 573-3141
Edwin Barr, *President*
Lisa Hyde, *Vice Pres*
Kevin Young, *Sales Staff*
◆ **EMP:** 15
SQ FT: 15,000
SALES (est): 4.4MM **Privately Held**
WEB: www.pnlspecialties.com
SIC: 3559 3556 Recycling machinery; beverage machinery

(P-15004)
PACIFIC GINNING COMPANY LLC
33370 W Nebraska Ave, Cantua Creek (93608)
PHONE......................559 829-9446
Matt Toste,
EMP: 23
SALES (est): 2.1MM **Privately Held**
SIC: 3559 Cotton ginning machinery

(P-15005)
PALOMAR TECHNOLOGIES INC (PA)
2728 Loker Ave W, Carlsbad (92010-6603)
PHONE......................760 931-3600
Bruce Hueners, *CEO*
Carl Hempel, *CFO*
Elena Isaia, *Admin Asst*
Shawn Rivera, *Info Tech Mgr*
William Forsyth, *Project Mgr*
EMP: 79
SQ FT: 40,000
SALES (est): 23.9MM **Privately Held**
WEB: www.palomartechnologies.com
SIC: 3559 Semiconductor manufacturing machinery

(P-15006)
PEABODY ENGINEERING & SUP INC
13435 Estelle St, Corona (92879-1877)
PHONE......................951 734-7711
Mark Peabody, *CEO*
Larry Peabody, *President*
Cheryl Peabody, *General Mgr*
Candice Brown, *Accountant*
Manvindar Singh, *Manager*
▲ **EMP:** 25
SQ FT: 32,400
SALES (est): 7.4MM **Privately Held**
WEB: www.etanks.com
SIC: 3559 5084 Chemical machinery & equipment; industrial machinery & equipment

(P-15007)
PERCEPTIMED INC
365 San Antonio Rd, Mountain View (94040-1213)
PHONE......................650 941-7000
Robert E Curry, *CEO*
Alan Jacobs, *President*
Hamutal Anavi Russo, *CFO*
Terry Cater, *VP Sls/Mktg*
EMP: 27
SALES (est): 1.9MM **Privately Held**
SIC: 3559 Pharmaceutical machinery

(P-15008)
PERSYS ENGINEERING INC
815 Swift St, Santa Cruz (95060-5851)
PHONE......................831 471-9300
Gideon Drimer, *CEO*
Ofer Molad, *President*
Oz Drimer, *COO*

Lior Yeshurun, *Project Mgr*
Mike Pitts, *Prdtn Mgr*
▲ **EMP:** 23
SQ FT: 12,000
SALES (est): 4.9MM **Privately Held**
WEB: www.persyseng.com
SIC: 3559 8711 7699 Semiconductor manufacturing machinery; engineering services; industrial equipment cleaning

(P-15009)
PHILLIPS 66 CO CARBON GROUP
2555 Willow Rd, Arroyo Grande (93420-5731)
PHONE......................805 489-4050
Glen Pericoli, *Vice Pres*
EMP: 16
SALES (est): 2.6MM **Privately Held**
SIC: 3559 Petroleum refinery equipment

(P-15010)
PICOTRACK
309 Laurelwood Rd Ste 21, Santa Clara (95054-2313)
PHONE......................408 988-7000
Thu Doan, *Partner*
Soang Nguyen, *Partner*
EMP: 10
SALES (est): 1.8MM **Privately Held**
SIC: 3559 Semiconductor manufacturing machinery

(P-15011)
PRECISION EUROPEAN INC
11594 Coley River Cir, Fountain Valley (92708-4219)
PHONE......................714 241-9657
Detlef Herrmann, *President*
Tanja Herrmann, *Vice Pres*
Dave Juergens, *Admin Sec*
▲ **EMP:** 13
SQ FT: 8,000
SALES: 1.5MM **Privately Held**
WEB: www.peius.com
SIC: 3559 7538 Automotive maintenance equipment; general automotive repair shops

(P-15012)
PROLINE CONCRETE TOOLS INC
2664 Vista Pacific Dr, Oceanside (92056-3514)
PHONE......................760 758-7240
Jeff Irwin, *CEO*
Paul Sowa, *CFO*
Liz Anderson, *Controller*
Nan Di Givanni, *Manager*
▼ **EMP:** 27
SALES (est): 6.2MM **Privately Held**
WEB: www.prolineconcretetools.com
SIC: 3559 Concrete products machinery

(P-15013)
PUROTECS INC
6678 Owens Dr Ste 104, Pleasanton (94588-3324)
PHONE......................925 215-0380
Ken Stevens, *Principal*
EMP: 10 **EST:** 2012
SALES (est): 1.7MM **Privately Held**
SIC: 3559 Chemical machinery & equipment

(P-15014)
QONTROL DEVICES INC
167 Mason Way Ste A7, City of Industry (91746-2338)
PHONE......................626 968-4268
Show Jow, *CEO*
Charles Jow, *President*
Terry Dowell, *Project Mgr*
Vinh Ly, *Project Mgr*
Wilson LI, *Senior Engr*
▲ **EMP:** 10
SQ FT: 30,000
SALES (est): 1.6MM **Privately Held**
WEB: www.qontroldevices.com
SIC: 3559

(P-15015)
QUALITY MACHINING & DESIGN INC
2857 Aiello Dr, San Jose (95111-2155)
PHONE......................408 224-7976
Ryszard Ott, *President*
EMP: 30
SQ FT: 23,000
SALES: 7.8MM **Privately Held**
WEB: www.qualitymd.com
SIC: 3559 3365 Semiconductor manufacturing machinery; aerospace castings, aluminum

(P-15016)
RAPID ANODIZING INC
1216 W Slauson Ave, Los Angeles (90044-2822)
PHONE......................323 753-5255
Florence Fratello, *Administration*
Jonathan Minter, *CEO*
EMP: 10
SALES (est): 653.2K **Privately Held**
SIC: 3559 Refinery, chemical processing & similar machinery

(P-15017)
RCH ASSOCIATES INC
4115 Business Center Dr, Fremont (94538-6355)
PHONE......................510 657-7846
Robert C Hoelsch, *President*
Chris Guiver, *Info Tech Dir*
Matthew Furlo, *Engineer*
Isidro Trujillo, *Prdtn Mgr*
EMP: 14
SQ FT: 8,000
SALES (est): 3.5MM **Privately Held**
SIC: 3559 Semiconductor manufacturing machinery

(P-15018)
REDLINE DETECTION LLC
828 W Taft Ave, Orange (92865-4232)
PHONE......................714 451-1411
Zachary Parker, *Principal*
Alex Parker, *Vice Pres*
Gene Stauffer, *General Mgr*
Jason Ouimette, *Purchasing*
▲ **EMP:** 10
SQ FT: 6,500
SALES (est): 2.3MM **Privately Held**
WEB: www.redlinedetection.com
SIC: 3559 Automotive maintenance equipment

(P-15019)
RICHARD VEECK
9966 Golf Link Rd, Hilmar (95324-9306)
PHONE......................209 667-0872
Richard Veeck, *Owner*
Jaince Veeck, *Treasurer*
EMP: 15
SALES (est): 943.3K **Privately Held**
SIC: 3559 Recycling machinery

(P-15020)
RICK PALENSHUS
Also Called: Pro Coat Powder Coating
560 3rd St, Lake Elsinore (92530-2729)
PHONE......................951 245-2100
Rick Palenshus, *Owner*
EMP: 18
SQ FT: 18,000
SALES (est): 3MM **Privately Held**
WEB: www.procoatpowdercoating.com
SIC: 3559 Metal finishing equipment for plating, etc.

(P-15021)
RITE TRACK EQUIPMENT SVCS INC
2151 Otoole Ave Ste 40, San Jose (95131-1330)
PHONE......................408 432-0131
Timothy Hayden, *Branch Mgr*
EMP: 15 **Privately Held**
WEB: www.ritetrack.com
SIC: 3559
PA: Rite Track Equipment Services, Inc.
    8655 Rite Track Way
    West Chester OH 45069

(P-15022)
ROCK & ROLL CUSTOM PAINT WORKS
1630 S Sunkist St Ste N, Anaheim (92806-5816)
PHONE......................714 744-0631
Randy Morton, *President*
EMP: 20 **EST:** 2004
SALES (est): 3MM **Privately Held**
WEB: www.rr-custompaintworks.com
SIC: 3559 Paint making machinery

(P-15023)
RUBICON EXPRESS (PA)
Also Called: Rubicon Manufacturing
3290 Monier Cir Ste 100, Rancho Cordova (95742-6804)
PHONE......................916 858-8575
Ryan Wallace, *President*
EMP: 10
SQ FT: 30,000
SALES (est): 3.8MM **Privately Held**
WEB: www.rubiconexpress.com
SIC: 3559 5013 Automotive related machinery; motor vehicle supplies & new parts

(P-15024)
RUCKER & KOLLS INC (HQ)
Also Called: Rucker & Knolls
1064 Yosemite Dr, Milpitas (95035-5410)
PHONE......................408 934-9875
Arlen Chou, *President*
Hsun Chou, *Director*
EMP: 27
SQ FT: 6,000
SALES: 3.2MM
SALES (corp-wide): 13.3MM **Privately Held**
WEB: www.ruckerkolls.com
SIC: 3559 3825 Semiconductor manufacturing machinery; instruments to measure electricity
PA: Eico, Inc.
    1054 Yosemite Dr
    Milpitas CA 95035
    408 945-9898

(P-15025)
RXSAFE LLC
2453 Cades Way Bldg A, Vista (92081-7858)
PHONE......................760 593-7161
William Holmes, *CEO*
David Wilkinson, *CFO*
Brian Kichler, *Vice Pres*
Maha Mossalam, *Manager*
Christine Taylor, *Consultant*
EMP: 15
SALES: 11.9MM **Privately Held**
SIC: 3559 Pharmaceutical machinery

(P-15026)
SAFETY-KLEEN SYSTEMS INC
3561 S Maple Ave, Fresno (93725-2415)
PHONE......................559 486-1960
Allan Calandra, *Manager*
Sam Pendergrass, *Cust Mgr*
EMP: 18
SQ FT: 2,000
SALES (corp-wide): 2.9B **Publicly Held**
SIC: 3559 7359 5172 4212 Degreasing machines, automotive & industrial; equipment rental & leasing; petroleum products; hazardous waste transport; solvents recovery service; industrial supplies
HQ: Safety-Kleen Systems, Inc.
    2600 N Central Expy # 400
    Richardson TX 75080
    972 265-2000

(P-15027)
SANDVIK THERMAL PROCESS INC
19500 Nugget Blvd, Sonora (95370-9248)
PHONE......................209 533-1990
James T Johnson, *CEO*
Darwin Tadena, *Project Engr*
Frank Figoni, *Finance*
Sue Westgate, *Human Res Dir*
Christy Munoz, *Purchasing*
▲ **EMP:** 75 **EST:** 1981
SQ FT: 100,000

SALES (est): 19.8MM
SALES (corp-wide): 10.7B Privately Held
SIC: 3559 Semiconductor manufacturing
machinery
HQ: Sandvik, Inc.
17-02 Nevins Rd
Fair Lawn NJ 07410
201 794-5000

(P-15028)
SANTUR CORPORATION (HQ)
40931 Encyclopedia Cir, Fremont
(94538-2436)
PHONE..................510 933-4100
Paul Meissner, President
George W Laplante, CFO
Bardia Pezeshki, CTO
Sabeur Siala, VP Engrg
Richard Wilmer, VP Opers
EMP: 28
SQ FT: 20,000
SALES (est): 4.5MM Publicly Held
WEB: www.santurcorp.com
SIC: 3559 Electronic component making
machinery

(P-15029)
**SEMICONDUCTOR EQUIPMENT
CORP**
Also Called: SEC
5154 Goldman Ave, Moorpark
(93021-1760)
PHONE..................805 529-2293
Donald I Moore, CEO
Richard Folsom, Treasurer
Chris Ryding, Sr Software Eng
Teresa Scruggs, Info Tech Mgr
Gloria Studley, Project Engr
▲ EMP: 16
SQ FT: 12,500
SALES (est): 3.4MM Privately Held
WEB: www.semicorp.com
SIC: 3559 Semiconductor manufacturing
machinery

(P-15030)
**SEMICONDUCTOR PROCESS
EQP CORP**
Also Called: Spec
27963 Franklin Pkwy, Valencia
(91355-4110)
PHONE..................661 257-0934
Arnold J Gustin, CEO
Robin Douglas, President
Veronica Luevano, President
Mike Loucks, COO
Kevin McGillivray, Vice Pres
◆ EMP: 35
SQ FT: 139,000
SALES (est): 10.3MM Privately Held
WEB: www.team-spec.com
SIC: 3559 Semiconductor manufacturing
machinery

(P-15031)
**SPT MICROTECHNOLOGIES
USA INC**
1150 Ringwood Ct, San Jose (95131-1726)
PHONE..................408 571-1400
Vivek RAO, COO
Seiichi Ogino, President
Takayoshi Kikuchi, Treasurer
Andy Bavin, General Mgr
Masayoshi Tanaka, Admin Sec
EMP: 43
SQ FT: 28,000
SALES (est): 6.6MM Privately Held
SIC: 3559 Semiconductor manufacturing
machinery

(P-15032)
**STARCO ENTERPRISES INC
(PA)**
Also Called: Four Star Chemical
3137 E 26th St, Vernon (90058-8006)
PHONE..................323 266-7111
Ross Sklar, CEO
Jerry Ulrich, CEO
Bill Edwards, IT/INT Sup
Rebecca Valdez, Human Res Mgr
Joe Lozano, Maintence Staff
▲ EMP: 75
SQ FT: 25,000

SALES (est): 18.8MM Privately Held
WEB: www.fourstarchemical.com
SIC: 3559 5169 5191 Degreasing machines, automotive & industrial; specialty
cleaning & sanitation preparations; farm
supplies

(P-15033)
SUPERIOR AUTOMATION INC
47770 Westinghouse Dr, Fremont
(94539-7475)
PHONE..................408 227-4898
Sean Kessinger, President
Donald Brosio, CFO
Lance Faure, Engineer
Roger Kessinger, Director
Chris Kieffer, Manager
EMP: 12
SQ FT: 11,000
SALES (est): 3.3MM Privately Held
WEB: www.superiorautomation.com
SIC: 3559 Semiconductor manufacturing
machinery

(P-15034)
SUSS MICROTEC INC (HQ)
220 Klug Cir, Corona (92880-5409)
PHONE..................408 940-0300
Frank Averdung, President
Franz Richter, Ch of Bd
Stefan Schneidewind, Ch of Bd
Wilfried Bair, President
Peter Szafir, President
EMP: 130
SQ FT: 37,000
SALES (est): 16.7MM
SALES (corp-wide): 196.3MM Privately
Held
SIC: 3559 3825 3674 Semiconductor
manufacturing machinery; instruments to
measure electricity; semiconductors & re-
lated devices
PA: SUss Microtec Se
SchleiBheimer Str. 90
Garching B. Munchen 85748
893 200-70

(P-15035)
SUVOLTA INC
130 Knowles Dr Ste D, Los Gatos
(95032-1832)
PHONE..................408 866-4125
Bruce McWilliams, President
Louis Parrillo, COO
Leslie Wilkinson, Director
EMP: 21
SALES (est): 3.7MM Privately Held
SIC: 3559 Semiconductor manufacturing
machinery

(P-15036)
**T ULTRA EQUIPMENT COMPANY
INC**
41980 Christy St, Fremont (94538-3161)
PHONE..................510 440-3900
John Flaagan, President
Bill Jepson, Project Engr
James Flaagan, Engineer
Christine Groves, Controller
Jesus Ortiz, Prdtn Mgr
◆ EMP: 12
SQ FT: 9,408
SALES (est): 3MM Privately Held
WEB: www.ultrat.com
SIC: 3559 7699 Semiconductor manufac-
turing machinery; plastics working ma-
chinery; industrial machinery & equipment
repair

(P-15037)
**TEMECULA QUALITY PLATING
INC**
43095 Black Deer Loop, Temecula
(92590-3413)
PHONE..................951 296-9875
Duc Vo, President
Dat Vo, Vice Pres
EMP: 18 EST: 2011
SQ FT: 10,000
SALES: 1.3MM Privately Held
SIC: 3559 Metal finishing equipment for
plating, etc.

(P-15038)
TRADEMARK PLASTICS INC
807 Palmyrita Ave, Riverside (92507-1805)
PHONE..................909 941-8810
Erin Carty, CEO
Carolyn Carty, President
Phil Estrada, Executive
▲ EMP: 150
SQ FT: 100,000
SALES (est): 76.6MM Privately Held
WEB: www.trademarkplastics.com
SIC: 3559 3089 Plastics working machin-
ery; injection molding of plastics

(P-15039)
TRI-C MANUFACTURING INC
517 Houston St, West Sacramento
(95691-2213)
PHONE..................916 371-1700
Lilburn Clyde Lamar, President
EMP: 20 EST: 1969
SALES (est): 3.9MM
SALES (corp-wide): 4.2MM Privately
Held
SIC: 3559 Rubber working machinery, in-
cluding tires
PA: Tri-C Machine Corporation
520 Harbor Blvd
West Sacramento CA 95691
916 371-8090

(P-15040)
**TRIO-TECH INTERNATIONAL
(PA)**
16139 Wyandotte St, Van Nuys
(91406-3423)
PHONE..................818 787-7000
Siew Wai Yong, President
A Charles Wilson, Ch of Bd
Victor H M Ting, CFO
Hwee Poh Lim, Vice Pres
S K Soon, Vice Pres
EMP: 10
SQ FT: 5,200
SALES: 42.3MM Publicly Held
WEB: www.triotech.com
SIC: 3559 3825 5084 3533 Semiconduc-
tor manufacturing machinery; semicon-
ductor test equipment; instruments &
control equipment; oil & gas field machin-
ery; real estate leasing & rentals

(P-15041)
**ULTRA TEC MANUFACTURING
INC**
1025 E Chestnut Ave, Santa Ana
(92701-6425)
PHONE..................714 542-0608
Joseph I Rubin, President
Maxine Rubin, Corp Secy
Robert Rubin, Vice Pres
EMP: 15
SQ FT: 7,000
SALES (est): 2.9MM Privately Held
WEB: www.ultratecusa.com
SIC: 3559 3541 Synthetic filament extrud-
ing machines; grinding, polishing, buffing,
lapping & honing machines

(P-15042)
ULTRATECH INC (HQ)
3050 Zanker Rd, San Jose (95134-2126)
PHONE..................408 321-8835
Arthur W Zafiropoulo, President
Bruce R Wright, CFO
Byoung-Ho Lee, Vice Pres
David Owen, Vice Pres
Masoud Safa, Vice Pres
EMP: 201
SQ FT: 100,000
SALES: 194MM
SALES (corp-wide): 484.7MM Publicly
Held
SIC: 3559 Semiconductor manufacturing
machinery
PA: Veeco Instruments Inc.
1 Terminal Dr
Plainview NY 11803
516 677-0200

(P-15043)
ULTRON SYSTEMS INC
5105 Maureen Ln, Moorpark (93021-1783)
PHONE..................805 529-1485
Aki Egerer, President

Aaron Chan, Vice Pres
▲ EMP: 17
SQ FT: 8,000
SALES (est): 3.9MM Privately Held
WEB: www.ultronsystems.com
SIC: 3559 Semiconductor manufacturing
machinery

(P-15044)
VA-TRAN SYSTEMS INC
677 Anita St Ste A, Chula Vista
(91911-4661)
PHONE..................619 423-4555
James E Sloan, President
Chris Sloan, Vice Pres
Daniel Madrigal, Accountant
▲ EMP: 10
SQ FT: 5,000
SALES (est): 1MM Privately Held
WEB: www.vatran.com
SIC: 3559 Cryogenic machinery, industrial

(P-15045)
VIBRATION IMPACT & PRES
Also Called: VIP Sensors
32242 Paseo Adelanto C, San Juan Capis-
trano (92675-3610)
PHONE..................949 429-3558
Alex Karolys, Owner
EMP: 10
SALES (est): 1.1MM Privately Held
WEB: www.vipsensors.com
SIC: 3559 Electronic component making
machinery

(P-15046)
**WAFER PROCESS SYSTEMS
INC**
3641 Charter Park Dr, San Jose
(95136-1312)
PHONE..................408 445-3010
Douglas H Caldwell, CEO
Christopher J Schmitz, Vice Pres
EMP: 15
SALES (est): 3.7MM Privately Held
WEB: www.waferprocess.com
SIC: 3559 Semiconductor manufacturing
machinery

(P-15047)
WALCO MACHINES CO
9017 Arrow Rte, Rancho Cucamonga
(91730-4412)
PHONE..................909 483-3333
James Wilkinson, Principal
EMP: 25
SALES (est): 5.3MM Privately Held
SIC: 3559 Ammunition & explosives, load-
ing machinery

(P-15048)
WESLAN SYSTEMS INC
1244 Commerce Ave, Woodland
(95776-5902)
PHONE..................530 668-3304
Richard Weston, President
Belma Weston, CFO
Larry Davis, Technology
Mark Brown, Electrical Engi
Jim Dittrich, Prdtn Mgr
EMP: 12
SQ FT: 15,000
SALES: 3MM Privately Held
WEB: www.weslan.com
SIC: 3559 Semiconductor manufacturing
machinery

(P-15049)
**WEST COAST CRYOGENICS
INC**
503 W Larch Rd Ste K, Tracy
(95304-1670)
PHONE..................209 914-6989
Danny Silveira, President
EMP: 19
SALES (est): 2MM Privately Held
SIC: 3559 Cryogenic machinery, industrial

3561 Pumps & Pumping

(P-15050)
ADVANCED RESULTS COMPANY INC
18760 Afton Ave, Saratoga (95070-4653)
PHONE..........................408 986-0123
Arkady Dorf, *President*
Jamie Wang, *Admin Sec*
EMP: 15
SQ FT: 2,200
SALES (est): 1.6MM **Privately Held**
SIC: 3561 Industrial pumps & parts

(P-15051)
AGGREGATE MINING PRODUCTS LLC
21780 Temescal Canyon Rd, Corona (92883-5669)
PHONE..........................951 277-1267
Bill Medina,
Frank Smith,
EMP: 12
SALES (est): 1.9MM **Privately Held**
SIC: 3561 Pump jacks & other pumping equipment

(P-15052)
AQUASTAR POOL PRODUCTS INC
Also Called: Aquastar Pool Productions
2340 Palma Dr Ste 104, Ventura (93003-8091)
PHONE..........................877 768-2717
Olaf Mjelde, *CEO*
Sarah Reimer, *Admin Sec*
▲ **EMP:** 16
SALES (est): 4MM **Privately Held**
SIC: 3561 Pumps, domestic: water or sump

(P-15053)
AQUATEC INTERNATIONAL INC
Also Called: Aquatec Water Systems
17422 Pullman St, Irvine (92614-5527)
PHONE..........................949 225-2200
Bryan Hausner, *CEO*
Sami Levi, *CFO*
Ivar Schoenmeyr, *Corp Secy*
Isak Levi, *Vice Pres*
Paul Renna, *Project Mgr*
▲ **EMP:** 95
SQ FT: 30,000
SALES (est): 28.9MM **Privately Held**
SIC: 3561 Pumps & pumping equipment

(P-15054)
BESTWAY HYDRAULICS CO INC
1518 S Santa Fe Ave, Compton (90221-4919)
PHONE..........................310 639-2507
Ehud Nahir, *President*
Alona Nahir, *Vice Pres*
EMP: 35
SQ FT: 7,000
SALES (est): 2.5MM **Privately Held**
WEB: www.bestwayhydraulics.com
SIC: 3561 5084 Cylinders, pump; industrial machinery & equipment

(P-15055)
BORIN MANUFACTURING INC
5741 Buckingham Pkwy B, Culver City (90230-6520)
PHONE..........................310 822-1000
Frank William Borin, *CEO*
Gregg Steele, *Vice Pres*
Luis Sanchez, *Admin Asst*
EMP: 40
SALES (est): 8.2MM **Privately Held**
WEB: www.borin.com
SIC: 3561 3443 3317 3494 Pumps & pumping equipment; fabricated plate work (boiler shop); steel pipe & tubes; valves & pipe fittings; telephone & telegraph apparatus; oil & gas field machinery

(P-15056)
CASCADE PUMP COMPANY
10107 Norwalk Blvd, Santa Fe Springs (90670-3354)
P.O. Box 2767 (90670-0767)
PHONE..........................562 946-1414

T W Summerfield, *CEO*
John Summerfield, *CFO*
Robert Gray, *Executive*
Brian Summerfield, *Engineer*
Scott Summerfield, *Human Res Dir*
EMP: 60
SQ FT: 120,000
SALES (est): 28.8MM **Privately Held**
WEB: www.cascadepump.com
SIC: 3561 3594 Pumps, domestic: water or sump; fluid power pumps & motors

(P-15057)
COASTAL PRODUCTS COMPANY INC
2157 Mohawk St, Bakersfield (93308-6020)
P.O. Box 1200 (93302-1200)
PHONE..........................661 323-0487
Dorothy Jones, *President*
Richard Jones, *General Mgr*
EMP: 14
SQ FT: 2,500
SALES (est): 1.6MM **Privately Held**
SIC: 3561 Pumps & pumping equipment

(P-15058)
CRYOSTAR USA LLC
13117 Meyer Rd, Whittier (90605-3555)
PHONE..........................562 903-1290
Randy Reynoso, *Manager*
Mark Sutton, *General Mgr*
Karen Danbar, *Admin Asst*
Bruno Brethes, *Technical Staff*
Sunny Liu, *Engineer*
▲ **EMP:** 41
SALES (est): 10.5MM **Privately Held**
SIC: 3561 Pump jacks & other pumping equipment

(P-15059)
DISCFLO CORPORATION
Also Called: Disc Pumps
10850 Hartley Rd, Santee (92071-2802)
PHONE..........................619 596-3181
Max Gurth, *CEO*
◆ **EMP:** 35
SQ FT: 50,000
SALES (est): 10.5MM **Privately Held**
WEB: www.discflo.com
SIC: 3561 Industrial pumps & parts

(P-15060)
DUONETICS
Also Called: Polynetics
809 E Parkridge Ave # 102, Corona (92879-6610)
PHONE..........................951 808-4903
Robert Pernice, *President*
Charles Pernice, *Vice Pres*
Charles A Pernice, *Vice Pres*
Sophia Pernice, *Admin Sec*
EMP: 10
SQ FT: 6,500
SALES (est): 2.5MM **Privately Held**
WEB: www.duonetics.com
SIC: 3561 3599 3728 Industrial pumps & parts; machine & other job shop work; dynetric balancing stands, aircraft

(P-15061)
EBARA INTERNATIONAL CORP
51 Main Ave, Sacramento (95838-2014)
PHONE..........................916 920-5451
Evertt Hylton, *Branch Mgr*
EMP: 85
SALES (corp-wide): 3.4B **Privately Held**
SIC: 3561 Pumps & pumping equipment
HQ: Ebara International Corp
350 Salomon Cir
Sparks NV 89434
775 356-2796

(P-15062)
FLOW CONTROL LLC
17942 Cowan, Irvine (92614-6026)
PHONE..........................949 608-3900
Sonia Hollies, *Mng Member*
EMP: 10 **Publicly Held**
SIC: 3561 Pumps, domestic: water or sump
HQ: Flow Control Llc
1 International Dr
Rye Brook NY 10573
914 323-5700

(P-15063)
FLOWSERVE CORPORATION
2300 E Vernon Ave Stop 76, Vernon (90058-1609)
PHONE..........................323 584-1890
Rick Soldo, *Branch Mgr*
Jama Meyer, *General Mgr*
Gerardo Galvan, *Planning*
Peter Downy, *Info Tech Dir*
Shiva Veera, *Info Tech Mgr*
EMP: 342
SALES (corp-wide): 3.6B **Publicly Held**
SIC: 3561 Pumps & pumping equipment
PA: Flowserve Corporation
5215 N Oconnor Blvd Connor
Irving TX 75039
972 443-6500

(P-15064)
FLOWSERVE CORPORATION
1909 E Cashdan St, Compton (90220-6422)
PHONE..........................310 667-4220
Dan Lattimore, *Manager*
Gary Mignacca, *General Mgr*
EMP: 50
SALES (corp-wide): 3.6B **Publicly Held**
SIC: 3561 Industrial pumps & parts
PA: Flowserve Corporation
5215 N Oconnor Blvd Connor
Irving TX 75039
972 443-6500

(P-15065)
FLOWSERVE CORPORATION
6077 Egret Ct, Benicia (94510-1205)
PHONE..........................707 745-4710
Keith Slothers, *Manager*
Jim Dobson, *Sales Staff*
John Ireland, *Sales Staff*
EMP: 18
SALES (corp-wide): 3.6B **Publicly Held**
SIC: 3561 Industrial pumps & parts
PA: Flowserve Corporation
5215 N Oconnor Blvd Connor
Irving TX 75039
972 443-6500

(P-15066)
FLOWSERVE CORPORATION
27455 Tierra Alta Way C, Temecula (92590-3498)
PHONE..........................951 296-2464
Paul Cortenbach, *Branch Mgr*
Jeannie Del Monte, *Engineer*
Chad Wagner, *Engineer*
Ian Jennings, *Manager*
EMP: 200
SALES (corp-wide): 3.6B **Publicly Held**
SIC: 3561 3053 Industrial pumps & parts; gaskets, packing & sealing devices
PA: Flowserve Corporation
5215 N Oconnor Blvd Connor
Irving TX 75039
972 443-6500

(P-15067)
GARDNER DENVER INC
28904 Scotsview Dr, Rancho Palos Verdes (90275-4744)
PHONE..........................310 544-5710
EMP: 180
SALES (corp-wide): 2.3B **Publicly Held**
SIC: 3561 Industrial pumps & parts
HQ: Gardner Denver, Inc.
222 E Erie St Ste 500
Milwaukee WI 53202

(P-15068)
GOULDS PUMPS
3951 Capitol Ave, City of Industry (90601-1734)
PHONE..........................562 949-2113
Mike Suess, *Manager*
▲ **EMP:** 22
SALES (est): 4.8MM **Privately Held**
SIC: 3561 Pumps & pumping equipment

(P-15069)
GRISWOLD PUMP COMPANY
22069 Van Buren St, Grand Terrace (92313-5607)
PHONE..........................909 422-1700
Dale Pavlovich, *President*
Michael Boul, *Vice Pres*

Dave Spitzer, *Vice Pres*
Edward Vaughn, *Vice Pres*
▲ **EMP:** 25
SQ FT: 25,000
SALES (est): 6MM
SALES (corp-wide): 7.8B **Publicly Held**
WEB: www.griswoldpump.com
SIC: 3561 5084 Industrial pumps & parts; industrial machinery & equipment
HQ: Wilden Pump And Engineering Llc
22069 Van Buren St
Grand Terrace CA 92313
909 422-1700

(P-15070)
GROVER SMITH MFG CORP
Also Called: Grover Manufacturing
620 S Vail Ave, Montebello (90640-4952)
P.O. Box 986 (90640-0986)
PHONE..........................323 724-3444
Marilyn Schirmer, *President*
W Michael Meeker, *Ch of Bd*
Lino Paras, *Treasurer*
Michael Meyer, *Manager*
EMP: 30 EST: 1925
SQ FT: 65,000
SALES (est): 7.1MM **Privately Held**
WEB: www.grovermfg.com
SIC: 3561 3569 Pumps & pumping equipment; lubrication equipment, industrial

(P-15071)
GRUNDFOS CBS INC
Also Called: Paco Pumps By Grundfos
25568 Seaboard Ln, Hayward (94545-3210)
PHONE..........................510 512-1300
Steve Wilson, *Branch Mgr*
EMP: 18
SALES (corp-wide): 4B **Privately Held**
WEB: www.us.grundfos.com
SIC: 3561 Pumps & pumping equipment
HQ: Grundfos Cbs Inc.
902 Koomey Rd
Brookshire TX 77423
281 994-2700

(P-15072)
HARBISON-FISCHER INC
2801 Pegasus Dr, Bakersfield (93308-6818)
PHONE..........................661 387-0166
Tom Demos, *Branch Mgr*
EMP: 20
SALES (corp-wide): 1.4B **Publicly Held**
WEB: www.hfpumps.com
SIC: 3561 Industrial pumps & parts
HQ: Harbison-Fischer, Inc.
901 N Crowley Rd
Crowley TX 76036
817 297-2211

(P-15073)
HASKEL INTERNATIONAL LLC (HQ)
100 E Graham Pl, Burbank (91502-2076)
PHONE..........................818 843-4000
Chris Krieps, *CEO*
Roy Todd, *Planning*
Veldma Crosby, *Info Tech Mgr*
Dave Arnold, *Technology*
Steve Quigley, *Engineer*
▲ **EMP:** 125
SQ FT: 78,000
SALES (est): 85.4MM
SALES (corp-wide): 415MM **Privately Held**
WEB: www.haskel.com
SIC: 3561 3594 5084 5085 Pumps & pumping equipment; fluid power pumps; hydraulic systems equipment & supplies; hose, belting & packing; valves, pistons & fittings; electrical equipment & supplies
PA: Accudyne Industries, Llc
2728 N Harwood St Ste 200
Dallas TX 75201
469 518-4777

(P-15074)
HI-FLO CORP
5161 E El Cedral St, Long Beach (90815-3903)
PHONE..........................562 468-0800
Alfred Brunella, *President*
Rick Brizendine, *Admin Sec*
EMP: 15

▲ = Import ▼=Export
◆ =Import/Export

SQ FT: 5,000
SALES (est): 2.1MM **Privately Held**
WEB: www.hiflocorp.com
SIC: 3561 Pumps, oil well & field

(P-15075)
HP WATER SYSTEMS INC
9338 W Whites Bridge Ave, Fresno
(93706-9515)
PHONE....................559 268-4751
Hollis Priest Jr, *President*
Joyce Priest, *Admin Sec*
EMP: 30
SQ FT: 3,000
SALES (est): 11.4MM **Privately Held**
SIC: 3561 1781 Pumps & pumping equipment; water well drilling

(P-15076)
HYDRAFORCE INCORPORATED
7383 Orangewood Dr, Riverside
(92504-1027)
PHONE....................951 689-3987
Javier Soto, *CEO*
Eric Lau, *Sales Associate*
Ricardo Michel, *Manager*
EMP: 14
SALES (est): 3.1MM **Privately Held**
SIC: 3561 Cylinders, pump

(P-15077)
HYDRAFORCE INCORPORATED
7383 Orangewood Dr, Riverside
(92504-1027)
PHONE....................951 689-3987
Javier Soto, *CEO*
Ricardo Michel, *Manager*
EMP: 14 **EST:** 1990
SQ FT: 4,000
SALES (est): 1.6MM **Privately Held**
SIC: 3561 Cylinders, pump

(P-15078)
HYDRAFORCE INCORPORATED
7383 Orangewood Dr, Riverside
(92504-1027)
PHONE....................951 689-3987
Javier Soto, *CEO*
Ricardo Michel, *Manager*
EMP: 14
SQ FT: 4,000
SALES (est): 673.6K **Privately Held**
SIC: 3561 Cylinders, pump

(P-15079)
HYDRAULIC TECHNOLOGY INC
3833 Cincinnati Ave, Rocklin (95765-1302)
PHONE....................916 645-3317
Daniel Stokes, *President*
Catherine Stokes, *Admin Sec*
Wendy Nathan, *Manager*
Julie Stokes, *Manager*
EMP: 10 **EST:** 1966
SQ FT: 10,400
SALES (est): 2.1MM **Privately Held**
WEB: www.hydraulictechnology.com
SIC: 3561 3823 Pumps & pumping equipment; pressure measurement instruments, industrial

(P-15080)
ITT LLC
3878 S Willow Ave Ste 104, Fresno
(93725-9015)
PHONE....................559 265-4730
Jeff Barrow, *Manager*
EMP: 15
SALES (corp-wide): 2.5B **Publicly Held**
WEB: www.ittind.com
SIC: 3561 Pumps & pumping equipment
HQ: Itt Llc
1133 Westchester Ave N-100
White Plains NY 10604
914 641-2000

(P-15081)
KEENE ENGINEERING INC (PA)
Also Called: Keene Industries
20201 Bahama St, Chatsworth
(91311-6204)
PHONE....................818 485-2681
Jerry Keene, *CEO*
Tina Ngo Shin, *CFO*
Patrick O Keene, *Treasurer*
Mark A Keene, *Vice Pres*
Chris Woods, *Purchasing*

▼ **EMP:** 10 **EST:** 1957
SQ FT: 22,000
SALES: 8MM **Privately Held**
WEB: www.keeneengineering.com
SIC: 3561 3531 Pumps & pumping equipment; dredging machinery

(P-15082)
LINDE LLC
Boc Edwards Systems Chemistry
2041 Mission College Blvd, Santa Clara
(95054-1518)
PHONE....................408 496-1177
Tom Haren, *Manager*
EMP: 80
SQ FT: 30,000
SALES (corp-wide): 20.1B **Privately Held**
SIC: 3561 Pumps & pumping equipment
HQ: Linde Llc
200 Somerset Corporate Bl
Bridgewater NJ 08807
908 464-8100

(P-15083)
LOCRIAN NETWORKS INC
120 San Lucar Ct, Sunnyvale
(94086-5213)
PHONE....................408 988-2288
William Kunz, *CEO*
EMP: 15
SALES: 100K **Privately Held**
WEB: www.locriannetworks.com
SIC: 3561 3661 Pumps & pumping equipment; telephone & telegraph apparatus

(P-15084)
LOS ANGLES PUMP VALVE PDTS INC
Also Called: Los Angeles Brass Products
2528 E 57th St, Huntington Park
(90255-2521)
P.O. Box 2007 (90255-1307)
PHONE....................323 277-7788
Santos J Pinto, *President*
Phil Pinto, *Vice Pres*
EMP: 20
SQ FT: 11,000
SALES (est): 4.1MM **Privately Held**
SIC: 3561 Pump jacks & other pumping equipment

(P-15085)
MJW INC
Also Called: American Lab and Systems
1328 W Slauson Ave, Los Angeles
(90044-2824)
PHONE....................323 778-8900
Mike Curry, *President*
Linda Curry, *Vice Pres*
Shane Curry, *General Mgr*
EMP: 65
SQ FT: 30,000
SALES (est): 13.5MM **Privately Held**
WEB: www.hydraulicsmall.com
SIC: 3561 Industrial pumps & parts

(P-15086)
N Z PUMP CO INC
Also Called: New Zealand Pump Company
801 S Palm Ave, Alhambra (91803-1426)
PHONE....................626 458-8023
Claire Jenkinson Johns, *Principal*
James Maines, *Vice Chairman*
Johnathan Hawkins, *General Mgr*
▲ **EMP:** 18
SALES (est): 4MM **Privately Held**
SIC: 3561 Industrial pumps & parts

(P-15087)
PENGUIN PUMPS INCORPORATED
Also Called: Filter Pump Industries
7932 Ajay Dr, Sun Valley (91352-5315)
PHONE....................818 504-2391
Jerome S Hollander, *President*
Larry Frederick, *COO*
Sonya E Hollander, *Corp Secy*
Mitchell A Hollander, *Vice Pres*
Mark Brien, *General Mgr*
▲ **EMP:** 50
SQ FT: 20,000
SALES (est): 16.6MM **Privately Held**
WEB: www.filterpump.com
SIC: 3561 3569 Pumps & pumping equipment; filters, general line: industrial

(P-15088)
POLARIS E-COMMERCE INC
1941 E Occidental St, Santa Ana
(92705-5115)
PHONE....................714 907-0582
Insoo Hwang, *CEO*
▲ **EMP:** 25 **EST:** 2010
SALES (est): 3.8MM **Privately Held**
SIC: 3561 Industrial pumps & parts

(P-15089)
PROVAC SALES INC
2535 7th Ave Ste 4, Santa Cruz
(95062-1676)
PHONE....................831 462-8900
David Hoyle, *Exec Dir*
Paul Flood, *Technology*
Katy Manning, *Opers Mgr*
EMP: 23
SQ FT: 3,000
SALES: 2.6MM **Privately Held**
WEB: www.provac.com
SIC: 3561 5084 Pumps & pumping equipment; pumps & pumping equipment

(P-15090)
REED LLC
Also Called: Reed Manufacturing
13822 Oaks Ave, Chino (91710-7008)
PHONE....................909 287-2100
James W Shea, *President*
Cliff KAO, *Vice Pres*
◆ **EMP:** 40
SQ FT: 69,000
SALES (est): 11.4MM **Privately Held**
WEB: www.reedmfg.com
SIC: 3561 3531 Pumps & pumping equipment; bituminous, cement & concrete related products & equipment

(P-15091)
SMITH PRECISION PRODUCTS CO
Also Called: Smith Pumps
1299 Lawrence Dr, Newbury Park
(91320-1306)
P.O. Box 276 (91319-0276)
PHONE....................805 498-6616
Walter W Smith, *President*
Warren Smith, *Treasurer*
Tiffany Ohara, *General Mgr*
Karen Bolyard, *Controller*
John Ives, *Sales Executive*
▲ **EMP:** 21
SQ FT: 16,000
SALES: 2.9MM **Privately Held**
WEB: www.smithpumps.com
SIC: 3561 Industrial pumps & parts

(P-15092)
STA-RITE INDUSTRIES LLC
Also Called: Pentair
16261 Tisbury Cir, Huntington Beach
(92649-2142)
PHONE....................714 371-1550
Wendy Inskeep, *Manager*
EMP: 430
SALES (corp-wide): 1.2B **Privately Held**
SIC: 3561 Pumps & pumping equipment
HQ: Sta-Rite Industries, Llc
293 S Wright St
Delavan WI 53115
888 782-7483

(P-15093)
SULZER PUMP SOLUTIONS US INC
1650 Bell Ave Ste 140, Sacramento
(95838-2869)
PHONE....................916 925-8508
Dale Gretzinger, *Manager*
EMP: 20
SALES (corp-wide): 17.3MM **Privately Held**
WEB: www.absgroup.com
SIC: 3561 Pumps & pumping equipment
PA: Sulzer Pump Solutions (Us) Inc.
140 Pond View Dr
Meriden CT 06450
203 238-2700

(P-15094)
TOMIKO INC
Also Called: American Industrial Pump
1615 W 10th St, Antioch (94509-1363)
P.O. Box 8056, Pittsburg (94565-8056)
PHONE....................925 754-5694
Michael Gianni, *CEO*
Enrique Pallado, *Corp Secy*
Tom Fox, *Director*
▲ **EMP:** 13
SALES (est): 3.4MM **Privately Held**
SIC: 3561 Industrial pumps & parts

(P-15095)
TOTAL PROCESS SOLUTIONS LLC
1400 Norris Rd, Bakersfield (93308-2232)
PHONE....................661 829-7910
Eddie L Rice, *Mng Member*
Stan Ellis, *Mng Member*
Travis Ellis, *Mng Member*
Joey L Taylor, *Mng Member*
EMP: 30
SALES (est): 9.4MM **Privately Held**
SIC: 3561 3563 Cylinders, pump; air & gas compressors including vacuum pumps

(P-15096)
TR ENGINEERING INC
1350 Green Hills Rd 10, Scotts Valley
(95066-4986)
PHONE....................831 430-9920
Robert J Romero, *President*
Jill Koering-Romero, *Vice Pres*
Carolina Perez, *Vice Pres*
Tarek Lutfi, *Software Dev*
Lisa Symonds, *Marketing Staff*
EMP: 10 **EST:** 1982
SQ FT: 8,800
SALES: 1MM **Privately Held**
WEB: www.trengineering.com
SIC: 3561 3491 Pumps & pumping equipment; industrial valves

(P-15097)
WEATHERFORD ARTIFICIA
21728 Rosedale Hwy, Bakersfield
(93314-9787)
PHONE....................661 654-8120
EMP: 32 **Privately Held**
SIC: 3561 Pumps, oil well & field
HQ: Weatherford Artificial Lift Systems, Llc
2000 Saint James Pl
Houston TX 77056
713 836-4000

(P-15098)
WEIR FLOWAY INC (HQ)
Also Called: Floway Pumps
2494 S Railroad Ave, Fresno (93706-5109)
P.O. Box 164 (93707-0164)
PHONE....................559 442-4000
Barry Cockerham, *President*
Vera Haitayan, *President*
Eric Smith, *Area Mgr*
Richard Debarry, *Software Dev*
Kevin Augusto, *Project Engr*
◆ **EMP:** 130 **EST:** 1932
SQ FT: 128,000
SALES (est): 49.8MM
SALES (corp-wide): 3.1B **Privately Held**
SIC: 3561 Industrial pumps & parts
PA: Weir Group Plc(The)
1 West Regent Street
Glasgow G2 1R
141 637-7111

(P-15099)
WESTCOAST ROTOR INC
119 W 154th St, Gardena (90248-2201)
PHONE....................310 327-5050
Vehan Mahdessian, *President*
Krikor Mahdessian, *CFO*
▲ **EMP:** 21
SQ FT: 15,625
SALES (est): 4.4MM **Privately Held**
WEB: www.westcoastrotor.com
SIC: 3561 Industrial pumps & parts

(P-15100)
WILDEN PUMP AND ENGRG LLC (DH)
22069 Van Buren St, Grand Terrace (92313-5651)
PHONE...............................909 422-1700
Denny L Buskirk, *Mng Member*
Daniel Anderson,
◆ EMP: 295 EST: 1956
SQ FT: 153,000
SALES (est): 60.6MM
SALES (corp-wide): 7.8B **Publicly Held**
WEB: www.wildenpump.com
SIC: 3561 Industrial pumps & parts
HQ: Canada Organization & Development Llc
3005 Highland Pkwy
Downers Grove IL 60515
630 743-2563

(P-15101)
XYLEM INC
3878 S Willow Ave, Fresno (93725-9015)
PHONE...............................559 265-4731
John Morales, *Manager*
Bridget Berardinelli, *Vice Pres*
Anna D'Errico, *Project Mgr*
Ilke McAliley, *Project Mgr*
Raffaella Novello, *Project Mgr*
▲ EMP: 13 EST: 2013
SALES (est): 2.8MM **Privately Held**
SIC: 3561 Pumps & pumping equipment

(P-15102)
XYLEM WATER SYSTEMS CAL INC
830 Bay Blvd Ste 101, Chula Vista (91911-1692)
PHONE...............................619 575-7466
Ken Napolitano, *CEO*
▲ EMP: 26
SALES (est): 2.5MM **Publicly Held**
SIC: 3561 3443
PA: Xylem Inc.
1 International Dr
Rye Brook NY 10573

(P-15103)
ZILIFT INC
3600 Pegasus Dr Unit 7, Bakersfield (93308-7089)
PHONE...............................661 369-8579
EMP: 10
SALES (est): 1.5MM
SALES (corp-wide): 342.6K **Privately Held**
SIC: 3561 Pumps & pumping equipment
HQ: Zilift Limited
Unit A
Aberdeen AB23

3562 Ball & Roller Bearings

(P-15104)
AMERICAN METAL BEARING COMPANY
7191 Acacia Ave, Garden Grove (92841-5297)
PHONE...............................714 892-5527
Alfred A Anawati, *CEO*
Jim Demaio, *Corp Secy*
Michael Litton, *Vice Pres*
Matthew Ghiassi, *QC Mgr*
▲ EMP: 21 EST: 1921
SQ FT: 40,000
SALES (est): 5.9MM
SALES (corp-wide): 21.9MM **Privately Held**
WEB: www.ambco.net
SIC: 3562 7699 3568 Ball bearings & parts; roller bearings & parts; rebabbitting; power transmission equipment
PA: Marisco, Ltd.
91-607 Malakole St
Kapolei HI 96707
808 682-1333

(P-15105)
CLEAN WAVE MANAGEMENT INC
Also Called: Impact Bearing
1291 Puerta Del Sol, San Clemente (92673-6310)
PHONE...............................949 361-5356
Richard D Kay Jr, *CEO*
Stanley Truong, *QC Mgr*
Randy Faber, *Sales Staff*
Michael Bartlett, *Manager*
Rick Kay, *Manager*
◆ EMP: 30
SQ FT: 20,000
SALES (est): 7.1MM **Privately Held**
SIC: 3562 Ball bearings & parts

(P-15106)
INDUSTRIAL TCTNICS BRINGS CORP (DH)
18301 S Santa Fe Ave, E Rncho Dmngz (90221-5519)
PHONE...............................310 537-3750
Michael J Hartnett, *CEO*
Ivica Fiamengo, *Executive*
Debbie Kanegawa, *General Mgr*
Malek Machta, *Senior Engr*
Ricardo Perez, *Manager*
EMP: 71
SQ FT: 70,000
SALES (est): 27.5MM
SALES (corp-wide): 674.9MM **Publicly Held**
SIC: 3562 5085 Roller bearings & parts; bearings
HQ: Roller Bearing Company Of America, Inc.
102 Willenbrock Rd
Oxford CT 06478
203 267-7001

(P-15107)
INTEGRATED ENERGY TECH INC
Also Called: Doncasters Gce Integrated
9335 Airway Rd Ste 206, San Diego (92154-7930)
PHONE...............................619 421-1151
Craig Gooding, *CEO*
Rey Dumlao, *Planning*
Olumayokun Olagbemi, *Engineer*
Ramon Garcia, *QC Mgr*
Jorge Bernal, *Opers Staff*
EMP: 160
SALES (est): 33.3MM **Privately Held**
SIC: 3562 Casters

(P-15108)
LINMARR ASSOCIATES INC
8 Hammond Ste 108, Irvine (92618-1601)
PHONE...............................949 215-5466
Sharon A Hoffman, *Owner*
William K Hoffman II, *Vice Pres*
Ryan Latka, *Sales Staff*
Ken Hoffman, *Manager*
Nancy Piper, *Manager*
EMP: 10
SQ FT: 5,500
SALES (est): 14.5MM **Privately Held**
WEB: www.linmarr.com
SIC: 3562 5063 5065 Ball & roller bearings; switches, except electronic; capacitors, electronic

(P-15109)
NOMA BEARING CORPORATION
1555 W Rosecrans Ave, Gardena (90249-3027)
PHONE...............................310 329-1800
Toshi Noma, *President*
Kevin Tanaka, *Vice Pres*
▲ EMP: 10
SQ FT: 15,000
SALES (est): 2.4MM **Privately Held**
SIC: 3562 Ball bearings & parts

(P-15110)
SCHAEFFLER GROUP USA INC
34700 Pacific Coast Hwy # 203, Capistrano Beach (92624-1349)
PHONE...............................949 234-9799
Rich Peterson, *Branch Mgr*
Kevin Marx, *Manager*
EMP: 342

SALES (corp-wide): 56.7B **Privately Held**
SIC: 3562 Ball & roller bearings
HQ: Schaeffler Group Usa Inc.
308 Springhill Farm Rd
Fort Mill SC 29715
803 548-8500

(P-15111)
SHEPHARD CASTERS
4451 Eucalyptus Ave, Chino (91710-9702)
PHONE...............................909 393-0597
David Onsurez, *Principal*
▲ EMP: 11 EST: 2009
SALES (est): 1.9MM **Privately Held**
SIC: 3562 5072 Casters; casters & glides

(P-15112)
SPECIALTY MOTIONS INC
5480 Smokey Mountain Way, Yorba Linda (92887-4247)
PHONE...............................951 735-8722
Thomas Corey, *CEO*
Dorothy Corey, *CFO*
EMP: 20
SQ FT: 13,000
SALES (est): 5.3MM **Privately Held**
WEB: www.smi4motion.com
SIC: 3562 5085 Ball & roller bearings; bearings

(P-15113)
TIMKEN COMPANY
4422 Corporate Center Dr, Los Alamitos (90720-2539)
PHONE...............................714 484-2400
Alma Cruz, *Info Tech Dir*
Doug Howland, *Controller*
Ed Esmaeili, *Buyer*
EMP: 277
SALES (corp-wide): 3B **Publicly Held**
SIC: 3562 Ball & roller bearings
PA: The Timken Company
4500 Mount Pleasant St Nw
North Canton OH 44720
234 262-3000

(P-15114)
U S BEARINGS
5001b Commerce Dr, Baldwin Park (91706-1424)
PHONE...............................626 358-0181
Michael Harnett, *President*
Denise Ceniceros, *General Mgr*
EMP: 20
SALES (est): 1.5MM
SALES (corp-wide): 674.9MM **Publicly Held**
SIC: 3562 Ball & roller bearings
HQ: Roller Bearing Company Of America, Inc.
102 Willenbrock Rd
Oxford CT 06478
203 267-7001

(P-15115)
UNITED STATES BALL CORPORATION
Also Called: Express Machining
15919 Phoebe Ave, La Mirada (90638-5628)
PHONE...............................714 521-6500
Tony Armas, *President*
Philip Armas, *Vice Pres*
EMP: 10
SALES (est): 2.6MM **Privately Held**
WEB: www.usball.com
SIC: 3562 Ball bearings & parts

(P-15116)
WEARTECH INTERNATIONAL INC (HQ)
1177 N Grove St, Anaheim (92806-2110)
PHONE...............................714 683-2430
George D Blankenship, *CEO*
Michael G Konieczny, *Treasurer*
Thomas Christie, *Vice Pres*
Enrique Sanchez, *Admin Sec*
▲ EMP: 40
SQ FT: 30,000

SALES (est): 12MM
SALES (corp-wide): 2.6B **Publicly Held**
WEB: www.weartech.net
SIC: 3562 3313 3548 3496 Ball bearings & parts; alloys, additive, except copper: not made in blast furnaces; welding apparatus; miscellaneous fabricated wire products; electrical or electronic engineering
PA: Lincoln Electric Holdings, Inc.
22801 Saint Clair Ave
Cleveland OH 44117
216 481-8100

3563 Air & Gas

(P-15117)
APOLLO SPRAYERS INTL INC
1040 Joshua Way, Vista (92081-7807)
PHONE...............................760 727-8300
John A Darroch, *President*
Bill Boxer, *Senior VP*
John B Darroch Sr, *Vice Pres*
▲ EMP: 11
SQ FT: 12,000
SALES (est): 2MM **Privately Held**
WEB: www.hvlp.com
SIC: 3563 5198 Spraying outfits: metals, paints & chemicals (compressor); paint brushes, rollers, sprayers

(P-15118)
ATLAS COPCO COMPRESSORS LLC
6094 Stewart Ave, Fremont (94538-3152)
PHONE...............................510 413-5200
Mark Kaebnick, *Mng Member*
Tim McNickle, *Mktg Dir*
Rawleigh Hedrick, *Sales Mgr*
Mark Kiser, *Sales Engr*
Kashmir Uppal, *Manager*
EMP: 17
SALES (corp-wide): 13.8B **Privately Held**
WEB: www.atlascopco.com
SIC: 3563 Air & gas compressors
HQ: Atlas Copco Compressors Llc
300 Technology
Rock Hill SC 29730
866 472-1015

(P-15119)
ATLAS COPCO COMPRESSORS LLC
48434 Milmont Dr, Fremont (94538-7326)
PHONE...............................510 413-5200
Howard Chantell, *Manager*
EMP: 19
SALES (corp-wide): 13.8B **Privately Held**
SIC: 3563 Air & gas compressors
HQ: Atlas Copco Compressors Llc
1059 Paragon Way
Rock Hill SC 29730
803 817-7000

(P-15120)
C M AUTOMOTIVE SYSTEMS INC (PA)
120 Commerce Way, Walnut (91789-2714)
PHONE...............................909 869-7912
Chander Mittal, *President*
Jorge Young, *Engineer*
Jack Ambegaokar, *Chief Engr*
Kamlesh Dave, *Production*
▲ EMP: 24
SQ FT: 20,370
SALES: 5.7MM **Privately Held**
WEB: www.cmautomotive.com
SIC: 3563 Air & gas compressors

(P-15121)
COMPRESSED AIR CONCEPTS
16207 Carmenita Rd, Cerritos (90703-2212)
PHONE...............................310 537-1350
Mark Hana, *Owner*
EMP: 25
SALES (est): 2MM **Privately Held**
SIC: 3563 Air & gas compressors

(P-15122)
COMPUVAC INDUSTRIES INC
18381 Mount Langley St, Fountain Valley (92708-6904)
PHONE...............................949 574-5085
David Donnelly, *President*

▲ = Import ▼=Export
◆ =Import/Export

Jean Yoo, *Office Mgr*
▲ EMP: 16
SQ FT: 13,000
SALES (est): 4.2MM **Privately Held**
WEB: www.compuvacind.com
SIC: 3563 Vacuum (air extraction) systems, industrial

(P-15123)
DRESSER-RAND COMPANY
18502 Dominguez Hill Dr, Rancho Dominguez (90220-6415)
PHONE..................................310 223-0600
Bob Lundeen, *Manager*
Kyle Nicklas, *Sales Executive*
EMP: 32
SALES (corp-wide): 97.7B **Privately Held**
WEB: www.dresser-rand.com
SIC: 3563 Air & gas compressors
HQ: Dresser-Rand Company
500 Paul Clark Dr
Olean NY 14760
716 375-3000

(P-15124)
DRESSER-RAND LLC
Also Called: Dresser-Rand Sales
5159 Commercial Cir Ste D, Concord (94520-8582)
PHONE..................................925 356-5700
Bob Lundeen, *Principal*
EMP: 31
SALES (corp-wide): 97.7B **Privately Held**
SIC: 3563 Air & gas compressors
HQ: Dresser-Rand Llc
1200 W Sam Houston Pkwy N
Houston TX 77043
713 354-6100

(P-15125)
EBARA TECHNOLOGIES INC (DH)
51 Main Ave, Sacramento (95838-2014)
PHONE..................................916 920-5451
Nasao Asami, *Ch of Bd*
Mitsuhiko Shirakashi, *President*
Tadashi Urata, *President*
Naoki Ando, *CEO*
Masumi Shionuma, *Corp Secy*
▲ EMP: 100
SQ FT: 160,000
SALES (est): 86.7MM
SALES (corp-wide): 3.4B **Privately Held**
WEB: www.ebaratech.com
SIC: 3563 Vacuum pumps, except laboratory

(P-15126)
FSI FIELD SPECIALTIES INC
2020 W 17th St, Long Beach (90813-1012)
PHONE..................................562 685-8300
Steve C James, *Branch Mgr*
EMP: 27 **Privately Held**
SIC: 3563 Vacuum (air extraction) systems, industrial
PA: Fsi Field Specialties, Inc.
7887 Fm 2004 Rd
Hitchcock TX 77563

(P-15127)
GS MANUFACTURING
985 W 18th St, Costa Mesa (92627-4541)
PHONE..................................949 642-1500
Gary L Smith, *CEO*
EMP: 10
SALES (est): 1.1MM **Privately Held**
SIC: 3563 Spraying & dusting equipment

(P-15128)
HUNTINGTON MECHANICAL LABS INC
Also Called: Huntington Mechanical Labs
13355 Nevada City Ave, Grass Valley (95945-9091)
PHONE..................................530 273-9533
Ronald Scott Hooper, *CEO*
Ron Hooper, *President*
Tamara Isaacson, *General Mgr*
EMP: 36
SQ FT: 45,000
SALES (est): 9.8MM **Privately Held**
WEB: www.huntvac.com
SIC: 3563 Vacuum pumps, except laboratory; vacuum (air extraction) systems, industrial

(P-15129)
KOBELCO COMPRESSORS AMER INC
301 N Smith Ave, Corona (92880-1742)
PHONE..................................951 739-3030
EMP: 75
SALES (corp-wide): 17.6B **Privately Held**
SIC: 3563 Air & gas compressors
HQ: Kobelco Compressors America, Inc.
1450 W Rincon St
Corona CA 92880
951 739-3030

(P-15130)
KOBELCO COMPRESSORS AMER INC (HQ)
1450 W Rincon St, Corona (92880-9205)
PHONE..................................951 739-3030
Makoto Motoyoshi, *President*
James Simpson, *Project Mgr*
Yu Tajima, *Project Engr*
Frank Tsui, *Engineer*
◆ EMP: 260
SALES (est): 99.7MM
SALES (corp-wide): 17.6B **Privately Held**
WEB: www.kobelcoedti.com
SIC: 3563 Air & gas compressors including vacuum pumps
PA: Kobe Steel, Ltd.
2-2-4, Wakinohamakaigandori, Chuo-Ku
Kobe HYO 651-0
782 615-111

(P-15131)
MAX SMT CORP
Also Called: Omxie
5675 Kimball Ct, Chino (91710-9121)
PHONE..................................877 589-9422
Shirlei Bi, *President*
Salvador Sandoval, *Electrical Engi*
Vee Smt, *Sales Mgr*
◆ EMP: 10
SQ FT: 12,000
SALES: 40K **Privately Held**
SIC: 3563 Air & gas compressors

(P-15132)
NU VENTURE DIVING CO
Also Called: Nuvair
1600 Beacon Pl, Oxnard (93033-2433)
PHONE..................................805 815-4044
Glenn A Huebner, *CEO*
Janet Huebner, *CFO*
◆ EMP: 28
SQ FT: 27,000
SALES (est): 4.5MM **Privately Held**
WEB: www.nuvair.com
SIC: 3563 Air & gas compressors

(P-15133)
PACIFIC TCHNICAL EQP ENGRG INC
Also Called: Pacific Tek
1298 N Blue Gum St, Anaheim (92806-2413)
PHONE..................................714 835-3088
Kirk Preston, *CEO*
Dan Skorcz, *President*
EMP: 10
SQ FT: 10,400
SALES (est): 2.6MM **Privately Held**
WEB: www.pacific-tek.com
SIC: 3563 Vacuum (air extraction) systems, industrial

(P-15134)
POOLE VENTURA INC
Also Called: P V I
321 Bernoulli Cir, Oxnard (93030-5164)
P.O. Box 5023 (93031-5023)
PHONE..................................805 981-1784
Henry Poole Jr, *President*
Nader Jamshidi, *Vice Pres*
Aaron Dingus, *Engineer*
Jamie Jamshidi, *Sales Mgr*
EMP: 12
SQ FT: 10,000
SALES (est): 2.7MM **Privately Held**
WEB: www.pvisystemtech.com
SIC: 3563 Vacuum (air extraction) systems, industrial

(P-15135)
PTB SALES INC (PA)
1361 Mountain View Cir, Azusa (91702-1649)
PHONE..................................626 334-0500
Patrick T Blackwell, *CEO*
John Varone, *President*
Brendan Riley, *Vice Pres*
Dean Scarborough, *Vice Pres*
Wesley Stupar, *General Mgr*
▲ EMP: 33
SQ FT: 16,000
SALES (est): 9.7MM **Privately Held**
WEB: www.ptbsales.com
SIC: 3563 3679 Vacuum (air extraction) systems, industrial; power supplies, all types: static

(P-15136)
RHINO LININGS CORPORATION (PA)
9747 Businesspark Ave, San Diego (92131-1661)
PHONE..................................858 450-0441
Pierre Gagnon, *President*
Bianca Williams, *Admin Asst*
Jenny Clifford, *Marketing Mgr*
Jeremy Searcy, *Regl Sales Mgr*
Jennifer Villalobos, *Marketing Staff*
◆ EMP: 65
SQ FT: 20,000
SALES (est): 42MM **Privately Held**
WEB: www.rhinolatino.com
SIC: 3563 3559 Air & gas compressors; automotive related machinery

(P-15137)
SPRAYLINE MANUFACTURING
10110 Greenleaf Ave, Santa Fe Springs (90670-3416)
PHONE..................................562 941-5313
Brady Wilson, *Owner*
EMP: 10 EST: 1997
SALES (est): 1.7MM **Privately Held**
WEB: www.sprayline.com
SIC: 3563 Spraying & dusting equipment

3564 Blowers & Fans

(P-15138)
ADVANTEC MFS INC
Also Called: Micro Filtration Systems
6723 Sierra Ct Ste A, Dublin (94568-2689)
PHONE..................................925 479-0625
Yoshioki Matsuo, *President*
Katsuhiro Shiotani, *Vice Pres*
Kazuo Matsumura, *Admin Sec*
Jill Teixeira, *Sales Mgr*
Debby Leglu, *Sales Staff*
▲ EMP: 13
SQ FT: 10,000
SALES (est): 3MM
SALES (corp-wide): 27.5MM **Privately Held**
SIC: 3564 Air purification equipment; filters, air: furnaces, air conditioning equipment, etc.
HQ: Toyo Roshi Kaisha, Ltd.
1-18-10, Otowa
Bunkyo-Ku TKY 112-0
359 810-571

(P-15139)
ADWEST TECHNOLOGIES INC (HQ)
4222 E La Palma Ave, Anaheim (92807-1816)
PHONE..................................714 632-8595
Brian Cannon, *Vice Pres*
Craig Bayer, *President*
Maryann Erickson, *Vice Pres*
Richard Whitford, *Vice Pres*
EMP: 35
SQ FT: 23,500
SALES (est): 7.2MM
SALES (corp-wide): 345MM **Publicly Held**
WEB: www.adwestusa.com
SIC: 3564 3585 3826 Air purification equipment; heating equipment, complete; thermal analysis instruments, laboratory type

PA: Ceco Environmental Corp.
14651 Dallas Pkwy
Dallas TX 75254
513 458-2600

(P-15140)
AIR BLAST INC
2050 Pepper St, Alhambra (91801-3162)
P.O. Box 367, San Gabriel (91778-0367)
PHONE..................................626 576-0144
Carl Von Wolffradt, *President*
Patty Von Wolffradt, *Corp Secy*
Judy Doland, *Opers Staff*
EMP: 11
SQ FT: 4,100
SALES (est): 2.3MM **Privately Held**
WEB: www.airblastinc.com
SIC: 3564 Turbo-blowers, industrial; blowing fans: industrial or commercial

(P-15141)
AIR FACTORS INC
4771 Arroyo Vis Ste D, Livermore (94551-4847)
PHONE..................................925 579-0040
Robert Browning, *President*
EMP: 12
SALES (est): 1.3MM **Privately Held**
WEB: www.airfactors.com
SIC: 3564 Blowers & fans

(P-15142)
AIRGARD INC (PA)
2190 Paragon Dr, San Jose (95131-1305)
PHONE..................................408 573-0701
Dan White, *President*
Dyana Chargin, *CFO*
Martin Johnson, *CFO*
Mark Johnsgard, *Officer*
Kevin McGinnis, *Vice Pres*
▲ EMP: 23
SQ FT: 13,000
SALES (est): 3.8MM **Privately Held**
WEB: www.airgard.com
SIC: 3564 Air purification equipment

(P-15143)
AMERICAN METAL FILTER COMPANY
611 Marsat Ct, Chula Vista (91911-4648)
PHONE..................................619 628-1917
Valentine C Deilgat, *President*
Michele Carter, *Technology*
Robert Duran, *Purchasing*
Brandon Deilgat, *Marketing Staff*
EMP: 17
SALES: 1.7MM **Privately Held**
WEB: www.amfco.com
SIC: 3564 Filters, air: furnaces, air conditioning equipment, etc.

(P-15144)
ATLAS COPCO MAFI-TRENCH CO LLC (DH)
3037 Industrial Pkwy, Santa Maria (93455-1807)
PHONE..................................805 352-0112
James T Reilly, *President*
Peter Wagner, *Ch of Bd*
Kevin Jordon, *Technology*
Jorgen Unemar, *Controller*
Brian Humbles, *Director*
◆ EMP: 208
SQ FT: 90,000
SALES (est): 81.1MM
SALES (corp-wide): 13.8B **Privately Held**
WEB: www.mafi-trench.com
SIC: 3564 3533 8744 Turbo-blowers, industrial; oil & gas field machinery; facilities support services

(P-15145)
CALIFORNIA TURBO INC
10721 Business Dr, Fontana (92337-8252)
PHONE..................................909 854-2800
Arthur May, *President*
Ram Iyer, *General Mgr*
Johnathan Alter, *Controller*
Dorothy Carr, *Controller*
Cameron Young, *Sales Staff*
▲ EMP: 10
SQ FT: 18,000
SALES (est): 2.3MM **Privately Held**
WEB: www.californiaturbo.com
SIC: 3564 Ventilating fans: industrial or commercial

(P-15146)
CAMFIL USA INC
3625 Del Amo Blvd Ste 260, Torrance
(90503-1688)
PHONE....................310 370-3673
EMP: 57
SALES (corp-wide): 864.2MM **Privately Held**
SIC: 3564 3569 Purification & dust collection equipment; air purification equipment; dust or fume collecting equipment, industrial; filters; filters, general line: industrial
HQ: Camfil Usa, Inc.
    1 N Corporate Dr
    Riverdale NJ 07457
    973 616-7300

(P-15147)
CAMFIL USA INC
500 Industrial Ave, Corcoran (93212-9629)
PHONE....................559 992-5118
Fausto Chavez, *Branch Mgr*
EMP: 64
SALES (corp-wide): 864.2MM **Privately Held**
SIC: 3564 Dust or fume collecting equipment, industrial
HQ: Camfil Usa, Inc.
    1 N Corporate Dr
    Riverdale NJ 07457
    973 616-7300

(P-15148)
CENTRAL BLOWER CO
211 S 7th Ave, City of Industry (91746-3288)
PHONE....................626 330-3182
David Roger Petersen, *President*
Mary Petersen, *Shareholder*
Eleanor Petersen, *Vice Pres*
EMP: 20
SQ FT: 24,000
SALES (est): 5.3MM **Privately Held**
WEB: www.centralblower.com
SIC: 3564 Exhaust fans: industrial or commercial; blowing fans: industrial or commercial

(P-15149)
CLARCOR AIR FILTRATION PDTS
1295 E Ontario Ave # 102, Corona (92881-6653)
PHONE....................951 272-1850
Larry Johnson, *Branch Mgr*
Doug Hamilton, *Vice Pres*
EMP: 66
SALES (corp-wide): 14.3B **Publicly Held**
WEB: www.airguard.com
SIC: 3564 Air cleaning systems
HQ: Clarcor Air Filtration Products, Inc
    100 River Ridge Cir
    Jeffersonville IN 47130
    502 969-2304

(P-15150)
CLOUDBURST INC
707 E Hueneme Rd, Oxnard (93033-8654)
PHONE....................805 986-4125
Michael Davis, *CEO*
▲ EMP: 30
SQ FT: 7,000
SALES (est): 6.6MM **Privately Held**
WEB: www.cloudburst.com
SIC: 3564 3585 Blowing fans: industrial or commercial; refrigeration & heating equipment

(P-15151)
DUST COLLECTOR SERVICES INC
1280 N Sunshine Way, Anaheim (92806-1746)
PHONE....................714 237-1690
Timothy Schlentz, *President*
Gregory Schlentz, *Vice Pres*
Jannie Schlentz, *Vice Pres*
Jeff Schlentz, *Vice Pres*
Greg Schlentz, *Sales Staff*
EMP: 20
SQ FT: 10,000
SALES (est): 6MM **Privately Held**
WEB: www.dustcollectorservices.com
SIC: 3564 Purification & dust collection equipment

(P-15152)
ECW TECHNOLOGY INC
609 Deep Valley Dr, Rllng HLS Est (90274-3629)
PHONE....................310 373-0082
REA-Tiing Liu, *President*
Wen Bow, *CFO*
EMP: 15
SQ FT: 3,000
SALES (est): 1.8MM **Privately Held**
WEB: www.ecwtechnology.com
SIC: 3564 5169 Air purification equipment; chemicals, industrial & heavy

(P-15153)
ENVION LLC
14724 Ventura Blvd Fl 200, Sherman Oaks (91403-3514)
PHONE....................818 217-2500
Craig Shandler,
▲ EMP: 100
SQ FT: 36,000
SALES (est): 17.8MM
SALES (corp-wide): 20MM **Privately Held**
WEB: www.ionicpro.com
SIC: 3564 Air purification equipment
PA: Sylmark Inc.
    7821 Orion Ave Ste 200
    Van Nuys CA 91406
    818 217-2000

(P-15154)
ENVIROCARE INTERNATIONAL INC
507 Green Island Rd, American Canyon (94503-9649)
PHONE....................707 638-6800
John Tate III, *President*
Russell Helfond, *COO*
Lisa Helfond, *Vice Pres*
Brian Higgins, *CTO*
David Ciabattari, *Project Engr*
EMP: 22
SQ FT: 10,000
SALES (est): 6.1MM **Privately Held**
SIC: 3564 Air cleaning systems; air purification equipment; dust or fume collecting equipment, industrial; precipitators, electrostatic

(P-15155)
EURAMCO SAFETY INC
Also Called: Ram Centrifical Products
2746 Via Orange Way, Spring Valley (91978-1744)
PHONE....................619 670-9590
Wayne Allen, *President*
Zachary Allen, *General Mgr*
Gary Clemons, *General Mgr*
Dirk Davidson, *Controller*
Gary- Thompson, *Buyer*
▲ EMP: 16
SQ FT: 15,000
SALES (est): 5.6MM **Privately Held**
WEB: www.euramcosafety.com
SIC: 3564 3429 Blowers & fans; marine hardware

(P-15156)
EXODUST COLLECTORS LLC
7045 Jackson St, Paramount (90723-4834)
PHONE....................562 808-0842
Daniel Meyers,
EMP: 10
SALES (est): 446.2K **Privately Held**
SIC: 3564 Purification & dust collection equipment

(P-15157)
FILTRATION GROUP LLC
498 Aviation Blvd, Santa Rosa (95403-1069)
PHONE....................707 525-8633
Dean Kerstetter, *Director*
Ernesto Muedano, *Engineer*
David Burmahl, *Maintence Staff*
Alison Huber, *Manager*
EMP: 80
SALES (corp-wide): 320.9MM **Privately Held**
WEB: www.filtrationgroup.com
SIC: 3564 Filters, air: furnaces, air conditioning equipment, etc.

PA: Filtration Group Llc
    912 E Washington St Ste 1
    Joliet IL 60433
    815 726-4600

(P-15158)
GREENHECK FAN CORPORATION
170 Cyber Ct, Rocklin (95765-1205)
PHONE....................916 626-3400
Mike Venturi, *Manager*
Amanda Irwin, *Accountant*
Andy Keil, *Maint Spvr*
Bill Cowen, *Manager*
EMP: 120
SALES (corp-wide): 1.3B **Privately Held**
WEB: www.greenheck.com
SIC: 3564 Blowers & fans
PA: Greenheck Fan Corporation
    1100 Greenheck Dr
    Schofield WI 54476
    715 359-6171

(P-15159)
HOCKIN DIVERSFD HOLDINGS INC
Also Called: Sonic Dry Clean
1672 Main St Ste E362, Ramona (92065-5257)
PHONE....................760 787-0510
John Hockins, *President*
▼ EMP: 10
SALES (est): 2MM **Privately Held**
SIC: 3564 Air cleaning systems

(P-15160)
INFICOLD INC
14654 Placida Ct, Saratoga (95070-5740)
PHONE....................408 464-8007
Himanshu Pokharna, *CEO*
EMP: 10
SALES (est): 653.3K **Privately Held**
SIC: 3564 3585 Filters, air: furnaces, air conditioning equipment, etc.; compressors for refrigeration & air conditioning equipment

(P-15161)
INTERTEX INC
Also Called: B-Air Blowers
550 S Ayon Ave, Azusa (91702-5121)
PHONE....................626 385-3300
Edward Demirdjian, *President*
Allan Guia, *Controller*
Chris Carducci, *Sales Staff*
Lynne Allen, *Manager*
◆ EMP: 25
SALES (est): 30MM **Privately Held**
WEB: www.b-air.com
SIC: 3564 Blowers & fans

(P-15162)
IQAIR NORTH AMERICA INC
14351 Firestone Blvd, La Mirada (90638-5527)
PHONE....................877 715-4247
Glory Z Dolphin, *CEO*
Frank Hammes, *President*
▲ EMP: 48
SQ FT: 40,000
SALES (est): 13.9MM **Privately Held**
WEB: www.iqair.com
SIC: 3564 8742 5999 Air cleaning systems; air purification equipment; materials mgmt. (purchasing, handling, inventory) consultant; air purification equipment
PA: Icleen Entwicklungs- Und Vertriebsanstalt Fur Umweltprodukte
    C/O Jgt Treuunternehmen Reg.
    Vaduz

(P-15163)
JETAIR TECHNOLOGIES LLC
1756 Eastman Ave Ste 100, Ventura (93003-5756)
PHONE....................805 654-7000
William Anderson, *Mng Member*
Kevin Beyer, *Mng Member*
Dan Snyder, *Mng Member*
▲ EMP: 19
SQ FT: 6,000
SALES (est): 5.6MM **Privately Held**
WEB: www.jetairtech.com
SIC: 3564 Turbo-blowers, industrial

(P-15164)
KIRK A SCHLIGER
Also Called: Bear Label Machines
11240 Pyrites Way, Gold River (95670-4481)
PHONE....................916 638-8433
Fax: 916 638-8209
EMP: 10
SALES (est): 1.4MM **Privately Held**
WEB: www.bearlabelmachine.com
SIC: 3564

(P-15165)
M D H BURNER & BOILER CO INC
12106 Center St, South Gate (90280-8046)
PHONE....................562 630-2875
Mauro Donate, *CEO*
EMP: 18
SQ FT: 5,000
SALES (est): 5.8MM **Privately Held**
SIC: 3564 7699 3443 3433 Air purification equipment; boiler repair shop; fabricated plate work (boiler shop); heating equipment, except electric

(P-15166)
MACROAIR TECHNOLOGIES INC (PA)
Also Called: Macro Air Technologies
794 S Allen St, San Bernardino (92408-2210)
PHONE....................909 890-2270
Edward Boyd, *CEO*
◆ EMP: 45
SQ FT: 15,000
SALES (est): 16.7MM **Privately Held**
SIC: 3564 Ventilating fans: industrial or commercial

(P-15167)
MARS AIR SYSTEMS LLC
14716 S Broadway, Gardena (90248-1814)
PHONE....................310 532-1555
EMP: 75 EST: 2009
SALES (est): 7.2MM **Privately Held**
SIC: 3564

(P-15168)
MEGGITT AIRDYNAMICS INC (DH)
2616 Research Dr, Corona (92882-6978)
PHONE....................951 734-0070
Lloyd Oshiro, *President*
David Cadman, *Engineer*
EMP: 31
SQ FT: 90,000
SALES (est): 10.8MM
SALES (corp-wide): 2.6B **Privately Held**
SIC: 3564 3563 Ventilating fans: industrial or commercial; air & gas compressors

(P-15169)
OPTIMIZATION CORPORATION
Also Called: McIntyre Industries
14680 Wicks Blvd, San Leandro (94577-6716)
PHONE....................510 614-5890
John-Paul Farsight, *CEO*
EMP: 13
SQ FT: 30,000
SALES (est): 2MM **Privately Held**
WEB: www.mcintyresg.com
SIC: 3564 Air purification equipment

(P-15170)
POLLUTION CONTROL SPECIALISTS
1354 Ritchey St, Santa Ana (92705-4727)
PHONE....................949 474-0137
Steve Fleischman, *President*
EMP: 22
SALES (est): 4.2MM **Privately Held**
SIC: 3564 Air cleaning systems

(P-15171)
PUROLATOR PDTS A FILTRATION CO
Also Called: Air Filter Sales
20671 Corsair Blvd, Hayward (94545-1007)
PHONE....................510 785-4800
Dave Lowinski, *Manager*
Valerie Ochoa, *Admin Asst*

EMP: 10
SALES (corp-wide): 14.3B **Publicly Held**
WEB: www.afss.net
SIC: 3564 Filters, air: furnaces, air conditioning equipment, etc.
HQ: Purolator Products Air Filtration Company
100 River Ridge Cir
Jeffersonville IN 47130
866 925-2247

(P-15172)
QC MANUFACTURING INC
43352 Business Park Dr, Temecula (92590-3665)
PHONE.....................951 325-6340
Dane Stevenson, *President*
Ted Greenman, *Executive*
Chris Bell, *Marketing Mgr*
Greg Breslen, *Sales Staff*
Andy McIntosh, *Director*
▲ **EMP:** 65
SQ FT: 43,000
SALES (est): 12.5MM **Privately Held**
SIC: 3564 Blowers & fans

(P-15173)
RAM CENTRIFUGAL PRODUCTS INC
2746 Via Orange Way, Spring Valley (91978-1744)
PHONE.....................619 670-9590
Wayne Allen, *President*
Gary Clemons, *Manager*
EMP: 10 **EST:** 1970
SALES: 3MM **Privately Held**
SIC: 3564 3429 Blowers & fans; marine hardware

(P-15174)
ROTRON INCORPORATED
Ametek Rotron
474 Raleigh Ave, El Cajon (92020-3138)
PHONE.....................619 593-7400
Fred Taylor, *Manager*
Scott McClure, *Materials Mgr*
EMP: 12
SALES (corp-wide): 4.3B **Publicly Held**
WEB: www.rotronmilaero.com
SIC: 3564 Blowers & fans
HQ: Rotron Incorporated
55 Hasbrouck Ln
Woodstock NY 12498
845 679-2401

(P-15175)
SONIC AIR SYSTEMS INC
1050 Beacon St, Brea (92821-2938)
PHONE.....................714 255-0124
Dan Vanderpyl, *CEO*
Terry Riley, *Vice Pres*
▲ **EMP:** 40
SQ FT: 50,000
SALES (est): 11.6MM **Privately Held**
WEB: www.sonicairsystems.com
SIC: 3564 Blowers & fans

(P-15176)
STANDARD FILTER CORPORATION (PA)
5928 Balfour Ct, Carlsbad (92008-7304)
PHONE.....................323 663-2184
Tobey Wiik, *President*
▼ **EMP:** 40
SQ FT: 30,000
SALES (est): 5.5MM **Privately Held**
WEB: www.standardfilter.com
SIC: 3564 5199 Filters, air: furnaces, air conditioning equipment, etc.; felt

(P-15177)
STERIL-AIRE INC
2840 N Lima St, Burbank (91504-2506)
PHONE.....................818 565-1128
Robert Scheir, *President*
Jose Barba, *Purchasing*
Dawn Kanno, *Regl Sales Mgr*
Randy Hansen, *Manager*
Robert O'Farrell, *Manager*
▲ **EMP:** 22
SQ FT: 15,000
SALES (est): 6.1MM **Privately Held**
WEB: www.steril-aire-usa.com
SIC: 3564 Filters, air: furnaces, air conditioning equipment, etc.

(P-15178)
SUNON INC (PA)
Also Called: Eme Fan & Motor
1075 W Lambert Rd Ste A, Brea (92821-2944)
PHONE.....................714 255-0208
Yin Su Hong, *CEO*
Jeannie Chen, *Accounting Mgr*
Christie Chin, *Marketing Mgr*
Ryan Chou, *Marketing Mgr*
Jared Lim, *Manager*
▲ **EMP:** 32 **EST:** 1998
SQ FT: 22,000
SALES (est): 4.8MM **Privately Held**
WEB: www.sunonusa.com
SIC: 3564 Blowers & fans

(P-15179)
SUPERIOR FILTRATION PDTS LLC
3401 Etiwanda Ave 811b, Mira Loma (91752-1132)
PHONE.....................951 681-1700
Julie Haight, *Manager*
EMP: 13
SALES (corp-wide): 18.4MM **Privately Held**
SIC: 3564 Blowers & fans
PA: Superior Filtration Products, Llc
160 N 400 W
North Salt Lake UT 84054
801 621-5200

(P-15180)
TEMPEST TECHNOLOGY CORPORATION
4708 N Blythe Ave, Fresno (93722-3930)
PHONE.....................559 277-7577
Leroy B Coffman III, *President*
Danette Dunn, *Officer*
Bruce Mahlmann, *Buyer*
Curt Johnson, *Sales Mgr*
▲ **EMP:** 25
SQ FT: 22,000
SALES (est): 6.7MM **Privately Held**
SIC: 3564 Ventilating fans: industrial or commercial

(P-15181)
TERRA UNIVERSAL INC
800 S Raymond Ave, Fullerton (92831-5234)
PHONE.....................714 526-0100
G H Sadaghiani, *CEO*
Ken Harms, *COO*
Lee Tran, *Software Dev*
Perry Chiang, *IT/INT Sup*
Leo Nguyen, *Design Engr*
▲ **EMP:** 195
SQ FT: 88,000
SALES (est): 73.6MM **Privately Held**
WEB: www.desiccator.com
SIC: 3564 3567 3569 3572 Purification & dust collection equipment; air purification equipment; filters, air: furnaces, air conditioning equipment, etc.; ventilating fans: industrial or commercial; heating units & devices, industrial: electric; filters; computer storage devices; refrigeration equipment, complete; clean room supplies

(P-15182)
TRI-DIM FILTER CORPORATION
15271 Fairfield Ranch Rd # 150, Chino Hills (91709-8865)
PHONE.....................626 826-5893
Scott Breckenridge, *Manager*
EMP: 30
SALES (corp-wide): 137.3MM **Privately Held**
WEB: www.tridim.com
SIC: 3564 Filters, air: furnaces, air conditioning equipment, etc.
PA: Tri-Dim Filter Corporation
93 Industrial Dr
Louisa VA 23093
540 967-2600

(P-15183)
US TOYO FAN CORPORATION (HQ)
16025 Arrow Hwy Ste F, Irwindale (91706-2063)
PHONE.....................626 338-1111
William Jacobs, *President*

Arnold Weisman, *Corp Secy*
Robert Rosenthal, *Vice Pres*
▲ **EMP:** 18
SQ FT: 10,000
SALES (est): 7.6MM
SALES (corp-wide): 66.3MM **Privately Held**
WEB: www.ustoyofan.com
SIC: 3564 Blowers & fans
PA: Desco Industries, Inc.
3651 Walnut Ave
Chino CA 91710
909 627-8178

(P-15184)
VENTUREDYNE LTD
Climet Instruments Company
1320 W Colton Ave, Redlands (92374-2864)
P.O. Box 1760 (92373-0543)
PHONE.....................909 793-2788
Ray Felbinger, *Manager*
Jim Strachan, *General Mgr*
Manuel Patino, *Technology*
David L Chandler, *Engineer*
Randy Grater, *Mfg Staff*
EMP: 65
SALES (corp-wide): 148.6MM **Privately Held**
SIC: 3564 3829 3825 3823 Blowing fans: industrial or commercial; measuring & controlling devices; instruments to measure electricity; industrial instrmnts msrmnt display/control process variable; relays & industrial controls
PA: Venturedyne, Ltd.
600 College Ave
Pewaukee WI 53072
262 691-9900

(P-15185)
VORTECH ENGINEERING INC
1650 Pacific Ave, Oxnard (93033-2746)
PHONE.....................805 247-0226
Jim Middlebrook, *CEO*
Randolf Riley, *President*
▲ **EMP:** 42
SALES (est): 12MM **Privately Held**
WEB: www.vortechsuperchargers.com
SIC: 3564 Blowing fans: industrial or commercial

(P-15186)
WEMS INC (PA)
Also Called: Wems Electronics
4650 W Rosecrans Ave, Hawthorne (90250-6898)
P.O. Box 528 (90251-0528)
PHONE.....................310 644-0251
Ronald Hood, *CEO*
Carroll Whitney, *President*
Mel Hughes, *Vice Pres*
Charles Wilson, *Admin Sec*
Nancy Howe, *IT/INT Sup*
EMP: 84
SQ FT: 78,000
SALES (est): 17.6MM **Privately Held**
WEB: www.wems.com
SIC: 3564 3612 6513 Blowers & fans; transformers, except electric; apartment building operators

(P-15187)
WHIPPLE INDUSTRIES INC
3292 N Weber Ave, Fresno (93722-4942)
PHONE.....................559 442-1261
Arthur Whipple, *CEO*
Sherry Anderson, *Admin Sec*
▲ **EMP:** 15
SQ FT: 5,258
SALES (est): 4.6MM **Privately Held**
WEB: www.whipplesuperchargers.com
SIC: 3564 3732 3724 3714 Turbo-blowers, industrial; boat building & repairing; aircraft engines & engine parts; motor vehicle parts & accessories

(P-15188)
XCELAERO CORPORATION
4540 Broad St Ste 120, San Luis Obispo (93401-8729)
PHONE.....................805 547-2660
Dennis Pfister, *President*
Molly Attala, *CFO*
Pat Lawless, *Vice Pres*
Chellatta Balan, *CTO*

EMP: 16
SQ FT: 7,500
SALES (est): 3.1MM **Privately Held**
SIC: 3564 Ventilating fans: industrial or commercial

3565 Packaging Machinery

(P-15189)
7 U P RC BOTTLING COMPANY
Also Called: 7-Up
1300 W Taft Ave, Orange (92865-4127)
PHONE.....................714 974-8560
Chuck Shanely, *President*
EMP: 60
SALES (est): 8MM **Privately Held**
SIC: 3565 2086 Bottling machinery: filling, capping, labeling; bottled & canned soft drinks

(P-15190)
ACCRAPLY INC
10860 6th St, Rancho Cucamonga (91730-5902)
PHONE.....................909 605-8200
Peter Nicholson, *Branch Mgr*
EMP: 30
SALES (corp-wide): 2.4B **Privately Held**
SIC: 3565 Packaging machinery
HQ: Accraply, Inc.
9350 W Broadway Ave # 190
Minneapolis MN 55445
763 557-1313

(P-15191)
ACCU-SEAL SENCORPWHITE INC
225 Bingham Dr Ste B, San Marcos (92069-1418)
PHONE.....................760 591-9800
Lesly Jensen, *President*
EMP: 19
SQ FT: 14,000
SALES (est): 7.6MM
SALES (corp-wide): 500MM **Privately Held**
WEB: www.accu-seal.com
SIC: 3565 Packaging machinery
HQ: Sencorpwhite, Inc.
400 Kidds Hill Rd
Hyannis MA 02601
508 771-9400

(P-15192)
ACCUTEK PACKAGING EQUIPMENT CO (PA)
Also Called: Kiss Packaging Systems
2685 S Melrose Dr, Vista (92081-8783)
PHONE.....................760 734-4177
Edward Chocholek, *Principal*
Darren Chocholek, *Vice Pres*
Drake Chocholek, *Vice Pres*
Drew Chocholek, *Vice Pres*
Daniel Kinnaman, *Technical Staff*
◆ **EMP:** 49
SQ FT: 103,000
SALES (est): 15.5MM **Privately Held**
WEB: www.accutekpackaging.com
SIC: 3565 Packaging machinery

(P-15193)
ADCO MANUFACTURING
2170 Academy Ave, Sanger (93657-3795)
PHONE.....................559 875-5563
Kate King, *President*
Glen Long, *COO*
Frank Hoffman, *Vice Pres*
◆ **EMP:** 150
SQ FT: 75,000
SALES (est): 57.8MM **Privately Held**
WEB: www.adcomfg.com
SIC: 3565 Carton packing machines

(P-15194)
AMERA MACHINE INC
Also Called: Biner Ellison Packg Systems
271 California Ter, Pasadena (91105-1514)
PHONE.....................626 577-2819
Thomas E Ellison, *President*
EMP: 14
SQ FT: 40,000
SALES (est): 1.7MM **Privately Held**
WEB: www.binerellison.com
SIC: 3565 Packaging machinery

(P-15195)
AVP TECHNOLOGY LLC
4140 Business Center Dr, Fremont
(94538-6354)
PHONE..................................510 683-0157
Hugh Chau, *CEO*
Thuc Tran, *Engineer*
Lynn Chau,
▲ EMP: 45
SQ FT: 4,000
SALES (est): 4.9MM **Privately Held**
WEB: www.avptechnology.com
SIC: 3565 Vacuum packaging machinery

(P-15196)
B & H MANUFACTURING CO INC (PA)
Also Called: B & H Labeling Systems
3461 Roeding Rd, Ceres (95307-9442)
P.O. Box 247 (95307-0247)
PHONE..................................209 537-5785
Roman M Eckols, *CEO*
Calvin E Bright, *Ch of Bd*
Lyn E Bright, *President*
Marjorie Bright, *Corp Secy*
Bob Adamson, *Vice Pres*
◆ EMP: 117
SQ FT: 65,000
SALES (est): 25.2MM **Privately Held**
WEB: www.bhlabeling.com
SIC: 3565 Labeling machines, industrial

(P-15197)
BELCO PACKAGING SYSTEMS INC
910 S Mountain Ave, Monrovia
(91016-3641)
PHONE..................................626 357-9566
Helen V Misik, *CEO*
A Michael Misik, *President*
▲ EMP: 25 EST: 1959
SQ FT: 35,000
SALES (est): 9.1MM **Privately Held**
WEB: www.belcomedical.com
SIC: 3565 Packing & wrapping machinery

(P-15198)
BEST LABEL COMPANY INC
Also Called: Imperial System
2900 Faber St, Union City (94587-1214)
PHONE..................................510 489-5400
John Kramer, *Branch Mgr*
Tim Koontz, *Marketing Staff*
EMP: 35
SALES (corp-wide): 21.2MM **Privately Held**
WEB: www.bestlabel.com
SIC: 3565 2679 3953 2672 Labeling machines, industrial; labels, paper: made from purchased material; marking devices; coated & laminated paper
PA: Best Label Company, Inc.
13260 Moore St
Cerritos CA 90703
562 926-1452

(P-15199)
BLICK INDUSTRIES LLC
2245 Laguna Canyon Rd, Laguna Beach
(92651-1141)
PHONE..................................949 499-5026
Beverly Wesley, *Mng Member*
Joshua Greenspoon, *Office Admin*
Klint Olsen, *Sales Mgr*
Dan Wacholder,
▼ EMP: 10
SQ FT: 750
SALES (est): 2.4MM **Privately Held**
SIC: 3565 Vacuum packaging machinery

(P-15200)
BOYD & BOYD INDUSTRIES (PA)
3500 Chester Ave, Bakersfield
(93301-1630)
PHONE..................................661 631-8400
Jerry Boyd, *Owner*
◆ EMP: 17
SQ FT: 30,000
SALES (est): 1MM **Privately Held**
SIC: 3565 5084 3535 Packaging machinery; packaging machinery & equipment; unit handling conveying systems

(P-15201)
CAN LINES ENGINEERING INC (PA)
Also Called: C L E
9839 Downey Norwalk Rd, Downey
(90241-5596)
P.O. Box 7039 (90241-7039)
PHONE..................................562 861-2996
Donald Koplien, *CEO*
Keenan Koplien, *President*
Erik Koplien, *Vice Pres*
Frank Snyder, *Vice Pres*
Darwin Smock, *Research*
EMP: 100 EST: 1960
SQ FT: 40,000
SALES (est): 19.2MM **Privately Held**
SIC: 3565 3556 Canning machinery, food; bottling machinery: filling, capping, labeling; food products machinery

(P-15202)
COLIMATIC USA INC
9272 Jeronimo Rd Ste 115, Irvine
(92618-1914)
PHONE..................................949 600-6440
Franceso Libretti, *President*
▲ EMP: 11
SALES (est): 1.7MM **Privately Held**
SIC: 3565 Packaging machinery

(P-15203)
CORASIA CORP
363 Fairview Way, Milpitas (95035-3024)
PHONE..................................408 321-8508
Chen Chin Hsien, *President*
▲ EMP: 10
SALES (est): 1.4MM **Privately Held**
SIC: 3565 Packaging machinery

(P-15204)
CVC TECHNOLOGIES INC
10861 Business Dr, Fontana (92337-8235)
PHONE..................................909 355-0311
Sheng Hui Yang, *CEO*
K Joe Yang, *President*
Peter Yang, *General Mgr*
▲ EMP: 21
SQ FT: 29,000
SALES (est): 6.5MM
SALES (corp-wide): 33.6MM **Privately Held**
WEB: www.cvcusa.com
SIC: 3565 Labeling machines, industrial
PA: Cvc Technologies Inc.
190, Gongye 9th Rd.,
Taichung City 41280
437 056-666

(P-15205)
ELLISON BINER
2685 S Melrose Dr, Vista (92081-8783)
PHONE..................................760 598-6500
Edward Chocholek, *President*
Drake Chochok, *Info Tech Dir*
EMP: 55
SALES (est): 6.4MM **Privately Held**
SIC: 3565 Packaging machinery

(P-15206)
FOOD MACHINERY SALES INC
Also Called: Serpa Packaging Solutions
7020 W Sunnyview Ave, Visalia
(93291-9639)
PHONE..................................559 651-2339
Fernando M Serpa, *President*
Joseph Scalia, *CFO*
Manuela Parreira, *Admin Sec*
Jessica Utsler, *Project Mgr*
Christopher Livingston, *Technology*
◆ EMP: 100
SQ FT: 62,000
SALES (est): 20.6MM **Privately Held**
WEB: www.fmsmfg.com
SIC: 3565 Carton packing machines

(P-15207)
GOLDEN W PPR CONVERTING CORP (PA)
Also Called: G W
16500 Worthley Dr, San Lorenzo
(94580-1812)
PHONE..................................510 317-0646
Shirley Hooi, *President*
David Hooi, *Vice Pres*
Henry Hooi, *Principal*

Michelle Walker, *Manager*
▼ EMP: 33
SQ FT: 42,000
SALES (est): 24.3MM **Privately Held**
WEB: www.goldenwestpaper.com
SIC: 3565 2657 Carton packing machines; folding paperboard boxes

(P-15208)
HANNAN PRODUCTS CORP (PA)
220 N Smith Ave, Corona (92880-1740)
PHONE..................................951 735-1587
Henry H Jenkins, *President*
Nancy P Jenkins, *Shareholder*
Alfred Ramos, *CFO*
Lawrence Jenkins, *Vice Pres*
Elena Nicklaus, *Office Mgr*
EMP: 16
SQ FT: 36,000
SALES (est): 3.4MM **Privately Held**
SIC: 3565 3053 3554 3549 Packaging machinery; packing materials; paper industries machinery; cutting & slitting machinery

(P-15209)
HASCO FABRICATION INC
13370 Monte Vista Ave, Chino
(91710-5147)
P.O. Box 519 (91708-0519)
PHONE..................................909 627-0326
Fred R Haskin, *President*
Thomas R Haskin, *Corp Secy*
Steven F Haskin, *Vice Pres*
EMP: 10
SQ FT: 12,000
SALES (est): 2MM **Privately Held**
SIC: 3565 3535 Canning machinery, food; belt conveyor systems, general industrial use

(P-15210)
HAUG MANUFACTURING CORPORATION
Also Called: Haug Quality Equipment
18443 Technology Dr, Morgan Hill
(95037-2822)
PHONE..................................408 842-1285
Brian Haug, *President*
Gale Kraft, *CFO*
Gale Craft, *Admin Sec*
Jason Haug, *Manager*
▲ EMP: 10
SQ FT: 5,800
SALES (est): 2.2MM **Privately Held**
WEB: www.haugquality.com
SIC: 3565 Packaging machinery

(P-15211)
HIS INDUSTRIES INC
Also Called: Phoenix Engineering
1202 W Shelley Ct, Orange (92868-1239)
PHONE..................................562 407-0512
Lynn Worthington, *President*
▲ EMP: 20
SQ FT: 6,000
SALES (est): 1.6MM **Privately Held**
SIC: 3565 Packaging machinery

(P-15212)
JACKSAM CORPORATION
Also Called: Jacksam Corp Blackout
30191 Avenida De Las, Rancho Santa Margari (92688)
PHONE..................................800 605-3580
Danny Davis, *Chairman*
Mark Adam, *President*
Mike Tequilla, *CFO*
Heather Wilson, *Admin Sec*
EMP: 25 EST: 2013
SQ FT: 4,000
SALES: 10MM **Privately Held**
SIC: 3565 Bottling machinery: filling, capping, labeling

(P-15213)
KETAN AUTOMATED EQUIPMENT INC
1451 S Cucamonga Ave, Ontario
(91761-4510)
PHONE..................................909 930-0780
Kenneth A Schultz, *CEO*
Ian Carver, *Vice Pres*
EMP: 10
SQ FT: 15,000

SALES (est): 3.5MM **Privately Held**
SIC: 3565 Packaging machinery

(P-15214)
KLIPPENSTEIN CORPORATION
5399 S Villa Ave, Fresno (93725-8903)
PHONE..................................559 834-4258
Kenneth Ray Klippenstein, *CEO*
Wendy Klippenstein, *Corp Secy*
Richard Klippenstein, *Vice Pres*
Francisco Iniguez, *Project Engr*
Conrad Reimer, *Engineer*
▲ EMP: 25 EST: 1979
SQ FT: 13,000
SALES (est): 4.2MM **Privately Held**
WEB: www.klippenstein.com
SIC: 3565 Packaging machinery

(P-15215)
KODIAK CARTONERS INC
2550 S East Ave Ste 101, Fresno
(93706-5121)
PHONE..................................559 266-4844
EMP: 50
SALES: 8.1MM **Privately Held**
SIC: 3565

(P-15216)
M & O PERRY INDUSTRIES INC
412 N Smith Ave, Corona (92880-6903)
PHONE..................................951 734-9838
Phillip Osterhaus, *CEO*
Robbin Driscoll, *Admin Asst*
Betty Hampton, *Purchasing*
Detlef Teubert, *Marketing Staff*
Paul Hradecky, *Manager*
▲ EMP: 40
SQ FT: 20,000
SALES (est): 10.4MM **Privately Held**
WEB: www.moperry.com
SIC: 3565 8711 7629 5084 Packaging machinery; engineering services; electrical repair shops; conveyor systems

(P-15217)
MAF INDUSTRIES INC (HQ)
36470 Highway 99, Traver (93673)
P.O. Box 218 (93673-0218)
PHONE..................................559 897-2905
Thomas Blanc, *President*
Philippe Blanc, *Vice Pres*
Raul Mejia, *Admin Sec*
Victor Macedo, *Technology*
Kevin Leong, *Electrical Engi*
◆ EMP: 80
SQ FT: 30,000
SALES (est): 23.1MM **Privately Held**
WEB: www.mafindustries.com
SIC: 3565 5084 Packing & wrapping machinery; food industry machinery

(P-15218)
MFG PACKAGING PRODUCTS
3200 Enterprise St, Brea (92821-6238)
PHONE..................................714 984-2300
Fax: 714 984-2350
EMP: 10
SALES (est): 1MM **Privately Held**
SIC: 3565

(P-15219)
NAFM LLC (PA)
Also Called: Nafm Engineering Service
1521 Pomona Rd Ste A, Corona
(92880-6925)
PHONE..................................951 738-1114
John Yamosaki, *Mng Member*
Jacek K Zdzienicki, *Vice Pres*
Kay Yamasaki,
▲ EMP: 10
SQ FT: 25,000
SALES (est): 1.5MM **Privately Held**
SIC: 3565 Packaging machinery

(P-15220)
P R P MULTISOURCE INC
3836 Wacker Dr, Mira Loma (91752-1147)
PHONE..................................951 681-6100
Phil Woss, *President*
Kurt Fisch, *Treasurer*
▲ EMP: 20
SQ FT: 25,000
SALES (est): 4.9MM **Privately Held**
SIC: 3565 5084 Vacuum packaging machinery; packaging machinery & equipment

▲ = Import ▼=Export
◆ =Import/Export

(P-15221)
PACKAGING AIDS CORPORATION (PA)
Also Called: P A C
25 Tiburon St, San Rafael (94901-4721)
P.O. Box 9144 (94912-9144)
PHONE..................................415 454-4868
Serge Berguig, *President*
Mark Goldman, *COO*
Estelle Dick, *Exec VP*
Adam Greenlief, *General Mgr*
Greg Quinn, *General Mgr*
▲ **EMP:** 35
SQ FT (est): 27,000
SALES (est): 6.5MM **Privately Held**
WEB: www.packagingaids.com
SIC: 3565 5084 Bag opening, filling & closing machines; industrial machinery & equipment

(P-15222)
PACKLINE TECHNOLOGIES INC
5929 Avenue 408, Dinuba (93618-9791)
P.O. Box 636, Kingsburg (93631-0636)
PHONE..................................559 591-3150
Lorin R Reed, *President*
Josh Lee, *Software Dev*
Ken Nikkel, *Sales Engr*
Brent Willems, *Sales Staff*
EMP: 30
SALES (est): 8.4MM **Privately Held**
SIC: 3565 5084 Packaging machinery; packaging machinery & equipment

(P-15223)
PNEUMATIC SCALE CORPORATION
Also Called: Pneumatic Scale Angelus
10860 6th St, Rancho Cucamonga (91730-5902)
PHONE..................................909 527-7600
Bob Chopman, *CEO*
Jim Foley, *Vice Pres*
Michelle Woodyard, *Analyst*
EMP: 10
SALES (corp-wide): 2.4B **Privately Held**
SIC: 3565 Packaging machinery
HQ: Pneumatic Scale Corporation
10 Ascot Pkwy
Cuyahoga Falls OH 44223
330 923-0491

(P-15224)
PRO PACK SYSTEMS INC
1354 Dayton St Ste A, Salinas (93901-4426)
P.O. Box 903, Monterey (93942-0903)
PHONE..................................831 771-1300
David Paul Zurlinden, *CEO*
Judy Zurlinden, *Vice Pres*
EMP: 12
SQ FT: 10,500
SALES (est): 2.8MM **Privately Held**
SIC: 3565 Carton packing machines

(P-15225)
PROMARKSVAC CORPORATION
1915 E Acacia St, Ontario (91761-7921)
PHONE..................................909 923-3888
Mohsin Syed, *President*
▲ **EMP:** 12 **EST:** 2009
SQ FT: 24,000
SALES (est): 2.5MM **Privately Held**
SIC: 3565 Packaging machinery

(P-15226)
RON UNGAR
Also Called: Ungar, Ron Engineering
4700 Aurora Dr Spc 114, Ventura (93003-8850)
PHONE..................................805 642-3555
Ron Ungar, *Owner*
EMP: 10
SALES (est): 1.7MM **Privately Held**
SIC: 3565 Bottling machinery: filling, capping, labeling

(P-15227)
SARDEE INDUSTRIES INC
2731 E Myrtle St, Stockton (95205-4718)
PHONE..................................209 466-1526
Alan Basset, *Branch Mgr*
EMP: 26

SALES (corp-wide): 13.5MM **Privately Held**
WEB: www.sardee.com
SIC: 3565 3536 Packaging machinery; hoists, cranes & monorails
PA: Sardee Industries, Inc.
5100 Academy Dr Ste 400
Lisle IL 60532
630 824-4200

(P-15228)
SHRINK WRAP PROS LLC
275 E Hillcrest Dr Ste 16, Thousand Oaks (91360-5827)
PHONE..................................805 207-9050
Cheryl Key, *President*
Chris Key,
Craig Key,
EMP: 10
SALES (est): 1.4MM **Privately Held**
SIC: 3565 5084 2392 Packaging machinery; processing & packaging equipment; slipcovers: made of fabric, plastic etc.

(P-15229)
SYSTEMS TECHNOLOGY INC
Also Called: Delaware Systems Technology
1350 Riverview Dr, San Bernardino (92408-2944)
PHONE..................................909 799-9950
David R Landon, *CEO*
John G Stjohn, *CEO*
Allyn Peterson, *Design Engr*
Tom Clauson, *Technology*
Grace Howard, *Purchasing*
▲ **EMP:** 65
SQ FT: 43,000
SALES (est): 18.9MM **Privately Held**
WEB: www.systems-technology-inc.com
SIC: 3565 Packing & wrapping machinery

(P-15230)
THIELE TECHNOLOGIES INC
1949 E Manning Ave, Reedley (93654-9462)
PHONE..................................559 638-8484
Ed Suarez, *Manager*
Dwight Turner, *Project Mgr*
James Lodridge, *Engineer*
Mark Reimer, *Engineer*
Kevin Wall, *Engineer*
EMP: 257
SALES (corp-wide): 2.4B **Privately Held**
SIC: 3565 Packaging machinery
HQ: Thiele Technologies, Inc.
315 27th Ave Ne
Minneapolis MN 55418
612 782-1200

(P-15231)
TRANSFER ENGINEERING & MFG INC
1100 La Avenida St Ste A, Mountain View (94043-1453)
PHONE..................................510 651-3000
Michael Ackert, *President*
Andrew Lunday, *President*
Jorg A Kaminsky, *CFO*
EMP: 25
SALES (est): 5.8MM **Privately Held**
WEB: www.transferengineering.com
SIC: 3565 Vacuum packaging machinery

(P-15232)
UNITED BAKERY EQUIPMENT CO INC (PA)
Also Called: Hartman Slicer Div
19216 S Laurel Park Rd, Compton (90220-6008)
PHONE..................................310 635-8121
Frank J Bastasch, *Owner*
Joyce Bastasch, *Treasurer*
Paul Bastasch, *Vice Pres*
Peggy Walker, *Personnel Exec*
Anita Nunez, *Human Res Mgr*
◆ **EMP:** 100 **EST:** 1966
SALES (est): 37MM **Privately Held**
SIC: 3565 3556 Packaging machinery; bakery machinery

(P-15233)
VISTECH MFG SOLUTIONS LLC (PA)
Also Called: Vis Tech
1156 Scenic Dr Ste 120, Modesto (95350-6100)
PHONE..................................209 544-9333
John Jacinto, *Mng Member*
Terry McLaughlin, *Vice Pres*
Scott Taylor, *Maintence Staff*
Don Vines, *Maintence Staff*
Lane Simpson,
EMP: 23
SQ FT: 32,500
SALES (est): 11.8MM **Privately Held**
SIC: 3565 Packaging machinery

(P-15234)
W E PLEMONS MCHY SVCS INC
13479 E Industrial Dr, Parlier (93648-9678)
P.O. Box 787 (93648-0787)
PHONE..................................559 646-6630
William Plemons, *President*
John Robinson, *Shareholder*
Edward Baskette, *CFO*
Olivia Kozera, *Vice Pres*
Jeff Winters, *Vice Pres*
▲ **EMP:** 25
SQ FT: 30,000
SALES (est): 9MM **Privately Held**
WEB: www.weplemons.com
SIC: 3565 7699 Packaging machinery; industrial machinery & equipment repair

(P-15235)
W J ELLISON CO INC
Also Called: Pack West Machinery Co
200 River Rd, Corona (92880-1435)
PHONE..................................626 814-4766
William J Ellison, *President*
Janice K Ellison, *Vice Pres*
EMP: 24
SQ FT: 20,000
SALES (est): 6.7MM **Privately Held**
SIC: 3565 Packaging machinery

(P-15236)
WILD HORSE INDUSTRIAL CORP
Also Called: Simplex Filler Co
640 Airpark Rd Ste A, NAPA (94558-7569)
PHONE..................................707 265-6801
G Donald Murray III, *President*
Edna Murray, *CFO*
Piper Quinones, *Marketing Staff*
EMP: 15
SQ FT: 15,500
SALES (est): 2MM **Privately Held**
WEB: www.simplexfiller.com
SIC: 3565 Packaging machinery

3566 Speed Changers, Drives & Gears

(P-15237)
AMERICAN CHAIN & GEAR COMPANY
3370 Paseo Halcon, San Clemente (92672-3523)
PHONE..................................323 581-9131
John Kyle, *President*
EMP: 13
SQ FT: 26,000
SALES (est): 2.1MM **Privately Held**
SIC: 3566 3568 5063 Gears, power transmission, except automotive; sprockets (power transmission equipment); power transmission equipment, electric

(P-15238)
AMERICAN PRECISION GEAR CO
365 Foster City Blvd, Foster City (94404-1104)
PHONE..................................650 627-8060
Steve W Lefczik, *President*
EMP: 20
SQ FT: 22,000
SALES (est): 6.1MM **Privately Held**
WEB: www.amgear.com
SIC: 3566 Gears, power transmission, except automotive

(P-15239)
HECO INC
Also Called: Pascal Systems
2350 Del Monte St, West Sacramento (95691-3807)
P.O. Box 1388 (95691-1388)
PHONE..................................916 372-5411
Michael H Jacobs, *President*
Allen Rasmussen, *Vice Pres*
Chris Bessette, *Plant Mgr*
John Woodhouse, *Opers Staff*
▲ **EMP:** 13 **EST:** 1975
SQ FT: 10,000
SALES (est): 6.5MM **Privately Held**
WEB: www.hecogear.com
SIC: 3566 Speed changers (power transmission equipment), except auto

(P-15240)
JETCO TORQUE TOOLS LLC
835 Meridian St, Duarte (91010-3587)
PHONE..................................626 359-2881
Bradley Jenkins, *Mng Member*
EMP: 10 **EST:** 2015
SALES: 1.5MM **Privately Held**
SIC: 3566 3621 Torque converters, except automotive; torque motors, electric

(P-15241)
MARPLES GEARS INC
808 W Santa Anita Ave, San Gabriel (91776-1017)
PHONE..................................626 570-1744
James A Phillips IV, *CEO*
Jeff Goff, *General Mgr*
EMP: 23
SQ FT: 5,000
SALES (est): 3.9MM **Privately Held**
WEB: www.marplesgears.com
SIC: 3566 Speed changers, drives & gears

(P-15242)
MARTIN SPROCKET & GEAR INC
1199 Vine St, Sacramento (95811-0426)
PHONE..................................916 441-7172
Steve Delay, *Branch Mgr*
Steve De Lay, *Manager*
EMP: 50
SQ FT: 100,000
SALES (corp-wide): 456MM **Privately Held**
SIC: 3566 3535 3534 3462 Gears, power transmission, except automotive; conveyors & conveying equipment; elevators & moving stairways; iron & steel forgings; hand & edge tools; sprockets (power transmission equipment)
PA: Martin Sprocket & Gear, Inc.
3100 Sprocket Dr
Arlington TX 76015
817 258-3000

(P-15243)
MARTIN SPROCKET & GEAR INC
5920 Triangle Dr, Commerce (90040-3688)
PHONE..................................323 728-8117
Gus Diaz, *Manager*
EMP: 12
SQ FT: 8,500
SALES (corp-wide): 456MM **Privately Held**
SIC: 3566 5085 3568 Gears, power transmission, except automotive; sprockets; power transmission equipment
PA: Martin Sprocket & Gear, Inc.
3100 Sprocket Dr
Arlington TX 76015
817 258-3000

(P-15244)
QUALITY GEARS INC
Also Called: Associated Gear
12139 Slauson Ave, Santa Fe Springs (90670-2603)
PHONE..................................562 921-9938
Stephany Castellanos, *President*
Bill Guillermo Castellanos, *Vice Pres*
Stephanie Castellanos, *Manager*
EMP: 12 **EST:** 2011
SALES (est): 100K **Privately Held**
SIC: 3566 Gears, power transmission, except automotive

(P-15245)
REXNORD LLC
3690 Jurupa St, Ontario (91761-2910)
PHONE...............................909 467-8102
EMP: 197 **Publicly Held**
SIC: **3566** Speed changers, drives & gears
HQ: Rexnord Llc
    3001 W Canal St
    Milwaukee WI 53208
    414 342-3131

(P-15246)
SEW-EURODRIVE INC
30599 San Antonio St, Hayward
(94544-7101)
PHONE...............................510 487-3560
Marvin Leeper, *Branch Mgr*
Keene Phonn, *Engineer*
Darwin Tindan, *Manager*
EMP: 44
SALES (corp-wide): 2.7B **Privately Held**
WEB: www.seweurodrive.com
SIC: **3566** Speed changers, drives & gears
HQ: Sew-Eurodrive, Inc.
    1295 Old Spartanburg Hwy
    Lyman SC 29365
    864 439-7537

(P-15247)
SOLAR TURBINES
INCORPORATED
2200 Pacific Hwy, San Diego (92101-1773)
PHONE...............................619 544-5352
Charles Chao, *Engineer*
Alick Lau, *Project Mgr*
EMP: 50
SQ FT: 45,000
SALES (corp-wide): 45.4B **Publicly Held**
WEB: www.esolar.cat.com
SIC: **3566** 3462 Gears, power transmission, except automotive; iron & steel forgings
HQ: Solar Turbines Incorporated
    2200 Pacific Hwy
    San Diego CA 92101
    619 544-5000

(P-15248)
US GEAR & PUMPS
1249 S Diamond Bar Blvd # 325, Diamond
Bar (91765-4122)
PHONE...............................909 525-3026
Eony Clark, *Owner*
EMP: 20
SALES (est): 1.4MM **Privately Held**
SIC: **3566** Speed changers, drives & gears

3567 Indl Process Furnaces & Ovens

(P-15249)
ALLEN MORGAN
Also Called: Tsi/Protherm
1233 W Collins Ave, Orange (92867-5412)
PHONE...............................714 538-7492
Allen Morgan, *Owner*
EMP: 12
SQ FT: 3,000
SALES (est): 2.1MM **Privately Held**
WEB: www.allenmorgan.com
SIC: **3567** Heating units & devices, industrial: electric

(P-15250)
AMARK INDUSTRIES INC (PA)
600 W Esplanade Ave, San Jacinto
(92583-4903)
PHONE...............................951 654-7351
Pepper Renshaw, *President*
Gordon Moss, *CFO*
EMP: 122
SALES (est): 14MM **Privately Held**
WEB: www.amarkindustries.com
SIC: **3567** Industrial furnaces & ovens

(P-15251)
AMERICAN INDUCTION TECH
INC
310 N Palm St Ste B, Brea (92821-2867)
PHONE...............................714 456-1122
Apolinar Rosas, *President*
▲ EMP: 14

SALES (est): 2.8MM **Privately Held**
SIC: **3567** Induction heating equipment

(P-15252)
ASC PROCESS SYSTEMS INC
28402 Livingston Ave, Valencia
(91355-4172)
PHONE...............................818 833-0088
David C Mason, *President*
Dave Mason, *President*
Gudrun Mason, *CFO*
◆ EMP: 250
SQ FT: 41,000
SALES: 55.9MM **Privately Held**
WEB: www.aschome.com
SIC: **3567** 3585 3563 7378 Industrial furnaces & ovens; heating & air conditioning combination units; vacuum pumps, except laboratory; computer peripheral equipment repair & maintenance; fabricated plate work (boiler shop)

(P-15253)
BAKER FURNACE INC
2680 Orbiter St, Brea (92821-6265)
PHONE...............................714 223-7262
Ernest E Bacon, *President*
Diane Bacon, *Treasurer*
Steve Pletcher, *Materials Mgr*
▼ EMP: 19
SQ FT: 25,000
SALES (est): 5.8MM
SALES (corp-wide): 94.7MM **Privately Held**
WEB: www.bakerfurnace.com
SIC: **3567** Heating units & devices, industrial: electric
HQ: Tps, Llc
    2821 Old Route 15
    New Columbia PA 17856
    570 538-7200

(P-15254)
BENCHMARK THERMAL
CORPORATION
13185 Nevada City Ave, Grass Valley
(95945-9568)
PHONE...............................530 477-5011
Vincent Palmieri, *CEO*
Gil Mathew, *President*
Laralee Hannah, *Admin Sec*
EMP: 52
SQ FT: 20,000
SALES (est): 11.4MM **Privately Held**
WEB: www.benchmarkthermal.com
SIC: **3567** Heating units & devices, industrial: electric

(P-15255)
CIRCLE INDUSTRIAL MFG CORP
(PA)
Also Called: Cim Services
1613 W El Segundo Blvd, Compton
(90222-1024)
PHONE...............................310 638-5101
Ronald M La Forest, *President*
Karen La Forest, *Treasurer*
John La Forest, *Vice Pres*
Debra Cosio, *Branch Mgr*
EMP: 23
SQ FT: 3,500
SALES (est): 5.1MM **Privately Held**
WEB: www.circleindustrial.com
SIC: **3567** 3542 3535 3444 Industrial furnaces & ovens; sheet metalworking machines; conveyors & conveying equipment; sheet metalwork

(P-15256)
CONCEPTS & METHODS CO
INC
Also Called: Camco Furnace
1017 Bransten Rd, San Carlos
(94070-4020)
PHONE...............................650 593-1064
Anthony Barulich, *President*
Kay Barulich, *Corp Secy*
Peter Sands, *Mfg Mgr*
EMP: 10
SQ FT: 12,000
SALES (est): 4.4MM **Privately Held**
WEB: www.camcoequipment.com
SIC: **3567** Vacuum furnaces & ovens

(P-15257)
DICK FARRELL INDUSTRIES
INC
Also Called: D.F. Industries
5071 Lindsay Ct, Chino (91710-5757)
PHONE...............................909 613-9424
Timothy Farrell, *Principal*
Richard Farrell, *Vice Pres*
Lisa Van Den Berg, *Admin Sec*
▲ EMP: 17
SQ FT: 25,000
SALES (est): 4.8MM **Privately Held**
WEB: www.dfindustries.com
SIC: **3567** 3312 7699 Industrial furnaces & ovens; ferroalloys, produced in blast furnaces; industrial machinery & equipment repair

(P-15258)
DS FIBERTECH CORP
Also Called: Interntonal Thermoproducts Div
11015 Mission Park Ct, Santee
(92071-5601)
PHONE...............................619 562-7001
Duong Minh Nguyen, *CEO*
Son Dinh Nguyen, *President*
Eric Ulrich, *Vice Pres*
Thomas Nguyen, *Prdtn Mgr*
▲ EMP: 45
SQ FT: 14,000
SALES (est): 10.7MM **Privately Held**
WEB: www.itp-dsf.com
SIC: **3567** Heating units & devices, industrial: electric

(P-15259)
ENERGY RECONNAISSANCE
INC
Also Called: California Heating Equipment
1270 N Red Gum St, Anaheim
(92806-1820)
PHONE...............................714 630-4491
John Tittelsitz, *President*
Bertha Hernandez, *Office Mgr*
EMP: 10
SALES (est): 2MM **Privately Held**
SIC: **3567** Electrical furnaces, ovens & heating devices, exc. induction

(P-15260)
FLUIDIX INC (PA)
1422 Mammoth Tav Rd C6, Mammoth
Lakes (93546)
P.O. Box 1807 (93546-1807)
PHONE...............................760 935-2016
Kent A Rianda, *President*
EMP: 11
SALES (est): 1MM **Privately Held**
WEB: www.thetroutfly.com
SIC: **3567** Heating units & devices, industrial: electric

(P-15261)
HEATER DESIGNS INC
2211 S Vista Ave, Bloomington
(92316-2921)
PHONE...............................909 421-0971
James Fan, *Chairman*
Tom Odendahl, *President*
EMP: 30
SQ FT: 14,500
SALES (est): 5.6MM **Privately Held**
WEB: www.heaterdesigns.net
SIC: **3567** Heating units & devices, industrial: electric

(P-15262)
INDUCTION TECHNOLOGY
CORP
22060 Bear Valley Rd, Apple Valley
(92308-7209)
PHONE...............................760 246-7333
Micahei T Dicken, *President*
Michael T Dicken, *President*
Marilyn Dicken, *Admin Sec*
Mike Bertelsen, *Engineer*
Adam Estrada, *Engineer*
EMP: 21
SQ FT: 25,000
SALES (est): 5.8MM **Privately Held**
WEB: www.inductiontech.com
SIC: **3567** 7699 Induction heating equipment; industrial machinery & equipment repair

(P-15263)
INDUSTRIAL FURNACE & INSUL
INC
2090 S Hellman Ave, Ontario (91761-8018)
PHONE...............................909 947-2449
Gobind Panjabi, *President*
Michael O'Rourke, *Vice Pres*
Michael O''rourke, *Vice Pres*
▲ EMP: 12
SQ FT: 10,200
SALES (est): 2.6MM **Privately Held**
WEB: www.indfurn.com
SIC: **3567** Ceramic kilns & furnaces

(P-15264)
INDUSTRIAL PROCESS EQP INC
Also Called: I P E
1700 Industrial Ave, Norco (92860-2949)
PHONE...............................714 447-0171
Michael J Waggoner, *CEO*
James Waggoner, *President*
Cody Waggoner, *Manager*
▼ EMP: 16
SQ FT: 30,220
SALES (est): 6.5MM **Privately Held**
SIC: **3567** Industrial furnaces & ovens

(P-15265)
JHAWAR INDUSTRIES INC (PA)
Also Called: G-M Enterprises
525 Klug Cir, Corona (92880-5452)
PHONE...............................951 340-4646
Suresh Jhawar, *CEO*
Paul Warg, *CFO*
Veena Jhawar, *Exec VP*
Dennis Trumpinski, *Director*
▼ EMP: 37 EST: 1975
SQ FT: 50,000
SALES (est): 16MM **Privately Held**
WEB: www.gmenterprises.com
SIC: **3567** Vacuum furnaces & ovens

(P-15266)
L C MILLER COMPANY
717 Monterey Pass Rd, Monterey Park
(91754-3606)
PHONE...............................323 268-3611
Dolores Naimy, *President*
EMP: 20
SALES (corp-wide): 2.3MM **Privately Held**
WEB: www.lcmiller.com
SIC: **3567** 3546 3625 3398 Heating units & devices, industrial: electric; saws & sawing equipment; industrial electrical relays & switches; metal heat treating
PA: L C Miller Company
    717 Monterey Pass Rd
    Monterey Park CA 91754
    323 268-3611

(P-15267)
L C MILLER COMPANY (PA)
717 Monterey Pass Rd, Monterey Park
(91754-3606)
PHONE...............................323 268-3611
Dolores Naimy, *President*
Dave Vito, *COO*
Victor De Lucia, *Vice Pres*
EMP: 14
SQ FT: 14,000
SALES (est): 2.3MM **Privately Held**
WEB: www.lcmiller.com
SIC: **3567** 3546 3625 3398 Heating units & devices, industrial: electric; saws & sawing equipment; industrial electrical relays & switches; metal heat treating

(P-15268)
LOCHABER CORNWALL INC
(PA)
Also Called: Furnace Pros
675 N Eckhoff St Ste D, Orange
(92868-1000)
PHONE...............................714 935-0302
James Clark, *President*
Katherine Clark, *Treasurer*
EMP: 13
SALES (est): 1.9MM **Privately Held**
SIC: **3567** Electrical furnaces, ovens & heating devices, exc. induction

(P-15269)
MESSANA INC
Also Called: Messana Radiant Cooling
4105 Soquel Dr Ste B, Soquel
(95073-2116)
PHONE..................855 729-6244
Alessandro Arnulfo, *CEO*
Francesco Marchesi, *Director*
▲ EMP: 15
SQ FT: 2,500
SALES: 1.4MM **Privately Held**
SIC: 3567 Radiant heating systems, indus-
trial process

(P-15270)
**MODULAR PROCESS TECH
CORP**
1675 Walsh Ave Ste E, Santa Clara
(95050-2626)
PHONE..................408 325-8640
Steven Shatas, *CTO*
Meiying Forney, *CIO*
Michael Menetto, *Director*
EMP: 12
SQ FT: 3,300
SALES (est): 1.7MM **Privately Held**
WEB: www.modularpro.com
SIC: 3567 3559

(P-15271)
PACIFIC KILN INSULATIONS INC
14370 Veterans Way, Moreno Valley
(92553-9058)
PHONE..................951 697-4422
Joel Fritz, *President*
▲ EMP: 12
SQ FT: 10,000
SALES (est): 3.4MM **Privately Held**
SIC: 3567 Fuel-fired furnaces & ovens

(P-15272)
PRIME HEAT INCORPORATED
1844 Friendship Dr Ste A, El Cajon
(92020-1115)
PHONE..................619 449-6623
Herb Boekamp, *President*
▲ EMP: 18
SQ FT: 20,500
SALES (est): 4.7MM **Privately Held**
SIC: 3567 Heating units & devices, indus-
trial: electric

(P-15273)
RAMA CORPORATION
600 W Esplanade Ave, San Jacinto
(92583-4999)
PHONE..................951 654-7351
Peggy Renshaw, *President*
Marilyn Renshaw, *Vice Pres*
Michael Dailey, *Administration*
Peggy Colebrook, *Accounting Mgr*
EMP: 45 EST: 1947
SQ FT: 25,000
SALES: 2MM
SALES (corp-wide): 14MM **Privately
Held**
WEB: www.amarkindustries.com
SIC: 3567 3634 Heating units & devices,
industrial: electric; electric housewares &
fans
PA: Amark Industries Inc
600 W Esplanade Ave
San Jacinto CA 92583
951 654-7351

(P-15274)
**SCHMID THERMAL SYSTEMS
INC**
200 Westridge Dr, Watsonville
(95076-4172)
PHONE..................831 763-0113
Thomas Stewart, *CEO*
William Daley, *Admin Sec*
◆ EMP: 110
SQ FT: 34,000
SALES: 25.7MM
SALES (corp-wide): 185.8K **Privately
Held**
WEB: www.sierratherm.com
SIC: 3567 3559 3674 Electrical furnaces,
ovens & heating devices, exc. induction;
broom making machinery; semiconduc-
tors & related devices

HQ: Gebr. Schmid Gmbh
Robert-Bosch-Str. 32-36
Freudenstadt 72250
744 153-80

(P-15275)
**THERMTRONIX CORPORATION
(PA)**
17129 Muskrat Ave, Adelanto
(92301-2260)
P.O. Box 100 (92301-0100)
PHONE..................760 246-4500
Robert Nealon, *President*
Deborah Nealon, *Admin Sec*
▲ EMP: 25
SQ FT: 12,000
SALES (est): 6.1MM **Privately Held**
WEB: www.thermtronix.com
SIC: 3567 Metal melting furnaces, indus-
trial: electric

(P-15276)
TP SOLAR INC
Also Called: Tpsi
16310 Downey Ave, Paramount
(90723-5500)
PHONE..................562 808-2171
Alex Rey, *President*
Peter Ragay, *Vice Pres*
▼ EMP: 26
SQ FT: 4,000
SALES: 3.2MM **Privately Held**
SIC: 3567 Industrial furnaces & ovens

(P-15277)
W P KEITH CO INC
8323 Loch Lomond Dr, Pico Rivera
(90660-2588)
PHONE..................562 948-3636
Carol N Keith, *CEO*
Wendell P Keith Jr, *President*
Charlie Birks, *Sales Mgr*
Dwain Davis,
▲ EMP: 25
SQ FT: 19,200
SALES (est): 7.8MM **Privately Held**
WEB: www.keithkilns.com
SIC: 3567 Kilns; metal melting furnaces,
industrial: fuel-fired; metal melting fur-
naces, industrial: electric

(P-15278)
WARMBOARD INC
8035 Soquel Dr Ste 41a, Aptos
(95003-3948)
PHONE..................831 685-9276
Terry Alberg, *President*
Mark Florez, *Manager*
EMP: 20
SQ FT: 1,250
SALES (est): 5.9MM **Privately Held**
WEB: www.warmboard.com
SIC: 3567 Radiant heating systems, indus-
trial process

**3568 Mechanical Power
Transmission Eqpt, NEC**

(P-15279)
ANACO INC
1001 El Camino Ave, Corona (92879-1756)
PHONE..................951 372-2732
Leon Nolen III, *President*
▲ EMP: 140
SALES (est): 41.3MM
SALES (corp-wide): 1.3B **Privately Held**
WEB: www.mcwane.com
SIC: 3568 Couplings, shaft: rigid, flexible,
universal joint, etc.
PA: Mcwane, Inc.
2900 Highway 280 S # 300
Birmingham AL 35223
205 414-3100

(P-15280)
ATR SALES INC
Also Called: Atra-Flex
110 E Garry Ave, Santa Ana (92707-4201)
PHONE..................714 432-8411
Jerry Hauck, *CEO*
Tom Arutunian, *Shareholder*
Raymond Hoyt, *Corp Secy*
Tony Hauck, *Opers Mgr*
EMP: 26

SQ FT: 12,000
SALES: 10MM **Privately Held**
WEB: www.atra-flex.com
SIC: 3568 Couplings, shaft: rigid, flexible,
universal joint, etc.

(P-15281)
**BALL SCREWS & ACTUATORS
COINC (HQ)**
Also Called: B S A
970 Mclaughlin Ave, San Jose
(95122-2611)
PHONE..................408 938-3031
Steve Randazzo, *President*
▲ EMP: 73
SQ FT: 30,000
SALES: 9.7MM
SALES (corp-wide): 18.3B **Publicly Held**
SIC: 3568 3625 3593 3562 Power trans-
mission equipment; actuators, industrial;
fluid power cylinders & actuators; ball &
roller bearings; bolts, nuts, rivets & wash-
ers
PA: Danaher Corporation
2200 Penn Ave Nw Ste 800w
Washington DC 20037
202 828-0850

(P-15282)
CLARKE ENGINEERING INC
8058 Lankershim Blvd, North Hollywood
(91605-1609)
PHONE..................818 768-0690
Roger D Clarke, *President*
Lee V Mason, *Vice Pres*
EMP: 12
SQ FT: 5,500
SALES (est): 2.3MM **Privately Held**
WEB: www.clarkgear.com
SIC: 3568 Power transmission equipment

(P-15283)
GEMINI BIO PRODUCTS
930 Riverside Pkwy Ste 50, Broderick
(95605-1511)
PHONE..................916 471-3540
EMP: 14
SALES (est): 289.6K **Privately Held**
SIC: 3568

(P-15284)
**HYSPAN PRECISION PRODUCTS
INC (PA)**
1685 Brandywine Ave, Chula Vista
(91911-6097)
PHONE..................619 421-1355
Donald R Heye, *President*
Eric Barnes, *CFO*
Phillip Ensz, *CFO*
◆ EMP: 100
SQ FT: 54,000
SALES (est): 96.5MM **Privately Held**
WEB: www.hyspan.com
SIC: 3568 3496 3441 Ball joints, except
aircraft & automotive; woven wire prod-
ucts; expansion joints (structural shapes),
iron or steel

(P-15285)
**INDU-ELECTRIC NORTH AMER
INC**
27756 Avenue Hopkins, Valencia
(91355-1222)
PHONE..................310 578-2144
Martin Gerber, *CEO*
▲ EMP: 50
SQ FT: 11,000
SALES (est): 22.5MM **Privately Held**
WEB: www.induelectric.com
SIC: 3568 5063 Power transmission
equipment; power transmission equip-
ment, electric

(P-15286)
**INDUSTRIAL SPROCKETS
GEARS INC**
13650 Rosecrans Ave, Santa Fe Springs
(90670-5025)
PHONE..................323 233-7221
Max R Patridge, *CEO*
Mark Partridge, *Treasurer*
Monty Patridge, *Vice Pres*
Connie Patridge-Eason, *Admin Sec*
EMP: 21
SQ FT: 18,000

SALES (est): 5MM **Privately Held**
SIC: 3568 3566 3462 Drives, chains &
sprockets; sprockets (power transmission
equipment); drives, high speed industrial,
except hydrostatic; iron & steel forgings

(P-15287)
KLA TENCOR
Also Called: Air Bearing Technology
2260 American Ave Ste 1, Hayward
(94545-1815)
PHONE..................510 887-2647
Art Cormier, *Principal*
Roger Peters, *Principal*
Jeff Rhoton, *Principal*
EMP: 25
SALES (est): 2.3MM **Privately Held**
WEB: www.airbearingtechnology.com
SIC: 3568 3545 Bearings, bushings &
blocks; machine tool accessories

(P-15288)
**LAUNCHPOINT TECHNOLOGIES
INC**
Also Called: Magnetic Moments
5735 Hollister Ave Ste B, Goleta
(93117-6410)
PHONE..................805 683-9659
Brad E Paden, *President*
Diana Hadjes, *CFO*
Dave Paden, *Vice Pres*
Alvin R Paden, *Admin Sec*
John Underhill, *Info Tech Mgr*
EMP: 15
SQ FT: 5,000
SALES (est): 4.3MM **Privately Held**
WEB: www.launchpnt.com
SIC: 3568 Bearings, plain

(P-15289)
PRECISION BABBITT CO INC
1007 S Whitemarsh Ave, Compton
(90220-4439)
PHONE..................562 531-9173
Michael Machala, *President*
EMP: 12
SQ FT: 3,200
SALES (est): 2.2MM **Privately Held**
WEB: www.precisionbabbitt.com
SIC: 3568 7699 Bearings, plain; rebabbit-
ting

(P-15290)
**RBC TRANSPORT DYNAMICS
CORP**
3131 W Segerstrom Ave, Santa Ana
(92704-5811)
PHONE..................203 267-7001
Michael Harnett, *President*
Alex Bautista, *Engineer*
Jose Bautista, *Engineer*
Jarrod Dezarn, *Engineer*
Tyler Heckendorn, *Engineer*
▲ EMP: 185
SQ FT: 75,000
SALES (est): 44MM
SALES (corp-wide): 674.9MM **Publicly
Held**
SIC: 3568 Power transmission equipment
HQ: Roller Bearing Company Of America,
Inc.
102 Willenbrock Rd
Oxford CT 06478
203 267-7001

(P-15291)
**REMANFCTURED CONVERTER
MBL LLC**
Also Called: Remanufactured Converter MBL
582 N Batavia St, Orange (92868-1219)
PHONE..................714 744-8988
Desmond Tan,
Jeronimo Bustillos,
Gustavo Magana,
EMP: 15
SQ FT: 7,000
SALES (est): 2.9MM **Privately Held**
SIC: 3568 Chain, power transmission

(P-15292)
REXNORD INDUSTRIES LLC
1150 Etiwanda Ave, Ontario (91761-8613)
PHONE..................602 682-1764
Santiago Rivera, *Manager*
EMP: 15 **Publicly Held**

SIC: 3568 Couplings, shaft: rigid, flexible, universal joint, etc.
HQ: Rexnord Industries, Llc
247 W Freshwater Way # 200
Milwaukee WI 53204
414 643-3000

(P-15293)
RNOVATE INC
Also Called: Rnc
834 S Broadway, Los Angeles
(90014-3501)
PHONE.....................213 489-1617
John Parros, CEO
▲ EMP: 32
SQ FT: 20,000
SALES (est): 8.3MM Privately Held
SIC: 3568 Belting, chain

3569 Indl Machinery & Eqpt, NEC

(P-15294)
A&D FIRE SPRINKLERS INC
2100 E Howell Ave Ste 209, Anaheim
(92806-6003)
PHONE.....................714 634-3923
Andrew Otero, CEO
EMP: 15 Privately Held
SIC: 3569 Sprinkler systems, fire: automatic
PA: A&D Fire Sprinklers, Inc.
7130 Convoy Ct
San Diego CA 92111

(P-15295)
A&D FIRE SPRINKLERS INC (PA)
7130 Convoy Ct, San Diego (92111-1019)
PHONE.....................858 277-3473
Andrew Otero, President
John Gonsalves, President
Debbie Allard, Chief Mktg Ofcr
Ron Devito, District Mgr
EMP: 35
SALES (est): 12.8MM Privately Held
SIC: 3569 Sprinkler systems, fire: automatic

(P-15296)
AEROSPACE FACILITIES GROUP INC
1590 Raleys Ct Ste 30, West Sacramento
(95691-3488)
PHONE.....................702 513-8336
Julie Robinson, President
Ji Chang, Principal
EMP: 18
SQ FT: 20,000
SALES (est): 690.7K Privately Held
SIC: 3569 1721 3812 Assembly machines, non-metalworking; aircraft painting; air traffic control systems & equipment, electronic

(P-15297)
AKM FIRE INC
18322 Oxnard St, Tarzana (91356-1502)
PHONE.....................818 343-8208
Yaakov Azran, President
Mary Azran, Admin Sec
EMP: 24
SALES: 1.5MM Privately Held
SIC: 3569 1711 Sprinkler systems, fire: automatic; fire sprinkler system installation

(P-15298)
AVX FILTERS CORPORATION
11144 Penrose St Ste 7, Sun Valley
(91352-2756)
PHONE.....................818 767-6770
John Gilbertson, President
Juan Arvizu, Engineer
Jody Jeppson, Cust Mgr
Bill Gerbing, Manager
▲ EMP: 90
SQ FT: 25,000
SALES (est): 18.4MM
SALES (corp-wide): 14.8B Publicly Held
WEB: www.avxcorp.com
SIC: 3569 3675 Filters; electronic capacitors

HQ: Avx Corporation
1 Avx Blvd
Fountain Inn SC 29644
864 967-2150

(P-15299)
BARDEX CORPORATION
6338 Lindmar Dr, Goleta (93117-3112)
PHONE.....................805 964-7747
Thomas Miller, CEO
Porter Spencer, General Mgr
Joanna Morgan, Office Mgr
Anita Elovitz, Admin Asst
Elizabeth Casteel, Administration
◆ EMP: 62
SQ FT: 80,000
SALES (est): 21.1MM Privately Held
WEB: www.bardex.com
SIC: 3569 Jacks, hydraulic

(P-15300)
BARON USA LLC
350 Baron Cir, Woodland (95776)
PHONE.....................931 528-8476
Derek L Baranowski, President
Diana M Baranowski, Admin Sec
EMP: 24
SQ FT: 28,000
SALES (est): 6.5MM Privately Held
WEB: www.baronusa.com
SIC: 3569 3567 Filters, general line: industrial; vacuum furnaces & ovens

(P-15301)
BAY AREA INDUS FILTRATION INC
6355 Coliseum Way, Oakland
(94621-3719)
P.O. Box 2071, San Leandro (94577-0207)
PHONE.....................510 562-6373
Thomas S Schneider, President
Diana E Schneider, Vice Pres
EMP: 24
SALES (est): 5.8MM Privately Held
SIC: 3569 5085 3564 2674 Filters, general line: industrial; filters, industrial; blowers & fans; bags: uncoated paper & multiwall

(P-15302)
BEAM ON TECHNOLOGY CORPORATION
2318 Calle De Luna, Santa Clara
(95054-1003)
PHONE.....................408 982-0161
Rajoo Venkat, President
Herbert Martinez, CFO
EMP: 27
SQ FT: 6,500
SALES (est): 6.3MM Privately Held
WEB: www.beamon.com
SIC: 3569 3544 3543 Assembly machines, non-metalworking; special dies, tools, jigs & fixtures; industrial patterns

(P-15303)
BLUELAB CORPORATION USA LTD
437 S Cataract Ave, San Dimas
(91773-2973)
PHONE.....................909 599-1940
Rick Jaries, President
EMP: 50
SALES (est): 6.3MM Privately Held
SIC: 3569 Testing chambers for altitude, temperature, ordnance, power

(P-15304)
BORETT AUTOMATION TECHNOLOGIES
3824 Bowsprit Cir, Westlake Village
(91361-3814)
PHONE.....................818 597-8664
Richard Boring, Partner
A W Charret, Partner
EMP: 14
SQ FT: 3,400
SALES (est): 1.7MM Privately Held
SIC: 3569 5084 Robots, assembly line: industrial & commercial; conveyor systems

(P-15305)
CAPSTONE FIRE MANAGEMENT INC (PA)
2240 Auto Park Way, Escondido
(92029-1249)
PHONE.....................760 839-2290
Jerry Dusa, President
Christopher Dusa, Vice Pres
Matthew Dusa, Vice Pres
Chris Dusa, Executive
Kristen Davis, Administration
EMP: 31 EST: 1989
SALES (est): 4.2MM Privately Held
WEB: www.fire-stop.com
SIC: 3569 Firefighting apparatus & related equipment

(P-15306)
CAPTIVE OCEAN REEF ENTERPRISES
Also Called: Ecosystem Aquarium
34135 Moongate Ct, Dana Point
(92629-2671)
PHONE.....................949 581-8888
Leng Sy, President
▲ EMP: 10
SQ FT: 10,800
SALES (est): 900K Privately Held
WEB: www.ecosystemaquarium.com
SIC: 3569 Filters

(P-15307)
CHAD INDUSTRIES INCORPORATED
1565 S Sinclair St, Anaheim (92806-5934)
PHONE.....................714 938-0080
Scott W Klimczak, President
Wayne Rapp, Admin Sec
Dennis Fischgrabe, Software Engr
Jeroen Bosboom, Engineer
Tatiana Major, Accounts Mgr
▲ EMP: 40
SQ FT: 31,000
SALES (est): 8.9MM Privately Held
WEB: www.chadindustries.com
SIC: 3569 Robots, assembly line: industrial & commercial

(P-15308)
CLAYTON MANUFACTURING COMPANY (PA)
Also Called: Clayton Industries
17477 Hurley St, City of Industry
(91744-5106)
PHONE.....................626 443-9381
John Clayton, President
Alexander Smirnoff, CFO
Boyd A Calvin, Senior VP
Allen L Cluer, Vice Pres
Phyllis Nielson, Vice Pres
▲ EMP: 147 EST: 1930
SQ FT: 215,000
SALES (est): 114.2MM Privately Held
WEB: www.claytonindustries.com
SIC: 3569 3829 3511 Generators: steam, liquid oxygen or nitrogen; dynamometer instruments; turbines & turbine generator sets

(P-15309)
CLAYTON MANUFACTURING INC (HQ)
17477 Hurley St, City of Industry
(91744-5106)
PHONE.....................626 443-9381
William Clayton Jr, CEO
John Clayton, President
Boyd A Calvin, Treasurer
Allen L Cluer, Vice Pres
Tim Pressley, Manager
▼ EMP: 80 EST: 1930
SQ FT: 215,000
SALES (est): 17.1MM
SALES (corp-wide): 114.2MM Privately Held
SIC: 3569 3829 Generators: steam, liquid oxygen or nitrogen; dynamometer instruments
PA: Clayton Manufacturing Company
17477 Hurley St
City Of Industry CA 91744
626 443-9381

(P-15310)
CLOUD COMPANY (PA)
4855 Morabito Pl, San Luis Obispo
(93401-8748)
PHONE.....................805 549-8093
James H Rucker, Ch of Bd
David L Rucker, President
Mike Kemp, Executive
Karen Rucker, Admin Sec
Seanah Muindi, Technology
EMP: 25
SQ FT: 7,000
SALES (est): 3.3MM Privately Held
WEB: www.cloudinc.com
SIC: 3569 Liquid automation machinery & equipment

(P-15311)
CODE-IN-MOTION LLC
232 Avenida Fabricante # 103, San
Clemente (92672-7553)
PHONE.....................949 361-2633
Jovan Zivkovic,
Hubert Schroeder, VP Sls/Mktg
Dan Popovich,
Wally Popovich,
Mark Stroud,
EMP: 15
SQ FT: 13,000
SALES (est): 2.2MM Privately Held
WEB: www.code-in-motion.com
SIC: 3569 3565 Robots, assembly line: industrial & commercial; labeling machines, industrial

(P-15312)
D & M FABRICATION INC
1615 S Stockton St, Lodi (95240-6353)
PHONE.....................209 334-0407
Byron Weisz, CEO
Debra Weisz, President
Michelle Weisz, Admin Sec
EMP: 27
SALES (est): 2.5MM Privately Held
SIC: 3569 3446 3444 3443 Sprinkler systems, fire: automatic; architectural metalwork; sheet metalwork; fabricated plate work (boiler shop)

(P-15313)
DELTA DESIGN INC (HQ)
12367 Crosthwaite Cir, Poway
(92064-6817)
PHONE.....................858 848-8000
Samer Aabbani, President
James A Donahue, President
Jeff Jose, CFO
Charles A Schwan, Chairman
James McFarlane, Senior VP
▲ EMP: 400
SQ FT: 334,000
SALES (est): 134.9MM
SALES (corp-wide): 352.7MM Publicly Held
SIC: 3569 3825 3674 Testing chambers for altitude, temperature, ordnance, power; test equipment for electronic & electrical circuits; semiconductors & related devices
PA: Cohu, Inc.
12367 Crosthwaite Cir
Poway CA 92064
858 848-8100

(P-15314)
DELTA TAU DATA SYSTEMS INC CAL (HQ)
21314 Lassen St, Chatsworth
(91311-4254)
PHONE.....................818 998-2095
Yasuto Ikuta, President
Tamara Dimitri, Treasurer
Dominic Dimitri, Vice Pres
Sandra Smith, Executive Asst
Ed Lay, Sr Software Eng
EMP: 130
SQ FT: 140,000
SALES: 41.8MM
SALES (corp-wide): 8B Privately Held
WEB: www.deltatau.com
SIC: 3569 7372 3625 3577 Robots, assembly line: industrial & commercial; prepackaged software; relays & industrial controls; computer peripheral equipment

PA: Omron Corporation
Minamifudondocho, Shiokojidori-
Horikawahigashiiru, Shimogyo-Ku
Kyoto KYO 600-8
753 447-000

(P-15315)
DELTA TAU INTERNATIONAL INC
21314 Lassen St, Chatsworth
(91311-4254)
PHONE..................................818 998-2095
Yasuto Ikuta, *President*
EMP: 14
SQ FT: 35,000
SALES (est): 1.8MM
SALES (corp-wide): 8B **Privately Held**
WEB: www.deltatau.com
SIC: 3569 Robots, assembly line: industrial
& commercial
HQ: Delta Tau Data Systems Inc Of Califor-
nia
21314 Lassen St
Chatsworth CA 91311
818 998-2095

(P-15316)
DESCHNER CORPORATION
3211 W Harvard St, Santa Ana
(92704-3976)
PHONE..................................714 557-1261
Joe Alessi, *President*
Toby Ryan, *CEO*
Frank Solis, *CFO*
EMP: 35
SQ FT: 21,600
SALES (est): 8MM **Privately Held**
WEB: www.deschner.com
SIC: 3569 3594 Liquid automation ma-
chinery & equipment; fluid power pumps
& motors

(P-15317)
EDEN EQUIPMENT COMPANY INC
5670 Wilshire Blvd # 1400, Los Angeles
(90036-5612)
PHONE..................................909 629-2217
Joe Kovach, *President*
Branden Crowe, *Opers Mgr*
EMP: 15 EST: 1982
SQ FT: 10,000
SALES (est): 3.8MM **Privately Held**
WEB: www.edenequipment.com
SIC: 3569 Filters, general line: industrial;
filters

(P-15318)
EKLAVYA LLC
Also Called: Nexus Automation
2021 Las Positas Ct # 141, Livermore
(94551-7304)
PHONE..................................925 443-3296
Sandeep Patel,
Vinita Chaturvedi, *Chief Mktg Ofcr*
EMP: 10
SQ FT: 4,000
SALES (est): 2MM **Privately Held**
SIC: 3569 3559 3565 5084 Robots, assembly line: industrial & commercial;
pharmaceutical machinery; semiconductor manufacturing machinery; packaging
machinery; labeling machines, industrial;
industrial machinery & equipment; machine shop, jobbing & repair

(P-15319)
FILBUR MANUFACTURING LLC
Also Called: Filbur Pool & Spa Filtration
20 Centerpointe Dr # 110, La Palma
(90623-2558)
PHONE..................................714 228-6000
Ching-Hsiung Lin, *Mng Member*
Bruce Stump, *Vice Pres*
Guadalupe Carillo, *Accounting Mgr*
Merced Pereda-Osorio, *Asst Controller*
Joe Marcotte, *Natl Sales Mgr*
▲ **EMP:** 42 EST: 1996
SQ FT: 93,000
SALES (est): 12.8MM **Privately Held**
WEB: www.filburmfg.com
SIC: 3569 Filters

(P-15320)
FIREBLAST GLOBAL INC
545 Monica Cir, Corona (92880-5447)
PHONE..................................951 277-8319

Richard Egelin, *CEO*
EMP: 25
SALES (est): 8.5MM **Privately Held**
WEB: www.fireblast.com
SIC: 3569 8711 Firefighting apparatus; en-
gineering services

(P-15321)
FIREQUICK PRODUCTS INC
1137 Red Rock Inyokern Rd, Inyokern
(93527)
P.O. Box 910 (93527-0910)
PHONE..................................760 371-4279
Beth J Sumners, *President*
Bill Sumners, *Vice Pres*
Deanne Kuppens, *Manager*
EMP: 15
SALES: 2.5MM **Privately Held**
WEB: www.firequick.com
SIC: 3569 Firefighting apparatus & related
equipment

(P-15322)
FIRST RESPONDER FIRE
Also Called: 1st Responder Fire Protection
19146 Stare St, Northridge (91324-1266)
PHONE..................................562 842-6602
John Flores, *President*
EMP: 11
SALES: 2.6MM **Privately Held**
SIC: 3569 7389 1711 1799 Sprinkler systems, fire: automatic; ; fire sprinkler system installation; irrigation sprinkler system
installation; coating, caulking & weather,
water & fireproofing; repairing fire damage, single-family houses

(P-15323)
FJA INDUSTRIES INC
1230 Coleman Ave, Santa Clara
(95050-4338)
P.O. Box 242 (95052-0242)
PHONE..................................408 727-0100
Frank J Ardezzone, *CEO*
▲ **EMP:** 14
SQ FT: 10,000
SALES: 600K **Privately Held**
SIC: 3569 Robots, assembly line: industrial
& commercial

(P-15324)
FLAME GARD INC
6825 E Washington Blvd, Los Angeles
(90040-1905)
PHONE..................................323 888-8707
Lawrence Capalbo, *President*
Thomas E Capalbo, *CFO*
Gary Barros, *VP Sales*
EMP: 67
SQ FT: 12,000
SALES (est): 7MM
SALES (corp-wide): 30MM **Privately
Held**
WEB: www.flamegard.com
SIC: 3569 3444 Filters; sheet metalwork
PA: Taylor Freezers Of Southern California,
Inc.
6825 E Washington Blvd
Commerce CA 90040
323 889-8700

(P-15325)
GENERON IGS INC
Also Called: M G Generon
992 Arcy Ln Bldg 992, Pittsburg (94565)
PHONE..................................925 431-1030
Karen Skala, *Manager*
EMP: 25
SALES (corp-wide): 35MM **Privately
Held**
WEB: www.generon-ca.com
SIC: 3569 2813 3081 Separators for
steam, gas, vapor or air (machinery); in-
dustrial gases; unsupported plastics film
& sheet
HQ: Generon Igs, Inc.
16250 State Highway 249
Houston TX 77086
713 937-5200

(P-15326)
GLASMAN SHIM & STAMPING INC
226 N Sherman Ave Ste B, Corona
(92882-7122)
PHONE..................................951 278-8197

Larry Glasman Jr, *CEO*
Diane Glasman, *General Mgr*
EMP: 10
SQ FT: 4,320
SALES (est): 1.6MM **Privately Held**
WEB: www.bolsanwestinc.com
SIC: 3569 Surveillance ovens for aging &
testing powder

(P-15327)
GUSMER ENTERPRISES INC
Also Called: Cellulo Co Division
81 M St, Fresno (93721-3215)
PHONE..................................908 301-1811
Fred Mazanec, *Opers Mgr*
Tom Whitling, *Prdtn Mgr*
EMP: 75
SQ FT: 18,644
SALES (corp-wide): 34MM **Privately
Held**
WEB: www.gusmerenterprises.com
SIC: 3569 Filters, general line: industrial
PA: Gusmer Enterprises, Inc.
1165 Globe Ave
Mountainside NJ 07092
908 301-1811

(P-15328)
HARTWICK COMBUSTION TECH INC
9426 Stewart And Gray Rd, Downey
(90241-5351)
PHONE..................................562 922-8300
Peter Hartwick, *President*
Andrea Hartwick, *Corp Secy*
EMP: 10
SALES (est): 1.9MM **Privately Held**
SIC: 3569 Cremating ovens

(P-15329)
HONEYBEE ROBOTICS LTD
398 W Washington Blvd, Pasadena
(91103-2000)
PHONE..................................510 207-4555
Stephen Gorvan, *Branch Mgr*
EMP: 11
SALES (corp-wide): 185.7MM **Privately
Held**
SIC: 3569 Filters
HQ: Honeybee Robotics, Ltd.
Suit Bldg 128
Brooklyn NY 11205
212 966-0661

(P-15330)
HYDRO-LOGIC PURIFICATION
370 Encinal St Ste 150, Santa Cruz
(95060-2182)
PHONE..................................888 426-5644
Rich Gellert, *CEO*
EMP: 12
SQ FT: 2,500
SALES (est): 1.9MM **Privately Held**
SIC: 3569 Filters

(P-15331)
IMERYS PERLITE USA INC
1450 Simpson Way, Escondido
(92029-1311)
P.O. Box 462908 (92046-2908)
PHONE..................................760 745-5900
Darin Jackman, *Manager*
EMP: 10
SQ FT: 13,288
SALES (corp-wide): 2.6MM **Privately
Held**
WEB: www.worldminerals.com
SIC: 3569 Filters, general line: industrial
HQ: Imerys Perlite Usa, Inc.
1732 N 1st St Ste 450
San Jose CA 95112
408 643-0215

(P-15332)
INDUSTRIAL EQP SOLUTIONS INC
Also Called: I E S
301 N Smith Ave, Corona (92880-1742)
PHONE..................................951 272-9540
Mohammad A Gauhar, *CEO*
Awais A Gauhar, *President*
Minhaj Khan, *Project Engr*
▲ **EMP:** 15 EST: 1998
SQ FT: 7,000

SALES (est): 9.1MM **Privately Held**
WEB: www.ies-corp.com
SIC: 3569 Filters

(P-15333)
INDUSTRIAL FIRE SPRNKLR CO INC
3845 Imperial Ave, San Diego
(92113-1702)
PHONE..................................619 266-6030
L David Sandage, *President*
Dave Sandage, *Manager*
EMP: 35
SALES (est): 8.4MM **Privately Held**
WEB: www.industrialfiresprinkler.com
SIC: 3569 1731 Sprinkler systems, fire:
automatic; fire detection & burglar alarm
systems specialization

(P-15334)
INVIA ROBOTICS INC (PA)
5701 Lindero Canyon Rd 3-100, Westlake
Village (91362-6487)
PHONE..................................818 597-1680
Lior Elazary, *CEO*
Dan Parks, *COO*
Randolph Voorhies, *CTO*
EMP: 10
SQ FT: 2,400
SALES: 2MM **Privately Held**
SIC: 3569 Robots, assembly line: industrial
& commercial

(P-15335)
J R SCHNEIDER CO INC
849 Jackson St, Benicia (94510-2994)
PHONE..................................707 745-0404
Bernice Schneider, *Ch of Bd*
J Stephen Schneider, *President*
Donna C Block, *CEO*
Chris Canada, *CFO*
◆ **EMP:** 13
SQ FT: 100,000
SALES (est): 3.5MM **Privately Held**
WEB: www.jrschneider.com
SIC: 3569 3471 3443 Filters, general line:
industrial; plating & polishing; fabricated
plate work (boiler shop)

(P-15336)
KINGS WAY SALES AND MKTG LLC
6680 Lockheed Dr, Redding (96002-9014)
PHONE..................................530 722-0272
David Mahrt, *Mng Member*
Charlin Mahrt,
EMP: 14
SQ FT: 4,500
SALES (est): 2.4MM **Privately Held**
SIC: 3569 Firefighting apparatus

(P-15337)
KNIGHT LLC (HQ)
15340 Barranca Pkwy, Irvine (92618-2215)
PHONE..................................949 595-4800
George Noa, *President*
Richard Yanez, *Vice Pres*
Jorge Del Portillo, *Engineer*
Chris March, *Regl Sales Mgr*
Wilson Wong, *Regl Sales Mgr*
▲ **EMP:** 100
SQ FT: 46,000
SALES (est): 18.6MM
SALES (corp-wide): 2.2B **Publicly Held**
WEB: www.knightequip.com
SIC: 3569 3582 3589 Liquid automation
machinery & equipment; commercial
laundry equipment; dishwashing ma-
chines, commercial
PA: Idex Corporation
1925 W Field Ct Ste 200
Lake Forest IL 60045
847 498-7070

(P-15338)
LA MAR INDUSTRIES INC
Also Called: Industrial Filtration
1500 Daisy Ave, Long Beach (90813-1523)
P.O. Box 2589 (90801-2589)
PHONE..................................562 436-4228
Jeffrey Greenemyer, *President*
Jeff Greenemeier, *Plant Mgr*
EMP: 12
SQ FT: 10,500

P R O D U C T S & S V C S

SALES (est): 2.7MM **Privately Held**
WEB: www.industrialfiltrationinc.com
SIC: 3569 Filters, general line: industrial

(P-15339)
LUBRICATION SCIENTICS LLC
17651 Armstrong Ave, Irvine (92614-5727)
PHONE...................714 557-0664
Richard Hanley, *Mng Member*
James Schoen, *Marketing Mgr*
EMP: 48
SALES (est): 6.6MM **Privately Held**
SIC: 3569 Lubricating equipment

(P-15340)
MAHMOOD IZADI INC
Also Called: Solatron Enterprises
3115 Lomita Blvd, Torrance (90505-5108)
PHONE...................310 325-0463
Mahmood Izadi, *President*
EMP: 14
SQ FT: 9,500
SALES: 850K **Privately Held**
WEB: www.solatron.com
SIC: 3569 Assembly machines, non-metal-
working; testing chambers for altitude,
temperature, ordnance, power

(P-15341)
MILLENNIUM AUTOMATION
1300 Fulton Pl, Fremont (94539-7990)
PHONE...................510 683-5942
Paul Adams, *President*
Jim Miller, *Treasurer*
David Miller, *Vice Pres*
Gerald Fedor, *Admin Sec*
Anthony Bauer, *Software Engr*
EMP: 16 EST: 1997
SQ FT: 5,500
SALES (est): 3.6MM
SALES (corp-wide): 988.5K **Privately
Held**
SIC: 3569 5084 Liquid automation ma-
chinery & equipment; robots, industrial
HQ: Marposs Spa
Via Saliceto 13
Bentivoglio BO 40010
051 899-111

(P-15342)
MYERS MIXERS LLC
8376 Salt Lake Ave, Cudahy (90201-5817)
PHONE...................323 560-4723
Gary Myers,
Cary Buller,
EMP: 41
SALES (est): 9.7MM **Privately Held**
SIC: 3569 Centrifuges, industrial

(P-15343)
NATIONAL FILTER MEDIA CORP
17130 Muskrat Ave Ste B, Adelanto
(92301-2473)
PHONE...................760 246-4551
EMP: 52
SALES (corp-wide): 658.7MM **Privately
Held**
SIC: 3569
HQ: The National Filter Media Corporation
691 N 400 W
Salt Lake City UT 84103
801 363-6736

(P-15344)
ONEX ENTERPRISES CORPORATION
Also Called: Onex Automation
1824 Flower Ave, Duarte (91010-2931)
PHONE...................626 358-6639
Onik Bogosyan, *President*
Edwin Thomassien, *CFO*
▲ EMP: 12
SALES (est): 1.3MM **Privately Held**
WEB: www.onexautomation.com
SIC: 3569 5084 Robots, assembly line: in-
dustrial & commercial; robots, industrial

(P-15345)
PACIFIC CONSOLIDATED INDS LLC
Also Called: PCI
12201 Magnolia Ave, Riverside
(92503-4820)
PHONE...................951 479-0860
Bob Eng, *Mng Member*
Tarik Naheiri, *President*

Paul Stevens, *CFO*
Soeren Schmitz, *Vice Pres*
Bonnie Gomez, *Administration*
◆ EMP: 77
SQ FT: 85,000
SALES (est): 31.1MM
SALES (corp-wide): 11.3MM **Privately
Held**
WEB: www.pci-intl.com
SIC: 3569 1382 Gas separators (machin-
ery); oil & gas exploration services
PA: Pci Holding Company, Inc.
12201 Magnolia Ave
Riverside CA 92503
951 479-0860

(P-15346)
PALL CORPORATION
4116 Sorrento Valley Blvd, San Diego
(92121-1407)
PHONE...................858 455-7264
Richard Mc Donald, *General Mgr*
Bill Nieman, *Engineer*
Chad Gannon, *Plant Mgr*
Dominico Garcia, *Opers Staff*
EMP: 70
SALES (corp-wide): 18.3B **Publicly Held**
WEB: www.pall.com
SIC: 3569 Filters
HQ: Pall Corporation
25 Harbor Park Dr
Port Washington NY 11050
516 484-5400

(P-15347)
PALL CORPORATION
1630 W Industrial Park St, Covina
(91722-3419)
PHONE...................626 339-7388
Sherman Tu, *Sales Engr*
EMP: 364
SALES (corp-wide): 18.3B **Publicly Held**
SIC: 3569 Filters
HQ: Pall Corporation
25 Harbor Park Dr
Port Washington NY 11050
516 484-5400

(P-15348)
PARKER-HANNIFIN CORPORATION
Racor Division
3400 Finch Rd, Modesto (95354-4125)
PHONE...................209 521-7860
Brian Hook, *Branch Mgr*
Roberto Jimenez, *Technician*
Bradley Harbur, *Design Engr*
Christopher Vandyke, *Design Engr*
Darren Anderson, *Engineer*
EMP: 700
SALES (corp-wide): 14.3B **Publicly Held**
WEB: www.parker.com
SIC: 3569 3561 3714 3564 Filters, gen-
eral line: industrial; pumps & pumping
equipment; motor vehicle parts & acces-
sories; blowers & fans
PA: Parker-Hannifin Corporation
6035 Parkland Blvd
Cleveland OH 44124
216 896-3000

(P-15349)
PARKER-HANNIFIN CORPORATION
Also Called: Process Advanced Filtration
2340 Eastman Ave, Oxnard (93030-5178)
PHONE...................805 604-3400
Aaron Zell, *Branch Mgr*
EMP: 187
SALES (corp-wide): 12B **Publicly Held**
WEB: www.parker.com
SIC: 3569 Filters
PA: Parker-Hannifin Corporation
6035 Parkland Blvd
Cleveland OH 44124
216 896-3000

(P-15350)
PCI HOLDING COMPANY INC (PA)
12201 Magnolia Ave, Riverside
(92503-4820)
PHONE...................951 479-0860
Bob Eng, *CEO*
Tarik Naheiri, *President*
EMP: 103 EST: 2012

SALES (est): 11.3MM **Privately Held**
SIC: 3569 1382 Gas separators (machinery); oil & gas exploration services

(P-15351)
PECOFACET (US) INC
Also Called: Clarcor Industrial Air
8314 Tiogawoods Dr, Sacramento
(95828-5048)
PHONE...................916 689-2328
Lori Radman, *Principal*
EMP: 12
SALES (corp-wide): 12B **Publicly Held**
SIC: 3569 3823 Filters, general line: in-
dustrial; separators for steam, gas, vapor
or air (machinery); flow instruments, in-
dustrial process type
HQ: Pecofacet (Us), Inc.
118 Washington Ave
Mineral Wells TX 76067
940 325-2575

(P-15352)
PIPELINE PRODUCTS INC
1650 Linda Vista Dr # 110, San Marcos
(92078-3810)
PHONE...................760 744-8907
Scott Higley, *President*
EMP: 17
SQ FT: 20,000
SALES (est): 4.8MM **Privately Held**
WEB: www.pipelineproducts.com
SIC: 3569 Filter elements, fluid, hydraulic
line

(P-15353)
PISTON HYDRAULIC SYSTEM INC
11614 Mcbean Dr, El Monte (91732-1105)
PHONE...................626 350-0100
Roobik Keshishian, *President*
Edwin Thomassian, *Vice Pres*
EMP: 10
SQ FT: 4,600
SALES (est): 820K **Privately Held**
SIC: 3569 8742 5084 Assembly ma-
chines, non-metalworking; robots, assem-
bly line: industrial & commercial;
automation & robotics consultant; con-
veyor systems

(P-15354)
POLLEY INC (PA)
Also Called: Kelco Sales & Engineering
11936 Front St, Norwalk (90650-2911)
P.O. Box 305 (90651-0305)
PHONE...................562 868-9861
Tracy Polley, *President*
John Polley, *Vice Pres*
Martin Blake, *Office Mgr*
Nyals Polley, *VP Prdtn*
Bill Mincher, *Sales Staff*
▲ EMP: 20 EST: 1950
SQ FT: 24,000
SALES (est): 3.3MM **Privately Held**
WEB: www.kelcosales.com
SIC: 3569 Blast cleaning equipment, dust-
less

(P-15355)
REC INC
Also Called: Ridgeline Engineering Company
2442 Cades Way, Vista (92081-7830)
PHONE...................760 727-8006
Patrick Falley, *President*
Anthony Moreau, *Vice Pres*
EMP: 10
SQ FT: 13,500
SALES (est): 2.6MM **Privately Held**
WEB: www.rec.com
SIC: 3569 Liquid automation machinery &
equipment

(P-15356)
RESCUE 42 INC
370 Ryan Ave Ste 120, Chico
(95973-9530)
P.O. Box 1242 (95927-1242)
PHONE...................530 891-3473
Tim Oconnell, *President*
EMP: 15
SALES (est): 3.9MM **Privately Held**
WEB: www.rescue42.com
SIC: 3569 Firefighting apparatus & related
equipment

(P-15357)
ROSTAR AUTO FILTER MFG CORP
Also Called: Rostar Filters
1278 Mercantile St, Oxnard (93030-7522)
PHONE...................805 278-2555
Jeff Starin, *President*
EMP: 141
SQ FT: 40,000
SALES (est): 5MM **Privately Held**
SIC: 3569 Filters

(P-15358)
SAES PURE GAS INC
4175 Santa Fe Rd, San Luis Obispo
(93401-8159)
PHONE...................805 541-9299
Timmothy Johnson, *CEO*
Giulio Canale, *President*
Paul Schrely, *Treasurer*
◆ EMP: 130
SQ FT: 50,000
SALES (est): 69.5MM
SALES (corp-wide): 62.1MM **Privately
Held**
WEB: www.puregastechnologies.com
SIC: 3569 Gas producers, generators &
other gas related equipment
HQ: S A E S Getters/U S A, Inc.
1122 E Cheyenne Mtn Blvd
Colorado Springs CO 80906
719 576-3200

(P-15359)
SEPARATION ENGINEERING INC
931 S Andreasen Dr Ste A, Escondido
(92029-1959)
PHONE...................760 489-0101
Charles E Hull, *President*
▲ EMP: 30
SQ FT: 20,000
SALES (est): 7.5MM **Privately Held**
SIC: 3569 Filters, general line: industrial

(P-15360)
SIEMENS INDUSTRY INC
5375 S Boyle Ave, Vernon (90058-3923)
PHONE...................323 277-1500
Ken Oldmixon, *Manager*
EMP: 33
SALES (corp-wide): 97.7B **Privately Held**
SIC: 3569 Filters
HQ: Siemens Industry, Inc.
100 Technology Dr
Alpharetta GA 30005
770 740-3000

(P-15361)
SIEMENS INDUSTRY INC
1441 E Washington Blvd, Los Angeles
(90021-3039)
PHONE...................724 772-1237
Aaron Boles, *Branch Mgr*
Mirko Giese, *Administration*
EMP: 33
SALES (corp-wide): 97.7B **Privately Held**
SIC: 3569 Filters
HQ: Siemens Industry, Inc.
100 Technology Dr
Alpharetta GA 30005
770 740-3000

(P-15362)
SOLARON POOL HEATING INC (PA)
3480 Sunrise Blvd Ste 100, Rancho Cor-
dova (95742-7371)
PHONE...................916 858-8146
Ron Harveck, *CEO*
Megan Deguerre, *Opers Staff*
Daron Mastainich, *Sales Associate*
Keith Langford, *Manager*
EMP: 10
SALES (est): 1.2MM **Privately Held**
SIC: 3569 Heaters, swimming pool: electric

(P-15363)
SP3 DIAMOND TECHNOLOGIES INC
1605 Wyatt Dr, Santa Clara (95054-1587)
PHONE...................877 773-9940
EMP: 15

SALES (est): 2.4MM
SALES (corp-wide): 7.8MM **Privately Held**
SIC: 3569
PA: Sp3, Inc.
1605 Wyatt Dr
Santa Clara CA 95054
408 492-0630

(P-15364)
SPINTEK FILTRATION INC
10863 Portal Dr, Los Alamitos
(90720-2508)
PHONE.............................714 236-9190
William A Greene, *CEO*
Patricia Kirk, *Vice Pres*
Donna Aubrey, *Office Mgr*
Jason D Gilmour, *Engineer*
Justin Rodriguez, *Marketing Staff*
◆ EMP: 15
SQ FT: 3,000
SALES (est): 4.3MM **Privately Held**
SIC: 3569 3069 8711 Filters & strainers, pipeline; roofing, membrane rubber; engineering services

(P-15365)
STEARNS PRODUCT DEV CORP (PA)
Also Called: Doughpro
20281 Harvill Ave, Perris (92570-7235)
PHONE.............................951 657-0379
Steven Raio, *President*
Tommy Srioudom, *Engineer*
Caroline De Jong, *Sales Staff*
Clete Fracchiolla, *Supervisor*
▲ EMP: 95
SQ FT: 5,000
SALES: 12MM **Privately Held**
SIC: 3569 3444 1721 Assembly machines, non-metalworking; sheet metalwork

(P-15366)
SUPPRESS FIRE ATMTC SPRINKLERS
363 Cliffwood Park St G, Brea
(92821-4106)
PHONE.............................714 671-5939
Oscar Delatorre, *President*
EMP: 10
SQ FT: 1,500
SALES (est): 850K **Privately Held**
SIC: 3569 Firefighting apparatus & related equipment

(P-15367)
SYNERGY OIL LLC
1201 Dove St Ste 475, Newport Beach
(92660-2812)
P.O. Box 993, Okmulgee OK (74447-0993)
PHONE.............................888 333-1933
Robert Falco, *Mng Member*
EMP: 30 EST: 2009
SQ FT: 4,000
SALES: 2.5MM **Privately Held**
SIC: 3569 5172 Gas producers, generators & other gas related equipment; fuel oil

(P-15368)
TRINET CONSTRUCTION INC
2560 Marin St, San Francisco
(94124-1015)
PHONE.. ....415 695-7814
Nora Mary Hickey, *President*
William Hickey, *Vice Pres*
Darcie Harper, *Program Mgr*
Abhishek Shrivastava, *Sr Software Eng*
John Ebert, *Engineer*
EMP: 12
SQ FT: 900
SALES (est): 6.1MM **Privately Held**
SIC: 3569 Firefighting apparatus & related equipment; firefighting apparatus

(P-15369)
TWIN DESIGN CO LLC
18458 Carlwyn Dr, Castro Valley
(94546-2030)
PHONE.............................510 329-4991
Zachary Hollis,
EMP: 10 EST: 2017
SALES (est): 446.2K **Privately Held**
SIC: 3569 Robots, assembly line: industrial & commercial

(P-15370)
TYCO FIRE PRODUCTS LP
Also Called: Tyco Fire Protection Products
6952 Preston Ave, Livermore (94551-9545)
PHONE.............................925 687-6957
Cedrick Ho, *Technical Staff*
EMP: 200 **Privately Held**
SIC: 3569 Sprinkler systems, fire: automatic; generators: steam, liquid oxygen or nitrogen
HQ: Tyco Fire Products Lp
1400 Pennbrook Pkwy
Lansdale PA 19446
215 362-0700

(P-15371)
TYCO SIMPLEXGRINNELL
3077 Wiljan Ct Ste B, Santa Rosa
(95407-5764)
PHONE.............................707 578-3212
Mark Watson, *District Mgr*
EMP: 40
SQ FT: 1,200
SALES (corp-wide): 1.3B **Privately Held**
SIC: 3569 1711 3498 3669 Sprinkler systems, fire: automatic; fire sprinkler system installation; pipe fittings, fabricated from purchased pipe; smoke detectors
PA: Tyco Simplexgrinnell
1501 Nw 51st St
Boca Raton FL 33431
561 988-3658

(P-15372)
VERTEX INDUSTRIAL INC
Also Called: Vertex Water Products
5138 Brooks St, Montclair (91763-4800)
PHONE.............................909 626-2100
Jean Voznick, *Ch of Bd*
Henry P Voznick, *President*
Hal Voznick, *Vice Pres*
Steven Voznick, *Vice Pres*
Steve Murphy, *Sales Staff*
▲ EMP: 10
SQ FT: 15,000
SALES (est): 1.9MM **Privately Held**
WEB: www.vertexwater.com
SIC: 3569 5074 Filters; water purification equipment

(P-15373)
WASSER FILTRATION INC (PA)
Also Called: Pacific Press
1215 N Fee Ana St, Anaheim (92807-1804)
PHONE.............................714 982-5600
Sean Duby, *President*
▲ EMP: 80
SQ FT: 20,000
SALES (est): 18.4MM **Privately Held**
WEB: www.pacpress.com
SIC: 3569 5084 Filters, general line: industrial; filters & strainers, pipeline; industrial machinery & equipment

(P-15374)
WATER FILTER EXCHANGE INC
980 Kirkton Pl, Glendale (91207-1550)
PHONE.............................818 808-2541
Mireille Chividian, *CEO*
EMP: 14
SQ FT: 5,000
SALES: 10MM **Privately Held**
SIC: 3569 Filters

(P-15375)
WEST BOND INC (PA)
1551 S Harris Ct, Anaheim (92806-5932)
PHONE.............................714 978-1551
John C Price, *President*
Gary Phillips, *Vice Pres*
Phyllis Eppig, *Admin Sec*
▼ EMP: 47
SQ FT: 38,000
SALES (est): 7.1MM **Privately Held**
WEB: www.westbond.com
SIC: 3569 Assembly machines, non-metalworking

(P-15376)
WOMACK INTERNATIONAL INC
3855 Cypress Dr Ste H, Petaluma
(94954-5690)
PHONE.............................707 763-1800
Thomas Womack, *President*
Michael Oakes, *Vice Pres*
Marv Guggemos, *Project Mgr*

▼ EMP: 20 EST: 1980
SQ FT: 130,000
SALES (est): 3.6MM **Privately Held**
SIC: 3569 Filter elements, fluid, hydraulic line

(P-15377)
YASKAWA AMERICA INC
1701 Kaiser Ave, Irvine (92614-5705)
PHONE.............................949 263-2640
Frank Bibas, *Branch Mgr*
EMP: 14
SALES (corp-wide): 4B **Privately Held**
WEB: www.motoman.com
SIC: 3569 Robots, assembly line: industrial & commercial
HQ: Yaskawa America, Inc.
2121 Norman Dr
Waukegan IL 60085
847 887-7000

3571 Electronic Computers

(P-15378)
3PAR INC (HQ)
4209 Technology Dr, Fremont
(94538-6339)
PHONE.............................510 445-1046
David C Scott, *President*
Adriel G Lares, *CFO*
Alastair A Short, *Vice Pres*
Ashok Singhal PHD, *CTO*
Kevin Minh Lam, *Technology*
EMP: 188
SQ FT: 263,000
SALES: 56.5MM
SALES (corp-wide): 28.8B **Publicly Held**
WEB: www.pardata.com
SIC: 3571 2542 Electronic computers; partitions & fixtures, except wood
PA: Hewlett Packard Enterprise Company
3000 Hanover St
Palo Alto CA 94304
650 687-5817

(P-15379)
A S A ENGINEERING INC
Also Called: Micro Express
8 Hammond Ste 105, Irvine (92618-1601)
PHONE.............................949 460-9911
Art Afshar, *President*
K C Shabak, *Vice Pres*
◆ EMP: 35
SQ FT: 2,000
SALES (est): 4.4MM **Privately Held**
WEB: www.microexpress.net
SIC: 3571 5963 Personal computers (microcomputers); direct selling establishments

(P-15380)
ACCURATE ALWAYS INC
127 Ocean Ave, Half Moon Bay
(94019-4042)
PHONE.............................650 728-9428
Yousef Shemisa, *CEO*
Kate Shemisa, *President*
Kate Haley, *Chief Mktg Ofcr*
EMP: 25
SQ FT: 3,500
SALES: 3.1MM **Privately Held**
WEB: www.accuratealways.com
SIC: 3571 Electronic computers

(P-15381)
ACME PORTABLE MACHINES INC
1330 Mountain View Cir, Azusa
(91702-1648)
PHONE.............................626 610-1888
James Cheng, *President*
Jay Hwang, *COO*
Henry Chandra, *General Mgr*
Myles Kelvin, *General Mgr*
Chih Kuo, *Mktg Dir*
▲ EMP: 30
SQ FT: 12,200
SALES (est): 7.3MM **Privately Held**
WEB: www.acmeportable.com
SIC: 3571 Electronic computers

(P-15382)
ADEGBESAN ADEFEMI
Also Called: Femi Data Telecommunication
1525 254th St, Harbor City (90710-2716)
PHONE.............................310 663-0789
Adefemi Adegbesan, *Owner*
EMP: 43
SALES: 100K **Privately Held**
SIC: 3571 Electronic computers

(P-15383)
ADVANCED KEYBOARD TECH INC
Also Called: Akt
2501 Golden Hill Rd # 200, Paso Robles
(93446-6391)
P.O. Box 186 (93447-0186)
PHONE.............................805 237-2055
Joel Stark, *President*
Jeffrey C Stark, *Vice Pres*
EMP: 11
SQ FT: 2,000
SALES (est): 1.6MM **Privately Held**
SIC: 3571 Electronic computers

(P-15384)
ADVANCED SCIENCE & NOVEL TECH (PA)
Also Called: Adsantec
2790 Skypark Dr Ste 104, Torrance
(90505-5331)
P.O. Box 2937, Pls Vrds Pnsl (90274-8937)
PHONE.............................310 530-9400
Vladimir Katzman, *Owner*
EMP: 20
SQ FT: 5,000
SALES: 1MM **Privately Held**
WEB: www.adsantec.com
SIC: 3571 Electronic computers

(P-15385)
ADVANSOR CORPORATION
380 Fairview Way, Milpitas (95035-3062)
PHONE.............................408 228-1008
Ker Chong Liou, *President*
▲ EMP: 10
SQ FT: 12,000
SALES (est): 1MM **Privately Held**
SIC: 3571 Mainframe computers

(P-15386)
AECHELON TECHNOLOGY INC (PA)
888 Brannan St Ste 210, San Francisco
(94103-4930)
PHONE.............................415 255-0120
Nacho Sanz-Pastor, *CEO*
Chris Blumenthal, *COO*
Bruce Johnson, *COO*
Luis Barcena, *Exec VP*
▲ EMP: 46 EST: 1998
SQ FT: 40,000
SALES (est): 18.4MM **Privately Held**
WEB: www.aechelon.com
SIC: 3571 Electronic computers

(P-15387)
AFFORDABLE GOODS
131 Cognac Cir, Sacramento (95835-2035)
PHONE.............................916 514-1049
Swarn Katyal, *Owner*
Vandana Katyal, *Owner*
EMP: 14
SALES: 575K **Privately Held**
SIC: 3571 5941 Electronic computers; sporting goods & bicycle shops

(P-15388)
ALLHEALTH INC
515 S Figueroa St # 1300, Los Angeles
(90071-3301)
PHONE.............................213 538-0762
John R Cochran, *CEO*
EMP: 250 EST: 1998
SALES (est): 22.4MM **Privately Held**
SIC: 3571 7381 Electronic computers; security guard service

(P-15389)
ALPHA RESEARCH & TECH INC
Also Called: Art
5175 Hillsdale Cir # 100, El Dorado Hills
(95762-5776)
PHONE.............................916 431-9340
Deann Kerr, *President*

Tom Bernritter, *President*
Nathan Brizzee, *Engineer*
Steve Totah, *Engineer*
Dawn Kelly, *Human Res Mgr*
EMP: 73
SQ FT: 22,000
SALES (est): 18.1MM **Privately Held**
WEB: www.artruggedsystems.com
SIC: 3571 Electronic computers

(P-15390)
AMERICAN CRCUIT CARD RETAINERS
2310 E Orangethorpe Ave, Anaheim
(92806-1231)
PHONE..........................714 738-6194
Dan Morales, *President*
Miguel D Nunez, *CFO*
Miguel Nunez, *Info Tech Mgr*
EMP: 10
SQ FT: 3,000
SALES (est): 732K **Privately Held**
SIC: 3571 Electronic computers

(P-15391)
AMERICAN RELIANCE INC
Also Called: Amrel
12941 Ramona Blvd Ste F, Baldwin Park
(91706-3756)
PHONE..........................626 443-6818
Edward Chen, *CEO*
Shelly Chen, *Admin Sec*
▲ **EMP:** 45
SQ FT: 72,000
SALES: 21.1MM **Privately Held**
WEB: www.amrel.com
SIC: 3571 Electronic computers

(P-15392)
AMPRO ADLINK TECHNOLOGY INC
Also Called: Ampro Computers, Inc.
5215 Hellyer Ave Ste 110, San Jose
(95138-1007)
PHONE..........................408 360-0200
Elizabeth Campbell, *CEO*
Mark Peterson, *Ch of Bd*
Joanne M Williams, *President*
Charles M Frank, *CFO*
Len Backus, *Vice Pres*
▲ **EMP:** 65
SQ FT: 25,000
SALES (est): 15.2MM
SALES (corp-wide): 354.4MM **Privately Held**
WEB: www.ampro.com
SIC: 3571 Electronic computers
PA: Adlink Technology Inc.
9f, 166, Jian Yi Rd.,
New Taipei City 23511
282 265-877

(P-15393)
AMTEK ELECTRONIC INC
Also Called: Manufacturers Import & Export
1150 N 5th St, San Jose (95112-4415)
PHONE..........................408 971-8787
Kathryn Yuen, *President*
John Yuen, *Vice Pres*
T C Yuen, *Vice Pres*
EMP: 35
SQ FT: 22,000
SALES: 2.5MM **Privately Held**
SIC: 3571 3679 3577 Electronic computers; power supplies, all types: static; computer peripheral equipment

(P-15394)
AP PARPRO INC
9565 Heinrich Hertz Dr # 1, San Diego
(92154-7920)
PHONE..........................760 931-7800
Thomas Sparrvik, *CEO*
EMP: 230 **EST:** 2010
SALES (est): 15MM **Privately Held**
SIC: 3571 3444 3548 3643 Electronic computers; sheet metalwork; welding apparatus; current-carrying wiring devices

(P-15395)
BOLD DATA TECHNOLOGY INC
Also Called: Crown Micro
48363 Fremont Blvd, Fremont
(94538-6580)
PHONE..........................510 490-8296
Eugene Kiang, *President*

Marco Yee, *CFO*
Winston Xia, *Exec VP*
Marvin Deleport, *Executive*
Bonnie Silva, *Administration*
▲ **EMP:** 45
SQ FT: 50,000
SALES (est): 38.3MM **Privately Held**
WEB: www.boldata.com
SIC: 3571 3577 3674 Personal computers (microcomputers); computer peripheral equipment; computer logic modules

(P-15396)
BORSOS ENGINEERING INC
5924 Balfour Ct Ste 102, Carlsbad
(92008-7378)
PHONE..........................760 930-0296
Steven D Borso, *President*
EMP: 25
SQ FT: 5,600
SALES (est): 4.1MM **Privately Held**
SIC: 3571 Electronic computers

(P-15397)
BULL HN INFO SYSTEMS INC
6077 Bristol Pkwy, Culver City
(90230-6601)
PHONE..........................310 337-3600
Tom Skelly, *Branch Mgr*
EMP: 20
SALES (corp-wide): 170.3MM **Privately Held**
SIC: 3571 3577 7378 7373 Mainframe computers; computer peripheral equipment; computer & data processing equipment repair/maintenance; computer peripheral equipment repair & maintenance; systems integration services
HQ: Bull Hn Information Systems Inc.
285 Billerica Rd Ste 200
Chelmsford MA 01824
978 294-6000

(P-15398)
CEMTROL INC
3035 E La Jolla St, Anaheim (92806-1303)
PHONE..........................714 666-6606
Sharon Paz, *President*
Marie Penton, *CEO*
Reuven Arad, *Info Tech Mgr*
Steve Smith, *Design Engr*
Samuel Paz, *Engineer*
EMP: 15
SALES: 3.3MM **Privately Held**
SIC: 3571 Electronic computers

(P-15399)
CENTENT COMPANY
3879 S Main St, Santa Ana (92707-5787)
PHONE..........................714 979-6491
August Freimanis, *Partner*
Mariss Freimanis, *Partner*
EMP: 20 **EST:** 1972
SQ FT: 2,500
SALES (est): 2.8MM **Privately Held**
WEB: www.centent.com
SIC: 3571 5063 Computers, digital, analog or hybrid; electrical apparatus & equipment

(P-15400)
COASTAL PVA OPCO LLC
1380 E Beamer St, Woodland
(95776-6003)
PHONE..........................530 406-3303
Joseph P Binkley,
Jeff Miller, *CFO*
EMP: 15
SALES (est): 709.6K **Privately Held**
SIC: 3571 Electronic computers

(P-15401)
COLFAX INTERNATIONAL
750 Palomar Ave, Sunnyvale (94085-2914)
PHONE..........................408 730-2275
Gautam Shah, *CEO*
Barbara Karvonen, *COO*
Danny Leung, *Business Anlyst*
Achim Wengeler, *Director*
▼ **EMP:** 31
SQ FT: 20,000
SALES: 48.5MM **Privately Held**
WEB: www.colfax-intl.com
SIC: 3571 Electronic computers

(P-15402)
COMPUTER ACCESS TECH CORP
3385 Scott Blvd, Santa Clara (95054-3115)
PHONE..........................408 727-6600
Fax: 408 727-6622
EMP: 67
SQ FT: 14,000
SALES (est): 6.1MM
SALES (corp-wide): 2.1B **Publicly Held**
SIC: 3571 7371 3577
HQ: Teledyne Lecroy, Inc.
700 Chestnut Ridge Rd
Chestnut Ridge NY 10977
845 425-2000

(P-15403)
CONTINUOUS COMPUTING CORP
Also Called: Ccpu
10431 Wtridge Cir Ste 110, San Diego
(92121)
PHONE..........................858 882-8800
Mike Dagenais, *CEO*
Ron Pyles, *President*
Bob Wise, *President*
Erez Barnavon, *CFO*
Robert Cagle, *Vice Pres*
EMP: 22
SQ FT: 48,000
SALES (est): 7.7MM
SALES (corp-wide): 133.7MM **Publicly Held**
WEB: www.ccpu.com
SIC: 3571 3661 4812 5045 Computers, digital, analog or hybrid; telephone & telegraph apparatus; radio telephone communication; computers, peripherals & software; computer integrated systems design
PA: Radisys Corporation
5435 Ne Dawson Creek Dr
Hillsboro OR 97124
503 615-1100

(P-15404)
CYBERNET MANUFACTURING INC
5 Holland Ste 201, Irvine (92618-2574)
PHONE..........................949 600-8000
Pouran Shoaee, *CEO*
Jeff Salem, *Purch Dir*
Tim Dalke, *Natl Sales Mgr*
Joe Divino, *VP Mktg*
Tina Jo Wentz, *Marketing Staff*
◆ **EMP:** 720
SALES (est): 112.6MM **Privately Held**
WEB: www.cybernetman.com
SIC: 3571 3577 Electronic computers; computer peripheral equipment

(P-15405)
DELL INC
Also Called: Enterprise Solutions Group
5450 Great America Pkwy, Santa Clara
(95054-3644)
PHONE..........................408 206-5466
Nariman Teymourian, *Exec Dir*
Deanna Kilbride, *Executive Asst*
Mike Chow, *Engineer*
Kenneth Coley, *Engineer*
Theodore Chen, *Counsel*
EMP: 11
SALES (corp-wide): 78.6B **Publicly Held**
SIC: 3571 Electronic computers
HQ: Dell Inc.
1 Dell Way
Round Rock TX 78682
800 289-3355

(P-15406)
EDGE SOLUTIONS CONSULTING INC (PA)
2801 Townsgate Rd Ste 111, Westlake Village (91361-3028)
P.O. Box 661480, Arcadia (91066-1480)
PHONE..........................818 591-3500
Marti R Hedge, *President*
Kathy Valencia, *Principal*
Kailee Holt, *Business Anlyst*
Robert Hedge, *VP Sales*
Sean Thomas, *Accounts Exec*
EMP: 28
SQ FT: 600

SALES (est): 9.4MM **Privately Held**
SIC: 3571 Mainframe computers

(P-15407)
ELECTRONIC COOLING SOLUTIONS
2344 Walsh Ave Ste B, Santa Clara
(95051-1327)
PHONE..........................408 738-8331
William Maltz, *President*
EMP: 15 **EST:** 2009
SALES (est): 2.4MM **Privately Held**
SIC: 3571 Electronic computers

(P-15408)
ELECTRONIC SYSTEMS INNOVATION
Also Called: Esi
5777 W Century Blvd # 1225, Los Angeles
(90045-5600)
PHONE..........................310 645-8400
Eli Cohen, *President*
EMP: 15
SALES (est): 1.9MM **Privately Held**
SIC: 3571 Electronic computers

(P-15409)
ELMA ELECTRONIC INC (HQ)
44350 S Grimmer Blvd, Fremont
(94538-6385)
PHONE..........................510 656-3400
Fred Ruegg, *CEO*
Shan Morgan, *President*
Peter Brunner, *Exec VP*
Ram Rajan, *Senior VP*
Sean Morgan, *Vice Pres*
▲ **EMP:** 150
SQ FT: 100,000
SALES (est): 73.1MM
SALES (corp-wide): 145.6MM **Privately Held**
SIC: 3571 3575 3577 Electronic computers; computer terminals; computer peripheral equipment
PA: Elma Electronic Ag
Hofstrasse 93
Wetzikon ZH 8620
449 334-111

(P-15410)
EMC CORPORATION
2201 Dupont Dr Ste 500, Irvine
(92612-7520)
PHONE..........................949 794-9999
Leonnard Iventosch, *Manager*
David Bryner, *Engineer*
Gary Bluhm, *Sales Mgr*
Joey Lei, *Manager*
Mike Reynolds, *Manager*
EMP: 85
SALES (corp-wide): 78.6B **Publicly Held**
WEB: www.emc.com
SIC: 3571 5045 Electronic computers; computers, peripherals & software
HQ: Emc Corporation
176 South St
Hopkinton MA 01748
508 435-1000

(P-15411)
EXPERT COMPUTER INTL INC (PA)
Also Called: Expertpower Direct
6437 Alondra Blvd, Paramount
(90723-3758)
PHONE..........................562 630-3002
Wen Cheng-Kan, *President*
Ruby Chu, *CFO*
Jesse Kan, *Vice Pres*
▲ **EMP:** 38
SQ FT: 13,000
SALES: 12MM **Privately Held**
WEB: www.expertcom.com
SIC: 3571 Electronic computers

(P-15412)
EXPORTECH WORLDWIDE LLC
Also Called: Imagictech
14310 Burning Tree Dr, Victorville
(92395-4368)
PHONE..........................909 278-9477
Carlos A Colin,
EMP: 10
SALES: 60K **Privately Held**
SIC: 3571 Electronic computers

▲ = Import ▼=Export
◆ =Import/Export

(P-15413)
GARNER HOLT PRODUCTIONS INC
825 E Cooley Ave, San Bernardino (92408-2823)
PHONE.....................909 799-3030
Garner L Holt, *President*
Andrew Garner, *Partner*
Michelle Berg, *Vice Pres*
Victor Martin, *Project Mgr*
Donna Jones, *Accountant*
EMP: 50
SQ FT: 50,000
SALES: 6.6MM **Privately Held**
WEB: www.garnerholt.com
SIC: 3571 Electronic computers

(P-15414)
GATEWAY INC (DH)
7565 Irvine Center Dr # 150, Irvine (92618-4933)
PHONE.....................949 471-7000
Ed Coleman, *CEO*
Bradly Shaw, *President*
John Goldsberry, *CFO*
Craig Calle, *Treasurer*
Michael R Tyler, *Senior VP*
▲ EMP: 250
SQ FT: 98,000
SALES (est): 333.2MM
SALES (corp-wide): 7.8B **Privately Held**
WEB: www.gateway.com
SIC: 3571 3577 Personal computers (microcomputers); computer peripheral equipment

(P-15415)
GATEWAY US RETAIL INC
7565 Irvine Center Dr, Irvine (92618-4918)
PHONE.....................949 471-7000
Wayne R Inouye, *President*
Brian Firestone, *Exec VP*
▲ EMP: 134 EST: 1998
SQ FT: 147,000
SALES (est): 10.5MM
SALES (corp-wide): 7.8B **Privately Held**
WEB: www.emachines.com
SIC: 3571 3577 5045 Electronic computers; computer peripheral equipment; computers, peripherals & software
HQ: Gateway, Inc.
7565 Irvine Center Dr # 150
Irvine CA 92618
949 471-7000

(P-15416)
GENERAL DYNMICS MSSION SYSTEMS
5922 Roseville Rd, Sacramento (95842-4030)
PHONE.....................916 339-3852
EMP: 151
SALES (corp-wide): 30.9B **Publicly Held**
SIC: 3571 Electronic computers
HQ: General Dynamics Mission Systems, Inc.
12450 Fair Lakes Cir # 200
Fairfax VA 22033
703 263-2800

(P-15417)
GENERAL MICRO SYSTEMS INC (PA)
Also Called: G M S
8358 Maple Pl, Rancho Cucamonga (91730-3839)
P.O. Box 3689 (91729-3689)
PHONE.....................909 980-4863
Benjamin K Sharfi, *President*
EMP: 80
SQ FT: 20,000
SALES (est): 24.9MM **Privately Held**
WEB: www.gms4sbc.com
SIC: 3571 Personal computers (microcomputers)

(P-15418)
GENESIS COMPUTER SYSTEMS INC
4055 E La Palma Ave Ste C, Anaheim (92807-1750)
PHONE.....................714 632-3648
Awaiz Akram, *President*
Shawn Dewan, *Vice Pres*
Sam Patel, *Purch Agent*

EMP: 31
SQ FT: 3,500
SALES (est): 6.6MM **Privately Held**
SIC: 3571 Electronic computers

(P-15419)
HEWLETT-PACKARD ENTPS LLC (HQ)
3000 Hanover St, Palo Alto (94304-1185)
PHONE.....................650 687-5817
Dion J Weisler, *CEO*
Tim Stonesifer, *Exec VP*
Brian Cumbra, *Vice Pres*
Jim Haring, *Vice Pres*
Laurel Krieger, *Vice Pres*
▲ EMP: 89
SALES (est): 1.8B
SALES (corp-wide): 52B **Publicly Held**
SIC: 3571 Electronic computers
PA: Hp Inc.
1501 Page Mill Rd
Palo Alto CA 94304
650 857-1501

(P-15420)
HP INC (PA)
1501 Page Mill Rd, Palo Alto (94304-1126)
P.O. Box 10301 (94303-0890)
PHONE.....................650 857-1501
Dion J Weisler, *President*
Carol Hamilton, *Partner*
Scott Strong, *Partner*
Charles V Bergh, *Ch of Bd*
Alex Cho, *President*
EMP: 2500 EST: 1939
SALES: 52B **Publicly Held**
SIC: 3571 7372 3861 3577 Personal computers (microcomputers); minicomputers; prepackaged software; cameras, still & motion picture (all types); diazotype (whiteprint) reproduction machines & equipment; printers, computer; optical scanning devices; computer storage devices; computer terminals

(P-15421)
HP INC
1140 Enterprise Way, Sunnyvale (94089-1412)
PHONE.....................978 687-1501
Bradley Lew, *Branch Mgr*
Jamie Marquez, *Partner*
Christoph Ruef, *President*
Fernando Moreno, *Business Dir*
Fred Van Buiten, *Comms Mgr*
EMP: 2000
SALES (corp-wide): 52B **Publicly Held**
SIC: 3571 Personal computers (microcomputers)
PA: Hp Inc.
1501 Page Mill Rd
Palo Alto CA 94304
650 857-1501

(P-15422)
HP INC
481 Cottonwood Dr, Milpitas (95035-7404)
PHONE.....................650 857-1501
Shengwu Luo, *Branch Mgr*
EMP: 1001
SALES (corp-wide): 52B **Publicly Held**
SIC: 3571 Personal computers (microcomputers)
PA: Hp Inc.
1501 Page Mill Rd
Palo Alto CA 94304
650 857-1501

(P-15423)
HP INC
1501 Page Mill Rd, Palo Alto (94304-1126)
PHONE.....................650 857-4946
Richard D Lampman, *Senior VP*
Brenda Tsang, *Research Analys*
Claudia Santos, *Accounts Mgr*
EMP: 3000
SALES (corp-wide): 52B **Publicly Held**
SIC: 3571 Personal computers (microcomputers)
PA: Hp Inc.
1501 Page Mill Rd
Palo Alto CA 94304
650 857-1501

(P-15424)
HP INC
130 Lytton Ave, Palo Alto (94301-1065)
PHONE.....................650 857-1501
Mark S Manasse, *Principal*
EMP: 80
SALES (corp-wide): 52B **Publicly Held**
SIC: 3571 Personal computers (microcomputers)
PA: Hp Inc.
1501 Page Mill Rd
Palo Alto CA 94304
650 857-1501

(P-15425)
HP INC
3495 Deer Creek Rd, Palo Alto (94304-1316)
P.O. Box 10301 (94303-0890)
PHONE.....................650 857-1501
Deidre Hoehn, *Branch Mgr*
EMP: 25
SALES (corp-wide): 52B **Publicly Held**
SIC: 3571 Personal computers (microcomputers)
PA: Hp Inc.
1501 Page Mill Rd
Palo Alto CA 94304
650 857-1501

(P-15426)
HP INC
303 2nd St Ste S500, San Francisco (94107-1373)
PHONE.....................415 979-3700
Ben Nelson, *General Mgr*
Chuck Zelanis, *Program Mgr*
EMP: 70
SALES (corp-wide): 52B **Publicly Held**
SIC: 3571 Personal computers (microcomputers)
PA: Hp Inc.
1501 Page Mill Rd
Palo Alto CA 94304
650 857-1501

(P-15427)
HPI FEDERAL LLC (HQ)
1501 Page Mill Rd, Palo Alto (94304-1126)
PHONE.....................650 857-1501
Mark T Prather, *President*
Dave Block, *Senior Mgr*
Jim Lindsey, *Manager*
EMP: 12
SALES (est): 1.5MM
SALES (corp-wide): 52B **Publicly Held**
SIC: 3571 Electronic computers
PA: Hp Inc.
1501 Page Mill Rd
Palo Alto CA 94304
650 857-1501

(P-15428)
INDUSTRIAL CPU SYSTEMS INTL
Also Called: Icpu
2225 S Grand Ave, Santa Ana (92705-5235)
P.O. Box 93445, Los Angeles (90093-0445)
PHONE.....................714 957-2815
Mehrdad Ayati, *President*
Mehran Ayali, *Exec Dir*
EMP: 15
SQ FT: 7,000
SALES (est): 1.4MM **Privately Held**
WEB: www.icpu.com
SIC: 3571 7371 Electronic computers; computer software systems analysis & design, custom

(P-15429)
INETWORK INC
575 6th Ave Unit 1402, San Diego (92101-8625)
PHONE.....................619 401-7334
Ernest Martinez, *President*
Stu Gross, *CIO*
Barry Brueseke, *VP Engrg*
Kelly May, *Marketing Mgr*
Brianne Martinez, *Marketing Staff*
EMP: 11
SQ FT: 1,000
SALES: 700K **Privately Held**
WEB: www.inetwork-west.com
SIC: 3571 Electronic computers

(P-15430)
INNOWI INC
3240 Scott Blvd, Santa Clara (95054-3011)
PHONE.....................408 609-9404
Zia Hasnain, *CEO*
Asis REO, *President*
Saisel Seed, *CIO*
EMP: 40 EST: 2014
SALES (est): 2.1MM **Privately Held**
SIC: 3571 Electronic computers

(P-15431)
INSPUR SYSTEMS INC (HQ)
47451 Fremont Blvd, Fremont (94538-6504)
PHONE.....................800 697-5893
Ziliang Leon Zheng, *President*
Meng Zhu, *CFO*
John Hu, *Vice Pres*
Kevin Huang, *Vice Pres*
Peter Peng, *Vice Pres*
▲ EMP: 50
SALES: 180MM **Privately Held**
SIC: 3571 Electronic computers
PA: Inspur Group Co., Ltd.
4f,North Floor No.5 Building,Langchao Technology Park, No.1036,L
Jinan 25000
531 851-0600

(P-15432)
INTERNATIONAL BUS MCHS CORP
Also Called: IBM
6033 W Century Blvd # 610, Los Angeles (90045-6410)
PHONE.....................310 412-8699
Paul King, *Partner*
Danny Brennan, *Administration*
Lee Armstrong, *Manager*
EMP: 923
SALES (corp-wide): 79.1B **Publicly Held**
WEB: www.ibm.com
SIC: 3571 Minicomputers
PA: International Business Machines Corporation
1 New Orchard Rd Ste 1 # 1
Armonk NY 10504
914 499-1900

(P-15433)
IPARIS LLC
10120 Wexted Way, Elk Grove (95757-5501)
PHONE.....................866 293-2872
Jacque Ojadidi,
EMP: 10 EST: 2017
SQ FT: 3,900
SALES: 2MM **Privately Held**
SIC: 3571 2741 Electronic computers;

(P-15434)
JAF INTERNATIONAL INC
2917 Bayview Dr, Fremont (94538-6520)
PHONE.....................510 656-1718
Yi Zhao, *CEO*
Joy Yan, *General Mgr*
Phuong Truong, *Accounting Mgr*
David Huang, *Marketing Staff*
Stephen Wong, *Consultant*
▲ EMP: 12 EST: 2008
SQ FT: 12,000
SALES (est): 3.7MM **Privately Held**
SIC: 3571 8748 Electronic computers; business consulting

(P-15435)
JETNEXUS LLC
3201 Great America Pkwy Ste 320, Santa Clara (95054)
PHONE.....................800 568-9921
Greg Howett, *Mng Member*
John Speraneo, *Vice Pres*
EMP: 50 EST: 2002
SQ FT: 200
SALES (est): 3.2MM **Privately Held**
SIC: 3571 Electronic computers

(P-15436)
JOINT TECHNOLOGIES LIMITED
5120 E La Palma Ave # 205, Anaheim (92807-2091)
PHONE.....................949 361-1158
Nigel Cheatle, *CEO*
Pamela Higbie, *Admin Sec*
EMP: 10

SQ FT: 4,500
SALES (est): 1.6MM **Privately Held**
WEB: www.jointtech.com
SIC: **3571** 7371 Personal computers (microcomputers); computer software systems analysis & design, custom

(P-15437)
KASER CORPORATION
801 Vista Hill Ter, Fremont (94539-3210)
PHONE.....................510 657-9002
Steve Hung, *President*
Manny Tang, *Vice Pres*
Wendy Salas, *Nurse*
▲ EMP: 15
SALES (est): 1.5MM **Privately Held**
WEB: www.kasercorp.com
SIC: **3571** Electronic computers

(P-15438)
KAZAN NETWORKS CORPORATION
1544 Eureka Rd Ste 250, Roseville (95661-3093)
PHONE.....................916 259-0087
Joe Steinmetz, *CEO*
Mike Thompson, *CTO*
EMP: 28 EST: 2014
SQ FT: 3,288
SALES (est): 1.9MM **Privately Held**
SIC: **3571** Electronic computers

(P-15439)
KONTRON AMERICA INC
9477 Waples St Ste 150, San Diego (92121-2937)
PHONE.....................800 822-7522
John Goode Jr, *President*
Thomas Sparrvik, *COO*
Ken Lowe, *CFO*
Kelly Jacobs, *Vice Pres*
Jim St John, *Engineer*
▲ EMP: 75
SQ FT: 40,000
SALES (est): 11.1MM
SALES (corp-wide): 1B **Privately Held**
WEB: www.aplabs.com
SIC: **3571** 7373 Electronic computers; computer integrated systems design
HQ: Kontron S&T Ag
Lise-Meitner-Str. 3-5
Augsburg 86156
821 408-60

(P-15440)
KONTRON AMERICA INCORPORATED (DH)
9477 Waples St Ste 150, San Diego (92121-2937)
PHONE.....................858 677-0877
Kevin Rhoads, *CEO*
Stefan Milnor, *President*
Stefan Milnov, *President*
Andy Mason, *Vice Pres*
Fran Moore, *Vice Pres*
▲ EMP: 163
SQ FT: 140,000
SALES (est): 72.1MM
SALES (corp-wide): 1B **Privately Held**
WEB: www.kontron.com
SIC: **3571** 3577 Electronic computers; computer peripheral equipment
HQ: Kontron S&T Ag
Lise-Meitner-Str. 3-5
Augsburg 86156
821 408-60

(P-15441)
KUNA SYSTEMS CORPORATION
883 Sneath Ln Ste 222, San Bruno (94066-2413)
PHONE.....................650 263-8257
Saiway Fu, *CEO*
Haomiao Huang, *Vice Pres*
Betty Tam, *Office Mgr*
EMP: 12 EST: 2012
SQ FT: 1,500
SALES (est): 659.4K **Privately Held**
SIC: **3571** Computers, digital, analog or hybrid

(P-15442)
L3 TECHNOLOGIES INC
Also Called: Winchester Electronics Div
9795 Bus Park Dr Ste K, Sacramento (95827-1708)
PHONE.....................916 363-6581
Herbert Russell, *Branch Mgr*
EMP: 55
SALES (corp-wide): 9.5B **Publicly Held**
SIC: **3571** Personal computers (microcomputers)
PA: L3 Technologies, Inc.
600 3rd Ave Fl 34
New York NY 10016
212 697-1111

(P-15443)
LD SMART INC
Also Called: Link Depot
1971 W Holt Ave, Pomona (91768-3352)
PHONE.....................626 581-8887
Benny Sun, *President*
▲ EMP: 12
SALES (est): 2.3MM **Privately Held**
WEB: www.link-depot.com
SIC: **3571** Electronic computers

(P-15444)
LEAP MOTION INC (PA)
321 11th St, San Francisco (94103-4313)
PHONE.....................954 234-6321
Michael Buckwald, *CEO*
Tom Kaweski General Counsel, *CFO*
Tom Kaweski, *CFO*
Eva Babiak, *Comms Dir*
Alex Marcolina, *Software Engr*
EMP: 36
SALES (est): 14MM **Privately Held**
SIC: **3571** Electronic computers

(P-15445)
M2 MARKETPLACE INC
2555 W 190th St 201, Torrance (90504-6002)
PHONE.....................310 354-3600
Sam Khulusi, *President*
Jeremy Laurenson, *Info Tech Dir*
Don Barnum, *Purch Dir*
Kevin Tchoreret, *Accounts Exec*
EMP: 15
SALES (est): 4.6MM
SALES (corp-wide): 2.1B **Publicly Held**
WEB: www.onsale.com
SIC: **3571** Electronic computers
PA: Pcm, Inc.
1940 E Mariposa Ave
El Segundo CA 90245
310 354-5600

(P-15446)
MAGNELL ASSOCIATE INC
Also Called: Newegg.com
17708 Rowland St, City of Industry (91748-1119)
PHONE.....................626 271-1320
Fred Chang, *President*
EMP: 13
SALES (corp-wide): 1.8B **Privately Held**
SIC: **3571** 5961 5045 Personal computers (microcomputers); computers & peripheral equipment, mail order; computers, peripherals & software
HQ: Magnell Associate, Inc.
17560 Rowland St
City Of Industry CA 91748
626 271-9700

(P-15447)
MANUTRONICS CO
Also Called: Liantronics
46722 Fremont Blvd, Fremont (94538-6538)
PHONE.....................510 438-0588
Thuha Dang, *Partner*
Nine-Ets Lu, *Partner*
Cuong Tran, *Manager*
EMP: 39
SALES (est): 4MM **Privately Held**
SIC: **3571** Electronic computers

(P-15448)
MATERIAL IN MOTION INC (PA)
385 Moffett Park Dr # 115, Sunnyvale (94089-1218)
PHONE.....................650 967-3300
Ted Salah, *CEO*

Minal Patel, *Info Tech Dir*
Rohit Kumar, *Info Tech Mgr*
Jignasa Patel, *Software Dev*
Ali Ghalandari, *Analyst*
◆ EMP: 200
SQ FT: 20,000
SALES (est): 134.4MM **Privately Held**
SIC: **3571** Electronic computers

(P-15449)
MC2 SABTECH HOLDINGS INC (PA)
Also Called: Ixi Technology
22705 Savi Ranch Pkwy, Yorba Linda (92887-4604)
PHONE.....................714 692-3800
Michael Carter, *CEO*
Thomas Bell, *CFO*
Karen Thomas Gibson, *Accountant*
Glenn Darrow, *Sales Mgr*
John Hope, *Manager*
EMP: 32
SQ FT: 40,000
SALES (est): 10.4MM **Privately Held**
WEB: www.sabtech.com
SIC: **3571** 3672 Electronic computers; printed circuit boards

(P-15450)
MCUBE INC (PA)
2570 N 1st St Ste 300, San Jose (95131-1018)
PHONE.....................408 637-5503
Ben Lee, *CEO*
Sanjay Bhandari, *Vice Pres*
EMP: 24
SALES (est): 7.8MM **Privately Held**
SIC: **3571** Personal computers (microcomputers)

(P-15451)
MEDIATEK USA INC (PA)
2840 Junction Ave, San Jose (95134-1922)
PHONE.....................408 526-1899
Ming-Kai Tsai, *Ch of Bd*
Jyh-Jer Cho, *Vice Chairman*
Ching-Jiang Hsieh, *President*
David Ku, *CFO*
Cheng-Te Chuang, *Senior VP*
▲ EMP: 102 EST: 1997
SALES (est): 75.8MM **Privately Held**
SIC: **3571** 3674 Electronic computers; semiconductors & related devices

(P-15452)
MEDIATEK USA INC
96 Corporate Park Ste 300, Irvine (92606-3107)
PHONE.....................408 526-1899
EMP: 11
SALES (corp-wide): 75.8MM **Privately Held**
SIC: **3571** 3674 Electronic computers; semiconductors & related devices
PA: Mediatek Usa Inc.
2840 Junction Ave
San Jose CA 95134
408 526-1899

(P-15453)
MELROSE MAC INC
2400 W Olive Ave, Burbank (91506-2630)
PHONE.....................818 840-8466
Sean Nasseri, *Branch Mgr*
EMP: 13
SALES (corp-wide): 12.2MM **Privately Held**
WEB: www.melrosemac.com
SIC: **3571** 5045 5734 8748 Electronic computers; computers, peripherals & software; computer & software stores; business consulting
PA: Melrose Mac, Inc.
6614 Melrose Ave
Los Angeles CA 90038
323 937-4600

(P-15454)
MERCURY SYSTMS-TRSTD MSSN SLTN (HQ)
Also Called: Themis
47200 Bayside Pkwy, Fremont (94538-6567)
PHONE.....................510 252-0870
Mark Aslett, *President*
Dennis Smith, *President*

Didier Mc Thibaud, *COO*
Michael D Ruppert, *CFO*
Christopher C Cambria, *Exec VP*
EMP: 65
SQ FT: 54,000
SALES (est): 34.4MM
SALES (corp-wide): 493.1MM **Publicly Held**
SIC: **3571** Electronic computers
PA: Mercury Systems, Inc.
50 Minuteman Rd
Andover MA 01810
978 256-1300

(P-15455)
MICILE INC
1225 S Shamrock Ave, Monrovia (91016-4244)
PHONE.....................626 381-9974
Naresh Menon, *CEO*
Jim Axtelle, *Project Mgr*
EMP: 15
SALES (est): 1.1MM **Privately Held**
SIC: **3571** Minicomputers

(P-15456)
MICRO/SYS INC
3730 Park Pl, Montrose (91020-1623)
PHONE.....................818 244-4600
Susan Wooley, *President*
James K Finster, *Vice Pres*
Alex Ayala, *Electrical Engi*
EMP: 30
SALES (est): 6MM **Privately Held**
WEB: www.embeddedsys.com
SIC: **3571** 3674 Electronic computers; semiconductors & related devices

(P-15457)
MIDERN COMPUTER INC
Also Called: Sager Co
18005 Cortney Ct, City of Industry (91748-1203)
PHONE.....................626 964-8682
Shooing Song Yuan, *President*
T Y Lee, *Vice Pres*
Frank Chu, *General Mgr*
Jim Hung, *Webmaster*
Tim LI, *Engineer*
▲ EMP: 40
SQ FT: 10,000
SALES (est): 12.7MM **Privately Held**
WEB: www.sager-midern.com
SIC: **3571** 5734 Personal computers (microcomputers); computer & software stores

(P-15458)
MILDEF INC (PA)
630 W Lambert Rd, Brea (92821-3139)
PHONE.....................703 224-8835
Nagnus Pyk, *President*
Wendy Cheng, *Manager*
EMP: 11
SQ FT: 5,000
SALES: 6MM **Privately Held**
SIC: **3571** Electronic computers

(P-15459)
MINTRONIX INC
6090 Cielo Vista Ct, Camarillo (93012-8210)
PHONE.....................805 482-1298
Robert Lee, *President*
Yaoling Lee, *Controller*
▲ EMP: 15
SQ FT: 10,000
SALES: 7MM **Privately Held**
WEB: www.mintronix.com
SIC: **3571** Electronic computers

(P-15460)
MITAC USA INC (DH)
Also Called: Mio Technology
47988 Fremont Blvd, Fremont (94538-6507)
PHONE.....................510 661-2800
Billy Ho, *President*
Matthew Miau, *Chairman*
Kent Dickerson, *Sales Dir*
Jack Wu, *Director*
Joanna Wang, *Manager*
EMP: 27

▲ = Import ▼=Export
◆ =Import/Export

SALES (est): 10.2MM
SALES (corp-wide): 1.6B **Privately Held**
WEB: www.mitacusa.com
SIC: 3571 Electronic computers

(P-15461)
MITXPC INC
Also Called: Mitxpc Embedded Sys Solutions
45437 Warm Springs Blvd, Fremont
(94539-6104)
PHONE.....................................510 226-6883
Eric Pang, *CEO*
John Ho, *Sales Mgr*
▲ EMP: 13
SQ FT: 10,000
SALES (est): 1MM **Privately Held**
SIC: 3571 8731 Computers, digital, analog
or hybrid; computer (hardware) develop-
ment

(P-15462)
MOCKINGBIRD NETWORKS
10040 Bubb Rd, Cupertino (95014-4132)
PHONE.....................................408 342-5300
Pong Lim, *CEO*
Ken Murray, *President*
John Chun, *COO*
Steve Y Kim, *Principal*
Alex Finch, *Finance*
EMP: 80
SQ FT: 8,000
SALES (est): 7.9MM **Privately Held**
WEB: www.mockingbirdnetworks.com
SIC: 3571 3672 3577 Electronic comput-
ers; printed circuit boards; computer pe-
ripheral equipment

(P-15463)
MPEG INDUSTRIES INC
Also Called: Enhance Electronics
1951 S Parco Ave Ste A, Ontario
(91761-8315)
PHONE.....................................562 677-1268
Douglas Su, *President*
Kevin Liu, *Vice Pres*
David Wang, *Vice Pres*
▲ EMP: 12
SQ FT: 12,800
SALES (est): 2MM **Privately Held**
WEB: www.enhanceusa.com
SIC: 3571 3648 Computers, digital, analog
or hybrid; searchlights

(P-15464)
MULFAT LLC
15835 Monte St Ste 103, Sylmar
(91342-7673)
PHONE.....................................818 367-0149
Daniel Mulcahey, *Principal*
EMP: 20
SALES (est): 1.4MM **Privately Held**
SIC: 3571 Electronic computers

(P-15465)
MYRICOM INC
3871 E Colo Blvd Ste 101, Pasadena
(91107)
PHONE.....................................626 821-5555
Nanette Boden, *President*
Robert Henigson, *Ch of Bd*
Rick Patton, *CFO*
Mike McPherson, *Vice Pres*
Dave Brandt, *Opers Staff*
▲ EMP: 45
SQ FT: 17,000
SALES (est): 10.2MM **Privately Held**
WEB: www.myri.com
SIC: 3571 Electronic computers

(P-15466)
NIXSYS INC
34 Mauchly Ste B, Irvine (92618-2357)
PHONE.....................................714 435-9610
Nicolas Szczedrin, *President*
Laura Lam, *Accountant*
Waleed Dahbour, *Production*
Andrew Martinovich, *Sales Mgr*
Brandon Lang, *Cust Mgr*
▲ EMP: 10
SALES (est): 2.6MM **Privately Held**
WEB: www.nixsys.com
SIC: 3571 7379 Electronic computers;
computer related consulting services

(P-15467)
OMNICELL INC
725 Sycamore Dr, Milpitas (95035-7411)
PHONE.....................................408 907-8868
EMP: 10 **Publicly Held**
SIC: 3571 Electronic computers
PA: Omnicell, Inc.
590 E Middlefield Rd
Mountain View CA 94043

(P-15468)
OMNICELL INC (PA)
590 E Middlefield Rd, Mountain View
(94043-4008)
PHONE.....................................650 251-6100
Randall A Lipps, *Ch of Bd*
J Christopher Drew, *President*
Robin G Seim, *President*
Peter J Kuipers, *CFO*
Rob Seim, *CFO*
▲ EMP: 273
SQ FT: 99,900
SALES (est): 716.1MM **Publicly Held**
WEB: www.omnicell.com
SIC: 3571 Electronic computers

(P-15469)
ORACLE AMERICA INC (HQ)
Also Called: Sun Microsystems
500 Oracle Pkwy, Redwood City
(94065-1677)
PHONE.....................................650 506-7000
Jeffrey O Henley, *Chairman*
Safra A Catz, *President*
Mark V Hurd, *President*
Kevin Melia, *CFO*
Michael A Dillon, *Exec VP*
▲ EMP: 3500
SALES (est): 11B
SALES (corp-wide): 39.8B **Publicly Held**
WEB: www.oracle.com
SIC: 3571 7379 7373 7372 Minicomput-
ers; computer related consulting services;
systems integration services; operating
systems computer software; microproces-
sors
PA: Oracle Corporation
500 Oracle Pkwy
Redwood City CA 94065
650 506-7000

(P-15470)
PARALLAX INCORPORATED
Also Called: Parallax Research
599 Menlo Dr Ste 100, Rocklin
(95765-3725)
PHONE.....................................916 624-8333
Charles Gracey III, *President*
Charles Gracey II, *Treasurer*
Carolyn Montzingo, *General Mgr*
Carolyn Heller, *Info Tech Mgr*
Mary Beth Gracey, *Controller*
▲ EMP: 33
SQ FT: 11,000
SALES (est): 8.5MM **Privately Held**
WEB: www.parallax.com
SIC: 3571 5045 3577 Minicomputers;
computers, peripherals & software; com-
puter peripheral equipment

(P-15471)
POLYWELL COMPANY INC
Also Called: Polywell Computers
1461 San Mateo Ave Ste 1, South San
Francisco (94080-6553)
PHONE.....................................650 583-7222
Chin Lo, *CEO*
Sam Chu, *Vice Pres*
Eva Loke, *Office Mgr*
Gerald Tighe, *CIO*
Samuel Yu, *Technician*
▲ EMP: 40
SQ FT: 20,000
SALES (est): 16.9MM **Privately Held**
WEB: www.polywell.com
SIC: 3571 Personal computers (microcom-
puters)

(P-15472)
PREMIO INC (PA)
918 Radecki Ct, City of Industry
(91748-1132)
PHONE.....................................626 839-3100
Crystal Tsao, *President*
Kevin Wu, *Exec VP*

Trevor Dodd, *Vice Pres*
Sammy Torky, *Vice Pres*
Brian Rock, *Branch Mgr*
▲ EMP: 120
SQ FT: 140,000
SALES: 43MM **Privately Held**
WEB: www.premioinc.com
SIC: 3571 7373 7378 Personal comput-
ers (microcomputers); computer inte-
grated systems design; computer
maintenance & repair

(P-15473)
PROBE-LOGIC INC
1885 Lundy Ave Ste 101, San Jose
(95131-1887)
PHONE.....................................408 416-0777
Hon Cheng, *CEO*
Luis Morales, *Sales Mgr*
Ken Chen, *Manager*
EMP: 92
SQ FT: 15,000
SALES (est): 17.1MM **Privately Held**
WEB: www.probelogic.com
SIC: 3571 Electronic computers

(P-15474)
PSITECH INC
18368 Bandilier Cir, Fountain Valley
(92708-7001)
PHONE.....................................714 964-7818
John T Kerr, *Ch of Bd*
John S Kerr, *Shareholder*
EMP: 12
SQ FT: 6,000
SALES (est): 2.3MM **Privately Held**
WEB: www.psitech.com
SIC: 3571 3577 Personal computers (mi-
crocomputers); computer peripheral
equipment

(P-15475)
QANTEL TECHNOLOGIES INC
3506 Breakwater Ct, Hayward
(94545-3611)
PHONE.....................................510 731-2080
Michael Galvin, *President*
Jerry Devries, *Vice Pres*
Barrie Moore, *Prgrmr*
Steven Wong, *Senior Engr*
Rick Morton, *Sales Staff*
EMP: 42
SQ FT: 12,000
SALES (est): 8.4MM **Privately Held**
WEB: www.qantel.com
SIC: 3571 7371 Electronic computers;
computer software development

(P-15476)
RAPT TOUCH INC
1875 S Grant St Ste 925, San Mateo
(94402-7036)
PHONE.....................................415 994-1537
Mark Anderson, *CEO*
EMP: 12
SALES (est): 1MM **Privately Held**
SIC: 3571 Electronic computers

(P-15477)
RAYTHEON COMPANY
26 Castilian Dr, Goleta (93117-5565)
PHONE.....................................805 562-2730
Robert Martinez, *Principal*
EMP: 18
SALES (corp-wide): 25.3B **Publicly Held**
SIC: 3571 Computers, digital, analog or
hybrid
PA: Raytheon Company
870 Winter St
Waltham MA 02451
781 522-3000

(P-15478)
ROSEWILL INC
17708 Rowland St, City of Industry
(91748-1119)
PHONE.....................................626 271-1420
Fred Chang, *CEO*
Rick Quiroga, *Treasurer*
Lee Cheng, *Admin Sec*
Devin Rose, *Manager*
Hip Lee, *Asst Sec*
▲ EMP: 22

SALES (est): 4.4MM
SALES (corp-wide): 1.8B **Privately Held**
SIC: 3571 5045 Electronic computers;
computers, peripherals & software
HQ: Magnell Associate, Inc.
17560 Rowland St
City Of Industry CA 91748
626 271-9700

(P-15479)
RUGGED SYSTEMS INC
Also Called: Core Systems
13000 Danielson St Ste Q, Poway
(92064-6827)
PHONE.....................................858 391-1006
Chris O Brien, *CEO*
Chris Alan Schaffner, *President*
EMP: 156
SQ FT: 63,000
SALES (est): 22MM **Privately Held**
WEB: www.coresystemsusa.com
SIC: 3571 7373 Electronic computers;
computer integrated systems design

(P-15480)
S E P E INC
Also Called: Fax Star
245 Fischer Ave Ste C4, Costa Mesa
(92626-4538)
PHONE.....................................714 241-7373
Michel J Remion, *President*
Patty King, *Admin Sec*
Pierre Steygers, *Info Tech Mgr*
EMP: 20
SQ FT: 5,000
SALES (est): 3MM **Privately Held**
WEB: www.faxstar.com
SIC: 3571 7371 4822 Electronic comput-
ers; computer software development; fac-
simile transmission services

(P-15481)
SERVERS DIRECT LLC
20480 Business Pkwy, Walnut
(91789-2938)
PHONE.....................................800 576-7931
Andy Juang, *CEO*
Howard Gilles, *CFO*
EMP: 139
SALES (est): 2.1MM **Privately Held**
WEB: www.equuscs.com
SIC: 3571 Mainframe computers
PA: Equus Computer Systems, Inc.
7725 Washington Ave S
Edina MN 55439

(P-15482)
SHASTA ELECTRONIC MFG SVCS INC
Also Called: Shasta Ems
525 E Brokaw Rd, San Jose (95112-1004)
PHONE.....................................408 436-1267
Vinh Nguyen, *President*
Rang Nguyen, *Vice Pres*
EMP: 20
SQ FT: 11,000
SALES (est): 4.7MM **Privately Held**
WEB: www.shastaems.com
SIC: 3571 Electronic computers

(P-15483)
SHUGART CORPORATION (PA)
Also Called: Interntnal Assmbly Specialists
25 Brookline, Aliso Viejo (92656-1461)
PHONE.....................................949 488-8779
Dennis Narlinger, *President*
Steve Alvey, *CFO*
EMP: 110
SQ FT: 2,500
SALES (est): 18.4MM **Privately Held**
WEB: www.ias-shugart.com
SIC: 3571 Computers, digital, analog or
hybrid

(P-15484)
SHUTTLE COMPUTER GROUP INC
17068 Evergreen Pl, City of Industry
(91745-1819)
PHONE.....................................626 820-9000
David Yu, *CEO*
Ray Lin, *President*
Simon Yu, *Corp Secy*
Peter Loiu, *General Mgr*
Tony Hsieh, *Opers Staff*

PRODUCTS & SVCS

▲ EMP: 30
SALES (est): 11.7MM
SALES (corp-wide): 158.1MM **Privately Held**
WEB: www.us.shuttle.com
SIC: 3571 Electronic computers
PA: Shuttle Inc.
  5f, 30, Lane 76, Rei Kuang Rd.,
  Taipei City TAP 11491
  287 926-168

(P-15485)
SIGMA MFG & LOGISTICS LLC
10050 Fthlls Blvd Ste 100, Roseville
(95747)
PHONE..............................916 781-3052
Ushadevi Chenna,
Tanuja Chenna,
Venkatasubbanna Chenna,
EMP: 20
SQ FT: 35,000
SALES (est): 3.5MM **Privately Held**
SIC: 3571 Computers, digital, analog or
  hybrid

(P-15486)
SIPIX IMAGING INC (DH)
47428 Fremont Blvd, Fremont
(94538-6503)
PHONE..............................510 743-2928
Felix Ho, *President*
Ching-Shon Ho, *CEO*
Mr Simon Nip, *CFO*
Ms Lynne C Garone, *Vice Pres*
▲ EMP: 40
SQ FT: 33,000
SALES (est): 7.3MM
SALES (corp-wide): 505.1MM **Privately Held**
WEB: www.sipix.com
SIC: 3571 7371 Computers, digital, analog
  or hybrid; custom computer programming
  services
HQ: Sipix Technology Inc.
  199, Hua Ya 2nd Rd.,
  Taoyuan City TAY 33383
  339 608-00

(P-15487)
SOLAR REGION INC
Also Called: Sumas Media
19575 E Walnut Dr S C16, City of Industry
(91748-2368)
PHONE..............................909 595-8500
Julie Shen, *President*
Alphonse Wu, *Vice Pres*
▲ EMP: 10
SALES (est): 1.8MM **Privately Held**
WEB: www.solarregion.net
SIC: 3571 5521 3823 Electronic comput-
  ers; used car dealers; industrial instrmnts
  msrmnt display/control process variable

(P-15488)
SOLARFLARE
COMMUNICATIONS INC
7505 Irvine Center Dr, Irvine (92618-2991)
PHONE..............................949 581-6830
Russell Stern, *President*
Bandel Carano, *Managing Prtnr*
David Parry, *President*
Mary Jane Abalos, *CFO*
John Graham, *Vice Pres*
EMP: 228
SQ FT: 22,097
SALES (est): 46.6MM **Privately Held**
WEB: www.solarflare.com
SIC: 3571 Electronic computers

(P-15489)
SONY CORPORATION OF
AMERICA (PA)
16530 Via Esprillo Mz7190, San Diego
(92127-1898)
PHONE..............................212 833-8000
Karen E Kelso, *Vice Pres*
EMP: 22
SALES (est): 1MM **Privately Held**
SIC: 3571 Computers, digital, analog or
  hybrid

(P-15490)
SUMICOM-USA
1729 Little Orchard St, San Jose
(95125-1055)
PHONE..............................408 385-2046

William Carey, *President*
EMP: 12
SALES (est): 865.7K **Privately Held**
SIC: 3571 Electronic computers

(P-15491)
SUPER MICRO COMPUTER INC
(PA)
Also Called: Supermicro
980 Rock Ave, San Jose (95131-1615)
PHONE..............................408 503-8000
Charles Liang, *Ch of Bd*
Kevin Bauer, *CFO*
Chiu-Chu Liu Liang, *Treasurer*
Phidias Chou, *Senior VP*
Yih-Shyan Liaw, *Senior VP*
▲ EMP: 1257
SQ FT: 46,000
SALES: 2.2B **Publicly Held**
WEB: www.supermicro.com
SIC: 3571 3572 7372 Electronic comput-
  ers; computer storage devices; prepack-
  aged software

(P-15492)
SYNERGY MICROSYSTEMS INC
(DH)
28965 Avenue Penn, Valencia
(91355-4185)
PHONE..............................858 452-0020
Chris Wiltsey, *Director*
EMP: 70
SALES (est): 6.7MM
SALES (corp-wide): 2.2B **Publicly Held**
WEB: www.synergymicro.com
SIC: 3571 Computers, digital, analog or
  hybrid
HQ: Curtiss-Wright Controls, Inc.
  15801 Brixham Hill Ave # 200
  Charlotte NC 28277
  704 869-4600

(P-15493)
SYNNEX CORPORATION
6551 W Schulte Rd Ste 100, Tracy
(95377-8130)
PHONE..............................510 656-3333
Simon Leung, *Branch Mgr*
Curtis Martin, *Opers Mgr*
EMP: 15
SALES (corp-wide): 17B **Publicly Held**
SIC: 3571 Personal computers (microcom-
  puters)
PA: Synnex Corporation
  44201 Nobel Dr
  Fremont CA 94538
  510 656-3333

(P-15494)
TANGENT COMPUTER INC
45800 Northport Loop W, Fremont
(94538-6413)
PHONE..............................650 342-9388
Doug Monsour, *President*
EMP: 80
SALES (est): 6MM
SALES (corp-wide): 33.2MM **Privately Held**
SIC: 3571 Personal computers (microcom-
  puters)
PA: Tangent Computer, Inc.
  191 Airport Blvd
  Burlingame CA 94010
  888 683-2881

(P-15495)
TANGENT COMPUTER INC (PA)
Also Called: Tanget Fastnet
191 Airport Blvd, Burlingame (94010-2006)
PHONE..............................888 683-2881
Douglas James Monsour, *CEO*
Ron Perkes, *President*
Maher Zabaneh, *Vice Pres*
Nick Haddad, *Technology*
Chris Lee, *Engineer*
EMP: 100
SQ FT: 80,000
SALES (est): 33.2MM **Privately Held**
SIC: 3571 5734 Personal computers (mi-
  crocomputers); computer & software
  stores

(P-15496)
THOUSANDSHORES INC
33442 Western Ave, Union City
(94587-3202)
PHONE..............................510 477-0249
Ding He, *CEO*
Zhi Liu, *President*
◆ EMP: 17
SALES (est): 3.2MM **Privately Held**
SIC: 3571 5999 Electronic computers; mo-
  bile telephones & equipment

(P-15497)
TOSHIBA AMER INFO SYSTEMS
INC
2 Musick, Irvine (92618-1631)
P.O. Box 19724 (92623-9724)
PHONE..............................949 587-6378
Dick Walker, *Project Mgr*
Bob Greenhalgh, *Vice Pres*
Angi Hoffend, *Human Res Mgr*
Leah Madrid, *HR Admin*
Ted Leblanc, *Sales Staff*
EMP: 85
SALES (corp-wide): 37B **Privately Held**
WEB: www.toshiba-components.com
SIC: 3571 Electronic computers
HQ: Toshiba America Information Systems,
  Inc.
  1251 Ave Of The
  New York NY 10020
  949 583-3000

(P-15498)
TOUCHPINT ELCTRNIC SLTIONS
LLC
38372 Innovation Ct # 306, Murrieta
(92563-2616)
PHONE..............................951 734-8083
EMP: 10
SQ FT: 10,000
SALES (est): 680K **Privately Held**
SIC: 3571

(P-15499)
TRANSLATTICE INC (PA)
3398 Londonderry Dr, Santa Clara
(95050-6619)
PHONE..............................408 749-8478
Frank Huerta, *CEO*
Michael Lyle, *President*
EMP: 20
SQ FT: 4,197
SALES (est): 2.5MM **Privately Held**
SIC: 3571 Electronic computers

(P-15500)
TREX ENTERPRISES
CORPORATION (PA)
Also Called: Ophthonix
10455 Pacific Center Ct, San Diego
(92121-4339)
PHONE..............................858 646-5300
Dr Kenneth Y Tang, *Ch of Bd*
Bill Dean, *Engineer*
Paul Kelleher, *Director*
EMP: 150
SQ FT: 90,000
SALES (est): 32.5MM **Privately Held**
WEB: www.trexenterprises.com
SIC: 3571 Electronic computers

(P-15501)
TRI MAP INTERNATIONAL INC
111 Val Dervin Pkwy, Stockton
(95206-4001)
PHONE..............................209 234-0100
Lee Jensen, *President*
Laura Jensen, *CFO*
David Jensen, *Exec VP*
EMP: 40
SQ FT: 36,000
SALES (est): 3.7MM **Privately Held**
WEB: www.trimapintl.com
SIC: 3571 Personal computers (microcom-
  puters)

(P-15502)
UNITEK TECHNOLOGY INC
10211 Bellegrave Ave, Mira Loma
(91752-1919)
PHONE..............................909 930-5700
Yubo Ho, *President*
EMP: 15
SQ FT: 21,000

SALES (est): 3.7MM **Privately Held**
SIC: 3571 5734 Electronic computers;
  computer & software stores

(P-15503)
VMC HOLDINGS GROUP CORP
9667 Owensmouth Ave # 202, Chatsworth
(91311-4818)
P.O. Box 7396, Northridge (91327-7396)
PHONE..............................818 993-1466
Pierre Yenokian, *President*
Chris Geudo, *CFO*
Dorothy Yenokian, *Vice Pres*
EMP: 49
SQ FT: 8,500
SALES (est): 6.1MM **Privately Held**
WEB: www.vmcholdings.com
SIC: 3571 Electronic computers

(P-15504)
VOICEBOARD CORPORATION
473 Post St, Camarillo (93010-8553)
PHONE..............................805 389-3100
Greg Peacock, *President*
EMP: 12
SQ FT: 10,000
SALES (est): 1.3MM **Privately Held**
WEB: www.voiceboard.com
SIC: 3571 Electronic computers

(P-15505)
WIZELINE INC
456 Montgomery St # 2200, San Francisco
(94104-1255)
PHONE..............................650 389-7272
Bismarck Lepe, *CEO*
Sung Kim, *Vice Pres*
Daniele Lasher, *Executive Asst*
Diego De Velasco, *Accounting Mgr*
Tom Gourhan, *Sales Staff*
EMP: 17
SALES (est): 2.7MM **Privately Held**
SIC: 3571 Computers, digital, analog or
  hybrid

(P-15506)
XMULTIPLE TECHNOLOGIES
(PA)
Also Called: Xmultiple/Xrjax
543 Country Club Dr B-128, Simi Valley
(93065-0637)
PHONE..............................805 579-1100
Alan Pocrass, *CEO*
Jeremy Chiu, *President*
Luke Flowers, *Vice Pres*
Emrich Kollar, *Vice Pres*
Drew Storberg, *Vice Pres*
▲ EMP: 13
SALES (est): 4.6MM **Privately Held**
SIC: 3571 3663 3661 3577 Electronic
  computers; multiplex equipment; tele-
  phone & telegraph apparatus; computer
  peripheral equipment

3572 Computer Storage Devices

(P-15507)
ABERDEEN LLC
10420 Pioneer Blvd, Santa Fe Springs
(90670-3734)
PHONE..............................562 903-1500
Menahem M Ovadya, *Mng Member*
Tracy Gardner, *President*
Jack Tateel, *COO*
Yuval Bymel, *Research*
Peter Liu, *Engineer*
▲ EMP: 48
SQ FT: 28,000
SALES (est): 19.7MM **Privately Held**
WEB: www.aberdeeninc.com
SIC: 3572 3571 Computer storage de-
  vices; electronic computers

(P-15508)
ADVANCED HPC INC
8228 Mercury Ct Ste 100, San Diego
(92111-1232)
PHONE..............................858 716-8262
Toni Falcone, *President*
Jeff Tomlinson, *Vice Pres*
Joe Lipman, *General Mgr*
Dave Hansen, *Sales Engr*
EMP: 15

SALES: 18MM **Privately Held**
SIC: **3572** 3571 Computer storage devices; electronic computers

(P-15509)
ALLSTAR MICROELECTRONICS INC
Also Called: Allstarshop.com
30191 Avendia De Las, Rancho Santa Margari (92688)
PHONE...................................949 546-0888
Ming-Chyi Chiang, *President*
Stephanie Hernandez, *COO*
Kris Pham, *Analyst*
EMP: 18
SQ FT: 12,843
SALES (est): 4.7MM **Privately Held**
WEB: www.allstarshop.com
SIC: **3572** Computer storage devices

(P-15510)
AMCAN USA LLC
8970 Crestmar Pt, San Diego (92121-3222)
PHONE...................................858 587-1032
Nils Forsmann,
▲ **EMP:** 15
SALES (est): 2.5MM **Privately Held**
SIC: **3572** Computer tape drives & components

(P-15511)
AMPEX DATA SYSTEMS CORPORATION (HQ)
26460 Corporate Ave, Hayward (94545-3914)
PHONE...................................650 367-2011
Gary Thom, *President*
David Lau, *Program Mgr*
Jim Orahood, *General Mgr*
Mike Bevington, *Sr Software Eng*
Peter Trinh, *Info Tech Mgr*
▲ **EMP:** 58
SQ FT: 15,661
SALES (est): 15.7MM
SALES (corp-wide): 20.9MM **Privately Held**
WEB: www.ampexdata.com
SIC: **3572** Computer storage devices
PA: Delta Information Systems, Inc.
747 Dresher Rd Ste 100
Horsham PA 19044
215 657-5270

(P-15512)
APPLIED MICRO CIRCUITS CORP
Amcc
455 W Maude Ave, Sunnyvale (94085-3540)
PHONE...................................408 523-1000
Faye Pairman, *Branch Mgr*
EMP: 42 **Publicly Held**
WEB: www.amcc.com
SIC: **3572** 8731 3613 3577 Computer auxiliary storage units; computer (hardware) development; switchgear & switchboard apparatus; computer peripheral equipment
HQ: Applied Micro Circuits Corp
4555 Great America Pkwy # 601
Santa Clara CA 95054
408 542-8600

(P-15513)
APPRO INTERNATIONAL INC (HQ)
Also Called: Cray Cluster Solutions
220 Devcon Dr, San Jose (95112-4210)
PHONE...................................408 941-8100
Daniel Kim, *President*
James Yi, *CFO*
Steve Lyness, *Vice Pres*
Jobeth Melvin, *General Mgr*
Robert Noska, *Sr Software Eng*
▲ **EMP:** 45
SQ FT: 40,000
SALES (est): 10.3MM
SALES (corp-wide): 392.5MM **Publicly Held**
WEB: www.appro.com
SIC: **3572** 3577 3571 Computer storage devices; computer peripheral equipment; electronic computers

PA: Cray Inc.
901 5th Ave Ste 1000
Seattle WA 98164
206 701-2000

(P-15514)
ATHANA INTERNATIONAL INC
602 Faye Ln, Redondo Beach (90277-4449)
PHONE...................................310 539-7280
John Wright, *President*
EMP: 12
SQ FT: 30,000
SALES (est): 2.3MM **Privately Held**
WEB: www.athana.com
SIC: **3572** Computer storage devices

(P-15515)
BITMICRO NETWORKS INC (PA)
47929 Fremont Blvd, Fremont (94538-6508)
PHONE...................................510 743-3124
David Shapowal, *CEO*
Dave Shapowal, *COO*
Stephen Uriarte, *Exec VP*
Gary Kohli, *Vice Pres*
Bharadwaj Pudipeddi, *Vice Pres*
EMP: 16
SQ FT: 14,000
SALES: 10MM **Privately Held**
WEB: www.bitmicro.com
SIC: **3572** Computer disk & drum drives & components; computer tape drives & components

(P-15516)
BNL TECHNOLOGIES INC
Also Called: Fantom Drives
20525 Manhattan Pl, Torrance (90501-1825)
PHONE...................................310 320-7272
Behzad Eshghieh, *CEO*
Hamid Khorsand, *Ch of Bd*
Nasser Ahdout, *CFO*
Monica Vicencio, *Info Tech Dir*
Tony Tan, *Technology*
▲ **EMP:** 26 **EST:** 1998
SALES (est): 9.4MM **Privately Held**
WEB: www.fantomdrives.com
SIC: **3572** Computer storage devices

(P-15517)
CALDIGIT INC
1941 E Miraloma Ave Ste B, Placentia (92870-6770)
PHONE...................................714 572-6668
PO Hung Chen, *CEO*
▲ **EMP:** 15
SALES (est): 3MM **Privately Held**
SIC: **3572** Disk drives, computer; magnetic storage devices, computer

(P-15518)
CAPSA SOLUTIONS LLC
14000 S Broadway, Los Angeles (90061-1018)
PHONE...................................800 437-6633
Jeff Strickler, *CFO*
EMP: 40
SALES (corp-wide): 202.6MM **Privately Held**
SIC: **3572** Computer storage devices
HQ: Capsa Solutions Llc
4253 Ne 189th Ave
Portland OR 97230
503 766-2324

(P-15519)
CELEROS CORP
559 Clyde Ave Ste 220, Mountain View (94043-2270)
PHONE...................................650 325-6900
Hossein Alaee, *CEO*
EMP: 20
SQ FT: 7,000
SALES (est): 2.7MM **Privately Held**
WEB: www.celeros.com
SIC: **3572** Computer storage devices

(P-15520)
CENTON ELECTRONICS INC (PA)
27412 Aliso Viejo Pkwy, Aliso Viejo (92656-3371)
PHONE...................................949 855-9111
Jennifer Miscione, *CEO*

Gene Miscione, *President*
Janet Miscione, *Vice Pres*
Laura Miscione, *Sales Staff*
▲ **EMP:** 60
SQ FT: 20,000
SALES (est): 17.7MM **Privately Held**
WEB: www.centon.com
SIC: **3572** 5734 7379 Computer storage devices; computer software & accessories; computer related consulting services

(P-15521)
CERTANCE LLC (HQ)
Also Called: Quantum Corporation
141 Innovation Dr, Irvine (92617-3211)
PHONE...................................949 856-7800
Howard L Matthews, *President*
Donald L Waite, *Chairman*
New Suez Aquisition Corp,
EMP: 300
SALES (est): 74MM
SALES (corp-wide): 505.3MM **Publicly Held**
WEB: www.quantum.com
SIC: **3572** Computer tape drives & components
PA: Quantum Corporation
224 Airport Pkwy Ste 550
San Jose CA 95110
408 944-4000

(P-15522)
CHENBRO MICOM (USA) INC
2800 Jurupa St, Ontario (91761-2903)
PHONE...................................909 937-0100
MEI CHI Chen, *President*
▲ **EMP:** 20 **EST:** 1983
SALES (est): 5.8MM
SALES (corp-wide): 183.1MM **Privately Held**
SIC: **3572** Computer storage devices
PA: Chenbro Micom Co., Ltd.
15f, 150, Chien 1st Rd.,
New Taipei City 23511
282 265-500

(P-15523)
CLOUD ENGINES INC
77 Geary St Ste 500, San Francisco (94108-5703)
PHONE...................................415 738-8076
Daniel Putterman, *President*
Gregory Smith, *CFO*
Jed Putterman, *Exec VP*
Adam Scolaro, *Vice Pres*
Brad Dietrich, *CTO*
EMP: 45
SALES (est): 6.4MM **Privately Held**
SIC: **3572** Computer storage devices

(P-15524)
CMS PRODUCTS INC
12 Mauchly Ste E, Irvine (92618-2398)
P.O. Box 2789, Capistrano Beach (92624-0789)
PHONE...................................714 424-5520
Kenneth Burke, *President*
Ronald C Harrell, *Shareholder*
Jim Sedin, *Shareholder*
Eric Robinson, *President*
Mark Balce, *Vice Pres*
▲ **EMP:** 40
SQ FT: 30,000
SALES (est): 8MM **Privately Held**
WEB: www.cmsstorage.com
SIC: **3572** 3577 7379 Computer storage devices; computer peripheral equipment; data processing consultant

(P-15525)
COMPUCASE CORPORATION
Also Called: Orion Tech
16720 Chestnut St Ste C, City of Industry (91748-1038)
PHONE...................................626 336-6588
Doung Fu Hsu, *President*
Aaron Tao, *COO*
Phillip Liu, *Manager*
▲ **EMP:** 1500
SQ FT: 30,000
SALES (est): 165.7MM
SALES (corp-wide): 237.9MM **Privately Held**
WEB: www.compucaseusa.com
SIC: **3572** Computer storage devices

PA: Compucase Enterprise Co., Ltd.
225, Lane 54, Anhe Rd., Sec. 2,
Tainan City 70967
635 606-06

(P-15526)
CORAID INC (PA)
255 Shoreline Dr Ste 650, Redwood City (94065-1431)
PHONE...................................650 517-9300
Dave Kresse, *CEO*
Audrey Maclean, *Ch of Bd*
Stewart Grierson, *CFO*
Carl Wright, *Exec VP*
Glenn Neufeld, *Foreman/Supr*
EMP: 100
SALES (est): 24MM **Privately Held**
WEB: www.coraid.com
SIC: **3572** Computer storage devices

(P-15527)
CUE TECHNOLOGIES INC
Also Called: Cuetech
823 Tumbleweed Ln, Fallbrook (92028-9447)
PHONE...................................949 362-4002
Jodi L Jenner, *CEO*
EMP: 15
SQ FT: 3,400
SALES (est): 3.6MM **Privately Held**
WEB: www.cuetech.com
SIC: **3572** Computer disk & drum drives & components

(P-15528)
DATADIRECT NETWORKS INC (PA)
Also Called: Ddn
9351 Deering Ave, Chatsworth (91311-5858)
PHONE...................................818 700-7600
Alex Bouzari, *CEO*
Paul Bloch, *President*
Gordon Manning, *President*
Ian Angelo, *CFO*
Bret Weber, *Exec VP*
▲ **EMP:** 120
SQ FT: 50,000
SALES (est): 231.8MM **Privately Held**
WEB: www.datadirectnet.com
SIC: **3572** 7374 Computer auxiliary storage units; data processing service

(P-15529)
DSSD INC
4025 Bohannon Dr, Menlo Park (94025-1004)
PHONE...................................775 773-8665
William Moore, *President*
Andreas Bechtolsheim, *Director*
EMP: 11
SQ FT: 7,500
SALES (est): 6.8MM **Privately Held**
SIC: **3572** Computer storage devices

(P-15530)
DUALCOR TECHNOLOGIES INC
1 Embarcadero Ctr Ste 500, San Francisco (94111-3610)
PHONE...................................831 684-2457
Tim Glass, *CEO*
Rob Howe, *President*
Bryan T Cupps, *CTO*
EMP: 25
SQ FT: 12,000
SALES (est): 1.9MM **Privately Held**
WEB: www.dualcor.com
SIC: **3572** Computer storage devices

(P-15531)
DURA MICRO INC
Also Called: Acom Data
901 E Cedar St, Ontario (91761-5572)
PHONE...................................909 947-4590
Titus Wu, *President*
▲ **EMP:** 46
SQ FT: 46,000
SALES (est): 7.1MM **Privately Held**
WEB: www.acomdata.com
SIC: **3572** 3577 Computer storage devices; computer peripheral equipment

(P-15532)
EMC CORPORATION
6800 Koll Center Pkwy # 200, Pleasanton
(94566-7053)
PHONE...................925 425-1400
Lucas Leslie, *Branch Mgr*
Kathy Wineger, *Senior VP*
Paul Ingham, *Program Mgr*
David Choy, *Sr Consultant*
EMP: 65
SALES (corp-wide): 78.6B **Publicly Held**
SIC: 3572 Computer storage devices
HQ: Emc Corporation
176 South St
Hopkinton MA 01748
508 435-1000

(P-15533)
EMC CORPORATION
6701 Koll Center Pkwy # 150, Pleasanton
(94566-8061)
PHONE...................925 948-9000
Rich Napolitano, *Principal*
Ken Sabino, *Engineer*
EMP: 75
SALES (corp-wide): 78.6B **Publicly Held**
SIC: 3572 Computer storage devices
HQ: Emc Corporation
176 South St
Hopkinton MA 01748
508 435-1000

(P-15534)
EMC CORPORATION
Also Called: Cloudscaling Group
455 Market St Fl 4, San Francisco
(94105-2486)
PHONE...................877 636-8589
Michael Grant, *Principal*
EMP: 40
SALES (corp-wide): 78.6B **Publicly Held**
SIC: 3572 Computer storage devices
HQ: Emc Corporation
176 South St
Hopkinton MA 01748
508 435-1000

(P-15535)
EMC CORPORATION
6801 Koll Center Pkwy, Pleasanton
(94566-7047)
PHONE...................925 600-6800
Kelly Campos, *Branch Mgr*
Kristina Austin, *Senior Partner*
Carol Joyce, *Vice Pres*
Nicki Crosswhite, *Admin Asst*
Sage Harvey, *Administration*
EMP: 65
SALES (corp-wide): 78.6B **Publicly Held**
SIC: 3572 Computer storage devices
HQ: Emc Corporation
176 South St
Hopkinton MA 01748
508 435-1000

(P-15536)
EP HOLDINGS INC
Also Called: Ep Memory
30442 Esperanza, Rcho STA Marg
(92688-2144)
PHONE...................949 713-4600
Eric Krantz, *CEO*
EMP: 20
SALES (est): 16.2MM **Privately Held**
SIC: 3572 Computer storage devices

(P-15537)
FORTASA MEMORY SYSTEMS INC
1111 Triton Dr Ste 100, Foster City
(94404-1284)
PHONE...................888 367-8588
Tatyana Nakhimovsky, *President*
Robert Noyes, *CFO*
Samuel Nakhimovsky, *General Mgr*
▼ EMP: 14 EST: 2009
SQ FT: 1,500
SALES (est): 1.8MM **Privately Held**
SIC: 3572 Computer storage devices

(P-15538)
FORTEMEDIA INC
Also Called: Fortemedia China
4051 Burton Dr, Santa Clara (95054-1585)
PHONE...................408 716-8011
May Ip, *Manager*

EMP: 65
SALES (corp-wide): 11.5MM **Privately Held**
WEB: www.fortemedia.com
SIC: 3572 Computer disk & drum drives & components
PA: Fortemedia, Inc.
4051 Burton Dr
Santa Clara CA 95054
408 716-8028

(P-15539)
FORTEMEDIA INC
4051 Burton Dr, Santa Clara (95054-1585)
PHONE...................408 716-8028
Minghua Chu, *Manager*
EMP: 65
SALES (corp-wide): 11.5MM **Privately Held**
WEB: www.fortemedia.com
SIC: 3572 Computer disk & drum drives & components
PA: Fortemedia, Inc.
4051 Burton Dr
Santa Clara CA 95054
408 716-8028

(P-15540)
GIGAMEM LLC
18375 Bandilier Cir, Fountain Valley
(92708-7001)
PHONE...................949 461-9999
Keller J Lee, *Mng Member*
▲ EMP: 15
SQ FT: 9,500
SALES (est): 2.2MM
SALES (corp-wide): 10.3MM **Privately Held**
WEB: www.gigaram.com
SIC: 3572 Computer storage devices
PA: Memoryten, Inc.
2800 Bowers Ave
Santa Clara CA 95051
408 516-4141

(P-15541)
GLOBALSCALE TECHNOLOGIES INC
1200 N Van Buren St Ste D, Anaheim
(92807-1638)
PHONE...................714 632-9239
Richard Cheng, *President*
John Meng, *Director*
▲ EMP: 11
SALES (est): 2.3MM **Privately Held**
SIC: 3572 Computer storage devices

(P-15542)
GLOBALVISION SYSTEMS INC
9401 Oakdale Ave Ste 100, Chatsworth
(91311-6512)
PHONE...................888 227-7967
Oliver Song, *CEO*
Robert Cohn, *Info Tech Mgr*
Mike Chen, *Opers Mgr*
EMP: 18
SALES (est): 3.3MM **Privately Held**
SIC: 3572 Computer disk & drum drives & components

(P-15543)
GOHARDDRIVE INC
Also Called: Goharddrive.com
137 S 8th Ave Ste E, La Puente
(91746-3247)
PHONE...................626 593-9927
Yee Wey Tan, *President*
▲ EMP: 12 EST: 2011
SALES: 19.9MM **Privately Held**
SIC: 3572 Disk drives, computer

(P-15544)
GRANDIS INC
1123 Cadillac Ct, Milpitas (95035-3055)
PHONE...................408 945-2160
Farhad Tabrizi, *President*
Mohamad Krounbi, *President*
Allen Morton, *CFO*
Alexander Driskill-Smith, *Vice Pres*
Adrian Ong, *Vice Pres*
EMP: 15
SALES (est): 3.2MM **Privately Held**
SIC: 3572 Magnetic storage devices, computer

PA: Samsung Group
11 Seocho-Daero 74-Gil, Seocho-Gu
Seoul
822 214-5211

(P-15545)
GST INC
3419 Via Lido Ste 164, Newport Beach
(92663-3908)
PHONE...................949 510-1142
David Breisacher, *CEO*
▼ EMP: 51
SQ FT: 10,000
SALES (est): 5.5MM **Privately Held**
WEB: www.gstinc.com
SIC: 3572 Computer storage devices

(P-15546)
H CO COMPUTER PRODUCTS
Also Called: Thinkcp Technologies
16812 Hale Ave, Irvine (92606-5021)
PHONE...................949 833-3222
Ali Hojreh, *CEO*
Mark Hojreh, *CFO*
Gary Richardson, *Vice Pres*
Saed Hojreh, *Admin Sec*
Sam Jazaerli, *Technical Mgr*
◆ EMP: 26
SQ FT: 15,600
SALES (est): 10MM **Privately Held**
WEB: www.thinkcp.com
SIC: 3572 3577 Computer storage devices; computer peripheral equipment

(P-15547)
HEADWAY TECHNOLOGIES INC (HQ)
682 S Hillview Dr, Milpitas (95035-5457)
PHONE...................408 934-5300
Mao-Min Chen, *President*
Thomas Surran, *CFO*
Moris Dovek, *Vice Pres*
Gary Pester, *Vice Pres*
Casey Moore, *Admin Asst*
▲ EMP: 200
SALES (est): 255.9MM
SALES (corp-wide): 11.9B **Privately Held**
WEB: www.headway.com
SIC: 3572 Magnetic storage devices, computer
PA: Tdk Corporation
3-9-1, Shibaura
Minato-Ku TKY 108-0
368 527-300

(P-15548)
HEADWAY TECHNOLOGIES INC
497 S Hillview Dr, Milpitas (95035-7702)
PHONE...................408 934-5300
Yoshiro Nakagawa, *VP Opers*
Eiki Narumi, *Human Resources*
EMP: 200
SALES (corp-wide): 11.9B **Privately Held**
SIC: 3572 Computer storage devices
HQ: Headway Technologies, Inc.
682 S Hillview Dr
Milpitas CA 95035
408 934-5300

(P-15549)
HEADWAY TECHNOLOGY
463 S Milpitas Blvd, Milpitas (95035-5438)
PHONE...................408 935-1020
Nabil Arnaout, *Principal*
Brenda Baltazar, *Administration*
Tony Nguyen, *Engineer*
Kazuki Sato, *Engineer*
Zunde Yang, *Engineer*
EMP: 12
SALES (est): 1.4MM **Privately Held**
SIC: 3572 Computer disk & drum drives & components

(P-15550)
HGST INC
Also Called: Skyera
5601 Great Oaks Pkwy, San Jose
(95119-1003)
PHONE...................408 418-4148
Craig Anderson, *Director*
EMP: 160
SALES (corp-wide): 20.6B **Publicly Held**
SIC: 3572 Computer storage devices

HQ: Hgst, Inc.
5601 Great Oaks Pkwy
San Jose CA 95119
408 717-6000

(P-15551)
HGST INC
951 Sandisk Dr, Milpitas (95035-7933)
PHONE...................408 801-2394
Michael Ray, *Principal*
EMP: 10
SALES (corp-wide): 20.6B **Publicly Held**
SIC: 3572 Computer storage devices
HQ: Hgst, Inc.
5601 Great Oaks Pkwy
San Jose CA 95119
408 717-6000

(P-15552)
HGST INC (DH)
5601 Great Oaks Pkwy, San Jose
(95119-1003)
PHONE...................408 717-6000
John Coyne, *CEO*
Stephen Milligan, *President*
Douglas A Gross, *COO*
Michael A Murray, *CFO*
Kevin Haughey, *Vice Pres*
▲ EMP: 14
SALES (est): 706.3MM
SALES (corp-wide): 20.6B **Publicly Held**
WEB: www.hitachigst.com
SIC: 3572 Computer storage devices

(P-15553)
HIGHPOINT TECHNOLOGIES INC
41650 Christy St, Fremont (94538-3114)
PHONE...................408 942-5800
Michael Whang, *President*
Yuan-Lang Chang, *CFO*
Susan Lin, *Accountant*
May Hwang, *Sales Dir*
Corey Baker, *Manager*
▲ EMP: 12
SQ FT: 14,500
SALES (est): 2.5MM **Privately Held**
SIC: 3572 8731 Computer disk & drum drives & components; computer (hardware) development

(P-15554)
HITACHI VANTARA CORPORATION (DH)
2845 Lafayette St, Santa Clara
(95050-2639)
PHONE...................408 970-1000
Jack Domme, *President*
Minoru Kosuge, *Ch of Bd*
Brian Householder, *President*
Rick Martig, *CFO*
Rex L Carter, *Exec VP*
▲ EMP: 450
SQ FT: 250,000
SALES (est): 2.1B
SALES (corp-wide): 87.9B **Privately Held**
WEB: www.hds.com
SIC: 3572 Computer storage devices
HQ: Hitachi Data Systems Holding Corporation
2845 Lafayette St
Santa Clara CA 95050
408 970-1000

(P-15555)
I-BUS CORPORATION (PA)
1138 Cadillac Ct, Milpitas (95035-3058)
PHONE...................408 942-1417
Johni Chan, *President*
Fred Chan, *Vice Pres*
EMP: 13
SALES (est): 3.6MM **Privately Held**
WEB: www.ibus.com
SIC: 3572 3571 Computer storage devices; electronic computers

(P-15556)
I-TECH COMPANY LTD LBLTY CO
42978 Osgood Rd, Fremont (94539-5627)
PHONE...................510 226-9226
Alan Chung, *Mng Member*
▲ EMP: 10

SALES (est): 1.3MM **Privately Held**
WEB: www.i-techcompany.com
SIC: **3572** 3577 Computer storage devices; computer peripheral equipment

(P-15557)
I/OMAGIC CORPORATION (PA)
20512 Crescent Bay Dr, Lake Forest (92630-8847)
PHONE..................................949 707-4800
Tony Shahbaz, *Ch of Bd*
Mary St George, *Treasurer*
Paula Lecossois, *Marketing Staff*
▲ EMP: 30
SQ FT: 52,000 **Privately Held**
WEB: www.iomagic.com
SIC: **3572** 3651 Computer storage devices; home entertainment equipment, electronic

(P-15558)
IN WIN DEVELOPMENT USA INC
188 Brea Canyon Rd, Walnut (91789-3086)
PHONE...................................909 348-0588
Wen Hsien Lai, *President*
Paul Hao, *Vice Pres*
▲ EMP: 20 EST: 1989
SQ FT: 50,000
SALES (est): 3.8MM
SALES (corp-wide): 63.9MM **Privately Held**
SIC: **3572** Computer tape drives & components
PA: In Win Development Inc.
57, Lane 350, Nan Shang Rd.,
Taoyuan City TAY 33392
332 298-98

(P-15559)
INNOVATIVE DIVERSFD TECH INC
Also Called: Disk Faktory
18062 Irvine Blvd Ste 304, Tustin (92780-3329)
PHONE...................................949 455-1701
EMP: 28
SQ FT: 7,800
SALES (est): 4.4MM **Privately Held**
WEB: www.burncd.com
SIC: **3572** 7371

(P-15560)
INTELLIGENT STORAGE SOLUTION
2073 Otoole Ave, San Jose (95131-1303)
PHONE...................................408 428-0105
Dat Do, *President*
Ian Wallace, *Engineer*
▲ EMP: 200
SALES (est): 24.7MM **Privately Held**
SIC: **3572** Computer disk & drum drives & components

(P-15561)
IOSAFE INC
10600 Industrial Ave # 120, Roseville (95678-6210)
PHONE...................................888 984-6723
Robb Moore, *CEO*
Christine Davis, *CFO*
Andrea Moore, *Treasurer*
Matt Eargis, *VP Sales*
Chris Wilson, *Sales Mgr*
▲ EMP: 18
SQ FT: 20,000
SALES (est): 5.5MM **Privately Held**
WEB: www.iosafe.com
SIC: **3572** Computer storage devices

(P-15562)
JMR ELECTRONICS INC
Also Called: J M R Components
8968 Fullbright Ave, Chatsworth (91311-6123)
PHONE...................................818 993-4801
Josef Rabinovitz, *President*
Judy Schoen, *CFO*
Mirit Rabinovitz, *Corp Secy*
▲ EMP: 22 EST: 1982
SQ FT: 24,000
SALES (est): 7.5MM **Privately Held**
SIC: **3572** Computer storage devices

(P-15563)
LGARDE INC
15181 Woodlawn Ave, Tustin (92780-6487)
PHONE..................................714 259-0771
Gayle D Bilyeu, *Ch of Bd*
Constantine Cassapakis, *President*
Alan R Hirasuna, *Treasurer*
Dwight Duston, *Bd of Directors*
Juan Ariza, *Business Dir*
EMP: 24
SQ FT: 19,000
SALES (est): 6.1MM **Privately Held**
WEB: www.lgarde.com
SIC: **3572** 8731 2822 3769 Tape recorders for computers; engineering laboratory, except testing; acrylic rubbers, polyacrylate; guided missile & space vehicle parts & auxiliary equipment; radio & TV communications equipment

(P-15564)
LOOKER DATA SCIENCES INC (PA)
101 Church St Fl 4, Santa Cruz (95060-3963)
PHONE..................................831 244-0340
Frank Bien, *CEO*
Lloyd Tabb, *Ch of Bd*
Joe Moran, *CFO*
Jen Grant, *Chief Mktg Ofcr*
Nick Caldwell,
EMP: 58
SALES (est): 13.8MM **Privately Held**
SIC: **3572** Computer tape drives & components

(P-15565)
MARANTI NETWORKS INC
1452 N Vasco Rd, Livermore (94551-9213)
PHONE..................................408 834-4000
Debbie Miller, *President*
Kuldeep Sandhu, *Security Dir*
Santosh Lolayekar, *CTO*
Harish Nayak, *VP Mktg*
EMP: 78
SQ FT: 20,000
SALES: 2MM **Privately Held**
SIC: **3572** Computer storage devices

(P-15566)
MAXTOR CORPORATION (DH)
4575 Scotts Valley Dr, Scotts Valley (95066-4517)
PHONE..................................831 438-6550
▲ EMP: 100
SALES (est): 418.7MM **Privately Held**
WEB: www.maxtor.com
SIC: **3572**
HQ: Seagate Technology (Us) Holdings, Inc
920 Disc Dr
Scotts Valley CA 95014
831 438-6550

(P-15567)
MEMORY EXPERTS INTL USA INC (HQ)
1651 E Saint Andrew Pl, Santa Ana (92705-4932)
PHONE..................................714 258-3000
Guadulupe Reusing, *Ch of Bd*
Lawrence Reusing, *President*
Gerard Reusing, *CEO*
Rino Lampasona, *Vice Pres*
Julian Reusing, *Vice Pres*
▲ EMP: 32
SQ FT: 40,000
SALES: 15MM **Privately Held**
WEB: www.memoryexpertsinc.com/
SIC: **3572** 3577 Computer storage devices; computer peripheral equipment
PA: Experts En Memoire Internationale Inc, Les
2321 Rue Cohen
Saint-Laurent QC H4R 2
514 333-5010

(P-15568)
MEMORYTEN INC (PA)
Also Called: Memoryx
2800 Bowers Ave, Santa Clara (95051-0918)
PHONE..................................408 516-4141
Kenneth Olsen, *President*
Gergia Law, *CFO*
Neil Kripalani, *Vice Pres*

Michael Rosito, *General Mgr*
Charles Kim, *Info Tech Mgr*
▲ EMP: 56
SQ FT: 4,500
SALES (est): 10.3MM **Privately Held**
WEB: www.memoryx.net
SIC: **3572** Computer storage devices

(P-15569)
MICRON CONSUMER PDTS GROUP INC (HQ)
540 Alder Dr, Fremont (94538)
PHONE..................................669 226-3000
Gerald Pittman, *President*
Vincent Nguyen, *Vice Pres*
Jon Halsey, *Director*
Fred Waddel, *Director*
EMP: 11 EST: 2000
SALES (est): 2.5MM
SALES (corp-wide): 30.3B **Publicly Held**
SIC: **3572** Computer storage devices
PA: Micron Technology, Inc.
8000 S Federal Way
Boise ID 83716
208 368-4000

(P-15570)
MITAC INFORMATION SYSTEMS CORP (DH)
39889 Eureka Dr, Newark (94560-4811)
PHONE..................................510 284-3000
Charlotte Chou, *President*
Billy Ho, *President*
Karen Soong, *CFO*
Matthew Miau, *Chairman*
Cliff Moon, *Director*
▲ EMP: 103
SQ FT: 240,000
SALES (est): 39.6MM
SALES (corp-wide): 1.6B **Privately Held**
WEB: www.mitac.com
SIC: **3572** Computer storage devices
HQ: Mitac International Corporation
No. 1, Yanfa 2nd Rd., Hsinchu Science Industrial Park Science Ba
Paoshan Hsiang HSI
357 792-50

(P-15571)
MTI TECHNOLOGY CORPORATION (PA)
15461 Red Hill Ave # 200, Tustin (92780-7314)
PHONE..................................949 251-1101
EMP: 200
SQ FT: 25,000
SALES (est): 54.8MM **Privately Held**
WEB: www.mti.com
SIC: **3572** 3571 7372 3674

(P-15572)
NETAPP INC (PA)
1395 Crossman Ave, Sunnyvale (94089-1114)
PHONE..................................408 822-6000
George Kurian, *President*
T Michael Nevens, *Ch of Bd*
Ronald J Pasek, *CFO*
Atish Gude, *Officer*
Joel D Reich, *Exec VP*
EMP: 1600
SQ FT: 700,000
SALES: 5.9B **Publicly Held**
WEB: www.netapp.com
SIC: **3572** 7373 7372 Computer storage devices; computer integrated systems design; systems software development services; computer system selling services; prepackaged software

(P-15573)
NEXSAN TECHNOLOGIES INC (DH)
325 E Hillcrest Dr # 150, Thousand Oaks (91360-7799)
PHONE..................................408 724-9809
Philip Black, *CEO*
Gene Spies, *CFO*
George Symons, *Officer*
Tony Craythorne, *Vice Pres*
James R Molenda, *Admin Sec*
▲ EMP: 40

SALES (est): 36.4MM
SALES (corp-wide): 41MM **Privately Held**
WEB: www.nexsan.com
SIC: **3572** Computer storage devices
HQ: Nexsan Corporation
900 E Hamilton Ave # 230
Campbell CA 95008
408 724-9809

(P-15574)
NEXSAN TECHNOLOGIES INC
302 Enterprise St, Escondido (92029-1235)
PHONE..................................760 745-3550
Fax: 760 745-3503
EMP: 25 **Publicly Held**
SIC: **3572**
HQ: Nexsan Technologies Incorporated
900 E Hamilton Ave # 230
Campbell CA 91360
408 724-9809

(P-15575)
NGD SYSTEMS INC
355 Goddard Ste 200, Irvine (92618-4642)
PHONE..................................949 510-6327
Mohammad Nader Salessi, *CEO*
Al Talavera, *CFO*
Eli Tiomkin, *VP Bus Dvlpt*
EMP: 30
SALES (est): 221.1K **Privately Held**
SIC: **3572** Computer storage devices

(P-15576)
NIMBLE STORAGE INC (HQ)
211 River Oaks Pkwy, San Jose (95134-1913)
PHONE..................................408 432-9600
Suresh Vasudevan, *CEO*
Anup Singh, *CFO*
Janet Matsuda, *Chief Mktg Ofcr*
Varun Mehta, *Security Dir*
Umesh Maheshwari, *CTO*
▲ EMP: 227
SQ FT: 165,000
SALES: 402.6MM
SALES (corp-wide): 28.8B **Publicly Held**
SIC: **3572** Computer storage devices
PA: Hewlett Packard Enterprise Company
3000 Hanover St
Palo Alto CA 94304
650 687-5817

(P-15577)
NIMBUS DATA INC
5151 California Ave # 100, Irvine (92617-3205)
PHONE..................................650 276-4500
Thomas Isakovich, *CEO*
◆ EMP: 50
SALES (est): 10.5MM **Privately Held**
WEB: www.nimbusdata.com
SIC: **3572** Computer storage devices

(P-15578)
NWE TECHNOLOGY INC
1688 Richard Ave, Santa Clara (95050-2844)
PHONE..................................408 919-6100
S C Huang, *President*
▲ EMP: 150
SQ FT: 63,000
SALES (est): 19.5MM **Privately Held**
WEB: www.nwetechnology.com
SIC: **3572** Computer disk & drum drives & components

(P-15579)
ORYX ADVANCED MATERIALS INC (PA)
46458 Fremont Blvd, Fremont (94538-6469)
PHONE..................................510 249-1158
Victor Tan, *CEO*
Kwei-San Teng, *Vice Pres*
Tan Geok San, *Director*
▲ EMP: 35
SQ FT: 7,000
SALES (est): 6.8MM **Privately Held**
WEB: www.oam-inc.com
SIC: **3572** Disk drives, computer

(P-15580)
OVERLAND STORAGE INC (HQ)
Also Called: S3d Acquisition II Company
4542 Ruffner St Ste 250, San Diego
(92111-2267)
PHONE...............................858 571-5555
Eric L Kelly, *CEO*
Kurt L Kalbfleisch, *CFO*
David Ochser, *Vice Pres*
Scott Petersen, *Vice Pres*
Andy Walsky, *Vice Pres*
◆ **EMP:** 102
SQ FT: 51,000
SALES (est): 87.4MM **Privately Held**
WEB: www.overlanddata.com
SIC: 3572 7372 Computer storage devices; prepackaged software
PA: Sphere 3d Inc
    240 Matheson Blvd E
    Mississauga ON L4Z 1
    416 749-5999

(P-15581)
OZMO INC
Also Called: Ozmo Devices
1600 Technology Dr, San Jose
(95110-1382)
PHONE...............................650 515-3524
Bill McLean, *CEO*
Jon Edney, *Vice Pres*
Jon Ewanich, *Vice Pres*
Mike Schwartz, *Vice Pres*
EMP: 24 **EST:** 2004
SALES (est): 3.5MM **Privately Held**
SIC: 3572 Computer disk & drum drives & components

(P-15582)
PACIFIC ALLIANCE CAPITAL INC
Also Called: Wct/Pac Data
27141 Aliso Creek Rd # 215, Aliso Viejo
(92656-3359)
PHONE...............................949 360-1796
Rick Crane, *CEO*
Susan Holloway, *Shareholder*
David Holloway, *Vice Pres*
Josh Moore, *Principal*
Dave Holloway, *General Mgr*
EMP: 12 **EST:** 2000
SQ FT: 28,000
SALES (est): 7.1MM **Privately Held**
WEB: www.pacdata.com
SIC: 3572 Computer storage devices

(P-15583)
PHILIPS & LITE-ON DIGITAL (DH)
Also Called: P L D S
726 S Hillview Dr, Milpitas (95035-5455)
PHONE...............................510 687-1800
Harlie Pseng, *President*
Charlie Pseng, *President*
Armando Abella, *CFO*
Walker Su, *Admin Sec*
Christine Hsing, *Marketing Mgr*
▲ **EMP:** 50
SQ FT: 17,088
SALES (est): 35MM
SALES (corp-wide): 20.9B **Privately Held**
WEB: www.liteonit.com
SIC: 3572 Disk drives, computer
HQ: Philips & Lite-On Digital Solutions Corporation
    16f, 392, Rueykuang Rd.,
    Taipei City TAP
    287 982-798

(P-15584)
PI-CORAL INC
600 California St Fl 6, San Francisco
(94108-2733)
PHONE...............................408 516-5150
Donpaul Stephens, *CEO*
Johnson Agogbua, *President*
Mary Martis, *Executive Asst*
EMP: 80
SQ FT: 15,000
SALES: 1MM **Privately Held**
SIC: 3572 Computer storage devices

(P-15585)
POSTVISION INC
Also Called: Archion
2120 Foothill Blvd # 111, La Verne
(91750-2941)
PHONE...............................818 840-0777
Mark Bianchi, *CEO*

Reuben Lima, *COO*
Daniel Stern, *Exec VP*
James A Tucci, *CTO*
James Tucci, *CTO*
EMP: 15
SQ FT: 6,000
SALES (est): 2.6MM **Privately Held**
WEB: www.archion.com
SIC: 3572 Computer storage devices

(P-15586)
PSSC LABS
20432 N Sea Cir, Lake Forest
(92630-8806)
PHONE...............................949 380-7288
Janice Lesser, *President*
Larry Lesser, *Vice Pres*
Harrison Angus, *Executive*
Kurtis Henderson, *Comp Tech*
▲ **EMP:** 15
SQ FT: 2,500
SALES (est): 18MM **Privately Held**
WEB: www.pssclabs.com
SIC: 3572 5734 Computer storage devices; computer & software stores

(P-15587)
PURE STORAGE INC (PA)
650 Castro St Ste 400, Mountain View
(94041-2081)
PHONE...............................800 379-7873
Charles H Giancarlo, *CEO*
Scott Dietzen, *Ch of Bd*
David Hatfield, *President*
Timothy Riitters, *CFO*
John Colgrove, *CTO*
EMP: 277
SALES: 1B **Publicly Held**
SIC: 3572 7372 Computer storage devices; prepackaged software

(P-15588)
QUALSTAR CORPORATION (PA)
130 W Cochran St Ste C, Simi Valley
(93065-6272)
PHONE...............................805 583-7744
Steven N Bronson, *President*
David J Wolenski, *Ch of Bd*
Louann L Negrete, *CFO*
Dale E Wallis, *Bd of Directors*
Nick Yarymovych, *Bd of Directors*
▲ **EMP:** 22
SQ FT: 15,160
SALES: 10.6MM **Publicly Held**
WEB: www.qualstar.com
SIC: 3572 3695 Tape storage units, computer; magnetic & optical recording media

(P-15589)
QUANTUM CORPORATION
Also Called: New Quantum Living
1441 Melanie Ln, Arcadia (91007-7908)
PHONE...............................213 248-2481
EMP: 110
SALES (corp-wide): 505.3MM **Publicly Held**
SIC: 3572 Computer storage devices
PA: Quantum Corporation
    224 Airport Pkwy Ste 550
    San Jose CA 95110
    408 944-4000

(P-15590)
QUANTUM CORPORATION
141 Innovation Dr Ste 100, Irvine
(92617-3212)
PHONE...............................949 856-7800
Lisa Ewbank, *Branch Mgr*
EMP: 90
SALES (corp-wide): 505.3MM **Publicly Held**
WEB: www.quantum.com
SIC: 3572 Computer storage devices
PA: Quantum Corporation
    224 Airport Pkwy Ste 550
    San Jose CA 95110
    408 944-4000

(P-15591)
QUANTUM DYNASTY
Also Called: Urban Empire
5934 Rancho Mission Rd # 118, San Diego
(92108-2530)
PHONE...............................347 469-1047
Milton Symister, *President*
David Symister, *Vice Pres*

EMP: 10
SALES (est): 1.2MM **Privately Held**
SIC: 3572 Computer storage devices

(P-15592)
QUANTUM PERFORMANCE DEVELOPMEN
32537 Jean Dr, Union City (94587-5017)
PHONE...............................510 870-6381
EMP: 13
SALES (est): 2.3MM **Privately Held**
SIC: 3572

(P-15593)
RANK TECHNOLOGY CORP
1190 Miraloma Way Ste Q, Sunnyvale
(94085-4607)
PHONE...............................408 737-1488
Fred Barez, *President*
Henry Barez, *Vice Pres*
EMP: 29
SQ FT: 6,000
SALES (est): 5.1MM **Privately Held**
SIC: 3572 Computer storage devices

(P-15594)
SACHS & ASSOCIATES INC
1230 Rosecrans Ave # 408, Manhattan Beach (90266-2436)
PHONE...............................310 356-7911
Greg T Sachs, *President*
EMP: 10
SALES (est): 1MM **Privately Held**
SIC: 3572 7379 Computer storage devices;

(P-15595)
SALE 121 CORP (PA)
1467 68th Ave, Sacramento (95822-4728)
P.O. Box 190969, Brooklyn NY (11219-0969)
PHONE...............................888 233-7667
Mohammad Naz, *Principal*
EMP: 99
SQ FT: 3,500
SALES (est): 3.5MM **Privately Held**
SIC: 3572 8748 7373 Disk drives, computer; systems engineering consultant, ex. computer or professional; systems software development services; office computer automation systems integration; turnkey vendors, computer systems

(P-15596)
SANDISK LLC
1101 Sandisk Dr Bldg 5, Milpitas
(95035-7936)
PHONE...............................408 801-2928
Michael Marks, *Principal*
EMP: 10
SALES (corp-wide): 20.6B **Publicly Held**
SIC: 3572 Computer storage devices
HQ: Sandisk Llc
    951 Sandisk Dr
    Milpitas CA 95035
    408 801-1000

(P-15597)
SANDISK LLC (DH)
Also Called: Western Digital
951 Sandisk Dr, Milpitas (95035-7933)
PHONE...............................408 801-1000
Sanjay Mehrotra, *President*
Michael Marks, *Ch of Bd*
Judy Bruner, *CFO*
John Joy, *Treasurer*
Sumit Sadana, *Exec VP*
▲ **EMP:** 141
SQ FT: 589,000
SALES (est): 2B
SALES (corp-wide): 20.6B **Publicly Held**
WEB: www.sdcard.com
SIC: 3572 Computer storage devices

(P-15598)
SANDISK LLC
Also Called: Ess Division
630 Alder Dr Ste 202, Milpitas
(95035-7435)
PHONE...............................408 321-0320
Greg Goles, *Manager*
EMP: 80
SALES (corp-wide): 20.6B **Publicly Held**
SIC: 3572 Computer storage devices

HQ: Sandisk Llc
    951 Sandisk Dr
    Milpitas CA 95035
    408 801-1000

(P-15599)
SAP AG
3410 Hillview Ave, Palo Alto (94304-1395)
PHONE...............................650 849-4000
John Schwarz, *CEO*
Michael Kiessle, *President*
Lori Mitchell-Keller, *Senior VP*
David Osborne, *Vice Pres*
Cliff Simpson, *Vice Pres*
EMP: 167
SALES (est): 17.1MM **Privately Held**
SIC: 3572 Computer storage devices

(P-15600)
SCALITY INC
555 California St # 3050, San Francisco
(94104-1503)
PHONE...............................650 356-8500
Jerome Lecat, *President*
Christopher Donohoe, *Partner*
Erwan Menard, *COO*
Philippe Mechanick, *CFO*
Paul Turner, *Chief Mktg Ofcr*
EMP: 45
SALES (est): 12.2MM
SALES (corp-wide): 14.7MM **Privately Held**
SIC: 3572 Computer storage devices
PA: Scality
    11 Rue Tronchet
    Paris 75008
    142 939-684

(P-15601)
SEAGATE SYSTEMS (US) INC (DH)
Also Called: Xyratex
46831 Lakeview Blvd, Fremont
(94538-6552)
PHONE...............................510 687-5200
Steve J Luczo, *Principal*
Ernest Sampias, *CEO*
Richard Pearce, *CFO*
Ken Claffey, *Senior VP*
Todd Gresham, *Senior VP*
▲ **EMP:** 70
SALES (est): 54.4MM **Privately Held**
SIC: 3572 Disk drives, computer
HQ: Seagate Technology Llc
    10200 S De Anza Blvd
    Cupertino CA 95014
    408 658-1000

(P-15602)
SEAGATE TECHNOLOGY LLC
10042 Wolf Rd, Grass Valley (95949-8192)
PHONE...............................530 410-6594
Martin Furuhjelm, *Principal*
EMP: 240 **Privately Held**
SIC: 3572 Computer storage devices
HQ: Seagate Technology Llc
    10200 S De Anza Blvd
    Cupertino CA 95014
    408 658-1000

(P-15603)
SEAGATE TECHNOLOGY LLC (DH)
Also Called: Seagate Tech Hdd Holdings
10200 S De Anza Blvd, Cupertino
(95014-3029)
P.O. Box 4030 (95015-4030)
PHONE...............................408 658-1000
Stephen J Luczo, *President*
Terry Cunningham, *President*
Robert Whitemore, *COO*
Robert Whitmore, *COO*
David A Wickershm, *COO*
▲ **EMP:** 3000
SQ FT: 383,000
SALES (est): 8.4B **Privately Held**
SIC: 3572 Computer storage devices
HQ: Seagate Technology (Us) Holdings, Inc.
    10200 S De Anza Blvd
    Cupertino CA 95014
    831 438-6550

▲ = Import ▼=Export
◆ =Import/Export

(P-15604)
SEAGATE TECHNOLOGY LLC
10200 S De Anza Blvd, Cupertino
(95014-3029)
PHONE..............................405 324-4799
Alan Shugart, *Branch Mgr*
Ed Zander, *Bd of Directors*
Glen Peterson, *Vice Pres*
Glenna W Heller, *Admin Asst*
Brian Doore, *Engineer*
EMP: 11 **Privately Held**
SIC: 3572 Disk drives, computer
HQ: Seagate Technology Llc
   10200 S De Anza Blvd
   Cupertino CA 95014
   408 658-1000

(P-15605)
SEAGATE US LLC
10200 S De Anza Blvd, Cupertino
(95014-3029)
PHONE..............................408 658-1000
Stephen J Luczo, *CEO*
EMP: 10
SALES (est): 1.9MM **Privately Held**
SIC: 3572 Magnetic storage devices, computer
PA: Seagate Technology Public Limited
   Company
   38/39 Fitzwilliam Square West
   Dublin 2
   -

(P-15606)
SHAXON INDUSTRIES INC
4852 E La Palma Ave, Anaheim
(92807-1911)
PHONE..............................714 779-1140
Benjamin S Wang, *CEO*
Rick Lawyer, *President*
Gilbert Wang, *President*
Thien Cao, *Purch Mgr*
Rick Trask, *Sales Mgr*
▲ **EMP:** 70
SQ FT: 30,000
SALES (est): 17.1MM **Privately Held**
WEB: www.shaxon.com
SIC: 3572 5045 3678 3661 Computer
   storage devices; computers & accessories, personal & home entertainment;
   electronic connectors; telephone & telegraph apparatus; pressed & blown glass

(P-15607)
SHOP4TECHCOM
Also Called: Leda Multimedia
13745 Seminole Dr, Chino (91710-5515)
PHONE..............................909 248-2725
Danny Wang, *President*
EMP: 45
SQ FT: 25,500
SALES (est): 5.9MM **Privately Held**
SIC: 3572 5731 Computer tape drives &
   components; video recorders, players,
   disc players & accessories
PA: Plc Multimedia, Inc.
   1226 E Lexington Ave
   Pomona CA 91766
   909 248-2680

(P-15608)
SILICON TECH INC
Also Called: Silicontech
3009 Daimler St, Santa Ana (92705-5812)
PHONE..............................949 476-1130
Manouch Moshayedi, *CEO*
Mark Moshayedi, *President*
Mike Moshayedi, *President*
EMP: 150
SALES (est): 7.7MM
SALES (corp-wide): 20.6B **Publicly Held**
SIC: 3572 Computer storage devices
HQ: Stec, Inc.
   3355 Michelson Dr Ste 100
   Irvine CA 92612
   415 222-9996

(P-15609)
SMART STORAGE SYSTEMS INC (DH)
39672 Eureka Dr, Newark (94560-4805)
PHONE..............................510 623-1231
Iain Mackenzie, *CEO*
Alan Marten, *President*
Ann T Nguyen, *CFO*
▲ **EMP:** 15 **EST:** 1985

SALES (est): 6.4MM
SALES (corp-wide): 20.6B **Publicly Held**
SIC: 3572 5045 Computer storage devices; computers, peripherals & software
HQ: Sandisk Llc
   951 Sandisk Dr
   Milpitas CA 95035
   408 801-1000

(P-15610)
SOLID DATA SYSTEMS INC
3542 Bassett St, Santa Clara (95054-2704)
P.O. Box 320095, Los Gatos (95032-0101)
PHONE..............................408 845-5700
EMP: 15
SQ FT: 3,500
SALES (est): 2.4MM **Privately Held**
WEB: www.soliddata.com
SIC: 3572

(P-15611)
SONY OPTICAL ARCHIVE INC
1730 N 1st St, San Jose (95112-4508)
PHONE..............................844 725-0398
Frank Frankovsky, *CEO*
EMP: 11
SALES (est): 602.7K **Privately Held**
SIC: 3572 Computer storage devices

(P-15612)
STEC INC (HQ)
3355 Michelson Dr Ste 100, Irvine
(92612-5694)
PHONE..............................415 222-9996
Stephen D Milligan, *President*
Faheem Hayat, *President*
▲ **EMP:** 340
SQ FT: 73,100
SALES (est): 70.3MM
SALES (corp-wide): 20.6B **Publicly Held**
WEB: www.stec-inc.com
SIC: 3572 3674 3577 Computer storage
   devices; semiconductors & related devices; computer peripheral equipment
PA: Western Digital Corporation
   5601 Great Oaks Pkwy
   San Jose CA 95119
   408 717-6000

(P-15613)
STEC INTERNATIONAL HOLDING INC
3001 Daimler St, Santa Ana (92705-5812)
PHONE..............................949 476-1180
Manouch Moshayedi, *Principal*
EMP: 70
SALES (est): 182.3K
SALES (corp-wide): 20.6B **Publicly Held**
SIC: 3572 Computer storage devices
HQ: Stec, Inc.
   3355 Michelson Dr Ste 100
   Irvine CA 92612
   415 222-9996

(P-15614)
SYNAPSENSE CORPORATION
340 Palladio Pkwy Ste 530, Folsom
(95630-8833)
PHONE..............................916 294-0110
Bart Tichelman, *President*
Dr Raju Pandey, *CTO*
EMP: 10
SALES (est): 2.7MM
SALES (corp-wide): 976.1MM **Privately Held**
SIC: 3572 Computer storage devices
PA: Panduit Corp.
   18900 Panduit Dr
   Tinley Park IL 60487
   708 532-1800

(P-15615)
SYPRIS DATA SYSTEMS INC (HQ)
160 Via Verde, San Dimas (91773-3901)
PHONE..............................909 962-9400
Darrell Robertson, *President*
▲ **EMP:** 50
SQ FT: 30,000
SALES (est): 198.1MM
SALES (corp-wide): 82.2MM **Publicly Held**
SIC: 3572 3651 Computer tape drives &
   components; tape recorders: cassette,
   cartridge or reel: household use

PA: Sypris Solutions, Inc.
   101 Bullitt Ln Ste 450
   Louisville KY 40222
   502 329-2000

(P-15616)
SYSTEMS UPGRADE INC
806 Avenida Pico Ste I, San Clemente
(92673-5693)
PHONE..............................949 429-8900
Deborah Allen, *President*
Robert Allen, *Vice Pres*
EMP: 12
SQ FT: 2,500
SALES (est): 2MM **Privately Held**
WEB: www.systemupgrade.com
SIC: 3572 Disk drives, computer

(P-15617)
TEKRAM USA INC
14228 Albers Way, Chino (91710-6940)
PHONE..............................714 961-0800
Woon Yei Kou, *President*
Kenny Ngo, *Manager*
▲ **EMP:** 10
SALES (est): 1.3MM **Privately Held**
SIC: 3572 Computer storage devices

(P-15618)
TOTAL PHASE INC
2350 Mission College Blvd # 1100, Santa
Clara (95054-1566)
PHONE..............................408 850-6500
Gil Ben-Dov, *CEO*
Annie Lu, *Technical Staff*
EMP: 16
SQ FT: 7,300
SALES (est): 1.3MM **Privately Held**
SIC: 3572 Computer storage devices

(P-15619)
TYPEHAUS INC
2262 Rutherford Rd # 103, Carlsbad
(92008-8818)
PHONE..............................760 334-3555
Nicole Gasperoni, *President*
Sarah Ly, *Production*
Joshua Jankowski, *Sales Mgr*
EMP: 15
SALES: 10MM **Privately Held**
SIC: 3572 Computer storage devices

(P-15620)
US CRITICAL LLC (PA)
Also Called: US Critical
6 Orchard Ste 150, Lake Forest
(92630-8352)
PHONE..............................949 916-9326
Thomas Horton, *Director*
John Lightman, *CEO*
Kurt Dunteman, *Vice Pres*
Angela Lunt, *Opers Mgr*
EMP: 24
SQ FT: 12,000
SALES (est): 64.1MM **Privately Held**
WEB: www.uscritical.com
SIC: 3572 Computer disk & drum drives &
   components

(P-15621)
US CRITICAL LLC
25422 Trabuco Rd 320, Lake Forest
(92630-2791)
PHONE..............................800 884-8945
Thomas Horton, *Director*
EMP: 41
SALES (corp-wide): 64.1MM **Privately Held**
SIC: 3572 Computer disk & drum drives &
   components
PA: U.S. Critical, Llc
   6 Orchard Ste 150
   Lake Forest CA 92630
   949 916-9326

(P-15622)
VICOM SYSTEMS INC
2336 Walsh Ave Ste H, Santa Clara
(95051-1313)
P.O. Box 6375 (95056-6375)
PHONE..............................408 588-1286
Samuel Tam, *President*
EMP: 25 **EST:** 1981
SQ FT: 13,000

SALES (est): 4.8MM **Privately Held**
SIC: 3572 7371 Computer storage devices; custom computer programming services

(P-15623)
VIOLIN SYSTEMS LLC
2560 N 1st St Ste 300, San Jose
(95131-1041)
PHONE..............................650 396-1501
Matthew Goh,
Hon Choe Lai,
Mark Lewis,
EMP: 137
SALES (est): 22.6MM **Privately Held**
SIC: 3572 Computer storage devices

(P-15624)
WESTERN DIGITAL CORPORATION (PA)
5601 Great Oaks Pkwy, San Jose
(95119-1003)
PHONE..............................408 717-6000
Stephen D Milligan, *CEO*
Matthew E Massengill, *Ch of Bd*
Michael D Cordano, *President*
Mark P Long, *CFO*
Michael C Ray,
▲ **EMP:** 1158
SQ FT: 2,750,000
SALES: 20.6B **Publicly Held**
WEB: www.wdc.com
SIC: 3572 Disk drives, computer

(P-15625)
WESTERN DIGITAL TECH INC (HQ)
Also Called: WD
5601 Great Oaks Pkwy, San Jose
(95119-1003)
PHONE..............................949 672-7000
Stephen D Milligan, *CEO*
John F Coyne, *President*
John Sawyer, *President*
Michael D Cordano, *COO*
Olivier C Leonetti, *CFO*
▲ **EMP:** 4300
SQ FT: 257,000
SALES (est): 4.7B
SALES (corp-wide): 20.6B **Publicly Held**
WEB: www.wdc.com
SIC: 3572 Disk drives, computer
PA: Western Digital Corporation
   5601 Great Oaks Pkwy
   San Jose CA 95119
   408 717-6000

(P-15626)
ZADARA STORAGE INC
6 Venture Ste 140, Irvine (92618-3742)
PHONE..............................949 251-0360
Nelson Nahum, *CEO*
Noam Shendar, *COO*
Yair Hershko, *Vice Pres*
Doug Jury, *Vice Pres*
Oded Kellner, *Vice Pres*
▲ **EMP:** 32
SALES (est): 7.3MM **Privately Held**
SIC: 3572 Computer storage devices

3575 Computer Terminals

(P-15627)
ACCO BRANDS USA LLC
Kensington Computer Pdts Group
1500 Fashion Island Blvd # 300, San Mateo
(94404-1597)
PHONE..............................650 572-2700
Patty Coffee, *Branch Mgr*
Ben Thacker, *Vice Pres*
Luciana Winter, *Executive*
Brian Bautista, *Engineer*
Charles J Froelich, *Opers Mgr*
EMP: 100
SALES (corp-wide): 1.9B **Publicly Held**
WEB: www.accobrands.com
SIC: 3575 Keyboards, computer, office machine
HQ: Acco Brands Usa Llc
   4 Corporate Dr
   Lake Zurich IL 60047
   800 222-6462

(P-15628)
ADVANCED DIGITAL RESEARCH INC
1813 E Dyer Rd Ste 410, Santa Ana (92705-5731)
PHONE..................949 252-1055
Dennis Childs, *President*
Robert Lasnik, *Vice Pres*
EMP: 10
SQ FT: 1,000
SALES (est): 1.2MM **Privately Held**
WEB: www.adrco.com
SIC: 3575 Computer terminals, monitors & components

(P-15629)
AG NEOVO TECHNOLOGY CORP
2362 Qume Dr Ste A, San Jose (95131-1841)
PHONE..................408 321-8210
Phillip Chang, *President*
Judy Sun, *Finance Mgr*
David Meng, *Sales Dir*
Curtis Liu, *Sales Mgr*
Tristarn Borgmann, *Manager*
▲ **EMP:** 18 **EST:** 1999
SALES (est): 3.6MM
SALES (corp-wide): 24.7MM **Privately Held**
WEB: www.neovo-usa.com
SIC: 3575 Computer terminals, monitors & components
PA: Associated Industries China, Inc.
5f-1, 3-1, Park St.,
Taipei City TAP 11503
226 558-080

(P-15630)
CORSAIR COMPONENTS INC (PA)
47100 Bayside Pkwy, Fremont (94538-6563)
PHONE..................510 657-8747
Andrew J Paul, *President*
Ronald Van Veen, *Vice Pres*
EMP: 35
SQ FT: 44,000
SALES (est): 41.5MM **Privately Held**
SIC: 3575 Computer terminals, monitors & components

(P-15631)
CYBERNETIC MICRO SYSTEMS INC
3000 La Honda Rd, San Gregorio (94074-9839)
PHONE..................650 726-3000
Edwin E Klingman, *President*
Karen Moty, *Treasurer*
EMP: 11
SQ FT: 6,960
SALES (est): 1.4MM **Privately Held**
WEB: www.controlchips.com
SIC: 3575 7371 Computer terminals, monitors & components; computer software development

(P-15632)
DIAMANTI INC
111 N Market St Ste 800, San Jose (95113-1102)
PHONE..................408 645-5111
Tom Barton, *CEO*
Karthik Govindhasamy, *COO*
EMP: 41
SALES (est): 9.6MM **Privately Held**
SIC: 3575 Keyboards, computer, office machine

(P-15633)
HPE GOVERNMENT LLC
46600 Landing Pkwy, Fremont (94538-6420)
PHONE..................916 435-9200
Pamela Jensen, *Branch Mgr*
EMP: 100
SALES (corp-wide): 28.8B **Publicly Held**
SIC: 3575 3572 7371 7378 Computer terminals; computer storage devices; custom computer programming services; computer maintenance & repair; electronic computers

HQ: Hpe Government, Llc.
420 Natl Bus Pkwy Ste 180
Annapolis Junction MD 20701
301 572-1980

(P-15634)
IMC NETWORKS CORP (PA)
25531 Commercentre Dr, Lake Forest (92630-8873)
PHONE..................949 465-3000
Jerry Roby, *Ch of Bd*
Michael Dailey, *President*
▲ **EMP:** 32
SQ FT: 35,000
SALES (est): 7.2MM **Privately Held**
WEB: www.imcnetworks.com
SIC: 3575 3577 Computer terminals, monitors & components; computer peripheral equipment

(P-15635)
INFORMER COMPUTER SYSTEMS
12711 Western Ave, Garden Grove (92841-4016)
PHONE..................714 899-2049
Wilfred R Little, *President*
Edward P Dailey, *Director*
EMP: 10
SQ FT: 14,000
SALES (est): 1.7MM **Privately Held**
WEB: www.informer911.com
SIC: 3575

(P-15636)
JUPITER SYSTEMS LLC
Also Called: Infocus Jupiter
31015 Huntwood Ave, Hayward (94544-7007)
PHONE..................510 675-1000
Jack Klingelhofer, *Ch of Bd*
Eric Wogsberg, *President*
Bob Worthington, *CFO*
Robert Worthington, *CFO*
Chuck Kelley, *Vice Pres*
▲ **EMP:** 65
SQ FT: 33,000
SALES (est): 15.2MM **Privately Held**
WEB: www.jupiter.com
SIC: 3575 Computer terminals
HQ: Infocus Corporation
13190 Sw 68th Pkwy # 200
Portland OR 97223
503 207-4700

(P-15637)
KEY SOURCE INTERNATIONAL (PA)
7711 Oakport St, Oakland (94621-2026)
PHONE..................510 562-5000
Robert A D Schwartz, *President*
Philip Bruno, *Senior VP*
Thil Brunl, *Vice Pres*
Kelly Chen, *Executive*
Tom Harkins, *Software Engr*
▲ **EMP:** 10
SALES (est): 2MM **Privately Held**
WEB: www.ksikeyboards.com
SIC: 3575 3993 2671 Keyboards, computer, office machine; signs & advertising specialties; packaging paper & plastics film, coated & laminated

(P-15638)
LANSTREETCOM
Also Called: Tricir Technologies
17050 Evergreen Pl, City of Industry (91745-1819)
PHONE..................626 964-2000
Michael Jen, *President*
EMP: 20
SALES: 8MM **Privately Held**
WEB: www.lanstreet.com
SIC: 3575 Computer terminals, monitors & components

(P-15639)
LIKOM CASEWORKS USA INC (DH)
17890 Castleton St # 309, City of Industry (91748-6789)
P.O. Box 370070, El Paso TX (79937-0070)
PHONE..................210 587-7824
Kim Ming Chow, *CEO*

Azmi Sulaiman, *Vice Pres*
◆ **EMP:** 26 **EST:** 1999
SALES (est): 12.8MM **Privately Held**
SIC: 3575 3469 Computer terminals, monitors & components; metal stampings
HQ: Likom Caseworks Sdn. Bhd.
19401-1 Jalan Ttc 12
Melaka MLC 75260
633 456-66

(P-15640)
MOTOROLA SOLUTIONS INC
6001 Shellmound St Fl 4th, Emeryville (94608-1968)
PHONE..................510 420-7400
EMP: 26
SALES (corp-wide): 5.7B **Publicly Held**
SIC: 3575
PA: Motorola Solutions, Inc.
1303 E Algonquin Rd
Schaumburg IL 60661
847 576-5000

(P-15641)
N-SYNCH TECHNOLOGIES
30100 Town Center Dr 0-204, Laguna Niguel (92677-2064)
PHONE..................949 218-7761
Tim Burke, *President*
Annamaria Burke, *Admin Sec*
EMP: 11
SQ FT: 11,000
SALES (est): 1.5MM **Privately Held**
WEB: www.n-synch.com
SIC: 3575 5045 Computer terminals, monitors & components; computer software

(P-15642)
NWT INFOTECH SERVICES
5779 Winfield Blvd Ste A2, San Jose (95123-2433)
PHONE..................831 335-6500
Mary Anderson, *CEO*
Marielle Martin, *COO*
EMP: 12
SALES (est): 900K **Privately Held**
WEB: www.nwtinfotech.com
SIC: 3575 Computer terminals

(P-15643)
OCP GROUP INC
7130 Engineer Rd, San Diego (92111-1422)
PHONE..................858 279-7400
Neil Gleason, *President*
Tracy Sommer, *CEO*
Margarita Carlsen, *Engineer*
Stan Walker, *Controller*
Leo Sanchez, *Purchasing*
▲ **EMP:** 22
SALES (est): 5.8MM **Privately Held**
SIC: 3575 5051 7549 Computer terminals, monitors & components; cable; wire; automotive maintenance services

(P-15644)
R G B DISPLAY CORPORATION
22525 Kingston Ln, Grass Valley (95949-7706)
PHONE..................530 268-2222
Lori Mc Laughlin, *President*
Michelle Hilger, *CFO*
Joan Mc Laughlin, *Corp Secy*
Mike Newman, *Engineer*
EMP: 12 **EST:** 1978
SQ FT: 14,000
SALES (est): 2.9MM **Privately Held**
WEB: www.rgbdisplay.com
SIC: 3575 Computer terminals, monitors & components

(P-15645)
SGB ENTERPRISES INC
24844 Anza Dr Ste A, Valencia (91355-1286)
PHONE..................661 294-8306
Joseph Padula, *President*
Chuck Burkholder, *CFO*
Jeff Mello, *Vice Pres*
Joe Padula, *Vice Pres*
Marvin Beiter, *General Mgr*
EMP: 22
SQ FT: 9,600

SALES (est): 7.3MM **Privately Held**
WEB: www.sgbent.com
SIC: 3575 5999 3728 3699 Cathode ray tube (CRT), computer terminal; training materials, electronic; aircraft training equipment; flight simulators (training aids), electronic

(P-15646)
SMK MANUFACTURING INC
1055 Tierra Del Rey Ste H, Chula Vista (91910-7875)
PHONE..................619 216-6400
Tetsuya Nakamura, *CEO*
Mathoru Hurukawa, *CFO*
Naomasa Miyata, *Vice Pres*
▲ **EMP:** 50
SQ FT: 14,688
SALES (est): 22.7MM
SALES (corp-wide): 561.1MM **Privately Held**
SIC: 3575 Keyboards, computer, office machine
HQ: Smk Electronics Corporation Usa
1055 Tierra Del Rey
Chula Vista CA 91910
619 216-6400

(P-15647)
SYSMASTER CORPORATION
2700 Ygnacio Valley Rd # 210, Walnut Creek (94598-3455)
PHONE..................925 891-7813
Kirk Iliev, *President*
Plamen Atanasov, *Mng Member*
▲ **EMP:** 49
SALES (est): 7.9MM **Privately Held**
WEB: www.sysmaster.com
SIC: 3575 3728 Computer terminals; aircraft parts & equipment

(P-15648)
TRANSPARENT PRODUCTS INC
28064 Avenue Stanford E, Valencia (91355-1160)
PHONE..................661 294-9787
Fred Bonyadian, *President*
John McVay, *President*
Debbie Merritt, *Finance*
Brenda Captol, *Manager*
▲ **EMP:** 50
SQ FT: 18,000
SALES (est): 15.3MM **Privately Held**
WEB: www.touchpage.com
SIC: 3575 7371 Computer terminals, monitors & components; computer software systems analysis & design, custom

(P-15649)
UNI-PIXEL DISPLAYS INC
4699 Old Ironsides Dr, Santa Clara (95054-1824)
PHONE..................281 825-4500
Jeff Hawthorne, *CEO*
Frank Delape, *Ch of Bd*
Reed Killion, *President*
Donna Grumgles, *COO*
Jim Tassone, *CFO*
▲ **EMP:** 14 **EST:** 1998
SQ FT: 30,000
SALES (est): 617.2K **Publicly Held**
WEB: www.uni-pixel.com
SIC: 3575 Computer terminals, monitors & components
PA: Uni-Pixel, Inc.
4699 Old Ironsides Dr
Santa Clara CA 95054

(P-15650)
WIDE USA CORPORATION
2210 E Winston Rd, Anaheim (92806-5536)
PHONE..................714 300-0540
Is Kang, *President*
Hyo Sung Lee, *Exec VP*
▲ **EMP:** 30
SQ FT: 8,700
SALES: 550K **Privately Held**
SIC: 3575 Computer terminals, monitors & components

▲ = Import ▼=Export
◆ =Import/Export

3577 Computer Peripheral Eqpt, NEC

(P-15651)
3DCONNEXION INC
6505 Kaiser Dr, Fremont (94555-3614)
PHONE....................510 713-6000
Rory Dooley, *President*
James V McCanna, *CFO*
Lew Epstein, *Vice Pres*
Niraj Swarup, *Vice Pres*
EMP: 71
SALES (est): 5.4MM
SALES (corp-wide): 2.2B **Privately Held**
WEB: www.3dconnexion.com
SIC: 3577 5045 Computer peripheral
equipment; computers & accessories,
personal & home entertainment
HQ: Logitech Inc.
7700 Gateway Blvd
Newark CA 94560
510 795-8500

(P-15652)
ACCES I/O PRODUCTS INC
10623 Roselle St, San Diego (92121-1506)
PHONE....................858 550-9559
John Persidok, *President*
Michael Pendleton, *Info Tech Mgr*
Roland Samson, *Design Engr*
Ellen Jing, *Accounting Mgr*
Gary Karns, *Sales Dir*
EMP: 28
SQ FT: 9,447
SALES (est): 6.6MM **Privately Held**
WEB: www.accesio.com
SIC: 3577 Computer peripheral equipment

(P-15653)
ACCURITE TECHNOLOGIES INC
15732 Los Gatos Blvd, Los Gatos
(95032-2504)
PHONE....................408 395-7100
Brad Baker, *President*
Elizabeth Dessuge, *Vice Pres*
Richard Kelly, *Vice Pres*
EMP: 10
SALES (est): 1.3MM **Privately Held**
WEB: www.accurite.com
SIC: 3577

(P-15654)
ACECAD INC
791 Foam St Ste 200, Monterey
(93940-1031)
P.O. Box 1071 (93942-1071)
PHONE....................831 655-1900
Todd Waldman, *President*
Megan Connolly, *Mktg Dir*
▲ EMP: 12
SQ FT: 4,500
SALES (est): 1.5MM **Privately Held**
SIC: 3577 5045 Computer peripheral
equipment; computers, peripherals & soft-
ware

(P-15655)
ACER AMERICAN HOLDINGS CORP (DH)
333 W San Carlos St # 1500, San Jose
(95110-2726)
PHONE....................408 533-7700
Emmanuel Fromont, *CEO*
J T Wang, *CEO*
Jon Chandler, *Telecomm Mgr*
Lynne Edgehill, *Accounts Mgr*
EMP: 13
SQ FT: 232,000
SALES (est): 333.5MM
SALES (corp-wide): 7.8B **Privately Held**
SIC: 3577 3571 Computer peripheral
equipment; electronic computers

(P-15656)
ACTIVEWIRE INC
1799 Silacci Dr, Campbell (95008-5130)
P.O. Box 60280, Palo Alto (94306-0280)
PHONE....................650 465-4000
Mato Hatori, *Branch Mgr*
EMP: 14
SALES (corp-wide): 1.2MM **Privately Held**
SIC: 3577 Computer peripheral equipment

PA: Activewire, Inc.
895 Commercial St Ste 700
Palo Alto CA 94303
650 969-4000

(P-15657)
ACUANT INC (HQ)
Also Called: Card Scanning Solutions
6080 Center Dr Ste 850, Los Angeles
(90045-9229)
PHONE....................213 867-2621
Yossi Zekri, *President*
Bruce Ackerman, *Exec VP*
Iuval Hatzav, *Exec VP*
Alexi Georghiou, *Vice Pres*
Luz Dimaculangan, *Office Mgr*
▲ EMP: 25
SALES (est): 4.4MM
SALES (corp-wide): 29.3MM **Privately Held**
SIC: 3577 Optical scanning devices
PA: Audax Management Company, Llc
101 Huntington Ave Fl 23
Boston MA 02199
617 859-1500

(P-15658)
ADD-ON COMPUTER PERIPHERAL INC
15775 Gateway Cir, Tustin (92780-6470)
PHONE....................949 546-8200
James Patton, *CEO*
Matthew McCormick, *Vice Pres*
Steven Pace, *Vice Pres*
Joe D'Esopo, *General Mgr*
Kim Couch, *Purchasing*
▲ EMP: 70
SQ FT: 11,000
SALES (est): 15.5MM **Privately Held**
WEB: www.addoncomputer.com
SIC: 3577 5045 Computer peripheral
equipment; computers, peripherals & soft-
ware

(P-15659)
ADVANCE MODULAR TECHNOLOGY INC
Also Called: A M T
2075 Bering Dr Ste C, San Jose
(95131-2011)
PHONE....................408 453-9880
Crispian SOO, *President*
Pauline SOO, *Vice Pres*
▲ EMP: 14
SALES (est): 3.5MM **Privately Held**
WEB: www.amchip.com
SIC: 3577 Computer peripheral equipment

(P-15660)
ALCATEL-LUCENT USA INC
2361 Rosecrans Ave # 150, El Segundo
(90245-4916)
PHONE....................310 297-2620
Marty Sanders, *Principal*
EMP: 12
SALES (corp-wide): 27.3B **Privately Held**
WEB: www.lucent.com
SIC: 3577 Computer peripheral equipment
HQ: Nokia Of America Corporation
600 Mountain Ave Ste 700
New Providence NJ 07974

(P-15661)
ALLEN SARAH &
Also Called: Lightprint Labs
560 Crestlake Dr, San Francisco
(94132-1325)
PHONE....................415 242-0906
Sarah Allen, *Partner*
Michele Henrion, *Partner*
EMP: 20
SALES (est): 1.9MM **Privately Held**
SIC: 3577 Graphic displays, except
graphic terminals

(P-15662)
ALLIED TELESIS INC
468 S Abbott Ave, Milpitas (95035-5258)
PHONE....................408 519-6700
Takayoshi Oshima, *Branch Mgr*
EMP: 70
SALES (corp-wide): 260.6MM **Privately Held**
SIC: 3577 Computer peripheral equipment

HQ: Allied Telesis, Inc.
19800 North Creek Pkwy # 100
Bothell WA 98011
408 519-8700

(P-15663)
ALLIED TELESIS INC
3041 Orchard Pkwy, San Jose
(95134-2017)
PHONE....................408 519-8700
Mike Dunbar, *President*
Kathy Schreiber, *Executive Asst*
Wendy Shrank, *Technical Staff*
Benny Barbero, *Engineer*
David Dunn, *Engineer*
EMP: 34
SALES (corp-wide): 260.6MM **Privately Held**
SIC: 3577 Computer peripheral equipment
HQ: Allied Telesis, Inc.
19800 North Creek Pkwy # 100
Bothell WA 98011
408 519-8700

(P-15664)
ALLIED TELESIS INC
3041 Orchard Pkwy, San Jose
(95134-2017)
PHONE....................408 519-8700
Taki Oshima, *Manager*
Lisa Rosetta, *Vice Pres*
Diem Doan, *CTO*
Joe Stelpflug, *Engineer*
Yun Wong, *Engineer*
EMP: 20
SALES (corp-wide): 260.6MM **Privately Held**
WEB: www.alliedtelesyn.com
SIC: 3577 Computer peripheral equipment
HQ: Allied Telesis, Inc.
19800 North Creek Pkwy # 100
Bothell WA 98011
408 519-8700

(P-15665)
AMAG TECHNOLOGY INC (DH)
20701 Manhattan Pl, Torrance
(90501-1829)
PHONE....................310 518-2380
Matt Barnette, *Ch of Bd*
N Keith Whitelock, *Ch of Bd*
Jeff Leblanc, *President*
Robert A Sawyer Jr, *President*
Robert Causee, *CFO*
▲ EMP: 50
SQ FT: 24,000
SALES (est): 12.3MM
SALES (corp-wide): 10.3B **Privately Held**
WEB: www.amagaccess.com
SIC: 3577 Decoders, computer peripheral
equipment
HQ: G4s Technology Limited
Challenge House
Tewkesbury GLOS GL20
168 427-7247

(P-15666)
ANOVA MICROSYSTEMS INC
173 Santa Rita Ct, Los Altos (94022-1096)
PHONE....................408 941-1888
Raymond S Chuang, *CEO*
Palm Nyu, *Shareholder*
Chao Huang, *Vice Pres*
Yukon Cherng, *Admin Sec*
Wayne Lu, *Controller*
◆ EMP: 10
SALES (est): 2.2MM **Privately Held**
WEB: www.anova.com
SIC: 3577 5045 Computer peripheral
equipment; computers & accessories,
personal & home entertainment

(P-15667)
ANTEC INC
47681 Lakeview Blvd, Fremont
(94538-6544)
PHONE....................510 770-1200
Yih Chung Andrew Lee, *CEO*
Lisa Lin, *Vice Pres*
▲ EMP: 50
SQ FT: 34,000
SALES (est): 11.8MM **Privately Held**
WEB: www.antec-inc.com
SIC: 3577 Computer peripheral equipment

(P-15668)
ANTEX ELECTRONICS CORPORATION
5483 E Oleta St, Long Beach
(90815-4432)
PHONE....................310 532-3092
David Antrim, *President*
Linda Edwards, *CFO*
Deri Antrim, *Admin Sec*
Rodney Dunbar, *Controller*
▲ EMP: 15
SQ FT: 12,000
SALES (est): 2.9MM **Privately Held**
WEB: www.antex.com
SIC: 3577 3663 3571 Computer periph-
eral equipment; radio & TV communica-
tions equipment; electronic computers

(P-15669)
AOT ELECTRONICS INC
Also Called: Orbit Systems
23172 Alcalde Dr Ste E, Laguna Hills
(92653-1452)
PHONE....................949 600-6335
Omar Turbi, *President*
Renee Laviolette, *CFO*
◆ EMP: 42
SQ FT: 40,000
SALES (est): 6.2MM **Privately Held**
WEB: www.aotelectronics.com
SIC: 3577 5065 Printers & plotters; com-
munication equipment; electronic parts

(P-15670)
APRICORN
12191 Kirkham Rd, Poway (92064-6870)
PHONE....................858 513-2000
Paul Brown, *President*
Michael Gordon, *Treasurer*
▲ EMP: 29
SQ FT: 21,000
SALES (est): 8.5MM **Privately Held**
WEB: www.apricorn.com
SIC: 3577 5734 Computer peripheral
equipment; computer & software stores

(P-15671)
ARIES RESEARCH INC
Also Called: Aries Solutions
46750 Fremont Blvd # 107, Fremont
(94538-6573)
P.O. Box 1112, Alamo (94507-7112)
PHONE....................925 818-1078
Lawrence T Kou, *CEO*
Ilain Kou, *President*
J Bar Houston, *Engineer*
EMP: 11
SQ FT: 8,600
SALES (est): 2.6MM **Privately Held**
SIC: 3577 3571 Computer peripheral
equipment; electronic computers

(P-15672)
ARUBA NETWORKS INC (HQ)
Also Called: Aruba Networks Cafe
3333 Scott Blvd, Santa Clara (95054-3103)
PHONE....................408 227-4500
Rishi Varma, *President*
Catherine A Lesjak, *CFO*
Robin Daniel, *Executive Asst*
Jason Cronin, *Engineer*
Christopher Victory, *Engineer*
EMP: 270
SALES (est): 717.5MM
SALES (corp-wide): 28.8B **Publicly Held**
WEB: www.arubanetworks.com
SIC: 3577 3663 7371 Computer periph-
eral equipment; mobile communication
equipment; computer software develop-
ment
PA: Hewlett Packard Enterprise Company
3000 Hanover St
Palo Alto CA 94304
650 687-5817

(P-15673)
ASANTE TECHNOLOGIES INC (PA)
2223 Oakland Rd, San Jose (95131-1402)
PHONE....................408 435-8388
Jeff Yuan-Kai Lin, *President*
David Kichar, *COO*
Y C Wang, *Exec VP*
Albert LI, *General Mgr*
Brian Lewis, *Engineer*

PRODUCTS & SVCS

EMP: 29
SQ FT: 7,000
SALES (est): 3.3MM **Privately Held**
WEB: www.asante.com
SIC: 3577 Computer peripheral equipment

(P-15674)
ASANTE TECHNOLOGIES INC
673 S Milpitas Blvd # 100, Milpitas (95035-5446)
PHONE..................................408 435-8388
Carmen Lopez Mngr, *Branch Mgr*
EMP: 16
SALES (corp-wide): 3.3MM **Privately Held**
SIC: 3577 Computer peripheral equipment
PA: Asante Technologies, Inc.
2223 Oakland Rd
San Jose CA 95131
408 435-8388

(P-15675)
ASANTE TECHNOLOGIES INC
47341 Bayside Pkwy, Fremont (94538-6574)
PHONE..................................408 435-8388
EMP: 23
SALES (corp-wide): 3.3MM **Privately Held**
SIC: 3577 Computer peripheral equipment
PA: Asante Technologies, Inc.
2223 Oakland Rd
San Jose CA 95131
408 435-8388

(P-15676)
AVERMEDIA TECHNOLOGIES INC
47358 Fremont Blvd, Fremont (94538-6501)
PHONE..................................510 403-0006
Michael Cooke, *President*
Ping Zhao, *Technology*
▲ EMP: 14
SALES (est): 2.2MM
SALES (corp-wide): 83.4MM **Privately Held**
SIC: 3577 Computer peripheral equipment
PA: Avermedia Technologies, Inc.
135, Jian 1st Rd.,
New Taipei City 23585
222 263-630

(P-15677)
BAJASYS LLC
9923 Via De La Amistad # 105, San Diego (92154-7215)
PHONE..................................619 661-0748
Jose Ramirez,
Roberto Lopez, *Sales Mgr*
▲ EMP: 13
SALES (est): 1.7MM **Privately Held**
SIC: 3577 Printers, computer

(P-15678)
BARRACUDA NETWORKS INC
5225 Hellyer Ave, San Jose (95138-1023)
PHONE..................................408 342-5400
William D Jenkins Jr, *President*
EMP: 10
SALES (corp-wide): 44.7MM **Privately Held**
SIC: 3577 Computer peripheral equipment
HQ: Barracuda Networks, Inc.
3175 Winchester Blvd
Campbell CA 95008
408 342-5400

(P-15679)
BDR INDUSTRIES INC
Also Called: Rnd Enterprises
9700 Owensmouth Ave Lbby, Chatsworth (91311-8073)
PHONE..................................818 341-2112
Scott Riddle, *Branch Mgr*
EMP: 20
SALES (corp-wide): 21.7MM **Privately Held**
WEB: www.rndcable.com
SIC: 3577 Computer peripheral equipment
PA: B.D.R. Industries, Inc.
820 E Avenue L12
Lancaster CA 93535
661 940-8554

(P-15680)
BERING TECHNOLOGY INC
1608 W Campbell Ave 328, Campbell (95008-1535)
PHONE..................................408 364-6500
Leung C Lok, *President*
Stephen Sun, *Admin Sec*
Roland F Aquino, *Engineer*
EMP: 45
SALES (est): 6.3MM **Privately Held**
WEB: www.bering.com
SIC: 3577 Computer peripheral equipment

(P-15681)
BEST DATA PRODUCTS INC
Also Called: Diamond Multimedia
21541 Blythe St, Canoga Park (91304-4910)
PHONE..................................818 534-1414
Bruce Zaman, *President*
Shirley Zaman, *CFO*
▲ EMP: 85
SALES (est): 19.8MM **Privately Held**
WEB: www.bestdata.com
SIC: 3577 Computer peripheral equipment

(P-15682)
BESTEK MANUFACTURING INC
675 Sycamore Dr, Milpitas (95035-7430)
PHONE..................................408 321-8834
Frank Dang, *President*
Tyler Dang, *Director*
EMP: 40
SQ FT: 8,000
SALES (est): 10.3MM **Privately Held**
WEB: www.bestekmfg.com
SIC: 3577 3679 3672 Computer peripheral equipment; harness assemblies for electronic use: wire or cable; printed circuit boards

(P-15683)
BIOMETRIC SOLUTIONS LLC
41829 Albrae St Unit 110, Fremont (94538-3144)
PHONE..................................408 625-7763
Danny Thakkar, *Manager*
EMP: 10
SALES: 60K **Privately Held**
SIC: 3577 Computer peripheral equipment

(P-15684)
BIOSTAR MICROTECH USA CORP
661 Brea Canyon Rd Ste 5, Walnut (91789-3044)
PHONE..................................909 444-3785
Chung Ming Wang, *President*
▲ EMP: 19
SQ FT: 13,000
SALES (est): 2.8MM **Privately Held**
WEB: www.biostar-usa.com
SIC: 3577 Computer peripheral equipment

(P-15685)
BIXOLON AMERICA INC
13705 Cimarron Ave, Gardena (90249-2463)
PHONE..................................858 764-4580
Chan Young Hwang, *CEO*
Yon H Son, *President*
David Roberts, *Senior VP*
Juan Salinas, *Sales Dir*
Rick Pino, *Sales Mgr*
▲ EMP: 18
SQ FT: 26,000
SALES (est): 3.1MM
SALES (corp-wide): 74MM **Privately Held**
SIC: 3577 Printers, computer
PA: Bixolon Co.,Ltd.
20 Pangyoyeok-Ro 241beon-Gil, Bundang-Gu
Seongnam 13494
823 121-8550

(P-15686)
BLACK DIAMOND VIDEO INC
503 Canal Blvd, Richmond (94804-3517)
PHONE..................................510 439-4500
Peter Metcalf, *CEO*
Jonathan Chao, *General Mgr*
Barrett Baird, *Administration*
Rod McArthur, *Project Mgr*
Anirrudh R Saddi, *Project Mgr*
▲ EMP: 90
SQ FT: 30,000
SALES: 25MM
SALES (corp-wide): 2.6B **Privately Held**
WEB: www.blackdiamondvideo.com
SIC: 3577 3679 Computer peripheral equipment; electronic switches
HQ: Steris Corporation
5960 Heisley Rd
Mentor OH 44060
440 354-2600

(P-15687)
BLASTRONIX INC
999 W Highway 4, Murphys (95247)
PHONE..................................209 795-0738
David A Barnes, *President*
Rebecca Barnes, *Vice Pres*
A C Barnes, *Director*
EMP: 10
SQ FT: 2,500
SALES (est): 2.5MM **Privately Held**
WEB: www.blastronix.com
SIC: 3577 8711 Input/output equipment, computer; engineering services

(P-15688)
BLUE CEDAR NETWORKS INC
325 Pacific Ave Fl 1, San Francisco (94111-1711)
PHONE..................................415 329-0401
John Aisien, *CEO*
Jeanne Angelo-Pardo, *CFO*
Chris Ford, *Officer*
Pam Brodt, *Vice Pres*
Adam Jacobs, *Vice Pres*
EMP: 36 EST: 2016
SQ FT: 8,000
SALES (est): 2.1MM **Privately Held**
SIC: 3577 Computer peripheral equipment

(P-15689)
BO-SHERREL CORPORATION
3340 Tree Swallow Pl, Fremont (94555-1330)
PHONE..................................510 744-3525
Fax: 510 792-0416
EMP: 13 EST: 1976
SQ FT: 2,000
SALES (est): 1.1MM **Privately Held**
SIC: 3577

(P-15690)
BRAVO COMMUNICATIONS INC
3463 Meadowlands Ln, San Jose (95135-1645)
PHONE..................................408 297-8700
Dennis L Mozingo, *President*
EMP: 29
SQ FT: 4,000
SALES (est): 3.9MM **Privately Held**
WEB: www.bravobravo.com
SIC: 3577 3612 Computer peripheral equipment; transformers, except electric

(P-15691)
BROCADE CMMNCTIONS SYSTEMS LLC
Also Called: Brocade It
120 Holger Way, San Jose (95134-1376)
PHONE..................................408 333-8000
Ken Bagley, *Partner*
Tim Lees, *Partner*
Shivanand Sawant, *Senior VP*
Marco Martinez, *Executive Asst*
Kenny Simpson, *Administration*
EMP: 14
SALES (corp-wide): 17.6B **Publicly Held**
SIC: 3577 4813 Computer peripheral equipment; telephone communication, except radio
HQ: Brocade Communications Systems Llc
130 Holger Way
San Jose CA 95134

(P-15692)
BROCADE CMMNCTIONS SYSTEMS LLC (DH)
130 Holger Way, San Jose (95134-1376)
PHONE..................................408 333-8000
Hock E Tan, *President*
Matt Wineberg, *Partner*
Thomas H Krause Jr, *CFO*
Jean Samuel Furter, *Treasurer*
Raymond Lee, *Vice Pres*
EMP: 800

SQ FT: 562,000
SALES: 2.3B
SALES (corp-wide): 17.6B **Publicly Held**
WEB: www.brocade.com
SIC: 3577 4813 Computer peripheral equipment;
HQ: Lsi Corporation
1320 Ridder Park Dr
San Jose CA 95131
408 433-8000

(P-15693)
BRUKER CORPORATION
1717 Dell Ave, Campbell (95008-6904)
PHONE..................................408 376-4040
Adrian Correa, *Engineer*
Andrew Lopez, *Engineer*
EMP: 30
SALES (corp-wide): 1.7B **Publicly Held**
SIC: 3577 8734 8731 Computer peripheral equipment; testing laboratories; commercial physical research
PA: Bruker Corporation
40 Manning Rd
Billerica MA 01821
978 663-3660

(P-15694)
C ENTERPRISES LP
2445 Cades Way, Vista (92081-7831)
PHONE..................................760 599-5111
Brian Tauber, *President*
Steven Yamasaki, *COO*
EMP: 64
SQ FT: 36,000
SALES (est): 14.3MM **Privately Held**
WEB: www.centerprises.com
SIC: 3577 5045 3357 3229 Computer peripheral equipment; computers & accessories, personal & home entertainment; nonferrous wiredrawing & insulating; pressed & blown glass

(P-15695)
CABLE DEVICES INCORPORATED (HQ)
Also Called: Cable Exchange
3008 S Croddy Way, Santa Ana (92704-6305)
PHONE..................................714 554-4370
Marvin S Edwards, *CEO*
Mark Olson, *CFO*
Joey Hynes, *Vice Pres*
Dan Bowlin, *Admin Sec*
Frank B Wyatt, *Admin Sec*
▲ EMP: 150
SQ FT: 24,516
SALES: 30MM **Publicly Held**
WEB: www.4cablex.com
SIC: 3577 Computer peripheral equipment

(P-15696)
CALIFORNIA DIGITAL INC (PA)
6 Saddleback Rd, Rolling Hills (90274-5141)
P.O. Box 3399, Torrance (90510-3399)
PHONE..................................310 217-0500
Terry Reiter, *President*
Floyd Pothoven, *Vice Pres*
Wade Wood, *Vice Pres*
EMP: 82
SQ FT: 30,000
SALES (est): 9.4MM **Privately Held**
SIC: 3577 3571 3699 Computer peripheral equipment; mainframe computers; electrical equipment & supplies

(P-15697)
CALIFORNIA SURVEYING & DRAFTIN
411 Russell Ave, Santa Rosa (95403-2219)
PHONE..................................707 293-9449
EMP: 17
SALES (corp-wide): 27.9MM **Privately Held**
SIC: 3577 5049 Computer peripheral equipment; surveyors' instruments
PA: California Surveying & Drafting Supply Inc.
4733 Auburn Blvd
Sacramento CA 95841
916 344-0232

▲ = Import ▼=Export
◆ =Import/Export

(P-15698)
CALIFORNIA SURVEYING & DRAFTIN (PA)
Also Called: CSDS
4733 Auburn Blvd, Sacramento (95841-3601)
PHONE.....................................916 344-0232
Bruce Gandelman, *CEO*
Tom Cardenas, *President*
Mike Woodel, *Vice Pres*
Dan Soldavini, *Principal*
Sean Davis, *Sales Associate*
EMP: 49
SQ FT: 17,500
SALES: 27.9MM **Privately Held**
SIC: 3577 7353 3993 5082 Printers & plotters; heavy construction equipment rental; displays & cutouts, window & lobby; general construction machinery & equipment; printers, computer; drafting supplies

(P-15699)
CARBON INC
1089 Mills Way, Redwood City (94063-3119)
PHONE.....................................650 285-6307
Joseph M Desimone, *CEO*
Elisa De Martel, *CFO*
Kirk Phelps, *Vice Pres*
Alan Mulally, *Principal*
Julius Yako, *Software Engr*
EMP: 210
SQ FT: 87,000
SALES (est): 912.1K **Privately Held**
SIC: 3577 Computer peripheral equipment

(P-15700)
CARDLOGIX
16 Hughes Ste 100, Irvine (92618-1948)
PHONE.....................................949 380-1312
Walter Lim, *Ch of Bd*
Bruce Ross, *President*
Ken indorf, *Vice Pres*
Arthur Krause, *Vice Pres*
Jean Pan, *Accountant*
▲ EMP: 19
SQ FT: 6,000
SALES (est): 4.7MM **Privately Held**
WEB: www.cardlogic.com
SIC: 3577 3089 Computer peripheral equipment; panels, building: plastic

(P-15701)
CD ALEXANDER LLC
2802 Willis St, Santa Ana (92705-5714)
P.O. Box 15101 (92735-0101)
PHONE.....................................949 250-3306
Anthony Gonzalez,
Robert Barraza, *Planning*
Michael Lenz, *Engineer*
Anthony Delgardo, *Opers Mgr*
Agustin Hernandez,
EMP: 27
SQ FT: 19,000
SALES (est): 6.5MM **Privately Held**
WEB: www.cdalexander.com
SIC: 3577 3444 Computer peripheral equipment; sheet metalwork

(P-15702)
CDC DATA LLC
9735 Lurline Ave, Chatsworth (91311-4404)
PHONE.....................................818 350-5070
Joe Varraveto, *Mng Member*
▲ EMP: 10
SALES (est): 1.6MM **Privately Held**
SIC: 3577 Optical scanning devices

(P-15703)
CIPHERTEX LLC
Also Called: Ciphertex Data Security
9301 Jordan Ave Ste 105a, Chatsworth (91311-5863)
PHONE.....................................818 773-8989
Jerry Kaner, *CEO*
Samantha Cosney, *Administration*
Paul Espinosa, *Info Tech Dir*
Matt Lind, *Marketing Staff*
Steve Crouch, *Sales Staff*
▲ EMP: 18
SALES (est): 3.6MM **Privately Held**
SIC: 3577 3572 Computer peripheral equipment; computer storage devices

(P-15704)
CISCO SYSTEMS INC
325 E Tasman Dr, San Jose (95134-1405)
PHONE.....................................408 526-7939
Steve Wogsland, *Engineer*
Francine Katsoudas, *Director*
EMP: 691
SALES (corp-wide): 48B **Publicly Held**
SIC: 3577 Data conversion equipment, media-to-media: computer
PA: Cisco Systems, Inc.
170 W Tasman Dr
San Jose CA 95134
408 526-4000

(P-15705)
CISCO SYSTEMS INC
771 Alder Dr, Milpitas (95035-7927)
PHONE.....................................408 570-9149
Bill Slime, *Manager*
Geoff Iverson, *Software Engr*
Hop Le, *Software Engr*
Larry Zhu, *Software Engr*
Dustin Pusatere, *Project Mgr*
EMP: 691
SALES (corp-wide): 48B **Publicly Held**
WEB: www.cisco.com
SIC: 3577 7379 Data conversion equipment, media-to-media: computer;
PA: Cisco Systems, Inc.
170 W Tasman Dr
San Jose CA 95134
408 526-4000

(P-15706)
CISCO SYSTEMS INC
500 Terry A Francois Blvd, San Francisco (94158-2354)
PHONE.....................................415 837-6261
EMP: 12
SALES (corp-wide): 48B **Publicly Held**
SIC: 3577
PA: Cisco Systems, Inc.
170 W Tasman Dr
San Jose CA 95134
408 526-4000

(P-15707)
CISCO SYSTEMS INC
3500 Hyland Ave, Costa Mesa (92626-1469)
PHONE.....................................714 434-2100
EMP: 10
SALES (corp-wide): 48B **Publicly Held**
SIC: 3577 Data conversion equipment, media-to-media: computer
PA: Cisco Systems, Inc.
170 W Tasman Dr
San Jose CA 95134
408 526-4000

(P-15708)
CISCO SYSTEMS INC
121 Theory, Irvine (92617-3209)
PHONE.....................................408 526-4000
J Pocock, *Exec VP*
Bob Shutack, *Partner*
Julie Ivask, *Software Dev*
Niki Lee, *Human Res Mgr*
Kelly Carlberg, *Sales Staff*
EMP: 691
SALES (corp-wide): 48B **Publicly Held**
SIC: 3577 Data conversion equipment, media-to-media: computer
PA: Cisco Systems, Inc.
170 W Tasman Dr
San Jose CA 95134
408 526-4000

(P-15709)
CISCO SYSTEMS INC
11 Great Oaks Blvd, San Jose (95119-1242)
PHONE.....................................408 225-5248
EMP: 678
SALES (corp-wide): 48B **Publicly Held**
SIC: 3577 Data conversion equipment, media-to-media: computer
PA: Cisco Systems, Inc.
170 W Tasman Dr
San Jose CA 95134
408 526-4000

(P-15710)
CISCO SYSTEMS INC
510 Mccarthy Blvd, Milpitas (95035-7908)
PHONE.....................................408 526-4000
Helder Antunes, *Principal*
Malini Vijayamohan, *Software Engr*
Abhijit Gujare, *Database Admin*
Naga Katragadda, *Technology*
Senthil Rajagopal, *Technology*
EMP: 691
SALES (corp-wide): 48B **Publicly Held**
SIC: 3577 7379 Data conversion equipment, media-to-media: computer;
PA: Cisco Systems, Inc.
170 W Tasman Dr
San Jose CA 95134
408 526-4000

(P-15711)
CISCO SYSTEMS INC
131 Meadowland Dr, Milpitas (95035-4416)
PHONE.....................................408 525-5669
EMP: 651
SALES (corp-wide): 49.3B **Publicly Held**
SIC: 3577 Computer peripheral equipment
PA: Cisco Systems, Inc.
170 W Tasman Dr
San Jose CA 95134
408 526-4000

(P-15712)
CISCO SYSTEMS INC
3650 Cisco Way Bldg 17, San Jose (95134-2205)
PHONE.....................................408 526-6698
Pags Krishnamoortly, *Systs Prg Mgr*
Christian Janoff, *Technology*
Joe Zhou, *Senior Mgr*
Chander Goyal, *Manager*
EMP: 649
SALES (corp-wide): 48B **Publicly Held**
SIC: 3577 Computer peripheral equipment
PA: Cisco Systems, Inc.
170 W Tasman Dr
San Jose CA 95134
408 526-4000

(P-15713)
CISCO SYSTEMS INC
4460 Rosewood Dr Ste 100, Pleasanton (94588-3082)
PHONE.....................................925 223-1006
Kevin Hodges, *Branch Mgr*
Yuyang Cao, *Software Engr*
James Maudlin, *Engineer*
Chris Tzortzis, *Regl Sales Mgr*
Kirsten Hazard, *Sales Mgr*
EMP: 691
SALES (corp-wide): 48B **Publicly Held**
WEB: www.cisco.com
SIC: 3577 Data conversion equipment, media-to-media: computer
PA: Cisco Systems, Inc.
170 W Tasman Dr
San Jose CA 95134
408 526-4000

(P-15714)
CISCO SYSTEMS INC (PA)
170 W Tasman Dr, San Jose (95134-1706)
PHONE.....................................408 526-4000
Charles H Robbins, *Ch of Bd*
Kelly A Kramer, *CFO*
Karen Walker, *Chief Mktg Ofcr*
David Goeckeler, *Exec VP*
Mark Chandler, *Senior VP*
EMP: 700
SALES: 49.3B **Publicly Held**
WEB: www.cisco.com
SIC: 3577 7379 Data conversion equipment, media-to-media: computer;

(P-15715)
CISCO SYSTEMS INC
3600 Cisco Way, San Jose (95134-2205)
PHONE.....................................408 434-1903
John Eira, *Branch Mgr*
Navdeep Johar, *Executive*
Denice Rodriguez, *Admin Asst*
Subadevi Pandian, *Software Engr*
Edgar Vo, *Software Engr*
EMP: 691
SALES (corp-wide): 48B **Publicly Held**
WEB: www.cisco.com
SIC: 3577 Data conversion equipment, media-to-media: computer

PA: Cisco Systems, Inc.
170 W Tasman Dr
San Jose CA 95134
408 526-4000

(P-15716)
CISCO SYSTEMS INC
110 W Tasman Dr, San Jose (95134-1700)
PHONE.....................................408 424-4050
David Holland, *Manager*
Sanjay Purandare, *Program Mgr*
Jackie Tang, *Info Tech Mgr*
Vinoth Ganapathy, *Software Engr*
Kirtee Yadav, *Project Mgr*
EMP: 7200
SQ FT: 147,000
SALES (corp-wide): 49.3B **Publicly Held**
WEB: www.cisco.com
SIC: 3577 Data conversion equipment, media-to-media: computer
PA: Cisco Systems, Inc.
170 W Tasman Dr
San Jose CA 95134
408 526-4000

(P-15717)
CISCO SYSTEMS INC
3700 Cisco Way, San Jose (95134-2206)
PHONE.....................................408 526-5999
John T Chambers, *Branch Mgr*
EMP: 691
SALES (corp-wide): 48B **Publicly Held**
SIC: 3577 Data conversion equipment, media-to-media: computer
PA: Cisco Systems, Inc.
170 W Tasman Dr
San Jose CA 95134
408 526-4000

(P-15718)
CLICKSCANSHARE INC
3631 Mt Diablo Blvd Ste C, Lafayette (94549-3788)
PHONE.....................................925 283-1400
Eva Dias, *Branch Mgr*
EMP: 14
SALES (corp-wide): 3.6MM **Privately Held**
SIC: 3577 Data conversion equipment, media-to-media: computer
PA: Clickscanshare, Inc.
8055 Clairemont Mesa Blvd # 101
San Diego CA 92111
619 461-5880

(P-15719)
CLICKSCANSHARE INC (PA)
8055 Clairemont Mesa Blvd # 101, San Diego (92111-1620)
PHONE.....................................619 461-5880
Troy Philip Langley, *Principal*
Nick Scalzo, *General Mgr*
Crystal Wilcox, *Opers Mgr*
Rose Zhao, *Senior Mgr*
Mimi Reschmeier, *Coordinator*
EMP: 11 EST: 2013
SALES (est): 3.6MM **Privately Held**
SIC: 3577 Data conversion equipment, media-to-media: computer

(P-15720)
CONVERGENT MANUFACTURING TECH
966 Shulman Ave, Santa Clara (95050-2822)
PHONE.....................................408 987-2770
Kevin C Lettire, *President*
Erin Lettire, *Office Mgr*
EMP: 12
SQ FT: 5,000
SALES: 4.9MM **Privately Held**
WEB: www.cmt-mtc.com
SIC: 3577 Computer peripheral equipment

(P-15721)
CONVERGING SYSTEMS INC
32420 Nautilus Dr Ste 100, Pls Vrds Pnsl (90275-6002)
PHONE.....................................310 544-2628
Craig Douglass, *President*
EMP: 12
SALES (est): 3MM **Privately Held**
WEB: www.convergingsystems.com
SIC: 3577 3679 Computer peripheral equipment; video triggers, except remote control TV devices

PRODUCTS & SVCS

(P-15722)
CPACKET NETWORKS INC
Also Called: Cwr Labs
765 Ravendale Dr, Mountain View
(94043-5219)
P.O. Box 430, Alviso (95002-0430)
PHONE..............................650 969-9500
Rony Kay, *CEO*
Hari Miriyala, *Vice Pres*
Ron Nevo, *Vice Pres*
Brendan O'Flaherty, *Vice Pres*
Juneed Ahamed, *Sr Software Eng*
EMP: 22
SALES (est): 6.9MM **Privately Held**
WEB: www.cwrlabs.com
SIC: 3577 Computer peripheral equipment

(P-15723)
CREAFORM USA INC
2031 Main St, Irvine (92614-6509)
PHONE..............................855 939-4446
Martin D Chader, *Manager*
EMP: 10
SALES (est): 1.6MM
SALES (corp-wide): 4.3B **Publicly Held**
SIC: 3577 Optical scanning devices
PA: Ametek, Inc.
1100 Cassatt Rd
Berwyn PA 19312
610 647-2121

(P-15724)
CRITICAL IO LLC
36 Executive Park Ste 150, Irvine
(92614-4715)
PHONE..............................949 553-2200
John Staub, *Mng Member*
Ron Godshalk, *Vice Pres*
Erich Fischer,
Ken Neeld,
EMP: 13
SQ FT: 2,500
SALES (est): 2.8MM **Privately Held**
WEB: www.criticalio.com
SIC: 3577 5045 Computer peripheral
equipment; computer software

(P-15725)
CS SYSTEMS INC
Also Called: Cs Electronics
16781 Noyes Ave, Irvine (92606-5123)
PHONE..............................949 475-9100
Christian Schwartz, *President*
Rebecca Martin, *CFO*
Gayle Schwartz, *CFO*
Eric Belson, *Accounts Mgr*
▲ **EMP:** 25
SQ FT: 33,200
SALES (est): 5.5MM **Privately Held**
WEB: www.cselex.com
SIC: 3577 3677 Computer peripheral
equipment; coil windings, electronic

(P-15726)
CSP INC
6250 N Paramount Blvd, Long Beach
(90805-3714)
P.O. Box 90964 (90809-0964)
PHONE..............................562 470-7236
EMP: 10
SALES (corp-wide): 111.4MM **Publicly
Held**
SIC: 3577 Computer peripheral equipment
PA: Csp, Inc.
175 Cabot St Ste 210
Lowell MA 01854
978 954-5038

(P-15727)
CYBERDATA CORPORATION
3 Justin Ct, Monterey (93940-5733)
PHONE..............................831 373-2601
Phil Lembo, *President*
▲ **EMP:** 33
SQ FT: 30,000
SALES (est): 6.8MM **Privately Held**
WEB: www.cyberdata.net
SIC: 3577 7379 Computer peripheral
equipment; computer related consulting
services

(P-15728)
DELPHI DISPLAY SYSTEMS INC
3550 Hyland Ave, Costa Mesa
(92626-1438)
PHONE..............................714 825-3400

Ken Neeld, *CEO*
Michael Deson, *CEO*
David Skinner, *Vice Pres*
Jaime Rivero, *Info Tech Mgr*
William Homan-Muise, *VP Engrg*
▲ **EMP:** 55 **EST:** 1997
SQ FT: 10,000
SALES (est): 15.2MM **Privately Held**
WEB: www.delphidisplaysystems.com
SIC: 3577 Computer peripheral equipment

(P-15729)
DIGITAL CHECK TECHNOLOGIES INC
10231 Trademark St Ste A, Rancho Cuca-
monga (91730-5821)
PHONE..............................909 204-4638
Thomas P Anderson, *President*
Tom Anderson Jr, *Treasurer*
Glenn Embury, *Vice Pres*
John Gainer, *Admin Sec*
◆ **EMP:** 48
SQ FT: 14,000
SALES (est): 6.9MM **Privately Held**
WEB: www.digitalcheck.com
SIC: 3577 3861 Computer peripheral
equipment; cameras & related equipment
PA: Digital Check Corp.
630 Dundee Rd Ste 210
Northbrook IL 60062

(P-15730)
DIVERSIFIED NANO CORPORATION (PA)
16885 W Bernardo Dr # 275, San Diego
(92127-1618)
PHONE..............................858 673-0387
James Danforth, *President*
▲ **EMP:** 10
SALES (est): 1.4MM **Privately Held**
SIC: 3577 Computer peripheral equipment

(P-15731)
DOCUMENT CAPTURE TECH INC (PA)
41332 Christy St, Fremont (94538-3115)
PHONE..............................408 436-9888
Michael J Campbell, *President*
Richard Dietl, *Ch of Bd*
M Carolyn Ellis, *CFO*
Edward M Straw, *Vice Ch Bd*
Karl Etzel, *Chief Mktg Ofcr*
▲ **EMP:** 25
SQ FT: 32,000
SALES (est): 17.3MM **Privately Held**
WEB: www.sysviewtech.com
SIC: 3577 Optical scanning devices

(P-15732)
DOUBLESIGHT DISPLAYS INC
2882 Walnut Ave Ste A, Tustin
(92780-7004)
PHONE..............................949 253-1535
Kang Lee, *President*
Patrick Bong, *Director*
▲ **EMP:** 10
SQ FT: 2,000
SALES (est): 2.8MM **Privately Held**
WEB: www.doublesight.com
SIC: 3577 Graphic displays, except
graphic terminals

(P-15733)
DSS NETWORKS INC
24462 Redlen St, Lake Forest
(92630-3848)
PHONE..............................949 981-3473
Anita Svay, *CEO*
Jerry Marcinko, *President*
Sam Svay, *Vice Pres*
EMP: 15 **EST:** 2000
SQ FT: 4,000
SALES (est): 2MM **Privately Held**
WEB: www.dssnetworks.com
SIC: 3577 Computer peripheral equipment

(P-15734)
E SEEK INC
9471 Ridgehaven Ct Ste E, San Diego
(92123-4357)
PHONE..............................714 832-7980
Larry H Anderson, *President*
Ken Waters, *CEO*
Ali Lebaschi, *Vice Pres*

EMP: 10
SALES (est): 1.1MM **Privately Held**
SIC: 3577 Bar code (magnetic ink) printers

(P-15735)
EFAXCOM (DH)
Also Called: Jetfax
6922 Hollywood Blvd Fl 5, Los Angeles
(90028-6125)
PHONE..............................323 817-3207
Ronald Brown, *President*
John H Harris, *Vice Pres*
Gary P Kapner, *Vice Pres*
Dan Gallo, *Risk Mgmt Dir*
Michael Dunford, *Manager*
EMP: 80
SALES (est): 11MM
SALES (corp-wide): 1.1B **Publicly Held**
WEB: www.efax.com
SIC: 3577 Computer peripheral equipment

(P-15736)
EFAXCOM
Also Called: J2 Global Communications
5385 Hollister Ave # 208, Santa Barbara
(93111-2389)
PHONE..............................805 692-0064
Stephen Zendjahas, *Manager*
EMP: 30
SALES (corp-wide): 1.1B **Publicly Held**
WEB: www.efax.com
SIC: 3577 Computer peripheral equipment
HQ: Efax.Com
6922 Hollywood Blvd Fl 5
Los Angeles CA 90028
323 817-3207

(P-15737)
ELECTRONIC RESOURCES NETWORK
Also Called: Tern
1950 5th St, Davis (95616-4018)
PHONE..............................530 758-0180
Tom Tang, *President*
Ning Lu, *CFO*
Ziqiang Tang, *Vice Pres*
EMP: 15
SQ FT: 6,000
SALES (est): 2.6MM **Privately Held**
WEB: www.tern.com
SIC: 3577 5045 3679 Computer periph-
eral equipment; computer peripheral
equipment; electronic circuits

(P-15738)
EPIC TECHNOLOGIES LLC
9340 Owensmouth Ave, Chatsworth
(91311-6915)
PHONE..............................423 461-2020
Louise Stump, *Manager*
EMP: 400
SALES (corp-wide): 1.2B **Privately Held**
SIC: 3577 3672 Computer peripheral
equipment; printed circuit boards
HQ: Epic Technologies, Llc
9340 Owensmouth Ave
Chatsworth CA 91311
818 734-6500

(P-15739)
EPICOR SOFTWARE CORPORATION
17320 Red Hill Ave # 250, Irvine
(92614-5669)
PHONE..............................949 585-4000
Mark Nyquist, *Director*
Dave Getty, *President*
Deb Tenenbaum, *Officer*
Bill Wilson, *Senior VP*
Paul Yaros, *Vice Pres*
EMP: 100 **Publicly Held**
SIC: 3577 5045 Computer peripheral
equipment; computers, peripherals & soft-
ware
HQ: Epicor Software Corporation
804 Las Cimas Pkwy # 200
Austin TX 78746

(P-15740)
EPSON AMERICA INC (DH)
Also Called: Seiko Epson
3840 Kilroy Airport Way, Long Beach
(90806-2452)
P.O. Box 93012 (90809-3012)
PHONE..............................800 463-7766

John Lang, *President*
John D Lang, *President*
Andrea Zoeckler, *CFO*
Keith Kratzberg, *Senior VP*
Alberto Arredondo, *Vice Pres*
◆ **EMP:** 510 **EST:** 1975
SQ FT: 163,000
SALES (est): 351.3MM
SALES (corp-wide): 10.3B **Privately Held**
WEB: www.presentersonline.com
SIC: 3577 Computer peripheral equipment

(P-15741)
ERICSSON INC
620 Newport Center Dr # 11, Newport
Beach (92660-6420)
PHONE..............................949 721-6604
Lucia Garcia, *Branch Mgr*
EMP: 65
SALES (corp-wide): 23.8B **Privately Held**
WEB: www.ericsson.com/us-ca
SIC: 3577 Computer peripheral equipment
HQ: Ericsson Inc.
6300 Legacy Dr
Plano TX 75024
972 583-0000

(P-15742)
FIRETIDE INC (DH)
2105 S Bascom Ave Ste 220, Campbell
(95008-3292)
PHONE..............................408 399-7771
Corry S Hong, *President*
Gordon Lowe, *Partner*
Charles Byrd, *Sales Engr*
Angela Zhou, *Manager*
▲ **EMP:** 100
SQ FT: 30,000
SALES (est): 12.6MM
SALES (corp-wide): 512.5MM **Privately
Held**
SIC: 3577 3825 4899 Computer periph-
eral equipment; network analyzers; com-
munication signal enhancement network
system
HQ: Unicom Systems Inc.
15535 San Fernando
Mission Hills CA 91345
818 838-0606

(P-15743)
FLEXTRONICS INTL USA INC
927 Gibraltar Dr, Milpitas (95035-6336)
PHONE..............................510 814-7000
EMP: 14
SALES (corp-wide): 23.8B **Privately Held**
SIC: 3577 Graphic displays, except
graphic terminals
HQ: Flextronics International Usa, Inc.
6201 America Center Dr
San Jose CA 95002

(P-15744)
FORESEESON CUSTOM DISPLAYS INC (PA)
2210 E Winston Rd, Anaheim
(92806-5536)
PHONE..............................714 300-0540
Insik Kang, *President*
Marie Kim, *General Mgr*
Robert Contreras, *Project Mgr*
Robert Tran, *Technology*
Majiid Imani, *QC Mgr*
▲ **EMP:** 21
SQ FT: 8,000
SALES (est): 4.7MM **Privately Held**
WEB: www.foreseesonusa.com
SIC: 3577 Computer peripheral equipment

(P-15745)
FUJIFILM DIMATIX INC (DH)
2250 Martin Ave, Santa Clara
(95050-2704)
PHONE..............................408 565-9150
Martin Schoeppler, *President*
Darren Imai, *Vice Pres*
Ray Gralak, *Software Engr*
Jay Ricci, *Network Tech*
Elizabeth Chabot, *Project Mgr*
◆ **EMP:** 230
SQ FT: 125,000

▲ = Import ▼=Export
◆ =Import/Export

SALES (est): 74.4MM
SALES (corp-wide): 22.8B **Privately Held**
WEB: www.dimatix.com
SIC: **3577** Printers, computer; readers, sorters or inscribers, magnetic ink
HQ: Fujifilm Corporation
9-7-3, Akasaka
Minato-Ku TKY 107-0
362 713-111

(P-15746)
GDCA INC
1799 Portola Ave Ste 1, Livermore (94551-7947)
PHONE..............................925 456-9900
Ethan Plotkin, *CEO*
Kip Kingsland, *Director*
Arlin Niernberger, *Director*
Kaye Porter, *Director*
Corinne Weber, *Director*
EMP: 38
SQ FT: 6,000
SALES (est): 11.1MM **Privately Held**
WEB: www.gdca.com
SIC: **3577 3571** Computer peripheral equipment; electronic computers

(P-15747)
GENOVATION INCORPRATED
17741 Mitchell N, Irvine (92614-6028)
PHONE..............................949 833-3355
Manouchehr Rahimzadeh, *President*
Jeanette Miyata, *Controller*
Barbara Sthrome, *Purch Agent*
Judy Chen, *Sales Staff*
▲ EMP: 10
SQ FT: 20,000
SALES (est): 2.3MM **Privately Held**
WEB: www.genovation.com
SIC: **3577 7371** Input/output equipment, computer; custom computer programming services

(P-15748)
GIZMAC ACCESSORIES LLC
20410 Earl St, Torrance (90503-2415)
PHONE..............................310 320-5563
Timothy Cave,
▲ EMP: 14
SALES (est): 2.2MM **Privately Held**
WEB: www.gizmac.com
SIC: **3577** Computer peripheral equipment

(P-15749)
GOLDENSOL MUSIC LLC
Also Called: Dj Tech Tools
200 Valley Dr Ste 14, Brisbane (94005-1222)
PHONE..............................877 246-8958
Ean Golden, *Owner*
Zachariah Alderson, *Creative Dir*
▲ EMP: 10
SALES (est): 1.4MM **Privately Held**
SIC: **3577** Computer peripheral equipment

(P-15750)
GOSUB 60
1334 3rd Street Promenade # 309, Santa Monica (90401-1378)
PHONE..............................310 394-4760
Josh Hartwell, *President*
Paul Bolten, *Vice Pres*
Kellie Hartwell, *Vice Pres*
Sean Foreman, *Webmaster*
EMP: 10
SQ FT: 1,000
SALES (est): 1.3MM **Privately Held**
WEB: www.gosub60.com
SIC: **3577** Computer peripheral equipment

(P-15751)
H45 TECHNOLOGY CORPORATION
Also Called: H 45 Technology
465 Fairchild Dr Ste 103, Mountain View (94043-2254)
PHONE..............................650 961-9114
Henryk Szejnwald, *President*
EMP: 10
SQ FT: 6,000
SALES (est): 1.5MM **Privately Held**
SIC: **3577** Computer peripheral equipment

(P-15752)
HALL RESEARCH TECHNOLOGIES LLC (PA)
1163 Warner Ave, Tustin (92780-6458)
PHONE..............................714 641-6607
Ali Haghjoo, *CEO*
Cirilo Garay, *Treasurer*
Gail Haghjoo, *Treasurer*
Lisa Nguyen, *Exec VP*
Nessie Mabini, *General Mgr*
◆ EMP: 17
SQ FT: 18,200
SALES (est): 12.2MM **Privately Held**
WEB: www.hallresearch.com
SIC: **3577** Computer peripheral equipment

(P-15753)
HANAPS ENTERPRISES (PA)
Also Called: Digital Storm
865 Jarvis Dr, Morgan Hill (95037-2858)
PHONE..............................669 235-3810
Paramjit Chana, *CEO*
Surnderjit Chana, *Vice Pres*
Harjit Chana, *General Mgr*
EMP: 50
SALES (est): 28MM **Privately Held**
SIC: **3577 7379** Computer peripheral equipment; computer related maintenance services

(P-15754)
HUNTER DIGITAL LTD
Also Called: Europian Investment
11999 San Vicente Blvd, Los Angeles (90049-5131)
PHONE..............................310 471-5852
Aaron H Sones, *President*
EMP: 15
SALES (est): 1.6MM **Privately Held**
SIC: **3577** Computer peripheral equipment

(P-15755)
IDENTIV INC (PA)
2201 Walnut Ave Ste 100, Fremont (94538-2334)
PHONE..............................949 250-8888
Steven Humphreys, *CEO*
James E Ousley, *Ch of Bd*
Steven Finney, *CFO*
Sandra Wallach, *CFO*
Gary Kremen, *Bd of Directors*
EMP: 305
SQ FT: 10,935
SALES (est): 60.2MM **Publicly Held**
WEB: www.scmmicro.com
SIC: **3577 7372** Computer peripheral equipment; prepackaged software

(P-15756)
IMAGING TECHNOLOGIES
15175 Innovation Dr, San Diego (92128-3401)
PHONE..............................858 487-8944
Brian Bonar, *President*
EMP: 10
SALES (est): 1.9MM
SALES (corp-wide): 3.3MM **Publicly Held**
WEB: www.dalrada.com
SIC: **3577** Printers, computer
PA: Dalrada Financial Corporation
11956 Bernardo Plaza Dr
San Diego CA 92128
877 325-7232

(P-15757)
IMMERSION CORPORATION (PA)
50 Rio Robles, San Jose (95134-1806)
PHONE..............................408 467-1900
Tom Lacey, *CEO*
Carl Schlachte, *CEO*
Nancy Erba, *CFO*
David Sugishita, *Bd of Directors*
Anne Marie Peters, *Senior VP*
EMP: 82
SQ FT: 42,000
SALES: 35MM **Publicly Held**
SIC: **3577 7371** Computer peripheral equipment; computer software development & applications

(P-15758)
INCAL TECHNOLOGY INC
46420 Fremont Blvd, Fremont (94538-6469)
PHONE..............................510 657-8405
Cary Caywood, *CEO*

Bruce Simikowski, *Vice Pres*
Naveed Syed, *Design Engr*
Hank Pedersen, *Technology*
Lillian Bledsaw, *Human Res Mgr*
EMP: 25
SQ FT: 7,500
SALES (est): 5.7MM **Privately Held**
SIC: **3577** Computer peripheral equipment

(P-15759)
INCIPIO TECHNOLOGIES INC (PA)
Also Called: Incipio Group
3347 Michelson Dr Ste 100, Irvine (92612-0661)
PHONE..............................949 250-4929
Tom Park, *CEO*
Jeff Buhrman, *Vice Pres*
Kevin Lin, *Principal*
Stacey Rozeil, *Credit Staff*
Cheryl Roberts, *Human Res Dir*
◆ EMP: 55
SALES (est): 71.4MM **Privately Held**
SIC: **3577** Computer peripheral equipment

(P-15760)
INDUSTRIAL ELECTRONIC ENGINEER
Also Called: Iee
7723 Kester Ave, Van Nuys (91405-1105)
PHONE..............................818 787-0311
Thomas Whinfrey, *President*
Steve Motter, *President*
Donald G Gumpertz, *Chairman*
Michael Tubbs, *Vice Pres*
Richard Pleasant, *Executive*
▲ EMP: 100 EST: 1947
SQ FT: 131,000
SALES (est): 54.4MM **Privately Held**
SIC: **3577 3575** Graphic displays, except graphic terminals; keyboards, computer, office machine

(P-15761)
INNOVATIVE TECH & ENGRG INC
Also Called: Innov8v
2691 Richter Ave Ste 124, Irvine (92606-5124)
PHONE..............................949 955-2501
Hassan Siddiqi, *President*
EMP: 12
SQ FT: 2,200
SALES (est): 1.3MM **Privately Held**
SIC: **3577 5961 1731 5999** Computer peripheral equipment; computers & peripheral equipment, mail order; safety & security specialization; audio-visual equipment & supplies

(P-15762)
INPUT/OUTPUT TECHNOLOGY INC
28415 Industry Dr Ste 520, Valencia (91355-4161)
PHONE..............................661 257-1000
Ted Drapala, *President*
Thad Drapala, *General Mgr*
Marilyn Joy, *Bookkeeper*
EMP: 20
SALES (est): 3.3MM **Privately Held**
WEB: www.iotechnology.com
SIC: **3577 3823** Input/output equipment, computer; industrial instrmnts msrmnt display/control process variable

(P-15763)
INSTRUMENTATION TECH SYSTEMS
Also Called: Its
19360 Business Center Dr, Northridge (91324-3547)
PHONE..............................818 886-2034
Paul Hightower, *CEO*
Don C Janess, *Vice Pres*
▼ EMP: 12
SQ FT: 8,200
SALES (est): 2.2MM **Privately Held**
WEB: www.itsamerica.com
SIC: **3577** Encoders, computer peripheral equipment

(P-15764)
INTEL CORPORATION (PA)
2200 Mission College Blvd, Santa Clara (95054-1549)
P.O. Box 58119 (95052-8119)
PHONE..............................408 765-8080
Robert H Swan, *CEO*
Andy D Bryant, *Ch of Bd*
Venkata S M Renduchintala, *Exec VP*
Navin Shenoy, *Exec VP*
Michael Mariani, *Technical Staff*
◆ EMP: 277
SALES: 62.7B **Publicly Held**
WEB: www.intel.com
SIC: **3577 7372 3674** Computer peripheral equipment; prepackaged software; application computer software; microprocessors

(P-15765)
INTEL CORPORATION
101 Innovation Dr, San Jose (95134-1941)
PHONE..............................408 544-7000
Dan McNamara, *Branch Mgr*
Hugh Atkinson, *Vice Pres*
Vincent Hu, *Vice Pres*
Dermot Hargaden, *General Mgr*
Kam Kasravi, *Sr Software Eng*
EMP: 3000
SALES (corp-wide): 62.7B **Publicly Held**
SIC: **3577** Computer peripheral equipment
PA: Intel Corporation
2200 Mission College Blvd
Santa Clara CA 95054
408 765-8080

(P-15766)
INTEL NETWORK SYSTEMS INC
12220 Scrps Summit Dr # 300, San Diego (92131-3698)
PHONE..............................858 877-4652
Seth Deyo, *Branch Mgr*
EMP: 13
SALES (corp-wide): 62.7B **Publicly Held**
SIC: **3577** Computer peripheral equipment
HQ: Intel Network Systems Inc
77 Reed Rd
Hudson MA 01749
978 553-4000

(P-15767)
INTELLIGENT PERIPHERALS
1123 Judah St, San Francisco (94122-1902)
PHONE..............................415 564-4366
Tennyson Lee, *Owner*
EMP: 12
SALES (est): 1MM **Privately Held**
SIC: **3577** Printers & plotters

(P-15768)
INTERMEC TECHNOLOGIES CORP
6960 Koll Center Pkwy, Pleasanton (94566-3160)
PHONE..............................925 738-1100
Tim Thul, *Branch Mgr*
EMP: 10
SALES (corp-wide): 40.5B **Publicly Held**
WEB: www.intermec.net
SIC: **3577** Bar code (magnetic ink) printers
HQ: Intermec Technologies Corporation
16201 25th Ave W
Lynnwood WA 98087
425 348-2600

(P-15769)
INTERNATIONAL TECHNOLOGIES
15445 Ventura Blvd # 780, Sherman Oaks (91403-3005)
PHONE..............................818 382-2087
Gordon Jones, *President*
EMP: 10
SALES (est): 1MM **Privately Held**
SIC: **3577** Computer peripheral equipment

(P-15770)
INTERNET MACHINES CORPORATION (PA)
30501 Agoura Rd Ste 203, Agoura Hills (91301-4389)
PHONE..............................818 575-2100
Christopher Hoogenboom, *CEO*
Frank Knuettel II, *CFO*

Michael Dubrow, *Exec VP*
Chris Haywood, *Vice Pres*
Aloke Gupta, *VP Mktg*
EMP: 70
SQ FT: 18,500
SALES (est): 6.7MM **Privately Held**
WEB: www.internetmachines.com
SIC: 3577 Computer peripheral equipment

(P-15771)
IRON SYSTEMS INC
980 Mission Ct, Fremont (94539-8202)
PHONE................................408 943-8000
Baljit Bath, *President*
Billy Bath, *President*
Kevin Singh, *President*
Garvy Singh, *CFO*
Harvey Bath, *Vice Pres*
▲ **EMP:** 75
SQ FT: 45,000
SALES (est): 35MM **Privately Held**
WEB: www.ironsystems.com
SIC: 3577 Computer peripheral equipment

(P-15772)
ISIGN SOLUTIONS INC (PA)
2025 Gateway Pl Ste 485, San Jose
(95110-1021)
PHONE................................650 802-7888
Philip S Sassower, *Ch of Bd*
Michael Engmann, *Ch of Bd*
Andrea Goren, *CFO*
EMP: 10
SQ FT: 2,400
SALES: 1MM **Publicly Held**
WEB: www.cic.com
SIC: 3577 7372 Computer peripheral
    equipment; prepackaged software

(P-15773)
ITUNER NETWORKS CORPORATION
47801 Fremont Blvd, Fremont
(94538-6506)
PHONE................................510 226-6033
Andrei Bulucea, *President*
Raluca Neacsu, *Vice Pres*
Nicu Pavel, *Technology*
Adina Pricop, *Technology*
▲ **EMP:** 15
SALES (est): 3.2MM **Privately Held**
WEB: www.ituner.com
SIC: 3577 5961 5045 Computer periph-
    eral equipment; computers & peripheral
    equipment, mail order; computer periph-
    eral equipment

(P-15774)
JEDITRON TECHNOLOGIES CORP
44137 Fremont Blvd, Fremont (94538)
PHONE................................510 226-1383
Jason Wang, *President*
Stone Chang, *Vice Pres*
EMP: 12
SQ FT: 11,000
SALES: 1.5MM **Privately Held**
SIC: 3577 Computer peripheral equipment

(P-15775)
JUNIPER NETWORKS INC (PA)
1133 Innovation Way, Sunnyvale
(94089-1228)
PHONE................................408 745-2000
Scott Kriens, *Ch of Bd*
Jeff Devore, *Partner*
Carl Glick, *Partner*
Brittnany Keenan, *Partner*
John Somm, *Partner*
EMP: 300
SALES: 5B **Publicly Held**
WEB: www.juniper.net
SIC: 3577 7372 Computer peripheral
    equipment; prepackaged software

(P-15776)
JUNIPER NETWORKS (US) INC
1133 Innovation Way, Sunnyvale
(94089-1228)
PHONE................................408 745-2000
Rami Rahim, *CEO*
Matt Brownell, *Partner*
Charles Cino, *Partner*
Scott Kriens, *Ch of Bd*
Rami Rahim, *CEO*
EMP: 8100

SALES (est): 228.8MM **Publicly Held**
WEB: www.juniper.net
SIC: 3577 Computer peripheral equipment
PA: Juniper Networks, Inc.
    1133 Innovation Way
    Sunnyvale CA 94089
    -

(P-15777)
KELLER ENTERTAINMENT GROUP INC
1093 Broxton Ave Ste 246, Los Angeles
(90024-2831)
PHONE................................818 981-4950
Max Keller, *Ch of Bd*
Micheline Keller, *President*
EMP: 10
SQ FT: 12,000
SALES (est): 1.4MM
SALES (corp-wide): 2.9MM **Privately
Held**
WEB: www.kellerentertainment.com
SIC: 3577 7922 Computer peripheral
    equipment; television program, including
    commercial producers
PA: American First Run
    14225 Ventura Blvd
    Sherman Oaks CA 91423
    818 981-4950

(P-15778)
KELLY COMPUTER SYSTEMS INC
1060 La Avenida St, Mountain View
(94043-1422)
PHONE................................650 960-1010
Larry Kelly, *President*
Tim Kelly, *Vice Pres*
EMP: 25
SQ FT: 20,000
SALES (est): 3.3MM **Privately Held**
SIC: 3577 7371 7373 Computer periph-
    eral equipment; computer software devel-
    opment; systems integration services

(P-15779)
KEMEERA INCORPORATED
Also Called: Oakland Production Center
315 Jefferson St, Oakland (94607-3537)
PHONE................................510 281-9000
Michelle Malia Mihevc, *CEO*
EMP: 17
SALES (corp-wide): 26.9MM **Privately
Held**
SIC: 3577 Printers, computer
PA: Kemeera Incorporated
    620 3rd St
    Oakland CA 94607
    510 281-9000

(P-15780)
KINGSTON DIGITAL INC (DH)
17600 Newhope St, Fountain Valley
(92708-4220)
PHONE................................714 435-2600
John Tu, *President*
David Sun, *Principal*
▲ **EMP:** 21
SALES (est): 17.5MM **Privately Held**
WEB: www.kingston.com
SIC: 3577 Computer peripheral equipment
HQ: Kingston Technology Company, Inc.
    17600 Newhope St
    Fountain Valley CA 92708
    714 435-2600

(P-15781)
KINGSTON TECHNOLOGY CORP (PA)
17600 Newhope St, Fountain Valley
(92708-4298)
PHONE................................714 445-3495
John Tu, *CEO*
David Hu, *Vice Pres*
David Sun, *Principal*
Daniel Chavez, *Admin Asst*
Kevin Chiu, *Planning*
▲ **EMP:** 500
SALES (est): 1.1B **Privately Held**
SIC: 3577 Computer peripheral equipment

(P-15782)
KURDEX CORPORATION
343 Gibraltar Dr, Sunnyvale (94089-1327)
PHONE................................408 734-8181

Bijan Pourmand, *President*
Mehrdad Pourmand, *Exec VP*
Christina Williams, *Purchasing*
▲ **EMP:** 11
SQ FT: 21,000
SALES (est): 3.5MM **Privately Held**
WEB: www.kurdex.com
SIC: 3577 Computer peripheral equipment

(P-15783)
L&H ENTERPRISES
2111 Montgomery Ave, Cardiff By The Sea
(92007-1817)
PHONE................................760 230-2275
Mark Laine,
EMP: 10
SALES (est): 1.2MM **Privately Held**
SIC: 3577 8731 7373 Computer periph-
    eral equipment; computer (hardware) de-
    velopment; computer integrated systems
    design

(P-15784)
LANTRONIX INC (PA)
7535 Irvine Center Dr # 100, Irvine
(92618-2966)
PHONE................................949 453-3990
Jeffrey W Benck, *President*
Bernhard Bruscha, *Ch of Bd*
Daryl R Miller, *President*
Jeremy R Whitaker, *CFO*
Hoshi Printer, *Bd of Directors*
EMP: 122
SQ FT: 27,000
SALES: 45.5MM **Publicly Held**
WEB: www.lantronix.com
SIC: 3577 Data conversion equipment,
    media-to-media: computer

(P-15785)
LASERGRAPHICS INC
Also Called: Lasergraphics General Business
20 Ada, Irvine (92618-2303)
PHONE................................949 753-8282
Mihai Demetrescu PHD, *President*
David Boyd, *CFO*
Stefan Demetrescu, *Senior VP*
Stefan Demetrescu PHD, *Senior VP*
Chris Olsen, *MIS Dir*
▲ **EMP:** 40
SQ FT: 20,000
SALES (est): 7MM **Privately Held**
WEB: www.lasergraphics.com
SIC: 3577 7371 3823 Graphic displays,
    except graphic terminals; custom com-
    puter programming services; industrial in-
    strmnts msrmnt display/control process
    variable

(P-15786)
LEICA GEOSYSTEMS HDS LLC
5000 Executive Pkwy # 500, San Ramon
(94583-4365)
PHONE................................925 790-2300
Kem Mooyman, *Director*
EMP: 72
SQ FT: 25,000
SALES (est): 13.9MM
SALES (corp-wide): 18.8MM **Privately
Held**
WEB: www.hds.leica-geosystems.com
SIC: 3577 Optical scanning devices
HQ: Leica Geosystems Ag
    Heinrich-Wild-Strasse 201
    Heerbrugg SG
    717 273-131

(P-15787)
LEIDOS INC
4025 Hancock St Ste 210, San Diego
(92110-5167)
PHONE................................619 524-2581
Daniel Shrum, *Branch Mgr*
EMP: 28
SALES (corp-wide): 10.1B **Publicly Held**
WEB: www.saic.com
SIC: 3577 Computer peripheral equipment
HQ: Leidos, Inc.
    11951 Freedom Dr Ste 500
    Reston VA 20190
    571 526-6000

(P-15788)
LEXMARK INTERNATIONAL INC
575 Anton Blvd Fl 3, Costa Mesa
(92626-7169)
PHONE................................714 641-1007
EMP: 35
SALES (corp-wide): 2.5B **Privately Held**
SIC: 3577
PA: Lexmark International, Inc.
    740 W New Circle Rd
    Lexington KY 40511
    859 232-2000

(P-15789)
LEXMARK INTERNATIONAL INC
2211 Michelson Dr Ste 600, Irvine
(92612-0300)
PHONE................................714 368-0015
Mike Johnson, *Branch Mgr*
EMP: 40 **Privately Held**
WEB: www.lexmark.com
SIC: 3577 Printers, computer
HQ: Lexmark International Inc.
    740 W New Circle Rd
    Lexington KY 40511
    859 232-2000

(P-15790)
LINKBIT INC
3180 De La Cruz Blvd # 200, Santa Clara
(95054-2434)
PHONE................................408 969-9940
Michael Sukhar, *President*
Dmitry Gorin, *Vice Pres*
EMP: 15 **EST:** 2000
SALES (est): 2.2MM **Privately Held**
WEB: www.linkbit.com
SIC: 3577 Input/output equipment, com-
    puter

(P-15791)
LITE ON TECHNOLOGY INTL INC (HQ)
720 S Hillview Dr, Milpitas (95035-5455)
PHONE................................408 945-0222
Kung Soong, *Principal*
Daisy Young, *Principal*
Daisy Yeung, *Credit Mgr*
Victoria Yu, *Human Resources*
Julian Sheu, *Marketing Staff*
▲ **EMP:** 30
SALES: 2.9MM
SALES (corp-wide): 7.1B **Privately Held**
WEB: www.liteontc.com
SIC: 3577 3572 Computer peripheral
    equipment; computer storage devices
PA: Lite-On Technology Corporation
    22f, 392, Ruey Kuang Rd.,
    Taipei City TAP 11492
    287 982-888

(P-15792)
LOGICUBE INC (PA)
19755 Nordhoff Pl, Chatsworth
(91311-6606)
PHONE................................818 700-8488
Farid Emrani, *President*
Jack M Schuster, *Ch of Bd*
Jeffrey Schuster, *CFO*
Chris Hernandez, *Opers Staff*
▲ **EMP:** 20
SALES: 8.5MM **Privately Held**
SIC: 3577 Computer peripheral equipment

(P-15793)
LOGITECH INC
3 Jenner Ste 180, Irvine (92618-3835)
PHONE................................510 795-8500
Darrell Bracken, *Branch Mgr*
Tim Griffin, *Senior Partner*
Abhishek Maheshwari, *Vice Pres*
Chantal Ocafrain, *Admin Asst*
Chris Robbins, *Producer*
EMP: 43
SALES (corp-wide): 2.2B **Privately Held**
SIC: 3577 Computer peripheral equipment
HQ: Logitech Inc.
    7700 Gateway Blvd
    Newark CA 94560
    510 795-8500

(P-15794)
LOGITECH INC (HQ)
7700 Gateway Blvd, Newark (94560-1046)
PHONE................................510 795-8500
Bracken P Darrell, *President*

Guerrino De Luca, *Ch of Bd*
Priti Kartik, *Treasurer*
Madhuri Peesapati, *Top Exec*
John Howard, *Exec Dir*
◆ **EMP:** 276 **EST:** 1982
SQ FT: 295,560
SALES (est): 1.6B
SALES (corp-wide): 2.2B **Privately Held**
WEB: www.logitech.com
SIC: 3577 Input/output equipment, computer
PA: Logitech International S.A.
Les Chatagnis
Apples VD
218 635-111

(P-15795)
LYNN PRODUCTS INC
Also Called: Pureformance Cables
2645 W 237th St, Torrance (90505-5269)
PHONE..................310 530-5966
Hsinyu Lin, *President*
Chun MEI Shei, *Treasurer*
Eric Tseng, *Vice Pres*
Chen Huei Tseng, *Admin Sec*
▲ **EMP:** 1000
SQ FT: 35,000
SALES (est): 146.3MM **Privately Held**
WEB: www.lynnprod.com
SIC: 3577 3357 Computer peripheral equipment; fiber optic cable (insulated)

(P-15796)
MACHINABLES INC
Also Called: Twindom
1101 Cowper St, Berkeley (94702-1813)
PHONE..................415 216-9467
David Ryan Pastewka, *CEO*
Will Brevno, *COO*
Richard Berwick, *Treasurer*
Peter Pastewka, *Principal*
Ali Alavi, *Software Engr*
EMP: 12
SQ FT: 5,600
SALES: 250K **Privately Held**
SIC: 3577 7374 7699 Optical scanning devices; optical scanning data service; industrial scanning services

(P-15797)
MAGTEK INC (PA)
1710 Apollo Ct, Seal Beach (90740-5617)
PHONE..................562 546-6400
Ann Marie Hart, *President*
Kiran Gandhi, *President*
Sam Kamel, *President*
Louis E Struett, *Exec VP*
Adriano Canzi, *Vice Pres*
▲ **EMP:** 200
SQ FT: 48,000
SALES (est): 57.4MM **Privately Held**
WEB: www.magtek.com
SIC: 3577 3674 Readers, sorters or inscribers, magnetic ink; encoders, computer peripheral equipment; semiconductors & related devices

(P-15798)
MAKEIT INC
612 S Marengo Ave, Alhambra (91803-1615)
PHONE..................626 470-7938
Salomo Murtonen, *CEO*
Shelley Sun, *President*
Russell Singer, *Development*
EMP: 10
SQ FT: 1,900
SALES: 350K **Privately Held**
SIC: 3577 5045 Computer peripheral equipment; computer peripheral equipment; accounting machines using machine readable programs

(P-15799)
MARBURG TECHNOLOGY INC
Also Called: Glide-Write
304 Turquoise St, Milpitas (95035-5431)
PHONE..................408 262-8400
Francis Burga, *CEO*
Mohammad Ebrahimi, *CFO*
Francis Guevara, *Vice Pres*
Lee Nguyen, *Engineer*
▲ **EMP:** 245
SALES (est): 33.4MM **Privately Held**
SIC: 3577 Disk & diskette equipment, except drives

(P-15800)
MARWAY POWER SYSTEMS INC (PA)
Also Called: Marway Power Solutions
1721 S Grand Ave, Santa Ana (92705-4808)
P.O. Box 30118 (92735-8118)
PHONE..................714 917-6200
Dan Richter, *President*
Mario Manriquez, *President*
Kevin Jacobs, *CFO*
Van Dang, *MIS Mgr*
Garen Manucharyan, *Electrical Engi*
◆ **EMP:** 43
SQ FT: 33,400
SALES (est): 10.7MM **Privately Held**
WEB: www.marway.com
SIC: 3577 8711 Computer peripheral equipment; engineering services

(P-15801)
MEGA FORCE CORPORATION
Also Called: Megaforce
2035 Otoole Ave, San Jose (95131-1301)
PHONE..................408 956-9989
Stanley Trenh, *President*
EMP: 45
SQ FT: 15,000
SALES (est): 12MM **Privately Held**
WEB: www.megaforcecorp.com
SIC: 3577 Computer peripheral equipment

(P-15802)
MEMJET LABELS INC (DH)
10920 Via Frontera # 120, San Diego (92127-1730)
PHONE..................858 798-3300
Len Lauer, *CEO*
Maureen Brock, *President*
Gail Partain, *President*
Aert Van De, *Engineer*
▲ **EMP:** 12
SALES (est): 1.9MM **Privately Held**
SIC: 3577 3555 Printers, computer; printing trades machinery

(P-15803)
MEMJET LABELS INC
10918 Technology Pl, San Diego (92127-1874)
PHONE..................858 798-3061
EMP: 24
SALES (est): 2.6MM **Privately Held**
SIC: 3577

(P-15804)
METROMEDIA TECHNOLOGIES INC
370 Amapola Ave Ste 200, Torrance (90501-7239)
PHONE..................818 552-6500
Paul Havig, *Branch Mgr*
Bill Ishida, *COO*
EMP: 41
SALES (corp-wide): 63.7MM **Privately Held**
WEB: www.mmt.com
SIC: 3577 Graphic displays, except graphic terminals
PA: Metromedia Technologies, Inc.
810 7th Ave Fl 29
New York NY 10019
212 273-2100

(P-15805)
MICRO CONNECTORS INC
2700 Mccone Ave, Hayward (94545-1615)
PHONE..................510 266-0299
Charlie Lin, *President*
▲ **EMP:** 29
SALES (est): 8MM **Privately Held**
WEB: www.microconnectors.com
SIC: 3577 Computer peripheral equipment

(P-15806)
MICROSOFT CORPORATION
680 Vaqueros Ave, Sunnyvale (94085-3523)
PHONE..................650 693-4000
Luis Salazar, *Branch Mgr*
EMP: 180
SALES (corp-wide): 110.3B **Publicly Held**
WEB: www.microsoft.com
SIC: 3577 Computer peripheral equipment

PA: Microsoft Corporation
1 Microsoft Way
Redmond WA 98052
425 882-8080

(P-15807)
MITAC INFORMATION SYSTEMS
39889 Eureka Dr, Newark (94560-4811)
PHONE..................510 668-3679
EMP: 50 **Privately Held**
SIC: 3577
HQ: Mitac Information Systems Corp.
44131 Nobel Dr
Fremont CA 94560
510 668-3679

(P-15808)
MOTION ENGINEERING INC (HQ)
Also Called: M E I
33 S La Patera Ln, Santa Barbara (93117-3214)
PHONE..................805 696-1200
Robert Steele, *CTO*
EMP: 60
SQ FT: 21,000
SALES (est): 4.7MM
SALES (corp-wide): 18.3B **Publicly Held**
WEB: www.synqnet.org
SIC: 3577 8711 3823 Computer peripheral equipment; engineering services; industrial instrmnts msrmnt display/control process variable
PA: Danaher Corporation
2200 Penn Ave Nw Ste 800w
Washington DC 20037
202 828-0850

(P-15809)
MOXA AMERICAS INC
601 Valencia Ave Ste 100, Brea (92823-6357)
PHONE..................714 528-6777
Tein Shun, *CEO*
Ben Chen, *President*
Steve Won, *Exec VP*
Clark Ko, *Vice Pres*
Bob Wolfe, *Vice Pres*
▲ **EMP:** 50
SQ FT: 8,000
SALES (est): 18.2MM **Privately Held**
WEB: www.moxausa.com
SIC: 3577 Input/output equipment, computer
HQ: Moxa Inc.
4f, 135, Lane 235, Pao Chiao Rd.,
New Taipei City
289 191-230

(P-15810)
MPD HOLDINGS INC
Also Called: Mousepad Designs
16200 Commerce Way, Cerritos (90703-2324)
PHONE..................562 777-1051
Glenn M Boghosian, *President*
◆ **EMP:** 34
SALES (est): 7.5MM **Privately Held**
SIC: 3577 Computer peripheral equipment

(P-15811)
NEWNEX TECHNOLOGY CORP
3041 Olcott St, Santa Clara (95054-3222)
PHONE..................408 986-9988
Sam Liu, *President*
Jean Tang, *CFO*
▲ **EMP:** 11
SQ FT: 3,800
SALES (est): 2.3MM **Privately Held**
WEB: www.newnex.com
SIC: 3577 Computer peripheral equipment

(P-15812)
NEWPACKET WIRELESS CORPORATION
1600 Wyatt Dr Ste 10, Santa Clara (95054-1525)
PHONE..................408 747-1003
Sanjay Gidwani, *President*
EMP: 10 **EST:** 2014
SALES (est): 751.9K **Privately Held**
SIC: 3577 Computer peripheral equipment

(P-15813)
NEXSYS ELECTRONICS INC (PA)
Also Called: Medweb
70 Zoe St Ste 100, San Francisco (94107-1753)
PHONE..................415 541-9980
Peter Killcommons, *President*
Ralph Peragine, *Admin Asst*
Cindy Newlove, *Administration*
David Hartmann, *Project Mgr*
Richard Hinesley, *Project Mgr*
EMP: 14
SQ FT: 2,700
SALES (est): 2.6MM **Privately Held**
WEB: www.nexsys.com
SIC: 3577 4813 Computer peripheral equipment;

(P-15814)
OLEA KIOSKS INC
13845 Artesia Blvd, Cerritos (90703-9000)
PHONE..................562 924-2644
Francisco Olea, *CEO*
Fernando Olea, *Ch of Bd*
Rene Olea, *Vice Pres*
Shauna Olea, *Admin Sec*
Craig Bennett, *Project Mgr*
▲ **EMP:** 29
SQ FT: 100,000
SALES: 9.9MM **Privately Held**
WEB: www.olea.com
SIC: 3577 Computer peripheral equipment

(P-15815)
OMNIPRINT INC
1923 E Deere Ave, Santa Ana (92705-5715)
PHONE..................949 833-0080
Fardin Mostafavi, *President*
▲ **EMP:** 24
SQ FT: 22,000
SALES: 8MM **Privately Held**
SIC: 3577 5045 Printers & plotters; printers, computer

(P-15816)
OMNITRON SYSTEMS TECH INC
38 Tesla, Irvine (92618-4603)
PHONE..................949 250-6510
Arie Goldberg, *CEO*
Heidi Cairns, *Vice Pres*
Barry Millman, *Sales Staff*
EMP: 75
SQ FT: 15,000
SALES (est): 16.6MM **Privately Held**
WEB: www.omnitron-systems.com
SIC: 3577 Data conversion equipment, media-to-media: computer

(P-15817)
ONE STOP SYSTEMS INC (PA)
Also Called: OSS
2235 Entp St Ste 110, Escondido (92029)
PHONE..................760 745-9883
Steve Cooper, *Ch of Bd*
John W Morrison Jr, *CFO*
William D Carpenter, *Bd of Directors*
Edgar Sanchez, *Area Mgr*
Mark Perrin, *Technical Staff*
EMP: 75
SQ FT: 17,911
SALES: 27.5MM **Publicly Held**
WEB: www.onestopsystems.com
SIC: 3577 Computer peripheral equipment

(P-15818)
ONE STOP SYSTEMS INC
Also Called: Magma
2235 Entp St Ste 110, Escondido (92029)
PHONE..................858 530-2511
Timothy Miller, *Principal*
Tom Fries, *General Mgr*
Matt Rackstein, *Technology*
Ariel Aquino, *Technical Staff*
EMP: 30
SALES (corp-wide): 27.5MM **Publicly Held**
SIC: 3577 Computer peripheral equipment
PA: One Stop Systems, Inc.
2235 Entp St Ste 110
Escondido CA 92029
760 745-9883

PRODUCTS & SVCS

(P-15819)
OPTIBASE INC (HQ)
931 Benecia Ave, Sunnyvale (94085-2805)
P.O. Box 448, Mountain View (94042-0448)
PHONE...............................800 451-5101
Shlomo Wyler, *CEO*
Michael Chorpash, *President*
EMP: 27
SQ FT: 15,000
SALES (est): 11.7MM
SALES (corp-wide): 15.2MM **Privately Held**
SIC: 3577 Computer peripheral equipment
PA: Optibase Ltd.
8 Hamanofim
Herzliya 46725
737 073-700

(P-15820)
OPTIMA TECHNOLOGY CORPORATION
17062 Murphy Ave, Irvine (92614-5914)
PHONE...............................949 253-5768
Barry Eisler, *Branch Mgr*
EMP: 343
SALES (corp-wide): 17.5MM **Privately Held**
SIC: 3577 Computer peripheral equipment
PA: Optima Technology Corporation
2222 Michelson Dr # 1830
Irvine CA
949 476-0515

(P-15821)
PALO ALTO NETWORKS INC (PA)
3000 Tannery Way, Santa Clara (95054-2832)
PHONE...............................408 753-4000
Nikesh Arora, *Ch of Bd*
Amit Singh, *President*
Kathleen Bonanno, *CFO*
Mark D McLaughlin, *Vice Ch Bd*
Rene Bonvanie, *Chief Mktg Ofcr*
EMP: 500
SQ FT: 941,000
SALES: 2.2B **Publicly Held**
WEB: www.paloaltonetworks.com
SIC: 3577 7371 Computer peripheral equipment; computer software development & applications

(P-15822)
PANO LOGIC INC
1100 La Avenida St Ste A, Mountain View (94043-1453)
PHONE...............................650 743-1773
John Kish, *President*
Parmeet S Chaddha, *Exec VP*
Aly Orady, *CTO*
Nils Bunger, *VP Engrg*
▲ EMP: 72
SQ FT: 11,800
SALES (est): 11.1MM **Privately Held**
WEB: www.attodevices.com
SIC: 3577 Computer peripheral equipment

(P-15823)
PHOTO SCIENCES INCORPORATED (PA)
2542 W 237th St, Torrance (90505-5217)
PHONE...............................310 634-1500
Kyle Stogsdill, *CEO*
L J Stogsdill, *Chairman*
Wade Walsh, *Treasurer*
Jeff Platts, *Vice Pres*
Maurice Muehle,
EMP: 34 EST: 1972
SQ FT: 35,000
SALES: 6MM **Privately Held**
WEB: www.photo-science.com
SIC: 3577 7335 Computer output to microfilm units; still & slide file production

(P-15824)
PLUSTEK TECHNOLOGY INC
9830 Norwalk Blvd Ste 155, Santa Fe Springs (90670-6107)
PHONE...............................562 777-1888
Karen Ku, *President*
▲ EMP: 13
SQ FT: 15,000
SALES (est): 2.7MM **Privately Held**
SIC: 3577 Optical scanning devices

(P-15825)
PRINCETON TECHNOLOGY INC
1691 Browning, Irvine (92606-4808)
PHONE...............................949 851-7776
Nasir Javed, *CEO*
▲ EMP: 30
SQ FT: 14,000
SALES (est): 7.1MM **Privately Held**
WEB: www.princetonusa.com
SIC: 3577 5045 3674 Computer peripheral equipment; computers, peripherals & software; semiconductors & related devices

(P-15826)
PRINKO IMAGE CO (USA) INC (HQ)
5021 Tyler Ave Ste D, Temple City (91780-3632)
PHONE...............................626 389-8988
Chunming Chen, *President*
▲ EMP: 16
SALES (est): 1.4MM **Privately Held**
SIC: 3577 Printers, computer
PA: Prinko Image Co.,Ltd.
4f,Building 1,Dongkeng No.2 Industrial Zone,No.2440,Lvyou Rd.
Zhuhai
756 852-6991

(P-15827)
PRINTRONIX LLC (PA)
6440 Oak Cyn Ste 200, Irvine (92618-5209)
PHONE...............................714 368-2300
Werner Heid, *CEO*
Norm Judd, *CFO*
Sean Irby, *Vice Pres*
Bill Matthewes, *Vice Pres*
Luis Magallanes, *Engineer*
▲ EMP: 108
SQ FT: 84,580
SALES (est): 53.5MM **Privately Held**
WEB: www.printronix.com
SIC: 3577 Printers, computer

(P-15828)
PRINTRONIX HOLDING CORP
6440 Oak Cyn Ste 200, Irvine (92618-5209)
PHONE...............................714 368-2300
Werner Heid, *CEO*
David Baylor, *COO*
EMP: 135
SALES (est): 5.9MM **Privately Held**
SIC: 3577 6719 Printers, computer; investment holding companies, except banks

(P-15829)
PRINTWORX INC
195 Aviation Way Ste 201, Watsonville (95076-2059)
PHONE...............................831 722-7147
James B Riches, *Ch of Bd*
David Willmon, *President*
Kevin Cardona, *General Mgr*
EMP: 17
SQ FT: 15,000
SALES (est): 3.2MM **Privately Held**
WEB: www.printworx.net
SIC: 3577 5112 7378 3861 Printers, computer; computer & photocopying supplies; computer & data processing equipment repair/maintenance; photographic equipment & supplies; commercial printing

(P-15830)
PROPHECY TECHNOLOGY LLC
Also Called: Maxus Group
339 Cheryl Ln, Walnut (91789-3003)
PHONE...............................909 598-7998
Juanito Pangalilingan,
▲ EMP: 30
SALES (est): 3.8MM **Privately Held**
SIC: 3577 Computer peripheral equipment

(P-15831)
PUREDEPTH INC (PA)
303 Twin Dolphin Dr Fl 6, Redwood City (94065-1497)
PHONE...............................408 394-9146
Darryl S K Singh, *CEO*
Andy L Wood, *Ch of Bd*
Michael Laycock, *CFO*
EMP: 12
SQ FT: 1,983
SALES (est): 1.1MM **Privately Held**
WEB: www.puredepth.com
SIC: 3577 Graphic displays, except graphic terminals

(P-15832)
R B S INC
31941 La Subida Dr, Trabuco Canyon (92679-3406)
PHONE...............................949 766-2924
Bob Ball, *President*
EMP: 19
SALES (est): 1.4MM **Privately Held**
SIC: 3577 Printers, computer

(P-15833)
R-QUEST TECHNOLOGIES LLC
4710 Oak Hill Rd, Placerville (95667-9104)
PHONE...............................530 621-9916
Larry Robertson, *President*
Jim Filkins, *VP Sales*
EMP: 12
SQ FT: 3,500
SALES: 2MM **Privately Held**
SIC: 3577 Disk & diskette equipment, except drives

(P-15834)
RANCHO TECHNOLOGY INC
10783 Bell Ct, Rancho Cucamonga (91730-4834)
PHONE...............................909 987-3966
Hari Gupta, *President*
John Fobel Jr, *Vice Pres*
EMP: 15
SALES (est): 2.1MM **Privately Held**
SIC: 3577 5045 Computer peripheral equipment; computers, peripherals & software

(P-15835)
RECORTEC INC
2231 Fortune Dr Ste A, San Jose (95131-1871)
PHONE...............................408 928-1488
Dr Lester H Lee, *President*
Eldon Corl, *Vice Pres*
▲ EMP: 13
SQ FT: 24,000
SALES (est): 2.1MM **Privately Held**
WEB: www.recortec.com
SIC: 3577 3571 Computer peripheral equipment; electronic computers

(P-15836)
REDLINE SOLUTIONS INC
3350 Scott Blvd Bldg 5, Santa Clara (95054-3108)
PHONE...............................408 562-1700
Todd N Baggett, *President*
Fritz Burnell, *Senior Engr*
Anthony Mattos, *Manager*
EMP: 18
SQ FT: 4,000
SALES (est): 4.5MM **Privately Held**
WEB: www.redlinesolutions.com
SIC: 3577 Bar code (magnetic ink) printers

(P-15837)
REVERA INCORPORATED
3090 Oakmead Village Dr, Santa Clara (95051-0862)
PHONE...............................408 510-7400
Glyn Davies, *President*
Timothy Welch, *CFO*
Dave Reed, *CTO*
David Mak, *Opers Staff*
Vincent Tabone, *Director*
▲ EMP: 40
SQ FT: 20,000
SALES (est): 11.5MM
SALES (corp-wide): 163.9MM **Privately Held**
WEB: www.revera.com
SIC: 3577 Optical scanning devices
PA: Nova Measuring Instruments Ltd
Ness Ziona
Ness Ziona 76100
893 875-05

(P-15838)
RGB SPECTRUM
950 Marina Village Pkwy, Alameda (94501-1047)
PHONE...............................510 814-7000
Robert Marcus, *CEO*
Scott Norder, *Senior VP*
Jed Deame, *Vice Pres*
Tony Spica, *Vice Pres*
Jason Tirado, *Vice Pres*
▲ EMP: 81
SQ FT: 27,326
SALES (est): 21.7MM **Privately Held**
WEB: www.rgb.com
SIC: 3577 5731 3679 Graphic displays, except graphic terminals; video cameras, recorders & accessories; recording & playback apparatus, including phonograph

(P-15839)
RGB SYSTEMS INC (PA)
Also Called: Extron Electronics
1025 E Ball Rd Ste 100, Anaheim (92805-5957)
PHONE...............................714 491-1500
Andrew C Edwards, *President*
Dave Pincek, *President*
Peter Knapp, *Program Mgr*
Bryan Tran, *Administration*
Oliver Montoya, *CTO*
▲ EMP: 185
SQ FT: 160,000
SALES (est): 85.4MM **Privately Held**
SIC: 3577 Computer output to microfilm units

(P-15840)
RGB SYSTEMS INC
Also Called: Extron Electronics
1025 E Ball Rd Ste 100, Anaheim (92805-5957)
PHONE...............................714 491-1500
Andrew Edwards, *President*
EMP: 93
SALES (corp-wide): 85.4MM **Privately Held**
SIC: 3577 Computer peripheral equipment
PA: Rgb Systems, Inc.
1025 E Ball Rd Ste 100
Anaheim CA 92805
714 491-1500

(P-15841)
RICOH PRTG SYSTEMS AMER INC (HQ)
2390 Ward Ave Ste A, Simi Valley (93065-1897)
PHONE...............................805 578-4000
Osamu Namikawa, *President*
Hiroyuki Kajiyama, *President*
Greg Grant, *Treasurer*
Leonard Stone, *Vice Pres*
Bill Barclay, *General Mgr*
▲ EMP: 400
SQ FT: 97,400
SALES: 99.3MM
SALES (corp-wide): 19.3B **Privately Held**
WEB: www.hitachi-printingsolutions.us
SIC: 3577 3861 3955 Printers, computer; toners, prepared photographic (not made in chemical plants); developers, photographic (not made in chemical plants); ribbons, inked: typewriter, adding machine, register, etc.
PA: Ricoh Company,Ltd.
1-3-6, Nakamagome
Ota-Ku TKY 143-0
337 778-111

(P-15842)
RIVERBED TECHNOLOGY INC (HQ)
680 Folsom St Ste 500, San Francisco (94107-2160)
PHONE...............................415 247-8800
Paul Mountford, *CEO*
John Tyler, *CFO*
Don Smoot, *Ch Credit Ofcr*
Subbu Iyer, *Chief Mktg Ofcr*
Mark Jopling, *Senior VP*
▲ EMP: 70
SQ FT: 167,000

SALES (est): 1B
SALES (corp-wide): 1.2B **Privately Held**
WEB: www.riverbed.com
SIC: 3577 5045 Computer peripheral
equipment; computer software
PA: Riverbed Holdings, Inc.
300 N La Salle Dr # 4350
Chicago IL 60654
312 254-3300

(P-15843)
ROUCHON INDUSTRIES INC
Also Called: Swiftech
3729 San Gabriel River Pk, Pico Rivera
(90660-1457)
PHONE....................310 763-0336
Gabriel Rouchon, *President*
▲ EMP: 12
SQ FT: 5,000
SALES (est): 2.7MM **Privately Held**
WEB: www.swiftech.com
SIC: 3577 Computer peripheral equipment

(P-15844)
RUGGED INFO TECH EQP CORP
(PA)
Also Called: Ritec
25 E Easy St, Simi Valley (93065-7707)
PHONE....................805 577-9710
Carl C Stella, *President*
Harry P Alteri, *Senior VP*
Roger Lazar, *Vice Pres*
Harry Alteri, *VP Bus Dvlpt*
Roger Lazer, *Admin Sec*
◆ EMP: 40
SQ FT: 25,000
SALES: 12MM **Privately Held**
WEB: www.ritecrugged.com
SIC: 3577 Computer peripheral equipment

(P-15845)
SAMSUNG SDI AMERICA INC
(HQ)
665 Clyde Ave, Mountain View
(94043-2235)
PHONE....................408 544-4470
Kikwon Yoon, *CEO*
Young Joon Gil, *President*
Duck Yun Kim, *President*
Ik Hyeon Kim, *CFO*
Mark Bernstein, *Senior VP*
▼ EMP: 14
SALES (est): 19.3MM
SALES (corp-wide): 4.9B **Privately Held**
SIC: 3577 5045 Computer peripheral
equipment; computer peripheral equip-
ment
PA: Samsung Sdi Co., Ltd.
150-20 Gongse-Ro, Giheung-Gu
Yongin-Gun 17084
318 006-3100

(P-15846)
SEAGRA TECHNOLOGY INC
816 W Ahwanee Ave, Sunnyvale
(94085-1409)
PHONE....................408 230-8706
EMP: 27 **Privately Held**
SIC: 3577 Computer peripheral equipment
PA: Seagra Technology Inc.
14252 Culver Dr
Irvine CA 92604

(P-15847)
SEAGRA TECHNOLOGY INC (PA)
14252 Culver Dr, Irvine (92604-0317)
PHONE....................949 419-6796
Atul Talati, *President*
Timothy Lipsky, *CEO*
Tim Lipsky, *CTO*
▲ EMP: 11
SQ FT: 1,200
SALES: 500K **Privately Held**
SIC: 3577 Computer peripheral equipment

(P-15848)
SECUGEN CORPORATION
2065 Martin Ave Ste 108, Santa Clara
(95050-2707)
PHONE....................408 834-7712
Won Lee, *President*
▲ EMP: 30

SALES (est): 5.8MM
SALES (corp-wide): 177.5K **Privately Held**
SIC: 3577 Computer peripheral equipment
PA: Pivotec Corporation
Rm 502 5/F
Seongnam
823 170-1022

(P-15849)
SEGMENTIO INC
100 California St Ste 700, San Francisco
(94111-4512)
PHONE....................844 611-0621
Peter Kristian Reinhardt, *President*
Sandra Smith, *CFO*
Laylee Asgari, *Office Mgr*
Mandy Adkins, *Admin Asst*
Andrey Bulgakov, *Software Engr*
EMP: 12
SALES (est): 713.3K **Privately Held**
SIC: 3577 Data conversion equipment,
media-to-media: computer

(P-15850)
SEMTEK INNVTIVE SOLUTIONS
CORP
12777 High Bludd Dr 225, San Diego
(92130)
PHONE....................858 436-2270
John Sarkisian, *Ch of Bd*
Patrick Hazel, *President*
Blake Wood, *Info Tech Dir*
▲ EMP: 22
SQ FT: 10,000
SALES (est): 4.1MM **Privately Held**
WEB: www.semtek.com
SIC: 3577 Readers, sorters or inscribers,
magnetic ink

(P-15851)
SENSATA TECHNOLOGIES INC
Also Called: BEI Industrial Encoders
1461 Lawrence Dr, Thousand Oaks
(91320-1303)
PHONE....................805 968-0782
Glenn Avolio, *Sales Mgr*
Eli Morales, *General Mgr*
Doug McGuire, *Engr R&D*
Tim Coronado, *Manager*
EMP: 70
SALES (corp-wide): 2.7MM **Privately Held**
SIC: 3577 3827 3663 Optical scanning
devices; optical instruments & lenses;
radio & TV communications equipment
HQ: Sensata Technologies, Inc.
529 Pleasant St
Attleboro MA 02703
508 236-3800

(P-15852)
SHARKRACK INC
23842 Cabot Blvd, Hayward (94545-1661)
PHONE....................510 477-7900
Seth Schalet, *President*
Jose Barragan, *VP Sales*
EMP: 10
SQ FT: 15,000
SALES (est): 4.2MM **Privately Held**
WEB: www.sharkrack.com
SIC: 3577

(P-15853)
SHARPDOTS LLC
Also Called: Sharp Dots.com
720 N Todd Ave, Azusa (91702-2227)
PHONE....................626 599-9696
John Tan, *President*
EMP: 12
SALES (est): 1.8MM **Privately Held**
WEB: www.sharpdots.com
SIC: 3577 Printers, computer

(P-15854)
SILICON GRAPHICS INTL CORP
(HQ)
940 N Mccarthy Blvd, Milpitas
(95035-5128)
PHONE....................669 900-8000
Jorge L Titinger, *CEO*
Cassio Conceicao, *COO*
Mack Asrat, *CFO*
Eng Lim Goh, *Senior VP*
Peter E Hilliard, *Senior VP*
▲ EMP: 276

SALES: 532.9MM
SALES (corp-wide): 28.8B **Publicly Held**
WEB: www.sgi.com
SIC: 3577 7371 Computer peripheral
equipment; computer software develop-
ment & applications
PA: Hewlett Packard Enterprise Company
3000 Hanover St
Palo Alto CA 94304
650 687-5817

(P-15855)
SKYMICRO INC
2060 E Ave Arboles 344, Thousand Oaks
(91362-1361)
PHONE....................805 491-8935
Rudy Lopez, *President*
▲ EMP: 20
SALES (est): 2.8MM **Privately Held**
WEB: www.skymicro.com
SIC: 3577 Computer peripheral equipment

(P-15856)
SOLFLOWER COMPUTER INC
3337 Kifer Rd, Santa Clara (95051-0719)
PHONE....................408 733-8100
Kim Vu, *President*
Janet Doan, *Vice Pres*
EMP: 15
SQ FT: 8,000
SALES (est): 3MM **Privately Held**
WEB: www.solflower.com
SIC: 3577 Computer peripheral equipment

(P-15857)
SONY ELECTRONICS INC
Also Called: Sony Broadcast Products
1730 N 1st St, San Jose (95112-4508)
PHONE....................408 352-4000
Elizabeth Boukis, *Manager*
EMP: 38
SALES (corp-wide): 80.1B **Privately Held**
SIC: 3577 3571 8731 8711 Computer pe-
ripheral equipment; electronic computers;
commercial physical research; engineer-
ing services
HQ: Sony Electronics Inc.
16535 Via Esprillo Bldg 1
San Diego CA 92127
858 942-2400

(P-15858)
SP CONTROLS INC
930 Linden Ave, South San Francisco
(94080-1754)
PHONE....................650 392-7880
Paul Anson Brown, *CEO*
Gary Arcudi, *Exec VP*
Chuck Conder, *Area Mgr*
Tim McGrew, *Technical Staff*
Lisa Roberts, *Marketing Staff*
▲ EMP: 15
SQ FT: 5,000
SALES (est): 3.1MM **Privately Held**
WEB: www.spcontrols.com
SIC: 3577 Computer peripheral equipment

(P-15859)
SPYRUS INC (PA)
103 Bonaventura Dr, San Jose
(95134-2106)
PHONE....................408 392-9131
Sue Pontius, *CEO*
Tom Dickens, *COO*
Ed Almojuela, *Treasurer*
EMP: 40
SQ FT: 15,000
SALES (est): 7.6MM **Privately Held**
WEB: www.spyrus.com
SIC: 3577 7371 7372 Computer periph-
eral equipment; computer software devel-
opment; prepackaged software

(P-15860)
SURFACE MOUNT TECH
CENTRE
Also Called: Smt Centre
431 Kato Ter, Fremont (94539-8333)
PHONE....................408 935-9548
Gary Walker, *Manager*
EMP: 350
SALES (corp-wide): 139.2MM **Privately Held**
SIC: 3577 3672 Computer peripheral
equipment; printed circuit boards

HQ: Smtc Manufacturing Corporation Of
Canada
7050 Woodbine Ave Suite 300
Markham ON L3R 4
905 479-1810

(P-15861)
SYMBOL TECHNOLOGIES LLC
208 Channing Way, Alameda (94502-6452)
PHONE....................510 684-2974
EMP: 140
SALES (corp-wide): 3.7B **Publicly Held**
SIC: 3577 Computer peripheral equipment
HQ: Symbol Technologies, Llc
1 Zebra Plz
Holtsville NY 11742
631 737-6851

(P-15862)
SYNAPTICS INCORPORATED
1109 Mckay Dr, San Jose (95131-1706)
PHONE....................408 904-1100
EMP: 10
SALES (corp-wide): 1.6B **Publicly Held**
SIC: 3577 7372 Computer peripheral
equipment; prepackaged software
PA: Synaptics Incorporated
1251 Mckay Dr
San Jose CA 95131
408 904-1100

(P-15863)
SYNAPTICS INCORPORATED
(PA)
1251 Mckay Dr, San Jose (95131-1709)
PHONE....................408 904-1100
Richard A Bergman, *President*
Francis F Lee, *Ch of Bd*
Wajid Ali, *CFO*
Jeffrey Buchanan, *Bd of Directors*
John McFarland, *Senior VP*
EMP: 277
SQ FT: 213,000
SALES: 1.6B **Publicly Held**
WEB: www.synaptics.com
SIC: 3577 7372 Computer peripheral
equipment; application computer software

(P-15864)
SYNCHRONIZED
TECHNOLOGIES INC
Also Called: Synchrotech
3333 Wilshire Blvd # 806, Los Angeles
(90010-4101)
PHONE....................213 368-3760
Eric Hartouni, *President*
John Melikian, *Treasurer*
▲ EMP: 15
SQ FT: 6,000
SALES (est): 2.5MM **Privately Held**
WEB: www.synchrotech.com
SIC: 3577 Computer peripheral equipment

(P-15865)
T S MICROTECH INC
17109 Gale Ave, City of Industry
(91745-1810)
PHONE....................626 839-8998
Steve Heung, *President*
David Huang, *General Mgr*
Joseph Lim, *Accounts Mgr*
▲ EMP: 10
SQ FT: 7,000
SALES (est): 1.8MM **Privately Held**
WEB: www.fancard.com
SIC: 3577 Computer peripheral equipment

(P-15866)
TELEPATHY INC
1202 Kifer Rd, Sunnyvale (94086-5304)
PHONE....................408 306-8421
EMP: 25 EST: 2013
SQ FT: 600
SALES (est): 2.5MM **Privately Held**
SIC: 3577

(P-15867)
TELESYNERGY RESEARCH USA
INC
40101 Spady St, Fremont (94538-2981)
PHONE....................408 200-9879
Hsueh-CHI Chin, *President*
EMP: 15 EST: 1993

SALES (est): 1.8MM Privately Held
WEB: www.telesynergy.com
SIC: 3577 Computer peripheral equipment

(P-15868)
TEMBO SYSTEMS INC
2933 Bunker Hill Ln # 100, Santa Clara
(95054-1124)
PHONE................408 300-9236
Simon Wright, *CEO*
EMP: 24
SALES (est): 1.1MM Privately Held
SIC: 3577 Computer peripheral equipment

(P-15869)
TERARECON INC (PA)
4000 E 3rd Ave Ste 200, Foster City
(94404-4825)
PHONE................650 372-1100
Jeff Sorenson, *President*
Jeffery Sorenson, *President*
Tiecheng Zhao, *Senior VP*
Dianne Oseto, *Admin Sec*
Jo Gutierrez, *Financial Exec*
▲ EMP: 80
SQ FT: 11,000
SALES (est): 50.7MM Privately Held
WEB: www.terarecon.com
SIC: 3577 5734 Computer peripheral equipment; computer peripheral equipment

(P-15870)
TONER2PRINT INC
9450 7th St Ste J, Rancho Cucamonga
(91730-5679)
PHONE................909 972-9656
Angel Granados, *CEO*
EMP: 10 EST: 2010
SQ FT: 1,100
SALES: 1.4MM Privately Held
SIC: 3577 2893 3955 Computer peripheral equipment; screen process ink; print cartridges for laser & other computer printers

(P-15871)
TOPAZ SYSTEMS INC (PA)
875 Patriot Dr Ste A, Moorpark
(93021-3351)
PHONE................805 520-8282
Anthony Zank, *President*
Tomlinson Rauscher, *President*
Tom Jacques, *Electrical Engi*
Josh Burkett, *Engineer*
Chelsea Ibanez, *Opers Mgr*
▲ EMP: 40
SQ FT: 16,000
SALES (est): 10.2MM Privately Held
WEB: www.topazsystems.com
SIC: 3577 7371 Graphic displays, except graphic terminals; custom computer programming services

(P-15872)
TOTALTHERMALIMAGINGCOM
8341 La Mesa Blvd, La Mesa
(91942-0217)
PHONE................619 303-5884
Britt Midgette, *Principal*
EMP: 10
SALES (est): 1MM Privately Held
SIC: 3577 Bar code (magnetic ink) printers

(P-15873)
TOYE CORPORATION
9230 Deering Ave, Chatsworth
(91311-5803)
P.O. Box 3997 (91313-3997)
PHONE................818 882-4000
Gordon Morris, *President*
▲ EMP: 12
SQ FT: 5,000
SALES (est): 1.2MM Privately Held
WEB: www.toyecorp.com
SIC: 3577 Computer peripheral equipment

(P-15874)
TRANSPARENT DEVICES INC
Also Called: Cybertouch
853 Lawrence Dr, Newbury Park
(91320-2232)
PHONE................805 499-5000
Abraham Gohari, *President*
Sima Walker, *Finance*
Dina De Falco, *Manager*

Jennifer Manzano, *Manager*
Jennifer Shoemaker, *Manager*
EMP: 20 EST: 1982
SQ FT: 25,000
SALES (est): 4.6MM Privately Held
WEB: www.cybertouch.com
SIC: 3577 Graphic displays, except graphic terminals

(P-15875)
TRI-NET TECHNOLOGY INC
21709 Ferrero, Walnut (91789-5209)
PHONE................909 598-8818
Tom Chung, *President*
Lisa Chung, *CFO*
Akinori Ogawa, *Vice Pres*
Cynthia Hsu, *Finance*
Johnny Honda, *Purchasing*
▲ EMP: 100
SQ FT: 35,000
SALES (est): 18.4MM Privately Held
SIC: 3577 3571 Computer peripheral equipment; electronic computers

(P-15876)
TURN-LUCKILY INTERNATIONAL INC
Also Called: Total Technologies
9710 Research Dr, Irvine (92618-4327)
PHONE................949 465-0200
George Huang, *President*
Vivien KAO, *Technology*
Nancy Tran, *Technology*
Brian McReavy, *Marketing Staff*
David Gutierrez, *Manager*
▲ EMP: 13
SQ FT: 16,000
SALES (est): 2.8MM Privately Held
WEB: www.total-technologies.com
SIC: 3577 Computer peripheral equipment

(P-15877)
ULTERA SYSTEMS INC
28241 Crown Valley Pkwy F115, Laguna Niguel (92677-4441)
PHONE................949 367-8800
MO Nourmohamadian, *President*
Cindy Karch, *CFO*
EMP: 17
SQ FT: 6,500
SALES: 5.2MM Privately Held
WEB: www.ultera.com
SIC: 3577 Key-tape equipment, except drives

(P-15878)
UNITED TOTE COMPANY
4205 Ponderosa Ave, San Diego
(92123-1525)
PHONE................858 279-4250
Scott Pfennighausen, *Engr R&D*
Roger Villarreal, *Senior Engr*
EMP: 20
SALES (corp-wide): 882.6MM Publicly Held
SIC: 3577 7378 Computer peripheral equipment; computer peripheral equipment repair & maintenance
HQ: United Tote Company
700 Central Ave
Louisville KY 40208

(P-15879)
US COMPUTERS INC
Also Called: U S Technical Institute
181 W Orangethorpe Ave C, Placentia
(92870-6931)
PHONE................714 528-0514
Uzma Sheikh, *President*
Saleem Sheikh, *Vice Pres*
EMP: 12
SQ FT: 3,500
SALES: 3MM Privately Held
SIC: 3577 8249 Computer peripheral equipment; vocational schools

(P-15880)
USI MANUFACTURING SERVICES INC
1255 E Arques Ave, Sunnyvale
(94085-4701)
PHONE................408 636-9600
Cherine Lyle, *Human Res Mgr*
EMP: 64

SALES (est): 39.7K Privately Held
WEB: www.usica.com
SIC: 3577 Computer peripheral equipment

(P-15881)
VERIFONE INC
10590 W Ocean Air Dr # 250, San Diego
(92130-4679)
PHONE................858 436-2270
John Sarkisian, *Branch Mgr*
EMP: 22
SALES (corp-wide): 1.8B Publicly Held
SIC: 3577 Readers, sorters or inscribers, magnetic ink
HQ: Verifone, Inc.
88 W Plumeria Dr
San Jose CA 95134
408 232-7800

(P-15882)
VIA MECHANICS (USA) INC (DH)
Also Called: Hitachi Via Mechanics USA Inc
150 Charcot Ave Ste C, San Jose
(95131-1131)
PHONE................408 392-9650
Noboru Matsuoka, *CEO*
Ted Saito, *Treasurer*
◆ EMP: 12
SQ FT: 8,000
SALES: 14.1MM
SALES (corp-wide): 756.2K Privately Held
WEB: www.hitachi-via-usa.com
SIC: 3577 Computer peripheral equipment
HQ: Via Mechanics,Ltd.
9-32, Tamuracho
Atsugi KNG 243-0
462 039-680

(P-15883)
VISIONEER INC (HQ)
5673 Gibraltar Dr Ste 150, Pleasanton
(94588-8569)
PHONE................925 251-6300
J Larry Smart, *Ch of Bd*
Walt Thinsen, *President*
John C Dexter, *Vice Pres*
Erik Banis, *Managing Dir*
Walt Thinfen, *CIO*
▲ EMP: 50 EST: 1994
SQ FT: 15,000
SALES (est): 9.4MM Privately Held
WEB: www.visioneer.com
SIC: 3577 Computer peripheral equipment

(P-15884)
VUZE INC
489 S El Camino Real, San Mateo
(94402-1727)
PHONE................650 963-4750
Gilles Bianrosa, *CEO*
Brian Sussman, *Manager*
EMP: 30
SQ FT: 10,000
SALES (est): 3.2MM Privately Held
WEB: www.azureus-inc.com
SIC: 3577 Data conversion equipment, media-to-media: computer

(P-15885)
WESTERN TELEMATIC INC
5 Sterling, Irvine (92618-2517)
PHONE................949 586-9950
Daniel Morrison, *CEO*
Herbert Hoover III, *Ch of Bd*
Everett Sykes, *Vice Pres*
Anthony Barrera, *Software Engr*
Donnie Glaser, *Engineer*
▲ EMP: 50
SQ FT: 24,000
SALES (est): 12.7MM Privately Held
WEB: www.wti.com
SIC: 3577 5065 Computer peripheral equipment; electronic parts & equipment

(P-15886)
WILLIAM HO
Also Called: MBA Electronics
40760 Encyclopedia Cir, Fremont
(94538-2473)
PHONE................510 226-9089
William Ho, *Owner*
EMP: 15
SQ FT: 21,000

SALES (est): 2.2MM Privately Held
WEB: www.mbaelectronics.com
SIC: 3577 Computer peripheral equipment

(P-15887)
WINTEC INDUSTRIES INC
8674 Thornton Ave, Newark (94560-3330)
PHONE................510 953-7400
Cecilia Chiao, *Manager*
EMP: 20
SALES (corp-wide): 76.5MM Privately Held
SIC: 3577 Computer peripheral equipment
PA: Wintec Industries, Inc.
8674 Thornton Ave
Newark CA 94560
510 953-7440

(P-15888)
WINTEC INDUSTRIES INC (PA)
8674 Thornton Ave, Newark (94560-3330)
PHONE................510 953-7440
Sanjay Bonde, *CEO*
Jennifer Chen, *Vice Pres*
Eric Wang, *Principal*
Kong Chen Chen, *Admin Sec*
Brandon Inabinet, *Info Tech Mgr*
▲ EMP: 160
SQ FT: 85,000
SALES (est): 68.8MM Privately Held
SIC: 3577 3674 3572 Computer peripheral equipment; semiconductors & related devices; computer storage devices

(P-15889)
XINGTERA INC
2953 Bunker Hill Ln # 202, Santa Clara
(95054-1131)
PHONE................408 916-4781
Ching Yu, *VP Engrg*
Yunzhentg Zhou, *CFO*
David Chin, *VP Mktg*
Alberto Feltstrom, *Chief*
◆ EMP: 10
SQ FT: 4,000
SALES (est): 900K Privately Held
SIC: 3577 Computer peripheral equipment

(P-15890)
ZEBRA TECHNOLOGIES CORPORATION
1440 Innovative Dr # 100, San Diego
(92154-6631)
PHONE................619 661-5465
Mark Wallace, *Branch Mgr*
Robert Beach, *Vice Pres*
Dennis Slattery, *Engineer*
Sean Stewart, *Opers Staff*
John Fay, *Senior Mgr*
EMP: 400
SALES (corp-wide): 3.7B Publicly Held
SIC: 3577 Bar code (magnetic ink) printers
PA: Zebra Technologies Corporation
3 Overlook Pt
Lincolnshire IL 60069
847 634-6700

(P-15891)
ZEBRA TECHNOLOGIES CORPORATION
Also Called: Eltron International
30601 Agoura Rd, Agoura Hills
(91301-2150)
PHONE................805 579-1800
Don Skinner, *Branch Mgr*
Mike Millman, *President*
Isidre Rosello-Martos, *Vice Pres*
Chuck Heiberger, *Info Tech Mgr*
Edward Dacey, *Software Engr*
EMP: 400
SALES (corp-wide): 3.7B Publicly Held
WEB: www.zebra.com
SIC: 3577 Bar code (magnetic ink) printers
PA: Zebra Technologies Corporation
3 Overlook Pt
Lincolnshire IL 60069
847 634-6700

(P-15892)
ZEBRA TECHNOLOGIES INTL LLC
2940 N 1st St, San Jose (95134-2021)
PHONE................408 473-8500
Jill Stelfox, *Manager*
Dongqing Chen, *Software Engr*

Joe Giordano, *Engineer*
Huong Hang, *Engineer*
Ed Weber, *Sales Staff*
EMP: 17
SALES (corp-wide): 3.7B **Publicly Held**
SIC: 3577 Computer peripheral equipment
HQ: Zebra Technologies International, Llc
3 Overlook Pt
Lincolnshire IL 60069
847 634-6700

3578 Calculating & Accounting Eqpt

(P-15893)
ASTERES INC (PA)
4110 Sorrento Valley Blvd, San Diego (92121-1429)
PHONE................................858 777-8600
Linda Pinney, *CEO*
Marc Thorstenson, *President*
Chris Juetten, *Senior VP*
Martin Bridges, *Vice Pres*
▲ **EMP:** 29
SALES (est): 4.5MM **Privately Held**
WEB: www.asteres.com
SIC: 3578 Cash registers

(P-15894)
AT SYSTEMS TECHNOLOGIES INC
301 N Lake Ave Ste 600, Pasadena (91101-5129)
PHONE................................317 591-2616
John Sims, *President*
Ronald Lambert, *Shareholder*
Thomas Wantz, *Treasurer*
Rex A Townsend, *Admin Sec*
Patricia Sims, *Asst Treas*
EMP: 35
SALES (est): 5.4MM **Privately Held**
WEB: www.autovend.com
SIC: 3578 Coin counters; change making machines
HQ: Garda Cl Technical Services, Inc.
700 S Federal Hwy Ste 300
Boca Raton FL 33432

(P-15895)
CAR ENTERPRISES INC
13100 Main St, Hesperia (92345-4625)
PHONE................................760 947-6411
Sam Anabi, *President*
EMP: 14
SALES (corp-wide): 132MM **Privately Held**
SIC: 3578 Automatic teller machines (ATM)
PA: C.A.R Enterprises, Inc.
1450 N Benson Ave Unit A
Upland CA 91786
909 932-9242

(P-15896)
COMMUNITY MERCH SOLUTIONS LLC
Also Called: CMS
27201 Puerta Real Ste 120, Mission Viejo (92691-8555)
PHONE................................877 956-9258
EMP: 35
SALES: 2.9MM **Privately Held**
SIC: 3578

(P-15897)
KOBUS BUSINESS SYSTEMS LLC
Also Called: Kobus Harmse
254 N Alta Ave, Dinuba (93618-1548)
P.O. Box 330 (93618-0330)
PHONE................................559 595-1915
Kobus Harmse,
EMP: 12
SQ FT: 1,800
SALES: 1.5MM **Privately Held**
SIC: 3578 Calculating & accounting equipment

(P-15898)
PAYMENTMAX PROCESSING INC
600 Hampshire Rd Ste 120, Westlake Village (91361-2584)
P.O. Box 3847, Thousand Oaks (91359-0847)
PHONE................................805 557-1692
Tony Shap, *President*
EMP: 60
SALES (est): 6.3MM **Privately Held**
SIC: 3578 Point-of-sale devices

(P-15899)
POS PORTAL INC (HQ)
180 Promenade Cir Ste 215, Sacramento (95834-2940)
PHONE................................530 695-3005
Mike Baur, *CEO*
Scott Agatep, *COO*
Gus Constancio, *Vice Pres*
Sarah Klose, *Vice Pres*
Bob Nicoson, *Vice Pres*
▲ **EMP:** 28
SQ FT: 12,500
SALES (est): 28.1MM **Publicly Held**
WEB: www.posportal.com
SIC: 3578 3699 Point-of-sale devices; security control equipment & systems

(P-15900)
SIERRA NATIONAL CORPORATION
5140 Alzeda Dr, La Mesa (91941-5725)
PHONE................................619 258-8200
Fred C Forbes, *President*
Gary Wadsworth, *Vice Pres*
EMP: 40 **EST:** 1968
SQ FT: 5,000
SALES (est): 5MM **Privately Held**
WEB: www.sierranational.com
SIC: 3578 7374 Point-of-sale devices; data processing service

(P-15901)
SUZHOU SOUTH
18351 Colima Rd Ste 82, Rowland Heights (91748-2791)
PHONE................................626 322-0101
Joel Wynne, *Director*
EMP: 300 **EST:** 2017
SALES: 16MM **Privately Held**
SIC: 3578 Banking machines

(P-15902)
VERIFONE INC (DH)
88 W Plumeria Dr, San Jose (95134-2134)
PHONE................................408 232-7800
Paul Galant, *CEO*
Doug Reed, *Treasurer*
Alok Bhanot, *Exec VP*
Albert Liu, *Exec VP*
Dave Turnbull, *Exec VP*
◆ **EMP:** 190 **EST:** 1981
SALES (est): 500MM
SALES (corp-wide): 137.5MM **Privately Held**
SIC: 3578 7372 3577 3575 Point-of-sale devices; operating systems computer software; application computer software; computer peripheral equipment; printers, computer; computer terminals; engineering services; current-carrying wiring devices
HQ: Verifone Systems, Inc.
88 W Plumeria Dr
San Jose CA 95134
408 232-7800

(P-15903)
VERIFONE INC
2455 Augustine Dr, Santa Clara (95054)
PHONE................................408 232-7800
Gene Hodges, *Branch Mgr*
Robert Henske, *Bd of Directors*
EMP: 155
SALES (corp-wide): 1.8B **Publicly Held**
SIC: 3578 Point-of-sale devices
HQ: Verifone, Inc.
88 W Plumeria Dr
San Jose CA 95134
408 232-7800

3579 Office Machines, NEC

(P-15904)
VERIFONE SYSTEMS INC (HQ)
88 W Plumeria Dr, San Jose (95134-2134)
PHONE................................408 232-7800
Mike Pulli, *CEO*
Marc E Rothman, *CFO*
Vin D'Agostino, *Exec VP*
Albert Liu, *Exec VP*
Glen Robson, *Exec VP*
▲ **EMP:** 74
SALES: 1.8B
SALES (corp-wide): 137.5MM **Privately Held**
SIC: 3578 7372 Point-of-sale devices; operating systems computer software; application computer software
PA: Vertex Holdco, Inc.
88 W Plumeria Dr
San Jose CA 95134
408 232-7800

(P-15905)
C-SCAN CORP
19630 Allendale Ave, Saratoga (95070-7799)
PHONE................................800 953-7888
Ata Khojasteh, *President*
EMP: 25
SALES (est): 2.9MM **Privately Held**
WEB: www.cscan.com
SIC: 3579 Dictating machines

(P-15906)
INTELMAIL USA INC
9965 Horn Rd Ste D, Sacramento (95827-1995)
PHONE................................916 361-9300
Heros Dilanchian, *President*
Cynthia Ferrario, *Treasurer*
Cindy Ferrario, *Corp Secy*
Bow Smith, *General Mgr*
▲ **EMP:** 13
SQ FT: 14,000
SALES: 4MM **Privately Held**
SIC: 3579 Mailing machines

(P-15907)
LYNDE-ORDWAY COMPANY INC
3308 W Warner Ave, Santa Ana (92704-5395)
P.O. Box 8709, Fountain Valley (92728-8709)
PHONE................................714 957-1311
Thomas Ordway, *President*
Penny Ordway, *Admin Sec*
EMP: 18 **EST:** 1925
SQ FT: 30,000
SALES (est): 3.6MM **Privately Held**
WEB: www.lynde-ordway.com
SIC: 3579 5999 5044 7359 Paper handling machines; coin wrapping machines; business machines & equipment; office equipment; equipment rental & leasing; industrial equipment services

(P-15908)
OLA CORPORATE SERVICES INC
6404 Wilshire Blvd # 525, Los Angeles (90048-5503)
PHONE................................323 655-1005
Ola Boykin, *CEO*
Mamon Boykin, *CFO*
EMP: 11 **EST:** 2000
SQ FT: 850
SALES: 177.9K **Privately Held**
SIC: 3579 7389 Typing & word processing machines; translation services

(P-15909)
OUTDOOR GALORE INC
5010 Young St, Bakersfield (93311-9899)
PHONE................................661 831-8662
Timothy Scott Clark, *Administration*
EMP: 16
SALES (corp-wide): 2.7MM **Privately Held**
SIC: 3579 Mailing, letter handling & addressing machines

PA: Outdoor Galore, Inc.
6801 White Ln Ste A1
Bakersfield CA 93309
661 831-8662

(P-15910)
PARKER POWIS INC
2929 5th St, Berkeley (94710-2736)
PHONE................................510 848-2463
Kevin Parker, *President*
Charles Marino, *COO*
Tony Cheng, *CFO*
Richard Lo, *Vice Pres*
Julie Banados, *Administration*
▲ **EMP:** 86
SQ FT: 54,000
SALES: 15MM **Privately Held**
WEB: www.powis.com
SIC: 3579 Binding machines, plastic & adhesive

(P-15911)
PITNEY BOWES INC
25531 Commercentre Dr # 110, Lake Forest (92630-8874)
PHONE................................949 855-7844
Olaf Jeziorek, *Branch Mgr*
Al Dettlings, *Principal*
EMP: 60
SALES (corp-wide): 3.5B **Publicly Held**
SIC: 3579 7359 Postage meters; business machine & electronic equipment rental services
PA: Pitney Bowes Inc.
3001 Summer St Ste 3
Stamford CT 06905
203 356-5000

(P-15912)
PITNEY BOWES INC
71 Park Ln, Brisbane (94005-1309)
PHONE................................415 330-9423
Tom Smith, *Manager*
EMP: 33
SALES (corp-wide): 3.5B **Publicly Held**
SIC: 3579 7359 Postage meters; business machine & electronic equipment rental services
PA: Pitney Bowes Inc.
3001 Summer St Ste 3
Stamford CT 06905
203 356-5000

(P-15913)
PITNEY BOWES INC
11355 W Olympic Blvd Fl 2, Los Angeles (90064-1656)
PHONE................................310 312-4288
Diane Poynter, *Branch Mgr*
EMP: 42
SALES (corp-wide): 3.5B **Publicly Held**
SIC: 3579 7359 Postage meters; business machine & electronic equipment rental services
PA: Pitney Bowes Inc.
3001 Summer St Ste 3
Stamford CT 06905
203 356-5000

(P-15914)
RESINA
27455 Bostik Ct, Temecula (92590-3698)
PHONE................................951 296-6585
Loonie Beltes, *President*
EMP: 15
SALES (est): 1.2MM **Privately Held**
SIC: 3579 Office machines

(P-15915)
RICOH ELECTRONICS INC
1100 Valencia Ave, Tustin (92780-6450)
PHONE................................714 259-1220
Paul Bakonyi, *Manager*
EMP: 300
SQ FT: 49,359
SALES (corp-wide): 19.3B **Privately Held**
WEB: www.ricohelectronicsinc.com
SIC: 3579 3571 Mailing, letter handling & addressing machines; typing & word processing machines; paper handling machines; electronic computers
HQ: Ricoh Electronics, Inc.
1100 Valencia Ave
Tustin CA 92780
714 566-2500

PRODUCTS & SVCS

(P-15916)
WHITTIER MAILING PRODUCTS INC (PA)
13019 Park St, Santa Fe Springs (90670-4005)
PHONE....................562 464-3000
Richard A Casford, *President*
EMP: 42
SQ FT: 5,000
SALES (est): 6.1MM **Privately Held**
WEB: www.traytag.com
SIC: 3579 Mailing, letter handling & addressing machines

(P-15917)
Y NISSIM INC
Also Called: Shear Tech
9424 Eton Ave Ste H, Chatsworth (91311-6937)
PHONE....................818 718-9024
Yosi Nissim, *President*
Ariela Nissim, *Vice Pres*
EMP: 10
SQ FT: 3,600
SALES (est): 1.5MM **Privately Held**
WEB: www.sheartech.net
SIC: 3579 Check writing, endorsing or signing machines

3581 Automatic Vending Machines

(P-15918)
AQUA PRODUCTS INC
6860 Oran Cir Ste 6351, Buena Park (90621-3304)
P.O. Box 5930 (90622-5930)
PHONE....................714 670-0691
Daniel Suh, *President*
Kathleen McClarnon, *CFO*
Don Mossing, *Administration*
◆ EMP: 30
SQ FT: 5,100
SALES (est): 3.6MM **Privately Held**
WEB: www.watervending.com
SIC: 3581 Automatic vending machines

(P-15919)
BVP DESIGNS INC
21354 Nordhoff St Ste 101, Chatsworth (91311-6910)
PHONE....................818 280-2900
Benjiman Grill, *President*
Shimon Grill, *Vice Pres*
EMP: 19
SALES: 2MM **Privately Held**
SIC: 3581 Automatic vending machines

(P-15920)
CARACAL ENTERPRISES LLC
Also Called: Ventek International
1260 Holm Rd Ste A, Petaluma (94954-7152)
PHONE....................707 773-3373
Gary Catt, *President*
Bill Paulin, *CFO*
Deb Swarthout, *Administration*
Bob Forsyth,
▲ EMP: 30
SALES: 5.3MM **Privately Held**
SIC: 3581 Automatic vending machines

(P-15921)
DIGITAL MEDIA VENDING INTL LLC
105 Duchess Ct, Windsor (95492-8043)
PHONE....................415 516-3243
David Ashforth, *Mng Member*
Raymond Tuzi,
▲ EMP: 12
SALES: 1.6MM **Privately Held**
SIC: 3581 Automatic vending machines

(P-15922)
GW SERVICES LLC (DH)
1385 Park Center Dr, Vista (92081-8338)
PHONE....................760 560-1111
Brian McInerney, *President*
Steven D Stringer, *CFO*
EMP: 41

SALES (est): 8.8MM
SALES (corp-wide): 286MM **Publicly Held**
SIC: 3581 Automatic vending machines
HQ: Primo Water Operations, Inc.
101 N Cherry St Ste 501
Winston Salem NC 27101
336 331-4000

(P-15923)
NUTRITION WITHOUT BORDERS LLC
Also Called: H.U.M.A.N. Healthy Vending
4641 Leahy St, Culver City (90232-3515)
PHONE....................310 845-7745
Sean Kelly,
Andrew Mackensen,
▼ EMP: 15
SQ FT: 10,000
SALES (est): 3.3MM **Privately Held**
SIC: 3581 5122 Automatic vending machines; vitamins & minerals

(P-15924)
OAK MANUFACTURING COMPANY INC
2850 E Vernon Ave, Vernon (90058-1804)
P.O. Box 58201, Los Angeles (90058-0201)
PHONE....................323 581-8087
James Hinton, *President*
EMP: 14
SQ FT: 12,000
SALES (est): 2.3MM **Privately Held**
WEB: www.oakmfg.com
SIC: 3581 Automatic vending machines

(P-15925)
PANTRY RETAIL INC
3095 Kerner Blvd Ste N, San Rafael (94901-5420)
PHONE....................415 234-3574
Russ Cohn, *CEO*
Alex Yancher, *COO*
Arnold Lee, *CFO*
EMP: 15
SALES (est): 3.1MM **Privately Held**
SIC: 3581 Automatic vending machines

(P-15926)
RNB VENDING INC
9353 Bolsa Ave Ste A49, Westminster (92683-5951)
PHONE....................714 548-6993
Ryan Donguyen, *President*
EMP: 10
SALES: 200K **Privately Held**
SIC: 3581 Automatic vending machines

3582 Commercial Laundry, Dry Clean & Pressing Mchs

(P-15927)
AMERICAN CLEANER AND LAUNDRY
Also Called: American Linen Rental
2230 S Depot St Ste D, Santa Maria (93455-1205)
PHONE....................805 925-1571
Chris Consorti, *Shareholder*
Steve Consorti, *Consultant*
EMP: 37
SALES (est): 1.3MM **Privately Held**
SIC: 3582 Commercial laundry equipment

(P-15928)
CONSOLIDATED LAUNDRY LLC
Also Called: Consolidated Laundry Machinery
211 Erie St, Pomona (91768-3328)
P.O. Box 2985 (91769-2985)
PHONE....................323 232-2417
Jason Farber,
Martin Pharis, *President*
Gabriel Camacho, *Opers Mgr*
John Alvarez, *Director*
EMP: 26
SQ FT: 20,000
SALES: 5MM **Privately Held**
SIC: 3582 Commercial laundry equipment

(P-15929)
DENIM-TECH LLC
2300 E 52nd St, Vernon (90058-3444)
PHONE....................323 277-8998
Toyoo Tashiro, *Mng Member*
Duane Dunbar, *General Mgr*
Ken Chen, *Technology*
Ken Nguyen, *Graphic Designe*
Deborah Marcotte, *Accounting Mgr*
▲ EMP: 100
SQ FT: 50,000
SALES (est): 19.8MM **Privately Held**
SIC: 3582 Commercial laundry equipment

(P-15930)
NEWBOLD CLEANERS
4211 Arden Way Ste A, Sacramento (95864-3037)
PHONE....................916 481-1130
Kil Cho, *CEO*
Shawn Cho, *Vice Pres*
EMP: 15
SALES (est): 900K **Privately Held**
SIC: 3582 Commercial laundry equipment

3585 Air Conditioning & Heating Eqpt

(P-15931)
ACCO ENGINEERED SYSTEMS INC
3121 N Sillect Ave # 104, Bakersfield (93308-6364)
PHONE....................661 631-1975
EMP: 17
SALES (corp-wide): 768.2MM **Privately Held**
SIC: 3585 Air conditioning equipment, complete
PA: Acco Engineered Systems, Inc.
6265 San Fernando Rd
Glendale CA 91201
818 244-6571

(P-15932)
ACE HEATERS LLC
130 Klug Cir, Corona (92880-5424)
PHONE....................951 738-2230
William Newbauer III, *President*
EMP: 20 EST: 2016
SQ FT: 40,000
SALES: 3MM
SALES (corp-wide): 9.1MM **Privately Held**
SIC: 3585 3443 Heating equipment, complete; boiler & boiler shop work; boiler shop products: boilers, smokestacks, steel tanks; industrial vessels, tanks & containers
PA: Heh Holdings Llc
45 Seymour St
Stratford CT

(P-15933)
ADVANCED AEROSPACE
10781 Forbes Ave, Garden Grove (92843-4977)
PHONE....................714 265-6200
Steve Flowers, *President*
Joe St Amand, *Controller*
EMP: 200
SALES (est): 14.9MM **Privately Held**
SIC: 3585 Refrigeration equipment, complete

(P-15934)
AIR SOLUTIONS LLC
37310 Cedar Blvd Ste J, Newark (94560-4156)
PHONE....................510 573-6474
Armando Mota, *Mng Member*
Jose Mota, *Sales Staff*
EMP: 10
SALES (est): 2.2MM **Privately Held**
SIC: 3585 3822 Refrigeration & heating equipment; thermostats & other environmental sensors

(P-15935)
ALLIANCE AIR PRODUCTS LLC
Also Called: Especializados Del Aire
2285 Michael Faraday Dr, San Diego (92154-7926)
PHONE....................619 428-9688
Thomas R Sieber, *Mng Member*
John Searsi,
John Staples,
Brenda Covarrubias, *Manager*
EMP: 113
SQ FT: 3,300
SALES: 25MM **Privately Held**
SIC: 3585 Air conditioning units, complete: domestic or industrial

(P-15936)
ANTHONY DOORS INC (DH)
Also Called: Anthony International
12391 Montero Ave, Sylmar (91342-5370)
PHONE....................818 365-9451
Jeffrey Clark, *CEO*
David Lautenschaelger, *CFO*
Craig Little, *Senior VP*
Michael Murth, *Vice Pres*
John Patterson, *General Mgr*
◆ EMP: 850
SQ FT: 350,000
SALES (est): 627.6MM
SALES (corp-wide): 7.8B **Publicly Held**
WEB: www.kramerusa.net
SIC: 3585 Refrigeration & heating equipment
HQ: Dover Printing & Identification, Inc.
3005 Highland Pkwy # 200
Downers Grove IL 60515
630 541-1540

(P-15937)
AQUA LOGIC INC
9558 Camino Ruiz, San Diego (92126-4435)
PHONE....................858 292-4773
Douglas Russell, *President*
Maralin Russell, *Vice Pres*
Curtis Epps, *Engineer*
Constantino Dimaano, *Purch Agent*
Louis Dang, *Sales Staff*
▼ EMP: 20
SQ FT: 20,000
SALES (est): 6.1MM **Privately Held**
WEB: www.aqualogicinc.com
SIC: 3585 Refrigeration & heating equipment

(P-15938)
ARI INDUSTRIES INC
Also Called: Airdyne Refrigeration
17018 Edwards Rd, Cerritos (90703-2422)
PHONE....................714 993-3700
R Tony Bedi, *President*
Ruth Lee Bedi, *Vice Pres*
Ruth Bedi, *Vice Pres*
Ruth Lee, *Vice Pres*
EMP: 80
SQ FT: 20,000
SALES (est): 17.9MM **Privately Held**
WEB: www.airdyne.com
SIC: 3585 Refrigeration equipment, complete

(P-15939)
AVIATE ENTERPRISES INC
5844 Price Ave, McClellan (95652-2407)
PHONE....................916 993-4000
Timothy Devine, *CEO*
Diane Devine, *Finance*
EMP: 27
SQ FT: 3,700
SALES (est): 519K **Privately Held**
SIC: 3585 3843 5599 3629 Refrigeration & heating equipment; dental equipment & supplies; golf cart, powered; electronic generation equipment; medical & hospital equipment

(P-15940)
BALTIMORE AIRCOIL COMPANY INC
B A C
15341 Road 28 1/2, Madera (93638-2395)
PHONE....................559 673-9231
Han Yen, *Branch Mgr*
Luke Rubino, *Executive*
Nicole Simms, *Administration*
Adam Garcia, *Info Tech Dir*

Javier Garcia, *Technology*
EMP: 150
SQ FT: 45,000
SALES (corp-wide): 2.4B **Privately Held**
WEB: www.baltimoreaircoil.com
SIC: 3585 Condensers, refrigeration; refrigeration equipment, complete
HQ: Baltimore Aircoil Company, Inc.
7600 Dorsey Run Rd
Jessup MD 20794
410 799-6200

(P-15941)
BIGFOGG INC (PA)
42095 Zevo Dr Ste A2, Temecula
(92590-3747)
PHONE..................951 587-2460
Christopher Miehl, *President*
Chris Miehl, *President*
EMP: 18
SQ FT: 4,000
SALES: 1.5MM **Privately Held**
WEB: www.bigfogg.com
SIC: 3585 Air conditioning condensers & condensing units

(P-15942)
BROOKS AUTOMATION INC
Also Called: Brooks Polycold Systems
46702 Bayside Pkwy, Fremont
(94538-6582)
PHONE..................510 498-8745
Steve Michaud, *Branch Mgr*
Ken Boyajian, *Finance Mgr*
EMP: 67
SALES (corp-wide): 692.8MM **Publicly Held**
SIC: 3585 3679 Refrigeration & heating equipment; electronic circuits
PA: Brooks Automation, Inc.
15 Elizabeth Dr
Chelmsford MA 01824
978 262-2400

(P-15943)
CALIFRNIA INDUS RFRGN MCHS INC
3197 Cornerstone Dr, Mira Loma
(91752-1028)
PHONE..................951 361-0040
Shahnaz Ghelani, *Corp Secy*
Rahim Ghelani, *President*
Mansoor Ghelani, *Vice Pres*
EMP: 15
SALES (est): 3.7MM **Privately Held**
WEB: www.caindustrial.com
SIC: 3585 5075 1711 1731 Air conditioning equipment, complete; compressors for refrigeration & air conditioning equipment; compressors, air conditioning; heating & air conditioning contractors; general electrical contractor

(P-15944)
CARRIER CORPORATION
600 Mccormick St Ste B, San Leandro
(94577-1128)
PHONE..................510 347-2000
Craig Sweeney, *General Mgr*
Chris Burns, *Sales Staff*
EMP: 280
SALES (corp-wide): 59.8B **Publicly Held**
SIC: 3585 Refrigeration & heating equipment
HQ: Carrier Corporation
13995 Pasteur Blvd
Palm Beach Gardens FL 33418
800 379-6484

(P-15945)
COMMERCIAL DISPLAY SYSTEMS LLC
Also Called: C D S
17341 Sierra Hwy, Canyon Country
(91351-1625)
PHONE..................818 361-8160
Fernando Calderon,
Nick Beswick, *Technology*
Robert Enriquez, *Technology*
Duane Beswick,
John T Karnes, *Mng Member*
EMP: 30
SQ FT: 17,000
SALES (est): 6.5MM **Privately Held**
SIC: 3585 Refrigeration & heating equipment

(P-15946)
COMPU AIRE INC
8167 Byron Rd, Whittier (90606-2615)
PHONE..................562 945-8971
Balbir Narang, *President*
Robert Narang, *Vice Pres*
Vincent Duong, *Office Admin*
Mahendra Ahir, *Engineer*
Jessica Desai, *Purchasing*
▲ EMP: 150
SQ FT: 75,000
SALES (est): 31.1MM **Privately Held**
WEB: www.compu-aire.com
SIC: 3585 Air conditioning units, complete: domestic or industrial

(P-15947)
COOLTEC REFRIGERATION CORP
1250 E Franklin Ave B, Pomona
(91766-5449)
P.O. Box 1150 (91769-1150)
PHONE..................909 865-2229
Paul Bedi, *CEO*
George Share, *Corp Secy*
Katherine Sanchez, *Office Mgr*
Sundeet Bedi, *Plant Mgr*
Fred Peppe, *Manager*
EMP: 22
SQ FT: 50,000
SALES (est): 6.3MM **Privately Held**
WEB: www.cooltecrefrigeration.com
SIC: 3585 Refrigeration equipment, complete

(P-15948)
CUSTOM MECHANICAL SYSTEMS LLC
1830 Embarcadero Ste 103, Oakland
(94606-5230)
PHONE..................510 347-5500
Daniel Hyman, *Mng Member*
EMP: 11 EST: 2008
SQ FT: 7,400
SALES (est): 1.8MM **Privately Held**
SIC: 3585 Refrigeration & heating equipment

(P-15949)
DATA AIRE INC (HQ)
230 W Blueridge Ave, Orange
(92865-4225)
PHONE..................800 347-2473
Duncan Moffatt, *President*
Edward J Altieri, *Corp Secy*
▲ EMP: 101
SALES (est): 36.4MM
SALES (corp-wide): 379MM **Privately Held**
WEB: www.dataaire.com
SIC: 3585 Air conditioning units, complete: domestic or industrial
PA: Construction Specialties Inc.
3 Werner Way Ste 100
Lebanon NJ 08833
908 236-0800

(P-15950)
DIVERSIFIED PANELS SYSTEMS INC
Also Called: Diversified Construction
2345 Statham Blvd, Oxnard (93033-3911)
PHONE..................805 487-9241
Richard C Bell, *CEO*
▲ EMP: 10
SALES: 6MM **Privately Held**
WEB: www.dpspanels.com
SIC: 3585 5064 Lockers, refrigerated; refrigerators & freezers

(P-15951)
DURO DYNE WEST CORP
10837 Commerce Way Ste C, Fontana
(92337-8202)
PHONE..................562 926-1774
Randall S Hinden, *President*
Bernard Hinden, *Director*
▲ EMP: 290
SQ FT: 41,000
SALES (est): 34.2MM
SALES (corp-wide): 125.5MM **Privately Held**
SIC: 3585 3444 Air conditioning units, complete: domestic or industrial; sheet metalwork

PA: Dyne Duro National Corp
81 Spence St
Bay Shore NY 11706

(P-15952)
ELCO RFRGN SOLUTIONS LLC
Also Called: Kulthorn North America
2554 Commercial St, San Diego
(92113-1132)
PHONE..................619 255-5251
Dean Rafiee, *Mng Member*
EMP: 5000 EST: 2014
SALES: 228.8MM
SALES (corp-wide): 243.3MM **Privately Held**
SIC: 3585 Compressors for refrigeration & air conditioning equipment
PA: Kulthorn Kirby Public Company Limited
126 Chalong Krung Road Soi Chalongkrung 31
Lat Krabang 10520
232 608-31

(P-15953)
ENERGY LABS INC (DH)
Also Called: E L I
1695 Cactus Rd, San Diego (92154-8102)
PHONE..................619 671-0100
Ray Irani, *President*
Miguel Reyes, *COO*
James Domholt, *Vice Pres*
Coral Pacheco, *Administration*
Moises Chilchoa, *MIS Staff*
▲ EMP: 400
SQ FT: 150,000
SALES (est): 201.9MM
SALES (corp-wide): 322.9MM **Privately Held**
WEB: www.energylabs.com
SIC: 3585 Heating & air conditioning combination units
HQ: Vertiv Corporation
1050 Dearborn Dr
Columbus OH 43085
614 888-0246

(P-15954)
ENLINK GEOENERGY SERVICES INC
2630 Homestead Pl, Rancho Dominguez
(90220-5610)
PHONE..................424 242-1200
Mark Mizrahi, *President*
Howard Johnson, *CIO*
EMP: 46
SQ FT: 12,000
SALES (est): 6.6MM **Privately Held**
WEB: www.enlinkgeoenergy.com
SIC: 3585 Heat pumps, electric

(P-15955)
ENVIRO-INTERCEPT INC
7327 Varna Ave Unit 5, North Hollywood
(91605-4183)
PHONE..................818 982-6063
Fred Bonamici, *President*
Jim Watt, *Shareholder*
Carlos Alverado, *Vice Pres*
EMP: 12
SQ FT: 11,500
SALES (est): 1.7MM **Privately Held**
SIC: 3585 Refrigeration & heating equipment

(P-15956)
EVAPCO INC
Also Called: Evapco West
1900 W Almond Ave, Madera (93637-5208)
PHONE..................559 673-2207
Steve Levake, *Manager*
John McCann, *Maint Spvr*
EMP: 150
SQ FT: 88,250
SALES (corp-wide): 384.1MM **Privately Held**
WEB: www.evapco.com
SIC: 3585 Air conditioning units, complete: domestic or industrial; refrigeration equipment, complete
PA: Evapco, Inc.
5151 Allendale Ln
Taneytown MD 21787
410 756-2600

(P-15957)
EVERIDGE INC
Also Called: Thermalrite
8886 White Oak Ave, Rancho Cucamonga
(91730-5106)
PHONE..................909 605-6419
Chris Kahler, *Branch Mgr*
EMP: 50 **Privately Held**
WEB: www.thermalrite.com
SIC: 3585 Refrigeration & heating equipment
PA: Everidge, Inc.
15600 37th Ave N Ste 100
Plymouth MN 55446

(P-15958)
FLUID INDUSTRIAL MFG INC
374 S Milpitas Blvd, Milpitas (95035-5421)
PHONE..................408 782-9900
Kerry Kirchenbauer, *President*
EMP: 23
SALES (est): 4.5MM **Privately Held**
WEB: www.fluidindmfg.com
SIC: 3585 Refrigeration equipment, complete

(P-15959)
HEAT TRANSFER PDTS GROUP LLC
Also Called: Htpg
8101 E Kaiser Blvd # 110, Anaheim
(92808-2661)
PHONE..................714 529-1935
Joe Sklencar,
J R Jones,
Chris Peel,
▼ EMP: 330
SALES (est): 38.1MM **Privately Held**
SIC: 3585 Refrigeration equipment, complete
HQ: American Refrigeration, Inc.
142 W 57th St Fl 17
New York NY 10019

(P-15960)
HILL PHOENIX INC
Walk-Ins Western Operations
14680 Monte Vista Ave, Chino
(91710-5744)
PHONE..................909 592-8830
Sangyup Steve Lee, *Manager*
EMP: 28
SALES (corp-wide): 7.8B **Publicly Held**
SIC: 3585 Parts for heating, cooling & refrigerating equipment
HQ: Hill Phoenix, Inc.
2016 Gees Mill Rd Ne
Conyers GA 30013

(P-15961)
HUSSMANN CORPORATION
13770 Ramona Ave, Chino (91710-5423)
P.O. Box 5133 (91708-5133)
PHONE..................909 590-4910
Mike Gleason, *General Mgr*
Nancy McElwee Taylor, *Manager*
EMP: 350
SALES (corp-wide): 74.9B **Privately Held**
WEB: www.hussmann.com
SIC: 3585 7623 Refrigeration & heating equipment; refrigeration service & repair
HQ: Hussmann Corporation
12999 St Charles Rock Rd
Bridgeton MO 63044
314 291-2000

(P-15962)
J P LAMBORN CO (PA)
Also Called: J P L
3663 E Wawona Ave, Fresno (93725-9236)
PHONE..................559 650-2120
John P Lamborn Jr, *CEO*
Pam Lamborn, *Admin Sec*
Chad Ward, *Technology*
Deeane Eltrich, *Accountant*
Dennis Carey, *Controller*
◆ EMP: 155 EST: 1961
SQ FT: 125,000
SALES (est): 53.4MM **Privately Held**
WEB: www.jplflex.com
SIC: 3585 Heating & air conditioning combination units

(P-15963)
KOCH FILTER CORPORATION
10290 Birtcher Dr, Mira Loma
(91752-1827)
PHONE....................951 361-9017
Dan Campbell, *General Mgr*
EMP: 15 **Privately Held**
WEB: www.kochfilter.com
SIC: 3585 Refrigeration & heating equipment
HQ: Koch Filter Corporation
8401 Air Commerce Dr
Louisville KY 40219
502 634-4796

(P-15964)
KOOLFOG INC (PA)
31290 Plantation Dr, Thousand Palms
(92276-6604)
PHONE....................760 321-9203
Bryan Roe, *President*
EMP: 11
SQ FT: 4,000
SALES (est): 3.1MM **Privately Held**
WEB: www.koolfog.com
SIC: 3585 7819 Humidifiers & dehumidifiers; visual effects production

(P-15965)
L3 CINCINNATI ELECTRONICS CORP
150 N San Gabriel Blvd, Pasadena
(91107-7109)
PHONE....................626 395-7460
Dan Kuo, *Manager*
Lizbeth Mollica, *Buyer*
EMP: 20
SALES (corp-wide): 9.5B **Publicly Held**
WEB: www.cinele.com
SIC: 3585 Room coolers, portable
HQ: L3 Cincinnati Electronics Corporation
7500 Innovation Way
Mason OH 45040
513 573-6100

(P-15966)
LENNOX
4000 Hamner Ave, Eastvale (91752-1022)
PHONE....................800 953-6669
EMP: 13
SALES (est): 2.1MM **Privately Held**
SIC: 3585 Refrigeration & heating equipment

(P-15967)
LENNOX INDUSTRIES INC
2221 Eastman Ave, Oxnard (93030-5185)
PHONE....................805 288-8200
Genero De Leon, *Branch Mgr*
EMP: 148
SALES (corp-wide): 3.8B **Publicly Held**
SIC: 3585 Furnaces, warm air: electric; air conditioning units, complete: domestic or industrial
HQ: Lennox Industries Inc.
2100 Lake Park Blvd
Richardson TX 75080
972 497-5000

(P-15968)
LMW ENTERPRISES LLC
Also Called: Lrc Coil Company
12309 Telegraph Rd, Santa Fe Springs
(90670-3309)
PHONE....................562 944-1969
Michael Williams,
George Aburto,
Linda Williams,
Chester Schaffer, *Mng Member*
▲ EMP: 35 EST: 2010
SQ FT: 35,000
SALES (est): 8MM **Privately Held**
WEB: www.lrccoil.com
SIC: 3585 Refrigeration equipment, complete; condensers, refrigeration; evaporative condensers, heat transfer equipment

(P-15969)
MARSAL PACKAGING & RFRGN
931 S Cypress St, La Habra (90631-6833)
PHONE....................714 812-6775
Salvatore Titone, *Principal*
Sal Titone, *President*
EMP: 16

SALES (est): 1.2MM **Privately Held**
SIC: 3585 Refrigeration equipment, complete

(P-15970)
MEE INDUSTRIES INC (PA)
16021 Adelante St, Irwindale (91702-3255)
PHONE....................626 359-4550
Thomas Rupert Mee III, *CEO*
Darcy Sloane, *President*
Mario Madrid, *Project Mgr*
Berklie Oscarson, *Project Mgr*
Inna Romanova, *Project Mgr*
▲ EMP: 10 EST: 1969
SQ FT: 26,000
SALES (est): 12.4MM **Privately Held**
WEB: www.meefog.com
SIC: 3585 0711 Humidifying equipment, except portable; soil preparation services

(P-15971)
MESTEK INC
Also Called: Anemostat Products
1220 E Watson Center Rd, Carson
(90745-4206)
PHONE....................310 835-7500
Chang Hung, *Plant Mgr*
Hari Thacker, *Controller*
Ben Cortez, *Mktg Dir*
Tim McCully, *Director*
Blanca Olvera, *Manager*
EMP: 200
SALES (corp-wide): 669.8MM **Privately Held**
SIC: 3585 3549 3542 3354 Heating equipment, complete; metalworking machinery; punching, shearing & bending machines; shapes, extruded aluminum; mainframe computers; manufactured hardware (general)
PA: Mestek, Inc.
260 N Elm St
Westfield MA 01085
413 568-9571

(P-15972)
MICRO MATIC USA INC
19761 Bahama St 19791, Northridge
(91324-3304)
PHONE....................818 701-9765
Torben Toffpegaard, *President*
Pamela Baldwin, *Human Res Mgr*
EMP: 20
SALES (corp-wide): 323.5MM **Privately Held**
SIC: 3585 Refrigeration & heating equipment
HQ: Micro Matic Usa, Inc.
2386 Simon Ct
Brooksville FL 34604
352 544-1081

(P-15973)
MYDAX INC
12260 Shale Ridge Ln # 4, Auburn
(95602-8400)
PHONE....................530 888-6662
Richard S Frankel, *CEO*
Gary Kramer, *President*
Thomas Spesick, *Vice Pres*
Mike Seibert, *Sales Executive*
Sandra Smith, *Sls & Mktg Exec*
EMP: 19
SQ FT: 15,000
SALES (est): 2.5MM **Privately Held**
WEB: www.mydax.com
SIC: 3585 Refrigeration equipment, complete

(P-15974)
R E MICHEL COMPANY LLC
Also Called: R E Michel
155 W Victoria St, Long Beach
(90805-2162)
PHONE....................310 885-9820
EMP: 24
SALES (corp-wide): 804MM **Privately Held**
SIC: 3585 Refrigeration equipment, complete
PA: R. E. Michel Company, Llc
1 Re Michel Dr
Glen Burnie MD 21060
410 760-4000

(P-15975)
R-COLD INC
1221 S G St, Perris (92570-2477)
PHONE....................951 436-5476
Michael Mulcahy, *President*
Ernest Gaston, *CFO*
Joshua Elder, *Sales Staff*
Karleen Hart, *Relations*
EMP: 65
SQ FT: 28,000
SALES (est): 16.1MM **Privately Held**
WEB: www.r-cold.com
SIC: 3585 1541 Refrigeration & heating equipment; industrial buildings & warehouses

(P-15976)
RAHN INDUSTRIES INCORPORATED (PA)
2630 Pacific Park Dr, Whittier (90601-1611)
PHONE....................562 908-0680
John Hancock, *President*
Jeff Meier, *Vice Pres*
Claudia Maytum, *Admin Sec*
Alberto Saucedo, *Sales Engr*
▲ EMP: 60
SQ FT: 25,000
SALES (est): 13.5MM **Privately Held**
WEB: www.rahnindustries.com
SIC: 3585 Refrigeration & heating equipment

(P-15977)
REFRIGERATOR MANUFACTURERS LLC
Also Called: Airdyne Refrigeration
17018 Edwards Rd, Cerritos (90703-2422)
PHONE....................562 926-2006
Tony Bedi, *President*
EMP: 47
SALES (est): 6.8MM **Privately Held**
SIC: 3585 Condensers, refrigeration

(P-15978)
SPRIZZI DRINK CO
897 Via Lata Ste C, Colton (92324-3922)
PHONE....................909 528-7779
Michael Breault, *CEO*
EMP: 10
SALES (est): 183K
SALES (corp-wide): 408.8K **Publicly Held**
SIC: 3585 Cold drink dispensing equipment (not coin-operated)
PA: Upper Street Marketing, Inc.
11445 E Via Linda
Scottsdale AZ 85259
844 535-8777

(P-15979)
TAYLOR COML FOODSERVICE INC
Tyler Refrigeration
221 S Berry St, Brea (92821-4829)
PHONE....................714 255-7200
Phil Herman, *Controller*
EMP: 40
SQ FT: 55,605
SALES (corp-wide): 2.3B **Publicly Held**
WEB: www.ccr.carrier.com
SIC: 3585 Cabinets, show & display, refrigerated
HQ: Taylor Commercial Foodservice Inc.
750 N Blackhawk Blvd
Rockton IL 61072
815 624-8333

(P-15980)
TEAM AIR INC (PA)
Also Called: Team Air Conditioning Eqp
12771 Brown Ave, Riverside (92509-1831)
PHONE....................909 823-1957
Thirusenthil Nathan, *President*
Oliver Corbala, *Vice Pres*
EMP: 35
SALES (est): 12.3MM **Privately Held**
SIC: 3585 Air conditioning equipment, complete

(P-15981)
THREE STAR RFRGN ENGRG INC
Also Called: Kool Star
21720 S Wilmington Ave # 309, Long
Beach (90810-1641)
PHONE....................310 327-9090
James Pak, *President*
William So, *CFO*
Kyung Lee, *Admin Sec*
◆ EMP: 50
SQ FT: 68,000
SALES (est): 6.4MM **Privately Held**
WEB: www.koolstar.com
SIC: 3585 4222 Air conditioning condensers & condensing units; condensers, refrigeration; refrigerated warehousing & storage

(P-15982)
TOM BENGARD RANCH INC
375 W Market St, Salinas (93901-1423)
PHONE....................831 758-5770
John Herrington, *Branch Mgr*
EMP: 12
SALES (corp-wide): 11.6MM **Privately Held**
SIC: 3585 Parts for heating, cooling & refrigerating equipment
PA: Tom Bengard Ranch, Inc.
375 W Market St
Salinas CA 93901
831 422-9021

(P-15983)
TRANE US INC
1601 S De Anza Blvd 235, Cupertino
(95014-5347)
PHONE....................408 257-5212
Tyler Clemmer, *Branch Mgr*
EMP: 15 **Privately Held**
SIC: 3585 Refrigeration & heating equipment
HQ: Trane U.S. Inc.
3600 Pammel Creek Rd
La Crosse WI 54601
608 787-2000

(P-15984)
TRANE US INC
310 Soquel Way, Sunnyvale (94085-4101)
PHONE....................408 481-3600
Don Druyanoff, *Manager*
EMP: 150 **Privately Held**
SIC: 3585 Refrigeration & heating equipment
HQ: Trane U.S. Inc.
3600 Pammel Creek Rd
La Crosse WI 54601
608 787-2000

(P-15985)
TRANE US INC
Also Called: Southern California Trane
3253 E Imperial Hwy, Brea (92821-6722)
PHONE....................626 913-7123
John Clark, *Branch Mgr*
EMP: 100 **Privately Held**
SIC: 3585 Heating & air conditioning combination units
HQ: Trane U.S. Inc.
3600 Pammel Creek Rd
La Crosse WI 54601
608 787-2000

(P-15986)
TRANE US INC
20450 E Walnut Dr N, Walnut
(91789-2921)
PHONE....................626 913-7913
Tyler Clemmer, *District Mgr*
Tim Dorsey, *Controller*
Louise Rasmussen, *Human Res Mgr*
Don La Marr, *Sales Staff*
EMP: 23 **Privately Held**
SIC: 3585 Refrigeration & heating equipment
HQ: Trane U.S. Inc.
3600 Pammel Creek Rd
La Crosse WI 54601
608 787-2000

(P-15987)
TRANE US INC
2222 Kansas Ave Ste C, Riverside
(92507-2635)
PHONE...................................951 801-6020
EMP: 62 Privately Held
SIC: 3585 Refrigeration & heating equipment
HQ: Trane U.S. Inc.
    3600 Pammel Creek Rd
    La Crosse WI 54601
    608 787-2000

(P-15988)
TRANE US INC
890 Service St Ste A, San Jose
(95112-1374)
PHONE...................................408 437-0390
EMP: 62 Privately Held
SIC: 3585 Refrigeration & heating equipment
HQ: Trane U.S. Inc.
    3600 Pammel Creek Rd
    La Crosse WI 54601
    608 787-2000

(P-15989)
TRANE US INC
1930 E Carson St Ste 101, Carson
(90810-1246)
PHONE...................................310 971-4555
EMP: 62 Privately Held
SIC: 3585 Refrigeration & heating equipment
HQ: Trane U.S. Inc.
    3600 Pammel Creek Rd
    La Crosse WI 54601
    608 787-2000

(P-15990)
TRANE US INC
3565 Corporate Ct Fl 1, San Diego
(92123-2415)
PHONE...................................858 292-0833
Tyler Clemmer, *Branch Mgr*
Lauren Stephens, *Marketing Staff*
EMP: 50 Privately Held
SIC: 3585 Refrigeration & heating equipment
HQ: Trane U.S. Inc.
    3600 Pammel Creek Rd
    La Crosse WI 54601
    608 787-2000

(P-15991)
TRANE US INC
3026 N Bus Park Ave # 104, Fresno
(93727-8647)
PHONE...................................559 271-4625
Tyler Clemmer, *Manager*
Cindy Taft, *Project Mgr*
EMP: 20 Privately Held
SIC: 3585 Refrigeration & heating equipment
HQ: Trane U.S. Inc.
    3600 Pammel Creek Rd
    La Crosse WI 54601
    608 787-2000

(P-15992)
TRMC SALE CORPORATION
4215 E Airport Dr, Ontario (91761-1565)
PHONE...................................800 290-7073
Joshua Klein, *President*
EMP: 56
SQ FT: 50,000
SALES: 5MM Privately Held
SIC: 3585 Room coolers, portable

(P-15993)
TRUMED SYSTEMS INCORPORATED
4350 Executive Dr Ste 120, San Diego
(92121-2140)
PHONE...................................844 878-6331
Jesper Jensen, *President*
Jim Martindale, *Vice Pres*
Joe Milkovits, *CTO*
Jacob Servantes, *Manager*
Lexie Kennedy, *Transportation*
EMP: 24
SQ FT: 2,000
SALES: 1MM Privately Held
SIC: 3585 5078 Refrigeration & heating equipment; commercial refrigeration equipment

(P-15994)
TURBO COIL INC
1532 Sinaloa Ave, Pasadena (91104-2744)
PHONE...................................626 644-6254
Hector Delgadillo, *CEO*
EMP: 12
SQ FT: 2,000
SALES (est): 1.1MM Privately Held
SIC: 3585 Compressors for refrigeration & air conditioning equipment

(P-15995)
TURBO REFRIGERATION SYSTEMS
1740 Evergreen St, Duarte (91010-2845)
PHONE...................................626 599-9777
Hector Delgadillo, *CEO*
Jose Carbajal, *Principal*
Roberta Delgadillo, *Principal*
EMP: 26
SQ FT: 4,000
SALES (est): 1.5MM Privately Held
SIC: 3585 Condensers, refrigeration

(P-15996)
UTILITY REFRIGERATOR
12160 Sherman Way, North Hollywood
(91605-5501)
P.O. Box 570782, Tarzana (91357-0782)
PHONE...................................818 764-6200
Michael Michrowski, *President*
Marshall Brown, *Officer*
Russ Geiger, *Sales Staff*
▲ **EMP: 15**
SALES (est): 2.5MM Privately Held
SIC: 3585 Parts for heating, cooling & refrigerating equipment

(P-15997)
VEGE-MIST INC
Also Called: Alco Designs
407 E Redondo Beach Blvd, Gardena
(90248-2312)
PHONE...................................310 353-2300
Samuel Cohen, *CEO*
Nava Cohen, *Sales Associate*
Dick Warden, *Sales Associate*
Antonio Ruvalcaba, *Sales Staff*
Dick Warde, *Sales Staff*
▲ **EMP: 24**
SQ FT: 8,000
SALES (est): 9.1MM Privately Held
WEB: www.alcodesigns.com
SIC: 3585 2541 5074 Humidifying equipment, except portable; store & office display cases & fixtures; water purification equipment

(P-15998)
VENSTAR INC
9250 Owensmouth Ave, Chatsworth
(91311-5853)
PHONE...................................818 341-8760
Steve Dushane, *President*
▲ **EMP: 15**
SALES (est): 6.3MM Privately Held
WEB: www.venstarusa.com
SIC: 3585 Refrigeration & heating equipment

(P-15999)
VINOTHEQUE WINE CELLARS
1738 E Alpine Ave, Stockton (95205-2505)
PHONE...................................209 466-9463
Thomas R Schneider, *CEO*
Franklin Pfaller-Martin, *Prdtn Mgr*
Manuel Keo, *Sales Mgr*
Adam Eigenberger, *Accounts Exec*
▼ **EMP: 16 EST:** 1999
SQ FT: 30,000
SALES (est): 5.5MM Privately Held
WEB: www.vinotheque.com
SIC: 3585 Refrigeration equipment, complete

(P-16000)
WESTAIRE ENGINEERING INC
5820 S Alameda St, Vernon (90058-3432)
PHONE...................................323 587-3347
Vazgen Galadjian, *President*
Shane Bekian, *Vice Pres*
Kevin Galadjian, *Vice Pres*
▲ **EMP: 15**
SQ FT: 50,000

SALES (est): 1.7MM Privately Held
SIC: 3585 5075 Air conditioning units, complete: domestic or industrial; ventilating equipment & supplies

(P-16001)
WHITES HVAC SERVICES INC
131 E Knotts St, Nipomo (93444-9423)
P.O. Box 365 (93444-0365)
PHONE...................................805 801-0167
Mike White, *President*
Georgia White, *CFO*
EMP: 11
SALES: 300K Privately Held
SIC: 3585 7389 Heating & air conditioning combination units;

(P-16002)
WILLIAMS FURNACE CO (HQ)
Also Called: Williams Comfort Products
250 W Laurel St, Colton (92324-1435)
PHONE...................................562 450-3602
Michael Markowich, *President*
Joseph Sum, *Treasurer*
Ruth Ann Davis, *Vice Pres*
James Gidwitz, *Vice Pres*
Jerry Miller, *Vice Pres*
◆ **EMP: 173**
SQ FT: 400,000
SALES (est): 34.1MM
SALES (corp-wide): 152.8MM Publicly Held
SIC: 3585 3433 Refrigeration & heating equipment; heating equipment, except electric
PA: Continental Materials Corporation
    440 S La Salle St # 3100
    Chicago IL 60605
    312 541-7200

(P-16003)
ZTECH
11481 Sunrise Gold Cir # 1, Rancho Cordova (95742-6545)
PHONE...................................916 635-6784
Michael Kuhlmann, *Owner*
EMP: 15
SQ FT: 9,000
SALES (est): 940K Privately Held
WEB: www.resconsys.com
SIC: 3585 5075 Parts for heating, cooling & refrigerating equipment; ventilating equipment & supplies

---

3589 Service Ind Machines, NEC

(P-16004)
AATECH
15342 Valencia Ave, Fontana
(92335-3284)
P.O. Box 366 (92334-0366)
PHONE...................................909 854-3200
Jerry McAuley, *President*
Darlene McAuley, *Vice Pres*
EMP: 22
SQ FT: 12,000
SALES (est): 7.9MM Privately Held
WEB: www.aatechwater.com
SIC: 3589 Water treatment equipment, industrial

(P-16005)
ACM RESEARCH INC
42307 Osgood Rd Ste I, Fremont
(94539-5062)
PHONE...................................510 445-3700
David H Wang, *Ch of Bd*
Min Xu, *CFO*
Lisa Feng, *Officer*
Mark McKechnie, *VP Finance*
EMP: 187
SALES: 36.5MM Privately Held
SIC: 3589 Commercial cleaning equipment

(P-16006)
ADS WATER INC
12 N Altadena Dr, Pasadena (91107-3345)
PHONE...................................415 448-6266
Adam Stein, *CEO*
EMP: 10 EST: 2014
SQ FT: 5,000

SALES: 8MM Privately Held
SIC: 3589 Water treatment equipment, industrial
PA: Advantageous Systems Llc
    525 S Hewitt St
    Los Angeles CA 90013
    -

(P-16007)
ADVANCED UV INC
16350 Manning Way, Cerritos
(90703-2224)
PHONE...................................562 407-0299
Kiyomitsu Kevin Toma, *CEO*
Kiyo Toma, *Business Anlyst*
▲ **EMP: 42 EST:** 1996
SQ FT: 30,000
SALES (est): 10.7MM Privately Held
WEB: www.advanceduv.com
SIC: 3589 Water purification equipment, household type; water treatment equipment, industrial

(P-16008)
AMIAD USA INC
Also Called: Amiad Filtration Systems
1251 Maulhardt Ave, Oxnard (93030-7990)
PHONE...................................805 988-3323
Tom Akehurst, *President*
Issac Orlans, *Shareholder*
Amos Shalev, *Bd of Directors*
Omry Levin, *Business Mgr*
Wendy Paul, *Opers Staff*
▲ **EMP: 35**
SQ FT: 30,000
SALES (est): 8.7MM
SALES (corp-wide): 3.7B Privately Held
WEB: www.amiadusa.com
SIC: 3589 Water treatment equipment, industrial
HQ: Amiad Water Systems Ltd
    Kibbutz
    Amiad 12335
    469 095-00

(P-16009)
APPLIED MEMBRANES INC (PA)
Also Called: Wateranywhere
2450 Business Park Dr, Vista (92081-8847)
PHONE...................................760 727-3711
Gulshan K Dhawan, *CEO*
◆ **EMP: 100**
SQ FT: 55,000
SALES (est): 30.2MM Privately Held
WEB: www.appliedmembranes.com
SIC: 3589 5074 Water purification equipment, household type; water heaters & purification equipment

(P-16010)
AQUA MAN INC (PA)
Also Called: Aqua Man Service
2568 Turquoise Cir, Newbury Park
(91320-1211)
P.O. Box 3906, Westlake Village (91359-0906)
PHONE...................................805 499-5707
Ray Hinton Sr, *President*
EMP: 10
SQ FT: 20,000
SALES (est): 1.7MM Privately Held
SIC: 3589 Water purification equipment, household type

(P-16011)
AQUAFINE CORPORATION (HQ)
29010 Avenue Paine, Valencia
(91355-4198)
PHONE...................................661 257-4770
Roberta Veloz, *Chairman*
Michael Murphy, *President*
Tomas Olivas, *Sales Staff*
Jiawei Zhang, *Manager*
Kyaw K Lwin, *Associate*
◆ **EMP: 75**
SQ FT: 100,000
SALES (est): 14MM
SALES (corp-wide): 18.3B Publicly Held
SIC: 3589 Water treatment equipment, industrial
PA: Danaher Corporation
    2200 Penn Ave Nw Ste 800w
    Washington DC 20037
    202 828-0850

(P-16012)
AQUEOUS TECHNOLOGIES CORP
1678 N Maple St, Corona (92880-1706)
PHONE..................................909 944-7771
Michael Konrad, *CEO*
Rosendo Ramirez, *Purch Mgr*
▲ EMP: 23
SQ FT: 15,000
SALES (est): 5.8MM **Privately Held**
WEB: www.aqueoustech.com
SIC: 3589 3829 5084 7699 High pressure cleaning equipment; water treatment equipment, industrial; physical property testing equipment; cleaning equipment, high pressure, sand or steam; industrial machinery & equipment repair

(P-16013)
AQUEOUS VETS
288 Jasmine Way, Danville (94506-4747)
PHONE..................................951 764-9384
Robert G Craw, *President*
Charles Wells, *Vice Pres*
Sarah Johnson, *General Mgr*
Chris Perry, *Mfg Staff*
EMP: 10
SALES (est): 2.1MM **Privately Held**
SIC: 3589 Sewage & water treatment equipment

(P-16014)
AUTO WASH CONCEPTS INC
11769 Telegraph Rd, Santa Fe Springs (90670-3657)
PHONE..................................562 948-2575
Douglas Wagner, *President*
Mimi Wagner, *Vice Pres*
EMP: 12
SQ FT: 5,400
SALES (est): 2.1MM **Privately Held**
SIC: 3589 5087 Car washing machinery; carwash equipment & supplies

(P-16015)
AXEON WATER TECHNOLOGIES
40980 County Center Dr # 110, Temecula (92591-6002)
PHONE..................................760 723-5417
Augustin R Pavel, *President*
Jeanette Pavel, *Corp Secy*
Patricia Hinrichs, *Controller*
Ryan Balogh, *Buyer*
Trish Caudillo, *Opers Mgr*
◆ EMP: 85
SQ FT: 47,000
SALES: 15.8MM **Privately Held**
WEB: www.roultratec.com
SIC: 3589 5999 Water filters & softeners, household type; water purification equipment, household type; water purification equipment

(P-16016)
B&W CUSTOM RESTAURANT EQP
541 E Jamie Ave, La Habra (90631-6842)
PHONE..................................714 578-0332
Nathan Bojorquez, *President*
EMP: 20
SALES (est): 5.2MM **Privately Held**
WEB: www.bwcustom.com
SIC: 3589 8711 2599 Cooking equipment, commercial; industrial engineers; carts, restaurant equipment

(P-16017)
BAKER FILTRATION
Also Called: Baker Tanks
2700 California Ave, Pittsburg (94565-4100)
PHONE..................................925 473-9659
EMP: 22
SALES (est): 3.8MM **Privately Held**
SIC: 3589 5074

(P-16018)
BARHENA INC
Also Called: Adamation
1085 Bixby Dr, Hacienda Heights (91745-1704)
PHONE..................................888 383-8800
EMP: 25 EST: 1957
SQ FT: 45,000

SALES (est): 2.7MM **Privately Held**
WEB: www.adamationinc.com
SIC: 3589 3952
PA: Flow Grinding Corp.
70 Conn St
Woburn MA 01801
-

(P-16019)
BAUER INTERNATIONAL CORP
9251 Irvine Blvd, Irvine (92618-1645)
PHONE..................................714 259-9800
Ernesto Cartojano, *CEO*
Mounia Dnoubi, *Project Engr*
John Livingston, *Business Mgr*
Ed Victoria, *Production*
EMP: 10
SALES (est): 1.8MM **Privately Held**
SIC: 3589 Water treatment equipment, industrial

(P-16020)
BLUE DESERT INTERNATIONAL INC
Also Called: Hydro Quip
510 N Sheridan St Ste A, Corona (92880-2024)
PHONE..................................951 273-7575
Christopher W Kuttig, *President*
Frank Briese, *Vice Pres*
Mike Staab, *Info Tech Mgr*
▲ EMP: 80
SQ FT: 31,000
SALES (est): 16.6MM **Privately Held**
WEB: www.hydroquip.com
SIC: 3589 Swimming pool filter & water conditioning systems

(P-16021)
CENTRAL COAST WATER AUTHORITY
5250 Annlope Rd, Cholame (93461)
P.O. Box 505, Shandon (93461-0505)
PHONE..................................805 463-2122
Darin Dargatc, *Manager*
EMP: 13 **Privately Held**
WEB: www.ccwa.com
SIC: 3589 9511 Sewage & water treatment equipment; air, water & solid waste management
PA: Central Coast Water Authority
255 Industrial Way
Buellton CA 93427

(P-16022)
CHEMICAL METHODS ASSOC LLC (DH)
Also Called: CMA Dish Machines
12700 Knott St, Garden Grove (92841-3938)
PHONE..................................714 898-8781
Fred G Palmer, *President*
Nancy Guzman, *General Mgr*
Candy Wagers, *Executive Asst*
Danny Abeleda, *Info Tech Dir*
Joseph Nudel, *Design Engr*
▲ EMP: 55
SQ FT: 50,000
SALES (est): 14.2MM **Privately Held**
WEB: www.cmadishmachines.com
SIC: 3589 Dishwashing machines, commercial
HQ: Ali Group North America Corporation
101 Corporate Woods Pkwy
Vernon Hills IL 60061
847 215-6565

(P-16023)
CHEMICAL TECHNOLOGIES INTL INC
Also Called: CTI
2747 Merc Dr Ste 200, Rancho Cordova (95742)
P.O. Box 968 (95741-0968)
PHONE..................................916 638-1315
Clint Townsend, *CEO*
Risa Townsend, *Corp Secy*
Diane Corey, *Human Resources*
April Weister, *Manager*
▲ EMP: 18
SQ FT: 50,000

SALES (est): 3.8MM **Privately Held**
SIC: 3589 2842 Commercial cleaning equipment; cleaning or polishing preparations

(P-16024)
CITY OF DELANO
Also Called: Delano Waste Water Treatment
1107 Lytle Ave, Delano (93215-9389)
PHONE..................................661 721-3352
Bill Hylton, *Manager*
EMP: 35 **Privately Held**
SIC: 3589 Water treatment equipment, industrial
PA: City Of Delano
1015 11th Ave
Delano CA 93215
661 721-3300

(P-16025)
CITY OF RIVERSIDE
Also Called: Water Treatment Plant
5950 Acorn St, Riverside (92504-1036)
PHONE..................................951 351-6140
Richard Pallante, *General Mgr*
EMP: 100 **Privately Held**
SIC: 3589 9111 Water treatment equipment, industrial; mayors' offices
PA: City Of Riverside
3900 Main St Fl 7
Riverside CA 92522
951 826-5311

(P-16026)
CLARITY H2O LLC
752 Pomelo Dr, Vista (92081-6307)
PHONE..................................619 993-4780
Peter Petersen, *CEO*
D Edward McGawley, *COO*
EMP: 12
SQ FT: 25,000
SALES: 3MM **Privately Held**
SIC: 3589 Water treatment equipment, industrial

(P-16027)
CLEAN WATER TECHNOLOGY INC
Also Called: CWT
151 W 135th St, Los Angeles (90061-1645)
PHONE..................................310 380-4648
Ariel Lechter, *CEO*
Colette Tassin, *Vice Pres*
Gerald Friedman, *Admin Sec*
Ray Guthrie, *Project Mgr*
Jonathan Salazar, *Project Mgr*
▲ EMP: 51 EST: 1996
SQ FT: 30,000
SALES (est): 15.1MM
SALES (corp-wide): 222.7MM **Privately Held**
WEB: www.cleanwatertech.com
SIC: 3589 Water treatment equipment, industrial
PA: Marvin Engineering Co., Inc.
261 W Beach Ave
Inglewood CA 90302
310 674-5030

(P-16028)
CLEAR WATER CORPORATION INC
14738 Oxnard St, Van Nuys (91411-3121)
PHONE..................................818 765-8293
Yarvin Gilboa, *President*
EMP: 12
SQ FT: 10,000
SALES (est): 2.4MM **Privately Held**
SIC: 3589 Water treatment equipment, industrial

(P-16029)
CM BREWING TECHNOLOGIES
Also Called: Ss Brewtech
13681 Newport Ave 8-261, Tustin (92780-4689)
PHONE..................................888 391-9990
Mitchell Thomson, *CEO*
EMP: 15
SALES: 12MM **Privately Held**
SIC: 3589 5046 Coffee brewing equipment; coffee brewing equipment & supplies

(P-16030)
COMCO INC
2151 N Lincoln St, Burbank (91504-3392)
PHONE..................................818 333-8500
Colin Weightman, *President*
Anders Pineiro, *Info Tech Mgr*
Carolyn Nouar, *Controller*
Sally Salazar, *Opers Mgr*
Ozzy Cuellar, *Production*
EMP: 36
SQ FT: 12,500
SALES (est): 8.9MM **Privately Held**
WEB: www.microabrasive.com
SIC: 3589 3291 Sandblasting equipment; abrasive products

(P-16031)
COMPASS WATER SOLUTIONS INC (PA)
15542 Mosher Ave, Tustin (92780-6425)
PHONE..................................949 222-5777
Thomas Farshler, *CEO*
Bill Tidmore, *CFO*
▲ EMP: 80
SQ FT: 3,000
SALES (est): 100MM **Privately Held**
WEB: www.cworldwater.com
SIC: 3589 Water treatment equipment, industrial

(P-16032)
COOK KING INC
15120 Desman Rd, La Mirada (90638-5737)
PHONE..................................714 739-0502
R C Miller, *President*
Glenna Miller, *Vice Pres*
EMP: 20
SQ FT: 15,000
SALES (est): 2.1MM **Privately Held**
SIC: 3589 Cooking equipment, commercial

(P-16033)
DE NORA WATER TECHNOLOGIES INC
1230 Rosecrans Ave # 300, Manhattan Beach (90266-2477)
PHONE..................................310 618-9700
Marwan Nesicolaci, *Vice Pres*
Wayne De Freest, *Purch Agent*
Steven Hinkle, *Manager*
EMP: 100 **Privately Held**
SIC: 3589 Water treatment equipment, industrial
HQ: De Nora Water Technologies, Inc.
3000 Advance Ln
Colmar PA 18915
215 997-4000

(P-16034)
DEL OZONE HOLDING COMPANY INC
Also Called: Del Industries
3580 Sueldo St, San Luis Obispo (93401-7338)
P.O. Box 4509 (93403-4509)
PHONE..................................805 541-1601
Mike Hawkins, *President*
Rick Totah, *CFO*
Joel Peterson, *Treasurer*
Dana Nelson, *Sales Associate*
Joe Mlnarik, *Marketing Staff*
◆ EMP: 42
SALES: 10.6MM
SALES (corp-wide): 80.2MM **Privately Held**
WEB: www.delozone.com
SIC: 3589 7389 8422 6719 Water purification equipment, household type; swimming pool & hot tub service & maintenance; water softener service; aquariums & zoological gardens; investment holding companies, except banks
PA: Custom Molded Products, Llc
36 Herring Rd
Newnan GA 30265
770 632-7112

(P-16035)
DYNAMIC COOKING SYSTEMS INC
Also Called: Fisher & Paykel
695 Town Center Dr # 180, Costa Mesa (92626-1924)
PHONE..................................714 372-7000

▲ = Import ▼=Export
◆ =Import/Export

Laurence Mawhinney, *CEO*
Marty Carrillo, *Bd of Directors*
Andrew Cooke, *Vice Pres*
Nick Derosa, *Vice Pres*
Esau Ramirez, *Executive*
▲ **EMP:** 700
SQ FT: 140,000
SALES (est): 118.9MM
SALES (corp-wide): 7.8K **Privately Held**
WEB: www.dcsappliances.com
SIC: 3589 Cooking equipment, commercial
HQ: Fisher & Paykel Appliances Usa Holdings Inc.
695 Town Center Dr # 180
Costa Mesa CA 92626
888 936-7872

(P-16036)
DYNGLOBAL CALIFORNIA CORP
1139 Baker St, Costa Mesa (92626-4114)
PHONE..................................949 584-6198
Albert V Wright, *CEO*
EMP: 30
SALES: 50MM **Privately Held**
SIC: 3589 3312 3674 Water purification equipment, household type; armor plate; solar cells

(P-16037)
ENAQUA
1350 Specialty Dr Ste D, Vista (92081-8565)
PHONE..................................760 599-2644
Manoj Kumar Jhawar, *CEO*
Mark Maki, *President*
Rudra Mishra, *CFO*
Paul Stewart, *Engineer*
Rick McIntyre, *Manager*
▲ **EMP:** 30
SQ FT: 26,000
SALES (est): 7.5MM
SALES (corp-wide): 4B **Privately Held**
WEB: www.enaqua.com
SIC: 3589 Water purification equipment, household type
HQ: Grundfos Ab
Lunnagardsgatan 6
Molndal 431 9
771 322-300

(P-16038)
ENGINEERED FOOD SYSTEMS
2490 Anselmo Dr, Corona (92879-8089)
P.O. Box 28321, Anaheim (92809-0144)
PHONE..................................714 921-9913
Martin Olguin, *President*
Irma Olguin, *CFO*
▲ **EMP:** 25 **EST:** 2008
SQ FT: 18,000
SALES (est): 5.9MM **Privately Held**
SIC: 3589 5084 Food warming equipment, commercial; food product manufacturing machinery

(P-16039)
ERG TRANSIT SYSTEMS (USA) INC
1800 Sutter St Ste 900, Concord (94520-2536)
PHONE..................................925 686-8233
Steve Gallagher, *President*
Richard Long, *CFO*
James Carroll, *Treasurer*
Min WEI, *Exec VP*
Larry Weissbach, *Vice Pres*
EMP: 115
SQ FT: 14,474
SALES (est): 16.6MM **Privately Held**
SIC: 3589 Servicing machines, except dry cleaning, laundry: coin-oper.

(P-16040)
EVOQUA WATER TECHNOLOGIES
960 Ames Ave, Milpitas (95035-6303)
PHONE..................................408 586-9745
Bill Johnson, *Manager*
EMP: 13
SALES (est): 2.8MM **Privately Held**
SIC: 3589 Water treatment equipment, industrial

(P-16041)
EVOQUA WATER TECHNOLOGIES LLC
199 Harris Ave Ste 1, Sacramento (95838-5012)
PHONE..................................916 564-1222
Steve Elliot, *Principal*
EMP: 15
SALES (corp-wide): 1.1B **Publicly Held**
SIC: 3589 Sewage & water treatment equipment
HQ: Evoqua Water Technologies Llc
210 6th Ave Ste 3300
Pittsburgh PA 15222
724 772-0044

(P-16042)
FILTRONICS INC
3726 E Miraloma Ave, Anaheim (92806-2107)
PHONE..................................714 630-5040
William R Hoyer, *President*
EMP: 12
SALES (est): 2.7MM **Privately Held**
WEB: www.filtronics.com
SIC: 3589 Water purification equipment, household type; water treatment equipment, industrial

(P-16043)
G A SYSTEMS INC
226 W Carleton Ave, Orange (92867-3608)
PHONE..................................714 848-7529
Steven Anderson, *President*
Pat Devalle, *CFO*
Lindsay Mattson, *Admin Asst*
Larry Wange, *Natl Sales Mgr*
EMP: 15
SQ FT: 19,400
SALES (est): 3.2MM **Privately Held**
WEB: www.speedeeserv.com
SIC: 3589 Commercial cooking & food-warming equipment

(P-16044)
G E M WATER SYSTEMS INTL LLC
6351 Orangethorpe Ave, Buena Park (90620-1340)
PHONE..................................714 736-9990
Jack Enkowitz,
Esther Enkowitz,
EMP: 15
SQ FT: 14,090
SALES (est): 1.9MM **Privately Held**
WEB: www.gemwater.com
SIC: 3589 Water treatment equipment, industrial

(P-16045)
GET
Also Called: Vita Science Health Products
2030 W 17th St, Long Beach (90813-1012)
PHONE..................................562 989-5400
Fax: 562 983-7717
EMP: 15
SQ FT: 28,000
SALES (est): 2.4MM **Privately Held**
WEB: www.get-inc.com
SIC: 3589

(P-16046)
GORLITZ SEWER & DRAIN INC
10132 Norwalk Blvd, Santa Fe Springs (90670-3326)
PHONE..................................562 944-3060
James Kruger, *CEO*
Gerd Kruger, *President*
Elba Kruger, *Vice Pres*
▲ **EMP:** 30
SQ FT: 33,300
SALES (est): 6.7MM **Privately Held**
SIC: 3589 Sewer cleaning equipment, power

(P-16047)
H2O ENGINEERING INC
189 Granada Dr, San Luis Obispo (93401-7316)
PHONE..................................805 542-9253
Charles Robert Moncrief III, *CEO*
Ben Corcoran, *Vice Pres*
Joseph Mendez, *Engineer*
Chris Nosti, *Engineer*
Art Wyrick, *Engineer*

EMP: 15
SQ FT: 8,000
SALES (est): 4.3MM **Privately Held**
SIC: 3589 8744 Water treatment equipment, industrial;

(P-16048)
HANNAH INDUSTRIES INC
Also Called: South Coast Water
401 S Santa Fe St, Santa Ana (92705-4139)
P.O. Box 247, Orange (92856-6247)
PHONE..................................714 939-7873
Roy Hall, *President*
Hayley Jackson, *Manager*
EMP: 15
SQ FT: 15,000
SALES: 4.3MM **Privately Held**
WEB: www.hannahbean.com
SIC: 3589 5074 Water treatment equipment, industrial; water purification equipment

(P-16049)
HORIZON INTERNATIONAL LTD
Also Called: Hydrokleen Systems
200 E Henderson Ave, Porterville (93257-1715)
PHONE..................................559 781-4640
Gordon Woods Jr, *General Mgr*
Peggy Milford, *Principal*
▼ **EMP:** 15
SALES (est): 1.3MM **Privately Held**
WEB: www.hydrokleensystems.com
SIC: 3589 Swimming pool filter & water conditioning systems

(P-16050)
HRUBY ORBITAL SYSTEMS INC
Also Called: Hos
3275 Corporate Vw, Vista (92081-8528)
PHONE..................................760 936-8054
Jeffrey Thomas Hruby, *CEO*
◆ **EMP:** 10
SALES (est): 4.4MM **Privately Held**
SIC: 3589 Commercial cleaning equipment

(P-16051)
HYDROCOMPONENTS & TECH INC
Also Called: Hydro Components and Tech
1175 Park Center Dr Ste H, Vista (92081-8303)
PHONE..................................760 598-0189
Robert Williamson, *President*
Elizabeth Pierce, *Corp Secy*
John Snyder, *Vice Pres*
▲ **EMP:** 15
SQ FT: 5,500
SALES (est): 2.3MM **Privately Held**
WEB: www.hcti.com
SIC: 3589 Water treatment equipment, industrial

(P-16052)
HYDRONOVATION INC
530 Howard St, San Francisco (94105-3007)
PHONE..................................800 778-5092
Bruce Stump, *President*
▲ **EMP:** 11
SALES (est): 2.1MM **Privately Held**
SIC: 3589 Water filters & softeners, household type

(P-16053)
ILLINOIS TOOL WORKS INC
Stero
3200 Lakeville Hwy, Petaluma (94954-5903)
PHONE..................................800 762-7600
Terry Goodfellow, *Director*
EMP: 65
SALES (corp-wide): 14.3B **Publicly Held**
SIC: 3589 3443 Dishwashing machines, commercial; fabricated plate work (boiler shop)
PA: Illinois Tool Works Inc.
155 Harlem Ave
Glenview IL 60025
847 724-7500

(P-16054)
IMPERIAL MANUFACTURING CO
Also Called: Imperial Coml Cooking Eqp
1128 Sherborn St, Corona (92879-2089)
PHONE..................................951 281-1830
Peter Spenuzza, *President*
EMP: 170
SALES (est): 15.5MM **Privately Held**
SIC: 3589 Cooking equipment, commercial

(P-16055)
INNOVATIVE CONTROL SYSTEMS INC
20992 Bake Pkwy Ste 106, Lake Forest (92630-2170)
PHONE..................................610 881-8061
Cindy Penchishen, *Branch Mgr*
EMP: 30 **Privately Held**
SIC: 3589 Car washing machinery
PA: Innovative Control Systems, Inc.
1349 Jacobsburg Rd
Wind Gap PA 18091

(P-16056)
INTEGRITY MUNICPL SYSTEMS LLC
13135 Danielson St # 204, Poway (92064-8874)
PHONE..................................858 486-1620
Roop Jain,
Zaw W Aung, *Project Mgr*
Conar Marcos, *Buyer*
Jim Pike,
▼ **EMP:** 16
SALES (est): 4.3MM **Privately Held**
SIC: 3589 1629 8711 Water treatment equipment, industrial; waste water & sewage treatment plant construction; engineering services

(P-16057)
J F DUNCAN INDUSTRIES INC (PA)
Also Called: Duray
9301 Stewart And Gray Rd, Downey (90241-5315)
PHONE..................................562 862-4269
Johnny F Wong, *CEO*
Don Durward, *Vice Pres*
Linda Joiner, *Manager*
▲ **EMP:** 100
SALES (est): 20.2MM **Privately Held**
WEB: www.duray.org
SIC: 3589 Cooking equipment, commercial

(P-16058)
J L WINGERT COMPANY (PA)
11800 Monarch St, Garden Grove (92841-2113)
P.O. Box 6207 (92846-6207)
PHONE..................................714 379-5519
Tommy Thomas, *CEO*
Reeve Thomas, *Principal*
EMP: 65
SQ FT: 16,000
SALES (est): 15.5MM **Privately Held**
WEB: www.jlwingert.com
SIC: 3589 5084 Water treatment equipment, industrial; industrial machinery & equipment

(P-16059)
JACUZZI INC (HQ)
Also Called: Jacuzzi Outdoor Products
14525 Monte Vista Ave, Chino (91710-5721)
PHONE..................................909 606-7733
Thomas Koos, *CEO*
Roy A Jacuzzi, *Ch of Bd*
Donald C Devine, *President*
Paul Van Slyke, *VP Finance*
◆ **EMP:** 110 **EST:** 1979
SQ FT: 30,000
SALES (est): 623.1MM
SALES (corp-wide): 1.6B **Privately Held**
WEB: www.jacuzzi.com
SIC: 3589 3088 Swimming pool filter & water conditioning systems; hot tubs, plastic or fiberglass
PA: Jacuzzi Brands Llc
13925 City Center Dr # 200
Chino Hills CA 91709
909 606-1416

(P-16060)
JANDY INDUSTRIES INC (DH)
6000 Condor Dr, Moorpark (93021-2601)
PHONE................805 529-2000
Robert Rasp, *President*
▲ EMP: 20
SALES (est): 6MM
SALES (corp-wide): 3.6B **Publicly Held**
SIC: 3589 Swimming pool filter & water conditioning systems
HQ: Zodiac Pool Systems Llc
2620 Commerce Way
Vista CA 92081
760 599-9600

(P-16061)
JWC ENVIRONMENTAL LLC
Also Called: Disposable Waste System
2600 S Garnsey St, Santa Ana (92707-3339)
PHONE................714 662-5829
Steve Glomb, *CFO*
EMP: 75
SQ FT: 45,637
SALES (corp-wide): 3B **Privately Held**
WEB: www.jwce.com
SIC: 3589 Sewage treatment equipment
HQ: Jwc Environmental Inc.
2850 Redhill Ave Ste 125
Santa Ana CA 92705
949 833-3888

(P-16062)
K2 PURE SOLUTIONS LP
950 Loveridge Rd, Pittsburg (94565-2808)
PHONE................925 203-1196
Richard Anthony, *Plant Mgr*
EMP: 60
SALES (corp-wide): 5.3MM **Privately Held**
SIC: 3589 Water purification equipment, household type
PA: K2 Pure Solutions, L.P.
3515 Massillon Rd Ste 290
Uniontown OH 44685
925 526-8112

(P-16063)
KATCHALL FLTRATION SYSTEMS LLC
263 W Fourth St, Beaumont (92223-2609)
PHONE................866 528-2425
Kip Searcy, *Mng Member*
EMP: 10
SALES (est): 1.4MM **Privately Held**
SIC: 3589 Water filters & softeners, household type

(P-16064)
KELLERMYER BERGENSONS SVCS LLC (PA)
1959 Avenida Plaza Real, Oceanside (92056-6024)
PHONE................760 631-5111
Arthur Long, *CFO*
Jay Garcia, *Exec VP*
Chris Knapp, *Exec VP*
Louise Smith, *Vice Pres*
Mark Grieco, *Regional Mgr*
EMP: 10
SALES (est): 61.7MM **Privately Held**
SIC: 3589 Commercial cleaning equipment

(P-16065)
LAS COLINAS
600 S Jefferson St Ste M, Placentia (92870-6634)
PHONE................714 528-8100
C Christine Licata, *President*
Catharine Christine Licata, *President*
Anthony Licata, *CFO*
EMP: 15
SALES (est): 3.3MM **Privately Held**
SIC: 3589 1711 Asbestos removal equipment; plumbing contractors

(P-16066)
LIFESOURCE WATER SYSTEMS INC (PA)
523 S Fair Oaks Ave, Pasadena (91105-2605)
PHONE................626 792-9996
B J Wright, *President*
Peter Hewitt, *Exec VP*
Tony Romaldo, *Vice Pres*

Nathan Anderson, *Regional Mgr*
Steven Edsinger, *District Mgr*
EMP: 22
SQ FT: 10,000
SALES (est): 10.6MM **Privately Held**
WEB: www.lifesourcewater.com
SIC: 3589 5074 Water purification equipment, household type; water filters & softeners, household type; plumbing & hydronic heating supplies

(P-16067)
LOPEZ WATER TREATMENT PLANT
2845 Lopez Dr, Arroyo Grande (93420-4998)
PHONE................805 473-7152
Ron Coleman, *Superintendent*
EMP: 11
SALES (est): 916.4K **Privately Held**
SIC: 3589 4952 Water treatment equipment, industrial; sewerage systems

(P-16068)
MAR COR PURIFICATION INC
6351 Orangethorpe Ave, Buena Park (90620-1340)
PHONE................800 633-3080
Sean West, *Principal*
EMP: 22
SALES (est): 2.5MM **Privately Held**
SIC: 3589 Water treatment equipment, industrial

(P-16069)
MAZZEI INJECTOR COMPANY LLC
500 Rooster Dr, Bakersfield (93307-9555)
PHONE................661 363-6500
Angelo Mazzei, *CEO*
Geofffrey Whynot, *President*
Mary Mazzei, *Bd of Directors*
Celia Cobar, *Vice Pres*
▲ EMP: 24
SALES: 8MM
SALES (corp-wide): 8MM **Privately Held**
SIC: 3589 Water treatment equipment, industrial
PA: Mazzei Injector Corporation
500 Rooster Dr
Bakersfield CA 93307
661 363-6500

(P-16070)
MCC CONTROLS LLC
Also Called: Primex
859 Cotting Ct Ste G, Vacaville (95688-9354)
P.O. Box 1708, Detroit Lakes MN (56502-1708)
PHONE................218 847-1317
David Thomas, *President*
Taunia Suckert, *Corp Secy*
EMP: 27
SALES (est): 2.9MM **Privately Held**
SIC: 3589 Sewage & water treatment equipment

(P-16071)
MD MANUFACTURING INC
34970 Mcmurtrey Ave, Bakersfield (93308-9578)
PHONE................661 283-7550
Raymond Stewart, *President*
Scott Hallmark, *Marketing Staff*
▲ EMP: 19
SQ FT: 34,000
SALES (est): 5.1MM **Privately Held**
SIC: 3589 Vacuum cleaners & sweepers, electric; industrial

(P-16072)
MEDIA BLAST & ABRASIVE INC
591 Apollo St, Brea (92821-3127)
PHONE................714 257-0484
Ronald Storer, *President*
EMP: 19
SALES (est): 3.7MM **Privately Held**
WEB: www.mediablast.com
SIC: 3589 3822 Sandblasting equipment; high pressure cleaning equipment; auto controls regulating residntl & coml environmt & applncs

(P-16073)
MICRODYN-NADIR US INC (DH)
Also Called: Trisep Corporation
93 S La Patera Ln, Goleta (93117-3246)
PHONE................805 964-8003
Peter Knappe, *President*
Kevin Edberg, *CFO*
Holly Wallis, *Planning*
Alfredo Rodriguez, *IT/INT Sup*
Jeffrey Flowers, *Design Engr*
◆ EMP: 90
SQ FT: 40,000
SALES: 23MM
SALES (corp-wide): 4.5B **Privately Held**
WEB: www.trisep.com
SIC: 3589 Water treatment equipment, industrial
HQ: Microdyn - Nadir Gmbh
Kasteler Str. 45
Wiesbaden 65203
611 962-6001

(P-16074)
MONTAGUE COMPANY
1830 Stearman Ave, Hayward (94545-1018)
P.O. Box 4954 (94540-4954)
PHONE................510 785-8822
Thomas M Whalen, *President*
Robert M Whalen, *Chairman*
George A Malloch, *Admin Sec*
◆ EMP: 105 EST: 1857
SQ FT: 100,000
SALES (est): 31.4MM **Privately Held**
WEB: www.montague-inc.com
SIC: 3589 Cooking equipment, commercial; commercial cooking & foodwarming equipment

(P-16075)
MYTEE PRODUCTS INC
13655 Stowe Dr, Poway (92064-6873)
PHONE................858 679-1191
John La Barbera, *President*
Gina La Barbera, *Corp Secy*
Paul La Barbera, *Vice Pres*
Melanie Alexander, *Department Mgr*
John Labarbera, *IT/INT Sup*
◆ EMP: 43
SQ FT: 45,000
SALES (est): 8.9MM **Privately Held**
WEB: www.mytee.com
SIC: 3589 Commercial cleaning equipment

(P-16076)
N/S CORPORATION (PA)
Also Called: NS Wash Systems
235 W Florence Ave, Inglewood (90301-1293)
PHONE................310 412-7074
G Thomas Ennis Sr, *CEO*
Francis Penggardjaja, *Exec VP*
Lumen Ong, *Controller*
◆ EMP: 87
SQ FT: 80,000
SALES: 20MM **Privately Held**
WEB: www.nswash.com
SIC: 3589 Car washing machinery

(P-16077)
NALCO WTR PRTRTMENT SLTONS LLC
704 Richfield Rd, Placentia (92870-6760)
PHONE................714 792-0708
EMP: 28
SALES (corp-wide): 13.8B **Publicly Held**
SIC: 3589 Water treatment equipment, industrial
HQ: Nalco Water Pretreatment Solutions, Llc
1601 W Diehl Rd
Naperville IL 60563
708 754-2550

(P-16078)
NEF TECH INC
Also Called: Ampac USA
5255 State St, Montclair (91763-6236)
PHONE................909 548-4900
Sammy Farag, *CEO*
Nevine Nakhla, *President*
John Gunn, *Office Admin*
▼ EMP: 17
SQ FT: 10,000

SALES (est): 3.2MM **Privately Held**
SIC: 3589 Water treatment equipment, industrial

(P-16079)
NEW WAVE INDUSTRIES LTD (PA)
Also Called: Pur-Clean Pressure Car Wash
3315 Orange Grove Ave, North Highlands (95660-5807)
PHONE................800 882-8854
Gary Hirsh, *CEO*
Charles Borchard, *Vice Pres*
Cheri Andresen, *Project Mgr*
Nicolle Hearne, *Project Mgr*
Richard Carpenter, *Technical Staff*
EMP: 18
SQ FT: 24,000
SALES (est): 3MM **Privately Held**
SIC: 3589 Car washing machinery

(P-16080)
NIECO CORPORATION
7950 Cameron Dr, Windsor (95492-8594)
PHONE................707 838-3226
Edward D Baker Sr, *President*
Edward Baker Jr, *Vice Pres*
Matthew Baker, *Vice Pres*
Patrick Baker, *Vice Pres*
Thomas Baker, *Vice Pres*
◆ EMP: 70
SQ FT: 80,000
SALES: 17.9MM
SALES (corp-wide): 2.3B **Publicly Held**
WEB: www.nieco.com
SIC: 3589 Commercial cooking & foodwarming equipment
PA: The Middleby Corporation
1400 Toastmaster Dr
Elgin IL 60120
847 741-3300

(P-16081)
NIMBUS WATER SYSTEMS
42445 Avenida Alvarado, Temecula (92590-3461)
P.O. Box 1478 (92593-1478)
PHONE................951 984-2800
Anthony Alexander Capone, *President*
Patricia Renee Capone, *CFO*
EMP: 15
SQ FT: 25,000
SALES (est): 4.1MM
SALES (corp-wide): 546.7MM **Privately Held**
SIC: 3589 Water purification equipment, household type; water treatment equipment, industrial
HQ: Kinetico Incorporated
10845 Kinsman Rd
Newbury OH 44065
440 564-9111

(P-16082)
OASIS STRUCTURES & WATER WORKS
273 Anker Ln, McKinleyville (95519-9710)
P.O. Box 2460 (95519-2460)
PHONE................707 839-1683
Timothy T White, *President*
Rene White, *Treasurer*
Nancy Custis, *Admin Sec*
EMP: 15
SALES (est): 724.7K **Privately Held**
SIC: 3589 Water filters & softeners, household type; water treatment equipment, industrial

(P-16083)
ORIGINCLEAR INC (PA)
525 S Hewitt St, Los Angeles (90013-2217)
PHONE................323 939-6645
T Riggs Eckelberry, *Ch of Bd*
Jean-Louis Kindler, *Ch Credit Ofcr*
EMP: 22 EST: 2007
SALES: 3.3MM **Publicly Held**
SIC: 3589 2869 Water treatment equipment, industrial; fuels

(P-16084)
OSMOSIS TECHNOLOGY INC
Also Called: Osmotik
6900 Hermosa Cir, Buena Park (90620-1151)
PHONE................714 670-9303
Mike Joulakian, *President*

▲ = Import ▼=Export
◆ =Import/Export

Sonia Joulakian, *Vice Pres*
EMP: 21
SQ FT: 13,000
SALES (est): 4.7MM **Privately Held**
WEB: www.osmotik.com
SIC: 3589 Water filters & softeners, household type

(P-16085)
OZOTECH INC (PA)
2401 E Oberlin Rd, Yreka (96097-9577)
PHONE................................530 842-4189
Stephen Christiansen, *President*
▲ **EMP:** 20
SQ FT: 6,000
SALES (est): 3.7MM **Privately Held**
WEB: www.ozotech.com
SIC: 3589 Water purification equipment, household type; water treatment equipment, industrial

(P-16086)
PENTAIR FLOW TECHNOLOGIES LLC
Also Called: Pentair Water Group
2445 S Gearhart Ave, Fresno
(93725-1300)
PHONE................................559 266-0516
Matt Miller, *Manager*
EMP: 128
SALES (corp-wide): 1.2B **Privately Held**
WEB: www.aurorapump.com
SIC: 3589 Water purification equipment, household type
HQ: Pentair Flow Technologies, Llc
1101 Myers Pkwy
Ashland OH 44805
419 289-1144

(P-16087)
PENTAIR WATER POOL AND SPA INC
Also Called: Pentair Aquatic Systems
13950 Mountain Ave, Chino (91710-9018)
PHONE................................909 287-7800
Raul Umali, *Branch Mgr*
EMP: 45
SALES (corp-wide): 1.2B **Privately Held**
WEB: www.pentairpool.com
SIC: 3589 Swimming pool filter & water conditioning systems
HQ: Pentair Water Pool And Spa, Inc.
1620 Hawkins Ave
Sanford NC 27330
919 566-8000

(P-16088)
PENTAIR WATER POOL AND SPA INC
Also Called: Pentair Pool Products
10951 W Los Angeles Ave, Moorpark
(93021-9744)
P.O. Box 8085 (93020-8085)
PHONE................................805 553-5003
Diane Larkin, *Manager*
Porfirio Piedra, *Engineer*
Tony Lukyn, *Marketing Staff*
Liz Mata, *Manager*
EMP: 45
SALES (corp-wide): 1.2B **Privately Held**
WEB: www.pentairpool.com
SIC: 3589 3561 3569 3648 Swimming pool filter & water conditioning systems; pumps, domestic: water or sump; heaters, swimming pool: electric; underwater lighting fixtures; sporting & athletic goods; swimming pool & hot tub service & maintenance
HQ: Pentair Water Pool And Spa, Inc.
1620 Hawkins Ave
Sanford NC 27330
919 566-8000

(P-16089)
PORIFERA INC
1575 Alvarado St, San Leandro
(94577-2640)
PHONE................................510 695-2775
Olgica Bakajin, *CEO*
Jeff Jensen, *Chairman*
Jeffrey Mendelssohn, *Vice Pres*
Alexsander Noy, *Security Dir*
Jennifer Klare, *Research*
EMP: 13
SQ FT: 5,000

SALES (est): 878.4K **Privately Held**
SIC: 3589 Water treatment equipment, industrial

(P-16090)
POWER KNOT LLC
2290 Ringwood Ave Ste A, San Jose
(95131-1718)
PHONE................................408 480-2758
Iain Milnes,
Lisa Shan, *Sales Mgr*
Lei Shan,
▲ **EMP:** 18
SQ FT: 1,600
SALES (est): 3.2MM **Privately Held**
SIC: 3589 Garbage disposers & compactors, commercial

(P-16091)
PRODUCT SOLUTIONS INC
1182 N Knollwood Cir, Anaheim
(92801-1307)
PHONE................................714 545-9757
Robert Kreaton, *CEO*
Judith Keaton, *Admin Sec*
▲ **EMP:** 50
SQ FT: 25,000
SALES (est): 9.8MM **Privately Held**
WEB: www.productsolutions.net
SIC: 3589 3631 Commercial cooking & foodwarming equipment; household cooking equipment

(P-16092)
PRONTO PRODUCTS CO (PA)
9850 Siempre Viva Rd, San Diego
(92154-7247)
PHONE................................619 661-6995
Carlos Matos, *CEO*
William E Parrot, *President*
Martha J Wagner, *Vice Pres*
Barbara Parrot, *Admin Sec*
EMP: 60
SALES (est): 12.5MM **Privately Held**
SIC: 3589 3496 Commercial cooking & foodwarming equipment; miscellaneous fabricated wire products

(P-16093)
PURE WATER CENTERS INC
Also Called: Absolute Aquasystems
8860 Corbin Ave Ste 382, Northridge
(91324-3309)
PHONE................................818 316-1250
Raymundo Abad, *President*
EMP: 11
SALES (est): 1MM **Privately Held**
SIC: 3589 Water purification equipment, household type

(P-16094)
PURI TECH INC
Also Called: Everfilt
3167 Progress Cir, Mira Loma
(91752-1112)
PHONE................................951 360-8380
Barbara J Andrew, *President*
EMP: 25
SQ FT: 10,600
SALES (est): 5.4MM **Privately Held**
WEB: www.everfilt.com
SIC: 3589 5074 Water treatment equipment, industrial; water purification equipment

(P-16095)
PURITY POOL INC
30411 Whitmore Rd, Whitmore
(96096-9548)
P.O. Box 160 (96096-0160)
PHONE................................530 472-3298
Julia Gross, *President*
Jason Gross, *Shareholder*
Richard S Gross, *Vice Pres*
EMP: 10
SQ FT: 3,600
SALES: 750K **Privately Held**
WEB: www.puritypool.com
SIC: 3589 Swimming pool filter & water conditioning systems

(P-16096)
PURONICS INCORPORATED
5775 Las Positas Rd, Livermore
(94551-7819)
PHONE................................925 456-7000

Scott A Batiste, *President*
EMP: 28
SALES (est): 7.7MM **Privately Held**
SIC: 3589 Swimming pool filter & water conditioning systems

(P-16097)
QMP INC
25070 Avenue Tibbitts, Valencia
(91355-3447)
PHONE................................661 294-6860
Freddy Vidal, *President*
Irma Vidal, *Vice Pres*
Michelle Vidal, *Admin Asst*
Tady Salaues, *VP Sales*
▲ **EMP:** 45
SQ FT: 40,000
SALES (est): 13MM **Privately Held**
WEB: www.qmpusa.com
SIC: 3589 Sewage & water treatment equipment; water purification equipment, household type; water treatment equipment, industrial

(P-16098)
RANKIN-DELUX INC (PA)
3245 Corridor Dr, Eastvale (91752-1030)
PHONE................................951 685-0081
L Vasan, *President*
William A Rankin, *Shareholder*
▲ **EMP:** 15
SQ FT: 25,000
SALES (est): 2.4MM **Privately Held**
SIC: 3589 Cooking equipment, commercial

(P-16099)
RAPID RAMEN INC
9381 E Stockton Blvd # 230, Elk Grove
(95624-5068)
PHONE................................916 479-7003
Christopher Alan Johnson, *CEO*
▲ **EMP:** 10 **EST:** 2010
SALES (est): 313.1K **Privately Held**
SIC: 3589 Commercial cooking & foodwarming equipment

(P-16100)
REMINGTON INC
28165 Avenue Crocker, Valencia
(91355-3440)
P.O. Box 800850, Santa Clarita (91380-0850)
PHONE................................661 257-9400
Bruce Burrows, *President*
Matt Houston, *Vice Pres*
Marat Bochkur, *Mfg Dir*
▲ **EMP:** 21
SALES (est): 3.7MM **Privately Held**
SIC: 3589 Water purification equipment, household type

(P-16101)
RENOVARE INTERNATIONAL INC (PA)
849 Balra Dr, El Cerrito (94530-3001)
PHONE................................510 748-9993
George Kniazewycz, *President*
Charles Lemon, *Vice Pres*
EMP: 10
SALES (est): 1MM **Privately Held**
WEB: www.renovare.com
SIC: 3589 Water treatment equipment, industrial

(P-16102)
ROBERT YICK COMPANY INC
261 Bay Shore Blvd, San Francisco
(94124-1386)
PHONE................................415 282-9707
Joseph Yick, *President*
Shew Yick, *Vice Pres*
EMP: 25
SQ FT: 10,000
SALES (est): 4.5MM **Privately Held**
SIC: 3589 3444 Cooking equipment, commercial; sheet metalwork

(P-16103)
RYKO SOLUTIONS INC
3939 W Capitol Ave Ste D, West Sacramento (95691-2105)
PHONE................................916 372-8815
EMP: 21
SALES (corp-wide): 2.3B **Privately Held**
SIC: 3589 5087

HQ: Ryko Solutions, Inc.
1500 Se 37th St
Grimes IA 50111
515 986-3700

(P-16104)
S & S INSTALLATIONS INC
Also Called: Pacific Stainless
294 W Olive St, Colton (92324-1757)
PHONE................................909 370-1730
Tom Skocilich, *President*
Ron Greg, *Vice Pres*
Robert Skocilich, *Vice Pres*
EMP: 23
SQ FT: 12,000
SALES (est): 3.8MM **Privately Held**
SIC: 3589 3556 3469 Food warming equipment, commercial; food products machinery; metal stampings

(P-16105)
SANTA MONICA CITY OF
Also Called: City of Santa Monica Wtr Trtmn
1228 S Bundy Dr, Los Angeles
(90025-1102)
PHONE................................310 826-6712
Myriam Cardenas, *Branch Mgr*
Gary Richinick, *Supervisor*
EMP: 12
SQ FT: 2,500 **Privately Held**
WEB: www.santamonicapd.org
SIC: 3589 Sewage & water treatment equipment
PA: City Of Santa Monica
1685 Main St
Santa Monica CA 90401
310 458-8411

(P-16106)
SEWER RODDING EQUIPMENT CO (PA)
Also Called: Flexible Video Systems
3217 Carter Ave, Marina Del Rey
(90292-5554)
PHONE................................310 301-9009
Patrick Crane, *CEO*
EMP: 25
SQ FT: 24,000
SALES (est): 17.6MM **Privately Held**
SIC: 3589 Sewer cleaning equipment, power

(P-16107)
SHEPARD BROS INC (PA)
503 S Cypress St, La Habra (90631-6126)
PHONE................................562 697-1366
Ronald Shepard, *CEO*
Duane Shepard, *President*
Jon Wynkoop, *CFO*
Carly Gonzalez, *Admin Asst*
Carly Shepard, *Admin Asst*
▲ **EMP:** 120 **EST:** 1976
SQ FT: 57,830
SALES: 44MM **Privately Held**
SIC: 3589 5169 Sewage & water treatment equipment; chemicals & allied products

(P-16108)
SJ ELECTRO SYSTEMS INC
Also Called: Primex
859 Cotting Ct Ste G, Vacaville
(95688-9354)
PHONE................................707 449-0341
Adam Vesely, *Branch Mgr*
EMP: 26
SALES (corp-wide): 87.3MM **Privately Held**
SIC: 3589 Water treatment equipment, industrial
PA: S.J. Electro Systems, Inc.
22650 County Highway 6
Detroit Lakes MN 56501
218 847-1317

(P-16109)
SNOWPURE LLC
Also Called: Snowpure Water Technologies
130 Calle Iglesia Ste A, San Clemente
(92672-7535)
P.O. Box 73368 (92673-0113)
PHONE................................949 240-2188
Michael Snow, *Mng Member*
Scott Panning, *Opers Staff*
Ron O'Hare, *Manager*
▲ **EMP:** 30

SALES: 5MM **Privately Held**
SIC: **3589** 5074 Water purification equipment, household type; water purification equipment

(P-16110)
SPECIALTY CAR WASH SYSTEM
146 Mercury Cir, Pomona (91768-3210)
PHONE...................................909 869-6300
Mike Martorano, *Owner*
EMP: 15
SALES (est): 2.2MM **Privately Held**
SIC: **3589** Car washing machinery

(P-16111)
SPECTRA WATERMAKERS INC (HQ)
2220 S Mcdowell Blvd Ext, Petaluma (94954-5659)
PHONE...................................415 526-2780
William Edinger, *President*
Kelly Donahue, *Controller*
◆ EMP: 12
SQ FT: 8,400
SALES (est): 2.5MM
SALES (corp-wide): 2.9MM **Privately Held**
WEB: www.spectrawatermakers.com
SIC: **3589** Water treatment equipment, industrial
PA: Katadyn North America, Inc.
4830 Azelia Ave N Ste 300
Minneapolis MN 55429
763 746-3500

(P-16112)
SPENUZZA INC (PA)
Also Called: Imperial Mfg Co
1128 Sherborn St, Corona (92879-2089)
PHONE...................................951 281-1830
Peter Spenuzza, *CEO*
Martina Molano, *Vice Pres*
Barry Tucker, *Admin Asst*
Jennifer Mullen, *Purchasing*
Miguel Betancourt, *Plant Mgr*
◆ EMP: 111
SQ FT: 100,000
SALES (est): 32MM **Privately Held**
WEB: www.imperialrange.com
SIC: **3589** 3556 Cooking equipment, commercial; food products machinery

(P-16113)
SPENUZZA INC
Also Called: Imperial Mfg Co
913 Oak Ave, Duarte (91010-1951)
PHONE...................................626 358-8063
Peter Spenuzza Jr, *President*
EMP: 40
SALES (corp-wide): 32MM **Privately Held**
WEB: www.imperialrange.com
SIC: **3589** Cooking equipment, commercial
PA: Spenuzza, Inc.
1128 Sherborn St
Corona CA 92879
951 281-1830

(P-16114)
SPIRAL WATER TECHNOLOGIES INC
999 Andersen Dr Ste 140, San Rafael (94901-5350)
PHONE...................................415 259-4929
Ashwin Gulati, *CEO*
David Dreessen, *CFO*
EMP: 15
SALES (est): 667K **Privately Held**
SIC: **3589** Water treatment equipment, industrial

(P-16115)
SPOTLESS WATER SYSTEMS LLC
Also Called: Cr Spotless
372 Coogan Way, El Cajon (92020-1902)
PHONE...................................858 530-9993
Chuck Dewent, *Mng Member*
Rochelle Asbell, *General Mgr*
John Fernandez, *General Mgr*
▲ EMP: 12
SQ FT: 20,000
SALES: 1MM **Privately Held**
SIC: **3589** Water filters & softeners, household type

(P-16116)
STANTEC CONSULTING SVCS INC
1245 Fiddyment Rd, Lincoln (95648-9504)
P.O. Box 1050 (95648-1050)
PHONE...................................916 434-5062
Sarah McKelroy, *Branch Mgr*
Lori Van Dermark, *Marketing Staff*
EMP: 12
SALES (corp-wide): 4B **Privately Held**
WEB: www.ecologicengineering.com
SIC: **3589** Water treatment equipment, industrial
HQ: Stantec Consulting Services Inc.
475 5th Ave Fl 12
New York NY 10017
212 352-5160

(P-16117)
STERNO GROUP LLC (DH)
1880 Compton Ave Ste 101, Corona (92881-2780)
PHONE...................................800 669-6699
John Clark, *Mng Member*
▼ SALES (est): 57.2MM **Publicly Held**
WEB: www.sterno.com
SIC: **3589** Commercial cooking & food-warming equipment
HQ: Sterno Products, Llc
1880 Compton Ave Ste 101
Corona CA 92881
951 682-9600

(P-16118)
STERNO PRODUCTS LLC (DH)
Also Called: Sternocandlelamp
1880 Compton Ave Ste 101, Corona (92881-2780)
PHONE...................................951 682-9600
Don Hinshaw, *CEO*
Mike Pacharis, *Vice Pres*
Shane Peck, *Vice Pres*
Scott Rylko, *Vice Pres*
Brett Witzel, *Info Tech Mgr*
▲ EMP: 50
SQ FT: 110,000
SALES (est): 137.7MM **Publicly Held**
WEB: www.candlelamp.com
SIC: **3589** 3634 2899 Food warming equipment, commercial; chafing dishes, electric; chemical preparations
HQ: Sternocandlelamp Holdings, Inc.
1880 Compton Ave Ste 101
Corona CA 92881
951 682-9600

(P-16119)
SUEZ WTS SERVICES USA INC
5900 Silver Creek Vly Rd, San Jose (95138-1083)
PHONE...................................408 360-5900
Thomas Hereda, *Branch Mgr*
EMP: 130
SALES (corp-wide): 51.4MM **Privately Held**
SIC: **3589** Water treatment equipment, industrial
HQ: Suez Wts Services Usa, Inc.
4545 Patent Rd
Norfolk VA 23502
757 855-9000

(P-16120)
SUEZ WTS SERVICES USA INC
7777 Industry Ave, Pico Rivera (90660-4303)
PHONE...................................562 942-2200
Michael Dimick, *Branch Mgr*
Willie Cisneros, *General Mgr*
Fred Valdes, *Sales Staff*
EMP: 60
SQ FT: 32,091
SALES (corp-wide): 86.1MM **Privately Held**
WEB: www.ecolochem.com
SIC: **3589** Water treatment equipment, industrial
HQ: Suez Wts Services Usa, Inc.
4545 Patent Rd
Norfolk VA 23502
757 855-9000

(P-16121)
SUEZ WTS SERVICES USA INC
11689 Pacific Ave, Fontana (92337-8225)
PHONE...................................951 681-5555
Dennis Holley, *Manager*
EMP: 19
SALES (corp-wide): 86.1MM **Privately Held**
WEB: www.ecolochem.com
SIC: **3589** Water treatment equipment, industrial
HQ: Suez Wts Services Usa, Inc.
4545 Patent Rd
Norfolk VA 23502
757 855-9000

(P-16122)
TESLAIRE
263 W Olive Ave 307, Burbank (91502-1825)
PHONE...................................310 590-5357
Albert Moran, *Partner*
EMP: 10 EST: 2010
SALES (est): 438.6K **Privately Held**
SIC: **3589** 5074 5999 Water purification equipment, household type; water purification equipment; water purification equipment

(P-16123)
THOUSANDS OAKS HAND WASH
Also Called: Auto Scrubber
2725 E Thousand Oaks Blvd, Thousand Oaks (91362-3257)
P.O. Box 7692, Westlake Village (91359-7692)
PHONE...................................805 379-2732
Kim Shirazi, *Owner*
EMP: 11
SALES (est): 853.6K **Privately Held**
SIC: **3589** 7542 Car washing machinery; carwashes

(P-16124)
TIMBUCKTOO MANUFACTURING INC
Also Called: T M I
1633 W 134th St, Gardena (90249-2013)
PHONE...................................310 323-1134
Juen Lee, *CEO*
Kyu Lee, *President*
Kevin Lee, *Prdtn Mgr*
▲ EMP: 43
SQ FT: 50,000
SALES (est): 8.5MM **Privately Held**
SIC: **3589** Car washing machinery

(P-16125)
TOPPER MANUFACTURING CORP
23880 Madison St, Torrance (90505-6009)
PHONE...................................310 375-5000
Timothy A Beall, *CEO*
EMP: 15 EST: 2015
SQ FT: 11,000
SALES (est): 4MM **Privately Held**
SIC: **3589** Water filters & softeners, household type; water purification equipment, household type

(P-16126)
TORAY MEMBRANE USA INC
Also Called: C S M
13435 Danielson St, Poway (92064-6825)
PHONE...................................714 678-8832
Kenneth Yoon, *Branch Mgr*
EMP: 15
SALES (corp-wide): 20.6B **Privately Held**
SIC: **3589** Water treatment equipment, industrial
HQ: Toray Membrane Usa, Inc.
13435 Danielson St
Poway CA 92064

(P-16127)
TST WATER LLC
Also Called: Watersentinel
42188 Rio Nedo Ste B, Temecula (92590-3717)
PHONE...................................951 541-9517
Michael T Baird, *President*
Mounir Ibrahim, *CFO*
Randy Parmley, *Design Engr*

Jay Julos, *Engineer*
Hassan Shurrab, *Engineer*
▲ EMP: 19
SALES (est): 8.5MM **Privately Held**
WEB: www.tstwater.com
SIC: **3589** Water filters & softeners, household type

(P-16128)
UNIVERSAL FILTRATION INC
914 Westminster Ave, Alhambra (91803-1229)
P.O. Box 400, Hamilton MT (59840-0400)
PHONE...................................626 308-1832
Brian Green, *President*
Ruth Green, *Corp Secy*
Clark R Green, *Vice Pres*
EMP: 16
SQ FT: 13,500
SALES: 2MM **Privately Held**
WEB: www.universalfiltration.com
SIC: **3589** 3999 Swimming pool filter & water conditioning systems; hot tub & spa covers

(P-16129)
VANDERLANS & SONS INC (PA)
Also Called: Lansas Products
1320 S Sacramento St, Lodi (95240-5705)
P.O. Box 758 (95241-0758)
PHONE...................................209 334-4115
Gerald Vanderlans, *President*
Nick Bettencourt, *Corp Secy*
Victor Schuh, *Corp Secy*
April Hayles, *Bookkeeper*
Scott Sanden, *Foreman/Supr*
▲ EMP: 49
SQ FT: 30,000
SALES (est): 6.7MM **Privately Held**
WEB: www.lansas.com
SIC: **3589** Sewer cleaning equipment, power

(P-16130)
WALTERS MANUFACTURING COMPANY
Also Called: Walters Steamworks
135 Aviation Way Ste 1, Watsonville (95076-2073)
PHONE...................................831 724-1377
Robert Bixby, *President*
▲ EMP: 12
SQ FT: 8,800
SALES: 2MM **Privately Held**
WEB: www.walterssteamworks.com
SIC: **3589** 5084 Water treatment equipment, industrial; cleaning equipment, high pressure, sand or steam
PA: Robert Bixby Associates, Inc.
135 Aviation Way Ste 1
Watsonville CA 95076
831 724-1377

(P-16131)
WATER ONE INDUSTRIES INC
2913 Pattern St Unit D, Brea (92821)
PHONE...................................707 747-4300
Mher Torossian, *Branch Mgr*
EMP: 10
SQ FT: 2,042 **Privately Held**
SIC: **3589** Water treatment equipment, industrial
PA: Water One Industries, Inc.
5410 Gateway Plaza Dr
Benicia CA 94510

(P-16132)
WATER ONE INDUSTRIES INC (PA)
5410 Gateway Plaza Dr, Benicia (94510-2122)
PHONE...................................707 747-4300
Hans-Erik Fuchs, *CEO*
Erin Steiger, *Treasurer*
Tim Russell, *Vice Pres*
EMP: 25
SQ FT: 3,500
SALES (est): 5.2MM **Privately Held**
SIC: **3589** Water treatment equipment, industrial

▲ = Import ▼=Export
◆ =Import/Export

(P-16133)
WATER PLANET ENGINEERING LLC
8915 S La Cienega Blvd C, Inglewood (90301-7423)
PHONE....................424 331-7700
Eric Hoek, *CEO*
Tony Wachinski, *President*
Tom Flynn, *Vice Pres*
Mark Harrington, *Engineer*
Rhys Marks, *Engineer*
EMP: 15
SQ FT: 6,000
SALES (est): 3.7MM **Privately Held**
SIC: 3589 Water treatment equipment, industrial

(P-16134)
WATERGURU INC
150 Post St Ste 650, San Francisco (94108-4719)
PHONE....................415 692-3310
Tadmor Shalon, *President*
EMP: 10
SALES (est): 530.7K **Privately Held**
SIC: 3589 Swimming pool filter & water conditioning systems

(P-16135)
WATERHEALTH INTERNATIONAL INC
9601 Irvine Center Dr, Irvine (92618-4652)
PHONE....................949 716-5790
Sanjay Bhatnagar, *CEO*
EMP: 125 EST: 1995
SQ FT: 2,000
SALES (est): 10.8MM **Privately Held**
WEB: www.waterhealth.com
SIC: 3589 Water treatment equipment, industrial

(P-16136)
WATERMAN VALVE LLC (HQ)
25500 Road 204, Exeter (93221-9655)
P.O. Box 458 (93221-0458)
PHONE....................559 562-4000
Marcus Shiveley, *President*
▲ EMP: 126
SQ FT: 175,000
SALES (est): 32MM
SALES (corp-wide): 1.3B **Privately Held**
WEB: www.watermanusa.com
SIC: 3589 Water treatment equipment, industrial
PA: Mcwane, Inc.
2900 Highway 280 S # 300
Birmingham AL 35223
205 414-3100

(P-16137)
WESFAC INC
Also Called: Wespac
9300 Hall Rd, Downey (90241-5309)
PHONE....................562 861-2160
Don Hyatt, *President*
Julie Hyatt, *Corp Secy*
EMP: 100 EST: 1982
SQ FT: 55,000
SALES (est): 8.4MM
SALES (corp-wide): 11.3MM **Privately Held**
WEB: www.omniteaminc.com
SIC: 3589 3431 Commercial cooking & foodwarming equipment; metal sanitary ware
PA: Omniment Industries, Inc
9300 Hall Rd
Downey CA 90241
562 923-9660

(P-16138)
WHITTIER FILTRATION INC (DH)
120 S State College Blvd, Brea (92821-5807)
PHONE....................714 986-5300
Jim Brown, *President*
John M Santelli, *Corp Secy*
Kenneth Severing, *Business Dir*
Richard Weiss, *Project Mgr*
◆ EMP: 24
SQ FT: 80,000

SALES (est): 7.1MM
SALES (corp-wide): 572.2MM **Privately Held**
SIC: 3589 Water treatment equipment, industrial

(P-16139)
WILBUR CURTIS CO INC
6913 W Acco St, Montebello (90640-5403)
PHONE....................323 837-2300
Kevin Curtis, *President*
Joe Laws, *COO*
Norman Fujitaki, *CFO*
Michael A Curtis, *Exec VP*
Steve Bradley, *Vice Pres*
◆ EMP: 280
SQ FT: 175,000
SALES: 90MM **Privately Held**
WEB: www.wilburcurtis.com
SIC: 3589 Coffee brewing equipment

(P-16140)
WILBUR CURTIS CO INC
6913 W Acco St, Montebello (90640-5403)
PHONE....................323 837-2300
EMP: 275 EST: 1946
SQ FT: 170,000
SALES: 75MM **Privately Held**
SIC: 3589

(P-16141)
YARDNEY WATER MGT SYSTEMS INC (PA)
Also Called: Yardney Water MGT Systems
6666 Box Springs Blvd, Riverside (92507-0736)
PHONE....................951 656-6716
Kenneth Phillips, *President*
Chris Phillips, *Vice Pres*
Kevin Hillger, *Admin Sec*
Sue Larsen, *Personnel Assit*
Brian Olson, *Sales Associate*
▲ EMP: 40
SQ FT: 55,000
SALES (est): 7.3MM **Privately Held**
WEB: www.yardneyfilters.com
SIC: 3589 Water treatment equipment, industrial

(P-16142)
YUBA CY WSTE WTR TRTMNT FCILTY
302 Burns Dr, Yuba City (95991-7205)
PHONE....................530 822-7698
John Buckland, *Mayor*
EMP: 24
SALES (est): 2.8MM **Privately Held**
SIC: 3589 Water treatment equipment, industrial

(P-16143)
ZODIAC POOL SOLUTIONS LLC (DH)
2620 Commerce Way, Vista (92081-8438)
PHONE....................760 599-9600
Francois Mirallie, *President*
EMP: 300
SALES (est): 28.7MM
SALES (corp-wide): 3.6B **Publicly Held**
SIC: 3589 Swimming pool filter & water conditioning systems
HQ: Zodiac Pool Systems Llc
2620 Commerce Way
Vista CA 92081
760 599-9600

(P-16144)
ZODIAC POOL SYSTEMS LLC (DH)
Also Called: Jandy Pool Products
2620 Commerce Way, Vista (92081-8438)
PHONE....................760 599-9600
Bruce Brooks, *CEO*
Anthony Prudhomme, *COO*
Mike Allanc, *CFO*
Scott Frost, *Vice Pres*
Michelle Kenyon, *Vice Pres*
◆ EMP: 250
SQ FT: 20,000
SALES (est): 544.4MM
SALES (corp-wide): 3.6B **Publicly Held**
WEB: www.jandy.com
SIC: 3589 3999 Swimming pool filter & water conditioning systems; hot tub & spa covers; atomizers, toiletry

---

3592 Carburetors, Pistons, Rings & Valves

(P-16145)
B & Y MACHINE CO
1060 5th St, Calimesa (92320-1512)
P.O. Box 1208, Redlands (92373-0401)
PHONE....................909 795-8588
John L Baker, *Manager*
EMP: 12
SQ FT: 10,000
SALES (est): 860K **Privately Held**
SIC: 3592 Valves

(P-16146)
CP-CARRILLO INC
17401 Armstrong Ave, Irvine (92614-5723)
PHONE....................949 567-9000
Barry Calvert, *Mng Member*
EMP: 30
SALES (corp-wide): 1.4B **Privately Held**
SIC: 3592 3714 Pistons & piston rings; connecting rods, motor vehicle engine
HQ Cp-Carrillo, Inc.
1902 Mcgaw Ave
Irvine CA 92614

(P-16147)
CP-CARRILLO INC (DH)
1902 Mcgaw Ave, Irvine (92614-0910)
PHONE....................949 567-9000
Barry Calvert, *CEO*
Peter Calvert, *President*
Harry Glieder, *CFO*
Nathan Cser, *Engineer*
Cindy Verkooij, *Marketing Staff*
▲ EMP: 120
SQ FT: 31,840
SALES: 28.8MM
SALES (corp-wide): 1.4B **Privately Held**
SIC: 3592 3714 Pistons & piston rings; connecting rods, motor vehicle engine

(P-16148)
NOEL BURT
Also Called: Recarbco
880 Howe Rd Ste F, Martinez (94553-3485)
PHONE....................925 439-7030
Noel Burt, *Owner*
EMP: 42
SQ FT: 20,000
SALES (est): 3.2MM **Privately Held**
WEB: www.recarbco.com
SIC: 3592 3714 Carburetors; motor vehicle parts & accessories

(P-16149)
PACIFIC PISTON RING CO INC
3620 Eastham Dr, Culver City (90232-2411)
P.O. Box 927 (90232-0927)
PHONE....................310 836-3322
Forest Shannon, *President*
Christina Davis, *Treasurer*
Michael Shannon, *Vice Pres*
EMP: 90
SQ FT: 35,000
SALES (est): 18.5MM **Privately Held**
SIC: 3592 Pistons & piston rings

(P-16150)
PROBE RACING COMPONENTS INC
Also Called: Kwikparts.com
5022 Onyx St, Torrance (90503-2742)
PHONE....................310 784-2977
Larry M O'Neal, *CEO*
▲ EMP: 28
SQ FT: 25,000
SALES (est): 5.5MM **Privately Held**
WEB: www.promustang.com
SIC: 3592 3463 Pistons & piston rings; engine or turbine forgings, nonferrous

(P-16151)
ROSS RACING PISTONS
625 S Douglas St, El Segundo (90245-4812)
PHONE....................310 536-0100
Ken Roble, *President*
Joy Roble, *Corp Secy*
J B Mills, *Vice Pres*

Chris Petrini, *Creative Dir*
Ivet Lopez, *Admin Asst*
EMP: 55
SQ FT: 25,000
SALES: 4.3MM **Privately Held**
WEB: www.rosspistons.com
SIC: 3592 Pistons & piston rings

(P-16152)
RTR INDUSTRIES LLC
Also Called: Grant Piston Rings
1360 N Jefferson St, Anaheim (92807-1614)
PHONE....................714 996-0050
Romy Laxamana,
Ramon Diaz,
Thom Nguyen,
Craig Marder, *Manager*
▲ EMP: 45
SQ FT: 44,000
SALES (est): 7.5MM **Privately Held**
SIC: 3592 Pistons & piston rings

(P-16153)
TOR C A M INDUSTRIES INC
Also Called: Venolia Pistons
2160 E Cherry Indus Cir, Long Beach (90805-4412)
PHONE....................562 531-8463
Frank Pisino, *President*
EMP: 31
SQ FT: 10,000
SALES (est): 4.1MM **Privately Held**
WEB: www.venolia.com
SIC: 3592 3354 Pistons & piston rings; aluminum rod & bar

3593 Fluid Power Cylinders & Actuators

(P-16154)
C & H MACHINE INC
Also Called: Support Equipment
943 S Andrsen Dr Escndido Escondido, Escondido (92029)
PHONE....................760 746-6459
Lyle J Anderson, *Exec VP*
Charles Gohlich, *Admin Sec*
EMP: 70 EST: 1964
SQ FT: 13,000
SALES (est): 16.8MM **Privately Held**
WEB: www.c-hmachine.com
SIC: 3593 3599 Fluid power cylinders & actuators; machine shop, jobbing & repair; electrical discharge machining (EDM)

(P-16155)
CAL-WEST MACHINING INC
1734 W Sequoia Ave, Orange (92868-1016)
PHONE....................714 637-4161
Larry Lewis Sr, *President*
Marleen Lewis, *Treasurer*
EMP: 10 EST: 1981
SQ FT: 11,000
SALES (est): 2.6MM **Privately Held**
WEB: www.calwestmachine.com
SIC: 3593 3599 Fluid power actuators, hydraulic or pneumatic; machine shop, jobbing & repair

(P-16156)
GENERAL DYNMICS OTS NCVLLE INC
511 Grove St, Healdsburg (95448-4747)
PHONE....................707 473-9200
Richard Schroeder, *General Mgr*
Tim Finks, *Engineer*
EMP: 60 EST: 1999
SQ FT: 28,000
SALES (est): 12.4MM
SALES (corp-wide): 30.9B **Publicly Held**
WEB: www.ver.gd-ots.com
SIC: 3593 Fluid power cylinders & actuators
HQ: General Dynamics Ordnance And Tactical Systems, Inc.
11399 16th Ct N Ste 200
Saint Petersburg FL 33716
727 578-8100

PRODUCTS & SVCS

(P-16157)
GENERAL GRINDING & MFG CO LLC
15100 Valley View Ave, La Mirada (90638-5226)
PHONE....................562 921-7033
SE Heung Kim,
Rich Kim,
Silas Pak,
EMP: 25
SQ FT: 25,000
SALES: 3MM **Privately Held**
WEB: www.generalgrinding.com
SIC: 3593 3599 3471 Fluid power cylinders, hydraulic or pneumatic; grinding castings for the trade; plating & polishing

(P-16158)
HYDRAULIC PNEUMATIC INC
Also Called: Hpi Cylinders
13766 Milroy Pl, Santa Fe Springs (90670-5131)
PHONE....................562 926-1122
James Whitney, *President*
EMP: 18 **EST:** 1946
SQ FT: 18,000
SALES: 2.2MM **Privately Held**
WEB: www.hydraulic-pneumatic.com
SIC: 3593 3599 Fluid power cylinders, hydraulic or pneumatic; machine shop, jobbing & repair

(P-16159)
ROBERTS TOOL COMPANY INC (PA)
20409 Prairie St, Chatsworth (91311-6029)
PHONE....................818 341-3344
James B Hart, *CEO*
BJ Schramm, *President*
Bill Hart, *Vice Pres*
Elizabeth Hart, *Vice Pres*
Robert McSweeney, *Engineer*
◆ **EMP:** 130
SQ FT: 42,000
SALES (est): 34MM **Privately Held**
SIC: 3593 3594 3599 Fluid power cylinders & actuators; fluid power pumps & motors; machine shop, jobbing & repair

(P-16160)
TURLOCK MACHINE WORKS
Also Called: Hypower Hydraulics
1240 S 1st St, Turlock (95380-6023)
PHONE....................209 632-2275
Vivian Manha, *CEO*
Konrad Hack, *Treasurer*
Judy Hunt, *Vice Pres*
Patti Nelson, *Office Mgr*
EMP: 20
SQ FT: 35,000
SALES (est): 4.7MM **Privately Held**
WEB: www.hypowerhydraulics.com
SIC: 3593 Fluid power cylinders, hydraulic or pneumatic

(P-16161)
VENTURA HYDRULIC MCH WORKS INC
1555 Callens Rd, Ventura (93003-5606)
PHONE....................805 656-1760
Fred H Malzacher, *President*
Ray Jenkins, *Vice Pres*
Elaine Z Malzacher, *Vice Pres*
EMP: 20
SQ FT: 15,700
SALES (est): 4.7MM **Privately Held**
WEB: www.venturahydraulics.com
SIC: 3593 Fluid power cylinders, hydraulic or pneumatic

3594 Fluid Power Pumps & Motors

(P-16162)
BERNELL HYDRAULICS INC (PA)
8810 Etiwanda Ave, Rancho Cucamonga (91739-9662)
P.O. Box 417 (91739-0417)
PHONE....................909 899-1751
Terrance B Jones Sr, *Ch of Bd*
Rhonda A Garness, *President*
John S Clemons, *Vice Pres*
EMP: 32
SQ FT: 6,000
SALES (est): 14.7MM **Privately Held**
WEB: www.bernellhydraulics.com
SIC: 3594 5084 3621 3593 Pumps, hydraulic power transfer; hydraulic systems equipment & supplies; motors & generators; fluid power cylinders & actuators; pumps & pumping equipment; machine tools, metal forming type

(P-16163)
CRISSAIR INC
28909 Avenue Williams, Valencia (91355-4183)
PHONE....................661 367-3300
Linda Bradley, *President*
Patrick Lacanfora, *Vice Pres*
Jack Mossman, *Executive*
Eric Grupp, *Business Dir*
Vivian Gonzales, *Administration*
EMP: 185
SQ FT: 40,000
SALES (est): 55.7MM
SALES (corp-wide): 685.7MM **Publicly Held**
WEB: www.crissair.com
SIC: 3594 3492 Motors, pneumatic; fluid power valves & hose fittings
PA: Esco Technologies Inc.
9900 Clayton Rd Ste A
Saint Louis MO 63124
314 213-7200

(P-16164)
DOW HYDRAULIC SYSTEMS INC
2895 Metropolitan Pl, Pomona (91767-1853)
PHONE....................909 596-6602
Richard Dow, *Principal*
Keith Dow, *Prdtn Mgr*
EMP: 10
SALES (est): 1.6MM
SALES (corp-wide): 12.9MM **Privately Held**
SIC: 3594 Fluid power pumps & motors
PA: Dow Hydraulic Systems, Inc.
1835 Wright Ave
La Verne CA 91750
909 596-6602

(P-16165)
EDDY PUMP CORPORATION (PA)
15405 Olde Highway 80, El Cajon (92021-2409)
PHONE....................619 258-7020
Harry P Weinrib, *President*
Peter Weinrib, *CFO*
James J Hamill, *Treasurer*
Dan Wahlgren, *Engineer*
EMP: 13
SQ FT: 5,000
SALES (est): 3.8MM **Privately Held**
WEB: www.eddypump.com
SIC: 3594 8731 Pumps, hydraulic power transfer; engineering laboratory, except testing

(P-16166)
ITT LLC
1400 S Shamrock Ave, Monrovia (91016-4267)
PHONE....................626 305-6100
EMP: 16
SALES (corp-wide): 2.5B **Publicly Held**
SIC: 3594 Fluid power pumps & motors
HQ: Itt Llc
1133 Westchester Ave N-100
White Plains NY 10604
914 641-2000

(P-16167)
KECO INC
Also Called: Pump-A-Head
3475 Kurtz St, San Diego (92110-4430)
P.O. Box 80308 (92138-0308)
PHONE....................619 546-9533
Anne Kenton Bleier, *President*
Andrew Bleier, *Vice Pres*
▼ **EMP:** 10
SQ FT: 2,000
SALES (est): 2.6MM **Privately Held**
WEB: www.pumpahead.com
SIC: 3594 5084 Fluid power pumps; industrial machinery & equipment

(P-16168)
OSTOICH DIESEL SERVICE
Also Called: Diesel Injection Service
1690 Ashley Way, Colton (92324-4000)
P.O. Box 11955, San Bernardino (92423-1955)
PHONE....................909 885-0590
Mark A Ostoich, *President*
Florence M Ostoich, *Treasurer*
Mark Ostoich, *Vice Pres*
EMP: 19
SQ FT: 5,000
SALES (est): 1.9MM **Privately Held**
SIC: 3594 Fluid power pumps & motors

(P-16169)
PARKER-HANNIFIN CORPORATION
Composite Sealing Systems Div
7664 Panasonic Way, San Diego (92154-8206)
PHONE....................619 661-7000
Jim Rando, *Manager*
Ramon Reyes, *Treasurer*
Laurie Phelts, *Program Mgr*
Frank Solis, *General Mgr*
Terry Ennis, *Administration*
EMP: 130
SALES (corp-wide): 12B **Publicly Held**
WEB: www.parker.com
SIC: 3594 Fluid power pumps & motors
PA: Parker-Hannifin Corporation
6035 Parkland Blvd
Cleveland OH 44124
216 896-3000

(P-16170)
PARKER-HANNIFIN CORPORATION
Also Called: Cylinder Division
221 Helicopter Cir, Corona (92880-2532)
PHONE....................951 280-3800
Donald P Szmania, *Branch Mgr*
Joi Martin, *Administration*
Tom Mitchell, *Sales Mgr*
Mary Zimmerman, *Sales Staff*
John Beam, *Manager*
EMP: 40
SALES (corp-wide): 14.3B **Publicly Held**
WEB: www.parker.com
SIC: 3594 3728 3593 Fluid power pumps & motors; aircraft parts & equipment; fluid power cylinders & actuators
PA: Parker-Hannifin Corporation
6035 Parkland Blvd
Cleveland OH 44124
216 896-3000

(P-16171)
PARKER-HANNIFIN CORPORATION
16666 Von Karman Ave, Irvine (92606-4997)
PHONE....................949 833-3000
Fax: 949 851-3341
EMP: 123
SALES (corp-wide): 13B **Publicly Held**
SIC: 3594
PA: Parker-Hannifin Corporation
6035 Parkland Blvd
Cleveland OH 44124
216 896-3000

(P-16172)
PARKER-HANNIFIN CORPORATION
3007 Bunsen Ave Ste K, Ventura (93003-7633)
PHONE....................805 658-2984
Russell Lanham, *Branch Mgr*
EMP: 12
SALES (corp-wide): 14.3B **Publicly Held**
SIC: 3594 Fluid power pumps & motors
PA: Parker-Hannifin Corporation
6035 Parkland Blvd
Cleveland OH 44124
216 896-3000

(P-16173)
WESTERN HYDROSTATICS INC (PA)
1956 Keats Dr, Riverside (92501-1747)
PHONE....................951 784-2133
John Starke Scott, *President*
Barnett Totten, *Treasurer*
Tandy W Scott, *Vice Pres*
Steve Moser, *Engineer*
Pat Maluso, *Plant Mgr*
▲ **EMP:** 30
SALES (est): 4.5MM **Privately Held**
WEB: www.weshyd.com
SIC: 3594 7699 5084 Hydrostatic drives (transmissions); hydraulic equipment repair; hydraulic systems equipment & supplies

3596 Scales & Balances, Exc Laboratory

(P-16174)
BIOMICROLAB INC
2500 Dean Lesher Dr Ste A, Concord (94520-1273)
PHONE....................925 689-1200
David B Miller, *President*
William Hess, *Vice Pres*
Brian Lechman, *Electrical Engi*
Peter Miller, *VP Opers*
Bill Hess, *VP Mktg*
EMP: 25
SALES (est): 2MM **Privately Held**
WEB: www.biomicrolab.com
SIC: 3596 Weighing machines & apparatus

(P-16175)
JONEL ENGINEERING
500 E Walnut Ave, Fullerton (92832-2540)
P.O. Box 798 (92836-0798)
PHONE....................714 879-2360
John Lawson, *CEO*
Mike Lawson, *President*
Christopher Haas, *Engineer*
Allen Wiggins, *Engineer*
Chris Crane, *Finance Mgr*
▼ **EMP:** 20
SQ FT: 8,000
SALES (est): 3.3MM **Privately Held**
SIC: 3596 5045 Weighing machines & apparatus; computers

(P-16176)
SCALE SERVICES INC
3553a N Perris Blvd Ste 8, Perris (92571-3149)
PHONE....................909 266-0896
Corey Stacy, *CEO*
EMP: 11
SQ FT: 1,300
SALES (est): 680.1K **Privately Held**
SIC: 3596 Counting scales; industrial scales; truck (motor vehicle) scales

3599 Machinery & Eqpt, Indl & Commercial, NEC

(P-16177)
2M MACHINE CORPORATION
13171 Rosecrans Ave, Santa Fe Springs (90670-4931)
PHONE....................562 404-4225
Michael Manspeaker, *Manager*
▲ **EMP:** 13
SQ FT: 8,650
SALES (est): 1.3MM **Privately Held**
WEB: www.2mmachining.com
SIC: 3599 Machine shop, jobbing & repair

(P-16178)
3B MACHINING CO INC
2292 Trade Zone Blvd 1a, San Jose (95131-1801)
PHONE....................408 719-9237
Bryan Bui, *President*
EMP: 10
SQ FT: 4,281
SALES (est): 1.5MM **Privately Held**
SIC: 3599 Machine shop, jobbing & repair

(P-16179)
3D MACHINE CO INC
4790 E Wesley Dr, Anaheim (92807-1941)
PHONE....................714 777-8985
Maria Falcusan, *President*
Constantine Falcusan, *Vice Pres*
EMP: 30
SQ FT: 3,300

▲ = Import ▼=Export
◆ =Import/Export

SALES (est): 5.9MM **Privately Held**
WEB: www.3dmachineco.com
SIC: 3599 Machine shop, jobbing & repair

(P-16180)
478826 LIMITED
Also Called: Zi Machine Manufacturing
5050 Hillsdale Cir, El Dorado Hills
(95762-5706)
PHONE..................................916 933-5280
Steve Zeldag, *CEO*
EMP: 21
SQ FT: 26,000
SALES (est): 3.1MM **Privately Held**
SIC: 3599 Machine shop, jobbing & repair

(P-16181)
A & B AEROSPACE INC
612 S Ayon Ave, Azusa (91702-5122)
PHONE..................................626 334-2976
Kenneth Smith, *President*
Malcolm Smith, *Vice Pres*
EMP: 35
SQ FT: 23,000
SALES (est): 6.7MM **Privately Held**
SIC: 3599 Machine shop, jobbing & repair

(P-16182)
A & D PRECISION MACHINING INC
4155 Business Center Dr, Fremont
(94538-6355)
PHONE..................................510 657-6781
David A Dreifort, *CEO*
Nicole Costanzo, *Info Tech Mgr*
Anson Nguyen, *Engineer*
Dan Shulda, *Business Mgr*
Nick Le, *Mfg Mgr*
EMP: 45
SQ FT: 28,000
SALES (est): 15.1MM **Privately Held**
WEB: www.adprecision.com
SIC: 3599 Machine & other job shop work

(P-16183)
A & D PRECISION MFG INC
4751 E Hunter Ave, Anaheim (92807-1940)
PHONE..................................714 779-2714
Dan Wiegel, *President*
Anthony Brown, *Vice Pres*
Tony Brown, *Vice Pres*
Allan Johnson, *QC Mgr*
EMP: 21
SQ FT: 9,000
SALES (est): 2.2MM **Privately Held**
WEB: www.adprecisionmfg.com
SIC: 3599 3728 Machine shop, jobbing & repair; aircraft parts & equipment

(P-16184)
A & H ENGINEERING & MFG INC
Also Called: A & H Tool Engineering
17109 Edwards Rd, Cerritos (90703-2423)
PHONE..................................562 623-9717
Asher Sharoni, *President*
Tova Sharoni, *CFO*
EMP: 27
SQ FT: 15,000
SALES: 1.6MM **Privately Held**
SIC: 3599 Grinding castings for the trade

(P-16185)
A & J MACHINING INC
16305 Vineyard Blvd Ste B, Morgan Hill
(95037-7132)
PHONE..................................903 566-0304
John Zekanoski, *Vice Pres*
John Boehme, *President*
Maryann Penwacesek, *Corp Secy*
EMP: 10
SALES (est): 1MM **Privately Held**
SIC: 3599 Machine shop, jobbing & repair

(P-16186)
A & M ENGINEERING INC
15854 Salvatierra St, Irwindale
(91706-6603)
PHONE..................................626 813-2020
Boris Beljak Sr, *President*
Anita Beljak, *Corp Secy*
Boris Beljak Jr, *Vice Pres*
Roy Beljak, *Vice Pres*
EMP: 80 EST: 1973
SQ FT: 25,000

SALES (est): 14.1MM **Privately Held**
WEB: www.amengineeringinc.com
SIC: 3599 3812 3537 Machine shop, jobbing & repair; search & navigation equipment; industrial trucks & tractors

(P-16187)
A & R ENGINEERING CO INC
1053 E Bedmar St, Carson (90746-3601)
PHONE..................................310 603-9060
Murat Sehidoglu, *President*
EMP: 44
SQ FT: 23,334
SALES (est): 10.6MM **Privately Held**
WEB: www.arengr.com
SIC: 3599 Machine shop, jobbing & repair

(P-16188)
A & V ENGINEERING INC
1155 W Mahalo Pl, Compton (90220-5444)
PHONE..................................310 637-9906
Vic Kuyumjian, *President*
Vartuhi Kuyumjian, *Vice Pres*
EMP: 12
SQ FT: 8,000
SALES (est): 2.5MM **Privately Held**
WEB: www.avengineering.com
SIC: 3599 Machine shop, jobbing & repair

(P-16189)
A A A ENGINEERING & MFG CO
2118 Huntington Dr, San Marino
(91108-2024)
P.O. Box 660273, Arcadia (91066-0273)
PHONE..................................626 447-5029
Lynn Akins, *Owner*
EMP: 37
SQ FT: 500
SALES (est): 2.1MM **Privately Held**
SIC: 3599 Machine shop, jobbing & repair

(P-16190)
A C MANUFACTURING INC
3023 Mount Whitney Rd, Escondido
(92029-1800)
PHONE..................................760 745-3717
Arley G Chugon, *President*
Billy Daniel, *Admin Sec*
EMP: 10
SQ FT: 12,000
SALES (est): 600K **Privately Held**
SIC: 3599 Machine shop, jobbing & repair

(P-16191)
A F M ENGINEERING INC
1313 E Borchard Ave, Santa Ana
(92705-4412)
PHONE..................................714 547-0194
Charles S Irwin, *President*
Jeffery Batchman, *Vice Pres*
EMP: 10
SQ FT: 10,000
SALES: 1MM **Privately Held**
WEB: www.afmeng.com
SIC: 3599 3089 Machine shop, jobbing & repair; plastic processing

(P-16192)
A H MACHINE INC
214 N Cedar Ave, Inglewood (90301-1009)
PHONE..................................310 672-0016
M P Desai, *President*
Sam Patel, *Vice Pres*
EMP: 12
SQ FT: 6,500
SALES (est): 2.5MM **Privately Held**
SIC: 3599 Machine shop, jobbing & repair

(P-16193)
A N TOOL & DIE INC
518 S Fair Oaks Ave, Pasadena
(91105-2690)
PHONE..................................626 795-3238
Dorothy Nettleton, *President*
John Nettleton, *Vice Pres*
EMP: 14
SQ FT: 6,000
SALES (est): 2.2MM **Privately Held**
SIC: 3599 Machine shop, jobbing & repair

(P-16194)
A&A ENGINEERING INC
158 Santa Felicia Dr, Goleta (93117-2804)
PHONE..................................805 685-4882
Hoa Truong, *President*
EMP: 10

SQ FT: 4,000
SALES (est): 1.2MM **Privately Held**
WEB: www.aaeng.com
SIC: 3599 Machine shop, jobbing & repair

(P-16195)
A&G MACHINE SHOP INC
1352 Burton Ave Ste B, Salinas
(93901-4417)
P.O. Box 6190 (93912-6190)
PHONE..................................831 759-2261
Anuar Molina, *President*
Edna Molina, *Vice Pres*
EMP: 16
SQ FT: 5,500
SALES (est): 1.7MM **Privately Held**
SIC: 3599 Machine shop, jobbing & repair

(P-16196)
A&T PRECISION MACHINING
330 Piercy Rd, San Jose (95138-1401)
PHONE..................................408 363-1198
James Le, *President*
An Le, *Partner*
Hieu Le, *Partner*
EMP: 12
SALES (est): 2.2MM **Privately Held**
SIC: 3599 Machine shop, jobbing & repair; machine & other job shop work

(P-16197)
A&W PRECISION MACHINING INC
17907 S Figueroa St Ste C, Gardena
(90248-4256)
PHONE..................................310 527-7242
Walter Galich, *President*
Adelfo Varela, *Vice Pres*
EMP: 15
SQ FT: 3,700
SALES (est): 1.1MM **Privately Held**
SIC: 3599 Machine shop, jobbing & repair

(P-16198)
A-1 JAYS MACHINING INC (PA)
2228 Oakland Rd, San Jose (95131-1414)
PHONE..................................408 262-1845
James K Machathil, *CEO*
Thomas Abraham, *General Mgr*
Shirley Barbary, *Accounting Mgr*
Shanmuga Ganesan, *Prdtn Mgr*
Nicole Cherry, *Mfg Staff*
EMP: 79
SQ FT: 10,000
SALES (est): 16.9MM **Privately Held**
WEB: www.a1jays.com
SIC: 3599 Machine shop, jobbing & repair

(P-16199)
A-1 MACHINE MANUFACTURING INC (PA)
490 Gianni St, Santa Clara (95054-2413)
PHONE..................................408 727-0880
Yong Kil, *President*
Yong Su Pak, *Vice Pres*
▲ EMP: 129
SQ FT: 250,000
SALES (est): 56.3MM **Privately Held**
WEB: www.a-1machine.com
SIC: 3599 Machine shop, jobbing & repair

(P-16200)
AAERO SWISS
22347 La Palma Ave # 105, Yorba Linda
(92887-3826)
PHONE..................................714 692-0558
Brandy Jones, *President*
Randy Jones, *Principal*
EMP: 10
SALES (est): 1.1MM **Privately Held**
SIC: 3599 Machine shop, jobbing & repair

(P-16201)
ABEN MACHINE PRODUCTS INC
6943 Eton Ave, Canoga Park (91303-2110)
PHONE..................................818 673-1627
Nabeel Saoud, *President*
Esdras Giron, *Vice Pres*
EMP: 17
SQ FT: 3,000
SALES (est): 1.5MM **Privately Held**
WEB: www.abenusa.com
SIC: 3599 Machine shop, jobbing & repair

(P-16202)
ABLE WIRE EDM INC
440 Atlas St Ste A, Brea (92821-3136)
PHONE..................................714 255-1967
John Marquardt, *President*
Kenny Snow, *Vice Pres*
Steven Stinnett, *Vice Pres*
Barbara Marquardt, *Admin Sec*
Chris Marks, *Manager*
EMP: 15
SQ FT: 5,500
SALES: 1MM **Privately Held**
SIC: 3599 Machine shop, jobbing & repair; electrical discharge machining (EDM)

(P-16203)
ABN INDUSTRIAL CO INC (PA)
5940 Dale St, Buena Park (90621-2150)
PHONE..................................714 521-9211
Jim C K Hsieh, *President*
▲ EMP: 12
SQ FT: 10,000
SALES: 750K **Privately Held**
SIC: 3599 Machine shop, jobbing & repair

(P-16204)
ABSOLUTE MACHINE
5020 Mountain Lakes Blvd, Redding
(96003-1457)
PHONE..................................530 242-6840
Alfred Madena, *President*
EMP: 20
SALES (est): 3.6MM **Privately Held**
SIC: 3599 Machine shop, jobbing & repair

(P-16205)
ACC PRECISION INC
321 Hearst Dr, Oxnard (93030-5158)
PHONE..................................805 278-9801
Arturo Alfaro, *President*
EMP: 15
SQ FT: 6,000
SALES (est): 1.2MM **Privately Held**
WEB: www.accprecision.com
SIC: 3599 Machine shop, jobbing & repair

(P-16206)
ACCU MACHINE INC
440 Aldo Ave, Santa Clara (95054-2301)
PHONE..................................408 855-8835
EMP: 29
SALES (est): 5.3MM **Privately Held**
SIC: 3599 Machine shop, jobbing & repair

(P-16207)
ACCUFAB INC
1326 E Francis St, Ontario (91761-5714)
PHONE..................................909 930-1751
Donna Mihovetz, *President*
EMP: 10
SQ FT: 9,000
SALES (est): 1.1MM **Privately Held**
SIC: 3599 Machine shop, jobbing & repair

(P-16208)
ACCURATE TECHNOLOGY MFG INC
930 Thompson Pl, Sunnyvale
(94085-4517)
PHONE..................................408 733-4344
Ivo Dukanovic, *CEO*
John Dukanovic, *Owner*
EMP: 60
SQ FT: 40,000
SALES (est): 9.8MM **Privately Held**
SIC: 3599 Machine shop, jobbing & repair

(P-16209)
ACCUTECH MANUFACTURING INC
13109 Los Nietos Rd, Santa Fe Springs
(90670-3027)
P.O. Box 6320, Anaheim (92816-0320)
PHONE..................................562 903-2365
Ramiro Perez, *President*
Maria Salafia, *Admin Sec*
EMP: 40
SQ FT: 24,000
SALES (est): 4.1MM **Privately Held**
WEB: www.accutechmfginc.com
SIC: 3599 Machine shop, jobbing & repair

PRODUCTS & SVCS

(P-16210)
ACE INDUSTRIES INC
738 Design Ct Ste 302, Chula Vista
(91911-6161)
PHONE..................................619 482-2700
Bobby Yoo, *President*
Joy Yoo, *CFO*
▲ EMP: 20
SQ FT: 15,000
SALES (est): 3.9MM **Privately Held**
WEB: www.aceindustries.com
SIC: 3599 Machine shop, jobbing & repair

(P-16211)
ACE MACHINE SHOP INC
11200 Wright Rd, Lynwood (90262-3124)
PHONE..................................310 608-2277
Pedro Gallinucci, *President*
Lucia Gallinucci, *Vice Pres*
Silvia Durell, *Office Mgr*
Jeff Ducas, *Purchasing*
Gustavo Velazquez, *Foreman/Supr*
EMP: 70 EST: 1956
SQ FT: 35,000
SALES (est): 13.3MM **Privately Held**
SIC: 3599 Machine shop, jobbing & repair

(P-16212)
ACKLEY METAL PRODUCTS INC
Also Called: Waco Products
1311 E Saint Gertrude Pl B, Santa Ana
(92705-5216)
PHONE..................................714 979-7431
Paul Ackley, *President*
Alan Ackley, *Vice Pres*
EMP: 12
SQ FT: 3,200
SALES (est): 2.3MM **Privately Held**
WEB: www.ackleymetal.com
SIC: 3599 Machine shop, jobbing & repair

(P-16213)
ACM MACHINING INC
Also Called: Alfred's Machining
240 State Highway 16 # 18, Plymouth
(95669-9701)
PHONE..................................916 804-9489
Carlos Balbacas, *Owner*
EMP: 32
SALES (corp-wide): 16.2MM **Privately Held**
SIC: 3599 3494 Machine shop, jobbing & repair; valves & pipe fittings
PA: Acm Machining, Inc.
11390 Gold Dredge Way
Rancho Cordova CA 95742
916 852-8600

(P-16214)
ACM MACHINING INC (PA)
11390 Gold Dredge Way, Rancho Cordova
(95742-6867)
PHONE..................................916 852-8600
Alfred Balbach, *President*
Carlos Balbachas, *Vice Pres*
Pete Reynen, *General Mgr*
Sherry Burnett, *Office Mgr*
Christina McWilliams, *Office Mgr*
▲ EMP: 41
SQ FT: 29,000
SALES (est): 16.2MM **Privately Held**
SIC: 3599 Machine shop, jobbing & repair

(P-16215)
ACRA ENTERPRISES INC
5760 Thornwood Dr, Goleta (93117-3802)
PHONE..................................805 964-4757
Jack Novak, *President*
Pam Kane, *Vice Pres*
EMP: 10
SQ FT: 4,000
SALES (est): 870K **Privately Held**
WEB: www.acraenterprises.com
SIC: 3599 Machine shop, jobbing & repair

(P-16216)
ACRATECH INC
2502 Supply St, Pomona (91767-2113)
PHONE..................................909 392-5722
Scott Dordick, *President*
Patty Dordick, *Vice Pres*
EMP: 12
SQ FT: 4,000

SALES (est): 1.9MM **Privately Held**
WEB: www.acratech.net
SIC: 3599 Machine & other job shop work

(P-16217)
ACRO-SPEC GRINDING CO INC
4134 Indus Way, Riverside (92503-4847)
PHONE..................................951 736-1199
Haskell Boss, *President*
Clifford Boss, *Vice Pres*
Michelle Austin, *Admin Sec*
EMP: 14
SQ FT: 7,000
SALES: 1.8MM **Privately Held**
SIC: 3599 Machine shop, jobbing & repair

(P-16218)
ACROMIL LLC
Also Called: Btl Machine
1168 Sherborn St, Corona (92879-2089)
PHONE..................................951 808-9929
David Nguyen, *President*
David Patterson, *Vice Pres*
▲ EMP: 65
SQ FT: 80,000
SALES (est): 24.9MM **Privately Held**
WEB: www.btlmachine.com
SIC: 3599 Machine shop, jobbing & repair
PA: Acromil Corporation
18421 Railroad St
City Of Industry CA 91748
626 964-2522

(P-16219)
ACROSCOPE LLC
3501 Thomas Rd Ste 7, Santa Clara
(95054-2037)
PHONE..................................408 727-6896
Gordon Erb, *Owner*
Michael Hadley, *General Mgr*
EMP: 12
SALES (est): 1.7MM **Privately Held**
WEB: www.acroscope.com
SIC: 3599 Machine shop, jobbing & repair

(P-16220)
ACTION BROACHING INC
Also Called: Action Gear & Broaching
1717 Monrovia Ave, Costa Mesa
(92627-4406)
P.O. Box 10007 (92627-0007)
PHONE..................................949 645-8212
Margaret Mackley, *President*
EMP: 10 EST: 1970
SQ FT: 2,800
SALES (est): 1.6MM **Privately Held**
SIC: 3599 Machine shop, jobbing & repair

(P-16221)
ACU SPEC INC
Also Called: Afi
990 Richard Ave Ste 103, Santa Clara
(95050-2828)
PHONE..................................408 748-8600
Fred Budde III, *President*
Amy Budde, *CFO*
EMP: 13
SQ FT: 9,900
SALES (est): 133.1K **Privately Held**
WEB: www.anchorsemi.com
SIC: 3599 Machine shop, jobbing & repair

(P-16222)
ACUNA DIONISIO ABLE
Also Called: A & L Engineering
12629 Prairie Ave, Hawthorne
(90250-4611)
PHONE..................................310 978-4741
Dionasio Abel Acuna, *Owner*
EMP: 15
SQ FT: 3,700
SALES: 300K **Privately Held**
SIC: 3599 8711 5049 Machine shop, jobbing & repair; industrial engineers; engineers' equipment & supplies

(P-16223)
ADC ENTERPRISES INC
633 W Katella Ave Ste T, Orange
(92867-4621)
PHONE..................................714 538-3102
Virginia Devois, *Owner*
EMP: 17
SALES (est): 1.1MM **Privately Held**
SIC: 3599 Machine shop, jobbing & repair

(P-16224)
ADEM LLC
Also Called: Advanced Design Engrg & Mfg
1040 Di Giulio Ave # 160, Santa Clara
(95050-2847)
PHONE..................................408 727-8955
Boris Kesil,
Jacob Obolsky,
Valery Sokolsky,
EMP: 30
SQ FT: 11,000
SALES (est): 5.1MM **Privately Held**
WEB: www.ademllc.com
SIC: 3599 8711 Machine shop, jobbing & repair; engineering services

(P-16225)
ADVANCED CERAMIC TECHNOLOGY
803 W Angus Ave, Orange (92868-1307)
PHONE..................................714 538-2524
Eric Andrew Roberts, *President*
William Roberts, *Vice Pres*
Kelly Roberts, *Program Mgr*
EMP: 16
SQ FT: 9,900
SALES: 1.7MM **Privately Held**
WEB: www.advancedceramictech.com
SIC: 3599 Machine shop, jobbing & repair

(P-16226)
ADVANCED COMPONENTS MFG
Also Called: A C M
1415 N Carolan Ave, Burlingame
(94010-2403)
PHONE..................................650 344-6272
Craig Corey, *President*
Jack Corey, *Treasurer*
Gloria Corey, *Admin Sec*
EMP: 20
SQ FT: 6,500
SALES (est): 3.3MM **Privately Held**
SIC: 3599 3444 Machine shop, jobbing & repair; sheet metalwork

(P-16227)
ADVANCED ENGINEERING & EDM INC
13007 Kirkham Way Ste A, Poway
(92064-7152)
PHONE..................................858 679-6800
Norm Turoff, *CEO*
Lindy Bauer, *Controller*
William J Bauer, *Manager*
EMP: 17
SALES (est): 1.6MM **Privately Held**
SIC: 3599 Machine shop, jobbing & repair

(P-16228)
ADVANCED ENGINERING AND EDM
13007 Kirkham Way Ste A, Poway
(92064-7152)
PHONE..................................858 679-6800
William J Bauer, *Managing Prtnr*
Norm Turoff, *Managing Prtnr*
Lindsey Bauer, *General Mgr*
EMP: 20 EST: 2011
SALES (est): 3.2MM **Privately Held**
SIC: 3599 Machine shop, jobbing & repair

(P-16229)
ADVANCED LASER CUTTING INC
Also Called: Advanced Laser & Wtr Jet Cutng
820 Comstock St, Santa Clara
(95054-3404)
PHONE..................................408 486-0700
Lester Gragg, *President*
Rick Linthicum, *Principal*
EMP: 13
SQ FT: 6,800
SALES (est): 2.3MM **Privately Held**
WEB: www.adv-laser.com
SIC: 3599 Machine shop, jobbing & repair

(P-16230)
ADVANCED MCHNING SOLUTIONS INC
3523 Main St Ste 606, Chula Vista
(91911-0803)
PHONE..................................619 671-3055
Pamela Yuhm, *President*
Mariana Bramba, *Purch Mgr*

Mariana Miller, *Purch Mgr*
EMP: 35
SALES (est): 4.8MM **Privately Held**
WEB: www.amsinc2005.com
SIC: 3599 Machine shop, jobbing & repair

(P-16231)
ADVANCED MCHNING TCHNIQUES INC
16205 Vineyard Blvd, Morgan Hill
(95037-7124)
PHONE..................................408 778-4500
Frank C Dutra, *President*
Susan Dutra, *Vice Pres*
Marla Abeyta, *Office Mgr*
Sharyn Gibbs, *Sales Staff*
EMP: 49
SQ FT: 24,000
SALES (est): 8MM **Privately Held**
WEB: www.advancedmachining.com
SIC: 3599 Machine shop, jobbing & repair

(P-16232)
ADVANCED PRCSION MACHINING INC
1649 Monrovia Ave, Costa Mesa
(92627-4404)
PHONE..................................949 650-6113
Sean McCaig, *CEO*
Russell Congelliere, *CFO*
Yasumi McCaig, *Admin Sec*
EMP: 12
SQ FT: 2,500
SALES (est): 1.3MM **Privately Held**
WEB: www.advanced-precision.com
SIC: 3599 Machine shop, jobbing & repair

(P-16233)
ADVANCED TECHNOLOGY MACHINING
28210 Avenue Crocker # 301, Valencia
(91355-3475)
PHONE..................................661 257-2313
Herbert Joe Howton, *CEO*
Vickie Howton, *President*
Joe Howton, *Vice Pres*
Steve R Riddle, *Managing Dir*
EMP: 15
SQ FT: 4,160
SALES (est): 2.9MM **Privately Held**
SIC: 3599 Machine shop, jobbing & repair

(P-16234)
AER-DAN PRECISION (PA)
1458 Seareel Pl, San Jose (95131-1572)
PHONE..................................408 954-8704
Steve Morton, *President*
Bob Burt, *Vice Pres*
EMP: 20 EST: 1979
SQ FT: 10,000
SALES (est): 2.3MM **Privately Held**
SIC: 3599 Machine shop, jobbing & repair

(P-16235)
AERO CHIP INC
13563 Freeway Dr, Santa Fe Springs
(90670-5633)
PHONE..................................562 404-6300
Solomon M Gavrila, *CEO*
Liviu Pribac, *Vice Pres*
George Stan, *QC Mgr*
EMP: 50
SQ FT: 17,000
SALES (est): 12.6MM **Privately Held**
WEB: www.aerochip.com
SIC: 3599 Machine shop, jobbing & repair

(P-16236)
AERO ENGINEERING INC
1020 E Elm Ave, Fullerton (92831-5022)
PHONE..................................714 879-6200
Brent Borden, *President*
EMP: 16
SQ FT: 5,500
SALES (est): 2.4MM **Privately Held**
WEB: www.aero-e.com
SIC: 3599 Machine shop, jobbing & repair

(P-16237)
AERO INDUSTRIES LLC
139 Industrial Way, Buellton (93427-9592)
P.O. Box 198 (93427-0198)
PHONE..................................805 688-6734
Dave Watkins, *Manager*
Francis Williams, *Site Mgr*

▲ = Import ▼=Export
◆ =Import/Export

EMP: 30
SALES (est): 4MM
SALES (corp-wide): 79.4MM **Privately Held**
SIC: 3599 Machine & other job shop work
PA: Gavial Holdings, Inc.
1435 W Mccoy Ln
Santa Maria CA 93455
805 614-0060

(P-16238)
AERO MECHANISM PRECISION INC
21700 Marilla St, Chatsworth (91311-4125)
PHONE................................818 886-1855
Palminder Sehmbey, *President*
EMP: 34 **EST:** 1996
SQ FT: 8,000
SALES (est): 5.3MM **Privately Held**
WEB: www.aeromechanism.com
SIC: 3599 Machine shop, jobbing & repair

(P-16239)
AERO-K INC
10764 Lower Azusa Rd, El Monte (91731-1306)
PHONE................................626 350-5125
Robert Krusic, *President*
Jeffrey Hines, *Info Tech Mgr*
Ryan Krusic, *Opers Staff*
EMP: 45
SQ FT: 14,000
SALES (est): 9.1MM **Privately Held**
WEB: www.aero-k.com
SIC: 3599 Machine shop, jobbing & repair

(P-16240)
AERO-MECHANICAL ENGRG INC
5945 Engineer Dr, Huntington Beach (92649-1129)
PHONE................................714 891-2423
Anders Ahlstrom, *Ch of Bd*
John Ahlstrom, *President*
EMP: 16 **EST:** 1974
SQ FT: 4,150
SALES (est): 1.5MM **Privately Held**
WEB: www.aero-mechanical.com
SIC: 3599 Machine shop, jobbing & repair

(P-16241)
AERODYNAMIC ENGINEERING INC
15495 Graham St, Huntington Beach (92649-1205)
PHONE................................714 891-2651
Bob Waddell, *CEO*
Alfred Mayer, *President*
Bob Waddell, *CEO*
Ewald Eisel, *Principal*
Bryan Deckner, *Human Res Dir*
▲ **EMP:** 40
SQ FT: 12,000
SALES (est): 8.5MM **Privately Held**
WEB: www.aerodynamic.net
SIC: 3599 3769 Machine shop, jobbing & repair; guided missile & space vehicle parts & auxiliary equipment

(P-16242)
AERODYNE PRCSION MACHINING INC
5471 Argosy Ave, Huntington Beach (92649-1038)
PHONE................................714 891-1311
Raymond Krispel, *President*
Veronica Schultz, *CFO*
Otto Schulz, *Vice Pres*
Jamie Krispel, *Human Resources*
Ron Whitlock, *Prdtn Mgr*
▲ **EMP:** 25
SQ FT: 20,000
SALES (est): 7.7MM **Privately Held**
WEB: www.aerodyneprecision.com
SIC: 3599 Machine shop, jobbing & repair

(P-16243)
AEROSTAR ENGINEERING & MFG INC
25514 Frampton Ave, Harbor City (90710-2907)
PHONE................................310 326-5098
Min Lee, *President*
Connie Lee, *Admin Sec*
EMP: 11

SQ FT: 4,680
SALES (est): 1.7MM **Privately Held**
SIC: 3599 Machine shop, jobbing & repair

(P-16244)
AF MACHINE & TOOL CO INC
950 W Hyde Park Blvd D, Inglewood (90302-3335)
PHONE................................310 674-1919
Malka Fogel, *President*
Aaron Fogel, *Vice Pres*
Eric Fogel, *Vice Pres*
EMP: 10
SQ FT: 5,500
SALES: 1.8MM **Privately Held**
WEB: www.afmach.com
SIC: 3599 Machine shop, jobbing & repair

(P-16245)
AGA PRECISION SYSTEMS INC
122 E Dyer Rd, Santa Ana (92707-3732)
PHONE................................714 540-3163
Ralph E Wilson, *President*
Wesley Wilson, *CFO*
EMP: 16
SQ FT: 14,100
SALES: 2.8MM **Privately Held**
WEB: www.agaprecision.com
SIC: 3599 Machine shop, jobbing & repair

(P-16246)
AIR CRAFTORS ENGINEERING INC
4040 Cheyenne Ct, Chino (91710-5457)
PHONE................................909 900-0635
Tim Boucher, *President*
John Boucher, *Vice Pres*
EMP: 14
SQ FT: 6,000
SALES (est): 1.1MM **Privately Held**
SIC: 3599 Machine shop, jobbing & repair

(P-16247)
AIRPOINT PRECISION INC
6221 Enterprise Dr Ste D, Diamond Springs (95619-9469)
PHONE................................530 622-0510
Will Fanning, *President*
Clem Fanning, *President*
Jason Hanks, *CFO*
EMP: 13
SQ FT: 7,200
SALES (est): 2.3MM **Privately Held**
WEB: www.airpointinc.com
SIC: 3599 Machine shop, jobbing & repair

(P-16248)
ALDO FRAGALE
Also Called: Turner Precision
17813 S Main St Ste 111, Gardena (90248-3542)
PHONE................................310 324-0050
Aldo Fragale, *President*
EMP: 12
SQ FT: 2,500
SALES: 1MM **Privately Held**
SIC: 3599 Machine shop, jobbing & repair

(P-16249)
ALFREDO HERNANDEZ
Also Called: A & H Wire EDM
474 W Arrow Hwy Ste K, San Dimas (91773-2919)
PHONE................................909 971-9320
Alfredo Hernandez, *Owner*
EMP: 10
SQ FT: 4,000
SALES (est): 1.5MM **Privately Held**
SIC: 3599 Machine shop, jobbing & repair

(P-16250)
ALL DIAMETER GRINDING INC
725 N Main St, Orange (92868-1105)
PHONE................................714 744-1200
Marvin W Goodwin, *President*
Barbara Goodwin, *Treasurer*
Jeff Goodwin, *Vice Pres*
EMP: 22
SQ FT: 9,500
SALES: 11MM **Privately Held**
WEB: www.alldiametergrinding.com
SIC: 3599 Machine shop, jobbing & repair

(P-16251)
ALL TIME MACHINE INC
2050 Del Rio Way, Ontario (91761-8037)
PHONE................................909 673-1899
Ronald J Gagnon, *President*
Allison Gagnon, *President*
EMP: 12
SQ FT: 13,000
SALES: 5.4MM **Privately Held**
WEB: www.alltimemachine.com
SIC: 3599 Machine shop, jobbing & repair

(P-16252)
ALL-TECH MACHINE & ENGRG INC
2700 Prune Ave, Fremont (94539-6780)
PHONE................................510 353-2000
Richard M Gale, *CEO*
Boydine Michaels, *Vice Pres*
Dave Abbley, *Marketing Staff*
EMP: 49
SALES (est): 7.1MM **Privately Held**
WEB: www.alltechinc.com
SIC: 3599 Machine shop, jobbing & repair

(P-16253)
ALLIED DISC GRINDING
2478 Maggio Cir Ste A, Lodi (95240-8815)
PHONE................................209 339-0333
Harry L Campbell, *President*
Kay Campbell, *Vice Pres*
EMP: 11
SQ FT: 9,000
SALES: 1MM **Privately Held**
WEB: www.softcom.com
SIC: 3599 Grinding castings for the trade

(P-16254)
ALLIED ENGINEERING & PROD CORP (PA)
2421 Blanding Ave, Alameda (94501-1503)
P.O. Box 1230 (94501-0134)
PHONE................................510 522-1500
Sharon L Miller, *CEO*
Kassi Miller, *Vice Pres*
Dave Belcher, *General Mgr*
◆ **EMP:** 27
SQ FT: 175,000
SALES (est): 2.6MM **Privately Held**
WEB: www.alliedeng.com
SIC: 3599 Machine shop, jobbing & repair

(P-16255)
ALLOY MACHINING AND HONING INC
2808 Supply Ave, Commerce (90040-2706)
PHONE................................323 726-8248
Paul Muscet, *President*
Nada Muscet, *Admin Sec*
EMP: 12
SQ FT: 12,000
SALES (est): 1.6MM **Privately Held**
SIC: 3599 Machine shop, jobbing & repair

(P-16256)
ALLOY MACHINING SERVICES INC
2808 Supply Ave, Commerce (90040-2706)
PHONE................................323 725-2545
EMP: 15
SALES (est): 2.3MM **Privately Held**
SIC: 3599

(P-16257)
ALPHA AVIATION COMPONENTS INC (PA)
16772 Schoenborn St, North Hills (91343-6108)
PHONE................................818 894-8801
Lidia Gorko, *President*
William Tudor, *Vice Pres*
Joanna Zapala, *Manager*
EMP: 36
SQ FT: 18,000
SALES: 3.8MM **Privately Held**
WEB: www.gorkoind.com
SIC: 3599 3451 3728 Machine shop, jobbing & repair; screw machine products; aircraft parts & equipment

(P-16258)
ALPHA AVIATION COMPONENTS INC
Cal-Swiss Mfg
16774 Schoenborn St, North Hills (91343-6108)
PHONE................................818 894-8468
Lidia Gorko, *President*
EMP: 15
SALES (corp-wide): 3.8MM **Privately Held**
WEB: www.gorkoind.com
SIC: 3599 Machine shop, jobbing & repair
PA: Alpha Aviation Components, Inc.
16772 Schoenborn St
North Hills CA 91343
818 894-8801

(P-16259)
ALPHA GRINDING INC
12402 Benedict Ave, Downey (90242-3112)
PHONE................................562 803-1509
Yanick Herrouin, *President*
Kay Marcy, *Corp Secy*
Marc Herrouin, *Vice Pres*
▲ **EMP:** 13 **EST:** 1964
SQ FT: 9,000
SALES (est): 1.6MM **Privately Held**
WEB: www.alphagrinding.com
SIC: 3599 Machine shop, jobbing & repair

(P-16260)
ALPHA MACHINE COMPANY INC
933 Chittenden Ln Ste A, Capitola (95010-3600)
PHONE................................831 462-7400
Pemo Saraliev, *President*
Marlene Saraliev, *Treasurer*
EMP: 18
SQ FT: 12,000
SALES (est): 5.1MM **Privately Held**
WEB: www.alphamco.com
SIC: 3599 Machine shop, jobbing & repair

(P-16261)
ALTA DESIGN AND MANUFACTURING
885 Auzerais Ave, San Jose (95126-3760)
PHONE................................408 450-5394
Steven E Hernandez, *President*
Paula Hernandez, *Vice Pres*
EMP: 13
SALES (est): 1.5MM **Privately Held**
SIC: 3599 Machine shop, jobbing & repair

(P-16262)
ALTEST CORPORATION
898 Faulstich Ct, San Jose (95112-1361)
PHONE................................408 436-9900
Savann Seng, *CEO*
Brian Sen, *President*
Amy Tung, *Vice Pres*
EMP: 29
SQ FT: 30,000
SALES (est): 6.5MM **Privately Held**
WEB: www.altestcorp.com
SIC: 3599 3672 Machine shop, jobbing & repair; printed circuit boards

(P-16263)
ALTS TOOL & MACHINE INC (PA)
10926 Woodside Ave N, Santee (92071-3272)
P.O. Box 712485 (92072-2485)
PHONE................................619 562-6653
Dean Alt, *President*
Kathleen Alt, *Treasurer*
Kelly Latislaw, *Accountant*
EMP: 55
SQ FT: 27,000
SALES (est): 10.3MM **Privately Held**
WEB: www.altstool.com
SIC: 3599 Machine shop, jobbing & repair

(P-16264)
ALVELLAN INC
Also Called: East Bay Machine and Shtmtl
1030 Shary Ct, Concord (94518-2409)
PHONE................................925 689-2421
Sean M McLellan, *CEO*
Tim Alvey, *CFO*
Jim Foster, *General Mgr*
EMP: 28

PRODUCTS & SVCS

SQ FT: 30,000
SALES (est): 3MM **Privately Held**
WEB: www.eastbaymachine.com
SIC: 3599 5083 Machine shop, jobbing & repair; lawn & garden machinery & equipment

(P-16265)
ALZIEBLER INCORPORATED (PA)
Also Called: Alziebler Jos Co
12734 Branford St Ste 12, Arleta
(91331-6828)
PHONE...................................800 430-7536
Robert Allen, *President*
EMP: 13 EST: 1959
SQ FT: 5,000
SALES (est): 2.4MM **Privately Held**
WEB: www.alziebler.com
SIC: 3599 Machine shop, jobbing & repair

(P-16266)
AM AND S MFG INC
Also Called: AM&s Mnufactruing Design Group
1283 Old Mountain View Al, Sunnyvale (94089)
PHONE...................................800 519-5709
Andrew Le, *CEO*
EMP: 10
SALES: 1.2MM **Privately Held**
SIC: 3599 3728 3541 3443 Machine shop, jobbing & repair; aircraft body & wing assemblies & parts; lathes; metal parts

(P-16267)
AM-PAR MANUFACTURING CO INC
959 Von Geldern Way, Yuba City
(95991-4215)
PHONE...................................530 671-1800
Frederick R Klamerus, *President*
Judith A Klamerus, *Vice Pres*
Karen A Coker, *Admin Sec*
EMP: 10 EST: 1962
SQ FT: 13,000
SALES: 761.4K **Privately Held**
SIC: 3599 Machine shop, jobbing & repair

(P-16268)
AM-TEK ENGINEERING INC
1180 E Francis St Ste C, Ontario
(91761-4802)
PHONE...................................909 673-1633
Boone Bounyaseng, *CEO*
EMP: 18 EST: 1998
SQ FT: 10,000
SALES (est): 3MM **Privately Held**
SIC: 3599 Machine shop, jobbing & repair

(P-16269)
AMERICAN CNC INC
12430 Montague St Ste 207, Pacoima
(91331-2149)
PHONE...................................818 890-3400
Patrick Talverdi Freidani, *CEO*
EMP: 10
SALES (est): 961.8K **Privately Held**
SIC: 3599 Machine shop, jobbing & repair

(P-16270)
AMERICAN DEBURRING INC
Also Called: A Fab
20742 Linear Ln, Lake Forest
(92630-7804)
PHONE...................................949 457-9790
Robert L Campbell, *President*
Theresa Cook, *Admin Sec*
EMP: 25
SQ FT: 11,000
SALES: 3MM **Privately Held**
WEB: www.afabcnc.com
SIC: 3599 Machine shop, jobbing & repair

(P-16271)
AMERICAN MFG NETWRK INC
Also Called: Amanet
7001 Eton Ave, Canoga Park (91303-2112)
PHONE 818 786-1113
Robert Barbour, *Chairman*
Sandip Desai, *President*
Natalia Garzo, *Accounting Mgr*
Maria Garcia, *Purch Mgr*
EMP: 14
SQ FT: 4,000

SALES (est): 2.4MM **Privately Held**
WEB: www.amanet.com
SIC: 3599 3469 Machine shop, jobbing & repair; metal stampings

(P-16272)
AMERICAN PRCISION GRINDING MCH
456 Gerona Ave, San Gabriel
(91775-2938)
PHONE...................................626 357-6610
Fax: 626 358-4365
EMP: 13
SQ FT: 3,500
SALES: 1.5MM **Privately Held**
SIC: 3599

(P-16273)
AMH INTERNATIONAL INC
1270 Avenida Acaso Ste J, Camarillo
(93012-8747)
PHONE...................................805 388-2082
Sam Grimaldo, *Principal*
EMP: 11
SALES (est): 1.3MM **Privately Held**
SIC: 3599 Amusement park equipment

(P-16274)
ANGULAR MACHINING INC
2040 Hartog Dr, San Jose (95131-2214)
PHONE...................................408 954-8326
Kiet Nguyen, *President*
Hieu Le, *Engineer*
Tina Tran, *Manager*
EMP: 24 EST: 2001
SALES (est): 4.5MM **Privately Held**
WEB: www.angularmachining.com
SIC: 3599 Machine shop, jobbing & repair

(P-16275)
APPLIED PROCESS EQUIPMENT
2620 Bay Rd, Redwood City (94063-3501)
PHONE...................................650 365-6895
Michael T Hertert, *Partner*
Chris Dale, *Partner*
EMP: 11
SQ FT: 5,000
SALES (est): 790K **Privately Held**
SIC: 3599 Machine shop, jobbing & repair

(P-16276)
ARAM PRECISION TOOL DIE INC
9758 Cozycroft Ave, Chatsworth
(91311-4417)
P.O. Box 3696 (91313-3696)
PHONE...................................818 998-1000
AVI Amichai, *President*
Rona Amichai, *Corp Secy*
EMP: 13
SQ FT: 12,000
SALES (est): 1MM **Privately Held**
WEB: www.aramprecision.com
SIC: 3599 3451 Machine shop, jobbing & repair; screw machine products

(P-16277)
ARANDA TOOLING INC
13950 Yorba Ave, Chino (91710-5520)
PHONE...................................714 379-6565
Pedro Aranda, *President*
Martha Aranda, *Corp Secy*
Sandra Galvan, *Human Res Mgr*
Robert Nunez, *Purchasing*
Bob Tucci, *Sales Staff*
▲ EMP: 70
SQ FT: 60,000
SALES (est): 35.1MM **Privately Held**
WEB: www.arandatooling.com
SIC: 3599 3469 3544 3465 Machine shop, jobbing & repair; metal stampings; special dies, tools, jigs & fixtures; automotive stampings

(P-16278)
AREMAC ASSOCIATES INC
2004 S Myrtle Ave, Monrovia (91016-4837)
PHONE...................................626 303-8795
Scott Sher, *CEO*
Mariela Vinas, *Vice Pres*
Mike Brunasso, *Manager*
EMP: 35
SQ FT: 12,500
SALES (est): 5.2MM **Privately Held**
SIC: 3599 3444 Machine shop, jobbing & repair; sheet metalwork

(P-16279)
ARGENTI INC
Also Called: J & R Engineering Company
2870 E Via Martens, Anaheim
(92806-1751)
PHONE...................................714 666-8084
Suyen Gutierrez, *President*
George Gutierrez Jr, *General Mgr*
EMP: 35
SQ FT: 8,000
SALES (est): 4.6MM **Privately Held**
WEB: www.argenti.com
SIC: 3599 3812 3728 Machine shop, jobbing & repair; search & navigation equipment; aircraft parts & equipment

(P-16280)
ARMS PRECISION INC
169 Radio Rd, Corona (92879-1724)
PHONE...................................951 273-1800
Dale O Banion, *President*
Robin O Banion, *CFO*
Landon O Banion, *Admin Sec*
Landon Obanion, *VP Engrg*
Matt Robinson, *Supervisor*
EMP: 10
SQ FT: 3,900
SALES (est): 323.8K **Privately Held**
SIC: 3599 Machine shop, jobbing & repair

(P-16281)
ARMSTRONG TECHNOLOGY INC
12780 Earhart Ave, Auburn (95602-9027)
PHONE...................................530 888-6262
Arthur Armstrong, *Branch Mgr*
Julie Armstrong, *Vice Pres*
Brandy Haring, *Office Mgr*
Jim Burkhart, *Plant Mgr*
EMP: 45
SALES (corp-wide): 20MM **Privately Held**
WEB: www.armstrong-tech.com
SIC: 3599 Machine shop, jobbing & repair
PA: Armstrong Technology, Inc.
   1121 Elko Dr
   Sunnyvale CA 94089
   408 734-4434

(P-16282)
ARNOLD-GONSALVES ENGRG INC
5731 Chino Ave, Chino (91710-5226)
PHONE...................................909 465-1579
Manuel Gonsalves, *President*
Mike Arnold, *Vice Pres*
EMP: 35
SQ FT: 10,000
SALES (est): 6MM **Privately Held**
SIC: 3599 3444 Machine shop, jobbing & repair; sheet metal specialties, not stamped

(P-16283)
ARROW ENGINEERING
4946 Azusa Canyon Rd, Irwindale
(91706-1940)
PHONE...................................626 960-2806
John Beaman, *President*
Jim Ballantyne, *Vice Pres*
Mark J Silk, *Agent*
Mark Silk, *Agent*
EMP: 36
SQ FT: 18,000
SALES (est): 7.7MM **Privately Held**
SIC: 3599 Machine shop, jobbing & repair

(P-16284)
ARROW SCREW PRODUCTS INC
941 W Mccoy Ln, Santa Maria
(93455-1109)
PHONE...................................805 928-2269
Robert Vine, *CEO*
Tim Vine, *Vice Pres*
Hoang Vine, *Admin Sec*
EMP: 33
SQ FT: 10,000
SALES (est): 5.9MM **Privately Held**
WEB: www.arrowscrew.com
SIC: 3599 3541 Machine shop, jobbing & repair; machine tools, metal cutting type

(P-16285)
ASIGMA CORPORATION
2930 San Luis Rey Rd, Oceanside
(92058-1220)
PHONE...................................760 966-3103
C Dale Chudomelka, *President*
Darryl Chudomelka, *Vice Pres*
Doug Chudomelka, *Vice Pres*
▲ EMP: 16
SQ FT: 6,500
SALES (est): 2.4MM **Privately Held**
WEB: www.asigmacorp.com
SIC: 3599 Custom machinery; machine shop, jobbing & repair

(P-16286)
ASTRO MACHINE CO INC
3734 W 139th St, Hawthorne (90250-7597)
PHONE...................................310 679-8291
William Skintauy, *President*
Ann Vellonakis, *Treasurer*
James Vellonakis, *Vice Pres*
Stas Vellonakis, *General Mgr*
Stasi Vellonakis, *Admin Sec*
EMP: 14 EST: 1965
SQ FT: 5,000
SALES (est): 2.7MM **Privately Held**
SIC: 3599 Machine shop, jobbing & repair

(P-16287)
ASTRODYNE GROUP INC (PA)
Also Called: Contour Machining
9555 Owensmouth Ave # 11, Chatsworth
(91311-4898)
PHONE...................................818 709-5440
Cathy Hayward, *President*
Herb Hayward, *Vice Pres*
EMP: 20
SQ FT: 12,000
SALES (est): 2.7MM **Privately Held**
WEB: www.astrodynegroupinc.com
SIC: 3599 Machine shop, jobbing & repair

(P-16288)
AUGER INDUSTRIES INC
390 E Crowther Ave, Placentia
(92870-6419)
PHONE...................................714 577-9350
John Auger, *President*
Francoise Auger, *Shareholder*
Cheryl Auger, *Executive*
EMP: 17 EST: 1969
SQ FT: 12,000
SALES (est): 3.3MM **Privately Held**
WEB: www.augerind.com
SIC: 3599 Machine shop, jobbing & repair

(P-16289)
AUTOCAM ACQUISITION INC
Also Called: Autocam California
1209 San Luis Obispo St, Hayward
(94544-7915)
PHONE...................................510 487-7600
John C Kennedy, *President*
Warren A Veltman, *Corp Secy*
Warren Veltman, *Exec VP*
EMP: 20
SQ FT: 27,000
SALES (est): 5.1MM
SALES (corp-wide): 619.7MM **Publicly Held**
SIC: 3599 7692 3545 Machine shop, jobbing & repair; welding repair; machine tool accessories
HQ: Autocam Corporation
   4180 40th St Se
   Kentwood MI 49512
   616 698-0707

(P-16290)
AUTOMATION WEST INC
Also Called: Cameron Metal Cutting
1605 E Saint Gertrude Pl, Santa Ana
(92705-5311)
PHONE...................................714 556-7381
George Danenhauer, *President*
David Roberts, *Vice Pres*
Linda Bingham, *Admin Sec*
▲ EMP: 15
SQ FT: 7,200
SALES (est): 1.5MM **Privately Held**
WEB: www.automationwest.se
SIC: 3599 7389 Machine shop, jobbing & repair; metal cutting services

(P-16291)
AVION TL MFG MACHINING CTR INC
29035 Tne Old Rd, Valencia (91355-1083)
PHONE..................................661 257-2915
Patrick Beaudoin, *President*
Alison Horne, *Manager*
EMP: 13
SQ FT: 6,000
SALES (est): 2.5MM **Privately Held**
SIC: 3599 Machine shop, jobbing & repair

(P-16292)
AXXIS CORPORATION
1535 Nandina Ave, Perris (92571-7010)
PHONE..................................951 436-9921
Brandy Tidball, *President*
Jo Olchawa, *Treasurer*
Susan Tidball, *Vice Pres*
David McClure, *Production*
EMP: 35
SALES (est): 6.5MM **Privately Held**
SIC: 3599 Machine shop, jobbing & repair

(P-16293)
AZTEC MACHINE CO INC
3156 Fitzgerald Rd Ste A, Rancho Cordova (95742-6889)
PHONE..................................916 638-4894
Alfredo Alvarez, *President*
EMP: 12
SQ FT: 7,200
SALES (est): 2.1MM **Privately Held**
SIC: 3599 Machine shop, jobbing & repair

(P-16294)
B & B MANUFACTURING CO (PA)
27940 Beale Ct, Santa Clarita (91355-1210)
PHONE..................................661 257-2161
Kenneth Gentry, *CEO*
Fred Duncan, *President*
Will Tiefuhr, *Vice Pres*
Kyla Kelly, *Program Mgr*
Wendy S Marroquin, *Administration*
▲ **EMP:** 200 **EST:** 1961
SQ FT: 180,000
SALES (est): 48.9MM **Privately Held**
WEB: www.bbmfg.com
SIC: 3599 Machine shop, jobbing & repair

(P-16295)
B & B PIPE AND TOOL CO (PA)
3035 Walnut Ave, Long Beach (90807-5221)
PHONE..................................562 424-0704
Craig Braly, *President*
Stephanie Braly, *Corp Secy*
▲ **EMP:** 23 **EST:** 1951
SQ FT: 2,000
SALES (est): 8.7MM **Privately Held**
WEB: www.pipesales.com
SIC: 3599 Machine shop, jobbing & repair

(P-16296)
B & B PIPE AND TOOL CO
2301 Parker Ln, Bakersfield (93308-6006)
PHONE..................................661 323-8208
Joe Keller, *General Mgr*
EMP: 12
SALES (corp-wide): 8.7MM **Privately Held**
WEB: www.pipesales.com
SIC: 3599 Machine shop, jobbing & repair
PA: B & B Pipe And Tool Co.
    3035 Walnut Ave
    Long Beach CA 90807
    562 424-0704

(P-16297)
B & G PRECISION INC
45450 Industrial Pl Ste 9, Fremont (94538-6474)
PHONE..................................510 438-9785
Daniel Datta, *CEO*
EMP: 19
SQ FT: 3,600
SALES (est): 3.5MM **Privately Held**
SIC: 3599 Machine shop, jobbing & repair; machine & other job shop work

(P-16298)
B & M MACHINE INC
8439 Cherry Ave, Fontana (92335-3027)
PHONE..................................909 355-0998
William Fay, *President*
Robynne Fay, *Treasurer*
Kevin Bing, *Vice Pres*
Manny Jorge, *Foreman/Supr*
EMP: 11
SQ FT: 7,000
SALES (est): 1.5MM **Privately Held**
WEB: www.bmmachine.com
SIC: 3599 7699 Machine shop, jobbing & repair; hydraulic equipment repair

(P-16299)
B & W PRECISION INC
1260 Pioneer St Ste A, Brea (92821-3725)
P.O. Box 674, Yucca Valley (92286-0674)
PHONE..................................714 447-0971
EMP: 19 **EST:** 1964
SQ FT: 25,000
SALES (est): 2.5MM **Privately Held**
WEB: www.bwprecision.com
SIC: 3599

(P-16300)
B P I CORP
Also Called: Banbury Precision
1208 Norman Ave Ste B, Santa Clara (95054-2068)
PHONE..................................408 988-7888
Gordon Banbury Jr, *President*
EMP: 15
SQ FT: 6,000
SALES (est): 1.4MM **Privately Held**
SIC: 3599 Machine shop, jobbing & repair

(P-16301)
B S K T INC
Also Called: S & S Precision Sheetmetal
8447 Canoga Ave, Canoga Park (91304-2607)
PHONE..................................818 349-1566
Steve Kim, *President*
Suzanne Kim, *Manager*
EMP: 20 **EST:** 1997
SQ FT: 12,000
SALES (est): 2.8MM **Privately Held**
WEB: www.snsprecision.com
SIC: 3599 Machine shop, jobbing & repair

(P-16302)
B&Z MANUFACTURING COMPANY INC
1478 Seareel Ln, San Jose (95131-1567)
PHONE..................................408 943-1117
Dennis Kimball, *President*
Thomas Simpson, *Treasurer*
Linda Franks, *Accounting Mgr*
EMP: 42 **EST:** 1960
SQ FT: 18,000
SALES (est): 8.1MM **Privately Held**
WEB: www.bzmfg.com
SIC: 3599 Machine shop, jobbing & repair

(P-16303)
B/E AEROSPACE INC
7155 Fenwick Ln, Westminster (92683-5218)
PHONE..................................714 896-9001
Amin Khoury, *Chairman*
Scott Reece, *Program Mgr*
Marshall Alvarado, *Engineer*
Maria Aguilar, *Purch Mgr*
EMP: 100 **Publicly Held**
SIC: 3599 3728 Machine shop, jobbing & repair; aircraft parts & equipment
HQ: B/E Aerospace, Inc.
    1400 Corporate Center Way
    Wellington FL 33414
    561 791-5000

(P-16304)
BABBITT BEARING CO INC
Also Called: B B C
1170 N 5th St, San Jose (95112-4483)
PHONE..................................408 298-1101
Stanley Sinn, *President*
Jerry Mann, *Vice Pres*
EMP: 25
SQ FT: 16,000
SALES (est): 4.3MM **Privately Held**
WEB: www.bbcmachine.com
SIC: 3599 Machine shop, jobbing & repair

(P-16305)
BAKERSFIELD MACHINE CO INC
Also Called: BMC Industries
5605 N Chester Ave Ext, Bakersfield (93308)
P.O. Box 122 (93302-0122)
PHONE..................................661 393-8441
John L Meyer, *President*
Alfred T Meyer Jr, *Vice Pres*
Robert Ruch, *Executive*
Roger Casulla, *Purch Mgr*
Dirk Bentz, *Sales Staff*
▲ **EMP:** 55
SQ FT: 8,276
SALES (est): 14MM **Privately Held**
WEB: www.bmcindustries.com
SIC: 3599 Machine shop, jobbing & repair

(P-16306)
BARBER WELDING AND MFG CO
7171 Scout Ave, Bell Gardens (90201-3252)
PHONE..................................562 928-2570
C Douglas Barber, *CEO*
Yvonne M Barber, *Vice Pres*
EMP: 25
SQ FT: 15,000
SALES (est): 5.7MM **Privately Held**
WEB: www.barberwelding.com
SIC: 3599 3443 Machine shop, jobbing & repair; tanks for tank trucks, metal plate

(P-16307)
BARRANGO (PA)
Also Called: American Rotoform
391 Forbes Blvd, South San Francisco (94080-2014)
PHONE..................................650 737-9206
William Barrango, *President*
John Barrango, *Vice Pres*
◆ **EMP:** 10 **EST:** 1911
SQ FT: 100,000
SALES (est): 3.3MM **Privately Held**
WEB: www.barrango.com
SIC: 3599 3299 3089 Carousels (merry-go-rounds); architectural sculptures: gypsum, clay, papier mache, etc.; plastic processing

(P-16308)
BAUMANN ENGINEERING INC
212 S Cambridge Ave, Claremont (91711-4843)
PHONE..................................909 621-4181
Fred Baumann, *President*
Isolde Doll, *Admin Sec*
Brad Siebert, *Buyer*
EMP: 85 **EST:** 1961
SQ FT: 18,057
SALES (est): 12.3MM **Privately Held**
WEB: www.baumannengineering.com
SIC: 3599 Machine shop, jobbing & repair

(P-16309)
BAY PRECISION MACHINING INC
Also Called: Emkay Mfg.
815 Sweeney Ave Ste D, Redwood City (94063-3029)
PHONE..................................650 365-3010
Anne Feher, *President*
George Koncz, *Vice Pres*
EMP: 25
SQ FT: 7,500
SALES (est): 3.9MM **Privately Held**
WEB: www.emkaymfg.com
SIC: 3599 Machine shop, jobbing & repair

(P-16310)
BAY TECH MANUFACTURING INC
23334 Bernhardt St, Hayward (94545-1678)
PHONE..................................510 783-0660
Mike Niklewski, *President*
Zbigniew Niklewski, *President*
Vicki Niklewski, *CFO*
Gus Concha, *Buyer*
EMP: 12
SQ FT: 9,700
SALES (est): 2.1MM **Privately Held**
WEB: www.baytechmfg.com
SIC: 3599 Machine shop, jobbing & repair

(P-16311)
BAYLESS ENGINEERING INC
Also Called: Bayless Engineering & Mfg
26100 Ave Hall Valencia, Valencia (91355)
P.O. Box 914 (91380-9014)
PHONE..................................661 257-3373
Earl Bayless, *President*
Rod Smith, *Vice Pres*
EMP: 235
SQ FT: 127,000
SALES (est): 37.2MM **Privately Held**
WEB: www.baylessengineering.com
SIC: 3599 3444 Machine shop, jobbing & repair; sheet metalwork

(P-16312)
BCI INC
Also Called: Upton Engineering & Mfg Co
1822 Belcroft Ave, South El Monte (91733-3703)
PHONE..................................626 579-4234
Adam Bondra, *President*
June Bondra, *Vice Pres*
EMP: 15
SQ FT: 6,500
SALES (est): 2.1MM **Privately Held**
SIC: 3599 5084 Machine & other job shop work; welding machinery & equipment

(P-16313)
BEDARD MACHINE INC
141 Viking Ave, Brea (92821-3817)
PHONE..................................714 990-4846
Dennis Bedard, *President*
Sue Bedard, *CFO*
Jaymie Marklevits, *Mfg Staff*
EMP: 13
SQ FT: 7,200
SALES (est): 2.1MM **Privately Held**
WEB: www.bedardmachineinc.com
SIC: 3599 Machine shop, jobbing & repair

(P-16314)
BEGOVIC INDUSTRIES INC
Also Called: B & H Engineering Company
1725 Old County Rd, San Carlos (94070-5206)
PHONE..................................650 594-2861
Bakir Begovic, *CEO*
Kenan Begovic, *President*
Hamida Begovic, *Vice Pres*
EMP: 20
SALES (est): 5.2MM **Privately Held**
SIC: 3599 3444 Machine shop, jobbing & repair; sheet metalwork

(P-16315)
BEL-AIR MACHINING CO
1514 E Edinger Ave Ste E, Santa Ana (92705-4918)
PHONE..................................714 953-6616
Moon H Choi, *Owner*
EMP: 15
SQ FT: 5,000
SALES (est): 2.7MM **Privately Held**
WEB: www.belairmachine.com
SIC: 3599 Machine shop, jobbing & repair

(P-16316)
BELLOWS MFG & RES INC
13596 Vaughn St, San Fernando (91340-3029)
PHONE..................................818 838-1333
Arteom Art Bulgadarian, *CEO*
David Galloway, *Engineer*
EMP: 13
SQ FT: 28,000
SALES (est): 1.6MM **Privately Held**
SIC: 3599 Bellows, industrial: metal

(P-16317)
BENDER CCP INC
Also Called: Bender US
2150 E 37th St Vernon, Vernon (90058)
P.O. Box 847, Benicia (94510-0847)
PHONE..................................707 745-9970
Michael A Potter, *President*
Randall Potter, *Vice Pres*
▲ **EMP:** 75
SALES (est): 13.3MM **Privately Held**
SIC: 3599 Custom machinery

(P-16318)
BENDICK PRECISION INC
56 La Porte St, Arcadia (91006-2827)
PHONE..................................626 445-0217

Christie Joseph, *President*
Benny Joseph, *Corp Secy*
Maria Salas, *QC Mgr*
Reyes Rosales, *Manager*
EMP: 12
SQ FT: 5,000
SALES (est): 1.8MM **Privately Held**
SIC: 3599 3061 Machine shop, jobbing & repair; medical & surgical rubber tubing (extruded & lathe-cut)

(P-16319)
BEONCA MACHINE INC
1680 Curtiss Ct, La Verne (91750-5848)
PHONE..........................909 392-9991
Johann Bock, *President*
Danny Bock, *President*
Dennis Bock, *Vice Pres*
Picture L Bock, *Office Mgr*
Jame Bock, *Admin Sec*
EMP: 17
SQ FT: 7,000
SALES (est): 2.9MM **Privately Held**
WEB: www.beoncamachine.com
SIC: 3599 Machine shop, jobbing & repair

(P-16320)
BERNS BROS INC
Also Called: De Berns Company
1250 W 17th St, Long Beach (90813-1310)
PHONE..........................562 437-0471
Steven Berns, *President*
Sue Porter, *Vice Pres*
▲ **EMP:** 17
SQ FT: 20,000
SALES (est): 2.4MM **Privately Held**
WEB: www.thebernsco.com
SIC: 3599 Machine & other job shop work

(P-16321)
BESTPRO MACHINING
45999 Warm Springs Blvd # 3, Fremont (94539-6766)
PHONE..........................510 490-6853
Duoqiang Loiang, *President*
Loi-Pin Zhao, *Partner*
EMP: 10 **EST:** 1997
SALES (est): 1.2MM **Privately Held**
WEB: www.bestpromachining.com
SIC: 3599 Machine shop, jobbing & repair

(P-16322)
BETTER-WAY & LOVELL GRINDING
Also Called: Better Way Grinding
8333 Chetle Ave, Santa Fe Springs (90670-2201)
PHONE..........................562 693-8722
Edward W Lovell, *President*
Pat Lovell, *Treasurer*
Fabb Fregoso, *Software Dev*
EMP: 12
SQ FT: 33,000
SALES (est): 2MM **Privately Held**
WEB: www.betterwaygrinding.com
SIC: 3599 Grinding castings for the trade

(P-16323)
BETTERLINE PRODUCTS INC
1101 E Elm Ave, Fullerton (92831-5003)
P.O. Box 3099, Riverside (92519-3099)
PHONE..........................760 535-5030
Byron Berkes, *President*
Bill W Berkes, *Ch of Bd*
Harriett Berkes, *Treasurer*
EMP: 23
SQ FT: 2,000
SALES (est): 2.1MM **Privately Held**
WEB: www.betterlineproducts.com
SIC: 3599 3949 3544 3469 Machine shop, jobbing & repair; sporting & athletic goods; special dies, tools, jigs & fixtures; metal stampings

(P-16324)
BISON ENGINEERING COMPANY
15535 Texaco Ave, Paramount (90723-3921)
PHONE..........................562 408-1525
Lothar Maertens, *President*
Neil Thompson, *Vice Pres*
EMP: 13
SQ FT: 40,000
SALES (est): 3MM **Privately Held**
SIC: 3599 3728 Machine shop, jobbing & repair; aircraft parts & equipment

(P-16325)
BLACK DIAMOND MANUFACTURING CO
755 Bliss Ave, Pittsburg (94565)
PHONE..........................925 439-9160
Pamela Kan, *President*
Shelley Galvin, *VP Finance*
EMP: 10
SALES (est): 1.3MM
SALES (corp-wide): 15.7MM **Privately Held**
SIC: 3599
PA: Bishop-Wisecarver Corporation
2104 Martin Way
Pittsburg CA 94565
925 439-8272

(P-16326)
BLAGA PRECISION INC
11650 Seaboard Cir, Stanton (90680-3426)
PHONE..........................714 891-9509
Gavril Blaga, *President*
▲ **EMP:** 15
SQ FT: 3,600
SALES (est): 3MM **Privately Held**
SIC: 3599 Machine shop, jobbing & repair

(P-16327)
BMC TECHNOLOGY
7968 Country Trail Dr, Orangevale (95662-2130)
PHONE..........................510 429-7000
Kris Bilski, *Owner*
Maria Bilski, *Co-Owner*
EMP: 12
SQ FT: 5,000
SALES (est): 2MM **Privately Held**
SIC: 3599 Machine shop, jobbing & repair

(P-16328)
BMW PRECISION MACHINING INC
2379 Industry St, Oceanside (92054-4803)
PHONE..........................760 439-6813
Richard Blakely, *President*
EMP: 25 **EST:** 1981
SQ FT: 17,400
SALES (est): 4.2MM **Privately Held**
WEB: www.bmwprecision.com
SIC: 3599 Machine shop, jobbing & repair

(P-16329)
BOB LEWIS MACHINE COMPANY INC
1324 W 135th St, Gardena (90247-1909)
PHONE..........................310 538-9406
Jeff Lewis, *President*
Helen Lewis, *Treasurer*
Joe Pinela, *Vice Pres*
Jose Angel Pinela, *Vice Pres*
Albert Young, *Admin Sec*
EMP: 12
SQ FT: 10,000
SALES (est): 1.1MM **Privately Held**
WEB: www.boblewismachine.com
SIC: 3599 Machine shop, jobbing & repair

(P-16330)
BOCK MACHINE COMPANY INC
2141 S Parco Ave, Ontario (91761-5769)
PHONE..........................909 947-7250
Jacob Bock, *President*
Jack Bock, *Vice Pres*
Roy Bock, *Vice Pres*
Wilma Bock, *Admin Sec*
EMP: 15
SQ FT: 10,000
SALES (est): 1.7MM **Privately Held**
WEB: www.bockmachine.com
SIC: 3599 Machine shop, jobbing & repair

(P-16331)
BRADFORD CANNING STAHL INC
Also Called: Piranha Propeller
250 Scottsville Blvd, Jackson (95642-2671)
PHONE..........................209 257-1535
Brad Stahl, *President*
Laura Griffiths, *Representative*
▼ **EMP:** 10
SQ FT: 4,000
SALES (est): 1.4MM **Privately Held**
WEB: www.piranhapropellers.com
SIC: 3599 5551 Propellers, ship & boat: machined; boat dealers

(P-16332)
BRONZE-WAY POWDER COATING INC
3301 E 14th St, Los Angeles (90023-3801)
PHONE..........................323 265-7024
Fiyodor Mikhael-Fard, *President*
Ben Mikhael-Fard, *Corp Secy*
Fred Mikhael-Fard, *Vice Pres*
EMP: 55
SQ FT: 37,000
SALES (est): 8.6MM **Privately Held**
SIC: 3599 Machine shop, jobbing & repair

(P-16333)
BROOKSHIRE TOOL & MFG CO INC
10654 Garfield Ave, South Gate (90280-7334)
PHONE..........................562 861-2567
Chrisman Chiang, *President*
▲ **EMP:** 10
SQ FT: 10,000
SALES (est): 1.4MM **Privately Held**
SIC: 3599 3544 3469 Machine shop, jobbing & repair; special dies, tools, jigs & fixtures; metal stampings

(P-16334)
BRUDER INDUSTRY
3920 Sandstone Dr, El Dorado Hills (95762-9652)
PHONE..........................916 939-6888
Rex Kamphfner, *General Mgr*
Sara Ports, *Accountant*
John Wallasch, *Purch Mgr*
EMP: 87
SQ FT: 35,000
SALES (est): 7.5MM
SALES (corp-wide): 39.6MM **Privately Held**
WEB: www.aero-metals.com
SIC: 3599 Machine shop, jobbing & repair
PA: Aerometals, Inc.
3920 Sandstone Dr
El Dorado Hills CA 95762
916 939-6888

(P-16335)
BTI AEROSPACE & ELECTRONICS
Also Called: B T I Areospace & Electronics
13546 Vintage Pl, Chino (91710-5243)
PHONE..........................909 465-1569
Gary Rindfleisch, *President*
Warren Hammers, *Vice Pres*
▲ **EMP:** 25
SQ FT: 25,000
SALES (est): 3.3MM **Privately Held**
SIC: 3599 3444 3769 Machine shop, jobbing & repair; sheet metalwork; guided missile & space vehicle parts & auxiliary equipment

(P-16336)
BUENA PARK TOOL & ENGINEERING
7661 Windfield Dr, Huntington Beach (92647-7140)
PHONE..........................714 843-6215
Leo Gomez, *CEO*
Teresa Gomez, *President*
Leo Gomez Jr, *Vice Pres*
EMP: 11
SQ FT: 11,000
SALES (est): 399.3K **Privately Held**
WEB: www.buenaparktool.com
SIC: 3599 7692 3544 Machine shop, jobbing & repair; welding repair; special dies, tools, jigs & fixtures

(P-16337)
BULLSEYE LEAK DETECTION INC
4015 Seaport Blvd, West Sacramento (95691-3416)
PHONE..........................916 760-8944
Daniel Spatz, *President*
EMP: 12
SALES: 500K **Privately Held**
SIC: 3599 1623 Water leak detectors; pipe laying construction

(P-16338)
BUNDY MANUFACTURING INC
Also Called: B M I
507 S Douglas St, El Segundo (90245-4810)
P.O. Box 3413 (90245-8513)
PHONE..........................323 772-3273
James Bundy, *President*
EMP: 25
SQ FT: 10,000
SALES (est): 4.2MM **Privately Held**
SIC: 3599 Machine shop, jobbing & repair

(P-16339)
BURNET MACHINING INC
330 S Kellogg Ave Ste N, Goleta (93117-3814)
PHONE..........................805 964-6321
Michael Schock, *President*
Laurie Schock, *CFO*
EMP: 10
SQ FT: 1,800
SALES (est): 1.3MM **Privately Held**
SIC: 3599 Machine shop, jobbing & repair

(P-16340)
BURTREE INC
13513 Sherman Way, Van Nuys (91405-2899)
PHONE..........................818 786-4276
Cyrus Massoudi, *President*
Farah Massoudi, *Vice Pres*
Shawn Massoudi, *Director*
EMP: 28 **EST:** 1955
SQ FT: 13,500
SALES (est): 3.7MM **Privately Held**
WEB: www.burtree.com
SIC: 3599 7699 Machine shop, jobbing & repair; professional instrument repair services

(P-16341)
BYRAN COMPANY INC
18092 Redondo Cir, Huntington Beach (92648-1326)
P.O. Box 466, Surfside (90743-0466)
PHONE..........................714 841-9808
Janell Dunagan, *President*
Kelly Dunagan, *Corp Secy*
EMP: 57
SQ FT: 21,000
SALES (est): 243.9K
SALES (corp-wide): 8.7MM **Publicly Held**
WEB: www.byranco.com
SIC: 3599 3842 3812 Machine shop, jobbing & repair; surgical appliances & supplies; search & navigation equipment
PA: M Line Holdings, Inc.
2214 Avalon St
Costa Mesa CA 92627
714 630-6253

(P-16342)
C & C DIE ENGRAVING
12510 Mccann Dr, Santa Fe Springs (90670-3337)
PHONE..........................562 944-3399
Salvador J Chavez, *Owner*
Estella Chavez, *Admin Sec*
EMP: 18
SQ FT: 10,000
SALES (est): 2.8MM **Privately Held**
WEB: www.cncdieengraving.com
SIC: 3599 Machine shop, jobbing & repair

(P-16343)
C & D PRECISION COMPONENTS
Also Called: Trimatic
969 S Raymond Ave, Pasadena (91105-3241)
PHONE..........................626 799-7109
Coleen Ganguin, *President*
Daniel A Ganguin, *Corp Secy*
EMP: 17 **EST:** 1964
SQ FT: 4,000
SALES (est): 1.1MM **Privately Held**
SIC: 3599 Machine shop, jobbing & repair

(P-16344)
C & D PRESCISION MACHINING INC
2031 Concourse Dr, San Jose (95131-1727)
PHONE..........................408 383-1888

Dong Nguyen, *President*
EMP: 20
SQ FT: 10,000
SALES (est): 1.9MM **Privately Held**
SIC: 3599 Machine shop, jobbing & repair

(P-16345)
C B MACHINE PRODUCTS INC
13735 Iroquois Pl, Chino (91710-5559)
PHONE...............................909 517-1828
Carl Brod, *President*
Cecilia Brod, *Vice Pres*
EMP: 13
SQ FT: 7,000
SALES (est): 1.9MM **Privately Held**
SIC: 3599 Machine shop, jobbing & repair

(P-16346)
C J PRECISION INDUSTRIES INC
2817 Cherry Ave, Signal Hill (90755-1908)
PHONE...............................562 426-3708
Mike Vedder, *President*
Michael Vedder, *Vice Pres*
Thomas Vedder, *Vice Pres*
Cynthia Vedder, *Admin Sec*
EMP: 15
SQ FT: 10,000
SALES (est): 2.2MM **Privately Held**
SIC: 3599 Machine shop, jobbing & repair

(P-16347)
C K TOOL COMPANY INC
1033 Wright Ave, Mountain View (94043-4535)
PHONE...............................650 968-0261
Louis Ammatuna, *President*
Sherry Ammatuna, *CFO*
EMP: 14
SQ FT: 5,352
SALES: 1.5MM **Privately Held**
WEB: www.cktool.com
SIC: 3599 Machine shop, jobbing & repair

(P-16348)
C L HANN INDUSTRIES INC
1020 Timothy Dr, San Jose (95133-1042)
PHONE...............................408 293-4800
Colin Edison Hann, *President*
Erich Von Shofstall, *COO*
Art Korp, *Engineer*
Mark Freitas, *Manager*
Cheyne Hann, *Manager*
EMP: 18
SQ FT: 30,000
SALES: 3.9MM **Privately Held**
WEB: www.clhann.com
SIC: 3599 Machine shop, jobbing & repair; machine & other job shop work

(P-16349)
C M MACHINE INC
560 S Grand Ave, San Jacinto (92582-3832)
PHONE...............................951 654-6019
Carmel Tomoni, *President*
Michael Tomoni, *General Mgr*
EMP: 15
SQ FT: 6,000
SALES: 910K **Privately Held**
SIC: 3599 Machine shop, jobbing & repair

(P-16350)
C N C ENGINEERING INC
518 N Riley St, Lake Elsinore (92530-3706)
PHONE...............................951 674-7486
Wayne Heinrichs, *President*
EMP: 18
SQ FT: 5,000
SALES: 1MM **Privately Held**
SIC: 3599 Machine shop, jobbing & repair

(P-16351)
C N C MACHINING INC
510 S Fairview Ave, Goleta (93117-3617)
PHONE...............................805 681-8855
Gary Brous, *President*
Greg Brous, *Vice Pres*
Shirley Brous, *Admin Sec*
EMP: 12
SQ FT: 2,000
SALES (est): 360.7K **Privately Held**
SIC: 3599 Machine shop, jobbing & repair

(P-16352)
C TEAM INC
Also Called: Team C High Performance Center
16706 Lakewood Blvd, Bellflower (90706-5127)
PHONE...............................562 866-3887
Herbert Cornelius, *President*
Mark Cornelius, *Corp Secy*
EMP: 13
SQ FT: 8,500
SALES: 3.6MM **Privately Held**
SIC: 3599 Machine shop, jobbing & repair

(P-16353)
CAE AUTOMATION AND TEST LLC
44368 Warm Springs Blvd, Fremont (94538)
PHONE...............................408 204-0006
Brady Quach, *Mng Member*
James Pak,
EMP: 10
SQ FT: 28,000
SALES: 2MM **Privately Held**
SIC: 3599 Custom machinery

(P-16354)
CAL PRECISION INC
1680 Commerce St, Corona (92880-1731)
PHONE...............................951 273-9901
Donna Loper, *President*
Andy Loper, *Vice Pres*
Charles Loper, *Vice Pres*
Tiffany Jordan, *Administration*
EMP: 14
SQ FT: 13,140
SALES (est): 3.6MM **Privately Held**
WEB: www.calprecision.com
SIC: 3599 Machine shop, jobbing & repair

(P-16355)
CALIFORNIA BROACH COMPANY
4815 Telegraph Rd, Los Angeles (90022-3720)
PHONE...............................323 260-4812
Fax: 323 263-0337
EMP: 12
SQ FT: 15,000
SALES (est): 1MM **Privately Held**
SIC: 3599 3545

(P-16356)
CALIFORNIA JIG GRINDING CO
861 N Holly Glen Dr, Long Beach (90815-4722)
PHONE...............................323 723-4017
Deryl R Craig, *President*
EMP: 16
SQ FT: 10,000
SALES (est): 1.9MM **Privately Held**
WEB: www.edmexcellence.com
SIC: 3599 Machine shop, jobbing & repair

(P-16357)
CALMAX TECHNOLOGY INC (PA)
526 Laurelwood Rd, Santa Clara (95054-2418)
PHONE...............................408 748-8660
Boguslaw J Marcinkowski, *CEO*
Gary Hintz, *General Mgr*
Katherine Marcinkowski, *Office Admin*
Mark Masterson, *Info Tech Mgr*
Matt Hintz, *Project Mgr*
EMP: 100
SQ FT: 78,822
SALES (est): 26.2MM **Privately Held**
WEB: www.calmaxtechnology.com
SIC: 3599 Machine shop, jobbing & repair

(P-16358)
CAMPBELL GRINDING INC
1003 E Vine St, Lodi (95240-3127)
PHONE...............................209 339-8838
Dan Fritz, *President*
EMP: 12
SQ FT: 17,000
SALES (est): 1.7MM **Privately Held**
WEB: www.campbellgrinding.com
SIC: 3599 Machine shop, jobbing & repair

(P-16359)
CANADY MANUFACTURING CO INC
500 5th St, San Fernando (91340-2299)
PHONE...............................818 365-9181
Brian Koehn, *President*
Rodney Hull, *Owner*
Rod Hull, *General Mgr*
Lyndi Carbajal, *Office Mgr*
Kimberlee Koehn, *Admin Asst*
EMP: 13 **EST:** 1943
SQ FT: 5,000
SALES (est): 2.2MM **Privately Held**
SIC: 3599 Machine shop, jobbing & repair

(P-16360)
CANAY MANUFACTURING INC
Also Called: Powder Coating Plus
26140 Avenue Hall, Valencia (91355-4808)
PHONE...............................661 295-0205
Earl T Bayless, *President*
EMP: 14
SALES (est): 1.5MM **Privately Held**
SIC: 3599 Machine shop, jobbing & repair

(P-16361)
CAPSTAN PERMAFLOW
16110 S Figueroa St, Gardena (90248-2617)
PHONE...............................310 366-5999
Robert Scow, *President*
Mark Paullin, *Admin Sec*
EMP: 10
SQ FT: 8,000
SALES (est): 1.3MM
SALES (corp-wide): 93.9MM **Privately Held**
WEB: www.capstanatlantic.com
SIC: 3599 Machine & other job shop work
PA: Capstan California, Inc.
16100 S Figueroa St
Gardena CA 90248
310 366-5999

(P-16362)
CARDIC MACHINE PRODUCTS INC
17000 Keegan Ave, Carson (90746-1309)
PHONE...............................310 884-3400
Joseph Trumpio, *CEO*
Calvin Crockett, *Vice Pres*
EMP: 15 **EST:** 1951
SQ FT: 10,900
SALES: 7MM **Privately Held**
WEB: www.cardicmachine.com
SIC: 3599 Machine shop, jobbing & repair

(P-16363)
CARLSON & BEAULOYE AIR PWR INC
2143 Newton Ave, San Diego (92113-2296)
P.O. Box 13622 (92170-3622)
PHONE...............................619 232-5719
Ronald Beauloye Jr, *President*
Eugenia B Coleman, *Treasurer*
Henry J Beauloye Jr, *Vice Pres*
Joe Bravo, *Foreman/Supr*
EMP: 10 **EST:** 1974
SQ FT: 13,000
SALES (est): 1.6MM **Privately Held**
WEB: www.carlsonassoc.com
SIC: 3599 Machine shop, jobbing & repair

(P-16364)
CARLSON & BEAULOYE MACH SP INC
2141 Newton Ave, San Diego (92113-2210)
P.O. Box 13622 (92170-3622)
PHONE...............................619 232-5719
Ronald Beauloye, *President*
Eugena Coleman, *Treasurer*
Alfred Beauloye, *Vice Pres*
Valerie Beauloye, *Admin Sec*
EMP: 10
SQ FT: 10,000
SALES: 1MM **Privately Held**
SIC: 3599 Machine shop, jobbing & repair

(P-16365)
CARTER PUMP & MACHINE INC
635 G St, Wasco (93280-2023)
PHONE...............................661 393-8620
Chet Grooman, *President*

EMP: 18
SQ FT: 6,000
SALES (est): 2.4MM **Privately Held**
SIC: 3599 7699 Machine shop, jobbing & repair; pumps & pumping equipment repair

(P-16366)
CASON ENGINEERING INC
4952 Windplay Dr Ste D, El Dorado Hills (95762-9338)
PHONE...............................916 939-9311
Bradford Cason, *President*
Michelle Cason, *Executive*
EMP: 34
SQ FT: 27,500
SALES (est): 4.3MM **Privately Held**
WEB: www.casoneng.com
SIC: 3599 Machine shop, jobbing & repair

(P-16367)
CAVALLO & CAVALLO INC
Also Called: Production Engineering & Mch
14955 Hilton Dr, Fontana (92336-2082)
PHONE...............................909 428-6994
Thomas H Kearns, *President*
EMP: 16
SQ FT: 16,400
SALES (est): 2.8MM **Privately Held**
WEB: www.cavallo-inc.com
SIC: 3599 Machine shop, jobbing & repair

(P-16368)
CAVANAUGH MACHINE WORKS INC
1540 Santa Fe Ave, Long Beach (90813-1239)
PHONE...............................562 437-1126
John Wells, *President*
Michael Wells, *Corp Secy*
Lisa Moore, *Manager*
Tim Wells, *Supervisor*
EMP: 40
SQ FT: 19,000
SALES (est): 7.2MM **Privately Held**
WEB: www.cavmachine.com
SIC: 3599 3731 3441 Machine shop, jobbing & repair; shipbuilding & repairing; fabricated structural metal

(P-16369)
CELESTICA PRCSION MCHINING LTD
40725 Encyclopedia Cir, Fremont (94538-2451)
PHONE...............................510 252-2100
EMP: 40
SALES (corp-wide): 3.1MM **Privately Held**
SIC: 3599 Machine shop, jobbing & repair
PA: Celestica Precision Machining Ltd.
49235 Milmont Dr
Fremont CA 94538
510 742-0500

(P-16370)
CENCAL CNC INC
2491 Simpson St, Kingsburg (93631-9501)
PHONE...............................559 897-8706
Abe Wiebe, *President*
Ann Wiebe, *Vice Pres*
EMP: 25
SQ FT: 5,000
SALES (est): 232.5K **Privately Held**
SIC: 3599 Electrical discharge machining (EDM)

(P-16371)
CENTERPOINT MFG CO INC
2625 N San Fernando Blvd, Burbank (91504-3220)
PHONE...............................818 842-2147
John C Rotunno, *President*
Carmen Rotunno, *Vice Pres*
Tony Rotunno, *Manager*
EMP: 40 **EST:** 1966
SQ FT: 12,000
SALES (est): 7MM **Privately Held**
SIC: 3599 Machine shop, jobbing & repair

(P-16372)
CENTURY PARTS INC
913 W 223rd St, Torrance (90502-2246)
PHONE...............................310 328-0281
Lynn Hale, *CEO*
EMP: 11

SQ FT: 12,500
SALES (est): 1.8MM **Privately Held**
SIC: 3599 Machine shop, jobbing & repair

(P-16373)
CENTURY PRECISION ENGRG INC
2141 W 139th St, Gardena (90249-2451)
PHONE..............................310 538-0015
Myron Yoo, *President*
Joe Kwon, *Executive*
Boo Lee, *Admin Sec*
Bruce Lee, *Admin Sec*
Jean Yoo, *Opers Mgr*
EMP: 25
SQ FT: 20,000
SALES (est): 5.4MM **Privately Held**
SIC: 3599 Machine shop, jobbing & repair

(P-16374)
CENTURY PRECISION MACHINE INC
Also Called: Century Industries
1130 W Grove Ave, Orange (92865-4131)
PHONE..............................714 637-3691
Donald R Bibona, *President*
Vera Bibona, *Corp Secy*
David Bibona, *Vice Pres*
EMP: 10
SQ FT: 7,800
SALES (est): 890K **Privately Held**
SIC: 3599 Machine shop, jobbing & repair

(P-16375)
CERAMIC TECH INC
46211 Research Ave, Fremont (94539-6113)
PHONE..............................510 252-8500
Kanu Gandhi, *President*
Vivek Gandhi, *Treasurer*
EMP: 28
SQ FT: 30,000
SALES (est): 5.2MM **Privately Held**
WEB: www.ceramictechinc.com
SIC: 3599 3264 Machine & other job shop work; porcelain electrical supplies

(P-16376)
CHANNEL ISL OPTO MECH
1595 Walter St Ste 1, Ventura (93003-5613)
PHONE..............................805 644-2153
Alan Cornelius, *President*
Roger Ransom, *Treasurer*
Mark Pennington, *Vice Pres*
Carri Jacobs, *Office Mgr*
EMP: 11
SQ FT: 5,000
SALES (est): 1MM **Privately Held**
SIC: 3599 3827 Machine shop, jobbing & repair; optical elements & assemblies, except ophthalmic

(P-16377)
CHAPMAN ENGINEERING CORP
2321 Cape Cod Way, Santa Ana (92703-3514)
PHONE..............................714 542-1942
Mary M Chapman, *CEO*
Ernest D Chapman, *Admin Sec*
Adam Diethrich, *Opers Mgr*
EMP: 40
SQ FT: 25,000
SALES (est): 6.4MM **Privately Held**
WEB: www.chapmanengineering.com
SIC: 3599 3469 Machine shop, jobbing & repair; metal stampings

(P-16378)
CHAVEZ WELDING & MACHINING
1115 Campbell Ave 1a, San Jose (95126-1004)
PHONE..............................408 247-4658
Ramon Chavez, *Owner*
EMP: 22
SALES (est): 1.5MM **Privately Held**
SIC: 3599 Machine & other job shop work

(P-16379)
CHE PRECISION INC
2640 Lavery Ct Ste C, Newbury Park (91320-1528)
PHONE..............................805 499-8885
Claude Holguin, *President*

Charlie Holguin, *Vice Pres*
▲ EMP: 15
SQ FT: 7,500
SALES (est): 3.1MM **Privately Held**
WEB: www.cheprecision.com
SIC: 3599 Machine shop, jobbing & repair

(P-16380)
CHECK YOURSELF INC
Also Called: Check Yourself Machining
5785 Thornwood Dr, Goleta (93117-3801)
PHONE..............................805 967-6190
Candice Wiesblott, *President*
Lorne Wiesblott, *CFO*
Justin Wiesblott, *Vice Pres*
EMP: 10
SQ FT: 2,300
SALES (est): 850K **Privately Held**
WEB: www.chkyourself.com
SIC: 3599 Custom machinery

(P-16381)
CHEEK MACHINE CORP
1312 S Allec St, Anaheim (92805-6303)
PHONE..............................714 279-9486
Tatiana Cheek, *President*
Christopher Cheek, *Vice Pres*
Hilario Herrera, *Prdtn Mgr*
EMP: 21
SQ FT: 5,000
SALES (est): 3.5MM **Privately Held**
WEB: www.cheekmachine.com
SIC: 3599 Machine shop, jobbing & repair

(P-16382)
CHIPCO MANUFACTURING CO INC
623 Bridge St, Yuba City (95991-3817)
PHONE..............................530 751-8150
Paul J Azzopardi, *President*
Lea Ann Roberts, *Office Mgr*
EMP: 14 EST: 1964
SQ FT: 22,000
SALES (est): 2.8MM **Privately Held**
SIC: 3599 Machine shop, jobbing & repair

(P-16383)
CHIPMASTERS MANUFACTURING INC (PA)
798 N Coney Ave, Azusa (91702-2239)
P.O. Box 697 (91702-0697)
PHONE..............................626 422-2053
Richard Jacobsen, *President*
Sal Hidalgo, *VP Opers*
Rick Standley, *Manager*
EMP: 16
SALES (est): 2.8MM **Privately Held**
SIC: 3599 Machine shop, jobbing & repair

(P-16384)
CISCO MFG INC
3185 De La Cruz Blvd, Santa Clara (95054-2405)
PHONE..............................510 584-9626
Francisco Nanez, *President*
EMP: 20
SQ FT: 500
SALES (est): 3.5MM **Privately Held**
SIC: 3599 Machine shop, jobbing & repair

(P-16385)
CLASSIC WIRE CUT COMPANY INC
28210 Constellation Rd, Valencia (91355-5000)
PHONE..............................661 257-0558
Brett Bannerman, *Principal*
▲ EMP: 150
SQ FT: 80,000
SALES (est): 33.2MM **Privately Held**
WEB: www.classicwirecut.com
SIC: 3599 3841 Electrical discharge machining (EDM); surgical instruments & apparatus

(P-16386)
CLINT PRECISION MFG INC
7665 Formula Pl Ste A, San Diego (92121-3429)
PHONE..............................858 271-4041
Michael Clint, *President*
Sharon Clint, *Treasurer*
Michael Gompper, *Vice Pres*
Rick Mills, *Prgrmr*
EMP: 14

SQ FT: 11,000
SALES (est): 3MM **Privately Held**
WEB: www.clintprecision.com
SIC: 3599 Machine shop, jobbing & repair

(P-16387)
CMI MFG INC
35370 Cedar Blvd, Newark (94560-1207)
PHONE..............................408 982-9580
Maria B Moreno, *Principal*
Sergio Basilio, *Materials Mgr*
EMP: 15
SALES (est): 644.6K **Privately Held**
SIC: 3599 Machine shop, jobbing & repair

(P-16388)
CMI PRECISION MACHINING LLC
527 Fee Ana St, Placentia (92870-6702)
PHONE..............................714 528-3000
EMP: 11
SALES (est): 1.7MM **Privately Held**
SIC: 3599

(P-16389)
CMI PRECISION MACHINING LLC
Also Called: CMI Precision Machining
527 Fee Ana St, Placentia (92870-6702)
PHONE..............................714 528-3000
Charles Cheek, *Principal*
EMP: 10
SALES (est): 1.4MM **Privately Held**
WEB: www.cmiprecision.com
SIC: 3599 Machine shop, jobbing & repair

(P-16390)
CNC INDUSTRIES INC
10635 Monte Vista Ave, Montclair (91763-4720)
PHONE..............................909 445-0300
Bob Evans, *President*
Stephanie Evans, *Treasurer*
EMP: 13 EST: 1980
SQ FT: 33,000
SALES (est): 2MM **Privately Held**
SIC: 3599 Machine shop, jobbing & repair

(P-16391)
CNI MFG INC
Also Called: Computer-Nozzles
15627 Arrow Hwy, Irwindale (91706-2004)
PHONE..............................626 962-6646
Toby Argandona, *President*
David Argandona, *Vice Pres*
Yolanda Pullen, *Admin Sec*
EMP: 20
SQ FT: 32,200
SALES (est): 4MM **Privately Held**
WEB: www.cni-mfg.com
SIC: 3599 3443 Custom machinery; fabricated plate work (boiler shop)

(P-16392)
COAST COMPOSITES LLC
7 Burroughs, Irvine (92618-2804)
PHONE..............................949 455-0665
Brendan Buckel, *Manager*
Tony Nhu, *Technology*
Colin Birtles, *Engineer*
Andy Close, *Engineer*
Cindy Camarillo, *Hum Res Coord*
EMP: 10
SALES (corp-wide): 385.4MM **Privately Held**
SIC: 3599 Machine shop, jobbing & repair
HQ: Coast Composites, Llc
5 Burroughs
Irvine CA 92618
949 455-0665

(P-16393)
COAST COMPOSITES LLC (DH)
Also Called: Aip Aerospace Holdings
5 Burroughs, Irvine (92618-2804)
PHONE..............................949 455-0665
Paul Walsh, *President*
Raphael Flores, *Exec VP*
Tim Shumate, *Business Dir*
Calvin Le, *Program Mgr*
Graham Mitchell, *Program Mgr*
◆ EMP: 101
SQ FT: 60,000

SALES (est): 58.4MM
SALES (corp-wide): 385.4MM **Privately Held**
WEB: www.coastcomposites.com
SIC: 3599 Machine shop, jobbing & repair
HQ: Ascent Aerospace, Llc
16445 23 Mile Rd
Macomb MI 48042
586 726-0500

(P-16394)
COLLEEN & HERB ENTERPRISES INC
Also Called: C & H Enterprises
46939 Bayside Pkwy, Fremont (94538-6527)
PHONE..............................510 226-6083
Herbert Schmidt, *CEO*
Colleen Schmidt, *President*
Jake Schmidt, *COO*
Steve Heredia, *Technology*
Greg Kerner, *Human Res Dir*
EMP: 60
SQ FT: 15,200
SALES (est): 14.6MM **Privately Held**
WEB: www.candhenterprises.com
SIC: 3599 7692 Machine shop, jobbing & repair; welding repair

(P-16395)
COMPLETE METAL DESIGN
154 S Valencia Ave, Glendora (91741-3262)
PHONE..............................626 335-3636
Robert Lane, *CEO*
Crystal Lane, *Admin Sec*
EMP: 12
SALES (est): 1.3MM **Privately Held**
SIC: 3599 Machine shop, jobbing & repair

(P-16396)
COMPUTER ASSSTED MFG TECH CORP
Also Called: CAM-Tech
8710 Research Dr, Irvine (92618-4222)
PHONE..............................949 263-8911
Lance Young, *President*
David Magnuson, *Treasurer*
Greg Scott, *Vice Pres*
Susan McKenzie, *Executive*
Susan Mc Kenzie, *Financial Exec*
EMP: 75
SQ FT: 50,000
SALES (est): 14.3MM **Privately Held**
WEB: www.camtechcorp.com
SIC: 3599 Custom machinery

(P-16397)
COMPUTER INTGRTED MCHINING INC
10940 Wheatlands Ave, Santee (92071-2857)
PHONE..............................619 596-9246
Michael J Brown, *President*
Terri Brock, *Opers Mgr*
Paul Vouaux, *Prdtn Mgr*
Timothy Hilliker, *Manager*
EMP: 21
SQ FT: 20,000
SALES (est): 4.5MM **Privately Held**
WEB: www.cimsd.com
SIC: 3599 Machine shop, jobbing & repair

(P-16398)
CONNELLY MACHINE WORKS
420 N Terminal St, Santa Ana (92701-4999)
PHONE..............................714 558-6855
Ray Connelly, *President*
Scott Connelly, *Vice Pres*
EMP: 22
SQ FT: 17,000
SALES (est): 4.4MM **Privately Held**
WEB: www.connellymachine.com
SIC: 3599 3492 Machine shop, jobbing & repair; fluid power valves & hose fittings

(P-16399)
CONNOR MANUFACTURING SVCS INC (PA)
1710 S Amphlett Blvd # 318, San Mateo (94402-2706)
PHONE..............................650 591-2026
Robert Sloss, *Ch of Bd*
Maxine Harmatta, *CFO*

Dennis Kwiecinski, *Exec VP*
Henry Chan, *General Mgr*
James Burns, *QA Dir*
▲ **EMP:** 100 **EST:** 1912
SQ FT: 3,000
SALES (est): 68.1MM **Privately Held**
WEB: www.connorms.com
SIC: 3599 Machine shop, jobbing & repair

(P-16400)
CONQUIP INC
11255 Pyrites Way Ste 100, Gold River
(95670-6336)
PHONE....................916 379-8200
Matthew Lind, *CEO*
Adam Zielenski, *President*
Charles Chuck Novak, *CFO*
Bruce Ballard, *Vice Pres*
Bob Wenning, *CTO*
▲ **EMP:** 54
SQ FT: 60,000
SALES (est): 21.8MM **Privately Held**
WEB: www.conquipinc.com
SIC: 3599 Custom machinery

(P-16401)
CONSOLDTED HNGE MNFCTURED PDTS
Also Called: Champ Co
1150b Dell Ave, Campbell (95008-6640)
PHONE....................408 379-6550
Karl L Herbst, *President*
Ursula Gueldner, *Treasurer*
Alfred Riesenhuber, *Vice Pres*
Rod Mourad, *General Mgr*
Tom Harris, *Business Mgr*
EMP: 17
SQ FT: 23,000
SALES (est): 2.9MM **Privately Held**
WEB: www.champcompany.com
SIC: 3599 Machine shop, jobbing & repair

(P-16402)
CONSTRUCTION TL & THREADING CO
8476 Garfield Ave, Bell Gardens
(90201-6125)
PHONE....................562 927-1326
James T Pokracki, *President*
Rita Pokracki, *Corp Secy*
EMP: 16
SQ FT: 8,800
SALES (est): 2.2MM **Privately Held**
WEB: www.constructiontool.com
SIC: 3599 Machine shop, jobbing & repair

(P-16403)
COORSTEK INC
Coorstek Fremont Division
42670 Albrae St, Fremont (94538-3391)
PHONE....................510 492-6600
Doug Coors, *Branch Mgr*
EMP: 70
SALES (corp-wide): 909.3MM **Privately Held**
SIC: 3599 Machine shop, jobbing & repair
HQ: Coorstek, Inc.
14143 Denver West Pkwy # 400
Lakewood CO 80401
303 271-7000

(P-16404)
COUGHRAN MECHANICAL SERVICES
3053 Liberty Island Rd, Rio Vista
(94571-1018)
P.O. Box 158 (94571-0158)
PHONE....................707 374-2100
Kirk Coughran, *President*
Karla Graham, *CFO*
EMP: 19
SQ FT: 2,400
SALES (est): 3.3MM **Privately Held**
SIC: 3599 Machine shop, jobbing & repair

(P-16405)
COZZA INC
9941 Prospect Ave, Santee (92071-4318)
PHONE....................619 749-5663
Frank Charles Cozza, *President*
Gerry Tailor, *Vice Pres*
EMP: 13
SQ FT: 10,000
SALES (est): 2.1MM **Privately Held**
SIC: 3599 Machine & other job shop work

(P-16406)
CPK MANUFACTURING INC
75 Phelan Ave Ste 3, San Jose
(95112-6120)
PHONE....................408 971-4019
Khamsy Syluangkhot, *President*
Paul Wendall, *Vice Pres*
Tony Syluangkhot, *Engineer*
EMP: 16
SQ FT: 17,500
SALES (est): 2.5MM **Privately Held**
WEB: www.cpkmfg.com
SIC: 3599 Machine shop, jobbing & repair;
machine & other job shop work

(P-16407)
CRAMER ENGINEERING INC
302 Elizabeth Ln, Corona (92880-2104)
PHONE....................562 903-5556
David Cramer, *President*
Barbara Cramer, *Treasurer*
EMP: 20
SALES: 1.3MM **Privately Held**
WEB: www.cramerengineering.com
SIC: 3599 Machine shop, jobbing & repair

(P-16408)
CREATIVE METAL PRODUCTS CORP
6284 San Ignacio Ave D, San Jose
(95119-1366)
PHONE....................408 281-0797
Kenneth Hutchinson, *President*
Shirley Hutchinson, *Corp Secy*
▲ **EMP:** 12
SQ FT: 4,606
SALES (est): 1.7MM **Privately Held**
WEB: www.creativemetalproducts.com
SIC: 3599 3544 Machine shop, jobbing &
repair; special dies, tools, jigs & fixtures

(P-16409)
CRESCO MANUFACTURING INC
Also Called: Crescomfg.com
1614 N Orangethorpe Way, Anaheim
(92801-1227)
PHONE....................714 525-2326
Jon Spielman, *President*
Alberta Spielman, *Vice Pres*
EMP: 40
SQ FT: 14,000
SALES (est): 4.9MM **Privately Held**
SIC: 3599 Machine shop, jobbing & repair

(P-16410)
CRUSH MASTER GRINDING CORP
755 Penarth Ave, Walnut (91789-3028)
PHONE....................909 595-2249
Sherman Durousseau, *President*
Jeanne Durousseau, *Admin Sec*
Donna Gilliam, *Mfg Staff*
EMP: 35
SQ FT: 11,800
SALES (est): 5.3MM **Privately Held**
WEB: www.crushmastergrinding.com
SIC: 3599 Machine shop, jobbing & repair

(P-16411)
CRYSTAL LAKE GRINDERS
1497 Menlo Ave Ste B, Clovis
(93611-0671)
P.O. Box 846, North Fork (93643-0846)
PHONE....................559 297-0737
Glenwood O'Dell, *Partner*
EMP: 95
SALES (est): 6.6MM **Privately Held**
WEB: www.crystallakegrinders.com
SIC: 3599 Machine shop, jobbing & repair

(P-16412)
CURLIN HEALTHCARE PRODUCTS INC
15751 Graham St, Huntington Beach
(92649-1630)
PHONE....................714 893-2200
Ahmad Momeni, *President*
Martin Reinders, *Engineer*
Michael Venegas, *Engineer*
▲ **EMP:** 55
SQ FT: 21,000
SALES (est): 6.5MM **Privately Held**
SIC: 3599 3841 Machine shop, jobbing &
repair; machine & other job shop work;
surgical & medical instruments

(P-16413)
CUSTOM MFG LLC
12946 Los Nietos Rd, Santa Fe Springs
(90670-3020)
PHONE....................562 944-0245
Walter Mason,
Laura McKenery,
EMP: 10
SQ FT: 5,000
SALES: 567.8K **Privately Held**
SIC: 3599 Machine shop, jobbing & repair

(P-16414)
CUSTOM MICRO MACHINING INC
707 Brown Rd, Fremont (94539-7014)
PHONE....................510 651-9434
Tao Chou, *President*
Victor Nguyen, *Vice Pres*
David Chow, *General Mgr*
Christina Le, *General Mgr*
EMP: 26
SQ FT: 8,000
SALES (est): 4.5MM **Privately Held**
WEB: www.cmmusa.com
SIC: 3599 Machine shop, jobbing & repair

(P-16415)
D & F STANDLER INC
195 Lewis Rd Ste 39, San Jose
(95111-2192)
PHONE....................408 226-8188
Dennis Styczynski, *President*
EMP: 12
SQ FT: 11,000
SALES (est): 1.7MM **Privately Held**
SIC: 3599 Machine shop, jobbing & repair

(P-16416)
D & T MACHINING INC
3360 Victor Ct, Santa Clara (95054-2316)
PHONE....................408 486-6035
Tom Nguyen, *President*
Thao Tran, *Office Mgr*
EMP: 15
SQ FT: 1,800
SALES (est): 2.1MM **Privately Held**
WEB: www.dtmachining.com
SIC: 3599 Machine shop, jobbing & repair

(P-16417)
D MILLS GRNDING MACHINING INC
6131 Quail Valley Ct, Riverside
(92507-0763)
PHONE....................951 697-6847
Anthony Puccio, *President*
Joe Puccio, *COO*
Gilles Madelmont, *CFO*
EMP: 30 **EST:** 1973
SQ FT: 14,000
SALES (est): 4.8MM
SALES (corp-wide): 14.7MM **Privately Held**
SIC: 3599 Grinding castings for the trade;
machine shop, jobbing & repair
PA: Manufacturing Solutions, Inc.
1738 N Neville St
Orange CA 92865
714 453-0100

(P-16418)
DAN R HUNT INC
Also Called: Hunt Enterprises
2030 S Susan St, Santa Ana (92704-4415)
PHONE....................714 850-9383
Dan R Hunt, *President*
EMP: 11
SQ FT: 6,000
SALES (est): 1.9MM **Privately Held**
WEB: www.huntenterprises.com
SIC: 3599 Machine shop, jobbing & repair

(P-16419)
DANVO MACHINING
2107 S Hathaway St, Santa Ana
(92705-5238)
PHONE....................714 751-1401
Diane Vosloo, *Owner*
EMP: 10 **EST:** 1971
SQ FT: 6,000
SALES (est): 1.3MM **Privately Held**
WEB: www.danvomachiningcompany.com
SIC: 3599 Machine shop, jobbing & repair

(P-16420)
DANWORTH MANUFACTURING CO
30991 Huntwood Ave # 401, Hayward
(94544-7047)
PHONE....................510 487-8290
Maria Barath, *Co-Owner*
Daniel Barath, *Co-Owner*
EMP: 10
SQ FT: 2,400
SALES (est): 1MM **Privately Held**
SIC: 3599 3451 3452 Machine & other
job shop work; machine shop, jobbing &
repair; screw machine products; bolts,
nuts, rivets & washers

(P-16421)
DARCY AK CORPORATION
Also Called: AK Darcy
1760 Monrovia Ave Ste A22, Costa Mesa
(92627-4433)
PHONE....................949 650-5566
Darrell Gilbert, *CEO*
EMP: 15
SALES: 16MM **Privately Held**
SIC: 3599 5085 Machine shop, jobbing &
repair; valves & fittings

(P-16422)
DARKO PRECISION INC
470 Gianni St, Santa Clara (95054-2413)
PHONE....................408 988-6133
Dardo Simunic, *President*
Vesna Simunic, *Vice Pres*
EMP: 78
SQ FT: 35,000
SALES (est): 20.7MM **Privately Held**
WEB: www.dp-inc.com
SIC: 3599 Machine shop, jobbing & repair

(P-16423)
DARMARK CORPORATION
13225 Gregg St, Poway (92064-7120)
PHONE....................858 679-3970
Darwin Mark Zavadil, *President*
Martin T Drake, *Vice Pres*
Lori Zavadil, *Admin Sec*
Shantia Gerard, *Buyer*
James Josafat, *Prdtn Mgr*
EMP: 90
SQ FT: 28,000
SALES (est): 19.4MM **Privately Held**
WEB: www.darmark.com
SIC: 3599 Machine shop, jobbing & repair

(P-16424)
DAVID A NEAL INC
9825 Bell Ranch Dr, Santa Fe Springs
(90670-2953)
PHONE....................562 941-5626
David A Neal, *President*
Debra Neal, *Admin Sec*
▲ **EMP:** 10
SQ FT: 12,800
SALES (est): 1.3MM **Privately Held**
WEB: www.davidoneal.com
SIC: 3599 Machine shop, jobbing & repair

(P-16425)
DAVIS GEAR & MACHINE CO
13625 S Normandie Ave, Gardena
(90249-2607)
PHONE....................310 337-9881
Phil Davis, *Owner*
EMP: 10
SQ FT: 12,000
SALES (est): 747.6K **Privately Held**
SIC: 3599 Machine shop, jobbing & repair

(P-16426)
DELAFIELD CORPORATION (PA)
Also Called: Delafield Fluid Technology
1520 Flower Ave, Duarte (91010-2925)
PHONE....................626 303-0740
Nik Ray, *President*
Henry Custodia, *CFO*
Jim Martin, *Vice Pres*
Hoa Le, *Info Tech Mgr*
Bill Bensing, *Engineer*
◆ **EMP:** 120
SQ FT: 90,000

SALES (est): 47MM **Privately Held**
WEB: www.dftcorp.com
SIC: **3599** 5085 3498 3492 Hose, flexible metallic; valves, pistons & fittings; tube fabricating (contract bending & shaping); fluid power valves & hose fittings; plumbing fixture fittings & trim; rubber & plastics hose & beltings

(P-16427)
DELONG MANUFACTURING CO INC
967 Parker Ct, Santa Clara (95050-2808)
PHONE.................................408 727-3348
David De Long, *CEO*
William A De Long Jr, *CFO*
EMP: 16
SQ FT: 8,400
SALES: 1.8MM **Privately Held**
SIC: **3599** Machine shop, jobbing & repair

(P-16428)
DELTA HI-TECH
9600 De Soto Ave, Chatsworth (91311-5012)
PHONE.................................818 407-4000
Joe Ostrowsky, *CEO*
Juan Casarrubias, *President*
Chava Ostrowsky, *CFO*
Ilan Ostrowsky, *Exec VP*
Gregory Elkhunovich, *Vice Pres*
▲ EMP: 130
SQ FT: 40,000
SALES (est): 31.5MM **Privately Held**
WEB: www.deltahitech.com
SIC: **3599** Machine shop, jobbing & repair

(P-16429)
DELTA MANUFACTURING INC
Also Called: Delta Engineering and Mfg
6260 Prescott Ct, Chino (91710-7111)
PHONE.................................909 590-4563
Ricardo Aguilar, *Owner*
Maria Aguilar, *Office Mgr*
EMP: 25
SQ FT: 1,500
SALES (est): 1.2MM **Privately Held**
WEB: www.deltamanufacturing.com
SIC: **3599** Machine shop, jobbing & repair

(P-16430)
DELTA MATRIX INC
Also Called: Delta Machine
2180 Oakland Rd, San Jose (95131-1571)
PHONE.................................408 955-9140
Tad Slowikowski, *President*
Yolanda Slowikowski, *Admin Sec*
EMP: 38
SQ FT: 9,000
SALES (est): 7.4MM **Privately Held**
WEB: www.deltamachine.com
SIC: **3599** Machine shop, jobbing & repair

(P-16431)
DESCO MANUFACTURING COMPANY (PA)
23031 Arroyo Vis Ste A, Rcho STA Marg (92688-2605)
PHONE.................................949 858-7400
Ralph L Fabian, *President*
William Cobble, *Vice Pres*
Ruth Sistrunk, *Executive*
Tom Sistrunk, *Info Tech Mgr*
Danny Perkins, *Mfg Staff*
▲ EMP: 16
SALES (est): 5.2MM **Privately Held**
WEB: www.descomfg.com
SIC: **3599** Custom machinery

(P-16432)
DESERT SKY MACHINING INC
Also Called: Progressive Concepts Machining
1236 Quarry Ln Ste 104, Pleasanton (94566-4730)
PHONE.................................925 426-0400
Chris Studzinski, *President*
Jane M Studzinski, *Vice Pres*
EMP: 25
SQ FT: 10,000
SALES (est): 3.6MM **Privately Held**
WEB: www.proconmach.com
SIC: **3599** Machine shop, jobbing & repair

(P-16433)
DETENTION DEVICE SYSTEMS
Also Called: DDS
25545 Seaboard Ln, Hayward (94545-3209)
PHONE.................................510 783-0771
Steven R Allington, *President*
Tom Heath, *Vice Pres*
Ron Blair, *Opers Staff*
Catherine Allington, *Marketing Mgr*
Susan Mariano, *Cust Mgr*
EMP: 45
SQ FT: 20,000
SALES (est): 7.6MM **Privately Held**
WEB: www.detentiondevicesystems.com
SIC: **3599** 3429 Machine shop, jobbing & repair; locks or lock sets

(P-16434)
DGA MACHINE SHOP INC
Also Called: D G A Mch Sp Blnchard Grinding
5825 Ordway St, Riverside (92504-1132)
PHONE.................................951 354-2113
Tony Diguglielmo, *President*
Angelo Diguglielmo, *COO*
Angelo Diguglielmo, *Admin Sec*
EMP: 15
SALES (est): 2.9MM **Privately Held**
WEB: www.dgamachineshop.com
SIC: **3599** Machine shop, jobbing & repair

(P-16435)
DIABLO PRECISION INC
500 Park Center Dr Ste 8, Hollister (95023-2539)
PHONE.................................831 634-0136
Conor Kelly, *CEO*
Bill Fixsen, *Vice Pres*
Kanwarjit Singh, *QC Mgr*
EMP: 11
SALES (est): 2.5MM **Privately Held**
WEB: www.diabloprecision.com
SIC: **3599** Machine shop, jobbing & repair

(P-16436)
DIAL PRECISION INC
17235 Darwin Ave, Hesperia (92345-5178)
P.O. Box 402259 (92340-2259)
PHONE.................................760 947-3557
Darryl L Tarullo, *Ch of Bd*
Bill Wolleson, *Prdtn Mgr*
Tom Jordon, *Accounts Mgr*
EMP: 95 EST: 1958
SQ FT: 15,000
SALES (est): 16.1MM **Privately Held**
WEB: www.dialprecision.com
SIC: **3599** 3545 Machine shop, jobbing & repair; machine tool accessories

(P-16437)
DIAMOND TOOL AND DIE INC
Also Called: Lab Clear
508 29th Ave, Oakland (94601-2198)
PHONE.................................510 534-7050
Darrell G Holt, *President*
Dan Welter, *Vice Pres*
Naya Pillazar, *Office Mgr*
Daniel Walter, *Admin Sec*
Larry Regas, *Prdtn Mgr*
▲ EMP: 32
SQ FT: 22,000
SALES (est): 6.7MM **Privately Held**
WEB: www.dtdjobshop.com
SIC: **3599** Machine shop, jobbing & repair

(P-16438)
DIE & TOOL PRODUCTS CO INC
1925 Ingalls St, San Francisco (94124-3350)
PHONE.................................415 822-2888
Victor Tschirky, *President*
Mariette Tschirky, *Corp Secy*
EMP: 16
SQ FT: 15,000
SALES (est): 2.6MM **Privately Held**
WEB: www.dieandtool.com
SIC: **3599** Machine shop, jobbing & repair

(P-16439)
DIECRAFT CORPORATION
5590 Naples Canal, Long Beach (90803-4018)
PHONE.................................323 728-2601
Ronald W Lamb, *President*
Donald R Lamb, *Corp Secy*
EMP: 30

SQ FT: 46,000
SALES (est): 3.2MM **Privately Held**
SIC: **3599** 3312 3544 3469 Machine shop, jobbing & repair; tool & die steel & alloys; special dies, tools, jigs & fixtures; metal stampings

(P-16440)
DILIGENT SOLUTIONS INC
Also Called: Absolute EDM
3240 Grey Hawk Ct, Carlsbad (92010-6651)
P.O. Box 985, Murrieta (92564-0985)
PHONE.................................760 814-8960
Stephen A Bowles, *President*
EMP: 20
SALES (est): 3.4MM **Privately Held**
SIC: **3599** Machine shop, jobbing & repair

(P-16441)
DILLON PRECISION INCORPORATED
3816 Maplewood Ln, Placerville (95667-7927)
PHONE.................................530 672-6794
Bradford W Dillon, *President*
Cheri Dillon, *Treasurer*
Cheri L Dillon, *Corp Secy*
EMP: 34
SQ FT: 13,700
SALES (est): 4.7MM **Privately Held**
WEB: www.dillonprec.net
SIC: **3599** Machine shop, jobbing & repair

(P-16442)
DIVERSIFIED MFG CAL INC
Also Called: Dmoc
2555 Progress St, Vista (92081-8423)
PHONE.................................760 599-9280
Thane D Rivers, *President*
Jerri Rivers, *Vice Pres*
▲ EMP: 10
SQ FT: 10,000
SALES (est): 1MM **Privately Held**
WEB: www.dmoc.us
SIC: **3599** Machine & other job shop work

(P-16443)
DKW PRECISION MACHINING INC
17731 Ideal Pkwy, Manteca (95336-8991)
PHONE.................................209 824-7899
Kurt Franklin, *President*
Brian Kott, *General Mgr*
EMP: 20
SQ FT: 10,000
SALES: 1.1MM **Privately Held**
SIC: **3599** Machine shop, jobbing & repair

(P-16444)
DOERKSEN PRECISION PRODUCTS
2725 Chanticleer Ave # 7, Santa Cruz (95065-1885)
PHONE.................................831 476-1843
Robert Doerksen Jr, *President*
Dan Doerksen, *President*
EMP: 11
SQ FT: 4,500
SALES (est): 1.5MM **Privately Held**
WEB: www.doerksenppi.com
SIC: **3599** Machine shop, jobbing & repair

(P-16445)
DOLSTRA AUTOMATIC PRODUCTS
14441 Edwards St, Westminster (92683-3607)
PHONE.................................714 894-2062
John Dolstra, *President*
Susan Dolstra, *Admin Sec*
EMP: 11
SQ FT: 3,400
SALES: 700K **Privately Held**
SIC: **3599** Machine shop, jobbing & repair

(P-16446)
DONAL MACHINE INC
591 N Mcdowell Blvd, Petaluma (94954-2340)
P.O. Box 750637 (94975-0637)
PHONE.................................707 763-6625
John Chris Bergstedt, *President*
Donna Bergstedt, *COO*
Robert Bergstedt, *Vice Pres*

EMP: 31
SQ FT: 30,000
SALES (est): 6.2MM **Privately Held**
WEB: www.donalmachine.com
SIC: **3599** 3444 3548 Machine shop, jobbing & repair; sheet metalwork; welding & cutting apparatus & accessories

(P-16447)
DOUBLE PRECISION MFG
2273 Calle De Luna, Santa Clara (95054-1002)
PHONE.................................408 727-7726
Michael D Corbo, *Owner*
EMP: 20
SQ FT: 8,000
SALES (est): 1.9MM **Privately Held**
WEB: www.doubleprecision.net
SIC: **3599** Machine shop, jobbing & repair

(P-16448)
DOW HYDRAULIC SYSTEMS INC (PA)
1835 Wright Ave, La Verne (91750-5817)
PHONE.................................909 596-6602
Richard P Dow, *President*
Bryan Dow, *Vice Pres*
Ryan K Dow, *Vice Pres*
Keith Dow, *Principal*
Jeramy Doyle, *QA Dir*
EMP: 60 EST: 1968
SQ FT: 11,000
SALES (est): 12.9MM **Privately Held**
WEB: www.dowprecision.com
SIC: **3599** 3594 Machine shop, jobbing & repair; fluid power pumps & motors

(P-16449)
DPM INC
Also Called: Datum Precision Machining
19641 Hirsch Ct, Anderson (96007-4941)
PHONE.................................530 378-3420
William E Holstein, *President*
Laurie Holstein, *Corp Secy*
EMP: 14
SQ FT: 6,000
SALES (est): 1.3MM **Privately Held**
SIC: **3599** Machine shop, jobbing & repair

(P-16450)
DU-ALL SAFETY LLC
45950 Hotchkiss St, Fremont (94539-7078)
PHONE.................................510 651-8289
Terry McCarthy,
Steve Pierre, *General Mgr*
Mike Connelly, *Director*
Sean Halpin, *Manager*
Richard Debusk, *Accounts Mgr*
EMP: 10
SALES (est): 1.4MM **Privately Held**
WEB: www.du-all.com
SIC: **3599** 8742 Machine shop, jobbing & repair; industrial & labor consulting services

(P-16451)
DUPLAN INDUSTRIES
Also Called: Gilbert Machine & Mfg
1265 Stone Dr, San Marcos (92078-4059)
PHONE.................................760 744-4047
Nancy Duplan, *President*
Carlton Duplan, *Corp Secy*
EMP: 20
SQ FT: 15,000
SALES (est): 3MM **Privately Held**
WEB: www.gilbertmachine.com
SIC: **3599** Machine shop, jobbing & repair

(P-16452)
DYELL MACHINE (PA)
160 S Linden Ave, Rialto (92376-6204)
P.O. Box 974 (92377-0974)
PHONE.................................909 350-4101
Tom Bradley, *Partner*
Edith Dyell, *Partner*
Donna Larson, *Office Mgr*
EMP: 30 EST: 1968
SQ FT: 20,000
SALES (est): 5.6MM **Privately Held**
WEB: www.dyellmachine.com
SIC: **3599** 5084 7699 Machine shop, jobbing & repair; hydraulic systems equipment & supplies; hydraulic equipment repair

▲ = Import ▼=Export
◆ =Import/Export

(P-16453)
DYELL MACHINE
Also Called: Dyell Machine & Hydraulic Shop
17499 Alder St, Hesperia (92345-5063)
PHONE..................................760 244-3333
Mike Coleman, *Manager*
EMP: 10
SQ FT: 10,000
SALES (est): 1.8MM
SALES (corp-wide): 5.6MM **Privately Held**
WEB: www.dyellmachine.com
SIC: 3599 5084 7699 Machine shop, jobbing & repair; hydraulic systems equipment & supplies; hydraulic equipment repair
PA: Dyell Machine
       160 S Linden Ave
       Rialto CA 92376
       909 350-4101

(P-16454)
DYLERN INCORPORATED
14444 Greenwood Cir, Nevada City (95959-9690)
PHONE..................................530 470-8785
EMP: 20
SQ FT: 9,000
SALES (est): 1.7MM **Privately Held**
SIC: 3599

(P-16455)
DYNAMIC ENTERPRISES INC
Also Called: D E I
10015 Greenleaf Ave, Santa Fe Springs (90670-3493)
PHONE..................................562 944-0271
Mildred Sudduth, *President*
Deanna Mansfield, *Corp Secy*
Alan Sudduth, *Vice Pres*
Frank McCluskie, *QC Mgr*
◆ EMP: 21
SQ FT: 50,000
SALES (est): 4.7MM **Privately Held**
WEB: www.dynamic-ent.com
SIC: 3599 Machine shop, jobbing & repair

(P-16456)
DYNAMIC MACHINE INC
3470 Randolph St, Huntington Park (90255-3259)
PHONE..................................323 585-0710
Brian Stevens, *President*
Mark Stevens, *Vice Pres*
EMP: 12
SQ FT: 15,000
SALES (est): 1.7MM **Privately Held**
SIC: 3599 Machine shop, jobbing & repair

(P-16457)
DYNATEC MFG INC
3326 Famille Ct, San Jose (95135-2307)
PHONE..................................408 265-8471
Hung Tieu, *President*
Thuy Vuong, *Vice Pres*
Tom Dang, *Admin Sec*
EMP: 10
SQ FT: 4,500
SALES (est): 1.3MM **Privately Held**
WEB: www.dynatecmfg.com
SIC: 3599 Machine shop, jobbing & repair

(P-16458)
E & S PRECISION MACHINE INC
4631 Enterprise Way, Modesto (95356-8715)
PHONE..................................209 545-6161
Jim Elzner, *President*
Donita Eizner, *CFO*
Alice Green, *Office Mgr*
Tim Weber, *Technology*
Dan Prado, *Sales Mgr*
EMP: 18
SQ FT: 5,000
SALES (est): 3.2MM **Privately Held**
WEB: www.esprecision.com
SIC: 3599 Machine shop, jobbing & repair

(P-16459)
E D M SACRAMENTO INC
Also Called: Sac EDM & Waterjet
11341 Sunrise Park Dr, Rancho Cordova (95742-6532)
PHONE..................................916 851-9285
Daniel Folk, *CEO*
EMP: 24

SQ FT: 20,000
SALES (est): 2.5MM **Privately Held**
WEB: www.sacedm.com
SIC: 3599 Machine shop, jobbing & repair

(P-16460)
E S M PLASTICS INC
13575 Yorba Ave, Chino (91710-5057)
P.O. Box 808 (91708-0808)
PHONE..................................909 591-7658
Earl D Silva, *CEO*
Cheryl Silva, *Admin Sec*
EMP: 15
SQ FT: 7,400
SALES (est): 2.3MM **Privately Held**
SIC: 3599 3089 Custom machinery; injection molding of plastics

(P-16461)
EASTWOOD MACHINE LLC
9346 Abraham Way, Santee (92071-2861)
PHONE..................................619 873-3660
Joseph Odneal,
Sara Odneal,
EMP: 11
SQ FT: 11,000
SALES (est): 1.3MM **Privately Held**
SIC: 3599 Machine shop, jobbing & repair; machine & other job shop work

(P-16462)
EDCO DIE INC
2199 W Arrow Rte, Upland (91786-7610)
PHONE..................................909 985-4417
Dennis Ortis, *President*
Joyce Ortis, *Corp Secy*
EMP: 15 EST: 1966
SQ FT: 23,000
SALES (est): 1.4MM **Privately Held**
SIC: 3599 Machine shop, jobbing & repair

(P-16463)
EH SUDA INC (PA)
Also Called: Fabtron
615 Industrial Rd, San Carlos (94070-3301)
PHONE..................................650 622-9700
Edwin H Suda, *CEO*
EMP: 15
SQ FT: 45,000
SALES (est): 3.2MM **Privately Held**
WEB: www.fabtron-usa.com
SIC: 3599 Machine shop, jobbing & repair

(P-16464)
EH SUDA INC
Also Called: Fabtron
210 Texas Ave, Lewiston (96052)
P.O. Box 171 (96052-0171)
PHONE..................................530 778-9830
Mark Suda, *Branch Mgr*
Tasha Suda, *Finance Mgr*
EMP: 25
SALES (est): 1.4MM
SALES (corp-wide): 3.2MM **Privately Held**
WEB: www.fabtron-usa.com
SIC: 3599 Machine shop, jobbing & repair
PA: E.H. Suda, Inc.
       615 Industrial Rd
       San Carlos CA 94070
       650 622-9700

(P-16465)
EJAYS MACHINE CO INC
1108 E Valencia Dr, Fullerton (92831-4627)
PHONE..................................714 879-0558
Denise Eastin, *President*
Schuyler Eastin, *Treasurer*
EMP: 20
SALES (est): 3.7MM **Privately Held**
SIC: 3599 Machine shop, jobbing & repair

(P-16466)
EL CAMINO MACHINE & WLDG LLC (PA)
296 El Camino Real S, Salinas (93901-4511)
PHONE..................................831 758-8309
Gordon Zook,
Jim Gnesa, *Accountant*
Yvette Gnesa,
Jane Zook,
EMP: 26
SQ FT: 4,800

SALES: 4MM **Privately Held**
SIC: 3599 7692 Machine shop, jobbing & repair; welding repair

(P-16467)
ELITE METAL FABRICATION INC
2299 Ringwood Ave Ste C1, San Jose (95131-1732)
PHONE..................................408 433-9926
Mario Flores, *Manager*
EMP: 21
SALES (est): 2.5MM **Privately Held**
WEB: www.eelitemetal.com
SIC: 3599 Machine & other job shop work

(P-16468)
ELLINGSON INC
119 W Santa Fe Ave, Fullerton (92832-1831)
PHONE..................................714 773-1923
Thomas Ellingson, *President*
T C Ellingson, *CEO*
Nancy Ellingson, *Treasurer*
Steven C Ellingson, *Admin Sec*
EMP: 12
SQ FT: 7,500
SALES (est): 1.6MM **Privately Held**
WEB: www.ellingson-inc.com
SIC: 3599 Machine shop, jobbing & repair; machine & other job shop work

(P-16469)
ELLIOTT MANUFACTURING COMPANY
2664 S Cherry Ave, Fresno (93706-5494)
P.O. Box 11277 (93772-1277)
PHONE..................................559 233-6235
Terry Aluisi, *CEO*
Thomas E Cole, *Ch of Bd*
Sarah Cole, *Bd of Directors*
Richard E Cole, *Vice Pres*
Richard Cole, *Vice Pres*
▼ EMP: 15 EST: 1929
SALES (est): 4.9MM **Privately Held**
WEB: www.elliott-mfg.com
SIC: 3599 3556 3565 7692 Machine shop, jobbing & repair; food products machinery; packaging machinery; welding repair; sheet metalwork

(P-16470)
ELY CO INC
3046 Kashiwa St, Torrance (90505-4083)
PHONE..................................310 539-5831
Walter Senff, *CEO*
Bill Senff, *Vice Pres*
Judith Senff, *Vice Pres*
Kurt Senff, *Admin Sec*
EMP: 36 EST: 1953
SQ FT: 11,500
SALES (est): 6.7MM **Privately Held**
WEB: www.elyco.com
SIC: 3599 Machine shop, jobbing & repair

(P-16471)
EMBERTON MACHINE & TOOL INC
1215 Pioneer Way Ste A, El Cajon (92020-1665)
PHONE..................................619 401-1870
Phyllis Oatman, *CEO*
Randy Emberton, *President*
EMP: 10
SQ FT: 10,000
SALES: 1.8MM **Privately Held**
WEB: www.embertonsmachine.com
SIC: 3599 Machine shop, jobbing & repair

(P-16472)
EME TECHNOLOGIES INC
3485 Victor St, Santa Clara (95054-2319)
PHONE..................................408 720-8817
Walter Nguyen, *President*
Rosario Bonilla, *Finance Mgr*
Lien Nguyen, *Manager*
▲ EMP: 40
SQ FT: 20,000
SALES (est): 6.4MM **Privately Held**
WEB: www.emetec.com
SIC: 3599 Machine shop, jobbing & repair

(P-16473)
ENERGY LINK INDUS SVCS INC
11439 S Enos Ln, Bakersfield (93311-9452)
P.O. Box 10716 (93389-0716)
PHONE..................................661 765-4444
James R Miller III, *CEO*
Matt Knight, *Shareholder*
West Moore, *Shareholder*
Ray Miller, *President*
Gary Winters, *District Mgr*
EMP: 34
SALES (est): 5.9MM **Privately Held**
SIC: 3599 7699 Bellows, industrial: metal; compressor repair

(P-16474)
ENERGY STEEL CORPORATION
Also Called: O'Brien Iron Works
2043 Arnold Indus Way, Concord (94520-5342)
PHONE..................................925 685-5300
Diane Monaghan, *President*
Kevin Monaghan, *CFO*
EMP: 10
SQ FT: 12,000
SALES (est): 2MM **Privately Held**
SIC: 3599 Machine shop, jobbing & repair

(P-16475)
ENGINEERED PRODUCTS BY LEE LTD
Also Called: Precision Engineered Products
10444 Mcvine Ave, Sunland (91040-3102)
PHONE..................................818 352-3322
Wallace K Lee, *President*
Christine Lee, *Office Mgr*
EMP: 12
SQ FT: 7,000
SALES (est): 1.3MM **Privately Held**
SIC: 3599 Machine shop, jobbing & repair

(P-16476)
ENGINEERING DESIGN INDS INC
Also Called: E D I
9649 Rush St, South El Monte (91733-1732)
PHONE..................................626 443-7741
Loc Tran, *President*
Denise Lee, *Treasurer*
EMP: 12
SQ FT: 5,000
SALES: 1.8MM **Privately Held**
WEB: www.go2edi.com
SIC: 3599 Machine shop, jobbing & repair

(P-16477)
ERB INVESTMENT COMPANY LLC
Also Called: 360 Manufacturing Solutions
3501 Thomas Rd Ste 7, Santa Clara (95054-2037)
PHONE..................................408 727-6908
Dick Brown, *General Mgr*
EMP: 10
SALES: 950K **Privately Held**
SIC: 3599 Industrial machinery

(P-16478)
ET BALANCING INC
12823 Athens Way, Los Angeles (90061-1146)
PHONE..................................310 538-9738
Michael Park, *President*
Jim Napora, *Corp Secy*
EMP: 10
SQ FT: 30,000
SALES (est): 1.5MM **Privately Held**
SIC: 3599 Machine shop, jobbing & repair

(P-16479)
EURO MACHINE INC
9627 Owensmouth Ave Ste 1, Chatsworth (91311-4842)
PHONE..................................818 998-5198
Juergen Schoellkopf, *President*
Gregory Calvano, *Vice Pres*
Mane Schoellkopf, *Admin Sec*
▲ EMP: 10
SQ FT: 6,300
SALES (est): 1.7MM **Privately Held**
SIC: 3599 Machine shop, jobbing & repair

(P-16480)
EVDEN ENTERPRISES INC
2000 Wellmar Dr, Ukiah (95482-3168)
PHONE..........................707 462-0375
Dennis Mc Grath, *President*
EMP: 15 EST: 1978
SQ FT: 8,000
SALES (est): 2.6MM Privately Held
WEB: www.evden.com
SIC: 3599 Machine shop, jobbing & repair

(P-16481)
EXACTA-TECHNOLOGY INC
378 Wright Brothers Ave, Livermore
(94551-9489)
PHONE..........................925 443-6200
Paul Speroni, *President*
Michelle Speroni, *Vice Pres*
EMP: 14 EST: 1961
SQ FT: 16,000
SALES (est): 2.3MM Privately Held
WEB: www.exacta-tech.com
SIC: 3599 3826 Machine shop, jobbing &
repair; liquid testing apparatus

(P-16482)
EXCEL CNC MACHINING INC
Also Called: Excel Machining
3185 De La Cruz Blvd, Santa Clara
(95054-2405)
PHONE..........................408 970-9460
Krzysztof Wisinski, *President*
EMP: 48
SALES (est): 9.2MM Privately Held
SIC: 3599 Machine shop, jobbing & repair

(P-16483)
EXCEL MANUFACTURING INC
20409 Prairie St, Chatsworth (91311-6029)
PHONE..........................661 257-1900
Susan Halliday, *President*
EMP: 45
SQ FT: 14,000
SALES (est): 7.5MM
SALES (corp-wide): 34MM Privately
Held
SIC: 3599 Machine & other job shop work
PA: Roberts Tool Company, Inc.
20409 Prairie St
Chatsworth CA 91311
818 341-3344

(P-16484)
EXPEDITE PRECISION WORKS INC
931 Berryessa Rd, San Jose (95133-1002)
PHONE..........................408 437-1893
Orlando Teixeira, *President*
EMP: 45
SQ FT: 5,500
SALES (est): 7.4MM Privately Held
WEB: www.expediteprecision.com
SIC: 3599 3089 Machine shop, jobbing &
repair; plastic hardware & building prod-
ucts

(P-16485)
EXPOL INC
2122 Ronald St, Santa Clara (95050-2820)
PHONE..........................408 567-9020
Josef Plata, *President*
EMP: 10
SQ FT: 6,000
SALES (est): 1MM Privately Held
WEB: www.expol.net
SIC: 3599 Machine shop, jobbing & repair

(P-16486)
EXTREME PRECISION INC
1717 Little Orchard St B, San Jose
(95125-1049)
PHONE..........................408 275-8365
Matthew Ellis, *President*
Rosa Pace, *General Mgr*
EMP: 15
SQ FT: 7,500
SALES (est): 2.1MM Privately Held
WEB: www.extremeprecision.com
SIC: 3599 Machine shop, jobbing & repair;
machine & other job shop work

(P-16487)
EXTREME PRECISION LLC
23266 Arroyo Vis, Rcho STA Marg
(92688-2610)
PHONE..........................949 459-1062
Eric Burgers,
Carrie Burgers,
EMP: 14
SALES (est): 2.2MM Privately Held
SIC: 3599 7539 Machine shop, jobbing &
repair; machine shop, automotive

(P-16488)
EXTRUDE HONE DEBURRING SERVICE
Also Called: Extrude Hone Abrsve Flw McHng
8800 Somerset Blvd, Paramount
(90723-4659)
PHONE..........................562 531-2976
William Melendez, *President*
EMP: 18
SQ FT: 11,000
SALES (est): 1.6MM Privately Held
SIC: 3599 5084 Machine shop, jobbing &
repair; machine tools & accessories; ma-
chinists' precision measuring tools

(P-16489)
F E W INC
Also Called: Western Fabrication & Eqp
420 30th St, Bakersfield (93301-2514)
PHONE..........................661 323-8319
Donald Bookout, *President*
Brent E Bookout, *Vice Pres*
EMP: 10
SQ FT: 21,000
SALES (est): 880K Privately Held
SIC: 3599 3549 3444 Machine shop, job-
bing & repair; metalworking machinery;
sheet metalwork

(P-16490)
FABRI-CORP
25850 Vinedo Ln, Los Altos Hills
(94022-4435)
P.O. Box 1019, Los Altos (94023-1019)
PHONE..........................650 941-2076
Ron E Essary, *Owner*
EMP: 20
SQ FT: 4,000
SALES (est): 1.4MM Privately Held
SIC: 3599 3542 Custom machinery; sheet
metalworking machines

(P-16491)
FABTRON
615 Industrial Rd, San Carlos
(94070-3301)
PHONE..........................650 622-9700
Edward Suda, *Principal*
EMP: 13
SALES (est): 2.3MM Privately Held
SIC: 3599 Machine shop, jobbing & repair

(P-16492)
FANTASY MANUFACTURING INC
7716 Bell Rd, Windsor (95492-8518)
PHONE..........................707 838-7686
Michael G Seeber, *President*
Cheryl Seeber, *Vice Pres*
EMP: 10
SQ FT: 12,000
SALES (est): 1.1MM Privately Held
SIC: 3599 Machine shop, jobbing & repair

(P-16493)
FARRELL BROTHERS HOLDING CORP
Also Called: Swiss Machine Products
1137 N Armando St, Anaheim
(92806-2609)
PHONE..........................714 630-3417
Doug Farrell, *President*
Myra Farrell, *Treasurer*
Ruby Farrell, *Admin Sec*
EMP: 16
SQ FT: 10,000
SALES (est): 2.5MM Privately Held
SIC: 3599 Machine shop, jobbing & repair

(P-16494)
FAST TURN MACHINING INC
3087 Lawrence Expy, Santa Clara
(95051-0713)
PHONE..........................408 720-6888
Tom Khuu, *President*
EMP: 10
SALES (est): 1MM Privately Held
WEB: www.fastturninc.com
SIC: 3599 Machine shop, jobbing & repair

(P-16495)
FERAL PRODUCTIONS LLC
1935 N Macarthur Dr, Tracy (95376-2833)
PHONE..........................510 791-5392
Robert Potts,
Lynn Potts,
EMP: 28
SQ FT: 10,400
SALES (est): 4MM Privately Held
SIC: 3599 Machine shop, jobbing & repair

(P-16496)
FIBREFORM ELECTRONICS INC
Also Called: Fibreform Precision Machining
5341 Argosy Ave, Huntington Beach
(92649-1036)
PHONE..........................714 898-9641
Zachary Fischer, *Ch of Bd*
Frank Mauro, *COO*
Todd Crow, *CFO*
Rovalier Thompson, *Vice Pres*
Joshua Ziegelhoefer, *Engineer*
EMP: 30
SQ FT: 30,000
SALES (est): 6.2MM Privately Held
SIC: 3599 Machine shop, jobbing & repair

(P-16497)
FIERRITO METAL STAMPING
12358 San Fernando Rd, Sylmar
(91342-5020)
PHONE..........................818 362-6136
Henry Avila, *President*
Rosie Avila, *Manager*
EMP: 30
SALES (est): 2.6MM Privately Held
SIC: 3599 3469 Machine shop, jobbing &
repair; metal stampings

(P-16498)
FIERRITOS INC
12358 San Fernando Rd, Sylmar
(91342-5020)
PHONE..........................818 362-6136
Henry Avila, *President*
EMP: 25
SALES (est): 2.3MM Privately Held
WEB: www.fierritos.com
SIC: 3599 Machine shop, jobbing & repair

(P-16499)
FIGUEROA MACHINING
1535 Nacimiento Lake Dr, Paso Robles
(93446-9770)
P.O. Box 399 (93447-0399)
PHONE..........................805 238-7704
Pedro Figueroa, *Owner*
Suzanne Figueroa, *Co-Owner*
EMP: 10
SQ FT: 10,000
SALES (est): 620K Privately Held
SIC: 3599 Machine shop, jobbing & repair

(P-16500)
FINNTECH INC
1930 W 169th St, Gardena (90247-5254)
PHONE..........................310 323-0790
Renny Laitio, *President*
Peter Laitio, *Chairman*
Leila Johnson, *Treasurer*
Kari Laitio, *Vice Pres*
EMP: 13 EST: 1978
SQ FT: 2,500
SALES (est): 800K Privately Held
WEB: www.finntech.com
SIC: 3599 Machine shop, jobbing & repair

(P-16501)
FIVE CORNER CONSERVATION INC
13654 Victory Blvd # 327, Van Nuys
(91401-1738)
PHONE..........................818 792-1805
Michael Ball, *President*
EMP: 10
SALES (est): 719.9K Privately Held
SIC: 3599 Water leak detectors

(P-16502)
FLATHERS PRECISION INC
1311 E Saint Gertrude Pl D, Santa Ana
(92705-5216)
PHONE..........................714 966-8505
Jerry Flathers, *President*
Linda Flathers, *Vice Pres*
EMP: 21
SALES (est): 3.4MM Privately Held
WEB: www.flathersprecision.com
SIC: 3599 Machine shop, jobbing & repair

(P-16503)
FLEXAUST COMPANY INC (HQ)
1200 Prospect St Ste 325, La Jolla
(92037-3660)
P.O. Box 4275, Warsaw IN (46581-4275)
PHONE..........................619 232-8429
Richard Meyer, *President*
Mike Harvey, *Vice Pres*
Sean O'Brien, *Regional Mgr*
Jim McGettrick, *Project Engr*
Mike Welk, *Regl Sales Mgr*
EMP: 22
SALES (est): 52.7MM
SALES (corp-wide): 177.3MM Privately
Held
SIC: 3599 Hose, flexible metallic
PA: Schauenburg International Gmbh
Weseler Str. 35
Mulheim An Der Ruhr 45478
208 999-10

(P-16504)
FM INDUSTRIES INC
331 E Warren Ave, Fremont (94539-7966)
PHONE..........................510 673-0192
Hidenori Nanto, *Ch of Bd*
EMP: 105
SALES (corp-wide): 4.2B Privately Held
SIC: 3599 Machine shop, jobbing & repair
HQ: Fm Industries, Inc.
221 E Warren Ave
Fremont CA 94539
510 668-1900

(P-16505)
FM INDUSTRIES INC (DH)
221 E Warren Ave, Fremont (94539-7916)
PHONE..........................510 668-1900
Hidenori Nanto, *Chairman*
Steven Nguyen, *Receiver*
David S Miller, *CEO*
Brian West, *Program Mgr*
Jeremy Ernest, *Admin Asst*
EMP: 110
SQ FT: 56,000
SALES (est): 41.7MM
SALES (corp-wide): 4.2B Privately Held
WEB: www.fmindustries.com
SIC: 3599 3544 3999 Machine shop, job-
bing & repair; special dies, tools, jigs &
fixtures; atomizers, toiletry
HQ: Ngk North America, Inc.
1105 N Market St Ste 1300
Wilmington DE 19801
302 654-1344

(P-16506)
FMW MACHINE SHOP
980 Obrien Dr, Menlo Park (94025-1407)
PHONE..........................650 363-1313
Humberto Fabris, *General Ptnr*
Annette Fabris, *Partner*
Maria Fabris, *Partner*
EMP: 18
SQ FT: 30,000
SALES (est): 2MM Privately Held
WEB: www.fmwmachineshop.com
SIC: 3599 Machine shop, jobbing & repair

(P-16507)
FONTAL CONTROLS INC
12725 Encinitas Ave, Sylmar (91342-3517)
PHONE..........................818 833-1127
Oscar Fontal, *President*
Gladys Fontal, *Treasurer*
Fernando Fontal, *Vice Pres*
Cristian Fontal, *Admin Sec*
EMP: 16
SQ FT: 14,200
SALES: 2.7MM Privately Held
WEB: www.fontalcontrols.com
SIC: 3599 Machine shop, jobbing & repair

▲ = Import ▼=Export
◆ =Import/Export

(P-16508)
FOREMOST PRECISION PDTS INC
Also Called: Diamond Precision Products
1940 Petra Ln Ste A, Placentia (92870-6750)
PHONE...................714 961-0165
Paul Lavoie, *President*
EMP: 10
SQ FT: 5,000
SALES (est): 1.3MM **Privately Held**
SIC: 3599 Machine shop, jobbing & repair

(P-16509)
FORM GRIND CORPORATION
Also Called: Form Products
30062 Aventura, Rcho STA Marg (92688-2010)
PHONE...................949 858-7000
Ernest Treichler, *CEO*
Gary Treichler, *Treasurer*
Joan Treichler, *Admin Sec*
Jeff Lee, *Senior Mgr*
EMP: 50 EST: 1963
SQ FT: 30,000
SALES (est): 9.2MM **Privately Held**
WEB: www.formgrind.com
SIC: 3599 5084 Machine shop, jobbing & repair; industrial machinery & equipment

(P-16510)
FOURWARD MACHINE INC
Also Called: Program Precision Co
5111 Santa Fe St Ste J&I, San Diego (92109-1614)
PHONE...................858 272-0601
Gary Ward, *President*
EMP: 10
SQ FT: 3,600
SALES: 750K **Privately Held**
SIC: 3599 Machine shop, jobbing & repair

(P-16511)
FOWLERS MACHINE WORKS INC
300 S Riverside Dr, Modesto (95354-4007)
PHONE...................209 522-5146
Andrew Fowler, *President*
Amanda Fowler, *Treasurer*
EMP: 11 EST: 1969
SQ FT: 5,000
SALES (est): 825K **Privately Held**
WEB: www.fowlersmachine.com
SIC: 3599 Machine shop, jobbing & repair

(P-16512)
FOX HILLS MACHINING INC
7431 Belva Dr Ste 102, Huntington Beach (92647-6261)
PHONE...................714 899-2211
Chris Machnicki, *President*
EMP: 10
SALES: 650K **Privately Held**
SIC: 3599 Machine shop, jobbing & repair

(P-16513)
FRANK RUSSELL INC
341 Pacific Ave, Shafter (93263-2046)
PHONE...................661 324-5575
Andrew Russell, *President*
Tim Wilkins, *Plant Mgr*
Cody Russell, *Parts Mgr*
EMP: 17
SQ FT: 13,000
SALES (est): 3.2MM **Privately Held**
SIC: 3599 5251 Machine shop, jobbing & repair; hardware

(P-16514)
FRANKLINS INDS SAN DIEGO INC
12135 Dearborn Pl, Poway (92064-7111)
PHONE...................858 486-9399
Kelly Franklin, *President*
Kim Craig, *Manager*
EMP: 44 EST: 1980
SQ FT: 20,000
SALES (est): 8.8MM **Privately Held**
WEB: www.franklin-ind.com
SIC: 3599 Machine shop, jobbing & repair

(P-16515)
FRED MATTER INC
Also Called: Alloy Metal Products
7801 Las Positas Rd, Livermore (94551-8206)
PHONE...................925 371-1234
Fred Matter, *President*
Chuck Bobek, *QC Mgr*
EMP: 21
SQ FT: 30,000
SALES: 5MM **Privately Held**
WEB: www.alloymp.com
SIC: 3599 Machine shop, jobbing & repair

(P-16516)
FRONTIER ENGRG & MFG TECH INC
Also Called: Frontier Technologies
800 W 16th St, Long Beach (90813-1413)
PHONE...................562 606-2655
John Tsai, *CEO*
Steve Hoekstra, *President*
▲ EMP: 46
SQ FT: 30,000
SALES: 12MM **Privately Held**
WEB: www.frontierfittings.com
SIC: 3599 8711 Machine shop, jobbing & repair; engineering services

(P-16517)
FUNTASTIC FACTORY INC
Also Called: Einflatables
19703 Meadows Cir, Cerritos (90703-7734)
PHONE...................562 777-1140
Ajay H Patel, *CEO*
Ross Andrizzi, *President*
EMP: 36
SQ FT: 20,000
SALES (est): 4.1MM **Privately Held**
WEB: www.einflatables.com
SIC: 3599 Carnival machines & equipment, amusement park

(P-16518)
FUTURE TECH METALS
2926 Rubidoux Blvd, Riverside (92509-2129)
PHONE...................951 781-4801
Tim Gearhardt, *Owner*
Art Medina, *Co-Owner*
EMP: 20
SQ FT: 3,000
SALES (est): 3.3MM **Privately Held**
SIC: 3599 Machine shop, jobbing & repair

(P-16519)
G & H PRECISION INC
11950 Vose St, North Hollywood (91605-5749)
P.O. Box 16123 (91615-6123)
PHONE...................818 982-3873
George Hallajian, *President*
Sevan Hallajian, *Vice Pres*
EMP: 14
SQ FT: 12,000
SALES: 3MM **Privately Held**
SIC: 3599 Machine shop, jobbing & repair

(P-16520)
G & S PROCESS EQUIPMENT INC
Also Called: G & S Enterprises
1700 N Broadway Ave, Stockton (95205-3049)
PHONE...................209 466-3630
Dave Goldsworth, *President*
▲ EMP: 10
SQ FT: 20,000
SALES (est): 1.4MM **Privately Held**
SIC: 3599 Machine shop, jobbing & repair

(P-16521)
G P MANUFACTURING INC
Also Called: Protype
541 W Briardale Ave, Orange (92865-4207)
PHONE...................714 974-0288
Greg Gilbert, *President*
Lewis Pearmain, *Vice Pres*
EMP: 16
SQ FT: 13,500
SALES (est): 2.5MM **Privately Held**
SIC: 3599 3444 Machine shop, jobbing & repair; sheet metalwork

(P-16522)
G V INDUSTRIES INC
1346 Cleveland Ave, National City (91950-4207)
PHONE...................619 474-3013
Gregory J Verdon, *President*
Joseph Verdon, *Vice Pres*
Linda Verdon, *Vice Pres*
EMP: 38
SQ FT: 14,000
SALES (est): 6.9MM **Privately Held**
SIC: 3599 Machine shop, jobbing & repair

(P-16523)
GABILAN WELDING INC
1091 San Felipe Rd, Hollister (95023-2813)
P.O. Box 370 (95024-0370)
PHONE...................831 637-3360
Fax: 831 637-8853
EMP: 12 EST: 1951
SQ FT: 20,000
SALES: 1.2MM **Privately Held**
SIC: 3599

(P-16524)
GALVIN PRECISION MACHINING INC
404 Yolanda Ave, Santa Rosa (95404-6323)
PHONE...................707 526-5359
Jim Galvin, *President*
Jennet Simanta, *Manager*
Greg Wetterman, *Supervisor*
EMP: 13
SQ FT: 7,500
SALES (est): 2.8MM **Privately Held**
WEB: www.galvinprecisionmachining.com
SIC: 3599 Machine shop, jobbing & repair

(P-16525)
GARABEDIAN BROS INC (PA)
Also Called: Valley Welding & Machine Works
2543 S Orange Ave, Fresno (93725-1329)
P.O. Box 2455 (93745-2455)
PHONE...................559 268-5014
Michael J Garabedian, *CEO*
Joanne Garabedian, *Corp Secy*
▼ EMP: 30
SQ FT: 45,000
SALES (est): 5.3MM **Privately Held**
WEB: www.vwmworks.com
SIC: 3599 3523 Machine shop, jobbing & repair; driers (farm): grain, hay & seed

(P-16526)
GARRETT PRECISION INC
25082 La Suen Rd, Laguna Hills (92653-5102)
PHONE...................949 855-9710
Justin S Osborn, *CEO*
Dean Garrett, *President*
Lynn Garrett, *Vice Pres*
EMP: 19 EST: 1978
SQ FT: 6,500
SALES (est): 5.1MM **Privately Held**
SIC: 3599 Machine shop, jobbing & repair

(P-16527)
GATEWAY PRECISION INC
2300 Calle De Luna, Santa Clara (95054-1003)
PHONE...................408 855-8849
Huy Nguyen, *President*
CHI To, *Manager*
EMP: 15
SQ FT: 10,283
SALES (est): 3.4MM **Privately Held**
WEB: www.gatewayprecision.com
SIC: 3599 Machine shop, jobbing & repair

(P-16528)
GBF ENTERPRISES INC
2709 Halladay St, Santa Ana (92705-5618)
PHONE...................714 979-7131
Cheryl Nowak, *President*
Lisa Garrison, *Business Mgr*
Candi Hart, *Consultant*
EMP: 25
SQ FT: 17,000
SALES (est): 4.4MM **Privately Held**
WEB: www.gbfenterprises.com
SIC: 3599 Machine shop, jobbing & repair

(P-16529)
GEIGER MANUFACTURING INC
1110 E Scotts Ave, Stockton (95205-6148)
P.O. Box 1449 (95201-1449)
PHONE...................209 464-7746
Roger Haack, *President*
Dennis D Geiger, *Treasurer*
EMP: 16 EST: 1904
SQ FT: 27,250
SALES (est): 2.7MM **Privately Held**
SIC: 3599 Custom machinery; machine shop, jobbing & repair

(P-16530)
GENERAL INDUSTRIAL REPAIR
7417 E Slauson Ave, Commerce (90040-3307)
PHONE...................323 278-0873
Henry Biazus, *President*
Richard Biazus, *CEO*
Bob Arconado, *Sales Staff*
Robert Biazus, *Sales Staff*
EMP: 25
SQ FT: 75,000
SALES (est): 4.7MM **Privately Held**
WEB: www.girepair.us
SIC: 3599 Machine shop, jobbing & repair

(P-16531)
GENERAL PRODUCTION SERVICES
670 Arroyo St, San Fernando (91340-2220)
PHONE...................818 365-4211
Maria Hall, *President*
Loren S Hall, *Vice Pres*
EMP: 11
SQ FT: 3,500
SALES (est): 1.5MM **Privately Held**
SIC: 3599 Machine shop, jobbing & repair

(P-16532)
GENESIS MCH & FABRICATION INC
4321 Turcon Ave, Bakersfield (93308-5263)
PHONE...................661 324-4366
Darko Skracic, *President*
▲ EMP: 19
SQ FT: 4,500
SALES (est): 2.5MM **Privately Held**
SIC: 3599 Machine shop, jobbing & repair

(P-16533)
GENTEC MANUFACTURING INC
2241 Ringwood Ave, San Jose (95131-1737)
PHONE...................408 432-6220
Mark Diaz, *President*
Delia Garcia, *Office Mgr*
Mike Elder, *Prdtn Mgr*
EMP: 15
SQ FT: 5,700
SALES (est): 2.9MM **Privately Held**
WEB: www.gentecmanufacturing.com
SIC: 3599 Machine shop, jobbing & repair

(P-16534)
GEORGE FISCHER INC (HQ)
3401 Aero Jet Ave, El Monte (91731-2801)
PHONE...................626 571-2770
Chris Blumer, *CEO*
Daniel Vaterlaus, *Vice Pres*
Ruben Rodriguez, *Research*
John Yates, *Project Engr*
Rudy Mangual, *Engineer*
◆ EMP: 46
SALES (est): 216MM
SALES (corp-wide): 4.2B **Privately Held**
SIC: 3599 5074 3829 3559 Electrical discharge machining (EDM); pipes & fittings, plastic; testing equipment: abrasion, shearing strength, etc.; foundry machinery & equipment
PA: Georg Fischer Ag
Amsler-Laffon-Strasse 9
Schaffhausen SH
526 311-111

(P-16535)
GERMAN MACHINED PRODUCTS INC
Also Called: German Machine Products
1415 W 178th St, Gardena (90248-3201)
PHONE...................310 532-4480

PRODUCTS & SVCS

Jonathan Minter, *CEO*
Jonathan James Minter, *CEO*
Karthik Shekar, *Program Mgr*
Jacob Minter, *General Mgr*
EMP: 32 **EST:** 1972
SQ FT: 12,000
SALES (est): 7.9MM **Privately Held**
SIC: 3599 Machine shop, jobbing & repair

(P-16536)
GLENGARRY MANUFACTURING INC
1535 Marlborough Ave, Riverside (92507-2029)
PHONE...................................951 248-1111
EMP: 10 **EST:** 2010
SQ FT: 5,000
SALES (est): 1.5MM **Privately Held**
SIC: 3599

(P-16537)
GOEPPNER INDUSTRIES INC
22924 Lockness Ave, Torrance (90501-5117)
PHONE...................................310 784-2800
Joanne Goeppner, *President*
EMP: 12
SQ FT: 12,000
SALES (est): 1.7MM **Privately Held**
SIC: 3599 Machine shop, jobbing & repair

(P-16538)
GOLDEN WEST MACHINE INC
9930 Jordan Cir, Santa Fe Springs (90670-3305)
PHONE...................................562 903-1111
Dan Goodman, *Principal*
Al Schlunegger, *Vice Pres*
Manny Ortega, *Purchasing*
Shane Downs, *Manager*
EMP: 35
SQ FT: 25,000
SALES: 5.4MM **Privately Held**
WEB: www.goldenwestmachine.com
SIC: 3599 7699 Machine shop, jobbing & repair; industrial machinery & equipment repair

(P-16539)
GOOSE MANUFACTURING INC
1853 Little Orchard St, San Jose (95125-1034)
PHONE...................................408 747-0940
Donald Goossens, *President*
Rosemary Goossens, *Info Tech Mgr*
EMP: 10
SALES (est): 1.4MM **Privately Held**
WEB: www.goosemfg.com
SIC: 3599 Machine shop, jobbing & repair

(P-16540)
GP MACHINING INC
94 Commerce Dr, Buellton (93427-9500)
P.O. Box 2006 (93427-2006)
PHONE...................................805 686-0852
Julian Guerra, *President*
Robert Place, *Vice Pres*
EMP: 34
SQ FT: 4,500
SALES (est): 7.1MM **Privately Held**
WEB: www.gpmachining.com
SIC: 3599 Machine shop, jobbing & repair

(P-16541)
GRACE MACHINE CO INC
4540 Cecilia St, Cudahy (90201-5812)
PHONE...................................323 771-6215
Guillermo Castellanos Sr, *President*
Ivon Rodriguez, *Treasurer*
Guillermo Castellanos Jr, *Vice Pres*
Grace Castellanos, *Admin Sec*
EMP: 20
SALES: 950K **Privately Held**
SIC: 3599 Machine shop, jobbing & repair

(P-16542)
GRAMBERG MACHINE INC
500 Spectrum Cir, Oxnard (93030-8988)
PHONE...................................805 278-4500
Carl Gramberg, *President*
EMP: 10
SQ FT: 5,000
SALES (est): 1.5MM **Privately Held**
SIC: 3599 Machinery, jobbing & repair

(P-16543)
GRICO PRECISION INC
128 S Valencia Ave Ste A, Glendora (91741-3271)
PHONE...................................626 963-0368
Thomas J Grisham, *President*
EMP: 12
SALES: 850K **Privately Held**
SIC: 3599 Industrial machinery

(P-16544)
GRICO PRECISION INC
Also Called: Swiss House
128 S Valencia Ave Ste A, Glendora (91741-3271)
PHONE...................................626 963-0368
Tom Grisham, *President*
Robert E Dill, *Vice Pres*
EMP: 12
SALES: 850K **Privately Held**
SIC: 3599 Machine shop, jobbing & repair

(P-16545)
GRIND FOOD COMPANY INC
Also Called: Goleta Coffee Company
177 S Turnpike Rd, Goleta (93111-2208)
PHONE...................................805 964-8344
Anne Breytsbrika, *President*
EMP: 10
SALES (est): 670K **Privately Held**
SIC: 3599 Grinding castings for the trade

(P-16546)
GSP PRECISION INC
650 Town Center Dr # 950, Costa Mesa (92626-7021)
PHONE...................................818 845-2212
George Gottardi, *President*
Walter D Prezioso, *CEO*
Pablo Prezioso, *Admin Sec*
EMP: 22
SQ FT: 6,000
SALES (est): 2.6MM **Privately Held**
WEB: www.gsp-precision.com
SIC: 3599

(P-16547)
GTR ENTERPRISES INCORPORATED
6352 Corte Del Abeto E, Carlsbad (92011-1408)
PHONE...................................760 931-1192
Kenneth Gray, *CEO*
Martin Randant, *President*
Mike Tedesco, *President*
Scott Lienhoop, *Info Tech Dir*
Shelly Roark, *Human Res Dir*
EMP: 40
SQ FT: 4,000
SALES (est): 6.3MM **Privately Held**
SIC: 3599 5531 Machine shop, jobbing & repair; truck equipment & parts

(P-16548)
GUNDRILL TECH INC
10030 Greenleaf Ave, Santa Fe Springs (90670-3414)
PHONE...................................562 946-9355
Joe Bati, *President*
Yolande Bati, *Vice Pres*
EMP: 22
SALES: 1.5MM **Privately Held**
SIC: 3599 Machine shop, jobbing & repair

(P-16549)
GUPTILL GEAR CORPORATION
874 S Rose Pl, Anaheim (92805-5337)
PHONE...................................714 956-2170
Ron Guptill, *President*
EMP: 10 **EST:** 1970
SQ FT: 4,000
SALES (est): 1.6MM **Privately Held**
WEB: www.guptillgear.com
SIC: 3599 Machine shop, jobbing & repair

(P-16550)
H & M FOUR-SLIDE INC
25779 Jefferson Ave, Murrieta (92562-6903)
PHONE...................................951 461-8244
Hans Klahr, *President*
EMP: 14
SQ FT: 11,600
SALES (est): 1.3MM **Privately Held**
SIC: 3599 Machine shop, jobbing & repair

(P-16551)
H FAM ENGINEERING INC
2131 S Hellman Ave Ste F, Ontario (91761-8004)
PHONE...................................909 930-5678
Joe Herrera, *President*
Raul Herrera, *Vice Pres*
EMP: 16
SQ FT: 7,000
SALES (est): 1MM **Privately Held**
SIC: 3599 Machine shop, jobbing & repair

(P-16552)
H Q MACHINE TECH INC
6900 8th St, Buena Park (90620-1036)
PHONE...................................714 956-3388
Jason Cho, *CEO*
EMP: 23
SALES (est): 3.7MM **Privately Held**
WEB: www.hqmachine.com
SIC: 3599 Machine & other job shop work

(P-16553)
H2J CORPORATION
Also Called: Kem-Mil-Co
3468 Diablo Ave, Hayward (94545-2745)
PHONE...................................510 785-2100
Max J Hill, *Ch of Bd*
M Lane Hill, *President*
L H Hill, *COO*
Douglas Soule, *Engineer*
EMP: 10
SQ FT: 7,500
SALES (est): 1.3MM **Privately Held**
WEB: www.kem-mil.com
SIC: 3599 Chemical milling job shop

(P-16554)
HAIG PRECISION MFG CORP
3616 Snell Ave, San Jose (95136-1305)
PHONE...................................408 378-4920
Daniel S Sarkisian, *CEO*
Paul Sarkisian, *Vice Pres*
Jack Edwards, *Executive*
Aaron Valenta, *Info Tech Mgr*
John Tower, *Design Engr*
▲ **EMP:** 60
SQ FT: 26,000
SALES (est): 12.9MM **Privately Held**
WEB: www.haig-mfg.com
SIC: 3599 7692 Machine shop, jobbing & repair; welding repair

(P-16555)
HANSEN HAULERS INC
Also Called: Hansen Machine Works
1628 N C St 1630, Sacramento (95811-0613)
PHONE...................................916 443-7755
Jodean Mc Millan, *President*
Duke Mc Millan, *Vice Pres*
Scott Mc Millan, *Admin Sec*
EMP: 10
SQ FT: 9,000
SALES (est): 1.2MM **Privately Held**
SIC: 3599 3715 Machine shop, jobbing & repair; truck trailers

(P-16556)
HASALA ENGINEERING INC
125 W 155th St, Gardena (90248-2203)
PHONE...................................310 538-4268
George Hasala, *President*
Emily Hasala, *Vice Pres*
EMP: 12
SQ FT: 5,000
SALES (est): 800K **Privately Held**
SIC: 3599 Machine shop, jobbing & repair

(P-16557)
HEIGHTEN AMERICA INC
Also Called: Heighten Manfacturing
1144 Post Rd, Oakdale (95361-9384)
PHONE...................................209 845-0455
Linda Smeck, *President*
Jerrold W Smeck, *Treasurer*
EMP: 21
SQ FT: 8,000
SALES (est): 3.9MM **Privately Held**
WEB: www.heightenamericainc.com
SIC: 3599 Machine shop, jobbing & repair

(P-16558)
HELFER ENTERPRISES
Also Called: Helfer Tool Co
3030 Oak St, Santa Ana (92707-4236)
PHONE...................................714 557-2733
Bennie L Helfer, *President*
EMP: 36 **EST:** 1973
SQ FT: 12,000
SALES (est): 5.2MM **Privately Held**
WEB: www.helfertool.com
SIC: 3599 5084 3545 3544 Machine shop, jobbing & repair; industrial machinery & equipment; machine tool accessories; special dies, tools, jigs & fixtures

(P-16559)
HENRY MACHINE INC
2316 La Mirada Dr, Vista (92081-7862)
PHONE...................................760 734-6792
Nhan Vo, *President*
Coung Quach, *Vice Pres*
Gene Grajek, *General Mgr*
Ivy Vuu, *Buyer*
Andrew Allen, *Opers Mgr*
EMP: 15
SALES (est): 3.2MM **Privately Held**
WEB: www.henrymachine.com
SIC: 3599 Machine shop, jobbing & repair

(P-16560)
HERITAGE CARBIDE INC
1591 N Main St, Orange (92867-3439)
PHONE...................................714 974-6377
Ronnie C Tipton, *President*
Paula Tipton, *CFO*
EMP: 10
SQ FT: 10,319
SALES (est): 2.5MM **Privately Held**
WEB: www.heritagecarbide.com
SIC: 3599 Machine shop, jobbing & repair; machine & other job shop work

(P-16561)
HI-TECH PRCISION MACHINING INC
Also Called: Htpmi Contract Manufacturing
1901 Las Plumas Ave # 50, San Jose (95133-1700)
PHONE...................................408 251-1269
Hiep Tran, *President*
Peter Lonero, *General Mgr*
EMP: 12
SQ FT: 15,000
SALES (est): 1.8MM **Privately Held**
SIC: 3599 3334 3354 Machine shop, jobbing & repair; primary aluminum; aluminum extruded products

(P-16562)
HI-TECH WELDING & FORMING INC
1327 Fayette St, El Cajon (92020-1512)
P.O. Box 1357 (92022-1357)
PHONE...................................619 562-5929
Aubrey Burer, *CEO*
John C Monsees, *President*
Amy Fitzgerald, *Admin Sec*
EMP: 35
SQ FT: 77,000
SALES (est): 4.7MM **Privately Held**
WEB: www.hi-techwelding.com
SIC: 3599 7692 3365 Machine shop, jobbing & repair; welding repair; aerospace castings, aluminum

(P-16563)
HI-TEMP FORMING CO INC
315 Arden Ave Ste 28, Glendale (91203-1150)
PHONE...................................714 529-6556
Marvin Rosenberg, *President*
Jay Rosenberg, *Treasurer*
Doris Rosenberg, *Vice Pres*
EMP: 65 **EST:** 1959
SQ FT: 36,000
SALES (est): 9.8MM **Privately Held**
SIC: 3599 3812 3769 Machine shop, jobbing & repair; search & navigation equipment; guided missile & space vehicle parts & auxiliary equipment

(P-16564)
HIGH PRECISION GRINDING
1130 Pioneer Way, El Cajon (92020-1925)
PHONE...................................619 440-0303

Keith Brawner, *President*
Ken Gerhart, *Vice Pres*
Shanda Brawner, *Admin Sec*
EMP: 32
SQ FT: 20,000
SALES (est): 4.6MM **Privately Held**
SIC: 3599 Machine shop, jobbing & repair

(P-16565)
HIGH SPEED CNC
3324 Victor Ct, Santa Clara   (95054-2316)
PHONE................................408 492-0331
Joe Munich, *President*
Deanna Schmelebeck, *CFO*
George Rodriguez, *Business Mgr*
Kim Schreckengost, *QC Mgr*
Duane Parsons, *Mfg Spvr*
EMP: 14
SQ FT: 12,000
SALES (est): 2.5MM **Privately Held**
WEB: www.highspeedcnc.com
SIC: 3599 Machine shop, jobbing & repair

(P-16566)
HIGH TECH ETCH (PA)
Also Called: High Tech Etch Research & Dev
17469 Lemon St, Hesperia   (92345-5151)
PHONE................................760 244-8916
Eric Harris, *President*
Will Ashford, *Vice Pres*
EMP: 15
SQ FT: 10,000
SALES (est): 528K **Privately Held**
SIC: 3599 Chemical milling job shop

(P-16567)
HIGHTOWER METAL PRODUCTS
2090 N Glassell St, Orange   (92865-3306)
P.O. Box 5586   (92863-5586)
PHONE................................714 637-7000
Kurt Koch, *President*
Mark Koch, *Vice Pres*
EMP: 66
SQ FT: 20,000
SALES (est): 16.3MM **Privately Held**
SIC: 3599 Machine shop, jobbing & repair

(P-16568)
HILL MARINE PRODUCTS LLC
Also Called: Signature Propellers
2683 Halladay St, Santa Ana   (92705-5617)
PHONE................................714 855-2986
Chad Hill, *Mng Member*
Ron Hill, *Partner*
▲ **EMP:** 14 **EST:** 2011
SALES (est): 972K **Privately Held**
SIC: 3599 7699 Propellers, ship & boat:
    machined; marine propeller repair

(P-16569)
HMCOMPANY
4464 Mcgrath St Ste 111, Ventura
(93003-7764)
PHONE................................805 650-2651
Mark Woellert, *Owner*
EMP: 18
SQ FT: 3,500
SALES (est): 1MM **Privately Held**
WEB: www.hmcompany.net
SIC: 3599 Machine shop, jobbing & repair

(P-16570)
HOEFNER CORPORATION
9722 Rush St, South El Monte
(91733-1777)
PHONE................................626 443-3258
Gerald Hoefner, *President*
Karen Hoefner, *Admin Sec*
EMP: 20
SQ FT: 14,800
SALES (est): 4MM **Privately Held**
WEB: www.hoefnercorp.com
SIC: 3599 3429 Machine shop, jobbing &
    repair; manufactured hardware (general)

(P-16571)
HOLLAND & HERRING MFG INC
Also Called: H & H MANUFACTURING
661 E Monterey Ave, Pomona
(91767-5607)
PHONE................................909 469-4700
Jerry C Holland, *President*
Anne M Herring, *Shareholder*
Bruce N Herring, *Shareholder*
Mark B Herring, *Shareholder*
Steven R Herring, *Shareholder*

EMP: 34
SQ FT: 15,000
SALES (est): 2.6MM **Privately Held**
SIC: 3599 3471 Machine shop, jobbing &
    repair; cleaning, polishing & finishing

(P-16572)
HONOMATIC INC
Also Called: Imperial Honing
10030 Greenleaf Ave, Santa Fe Springs
(90670-3414)
PHONE................................562 941-3295
Ezra Bati, *President*
ARI Bati, *Vice Pres*
EMP: 12
SQ FT: 11,000
SALES (est): 990K **Privately Held**
SIC: 3599 Machine shop, jobbing & repair

(P-16573)
HORIZON ENGINEERING INC
13200 Kirkham Way Ste 109, Poway
(92064-7126)
PHONE................................858 679-0785
Michael Castle, *President*
Dennis Baros, *Vice Pres*
EMP: 10
SQ FT: 4,103
SALES (est): 800K **Privately Held**
WEB: www.horizon-eng.com
SIC: 3599 Machine shop, jobbing & repair

(P-16574)
HORVATH PRECISION MACHINING
Also Called: H P M
930 Thompson Pl, Sunnyvale
(94085-4517)
PHONE................................510 683-0810
Fax: 510 683-0815
EMP: 12
SQ FT: 5,000
SALES (est): 1.2MM **Privately Held**
WEB: www.hpmquality.com
SIC: 3599

(P-16575)
HUNG TUNG
Also Called: Quality Tech Machining
3672 Bassett St, Santa Clara   (95054-2001)
PHONE................................408 496-1818
Tung Hung, *Owner*
EMP: 10
SQ FT: 1,000
SALES (est): 650K **Privately Held**
WEB: www.qualitytechmachining.com
SIC: 3599 Machine shop, jobbing & repair

(P-16576)
HYTRON MFG CO INC
15582 Chemical Ln, Huntington Beach
(92649-1505)
PHONE................................714 903-6701
James C Rehling, *President*
Cheryll Rehling, *Corp Secy*
Robert Rehling, *Vice Pres*
Deborah Strickland, *Vice Pres*
Ken Rehling, *Sales Executive*
EMP: 50
SQ FT: 13,370
SALES (est): 8.7MM **Privately Held**
WEB: www.hytronmanufacturing.com
SIC: 3599 Machine shop, jobbing & repair

(P-16577)
IMG COMPANIES LLC
225 Mountain Vista Pkwy, Livermore
(94551-8210)
PHONE................................925 273-1100
Kam Pasha, *CEO*
Kiran Mukkamala, *CFO*
Mahesh Kumar, *Vice Pres*
▲ **EMP:** 135
SALES (est): 20MM **Privately Held**
SIC: 3599 Machine shop, jobbing & repair

(P-16578)
IMT PRECISION INC
31902 Hayman St, Hayward   (94544-7925)
PHONE................................510 324-8926
Timoteo Ilario, *President*
Jeff Nordloff, *Business Mgr*
Bekki Nguyen, *Accountant*
Peter Kunze, *QC Mgr*
Zack Lemley, *Opers Staff*
EMP: 50

SQ FT: 50,000
SALES (est): 6.5MM **Privately Held**
WEB: www.imtp.com
SIC: 3599 Machine shop, jobbing & repair

(P-16579)
INDUSTRIAL DESIGN FABRICATION
802 S San Joaquin St B, Stockton
(95206-1461)
P.O. Box 268   (95201-0268)
PHONE................................209 937-9128
Laurie Cornell, *President*
Jerry Hicks, *Vice Pres*
▼ **EMP:** 13
SQ FT: 13,200
SALES (est): 2.8MM **Privately Held**
SIC: 3599 3589 Custom machinery; com-
    mercial cleaning equipment

(P-16580)
INDUSTRIAL POWER PRODUCTS
Also Called: Kubota Authorized Dealer
355 E Park Ave, Chico   (95928-7125)
PHONE................................530 893-0584
Tim Adkins, *President*
Robert Berger, *Vice Pres*
Shannon Palo, *General Mgr*
Rob Rice, *Sales Mgr*
Duane Brock, *Manager*
EMP: 30
SQ FT: 7,541
SALES (est): 2.8MM **Privately Held**
SIC: 3599 5084 5085 Machine shop, job-
    bing & repair; engines, gasoline; industrial
    supplies

(P-16581)
INFINITE ENGINEERING INC
13682 Newhope St, Garden Grove
(92843-3712)
PHONE................................714 534-4688
Simon Ho, *President*
Kelly Ho, *Vice Pres*
EMP: 12
SALES (est): 605.7K **Privately Held**
WEB: www.infinite-eng.com
SIC: 3599 Machine shop, jobbing & repair

(P-16582)
INFINITY PRECISION INC
Also Called: Design Engineering
6919 Eton Ave, Canoga Park   (91303-2110)
PHONE................................818 447-3008
Evelina Martirosova, *President*
Armen Khachaturov, *Foreman/Supr*
EMP: 10
SQ FT: 6,000
SALES (est): 1.1MM **Privately Held**
SIC: 3599 3441 Machine & other job shop
    work; fabricated structural metal

(P-16583)
INFINITY SYSTEMS INC
22715 La Palma Ave, Yorba Linda
(92887-4772)
PHONE................................714 692-1722
Zoltan Karpati, *President*
Tony Karpati, *Corp Secy*
Mark Robbins, *General Mgr*
EMP: 10
SQ FT: 6,300
SALES (est): 2.1MM **Privately Held**
WEB: www.infinitysystemsinc.com
SIC: 3599 Machine shop, jobbing & repair

(P-16584)
INNO TECH MACHINING INC
8276 Ronson Rd, San Diego   (92111-2015)
PHONE................................858 565-4556
Marek Prochazka, *President*
Gail Prochazka, *CFO*
Michael Jenny, *Opers Mgr*
▲ **EMP:** 14
SQ FT: 5,000
SALES (est): 2.6MM **Privately Held**
WEB: www.innotechmachining.com
SIC: 3599 Machine shop, jobbing & repair

(P-16585)
INNOVATIVE MACHINING INC
845 Yosemite Way, Milpitas   (95035-6329)
PHONE................................408 262-2270
Thang Vo, *President*
Bich Nguyen, *Vice Pres*

EMP: 25
SQ FT: 3,000
SALES (est): 3.7MM **Privately Held**
SIC: 3599 Machine shop, jobbing & repair

(P-16586)
INSERTS & KITS INC
1811 Carnegie Ave, Santa Ana
(92705-5502)
PHONE................................714 708-2888
Reinaldo J Ayala, *President*
Debbie Hookey, *Manager*
EMP: 10
SALES (est): 800K **Privately Held**
SIC: 3599 Machine shop, jobbing & repair

(P-16587)
INTEGRATED MFG TECH INC
Also Called: IMT
1477 N Milpitas Blvd, Milpitas
(95035-3160)
PHONE................................510 366-8793
Andy Luong, *President*
Whyemun Chan, *Treasurer*
Sally Luong, *Vice Pres*
Dave Gonzalez, *General Mgr*
EMP: 27
SALES (est): 10MM **Privately Held**
SIC: 3599 3471 3498 7692 Machine
    shop, jobbing & repair; polishing, metals
    or formed products; fabricated pipe & fit-
    tings; welding repair

(P-16588)
INTER CITY MANUFACTURING INC
507 Redwood Ave, Seaside   (93955-3029)
PHONE................................831 899-3636
Douglas A Learned, *President*
Karen Learned, *Executive*
EMP: 24
SQ FT: 12,000
SALES (est): 3.3MM **Privately Held**
SIC: 3599 Machine shop, jobbing & repair

(P-16589)
INTERCITY CENTERLESS GRINDING
11546 Coley River Cir, Fountain Valley
(92708-4219)
PHONE................................714 546-5644
Mike Bell, *Owner*
Ellen Marie Gutierrez, *President*
Michael Gutierrez, *Vice Pres*
EMP: 10
SQ FT: 7,800
SALES (est): 1.1MM **Privately Held**
SIC: 3599 Machine shop, jobbing & repair

(P-16590)
INTERNATIONAL PRECISION INC
Also Called: I P
9526 Vassar Ave, Chatsworth
(91311-4168)
P.O. Box 4839   (91313-4839)
PHONE................................818 882-3933
Renee M Brendel-Konrad, *CEO*
Robert Ciccone, *Administration*
Giovanni Passarelli, *Engineer*
Rene Konrad, *Purch Mgr*
Juan Passarelli, *Mfg Mgr*
◆ **EMP:** 22
SQ FT: 12,000
SALES (est): 4.9MM **Privately Held**
WEB: www.intlprecision.com
SIC: 3599 3728 Machine shop, jobbing &
    repair; aircraft parts & equipment

(P-16591)
INVERSE SOLUTIONS INC
3922 Valley Ave Ste A, Pleasanton
(94566-4873)
PHONE................................925 931-9500
David Jordan, *Principal*
Ronda Jordan, *Admin Sec*
EMP: 24
SQ FT: 12,500
SALES (est): 4.4MM **Privately Held**
SIC: 3599 Machine shop, jobbing & repair

(P-16592)
IRONCLAD TOOL AND MACHINE INC
120 Old Yard Dr, Bakersfield (93307-4295)
P.O. Box 42707 (93384-2707)
PHONE..................................661 833-9990
Joseph Williams, *President*
EMP: 10 EST: 2016
SALES (est): 548K **Privately Held**
SIC: 3599 7692 1389 Machine & other job shop work; machine shop, jobbing & repair; welding repair; mud service, oil field drilling

(P-16593)
ISI DETENTION CONTG GROUP INC
Also Called: Argyle Precision
577 N Batavia St, Orange (92868-1218)
PHONE..................................714 288-1770
Zach Greene, *President*
Joe Chavez, *Vice Pres*
▲ EMP: 90
SQ FT: 25,000
SALES (est): 16.7MM **Privately Held**
WEB: www.petersondetention.com
SIC: 3599 3444 Machine & other job shop work; sheet metal specialties, not stamped

(P-16594)
J & F MACHINE INC
6401 Global Dr, Cypress (90630-5227)
PHONE..................................714 527-3499
Micheline Varnum, *President*
Richard Varnum, *Vice Pres*
Oscar Ocampo, *Finance*
EMP: 22
SQ FT: 8,500
SALES (est): 4.5MM **Privately Held**
SIC: 3599 Machine shop, jobbing & repair

(P-16595)
J & R MACHINE WORKS
45420 60th St W, Lancaster (93536-8322)
PHONE..................................661 945-8826
Jesse Alvarado, *Partner*
Rudy Alvarado, *Partner*
Jonathan Varela, *QC Mgr*
EMP: 20
SQ FT: 3,500
SALES (est): 3.4MM **Privately Held**
SIC: 3599 Machine shop, jobbing & repair

(P-16596)
J & R MACHINING INC
164 Martinvale Ln, San Jose (95119-1355)
PHONE..................................408 365-7314
Ashur Peera, *President*
Anna Peera, *Vice Pres*
Edisson Haghnazari, *Manager*
EMP: 11
SQ FT: 5,000
SALES (est): 1.4MM **Privately Held**
SIC: 3599 Machine shop, jobbing & repair

(P-16597)
J & S INC
229 E Gardena Blvd, Gardena (90248-2800)
PHONE..................................310 719-7144
Joseph Brown, *President*
Sheryl Zamora, *CEO*
Margaret Brown, *Corp Secy*
EMP: 33
SQ FT: 6,141
SALES (est): 4.4MM **Privately Held**
SIC: 3599 Machine shop, jobbing & repair

(P-16598)
J & S MACHINE
Also Called: J and S Machine
8112 Freestone Ave, Santa Fe Springs (90670-2114)
PHONE..................................562 945-6419
EMP: 30
SQ FT: 7,200
SALES (est): 1.5MM **Privately Held**
SIC: 3599

(P-16599)
J A-CO MACHINE WORKS LLC
Also Called: Jaco Machine Works
4 Carbonero Way, Scotts Valley (95066-4200)
PHONE..................................831 429-8175
Andy Smith, *Mng Member*
Jeffrey A Smith, *Managing Prtnr*
Jeff Smith, *VP Opers*
EMP: 20
SQ FT: 9,000
SALES (est): 3.2MM **Privately Held**
WEB: www.jacoworks.com
SIC: 3599 Machine shop, jobbing & repair

(P-16600)
J B TOOL INC
350 E Orngthrp Ave Ste 6, Placentia (92870-6504)
PHONE..................................714 993-7173
Robert Barna, *President*
EMP: 11
SQ FT: 12,000
SALES (est): 800K **Privately Held**
WEB: www.jbtoolinc.com
SIC: 3599 Machine shop, jobbing & repair

(P-16601)
J C GRINDING (PA)
Also Called: J C Machining
10923 Painter Ave, Santa Fe Springs (90670-4528)
PHONE..................................562 944-3025
Paul Caringella, *Owner*
EMP: 12 EST: 1975
SQ FT: 10,000
SALES (est): 2MM **Privately Held**
SIC: 3599 Machine shop, jobbing & repair

(P-16602)
J D INDUSTRIES
1636 E Edinger Ave Ste P, Santa Ana (92705-5020)
PHONE..................................714 542-5517
Fax: 714 542-3430
EMP: 10
SQ FT: 4,000
SALES (est): 650K **Privately Held**
SIC: 3599

(P-16603)
J E S DISC GRINDING INC
2824 Metropolitan Pl, Pomona (91767-1854)
PHONE..................................909 596-3823
John Schmidt, *President*
Ray Schmidt, *Vice Pres*
EMP: 13
SQ FT: 12,000
SALES (est): 1.4MM **Privately Held**
SIC: 3599 Machine shop, jobbing & repair

(P-16604)
J L HALEY ENTERPRISES
3510 Luyung Dr, Rancho Cordova (95742-6872)
PHONE..................................916 631-6375
James L Haley, *CEO*
Julie Haley, *Manager*
▲ EMP: 140
SQ FT: 67,000
SALES (est): 27.1MM **Privately Held**
SIC: 3599 3312 7692 Machine shop, jobbing & repair; blast furnaces & steel mills; welding repair

(P-16605)
J&E PRECISION MACHINING INC
2814 Aiello Dr Ste A, San Jose (95111-2197)
PHONE..................................408 281-1195
Eva M Sousa, *President*
Jorge Sousa, *Vice Pres*
Al Furtado, *Manager*
EMP: 12
SQ FT: 6,000
SALES (est): 1.3MM **Privately Held**
WEB: www.jandeprecision.com
SIC: 3599 Machine shop, jobbing & repair

(P-16606)
J&J PRODUCTS
835 Capitolio Way Ste 4, San Luis Obispo (93401-7127)
PHONE..................................805 544-4288
Earl Jeffries, *Owner*
EMP: 12
SQ FT: 3,000
SALES (est): 938.3K **Privately Held**
WEB: www.j-jproducts.com
SIC: 3599 7692 Machine & other job shop work; welding repair

(P-16607)
J3 ASSOCIATES INC
2751 Aiello Dr, San Jose (95111-2156)
PHONE..................................408 281-4412
John Vasapollo, *President*
James Catron, *Vice Pres*
EMP: 10
SQ FT: 10,000
SALES (est): 1.6MM **Privately Held**
WEB: www.j3associates.com
SIC: 3599 Machine shop, jobbing & repair

(P-16608)
JACK C DREES GRINDING CO INC
11815 Vose St B, North Hollywood (91605-5748)
PHONE..................................818 764-8301
Jack C Drees, *President*
Dann Drees, *Vice Pres*
EMP: 20 EST: 1957
SQ FT: 12,000
SALES (est): 2MM **Privately Held**
SIC: 3599 7389 Grinding castings for the trade; grinding, precision: commercial or industrial

(P-16609)
JACK WEST CNC INC
3451 Main St Ste 111, Chula Vista (91911-5894)
PHONE..................................619 421-1695
Jack West, *President*
Jenny West, *Vice Pres*
▲ EMP: 10
SALES (est): 1.8MM **Privately Held**
SIC: 3599 Machine shop, jobbing & repair

(P-16610)
JACO ENGINEERING
879 S East St, Anaheim (92805-5391)
PHONE..................................714 991-1680
H J Meagher, *President*
Barbara Meagher, *Vice Pres*
Kathy Gordon, *General Mgr*
Patrick Meagher, *General Mgr*
Sharon Maloney, *Office Mgr*
EMP: 35
SQ FT: 10,000
SALES (est): 7MM **Privately Held**
WEB: www.jacoengineering.com
SIC: 3599 Machine shop, jobbing & repair

(P-16611)
JAFFA PRECISION ENGRG INC
12117 Madera Way, Riverside (92503-4849)
PHONE..................................951 278-8797
Raida Sayegh, *President*
Mark Sayegh, *Manager*
EMP: 15
SQ FT: 12,500
SALES (est): 2.1MM **Privately Held**
SIC: 3599 Machine shop, jobbing & repair

(P-16612)
JAMES JACKSON
Also Called: J J Engineering
11021 Via El Mercado, Los Alamitos (90720-2811)
PHONE..................................562 493-1402
James Jackson, *Owner*
EMP: 10
SQ FT: 7,050
SALES (est): 1.1MM **Privately Held**
SIC: 3599 Machine shop, jobbing & repair

(P-16613)
JAMES L CRAFT INC
Also Called: Genenco
1101 33rd St, Bakersfield (93301-2121)
PHONE..................................661 323-8251
James L Craft, *President*
EMP: 25
SALES (est): 2MM **Privately Held**
SIC: 3599 Machine shop, jobbing & repair

(P-16614)
JAMES STOUT
Also Called: Stg Machine
481 Gianni St, Santa Clara (95054-2414)
PHONE..................................408 988-8582
Jim Stout, *Owner*
Robert Fernandez, *General Mgr*
Debra Stout, *Technology*
Vince Tran, *Accounts Mgr*
EMP: 30
SQ FT: 15,000
SALES (est): 3.9MM **Privately Held**
SIC: 3599 Machine shop, jobbing & repair

(P-16615)
JARVIS MANUFACTURING INC
195 Lewis Rd Ste 36, San Jose (95111-2192)
PHONE..................................408 226-2600
Tony Grewal, *CEO*
EMP: 17
SQ FT: 6,000
SALES (est): 2.9MM **Privately Held**
WEB: www.jarvismfg.com
SIC: 3599 Machine shop, jobbing & repair

(P-16616)
JAY BELLACH CUSTOM HARVESTING
4140 N Madera Ave, Kerman (93630-9739)
PHONE..................................559 846-9785
Jay Wayne Bellach, *Owner*
EMP: 15
SALES (est): 1.3MM **Privately Held**
SIC: 3599 Industrial machinery

(P-16617)
JCPM INC
Also Called: J C Precision
8576 Red Oak St, Rancho Cucamonga (91730-4822)
PHONE..................................909 484-9040
Carlos Cajas, *President*
EMP: 14
SQ FT: 5,200
SALES (est): 2.9MM **Privately Held**
WEB: www.jcpm-inc.com
SIC: 3599 Machine shop, jobbing & repair

(P-16618)
JD ENGINEERING & ASSOC INC
905 Dell Ave, Campbell (95008-4120)
PHONE..................................408 866-0822
Bill Akers, *President*
EMP: 28
SALES (est): 3.8MM **Privately Held**
SIC: 3599 Machine shop, jobbing & repair

(P-16619)
JENSON MECHANICAL INC
Also Called: J M I
32420 Central Ave, Union City (94587-2007)
PHONE..................................510 429-8078
Greg Jenson, *President*
Sidne Margolis, *Controller*
EMP: 20 EST: 1976
SQ FT: 30,000
SALES (est): 4.5MM **Privately Held**
SIC: 3599 7699 Custom machinery; industrial machinery & equipment repair

(P-16620)
JERAMES INDUSTRIES INC
Also Called: Jerames Tool & Mfg
460 Cypress Ln Ste F, El Cajon (92020-1647)
PHONE..................................619 334-2204
Matthew Fromm, *President*
Harry Railton, *Shareholder*
Josiah Gibson, *Treasurer*
Gary Sanchez, *General Mgr*
EMP: 20
SQ FT: 10,600
SALES (est): 4.2MM **Privately Held**
WEB: www.jerames.com
SIC: 3599 Machine shop, jobbing & repair

(P-16621)
JERRY CARROLL MACHINERY INC
Also Called: Electrocut-Pacific
993 E San Carlos Ave, San Carlos
(94070-2528)
PHONE..................................650 591-3302
Fax: 650 591-2149
EMP: 12
SQ FT: 10,000
SALES (est): 1.3MM **Privately Held**
SIC: 3599

(P-16622)
JESSEE BROTHERS MACHINE SP INC
Also Called: J B Precision
1640 Dell Ave, Campbell (95008-6901)
PHONE..................................408 866-1755
Chett Jessee, *President*
Thomas Cundiff, *Sales Mgr*
Rick Vasquez, *Manager*
EMP: 16
SQ FT: 12,500
SALES (est): 1.8MM **Privately Held**
WEB: www.jesseebrothersinc.com
SIC: 3599 Machine shop, jobbing & repair

(P-16623)
JESSOP INDUSTRIES
4645 Industrial St Ste 2c, Simi Valley
(93063-3466)
PHONE..................................805 581-6976
EMP: 11
SALES: 200K **Privately Held**
SIC: 3599

(P-16624)
JIMACHINE COMPANY INC
9720 Distribution Ave, San Diego
(92121-2310)
PHONE..................................858 695-1787
Ila Ree Piel, *President*
James Piel, *Vice Pres*
Mark Jay Piel, *Vice Pres*
Wendy Anne Piel, *Vice Pres*
▲ EMP: 20
SQ FT: 15,400
SALES (est): 3.6MM **Privately Held**
WEB: www.jimachine.com
SIC: 3599 3812 Machine shop, jobbing & repair; search & navigation equipment

(P-16625)
JMG MACHINE INC
17037 Industry Pl, La Mirada (90638-5819)
PHONE..................................562 926-2848
Juan Manuel Guillen, *President*
Ben Sanchez, *Manager*
EMP: 20
SQ FT: 10,000
SALES (est): 4MM **Privately Held**
WEB: www.jobshoppowersites.com
SIC: 3599 Machine shop, jobbing & repair

(P-16626)
JMT INC
14926 Bloomfield Ave, Norwalk
(90650-6065)
PHONE..................................562 404-2014
Juan Barajas, *President*
Juan C Barajas, *General Mgr*
◆ EMP: 12
SQ FT: 6,000
SALES (est): 2.5MM **Privately Held**
SIC: 3599 Machine shop, jobbing & repair

(P-16627)
JNC MACHINING
1834 Stone Ave, San Jose (95125-1306)
PHONE..................................408 920-2520
Jesus Castillon, *Owner*
EMP: 10
SALES: 700K **Privately Held**
SIC: 3599 Machine shop, jobbing & repair

(P-16628)
JNS INDUSTRIES INC
2320 S Vineyard Ave, Ontario
(91761-7767)
PHONE..................................909 923-8334
Janet Sheikh, *President*
Pamela Oates Sanders, *Manager*
EMP: 15
SQ FT: 5,000

SALES (est): 2.2MM **Privately Held**
WEB: www.jnsindustries.com
SIC: 3599 Machine shop, jobbing & repair

(P-16629)
JOHNSON MANUFACTURING INC
15201 Connector Ln, Huntington Beach
(92649-1117)
PHONE..................................714 903-0393
Colleen Johnson, *CEO*
Allan Johnson, *Vice Pres*
Sylvia Culling, *Manager*
EMP: 35
SQ FT: 13,000
SALES: 5.6MM **Privately Held**
WEB: www.johnsonmfginc.com
SIC: 3599 Machine shop, jobbing & repair

(P-16630)
JOHNSON PRECISION PRODUCTS INC
1308 E Wakeham Ave, Santa Ana
(92705-4145)
PHONE..................................714 824-6971
Paul Cronin, *President*
EMP: 19 EST: 1961
SQ FT: 4,000
SALES (est): 3.7MM **Privately Held**
SIC: 3599 Machine shop, jobbing & repair

(P-16631)
JOLLY JUMPS INC
600 Via Alondra, Camarillo (93012-8733)
PHONE..................................805 484-0026
Ted Schwochow, *President*
Don Arndorfer, *Corp Secy*
EMP: 45
SQ FT: 26,000
SALES (est): 4.9MM **Privately Held**
SIC: 3599 7999 Carnival machines & equipment, amusement park; exhibition & carnival operation services

(P-16632)
JOT ENGINEERING INC
8385 Canoga Ave, Canoga Park
(91304-2605)
PHONE..................................818 727-7572
Balwinder Riat, *President*
EMP: 12
SQ FT: 2,000
SALES (est): 1.4MM **Privately Held**
SIC: 3599 Amusement park equipment

(P-16633)
JR MACHINE COMPANY INC
13245 Florence Ave, Santa Fe Springs
(90670-4509)
PHONE..................................562 903-9477
Gilbert Reyes, *President*
Gene Reyes, *Manager*
EMP: 29
SQ FT: 12,000
SALES (est): 2.8MM **Privately Held**
SIC: 3599 Machine shop, jobbing & repair

(P-16634)
JRD PRECISION MACHINING INC
1158 Campbell Ave, San Jose
(95126-1063)
PHONE..................................408 246-9327
Rene Diaz, *President*
EMP: 10
SALES (est): 790K **Privately Held**
SIC: 3599 Machine shop, jobbing & repair

(P-16635)
JUELL MACHINE COINC
150 Pacific St, Pomona (91768-3214)
PHONE..................................909 594-8164
Michael Starr, *President*
Ronald Starr, *Vice Pres*
Sharon Starr, *Vice Pres*
Ernie Manriquez, *Sales Staff*
EMP: 12
SQ FT: 12,000
SALES (est): 2.2MM **Privately Held**
WEB: www.juellmachine.com
SIC: 3599 Machine shop, jobbing & repair

(P-16636)
JWP MANUFACTURING LLC
3500 De La Cruz Blvd, Santa Clara
(95054-2111)
PHONE..................................408 970-0641
Jerzy W Prokop, *Mng Member*
Peter Prokop, *Engineer*
Chris Heider, *Mfg Mgr*
Carl Madau, *Opers Mgr*
Andy Eden, *Sales Staff*
EMP: 25
SQ FT: 12,000
SALES (est): 4.9MM **Privately Held**
WEB: www.jwpmfg.com
SIC: 3599 Machine shop, jobbing & repair

(P-16637)
K & L PRECISION GRINDING CO
9309 Atlantic Ave, South Gate
(90280-3522)
PHONE..................................323 564-5151
Kadri Hakaj, *President*
Kadilja Hakaj, *Vice Pres*
EMP: 12
SQ FT: 6,000
SALES (est): 1.5MM **Privately Held**
SIC: 3599 Machine shop, jobbing & repair

(P-16638)
K A TOOL & TECHNOLOGY INC
1700 Sango Ct, Milpitas (95035-6838)
PHONE..................................408 957-9600
Henry Chung, *President*
▲ EMP: 30
SQ FT: 9,600
SALES (est): 3.4MM **Privately Held**
SIC: 3599 Machine shop, jobbing & repair

(P-16639)
K-P ENGINEERING CORP
2126 S Lyon St Ste A, Santa Ana
(92705-5328)
PHONE..................................714 545-7045
Kemal Pepic, *CEO*
EMP: 18
SQ FT: 7,000
SALES (est): 3.9MM **Privately Held**
SIC: 3599 8711 Machine shop, jobbing & repair; professional engineer

(P-16640)
K-TECH MACHINE INC
1377 Armorlite Dr, San Marcos
(92069-1341)
PHONE..................................800 274-9424
Kenneth Russell, *President*
Stuart John Russell, *CFO*
EMP: 134
SQ FT: 16,000
SALES (est): 32.8MM **Privately Held**
WEB: www.k-techmachine.com
SIC: 3599 3444 Machine shop, jobbing & repair; sheet metalwork

(P-16641)
KACEE COMPANY
Also Called: Kacee Discount Abrasives
3570 Hiawatha, North Highlands (95660)
PHONE..................................916 348-3204
Kenneth Cramer, *Owner*
Elizabeth Cramer, *Owner*
EMP: 10
SALES (est): 600K **Privately Held**
WEB: www.kacee.com
SIC: 3599 5084 5085 Machine shop, jobbing & repair; industrial machinery & equipment; abrasives

(P-16642)
KADAN CONSULTANTS INCORPORATED
5662 Research Dr, Huntington Beach
(92649-1615)
PHONE..................................562 988-1165
Rhoda Sjoberg, *CEO*
Denise Caredes, *Office Mgr*
Joseph Arambula, *Engineer*
EMP: 15
SQ FT: 17,000
SALES: 1.6MM **Privately Held**
WEB: www.kadaninc.net
SIC: 3599 3728 3544 8711 Machine shop, jobbing & repair; aircraft parts & equipment; special dies, tools, jigs & fixtures; engineering services

(P-16643)
KAL MACHINING INC
18450 Sutter Blvd, Morgan Hill
(95037-2819)
PHONE..................................408 782-8989
Qing Ye, *President*
David Long, *Vice Pres*
James Swartzbaugh, *QC Mgr*
▲ EMP: 13
SQ FT: 10,000
SALES (est): 2.2MM **Privately Held**
WEB: www.kalmachining.com
SIC: 3599 Machine shop, jobbing & repair

(P-16644)
KALMAN MANUFACTURING INC
780 Jarvis Dr Ste 150, Morgan Hill
(95037-2886)
PHONE..................................408 776-7664
Alan D Kalman, *President*
Freia Kalman, *Vice Pres*
Rosa Esparza, *Office Mgr*
EMP: 43
SQ FT: 35,000
SALES: 5MM **Privately Held**
SIC: 3599 Machine shop, jobbing & repair

(P-16645)
KARAPET ENGINEERING INC
Also Called: Best Engineering
11455 Vanowen St, North Hollywood
(91605-6219)
PHONE..................................818 255-0838
Arthur Alajajyan, *President*
Arthur Alajayan, *President*
EMP: 12
SQ FT: 8,700
SALES (est): 1.9MM **Privately Held**
SIC: 3599 Machine & other job shop work

(P-16646)
KATCH PRECISION MACHINING INC
3953 W 139th St, Hawthorne (90250-7404)
PHONE..................................310 676-4989
George Lopez, *Owner*
Rossie Dominguez, *Executive Asst*
EMP: 10
SQ FT: 5,088
SALES (est): 928.5K **Privately Held**
WEB: www.katchdesign.com
SIC: 3599 Machine shop, jobbing & repair

(P-16647)
KAY & JAMES INC
Also Called: J&S Machine Works
14062 Balboa Blvd, Sylmar (91342-1005)
PHONE..................................818 998-0357
Kye Sook So, *CEO*
Jung M So, *Vice Pres*
EMP: 75
SQ FT: 25,000
SALES (est): 14.8MM **Privately Held**
WEB: www.jandsmachineworks.com
SIC: 3599 Machine shop, jobbing & repair

(P-16648)
KEITHCO MANUFACTURING INC
15031 Parkway Loop Ste C, Tustin
(92780-6527)
PHONE..................................714 258-8933
Bernard Steel, *President*
EMP: 10 EST: 1978
SQ FT: 10,100
SALES (est): 1.4MM **Privately Held**
WEB: www.keithco-mfg.com
SIC: 3599 Machine shop, jobbing & repair

(P-16649)
KELLER ENGINEERING
136 W 157th St, Gardena (90248-2226)
PHONE..................................310 532-0554
Fax: 310 532-1086
EMP: 12
SQ FT: 12,000
SALES (est): 640K **Privately Held**
WEB: www.kellerengineering.com
SIC: 3599

(P-16650)
KELLER ENGINEERING INC
3203 Kashiwa St, Torrance (90505-4020)
PHONE..................................310 326-6291
Kathy Keller, *President*
Claudia Keller Abate, *Treasurer*

Maya Keller Navarra, *Admin Sec*
EMP: 28
SQ FT: 20,000
SALES (est): 3.5MM **Privately Held**
WEB: www.kellereng.com
SIC: 3599 Machine shop, jobbing & repair

(P-16651)
KELLY & THOME
228 San Lorenzo St, Pomona
(91766-2336)
PHONE..................909 623-2559
Warren C Kelly, *President*
Martha Lehr, *Office Mgr*
EMP: 20
SQ FT: 6,000
SALES (est): 2.7MM **Privately Held**
WEB: www.kandt.com
SIC: 3599 Machine shop, jobbing & repair

(P-16652)
KEYSTONE ENGINEERING COMPANY (HQ)
4401 E Donald Douglas Dr, Long Beach
(90808-1732)
PHONE..................562 497-3200
Ian Ballinger, *CEO*
Lili Zhou, *CFO*
David Puckett, *Opers Staff*
◆ **EMP:** 37
SQ FT: 60,000
SALES (est): 9.8MM **Privately Held**
WEB: www.hamilton-standard.com
SIC: 3599 Air intake filters, internal combustion engine, except auto
PA: Ke Company Acquisition Corp.
    4401 E Donald Douglas Dr
    Long Beach CA 90808
    562 497-3200

(P-16653)
KHUUS INC
Also Called: Kamet
1778 Mccarthy Blvd, Milpitas (95035-7421)
PHONE..................408 522-8000
Peter Khuu, *President*
Neary Hem, *Executive*
Donald Cheng, *General Mgr*
Chris Todd, *Project Mgr*
Kelly Quach, *Human Res Mgr*
▲ **EMP:** 60
SQ FT: 25,000
SALES (est): 14.4MM **Privately Held**
WEB: www.kamet.com
SIC: 3599 Machine shop, jobbing & repair

(P-16654)
KILGORE MACHINE COMPANY INC
2312 S Susan St, Santa Ana (92704-4421)
PHONE..................714 540-3659
Bryant Kilgore, *President*
Karen Sullivan, *CFO*
Doree Kilgore, *Vice Pres*
Lisa Damico, *Principal*
Linda McKenzie, *Principal*
EMP: 22
SQ FT: 8,000
SALES (est): 2.1MM **Privately Held**
WEB: www.kilgoremachinecompany.com
SIC: 3599 Machine shop, jobbing & repair

(P-16655)
KIMBERLY MACHINE INC
12822 Joy St, Garden Grove (92840-6350)
PHONE..................714 539-1360
Kary L Laursen, *CEO*
Lynne Laursen, *Corp Secy*
EMP: 17
SQ FT: 10,300
SALES: 4MM **Privately Held**
SIC: 3599 Machine shop, jobbing & repair

(P-16656)
KIMZEY WELDING WORKS INC
164 Kentucky Ave, Woodland
(95695-2743)
PHONE..................530 662-9331
John W Kimzey, *President*
Edith Kimzey, *Corp Secy*
EMP: 13
SQ FT: 14,400

SALES (est): 2.1MM **Privately Held**
WEB: www.kimzeymetalproducts.com
SIC: 3599 7692 5251 3842 Custom machinery; welding repair; hardware; surgical appliances & supplies; surgical & medical instruments

(P-16657)
KITCH ENGINEERING INC
12320 Montague St, Pacoima
(91331-2213)
PHONE..................818 897-7133
Steven Kitching, *President*
Terry Kitching, *Treasurer*
Kerri Kitching, *Vice Pres*
Cynthia George, *Admin Sec*
EMP: 30
SQ FT: 6,000
SALES (est): 5.3MM **Privately Held**
WEB: www.kitchengineering.com
SIC: 3599 3751 Machine shop, jobbing & repair; motorcycles, bicycles & parts

(P-16658)
KLEIN INDUSTRIES INC
Also Called: Production Specialties
2380 Jerrold Ave, San Francisco
(94124-1013)
PHONE..................415 695-9117
Lloyd Klein, *President*
EMP: 13
SQ FT: 16,000
SALES (est): 1.4MM **Privately Held**
WEB: www.kleinindustries.com
SIC: 3599 Machine shop, jobbing & repair

(P-16659)
KLN PRECISION MACHINING CORP
40725 Encyclopedia Cir, Fremont
(94538-2451)
PHONE..................510 770-5001
Kiet Nguyen, *President*
Rinado Garofani, *Vice Pres*
EMP: 100
SQ FT: 80,000
SALES (est): 10.3MM **Privately Held**
WEB: www.klncorp.com
SIC: 3599 Machine shop, jobbing & repair

(P-16660)
KNT INC
Also Called: Knt Manufacturing
39760 Eureka Dr, Newark (94560-4808)
PHONE..................510 651-7163
Keith Ngo, *CEO*
Matthew Deye, *Program Mgr*
EMP: 150
SQ FT: 50,000
SALES (est): 29.6MM **Privately Held**
WEB: www.knt.com
SIC: 3599 Machine shop, jobbing & repair

(P-16661)
KODIAK PRECISION INC (PA)
444 S 1st St, Richmond (94804-2107)
PHONE..................510 234-4165
Paul Bacchi, *President*
Neil Divers, *Vice Pres*
Dave Harris, *Vice Pres*
EMP: 18 EST: 1976
SQ FT: 10,000
SALES: 3MM **Privately Held**
WEB: www.kodiakprecision.com
SIC: 3599 Machine shop, jobbing & repair

(P-16662)
KOHLER & CLARK SCREW PRODUCTS
4088 S K St, Tulare (93274-7183)
PHONE..................559 688-1194
Arthur Clark, *President*
EMP: 30 EST: 1977
SALES (est): 3.6MM **Privately Held**
SIC: 3599 3451 Machine shop, jobbing & repair; screw machine products

(P-16663)
KORDA & GEIS ENGINEERING LLC
132 Easy St Ste D, Buellton (93427-9561)
PHONE..................805 968-5648
Jim Geis,
Michael Korda,
Tony Korda,

EMP: 22
SQ FT: 4,000
SALES (est): 4.1MM **Privately Held**
WEB: www.kordaandgeis.com
SIC: 3599 Machine shop, jobbing & repair

(P-16664)
KRAMARZ ENTERPRISES
1065 Delmas Ave, San Jose (95125-1635)
PHONE..................408 293-1187
Mike Kramarz, *Owner*
EMP: 10
SQ FT: 1,000
SALES (est): 641.6K **Privately Held**
SIC: 3599 Machine shop, jobbing & repair

(P-16665)
KRISALIS INC
Also Called: Marler Precision
3366 Golden Gate Ct, San Andreas
(95249-9625)
PHONE..................209 286-1637
Charlie Timmy, *Manager*
EMP: 10
SALES (corp-wide): 2MM **Privately Held**
WEB: www.krisalis.com
SIC: 3599 Custom machinery
PA: Krisalis, Inc.
    28216 Industrial Blvd
    Hayward CA 94545
    510 786-0858

(P-16666)
KRISALIS INC (PA)
Also Called: Krisalis Precision Machining
28216 Industrial Blvd, Hayward
(94545-4432)
PHONE..................510 786-0858
William L Kannenberg, *CEO*
EMP: 10
SQ FT: 10,000
SALES: 2MM **Privately Held**
WEB: www.krisalis.com
SIC: 3599 Custom machinery

(P-16667)
KSD INC
161 W Lincoln St, Banning (92220-4976)
PHONE..................951 849-7669
Robert S Anderson, *President*
EMP: 10
SQ FT: 20,000
SALES (est): 3MM **Privately Held**
WEB: www.ksdinc.net
SIC: 3599 Machine shop, jobbing & repair

(P-16668)
KT ENGINEERING CORPORATION
2016 E Vista Bella Way, Rancho
Dominguez (90220-6109)
PHONE..................310 537-3818
John Tajirian, *CEO*
Shahan Zakarian, *General Mgr*
EMP: 16
SQ FT: 3,500
SALES (est): 4.8MM **Privately Held**
WEB: www.ktengineering.com
SIC: 3599 8711 Machine shop, jobbing & repair; aviation &/or aeronautical engineering

(P-16669)
L & M MACHINING CENTER INC
1497 Poinsettia Ave # 156, Vista
(92081-8542)
PHONE..................760 437-3810
Mike Slavinski, *President*
EMP: 14
SQ FT: 5,400
SALES: 500K **Privately Held**
WEB: www.landmmachining.com
SIC: 3599 Machine shop, jobbing & repair

(P-16670)
L & T PRECISION ENGRG INC
2395 Qume Dr, San Jose (95131-1813)
PHONE..................408 441-1890
Luc Tran, *President*
My Truong, *General Mgr*
Sau Pham, *Administration*
Thai Le, *Manager*
EMP: 40

SALES (est): 8.9MM **Privately Held**
WEB: www.lt-engineering.com
SIC: 3599 8711 Machine shop, jobbing & repair; consulting engineer

(P-16671)
L J R GRINDING CORP
Also Called: Ljr Blanchard Grinding
445 W 164th St, Gardena (90248-2726)
PHONE..................310 532-7232
James Garon, *President*
Robert Margolis Jr, *Vice Pres*
EMP: 13
SQ FT: 4,000
SALES (est): 1.9MM **Privately Held**
WEB: www.ljrgrinding.com
SIC: 3599 Machine shop, jobbing & repair

(P-16672)
LA GAUGE CO INC
7440 San Fernando Rd, Sun Valley
(91352-4398)
PHONE..................818 767-7193
Harbans Bawa, *President*
Juan Calle, *Info Tech Mgr*
Manny Lozano, *QC Mgr*
JD Caravantes, *Sales Associate*
Bob Bawa, *Marketing Staff*
EMP: 74
SQ FT: 26,682
SALES (est): 31.8MM **Privately Held**
WEB: www.lagauge.com
SIC: 3599 Machine shop, jobbing & repair

(P-16673)
LANDMARK MFG INC
Also Called: Landmark Motor Cycle ACC
4112 Avenida De La Plata, Oceanside
(92056-6099)
PHONE..................760 941-6626
Tom Allen, *President*
Maggie McEniry, *CFO*
Lowell Allen, *Vice Pres*
Pat Allen, *Admin Sec*
EMP: 23
SQ FT: 17,000
SALES (est): 4.3MM **Privately Held**
WEB: www.landmarkmfg.com
SIC: 3599 3751 Machine shop, jobbing & repair; motorcycle accessories

(P-16674)
LANGE PRECISION INC
1106 E Elm Ave, Fullerton (92831-5024)
PHONE..................714 870-5420
Gregory R Lange, *President*
Lisa Lange, *CFO*
EMP: 18
SQ FT: 35,000
SALES (est): 3.8MM **Privately Held**
WEB: www.lantma.org
SIC: 3599 Machine shop, jobbing & repair

(P-16675)
LANGILLS GENERAL MACHINE INC
7850 14th Ave, Sacramento (95826-4302)
PHONE..................916 452-0167
James Langill Sr, *President*
EMP: 35
SQ FT: 10,000
SALES (est): 6.2MM **Privately Held**
WEB: www.langills.com
SIC: 3599 Machine shop, jobbing & repair

(P-16676)
LANSAIR CORPORATION
25228 Anza Dr, Santa Clarita (91355-3496)
PHONE..................661 294-9503
John Voshell, *President*
Eleanor Voshell, *Vice Pres*
EMP: 14
SQ FT: 15,000
SALES (est): 2.2MM **Privately Held**
SIC: 3599 Machine shop, jobbing & repair

(P-16677)
LANTIN ENTERPRISE INC
Also Called: Cee & Gee Precision
2290 Trade Zone Blvd, San Jose
(95131-1801)
PHONE..................408 935-9327
Cecil Lantin, *President*
Maria Lantin, *Vice Pres*
EMP: 12
SQ FT: 4,200

SALES (est): 1.6MM **Privately Held**
WEB: www.ceegeeprecision.com
SIC: 3599 Machine shop, jobbing & repair

(P-16678)
LARKIN PRECISION MACHINING
Also Called: Precision Cnc Mil & Turning
175 El Pueblo Rd Ste 10, Scotts Valley
(95066-4260)
PHONE.............................831 438-2700
Robert Larkin, *President*
Rob Larkin, *CEO*
Jon Larkin, *CFO*
Jonathon Larkin, *CFO*
Seth Larkin, *Admin Sec*
EMP: 35
SQ FT: 20,000
SALES (est): 6.4MM **Privately Held**
WEB: www.lpmachining.com
SIC: 3599 Amusement park equipment;
machine shop, jobbing & repair

(P-16679)
LASER INDUSTRIES INC
1351 Manhattan Ave, Fullerton
(92831-5216)
PHONE.............................714 532-3271
Robert Karim, *President*
Joseph Butterly, *Corp Secy*
John Krickl, *Vice Pres*
Gary Nadau, *Vice Pres*
Gary Nadeau, *Vice Pres*
EMP: 65
SQ FT: 17,500
SALES (est): 18MM **Privately Held**
WEB: www.laserindusties.com
SIC: 3599 Machine shop, jobbing & repair

(P-16680)
LASERTRON INC
909 Summit Way, Laguna Beach
(92651-3438)
PHONE.............................954 846-8600
Gary Geller, *President*
▲ EMP: 26 EST: 1979
SQ FT: 18,750
SALES (est): 4.3MM **Privately Held**
SIC: 3599 3769 3444 3429 Machine
shop, jobbing & repair; guided missile &
space vehicle parts & auxiliary equipment; sheet metalwork; manufactured
hardware (general); porcelain electrical
supplies

(P-16681)
LASZLO J LAK
Also Called: L J L Engineering Co
3621 W Moore Ave, Santa Ana
(92704-6834)
PHONE.............................714 850-0141
Laszlo J Lak, *Owner*
Rosa Vaca, *Admin Asst*
EMP: 10
SQ FT: 17,000
SALES (est): 1.2MM **Privately Held**
SIC: 3599 Machine shop, jobbing & repair

(P-16682)
LAURELWOOD INDUSTRIES INC
Also Called: Automation Gt
1939 Palomar Oaks Way B, Carlsbad
(92011-1311)
PHONE.............................760 705-1649
Simon Grant, *President*
EMP: 20
SALES (est): 3MM **Privately Held**
SIC: 3599 8734 3545 Custom machinery;
product testing laboratory, safety or per-
formance; precision measuring tools

(P-16683)
LE HUNG TUAN
Also Called: Vinaco Engineering Company
20952 Itasca St, Chatsworth (91311-4915)
PHONE.............................818 700-1008
Hung Le, *Owner*
EMP: 10
SALES (est): 600K **Privately Held**
SIC: 3599 Machine shop, jobbing & repair

(P-16684)
LEES PRECISION TOOLING
16751 Parkside Ave, Cerritos (90703-1840)
PHONE.............................562 926-1302
Jimmy Yoon, *Owner*
EMP: 19

SQ FT: 10,000
SALES: 3MM **Privately Held**
SIC: 3599 Machine shop, jobbing & repair

(P-16685)
LENZ PRECISION TECHNOLOGY INC
Also Called: Lenz Technology
355 Pioneer Way Ste A, Mountain View
(94041-1542)
PHONE.............................650 966-1784
Eric Lenz, *President*
Valerie Lenz, *Corp Secy*
EMP: 23
SQ FT: 18,000
SALES (est): 3.7MM **Privately Held**
SIC: 3599 Machine shop, jobbing & repair

(P-16686)
LF INDUSTRIES INC
6352 Corte Del Abeto G, Carlsbad
(92011-1408)
PHONE.............................951 471-0372
Lucenda Oline, *President*
Frank Harton, *General Mgr*
Julian Harton, *Opers Mgr*
Allison Harton, *Manager*
EMP: 10
SALES (est): 424.1K **Privately Held**
SIC: 3599 Machine shop, jobbing & repair

(P-16687)
LIBERTY INDUSTRIES
10754 Lower Azusa Rd, El Monte
(91731-1391)
PHONE.............................626 575-3206
William Carter, *President*
Sandra Smith, *Admin Asst*
EMP: 15
SQ FT: 9,000
SALES (est): 2MM **Privately Held**
SIC: 3599 Machine shop, jobbing & repair;
machine & other job shop work

(P-16688)
LLOYD E HENNESSEY JR
Also Called: Machinist Cooperative
7200 Alexander St, Gilroy (95020-6907)
PHONE.............................408 842-8437
Lloyd E Hennessey Jr, *Owner*
Bill Horst, *General Mgr*
EMP: 45 EST: 1979
SALES (est): 4.2MM **Privately Held**
WEB: www.machinistcoop.com
SIC: 3599 Machine shop, jobbing & repair

(P-16689)
LMM ENTERPRISES
Also Called: Freeway Machine & Welding
Shop
1348 E Sunview Dr, Orange (92865-1739)
PHONE.............................714 543-8044
Leslie M Maude, *President*
Bill Barrett, *Principal*
Ronald Cardiel, *Principal*
EMP: 10 EST: 1951
SQ FT: 7,440
SALES (est): 1.3MM **Privately Held**
SIC: 3599 Machine shop, jobbing & repair

(P-16690)
LOGAN SMITH MACHINE CO
4190 Citrus Ave, Rocklin (95677-4000)
PHONE.............................916 632-2692
Logan Smith, *President*
Tim Smith, *Vice Pres*
EMP: 10
SQ FT: 1,200
SALES (est): 1.5MM **Privately Held**
SIC: 3599 Custom machinery; machine
shop, jobbing & repair

(P-16691)
LONG BAR GRINDING INC
13121 Arctic Cir, Santa Fe Springs
(90670-5571)
PHONE.............................562 921-1983
Joseph Kudron, *President*
Kade Kudron, *Finance Mgr*
EMP: 15
SQ FT: 25,000
SALES (est): 1.8MM **Privately Held**
SIC: 3599 Machine shop, jobbing & repair

(P-16692)
LONG MACHINE INC
27450 Colt Ct, Temecula (92590-3673)
PHONE.............................951 296-0194
Larry Long, *President*
Vicki Long, *Vice Pres*
EMP: 21
SQ FT: 15,000
SALES (est): 3.8MM **Privately Held**
WEB: www.longmachine.com
SIC: 3599 Machine shop, jobbing & repair

(P-16693)
LOWERS WLDG & FABRICATION INC
Also Called: Lowers Industrial Supply
10847 Painter Ave, Santa Fe Springs
(90670-4526)
P.O. Box 2985 (90670-0985)
PHONE.............................562 946-4521
Dawn Davis, *President*
Nora Lowers, *Treasurer*
Sheri Lowers, *Sales Mgr*
EMP: 13
SQ FT: 4,669
SALES (est): 3.7MM **Privately Held**
WEB: www.lowerswelding.com
SIC: 3599 7692 5085 5719 Machine
shop, jobbing & repair; welding repair; in-
dustrial supplies; metalware

(P-16694)
LURAN INC
24927 Avenue Tibbitts K, Valencia
(91355-1268)
PHONE.............................661 257-6303
Terry Decker, *President*
EMP: 18
SQ FT: 20,000
SALES (est): 2.7MM **Privately Held**
WEB: www.luraninc.com
SIC: 3599 Machine shop, jobbing & repair

(P-16695)
LUSK QUALITY MACHINE PRODUCTS
39457 15th St E, Palmdale (93550-3445)
P.O. Box 901030 (93590-1030)
PHONE.............................661 272-0630
Randall J Lusk, *CEO*
Lloyd Lusk, *President*
EMP: 27
SQ FT: 25,000
SALES (est): 5.2MM **Privately Held**
SIC: 3599 3451 Machine shop, jobbing &
repair; screw machine products

(P-16696)
LYNCO GRINDING COMPANY INC
5950 Clara St, Bell (90201-4798)
P.O. Box 2127 (90202-2127)
PHONE.............................562 927-2631
Wayne Hogarth, *President*
Mary E Hogarth, *Vice Pres*
Jeri Hogarth, *Info Tech Mgr*
EMP: 10
SQ FT: 16,500
SALES (est): 1.7MM **Privately Held**
SIC: 3599 Machine shop, jobbing & repair

(P-16697)
LYRU ENGINEERING INC
965 San Leandro Blvd, San Leandro
(94577-1532)
PHONE.............................510 357-5951
Jeff Snyder, *President*
Greg A Snyder, *Admin Sec*
EMP: 15
SQ FT: 12,500
SALES (est): 1.4MM **Privately Held**
SIC: 3599 Machine shop, jobbing & repair

(P-16698)
M & L PRECISION MACHINING INC (PA)
18665 Madrone Pkwy, Morgan Hill
(95037-2868)
PHONE.............................408 436-3955
Mark Laisure, *President*
Harold Laisure, *Vice Pres*
Karen Laisure, *Vice Pres*
Ross Laisure, *Vice Pres*
David Gonzales, *QC Dir*
▲ EMP: 20

SQ FT: 10,000
SALES (est): 7.2MM **Privately Held**
SIC: 3599 3451 3444 Machine shop, jobbing & repair; screw machine products;
sheet metalwork

(P-16699)
M & R ENGINEERING CO
227 E Meats Ave, Orange (92865-3311)
PHONE.............................714 991-8480
Dick Wilmont, *President*
EMP: 15 EST: 1973
SQ FT: 32,000
SALES (est): 3.6MM **Privately Held**
WEB: www.m-reng.com
SIC: 3599 3451 Screw machine products;
lathes; lathes, metal cutting & polishing

(P-16700)
M & W ENGINEERING INC
3880 Dividend Dr Ste 100, Shingle Springs
(95682-7229)
PHONE.............................530 676-7185
Frank E Marsh, *President*
Kim Waters, *Treasurer*
EMP: 20
SQ FT: 10,800
SALES (est): 4.2MM **Privately Held**
SIC: 3599 Machine shop, jobbing & repair

(P-16701)
M & W MACHINE CORPORATION
Also Called: Capitol Machine Co
1642 E Edinger Ave Ste A, Santa Ana
(92705-5002)
PHONE.............................714 541-2652
George Nys, *President*
Sandra Nys, *Treasurer*
Jason Nys, *Admin Sec*
EMP: 15 EST: 1965
SQ FT: 6,000
SALES (est): 2.5MM **Privately Held**
WEB: www.capitolmachineco.com
SIC: 3599 Machine shop, jobbing & repair

(P-16702)
M G DEANZA ACQUISITION INC
Also Called: Deanza Tool & Manufacturing
4010 Garner Rd, Riverside (92501-1006)
PHONE.............................951 683-3080
Mike Greenawalt, *President*
EMP: 10
SQ FT: 9,300
SALES (est): 1.3MM **Privately Held**
SIC: 3599 Machine shop, jobbing & repair

(P-16703)
MACHINE ARTS INCORPORATED
2105 S Hathaway St, Santa Ana
(92705-5238)
PHONE.............................805 965-5344
Fax: 805 564-7889
EMP: 12
SQ FT: 4,000
SALES (est): 1.2MM **Privately Held**
WEB: www.machinearts.com
SIC: 3599

(P-16704)
MACHINE CRAFT OF SAN DIEGO
9822 Waples St, San Diego (92121-2921)
PHONE.............................858 642-0509
Chinta M Sawh, *President*
Deo Sawh, *Vice Pres*
Indra Starr, *Admin Sec*
EMP: 35
SQ FT: 4,500
SALES (est): 4.5MM **Privately Held**
WEB: www.bingoandmore.com
SIC: 3599 3812 Machine shop, jobbing &
repair; search & navigation equipment

(P-16705)
MACHINE EXPRNCE & DESIGN INC
Also Called: Med
2964 Phillip Ave, Clovis (93612-3934)
PHONE.............................559 291-7710
David Bobbitt, *President*
Debbie Bobbitt, *Vice Pres*
EMP: 21
SQ FT: 7,100

SALES (est): 3MM **Privately Held**
SIC: **3599** Machine shop, jobbing & repair

(P-16706)
MACHINE PRECISION COMPONENTS
14014 Dinard Ave, Santa Fe Springs (90670-4923)
PHONE.................................562 404-0500
Mauro Michel, *CEO*
EMP: 18
SALES (est): 2.6MM **Privately Held**
SIC: **3599** Machine shop, jobbing & repair

(P-16707)
MACHINING SPECIALIST CORP
7125 Fenwick Ln Ste O, Westminster (92683-5239)
PHONE.................................714 847-1214
EMP: 20
SQ FT: 8,500
SALES (est): 197.2K **Privately Held**
SIC: **3599**

(P-16708)
MADSEN PRODUCTS INCORPORATED
Also Called: Huntington Beach Machining
15321 Connector Ln, Huntington Beach (92649-1119)
PHONE.................................714 894-1816
Robert Madsen, *President*
Linda Adkison, *Vice Pres*
Erik Madsen, *Vice Pres*
Angela Cardenas, *Accountant*
EMP: 16
SQ FT: 11,345
SALES (est): 3.7MM **Privately Held**
WEB: www.madsenproductions.com
SIC: **3599** 5961 Machine shop, jobbing & repair; mail order house

(P-16709)
MAGNA TOOL INC
5594 Market Pl, Cypress (90630-4710)
PHONE.................................714 826-2500
Bob Melton, *President*
Cindy Melton, *CFO*
EMP: 20
SQ FT: 8,500
SALES (est): 3.3MM **Privately Held**
WEB: www.magnatoolinc.com
SIC: **3599** Machine shop, jobbing & repair

(P-16710)
MAINLAND MACHINE
2930 Mcmillan Ave Ste E, San Luis Obispo (93401-6790)
PHONE.................................805 543-7149
Mark W Ames, *Owner*
Todd Helgeson, *Engineer*
Ted Engdahl, *Opers Mgr*
EMP: 20
SQ FT: 6,000
SALES (est): 3.4MM **Privately Held**
WEB: www.mainlandmachine.com
SIC: **3599** Machine shop, jobbing & repair

(P-16711)
MANTI-MACHINE CO INC
11782 Western Ave Ste 15, Stanton (90680-3466)
PHONE.................................714 902-1465
William G Vlieland, *President*
Dawn Harlow, *CFO*
BJ Vlieland, *Corp Secy*
EMP: 12
SQ FT: 3,400
SALES (est): 752.8K **Privately Held**
SIC: **3599** Machine & other job shop work

(P-16712)
MAR ENGINEERING COMPANY
7350 Greenbush Ave, North Hollywood (91605-4003)
PHONE.................................818 765-4805
Monte Markowitz, *CEO*
Samuel Markowitz, *President*
Barbara Markowitz, *Corp Secy*
Robert Markowitz, *Engineer*
Jeff Markowitz, *Mfg Staff*
EMP: 27
SQ FT: 12,000
SALES: 3.2MM **Privately Held**
WEB: www.marengineering.com
SIC: **3599** Machine shop, jobbing & repair

(P-16713)
MARATHON MACHINE INC
7588 Trade St, San Diego (92121-2412)
PHONE.................................858 578-8670
Donald R Adcock, *President*
EMP: 11 EST: 1967
SQ FT: 5,000
SALES: 1MM **Privately Held**
SIC: **3599** 8711 Machine shop, jobbing & repair; engineering services

(P-16714)
MARLIN MACHINE PRODUCTS
4071 Brewster Way, Riverside (92501-1060)
PHONE.................................951 275-0050
Juan Tellez, *Partner*
Candido Tellez, *Partner*
EMP: 10
SQ FT: 5,000
SALES (est): 820K **Privately Held**
SIC: **3599** Machine shop, jobbing & repair

(P-16715)
MARONEY COMPANY
9016 Winnetka Ave, Northridge (91324-3235)
PHONE.................................818 882-2722
John C Maroney Sr, *President*
Francine L Maroney, *Senior VP*
EMP: 17
SQ FT: 12,500
SALES (est): 2.9MM **Privately Held**
WEB: www.maroneycompany.com
SIC: **3599** Machine shop, jobbing & repair

(P-16716)
MARTIN-CHANDLER INC
122 E Alondra Blvd, Gardena (90248-2883)
PHONE.................................323 321-5119
Paul Fihn, *CEO*
Hans Haag, *Treasurer*
EMP: 11
SQ FT: 5,000
SALES (est): 1.1MM **Privately Held**
SIC: **3599** Machine shop, jobbing & repair

(P-16717)
MARTINEK MANUFACTURING
42650 Osgood Rd, Fremont (94539-5603)
PHONE.................................510 438-0357
Mark Martinek, *Partner*
Charles Martinek, *Partner*
Mardell Martinek, *Partner*
EMP: 25
SQ FT: 40,000
SALES (est): 2.4MM **Privately Held**
WEB: www.martinek.com
SIC: **3599** Machine shop, jobbing & repair

(P-16718)
MARTINEZ AND TUREK INC
Also Called: Martinez & Turek
300 S Cedar Ave, Rialto (92376-9100)
PHONE.................................909 820-6800
Larry Tribe, *President*
Donald A Turek, *CFO*
Thomas J Martinez, *Vice Pres*
John Romero, *Vice Pres*
Tony Elizondo, *Engineer*
EMP: 120 EST: 1980
SQ FT: 139,000
SALES (est): 32.1MM **Privately Held**
WEB: www.martinezandturek.com
SIC: **3599** Machine shop, jobbing & repair

(P-16719)
MARTINIC ENGINEERING INC (DH)
10932 Chestnut Ave, Stanton (90680-3241)
PHONE.................................714 527-8988
Tony Martinic, *President*
Claudia Martinic, *Vice Pres*
EMP: 29
SQ FT: 6,200
SALES (est): 8.3MM
SALES (corp-wide): 817.7MM **Publicly Held**
SIC: **3599** Machine shop, jobbing & repair

(P-16720)
MARX DIGITAL MFG INC (PA)
Also Called: Marx Digital Cnc Machine Shop
3551 Victor St, Santa Clara (95054-2321)
PHONE.................................408 748-1783
Marek Smiech, *President*
Krzysztof Juszczynski, *Treasurer*
Shane Johnson, *General Mgr*
EMP: 30
SALES (est): 9.4MM **Privately Held**
SIC: **3599** 3639 3829 Machine shop, jobbing & repair; sewing machines & attachments, domestic; drafting instruments & machines: t-square, template, etc.

(P-16721)
MASTER PRECISION MACHINING
2199 Ronald St, Santa Clara (95050-2883)
PHONE.................................408 727-0185
Richard Rossi, *President*
Robert Paolinetti, *Corp Secy*
William Regnani, *Vice Pres*
EMP: 30 EST: 1969
SQ FT: 10,000
SALES (est): 4.8MM **Privately Held**
WEB: www.master-precision.com
SIC: **3599** Machine shop, jobbing & repair

(P-16722)
MAUL MFG INC (PA)
3041 S Shannon St, Santa Ana (92704-6320)
PHONE.................................714 641-0727
Tony Johnson, *President*
Lori Deorio, *Admin Sec*
EMP: 28
SQ FT: 10,080
SALES (est): 4.3MM **Privately Held**
SIC: **3599** 3491 3492 Machine shop, jobbing & repair; solenoid valves; control valves, aircraft: hydraulic & pneumatic

(P-16723)
MAX PRECISION MACHINE INC
2467 Autumnvale Dr, San Jose (95131-1802)
PHONE.................................408 956-8986
Kevin Nguyen, *President*
Alvin Nguyen, *Treasurer*
Donovan Son, *Vice Pres*
Cuong Nguyen, *Admin Sec*
EMP: 10
SALES (est): 571.3K **Privately Held**
SIC: **3599** Machine & other job shop work

(P-16724)
MC CAIN & MC CAIN INC
Also Called: B&G Machine Shop
3801 Gilmore Ave, Bakersfield (93308-6211)
PHONE.................................661 322-7764
Jim McCain, *President*
Gary McCain, *Vice Pres*
Steven Glover, *General Mgr*
Yvonne Jennings, *Office Mgr*
EMP: 15 EST: 1951
SQ FT: 10,000
SALES (est): 2.4MM **Privately Held**
WEB: www.hobble-clamp.com
SIC: **3599** Machine shop, jobbing & repair

(P-16725)
MC CORMICK G R ENGRG & MFG CO
416 N Varney St, Burbank (91502-1732)
PHONE.................................818 848-8511
Larry Mc Cormick, *President*
EMP: 11
SQ FT: 5,000
SALES (est): 870K **Privately Held**
SIC: **3599** Machine shop, jobbing & repair

(P-16726)
MCAERO LLC
Also Called: McCullough Aero Company
12711 Imperial Hwy, Santa Fe Springs (90670-4711)
PHONE.................................310 787-9911
Peter Lake, *CEO*
EMP: 10
SALES (est): 1.4MM **Privately Held**
SIC: **3599** 3429 Machine shop, jobbing & repair; manufactured hardware (general)

(P-16727)
MCCOPPIN ENTERPRISES
Also Called: Accurate Manufacturing Company
6641 San Fernando Rd, Glendale (91201-1702)
PHONE.................................818 240-4840
Richard J Mc Coppin, *President*
Carol Park, *Shareholder*
John Gagliardi, *Vice Pres*
Robert R Gagliardi, *Vice Pres*
EMP: 22
SQ FT: 25,000
SALES: 3MM **Privately Held**
WEB: www.acc-mfg.com
SIC: **3599** 3544 3441 Machine & other job shop work; machine shop, jobbing & repair; dies & die holders for metal cutting, forming, die casting; industrial molds; fabricated structural metal

(P-16728)
MCKENZIE MACHINING INC
481 Perry Ct, Santa Clara (95054-2624)
PHONE.................................408 748-8885
Scott McKenzie, *Owner*
EMP: 14
SQ FT: 10,400
SALES (est): 2.6MM **Privately Held**
SIC: **3599** Machine shop, jobbing & repair

(P-16729)
MD ENGINEERING INC
1550 Consumer Cir, Corona (92880-1725)
PHONE.................................951 736-5390
Mike Morgan, *President*
Wendy Li-Bertrams, *Officer*
Ryan Cortes, *Vice Pres*
Danny Vu, *QC Mgr*
EMP: 37
SQ FT: 16,000
SALES (est): 3.9MM **Privately Held**
SIC: **3599** Machine shop, jobbing & repair

(P-16730)
MECHANICAL AND MCH REPR SVCS
10584 Silicon Ave, Montclair (91763-4617)
PHONE.................................909 625-8705
Jose Farsaci, *President*
Hector Pinasco, *Vice Pres*
EMP: 10
SQ FT: 15,000
SALES: 2MM **Privately Held**
WEB: www.mechandmachinerepair.com
SIC: **3599** Machine shop, jobbing & repair

(P-16731)
MECHANIZED ENTERPRISES INC
1140 N Kraemer Blvd Ste M, Anaheim (92806-1919)
PHONE.................................714 630-5512
George Hansel, *President*
Don Plum, *Mktg Dir*
EMP: 13
SQ FT: 12,000
SALES (est): 2.1MM **Privately Held**
WEB: www.mechanizedenterprises.com
SIC: **3599** Machine shop, jobbing & repair

(P-16732)
MECOPTRON INC
3115 Osgood Ct, Fremont (94539-5652)
PHONE.................................510 226-9966
Andy Law, *Founder*
Chris Law, *Human Res Mgr*
EMP: 45
SQ FT: 12,000
SALES (est): 5.8MM **Privately Held**
WEB: www.mecoptron.com
SIC: **3599** 3444 Machine shop, jobbing & repair; sheet metalwork

(P-16733)
MECPRO INC
980 George St, Santa Clara (95054-2705)
PHONE.................................408 727-9757
Son Ho, *President*
Kelly Ho, *Vice Pres*
Colin Wintrup, *Vice Pres*
Sun H Ho, *General Mgr*
Daniel Diep, *Purch Mgr*
EMP: 26
SQ FT: 15,000

SALES (est): 5.1MM **Privately Held**
WEB: www.mecpro.com
SIC: 3599 Machine shop, jobbing & repair

(P-16734)
MEDLIN & SON ENGRG SERVINC
Also Called: Medlin & Sons
12484 Whittier Blvd, Whittier (90602-1017)
PHONE..................................562 464-5889
George W Medlin II, *CEO*
Susan Medlin, *Admin Sec*
EMP: 60 EST: 1959
SQ FT: 26,000
SALES (est): 9.7MM **Privately Held**
SIC: 3599 Machine shop, jobbing & repair

(P-16735)
MEERKAT INC
434 S Yucca Ave, Rialto (92376-6300)
PHONE..................................909 877-0093
Ronald J Vangrouw, *President*
Dave Vangrouw, *Treasurer*
Cindy Vangrouw, *Admin Sec*
EMP: 14
SQ FT: 11,000
SALES (est): 2.1MM **Privately Held**
SIC: 3599 Machine shop, jobbing & repair

(P-16736)
MEGA PRECISION O RINGS INC
23206 Normandie Ave Ste 5, Torrance
(90502-2614)
PHONE..................................310 530-1166
Gerardo Sandoval, *President*
EMP: 14
SQ FT: 4,500
SALES (est): 1.7MM **Privately Held**
WEB: www.megaprecisiono-rings.com
SIC: 3599 3089 Machine shop, jobbing & repair; plastic processing

(P-16737)
MELFRED BORZALL INC
12115 Shoemaker Ave, Santa Fe Springs
(90670-4719)
PHONE..................................562 946-7524
Fax: 562 946-2014
EMP: 12
SQ FT: 7,800
SALES (est): 920K **Privately Held**
WEB: www.melfredborzall.com
SIC: 3599

(P-16738)
MELKES MACHINE INC
9928 Hayward Way, South El Monte
(91733-3114)
PHONE..................................626 448-5062
Isabelle Melkesian, *President*
Brent Melkesian, *Vice Pres*
EMP: 50
SQ FT: 24,000
SALES (est): 6.3MM **Privately Held**
WEB: www.melkes.com
SIC: 3599 Machine shop, jobbing & repair

(P-16739)
MERCURY ENGINEERING CORP
5630 Imperial Hwy, South Gate
(90280-7420)
PHONE..................................562 861-7816
David Barker, *President*
EMP: 13 EST: 1949
SQ FT: 10,000
SALES (est): 1.8MM **Privately Held**
SIC: 3599 Machine shop, jobbing & repair

(P-16740)
METAL CUTTING SERVICE INC
16233 Gale Ave, City of Industry
(91745-1719)
PHONE..................................626 968-4764
David Viel, *President*
Milon Viel, *CEO*
Earl Viel, *Corp Secy*
Curt Steen, *Plant Mgr*
EMP: 18
SQ FT: 32,000
SALES (est): 2.7MM **Privately Held**
WEB: www.metalcut.com
SIC: 3599 Machine shop, jobbing & repair

(P-16741)
METALORE INC
750 S Douglas St, El Segundo
(90245-4901)
PHONE..................................310 643-0360
Kenneth Hill, *President*
▲ EMP: 30
SALES (est): 5.1MM **Privately Held**
WEB: www.metalore.com
SIC: 3599 Machine shop, jobbing & repair

(P-16742)
MEZIERE ENTERPRISES INC
220 S Hale Ave Ste A, Escondido
(92029-1719)
PHONE..................................800 208-1755
Michael Meziere, *President*
Don Meziere, *Vice Pres*
Marie Meziere, *Office Mgr*
Dave Meziere, *Admin Sec*
Joel Meziere, *Admin Asst*
▲ EMP: 30
SQ FT: 15,000
SALES (est): 6.8MM **Privately Held**
WEB: www.meziere.com
SIC: 3599 Machine shop, jobbing & repair

(P-16743)
MICRON MACHINE COMPANY
12530 Stowe Dr, Poway (92064-6804)
PHONE..................................858 486-5900
Mark Conley, *CEO*
Donna Conley, *Vice Pres*
EMP: 22
SQ FT: 16,000
SALES (est): 4.3MM **Privately Held**
SIC: 3599 8731 3462 3369 Machine shop, jobbing & repair; commercial physical research; iron & steel forgings; nonferrous foundries

(P-16744)
MID VALLEY MFG INC
2039 W Superior Ave, Caruthers
(93609-9531)
P.O. Box 295 (93609-0295)
PHONE..................................559 864-9441
Robert Smith, *President*
Rex Tyler, *Vice Pres*
EMP: 15
SQ FT: 7,200
SALES (est): 1.2MM **Privately Held**
WEB: www.midvalleymanufacturing.com
SIC: 3599 Machine shop, jobbing & repair

(P-16745)
MIKE KENNEY TOOL INC
Also Called: Mkt Innovations
2900 Saturn St Ste A, Brea (92821-1702)
PHONE..................................714 577-9262
Mike Kenney, *President*
Julie Kenney, *Admin Sec*
▲ EMP: 37
SALES (est): 6.2MM **Privately Held**
WEB: www.cooljet.com
SIC: 3599 Machine shop, jobbing & repair

(P-16746)
MIKES MICRO PARTS INC
1901 Potrero Ave, South El Monte
(91733-3024)
PHONE..................................626 443-0675
Robert Oganesian, *CEO*
Mike Oganesian, *President*
Henry Oganesian, *Vice Pres*
Araxi Oganesian, *Admin Sec*
EMP: 35 EST: 1964
SQ FT: 10,000
SALES (est): 5MM **Privately Held**
SIC: 3599 Machine shop, jobbing & repair

(P-16747)
MILCO WIRE EDM INC
Also Called: Milco Waterjet
15221 Connector Ln, Huntington Beach
(92649-1117)
PHONE..................................714 373-0098
Steven R Miller, *President*
John Fuhr, *QC Mgr*
Chadd Miller, *Manager*
EMP: 17
SQ FT: 14,000

SALES: 2.2MM **Privately Held**
WEB: www.milcowireedm.com
SIC: 3599 3541 Electrical discharge machining (EDM); machine tools, metal cutting type

(P-16748)
MILITARY AIRCRAFT PARTS
11265 Sunrise Gold Cir G, Rancho Cordova
(95742-6560)
PHONE..................................916 635-8010
Robert E Marin, *President*
Robert Marin, *President*
EMP: 22
SALES (corp-wide): 5.4MM **Privately Held**
SIC: 3599 Air intake filters, internal combustion engine, except auto
PA: Military Aircraft Parts
116 Oxburough Dr
Folsom CA 95630
916 635-8010

(P-16749)
MILITARY AIRCRAFT PARTS (PA)
116 Oxburough Dr, Folsom (95630-3293)
PHONE..................................916 635-8010
Robert E Marin, *President*
EMP: 28
SALES (est): 5.4MM **Privately Held**
SIC: 3599 Machine shop, jobbing & repair

(P-16750)
MILLER MACHINE INC
4055 Calle Platino # 200, Oceanside
(92056-5861)
PHONE..................................814 723-5700
Fax: 760 723-4202
EMP: 25 EST: 1981
SQ FT: 11,000
SALES (est): 4MM **Privately Held**
WEB: www.millermachine.net
SIC: 3599

(P-16751)
MILLER MACHINE WORKS LLC
Also Called: Miller Cnc
1905 Broadway, San Diego (92102-1824)
PHONE..................................619 501-9866
Todd Cuffaro, *CEO*
Dave Miller, *President*
Gregory Hansen, *CFO*
EMP: 17
SQ FT: 7,500
SALES (est): 3.6MM **Privately Held**
WEB: www.millermachineworks.net
SIC: 3599 Machine shop, jobbing & repair

(P-16752)
MILLIPART INC (PA)
412 W Carter Dr, Glendora (91740-5998)
PHONE..................................626 963-4101
Scot Jamison, *President*
EMP: 18 EST: 1954
SQ FT: 4,000
SALES (est): 4.1MM **Privately Held**
WEB: www.millipart.com
SIC: 3599 Machine shop, jobbing & repair

(P-16753)
MILLWORX PRCSION MACHINING INC
506 Malloy Ct, Corona (92880-2045)
PHONE..................................951 371-2683
Stacy Wilson, *President*
Terry Windust, *Vice Pres*
EMP: 22
SQ FT: 3,500
SALES (est): 6MM **Privately Held**
WEB: www.millworxprecision.com
SIC: 3599 Machine shop, jobbing & repair

(P-16754)
MILO MACHINING INC
Also Called: Milo Engineering
2675 Skypark Dr Ste 304, Torrance
(90505-5330)
PHONE..................................310 530-0925
Herman Hofer, *President*
Raymond Hofer, *Vice Pres*
EMP: 10
SQ FT: 5,000
SALES (est): 1.7MM **Privately Held**
WEB: www.miloeng.com
SIC: 3599 Machine shop, jobbing & repair

(P-16755)
MINI-FLEX CORPORATION
2472 Eastman Ave Ste 29, Ventura
(93003-5774)
PHONE..................................805 644-1474
Paul Jorgensen, *President*
Patrick T Loughman, *Agent*
◆ EMP: 13
SQ FT: 8,500
SALES (est): 2.1MM **Privately Held**
WEB: www.mini-flex.com
SIC: 3599 Bellows, industrial: metal

(P-16756)
MINIATURE PRECISION INC
4488 Mountain Lakes Blvd, Redding
(96003-1445)
PHONE..................................530 244-4131
Don Anderson, *President*
Diana Anderson, *Vice Pres*
Mike Twoney, *QC Mgr*
EMP: 13
SQ FT: 8,000
SALES: 1.1MM **Privately Held**
WEB: www.mpcomponents.com
SIC: 3599 Machine shop, jobbing & repair

(P-16757)
MISSION TOOL AND MFG CO INC
3440 Arden Rd, Hayward (94545-3906)
PHONE..................................510 782-8383
Gary W Smith, *President*
Carol Smith, *Vice Pres*
Sheri Albright, *General Mgr*
Tom Gazsi, *Project Mgr*
Thomas Zaw, *QC Mgr*
▲ EMP: 40 EST: 1968
SQ FT: 28,000
SALES (est): 7.5MM **Privately Held**
WEB: www.missiontool.com
SIC: 3599 3465 3469 3544 Machine & other job shop work; automotive stampings; metal stampings; special dies, tools, jigs & fixtures

(P-16758)
MITCHELL-DUCKETT CORPORATION
Also Called: M & M Machine & Tool
10074 Streeter Rd Ste B, Auburn
(95602-8559)
PHONE..................................530 268-2112
Chris Duckett, *President*
Janis Duckett, *Vice Pres*
EMP: 10
SQ FT: 4,800
SALES (est): 1.5MM **Privately Held**
SIC: 3599 Machine shop, jobbing & repair

(P-16759)
MITCO INDUSTRIES INC (PA)
2235 S Vista Ave, Bloomington
(92316-2921)
PHONE..................................909 877-0800
Larry Mitchell, *President*
Sammy Mitchell, *Corp Secy*
EMP: 34
SQ FT: 11,000
SALES (est): 4.8MM **Privately Held**
WEB: www.mitcoind.com
SIC: 3599 3533 Machine shop, jobbing & repair; drilling tools for gas, oil or water wells

(P-16760)
MKT INNOVATIONS
Also Called: Cooljet Systems
2900 Saturn St Ste A, Brea (92821-1702)
PHONE..................................714 524-7668
Mike Kenney, *CEO*
Kathy Jackson, *CFO*
▲ EMP: 68
SALES (est): 11MM **Privately Held**
WEB: www.mkti.com
SIC: 3599 3523 Machine shop, jobbing & repair; farm machinery & equipment

(P-16761)
MODERN ENGINE INC
701 Sonora Ave, Glendale (91201-2431)
PHONE..................................818 409-9494
Vachagan Aslanian, *President*
Armond Aslanian, *Treasurer*
Razmik Aslanian, *Vice Pres*

Nora Aslanian, *Admin Sec*
▲ EMP: 43
SQ FT: 26,000
SALES (est): 6.5MM **Privately Held**
WEB: www.modernengine.com
SIC: 3599 7539 Machine & other job shop work; machine shop, automotive

(P-16762)
MODERN MANUFACTURING INC
4110 E La Palma Ave, Anaheim (92807-1814)
PHONE..................................714 254-0156
▲ EMP: 26 EST: 2002
SQ FT: 20,000
SALES (est): 2.5MM **Privately Held**
WEB: www.modernmfginc.com
SIC: 3599

(P-16763)
MOLNAR ENGINEERING INC
Also Called: Lee's Enterprise
20731 Marilla St, Chatsworth (91311-4408)
PHONE..................................818 734-5685
Laszlo Molnar, *CEO*
Tom Molnar, *President*
Linda D Molnar, *Corp Secy*
Michael Molnar, *Manager*
▲ EMP: 37
SQ FT: 12,000
SALES (est): 6.7MM **Privately Held**
WEB: www.leesenterprise.com
SIC: 3599 Machine shop, jobbing & repair

(P-16764)
MOMENI ENGINEERING LLC
15662 Commerce Ln, Huntington Beach (92649-1604)
PHONE..................................714 897-9301
Ahmad Momeni, *Mng Member*
EMP: 28
SQ FT: 14,000
SALES: 4.7MM **Privately Held**
SIC: 3599 3841 Machine & other job shop work; surgical & medical instruments

(P-16765)
MONO ENGINEERING CORP
20977 Knapp St, Chatsworth (91311-5926)
PHONE..................................818 772-4998
Siamak Morini, *CEO*
David Chavez, *Engineer*
Roujebeh Azarahishin, *Controller*
Siegfried Treichel, *Prdtn Mgr*
Antonio Aragon, *QC Mgr*
EMP: 50
SQ FT: 40,000
SALES: 4.5MM **Privately Held**
WEB: www.monoengineering.com
SIC: 3599 3444 8711 Machine shop, jobbing & repair; sheet metalwork; industrial engineers

(P-16766)
MONSON MACHINE INC
1802 Pomona Rd, Corona (92880-1777)
PHONE..................................951 736-6615
Kathy Monson, *President*
EMP: 18
SQ FT: 12,500
SALES (est): 1.8MM **Privately Held**
WEB: www.monsonmachine.com
SIC: 3599 Machine shop, jobbing & repair

(P-16767)
MONTCLAIR MACHINE SHOP INC
5621 State St, Montclair (91763-6241)
P.O. Box 2009 (91763-0509)
PHONE..................................909 986-2664
Wayne Freeberg, *President*
Thomas Freeberg, *Vice Pres*
David Peterson, *General Mgr*
EMP: 11
SQ FT: 10,000
SALES (est): 948.6K
SALES (corp-wide): 4.5MM **Privately Held**
SIC: 3599 Machine shop, jobbing & repair
PA: Montclair Bronze Inc.,
5621 State St
Montclair CA 91763
909 986-2664

(P-16768)
MONTEREY MACHINE PRODUCTS
1504 W Industrial Park St, Covina (91722-3417)
PHONE..................................626 967-2242
David Griffits, *Owner*
Dave Griffith, *Partner*
EMP: 14 EST: 1953
SQ FT: 2,400
SALES (est): 2MM **Privately Held**
WEB: www.montereymachine.com
SIC: 3599 Machine shop, jobbing & repair

(P-16769)
MOONEY INDUSTRIES
8744 Remmet Ave, Canoga Park (91304-1588)
PHONE..................................818 998-0199
Alan Mooney, *CFO*
Brian Mooney, *President*
Joyce Mooney, *Vice Pres*
EMP: 15 EST: 1962
SQ FT: 9,000
SALES: 1.5MM **Privately Held**
SIC: 3599 Machine shop, jobbing & repair

(P-16770)
MORGAN HILL PRECISION INC
15500 Concord Cir Ste 100, Morgan Hill (95037-7109)
PHONE..................................408 778-7895
Michelle Rasmussen, *CEO*
George King, *President*
Janet King, *Vice Pres*
EMP: 12
SQ FT: 7,336
SALES: 1.7MM **Privately Held**
WEB: www.morganhillprecision.com
SIC: 3599 Machine shop, jobbing & repair

(P-16771)
MORGAN PRODUCTS INC
28103 Avenue Stanford, Santa Clarita (91355-1106)
PHONE..................................661 257-3022
Morris E Morgan, *President*
Mary O Morgan, *CFO*
William A Morgan, *Vice Pres*
▲ EMP: 18 EST: 1966
SQ FT: 3,250
SALES: 2MM **Privately Held**
WEB: www.morganproducts.com
SIC: 3599 3561 Machine shop, jobbing & repair; pumps & pumping equipment

(P-16772)
MORRISON ENGINEERING
9879 Juniper Ct, Yucaipa (92399-2939)
PHONE..................................909 796-5319
James Morrison, *President*
Jam Morrison, *CFO*
EMP: 10 EST: 1981
SALES: 1MM **Privately Held**
SIC: 3599 Machine shop, jobbing & repair

(P-16773)
MOTEK INDUSTRIES
14434 Joanbridge St, Baldwin Park (91706-1746)
PHONE..................................626 960-6005
Julio Enriquez, *Owner*
EMP: 13
SQ FT: 5,000
SALES (est): 1.4MM **Privately Held**
SIC: 3599 Machine shop, jobbing & repair

(P-16774)
MP TOOL INC
28110 Avenue Stanford E, Valencia (91355-1161)
PHONE..................................661 294-7711
Ed Pimentel, *President*
Dave Miller, *Vice Pres*
Sandy Pimentel, *Office Mgr*
EMP: 12
SQ FT: 26,000
SALES: 1.7MM **Privately Held**
SIC: 3599 7699 Grinding castings for the trade; industrial tool grinding

(P-16775)
MR GEARS INC
428 Stanford Ave, Redwood City (94063-3423)
PHONE..................................650 364-7793
Jack Hybl, *President*
EMP: 11
SQ FT: 4,100
SALES (est): 640K **Privately Held**
WEB: www.mrgears.com
SIC: 3599 3751 3462 3714 Machine shop, jobbing & repair; gears, motorcycle & bicycle; gears, forged steel; gears, motor vehicle

(P-16776)
MTM INDUSTRIAL INC
3230 Production Ave Ste B, Oceanside (92058-1305)
PHONE..................................760 967-1346
Mark Meddock, *President*
EMP: 14
SQ FT: 7,000
SALES (est): 2.9MM **Privately Held**
WEB: www.oilguard.com
SIC: 3599 Machine shop, jobbing & repair

(P-16777)
MUFICH ENGINEERING INC
341 W Blueridge Ave, Orange (92865-4201)
PHONE..................................714 283-0599
Mike Mufich, *President*
EMP: 20
SQ FT: 2,000
SALES (est): 2MM **Privately Held**
SIC: 3599 3444 Machine shop, jobbing & repair; sheet metalwork

(P-16778)
MUTH MACHINE WORKS (HQ)
8042 Katella Ave, Stanton (90680-3207)
PHONE..................................714 527-2239
Richard Muth, *President*
Peter G Muth, *Treasurer*
Lynn Muth, *Vice Pres*
Dwayne Gleason, *VP Opers*
▲ EMP: 20
SQ FT: 2,000
SALES (est): 6.8MM
SALES (corp-wide): 33.4MM **Privately Held**
WEB: www.orco.com
SIC: 3599 Machine & other job shop work
PA: Orco Block & Hardscape
11100 Beach Blvd
Stanton CA 90680
714 527-2239

(P-16779)
MY MACHINE INC
5140 Commerce Dr, Baldwin Park (91706-1450)
PHONE..................................626 214-9223
Jamie Scott Young, *CEO*
Pedro Ignico Martinez, *Vice Pres*
Helene Orban, *Office Mgr*
EMP: 15
SALES (est): 3.2MM **Privately Held**
SIC: 3599 Machine shop, jobbing & repair

(P-16780)
N C INDUSTRIES
42147 Roick Dr, Temecula (92590-3695)
PHONE..................................951 296-9603
Richard Waltz, *Owner*
EMP: 10
SALES (est): 660K **Privately Held**
WEB: www.ncindustries.com
SIC: 3599 5112 Machine shop, jobbing & repair; stationery & office supplies

(P-16781)
NC DYNAMICS LLC
3401 E 69th St, Long Beach (90805-1872)
PHONE..................................562 634-7392
Phillip Friedman, *Principal*
Anthony Rinauro, *Vice Pres*
Chris Thompson, *Vice Pres*
EMP: 150
SALES (est): 8MM
SALES (corp-wide): 118.6MM **Privately Held**
SIC: 3599 Machine shop, jobbing & repair

PA: Harlow Aerostructures Llc
1501 S Mclean Blvd
Wichita KS 67213
316 265-5268

(P-16782)
NC ENGINEERING INC
13439 S Budlong Ave, Gardena (90247-1995)
PHONE..................................310 532-4810
Patrick Mason, *President*
Gerald Fazis, *Vice Pres*
▲ EMP: 11
SQ FT: 8,000
SALES (est): 1.8MM **Privately Held**
SIC: 3599 Machine shop, jobbing & repair

(P-16783)
NELGO INDUSTRIES INC
Also Called: Nelgo Manufacturing
3265 Production Ave Ste A, Oceanside (92058-1361)
PHONE..................................760 433-6434
Peter Edward Goethel, *CEO*
EMP: 32 EST: 1966
SQ FT: 5,000
SALES (est): 6.4MM **Privately Held**
WEB: www.nelgo.com
SIC: 3599 Machine shop, jobbing & repair

(P-16784)
NELSON ENGINEERING LLC
11600 Monarch St, Garden Grove (92841-1817)
PHONE..................................714 893-7999
Ed McKenna,
▲ EMP: 48
SQ FT: 17,600
SALES (est): 6MM **Privately Held**
WEB: www.nel-eng.com
SIC: 3599 Machine shop, jobbing & repair

(P-16785)
NELSON THREAD GRINDING INC
8205 Lankershim Blvd, North Hollywood (91605-1614)
PHONE..................................818 768-2578
Raymond Nelson, *President*
Phyllis Nelson, *CEO*
Brian Nelson, *Manager*
▲ EMP: 10
SQ FT: 5,000
SALES (est): 1.5MM **Privately Held**
WEB: www.nelsonthread.com
SIC: 3599 Machine shop, jobbing & repair

(P-16786)
NEW WORLD MACHINING INC
2799 Aiello Dr, San Jose (95111-2156)
PHONE..................................408 227-3810
Marvin Elsten, *President*
Dianne Elsten, *Vice Pres*
EMP: 25 EST: 1973
SQ FT: 30,000
SALES (est): 3.9MM **Privately Held**
WEB: www.newworldmachining.com
SIC: 3599 5084 Machine shop, jobbing & repair; industrial machinery & equipment

(P-16787)
NEXT INTENT INC
865 Via Esteban, San Luis Obispo (93401-7178)
PHONE..................................805 781-6755
Rodney Babcock, *CEO*
Catherine B Babcock, *CFO*
EMP: 30
SQ FT: 8,500
SALES (est): 6.7MM **Privately Held**
WEB: www.nextintent.com
SIC: 3599 Machine shop, jobbing & repair

(P-16788)
NGUYEN HIEP CORP
Also Called: Silicon Valley Precision Mch
1641 Rogers Ave, San Jose (95112-1126)
PHONE..................................408 451-9042
Hen Tran, *President*
Hua Tran, *Vice Pres*
Buu Thai, *Admin Sec*
EMP: 22
SQ FT: 6,400
SALES (est): 3.6MM **Privately Held**
SIC: 3599 Machine & other job shop work

(P-16789)
NICHOLS MANUFACTURING INC
913 Hanson Ct, Milpitas (95035-3166)
PHONE..................408 945-0911
Lettie Nichols, *President*
John Nichols, *Vice Pres*
Jon Nichols, *Vice Pres*
Nick Rodriguez, *Systems Mgr*
EMP: 14
SQ FT: 11,000
SALES (est): 2.6MM **Privately Held**
WEB: www.nicholsmfg.com
SIC: 3599 Machine shop, jobbing & repair

(P-16790)
NICKSONS MACHINE SHOP INC
914 W Betteravia Rd, Santa Maria (93455-1194)
P.O. Box 5200 (93456-5200)
PHONE..................805 925-2525
Dennis William Leal, *CEO*
Barbara Leal, *Corp Secy*
Gary Winters, *Vice Pres*
EMP: 24
SQ FT: 23,800
SALES (est): 4MM **Privately Held**
WEB: www.nicksons.com
SIC: 3599 Machine shop, jobbing & repair

(P-16791)
NIEDWICK CORPORATION
Also Called: Niedwick Machine Co
967 N Eckhoff St, Orange (92867-5432)
PHONE..................714 771-9999
Theodore R Niedwick, *President*
EMP: 45
SQ FT: 8,200
SALES (est): 8.4MM **Privately Held**
WEB: www.niedwickmachine.com
SIC: 3599 Machine shop, jobbing & repair

(P-16792)
NM MACHINING INC
175 Lewis Rd Ste 25, San Jose (95111-2175)
PHONE..................408 972-8978
Mike Tran, *President*
Tony Lee, *Accountant*
EMP: 27
SQ FT: 8,272
SALES (est): 5.1MM **Privately Held**
WEB: www.nmmachining.com
SIC: 3599 Machine shop, jobbing & repair

(P-16793)
NOROTOS INC
201 E Alton Ave, Santa Ana (92707-4416)
PHONE..................714 662-3113
Ronald Soto, *President*
John Soto, *Vice Pres*
Linda Soto, *Human Res Mgr*
Rob Prendergast, *Mfg Staff*
▲ EMP: 116
SQ FT: 12,000
SALES (est): 16.2MM **Privately Held**
WEB: www.norotos.com
SIC: 3599 3842 Machine shop, jobbing & repair; surgical appliances & supplies

(P-16794)
NOTRON MANUFACTURING INC
801 Milford St, Glendale (91203-1520)
PHONE..................818 247-7739
Theone Notron, *President*
David Notron Jr, *CFO*
James Notron, *Treasurer*
David Norton, *Office Mgr*
▲ EMP: 15
SQ FT: 13,000
SALES (est): 2MM **Privately Held**
SIC: 3599 5084 Machine & other job shop work; pneumatic tools & equipment

(P-16795)
NQ ENGINEERING INC
1852 W 11th St Pmb 532, Tracy (95376-3736)
PHONE..................209 836-3255
Noel C Quigg, *President*
Loretta Quigg, *Admin Sec*
EMP: 10
SQ FT: 4,000
SALES: 900K **Privately Held**
WEB: www.inrich.com
SIC: 3599 Machine shop, jobbing & repair

(P-16796)
NSD INDUSTRIES INC
5027 Gayhurst Ave, Baldwin Park (91706-1813)
PHONE..................626 813-2001
Ed Siapno, *President*
Chona Siapno, *Vice Pres*
EMP: 14
SQ FT: 2,496
SALES (est): 1.6MM **Privately Held**
SIC: 3599 Machine shop, jobbing & repair

(P-16797)
NTL PRECISION MACHINING INC
1355 Vander Way, San Jose (95112-2809)
PHONE..................408 298-6650
Henry Ngo, *CEO*
Hai Ngo, *Vice Pres*
Thao Ngo, *Admin Sec*
EMP: 15
SQ FT: 7,500
SALES (est): 2.5MM **Privately Held**
WEB: www.ntlprecision.com
SIC: 3599 Machine shop, jobbing & repair

(P-16798)
NU ENGINEERING
12121 Bartlett St, Garden Grove (92845-1525)
PHONE..................714 894-1206
Robert Kozlowski, *Owner*
EMP: 26
SQ FT: 4,500
SALES (est): 1.3MM **Privately Held**
SIC: 3599 8742 Machine shop, jobbing & repair; automation & robotics consultant

(P-16799)
NUMERI TECH INC
124 N E St, Stockton (95205-5015)
P.O. Box 5847 (95205-0847)
PHONE..................209 463-1910
Don King, *CEO*
EMP: 10
SQ FT: 12,000
SALES: 1.2MM **Privately Held**
SIC: 3599 Machine shop, jobbing & repair

(P-16800)
O & S PRECISION INC
20630 Nordhoff St, Chatsworth (91311-6114)
PHONE..................818 718-8876
Scott Onasch, *CEO*
Chris James, *General Mgr*
EMP: 20
SQ FT: 5,000
SALES (est): 5.2MM **Privately Held**
WEB: www.oands.com
SIC: 3599 Machine shop, jobbing & repair

(P-16801)
O-S INC
Also Called: All Weld Mch & Fabrication Co
541 W Capitol Expy Ste 10, San Jose (95136-3962)
PHONE..................408 946-5890
Kim Green, *President*
Ann Owen, *Treasurer*
John Heywood, *Plant Mgr*
EMP: 13
SQ FT: 12,000
SALES (est): 2.4MM **Privately Held**
WEB: www.allweld.com
SIC: 3599 7692 3444 Machine shop, jobbing & repair; welding repair; sheet metal specialties, not stamped

(P-16802)
ODONNELL MANUFACTURING INC
14811 Via Defrancesco Ave, Riverside (92508-9005)
P.O. Box 6245, Norco (92860-8041)
PHONE..................562 944-9671
Steve O'Donnell, *President*
▲ EMP: 12
SQ FT: 10,000
SALES (est): 1.5MM **Privately Held**
WEB: www.odonnellracing.com
SIC: 3599 Machine shop, jobbing & repair

(P-16803)
OEM LLC
311 S Highland Ave, Fullerton (92832-2305)
PHONE..................714 449-7500
John B Copp, *CEO*
Mary Quinlan, *Vice Pres*
Cheryl Bell, *Human Res Mgr*
▲ EMP: 23
SQ FT: 40,000
SALES (est): 4.6MM **Privately Held**
WEB: www.oempresssystems.com
SIC: 3599 Machine shop, jobbing & repair

(P-16804)
OFFERMAN INDUSTRIES
43154 Via Dos Picos Ste F, Temecula (92590-3478)
P.O. Box 2000 (92593-2000)
PHONE..................951 676-5016
Fax: 951 676-5031
EMP: 10
SQ FT: 2,000
SALES (est): 1.4MM **Privately Held**
SIC: 3599 3769

(P-16805)
OMEGA INTERCONNECT INC
1207 Brooks St, Ontario (91762-3609)
PHONE..................909 986-1933
Eric Vasquez, *President*
EMP: 10
SALES (est): 1.2MM **Privately Held**
SIC: 3599 Machine shop, jobbing & repair

(P-16806)
OMEGA PRECISION
13040 Telegraph Rd, Santa Fe Springs (90670-4078)
PHONE..................562 946-2491
Richard Venegas, *CEO*
Joseph M Venegas, *President*
Steve Venegas, *COO*
Richard M Venegas, *Corp Secy*
Chris Klowsowski, *Admin Asst*
EMP: 25 EST: 1965
SQ FT: 16,332
SALES (est): 4.8MM **Privately Held**
WEB: www.omegaprecision.com
SIC: 3599 Machine shop, jobbing & repair

(P-16807)
OMEGA PRECISION MACHINE
Also Called: Opmp
320 W Larch Rd Ste 15, Tracy (95304-1646)
PHONE..................209 833-6502
Mark Orner, *President*
EMP: 12
SQ FT: 5,000
SALES (est): 2.1MM **Privately Held**
WEB: www.omegaprecisionmachine.com
SIC: 3599 Machine shop, jobbing & repair

(P-16808)
OMICRON ENGINEERING INC
1513 Plaza Del Amo, Torrance (90501-4935)
PHONE..................310 328-4017
Alfons Ribitsch, *President*
Louis Ribitsch, *Vice Pres*
EMP: 10 EST: 1970
SQ FT: 12,500
SALES (est): 2MM **Privately Held**
WEB: www.omicron-eng.com
SIC: 3599 Machine shop, jobbing & repair

(P-16809)
OMNITEC PRECISION MFG INC
435 Queens Ln, San Jose (95112-4309)
PHONE..................408 437-9056
Eric Thomas Kawano, *President*
EMP: 15
SQ FT: 22,000
SALES (est): 3.4MM **Privately Held**
SIC: 3599 Machine & other job shop work

(P-16810)
OPTEL-MATIC INC
11221 Thienes Ave, El Monte (91733-3777)
PHONE..................626 444-2671
Max Buettiker, *President*
Justina Buettiker, *Vice Pres*
Elizabeth Buettiker, *Admin Sec*
EMP: 13 EST: 1966
SQ FT: 10,000
SALES: 900K **Privately Held**
WEB: www.optelmatic.com
SIC: 3599 Machine shop, jobbing & repair

(P-16811)
ORANGE COUNTY SCREW PRODUCTS
2993 E La Palma Ave, Anaheim (92806-2620)
PHONE..................714 630-7433
Robert Andri, *President*
EMP: 20
SQ FT: 8,000
SALES (est): 2.5MM **Privately Held**
SIC: 3599 3451 Machine shop, jobbing & repair; screw machine products

(P-16812)
OT PRECISION INC
1450 Seareel Ln, San Jose (95131-1580)
PHONE..................408 435-8818
Tam Dang, *President*
EMP: 25
SQ FT: 2,000
SALES (est): 4MM **Privately Held**
WEB: www.otprecision.com
SIC: 3599 Machine shop, jobbing & repair

(P-16813)
OVERBECK MACHINE
2620 Mission St, Santa Cruz (95060-5703)
PHONE..................831 425-5912
Wayne Overbeck, *Owner*
Wayne O Overbeck, *COO*
EMP: 20
SQ FT: 2,700
SALES (est): 1.9MM **Privately Held**
WEB: www.overbeckmachine.com
SIC: 3599 Machine shop, jobbing & repair

(P-16814)
OWENS DESIGN INCORPORATED
47427 Fremont Blvd, Fremont (94538-6504)
PHONE..................510 659-1800
John Apgar, *President*
EMP: 45
SQ FT: 30,000
SALES (est): 13.8MM **Privately Held**
SIC: 3599 Custom machinery

(P-16815)
P & F MACHINE INC
301 S Broadway, Turlock (95380-5414)
PHONE..................209 667-2515
Wayne D Rickey, *President*
Robert Finnegan, *Treasurer*
EMP: 10
SQ FT: 2,000
SALES (est): 1.6MM **Privately Held**
WEB: www.pfmetals.com
SIC: 3599 Machine shop, jobbing & repair

(P-16816)
P J MACHINING CO INC
17056 Hercules St Ste 101, Hesperia (92345-7608)
PHONE..................760 948-2722
EMP: 11
SQ FT: 5,000
SALES (est): 1.7MM **Privately Held**
SIC: 3599

(P-16817)
P M S D INC
Also Called: Danco Machine
950 George St, Santa Clara (95054-2705)
PHONE..................408 988-5235
Timothy Rohr, *CEO*
Jodie Lim, *Program Mgr*
Linh Nguyen, *Human Res Mgr*
Rod Dincoff, *Manager*
EMP: 92
SQ FT: 20,000
SALES: 14MM **Privately Held**
WEB: www.dancomachine.com
SIC: 3599 Machine shop, jobbing & repair

PRODUCTS & SVCS

(P-16818)
PACIFIC AEROSPACE MACHINE INC
3002 S Rosewood Ave, Santa Ana (92707-3822)
PHONE.....................714 534-1444
Paul Nguyen, *CEO*
Kirk Nguyen, *CFO*
EMP: 40
SQ FT: 50,000
SALES: 7MM **Privately Held**
WEB: www.pacificmachine.net
SIC: 3599 Machine shop, jobbing & repair

(P-16819)
PACIFIC BROACH & ENGRG ASSOC
1513 N Kraemer Blvd, Anaheim (92806-1407)
PHONE.....................714 632-5678
Steven R Yetzke, *President*
Michael Yetzke, *Vice Pres*
Elaine Montgomery, *Admin Sec*
▲ EMP: 19
SQ FT: 18,000
SALES (est): 2.8MM **Privately Held**
SIC: 3599 Machine shop, jobbing & repair

(P-16820)
PACIFIC CNC MACHINE CO
2702 Gateway Rd, Carlsbad (92009-1730)
PHONE.....................760 431-7558
John McClain, *Owner*
EMP: 12
SQ FT: 2,500
SALES (est): 825K **Privately Held**
SIC: 3599 Machine shop, jobbing & repair

(P-16821)
PACIFIC MFG INC SAN DIEGO
1520 Corporate Center Dr, San Diego (92154-6634)
PHONE.....................619 423-0316
Raymundo Montalvo, *President*
Maria A Montalvo, *Vice Pres*
Richard Valenzuele, *Sales Executive*
EMP: 20
SQ FT: 9,500
SALES (est): 3.5MM **Privately Held**
SIC: 3599 Machine shop, jobbing & repair

(P-16822)
PACIFIC WSTN AROSTRUCTURES INC
27771 Avenue Hopkins, Valencia (91355-1223)
PHONE.....................661 607-0100
Steve Cormier, *CEO*
EMP: 12 EST: 2015
SALES (est): 580K **Privately Held**
SIC: 3599 Machine shop, jobbing & repair

(P-16823)
PACON MFG INC
4777 Bennett Dr Ste H, Livermore (94551-4860)
PHONE.....................925 961-0445
Steven McClure, *CEO*
EMP: 20 EST: 2013
SALES (est): 3.2MM **Privately Held**
SIC: 3599 Machine shop, jobbing & repair

(P-16824)
PAMCO MACHINE WORKS INC
9359 Feron Blvd, Rancho Cucamonga (91730-4516)
PHONE.....................909 941-7260
James Fredrick Wilkinson, *CEO*
Diane Wilkinson, *Admin Sec*
EMP: 20
SQ FT: 17,000
SALES: 5MM **Privately Held**
WEB: www.pamcomachine.com
SIC: 3599 3462 Machine shop, jobbing & repair; iron & steel forgings

(P-16825)
PAPADATOS ENTERPRISES INC
Also Called: Dp Products
2015 Stone Ave, San Jose (95125-1447)
PHONE.....................408 299-0190
Danny Papadatos, *President*
Robert Cobb, *Vice Pres*
EMP: 10
SQ FT: 3,500
SALES: 650K **Privately Held**
WEB: www.dpprod.com
SIC: 3599 3089 Machine shop, jobbing & repair; plastic processing

(P-16826)
PARAGON MACHINE WORKS INC
253 S 25th St, Richmond (94804-2856)
PHONE.....................510 232-3223
Mark Norstad, *Owner*
Donna Norstad, *Manager*
EMP: 60
SQ FT: 55,000
SALES (est): 6.9MM **Privately Held**
WEB: www.paragonmachineworks.com
SIC: 3599 Machine shop, jobbing & repair

(P-16827)
PARAGON SWISS INC
545 Aldo Ave Ste 1, Santa Clara (95054-2206)
PHONE.....................408 748-1617
Kevin Beatty, *President*
David R Beatty, *Vice Pres*
Joanne Beatty, *Admin Sec*
Michael Gonzales, *Technology*
Laura Kay, *Technology*
EMP: 30
SQ FT: 10,200
SALES (est): 5.1MM **Privately Held**
WEB: www.paragonswiss.com
SIC: 3599 3451 Machine shop, jobbing & repair; screw machine products

(P-16828)
PARAMETRIC MANUFACTURING INC
3465 Edward Ave, Santa Clara (95054-2131)
PHONE.....................408 654-9845
Jon Drury, *President*
EMP: 16
SQ FT: 7,500
SALES: 2MM **Privately Held**
SIC: 3599 Machine shop, jobbing & repair

(P-16829)
PARAMOUNT GRINDING SERVICE
7311 Madison St Ste C, Paramount (90723-4038)
P.O. Box 893 (90723-0893)
PHONE.....................562 630-6940
John F Jaramillo, *President*
Lisa Jaramillo, *Vice Pres*
EMP: 12
SQ FT: 3,000
SALES: 740K **Privately Held**
SIC: 3599 Grinding castings for the trade

(P-16830)
PARAMOUNT MACHINE CO INC
10824 Edison Ct, Rancho Cucamonga (91730-3868)
PHONE.....................909 484-3600
Gregory A Harsen, *President*
Gail Harsen, *Vice Pres*
Maree Guest, *Office Mgr*
Sally Miller, *Manager*
EMP: 36
SQ FT: 12,000
SALES (est): 6.2MM **Privately Held**
WEB: www.paramountmachine.com
SIC: 3599 Machine shop, jobbing & repair

(P-16831)
PARK ENGINEERING AND MFG CO
Also Called: Pem
6430 Roland St, Buena Park (90621-3122)
PHONE.....................714 521-4660
Joanna Tenney, *CEO*
Jeff Tenney, *President*
Harold Tipton, *Purch Agent*
Rod Ordonez, *QC Mgr*
EMP: 30
SQ FT: 6,000
SALES (est): 5MM **Privately Held**
WEB: www.park-engineering.com
SIC: 3599 Machine shop, jobbing & repair

(P-16832)
PARKER-HANNIFIN CORPORATION
Also Called: X Cell Tool & Manufacturing Co
13850 Van Ness Ave, Gardena (90249-2476)
PHONE.....................310 308-0389
Art Siler, *Manager*
Ken Her, *Technology*
EMP: 80
SALES (corp-wide): 14.3B **Publicly Held**
WEB: www.parker.com
SIC: 3599 3769 Machine shop, jobbing & repair; guided missile & space vehicle parts & auxiliary equipment
PA: Parker-Hannifin Corporation
6035 Parkland Blvd
Cleveland OH 44124
216 896-3000

(P-16833)
PAULCO PRECISION INC
Also Called: Precision Resources
13916 Cordary Ave, Hawthorne (90250-7916)
PHONE.....................310 679-4900
Paul Ruby, *President*
Erika Mageo, *Office Mgr*
EMP: 16
SQ FT: 15,000
SALES (est): 2.4MM **Privately Held**
SIC: 3599 Machine shop, jobbing & repair

(P-16834)
PAULI SYSTEMS INC
1820 Walters Ct, Fairfield (94533-2759)
PHONE.....................707 429-2434
Robert Pauli, *CEO*
EMP: 22
SQ FT: 13,500
SALES: 3MM **Privately Held**
WEB: www.paulisystems.com
SIC: 3599 Custom machinery

(P-16835)
PCS MACHINING SERVICE INC
Also Called: Pcs Company
784 Edale Dr, Sunnyvale (94087-2316)
PHONE.....................408 735-9974
Paul V Camenzind, *President*
Barbara Camenzind, *Treasurer*
▲ EMP: 12
SQ FT: 6,300
SALES: 1MM **Privately Held**
SIC: 3599 Machine shop, jobbing & repair

(P-16836)
PEDAVENA MOULD AND DIE CO INC
Also Called: P M D
12464 Mccann Dr, Gardena (90249)
PHONE.....................310 327-2814
Steve Scardenzan, *President*
Anthony Scardenzan, *Shareholder*
Franca Scardenzan, *Admin Sec*
▲ EMP: 25
SQ FT: 10,000
SALES (est): 4.4MM **Privately Held**
WEB: www.pmd-inc.net
SIC: 3599 Machine & other job shop work

(P-16837)
PENDARVIS MANUFACTURING INC
1808 N American St, Anaheim (92801-1001)
PHONE.....................714 992-0950
Robert D Pendarvis, *CEO*
Brian Pendarvis, *General Mgr*
EMP: 25
SQ FT: 8,000
SALES (est): 5.5MM **Privately Held**
WEB: www.pendarvismanufacturing.com
SIC: 3599 Machine shop, jobbing & repair

(P-16838)
PEREZ MACHINE INC
1501 W 134th St, Gardena (90249-2215)
PHONE.....................310 217-9090
Mario Perez, *President*
Marcia Perez, *Vice Pres*
EMP: 10
SQ FT: 10,000
SALES (est): 1.7MM **Privately Held**
SIC: 3599 Machine shop, jobbing & repair

(P-16839)
PERFECTION MACHINE AND TL WORK
Also Called: Perfection Machine & TI Works
1568 E 22nd St, Los Angeles (90011-1389)
PHONE.....................213 749-5095
Steve Hix, *President*
▲ EMP: 50
SQ FT: 93,000
SALES (est): 7.5MM **Privately Held**
WEB: www.pmtw.com
SIC: 3599 3469 3544 Machine shop, jobbing & repair; stamping metal for the trade; special dies, tools, jigs & fixtures

(P-16840)
PERFORMANCE CNC INC
3210 Production Ave Ste A, Oceanside (92058-1306)
PHONE.....................760 722-1129
Michael Stark, *CEO*
EMP: 10
SQ FT: 1,600
SALES (est): 783.7K **Privately Held**
WEB: www.performancecnc.com
SIC: 3599 Machine shop, jobbing & repair

(P-16841)
PERFORMANCE MACHINE TECH INC
25141 Avenue Stanford, Valencia (91355-1227)
PHONE.....................661 294-8617
Dennis Moran, *President*
Carolyn Moran, *Corp Secy*
EMP: 33
SQ FT: 10,000
SALES (est): 5.3MM **Privately Held**
SIC: 3599 Machine shop, jobbing & repair

(P-16842)
PERFORMEX MACHINING INC
963 Terminal Way, San Carlos (94070-3224)
PHONE.....................650 595-2228
Joseph Iffla, *Owner*
EMP: 20
SQ FT: 5,600
SALES (est): 3.9MM **Privately Held**
WEB: www.performexmachining.com
SIC: 3599 Machine shop, jobbing & repair

(P-16843)
PETERSEN PRECISION ENGRG LLC
611 Broadway St, Redwood City (94063-3102)
PHONE.....................650 365-4373
Fred Petersen, *Mng Member*
Sunil Chandar, *Engineer*
Brian Malenfant, *Engineer*
Milton Philip Olson,
EMP: 120
SQ FT: 55,000
SALES (est): 19.1MM **Privately Held**
SIC: 3599 Machine shop, jobbing & repair

(P-16844)
PISOR INDUSTRIES INC
7201 32nd St, North Highlands (95660-2500)
PHONE.....................916 944-2851
Tony Free, *President*
Joy Pisor, *Corp Secy*
EMP: 20
SQ FT: 4,500
SALES (est): 3MM **Privately Held**
SIC: 3599 3498 Machine shop, jobbing & repair; fabricated pipe & fittings; architectural metalwork

(P-16845)
PLASMA COATING CORPORATION
13309 S Western Ave, Gardena (90249-1925)
PHONE.....................310 532-1951
James M Emery, *President*
Willard A Emery, *Vice Pres*
EMP: 22
SQ FT: 25,000

SALES (est): 4.2MM
SALES (corp-wide): 242.1B **Publicly Held**
WEB: www.plasmacoatingcorp.com
SIC: 3599 Machine shop, jobbing & repair
HQ: Southwest United Industries, Inc.
422 S Saint Louis Ave
Tulsa OK 74120
918 587-4161

(P-16846)
PLATRON COMPANY WEST
26260 Eden Landing Rd, Hayward (94545-3717)
PHONE..................................510 781-5588
Tim Martin, *Partner*
Bruce Garratt, *Partner*
Lizet Estrada, *Human Resources*
James White, *Prdtn Mgr*
EMP: 17
SALES (est): 2.4MM **Privately Held**
WEB: www.platron.com
SIC: 3599 Machine shop, jobbing & repair

(P-16847)
PLAYA TOOL & MARINE INC
1746 E Borchard Ave, Santa Ana (92705-4695)
PHONE..................................714 972-2722
Kirk Schroeder, *President*
EMP: 8
SQ FT: 8,400
SALES (est): 990K **Privately Held**
SIC: 3599 Machine shop, jobbing & repair

(P-16848)
PLEASANTON TOOL & MFG INC
1181 Quarry Ln Ste 450, Pleasanton (94566-8460)
PHONE..................................925 426-0500
Chester Thomas, *President*
Rich Thomas, *President*
Shirley Thomas, *CFO*
Steve Hallock, *Vice Pres*
Ray Forbes, *General Mgr*
EMP: 25
SQ FT: 18,000
SALES (est): 4.3MM **Privately Held**
WEB: www.pleasantontool.com
SIC: 3599 Machine shop, jobbing & repair

(P-16849)
PNM COMPANY
2547 N Business Park Ave, Fresno (93727-8637)
PHONE..................................559 291-1986
Dave Counts, *Partner*
Precision Numeric Machine, *Partner*
Mark Winters, *Partner*
Mario Persicone, *Director*
Bev Caldwell, *Manager*
▲ EMP: 48
SQ FT: 5,500
SALES (est): 8.6MM **Privately Held**
WEB: www.pnmcnc.com
SIC: 3599 Machine shop, jobbing & repair

(P-16850)
POLYTEC PRODUCTS CORPORATION
1190 Obrien Dr, Menlo Park (94025-1411)
PHONE..................................650 322-7555
John Parissenti, *President*
Tony Hertado, *Principal*
EMP: 45
SQ FT: 12,000
SALES (est): 8MM **Privately Held**
WEB: www.polytecproducts.com
SIC: 3599 Machine shop, jobbing & repair

(P-16851)
POWERS BROS MACHINE INC
8100 Slauson Ave, Montebello (90640-6622)
PHONE..................................323 728-2010
Mitchell Power, *President*
Casey Powers, *Treasurer*
Charles Powers, *Treasurer*
EMP: 12
SQ FT: 21,300
SALES (est): 2.1MM **Privately Held**
SIC: 3599 Machine shop, jobbing & repair

(P-16852)
PPM PRODUCTS INC
1538 Gladding Ct, Milpitas (95035-6814)
PHONE..................................408 946-4710
Yasuhiro Hayashi, *President*
Kathy Sato, *Executive Asst*
Clifford Hayashi, *Info Tech Dir*
EMP: 13
SQ FT: 3,000
SALES (est): 2.2MM **Privately Held**
WEB: www.ppmproducts.com
SIC: 3599 Machine shop, jobbing & repair

(P-16853)
PRECISION ARCFT MACHINING INC
Also Called: Pamco
10640 Elkwood St, Sun Valley (91352-4631)
PHONE..................................818 768-5900
Donald A Pisano, *President*
Kimberly Pisano, *CFO*
Joyce Pisano, *Treasurer*
Felicia Gomez, *Technology*
Jim Asseltyne, *Sales Mgr*
▲ EMP: 50
SQ FT: 6,500
SALES (est): 9MM **Privately Held**
SIC: 3599 3678 Machine shop, jobbing & repair; electronic connectors

(P-16854)
PRECISION IDENTITY CORPORATION
804 Camden Ave, Campbell (95008-4119)
PHONE..................................408 374-2346
Karl Kamber, *President*
Pierre Kamber, *Vice Pres*
Roland Kamber, *Vice Pres*
Jennifer Birch, *Bookkeeper*
EMP: 24
SQ FT: 12,000
SALES (est): 3.5MM **Privately Held**
WEB: www.precisionidentity.com
SIC: 3599 3451 Machine shop, jobbing & repair; screw machine products

(P-16855)
PRECISION WATERJET INC
880 W Crowther Ave, Placentia (92870-6348)
PHONE..................................888 538-9287
Shane Strowski, *President*
EMP: 39 EST: 2011
SALES: 7.8MM **Privately Held**
SIC: 3599 Machine shop, jobbing & repair

(P-16856)
PREFERRED MFG SVCS INC (PA)
Also Called: Snowline Engineering
4261 Business Dr, Cameron Park (95682-7217)
PHONE..................................530 677-2675
Calvin Reynolds, *President*
Debora Reynolds, *Treasurer*
Lee Block, *Exec VP*
Dave Greenace, *General Mgr*
Sue Belcher, *Office Mgr*
EMP: 85
SQ FT: 34,000
SALES (est): 13MM **Privately Held**
WEB: www.snowlineengineering.com
SIC: 3599 Machine shop, jobbing & repair

(P-16857)
PREMAC INC
Also Called: Precision Machining
625 Thompson Ave, Glendale (91201-2032)
PHONE..................................818 241-8370
Michael Warme, *CEO*
Victoria Warme, *CFO*
Rainer H Warme, *Principal*
EMP: 14
SQ FT: 6,000
SALES (est): 2.8MM **Privately Held**
SIC: 3599 Machine shop, jobbing & repair

(P-16858)
PRICE PRODUCTS INCORPORATED
106 State Pl, Escondido (92029-1323)
PHONE..................................760 233-8704
John Price, *President*

Jeanne Price, *Partner*
Shirley L Price, *Corp Secy*
Robert Price, *Vice Pres*
Barry Beatty, *Production*
EMP: 34
SQ FT: 15,000
SALES (est): 7.2MM **Privately Held**
WEB: www.priceproducts.com
SIC: 3599 Machine shop, jobbing & repair

(P-16859)
PRODUCTION LAPPING COMPANY
124 E Chestnut Ave, Monrovia (91016-3432)
PHONE..................................626 359-0611
Hans Herzig, *President*
Steve Herzig, *President*
Vangie Lozada, *Office Mgr*
Trudy Herzig, *Admin Sec*
George Avelar, *Supervisor*
EMP: 20 EST: 1959
SQ FT: 4,500
SALES (est): 3MM **Privately Held**
SIC: 3599 Machine shop, jobbing & repair

(P-16860)
PROFESSIONAL BEARING SVC INC
3831 Catalina St Ste K, Los Alamitos (90720-5447)
PHONE..................................562 596-5023
Christopher Mandryk, *CEO*
Martina Mandryk, *CFO*
EMP: 24
SQ FT: 10,840
SALES (est): 2.4MM **Privately Held**
SIC: 3599 Machine shop, jobbing & repair

(P-16861)
PRONTO DRILLING INC (PA)
9501 Santa Fe Springs Rd, Santa Fe Springs (90670-2624)
PHONE..................................562 777-0900
Miguel A Montanez, *President*
Orlando M Montanez, *Purch Mgr*
EMP: 24 EST: 1976
SALES (est): 3.8MM **Privately Held**
SIC: 3599 Machine shop, jobbing & repair

(P-16862)
PROTO SPACE ENGINEERING INC
2214 Loma Ave, South El Monte (91733-2518)
PHONE..................................626 442-8273
Linda Dabbs, *CEO*
Michael Dabbs, *President*
EMP: 30
SQ FT: 24,000
SALES (est): 5.5MM **Privately Held**
WEB: www.psengr.com
SIC: 3599 Machine shop, jobbing & repair

(P-16863)
PROTOQUICK INC
3412 Investment Blvd, Hayward (94545-3811)
PHONE..................................510 264-0101
Carl Anderson, *President*
John Harrigan, *Vice Pres*
Ken Staal, *Vice Pres*
Ken Stall, *Vice Pres*
Ryan Palo, *Engineer*
EMP: 10 EST: 2009
SQ FT: 7,000
SALES (est): 1.7MM **Privately Held**
SIC: 3599 Machine shop, jobbing & repair

(P-16864)
PTEC SOLUTIONS INC
48633 Warm Springs Blvd, Fremont (94539-7782)
PHONE..................................510 358-3578
Peter Pham, *President*
▲ EMP: 67
SQ FT: 25,000
SALES (est): 9MM **Privately Held**
WEB: www.pthsolutions.com
SIC: 3599 8711 3357 Machine shop, jobbing & repair; engineering services; fiber optic cable (insulated)

(P-16865)
PTR MANUFACTURING INC
Also Called: Ptr Sheet Metal & Fabrication
33390 Transit Ave, Union City (94587-2014)
PHONE..................................510 477-9654
SAI La, *President*
Phong La, *General Mgr*
EMP: 40
SQ FT: 45,000
SALES (est): 6.6MM **Privately Held**
SIC: 3599 3444 Machine shop, jobbing & repair; sheet metalwork

(P-16866)
PVA TEPLA AMERICA INC (HQ)
Also Called: Plasma Division
251 Corporate Terrace St, Corona (92879-6000)
PHONE..................................951 371-2500
Bill Marsh, *President*
Jeremy Detagle, *Accountant*
Monica Gatdula, *Accountant*
Stephen K Wilson, *Sales Mgr*
Andrea Babcock, *Marketing Staff*
EMP: 20
SQ FT: 15,000
SALES: 9MM
SALES (corp-wide): 100.6MM **Privately Held**
WEB: www.plasmapen.com
SIC: 3599 Custom machinery
PA: Pva Tepla Ag
Im Westpark 10-12
Wettenberg 35435
641 686-900

(P-16867)
PYRAMID PRECISION MACHINE INC
6721 Cobra Way, San Diego (92121-4110)
PHONE..................................858 642-0713
Robert Taylor, *President*
Walter Gieffels, *COO*
Stephanie Mills, *CFO*
Arnie Amaya, *Prgrmr*
Stephanie Rosalas, *Controller*
EMP: 100
SQ FT: 23,800
SALES (est): 27.9MM **Privately Held**
WEB: www.pyramidprecision.com
SIC: 3599 Machine shop, jobbing & repair

(P-16868)
Q3-CNC INC
9091 Kenamar Dr, San Diego (92121-2421)
PHONE..................................858 790-0002
David Trainor, *President*
Christopher Campbell, *Treasurer*
Luis Ramos, *Admin Sec*
EMP: 13
SQ FT: 10,000
SALES (est): 2.2MM **Privately Held**
WEB: www.q3cnc.com
SIC: 3599 Machine shop, jobbing & repair

(P-16869)
QUALITASK INCORPORATED
2840 E Gretta Ln, Anaheim (92806-2512)
PHONE..................................714 237-0900
Som Suntharaphat, *President*
Eduvigis Suntharaphat, *Principal*
Deb Beds, *Admin Sec*
EMP: 17
SQ FT: 13,100
SALES (est): 3.1MM **Privately Held**
WEB: www.qualitask.net
SIC: 3599 Machine shop, jobbing & repair

(P-16870)
QUALITY CONTROLLED MFG INC
9429 Abraham Way, Santee (92071-2854)
PHONE..................................619 443-3997
William Grande, *President*
Jane Currie, *Treasurer*
James Hiebing, *Vice Pres*
EMP: 70 EST: 1978
SQ FT: 25,000
SALES (est): 8.8MM **Privately Held**
SIC: 3599 Machine shop, jobbing & repair

PRODUCTS & SVCS

(P-16871)
QUALITY EDM INC
8025 E Crystal Dr, Anaheim (92807-2523)
PHONE..............................714 283-9220
Michael Gervais, *President*
EMP: 10
SQ FT: 8,000
SALES: 2.2MM **Privately Held**
SIC: 3599 Machine shop, jobbing & repair

(P-16872)
QUALITY MACHINE ENGRG INC
2559 Grosse Ave, Santa Rosa
(95404-2608)
PHONE..............................707 528-1900
Rudy Hirschnitz, *President*
Shawn Barnett, *Vice Pres*
John F Wright, *Vice Pres*
EMP: 40
SQ FT: 13,500
SALES (est): 6MM **Privately Held**
WEB: www.qme1.com
SIC: 3599 Machine shop, jobbing & repair

(P-16873)
QUALITY MACHINE SHOP INC
1676 N Ventura Ave, Ventura (93001-1576)
PHONE..............................805 653-7944
David V Gudino, *President*
EMP: 10
SQ FT: 4,800
SALES: 250K **Privately Held**
SIC: 3599 Machine shop, jobbing & repair

(P-16874)
QUALONTIME CORPORATION
19 Senisa, Irvine (92612-2112)
PHONE..............................714 523-4751
Douglas J Siemer, *President*
EMP: 16
SQ FT: 7,500
SALES (est): 1.6MM **Privately Held**
SIC: 3599 Machine shop, jobbing & repair

(P-16875)
QUANTECH MACHINING INC
25647 Rye Canyon Rd, Valencia
(91355-1110)
PHONE..............................661 775-3990
Riad Hussein, *President*
Josie Muniz, *Office Mgr*
Jocelane Fanol, *Contract Mgr*
Raul R Serrato, *Purch Mgr*
Jamaal Hussein, *QC Mgr*
EMP: 45
SALES: 8MM **Privately Held**
SIC: 3599 Machine shop, jobbing & repair

(P-16876)
R & B PLASTICS INC
227 E Meats Ave, Orange (92865-3311)
PHONE..............................714 229-8419
Richard T Young, *President*
Nancy Young, *Vice Pres*
EMP: 14
SQ FT: 10,000
SALES (est): 3.1MM **Privately Held**
SIC: 3599 Machine shop, jobbing & repair

(P-16877)
R & L ENTERPRISES INC
Also Called: Rand Machine Works
1955 S Mary St, Fresno (93721-3309)
PHONE..............................559 233-1608
Robert Rand, *President*
Linda Rand, *Vice Pres*
Kristin Henson, *Executive*
EMP: 26
SQ FT: 27,000
SALES: 2.7MM **Privately Held**
WEB: www.randmachineworks.com
SIC: 3599 7692 Machine shop, jobbing &
repair; welding repair

(P-16878)
R A INDUSTRIES LLC
3207 W Pendleton Ave, Santa Ana
(92704-4481)
PHONE..............................714 557-2322
Robert J Follman, *Mng Member*
Thomas Hyland,
Carole A Follman, *Mng Member*
▲ EMP: 30 EST: 1969
SQ FT: 30,000

SALES: 6.4MM **Privately Held**
WEB: www.ra-industries.com
SIC: 3599 3593 Machine shop, jobbing &
repair; fluid power cylinders & actuators

(P-16879)
R C I P INC
Also Called: R C Industries
1476 N Hundley St, Anaheim (92806-1322)
PHONE..............................714 630-1239
Robert Champlin, *CEO*
EMP: 16
SQ FT: 4,400
SALES (est): 3.4MM **Privately Held**
WEB: www.rcip.com
SIC: 3599 Machine shop, jobbing & repair

(P-16880)
R M BAKER MACHINE & TOOL INC
815 W Front St, Covina (91722-3613)
PHONE..............................562 697-4007
Richard Baker, *President*
Faith Baker, *Admin Sec*
Candis Bright, *Accounting Mgr*
EMP: 16
SQ FT: 6,700
SALES (est): 2.7MM **Privately Held**
SIC: 3599 Machine shop, jobbing & repair

(P-16881)
R STEPHENSON & D CRAM MFG INC
Also Called: R & D Mfg Services
800 Faulstich Ct, San Jose (95112-1361)
PHONE..............................408 452-0882
Rick Stephenson, *President*
EMP: 30 EST: 1976
SQ FT: 14,000
SALES (est): 5.1MM **Privately Held**
SIC: 3599 3369 3324 Machine shop, job-
bing & repair; nonferrous foundries; steel
investment foundries

(P-16882)
RA-WHITE INC
2736 W Industry Rd, Delano (93215-9565)
PHONE..............................661 725-1840
Debbie Bushnell, *President*
Carl Bushnell, *Vice Pres*
EMP: 10
SQ FT: 20,000
SALES: 1MM **Privately Held**
WEB: www.rawhite.com
SIC: 3599 Machine & other job shop work

(P-16883)
RALPH E AMES MACHINE WORKS
2301 Dominguez Way, Torrance
(90501-6200)
PHONE..............................310 328-8523
Mike Ames, *President*
Ron Ames, *Vice Pres*
EMP: 45
SQ FT: 11,000
SALES (est): 8.8MM **Privately Held**
WEB: www.amesmachine.com
SIC: 3599 Machine shop, jobbing & repair

(P-16884)
RAPID PRECISION MFG INC
1516 Montague Expy, San Jose
(95131-1408)
PHONE..............................408 617-0771
Paul Yi, *CEO*
Jane Yi, *CFO*
EMP: 35
SQ FT: 11,000
SALES (est): 6.1MM **Privately Held**
SIC: 3599 Machine shop, jobbing & repair

(P-16885)
RAPID PRODUCT SOLUTIONS INC
2240 Celsius Ave Ste D, Oxnard
(93030-8015)
PHONE..............................805 485-7234
Max Gerdts, *President*
Richard Fitch, *President*
Douglas Wallis, *President*
Sarah Phelps, *Technical Staff*
Shawn Tester, *Sales Associate*
▲ EMP: 30
SQ FT: 10,000

SALES (est): 5.5MM **Privately Held**
WEB: www.rapid-products.com
SIC: 3599 Machine shop, jobbing & repair

(P-16886)
RB MACHINING INC
39360 3rd St E Ste B203, Palmdale
(93550-3256)
PHONE..............................661 274-4611
Barbara Mc Millan, *CEO*
Robert McMillan, *Owner*
EMP: 10
SALES (est): 1.3MM **Privately Held**
SIC: 3599 Machine shop, jobbing & repair

(P-16887)
RDC MACHINE INC
384 Laurelwood Rd, Santa Clara
(95054-2311)
PHONE..............................408 970-0721
Randolph D Cuilla, *President*
Janene Cuilla, *Treasurer*
Mark Cuilla, *Vice Pres*
EMP: 41
SQ FT: 30,000
SALES (est): 7.5MM **Privately Held**
SIC: 3599 Machine shop, jobbing & repair

(P-16888)
RDL MACHINE INC
Also Called: Hall Machine
7775 Arjons Dr, San Diego (92126-4366)
PHONE..............................858 693-3975
Richard G Hall, *President*
Debbie Hall, *Corp Secy*
Richard Hall, *CIO*
Roma Candelaria, *Purchasing*
Dave Lopez, *Sales Executive*
EMP: 30
SQ FT: 12,200
SALES: 2.7MM **Privately Held**
WEB: www.hallmachinesd.com
SIC: 3599 Machine shop, jobbing & repair

(P-16889)
RE BILT METALIZING CO
Also Called: Rebuilt Metalizing Chrome Pltg
2229 E 38th St, Vernon (90058-1628)
P.O. Box 58808, Los Angeles (90058-0808)
PHONE..............................323 277-8200
Dave Dehota, *Owner*
EMP: 14
SQ FT: 18,000
SALES (est): 1.4MM **Privately Held**
SIC: 3599 Machine shop, jobbing & repair

(P-16890)
RED LINE ENGINEERING INC
4616 Weed Patch Ct, Greenwood
(95635-9507)
P.O. Box 399 (95635-0399)
PHONE..............................530 333-2134
Matt Johnson, *CEO*
Michaela Johnson, *Vice Pres*
EMP: 14
SQ FT: 15,000
SALES (est): 1MM **Privately Held**
WEB: www.randyjohnson.com
SIC: 3599 Machine shop, jobbing & repair

(P-16891)
REGAL MACHINE & ENGRG INC
5200 E 60th St, Maywood (90270-3557)
PHONE..............................323 773-7462
Val Darie, *President*
Ben Dang, *Prgrmr*
EMP: 27
SQ FT: 20,500
SALES (est): 5MM **Privately Held**
WEB: www.regalmachine.com
SIC: 3599 3769 Machine shop, jobbing &
repair; guided missile & space vehicle
parts & auxiliary equipment

(P-16892)
REID PRODUCTS INC
21430 Waalew Rd, Apple Valley
(92307-1026)
P.O. Box 1507 (92307-0028)
PHONE..............................760 240-1355
Kevin Reid, *President*
Cliff R Carter, *Treasurer*
Shelby Reid, *Vice Pres*
Steve Childs, *General Mgr*
Lisa Grinser, *Admin Sec*
EMP: 48

SALES (est): 15,000
SALES: 8.9MM **Privately Held**
SIC: 3599 Machine shop, jobbing & repair

(P-16893)
REISNER ENTERPRISES INC
Also Called: Westcorp Engineering
1403 W Linden St, Riverside (92507-6804)
PHONE..............................951 786-9478
Tom Reisner, *President*
EMP: 12
SQ FT: 9,000
SALES (est): 1.3MM **Privately Held**
SIC: 3599 Machine shop, jobbing & repair

(P-16894)
RELIANCE MACHINE PRODUCTS INC
4265 Solar Way, Fremont (94538-6389)
PHONE..............................510 438-6760
Kelly L Hill, *President*
EMP: 45
SQ FT: 12,000
SALES (est): 7.9MM **Privately Held**
SIC: 3599 Machine shop, jobbing & repair

(P-16895)
REMCO MCH & FABRICATION INC
1966 S Date Ave, Bloomington
(92316-2442)
PHONE..............................909 877-3530
Jacque Lewis Russell, *CEO*
Jerry Gilson, *Vice Pres*
▲ EMP: 19 EST: 1979
SALES (est): 4.2MM **Privately Held**
SIC: 3599 3441 Machine shop, jobbing &
repair; fabricated structural metal; building
components, structural steel

(P-16896)
RENAISSANCE PRECISION MFG INC
Also Called: R P M
2551 Stanwell Dr Concord, Concord
(94520-4818)
PHONE..............................925 691-5997
Wade Carbone, *CEO*
Bill Burmeister, *President*
Kelly Burmeister, *Corp Secy*
EMP: 10
SQ FT: 10,000
SALES (est): 1.8MM **Privately Held**
SIC: 3599 Machine shop, jobbing & repair

(P-16897)
RESEARCH METAL INDUSTRIES INC
1970 W 139th St, Gardena (90249-2408)
PHONE..............................310 352-3200
Harish Brahmbhatt, *President*
Kamla Brahmbhatt, *Vice Pres*
Leigh Thompson, *General Mgr*
Steve Oldakowski, *Technology*
◆ EMP: 35
SQ FT: 24,000
SALES (est): 9.1MM **Privately Held**
WEB: www.researchmetal.com
SIC: 3599 3469 Electrical discharge ma-
chining (EDM); spinning metal for the
trade

(P-16898)
RICAURTE PRECISION INC
1550 E Mcfadden Ave, Santa Ana
(92705-4308)
PHONE..............................714 667-0632
Luis Ricaurte, *CEO*
Marina Ricaurte, *President*
EMP: 22
SQ FT: 72,000
SALES (est): 4.1MM **Privately Held**
SIC: 3599 Machine shop, jobbing & repair

(P-16899)
RICHARDS MACHINING CO INC
2161 Del Franco St, San Jose
(95131-1570)
PHONE..............................408 526-9219
Gustavo Chavez, *President*
Odin Chavez, *Vice Pres*
Yamir Chavez, *Admin Sec*
Yovannah Chavez, *Administration*
EMP: 16
SQ FT: 6,500

▲ = Import ▼ =Export
◆ =Import/Export

SALES: 1.2MM **Privately Held**
SIC: 3599 Machine shop, jobbing & repair

(P-16900)
RICMAN MFG INC
2273 American Ave Ste 1, Hayward
(94545-1813)
PHONE..................................510 670-1785
Richard Mann, *President*
EMP: 20
SQ FT: 5,000
SALES (est): 3.7MM **Privately Held**
SIC: 3599 Machine shop, jobbing & repair

(P-16901)
RIGGINS ENGINEERING INC
13932 Saticoy St, Van Nuys (91402-6587)
PHONE..................................818 782-7010
Joe Grossnickle, *President*
Michael Riggins, *Vice Pres*
Mike Riggins, *Vice Pres*
Casey Evans, *Office Mgr*
Nana Grossnickle, *Admin Sec*
EMP: 40
SQ FT: 18,000
SALES (est): 6.4MM **Privately Held**
WEB: www.rigginseng.com
SIC: 3599 Machine shop, jobbing & repair

(P-16902)
RINCON ENGINEERING CORPORATION
6325 Carpinteria Ave, Carpinteria
(93013-2901)
P.O. Box 87 (93014-0087)
PHONE..................................805 684-0935
Alberto Hugo, *CEO*
Roger Hugo, *President*
Richard Hugo, *Vice Pres*
Rick Sanchez, *Executive*
Colleen Hugo CPA, *General Mgr*
EMP: 43
SQ FT: 12,000
SALES (est): 9.7MM **Privately Held**
WEB: www.rinconeng.com
SIC: 3599 3444 3441 Machine shop, jobbing & repair; sheet metalwork; fabricated structural metal

(P-16903)
RIVERSIDE MACHINE WORKS INC
6301 Baldwin Ave, Riverside (92509-6014)
PHONE..................................951 685-7416
Kerry Townsend, *President*
EMP: 14
SQ FT: 7,500
SALES (est): 1.9MM **Privately Held**
SIC: 3599 7692 3444 Machine shop, jobbing & repair; welding repair; sheet metalwork

(P-16904)
RJ MACHINE INC
7985 Dunbrook Rd Ste E, San Diego
(92126-6307)
PHONE..................................858 547-9482
Reed Jackson, *President*
Sandra Jackson, *CFO*
Jonathan Jackson, *Prdtn Mgr*
EMP: 10
SQ FT: 7,000
SALES (est): 1.7MM **Privately Held**
WEB: www.rjmachine.net
SIC: 3599 Machine shop, jobbing & repair

(P-16905)
RMC ENGINEERING CO INC (PA)
255 Mayock Rd, Gilroy (95020-7032)
P.O. Box 575 (95021-0575)
PHONE..................................408 842-2525
Betty Mc Kenzie, *President*
Brian Shonebarger, *COO*
Shawna Mc Kenzie, *Corp Secy*
Kevin Mc Kenzie, *Vice Pres*
Scott Mc Kenzie, *Vice Pres*
▲ EMP: 30
SQ FT: 14,000
SALES (est): 7.5MM **Privately Held**
SIC: 3599 7692 7538 3715 Machine shop, jobbing & repair; automotive welding; general automotive repair shops; truck trailers

(P-16906)
ROBERT H OLIVA INC
Also Called: Romakk Engineering
19863 Nordhoff St, Northridge
(91324-3331)
PHONE..................................818 700-1035
Robert Oliva, *President*
Kim Oliva, *Vice Pres*
EMP: 25
SQ FT: 4,000
SALES (est): 4.2MM **Privately Held**
SIC: 3599 Machine shop, jobbing & repair

(P-16907)
ROBERT J ALANDT & SONS
Also Called: Central Cal Metals
4692 N Brawley Ave, Fresno (93722-3921)
PHONE..................................559 275-1391
Frank Alandt, *President*
Joseph Alandt, *Corp Secy*
Robert Alandt, *Vice Pres*
EMP: 45 EST: 1950
SQ FT: 50,000
SALES (est): 10MM **Privately Held**
SIC: 3599 Machine shop, jobbing & repair

(P-16908)
ROBERT W WIESMANTEL
Also Called: Cebe Co
15345 Allen St, Paramount (90723-4011)
P.O. Box 620 (90723-0620)
PHONE..................................562 634-0442
Robert W Wiesmantel, *Owner*
EMP: 14
SQ FT: 24,000
SALES (est): 1.2MM **Privately Held**
SIC: 3599 Machine shop, jobbing & repair

(P-16909)
ROBERTS PRECISION ENGRG INC
Also Called: Robert's Engineering
1345 S Allec St, Anaheim (92805-6304)
PHONE..................................714 635-4485
Robert Flores II, *President*
EMP: 25
SQ FT: 23,000
SALES (est): 5.8MM **Privately Held**
SIC: 3599 Machine shop, jobbing & repair

(P-16910)
ROBSON TECHNOLOGIES INC
Also Called: R T I
135 E Main Ave Ste 130, Morgan Hill
(95037-7522)
PHONE..................................408 779-8008
William W Robson, *President*
Ryan Block, *Manager*
Lori Robson, *Vice Pres*
EMP: 27
SQ FT: 3,000
SALES (est): 5.9MM **Privately Held**
WEB: www.geminiwriter.com
SIC: 3599 3823 Machine shop, jobbing & repair; computer interface equipment for industrial process control

(P-16911)
ROC-AIRE CORP
2198 Pomona Blvd, Pomona (91768-3332)
PHONE..................................909 784-3385
Thomas L Collins, *CEO*
Jason Collins, *Corp Secy*
EMP: 22
SQ FT: 52,000
SALES (est): 4.5MM **Privately Held**
WEB: www.rocaire.com
SIC: 3599 Machine shop, jobbing & repair

(P-16912)
ROMI INDUSTRIES INC
Also Called: Romi Machine Shop
25443 Rye Canyon Rd, Valencia
(91355-1206)
PHONE..................................661 294-1142
Jay Patel, *President*
EMP: 10
SQ FT: 6,000
SALES (est): 1.2MM **Privately Held**
SIC: 3599 Machine shop, jobbing & repair

(P-16913)
RON GROSE RACING INC
488 E Kettleman Ln, Lodi (95240-5945)
PHONE..................................209 368-2571

Joey Grose, *President*
EMP: 10
SQ FT: 8,600
SALES (est): 860K **Privately Held**
WEB: www.rgracing.com
SIC: 3599 5531 7539 Machine shop, jobbing & repair; speed shops, including race car supplies; machine shop, automotive

(P-16914)
RON WITHERSPOON INC
13525 Blackie Rd, Castroville
(95012-3211)
PHONE..................................831 633-3568
Les Oglesby, *Manager*
EMP: 85
SALES (corp-wide): 18.7MM **Privately Held**
SIC: 3599 Machine shop, jobbing & repair
PA: Ron Witherspoon Inc.
1551 Dell Ave
Campbell CA 95008
408 370-6620

(P-16915)
RONLO ENGINEERING LTD
955 Flynn Rd, Camarillo (93012-8704)
PHONE..................................805 388-3227
Ronnie Lowe, *CEO*
Rick Slaney, *President*
Tracy Slaney, *Treasurer*
Karen Mc Master, *Vice Pres*
EMP: 30
SQ FT: 23,650
SALES (est): 5.3MM **Privately Held**
WEB: www.ronlo.com
SIC: 3599 Machine shop, jobbing & repair

(P-16916)
ROOKE MANUFACTURING CO
3360 W Harvard St, Santa Ana
(92704-3920)
PHONE..................................714 540-6943
Deward Rooke, *Owner*
EMP: 10 EST: 1977
SQ FT: 5,000
SALES: 600K **Privately Held**
SIC: 3599 Machine shop, jobbing & repair

(P-16917)
ROTHLISBERGER MFG A CAL CORP
Also Called: R M I
14718 Arminta St, Van Nuys (91402-5904)
PHONE..................................818 786-9462
Jerry Rothlisberger, *President*
Korena Rothlisberger, *Admin Sec*
EMP: 16
SQ FT: 8,000
SALES (est): 2.2MM **Privately Held**
WEB: www.mag-hytec.com
SIC: 3599 Machine shop, jobbing & repair

(P-16918)
ROY & VAL TOOL GRINDING INC
10131 Canoga Ave, Chatsworth
(91311-3006)
PHONE..................................818 341-2434
Val Goelz, *President*
Jim Tweety, *Vice Pres*
Mark Goelz, *Admin Sec*
EMP: 11
SQ FT: 4,800
SALES: 500K **Privately Held**
SIC: 3599 7389 Machine shop, jobbing & repair; grinding, precision: commercial or industrial

(P-16919)
ROZAK ENGINEERING INC
556 S State College Blvd, Fullerton
(92831-5114)
PHONE..................................714 446-8855
Solomon Kilaghbian, *President*
EMP: 11
SQ FT: 1,920
SALES (est): 1.1MM **Privately Held**
SIC: 3599 Machine shop, jobbing & repair

(P-16920)
RPM GRINDING CO INC
Also Called: R P M Centerless Grinding
1755 Commerce St, Norco (92860-2934)
PHONE..................................951 273-0602
Rudy Miller, *CEO*

EMP: 13
SQ FT: 10,500
SALES (est): 1.7MM **Privately Held**
WEB: www.rudymiller.com
SIC: 3599 Machine shop, jobbing & repair

(P-16921)
RS MACHINING CO INC
9726 Cozycroft Ave, Chatsworth
(91311-4401)
PHONE..................................818 718-0097
Crystal C Crawford, *CEO*
Amado J Edghill, *CFO*
Dennis Germann, *QC Mgr*
EMP: 10
SQ FT: 4,500
SALES: 1.3MM **Privately Held**
SIC: 3599 Machine shop, jobbing & repair

(P-16922)
S & H MACHINE INC (PA)
900 N Lake St, Burbank (91502-1622)
PHONE..................................818 846-9847
Fisher, *Principal*
Kenneth Fisher, *Vice Pres*
Pamela Fisher, *Vice Pres*
Art Martinez, *Mfg Mgr*
EMP: 13
SQ FT: 17,107
SALES (est): 7.6MM **Privately Held**
WEB: www.shmachine.com
SIC: 3599 Machine shop, jobbing & repair

(P-16923)
S & S NUMERICAL CONTROL INC
19841 Nordhoff St, Northridge
(91324-3331)
PHONE..................................818 341-4141
John Satterfield, *President*
Roberta J Satterfield, *Admin Sec*
EMP: 20
SQ FT: 9,000
SALES (est): 3.1MM **Privately Held**
WEB: www.ssnumerical.com
SIC: 3599 Machine shop, jobbing & repair

(P-16924)
S & S PRECISION MFG INC
2509 S Broadway, Santa Ana (92707-3411)
PHONE..................................714 754-6664
David Mosier, *President*
Lucille Goudreault, *Manager*
EMP: 45
SQ FT: 10,000
SALES (est): 9MM **Privately Held**
SIC: 3599 Machine shop, jobbing & repair

(P-16925)
S F ENTERPRISES INCORPORATED
707 Warrington Ave, Redwood City
(94063-3525)
PHONE..................................650 455-3223
Ben Schloss, *President*
EMP: 12
SQ FT: 4,000
SALES: 2MM **Privately Held**
SIC: 3599 Air intake filters, internal combustion engine, except auto

(P-16926)
S R MACHINING-PROPERTIES LLC
640 Parkridge Ave, Norco (92860-3124)
PHONE..................................951 520-9486
Lawrence Kaford, *President*
Larry Novak, *Vice Pres*
▲ EMP: 134
SQ FT: 28,000
SALES (est): 30.2MM **Privately Held**
WEB: www.srmachining.com
SIC: 3599 3089 Machine shop, jobbing & repair; injection molding of plastics

(P-16927)
SAMAX PRECISION INC
926 W Evelyn Ave, Sunnyvale
(94086-5957)
PHONE..................................408 245-9555
Vicki Murray, *President*
Michelle Beroza, *Office Mgr*
Jodi McCash, *Admin Sec*
Scott McClung, *QC Dir*
EMP: 36 EST: 1963

PRODUCTS & SVCS

SQ FT: 10,000
SALES (est): 7.8MM Privately Held
WEB: www.samaxinc.com
SIC: 3599 Custom machinery

(P-16928)
SANTA FE MACHINE WORKS INC
14578 Rancho Vista Dr, Fontana (92335-4277)
PHONE......................909 350-6877
Dennis Kelly, *President*
Scott Kelly, *CFO*
Todd Kelly, *Corp Secy*
Patricia Kelly, *Vice Pres*
Gilbert Robinson, *Vice Pres*
EMP: 24
SQ FT: 30,000
SALES (est): 4.8MM Privately Held
WEB: www.santafemachine-phoenix.com
SIC: 3599 Machine shop, jobbing & repair

(P-16929)
SARR INDUSTRIES INC
8975 Fullbright Ave, Chatsworth (91311-6124)
PHONE......................818 998-7735
Richard L Joice Jr, *President*
Angela Suszka, *Corp Secy*
Sharon Mills-Roche, *Accountant*
EMP: 14
SQ FT: 5,500
SALES (est): 2.4MM Privately Held
SIC: 3599 Machine shop, jobbing & repair

(P-16930)
SCHNEIDERS MANUFACTURING INC
11122 Penrose St, Sun Valley (91352-2724)
PHONE......................818 771-0082
Nick Schneider, *President*
Trudy Schneider, *Corp Secy*
Tom Schneider, *Vice Pres*
EMP: 30 EST: 1967
SQ FT: 18,000
SALES (est): 5.1MM Privately Held
SIC: 3599 Machine shop, jobbing & repair

(P-16931)
SCHROEDER TOOL & DIE CORP
25448 Cumberland Ln, Calabasas (91302-3156)
PHONE......................818 786-9360
Steve Schroeder, *President*
Patricia Schroeder-Deckard, *Shareholder*
EMP: 40
SQ FT: 45,000
SALES (est): 3.7MM Privately Held
SIC: 3599 3545 3544 Machine shop, jobbing & repair; machine tool accessories; special dies, tools, jigs & fixtures

(P-16932)
SCOTT CRAFT CO (PA)
4601 Cecilia St, Cudahy (90201-5813)
P.O. Box 430, Bell (90201-0430)
PHONE......................323 560-3949
Merry An Cejka, *Owner*
Robert Cejka, *Sales Staff*
EMP: 15 EST: 1966
SQ FT: 12,000
SALES (est): 3.3MM Privately Held
WEB: www.scottcraft.com
SIC: 3599 3544 Custom machinery; machine shop, jobbing & repair; special dies, tools, jigs & fixtures

(P-16933)
SCOTT CRAFT CO
Also Called: Scott Craft Co & STC
5 Stallion Rd, Rancho Palos Verdes (90275-5257)
PHONE......................323 560-3949
Merry An Cejka, *Branch Mgr*
EMP: 10
SALES (corp-wide): 3.3MM Privately Held
WEB: www.scottcraft.com
SIC: 3599 Custom machinery
PA: Scott Craft Co
    4601 Cecilia St
    Cudahy CA 90201
    323 560-3949

(P-16934)
SCREWMATIC INC
925 W 1st St, Azusa (91702-4222)
P.O. Box 518 (91702-0518)
PHONE......................626 334-7831
Louis E Zimmerli, *CEO*
Alice Zimmerli, *Vice Pres*
Jeff Clow, *Admin Sec*
Wayne Dobloer, *Prdtn Mgr*
EMP: 65
SQ FT: 40,000
SALES (est): 10.2MM Privately Held
WEB: www.screwmaticinc.com
SIC: 3599 Machine shop, jobbing & repair

(P-16935)
SDI LLC
21 Morgan Ste 150, Irvine (92618-2086)
PHONE......................949 351-1866
Jon Korbonski, *President*
Vic Klashorst, *Natl Sales Mgr*
EMP: 20
SALES (est): 1.2MM Privately Held
SIC: 3599 Custom machinery

(P-16936)
SENGA ENGINEERING INC
1525 E Warner Ave, Santa Ana (92705-5419)
PHONE......................714 549-8011
Roy Jones, *President*
EMP: 48
SQ FT: 25,000
SALES (est): 8.4MM Privately Held
WEB: www.senga-eng.com
SIC: 3599 Machine shop, jobbing & repair

(P-16937)
SENIOR OPERATIONS LLC
Also Called: Senior Flexonics
9106 Balboa Ave, San Diego (92123-1512)
PHONE......................858 278-8400
James Young, *Vice Pres*
EMP: 258
SALES (corp-wide): 1.3B Privately Held
SIC: 3599 Bellows, industrial: metal; hose, flexible metallic; tubing, flexible metallic
HQ: Senior Operations Llc
    300 E Devon Ave
    Bartlett IL 60103
    630 837-1811

(P-16938)
SENIOR OPERATIONS LLC
Also Called: Capo Industries Division
790 Greenfield Dr, El Cajon (92021-3101)
PHONE......................909 627-2723
Jim Watkins, *Branch Mgr*
EMP: 70
SALES (corp-wide): 1.3B Privately Held
SIC: 3599 Hose, flexible metallic; tubing, flexible metallic; bellows, industrial: metal
HQ: Senior Operations Llc
    300 E Devon Ave
    Bartlett IL 60103
    630 837-1811

(P-16939)
SENIOR OPERATIONS LLC
Also Called: Jet Products
9106 Balboa Ave, San Diego (92123-1512)
PHONE......................858 278-8400
Damon Evans, *Branch Mgr*
Daniel Fee, *Engineer*
Barbara Wagner, *Asst Controller*
Roman Salas, *Opers Staff*
EMP: 160
SALES (corp-wide): 1.3B Privately Held
SIC: 3599 Hose, flexible metallic; tubing, flexible metallic; bellows, industrial: metal
HQ: Senior Operations Llc
    300 E Devon Ave
    Bartlett IL 60103
    630 837-1811

(P-16940)
SERRANO INDUSTRIES INC
9922 Tabor Pl, Santa Fe Springs (90670-3300)
PHONE......................562 777-8180
Hoberto Serrano Jr, *President*
Bobby Serrano, *Vice Pres*
Maria Serrano, *Vice Pres*
Daniel Mota, *General Mgr*
Jorge Ballesteros, *Purchasing*
EMP: 34

SQ FT: 30,000
SALES (est): 8.1MM Privately Held
WEB: www.serrano-ind.com
SIC: 3599 Machine shop, jobbing & repair

(P-16941)
SHARKEY TECHNOLOGY GROUP INC
Also Called: C and T Machining
39450 3rd St E Ste 154, Palmdale (93550-3253)
PHONE......................661 267-2118
John P Sharkey, *Treasurer*
Judy Sharkey, *President*
EMP: 10
SQ FT: 5,000
SALES (est): 1.2MM Privately Held
SIC: 3599 Machine shop, jobbing & repair

(P-16942)
SHARP DIMENSION INC
4240 Business Center Dr, Fremont (94538-6356)
PHONE......................510 656-8938
Scott Vo, *President*
Tracy Tran, *Human Res Mgr*
EMP: 21
SQ FT: 12,000
SALES (est): 4.4MM Privately Held
WEB: www.sharpdimension.com
SIC: 3599 Machine shop, jobbing & repair

(P-16943)
SHEFFIELD MANUFACTURING INC
13849 Magnolia Ave, Chino (91710-7028)
PHONE......................818 767-4948
Dave Hilton, *CEO*
EMP: 40 EST: 2013
SALES (est): 6.8MM Privately Held
SIC: 3599 3444 Machine shop, jobbing & repair; sheet metalwork

(P-16944)
SHERMAN CORPORATION
10803 Los Jardines E, Fountain Valley (92708-3936)
PHONE......................310 671-2117
Helen Sherman, *President*
Darlene Williams, *Vice Pres*
Barbara Halvorsen, *Admin Sec*
EMP: 27
SQ FT: 14,000
SALES (est): 3.8MM Privately Held
SIC: 3599

(P-16945)
SHORT RUN SWISS INC
714 E Edna Pl, Covina (91723-1408)
PHONE......................626 974-9373
Paul Ellis, *President*
Bud Ellis, *Vice Pres*
EMP: 10
SQ FT: 4,650
SALES (est): 800K Privately Held
WEB: www.shortrunswiss.com
SIC: 3599 Machine shop, jobbing & repair

(P-16946)
SIERRA PACIFIC MACHINING INC
530 Parrott St, San Jose (95112-4120)
PHONE......................408 924-0281
Richard Wagner, *President*
Steven Young, *Vice Pres*
EMP: 18
SALES (est): 2.7MM Privately Held
SIC: 3599 Machine shop, jobbing & repair

(P-16947)
SIX SIGMA PRECISION INC
7706 Bell Rd Ste C, Windsor (95492-8546)
PHONE......................707 836-0869
Dan E McCrady, *CEO*
Patrick A McCrady, *CFO*
EMP: 10
SQ FT: 4,000
SALES (est): 1.8MM Privately Held
SIC: 3599 Machine shop, jobbing & repair

(P-16948)
SMI CA INC
Also Called: Saeilo Manufacturing Inds
14340 Iseli Rd, Santa Fe Springs (90670-5204)
PHONE......................562 926-9407
Katsuhiko Tsukamoto, *CEO*
David Tsukamoto, *President*
Erik Kawakami, *Corp Secy*
EMP: 26
SQ FT: 10,000
SALES (est): 4.4MM
SALES (corp-wide): 18.4MM Privately Held
WEB: www.saeilo-smi.com
SIC: 3599 Machine & other job shop work
PA: Saeilo Enterprises Inc
    105 Kahr Ave
    Greeley PA 18425
    845 735-6500

(P-16949)
SMITH BROTHERS MANUFACTURING
5304 Banks St, San Diego (92110-4008)
PHONE......................619 296-3171
Larry D Smith, *President*
Karen Amberg, *Treasurer*
Billie L Mc Farland, *Vice Pres*
EMP: 18 EST: 1945
SQ FT: 5,700
SALES (est): 2.8MM Privately Held
WEB: www.smithbrosmfg.com
SIC: 3599 3548 Machine shop, jobbing & repair; electrodes, electric welding

(P-16950)
SOLO ENTERPRISE CORP
Also Called: Solo Golf
220 N California Ave, City of Industry (91744-4323)
PHONE......................626 961-3591
Richard F Mugica, *CEO*
Edward A Mugica, *VP Mfg*
EMP: 50
SQ FT: 20,000
SALES (est): 8MM Privately Held
SIC: 3599 3812 Machine shop, jobbing & repair; search & navigation equipment

(P-16951)
SONFARREL INC
3000 E La Jolla St 3010, Anaheim (92806-1388)
PHONE......................714 630-7286
Kent Andersson, *COO*
Aurora Kerley, *President*
EMP: 100 EST: 1956
SQ FT: 120,000
SALES (est): 21.8MM Privately Held
WEB: www.sonfarrel.com
SIC: 3599 3469 3444 3061 Machine & other job shop work; machine parts, stamped or pressed metal; sheet metalwork; mechanical rubber goods

(P-16952)
SOUTH ALLIANCE INDUSTRIAL MCH
2423 Troy Ave, South El Monte (91733-1431)
PHONE......................626 442-3744
Miguel Hidalgo, *President*
EMP: 10
SQ FT: 9,000
SALES: 1MM Privately Held
SIC: 3599 Machine shop, jobbing & repair

(P-16953)
SOUTH BAY SOLUTIONS INC (PA)
Also Called: SBS
37399 Centralmont Pl, Fremont (94536-6549)
PHONE......................650 843-1800
Adam Drewniany, *CEO*
George Chow, *CFO*
Parveen Johal, *CTO*
Renato Garofani, *Mfg Mgr*
EMP: 30
SQ FT: 20,000
SALES (est): 16.6MM Privately Held
WEB: www.southbaysolutions.com
SIC: 3599 Machine shop, jobbing & repair

(P-16954)
SOUTHERN CAL TCHNICAL ARTS INC
370 E Crowther Ave, Placentia (92870-6419)
PHONE.....................714 524-2626
John H Robson IV, *President*
Matt Robson, *COO*
Kristi A Robson, *CFO*
Christine Robson, *Corp Secy*
Paul Kiralla, *Admin Asst*
EMP: 48
SQ FT: 9,400
SALES (est) 8.9MM **Privately Held**
WEB: www.technicalarts.com
SIC: 3599 3827 Machine shop, jobbing & repair; optical instruments & lenses

(P-16955)
SPACETRON METAL BILLOWS CORP
15303 Ventura Blvd # 900, Sherman Oaks (91403-3110)
PHONE.....................818 633-1075
Naborina Martinez, *President*
Lawrence Miller, *CFO*
Rick Montoya, *Senior VP*
EMP: 15
SQ FT: 12,000
SALES (est): 1.1MM **Privately Held**
SIC: 3599 Bellows, industrial: metal

(P-16956)
SPARTAN MANUFACTURING CO
7081 Patterson Dr, Garden Grove (92841-1435)
PHONE.....................714 894-1955
R J Horton, *President*
Terry Danielson, *Vice Pres*
EMP: 26 **EST:** 1957
SQ FT: 16,000
SALES (est): 5.4MM **Privately Held**
WEB: www.spartanmfg.com
SIC: 3599 Machine shop, jobbing & repair

(P-16957)
SPEC ENGINEERING CO INC
13754 Saticoy St, Van Nuys (91402-6518)
PHONE.....................818 780-3045
Gregory Viksman, *President*
Anna Viksman, *Vice Pres*
EMP: 25
SQ FT: 5,200
SALES: 3.5MM **Privately Held**
SIC: 3599 3412 Machine shop, jobbing & repair; metal barrels, drums & pails

(P-16958)
SPECIALTY SURFACE GRINDING
345 W 131st St, Los Angeles (90061-1103)
PHONE.....................310 538-4352
Piero Casadio, *President*
Jone Casadio, *Corp Secy*
EMP: 15
SQ FT: 11,000
SALES: 700K **Privately Held**
SIC: 3599 Grinding castings for the trade; machine shop, jobbing & repair

(P-16959)
SPENCO MACHINE & MANUFACTURING
27556 Commerce Center Dr, Temecula (92590-2518)
PHONE.....................951 699-5566
Robert L Spencer, *Owner*
EMP: 14
SQ FT: 11,000
SALES (est): 1.9MM **Privately Held**
WEB: www.spencomachine.com
SIC: 3599 Machine shop, jobbing & repair

(P-16960)
SPIN TEK MACHINING INC
540 Parrott St Ste A, San Jose (95112-4124)
PHONE.....................408 298-8223
Trung Nguyen, *Principal*
EMP: 15
SALES (est): 1.9MM **Privately Held**
SIC: 3599 Machine shop, jobbing & repair

(P-16961)
SQUAGLIA MANUFACTURING (PA)
275 Polaris Ave, Mountain View (94043-4588)
PHONE.....................650 965-9644
Pat Pellizzari, *President*
Ken Pellizzari, *Vice Pres*
EMP: 22 **EST:** 1962
SQ FT: 10,000
SALES (est): 4.2MM **Privately Held**
WEB: www.squaglia.com
SIC: 3599 Machine shop, jobbing & repair

(P-16962)
SR MACHINING INC
692 Parkridge Ave, Norco (92860-3124)
PHONE.....................951 520-9486
EMP: 10 **EST:** 2017
SALES (est): 1.1MM **Privately Held**
SIC: 3599 Machine shop, jobbing & repair

(P-16963)
SRCO INC
2305 Merced Ave, El Monte (91733-2624)
PHONE.....................626 350-8321
John Barkune, *President*
Van Roush, *Vice Pres*
Ann Skinner, *Office Mgr*
EMP: 10 **EST:** 1975
SQ FT: 6,200
SALES (est): 1.7MM **Privately Held**
SIC: 3599 Machine shop, jobbing & repair

(P-16964)
STAR PRODUCTS
312 Brokaw Rd, Santa Clara (95050-4336)
PHONE.....................408 727-8421
Jody Kidambi,
EMP: 35
SALES: 950K **Privately Held**
SIC: 3599 Machine shop, jobbing & repair

(P-16965)
STAR TOOL & ENGINEERING CO INC
49235 Milmont Dr, Fremont (94538-7349)
PHONE.....................510 742-0500
Darren Myers, *CEO*
Angelo Grestoni, *President*
John S Winter, *Vice Pres*
EMP: 48
SQ FT: 40,000
SALES (est): 4.2MM **Privately Held**
WEB: www.startoolusa.com
SIC: 3599 3566 3469 3544 Gears, power transmission, except automotive; machine shop, jobbing & repair; stamping metal for the trade; special dies & tools

(P-16966)
STEVEN VARRATI
Also Called: Acme Machine Products
5237 American Ave, Modesto (95356-9022)
PHONE.....................209 545-0107
Steven Varrati, *Owner*
EMP: 10 **EST:** 1957
SQ FT: 10,000
SALES (est): 747.6K **Privately Held**
SIC: 3599 Machine shop, jobbing & repair

(P-16967)
STIGTEC MANUFACTURING LLC
1125 Linda Vista Dr # 110, San Marcos (92078-3819)
PHONE.....................760 744-7239
Ed Stiglic,
Teresa Stiglic, *Co-Owner*
Jennifer Welch, *CFO*
Shaylee Welch, *General Mgr*
Lance Guddee, *Prgrmr*
EMP: 19
SQ FT: 10,000
SALES (est): 2.2MM **Privately Held**
WEB: www.stigtec.com
SIC: 3599 Machine shop, jobbing & repair

(P-16968)
STINES MACHINE INC
2481 Coral St, Vista (92081-8431)
PHONE.....................760 599-9955
Edward L Huston, *President*
Tri Tran, *Vice Pres*
EMP: 35

SQ FT: 15,000
SALES (est): 6.4MM **Privately Held**
WEB: www.stinesmachine.com
SIC: 3599 Machine shop, jobbing & repair

(P-16969)
SUMMIT MACHINE LLC
2880 E Philadelphia St, Ontario (91761-8523)
PHONE.....................909 923-2744
▼ **EMP:** 120
SQ FT: 103,000
SALES: 20MM
SALES (corp-wide): 242.1B **Publicly Held**
WEB: www.summitmachining.com
SIC: 3599 3728 Machine shop, jobbing & repair; aircraft parts & equipment
HQ: Precision Castparts Corp.
4650 Sw Mcdam Ave Ste 300
Portland OR 97239
503 946-4800

(P-16970)
SUN PRECISION MACHINING INC
1651 Market St Ste A, Corona (92880-1710)
PHONE.....................951 817-0056
Eric Zembower, *President*
EMP: 17
SALES (est): 2.6MM **Privately Held**
SIC: 3599 Machine shop, jobbing & repair

(P-16971)
SUNLAND TOOL INC
1819 N Case St, Orange (92865-4234)
PHONE.....................714 974-6500
Douglas P Brown, *President*
EMP: 10 **EST:** 1967
SQ FT: 10,000
SALES (est): 760K **Privately Held**
SIC: 3599 Machine shop, jobbing & repair

(P-16972)
SUNVAIR INC (HQ)
29145 The Old Rd, Valencia (91355-1015)
PHONE.....................661 294-3777
Robert Dann, *President*
Melba Waschak, *Corp Secy*
Edward Waschak, *Vice Pres*
Seth Schornick, *QC Mgr*
Bob Byrd, *Production*
EMP: 65
SQ FT: 26,000
SALES (est): 19.9MM
SALES (corp-wide): 30MM **Privately Held**
WEB: www.sunvair.com
SIC: 3599 7699 Machine shop, jobbing & repair; aircraft & heavy equipment repair services
PA: Sunvair Aerospace Group, Inc.
29145 The Old Rd
Valencia CA 91355
661 294-3777

(P-16973)
SUPER MACHINING INC
2008 S Susan St, Santa Ana (92704-4415)
PHONE.....................714 662-2021
Tony Cao, *President*
Tian Tsu, *Shareholder*
Mort Evans, *Vice Pres*
Mindyv Ha, *Vice Pres*
EMP: 10
SQ FT: 9,000
SALES (est): 800K **Privately Held**
SIC: 3599 Machine shop, jobbing & repair

(P-16974)
SUPREME MACHINE PRODUCTS INC
302 Sequoia Ave, Ontario (91761-1543)
PHONE.....................909 974-0349
Harold Hal Peterson, *President*
Isac Gomez, *Vice Pres*
Lyn Kaplan, *Manager*
EMP: 18
SQ FT: 7,800
SALES (est): 2.9MM **Privately Held**
SIC: 3599 Machine shop, jobbing & repair

(P-16975)
SURFACE MANUFACTURING INC
2025 Airpark Ct Ste 10, Auburn (95602-9069)
PHONE.....................530 885-0700
Lee Baker, *President*
Richard Peattie, *CFO*
Jane Peattie, *Corp Secy*
EMP: 16
SQ FT: 10,000
SALES (est): 2.2MM **Privately Held**
WEB: www.surfacemfg.com
SIC: 3599 3577 Machine shop, jobbing & repair; computer peripheral equipment

(P-16976)
SUST MANUFACTURING COMPANY
2380 Wilcox Rd, Stockton (95215-2318)
PHONE.....................209 931-9571
Peter Sust, *President*
EMP: 10
SQ FT: 5,000
SALES (est): 1.2MM **Privately Held**
SIC: 3599 Machine shop, jobbing & repair

(P-16977)
SUTTER P DAHLGLEN ENTPS INC
Also Called: Metalfab
1650 Grant St, Santa Clara (95050-3981)
PHONE.....................408 727-4640
Linda Terestra, *President*
Jack Paravagna, *President*
EMP: 16
SQ FT: 16,000
SALES (est): 2.8MM **Privately Held**
SIC: 3599 1611 Machine & other job shop work; grading

(P-16978)
SWISS SCREW PRODUCTS INC
339 Mathew St, Santa Clara (95050-3113)
PHONE.....................408 748-8400
Sung H Hwang, *President*
Mike Hwang, *Vice Pres*
Young S Hwang, *Vice Pres*
EMP: 25
SQ FT: 12,750
SALES (est): 4.2MM **Privately Held**
WEB: www.swissscrew.com
SIC: 3599 3541 3451 Machine shop, jobbing & repair; machine tools, metal cutting type; screw machine products

(P-16979)
SWISS WIRE EDM
3505 Cadillac Ave Ste J1, Costa Mesa (92626-1432)
PHONE.....................714 540-2903
Malcolm Schneer, *President*
Nola Schneer, *Vice Pres*
Wazida Muneshwar, *Manager*
EMP: 15
SQ FT: 10,000
SALES (est): 3.2MM **Privately Held**
WEB: www.swedm.com
SIC: 3599 Electrical discharge machining (EDM); machine shop, jobbing & repair

(P-16980)
T & M MACHINING INC
331 Irving Dr, Oxnard (93030-5172)
PHONE.....................805 983-6716
Mario Mangone, *President*
Kay Mangone, *Controller*
EMP: 20
SALES (est): 2.5MM **Privately Held**
SIC: 3599 3544 Machine shop, jobbing & repair; special dies, tools, jigs & fixtures

(P-16981)
T C QUALITY MACHINING INC
12155 Magnolia Ave 10d, Riverside (92503-4905)
PHONE.....................951 509-4633
Dale Caldwell, *President*
Michael Taylor, *CEO*
Theresa A Taylor, *Principal*
Ronda A Caldwell, *Admin Sec*
EMP: 12 **EST:** 1997
SQ FT: 6,500
SALES (est): 1.9MM **Privately Held**
SIC: 3599 Machine shop, jobbing & repair

(P-16982)
T E B INC
8754 Lion St, Rancho Cucamonga
(91730-4427)
PHONE.................................909 941-8100
Michael Harding, *President*
EMP: 15 **EST:** 1961
SQ FT: 8,500
SALES (est): 2MM **Privately Held**
SIC: 3599 Machine shop, jobbing & repair

(P-16983)
T T E PRODUCTS INC
1701 Fortune Dr Ste N, San Jose
(95131-1702)
PHONE.................................408 955-0100
Sherman K Chu, *President*
EMP: 10
SQ FT: 2,500
SALES (est): 1.2MM **Privately Held**
SIC: 3599 Machine & other job shop work

(P-16984)
T&T PRECISION MACHINING
9812 Atlantic Ave, South Gate
(90280-5219)
PHONE.................................323 583-0064
German Torres, *Principal*
EMP: 11
SALES (est): 1.2MM **Privately Held**
SIC: 3599 Machine shop, jobbing & repair

(P-16985)
T/Q SYSTEMS INC
25131 Arctic Ocean Dr, Lake Forest
(92630-8852)
PHONE.................................949 455-0478
Victor Buytkus, *President*
Scott Moebius, *Vice Pres*
EMP: 42
SALES: 7.1MM **Privately Held**
WEB: www.tqsystems.net
SIC: 3599 Machine shop, jobbing & repair

(P-16986)
TALOS CORPORATION
Also Called: Paramount Tool & Machine Co
512 2nd Ave, Redwood City (94063-3848)
PHONE.................................650 364-7364
Gerald G Popplewell, *President*
Adelina Popplewell, *Treasurer*
EMP: 20
SQ FT: 20,000
SALES: 1.5MM **Privately Held**
WEB: www.talosinstruments.com
SIC: 3599 Machine shop, jobbing & repair

(P-16987)
TAPEMATION MACHINING INC (PA)
13 Janis Way, Scotts Valley (95066-3537)
PHONE.................................831 438-3069
Ericka Stevens, *President*
Josolyn Bradshaw, *Vice Pres*
EMP: 12 **EST:** 1961
SALES (est): 4.2MM **Privately Held**
WEB: www.tapemation.com
SIC: 3599 Machine shop, jobbing & repair

(P-16988)
TCT ADVANCED MACHINING INC
2454 Fender Ave Ste C, Fullerton
(92831-4320)
PHONE.................................714 871-9371
James Chang, *President*
EMP: 14
SQ FT: 2,400
SALES (est): 878.4K **Privately Held**
SIC: 3599 Machine shop, jobbing & repair

(P-16989)
TECFAR MANUFACTURING INC
8525 Telfair Ave, Sun Valley (91352-3928)
PHONE.................................818 767-0677
Joe Simpson, *President*
Charles Ahn, *CEO*
Sandy Ahn, *CFO*
Oscar Echeverry, *Executive*
Joe Richardson, *Prdtn Mgr*
EMP: 17
SQ FT: 8,500
SALES: 900K **Privately Held**
WEB: www.tecfar.net
SIC: 3599 Machine shop, jobbing & repair

(P-16990)
TECH-STAR INDUSTRIES INC
1171 Sonora Ct, Sunnyvale (94086-5384)
PHONE.................................650 369-7214
James Stephens, *President*
Lolo Stephens, *CFO*
Mike Walker, *General Mgr*
▲ **EMP:** 12
SQ FT: 9,000
SALES (est): 2.1MM **Privately Held**
WEB: www.techstarindustries.com
SIC: 3599 Machine shop, jobbing & repair

(P-16991)
TECHNICAL TROUBLE SHOOTING INC
27822 Fremont Ct B, Valencia
(91355-1130)
PHONE.................................661 257-1202
Sergey Levkov, *President*
EMP: 20
SQ FT: 15,000
SALES (est): 3.1MM **Privately Held**
SIC: 3599 Bellows, industrial: metal; propellers, ship & boat: machined

(P-16992)
TECHNIFORM INTERNATIONAL CORP
375 S Cactus Ave, Rialto (92376-6320)
PHONE.................................909 877-6886
Richard S Jones, *President*
Jon Harrison, *VP Opers*
EMP: 105
SQ FT: 60,000
SALES (est): 12.7MM **Privately Held**
SIC: 3599 3469 3444 Machine shop, jobbing & repair; metal stampings; sheet metalwork

(P-16993)
TECNO INDUSTRIAL ENGINEERING
13528 Pumice St, Norwalk (90650-5249)
PHONE.................................562 623-4517
Juan Giner, *President*
Enrique Viano, *Vice Pres*
EMP: 45
SQ FT: 17,000
SALES (est): 2.2MM **Privately Held**
WEB: www.tecnoest.net
SIC: 3599 3728 Machine shop, jobbing & repair; aircraft parts & equipment

(P-16994)
TEMPCO ENGINEERING INC
8866 Laurel Canyon Blvd A, Sun Valley
(91352-2998)
PHONE.................................818 767-2326
David Shushereba, *Principal*
EMP: 102 **EST:** 1966
SQ FT: 26,000
SALES: 12.9MM
SALES (corp-wide): 1MM **Privately Held**
WEB: www.lmiaerospace.com
SIC: 3599 Machine shop, jobbing & repair
HQ: Lmi Aerospace, Inc.
411 Fountain Lakes Blvd
Saint Charles MO 63301
636 946-6525

(P-16995)
TER INC
Also Called: T E R
306 Mathew St, Santa Clara (95050-3104)
PHONE.................................408 986-9920
Edward Cech III, *President*
Tom Cech, *Vice Pres*
Douglas Cech, *Prgrmr*
EMP: 30
SQ FT: 12,000
SALES (est): 4.2MM **Privately Held**
SIC: 3599 3444 Machine shop, jobbing & repair; sheet metalwork

(P-16996)
TER PRECISION MACHINING INC
306 Mathew St, Santa Clara (95050-3104)
PHONE.................................408 986-9920
Thomas Cech, *President*
Edward Cech III, *Principal*
Randall Cech, *Principal*
Daryl Gillum, *Sales Staff*
EMP: 25
SQ FT: 12,000

SALES (est): 4.2MM **Privately Held**
SIC: 3599 Machine shop, jobbing & repair

(P-16997)
TETRAD SERVICES INC
960 Diamond Ave, Red Bluff (96080-4358)
P.O. Box 8099 (96080-8099)
PHONE.................................530 527-5889
Roger Meyer, *CEO*
EMP: 12
SQ FT: 20,000
SALES (est): 2.4MM **Privately Held**
WEB: www.tetradservice.com
SIC: 3599 Machine shop, jobbing & repair

(P-16998)
THIESSEN PRODUCTS INC
Also Called: Jim's Machining
555 Dawson Dr Ste A, Camarillo
(93012-5085)
PHONE.................................805 482-6913
Jim Thiessen, *President*
Jay R Thiessen, *Treasurer*
Debra Thiessen, *Vice Pres*
David Whitaker, *Engineer*
Paul Platts, *Sls & Mktg Exec*
EMP: 130
SQ FT: 44,000
SALES (est): 26.1MM **Privately Held**
WEB: www.jimsusa.com
SIC: 3599 Machine shop, jobbing & repair

(P-16999)
THOMAS CNC MACHINING
23650 Via Del Rio, Yorba Linda
(92887-2714)
PHONE.................................714 692-9373
Kim Rose, *Owner*
EMP: 10
SQ FT: 11,000
SALES (est): 1MM **Privately Held**
SIC: 3599 Machine shop, jobbing & repair

(P-17000)
THUNDERBOLT MANUFACTURING INC
641 S State College Blvd, Fullerton
(92831-5115)
PHONE.................................714 632-0397
Minh Son To, *President*
EMP: 26
SQ FT: 5,800
SALES: 3MM **Privately Held**
SIC: 3599 Machine shop, jobbing & repair

(P-17001)
TIM GUZZY SERVICES INC
5136 Calmview Ave, Baldwin Park
(91706-1803)
P.O. Box 1457 (91706-7457)
PHONE.................................626 813-0626
Tim Guzzy, *President*
Mariana Guzzy, *Vice Pres*
Helene Pichardo, *Bookkeeper*
EMP: 11
SQ FT: 5,500
SALES (est): 1.9MM **Privately Held**
SIC: 3599 Machine shop, jobbing & repair

(P-17002)
TMX ENGINEERING AND MFG CORP
2141 S Standard Ave, Santa Ana
(92707-3034)
PHONE.................................714 641-5884
Souhil Toubia, *CEO*
Gus Toubia, *President*
Mauricio Escarcega, *Principal*
Steve Korn, *Principal*
Ali Ossaily, *General Mgr*
EMP: 75
SQ FT: 23,000
SALES (est): 16.5MM **Privately Held**
WEB: www.tmxengineering.com
SIC: 3599 3728 3544 Machine shop, jobbing & repair; aircraft parts & equipment; special dies, tools, jigs & fixtures

(P-17003)
TOMI ENGINEERING INC
414 E Alton Ave, Santa Ana (92707-4242)
PHONE.................................714 556-1474
Michael F Falbo, *CEO*
Anthony Falbo, *President*
EMP: 52 **EST:** 1975
SQ FT: 15,000

SALES (est): 10.4MM **Privately Held**
WEB: www.tomiengineering.com
SIC: 3599 Machine shop, jobbing & repair

(P-17004)
TORRANCE PRECISION MACHINING
Also Called: Torrance Manufacturing
9530 Owensmouth Ave Ste 8, Chatsworth
(91311-8026)
PHONE.................................818 709-7838
Fred Torrance, *President*
Lajauna Torrance, *CFO*
EMP: 13
SQ FT: 8,000
SALES (est): 1.9MM **Privately Held**
WEB: www.torranceprecision.com
SIC: 3599 Machine shop, jobbing & repair

(P-17005)
TOWER INDUSTRIES INC
Also Called: Allied Mechanical Products
1720 S Bon View Ave, Ontario
(91761-4411)
PHONE.................................909 947-2723
Mark Slater, *Manager*
EMP: 110
SQ FT: 60,794
SALES (corp-wide): 34.2MM **Privately Held**
SIC: 3599 Machine shop, jobbing & repair
PA: Tower Industries, Inc.
1518 N Endeavor Ln Ste C
Anaheim CA 92801
714 630-8145

(P-17006)
TRACET MANUFACTURING INC
40 Kirby Ave, Morgan Hill (95037-9391)
PHONE.................................408 779-8846
Tim Westmoreland, *President*
William Lattin, *Vice Pres*
EMP: 10
SQ FT: 5,000
SALES (est): 1.4MM **Privately Held**
WEB: www.tracet.com
SIC: 3599 Machine shop, jobbing & repair

(P-17007)
TREPANNING SPCIALTY A CAL CORP
Also Called: Trepanning Specialties
16201 Illinois Ave, Paramount
(90723-4903)
PHONE.................................562 408-0044
Donald B Laughlin, *President*
Patricia Laughlin, *Vice Pres*
▲ **EMP:** 23
SQ FT: 7,000
SALES: 2.1MM **Privately Held**
WEB: www.trepanningspec.com
SIC: 3599 Machine shop, jobbing & repair

(P-17008)
TRI STATE MANUFACTURING INC
27212 Burbank, El Toro (92610-2504)
PHONE.................................949 855-9121
Bill Smith, *President*
Deanna Smith, *Corp Secy*
EMP: 10
SQ FT: 5,000
SALES (est): 1.5MM **Privately Held**
SIC: 3599 Machine shop, jobbing & repair

(P-17009)
TRI-C MACHINE CORPORATION (PA)
Also Called: Tri C Machine Shop
520 Harbor Blvd, West Sacramento
(95691-2227)
PHONE.................................916 371-8090
Lilburn C Lamar Jr, *Principal*
L Lamar, *CFO*
Marion Lamar, *Vice Pres*
EMP: 10 **EST:** 1970
SQ FT: 12,000
SALES (est): 4.2MM **Privately Held**
SIC: 3599 3552 7389 Machine shop, jobbing & repair; fabric forming machinery & equipment; design services

(P-17010)
TRIAD BELLOWS DESIGN & MFG INC
2897 E La Cresta Ave, Anaheim (92806-1817)
PHONE..................................714 204-4444
Michael G Moore, *President*
Julianne Moore, *CFO*
EMP: 26
SALES (est): 1.6MM Privately Held
SIC: 3599 Bellows, industrial: metal

(P-17011)
TRIANGLE TOOL & DIE CORP
13189 Flores St, Santa Fe Springs (90670-4041)
PHONE..................................562 944-2117
Michael J Beyer, *Principal*
Barbara Beyer, *Vice Pres*
EMP: 15
SQ FT: 14,000
SALES (est): 2.2MM Privately Held
SIC: 3599 3542 Electrical discharge machining (EDM); die casting & extruding machines

(P-17012)
TRIDECS CORPORATION
3513 Arden Rd, Hayward (94545-3907)
PHONE..................................510 785-2620
Frank Schenkhuizen Sr, *Ch of Bd*
Frank Schenkhuizen Jr, *President*
Emma J Schenkhuizen, *Admin Sec*
John Homa, *QC Mgr*
EMP: 25
SQ FT: 15,000
SALES: 3MM Privately Held
WEB: www.tridecs.com
SIC: 3599 Machine shop, jobbing & repair

(P-17013)
TRONSON MANUFACTURING INC
3421 Yale Way, Fremont (94538-6171)
PHONE..................................408 533-0369
Michael Lieu, *President*
Jessica Lieu, *Manager*
▲ EMP: 20
SQ FT: 11,040
SALES (est): 2.6MM Privately Held
SIC: 3599 Machine shop, jobbing & repair

(P-17014)
TRU MACHINING
45979 Warm Springs Blvd, Fremont (94539-6765)
PHONE..................................510 573-3408
Quocthuy Truong, *President*
Diep Nguyen, *Director*
EMP: 15 EST: 2013
SALES (est): 122.7K Privately Held
SIC: 3599 3569 Industrial machinery; liquid automation machinery & equipment

(P-17015)
TRUE POSITION TECHNOLOGIES LLC
24900 Avenue Stanford, Valencia (91355-1272)
PHONE..................................661 294-0030
Allen Sumian, *President*
EMP: 82
SQ FT: 25,000
SALES (est): 11.9MM
SALES (corp-wide): 223.8MM Privately Held
WEB: www.truepositiontech.com
SIC: 3599 Machine shop, jobbing & repair
PA: Hbd Industries Inc
5200 Upper Metro
Dublin OH 43017
614 526-7000

(P-17016)
TRUE PRECISION MACHINING INC
175 Indstrial Way Bellton Buellton, Buellton (93427)
PHONE..................................805 964-4545
Todd Ackert, *President*
EMP: 22
SQ FT: 6,600
SALES: 3MM Privately Held
WEB: www.trueprecision.net
SIC: 3599 Machine shop, jobbing & repair

(P-17017)
TSCHIDA ENGINEERING
1812 Yajome St, NAPA (94559-1306)
PHONE..................................707 224-4482
Bruce Tschida, *President*
EMP: 10
SQ FT: 3,600
SALES (est): 1.7MM Privately Held
WEB: www.tschidaeng.com
SIC: 3599 Machine shop, jobbing & repair

(P-17018)
TTN MACHINING INC
9105 Olive Dr, Spring Valley (91977-2304)
PHONE..................................619 303-4573
Hung Troung, *President*
Thuy Truong, *Planning Mgr*
Phuc Truong, *VP Opers*
Samantha Truong, *Sales Staff*
EMP: 16
SALES (est): 2.5MM Privately Held
WEB: www.ttnmachining.com
SIC: 3599 Machine shop, jobbing & repair

(P-17019)
TURNKEY TECHNOLOGIES INC
Also Called: Accuvac Technology Division
4650 E 2nd St Ste C, Benicia (94510-1038)
P.O. Box 205 (94510-0205)
PHONE..................................707 745-9520
Satish Chohan, *President*
EMP: 21 EST: 1969
SQ FT: 24,000
SALES (est): 2MM Privately Held
WEB: www.accuvac.com
SIC: 3599 Machine shop, jobbing & repair

(P-17020)
TURRET LATHE SPECIALISTS INC
875 S Rose Pl, Anaheim (92805-5337)
PHONE..................................714 520-0058
Robert McBride, *President*
EMP: 18
SQ FT: 6,000
SALES (est): 2.9MM Privately Held
SIC: 3599 Machine shop, jobbing & repair

(P-17021)
TWO BEARS METAL PRODUCTS
723 N Meyler St, San Pedro (90731-1428)
PHONE..................................310 326-2533
Jeffrey Allen, *Owner*
EMP: 20
SALES (est): 1.5MM Privately Held
SIC: 3599 Machine shop, jobbing & repair

(P-17022)
UNITECH TOOL & MACHINE INC
3025 Stender Way, Santa Clara (95054-3216)
PHONE..................................408 566-0333
Ramin Lak, *CEO*
▲ EMP: 20
SALES (est): 3.2MM Privately Held
SIC: 3599 Machine shop, jobbing & repair

(P-17023)
UNITED DRILLING CO
11807 Slauson Ave, Santa Fe Springs (90670-2219)
PHONE..................................562 945-8833
Peter Arjona, *Owner*
Tony Flota, *Finance Mgr*
EMP: 24
SQ FT: 6,500
SALES (est): 2MM Privately Held
SIC: 3599 Machine shop, jobbing & repair

(P-17024)
UNITED WESTERN INDUSTRIES INC
3515 N Hazel Ave, Fresno (93722-4995)
PHONE..................................559 226-7236
L G Simmons, *President*
Bruce Ketch, *Purchasing*
EMP: 49 EST: 1971
SQ FT: 15,000
SALES (est): 8.3MM Privately Held
SIC: 3599 3469 3544 Custom machinery; machine shop, jobbing & repair; metal stampings; die sets for metal stamping (presses)

(P-17025)
UNIVERSAL PLANT SVCS CAL INC (HQ)
20545a Belshaw Ave, Carson (90746-3505)
PHONE..................................310 618-1600
Bradley Jones, *CEO*
Stewart Jones, *President*
Reagan Busbee, *COO*
EMP: 18
SALES (est): 8.9MM
SALES (corp-wide): 166.7MM Privately Held
SIC: 3599 Custom machinery
PA: Jones Industrial Holdings, Inc.
806 Seaco Ct
Deer Park TX 77536
281 479-6000

(P-17026)
URABE INCORPORATED
Also Called: Precision Plus
16742 Westfield Ln, Huntington Beach (92649-3689)
PHONE..................................714 377-9701
Dave Urabe, *President*
EMP: 12
SALES (est): 990K Privately Held
SIC: 3599 Machine shop, jobbing & repair

(P-17027)
V & S ENGINEERING COMPANY LTD
5766 Research Dr, Huntington Beach (92649-1617)
PHONE..................................714 898-7869
Dino Dukovic, *President*
Dino Dokovic, *President*
EMP: 15
SQ FT: 10,000
SALES (est): 2.5MM Privately Held
SIC: 3599 Machine shop, jobbing & repair

(P-17028)
V-TECH MANUFACTURING INC
Also Called: V Tech
1140 W Evelyn Ave, Sunnyvale (94086-5742)
PHONE..................................408 730-9200
Robert Gluchowski, *President*
Jamie Sandidge, *Office Mgr*
EMP: 15
SQ FT: 2,000
SALES (est): 2.1MM Privately Held
WEB: www.vtechmanufacturing.com
SIC: 3599 Machine shop, jobbing & repair

(P-17029)
VAL-AERO INDUSTRIES INC
25319 Rye Canyon Rd, Valencia (91355-1205)
PHONE..................................661 252-1047
EMP: 12
SQ FT: 4,800
SALES (est): 1.2MM Privately Held
SIC: 3599

(P-17030)
VALLEY PERFORATING LLC
3201 Gulf St, Bakersfield (93308-4905)
PHONE..................................661 324-4964
Mike Dover, *President*
Dorothy Reynolds, *Vice Pres*
Alice Lomas, *Admin Sec*
EMP: 65
SQ FT: 10,440
SALES (est): 10.7MM Privately Held
WEB: www.valleyperf.com
SIC: 3599 Machine shop, jobbing & repair

(P-17031)
VALLEY PRECISION INC
536 Hi Tech Pkwy, Oakdale (95361-9371)
PHONE..................................209 847-1758
Donald R Faubion, *President*
Michael P Faubion, *Admin Sec*
EMP: 11 EST: 1977
SQ FT: 5,000
SALES (est): 4.3MM Privately Held
SIC: 3599 3545 3544 Machine shop, jobbing & repair; machine tool accessories; special dies, tools, jigs & fixtures

(P-17032)
VALLEY TOOL & MFG CO INC
2507 Tully Rd, Hughson (95326-9824)
P.O. Box 220 (95326-0220)
PHONE..................................209 883-4093
Fred G Brenda, *CEO*
Carol Finn, *Corp Secy*
Vaughn Brenda, *Vice Pres*
Daniel C Finn, *Vice Pres*
Richard Kohl, *VP Opers*
▲ EMP: 40
SQ FT: 50,000
SALES (est): 9.8MM Privately Held
WEB: www.valleytoolmfg.com
SIC: 3599 Machine shop, jobbing & repair

(P-17033)
VALLEY TOOL AND MACHINE CO INC
111 Explorer St, Pomona (91768-3278)
PHONE..................................909 595-2205
Chuck Rogers, *CEO*
Jim Rogers, *President*
Nancy Larson, *Corp Secy*
EMP: 32 EST: 1982
SQ FT: 34,000
SALES (est): 5.8MM Privately Held
WEB: www.valleytool-inc.com
SIC: 3599 7692 3544 Machine shop, jobbing & repair; welding repair; special dies, tools, jigs & fixtures

(P-17034)
VALLIN ALIDA
Also Called: Mnd Engineering
12473 Gladstone Ave, Sylmar (91342-5300)
PHONE..................................818 361-9020
Daniel Vallin, *President*
Alida Vallin, *Principal*
EMP: 15
SQ FT: 5,000
SALES (est): 2MM Privately Held
SIC: 3599 Machine shop, jobbing & repair

(P-17035)
VALVEX ENTERPRISES INC
Also Called: DC Valve Mfg & Precision Mchs
885 Jarvis Dr, Morgan Hill (95037-2858)
PHONE..................................408 928-2510
Cuu Banh, *CEO*
Christine Dong, *Purch Agent*
EMP: 43
SQ FT: 3,200
SALES (est): 8.3MM Privately Held
WEB: www.dcvalvemfg.com
SIC: 3599 Machine shop, jobbing & repair

(P-17036)
VANDERHULST ASSOCIATES INC
3300 Victor Ct, Santa Clara (95054-2316)
PHONE..................................408 727-1313
Hank Vanderhulst, *CEO*
Sandy Thompson, *Vice Pres*
Corrie Vanderhulst, *Admin Sec*
EMP: 30 EST: 1975
SQ FT: 11,000
SALES (est): 3.5MM Privately Held
WEB: www.vanderhulst.com
SIC: 3599 Machine shop, jobbing & repair

(P-17037)
VANS MANUFACTURING INC
330 E Easy St Ste C, Simi Valley (93065-7526)
PHONE..................................805 522-6267
Louis Tignac, *President*
EMP: 19
SQ FT: 8,500
SALES (est): 2.4MM Privately Held
SIC: 3599 Custom machinery

(P-17038)
VEECO PROCESS EQUIPMENT INC
Slider Process Division
112 Robin Hill Rd, Goleta (93117-3107)
PHONE..................................805 967-2700
Ed Wagner, *Manager*
Peter Simone, *Bd of Directors*
Richard D'Amore, *Director*
Jim Young, *Director*
EMP: 70

PRODUCTS & SVCS

SALES (corp-wide): 484.7MM **Publicly Held**
SIC: 3599 3545 3544 3291 Machine shop, jobbing & repair; machine tool accessories; special dies, tools, jigs & fixtures; abrasive products
HQ: Veeco Process Equipment Inc.
1 Terminal Dr
Plainview NY 11803

(P-17039)
VELLIOS MACHINE SHOP INC
Also Called: Vellios Automotive Machine Sp
4625 29th Mnhattan Bch Bl, Lawndale (90260)
PHONE................................310 643-8540
Harry Vellios, *President*
Carolyn Vellios, *Corp Secy*
Mark Vellios, *Vice Pres*
EMP: 12
SQ FT: 6,500
SALES (est): 1.6MM **Privately Held**
SIC: 3599 3714 5013 Machine shop, jobbing & repair; rebuilding engines & transmissions, factory basis; automotive supplies & parts

(P-17040)
VESCIO THREADING CO
Also Called: Vescio Manufacturing Intl
14002 Anson Ave, Santa Fe Springs (90670-5202)
PHONE................................562 802-1868
Gregory Vescio, *CEO*
Robert Vescio, *President*
Greg Vescio, *CEO*
Bob Vescio, *CFO*
Verna Vescio, *Corp Secy*
EMP: 73
SQ FT: 13,000
SALES (est): 15.3MM **Privately Held**
WEB: www.vesciothreading.com
SIC: 3599 Machine shop, jobbing & repair

(P-17041)
VI-TEC MANUFACTURING INC
288 Boeing Ct, Livermore (94551-9258)
PHONE................................925 447-8200
James Vice, *President*
Linda Vice, *CFO*
EMP: 10
SQ FT: 12,000
SALES (est): 1.4MM **Privately Held**
WEB: www.vi-tec.com
SIC: 3599 Machine shop, jobbing & repair

(P-17042)
VIANH COMPANY INC
13841 A Better Way 10c, Garden Grove (92843-3930)
PHONE................................714 590-9808
Tam Nguyen, *President*
Vianh Nguyen, *CFO*
Jimmy Nguyen, *CTO*
Ann P Parras, *Manager*
EMP: 25
SQ FT: 8,000
SALES: 300K **Privately Held**
WEB: www.vianhcompany.com
SIC: 3599 Machine shop, jobbing & repair

(P-17043)
VISGER PRECISION INC
1815 Russell Ave, Santa Clara (95054-2035)
PHONE................................408 988-0184
Terrance M Visger, *President*
EMP: 18
SQ FT: 10,000
SALES (est): 2.8MM **Privately Held**
WEB: www.visger.com
SIC: 3599 Machine shop, jobbing & repair

(P-17044)
VMG ENGINEERING INC
1046 Griswold Ave, San Fernando (91340-1455)
P.O. Box 507 (91341-0507)
PHONE................................818 837-6320
Vicente Corona, *President*
Maribel Corona, *Corp Secy*
Marie Corona, *Vice Pres*
EMP: 10
SQ FT: 8,000

SALES (est): 1.7MM **Privately Held**
WEB: www.vmgengineering.com
SIC: 3599 3429 Machine shop, jobbing & repair; manufactured hardware (general)

(P-17045)
VULTURES ROW AVIATION LLC
Also Called: Vra Manufacturing
3152 Cameron Park Dr, Cameron Park (95682-7623)
PHONE................................530 676-9245
Charles Wahl, *Owner*
Carol Wahl,
EMP: 11 **EST:** 2010
SQ FT: 15,000
SALES (est): 1.4MM **Privately Held**
SIC: 3599 3724 3728 Machine & other job shop work; aircraft engines & engine parts; ailerons, aircraft

(P-17046)
W MACHINE WORKS INC
13814 Del Sur St, San Fernando (91340-3440)
PHONE................................818 890-8049
Marzel Neckien, *President*
Randy Neckien, *Vice Pres*
Omar Espinoza, *QC Mgr*
Cary Sklar, *Manager*
Anna Martirosyan, *Accounts Mgr*
EMP: 45
SQ FT: 25,000
SALES (est): 9MM **Privately Held**
WEB: www.wmachineworksinc.com
SIC: 3599 Machine shop, jobbing & repair

(P-17047)
WACKER DEVELOPMENT INC
36 Hollywood Ave, Los Gatos (95030-6235)
PHONE................................408 356-0208
Roland Wacker, *President*
Doris Wacker, *Treasurer*
EMP: 10
SQ FT: 16,000
SALES (est): 750K **Privately Held**
SIC: 3599 Machine shop, jobbing & repair

(P-17048)
WAHLCO INC
15 Marconi Ste B, Irvine (92618-2779)
PHONE................................714 979-7300
Alonso Munoz, *CEO*
Robert R Wahler, *CEO*
Dennis Nickel, *CFO*
Barry J Southam, *Exec VP*
Jeremy Vana, *Project Mgr*
◆ **EMP:** 106
SQ FT: 54,000
SALES (est): 36.7MM **Privately Held**
WEB: www.wahlcc.com
SIC: 3599 Custom machinery

(P-17049)
WALLACE E MILLER INC
Also Called: Micro-TEC
9155 Alabama Ave Ste B, Chatsworth (91311-5867)
PHONE................................818 998-0444
Gary Case, *President*
Roxanne Case, *Vice Pres*
EMP: 19
SQ FT: 8,000
SALES: 1.4MM **Privately Held**
WEB: www.microtecmfg.com
SIC: 3599 Machine shop, jobbing & repair

(P-17050)
WARD ENTERPRISES
10332 Trumbull St, California City (93505-1550)
P.O. Box 803231, Santa Clarita (91380-3231)
PHONE................................661 251-4890
Harry L Ward, *Owner*
EMP: 15
SQ FT: 16,000
SALES: 1.1MM **Privately Held**
SIC: 3599

(P-17051)
WARMELIN PRECISION PDTS LLC
12705 Daphne Ave, Hawthorne (90250-3311)
PHONE................................323 777-5003

Doug Horton, *President*
Avner Applbaum, *CFO*
Ron Bohannon, *Vice Pres*
Nelia Azelano, *Credit Mgr*
Sherri Henkel, *Senior Buyer*
EMP: 65
SQ FT: 50,000
SALES (est): 8.2MM
SALES (corp-wide): 21MM **Privately Held**
SIC: 3599 Machine shop, jobbing & repair
PA: Aerostar Aerospace Manufacturing, Llc
2688 E Rose Garden Ln
Phoenix AZ 85050
602 861-1145

(P-17052)
WATSONS PROFILING CORP
1460 S Balboa Ave, Ontario (91761-7609)
PHONE................................909 923-5500
James Watson, *President*
EMP: 13
SALES (est): 3MM **Privately Held**
SIC: 3599 Machine shop, jobbing & repair

(P-17053)
WATTS MACHINING INC
2339 Calle Del Mundo, Santa Clara (95054-1008)
PHONE................................408 654-9300
Doug Watts, *President*
Karen Watts, *Office Mgr*
EMP: 30
SQ FT: 17,000
SALES (est): 3.7MM **Privately Held**
WEB: www.wattsmachining.com
SIC: 3599 Machine shop, jobbing & repair

(P-17054)
WB MACHINING & MECH DESIGN
1670 Zanker Rd, San Jose (95112-1134)
PHONE................................408 453-5005
Max Ho, *CEO*
EMP: 22
SQ FT: 20,000
SALES: 5MM **Privately Held**
WEB: www.wema.com
SIC: 3599 3569 3699 Machine shop, jobbing & repair; assembly machines, nonmetalworking; electrical equipment & supplies

(P-17055)
WEBB-STOTLER ENGINEERING
1701 Commerce St, Corona (92880-1734)
PHONE................................951 735-2040
David Stotler, *Owner*
EMP: 10
SQ FT: 5,700
SALES (est): 740K **Privately Held**
SIC: 3599 Machine shop, jobbing & repair

(P-17056)
WELDMAC MANUFACTURING COMPANY
1451 N Johnson Ave, El Cajon (92020-1615)
PHONE................................619 440-2300
Marshall J Rugg, *President*
Barbara Bloomfield, *Corp Secy*
Robert L Rugg, *Vice Pres*
EMP: 122
SQ FT: 100,000
SALES (est): 29.6MM **Privately Held**
WEB: www.weldmac.com
SIC: 3599 3444 7692 Machine shop, jobbing & repair; sheet metalwork; brazing

(P-17057)
WES MANUFACTURING INC
3241 Keller St, Santa Clara (95054-2646)
PHONE................................408 727-0750
Garn Nelson, *CEO*
Carl Michaels, *Vice Pres*
Dennis Whightman, *Vice Pres*
EMP: 20
SALES (est): 4MM **Privately Held**
SIC: 3599 8711 Machine shop, jobbing & repair; consulting engineer

(P-17058)
WEST COAST FORM GRINDING
Also Called: Precision Corepins
2548 S Fairview St, Santa Ana (92704-5335)
PHONE................................714 540-5621
Adrian Calderon, *President*
Danny Deu Tran, *Treasurer*
Henry Busane, *Admin Sec*
EMP: 10
SQ FT: 3,000
SALES (est): 869.4K **Privately Held**
SIC: 3599 Grinding castings for the trade; machine shop, jobbing & repair

(P-17059)
WEST COAST MACHINING INC
14560 Marquardt Ave, Santa Fe Springs (90670-5121)
PHONE................................562 229-1087
Sonia Duran, *CEO*
Carolina Beas, *CFO*
EMP: 15
SQ FT: 18,000
SALES (est): 3.3MM **Privately Held**
WEB: www.westcoastmachining.com
SIC: 3599 Machine shop, jobbing & repair

(P-17060)
WESTCOAST GRINDING CORPORATION
Also Called: Accurate Double Disc Grinding
10517 San Fernando Rd, Pacoima (91331-2624)
PHONE................................818 890-1841
William C Birch, *President*
EMP: 15
SQ FT: 6,000
SALES: 1MM **Privately Held**
SIC: 3599 Machine shop, jobbing & repair

(P-17061)
WESTCOAST PRECISION INC
2091 Fortune Dr, San Jose (95131-1824)
PHONE................................408 943-9998
Sang A Nhin, *President*
Helen Nhin, *Principal*
Chieu Hoang, *Bookkeeper*
EMP: 45
SALES (est): 8.2MM **Privately Held**
SIC: 3599 3559 Machine shop, jobbing & repair; semiconductor manufacturing machinery

(P-17062)
WESTERN CNC INC
1001 Park Center Dr, Vista (92081-8340)
PHONE................................760 597-7000
Danny Ashcraft, *President*
April Ashcraft Ramirez, *Vice Pres*
Carolyn Ashcraft, *Admin Sec*
Tommy Asaro, *Engineer*
Wences De La Mora, *Engineer*
EMP: 100
SQ FT: 57,000
SALES (est): 20.2MM **Privately Held**
WEB: www.westerncnc.com
SIC: 3599 Machine shop, jobbing & repair

(P-17063)
WESTERN WIDGETS CNC INC
915 Commercial St, San Jose (95112-1440)
PHONE................................408 436-1230
Laszlo Molnar, *President*
Tony Fricano, *CEO*
EMP: 10
SQ FT: 7,000
SALES (est): 1.5MM **Privately Held**
SIC: 3599 Machine shop, jobbing & repair

(P-17064)
WESVAL INC
1621 N Orangethorpe Way, Anaheim (92801-1228)
P.O. Box 25508, Santa Ana (92799-5508)
PHONE................................714 870-0990
Norton Graham Jr, *President*
Norton L Graham Sr, *Treasurer*
EMP: 13
SQ FT: 7,000
SALES (est): 1.9MM **Privately Held**
WEB: www.wesval.com
SIC: 3599 Machine shop, jobbing & repair

(P-17065)
WHITTEN MACHINE SHOP
4770 S K St, Tulare (93274-7149)
PHONE....................559 686-3428
John Whitten, *President*
Larry Whitten, *Shareholder*
Steve Whitten, *Shareholder*
Geraldine Whitten, *Corp Secy*
Ron Whitten, *Vice Pres*
EMP: 13
SALES: 1.4MM **Privately Held**
WEB: www.whittenmachine.com
SIC: 3599 Machine shop, jobbing & repair

(P-17066)
WILCOX MACHINE CO
7180 Scout Ave, Bell Gardens
(90201-3202)
P.O. Box 2159, Bell (90202-2159)
PHONE....................562 927-5353
George Schofhauser, *President*
Jill Wigney, *Corp Secy*
Kurt Anderegg, *Vice Pres*
Tom Anderegg, *Vice Pres*
◆ **EMP:** 60 **EST:** 1955
SALES (est): 12.1MM **Privately Held**
WEB: www.wilcoxmachine.com
SIC: 3599 Machine shop, jobbing & repair;
  custom machinery

(P-17067)
WILKINSON MFG INC
332 Piercy Rd, San Jose (95138-1401)
PHONE....................408 809-7341
Douglas M Greene, *President*
EMP: 13
SQ FT: 4,400
SALES (est): 2.1MM **Privately Held**
WEB: www.wilkinsonmfg.com
SIC: 3599 Machine shop, jobbing & repair

(P-17068)
WILLIS MACHINE INC
200 Kinetic Dr, Oxnard (93030-7920)
PHONE....................805 604-4500
Harlan Willis, *President*
Allison Napp, *Opers Spvr*
Scott Ketchum, *Manager*
EMP: 23
SQ FT: 20,000
SALES (est): 3.9MM **Privately Held**
WEB: www.willismachine.com
SIC: 3599 Machine shop, jobbing & repair

(P-17069)
WILMINGTON MACHINE INC
Also Called: Wilmington Ironworks
432 W C St, Wilmington (90744-5714)
PHONE....................310 518-3213
Walter C Richards III, *President*
Elva Richards, *Treasurer*
J W Richards, *Admin Sec*
EMP: 14
SQ FT: 13,000
SALES (est): 2.4MM **Privately Held**
WEB: www.wilmingtonironworks.com
SIC: 3599 Machine shop, jobbing & repair

(P-17070)
WILSHIRE PRECISION PDTS INC
7353 Hinds Ave, North Hollywood
(91605-3704)
PHONE....................818 765-4571
Thomas G Lewis, *President*
Dana Lewis, *Corp Secy*
Shoshona Lewis, *Corp Secy*
Wendy Lewis, *Vice Pres*
John Seeley, *Managing Dir*
EMP: 31 **EST:** 1951
SQ FT: 10,000
SALES (est): 5.7MM **Privately Held**
WEB: www.wilshireprecision.com
SIC: 3599 3621 Machine shop, jobbing &
  repair; motors, electric; electric motor &
  generator auxiliary parts

(P-17071)
WIRE CUT COMPANY INC
6750 Caballero Blvd, Buena Park
(90620-1134)
PHONE....................714 994-1170
Milton M Thomas, *CEO*
Tina Thomas, *Corp Secy*
EMP: 30
SQ FT: 20,000

SALES (est): 5.8MM **Privately Held**
WEB: www.wirecut-co.com
SIC: 3599 Machine shop, jobbing & repair

(P-17072)
WMC PRECISION MACHINING
1234 E Ash Ave Ste A, Fullerton
(92831-5013)
PHONE....................714 773-0059
Richard Mourey, *President*
Leigh Thompson, *General Mgr*
EMP: 15
SQ FT: 10,000
SALES (est): 2.7MM **Privately Held**
SIC: 3599 Machine shop, jobbing & repair

(P-17073)
WOLFS PRECISION WORKS INC
3549 Haven Ave Ste F, Menlo Park
(94025-1070)
PHONE....................650 364-1341
Wolfgang Pohl, *President*
Karen Pohl, *Corp Secy*
EMP: 15
SQ FT: 5,000
SALES (est): 2.2MM **Privately Held**
WEB: www.wpw-inc.com
SIC: 3599 Machine shop, jobbing & repair

(P-17074)
WOODRUFF CORPORATION
109 Calle Mayor, Redondo Beach
(90277-6509)
PHONE....................310 378-1611
Ronald D Woodruff, *President*
Dan Watts, *Vice Pres*
EMP: 32
SQ FT: 16,000
SALES (est): 3.5MM **Privately Held**
SIC: 3599 Machine shop, jobbing & repair

(P-17075)
YOUNG MACHINE INC
Also Called: California Machine Specialties
12282 Colony Ave, Chino (91710-2095)
PHONE....................909 464-0405
Anand Jagani, *President*
Sofia Gomez, *Manager*
Gilbert Fresquez, *Consultant*
EMP: 19
SQ FT: 11,000
SALES (est): 3.6MM **Privately Held**
SIC: 3599 Machine shop, jobbing & repair

(P-17076)
YUHAS TOOLING & MACHINING
Also Called: Slawomira Sobczyk
1031 Pecten Ct, Milpitas (95035-6804)
PHONE....................408 934-9196
Slava Sobczyk, *CEO*
EMP: 13
SQ FT: 6,000
SALES: 1MM **Privately Held**
WEB: www.yuhasmachining.com
SIC: 3599 Machine shop, jobbing & repair

(P-17077)
ZET-TEK PRECISION MACHINING (PA)
Also Called: Zet-Tek Machining
22951 La Palma Ave, Yorba Linda
(92887-6701)
PHONE....................714 777-8770
Daniel Zettler, *CEO*
Sandra Rubino, *Vice Pres*
EMP: 15
SQ FT: 25,000
SALES (est): 3.8MM **Privately Held**
WEB: www.zet-tek.com
SIC: 3599 3444 Machine shop, jobbing &
  repair; sheet metalwork

**3612 Power, Distribution &
Specialty Transformers**

(P-17078)
ABBOTT TECHNOLOGIES INC
8203 Vineland Ave, Sun Valley
(91352-3956)
PHONE....................818 504-0644
Kerima Marie Batte, *CEO*

Yasmin Morales, *Admin Asst*
Lisa Daniels, *Purch Mgr*
Albert Rieker, *Opers Mgr*
John Batte, *Sales Associate*
EMP: 50
SQ FT: 12,000
SALES (est): 9.9MM **Privately Held**
WEB: www.abbott-tech.com
SIC: 3612 3559 3677 Transformers, ex-
  cept electric; electronic component mak-
  ing machinery; transformers power
  supply, electronic type

(P-17079)
ALECTRO INC
Also Called: Protech Systems
6770 Central Ave Ste B, Riverside
(92504-1443)
PHONE....................909 590-9521
Tim Stevens, *CEO*
Gail A Stephens, *President*
EMP: 15 **EST:** 1978
SQ FT: 18,000
SALES (est): 2.1MM **Privately Held**
WEB: www.protechsystems.com
SIC: 3612 1731 Transformers, except
  electric; safety & security specialization

(P-17080)
**ALGONQUIN POWER SANGER
LLC**
1125 Muscat Ave, Sanger (93657-4000)
P.O. Box 397 (93657-0397)
PHONE....................559 875-0800
Ian Robertson, *Mng Member*
Debra Garrison, *Admin Asst*
Bernie Reed, *Plant Mgr*
EMP: 22
SQ FT: 16,225
SALES (est): 5MM
SALES (corp-wide): 810.6MM **Privately
Held**
SIC: 3612 Power transformers, electric
PA: Algonquin Power & Utilities Corp
  354 Davis Rd
  Oakville ON L6J 2
  905 465-4500

(P-17081)
BERKELEY MAGNETICS INC
Also Called: B M I
1836 Stone Ave, San Jose (95125-1306)
PHONE....................408 292-2023
Suresh Sansguiri, *President*
Nahid Saman, *Corp Secy*
EMP: 25
SQ FT: 4,000
SALES (est): 2.9MM **Privately Held**
WEB: www.berkeleymagnetics.com
SIC: 3612 8711 Transformers, except
  electric; consulting engineer

(P-17082)
CALIFORNIA PAK INTL INC
1700 S Wilmington Ave, Compton
(90220-5116)
PHONE....................310 223-2500
Edward Kwon, *President*
Barry Casper, *Vice Pres*
Judy Kwon, *Finance Mgr*
Kevin Reagan, *Director*
▲ **EMP:** 20
SQ FT: 15,000
SALES (est): 3.5MM **Privately Held**
WEB: www.calpaks.com
SIC: 3612 Distribution transformers, elec-
  tric

(P-17083)
**CALIFORNIA ST UNI CHANNEL
ISLA**
45 Rincon Dr Unit 104a, Camarillo
(93012-8423)
PHONE....................805 437-2670
Erik Blaine, *Exec Dir*
EMP: 25
SQ FT: 5,000
SALES (est): 2.7MM **Privately Held**
SIC: 3612 Power & distribution transform-
  ers

(P-17084)
**CGR/THOMPSON INDUSTRIES
INC**
7155 Fenwick Ln, Westminster
(92683-5218)
PHONE....................714 678-4200
Michael B Baughan, *CEO*
Vince Corti, *General Mgr*
Kevin Rowan, *Sales Staff*
Diana McCullough, *Manager*
EMP: 70
SQ FT: 10,000
SALES (est): 11.7MM **Publicly Held**
SIC: 3612 Machine tool transformers
HQ: B/E Aerospace, Inc.
  1400 Corporate Center Way
  Wellington FL 33414
  561 791-5000

(P-17085)
CPI ADVANCED INC
Also Called: Enaba-Kbw USA
14708 Central Ave, Chino (91710-9502)
PHONE....................909 597-5533
Charles Pyong Cha, *President*
Yarnee Arias, *Manager*
▲ **EMP:** 120
SQ FT: 2,500
SALES (est): 14.4MM **Privately Held**
WEB: www.cpipower.com
SIC: 3612 Fluorescent lighting transform-
  ers

(P-17086)
**DATATRONIC DISTRIBUTION
INC**
28151 Us Highway 74, Romoland
(92585-8915)
P.O. Box 1580, Sun City (92585-1580)
PHONE....................951 928-2058
Paul Siu, *President*
Mark Robinson, *Vice Pres*
Randy Eller, *Admin Sec*
Gisela Anderson, *Controller*
Julie Henderson, *Purch Mgr*
▲ **EMP:** 19
SQ FT: 8,200
SALES (est): 4MM
SALES (corp-wide): 32.2MM **Privately
Held**
WEB: www.datatronics.com
SIC: 3612 Transformers, except electric
PA: Datatronic Limited
  19/F North Point Indl Bldg
  North Point HK
  256 484-77

(P-17087)
DATATRONICS ROMOLAND INC
28151 Us Highway 74, Menifee
(92585-8916)
P.O. Box 1579 (92585-1579)
PHONE....................951 928-7700
Paul Y Siu, *CEO*
Gisela Anderson, *Info Tech Mgr*
Kelly Casey, *Controller*
Dick Hewitt, *Plant Mgr*
Richard Holcomb, *QC Mgr*
▲ **EMP:** 75
SQ FT: 38,800
SALES: 12.2MM **Privately Held**
WEB: www.datatronicsromoland.com
SIC: 3612 3677 Transformers, except
  electric; inductors, electronic

(P-17088)
DELTA STAR INC
270 Industrial Rd, San Carlos
(94070-6212)
PHONE....................650 508-2850
Ivan Tepper, *President*
EMP: 275
SALES (corp-wide): 422.9MM **Privately
Held**
SIC: 3612 Transformers, except electric
PA: Delta Star, Inc.
  3550 Mayflower Dr
  Lynchburg VA 24501
  434 845-0921

(P-17089)
DIMA-TECH INC
301 W 28th St Ste W, National City
(91950-8734)
PHONE....................619 474-7006

(PA)=Parent Co (HQ)=Headquarters (DH)=Div Headquarters
✿ = New Business established in last 2 years

3612 - Power, Distribution & Specialty Transformers County (P-17090)

Paul Dimatteo, *President*
Thierry Dimatteo, *Vice Pres*
EMP: 22
SALES (est): 2MM **Privately Held**
WEB: www.dimatech.com
SIC: 3612 Control transformers

(P-17090)
DOW-ELCO INC
1313 W Olympic Blvd, Montebello
(90640-5010)
P.O. Box 669 (90640-0669)
PHONE....................................323 723-1288
Linda Su, *President*
Cecile SE Kay, *Vice Pres*
Grace Park, *Admin Sec*
Ronald Cheung, *Director*
Annie Su, *Director*
EMP: 25
SQ FT: 8,100
SALES (est): 4.9MM **Privately Held**
SIC: 3612 3829 3061 Vibrators, inter-
rupter; measuring & controlling devices;
mechanical rubber goods

(P-17091)
ENERGY CNVRSION
APPLCTIONS INC
Also Called: Eca
582 Explorer St, Brea (92821-3108)
PHONE....................................714 256-2166
Akbal Grewal, *CEO*
Robert De Luca, *Business Mgr*
Zafar Arain, *Mktg Dir*
EMP: 17
SQ FT: 10,000
SALES (est): 3.9MM **Privately Held**
WEB: www.eca-mfg.com
SIC: 3612 8748 Transformers, except
electric; telecommunications consultant

(P-17092)
FALCON ELECTRIC INC
5116 Azusa Canyon Rd, Baldwin Park
(91706-1846)
PHONE....................................626 962-7770
Arthur Seredian, *CEO*
Tina Banh, *Admin Asst*
Ron Seredian, *Sales Staff*
▲ **EMP:** 13
SALES (est): 3.1MM **Privately Held**
SIC: 3612 Transformers, except electric

(P-17093)
FENIX INTERNATIONAL INC
30 Cleveland St, San Francisco
(94103-4014)
PHONE....................................415 754-9222
Lyndsay Handler, *CEO*
Brian Warshawsky, *COO*
Jit Bhattacharya, *CTO*
Luke Hodgkinson, *Engineer*
Azra Skeljo, *Engineer*
EMP: 350
SALES (est): 4.8MM
SALES (corp-wide): 24.2B **Privately Held**
SIC: 3612 Transformers, except electric
PA: Engie
1 Place Samuel De Champlain
Courbevoie
144 220-000

(P-17094)
FORTRON/SOURCE
CORPORATION (PA)
23181 Antonio Pkwy, Rcho STA Marg
(92688-2652)
PHONE....................................949 766-9240
Jackson Wang, *President*
Tom Sullivan, *COO*
Charlie Shih, *Vice Pres*
Jeff Tseng, *Vice Pres*
Monica Mao, *Executive*
▲ **EMP:** 24
SQ FT: 10,000
SALES (est): 2.4MM **Privately Held**
SIC: 3612 3679 3577 Transformers, ex-
cept electric; power supplies, all types:
static; computer peripheral equipment

(P-17095)
FULHAM CO INC (DH)
12705 S Van Ness Ave, Hawthorne
(90250-3322)
PHONE....................................323 779-2980
Brian Wald, *President*

James Cooke, *CFO*
Deborah Knuckles, *CFO*
Mike Hu, *Vice Pres*
Harry Libby, *Vice Pres*
◆ **EMP:** 40
SQ FT: 48,000
SALES (est): 7MM
SALES (corp-wide): 1MM **Privately Held**
WEB: www.fulham.com
SIC: 3612 Ballasts for lighting fixtures

(P-17096)
GRAND GENERAL
ACCESSORIES MFG
1965 E Vista Bella Way, Rancho
Dominguez (90220-6106)
PHONE....................................310 631-2589
Shu-Hui Lin Huang, *CEO*
Sophia Huang, *Vice Pres*
Nan-Huang Huang, *Admin Sec*
Dinora Rivera, *Admin Asst*
Maggie Huang, *Info Tech Mgr*
▲ **EMP:** 39
SALES (est): 7.7MM **Privately Held**
SIC: 3612 5531 3713 Transformers, ex-
cept electric; truck equipment & parts;
truck & bus bodies

(P-17097)
HAMMOND POWER SOLUTIONS
INC
17715 S Susana Rd, Compton
(90221-5409)
PHONE....................................310 537-4690
Raymundo Regalado, *Manager*
EMP: 25
SALES (corp-wide): 203.2MM **Privately**
Held
WEB: www.hammondpowersolutions.com
SIC: 3612 Power transformers, electric
HQ: Hammond Power Solutions, Inc.
1100 Lake St
Baraboo WI 53913
608 356-3921

(P-17098)
HOME PORTAL LLC
Also Called: Future Home
3351 La Cienega Pl, Los Angeles
(90016-3116)
PHONE....................................310 559-6100
Murray S Kunis, *President*
EMP: 10
SQ FT: 5,000
SALES (est): 2.5MM **Privately Held**
WEB: www.futurehome.net
SIC: 3612 Voltage regulators, transmission
& distribution

(P-17099)
HYBRINETICS INC
Also Called: Voltage Valet Division
225 Sutton Pl, Santa Rosa (95407-8123)
P.O. Box 14399 (95402-6399)
PHONE....................................707 585-0333
Richard Rosa, *President*
▲ **EMP:** 95 **EST:** 1965
SQ FT: 15,000
SALES (est): 11.2MM **Privately Held**
WEB: www.voltagevalet.com
SIC: 3612 5064 3634 Voltage regu-
lating transformers, electric power; elec-
tric household appliances; irons; motors &
generators; irons, electric: household

(P-17100)
INTERCOM ENERGY INC
1330 Orange Ave 300-30, Coronado
(92118-2949)
PHONE....................................619 863-9644
Ernesto Pallares, *CEO*
EMP: 13
SALES (est): 1.2MM **Privately Held**
SIC: 3612 Transformers, except electric

(P-17101)
IXIA INC
5301 Stevens Creek Blvd, Santa Clara
(95051-7201)
PHONE....................................408 988-8703
Jack Harding, *Principal*
EMP: 26
SALES (est): 3.9MM **Privately Held**
SIC: 3612 Transformers, except electric

(P-17102)
JACKSON ENGINEERING
COMPANY
9411 Winnetka Ave A, Chatsworth
(91311-6035)
PHONE....................................818 886-9567
Ron Jackson, *President*
Dennis Elliott, *Vice Pres*
EMP: 40
SQ FT: 10,000
SALES (est): 9MM **Privately Held**
WEB: www.jacksonengineering.com
SIC: 3612 Electronic meter transformers

(P-17103)
JUSTIN INC
2663 Lee Ave, El Monte (91733-1411)
PHONE....................................626 444-4516
Frank Justin Jr, *President*
Jeffrey Ross Justin, *CEO*
Jeff Justin, *Vice Pres*
EMP: 50
SQ FT: 4,000
SALES (est): 11.3MM **Privately Held**
WEB: www.justininc.com
SIC: 3612 Specialty transformers

(P-17104)
LORAN INC
Also Called: Nightscaping Outdoor Lighting
1705 E Colton Ave, Redlands
(92374-4971)
PHONE....................................405 340-0660
Lavesta Locklin, *President*
▲ **EMP:** 42
SQ FT: 100,000
SALES (est): 6MM **Privately Held**
WEB: www.loraninc.com
SIC: 3612 3645 Transformers, except
electric; garden, patio, walkway & yard
lighting fixtures: electric

(P-17105)
MAGCOMP INC
1020 N Batavia St Ste T, Orange
(92867-5529)
PHONE....................................714 532-3584
Thang Nguyen, *Partner*
Huong Vu, *Partner*
John Nguyen, *Prdtn Mgr*
EMP: 10
SQ FT: 6,000
SALES (est): 1MM **Privately Held**
WEB: www.magcomp.com
SIC: 3612 Specialty transformers

(P-17106)
MGM TRANSFORMER CO
5701 Smithway St, Commerce
(90040-1583)
PHONE....................................323 726-0888
Patrick Gogerchin, *President*
Luis Otero, *Vice Pres*
Bianca Kaveh, *Director*
◆ **EMP:** 70
SQ FT: 40,000
SALES (est): 34.8MM **Privately Held**
WEB: www.mgm-transformer.com
SIC: 3612 Transformers, except electric

(P-17107)
MPS INDUSTRIES
INCORPORATED (PA)
19210 S Vermont Ave # 405, Gardena
(90248-4431)
PHONE....................................310 325-1043
Chiging Jean Wang, *President*
▲ **EMP:** 25
SQ FT: 25,000
SALES (est): 7.2MM **Privately Held**
SIC: 3612 3499 Power transformers, elec-
tric; magnets, permanent: metallic

(P-17108)
NRG ENERGY SERVICES LLC
100302 Yates Well Rd, Nipton (92364)
PHONE....................................702 815-2023
Dick Dusmely, *Manager*
EMP: 60 **Publicly Held**
SIC: 3612 Machine tool transformers
HQ: Nrg Energy Services Llc
990 Peiffers Ln
Harrisburg PA 17109

(P-17109)
ON-LINE POWER
INCORPORATED (PA)
Also Called: Power Services
14000 S Broadway, Los Angeles
(90061-1018)
PHONE....................................323 721-5017
Abbie Gougerchian, *President*
Brad Goodman, *General Mgr*
Vivian Meza, *Admin Asst*
Henry Baik, *Design Engr*
Sharon Fischer, *Natl Sales Mgr*
▲ **EMP:** 46
SQ FT: 36,000
SALES (est): 17.6MM **Privately Held**
WEB: www.onlinepower.com
SIC: 3612 3621 3613 3677 Transform-
ers, except electric; motors & generators;
regulators, power; electronic coils, trans-
formers & other inductors

(P-17110)
ON-LINE POWER
INCORPORATED
14000 S Broadway, Los Angeles
(90061-1018)
PHONE....................................323 720-4125
Raymond Clary, *Manager*
EMP: 60
SALES (corp-wide): 17.6MM **Privately**
Held
WEB: www.onlinepower.com
SIC: 3612 3679 Transformers, except
electric; power supplies, all types: static
PA: On-Line Power, Incorporated
14000 S Broadway
Los Angeles CA 90061
323 721-5017

(P-17111)
PACIFIC TRANSFORMER CORP
5399 E Hunter Ave, Anaheim (92807-2054)
PHONE....................................714 779-0450
Patrick A Thomas, *CEO*
Jim Richardson, *CFO*
Jackie Wood, *Executive*
Ray Artsdalen, *General Mgr*
Patrick Thomas, *General Mgr*
▲ **EMP:** 205
SQ FT: 37,000
SALES (est): 16.9MM **Privately Held**
WEB: www.pactran.com
SIC: 3612 Power transformers, electric

(P-17112)
PIONEER CUSTOM ELEC PDTS
CORP
10640 Springdale Ave, Santa Fe Springs
(90670-3843)
PHONE....................................562 944-0626
Geo Murickan, *President*
Stephen Paul, *COO*
Ian Ross, *Bd of Directors*
Richard Guerrero, *Regional Mgr*
Wilfredo Gonzalez, *Administration*
EMP: 68 **EST:** 2013
SALES: 18MM **Publicly Held**
SIC: 3612 Electronic meter transformers
PA: Pioneer Power Solutions, Inc.
400 Kelby St Ste 12
Fort Lee NJ 07024

(P-17113)
POWER PARAGON INC (HQ)
Also Called: Power Systems Group
901 E Ball Rd, Anaheim (92805-5916)
PHONE....................................714 956-9200
David R Riley, *President*
Bruce Moore, *President*
Michael R Allen, *Vice Pres*
Michael Benthale, *Vice Pres*
Klaus Kahrs, *Vice Pres*
▼ **EMP:** 585
SQ FT: 120,000
SALES (est): 155.8MM
SALES (corp-wide): 9.5B **Publicly Held**
WEB: www.powerparagon.com
SIC: 3612 3613 3621 3643 Transform-
ers, except electric; switchgear & switch-
board apparatus; motors & generators;
current-carrying wiring devices

▲ = Import ▼=Export
◆ =Import/Export

PA: L3 Technologies, Inc.
600 3rd Ave Fl 34
New York NY 10016
212 697-1111

(P-17114)
POWER PARAGON INC
Also Called: Power Magnetics
711 W Knox St, Gardena (90248-4410)
PHONE..................................310 523-4443
J J Garcia, *Manager*
EMP: 17
SALES (corp-wide): 9.5B **Publicly Held**
WEB: www.powerparagon.com
SIC: 3612 Transformers, except electric
HQ: Power Paragon, Inc.
901 E Ball Rd
Anaheim CA 92805
714 956-9200

(P-17115)
POWERTRONIX CORPORATION
1120 Chess Dr, Foster City (94404-1103)
PHONE..................................650 345-6800
Carl A Svensson, *CEO*
Mike Bradley, *Vice Pres*
John Scott, *Vice Pres*
Anita Svensson, *Admin Sec*
Milana Ram, *Electrical Engi*
◆ **EMP:** 25
SQ FT: 1,800
SALES (est): 5.9MM **Privately Held**
WEB: www.powertronix.com
SIC: 3612 Power & distribution transform-
ers

(P-17116)
PULSE ELECTRONICS INC (DH)
15255 Innovation Dr # 100, San Diego
(92128-3410)
PHONE..................................858 674-8100
Mark Twaalfhoven, *CEO*
Renuka Ayer, *CFO*
Mike Bond, *Senior VP*
John R D Dickson, *Senior VP*
John Houston, *Senior VP*
▲ **EMP:** 270
SQ FT: 49,750
SALES (est): 336.2MM
SALES (corp-wide): 652.7MM **Privately
Held**
WEB: www.pulseeng.com
SIC: 3612 3674 3677 Specialty trans-
formers; modules, solid state; filtration de-
vices, electronic
HQ: Pulse Electronics Corporation
15255 Innovation Dr # 100
San Diego CA 92128
858 674-8100

(P-17117)
QUALITY TRANSFORMER & ELEC
Also Called: Quality Transformer & Elec Co
963 Ames Ave, Milpitas (95035-6326)
PHONE..................................408 935-0231
Carl Clift, *CEO*
Frank W Hendershot, *President*
Adam Clouse, *General Mgr*
Dwight Ennis, *Info Tech Mgr*
Preston Hullen, *Design Engr*
EMP: 40 **EST:** 1964
SQ FT: 32,500
SALES (est): 12.3MM **Privately Held**
WEB: www.qte.com
SIC: 3612 Transformers, except electric

(P-17118)
RING LLC (HQ)
1523 26th St, Santa Monica (90404-3507)
PHONE..................................800 656-1918
Jamie Siminoff, *CEO*
▲ **EMP:** 300
SQ FT: 40,000
SALES (est): 165MM **Publicly Held**
SIC: 3612 5065 Doorbell transformers,
electric; security control equipment & sys-
tems

(P-17119)
RWNM INC
1240 Simpson Way, Escondido
(92029-1406)
PHONE..................................760 489-1245
Randy Allen Weisser, *President*
Nate Mullen, *Vice Pres*

▲ **EMP:** 55
SQ FT: 2,200
SALES (est): 9.1MM **Privately Held**
WEB: www.uniquelighting.com
SIC: 3612 Transformers, except electric

(P-17120)
SEMPRA GLOBAL (HQ)
488 8th Ave, San Diego (92101-7123)
PHONE..................................619 696-2000
Debra L Reed, *CEO*
Teresa Sasaki, *Executive Asst*
Jason Neely, *Database Admin*
Chris Ward, *Project Mgr*
Jennifer Ramp, *Manager*
EMP: 65
SALES (est): 44.2MM
SALES (corp-wide): 11.2B **Publicly Held**
SIC: 3612 Transformers, except electric
PA: Sempra Energy
488 8th Ave
San Diego CA 92101
619 696-2000

(P-17121)
SOMA MAGNETICS CORPORATION
585 S State College Blvd, Fullerton
(92831-5113)
PHONE..................................714 447-0782
Harry Sidhu, *President*
Soma Sidhu, *Vice Pres*
EMP: 20
SQ FT: 10,000
SALES (est): 1.1MM **Privately Held**
WEB: www.somamagnetics.com
SIC: 3612 3677 3496 5999 Transform-
ers, except electric; inductors, electronic;
cable, uninsulated wire: made from pur-
chased wire; electronic parts & equip-
ment; transformers, electric

(P-17122)
STARLINEOEM INC
3183 Airway Ave Ste 112f, Costa Mesa
(92626-4629)
PHONE..................................949 342-8889
Rosario Pozzi, *President*
EMP: 12
SALES (est): 1.7MM **Privately Held**
SIC: 3612 3613 Distribution transformers,
electric; panelboards & distribution
boards, electric

(P-17123)
STEWARD TERRA INC
4323 Palm Ave, La Mesa (91941-6528)
PHONE..................................619 713-0028
Christopher D'Avignon, *CEO*
EMP: 25
SALES (est): 1.6MM **Privately Held**
SIC: 3612 Transformers, except electric

(P-17124)
STREAMLINE AVIONICS INC
17672 Armstrong Ave, Irvine (92614-5728)
PHONE..................................949 861-8151
Daniel Frahm, *President*
Wally Sandberg, *Engineer*
EMP: 22
SALES (est): 3.8MM **Privately Held**
SIC: 3612 Transformers, except electric

(P-17125)
UTOPIA LIGHTING
2329 E Pacifica Pl, Compton (90220-6210)
PHONE..................................310 327-7711
▲ **EMP:** 14
SALES (est): 2.4MM **Privately Held**
SIC: 3612

(P-17126)
ZETTLER MAGNETICS INC
75 Columbia, Aliso Viejo (92656-1498)
PHONE..................................949 831-5000
Gunther Rueb, *CEO*
▲ **EMP:** 50
SQ FT: 80,000
SALES (est): 5.8MM **Privately Held**
WEB: www.buytransformers.com
SIC: 3612 Transformers, except electric
PA: Zettler Components, Inc.
75 Columbia
Orange CA 92868

3613 Switchgear & Switchboard Apparatus

(P-17127)
3M COMPANY
8357 Canoga Ave, Canoga Park
(91304-2605)
PHONE..................................818 882-0606
Clint Hinze, *Branch Mgr*
Chuck Brummer, *Engineer*
Howard Kaplan, *Engineer*
Debra Ladehoffguiles, *QC Mgr*
EMP: 10
SALES (corp-wide): 31.6B **Publicly Held**
SIC: 3613 Switchgear & switchboard appa-
ratus
PA: 3m Company
3m Center
Saint Paul MN 55144
651 733-1110

(P-17128)
ABD EL & LARSON HOLDINGS LLC (PA)
Also Called: Industrial Electric Mfg
48205 Warm Springs Blvd, Fremont
(94539-7654)
PHONE..................................510 656-1600
Ed Rossi, *President*
Cindy Goodsell, *CFO*
Bruce Baumann, *Exec VP*
Frank Cavezza, *Exec VP*
Doug Kristensen, *Exec VP*
▲ **EMP:** 25
SALES (est): 45MM **Privately Held**
SIC: 3613 Switchboards & parts, power;
switchboard apparatus, except instru-
ments; control panels, electric; switchgear
& switchgear accessories

(P-17129)
AEM (HOLDINGS) INC
6610 Cobra Way, San Diego (92121-4107)
PHONE..................................858 481-0210
Daniel H Chang, *Ch of Bd*
Xiang Ming LI, *Senior VP*
Caili Chang, *Vice Pres*
▲ **EMP:** 77
SQ FT: 45,000
SALES (est): 20.2MM **Privately Held**
WEB: www.aem-usa.com
SIC: 3613 3677 7699 Fuses & fuse
equipment; inductors, electronic; metal re-
shaping & replating services

(P-17130)
AGE INCORPORATED
14423 Marquardt Ave, Santa Fe Springs
(90670-5118)
PHONE..................................562 483-7300
Vasken Imasdounian, *President*
Annie Imasdounian, *Corp Secy*
Daniel Imasdounian, *Vice Pres*
▲ **EMP:** 35
SQ FT: 8,000
SALES (est): 3.8MM **Privately Held**
SIC: 3613 3625 Control panels, electric;
electric controls & control accessories, in-
dustrial

(P-17131)
BRILLIANT HOME TECHNOLOGY INC
241a S San Mateo Dr, San Mateo
(94401-4037)
PHONE..................................650 539-5320
Aaron Emigh, *CEO*
Brian Cardanha, *Vice Pres*
Steven Stanek, *CTO*
EMP: 11 **EST:** 2016
SQ FT: 2,000
SALES: 500K **Privately Held**
SIC: 3613 Switchgear & switchboard appa-
ratus

(P-17132)
BUFFALO DISTRIBUTION INC
30750 San Clemente St, Hayward
(94544-7131)
PHONE..................................510 324-3800
Earl I Ramer Jr, *CEO*
▲ **EMP:** 40

SALES (est): 3.5MM **Privately Held**
SIC: 3613 Distribution cutouts

(P-17133)
C M COMMON GROUND INC
888 Production Pl, Newport Beach
(92663-2810)
PHONE..................................949 646-9468
Mary Blair, *President*
Rich Labonte, *Vice Pres*
EMP: 12
SQ FT: 3,650
SALES: 1.7MM **Privately Held**
WEB: www.commongroundmarine.com
SIC: 3613 Control panels, electric

(P-17134)
CALHOUN & POXON COMPANY INC
5330 Alhambra Ave, Los Angeles
(90032-3485)
PHONE..................................323 225-2328
Garrett Calhoun, *President*
Lois Calhoun, *Vice Pres*
EMP: 15
SQ FT: 22,000
SALES (est): 1.7MM **Privately Held**
WEB: www.calhounandpoxon.com
SIC: 3613 Control panels, electric

(P-17135)
CHRONTROL CORPORATION (PA)
Also Called: Chron Trol
6611 Jackson Dr, San Diego (92119-3333)
P.O. Box 19537 (92159-0537)
PHONE..................................619 282-8686
James Durham, *CEO*
EMP: 10
SQ FT: 4,461
SALES (est): 950.8K **Privately Held**
WEB: www.chrontrol.com
SIC: 3613 3625 Time switches, electrical
switchgear apparatus; relays & industrial
controls

(P-17136)
COBEL TECHNOLOGIES INC
822 N Grand Ave, Covina (91724-2418)
PHONE..................................626 332-2100
Mike Warner, *President*
EMP: 20
SQ FT: 5,600
SALES (est): 1.4MM **Privately Held**
WEB: www.cobeltech.com
SIC: 3613 3625 Control panels, electric;
relays & industrial controls

(P-17137)
CROWN TECHNICAL SYSTEMS
13470 Philadelphia Ave, Fontana
(92337-7700)
PHONE..................................909 923-0900
Naim Siddiqui, *President*
Howard Siddiqui, *Vice Pres*
Jake Tibbetts, *Project Mgr*
Nabil Samara, *Electrical Engi*
Christopher Boyer, *Engineer*
▲ **EMP:** 210
SQ FT: 92,000
SALES: 42MM **Privately Held**
SIC: 3613 Control panels, electric

(P-17138)
CUSTOM CONTROL SENSORS LLC (PA)
Also Called: Custom Aviation Supply
21111 Plummer St, Chatsworth
(91311-4905)
P.O. Box 2516 (91313-2516)
PHONE..................................818 341-4610
Henry P Acuff, *President*
Thomas Pilgrim, *CFO*
Tom Pilgrim, *CFO*
Joann D Acuff, *Corp Secy*
Linda Ruiz, *Executive Asst*
EMP: 153
SALES (est): 31.4MM **Privately Held**
WEB: www.ccsdualsnap.com
SIC: 3613 3643 3625 Switches, electric
power except snap, push button, etc.; cur-
rent-carrying wiring devices; relays & in-
dustrial controls

(P-17139)
DAZ INC
Also Called: Duramar Interior Surfaces
2500 White Rd Ste B, Irvine (92614-6276)
PHONE.............................949 724-8800
Farhad Abdollahi, *President*
Tom Belcher, *Vice Pres*
Nikkisa Abdollahi, *Exec Dir*
EMP: 15
SQ FT: 60,000
SALES: 10MM **Privately Held**
SIC: 3613 Panelboards & distribution
boards, electric

(P-17140)
DIGITAL LOGGERS INC
2695 Walsh Ave, Santa Clara
(95051-0920)
PHONE.............................408 330-5599
▲ EMP: 34 EST: 2009
SQ FT: 21,000
SALES (est): 2.8MM **Privately Held**
SIC: 3613 3679

(P-17141)
**DOBLE ENGINEERING
COMPANY**
Also Called: Vanguard Instruments
1520 S Hellman Ave, Ontario (91761-7634)
PHONE.............................909 923-9390
Hai Nguyen, *Director*
EMP: 10
SALES (corp-wide): 685.7MM **Publicly
Held**
SIC: 3613 3825 Power circuit breakers;
electrical energy measuring equipment
HQ: Doble Engineering Company
85 Walnut St
Watertown MA 02472
617 926-4900

(P-17142)
DVTECH SOLUTION CORP
Also Called: Dvxtreme
13937 Magnolia Ave, Chino (91710-7033)
PHONE.............................909 308-0358
Daniel Wang, *CEO*
EMP: 10
SALES: 100K **Privately Held**
SIC: 3613 Switchboard apparatus, except
instruments; control panels, electric; dis-
tribution boards, electric

(P-17143)
ELECTRO SWITCH CORP
Also Called: Digitran
10410 Trademark St, Rancho Cucamonga
(91730-5826)
PHONE.............................909 581-0855
Robert M Pineau, *President*
George Nguyen, *Engineer*
Edgar Mancenido, *Purch Mgr*
Richard Zalac, *VP Sales*
EMP: 140
SALES (corp-wide): 88.3MM **Privately
Held**
WEB: www.electroswitch.com
SIC: 3613 3625 Switches, electric power
except snap, push button, etc.; control
panels, electric; industrial controls: push
button, selector switches, pilot
HQ: Electro Switch Corp.
775 Pleasant St Ste 1
Weymouth MA 02189
781 335-1195

(P-17144)
**ELECTRO-MECH COMPONENTS
INC (PA)**
1826 Floradale Ave, South El Monte
(91733-3689)
PHONE.............................626 442-7180
Walter Trumbull Jr, *President*
Terry Trumbull, *Vice Pres*
EMP: 10 EST: 1963
SQ FT: 7,500
SALES (est): 1.6MM **Privately Held**
WEB: www.electromechcomp.com
SIC: 3613 Switchgear & switchboard appa-
ratus

(P-17145)
ELECTRONIC STAMPING CORP
Also Called: Esc
19920 S Alameda St, Compton
(90221-6210)
PHONE.............................310 639-2120
Hang Up Moon, *President*
Madhu RAO, *CEO*
▲ EMP: 24
SQ FT: 42,000
SALES (est): 4MM **Privately Held**
WEB: www.electronic-stamping.com
SIC: 3613 3678 3469 Bus bar structures;
electronic connectors; metal stampings

(P-17146)
**HYDRA-ELECTRIC COMPANY
(PA)**
3151 N Kenwood St, Burbank
(91505-1052)
PHONE.............................818 843-6211
David E Schmidt, *CEO*
Len Torres, *COO*
Gerry Schauer, *CFO*
Austin Reed, *Design Engr*
Tim Wright, *Project Mgr*
EMP: 178
SQ FT: 90,000
SALES: 18.5MM **Privately Held**
SIC: 3613 Switches, electric power except
snap, push button, etc.

(P-17147)
**INERTIA ENGRG & MCH WORKS
INC**
6665 Hardaway Rd, Stockton
(95215-9700)
PHONE.............................800 791-9997
Dean C Sanders, *President*
Renee Arlt, *Manager*
EMP: 30
SQ FT: 100,000
SALES (est): 7.1MM **Privately Held**
WEB: www.inertiaworks.com
SIC: 3613 Switchgear & switchgear acces-
sories

(P-17148)
KREGO CORPORATION
Also Called: Panel Shop, The
12971 Arroyo St, San Fernando
(91340-1548)
PHONE.............................818 837-1494
Walter Krego, *President*
Cynthia Krego, *Treasurer*
Michael E Godinez, *Business Mgr*
Ann Baker, *Purchasing*
EMP: 10
SQ FT: 8,232
SALES (est): 2.5MM **Privately Held**
SIC: 3613 Panelboards & distribution
boards, electric

(P-17149)
KT INDUSTRIES INC
3203 Fletcher Dr, Los Angeles
(90065-2919)
PHONE.............................323 255-7143
Leonor Vaca, *President*
Frank Vaca, *Admin Sec*
EMP: 12
SQ FT: 3,500
SALES: 2.3MM **Privately Held**
WEB: www.ktiengineering.com
SIC: 3613 Switchgear & switchgear acces-
sories; control panels, electric

(P-17150)
MACHINE CONTROL TECH INC
210 Crouse Dr, Corona (92879-8093)
PHONE.............................951 808-0973
Sam Yu, *President*
EMP: 10
SALES (est): 780K **Privately Held**
SIC: 3613 Control panels, electric

(P-17151)
MARWELL CORPORATION
1094 Wabash Ave, Mentone (92359)
P.O. Box 139 (92359-0139)
PHONE.............................909 794-4192
Larry R Blackwell, *President*
Kelle A Blackwell, *Corp Secy*
Robert Ashford, *Manager*
Karrie Matcham, *Supervisor*
EMP: 18
SQ FT: 3,500
SALES (est): 3.6MM **Privately Held**
WEB: www.marwellcorp.com
SIC: 3613 Panel & distribution boards &
other related apparatus

(P-17152)
NEW IEM LLC
Also Called: Industrial Electric Mfg
48205 Warm Springs Blvd, Fremont
(94539-7654)
PHONE.............................510 656-1600
Edward Rossi, *President*
John Hulme, *CFO*
Dan Hulme, *Webmaster*
Jim Horner, *Project Mgr*
Erica Mamone, *Project Mgr*
▲ EMP: 90
SQ FT: 100,000
SALES (est): 45MM **Privately Held**
SIC: 3613 Switchboards & parts, power;
switchboard apparatus, except instru-
ments; control panels, electric; switchgear
& switchgear accessories
PA: Abd El & Larson Holdings, Llc
48205 Warm Springs Blvd
Fremont CA 94539
510 656-1600

(P-17153)
PANEL SHOP INC
Also Called: Electrical Systems
2800 Palisades Dr, Corona (92880-9427)
PHONE.............................951 739-7000
Michael Hellmers, *President*
Carol Crawford, *President*
David Hellmers, *President*
EMP: 30
SQ FT: 36,000
SALES (est): 4.1MM **Privately Held**
WEB: www.eslsys.com
SIC: 3613 3625 Control panels, electric;
relays & industrial controls

(P-17154)
**PEC OF AMERICA
CORPORATION (HQ)**
2320 Pso De Las Amer # 107, San Diego
(92154-7281)
PHONE.............................619 710-8131
Takahisa Ogawa, *CEO*
Koichiro Mabuchi, *CFO*
▲ EMP: 15
SQ FT: 1,200
SALES: 50MM
SALES (corp-wide): 7.6MM **Privately
Held**
SIC: 3613 3469 Fuses, electric; machine
parts, stamped or pressed metal
PA: Pec Holdings Corporation
450, Hinokicho
Ogaki GIF 503-0
584 913-131

(P-17155)
**PHAOSTRON INSTR
ELECTRONIC CO**
Also Called: Phaostron Instr Electronic Co
717 N Coney Ave, Azusa (91702-2205)
PHONE.............................626 969-6801
Paul R Mc Guirk, *President*
Jackie Cangialosi, *CFO*
Andrew McGuirk, *Vice Pres*
Jacqueline Cangialosi, *Admin Sec*
Richard White, *Prdtn Mgr*
EMP: 80
SQ FT: 50,000
SALES (est): 12.4MM **Privately Held**
SIC: 3613 Metering panels, electric; bus
bar structures
PA: Westbase Inc
717 N Coney Ave
Azusa CA 91702

(P-17156)
POWER AIRE INC
8055 E Crystal Dr, Anaheim (92807-2523)
PHONE.............................800 526-7661
Harry Ellis Sr, *President*
Jean Blasko, *Treasurer*
Harry Ellis Jr, *Vice Pres*
Michael Ellis, *Vice Pres*
EMP: 20
SQ FT: 3,800
SALES (est): 1.6MM **Privately Held**
WEB: www.poweraire.com
SIC: 3613 5084 Panel & distribution
boards & other related apparatus; indus-
trial machinery & equipment

(P-17157)
POWERTYE MANUFACTURING
1640 E Miraloma Ave, Placentia
(92870-6622)
P.O. Box 17904, Anaheim (92817-7904)
PHONE.............................714 993-7400
Linda Carrillo, *President*
▲ EMP: 10
SALES (est): 1.3MM **Privately Held**
SIC: 3613 5571

(P-17158)
**R & J WLDG MET FABRICATION
INC**
2182 Maple Privado, Ontario (91761-7602)
PHONE.............................909 930-2900
Jose Fregoso, *CEO*
EMP: 11
SALES (est): 2.3MM **Privately Held**
SIC: 3613 3444 Generator control & me-
tering panels; sheet metalwork

(P-17159)
RELECTRIC INC
2390 Zanker Rd, San Jose (95131-1115)
PHONE.............................408 467-2222
Anthony Robinson, *President*
Kelly Pihera, *Purch Agent*
Jessica Clifford, *Accounts Exec*
▲ EMP: 30
SQ FT: 35,000
SALES (est): 9.9MM **Privately Held**
WEB: www.allbreakers.com
SIC: 3613 3625 5063 8734 Switchgear &
switchboard apparatus; relays & industrial
controls; electrical apparatus & equip-
ment; testing laboratories

(P-17160)
ROMAC SUPPLY CO INC
7400 Bandini Blvd, Commerce
(90040-3339)
PHONE.............................323 721-5810
David B Rosenfield, *President*
Payman Salamati, *COO*
Victoria Rosenfield, *Treasurer*
Lisa R Podolsky, *Vice Pres*
Phillip Rosenfield, *Vice Pres*
EMP: 60
SQ FT: 105,000
SALES (est): 22.2MM **Privately Held**
WEB: www.romacsupply.com
SIC: 3613 3621 3612 5063 Switchgear &
switchgear accessories; motors & genera-
tors; transformers, except electric; mo-
tors, electric

(P-17161)
SCHNEIDER ELECTRIC USA INC
10805 Thornmint Rd # 140, San Diego
(92127-2429)
PHONE.............................858 385-5040
Rusty King, *Manager*
Steven McGovern, *Engineer*
EMP: 136
SALES (corp-wide): 200.4K **Privately
Held**
WEB: www.squared.com
SIC: 3613 Switchgear & switchboard appa-
ratus
HQ: Schneider Electric Usa, Inc.
800 Federal St
Andover MA 01810
978 975-9600

(P-17162)
SIEMENS INDUSTRY INC
10855 Business Center Dr, Cypress
(90630-5252)
PHONE.............................714 252-3100
Donald House, *Principal*
EMP: 92
SALES (corp-wide): 97.7B **Privately Held**
WEB: www.sea.siemens.com
SIC: 3613 Switchboard apparatus, except
instruments
HQ: Siemens Industry, Inc.
100 Technology Dr
Alpharetta GA 30005
770 740-3000

▲ = Import ▼=Export
◆ =Import/Export

(P-17163)
SILICON VLY WORLD TRADE CORP
Also Called: American Skynet Electronics
1474 Gladding Ct, Milpitas (95035-6831)
PHONE...................................408 945-6355
Ching-Hung Liang, *President*
▲ EMP: 17
SQ FT: 10,000
SALES (est): 1.5MM **Privately Held**
WEB: www.skynetusa.com
SIC: 3613 7379 Power switching equipment; computer related maintenance services
PA: Skynet Electronic Co., Ltd.
4f, 76, 78, 80, Cheng Kung Rd., Sec. 1,
Taipei City TAP
227 882-403

(P-17164)
SOLARBOS
310 Stealth Ct, Livermore (94551-9303)
PHONE...................................925 456-7744
William Lawrence Vietas, *CEO*
EMP: 53
SQ FT: 20,000
SALES (est): 26.1MM **Privately Held**
SIC: 3613 Switchgear & switchboard apparatus

(P-17165)
SPECIALTY CONCEPTS INC
2393 Teller Rd Ste 106, Newbury Park (91320-6092)
PHONE...................................818 998-5238
Terry Staler, *President*
EMP: 12 EST: 1981
SQ FT: 7,200
SALES (est): 1.9MM **Privately Held**
WEB: www.specialtyconcepts.com
SIC: 3613 Metering panels, electric

(P-17166)
STACO SYSTEMS INC (HQ)
Also Called: Staco Switch
7 Morgan, Irvine (92618-2005)
PHONE...................................949 297-8700
Patrick Hutchins, *President*
Andy Bain, *Vice Pres*
Jeff Bowen, *Vice Pres*
Tom Lanni, *Vice Pres*
Brett Meinsen, *Vice Pres*
◆ EMP: 69
SQ FT: 35,000
SALES (est): 12.3MM
SALES (corp-wide): 44.2MM **Privately Held**
WEB: www.stacoswitch.com
SIC: 3613 Switches, electric power except snap, push button, etc.; panelboards & distribution boards, electric
PA: Components Corporation Of America
5950 Berkshire Ln # 1500
Dallas TX 75225
214 969-0166

(P-17167)
TE CONNECTIVITY CORPORATION
Te Circuit Protection
308 Constitution Dr, Menlo Park (94025-1111)
PHONE...................................650 361-3333
John McGraw,
EMP: 400
SALES (corp-wide): 13.1B **Privately Held**
WEB: www.raychem.com
SIC: 3613 Switchgear & switchboard apparatus
HQ: Te Connectivity Corporation
1050 Westlakes Dr
Berwyn PA 19312
610 893-9800

(P-17168)
TRAYER ENGINEERING CORPORATION
1569 Alvarado St, San Leandro (94577-2640)
PHONE...................................415 285-7770
John Trayer, *President*
Kirit Patel, *COO*
Ben Wong, *CFO*
Andrew Bond, *Officer*

Joe Stemmerich, *Vice Pres*
▼ EMP: 84
SQ FT: 21,000
SALES (est): 35.4MM **Privately Held**
WEB: www.trayer.com
SIC: 3613 Switchgear & switchgear accessories

(P-17169)
VERTIV CORPORATION
6960 Koll Center Pkwy # 300, Pleasanton (94566-3160)
PHONE...................................925 734-8660
Tony Thomas, *Manager*
EMP: 268
SALES (corp-wide): 322.9MM **Privately Held**
SIC: 3613 Regulators, power
HQ: Vertiv Corporation
1050 Dearborn Dr
Columbus OH 43085
614 888-0246

(P-17170)
VERTIV CORPORATION
2340 Rockwood Ave, Calexico (92231-1726)
P.O. Box 2887 (92232-2887)
PHONE...................................760 768-7522
Steve Benton, *Branch Mgr*
EMP: 10
SALES (corp-wide): 322.9MM **Privately Held**
SIC: 3613 3585 7629 3625 Regulators, power; air conditioning equipment, complete; electronic equipment repair; relays & industrial controls; computer peripheral equipment; blowers & fans
HQ: Vertiv Corporation
1050 Dearborn Dr
Columbus OH 43085
614 888-0246

(P-17171)
WABENJAMIN ELECTRIC CO
1615 Staunton Ave, Los Angeles (90021-3118)
PHONE...................................213 749-7731
D E Benjamin, *President*
Mauricio Mena, *CIO*
Jeff Hill, *Design Engr*
Jack Clark, *Marketing Staff*
EMP: 50
SALES (est): 11.7MM **Privately Held**
WEB: www.benjaminelectric.com
SIC: 3613 Panelboards & distribution boards, electric; switchgear & switchgear accessories

(P-17172)
WEST COAST SWITCHGEAR (HQ)
13837 Bettencourt St, Cerritos (90703-1009)
PHONE...................................562 802-3441
Alfred P Cisternelli, *CEO*
▲ EMP: 93
SQ FT: 20,000
SALES: 20MM
SALES (corp-wide): 70MM **Privately Held**
WEB: www.westcoastswitchgear.com
SIC: 3613 5063 Power circuit breakers; switchgear
PA: Resa Power, Llc
19500 Tx St Hwy 249 440
Houston TX 77070
832 876-7372

(P-17173)
WESTBASE INC (PA)
717 N Coney Ave, Azusa (91702-2205)
PHONE...................................626 969-6801
Paul R McGuirk, *President*
EMP: 10
SQ FT: 50,000
SALES (est): 13.8MM **Privately Held**
SIC: 3613 Metering panels, electric

3621 Motors & Generators

(P-17174)
ABB MOTORS AND MECHANICAL INC
Also Called: Golden Gate Baldor
21056 Forbes Ave, Hayward (94545-1116)
PHONE...................................510 785-9900
Deryl Rippy, *Manager*
EMP: 10
SALES (corp-wide): 34.3B **Privately Held**
WEB: www.baldor.com
SIC: 3621 Motors, electric
HQ: Abb Motors And Mechanical Inc.
5711 Rs Boreham Jr St
Fort Smith AR 72901
479 646-4711

(P-17175)
AC PROPULSION
446 Borrego Ct, San Dimas (91773-2937)
PHONE...................................909 592-5399
EMP: 20
SALES (est): 903.7K **Privately Held**
SIC: 3621 Motors & generators

(P-17176)
ACTON INC
2400 Lincoln Ave Ste 238, Altadena (91001-5436)
PHONE...................................323 250-0685
Janelle Wang, *CEO*
▲ EMP: 10
SALES: 120K **Privately Held**
SIC: 3621 7519 Generators for gas-electric or oil-electric vehicles; recreational vehicle rental

(P-17177)
ADVANCED POWER & CONTROLS LLC
605 E Alton Ave Ste A, Santa Ana (92705-5647)
PHONE...................................714 540-9010
David Tavares, *Mng Member*
Gary Rasmussen,
▲ EMP: 12
SQ FT: 3,600
SALES (est): 2.4MM **Privately Held**
WEB: www.advancedpowercontrols.com
SIC: 3621 3625 7629 Motor generator sets; motor controls, electric; generator repair

(P-17178)
ADVANTAGE MANUFACTURING INC
616 S Santa Fe St, Santa Ana (92705-4109)
PHONE...................................714 505-1166
Craig Ashmore, *Manager*
EMP: 30 **Privately Held**
WEB: www.advantageman.com
SIC: 3621 Motors, electric
PA: Advantage Manufacturing, Inc.
616 S Santa Fe St
Santa Ana CA 92705

(P-17179)
AMERICAN SD POWER INC
14181 Fern Ave, Chino (91710-9013)
PHONE...................................909 947-0673
Xin Wang, *President*
▲ EMP: 10
SALES (est): 1.8MM **Privately Held**
SIC: 3621 Generator sets: gasoline, diesel or dual-fuel

(P-17180)
AMETEK INC
Aerospace Gst
17032 Armstrong Ave, Irvine (92614-5716)
PHONE...................................949 642-2400
Dave McGinley, *Vice Pres*
Don Monte, *IT/INT Sup*
Mitra Mosallaie, *Analyst*
Mary Boris, *Sales Staff*
Umesh Kamalanathan, *Manager*
EMP: 68

SALES (corp-wide): 4.3B **Publicly Held**
SIC: 3621 3823 Motors & generators; industrial instrmnts msrmnt display/control process variable
PA: Ametek, Inc.
1100 Cassatt Rd
Berwyn PA 19312
610 647-2121

(P-17181)
BARTA-SCHOENEWALD INC (PA)
Also Called: Advanced Motion Controls
3805 Calle Tecate, Camarillo (93012-5068)
PHONE...................................805 389-1935
Sandor Barta, *President*
Daniel Schoenewald, *Exec VP*
▲ EMP: 120
SQ FT: 86,000
SALES (est): 27.5MM **Privately Held**
WEB: www.a-m-c.com
SIC: 3621 3699 Servomotors, electric; electric motor & generator parts; electrical equipment & supplies

(P-17182)
BOSCH ENRGY STOR SOLUTIONS LLC
Also Called: Robert Bosch Stiftung GMBH
4005 Miranda Ave Ste 200, Palo Alto (94304-1232)
PHONE...................................650 320-2933
Jasim Ahmed, *Vice Pres*
Jake Christensen, *Senior Mgr*
EMP: 11
SALES (est): 1.1MM
SALES (corp-wide): 261.7MM **Privately Held**
SIC: 3621
PA: R O B E R T B O S C H S T I F T U N G Gesellschaft Mit Beschrankter Haftung
Heidehofstr. 31
Stuttgart 70184
711 460-840

(P-17183)
CALNETIX INC (PA)
Also Called: Calnetix Technologies
16323 Shoemaker Ave, Cerritos (90703-2244)
PHONE...................................562 293-1660
Vatche Artinian, *President*
Dennis Strouse, *COO*
Ian Hart, *CFO*
Herman Artinian, *Vice Pres*
Frank Delattre, *Senior Mgr*
▲ EMP: 110
SQ FT: 68,000
SALES: 22MM **Privately Held**
WEB: www.calnetix.com
SIC: 3621 Motors & generators

(P-17184)
CALNETIX TECHNOLOGIES LLC
16323 Shoemaker Ave, Cerritos (90703-2244)
PHONE...................................562 293-1660
Vatche Artinian, *Chairman*
Herman Artinian, *CEO*
Ian Hart, *CFO*
Pana Shenoy, *Vice Pres*
Andrea Matiauda, *Admin Sec*
EMP: 82
SALES: 22MM **Privately Held**
SIC: 3621 Motors & generators
PA: Calnetix, Inc.
16323 Shoemaker Ave
Cerritos CA 90703
562 293-1660

(P-17185)
CLO SYSTEMS LLC
15312 Valley Blvd, City of Industry (91746-3324)
P.O. Box 360752, Los Angeles (90036-1251)
PHONE...................................626 939-4226
Sung OH, *CEO*
Sam Kim, *Accountant*
▲ EMP: 10
SQ FT: 6,000
SALES (est): 2.1MM **Privately Held**
WEB: www.closystems.com
SIC: 3621

PRODUCTS & SVCS

(P-17186)
CMI INTEGRATED TECH INC
11248 Playa Ct, Culver City (90230-6127)
PHONE....................................760 431-7003
Anil Nanji, *President*
Shankar RAO, *COO*
Gary Hooper, *CFO*
EMP: 35
SQ FT: 6,600
SALES (est): 4.3MM **Privately Held**
WEB: www.carlsbadmagnetics.com
SIC: 3621 3825

(P-17187)
COLE INSTRUMENT CORP
2650 S Croddy Way, Santa Ana
(92704-5238)
P.O. Box 25063 (92799-5063)
PHONE....................................714 556-3100
Ric Garcia, *President*
Manuel Garcia, *Exec VP*
Greg Hendrick, *Design Engr*
Roshan Sarode, *Design Engr*
Ed Brigham, *Safety Mgr*
EMP: 70 **EST:** 1965
SQ FT: 16,000
SALES (est): 17MM **Privately Held**
WEB: www.cole-switches.com
SIC: 3621 3679 Motors & generators;
electronic switches

(P-17188)
**CONCENTRIC COMPONENTS
INC**
913 5th St, Modesto (95351-2809)
PHONE....................................209 529-4840
Phillip Nachatelo, *President*
EMP: 10
SALES (est): 1.2MM **Privately Held**
SIC: 3621 7537 5531 Torque motors,
electric; automotive transmission repair
shops; automobile & truck equipment &
parts

(P-17189)
DIRECT DRIVE SYSTEMS INC
621 Burning Tree Rd, Fullerton
(92833-1448)
PHONE....................................714 872-5500
James Pribble, *CEO*
Michael Slater, *COO*
Robert Clark, *CFO*
Daryl Kobayashi, *Engineer*
EMP: 57
SALES (est): 11.2MM
SALES (corp-wide): 15B **Privately Held**
WEB: www.directdrivesystems.net
SIC: 3621 Electric motor & generator parts
HQ: Fmc Technologies, Inc.
11740 Katy Fwy Energy Tow
Houston TX 77079
281 591-4000

(P-17190)
ECO-GEN DISTRIBUTORS INC
340 Goddard, Irvine (92618-4601)
PHONE....................................760 712-7460
Bruce Kaylor, *President*
Robert Zannasdale, *CEO*
Garrtt Adams, *COO*
Stacey Zannasdale, *Vice Pres*
EMP: 12
SALES (est): 2.8MM **Privately Held**
SIC: 3621 Motors & generators

(P-17191)
ECO-GEN ENERGY INC
7247 Hayvenhurst Ave A6, Van Nuys
(91406-2871)
PHONE....................................818 756-4700
Raoul Hamilton, *President*
Julia A Otey, *Corp Secy*
▲ **EMP:** 11
SALES (est): 1.7MM **Privately Held**
SIC: 3621 Motors & generators

(P-17192)
ELITE GENERATORS INC
9007 De Soto Ave, Canoga Park
(91304-1968)
PHONE....................................818 718-0200
Jeffrey Peter Giedt, *CEO*
Lupean Campos, *CFO*
Lupeann Campos, *Manager*
EMP: 11
SQ FT: 1,500

SALES (est): 1.4MM **Privately Held**
SIC: 3621 7629 Power generators; generator repair

(P-17193)
ENER-CORE INC (PA)
8965 Research Dr Ste 100, Irvine
(92618-4246)
PHONE....................................949 616-3300
Alain J Castro, *CEO*
Michael J Hammons, *Ch of Bd*
Domonic J Carney, *CFO*
Douglas A Hamrin, *VP Engrg*
EMP: 13
SQ FT: 4,960
SALES (est): 11.2MM **Publicly Held**
SIC: 3621 Power generators

(P-17194)
ES WEST COAST LLC
Also Called: Energy Systems
7100 Longe St Ste 300, Stockton
(95206-3962)
PHONE....................................209 870-1900
Don Richter, *President*
EMP: 45
SALES (est): 5.5MM
SALES (corp-wide): 68.1MM **Privately
Held**
SIC: 3621 Electric motor & generator auxil-
lary parts
HQ: The Shane Group Llc
215 W Mechanic St
Hillsdale MI 49242
517 439-4316

(P-17195)
**EURUS ENERGY AMERICA
CORP (DH)**
9255 Towne Centre Dr # 840, San Diego
(92121-3041)
PHONE....................................858 638-7115
Mark E Anderson, *President*
Michael Whittle, *Vice Pres*
Yoko Rover, *Executive Asst*
Landon Boisclair, *Finance Mgr*
Hidetoshi Koshiya, *Finance Mgr*
EMP: 16
SQ FT: 3,000
SALES (est): 15MM
SALES (corp-wide): 60.9B **Privately Held**
WEB: www.eurusenergy.com
SIC: 3621 Windmills, electric generating
HQ: Eurus Energy Holdings Corporation
4-3-13, Toranomon
Minato-Ku TKY 105-0
354 045-300

(P-17196)
FLAMESTOWER INC
127 Kissling St, San Francisco
(94103-3726)
PHONE....................................415 699-8650
Andrew Gordon Byrnes, *CEO*
EMP: 55
SQ FT: 2,000
SALES (est): 6.5MM **Privately Held**
SIC: 3621 Generators & sets, electric

(P-17197)
FRANKLIN ELECTRIC CO INC
1129 Brussels St, San Francisco
(94134-2105)
PHONE....................................415 467-2693
EMP: 563
SALES (corp-wide): 1.1B **Publicly Held**
SIC: 3621 Motors, electric
PA: Franklin Electric Co., Inc.
9255 Coverdale Rd
Fort Wayne IN 46809
260 824-2900

(P-17198)
GLENTEK INC
208 Standard St, El Segundo
(90245-3818)
PHONE....................................310 322-3026
Richard C Vasak, *CEO*
Helen Sysel, *CFO*
Helen M Vasak, *Corp Secy*
Bill Vasak, *Information Mgr*
Roxy Escoto, *Accountant*
▲ **EMP:** 71
SQ FT: 105,000

SALES: 6MM **Privately Held**
WEB: www.glentek.com
SIC: 3621 Motors & generators

(P-17199)
GLOBE MOTORS INC
1507 Gladding Ct, Milpitas (95035-6813)
PHONE....................................408 935-8989
Surinder Singh, *General Mgr*
EMP: 175
SALES (corp-wide): 252MM **Publicly
Held**
SIC: 3621 Motors, electric
HQ: Globe Motors, Inc.
2275 Stanley Ave
Dayton OH 45404
334 983-3542

(P-17200)
**GO GREEN MOBILE POWER
LLC**
171 Pier Ave Ste 105, Santa Monica
(90405-5311)
PHONE....................................877 800-4467
James P Caulfield, *Mng Member*
James Montoya, *Exec VP*
EMP: 10
SALES (est): 3MM **Privately Held**
SIC: 3621 3648 Power generators; lighting
equipment

(P-17201)
HARMONIC DESIGN INC
13367 Krkrham Way Ste 110, Poway
(92064)
PHONE....................................858 391-9085
Michel Pouvreau, *CEO*
▲ **EMP:** 32
SALES (est): 5.6MM **Privately Held**
SIC: 3621 Motors & generators

(P-17202)
HEEGER INC
Also Called: Lmb Heeger
6446 Flotilla St, Commerce (90040-1712)
PHONE....................................323 728-5108
Robert Heeger, *President*
Christine Avila, *Vice Pres*
EMP: 19 **EST:** 1946
SQ FT: 16,000
SALES (est): 1.5MM **Privately Held**
SIC: 3621 3469 3444 Motors & genera-
tors; metal stampings; sheet metalwork

(P-17203)
**HI PERFORMANCE ELECTRIC
VEHICL**
620 S Magnolia Ave Ste B, Ontario
(91762-4030)
PHONE....................................909 923-1973
Brian Guy Seymour, *CEO*
Toni Seymour, *Treasurer*
Bill Ritchie, *Sales Staff*
▲ **EMP:** 15
SQ FT: 9,000
SALES (est): 3.4MM **Privately Held**
WEB: www.hiperformancegolfcars.com
SIC: 3621 Motors, electric

(P-17204)
**HITACHI AUTOMOTIVE
SYSTEMS**
Also Called: Los Angeles Plant
6200 Gateway Dr, Cypress (90630-4842)
PHONE....................................310 212-0200
Fred Pakshir, *Branch Mgr*
EMP: 100
SALES (corp-wide): 87.9B **Privately Held**
SIC: 3621 3714 Electric motor & generator
parts; motor vehicle parts & accessories
HQ: Hitachi Automotive Systems Americas,
Inc.
955 Warwick Rd
Harrodsburg KY 40330
859 734-9451

(P-17205)
INTEGRATED MAGNETICS INC
11250 Playa Ct, Culver City (90230-6127)
PHONE....................................310 391-7213
Anil Nanji, *President*
EMP: 40
SQ FT: 120,000

SALES (est): 7.1MM
SALES (corp-wide): 47.2MM **Privately
Held**
SIC: 3621 3679 3764 Rotors, for motors;
servomotors, electric; cores, magnetic;
rocket motors, guided missiles
PA: Integrated Technologies Group, Inc.
11250 Playa Ct
Culver City CA 90230
310 391-7213

(P-17206)
KOLLMORGEN CORPORATION
33 S La Patera Ln, Santa Barbara
(93117-3214)
PHONE....................................805 696-1236
EMP: 383
SALES (corp-wide): 6.6B **Publicly Held**
SIC: 3621 Servomotors, electric
HQ: Kollmorgen Corporation
203a W Rock Rd
Radford VA 24141
540 639-9045

(P-17207)
**LEOCH BATTERY
CORPORATION (PA)**
19751 Descartes Unit A, Foothill Ranch
(92610-2620)
PHONE....................................949 588-5853
Hui Peng, *President*
Crystal He, *Sales Mgr*
Kelly Liu, *Sales Mgr*
Shawn Smith, *Marketing Staff*
Catherine Binette, *Sales Staff*
▲ **EMP:** 39
SALES (est): 34MM **Privately Held**
SIC: 3621 Storage battery chargers, motor
& engine generator type

(P-17208)
LIN ENGINEERING INC
16245 Vineyard Blvd, Morgan Hill
(95037-7123)
PHONE....................................408 919-0200
Ted T Lin, *President*
Rouyu Loughry, *CFO*
Cynthia Lin, *Corp Secy*
Mindy Lin, *Research*
Harlan Nguyen, *Research*
▲ **EMP:** 125
SQ FT: 16,000
SALES (est): 26.6MM **Privately Held**
WEB: www.linengineering.com
SIC: 3621 Motors, electric
HQ: Moons' International Trading (Shang-
hai) Co., Ltd.
Caohejing Hi-Tech Tech. Zone
Shanghai 20023
216 495-2755

(P-17209)
MAGICALL INC
4550 Calle Alto, Camarillo (93012-8509)
P.O. Box 3730 (93011-3730)
PHONE....................................805 484-4300
Joel Wacknov, *CEO*
Dan Qin, *President*
Randy Martin, *Vice Pres*
Vicki Clifford, *Purch Mgr*
Matt Cullinane, *VP Sales*
▲ **EMP:** 33
SALES (est): 6.7MM **Privately Held**
SIC: 3621 3612 3677 3679 Motors &
generators; power transformers, electric;
electronic coils, transformers & other in-
ductors; static power supply converters
for electronic applications

(P-17210)
**MC CULLY MAC M
CORPORATION**
Also Called: Mac M McCully Co
12012 Hertz Ave, Moorpark (93021-7130)
PHONE....................................805 529-0661
Guy Mc Cully, *President*
Martha L McCully, *Corp Secy*
EMP: 35
SQ FT: 8,000
SALES (est): 5.6MM **Privately Held**
SIC: 3621 Motors, electric

(P-17211)
MOTOR TECHNOLOGY INC
2301 Wardlow Cir, Corona (92880-2801)
PHONE....................................951 270-6200

▲ = Import ▼=Export
◆ =Import/Export

Robert Buchwalder, *President*
Phyllis Buchwalder, *Corp Secy*
George Teets, *Manager*
EMP: 37
SQ FT: 12,600
SALES (est) 5.1MM
SALES (corp-wide): 661.7MM **Publicly Held**
WEB: www.motortech.com
SIC: 3621 Motors, electric
PA: Circor International, Inc.
30 Corporate Dr Ste 200
Burlington MA 01803
781 270-1200

(P-17212)
MOTRAN INDUSTRIES INC
3037 Golf Course Dr Ste 4, Ventura
(93003-7608)
PHONE..........................661 257-4995
Charles Willard, *President*
▲ **EMP:** 10
SQ FT: 8,200
SALES: 1.7MM **Privately Held**
WEB: www.motran.com
SIC: 3621 Electric motor & generator parts

(P-17213)
NATURENER USA LLC (DH)
435 Pacific Ave Fl 4, San Francisco
(94133-4611)
PHONE..........................415 217-5500
Jose M S Seara,
Greg Copeland, *Vice Pres*
Scott Hooper, *Vice Pres*
Marc Denarie, *CIO*
Antonio Utrillas, *Engineer*
EMP: 36
SALES (est): 10.6MM **Privately Held**
SIC: 3621 Windmills, electric generating
HQ: Grupo Naturener, Sa
Calle Nulez De Balboa, 120 - 7
Madrid 28006
915 625-410

(P-17214)
NORTHERN CALIFORNIA POWER AGCY
477 Bret Harte Ln, Murphys (95247-9537)
P.O. Box 2280 (95247-2280)
PHONE..........................209 728-1387
Kevin Cunningham, *Manager*
EMP: 17
SALES (est): 1.9MM
SALES (corp-wide): 113.4MM **Privately Held**
SIC: 3621 Power generators
PA: Northern California Power Agency
651 Commerce Dr
Roseville CA 95678
916 781-3636

(P-17215)
NOVATORQUE INC
281 Greenoaks Dr, Atherton (94027-2114)
PHONE..........................510 933-2700
Emily Liggett, *CEO*
Tim McNally, *CFO*
Kim Baker, *Vice Pres*
Scott Johnson, *Vice Pres*
Joe Weber, *Vice Pres*
▲ **EMP:** 40
SQ FT: 27,000
SALES (est): 9MM **Privately Held**
WEB: www.novatorque.com
SIC: 3621 Motors & generators

(P-17216)
OUPIIN AMERICA INC
27795 Avenue Hopkins, Valencia
(91355-1223)
PHONE..........................661 294-0228
Rebecca Chong Ryan, *Principal*
Randy Ryan, *Vice Pres*
▲ **EMP:** 13
SALES (est): 1.7MM **Privately Held**
SIC: 3621 Motors & generators

(P-17217)
POWER EFFICIENCY CORPORATION
5744 Pcf Ctr Blvd Ste 311, San Diego
(92121)
PHONE..........................858 750-3875
Steven Z Strasser, *CEO*
Thomas A Mills Jr, *Vice Pres*

Brian C Chan, *Admin Sec*
▲ **EMP:** 13
SALES (est): 1.6MM **Privately Held**
WEB: www.powerefficiency.com
SIC: 3621 Motors & generators

(P-17218)
R K LARRABEE COMPANY INC
Also Called: Construction Electrical Pdts
7800 Las Positas Rd, Livermore
(94551-8240)
PHONE..........................925 828-9420
Robert Larrabee, *President*
Colin Christian, *Vice Pres*
Nancy Larrabee, *Vice Pres*
Christine Jeffery, *Credit Mgr*
Scott Larrabee, *Mfg Dir*
▲ **EMP:** 65
SALES (est): 15.8MM **Privately Held**
WEB: www.cepnow.com
SIC: 3621 3699 3648 3646 Power generators; electrical equipment & supplies; lighting equipment; commercial indusl & institutional electric lighting fixtures; non-current-carrying wiring services; nonferrous wiredrawing & insulating

(P-17219)
RESMED MOTOR TECHNOLOGIES INC
9540 De Soto Ave, Chatsworth
(91311-5010)
PHONE..........................818 428-6400
David B Sears, *CEO*
Michael Fliss, *President*
Jean Ellis, *Vice Pres*
Paul Yacoob, *Engineer*
▲ **EMP:** 170
SQ FT: 35,000
SALES (est): 34.6MM **Publicly Held**
WEB: www.resmed.com
SIC: 3621 3714 3841 Coils, for electric motors or generators; collector rings, for electric motors or generators; propane conversion equipment, motor vehicle; surgical & medical instruments
PA: Resmed Inc.
9001 Spectrum Center Blvd
San Diego CA 92123
-

(P-17220)
REULAND ELECTRIC CO (PA)
17969 Railroad St, City of Industry
(91748-1192)
P.O. Box 1464, La Puente (91749-1464)
PHONE..........................626 964-6411
Noel C Reuland, *President*
Bill Kramer, *CFO*
William Kramer III, *CFO*
Marie Ponia, *Executive*
Phor Engstrom, *Info Tech Mgr*
▲ **EMP:** 130 **EST:** 1937
SQ FT: 100,000
SALES (est): 42.4MM **Privately Held**
WEB: www.reuland.com
SIC: 3621 3566 3363 3625 Motors, electric; drives, high speed industrial, except hydrostatic; aluminum die-castings; electric controls & control accessories, industrial; fluid power motors

(P-17221)
ROCKETSTAR ROBOTICS INC
177 Estaban Dr, Camarillo (93010-1611)
PHONE..........................805 529-7769
EMP: 10
SALES (est): 640K **Privately Held**
WEB: www.rocketstarrobotics.com
SIC: 3621 Motors & generators

(P-17222)
SENSATA TECHNOLOGIES INC
Also Called: Kimco Magnetics
1499 Poinsettia Ave # 160, Vista
(92081-8543)
PHONE..........................760 597-7042
D Mallet, *Branch Mgr*
Jerry Brierton, *Natl Sales Mgr*
Don Fontaine, *Regl Sales Mgr*
Eric Blythe, *Sales Staff*
Dennis Cooper, *Sales Staff*
EMP: 89

SALES (corp-wide): 2.7MM **Privately Held**
SIC: 3621 3593 Motors, electric; fluid power cylinders & actuators
HQ: Sensata Technologies, Inc.
529 Pleasant St
Attleboro MA 02703
508 236-3800

(P-17223)
SKURKA AEROSPACE INC (DH)
4600 Calle Bolero, Camarillo (93012-8575)
P.O. Box 2869 (93011-2869)
PHONE..........................216 706-2939
Sean Magee, *General Mgr*
Victoria Alonzo, *Administration*
Georgia Gonzalez, *Administration*
Monica Nunez, *Administration*
Christie Morris, *Info Tech Dir*
EMP: 140 **EST:** 1950
SQ FT: 70,000
SALES (est): 37.3MM
SALES (corp-wide): 3.5B **Publicly Held**
WEB: www.skurka-aero.com
SIC: 3621 3679 Motors, electric; transducers, electrical

(P-17224)
SOFTWARE MOTOR COMPANY
1295 Forgewood Ave, Sunnyvale
(94089-2216)
PHONE..........................408 601-7781
Mark Johnston, *CEO*
Mike Petouhoff, *Vice Pres*
EMP: 10
SALES (est): 2.1MM **Privately Held**
SIC: 3621 7389 Motors, electric; design services

(P-17225)
SOUTH AMRCN IMGING SLTIONS INC
2360 Eastman Ave Ste 110, Oxnard
(93030-7287)
PHONE..........................805 824-4036
Rogelio Zavala, *CEO*
EMP: 10
SALES (est): 636.8K **Privately Held**
SIC: 3621 Electric motor & generator parts

(P-17226)
THINGAP LLC
4035 Via Pescador, Camarillo
(93012-5050)
PHONE..........................805 477-9741
Sarah Gallagher, *President*
Len Wedman, *President*
Jannelle Taylor, *Office Mgr*
Donnie Harris, *Project Engr*
Carlos Sanchez, *Engineer*
EMP: 20
SALES: 2.5MM **Privately Held**
SIC: 3621 Coils, for electric motors or generators

(P-17227)
THINGAP HOLDINGS LLC
Also Called: Thingap.com
4035 Via Pescador, Camarillo
(93012-5050)
PHONE..........................805 477-9741
Sarah Gallagher, *CEO*
Evan Frank, *Director*
▲ **EMP:** 10
SQ FT: 6,826
SALES (est): 1.7MM **Privately Held**
WEB: www.thingap.com
SIC: 3621 Motors, electric

(P-17228)
VALLEY POWER SERVICES INC
425 S Hacienda Blvd, City of Industry
(91745-1123)
PHONE..........................909 969-9345
Clark Lee, *President*
▲ **EMP:** 20
SQ FT: 17,802
SALES (est): 3.9MM **Privately Held**
SIC: 3621 Motor housings

(P-17229)
YASKAWA AMERICA INC
4101 Burton Dr, Santa Clara (95054-1510)
PHONE..........................408 748-4400
Jody Kurtzhalts, *CEO*
EMP: 225

SALES (corp-wide): 4B **Privately Held**
WEB: www.methodsmachine.com
SIC: 3621 Motors, electric
HQ: Yaskawa America, Inc.
2121 Norman Dr
Waukegan IL 60085
847 887-7000

(P-17230)
ZAPWORLDCOM (PA)
300 Stony Point Rd # 249, Petaluma
(94952-8113)
PHONE..........................707 525-8658
Alex Wang, *CEO*
Michael Ringstad, *CFO*
▲ **EMP:** 13
SQ FT: 10,000
SALES: 10.7MM **Publicly Held**
WEB: www.zapworld.com
SIC: 3621 3751 Motors, electric; motorcycles, bicycles & parts

---

3624 Carbon & Graphite Prdts

(P-17231)
ADVANCE CARBON PRODUCTS INC
2036 National Ave, Hayward (94545-1712)
PHONE..........................510 293-5930
Ronald D Crader, *President*
James Michael Crader, *Vice Pres*
Gary Kloss, *Vice Pres*
Bill Crader, *Manager*
EMP: 40
SQ FT: 20,000
SALES (est): 7.2MM **Privately Held**
WEB: www.advancecarbon.com
SIC: 3624 3678 3643 3568 Brush blocks, carbon or molded graphite; electronic connectors; current-carrying wiring devices; power transmission equipment; gaskets, packing & sealing devices; industrial inorganic chemicals

(P-17232)
ALLIANCE SPACESYSTEMS LLC
4398 Corporate Center Dr, Los Alamitos
(90720-2537)
PHONE..........................714 226-1400
Rick Byrens, *President*
Steve Gort, *Program Mgr*
Mike Chernobieff, *Engineer*
Chris Thayer, *Engineer*
Robert A Crane, *Analyst*
EMP: 155
SQ FT: 101,000
SALES: 25MM
SALES (corp-wide): 125.5MM **Privately Held**
SIC: 3624 Carbon & graphite products
PA: Solaero Technologies Corp.
10420 Res Rd Se Bldg 1
Albuquerque NM 87123
505 332-5000

(P-17233)
AMERICAN ACTIVATED CARBON CORP
7310 Deering Ave, Canoga Park
(91303-1503)
PHONE..........................310 491-2842
Anthony Pathirana, *CEO*
Tony Pathirana, *Marketing Staff*
▲ **EMP:** 10
SALES (est): 1.8MM **Privately Held**
SIC: 3624 Fibers, carbon & graphite

(P-17234)
BAKERCORP
Also Called: Baker Filtration
5500 Rawlings Ave, South Gate
(90280-7412)
PHONE..........................562 904-3680
Chris Ritchie, *Branch Mgr*
Todd Williams, *Opers Mgr*
EMP: 15
SALES (corp-wide): 6.6B **Publicly Held**
SIC: 3624 Carbon & graphite products
HQ: Bakercorp
3020 Old Ranch Pkwy # 220
Seal Beach CA 90740
562 430-6262

PRODUCTS & SVCS

(P-17235)
CARBON SOLUTIONS INC
5094 Victoria Hill Dr, Riverside
(92506-1450)
PHONE.....................................909 234-2738
Robert Haddon, *President*
EMP: 12 EST: 1999
SALES (est): 990K Privately Held
WEB: www.carbonsolution.com
SIC: 3624 Carbon & graphite products

(P-17236)
CDG TECHNOLOGY LLC
779 Twin View Blvd, Redding (96003-2008)
PHONE.....................................530 243-4451
Manny Ornellas,
EMP: 15
SALES: 1MM Privately Held
SIC: 3624 Fibers, carbon & graphite

(P-17237)
FRONTERA SOLUTIONS INC
1913 E 17th St Ste 210, Santa Ana
(92705-8627)
PHONE.....................................714 368-1631
Earl B Johnson, *President*
John Drake, *CFO*
Ben Rawski, *Vice Pres*
EMP: 100
SALES: 450K Privately Held
WEB: www.mtidebaja.com
SIC: 3624 3231 Fibers, carbon & graphite;
insulating glass: made from purchased
glass

(P-17238)
KBR INC
Also Called: Electro-Tech Machining Div
2000 W Gaylord St, Long Beach
(90813-1032)
P.O. Box 92610, Rochester NY (14692-
0610)
PHONE.....................................562 436-9281
Kevin McMahon, *Vice Pres*
David R McMahon, *President*
Karen McMahon, *Admin Sec*
▲ EMP: 32
SQ FT: 39,000
SALES (est): 6.1MM Privately Held
SIC: 3624 Carbon & graphite products

(P-17239)
**MITSUBISHI CHEMICAL CRBN
FBR (DH)**
5900 88th St, Sacramento (95828-1109)
PHONE.....................................916 386-1733
Susumu Sasaki, *CEO*
Donald Carter, *CFO*
Masayoshi Ozeki, *Vice Pres*
Takeshi Sasaki, *Vice Pres*
Denise Di Fabbio, *Admin Asst*
▲ EMP: 125
SQ FT: 60,000
SALES (est): 50.6MM
SALES (corp-wide): 34.9B Privately Held
WEB: www.grafil.com
SIC: 3624 Fibers, carbon & graphite
HQ: Mitsubishi Chemical Corporation
1-1-1, Marunouchi
Chiyoda-Ku TKY 100-0
367 487-300

(P-17240)
MOTIV DESIGN GROUP INC
430 Perrymont Ave, San Jose
(95125-1444)
PHONE.....................................408 441-0611
Lino R Covarrubias, *CEO*
Carbs Barrientos, *Vice Pres*
EMP: 25
SQ FT: 2,400
SALES (est): 4.2MM Privately Held
SIC: 3624 Carbon & graphite products

(P-17241)
QUATRO COMPOSITES LLC
13250 Gregg St Ste A1, Poway
(92064-7164)
PHONE.....................................712 707-9200
Karash Quepin, *Manager*
EMP: 35
SALES (corp-wide): 168.2MM Privately
Held
SIC: 3624 Carbon & graphite products

HQ: Quatro Composites, L.L.C.
403 14th St Se
Orange City IA 51041
712 707-9200

(P-17242)
**SIGMATEX HIGH TECH FABRICS
INC (HQ)**
6001 Egret Ct, Benicia (94510-1205)
PHONE.....................................707 751-0573
Scott Tolson, *President*
Jonah Jimemez, *President*
Russ Pancio, *Info Tech Mgr*
Mary Ann Reyes, *Controller*
Pamela Butala, *Human Resources*
▲ EMP: 52
SQ FT: 10,000
SALES: 28MM
SALES (corp-wide): 78MM Privately
Held
WEB: www.sigmatex.com
SIC: 3624 Carbon & graphite products
PA: Sigmatex (Uk) Limited
Manor Farm Road
Runcorn WA7 1
192 857-0050

(P-17243)
**SPACESYSTEMS HOLDINGS
LLC**
4398 Corporate Center Dr, Los Alamitos
(90720-2537)
PHONE.....................................714 226-1400
Terence Lyons, *CEO*
Rick Byrens, *President*
Jeffrey David Lassiter, *CFO*
EMP: 144 EST: 2012
SQ FT: 101,000
SALES: 30MM Privately Held
SIC: 3624 Carbon & graphite products

(P-17244)
ZEPTOR CORPORATION
3087 N 1st St, San Jose (95134-2006)
PHONE.....................................408 432-6001
Tatsunori Suzuki, *President*
Charles Consorte, *Vice Pres*
Zhihui Wang, *Senior Engr*
EMP: 15
SALES (est): 328.4K Privately Held
SIC: 3624 Carbon & graphite products

3625 Relays & Indl Controls

(P-17245)
**A P SEEDORFF & COMPANY
INC**
Also Called: Seedorff Acme
1338 N Knollwood Cir, Anaheim
(92801-1311)
PHONE.....................................714 252-5330
Kurt Simon, *President*
Helmut Simon, *Treasurer*
EMP: 15
SQ FT: 10,000
SALES (est): 4.4MM Privately Held
WEB: www.acmewelders.com
SIC: 3625 Resistance welder controls

(P-17246)
**ABSOLUTE GRAPHIC TECH USA
INC**
Also Called: Agt
235 Jason Ct, Corona (92879-6199)
PHONE.....................................909 597-1133
Steven J Barberi, *President*
Socorell Fog, *Manager*
EMP: 49
SQ FT: 25,800
SALES: 10MM Privately Held
SIC: 3625 3577 Industrial electrical relays
& switches; printers & plotters

(P-17247)
AIRSPACE SYSTEMS INC
1933 Davis St Ste 229, San Leandro
(94577-1260)
PHONE.....................................310 704-7155
Jasminder Banga, *CEO*
Guy Bar-Nahum, *Vice Pres*
Rob Coneybeer, *Director*
Steve Schimmel, *Director*

EMP: 30
SALES (est): 421K Privately Held
SIC: 3625 Control equipment, electric

(P-17248)
AISIN ELECTRONICS INC
199 Frank West Cir, Stockton
(95206-4002)
PHONE.....................................209 983-4988
Yasuhito Mori, *President*
Yuji Tomisawa, *Admin Sec*
Timothy Willis, *Engineer*
Rob Pointer, *QC Mgr*
Matt Owens, *Manager*
EMP: 230
SQ FT: 22,000
SALES (est): 63.6MM
SALES (corp-wide): 36.6B Privately Held
WEB: www.aisin-electronics.com
SIC: 3625 3714 Control circuit relays, in-
dustrial; relays, electric power; relays, for
electronic use; switches, electronic appli-
cations; motor vehicle parts & acces-
sories
HQ: Aisin Holdings Of America, Inc.
1665 E 4th Street Rd
Seymour IN 47274
812 524-8144

(P-17249)
AMERICAN RELAYS INC
15537 Blackburn Ave, Norwalk
(90650-6846)
PHONE.....................................562 944-0447
Hyo Lee, *President*
Richard Lenning, *Vice Pres*
Sue Lee, *Buyer*
EMP: 40
SQ FT: 12,000
SALES (est): 5.7MM Privately Held
WEB: www.americanrelays.com
SIC: 3625 Relays, for electronic use

(P-17250)
AMES FIRE WATERWORKS
1485 Tanforan Ave, Woodland
(95776-6108)
PHONE.....................................530 666-2493
Nancy West, *CEO*
Christine Hartman, *Human Res Mgr*
Steve Loya, *Prdtn Mgr*
▲ EMP: 88
SQ FT: 10,000
SALES (est): 18.2MM
SALES (corp-wide): 1.4B Publicly Held
WEB: www.amesfirewater.com
SIC: 3625 3494 Relays & industrial con-
trols; valves & pipe fittings
PA: Watts Water Technologies, Inc.
815 Chestnut St
North Andover MA 01845
978 688-1811

(P-17251)
ANAHEIM AUTOMATION INC
4985 E Landon Dr, Anaheim (92807-1972)
PHONE.....................................714 992-6990
Faithe Reimbold, *Vice Pres*
Nannette Israel, *CFO*
John Witt, *Vice Pres*
Alan Harmon, *General Mgr*
Joann Witt, *Admin Sec*
▲ EMP: 47
SQ FT: 9,000
SALES (est): 9.8MM Privately Held
WEB: www.anaheimautomation.com
SIC: 3625 3545 3566 Control equipment,
electric; machine tool accessories; speed
changers, drives & gears

(P-17252)
**APPLIED CONTROL
ELECTRONICS**
5480 Merchant Cir, Placerville
(95667-8250)
PHONE.....................................530 626-5181
Terry Burke, *President*
Natalie Burke, *CFO*
Gaylyn Burke, *Office Mgr*
Edd Todd, *Prdtn Mgr*
EMP: 12
SQ FT: 10,000
SALES (est): 1.1MM Privately Held
SIC: 3625 8711 Motor controls & acces-
sories; electrical or electronic engineer-
ing; consulting engineer

(P-17253)
**AQUADYNE COMPUTER
CORPORATION**
9434 Chesapeake Dr # 1204, San Diego
(92123-1390)
PHONE.....................................858 495-1040
Dean McDaniel, *President*
EMP: 16
SQ FT: 2,100
SALES (est): 2MM Privately Held
WEB: www.aquadyne.com
SIC: 3625 Control equipment, electric

(P-17254)
ASCOR INC (HQ)
4650 Norris Canyon Rd, San Ramon
(94583-1320)
PHONE.....................................925 328-4650
Jeffrey Lum, *President*
John Regazzi, *CEO*
EMP: 25
SQ FT: 19,000
SALES: 3.8MM
SALES (corp-wide): 9.8MM Publicly Held
WEB: www.ascor.com
SIC: 3625 Switches, electronic applications
PA: Giga-Tronics Incorporated
5990 Gleason Dr
Dublin CA 94568
925 328-4650

(P-17255)
AVAB AMERICA INC
11078 Fleetwood St, Sun Valley
(91352-2708)
PHONE.....................................707 778-8990
Frantz Lau, *CEO*
EMP: 25
SQ FT: 7,500
SALES (est): 3.5MM Privately Held
WEB: www.avab.com
SIC: 3625 Control equipment, electric

(P-17256)
**BALBOA WATER GROUP LLC
(PA)**
Also Called: Controlmyspa
1382 Bell Ave, Tustin (92780-6430)
PHONE.....................................714 384-0384
David J Cline, *President*
▲ EMP: 182 EST: 2007
SQ FT: 35,000
SALES (est): 82.1MM Privately Held
WEB: www.balboainstruments.com
SIC: 3625 3599 Electric controls & control
accessories, industrial; machine shop,
jobbing & repair

(P-17257)
BASIC MICROCOM INC
38595 Rancho Christina Rd, Temecula
(92592-8025)
PHONE.....................................951 708-1268
Lisa M Kubin, *Administration*
Lisa Kubin, *President*
EMP: 10 EST: 2011
SALES (est): 1.3MM Privately Held
SIC: 3625 Control equipment, electric

(P-17258)
CALIFORNIA ECONOMIZER
Also Called: Zonex Systems
5622 Engineer Dr, Huntington Beach
(92649-1124)
PHONE.....................................714 898-9963
Jeff Osheroff, *President*
▲ EMP: 50
SQ FT: 16,000
SALES (est): 9MM Privately Held
WEB: www.hvaccomfort.com
SIC: 3625 3822 Control equipment, elec-
tric; auto controls regulating residntl &
coml environmt & applncs

(P-17259)
**CALIFORNIA MOTOR
CONTROLS INCO**
3070 Bay Vista Ct, Benicia (94510-1235)
PHONE.....................................707 746-6255
Tom Duling, *President*
Susan Duling, *Vice Pres*
Kristi Duling, *Office Mgr*
Jarrod Slate, *Opers Mgr*
Mike Loden, *Cust Mgr*
EMP: 13

SQ FT: 8,000
SALES (est): 4.3MM **Privately Held**
SIC: **3625** Motor controls, electric

(P-17260)
COMSTAR INDUSTRIES INC
Also Called: Industrial Graphic
4009 W Segerstrom Ave, Santa Ana
(92704-6326)
PHONE..................................714 556-1400
David Goff, *President*
Ernie Riddle-Duarte, *Sales Staff*
Ernie Riddle, *Manager*
EMP: 30
SQ FT: 9,500
SALES (est): 4.4MM **Privately Held**
WEB: www.comstarindustries.com
SIC: **3625** 3674 3643 3613 Relays & industrial controls; semiconductors & related devices; current-carrying wiring devices; switchgear & switchboard apparatus; screen printing

(P-17261)
CONTROL SWITCHES INC (PA)
2425 Mira Mar Ave, Long Beach
(90815-1757)
PHONE..................................562 498-7331
Susana Moore, *Principal*
Donald J Armstrong, *President*
Susan Moore, *CFO*
EMP: 15
SALES (est): 10.4MM **Privately Held**
SIC: **3625** 5063 Industrial electrical relays & switches; electrical apparatus & equipment

(P-17262)
CONTROL SWITCHES INTL INC
2425 Mira Mar Ave, Long Beach
(90815-1757)
P.O. Box 92349 (90809-2349)
PHONE..................................562 498-7331
Margerate Turner, *Exec VP*
Susan Moore, *CFO*
Susan A Moore, *CFO*
Judith Steward, *Vice Pres*
Peggy Turner, *Vice Pres*
EMP: 25
SQ FT: 10,000
SALES (est): 3.4MM
SALES (corp-wide): 10.4MM **Privately Held**
WEB: www.controlswitches.com
SIC: **3625** Switches, electronic applications
PA: Control Switches, Inc.
  2425 Mira Mar Ave
  Long Beach CA 90815
  562 498-7331

(P-17263)
CRYDOM INC (DH)
2320 Paseo Delas Amer 2, San Diego
(92154)
PHONE..................................619 210-1590
Martha Sullivan, *President*
Oscar Fernandez, *CFO*
Jeffrey Cote, *Director*
▲ EMP: 296
SQ FT: 20,000
SALES (est): 118MM
SALES (corp-wide): 2.7MM **Privately Held**
WEB: www.crydom.com
SIC: **3625** 5065 3674 3643 Control equipment, electric; electronic parts & equipment; semiconductors & related devices; current-carrying wiring devices
HQ: Sensata Technologies, Inc.
  529 Pleasant St
  Attleboro MA 02703
  508 236-3800

(P-17264)
CTI-CONTROLTECH INC
22 Beta Ct, San Ramon (94583-1202)
PHONE..................................925 208-4250
George P Constas, *President*
EMP: 15
SQ FT: 5,000
SALES (est): 4.6MM **Privately Held**
WEB: www.cticontroltech.com
SIC: **3625** 5084 Relays & industrial controls; controlling instruments & accessories

(P-17265)
CYNERGY3 COMPONENTS CORP (PA)
2475 Pseo De Las Americas, San Diego
(92154-7255)
PHONE..................................858 715-7200
John Royan, *CEO*
Wilfred Corrigan, *Ch of Bd*
Wayne Carlyle, *COO*
Bob Fenton, *Exec VP*
Robert T Borawski, *Admin Sec*
▲ EMP: 10
SQ FT: 12,000
SALES (est): 50.3MM **Privately Held**
WEB: www.ampsabundant.com
SIC: **3625** Relays & industrial controls

(P-17266)
DOW-KEY MICROWAVE CORPORATION
4822 Mcgrath St, Ventura (93003-7718)
PHONE..................................805 650-0260
David Wightman, *President*
Sonia Cole, *Human Res Dir*
EMP: 150
SQ FT: 26,000
SALES (est): 32MM
SALES (corp-wide): 7.8B **Publicly Held**
WEB: www.dowkey.com
SIC: **3625** 3678 3643 3613 Switches, electronic applications; electronic connectors; current-carrying wiring devices; switchgear & switchboard apparatus
PA: Dover Corporation
  3005 Highland Pkwy # 200
  Downers Grove IL 60515
  630 541-1540

(P-17267)
EAGLE ACCESS CONTROL SYSTEMS
12953 Foothill Blvd, Sylmar (91342-4929)
PHONE..................................818 837-7900
Yossi Afriat, *CEO*
Oren Afriat, *CFO*
AVI Afriat, *Vice Pres*
◆ EMP: 22 EST: 1996
SQ FT: 13,000
SALES (est): 5MM **Privately Held**
WEB: www.eagleoperators.com
SIC: **3625** Control equipment, electric

(P-17268)
EATON CORPORATION
200 New Stine Rd, Bakersfield
(93309-2651)
PHONE..................................661 396-2557
David Madrid, *Branch Mgr*
EMP: 218 **Privately Held**
SIC: **3625** Motor controls & accessories
HQ: Eaton Corporation
  1000 Eaton Blvd
  Cleveland OH 44122
  440 523-5000

(P-17269)
EMBEDDED SYSTEMS INC
Also Called: Esi Motion
2250a Union Pl, Simi Valley (93065-1660)
PHONE..................................805 624-6030
Earnie Beem, *President*
Sheila D'Angelo, *Vice Pres*
Frank Rosado, *Director*
EMP: 40
SALES (est): 530.9K **Privately Held**
WEB: www.esimotion.com
SIC: **3625** Motor starters & controllers, electric

(P-17270)
FIRE & SAFETY ELECTRONICS INC
Also Called: Phase Research
3160 Pullman St, Costa Mesa
(92626-3315)
PHONE..................................714 850-1320
John M Ludutsky, *President*
Thomas M Mitchell, *Chairman*
▼ EMP: 25
SQ FT: 5,400
SALES (est): 3.5MM **Privately Held**
WEB: www.phaseresearch.com
SIC: **3625** 3873 Timing devices, electronic; watches, clocks, watchcases & parts

(P-17271)
GENERAL DYNAMICS GLBL IMG TECH
7603 Saint Andrews Ave H, San Diego
(92154-8216)
PHONE..................................619 671-5400
Bud Jenkins, *Executive*
John Schulz, *Director*
Barbara Coats, *Manager*
EMP: 70
SALES (corp-wide): 30.9B **Publicly Held**
WEB: www.axsys.com
SIC: **3625** 3824 3825 3621 Relays & industrial controls; fluid meters & counting devices; instruments to measure electricity; motors & generators
HQ: General Dynamics Global Imaging Technologies, Inc.
  24 Simon St
  Nashua NH 03060

(P-17272)
GENERAL DYNMICS MTION CTRL LLC
7603 Saint Andrews Ave H, San Diego
(92154-8216)
PHONE..................................619 671-5400
Firat Gezen, *Mng Member*
Del Dameron, *Mng Member*
EMP: 12
SALES (est): 732.6K
SALES (corp-wide): 30.9B **Publicly Held**
SIC: **3625** Motor control centers
HQ: General Dynamics Ots (Niceville), Inc.
  115 Hart St
  Niceville FL 32578
  850 897-9700

(P-17273)
GIGAVAC LLC
6382 Rose Ln, Carpinteria (93013-2922)
P.O. Box 4428, Santa Barbara (93140-4428)
PHONE..................................805 684-8401
Mike Molyneux,
Scott Hickman, *President*
Rick Danchuk, *CFO*
Markus Beck, *Vice Pres*
Jim Lanum, *Vice Pres*
▲ EMP: 15
SALES (est): 5.4MM **Privately Held**
WEB: www.gigavac.com
SIC: **3625** Relays, electric power

(P-17274)
GNA INDUSTRIES INC
Also Called: Alex Tronix
4761 W Jacquelyn Ave, Fresno
(93722-6438)
PHONE..................................559 276-0953
George Alexanian, *President*
Dominic Shows, *CFO*
EMP: 29 EST: 1976
SQ FT: 5,000
SALES (est): 4.8MM **Privately Held**
WEB: www.alex-tronix.com
SIC: **3625** Timing devices, electronic; motor starters & controllers, electric

(P-17275)
H2W TECHNOLOGIES INC
26380 Ferry Ct, Santa Clarita
(91350-2998)
PHONE..................................661 291-1620
Fred Wilson, *CEO*
Mark Wilson, *President*
Alexander Hinds, *Exec VP*
EMP: 16 EST: 2000
SQ FT: 12,000
SALES (est): 5.2MM **Privately Held**
WEB: www.h2wtech.com
SIC: **3625** Relays & industrial controls

(P-17276)
HARRIS CORPORATION
7821 Orion Ave, Van Nuys (91406-2029)
PHONE..................................408 201-8000
Anthony Nigara, *Branch Mgr*
EMP: 38
SALES (corp-wide): 6.1B **Publicly Held**
WEB: www.ittind.com
SIC: **3625** Control equipment, electric

PA: Harris Corporation
  1025 W Nasa Blvd
  Melbourne FL 32919
  321 727-9100

(P-17277)
I/O CONTROLS CORPORATION (PA)
1357 W Foothill Blvd, Azusa (91702-2853)
PHONE..................................626 812-5353
Jeffrey Ying, *President*
Michael Kuang, *President*
Renee Chen, *Treasurer*
Renee Hsiaspin Ying, *Vice Pres*
Kody Wu, *Project Leader*
▲ EMP: 65
SALES (est): 14.3MM **Privately Held**
WEB: www.iocontrols.com
SIC: **3625** 3621 Control equipment, electric; control equipment for buses or trucks, electric

(P-17278)
ITS GROUP INC
Also Called: Its
266 Viking Ave, Brea (92821-3821)
PHONE..................................714 256-4100
Art Yee, *President*
EMP: 10
SQ FT: 2,400
SALES (est): 2.4MM **Privately Held**
SIC: **3625** Solenoid switches (industrial controls)

(P-17279)
ITT CORPORATION
I T T Cannon
56 Technology Dr, Irvine (92618-2301)
PHONE..................................714 557-4700
Mike Kuchenbrod, *Branch Mgr*
Mimi Ohara, *General Mgr*
John Gruppetta, *Design Engr*
Neil Mahaffy, *Design Engr*
Russ Gross, *Project Engr*
EMP: 500
SQ FT: 100,000
SALES (corp-wide): 2.5B **Publicly Held**
WEB: www.ittind.com
SIC: **3625** Control equipment, electric
HQ: Itt Llc
  1133 Westchester Ave N-100
  White Plains NY 10604
  914 641-2000

(P-17280)
ITT LLC
ITT Goulds Pumps
3951 Capitol Ave, City of Industry
(90601-1734)
P.O. Box 1254, La Puente (91749-1254)
PHONE..................................562 908-4144
Shashank Patel, *General Mgr*
Marco Garcia, *Electrical Engi*
Grace Lin, *Manager*
EMP: 75
SQ FT: 85,000
SALES (corp-wide): 2.5B **Publicly Held**
WEB: www.ittind.com
SIC: **3625** Control equipment, electric
HQ: Itt Llc
  1133 Westchester Ave N-100
  White Plains NY 10604
  914 641-2000

(P-17281)
KAPSCH TRAFFICCOM USA INC
4256 Hacienda Dr Ste 100, Pleasanton
(94588-8595)
PHONE..................................925 225-1600
David Dimlich, *President*
Thien Nguyen, *Sr Software Eng*
Peter Smith, *Engineer*
EMP: 18
SALES (corp-wide): 1.1B **Privately Held**
SIC: **3625** Industrial electrical relays & switches
HQ: Kapsch Trafficcom Usa, Inc.
  8201 Greensboro Dr # 1002
  Mc Lean VA 22102
  703 885-1976

(P-17282)
KENSINGTON LABORATORIES LLC (PA)
6200 Village Pkwy, Dublin (94568-3004)
PHONE..................................510 324-0126

P
R
O
D
U
C
T
S

&

S
V
C
S

Raj Kaul, *Mng Member*
EMP: 17
SQ FT: 72,000
SALES (est): 6MM **Privately Held**
WEB: www.kenlabs.com
SIC: 3625 3825 3674 Positioning controls, electric; measuring instruments & meters, electric; semiconductors & related devices

(P-17283)
LEACH INTERNATIONAL CORP
Also Called: Reach International
6900 Orangethorpe Ave, Buena Park
(90620-1390)
PHONE......................714 739-0770
Mark Chek, *President*
EMP: 386
SALES (corp-wide): 2B **Publicly Held**
SIC: 3625 3679 3674 Relays, electric power; relays, for electronic use; electronic switches; semiconductors & related devices
HQ: Leach International Corporation
   6900 Orangethorpe Ave
   Buena Park CA 90620
   714 736-7537

(P-17284)
LEFTON TECHNOLOGIES INC
1140 Brooklawn Dr, Los Angeles
(90077-3509)
PHONE......................818 986-1728
Norman Lefton, *CEO*
EMP: 30
SQ FT: 100,000
SALES: 5MM **Privately Held**
SIC: 3625 Motor control centers

(P-17285)
LIGHT GUARD SYSTEMS INC
2292 Airport Blvd, Santa Rosa
(95403-1003)
PHONE......................707 542-4547
Michael A Harrison, *President*
▼ **EMP:** 11
SQ FT: 2,500
SALES (est): 1.9MM **Privately Held**
WEB: www.lightguardsystems.com
SIC: 3625 Relays & industrial controls

(P-17286)
LOCIX INC
1150 Bayhill Dr Ste 205, San Bruno
(94066-3004)
PHONE......................650 231-2180
Vikram Pavate, *CEO*
Elad Alon, *Principal*
Vivek Subramanian, *Principal*
EMP: 10
SQ FT: 3,450
SALES (est): 622.8K **Privately Held**
SIC: 3625 5084 8731 Control equipment, electric; controlling instruments & accessories; electronic research

(P-17287)
MICROSEMI CORP-POWER MGT GROUP
11861 Western Ave, Garden Grove
(92841-2119)
PHONE......................714 994-6500
James J Peterson, *President*
John W Hohener, *CFO*
Rob Warren, *Vice Pres*
David Goren, *Asst Sec*
EMP: 250 **EST:** 1977
SQ FT: 135,000
SALES (est): 31.7MM **Privately Held**
SIC: 3625 3677 3679 3613 Relays, for electronic use; electronic transformers; liquid crystal displays (LCD); switchgear & switchboard apparatus; transformers, except electric; computer peripheral equipment
PA: Microsemi Corp.-Power Management
   Group Holding
   11861 Western Ave
   Garden Grove CA 92841
   714 994-6500

(P-17288)
MOOG INC
Also Called: Moog Jon Street Warehouse
1218 W Jon St, Torrance (90502-1208)
PHONE......................310 533-1178

Alberto Bilalon, *Manager*
Keith Pryor, *Info Tech Mgr*
Wilma Whitley, *Info Tech Mgr*
Alex Perelman, *Software Engr*
Julie Mazzu, *Project Mgr*
EMP: 500
SALES (corp-wide): 2.7B **Publicly Held**
SIC: 3625 8711 3812 Relays & industrial controls; aviation &/or aeronautical engineering; aircraft/aerospace flight instruments & guidance systems
PA: Moog Inc.
   400 Jamison Rd
   Elma NY 14059
   716 652-2000

(P-17289)
MWSAUSSE & CO INC (PA)
Also Called: Vibrex
28744 Witherspoon Pkwy, Valencia
(91355-5425)
PHONE......................661 257-3311
Torbjorn Helland, *President*
Paul Azevedo, *Vice Pres*
Gregory Hall, *Vice Pres*
Dan Robinson, *Vice Pres*
▲ **EMP:** 59
SQ FT: 12,000
SALES (est): 10.4MM **Privately Held**
WEB: www.mwsausse.com
SIC: 3625 Control equipment, electric

(P-17290)
NEXTINPUT INC (PA)
980 Linda Vista Ave, Mountain View
(94043-1903)
PHONE......................408 770-9293
Ali Foughi, *CEO*
Philip Thach, *Vice Pres*
EMP: 18
SALES: 5MM **Privately Held**
SIC: 3625 Switches, electronic applications

(P-17291)
PARKER-HANNIFIN CORPORATION
Compumotor
5500 Business Park Dr, Rohnert Park
(94928-7904)
PHONE......................707 584-7558
Kenneth Sweet, *Branch Mgr*
Ken Sweet, *General Mgr*
Bud Parer, *MIS Dir*
CHI Hua, *Design Engr*
Mark Calahan, *Engineer*
EMP: 200
SQ FT: 32,000
SALES (corp-wide): 14.3B **Publicly Held**
WEB: www.parker.com
SIC: 3625 3823 Motor controls, electric; industrial instrmnts msrmnt display/control process variable
PA: Parker-Hannifin Corporation
   6035 Parkland Blvd
   Cleveland OH 44124
   216 896-3000

(P-17292)
PEAK SERVO CORPORATION
Also Called: Peak Servo Corp / Eltrol
5931 Sea Lion Pl Ste 108, Carlsbad
(92010-6622)
PHONE......................760 438-4986
David Olstad, *President*
EMP: 10
SQ FT: 2,000
SALES (est): 1.1MM **Privately Held**
WEB: www.peakservo.com
SIC: 3625 Motor controls, electric

(P-17293)
PECO CONTROLS CORPORATION
Also Called: Peco Inspx
1616 Culpepper Ave Ste A, Modesto
(95351-1220)
PHONE......................209 576-3345
Dan Kemnitz, *Manager*
EMP: 14
SALES (corp-wide): 7.3MM **Privately Held**
WEB: www.pecocontrols.com
SIC: 3625 Relays & industrial controls

PA: Peco Inspx
   1050 Commercial St
   San Carlos CA 94070
   209 576-3345

(P-17294)
PIVOTAL SYSTEMS CORPORATION
48389 Fremont Blvd # 100, Fremont
(94538-6559)
PHONE......................510 770-9125
John Hoffman, *CEO*
EMP: 20
SQ FT: 1,000
SALES (est): 4.8MM **Privately Held**
WEB: www.pivotalsys.com
SIC: 3625 Control equipment, electric

(P-17295)
PULVER LABORATORIES INC
Also Called: Electromagnetics Division
320 N Santa Cruz Ave, Los Gatos
(95030-7243)
PHONE......................408 399-7000
Lee J Pulver, *President*
EMP: 12
SALES (est): 970K **Privately Held**
WEB: www.pulverlabs.com
SIC: 3625 8742 8734 Brakes, electromagnetic; marketing consulting services; product testing laboratories

(P-17296)
QULSAR INC (PA)
1798 Tech Dr Ste 139, San Jose (95110)
PHONE......................408 715-1098
Rajen Datta, *CEO*
Ola Andersson, *COO*
Jim Werner, *CFO*
Kishan Shenoi, *CTO*
Minoo Mehta, *VP Mktg*
EMP: 10 **EST:** 2014
SALES (est): 994.5K **Privately Held**
SIC: 3625 Relays & industrial controls

(P-17297)
RCD ENGINEERING INC
17100 Salmon Mine Rd, Nevada City
(95959-9350)
P.O. Box 119, North San Juan (95960-0119)
PHONE......................530 292-3133
Steve Leach, *CEO*
Pat Leach, *Admin Sec*
EMP: 22
SQ FT: 12,000
SALES (est): 4MM **Privately Held**
WEB: www.rcdengineering.com
SIC: 3625 3714 Motor controls & accessories; motor starters & controllers, electric; motor vehicle parts & accessories

(P-17298)
RF-LAMBDA USA LLC
10509 Vista Sorrento Pkwy # 120, San Diego (92121-2743)
PHONE......................972 767-5998
Jon Abalos, *Mfg Staff*
EMP: 10
SALES (corp-wide): 5.3MM **Privately Held**
SIC: 3625 Switches, electronic applications
PA: Rf-Lambda Usa, Llc
   4300 Marsh Ridge Rd # 110
   Carrollton TX 75010
   972 767-5998

(P-17299)
RIGHT HAND MANUFACTURING INC
180 Otay Lakes Rd Ste 205, Bonita
(91902-2444)
PHONE......................619 819-5056
Pedro Zaragoza, *CEO*
Jorge Vargas, *Purch Mgr*
Luis Resendiz, *QC Mgr*
▲ **EMP:** 150
SALES: 7MM **Privately Held**
WEB: www.rightandsynergy.com
SIC: 3625 Control circuit devices, magnet & solid state

(P-17300)
ROCKWELL AUTOMATION INC
2125 E Katella Ave # 250, Anaheim
(92806-6024)
PHONE......................714 938-9000
Brian Holte, *Branch Mgr*
Paul Steiner, *Sales Staff*
EMP: 67 **Publicly Held**
SIC: 3625 Electric controls & control accessories, industrial
PA: Rockwell Automation, Inc.
   1201 S 2nd St
   Milwaukee WI 53204
   -

(P-17301)
ROCKWELL AUTOMATION INC
5836 Corporate Ave, Cypress
(90630-4742)
PHONE......................714 828-1800
Rick Johnston, *Branch Mgr*
EMP: 40 **Publicly Held**
SIC: 3625 Relays & industrial controls
PA: Rockwell Automation, Inc.
   1201 S 2nd St
   Milwaukee WI 53204

(P-17302)
ROCKWELL AUTOMATION INC
111 N Market St Ste 200, San Jose
(95113-1116)
PHONE......................408 443-5425
Vladimir Preysman, *Branch Mgr*
Steve Byrnes, *Admin Sec*
Wayne J Leideker, *Technical Staff*
Peter A Newman, *Engineer*
Laura J Wynn, *Analyst*
EMP: 67 **Publicly Held**
SIC: 3625
PA: Rockwell Automation, Inc.
   1201 S 2nd St
   Milwaukee WI 53204

(P-17303)
ROCKWELL AUTOMATION INC
3000 Executive Pkwy # 210, San Ramon
(94583-2300)
PHONE......................925 242-5700
Mary P Farrell, *Branch Mgr*
Nirpal Sihota, *Accounts Mgr*
EMP: 35 **Publicly Held**
SIC: 3625 Electric controls & control accessories, industrial
PA: Rockwell Automation, Inc.
   1201 S 2nd St
   Milwaukee WI 53204
   -

(P-17304)
ROTORK CONTROLS INC
419 1st St, Petaluma (94952-4226)
PHONE......................707 769-4880
Howard Williams, *Branch Mgr*
EMP: 12
SALES (corp-wide): 848.5MM **Privately Held**
SIC: 3625 Actuators, industrial
HQ: Rotork Controls Inc.
   675 Mile Crossing Blvd
   Rochester NY 14624
   585 247-2304

(P-17305)
S & C ELECTRIC COMPANY
1135 Atlantic Ave Ste 100, Alameda
(94501-1174)
PHONE......................510 864-9300
Witold Bik, *Vice Pres*
Jennifer Tacdol, *Human Res Dir*
EMP: 50
SALES (corp-wide): 683.9MM **Privately Held**
SIC: 3625 3823 3822 Relays & industrial controls; industrial instrmnts msrmnt display/control process variable; auto controls regulating residntl & coml environmt & applncs
PA: S & C Electric Company
   6601 N Ridge Blvd
   Chicago IL 60626
   773 338-1000

(P-17306)
S R C DEVICES INCCUSTOMER (PA)
6295 Ferris Sq Ste D, San Diego (92121-3248)
PHONE..................866 772-8668
Richard W Carlyle, *President*
Mark McCabe, *Senior VP*
EMP: 10
SQ FT: 2,000
SALES (est): 16.1MM **Privately Held**
SIC: 3625 3643 5065 Switches, electronic applications; current-carrying wiring devices; electronic parts & equipment

(P-17307)
SCHMARTBOARD INC
37423 Fremont Blvd, Fremont (94536-3704)
PHONE..................510 744-9900
Andrew Yaung, *President*
Neal Greenberg, *Principal*
EMP: 10
SALES (est): 1.4MM **Privately Held**
WEB: www.schmartboard.com
SIC: 3625 Switches, electronic applications

(P-17308)
SILICON MICROSTRUCTURES INC
1701 Mccarthy Blvd, Milpitas (95035-7416)
PHONE..................408 473-9700
Rainer Cholewa, *CEO*
Omar Abed, *CEO*
Holger Doering, *COO*
Friedrich Holz, *CFO*
Henry Allen, *Vice Pres*
▲ EMP: 76
SQ FT: 34,000
SALES (est): 18.8MM
SALES (corp-wide): 295.3MM **Privately Held**
WEB: www.si-micro.com
SIC: 3625 3823 Relays & industrial controls; industrial instrmnts msrmnt display/control process variable
PA: Elmos Semiconductor Ag
Heinrich-Hertz-Str. 1
Dortmund 44227
231 754-90

(P-17309)
SILVERON INDUSTRIES INC
182 S Brent Cir, City of Industry (91789-3050)
PHONE..................909 598-4533
Steve Lee, *President*
Richard Lee, *General Mgr*
Jae Lee, *Business Mgr*
Wendy Sun, *Controller*
Brad Yi, *Purchasing*
▲ EMP: 16
SQ FT: 24,000
SALES (est): 5.2MM **Privately Held**
WEB: www.silveronusa.com
SIC: 3625 5065 Industrial controls: push button, selector switches, pilot; electronic parts

(P-17310)
SKJONBERG CONTROLS INC
1363 Donlon St Ste 6, Ventura (93003-8387)
PHONE..................805 650-0877
Knut Skjonberg, *President*
Monica Skjonberg, *Corp Secy*
EMP: 12
SQ FT: 3,600
SALES (est): 2.9MM **Privately Held**
WEB: www.skjonberg.com
SIC: 3625 Motor controls, electric

(P-17311)
SOUNDCOAT COMPANY INC
16901 Armstrong Ave, Irvine (92606-4914)
PHONE..................631 242-2200
Clay Simpson, *Branch Mgr*
EMP: 30
SALES (corp-wide): 385.7MM **Privately Held**
WEB: www.soundcoat.com
SIC: 3625 3086 3296 Noise control equipment; plastics foam products; mineral wool

HQ: The Soundcoat Company Inc
1 Burt Dr
Deer Park NY 11729
631 242-2200

(P-17312)
SURFACE TECHNOLOGIES CORP
3170 Commercial St, San Diego (92113-1427)
PHONE..................619 564-8320
Bernard Meartz, *Manager*
EMP: 35
SQ FT: 29,617
SALES (corp-wide): 42.6MM **Privately Held**
WEB: www.surfacetechcorp.net
SIC: 3625 Marine & navy auxiliary controls
PA: Surface Technologies Corporation
2440 Mayport Rd Ste 7
Jacksonville FL 32233
904 241-1501

(P-17313)
SYSTEM TECHNICAL SUPPORT CORP
Also Called: STS
13826 Prairie Ave, Hawthorne (90250-7309)
PHONE..................310 845-9400
Eric Leskly, *President*
▲ EMP: 20
SQ FT: 10,000
SALES (est): 5.5MM **Privately Held**
WEB: www.stscorp.net
SIC: 3625 Relays & industrial controls

(P-17314)
SYSTEMS MACHINES AUTOMATIO (PA)
Also Called: Smac
5807 Van Allen Way, Carlsbad (92008-7309)
PHONE..................760 929-7575
Ed Neff, *CEO*
Robert Berry, *CFO*
Mike Ferris, *Chief Mktg Ofcr*
Ken Clough, *Branch Mgr*
Mark Cato, *Engineer*
◆ EMP: 165
SQ FT: 102,000
SALES (est): 51MM **Privately Held**
WEB: www.smac-mca.com
SIC: 3625 2822 3549 Actuators, industrial; synthetic rubber; assembly machines, including robotic

(P-17315)
TE CONNECTIVITY CORPORATION
Also Called: Kilovac
550 Linden Ave, Carpinteria (93013-2038)
PHONE..................805 684-4560
Mike Moschitto, *Branch Mgr*
EMP: 110
SALES (corp-wide): 13.1B **Privately Held**
WEB: www.raychem.com
SIC: 3625 Relays, for electronic use
HQ: Te Connectivity Corporation
1050 Westlakes Dr
Berwyn PA 19312
610 893-9800

(P-17316)
TEAL ELECTRONICS CORPORATION (PA)
10350 Sorrento Valley Rd, San Diego (92121-1642)
PHONE..................858 558-9000
Glen Kassan, *Ch of Bd*
Donald Klein, *CEO*
David Nuzzo, *Treasurer*
William Bickel, *Vice Pres*
◆ EMP: 79
SQ FT: 36,059
SALES (est): 30MM **Privately Held**
WEB: www.teal.com
SIC: 3625 2631 3612 Noise control equipment; transformer board; transformers, except electric

(P-17317)
UNIVERSAL CTRL SOLUTIONS CORP
Also Called: Dnfcontrols
19770 Bahama St, Northridge (91324-3303)
PHONE..................818 898-3380
Daniel Fogel, *CEO*
Rochelle Perito, *General Mgr*
Kent Stork, *Engineer*
Fred E Scott, *Sales Staff*
▲ EMP: 15
SALES (est): 3.2MM **Privately Held**
WEB: www.dnfcontrols.com
SIC: 3625 Control equipment, electric

(P-17318)
VAREDAN TECHNOLOGIES LLC
3860 Del Amo Blvd Ste 401, Torrance (90503-7704)
PHONE..................310 542-2320
John Vasak,
Craig Hammond, *CFO*
EMP: 11
SQ FT: 1,350
SALES (est): 2MM **Privately Held**
SIC: 3625 Control equipment, electric

(P-17319)
VARIOUS TECHNOLOGIES INC
2720 Aiello Dr Ste C, San Jose (95111-2186)
PHONE..................408 972-4460
Kurt Sebben, *President*
Yolanda Sebben, *Office Mgr*
EMP: 40
SQ FT: 8,300
SALES (est): 5MM **Privately Held**
WEB: www.vari-tech.com
SIC: 3625 Solenoid switches (industrial controls); electric controls & control accessories, industrial

(P-17320)
VISHAY TECHNO COMPONENTS LLC
Also Called: Vishay Techno Components Corp
4051 Greystone Dr, Ontario (91761-3100)
PHONE..................909 923-3313
Felix Zandman PHD, *President*
Robert A Freece, *Vice Pres*
William J Spiers, *Admin Sec*
▲ EMP: 100
SQ FT: 30,000
SALES (est): 10.7MM
SALES (corp-wide): 2.6B **Publicly Held**
SIC: 3625 Resistors & resistor units
HQ: Dale Vishay Electronics Llc
1122 23rd St
Columbus NE 68601
605 665-9301

(P-17321)
WABASH TECHNOLOGIES INC
1778 Carr Rd, Calexico (92231-9764)
PHONE..................760 768-9343
EMP: 12
SALES (corp-wide): 2.7MM **Privately Held**
SIC: 3625 Flow actuated electrical switches
HQ: Wabash Technologies, Inc.
529 Pleasant St
Attleboro MA 02703
260 355-4100

(P-17322)
WARTSILA DYNMC POSITIONING INC (DH)
12131 Community Rd Ste A, Poway (92064-8893)
PHONE..................858 679-5500
Anthony Gardiner, *President*
Bryan Taylor, *CFO*
Mika Verronen, *Treasurer*
Aaron Bresmahan, *Vice Pres*
Martha Vasquez, *Finance Dir*
◆ EMP: 38
SQ FT: 50,000
SALES: 12MM
SALES (corp-wide): 5.8B **Privately Held**
SIC: 3625 3699 Marine & navy auxiliary controls; underwater sound equipment

HQ: Wartsila Holding, Inc.
11710 N Gessner Rd Ste A
Houston TX 77064
281 233-6200

(P-17323)
WEMS INC
Vacuum Atmospheres Co
4652 W Rosecrans Ave, Hawthorne (90250-6841)
P.O. Box 528 (90251-0528)
PHONE..................310 644-0255
Terry Sweem, *Branch Mgr*
Teresa Dougherty, *Buyer*
EMP: 50
SALES (corp-wide): 17.6MM **Privately Held**
WEB: www.wems.com
SIC: 3625 Relays & industrial controls
PA: Wems Inc.
4650 W Rosecrans Ave
Hawthorne CA 90250
310 644-0251

(P-17324)
WOODWARD HRT INC (HQ)
25200 Rye Canyon Rd, Santa Clarita (91355-1204)
PHONE..................661 294-6000
Thomas A Gendron, *CEO*
Martin V Glass, *President*
Lisa Tanner, *Vice Pres*
Daniel Nguyen, *General Mgr*
Sonia Saldana, *General Mgr*
▲ EMP: 650 EST: 1954
SQ FT: 200,000
SALES (est): 214.8MM
SALES (corp-wide): 2.3B **Publicly Held**
SIC: 3625 3492 Actuators, industrial; electrohydraulic servo valves, metal
PA: Woodward, Inc.
1081 Woodward Way
Fort Collins CO 80524
970 482-5811

(P-17325)
WOODWARD HRT INC
25200 Rye Canyon Rd, Santa Clarita (91355-1204)
PHONE..................661 702-5552
Ronald Delet, *Manager*
Sally Lillard, *Personnel*
Jayme Rodela, *Buyer*
EMP: 70
SALES (corp-wide): 2.3B **Publicly Held**
SIC: 3625 3492 Actuators, industrial; electrohydraulic servo valves, metal
HQ: Woodward Hrt, Inc.
25200 Rye Canyon Rd
Santa Clarita CA 91355
661 294-6000

(P-17326)
ZBE INC
1035 Cindy Ln, Carpinteria (93013-2905)
PHONE..................805 576-1600
Zac Bogart, *President*
Rod Martinez, *Engineer*
Tim Sexton, *Sales Executive*
Mia Rodgers, *Marketing Mgr*
Tony Baker, *Sales Staff*
▲ EMP: 45
SQ FT: 7,500
SALES (est): 7.5MM **Privately Held**
WEB: www.zbe.com
SIC: 3625 3861 3577 Electric controls & control accessories, industrial; photographic equipment & supplies; computer peripheral equipment

(P-17327)
ZMP AQUISITION CORPORATION
Also Called: Adams Rite Aerospace
4141 N Palm St, Fullerton (92835-1025)
PHONE..................714 278-6500
Charles Collins, *President*
Glen Anders, *MIS Dir*
EMP: 200
SQ FT: 100,000

P R O D U C T S & S V C S

SALES (est): 17.9MM **Privately Held**
WEB: www.adamsriteaerospace.org
SIC: **3625** 3743 3728 3429 Electric controls & control accessories, industrial; marine & navy auxiliary controls; railroad locomotives & parts, electric or nonelectric; aircraft parts & equipment; aircraft hardware; marine hardware

---

**3629 Electrical Indl
Apparatus, NEC**

(P-17328)
ADVANCED CHARGING TECH INC
Also Called: A C T
16855 Knott Ave, La Mirada (90638-6014)
PHONE...................................877 228-5922
Robert J Istwan, *President*
Anthony Capalino, *Admin Sec*
▲ EMP: 21
SALES (est): 14MM **Privately Held**
SIC: **3629** 3691 Battery chargers, rectifying or nonrotating; alkaline cell storage batteries

(P-17329)
ALTERGY SYSTEMS
140 Blue Ravine Rd, Folsom (95630-4703)
PHONE...................................916 458-8590
Eric S Mettler, *President*
Nate Cammack, *CFO*
Nathan Cammack, *CFO*
Mickey Oros, *Vice Pres*
Al Stevens, *Vice Pres*
▼ EMP: 29
SQ FT: 37,000
SALES (est): 7.7MM **Privately Held**
WEB: www.altergysystems.com
SIC: **3629** Electrochemical generators (fuel cells)

(P-17330)
AMERICAN BATTERY CHARGING INC
15272 Newsboy Cir, Huntington Beach (92649-1202)
PHONE...................................401 231-5227
Ronald J Stutzbach, *President*
Joan Stutzbach, *Admin Sec*
▼ EMP: 20
SQ FT: 20,000
SALES (est): 3.7MM **Privately Held**
WEB: www.abc-chargers.com
SIC: **3629** Battery chargers, rectifying or nonrotating

(P-17331)
APOLLO MANUFACTURING SERVICES
10360 Sorrento Valley Rd A, San Diego (92121-1600)
PHONE...................................858 271-8009
Jenny Truong, *President*
EMP: 15
SQ FT: 5,000
SALES (est): 1.5MM **Privately Held**
SIC: **3629** 8742 Battery chargers, rectifying or nonrotating; manufacturing management consultant

(P-17332)
ARECONT VISION COSTAR LLC
425 E Colorado St Fl 7700, Glendale (91205-5117)
PHONE...................................818 937-0700
Raul Calderon, *President*
Edmond Deravanessian, *CFO*
EMP: 100
SALES (est): 2.8MM
SALES (corp-wide): 20.2MM **Publicly Held**
SIC: **3629** Electronic generation equipment
PA: Costar Technologies, Inc.
    101 Wrangler Dr Ste 201
    Coppell TX 75019
    469 635-6800

(P-17333)
AVEOX INC
2265 Ward Ave Ste A, Simi Valley (93065-1864)
PHONE...................................805 915-0200

David Palombo, *President*
Tom Sievers, *Exec VP*
Tony Dematteis, *Engineer*
Wayne Hay, *Engineer*
Balazs Szoke, *Engineer*
EMP: 35
SQ FT: 22,000
SALES (est): 7.7MM **Privately Held**
WEB: www.aveox.com
SIC: **3629** Electronic generation equipment

(P-17334)
BLUE SKY ENERGY INC
2598 Fortune Way Ste K, Vista (92081-8442)
PHONE...................................760 597-1642
Alex Mevay, *President*
Jared Craft, *Officer*
Kristen Antrim, *Marketing Staff*
Stefano Luciani, *Marketing Staff*
Ernesto Fernandez, *Manager*
▲ EMP: 10
SQ FT: 2,500
SALES (est): 2.1MM **Privately Held**
WEB: www.blueskyenergyinc.com
SIC: **3629** Battery chargers, rectifying or nonrotating

(P-17335)
CAPAX TECHNOLOGIES INC
24842 Avenue Tibbitts, Valencia (91355-3404)
PHONE...................................661 257-7666
Jagdish Patel, *President*
Nina Patel, *Corp Secy*
Jagdish C Patel, *Engineer*
Kira Patel, *VP Mktg*
EMP: 28
SQ FT: 17,000
SALES (est): 4.7MM **Privately Held**
WEB: www.capaxtechnologies.com
SIC: **3629** 3675 Capacitors, fixed or variable; electronic capacitors

(P-17336)
CHARGEPOINT INC (PA)
240 E Hacienda Ave, Campbell (95008-6617)
PHONE...................................408 841-4500
Pasquale Romano, *President*
Antonio Canova, *COO*
Rex Jackson, *CFO*
Colleen Jansen, *Chief Mktg Ofcr*
Bill Loewenthal, *Senior VP*
◆ EMP: 200
SQ FT: 37,000
SALES (est): 88.3MM **Privately Held**
SIC: **3629** Battery chargers, rectifying or nonrotating

(P-17337)
CHARGETEK INC
409 Calle San Pablo # 104, Camarillo (93012-8565)
PHONE...................................805 444-7792
Louis C Josephs, *President*
Terri Shackelford, *Sales Staff*
▲ EMP: 20
SALES (est): 3.4MM **Privately Held**
WEB: www.chargetek.com
SIC: **3629** 3679 3677 Battery chargers, rectifying or nonrotating; static power supply converters for electronic applications; transformers power supply, electronic type

(P-17338)
COOPER BUSSMANN LLC
5735 W Las Positas Blvd # 100, Pleasanton (94588-4002)
PHONE...................................925 924-8500
Hundi Kamath, *Manager*
EMP: 15 **Privately Held**
WEB: www.bussmann.com
SIC: **3629** 5065 Capacitors & condensers; capacitors, electronic
HQ: Cooper Bussmann, Llc
    114 Old State Rd
    Ellisville MO 63021
    636 527-1324

(P-17339)
CURRENT WAYS INC
10221 Buena Vista Ave, Santee (92071-4484)
PHONE...................................619 596-3984

James Gevarges, *President*
Forest Tracko, *CFO*
Craig Miller, *Admin Sec*
EMP: 15
SQ FT: 26,000
SALES (est): 2MM **Privately Held**
WEB: www.CurrentWays.com
SIC: **3629** Battery chargers, rectifying or nonrotating

(P-17340)
ENGINEERED MAGNETICS INC
Also Called: Aap Division
10524 S La Cienega Blvd, Inglewood (90304-1116)
PHONE...................................310 649-9000
Josh Shachar, *Ch of Bd*
Kathy Tran, *President*
Tony Truong, *Project Mgr*
Isabella Yi Sha Li, *Director*
Maya Vu, *Director*
EMP: 26
SQ FT: 57,000
SALES (est): 7.4MM **Privately Held**
SIC: **3629** 3812 3369 Power conversion units, a.c. to d.c.: static-electric; missile guidance systems & equipment; aerospace castings, nonferrous: except aluminum

(P-17341)
EPC POWER CORP
13125 Danielson St # 112, Poway (92064-8873)
PHONE...................................858 748-5590
Devin Dilley, *CEO*
Allan Abela, *COO*
William Granham, *CFO*
Ryan Smith, *General Mgr*
Marc Hoffman, *Engineer*
▼ EMP: 20
SQ FT: 10,000
SALES (est): 2.1MM **Privately Held**
WEB: www.epcpower.com
SIC: **3629** Battery chargers, rectifying or nonrotating; inverters, nonrotating: electrical

(P-17342)
HI-Z TECHNOLOGY INC
Also Called: Ethernal Electric Company
7606 Miramar Rd Ste 7400, San Diego (92126-4210)
PHONE...................................858 695-6660
Jill Elsner, *CEO*
Dan Krommenhoek, *President*
Alexander Kushch, *Vice Pres*
Bing Xiao, *Research*
Frederick Leavitt, *Opers Mgr*
◆ EMP: 20
SQ FT: 6,800
SALES (est): 4.4MM **Privately Held**
WEB: www.hi-z.com
SIC: **3629** Thermo-electric generators

(P-17343)
INTELLIGENT TECHNOLOGIES LLC
Also Called: Itech
9454 Waples St, San Diego (92121-2919)
PHONE...................................858 458-1500
Rod Bolton, *President*
Frank Cooper, *Exec VP*
▲ EMP: 125
SQ FT: 17,846
SALES (est): 33.9MM
SALES (corp-wide): 90.9MM **Privately Held**
WEB: www.itecheng.com
SIC: **3629** 3356 Battery chargers, rectifying or nonrotating; battery metal
PA: Universal Power Group, Inc.
    488 S Royal Ln
    Coppell TX 75019
    469 892-1122

(P-17344)
ISC ENGINEERING LLC
4351 Schaefer Ave, Chino (91710-5451)
PHONE...................................909 596-3315
Steve Burk, *Mng Member*
▲ EMP: 70 EST: 1999
SQ FT: 15,000
SALES (est): 14MM **Privately Held**
WEB: www.iscengineering.com
SIC: **3629** Electronic generation equipment

(P-17345)
KINDER SCIENTIFIC COMPANY LLC
12675 Danielson Ct # 406, Poway (92064-6835)
PHONE...................................858 679-1515
J Michael Kinder,
Robert Van Die, *Vice Pres*
▼ EMP: 10
SQ FT: 3,000
SALES (est): 1.1MM **Privately Held**
SIC: **3629** Electronic generation equipment

(P-17346)
LUMATRONIX MFG INC
1141 Ringwood Ct Ste 150, San Jose (95131-1759)
PHONE...................................408 435-7820
Paul E Shin, *President*
▲ EMP: 15
SQ FT: 7,000
SALES (est): 3.2MM **Privately Held**
SIC: **3629** Capacitors, a.c., for motors or fluorescent lamp ballasts

(P-17347)
MDE SEMICONDUCTOR INC
78150 Calle Tampico # 210, La Quinta (92253-2907)
PHONE...................................760 564-8656
Bill Morgan, *President*
▲ EMP: 75
SALES (est): 5MM **Privately Held**
WEB: www.mdesemiconductor.com
SIC: **3629** Electronic generation equipment

(P-17348)
MULTIMETRIXS LLC
1025 Solano Ave, Albany (94706-1617)
PHONE...................................510 527-6769
Boris Kesil,
EMP: 15
SALES (est): 1.3MM **Privately Held**
SIC: **3629** Electronic generation equipment

(P-17349)
PINNACLE WORLDWIDE INC
435 S Detroit St Apt 209, Los Angeles (90036-6402)
PHONE...................................909 628-2200
Vishal Uttamchandani, *CEO*
EMP: 15
SALES (est): 1.6MM **Privately Held**
SIC: **3629** Electronic generation equipment

(P-17350)
PIRANHA EMS INC
2681 Zanker Rd Ste B, San Jose (95134-2137)
PHONE...................................408 520-3963
Roger Malmrose, *CEO*
Richard Walkup, *Exec VP*
Kiu Chong, *Buyer*
Mary Briggs, *Mktg Dir*
EMP: 35
SALES (est): 7.5MM **Privately Held**
SIC: **3629** Electronic generation equipment

(P-17351)
PRO POWER PRODUCTS INC
Also Called: Battery Hut
913 S Victory Blvd, Burbank (91502-2430)
PHONE...................................818 558-6222
Bernard A Tessmar, *President*
James L Tessmar, *Vice Pres*
EMP: 10
SQ FT: 2,000
SALES (est): 1MM **Privately Held**
SIC: **3629** 3691 7699 5531 Electronic generation equipment; storage batteries; battery service & repair; batteries, automotive & truck; batteries, dry cell

(P-17352)
Q C M INC
Also Called: Veris Manufacturing
285 Gemini Ave, Brea (92821-3704)
PHONE...................................714 414-1173
Jay Cadler, *CEO*
Larry Ching, *Exec VP*
Sandra Martinez, *Engineer*
Rob Rios, *Buyer*
Breanna Rorer, *Buyer*
▲ EMP: 45

SALES (est): 18.9MM **Privately Held**
WEB: www.verismfg.com
SIC: 3629 Electronic generation equipment

(P-17353)
SCOTT ENGINEERING INC
5051 Edison Ave, Chino (91710-5716)
PHONE...............................909 594-9637
Luis Ernesto Lujan, *CEO*
Kathy Meyer, *Planning*
Ed Kamiab, *Engineer*
Matt Knowles, *Engineer*
Jennifer Galvan, *Materials Mgr*
▲ EMP: 50 EST: 1967
SQ FT: 102,660
SALES (est): 21.9MM **Privately Held**
SIC: 3629 3613 Electronic generation
equipment; switchgear & switchboard apparatus

(P-17354)
SIMCO-ION TECHNOLOGY GROUP (PA)
1601 Harbor Bay Pkwy # 150, Alameda
(94502-3028)
PHONE...............................510 217-0600
Craig Hindman, *CEO*
Ronald Weigner, *President*
Michael Sheperia, *Managing Dir*
Berry Brown, *General Mgr*
▲ EMP: 110
SQ FT: 55,000
SALES (est): 10.9MM **Privately Held**
WEB: www.mksinst.com
SIC: 3629 Static elimination equipment, industrial

(P-17355)
SKYWORKS SOLUTIONS
1767 Carr Rd Ste 105, Calexico
(92231-9506)
PHONE...............................301 874-6408
David J Aldrich, *President*
▲ EMP: 18
SALES (est): 2.9MM **Privately Held**
SIC: 3629 Capacitors & condensers

(P-17356)
SOLAREDGE TECHNOLOGIES INC (PA)
47505 Seabridge Dr, Fremont
(94538-6546)
PHONE...............................510 498-3200
Guy Sella, *CEO*
Ronen Faier, *CFO*
Amir Cohen, *Vice Pres*
Yoav Galin, *Vice Pres*
Lior Handelsman, *Vice Pres*
EMP: 93
SALES (est): 97.4MM **Privately Held**
SIC: 3629 Power conversion units, a.c. to
d.c.: static-electric

(P-17357)
SOUTH BAY SOLUTIONS TEXAS LLC
37399 Centralmont Pl, Fremont
(94536-6549)
PHONE...............................936 494-0180
Theresa Brooks, *Vice Pres*
▲ EMP: 35
SALES (est): 5.2MM **Privately Held**
SIC: 3629 Electronic generation equipment

(P-17358)
SPARQTRON CORPORATION
5079 Brandin Ct, Fremont (94538-3140)
PHONE...............................510 657-7198
Shu Hung Kung, *CEO*
Mitchell Kung, *President*
Stephanie Nelson, *CFO*
Johnny Chen, *Vice Pres*
Gena Mu, *Program Mgr*
▲ EMP: 100 EST: 1998
SQ FT: 70,000
SALES (est): 33.6MM **Privately Held**
SIC: 3629 3672 Static elimination equipment, industrial; printed circuit boards

(P-17359)
STRATA TECHNOLOGIES
1800 Irvine Blvd Ste 205, Tustin (92780)
PHONE...............................714 368-9785
Jack Mazarone, *President*
EMP: 45 EST: 1997

SALES (est): 4.8MM **Privately Held**
WEB: www.strata-tech.net
SIC: 3629 Electronic generation equipment

(P-17360)
TOMAHAWK POWER LLC
402 W Broadway Ste 810, San Diego
(92101-3553)
PHONE...............................619 255-7478
Lawrence S Nora, *President*
▲ EMP: 12
SALES (est): 912.6K **Privately Held**
SIC: 3629 Electronic generation equipment

(P-17361)
YUTAKA ELECTRIC INTL INC
Also Called: Falcon Electric
5116 Azusa Canyon Rd, Baldwin Park
(91706-1846)
PHONE...............................626 962-7770
Arthur Seredian, *President*
Jitsuo Mase, *Vice Pres*
▲ EMP: 11
SQ FT: 10,000
SALES (est): 1.6MM **Privately Held**
SIC: 3629 3612 Power conversion units,
a.c. to d.c.: static-electric; power & distribution transformers

(P-17362)
ZPOWER LLC
4765 Calle Quetzal, Camarillo
(93012-8546)
PHONE...............................805 445-7789
Ross E Dueber, *President*
Herbert V Weigel II, *COO*
Dennis Dugan, *CFO*
Dennis J Dugan, *Vice Pres*
Barry A Freeman, *Vice Pres*
EMP: 210
SALES (est): 28.4MM **Privately Held**
WEB: www.zincmatrix.com
SIC: 3629 Battery chargers, rectifying or
nonrotating

3631 Household Cooking Eqpt

(P-17363)
BAKERSTONE INTERNATIONAL LLC
3617 W Macarthur Blvd, Santa Ana
(92704-6847)
PHONE...............................855 657-6836
Timothy Case,
▲ EMP: 10
SALES (est): 1.8MM **Privately Held**
SIC: 3631 Household cooking equipment

(P-17364)
CONAIR CORPORATION
Also Called: Allegro
9350 Rayo Ave, South Gate (90280-3613)
PHONE...............................323 724-0101
Pjbrice, *Branch Mgr*
Teresa Dionsio, *Info Tech Dir*
Cheryl Vance, *Director*
EMP: 80
SALES (corp-wide): 2B **Privately Held**
SIC: 3631 3639 3999 3634 Household
cooking equipment; major kitchen appliances, except refrigerators & stoves; barber & beauty shop equipment; hair dryers,
electric
PA: Conair Corporation
1 Cummings Point Rd
Stamford CT 06902
203 351-9000

(P-17365)
DACOR
14425 Clark Ave, City of Industry
(91745-1235)
PHONE...............................626 799-1000
EMP: 55
SALES (corp-wide): 148.1B **Privately
Held**
SIC: 3631 Convection ovens, including
portable: household
HQ: Dacor
14425 Clark Ave
City Of Industry CA 91745
626 799-1000

(P-17366)
DACOR
Also Called: Dacor Purchasing Industry
14425 Clark Ave, City of Industry
(91745-1235)
PHONE...............................626 799-1000
Jaime Morales, *Branch Mgr*
EMP: 12
SALES (corp-wide): 148.1B **Privately
Held**
SIC: 3631 Convection ovens, including
portable: household
HQ: Dacor
14425 Clark Ave
City Of Industry CA 91745
626 799-1000

(P-17367)
DACOR
14525 Clark Ave, City of Industry
(91745-1236)
PHONE...............................626 961-2256
Jaime Morales, *Branch Mgr*
EMP: 53
SALES (corp-wide): 148.1B **Privately
Held**
SIC: 3631 Convection ovens, including
portable: household
HQ: Dacor
14425 Clark Ave
City Of Industry CA 91745
626 799-1000

(P-17368)
DURO CORPORATION
Also Called: Nexrange Industries
17018 Evergreen Pl, City of Industry
(91745-1819)
PHONE...............................626 839-6541
Saban Chang, *President*
Grace Cho,
▲ EMP: 15
SQ FT: 10,000
SALES: 22MM **Privately Held**
SIC: 3631 Gas ranges, domestic

(P-17369)
FILTHY GRILL INC
70 N Dewey Ave, Newbury Park
(91320-4359)
PHONE...............................818 282-2017
Thomas Hudgins, *Principal*
EMP: 15
SALES (est): 2.3MM **Privately Held**
SIC: 3631 Barbecues, grills & braziers
(outdoor cooking)

(P-17370)
JADE RANGE LLC
Also Called: Jade Products
2650 Orbiter St, Brea (92821-6265)
PHONE...............................714 961-2400
Selim A Bassoul, *CFO*
Selim Bassoul, *CFO*
Timothy J Fitzgerald, *CFO*
Martin M Lindsay, *Treasurer*
Deanna Cook, *Administration*
▲ EMP: 120
SALES (est): 23.3MM
SALES (corp-wide): 2.3B **Publicly Held**
WEB: www.jaderange.com
SIC: 3631 3589 Household cooking equipment; commercial cooking & foodwarming
equipment
PA: The Middleby Corporation
1400 Toastmaster Dr
Elgin IL 60120
847 741-3300

(P-17371)
LYNX GRILLS INC (HQ)
7300 Flores St, Downey (90242-4010)
PHONE...............................323 722-4324
James Buch, *CEO*
Kirk Cleveland, *President*
Fred Heldreth, *Technical Staff*
Russ Morgan, *Controller*
Farah Marinero, *Human Res Dir*
▲ EMP: 17
SALES (est): 6.7MM
SALES (corp-wide): 2.3B **Publicly Held**
SIC: 3631 Barbecues, grills & braziers
(outdoor cooking)

PA: The Middleby Corporation
1400 Toastmaster Dr
Elgin IL 60120
847 741-3300

(P-17372)
LYNX GRILLS INC
7300 Flores St, Downey (90242-4010)
PHONE...............................323 838-1770
James Buch, *Branch Mgr*
Noel Crain, *Executive*
Carlos Torres, *Info Tech Dir*
Tim French, *Engineer*
Becky Scherrer, *Sales Staff*
EMP: 17
SALES (corp-wide): 2.3B **Publicly Held**
SIC: 3631 Barbecues, grills & braziers
(outdoor cooking)
HQ: Lynx Grills, Inc.
7300 Flores St
Downey CA 90242
323 722-4324

(P-17373)
MAGMA PRODUCTS INC
3940 Pixie Ave, Lakewood (90712-4136)
PHONE...............................562 627-0500
Jerry Mashburn, *President*
James Mashburn, *Vice Pres*
Gordon Andresen, *Info Tech Mgr*
Sheila Comeau, *Financial Exec*
Greg Schicora, *VP Opers*
◆ EMP: 70
SQ FT: 22,000
SALES (est): 10.4MM **Privately Held**
WEB: www.magmaproducts.com
SIC: 3631 3634 Barbecues, grills & braziers (outdoor cooking); griddles or grills,
electric: household

(P-17374)
PACIFIC COAST MFG INC
5270 Edison Ave, Chino (91710-5719)
PHONE...............................909 627-7040
Bruce Doran, *President*
James Poremba, *Vice Pres*
▲ EMP: 72
SQ FT: 40,000
SALES: 15MM **Privately Held**
SIC: 3631 Barbecues, grills & braziers
(outdoor cooking)

(P-17375)
ROYAL RANGE CALIFORNIA INC
Also Called: Royal Industries
3245 Corridor Dr, Eastvale (91752-1030)
PHONE...............................951 360-1600
L Vasan, *CEO*
Patricia Woods, *Vice Pres*
▼ EMP: 65
SQ FT: 52,000
SALES (est): 13.9MM **Privately Held**
WEB: www.royalranges.com
SIC: 3631 Household cooking equipment

(P-17376)
SUPERIOR EQUIPMENT SOLUTIONS
1085 Bixby Dr, Hacienda Heights
(91745-1704)
PHONE...............................323 722-7900
Jeffrey Bernstein, *CEO*
Stephan Bernstein, *Principal*
Neil Silcock, *Engineer*
▲ EMP: 60
SQ FT: 45,000
SALES: 750MM **Privately Held**
WEB: www.bestgrille.com
SIC: 3631 5046 Household cooking equipment; restaurant equipment & supplies

(P-17377)
TELEDYNE WIRELESS INC
Also Called: Teledyne Microwave
3236 Scott Blvd, Santa Clara (95054-3011)
PHONE...............................408 986-5060
EMP: 110
SALES (corp-wide): 2.3B **Publicly Held**
SIC: 3631
HQ: Teledyne Wireless, Llc
1274 Terra Bella Ave
Mountain View CA 94043
650 691-9800

(P-17378)
TWIN EAGLES INC
13259 166th St, Cerritos (90703-2203)
PHONE..................562 802-3488
Dante L Cantal, *CEO*
Epifania Cantal, *Vice Pres*
▲ EMP: 85
SQ FT: 45,000
SALES (est): 31.3MM **Privately Held**
WEB: www.twineaglesinc.com
SIC: 3631 Barbecues, grills & braziers (outdoor cooking)

3632 Household Refrigerators & Freezers

(P-17379)
LARRY SCHLUSSLER
Also Called: Sun Frost
824 L St Ste 7, Arcata (95521-5766)
P.O. Box 1101 (95518-1101)
PHONE..................707 822-9095
Larry Schussler, *Owner*
▼ EMP: 16
SQ FT: 6,000
SALES (est): 1.6MM **Privately Held**
WEB: www.sunfrost.com
SIC: 3632 Household refrigerators & freezers

(P-17380)
PANASONIC APPLIANCES REF
Also Called: Paprsa
2001 Sanyo Ave, San Diego (92154-6212)
PHONE..................619 661-1134
Shusaku Nagae, *CEO*
Kazuya Jinno, *President*
Hiroyuki Maotani, *Treasurer*
Shigeki Muneyasu, *Treasurer*
◆ EMP: 64
SALES (est): 60.6MM
SALES (corp-wide): 74.9B **Privately Held**
WEB: www.sanyousa.com
SIC: 3632 3821 3585 Household refrigerators & freezers; freezers, laboratory; cabinets, show & display, refrigerated
HQ: Panasonic Corporation Of North America
2 Riverfront Plz Ste 200
Newark NJ 07102
201 348-7000

(P-17381)
PAR ENGINEERING INC
Also Called: Commercial Cooling
17855 Arenth Ave, City of Industry (91748-1129)
PHONE..................626 964-8700
Hassan John Milani, *President*
EMP: 50 EST: 1965
SQ FT: 70,000
SALES (est): 13.7MM **Privately Held**
SIC: 3632 Freezers, home & farm

(P-17382)
REFRIGERATOR MANUFACTERS INC (PA)
Also Called: Econocold Refrigerators
17018 Edwards Rd, Cerritos (90703-2422)
PHONE..................562 926-2006
Lawrence E Jaffe, *President*
Paula Donohoo, *President*
Russell E Anthony, *Exec VP*
Leo R Lewis, *Exec VP*
EMP: 24
SQ FT: 40,000
SALES (est): 4.9MM **Privately Held**
WEB: www.rmi-econocold.com
SIC: 3632 3585 Household refrigerators & freezers; refrigeration & heating equipment

(P-17383)
RITEMP REFRIGERATION INC
9155 Archibald Ave # 503, Rancho Cucamonga (91730-5255)
PHONE..................909 941-0444
Jesse A Saldamando, *President*
Angelina Saldamando, *Treasurer*
EMP: 10
SQ FT: 7,000

SALES: 188K **Privately Held**
SIC: 3632 1711 Refrigerator cabinets, household: metal & wood; refrigeration contractor

3634 Electric Household Appliances

(P-17384)
AG GLOBAL PRODUCTS LLC
Also Called: Fhi Brands
15301 Blackburn Ave, Norwalk (90650-6842)
PHONE..................323 334-2900
Shauky Gulamani, *President*
Jayson Dodo, *CFO*
Nicolas Bobroff, *Senior VP*
Daniel Bobroff, *Mng Member*
▲ EMP: 35
SALES (est): 6.8MM **Privately Held**
SIC: 3634 3999 Hair curlers, electric; hair & hair-based products

(P-17385)
ALL RISE RECORDS INC
3175 Palisades Dr, Corona (92880-9432)
PHONE..................951 279-2507
Raphael Watkins, *President*
EMP: 16
SQ FT: 8,400
SALES (corp-wide): 2.7MM **Privately Held**
SIC: 3634 Vaporizers, electric: household
PA: All Rise Records Inc.
3175 Palisades Dr
Corona CA 92880
951 279-2507

(P-17386)
BODY CARE RESORT INC
22125 S Vermont Ave, Torrance (90502-2132)
PHONE..................310 328-8888
David Hsiung, *President*
EMP: 10
SALES (est): 132.2K **Privately Held**
WEB: www.bodycareonline.com
SIC: 3634 Massage machines, electric, except for beauty/barber shops

(P-17387)
BRAVA HOME INC
312 Chestnut St, Redwood City (94063-2222)
PHONE..................408 675-2569
John Pleasants, *CEO*
Shih Yu Cheng, *COO*
Dan Yue,
Mark Janoff, *Admin Sec*
EMP: 26
SALES (est): 220.6K **Privately Held**
SIC: 3634 Ovens, portable: household

(P-17388)
CAPITAL TECHNOLOGY INC
13980 Central Ave, Chino (91710-5529)
PHONE..................909 293-8887
Kevin Chih, *CEO*
Julia Akman Chih, *COO*
EMP: 10
SQ FT: 25,000
SALES (est): 2.8MM **Privately Held**
SIC: 3634 Personal electrical appliances

(P-17389)
FOLDIMATE INC
879 White Pine Ct, Oak Park (91377-4769)
PHONE..................805 876-4418
Gal Rozov, *CEO*
Ori Kaplan, *COO*
EMP: 22 EST: 2012
SALES (est): 1MM **Privately Held**
SIC: 3634 Personal electrical appliances

(P-17390)
INNOVATIVE HEARTH PRODUCTS LLC (PA)
Also Called: Lennox
2701 S Harbor Blvd, Santa Ana (92704-5838)
PHONE..................615 925-3417
Mark Klein, *President*
Linda Pahl, *CFO*
Omer Khan, *Administration*

▲ EMP: 33 EST: 2010
SALES (est): 113.1MM **Privately Held**
WEB: www.lennoxhearthproducts.com
SIC: 3634 3433 Heating units, electric (radiant heat): baseboard or wall; heating equipment, except electric

(P-17391)
INNOVATIVE HEARTH PRODUCTS LLC
2701 S Harbor Blvd, Santa Ana (92704-5838)
PHONE..................714 549-7782
EMP: 42
SALES (corp-wide): 113.1MM **Privately Held**
SIC: 3634 Heating units, electric (radiant heat): baseboard or wall
PA: Innovative Hearth Products Llc
2701 S Harbor Blvd
Santa Ana CA 92704
615 925-3417

(P-17392)
INSEAT SOLUTIONS LLC
1871 Wright Ave, La Verne (91750-5817)
PHONE..................562 447-1780
Arthur Liu,
Dickson Liu,
▲ EMP: 22
SALES (est): 4MM **Privately Held**
WEB: www.relaxor.com
SIC: 3634 Massage machines, electric, except for beauty/barber shops

(P-17393)
J & J ACTION INC
3210 S Standard Ave, Santa Ana (92705-5630)
PHONE..................877 327-5268
Przemyslaw Maslowiec, *President*
EMP: 10 EST: 2012
SQ FT: 30,000
SALES: 2.5MM **Privately Held**
SIC: 3634 Toothbrushes, electric

(P-17394)
KATADYN DESALINATION LLC
Also Called: Spectra Watermakers
2220 S Mcdowell Blvd Ext, Petaluma (94954-5659)
PHONE..................415 526-2780
Shawn Hostetter, *Mng Member*
Chris Voxland,
EMP: 20
SQ FT: 8,400
SALES: 4MM **Privately Held**
SIC: 3634 3732 Water pulsating devices, electric; yachts, building & repairing

(P-17395)
KIZURE PRODUCT CO INC
Also Called: Kizure Hair Products & Irons
1950 N Central Ave, Compton (90222-3102)
P.O. Box 2556, Gardena (90247-0120)
PHONE..................310 604-0058
Jerry White, *President*
Lucky White, *Exec VP*
EMP: 33
SQ FT: 40,000
SALES: 2.3MM **Privately Held**
SIC: 3634 2844 Hair dryers, electric; shampoos, rinses, conditioners: hair

(P-17396)
LUMA COMFORT LLC
6600 Katella Ave, Cypress (90630-5104)
PHONE..................855 963-9247
Luke Peters, *President*
Mariella Peters, *Admin Sec*
▲ EMP: 50
SQ FT: 30,000
SALES (est): 3.6MM **Privately Held**
SIC: 3634 Electric housewares & fans

(P-17397)
MILA USA INC
11 Laurel Ave, Belvedere Tiburon (94920-2305)
PHONE..................415 734-8540
Grant Prigge, *CEO*
EMP: 20
SALES (est): 746.9K **Privately Held**
SIC: 3634 7389 Air purifiers, portable;

(P-17398)
MIST & COOL LLC
707 E Hueneme Rd, Oxnard (93033-8654)
PHONE..................805 986-4125
Mike Davis, *Mng Member*
Barry Hanish, *Mng Member*
▲ EMP: 18
SQ FT: 9,500
SALES (est): 2.3MM **Privately Held**
SIC: 3634 Water pulsating devices, electric

(P-17399)
OLISO INC
1200 Harbour Way S 215, Richmond (94804-3636)
PHONE..................415 864-7600
Ehsan Alipour, *CEO*
John Melot, *CFO*
Janice Wong, *Administration*
Sid Keshari, *Opers Staff*
Shann Alipour, *Sales Executive*
▲ EMP: 16
SQ FT: 7,000
SALES (est): 3.4MM **Privately Held**
WEB: www.oliso.com
SIC: 3634 Personal electrical appliances

(P-17400)
OMEGA 2000 GROUP CORP
160 S Carmalita St, Hemet (92543-4230)
PHONE..................951 775-5815
George E Sararu, *President*
Burlacu Lilioara, *CFO*
William Hull, *Director*
▲ EMP: 95
SQ FT: 5,200
SALES: 12.4MM **Privately Held**
WEB: www.omega2000group.com
SIC: 3634 Heating units, for electric appliances

(P-17401)
PACIFIC ACCENT INCORPORATED
623 S Doubleday Ave, Ontario (91761-1520)
PHONE..................909 563-1600
Sophia Juang, *CEO*
▲ EMP: 14 EST: 2010
SQ FT: 600
SALES: 4MM **Privately Held**
SIC: 3634 Housewares, excluding cooking appliances & utensils

(P-17402)
QYK BRANDS LLC
Also Called: Qyksonic
9 Macarthur Pl, Santa Ana (92707-6738)
PHONE..................949 312-7119
Rakesh Tammabattula,
Alexandra Aldana, *Executive Asst*
EMP: 35
SQ FT: 2,000
SALES: 350K **Privately Held**
SIC: 3634 Massage machines, electric, except for beauty/barber shops

(P-17403)
REPOSE CORP
16826 Edwards Rd, Cerritos (90703-2418)
PHONE..................562 921-9299
Johnny Lee, *Principal*
EMP: 10
SALES (est): 861.9K **Privately Held**
SIC: 3634 Massage machines, electric, except for beauty/barber shops

(P-17404)
TOUCH COFFEE & BEVERAGES LLC
15312 Valley Blvd, City of Industry (91746-3324)
P.O. Box 360752, Los Angeles (90036-1251)
PHONE..................626 968-0300
Samuel Kim, *Mng Member*
▲ EMP: 14 EST: 2013
SALES (est): 2.2MM **Privately Held**
SIC: 3634 5149 Coffee makers, electric: household; coffee & tea

(P-17405)
VAPORBROTHERS INC
2908 Oregon Ct Ste I9, Torrance
(90503-2651)
PHONE..............................310 618-1188
Bertram Balch, *President*
Michelle Gilpin, *Office Mgr*
Naomi Hinzo, *Sales Staff*
EMP: 12
SALES (est): 2.1MM **Privately Held**
WEB: www.vaporbrothers.com
SIC: 3634 Electric housewares & fans

3635 Household Vacuum Cleaners

(P-17406)
BETTER CLEANING SYSTEMS INC
Also Called: Kleenrite
1122 Maple St, Madera (93637-5368)
P.O. Box 359 (93639-0359)
PHONE..............................559 673-5700
William Hachtmann, *CEO*
Bill Hachtmann, *President*
Pat Hibben, *Controller*
Christine Farinelli, *Purch Mgr*
Jeremy Wheeler, *Opers Staff*
▲ EMP: 37
SQ FT: 27,620
SALES (est): 4.1MM **Privately Held**
SIC: 3635 Carpet shampooer

(P-17407)
MINI VAC INC
634 E Colorado St, Glendale (91205-1710)
P.O. Box 10850 (91209-3850)
PHONE..............................818 244-6777
Eric Miglins, *CEO*
▲ EMP: 12
SALES (est): 774.9K **Privately Held**
WEB: www.mini-vac.com
SIC: 3635 5064 Household vacuum cleaners; vacuum cleaners

(P-17408)
S & J CARPET CLEANING
1911 Douglas Blvd 85394, Roseville
(95661-3811)
PHONE..............................916 630-9330
John Lizesy, *Partner*
Scott Bailey, *Partner*
Nicole Lizesy, *Admin Sec*
EMP: 16
SALES (est): 1.7MM **Privately Held**
SIC: 3635 Carpet shampooer

(P-17409)
TECHKO KOBOT INC
Also Called: Techko Maid
11 Marconi Ste A, Irvine (92618-2786)
PHONE..............................949 380-7300
Joseph Ko, *President*
▲ EMP: 12
SQ FT: 4,500
SALES (est): 2.5MM **Privately Held**
SIC: 3635 5065 Household vacuum cleaners; security control equipment & systems

(P-17410)
UNOVO LLC
Also Called: Oliso
1200 Hrbour Way S Ste 215, Richmond
(94804)
PHONE..............................415 864-7600
Ehsan Alipour, *Mng Member*
EMP: 10 EST: 2015
SQ FT: 1,400
SALES (est): 2.3MM **Privately Held**
SIC: 3635 3634 Household vacuum cleaners; irons, electric: household

3639 Household Appliances, NEC

(P-17411)
BRENTWOOD APPLIANCES INC
3088 E 46th St, Vernon (90058-2422)
PHONE..............................323 266-4600
Poorad B Panahi, *President*
Maurice Araghi, *Vice Pres*
John Yadgari, *Vice Pres*

▲ EMP: 13
SQ FT: 65,000
SALES (est): 2.1MM **Privately Held**
SIC: 3639 Major kitchen appliances, except refrigerators & stoves

(P-17412)
BSH HOME APPLIANCES CORP (DH)
1901 Main St Ste 600, Irvine (92614-0521)
PHONE..............................949 440-7100
Michael Traub, *President*
Christofer Von Nagel, *President*
Stefan Koss, *CFO*
Christie James, *Treasurer*
Bob Eustice, *Vice Pres*
◆ EMP: 220
SQ FT: 52,000
SALES (est): 543.1MM
SALES (corp-wide): 261.7MM **Privately Held**
WEB: www.bsh-group.us
SIC: 3639 Major kitchen appliances, except refrigerators & stoves
HQ: Bsh Hausgerate Gmbh
Carl-Wery-Str. 34
Munchen 81739
894 590-01

(P-17413)
CNP INDUSTRIES INC
351 Thor Pl, Brea (92821-4133)
PHONE..............................714 482-2320
Harold R Piszczek, *CEO*
Steven L Kirkley, *President*
▲ EMP: 12
SQ FT: 10,000
SALES (est): 2.7MM **Privately Held**
WEB: www.windcrestcnp.com
SIC: 3639 Major kitchen appliances, except refrigerators & stoves

(P-17414)
FISHER & PAYKEL APPLIANCES INC (DH)
695 Town Center Dr # 180, Costa Mesa
(92626-1902)
PHONE..............................949 790-8900
Peter Lockwell, *President*
Matt McConnell, *President*
Sean Robinson, *Vice Pres*
Tina Ngo, *Credit Staff*
Kristy Faulkner, *Accountant*
▲ EMP: 190
SQ FT: 26,000
SALES (est): 41.7MM
SALES (corp-wide): 7.8K **Privately Held**
WEB: www.fisherandpaykelappliances.com
SIC: 3639 3631 5064 5078 Dishwashing machines, household; household cooking equipment; electric household appliances; refrigeration equipment & supplies
HQ: Fisher & Paykel Appliances Usa Holdings Inc.
695 Town Center Dr # 180
Costa Mesa CA 92626
888 936-7872

(P-17415)
HESTAN COMMERCIAL CORPORATION
3375 E La Palma Ave, Anaheim
(92806-2815)
PHONE..............................714 869-2380
Stanley Kin Sui Cheng, *CEO*
Eric Deng, *President*
Steve Pak, *Finance*
Barry Needleman, *Controller*
▲ EMP: 125 EST: 2013
SQ FT: 70,000
SALES (est): 8.4MM **Privately Held**
SIC: 3639 Major kitchen appliances, except refrigerators & stoves
HQ: Meyer Corporation, U.S.
1 Meyer Plz
Vallejo CA 94590
707 551-2800

(P-17416)
NRC USA INC
3700 Wilshire Blvd # 300, Los Angeles
(90010-2919)
PHONE..............................213 325-2780
Jibaek Heo, *President*
Kweon Lee, *Vice Pres*

▲ EMP: 14
SALES: 3.5MM **Privately Held**
SIC: 3639 Major kitchen appliances, except refrigerators & stoves
PA: Nr Communication
648-1 Yeoksam-Dong, Kangnam-Gu
Seoul

(P-17417)
THERMA-TEK RANGE CORP
9121 Atlanta Ave Ste 331, Huntington
Beach (92646-6309)
PHONE..............................570 455-9491
EMP: 25
SQ FT: 30,000
SALES (est): 3.1MM **Privately Held**
SIC: 3639

(P-17418)
TLM INTERNATIONAL INC
Also Called: Dr Heater USA
239 Harbor Way, South San Francisco
(94080-6811)
PHONE..............................650 952-2257
Mr Vincent MA, *President*
James Tan, *Owner*
EMP: 12
SQ FT: 17,000
SALES: 500K **Privately Held**
SIC: 3639 2519 3634 Hot water heaters, household; household furniture, except wood or metal: upholstered; massage machines, electric, except for beauty/barber shops

3641 Electric Lamps

(P-17419)
ALERTLITE NEON CO INC
11116 Tuxford St, Sun Valley (91352-2631)
PHONE..............................818 767-2059
Rio Lee Score Sr, *CEO*
Eric J Score, *President*
Patty Score, *Treasurer*
Edith R 'kitty' Score, *Admin Sec*
EMP: 10 EST: 1946
SQ FT: 7,000
SALES (est): 1.1MM **Privately Held**
SIC: 3641 3645 3446 Tubes, electric light; residential lighting fixtures; ornamental metalwork

(P-17420)
APPLIED PHOTON TECHNOLOGY INC
3346 Arden Rd, Hayward (94545-3923)
PHONE..............................510 780-9500
Leonard Goldfine, *President*
Rafael Olano, *Vice Pres*
Rodney Romero, *Vice Pres*
▲ EMP: 29
SQ FT: 9,300
SALES (est): 5MM **Privately Held**
WEB: www.appliedphoton.com
SIC: 3641 Ultraviolet lamps

(P-17421)
BHK INC
760 E Sunkist St, Ontario (91761-1861)
PHONE..............................909 983-2973
Steve Boland, *President*
Walter Chapman, *Engineer*
▲ EMP: 24
SALES (est): 4.4MM **Privately Held**
SIC: 3641 Health lamps, infrared or ultraviolet

(P-17422)
CASUAL LAMPS CALIFORNIA INC (PA)
15000 S Broadway, Gardena (90248-1820)
PHONE..............................310 323-0105
Steven L Koch, *President*
EMP: 37
SALES (est): 2.1MM **Privately Held**
SIC: 3641 3645 2511 Lamps, fluorescent, electric; table lamps; coffee tables: wood

(P-17423)
DA GLOBAL ENERGY INC
548 Market St Ste 32810, San Francisco
(94104-5401)
PHONE..............................408 916-6303

Donald James Ashley, *CEO*
EMP: 13
SALES (est): 1.1MM **Privately Held**
SIC: 3641 5063 7389 Electric light bulbs, complete; lamps, fluorescent, electric; light bulbs & related supplies

(P-17424)
DASOL INC
Also Called: Coronet Lighting
16210 S Avalon Blvd, Gardena
(90248-2908)
P.O. Box 2065 (90247-0010)
PHONE..............................310 327-6700
Sol Smith, *Ch of Bd*
David Smith, *President*
Mark Smith, *Vice Pres*
▲ EMP: 225 EST: 1944
SQ FT: 120,000
SALES (est): 37.3MM **Privately Held**
WEB: www.coronetlighting.com
SIC: 3641 Electric lamps & parts for generalized applications

(P-17425)
DURALED LTG TECHNOLGIES CORP
15285 Alton Pkwy Ste 200, Irvine
(92618-2372)
PHONE..............................949 753-0162
Allen Fann, *President*
EMP: 16 EST: 2000
SQ FT: 10,000
SALES (est): 1.5MM **Privately Held**
WEB: www.duraled.com
SIC: 3641 3674 Electric lamps; semiconductors & related devices

(P-17426)
ENVISION LED LIGHTING INC
4845 Eastern Ave, Bell (90201-6405)
PHONE..............................213 741-1550
Faramarz Mehrabanian, *CEO*
Joshua Mehraban, *Manager*
EMP: 14
SALES (est): 166.2K **Privately Held**
SIC: 3641 3648 Electric lamps; lighting equipment

(P-17427)
ESTAR LIMITED
15216 Daphne Ave, Gardena (90249-4122)
PHONE..............................310 989-6265
Rick McCoy, *President*
EMP: 50
SALES (est): 5.2MM **Privately Held**
SIC: 3641 5047 Electric lamps; hospital equipment & supplies; dental equipment & supplies; industrial safety devices: first aid kits & masks

(P-17428)
FANLIGHT CORPORATION INC (DH)
Also Called: Plusrite and Ledirect
2000 Sgrove Ave Bldg B, Ontario (91761)
PHONE..............................909 930-6868
Song Qian, *CEO*
Koji Sasaki, *President*
Cecilia Liem, *Treasurer*
Mortimer Zhang, *Project Mgr*
Winsome Lo, *Graphic Designe*
▲ EMP: 15
SQ FT: 32,000
SALES (est): 8.1MM **Privately Held**
WEB: www.fanlightinc.com
SIC: 3641 Electric lamps & parts for generalized applications; electric lamp (bulb) parts; electric light bulbs, complete; glow lamp bulbs
HQ: Plusrite Electric (China) Co., Ltd.
27 Teng Long Road, Wujin
Changzhou 21300
519 863-9702

(P-17429)
HOLLYWOOD LAMP & SHADE CO
Also Called: Kimberly Lighting
2928 Leonis Blvd, Vernon (90058-2916)
PHONE..............................323 585-3999
Fred Nadal, *President*
EMP: 15

SALES (est): 2.1MM **Privately Held**
WEB: www.hollywoodshades.com
SIC: **3641** 3648 3645 Lamps, fluorescent, electric; lamps, incandescent filament, electric; lighting equipment; lamp shades, metal

(P-17430)
IRTRONIX INC
Also Called: Euri Lighting
20900 Normandie Ave B, Torrance
(90502-1602)
PHONE................................310 787-1100
Danny J OH, *President*
Suk J OH, *CFO*
Claudia Funk, *Sales Executive*
Alfredo Zamora, *Manager*
▲ EMP: 12 EST: 2000
SQ FT: 23,000
SALES (est): 7MM **Privately Held**
WEB: www.irtronix.com
SIC: **3641** 5065 Electric lamps & parts for generalized applications; semiconductor devices

(P-17431)
LITEPANELS INC
20600 Plummer St, Chatsworth
(91311-5111)
PHONE................................818 752-7009
Rudy Pohlert, *President*
Tim Latham, *Project Mgr*
Kevin Baxter, *Director*
Byron Brown, *Manager*
▲ EMP: 11
SALES (est): 1.1MM
SALES (corp-wide): 466.8MM **Privately Held**
WEB: www.litepanels.com
SIC: **3641** Electric lamps
HQ: Vitec Group Holdings Limited
Bridge House
Richmond TW9 1
208 332-4600

(P-17432)
NIA ENERGY LLC
23679 Calabasas Rd, Calabasas
(91302-1502)
PHONE................................818 422-8000
Linying Du,
Angelina Leo, *Mng Member*
EMP: 10 EST: 2012
SQ FT: 10,000
SALES: 20MM **Privately Held**
SIC: **3641** Electric lamp (bulb) parts

(P-17433)
OPTIC ARTS INC
1130 Monterey Pass Rd, Monterey Park
(91754-3615)
PHONE................................213 250-6069
Jason Mullen, *CEO*
Mason Barker, *Exec VP*
Dorian L Hicklin, *Exec VP*
Christy Lee, *General Mgr*
Lawrence Wong, *Engineer*
EMP: 26 EST: 2011
SQ FT: 4,000
SALES (est): 8MM **Privately Held**
SIC: **3641** Electric lamps & parts for specialized applications

(P-17434)
OSRAM SYLVANIA INC
13350 Gregg St Ste 101, Poway
(92064-7137)
PHONE................................858 748-5077
Dennis Cohen, *Branch Mgr*
EMP: 377
SALES (corp-wide): 4.8B **Privately Held**
SIC: **3641** Electric lamps
HQ: Osram Sylvania Inc
200 Ballardvale St # 305
Wilmington MA 01887
978 570-3000

(P-17435)
TIVOLI LLC
15602 Mosher Ave, Tustin (92780-6427)
PHONE................................714 957-6101
Marie Paris, *CEO*
Susan Larson, *CEO*
Carrie Verkuil, *Natl Sales Mgr*
Eric Kramer, *Mng Member*
Targetti Poulsen, *Mng Member*

◆ EMP: 50
SALES (est): 15.3MM **Privately Held**
SIC: **3641** 3646 Tubes, electric light; ceiling systems, luminous; fluorescent lighting fixtures, commercial; ornamental lighting fixtures, commercial

(P-17436)
TOPSTAR INTERNATIONAL INC
13668 Valley Blvd Unit D2, City of Industry
(91746-2572)
PHONE................................909 595-8807
Sheng Wang, *CEO*
▲ EMP: 11
SQ FT: 20,000
SALES (est): 1.6MM **Privately Held**
SIC: **3641** Electric light bulbs, complete

3643 Current-Carrying Wiring Devices

(P-17437)
1891 ALTON A CALIFORNIA CO
1891 Alton Pkwy Ste A, Irvine
(92606-4985)
PHONE................................949 261-6402
Elias Khamis, *Owner*
EMP: 15
SALES (est): 1MM **Privately Held**
SIC: **3643** Power line cable

(P-17438)
ABRAMS ELECTRONICS INC
Also Called: Thor Electronics of California
420 W Market St, Salinas (93901-1422)
PHONE................................831 758-6400
Stephen Abrams, *President*
Jeff Abrams, *Vice Pres*
Carol Villagran, *Accounting Mgr*
Estella Saucedo, *Purchasing*
EMP: 42
SQ FT: 28,000
SALES (est): 8MM **Privately Held**
SIC: **3643** 3496 Connectors & terminals for electrical devices; cable, uninsulated wire: made from purchased wire

(P-17439)
AEI MANUFACTURING INC
Also Called: Air Electro
9452 De Soto Ave, Chatsworth
(91311-4910)
P.O. Box 2231 (91313-2231)
PHONE................................818 407-5400
Steven Strull, *President*
EMP: 10
SALES (est): 1.1MM **Privately Held**
WEB: www.aeimanufacturing.com
SIC: **3643** Current-carrying wiring devices

(P-17440)
AERO-ELECTRIC CONNECTOR INC
2280 W 208th St, Torrance (90501-1452)
PHONE................................310 618-3737
Bob Dasilva, *Branch Mgr*
John Vinke, *CFO*
Bea Jamshidian, *Sales Mgr*
Merly Rosario, *Marketing Staff*
Rolando Hernandez, *Manager*
EMP: 15
SALES (corp-wide): 76.6MM **Privately Held**
SIC: **3643** Connectors & terminals for electrical devices
PA: Aero-Electric Connector, Inc.
2280 W 208th St
Torrance CA 90501
310 618-3737

(P-17441)
AERO-ELECTRIC CONNECTOR INC (PA)
2280 W 208th St, Torrance (90501-1452)
PHONE................................310 618-3737
Walter Neubauer, *Chairman*
Walter Neubauer Jr, *CEO*
Mark Edwards, *Info Tech Mgr*
Thinh Nguyen, *Design Engr*
Charles Gelm, *Train & Dev Mgr*
EMP: 360
SQ FT: 65,000

SALES (est): 76.6MM **Privately Held**
WEB: www.aero-electric.com
SIC: **3643** 3678 Connectors & terminals for electrical devices; electronic connectors

(P-17442)
ALLAN KIDD
Also Called: AK Industries
3115 E Las Hermanas St, Compton
(90221-5512)
PHONE................................310 762-1600
Allan Kidd, *Owner*
Loni Miller, *Marketing Mgr*
EMP: 20
SQ FT: 17,000
SALES: 2MM **Privately Held**
WEB: www.ak-ind.com
SIC: **3643** Electric connectors

(P-17443)
AMPHENOL DC ELECTRONICS INC
1870 Little Orchard St, San Jose
(95125-1041)
P.O. Box 28463 (95159-8463)
PHONE................................408 947-4500
David Cianciulli Sr, *CEO*
David Cianciulli Jr, *President*
Ruben Macias, *General Mgr*
Alex Friedrich, *Info Tech Mgr*
Rio Ebbah, *Technology*
EMP: 300
SQ FT: 33,000
SALES (est): 58.2MM
SALES (corp-wide): 7B **Publicly Held**
WEB: www.dcelectronics.com
SIC: **3643** Current-carrying wiring devices
PA: Amphenol Corporation
358 Hall Ave
Wallingford CT 06492
203 265-8900

(P-17444)
AUTOSPLICE INC (PA)
10431 Wtridge Cir Ste 110, San Diego
(92121)
PHONE................................858 535-0077
Santosh RAO, *CEO*
Kevin Barry, *COO*
Jeffrey Cartwright, *CFO*
Ken Krone, *VP Mktg*
▲ EMP: 200 EST: 1954
SQ FT: 20,000
SALES (est): 151.2MM **Privately Held**
SIC: **3643** Electric connectors

(P-17445)
BIZLINK TECHNOLOGY INC (HQ)
47211 Bayside Pkwy, Fremont
(94538-6517)
PHONE................................510 252-0786
Annie Kuo, *President*
Lorena Cinotti, *Officer*
Ted Hsiao, *Vice Pres*
Roger Liang, *Vice Pres*
Anders Peterson, *Vice Pres*
▲ EMP: 80 EST: 1996
SQ FT: 62,000
SALES (est): 32.8MM **Privately Held**
WEB: www.bizlinktech.com
SIC: **3643** Current-carrying wiring devices

(P-17446)
CABLE CONNECTION INC
Also Called: Lorom West
1035 Mission Ct, Fremont (94539-8203)
PHONE................................510 249-9000
Greg Gaches, *President*
Nikki Del Campo, *Administration*
Vince Truong, *QA Dir*
Jay Judoprasetijo, *Project Dir*
Pat Matthews, *Technology*
▲ EMP: 100
SQ FT: 55,000
SALES (est): 26.6MM **Privately Held**
WEB: www.cable-connection.com
SIC: **3643** Current-carrying wiring devices

(P-17447)
CABLETEK INC
525 Finney Ct, Gardena (90248-2037)
P.O. Box 39 (90248-0039)
PHONE................................310 523-5000
Rosa G Lockwood, *President*

Rosa M Garcia, *General Mgr*
▲ EMP: 10
SALES (est): 1.4MM **Privately Held**
SIC: **3643** Current-carrying wiring devices

(P-17448)
CALPICO INC
1387 San Mateo Ave, South San Francisco
(94080-6511)
PHONE................................650 588-2241
Carey Wilson, *President*
Edna Wilson, *Treasurer*
Karen Perazzo, *Sales Staff*
▲ EMP: 23
SQ FT: 20,000
SALES (est): 3.9MM **Privately Held**
WEB: www.calpicoinc.com
SIC: **3643** 3317 3089 3498 Current-carrying wiring devices; steel pipe & tubes; plastic hardware & building products; fabricated pipe & fittings; gaskets, packing & sealing devices

(P-17449)
CARR MANUFACTURING COMPANY INC
19675 Descartes, Foothill Ranch
(92610-2609)
PHONE................................949 215-7952
Michelle R Carraway, *CEO*
Gregory J Carraway, *Admin Sec*
▲ EMP: 11
SQ FT: 5,000
SALES (est): 2.4MM **Privately Held**
WEB: www.carrmfg.com
SIC: **3643** 3679 Power line cable; printed circuit boards; harness assemblies for electronic use: wire or cable

(P-17450)
CELESTICA LLC
280 Campillo St Ste G, Calexico
(92231-3200)
PHONE................................760 357-4880
Michael Garmon, *Principal*
EMP: 400
SALES (est): 214.9K **Privately Held**
SIC: **3643** Current-carrying wiring devices

(P-17451)
CHIPSTART LLC
5537 Blossom Vista Ave, San Jose
(95124-6059)
PHONE................................650 204-7883
Howard Pakosh, *Mng Member*
Bob Lynch, *Sales Dir*
EMP: 19
SQ FT: 100
SALES: 1.9MM **Privately Held**
SIC: **3643** 3823 3826 3674 Bus bars (electrical conductors); electrolytic conductivity instruments, industrial process; thermal conductivity instruments, industrial process type; electrolytic conductivity instruments; semiconductors & related devices

(P-17452)
COAST AIR SUPPLY CO INC
26501 Summit Cir, Santa Clarita
(91350-3049)
PHONE................................818 898-2288
Fred W Sutherland, *CEO*
EMP: 12
SQ FT: 15,000
SALES (est): 2MM **Privately Held**
WEB: www.coastair.com
SIC: **3643**

(P-17453)
CONNECTEC COMPANY INC (PA)
1701 Reynolds Ave, Irvine (92614-5711)
PHONE................................949 252-1077
Rassool Kavezade, *CEO*
Lora Taleb, *CFO*
Mike Taleb, *Treasurer*
▲ EMP: 90
SQ FT: 12,000
SALES (est): 12.8MM **Privately Held**
WEB: www.connectecco.com
SIC: **3643** 3678 Electric connectors; electronic connectors

(P-17454)
CONNECTEC COMPANY INC
3901 S Main St, Santa Ana (92707-5711)
PHONE....................949 252-1077
Lora Taleb, *Branch Mgr*
EMP: 10
SALES (corp-wide): 12.8MM **Privately Held**
SIC: 3643 3678 Electric connectors; electronic connectors
PA: Connectec Company, Inc.
1701 Reynolds Ave
Irvine CA 92614
949 252-1077

(P-17455)
CONNECTION ENTERPRISES INC
4130 Flat Rock Dr Ste 140, Riverside (92505-5864)
PHONE....................951 688-8133
Marabell Lucioto, *Principal*
EMP: 10
SALES (est): 1MM **Privately Held**
SIC: 3643 3679 Current-carrying wiring devices; electronic circuits; electronic loads & power supplies

(P-17456)
COOPER INTERCONNECT INC (DH)
750 W Ventura Blvd, Camarillo (93010-8382)
PHONE....................805 484-0543
Revathi Advaithi, *President*
EMP: 70 **EST:** 1945
SQ FT: 113,000
SALES (est): 23.1MM **Privately Held**
WEB: www.ghtech.com
SIC: 3643 3678 Electric connectors; electronic connectors
HQ: Eaton Corporation
1000 Eaton Blvd
Cleveland OH 44122
440 523-5000

(P-17457)
CTC GLOBAL CORPORATION (PA)
2026 Mcgaw Ave, Irvine (92614-0911)
PHONE....................949 428-8500
J D Sitton, *CEO*
John Mansfield, *President*
Anne McDowell, *President*
Marvin Sepe, *COO*
Gabriel Tashjian, *COO*
▲ **EMP:** 112
SALES (est): 40.2MM **Privately Held**
SIC: 3643 Power line cable

(P-17458)
DATA SOLDER INC
2915 Kilson Dr, Santa Ana (92707-3716)
PHONE....................714 429-9866
Irma Gomez, *President*
Guillermo Gomez, *Vice Pres*
EMP: 14 **EST:** 1997
SQ FT: 4,000
SALES (est): 1.7MM **Privately Held**
WEB: www.solddata.com
SIC: 3643 Solderless connectors (electric wiring devices)

(P-17459)
DC ELECTRONICS INC
1870 Little Orchard St, San Jose (95125-1041)
P.O. Box 67126, Scotts Valley (95067-7126)
PHONE....................408 947-4531
Dave Cianciulli, *President*
Ruben Macias Jr, *COO*
Eric Hynes, *CFO*
Steve Gulesserian, *Vice Pres*
Tuyen Tran, *Engineer*
EMP: 15 **EST:** 1983
SALES (est): 5.2MM **Privately Held**
SIC: 3643 Current-carrying wiring devices

(P-17460)
DDH ENTERPRISE INC (PA)
2220 Oak Ridge Way, Vista (92081-8341)
PHONE....................760 599-0171
David Du, *CEO*
Danny Du, *President*

Jim Wilhelm, *Program Mgr*
Monika Friend, *Office Mgr*
Mike Schold, *MIS Dir*
▲ **EMP:** 160
SQ FT: 42,000
SALES: 30.5MM **Privately Held**
WEB: www.ddhent.com
SIC: 3643 3644 3699 Current-carrying wiring devices; noncurrent-carrying wiring services; electrical equipment & supplies

(P-17461)
DIGGIMAC INC DBA LTG ELEMENT
16885 W Bernardo Dr # 380, San Diego (92127-1618)
PHONE....................858 322-6000
Madeleine Kent, *CEO*
EMP: 10
SALES: 8MM **Privately Held**
SIC: 3643 8748 Lightning protection equipment; lighting consultant

(P-17462)
DMC POWER INC (PA)
623 E Artesia Blvd, Carson (90746-1201)
PHONE....................310 323-1616
Tony Ward, *CEO*
Eben Kane, *CFO*
Ed Cox, *Vice Pres*
Michael Yazdanpanah, *Vice Pres*
Jenny Huo, *Planning*
▲ **EMP:** 77
SQ FT: 40,000
SALES (est): 25.5MM **Privately Held**
SIC: 3643 Current-carrying wiring devices

(P-17463)
ELECTRO ADAPTER INC
Also Called: Plating
20640 Nordhoff St, Chatsworth (91311-6189)
P.O. Box 2560 (91313-2560)
PHONE....................818 998-1198
Ray Fish, *President*
Terrill Fish, *Admin Sec*
Sam Clarke, *Info Tech Mgr*
Ken Ivers, *Info Tech Mgr*
Tonie Melendez, *Info Tech Mgr*
EMP: 67
SQ FT: 54,000
SALES (est): 12.1MM
SALES (corp-wide): 15.5MM **Privately Held**
WEB: www.electroadapter.com
SIC: 3643 Electric connectors
PA: Intritec
20640 Nordhoff St
Chatsworth CA 91311
818 998-1198

(P-17464)
ELECTRONIC CONNECTOR SVC INC
Also Called: Ecs
10541 Ashdale St, Stanton (90680-2621)
PHONE....................714 750-9420
Edward J Stout, *President*
▲ **EMP:** 45
SQ FT: 10,000
SALES (est): 5.5MM **Privately Held**
WEB: www.ecsconn.com
SIC: 3643 Connectors & terminals for electrical devices

(P-17465)
EMP CONNECTORS INC
548 Amapola Ave, Torrance (90501-1472)
PHONE....................310 533-6799
EMP: 20
SQ FT: 39,000
SALES (est): 3.8MM **Privately Held**
WEB: www.empconnectors.com
SIC: 3643 3678 3612

(P-17466)
ESL POWER SYSTEMS INC
2800 Palisades Dr, Corona (92880-9427)
PHONE....................800 922-4188
Michael Hellmers, *President*
David Hellmers, *Vice Pres*
◆ **EMP:** 55
SQ FT: 36,000
SALES (est): 15.5MM **Privately Held**
WEB: www.eslpwr.com
SIC: 3643 Outlets, electric: convenience

(P-17467)
FOXLINK INTERNATIONAL INC (HQ)
925 W Lambert Rd Ste C, Brea (92821-2943)
PHONE....................714 256-1777
Ching Fan Pu, *CEO*
James Lee, *President*
▲ **EMP:** 44
SQ FT: 22,590
SALES (est): 14.2MM
SALES (corp-wide): 3.1B **Privately Held**
WEB: www.foxlink.com
SIC: 3643 3678 3679 3691 Current-carrying wiring devices; electronic connectors; electronic circuits; storage batteries; household audio & video equipment; computer peripheral equipment
PA: Cheng Uei Precision Industry Co., Ltd.
18, Chung Shan Rd.,
New Taipei City 23680
222 699-888

(P-17468)
G D M ELECTRONIC ASSEMBLY INC
Also Called: Gdm Electronic & Medical
2070 Ringwood Ave, San Jose (95131-1745)
PHONE....................408 945-4100
Grant Murphy, *Partner*
Susie Perches, *Partner*
Tamee Pires, *Executive*
Shawn Gorham, *General Mgr*
Karen Guerrero, *Opers Staff*
EMP: 77
SQ FT: 24,000
SALES (est): 20.1MM **Privately Held**
WEB: www.gdm1.com
SIC: 3643 3565 Current-carrying wiring devices; packaging machinery

(P-17469)
GOLD TECHNOLOGIES INC
Also Called: Goldtec USA
1648 Mabury Rd Ste A, San Jose (95133-1097)
PHONE....................408 321-9568
Patricia Tran, *President*
EMP: 25 **EST:** 1998
SQ FT: 12,000
SALES (est): 4.1MM **Privately Held**
WEB: www.goldtec.com
SIC: 3643 Electric connectors

(P-17470)
HI REL CONNECTORS INC
Also Called: Hirel Connectors
760 Wharton Dr, Claremont (91711-4800)
PHONE....................909 626-1820
Fred Baumann, *CEO*
Frederick Bb Baumann, *CEO*
Scott Snedigar, *CFO*
Will Williams, *Division Mgr*
Joshua Kling, *Design Engr*
EMP: 300
SQ FT: 25,000
SALES (est): 60.8MM **Privately Held**
WEB: www.hirelco.net
SIC: 3643 3678 Connectors & terminals for electrical devices; electronic connectors

(P-17471)
HUBBELL INCORPORATED
Also Called: Hubbel Wiring Device Kellems
1392 Sarah Pl Ste A, Ontario (91761-1433)
PHONE....................909 390-8002
Les Green, *Manager*
EMP: 30
SALES (corp-wide): 3.6B **Publicly Held**
WEB: www.hubbell.com
SIC: 3643 Current-carrying wiring devices
PA: Hubbell Incorporated
40 Waterview Dr
Shelton CT 06484
475 882-4000

(P-17472)
HUBBELL INCORPORATED
1829 Thunderbolt Dr, Porterville (93257-9300)
PHONE....................559 783-0470
Mona Satterfield, *Branch Mgr*
EMP: 40

SALES (corp-wide): 3.6B **Publicly Held**
WEB: www.hubbell.com
SIC: 3643 Current-carrying wiring devices
PA: Hubbell Incorporated
40 Waterview Dr
Shelton CT 06484
475 882-4000

(P-17473)
IMPULSE ENTERPRISE
Also Called: Teledyne Impulse
9855 Carroll Canyon Rd, San Diego (92131-1103)
PHONE....................858 565-7050
Paula Ciavarelli, *Human Resources*
Andy Gardner, *Sales Dir*
▲ **EMP:** 19
SALES (est): 3.6MM **Privately Held**
SIC: 3643 Connectors & terminals for electrical devices

(P-17474)
IMPULSE ENTERPRISE
Also Called: Teledyne Impulse
8254 Ronson Rd, San Diego (92111-2015)
PHONE....................858 565-7050
Francis G Faber, *President*
Lois Faber, *CFO*
Raymond Hom, *Vice Pres*
Heather Butler, *Admin Sec*
Som Faramarzi, *Engineer*
▲ **EMP:** 55
SQ FT: 20,000
SALES (est): 9.5MM **Privately Held**
SIC: 3643 Connectors & terminals for electrical devices

(P-17475)
ITT LLC
ITT BIW Connector Systems
500 Tesconi Cir, Santa Rosa (95401-4665)
PHONE....................707 523-2300
Robert Roeser, *Branch Mgr*
Eckhard Konkel, *Vice Pres*
Volodymyr Skrypka, *Project Engr*
Pedro Andrade, *Warehouse Mgr*
Scot Switzer, *Manager*
EMP: 109
SQ FT: 35,000
SALES (corp-wide): 2.5B **Publicly Held**
SIC: 3643 Connectors & terminals for electrical devices
HQ: Itt Llc
1133 Westchester Ave N-100
White Plains NY 10604
914 641-2000

(P-17476)
JOY SIGNAL TECHNOLOGY LLC
1020 Marauder St Ste A, Chico (95973-9028)
PHONE....................530 891-3551
John Joy, *Mng Member*
Gerry Hill, *Buyer*
EMP: 50
SQ FT: 21,000
SALES (est): 10.6MM **Privately Held**
SIC: 3643 Power line cable

(P-17477)
KCB PRECISION
Also Called: K C B
29009 Avenue Penn, Valencia (91355-5426)
PHONE....................661 295-5695
Kenny Bayer, *Principal*
Chris Bayer, *Principal*
EMP: 10
SQ FT: 5,000
SALES (est): 950K **Privately Held**
WEB: www.kcbprecision.com
SIC: 3643 Contacts, electrical; power outlets & sockets

(P-17478)
LEVITON MANUFACTURING CO INC
3760 Kilroy Airport Way # 660, Long Beach (90806-6832)
PHONE....................631 812-6041
Joann Parks, *Manager*
EMP: 25
SALES (corp-wide): 1.7B **Privately Held**
SIC: 3643 Plugs, electric

PA: Leviton Manufacturing Co., Inc.
201 N Service Rd
Melville NY 11747
631 812-6000

(P-17479)
LEVITON MANUFACTURING CO INC
860 Harold Pl, Chula Vista (91914-3550)
PHONE................................619 205-8600
John Nelson, *Principal*
EMP: 319
SALES (corp-wide): 1.7B **Privately Held**
SIC: 3643 Current-carrying wiring devices
PA: Leviton Manufacturing Co., Inc.
201 N Service Rd
Melville NY 11747
631 812-6000

(P-17480)
LIGHTNING DVERSION SYSTEMS LLC
16572 Burke Ln, Huntington Beach (92647-4538)
PHONE................................714 841-1080
Dave Wilmot, *President*
EMP: 14
SQ FT: 6,284
SALES (est): 2.9MM
SALES (corp-wide): 558.1MM **Publicly Held**
WEB: www.lightningdiversion.com
SIC: 3643 3812 Lightning protection equipment; antennas, radar or communications; radar systems & equipment
HQ: Ls Holdings Company, Llc
16572 Burke Ln
Huntington Beach CA 92647
714 841-1080

(P-17481)
LUCIDPORT TECHNOLOGY INC
19287 San Marcos Rd, Saratoga (95070-5677)
PHONE................................408 720-8800
WEI T Liu, *CEO*
EMP: 11
SALES (est): 1.3MM **Privately Held**
SIC: 3643 Bus bars (electrical conductors)

(P-17482)
LYNCOLE GRUNDING SOLUTIONS LLC
Also Called: Lyncole Xit Grounding
3547 Voyager St Ste 204, Torrance (90503-1673)
PHONE................................310 214-4000
Elizabeth B Robertson,
Benjamin Du, *Engineer*
Helen Knapp,
EMP: 25
SQ FT: 10,000
SALES (est): 5.4MM **Privately Held**
WEB: www.lyncole.com
SIC: 3643 8711 Current-carrying wiring devices; consulting engineer

(P-17483)
MERCOTAC INC
6195 Corte Del Cedro # 100, Carlsbad (92011-1549)
PHONE................................760 431-7723
Timothy Leslie, *President*
Dave Brunet, *Treasurer*
Chris Rechlin, *Admin Sec*
Brian Schultz, *Engineer*
Katie Wells, *Prdtn Mgr*
▼ **EMP:** 17
SQ FT: 12,000
SALES (est): 3.9MM **Privately Held**
WEB: www.mercotac.com
SIC: 3643 Connectors & terminals for electrical devices

(P-17484)
MICRO PLASTICS INC
20821 Dearborn St, Chatsworth (91311-5916)
PHONE................................818 882-0244
Lynda Eurton, *President*
Anacleto Gonzalez, *Vice Pres*
Agripina Eurton, *Admin Sec*
EMP: 20 EST: 1956
SQ FT: 11,000

SALES: 2MM **Privately Held**
WEB: www.microplastics.net
SIC: 3643 3089 Connectors & terminals for electrical devices; molding primary plastic

(P-17485)
PASS & SEYMOUR INC
9415 Kruse Rd, Pico Rivera (90660-1430)
PHONE................................562 505-4072
EMP: 534
SALES (corp-wide): 20.7MM **Privately Held**
SIC: 3643 Current-carrying wiring devices
HQ: Pass & Seymour, Inc.
50 Boyd Ave
Syracuse NY 13209
315 468-6211

(P-17486)
PLT ENTERPRISES INC
Also Called: So-Cal Value Added
809 Calle Plano, Camarillo (93012-8516)
PHONE................................805 389-5335
Pamela L Tunis, *President*
Peter L Tunis, *Vice Pres*
Peter Tunis Jr, *General Mgr*
Maribel Alejandre, *Purchasing*
EMP: 75
SQ FT: 41,000
SALES (est): 12.7MM **Privately Held**
WEB: www.so-calvalueadded.com
SIC: 3643 3679 Current-carrying wiring devices; harness assemblies for electronic use: wire or cable

(P-17487)
PRECISION STAMPINGS INC (PA)
Also Called: P S I
500 Egan Ave, Beaumont (92223-2132)
PHONE................................951 845-1174
Herman Viets, *Ch of Bd*
Peter Gailing, *Shareholder*
Frauke Roth, *Shareholder*
Keith Roth, *Shareholder*
Herta Viets, *Shareholder*
EMP: 32
SQ FT: 25,000
SALES (est): 4.9MM **Privately Held**
WEB: www.precisionstampingsinc.com
SIC: 3643 5084 7539 Contacts, electrical; tool & die makers' equipment; machine shop, automotive

(P-17488)
Q-LITE USA LLC
3691 Lenawee Ave, Los Angeles (90016-4310)
PHONE................................310 736-2977
Halston Mikail, *Mng Member*
EMP: 220 EST: 2013
SQ FT: 80,000
SALES: 27MM **Privately Held**
SIC: 3643 Lightning arrestors & coils

(P-17489)
SIMPLY AUTOMATED INC
6108 Avd Encinas Ste B, Carlsbad (92011-1044)
PHONE................................760 431-2100
Frederick J Kiko, *President*
▲ **EMP:** 11
SQ FT: 7,300
SALES (est): 1.8MM **Privately Held**
WEB: www.simply-automated.com
SIC: 3643

(P-17490)
SOURIAU USA INC (DH)
1750 Commerce Way, Paso Robles (93446-3620)
PHONE................................805 238-2840
Rob Hanes, *President*
◆ **EMP:** 46
SQ FT: 55,000
SALES: 35MM
SALES (corp-wide): 2B **Publicly Held**
SIC: 3643 Bus bars (electrical conductors)
HQ: Souriau
9 Rue De La Porte De Buc
Versailles 78000
130 847-799

(P-17491)
SPIRE MANUFACTURING INC
49016 Milmont Dr, Fremont (94538-7301)
PHONE................................510 226-1070
Christine Bui, *CEO*
Achilleas Vezirir, *President*
▲ **EMP:** 20
SALES (est): 3.3MM **Privately Held**
SIC: 3643 3674 Power outlets & sockets; lamp sockets & receptacles (electric wiring devices); integrated circuits, semiconductor networks, etc.

(P-17492)
SULLINS ELECTRONICS CORP (PA)
Also Called: Sullins Connector Solutions
801 E Mission Rd B, San Marcos (92069-3002)
PHONE................................760 744-0125
Kayvan Sullins, *CEO*
▲ **EMP:** 44
SQ FT: 33,000
SALES (est): 9.9MM **Privately Held**
WEB: www.edgecards.com
SIC: 3643 3678 Connectors & terminals for electrical devices; electronic connectors

(P-17493)
SUPERIOR GROUNDING SYSTEMS
Also Called: S G S
16021 Arrow Hwy Ste A, Baldwin Park (91706-2062)
P.O. Box 2171, Irwindale (91706-1112)
PHONE................................626 814-1981
Steve Phan, *General Ptnr*
EMP: 50
SQ FT: 15,000
SALES (est): 6.1MM **Privately Held**
WEB: www.sgscorp.com
SIC: 3643 Connectors & terminals for electrical devices

(P-17494)
T MCGEE ELECTRIC INC
12375 Mills Ave Ste 2, Chino (91710-2082)
PHONE................................909 591-6461
Trent McGee, *President*
EMP: 10
SQ FT: 15,000
SALES (est): 1.5MM **Privately Held**
SIC: 3643 Solderless connectors (electric wiring devices); ground clamps (electric wiring devices)

(P-17495)
TE CONNECTIVITY CORPORATION
305 Constitution Dr, Menlo Park (94025-1110)
PHONE................................650 361-3333
Thomas Lynch, *President*
EMP: 800
SALES (corp-wide): 13.1B **Privately Held**
SIC: 3643 Connectors & terminals for electrical devices
HQ: Te Connectivity Corporation
1050 Westlakes Dr
Berwyn PA 19312
610 893-9800

(P-17496)
TE CONNECTIVITY CORPORATION
Also Called: Raychem Product Division
501 Oakside Ave Side, Redwood City (94063-3800)
PHONE................................650 361-2495
EMP: 14
SALES (corp-wide): 13.1B **Privately Held**
SIC: 3643 Connectors & terminals for electrical devices
HQ: Te Connectivity Corporation
1050 Westlakes Dr
Berwyn PA 19312
610 893-9800

(P-17497)
TE CONNECTIVITY CORPORATION
Also Called: Elcon Power Conectr Pdts Group
307 Constitution Dr, Menlo Park (94025-1110)
PHONE................................650 361-3306
Don Wood, *Branch Mgr*
EMP: 20
SALES (corp-wide): 13.1B **Privately Held**
WEB: www.raychem.com
SIC: 3643 Current-carrying wiring devices
HQ: Te Connectivity Corporation
1050 Westlakes Dr
Berwyn PA 19312
610 893-9800

(P-17498)
TE CONNECTIVITY CORPORATION
Also Called: Raychem Wire Division
501 Oakside Ave Side, Redwood City (94063-3800)
PHONE................................650 361-2495
Don Reed, *Director*
EMP: 400
SALES (corp-wide): 13.1B **Privately Held**
WEB: www.raychem.com
SIC: 3643 Connectors & terminals for electrical devices
HQ: Te Connectivity Corporation
1050 Westlakes Dr
Berwyn PA 19312
610 893-9800

(P-17499)
TECHNICAL RESOURCE INDUSTRIES (PA)
Also Called: T R I
12854 Daisy Ct, Yucaipa (92399-2026)
PHONE................................909 446-1109
Reinhard Thalmayer, *President*
EMP: 25
SQ FT: 5,000
SALES: 3MM **Privately Held**
SIC: 3643 Electric connectors

(P-17500)
TELEDYNE INSTRUMENTS INC
Also Called: Teledyne Impulse
9855 Carroll Canyon Rd, San Diego (92131-1103)
PHONE................................858 565-7050
Raymond Hom, *Manager*
Heather Butler, *General Mgr*
Michael Solorzano, *QC Mgr*
Andy Gardner, *Sales Staff*
Stan Logan, *Cust Mgr*
EMP: 67
SALES (corp-wide): 2.6B **Publicly Held**
WEB: www.teledyne.com
SIC: 3643 Connectors & terminals for electrical devices
HQ: Teledyne Instruments, Inc.
1049 Camino Dos Rios
Thousand Oaks CA 91360
805 373-4545

(P-17501)
TOBAR INDUSTRIES
912 Olinder Ct, San Jose (95122-2619)
PHONE................................408 494-3530
Elias Antoun, *CEO*
Farid Ghantous, *COO*
William Delaney, *CFO*
EMP: 95
SQ FT: 58,516
SALES (est): 11.3MM **Privately Held**
WEB: www.tobar-ind.com
SIC: 3643 3444 Current-carrying wiring devices; sheet metalwork

(P-17502)
TRI-STAR ELECTRONICS INTL INC (HQ)
Also Called: Carlisle Interconnect
2201 Rosecrans Ave, El Segundo (90245-4910)
PHONE................................310 536-0444
John Berlin, *President*
Amelia Murillo, *Vice Pres*
Ben Damon, *Info Tech Dir*
Henry Le, *Business Mgr*
◆ **EMP:** 270
SQ FT: 80,000

▲ = Import ▼=Export
◆ =Import/Export

SALES (est): 96MM
SALES (corp-wide): 4B **Publicly Held**
WEB: www.tri-starelectronics.com
SIC: 3643 Connectors, electric cord
PA: Carlisle Companies Incorporated
16430 N Scottsdale Rd # 400
Scottsdale AZ 85254
480 781-5000

(P-17503)
TRS INTERNATIONAL MFG INC
27152 Burbank, Foothill Ranch
(92610-2503)
PHONE...................................949 855-0673
Kevin Yin, *President*
Y P Ting, *Shareholder*
Ling Yin, *Treasurer*
▲ EMP: 10
SQ FT: 7,500
SALES (est): 2.2MM **Privately Held**
WEB: www.trsintl.com
SIC: 3643 Power line cable

(P-17504)
WASCO SALES & MARKETING INC
2245 A St, Santa Maria (93455-1008)
PHONE...................................805 739-2747
Ronald Way, *President*
Brenda Way, *Shareholder*
Dave Way, *Shareholder*
Dana Way, *Admin Sec*
Carrie Way, *Manager*
◆ EMP: 20
SQ FT: 9,000
SALES (est): 3.1MM **Privately Held**
WEB: www.wascoinc.com
SIC: 3643 Electric switches

(P-17505)
WATT STOPPER INC (DH)
Also Called: Watt Stopper Le Grand
2700 Zanker Rd Ste 168, San Jose
(95134-2140)
PHONE...................................408 988-5331
Tom Lowery, *CEO*
Aaron Lee, *Admin Sec*
Bryan Pike, *Manager*
▲ EMP: 30
SQ FT: 16,000
SALES (est): 54.5MM
SALES (corp-wide): 20.7MM **Privately Held**
WEB: www.wattstopper.com
SIC: 3643 3646 3645 Current-carrying wiring devices; commercial indusl & institutional electric lighting fixtures; residential lighting fixtures
HQ: Legrand Holding, Inc.
60 Woodlawn St
West Hartford CT 06110
860 233-6251

(P-17506)
XMULTIPLE TECHNOLOGIES INC
Also Called: Slashpoint Share Drive
1060 E Los Angeles Ave, Simi Valley
(93065-1827)
PHONE...................................805 579-1100
Alan Pocrass, *CEO*
Jeremy Chu, *President*
Mr Drew Stoiberg, *VP Sales*
Mike Basowski, *Manager*
Don Diamond, *Manager*
EMP: 1500 EST: 2001
SALES (est): 80.6MM **Privately Held**
WEB: www.starburosthomepage.com
SIC: 3643 Connectors & terminals for electrical devices

3644 Noncurrent-Carrying Wiring Devices

(P-17507)
CHASE CORPORATION
132 E Colorado Blvd, Pasadena
(91105-1919)
PHONE...................................626 395-7706
Paul Schwab, *Branch Mgr*
EMP: 11

SALES (corp-wide): 252.5MM **Publicly Held**
SIC: 3644 Noncurrent-carrying wiring services
PA: Chase Corporation
295 University Ave
Westwood MA 02090
781 332-0700

(P-17508)
CHASE CORPORATION
20001 Brookhurst St, Huntington Beach
(92646-4922)
PHONE...................................714 964-6268
EMP: 11
SALES (corp-wide): 252.5MM **Publicly Held**
SIC: 3644 Noncurrent-carrying wiring services
PA: Chase Corporation
295 University Ave
Westwood MA 02090
781 332-0700

(P-17509)
COOPER INTERCONNECT INC
Burton Electrical Engineering
750 W Ventura Blvd, Camarillo
(93010-8382)
PHONE...................................805 553-9632
Richard Busch, *Branch Mgr*
Terry Storms, *Info Tech Mgr*
EMP: 40 **Privately Held**
WEB: www.vikcon.com
SIC: 3644 3643 3728 3699 Outlet boxes (electric wiring devices); current-carrying wiring devices; aircraft parts & equipment; electrical equipment & supplies; electronic connectors
HQ: Cooper Interconnect, Inc.
750 W Ventura Blvd
Camarillo CA 93010
805 484-0543

(P-17510)
CREFTCON INDUSTRIES INC
Also Called: Regal Mfg Co
900 Ajax Ave, City of Industry (91748-1128)
P.O. Box 1269, La Puente (91749-1269)
PHONE...................................203 377-5944
Leonard W Freibott, *President*
Win Freibott, *Corp Secy*
Mary M Butler, *Vice Pres*
Kathy Freibott, *Vice Pres*
Michael E Freibott, *Vice Pres*
EMP: 160
SQ FT: 85,000
SALES (est): 17.4MM **Privately Held**
WEB: www.regalfittings.com
SIC: 3644 3432 Electric conduits & fittings; plumbers' brass goods: drain cocks, faucets, spigots, etc.

(P-17511)
CWI TRADING
714 Elaine Dr, Stockton (95207-4803)
PHONE...................................209 981-7023
Richard Chu, *Principal*
EMP: 10
SALES (est): 500K **Privately Held**
SIC: 3644 Noncurrent-carrying wiring services

(P-17512)
DRIVEN RACEWAY AND FAMILY ENTE
4601 Redwood Dr, Rohnert Park
(94928-7941)
PHONE...................................707 585-3748
Rodney Towery, *Principal*
EMP: 17
SALES (est): 2.6MM **Privately Held**
SIC: 3644 Raceways

(P-17513)
ENOVA ENGINEERING LLC (PA)
Also Called: Garlord Manufacturing Company
1088 Mt Clair Dr, Ceres (95307)
P.O. Box 547 (95307-0547)
PHONE...................................209 538-3313
Howard Logsdon,
Vickie Ewald, *Office Mgr*
Keith Mello,
EMP: 16
SQ FT: 30,000

SALES (est): 2.9MM **Privately Held**
SIC: 3644 3469 Fuse boxes, electric; metal stampings

(P-17514)
FRASE ENTERPRISES
Also Called: Kortick Manufacturer Co
2261 Carion Ct, Pittsburg (94565-4029)
PHONE...................................510 856-3600
Robert C Frase, *CEO*
Robert Spigel, *President*
Lily Frey, *Controller*
Ron Matthews, *Sales Staff*
Gloria Recchioni,
▲ EMP: 26 EST: 1891
SQ FT: 90,000
SALES (est): 7MM **Privately Held**
WEB: www.kortick.com
SIC: 3644 3462 Insulators & insulation materials, electrical; pole line hardware forgings, ferrous

(P-17515)
GUND COMPANY INC
4701 E Airport Dr, Ontario (91761-7817)
PHONE...................................909 890-9300
Ricardo Beinar, *Manager*
EMP: 15
SALES (corp-wide): 70MM **Privately Held**
WEB: www.thegundcompany.com
SIC: 3644 Insulators & insulation materials, electrical
PA: The Gund Company Inc
2121 Walton Rd
Saint Louis MO 63114
314 423-5200

(P-17516)
ONE TIME UTILITY SALES INC
Also Called: One Time Utilities Sales
501 N Garfield St, Santa Ana (92701-4756)
PHONE...................................714 953-5700
Brian Elliott, *President*
Denisse Elliott, *CFO*
Joe Castro, *General Mgr*
EMP: 20 EST: 2011
SALES (est): 2.1MM **Privately Held**
SIC: 3644 5051 5063 5087 Electric conduits & fittings; cable, wire; rods, wire (not insulated); electrical fittings & construction materials; cable conduit; concrete burial vaults & boxes

(P-17517)
PRECISION FIBERGLASS PRODUCTS
3105 Kashiwa St, Torrance (90505-4089)
PHONE...................................310 539-7470
Robby D Ross, *President*
Lucille Ross, *Vice Pres*
Randal A Ross, *Vice Pres*
Loretta Mora, *Financial Exec*
EMP: 25
SQ FT: 13,300
SALES (est): 4.2MM **Privately Held**
SIC: 3644 Insulators & insulation materials, electrical

(P-17518)
SAF-T-CO SUPPLY
Also Called: All American Pipe Bending
1300 E Normandy Pl, Santa Ana
(92705-4138)
PHONE...................................714 547-9975
Patricia McDonald, *President*
Paul McDonald, *Corp Secy*
Robyn Dague, *Vice Pres*
EMP: 50
SQ FT: 24,000
SALES (est): 15.2MM **Privately Held**
WEB: www.saftco.com
SIC: 3644 5032 5251 5074 Noncurrent-carrying wiring services; brick, stone & related material; hardware; pipes & fittings, plastic; electrical apparatus & equipment

(P-17519)
TODAY PVC BENDING INC
501 N Garfield St, Santa Ana (92701-4756)
PHONE...................................714 953-5707
Joe Castro, *President*
Juan Martinez, *Principal*
Marcellino Rios, *Principal*
EMP: 14

SALES (est): 1.3MM **Privately Held**
SIC: 3644 Electric conduits & fittings

(P-17520)
WESTERN TUBE & CONDUIT CORP (HQ)
2001 E Dominguez St, Long Beach
(90810-1088)
PHONE...................................310 537-6300
Barry Zekelman, *CEO*
Irene Davis, *CFO*
Andy Hardesty, *Regional Mgr*
Joe Sheridan, *Regional Mgr*
Kathy Bowden, *Prgrmr*
▲ EMP: 216 EST: 2004
SQ FT: 420,000
SALES (est): 200MM **Privately Held**
WEB: www.westerntube.com
SIC: 3644 3446 3317 Electric conduits & fittings; fences or posts, ornamental iron or steel; tubing, mechanical or hypodermic sizes: cold drawn stainless

(P-17521)
WIRE GUARD SYSTEMS INC
2050 E Slauson Ave, Huntington Park
(90255-2799)
PHONE...................................323 588-2166
Frank Spitzer, *President*
Ann Spitzer, *Vice Pres*
EMP: 10
SALES (est): 1.6MM **Privately Held**
SIC: 3644 Junction boxes, electric

3645 Residential Lighting Fixtures

(P-17522)
ALGER-TRITON INC
Also Called: Alger International
5600 W Jefferson Blvd, Los Angeles
(90016)
PHONE...................................310 229-9500
Mishel Michael, *Principal*
◆ EMP: 28
SALES (est): 6.3MM **Privately Held**
WEB: www.algerco.com
SIC: 3645 Residential lighting fixtures

(P-17523)
AMERICAN NAIL PLATE LTG INC
Also Called: Anp Lighting
9044 Del Mar Ave, Montclair (91763-1627)
PHONE...................................909 982-1807
Harry Foster, *CEO*
Ron Foster, *Treasurer*
Joan Foster, *Vice Pres*
Bob Foster, *Admin Sec*
▲ EMP: 70
SQ FT: 13,000
SALES (est): 13.2MM **Privately Held**
SIC: 3645 3646 Residential lighting fixtures; commercial indusl & institutional electric lighting fixtures

(P-17524)
ANTHONY CALIFORNIA INC (PA)
14485 Monte Vista Ave, Chino
(91710-5728)
PHONE...................................909 627-0351
Kuei-Lan Yeh, *CEO*
Cindy Chang, *Treasurer*
Darien Chung, *Sales Mgr*
◆ EMP: 30
SALES (est): 3.2MM **Privately Held**
SIC: 3645 5063 5023 Residential lighting fixtures; lighting fixtures; lamps: floor, boudoir, desk

(P-17525)
APEX DIGITAL INC
4401 Eucalyptus Ave # 110, Chino
(91710-9707)
PHONE...................................909 923-8686
David Ji, *CEO*
Alice Hsu, *COO*
Scott Popovich, *Exec VP*
Shannon Tang, *Human Res Mgr*
Linda Smith, *Purch Dir*
▲ EMP: 18
SQ FT: 14,000

SALES (est): 4.3MM **Privately Held**
WEB: www.apexdigitalinc.com
SIC: 3645 Residential lighting fixtures

(P-17526)
ART MANUFACTURERS INC
623 Young St, Santa Ana (92705-5633)
PHONE..............................714 540-9125
Rafio Franco, *President*
EMP: 30
SQ FT: 11,000
SALES (est): 2.1MM **Privately Held**
SIC: 3645 3648 Residential lighting fix-
tures; lighting equipment

(P-17527)
ARTIVA USA INC
12866 Ann St Ste 1, Santa Fe Springs
(90670-3064)
PHONE..............................562 298-8968
Jane Wang, *Manager*
EMP: 50 **Privately Held**
SIC: 3645 5063 Residential lighting fix-
tures; lighting fixtures
PA: Artiva Usa Inc.
13901 Magnolia Ave
Chino CA 91710

(P-17528)
ARTIVA USA INC (PA)
13901 Magnolia Ave, Chino (91710-7030)
PHONE..............................909 628-1388
PO Y Webb, *President*
▲ EMP: 35
SQ FT: 20,000
SALES: 12MM **Privately Held**
SIC: 3645 5063 Residential lighting fix-
tures; lighting fixtures

(P-17529)
B-K LIGHTING INC
40429 Brickyard Dr, Madera (93636-9515)
PHONE..............................559 438-5800
Douglas W Hagen, *President*
Nathan Sloan, *President*
Douglas Hagen, *Vice Pres*
Craig Reed, *Technical Staff*
▲ EMP: 90
SQ FT: 70,000
SALES (est): 20.2MM **Privately Held**
WEB: www.bklighting.com
SIC: 3645 3646 5063 Residential lighting
fixtures; commercial indusl & institutional
electric lighting fixtures; electrical appara-
tus & equipment

(P-17530)
BASE LITE CORPORATION
Also Called: Baselite
12260 Eastend Ave, Chino (91710-2008)
PHONE..............................909 444-2776
Moaaa A Teixeira, *CEO*
Nick Jones, *Sales Executive*
EMP: 38
SQ FT: 10,000
SALES (est): 10.2MM **Privately Held**
WEB: www.baselite.com
SIC: 3645 3646 Residential lighting fix-
tures; commercial indusl & institutional
electric lighting fixtures

(P-17531)
BRUCE EICHER INC (PA)
8755 Melrose Ave, Los Angeles
(90069-5014)
PHONE..............................310 657-4630
Hugh Duff Rubertson, *President*
Evan James Buchannan, *Vice Pres*
EMP: 15
SQ FT: 7,500
SALES (est): 2.2MM **Privately Held**
SIC: 3645 3646 Residential lighting fix-
tures; commercial indusl & institutional
electric lighting fixtures

(P-17532)
CRAFTSMAN LIGHTING
14266 Valley Blvd Ste A, La Puente
(91746-2927)
PHONE..............................626 330-8512
Gilbert Orosco, *Owner*
Onelio Orozco, *General Mgr*
EMP: 11
SQ FT: 5,000

SALES: 500K **Privately Held**
WEB: www.craftsmanoutdoorlighting.com
SIC: 3645 Residential lighting fixtures

(P-17533)
DAB INC
Also Called: Spectrum Lighting
13415 Marquardt Ave, Santa Fe Springs
(90670-5012)
PHONE..............................562 623-4773
David A Boose, *President*
▲ EMP: 52
SQ FT: 31,000
SALES (est): 9.3MM **Privately Held**
SIC: 3645 3648 3646 Residential lighting
fixtures; decorative area lighting fixtures;
commercial indusl & institutional electric
lighting fixtures

(P-17534)
ELATION LIGHTING INC
6122 S Eastern Ave, Commerce
(90040-3402)
PHONE..............................323 213-4552
John Lopez, *Principal*
Ray Villasenor, *Sales Staff*
▲ EMP: 17
SALES (est): 2.7MM **Privately Held**
SIC: 3645 Residential lighting fixtures

(P-17535)
FEIT ELECTRIC COMPANY INC
(PA)
4901 Gregg Rd, Pico Rivera (90660-2108)
PHONE..............................562 463-2852
Aaron Feit, *CEO*
Toby Feit, *CFO*
Alan Feit, *Exec VP*
Daisy Soza, *Technology*
Mandy Dominguez, *Analyst*
◆ EMP: 160 EST: 1978
SQ FT: 300,000
SALES (est): 50MM **Privately Held**
WEB: www.feit.com
SIC: 3645 3641 5023 3646 Residential
lighting fixtures; electric light bulbs, com-
plete; lamps, fluorescent, electric; home
furnishings; commercial indusl & institu-
tional electric lighting fixtures; pressed &
blown glass

(P-17536)
GENERATION ALPHA INC
853 Sandhill Ave, Carson (90746-1210)
PHONE..............................888 998-8881
Alan Lien, *CEO*
Alvin Hao, *President*
Tiffany Davis, *COO*
Simon Siu, *General Mgr*
Josh Armitage, *Sales Mgr*
EMP: 15
SQ FT: 19,060
SALES: 8.9MM **Privately Held**
SIC: 3645 Garden, patio, walkway & yard
lighting fixtures: electric

(P-17537)
GLOBALUX LIGHTING LLC
2037 S Vineyard Ave, Ontario
(91761-8066)
PHONE..............................909 591-7506
Esmail K Parekh, *Mng Member*
Nausheen Tabani,
Esamail K Parekh, *Mng Member*
▲ EMP: 16
SQ FT: 22,000
SALES (est): 2.7MM **Privately Held**
SIC: 3645 3646 Residential lighting fix-
tures; commercial indusl & institutional
electric lighting fixtures

(P-17538)
GREEN CREATIVE LLC
1200 Bayhill Dr Ste 220, San Bruno
(94066-3006)
PHONE..............................866 774-5433
Cole Zucker, *Mng Member*
Michael P Santoni, *Treasurer*
Guillume Vidal,
▲ EMP: 50
SALES (est): 11.9MM
SALES (corp-wide): 1.4B **Privately Held**
SIC: 3645 Fluorescent lighting fixtures,
residential; floor lamps

PA: Harbour Group Ltd.
7733 Forsyth Blvd Fl 23
Saint Louis MO 63105
314 727-5550

(P-17539)
HIVE LIGHTING INC
525 S Hewitt St, Los Angeles (90013-2217)
PHONE..............................310 773-4362
Robert Bruce Rutherford, *President*
Jamie Patterson, *Mktg Dir*
Mitch Gross, *Consultant*
EMP: 12
SALES (est): 962K **Privately Held**
SIC: 3645 Residential lighting fixtures

(P-17540)
KABUSHIKI KISHA HIGUCHI
SHOKAI
Also Called: Higuchi Inc., USA
2281 W 205th St Ste 107, Torrance
(90501-1450)
PHONE..............................310 212-7234
Mikio Morinaga, *Principal*
Kabushiki Shokai, *Principal*
Carmine Sapienza, *Manager*
▲ EMP: 11
SALES (est): 1.5MM **Privately Held**
SIC: 3645 Residential lighting fixtures

(P-17541)
KONCEPT TECHNOLOGIES INC
429 E Huntington Dr, Monrovia
(91016-3632)
PHONE..............................323 261-8999
Kenneth Ng, *President*
Edmund Ng, *Vice Pres*
William Lam, *Opers Spvr*
Billy Yu, *Sales Staff*
▲ EMP: 10
SQ FT: 14,000
SALES (est): 8.6MM **Privately Held**
WEB: koncept.com
SIC: 3645 3646 Residential lighting fix-
tures; commercial indusl & institutional
electric lighting fixtures

(P-17542)
LIGHTCRAFT OUTDOOR
ENVIRONMNTS
Also Called: Lightclub USA
9811 Owensmouth Ave Ste 1, Chatsworth
(91311-3800)
PHONE..............................818 349-2663
Bruce Dennis, *President*
Jorge Fuentes, *Admin Asst*
▲ EMP: 16
SQ FT: 5,000
SALES: 3.5MM **Privately Held**
SIC: 3645 5063 Garden, patio, walkway &
yard lighting fixtures: electric; lighting fit-
tings & accessories

(P-17543)
LIGHTS OF AMERICA INC (PA)
611 Reyes Dr, Walnut (91789-3098)
PHONE..............................909 594-7883
Usman Vakil, *CEO*
Brian Halliwell, *Chief Mktg Ofcr*
Farooq Vakil, *Exec VP*
Chin Tara, *Vice Pres*
Rosa Anguiano, *Purchasing*
▲ EMP: 500
SQ FT: 210,000
SALES (est): 247.5MM **Privately Held**
WEB: www.lightsofamerica.com
SIC: 3645 3646 3641 Fluorescent lighting
fixtures, residential; fluorescent lighting
fixtures, commercial; electric lamps

(P-17544)
LIGHTWAVE PDL INC
1246 E Lexington Ave, Pomona
(91766-5561)
PHONE..............................909 548-3677
Paul Loh, *President*
Peter Lau, *CFO*
Ginger Patton, *Office Mgr*
▲ EMP: 10
SQ FT: 7,500
SALES (est): 1.7MM **Privately Held**
WEB: www.lwlight.com
SIC: 3645 Fluorescent lighting fixtures,
residential

(P-17545)
LUNA SCIENCES CORPORATION
18218 Mcdurmott E Ste A, Irvine
(92614-4746)
PHONE..............................949 225-0000
▲ EMP: 13 EST: 2010
SALES (est): 1.8MM **Privately Held**
SIC: 3645 Residential lighting fixtures

(P-17546)
MAXIM LIGHTING
253 Vineland Ave, City of Industry
(91746-2319)
PHONE..............................626 956-4200
Jacob Sperling, *President*
Zvi Sperling, *Vice Pres*
▲ EMP: 103
SQ FT: 285,000
SALES (est): 15.7MM **Privately Held**
WEB: www.maximlighting.com
SIC: 3645 Residential lighting fixtures

(P-17547)
MAXIM LIGHTING INTL INC (PA)
253 Vineland Ave, City of Industry
(91746-2319)
PHONE..............................626 956-4200
Jacob Sperling, *CEO*
Michael S Andrews, *CFO*
Zvi Sperling, *Corp Secy*
Jessica Tseng, *Admin Asst*
Louis Pinelo, *Marketing Staff*
▲ EMP: 250
SQ FT: 26,000
SALES (est): 75MM **Privately Held**
SIC: 3645 Residential lighting fixtures

(P-17548)
MAXIM LIGHTING INTL INC
247 Vineland Ave, City of Industry
(91746-2319)
PHONE..............................626 956-4200
EMP: 51
SALES (corp-wide): 75MM **Privately
Held**
SIC: 3645 Residential lighting fixtures
PA: Maxim Lighting International, Inc.
253 Vineland Ave
City Of Industry CA 91746
626 956-4200

(P-17549)
NIC PROTECTION INC
7135 Foothill Blvd, Tujunga (91042-2716)
PHONE..............................818 249-2539
Vahik Arzoomanian, *President*
EMP: 12
SALES (est): 1.5MM **Privately Held**
SIC: 3645 1521 Residential lighting fix-
tures; repairing fire damage, single-family
houses

(P-17550)
NL&A COLLECTIONS INC
Also Called: Nova
6323 Maywood Ave, Huntington Park
(90255-4531)
P.O. Box 661820, Los Angeles (90066-
8820)
PHONE..............................323 277-6266
Daniel Edelist, *President*
Minal Chaudhary, *Vice Pres*
Sohail Rajani, *Accountant*
▲ EMP: 40
SQ FT: 48,675
SALES (est): 8MM **Privately Held**
WEB: www.novalamps.com
SIC: 3645 5023 Boudoir lamps; lamps:
floor, boudoir, desk

(P-17551)
ORIGINALS 22 INC
3675 Placentia Ct, Chino (91710-2900)
PHONE..............................909 993-5050
Andrew Braden, *Principal*
EMP: 10
SALES (est): 1.4MM **Privately Held**
SIC: 3645 Light shades, metal

(P-17552)
ORION CHANDELIER INC
2202 S Wright St, Santa Ana (92705-5316)
PHONE..............................714 668-9668
Paul Depersis, *President*
Kirk Fisher, *Assistant VP*
◆ EMP: 17 EST: 1998

▲ = Import ▼=Export
◆ =Import/Export

SQ FT: 3,000
SALES (est): 3MM **Privately Held**
WEB: www.orionchandelier.com
SIC: 3645 Chandeliers, residential

(P-17553)
PATIO PARADISE INC
444 Athol St, San Bernardino (92401-1907)
PHONE..................................626 715-4869
Peng Sun, *CEO*
EMP: 10
SALES (est): 419K **Privately Held**
SIC: 3645 Garden, patio, walkway & yard
lighting fixtures: electric

(P-17554)
PHILIPS NORTH AMERICA LLC
11201 Iberia St Ste A, Jurupa Valley
(91752-3280)
PHONE..................................909 574-1800
Kenneth Parivar, *Branch Mgr*
EMP: 20
SALES (corp-wide): 20.9B **Privately Held**
WEB: www.lightguard.com
SIC: 3645 3648 3646 Residential lighting
fixtures; garden, patio, walkway & yard
lighting fixtures: electric; fluorescent lighting fixtures, residential; outdoor lighting
equipment; decorative area lighting fixtures; underwater lighting systems; ceiling
systems, luminous
HQ: Philips North America Llc
3000 Minuteman Rd Ms1203
Andover MA 01810
978 659-3000

(P-17555)
PHOENIX DAY CO INC
3431 Regatta Blvd, Richmond
(94804-4594)
PHONE..................................415 822-4414
Tony Brenta, *President*
▲ EMP: 15
SQ FT: 8,000
SALES (est): 2.4MM **Privately Held**
WEB: www.phoenixday.com
SIC: 3645 3646 3446 Residential lighting
fixtures; commercial indusl & institutional
electric lighting fixtures; ornamental met-
alwork

(P-17556)
PRIMA LIGHTING CORP
13615 Marquardt Ave, Santa Fe Springs
(90670-5014)
PHONE..................................562 407-3079
Adam Y Lee, *President*
▲ EMP: 17 EST: 1998
SQ FT: 18,000
SALES (est): 2.4MM **Privately Held**
WEB: www.primalighting.com
SIC: 3645 Residential lighting fixtures

(P-17557)
RICHARD RAY CUSTOM DESIGNS
11350 Alethea Dr, Sunland (91040-2206)
PHONE..................................323 937-5685
Richard Ray, *Owner*
EMP: 17
SQ FT: 4,500
SALES (est): 1.9MM **Privately Held**
WEB: www.richardraycustomdesigns.com
SIC: 3645 Residential lighting fixtures

(P-17558)
S&H INTERNATIONAL INC
1240 Palmetto St, Los Angeles
(90013-2227)
PHONE..................................213 626-7112
Loan L Tran, *President*
▲ EMP: 12 EST: 2006
SALES (est): 1.5MM **Privately Held**
SIC: 3645 Residential lighting fixtures

(P-17559)
SEASCAPE LAMPS INC
125a Lee Rd, Watsonville (95076-9422)
PHONE..................................831 728-5699
Michael Shenk, *President*
▲ EMP: 17
SQ FT: 16,000
SALES (est): 3.1MM **Privately Held**
WEB: www.seascapelamps.com
SIC: 3645 Boudoir lamps; lamp & light
shades

(P-17560)
SEESMART INC
Also Called: Revolution Lighting
2280 Ward Ave, Simi Valley (93065-1859)
PHONE..................................203 504-1111
James Depalma, *President*
Jonathan Miller, *CFO*
Patrick Doehner, *Treasurer*
Ken Ames, *Vice Pres*
Joey Leon, *Manager*
▲ EMP: 27
SALES (est): 5.8MM
SALES (corp-wide): 152.3MM **Publicly
Held**
SIC: 3645 3646 Residential lighting fix-
tures; commercial indusl & institutional
electric lighting fixtures
PA: Revolution Lighting Technologies, Inc.
177 Broad St Fl 12
Stamford CT 06901
203 504-1111

(P-17561)
SILVER MOON LIGHTING INC
12225 World Trade Dr F, San Diego
(92128-3768)
PHONE..................................858 613-3600
Kyle R Finley, *CEO*
EMP: 14 EST: 2005
SALES (est): 2.1MM **Privately Held**
SIC: 3645 Garden, patio, walkway & yard
lighting fixtures: electric

(P-17562)
SPADIA INC
Also Called: Vortex Enterprise
10440 Pioneer Blvd Ste 1, Santa Fe
Springs (90670-8234)
PHONE..................................562 206-2505
Jihoon Park, *President*
▲ EMP: 10 EST: 2012
SALES (est): 1MM **Privately Held**
SIC: 3645 3646 5719 3634 Desk lamps;
desk lamps, commercial; lighting, lamps &
accessories; air purifiers, portable; light-
ing fixtures

(P-17563)
TECHTRON PRODUCTS INC
2694 W Winton Ave, Hayward
(94545-1108)
PHONE..................................510 293-3500
William Swen, *President*
Shiow Shya Swen, *Vice Pres*
EMP: 43
SQ FT: 50,500
SALES (est): 8.7MM **Privately Held**
WEB: www.techtronproducts.com
SIC: 3645 5063 Residential lighting fix-
tures; lighting fixtures, residential

(P-17564)
TROY-CSL LIGHTING INC
14508 Nelson Ave, City of Industry
(91744-3514)
P.O. Box 514310, Los Angeles (90051-
4310)
PHONE..................................626 336-4511
David Littman, *CEO*
Steve Nadell, *President*
Anne Wilcox, *CFO*
Ian Wilcox, *Admin Sec*
▲ EMP: 80
SALES (est): 26.2MM **Privately Held**
WEB: www.troycsl.com
SIC: 3645 3646 Wall lamps; ornamental
lighting fixtures, commercial

(P-17565)
TYLERCO INC
17831 Sky Park Cir Ste A, Irvine
(92614-6105)
PHONE..................................949 769-3991
Richard D Ashoff, *President*
◆ EMP: 45
SQ FT: 5,500
SALES (est): 5.2MM **Privately Held**
SIC: 3645 Residential lighting fixtures

(P-17566)
USPAR ENTERPRISES INC
2037 S Vineyard Ave, Ontario
(91761-8066)
PHONE..................................909 591-7506
Khalid Parekh, *President*
Esmail K Parekh, *CEO*

Irfan Parekh, *Vice Pres*
▲ EMP: 25
SQ FT: 50,000
SALES (est): 4.8MM **Privately Held**
WEB: www.uspar.com
SIC: 3645 3646 3641 5063 Fluorescent
lighting fixtures, residential; fluorescent
lighting fixtures, commercial; electric
lamps; lighting fixtures

(P-17567)
VIDESSENCE LLC (PA)
10768 Lower Azusa Rd, El Monte
(91731-1306)
PHONE..................................626 579-0943
Toni Swarens, *President*
Gary Thomas, *Regl Sales Mgr*
Brian Fraser, *Sales Staff*
Lee Hedberg, *Manager*
Amanda McGinnis, *Manager*
▲ EMP: 25 EST: 1951
SQ FT: 35,000
SALES (est): 4.4MM **Privately Held**
WEB: www.elplighting.com
SIC: 3645 3648 Residential lighting fix-
tures; stage lighting equipment

(P-17568)
VODE LIGHTING LLC
21684 8th St E Ste 700, Sonoma
(95476-2818)
PHONE..................................707 996-9898
Thomas Warton, *President*
George Mieling, *COO*
George Santana, *Managing Dir*
Lauren Schuyler, *Project Mgr*
Jonathan Jones, *Engineer*
▲ EMP: 19
SALES (est): 7.4MM **Privately Held**
WEB: www.vode.com
SIC: 3645 3646 Residential lighting fix-
tures; commercial indusl & institutional
electric lighting fixtures

(P-17569)
WANGS ALLIANCE CORPORATION
Also Called: Wac Lighting
1750 S Archibald Ave, Ontario
(91761-1239)
PHONE..................................909 230-9401
Nina Chou, *Principal*
EMP: 20
SALES (corp-wide): 70.4MM **Privately
Held**
SIC: 3645 Residential lighting fixtures
PA: Wangs Alliance Corporation
44 Harbor Park Dr
Port Washington NY 11050
516 515-5000

(P-17570)
WASHOE EQUIPMENT INC
Also Called: Sunoptics Prismatic Skylights
6201 27th St, Sacramento (95822-3712)
PHONE..................................916 395-4700
Jim Blomberg, *President*
Jerry Blomberg, *Treasurer*
Thomas Blomberg, *Vice Pres*
Grant Grabble, *VP Sales*
Manosh Singh, *Accounts Mgr*
▼ EMP: 34
SQ FT: 16,000
SALES (est): 11.1MM
SALES (corp-wide): 3.6B **Publicly Held**
SIC: 3645 3646 5031 Residential lighting
fixtures; commercial indusl & institutional
electric lighting fixtures; skylights, all ma-
terials
PA: Acuity Brands, Inc.
1170 Peachtree St Ne
Atlanta GA 30309
404 853-1400

(P-17571)
WESTERN LIGHTING INDS INC
Also Called: Orgatech Omegalux
205 W Blueridge Ave, Orange
(92865-4226)
PHONE..................................626 969-6820
Lawrence St Ives, *CEO*
Victor Ortiz, *Opers Staff*
▲ EMP: 22
SQ FT: 16,000

SALES (est): 4.4MM **Privately Held**
WEB: www.orgatechomegalux.com
SIC: 3645 Residential lighting fixtures

(P-17572)
XICATO INC (PA)
101 Daggett Dr, San Jose (95134-2110)
PHONE..................................408 829-4758
Menko Deroos, *CEO*
Mark Pugh, *President*
John Yriberri, *President*
Steve Workman, *CFO*
Joanna Brace, *Exec VP*
▲ EMP: 39
SALES (est): 10.6MM **Privately Held**
SIC: 3645 Garden, patio, walkway & yard
lighting fixtures: electric

(P-17573)
YAWITZ INC
Also Called: Evergreen Lighting
1379 Ridgeway St, Pomona (91768-2701)
PHONE..................................909 865-5599
John Klena, *CEO*
Victor Rosen, *Corp Secy*
George Cole III, *Vice Pres*
Mayte Arias, *Office Mgr*
Robert Allen, *Natl Sales Mgr*
▲ EMP: 42
SQ FT: 23,000
SALES (est): 10.4MM **Privately Held**
WEB: www.evergreenlighting.com
SIC: 3645 3646 Fluorescent lighting fix-
tures, residential; fluorescent lighting fix-
tures, commercial

3646 Commercial, Indl & Institutional Lighting Fixtures

(P-17574)
1LE CALIFORNIA INC
3224 Mchenry Ave Ste F, Modesto
(95350-1400)
PHONE..................................209 846-7541
EMP: 40
SALES (est): 5MM **Privately Held**
SIC: 3646 3645

(P-17575)
515 W SEVENTH LLC
Also Called: Candella Lighting Company
430 S Pecan St, Los Angeles
(90033-4212)
PHONE..................................323 278-8116
Luis A Flores Avalos, *Principal*
EMP: 11
SALES (est): 1.1MM **Privately Held**
SIC: 3646 3645 Ornamental lighting fix-
tures, commercial; residential lighting fix-
tures

(P-17576)
A V POLES AND LIGHTING INC
43827 Division St, Lancaster (93535-4061)
P.O. Box 9054 (93539-9054)
PHONE..................................661 945-2731
Luis Romero, *CEO*
Roberta Wood, *President*
EMP: 20
SQ FT: 12,000
SALES (est): 1.3MM **Privately Held**
SIC: 3646 Commercial indusl & institu-
tional electric lighting fixtures

(P-17577)
ACCLAIM LIGHTING LLC
6122 S Eastern Ave, Commerce
(90040-3402)
PHONE..................................323 213-4626
Charles J Davies, *Principal*
Blaine Engle, *Natl Sales Mgr*
▲ EMP: 11
SALES (est): 1.6MM **Privately Held**
SIC: 3646 3679 5063 Commercial indusl
& institutional electric lighting fixtures;
electronic loads & power supplies; wire &
cable

(P-17578)
ACUITY BRANDS LIGHTING INC
Hydrel Lighting
9144 Deering Ave, Chatsworth
(91311-5801)
PHONE..................................818 576-9774
Craig Jennings, *Branch Mgr*
EMP: 23
SALES (corp-wide): 3.6B **Publicly Held**
SIC: 3646 Commercial indusl & institutional electric lighting fixtures
HQ: Acuity Brands Lighting, Inc.
1 Acuity Way
Conyers GA 30012
-

(P-17579)
ACUITY BRANDS LIGHTING INC
Peerless Lighting
2246 5th St, Berkeley (94710-2217)
PHONE..................................510 845-2760
Thor Scordelis, *Manager*
Mike Lu, *Director*
EMP: 40
SALES (corp-wide): 3.6B **Publicly Held**
SIC: 3646 Fluorescent lighting fixtures, commercial
HQ: Acuity Brands Lighting, Inc.
1 Acuity Way
Conyers GA 30012

(P-17580)
ACUITY BRANDS LIGHTING INC
Also Called: Lithonia Lighting
1405 Locust Ave, Ontario (91761)
PHONE..................................909 395-9009
Ruth Parsons, *Branch Mgr*
Eugene Mazo, *Vice Pres*
Nicholas Chapman, *Technical Staff*
EMP: 30
SALES (corp-wide): 3.6B **Publicly Held**
SIC: 3646 Commercial indusl & institutional electric lighting fixtures
HQ: Acuity Brands Lighting, Inc.
1 Acuity Way
Conyers GA 30012
-

(P-17581)
ALPHABET LIGHTING
15774 Gateway Cir, Tustin (92780-6469)
PHONE..................................714 259-0990
Alex Ladjevardi,
Vahid Ladjevardi,
Helmuth Unger,
▲ **EMP:** 11
SQ FT: 3,000
SALES (est): 1.5MM **Privately Held**
SIC: 3646 Commercial indusl & institutional electric lighting fixtures

(P-17582)
ALUMAFAB
Also Called: Showcase Components
14335 Iseli Rd, Santa Fe Springs
(90670-5203)
PHONE..................................562 630-6440
Robert Lockwood, *President*
Art Lockwood, *Vice Pres*
Gary Lockwood, *Vice Pres*
EMP: 12 **EST:** 1978
SQ FT: 12,000
SALES (est): 1.9MM **Privately Held**
WEB: www.showcasecomponents.com
SIC: 3646 Commercial indusl & institutional electric lighting fixtures

(P-17583)
AMERICA ASIAN TRADE ASSN PROM
4633 Old Ironside Ste 308, Santa Rosa
(95404)
PHONE..................................408 588-0008
Jeff Barrera, *Sales Mgr*
EMP: 99
SALES (est): 4.2MM **Privately Held**
SIC: 3646 Commercial indusl & institutional electric lighting fixtures

(P-17584)
ARTE DE MEXICO INC
5506 Riverton Ave, North Hollywood
(91601)
PHONE..................................818 753-4510
David Staffers, *Manager*
EMP: 30
SALES (corp-wide): 22.5MM **Privately Held**
WEB: www.artedemexico.com
SIC: 3646 3446 Commercial indusl & institutional electric lighting fixtures; architectural metalwork
PA: Arte De Mexico, Inc.
1000 Chestnut St
Burbank CA 91506
818 753-4559

(P-17585)
AXP TECHNOLOGY INC
41041 Trimboli Way # 1761, Fremont
(94538-8001)
PHONE..................................510 683-1180
Justin Wang, *President*
EMP: 10
SALES: 600K **Privately Held**
SIC: 3646 Commercial indusl & institutional electric lighting fixtures

(P-17586)
B-EFFICIENT INC
11545 W Bernardo Ct # 209, San Diego
(92127-1631)
PHONE..................................209 663-9199
Tom Comery, *President*
EMP: 20 **EST:** 2012
SQ FT: 3,000
SALES (est): 2.4MM **Privately Held**
SIC: 3646 5063 Commercial indusl & institutional electric lighting fixtures; lighting fixtures, commercial & industrial

(P-17587)
BLUE PLANET ENERGY SOLUTIONS
6540 Lusk Blvd Ste C204, San Diego
(92121-6716)
P.O. Box 910757 (92191-0757)
PHONE..................................858 947-0100
Michael Lance Copelin, *CEO*
EMP: 15
SALES (est): 2.3MM **Privately Held**
SIC: 3646 Commercial indusl & institutional electric lighting fixtures

(P-17588)
BORDEN LIGHTING
460 Roland Way, Oakland (94621-2013)
PHONE..................................510 357-0171
Randy Borden, *Principal*
James Borden, *CEO*
EMP: 24 **EST:** 1962
SQ FT: 16,600
SALES (est): 5.8MM **Privately Held**
WEB: www.bordenlighting.com
SIC: 3646 3645 Fluorescent lighting fixtures, commercial; ornamental lighting fixtures, commercial; fluorescent lighting fixtures, residential

(P-17589)
BOYD LIGHTING FIXTURE CO (PA)
30 Liberty Ship Way # 3150, Sausalito
(94965-3306)
PHONE..................................415 778-4300
John S Sweet Jr, *President*
Udell Blackham, *CFO*
Isma Khan, *Office Mgr*
Michele Kurvink, *Office Mgr*
Dave Votava, *Engineer*
▲ **EMP:** 20
SQ FT: 13,000
SALES (est): 12.9MM **Privately Held**
WEB: www.boydlighting.com
SIC: 3646 3645 Commercial indusl & institutional electric lighting fixtures; residential lighting fixtures

(P-17590)
C W COLE & COMPANY INC
Also Called: Cole Lighting
2560 Rosemead Blvd, South El Monte
(91733-1593)
PHONE..................................626 443-2473
Russell W Cole, *Ch of Bd*
Stephen W Cole, *President*
Donald Cole, *Vice Pres*
Zach De La Rosa, *Executive Asst*
Eric Vargas, *Design Engr*
EMP: 41
SQ FT: 25,000

SALES (est): 10.4MM **Privately Held**
WEB: www.colelighting.com
SIC: 3646 Commercial indusl & institutional electric lighting fixtures

(P-17591)
CAL BEST CEILINGS INC
979 Seaboard Ct, Upland (91786-4572)
PHONE..................................909 946-1565
Karen Doi Parker, *President*
Jennifer Doi, *Vice Pres*
EMP: 10
SQ FT: 12,500
SALES: 960K **Privately Held**
SIC: 3646 3446 1742 Ceiling systems, luminous; acoustical suspension systems, metal; acoustical & ceiling work

(P-17592)
CANDELLA LIGHTING CO INC
430 S Pecan St, Los Angeles
(90033-4212)
PHONE..................................323 798-1091
Eva Axelsson, *President*
Lillemor Greenhut, *Admin Sec*
▲ **EMP:** 10
SQ FT: 30,000
SALES: 174K **Privately Held**
WEB: www.candella.com
SIC: 3646 3645 2514 3648 Commercial indusl & institutional electric lighting fixtures; residential lighting fixtures; metal household furniture; lighting equipment

(P-17593)
CONTRACT ILLUMINATION
Also Called: Old California Lantern Company
975 N Enterprise St, Orange (92867-5448)
PHONE..................................714 771-5223
Tom Richard, *President*
Leslie Richard, *Corp Secy*
EMP: 20
SQ FT: 6,000
SALES (est): 4.4MM **Privately Held**
WEB: www.oldcalifornia.com
SIC: 3646 Commercial indusl & institutional electric lighting fixtures

(P-17594)
COOL LUMENS INC
1334 Brommer St Ste B6, Santa Cruz
(95062-2955)
PHONE..................................831 471-8084
Thomas D McClellan, *President*
EMP: 12
SQ FT: 3,500
SALES (est): 1.9MM **Privately Held**
SIC: 3646 Commercial indusl & institutional electric lighting fixtures

(P-17595)
CRYSTAL LIGHTING CORP
13182 Flores St, Santa Fe Springs
(90670-4023)
PHONE..................................562 944-0223
Manolo Naranjo, *CEO*
Fabian Naranjo, *Treasurer*
Robert Naranjo, *Vice Pres*
◆ **EMP:** 14
SQ FT: 10,000
SALES (est): 4.1MM **Privately Held**
WEB: www.crystallighting.us
SIC: 3646 3645 Ornamental lighting fixtures, commercial; residential lighting fixtures

(P-17596)
DECO ENTERPRISES INC
Also Called: DECO LIGHTING
2917 Vail Ave, Commerce (90040-2615)
PHONE..................................323 726-2575
Saman Sinai, *CEO*
Benjamin Pouladian, *President*
Craig Allen, *COO*
Ben Peterson, *Vice Pres*
Sheree Nelson, *Executive Asst*
▲ **EMP:** 60
SQ FT: 100,000
SALES (est): 47.4MM **Privately Held**
SIC: 3646 Commercial indusl & institutional electric lighting fixtures

(P-17597)
DEXIN INTERNATIONAL INC
677 Arrow Grand Cir, Covina (91722-2146)
PHONE..................................626 859-7475

Simon LI, *President*
May Lee, *Vice Pres*
▲ **EMP:** 200
SQ FT: 2,500
SALES (est): 16.8MM **Privately Held**
WEB: www.dexinintl.com
SIC: 3646 5063 5199 Commercial indusl & institutional electric lighting fixtures; lighting fixtures; bags, baskets & cases

(P-17598)
ECO WORLD USA LLC
9950 Baldwin Pl, El Monte (91731-2204)
PHONE..................................626 433-1333
Shen Yen,
EMP: 12
SALES (est): 1.2MM **Privately Held**
SIC: 3646 Commercial indusl & institutional electric lighting fixtures

(P-17599)
ELATION LIGHTING INC
Also Called: Elation Professional
6122 S Eastern Ave, Commerce
(90040-3402)
PHONE..................................323 582-3322
Toby Velazquez, *President*
John Dunn, *Regl Sales Mgr*
Chuck Green, *Sales Mgr*
Patrick Nadjarians, *Marketing Staff*
Larry Beck, *Corp Comm Staff*
▲ **EMP:** 60
SQ FT: 50,000
SALES: 15MM **Privately Held**
SIC: 3646 Commercial indusl & institutional electric lighting fixtures

(P-17600)
ENERTRON TECHNOLOGIES INC
3030 Enterprise Ct Ste D, Vista
(92081-8358)
PHONE..................................800 537-7649
Ronald Curley, *President*
EMP: 50
SQ FT: 80,000
SALES (est): 8.9MM **Privately Held**
SIC: 3646 3645 Fluorescent lighting fixtures, commercial; fluorescent lighting fixtures, residential

(P-17601)
ENLIGHTED INC (PA)
930 Benecia Ave, Sunnyvale (94085-2804)
PHONE..................................650 964-1094
Joe Costello, *Ch of Bd*
Mike Martini, *CFO*
Tanuj Mohan, *CTO*
▲ **EMP:** 39
SALES (est): 25MM **Privately Held**
SIC: 3646 Commercial indusl & institutional electric lighting fixtures

(P-17602)
ENVEL DESIGN CORPORATION
3579 Old Conejo Rd, Newbury Park
(91320-2122)
PHONE..................................805 376-8111
Quinn B Mayer, *President*
Pamela K Mayer, *Exec VP*
EMP: 10
SALES (est): 1.8MM **Privately Held**
WEB: www.enveldesign.com
SIC: 3646 Ceiling systems, luminous

(P-17603)
ENVIRONMENTAL LTG FOR ARCH INC
Also Called: E L A Custom Architectural Div
17891 Arenth Ave, City of Industry
(91748-1129)
PHONE..................................626 965-0821
Elsie U Dahlin, *CEO*
Scott Jones, *President*
▲ **EMP:** 42
SQ FT: 50,000
SALES: 8MM **Privately Held**
WEB: www.ela-lighting.com
SIC: 3646 Commercial indusl & institutional electric lighting fixtures

(P-17604)
EPTRONICS INC
19210 S Vermont Ave # 300, Gardena
(90248-4426)
PHONE..................................310 536-0700

▲ = Import ▼=Export
◆ =Import/Export

Chris Chen, *President*
Quincie Lane, *Office Admin*
Lee Chiang, *Engineer*
Steve Turner, *VP Sls/Mktg*
Christian Chung, *Marketing Staff*
EMP: 18
SALES (est): 3MM **Privately Held**
SIC: 3646 Commercial indusl & institutional electric lighting fixtures

(P-17605)
EXIT LIGHT CO INC
Also Called: Light Fixture Industries
3170 Scott St, Vista (92081-8318)
PHONE..............................877 352-3948
Jeannette L Carrico, *President*
Paul Carrico, *CFO*
◆ **EMP:** 15
SQ FT: 11,000
SALES (est): 3MM **Privately Held**
WEB: www.exitlightco.com
SIC: 3646 5063 3993 Commercial indusl & institutional electric lighting fixtures; signaling equipment, electrical; electric signs

(P-17606)
EXIT SIGN WAREHOUSE INC
16123 Cohasset St, Van Nuys (91406-2908)
PHONE..............................888 953-3948
Josh Roman, *CEO*
John Scalco, *President*
EMP: 12
SALES: 1MM **Privately Held**
SIC: 3646 Commercial indusl & institutional electric lighting fixtures

(P-17607)
FARLIGHT LLC
460 W 5th St, San Pedro (90731-2616)
PHONE..............................310 830-0181
Robert Wolfenden, *General Mgr*
Steve Becerra, *Engineer*
Western Land and Investment LL,
▲ **EMP:** 10
SQ FT: 5,000
SALES (est): 2MM **Privately Held**
WEB: www.farlight.com
SIC: 3646 Commercial indusl & institutional electric lighting fixtures

(P-17608)
FINELITE INC
30500 Whipple Rd, Union City (94587-1530)
PHONE..............................510 441-1100
Jerome Mix, *CEO*
Mark Benguerel, *COO*
Attila Bardos, *CFO*
Margaret Fenton, *CFO*
Walter B Clark, *Chairman*
▲ **EMP:** 138
SQ FT: 140,132
SALES (est): 51.9MM **Privately Held**
WEB: www.finelite.com
SIC: 3646 Commercial indusl & institutional electric lighting fixtures

(P-17609)
FLUORESCENT SUPPLY CO INC
Also Called: Fsc Lighting
9120 Center Ave, Rancho Cucamonga (91730-5310)
PHONE..............................909 948-8878
Edward Yawitz, *CEO*
John Watkins, *President*
Chad Treadwell, *Senior VP*
Janet Johansen, *Vice Pres*
Greg Lechtenberg, *Vice Pres*
▲ **EMP:** 40
SQ FT: 80,000
SALES: 20MM **Privately Held**
WEB: www.fsclighting.com
SIC: 3646 3645 Commercial indusl & institutional electric lighting fixtures; residential lighting fixtures

(P-17610)
FOCUS INDUSTRIES INC
Also Called: Focus Landscape
25301 Commercentre Dr, Lake Forest (92630-8808)
PHONE..............................949 830-1350
Stan Shibata, *President*
Luis Mejia, *CFO*
June Shibata, *Vice Pres*

James Christopher, *Graphic Designe*
Linda Lindgren, *Human Res Mgr*
▲ **EMP:** 100
SQ FT: 40,000
SALES (est): 24.9MM **Privately Held**
WEB: www.focusindustries.com
SIC: 3646 5063 Commercial indusl & institutional electric lighting fixtures; electrical apparatus & equipment

(P-17611)
GARA INC
Also Called: First Source Lighting
1730 Industrial Dr, Auburn (95603-9587)
PHONE..............................530 887-1110
Robert Glenn Gara, *CEO*
Laurie Lerea Gara, *Vice Pres*
▲ **EMP:** 16
SQ FT: 10,000
SALES (est): 4.1MM **Privately Held**
WEB: www.1stsourcelight.com
SIC: 3646 Fluorescent lighting fixtures, commercial

(P-17612)
GENERAL ELECTRIC COMPANY
11600 Philadelphia Ave, Mira Loma (91752-1135)
PHONE..............................951 360-2400
Fax: 951 360-3235
EMP: 50
SALES (corp-wide): 122B **Publicly Held**
SIC: 3646
PA: General Electric Company
41 Farnsworth St
Boston MA 02210
617 443-3000

(P-17613)
HALLMARK LIGHTING LLC
9631 De Soto Ave, Chatsworth (91311-5013)
PHONE..............................818 885-5010
Christopher Larocca, *CEO*
Eric Allen, *President*
Cory Trunnell, *President*
Julie Winfield, *CFO*
Isaac Clark, *Design Engr*
▲ **EMP:** 80
SQ FT: 56,320
SALES (est): 18MM **Privately Held**
WEB: www.hallmarklighting.com
SIC: 3646 3645 3641 Commercial indusl & institutional electric lighting fixtures; wall lamps; electric lamps

(P-17614)
HAMILTON TECHNOLOGY CORP
14900 S Figueroa St, Gardena (90248-1715)
PHONE..............................310 217-1191
Mark Rambod, *President*
▲ **EMP:** 13
SQ FT: 2,000
SALES (est): 2MM **Privately Held**
SIC: 3646 Commercial indusl & institutional electric lighting fixtures

(P-17615)
HARVATEK INTERNATIONAL CORP
3350 Scott Blvd Ste 4101, Santa Clara (95054-3120)
PHONE..............................408 844-9698
Jitfu Lim, *CEO*
Putt Choon Yong, *President*
EMP: 10
SALES (est): 1.4MM **Privately Held**
SIC: 3646 Commercial indusl & institutional electric lighting fixtures

(P-17616)
HI-LITE MANUFACTURING CO INC
13450 Monte Vista Ave, Chino (91710-5149)
PHONE..............................909 465-1999
Dorothy A Ohai, *President*
Lava Bobbermin, *Human Resources*
David McAdam, *Marketing Staff*
Jeffrey Ohai, *Manager*
▲ **EMP:** 90 **EST:** 1959
SQ FT: 157,000

SALES (est): 18.7MM **Privately Held**
SIC: 3646 3645 Commercial indusl & institutional electric lighting fixtures; residential lighting fixtures

(P-17617)
HUBBELL LIGHTING INC
Precision-Paragon
17760 Rowland St, Rowland Heights (91748-1119)
PHONE..............................714 386-5550
Joe Martin, *General Mgr*
EMP: 70
SALES (corp-wide): 3.6B **Publicly Held**
SIC: 3646 Commercial indusl & institutional electric lighting fixtures
HQ: Hubbell Lighting, Inc.
701 Millennium Blvd
Greenville SC 29607

(P-17618)
INTENSE LIGHTING LLC
3340 E La Palma Ave, Anaheim (92806-2814)
PHONE..............................714 630-9877
Kenny Eidsvold, *President*
Kenneth Eidsvold, *President*
Tom Elam, *Vice Pres*
Janet Yuzon, *Accounting Mgr*
Christine Cortez, *Human Res Mgr*
▲ **EMP:** 80 **EST:** 2001
SQ FT: 153,000
SALES (est): 30.5MM
SALES (corp-wide): 1.7B **Privately Held**
WEB: www.intenselighting.com
SIC: 3646 3645 Commercial indusl & institutional electric lighting fixtures; residential lighting fixtures
PA: Leviton Manufacturing Co., Inc.
201 N Service Rd
Melville NY 11747
631 812-6000

(P-17619)
J & J ELECTRONICS LLC
6 Bendix, Irvine (92618-2006)
PHONE..............................949 455-4460
James T Rafferty, *President*
Richard Reilly, *Vice Pres*
◆ **EMP:** 30
SQ FT: 30,000
SALES (est): 6.9MM **Privately Held**
SIC: 3646 Commercial indusl & institutional electric lighting fixtures
PA: Halco Lighting Technologies Llc
2940 Pacific Dr Ste A
Norcross GA 30071

(P-17620)
JISHAN USA INC
Also Called: Kerilgithing
15257 Don Julian Rd, City of Industry (91745-1002)
PHONE..............................408 609-3286
Weiping Wang, *CEO*
EMP: 10
SQ FT: 15,000
SALES (est): 736.2K **Privately Held**
SIC: 3646 Commercial indusl & institutional electric lighting fixtures

(P-17621)
JOHNSON ART STUDIO INC
Also Called: Johnson Art Studio
375 W Beach St, Watsonville (95076-4508)
PHONE..............................831 763-2744
Roy F Johnson, *President*
Roy Johnson, *Owner*
EMP: 14
SQ FT: 3,000
SALES (est): 1.2MM **Privately Held**
WEB: www.johnsonartstudio.com
SIC: 3646 Commercial indusl & institutional electric lighting fixtures

(P-17622)
KONTECH USA LLC
18045 Rowland St, City of Industry (91748-1205)
PHONE..............................626 622-1325
Miguel Martinez, *Branch Mgr*
EMP: 10

SALES (corp-wide): 2.5MM **Privately Held**
SIC: 3646 3663 Commercial indusl & institutional electric lighting fixtures; television monitors
PA: Kontech Usa Llc
600 W Owens Ave
Las Vegas NV 89106
626 321-8741

(P-17623)
LA SPEC INDUSTRIES INC
Also Called: Laspec Lighting
2315 E 52nd St, Vernon (90058-3499)
PHONE..............................323 588-8746
Jacob Melamed, *Principal*
J Melamed, *President*
▲ **EMP:** 15
SQ FT: 30,000
SALES: 3MM **Privately Held**
WEB: www.laspec.com
SIC: 3646 3648 Commercial indusl & institutional electric lighting fixtures; decorative area lighting fixtures

(P-17624)
LAMPS PLUS INC
Also Called: Pacific Coast Lighting
4723 Telephone Rd, Ventura (93003-5254)
PHONE..............................805 642-9007
David Hillard, *Manager*
EMP: 13
SALES (corp-wide): 297.4MM **Privately Held**
WEB: www.lampsplus.com
SIC: 3646 5719 5064 Commercial indusl & institutional electric lighting fixtures; lamps & lamp shades; fans, household: electric
PA: Lamps Plus, Inc.
20250 Plummer St
Chatsworth CA 91311
818 886-5267

(P-17625)
LEXSTAR INC (PA)
Also Called: Lites On West Soho
4959 Kalamis Way, Oceanside (92056-7411)
PHONE..............................845 947-1415
Uri Redlich, *President*
▲ **EMP:** 30
SQ FT: 15,000
SALES (est): 2.9MM **Privately Held**
WEB: www.lexstar.com
SIC: 3646 Commercial indusl & institutional electric lighting fixtures

(P-17626)
LF ILLUMINATION LLC
9200 Deering Ave, Chatsworth (91311-5803)
PHONE..............................818 885-1335
Jack Zukerman, *CEO*
Loren Kessel, *President*
Eileen S Cheng, *CFO*
▲ **EMP:** 51 **EST:** 2013
SALES (est): 11.3MM **Privately Held**
SIC: 3646 3645 5719 Commercial indusl & institutional electric lighting fixtures; residential lighting fixtures; lighting fixtures; lighting, lamps & accessories

(P-17627)
LIANTRONICS LLC
46722 Fremont Blvd, Fremont (94538-6538)
PHONE..............................510 438-0588
Alice Wang,
Cynthia Huang, *COO*
▲ **EMP:** 10 **EST:** 2009
SALES (est): 1MM
SALES (corp-wide): 596.5MM **Privately Held**
SIC: 3646 Commercial indusl & institutional electric lighting fixtures
PA: Shenzhen Liantronics Co.,Ltd.
Floor 2, Factory Building 4, Antongda Industry Premise, Liuxian
Shenzhen 51810
755 297-4662

(P-17628)
LIGHTWAY INDUSTRIES INC
28435 Industry Dr, Valencia (91355-4107)
PHONE..............................661 257-0286

P R O D U C T S & S V C S

Jeffrey Bargman, *President*
Gary N Patten, *Vice Pres*
EMP: 28 **EST:** 1980
SQ FT: 22,300
SALES: 5.5MM **Privately Held**
WEB: www.lightwayind.com
SIC: 3646 3645 Commercial indusl & institutional electric lighting fixtures; residential lighting fixtures

(P-17629)
LOS ANGELES LTG MFG CO INC
Also Called: L A Lighting
10141 Olney St, El Monte (91731-2311)
PHONE..................................626 454-8300
William D Shapiro, *President*
Mieko Shapiro, *Treasurer*
◆ **EMP:** 55
SQ FT: 50,000
SALES (est): 15.3MM **Privately Held**
WEB: www.lalighting.com
SIC: 3646 Commercial indusl & institutional electric lighting fixtures

(P-17630)
LUMASCAPE USA INC
1300 Industrial Rd Ste 19, San Carlos
(94070-4130)
PHONE..................................650 595-5862
Michael Agustin, *President*
Deepak Varma, *Engineer*
Matthew Anderson, *Marketing Mgr*
Alex Schlemer, *Manager*
Taylor Graham, *Assistant*
▲ **EMP:** 10
SQ FT: 7,000
SALES (est): 2.8MM **Privately Held**
WEB: www.lumascape.com
SIC: 3646 Commercial indusl & institutional electric lighting fixtures
PA: Lumascape Pty Ltd
18 Brandl St
Eight Mile Plains QLD 4113

(P-17631)
LUMIGROW INC
1480 64th St Ste 150, Emeryville
(94608-2267)
PHONE..................................800 514-0487
Kevin Wells, *President*
EMP: 28 **EST:** 2008
SALES (est): 8.4MM **Privately Held**
WEB: www.lumigrow.com
SIC: 3646 Ornamental lighting fixtures, commercial

(P-17632)
LUMINATION LIGHTING & TECH INC
1515 240th St, Harbor City (90710-1308)
PHONE..................................855 283-1100
EMP: 150
SALES (est): 4.9MM **Privately Held**
SIC: 3646

(P-17633)
LUMINUS INC (HQ)
Also Called: Lightera
1145 Sonora Ct, Sunnyvale (94086-5384)
PHONE..................................408 708-7000
Decai Sun, *CEO*
Tao T Tong, *Vice Pres*
Stephen Blasich, *Finance*
EMP: 120
SALES (est): 24.1MM
SALES (corp-wide): 1.2B **Privately Held**
SIC: 3646 Fluorescent lighting fixtures, commercial
PA: Sanan Optoelectronics Co., Ltd.
No.1721-1725,Lvling Road,Siming Dist.
Xiamen 36100
592 593-7117

(P-17634)
NOELS LIGHTING INC
9335 Stephens St Unit I, Pico Rivera
(90660-2160)
PHONE..................................562 908-6181
Humberto Arguelles, *President*
EMP: 30
SQ FT: 15,000

SALES (est): 4.9MM **Privately Held**
SIC: 3646 3648 Commercial indusl & institutional electric lighting fixtures; lighting equipment

(P-17635)
PACIFIC LTG & STANDARDS CO
2815 Los Flores Blvd, Lynwood
(90262-2416)
PHONE..................................310 603-9344
Frank Munoz, *President*
Enrique Garcia, *Vice Pres*
Candy Rodriquez, *Admin Asst*
John Moore, *Sales Staff*
▲ **EMP:** 34
SQ FT: 17,000
SALES (est): 9.1MM **Privately Held**
WEB: www.pacificlighting.com
SIC: 3646 Commercial indusl & institutional electric lighting fixtures

(P-17636)
PACLIGHTS LLC (PA)
15830 El Prado Rd Ste F, Chino
(91708-9127)
P.O. Box 928, Chino Hills (91709-0031)
PHONE..................................888 983-2165
Tommy Zhen, *CEO*
Fiona Zhao, *President*
Rudan Zhao, *Principal*
Rick Acevedo, *Sales Dir*
▲ **EMP:** 20
SQ FT: 20,000
SALES (est): 2.7MM **Privately Held**
SIC: 3646 Commercial indusl & institutional electric lighting fixtures

(P-17637)
PATRIOT LIGHTING INC
Also Called: U.S. Patriot Lite
2305 S Main St, Los Angeles (90007-2725)
PHONE..................................213 741-9757
Young E Lee, *President*
▲ **EMP:** 10
SALES (est): 910K **Privately Held**
WEB: www.patriotltg.com
SIC: 3646 5063 Commercial indusl & institutional electric lighting fixtures; lighting fixtures

(P-17638)
PRECISION FLUORESCENT WEST INC (DH)
Also Called: Precision Energy Efficient Ltg
23281 La Palma Ave, Yorba Linda
(92887-4768)
PHONE..................................352 692-5900
Raymond Pustinger, *President*
Dan Rodriguez, *Vice Pres*
Kelly Khuu, *Manager*
▲ **EMP:** 67
SQ FT: 31,000
SALES (est): 14.6MM
SALES (corp-wide): 3.6B **Publicly Held**
WEB: www.precisionfluorescent.com
SIC: 3646 Commercial indusl & institutional electric lighting fixtures

(P-17639)
PRUDENTIAL LIGHTING CORP (PA)
Also Called: P L M
1774 E 21st St, Los Angeles (90058-1082)
P.O. Box 58736 (90058-0736)
PHONE..................................213 477-1694
Stanely J Ellis, *CEO*
Jeffrey Ellis, *President*
Jolie Ellis, *Corp Secy*
Elliot Ellis, *Vice Pres*
Ron Marler, *Vice Pres*
▲ **EMP:** 120 **EST:** 1955
SQ FT: 112,000
SALES (est): 27.4MM **Privately Held**
WEB: www.prulite.com
SIC: 3646 Fluorescent lighting fixtures, commercial

(P-17640)
R W SWARENS ASSOCIATES INC
Also Called: Engineered Lighting Products
10768 Lower Azusa Rd, El Monte
(91731-1306)
PHONE..................................626 579-0943
Toni Swarens, *CEO*

Lauri Maines, *President*
Jon Divall, *Executive*
Mandy McGinnis, *Executive*
Jerry Caron, *Purch Agent*
▲ **EMP:** 45 **EST:** 1984
SALES (est): 7.1MM **Privately Held**
SIC: 3646 Commercial indusl & institutional electric lighting fixtures

(P-17641)
SAPPHIRE CHANDELIER LLC
505 Porter Way, Placentia (92870-6454)
PHONE..................................714 630-3660
Hector Garibay, *Mng Member*
Hayley Hustedt,
▲ **EMP:** 13
SQ FT: 10,000
SALES (est): 3.2MM **Privately Held**
SIC: 3646 Commercial indusl & institutional electric lighting fixtures

(P-17642)
SCIENTIFIC COMPONENTS SYSTEMS
1514 N Susan St Ste C, Santa Ana
(92703-1435)
PHONE..................................714 554-3960
Juan L Flores, *President*
Juan Flores, *President*
Elizabeth Flores, *Admin Sec*
EMP: 10 **EST:** 1983
SQ FT: 5,000
SALES (est): 726K **Privately Held**
WEB: www.scsix18.com
SIC: 3646 5063 Commercial indusl & institutional electric lighting fixtures; lighting fixtures

(P-17643)
SCOTT LAMP COMPANY INC
Also Called: Scott Architectural
355 Watt Dr, Fairfield (94534-4207)
PHONE..................................707 864-2066
Dennis J Scott, *CEO*
Dennis Scott, *CEO*
Paul R Scott, *Vice Pres*
Eileen Emerson, *Office Mgr*
Eileen K Scott-Emerson, *Admin Sec*
▲ **EMP:** 90
SQ FT: 71,000
SALES (est): 18MM **Privately Held**
WEB: www.scottlamp.com
SIC: 3646 3645 Ceiling systems, luminous; chandeliers, commercial; desk lamps, commercial; ornamental lighting fixtures, commercial; residential lighting fixtures

(P-17644)
SPOTLITE POWER CORPORATION
9937 Jefferson Blvd # 110, Culver City
(90232-3505)
PHONE..................................310 838-2367
Halston Mikail, *President*
▲ **EMP:** 30
SALES (est): 1.8MM
SALES (corp-wide): 27.5MM **Privately Held**
SIC: 3646 Commercial indusl & institutional electric lighting fixtures
PA: Spotlite America Corporation
9937 Jefferson Blvd # 110
Culver City CA 90232
310 829-0200

(P-17645)
STACK LABS INC
Also Called: Stack Lighting
10052 Pasadena Ave Ste A, Cupertino
(95014-5956)
PHONE..................................503 453-5172
Neil Joseph, *CEO*
Jack McFarland, *CFO*
Scott Cypher, *Info Tech Mgr*
Pedraam Behroozi, *Technical Staff*
EMP: 20
SQ FT: 5,000
SALES: 7.5MM **Privately Held**
SIC: 3646 Commercial indusl & institutional electric lighting fixtures

(P-17646)
SUN & SUN INDUSTRIES INC
2101 S Yale St, Santa Ana (92704-4424)
PHONE..................................714 210-5141

Lynda Sun-Frederick, *CEO*
Duncan Frederick, *President*
Ken Flockblower, *Vice Pres*
EMP: 100
SQ FT: 11,000
SALES (est): 18.3MM **Privately Held**
WEB: www.sunindustriesinc.com
SIC: 3646 Fluorescent lighting fixtures, commercial
PA: Eco-Shift Power Corp
125 Mcgovern Dr Unit 10
Cambridge ON N3H 4

(P-17647)
SUN VALLEY LTG STANDARDS INC
Also Called: US Architectural Lighting
660 W Avenue O, Palmdale (93551-3610)
PHONE..................................661 233-2000
Joseph Straus, *President*
Judith Straus, *Vice Pres*
EMP: 260
SQ FT: 30,000
SALES (est): 26.7MM
SALES (corp-wide): 83.4MM **Privately Held**
WEB: www.usaltg.com
SIC: 3646 5063 3648 Ornamental lighting fixtures, commercial; electrical apparatus & equipment; lighting equipment
PA: U.S. Pole Company, Inc.
660 W Avenue O
Palmdale CA 93551
800 877-6537

(P-17648)
T-1 LIGHTING INC
9929 Pioneer Blvd, Santa Fe Springs
(90670-3219)
PHONE..................................626 234-2328
Artur Saakyan, *CEO*
An Bao Vu, *COO*
Pang Chun Zhang, *CFO*
EMP: 14
SQ FT: 19,660
SALES (est): 554.8K **Privately Held**
SIC: 3646 Commercial indusl & institutional electric lighting fixtures

(P-17649)
TANKO STREETLIGHTING INC
Also Called: Tanko Streetlighting Services
220 Bay Shore Blvd, San Francisco
(94124-1323)
PHONE..................................415 254-7579
Jason Tanko, *President*
Clare Bressani, *Vice Pres*
Jaclyn Blackwell, *Project Mgr*
Alex Wurzel, *Sales Associate*
Joe Bollinger, *Sales Staff*
▲ **EMP:** 31
SQ FT: 5,000
SALES (est): 5.5MM **Privately Held**
SIC: 3646 Commercial indusl & institutional electric lighting fixtures

(P-17650)
TEMPO LIGHTING INC
Also Called: Tempo Industries
1961 Mcgaw Ave, Irvine (92614-0909)
PHONE..................................949 442-1601
Dennis Pearson, *CEO*
Michael Bremser, *Vice Pres*
Ray Letasi, *Vice Pres*
Dennis Barton, *Electrical Engi*
Tom Lueken, *Engineer*
▲ **EMP:** 31 **EST:** 1986
SQ FT: 27,000
SALES (est): 9MM **Privately Held**
WEB: www.tempoindustries.com
SIC: 3646 Commercial indusl & institutional electric lighting fixtures

(P-17651)
TRITON CHANDELIER INC
1301 Dove St Ste 900, Newport Beach
(92660-2473)
PHONE..................................714 957-9600
Richard Cooley, *President*
▲ **EMP:** 43
SQ FT: 10,000
SALES (est): 5.4MM **Privately Held**
WEB: www.tritonchandelier.com
SIC: 3646 Chandeliers, commercial

▲ = Import ▼=Export
◆ =Import/Export

(P-17652)
TUJAYAR ENTERPRISES INC
Also Called: Tube Lighting Products
1346 Pioneer Way, El Cajon (92020-1626)
PHONE..............................619 442-0577
Rick Tempkin, *President*
Donna Rogers, *General Mgr*
Jake Valenzuela, *Prdtn Mgr*
Pete Olson, *Natl Sales Mgr*
Sue Hebert,
▲ EMP: 21
SQ FT: 9,000
SALES (est): 3.9MM **Privately Held**
WEB: www.tubelightingproducts.com
SIC: 3646 3645 Commercial indusl & institutional electric lighting fixtures; residential lighting fixtures

(P-17653)
UNIVERSAL METAL SPINNING INC
2543 W Winton Ave Ste 5j, Hayward (94545-1153)
PHONE..............................510 782-0980
Stewart Blunck, *President*
Maria Blunck, *Treasurer*
Rudolf Blunck, *Vice Pres*
EMP: 11
SALES (est): 1.1MM **Privately Held**
WEB: www.universalmetalspinning.com
SIC: 3646 Commercial indusl & institutional electric lighting fixtures

(P-17654)
USHIO AMERICA INC
14 Mason, Irvine (92618-2705)
PHONE..............................714 236-8600
Holger Claus, *Vice Pres*
EMP: 30
SALES (corp-wide): 1.6B **Privately Held**
SIC: 3646 Fluorescent lighting fixtures, commercial
HQ: Ushio America, Inc.
5440 Cerritos Ave
Cypress CA 90630
714 236-8600

(P-17655)
VISION ENGRG MET STAMPING INC
114 Grand Cypress Ave, Palmdale (93551-3617)
PHONE..............................661 575-0933
Joseph Avila, *CEO*
EMP: 100
SQ FT: 72,000
SALES (est): 8MM **Privately Held**
SIC: 3646 Ceiling systems, luminous

(P-17656)
VISIONAIRE LIGHTING LLC
19645 S Rancho Way, Compton (90220-6028)
PHONE..............................310 512-6480
Fred Kayne, *CEO*
Cheryl Moorman, *CFO*
Paul Arrieta, *Vice Pres*
Erik Van Wier, *Vice Pres*
Calvin Wong, *Managing Dir*
◆ EMP: 650
SQ FT: 36,000
SALES (est): 50MM **Privately Held**
WEB: www.visionairelighting.com
SIC: 3646 Commercial indusl & institutional electric lighting fixtures

(P-17657)
WESTERN ILLUMINATED PLAS INC
14451 Edwards St, Westminster (92683-3607)
PHONE..............................714 895-3067
Cornelius Crompvoets, *President*
Irene Crompvoets, *Treasurer*
Charles Crompvoets, *Vice Pres*
Sandra Crompvoets-Katanjian, *Admin Sec*
EMP: 18
SQ FT: 8,800
SALES (est): 3.4MM **Privately Held**
WEB: www.westernplastics.com
SIC: 3646 1761 Ceiling systems, luminous; ceilings, metal: erection & repair

(P-17658)
YANKON INDUSTRIES INC
Also Called: Energetic Lighting
13445 12th St, Chino (91710-5206)
PHONE..............................909 591-2345
WEI Chen, *CEO*
David Liu, *CEO*
Kristen Tai, *CFO*
▲ EMP: 25
SQ FT: 100,627
SALES (est): 4.7MM **Privately Held**
SIC: 3646 Commercial indusl & institutional electric lighting fixtures

3647 Vehicular Lighting Eqpt

(P-17659)
AMP PLUS INC
Also Called: Elco Lighting
2042 E Vernon Ave, Vernon (90058-1613)
PHONE..............................323 231-2600
Steve Cohen, *President*
Ryan Cohen, *Representative*
▲ EMP: 55
SQ FT: 100,000
SALES (est): 9.1MM **Privately Held**
SIC: 3647 5063 3645 Vehicular lighting equipment; electrical apparatus & equipment; residential lighting fixtures

(P-17660)
DELTA TECH INDUSTRIES LLC
1901 S Vineyard Ave, Ontario (91761-7747)
PHONE..............................909 673-1900
Bogdan G Durian, *Mng Member*
James Jimenez, *Executive*
▲ EMP: 14
SQ FT: 12,000
SALES (est): 2.1MM **Privately Held**
WEB: www.deltalights.com
SIC: 3647 Automotive lighting fixtures

(P-17661)
ELDEMA PRODUCTS
10145 Via De La Amistad # 5, San Diego (92154-5217)
PHONE..............................619 661-5113
Chuy Valles, *Owner*
Maria Valles, *Co-Owner*
Mayra Valles, *Executive*
EMP: 10
SALES (est): 560K **Privately Held**
SIC: 3647 3825 Parking lights, automotive; indicating instruments, electric

(P-17662)
JKL COMPONENTS CORPORATION
13343 Paxton St, Pacoima (91331-2340)
PHONE..............................818 896-0019
Joseph Velas, *President*
Kent Koerting, *Shareholder*
Makoto Hori, *Treasurer*
Sara Velas, *Chief Mktg Ofcr*
Percy Andres, *Info Tech Mgr*
EMP: 32
SQ FT: 7,000
SALES (est): 5.8MM **Privately Held**
WEB: www.jklamps.com
SIC: 3647 3827 3699 Automotive lighting fixtures; optical instruments & lenses; electrical equipment & supplies

(P-17663)
SIERRA DESIGN MFG INC (PA)
Also Called: Dry Launch Light Co
1113 Greenville Rd, Livermore (94550-9714)
PHONE..............................925 443-3140
Dennis Moore, *President*
Cindy Moore, *Treasurer*
▲ EMP: 40
SQ FT: 15,000
SALES (est): 3.1MM **Privately Held**
WEB: www.dry-launch.com
SIC: 3647 Taillights, motor vehicle

(P-17664)
SODERBERG MANUFACTURING CO INC
20821 Currier Rd, Walnut (91789-3018)
PHONE..............................909 595-1291
B W Soderberg, *CEO*
Kathy Kirkeby, *Corp Secy*
Kari Levario, *Vice Pres*
Rick Soderberg, *Vice Pres*
Sam Tapia, *Project Engr*
EMP: 85
SALES (est): 16.5MM **Privately Held**
WEB: www.soderberg-mfg.com
SIC: 3647 3812 Aircraft lighting fixtures; search & navigation equipment

(P-17665)
STREET GLOW INC
2710 E El Presidio St, Carson (90810-1117)
PHONE..............................310 631-1881
EMP: 60 **Privately Held**
SIC: 3647
PA: Street Glow Inc
160 Gregg St Ste 7
Lodi NJ
973 709-9000

(P-17666)
SUNBEAM TRAILER PRODUCTS INC
5312 Production Dr, Huntington Beach (92649-1523)
PHONE..............................714 373-5000
Fred A Muzic, *President*
Lynne Muzic, *Treasurer*
EMP: 20 EST: 1939
SQ FT: 11,000
SALES (est): 1.7MM **Privately Held**
SIC: 3647

3648 Lighting Eqpt, NEC

(P-17667)
A&R LIGHTING CO
7644 Emil Ave, Bell (90201-4940)
PHONE..............................562 927-8617
Rosemary Picon, *Owner*
EMP: 12
SALES (est): 1.3MM **Privately Held**
WEB: www.arlighting.com
SIC: 3648 3999 Lighting equipment; advertising display products

(P-17668)
AL KRAMP SPECIALTIES
Also Called: J K Lighting Systems
1707 El Pinal Dr, Stockton (95205-2553)
P.O. Box 8867 (95208-0867)
PHONE..............................209 464-7539
Al Kramp, *Owner*
EMP: 25
SQ FT: 67,000
SALES (est): 3.6MM **Privately Held**
WEB: www.jk-lighting.com
SIC: 3648 5063 3699 Lighting equipment; lighting fixtures; electrical equipment & supplies

(P-17669)
ALL ACCESS STGING PRDCTONS INC (PA)
1320 Storm Pkwy, Torrance (90501-5041)
PHONE..............................310 784-2464
Clive Forrester, *CEO*
Erik Eastland, *President*
Robert Achlimbari, *Vice Pres*
Mishele Bacon, *Controller*
Larry Smythe, *Opers Mgr*
▲ EMP: 71
SQ FT: 42,000
SALES (est): 15.9MM **Privately Held**
SIC: 3648 Stage lighting equipment

(P-17670)
ALL ENERGY INC
3401 Adams Ave A28, San Diego (92116-2490)
PHONE..............................619 988-7030
Kenneth Ramcharan, *President*
EMP: 15
SALES (est): 1.2MM **Privately Held**
SIC: 3648 Area & sports luminaries

(P-17671)
AMERICAN GRIP INC
8468 Kewen Ave, Sun Valley (91352-3118)
PHONE..............................818 768-8922
Lance Snoke, *President*
EMP: 25
SQ FT: 15,000
SALES (est): 3MM **Privately Held**
WEB: www.americangrip.com
SIC: 3648 3861 Stage lighting equipment; stands, camera & projector

(P-17672)
AMERILLUM LLC
Also Called: Alumen-8
3728 Maritime Way, Oceanside (92056-2702)
PHONE..............................760 727-7675
Ronald S Lancial, *Mng Member*
Serge Lambert,
Guy St Pierre,
▲ EMP: 54
SQ FT: 27,000
SALES (est): 15.6MM **Privately Held**
WEB: www.amerillum.com
SIC: 3648 Lighting equipment

(P-17673)
ARCHITECTURAL CATHODE LIGHTING
Also Called: Archigraphics
12123 Pantheon St, Norwalk (90650-1822)
PHONE..............................323 581-8800
Eric Zimmerman, *President*
Stephanie Baxter, *Office Mgr*
Leo Silva, *Manager*
EMP: 12
SQ FT: 8,000
SALES (est): 2MM **Privately Held**
WEB: www.archigraphics.com
SIC: 3648 3641 Decorative area lighting fixtures; electric lamps

(P-17674)
BEGA/US INC
1000 Bega Way, Carpinteria (93013-2902)
PHONE..............................805 684-0533
Don Kinderdick, *CEO*
Mark Reed, *Vice Pres*
Scott Sorensen, *Vice Pres*
Kenneth Neppach, *Regional Mgr*
Kamie Mulroy, *Office Admin*
▲ EMP: 100
SQ FT: 60,000
SALES (est): 34MM **Privately Held**
WEB: www.bega-us.com
SIC: 3648 3646 Outdoor lighting equipment; commercial indusl & institutional electric lighting fixtures

(P-17675)
BIRCHWOOD LIGHTING INC
3340 E La Palma Ave, Anaheim (92806-2814)
PHONE..............................714 550-7118
Darrin Weedon, *President*
Linda Allen, *Admin Sec*
EMP: 25
SQ FT: 1,900
SALES (est): 5.8MM
SALES (corp-wide): 1.7B **Privately Held**
WEB: www.birchwoodlighting.com
SIC: 3648 3646 3645 Decorative area lighting fixtures; commercial indusl & institutional electric lighting fixtures; residential lighting fixtures
PA: Leviton Manufacturing Co., Inc.
201 N Service Rd
Melville NY 11747
631 812-6000

(P-17676)
BLISS HOLDINGS LLC
745 S Vinewood St, Escondido (92029-1928)
PHONE..............................626 506-8696
Allan Lee,
▲ EMP: 50
SALES (est): 992.4K **Privately Held**
SIC: 3648 Lighting equipment

(P-17677)
BLISSLIGHTS LLC
100 E San Marcos Blvd # 308, San Marcos (92069-2989)
PHONE..............................888 868-4603

P R O D U C T S & S V C S

Ravi Bhagavatula,
Brent Hunter, *Finance Dir*
EMP: 20
SQ FT: 4,573
SALES (est): 1.2MM **Privately Held**
SIC: 3648 Lighting equipment

(P-17678)
C W ENTERPRISES INC
2111 Iowa Ave Ste D, Riverside
(92507-7414)
PHONE..............................951 786-9999
William Noyes, *CEO*
Charlotte Noyes, *CFO*
EMP: 10
SALES: 1.6MM **Privately Held**
SIC: 3648 Lighting equipment

(P-17679)
CINEMILLS CORPORATION (PA)
2021 N Lincoln St, Burbank (91504-3334)
PHONE..............................818 843-4560
Marcos M Demattos, *CEO*
Carlos Demattos, *President*
▲ **EMP:** 10 **EST:** 1976
SQ FT: 5,000
SALES (est): 1.9MM **Privately Held**
WEB: www.cinemills.com
SIC: 3648 7359 3646 Lighting equipment;
sound & lighting equipment rental; com-
mercial indusl & institutional electric light-
ing fixtures

(P-17680)
CLARUS LIGHTING LLC
Also Called: Casella
10183 Croydon Way Ste C, Sacramento
(95827-2103)
PHONE..............................916 363-2888
▲ **EMP:** 11
SQ FT: 5,000
SALES (est): 1.5MM **Privately Held**
WEB: www.claruslighting.com
SIC: 3648 Lighting equipment

(P-17681)
COOPER LIGHTING LLC
3350 Enterprise Dr, Bloomington
(92316-3538)
PHONE..............................909 605-6615
John Seiler, *Manager*
EMP: 35 **Privately Held**
WEB: www.corelite.com
SIC: 3648 Lighting equipment
HQ: Cooper Lighting, Llc
    1121 Highway 74 S
    Peachtree City GA 30269
    770 486-4800

(P-17682)
CYRON INC
21029 Itasca St Ste C, Chatsworth
(91311-8510)
PHONE..............................818 772-1900
Al Javadi, *President*
Shell Reinish, *Vice Pres*
Jim Adair, *Sales Staff*
▲ **EMP:** 10
SQ FT: 5,700
SALES: 1.4MM **Privately Held**
WEB: www.cyron.com
SIC: 3648 Lighting equipment

(P-17683)
DABMAR LIGHTING INC (PA)
2140 Eastman Ave, Oxnard (93030-5168)
PHONE..............................805 604-9090
Dan Davidson, *President*
Bilha Davidson, *Vice Pres*
◆ **EMP:** 23
SQ FT: 50,000
SALES (est): 4.5MM **Privately Held**
WEB: www.dabmar.com
SIC: 3648 Lighting equipment

(P-17684)
DANA CREATH DESIGNS LTD
3030 Kilson Dr, Santa Ana (92707-4203)
PHONE..............................714 662-0111
Dana E Creath, *Partner*
James K Creath, *Partner*
Raylene R Creath, *Partner*
EMP: 30

SALES (est): 4.2MM **Privately Held**
WEB: www.danacreathdesigns.com
SIC: 3648 3646 3645 Lighting equipment;
commercial indusl & institutional electric
lighting fixtures; residential lighting fixtures

(P-17685)
DELRAY LIGHTING INC
7545 N Lockheed Dr, Burbank
(91505-1045)
PHONE..............................818 767-3793
Steven Feig, *CEO*
Steve Babbitt, *Engineer*
Adam Lamar, *Sales Dir*
Mark Rorrison, *Sales Staff*
Mindy Kindhart, *Manager*
▲ **EMP:** 28
SQ FT: 20,000
SALES (est): 7.1MM **Privately Held**
WEB: www.delraylighting.com
SIC: 3648 Lighting equipment

(P-17686)
E2 LIGHTING INC
1460 Yosemite Ave, San Francisco
(94124-3322)
PHONE..............................415 760-7793
John Lowe, *CEO*
Mike Kwong, *Admin Sec*
EMP: 20
SALES (est): 1.9MM **Privately Held**
SIC: 3648 Lighting equipment

(P-17687)
ECHO LIGHTING INCORPORATED
5618 E Washington Blvd, Commerce
(90040-1406)
PHONE..............................323 890-9008
Armando Garcia, *President*
Silvia Garcia, *Admin Sec*
EMP: 10
SQ FT: 4,000
SALES (est): 1.6MM **Privately Held**
SIC: 3648 Outdoor lighting equipment

(P-17688)
EEMA INDUSTRIES INC
Also Called: Liton Lighting
5461 W Jefferson Blvd, Los Angeles
(90016-3715)
PHONE..............................323 904-0200
Amir Esmail Zadeh, *President*
Tony Phan, *Marketing Staff*
◆ **EMP:** 40
SQ FT: 40,000
SALES (est): 8.1MM **Privately Held**
WEB: www.eema.net
SIC: 3648 5063 Lighting equipment; elec-
trical apparatus & equipment

(P-17689)
ELECTRONIC THEATRE CONTRLS INC
Also Called: Etc
6640 W Sunset Blvd # 200, Los Angeles
(90028-7104)
PHONE..............................323 461-0216
Randy Pybas, *Regional Mgr*
EMP: 18
SALES (corp-wide): 317.6MM **Privately Held**
WEB: www.etcasia.com
SIC: 3648 5049 Lighting equipment; the-
atrical equipment & supplies
PA: Electronic Theatre Controls, Inc.
    3031 Pleasant View Rd
    Middleton WI 53562
    608 831-4116

(P-17690)
ELITE LIGHTING
Also Called: Elite Lighting Corp.
5424 E Slauson Ave, Commerce
(90040-2919)
PHONE..............................323 888-1973
Babak Rashididoust, *CEO*
Daniel Lubin, *Project Engr*
Monica Pour, *Purchasing*
Hamid Rashidi, *Natl Sales Mgr*
Natalie Bravo, *Regl Sales Mgr*
▲ **EMP:** 200
SQ FT: 25,000

SALES (est): 57.5MM **Privately Held**
SIC: 3648 3646 3645 Lighting equipment;
commercial indusl & institutional electric
lighting fixtures; boudoir lamps

(P-17691)
EMAZING LIGHTS LLC
240 S Loara St, Anaheim (92802-1020)
PHONE..............................626 628-6482
Brian Lim, *Principal*
Scott Elliott, *COO*
Joel Ruiz, *Store Mgr*
Sean Okita, *Manager*
▲ **EMP:** 13
SALES (est): 2.6MM **Privately Held**
SIC: 3648 3229 Spotlights; bulbs for elec-
tric lights

(P-17692)
ENERGY MANAGEMENT GROUP INC (PA)
Also Called: Lighting Company, The
1621 Browning, Irvine (92606-4828)
PHONE..............................949 296-0764
Steve Espinosa, *President*
Arnold Irizar, *Sales Staff*
EMP: 13
SQ FT: 16,000
SALES (est): 2.6MM **Privately Held**
SIC: 3648 Lighting fixtures, except electric:
residential

(P-17693)
EXCELITAS TECHNOLOGIES CORP
44370 Christy St, Fremont (94538-3180)
PHONE..............................510 979-6500
John Lucero, *Branch Mgr*
Nam Dao, *Project Engr*
Mauro Manzano, *Facilities Mgr*
Joseph Low, *Director*
EMP: 93 **Privately Held**
SIC: 3648 3845 Lighting equipment; elec-
tromedical apparatus
HQ: Excelitas Technologies Corp.
    200 West St
    Waltham MA 02451

(P-17694)
FNTECH
18107 Mount Washington St, Fountain Val-
ley (92708-6120)
PHONE..............................714 429-1686
EMP: 15
SALES: 2.5MM **Privately Held**
SIC: 3648 Stage lighting equipment

(P-17695)
FOXFURY LLC
Also Called: Foxfury Lighting Solution
3528 Seagate Way Ste 100, Oceanside
(92056-6040)
PHONE..............................760 945-4231
Mario A Cugini,
▲ **EMP:** 24
SALES (est): 4.7MM **Privately Held**
WEB: www.foxfury.com
SIC: 3648 Lighting equipment

(P-17696)
GALLAGHER RENTAL INC
15701 Heron Ave, La Mirada (90638-5206)
PHONE..............................714 690-1559
Joseph Gallagher, *CEO*
Megan Gallagher, *Manager*
EMP: 30 **EST:** 2012
SALES (est): 4.7MM **Privately Held**
SIC: 3648 Stage lighting equipment

(P-17697)
GAMMALUX LIGHTING SYSTEMS
248 E Arrow Hwy, San Dimas
(91773-3359)
PHONE..............................909 599-9669
Mehmet K Incikaya, *CEO*
Philip Incikaya, *Vice Pres*
Joe Napoli, *Vice Pres*
Connie Incikaya, *Finance Mgr*
Amir Abdabhai, *VP Sales*
EMP: 40
SQ FT: 25,000

SALES (est): 9.2MM **Privately Held**
WEB: www.gammalux.com
SIC: 3648 Lighting equipment

(P-17698)
GREENSHINE NEW ENERGY LLC
Also Called: Greenshine New Energy Co
23661 Birtcher Dr, Lake Forest
(92630-1770)
PHONE..............................949 609-9636
Alex Chen, *Sales Mgr*
Scott Douglas, *General Mgr*
Kevin Laurent, *Project Mgr*
▲ **EMP:** 100
SQ FT: 200
SALES: 1MM **Privately Held**
SIC: 3648 Lighting equipment

(P-17699)
H K LIGHTING GROUP INC
3529 Old Conejo Rd # 118, Newbury Park
(91320-6152)
PHONE..............................805 480-4881
Hiroshi Kira, *President*
Shirley Zien, *CFO*
William Steinbrink, *Sales Staff*
Allen Cheng,
◆ **EMP:** 12
SALES (est): 2.3MM **Privately Held**
SIC: 3648 Decorative area lighting fixtures

(P-17700)
HITEK LIGHTING INC
1172 Pradera Ct, Arroyo Grande
(93420-2900)
PHONE..............................805 481-6006
Kellena Henwood, *President*
EMP: 14
SALES (est): 1.3MM **Privately Held**
SIC: 3648 Lighting equipment

(P-17701)
HUBBELL LIGHTING INC
2498 Roll Dr, San Diego (92154-7213)
PHONE..............................619 946-1800
EMP: 252
SALES (corp-wide): 3.6B **Publicly Held**
SIC: 3648 Outdoor lighting equipment
HQ: Hubbell Lighting, Inc.
    701 Millennium Blvd
    Greenville SC 29607

(P-17702)
ILOS CORP
Also Called: Meteor Lighting
1300 John Reed Ct Ste B, City of Industry
(91745-2422)
PHONE..............................213 255-2060
Ming Hsin Lu, *President*
▲ **EMP:** 10 **EST:** 2008
SALES (est): 740.8K **Privately Held**
SIC: 3648 Lighting equipment

(P-17703)
IN PRO CAR WEAR INC
Also Called: I P C W
6363 Corsair St, Commerce (90040-2503)
PHONE..............................323 724-0568
Ken Liao, *Vice Pres*
▲ **EMP:** 11
SALES (est): 1.2MM **Privately Held**
WEB: www.inprocarwear.com
SIC: 3648 Lighting equipment

(P-17704)
INNOVALIGHT INC
965 W Maude Ave, Sunnyvale
(94085-2802)
PHONE..............................408 419-4400
Thomas Linn, *CEO*
Michael Johnson, *CFO*
Conrad Burke, *Principal*
▲ **EMP:** 40
SALES (est): 7.1MM
SALES (corp-wide): 62.4B **Publicly Held**
WEB: www.innovalight.com
SIC: 3648 Lighting equipment
HQ: E. I. Du Pont De Nemours And Com-
pany
    974 Centre Rd
    Wilmington DE 19805
    302 774-1000

▲ = Import ▼=Export
◆ =Import/Export

(P-17705)
JIMWAY INC
Also Called: Altair Lighting
20101 S Santa Fe Ave, Compton
(90221-5917)
PHONE...............................310 886-3718
Hsing-Min Keng, *CEO*
Irene Wang, *Admin Sec*
Singh Chang, *Info Tech Mgr*
Jay Spowart, *VP Finance*
Hao Rocks, *Manager*
▲ EMP: 100
SQ FT: 200,000
SALES (est): 20.3MM **Privately Held**
SIC: 3648 3221 5063 Lighting equipment;
glass containers; electrical apparatus &
equipment

(P-17706)
KUSTOM LIGHTING PRODUCTS INC
2107 Chico Ave, South El Monte
(91733-1606)
PHONE...............................626 443-0166
Paul Lestz, *President*
Augustine Haro, *Shareholder*
Brett Browning, *Vice Pres*
▲ EMP: 50
SQ FT: 11,500
SALES (est): 6.7MM **Privately Held**
SIC: 3648 Lighting equipment

(P-17707)
LIGHT & MOTION INDUSTRIES
711 Neeson Rd, Marina (93933-5104)
PHONE...............................831 645-1525
Daniel T Emerson, *President*
Ryan Stokey, *Marketing Staff*
Adriane Fells, *Manager*
▲ EMP: 55
SALES (est): 12MM **Privately Held**
WEB: www.lightandmotion.com
SIC: 3648 Underwater lighting fixtures

(P-17708)
LIGHTING CONTROL & DESIGN INC (HQ)
Also Called: LCD&d
9144 Deering Ave, Chatsworth
(91311-5801)
PHONE...............................323 226-0000
J David Wilson, *President*
William Lahey, *Vice Pres*
Jon Stachelrodt, *Vice Pres*
EMP: 29
SQ FT: 10,000
SALES (est): 4.6MM
SALES (corp-wide): 3.6B **Publicly Held**
WEB: www.lcdtest.com
SIC: 3648 3643 5719 Lighting equipment;
current-carrying wiring devices; lighting
fixtures
PA: Acuity Brands, Inc.
1170 Peachtree St Ne
Atlanta GA 30309
404 853-1400

(P-17709)
LUMENTON INC
Also Called: Lumenton Lighting
5461 W Jefferson Blvd, Los Angeles
(90016-3715)
PHONE...............................323 904-0202
A J Esmailzadeh, *President*
Sonny Guerrero, *Purchasing*
George Pizzo, *Natl Sales Mgr*
▲ EMP: 26
SQ FT: 100,000
SALES (est): 4.3MM **Privately Held**
SIC: 3648 Outdoor lighting equipment

(P-17710)
LUMENYTE INTERNATIONAL CORP
535 4th St, San Fernando (91340-2521)
PHONE...............................949 279-8687
Peter D Costigan, *President*
Peter Costigan, *Executive*
Steven Strickler, *Principal*
Paul Robbins, *Manager*
▲ EMP: 10
SQ FT: 5,000

SALES (est): 2.2MM **Privately Held**
WEB: www.lumenyte.com
SIC: 3648 8748 Lighting equipment; light-
ing consultant

(P-17711)
LUMINUS DEVICES INC
1145 Sonora Ct, Sunnyvale (94086-5384)
PHONE...............................978 528-8000
Kechuang Lin, *Chairman*
Decai Sun, *President*
Kevin Shih, *CFO*
Mark Pugh, *Exec VP*
▲ EMP: 48
SALES (est): 19.4MM
SALES (corp-wide): 1.2B **Privately Held**
WEB: www.luminusdevices.com
SIC: 3648 Lighting equipment
HQ: Luminus, Inc.
1145 Sonora Ct
Sunnyvale CA 94086
408 708-7000

(P-17712)
MAG INSTRUMENT INC (PA)
2001 S Hellman Ave, Ontario (91761-8019)
P.O. Box 50600 (91761-1083)
PHONE...............................909 947-1006
Anthony Maglica, *CEO*
Jim Zecchini, *COO*
Brent Flaharty, *Officer*
Malissa Peace, *Officer*
David Hefner, *Vice Pres*
▲ EMP: 277 EST: 1955
SQ FT: 1,000,000
SALES (est): 175.8MM **Privately Held**
WEB: www.maglite.com
SIC: 3648 Flashlights

(P-17713)
MAXLITE INC
1148 N Ocean Cir, Anaheim (92806-1939)
PHONE...............................714 678-5000
David Delgado, *Technical Staff*
EMP: 14
SALES (est): 2.8MM **Privately Held**
SIC: 3648 Lighting equipment
PA: Maxlite, Inc.
12 York Ave
West Caldwell NJ 07006

(P-17714)
MICA LIGHTING COMPANY INC
717 S State College Blvd K, Fullerton
(92831-5119)
PHONE...............................714 738-8448
Gayle Von Eissler, *President*
George Von Eissler, *CFO*
Francisco Briseno, *Vice Pres*
EMP: 15
SQ FT: 2,200
SALES (est): 865.1K **Privately Held**
WEB: www.micalighting.com
SIC: 3648 Decorative area lighting fixtures

(P-17715)
MIDMARK CORPORATION
690 Knox St, Torrance (90502-1337)
PHONE...............................310 516-5100
EMP: 12
SALES (corp-wide): 322.2MM **Privately Held**
SIC: 3648 3842 3843 Lighting equipment;
stretchers; dental equipment & supplies
PA: Midmark Corporation
1700 S Patterson Blvd # 400
Kettering OH 45409
937 526-3662

(P-17716)
MNC BLISS ENTERPRISES INC
1715 Fulton Ave, Sacramento
(95825-2415)
PHONE...............................916 483-1167
Marshall Bliss, *CEO*
Cassie Bliss, *CFO*
EMP: 13
SQ FT: 10,000
SALES: 4MM **Privately Held**
SIC: 3648 Outdoor lighting equipment

(P-17717)
MW MCWONG INTERNATIONAL INC
Also Called: Pacific Lighting & Electrical
1921 Arena Blvd, Sacramento
(95834-3770)
PHONE...............................916 371-8080
Margaret Y Wong, *CEO*
Emily MEI, *CFO*
Blane Goettle, *Vice Pres*
Stephen Zhou, *Vice Pres*
▲ EMP: 90
SQ FT: 47,430
SALES (est): 17.6MM **Privately Held**
SIC: 3648 Lighting fixtures, except electric:
residential

(P-17718)
NATIONAL BRIGHT LIGHTING INC
1480 Adelia Ave, South El Monte
(91733-3003)
PHONE...............................909 818-9188
Helen Lin, *President*
EMP: 22
SALES (est): 3MM **Privately Held**
SIC: 3648 3646 Street lighting fixtures; air-
port lighting fixtures: runway approach,
taxi or ramp; commercial indusl & institu-
tional electric lighting fixtures

(P-17719)
NEW BEDFORD PANORAMEX CORP
Also Called: Nbp
1480 N Claremont Blvd, Claremont
(91711-3538)
PHONE...............................909 982-9806
Steven Robert Ozuna, *President*
Bryce Nielsen, *Admin Sec*
Victor Zamora, *Project Engr*
Saswata Mondal, *Engineer*
James Casso, *Director*
EMP: 35 EST: 1966
SQ FT: 65,000
SALES (est): 10.4MM **Privately Held**
WEB: www.nbpcorp.com
SIC: 3648 Airport lighting fixtures: runway
approach, taxi or ramp

(P-17720)
NITERIDER TECHNICAL LIGHTING &
8295 Aero Pl Ste 200, San Diego
(92123-2001)
PHONE...............................858 268-9316
Thomas Edward Carroll, *CEO*
Mark Schultz, *COO*
Mark Ortega, *Accounts Mgr*
▲ EMP: 35
SQ FT: 15,000
SALES (est): 7MM **Privately Held**
WEB: www.niterideroffroad.com
SIC: 3648 3646 Lighting equipment; com-
mercial indusl & institutional electric light-
ing fixtures

(P-17721)
ONESOLUTION LIGHT AND CONTROL
Also Called: Nsi Architectural
225 S Loara St, Anaheim (92802-1019)
PHONE...............................714 490-5540
John C Ortiz, *President*
EMP: 20
SQ FT: 14,000
SALES (est): 3.2MM **Privately Held**
WEB: www.nsi-inc.com
SIC: 3648 Lighting equipment

(P-17722)
PACIFIC COAST LIGHTING INC (PA)
20238 Plummer St, Chatsworth
(91311-5365)
PHONE...............................818 886-9751
Dennis K Swanson, *CEO*
Dick Idol, *Partner*
Clark Linstone, *CEO*
Linda Clayton, *Executive*
Manja Swanson, *Admin Sec*
◆ EMP: 240
SQ FT: 100,000

SALES (est): 38.2MM **Privately Held**
WEB: www.pacificcoastlighting.com
SIC: 3648 3641 5719 Lighting equipment;
electric lamps; lighting fixtures

(P-17723)
PAN-A-LITE PRODUCTS INC
1601 Ritchey St, Santa Ana (92705-5123)
PHONE...............................714 258-7111
Nina Rahe, *President*
EMP: 15
SQ FT: 3,200
SALES (est): 1.9MM **Privately Held**
SIC: 3648 Lighting equipment

(P-17724)
PELICAN PRODUCTS INC (PA)
23215 Early Ave, Torrance (90505-4002)
PHONE...............................310 326-4700
Lyndon J Faulkner, *CEO*
Peter Pace, *Ch of Bd*
Phil Gyori, *President*
Dave Williams, *President*
John Padian, *COO*
▲ EMP: 277
SQ FT: 150,000
SALES (est): 214.2MM **Privately Held**
WEB: www.pelican.com
SIC: 3648 3161 3089 Flashlights; lug-
gage; plastic containers, except foam

(P-17725)
POWERLUX CORPORATION
1260 Liberty Way Ste E, Vista
(92081-8320)
PHONE...............................760 727-2360
Kenneth Lau, *President*
Theodora Lau, *Vice Pres*
Donald Maund, *Director*
EMP: 13
SQ FT: 6,000
SALES (est): 2.2MM **Privately Held**
WEB: www.powerlux.com
SIC: 3648 Lighting equipment

(P-17726)
PRIMUS LIGHTING INC
3570 Lexington Ave, El Monte
(91731-2608)
PHONE...............................626 442-4600
Jaime Calderon, *President*
EMP: 13
SQ FT: 5,300
SALES (est): 1.9MM **Privately Held**
WEB: www.primuslighting.com
SIC: 3648 Outdoor lighting equipment

(P-17727)
RAXIUM INC
1250 Reliance Way, Fremont (94539-6100)
PHONE...............................408 712-1648
EMP: 20
SALES (est): 4MM **Privately Held**
SIC: 3648 Lighting equipment

(P-17728)
REMOTE OCEAN SYSTEMS INC (PA)
Also Called: R O S
5618 Copley Dr, San Diego (92111-7902)
PHONE...............................858 565-8500
Robert Acks, *CEO*
Christine Acks, *Admin Sec*
Kenna Thompson, *Info Tech Dir*
EMP: 34
SQ FT: 27,000
SALES (est): 5.5MM **Privately Held**
WEB: www.rosys.com
SIC: 3648 3861 3812 3643 Underwater
lighting fixtures; photographic equipment
& supplies; search & navigation equip-
ment; current-carrying wiring devices; ve-
hicular lighting equipment

(P-17729)
RICHEE LIGHTING INC
1600 W Washington Blvd, Los Angeles
(90007-1115)
PHONE...............................213 814-1638
James Lee, *Administration*
Angela Yi, *Admin Sec*
EMP: 10
SALES (est): 956.6K **Privately Held**
SIC: 3648 Public lighting fixtures

(P-17730)
S T E U INC
Also Called: Vista Landscape Lighting
1625 Surveyor Ave, Simi Valley
(93063-3387)
PHONE..........................805 527-0987
Dan Cunado, *President*
Tony Rolando, *CFO*
Ankur Vyas, *Design Engr*
Bryan Tanger, *Technology*
Omar Alcantara, *Technical Staff*
▲ EMP: 30
SALES (est): 11.9MM **Privately Held**
WEB: www.vistapro.com
SIC: 3648 Decorative area lighting fixtures

(P-17731)
SHIMADA ENTERPRISES INC
Also Called: Celestial Lighting
14009 Dinard Ave, Santa Fe Springs
(90670-4922)
PHONE..........................562 802-8811
Tak Shimada, *President*
Mick Shimada, *Vice Pres*
Alex Gaxiola, *Sales Mgr*
▲ EMP: 30
SQ FT: 11,000
SALES (est): 5.6MM **Privately Held**
WEB: www.celestiallighting.com
SIC: 3648 Decorative area lighting fixtures

(P-17732)
SPIN SHADES CORPORATION
3115 Breaker Dr, Ventura (93003-1009)
PHONE..........................805 650-4849
Wendy Gayner, *President*
▲ EMP: 20
SALES (est): 3MM **Privately Held**
WEB: www.spinshades.com
SIC: 3648 Lighting equipment

(P-17733)
SUN POWER SOURCE (PA)
1650 Palma Dr, Ventura (93003-5749)
PHONE..........................805 644-2520
Sean Frye, *President*
Tammy Frye, *Vice Pres*
EMP: 15
SQ FT: 1,850
SALES (est): 2.4MM **Privately Held**
SIC: 3648 7299 Sun tanning equipment,
incl. tanning beds; tanning salon

(P-17734)
SUREFIRE LLC
18300 Mount Baldy Cir, Fountain Valley
(92708-6122)
PHONE..........................714 545-9444
Joel Smith, *Manager*
Matt Richardson, *Engineer*
William Wells, *Engineer*
EMP: 25 **Privately Held**
SIC: 3648 Lighting equipment

(P-17735)
TEC LIGHTING INC
115 Arovista Cir, Brea (92821-3830)
PHONE..........................714 529-5068
Kamal S Hodhodc, *CEO*
David Hodhod, *President*
Paul Hebert, *COO*
Daniel Hodhod, *Vice Pres*
Moses Nuno, *Engineer*
◆ EMP: 15
SALES: 7.5MM **Privately Held**
WEB: www.teclighting.com
SIC: 3648 Lighting equipment

(P-17736)
TEKA ILLUMINATION INC
40429 Brickyard Dr, Madera (93636-9515)
PHONE..........................559 438-5800
Douglas W Hagen, *President*
EMP: 15
SQ FT: 3,000
SALES (est): 2.8MM **Privately Held**
WEB: www.tekaillumination.com
SIC: 3648 Lighting equipment

(P-17737)
THE SLOAN COMPANY INC (PA)
Also Called: Sloanled
5725 Olivas Park Dr, Ventura (93003-7697)
PHONE..........................805 676-3200
Tom Beyer, *President*
Angela Delonzo, *CFO*

Kevin Stoll, *Vice Pres*
Allen Kim, *Executive*
Sheryl Ramirez, *General Mgr*
▲ EMP: 120
SQ FT: 25,545
SALES: 55MM **Privately Held**
WEB: www.sloanled.com
SIC: 3648 Lighting equipment

(P-17738)
THIN-LITE CORPORATION
530 Constitution Ave, Camarillo
(93012-8595)
PHONE..........................805 987-5021
Alan Griffin, *President*
Lilian Cross Szymanek, *Co-President*
▲ EMP: 47 EST: 1970
SQ FT: 27,000
SALES (est): 7MM **Privately Held**
WEB: www.thinlite.com
SIC: 3648 3612 3646 Lighting equipment;
transformers, except electric; fluorescent
lighting fixtures, commercial

(P-17739)
TIVOLI INDUSTRIES INC
1550 E Saint Gertrude Pl, Santa Ana
(92705-5310)
PHONE..........................714 957-6101
Peter Jang, *CEO*
Nigel Coppins, *CFO*
▲ EMP: 50
SALES: 1MM **Privately Held**
SIC: 3648 Lighting equipment

(P-17740)
TOTAL STRUCTURES INC
1696 Walter St, Ventura (93003-5619)
PHONE..........................805 676-3322
Martijn Kuijper, *President*
◆ EMP: 32
SQ FT: 24,000
SALES (est): 14.6MM **Privately Held**
WEB: www.newwavetruss.com
SIC: 3648 3441 Lighting equipment; fabri-
cated structural metal

(P-17741)
TRULY GREEN SOLUTIONS LLC
9601 Variel Ave, Chatsworth (91311-4914)
PHONE..........................818 206-4404
Rubina Jadwet, *CEO*
John Woodman, *Vice Pres*
Jennifer Cataffo, *Admin Asst*
Johana Romero, *Admin Asst*
Scott Marshall, *Natl Sales Mgr*
▲ EMP: 25 EST: 2010
SALES (est): 5.4MM **Privately Held**
SIC: 3648 Lighting equipment

(P-17742)
US POLE COMPANY INC (PA)
Also Called: U S Architectural Lighting
660 W Avenue O, Palmdale (93551-3610)
PHONE..........................800 877-6537
Joseph Straus, *President*
Lucas Peters, *Technology*
Harvey Solis, *Purch Mgr*
Roger Rosales, *Production*
Ted Tracy, *Regl Sales Mgr*
◆ EMP: 140
SQ FT: 112,000
SALES (est): 83.4MM **Privately Held**
WEB: www.usaltg.com
SIC: 3648 Outdoor lighting equipment

(P-17743)
V2 LIGHTING GROUP INC
276 E Gish Rd, San Jose (95112-4706)
PHONE..........................707 383-4600
Chris Varrin, *CEO*
Michelle Varrin, *Admin Sec*
▲ EMP: 12 EST: 2010
SQ FT: 1,200
SALES (est): 2.7MM **Privately Held**
SIC: 3648 Lighting equipment

(P-17744)
VARIANT TECHNOLOGY INC
635 Hampton Rd, Arcadia (91006-2102)
PHONE..........................626 278-4343
Kamran Sarmadi, *President*
Maryam Mosallaie, *CFO*
EMP: 10
SALES: 2MM **Privately Held**
SIC: 3648 Lighting equipment

(P-17745)
VIDESSENCE LLC
10768 Lower Azusa Rd, El Monte
(91731-1306)
PHONE..........................626 579-0943
Toni Warrens, *Owner*
EMP: 20
SALES (corp-wide): 4.4MM **Privately Held**
WEB: www.elplighting.com
SIC: 3648 Stage lighting equipment
PA: Videssence Llc
10768 Lower Azusa Rd
El Monte CA 91731
626 579-0943

(P-17746)
XENONICS HOLDINGS INC
3186 Lionshead Ave # 100, Carlsbad
(92010-4700)
PHONE..........................760 477-8900
Alan P Magerman, *Ch of Bd*
Jeffrey P Kennedy, *President*
Richard S Kay, *CFO*
EMP: 10
SQ FT: 13,200
SALES: 830K **Privately Held**
WEB: www.xenonics.com
SIC: 3648 Infrared lamp fixtures

3651 Household Audio & Video Eqpt

(P-17747)
360 SYSTEMS
3281 Grande Vista Dr, Newbury Park
(91320-1193)
PHONE..........................818 991-0360
Robert Easton, *President*
Freddie Hamilton, *Technician*
Daren Francom, *Controller*
John Hall, *Sales Dir*
Robert Nilo, *Sales Mgr*
EMP: 12
SQ FT: 17,000
SALES (est): 2.5MM **Privately Held**
WEB: www.360systems.com
SIC: 3651 Audio electronic systems

(P-17748)
ABCRON CORPORATION
3002 Dow Ave Ste 408, Tustin
(92780-7236)
PHONE..........................714 730-9988
Sopa Ker, *Office Mgr*
Mike Chen, *President*
▲ EMP: 12
SQ FT: 2,100
SALES: 9MM **Privately Held**
WEB: www.abcron.com
SIC: 3651 Household audio & video equip-
ment

(P-17749)
ABSOLUTE USA INC
1800 E Washington Blvd, Los Angeles
(90021-3127)
PHONE..........................213 744-0044
Mohammad K Razipour, *President*
Gerardo Malara, *Buyer*
Maria Martinez, *Sales Executive*
Jesse Rosales, *Sales Staff*
Sam Farzan, *Manager*
◆ EMP: 47
SQ FT: 35,000
SALES (est): 11.1MM **Privately Held**
WEB: www.absoluteusa.com
SIC: 3651 Audio electronic systems

(P-17750)
ACTI CORPORATION INC
Also Called: California Acti
3 Jenner Ste 160, Irvine (92618-3834)
PHONE..........................949 753-0352
Juber Chu, *President*
Kelvin Wong, *CFO*
Ingrid Lin, *Administration*
Adrian Garcia, *Technical Mgr*
Yen Andy, *Technical Staff*
EMP: 20

SALES (est): 3.7MM
SALES (corp-wide): 25.7MM **Privately
Held**
SIC: 3651 3663 3699 Household audio &
video equipment; cameras, television; se-
curity devices
PA: Acti Corporation
7f, 1, Alley 20, Lane 407, Ti Ting Blvd.,
Sec. 2,
Taipei City TAP 11493
226 562-588

(P-17751)
ACTIVEON INC (PA)
10905 Technology Pl, San Diego
(92127-1811)
PHONE..........................858 798-3300
John Lee, *CEO*
Jonathan Zupnik, *Vice Pres*
Alan Erickson, *Manager*
▲ EMP: 17
SALES (est): 3.5MM **Privately Held**
SIC: 3651 Household audio & video equip-
ment

(P-17752)
ACTODYNE GENERAL INC
Also Called: Lace Music Products
5596 Corporate Ave, Cypress
(90630-4709)
PHONE..........................714 898-2776
Donald Lace Jr, *President*
Jeff Lace, *Vice Pres*
▲ EMP: 15
SQ FT: 12,000
SALES (est): 2.4MM **Privately Held**
WEB: www.agi-lace.com
SIC: 3651 Household audio & video equip-
ment

(P-17753)
**ADVANCE ENGINEERING RES
INC**
1012 W Beverly Blvd # 857, Montebello
(90640-4139)
PHONE..........................626 354-9282
Kenny Fung, *President*
Yali RAO, *Admin Sec*
EMP: 10
SALES (est): 1.4MM **Privately Held**
SIC: 3651 5065 5731 Home entertain-
ment equipment, electronic; communica-
tion equipment; consumer electronic
equipment

(P-17754)
AEA RIBBON MICS
1029 N Allen Ave, Pasadena (91104-3202)
PHONE..........................626 798-9128
Wes Dooley, *Owner*
Charlene Gibbs, *Marketing Staff*
Sammy Rothman, *Mktg Coord*
EMP: 12
SALES (est): 760.7K **Privately Held**
SIC: 3651 Microphones

(P-17755)
AFTER HOURS
7310 Adams St Ste F, Paramount
(90723-4043)
PHONE..........................562 925-5737
Raul Uc, *Owner*
Kimzie Garland, *Manager*
Isiah Macon, *Manager*
EMP: 16
SALES (est): 1.6MM **Privately Held**
SIC: 3651 Video camera-audio recorders,
household use

(P-17756)
AL SHELLCO LLC (HQ)
9330 Scranton Rd Ste 600, San Diego
(92121-7706)
PHONE..........................570 296-6444
Mark Lucas, *Facilities Mgr*
George Stelling, *President*
Ross Gatlin, *CEO*
Richard P Horner, *CFO*
Edward Anchel,
▲ EMP: 160
SQ FT: 120,000

▲ = Import ▼=Export
◆ =Import/Export

SALES (est): 84.1MM
SALES (corp-wide): 869.1MM **Privately Held**
WEB: www.alteclansing.com
SIC: 3651 3577 Radio receiving sets; computer peripheral equipment
PA: Prophet Equity Lp
1460 Main St Ste 200
Southlake TX 76092
817 898-1500

(P-17757)
ALPHA ALARM & AUDIO INC
1400 Belden Ct, Dixon (95620-4823)
P.O. Box 911 (95620-0911)
PHONE.....................707 452-8334
Loren Dougherty, *CEO*
EMP: 14
SALES (est): 2.3MM **Privately Held**
SIC: 3651 Household audio & video equipment

(P-17758)
ALURATEK INC
15241 Barranca Pkwy, Irvine (92618-2201)
PHONE.....................949 468-2046
John Wolikow, *CEO*
Akash Patel, *CFO*
Kamal Panda, *Vice Pres*
Dave Song, *Vice Pres*
Victor Wang, *Principal*
▲ EMP: 25
SQ FT: 5,000
SALES (est): 4.9MM **Privately Held**
SIC: 3651 5045 Home entertainment equipment, electronic; audio electronic systems; computers, peripherals & software

(P-17759)
ANACOM GENERAL CORPORATION
Also Called: Anacom Medtek
1240 S Claudina St, Anaheim (92805-6232)
PHONE.....................714 774-8484
Daniel S Haines, *President*
William K Haines, *Chairman*
Joe Kuciera, *General Mgr*
Paul Lau, *Manager*
▲ EMP: 48
SQ FT: 20,000
SALES (est): 11.4MM **Privately Held**
WEB: www.anacom-medtek.com
SIC: 3651 3577 Speaker monitors; computer peripheral equipment

(P-17760)
ANCHOR AUDIO INC
5931 Darwin Ct, Carlsbad (92008-7302)
PHONE.....................760 827-7100
Janet Jacobs, *CEO*
David Jacobs, *President*
Dwight Garbe, *CFO*
Mario Granados, *Engineer*
Jennifer Truong, *Controller*
◆ EMP: 58
SQ FT: 31,200
SALES (est): 13.6MM **Privately Held**
WEB: www.anchoraudio.com
SIC: 3651 Public address systems

(P-17761)
APOGEE ELECTRONICS CORPORATION
1715 Berkeley St, Santa Monica (90404-4104)
PHONE.....................310 584-9394
Betty A Bennett, *CEO*
Jack Shady, *Technician*
Pieter Kelchtermans, *Electrical Engi*
Rob Clark, *Business Mgr*
Tara Nader, *Human Resources*
▲ EMP: 35
SQ FT: 5,000
SALES (est): 7.8MM **Privately Held**
WEB: www.apogeedigital.com
SIC: 3651 3621 8748 Audio electronic systems; motors & generators; communications consulting

(P-17762)
AQUATIC AV INC
282 Kinney Dr, San Jose (95112-4433)
PHONE.....................408 559-1668
Robert Fils, *CEO*

Janet Goldstein, *Treasurer*
▲ EMP: 12 EST: 2005
SQ FT: 3,000
SALES (est): 2MM **Privately Held**
SIC: 3651 Audio electronic systems

(P-17763)
ATLONA INC
70 Daggett Dr, San Jose (95134-2108)
P.O. Box 642015 (95164-2015)
PHONE.....................408 962-0515
Ilya Khayn, *CEO*
Michael Khain, *CEO*
Jeff Meyer, *Business Dir*
Ronnie Guggenheim, *General Mgr*
Danielle Welch, *Administration*
▲ EMP: 60
SQ FT: 21,000
SALES (est): 13.6MM **Privately Held**
WEB: www.lenexpo-electronics.com
SIC: 3651 Household audio & video equipment

(P-17764)
AUDEZE LLC (PA)
3410 S Susan St, Santa Ana (92704-6936)
PHONE.....................714 581-8010
Alexander Rosson, *CEO*
Sankar Thiagasamudram, *President*
Mark Harper, *Chief Mktg Ofcr*
Mark Cohen, *Vice Pres*
Drag Colich, *CTO*
▲ EMP: 15 EST: 2012
SALES (est): 3MM **Privately Held**
SIC: 3651 Audio electronic systems

(P-17765)
AUDIO DYNAMIX INC
2770 S Harbor Blvd Ste D, Santa Ana (92704-5828)
PHONE.....................714 549-5100
Teresa Schmidt, *President*
Denise Denicola, *Sls & Mktg Exec*
EMP: 10
SQ FT: 3,645
SALES (est): 1.6MM **Privately Held**
WEB: www.audiodynamix.com
SIC: 3651 5065 Audio electronic systems; electronic parts & equipment

(P-17766)
AUDIO FX LLC
Also Called: Audio Fx Home Theater
1415 Howe Ave, Sacramento (95825-3203)
PHONE.....................916 929-2100
Chris Malone,
William Chrisman,
EMP: 11
SQ FT: 4,000
SALES (est): 1.4MM **Privately Held**
WEB: www.audiofx.com
SIC: 3651 5735 Household audio equipment; records, audio discs & tapes

(P-17767)
AUDIONICS SYSTEM INC
6860 Canby Ave Ste 104, Reseda (91335-8725)
PHONE.....................818 345-9599
Khalid Jaffer, *President*
▲ EMP: 14
SALES: 2.5MM **Privately Held**
SIC: 3651 Household audio & video equipment

(P-17768)
AUERNHEIMER LABS INC
Also Called: ALC
4561 E Florence Ave, Fresno (93725-1197)
PHONE.....................559 442-1048
Clarence Auernheimer, *President*
Dwayne Auernheimer, *Corp Secy*
Warren Auernheimer, *Vice Pres*
EMP: 11
SQ FT: 40,000
SALES (est): 1.1MM **Privately Held**
SIC: 3651 5169 Household audio & video equipment; chemicals & allied products

(P-17769)
AV NOW INC
100 Pioneer St Ste B, Santa Cruz (95060-2181)
PHONE.....................831 425-2500
Robert Dehart, *President*
Brad Freitas, *Opers Spvr*

▲ EMP: 20
SQ FT: 2,000
SALES (est): 4.6MM **Privately Held**
WEB: www.avnow.com
SIC: 3651 7929 Audio electronic systems; disc jockey service

(P-17770)
AXESS PRODUCTS CORP
9409 Owensmouth Ave, Chatsworth (91311-6904)
PHONE.....................818 785-4000
David Bakhaj, *President*
Danny Aghaee, *COO*
Kevin Hedvat, *CFO*
Sion Nabati,
Hector Guardado, *Accounts Exec*
EMP: 10
SQ FT: 20,000
SALES (est): 14MM **Privately Held**
SIC: 3651 Home entertainment equipment, electronic

(P-17771)
BEATS ELECTRONICS LLC (HQ)
Also Called: Beats By Dre
8600 Hayden Pl, Culver City (90232-2902)
PHONE.....................424 326-4679
Timothy Cook, *CEO*
▲ EMP: 92
SALES (est): 135MM
SALES (corp-wide): 265.6B **Publicly Held**
SIC: 3651 3679 Speaker systems; headphones, radio
PA: Apple Inc.
1 Apple Park Way
Cupertino CA 95014
408 996-1010

(P-17772)
BEGA SUPPLY INC
Also Called: Bega Video Supplies
1613 W 134th St Ste 3, Gardena (90249-2036)
PHONE.....................310 719-1252
Hae Won Kim, *President*
Charlie Kim, *Vice Pres*
Sung J Kim, *Admin Sec*
EMP: 11
SQ FT: 5,000
SALES (est): 1.2MM **Privately Held**
SIC: 3651 5099 2759 Video cassette recorders/players & accessories; video cassettes, accessories & supplies; labels & seals; printing

(P-17773)
BELKIN INC
12045 Waterfront Dr, Playa Vista (90094-2999)
PHONE.....................800 223-5546
Chester J Pipkin, *President*
George Platisa, *CFO*
Maggie Curran, *Vice Pres*
Ryan Kim, *Vice Pres*
Jenny Ng, *Vice Pres*
▲ EMP: 145
SALES (est): 47.2MM **Privately Held**
SIC: 3651 Electronic kits for home assembly: radio, TV, phonograph

(P-17774)
BETA BOX INC
12021 Wilshire Blvd, Los Angeles (90025-1206)
PHONE.....................323 383-9820
Guy Fleming, *Principal*
EMP: 15
SALES (est): 1MM **Privately Held**
SIC: 3651 Home entertainment equipment, electronic

(P-17775)
BIG 5 ELECTRONICS INC
Also Called: Big Five Electronics
13452 Alondra Blvd, Cerritos (90703-2315)
PHONE.....................562 941-4669
Amina Bawaney, *CEO*
Latif Bawaney, *President*
Rizwan Bawaney, *CFO*
Carlos Ibarra, *Sales Mgr*
Jay Lopez, *Sales Mgr*
▲ EMP: 22
SQ FT: 4,500

SALES (est): 6.3MM **Privately Held**
WEB: www.big5electronics.net
SIC: 3651 5099 5065 Audio electronic systems; video & audio equipment; electronic parts & equipment

(P-17776)
BLUE MICROPHONES LLC
5706 Corsa Ave Ste 102, Westlake Village (91362-4057)
PHONE.....................818 879-5200
Fax: 818 879-7258
EMP: 17 EST: 2008
SALES (est): 2.4MM **Privately Held**
SIC: 3651

(P-17777)
BOGNER AMPLIFICATION
11411 Vanowen St, North Hollywood (91605-6219)
PHONE.....................818 765-8929
Jorg Dorschner, *Partner*
Gregory Bayeles, *Partner*
Reinhold Bogner, *Partner*
EMP: 10
SQ FT: 5,000
SALES: 1.2MM **Privately Held**
WEB: www.bogneramplification.com
SIC: 3651 5099 Amplifiers: radio, public address or musical instrument; musical instruments

(P-17778)
BOOM MOVEMENT LLC
1 Viper Way Ste 3, Vista (92081-7811)
PHONE.....................410 358-3600
Jim Minark, *CEO*
EMP: 100
SALES (est): 7MM **Privately Held**
SIC: 3651 Household audio equipment

(P-17779)
BRISTOL SOUNDS ELECTRONICS
Also Called: Bristol Sounds Elec Whse
2604 S Bristol St, Santa Ana (92704-5727)
PHONE.....................714 549-5923
Mike Khan, *Owner*
▲ EMP: 14
SALES (est): 1.4MM **Privately Held**
SIC: 3651 5731 Sound reproducing equipment; sound equipment, automotive

(P-17780)
BRITE LITE ENTERPRISES
11661 San Vicente Blvd, Los Angeles (90049-5103)
PHONE.....................310 363-7120
Arash Shamoeil, *President*
Ray Oribello, *Senior VP*
◆ EMP: 12
SALES (est): 20.2MM **Privately Held**
SIC: 3651 Household audio equipment

(P-17781)
CEENEE INC
683 River Oaks Pkwy, San Jose (95134-1907)
PHONE.....................408 890-5018
Kim Tran, *President*
Kiwi Dang, *Sales Mgr*
EMP: 27
SQ FT: 15,000
SALES (est): 1.7MM **Privately Held**
SIC: 3651 Home entertainment equipment, electronic

(P-17782)
CLARKE PB & ASSOCIATES INC
Also Called: Pacific Accesory
2500 E Francis St, Ontario (91761-7730)
PHONE.....................714 835-3022
Bob Clarke, *President*
Brett Riggs, *President*
▲ EMP: 25
SQ FT: 10,000
SALES: 3MM **Privately Held**
SIC: 3651 Audio electronic systems

(P-17783)
COHUHD COSTAR LLC
7330 Trade St, San Diego (92121-2456)
PHONE.....................858 391-1800
Doug Means, *President*
James Arbuckle, *President*
Phil Cutler, *Vice Pres*

P
R
O
D
U
C
T
S

&

S
V
C
S

Jennifer Himes, *Admin Asst*
Kris Amundson, *Administration*
EMP: 70
SQ FT: 26,304
SALES: 5MM
SALES (corp-wide): 19.7MM **Publicly Held**
SIC: 3651 Video camera-audio recorders, household use
PA: Costar Technologies, Inc.
101 Wrangler Dr Ste 201
Coppell TX 75019
469 635-6800

(P-17784)
COUNTRYMAN ASSOCIATES INC
195 Constitution Dr, Menlo Park (94025-1106)
PHONE.................................650 364-9988
Carl Countryman, *President*
Carolyn Countryman, *Treasurer*
Rosa Pimentel, *General Mgr*
▲ **EMP:** 17
SQ FT: 4,000
SALES (est): 2.7MM **Privately Held**
SIC: 3651 5065 Audio electronic systems; electronic parts & equipment

(P-17785)
COVAN SYSTEMS INC
Also Called: Covan Alarm Company
569 Leisure St, Livermore (94551-5148)
P.O. Box 4237, Manteca (95337-0004)
PHONE.................................510 226-9886
David Coon, *President*
Leilani Coon, *Vice Pres*
Timothy Coon, *Admin Sec*
EMP: 12
SQ FT: 1,500
SALES (est): 1.6MM **Privately Held**
WEB: www.covansystems.com
SIC: 3651 1731 Home entertainment equipment, electronic; fire detection & burglar alarm systems specialization

(P-17786)
CRAZYONDIGITAL INC
907 Sunny Brook Way, Pleasanton (94566-3823)
PHONE.................................925 294-9432
Sanjay Singh, *President*
Binita Singh, *Shareholder*
EMP: 12
SALES (est): 3.5MM **Privately Held**
SIC: 3651 5961 Home entertainment equipment, electronic; computer equipment & electronics, mail order

(P-17787)
DANA INNOVATIONS
Also Called: Sonance
991 Calle Amanecer, San Clemente (92673-6212)
PHONE.................................949 492-7777
ARI Supran, *CEO*
Scott Struthers, *President*
Mike Simmons, *CFO*
Geoffrey L Spencer, *Corp Secy*
Rob Roland, *Exec VP*
▲ **EMP:** 59 **EST:** 1981
SQ FT: 42,320
SALES (est): 15.4MM **Privately Held**
WEB: www.sonance.com
SIC: 3651 5731 7629 Speaker systems; radio, television & electronic stores; electrical repair shops

(P-17788)
DAVENPORT INTERNATIONAL CORP
7230 Coldwater Canyon Ave, North Hollywood (91605-4203)
P.O. Box 16539 (91615-6539)
PHONE.................................818 765-6400
Daniel Mamane, *President*
▲ **EMP:** 50
SQ FT: 50,000
SALES (est): 6.3MM **Privately Held**
SIC: 3651 7819 7812 7334 Household audio & video equipment; reproduction services, motion picture production; motion picture & video production; photocopying & duplicating services

(P-17789)
DIGITAL PERIPH SOLUTIONS INC
Also Called: Q-See
8015 E Crystal Dr Bldg J, Anaheim (92807-2523)
PHONE.................................714 998-3440
Priti Sharma, *President*
Rajeev Sharma, *CFO*
▲ **EMP:** 40
SQ FT: 30,000
SALES (est): 26.2MM **Privately Held**
WEB: www.q-see.com
SIC: 3651 7382 Video camera-audio recorders, household use; confinement surveillance systems maintenance & monitoring

(P-17790)
DIGITAL VIDEO SYSTEMS INC (PA)
357 Castro St Ste 5, Mountain View (94041-1258)
PHONE.................................650 938-8815
Mali Kuo, *Ch of Bd*
Shaun Kang, *President*
Dean Clarke Seniff, *CFO*
Delle V Vedove, *Marketing Mgr*
EMP: 40
SQ FT: 2,130
SALES (est): 14.8MM **Privately Held**
WEB: www.dvsystems.com
SIC: 3651 Household video equipment

(P-17791)
DOLBY LABORATORIES INC
Also Called: Doremi Labs
1020 Chestnut St, Burbank (91506-1623)
PHONE.................................818 562-1101
EMP: 40
SALES (corp-wide): 1.1B **Publicly Held**
SIC: 3651 Audio electronic systems
PA: Dolby Laboratories, Inc.
1275 Market St
San Francisco CA 94103
415 558-0200

(P-17792)
DOLBY LABORATORIES INC (PA)
1275 Market St, San Francisco (94103-1410)
PHONE.................................415 558-0200
Peter Gotcher, *Ch of Bd*
Kevin Yeaman, *President*
Lewis Chew, *CFO*
Bob Borchers, *Chief Mktg Ofcr*
Robert Borchers, *Chief Mktg Ofcr*
EMP: 277
SALES: 1.1B **Publicly Held**
WEB: www.dolby.com
SIC: 3651 7819 Audio electronic systems; laboratory service, motion picture

(P-17793)
DTS LLC
5220 Las Virgenes Rd, Calabasas (91302-1064)
PHONE.................................818 436-1000
Jon Kirchner,
EMP: 100
SALES (est): 7.6MM
SALES (corp-wide): 373.7MM **Publicly Held**
SIC: 3651 3845 Audio electronic systems; audiological equipment, electromedical
HQ: Dts, Inc.
5220 Las Virgenes Rd
Calabasas CA 91302

(P-17794)
DWI ENTERPRISES
11081 Winners Cir Ste 100, Los Alamitos (90720-2894)
PHONE.................................714 842-2236
Fred Delgleize, *President*
Amanda Delgleize, *CFO*
Dave Dain, *Vice Pres*
Dan Delgleize, *Vice Pres*
Mike Delgleize, *Vice Pres*
◆ **EMP:** 25
SQ FT: 9,500

SALES: 1.9MM **Privately Held**
WEB: www.dwienterprises.com
SIC: 3651 3669 Audio electronic systems; visual communication systems

(P-17795)
E VIRTUAL CORPORATION
Also Called: Product Virtual Gt
192 22nd St Apt D, Costa Mesa (92627-6726)
PHONE.................................949 515-3670
Paul Stary, *President*
John Coute, *Vice Pres*
EMP: 10
SALES: 1MM **Privately Held**
SIC: 3651 Home entertainment equipment, electronic

(P-17796)
ECOLINK INTELLIGENT TECH INC
2055 Corte Del Nogal, Carlsbad (92011-1412)
PHONE.................................855 432-6546
Michael Lamb, *CEO*
Dave Doney, *Sales Mgr*
EMP: 18
SALES (est): 2.8MM
SALES (corp-wide): 695.7MM **Publicly Held**
SIC: 3651 Video triggers (remote control TV devices)
PA: Universal Electronics Inc.
201 Sandpointe Ave Fl 8
Santa Ana CA 92707
714 918-9500

(P-17797)
EIGEN INC
13355 Grass Valley Ave A, Grass Valley (95945-9521)
PHONE.................................530 274-1240
Mahtab Damda, *President*
Syed Zaidi, *CFO*
Michael Ahmadi, *Exec VP*
William Mandel, *Vice Pres*
Ram Narayanan, *Vice Pres*
EMP: 31
SQ FT: 27,000
SALES (est): 6MM **Privately Held**
WEB: www.eigen.com
SIC: 3651 3845 3841 Recording machines, except dictation & telephone answering; electromedical equipment; surgical & medical instruments

(P-17798)
ELECTRONIC AUTO SYSTEMS INC
9855 Joe Vargas Way, South El Monte (91733-3107)
PHONE.................................626 280-3855
Chang Ye Tong, *President*
Virginia Young, *Treasurer*
Eduardo Lo, *Exec VP*
Julio Young, *Vice Pres*
◆ **EMP:** 15
SQ FT: 9,000
SALES (est): 2MM **Privately Held**
SIC: 3651 Speaker systems

(P-17799)
ETI SOUND SYSTEMS INC
Also Called: Eti B Si Professional
3383 E Gage Ave, Huntington Park (90255-5530)
PHONE.................................323 835-6660
Eli El-Kiss, *President*
AVI El-Kiss, *Vice Pres*
Delio Tocong, *Accountant*
Todd Vucins, *Manager*
▲ **EMP:** 45
SQ FT: 73,000
SALES (est): 8.3MM **Privately Held**
WEB: www.b-52pro.com
SIC: 3651 Speaker monitors

(P-17800)
EUREKA RECORD WORKS INC (PA)
Also Called: Works, The
210 C St, Eureka (95501-0339)
PHONE.................................707 442-8121
Larry Glass, *President*
EMP: 10

SQ FT: 1,200
SALES (est): 1MM **Privately Held**
SIC: 3651 Compact disk players; video camera-audio recorders, household use; video cassette recorders/players & accessories

(P-17801)
FRESNO DISTRIBUTING CO
Also Called: Fresno D"
2055 E Mckinley Ave, Fresno (93703-2997)
P.O. Box 6078 (93703-6078)
PHONE.................................559 442-8800
Stephen Ronald Cloud, *CEO*
Mary Iness, *Corp Secy*
Ryan Cloud, *Vice Pres*
Steve Cloud Jr, *Vice Pres*
Tim Monroe, *Sales Staff*
EMP: 33
SALES (est): 13.1MM **Privately Held**
WEB: www.fresnodistributing.com
SIC: 3651 3494 Home entertainment equipment, electronic; plumbing & heating valves

(P-17802)
GALLIEN TECHNOLOGY INC (PA)
Also Called: Galliien Krueger
2234 Industrial Dr, Stockton (95206-4937)
PHONE.................................209 234-7300
Robert Gallien, *President*
Christine Simpson, *Sales Staff*
Veronica Almada,
Ricardo Almada, *Manager*
▲ **EMP:** 59
SQ FT: 21,000
SALES (est): 9.8MM **Privately Held**
WEB: www.gallien-krueger.com
SIC: 3651 Amplifiers: radio, public address or musical instrument

(P-17803)
GILDERFLUKE & COMPANY INC (PA)
205 S Flower St, Burbank (91502-2102)
PHONE.................................818 840-9484
Douglas Mobley, *President*
Carolyn Rowley, *CFO*
Richard Smith, *Technician*
Sofia Vilner, *Accountant*
EMP: 10
SQ FT: 6,599
SALES (est): 989.9K **Privately Held**
WEB: www.gilderfluke.com
SIC: 3651 7819 7999 Audio electronic systems; sound reproducing equipment; sound (effects & music production); motion picture; visual effects production; tourist attractions, amusement park concessions & rides

(P-17804)
GOTO CALIFORNIA INC (HQ)
Also Called: GCI
6120 Bus Ctr Ct Ste F200, San Diego (92154)
PHONE.................................619 691-8722
Saburo Goto, *CEO*
▲ **EMP:** 200
SALES (est): 22MM
SALES (corp-wide): 143.3K **Privately Held**
WEB: www.goto-california.com
SIC: 3651 Speaker systems
PA: Goto Densan, Y.K.
1-2-44, Minamiharamachi
Yamagata YGT
236 265-255

(P-17805)
GRAFFITI ENTERTAINMENT LLC
3000 Bridge Pkwy Ste 101, Redwood City (94065-1189)
PHONE.................................650 654-4800
Kenneth Hurley, *Officer*
Signature Devices,
EMP: 15
SQ FT: 3,500
SALES (est): 1MM **Privately Held**
WEB: www.signaturedevices.com
SIC: 3651 Video cassette recorders/players & accessories

▲ = Import ▼=Export
◆ =Import/Export

(P-17806)
GUY G VERALRUD
Also Called: Vertek
10141 Evening Star Dr # 1, Grass Valley (95945-9060)
P.O. Box 1437, Cedar Ridge (95924-1437)
PHONE...............................530 477-7323
Guy G Veralrud, *Owner*
EMP: 16
SQ FT: 20,000
SALES (est): 490K **Privately Held**
WEB: www.vertek.com
SIC: 3651 Household audio & video equipment

(P-17807)
H&F TECHNOLOGIES INC
Also Called: Audio 2000's
650 Flinn Ave Unit 4, Moorpark (93021-2004)
PHONE...............................805 523-2759
Haw-Renn Chen, *President*
Faye Chen, *Vice Pres*
▲ EMP: 10
SQ FT: 2,000
SALES (est): 2MM **Privately Held**
WEB: www.audio2000s.com
SIC: 3651 5099 Audio electronic systems; video & audio equipment

(P-17808)
HARMAN PROFESSIONAL INC
24950 Grove View Rd, Moreno Valley (92551-9552)
PHONE...............................951 242-2927
Edward Kamp, *Manager*
EMP: 405
SALES (corp-wide): 148.1B **Privately Held**
SIC: 3651 Household audio equipment
HQ: Harman Professional, Inc.
8500 Balboa Blvd
Northridge CA 91329
818 893-8411

(P-17809)
HARMAN PROFESSIONAL INC (DH)
8500 Balboa Blvd, Northridge (91329-0003)
P.O. Box 2200 (91328-2200)
PHONE...............................818 893-8411
Mohit Parasher, *President*
Ricardo Torres, *Technician*
Kevin Vass, *Controller*
David Cabrera, *QC Mgr*
Kerry Kapin, *Marketing Staff*
◆ EMP: 300
SALES (est): 191.9MM
SALES (corp-wide): 148.1B **Privately Held**
SIC: 3651 Audio electronic systems
HQ: Harman International Industries Incorporated
400 Atlantic St Ste 15
Stamford CT 06901
203 328-3500

(P-17810)
HDKARAOKE LLC
2400 Lincoln Ave, Altadena (91001-5436)
PHONE...............................626 296-6200
Meng Guo,
Wayne Sheng, *Manager*
▲ EMP: 12
SALES (est): 500K **Privately Held**
SIC: 3651 Home entertainment equipment, electronic

(P-17811)
HENRYS ADIO VSUAL SLUTIONS INC
Also Called: Audio Images
1582 Parkway Loop Ste F, Tustin (92780-6505)
PHONE...............................714 258-7238
Mark Ontiveros, *CEO*
Chris Corrigan, *Project Engr*
EMP: 30
SQ FT: 5,400
SALES (est): 6.4MM **Privately Held**
SIC: 3651 Household audio & video equipment

(P-17812)
HILL PRODUCTS INC
19160 Arminta St, Reseda (91335-1105)
PHONE...............................818 877-9256
Jerry Hill, *President*
Kim Hill, *Corp Secy*
EMP: 10
SQ FT: 1,500
SALES (est): 666.9K **Privately Held**
SIC: 3651 Video camera-audio recorders, household use

(P-17813)
HILLO AMERICA INC
9094 Las Tunas Dr, Temple City (91780-1902)
PHONE...............................626 570-8899
Jeff Chang, *CEO*
Chengjia Wang, *President*
▲ EMP: 12
SQ FT: 47,000
SALES (est): 5MM **Privately Held**
SIC: 3651 Household audio equipment

(P-17814)
HITACHI HOME ELEC AMER INC (DH)
2420 Fenton St 200, Chula Vista (91914-3516)
PHONE...............................619 591-5200
Kenji Nakamura, *CEO*
Tomomi ITOH, *President*
Tsuneo Yuki, *Treasurer*
Gary Bennett, *Exec VP*
Tatsou Hagiwara, *Exec VP*
EMP: 170
SQ FT: 260,000
SALES (est): 54.5MM
SALES (corp-wide): 87.9B **Privately Held**
WEB: www.hitachiserviceusa.com
SIC: 3651 Television receiving sets; tape recorders: cassette, cartridge or reel: household use; video cassette recorders/players & accessories
HQ: Hitachi America Ltd
50 Prospect Ave
Tarrytown NY 10591
914 332-5800

(P-17815)
HPV TECHNOLOGIES INC
301 E Alton Ave, Santa Ana (92707-4418)
PHONE...............................949 476-7000
Vahan Simidian, *President*
Phillip Hamilton, *Vice Pres*
▲ EMP: 20
SQ FT: 6,250
SALES (est): 2MM **Privately Held**
WEB: www.hpvtech.com
SIC: 3651 Speaker systems

(P-17816)
IMATTE INC
20945 Plummer St, Chatsworth (91311-4902)
PHONE...............................818 993-8007
Paul E Vlahos, *President*
Joesph Parker, *COO*
Alan Dadourian, *Vice Pres*
Michael Vlahos, *Software Engr*
Lynne Sauve, *Sales Mgr*
EMP: 10
SALES (est): 1.2MM **Privately Held**
WEB: www.imatte.com
SIC: 3651 Audio electronic systems; video camera-audio recorders, household use

(P-17817)
INTEC VIDEO SYSTEMS INC (PA)
23301 Vista Grande Dr, Laguna Hills (92653-1497)
PHONE...............................949 859-3800
Donald E Nama II, *President*
Selene A Nama, *Corp Secy*
Selene A Musgrave, *Admin Asst*
Jazmin Medel, *Marketing Staff*
John Defazio, *Sales Staff*
▲ EMP: 20 EST: 1970
SALES (est): 2.5MM **Privately Held**
SIC: 3651 Household audio & video equipment

(P-17818)
INTERMED VIDEO TECH INC
38 Waterworks Way, Irvine (92618-3107)
PHONE...............................203 270-9100
Harry Davies, *President*
EMP: 11
SQ FT: 10,000
SALES (est): 1.8MM **Privately Held**
SIC: 3651 3844 Household audio & video equipment; X-ray apparatus & tubes

(P-17819)
ISOLATION NETWORK INC (PA)
Also Called: Ingrooves
55 Francisco St Ste 350, San Francisco (94133-2112)
PHONE...............................415 489-7000
Jay Boberg, *Ch of Bd*
Adam Hiles, *President*
Bob Roback, *CEO*
Vincent Freda, *COO*
Clifton Wong, *CFO*
EMP: 28
SQ FT: 5,000
SALES (est): 5.6MM **Privately Held**
SIC: 3651 7929 Music distribution apparatus; musical entertainers

(P-17820)
JEFF BURGESS & ASSOCIATES INC (PA)
Also Called: JB&a Distribution
1050 Northgate Dr Ste 200, San Rafael (94903-2562)
PHONE...............................415 256-2800
Jeff Burgess, *CEO*
Gregory Burgess, *President*
Brad Tabata, *Senior Mgr*
Nick Smith, *Director*
EMP: 45
SQ FT: 10,000
SALES (est): 19.4MM **Privately Held**
WEB: www.jbanda.com
SIC: 3651 Household audio equipment

(P-17821)
JODEL ENTERPRISES
340 Gateway Dr Apt 105, Pacifica (94044-1155)
PHONE...............................650 343-4510
Josh Jodel, *Owner*
EMP: 10
SALES (est): 663.3K **Privately Held**
SIC: 3651 Audio electronic systems

(P-17822)
KAZMERE ENTERTAINMENT
400 N La Brea Ave Ste 500, Inglewood (90302-5145)
PHONE...............................323 448-9009
Shameka Peters, *Owner*
EMP: 10
SALES (est): 528.5K **Privately Held**
WEB: www.kazmereentertainment.com
SIC: 3651 Household audio & video equipment

(P-17823)
KEYFAX NEWMEDIA INC
911 Center St Ste A, Santa Cruz (95060-3831)
P.O. Box 1151, Aptos (95001-1151)
PHONE...............................831 477-1205
Julian K C Colbeck, *President*
Rachel Dean, *Opers Mgr*
EMP: 15
SALES (est): 2MM **Privately Held**
WEB: www.keyfaxnewmedia.com
SIC: 3651 Music distribution apparatus

(P-17824)
KSC INDUSTRIES INC
9771 Clairemont Mesa Blvd E, San Diego (92124-1300)
PHONE...............................619 671-0110
Jeffrey W King Jr, *President*
Bill McCarty, *President*
Malcolm Hollombe, *Exec VP*
William McCarty, *Vice Pres*
Lisa Michaud, *Vice Pres*
▲ EMP: 25
SQ FT: 10,000
SALES (est): 4.9MM **Privately Held**
WEB: www.kscind.com
SIC: 3651 Speaker systems

(P-17825)
LRAD CORPORATION (PA)
16262 W Bernardo Dr, San Diego (92127-1879)
PHONE...............................858 676-1112
Richard S Danforth, *CEO*
John G Coburn, *Ch of Bd*
Dennis D Klahn, *CFO*
Scott Anchin, *Bd of Directors*
Laura Clague, *Bd of Directors*
EMP: 50
SQ FT: 31,360
SALES: 20.3MM **Publicly Held**
WEB: www.lradx.com
SIC: 3651 Sound reproducing equipment; speaker systems; loudspeakers, electro-dynamic or magnetic

(P-17826)
LYNX STUDIO TECHNOLOGY INC
190 Mccormick Ave, Costa Mesa (92626-3307)
PHONE...............................714 545-4700
Robert J Bauman, *President*
David A Hoatson, *CFO*
Phil Moon, *Vice Pres*
Albert Margolis, *VP Sls/Mktg*
Paul Erlandson, *Director*
EMP: 11
SQ FT: 6,400
SALES (est): 2.3MM **Privately Held**
WEB: www.lynxstudio.com
SIC: 3651 Audio electronic systems

(P-17827)
M KLEMME TECHNOLOGY CORP
Also Called: K-Tek
1384 Poinsettia Ave Ste F, Vista (92081-8505)
PHONE...............................760 727-0593
Brenda L Parker, *President*
▲ EMP: 12
SALES (est): 2.5MM **Privately Held**
SIC: 3651 Audio electronic systems

(P-17828)
MAGICO LLC
3170 Corporate Pl, Hayward (94545-3916)
PHONE...............................510 649-9700
Alon Wolf, *CEO*
Pete Maher, *CFO*
Peter Maher, *CFO*
Tuan Trinh, *CFO*
Peter Mackay, *Vice Pres*
◆ EMP: 26 EST: 1996
SQ FT: 12,000
SALES (est): 6.2MM **Privately Held**
WEB: www.magico.net
SIC: 3651 Speaker systems

(P-17829)
MANLEY LABORATORIES INC
13880 Magnolia Ave, Chino (91710-7027)
PHONE...............................909 627-4256
Eveanna Manley-Collins, *CEO*
Zia Faruqi, *Vice Pres*
Baltazar Hernandez, *Human Res Mgr*
Rick McClendon, *VP Sales*
▲ EMP: 40
SQ FT: 11,000
SALES (est): 8.6MM **Privately Held**
WEB: www.manleylabs.com
SIC: 3651 3312 3663 Audio electronic systems; tool & die steel; radio & TV communications equipment

(P-17830)
MEDIAPOINTE INC
3952 Camino Ranchero, Camarillo (93012-5066)
PHONE...............................805 480-3700
Stephen Villoria, *CEO*
EMP: 11 EST: 2011
SALES (est): 1.9MM **Privately Held**
SIC: 3651 Audio electronic systems

(P-17831)
MESA/BOOGIE LIMITED (PA)
1317 Ross St, Petaluma (94954-1124)
PHONE...............................707 765-1805
Randall Smith, *President*
Jo Leach, *Controller*
Tien Lawrence, *Purch Mgr*

PRODUCTS & SVCS

Doug West, *Mktg Dir*
Shawn Farbman, *Sales Mgr*
▲ EMP: 100 EST: 1975
SQ FT: 47,000
SALES (est): 16.4MM **Privately Held**
WEB: www.mesaboogie.com
SIC: 3651 5736 Amplifiers: radio, public
address or musical instrument; musical
instrument stores

(P-17832)
**MEYER SOUND LABORATORIES
INC (PA)**
Also Called: Meyer Sound Labs
2832 San Pablo Ave, Berkeley
(94702-2258)
PHONE....................510 486-1166
John D Meyer, *President*
Brad Friedman, *CFO*
John McMahon, *Senior VP*
Helen Meyer, *Admin Sec*
Ian Steinberg, *Technical Staff*
◆ EMP: 140 EST: 1978
SQ FT: 15,800
SALES (est): 31.9MM **Privately Held**
WEB: www.msli.com
SIC: 3651 Loudspeakers, electrodynamic
or magnetic

(P-17833)
MICRONAS USA INC
560 S Winchester Blvd, San Jose
(95128-2560)
PHONE....................408 625-1200
James Mannos, *President*
Rainer Hoffmann, *President*
Frank Brooks, *CFO*
EMP: 115
SQ FT: 39,000
SALES (est): 11.3MM **Privately Held**
WEB: www.micronas.com
SIC: 3651 Household audio & video equip-
ment

(P-17834)
MIDAS TECHNOLOGY INC
Also Called: Phoenix Audio Technologies
16 Goodyear Ste 120, Irvine (92618-3757)
PHONE....................818 937-4774
Jacob Marash, *CEO*
Joseph Marash, *Ch of Bd*
Baruch Berdugo, *CTO*
Zachary Flanagan, *Manager*
▲ EMP: 22
SALES (est): 4.1MM **Privately Held**
SIC: 3651 Speaker systems

(P-17835)
**MOKI INTERNATIONAL (USA)
INC**
21700 Oxnard St Ste 850, Woodland Hills
(91367-7566)
PHONE....................205 208-0179
Michael Smit, *CEO*
EMP: 20 EST: 2011
SALES (est): 1.1MM **Privately Held**
SIC: 3651 3678 Audio electronic systems;
electronic connectors

(P-17836)
NADY SYSTEMS INC
870 Harbour Way S, Richmond
(94804-3613)
PHONE....................510 652-2411
John Nady, *President*
Cora Racher, *Marketing Staff*
Joy Ferrer, *Manager*
▲ EMP: 30
SQ FT: 80,000
SALES (est): 5.8MM **Privately Held**
WEB: www.nady.com
SIC: 3651 3669 Audio electronic systems;
intercommunication systems, electric

(P-17837)
NCA LABORATORIES INC
Also Called: The Clearwater Company
11305 Sunrise Gold Cir D, Rancho Cordova
(95742-7213)
P.O. Box 428, Folsom (95763-0428)
PHONE....................916 852-7029
Glenn A Stasky, *President*
▲ EMP: 17
SALES (est): 2.8MM **Privately Held**
WEB: www.clearwateraudio.com
SIC: 3651 Audio electronic systems

(P-17838)
NIMA LLC
Also Called: Nima Sports
3857 Birch St Ste 406, Newport Beach
(92660-2616)
PHONE....................949 404-1990
Amir Saati, *Mng Member*
EMP: 20
SQ FT: 2,600
SALES: 6MM **Privately Held**
SIC: 3651 Speaker systems

(P-17839)
NO STATIC PRO AUDIO INC
3223 Burton Ave, Burbank (91504-3104)
PHONE....................818 729-8554
Eugene Gordon, *President*
Steven Barnes, *Finance Mgr*
Dare Gaskin, *Director*
EMP: 11 EST: 1985
SQ FT: 12,000
SALES (est): 3.7MM **Privately Held**
WEB: www.nsav.com
SIC: 3651 Audio electronic systems

(P-17840)
O W I INC
Also Called: Movits
17141 Kingsview Ave, Carson
(90746-1207)
PHONE....................310 515-1900
Ned Morioka, *CEO*
Craig Morioka, *President*
Kristin Martinez, *Treasurer*
Joseph Martinez, *Vice Pres*
June Morioka, *Admin Sec*
▲ EMP: 13
SQ FT: 17,000
SALES (est): 3MM **Privately Held**
WEB: www.owi-inc.com
SIC: 3651 5064 3944 5099 Speaker sys-
tems; high fidelity equipment; electronic
toys; robots, service or novelty

(P-17841)
PARASOUND PRODUCTS INC
2250 Mckinnon Ave, San Francisco
(94124-1327)
PHONE....................415 397-7100
Richard Schram, *President*
Jean Schram PHD, *Vice Pres*
▲ EMP: 13
SQ FT: 2,500
SALES (est): 2.2MM **Privately Held**
WEB: www.parasound.com
SIC: 3651 Audio electronic systems

(P-17842)
PASS LABORATORIES INC
13395 New Airport Rd, Auburn
(95602-7419)
PHONE....................530 878-5350
Desmond Harrinton, *President*
Desmond Harrington, *President*
Joseph Sammutt, *Finance Mgr*
Kent English, *Director*
Sherilyn Spiva, *Manager*
▲ EMP: 15
SQ FT: 4,000
SALES (est): 3MM **Privately Held**
SIC: 3651 Amplifiers: radio, public address
or musical instrument

(P-17843)
PHORUS LLC
16255 Ventura Blvd # 310, Encino
(91436-2327)
PHONE....................310 995-2521
Jon Kirchner,
Melvin Flanigan,
Sharon Graves,
Brian Towne,
▲ EMP: 14
SALES (est): 1.3MM **Privately Held**
SIC: 3651 Audio electronic systems

(P-17844)
**PIONEER ELECTRONICS (USA)
INC (DH)**
2050 W 190th St Ste 100, Torrance
(90504-6229)
P.O. Box 1720, Long Beach (90801-1720)
PHONE....................310 952-2000
Hajime Wada, *CEO*
Kevan Morris, *Exec VP*
Gary Jordahl, *Vice Pres*

Brenda Pioneer, *Vice Pres*
Dennis Stepien, *Vice Pres*
◆ EMP: 300 EST: 1982
SQ FT: 86,485
SALES (est): 69.4MM
SALES (corp-wide): 3.4B **Privately Held**
SIC: 3651 Household audio & video equip-
ment
HQ: Pioneer North America, Inc.
2050 W 190th St Ste 100
Torrance CA 90504
310 952-2000

(P-17845)
PIONEER SPEAKERS INC (DH)
2050 W 190th St Ste 100, Torrance
(90504-6229)
PHONE....................310 952-2000
Hiroyuki Mineta, *CEO*
Kazuo Goto, *CFO*
Makoto Takano, *Principal*
Nobuhiko Yamaguchi, *Principal*
▲ EMP: 50
SQ FT: 2,500
SALES (est): 91.8MM
SALES (corp-wide): 3.4B **Privately Held**
WEB: www.piomsystems.com
SIC: 3651 Speaker systems
HQ: Tohoku Pioneer Corporation
1105, Azanikko, Kunomoto
Tendo YGT 994-0
236 541-211

(P-17846)
PLUOT COMMUNICATIONS INC
1925 48th Ave, San Francisco
(94116-1050)
PHONE....................202 258-9223
Kwindla Hultman Kramer, *CEO*
EMP: 10 EST: 2015
SALES: 100K **Privately Held**
SIC: 3651 7371 Household video equip-
ment; computer software development &
applications

(P-17847)
POLK AUDIO LLC
1 Viper Way Ste 3, Vista (92081-7811)
PHONE....................888 267-5495
Peter Kriz, *Manager*
EMP: 50 **Privately Held**
SIC: 3651 Audio electronic systems
HQ: Polk Audio, Llc
11500 Cronridge Dr # 110
Owings Mills MD 21117
410 358-3600

(P-17848)
QSC LLC (PA)
1675 Macarthur Blvd, Costa Mesa
(92626-1468)
PHONE....................714 754-6175
Joe Pham, *CEO*
Jatan Shah, *COO*
Aravind Yarlagadda, *Exec VP*
Barry Ferrell, *Senior VP*
Eric Andersen, *Vice Pres*
◆ EMP: 277 EST: 1979
SQ FT: 180,000
SALES (est): 91.4MM **Privately Held**
WEB: www.qscaudio.com
SIC: 3651 Audio electronic systems

(P-17849)
RENKUS-HEINZ INC
19201 Cook St, Foothill Ranch
(92610-3501)
PHONE....................949 588-9997
Harro Heinz, *President*
Roscoe L Anthony III, *CEO*
Erika Heinz, *Admin Sec*
Gregg Lewis, *Technician*
Joe Fustolo, *Technology*
▲ EMP: 80
SQ FT: 48,500
SALES (est): 22.6MM **Privately Held**
WEB: www.renkus-heinz.com
SIC: 3651 Audio electronic systems

(P-17850)
**ROCK-OLA MANUFACTURING
CORP**
Also Called: Antique Apparatus Company
2335 W 208th St, Torrance (90501-1443)
PHONE....................310 328-1306
Glenn S Streeter, *President*

▲ EMP: 80
SQ FT: 60,000
SALES (est): 13.3MM **Privately Held**
SIC: 3651 Coin-operated phonographs,
juke boxes; speaker systems

(P-17851)
RODE MICROPHONES LLC
2745 Raymond Ave, Signal Hill
(90755-2129)
P.O. Box 91028, Long Beach (90809-1028)
PHONE....................310 328-7456
Mark Ludmer, *CEO*
Peter Freedmon, *President*
Brian Swbaringen, *District Mgr*
▲ EMP: 140
SALES (est): 18.8MM **Privately Held**
WEB: www.rodemicrophones.com
SIC: 3651 Microphones
HQ: Freedman Electronics Pty Ltd
107 Carnarvon St
Silverwater NSW 2128

(P-17852)
S2E INC
Also Called: Mee Audio
817 Lawson St, City of Industry
(91748-1104)
PHONE....................626 965-1008
Martie Shieh, *President*
Jerry Hsieh, *Vice Pres*
Jerry Shieh, *Vice Pres*
▲ EMP: 15
SQ FT: 7,000
SALES (est): 2.9MM **Privately Held**
SIC: 3651 Household audio & video equip-
ment

(P-17853)
SARGAM INTERNATIONAL INC
Also Called: Agent 18
719 Huntley Dr, West Hollywood
(90069-5043)
PHONE....................310 855-9694
Sargam Patel, *President*
▲ EMP: 11
SALES (est): 1.8MM **Privately Held**
SIC: 3651 Audio electronic systems

(P-17854)
SCOSCHE INDUSTRIES INC
1550 Pacific Ave, Oxnard (93033-2451)
P.O. Box 2901 (93034-2901)
PHONE....................805 486-4450
Roger Alves, *CEO*
Steve Klinger, *CFO*
Steven R Klinger, *CFO*
Kasidy Alves, *Exec VP*
Vincent Alves, *Exec VP*
▲ EMP: 150
SQ FT: 83,000
SALES: 150MM **Privately Held**
WEB: www.scosche.com
SIC: 3651 Audio electronic systems

(P-17855)
SECOND GENERATION INC
Also Called: Fish Bowl
4433 Pacific Blvd, Vernon (90058-2205)
PHONE....................213 743-8700
Michael Weisberg, *CEO*
Dale Kaufman, *CFO*
▲ EMP: 68
SQ FT: 11,000
SALES (est): 15.8MM **Privately Held**
SIC: 3651 2339 Audio electronic systems;
women's & misses' athletic clothing &
sportswear

(P-17856)
**SERVO DYNAMICS
CORPORATION**
28231 Avenue Crocker # 10, Valencia
(91355-1276)
PHONE....................818 700-8600
Gary Robert, *President*
Jeff Roberts, *Vice Pres*
EMP: 25
SQ FT: 5,839
SALES (est): 3.5MM **Privately Held**
WEB: www.servodynamics.com
SIC: 3651 3679 Household audio & video
equipment; parametric amplifiers

(P-17857)
SIGMATRONIX INC
2109 S Susan St, Santa Ana (92704-4416)
PHONE..................714 436-1618
Michael Dang, *President*
EMP: 15
SQ FT: 5,600
SALES: 1MM **Privately Held**
WEB: www.sigmatronix.com
SIC: **3651** Electronic kits for home assembly: radio, TV, phonograph

(P-17858)
SONOS INC (PA)
614 Chapala St, Santa Barbara (93101-3312)
PHONE..................805 965-3001
Patrick Spence, *President*
Michelangelo Volpi, *Ch of Bd*
Michael Giannetto, *CFO*
Matthew Siegel, *Ch Credit Ofcr*
Nicholas Millington,
◆ EMP: 91
SQ FT: 33,280
SALES: 992.5MM **Publicly Held**
WEB: www.sonos.com
SIC: **3651** Household audio & video equipment

(P-17859)
SONY ELECTRONICS INC (DH)
16535 Via Esprillo Bldg 1, San Diego (92127-1738)
PHONE..................858 942-2400
Phil Molyneux, *President*
Hideki Komiyama, *Ch of Bd*
Charles Gregory, *President*
Rintaro Miyoshi, *CFO*
Frank M Lesher, *Exec VP*
▲ EMP: 1000 EST: 1960
SALES (est): 4.7B
SALES (corp-wide): 80.1B **Privately Held**
WEB: news.sel.sony.com/en
SIC: **3651** 5064 3695 3671 Household audio & video equipment; television receiving sets; radio receiving sets; tape recorders: cassette, cartridge or reel: household use; electrical appliances, television & radio; television sets; radios; video cassette recorders & accessories; video recording tape, blank; audio range tape, blank; television tubes; computer tape drives & components; semiconductors & related devices
HQ: Sony Corporation Of America
25 Madison Ave Fl 27
New York NY 10010
212 833-8000

(P-17860)
SONY ELECTRONICS INC
Also Called: Sony Style
16530 Via Esprillo, San Diego (92127-1708)
PHONE..................858 942-2400
Bill Lunger, *Principal*
EMP: 159
SALES (corp-wide): 80.1B **Privately Held**
SIC: **3651** Household audio & video equipment
HQ: Sony Electronics Inc.
16535 Via Esprillo Bldg 1
San Diego CA 92127
858 942-2400

(P-17861)
SOUND STORM LABORATORY LLC
3451 Lunar Ct, Oxnard (93030-8976)
PHONE..................805 983-8008
Nasrin Rouhani,
Cameron Arbani,
▲ EMP: 50
SQ FT: 72,000
SALES (est): 4.8MM **Privately Held**
SIC: **3651** 5731 Audio electronic systems; radio, television & electronic stores

(P-17862)
SOUNDVIEW APPLICATIONS INC
2390 Lindbergh St Ste 101, Auburn (95602-9529)
PHONE..................530 888-7593
Robert Lazor, *President*
EMP: 10

SALES (est): 850K **Privately Held**
WEB: www.svatech.com
SIC: **3651** Microphones

(P-17863)
TECHNICOLOR THOMSON GROUP
Also Called: Thompson Multimedia
3233 Mission Oaks Blvd, Camarillo (93012-5097)
PHONE..................805 445-7652
Marjorie Martinez, *Human Resources*
EMP: 2000
SALES (corp-wide): 63.6MM **Privately Held**
WEB: www.technicolor.com
SIC: **3651** 3652 Household video equipment; pre-recorded records & tapes
HQ: Technicolor Thomson Group, Inc
2233 N Ontario St Ste 300
Burbank CA 91504
818 260-3600

(P-17864)
TECHNICOLOR USA INC
Also Called: Technicolor Connected USA
4049 Industrial Pkwy Dr, Lebec (93243-9719)
PHONE..................661 496-1309
EMP: 143
SALES (corp-wide): 63.6MM **Privately Held**
SIC: **3651** Household audio & video equipment
HQ: Technicolor Usa, Inc.
101 W 103rd St
Indianapolis IN 46290
818 260-3651

(P-17865)
TECHNICOLOR USA INC
1507 Railroad St, Glendale (91204-2774)
PHONE..................818 500-9090
EMP: 143
SALES (corp-wide): 82MM **Privately Held**
SIC: **3651**
HQ: Technicolor Usa, Inc.
4 Research Way
Princeton NJ 46290
317 587-3000

(P-17866)
TECHNICOLOR USA INC
Also Called: Technicolor Content Services
440 W Los Feliz Rd, Glendale (91204-2776)
PHONE..................818 260-3651
EMP: 143
SALES (corp-wide): 115.5MM **Privately Held**
SIC: **3651** 3861 3661
HQ: Technicolor Usa, Inc.
101 W 103rd St
Indianapolis IN 46290
317 587-3000

(P-17867)
THETA DIGITAL CORPORATION
1749 Chapin Rd, Montebello (90640-6609)
PHONE..................818 572-4300
Neil Sinclair, *President*
▲ EMP: 21
SQ FT: 12,000
SALES (est): 3.3MM **Privately Held**
WEB: www.thetadigital.com
SIC: **3651** 5731 Audio electronic systems; radio, television & electronic stores

(P-17868)
TOSHIBA AMERICA ELECTRONIC (DH)
5231 California Ave, Irvine (92617-3073)
PHONE..................949 462-7700
Hideya Yamaguchi, *CEO*
Hitoshi Otsuka, *President*
Ichiro Hirata, *Exec VP*
Farhad Mafie, *Vice Pres*
Richard Tobias, *Vice Pres*
▲ EMP: 300
SQ FT: 100,000

SALES (est): 3B
SALES (corp-wide): 37B **Privately Held**
SIC: **3651** 3631 3674 3679 Television receiving sets; video cassette recorders/players & accessories; microwave ovens, including portable: household; semiconductors & related devices; electronic circuits; electronic parts & equipment; video cassette recorders & accessories; high fidelity equipment
HQ: Toshiba America Inc
1251 Ave Of Ameri
New York NY 10020
212 596-0600

(P-17869)
TR THEATER RESEARCH INC (PA)
Also Called: Dogg Digital
11150 Hope St, Cypress (90630-5236)
PHONE..................714 894-5888
Glenn Smith, *President*
▲ EMP: 12
SQ FT: 15,000
SALES: 10.5MM **Privately Held**
WEB: www.dcssound.com
SIC: **3651** 5099 Speaker systems; video & audio equipment

(P-17870)
ULTIMATE GAME CHAIR INC
5089 Lone Tree Way, Antioch (94531-8016)
PHONE..................925 756-6944
Jamie Duran, *CEO*
Richard Florez, *CEO*
▲ EMP: 25
SQ FT: 3,000
SALES: 12MM **Privately Held**
WEB: www.ultimategamechair.com
SIC: **3651** Home entertainment equipment, electronic

(P-17871)
ULTIMATE SOUND INC
1200 S Diamond Bar Blvd # 200, Diamond Bar (91765-2298)
PHONE..................909 861-6200
Robert Chiu, *President*
Cindy Chiu, *Vice Pres*
Alex Chiu, *Bus Dvlpt Dir*
▼ EMP: 300
SQ FT: 20,000
SALES (est): 10.3MM **Privately Held**
WEB: www.ultimate-sound.com
SIC: **3651** 5731 Loudspeakers, electrodynamic or magnetic; amplifiers: radio, public address or musical instrument; radio, television & electronic stores

(P-17872)
UME VOICE INC
Also Called: Theboom Headsets
1435 Technology Ln Ste B4, Petaluma (94954-7615)
PHONE..................707 939-8607
Adithya Padala, *President*
Jill Devos, *Admin Mgr*
▲ EMP: 13
SQ FT: 2,000
SALES (est): 2.1MM **Privately Held**
WEB: www.umevoice.com
SIC: **3651** Microphones

(P-17873)
UNIVERSAL ELECTRONICS INC (PA)
201 Sandpointe Ave Fl 8, Santa Ana (92707-5778)
PHONE..................714 918-9500
Paul D Arling, *Ch of Bd*
Louis S Hughes, *COO*
Bryan M Hackworth, *CFO*
Satjiv Chahil, *Bd of Directors*
Gregory Stapleton, *Bd of Directors*
▲ EMP: 231
SQ FT: 36,184
SALES: 695.7MM **Publicly Held**
WEB: www.ezremote.com
SIC: **3651** 3625 7372 Video triggers (remote control TV devices); relays & industrial controls; prepackaged software

(P-17874)
VANDERSTEEN AUDIO INC
116 W 4th St, Hanford (93230-5021)
PHONE..................559 582-0324
Richard J Vandersteen, *President*
Eneke Vandersteen, *Principal*
▲ EMP: 21 EST: 1977
SQ FT: 20,000
SALES: 2MM **Privately Held**
SIC: **3651** 5731 Speaker systems; radio, television & electronic stores

(P-17875)
VANTAGE POINT PRODUCTS CORP (PA)
Also Called: Vpt Direct
9115 Dice Rd Ste 18, Santa Fe Springs (90670-2538)
P.O. Box 2485 (90670-0485)
PHONE..................562 946-1718
Donald R Burns, *CEO*
Mick Mulcahey, *President*
▲ EMP: 60
SQ FT: 62,000
SALES (est): 10.3MM **Privately Held**
WEB: www.vanptc.com
SIC: **3651** Audio electronic systems

(P-17876)
VELODYNE ACOUSTICS INC
345 Digital Dr, Morgan Hill (95037-2878)
PHONE..................408 465-2800
David Hall, *CEO*
Joseph B Culkin, *Shareholder*
Vincent C Hall, *Shareholder*
Bruce Hall, *President*
Michael Jellen, *President*
▲ EMP: 70
SQ FT: 48,000
SALES (est): 28.8MM **Privately Held**
WEB: www.velodyne.com
SIC: **3651** 5731 Speaker systems; radio, television & electronic stores

(P-17877)
VIBES AUDIO LLC
15635 Alton Pkwy Ste 475, Irvine (92618-7361)
PHONE..................949 769-6806
Shane Wilder, *President*
Charles Wilder, *CTO*
EMP: 12 EST: 2016
SQ FT: 40,068
SALES (est): 590.3K **Privately Held**
SIC: **3651** Audio electronic systems

(P-17878)
VIZIO INC (PA)
39 Tesla, Irvine (92618-4603)
PHONE..................949 428-2525
William Wang, *CEO*
Ken Lowe, *President*
Derrick Beard, *Vice Pres*
Jodie McAfee, *Vice Pres*
Mark Nelson, *Vice Pres*
◆ EMP: 154
SQ FT: 27,300
SALES (est): 113.4MM **Privately Held**
SIC: **3651** Television receiving sets; compact disk players

(P-17879)
VTL AMPLIFIERS INC
4774 Murietta St Ste 10, Chino (91710-5155)
PHONE..................909 627-5944
Luke Manley, *President*
▲ EMP: 24
SQ FT: 6,000
SALES (est): 3.6MM **Privately Held**
SIC: **3651** Audio electronic systems

(P-17880)
WINNOV INC
3910 Freedom Cir Ste 102, Santa Clara (95054-1205)
PHONE..................888 315-9460
Olivier Garbe, *CEO*
EMP: 16
SQ FT: 10,200
SALES (est): 3.2MM **Privately Held**
WEB: www.winnov.com
SIC: **3651** Household audio & video equipment

(PA)=Parent Co (HQ)=Headquarters (DH)=Div Headquarters
✿ = New Business established in last 2 years

(P-17881)
WIRELESS TECHNOLOGY INC
Also Called: Wti
2064 Eastman Ave Ste 113, Ventura
(93003-7787)
PHONE....................................805 339-9696
Phil Fancher, *CEO*
Arlene Fancher, *CFO*
David Malackowskit, *CIO*
Margie Blake, *Controller*
Hal Campbell, *QC Mgr*
EMP: 30
SQ FT: 7,000
SALES: 10.7MM **Privately Held**
SIC: **3651** Household audio & video equipment

(P-17882)
WYRED 4 SOUND LLC
4235 Traffic Way, Atascadero (93422-3002)
PHONE....................................805 466-9973
Ej Sarmento, *Mng Member*
Clint Hartman,
Janice Huntington, *Manager*
▲ EMP: 11
SALES (est): 1.9MM **Privately Held**
SIC: **3651** Audio electronic systems

(P-17883)
YAWA INC
1706 E Francis St, Ontario (91761-5722)
PHONE....................................909 391-8888
David Yan, *President*
Xinwen David, *Sales Associate*
▲ EMP: 10
SALES (est): 1.2MM **Privately Held**
WEB: www.yawaaudio.com
SIC: **3651** Household audio & video equipment

(P-17884)
ZAOLLA
6650 Caballero Blvd, Buena Park
(90620-1132)
PHONE....................................714 736-9270
Sho Sato, *Owner*
EMP: 30
SALES (est): 2.5MM **Privately Held**
WEB: www.zaolla.com
SIC: **3651** Audio electronic systems

(P-17885)
ZED AUDIO CORPORATION
2624 Lavery Ct Ste 203, Newbury Park
(91320-1500)
PHONE....................................805 499-5559
Stephen Mantz, *President*
Joyce Mantz, *Corp Secy*
▲ EMP: 10
SALES (est): 1.4MM **Privately Held**
WEB: www.zedaudiocorp.com
SIC: **3651** Audio electronic systems

3652 Phonograph Records & Magnetic Tape

(P-17886)
AUDIO PARTNERS PUBLISHING
131 E Placer St, Auburn (95603-5241)
P.O. Box 6930 (95604-6930)
PHONE....................................530 888-7803
Linda D Olsen, *President*
Grady Hesters, *CEO*
EMP: 10
SQ FT: 6,000
SALES (est): 940K **Privately Held**
WEB: www.audiopartners.com
SIC: **3652** Pre-recorded records & tapes

(P-17887)
C M H RECORDS INC
Also Called: Dwell Records
2898 Rowena Ave Ste 201, Los Angeles
(90039-2096)
P.O. Box 39439 (90039-0439)
PHONE....................................323 663-8098
David Haerle, *President*
EMP: 20
SQ FT: 3,303
SALES (est): 2.7MM **Privately Held**
WEB: www.cmhrecords.com
SIC: **3652** 7929 Phonograph records, pre-recorded; entertainers & entertainment groups

(P-17888)
CAV DISTRIBUTING CORPORATION
Also Called: California Audio Video Distrg
253 Utah Ave, South San Francisco
(94080-6802)
PHONE....................................650 588-2228
Stanford Martin Jr, *President*
Jay Douglas, *Vice Pres*
Fred Eggink, *Sales Mgr*
▲ EMP: 13
SQ FT: 32,000
SALES (est): 2.6MM **Privately Held**
WEB: www.cavd.com
SIC: **3652** 5099 Compact laser discs, pre-recorded; video & audio equipment

(P-17889)
CORD INTRNATIONAL/HANA OLA REC
1874 Terrace Dr, Ventura (93001-2351)
P.O. Box 152 (93002-0152)
PHONE....................................805 648-7881
Michael Cord, *Owner*
EMP: 12
SQ FT: 6,000
SALES: 2MM **Privately Held**
WEB: www.cordinternational.com
SIC: **3652** Pre-recorded records & tapes

(P-17890)
DICARLO CONCRETE INC
8657 Pecan Ave Ste 100, Rancho Cucamonga (91739-9465)
PHONE....................................909 261-4294
Mario Dicarlo, *President*
EMP: 12
SQ FT: 10,000
SALES (est): 3.6MM **Privately Held**
SIC: **3652** Master records or tapes, preparation of

(P-17891)
DISC REPLICATOR INC
21137 Commerce Point Dr, Walnut
(91789-3054)
PHONE....................................909 385-0118
Jingtao Xie, *CEO*
Amelyn Binagy, *Manager*
EMP: 15
SALES (est): 1.8MM **Privately Held**
SIC: **3652** Compact laser discs, pre-recorded

(P-17892)
DISCOPYLABS (PA)
Also Called: Dcl
48641 Milmont Dr, Fremont (94538-7354)
PHONE....................................510 651-5100
Norman Tu, *CEO*
Dave Tu, *President*
Antonia Tu, *Treasurer*
Shahid Masood, *Vice Pres*
David Tu, *Vice Pres*
▲ EMP: 50
SQ FT: 300,000
SALES (est): 26.1MM **Privately Held**
WEB: www.dclcorp.com
SIC: **3652** 4225 7379 7389 Pre-recorded records & tapes; general warehousing & storage; ; ; materials mgmt. (purchasing, handling, inventory) consultant

(P-17893)
DISCOPYLABS
4455 E Philadelphia St, Ontario
(91761-2329)
PHONE....................................909 390-3800
Larry Shaker, *Director*
EMP: 30
SALES (corp-wide): 26.1MM **Privately Held**
WEB: www.dclcorp.com
SIC: **3652** 4225 7379 7389 Pre-recorded records & tapes; general warehousing & storage; ; ; materials mgmt. (purchasing, handling, inventory) consultant
PA: Discopylabs
48641 Milmont Dr
Fremont CA 94538
510 651-5100

(P-17894)
ENAS MEDIA INC
1316 Michillinda Ave, Arcadia
(91006-1921)
PHONE....................................626 962-1115
Nagapet Keshishian, *President*
Avetis Keshishian, *Vice Pres*
Serop Keshishian, *Vice Pres*
Nick Keshian, *Mfg Staff*
EMP: 34
SALES (est): 5.1MM **Privately Held**
SIC: **3652** Phonograph records, pre-recorded

(P-17895)
ERIKA RECORDS INC
6300 Caballero Blvd, Buena Park
(90620-1126)
PHONE....................................714 228-5420
Liz Dunster, *President*
Erzsebet Dunster, *CEO*
Timarie Bryant, *Manager*
▲ EMP: 20
SALES (est): 3.9MM **Privately Held**
WEB: www.erikarecords.com
SIC: **3652** 5735 Phonograph records, pre-recorded; compact laser discs, pre-recorded; records

(P-17896)
EXTREME GROUP HOLDINGS LLC
Also Called: Extreme Production Music
1531 14th St, Santa Monica (90404-3302)
PHONE....................................310 899-3200
Emanuel Russell, *Branch Mgr*
EMP: 20
SALES (corp-wide): 80.1B **Privately Held**
WEB: www.extrememusic.com
SIC: **3652** Pre-recorded records & tapes
HQ: Extreme Group Holdings Llc
550 Madison Ave Fl 6
New York NY 10022

(P-17897)
FANTASY INC
Also Called: Contemporary Records
2600 10th St Ste 100, Berkeley
(94710-2512)
PHONE....................................510 486-2038
Saul Zaentz, *Ch of Bd*
Ralph Kaffel, *President*
Frank Noonan, *Treasurer*
Bill Jarrell, *Exec VP*
Albert M Bendich, *Admin Sec*
EMP: 100
SQ FT: 40,000
SALES (est): 10.7MM **Privately Held**
SIC: **3652** 2741 7389 Pre-recorded records & tapes; music book & sheet music publishing; recording studio, non-commercial records

(P-17898)
FAT WRECK CHORDS INC
2196 Palou Ave, San Francisco
(94124-1503)
PHONE....................................415 284-1790
Michael Burkett, *President*
Erin Kelly-Burkett, *Vice Pres*
▲ EMP: 14
SALES (est): 1.3MM **Privately Held**
SIC: **3652** Master records or tapes, preparation of

(P-17899)
GC INTERNATIONAL INC (PA)
Also Called: Alj
4671 Calle Carga, Camarillo (93012-8560)
PHONE....................................805 389-4631
Richard R Carlson, *President*
F Willard Griffith, *CEO*
Terry Carlson, *Vice Pres*
Mark R Griffith, *Vice Pres*
Marilyn Good, *Controller*
▼ EMP: 43
SQ FT: 45,000
SALES: 7MM **Publicly Held**
WEB: www.aljcast.com
SIC: **3652** 3365 3695 3369 Phonograph record blanks; aluminum & aluminum-based alloy castings; magnetic & optical recording media; nonferrous foundries; mechanical rubber goods

(P-17900)
GC INTERNATIONAL INC
Also Called: Al Johnson Company
4671 Calle Carga, Camarillo (93012-8560)
PHONE....................................805 389-4631
Mark Griffith, *Principal*
Ricardo Garcia, *QC Mgr*
EMP: 43
SALES (corp-wide): 7MM **Publicly Held**
SIC: **3652** 3369 Phonograph record blanks; lead, zinc & white metal
PA: Gc International, Inc.
4671 Calle Carga
Camarillo CA 93012
805 389-4631

(P-17901)
GOSPEL RECORDINGS INC
41823 Enterprise Cir N, Temecula
(92590-5681)
PHONE....................................951 719-1650
Colin Stott, *Exec Dir*
Mac Timm, *President*
Bill Cornthwaite, *Vice Pres*
Doug Fletcher, *Technology*
EMP: 35 EST: 1943
SQ FT: 20,000
SALES: 1.7MM **Privately Held**
WEB: www.grnusa.net
SIC: **3652** Pre-recorded records & tapes

(P-17902)
GRAND MOTIF RECORDS
Also Called: Monopoly Music
8304 Enramada Ave, Whittier
(90605-1207)
PHONE....................................562 698-8538
David Esterson, *Owner*
EMP: 11
SALES (est): 955.3K **Privately Held**
SIC: **3652** Pre-recorded records & tapes

(P-17903)
HOLLYWOOD RECORDS INC
500 S Buena Vista St, Burbank
(91521-0002)
PHONE....................................818 560-5670
Abbey Konowitch, *General Mgr*
EMP: 50
SALES (est): 6.1MM **Publicly Held**
SIC: **3652** Pre-recorded records & tapes
HQ: Walt Disney Music Company
500 S Buena Vista St
Burbank CA 91521
818 560-1000

(P-17904)
INSIGHT MANAGEMENT CORPORATION (PA)
1130 E Clark Ave, Santa Maria
(93455-5178)
PHONE....................................866 787-3588
Kevin Jasper, *CEO*
EMP: 50
SALES (est): 3.2MM **Privately Held**
SIC: **3652** Pre-recorded records & tapes

(P-17905)
INTERNATIONAL DISC MFR INC
Also Called: IDM
4906 W 1st St, Santa Ana (92703-3110)
PHONE....................................714 210-1780
Thoai Tang, *President*
Tri Tang, *Vice Pres*
EMP: 25
SQ FT: 50,000
SALES (est): 3.6MM **Privately Held**
WEB: www.idmdvd.com
SIC: **3652** Compact laser discs, pre-recorded

(P-17906)
ISOMEDIA LLC
41380 Christy St, Fremont (94538-3115)
PHONE....................................510 668-1656
Howard Xu,
Greg Evans, *Accounts Exec*
▲ EMP: 25
SQ FT: 15,000
SALES: 2.2MM **Privately Held**
WEB: www.isoptix.com
SIC: **3652** Compact laser discs, pre-recorded

▲ = Import ▼=Export
◆ =Import/Export

(P-17907)
MASTERING LAB INC
911 Bryant Pl, Ojai (93023-3321)
PHONE..................................805 640-2900
EMP: 10
SQ FT: 2,000
SALES (est): 850K **Privately Held**
WEB: www.masteringlab.com
SIC: 3652

(P-17908)
NUTRITION RESOURCE CONNECTION
Also Called: Exxel Media
254 May Ct, Cardiff By The Sea (92007-2411)
PHONE..................................760 803-8234
Carol Venditti, *President*
EMP: 10
SALES (est): 960K **Privately Held**
SIC: 3652 Pre-recorded records & tapes

(P-17909)
PIRATES PRESS INC
1260 Powell St, Emeryville (94608-2641)
PHONE..................................415 738-2268
Eric Mueller, *President*
Damon Beebe, *Sales Staff*
Sam Paris, *Editor*
EMP: 17
SALES: 10MM **Privately Held**
SIC: 3652 7384 Phonograph record blanks; film developing & printing

(P-17910)
PRECISE MEDIA SERVICES INC
Also Called: Precise-Full Service Media
888 Vintage Ave, Ontario (91764-5392)
PHONE..................................909 481-3305
Choy Tim Lee, *CEO*
Robert Miller, *President*
▲ EMP: 25
SQ FT: 112,000
SALES (est): 5.4MM **Privately Held**
SIC: 3652 7819 Pre-recorded records & tapes; video tape or disk reproduction

(P-17911)
RAINBO RECORD MFG CORP (PA)
Also Called: Rainbo Records & Cassettes
8960 Eton Ave, Canoga Park (91304-1621)
PHONE..................................818 280-1100
Jack Brown, *Principal*
David Dickinson, *CFO*
Chris Ambriz, *Branch Mgr*
Darren Norton, *General Mgr*
Jacob Gularine, *Purch Mgr*
▲ EMP: 150
SQ FT: 50,000
SALES (est): 45.7MM **Privately Held**
WEB: www.rainborecords.com
SIC: 3652 5099 Compact laser discs, pre-recorded; compact discs

(P-17912)
RECORD TECHNOLOGY INC
486 Dawson Dr Ste 4s, Camarillo (93012-8049)
PHONE..................................805 484-2747
Don Mac Innis, *President*
Melodie Innis, *Vice Pres*
Melodie Mac Innis, *Vice Pres*
Sharon Waldron, *Admin Asst*
Rick Hoshamoto, *Plant Mgr*
▲ EMP: 28 EST: 1972
SQ FT: 30,000
SALES (est): 5.2MM **Privately Held**
WEB: www.recordtech.com
SIC: 3652 Master records or tapes, preparation of; phonograph record blanks; compact laser discs, prerecorded

(P-17913)
SONY ELECTRONICS INC
Also Called: Sony Network Studios Division
5510 Morehouse Dr Ste 100, San Diego (92121-3721)
PHONE..................................858 824-6960
Komei Kataoka, *Director*
EMP: 20
SALES (corp-wide): 80.1B **Privately Held**
SIC: 3652 Pre-recorded records & tapes

HQ: Sony Electronics Inc.
16535 Via Esprillo Bldg 1
San Diego CA 92127
858 942-2400

(P-17914)
UNIQUE MEDIA INC
2991 Corvin Dr, Santa Clara (95051-0705)
PHONE..................................408 733-9999
Champion Chen, *President*
Katie Yang, *Accountant*
▲ EMP: 10
SQ FT: 2,000
SALES (est): 1.6MM **Privately Held**
WEB: www.unimediainc.com
SIC: 3652 Pre-recorded records & tapes

(P-17915)
WARNER MUSIC GROUP CORP
3300 Warner Blvd, Burbank (91505-4632)
PHONE..................................818 846-9090
Todd Moscowitz, *Branch Mgr*
EMP: 13 **Privately Held**
SIC: 3652 Pre-recorded records & tapes
HQ: Warner Music Group Corp.
1633 Broadway
New York NY 10019
212 275-2000

(P-17916)
WARNER MUSIC INC
3400 W Riverside Dr # 900, Burbank (91505-4669)
PHONE..................................818 953-2600
David Archambault, *Technology*
James Theodoulou, *Manager*
EMP: 60 **Privately Held**
SIC: 3652 Pre-recorded records & tapes
HQ: Warner Music Inc.
1633 Broadway
New York NY 10019
-

3661 Telephone & Telegraph Apparatus

(P-17917)
AEI COMMUNICATIONS CORP
1001 Broadway Ste 2d, Millbrae (94030-1977)
PHONE..................................650 552-9416
Mario Jauryegui, *CEO*
Mario Jauregui, *CTO*
Peter Chen, *Engineer*
Abel Soria, *Manager*
▲ EMP: 20
SALES (est): 2.5MM **Privately Held**
SIC: 3661 Telephones & telephone apparatus

(P-17918)
ALCATEL-LUCENT USA INC
30971a San Benito St, Hayward (94544-7936)
PHONE..................................510 475-5000
Richard McGinn, *CEO*
EMP: 25
SALES (corp-wide): 27.3B **Privately Held**
WEB: www.lucent.com
SIC: 3661
HQ: Nokia Of America Corporation
600 Mountain Ave Ste 700
New Providence NJ 07974

(P-17919)
ALCATEL-LUCENT USA INC
26801 Agoura Rd, Calabasas (91301-5122)
PHONE..................................818 880-3500
Menandro Canelo, *Executive*
Steve Skolnick, *Program Mgr*
Rishi Bhaskar, *Research*
Pierre Chaume, *Sales Dir*
Darren Fowlie, *Director*
EMP: 20
SALES (corp-wide): 27.3B **Privately Held**
WEB: www.rfsworld.com
SIC: 3661 Telephone & telegraph apparatus
HQ: Nokia Of America Corporation
600 Mountain Ave Ste 700
New Providence NJ 07974
-

(P-17920)
ALSTON TASCOM INC
5171 Edison Ave Ste C, Chino (91710-5758)
PHONE..................................909 517-3660
Wayne Scaggs, *President*
Susan Reinhart, *Admin Asst*
Richard Fung, *Software Dev*
Joanne Scaggs, *Marketing Mgr*
EMP: 20
SQ FT: 7,500
SALES (est): 3.2MM **Privately Held**
WEB: www.alstontascom.com
SIC: 3661 Telephones & telephone apparatus

(P-17921)
ALTIGEN COMMUNICATIONS INC
679 River Oaks Pkwy, San Jose (95134-1907)
PHONE..................................408 597-9000
Jeremiah J Fleming, *President*
Philip M McDermott, *CFO*
Simon Chouldjian, *Vice Pres*
Mike Plumer, *Vice Pres*
Shirley Sun, *Vice Pres*
▲ EMP: 115
SQ FT: 27,576
SALES (est): 21.2MM **Privately Held**
SIC: 3661 1731 Telephone & telegraph apparatus; communications specialization

(P-17922)
ANDA NETWORKS INC
1100 La Avenida St Ste A, Mountain View (94043-1453)
PHONE..................................408 519-4900
Charles R Kenmore, *President*
Wufu Chen, *Ch of Bd*
Tracy Tang, *Principal*
EMP: 185
SQ FT: 102,291
SALES (est): 22.9MM **Privately Held**
WEB: www.andanetworks.com
SIC: 3661 Telephone & telegraph apparatus

(P-17923)
AVAYA HOLDINGS CORP (PA)
4655 Great America Pkwy, Santa Clara (95054-1236)
PHONE..................................908 953-6000
Charles H Giancarlo, *Ch of Bd*
Dino Di Palma, *Partner*
Kevin J Kennedy, *President*
Ed Nalbandian, *President*
Gaurav Passi, *President*
EMP: 44
SALES: 3.7B **Publicly Held**
SIC: 3661 7372 Prepackaged software; telephones & telephone apparatus

(P-17924)
AYANTRA INC
47873 Fremont Blvd, Fremont (94538-6506)
PHONE..................................510 623-7526
Ashok Teckchandani, *President*
Harbans Rattia, *Vice Pres*
Andy Rogers, *Vice Pres*
Albert Calpito, *Technical Staff*
Ravi Koppula,
▲ EMP: 15
SQ FT: 2,300
SALES (est): 2.6MM **Privately Held**
WEB: www.ayantra.com
SIC: 3661 Telephone & telegraph apparatus

(P-17925)
BALAJI TRADING INC
Also Called: City of Industry
4850 Eucalyptus Ave, Chino (91710-9255)
PHONE..................................909 444-7999
Mukesh Batta, *CEO*
▲ EMP: 91
SALES (est): 14MM **Privately Held**
SIC: 3661 Headsets, telephone; telephone cords, jacks, adapters, etc.

(P-17926)
BLACK POINT PRODUCTS INC
2000 Wright Ave, Richmond (94804-3849)
P.O. Box 70074 (94807-0074)
PHONE..................................510 232-7723

Thomas Tognetti, *President*
Karin M Ashford, *Vice Pres*
▲ EMP: 30
SQ FT: 6,985
SALES (est): 3.3MM **Privately Held**
WEB: www.blkpoint.com
SIC: 3661 3651 Telephones & telephone apparatus; video cassette recorders/players & accessories

(P-17927)
CALIENT TECHNOLOGIES INC
25 Castilian Dr, Goleta (93117-3026)
PHONE..................................805 562-5500
John Bowers, *Manager*
EMP: 55
SALES (est): 4.1MM
SALES (corp-wide): 65.6MM **Privately Held**
WEB: www.calient.net
SIC: 3661 Fiber optics communications equipment
PA: Calient Technologies, Inc.
27 Castilian Dr
Goleta CA 93117
805 562-5500

(P-17928)
CALIENT TECHNOLOGIES INC (PA)
27 Castilian Dr, Goleta (93117)
PHONE..................................805 562-5500
Atiq Raza, *CEO*
Saiyed Atiq Raza, *CEO*
Jag Setlur, *COO*
Kevin Welsh, *Senior VP*
Shannon Carr, *Vice Pres*
▲ EMP: 285 EST: 1999
SQ FT: 150,000
SALES (est): 65.6MM **Privately Held**
WEB: www.calient.net
SIC: 3661 Fiber optics communications equipment

(P-17929)
CALMAR OPTCOM INC
Also Called: Calmar Laser
951 Commercial St, Palo Alto (94303-4908)
PHONE..................................408 733-7800
Anthony Lin, *President*
Sha Tong, *Director*
Tony Lin, *Manager*
EMP: 20
SQ FT: 7,000
SALES (est): 3.5MM **Privately Held**
WEB: www.calmaropt.com
SIC: 3661 3699 Fiber optics communications equipment; pulse amplifiers; laser systems & equipment

(P-17930)
CELLSCOPE INC
5537 Claremont Ave Apt 1, Oakland (94618-1151)
PHONE..................................510 282-0674
Erik Scott Douglas, *CEO*
EMP: 11
SALES (est): 1.3MM **Privately Held**
SIC: 3661 Telephones & telephone apparatus

(P-17931)
CHANNELL COMMERCIAL CORP (PA)
26040 Ynez Rd, Temecula (92591-6036)
P.O. Box 9022 (92589-9022)
PHONE..................................951 719-2600
William H Channell Jr, *CEO*
Jacqueline M Channell, *Ch of Bd*
Guy E Marge, *President*
Michael Perica, *Treasurer*
Ed Burke, *Vice Pres*
◆ EMP: 100
SQ FT: 210,000
SALES (est): 81.6MM **Privately Held**
WEB: www.channellcomm.com
SIC: 3661 3663 3088 3083 Telephone & telegraph apparatus; television broadcasting & communications equipment; plastics plumbing fixtures; laminated plastics plate & sheet; thermoplastic laminates: rods, tubes, plates & sheet

(P-17932)
CISCO SYSTEMS INC
121 Theory Ste 100, Irvine (92617-3209)
PHONE..............................949 823-1200
Chris White, *Vice Pres*
EMP: 278
SALES (corp-wide): 49.3B **Publicly Held**
WEB: www.cisco.com
SIC: **3661** 5045 3577 Telephone & tele-
graph apparatus; computers, peripherals
& software; computer peripheral equip-
ment
PA: Cisco Systems, Inc.
170 W Tasman Dr
San Jose CA 95134
408 526-4000

(P-17933)
COADNA PHOTONICS INC (DH)
1012 Stewart Dr, Sunnyvale (94085-3914)
PHONE..............................408 736-1100
Jim Yuan, *CEO*
Fang Wang, *COO*
Irene Yum, *CFO*
Jack Kelly, *Vice Pres*
▲ EMP: 60
SQ FT: 12,000
SALES (est): 9.1MM
SALES (corp-wide): 1.1B **Publicly Held**
SIC: **3661** Fiber optics communications
equipment
HQ: Coadna Holdings, Inc.
1020 Stewart Dr
Sunnyvale CA 94085
408 736-1100

(P-17934)
COASTAL CONNECTIONS
2085 Sperry Ave Ste B, Ventura
(93003-7452)
PHONE..............................805 644-5051
Andy Devine, *President*
Nancy Devine, *Treasurer*
Ryan Laudato, *Executive*
Marisol Diaz, *Project Mgr*
◆ EMP: 31
SQ FT: 9,000
SALES (est): 2.4MM **Privately Held**
SIC: **3661** Fiber optics communications
equipment

(P-17935)
CONVEYANT SYSTEMS INC
1901 Carnegie Ave Ste 1I, Santa Ana
(92705-5504)
PHONE..............................949 756-7100
Timothy Kenyon, *CEO*
Brien Amspoker, *Director*
Gordon Drew, *Director*
EMP: 10
SQ FT: 4,230
SALES (est): 1.7MM **Privately Held**
WEB: www.conveyant.com
SIC: **3661** Telephones & telephone appara-
tus

(P-17936)
DANTEL
2991 N Argyle Ave, Fresno (93727-1388)
PHONE..............................559 292-1111
Alan J Brown, *Chairman*
Alan G Hutcheson, *CEO*
Mary Papadopoulus, *CFO*
Paul Wright, *CTO*
Ifty Husain, *Research*
EMP: 23
SQ FT: 60,500
SALES (est): 5.6MM **Privately Held**
WEB: www.dantel.com
SIC: **3661** Telephones & telephone appara-
tus

(P-17937)
DARE TECHNOLOGIES INC (HQ)
674 Via De La Valle # 100, Solana Beach
(92075-3405)
PHONE..............................714 634-5900
Xinyue Huang, *CEO*
Xinkang Chen, *Chairman*
Liyao LI, *Senior VP*
EMP: 13

SALES (est): 928.8K **Privately Held**
WEB: www.usdare.com
SIC: **3661** 5021 5023 5085 Fiber optics
communications equipment; household
furniture; office furniture; floor coverings;
bearings, bushings, wheels & gears;
packaging materials; computers, periph-
erals & software
PA: Shanghai Dareglobal Technologies Co.,
Ltd.
Block B, Floor 1, No.1555, Kongjiang
Rd.
Shanghai 20009
216 563-5566

(P-17938)
DASAN ZHONE SOLUTIONS INC (HQ)
7195 Oakport St, Oakland (94621-1947)
PHONE..............................510 777-7000
IL Yung Kim, *President*
Min Woo Nam, *Ch of Bd*
Michael Golomb, *CFO*
Michael Connors, *Bd of Directors*
Seonggyun Kim, *Bd of Directors*
◆ EMP: 167
SALES: 247.1MM
SALES (corp-wide): 27.2MM **Publicly
Held**
WEB: www.tellium.com
SIC: **3661** 4813 Fiber optics communica-
tions equipment;
PA: Dasan Networks, Inc.
700 Daewangpangyo-Ro 644beon-Gil,
Bundang-Gu
Seongnam 13493
707 010-1189

(P-17939)
DIALOGIC INC
2890 Zanker Rd Ste 107, San Jose
(95134-2118)
PHONE..............................800 755-4444
Huw Carpenter, *Engineer*
Jennifer Kimmell, *Accounts Mgr*
Carmen Lopez, *Supervisor*
EMP: 82 **Privately Held**
SIC: **3661** 3577 7371 Telephone & tele-
graph apparatus; data conversion equip-
ment, media-to-media: computer;
computer software development & appli-
cations
HQ: Dialogic Inc.
4 Gatehall Dr Ste 9
Parsippany NJ 07054
973 967-6000

(P-17940)
DITECH NETWORKS INC (HQ)
3099 N 1st St, San Jose (95134-2006)
PHONE..............................408 883-3636
Thomas L Beaudoin, *President*
Paul A Ricci, *CEO*
William Tamblyn, *Vice Pres*
EMP: 29
SQ FT: 20,100
SALES (est): 7.7MM **Publicly Held**
WEB: www.ditechcom.com
SIC: **3661** Telephones & telephone appara-
tus

(P-17941)
DYNAMETRIC INC
1715 Business Center Dr, Duarte
(91010-2860)
PHONE..............................626 358-2559
Alan Morse, *CEO*
EMP: 10 EST: 1958
SQ FT: 8,500
SALES: 1MM **Privately Held**
WEB: www.dynametric.com
SIC: **3661** Telephones & telephone appara-
tus

(P-17942)
EARLY BIRD ALERT INC
70 Mitchell Blvd Ste 106, San Rafael
(94903-2019)
PHONE..............................415 479-7902
Andrew Kluger, *CEO*
MI Kosasa, *Treasurer*
Gen Ronald Blank, *Vice Pres*
Michael Pecht PHD, *Vice Pres*
Patrick Souter, *Admin Sec*
EMP: 11

SALES (est): 1.4MM **Privately Held**
SIC: **3661** Telephone & telegraph apparatus

(P-17943)
**ENABLENCE USA
COMPONENTS INC**
2933 Bayview Dr, Fremont (94538-6520)
PHONE..............................510 226-8900
Evan Chen, *CEO*
Andy Spector, *Surgery Dir*
Jacob Sun, *Principal*
Peter Sung, *Finance Dir*
Fang Wang, *Sales Staff*
EMP: 98
SQ FT: 26,000
SALES (est): 17.1MM
SALES (corp-wide): 3.4MM **Privately
Held**
WEB: www.andevices.com
SIC: **3661** Fiber optics communications
equipment
PA: Enablence Technologies Inc
390 March Rd Suite 119
Kanata ON K2K 0
613 656-2850

(P-17944)
**ENGAGE COMMUNICATION INC
(PA)**
9565 Soquel Dr Ste 201, Aptos
(95003-4155)
PHONE..............................831 688-1021
Mark Doyle, *President*
Edmund Doyle, *Ch of Bd*
Chris Copus, *Administration*
Shaun Tomaszewski, *Sr Software Eng*
Salvador Lara, *Technology*
EMP: 24
SQ FT: 3,000
SALES (est): 3.8MM **Privately Held**
WEB: www.engageinc.com
SIC: **3661** Modems

(P-17945)
EPIC TECHNOLOGIES LLC (HQ)
Also Called: Natel
9340 Owensmouth Ave, Chatsworth
(91311-6915)
PHONE..............................818 734-6500
Bhawnesh Mathur, *Mng Member*
Robert T Howard,
Jochen Lipp,
John J Sammut,
Marcus Wedner,
▲ EMP: 200
SQ FT: 52,000
SALES (est): 638.1MM
SALES (corp-wide): 1.2B **Privately Held**
SIC: **3661** 3577 3679 Telephone & tele-
graph apparatus; computer peripheral
equipment; electronic circuits
PA: Natel Engineering Company Inc
9340 Owensmouth Ave
Chatsworth CA 91311
818 734-6523

(P-17946)
EXTREME NETWORKS INC (PA)
6480 Via Del Oro, San Jose (95119-1208)
PHONE..............................408 579-2800
Edward B Meyercord, *President*
John C Shoemaker, *Ch of Bd*
Benjamin Drew Davies, *CFO*
Raj Khanna, *Bd of Directors*
Bob Gault, *Exec VP*
◆ EMP: 400
SQ FT: 102,139
SALES: 983.1MM **Publicly Held**
WEB: www.extremenetworks.com
SIC: **3661** 7373 7372 Telephone & tele-
graph apparatus; computer integrated
systems design; systems integration serv-
ices; prepackaged software

(P-17947)
**FERMINICS OPTO-
TECHNOLOGY CORP**
4555 Runway St, Simi Valley (93063-3586)
PHONE..............................805 582-0155
Ock-KY Kim, *President*
Larry Perillo, *Corp Secy*
Lawrence Perillo, *Vice Pres*
EMP: 12
SQ FT: 23,000

SALES (est): 3MM **Privately Held**
WEB: www.ferminics.com
SIC: **3661** Telegraph & related apparatus

(P-17948)
**FIBER NETWORK ENGINEERING
CO (PA)**
2085 Touraine Ln, Half Moon Bay
(94019-1444)
PHONE..............................650 726-2639
Sara Nebeling, *President*
Marcus Nebeling, *Officer*
William Hansen, *General Mgr*
EMP: 10 EST: 1998
SQ FT: 2,000
SALES: 500K **Privately Held**
WEB: www.fn-eng.com
SIC: **3661** Fiber optics communications
equipment

(P-17949)
FIBER SYSTEMS INC
380 Encinal St Ste 150, Santa Cruz
(95060-2183)
PHONE..............................831 430-0700
Mitchell K Hutchison, *President*
▲ EMP: 21
SQ FT: 3,000
SALES (est): 3.1MM **Privately Held**
WEB: www.fibersys.com
SIC: **3661** Fiber optics communications
equipment

(P-17950)
FIBERSENSE & SIGNALS INC
4423 Fortran Ct Ste 111, San Jose
(95134-2323)
PHONE..............................408 941-1900
Joan Davies, *President*
EMP: 15
SALES (est): 1.5MM **Privately Held**
WEB: www.fibersensefirst.com
SIC: **3661** Fiber optics communications
equipment

(P-17951)
FINISAR CORPORATION (PA)
1389 Moffett Park Dr, Sunnyvale
(94089-1134)
PHONE..............................408 548-1000
Michael Hurlston, *CEO*
Robert N Stephens, *Ch of Bd*
Todd Swanson, *COO*
Kurt Adzema, *CFO*
Roger Ferguson, *Bd of Directors*
EMP: 24
SQ FT: 92,000
SALES: 1.3B **Publicly Held**
WEB: www.finisar.com
SIC: **3661** 3663 Fiber optics communica-
tions equipment; antennas, transmitting &
communications; receiver-transmitter
units (transceiver)

(P-17952)
FRANKLIN WIRELESS CORP
9707 Waples St Ste 150, San Diego
(92121-2954)
PHONE..............................858 623-0000
Oc Kim, *President*
Gary Nelson, *Ch of Bd*
Yun J Lee, *COO*
▲ EMP: 76 EST: 1982
SQ FT: 12,775
SALES: 30MM **Privately Held**
WEB: www.franklin-wireless.com
SIC: **3661** Modems

(P-17953)
GENERAL PHOTONICS CORP
14351 Pipeline Ave, Chino (91710-5642)
PHONE..............................909 590-5473
Steve Yao, *President*
James Shen, *President*
James Chen, *Vice Pres*
Mary Fang, *Vice Pres*
Kevin Hsu, *Vice Pres*
▲ EMP: 50
SQ FT: 20,000
SALES: 6.2MM **Privately Held**
WEB: www.generalphotonics.com
SIC: **3661** Fiber optics communications
equipment

▲ = Import ▼=Export
◆ =Import/Export

(P-17954)
GREENBERG TELEPRMPT
868 N Main St, Orange (92868-1108)
PHONE................................714 633-1111
EMP: 16
SALES (corp-wide): 286.2K Privately Held
SIC: 3661 Telephone dialing devices, automatic
PA: Greenberg Teleprmpt
1431 Truman St
San Fernando CA 91340
818 838-4437

(P-17955)
HOTRONIC INC
1875 Winchester Blvd # 100, Campbell (95008-1168)
PHONE................................408 378-3883
Andy Ho, President
EMP: 25
SQ FT: 841
SALES (est): 4.4MM Privately Held
WEB: www.hotronics.com
SIC: 3661 Carrier equipment, telephone or telegraph

(P-17956)
INFINERA CORPORATION (PA)
140 Caspian Ct, Sunnyvale (94089-1000)
PHONE................................408 572-5200
Thomas J Fallon, CEO
Kambiz Y Hooshmand, Ch of Bd
David W Heard, COO
David Heard, COO
Brad D Feller, CFO
▼ EMP: 450
SQ FT: 321,000
SALES: 740.7MM Publicly Held
SIC: 3661 7372 Fiber optics communications equipment; prepackaged software

(P-17957)
INSIEME NETWORKS LLC
210 W Tasman Dr Bldg F, San Jose (95134-1714)
PHONE................................408 424-1227
Luca Cafiero, Principal
Phuong Than, Office Mgr
EMP: 13 EST: 2012
SALES (est): 1.7MM
SALES (corp-wide): 49.3B Publicly Held
SIC: 3661 Telephone & telegraph apparatus
PA: Cisco Systems, Inc.
170 W Tasman Dr
San Jose CA 95134
408 526-4000

(P-17958)
INTERNTNAL CNNCTORS CABLE CORP
Also Called: I C C
2100 E Valencia Dr Ste D, Fullerton (92831-4811)
PHONE................................888 275-4422
Mike Lin, President
Eugene Chyun Tsai, Shareholder
John Zafra, Accounts Mgr
▲ EMP: 110
SQ FT: 38,720
SALES (est): 18.8MM Privately Held
WEB: www.cat6.com
SIC: 3661 5065 Telephone & telegraph apparatus; telephone & telegraphic equipment; communication equipment

(P-17959)
INTERNTNAL VIRTUAL PDT MGT INC
Also Called: I V P
8957 De Soto Ave, Canoga Park (91304-5901)
PHONE................................818 812-9500
Sergey Tishkin, CEO
EMP: 11
SQ FT: 1,200
SALES (est): 2.4MM
SALES (corp-wide): 97.1MM Privately Held
SIC: 3661 2813 Autotransformers for telephone switchboards; oxygen, compressed or liquefied

HQ: Ivp Group Germany Gmbh
Gewerbestr. 3
Buchenbach
766 190-160

(P-17960)
K S TELECOM INC
2350 Humphrey Rd, Penryn (95663-9500)
P.O. Box 330 (95663-0330)
PHONE................................916 652-4735
Kent Vander Linden, President
Suzan Vander Linden, CFO
Eric V Linden, General Mgr
Ian V Linden, General Mgr
EMP: 10 EST: 1995
SALES: 1MM Privately Held
WEB: www.kstelecom.com
SIC: 3661 Fiber optics communications equipment

(P-17961)
LG-ERICSSON USA INC
20 Mason, Irvine (92618-2706)
PHONE................................877 828-2673
Seok B Mun, President
Pierre Kerbage, Vice Pres
Jack Weaver, Admin Sec
Bernd Hesse, Director
▲ EMP: 47
SQ FT: 22,000
SALES (est): 6MM Privately Held
WEB: www.lgericssonus.com
SIC: 3661 5065 Telephone sets, all types except cellular radio; modems, computer

(P-17962)
LYNX PHTNIC NTWORKS A DEL CORP
6303 Owensmouth Ave Fl 10, Woodland Hills (91367-2262)
PHONE................................818 878-7500
Daniel Tal, CEO
Michael Leigh, President
Beni Kopelovitz, Officer
EMP: 13 EST: 1998
SQ FT: 30,000
SALES (est): 1.7MM Privately Held
WEB: www.lynxpn.com
SIC: 3661

(P-17963)
METROPHONES UNLIMITED INC
15675 La Jolla Ct, Morgan Hill (95037-5679)
PHONE................................650 630-5400
Gregg James, CEO
EMP: 28
SALES (est): 3.4MM Privately Held
SIC: 3661 Telephone sets, all types except cellular radio

(P-17964)
MICROSEMI FREQUENCY TIME CORP
3750 Westwind Blvd, Santa Rosa (95403-9072)
PHONE................................707 528-1230
John Dutil, Manager
EMP: 100
SALES (corp-wide): 3.9B Publicly Held
WEB: www.symmetricom.com
SIC: 3661 Telephone & telegraph apparatus
HQ: Microsemi Frequency And Time Corporation
3870 N 1st St
San Jose CA 95134

(P-17965)
MITEL NETWORKS INC (DH)
Also Called: Shorecare
960 Stewart Dr, Sunnyvale (94085-3912)
PHONE................................613 592-2122
Richard D McBee, President
Michael Baillargeon, Partner
Victoria Hassenauer, Partner
Shelley Stratton, Partner
Steven E Spooner, President
▲ EMP: 250
SQ FT: 63,781

SALES: 357.7MM
SALES (corp-wide): 987.6MM Privately Held
WEB: www.shoretel.com
SIC: 3661 3663 7372 Telephone & telegraph apparatus; radio & TV communications equipment; television broadcasting & communications equipment; mobile communication equipment; prepackaged software

(P-17966)
MYNTAHL CORPORATION
Also Called: East Electronics
48273 Lakeview Blvd, Fremont (94538-6519)
PHONE................................510 413-0002
Tingyi Xu, CEO
Jay Prakash, Sales Staff
Ben Lawrence, Director
▲ EMP: 30
SQ FT: 7,000
SALES (est): 5.8MM Privately Held
WEB: www.myntahl.com
SIC: 3661 Communication headgear, telephone

(P-17967)
NANOMETER TECHNOLOGIES INC
2985 Theatre Dr Ste 3, Paso Robles (93446-4500)
PHONE................................805 226-7332
Mike Buzzetti, President
Mike Mowrey, Vice Pres
Terri Bonnema, Admin Sec
▲ EMP: 10
SQ FT: 10,000
SALES (est): 1.2MM Privately Held
WEB: www.nanometer.com
SIC: 3661 3679 3827 Fiber optics communications equipment; attenuators; optical instruments & lenses

(P-17968)
NETGEAR INC (PA)
350 E Plumeria Dr, San Jose (95134-1911)
PHONE................................408 907-8000
Patrick C S Lo, Ch of Bd
Christine M Gorjanc, CFO
Bryan Murray, CFO
Cheryl Myint, Treasurer
Barbara Scherer, Bd of Directors
◆ EMP: 130
SQ FT: 142,700
SALES: 1.4B Publicly Held
WEB: www.netgear.com
SIC: 3661 3577 Modems; carrier equipment, telephone or telegraph; computer peripheral equipment

(P-17969)
NOKIA OF AMERICA CORPORATION
Also Called: Alcatel-Lucent USA
5390 Hellyer Ave, San Jose (95138-1003)
PHONE................................408 363-5906
EMP: 13
SALES (corp-wide): 27.3B Privately Held
SIC: 3661
HQ: Nokia Of America Corporation
600 Mountain Ave Ste 700
New Providence NJ 07974

(P-17970)
OCCAM NETWORKS INC (HQ)
6868 Cortona Dr, Santa Barbara (93117-1360)
PHONE................................805 692-2900
Carl Russo, CEO
Michael Ashby, Exec VP
EMP: 23 EST: 1996
SQ FT: 51,000
SALES (est): 11.4MM
SALES (corp-wide): 510.3MM Publicly Held
WEB: www.acceleratednetworks.com
SIC: 3661 Carrier equipment, telephone or telegraph
PA: Calix, Inc.
2777 Orchard Pkwy
San Jose CA 95134
408 514-3000

(P-17971)
OCLARO (NORTH AMERICA) INC (HQ)
252 Charcot Ave, San Jose (95131)
PHONE................................408 383-1400
Jerry Turin, CEO
Pete Mangan, CEO
Paul Jiang, Senior VP
Kate Rundle, Admin Sec
EMP: 433 EST: 2000
SQ FT: 54,000
SALES: 38MM
SALES (corp-wide): 600.9MM Publicly Held
WEB: www.avanex.com
SIC: 3661 Fiber optics communications equipment
PA: Oclaro, Inc.
225 Charcot Ave
San Jose CA 95131
408 383-1400

(P-17972)
OCLARO SUBSYSTEMS INC
225 Charcot Ave, San Jose (95131-1107)
PHONE................................408 383-1400
Jerry Turin, CEO
Bob Barron, Partner
Shri Dodani, President
Bruce D Horn, CFO
John Ralston, Vice Pres
▲ EMP: 200
SALES (est): 38.2MM
SALES (corp-wide): 600.9MM Publicly Held
WEB: www.stratalight.com
SIC: 3661 Fiber optics communications equipment
HQ: Oclaro Fiber Optics, Inc.
225 Charcot Ave
San Jose CA 95131
408 383-1400

(P-17973)
OCLARO TECHNOLOGY INC (HQ)
225 Charcot Ave, San Jose (95131-1107)
PHONE................................408 383-1400
Greg Dougherty, CEO
Jim Haynes, President
Terry Unter, COO
Pete Mangan, CFO
Claudio Bellu, Project Mgr
EMP: 74
SQ FT: 150,000
SALES (est): 67.9MM
SALES (corp-wide): 543.1MM Publicly Held
WEB: www.bookham.com
SIC: 3661 Fiber optics communications equipment
PA: Oclaro, Inc.
225 Charcot Ave
San Jose CA 95131
408 383-1400

(P-17974)
OPTICAL COMMUNICATION PDTS INC
Also Called: O C P
26850 Agoura Rd Fl 1, Calabasas (91301-5129)
PHONE................................818 876-8700
Philip F Otto, President
Frederic T Boyer MBA, CFO
Liew-Chuang Chiu PHD, VP Mfg
EMP: 736
SQ FT: 149,000
SALES (est): 50.2MM
SALES (corp-wide): 42.9B Privately Held
WEB: www.ocp-inc.com
SIC: 3661 Fiber optics communications equipment
HQ: Oplink Communications, Inc.
46360 Fremont Blvd
Fremont CA 94538

(P-17975)
OPTICAL ZONU CORPORATION
7510 Hazeltine Ave, Van Nuys (91405-1419)
PHONE................................818 780-9701
Meir Bartur, President
Frazad Ghadooshay, Vice Pres

Hanoch Eldar, *VP Opers*
▲ **EMP:** 18
SALES (est): 4.2MM **Privately Held**
WEB: www.zonu.com
SIC: 3661 Fiber optics communications equipment

(P-17976)
OPTOPLEX CORPORATION (PA)
48500 Kato Rd, Fremont (94538-7338)
PHONE..........................510 490-9930
James C Sha, *President*
Dar-Yuan Song, *Exec VP*
James Pang, *Business Dir*
Emily Wang, *Office Mgr*
Yung-Chieh Hsieh, *CTO*
EMP: 69 **EST:** 2000
SQ FT: 16,000
SALES (est): 44.5MM **Privately Held**
WEB: www.optoplex.com
SIC: 3661 7361 3827 Fiber optics communications equipment; employment agencies; optical instruments & lenses

(P-17977)
PLANTRONICS INC (PA)
345 Encinal St, Santa Cruz (95060-2146)
PHONE..........................831 426-5858
Joe Burton, *President*
Robert Hagerty, *Ch of Bd*
Pamela Strayer, *CFO*
Marv Tseu, *Vice Ch Bd*
Anja Hamilton, *Officer*
▲ **EMP:** 277
SQ FT: 183,653
SALES: 856.9MM **Publicly Held**
WEB: www.plantronics.com
SIC: 3661 3679 Telephones & telephone apparatus; headsets, telephone; telephone sets, all types except cellular radio; headphones, radio

(P-17978)
PLANTRONICS INC
Also Called: Plantronics BV
1470 Expo Way Ste 130, San Diego (92154)
PHONE..........................831 458-7089
Jesus Barrera, *Branch Mgr*
EMP: 16
SALES (corp-wide): 856.9MM **Publicly Held**
SIC: 3661 Telephone & telegraph apparatus
PA: Plantronics, Inc.
345 Encinal St
Santa Cruz CA 95060
831 426-5858

(P-17979)
PLANTRONICS INC
Also Called: Plantronics BV
345 Encinal St, Santa Cruz (95060-2146)
P.O. Box 635 (95061-0635)
PHONE..........................831 426-5858
Robert Cecil, *President*
Kenneth Koll, *Sales Engr*
Chidambaram Ramaswamy, *Director*
EMP: 34
SALES (corp-wide): 856.9MM **Publicly Held**
SIC: 3661 Telephone & telegraph apparatus
PA: Plantronics, Inc.
345 Encinal St
Santa Cruz CA 95060
831 426-5858

(P-17980)
POLYCOM INC
25212 S Schulte Rd, Tracy (95377-9703)
PHONE..........................209 830-5083
Wendy Wam, *Branch Mgr*
Dipto Mukherjee, *Manager*
EMP: 38
SALES (corp-wide): 856.9MM **Publicly Held**
WEB: www.polycom.com
SIC: 3661 Telephones & telephone apparatus
HQ: Polycom, Inc.
6001 America Center Dr
San Jose CA 95002
408 586-6000

(P-17981)
POLYCOM INC (HQ)
6001 America Center Dr, San Jose (95002-2562)
PHONE..........................408 586-6000
Mary T McDowell, *CEO*
Marco Landi, *President*
Laura J Durr, *CFO*
Amy Barzdukas, *Chief Mktg Ofcr*
Jim Kruger, *Chief Mktg Ofcr*
▲ **EMP:** 277
SALES (est): 738.7MM
SALES (corp-wide): 856.9MM **Publicly Held**
WEB: www.polycom.com
SIC: 3661 3679 Telephones & telephone apparatus; headphones, radio
PA: Plantronics, Inc.
345 Encinal St
Santa Cruz CA 95060
831 426-5858

(P-17982)
POLYCOM INC
4750 Willow Rd, Pleasanton (94588-2959)
PHONE..........................925 924-6151
Tom Carhart, *Vice Pres*
Shawn Puddester, *Vice Pres*
Jack Shemavon, *Vice Pres*
Diane Enes, *Admin Asst*
Ray Giles, *Administration*
EMP: 221
SALES (est): 28.9MM **Privately Held**
SIC: 3661 Telephones & telephone apparatus

(P-17983)
PSS COMMUNICATIONS INC
Also Called: Data Line
3066 Scott Blvd, Santa Clara (95054-3325)
PHONE..........................408 496-3330
Paul R Fales, *CEO*
Marlene C Fales, *President*
Mathew Vieira, *Technician*
Justin Carey, *Business Mgr*
EMP: 16
SALES (est): 2MM **Privately Held**
SIC: 3661 Telephones & telephone apparatus

(P-17984)
QUAKE GLOBAL INC (PA)
4711 Vewridge Ave Ste 150, San Diego (92123)
PHONE..........................858 277-7290
George Lingenbrink, *Chairman*
Polina Braunstein, *President*
William Ater, *CFO*
Charlie Maneval, *CFO*
Michael Geffroy, *Vice Pres*
▲ **EMP:** 77
SQ FT: 8,700
SALES (est): 19.1MM **Privately Held**
WEB: www.quakeglobal.com
SIC: 3661 Modems

(P-17985)
QUINTRON SYSTEMS INC (PA)
2105 S Blosser Rd, Santa Maria (93458-7300)
PHONE..........................805 928-4343
James E Mc Glothlin, *CEO*
David Wilhite, *President*
Sharon Lewis, *CFO*
Elton L Hammers, *Treasurer*
Amy Adams, *Info Tech Mgr*
EMP: 70
SQ FT: 20,000
SALES: 16.8MM **Privately Held**
WEB: www.quintron.com
SIC: 3661 1731 Telephone & telegraph apparatus; telephone & telephone equipment installation

(P-17986)
RADICOM RESEARCH INC (PA)
671 E Brokaw Rd, San Jose (95112-1005)
PHONE..........................408 383-9006
Ming Hsieh, *President*
Kathy Huynh, *Marketing Staff*
▲ **EMP:** 10
SQ FT: 5,000
SALES (est): 1.6MM **Privately Held**
WEB: www.radi.com
SIC: 3661 8732 Modems; research services, except laboratory

(P-17987)
RAYMAR INFORMATION TECH INC (PA)
Also Called: Computer Exchange, The
7325 Roseville Rd, Sacramento (95842-1600)
PHONE..........................916 783-1951
Donald L Breidenbach, *CEO*
David Figueroa, *CFO*
Corinna Gross, *Technology*
David Green, *Materials Mgr*
Michial Trayler, *Marketing Staff*
EMP: 14
SALES (est): 6.3MM **Privately Held**
WEB: www.raymarinc.com
SIC: 3661 5045 Telephone & telegraph apparatus; computers

(P-17988)
RAYSPAN CORPORATION
1493 Poinsettia Ave # 139, Vista (92081-8544)
PHONE..........................858 259-9596
EMP: 13
SALES (est): 1.6MM **Privately Held**
SIC: 3661

(P-17989)
RLH INDUSTRIES INC (PA)
936 N Main St, Orange (92867-5403)
PHONE..........................714 532-1672
James B Harris, *CEO*
Tristan A Harris, *Vice Pres*
Thomas Vo, *Vice Pres*
Tim Harris, *General Mgr*
Carol E Harris, *Admin Sec*
▲ **EMP:** 40
SQ FT: 16,000
SALES: 8MM **Privately Held**
WEB: www.fiberopticlink.com
SIC: 3661 5065 5999 Telephone & telegraph apparatus; communication equipment; telephone equipment & systems

(P-17990)
RUCKUS WIRELESS INC
Also Called: General Instrument
2450 Walsh Ave, Santa Clara (95051-1303)
PHONE..........................408 235-5500
EMP: 43
SALES (corp-wide): 6.6B **Privately Held**
WEB: www.motorola.com
SIC: 3661 Telephone & telegraph apparatus
HQ: Ruckus Wireless, Inc.
350 W Java Dr
Sunnyvale CA 94089
650 265-4200

(P-17991)
SIEMENS HLTHCARE DGNOSTICS INC
Also Called: Siemens Medical Systems
725 Potter St, Berkeley (94710-2722)
P.O. Box 2466 (94702-0466)
PHONE..........................510 982-4000
Jan Turczyn, *Principal*
Maria Silveira, *Mfg Staff*
EMP: 12
SALES (corp-wide): 97.7B **Privately Held**
WEB: www.dpcweb.com
SIC: 3661 Telephones & telephone apparatus
HQ: Siemens Healthcare Diagnostics Inc.
511 Benedict Ave
Tarrytown NY 10591
914 631-8000

(P-17992)
SOLONICS INC (PA)
31082 San Antonio St, Hayward (94544-7904)
PHONE..........................650 589-9798
Eddy Lee, *President*
▲ **EMP:** 10
SQ FT: 15,000
SALES (est): 1MM **Privately Held**
WEB: www.solonics.com
SIC: 3661 Telephone & telegraph apparatus

(P-17993)
SONANT CORPORATION
6215 Ferris Sq Ste 220, San Diego (92121-3251)
PHONE..........................858 623-8180
Charles W Smith, *President*
James B Reeg, *CFO*
Jack A Buell Jr, *Vice Pres*
Murray S Judy, *Vice Pres*
EMP: 15
SQ FT: 7,000
SALES (est): 2.1MM **Privately Held**
WEB: www.sonant.com
SIC: 3661 Computer software development & applications; systems software development services

(P-17994)
SORRENTO NETWORKS CORPORATION (DH)
7195 Oakport St, Oakland (94621-1947)
PHONE..........................510 577-1400
Phillip W Arneson, *President*
Joe R Armstrong, *CFO*
Richard L Jacobson, *Senior VP*
EMP: 18
SQ FT: 36,000
SALES (est): 10.3MM
SALES (corp-wide): 27.2MM **Publicly Held**
WEB: www.sorrentonet.com
SIC: 3661 Telephones & telephone apparatus; switching equipment, telephone; multiplex equipment, telephone & telegraph; fiber optics communications equipment
HQ: Dasan Zhone Solutions, Inc.
7195 Oakport St
Oakland CA 94621
510 777-7000

(P-17995)
SPECTRASWITCH INC
445 Tesconi Cir, Santa Rosa (95401-4619)
PHONE..........................707 568-7000
Nick Lawrence, *President*
EMP: 41
SALES (est): 2.5MM **Privately Held**
WEB: www.spectraswitch.com
SIC: 3661 Fiber optics communications equipment; switching equipment, telephone

(P-17996)
SPROUTLING INC
8 California St Ste 300, San Francisco (94111-4822)
PHONE..........................415 323-3270
Christopher Sinclair, *CEO*
EMP: 10
SQ FT: 335,000
SALES (est): 1.7MM
SALES (corp-wide): 4.8B **Publicly Held**
SIC: 3661 Switching equipment, telephone
PA: Mattel, Inc.
333 Continental Blvd
El Segundo CA 90245
310 252-2000

(P-17997)
SWEDCOM CORPORATION
851 Burlway Rd Ste 300, Burlingame (94010-1712)
PHONE..........................650 348-1190
Sven E Kjaersgaard, *President*
Kersin Kjaersgaard, *Vice Pres*
Lola Cornell, *Office Mgr*
Dan Leonetti, *Purchasing*
▲ **EMP:** 16
SQ FT: 2,400
SALES (est): 1.7MM **Privately Held**
SIC: 3661 5063 Multiplex equipment, telephone & telegraph; antennas, receiving, satellite dishes

(P-17998)
SYMMETRICOM INC
3870 N 1st St, San Jose (95134-1702)
PHONE..........................408 433-0910
EMP: 20
SALES (est): 3.6MM **Privately Held**
SIC: 3661 Telephone & telegraph apparatus

(P-17999)
SYSTEM STUDIES
INCORPORATED (PA)
21340 E Cliff Dr, Santa Cruz (95062-4800)
PHONE..............................831 475-5777
Robert A Simpkins, *President*
Diane Bordoni, *CFO*
William D Simpkins, *Vice Pres*
Sheryll Hiatt, *Sales Mgr*
EMP: 42 **EST:** 1980
SQ FT: 11,000
SALES (est): 8.2MM **Privately Held**
WEB: www.airtalk.com
SIC: 3661 Telephone & telegraph apparatus

(P-18000)
TATUNG TELECOM
CORPORATION
2660 Marine Way, Mountain View (94043-1124)
P.O. Box 2012, Menlo Park (94026-2012)
PHONE..............................650 961-2288
Douglas Lau, *President*
T S Lin, *Ch of Bd*
Grace Lau, *CFO*
Sue J Lau, *Admin Sec*
EMP: 100
SQ FT: 10,000
SALES (est): 8MM
SALES (corp-wide): 2.5B **Privately Held**
SIC: 3661 Telephone & telegraph apparatus
PA: Tatung Co.
22, Zhongshan N. Rd., Sec. 3,
Taipei City TAP 10435
225 925-252

(P-18001)
TITAN PHOTONICS INC
1241 Quarry Ln Ste 140, Pleasanton (94566-8462)
PHONE..............................510 687-0488
Eric Liu, *President*
Charlie Chen, *Treasurer*
Katherine Liang, *Project Mgr*
Sam Tung, *Opers Mgr*
Jim McGowan, *Manager*
▲ **EMP:** 25
SQ FT: 2,000
SALES (est): 6MM **Privately Held**
WEB: www.titanphotonics.com
SIC: 3661 Telephone & telegraph apparatus

(P-18002)
U-BLOX SAN DIEGO INC
12626 High Bluff Dr, San Diego (92130-2070)
PHONE..............................858 847-9611
David W Carey, *President*
Brian N Richardson, *President*
James Gibson, *Sr Software Eng*
EMP: 16
SALES (est): 2.6MM
SALES (corp-wide): 408.3MM **Privately Held**
SIC: 3661 3571 5045 Modems; personal computers (microcomputers); computers, peripherals & software
HQ: U-Blox Ag
Zurcherstrasse 68
Thalwil ZH 8800
447 227-444

(P-18003)
UNITED OPTRONICS INC
1323 Great Mall Dr, Milpitas (95035-8013)
PHONE..............................408 503-8900
J J Pang, *Ch of Bd*
EMP: 10
SQ FT: 50,000
SALES (est): 1MM **Privately Held**
WEB: www.unitedoptronics.com
SIC: 3661 Fiber optics communications equipment

(P-18004)
VELLO SYSTEMS INC
1530 Obrien Dr, Menlo Park (94025-1454)
PHONE..............................650 324-7688
Karl May, *CEO*
Armineh Baghoomian, *CFO*
EMP: 85

SALES (est): 13.5MM **Privately Held**
SIC: 3661 5999 5065 7622 Telephone station equipment & parts, wire; communication equipment; communication equipment; communication equipment repair

(P-18005)
VERTICAL COMMUNICATION
(HQ)
3979 Freedom Cir Ste 400, Santa Clara (95054-1257)
PHONE..............................408 969-9600
William Tauscher, *CEO*
Janice Dow, *Partner*
Bill Meyer, *Officer*
Richard Anderson, *Exec VP*
Al Loaiza, *Vice Pres*
▲ **EMP:** 65
SALES (est): 9.9MM
SALES (corp-wide): 67.7MM **Privately Held**
WEB: www.vertical.com
SIC: 3661 Telephones & telephone apparatus
PA: Vertical Communications, Inc.
1000 Holcomb Wds Pkwy # 300
Roswell GA 30076
408 404-1600

(P-18006)
VESTA SOLUTIONS INC (DH)
42555 Rio Nedo, Temecula (92590-3726)
P.O. Box 9007 (92589-9007)
PHONE..............................951 719-2100
Jeff Robertson, *President*
Mage Hernandez, *Partner*
Louis Albatro, *CFO*
Philippe Devos, *Vice Pres*
Mike Pavick, *Vice Pres*
▲ **EMP:** 277
SQ FT: 100,000
SALES (est): 119MM
SALES (corp-wide): 78.7B **Privately Held**
WEB: www.peinc.com
SIC: 3661 Telephone station equipment & parts, wire
HQ: Airbus Defense And Space, Inc.
2550 Wasser Ter Ste 9000
Herndon VA 20171
703 466-5600

(P-18007)
VIAVI SOLUTIONS INC
3601 Calle Tecate, Camarillo (93012-5056)
PHONE..............................805 465-1875
Bobby Donaldson, *Manager*
EMP: 75
SALES (corp-wide): 811.4MM **Publicly Held**
WEB: www.jdsuniphase.com
SIC: 3661
PA: Viavi Solutions Inc.
6001 America Center Dr # 6
San Jose CA 95002
408 404-3600

(P-18008)
VSR NETWORK TECHNOLOGIES
LLC
11760 Atwood Rd, Auburn (95603-9075)
PHONE..............................530 889-1500
Mark Cederloff, *Mng Member*
Rhonda Cederloff,
EMP: 21
SQ FT: 2,000
SALES (est): 1.9MM **Privately Held**
WEB: www.vsrusa.com
SIC: 3661 Telephones & telephone apparatus

(P-18009)
WEST COAST VENTURE
CAPITAL LLC (PA)
10050 Bandley Dr, Cupertino (95014-2102)
PHONE..............................408 725-0700
Carl Berg, *President*
EMP: 700
SALES (est): 52MM **Privately Held**
SIC: 3661 Telephone & telegraph apparatus

(P-18010)
Y B S ENTERPRISES INC
Also Called: Electro-Comm
3116 W Vanowen St, Burbank (91505-1237)
PHONE..............................818 848-7790
Y B Song, *President*
Grace Song, *Admin Sec*
EMP: 13
SQ FT: 30,000
SALES (est): 6.5MM **Privately Held**
SIC: 3661 Communication headgear, telephone

3663 Radio & T V Communications, Systs & Eqpt, Broadcast/Studio
---

(P-18011)
24/7 STUDIO EQUIPMENT INC
Also Called: Hertz Entertainment Services
3111 N Kenwood St, Burbank (91505-1041)
PHONE..............................818 840-8247
Lance Sorenson, *President*
Gary Mielke, *Vice Pres*
EMP: 92
SALES (est): 21.8MM
SALES (corp-wide): 8.8B **Publicly Held**
WEB: www.247studioequipment.com
SIC: 3663 Studio equipment, radio & television broadcasting
PA: Hertz Global Holdings, Inc.
8501 Williams Rd Fl 3
Estero FL 33928
239 301-7000

(P-18012)
2XWIRELESS INC
1065 Marauder St, Chico (95973-9039)
PHONE..............................877 581-8002
James Higgins, *CEO*
EMP: 60
SALES (est): 4.9MM **Privately Held**
SIC: 3663 Television antennas (transmitting) & ground equipment

(P-18013)
ABEKAS INC
1233 Midas Way, Sunnyvale (94085-4021)
PHONE..............................650 470-0900
Junaid Sheikh, *President*
Phil Bennett, *Engineer*
Atul Vaidya, *Engineer*
Kathleen Alpi, *Sales Staff*
Douglas Johnson, *Manager*
EMP: 12
SQ FT: 5,700
SALES (est): 2.7MM **Privately Held**
WEB: www.abekas.com
SIC: 3663 Television broadcasting & communications equipment
HQ: Ross Europe B.V.
Strawinskylaan 411
Amsterdam
205 752-727

(P-18014)
ACROAMATICS INC
7230 Hollister Ave, Goleta (93117-2807)
PHONE..............................805 967-9909
Geoffrey Johnson, *President*
Patricia Johnson, *CFO*
Robert Danford, *Vice Pres*
John Foondle, *Vice Pres*
John Hooper, *Business Dir*
EMP: 24
SALES (est): 4.6MM **Privately Held**
WEB: www.acroamatics.com
SIC: 3663 Telemetering equipment, electronic

(P-18015)
ADAPTIVE DIGITAL SYSTEMS
INC
20322 Sw Acacia St # 200, Newport Beach (92660-1504)
PHONE..............................949 955-3116
Attila W Mathe, *President*
Ralph Boehringer, *Vice Pres*
Emmanuel Ladsous, *Vice Pres*
Susan Cameron, *Admin Sec*

Christian Corb, *Engineer*
▲ **EMP:** 27
SQ FT: 6,500
SALES: 9.5MM **Privately Held**
WEB: www.adaptivedigitalsystems.com
SIC: 3663 Marine radio communications equipment

(P-18016)
ADVANCED ENTERPRISES LLC
Also Called: Advanced Dealer Services
48511 Warm Springs Blvd # 202, Fremont (94539-7746)
PHONE..............................408 923-5000
James Landes, *Principal*
EMP: 11 **EST:** 1998
SQ FT: 1,600
SALES (est): 1.1MM **Privately Held**
WEB: www.adsmobile.net
SIC: 3663 Mobile communication equipment

(P-18017)
AETHERCOMM INC
3205 Lionshead Ave, Carlsbad (92010-4710)
PHONE..............................760 208-6002
William Todd Thornton, *CEO*
Todd Thornton, *President*
Richard Martinez, *CFO*
Terri Thornton, *Vice Pres*
Mark Bahu, *Chief Engr*
EMP: 125
SQ FT: 46,000
SALES: 30.5MM **Privately Held**
WEB: www.aethercomm.com
SIC: 3663 Radio & TV communications equipment

(P-18018)
AGUDA WILSON RAMOS
Also Called: Filipino Channel
5409 Asbury Way, Stockton (95219-7163)
PHONE..............................209 942-2446
Wilson Aguda, *Owner*
EMP: 13
SALES: 100K **Privately Held**
SIC: 3663 Satellites, communications

(P-18019)
AIR-TRAK
15090 Avenue Of Science # 103, San Diego (92128-3412)
PHONE..............................858 677-9950
Greg White, *President*
Dennis Clark, *Chairman*
Marc Bernard, *Vice Pres*
Steve Porter, *Vice Pres*
EMP: 17
SQ FT: 5,600
SALES: 5MM **Privately Held**
WEB: www.air-trak.com
SIC: 3663

(P-18020)
AIRAYA CORP
18434 Technology Dr, Morgan Hill (95037-2844)
PHONE..............................408 776-2846
Mike Nydam, *President*
Bill Pabst, *Vice Pres*
EMP: 15
SQ FT: 10,000
SALES (est): 2.4MM **Privately Held**
WEB: www.airaya.com
SIC: 3663 Radio & TV communications equipment

(P-18021)
AIRGAIN INC (PA)
3611 Valley Centre Dr # 150, San Diego (92130-3331)
PHONE..............................760 579-0200
James K Sims, *Ch of Bd*
Charles Myers, *President*
Glenn Selbo, *COO*
Anil Doradla, *CFO*
Leah Cook, *Admin Asst*
EMP: 38
SQ FT: 10,300
SALES: 49.5MM **Publicly Held**
WEB: www.airgain.com
SIC: 3663 5731 Antennas, transmitting & communications; antennas, satellite dish

(P-18022)
AJA VIDEO SYSTEMS INC (PA)
180 Litton Dr, Grass Valley (95945-5076)
P.O. Box 1033 (95945-1033)
PHONE..................................530 274-2048
John O ABT, *Principal*
Darlene ABT, *CFO*
Dustin Graham, *Web Dvlpr*
David Palley, *General Counsel*
▲ **EMP:** 30
SQ FT: 9,800
SALES (est): 7.5MM **Privately Held**
WEB: www.aja.com
SIC: 3663 Television broadcasting & communications equipment

(P-18023)
ALDETEC INC
3560 Business Dr Ste 100, Sacramento (95820-2161)
PHONE..................................916 453-3382
Jeff Russ, *President*
David Dwssem, *Purch Mgr*
John Esguerra, *QC Mgr*
Lenore Minasian, *Manager*
Tram Le, *Assistant*
EMP: 45
SQ FT: 16,038
SALES (est): 4.4MM **Privately Held**
WEB: www.aldetec.com
SIC: 3663 Amplifiers, RF power & IF

(P-18024)
ALE USA INC
26801 Agoura Rd, Calabasas (91301-5122)
PHONE..................................818 878-4816
Stanley Stopka, *Principal*
Michel Emelianoff, *CEO*
Stan Stopka, *Vice Pres*
Tim Ballew, *Director*
EMP: 550
SQ FT: 50,000
SALES: 130MM **Privately Held**
SIC: 3663 3613 Mobile communication equipment; switchgear & switchboard apparatus
HQ: China Huaxin Post And Telecom Technologies Co.,Ltd.
    Building 4(West Building), Chang An
    Xing Rong Center, No.1 Court
    Beijing
    105 852-8866

(P-18025)
ALIEN TECHNOLOGY LLC (PA)
845 Embedded Way, San Jose (95138-1030)
PHONE..................................408 782-3900
Weijie Yun, *CEO*
Duane E Zitzner, *Ch of Bd*
Patrick Ervin, *President*
Glenn Gengel, *President*
John Payne, *COO*
▲ **EMP:** 50
SQ FT: 81,000
SALES (est): 28.6MM **Privately Held**
WEB: www.alientechnology.com
SIC: 3663 Radio broadcasting & communications equipment; transmitting apparatus, radio or television

(P-18026)
ALTINEX INC
592 Apollo St Ste A, Brea (92821-3133)
PHONE..................................714 990-0877
Jack Gershfeld, *President*
Keyur Sheth, *Managing Dir*
Sergey Alayev, *Project Engr*
▲ **EMP:** 50
SQ FT: 28,000
SALES (est): 19.6MM **Privately Held**
SIC: 3663 3577 3651 5099 Radio & TV communications equipment; computer peripheral equipment; household audio & video equipment; video & audio equipment

(P-18027)
AMEBA TECHNOLOGY INC
4700 Miller Dr Ste B5, Temple City (91780-3756)
P.O. Box 990 (91780-0990)
PHONE..................................626 575-8811
Chin Jung Wu, *President*
◆ **EMP:** 10

SQ FT: 5,700
SALES (est): 1MM **Privately Held**
WEB: www.amebacctv.com
SIC: 3663 Television broadcasting & communications equipment

(P-18028)
AMINO TECHNOLOGIES (US) LLC (HQ)
20823 Stevens Creek Blvd, Cupertino (95014-2108)
PHONE..................................408 861-1400
Steve D McKay, *Mng Member*
Brian Garrett, *Partner*
Ming Hui, *Manager*
◆ **EMP:** 60
SALES (est): 9.1MM
SALES (corp-wide): 99.1MM **Privately Held**
SIC: 3663 5064 Television broadcasting & communications equipment; electrical appliances, television & radio; television sets
PA: Amino Technologies Plc
    Prospect House
    Cambridge CAMBS CB24
    195 423-4100

(P-18029)
AMPLIFIER TECHNOLOGIES INC
1749 Chapin Rd, Montebello (90640-6609)
PHONE..................................323 278-0001
Morris Kessler, *President*
Jeff Hipps, *Vice Pres*
▲ **EMP:** 25
SQ FT: 84,000
SALES (est): 4.9MM **Privately Held**
WEB: www.ati-amp.com
SIC: 3663 Television broadcasting & communications equipment
PA: Macey Investment Corp
    1749 Chapin Rd
    Montebello CA 90640
    323 278-0001

(P-18030)
ANACOM INC
1961 Concourse Dr, San Jose (95131-1708)
PHONE..................................408 519-2062
James Tom, *CEO*
May Tom, *President*
Christopher Nguyen, *CFO*
Ram Chandran, *Vice Pres*
Ron Fischler, *Vice Pres*
▲ **EMP:** 40
SQ FT: 5,000
SALES (est): 9.9MM **Privately Held**
WEB: www.anacominc.com
SIC: 3663 Receiver-transmitter units (transceiver)

(P-18031)
ANRITSU COMPANY (DH)
490 Jarvis Dr, Morgan Hill (95037-2834)
P.O. Box 39000, San Francisco (94139-0001)
PHONE..................................408 201-1551
Hirokazu Hashimoto, *President*
Andrea Culler, *Sr Corp Ofcr*
Kenji Tanaka, *Exec VP*
Toshihiko Takahashi, *Senior VP*
Wade Hulon, *Vice Pres*
▲ **EMP:** 485
SQ FT: 242,000
SALES: 228.6MM
SALES (corp-wide): 806.8MM **Privately Held**
WEB: www.us.anritsu.com
SIC: 3663 3825 5065 Radio & TV communications equipment; test equipment for electronic & electric measurement; electronic parts & equipment
HQ: Anritsu U.S. Holding, Inc.
    490 Jarvis Dr
    Morgan Hill CA 95037
    408 778-2000

(P-18032)
ANTCOM CORPORATION
367 Van Ness Way Ste 602, Torrance (90501-6246)
PHONE..................................310 782-1076
Michael Ritter, *CEO*
Sean Huynh, *Vice Pres*

Doug Reid, *General Mgr*
Phil Tran, *Engineer*
Gina Lansing, *Controller*
EMP: 45 **EST:** 1997
SQ FT: 15,000
SALES (est): 11.4MM **Privately Held**
WEB: www.antcom.com
SIC: 3663 Antennas, transmitting & communications

(P-18033)
ANTYPAS & ASSOCIATES INC
749 Thorsen Ct, Los Altos (94024-6630)
PHONE..................................650 961-4311
EMP: 12
SQ FT: 20,000
SALES (est): 1.1MM **Privately Held**
WEB: www.crystacomm.com
SIC: 3663 3661

(P-18034)
ANYDATA CORPORATION (PA)
5405 Alton Pkwy, Irvine (92604-3717)
PHONE..................................949 900-6040
Soon B Shin, *CEO*
John Scott, *President*
Ulrich Gottschling, *COO*
Zion Kim, *Vice Pres*
Chilsam Lee, *Research*
EMP: 29
SALES (est): 15MM **Privately Held**
WEB: www.uct.net
SIC: 3663 Mobile communication equipment

(P-18035)
APHEX LLC
820 S Palm Ave Ste 21, Alhambra (91803-1544)
P.O. Box 680038, Park City UT (84068-0038)
PHONE..................................818 767-2929
David M Wiener, *CEO*
Robin Sibucao, *COO*
Julie Garcia, *Manager*
EMP: 12
SQ FT: 6,402
SALES (est): 1.1MM **Privately Held**
SIC: 3663 Television broadcasting & communications equipment

(P-18036)
APHEX SYSTEMS LTD
3500 N San Fernando Blvd, Burbank (91505-1000)
PHONE..................................818 767-2929
Marvin Caesar, *President*
Robbie Jo Dungey, *Manager*
EMP: 27
SALES (est): 3.9MM **Privately Held**
WEB: www.aphex.com
SIC: 3663 Radio & TV communications equipment

(P-18037)
APPLE INC (PA)
1 Apple Park Way, Cupertino (95014-0642)
PHONE..................................408 996-1010
Timothy D Cook, *CEO*
Arthur D Levinson, *Ch of Bd*
Jeff Williams, *COO*
Luca Maestri, *CFO*
Katherine Adams, *Senior VP*
◆ **EMP:** 2000
SALES: 265.6B **Publicly Held**
WEB: www.apple.com
SIC: 3663 3571 3575 3577 Mobile communication equipment; personal computers (microcomputers); computer terminals, monitors & components; printers, computer; sound reproducing equipment; operating systems computer software; application computer software

(P-18038)
APPLE INC
1 Infinite Loop, Cupertino (95014-2083)
PHONE..................................408 606-5775
EMP: 12
SALES (corp-wide): 265.6B **Publicly Held**
SIC: 3663 Cellular radio telephone
PA: Apple Inc.
    1 Apple Park Way
    Cupertino CA 95014
    408 996-1010

(P-18039)
APPLICA INC
11651 Vanowen St, North Hollywood (91605-6128)
PHONE..................................818 565-0011
Albert Cohen, *President*
Shlomo Barash, *Treasurer*
James Viray, *General Mgr*
EMP: 20
SALES (est): 3.1MM **Privately Held**
SIC: 3663 Radio & TV communications equipment

(P-18040)
AQUILA SPACE INC
Nasa Ames Research Park, Moffett Field (94035)
PHONE..................................650 224-8559
Chris Biddy, *President*
EMP: 13
SALES (est): 1.5MM **Privately Held**
SIC: 3663 Space satellite communications equipment

(P-18041)
ARDAX SYSTEMS INC
1669 Industrial Rd, San Carlos (94070-4112)
PHONE..................................650 591-2656
Fax: 650 591-8249
EMP: 10
SQ FT: 5,800
SALES (est): 960K **Privately Held**
WEB: www.ardax.com
SIC: 3663

(P-18042)
ARUBA NETWORKS INC
392 Acoma Way, Fremont (94539-7508)
PHONE..................................408 227-4500
EMP: 29
SALES (corp-wide): 50.1B **Publicly Held**
SIC: 3663
HQ: Aruba Networks, Inc.
    3333 Scott Blvd
    Santa Clara CA 95054
    408 227-4500

(P-18043)
ARUBA NETWORKS INC
390 W Caribbean Dr, Sunnyvale (94089-1010)
PHONE..................................408 227-4500
EMP: 10
SALES (corp-wide): 28.8B **Publicly Held**
SIC: 3663 3577 7371 Mobile communication equipment; data conversion equipment, media-to-media: computer; graphic displays, except graphic terminals; computer software development
HQ: Aruba Networks, Inc.
    3333 Scott Blvd
    Santa Clara CA 95054
    408 227-4500

(P-18044)
ASTRA COMMUNICATIONS INC
1101 Chestnut St, Burbank (91506-1624)
P.O. Box 391 (91503-0391)
PHONE..................................818 859-7305
EMP: 12
SQ FT: 11,000
SALES (est): 1.7MM **Privately Held**
WEB: www.astracomm.com
SIC: 3663

(P-18045)
AVIAT NETWORKS INC (PA)
860 N Mccarthy Blvd, Milpitas (95035-5110)
PHONE..................................408 941-7100
Michael A Pangia, *President*
John Mutch, *Ch of Bd*
Stan Gallagher, *COO*
Shaun McFall, *Senior VP*
Heinz H Stumpe, *Senior VP*
EMP: 98
SQ FT: 19,000
SALES: 242.5MM **Publicly Held**
WEB: www.harrisstratex.com
SIC: 3663 Radio broadcasting & communications equipment

▲ = Import ▼=Export
◆ =Import/Export

(P-18046)
AVIAT US INC (HQ)
860 N Mccarthy Blvd # 200, Milpitas
(95035-5117)
PHONE..................................408 941-7100
Michael A Pangia, *President*
John Mutch, *Ch of Bd*
Ralph Marimon, *CFO*
Shaun McFall, *Chief Mktg Ofcr*
Meena L Elliott, *Senior VP*
▼ EMP: 450
SQ FT: 60,000
SALES (est): 129.7MM **Publicly Held**
SIC: 3663 3661 Radio broadcasting &
  communications equipment; transmitter-
  receivers, radio; mobile communication
  equipment; fiber optics communications
  equipment

(P-18047)
AVID SYSTEMS INC (HQ)
280 Bernardo Ave, Mountain View
(94043-5238)
PHONE..................................650 526-1600
Ken A Sexton, *CEO*
Patti S Hart, *Ch of Bd*
Georg Blinn, *President*
Ajay Chopra, *President*
Arthur D Chadwick, *CFO*
EMP: 225
SQ FT: 106,000
SALES (est): 81MM
SALES (corp-wide): 419MM **Publicly
Held**
WEB: www.ipinnacle.com
SIC: 3663 3577 Radio & TV communica-
  tions equipment; computer peripheral
  equipment
PA: Avid Technology, Inc.
  75 Network Dr
  Burlington MA 01803
  978 640-6789

(P-18048)
AVX ANTENNA INC (DH)
5501 Oberlin Dr Ste 100, San Diego
(92121-1718)
PHONE..................................858 550-3820
Laurent Desclos, *President*
Vahid Manian, *COO*
Rick Johnson, *CFO*
Sung-Ki Jung, *Officer*
Feng Niu, *Vice Pres*
▲ EMP: 23
SALES (est): 5.8MM
SALES (corp-wide): 14.8B **Publicly Held**
WEB: www.ethertronics.com
SIC: 3663 Antennas, transmitting & com-
  munications
HQ: Avx Corporation
  1 Avx Blvd
  Fountain Inn SC 29644
  864 967-2150

(P-18049)
**AXXCELERA BRDBAND
WIRELESS INC (DH)**
82 Coromar Dr, Santa Barbara
(93117-3024)
PHONE..................................805 968-9621
Jamal Hamdani, *CEO*
Bruce Tarr, *CFO*
Tony Masters, *Senior VP*
Philip Rushton, *Senior VP*
Alex Clamann, *Sr Software Eng*
▲ EMP: 16
SQ FT: 56,000
SALES (est): 1.7MM
SALES (corp-wide): 32.2MM **Privately
Held**
WEB: www.axxcelera.com
SIC: 3663 Radio & TV communications
  equipment
HQ: Moseley Associates, Inc.
  82 Coromar Dr
  Goleta CA 93117
  805 968-9621

(P-18050)
BIG SHINE LOS ANGELES INC
27211 Branbury Ct, Valencia (91354-2112)
PHONE..................................818 346-0770
Jae Ho Lee, *President*
EMP: 10

SALES (est): 1.1MM **Privately Held**
SIC: 3663 Telemetering equipment, electronic

(P-18051)
BLITZZ TECHNOLOGY INC
53 Parker, Irvine (92618-1605)
PHONE..................................949 380-7709
▲ EMP: 25
SQ FT: 10,000
SALES: 4MM **Privately Held**
SIC: 3663 5065

(P-18052)
**BLUE DANUBE SYSTEMS INC
(PA)**
3131 Jay St Ste 201, Santa Clara
(95054-3340)
PHONE..................................650 316-5010
Mark Pinto, *CEO*
Mihai Banu, *Vice Pres*
Bart Rizzolo, *Business Dir*
John Caruso, *Technician*
James Emerick, *Engineer*
EMP: 15
SALES (est): 3.3MM **Privately Held**
SIC: 3663 Radio broadcasting & communi-
  cations equipment

(P-18053)
BOEING COMPANY
900 N Sepulveda Blvd, El Segundo
(90245-2710)
P.O. Box 92919, Los Angeles (90009-2919)
PHONE..................................310 662-9000
EMP: 25
SALES (corp-wide): 93.3B **Publicly Held**
SIC: 3663 Satellites, communications;
  space satellite communications equip-
  ment
PA: The Boeing Company
  100 N Riverside Plz
  Chicago IL 60606
  312 544-2000

(P-18054)
BOEING COMPANY
2201 Seal Beach Blvd, Seal Beach
(90740-5603)
PHONE..................................714 372-5361
Arthur Cohen, *Branch Mgr*
EMP: 1000
SALES (corp-wide): 93.3B **Publicly Held**
SIC: 3663 3812 Satellites, communica-
  tions; search & navigation equipment
PA: The Boeing Company
  100 N Riverside Plz
  Chicago IL 60606
  312 544-2000

(P-18055)
**BOEING SATELLITE SYSTEMS
INC (HQ)**
900 N Pacific Coast Hwy, El Segundo
(90245-2710)
P.O. Box 92919, Los Angeles (90009-2919)
PHONE..................................310 791-7450
Craig R Cooning, *President*
Dave Ryan, *Vice Pres*
Charles Toups, *Vice Pres*
Eric Glass, *Meeting Planner*
Michael Cook, *Network Enginr*
◆ EMP: 25
SALES (est): 1.1B
SALES (corp-wide): 93.3B **Publicly Held**
SIC: 3663 Satellites, communications;
  space satellite communications equip-
  ment
PA: The Boeing Company
  100 N Riverside Plz
  Chicago IL 60606
  312 544-2000

(P-18056)
**BROADCAST MICROWAVE
SERVICES (PA)**
12305 Crosthwaite Cir, Poway
(92064-6817)
PHONE..................................858 391-3050
Graham Bunney, *CEO*
Sharon Desuacido, *Vice Pres*
Jeff Jones, *Admin Sec*
Randy Angelito, *Software Engr*
Jason Moses, *Technology*
EMP: 109

SQ FT: 37,000
SALES (est): 27.6MM **Privately Held**
WEB: www.bms-inc.com
SIC: 3663 Microwave communication
  equipment

(P-18057)
CABLE AML INC (PA)
2271 W 205th St Ste 101, Torrance
(90501-1449)
PHONE..................................310 222-5599
Francisco Bernues, *President*
Eddie Nakamura, *CFO*
Norman Woods, *Admin Sec*
▼ EMP: 14
SQ FT: 15,000
SALES (est): 2.5MM **Privately Held**
SIC: 3663 8711 Radio & TV communica-
  tions equipment; consulting engineer

(P-18058)
CALAMP CORP (PA)
15635 Alton Pkwy Ste 250, Irvine
(92618-7328)
PHONE..................................949 600-5600
Michael Burdiek, *President*
A J Moyer, *Ch of Bd*
Kurtis Binder, *CFO*
Kimberly Alexy, *Bd of Directors*
Jeffery Gardner, *Bd of Directors*
◆ EMP: 265
SQ FT: 16,000
SALES: 365.9MM **Publicly Held**
SIC: 3663 Microwave communication
  equipment

(P-18059)
CALAMP CORP
2231 Rutherford Rd # 110, Carlsbad
(92008-8811)
PHONE..................................760 438-9010
Frank Perna Jr, *Chairman*
EMP: 12 EST: 2012
SALES (est): 1.5MM
SALES (corp-wide): 365.9MM **Publicly
Held**
SIC: 3663 Radio & TV communications
  equipment
PA: Calamp Corp.
  15635 Alton Pkwy Ste 250
  Irvine CA 92618
  949 600-5600

(P-18060)
CALIX INC (PA)
2777 Orchard Pkwy, San Jose
(95134-2008)
PHONE..................................408 514-3000
Carl Russo, *President*
Don Listwin, *Ch of Bd*
Gregory Billings, *President*
Cory Sindelar, *CFO*
Chris Bowick, *Bd of Directors*
◆ EMP: 277
SQ FT: 82,100
SALES: 510.3MM **Publicly Held**
WEB: www.calix-networks.com
SIC: 3663 4899 4813 Radio & TV com-
  munications equipment; data communica-
  tion services; communication signal
  enhancement network system; telephone
  communication, except radio

(P-18061)
CANAM TECHNOLOGY INC
5318 E 2nd St Ste 700, Long Beach
(90803-5324)
PHONE..................................562 856-0178
Michael Martinez, *President*
▲ EMP: 10
SQ FT: 2,200
SALES (est): 2.3MM **Privately Held**
WEB: www.canamtechnology.com
SIC: 3663 8711 Antennas, transmitting &
  communications; consulting engineer

(P-18062)
**CANARY COMMUNICATIONS
INC**
6040 Hellyer Ave Ste 150, San Jose
(95138-1041)
PHONE..................................408 365-0609
Vinh Tran, *President*
Roland Yamaguchi, *Vice Pres*
Charles McKee, *Executive*
▲ EMP: 15

SALES (est): 2.2MM **Privately Held**
WEB: www.canarycom.com
SIC: 3663 Receiver-transmitter units
  (transceiver)

(P-18063)
CARLSON WIRELESS TECH INC
3134 Jacobs Ave Ste C, Eureka
(95501-0960)
PHONE..................................707 822-7000
James R Carlson, *CEO*
Chris Spoerle, *Vice Pres*
Sebastien Amiot, *CTO*
Shamus Jennings, *Technical Staff*
Mindy Hiley, *Opers Staff*
EMP: 15
SQ FT: 6,000
SALES (est): 3.4MM **Privately Held**
WEB: www.carlsonwireless.com
SIC: 3663 Airborne radio communications
  equipment; receivers, radio communica-
  tions; transmitter-receivers, radio

(P-18064)
CARRIERCOMM INC
82 Coromar Dr, Goleta (93117-3024)
PHONE..................................805 968-9621
Jamal N Hamdani, *President*
Bruce Tarr, *CFO*
EMP: 50
SQ FT: 18,000
SALES (est): 6.9MM
SALES (corp-wide): 32.2MM **Privately
Held**
WEB: www.carriercom.com
SIC: 3663 Radio & TV communications
  equipment
PA: Axxcss Wireless Solutions Inc
  82 Coromar Dr
  Goleta CA 93117
  805 968-9621

(P-18065)
CELLCO PARTNERSHIP
Also Called: Verizon
3770 W Mcfadden Ave Ste H, Santa Ana
(92704-1395)
PHONE..................................714 775-0600
Roberto Espinosa, *Manager*
Johnny Yepez, *Sales Staff*
EMP: 20
SALES (corp-wide): 126B **Publicly Held**
SIC: 3663 5999 3661 Mobile communica-
  tion equipment; telephone equipment &
  systems; telephone & telegraph appara-
  tus
HQ: Cellco Partnership
  1 Verizon Way
  Basking Ridge NJ 07920

(P-18066)
CELLPHONE-MATE INC
Also Called: Surecall
48346 Milmont Dr, Fremont (94538-7324)
PHONE..................................510 770-0469
Hongtao Zhan, *President*
Mark Galang, *Info Tech Mgr*
Eric Mercil, *Sales Dir*
Bethany Mangold, *Marketing Mgr*
Roman Vizvary, *Marketing Staff*
▲ EMP: 52
SQ FT: 22,800
SALES: 7MM **Privately Held**
SIC: 3663 Amplifiers, RF power & IF; an-
  tennas, transmitting & communications;
  cable television equipment

(P-18067)
CENTRON INDUSTRIES INC
441 W Victoria St, Gardena (90248-3528)
PHONE..................................310 324-6443
Yong W Kim, *CEO*
Erin Roche, *Senior VP*
Hye S Kim, *Admin Sec*
Joe Thurber, *Graphic Designe*
Mandeep Kaur, *Accountant*
▲ EMP: 37
SQ FT: 10,000
SALES (est): 8.8MM **Privately Held**
WEB: www.centronind.com
SIC: 3663 Radio & TV communications
  equipment

(PA)=Parent Co (HQ)=Headquarters (DH)=Div Headquarters
✿ = New Business established in last 2 years

2019 California
Manufacturers Register

735

PRODUCTS & SVCS

(P-18068)
CLEAR-COM LLC
Also Called: Clear-Com Communications
1301 Marina Vil Pkwy 10, Alameda (94501)
PHONE..................................510 337-6600
Mitzi Dominguez, *CEO*
Bob Boster, *President*
Harry Miyahira, *Chairman*
Simon Browne, *Vice Pres*
Peter Giddings, *Vice Pres*
▲ **EMP:** 801
SQ FT: 23,700
SALES (est): 66.7MM
SALES (corp-wide): 515.5MM **Privately Held**
WEB: www.clearcom.com
SIC: 3663 Radio & TV communications equipment
PA: H. M. Electronics, Inc.
2848 Whiptail Loop
Carlsbad CA 92010
858 535-6000

(P-18069)
COASTLINE HIGH PRFMCE COATINGS
7181 Orangewood Ave, Garden Grove (92841-1409)
PHONE..................................714 372-3263
Phil Viljoen, *President*
Mayra Torres, *Office Mgr*
EMP: 15
SALES (est): 2MM **Privately Held**
SIC: 3663 Satellites, communications

(P-18070)
COLUMBIA COMMUNICATIONS INC
22480 Parrotts Ferry Rd, Columbia (95310-9731)
PHONE..................................203 533-0252
Wallace Ratzlaff, *President*
Carolyn Ratzlaff, *Vice Pres*
Heidi Perlewitz, *Admin Sec*
EMP: 10
SQ FT: 3,000
SALES: 1MM **Privately Held**
WEB: www.columbia-comm.com
SIC: 3663 Radio broadcasting & communications equipment

(P-18071)
COMANT INDUSTRIES INCORPORATED (DH)
577 Burning Tree Rd, Fullerton (92833-1445)
PHONE..................................714 870-2420
Walter G Stierhoff, *CEO*
Josh Jones, *Engineer*
Irwin Bettman, *Controller*
EMP: 30
SQ FT: 30,000
SALES (est): 5MM
SALES (corp-wide): 2.7B **Privately Held**
WEB: www.comant.com
SIC: 3663 Antennas, transmitting & communications
HQ: Chelton Avionics, Inc.
6400 Wilkinson Dr
Prescott AZ 86301
928 708-1500

(P-18072)
COMMSYSTEMS LLC
12225 World Trade Dr I, San Diego (92128-3768)
PHONE..................................858 824-0056
Karl Kapusta, *President*
Preston Vorlicek,
EMP: 10 EST: 1996
SQ FT: 1,500
SALES: 2.9MM **Privately Held**
WEB: www.comm-systems.com
SIC: 3663 Satellites, communications

(P-18073)
COMMUNICATIONS & PWR INDS LLC
Also Called: CPI
811 Hansen Way, Palo Alto (94304-1031)
PHONE..................................650 846-3729
Robert Sickett, *Manager*
Andy Tafler, *President*
Dee Camacho, *Executive*
Michael Arimas, *Engineer*

Gerry Burton, *Engineer*
EMP: 1500
SQ FT: 25,000 **Privately Held**
WEB: www.cpii.com
SIC: 3663 Radio & TV communications equipment
HQ: Communications & Power Industries Llc
607 Hansen Way
Palo Alto CA 94304

(P-18074)
COMMUNICATIONS & PWR INDS LLC
CPI
6385 San Ignacio Ave, San Jose (95119-1206)
P.O. Box 51110, Palo Alto (94303-0687)
PHONE..................................650 846-2900
EMP: 130 **Privately Held**
SIC: 3663 Radio & TV communications equipment
HQ: Communications & Power Industries Llc
607 Hansen Way
Palo Alto CA 94304

(P-18075)
COMSAT INC
7676 Pine Grove Rd, Santa Paula (93060-9628)
P.O. Box 150 (93061-0150)
PHONE..................................805 933-4080
Mike Whiteford, *Manager*
EMP: 17
SALES (corp-wide): 20.8MM **Privately Held**
SIC: 3663 Radio & TV communications equipment
HQ: Comsat Inc.
2550 Wasser Ter Ste 600
Herndon VA 20171
571 599-3600

(P-18076)
COMTECH XICOM TECHNOLOGY INC (HQ)
3550 Bassett St, Santa Clara (95054-2704)
PHONE..................................408 213-3000
Fred Kornberg, *CEO*
John Branscum, *President*
Kevin Kirkpatrick, *General Mgr*
Karen Horvath, *Financial Exec*
Paula Miranda, *Human Res Dir*
EMP: 141
SQ FT: 40,000
SALES (est): 49.2MM
SALES (corp-wide): 570.5MM **Publicly Held**
WEB: www.xicomtech.com
SIC: 3663 3679 Amplifiers, RF power & IF; power supplies, all types: static
PA: Comtech Telecommunications Corp.
68 S Service Rd Ste 230
Melville NY 11747
631 962-7000

(P-18077)
CONNECT SYSTEMS INC
1802 Eastman Ave Ste 116, Ventura (93003-5759)
PHONE..................................805 642-7184
Jerry Wanger, *President*
▲ **EMP:** 22
SQ FT: 10,000
SALES (est): 3.5MM **Privately Held**
WEB: www.connectsystems.com
SIC: 3663

(P-18078)
CPI MALIBU DIVISION
3760 Calle Tecate Ste A, Camarillo (93012-5060)
PHONE..................................805 383-1829
Joel Littman, *CFO*
Danielle Montelongo, *Administration*
Elizabeth McKenzie, *QA Dir*
Kathleen Allen, *Info Tech Dir*
Scott Hanchar, *Project Engr*
EMP: 80
SQ FT: 32,500

SALES (est): 17.1MM **Privately Held**
WEB: www.maliburesearch.com
SIC: 3663 Antennas, transmitting & communications
HQ: Communications & Power Industries Llc
607 Hansen Way
Palo Alto CA 94304

(P-18079)
CREDENCE ID LLC
5801 Christie Ave Ste 500, Emeryville (94608-1938)
PHONE..................................888 243-5452
Bruce D Hanson, *CEO*
Robert Carrigan, *Vice Pres*
Yash Shah, *Vice Pres*
Aranesh Chandra, *Opers Staff*
Machiel Vander Harst, *VP Sales*
EMP: 32
SALES (est): 4MM **Privately Held**
SIC: 3663 Mobile communication equipment

(P-18080)
CRL SYSTEMS INC
Also Called: Orban
14798 Wicks Blvd, San Leandro (94577-6718)
PHONE..................................510 351-3500
Derek Pilkington, *President*
C J Brentlinger, *President*
Robert McMartin, *CFO*
EMP: 65 EST: 1969
SQ FT: 75,000
SALES (est): 8.3MM
SALES (corp-wide): 9.2MM **Publicly Held**
WEB: www.orban.com
SIC: 3663 Radio & TV communications equipment
PA: Circuit Research Labs, Inc.
7970 S Kyrene Rd
Tempe AZ 85284
480 403-8300

(P-18081)
CTT INC (PA)
5870 Hellyer Ave Ste 70, San Jose (95138-1004)
PHONE..................................408 541-0596
David Tai, *President*
Thanh Thai, *Vice Pres*
John Campbell, *Admin Sec*
Ken Pickard, *Technical Mgr*
Cw Lau, *Engineer*
▼ **EMP:** 81
SQ FT: 45,000
SALES (est): 8.2MM **Privately Held**
WEB: www.cttinc.com
SIC: 3663 Microwave communication equipment; amplifiers, RF power & IF

(P-18082)
D X COMMUNICATIONS INC
Also Called: Tpl Communications
3825 Foothill Blvd, La Crescenta (91214-1619)
PHONE..................................323 256-3000
Richard H Myers, *CEO*
John Ehret, *President*
Lenny Uchenik, *President*
Richard Myers, *CEO*
Mitch Friedman, *Technology*
EMP: 28
SQ FT: 12,500
SALES (est): 10.4MM **Privately Held**
WEB: www.tplcom.com
SIC: 3663 Satellites, communications

(P-18083)
DATRON WRLD COMMUNICATIONS INC (PA)
3055 Enterprise Ct, Vista (92081-8347)
PHONE..................................760 597-1500
Art Barter, *President*
John C Goehring, *CFO*
Jimmy Diaz, *Bd of Directors*
Christopher Barter, *Program Mgr*
Lisa Courtemanche, *Executive Asst*
◆ **EMP:** 122 EST: 1971
SQ FT: 62,100
SALES (est): 56.2MM **Privately Held**
WEB: www.dtwc.com
SIC: 3663 Receiver-transmitter units (transceiver)

(P-18084)
DELTA-SIGMA INC
6690 Doolittle Ave, Riverside (92503-1432)
PHONE..................................951 343-4005
Ernesto G F Starri, *President*
Lisa K Starri, *Vice Pres*
Clive Winkler, *CTO*
EMP: 15
SQ FT: 12,000
SALES (est): 3.3MM **Privately Held**
WEB: www.111rfpower.com
SIC: 3663 Amplifiers, RF power & IF

(P-18085)
DENSO WRELESS SYSTEMS AMER INC
3250 Business Park Dr, Vista (92081-8511)
PHONE..................................760 734-4600
Yoshihaku Kokubo, *President*
Kazuaki Nanmo, *Vice Pres*
Dave Redden, *Vice Pres*
David Shiffman, *Admin Sec*
Jason Graves, *Software Engr*
◆ **EMP:** 191
SQ FT: 200,000
SALES (est): 73.1MM
SALES (corp-wide): 47.9B **Privately Held**
WEB: www.densocorp-na.com
SIC: 3663 3714 Cellular radio telephone; motor vehicle electrical equipment
HQ: Denso International America, Inc.
24777 Denso Dr
Southfield MI 48033
248 350-7500

(P-18086)
DIGI GROUP LLC
Also Called: Thor Fiber
2421 W 205th St Ste D204, Torrance (90501-6263)
PHONE..................................800 521-8467
Slawomir Sochur, *Principal*
EMP: 10 EST: 1997
SALES (est): 881.1K **Privately Held**
SIC: 3663 Television broadcasting & communications equipment

(P-18087)
DIGITAL PROTOTYPE SYSTEMS INC
Also Called: Dps Telecom
4955 E Yale Ave, Fresno (93727-1523)
PHONE..................................559 454-1600
Robert A Berry, *CEO*
Marshall Denhartog, *President*
Jeff Pierce, *Officer*
Ron Stover, *Vice Pres*
Samantha Johnson, *Executive Asst*
EMP: 46
SQ FT: 50,000
SALES (est): 11.2MM **Privately Held**
WEB: www.dpstele.com
SIC: 3663 Telemetering equipment, electronic

(P-18088)
DJH ENTERPRISES
Also Called: Channel Vision Technology
234 Fischer Ave, Costa Mesa (92626-4515)
PHONE..................................714 424-6500
Darrel Eugene Hauk, *President*
▲ **EMP:** 35
SALES (est): 5.7MM **Privately Held**
WEB: www.channelvision.com
SIC: 3663 Radio & TV communications equipment

(P-18089)
DOLBY LABORATORIES INC
432 Lakeside Dr, Sunnyvale (94085-4703)
PHONE..................................408 730-5543
Carlo Basile, *President*
EMP: 14
SALES (corp-wide): 1.1B **Publicly Held**
SIC: 3663 Radio & TV communications equipment
PA: Dolby Laboratories, Inc.
1275 Market St
San Francisco CA 94103
415 558-0200

(P-18090)
DOLBY LABORATORIES INC
Also Called: Dolby Labs
175 S Hill Dr, Brisbane (94005-1203)
PHONE..............................415 715-2500
Jeff Griffith, *Vice Pres*
Cory Iwatsu, *Manager*
EMP: 76
SALES (corp-wide): 1.1B Publicly Held
WEB: www.dolby.com
SIC: 3663 3651 Radio broadcasting &
   communications equipment; household
   audio & video equipment
PA: Dolby Laboratories, Inc.
   1275 Market St
   San Francisco CA 94103
   415 558-0200

(P-18091)
DSS-CCTV INC
1280 Activity Dr Ste A, Vista (92081-8508)
PHONE...................................609 850-9498
Jiang Cheng, *President*
▲ EMP: 10
SALES: 6MM Privately Held
SIC: 3663 5065 Television closed circuit
   equipment; closed circuit television

(P-18092)
DYNAMIC SCIENCES INTL INC
9400 Lurline Ave Unit B, Chatsworth
(91311-6022)
PHONE..............................818 226-6262
Eli Shiri, *President*
Robert Cook, *Vice Pres*
Oren Shiri, *VP Sales*
Sylvia Shuter, *Director*
EMP: 35
SQ FT: 20,000
SALES (est): 5.7MM Privately Held
WEB: www.dynamicsciences.com
SIC: 3663 Radio receiver networks

(P-18093)
**E-BAND COMMUNICATIONS
LLC**
17034 Camino San Bernardo, San Diego
(92127-5708)
PHONE..............................858 408-0660
Sam Smookler, *CEO*
Russ Kinsch, *CFO*
Saul Umbrasas, *Senior VP*
Susan Fanno, *Office Mgr*
Andrew Pavelchek, *VP Engrg*
EMP: 30
SALES (est): 6.1MM
SALES (corp-wide): 32.2MM Privately
Held
WEB: www.ebandcom.com
SIC: 3663 Carrier equipment, radio com-
   munications; microwave communication
   equipment
PA: Axxcss Wireless Solutions Inc
   82 Coromar Dr
   Goleta CA 93117
   805 968-9621

(P-18094)
ECTRON CORPORATION
8159 Engineer Rd, San Diego
(92111-1980)
PHONE..............................858 278-0600
E Earl Cunningham, *President*
Karl E Cunningham, *CEO*
Carol C Cunningham, *Admin Sec*
EMP: 35
SQ FT: 9,500
SALES (est): 6.3MM Privately Held
WEB: www.ectron.com
SIC: 3663 3829 3577 3823 Amplifiers,
   RF power & IF; measuring & controlling
   devices; data conversion equipment,
   media-to-media: computer; industrial in-
   strmnts msrmnt display/control process
   variable

(P-18095)
EIGER VISION CORPORATION
7714a Lankershim Blvd, North Hollywood
(91605-2815)
PHONE..............................818 201-0471
Arnold John Kim, *CEO*
▲ EMP: 11
SQ FT: 5,000

SALES (est): 1.5MM Privately Held
WEB: www.eigervision.net
SIC: 3663 Radio broadcasting & communi-
   cations equipment

(P-18096)
EKA TECHNOLOGIES INC
Also Called: EKA Designs
2985 E Hillcrest Dr # 203, Westlake Village
(91362-3192)
PHONE..............................805 379-8668
Arun Madhav, *President*
▲ EMP: 20
SQ FT: 800
SALES: 268K Privately Held
SIC: 3663 7336 Cameras, television; art
   design services

(P-18097)
EMCORE CORPORATION
Emcore-Ortel Division
2015 Chestnut St, Alhambra (91803-1542)
PHONE..............................626 293-3400
Hone Hu, *Vice Pres*
EMP: 175
SALES (corp-wide): 122.9MM Publicly
Held
WEB: www.emcore.com
SIC: 3663 Television broadcasting & com-
   munications equipment
PA: Emcore Corporation
   2015 Chestnut St
   Alhambra CA 91803
   626 293-3400

(P-18098)
**EMPOWER RF SYSTEMS INC
(PA)**
316 W Florence Ave, Inglewood
(90301-1104)
PHONE..............................310 412-8100
Barry Phelps, *Ch of Bd*
Jon Jacocks, *President*
Larisa Spanisic, *CFO*
Efraim Bainvoll, *Founder*
EMP: 90
SQ FT: 30,000
SALES: 20MM Privately Held
WEB: www.empowerrf.com
SIC: 3663 Amplifiers, RF power & IF

(P-18099)
ENERGOUS CORPORATION
3590 N 1st St Ste 210, San Jose
(95134-1812)
PHONE..............................408 963-0200
Stephen R Rizzone, *President*
Robert J Griffin, *Ch of Bd*
Brian Sereda, *CFO*
Cesar Johnston, *Senior VP*
Neeraj Sahejpal, *Senior VP*
EMP: 68
SALES: 1.1MM Privately Held
SIC: 3663 3674 Radio broadcasting &
   communications equipment; antennas,
   transmitting & communications; semicon-
   ductors & related devices

(P-18100)
ERICSSON INC
426 Appleton Rd, Simi Valley (93065-6005)
PHONE..............................805 584-6890
Patrick Ferrari, *Manager*
EMP: 15
SALES (corp-wide): 23.8B Privately Held
SIC: 3663 Radio & TV communications
   equipment
HQ: Ericsson Inc.
   6300 Legacy Dr
   Plano TX 75024
   972 583-0000

(P-18101)
ERICSSON INC
1055 La Avenida St, Mountain View
(94043-1421)
PHONE..............................972 583-0000
Flicka Enloe, *Branch Mgr*
EMP: 29
SALES (corp-wide): 23.8B Privately Held
SIC: 3663 Radio & TV communications
   equipment
HQ: Ericsson Inc.
   6300 Legacy Dr
   Plano TX 75024
   972 583-0000

(P-18102)
ERICSSON INC
18275 Serene Dr, Morgan Hill
(95037-2860)
PHONE..............................408 776-0600
Henrik Hoyer, *Systems Dir*
Jeff Olson, *Engineer*
Bo Liljeberg, *Opers Staff*
Terry Simons, *Marketing Staff*
Nick Turk, *Manager*
EMP: 15
SALES (corp-wide): 23.8B Privately Held
WEB: www.ericsson.com/us-ca
SIC: 3663 Radio & TV communications
   equipment
HQ: Ericsson Inc.
   6300 Legacy Dr
   Plano TX 75024
   972 583-0000

(P-18103)
ERICSSON INC
250 Holger Way, San Jose (95134-1300)
PHONE..............................408 970-2000
EMP: 24
SALES (corp-wide): 30.8B Publicly Held
SIC: 3663
HQ: Ericsson Inc.
   6300 Legacy Dr
   Plano TX 75024
   972 583-0000

(P-18104)
**ESCAPE COMMUNICATIONS
INC**
2790 Skypark Dr Ste 203, Torrance
(90505-5345)
PHONE..............................310 997-1300
Micheal Stewart, *President*
Gregory Caso PHD, *Exec VP*
James Nadeau, *Admin Sec*
Jim Nadeau, *Engineer*
EMP: 17
SQ FT: 5,300
SALES (est): 2.1MM Privately Held
WEB: www.escapecom.com
SIC: 3663 8711 8731 Microwave commu-
   nication equipment; engineering services;
   commercial physical research

(P-18105)
ETM—ELECTROMATIC INC (PA)
35451 Dumbarton Ct, Newark
(94560-1100)
PHONE..............................510 797-1100
Thomas M Hayse, *CEO*
Ramesh Garg, *Vice Pres*
Jesse Iverson, *Vice Pres*
Kayte Mariani, *Vice Pres*
Richard Marquez, *Vice Pres*
◆ EMP: 100
SQ FT: 56,000
SALES (est): 23.44MM Privately Held
WEB: www.etm-inc.com
SIC: 3663 3825 Microwave communica-
   tion equipment; amplifiers, RF power &
   IF; test equipment for electronic & electric
   measurement

(P-18106)
EUPHONIX INC (HQ)
280 Bernardo Ave, Mountain View
(94043-5238)
PHONE..............................650 526-1600
Jeffrey A Chew, *CEO*
Paul L Hammel, *Senior VP*
▲ EMP: 95
SQ FT: 40,000
SALES: 8.4MM
SALES (corp-wide): 419MM Publicly
Held
WEB: www.euphonix.com
SIC: 3663 Studio equipment, radio & tele-
   vision broadcasting
PA: Avid Technology, Inc.
   75 Network Dr
   Burlington MA 01803
   978 640-6789

(P-18107)
EVISSAP INC
800 Charcot Ave, San Jose (95131-2211)
PHONE..............................408 432-7393
Hong Yin Wang, *Branch Mgr*
EMP: 25

SALES (corp-wide): 6.4MM Privately
Held
SIC: 3663 Radio & TV communications
   equipment
PA: Evissap Inc.
   812 Charcot Ave
   San Jose CA 95131
   408 943-8266

(P-18108)
FEI-ZYFER INC (HQ)
7321 Lincoln Way, Garden Grove
(92841-1428)
PHONE..............................714 933-4000
Steve Strang, *President*
David Williamson, *Vice Pres*
Long Pham, *Engineer*
Heinz Badura, *VP Mktg*
David Cole, *Regl Sales Mgr*
EMP: 41
SQ FT: 50,000
SALES (est): 44.6MM
SALES (corp-wide): 39.4MM Publicly
Held
WEB: www.fei-zyfer.com
SIC: 3663 Television broadcasting & com-
   munications equipment; encryption de-
   vices
PA: Frequency Electronics, Inc.
   55 Charles Lindbergh Blvd # 2
   Uniondale NY 11553
   516 794-4500

(P-18109)
**FLEET MANAGEMENT
SOLUTIONS INC**
7391 Lincoln Way, Garden Grove
(92841-1428)
PHONE..............................800 500-6009
Tony Eales, *CEO*
Sheila Henley Roth, *CFO*
EMP: 26
SALES (est): 2.5MM
SALES (corp-wide): 6.6B Publicly Held
WEB: www.fmsgps.com
SIC: 3663 4899 Radio & TV communica-
   tions equipment; satellite earth stations
HQ: Teletrac Navman (Uk) Ltd
   K1 Business Park
   Milton Keynes BUCKS MK7 6
   123 475-9000

(P-18110)
FLO TV INCORPORATED
5775 Morehouse Dr, San Diego
(92121-1714)
PHONE..............................858 651-1645
Gilbert P John, *Principal*
EMP: 15
SALES (est): 2.2MM
SALES (corp-wide): 22.2B Publicly Held
WEB: www.mediaflousa.com
SIC: 3663 Transmitting apparatus, radio or
   television
PA: Qualcomm Incorporated
   5775 Morehouse Dr
   San Diego CA 92121
   858 587-1121

(P-18111)
FM SYSTEMS INC
3877 S Main St, Santa Ana (92707-5710)
PHONE..............................714 979-0537
Donald Mc Clatchie, *CFO*
Frank Mc Clatchie, *President*
EMP: 10
SQ FT: 3,300
SALES: 300K Privately Held
WEB: www.fmsystems-inc.com
SIC: 3663 Radio broadcasting & communi-
   cations equipment

(P-18112)
**GENERAL DYNMICS STCOM
TECH INC**
3111 Fujita St, Torrance (90505-4006)
PHONE..............................310 539-6704
Sandra Seto, *Branch Mgr*
Gary Peale, *Sales Mgr*
EMP: 67
SALES (corp-wide): 30.9B Publicly Held
WEB: www.tripointglobal.com
SIC: 3663 Antennas, transmitting & com-
   munications

P
R
O
D
U
C
T
S

&

S
V
C
S

HQ: General Dynamics Satcom Technologies, Inc.
1700 Cable Dr Ne
Conover NC 28613
704 462-7330

(P-18113)
GPS LOGIC LLC
1327 Calle Avanzado, San Clemente
(92673-6351)
P.O. Box 999, San Juan Capistrano
(92693-0999)
PHONE..................................949 812-6942
Ronald Cedillos, *CEO*
Nicole Pete, *Office Mgr*
EMP: 13
SALES (est): 1.6MM **Privately Held**
SIC: 3663 Space satellite communications
equipment

(P-18114)
GRASS VALLEY INC
125 Crown Point Ct, Grass Valley
(95945-9515)
P.O. Box 599000, Nevada City (95959-
7900)
PHONE..................................530 478-3000
Marc Valentine, *President*
Donald Childers, *Engineer*
Bret Jones, *Senior Engr*
Katy Hanna, *Opers Mgr*
Kevin Basquill, *Sales Staff*
▲ **EMP:** 750
SALES (est): 128.8MM **Privately Held**
WEB: www.grassvalley.com
SIC: 3663 Radio & TV communications
equipment
PA: Grass Valley Canada
3499 Rue Douglas-B.-Floreani
Saint-Laurent QC H4S 2
514 333-1772

(P-18115)
GRASS VALLEY INC (HQ)
Also Called: Miranda
125 Crown Point Ct, Grass Valley
(95945-9515)
P.O. Box 1658, Nevada City (95959-1658)
PHONE..................................530 265-1000
Strath Goodship, *CEO*
Marco Lopez, *President*
Charles Meyer, *President*
Luc St-Georges, *COO*
Mario Settinio, *Principal*
EMP: 108
SQ FT: 42,000
SALES (est): 19.3MM **Privately Held**
WEB: www.nvision1.com
SIC: 3663 Radio & TV communications
equipment
PA: Grass Valley Canada
3499 Rue Douglas-B.-Floreani
Saint-Laurent QC H4S 2
514 333-1772

(P-18116)
GRASS VALLEY USA LLC (HQ)
125 Crown Point Ct, Grass Valley
(95945-9515)
P.O. Box 599000, Nevada City (95959-
7900)
PHONE..................................800 547-8949
Marco Lopez, *President*
Nahuel Villegas, *Vice Pres*
Kc Najarian, *Executive*
Richard Tyrrell, *General Mgr*
David Meltz, *Planning Mgr*
▲ **EMP:** 300
SALES (est): 238.8MM
SALES (corp-wide): 2.3B **Publicly Held**
SIC: 3663 3661 3651 Radio & TV com-
munications equipment; telephone sets,
all types except cellular radio; television
receiving sets
PA: Belden Inc.
1 N Brentwood Blvd Fl 15
Saint Louis MO 63105
314 854-8000

(P-18117)
**GROUND CONTROL SYSTEMS
INC**
3100 El Camino Real, Atascadero
(93422-2544)
P.O. Box 4459, San Luis Obispo (93403-
4459)
PHONE..................................805 783-4600
Jeff Staples, *CEO*
Mark Wright, *Shareholder*
Kurt Wright, *COO*
Branden Jenkins, *CFO*
Mike Hendricks, *CTO*
EMP: 17
SQ FT: 20,200
SALES (est): 4.2MM **Privately Held**
WEB: www.groundcontrol.com
SIC: 3663 Satellites, communications

(P-18118)
**GRYPHON MOBILE
ELECTRONICS LLC**
2664 Saturn St Ste B, Brea (92821-6789)
PHONE..................................626 810-7770
Nelson Yen, *CEO*
Carol Ko, *CFO*
Mark Elkins, *Mng Member*
▲ **EMP:** 15
SALES (est): 322.1K **Privately Held**
SIC: 3663 Mobile communication equip-
ment

(P-18119)
GTX CORP
117 W 9th St Ste 1214, Los Angeles
(90015-1524)
PHONE..................................213 489-3019
Patrick E Bertagna, *Ch of Bd*
Alex McKean, *CFO*
Andrew Duncan, *Treasurer*
Louis Rosenbaum, *Vice Pres*
EMP: 10
SQ FT: 1,230
SALES: 538.3K **Privately Held**
SIC: 3663 ; light communications equip-
ment

(P-18120)
HARMONIC INC
4300 N 1st St, San Jose (95134-1258)
PHONE..................................800 788-1330
Carolyn Aver, *CFO*
Krutik Patel, *Software Engr*
EMP: 19
SALES (corp-wide): 358.2MM **Publicly
Held**
SIC: 3663 Television broadcasting & com-
munications equipment
PA: Harmonic Inc.
4300 N 1st St
San Jose CA 95134
408 542-2500

(P-18121)
HARMONIC INC (PA)
4300 N 1st St, San Jose (95134-1258)
PHONE..................................408 542-2500
Patrick J Harshman, *President*
Patrick Gallagher, *Ch of Bd*
Sanjay Kalra, *CFO*
Nimrod Ben-Natan, *Senior VP*
Neven Haltmayer, *Senior VP*
EMP: 277
SQ FT: 160,000
SALES: 358.2MM **Publicly Held**
WEB: www.harmonicinc.com
SIC: 3663 3823 Television broadcasting &
communications equipment; industrial in-
strmnts msrmnt display/control process
variable

(P-18122)
HARMONIC INC
641 Baltic Way, Sunnyvale (94089-1140)
PHONE..................................408 542-2500
Anthony Ley, *President*
Ian Graham, *Vice Pres*
Sam Organ, *Vice Pres*
Baruch Levi, *Research*
Doron Cohen, *Technical Staff*
EMP: 18
SALES (corp-wide): 358.2MM **Publicly
Held**
SIC: 3663 Television broadcasting & com-
munications equipment

PA: Harmonic Inc.
4300 N 1st St
San Jose CA 95134
408 542-2500

(P-18123)
HAWAII PACIFIC TELEPORT LP
1145 Beasley Way, Sonoma (95476-7466)
PHONE..................................707 938-7057
Christopher Guthrie, *Managing Prtnr*
EMP: 10
SQ FT: 200
SALES: 1MM **Privately Held**
SIC: 3663 8999 Satellites, communica-
tion; communication services

(P-18124)
**HBC SOLUTIONS HOLDINGS
LLC**
10877 Wilshire Blvd Fl 18, Los Angeles
(90024-4373)
PHONE..................................321 727-9100
Daniel Abrams, *Mng Member*
EMP: 1002 **EST:** 2013
SALES (est): 54.9MM **Privately Held**
SIC: 3663 Radio broadcasting & communi-
cations equipment; television broadcast-
ing & communications equipment

(P-18125)
HEROTEK INC
155 Baytech Dr, San Jose (95134-2303)
PHONE..................................408 941-8399
Cheng W Lai, *President*
James Wong, *Engineer*
Michael Lau, *Purchasing*
Ted Wadholm, *Sales Mgr*
Susan Hartman, *Sales Staff*
EMP: 46
SQ FT: 9,600
SALES (est): 8.3MM **Privately Held**
WEB: www.herotek.com
SIC: 3663 3812 Microwave communica-
tion equipment; search & navigation
equipment

(P-18126)
HILLSIDE CAPITAL INC
6222 Fallbrook Ave, Woodland Hills
(91367-1601)
PHONE..................................650 367-2011
Becky Tran, *President*
EMP: 115
SALES (est): 7.5MM **Privately Held**
SIC: 3663 Radio & TV communications
equipment

(P-18127)
**HUGHES NETWORK SYSTEMS
LLC**
Also Called: H N S
9605 Scranton Rd Ste 500, San Diego
(92121-1770)
PHONE..................................858 455-9550
Douglas H Austin, *President*
Graham Avis, *Vice Pres*
Janet Williamson, *Vice Pres*
Tarun Rawat, *Admin Asst*
Jeremy McGuinn, *Administration*
EMP: 50 **Publicly Held**
WEB: www.hnseu.com
SIC: 3663 Satellites, communications
HQ: Hughes Network Systems, Llc
11717 Exploration Ln
Germantown MD 20876
301 428-5500

(P-18128)
IGO INC (PA)
6001 Oak Cyn, Irvine (92618-5200)
PHONE..................................888 205-0093
Terry R Gibson, *President*
Jack L Howard, *Ch of Bd*
Leonard J McGill, *Vice Pres*
◆ **EMP:** 10
SALES (est): 15.2MM **Privately Held**
WEB: www.mobilityelectronics.com
SIC: 3663 Mobile communication equip-
ment

(P-18129)
**IMAGINE COMMUNICATIONS
CORP**
1493 Poinsettia Ave # 143, Vista
(92081-8544)
PHONE..................................760 936-4000
Jack Williams, *Branch Mgr*
EMP: 11
SALES (corp-wide): 4.5B **Privately Held**
SIC: 3663 Radio broadcasting & communi-
cations equipment; television broadcast-
ing & communications equipment
HQ: Imagine Communications Corp.
7950 Legacy Dr 400-485
Plano TX 75024
469 803-4900

(P-18130)
IMPAC TECHNOLOGIES INC
3050 Red Hill Ave, Costa Mesa
(92626-4524)
PHONE..................................714 427-2000
Louis Parker, *President*
EMP: 89
SQ FT: 24,000
SALES (est): 8.2MM **Privately Held**
SIC: 3663 Radio & TV communications
equipment

(P-18131)
INGENU INC (PA)
10301 Meanley Dr, San Diego
(92131-3011)
PHONE..................................858 201-6000
John Horn, *CEO*
Tom Gregor, *President*
Dan Halvorson, *CFO*
Jason Wilson, *Senior VP*
Josh Builta, *Vice Pres*
EMP: 50
SALES (est): 13.9MM **Privately Held**
SIC: 3663 Radio & TV communications
equipment

(P-18132)
INTERDIGITAL INC
9276 Scranton Rd Ste 300, San Diego
(92121-7700)
PHONE..................................858 210-4800
Julie McDonough, *Branch Mgr*
EMP: 21 **Publicly Held**
SIC: 3663 Mobile communication equip-
ment
PA: Interdigital, Inc.
200 Bellevue Pkwy Ste 300
Wilmington DE 19809

(P-18133)
**INTERSTATE ELECTRONICS
CORP**
604 E Vermont Ave, Anaheim
(92805-5607)
PHONE..................................714 758-3395
Thomas Jackson, *Branch Mgr*
EMP: 50
SALES (corp-wide): 9.5B **Publicly Held**
WEB: www.iechome.com
SIC: 3663 3621 Telemetering equipment,
electronic; motors & generators
HQ: Interstate Electronics Corporation
602 E Vermont Ave
Anaheim CA 92805
714 758-0500

(P-18134)
IPITEK GROUP INC
2330 Faraday Ave, Carlsbad (92008-7243)
P.O. Box 130878 (92013-0878)
PHONE..................................760 438-8362
Michael Salour, *Ch of Bd*
EMP: 150
SALES (est): 15.5MM **Privately Held**
SIC: 3663 Television broadcasting & com-
munications equipment

(P-18135)
**J M MILLS COMMUNICATIONS
INC (HQ)**
4686 Mission Gorge Pl, San Diego
(92120-4133)
PHONE..................................613 321-2100
John Mills, *President*
Lisa Mills, *Vice Pres*
Michele Boehme, *Project Mgr*

Erin Maes, *Sales Staff*
EMP: 21
SQ FT: 9,000
SALES (est): 2.2MM
SALES (corp-wide): 6.2MM **Privately Held**
WEB: www.millscom.com
SIC: 3663 Radio & TV communications equipment
PA: Protel Communications Inc.
13851 Danielson St
Poway CA 92064
858 391-9031

(P-18136)
JAMPRO ANTENNAS INC
6340 Sky Creek Dr, Sacramento (95828-1025)
PHONE.................................916 383-1177
Alex Perchevitch, *President*
Doug McCabe, *COO*
Ken Mueller, *CFO*
Cyndi Sanderson, *Vice Pres*
◆ **EMP:** 60
SQ FT: 12,000
SALES (est): 13.8MM **Privately Held**
WEB: www.jampro.com
SIC: 3663 Antennas, transmitting & communications; television antennas (transmitting) & ground equipment

(P-18137)
JANTEQ CORP (PA)
9975 Toledo Way Ste 150, Irvine (92618-1827)
PHONE.................................949 215-2603
John A Porter, *President*
Andrew Fox, *Director*
Nigel Pedersen, *Director*
EMP: 24
SQ FT: 33,000
SALES: 29.3MM **Privately Held**
SIC: 3663 Radio & TV communications equipment

(P-18138)
JEI
3087 Alhambra Dr, Cameron Park (95682-8849)
PHONE.................................530 677-3210
Jack Mahoney, *President*
Steve Vodoklys, *CFO*
Candie White, *Marketing Staff*
Roxane Novikoff, *Asst Mgr*
▲ **EMP:** 20
SQ FT: 4,400
SALES (est): 2.9MM **Privately Held**
WEB: www.jei-inc.com
SIC: 3663 Receivers, radio communications

(P-18139)
JUST CELLULAR INC
9327 Deering Ave, Chatsworth (91311-5858)
PHONE.................................818 701-3039
James Eric Kirkland, *President*
▲ **EMP:** 35
SQ FT: 6,700
SALES (est): 7.3MM **Privately Held**
SIC: 3663 Cellular radio telephone; mobile communication equipment

(P-18140)
JW WIRELESS
846 E Valley Blvd Ste A, San Gabriel (91776-4602)
PHONE.................................626 532-2511
Leo Lee, *Owner*
Ben Her, *Partner*
EMP: 10
SALES (est): 1.3MM **Privately Held**
SIC: 3663 Cellular radio telephone

(P-18141)
K TECH TELECOMMUNICATIONS INC
28231 Avenue Crocker # 90, Santa Clarita (91355-1299)
PHONE.................................818 773-0333
Steve Kuh, *President*
EMP: 10
SALES (est): 2MM **Privately Held**
SIC: 3663 Radio & television switching equipment

(P-18142)
KATEEVA INC
7015 Gateway Blvd, Newark (94560-1011)
PHONE.................................510 953-7600
Alain Harrus, *CEO*
Conor Madigan, *President*
Eli Vronsky,
May Su, *Officer*
Tom Wu, *Exec VP*
▲ **EMP:** 300
SQ FT: 11,000
SALES (est): 17.8MM **Privately Held**
SIC: 3663 Cable television equipment

(P-18143)
KATZ MILLENNIUM SLS & MKTG INC
Also Called: Clear Channel Radio Sales
5700 Wilshire Blvd # 100, Los Angeles (90036-3659)
PHONE.................................323 966-5066
Nathan Brown, *Manager*
EMP: 100 **Publicly Held**
WEB: www.millenniumtvsales.com
SIC: 3663 Radio receiver networks
HQ: Katz Millennium Sales & Marketing Inc.
125 W 55th St Frnt 3
New York NY 10019

(P-18144)
KEOPSYS INC (HQ)
7001 Briza Loop, San Ramon (94582-5047)
P.O. Box 305, Whitehall PA (18052-0305)
PHONE.................................610 758-8428
Jean-Marc Delavaux, *Vice Pres*
Yves Deiss, *General Mgr*
Eugene Gueroguiee, *General Mgr*
EMP: 11
SALES (est): 952.4K
SALES (corp-wide): 11MM **Privately Held**
WEB: www.keopsys.com
SIC: 3663 Amplifiers, RF power & IF
PA: Keopsys
Optocom Innovation
Lannion 22300
296 050-800

(P-18145)
KIRSEN TECHNOLOGIES INC
2041 Bancroft Way Ste 201, Berkeley (94704-1443)
PHONE.................................510 540-5383
Kirill Mostov, *President*
EMP: 10
SALES (est): 1.4MM **Privately Held**
WEB: www.kirsentech.com
SIC: 3663

(P-18146)
KLEIN ELECTRONICS INC
349 N Vinewood St, Escondido (92029-1338)
PHONE.................................760 781-3220
Richard Klein, *President*
Ken Sampson, *Executive*
Betty Randolph, *Admin Asst*
Janae Marcink, *Technology*
Matthew Marjanovic, *Technology*
▲ **EMP:** 23
SQ FT: 13,700
SALES (est): 7MM **Privately Held**
WEB: www.headsetusa.com
SIC: 3663 Radio & TV communications equipment

(P-18147)
KMIC TECHNOLOGY INC
2095 Ringwood Ave Ste 10, San Jose (95131-1786)
PHONE.................................408 240-3600
David Kim, *President*
Jinho Park, *Opers Mgr*
EMP: 28
SQ FT: 15,800
SALES (est): 5.2MM **Privately Held**
SIC: 3663 Receivers, radio communications

(P-18148)
KRATOS DEF & SEC SOLUTIONS INC (PA)
10680 Treena St Ste 600, San Diego (92131-2487)
PHONE.................................858 812-7300
Eric M Demarco, *President*
William Hoglund, *Ch of Bd*
Jonah Adelman, *President*
Phillip Carrai, *President*
David Carter, *President*
EMP: 300
SALES: 751.9MM **Publicly Held**
WEB: www.kratosdefense.com/
SIC: 3663 3761 7382 8711 Microwave communication equipment; satellites, communications; guided missiles & space vehicles; security systems services; engineering services; facilities support services

(P-18149)
KWORLD (USA) COMPUTER INC
499 Nibus Ste D, Brea (92821-3211)
PHONE.................................626 581-0867
Chung-Chieh Wang, *President*
▲ **EMP:** 12
SQ FT: 4,600
SALES (est): 2.8MM
SALES (corp-wide): 10.8MM **Privately Held**
WEB: www.kworldcomputer.com
SIC: 3663 Cable television equipment
PA: Kworld Computer Co., Ltd.
6f, 113, Chien 2nd Rd.,
New Taipei City 23585
282 286-088

(P-18150)
L-3 COMMUNICATIONS CORPORATION
Telemetry & Rf Products
9020 Balboa Ave, San Diego (92123-1510)
PHONE.................................858 694-7500
Fax: 619 670-0127
EMP: 16
SALES (corp-wide): 10.4B **Publicly Held**
SIC: 3663
HQ: L-3 Communications Corporation
600 3rd Ave
New York NY 10016
212 697-1111

(P-18151)
L3 APPLIED TECHNOLOGIES INC (HQ)
Also Called: L-3 Applied Technologies, Inc.
10180 Barnes Canyon Rd, San Diego (92121-2724)
PHONE.................................858 404-7824
Michael T Strainese, *CEO*
Robert A Huffman, *President*
▼ **EMP:** 104
SALES (est): 16.6MM
SALES (corp-wide): 9.5B **Publicly Held**
SIC: 3663 3669 3769 Telemetering equipment, electronic; receiver-transmitter units (transceiver); amplifiers, RF power & IF; signaling apparatus, electric; intercommunication systems, electric; guided missile & space vehicle parts & auxiliary equipment
PA: L3 Technologies, Inc.
600 3rd Ave Fl 34
New York NY 10016
212 697-1111

(P-18152)
L3 APPLIED TECHNOLOGIES INC
10180 Barnes Canyon Rd, San Diego (92121-2724)
PHONE.................................858 404-7824
Janet Luna, *Controller*
Pat Hernandez, *Executive Asst*
EMP: 113
SALES (corp-wide): 9.5B **Publicly Held**
SIC: 3663 3669 3769 Telemetering equipment, electronic; receiver-transmitter units (transceiver); amplifiers, RF power & IF; signaling apparatus, electric; intercommunication systems, electric; guided missile & space vehicle parts & auxiliary equipment

HQ: L3 Applied Technologies, Inc.
10180 Barnes Canyon Rd
San Diego CA 92121
858 404-7824

(P-18153)
L3 TECHNOLOGIES INC
Also Called: L-3 Telemetry & Rf Products
9020 Balboa Ave, San Diego (92123-1510)
PHONE.................................858 279-0411
Burt Smith, *Branch Mgr*
Edward Christensen, *Vice Pres*
Bill Saputo, *Information Mgr*
Gary Frost, *Engineer*
John Tomasso, *Engineer*
EMP: 358
SALES (corp-wide): 9.5B **Publicly Held**
SIC: 3663 3669 3812 3679 Telemetering equipment, electronic; receiver-transmitter units (transceiver); amplifiers, RF power & IF; signaling apparatus, electric; intercommunication systems, electric; search & navigation equipment; aircraft control systems, electronic; microwave components; guided missile & space vehicle parts & auxiliary equipment
PA: L3 Technologies, Inc.
600 3rd Ave Fl 34
New York NY 10016
212 697-1111

(P-18154)
L3 TECHNOLOGIES INC
Electron Devices
3100 Lomita Blvd, Torrance (90505-5104)
PHONE.................................650 591-8411
James D Benham, *President*
Ewa Kantorczyk, *Engineer*
Conrad Marotta, *Engineer*
Mike Martin, *Engineer*
John Marzillo, *Engineer*
EMP: 398
SALES (corp-wide): 9.5B **Publicly Held**
SIC: 3663 Telemetering equipment, electronic
PA: L3 Technologies, Inc.
600 3rd Ave Fl 34
New York NY 10016
212 697-1111

(P-18155)
L3 TECHNOLOGIES INC
602 E Vermont Ave, Anaheim (92805-5607)
PHONE.................................714 758-4222
Robert Vanwechel, *Branch Mgr*
Aaron Castillo, *Software Engr*
Jesse Lopez, *Software Engr*
Tracy Quevedo, *HR Admin*
Curt Hiu, *Senior Mgr*
EMP: 220
SALES (corp-wide): 9.5B **Publicly Held**
SIC: 3663 Telemetering equipment, electronic
PA: L3 Technologies, Inc.
600 3rd Ave Fl 34
New York NY 10016
212 697-1111

(P-18156)
L3 TECHNOLOGIES INC
Narda Microwave West
107 Woodmere Rd, Folsom (95630-4706)
PHONE.................................916 351-4556
Michael Claggett, *Division Pres*
EMP: 165
SALES (corp-wide): 9.5B **Publicly Held**
SIC: 3663 Telemetering equipment, electronic
PA: L3 Technologies, Inc.
600 3rd Ave Fl 34
New York NY 10016
212 697-1111

(P-18157)
L3 TECHNOLOGIES INC
L3 Rccs
10180 Barnes Canyon Rd, San Diego (92121-2724)
PHONE.................................858 552-9716
Jonathan Roy, *CFO*
David Duggan, *CEO*
EMP: 100
SALES (corp-wide): 9.5B **Publicly Held**
SIC: 3663 Telemetering equipment, electronic

PA: L3 Technologies, Inc.
600 3rd Ave Fl 34
New York NY 10016
212 697-1111

(P-18158)
L3 TECHNOLOGIES INC
Datron Advanced Tech Div
200 W Los Angeles Ave, Simi Valley
(93065-1650)
PHONE..................................805 584-1717
John Digioia, *Branch Mgr*
Stephen Clift, *Engineer*
Lindsey Calderon, *Purchasing*
EMP: 100
SALES (corp-wide): 9.5B Publicly Held
SIC: 3663 Satellites, communications
PA: L3 Technologies, Inc.
600 3rd Ave Fl 34
New York NY 10016
212 697-1111

(P-18159)
L3 TECHNOLOGIES INC
Also Called: Communction Systms-Wst/Lnk-abit
9890 Towne Centre Dr # 100, San Diego
(92121-1983)
PHONE..................................858 552-9500
Andrew Ivers, *Branch Mgr*
Ralph Williams, *President*
EMP: 325
SALES (corp-wide): 9.5B Publicly Held
SIC: 3663 Space satellite communications
equipment
PA: L3 Technologies, Inc.
600 3rd Ave Fl 34
New York NY 10016
212 697-1111

(P-18160)
L3 TECHNOLOGIES INC
Also Called: Randtron Antenna Systems
130 Constitution Dr, Menlo Park
(94025-1141)
PHONE..................................650 326-9500
Robert Friedman, *Branch Mgr*
Kevin McCullough, *President*
David Butler, *Vice Pres*
Elpidio Baltazar, *Engineer*
Mike De Mello, *Manager*
EMP: 160
SALES (corp-wide): 9.5B Publicly Held
SIC: 3663 Telemetering equipment, electronic; antennas, transmitting & communications
PA: L3 Technologies, Inc.
600 3rd Ave Fl 34
New York NY 10016
212 697-1111

(P-18161)
L3 TECHNOLOGIES INC
15825 Roxford St, Sylmar (91342-3537)
PHONE..................................818 367-0111
EMP: 208
SALES (corp-wide): 9.5B Publicly Held
SIC: 3663 Radio & TV communications
equipment
PA: L3 Technologies, Inc.
600 3rd Ave Fl 34
New York NY 10016
212 697-1111

(P-18162)
L3 TECHNOLOGIES INC
Also Called: L-3 Communication
2700 Merced St, San Leandro
(94577-5602)
PHONE..................................858 499-0284
Jim Clemmons, *Branch Mgr*
EMP: 208
SALES (corp-wide): 9.5B Publicly Held
SIC: 3663 Telemetering equipment, electronic; receiver-transmitter units (transceiver); amplifiers, RF power & IF
PA: L3 Technologies, Inc.
600 3rd Ave Fl 34
New York NY 10016
212 697-1111

(P-18163)
LEGEND SILICON CORP
22 Stirling Way, Hayward (94542-7945)
PHONE..................................408 735-9888
Zhengyu Zhang, *President*

Hong Dong, *Vice Chairman*
Lin Yang, *Chairman*
Derek Huo, *Technology*
EMP: 50
SQ FT: 8,000
SALES (est): 5.8MM Privately Held
WEB: www.legendsilicon.com
SIC: 3663 8733 Antennas, transmitting &
communications; research institute

(P-18164)
LENNTEK CORPORATION
Also Called: Sonix
1610 Lockness Pl, Torrance (90501-5119)
PHONE..................................310 534-2738
Danny Tsai, *Principal*
Mallory Molinski, *Pub Rel Mgr*
Steven Reymond, *Sales Staff*
▲ EMP: 50
SQ FT: 15,000
SALES: 20MM Privately Held
SIC: 3663 Mobile communication equipment

(P-18165)
LGC WIRELESS INC
541 E Trimble Rd, San Jose (95131-1224)
PHONE..................................408 952-2400
Ian Sugarbroad, *President*
John Niedermaier, *CFO*
Michael Frausing, *Senior VP*
Dermot Conlon, *Vice Pres*
▲ EMP: 227
SQ FT: 30,000
SALES (est): 21.7MM Publicly Held
WEB: www.lgcwireless.com
SIC: 3663 Carrier equipment, radio communications
HQ: Commscope Connectivity Solutions Llc
1100 Commscope Pl Se
Hickory NC 28602
828 324-2200

(P-18166)
LINKUS CORP
13251 Whitchurch Ln, Chico (95973-9071)
PHONE..................................530 342-0738
Kevin Thomas, *Manager*
EMP: 19
SALES (corp-wide): 10.9MM Privately Held
SIC: 3663 Satellites, communications
PA: Linkus Corp.
5595 W San Madele Ave
Fresno CA 93722
559 256-6636

(P-18167)
LOCKHEED MARTIN CORPORATION
3130 Zanker Rd, San Jose (95134-1965)
P.O. Box 3504, Sunnyvale (94088-3504)
PHONE..................................408 473-3000
Magda Clyne, *Manager*
Steve Billmire, *Software Engr*
Sandra Frazier, *Design Engr*
Jeffry Hartman, *Design Engr*
Carlos Bettencourt, *Engineer*
EMP: 1665 Publicly Held
WEB: www.lockheedmartin.com
SIC: 3663 7373 8711 Satellites, communications; computer integrated systems design; engineering services
PA: Lockheed Martin Corporation
6801 Rockledge Dr
Bethesda MD 20817

(P-18168)
LOCKHEED MARTIN CORPORATION
Bldg 8310, Lompoc (93437)
PHONE..................................805 606-4860
John Goodwin, *Administration*
EMP: 300 Publicly Held
WEB: www.lockheedmartin.com
SIC: 3663 3761 Satellites, communications; space vehicles, complete; guided missiles, complete; ballistic missiles, complete; guided missiles & space vehicles, research & development
PA: Lockheed Martin Corporation
6801 Rockledge Dr
Bethesda MD 20817

(P-18169)
LOMA SCIENTIFIC INTERNATIONAL
3115 Kashiwa St, Torrance (90505-4010)
PHONE..................................310 539-8655
J Patrick Loughboro, *President*
Jeff Loughboro, *Vice Pres*
EMP: 20
SQ FT: 16,000
SALES (est): 3.1MM Privately Held
WEB: www.lomasci.com
SIC: 3663 Transmitting apparatus, radio or
television

(P-18170)
LORIMAR GROUP INC
Also Called: Lorimar Communications
1488 Pioneer Way Ste 14, El Cajon
(92020-1633)
PHONE..................................619 954-9300
George M Johnson, *CEO*
Sue Cole, *CFO*
Mike Johnson, *CFO*
Jordan Skip, *Manager*
EMP: 13
SQ FT: 2,400
SALES (est): 2.6MM Privately Held
SIC: 3663 7622 Radio & TV communications equipment; radio repair & installation

(P-18171)
LPN WIRELESS INC
4170 Redwood Hwy, San Rafael
(94903-2618)
PHONE..................................707 781-9210
Jerry Hinshaw, *President*
EMP: 12
SQ FT: 2,500
SALES (est): 1.1MM Privately Held
SIC: 3663

(P-18172)
M G WATANABE INC
Also Called: West Coast Microwave
17031 Roseton Ave, Artesia (90701-2642)
PHONE..................................562 402-8989
Mike Watanabe, *President*
Angeline Joseph, *QC Mgr*
EMP: 13
SQ FT: 1,500
SALES (est): 1.8MM Privately Held
SIC: 3663 Microwave communication
equipment

(P-18173)
MACOM TECHNOLOGY SOLUTIONS INC
Also Called: Commercial Electronics Pho
4000 Macarthur Blvd # 101, Newport Beach
(92660-2546)
PHONE..................................310 320-6160
Gary Lopes, *Principal*
Scott Murphy, *Opers Staff*
EMP: 16 Publicly Held
WEB: www.macom.com
SIC: 3663 2752 3674 Radio & TV communications equipment; catalogs, lithographed; semiconductors & related devices
HQ: Macom Technology Solutions Inc.
100 Chelmsford St
Lowell MA 01851

(P-18174)
MAINLINE EQUIPMENT INC
20917 Higgins Ct, Torrance (90501-1723)
PHONE..................................800 444-2288
Mark E Lipp, *President*
EMP: 52
SQ FT: 36,000
SALES (est): 8.7MM Privately Held
SIC: 3663 7629 Radio & TV communications equipment; electrical equipment repair services

(P-18175)
MATCHLESS LLC
8423 Wilshire Blvd, Beverly Hills
(90211-3202)
PHONE..................................310 473-5100
Geoff Emery, *Manager*
EMP: 23
SALES (est): 2MM Privately Held
SIC: 3663 Amplifiers, RF power & IF

(P-18176)
MCV TECHNOLOGIES INC
Also Called: McV Microwave
6349 Nancy Ridge Dr, San Diego
(92121-6203)
PHONE..................................858 450-0468
Edward Liang, *President*
Marian Liang, *President*
▲ EMP: 15
SQ FT: 5,000
SALES: 3MM Privately Held
WEB: www.mcvtech.com
SIC: 3663 3679 3629 Microwave communication equipment; microwave components; power conversion units, a.c. to d.c.: static-electric

(P-18177)
MDA CMMUNICATIONS HOLDINGS LLC
3825 Fabian Way, Palo Alto (94303-4604)
PHONE..................................650 852-4000
Anil Wirasekara,
William McCombe,
EMP: 2800 EST: 2015
SALES (est): 144.8MM Privately Held
SIC: 3663 Satellites, communications

(P-18178)
MERCURY NETWORKS LLC
1800 Wyatt Dr Ste 2, Santa Clara
(95054-1527)
PHONE..................................408 859-1345
Matt Cox, *Principal*
▲ EMP: 16 EST: 2014
SQ FT: 3,000
SALES: 1.4MM Privately Held
SIC: 3663 Light communications equipment

(P-18179)
METRIC SYSTEMS CORPORATION
3055 Enterprise Ct, Vista (92081-8347)
PHONE..................................760 560-0348
William M Brown, *President*
Lori Daub, *General Mgr*
John Clark, *Software Engr*
EMP: 10
SQ FT: 5,500
SALES (est): 1.7MM Privately Held
WEB: www.metricsystems.com
SIC: 3663 Mobile communication equipment

(P-18180)
MICRO-MODE PRODUCTS INC
1870 John Towers Ave, El Cajon
(92020-1193)
PHONE..................................619 449-3844
Vincent De Marco, *President*
Dick Robinson, *President*
Michael Cuban, *CEO*
Ruby Marco, *Treasurer*
Emily Clagett, *Department Mgr*
EMP: 110 EST: 1971
SALES (est): 24.3MM Privately Held
WEB: www.micromode.com
SIC: 3663 3678 7389 Microwave communication equipment; electronic connectors;

(P-18181)
MICROTEK ELECTRONICS INC
25691 Atlantic Ocean Dr, Lake Forest
(92630-8842)
PHONE..................................949 297-4930
Michael Henkoski, *Chairman*
Steve Kurtz, *Vice Pres*
EMP: 16
SQ FT: 4,994
SALES (est): 1.5MM Privately Held
WEB: www.microtekelectronics.com
SIC: 3663 8748 8731 Microwave communication equipment; communications consulting; electronic research

(P-18182)
MICROVOICE CORPORATION
Also Called: Microvoice Systems
345 Willis Ave, Camarillo (93010-8558)
PHONE..................................805 389-2922
Larry Tomon, *President*
Vic Weiers, *Controller*
EMP: 50

▲ = Import ▼=Export
◆ =Import/Export

SQ FT: 10,000
SALES (est): 4.1MM **Privately Held**
WEB: www.microvoice.com
SIC: 3663

(P-18183)
MICROWAVE DYNAMICS
16541 Scientific, Irvine (92618-4356)
PHONE............................949 679-7788
Shoja Peter Adel, *CEO*
Brian Adel, *Admin Sec*
EMP: 18
SQ FT: 10,000
SALES (est): 3.8MM **Privately Held**
WEB: www.microwave-dynamics.com
SIC: 3663 5065 Microwave communication equipment; electronic parts & equipment

(P-18184)
MIRAPOINT SOFTWARE, INC.
1600 Seaport Blvd Ste 400, Redwood City (94063-5564)
PHONE............................650 286-7200
EMP: 96
SQ FT: 30,000
SALES (est): 11.6MM **Privately Held**
WEB: www.mirapoint.com
SIC: 3663 Radio & TV communications equipment

(P-18185)
MISSION MICROWAVE TECH LLC
9924 Norwalk Blvd, Santa Fe Springs (90670-3322)
PHONE............................951 893-4925
Francis Auricchio, *President*
Michael Delisio, *CTO*
EMP: 23 EST: 2014
SALES: 210K **Privately Held**
SIC: 3663 Satellites, communications

(P-18186)
MOBILE TONE INC
5430 Westhaven St, Los Angeles (90016-3314)
PHONE............................323 939-6928
Michael Towner, *President*
EMP: 12
SALES (est): 1.1MM **Privately Held**
SIC: 3663 Mobile communication equipment

(P-18187)
MODULAR COMMUNICATIONS SYSTEMS
Also Called: Moducom
373 N Western Ave Ste 15, Los Angeles (90004-2616)
PHONE............................818 764-1333
Robert A Moesch, *President*
Bernard Brandt, *Vice Pres*
Peter Hong, *Vice Pres*
Steve Simpkins, *Managing Dir*
Linda Hong, *Executive Asst*
EMP: 21
SQ FT: 10,000
SALES (est): 4MM **Privately Held**
WEB: www.moducom.com
SIC: 3663 Radio & TV communications equipment

(P-18188)
MOPHIE INC (HQ)
15101 Red Hill Ave, Tustin (92780-6503)
PHONE............................888 866-7443
Daniel Huang, *CEO*
▲ EMP: 28
SALES (est): 21.8MM **Publicly Held**
SIC: 3663 Mobile communication equipment

(P-18189)
MOSELEY ASSOCIATES INC (HQ)
82 Coromar Dr, Goleta (93117-3024)
PHONE............................805 968-9621
Jamal N Hamdani, *President*
Bruce Tarr, *CFO*
Raffi Kaprelian, *Engineer*
▲ EMP: 115
SQ FT: 56,000

SALES (est): 65.2MM
SALES (corp-wide): 32.2MM **Privately Held**
WEB: www.moseleysb.com
SIC: 3663 Radio & TV communications equipment
PA: Axxcss Wireless Solutions Inc
    82 Coromar Dr
    Goleta CA 93117
    805 968-9621

(P-18190)
MOTOROLA MOBILITY LLC
1633 Bayshore Hwy, Burlingame (94010-1544)
PHONE............................206 383-7785
David Zhao, *Branch Mgr*
EMP: 58
SALES (corp-wide): 43B **Privately Held**
SIC: 3663 Radio & TV communications equipment
HQ: Motorola Mobility Llc
    222 Merchandise Mart Plz # 1800
    Chicago IL 60654
    -

(P-18191)
MOTOROLA MOBILITY LLC
809 Eleventh Ave Bldg 4, Sunnyvale (94089-4731)
PHONE............................847 576-5000
EMP: 58
SALES (corp-wide): 43B **Privately Held**
WEB: www.motorola.com
SIC: 3663 Radio & TV communications equipment
HQ: Motorola Mobility Llc
    222 Merchandise Mart Plz # 1800
    Chicago IL 60654
    -

(P-18192)
MOTOROLA SOLUTIONS INC
1101 Marina Village Pkwy # 200, Alameda (94501-6472)
PHONE............................510 217-7400
EMP: 142
SALES (corp-wide): 6.3B **Publicly Held**
SIC: 3663 5046 3674 3571
PA: Motorola Solutions, Inc.
    500 W Monroe St Ste 4400
    Chicago IL 60661
    847 576-5000

(P-18193)
MOTOROLA SOLUTIONS INC
725 S Figueroa St # 1855, Los Angeles (90017-5458)
PHONE............................213 362-6706
Jim Hardimon, *General Mgr*
EMP: 40
SALES (corp-wide): 6.3B **Publicly Held**
SIC: 3663 Transmitter-receivers, radio
PA: Motorola Solutions, Inc.
    500 W Monroe St Ste 4400
    Chicago IL 60661
    847 576-5000

(P-18194)
MOTOROLA SOLUTIONS INC
6101 W Century Blvd, Los Angeles (90045-5310)
PHONE............................954 723-4730
EMP: 142
SALES (corp-wide): 5.7B **Publicly Held**
SIC: 3663
PA: Motorola Solutions, Inc.
    1303 E Algonquin Rd
    Schaumburg IL 60661
    847 576-5000

(P-18195)
MTI LABORATORY INC
Also Called: Mtil
201 Continental Blvd # 300, El Segundo (90245-4500)
PHONE............................310 955-3700
Ger Ling, *President*
Nolan Clark, *Engineer*
▼ EMP: 61

SALES (est): 11.3MM
SALES (corp-wide): 250.8MM **Privately Held**
SIC: 3663 Microwave communication equipment; mobile communication equipment; radio broadcasting & communications equipment
PA: Microelectronics Technology, Inc.
    1, Innovation 2nd Rd., Science-Based Industrial Park,
    Hsinchu City 30076
    357 733-35

(P-18196)
NAVCOM TECHNOLOGY INC (HQ)
20780 Madrona Ave, Torrance (90503-3777)
PHONE............................310 381-2000
Tony Thelen, *CEO*
Craig Fawcept, *President*
Michael Linzy, *COO*
Alisobhani Jalal, *Principal*
Paul Galyean, *Director*
EMP: 49
SQ FT: 55,000
SALES (est): 9.6MM
SALES (corp-wide): 29.7B **Publicly Held**
WEB: www.navcomtech.com
SIC: 3663 8748 Satellites, communications; communications consulting
PA: Deere & Company
    1 John Deere Pl
    Moline IL 61265
    309 765-8000

(P-18197)
NERDIST CHANNEL LLC
Also Called: Nerdist Industries
2525 N Naomi St, Burbank (91504-3236)
PHONE............................818 333-2705
Peter Levin,
EMP: 30
SALES (est): 2.9MM **Privately Held**
SIC: 3663 Digital encoders

(P-18198)
NEVION USA INC
400 W Ventura Blvd # 155, Camarillo (93010-9137)
PHONE............................805 247-8575
Geir Bryn-Jensen, *CEO*
Eugene Keane, *President*
Petter Kvaal Djupvik, *COO*
Nils Fredriksen, *CFO*
Hans Hasselbach, *Officer*
EMP: 61
SQ FT: 12,000
SALES (est): 11.9MM
SALES (corp-wide): 45.1MM **Privately Held**
WEB: www.nevion.com
SIC: 3663 3669 3661 Radio & TV communications equipment; emergency alarms; telephones & telephone apparatus
HQ: Network Electronics Holdings, Inc.
    1600 Emerson Ave
    Oxnard CA 93033
    -

(P-18199)
NEXTEC MICROWAVE & RF INC
3010 Scott Blvd, Santa Clara (95054-3323)
PHONE............................408 727-1189
Dongwook Lee, *President*
EMP: 10
SALES (est): 2.2MM **Privately Held**
WEB: www.nextec-rf.com
SIC: 3663 Radio & TV communications equipment

(P-18200)
NEXTIVITY INC (PA)
16550 W Bernardo Dr # 550, San Diego (92127-1889)
PHONE............................858 485-9442
Werner Sievers, *CEO*
Tom Cooper, *President*
Thomas Cooper, *Vice Pres*
George Lamb, *Vice Pres*
Carol Lee, *Vice Pres*
▲ EMP: 69
SALES (est): 13.9MM **Privately Held**
SIC: 3663 Airborne radio communications equipment

(P-18201)
NORDEN MILLIMETER INC
5441 Merchant Cir Ste C, Placerville (95667-8643)
PHONE............................530 642-9123
JC Rosenberg, *Chairman*
Duncan Smith, *President*
Kary Robertson, *Treasurer*
John Rosenberg, *Info Tech Mgr*
Ross Ecker, *Senior Engr*
EMP: 22
SQ FT: 10,000
SALES (est): 4.4MM **Privately Held**
WEB: www.nordengroup.com
SIC: 3663 Amplifiers, RF power & IF

(P-18202)
NORTHROP GRUMMAN SYSTEMS CORP
Aerospace Systems
1 Space Park Blvd, Redondo Beach (90278-1071)
PHONE............................310 812-5149
Ronald Tom, *Branch Mgr*
Dennis Long, *Info Tech Dir*
Scott Ninegar, *Info Tech Dir*
Steve Schwarzbek, *Info Tech Mgr*
Steven Cohn, *Prgrmr*
EMP: 101 **Publicly Held**
WEB: www.trw.com
SIC: 3663 3674 3679 3761 Airborne radio communications equipment; satellites, communications; semiconductors & related devices; antennas, satellite; household use; guided missiles & space vehicles; guided missile & space vehicle propulsion unit parts; navigational systems & instruments
HQ: Northrop Grumman Systems Corporation
    2980 Fairview Park Dr
    Falls Church VA 22042
    703 280-2900

(P-18203)
NVIDIA US INVESTMENT COMPANY
2701 San Tomas Expy, Santa Clara (95050-2519)
PHONE............................408 615-2500
Jen-Hsun Huang, *President*
EMP: 850 EST: 2000
SALES (est): 44.8MM **Publicly Held**
WEB: www.nvidia.com
SIC: 3663 Radio & TV communications equipment
PA: Nvidia Corporation
    2788 San Tomas Expy
    Santa Clara CA 95051
    -

(P-18204)
OLSON TECHNOLOGY INC
24926 State Highway 108, MI Wuk Village (95346-9714)
PHONE............................209 586-1022
Thomas A Olson, *CEO*
Janice Sue Olson, *Vice Pres*
EMP: 30
SQ FT: 2,600
SALES (est): 4.9MM **Privately Held**
WEB: www.olson-technology.com
SIC: 3663 Cable television equipment

(P-18205)
OMNEON INC (HQ)
4300 N 1st St, San Jose (95134-1258)
PHONE............................408 585-5000
Suresh Vasudevan, *President*
Darwin Kuan, *President*
Laura Perrone, *CFO*
Ron Howe, *Senior VP*
Denis R Maynard, *Senior VP*
▲ EMP: 117
SQ FT: 68,000
SALES (est): 9.8MM
SALES (corp-wide): 358.2MM **Publicly Held**
SIC: 3663 7375 Television broadcasting & communications equipment; information retrieval services
PA: Harmonic Inc.
    4300 N 1st St
    San Jose CA 95134
    408 542-2500

(P-18206)
OPHIR RF INC
5300 Beethoven St Fl 3, Los Angeles
(90066-7068)
PHONE.................................310 306-5556
Ilan Israely, *President*
Albert Barrios, *Vice Pres*
Mary Ellen Smith, *Materials Mgr*
EMP: 42
SQ FT: 11,800
SALES: 6.9MM **Privately Held**
WEB: www.ophirrf.com
SIC: 3663 Amplifiers, RF power & IF

(P-18207)
OPTIM MICROWAVE INC
4020 Adolfo Rd, Camarillo (93012-6793)
PHONE.................................805 482-7093
Jack Peterson, *President*
Cynthia Espino, *Shareholder*
John Mahon, *Vice Pres*
William Faust, *Admin Sec*
Tom Bohner, *Prdtn Mgr*
EMP: 23
SQ FT: 15,000
SALES (est): 3.7MM **Privately Held**
WEB: www.optim-microwave.com
SIC: 3663 Antennas, transmitting & com-
munications

(P-18208)
OPTODYNE INCORPORATION
1180 W Mahalo Pl, Rancho Dominguez
(90220-5443)
PHONE.................................310 635-7481
Charles Wang, *CEO*
Lily Wang, *Corp Secy*
Wang Lichen, *Vice Pres*
Lichen Wang, *Vice Pres*
▲ **EMP:** 25
SQ FT: 7,500
SALES (est): 4.9MM **Privately Held**
WEB: www.optodyne.com
SIC: 3663 3829 3827 Light communica-
tions equipment; measuring & controlling
devices; optical instruments & lenses

(P-18209)
OVATION R&G LLC (PA)
2850 Ocean Park Blvd # 225, Santa Monica
(90405-2955)
PHONE.................................310 430-7575
Charles D D Segars,
Ken Solomon, *Ch of Bd*
Phil Gilligan, *CFO*
Liz Janneman, *Exec VP*
Brad Samuels, *Exec VP*
EMP: 42
SALES (est): 12.1MM **Privately Held**
SIC: 3663 Satellites, communications; tele-
vision broadcasting & communications
equipment

(P-18210)
**P C I MANUFACTURING
DIVISION**
Also Called: Pagecorp Industries
2103 N Ross St, Santa Ana (92706-2507)
PHONE.................................714 543-3496
Sue Edwards, *President*
Jamie Edwards, *Admin Sec*
▲ **EMP:** 10
SQ FT: 3,500
SALES: 1.2MM **Privately Held**
WEB: www.pagecorp.com
SIC: 3663 3823 5065 Pagers (one-way);
programmers, process type; paging & sig-
naling equipment

(P-18211)
P H MACHINING INC
1099 N 5th St, San Jose (95112-4414)
PHONE.................................408 980-9895
EMP: 11
SQ FT: 4,000
SALES (est): 3.4MM **Privately Held**
WEB: www.euro-inter-pharma.com
SIC: 3663

(P-18212)
PACE AMERICAS INC
887 N Douglas St 200, El Segundo
(90245-2801)
PHONE.................................310 606-8300
Bill Ryan, *Vice Pres*
▲ **EMP:** 27 **EST:** 2007

SALES (est): 2MM **Privately Held**
SIC: 3663 Cable television equipment

(P-18213)
PACIFIC WAVE SYSTEMS INC
7151 Patterson Dr, Garden Grove
(92841-1415)
PHONE.................................714 893-0152
Carl Esposito, *CEO*
John J Tus, *CFO*
Victor Jay Miller, *Admin Sec*
Robert B Topolski, *Director*
EMP: 68
SALES (est): 11.5MM **Privately Held**
WEB: www.pacificwavesystems.com
SIC: 3663 Satellites, communications

(P-18214)
PACIFITEK SYSTEMS INC
344 Coogan Way, El Cajon (92020-1902)
PHONE.................................619 401-1968
Sam Eulmi, *President*
EMP: 10
SQ FT: 3,300
SALES (est): 1.1MM **Privately Held**
SIC: 3663

(P-18215)
PALM INC (DH)
950 W Maude Ave, Sunnyvale
(94085-2801)
PHONE.................................408 617-7000
Jonathan J Rubinstein, *President*
Alex Stroessner, *COO*
Lidia Gorzelany, *Vice Pres*
Lovina Kodwaney, *Vice Pres*
Ray Thietten, *Vice Pres*
▲ **EMP:** 400
SQ FT: 347,144
SALES (est): 183.3MM
SALES (corp-wide): 16.8B **Privately Held**
WEB: www.palm.com
SIC: 3663 Mobile communication equip-
ment
HQ: Tcl Communications Technology Co.,
Ltd.
No.15, Suite B, Tcl Mansion, High-
Tech South No.1 Road, Nanshan
Shenzhen 51805
755 333-1300

(P-18216)
PEARPOINT INC
39740 Garand Ln Ste B, Palm Desert
(92211-7176)
PHONE.................................760 343-7350
Paul Tistai, *CEO*
Vince Monteleone, *CFO*
EMP: 33
SQ FT: 15,000
SALES (est): 4.4MM
SALES (corp-wide): 1.9B **Publicly Held**
WEB: www.pearpoint.com
SIC: 3663 3829 5065 Television closed
circuit equipment; measuring & controlling
devices; closed circuit television
HQ: Radiodetection Limited
Western Drive
Bristol BS14

(P-18217)
**PENINSULA ENGRG SOLUTIONS
INC**
288 Love Ln, Danville (94526-2447)
P.O. Box 1095 (94526-1095)
PHONE.................................925 837-2243
Frank Martens, *President*
EMP: 10
SQ FT: 1,200
SALES: 1.6MM **Privately Held**
WEB: www.peninsulaengineering.com
SIC: 3663 Microwave communication
equipment

(P-18218)
PHONESUIT INC
1431 7th St Ste 201, Santa Monica
(90401-2638)
PHONE.................................310 774-0282
Sumeet Gupta, *CEO*
Christopher Folk, *Vice Pres*
EMP: 25
SQ FT: 4,000

SALES (est): 10MM **Privately Held**
SIC: 3663 Mobile communication equipment

(P-18219)
PICO DIGITAL INC (DH)
8880 Rehco Rd, San Diego (92121-3265)
PHONE.................................858 546-5050
Charlie Vogp, *President*
Carlos Shteremberg, *COO*
Ian A Lerner, *Officer*
Stephen Blake, *Vice Pres*
Peter Neuman, *Vice Pres*
▲ **EMP:** 90
SQ FT: 7,000
SALES (est): 26.1MM
SALES (corp-wide): 141.8MM **Privately
Held**
WEB: www.picomacom.com
SIC: 3663 5065 3678 Radio & TV com-
munications equipment; electronic parts &
equipment; electronic connectors
HQ: Atx Networks Corp
501 Clements Rd W Suite 1
Ajax ON L1S 7
905 428-6068

(P-18220)
PINNACLE SYSTEMS INC
280 Bernardo Ave, Mountain View
(94043-5238)
PHONE.................................650 237-1900
EMP: 12
SALES (est): 1.1MM **Privately Held**
SIC: 3663 Radio & TV communications
equipment

(P-18221)
**PIONEER AUTOMOTIVE TECH
INC**
8701 Siempre Viva Rd, San Diego
(92154-6294)
PHONE.................................937 746-6600
Jenna Heaston, *Branch Mgr*
EMP: 10
SALES (corp-wide): 3.4B **Privately Held**
SIC: 3663 Cable television equipment
HQ: Pioneer Automotive Technologies, Inc.
100 S Pioneer Blvd
Springboro OH 45066

(P-18222)
**POSITRON ACCESS SOLUTIONS
INC**
1640 2nd St Ste 207, Norco (92860-2983)
PHONE.................................951 272-9100
Reginald Weiser, *CEO*
Pierre Trudeau, *President*
Claude Samson, *CFO*
Alan W Pritchard, *Senior VP*
EMP: 10
SALES (est): 1.4MM **Privately Held**
SIC: 3663 4899 Mobile communication
equipment; data communication services
HQ: Positron Access Solutions Corporation
5101 Rue Buchan Bureau 220
Montreal QC H4P 2
514 345-2220

(P-18223)
PRECISION CONTACTS INC
990 Suncast Ln, El Dorado Hills
(95762-9626)
PHONE.................................916 939-4147
Mat Wroblewski, *President*
Mathew Wroblewski, *President*
Nancy Wroblewski, *Corp Secy*
Dean Wroblewski, *Vice Pres*
Steven Wroblewski, *Vice Pres*
EMP: 37
SQ FT: 24,000
SALES (est): 5.3MM **Privately Held**
WEB: www.precisioncontacts.com
SIC: 3663 3829 Radio & TV communica-
tions equipment; measuring & controlling
devices

(P-18224)
PRISM SKYLABS INC
799 Market St Fl 8, San Francisco
(94103-2044)
PHONE.................................415 243-0834
Stephen Russell, *CEO*
Bob Cutting, *COO*
Bethany Cavender, *Admin Asst*

Justina Pupiene, *QA Dir*
Constantin Kisly, *Engineer*
EMP: 14
SALES (est): 1.4MM **Privately Held**
SIC: 3663 Space satellite communications
equipment

(P-18225)
PROMPTER PEOPLE INC
Also Called: Flolight
126 Dillon Ave, Campbell (95008-3002)
PHONE.................................408 353-6000
Mark R Ditmanson, *CEO*
Renee Rios, *Technology*
▲ **EMP:** 12
SALES: 5MM **Privately Held**
SIC: 3663 3651 Telemetering equipment,
electronic; household video equipment

(P-18226)
PROSHOT INVESTORS LLC
Also Called: Proshot Golf
13865 Alton Pkwy Ste 100, Irvine
(92618-1687)
PHONE.................................949 586-9500
David Kuhn, *President*
▲ **EMP:** 15
SQ FT: 6,000
SALES (est): 1.6MM
SALES (corp-wide): 1.8MM **Privately
Held**
SIC: 3663
PA: Izon Network, Inc.
2600 N Central Ave # 1700
Phoenix AZ 85004
480 626-2423

(P-18227)
PUREWAVE NETWORKS INC
3951 Burton Dr, Santa Clara (95054-1583)
P.O. Box 970, Pleasanton (94566-0970)
PHONE.................................650 528-5200
Don Meiners, *CEO*
Chris Sommers, *President*
Mike Seifert, *CFO*
Peter Carson, *Senior VP*
Reza Golshan, *Vice Pres*
▲ **EMP:** 35
SALES (est): 7.5MM **Privately Held**
WEB: www.purewavenetworks.com
SIC: 3663 Light communications equip-
ment

(P-18228)
QUALCOMM INCORPORATED
3165 Kifer Rd, Santa Clara (95051-0804)
PHONE.................................408 216-2500
Melinda Barlow, *Branch Mgr*
Nancy May, *Executive Asst*
EMP: 125
SALES (corp-wide): 22.2B **Publicly Held**
SIC: 3663 Space satellite communications
equipment
PA: Qualcomm Incorporated
5775 Morehouse Dr
San Diego CA 92121
858 587-1121

(P-18229)
**QUALCOMM INCORPORATED
(PA)**
5775 Morehouse Dr, San Diego
(92121-1714)
PHONE.................................858 587-1121
Steve Mollenkopf, *CEO*
Jeffrey W Henderson, *Ch of Bd*
Cristiano R Amon, *President*
Alexander H Rogers, *President*
George S Davis, *CFO*
EMP: 277
SALES: 22.2B **Publicly Held**
WEB: www.qualcomm.com
SIC: 3663 3674 7372 6794 Mobile com-
munication equipment; semiconductors &
related devices; integrated circuits, semi-
conductor networks, etc.; hybrid inte-
grated circuits; business oriented
computer software; patent buying, licens-
ing, leasing

(P-18230)
QUALCOMM INCORPORATED
5525 Morehouse Dr, San Diego
(92121-1710)
PHONE.................................858 587-1121
Derek May, *Vice Pres*

Peter Bzenich, *Manager*
EMP: 100
SALES (corp-wide): 22.2B **Publicly Held**
SIC: 3663 Space satellite communications equipment
PA: Qualcomm Incorporated
5775 Morehouse Dr
San Diego CA 92121
858 587-1121

(P-18231)
QULSAR USA INC
1798 Tech Dr Ste 292, San Jose (95110)
PHONE..................408 715-1098
Rajendra Datta, *CEO*
Ola Andersson, *COO*
James Werner, *CFO*
EMP: 12
SQ FT: 1,400
SALES (est): 714.3K **Privately Held**
SIC: 3663 3661 3625 Mobile communication equipment; carrier equipment, telephone or telegraph; timing devices, electronic

(P-18232)
RADIAN AUDIO ENGINEERING INC
600 N Batavia St, Orange (92868-1221)
PHONE..................714 288-8900
Richard Kontrimas, *CEO*
Raimonda Kontrimas, *Admin Sec*
▲ **EMP:** 26
SQ FT: 17,000
SALES (est): 4.9MM **Privately Held**
WEB: www.radianaudio.com
SIC: 3663 5731 3651 Radio broadcasting & communications equipment; radio, television & electronic stores; household audio & video equipment

(P-18233)
RADIO FREQUENCY SYSTEMS INC
Also Called: Radio Frqency Systems Ferrocom
6276 San Ignacio Ave E, San Jose (95119-1363)
PHONE..................408 281-6100
Tam Nguyen, *Branch Mgr*
Dalila Samatua, *Production*
EMP: 12
SALES (corp-wide): 27.3B **Privately Held**
WEB: www.rfsworld.com
SIC: 3663 Radio & TV communications equipment
HQ: Radio Frequency Systems, Inc.
200 Pond View Dr
Meriden CT 06450
203 630-3311

(P-18234)
RADITEK INC (PA)
1702 Meridian Ave Ste L, San Jose (95125-5586)
PHONE..................408 266-7404
Malcolm R Lee, *President*
Peter Corbett, *COO*
▲ **EMP:** 79
SALES: 5.5MM **Privately Held**
WEB: www.raditek.com
SIC: 3663 Microwave communication equipment

(P-18235)
RADITEK INC
44253 Old Warm Sprng Blvd, Fremont (94538-6168)
PHONE..................408 266-7404
Peter Corbett, *COO*
EMP: 15
SALES (est): 765.1K **Privately Held**
SIC: 3663 Microwave communication equipment
PA: Raditek Inc.
1702 Meridian Ave Ste L
San Jose CA 95125

(P-18236)
RAVEON TECHNOLOGIES CORP
2320 Cousteau Ct, Vista (92081-8363)
PHONE..................760 444-5995
John Richard Sonnenberg, *President*
Eunice Hanson, *Accountant*
Curt Buck, *Sales Mgr*

Larry Topp, *Sales Staff*
EMP: 37
SQ FT: 7,300
SALES (est): 6.7MM **Privately Held**
WEB: www.raveontech.com
SIC: 3663 Airborne radio communications equipment

(P-18237)
RECOMAX SOFTWARE INC
706 La Para Ave, Palo Alto (94306-3157)
PHONE..................408 592-0851
Vladimir Kardonskiy, *President*
EMP: 11
SALES (est): 1.1MM **Privately Held**
SIC: 3663

(P-18238)
REMEC BROADBAND WIRE
17034 Camino San Bernardo, San Diego (92127-5708)
PHONE..................858 312-6900
Jamal Hamdani, *CEO*
Bruce Tarr, *CFO*
EMP: 180
SALES (est): 8.2MM
SALES (corp-wide): 32.2MM **Privately Held**
SIC: 3663 Mobile communication equipment
PA: Axxcss Wireless Solutions Inc
82 Coromar Dr
Goleta CA 93117
805 968-9621

(P-18239)
REMEC BROADBAND WIRELESS LLC (PA)
17034 Camino San Bernardo, San Diego (92127-5708)
PHONE..................858 312-6900
David K Newman, *Mng Member*
Behzad Ziai, *President*
Jon Opalski, *COO*
Byoung Lee, *CFO*
Sanjay Nagpal, *Senior VP*
EMP: 102
SALES (est): 17.6MM **Privately Held**
SIC: 3663 Radio & TV communications equipment

(P-18240)
ROSELM INDUSTRIES INC
2510 Seaman Ave, South El Monte (91733-1928)
PHONE..................626 442-6840
Conrad Arguiz, *President*
EMP: 20 **EST:** 1965
SQ FT: 13,000
SALES (est): 3.2MM **Privately Held**
WEB: www.socaltech.com
SIC: 3663 Radio & TV communications equipment

(P-18241)
ROTATING PRCSION MCHANISMS INC
Also Called: RPM
8750 Shirley Ave, Northridge (91324-3409)
PHONE..................818 349-9774
Kathy Flynn-Nikolai, *CEO*
Jerome Smith, *Shareholder*
Daniel P Flynn, *President*
Yuki Matsumura, *General Mgr*
James Nikolai, *Sr Software Eng*
EMP: 46
SQ FT: 40,000
SALES (est): 12.5MM **Privately Held**
WEB: www.rpm-psi.com
SIC: 3663 Radio & TV communications equipment

(P-18242)
RUDEX BROADCASTING LTD CORP
12272 Sarazen Pl, Granada Hills (91344-2635)
PHONE..................213 494-3377
John Cooper, *CEO*
EMP: 12
SALES (est): 1.2MM **Privately Held**
SIC: 3663 Radio broadcasting & communications equipment

(P-18243)
RURISOND INC
2725 Ohio Ave, Redwood City (94061-3237)
PHONE..................650 395-7136
Robert Stevenson, *CEO*
EMP: 10
SALES (est): 503K **Privately Held**
SIC: 3663 Carrier equipment, radio communications

(P-18244)
SATELLITE 2000 SYSTEMS
741 Lakefield Rd Ste I, Westlake Village (91361-2677)
P.O. Box 4453, Thousand Oaks (91359-1453)
PHONE..................818 991-9794
Fred Joubert, *CEO*
EMP: 10
SQ FT: 7,500
SALES (est): 2.3MM **Privately Held**
SIC: 3663 Radio & TV communications equipment

(P-18245)
SAVI TECHNOLOGY HOLDINGS INC (PA)
615 Tasman Dr, Sunnyvale (94089-1707)
PHONE..................650 316-4950
Vikram Verma, *President*
Rohit Verma, *President*
Jerry Beckwith, *COO*
George De Urioste, *CFO*
Brian Daum, *Senior VP*
▲ **EMP:** 43
SQ FT: 35,000
SALES (est): 23.9MM **Privately Held**
SIC: 3663 3999 Radio & TV communications equipment; identification tags, except paper

(P-18246)
SEASPACE CORPORATION
13000 Gregg St Ste A, Poway (92064-7151)
PHONE..................858 746-1100
Erik Park, *CEO*
Daniel Lee, *Vice Pres*
Jihong Park, *Admin Sec*
Peter Nowak, *Software Dev*
Anthony Burunoff, *Project Engr*
EMP: 25
SQ FT: 24,000
SALES (est): 6.1MM **Privately Held**
WEB: www.seaspace.com
SIC: 3663 3829 Satellites, communications; measuring & controlling devices

(P-18247)
SECURE COMM SYSTEMS INC (HQ)
Also Called: Rugged Portable Systems
1740 E Wilshire Ave, Santa Ana (92705-4615)
PHONE..................714 547-1174
Allen B Ronk, *CEO*
Robert Korb, *President*
Andrew Lewes, *CFO*
Mike Boice, *Vice Pres*
Richard Crowell, *Principal*
▲ **EMP:** 161
SQ FT: 38,000
SALES (est): 133.7MM
SALES (corp-wide): 2.4B **Publicly Held**
WEB: www.securecomm.com
SIC: 3663 3829 3577 3571 Encryption devices; vibration meters, analyzers & calibrators; computer peripheral equipment; electronic computers
PA: Benchmark Electronics, Inc.
4141 N Scottsdale Rd
Scottsdale AZ 85251
623 300-7000

(P-18248)
SECURE COMM SYSTEMS INC
1740 E Wilshire Ave, Santa Ana (92705-4615)
PHONE..................714 547-1174
Allen Ronk, *Branch Mgr*
EMP: 15

SALES (corp-wide): 2.4B **Publicly Held**
WEB: www.securecomm.com
SIC: 3663 3829 Encryption devices; vibration meters, analyzers & calibrators
HQ: Secure Communication Systems, Inc.
1740 E Wilshire Ave
Santa Ana CA 92705
714 547-1174

(P-18249)
SEKAI ELECTRONICS INC (PA)
38 Waterworks Way, Irvine (92618-3107)
PHONE..................949 783-5740
Roland Soohoo, *CEO*
Mattias Nilsson,
EMP: 30
SQ FT: 7,000
SALES (est): 5.3MM **Privately Held**
WEB: www.sekai-electronics.com
SIC: 3663 5065 Radio & TV communications equipment; video equipment, electronic

(P-18250)
SHELDONS HOBBY SHOP
2135 Oakland Rd, San Jose (95131-1578)
P.O. Box 611147 (95161-1147)
PHONE..................408 943-0220
Ronald Sheldon, *Owner*
EMP: 19
SQ FT: 21,000
SALES (est): 1.7MM **Privately Held**
WEB: www.sheldonshobbies.com
SIC: 3663 5945 Radio & TV communications equipment; hobbies

(P-18251)
SIERRA AUTOMATED SYS/ENG CORP
2821 Burton Ave, Burbank (91504-3224)
PHONE..................818 840-6749
Edward O Fritz, *President*
Al Salci, *Vice Pres*
Richard Schumeyer, *Regional Mgr*
Giovanni Morales, *General Mgr*
Daniel Gaylord, *Software Engr*
EMP: 20
SALES (est): 3.9MM **Privately Held**
WEB: www.sasaudio.com
SIC: 3663 Radio broadcasting & communications equipment

(P-18252)
SIERRA NEVADA CORPORATION
39465 Paseo Padre Pkwy # 2900, Fremont (94538-5350)
PHONE..................510 446-8400
Fatih Ozmen, *CEO*
Eren Ozmen, *President*
Lisa Brown, *Controller*
EMP: 30
SALES (corp-wide): 1.5B **Privately Held**
WEB: www.sncorp.com
SIC: 3663 4812 Radio & TV communications equipment; radio telephone communication
PA: Sierra Nevada Corporation
444 Salomon Cir
Sparks NV 89434
775 331-0222

(P-18253)
SILVUS TECHNOLOGIES INC (PA)
10990 Wilshire Blvd # 1500, Los Angeles (90024-3913)
PHONE..................310 479-3333
Babak Daneshrad, *Chairman*
Phillip Duncan, *COO*
Jimi Henderson, *Vice Pres*
Weijun Zhu, *Vice Pres*
Amanda Kahenasa, *Office Admin*
EMP: 30
SQ FT: 7,200
SALES (est): 4.8MM **Privately Held**
SIC: 3663 8731 Radio & TV communications equipment; commercial physical research

(P-18254)
SMARTRUNK SYSTEMS INC
867 Bowsprit Rd, Chula Vista (91914-4529)
PHONE..................619 426-3781
Joe Banos, *President*
EMP: 25

SQ FT: 11,300
SALES (est): 2.6MM **Privately Held**
WEB: www.smarttrunk.com
SIC: 3663

(P-18255)
SOCKET MOBILE INC
39700 Eureka Dr, Newark (94560-4808)
PHONE....................510 933-3000
Kevin J Mills, *President*
Charlie Bass, *Ch of Bd*
David W Dunlap, *CFO*
Nelson Chan, *Bd of Directors*
Brenton Macdonald, *Bd of Directors*
▲ EMP: 50
SQ FT: 37,100
SALES: 21.2MM **Privately Held**
WEB: www.socketcom.com
SIC: 3663 Mobile communication equipment

(P-18256)
SOLECTEK CORPORATION
8375 Cmino Santa Fe Ste A, San Diego
(92121)
PHONE....................858 450-1220
Seung Joon Lee, *CEO*
Eric Lee, *President*
Helena Adams, *COO*
Seung Lee, *Executive*
Gene Swank, *Sr Software Eng*
▲ EMP: 20
SQ FT: 10,000
SALES (est): 4.1MM **Privately Held**
WEB: www.solectek.com
SIC: 3663 Television broadcasting & communications equipment

(P-18257)
SONY MOBILE COMMUNICATIONS USA
2207 Bridgepoint Pkwy, San Mateo
(94404)
PHONE....................866 766-9374
Kunihiko Shiomi, *CEO*
Hideki Komiyama, *President*
Francisco Lazardi, *CFO*
Paul Hamnett, *Vice Pres*
Ron Louks, *Vice Pres*
▲ EMP: 170
SQ FT: 10,000
SALES (est): 107.6MM **Privately Held**
WEB: www.ericsson.se
SIC: 3663 5999 Mobile communication equipment; mobile telephones & equipment

(P-18258)
SPACE MICRO INC
10237 Flanders Ct, San Diego
(92121-2901)
PHONE....................858 332-0700
David J Strobel, *CEO*
David R Czajkowski, *President*
David Czajkowski, *COO*
Patricia Ellison, *Vice Pres*
Michael Jacox, *Vice Pres*
EMP: 100
SALES: 18.6MM **Privately Held**
WEB: www.spacemicro.com
SIC: 3663 Space satellite communications equipment

(P-18259)
SPACE SYSTEMS/LORAL LLC
5130 Rbert J Mathews Pkwy, El Dorado
Hills (95762-5703)
PHONE....................916 605-5448
Bob White, *Plant Mgr*
Larry Wray, *Vice Pres*
EMP: 20
SALES (corp-wide): 581.1MM **Publicly Held**
SIC: 3663 Space satellite communications equipment
HQ: Space Systems/Loral, Llc
3825 Fabian Way
Palo Alto CA 94303
650 852-7320

(P-18260)
SPIRENT COMMUNICATIONS INC (HQ)
27349 Agoura Rd, Calabasas
(91301-2413)
PHONE....................818 676-2300

Eric G Hutchinson, *CEO*
Bill Burns, *President*
Matthew Philpott, *Engineer*
▲ EMP: 350
SALES (est): 300.1MM
SALES (corp-wide): 454.8MM **Privately Held**
SIC: 3663 3829 3825 Radio & TV communications equipment; measuring & controlling devices; instruments to measure electricity
PA: Spirent Communications Plc
Northwood Park
Crawley W SUSSEX RH10
129 376-7676

(P-18261)
SPIRENT COMMUNICATIONS INC
2708 Orchard Pkwy Ste 20, San Jose
(95134-1968)
PHONE....................408 894-7015
Barry Phelps, *Branch Mgr*
EMP: 35
SALES (corp-wide): 454.8MM **Privately Held**
SIC: 3663 Radio & TV communications equipment
HQ: Spirent Communications Inc.
27349 Agoura Rd
Calabasas CA 91301
818 676-2300

(P-18262)
SPOSATO JOHN
Also Called: Silicon Valley Launch
257 Vera Ave, Redwood City (94061-1702)
PHONE....................408 215-8727
John Sposato, *Owner*
EMP: 10
SALES (est): 677.6K **Privately Held**
SIC: 3663 3761 3812 3825 Radio receiver networks; guided missiles & space vehicles, research & development; antennas, radar or communications; oscillators, audio & radio frequency (instrument types); energy research;

(P-18263)
STARIX TECHNOLOGY INC
9120 Irvine Center Dr # 200, Irvine
(92618-4682)
PHONE....................949 387-8120
Ran-Hong Yan, *CEO*
Frederic Battaglia, *General Mgr*
Nancy Chiang, *General Mgr*
Inanc Inan, *Technical Mgr*
Andrei Miclea, *Software Engr*
EMP: 20
SALES: 950K **Privately Held**
SIC: 3663 Radio & TV communications equipment

(P-18264)
STM NETWORKS INC
Also Called: Stm Wireless
2 Faraday, Irvine (92618-2737)
PHONE....................949 273-6800
Emil Youssefzadeh, *CEO*
Faramarz Yousefzaheh, *Ch of Bd*
Gene Meistad, *COO*
Albert Yousefzaheh, *Treasurer*
Umar Javed, *Senior VP*
▲ EMP: 27
SQ FT: 22,000
SALES (est): 4.6MM **Privately Held**
WEB: www.stmnetworks.com
SIC: 3663 Satellites, communications

(P-18265)
STONECROP TECHNOLOGIES LLC
103 H St Ste B, Petaluma (94952-5125)
PHONE....................781 659-0007
Jeff Baum, *VP Bus Dvlpt*
Roya Platsis, *Human Res Dir*
EMP: 29
SALES (corp-wide): 1.5MM **Privately Held**
SIC: 3663 Microwave communication equipment
PA: Stonecrop Technologies, Llc
80 Washington St Ste M50
Norwell MA 02061
781 829-9919

(P-18266)
SUNAR RF MOTION INC
6780 Sierra Ct Ste R, Dublin (94568-2600)
PHONE....................925 833-9936
Jason Fong, *General Mgr*
Donald R Shepherd, *Shareholder*
EMP: 10
SALES: 1MM **Privately Held**
SIC: 3663 Amplifiers, RF power & IF

(P-18267)
SUNBRITETV LLC
2001 Anchor Ct, Thousand Oaks
(91320-1614)
PHONE....................805 214-7250
Cameron Hill, *CEO*
Jonathan Johnson, *Manager*
▲ EMP: 50
SALES (est): 11.4MM **Privately Held**
SIC: 3663 Transmitting apparatus, radio or television
HQ: Sunbrite Holding Corporation
2001 Anchor Ct
Thousand Oaks CA 91320
805 214-7250

(P-18268)
SWIFT NAVIGATION INC
650 Townsend St Ste 410, San Francisco
(94103-6246)
PHONE....................415 484-9026
Timothy Harris, *CEO*
Mark Fine, *Software Engr*
Josh Kretzmer, *Engineer*
Stefan Witanis, *Engineer*
Dennis Zollo, *Engineer*
EMP: 65
SQ FT: 15,000
SALES (est): 2.5MM **Privately Held**
SIC: 3663 Radio & TV communications equipment

(P-18269)
SYNTONIC MICROWAVE INC
275 E Hacienda Ave, Campbell
(95008-6616)
P.O. Box 12228, Portland OR (97212-0228)
PHONE....................408 866-5900
Frederic Storke, *Chairman*
Jay Goodfriend, *President*
Jerry McCoy, *President*
Kathleen Goodfriend, *Info Tech Mgr*
EMP: 12
SALES (est): 2MM **Privately Held**
WEB: www.syntonicmicrowave.com
SIC: 3663 Microwave communication equipment

(P-18270)
TACHYON NETWORKS INCORPORATED
9339 Carroll Park Dr # 150, San Diego
(92121-3278)
PHONE....................858 882-8100
Peter A Carides, *CEO*
Laurence A Hinz, *CFO*
EMP: 52
SQ FT: 18,000
SALES (est): 8.2MM **Privately Held**
WEB: www.tachyon.net
SIC: 3663 Antennas, transmitting & communications

(P-18271)
TANGOME INC
440 N Wolfe Rd, Sunnyvale (94085-3869)
PHONE....................650 375-2620
Eric Setton, *CEO*
Uri Raz, *Ch of Bd*
Gary Chevsky, *Vice Pres*
Gregory Dorso, *Vice Pres*
Uli Galoz, *Vice Pres*
▲ EMP: 42
SALES (est): 13MM **Privately Held**
SIC: 3663 Mobile communication equipment

(P-18272)
TARANA WIRELESS INC
2105 M L King Jr Way J, Berkeley
(94704-1108)
PHONE....................510 868-3359
Sergiu Nedeski, *President*
Rabin K Patra, *Vice Pres*
Rj Honicky, *Sr Software Eng*

Dale Branlund, *CTO*
Steven Good, *Engineer*
EMP: 22
SALES (est): 3.5MM **Privately Held**
SIC: 3663 Radio & TV communications equipment

(P-18273)
TATUNG COMPANY AMERICA INC (HQ)
2850 E El Presidio St, Long Beach
(90810-1119)
PHONE....................310 637-2105
Huei-Jihn Jih, *President*
Danny Huang, *CFO*
Mike Lee, *Vice Pres*
Alvin Ramali, *Info Tech Mgr*
Vivien Ho, *Project Mgr*
▲ EMP: 98
SQ FT: 95,000
SALES (est): 26.1MM
SALES (corp-wide): 2.5B **Privately Held**
WEB: www.tatungusa.com
SIC: 3663 3575 3944 3651 Television closed circuit equipment; computer terminals, monitors & components; video game machines, except coin-operated; television receiving sets; video cassette recorders/players & accessories; refrigerators, mechanical & absorption: household; microwave ovens (cooking equipment), commercial
PA: Tatung Co.
22, Zhongshan N. Rd., Sec. 3,
Taipei City TAP 10435
225 925-252

(P-18274)
TCI INTERNATIONAL INC (HQ)
3541 Gateway Blvd, Fremont
(94538-6585)
PHONE....................510 687-6100
Slobodan Tkalcevic, *Vice Pres*
Stephen Stein, *Vice Pres*
Roy Woolsey, *Vice Pres*
▲ EMP: 103
SQ FT: 60,000
SALES (est): 17.3MM
SALES (corp-wide): 1.4B **Publicly Held**
WEB: www.tcibr.com
SIC: 3663 3812 3661 Radio broadcasting & communications equipment; antennas, transmitting & communications; antennas, radar or communications; modems
PA: Spx Corporation
13320a Balntyn Corp Pl
Charlotte NC 28277
980 474-3700

(P-18275)
TCOMT INC
111 N Market St Ste 670, San Jose
(95113-1112)
PHONE....................408 351-3340
Clifford Rhee, *President*
Michael Luther, *Chairman*
Vito Picicci, *Vice Pres*
EMP: 89
SALES: 90MM **Privately Held**
WEB: www.tcomt.net
SIC: 3663 Mobile communication equipment

(P-18276)
TECHNICOLOR USA INC
400 Providence Mine Rd, Nevada City
(95959-2953)
PHONE....................530 478-3000
Jeff Rosica, *Senior VP*
EMP: 513
SALES (corp-wide): 63.6MM **Privately Held**
SIC: 3663 Radio & TV communications equipment
HQ: Technicolor Usa, Inc.
101 W 103rd St
Indianapolis IN 46290
818 260-3651

(P-18277)
TELECOMMUNICATIONS ENGRG ASSOC
1160 Industrial Rd Ste 15, San Carlos
(94070-4128)
PHONE....................650 590-1801
Daryl Jones, *President*

Walt Gradzki, *Manager*
EMP: 13
SQ FT: 5,500
SALES (est): 1.9MM **Privately Held**
WEB: www.tcomeng.com
SIC: 3663 7622 Radio & TV communications equipment; communication equipment repair

(P-18278)
TELEDESIGN SYSTEMS
1729 S Main St, Milpitas (95035-6756)
PHONE....................408 941-1808
Mark Hubbard, *CEO*
Bruce Delevaux, *Vice Pres*
Oscar Nevarez, *Production*
Hazel Wolfe, *Manager*
EMP: 10
SQ FT: 5,000
SALES (est): 1.8MM **Privately Held**
WEB: www.teledesignsystems.com
SIC: 3663 Radio & TV communications equipment

(P-18279)
TELEMTRY CMMNCTONS SYSTEMS INC
Also Called: TCS
10020 Remmet Ave, Chatsworth (91311-3854)
PHONE....................818 718-6248
Sarin Michel Roy, *President*
Mihail Mateescu, *Vice Pres*
EMP: 24
SQ FT: 14,500
SALES: 7MM **Privately Held**
WEB: www.telcoms.com
SIC: 3663 Antennas, transmitting & communications

(P-18280)
TELEWAVE INC
660 Giguere Ct, San Jose (95133-1742)
PHONE....................408 929-4400
Roberta Boward, *President*
Allen Collins, *COO*
Jeff Cornehl, *Engineer*
Dave Mexicano, *Mfg Staff*
Bradley Senge, *Sales Mgr*
◆ **EMP:** 46
SQ FT: 30,000
SALES: 9MM **Privately Held**
SIC: 3663 Radio broadcasting & communications equipment

(P-18281)
TERABIT RADIOS INC
1551 Mccarthy Blvd # 210, Milpitas (95035-7442)
PHONE....................408 431-6032
Srinivas Sivaprakasam, *President*
Carpenter Bruce, *Vice Pres*
EMP: 14 **EST:** 2014
SALES (est): 2.2MM **Privately Held**
SIC: 3663 Radio broadcasting & communications equipment

(P-18282)
TERRALINK COMMUNICATIONS INC
5145 Golden Foothill Pkwy # 140, El Dorado Hills (95762-9656)
PHONE....................916 439-4367
Casey Janssen, *President*
Loni Cooke, *Accountant*
EMP: 10
SQ FT: 3,525
SALES: 6.7MM **Privately Held**
WEB: www.terralinkcommunications.com
SIC: 3663 Antennas, transmitting & communications

(P-18283)
TERRASAT COMMUNICATIONS INC
315 Digital Dr, Morgan Hill (95037-2878)
PHONE....................408 782-5911
Jit Patel, *President*
Mike Gold, *President*
Rod Benson, *Vice Pres*
Jose Hecht, *Vice Pres*
Carl Hurst, *Vice Pres*
▲ **EMP:** 47

SALES (est): 14.7MM **Privately Held**
WEB: www.terrasatinc.com
SIC: 3663 Satellites, communications

(P-18284)
THAWTE INC
Also Called: Thawte Consulting USA
487 E Middlefield Rd, Mountain View (94043-4047)
PHONE....................650 426-7400
Mark Shuttleworth, *President*
EMP: 20 **EST:** 1995
SQ FT: 5,000
SALES (est): 1.7MM
SALES (corp-wide): 4.8B **Publicly Held**
WEB: www.thawte.com
SIC: 3663 7371 Digital encoders; custom computer programming services
PA: Symantec Corporation
350 Ellis St
Mountain View CA 94043
650 527-8000

(P-18285)
THEFT PATROL LLC
4740 Von Karman Ave, Newport Beach (92660-8109)
PHONE....................858 880-5841
Brian Boling, *CEO*
EMP: 12
SALES: 2MM **Privately Held**
SIC: 3663

(P-18286)
THOMSON REUTERS CORPORATION
Also Called: Reuters Television La
633 W 5th St Ste 2300, Los Angeles (90071-2049)
PHONE....................877 518-2761
Kevin Regan, *Principal*
EMP: 15 **Publicly Held**
SIC: 3663 Satellites, communications
HQ: Thomson Reuters Corporation
3 Times Sq
New York NY 10036
646 223-4000

(P-18287)
TIM HOOVER ENTERPRISES
8532 Yarrow Ln, Riverside (92508-2926)
PHONE....................951 237-9210
Tim Hoover, *Owner*
EMP: 60
SALES (est): 3.5MM **Privately Held**
SIC: 3663 Space satellite communications equipment

(P-18288)
TINI AEROSPACE INC
2505 Kerner Blvd, San Rafael (94901-5571)
PHONE....................415 524-2124
Michael Bokaie, *President*
Vicki Lasky, *Treasurer*
David Bokaie, *Vice Pres*
Trudy Sachs, *Vice Pres*
Evelyn Cabrera, *Office Mgr*
▼ **EMP:** 30 **EST:** 1996
SQ FT: 5,400
SALES (est): 6.1MM **Privately Held**
WEB: www.tiniaerospace.com
SIC: 3663 Space satellite communications equipment

(P-18289)
TJEKER LLC
730 Arizona Ave, Santa Monica (90401-1702)
PHONE....................424 240-7696
Brent Morgan,
EMP: 25
SALES: 12.6MM **Privately Held**
SIC: 3663 Mobile communication equipment

(P-18290)
TREXTA INC
Also Called: Wireless Products
8969 Kenamar Dr Ste 105, San Diego (92121-2441)
PHONE....................858 536-9100
Attila F Kutbay, *President*
▲ **EMP:** 10
SQ FT: 6,000

SALES (est): 2MM **Privately Held**
WEB: www.trexta.com
SIC: 3663 Mobile communication equipment

(P-18291)
TRICOM RESEARCH INC
17791 Sky Park Cir Ste J, Irvine (92614-6150)
PHONE....................949 250-6024
Paula Wright, *President*
John W Wright, *CFO*
Chang Ju, *Engineer*
Scott Snyder, *Director*
John Boos, *Manager*
EMP: 64
SALES (est): 9.4MM **Privately Held**
SIC: 3663 Radio & TV communications equipment

(P-18292)
TRIQUINT WJ INC
3099 Orchard Dr, San Jose (95134-2005)
PHONE....................408 577-6200
W Dexter Paine III, *Ch of Bd*
Bruce W Diamond, *President*
Ralph G Quinsey, *CEO*
R Gregory Miller, *CFO*
Haresh P Patel, *Senior VP*
EMP: 24
SQ FT: 124,000
SALES (est): 7.7MM
SALES (corp-wide): 2.9B **Publicly Held**
WEB: www.triquint.com
SIC: 3663 3674 Radio broadcasting & communications equipment; semiconductors & related devices
HQ: Qorvo Us, Inc.
7628 Thorndike Rd
Greensboro NC 27409
336 664-1233

(P-18293)
TRIVEC-AVANT CORPORATION
17831 Jamestown Ln, Huntington Beach (92647-7136)
PHONE....................714 841-4976
Jill Kale, *CEO*
Mike Berberet, *Vice Pres*
David Macy, *Vice Pres*
▲ **EMP:** 45
SQ FT: 15,000
SALES (est): 9.9MM
SALES (corp-wide): 2.7B **Privately Held**
WEB: www.trivec.com
SIC: 3663 Antennas, transmitting & communications
HQ: Cobham Aes Holdings Inc.
2121 Crystal Dr Ste 625
Arlington VA 22202

(P-18294)
ULTIMATTE CORPORATION
20945 Plummer St, Chatsworth (91311-4902)
PHONE....................818 993-8007
Lynne Sauve, *President*
Petro Vlahos, *Shareholder*
Paul Vlahos, *Treasurer*
Paul E Vlahos, *Treasurer*
Nina Michalko, *Admin Sec*
▲ **EMP:** 26
SQ FT: 17,700
SALES (est): 4.6MM
SALES (corp-wide): 230MM **Privately Held**
SIC: 3663 3651 7371 Television broadcasting & communications equipment; household audio & video equipment; computer software development & applications
PA: Blackmagic Design Pty Ltd
11 Gateway Ct
Port Melbourne VIC 3207
396 824-770

(P-18295)
USGLOBALSAT INC
14740 Yorba Ct, Chino (91710-9210)
PHONE....................909 597-8525
Shirley Cheng, *President*
▲ **EMP:** 10
SQ FT: 62,000

SALES (est): 3.2MM **Privately Held**
WEB: www.usglobalsat.com
SIC: 3663 Radio & TV communications equipment

(P-18296)
VIASAT INC (PA)
6155 El Camino Real, Carlsbad (92009-1602)
PHONE....................760 476-2200
Mark Dankberg, *Ch of Bd*
Richard Baldridge, *President*
Ken Peterman, *President*
David Ryan, *President*
Shawn Duffy, *CFO*
▲ **EMP:** 277
SQ FT: 695,000
SALES: 1.5B **Publicly Held**
WEB: www.viasat.com
SIC: 3663 Space satellite communications equipment; receiver-transmitter units (transceiver); mobile communication equipment; antennas, transmitting & communications

(P-18297)
VIGOR SYSTEMS INC
4660 La Jolla Village Dr # 500, San Diego (92122-4605)
PHONE....................866 748-4467
Magnus Sorlander, *CEO*
Shayna Smith, *COO*
Ian Loyo, *Info Tech Mgr*
Misung Kwon, *Software Engr*
▲ **EMP:** 35
SALES (est): 4.1MM **Privately Held**
WEB: www.vigorsys.com
SIC: 3663 Studio equipment, radio & television broadcasting

(P-18298)
WATER ASSOCIATES LLC
Also Called: Redtrac
34929 Flyover Ct, Bakersfield (93308-9725)
PHONE....................661 281-6077
Jeff Young, *Managing Prtnr*
Michael McAllister, *Business Mgr*
Bob Simonian, *Sales Mgr*
Michael Young,
EMP: 20
SQ FT: 7,000
SALES (est): 4MM **Privately Held**
SIC: 3663 3523 Radio & TV communications equipment; irrigation equipment, self-propelled

(P-18299)
WBWALTON ENTERPRISES INC
4185 Hallmark Pkwy, San Bernardino (92407-1832)
P.O. Box 9010 (92427-0010)
PHONE....................951 683-0930
William B Walton Jr, *President*
Jane Walton, *Corp Secy*
EMP: 26
SQ FT: 30,000
SALES (est): 5.3MM **Privately Held**
WEB: www.de-ice.com
SIC: 3663 1731 Satellites, communications; electrical work

(P-18300)
WEST-COM NRSE CALL SYSTEMS INC (PA)
Also Called: Wc
2200 Cordelia Rd, Fairfield (94534-1912)
PHONE....................707 428-5900
C Larry Peters, *CEO*
Dania Atanassova-Een, *CFO*
David Daum, *Regional Mgr*
Joe Edwards, *Regional Mgr*
Denise Peters, *General Mgr*
EMP: 44
SQ FT: 15,000
SALES (est): 8.5MM **Privately Held**
WEB: www.westcall.com
SIC: 3663 Radio broadcasting & communications equipment

(P-18301)
WI2WI INC (PA)
2107 N 1st St Ste 680, San Jose (95131-2027)
PHONE....................408 416-4200
Zachariah J Mathews, *President*

Sharad Mistry, *Director*
EMP: 28
SALES (est): 8.3MM **Privately Held**
SIC: 3663 Radio & TV communications equipment

(P-18302)
WILMANCO
5350 Kazuko Ct, Moorpark (93021-1790)
PHONE.................................805 523-2390
Harold B Williams, *Owner*
Harold Williams Jr, *Co-Owner*
Marie Williams, *Co-Owner*
Marci Padgett, *Graphic Designe*
EMP: 16
SQ FT: 11,000
SALES (est): 1.9MM **Privately Held**
WEB: www.wilmanco.com
SIC: 3663 Microwave communication equipment

(P-18303)
WOHLER TECHNOLOGIES INC
1280 San Luis Obispo St, Hayward (94544-7916)
PHONE.................................510 870-0810
Michael Kelly, *President*
John Palmer, *Chairman*
Craig Newbury, *Vice Pres*
Aaron Aiken, *Admin Sec*
Mohamad Azam, *Sales Mgr*
▲ **EMP:** 25
SALES (est): 10.2MM **Privately Held**
WEB: www.wohler.com
SIC: 3663 Radio & TV communications equipment

(P-18304)
WV COMMUNICATIONS INC
1125 Bus Ctr Cir Ste A, Newbury Park (91320)
PHONE.................................805 376-1820
Uri Yulzari, *President*
Jim Tranovich, *Vice Pres*
Ron Bosi, *Admin Sec*
David Aubertin, *Software Dev*
Gerri Yulzari, *QC Mgr*
▲ **EMP:** 40
SQ FT: 18,000
SALES (est): 10MM **Privately Held**
WEB: www.wv-comm.com
SIC: 3663 Microwave communication equipment

(P-18305)
XCOM WIRELESS INC
2700 Rose Ave Ste E, Signal Hill (90755-1929)
PHONE.................................562 981-0077
Dan Hyman, *President*
Peter Bogdanoff, *Shareholder*
Ardesta LLC, *Shareholder*
Mark Hyman, *Corp Secy*
Michele Holden, *Office Mgr*
EMP: 12
SQ FT: 3,500
SALES (est): 1.3MM **Privately Held**
WEB: www.xcomwireless.net
SIC: 3663 Mobile communication equipment

(P-18306)
ZYPCOM INC
29400 Kohoutek Way # 170, Union City (94587-1212)
PHONE.................................510 324-2501
Karl Zorzi, *President*
Heidi Zorzi, *Manager*
▲ **EMP:** 11
SQ FT: 7,200
SALES (est): 2.7MM **Privately Held**
SIC: 3663 3661 Multiplex equipment; modems

3669 Communications Eqpt, NEC

(P-18307)
ALSTOM SIGNALING OPERATION LLC
7337 Central Ave, Riverside (92504-1440)
PHONE.................................951 343-9699
Jeff Utterbach, *Manager*
EMP: 192

SALES (corp-wide): 1.5B **Privately Held**
WEB: www.proyard.com
SIC: 3669 Railroad signaling devices, electric
PA: Alstom Signaling Operation, Llc
2901 E Lake Rd Bldg 122
Erie PA 16531
800 825-3178

(P-18308)
AMERICAN TECH SUPPLY INC (PA)
1250 Pine St Ste 105, Walnut Creek (94596-3633)
PHONE.................................925 944-0777
Gil Hunter, *President*
EMP: 25
SQ FT: 2,100
SALES (est): 8MM **Privately Held**
WEB: www.americantechsupply.com
SIC: 3669 3357 4813 Intercommunication systems, electric; aircraft wire & cable, nonferrous; telephone communication, except radio

(P-18309)
ATI SOLUTIONS INC (PA)
Also Called: Ucview
18425 Napa St, Northridge (91325-3619)
PHONE.................................818 772-7900
Guy Avital, *CEO*
Leah Avital, *Vice Pres*
Eileen Dela Cruz, *Accountant*
EMP: 15
SALES (est): 2.8MM **Privately Held**
WEB: www.atisol.com
SIC: 3669 Visual communication systems

(P-18310)
BDFCO INC
Also Called: Damac
1926 Kauai Dr, Costa Mesa (92626-3542)
PHONE.................................714 228-2900
Frank J Kubat Jr, *CEO*
Robert Mc Clory, *Shareholder*
Daniel L Davis, *Admin Sec*
▲ **EMP:** 80
SQ FT: 120,000
SALES (est): 14.3MM **Privately Held**
WEB: www.damac.com
SIC: 3669 Intercommunication systems, electric

(P-18311)
BITMAX LLC (PA)
6255 W Sunset Blvd # 1515, Los Angeles (90028-7416)
PHONE.................................323 978-7878
Nancy Bennett, *Mng Member*
Tony Rizkallah, *CTO*
Kathyren Dugenia, *Project Mgr*
Norma Troke, *Controller*
David Baker, *Opers Mgr*
EMP: 22
SQ FT: 7,500
SALES (est): 2.3MM **Privately Held**
WEB: www.bitmax.net
SIC: 3669 7929 Visual communication systems; entertainment service

(P-18312)
BLUE SKY REMEDIATION SVCS INC
Also Called: United Traffic Services & Sup
14000 Valley Blvd, La Puente (91746-2801)
PHONE.................................626 961-5736
Dora Pina, *President*
EMP: 14
SQ FT: 15,000
SALES (est): 2.5MM **Privately Held**
SIC: 3669 Pedestrian traffic control equipment; traffic signals, electric

(P-18313)
BLUE SQUIRREL INC
8295 Aero Pl, San Diego (92123-2031)
PHONE.................................858 268-0717
Steve Deal, *CEO*
Derek Morikawa, *COO*
James Doss, *CFO*
Jack Hetzel, *CFO*
Larry Cleary, *Vice Pres*
▲ **EMP:** 80
SQ FT: 20,000

SALES (est): 13MM **Privately Held**
WEB: www.indyme.com
SIC: 3669 3663 Burglar alarm apparatus, electric; airborne radio communications equipment

(P-18314)
CAL SIGNAL CORP
384 Beach Rd, Burlingame (94010-2004)
PHONE.................................650 343-6100
Tom Mori, *Vice Pres*
EMP: 11
SALES (est): 2.2MM **Privately Held**
SIC: 3669 Traffic signals, electric

(P-18315)
CANOGA PERKINS CORPORATION (HQ)
20600 Prairie St, Chatsworth (91311-6008)
PHONE.................................818 718-6300
Alfred Tim Champion, *President*
Mercedes Agta Soa, *Human Resources*
James Heney, *Director*
◆ **EMP:** 100 **EST:** 1965
SQ FT: 64,000
SALES (est): 24.2MM
SALES (corp-wide): 928.2MM **Privately Held**
WEB: www.canoga.com
SIC: 3669 Intercommunication systems, electric
PA: Rowan Technologies, Inc.
10 Indel Ave
Rancocas NJ 08073
609 267-9000

(P-18316)
CONTINENTAL SECURITY INDS
19425b Soledad Canyon Rd # 126, Canyon Country (91351-2632)
PHONE.................................661 251-8800
Gregory Basse, *President*
EMP: 15
SALES (est): 1.7MM **Privately Held**
SIC: 3669 Fire alarm apparatus, electric

(P-18317)
COTT MANUFACTURING COMPANY
19755 Nordhoff Pl, Chatsworth (91311-6606)
P.O. Box 596, Wexford PA (15090-0596)
PHONE.................................818 988-9500
Jeffrey Thomas, *Owner*
EMP: 20
SALES (est): 1.1MM **Privately Held**
SIC: 3669 Signaling apparatus, electric

(P-18318)
D-TECH OPTOELECTRONICS INC (DH)
18062 Rowland St, City of Industry (91748-1205)
PHONE.................................626 956-1100
An Baoxin, *President*
EMP: 20
SALES: 20MM **Privately Held**
SIC: 3669 Intercommunication systems, electric
HQ: Global Communication Semiconductors, Llc
23155 Kashiwa Ct
Torrance CA 90505
310 530-7274

(P-18319)
DEI HEADQUARTERS INC
Also Called: Sound United
1 Viper Way, Vista (92081-7809)
PHONE.................................760 598-6200
James E Minarik, *President*
Kevin P Duffy, *President*
Blair Tripodi, *President*
Veysel P Goker, *CFO*
Josh Talge, *Chief Mktg Ofcr*
▲ **EMP:** 385
SQ FT: 50,000
SALES (est): 34.5MM **Privately Held**
WEB: www.directed.com
SIC: 3669 Burglar alarm apparatus, electric
HQ: Dei Holdings, Inc.
1 Viper Way Ste 3
Vista CA 92081
760 598-6200

(P-18320)
DEI HOLDINGS INC (HQ)
1 Viper Way Ste 3, Vista (92081-7811)
PHONE.................................760 598-6200
Kevin P Duffy, *CEO*
Robert J Struble, *CEO*
Veysel Goker, *CFO*
Dan Brockman, *Treasurer*
Michael S Simmons, *Exec VP*
▲ **EMP:** 156
SQ FT: 198,000
SALES (est): 205.9MM **Privately Held**
WEB: www.directed.com
SIC: 3669 3651 Burglar alarm apparatus, electric; amplifiers: radio, public address or musical instrument

(P-18321)
DULCE SYSTEMS INC
26893 Bouquet Canyon Rd L, Santa Clarita (91350-2374)
PHONE.................................818 435-6007
Carmen Palacios, *President*
Greg Farrin, *Engineer*
▲ **EMP:** 10
SALES (est): 1.4MM **Privately Held**
WEB: www.dulcesystems.com
SIC: 3669 3572 Sirens, electric: vehicle, marine, industrial & air raid; signaling apparatus, electric; visual communication systems; computer storage devices; tape storage units, computer; computer auxiliary storage units

(P-18322)
ECONOLITE CONTROL PRODUCTS INC (PA)
1250 N Tustin Ave, Anaheim (92807-1617)
P.O. Box 6150 (92816-0150)
PHONE.................................714 630-3700
Michael C Doyle, *CEO*
David St Amant, *President*
Douglas Wiersig, *Vice Pres*
Peter Sweatman, *Principal*
Peter Shuttleworth, *Director*
▼ **EMP:** 160
SQ FT: 95,000
SALES (est): 73MM **Privately Held**
WEB: www.econolite.com
SIC: 3669 Traffic signals, electric

(P-18323)
EXCELLENCE OPTO INC
20047 Tipico St, Chatsworth (91311-3443)
PHONE.................................818 674-1921
Fanny Huang, *President*
Kuo Hsin Huang, *President*
Tyson Tien, *Director*
EMP: 10
SQ FT: 7,000
SALES (est): 781.5K **Privately Held**
SIC: 3669 Traffic signals, electric

(P-18324)
FTC - FORWARD THREAT CONTROL
234 Jason Way, Mountain View (94043-4866)
PHONE.................................650 906-7917
Frank Zajac, *Principal*
EMP: 14
SALES (est): 1.7MM **Privately Held**
WEB: www.threatcon.info
SIC: 3669 Communications equipment

(P-18325)
GENERAL DYNMICS MSSION SYSTEMS
2688 Orchard Pkwy, San Jose (95134-2020)
PHONE.................................408 908-7300
Christopher Marzilli, *President*
Jeffrey Chan, *Engineer*
Roy Reyes, *Engineer*
Fernando Ruiz, *Engineer*
Brenda Tolan, *Engineer*
EMP: 449
SALES (corp-wide): 30.9B **Publicly Held**
SIC: 3669 3812 Transportation signaling devices; search & navigation equipment
HQ: General Dynamics Mission Systems, Inc.
12450 Fair Lakes Cir # 200
Fairfax VA 22033
703 263-2800

(P-18326)
GENERAL DYNMICS MSSION SYSTEMS
112 S Lakeview Canyon Rd, Westlake Village (91362-3925)
PHONE..................................805 497-5042
Tom Melatis, *Branch Mgr*
Christopher Marzilli, *President*
Yaron Goldstein, *Software Engr*
EMP: 209
SALES (corp-wide): 30.9B **Publicly Held**
SIC: 3669 3812 7373 8711 Intercommunication systems, electric; search & navigation equipment; computer integrated systems design; engineering services
HQ: General Dynamics Mission Systems, Inc.
12450 Fair Lakes Cir # 200
Fairfax VA 22033
703 263-2800

(P-18327)
GENERAL DYNMICS MSSION SYSTEMS
Also Called: General Dynamics Adv Info Sys
4235 Forcum Ave Ste 200, McClellan (95652-2105)
PHONE..................................916 565-5316
Bob Hauser, *Branch Mgr*
Raymond Moya, *Project Mgr*
EMP: 13
SALES (corp-wide): 30.9B **Publicly Held**
SIC: 3669 3812 Transportation signaling devices; search & navigation equipment
HQ: General Dynamics Mission Systems, Inc.
12450 Fair Lakes Cir # 200
Fairfax VA 22033
703 263-2800

(P-18328)
GENERAL DYNMICS MSSION SYSTEMS
2205 Fortune Dr, San Jose (95131-1806)
PHONE..................................408 955-1900
Steve Michaud, *Branch Mgr*
Christopher Marzilli, *President*
EMP: 70
SALES (corp-wide): 30.9B **Publicly Held**
WEB: www.tripointglobal.com
SIC: 3669 Intercommunication systems, electric
HQ: General Dynamics Mission Systems, Inc.
12450 Fair Lakes Cir # 200
Fairfax VA 22033
703 263-2800

(P-18329)
GENERAL MONITORS INC (DH)
26776 Simpatica Cir, Lake Forest (92630-8128)
PHONE..................................949 581-4464
Nish Vartanian, *Vice Pres*
Richard Lamishaw, *CFO*
◆ EMP: 110
SQ FT: 60,000
SALES (est): 63.1MM
SALES (corp-wide): 1.2B **Publicly Held**
WEB: www.generalmonitors.com
SIC: 3669 1799 3812 Fire detection systems, electric; gas leakage detection; infrared object detection equipment
HQ: Mine Safety Appliances Company, Llc
1000 Cranberry Woods Dr
Cranberry Township PA 16066
724 776-8600

(P-18330)
HIGHBALL SIGNAL INC
1871 N Gaffey St Ste C, San Pedro (90731-1260)
PHONE..................................909 341-5367
Lupita Mejia, *President*
Miguel Mejia Jr, *Vice Pres*
EMP: 12
SALES (est): 2.2MM **Privately Held**
SIC: 3669 Railroad signaling devices, electric

(P-18331)
HME HOSPITALITY & SPECIALTY CO
14110 Stowe Dr, Poway (92064-7147)
PHONE..................................858 535-6139
Mike Grell, *Director*
Jennifer Styer, *Manager*
EMP: 21
SALES (est): 971.5K **Privately Held**
SIC: 3669 Intercommunication systems, electric

(P-18332)
ISMART ALARM INC
120 San Lucar Ct, Sunnyvale (94086-5213)
PHONE..................................408 245-2551
Qingwei Meng, *President*
Justin CHI, *Technology*
Grace Khor, *Accountant*
Janine Wong, *Cust Mgr*
Jake Fox, *Manager*
▲ EMP: 20
SALES (est): 1.2MM **Privately Held**
SIC: 3669 5063 7382 Burglar alarm apparatus, electric; burglar alarm systems; security systems services

(P-18333)
JOHNSON CONTROLS
3568 Ruffin Rd, San Diego (92123-2597)
PHONE..................................858 633-9100
Bob Jamieson, *Branch Mgr*
Brian Lyle, *Business Mgr*
James Potter, *Manager*
EMP: 150 **Privately Held**
WEB: www.simplexgrinnell.com
SIC: 3669 1731 1711 3873 Emergency alarms; fire detection & burglar alarm systems specialization; fire sprinkler system installation; watches, clocks, watchcases & parts; surgical appliances & supplies
HQ: Johnson Controls Fire Protection Lp
4700 Exchange Ct Ste 300
Boca Raton FL 33431
561 988-7200

(P-18334)
JOHNSON CONTROLS
6952 Preston Ave Ste A, Livermore (94551-9545)
PHONE..................................925 273-0100
Michael Fisher, *Branch Mgr*
Silvestre Cruz, *Manager*
Marji Viceral, *Manager*
EMP: 185 **Privately Held**
WEB: www.simplexgrinnell.com
SIC: 3669 1731 1711 Emergency alarms; fire detection & burglar alarm systems specialization; fire sprinkler system installation
HQ: Johnson Controls Fire Protection Lp
4700 Exchange Ct Ste 300
Boca Raton FL 33431
561 988-7200

(P-18335)
JOHNSON CONTROLS
13504 Skypark Industrial, Chico (95973-8859)
PHONE..................................530 893-0110
Christine Gilbert, *Branch Mgr*
EMP: 15 **Privately Held**
WEB: www.simplexgrinnell.com
SIC: 3669 3569 Fire alarm apparatus, electric; fire detection systems, electric; firefighting apparatus
HQ: Johnson Controls Fire Protection Lp
4700 Exchange Ct Ste 300
Boca Raton FL 33431
561 988-7200

(P-18336)
JOHNSON CONTROLS
4650 Beloit Dr, Sacramento (95838-2426)
PHONE..................................916 283-0300
Ron Ricketts, *General Mgr*
Joey Turner, *Controller*
Randy Low, *Sales Staff*
Justin Bradshaw, *Supervisor*
EMP: 85 **Privately Held**
WEB: www.simplexgrinnell.com
SIC: 3669 Emergency alarms
HQ: Johnson Controls Fire Protection Lp
4700 Exchange Ct Ste 300
Boca Raton FL 33431
561 988-7200

(P-18337)
JTB SUPPLY COMPANY INC
1030 N Batavia St Ste A, Orange (92867-5541)
PHONE..................................714 639-9558
Jeff York, *President*
Matt Pieper, *Regl Sales Mgr*
Mindy Myers, *Sales Staff*
EMP: 13
SQ FT: 10,000
SALES (est): 3.9MM **Privately Held**
WEB: www.jtbsupplyco.com
SIC: 3669 Traffic signals, electric

(P-18338)
KENDRA GROUP INC
Also Called: Bell Enterprise
2394 Saratoga Way, San Bernardino (92407-1861)
PHONE..................................909 473-7206
Ed Campana, *CFO*
Debbie Campana, *President*
Brian Linton, *Office Mgr*
Brandon Bell, *Opers Staff*
Sue Ingalls, *VP Mktg*
▼ EMP: 11
SALES (est): 5MM **Privately Held**
SIC: 3669 4953 Intercommunication systems, electric; recycling, waste materials

(P-18339)
L3 TECHNOLOGIES INC
Also Called: Photonics Division
5957 Landau Ct, Carlsbad (92008-8803)
PHONE..................................760 431-6800
Tim Call, *Vice Pres*
EMP: 150
SALES (corp-wide): 9.5B **Publicly Held**
SIC: 3669 Intercommunication systems, electric
PA: L3 Technologies, Inc.
600 3rd Ave Fl 34
New York NY 10016
212 697-1111

(P-18340)
LIFELINE SYSTEMS COMPANY
450 E Romie Ln, Salinas (93901-4029)
PHONE..................................831 755-0788
Lynn Brooks, *Director*
EMP: 150
SALES (corp-wide): 20.9B **Privately Held**
SIC: 3669 Emergency alarms
HQ: Lifeline Systems Company
111 Lawrence St
Framingham MA 01702
508 988-1000

(P-18341)
LOCTRONICS INC
3212 Luyung Dr, Rancho Cordova (95742-6830)
PHONE..................................916 638-4900
Earl R Lobley, *President*
Richard Lobley, *Vice Pres*
EMP: 50
SQ FT: 5,500
SALES: 4.4MM **Privately Held**
SIC: 3669 7539 Burglar alarm apparatus, electric; electrical services

(P-18342)
LUMENS AUDIO VISUAL INC
127 27th St Apt A, Newport Beach (92663-3461)
PHONE..................................970 988-6268
Thomas Vanden Berge, *President*
EMP: 15
SALES (est): 1.2MM **Privately Held**
SIC: 3669 Communications equipment

(P-18343)
LUMENTUM HOLDINGS INC (PA)
400 N Mccarthy Blvd, Milpitas (95035-5112)
PHONE..................................408 546-5483
Alan S Lowe, *President*
Martin A Kaplan, *Ch of Bd*
Vincent Retort, *COO*
Chris Coldren, *CFO*
Brian Lillie, *Bd of Directors*
EMP: 154
SQ FT: 126,000
SALES: 1.2B **Publicly Held**
SIC: 3669 3674 3826 Emergency alarms; semiconductors & related devices; optical isolators; analytical instruments; laser scientific & engineering instruments

(P-18344)
LUMENTUM OPERATIONS LLC (HQ)
400 N Mccarthy Blvd, Milpitas (95035-5112)
PHONE..................................408 546-5483
Alan Lowe, *CEO*
Aaron Tachibana, *CFO*
Craig Cocchi, *Senior VP*
Sharon Parker, *Senior VP*
Vince Retort, *Senior VP*
▲ EMP: 215
SALES (est): 6.9MM
SALES (corp-wide): 1.2B **Publicly Held**
SIC: 3669 8748 3999 Emergency alarms; telecommunications consultant; atomizers, toiletry
PA: Lumentum Holdings Inc.
400 N Mccarthy Blvd
Milpitas CA 95035
408 546-5483

(P-18345)
MERU NETWORKS INC (HQ)
894 Ross Dr, Sunnyvale (94089-1403)
PHONE..................................408 215-5300
Ken Xie, *CEO*
Michael Xie, *President*
Andrew Del Matto, *CFO*
Kishore Reddy, *Vice Pres*
Saurabh Bhargava, *Engineer*
▲ EMP: 92
SQ FT: 44,000
SALES (est): 100.1MM
SALES (corp-wide): 1.4B **Publicly Held**
WEB: www.merunetworks.com
SIC: 3669 Intercommunication systems, electric
PA: Fortinet, Inc.
899 Kifer Rd
Sunnyvale CA 94086
408 235-7700

(P-18346)
MICROUNITY SYSTEMS ENGINEERING
2010 El Camino Real, Santa Clara (95050-4051)
PHONE..................................408 734-8100
John Moussouris, *Ch of Bd*
Tom Buckmaster, *President*
EMP: 27
SQ FT: 6,800
SALES (est): 3.8MM **Privately Held**
WEB: www.microunity.com
SIC: 3669 3663 Intercommunication systems, electric; radio & TV communications equipment

(P-18347)
MOBILE WIRELESS TECH LLC
125 W Cerritos Ave, Anaheim (92805-6547)
PHONE..................................714 239-1535
Charles Jones, *CEO*
Harold Sabbagh, *Vice Pres*
Richard Succa, *Vice Pres*
EMP: 15
SQ FT: 5,000
SALES (est): 1MM **Privately Held**
WEB: www.gomobilewireless.com
SIC: 3669 Transportation signaling devices; intercommunication systems, electric

(P-18348)
MYERS & SONS HI-WAY SAFETY INC
520 W Grand Ave, Escondido (92025-2502)
P.O. Box 1030, Chino (91708-1030)
PHONE..................................909 591-1781
Rod Lowry, *Manager*
EMP: 30
SALES (corp-wide): 47.8MM **Privately Held**
WEB: www.hiwaysafety.com
SIC: 3669 3499 Transportation signaling devices; barricades, metal

PRODUCTS & SVCS

PA: Myers & Son's Hi-Way Safety Inc.
13310 5th St
Chino CA 91710
909 591-1781

(P-18349)
MYERS & SONS HI-WAY SAFETY INC (PA)
13310 5th St, Chino (91710-5125)
P.O. Box 1030 (91708-1030)
PHONE..................................909 591-1781
Michael Rodgers, *CEO*
Brandon Myer, *Exec VP*
Kevin Keith, *Purchasing*
▲ EMP: 120 EST: 1975
SQ FT: 36,400
SALES (est): 47.8MM **Privately Held**
WEB: www.hiwaysafety.com
SIC: 3669 Pedestrian traffic control equipment

(P-18350)
NIGHT OPTICS USA INC
605 Oro Dam Blvd E, Oroville (95965-5718)
PHONE..................................714 899-4475
Ilya Reyngold, *CEO*
Rimma Epelbaum, *CFO*
Israel Reyngold, *Vice Pres*
◆ EMP: 13
SQ FT: 4,600
SALES (est): 2.1MM
SALES (corp-wide): 2.3B **Publicly Held**
WEB: www.nightopticsusa.com
SIC: 3669 3827 Visual communication systems; optical instruments & apparatus
PA: Vista Outdoor Inc.
262 N University Ave
Farmington UT 84025
801 447-3000

(P-18351)
OPTEX INCORPORATED
18730 S Wilmington Ave # 100, Compton (90220-5924)
PHONE..................................800 966-7839
Makoto Kokobo, *CEO*
Tohru Kobayashi, *Ch of Bd*
James Quick, *President*
Michael La Chere, *CFO*
Clint Choate, *Vice Pres*
▲ EMP: 17
SQ FT: 35,000
SALES (est): 3.2MM
SALES (corp-wide): 334.7MM **Privately Held**
WEB: www.optexamerica.com
SIC: 3669 Emergency alarms
PA: Optex Group Company, Limited
5-8-12, Ogoto
Otsu SGA 520-0
775 798-000

(P-18352)
PALOMAR PRODUCTS INC
23042 Arroyo Vis, Rcho STA Marg (92688-2604)
PHONE..................................949 858-8836
Kevin Moschetti, *CEO*
Val Policky, *President*
Fred Ekstein, *Vice Pres*
Karen Tayler, *General Mgr*
Christopher Jones, *Project Mgr*
EMP: 79 EST: 1997
SQ FT: 35,000
SALES (est): 16.8MM
SALES (corp-wide): 2B **Publicly Held**
WEB: www.palpro.com
SIC: 3669 Intercommunication systems, electric
PA: Esterline Technologies Corp
500 108th Ave Ne Ste 1500
Bellevue WA 98004
425 453-9400

(P-18353)
PROTO SERVICES INC
Also Called: PSI
1991 Concourse Dr, San Jose (95131-1708)
PHONE..................................408 321-8688
Nicky Wu, *CEO*
EMP: 40
SQ FT: 25,000

SALES: 4MM **Privately Held**
WEB: www.protoservices.com
SIC: 3669 Visual communication systems

(P-18354)
PROXIM WIRELESS CORPORATION (PA)
2114 Ringwood Ave, San Jose (95131-1715)
PHONE..................................408 383-7600
Greg Marzullo, *President*
Steve Button, *CFO*
David Porte, *Senior VP*
David L Renauld, *Vice Pres*
David Sumi, *Vice Pres*
▲ EMP: 55
SQ FT: 42,500
SALES (est): 34.1MM **Publicly Held**
SIC: 3669 Signaling apparatus, electric

(P-18355)
Q I S INC
28005 Oregon Pl, Quail Valley (92587-9045)
P.O. Box 1220, Garden Grove (92842-1220)
PHONE..................................951 244-0500
Dennis Daigle, *President*
Shelly Daigle, *Admin Sec*
EMP: 10
SQ FT: 2,000
SALES (est): 1.3MM **Privately Held**
SIC: 3669 Intercommunication systems, electric

(P-18356)
QUALCOMM MEMS TECHNOLOGIES INC
5775 Morehouse Dr, San Diego (92121-1714)
PHONE..................................858 587-1121
Greg Heinzinger, *Senior VP*
Adrian Ong, *President*
Derek Aberle, *Exec VP*
Junchen Du, *Engineer*
Jenny Gong, *Engineer*
EMP: 31
SQ FT: 9,000
SALES (est): 17.9MM
SALES (corp-wide): 22.2B **Publicly Held**
WEB: www.iridigm.com
SIC: 3669 Visual communication systems
PA: Qualcomm Incorporated
5775 Morehouse Dr
San Diego CA 92121
858 587-1121

(P-18357)
RAYTHEON APPLIED SIGNAL (HQ)
460 W California Ave, Sunnyvale (94086-5148)
PHONE..................................408 749-1888
John R Treichler, *CEO*
William B Van Vleet III, *CEO*
Mark M Andersson, *COO*
James E Doyle, *CFO*
R Fred Roscher, *Exec VP*
EMP: 208
SQ FT: 266,077
SALES (est): 164MM
SALES (corp-wide): 25.3B **Publicly Held**
SIC: 3669 Signaling apparatus, electric
PA: Raytheon Company
870 Winter St
Waltham MA 02451
781 522-3000

(P-18358)
RAYTHEON APPLIED SIGNAL
160 N Rverview Dr Ste 300, Anaheim (92808)
PHONE..................................714 917-0255
John McGrory, *Branch Mgr*
EMP: 10
SALES (corp-wide): 25.3B **Publicly Held**
SIC: 3669 Signaling apparatus, electric
HQ: Raytheon Applied Signal Technology, Inc.
460 W California Ave
Sunnyvale CA 94086
408 749-1888

(P-18359)
RIEDEL COMMUNICATIONS INC
2508 N Ontario St, Burbank (91504-2512)
PHONE..................................818 559-6900
Thomas Riedel, *President*
Janis Fontein, *Finance Mgr*
EMP: 19
SALES (est): 3.8MM
SALES (corp-wide): 117.2MM **Privately Held**
WEB: www.riedel.net
SIC: 3669 Emergency alarms
PA: Riedel Communications Gmbh & Co. Kg
Uellendahler Str. 353
Wuppertal 42109
202 292-90

(P-18360)
RSG/AAMES SECURITY INC
3300 E 59th St, Long Beach (90805-4504)
PHONE..................................562 529-5100
Louis J Finkle, *President*
Danielle Roberts, *Shareholder*
Michelle Reuven, *Office Mgr*
▲ EMP: 20
SQ FT: 17,000
SALES (est): 3.2MM **Privately Held**
WEB: www.rsgsecurity.com
SIC: 3669 Fire alarm apparatus, electric

(P-18361)
SAFARILAND LLC (DH)
3120 E Mission Blvd, Ontario (91761-2900)
PHONE..................................925 219-1097
Scott O'Brien, *President*
Scott Harris, *CFO*
Michelle Boyer, *Vice Pres*
Roger Cox, *Vice Pres*
Jim Duncan, *Vice Pres*
EMP: 22 EST: 1996
SQ FT: 2,000
SALES (est): 2.6MM
SALES (corp-wide): 875.1MM **Privately Held**
WEB: www.tacticalcommand.com
SIC: 3669 Intercommunication systems, electric
HQ: Safariland, Llc
13386 International Pkwy
Jacksonville FL 32218
904 741-5400

(P-18362)
SENSYS NETWORKS INC (PA)
Also Called: Senetrics International
1608 4th St Ste 200, Berkeley (94710-1749)
PHONE..................................510 548-4620
Amine Haoui, *President*
Brian Fuller, *President*
Karen Camp, *CFO*
Robert Kavaler, *Senior VP*
Hamed Benouar, *Vice Pres*
▲ EMP: 64
SALES (est): 12.7MM **Privately Held**
SIC: 3669 Transportation signaling devices

(P-18363)
SIEMENS RAIL AUTOMATION CORP
9568 Archibald Ave, Rancho Cucamonga (91730-5710)
PHONE..................................909 532-5405
Jay Aslam, *Opers Mgr*
Elizabeth Teague, *Human Res Mgr*
John Rouse, *Purch Mgr*
Richard V Peel, *Mfg Staff*
Gary Thompson, *Manager*
EMP: 250
SALES (corp-wide): 97.7B **Privately Held**
SIC: 3669 Railroad signaling devices, electric
HQ: Siemens Rail Automation Corporation
2400 Nelson Miller Pkwy
Louisville KY 40223
502 244-7400

(P-18364)
SIERRA PHOTONICS INC
Also Called: S P I
7563 Southfront Rd, Livermore (94551-8226)
PHONE..................................925 290-2930
Anthony Ruggiero, *President*
Eileen Bettman, *Treasurer*

Darlene Litcher, *Treasurer*
EMP: 25
SQ FT: 20,000
SALES: 1.8MM **Privately Held**
SIC: 3669 Intercommunication systems, electric

(P-18365)
SIERRA TRAFFIC SERVICE INC
225 W Loop Dr, Camarillo (93010-2038)
P.O. Box 222, Somis (93066-0222)
PHONE..................................805 388-2474
Terry Quinones, *President*
EMP: 12
SALES (est): 1.9MM **Privately Held**
SIC: 3669 Pedestrian traffic control equipment

(P-18366)
SIGTRONICS CORPORATION
178 E Arrow Hwy, San Dimas (91773-3336)
PHONE..................................909 305-9399
Mark Kelley, *President*
Tim Theis, *Vice Pres*
Frank M Sigona, *Principal*
Jane Sigona, *Principal*
Steve Daw, *Info Tech Mgr*
EMP: 20
SQ FT: 12,000
SALES (est): 4.1MM **Privately Held**
WEB: www.sigtronics.com
SIC: 3669 Intercommunication systems, electric

(P-18367)
STATEWIDE SAFETY AND SIGNS I
522 Lindon Ln, Nipomo (93444-9222)
PHONE..................................714 468-1919
Greg Grosch, *CEO*
Don Nicholas, *President*
Chris Burns, *CFO*
Kenneth Haley, *Accounts Mgr*
Eric Marquez, *Accounts Mgr*
EMP: 300
SALES (est): 69.2MM **Privately Held**
SIC: 3669 Pedestrian traffic control equipment

(P-18368)
SYSTECH CORPORATION
10908 Technology Pl, San Diego (92127-1874)
PHONE..................................858 674-6500
D Mark Fowler, *President*
Don Armerding, *Vice Pres*
Zenon Barelka, *Vice Pres*
Jon Goby, *Vice Pres*
Cheri Houchin, *Vice Pres*
▲ EMP: 35 EST: 1980
SQ FT: 25,000
SALES (est): 6.9MM **Privately Held**
WEB: www.systech.com
SIC: 3669 7371 3661 3577 Intercommunication systems, electric; custom computer programming services; telephone & telegraph apparatus; computer peripheral equipment

(P-18369)
TACTICAL COMMUNICATIONS CORP
473 Post St, Camarillo (93010-8553)
PHONE..................................805 987-4100
Gregory Peacock, *Ch of Bd*
E Carey Walter, *CEO*
Doug Fuller, *Info Tech Mgr*
Carey Walters, *Info Tech Mgr*
Lop Ng, *Engineer*
EMP: 25
SQ FT: 11,000
SALES (est): 4.6MM **Privately Held**
SIC: 3669 Intercommunication systems, electric

(P-18370)
TC COMMUNICATIONS INC
17881 Cartwright Rd, Irvine (92614-6216)
PHONE..................................949 852-1972
Kai Liang, *President*
Daphne Wang, *CFO*
Fredrick Chow, *Technical Staff*
Chin Tang, *Senior Buyer*
Alex Hernandez, *Sales Staff*
◆ EMP: 42

▲ = Import ▼ =Export
◆ =Import/Export

SQ FT: 54,000
SALES (est): 7.2MM Privately Held
WEB: www.tccomm.com
SIC: 3669 Visual communication systems

(P-18371)
TEAM ECONOLITE
Also Called: Aegis Its
1810 Oakland Rd Ste E, San Jose
(95131-2316)
PHONE.....................408 577-1733
John Cane, General Mgr
EMP: 10
SALES (est): 1.4MM Privately Held
WEB: www.teameconolite.com
SIC: 3669 Traffic signals, electric

(P-18372)
TRAFFIX DEVICES INC (PA)
160 Avenida La Pata, San Clemente
(92673-6304)
PHONE.....................949 361-5663
Jack H Kulp, President
Suzanne Kulp, Corp Secy
Brent M Kulp, Vice Pres
Maurice Havens, General Mgr
Andrew Maxwell, Web Dvlpr
◆ EMP: 15
SQ FT: 10,000
SALES (est): 13MM Privately Held
WEB: www.traffixdevices.com
SIC: 3669 Transportation signaling devices

(P-18373)
TTB PRODUCTS INC (PA)
220 Calle Pintoresco, San Clemente
(92672-7505)
PHONE.....................949 369-1475
Bob Wielenga, President
▲ EMP: 12
SALES (est): 7.5MM Privately Held
WEB: www.ttbproducts.com
SIC: 3669 2759 Transportation signaling
devices; screen printing

(P-18374)
UNICOM ELECTRIC INC
565 Brea Canyon Rd Ste A, Walnut
(91789-3004)
PHONE.....................626 964-7873
Jeffrey Lo, President
Christopher Lin, Manager
▲ EMP: 32
SQ FT: 25,000
SALES: 1.5MM Privately Held
WEB: www.unicomlink.com
SIC: 3669 3678 3577 Intercommunication
systems, electric; electronic connectors;
computer peripheral equipment

(P-18375)
**VANGUARD NETWORING
PRODUCTS**
Also Called: Vanguard Elect
7412 Prince Dr, Huntington Beach
(92647-4553)
PHONE.....................714 842-3330
Ken Finley, President
John Kooklan, Exec VP
Nasir Mahmood, Vice Pres
Sandy Lowe, Sales Staff
EMP: 325
SALES (est): 22.1MM
SALES (corp-wide): 23.4MM Privately
Held
SIC: 3669 Visual communication systems
PA: Vanguard Electronics Company
17941 Brookshire Ln
Huntington Beach CA 92647
714 842-3330

(P-18376)
**VERSACALL TECHNOLOGIES
INC**
7047 Carroll Rd, San Diego (92121-3273)
PHONE.....................858 677-6766
Robert A Giese, President
EMP: 11 EST: 2000
SQ FT: 5,000
SALES (est): 2.6MM Privately Held
WEB: www.versacall.com
SIC: 3669 Visual communication systems

(P-18377)
**VOCERA COMMUNICATIONS
INC (PA)**
525 Race St Ste 150, San Jose
(95126-3497)
PHONE.....................408 882-5100
Brent D Lang, Ch of Bd
Justin R Spencer, CFO
M Bridget Duffy, Chief Mktg Ofcr
Paul T Johnson, Exec VP
Douglas A Carlen, Vice Pres
EMP: 186
SQ FT: 70,000
SALES: 162.5MM Publicly Held
WEB: www.vocera.com
SIC: 3669 Intercommunication systems,
electric

(P-18378)
WESTEK ELECTRONICS INC
185 Westridge Dr, Watsonville
(95076-4167)
PHONE.....................831 740-6300
Kevin Larkin, CEO
Amy Eades, Principal
Susie Freitas, Principal
Javier Ramirez, Principal
▲ EMP: 40
SQ FT: 1,220
SALES (est): 8.1MM Privately Held
WEB: www.westekelectronics.com
SIC: 3669 Intercommunication systems,
electric

(P-18379)
WESTERN PACIFIC SIGNAL LLC
15890 Foothill Blvd, San Leandro
(94578-2101)
PHONE.....................510 276-6400
Heidi Shupp, President
Donald R Shupp, Vice Pres
Karen Gonzalez, Executive
Erica Casillas, Technician
Elizabeth Aziz, Sales Staff
EMP: 15
SQ FT: 6,500
SALES (est): 3.9MM Privately Held
WEB: www.wpsignal.com
SIC: 3669 Traffic signals, electric

**3671 Radio & T V Receiving
Electron Tubes**

(P-18380)
ACCURATE SOLUTIONS INC
2273 Wales Dr, Cardiff By The Sea
(92007-1509)
PHONE.....................760 753-6524
Tod Kilgore, President
Steven Freeman, Corp Secy
Eric Pinson, Vice Pres
EMP: 10
SQ FT: 2,400
SALES (est): 714.2K Privately Held
SIC: 3671 Electronic tube parts, except
glass blanks

(P-18381)
**AQUA BACKFLOW AND
CHLORINATION**
1060 Northgate St Ste C, Riverside
(92507-2172)
PHONE.....................909 598-7251
Shirley Rogers, President
Duane Rogers, Treasurer
Chris Spaulding, Principal
Nicole Spaulding, Director
EMP: 10
SQ FT: 1,200
SALES (est): 2MM Privately Held
SIC: 3671 7699 Electron tubes, industrial;
industrial equipment services

(P-18382)
**COMMUNICATIONS & PWR INDS
LLC**
Also Called: CPI
607 Hansen Way, Palo Alto (94304-1015)
PHONE.....................650 846-3494
Michael Cheng, Branch Mgr
EMP: 150
SQ FT: 25,000 Privately Held
WEB: www.cpii.com

SIC: 3671 Electron tubes
HQ: Communications & Power Industries
Llc
607 Hansen Way
Palo Alto CA 94304
-

(P-18383)
**COMMUNICATIONS & PWR INDS
LLC (DH)**
Also Called: CPI
607 Hansen Way, Palo Alto (94304-1015)
PHONE.....................650 846-2900
Robert A Fickett, President
Joel A Littman, CFO
John Beighley, Vice Pres
Don C Coleman, Vice Pres
Andrew Tafler, Principal
◆ EMP: 720
SQ FT: 429,000
SALES (est): 419.8MM Privately Held
WEB: www.cpii.com
SIC: 3671 3679 3699 3663 Vacuum
tubes; microwave components; power
supplies, all types: static; electrical equip-
ment & supplies; radio & TV communica-
tions equipment
HQ: Cpi International, Inc.
811 Hansen Way
Palo Alto CA 94304
650 846-2801

(P-18384)
**COMMUNICATIONS & PWR INDS
LLC**
Also Called: Microwave Power Products Div
811 Hansen Way, Palo Alto (94304-1031)
PHONE.....................650 846-2900
Rasheda Begum, Engineer
Greg Rey, Engineer
EMP: 130 Privately Held
SIC: 3671 Vacuum tubes
HQ: Communications & Power Industries
Llc
607 Hansen Way
Palo Alto CA 94304
-

(P-18385)
CPI INTERNATIONAL INC (HQ)
811 Hansen Way, Palo Alto (94304-1031)
PHONE.....................650 846-2801
Robert A Fickett, CEO
Joe Caldarelli, Ch of Bd
Joel A Littman, CFO
Veronica Tsui, Treasurer
John R Beighley, Vice Pres
EMP: 10
SQ FT: 418,300
SALES (est): 397.1MM Privately Held
WEB: www.cpiinternational.net
SIC: 3671 3679 3699 3825 Traveling
wave tubes; vacuum tubes; microwave
components; power supplies, all types:
static; electrical equipment & supplies;
radio frequency measuring equipment

(P-18386)
**DCX-CHOL ENTERPRISES INC
(PA)**
Also Called: Smi, Scb
12831 S Figueroa St, Los Angeles
(90061-1157)
PHONE.....................310 516-1692
Neal Castleman, President
Chanti Mahasena, Partner
Jack Cate, CFO
Brian Gamberg, Vice Pres
Garret Hoffman, Vice Pres
▲ EMP: 80
SQ FT: 50,000
SALES (est): 145.3MM Privately Held
SIC: 3671 Electron tubes

(P-18387)
DCX-CHOL ENTERPRISES INC
Teletronic Div Dcx-Chol Entp
12831 S Figueroa St, Los Angeles
(90061-1157)
PHONE.....................310 516-1692
Neil Levy, Director
EMP: 80

SALES (corp-wide): 145.3MM Privately
Held
SIC: 3671 3679 Electron tubes; harness
assemblies for electronic use: wire or
cable
PA: Dcx-Chol Enterprises, Inc.
12831 S Figueroa St
Los Angeles CA 90061
310 516-1692

(P-18388)
DCX-CHOL ENTERPRISES INC
New-Vac Division
9330 Desoto Ave, Chatsworth (91311)
PHONE.....................310 516-1692
Garrett Hoffman, Branch Mgr
Alex Benavidez, IT/INT Sup
Ed Castillo, Design Engr
Lola Herron, VP Finance
Ruben Crespo, Opers Mgr
EMP: 80
SALES (corp-wide): 145.3MM Privately
Held
SIC: 3671 3678 3679 Electron tubes;
electronic connectors; harness assem-
blies for electronic use: wire or cable
PA: Dcx-Chol Enterprises, Inc.
12831 S Figueroa St
Los Angeles CA 90061
310 516-1692

(P-18389)
DCX-CHOL ENTERPRISES INC
Also Called: Masterite Division
12831 S Figueroa St, Los Angeles
(90061-1157)
PHONE.....................310 516-1692
Brian Gamberg, Branch Mgr
EMP: 16
SALES (corp-wide): 145.3MM Privately
Held
SIC: 3671 3365 Electron tubes; aerospace
castings, aluminum
PA: Dcx-Chol Enterprises, Inc.
12831 S Figueroa St
Los Angeles CA 90061
310 516-1692

(P-18390)
DCX-CHOL ENTERPRISES INC
12831 S Figueroa St, Los Angeles
(90061-1157)
PHONE.....................310 525-1205
Neil Castleman, President
EMP: 46
SALES (corp-wide): 145.3MM Privately
Held
SIC: 3671 3365 Electron tubes; aerospace
castings, aluminum
PA: Dcx-Chol Enterprises, Inc.
12831 S Figueroa St
Los Angeles CA 90061
310 516-1692

(P-18391)
DCX-CHOL ENTERPRISES INC
Also Called: Dcx Division
9330 De Soto Ave, Chatsworth
(91311-4926)
PHONE.....................310 715-6946
Allan Swanson, General Mgr
EMP: 50
SALES (corp-wide): 145.3MM Privately
Held
SIC: 3671 3672 3429 Electron tubes;
printed circuit boards; manufactured hard-
ware (general)
PA: Dcx-Chol Enterprises, Inc.
12831 S Figueroa St
Los Angeles CA 90061
310 516-1692

(P-18392)
**L3 ELECTRON DEVICES INC
(HQ)**
3100 Lomita Blvd, Torrance (90505-5104)
P.O. Box 2999 (90509-2999)
PHONE.....................310 517-6000
Michael Strianese, CEO
Robert Vasquez, General Mgr
Gary Wise, Technical Staff
Ray Robinson, Manager
▲ EMP: 658

(PA)=Parent Co (HQ)=Headquarters (DH)=Div Headquarters
♻ = New Business established in last 2 years

SALES (est): 170MM
SALES (corp-wide): 9.5B **Publicly Held**
SIC: 3671 3764 Traveling wave tubes; guided missile & space vehicle propulsion unit parts
PA: L3 Technologies, Inc.
600 3rd Ave Fl 34
New York NY 10016
212 697-1111

(P-18393)
LEEMAH CORPORATION (PA)
155 S Hill Dr, Brisbane (94005-1203)
PHONE....................................415 394-1288
Efrem Mah, *CEO*
Bing Hong Mah, *President*
Warren Gee, *CFO*
Dick Wong, *Admin Sec*
▲ EMP: 150
SQ FT: 60,000
SALES (est): 101MM **Privately Held**
WEB: www.leemah.com
SIC: 3671 3672 3669 3663 Electron tubes; printed circuit boards; intercommunication systems, electric; radio & TV communications equipment; computer peripheral equipment

(P-18394)
PENTA FINANCIAL INC
Also Called: Penta Laboratories
7868 Deering Ave, Canoga Park (91304-5005)
PHONE....................................818 882-3872
Steve Sanett, *CEO*
Susan Sanett, *President*
▲ EMP: 24
SQ FT: 24,000
SALES (est): 2.8MM **Privately Held**
WEB: www.pentalabs.com
SIC: 3671 7699 Electron tubes; stove repair shop; restaurant equipment repair

(P-18395)
PENTA LABORATORIES LLC
7868 Deering Ave, Canoga Park (91304-5005)
PHONE....................................818 882-3872
Susan E Sanett, *President*
Wayne Coturri, *President*
Neil Towey, *Vice Pres*
John Grandinetti, *Sales Staff*
Holly Koenigsaecker, *Sales Staff*
▲ EMP: 15
SALES (est): 4.5MM **Privately Held**
SIC: 3671 5065 Electron tubes; electronic tubes: receiving & transmitting or industrial

(P-18396)
SONY ELECTRONICS INC
Sony Display Device Pdts Div
16530 Via Esprillo, San Diego (92127-1708)
PHONE....................................858 942-2400
Fred Ishii, *Senior VP*
Debbie Zerbini, *IT/INT Sup*
Catherine Wozney, *Manager*
EMP: 250
SALES (corp-wide): 80.1B **Privately Held**
SIC: 3671 3651 Electron tubes; household audio & video equipment
HQ: Sony Electronics Inc.
16535 Via Esprillo Bldg 1
San Diego CA 92127
858 942-2400

(P-18397)
THERMO KEVEX X-RAY INC
320 El Pueblo Rd, Scotts Valley (95066-4219)
PHONE....................................831 438-5940
Marijn Dekkers, *President*
Mark Chatfield, *Director*
EMP: 34
SQ FT: 16,800
SALES (est): 5.6MM
SALES (corp-wide): 20.9B **Publicly Held**
WEB: www.thermo.com
SIC: 3671 3679 3844 Transmittal, industrial & special purpose electron tubes; power supplies, all types: static; X-ray apparatus & tubes

PA: Thermo Fisher Scientific Inc.
168 3rd Ave
Waltham MA 02451
781 622-1000

(P-18398)
VACUUM TUBE LOGIC OF AMERICA
4774 Murietta St Ste 10, Chino (91710-5155)
P.O. Box 2604, Sunnyvale (94087-0604)
PHONE....................................909 627-5944
Luke Manley, *President*
EMP: 15
SALES (est): 1.5MM **Privately Held**
SIC: 3671 Electron tubes

(P-18399)
VARIAN MEDICAL SYSTEMS INC
Also Called: Varian Thin Film Systems
3175 Hanover St, Palo Alto (94304-1130)
P.O. Box 10032 (94303-0896)
PHONE....................................650 493-4000
Boris Lipkin, *General Mgr*
EMP: 15
SALES (corp-wide): 2.6B **Publicly Held**
SIC: 3671 3663 3699 3563 Electron tubes, special purpose; transmitting apparatus, radio or television; amplifiers, RF power & IF; electrical equipment & supplies; linear accelerators; air & gas compressors; vacuum pumps, except laboratory; industrial instrmnts msrmnt display/control process variable; chromatographs, industrial process type; analytical instruments; spectrometers; photometers
PA: Varian Medical Systems, Inc.
3100 Hansen Way
Palo Alto CA 94304
650 493-4000

3672 Printed Circuit Boards

(P-18400)
A & M ELECTRONICS INC
25018 Avenue Kearny, Valencia (91355-1253)
PHONE....................................661 257-3680
Ron Simpson, *President*
Tiffiny Simpson, *Vice Pres*
Dan Simpson, *Manager*
EMP: 30
SQ FT: 12,000
SALES (est): 7MM **Privately Held**
WEB: www.aandmelectronics.com
SIC: 3672 Circuit boards, television & radio printed

(P-18401)
A AND C ELECTRONICS
18153 Napa St, Northridge (91325-3377)
PHONE....................................818 886-8900
Frank Sampo, *President*
Louis Pacent III, *Treasurer*
EMP: 10
SQ FT: 6,000
SALES (est): 4.7MM **Privately Held**
WEB: www.acelectronics.com
SIC: 3672 Circuit boards, television & radio printed

(P-18402)
ABSOLUTE TURNKEY SERVICES INC
555 Aldo Ave, Santa Clara (95054-2205)
PHONE....................................408 850-7530
Jeffrey Bullis, *CEO*
Michelle Gaynor, *Vice Pres*
Dorothy Gonzalez, *Purch Mgr*
Dorothy Litle, *Purch Mgr*
EMP: 40
SQ FT: 17,000
SALES (est): 8.7MM **Privately Held**
WEB: www.absoluteturnkey.com
SIC: 3672 Printed circuit boards

(P-18403)
ACCU-SEMBLY INC
1835 Huntington Dr, Duarte (91010-2635)
PHONE....................................626 357-3447

John Hykes, *CEO*
Jan Shimmin, *Shareholder*
John Shimmin, *Shareholder*
Marilyn Hykes, *Admin Dir*
Joseph Santana, *Program Mgr*
▲ EMP: 95
SQ FT: 15,000
SALES (est): 29.3MM **Privately Held**
WEB: www.accu-sembly.com
SIC: 3672 Printed circuit boards

(P-18404)
ACCURATE CIRCUIT ENGRG INC
Also Called: Ace
3019 Kilson Dr, Santa Ana (92707-4202)
PHONE....................................714 546-2162
Charles Lowe, *CEO*
James Hofer, *General Mgr*
Charels Lowe, *Info Tech Mgr*
Tim Waddell, *Engineer*
Frank Yuen, *Engineer*
▲ EMP: 70
SQ FT: 15,000
SALES: 7.2MM **Privately Held**
WEB: www.ace-pcb.com
SIC: 3672 Printed circuit boards

(P-18405)
ACCURATE ENGINEERING INC
8710 Telfair Ave, Sun Valley (91352-2530)
PHONE....................................818 768-3919
Rush Patel, *President*
Ramesh Jasani, *Shareholder*
Gautam Jasani, *CFO*
Suresh Jasani, *Treasurer*
Hiten Golakiea, *Vice Pres*
EMP: 25
SQ FT: 15,000
SALES (est): 4.7MM
SALES (corp-wide): 10.2MM **Privately Held**
WEB: www.accueng.com
SIC: 3672 Printed circuit boards
PA: Austin Engineering Company Limited
Village Patla, Taluka Bhesan
Junagadh GJ 36203
287 325-2223

(P-18406)
ACTION ELECTRONIC ASSEMBLY INC
Also Called: Prowave Manufacturing
2872 S Santa Fe Ave, San Marcos (92069-6046)
PHONE....................................760 510-0003
Salim Khalfan, *President*
Deborah A Walker, *Treasurer*
EMP: 25
SQ FT: 4,000
SALES: 2.7MM **Privately Held**
WEB: www.prowavemfg.com
SIC: 3672 Printed circuit boards

(P-18407)
ADDISON TECHNOLOGY INC
Also Called: Addison Engineering
150 Nortech Pkwy, San Jose (95134-2305)
PHONE....................................408 749-1000
Gibson Cobb, *President*
Jim Landis, *Vice Pres*
Jeff Besterman, *Accounts Mgr*
▲ EMP: 45
SQ FT: 40,000
SALES (est): 4.7MM **Privately Held**
WEB: www.addisonengineering.com
SIC: 3672 5065 Printed circuit boards; semiconductor devices

(P-18408)
ADURA LED SOLUTIONS LLC
511 Princeland Ct, Corona (92879-1383)
PHONE....................................714 660-2944
Kris Vasoya,
▲ EMP: 10
SALES (est): 1.4MM **Privately Held**
SIC: 3672 5719 Printed circuit boards; lighting fixtures

(P-18409)
ADVANCE ELECTRONIC SERVICE
44141 Fremont Blvd, Fremont (94538-6044)
PHONE....................................510 490-1065
Patrick Chan, *President*
EMP: 20

SALES (est): 500K **Privately Held**
SIC: 3672 Circuit boards, television & radio printed

(P-18410)
ADVANCED ASSEMBLIES INC
990 Richard Ave Ste 109, Santa Clara (95050-2828)
PHONE....................................408 988-1016
Kim N Tran, *President*
Charles Mosqueda, *Sales Staff*
EMP: 12
SQ FT: 7,450
SALES (est): 805.2K **Privately Held**
WEB: www.advancedassemblies.net
SIC: 3672 Circuit boards, television & radio printed

(P-18411)
ALL QUALITY & SERVICES INC
Also Called: Aqs
401 Kato Ter, Fremont (94539-8333)
PHONE....................................510 249-5800
So Jin Lee, *President*
John Park, *Chief Mktg Ofcr*
Raymond Luk, *Business Dir*
Hans Krasnow, *MIS Dir*
Dawn Lauterbach, *Business Anlyst*
▲ EMP: 120
SQ FT: 82,000
SALES (est): 47.1MM **Privately Held**
WEB: www.aqs-inc.com
SIC: 3672 3651 Printed circuit boards; electronic kits for home assembly: radio, TV, phonograph

(P-18412)
ALLIED ELECTRONIC SERVICES
1342 E Borchard Ave, Santa Ana (92705-4413)
PHONE....................................714 245-2500
Dave Vadodaria, *President*
Bharati Vadodaria, *CFO*
Susan Henry, *Representative*
EMP: 15
SQ FT: 6,000
SALES (est): 2.1MM **Privately Held**
SIC: 3672 Printed circuit boards

(P-18413)
ALMATRON ELECTRONICS INC
644 Young St, Santa Ana (92705-5633)
PHONE....................................714 557-6000
Margarito Alvarez, *President*
Margarita Alvarez, *Owner*
Sergio Rivera, *Purch Agent*
EMP: 30
SQ FT: 11,500
SALES (est): 4.8MM **Privately Held**
WEB: www.almatron.com
SIC: 3672 Circuit boards, television & radio printed

(P-18414)
ALPHA EMS CORPORATION
44419 S Grimmer Blvd, Fremont (94538-6350)
PHONE....................................510 498-8788
Eric Chang, *President*
Dave Kichar, *Senior VP*
Shu-Lin Chen, *Vice Pres*
Jim Creel, *Vice Pres*
Ben Wang, *Vice Pres*
EMP: 150
SQ FT: 50,000
SALES: 13.3MM **Privately Held**
SIC: 3672 Printed circuit boards

(P-18415)
ALTA MANUFACTURING INC
47650 Westinghouse Dr, Fremont (94539-7473)
PHONE....................................510 668-1870
Anne Lee, *CEO*
EMP: 30
SQ FT: 24,000
SALES (est): 8MM **Privately Held**
WEB: www.altamfg.com
SIC: 3672 Printed circuit boards

(P-18416)
ALTAFLEX
336 Martin Ave, Santa Clara (95050-3112)
PHONE....................................408 727-6614
Shawn Thompson, *President*
Shawn Thompson, *President*

▲ = Import ▼=Export
◆ =Import/Export

Robert Jung, *General Mgr*
EMP: 52 **EST:** 2000
SQ FT: 20,200
SALES: 13MM
SALES (corp-wide): 1B **Publicly Held**
WEB: www.altaflex.com
SIC: 3672 Printed circuit boards
HQ: Osi Electronics, Inc.
   12533 Chadron Ave
   Hawthorne CA 90250
   310 978-0516

(P-18417)
AMBAY CIRCUITS INC
Also Called: Delta Dvh Circuits
16117 Leadwell St, Van Nuys
(91406-3417)
PHONE..........................818 786-8241
Kana Khunti, *President*
EMP: 12 **EST:** 1973
SQ FT: 5,500
SALES (est): 1.9MM **Privately Held**
SIC: 3672 Circuit boards, television & radio printed

(P-18418)
AMERICAN BOARD ASSEMBLY INC
5456 Endeavour Ct, Moorpark
(93021-1705)
PHONE..........................805 523-0274
Gene Difabritis, *President*
Cindy Murray, *COO*
Bob Swet, *Engineer*
▲ **EMP:** 140
SQ FT: 11,000
SALES (est): 45.1MM **Privately Held**
WEB: www.americanboard.com
SIC: 3672 Printed circuit boards

(P-18419)
AMERICAN CIRCUIT TECH INC (PA)
5330 E Hunter Ave, Anaheim (92807-2053)
PHONE..........................714 777-2480
Ravi Kheni, *President*
Labheu Zalavadia, *Vice Pres*
Kanu Patel, *Executive*
Giradhar Butani, *General Mgr*
EMP: 40
SQ FT: 22,000
SALES (est): 6.3MM **Privately Held**
WEB: www.act-cw.com
SIC: 3672 Circuit boards, television & radio printed

(P-18420)
AMPRO SYSTEMS INC
1000 Page Ave, Fremont (94538-7340)
PHONE..........................510 624-9000
Elliot Wang, *President*
▲ **EMP:** 45 **EST:** 1997
SQ FT: 21,000
SALES (est): 7.5MM **Privately Held**
WEB: www.amprosystems.com
SIC: 3672 Printed circuit boards

(P-18421)
AMTECH MICROELECTRONICS INC
485 Cochrane Cir, Morgan Hill
(95037-2831)
PHONE..........................408 612-8888
Walter Chavez, *President*
Chris Wright, *Engineer*
Dave Bringuel, *Sales Staff*
EMP: 42
SQ FT: 14,500
SALES (est): 6.8MM **Privately Held**
WEB: www.amtechmicro.com
SIC: 3672 Printed circuit boards

(P-18422)
ANC TECHNOLOGY
Also Called: Shanghai Anc Electronic Tech
10195 Stockton Rd, Moorpark
(93021-9755)
PHONE..........................805 530-3958
Dennis Noble, *Owner*
▲ **EMP:** 100
SQ FT: 60,000
SALES: 10MM **Privately Held**
WEB: www.anctech.com
SIC: 3672 5083 Printed circuit boards; irrigation equipment

(P-18423)
APCT INC (PA)
Also Called: (FORMER: ADVANCED PRINTED CIRCUIT TECHNOLOGY)
3495 De La Cruz Blvd, Santa Clara (95054-2110)
PHONE..........................408 727-6442
Steve Robinson, *CEO*
Greg Elder, *CFO*
Eduardo Hernandez, *Electrical Engi*
John Newbrough, *Engineer*
Susan Davis, *Human Res Mgr*
▲ **EMP:** 77
SQ FT: 30,000
SALES (est): 23.4MM **Privately Held**
WEB: www.apctcircuits.com
SIC: 3672 Circuit boards, television & radio printed

(P-18424)
APT ELECTRONICS INC
241 N Crescent Way, Anaheim
(92801-6704)
PHONE..........................714 687-6760
Tae Myoung Kim, *CEO*
DH Song, *Shareholder*
Sj Song, *Shareholder*
Y B Song, *Shareholder*
EMP: 112
SQ FT: 20,000
SALES (est): 21.3MM **Privately Held**
WEB: www.aptelectronics.com
SIC: 3672 Printed circuit boards

(P-18425)
ARDENT SYSTEMS INC
2040 Ringwood Ave, San Jose
(95131-1728)
PHONE..........................408 526-0100
Thomas Han, *President*
Young C Kang, *Admin Sec*
EMP: 24
SQ FT: 8,000
SALES (est): 3.9MM **Privately Held**
SIC: 3672 Printed circuit boards

(P-18426)
ARNOLD ELECTRONICS INC
1907 Nancita Cir, Placentia (92870-6737)
PHONE..........................714 646-8343
Sam Z Bhayani, *President*
Tushar Patel, *Vice Pres*
Kim Hack, *Manager*
▲ **EMP:** 12
SQ FT: 2,500
SALES (est): 5.8MM **Privately Held**
WEB: www.arnoldelectronics.com
SIC: 3672 Circuit boards, television & radio printed

(P-18427)
ASROCK AMERICA INC
13848 Magnolia Ave, Chino (91710-7027)
PHONE..........................909 590-8308
James Teng, *President*
▲ **EMP:** 20
SALES (est): 2.8MM
SALES (corp-wide): 306MM **Privately Held**
SIC: 3672 Printed circuit boards
HQ: Firstplace International Limited
   C/O: Offshore Incorporations Limited
   Road Town
   -

(P-18428)
ASSEMBLY TECHNOLOGIES CO LLC
Also Called: Atc
2921 W Central Ave Ste B, Santa Ana
(92704-5336)
PHONE..........................714 979-4400
David Mathisen,
Esther Mathisen, *Partner*
Rick Mathisen, *General Mgr*
EMP: 11
SQ FT: 2,000
SALES (est): 1.1MM **Privately Held**
SIC: 3672 Printed circuit boards

(P-18429)
ASTEELFLASH USA CORP (HQ)
4211 Starboard Dr, Fremont (94538-6427)
PHONE..........................510 440-2840
Gilles Benhamou, *President*
Craig Young, *President*

Claude Savard, *CFO*
Pierre Laboisse, *Exec VP*
Vince Pradia, *Exec VP*
▲ **EMP:** 211 **EST:** 2011
SALES (est): 134.5MM
SALES (corp-wide): 5.8MM **Privately Held**
SIC: 3672 3679 Printed circuit boards; electronic circuits
PA: Asteelflash Group
   6 Rue Vincent Van Gogh
   Neuilly Plaisance 93360
   149 445-301

(P-18430)
ASTRONIC
2 Orion, Aliso Viejo (92656-4200)
PHONE..........................949 454-1180
Sang H Choi, *CEO*
Kristine Cynn, *COO*
OK Kay Choi, *Corp Secy*
Patrick McBride, *Engineer*
Dolores Carreon, *Controller*
▲ **EMP:** 143 **EST:** 1976
SQ FT: 41,000
SALES (est): 38.4MM **Privately Held**
SIC: 3672 1742 Printed circuit boards; acoustical & insulation work

(P-18431)
AURUM ASSEMBLY PLUS INC
8829 Production Ave, San Diego
(92121-2220)
PHONE..........................858 578-8710
Karl Northwang, *President*
Karl E Nothwang, *CFO*
Robert Mosley, *Vice Pres*
Robert Nothwang, *Vice Pres*
Bobby Northwang, *General Mgr*
EMP: 20
SQ FT: 7,000
SALES (est): 3.7MM **Privately Held**
WEB: www.aurumassembly.com
SIC: 3672 2298 Circuit boards, television & radio printed; wire rope centers

(P-18432)
AVALENT TECHNOLOGIES INC (PA)
920 Hillview Ct Ste 195, Milpitas
(95035-4500)
PHONE..........................408 727-6323
Duen-Shun Wen, *President*
Mazin Khurshid, *VP Engrg*
EMP: 15
SALES (est): 2.2MM **Privately Held**
WEB: www.avalent.com
SIC: 3672 Circuit boards, television & radio printed

(P-18433)
AVANTEC MANUFACTURING INC
1811 N Case St, Orange (92865-4234)
PHONE..........................714 532-6197
Alan E McNeeney, *CEO*
▲ **EMP:** 20
SALES (est): 5.7MM **Privately Held**
WEB: www.avantecusa.com
SIC: 3672 Printed circuit boards

(P-18434)
BAY AREA CIRCUITS INC
44358 Old Warm Sprng Blvd, Fremont
(94538-6148)
PHONE..........................510 933-9000
Barbara Nobriga, *President*
Brian Paper, *COO*
Cassandra Mubayed, *Office Mgr*
James Vansant, *Info Tech Mgr*
Ron De Franco, *Business Mgr*
▲ **EMP:** 48
SQ FT: 7,500
SALES (est): 8.6MM **Privately Held**
WEB: www.bacircuits.com
SIC: 3672 Circuit boards, television & radio printed

(P-18435)
BAY AREA EMS SOLUTIONS LLC
Also Called: Baems
147 Walker Ranch Pkwy, Patterson
(95363-8811)
PHONE..........................408 753-3651

Mueed Khan,
Asad Hameed,
Arif Saeed,
Neil Boylan, *Mng Member*
EMP: 11 **EST:** 2011
SQ FT: 12,000
SALES (est): 1.4MM **Privately Held**
SIC: 3672

(P-18436)
BAY ELCTRNIC SPPORT TRNICS INC
Also Called: Bestronics
2090 Fortune Dr, San Jose (95131-1823)
PHONE..........................408 432-3222
Nat Mani, *CEO*
Ben Calub, *Vice Pres*
Ron Menigoz, *Vice Pres*
Steve Yetso, *Vice Pres*
Salvador Daunell, *Business Dir*
▲ **EMP:** 155
SQ FT: 150,000
SALES (est): 65MM **Privately Held**
WEB: www.bestronicsinc.com
SIC: 3672 Circuit boards, television & radio printed
PA: Bestronics Holdings, Inc.
   2090 Fortune Dr
   San Jose CA 95131
   408 385-7777

(P-18437)
BENCHMARK ELEC MFG SLTIONS INC (HQ)
5550 Hellyer Ave, San Jose (95138-1005)
PHONE..........................408 754-9800
Jayne Desorcie, *Administration*
Tom Dineen, *General Mgr*
Thomas Nye, *Technology*
Carmen Shahrokhfar, *Buyer*
Abraham Abrahan, *Maint Spvr*
▲ **EMP:** 100
SQ FT: 80,000
SALES (est): 119.5MM
SALES (corp-wide): 2.4B **Publicly Held**
WEB: www.smtek.com
SIC: 3672 Printed circuit boards
PA: Benchmark Electronics, Inc.
   4141 N Scottsdale Rd
   Scottsdale AZ 85251
   623 300-7000

(P-18438)
BENCHMARK ELECTRONICS INC
42701 Christy St, Fremont (94538-3146)
PHONE..........................510 360-2800
Robert Pruett, *Vice Pres*
John Ratkovich, *Program Mgr*
Jay Blanpied, *Engineer*
Wilson Eng, *Engineer*
Sathish Sakthivelan, *Engineer*
EMP: 100
SALES (corp-wide): 2.4B **Publicly Held**
SIC: 3672 Printed circuit boards
PA: Benchmark Electronics, Inc.
   4141 N Scottsdale Rd
   Scottsdale AZ 85251
   623 300-7000

(P-18439)
BENCHMARK ELECTRONICS INC
2301 Arnold Ind Way Ste G, Concord
(94520-5379)
PHONE..........................925 363-1151
Steve Tate, *Branch Mgr*
Emily Huang, *Accountant*
EMP: 257
SALES (corp-wide): 2.4B **Publicly Held**
SIC: 3672 Printed circuit boards
PA: Benchmark Electronics, Inc.
   4141 N Scottsdale Rd
   Scottsdale AZ 85251
   623 300-7000

(P-18440)
BINH-NHAN D NGO
Also Called: Prototype Solutions
1751 Fortune Dr Ste F, San Jose
(95131-1705)
PHONE..........................408 641-1721
Binh-Nhan Ngo, *Owner*
EMP: 10

SALES (est): 757.3K **Privately Held**
SIC: 3672 Printed circuit boards

(P-18441)
CAL-COMP USA (SAN DIEGO) INC
1940 Camino Vida Roble, Carlsbad (92008-6516)
PHONE..................................858 587-6900
Peter Pan, *President*
Marlena Aragon, *Program Mgr*
John Wolfe, *Senior Buyer*
EMP: 215
SQ FT: 65,000
SALES (est): 59.7MM **Privately Held**
WEB: www.smstech.com
SIC: 3672 Circuit boards, television & radio printed

(P-18442)
CALIFORNIA INTEGRATION COORDIN
2929 Grandview St, Placerville (95667-4635)
PHONE..................................530 626-6168
Cherie Myers, *President*
Patricia Presgrave, *CFO*
Kim Ishmael, *Office Mgr*
Ray Presgrave, *Admin Sec*
Debby Verry, *Manager*
EMP: 14
SQ FT: 7,500
SALES: 5MM **Privately Held**
WEB: www.cic-inc.com
SIC: 3672 Circuit boards, television & radio printed

(P-18443)
CALPAK USA INC
2110 Artesia Blvd B202, Redondo Beach (90278-3073)
PHONE..................................310 937-7335
Danish Qureshi, *President*
▲ EMP: 20
SALES: 5MM **Privately Held**
WEB: www.calpak-usa.com
SIC: 3672 3679 8742 4813 Printed circuit boards; commutators, electronic; management consulting services; telephone communication, except radio

(P-18444)
CAPELLA MICROSYSTEMS INC
2201 Laurelwood Rd, Santa Clara (95054-1516)
PHONE..................................408 988-8000
Cheng-Chung Shih, *CEO*
EMP: 22
SQ FT: 6,600
SALES (est): 2MM
SALES (corp-wide): 2.6B **Publicly Held**
WEB: www.capellamicro.com
SIC: 3672 3674 Circuit boards, television & radio printed; semiconductors & related devices
HQ: Vishay Capella Microsystems (Taiwan) Limited
6f, 43, Fuxing Rd.,
New Taipei City
282 186-600

(P-18445)
CELESTICA AEROSPACE TECH CORP
Also Called: Celestica-Aerospace
895 S Rockefeller Ave, Ontario (91761-8145)
PHONE..................................512 310-7540
Jeffrey Bain, *President*
Thomas Lovelock, *President*
Leslie K Sladek, *Admin Sec*
Barry Trejo, *Technology*
Armin Bogosian, *QC Mgr*
▲ EMP: 200
SQ FT: 55,000
SALES (est): 47MM
SALES (corp-wide): 24.5B **Privately Held**
WEB: www.celestica.com
SIC: 3672 Printed circuit boards
HQ: Celestica Inc
844 Don Mills Rd
Toronto ON M3C 1
416 448-5800

(P-18446)
CENTURY TECHNOLOGY INC
225 Harris Ct, South San Francisco (94080-6004)
PHONE..................................650 583-8908
Henry Han Ho, *President*
Kayle Hoad, *Vice Pres*
Lily Jriyasetapong, *Sales Mgr*
▲ EMP: 15 EST: 1993
SQ FT: 7,000
SALES: 2MM **Privately Held**
WEB: www.century-technology.com
SIC: 3672 Printed circuit boards

(P-18447)
CHINA CIRCUIT TECH CORP N AMER
Also Called: C C T C North America
11 Thomas Owens Way, Monterey (93940-5816)
PHONE..................................831 646-2194
Doug Humble, *President*
▲ EMP: 10
SALES (est): 25.9MM
SALES (corp-wide): 653.9MM **Privately Held**
WEB: www.cctcna.com
SIC: 3672 Printed circuit boards
HQ: China Circuit Technology(Shantou) Corporation
Wanji Industrial Zone, Longhu Dist.
Shantou
754 883-9421

(P-18448)
CHOOSE MANUFACTURING CO LLC
17925 Sky Park Cir Ste G, Irvine (92614-4325)
PHONE..................................714 327-1698
Herbert Chiu, *Mng Member*
Heidi Cheng, *Accounting Mgr*
Tim Lynch, *Purch Agent*
Doreen Swaze, *QC Dir*
Anthony Chiu, *Manager*
▲ EMP: 20 EST: 2000
SQ FT: 13,000
SALES: 3MM **Privately Held**
WEB: www.choosemfg.com
SIC: 3672 Printed circuit boards

(P-18449)
CIRCUIT CONNECTIONS
Also Called: Innovative Circuits Engrg
2310 Lundy Ave, San Jose (95131-1827)
PHONE..................................408 955-9505
Narendra Narayan, *President*
EMP: 30
SALES (est): 3.8MM **Privately Held**
WEB: www.circuitconnections.com
SIC: 3672 Circuit boards, television & radio printed

(P-18450)
CIRCUIT EXPRESS INC
67 W Easy St Ste 129, Simi Valley (93065-6204)
PHONE..................................805 581-2172
Himmat Desai, *CEO*
Vinny Kathrota, *Admin Sec*
EMP: 12
SQ FT: 5,000
SALES: 1.2MM **Privately Held**
WEB: www.circuitexpressinc.com
SIC: 3672 Circuit boards, television & radio printed

(P-18451)
CIRCUIT SERVICES LLC
Also Called: Career Tech Circuit Services
18646 Parthenia St, Northridge (91324-4027)
PHONE..................................818 701-5391
Theodore Brudzinski, *CEO*
Elcid Aranas, *Engineer*
Anahit Stepanian, *Purch Mgr*
Tim Blackburn, *Marketing Mgr*
Artin Minas, *Marketing Staff*
EMP: 43
SQ FT: 9,000
SALES (est): 10.3MM **Privately Held**
WEB: www.careertech-usa.com
SIC: 3672 Printed circuit boards

(P-18452)
CIRCUIT SPECTRUM INC
988 Morse St, San Jose (95126-1414)
PHONE..................................408 946-8484
Zaven Tashjian, *President*
EMP: 10
SQ FT: 75,000
SALES (est): 1.6MM **Privately Held**
WEB: www.circuitspectrum.com
SIC: 3672 Printed circuit boards

(P-18453)
CIREXX CORPORATION
791 Nuttman St, Santa Clara (95054-2623)
PHONE..................................408 988-3980
Phillip Menges, *President*
EMP: 49
SQ FT: 22,000
SALES (est): 9.3MM **Privately Held**
WEB: www.cirexx.com
SIC: 3672 8711 Printed circuit boards; engineering services

(P-18454)
CIREXX INTERNATIONAL INC (PA)
791 Nuttman St, Santa Clara (95054-2623)
PHONE..................................408 988-3980
Philip Menges, *President*
Kurt H Menges, *Vice Pres*
Carlo Dominguez, *Data Proc Staff*
Ed Correa, *Engineer*
EMP: 115
SALES (est): 34.4MM **Privately Held**
WEB: www.cirexxintl.com
SIC: 3672 Circuit boards, television & radio printed

(P-18455)
COAST TO COAST CIRCUITS INC (PA)
Also Called: Speedy Circuits
5331 Mcfadden Ave, Huntington Beach (92649-1204)
PHONE..................................585 254-2980
Walter Stender, *CEO*
Ronald Scott Lawhead, *CFO*
Mike Schlehr, *CFO*
Albert Martinez, *Vice Pres*
Juan Lopez, *Engineer*
◆ EMP: 102
SQ FT: 40,000
SALES (est): 21.3MM **Privately Held**
WEB: www.speedycircuits.com
SIC: 3672 Circuit boards, television & radio printed

(P-18456)
COAST TO COAST CIRCUITS INC
Speedy Circuits
5331 Mcfadden Ave, Huntington Beach (92649-1204)
PHONE..................................714 898-4901
Peter Casson, *President*
EMP: 65
SALES (corp-wide): 21.3MM **Privately Held**
WEB: www.speedycircuits.com
SIC: 3672 8711 Printed circuit boards; engineering services
PA: Coast To Coast Circuits, Inc.
5331 Mcfadden Ave
Huntington Beach CA 92649
585 254-2980

(P-18457)
CONCEPT DEVELOPMENT LLC
Also Called: CDI
1881 Langley Ave, Irvine (92614-5623)
PHONE..................................949 623-8000
James M Reardon, *President*
Young Ha, *Engineer*
Daniel Lotocky, *Engineer*
Teresa Brown, *Mktg Coord*
EMP: 20 EST: 1972
SQ FT: 12,880
SALES (est): 4.5MM
SALES (corp-wide): 27.5MM **Publicly Held**
WEB: www.cdvinc.com
SIC: 3672 8711 Printed circuit boards; consulting engineer

PA: One Stop Systems, Inc.
2235 Entp St Ste 110
Escondido CA 92029
760 745-9883

(P-18458)
CREATION TECH CALEXICO INC (HQ)
Also Called: Aisling Industries
1778 Zinetta Rd Ste A, Calexico (92231-9511)
P.O. Box 1833, El Centro (92244-1833)
PHONE..................................760 336-8543
Bhawnesh Mathur, *CEO*
Michael J Logue, *President*
Sergio Quiroz, *Vice Pres*
▲ EMP: 205
SQ FT: 10,000
SALES (est): 39.4MM **Privately Held**
WEB: www.aislinginc.com
SIC: 3672 3679 Printed circuit boards; electronic circuits
PA: Creation Technologies Inc
8999 Fraserton Crt
Burnaby BC V5J 5
604 430-4336

(P-18459)
CREATION TECH SAN JOSE INC
1873 Barber Ln, Milpitas (95035-7419)
PHONE..................................408 954-8055
Bhawnesh Mathur, *CEO*
Arthur Tymos, *President*
EMP: 200
SQ FT: 17,000
SALES (est): 15.6MM **Privately Held**
SIC: 3672 Printed circuit boards
PA: Creation Technologies Lp
8999 Fraserton Crt
Burnaby BC V5J 5
604 430-4336

(P-18460)
CREATION TECH SANTA CLARA INC
2801 Northwestern Pkwy, Santa Clara (95051-0903)
PHONE..................................408 235-7500
Arthur Tymos, *CEO*
Dennis Kottke, *Ch of Bd*
Simon Ip, *Vice Pres*
Kurt Pagnini, *Vice Pres*
▲ EMP: 275
SQ FT: 32,000
SALES (est): 50.3MM **Privately Held**
WEB: www.pro-works.com
SIC: 3672 Printed circuit boards
PA: Creation Technologies Inc
8999 Fraserton Crt
Burnaby BC V5J 5
604 430-4336

(P-18461)
CROWN CIRCUITS INC
6070 Avenida Encinas, Carlsbad (92011-1001)
PHONE..................................949 922-0144
Kamran A Saffari, *CEO*
Nilofar Saffari, *Ch of Bd*
Bert Arucnn, *President*
EMP: 70
SQ FT: 20,000
SALES (est): 5.9MM **Privately Held**
SIC: 3672 Printed circuit boards

(P-18462)
CTS CORPORATION
2271 Ringwood Ave, San Jose (95131-1717)
PHONE..................................408 955-9001
Richard Dinh, *Manager*
EMP: 125
SALES (corp-wide): 422.9MM **Publicly Held**
WEB: www.ctscorp.com
SIC: 3672 Printed circuit boards
PA: Cts Corporation
4925 Indiana Ave
Lisle IL 60532
630 577-8800

(P-18463)
D Y U INC
223 N Crescent Way, Anaheim (92801-6704)
PHONE..................................714 239-2433

Young Bae Song, *President*
Hyun Jung Song, *Treasurer*
Yound Hee Song, *Admin Sec*
EMP: 170
SALES (est): 6.8MM **Privately Held**
SIC: 3672 Printed circuit boards

(P-18464)
DALLAS ELECTRONICS INC
2151 Delaware Ave Ste A, Santa Cruz
(95060-5788)
P.O. Box 2489 (95063-2489)
PHONE..........................831 457-3610
Geneva Matta, *President*
Dallas Matta, *Vice Pres*
▲ **EMP:** 50
SQ FT: 16,000
SALES (est): 9.5MM **Privately Held**
WEB: www.dallaselectronics.com
SIC: 3672 3674 Printed circuit boards;
semiconductors & related devices

(P-18465)
DE LEON ENTPS ELEC SPCLIST INC
11934 Allegheny St, Sun Valley
(91352-1833)
PHONE..........................818 252-6690
Miguel De Leon, *President*
Ray Payne, *Manager*
▲ **EMP:** 24
SQ FT: 11,000
SALES (est): 4.5MM **Privately Held**
SIC: 3672 Printed circuit boards

(P-18466)
DELTA D V H CIRCUITS INC
16117 Leadwell St, Van Nuys
(91406-3417)
PHONE..........................818 786-8241
Kana Khunai, *Owner*
EMP: 20
SQ FT: 10,000
SALES (est): 2.4MM **Privately Held**
WEB: www.deltacircuittech.com
SIC: 3672 Printed circuit boards

(P-18467)
DIAMOND MULTIMEDIA SYSTEMS
2880 Junction Ave, San Jose (95134-1922)
PHONE..........................408 868-9613
William J Schroeder, *President*
Franz Fichtner, *President*
James M Walker, *CFO*
C Scott Holt, *Senior VP*
Hyung Hwe Huh, *Senior VP*
EMP: 290
SQ FT: 80,000
SALES: 608.5MM **Privately Held**
SIC: 3672 3577 3661 Printed circuit
boards; computer peripheral equipment;
modems

(P-18468)
DIGICOM ELECTRONICS INC
7799 Pardee Ln, Oakland (94621-1425)
PHONE..........................510 639-7003
Mohammed R Ohady, *CEO*
MO Ohady, *General Mgr*
Arthur Fung, *Manager*
EMP: 27
SALES (est): 6.6MM **Privately Held**
WEB: www.de-crypt.com
SIC: 3672 Printed circuit boards

(P-18469)
DYNASTY ELECTRONIC COMPANY LLC
Also Called: Dec
1790 E Mcfadden Ave, Santa Ana
(92705-4638)
PHONE..........................714 550-1197
Fredrick Rodenhuis, *Mng Member*
Mark Clark,
EMP: 65
SQ FT: 10,000
SALES (est): 8.2MM **Privately Held**
SIC: 3672 Printed circuit boards

(P-18470)
ELECTRO SURFACE TECH INC
Also Called: E S T
2281 Las Palmas Dr 101, Carlsbad
(92011-1527)
PHONE..........................760 431-8306
Hiroo Kirpalani, *President*
EMP: 61
SQ FT: 31,500
SALES (est): 9MM **Privately Held**
WEB: www.est.com
SIC: 3672 Circuit boards, television & radio
printed

(P-18471)
ELECTROMAX INC
1960 Concourse Dr, San Jose
(95131-1719)
PHONE..........................408 428-9474
Aaron Wong, *President*
Ken Wong, *Vice Pres*
▲ **EMP:** 50
SQ FT: 30,000
SALES (est): 10.9MM **Privately Held**
WEB: www.electromaxinc.com
SIC: 3672 Printed circuit boards

(P-18472)
ELECTRONIC MFG TECH INC
Also Called: Emti
16464 Via Esprillo, San Diego
(92127-1702)
PHONE..........................858 613-1040
Greg Lobdell, *President*
Chris Lobdell, *Corp Secy*
EMP: 20
SQ FT: 11,000
SALES (est): 3MM **Privately Held**
WEB: www.emtiusa.com
SIC: 3672 Printed circuit boards

(P-18473)
ELECTRONIC SURFC MOUNTED INDS
Also Called: Esmi
6731 Cobra Way, San Diego (92121-4110)
PHONE..........................858 455-1710
Henry Kim, *President*
Lynn Kim, *Vice Pres*
▼ **EMP:** 40
SQ FT: 25,000
SALES: 4MM **Privately Held**
WEB: www.esmiinc.com
SIC: 3672 Printed circuit boards

(P-18474)
EMD SPECIALTY MATERIALS LLC
Also Called: Arlon EMD
9433 Hyssop Dr, Rancho Cucamonga
(91730-6107)
PHONE..........................909 987-9533
Matt Young,
Charles Huard, *Supervisor*
EMP: 10
SALES (est): 347.8K **Privately Held**
SIC: 3672 Circuit boards, television & radio
printed

(P-18475)
EMSOLUTIONS INC
2152 Zanker Rd, San Jose (95131-2113)
PHONE..........................510 668-1118
Jun Huo, *President*
EMP: 10
SQ FT: 5,000
SALES (est): 1.8MM **Privately Held**
SIC: 3672 Printed circuit boards

(P-18476)
EXCELLO CIRCUITS INC
1924 Nancita Cir, Placentia (92870-6737)
PHONE..........................714 993-0560
Sam Bhayani, *President*
Tushar Patel, *Vice Pres*
Rax Ribadia, *Vice Pres*
EMP: 30
SQ FT: 11,000
SALES (est): 5.1MM **Privately Held**
WEB: www.excello.com
SIC: 3672 Circuit boards, television & radio
printed

(P-18477)
EXPERT ASSEMBLY SERVICES INC
1183 Warner Ave, Tustin (92780-6458)
PHONE..........................714 258-8880
Jack Quinn, *CEO*
EMP: 30
SQ FT: 8,000
SALES (est): 6.1MM **Privately Held**
WEB: www.expertassembly.com
SIC: 3672 Printed circuit boards

(P-18478)
FABRICATED COMPONENTS CORP
Also Called: Summit Interconnect Orange
130 W Bristol Ln, Orange (92865-2640)
PHONE..........................714 974-8590
Shane Whiteside, *President*
▼ **EMP:** 140 **EST:** 1979
SQ FT: 40,000
SALES (est): 25.3MM **Privately Held**
WEB: www.mei4pcbs.com
SIC: 3672 Printed circuit boards

(P-18479)
FINE ELECTRONIC ASSEMBLY INC
4887 Mercury St, San Diego (92111-2104)
PHONE..........................858 573-0887
Rick Bajaria, *President*
David Nason, *Principal*
EMP: 20
SQ FT: 10,000
SALES: 1.5MM **Privately Held**
WEB: www.fineelectronic.com
SIC: 3672 3699 Printed circuit boards;
electrical equipment & supplies

(P-18480)
FINE PTCH ELCTRNIC ASSMBLY LLC
5106 Azusa Canyon Rd, Irwindale
(91706-1846)
PHONE..........................626 337-2800
Ashish Sheladiya, *General Mgr*
Mayur Savalia,
EMP: 20
SQ FT: 15,000
SALES: 2.5MM **Privately Held**
WEB: www.finepitchassembly.com
SIC: 3672 Printed circuit boards

(P-18481)
FINELINE CIRCUITS & TECHNOLOGY
594 Apollo St Ste A, Brea (92821-3134)
PHONE..........................714 529-2942
Rick Bajaria, *President*
Ken Pansuria, *Vice Pres*
Vinny Kathrotia, *General Mgr*
Andy Kumar, *Design Engr*
Sharon Long, *Accounting Mgr*
EMP: 30
SQ FT: 20,000
SALES (est): 4.5MM **Privately Held**
WEB: www.finelinecircuits.com
SIC: 3672 Circuit boards, television & radio
printed

(P-18482)
FIRST CIRCUIT INC
Also Called: Precision Circuits San Diego
7701 Garboso Pl, Carlsbad (92009-8325)
PHONE..........................760 560-0530
Tom Smiley, *President*
Christine Smiley, *Admin Sec*
EMP: 12
SALES: 1MM **Privately Held**
WEB: www.precisionpcbs.com
SIC: 3672 Printed circuit boards

(P-18483)
FLEXTRONICS AMERICA LLC (DH)
6201 America Center Dr, San Jose
(95002-2563)
PHONE..........................408 576-7000
David Bennett, *Mng Member*
Chris Collier,
▲ **EMP:** 230 **EST:** 2001
SALES (est): 1.1B
SALES (corp-wide): 25.4B **Privately Held**
SIC: 3672 Printed circuit boards

(P-18484)
FLEXTRONICS INTERNATIONAL USA
260 S Milpitas Blvd # 15, Milpitas
(95035-5420)
PHONE..........................408 576-7000
Matt Bryan, *Branch Mgr*
Bernard Bareis, *Vice Pres*
David Gessler, *Vice Pres*
Steven Proctor, *Vice Pres*
Majid Sairafi, *Vice Pres*
EMP: 650
SALES (corp-wide): 25.4B **Privately Held**
SIC: 3672 3679 Printed circuit boards;
power supplies, all types: static; harness
assemblies for electronic use: wire or
cable
HQ: Flextronics International Usa, Inc.
6201 America Center Dr
San Jose CA 95002

(P-18485)
FLEXTRONICS INTL USA INC
1177 Gibraltar Dr Bldg 9, Milpitas
(95035-6337)
PHONE..........................408 678-3268
EMP: 11
SALES (corp-wide): 23.8B **Privately Held**
SIC: 3672 Printed circuit boards
HQ: Flextronics International Usa, Inc.
6201 America Center Dr
San Jose CA 95002

(P-18486)
FLEXTRONICS INTL USA INC
925 Lightpost Way, Morgan Hill
(95037-2869)
PHONE..........................408 577-2262
EMP: 298
SALES (corp-wide): 23.8B **Privately Held**
SIC: 3672 Printed circuit boards
HQ: Flextronics International Usa, Inc.
6201 America Center Dr
San Jose CA 95002

(P-18487)
FLEXTRONICS INTL USA INC (HQ)
6201 America Center Dr, San Jose
(95002-2563)
PHONE..........................408 576-7000
Michael McNamara, *CEO*
Christopher Collier, *CFO*
Vivek Bharti, *Vice Pres*
Thomas Conelly, *Vice Pres*
Kelly Hampton, *Vice Pres*
▲ **EMP:** 892
SQ FT: 100,000
SALES (est): 39.4B
SALES (corp-wide): 25.4B **Privately Held**
SIC: 3672 Printed circuit boards
PA: Flex Ltd.
2 Changi South Lane
Singapore 48612
629 988-88

(P-18488)
FOXLINK WORLD CIRCUIT TECH
925 W Lambert Rd Ste C, Brea
(92821-2943)
PHONE..........................714 256-0877
EMP: 20
SQ FT: 6,000
SALES (est): 1.6MM **Privately Held**
SIC: 3672

(P-18489)
FTG CIRCUITS INC (DH)
20750 Marilla St, Chatsworth (91311-4407)
PHONE..........................818 407-4024
Brad Bourne, *CEO*
Michael Labrador, *President*
Joe Ricci, *CFO*
Ed Hanna, *Director*
▼ **EMP:** 100
SQ FT: 38,000
SALES (est): 31.1MM
SALES (corp-wide): 74.8MM **Privately Held**
SIC: 3672 3644 Printed circuit boards; terminal boards

HQ: Firan Technology Group (Usa) Corporation
20750 Marilla St
Chatsworth CA 91311
818 407-4024

(P-18490)
GAVIAL ENGINEERING & MFG INC (HQ)
1435 W Mccoy Ln, Santa Maria (93455-1002)
PHONE...............805 614-0060
Don Connors, *President*
Stanley D Connors, *CEO*
Ramona Castano, *Division Mgr*
Ken Hicks, *General Mgr*
Cathy Castor, *Office Mgr*
EMP: 45 **EST:** 2012
SQ FT: 25,000
SALES (est): 6.8MM
SALES (corp-wide): 79.4MM **Privately Held**
SIC: 3672 3679 Printed circuit boards; electronic circuits
PA: Gavial Holdings, Inc.
1435 W Mccoy Ln
Santa Maria CA 93455
805 614-0060

(P-18491)
GEERIRAJ INC
Also Called: Mer-Mar Electronics
7042 Santa Fe Ave E A1, Hesperia (92345-5711)
PHONE...............760 244-6149
Kanjibhai Ghadia, *President*
Suresh Patel, *Vice Pres*
EMP: 28 **EST:** 1974
SQ FT: 22,000
SALES: 450K **Privately Held**
WEB: www.mermarinc.com
SIC: 3672 Printed circuit boards

(P-18492)
GEMINI CONSULTANTS INC
Also Called: Twin Industries
2303 Camino Ramon Ste 106, San Ramon (94583-1389)
PHONE...............925 866-8946
David M Wisser, *President*
David Wisser, *General Mgr*
▲ **EMP:** 10
SALES: 650K **Privately Held**
SIC: 3672 3825 Printed circuit boards; instruments to measure electricity

(P-18493)
GENERAL ELEC ASSEMBLY INC
1525 Atteberry Ln, San Jose (95131-1412)
PHONE...............408 980-8819
Eric Chang, *President*
Matthew McClendon, *Program Mgr*
Grace Ling, *Human Res Mgr*
Carmen Lee, *Supervisor*
EMP: 45
SQ FT: 16,000
SALES (est): 9.6MM **Privately Held**
WEB: www.geamfg.com
SIC: 3672 Wiring boards

(P-18494)
GENERATION CIRCUITS LLC
Also Called: RB Design
621 S Andreasen Dr Ste B, Escondido (92029-1904)
PHONE...............760 743-7459
David E Maudlin, *CEO*
Max P Henzi, *Ch of Bd*
Thomas F Beales, *President*
EMP: 20
SQ FT: 7,000
SALES: 2MM **Privately Held**
WEB: www.rbdpcb.com
SIC: 3672 Circuit boards, television & radio printed

(P-18495)
GLOBAL CIRCUIT SOLUTIONS INC
4130 Flat Rock Dr Unit 1, Riverside (92505-5867)
PHONE...............951 353-2780
Raul Barragan, *President*
▲ **EMP:** 15 **EST:** 2001
SQ FT: 2,800

SALES: 8MM **Privately Held**
SIC: 3672 Printed circuit boards

(P-18496)
GOLDEN WEST TECHNOLOGY
1180 E Valencia Dr, Fullerton (92831-4627)
PHONE...............714 738-3775
Dan P Rieth, *President*
Russ Rieth, *Info Tech Mgr*
Bill Frye, *Engineer*
Mike Kutzle, *Purch Dir*
EMP: 60 **EST:** 1974
SQ FT: 30,000
SALES (est): 12.4MM **Privately Held**
SIC: 3672 Printed circuit boards

(P-18497)
GORILLA CIRCUITS (PA)
1445 Oakland Rd, San Jose (95112-1203)
PHONE...............408 294-9897
Fermin Aviles, *Managing Prtnr*
Hershel Petty, *President*
Jaime Gutierrez, *Vice Pres*
▲ **EMP:** 166
SQ FT: 60,000
SALES: 36.2MM **Privately Held**
WEB: www.gorillacircuits.com
SIC: 3672 Circuit boards, television & radio printed

(P-18498)
GRAPHIC RESEARCH INC
9334 Mason Ave, Chatsworth (91311-5295)
PHONE...............818 886-7340
Govind R Vaghashia, *President*
Pete Vaghashia, *Vice Pres*
▲ **EMP:** 50
SQ FT: 42,000
SALES (est): 9.7MM **Privately Held**
WEB: www.graphicresearch.com
SIC: 3672 Printed circuit boards

(P-18499)
HI-TECH ELECTRONIC MFG CORP
Also Called: Hitem
7420 Carroll Rd, San Diego (92121-2304)
PHONE...............858 657-0908
Vinh Lam, *President*
Tran Vu, *Vice Pres*
Yoshi Otani, *Program Mgr*
Sherry Nguyen, *Senior Buyer*
Dan Shepard, *VP Sales*
▲ **EMP:** 80
SQ FT: 20,000
SALES (est): 29.4MM **Privately Held**
WEB: www.hitem.com
SIC: 3672 Circuit boards, television & radio printed

(P-18500)
HUGHES CIRCUITS INC (PA)
Also Called: Hci
546 S Pacific St, San Marcos (92078-4070)
PHONE...............760 744-0300
Barbara Hughes, *CEO*
Jerry Hughes, *President*
Michelle Glatts, *Vice Pres*
Joe Hughes, *Vice Pres*
Steve Hughes, *Vice Pres*
EMP: 45 **EST:** 1999
SQ FT: 50,000
SALES (est): 32.7MM **Privately Held**
WEB: www.hughescircuits.com
SIC: 3672 Circuit boards, television & radio printed

(P-18501)
HUGHES CIRCUITS INC
Also Called: Pcb Fabrication Facility
540 S Pacific St, San Marcos (92078-4050)
PHONE...............760 744-0300
Barbara Hughes, *Branch Mgr*
Jeff Hughes, *Principal*
EMP: 115
SALES (corp-wide): 32.7MM **Privately Held**
SIC: 3672 Circuit boards, television & radio printed
PA: Hughes Circuits, Inc.
546 S Pacific St
San Marcos CA 92078
760 744-0300

(P-18502)
HYTEK R&D INC (PA)
Also Called: R & D Tech
2044 Corporate Ct, Milpitas (95035)
PHONE...............408 761-5271
Richard Hernandez, *President*
EMP: 22
SALES (est): 2.1MM **Privately Held**
SIC: 3672 5063 Printed circuit boards; electrical supplies

(P-18503)
IMPACT PROJECT MANAGEMENT INC
2872 S Santa Fe Ave, San Marcos (92069-6046)
PHONE...............760 747-6616
Randy Scott Walker, *President*
Debbie Walker, *Vice Pres*
EMP: 25
SALES (est): 5MM **Privately Held**
WEB: www.impactprojects.com
SIC: 3672 Printed circuit boards

(P-18504)
INDTEC CORPORATION
3348 Paul Davis Dr # 109, Marina (93933-2258)
P.O. Box 1998, Seaside (93955-1998)
PHONE...............831 582-9388
Dung Van Trinh, *President*
Lily Pham, *Admin Sec*
Pualani Visesio, *Purch Mgr*
Hoan Phan, *Manager*
EMP: 20
SQ FT: 5,000
SALES (est): 3.4MM **Privately Held**
WEB: www.indtec.net
SIC: 3672 Circuit boards, television & radio printed

(P-18505)
INFINITI SOLUTIONS USA INC (PA)
Also Called: Adec
3910 N 1st St, San Jose (95134-1501)
PHONE...............408 923-7300
Inderjit Singh, *President*
Kumar Patel, *President*
Pin Patel, *Vice Pres*
EMP: 78 **EST:** 1975
SQ FT: 70,000
SALES (est): 21.5MM **Privately Held**
WEB: www.adaptivecircuits.com
SIC: 3672 3825 8711 Printed circuit boards; test equipment for electronic & electrical circuits; engineering services

(P-18506)
INFINITI SOLUTIONS USA INC
3910 N 1st St, San Jose (95134-1501)
PHONE...............408 923-7300
EMP: 60
SALES (corp-wide): 21.5MM **Privately Held**
SIC: 3672 Printed circuit boards
PA: Infiniti Solutions Usa, Inc.
3910 N 1st St
San Jose CA 95134
408 923-7300

(P-18507)
INNERSTEP BSE (PA)
4742 Scotts Valley Dr, Scotts Valley (95066-4231)
PHONE...............831 461-5600
Don Landry, *CEO*
Jim Kingman, *President*
James Kingman, *CEO*
Trung Vu, *Engineer*
Caleb Hunt, *Manager*
▲ **EMP:** 11
SQ FT: 25,000
SALES (est): 14.8MM **Privately Held**
WEB: www.innerstep.com
SIC: 3672 3679 Printed circuit boards; power supplies, all types: static

(P-18508)
IPC CAL FLEX INC
13337 South St 307, Cerritos (90703-7308)
PHONE...............714 952-0373
Scott Kohno, *President*
EMP: 40
SQ FT: 25,000

SALES (est): 5.4MM **Privately Held**
WEB: www.calflex.com
SIC: 3672 Printed circuit boards

(P-18509)
IRVINE ELECTRONICS INC
1601 Alton Pkwy Ste A, Irvine (92606-4843)
PHONE...............949 250-0315
Jane Zerounian, *President*
Onnig Zerounian, *Vice Pres*
Michael Mukund, *Program Mgr*
Phillip Tran, *Technician*
David Bossley, *Engineer*
EMP: 100
SQ FT: 48,000
SALES: 14.1MM **Privately Held**
WEB: www.irvine-electronics.com
SIC: 3672 Circuit boards, television & radio printed

(P-18510)
ISU PETASYS CORP
12930 Bradley Ave, Sylmar (91342-3829)
PHONE...............818 833-5800
Yong Kyoun Kim, *President*
Arleen Masangkay, *Executive*
John Lyday, *Purch Mgr*
Simeon Requidan, *QC Mgr*
Don Van Patten, *Sales Dir*
▲ **EMP:** 95
SQ FT: 50,000
SALES: 17.8MM
SALES (corp-wide): 960MM **Privately Held**
WEB: www.isupetasys.com
SIC: 3672 Printed circuit boards
PA: Isu Chemical Co., Ltd.
84 Sapyeong-Daero, Seocho-Gu
Seoul 06575
822 590-6600

(P-18511)
JABIL CIRCUIT INC
1925 Lundy Ave, San Jose (95131-1847)
PHONE...............408 361-3200
Thomas Costkel, *Manager*
EMP: 100
SALES (corp-wide): 22.1B **Publicly Held**
SIC: 3672 Printed circuit boards
PA: Jabil Inc.
10560 Dr Martin Luther
Saint Petersburg FL 33716
727 577-9749

(P-18512)
JABIL INC
Also Called: Jabil Chad Automation
1565 S Sinclair St, Anaheim (92806-5934)
PHONE...............714 938-0080
Babak Naderi, *Director*
Richard Munro, *Business Mgr*
EMP: 50
SALES (corp-wide): 22.1B **Publicly Held**
SIC: 3672 Printed circuit boards
PA: Jabil Inc.
10560 Dr Martin Luther
Saint Petersburg FL 33716
727 577-9749

(P-18513)
JABIL INC
30 Great Oaks Blvd, San Jose (95119-1309)
PHONE...............408 361-3200
EMP: 500
SALES (corp-wide): 22.1B **Publicly Held**
WEB: www.jabil.com
SIC: 3672 Printed circuit boards
PA: Jabil Inc.
10560 Dr Martin Luther
Saint Petersburg FL 33716
727 577-9749

(P-18514)
JATON CORPORATION
47677 Lakeview Blvd, Fremont (94538-6544)
PHONE...............510 933-8888
Vicky Hong, *President*
J S Chiang, *CEO*
George Cheng, *Manager*
▲ **EMP:** 255
SQ FT: 85,000

▲ = Import ▼=Export
◆ =Import/Export

SALES (est): 28.5MM **Privately Held**
WEB: www.jaton.com
SIC: 3672 3674 3661 3577 Printed circuit boards; modules, solid state; modems; computer peripheral equipment

(P-18515)
JMP ELECTRONICS INC
2685 Dow Ave Ste A1, Tustin (92780-7241)
PHONE....................714 730-2086
Joseph Manea, *President*
Martha Manea, *Senior VP*
Petru Pantis, *Vice Pres*
Dorel Bila, *Manager*
▲ **EMP:** 18
SQ FT: 12,500
SALES (est): 4.1MM **Privately Held**
WEB: www.jmpelectronics.com
SIC: 3672 Printed circuit boards

(P-18516)
KCA ELECTRONICS INC
Also Called: Summit Interconnect - Anaheim
223 N Crescent Way, Anaheim (92801-6704)
PHONE....................714 239-2433
Shane Whiteside, *President*
▲ **EMP:** 180
SQ FT: 60,000
SALES (est): 38.6MM **Privately Held**
WEB: www.kcamerica.com
SIC: 3672 Circuit boards, television & radio printed
HQ: Equity Hci Management L P
1730 Pennsylvania Ave Nw
Washington DC
-

(P-18517)
KL ELECTRONICS INC
3083 S Harbor Blvd, Santa Ana (92704-6448)
PHONE....................714 751-5611
Khanh Ton, *President*
Michael Ton, *CEO*
Luon Ton, *Corp Secy*
Charlie Tran, *Mfg Staff*
EMP: 20
SQ FT: 4,000
SALES (est): 3.3MM **Privately Held**
WEB: www.klelectronics.com
SIC: 3672 Printed circuit boards

(P-18518)
LAMINATING COMPANY OF AMERICA
Also Called: Lcoa
20322 Windrow Dr Ste 100, Lake Forest (92630-8150)
PHONE....................949 587-3300
Tim Redfern, *President*
Brad Biddol, *CFO*
David Klebba, *Sales Staff*
▲ **EMP:** 50
SALES (est): 8.4MM **Privately Held**
WEB: www.tristarlaminates.com
SIC: 3672 Printed circuit boards

(P-18519)
LARITECH INC
387 Zachary St Unit 102, Moorpark (93021-2071)
PHONE....................805 529-5000
William C Larrick, *CEO*
Joel Butler, *COO*
Terry Gonzales, *Treasurer*
Carson Derry, *Program Mgr*
Jody Martin, *Program Mgr*
EMP: 51 **EST:** 2001
SQ FT: 13,000
SALES: 10MM **Privately Held**
WEB: www.laritech.com
SIC: 3672 Printed circuit boards

(P-18520)
LIFETIME MEMORY PRODUCTS INC
2505 Da Vinci Ste A, Irvine (92614-0170)
P.O. Box 1207, Laguna Beach (92652-1207)
PHONE....................949 794-9000
Paul Columbus, *CEO*
Cameron Hum, *President*
◆ **EMP:** 40
SQ FT: 16,000

SALES (est): 7.6MM **Privately Held**
WEB: www.lifetimememory.com
SIC: 3672 5045 3674 Printed circuit boards; computers, peripherals & software; semiconductors & related devices

(P-18521)
LOGI GRAPHICS INCORPORATED
17592 Metzler Ln, Huntington Beach (92647-6241)
PHONE....................714 841-3686
Greg Otterbach, *President*
Terri Otterbach, *Admin Sec*
EMP: 17
SQ FT: 12,000
SALES: 1.3MM **Privately Held**
SIC: 3672 Printed circuit boards

(P-18522)
LUMISTAR INC (DH)
2270 Camino Vida Roble L, Carlsbad (92011-1503)
PHONE....................760 431-2181
Eric Demarco, *President*
Deanna Lund, *CEO*
Laura Siegal, *Treasurer*
Michael Fink, *Vice Pres*
Bryan Graber, *Principal*
EMP: 13 **EST:** 2000
SQ FT: 6,000
SALES (est): 1.5MM **Publicly Held**
WEB: www.lumi-star.com
SIC: 3672 Printed circuit boards
HQ: Real Time Logic, Inc.
12515 Academy Ridge Vw
Colorado Springs CO 80921
719 598-2801

(P-18523)
MARCEL ELECTRONICS INC
240 W Bristol Ln, Orange (92865-2645)
PHONE....................714 974-8590
EMP: 15
SALES (est): 2.2MM **Privately Held**
SIC: 3672 Printed circuit boards

(P-18524)
MARCEL ELECTRONICS INC
130 W Bristol Ln, Orange (92865-2637)
PHONE....................714 974-8590
Chris Lewarn, *Technology*
John Dipalo, *Purch Agent*
John Dipaolo, *Purch Agent*
Chris Ogle, *Maint Spvr*
EMP: 14
SALES (est): 2MM **Privately Held**
SIC: 3672 Printed circuit boards

(P-18525)
MATRIX USA INC
2730 S Main St, Santa Ana (92707-3435)
PHONE....................714 825-0404
Kieran Healy, *President*
George Potocska, *Controller*
▲ **EMP:** 25 **EST:** 2005
SALES (est): 5.1MM **Privately Held**
SIC: 3672 Printed circuit boards
HQ: Matrix Electronics Limited
1124 Mid-Way Blvd
Mississauga ON L5T 2
905 670-8400

(P-18526)
MEGA PLUS PCB INCORPORATED
4091 E La Palma Ave Ste M, Anaheim (92807-1703)
PHONE....................714 550-0265
Nadim S Kazempoor, *CEO*
Noorya Kazempoor, *Vice Pres*
EMP: 15
SQ FT: 1,500
SALES: 500K **Privately Held**
SIC: 3672 Printed circuit boards

(P-18527)
MERCURY SYSTEMS INC
1000 Avenida Acaso, Camarillo (93012-8712)
PHONE....................805 388-1345
Stephen Bouchard, *CEO*
EMP: 110
SALES (corp-wide): 493.1MM **Publicly Held**
SIC: 3672 Printed circuit boards

PA: Mercury Systems, Inc.
50 Minuteman Rd
Andover MA 01810
978 256-1300

(P-18528)
MERCURY SYSTEMS INC
85 Nicholson Ln, San Jose (95134-1366)
PHONE....................669 226-5800
Charles Leader, *CEO*
EMP: 10
SQ FT: 3,990
SALES (corp-wide): 493.1MM **Publicly Held**
WEB: www.amlj.com
SIC: 3672 Printed circuit boards
PA: Mercury Systems, Inc.
50 Minuteman Rd
Andover MA 01810
978 256-1300

(P-18529)
MERITRONICS INC (PA)
500 Yosemite Dr Ste 108, Milpitas (95035)
PHONE....................408 969-0888
Cherng Dior Wu, *President*
Pat Penparkgoon, *Engineer*
▲ **EMP:** 43
SQ FT: 34,000
SALES (est): 16.3MM **Privately Held**
WEB: www.meritronics.com
SIC: 3672 Printed circuit boards

(P-18530)
MI TECHNOLOGIES INC
Also Called: Discount Merchant.com
2215 Pseo De Las Americas, San Diego (92154-7908)
PHONE....................619 710-2637
Amir Tafreshi, *CEO*
John Celms, *CFO*
Ricardo Cazares, *Vice Pres*
Ali Irani-Tehrani, *Principal*
Miguel Nava, *Technician*
▲ **EMP:** 130
SQ FT: 8,000
SALES: 21.6MM **Privately Held**
WEB: www.mitechnologies.net
SIC: 3672 3469 3089 Printed circuit boards; metal stampings; injection molding of plastics

(P-18531)
MICRO ANALOG INC
1861 Puddingstone Dr, La Verne (91750-5825)
PHONE....................909 392-8277
Hung T Nguyen, *CEO*
Khanh Van Nguyen, *CFO*
KV Nguyen, *Vice Pres*
Binh Pham, *Human Resources*
Hai Nguyen, *Manager*
▲ **EMP:** 160
SQ FT: 27,000
SALES (est): 52.9MM **Privately Held**
SIC: 3672 Printed circuit boards

(P-18532)
MODULUS INC
518 Sycamore Dr, Milpitas (95035-7412)
PHONE....................408 457-3712
Mir Imran, *CEO*
Marvin Ackerman, *Shareholder*
Syed Zaidi, *Vice Pres*
▲ **EMP:** 10
SQ FT: 85,040
SALES (est): 2.5MM **Privately Held**
WEB: www.modulusinc.com
SIC: 3672 Printed circuit boards

(P-18533)
MULTI-FINELINE ELECTRONIX INC (HQ)
101 Academy Ste 250, Irvine (92617-3035)
PHONE....................949 453-6800
Reza Meshgin, *President*
Tom Kampfer, *CFO*
Christine Besnard, *Exec VP*
Lance Jin, *Exec VP*
Thomas Lee, *Exec VP*
EMP: 583
SQ FT: 20,171
SALES (est): 572.9MM
SALES (corp-wide): 2.3B **Privately Held**
WEB: www.mflex.com
SIC: 3672 Printed circuit boards

PA: Suzhou Dongshan Precision Manufacturing Co., Ltd.
No.8, Shiheshan Road, Dongshan Industrial Park, Wuzhong District
Suzhou 21510
512 662-8121

(P-18534)
MULTILAYER PROTOTYPES INC
Also Called: Mpi
2513 Teller Rd, Newbury Park (91320-2220)
PHONE....................805 498-9390
Steve Ferris, *President*
Dara Garza, *Corp Secy*
EMP: 19
SQ FT: 11,000
SALES (est): 3.1MM **Privately Held**
WEB: www.mpi-pcb.com
SIC: 3672 Circuit boards, television & radio printed

(P-18535)
MULTIMEK INC
357 Reed St, Santa Clara (95050-3107)
PHONE....................408 653-1300
Doug McCown, *President*
Doug Mc Cown, *VP Human Res*
EMP: 20
SQ FT: 8,000
SALES (est): 3.2MM **Privately Held**
WEB: www.multimek.com
SIC: 3672 Printed circuit boards

(P-18536)
N D E INC
Also Called: New Dimension Electronics
3301 Keller St, Santa Clara (95054-2601)
PHONE....................408 727-3955
Richard Le, *CEO*
Lana Le, *Office Mgr*
EMP: 30
SQ FT: 6,000
SALES (est): 4MM **Privately Held**
SIC: 3672 3679 Printed circuit boards; harness assemblies for electronic use: wire or cable

(P-18537)
NAPROTEK INC
90 Rose Orchard Way, San Jose (95134-1356)
PHONE....................408 830-5000
Najat Badriyeh, *CEO*
Liz Davidson, *Vice Pres*
James Handyside, *Business Mgr*
EMP: 60
SQ FT: 24,000
SALES: 14.1MM **Privately Held**
WEB: www.naprotek.com
SIC: 3672 Circuit boards, television & radio printed

(P-18538)
NASO INDUSTRIES CORPORATION
Also Called: Naso Technologies
3007 Bunsen Ave Ste Q, Ventura (93003-7634)
PHONE....................805 650-1231
Jahansooz Saleh, *CEO*
Bill Thorpe, *President*
Soraya Saleh, *CEO*
Bryan Howe, *Vice Pres*
Namdar Saleh, *Vice Pres*
EMP: 40
SQ FT: 20,000
SALES (est): 15MM **Privately Held**
WEB: www.naso.com
SIC: 3672 3599 Printed circuit boards; machine shop, jobbing & repair

(P-18539)
NATEL ENGINEERING COMPANY INC
Also Called: Powercube
9340 Owensmouth Ave, Chatsworth (91311-6915)
PHONE....................818 734-6552
Sudesh Arora, *Branch Mgr*
EMP: 20
SALES (corp-wide): 1.2B **Privately Held**
WEB: www.natelengr.com
SIC: 3672 Printed circuit boards

PA: Natel Engineering Company Inc
9340 Owensmouth Ave
Chatsworth CA 91311
818 734-6523

(P-18540)
NATEL ENGINEERING COMPANY INC
2243 Lundy Ave, San Jose (95131-1822)
PHONE...................................408 228-5462
EMP: 130
SALES (corp-wide): 1.2B Privately Held
SIC: 3672 Printed circuit boards
PA: Natel Engineering Company Inc
9340 Owensmouth Ave
Chatsworth CA 91311
818 734-6523

(P-18541)
NATEL ENGINEERING COMPANY INC
2066 Aldergrove Ave, Escondido (92029-1901)
PHONE...................................760 737-6777
Keith Butler, Branch Mgr
EMP: 130
SALES (corp-wide): 1.2B Privately Held
SIC: 3672 Printed circuit boards
PA: Natel Engineering Company Inc
9340 Owensmouth Ave
Chatsworth CA 91311
818 734-6523

(P-18542)
NELCO PRODUCTS INC
1100 E Kimberly Ave, Anaheim (92801-1101)
PHONE...................................714 879-4293
Ronald B Hart, President
EMP: 20
SALES (corp-wide): 111.2MM Publicly Held
WEB: www.nelcoproducts.com
SIC: 3672 Printed circuit boards
HQ: Nelco Products, Inc
1100 E Kimberly Ave
Anaheim CA 92801
714 879-4293

(P-18543)
NETWORK PCB INC
1914 Otoole Way, San Jose (95131-2237)
PHONE...................................408 943-8760
Kevin Le, President
Pauline Vo, Accounts Mgr
EMP: 30
SALES (est): 4.8MM Privately Held
WEB: www.networkpcb.com
SIC: 3672 Circuit boards, television & radio printed

(P-18544)
NEW BRUNSWICK INDUSTRIES INC
1850 Gillespie Way, El Cajon (92020-1094)
PHONE...................................619 448-4900
Jim Krehbiel, President
Sue Harnack, Vice Pres
Sue Krehbiel, Vice Pres
EMP: 30
SALES (est): 7MM Privately Held
WEB: www.nbiinc.com
SIC: 3672 Circuit boards, television & radio printed

(P-18545)
NEXLOGIC TECHNOLOGIES INC
2085 Zanker Rd, San Jose (95131-2107)
PHONE...................................408 436-8150
Zulki Khan, President
Tariq Nisar, Program Mgr
Sanam Shaikh, Sr Software Eng
Johnny Hasan, Engineer
Yaseen Haroon, Controller
▲ EMP: 76
SALES (est): 16.1MM Privately Held
WEB: www.nxtcommercial.com
SIC: 3672 Printed circuit boards

(P-18546)
NORTHWEST CIRCUITS CORP
8660 Avenida Costa Blanca, San Diego (92154-6232)
PHONE...................................619 661-1701
Toribio Lobato, President

▲ EMP: 65
SQ FT: 12,000
SALES (est): 19.1MM Privately Held
WEB: www.northwestcircuitscorp.com
SIC: 3672 Printed circuit boards

(P-18547)
NOVA DRILLING SERVICES INC
1500 Buckeye Dr, Milpitas (95035-7418)
PHONE...................................408 732-6682
Mike McKibbin, President
Michael Doherty, Vice Pres
Stephanie Bell, Admin Sec
Kathleen McKibbin, Admin Sec
CAM Smith, Purch Agent
EMP: 32
SQ FT: 15,000
SALES (est): 4.1MM Privately Held
WEB: www.novadrill-fab.com
SIC: 3672 3083 Printed circuit boards; laminated plastics plate & sheet

(P-18548)
NPI SERVICES INC
1580 Corporate Dr Ste 124, Costa Mesa (92626-1460)
PHONE...................................714 850-0550
Judith Greenspon, President
Bente Fajardo, Business Mgr
EMP: 11
SQ FT: 5,880
SALES: 2.8MM Privately Held
WEB: www.npiservices.com
SIC: 3672 Printed circuit boards

(P-18549)
ONCORE MANUFACTURING LLC
Also Called: Oncore Velocity
237 Via Vera Cruz, San Marcos (92078-2617)
PHONE...................................760 737-6777
Arnulfo Villa, Principal
EMP: 130
SALES (corp-wide): 1.2B Privately Held
SIC: 3672 Printed circuit boards
HQ: Oncore Manufacturing Llc
9340 Owensmouth Ave
Chatsworth CA 91311

(P-18550)
ONCORE MANUFACTURING SVCS INC
Also Called: Neo Tech Natel Epic Oncore
9340 Owensmouth Ave, Chatsworth (91311-6915)
PHONE...................................510 360-2222
Sudesh Arora, CEO
Walt Hussey, COO
Sajjad Malik, Exec VP
David Brakenwagen, Senior VP
Magdy Henry, Vice Pres
▲ EMP: 230
SALES: 117.8MM
SALES (corp-wide): 1.2B Privately Held
WEB: www.victron.com
SIC: 3672 Printed circuit boards
PA: Natel Engineering Company Inc
9340 Owensmouth Ave
Chatsworth CA 91311
818 734-6523

(P-18551)
ORCA SYSTEMS INC
3990 Old Town Ave, San Diego (92110-2930)
PHONE...................................858 679-9295
Guruswami Sridharan, President
Kartik Sridharan, Vice Pres
EMP: 35
SALES (est): 6.4MM Privately Held
WEB: www.orcasystems.com
SIC: 3672 Circuit boards, television & radio printed

(P-18552)
ORION MANUFACTURING INC
5550 Hellyer Ave, San Jose (95138-1005)
PHONE...................................408 955-9001
Matthew L Davis, President
EMP: 125
SALES (est): 1.4MM Privately Held
SIC: 3672 Printed circuit boards

(P-18553)
OSI ELECTRONICS INC (HQ)
12533 Chadron Ave, Hawthorne (90250-4807)
PHONE...................................310 978-0516
Paul Morben, President
Bruce Macdonald, President
Alex Colquhoun, COO
Lou Campana, Vice Pres
Connie Spence, Technology
▲ EMP: 166
SQ FT: 60,000
SALES (est): 28.2MM
SALES (corp-wide): 1B Publicly Held
WEB: www.osielectronics.com
SIC: 3672 Printed circuit boards
PA: Osi Systems, Inc.
12525 Chadron Ave
Hawthorne CA 90250
310 978-0516

(P-18554)
PALPILOT INTERNATIONAL CORP
15991 Red Hill Ave # 102, Tustin (92780-7320)
PHONE...................................714 460-0718
Bruce Lee, Branch Mgr
Win Cheng, President
Paul Laliberty, Business Mgr
Jeff Berger, Sales Mgr
EMP: 33 Privately Held
SIC: 3672 Printed circuit boards
PA: Palpilot International Corporation
500 Yosemite Dr
Milpitas CA 95035

(P-18555)
PALPILOT INTERNATIONAL CORP (PA)
500 Yosemite Dr, Milpitas (95035)
PHONE...................................408 855-8866
Eddy C Niu, President
Alex Shih, Officer
Yichien Hwang, Vice Pres
Bruce Lee, Vice Pres
David Bainbridge, Regional Mgr
▲ EMP: 40
SQ FT: 7,000
SALES (est): 70.5MM Privately Held
SIC: 3672 3089 Printed circuit boards; injection molding of plastics

(P-18556)
PARK ELECTROCHEMICAL CORP
1100 E Kimberly Ave, Anaheim (92801-1101)
PHONE...................................714 459-4400
George Frantz, Branch Mgr
EMP: 40
SALES (corp-wide): 111.2MM Publicly Held
WEB: www.parkelectro.com
SIC: 3672 Printed circuit boards
PA: Park Electrochemical Corp.
48 S Service Rd Ste 300
Melville NY 11747
631 465-3600

(P-18557)
PARPRO TECHNOLOGIES INC
Also Called: P T I
2700 S Fairview St, Santa Ana (92704-5947)
PHONE...................................714 545-8886
Thomas Sparrvik, CEO
Keith Knight, President
Ken Haney, Vice Pres
Tucky Wong, Vice Pres
Cuong Hoang, Engineer
EMP: 180
SALES: 34.2MM
SALES (corp-wide): 185.1MM Privately Held
SIC: 3672 Printed circuit boards
PA: Parpro Corporation
67-1, Tung Yuan Rd., Chung Li Ind. Park,
Taoyuan City TAY 32063
345 255-35

(P-18558)
PDM SOLUTIONS INC
Also Called: Protech Design & Manufacturing
8451 Miralani Dr Ste J, San Diego (92126-4388)
PHONE...................................858 348-1000
James O'Shea, President
Michelle Kim, Vice Pres
Basman Musa, Engineer
EMP: 20
SQ FT: 5,700
SALES (est): 4.6MM Privately Held
SIC: 3672 Printed circuit boards

(P-18559)
PHOTO FABRICATORS INC
7648 Burnet Ave, Van Nuys (91405-1043)
PHONE...................................818 781-1010
Steve L Brooks, President
John R Brooks, Chairman
Susan Brooks, Corp Secy
▲ EMP: 75
SQ FT: 14,000
SALES (est): 11.2MM Privately Held
WEB: www.photofabricators.com
SIC: 3672 Circuit boards, television & radio printed

(P-18560)
PIONEER CIRCUITS INC
3000 S Shannon St, Santa Ana (92704-6387)
PHONE...................................714 641-3132
James Y Lee, President
EMP: 260
SQ FT: 50,000
SALES (est): 32.4MM Privately Held
WEB: www.pioneercircuits.com
SIC: 3672 Circuit boards, television & radio printed

(P-18561)
PLEXUS CORP
431 Kato Ter, Fremont (94539-8333)
P.O. Box 156, Neenah WI (54957-0156)
PHONE...................................510 668-9000
Fax: 510 668-9090
EMP: 120
SALES (corp-wide): 2.6B Publicly Held
SIC: 3672
PA: Plexus Corp.
1 Plexus Way
Neenah WI 54956
920 969-6000

(P-18562)
POWER CIRCUITS INC
2630 S Harbor Blvd, Santa Ana (92704-5829)
PHONE...................................714 327-3000
Kenton K Alder, President
EMP: 350
SALES (est): 32MM
SALES (corp-wide): 2.6B Publicly Held
WEB: www.ttmtek.com
SIC: 3672 Printed circuit boards
PA: Ttm Technologies, Inc.
1665 Scenic Ave Ste 250
Costa Mesa CA 92626
714 327-3000

(P-18563)
POWER DESIGN MANUFACTURING LLC
Also Called: Power Design Services
121 E Brokaw Rd, San Jose (95112-4204)
PHONE...................................408 437-1931
Keith Schenk, CEO
Tuan Tran, Vice Pres
Joann Bryant, Purchasing
Joe Wilcox, Opers Staff
Eric Willson, Regl Sales Mgr
EMP: 23
SQ FT: 6,800
SALES (est): 7.2MM Privately Held
WEB: www.powerdesignservices.com
SIC: 3672 Circuit boards, television & radio printed

(P-18564)
PRECISION CIRCUITS WEST INC
3310 W Harvard St, Santa Ana (92704-3920)
PHONE...................................714 435-9670
Chatur Patel, President
Sam Akbari, Executive

▲ = Import ▼=Export
◆ =Import/Export

Prabhudas Patel, *Admin Sec*
Kelly Akbari, *Controller*
John Sunu, *Opers Staff*
EMP: 15
SQ FT: 12,000
SALES (est): 1.2MM **Privately Held**
WEB: www.pcwesti.com
SIC: 3672 Circuit boards, television & radio printed

(P-18565)
PRECISION DESIGN INC
Also Called: Pdi
1160 Industrial Rd Ste 16, San Carlos (94070-4128)
PHONE..................................650 508-8041
Alexandra Sgolombis, *President*
EMP: 25
SQ FT: 5,030
SALES (est): 3.4MM **Privately Held**
SIC: 3672 7373 Printed circuit boards; computer integrated systems design

(P-18566)
PRINTED CIRCUIT SOLUTIONS INC
2040 S Yale St, Santa Ana (92704-3923)
PHONE..................................714 825-1090
Jose Lara, *CEO*
Ofelia Lara, *COO*
Joe Lara, *VP Bus Dvlpt*
EMP: 10 **EST:** 2012
SALES (est): 1.1MM **Privately Held**
SIC: 3672 Printed circuit boards

(P-18567)
PRINTED CIRCUIT TECHNOLOGY
Also Called: Pct
44081 Old Warm Sprng Blvd, Fremont (94538-6158)
PHONE..................................510 659-1866
Scott Lew, *President*
EMP: 80
SQ FT: 13,000
SALES (est): 9.1MM **Privately Held**
WEB: www.pctnet.com
SIC: 3672 Printed circuit boards

(P-18568)
Q-FLEX INC
1301 E Hunter Ave, Santa Ana (92705-4133)
PHONE..................................714 664-0101
Nayna Uka, *President*
Nalini Celio, *Corp Secy*
Pete Uka, *Vice Pres*
▲ **EMP:** 22 **EST:** 1988
SQ FT: 7,200
SALES (est): 3.4MM **Privately Held**
SIC: 3672 Printed circuit boards

(P-18569)
QOSTRONICS INC
2044 Corporate Ct, San Jose (95131-1753)
PHONE..................................408 719-1286
Shawn Do, *Principal*
MAI Tran, *Admin Sec*
EMP: 33
SQ FT: 5,500
SALES: 4MM **Privately Held**
WEB: www.qostronics.com
SIC: 3672 3845 Circuit boards, television & radio printed; electromedical equipment

(P-18570)
QUAL-PRO CORPORATION (HQ)
18510 S Figueroa St, Gardena (90248-4519)
PHONE..................................310 329-7535
Brian Jeffrey Shane, *CEO*
David Soden, *President*
Richard Fitzgerald, *COO*
Kirk Waldron, *Exec VP*
Kevin Vincent, *Prgrmr*
EMP: 200
SQ FT: 55,000
SALES (est): 40.5MM
SALES (corp-wide): 167.5MM **Privately Held**
WEB: www.qual-pro.com
SIC: 3672 Circuit boards, television & radio printed

PA: Sfo Technologies Private Limited
Plot No. 2, Cochin Special Economic Zone
Kochi KL 68203
484 661-4300

(P-18571)
QUALITEK INC (HQ)
1116 Elko Dr, Sunnyvale (94089-2207)
PHONE..................................408 734-8686
Louise Crisham, *CEO*
▲ **EMP:** 75
SQ FT: 20,000
SALES (est): 8.8MM
SALES (corp-wide): 64.1MM **Privately Held**
SIC: 3672 Printed circuit boards
PA: Westak, Inc
1116 Elko Dr
Sunnyvale CA 94089
408 734-8686

(P-18572)
QUALITEK INC
Also Called: Westak
1272 Forgewood Ave, Sunnyvale (94089-2215)
PHONE..................................408 752-8422
Ray Giancola, *Manager*
EMP: 90
SALES (corp-wide): 64.1MM **Privately Held**
SIC: 3672 Printed circuit boards
HQ: Qualitek Inc
1116 Elko Dr
Sunnyvale CA 94089
408 734-8686

(P-18573)
QUALITY CIRCUIT ASSEMBLY INC
Also Called: Q C A
1709 Junction Ct Ste 380, San Jose (95112-1044)
PHONE..................................408 441-1001
Jeff Moss, *President*
Dwight Hargrave, *Vice Pres*
Nancy Moss, *Sales Dir*
EMP: 65
SQ FT: 30,000
SALES (est): 20.6MM **Privately Held**
WEB: www.qcamfg.com
SIC: 3672 Circuit boards, television & radio printed

(P-18574)
QUALITY SYSTEMS INTGRATED CORP (PA)
6720 Cobra Way, San Diego (92121-4109)
PHONE..................................858 587-9797
Kiem T Le, *CEO*
Cecile Le, *CFO*
Hai Bach, *Principal*
Thui Trong, *Principal*
Mike Gallegher, *Info Tech Mgr*
▲ **EMP:** 275
SQ FT: 50,000
SALES (est): 81.4MM **Privately Held**
WEB: www.qsic.com
SIC: 3672 Printed circuit boards

(P-18575)
QUALTECH CIRCUITS INC
1101 Comstock St, Santa Clara (95054-3407)
PHONE..................................408 727-4125
Jim Khosh, *President*
EMP: 12
SQ FT: 25,000
SALES (est): 1.8MM **Privately Held**
SIC: 3672 Circuit boards, television & radio printed

(P-18576)
R F CIRCUITS AND ASSEMBLY INC
3533 Old Conejo Rd # 107, Newbury Park (91320-6163)
PHONE..................................805 499-7788
Pankaj Patell, *President*
EMP: 12
SALES: 500K **Privately Held**
WEB: www.rfassembly.com
SIC: 3672 Printed circuit boards

(P-18577)
R&D ALTANOVA INC
6389 San Ignacio Ave, San Jose (95119-1206)
PHONE..................................408 225-7011
James Russell, *CEO*
Ken Pawloski, *CFO*
Khurram Aziz, *Engineer*
Patricia Olah, *Controller*
Jizel Alvand, *Buyer*
EMP: 38
SQ FT: 15,000
SALES (est): 7.9MM
SALES (corp-wide): 33.4MM **Privately Held**
WEB: www.altanova1.com
SIC: 3672 7389 Printed circuit boards; design services
PA: R & D Circuits Inc
3601 S Clinton Ave
South Plainfield NJ 07080
732 549-4554

(P-18578)
RACAAR CIRCUIT INDUSTRIES INC
9225 Alabama Ave Ste F, Chatsworth (91311-5843)
PHONE..................................818 998-7566
Stephen Serup, *President*
Julie Serup, *Corp Secy*
EMP: 40
SQ FT: 4,000
SALES (est): 1.5MM **Privately Held**
SIC: 3672 3433 Printed circuit boards; heating equipment, except electric

(P-18579)
RASTERGRAF INC (PA)
7145 Marlborough Ter, Berkeley (94705-1736)
PHONE..................................510 849-4801
Victor R Gold Jr, *President*
EMP: 15
SALES (est): 2.2MM **Privately Held**
WEB: www.rastergraf.com
SIC: 3672 Printed circuit boards

(P-18580)
RIGIFLEX TECHNOLOGY INC
1166 N Grove St, Anaheim (92806-2109)
PHONE..................................714 688-1500
Dhiru Sorathia, *President*
EMP: 25
SQ FT: 15,000
SALES (est): 4.4MM **Privately Held**
SIC: 3672 Printed circuit boards

(P-18581)
ROADRUNNER CIRCUIT TECHNOLOGY
23201 Mill Creek Dr, Laguna Hills (92653-7905)
PHONE..................................714 671-9517
Han Peng, *President*
Gary Reese, *Vice Pres*
EMP: 11
SQ FT: 12,000
SALES (est): 1.3MM **Privately Held**
WEB: www.rrcircuits.com
SIC: 3672 Circuit boards, television & radio printed

(P-18582)
ROCKET EMS INC
2950 Patrick Henry Dr, Santa Clara (95054-1813)
PHONE..................................408 727-3700
Craig Arcuri, *CEO*
Michael Kottke, *President*
EMP: 140
SQ FT: 40,000
SALES (est): 62.2MM **Privately Held**
SIC: 3672 Printed circuit boards

(P-18583)
ROGER INDUSTRY
11552 Knott St Ste 5, Garden Grove (92841-1833)
PHONE..................................714 896-0765
Shann-Mou Lee, *President*
Jiin-Sheue Lee, *Vice Pres*
▲ **EMP:** 16
SQ FT: 10,000

SALES (est): 1.3MM **Privately Held**
WEB: www.rogerindustry.com
SIC: 3672 3479 Printed circuit boards; coating of metals with plastic or resins

(P-18584)
ROYAL CIRCUIT SOLUTIONS INC (PA)
21 Hamilton Ct, Hollister (95023-2535)
PHONE..................................831 636-7789
Milan Shah, *President*
Mary Nydegger, *Accountant*
Amber Marini, *Regl Sales Mgr*
Johnny Dearmas, *Sales Staff*
Tara Jewell, *Director*
▲ **EMP:** 33
SQ FT: 15,000
SALES (est): 5.5MM **Privately Held**
SIC: 3672 Circuit boards, television & radio printed

(P-18585)
ROYAL FLEX CIRCUITS INC
15320 Cornet St, Santa Fe Springs (90670-5532)
PHONE..................................562 404-0626
Milan Shah, *CEO*
EMP: 27 **EST:** 2013
SQ FT: 15,000
SALES (est): 4.3MM
SALES (corp-wide): 5.5MM **Privately Held**
SIC: 3672 Wiring boards
PA: Royal Circuit Solutions, Inc.
21 Hamilton Ct
Hollister CA 95023
831 636-7789

(P-18586)
RUSH PCB INC
2149 Otoole Ave Ste 20, San Jose (95131-1341)
PHONE..................................408 469-6013
Neelkanta R Dantu, *Principal*
Roy Akber, *Administration*
Padma Dantu, *Manager*
Imran Valiani, *Accounts Mgr*
EMP: 10 **EST:** 2007
SALES (est): 10MM **Privately Held**
SIC: 3672 7389 Printed circuit boards;

(P-18587)
SAEHAN ELECTRONICS AMERICA INC (PA)
7880 Airway Rd Ste B5g, San Diego (92154-8308)
PHONE..................................858 496-1500
Bongsu Jeong, *CEO*
John Kim, *President*
Maria Bravo, *Human Res Mgr*
▲ **EMP:** 12
SALES (est): 7.8MM **Privately Held**
WEB: www.saehanusa.com
SIC: 3672 Printed circuit boards

(P-18588)
SAN DIEGO PCB DESIGN LLC
9909 Mira Mesa Blvd # 250, San Diego (92131-1056)
PHONE..................................858 271-5722
P Michael Stoehr, *Mng Member*
EMP: 18
SALES (est): 718K **Privately Held**
SIC: 3672 Circuit boards, television & radio printed

(P-18589)
SAN FRANCISCO CIRCUITS INC
1660 S Amphlett Blvd # 200, San Mateo (94402-2525)
PHONE..................................650 655-7202
Alex Danovich, *President*
Sam Danovich, *Vice Pres*
Andrew Gonzales, *Vice Pres*
Victor Bilandzic, *General Mgr*
Robert Boten, *QA Dir*
EMP: 12
SQ FT: 1,000
SALES (est): 2.7MM **Privately Held**
SIC: 3672 7379 Circuit boards, television & radio printed; computer related consulting services

(P-18590)
SANMINA CORPORATION
425 El Camino Real Bldg A, Santa Clara
(95050-4366)
PHONE..........................408 244-0266
Ed Carignan, *Manager*
EMP: 1200 **Publicly Held**
SIC: 3672 Printed circuit boards
PA: Sanmina Corporation
2700 N 1st St
San Jose CA 95134
-

(P-18591)
SANMINA CORPORATION
San Jose Plant 1337
2700 N 1st St, San Jose (95134-2015)
PHONE..........................408 964-3500
Thomas Mosier, *President*
Bob Moffat, *Vice Pres*
Erik Swennumson, *Vice Pres*
Jan Finkas, *Business Dir*
Brian Chaput, *Engineer*
EMP: 20 **Publicly Held**
WEB: www.sanmina.com
SIC: 3672 Printed circuit boards
PA: Sanmina Corporation
2700 N 1st St
San Jose CA 95134
-

(P-18592)
SANMINA CORPORATION
2701 Zanker Rd, San Jose (95134-2112)
PHONE..........................408 964-3500
Paul Hopwood, *Branch Mgr*
Gene Delaney, *Bd of Directors*
Tracy Trahan, *Engineer*
EMP: 20
SQ FT: 77,712 **Publicly Held**
WEB: www.sanmina.com
SIC: 3672 Printed circuit boards
PA: Sanmina Corporation
2700 N 1st St
San Jose CA 95134
-

(P-18593)
SANMINA CORPORATION
2050 Bering Dr, San Jose (95131-2009)
PHONE..........................408 964-6400
Eileen Card, *Branch Mgr*
Dale Kersten, *President*
William Quinn, *President*
Jure Sola, *CEO*
Raul Hernandez, *Program Mgr*
EMP: 375 **Publicly Held**
WEB: www.sanmina.com
SIC: 3672 Printed circuit boards
PA: Sanmina Corporation
2700 N 1st St
San Jose CA 95134
-

(P-18594)
SANMINA CORPORATION
Also Called: Sanmina-Sci
2036 Bering Dr, San Jose (95131-2009)
PHONE..........................408 964-3500
Norman Evans, *Branch Mgr*
Ed Attanasio, *President*
Dennis Young, *President*
Patrick Macdonald, *Senior VP*
Alan Abatte, *Vice Pres*
EMP: 300 **Publicly Held**
SIC: 3672 Printed circuit boards
PA: Sanmina Corporation
2700 N 1st St
San Jose CA 95134
-

(P-18595)
SANMINA CORPORATION
60 E Plumeria Dr B2db, San Jose
(95134-2102)
PHONE..........................408 557-7210
Randy Furr, *President*
David Anderson, *Vice Pres*
Tim McGinnis, *Vice Pres*
Girish Nair, *Program Mgr*
Shannon Wesley, *Administration*
EMP: 300 **Publicly Held**
WEB: www.sanmina.com
SIC: 3672 3643 Printed circuit boards;
current-carrying wiring devices

PA: Sanmina Corporation
2700 N 1st St
San Jose CA 95134

(P-18596)
SANMINA CORPORATION
42735 Christy St, Fremont (94538-3146)
PHONE..........................510 897-2000
Tony Princiotta, *Branch Mgr*
Eduardo Davalos, *Technology*
Jeannie Chua, *Engineer*
Vineeth Nair, *Engineer*
Younes Shabany, *Engineer*
EMP: 500
SQ FT: 155,000 **Publicly Held**
WEB: www.sanmina.com
SIC: 3672 Printed circuit boards
PA: Sanmina Corporation
2700 N 1st St
San Jose CA 95134

(P-18597)
SANMINA CORPORATION
60 E Plumeria Dr, San Jose (95134-2102)
PHONE..........................408 964-3000
Kishan Patel, *Manager*
Jackie Ward, *Bd of Directors*
Adil Mohammad, *Vice Pres*
Arnel Diesta, *Info Tech Mgr*
Janice Bass, *Engineer*
EMP: 56 **Publicly Held**
WEB: www.sanmina.com
SIC: 3672 3679 Circuit boards, television
& radio printed; harness assemblies for
electronic use: wire or cable
PA: Sanmina Corporation
2700 N 1st St
San Jose CA 95134

(P-18598)
SANMINA CORPORATION
2945 Airway Ave, Costa Mesa
(92626-6007)
PHONE..........................714 371-2800
Dox Scream, *Manager*
Ellen Mattox, *Prgrmr*
Jack Youil, *Mfg Mgr*
George Trinite, *Director*
Doug Scrimes, *Manager*
EMP: 100
SQ FT: 60,580 **Publicly Held**
WEB: www.sanmina.com
SIC: 3672 Printed circuit boards
PA: Sanmina Corporation
2700 N 1st St
San Jose CA 95134
-

(P-18599)
SANMINA CORPORATION (PA)
2700 N 1st St, San Jose (95134-2015)
P.O. Box 7, Huntsville AL (35804-0007)
PHONE..........................408 964-3500
Robert K Eulau, *CEO*
Jure Sola, *Ch of Bd*
David R Anderson, *CFO*
Nick Ravlich, *Treasurer*
Neil Bonke, *Bd of Directors*
EMP: 318
SALES: 7.1B **Publicly Held**
WEB: www.sanmina.com
SIC: 3672 3674 Printed circuit boards;
semiconductors & related devices; light
emitting diodes

(P-18600)
SANMINA CORPORATION
Viking Modular Solutions
2950 Red Hill Ave, Costa Mesa
(92626-5935)
PHONE..........................714 913-2200
Hamid Shokrgovar, *President*
Andy Reinelt, *Project Engr*
Sandra Saavedra, *Manager*
EMP: 110 **Publicly Held**
WEB: www.sanmina.com
SIC: 3672 Printed circuit boards
PA: Sanmina Corporation
2700 N 1st St
San Jose CA 95134

(P-18601)
SELECT CIRCUITS
3700 W Segerstrom Ave, Santa Ana
(92704-6410)
PHONE..........................714 825-1090
Esther Lara, *Partner*
Jose Lara, *Partner*
Ofelia Lara, *Partner*
EMP: 10
SALES (est): 703.8K **Privately Held**
WEB: www.selectcircuits.com
SIC: 3672 Printed circuit boards

(P-18602)
SEMI-KINETICS INC
20191 Windrow Dr Ste A, Lake Forest
(92630-8161)
PHONE..........................949 830-7364
Gary H Gonzalez, *CEO*
Kevin Loomans, *Buyer*
Michael Perdue, *Marketing Staff*
▲ **EMP:** 95 **EST:** 1981
SALES: 9.9MM
SALES (corp-wide): 57.7MM **Privately
Held**
WEB: www.semi-kinetics.com
SIC: 3672 Circuit boards, television & radio
printed
PA: Gonzalez Production Systems, Inc.
1670 Highwood E
Pontiac MI 48340
248 548-6010

(P-18603)
SIERRA CIRCUITS INC
Also Called: Sierra Proto Express
1108 W Evelyn Ave, Sunnyvale
(94086-5745)
PHONE..........................408 735-7137
Kenneth Bahl, *CEO*
Steve Arobio, *Vice Pres*
S Bala Bahl, *Vice Pres*
Ron Burns, *Executive*
Nilesh Parate, *General Mgr*
▲ **EMP:** 105 **EST:** 1978
SQ FT: 22,000
SALES (est): 58MM **Privately Held**
WEB: www.protoexpress.com
SIC: 3672 Printed circuit boards

(P-18604)
**SIGMA CIRCUIT TECHNOLOGY
LLC**
4624 Calle Mar De Armonia, San Diego
(92130-2689)
PHONE..........................858 523-0146
Daniel Duong,
EMP: 99
SALES: 800K **Privately Held**
SIC: 3672 Printed circuit boards

(P-18605)
**SIGMATRON INTERNATIONAL
INC**
30000 Eigenbrodt Way, Union City
(94587-1226)
PHONE..........................510 477-5000
Raj Upadhyaya, *Vice Pres*
Eric Chan, *Info Tech Mgr*
Erwin Rivera, *Senior Buyer*
EMP: 185 **Publicly Held**
WEB: www.sigmatronintl.com
SIC: 3672 Printed circuit boards
PA: Sigmatron International, Inc.
2201 Landmeier Rd
Elk Grove Village IL 60007

(P-18606)
SLP LIMITED LLC
Also Called: Www.slp-Formx.com
2031 E Cerritos Ave Ste H, Anaheim
(92806-5705)
PHONE..........................714 517-1955
Bruce Stuart, *Manager*
▲ **EMP:** 10
SQ FT: 5,000
SALES: 500K **Privately Held**
WEB: www.form-x.com
SIC: 3672 Circuit boards, television & radio
printed

(P-18607)
SMART ELEC & ASSEMBLY INC
2000 W Corporate Way, Anaheim
(92801-5373)
PHONE..........................714 772-2651
Robert Swelgin, *President*
Shou-Lee Wang, *CEO*
Patrick Huang, *COO*
Dave Wopschall, *CFO*
Getaneh Bekele, *Vice Pres*
▲ **EMP:** 120
SQ FT: 34,500
SALES: 100.2MM
SALES (corp-wide): 2.4B **Publicly Held**
WEB: www.smartelec.com
SIC: 3672 Circuit boards, television & radio
printed
HQ: Secure Communication Systems, Inc.
1740 E Wilshire Ave
Santa Ana CA 92705
714 547-1174

(P-18608)
**SMTC MANUFACTURING CORP
CAL**
2302 Trade Zone Blvd, San Jose
(95131-1819)
PHONE..........................408 934-7100
Larry Silber, *CEO*
John Caldwell, *President*
Claude Germain, *President*
Alex Walker, *President*
Jane Todd, *CFO*
▲ **EMP:** 1875
SALES (est): 188.6MM
SALES (corp-wide): 139.2MM **Privately
Held**
SIC: 3672 Printed circuit boards
HQ: Smtc Manufacturing Corporation Of
Canada
7050 Woodbine Ave Suite 300
Markham ON L3R 4
905 479-1810

(P-18609)
SNA ELECTRONICS INC
3249 Laurelview Ct, Fremont (94538-6535)
PHONE..........................510 656-3903
Sung W Shin, *CEO*
CHI Shin, *CFO*
Luis Hernandez, *Vice Pres*
Jae Song, *VP Bus Dvlpt*
Jae Kang, *Technician*
EMP: 44
SQ FT: 40,800
SALES: 5MM **Privately Held**
WEB: www.sna-electronic.com/
SIC: 3672 Printed circuit boards

(P-18610)
SOLDERMASK INC
17905 Metzler Ln, Huntington Beach
(92647-6258)
PHONE..........................714 842-1987
Frank S Kurisu, *President*
Son Pham, *General Mgr*
▲ **EMP:** 15
SQ FT: 10,000
SALES (est): 2.4MM **Privately Held**
SIC: 3672 3577 Printed circuit boards;
printers & plotters

(P-18611)
SOMACIS INC
13500 Danielson St, Poway (92064-6874)
PHONE..........................858 513-2200
Giovanni Tridenti, *CEO*
Carl Charleston, *Administration*
Cindy Burns, *Human Res Mgr*
Sean Cowan, *Opers Dir*
Michael Gleason, *Regl Sales Mgr*
▲ **EMP:** 120
SQ FT: 76,000
SALES (est): 17.5MM
SALES (corp-wide): 117.9K **Privately
Held**
SIC: 3672 Circuit boards, television & radio
printed
HQ: So.Ma.Ci.S. Spa
Via Jesina 17
Castelfidardo AN 60022
071 721-531

▲ = Import ▼=Export
◆ =Import/Export

(P-18612)
SONIC MANUFACTURING TECH INC
47951 Westinghouse Dr, Fremont (94539-7483)
PHONE...........................510 580-8500
Kenneth Raab, *President*
Robert Pereyda, *Vice Pres*
Henry Woo, *Vice Pres*
Norma Hirle, *Prdtn Mgr*
Matt Cavender, *Manager*
▲ EMP: 300
SQ FT: 80,000
SALES (est): 120.8MM **Privately Held**
WEB: www.sonicmfg.com
SIC: 3672 Printed circuit boards

(P-18613)
SOUTH COAST CIRCUITS INC
3506 W Lake Center Dr A, Santa Ana (92704-6985)
PHONE...........................714 966-2108
Charles R Benson, *CEO*
Daniel Alderete, *Purch Agent*
Jeff Rice, *Mfg Dir*
Patrick Bacon, *Mfg Staff*
Brad Harline, *Sales Staff*
▲ EMP: 68
SQ FT: 30,000
SALES: 9MM **Privately Held**
WEB: www.sccircuits.com
SIC: 3672 Circuit boards, television & radio printed

(P-18614)
SPECIALIZED COATING SERVICES
42680 Christy St, Fremont (94538-3135)
PHONE...........................510 226-8700
Richard Ramirez, *President*
Kim Atkins, *Vice Pres*
EMP: 62
SALES (est): 1.8MM **Privately Held**
WEB: www.speccoat.com
SIC: 3672 Circuit boards, television & radio printed

(P-18615)
SPECTRUM ASSEMBLY INC
Also Called: Spectrum Electronics
6300 Yarrow Dr Ste 100, Carlsbad (92011-1542)
PHONE...........................760 930-4000
Ronald Tupp, *President*
Michael Baldwin, *Vice Pres*
Mike Baldwin, *Vice Pres*
Jordan Topp, *Info Tech Mgr*
Stephen Wong, *Purchasing*
EMP: 85
SQ FT: 20,000
SALES (est): 25.8MM **Privately Held**
WEB: www.saicorp.com
SIC: 3672 Printed circuit boards

(P-18616)
STREAMLINE CIRCUITS CORP
1410 Martin Ave, Santa Clara (95050-2621)
PHONE...........................408 727-1418
Chuck D Dimick, *CEO*
Greg Halvorson, *President*
Tom Doslak, *Senior VP*
Linda Miyahara, *Engineer*
Ed Pitney, *Manager*
◆ EMP: 240
SQ FT: 30,000
SALES (est): 52.5MM **Privately Held**
WEB: www.streamlinecircuits.com
SIC: 3672 Printed circuit boards

(P-18617)
STREAMLINE ELECTRONICS MFG INC
Also Called: S E M
4285 Technology Dr, Fremont (94538-6339)
PHONE...........................408 263-3600
Shahab Jafri, *President*
Stephanie Broussard, *Project Mgr*
Ali Jamal, *Engineer*
Pierre Voreux, *Engineer*
Michelle Lee, *Opers Staff*
EMP: 50 EST: 1975
SQ FT: 26,000

SALES (est): 506.4K **Privately Held**
WEB: www.sem-inc.com
SIC: 3672 8711 2542 Printed circuit boards; engineering services; partitions & fixtures, except wood

(P-18618)
SUBA TECHNOLOGY INC
551 Lundy Pl, Milpitas (95035-6833)
PHONE...........................408 434-6500
Rolando M Suba, *CEO*
Alex Obice, *COO*
EMP: 25
SQ FT: 35,000
SALES (est): 3.8MM **Privately Held**
WEB: www.subatech.com
SIC: 3672 Printed circuit boards

(P-18619)
SUMITRONICS USA INC
9335 Airway Rd Ste 203c, San Diego (92154-7930)
PHONE...........................619 661-0450
Yukio Nagata, *President*
Ryuji Sumi, *CFO*
▲ EMP: 30
SQ FT: 800
SALES (est): 9.1MM
SALES (corp-wide): 45.3B **Privately Held**
SIC: 3672 Printed circuit boards
HQ: Sumitronics Corporation
1-2-2, Hitotsubashi
Chiyoda-Ku TKY 100-0
362 591-411

(P-18620)
SUNNYTECH
2243 Ringwood Ave, San Jose (95131-1737)
PHONE...........................408 943-8100
Siu Fong Chow, *President*
Virgil Chen, *Vice Pres*
Winny Chow, *Finance*
▲ EMP: 18
SQ FT: 5,500
SALES (est): 3.5MM **Privately Held**
SIC: 3672 Printed circuit boards

(P-18621)
SYMPROTEK CO
950 Yosemite Dr, Milpitas (95035-5452)
PHONE...........................408 956-0700
Eric Chon, *President*
Sangkyoo Jang, *Senior Buyer*
Harry La, *Director*
▲ EMP: 35
SQ FT: 36,000
SALES (est): 7.1MM **Privately Held**
WEB: www.symprotek.com
SIC: 3672 Printed circuit boards

(P-18622)
TC COSMOTRONIC INC
4663 E Guasti Rd Ste A, Ontario (91761-8196)
PHONE...........................949 660-0740
James R Savage, *CEO*
Tracyconrad Enriquez, *CFO*
EMP: 100
SALES (est): 16.3MM **Privately Held**
SIC: 3672 Printed circuit boards

(P-18623)
TECHNOTRONIX INC
1381 N Hundley St, Anaheim (92806-1301)
PHONE...........................714 630-9200
Jayshree Kapuria, *CEO*
Chris Paris, *Sales Engr*
Ken Ghadia, *Manager*
EMP: 20
SALES (est): 2.3MM **Privately Held**
SIC: 3672 Printed circuit boards

(P-18624)
TECHSERVE INDUSTRIES INC
6032 E West View Dr, Orange (92869-4357)
PHONE...........................714 505-2755
Al Aryamane, *President*
▲ EMP: 40
SQ FT: 4,500
SALES (est): 6.7MM **Privately Held**
SIC: 3672 Printed circuit boards

(P-18625)
TELIRITE TECHNICAL SVCS INC
2857 Lakeview Ct, Fremont (94538-6534)
PHONE...........................510 440-3888
Patrick Chan, *CEO*
Kue Chau Loh, *CFO*
Melissa Chow, *Accountant*
Ivy Tang, *Purchasing*
▲ EMP: 22
SQ FT: 12,000
SALES (est): 6.4MM **Privately Held**
WEB: www.telirite.com
SIC: 3672 Printed circuit boards

(P-18626)
TRANSLINE TECHNOLOGY INC
1106 S Technology Cir, Anaheim (92805-6329)
PHONE...........................714 533-8300
Kishor Patel, *President*
Larry Padmani, *Vice Pres*
▲ EMP: 33 EST: 1996
SQ FT: 20,000
SALES (est): 1.9MM **Privately Held**
WEB: www.translinetech.com
SIC: 3672 Printed circuit boards

(P-18627)
TRANTRONICS INC
1822 Langley Ave, Irvine (92614-5624)
PHONE...........................949 553-1234
Tom Tran, *President*
EMP: 32
SALES (est): 7MM **Privately Held**
WEB: www.trantronics.com
SIC: 3672 3599 Printed circuit boards; machine & other job shop work

(P-18628)
TRI-PHASE INC
Also Called: Valley Services Electronics
6190 San Ignacio Ave, San Jose (95119-1378)
PHONE...........................408 284-7700
Andy Pecota, *CEO*
Beth Kendrick, *President*
Jeff Trambley, *Exec VP*
Tamara Verrette, *Program Mgr*
Martin Nile, *Info Tech Dir*
EMP: 160
SQ FT: 52,000
SALES (est): 36.7MM **Privately Held**
WEB: www.boinglures.com
SIC: 3672 Printed circuit boards

(P-18629)
TRI-STAR LAMINATES INC
Also Called: Laminating Company of America
20322 Windrow Dr Ste 100, Lake Forest (92630-8150)
PHONE...........................949 587-3200
Patrick Redfern, *President*
Rob Wassem, *President*
Brad Biddle, *CFO*
Ethan Morgan, *Technology*
Adriana Gallegos, *Accounting Mgr*
EMP: 45
SQ FT: 50,000
SALES (est): 8MM **Privately Held**
WEB: www.lcoa.com
SIC: 3672 Printed circuit boards

(P-18630)
TTM PRINTED CIRCUIT GROUP INC
407 Mathew St, Santa Clara (95050-3105)
PHONE...........................408 486-3100
Jeff Gonsman, *Manager*
April Xu, *Officer*
Shaowei Zhang, *Officer*
Amy Feng, *Executive*
Raymond Ho, *Engineer*
EMP: 250
SALES (corp-wide): 2.6B **Publicly Held**
SIC: 3672 Printed circuit boards
HQ: Ttm Printed Circuit Group, Inc.
2630 S Harbor Blvd
Santa Ana CA 92704

(P-18631)
TTM PRINTED CIRCUIT GROUP INC (HQ)
2630 S Harbor Blvd, Santa Ana (92704-5829)
PHONE...........................714 327-3000
Thomas T Edman, *President*
Steve Richards, *CFO*
▲ EMP: 52
SALES (est): 137.5MM
SALES (corp-wide): 2.6B **Publicly Held**
WEB: www.ttmtechnologies.com
SIC: 3672 Printed circuit boards
PA: Ttm Technologies, Inc.
1665 Scenic Ave Ste 250
Costa Mesa CA 92626
714 327-3000

(P-18632)
TTM TECHNOLOGIES INC
407 Mathew St, Santa Clara (95050-3105)
PHONE...........................408 486-3100
Kate Lim, *Executive*
Rick Galeazzo, *Manager*
Scott Curry, *Accounts Mgr*
Jim Mills, *Accounts Mgr*
EMP: 260
SALES (corp-wide): 2.6B **Publicly Held**
SIC: 3672 Printed circuit boards
PA: Ttm Technologies, Inc.
1665 Scenic Ave Ste 250
Costa Mesa CA 92626
714 327-3000

(P-18633)
TTM TECHNOLOGIES INC (PA)
1665 Scenic Ave Ste 250, Costa Mesa (92626-1455)
PHONE...........................714 327-3000
Thomas T Edman, *President*
Robert E Klatell, *Ch of Bd*
Brian W Barber, *COO*
Todd B Schull, *CFO*
Chung Tai Keung Canice, *Exec VP*
EMP: 500
SQ FT: 11,775
SALES: 2.6B **Publicly Held**
WEB: www.ttmtechnologies.com
SIC: 3672 Printed circuit boards

(P-18634)
TTM TECHNOLOGIES INC
3140 E Coronado St, Anaheim (92806-1914)
PHONE...........................714 688-7200
Ruben Zepeda, *General Mgr*
EMP: 290
SALES (corp-wide): 2.6B **Publicly Held**
WEB: www.ddiglobal.com
SIC: 3672 Printed circuit boards
PA: Ttm Technologies, Inc.
1665 Scenic Ave Ste 250
Costa Mesa CA 92626
714 327-3000

(P-18635)
TTM TECHNOLOGIES INC
5037 Ruffner St, San Diego (92111-1107)
PHONE...........................858 874-2701
Mark Micale, *Manager*
EMP: 100
SALES (corp-wide): 2.6B **Publicly Held**
WEB: www.ttmtechnologies.com
SIC: 3672 Printed circuit boards
PA: Ttm Technologies, Inc.
1665 Scenic Ave Ste 250
Costa Mesa CA 92626
714 327-3000

(P-18636)
TTM TECHNOLOGIES INC
2630 S Harbor Blvd, Santa Ana (92704-5829)
PHONE...........................714 327-3000
Joe Ruane, *Vice Pres*
Kian Boloori, *Analyst*
Brandon Borland, *Human Res Mgr*
Kevin Mullin, *Purch Mgr*
Andrew Kozlak, *Maintence Staff*
EMP: 330
SALES (corp-wide): 2.6B **Publicly Held**
WEB: www.ttmtechnologies.com
SIC: 3672 Printed circuit boards

PA: Ttm Technologies, Inc.
1665 Scenic Ave Ste 250
Costa Mesa CA 92626
714 327-3000

(P-18637)
TTM TECHNOLOGIES INC
355 Turtle Creek Ct, San Jose
(95125-1316)
PHONE.....................408 280-0422
Arnold Amaral, *Branch Mgr*
Hieu Pham, *Manager*
EMP: 118
SALES (corp-wide): 2.6B **Publicly Held**
SIC: 3672 Printed circuit boards
PA: Ttm Technologies, Inc.
1665 Scenic Ave Ste 250
Costa Mesa CA 92626
714 327-3000

(P-18638)
TTM TECHNOLOGIES N AMER LLC
355 Turtle Creek Ct, San Jose
(95125-1316)
PHONE.....................408 719-4000
EMP: 118
SALES (corp-wide): 2.6B **Publicly Held**
WEB: www.ddiglobal.com
SIC: 3672 Printed circuit boards
HQ: Ttm Technologies North America, Llc
520 Maryville Centre Dr
Saint Louis MO 63141
314 719-1845

(P-18639)
TWIN INDUSTRIES INC
2303 Camino Ramon Ste 106, San Ramon
(94583-1389)
PHONE.....................925 866-8946
Joe O'Neil, *General Mgr*
Adom Moutafian, *President*
John Lagrasso, *Creative Dir*
▲ **EMP:** 85
SQ FT: 26,000
SALES (est): 8.1MM **Privately Held**
SIC: 3672 Printed circuit boards

(P-18640)
UNITED SUPERTEK INC
Also Called: U S I
14930 Vintner Ct, Saratoga (95070-9712)
PHONE.....................408 922-0730
Samson Zarnegar, *President*
EMP: 35
SQ FT: 25,000
SALES (est): 4.6MM **Privately Held**
SIC: 3672 Printed circuit boards

(P-18641)
URI TECH INC
1340 Norman Ave, Santa Clara
(95054-2056)
PHONE.....................408 456-0115
Sea Heon Kim, *President*
EMP: 13
SQ FT: 20,000
SALES: 1.2MM **Privately Held**
WEB: www.uritech.net
SIC: 3672 Printed circuit boards

(P-18642)
VALLEY CIRCUITS
Also Called: Valley Syncom Circuits
24940 Avenue Tibbitts, Valencia
(91355-3426)
PHONE.....................661 294-0077
Christine Janes, *President*
Drew Janes, *Vice Pres*
EMP: 12
SALES (est): 3.2MM **Privately Held**
WEB: www.valleycircuits.com
SIC: 3672 Circuit boards, television & radio
printed

(P-18643)
VECTOR ELECTRONICS & TECH INC
11115 Vanowen St, North Hollywood
(91605-6371)
PHONE.....................818 985-8208
Rakesh Bajaria, *CEO*
Ken Pansuriah, *Vice Pres*
Jerry Rodriguez, *Vice Pres*
Viny Kathrotia, *Admin Sec*
Maha Subra, *Accountant*

▲ **EMP:** 25 **EST:** 2001
SALES (est): 4.8MM **Privately Held**
WEB: www.vectorelect.com
SIC: 3672 Printed circuit boards

(P-18644)
VECTOR FABRICATION INC (PA)
1629 Watson Ct, Milpitas (95035-6806)
PHONE.....................408 942-9800
Quang Luong, *President*
Issac Stringer, *Vice Pres*
▲ **EMP:** 20
SQ FT: 18,000
SALES (est): 2.4MM **Privately Held**
WEB: www.vectorfab.com
SIC: 3672 Printed circuit boards

(P-18645)
VEECO ELECTRO FAB INC (PA)
1176 N Osprey Cir, Anaheim (92807-1709)
PHONE.....................714 630-8020
Jagjit Singh, *President*
Joginda Singh, *Vice Pres*
EMP: 16
SQ FT: 10,000
SALES (est): 1.4MM **Privately Held**
SIC: 3672 7629 Printed circuit boards; circuit board repair

(P-18646)
VENTURE ELECTRONICS INTL INC
6701 Mowry Ave, Newark (94560-4927)
PHONE.....................510 744-3720
C T Wong, *President*
EMP: 19
SALES (est): 2.6MM
SALES (corp-wide): 2.9B **Privately Held**
WEB: www.venture.com.sg
SIC: 3672 Printed circuit boards
PA: Venture Corporation Limited
5006 Ang Mo Kio Avenue 5
Singapore 56987
648 217-55

(P-18647)
VINATRONIC INC
15571 Industry Ln, Huntington Beach
(92649-1534)
PHONE.....................714 845-3480
Lan Nguyen, *CEO*
Kem Strano, *President*
EMP: 30
SQ FT: 13,000
SALES (est): 4.3MM **Privately Held**
WEB: www.vinatronic.com
SIC: 3672 Printed circuit boards

(P-18648)
VITRON ELECTRONIC SERVICES INC
Also Called: Vitron Electronics Mfg & Svcs
5400 Hellyer Ave, San Jose (95138-1019)
PHONE.....................408 251-1600
Huan Cong Tran, *CEO*
Hien Duong, *Purchasing*
▲ **EMP:** 60
SQ FT: 3,500
SALES: 15MM **Privately Held**
WEB: www.vitronmfg.com
SIC: 3672 Printed circuit boards

(P-18649)
VYCOM AMERICA INC
39252 Winchester Rd 107-3, Murrieta
(92563-3509)
PHONE.....................800 235-9195
Roberto Simeon, *CEO*
Sonny Dawoodjee, *Principal*
Tammy Ginsburg, *Principal*
EMP: 35 **EST:** 2013
SALES (est): 1.3MM **Privately Held**
SIC: 3672 Circuit boards, television & radio
printed

(P-18650)
WE IMAGINE INC
9371 Canoga Ave, Chatsworth
(91311-5879)
P.O. Box 5696 (91313-5696)
PHONE.....................818 709-0064
Barry Henley, *President*
Diana Reiter, *COO*
Claudia Henley, *Corp Secy*
EMP: 53

SQ FT: 65,000
SALES (est): 8.7MM **Privately Held**
WEB: www.weimagineinc.com
SIC: 3672 Printed circuit boards

(P-18651)
WESTAK INC (PA)
Also Called: A2
1116 Elko Dr, Sunnyvale (94089-2207)
PHONE.....................408 734-8686
Louise Crisham, *CEO*
Lou George, *COO*
Dicie Hinaga, *CFO*
Jay Latin, *Vice Pres*
Lisa Kennedy, *Office Mgr*
EMP: 100 **EST:** 1972
SQ FT: 20,000
SALES (est): 64.1MM **Privately Held**
WEB: www.westak.com
SIC: 3672 Circuit boards, television & radio
printed

(P-18652)
WHIZZ SYSTEMS INC
3240 Scott Blvd, Santa Clara (95054-3011)
PHONE.....................408 207-0400
Munawar Karimjee, *CEO*
Muhammad Irfan, *President*
Yome Salinas, *Administration*
▲ **EMP:** 50 **EST:** 1999
SQ FT: 35,000
SALES (est): 32MM **Privately Held**
WEB: www.whizzsystems.com
SIC: 3672 Printed circuit boards

(P-18653)
WINONICS INC
Also Called: Bench 2 Bench Technologies
1257 S State College Blvd, Fullerton
(92831-5336)
PHONE.....................714 626-3755
Tom Sciulli, *General Mgr*
Robert Froehlich, *Admin Mgr*
Octavio Ruelas, *Prdtn Mgr*
Xavier Pacheco, *Manager*
EMP: 120
SALES (corp-wide): 42MM **Privately Held**
WEB: www.winonics.com
SIC: 3672 Printed circuit boards
HQ: Winonics Inc.
660 N Puente St
Brea CA
714 256-8700

(P-18654)
XILINX INC (PA)
2100 All Programable, San Jose
(95124-4355)
PHONE.....................408 559-7778
Victor Peng, *President*
Dennis Segers, *Ch of Bd*
Lorenzo A Flores, *CFO*
Thomas Lee, *Bd of Directors*
Marshall Turner, *Bd of Directors*
EMP: 988
SQ FT: 588,000
SALES: 2.5B **Publicly Held**
WEB: www.xilinx.com
SIC: 3672 3674 7372 Printed circuit
boards; microcircuits, integrated (semi-
conductor); application computer software

(P-18655)
YAMAMOTO MANUFACTURING USA INC (HQ)
2025 Gateway Pl Ste 220, San Jose
(95110-1000)
PHONE.....................408 387-5250
Takashi Toshishige, *President*
Carl Olin, *Director*
EMP: 12
SQ FT: 5,000
SALES (est): 998.4K
SALES (corp-wide): 166.7MM **Privately Held**
WEB: www.yusa.com
SIC: 3672 8711 Printed circuit boards; en-
gineering services
PA: Yamamoto Mfg Co., Ltd.
4-4, Shimizucho
Itabashi-Ku TKY 174-0
339 614-601

(P-18656)
YUN INDUSTRIAL CO LTD
Also Called: Y I C
161 Selandia Ln, Carson (90746-1412)
PHONE.....................310 715-1898
Ilun Yun, *President*
Stephen Yun, *Vice Pres*
William Yun, *Admin Sec*
◆ **EMP:** 40
SQ FT: 16,000
SALES (est): 7.4MM **Privately Held**
WEB: www.yic-assm.com
SIC: 3672 Printed circuit boards

(P-18657)
ZOLLNER ELECTRONICS INC
575 Cottonwood Dr, Milpitas (95035-7402)
PHONE.....................408 434-5400
Stephan Weiss, *COO*
Michael Diep, *Program Mgr*
Nessa Hunt, *Admin Sec*
Andy Ying, *Engineer*
Charlie Ha, *Purchasing*
▲ **EMP:** 29
SALES (est): 19.5MM
SALES (corp-wide): 1.3B **Privately Held**
SIC: 3672 Printed circuit boards
PA: Zollner Elektronik Ag
Manfred-Zollner-Str. 1
Zandt 93499
994 420-10

(P-18658)
ZYREL INC
15322 Lkeshore Dr Ste 301, Clearlake
(95422)
P.O. Box 54157, San Jose (95154-0157)
PHONE.....................707 995-2551
Don Hargrave, *CEO*
Takako Hargrave, *Corp Secy*
▲ **EMP:** 11
SQ FT: 1,100
SALES (est): 1.9MM **Privately Held**
WEB: www.zyrel.com
SIC: 3672

(P-18659)
ZYTEK CORP
Also Called: Zytek Ems
1755 Mccarthy Blvd, Milpitas (95035-7416)
PHONE.....................408 520-4287
Rabia Khan, *President*
Zubair Ahmed, *Program Mgr*
Carmen Aguirre, *Senior Buyer*
EMP: 40
SQ FT: 21,000
SALES (est): 8.3MM **Privately Held**
SIC: 3672 Printed circuit boards

3674 Semiconductors

(P-18660)
ACCELERATED MEMORY PROD INC
Also Called: AMP
1317 E Edinger Ave, Santa Ana
(92705-4416)
PHONE.....................714 460-9800
Richard McCauley, *President*
Cathleen McCauley, *Vice Pres*
◆ **EMP:** 49
SQ FT: 10,000
SALES (est): 11.7MM **Privately Held**
WEB: www.ampinc.biz
SIC: 3674 Memories, solid state

(P-18661)
ACHRONIX SEMICONDUCTOR CORP
2903 Bunker Hill Ln # 200, Santa Clara
(95054-1148)
PHONE.....................408 889-4100
Robert Blake, *President*
John Holt, *Ch of Bd*
Howard Brodsky, *CFO*
Kamal Chaudhary, *Vice Pres*
Virantha Ekanayake, *Vice Pres*
EMP: 75
SQ FT: 25,000
SALES (est): 14.8MM **Privately Held**
SIC: 3674 Integrated circuits, semiconduc-
tor networks, etc.

(P-18662)
ADESTO TECHNOLOGIES CORP (PA)
3600 Peterson Way, Santa Clara
(95054-2808)
PHONE....................408 400-0578
Narbeh Derhacobian, *CEO*
Barry L Cox, *Ch of Bd*
Shane Hollmer, *President*
Ron Shelton, *CFO*
Ishai Naveh, *Vice Pres*
◆ **EMP:** 51
SQ FT: 34,000
SALES: 56.1MM **Publicly Held**
SIC: 3674 8731 Semiconductors & related devices; commercial research laboratory

(P-18663)
ADEX ELECTRONICS INC
3 Watson, Irvine (92618-2716)
PHONE....................949 597-1772
Casey Huang, *President*
Cheryl Roberts, *Treasurer*
▲ **EMP:** 15
SQ FT: 10,330
SALES (est): 1.4MM **Privately Held**
WEB: www.adexelec.com
SIC: 3674 8711 Semiconductors & related devices; engineering services

(P-18664)
ADVANCE DISPLAY TECH INC
Also Called: (A DEVELOPMENT STAGE COMPANY)
42230 Zevo Dr, Temecula (92590-3732)
PHONE....................951 757-0469
Matthew W Shankle, *President*
James P Martindale, *COO*
Gregory L Heacock, *Vice Pres*
Robert Ridgeway, *Vice Pres*
Rebecca McCall, *VP Accounting*
▲ **EMP:** 28
SQ FT: 1,411
SALES (est): 4.1MM **Privately Held**
WEB:
www.advancedisplaytechnologies.com
SIC: 3674 Light emitting diodes

(P-18665)
ADVANCED ANALOGIC TECH INC
2740 Zanker Rd, San Jose (95134-2128)
PHONE....................408 330-1400
Richard K Williams, *President*
David J Aldrich, *CEO*
Parviz Ghaffaripour, *COO*
Ashok Chandran, *CFO*
Bijan Mohandes, *Exec VP*
EMP: 52 **EST:** 1962
SQ FT: 42,174
SALES (est): 11.7MM
SALES (corp-wide): 3.8B **Publicly Held**
SIC: 3674 Integrated circuits, semiconductor networks, etc.
PA: Skyworks Solutions, Inc.
20 Sylvan Rd
Woburn MA 01801
781 376-3000

(P-18666)
ADVANCED COMPONENT LABS INC
Also Called: A C L
990 Richard Ave Ste 118, Santa Clara
(95050-2828)
PHONE....................408 327-0200
Michael J Oswald, *CEO*
Nerissa De Ramos, *Sales Mgr*
EMP: 20
SQ FT: 20,000
SALES (est): 3.6MM **Privately Held**
WEB: www.aclusa.com
SIC: 3674 Semiconductor circuit networks

(P-18667)
ADVANCED LINEAR DEVICES INC
415 Tasman Dr, Sunnyvale (94089-1706)
PHONE....................408 747-1155
Robert L Chao, *President*
EMP: 20
SQ FT: 12,000

SALES (est): 2.8MM **Privately Held**
WEB: www.aldinc.com
SIC: 3674 8711 Integrated circuits, semiconductor networks, etc.; engineering services

(P-18668)
ADVANCED MICRO DEVICES INC (PA)
2485 Augustine Dr, Santa Clara
(95054-3002)
PHONE....................408 749-4000
Lisa T Su, *President*
John E Caldwell, *Ch of Bd*
Devinder Kumar, *CFO*
Robert Gama, *Officer*
Darren Grasby, *Senior VP*
EMP: 277
SALES: 5.3B **Publicly Held**
WEB: www.amd.com
SIC: 3674 Integrated circuits, semiconductor networks, etc.; microprocessors; memories, solid state; microcircuits, integrated (semiconductor)

(P-18669)
ADVANCED SEMICONDUCTOR INC (PA)
Also Called: A S I
7525 Ethel Ave Ste I, North Hollywood
(91605-1912)
PHONE....................818 982-1200
Fred Golob, *CEO*
Don Wolf, *Executive*
Maria Arias, *Purch Mgr*
▲ **EMP:** 58
SQ FT: 9,000
SALES (est): 8.8MM **Privately Held**
WEB: www.advancedsemiconductor.com
SIC: 3674 Integrated circuits, semiconductor networks, etc.

(P-18670)
ADVANCED THERMAL SCIENCES
3355 E La Palma Ave, Anaheim
(92806-2815)
PHONE....................714 688-4200
Bruce Thayer, *President*
Masashi Iwao, *Vice Pres*
▲ **EMP:** 14
SALES (est): 2.2MM **Publicly Held**
SIC: 3674 Semiconductors & related devices
HQ: B/E Aerospace, Inc.
1400 Corporate Center Way
Wellington FL 33414
561 791-5000

(P-18671)
ADVANTEST AMERICA INC (HQ)
3061 Zanker Rd, San Jose (95134-2127)
P.O. Box 7247-6495, Philadelphia PA
(19170-0001)
PHONE....................408 456-3600
Debbora Ahlgren, *Vice Pres*
Michael Jung, *CFO*
Tony Loi, *Treasurer*
▲ **EMP:** 90
SALES (est): 64.8MM
SALES (corp-wide): 1.9B **Privately Held**
SIC: 3674 Semiconductors & related devices
PA: Advantest Corporation
1-6-2, Marunouchi
Chiyoda-Ku TKY 100-0
332 147-500

(P-18672)
ADVIN SYSTEMS INC
11693 Vineyard Spring Ct, Cupertino
(95014-5135)
PHONE....................408 243-7000
Wing F Hui, *President*
Christine Hung, *COO*
Carl Buck, *VP Mktg*
EMP: 10
SQ FT: 2,680
SALES (est): 970K **Privately Held**
WEB: www.advin.com
SIC: 3674 Integrated circuits, semiconductor networks, etc.

(P-18673)
AGILE TECHNOLOGIES INC
2 Orion, Aliso Viejo (92656-4200)
PHONE....................949 454-8030
Martin Munzer, *CEO*
David A Krohn, *President*
Rick Brooks, *Vice Pres*
EMP: 19
SQ FT: 40,000
SALES (est): 4.7MM **Privately Held**
WEB: www.agiletech.org
SIC: 3674 Photoelectric magnetic devices

(P-18674)
AIXTRON INC
1700 Wyatt Dr Ste 15, Santa Clara
(95054-1526)
PHONE....................669 228-3759
Martin Goetzeler, *CEO*
Johannes Lindner, *President*
Randy Singh, *CFO*
Zia Karim, *Vice Pres*
Brian Lu, *Vice Pres*
▲ **EMP:** 156
SQ FT: 100,500
SALES: 196.4K
SALES (corp-wide): 271.6MM **Privately Held**
WEB: www.genus.com
SIC: 3674 Semiconductors & related devices
PA: Aixtron Se
Dornkaulstr. 2
Herzogenrath 52134
240 790-300

(P-18675)
AJILE SYSTEMS INC (PA)
920 Saratoga Ave Ste 104, San Jose
(95129-3408)
PHONE....................408 557-0829
George Hwang, *President*
Danh Lengoc, *Vice Pres*
EMP: 20
SQ FT: 3,000
SALES (est): 1.2MM **Privately Held**
WEB: www.ajile.com
SIC: 3674 Semiconductors & related devices

(P-18676)
AKM SEMICONDUCTOR INC
Also Called: A K M
1731 Tech Dr Ste 500, San Jose (95110)
PHONE....................408 436-8580
S Kido, *President*
Makoto Konosu, *CEO*
Lyle Knudsen, *Vice Pres*
Chris Baltar, *Technology*
▲ **EMP:** 22
SQ FT: 5,402
SALES (est): 3.9MM
SALES (corp-wide): 19.1B **Privately Held**
WEB: www.akm.com
SIC: 3674 Semiconductors & related devices
HQ: Asahi Kasei Microdevices Corporation
1-1-2, Yurakucho
Chiyoda-Ku TKY 100-0
366 993-933

(P-18677)
ALCATEL-LUCENT USA INC
701 E Middlefield Rd, Mountain View
(94043-4079)
PHONE....................408 878-6500
Oscar Rodriguez, *Manager*
SRI Reddy, *Vice Pres*
Mike McKeon, *Business Dir*
Kevin Kulhanek, *CIO*
Fabrizio Boggio, *Engineer*
EMP: 421
SALES (corp-wide): 27.3B **Privately Held**
WEB: www.lucent.com
SIC: 3674 Integrated circuits, semiconductor networks, etc.
HQ: Nokia Of America Corporation
600 Mountain Ave Ste 700
New Providence NJ 07974

(P-18678)
ALION ENERGY INC
870 Harbour Way S, Richmond
(94804-3613)
PHONE....................510 965-0868

Mark Kingsley, *President*
Jesse Atkinson, *Vice Pres*
Linda Ramos, *Office Mgr*
Thomas Goehring, *Design Engr*
Soren Jensen, *VP Engrg*
▲ **EMP:** 51
SQ FT: 65,000
SALES (est): 10.3MM **Privately Held**
SIC: 3674 Solar cells

(P-18679)
ALL SENSORS CORPORATION
16035 Vineyard Blvd, Morgan Hill
(95037-5480)
PHONE....................408 776-9434
Dennis Dauenhauer, *President*
Danny Bernier, *Vice Pres*
Dale Dauenhauer, *Vice Pres*
Paiva Delly, *Administration*
Stephen Johnson, *Engineer*
▲ **EMP:** 38
SQ FT: 20,000
SALES (est): 9.4MM **Privately Held**
WEB: www.allsensors.com
SIC: 3674 Infrared sensors, solid state

(P-18680)
ALLIANCE MEMORY INC
511 Taylor Way, San Carlos (94070-6201)
PHONE....................650 610-6800
David A Bagby, *President*
Kim Bagby, *CFO*
Anny Qin, *Adv Dir*
Sue Macedo, *Sales Dir*
Mitch Labbie, *Marketing Staff*
▲ **EMP:** 15
SQ FT: 3,000
SALES (est): 2MM **Privately Held**
WEB: www.alliancememory.com
SIC: 3674 Semiconductors & related devices

(P-18681)
ALLTEQ INDUSTRIES INC
215 Rustic Pl, San Ramon (94582-5618)
PHONE....................925 833-7666
Phil Davies, *President*
Tony Draga, *Vice Pres*
William Miller, *Vice Pres*
EMP: 14
SQ FT: 11,000
SALES (est): 1.3MM **Privately Held**
WEB: www.allteq.com
SIC: 3674 3825 Semiconductors & related devices; integrated circuit testers

(P-18682)
ALLVIA INC
657 N Pastoria Ave, Sunnyvale
(94085-2917)
PHONE....................408 720-3333
Sergey Savastiouk, *CEO*
EMP: 20
SQ FT: 17,900
SALES (est): 4.1MM **Privately Held**
WEB: www.trusi.com
SIC: 3674 Integrated circuits, semiconductor networks, etc.

(P-18683)
ALPHA AND OMEGA SEMICDTR INC (HQ)
475 Oakmead Pkwy, Sunnyvale
(94085-4709)
PHONE....................408 789-0008
Mike F Chang, *CEO*
Sophie Chan, *CFO*
Mary Dotz, *CFO*
Rachel Xun, *Treasurer*
King Owyang PHD, *Bd of Directors*
▲ **EMP:** 120
SQ FT: 50,000
SALES (est): 30.7MM **Privately Held**
WEB: www.aos.com
SIC: 3674 Semiconductors & related devices

(P-18684)
ALTA DEVICES INC
545 Oakmead Pkwy, Sunnyvale
(94085-4023)
PHONE....................408 988-8600
Jian Ding, *CEO*
Mallorie Burak, *CFO*
Harry Atwater, *Bd of Directors*
Eli Yablonovitch, *Bd of Directors*

P R O D U C T S & S V C S

Raymond Milano, *Vice Pres*
EMP: 250
SQ FT: 115,000
SALES (est): 3MM **Privately Held**
SIC: 3674 Semiconductors & related devices
PA: Hanergy Holding Group Limited
No.0-A, Anli Road, Chaoyang Dist.
Beijing
108 391-4567

(P-18685)
ALTASENS INC (HQ)
2201 E Dominguez St, Long Beach
(90810-1009)
PHONE................................818 338-9400
Kensuke Kawai, *CEO*
Clint Elsemore, *CFO*
Giuseppe Rossi, *Vice Pres*
John Von Colln, *Program Mgr*
Lester Kozlowski, *CTO*
▲ **EMP:** 48
SQ FT: 15,000
SALES (est): 6.9MM
SALES (corp-wide): 2.8B **Privately Held**
WEB: www.altasens.com
SIC: 3674 Semiconductors & related devices
PA: Jvc Kenwood Corporation
3-12, Moriyacho, Kanagawa-Ku
Yokohama KNG 221-0
454 445-232

(P-18686)
ALTERA CORPORATION (HQ)
101 Innovation Dr, San Jose (95134-1941)
PHONE................................408 544-7000
John P Daane, *Ch of Bd*
Ronald J Pasek, *CFO*
Rashmi Dhruvakumar, *Bd of Directors*
Danny Biran, *Senior VP*
William Y Hata, *Senior VP*
▲ **EMP:** 277
SQ FT: 505,000
SALES: 1.9B
SALES (corp-wide): 62.7B **Publicly Held**
WEB: www.altera.com
SIC: 3674 7371 Semiconductors & related devices; computer software development & applications
PA: Intel Corporation
2200 Mission College Blvd
Santa Clara CA 95054
408 765-8080

(P-18687)
ALTIERRE CORPORATION
1980 Concourse Dr, San Jose
(95131-1719)
PHONE................................408 435-7343
Tony Alvarez, *CEO*
Anurag Goel, *COO*
Shan Kumar, *CFO*
Dave Wetle, *Vice Pres*
Howard Feger, *Info Tech Dir*
▲ **EMP:** 50
SQ FT: 85,367
SALES (est): 17.2MM **Privately Held**
WEB: www.altierre.com
SIC: 3674 Integrated circuits, semiconductor networks, etc.

(P-18688)
AMBARELLA INC
3101 Jay St, Santa Clara (95054-3329)
PHONE................................408 734-8888
Feng-Ming Wang, *Ch of Bd*
Yun-Lung Chen, *President*
Kevin C Eichler, *CFO*
Chenming Hu, *Bd of Directors*
Christopher Paisley, *Bd of Directors*
EMP: 669
SQ FT: 49,000
SALES: 295.4MM **Privately Held**
SIC: 3674 Semiconductors & related devices

(P-18689)
AMD INTERNATIONAL SLS SVC LTD (HQ)
1 Amd Pl, Sunnyvale (94085-3905)
P.O. Box 3453 (94088-3453)
PHONE................................408 749-4000
Lisa Su, *President*
Bob Rivet, *CFO*
Chekib Akrout, *Senior VP*

John Byrne, *Senior VP*
Darrell L Ford, *Senior VP*
◆ **EMP:** 26
SALES (est): 26.4MM
SALES (corp-wide): 5.3B **Publicly Held**
SIC: 3674 Semiconductors & related devices
PA: Advanced Micro Devices, Inc.
2485 Augustine Dr
Santa Clara CA 95054
408 749-4000

(P-18690)
AMD VENTURES LLC
1 Amd Pl, Sunnyvale (94085-3905)
P.O. Box 3453 (94088-3453)
PHONE................................408 749-4000
Rory Read, *Principal*
Rory P Read, *Principal*
EMP: 115
SALES (est): 11.4MM **Privately Held**
SIC: 3674 Semiconductors & related devices

(P-18691)
AMERICA TECHCODE SEMICDTR INC
10456 San Fernando Ave, Cupertino
(95014-2867)
PHONE................................408 910-2028
Fong Lok-Cheung, *President*
EMP: 20 **EST:** 2010
SALES (est): 1.2MM **Privately Held**
SIC: 3674 Semiconductors & related devices

(P-18692)
AMERICAN SOLAR ADVANTAGE INC
7056 Archibald St 102-432, Corona
(92880-8713)
PHONE................................951 496-1075
Bobby D Harris, *President*
EMP: 20
SALES: 800K **Privately Held**
SIC: 3674 1731 Solar cells; electrical work

(P-18693)
AMEST CORPORATION
30394 Esperanza, Rcho STA Marg
(92688-2118)
PHONE................................949 766-9692
John P Iest, *President*
Linda Iest, *Admin Sec*
EMP: 10 **EST:** 1975
SQ FT: 5,400
SALES (est): 1.8MM **Privately Held**
WEB: www.amestcorp.com
SIC: 3674 Microprocessors

(P-18694)
AMKOR TECHNOLOGY INC
5465 Morehouse Dr Ste 210, San Diego
(92121-4764)
PHONE................................858 320-6280
Susan Kim, *Bd of Directors*
John Osborne, *Bd of Directors*
John Stone, *Exec VP*
Ray Miranda, *Systems Dir*
Howard Ushkow, *Sales Staff*
EMP: 84
SALES (corp-wide): 4.1B **Publicly Held**
SIC: 3674 Semiconductors & related devices
PA: Amkor Technology, Inc.
2045 E Innovation Cir
Tempe AZ 85284
480 821-5000

(P-18695)
AMKOR TECHNOLOGY INC
3 Corporate Park Ste 230, Irvine
(92606-5161)
PHONE................................949 724-9370
Davren Mc Millan, *Manager*
EMP: 25
SALES (corp-wide): 4.1B **Publicly Held**
WEB: www.amkor.com
SIC: 3674 Semiconductors & related devices
PA: Amkor Technology, Inc.
2045 E Innovation Cir
Tempe AZ 85284
480 821-5000

(P-18696)
AMLOGIC INC
2518 Mission College Blvd, Santa Clara
(95054-1239)
PHONE................................408 850-9688
John Zhong, *President*
Mike Yip, *President*
James Xie, *Vice Pres*
Yeeping Zhong, *Vice Pres*
Rose Kung, *Office Mgr*
EMP: 20
SALES (est): 3.7MM **Privately Held**
SIC: 3674 Integrated circuits, semiconductor networks, etc.

(P-18697)
ANALOG BITS
945 Stewart Dr, Sunnyvale (94085-3913)
PHONE................................650 279-9323
Alan Rogers, *Owner*
Jessica Huang, *Technology*
Liting Huang, *Engineer*
Katherine Ryan, *VP Human Res*
Mahesh Tirupattur, *Sales Executive*
EMP: 30
SALES (est): 3.8MM **Privately Held**
WEB: www.analogbits.com
SIC: 3674 Semiconductors & related devices

(P-18698)
ANALOG DEVICES INC
3550 N 1st St, San Jose (95134-1805)
PHONE................................408 727-9222
Jerry Fishman, *Sales/Mktg Mgr*
EMP: 300
SALES (corp-wide): 5.1B **Publicly Held**
WEB: www.analog.com
SIC: 3674 Integrated circuits, semiconductor networks, etc.
PA: Analog Devices, Inc.
1 Technology Way
Norwood MA 02062
781 329-4700

(P-18699)
ANALOG DEVICES INC
940 S Coast Dr Ste 230, Costa Mesa
(92626-7802)
PHONE................................714 641-9391
Jay Feldman, *Manager*
EMP: 20
SALES (corp-wide): 5.1B **Publicly Held**
WEB: www.analog.com
SIC: 3674 Integrated circuits, semiconductor networks, etc.
PA: Analog Devices, Inc.
1 Technology Way
Norwood MA 02062
781 329-4700

(P-18700)
ANALOGIX SEMICONDUCTOR INC
Also Called: Pacific Analogix Semiconductor
3211 Scott Blvd Ste 100, Santa Clara
(95054-3009)
PHONE................................408 988-8686
Kewei Yang, *Ch of Bd*
Bill Eichen, *President*
Michael Seifert, *CFO*
Mike Seifert, *CFO*
Hing Chu, *Vice Pres*
▲ **EMP:** 24
SALES (est): 7.1MM **Privately Held**
WEB: www.analogixsemi.com
SIC: 3674 Integrated circuits, semiconductor networks, etc.

(P-18701)
ANOKIWAVE INC (PA)
11236 El Camino Real # 100, San Diego
(92130-2617)
PHONE................................858 792-9910
Nitin Jain, *Officer*
Robert S Donahue, *CEO*
Carl Frank, *COO*
William Boecke, *CFO*
Andrew Crofts, *Vice Pres*
EMP: 34
SQ FT: 5,766
SALES (est): 9MM **Privately Held**
WEB: www.anokiwave.com
SIC: 3674 Semiconductors & related devices

(P-18702)
APIC CORPORATION
5800 Uplander Way, Culver City
(90230-6608)
PHONE................................310 642-7975
James Chan, *Officer*
Birendra Dutt, *President*
Denise Lortie, *Vice Pres*
Anguel Nikolov, *Vice Pres*
Koichi Sayano, *Vice Pres*
EMP: 58
SQ FT: 14,416
SALES (est): 11.2MM **Privately Held**
WEB: www.apichip.com
SIC: 3674 Semiconductors & related devices

(P-18703)
APLUS FLASH TECHNOLOGY INC
780 Montague Expy Ste 103, San Jose
(95131-1315)
PHONE................................408 382-1100
Peter W Lee, *President*
EMP: 15 **EST:** 1998
SQ FT: 7,000
SALES (est): 1.9MM **Privately Held**
WEB: www.aplusflash.com
SIC: 3674 Monolithic integrated circuits (solid state)

(P-18704)
APPLIED CERAMICS INC (PA)
48630 Milmont Dr, Fremont (94538-7353)
PHONE................................510 249-9700
Matt Darko Sertic, *CEO*
Rick Le, *Engineer*
Adriana Armstrong, *Accounts Mgr*
▲ **EMP:** 13
SQ FT: 57,000
SALES (est): 17.4MM **Privately Held**
WEB: www.aceramic.com
SIC: 3674 3264 Semiconductors & related devices; porcelain electrical supplies

(P-18705)
APPLIED FILMS CORPORATION
3050 Bowers Ave, Santa Clara
(95054-3201)
PHONE................................408 727-5555
Thomas T Edman, *President*
Richard P Beck, *Ch of Bd*
Lawrence D Firestone, *CFO*
Joachim Nell, *Exec VP*
James P Scholhamer, *Senior VP*
▲ **EMP:** 28
SQ FT: 87,000
SALES (est): 2.7MM
SALES (corp-wide): 14.5B **Publicly Held**
SIC: 3674 Semiconductors & related devices
PA: Applied Materials, Inc.
3050 Bowers Ave
Santa Clara CA 95054
408 727-5555

(P-18706)
APPLIED MATERIALS INC
1285 Walsh Ave, Santa Clara
(95050-2662)
PHONE................................406 752-2107
Gary Dickerson, *President*
Satoru Kobayashi, *Technical Staff*
Beth Rosal, *Engineer*
Tugrul Samir PHD, *Engineer*
EMP: 48
SALES (corp-wide): 14.5B **Publicly Held**
SIC: 3674 Semiconductors & related devices
PA: Applied Materials, Inc.
3050 Bowers Ave
Santa Clara CA 95054
408 727-5555

(P-18707)
APPLIED MATERIALS INC
3340 Scott Blvd, Santa Clara (95054-3101)
PHONE................................408 727-5555
Gary E Dickerson, *President*
Murali Narasimhan, *General Mgr*
Aron Rosenfeld, *Info Tech Dir*
Wen Chang, *Systems Dir*
Vijay Radhakrishnan, *Info Tech Mgr*
EMP: 56

▲ = Import ▼=Export
◆ =Import/Export

SALES (est): 5.9MM **Privately Held**
SIC: **3674** Semiconductors & related devices

(P-18708)
APPLIED MATERIALS INC
44050 Fremont Blvd, Fremont
(94538-6042)
PHONE..................510 687-8018
Dianne Dougherty, *Manager*
EMP: 48
SALES (corp-wide): 14.5B **Publicly Held**
WEB: www.appliedmaterials.com
SIC: **3674** Semiconductors & related devices
PA: Applied Materials, Inc.
3050 Bowers Ave
Santa Clara CA 95054
408 727-5555

(P-18709)
APPLIED MATERIALS INC
1285 Walsh Ave Bldg 21, Santa Clara
(95050-2662)
PHONE..................408 727-5555
Diann Wiggins, *Manager*
EMP: 48
SALES (corp-wide): 14.5B **Publicly Held**
WEB: www.appliedmaterials.com
SIC: **3674** Semiconductors & related devices
PA: Applied Materials, Inc.
3050 Bowers Ave
Santa Clara CA 95054
408 727-5555

(P-18710)
APPLIED MATERIALS INC
2821 Scott Blvd Bldg 17, Santa Clara
(95050-2549)
P.O. Box 58039 (95052-8039)
PHONE..................408 727-5555
Johnny Singh, *Principal*
John Busch, *Vice Pres*
Sharon Timoner, *Managing Dir*
Donn Turner, *General Mgr*
Yvonne Tai, *Info Tech Mgr*
EMP: 100
SALES (corp-wide): 14.5B **Publicly Held**
WEB: www.appliedmaterials.com
SIC: **3674** Semiconductors & related devices
PA: Applied Materials, Inc.
3050 Bowers Ave
Santa Clara CA 95054
408 727-5555

(P-18711)
APPLIED MICRO CIRCUITS CORP (HQ)
4555 Great America Pkwy # 601, Santa
Clara (95054-1288)
PHONE..................408 542-8600
Paramesh Gopi, *President*
Alan Sorgi, *Owner*
Martin S McDermut, *CFO*
L William Caraccio, *Vice Pres*
Seyed Attaran, *Vice Pres*
▲ EMP: 221
SQ FT: 55,000
SALES: 159.2MM **Publicly Held**
WEB: www.amcc.com
SIC: **3674** Microcircuits, integrated (semiconductor)

(P-18712)
APPLIED MICRO CIRCUITS CORP
Also Called: Amcc Sales
4555 Great America Pkwy # 601, Santa
Clara (95054-1288)
PHONE..................408 542-8600
Kambiz Hooshmand, *Manager*
Brian Chase, *Design Engr*
Allen Merrill, *Design Engr*
Bhaskara Avula, *Engineer*
Ashish Ganbavale, *Engineer*
EMP: 27 **Publicly Held**
WEB: www.amcc.com
SIC: **3674** Microcircuits, integrated (semiconductor)
HQ: Applied Micro Circuits Corp
4555 Great America Pkwy # 601
Santa Clara CA 95054
408 542-8600

(P-18713)
APTA GROUP INC (PA)
Also Called: Advanced Packaging Tech Amer
7580 Britannia Ct, San Diego
(92154-7424)
PHONE..................619 710-8170
Per Tonnesen, *President*
EMP: 21
SQ FT: 25,000
SALES (est): 2.3MM **Privately Held**
WEB: www.aptagroup.com
SIC: **3674** Hybrid integrated circuits; modules, solid state

(P-18714)
AQUANTIA CORP (PA)
91 E Tasman Dr Ste 100, San Jose
(95134-1620)
PHONE..................408 228-8300
Faraj Aalaei, *Ch of Bd*
Pirooz Parvarandeh, *COO*
Mark Voll, *CFO*
Sam Srinivasan, *Bd of Directors*
Anders Swahn, *Bd of Directors*
EMP: 89
SQ FT: 36,595
SALES: 103.3MM **Publicly Held**
WEB: www.aquantia.com
SIC: **3674** Semiconductors & related devices

(P-18715)
ARDICA TECHNOLOGIES INC
2325 3rd St Ste 424, San Francisco
(94107-4305)
PHONE..................415 568-9270
Jeff Scheinrock, *CEO*
Daniel Braithwaite, *President*
Dick Martin, *President*
Blaine Klusky, *CFO*
Jim Retzlaff, *CFO*
EMP: 12
SQ FT: 5,000
SALES: 50K **Privately Held**
WEB: www.ardica.com
SIC: **3674** Fuel cells, solid state

(P-18716)
ARM INC
150 Rose Orchard Way, San Jose
(95134-1358)
PHONE..................408 576-1500
Vojin Zivojnovic, *Manager*
EMP: 12 **Privately Held**
SIC: **3674** Integrated circuits, semiconductor networks, etc.
HQ: Arm, Inc.
150 Rose Orchard Way
San Jose CA 95134
-

(P-18717)
ARM INC (HQ)
150 Rose Orchard Way, San Jose
(95134-1358)
PHONE..................408 576-1500
Simon Segars, *CEO*
Graham Budd, *COO*
R Keith Hopkins, *Vice Pres*
EMP: 270
SQ FT: 54,489
SALES (est): 205.5MM **Privately Held**
SIC: **3674** Integrated circuits, semiconductor networks, etc.

(P-18718)
ARM INC
5375 Mira Sorrento Pl # 540, San Diego
(92121-3809)
PHONE..................858 453-1900
Todd Vierra, *Branch Mgr*
EMP: 127 **Privately Held**
SIC: **3674** Integrated circuits, semiconductor networks, etc.
HQ: Arm, Inc.
150 Rose Orchard Way
San Jose CA 95134

(P-18719)
ARRIVE TECHNOLOGIES INC
3693 Westchester Dr, Roseville
(95747-6353)
PHONE..................888 864-6959
Peter W Keeler, *Ch of Bd*
Murat Uraz, *President*

EMP: 15 EST: 2001
SALES: 11K **Privately Held**
SIC: **3674** Integrated circuits, semiconductor networks, etc.

(P-18720)
ART MICROELECTRONICS CORP
5917 Oak Ave Ste 201, Temple City
(91780-2028)
PHONE..................626 447-7503
Richard King, *President*
▲ EMP: 15
SQ FT: 800
SALES (est): 1.4MM **Privately Held**
WEB: www.alpha-sci.com
SIC: **3674** 5065 Semiconductors & related devices; semiconductor devices

(P-18721)
ARTERIS INC
595 Millich Dr Ste 200, Campbell
(95008-0550)
PHONE..................408 470-7300
Charles K Janac, *President*
Stephane Mehat, *CFO*
EMP: 40
SQ FT: 6,287
SALES: 10.4MM **Privately Held**
SIC: **3674** Semiconductors & related devices

(P-18722)
ARTERIS HOLDINGS INC
591 W Hamilton Ave # 250, Campbell
(95008-0559)
PHONE..................408 470-7300
Charles K Janac, *President*
Stephane Mehat, *CFO*
Ty Garibay, *CTO*
Bhavin Vaidya, *Technology*
Farnaz Alim, *Technical Staff*
EMP: 45
SQ FT: 4,500
SALES (est): 5.8MM **Privately Held**
WEB: www.arteris.com
SIC: **3674** Semiconductors & related devices

(P-18723)
ASC GROUP INC
12243 Branford St, Sun Valley
(91352-1010)
P.O. Box 1367 (91353-1367)
PHONE..................818 896-1101
Chuck Rogers, *President*
EMP: 250
SQ FT: 80,000
SALES (est): 12.5MM
SALES (corp-wide): 2.5B **Privately Held**
WEB: www.ascgroup.com
SIC: **3674** Semiconductors & related devices
HQ: Pmc, Inc.
12243 Branford St
Sun Valley CA 91352
818 896-1101

(P-18724)
ASI SEMICONDUCTOR INC
Also Called: A S I
7525 Ethel Ave, North Hollywood
(91605-1912)
PHONE..................818 982-1200
Steve Golob, *Principal*
Mike Lincoln, *COO*
Fred Golob, *Principal*
EMP: 25
SQ FT: 15,000
SALES (est): 4.3MM **Privately Held**
SIC: **3674** Semiconductors & related devices

(P-18725)
ASIC ADVANTAGE INC
3850 N 1st St, San Jose (95134-1702)
PHONE..................408 541-8686
EMP: 52
SQ FT: 20,077
SALES (est): 6.7MM **Privately Held**
WEB: www.asicadvantage.com
SIC: **3674**

(P-18726)
ATMEL CORPORATION (HQ)
1600 Technology Dr, San Jose
(95110-1382)
PHONE..................408 735-9110
Steven Laub, *President*
Steve Skaggs, *CFO*
Scott M Wornow, *Officer*
Maria L Corradini, *Officer*
Alfredo Sanz, *Officer*
EMP: 277
SALES: 1.1B
SALES (corp-wide): 3.9B **Publicly Held**
WEB: www.atmel.com
SIC: **3674** 3714 3545 Microcircuits, integrated (semiconductor); memories, solid state; solid state electronic devices; motor vehicle electrical equipment; wheel turning equipment, diamond point or other
PA: Microchip Technology Inc
2355 W Chandler Blvd
Chandler AZ 85224
480 792-7200

(P-18727)
ATMEL WIRELESS MCU TECH CORP
1 Spectrum Pointe Dr # 225, Lake Forest
(92630-2282)
PHONE..................949 525-4481
Steven Laub, *CEO*
Mohy Abdelgany, *President*
Scott Blouin, *CFO*
Tsung Ching Wu, *Exec VP*
Reza Kazerounian, *Senior VP*
▼ EMP: 52
SQ FT: 10,000
SALES (est): 7.7MM
SALES (corp-wide): 3.9B **Publicly Held**
WEB: www.newportmediainc.com
SIC: **3674** Semiconductors & related devices
HQ: Atmel Corporation
1600 Technology Dr
San Jose CA 95110
408 735-9110

(P-18728)
ATOMERA INCORPORATED
750 University Ave # 280, Los Gatos
(95032-7698)
PHONE..................408 442-5248
Scott Bibaud, *President*
John Gerber, *Ch of Bd*
Steven Shevick, *Bd of Directors*
Rolf Stadheim, *Bd of Directors*
Francis Laurencio, *Officer*
EMP: 12 EST: 2001
SQ FT: 3,396
SALES: 110K **Privately Held**
SIC: **3674** Semiconductors & related devices

(P-18729)
ATP ELECTRONICS INC
2590 N 1st St Ste 150, San Jose
(95131-1049)
PHONE..................408 732-5000
Dean Chang, *Ch of Bd*
Jeffray W Hsieh, *CEO*
Russell Shyur, *General Mgr*
Winnie Chan, *Human Res Dir*
Hollie Lee, *Sales Mgr*
▲ EMP: 33
SQ FT: 10,000
SALES (est): 8.7MM **Privately Held**
WEB: www.atpinc.com
SIC: **3674** Semiconductors & related devices
PA: Atp Electronics Taiwan Inc.
10f, 185, Tiding Blvd., Sec. 2,
Taipei City TAP
226 596-368

(P-18730)
AUDIENCE INC (HQ)
331 Fairchild Dr, Mountain View
(94043-2200)
PHONE..................650 254-2800
Jeffrey Niew, *President*
Paul Dickinson, *President*
Christian Scherp, *President*
Gordon Walker, *President*
David Wightman, *President*
EMP: 57
SQ FT: 87,565

SALES (est): 74.3MM
SALES (corp-wide): 744.2MM **Publicly Held**
SIC: 3674 Microprocessors
PA: Knowles Corporation
1151 Maplewood Dr
Itasca IL 60143
630 250-5100

(P-18731)
AUXIN SOLAR INC
6835 Via Del Oro, San Jose (95119-1315)
PHONE..................408 225-4380
Sherry Tai, *CEO*
Mamum Rashid, *Vice Pres*
▲ **EMP:** 45
SQ FT: 100,000
SALES (est): 5.1MM **Privately Held**
SIC: 3674 Solar cells; modules, solid state

(P-18732)
AVAGO TECHNOLOGIES
1730 Fox Dr, San Jose (95131-2311)
PHONE..................408 433-4068
Hock E Tan, *President*
EMP: 14
SALES (est): 2.1MM **Privately Held**
SIC: 3674 Semiconductors & related devices

(P-18733)
AVAGO TECHNOLOGIES US INC (HQ)
1320 Ridder Park Dr, San Jose (95131-2313)
P.O. Box 3643, Santa Clara (95055-3643)
PHONE..................800 433-8778
Hock E Tan, *President*
Dick Chang, *Ch of Bd*
Douglas R Bettinger, *CFO*
Jeff Henderson, *Senior VP*
Bryan Ingram, *Senior VP*
EMP: 400
SALES (est): 1.2B
SALES (corp-wide): 17.6B **Publicly Held**
WEB: www.avagotech.com
SIC: 3674 Semiconductor diodes & rectifiers
PA: Broadcom Inc.
1320 Ridder Park Dr
San Jose CA 95131
408 433-8000

(P-18734)
AVALANCHE TECHNOLOGY INC
3450 W Warren Ave, Fremont (94538-6425)
PHONE..................510 438-0148
Petro Estakhn, *President*
Ebi Abedifard, *President*
Yiming Huai, *President*
Bob Netter, *CFO*
Robert Netter, *CFO*
EMP: 25
SALES (est): 4.7MM **Privately Held**
SIC: 3674 Magnetic bubble memory device

(P-18735)
AVID IDNTIFICATION SYSTEMS INC (PA)
3185 Hamner Ave, Norco (92860-1937)
PHONE..................951 371-7505
Hannis L Stoddard, *CEO*
Peter Troesch, *Vice Pres*
Mary Metzner, *Administration*
Neil King, *Info Tech Mgr*
Mark Blair, *Engineer*
▲ **EMP:** 100
SQ FT: 30,000
SALES (est): 15.4MM **Privately Held**
WEB: www.avidplc.com
SIC: 3674 5999 Semiconductors & related devices; pets & pet supplies

(P-18736)
AVOGY INC
677 River Oaks Pkwy, San Jose (95134-1907)
PHONE..................408 684-5200
Dinesh Ramanathan, *CEO*
Pierre Lamond, *Ch of Bd*
Isik Kizilyalli, *CEO*
Jeff Shealy, *Vice Pres*
Eve Cohen, *Finance Dir*
EMP: 20

SALES (est): 6.3MM **Privately Held**
SIC: 3674 Semiconductor diodes & rectifiers

(P-18737)
AXIS GROUP INC
1220 Whipple Rd, Union City (94587-2026)
P.O. Box 1192 (94587-1192)
PHONE..................510 487-7393
Kofi A Tawiah, *President*
EMP: 17
SQ FT: 15,000
SALES (est): 1.5MM **Privately Held**
WEB: www.theaxisgroup.com
SIC: 3674 Semiconductors & related devices

(P-18738)
AXT INC
Also Called: American Etal Technology
4311 Solar Way, Fremont (94538-6389)
PHONE..................510 683-5900
Maureen Wang, *Manager*
EMP: 23
SALES (corp-wide): 98.6MM **Publicly Held**
SIC: 3674 Integrated circuits, semiconductor networks, etc.
PA: Axt, Inc.
4281 Technology Dr
Fremont CA 94538
510 438-4700

(P-18739)
AXT INC (PA)
4281 Technology Dr, Fremont (94538-6339)
PHONE..................510 438-4700
Morris S Young, *CEO*
Jesse Chen, *Ch of Bd*
Wilson Lin, *COO*
Gary L Fischer, *CFO*
David Chang, *Bd of Directors*
▲ **EMP:** 25
SQ FT: 19,467
SALES (est): 98.6MM **Publicly Held**
WEB: www.axt.com
SIC: 3674 Integrated circuits, semiconductor networks, etc.; diodes, solid state (germanium, silicon, etc.)

(P-18740)
AZIMUTH INDUSTRIAL CO INC
Also Called: Azimuth Semiconductor Assembly
30593 Un Cy Blvd Ste 110, Union City (94587)
PHONE..................510 441-6000
David Lee, *President*
Sandra Lee, *Officer*
▲ **EMP:** 20
SQ FT: 16,000
SALES (est): 3.5MM **Privately Held**
SIC: 3674 Semiconductors & related devices

(P-18741)
BAE SYSTEMS IMGING SLTIONS INC
1841 Zanker Rd Ste 50, San Jose (95112-4223)
PHONE..................408 433-2500
Terry Crimmins, *President*
Henry Silveira, *Design Engr*
Wil Chen, *Technology*
George Wang, *Engineer*
Colin Earle, *Manager*
EMP: 140
SQ FT: 60,000
SALES (est): 34.3MM
SALES (corp-wide): 24.2B **Privately Held**
WEB: www.fairchildimaging.com
SIC: 3674 3577 Semiconductors & related devices; computer peripheral equipment
HQ: Bae Systems Information And Electronic Systems Integration Inc.
65 Spit Brook Rd
Nashua NH 03060
603 885-4321

(P-18742)
BAR MANUFACTURING INC
3921 Sandstone Dr Ste 1, El Dorado Hills (95762-9343)
P.O. Box 4664 (95762-0022)
PHONE..................916 939-0551

S S Wong, *Ch of Bd*
▲ **EMP:** 68
SALES: 14MM
SALES (corp-wide): 458.3MM **Privately Held**
WEB: www.barmfg.us
SIC: 3674 Semiconductor circuit networks
HQ: Compart Engineering, Inc.
1730 E Philadelphia St
Ontario CA 91761
909 947-6688

(P-18743)
BAYWA RE SOLAR PROJECTS LLC
Also Called: Baywa R.E.renewable Energy
17901 Von Karman Ave # 1050, Irvine (92614-5254)
PHONE..................949 398-3915
Jam Attari, *CEO*
David Sanders, *COO*
Gaby Grullon, *Office Mgr*
David Dunlap, *Opers Staff*
Tom Miller, *Mktg Dir*
▲ **EMP:** 40 EST: 2014
SALES (est): 8.4MM
SALES (corp-wide): 18.9B **Privately Held**
SIC: 3674 Solar cells
HQ: Baywa R.E. Renewable Energy Gmbh
Arabellastr. 4
Munchen 81925
893 839-320

(P-18744)
BENTEK CORPORATION
1911 Lundy Ave, San Jose (95131-1847)
PHONE..................408 954-9600
EMP: 13
SALES (est): 2MM **Privately Held**
SIC: 3674 Semiconductors & related devices

(P-18745)
BERKELEY DESIGN AUTOMATION INC
46871 Bayside Pkwy, Fremont (94538-6572)
PHONE..................408 496-6600
Ravi Subramanian PH D, *President*
Paul Estrada, *COO*
Kelly Perey, *Vice Pres*
Nafees Qureshy, *Vice Pres*
EMP: 25
SQ FT: 25,000
SALES (est): 2.6MM
SALES (corp-wide): 97.7B **Privately Held**
WEB: www.berkeley-da.com
SIC: 3674 Integrated circuits, semiconductor networks, etc.
HQ: Mentor Graphics Corporation
8005 Sw Boeckman Rd
Wilsonville OR 97070
503 685-7000

(P-18746)
BIPOLARICS INC
1620 Oakland Rd Ste D103, San Jose (95131-2447)
PHONE..................408 372-7574
Dr Charles Leung, *President*
Colin Levy, *Treasurer*
Jessica Leung, *Controller*
EMP: 50
SALES (est): 5.8MM **Privately Held**
WEB: www.bipolarics.com
SIC: 3674 3677 Integrated circuits, semiconductor networks, etc.; electronic coils, transformers & other inductors

(P-18747)
BLACK HILLS NANOSYSTEMS CORP
1941 Jackson St 9, Oakland (94612-4600)
PHONE..................605 341-3641
EMP: 10
SQ FT: 4,000
SALES (est): 790K **Privately Held**
WEB: www.blackhillsnano.com
SIC: 3674

(P-18748)
BLOOM ENERGY CORPORATION (PA)
1299 Orleans Dr, Sunnyvale (94089-1138)
PHONE..................408 543-1500

Kr Sridhar, *Ch of Bd*
Susan Brennan, *COO*
Randy Furr, *CFO*
Matt Ross, *Chief Mktg Ofcr*
Bill Kurtz, *Officer*
▲ **EMP:** 300
SQ FT: 31,000
SALES: 376MM **Publicly Held**
WEB: www.bloomenergy.com
SIC: 3674 Fuel cells, solid state

(P-18749)
BOUNDARY DEVICES LLC
7 Orchard Ste 102, Lake Forest (92630-8334)
PHONE..................602 212-6744
Pejman Kalkhoran,
Jeff Broadhead, *Controller*
Parviz Kalkhoran,
Troy Kisky,
Jordan Tate,
EMP: 29
SQ FT: 7,100
SALES: 20MM **Privately Held**
SIC: 3674 Computer logic modules

(P-18750)
BRIDGELUX INC (PA)
46430 Fremont Blvd, Fremont (94538-6469)
PHONE..................925 583-8400
Tim Lester, *CEO*
Steve Scannell, *COO*
Brian Cumpston, *Vice Pres*
Keith Scott, *VP Bus Dvlpt*
Aneta Davis, *Managing Dir*
▲ **EMP:** 90
SALES (est): 29.9MM **Privately Held**
WEB: www.bridgelux.com
SIC: 3674 Light emitting diodes

(P-18751)
BRION TECHNOLOGIES INC
399 W Trimble Rd, San Jose (95131-1028)
PHONE..................408 653-1500
Jim Koonmen, *General Mgr*
Tadahiro Takigawa, *Ch of Bd*
Ken Dasso, *Vice Pres*
Christian Desplat, *Vice Pres*
Yen-Wen Lu, *Vice Pres*
▲ **EMP:** 17
SQ FT: 12,439
SALES (est): 2.8MM
SALES (corp-wide): 10.6B **Privately Held**
WEB: www.brion.com
SIC: 3674 Integrated circuits, semiconductor networks, etc.
PA: Asml Holding N.V.
De Run 6501
Veldhoven 5504
402 683-000

(P-18752)
BROADCOM CORPORATION
250 Innovation Dr, San Jose (95134-3390)
PHONE..................408 922-7000
Carol Barrett, *Branch Mgr*
Huan Phan, *Design Engr*
Sarin Chandran, *Engineer*
Bo Wang, *Engineer*
Jim McKeon, *Mktg Dir*
EMP: 39
SALES (corp-wide): 17.6B **Publicly Held**
SIC: 3674 Integrated circuits, semiconductor networks, etc.
HQ: Broadcom Corporation
1320 Ridder Park Dr
San Jose CA 95131

(P-18753)
BROADCOM CORPORATION (HQ)
Also Called: Broadcom Limited
1320 Ridder Park Dr, San Jose (95131-2313)
P.O. Box 57013, Irvine (92619-7013)
PHONE..................408 433-8000
Hock E Tan, *President*
Anthony Maslowski, *CFO*
Charlie Kawwas, *Senior VP*
Bryan Ingram, *Vice Pres*
Vijay Janapaty, *Vice Pres*
▲ **EMP:** 277

SALES (est): 3.8B
SALES (corp-wide): 17.6B **Publicly Held**
WEB: www.broadcom.com
SIC: 3674 Integrated circuits, semiconductor networks, etc.
PA: Broadcom Inc.
1320 Ridder Park Dr
San Jose CA 95131
408 433-8000

(P-18754)
BROADCOM CORPORATION
250 Innovation Dr, San Jose (95134-3390)
PHONE..................408 501-8200
Henry Samueli, *Chairman*
David Brown, *President*
Deon Carr, *Executive*
Gary Goodman, *Program Mgr*
Barbara Fiedler, *Executive Asst*
EMP: 38
SALES (corp-wide): 17.6B **Publicly Held**
WEB: www.broadcom.com
SIC: 3674 Integrated circuits, semiconductor networks, etc.
HQ: Broadcom Corporation
1320 Ridder Park Dr
San Jose CA 95131
-

(P-18755)
BROADCOM CORPORATION
16340 W Bernardo Dr A, San Diego (92127-1802)
PHONE..................858 385-8800
Bell Philip Andrew, *Branch Mgr*
Mark Erikson, *Engineer*
Syd Logan, *Engineer*
Chris Pikus, *Engineer*
WEI Chen, *Senior Engr*
EMP: 860
SALES (corp-wide): 17.6B **Publicly Held**
WEB: www.broadcom.com
SIC: 3674 Integrated circuits, semiconductor networks, etc.
HQ: Broadcom Corporation
1320 Ridder Park Dr
San Jose CA 95131

(P-18756)
BROADLIGHT INC (DH)
2901 Tasman Dr Ste 218, Santa Clara (95054-1138)
PHONE..................408 982-4210
Raanan Gewirtzman, *CEO*
Dror Heldenberg, *CFO*
Didi Ivancovsky, *Vice Pres*
Eli Weitz, *CTO*
EMP: 10
SALES (est): 1.1MM
SALES (corp-wide): 17.6B **Publicly Held**
WEB: www.broadlight.com
SIC: 3674 Semiconductors & related devices

(P-18757)
C & D SEMICONDUCTOR SVCS INC (PA)
Also Called: C&D Precision Machining
2031 Concourse Dr, San Jose (95131-1727)
PHONE..................408 383-1888
Dong Van Nguyen, *CEO*
Tien Nguyen, *Vice Pres*
Hieu Nguyen, *General Mgr*
Thuy Truong, *Personnel Assit*
Richard Shin, *Mfg Dir*
▲ **EMP:** 45
SQ FT: 3,600
SALES: 11.1MM **Privately Held**
WEB: www.cdsemi.com
SIC: 3674 Semiconductors & related devices

(P-18758)
C-CUBE US INC
1778 Mccarthy Blvd, Milpitas (95035-7421)
PHONE..................408 944-6300
Alexandre A Balkanski, *President*
Tom Lookabaugh, *President*
Umesh Padval, *President*
Howard Bailey, *CFO*
Fred Brown, *Senior VP*
EMP: 929
SQ FT: 33,000

SALES (est): 39.5MM
SALES (corp-wide): 17.6B **Publicly Held**
SIC: 3674 Microprocessors
HQ: Lsi Corporation
1320 Ridder Park Dr
San Jose CA 95131
408 433-8000

(P-18759)
CAMTEK USA INC
48389 Fremont Blvd # 112, Fremont (94538-6558)
PHONE..................510 624-9905
Cathy Hamilton, *Principal*
Amy Zhong, *Treasurer*
Tommy Weiss, *Vice Pres*
EMP: 28
SQ FT: 10,000
SALES (est): 4.8MM
SALES (corp-wide): 99.2MM **Privately Held**
WEB: www.camtekusa.com
SIC: 3674 Integrated circuits, semiconductor networks, etc.
PA: Camtek Ltd
Ramat Gavriel Ind Zone Migdal Ha'emek
Migdal Haemek
460 481-00

(P-18760)
CANADIAN SOLAR (USA) INC
3000 Oak Rd Ste 400, Walnut Creek (94597-2051)
PHONE..................925 807-7499
Shawn Qu, *CEO*
Robert Patterson, *President*
Guangchun Zhang, *COO*
Michael G Potter, *CFO*
Yan Zhuang, *Senior VP*
◆ **EMP:** 10
SQ FT: 2,000
SALES (est): 5.5MM
SALES (corp-wide): 3.3B **Privately Held**
SIC: 3674 Solar cells
PA: Canadian Solar Inc
545 Speedvale Ave W
Guelph ON N1K 1
519 837-1881

(P-18761)
CATALYST SEMICONDUCTOR INC
2975 Stender Way, Santa Clara (95054-3214)
PHONE..................408 542-1000
Gelu Voicu, *Principal*
Doug Eddleman, *Engineer*
EMP: 13
SALES (est): 1.6MM
SALES (corp-wide): 5.5B **Publicly Held**
WEB: www.onsemi.com
SIC: 3674 Semiconductors & related devices
HQ: Semiconductor Components Industries, Llc
5005 E Mcdowell Rd
Phoenix AZ 85008
800 282-9855

(P-18762)
CAVIUM INC (HQ)
5488 Marvell Ln, Santa Clara (95054-3606)
P.O. Box 67151, Scotts Valley (95067-7151)
PHONE..................408 943-7100
Jean Hu, *President*
Muhammad Hussain, *COO*
Amer Haider, *Vice Pres*
Raj Singh, *General Mgr*
Chenchi Kuo, *Info Tech Dir*
EMP: 225
SALES: 984MM **Privately Held**
WEB: www.cavium.com
SIC: 3674 Semiconductors & related devices

(P-18763)
CAVIUM NETWORKS INTL INC (DH)
2315 N 1st St, San Jose (95131-1010)
PHONE..................650 625-7000
Syed Ali, *CEO*
Arthur D Chadwick, *Senior VP*
Gopal Hegde, *Vice Pres*

Prasun Kapoor, *Systs Prg Mgr*
Len Cabeceiras, *Tech Recruiter*
EMP: 12
SALES (est): 8MM **Privately Held**
WEB: www.cavium.com
SIC: 3674 Semiconductor diodes & rectifiers

(P-18764)
CBC DISTRIBUTION INC
17352 Daimler St, Irvine (92614-5512)
PHONE..................949 553-4240
Nancy D Feldman, *CEO*
Greg T Harper, *CFO*
David W Moore, *Admin Sec*
▲ **EMP:** 37 **EST:** 1997
SQ FT: 3,500
SALES: 5.1MM **Privately Held**
SIC: 3674 Semiconductors & related devices

(P-18765)
CELESTICA LLC
5325 Hellyer Ave, San Jose (95138-1013)
PHONE..................408 574-6000
Joel Bustos, *General Mgr*
Arnold Villanueva, *Engineer*
Donald Fradette, *Manager*
John Nojeim, *Manager*
EMP: 250
SALES (corp-wide): 24.5B **Privately Held**
SIC: 3674 Semiconductors & related devices
HQ: Celestica Llc
11 Continental Blvd # 103
Merrimack NH 03054

(P-18766)
CHRONTEL INC (PA)
2210 Otoole Ave Ste 100, San Jose (95131-1300)
PHONE..................408 383-9328
Bruce Wooley, *Ch of Bd*
David C SOO, *President*
James Lin, *CFO*
Demonder Chan, *Officer*
Teh Lee, *Office Mgr*
EMP: 150
SQ FT: 40,000
SALES (est): 30.2MM **Privately Held**
WEB: www.chrontel.com
SIC: 3674 8711 Integrated circuits, semiconductor networks, etc.; engineering services

(P-18767)
CIRRUS LOGIC INC
45630 Northport Loop E, Fremont (94538-6477)
PHONE..................510 226-1204
Halappa Ravindra, *Branch Mgr*
David D French, *President*
EMP: 100
SQ FT: 57,952
SALES (corp-wide): 1.5B **Publicly Held**
WEB: www.cirrus.com
SIC: 3674 7371 Integrated circuits, semiconductor networks, etc.; custom computer programming services
PA: Cirrus Logic, Inc.
800 W 6th St
Austin TX 78701
512 851-4000

(P-18768)
CISC SEMICONDUCTOR CORP
800 W El Camino Real, Mountain View (94040-2567)
PHONE..................847 553-4204
Markus Pistauer, *President*
EMP: 10
SALES (est): 779.8K **Privately Held**
SIC: 3674 Integrated circuits, semiconductor networks, etc.

(P-18769)
CLARIPHY COMMUNICATIONS INC (HQ)
7585 Irvine Center Dr # 100, Irvine (92618-2985)
PHONE..................949 861-3074
Nariman Yousefi, *President*
William J Ruehle, *CFO*
Tim Heenan, *Vice Pres*
Brandon Ferguson, *Office Admin*

Norman L Swenson, *CTO*
EMP: 91
SALES (est): 35.9MM
SALES (corp-wide): 348.2MM **Publicly Held**
WEB: www.clariphy.com
SIC: 3674 Integrated circuits, semiconductor networks, etc.
PA: Inphi Corporation
2953 Bunker Hill Ln # 300
Santa Clara CA 95054
408 217-7300

(P-18770)
CM MANUFACTURING INC (HQ)
6321 San Ignacio Ave, San Jose (95119-1202)
PHONE..................408 284-7200
Chet Farris, *CEO*
Vineet Dharmadhikari, *COO*
Morris Alexander, *Vice Pres*
Garrett Hickey, *Vice Pres*
Howard Lee, *Vice Pres*
▲ **EMP:** 142
SALES (est): 75.9MM **Privately Held**
WEB: www.stion.com
SIC: 3674 Semiconductors & related devices
PA: Stion Corporation
333 S Grand Ave Ste 4070
Los Angeles CA 90071
408 284-7200

(P-18771)
CMOS SENSOR INC
20045 Stevens Creek Blvd 1a, Cupertino (95014-2355)
PHONE..................408 366-2898
Bill Wang, *President*
Michael Chern, *Vice Pres*
Shirley Cheng, *Finance Mgr*
EMP: 10
SALES: 2.2MM **Privately Held**
SIC: 3674 Semiconductors & related devices

(P-18772)
CNEX LABS INC
2880 Stevens Creek Blvd, San Jose (95128-4622)
PHONE..................408 695-1045
Alan Armstrong, *CEO*
Joe Defranco, *Vice Pres*
Ronnie Huang, *Vice Pres*
EMP: 50
SALES: 10MM **Privately Held**
SIC: 3674 Semiconductors & related devices

(P-18773)
COLLECTION DEVELOPMENT
Also Called: Collection Led
710 Nogales St, City of Industry (91748-1306)
PHONE..................909 595-8588
▲ **EMP:** 12
SALES: 950K **Privately Held**
SIC: 3674

(P-18774)
COMMNEXUS SAN DIEGO
4225 Executive Sq # 1110, La Jolla (92037-1486)
PHONE..................888 926-3987
Rory Moore, *Principal*
Danielle Tavshanjian, *Controller*
EMP: 17
SALES: 1.2MM **Privately Held**
SIC: 3674 Semiconductor circuit networks

(P-18775)
COMPONENT RE-ENGINEERING INC
Also Called: C. R. C
3508 Bassett St, Santa Clara (95054-2704)
PHONE..................408 562-4000
Brent Elliot, *President*
Frank Balma, *COO*
EMP: 12
SALES (est): 4.7MM **Privately Held**
SIC: 3674 Integrated circuits, semiconductor networks, etc.

(P-18776)
COMPUGRAPHICS USA INC (HQ)
43455 Osgood Rd, Fremont (94539-5609)
PHONE.................................510 249-2600
Lawrence Amon, *President*
Mark Crownover, *Administration*
Mark Nehrenz, *Manager*
Cathy Widner, *Manager*
Craig Durgy, *Accounts Mgr*
EMP: 56
SQ FT: 25,000
SALES (est): 11MM
SALES (corp-wide): 1.7B **Privately Held**
SIC: 3674 Integrated circuits, semiconductor networks, etc.

(P-18777)
CONCEPT SYSTEMS MFG INC
2047 Zanker Rd, San Jose (95131-2107)
PHONE.................................408 855-8595
Richard Diehl, *President*
Shannon Christie, *CTO*
Perry Hough, *Engineer*
▲ **EMP:** 15
SALES (est): 3.8MM **Privately Held**
SIC: 3674 Semiconductors & related devices

(P-18778)
CONDOR RELIABILITY SERVICES
2175 De La Cruz Blvd # 8, Santa Clara
(95050-3036)
PHONE.................................408 486-9600
Punam Patel, *President*
Tushar Patel, *Executive*
EMP: 120 **EST:** 1980
SQ FT: 5,000
SALES (est): 11.3MM **Privately Held**
SIC: 3674 8999 8734 8731 Semiconductors & related devices; weather related services; testing laboratories; commercial physical research

(P-18779)
CONEXANT HOLDINGS INC
4000 Macarthur Blvd, Newport Beach
(92660-2558)
PHONE.................................415 983-2706
David Dominik, *CEO*
Carl Mills, *CFO*
Saleel Awsare, *Vice Pres*
Nic Rossi, *Vice Pres*
John Knoll, *Admin Sec*
EMP: 600
SALES (est): 30.2MM **Privately Held**
SIC: 3674 5065 Semiconductors & related devices; semiconductor devices

(P-18780)
CONEXANT SYSTEMS LLC (HQ)
1901 Main St Ste 300, Irvine (92614-0512)
PHONE.................................949 483-4600
Jan Johannessen, *CEO*
Jennifer Jensen, *Senior Buyer*
EMP: 45
SQ FT: 140,000
SALES (est): 50.4MM
SALES (corp-wide): 1.7B **Publicly Held**
SIC: 3674 5065 Semiconductors & related devices; semiconductor devices
PA: Synaptics Incorporated
1251 Mckay Dr
San Jose CA 95131
408 904-1100

(P-18781)
CONEXANT SYSTEMS WORLDWIDE INC
4000 Macarthur Blvd, Newport Beach
(92660-2558)
PHONE.................................949 483-4600
Sailesh Chittipeddi, *President*
Scott Martin, *Exec Dir*
Greg Meyer, *Info Tech Dir*
Leslie Woodard, *Engineer*
David Chang, *Director*
EMP: 86
SALES (est): 14.4MM **Privately Held**
SIC: 3674 Semiconductors & related devices

(P-18782)
CONTECH SOLUTIONS INCORPORATED
631 Montague St, San Leandro
(94577-4323)
PHONE.................................510 357-7900
Afshin Nouri, *President*
Mehran Jafarcadeh, *Vice Pres*
Jafarzaden Mehran, *Director*
EMP: 21
SQ FT: 4,000
SALES: 2.6MM **Privately Held**
WEB: www.contechsolutions.com
SIC: 3674 Semiconductors & related devices

(P-18783)
CONVERGENT MOBILE INC
870 Knight St, Sonoma (95476-7258)
PHONE.................................707 343-1200
Mickey Breen, *CEO*
Tom Conery, *CEO*
EMP: 12 **EST:** 2007
SALES (est): 1.3MM **Privately Held**
SIC: 3674 Semiconductors & related devices

(P-18784)
COOPER MICROELECTRONICS INC
Also Called: CMI
1671 Reynolds Ave, Irvine (92614-5709)
PHONE.................................949 553-8352
Kenneth B Cooper III, *President*
Lily Cooper, *Vice Pres*
Tim Delpadre, *Prdtn Mgr*
▲ **EMP:** 37
SQ FT: 10,000
SALES (est): 5.9MM **Privately Held**
WEB: www.coopermicro.com
SIC: 3674 7371 Semiconductors & related devices; custom computer programming services

(P-18785)
CORPORATECOUCH
Also Called: Corp Couch
260 Vicente St, San Francisco
(94127-1331)
PHONE.................................415 312-6078
Farzaneh Amini, *CEO*
Fatemh Amini, *Admin Sec*
EMP: 25 **EST:** 2011
SALES (est): 2MM **Privately Held**
SIC: 3674 Integrated circuits, semiconductor networks, etc.

(P-18786)
CORSAIR MEMORY INC
47100 Bayside Pkwy, Fremont
(94538-6563)
PHONE.................................510 657-8747
Andrew J Paul, *President*
Ronald Van Veen, *Vice Pres*
Don Lieberman, *CTO*
Paul Snell, *Engineer*
▲ **EMP:** 150
SQ FT: 44,000
SALES (est): 41.5MM **Privately Held**
WEB: www.corsairmicro.com
SIC: 3674 7373 8731 Memories, solid state; computer integrated systems design; computer (hardware) development
PA: Corsair Components, Inc.
47100 Bayside Pkwy
Fremont CA 94538

(P-18787)
CORTINA SYSTEMS INC (HQ)
2953 Bunker Hill Ln # 300, Santa Clara
(95054-1131)
PHONE.................................408 481-2300
Amir Nayyerhabibi, *President*
Bruce Margtson, *CFO*
Randy Raymond, *Manager*
EMP: 120
SQ FT: 41,645
SALES (est): 45.9MM
SALES (corp-wide): 348.2MM **Publicly Held**
WEB: www.cortina-systems.com
SIC: 3674 Integrated circuits, semiconductor networks, etc.

PA: Inphi Corporation
2953 Bunker Hill Ln # 300
Santa Clara CA 95054
408 217-7300

(P-18788)
COSEMI TECHNOLOGIES INC
1370 Reynolds Ave Ste 100, Irvine
(92614-5504)
PHONE.................................949 623-9816
Samir Desai, *President*
David Kosanke, *Vice Pres*
John Marcin, *Executive*
Nanette Young, *Administration*
Wenbin Jiang, *CTO*
EMP: 15
SQ FT: 3,000
SALES (est): 4.1MM **Privately Held**
WEB: www.cosemi.com
SIC: 3674 Light sensitive devices

(P-18789)
COVE20 LLC
Also Called: Kbc Networks USA
15 Brookline, Aliso Viejo (92656-1461)
PHONE.................................949 297-4930
Steve Kuntz, *President*
▲ **EMP:** 11
SALES (est): 1.3MM **Privately Held**
SIC: 3674 3663 Integrated circuits, semiconductor networks, etc.; radio & TV communications equipment

(P-18790)
CREATIVE INTGRATED SYSTEMS INC
Also Called: CIS
1700 E Garry Ave Ste 112, Santa Ana
(92705-5828)
PHONE.................................949 261-6577
Jim Komarek, *President*
Shiro Fujioka, *Vice Pres*
Jack Minney, *Manager*
EMP: 25
SQ FT: 4,500
SALES: 1MM **Privately Held**
WEB: www.cisdesign.com
SIC: 3674 7371 3672 3661 Microcircuits, integrated (semiconductor); custom computer programming services; printed circuit boards; telephone & telegraph apparatus; electrical or electronic engineering; computer integrated systems design

(P-18791)
CREE INC
340 Storke Rd Ste 100, Goleta
(93117-2993)
PHONE.................................805 968-9460
Bernd Keller, *Branch Mgr*
EMP: 30
SALES (corp-wide): 1.4B **Publicly Held**
WEB: www.cree.com
SIC: 3674 Semiconductors & related devices
PA: Cree, Inc.
4600 Silicon Dr
Durham NC 27703
919 407-5300

(P-18792)
CROSSBAR INC
3200 Patrick Henry Dr # 110, Santa Clara
(95054-1865)
PHONE.................................408 884-0281
George Minassian, *CEO*
Sundar Narayanan, *Vice Pres*
Hagop Nazarian, *Vice Pres*
Ashish Pancholy, *General Mgr*
Zorina Mercado, *Executive Asst*
EMP: 20
SALES (est): 3.2MM **Privately Held**
SIC: 3674 Semiconductors & related devices

(P-18793)
CRYSTAL SOLAR INC
3050 Coronado Dr, Santa Clara
(95054-3203)
PHONE.................................408 490-1340
Tirunelveli S Ravi, *CEO*
David Bostwick, *CFO*
V Siva, *Exec VP*
Melissa Cayabyab, *Office Mgr*
Alex Berger, *Technical Staff*

EMP: 16 **EST:** 2008
SALES (est): 3.4MM **Privately Held**
SIC: 3674 Semiconductors & related devices

(P-18794)
CSDR INTERNATIONAL INC
7701 Woodley Ave, Van Nuys
(91406-1732)
PHONE.................................844 330-0664
Randall H Roth, *President*
EMP: 10
SQ FT: 1,000
SALES (est): 27.3K **Privately Held**
SIC: 3674 Solar cells

(P-18795)
CYPRESS SEMICONDUCTOR CORP
195 Champion Ct Bldg 2, San Jose
(95134-1709)
PHONE.................................408 943-2600
Emmanuel Hernandez, *Principal*
EMP: 13
SQ FT: 60,370
SALES (corp-wide): 2.3B **Publicly Held**
WEB: www.cypress.com
SIC: 3674 Integrated circuits, semiconductor networks, etc.
PA: Cypress Semiconductor Corporation
198 Champion Ct
San Jose CA 95134
408 943-2600

(P-18796)
CYPRESS SEMICONDUCTOR CORP (PA)
198 Champion Ct, San Jose (95134-1709)
PHONE.................................408 943-2600
Hassane El-Khoury, *President*
W Steve Albrecht, *Ch of Bd*
Thad Trent, *CFO*
Camillo Martino, *Bd of Directors*
Jeffrey Owens, *Bd of Directors*
◆ **EMP:** 1149
SQ FT: 171,370
SALES: 2.3B **Publicly Held**
WEB: www.cypress.com
SIC: 3674 Integrated circuits, semiconductor networks, etc.

(P-18797)
D-TEK MANUFACTURING
3245 Woodward Ave, Santa Clara
(95054-2626)
PHONE.................................408 588-1574
Dung Nguyen, *President*
Thanh L Dang, *Vice Pres*
EMP: 20 **EST:** 2010
SQ FT: 5,000
SALES (est): 5.7MM **Privately Held**
SIC: 3674 Semiconductors & related devices

(P-18798)
DATA CIRCLE INC
3333 Michelson Dr Ste 735, Irvine
(92612-7679)
PHONE.................................949 260-6569
Steve Oren, *CEO*
EMP: 13
SQ FT: 12,000
SALES (est): 1.2MM **Privately Held**
WEB: www.datacircle.com
SIC: 3674 Integrated circuits, semiconductor networks, etc.

(P-18799)
DAYLIGHT SOLUTIONS INC (DH)
Also Called: Drs Daylight Solutions
15378 Ave Of Science # 200, San Diego
(92128-3451)
PHONE.................................858 432-7500
Timothy Day, *CEO*
Paul Larson, *President*
Michelle Molina, *Office Mgr*
Matthew Dickerman, *Administration*
Enrique Lopez, *Research*
EMP: 175
SALES (est): 60.2MM
SALES (corp-wide): 9.2B **Privately Held**
WEB: www.daylightsolutions.net
SIC: 3674 5084 Molecular devices, solid state; instruments & control equipment

HQ: Leonardo Drs, Inc.
2345 Crystal Dr Ste 1000
Arlington VA 22202
703 416-8000

(P-18800)
DIALOG SEMICONDUCTOR INC (DH)
2560 Mission College Blvd # 110, Santa Clara (95054-1217)
P.O. Box 2369, Clifton NJ (07015-2369)
PHONE..............................408 845-8500
Jalal Bagherli, *CEO*
Wissam Jabre, *CFO*
Tom Sandoval, *Senior VP*
Karim Arabi, *Vice Pres*
Andrew Austin, *Vice Pres*
EMP: 235
SALES (est): 30.4MM
SALES (corp-wide): 1.3B **Privately Held**
SIC: 3674 Semiconductors & related devices
HQ: Dialog Semiconductor Gmbh
Neue Str. 95
Kirchheim Unter Teck 73230
702 180-50

(P-18801)
DIGITAL LIGHT LLC
1801 Century Park E # 2400, Los Angeles (90067-2302)
PHONE..............................310 551-9999
Steven Nia, *Mng Member*
George Shalhoub,
Jessica Chon, *Mng Member*
Kaveh Esmael, *Director*
▲ EMP: 21 EST: 2000
SQ FT: 600
SALES (est): 1.4MM **Privately Held**
WEB: www.edigitallight.com
SIC: 3674 5065 Semiconductors & related devices; semiconductor devices

(P-18802)
DNP AMERICA LLC
2099 Gateway Pl Ste 490, San Jose (95110-1087)
PHONE..............................408 616-1200
Yasuhiro Yamamura, *Principal*
EMP: 12
SALES (corp-wide): 13.2B **Privately Held**
SIC: 3674 5084 Semiconductors & related devices; industrial machinery & equipment
HQ: Dnp America, Llc
335 Madison Ave Fl 3
New York NY 10017
212 503-1060

(P-18803)
DONGBU ELECTRONICS CO
Also Called: Dongbu Hi-Tech
2953 Bunker Hill Ln # 206, Santa Clara (95054-1131)
PHONE..............................408 330-0330
B J Yoon, *Manager*
EMP: 13 **Privately Held**
SIC: 3674 Wafers (semiconductor devices)

(P-18804)
DPA LABS INC
Also Called: Dpa Components International
2251 Ward Ave, Simi Valley (93065-7556)
PHONE..............................805 581-9200
Douglas Young, *President*
Philip Young, *Vice Pres*
Doug Schweitzer, *General Mgr*
Steve Greene, *MIS Dir*
Hector Aponte, *Technician*
EMP: 50
SQ FT: 38,000
SALES (est): 12MM **Privately Held**
WEB: www.dpaci.com
SIC: 3674 8734 Semiconductors & related devices; testing laboratories

(P-18805)
DRS ADVANCED ISR LLC
10600 Valley View St, Cypress (90630-4833)
PHONE..............................714 220-3800
Jim Womble, *Branch Mgr*
Gary Roberts, *General Mgr*
Cathie Meister, *Info Tech Mgr*
Al Hoblit, *Engineer*
EMP: 200

SALES (corp-wide): 9.2B **Privately Held**
SIC: 3674 8731 Infrared sensors, solid state; commercial physical research
HQ: Drs Icas, Llc
2601 Mission Point Blvd
Beavercreek OH 45431
-

(P-18806)
DRS NTWORK IMAGING SYSTEMS LLC
Also Called: Drs Snsors Trgting Systems Inc
10600 Valley View St, Cypress (90630-4833)
PHONE..............................714 220-3800
Shawn Black,
Timothy Harrison, *President*
EMP: 100
SALES (est): 34.4MM
SALES (corp-wide): 9.2B **Privately Held**
SIC: 3674 8731 Infrared sensors, solid state; commercial physical research
HQ: Leonardo Drs, Inc.
2345 Crystal Dr Ste 1000
Arlington VA 22202
703 416-8000

(P-18807)
DYNAMIC ENGINEERING
150 Dubois St Ste C, Santa Cruz (95060-2114)
PHONE..............................831 457-8891
Keith V Leisses, *CEO*
Vicki C Leisses, *Vice Pres*
▼ EMP: 12
SQ FT: 4,000
SALES (est): 3MM **Privately Held**
SIC: 3674 8711 5734 Integrated circuits, semiconductor networks, etc.; engineering services; computer peripheral equipment

(P-18808)
DYNAMIC INTGRTED SOLUTIONS LLC
1710 Fortune Dr, San Jose (95131-1744)
PHONE..............................408 737-3400
EMP: 12
SALES (corp-wide): 8.7MM **Privately Held**
SIC: 3674
PA: Dynamic Integrated Solutions Llc
3964 Rivermark Plz # 104
Santa Clara CA 95054
408 727-3400

(P-18809)
DYNAMIC INTGRTED SOLUTIONS LLC (PA)
3964 Rivermark Plz # 104, Santa Clara (95054-4155)
PHONE..............................408 727-3400
David Diep,
EMP: 32
SALES (est): 8.6MM **Privately Held**
SIC: 3674 Semiconductors & related devices

(P-18810)
E/G ELECTRO-GRAPH INC
Also Called: Electrograph
1491 Poinsettia Ave # 138, Vista (92081-8541)
PHONE..............................760 438-9090
Mike Reilly, *President*
Mary Poniktera, *CFO*
EMP: 60
SQ FT: 24,500
SALES (est): 11.4MM **Privately Held**
WEB: www.egraph.com
SIC: 3674 Semiconductor diodes & rectifiers
HQ: Plansee Se
Metallwerk Plansee-StraBe 71
Reutte 6600
567 260-00

(P-18811)
EASIC CORPORATION
3940 Freedom Cir 100, Santa Clara (95054-1204)
PHONE..............................408 855-9200
Ronnie Vasishta, *President*
Kaushik Banerjee, *President*
Patrick Little, *President*

Richard Heye, *COO*
Richard Deranleau, *CFO*
EMP: 30
SQ FT: 12,195
SALES (est): 8.2MM **Privately Held**
SIC: 3674 Semiconductors & related devices

(P-18812)
EDISON OPTO USA CORPORATION
1809 Excise Ave Ste 201, Ontario (91761-8558)
PHONE..............................909 284-9710
Wen-Jui Cheng, *CEO*
Adrian Cheng, *Executive*
▲ EMP: 12
SALES (est): 1.2MM **Privately Held**
SIC: 3674 Light emitting diodes

(P-18813)
EG SYSTEMS LLC (PA)
Also Called: Electroglas
6200 Village Pkwy, Dublin (94568-3004)
PHONE..............................510 324-0126
Raj Kaul, *Mng Member*
▲ EMP: 24
SALES (est): 30.4MM **Privately Held**
SIC: 3674 Semiconductors & related devices

(P-18814)
ELANTEC SEMICONDUCTOR INC (DH)
675 Trade Zone Blvd, Milpitas (95035-6803)
PHONE..............................408 945-1323
Richard Beyer, *President*
James V Diller, *Ch of Bd*
Brian McDonald, *CFO*
Rajeeva Lahri, *Senior VP*
Ralph S Granchelli Jr, *Vice Pres*
EMP: 201
SQ FT: 39,000
SALES (est): 14.7MM
SALES (corp-wide): 4.5B **Privately Held**
WEB: www.elantec.com
SIC: 3674 Integrated circuits, semiconductor networks, etc.
HQ: Renesas Electronics America Inc.
1001 Murphy Ranch Rd
Milpitas CA 95035
408 432-8888

(P-18815)
ELEKTRON TECHNOLOGY CORP
11849 Telegraph Rd, Santa Fe Springs (90670-3716)
PHONE..............................760 343-3650
John Wilson, *President*
Andy P Weatherstone, *CFO*
Charlie Fixa, *Vice Pres*
Mark Milmine, *Admin Asst*
Paul Thatcher, *Project Engr*
▲ EMP: 10 EST: 1966
SALES (est): 1.6MM
SALES (corp-wide): 39.8MM **Privately Held**
WEB: www.arcolectric.com
SIC: 3674 3613 3648 3641 Semiconductors & related devices; switches, electric power except snap, push button, etc.; lighting equipment; electric lamps
PA: Elektron Technology Plc
Broers Building
Cambridge CAMBS CB3 0
122 337-1000

(P-18816)
ELEMENTCXI
25 E Trimble Rd, San Jose (95131-1108)
PHONE..............................408 935-8090
Jaime Cummins, *President*
EMP: 20
SALES (est): 2.4MM **Privately Held**
WEB: www.elementcxi.com
SIC: 3674

(P-18817)
EMCORE CORPORATION
8674 Thornton Ave, Newark (94560-3330)
PHONE..............................510 896-2139
EMP: 13

SALES (corp-wide): 174.7MM **Publicly Held**
SIC: 3674
PA: Emcore Corporation
2015 Chestnut St
Alhambra CA 91803
626 293-3400

(P-18818)
EMCORE CORPORATION (PA)
2015 Chestnut St, Alhambra (91803-1542)
PHONE..............................626 293-3400
Jeffrey Rittichier, *CEO*
Gerald J Fine, *Ch of Bd*
Jikun Kim, *CFO*
Stephen Domenik, *Bd of Directors*
Albert Lu, *Senior VP*
▲ EMP: 230
SQ FT: 75,000
SALES: 122.9MM **Publicly Held**
WEB: www.emcore.com
SIC: 3674 3559 Integrated circuits, semiconductor networks, etc.; metal oxide silicon (MOS) devices; wafers (semiconductor devices); semiconductor manufacturing machinery

(P-18819)
EMISENSE TECHNOLOGIES LLC (PA)
Also Called: Emisense CA
999 Corporate Dr Ste 100, Ladera Ranch (92694-2149)
PHONE..............................949 502-8440
Patrick Thompson, *CEO*
Joe Fitzpatrick, *Engineer*
EMP: 11
SALES (est): 915.1K **Privately Held**
SIC: 3674 Radiation sensors

(P-18820)
EMULEX DESIGN & MFG CORP
3333 Susan St, Costa Mesa (92626-1632)
PHONE..............................714 662-5600
Paul Folino, *Chairman*
Jim Mc'cluney, *CEO*
Michael J Rockenbach, *Vice Pres*
EMP: 339
SQ FT: 100,000
SALES (est): 31.7MM
SALES (corp-wide): 17.6B **Publicly Held**
WEB: www.emlx.com
SIC: 3674 Semiconductors & related devices
HQ: Emulex Corporation
5300 California Ave
Irvine CA 92617

(P-18821)
ENCOMPASS DIST SVCS LLC
Also Called: EDS
3502 Mars Way Ste 161, Tracy (95377-8002)
PHONE..............................925 249-0988
Bob Swor, *President*
▲ EMP: 12
SQ FT: 3,500
SALES (est): 1.8MM **Privately Held**
SIC: 3674 Silicon wafers, chemically doped

(P-18822)
ENDURA TECHNOLOGIES LLC
7310 Miramar Rd Fl 5, San Diego (92126-4222)
P.O. Box 928769 (92192-8769)
PHONE..............................858 412-2135
Massih Tayebi, *CEO*
EMP: 13
SQ FT: 55,000
SALES (est): 1MM **Privately Held**
SIC: 3674 Microcircuits, integrated (semiconductor)

(P-18823)
ENGINEERED OUTSOURCE SOLUTIONS
557 E California Ave, Sunnyvale (94086-5147)
PHONE..............................408 617-2800
Lance Nelson, *CEO*
Scott Mobley, *President*
EMP: 23
SQ FT: 44,000

(PA)=Parent Co (HQ)=Headquarters (DH)=Div Headquarters
✿ = New Business established in last 2 years

SALES (est): 5.7MM **Privately Held**
WEB: www.engrsolutions.com
SIC: 3674 Computer logic modules

(P-18824)
ENPHASE ENERGY INC (PA)
1420 N Mcdowell Blvd, Petaluma
(94954-6515)
PHONE..................................707 774-7000
Badrinarayanan, *CEO*
Badrinarayanan Kothandaraman, *President*
Eric Branderiz, *CFO*
Humberto Garcia, *CFO*
David Ranhoff, *Ch Credit Ofcr*
▲ EMP: 259
SQ FT: 100,000
SALES: 286.1MM **Publicly Held**
WEB: www.enphaseenergy.com
SIC: 3674 Semiconductors & related devices

(P-18825)
ENPIRION
101 Innovation Dr, San Jose (95134-1941)
PHONE..................................408 904-2800
Juinn Chen, *Vice Pres*
EMP: 12
SALES: 630K **Privately Held**
SIC: 3674 Semiconductors & related devices

(P-18826)
ENSPHERE SOLUTIONS INC
2870 Briarwood Dr, San Jose
(95125-5020)
PHONE..................................408 598-2441
Hessam Mohajeri, *President*
Emad Afifi, *Vice Pres*
EMP: 14
SALES (est): 2.1MM **Privately Held**
SIC: 3674 Semiconductors & related devices

(P-18827)
ENTROPIC COMMUNICATIONS LLC (HQ)
5966 La Place Ct Ste 100, Carlsbad
(92008-8830)
PHONE..................................858 768-3600
Kishore Seendripu, *President*
Andrew Chartrand, *President*
Ted Tewksbury, *President*
Adam Spice, *Treasurer*
William R Bradford, *Senior VP*
▲ EMP: 83
SQ FT: 90,000
SALES (est): 60.1MM
SALES (corp-wide): 420.3MM **Publicly Held**
WEB: www.entropic.com
SIC: 3674 7372 Semiconductor circuit networks; prepackaged software
PA: Maxlinear, Inc.
5966 La Place Ct Ste 100
Carlsbad CA 92008
760 692-0711

(P-18828)
ENVIRON-CLEAN TECHNOLOGY INC
Also Called: Environ Clean Technology
1710 Ringwood Ave, San Jose
(95131-1711)
PHONE..................................408 487-1770
Christopher Tracey, *Manager*
EMP: 16
SALES (corp-wide): 213.5MM **Privately Held**
SIC: 3674 Semiconductors & related devices
HQ: Environ-Clean Technology Inc
3844 E University Dr # 2
Phoenix AZ 85034
602 438-9131

(P-18829)
EOPLLY USA INC
1670 S Amphlett Blvd # 140, San Mateo
(94402-2533)
PHONE..................................650 225-9400
Warren Nishikawa, *CEO*
EMP: 10 EST: 2012
SALES (est): 1.2MM **Privately Held**
SIC: 3674

(P-18830)
EPSON ELECTRONICS AMERICA INC (DH)
214 Devcon Dr, San Jose (95112-4210)
PHONE..................................408 922-0200
Koji Abe, *President*
Craig Hodowski, *Admin Sec*
▲ EMP: 32
SQ FT: 28,000
SALES (est): 12.3MM
SALES (corp-wide): 10.3B **Privately Held**
SIC: 3674 5065 8731 Semiconductors & related devices; electronic parts & equipment; commercial physical research

(P-18831)
ESILICON CORPORATION (PA)
2130 Gold St Ste 100, Alviso (95002-3700)
PHONE..................................408 635-6300
Seth Neiman, *Ch of Bd*
Jens Andersen, *President*
Jack Harding, *President*
Hugh Durdan, *COO*
Dennis Hollenbeck, *COO*
EMP: 102
SALES (est): 58MM **Privately Held**
WEB: www.esilicon.com
SIC: 3674 Integrated circuits, semiconductor networks, etc.; hybrid integrated circuits

(P-18832)
ESS TECHNOLOGY INC (HQ)
237 S Hillview Dr, Milpitas (95035-5417)
PHONE..................................408 643-8818
Robert L Blair, *President*
Robert Plachno, *President*
John A Marsh, *CFO*
Dan Christman, *Chief Mktg Ofcr*
Peter Frith, *Officer*
▲ EMP: 135
SQ FT: 35,000
SALES (est): 31MM
SALES (corp-wide): 14.4MM **Privately Held**
WEB: www.esstech.com
SIC: 3674 Microcircuits, integrated (semiconductor); semiconductor circuit networks
PA: Imperium Partners Group, Llc
509 Madison Ave
New York NY 10022
212 433-1360

(P-18833)
ESSEX ELECTRONICS INC
1130 Mark Ave, Carpinteria (93013-2918)
PHONE..................................805 684-7601
Stewart Frisch, *Ch of Bd*
Garrett Kaufman, *President*
Fred Zimmermann, *President*
Jesse Moore, *CEO*
Dean Benjamin, *Vice Pres*
▲ EMP: 23
SQ FT: 7,000
SALES (est): 4.6MM **Privately Held**
WEB: www.keyless.com
SIC: 3674 Semiconductors & related devices

(P-18834)
ETD PRECISION CERAMICS CORP
580 Charcot Ave, San Jose (95131-2201)
PHONE..................................408 577-0405
Thanh Duong, *President*
EMP: 10
SQ FT: 7,000
SALES (est): 1.8MM **Privately Held**
SIC: 3674 Semiconductors & related devices

(P-18835)
EVERGREEN AVIONICS INC (PA)
Also Called: Evergreen Systems Intl
880 Calle Plano Ste J, Camarillo
(93012-8573)
P.O. Box 1656 (93011-1656)
PHONE..................................805 445-6492
Robert Hulle, *President*
Linda Magallanes, *Vice Pres*
EMP: 12
SQ FT: 6,500

SALES (est): 1.5MM **Privately Held**
WEB: www.trackballs.com
SIC: 3674 Semiconductors & related devices

(P-18836)
EXAR CORPORATION (HQ)
1060 Rincon Cir, San Jose (95131-1325)
PHONE..................................669 265-6100
Ryan A Benton, *CEO*
Keith Tainsky, *CFO*
David Matteucci, *Division VP*
Sherry Lin,
Cora Abuan, *Executive Asst*
EMP: 201 EST: 1971
SQ FT: 151,000
SALES: 149.3MM
SALES (corp-wide): 420.3MM **Publicly Held**
WEB: www.exar.com
SIC: 3674 Integrated circuits, semiconductor networks, etc.; metal oxide silicon (MOS) devices; microcircuits, integrated (semiconductor)
PA: Maxlinear, Inc.
5966 La Place Ct Ste 100
Carlsbad CA 92008
760 692-0711

(P-18837)
EXAR CORPORATION
SIPEX
48760 Kato Rd, Fremont (94538-7312)
PHONE..................................408 927-9975
Jim Donegan, *Branch Mgr*
Lizzy Yu, *COO*
Sherry Lin, *Officer*
Dan Wark, *Division VP*
Thomas R Melendrez, *Exec VP*
EMP: 280
SALES (corp-wide): 420.3MM **Publicly Held**
WEB: www.sipex.com
SIC: 3674 Semiconductors & related devices
HQ: Exar Corporation
1060 Rincon Cir
San Jose CA 95131
669 265-6100

(P-18838)
EXCLARA INC
4701 Patrick Henry Dr # 1701, Santa Clara
(95054-1819)
PHONE..................................408 329-9319
Shrichand Dodani, *President*
Stephanie Leung, *CFO*
Phil Hamister, *Director*
Tony Suzer, *Director*
▲ EMP: 20 EST: 2006
SALES (est): 2.1MM **Privately Held**
SIC: 3674 3677 Semiconductors & related devices; transformers power supply, electronic type

(P-18839)
EXPONENTIAL TECHNOLOGY INC
685 Budd Ct, Campbell (95008-4600)
PHONE..................................408 378-1850
Rick Shriner, *President*
Stephanie C Dorris, *Vice Pres*
George Taylor, *Vice Pres*
Jeffrey A Thomas, *Vice Pres*
EMP: 75
SQ FT: 26,800
SALES (est): 6.8MM **Privately Held**
SIC: 3674 Microprocessors

(P-18840)
FAIRCHILD SEMICDTR INTL INC (HQ)
1272 Borregas Ave, Sunnyvale
(94089-1310)
PHONE..................................408 822-2000
Keith D Jackson, *President*
William A Schromm, *COO*
Bernard Gutmann, *CFO*
George H Cave, *Exec VP*
William M Hall, *Exec VP*
EMP: 27
SALES: 1.3B
SALES (corp-wide): 5.5B **Publicly Held**
WEB: www.fairchildsemi.com
SIC: 3674 Semiconductors & related devices

PA: On Semiconductor Corporation
5005 E Mcdowell Rd
Phoenix AZ 85008
602 244-6600

(P-18841)
FALKOR PARTNERS LLC
Also Called: Semicoa
333 Mccormick Ave, Costa Mesa
(92626-3422)
PHONE..................................714 721-8772
Allen Ronk, *CEO*
John Park, *Principal*
EMP: 62
SQ FT: 24,000
SALES (est): 5.5MM **Privately Held**
SIC: 3674 Semiconductors & related devices

(P-18842)
FINISAR CORPORATION
41762 Christy St, Fremont (94538-5106)
PHONE..................................408 548-1000
Fariba Daneh, *Manager*
Jing Chai, *Engineer*
Weizhong W Sun PHD, *Engineer*
Hee Park, *Senior Engr*
Ken Falta, *Director*
EMP: 13
SALES (corp-wide): 1.3B **Publicly Held**
SIC: 3674 Semiconductors & related devices
PA: Finisar Corporation
1389 Moffett Park Dr
Sunnyvale CA 94089
408 548-1000

(P-18843)
FIRST SOLAR INC
Also Called: First Solar Electric
135 Main St Fl 6, San Francisco
(94105-8113)
PHONE..................................415 935-2500
Sina Maghsoodi, *Director*
EMP: 17
SALES (corp-wide): 2.9B **Publicly Held**
SIC: 3674 3433 Solar cells; heating equipment, except electric
PA: First Solar, Inc.
350 W Washington St # 600
Tempe AZ 85281
602 414-9300

(P-18844)
FLEXTRONICS SEMICONDUCTOR (DH)
2241 Lundy Ave Bldg 2, San Jose
(95131-1822)
PHONE..................................408 576-7000
Ash Bhardwaj, *President*
Vikas Desai, *Vice Pres*
Duncan Robertson, *Vice Pres*
Eric Sislian, *Vice Pres*
Angela Wright, *Vice Pres*
EMP: 40
SQ FT: 54,000
SALES (est): 9.8MM
SALES (corp-wide): 23.8B **Privately Held**
SIC: 3674 8711 Semiconductors & related devices; engineering services

(P-18845)
FOCUS ENHANCEMENTS INC (DH)
Also Called: Focus Enhncments Systems Group
931 Benecia Ave, Sunnyvale (94085-2805)
PHONE..................................650 230-2400
Brett A Moyer, *President*
Gary Williams, *CFO*
▲ EMP: 27
SQ FT: 27,500
SALES (est): 5.7MM **Privately Held**
WEB: www.focusinfo.com
SIC: 3674 3861 Semiconductors & related devices; wafers (semiconductor devices); editing equipment, motion picture: viewers, splicers, etc.
HQ: Vitec Multimedia, Inc.
2200 Century Pkwy Ne # 900
Atlanta GA 30345
404 320-0110

(P-18846)
FORMFACTOR INC
7545 Longard Rd, Livermore (94551)
PHONE..................................925 290-4000
Tom St Dennis, *CEO*
EMP: 13 **Publicly Held**
SIC: 3674 Semiconductors & related devices
PA: Formfactor, Inc.
     7005 Southfront Rd
     Livermore CA 94551
     -

(P-18847)
FORMFACTOR INC (PA)
7005 Southfront Rd, Livermore
(94551-8201)
PHONE..................................925 290-4000
Michael D Slessor, *CEO*
Thomas St Dennis, *Ch of Bd*
Michael M Ludwig, *CFO*
Tom Begley, *Vice Pres*
Rahul Jairath, *Vice Pres*
▲ **EMP:** 200
SQ FT: 168,636
SALES: 548.4MM **Publicly Held**
WEB: www.formfactor.com
SIC: 3674 Thermoelectric devices, solid state

(P-18848)
FORTEMEDIA INC (PA)
4051 Burton Dr, Santa Clara (95054-1585)
PHONE..................................408 716-8028
Paul Huang, *CEO*
Elaine Yeh, *Manager*
▲ **EMP:** 25
SQ FT: 9,000
SALES (est): 11.5MM **Privately Held**
WEB: www.fortemedia.com
SIC: 3674 Semiconductors & related devices

(P-18849)
FOVEON INC
2249 Zanker Rd, San Jose (95131-1120)
PHONE..................................408 855-6800
Carver A Mead, *Ch of Bd*
Jim Lau, *President*
Rudy Guttosch, *Vice Pres*
Hien Truong, *Technician*
Tony Velazquez, *Engineer*
EMP: 50 **EST:** 1997
SALES (est): 7.4MM **Privately Held**
WEB: www.foveon.com
SIC: 3674 7221 Light sensitive devices, solid state; photographic studios, portrait

(P-18850)
FOXSEMICON INTEGRATED TECH INC
96 Bonaventura Dr, San Jose
(95134-2124)
PHONE..................................408 383-9880
Jackson C Hwang, *CEO*
Charles Tao, *Manager*
▲ **EMP:** 13
SQ FT: 3,000
SALES (est): 4.3MM
SALES (corp-wide): 60.3B **Privately Held**
SIC: 3674 Semiconductors & related devices
PA: Hon Hai Precision Industry Co., Ltd.
     66, Zhongshan Rd.,
     New Taipei City 23680
     222 683-477

(P-18851)
FRESCO SOLAR INC
Also Called: Alfresco Concepts
16875 Joleen Way Unit 170, Morgan Hill
(95037-4604)
PHONE..................................408 497-1579
Sean Kenny, *CEO*
EMP: 15
SALES: 2MM **Privately Held**
SIC: 3674 Solar cells

(P-18852)
FRONTIER SEMICONDUCTOR (PA)
Also Called: Fsm
165 Topaz St, Milpitas (95035-5430)
PHONE..................................408 432-8338
Yuen F Lim, *CEO*

Aruna Aiyer, *CIO*
Wojtek Walecki, *CTO*
Jae Ryu, *Technology*
Jason Yeung, *Technology*
EMP: 35
SQ FT: 40,000
SALES (est): 3.6MM **Privately Held**
WEB: www.frontiersemi.com
SIC: 3674 Integrated circuits, semiconductor networks, etc.

(P-18853)
FULCRUM MICROSYSTEMS INC
26630 Agoura Rd, Calabasas
(91302-1954)
PHONE..................................818 871-8100
Robert R Nunn, *CEO*
Mike Zeile, *President*
Dale Bartos, *CFO*
Uri Cummings, *CTO*
EMP: 58 **EST:** 1999
SQ FT: 17,077
SALES (est): 6MM
SALES (corp-wide): 62.7B **Publicly Held**
WEB: www.fulcrummicro.com
SIC: 3674 Semiconductors & related devices
PA: Intel Corporation
     2200 Mission College Blvd
     Santa Clara CA 95054
     408 765-8080

(P-18854)
GAZE INC
1 Market Spear Twr, San Francisco
(94105)
PHONE..................................415 374-9193
Tero Heinonen, *CEO*
EMP: 10
SALES (est): 398.2K **Privately Held**
SIC: 3674 7371 Radiation sensors; computer software development

(P-18855)
GENERAL TRANSISTOR CORPORATION (PA)
Also Called: G T C
12449 Putnam St, Whittier (90602-1023)
PHONE..................................310 578-7344
Albert A Barrios, *President*
Ilan Israely, *Vice Pres*
EMP: 30
SALES (est): 6.4MM **Privately Held**
WEB: www.gtcelectronics.com
SIC: 3674 5065 Semiconductor devices; semiconductor circuit networks

(P-18856)
GENOA CORPORATION
41762 Christy St, Fremont (94538-5106)
PHONE..................................510 979-3000
Fariba Danesh, *CEO*
August Capital LLC, *Shareholder*
Jeff Walker, *Shareholder*
Jim Witham, *Senior VP*
Deborah Witt, *Accountant*
EMP: 45 **EST:** 1998
SQ FT: 44,000
SALES (est): 3.9MM **Privately Held**
SIC: 3674 Semiconductors & related devices

(P-18857)
GEO SEMICONDUCTOR INC (PA)
101 Metro Dr Ste 620, San Jose
(95110-1342)
PHONE..................................408 638-0400
Paul Russo, *CEO*
John Casey, *President*
Simon Westbrook, *CFO*
Ronald Allard, *Vice Pres*
Michael Hopton, *Vice Pres*
EMP: 25
SALES (est): 9.4MM **Privately Held**
SIC: 3674 Semiconductors & related devices

(P-18858)
GLO-USA INC
Also Called: G L O
1225 Bordeaux Dr, Sunnyvale
(94089-1203)
PHONE..................................408 598-4400
Fariba Danesh, *CEO*
Christian Wittmann, *President*
James McCanna, *CFO*

Monier Nessim, *VP Opers*
Henry Chiu, *VP Sales*
EMP: 55
SALES (est): 13.7MM **Privately Held**
WEB: www.glo.se
SIC: 3674 Light emitting diodes

(P-18859)
GLOBAL COMM SEMICONDUCTORS LLC (HQ)
Also Called: G C S
23155 Kashiwa Ct, Torrance (90505-4026)
PHONE..................................310 530-7274
Bau-Hsing Ann, *President*
Dave Wang, *COO*
Ta-Lun Huang, *Chairman*
Sam Wang, *Vice Pres*
Armando Gutierrez, *Managing Dir*
EMP: 20
SQ FT: 38,000
SALES (est): 20MM **Privately Held**
WEB: www.gcsincorp.com
SIC: 3674 Semiconductors & related devices

(P-18860)
GLOBAL POWER TECH GROUP INC
20692 Prism Pl, Lake Forest (92630-7803)
PHONE..................................949 273-4373
Sung Joon Kim, *President*
Brian Patterson, *Electrical Engi*
Tami Williams, *Controller*
EMP: 16
SALES: 450K **Privately Held**
SIC: 3674 7389 Semiconductors & related devices;

(P-18861)
GOLD COAST SOLAR LLC
Also Called: Colored Solar
1975 Hillgate Way Apt G, Simi Valley
(93065-2977)
PHONE..................................310 351-7229
Michael Mrozek, *CEO*
Paul Wise, *COO*
Paul Meyer, *CFO*
EMP: 42
SQ FT: 10,000
SALES: 4MM **Privately Held**
SIC: 3674 7373 3861 Solar cells; modules, solid state; systems integration services; photographic equipment & supplies

(P-18862)
GREENLIANT SYSTEMS INC
3970 Freedom Cir Ste 100, Santa Clara
(95054-1204)
PHONE..................................408 217-7400
Bing Yeh, *CEO*
Arthur Hsu, *President*
Yoshinobu Higuchi, *Vice Pres*
Marisa Lin, *Accountant*
Gary Brown, *Senior Mgr*
EMP: 105 **EST:** 2010
SALES (est): 14.4MM **Privately Held**
SIC: 3674 5065 Semiconductors & related devices; electronic parts & equipment

(P-18863)
GRINDING & DICING SERVICES INC
Also Called: Gdsi
925 Berryessa Rd, San Jose (95133-1002)
PHONE..................................408 451-2000
Joe D Collins, *CEO*
Laila H Collins, *Vice Pres*
Saira Haq, *Vice Pres*
Glenn Sebastian, *Project Engr*
Rey Sana, *Engineer*
▲ **EMP:** 24
SQ FT: 14,500
SALES (est): 3.9MM **Privately Held**
SIC: 3674 2672 Semiconductors & related devices; adhesive papers, labels or tapes: from purchased material

(P-18864)
GSI TECHNOLOGY INC
2360 Owen St, Santa Clara (95054-3210)
PHONE..................................408 980-8388
Shu Lee-Lean, *Branch Mgr*
EMP: 81 **Publicly Held**
SIC: 3674 Semiconductors & related devices

PA: Gsi Technology, Inc.
     1213 Elko Dr
     Sunnyvale CA 94089
     -

(P-18865)
GSI TECHNOLOGY INC (PA)
1213 Elko Dr, Sunnyvale (94089-2211)
PHONE..................................408 331-8800
Lee-Lean Shu, *Ch of Bd*
Douglas M Schirle, *CFO*
Ruey Lu, *Bd of Directors*
Didier Lasserre, *Vice Pres*
Bor-Tay Wu, *Vice Pres*
EMP: 58
SQ FT: 44,277
SALES: 42.6MM **Publicly Held**
WEB: www.gsitechnology.com
SIC: 3674 3572 Integrated circuits, semiconductor networks, etc.; computer storage devices

(P-18866)
GULSHAN INTERNATIONAL CORP
Also Called: Invax Technologies
1355 Geneva Dr, Sunnyvale (94089-1121)
PHONE..................................408 745-6090
Abid Khan, *President*
Susy Khan, *Office Mgr*
Brandon Shalin, *Engineer*
EMP: 14 **EST:** 1980
SALES (est): 2.4MM **Privately Held**
WEB: www.invax.com
SIC: 3674 Modules, solid state

(P-18867)
H-SQUARE CORPORATION
Also Called: H2 Co
3100 Patrick Henry Dr, Santa Clara
(95054-1850)
PHONE..................................408 732-1240
Bud Barclay, *President*
Larry Dean, *Shareholder*
▲ **EMP:** 42 **EST:** 1975
SQ FT: 20,000
SALES (est): 8MM **Privately Held**
WEB: www.h-square.com
SIC: 3674 Semiconductor circuit networks; solid state electronic devices; stud bases or mounts for semiconductor devices

(P-18868)
HALCYON MICROELECTRONICS INC
5467 2nd St, Irwindale (91706-2072)
PHONE..................................626 814-4688
Patricia Martin, *CEO*
Dennis Martin, *President*
John Truong, *Senior Engr*
EMP: 16
SQ FT: 9,100
SALES (est): 1.7MM **Privately Held**
WEB: www.halcyonmicro.com
SIC: 3674 Microcircuits, integrated (semiconductor)

(P-18869)
HANERGY HOLDING (AMERICA) LLC (HQ)
1350 Bayshore Hwy, Burlingame
(94010-1823)
PHONE..................................650 288-3722
Yi Wu, *CEO*
EMP: 17
SALES (est): 38MM **Privately Held**
SIC: 3674 6719 Solar cells; investment holding companies, except banks
PA: Hanergy Holding Group Limited
     No.0-A, Anli Road, Chaoyang Dist.
     Beijing
     108 391-4567

(P-18870)
HAYWARD QUARTZ TECHNOLOGY
Also Called: Hayward Quartz Machining Co
1700 Corporate Way, Fremont
(94539-6107)
PHONE..................................510 657-9605
Nhe Thi Le, *CEO*
Ha Vinh Ly, *President*
Ken Jacoby, *Project Mgr*
Kin Kuan, *Engineer*
Dean Gehrman, *Sales Mgr*

P
R
O
D
U
C
T
S

&

S
V
C
S

▲ **EMP:** 250
SQ FT: 250,000
SALES (est): 62.4MM **Privately Held**
WEB: www.haywardquartz.com
SIC: 3674 Semiconductor circuit networks

(P-18871)
HELITEK COMPANY LTD
4033 Clipper Ct, Fremont (94538-6540)
PHONE...................................510 933-7688
Ping-Hai Chiao, *President*
Art Tao, *Project Mgr*
Nancy Lin, *Purchasing*
▲ **EMP:** 15
SQ FT: 30,000
SALES (est): 2.7MM
SALES (corp-wide): 211.8MM **Privately Held**
SIC: 3674 Semiconductors & related devices
PA: Wafer Works Corporation
100, Longyuan 1st Rd.,
Taoyuan City TAY 32542
348 150-01

(P-18872)
HERMES-MICROVISION INC
1762 Automation Pkwy, San Jose (95131-1873)
PHONE...................................408 597-8600
Jack Jau, *CEO*
Chung Shih Pan, *President*
Kevin Liu, *Vice Pres*
Cynthia Gao, *Administration*
Darman Ding, *Sr Software Eng*
▲ **EMP:** 25
SQ FT: 80,000
SALES (est): 9.5MM
SALES (corp-wide): 10.6B **Privately Held**
WEB: www.hermesmicrovision.com
SIC: 3674 Integrated circuits, semiconductor networks, etc.
HQ: Hermes Microvision, Inc.
7f, 18, Pu Ting Rd.,
Hsinchu City 30072
366 692-29

(P-18873)
HI RELBLITY MCRELECTRONICS INC
1804 Mccarthy Blvd, Milpitas (95035-7410)
PHONE...................................408 764-5500
Zafar Malik, *President*
Alex Barrios, *Vice Pres*
Larry Jorstad, *CTO*
Catherine Tijo, *Finance Mgr*
EMP: 32
SALES (est): 4.7MM
SALES (corp-wide): 87.1MM **Privately Held**
SIC: 3674 7389 Semiconductors & related devices; inspection & testing services
HQ: Silicon Turnkey Solutions, Inc.
1804 Mccarthy Blvd
Milpitas CA 95035
408 904-0200

(P-18874)
HI/FN INC (DH)
48720 Kato Rd, Fremont (94538-7312)
PHONE...................................408 778-2944
Albert E Sisto, *Ch of Bd*
William R Walker, *CFO*
Russell S Dietz, *Vice Pres*
John Matze, *Vice Pres*
Dr Jiebing Wang, *Vice Pres*
EMP: 14
SQ FT: 20,000
SALES (est): 6.2MM
SALES (corp-wide): 420.3MM **Publicly Held**
WEB: www.hifn.com
SIC: 3674 7372 Semiconductors & related devices; prepackaged software
HQ: Exar Corporation
1060 Rincon Cir
San Jose CA 95131
669 265-6100

(P-18875)
HITECH GLOBAL DISTRIBUTION LLC
2059 Camden Ave Ste 160, San Jose (95124-2024)
PHONE...................................408 781-8043
Samantha Alimardani, *General Mgr*

Cyrus Mousavi, *General Mgr*
◆ **EMP:** 29
SALES (est): 6.4MM **Privately Held**
WEB: www.hitechglobal.com
SIC: 3674 Semiconductors & related devices

(P-18876)
HOTECH CORPORATION
9320 Santa Anita Ave # 100, Rancho Cucamonga (91730-6147)
PHONE...................................909 987-8828
David Ho, *President*
Hai CHI Yang, *Manager*
▲ **EMP:** 20
SQ FT: 3,000
SALES (est): 1.8MM **Privately Held**
WEB: www.hotechusa.com
SIC: 3674 Semiconductors & related devices

(P-18877)
I2A TECHNOLOGIES INC
3399 W Warren Ave, Fremont (94538-6424)
PHONE...................................510 770-0322
Victor Batinovich, *President*
Ann Batinovich, *Ch of Bd*
▲ **EMP:** 40
SQ FT: 35,000
SALES (est): 15.3MM **Privately Held**
SIC: 3674 8711 Semiconductors & related devices; engineering services

(P-18878)
IC SENSORS INC
45738 Northport Loop W, Fremont (94538-6476)
PHONE...................................510 498-1570
Frank Guibone, *President*
Victor Chatigny, *General Mgr*
EMP: 100
SQ FT: 34,000
SALES (est): 7.9MM
SALES (corp-wide): 13.1B **Privately Held**
SIC: 3674 8711 3625 Semiconductors & related devices; engineering services; switches, electronic applications
HQ: Measurement Specialties, Inc.
1000 Lucas Way
Hampton VA 23666
757 766-1500

(P-18879)
ICHIA USA INC
509 Telegraph Canyon Rd, Chula Vista (91910-6436)
PHONE...................................619 482-2222
Simon Goh, *General Mgr*
▲ **EMP:** 200
SQ FT: 3,000
SALES (est): 22.4MM
SALES (corp-wide): 238.5MM **Privately Held**
WEB: www.ichia.com
SIC: 3674 Semiconductors & related devices
PA: Ichia Technologies, Inc.
268, Hua Ya 2nd Rd.,
Taoyuan City TAY 33383
339 733-45

(P-18880)
ICHOR SYSTEMS INC (HQ)
3185 Laurelview Ct, Fremont (94538-6535)
PHONE...................................510 897-5200
Thomas M Rohrs, *CEO*
Maurice Carson, *President*
Peter English, *President*
Mark Hutson, *COO*
Phil R Barros, *CTO*
▲ **EMP:** 20
SALES: 371.3MM
SALES (corp-wide): 655.8MM **Publicly Held**
SIC: 3674 Semiconductors & related devices
PA: Ichor Holdings, Ltd.
3185 Laurelview Ct
Fremont CA 94538
510 897-5200

(P-18881)
IKANOS COMMUNICATIONS INC (DH)
5775 Morehouse Dr, San Diego (92121-1714)
PHONE...................................858 587-1121
Rahul Patel, *President*
Sanjay Mehta, *CFO*
Kevin Wang, *Director*
Ning Zhang, *Director*
Chen Shen, *Contractor*
▲ **EMP:** 155
SQ FT: 73,500
SALES: 48.3MM
SALES (corp-wide): 22.2B **Publicly Held**
WEB: www.ikanos.com
SIC: 3674 Semiconductors & related devices
HQ: Qualcomm Atheros, Inc.
1700 Technology Dr
San Jose CA 95110
408 773-5200

(P-18882)
ILLINOIS TOOL WORKS INC
Also Called: ITW-Opto Diode
1260 Calle Suerte, Camarillo (93012-8053)
PHONE...................................805 499-0335
Russ Dahl, *General Mgr*
EMP: 40
SALES (corp-wide): 14.3B **Publicly Held**
SIC: 3674 Semiconductors & related devices
PA: Illinois Tool Works Inc.
155 Harlem Ave
Glenview IL 60025
847 724-7500

(P-18883)
ILLINOIS TOOL WORKS INC
ITW Rippey
5000 Hillsdale Cir, El Dorado Hills (95762-5706)
PHONE...................................916 939-4332
Brent Best, *Manager*
EMP: 69
SALES (corp-wide): 14.3B **Publicly Held**
SIC: 3674 Semiconductors & related devices
PA: Illinois Tool Works Inc.
155 Harlem Ave
Glenview IL 60025
847 724-7500

(P-18884)
IMAGERLABS INC
1995 S Myrtle Ave, Monrovia (91016-4854)
PHONE...................................949 310-9560
Eugene Atlas, *CEO*
Mark Wadsworth, *CTO*
◆ **EMP:** 10
SQ FT: 4,500
SALES: 750K **Privately Held**
SIC: 3674 Infrared sensors, solid state; radiation sensors; ultra-violet sensors, solid state

(P-18885)
INFINEON TECH AMERICAS CORP (HQ)
Also Called: I R
101 N Pacific Coast Hwy, El Segundo (90245-4318)
PHONE...................................310 726-8000
Oleg Khaykin, *CEO*
Gary Tanner, *COO*
Ilan Daskal, *CFO*
Fred Farris, *Vice Pres*
Alex Garcia, *Vice Pres*
▲ **EMP:** 900
SALES (est): 1.1B
SALES (corp-wide): 8.3B **Privately Held**
WEB: www.irf.com
SIC: 3674 Integrated circuits, semiconductor networks, etc.
PA: Infineon Technologies Ag
Am Campeon 1-15
Neubiberg 85579
892 340-

(P-18886)
INFINEON TECH AMERICAS CORP
233 Kansas St, El Segundo (90245-4316)
PHONE...................................951 375-2254

Alvin Guzon, *Vice Pres*
Tim Phillips, *Vice Pres*
Jim Jiang, *Exec Dir*
Rick Sivon, *Exec Dir*
Chris Toth, *Exec Dir*
EMP: 534
SALES (corp-wide): 8.3B **Privately Held**
SIC: 3674 Integrated circuits, semiconductor networks, etc.
HQ: Infineon Technologies Americas Corp.
101 N Pacific Coast Hwy
El Segundo CA 90245
310 726-8000

(P-18887)
INFINEON TECH AMERICAS CORP
Crydom Controls
233 Kansas St, El Segundo (90245-4316)
PHONE...................................310 726-8000
Derek Lidow, *Manager*
EMP: 1200
SALES (corp-wide): 8.3B **Privately Held**
SIC: 3674 Semiconductor circuit networks; rectifiers, solid state
HQ: Infineon Technologies Americas Corp.
101 N Pacific Coast Hwy
El Segundo CA 90245
310 726-8000

(P-18888)
INFINEON TECH AMERICAS CORP
640 N Mccarthy Blvd, Milpitas (95035-5113)
PHONE...................................866 951-9519
Robert Lefort, *President*
Daniel Lai, *Engineer*
Christian Rosengarten, *Purchasing*
Spencer Allan, *Regl Sales Mgr*
Kathlee Kok, *Director*
EMP: 1200
SALES (corp-wide): 8.3B **Privately Held**
SIC: 3674 Semiconductors & related devices
HQ: Infineon Technologies Americas Corp.
101 N Pacific Coast Hwy
El Segundo CA 90245
310 726-8000

(P-18889)
INFINEON TECH AMERICAS CORP
Interntnal Rctfier/Hexget Amer
41915 Business Park Dr, Temecula (92590-3637)
PHONE...................................951 375-6008
Marc Rougee, *Branch Mgr*
Dale Suddon, *Treasurer*
Patrick Schreffler, *Vice Pres*
Marti Jarsey, *Pharmacy Dir*
Tony Dugdale, *Exec Dir*
EMP: 710
SALES (corp-wide): 8.3B **Privately Held**
WEB: www.irf.com
SIC: 3674 3577 Computer peripheral equipment; semiconductor circuit networks
HQ: Infineon Technologies Americas Corp.
101 N Pacific Coast Hwy
El Segundo CA 90245
310 726-8000

(P-18890)
INFINEON TECH N AMER CORP (DH)
640 N Mccarthy Blvd, Milpitas (95035-5113)
PHONE...................................408 503-2642
Robert Lefort, *President*
Andrew Prillwitz, *CFO*
Alexander Peschke, *Vice Pres*
Yaneth Hernandez, *Executive Asst*
Diana Quintana, *Admin Asst*
EMP: 500
SQ FT: 400,000
SALES: 719MM
SALES (corp-wide): 8.3B **Privately Held**
WEB: www.infineon-ncs.com
SIC: 3674 Semiconductors & related devices
HQ: Infineon Technologies Us Holdco Inc.
640 N Mccarthy Blvd
Milpitas CA 95035
866 951-9519

(P-18891)
INFINEON TECH US HOLDCO INC (HQ)
Also Called: Infineon Technologies AG
640 N Mccarthy Blvd, Milpitas
(95035-5113)
PHONE....................866 951-9519
David Lewis, *CEO*
Stefan Marquardt, *Partner*
Andrew Prillwitz, *CFO*
Gernot Langguth, *Sr Corp Ofcr*
Kurt Mayer, *Business Dir*
EMP: 75
SQ FT: 62,874
SALES (est): 739.1MM
SALES (corp-wide): 8.3B **Privately Held**
SIC: 3674 Integrated circuits, semiconductor networks, etc.
PA: Infineon Technologies Ag
Am Campeon 1-15
Neubiberg 85579
892 340-

(P-18892)
INFINERA CORPORATION
1338 Bordeaux Dr, Sunnyvale
(94089-1005)
PHONE....................408 572-5200
Debby Schuster, *Branch Mgr*
Chris Liou, *Vice Pres*
Dave Mehuys, *Vice Pres*
Serge Melle, *Vice Pres*
Jeffrey Bostak, *Executive*
EMP: 20
SALES (corp-wide): 740.7MM **Publicly Held**
SIC: 3674 Light sensitive devices
PA: Infinera Corporation
140 Caspian Ct
Sunnyvale CA 94089
408 572-5200

(P-18893)
INFORMATION STORAGE DVCS INC
2727 N 1st St, San Jose (95134-2029)
PHONE....................408 943-6666
David L Angel, *CEO*
Jock Ochiltree, *President*
Felix J Rosengarten, *CFO*
James Brennan Jr, *Vice Pres*
Michael Geilhufe, *Vice Pres*
▲ EMP: 165
SQ FT: 60,000
SALES (est): 10.7MM
SALES (corp-wide): 1.5B **Privately Held**
WEB: www.isd.com
SIC: 3674 Semiconductors & related devices
PA: Winbond Electronics Corp.
8, Keya 1st Rd.,
Taichung City 42881
425 218-168

(P-18894)
INFRAREDVISION TECHNOLOGY CORP
Also Called: L-3 Communications Infrared
140 Industrial Way, Buellton (93427-9507)
P.O. Box 1727 (93427-1727)
PHONE....................805 686-8848
James Giacobazzi, *President*
Kenneth Hay, *Vice Pres*
Adrew Wallis, *Engineer*
EMP: 20
SALES (est): 2.2MM
SALES (corp-wide): 671MM **Publicly Held**
SIC: 3674 Infrared sensors, solid state
HQ: Lumasense Technologies Holdings, Inc.
3301 Leonard Ct
Santa Clara CA 95054
408 727-1600

(P-18895)
INITIO CORPORATION
2050 Ringwood Ave Ste A, San Jose
(95131-1783)
PHONE....................408 943-3189
Jui liang, *President*
▲ EMP: 26
SQ FT: 14,000

SALES (est): 4.6MM
SALES (corp-wide): 11MM **Privately Held**
SIC: 3674 7371 3577 Semiconductors & related devices; custom computer programming services; computer peripheral equipment
PA: Initio Semiconductor Corporation
8f, 192, Jui Kuang Rd.,
Taipei City TAP 11491
287 516-377

(P-18896)
INNODISK USA CORPORATION
42996 Osgood Rd, Fremont (94539-5627)
PHONE....................510 770-9421
Victor Le, *President*
▲ EMP: 30
SALES (est): 3.4MM
SALES (corp-wide): 217.4MM **Privately Held**
SIC: 3674 Random access memory (RAM)
PA: Innodisk Corporation
5f, 237, Ta Tung Rd., Sec. 1,
New Taipei City 22161
277 033-000

(P-18897)
INNOPHASE INC
6815 Flanders Dr Ste 150, San Diego
(92121-3925)
PHONE....................619 541-8280
Yang Xu, *CEO*
Thomas Lee, *Vice Pres*
EMP: 100 EST: 2011
SALES (est): 8.7MM **Privately Held**
SIC: 3674 Semiconductors & related devices

(P-18898)
INNOVATIVE MICRO TECH INC
Also Called: IMT Analytical
75 Robin Hill Rd, Goleta (93117-3108)
PHONE....................805 681-2807
Craig H Ensley, *President*
Peter Altavilla, *CFO*
Richard Brossart, *Vice Pres*
Dave Chrishna, *Vice Pres*
Chris Gudeman, *Vice Pres*
EMP: 115
SQ FT: 130,000
SALES (est): 20MM **Privately Held**
WEB: www.imtmems.com
SIC: 3674 Semiconductors & related devices

(P-18899)
INPHENIX INC
250 N Mines Rd, Livermore (94551-2238)
PHONE....................925 606-8809
David Eu, *President*
Tao Huang, *Engineer*
Vincent Ji, *Engineer*
Zhenghua Wu, *Engineer*
Steve Vitkovsky, *Sales Mgr*
EMP: 25
SALES (est): 5.9MM **Privately Held**
WEB: www.inphenix.com
SIC: 3674 Semiconductors & related devices

(P-18900)
INPHI CORPORATION (PA)
2953 Bunker Hill Ln # 300, Santa Clara
(95054-1131)
PHONE....................408 217-7300
Ford Tamer, *President*
Diosdado P Banatao, *Ch of Bd*
John Edmunds, *CFO*
Charles Roach, *Senior VP*
Ron Torten, *Senior VP*
EMP: 229
SQ FT: 57,914
SALES: 348.2MM **Publicly Held**
WEB: www.inphi-corp.com
SIC: 3674 Integrated circuits, semiconductor networks, etc.

(P-18901)
INPHI INTERNATIONAL PTE LTD
112 S Lakeview Canyon Rd, Westlake Village (91362-3925)
PHONE....................805 719-2300
Ford Tamer, *President*
John Edmunds, *CFO*
EMP: 21

SALES (est): 922.2K **Privately Held**
SIC: 3674 Semiconductors & related devices

(P-18902)
INSILIXA INC
1000 Hamlin Ct, Sunnyvale (94089-1400)
PHONE....................408 809-3000
Arjang Hassibi, *CEO*
Nader Gamini, *COO*
EMP: 12
SQ FT: 1,500
SALES (est): 2.6MM **Privately Held**
SIC: 3674 Semiconductors & related devices

(P-18903)
INTEGRA TECH SILICON VLY LLC (DH)
1635 Mccarthy Blvd, Milpitas (95035-7415)
PHONE....................408 618-8700
Matt Bergeron, *CEO*
Joe Foerstel, *Vice Pres*
Joseph Foerstel, *Vice Pres*
Benedicta Eli, *Program Mgr*
Irma Marquez, *Program Mgr*
EMP: 109
SQ FT: 48,000
SALES (est): 22.4MM **Privately Held**
WEB: www.corwil.com
SIC: 3674 3825 Semiconductors & related devices; semiconductor test equipment
HQ: Integra Technologies Llc
3450 N Rock Rd Ste 100
Wichita KS 67226
316 630-6800

(P-18904)
INTEGRA TECHNOLOGIES INC
321 Coral Cir, El Segundo (90245-4620)
PHONE....................310 606-0855
Paul Aken, *President*
Jeff Burger, *Vice Pres*
Gerry Obrien, *Vice Pres*
Apet Barsegyan, *Engineer*
Richard Keshishian, *Senior Engr*
EMP: 50 EST: 1997
SQ FT: 15,000
SALES (est): 17.5MM **Privately Held**
WEB: www.integratech.com
SIC: 3674 Modules, solid state; transistors

(P-18905)
INTEGRA TECHNOLOGIES LLC
Also Called: Viko Test Labs
2006 Martin Ave, Santa Clara
(95050-2700)
PHONE....................408 923-7300
Ed Nunes, *Principal*
George Liu, *Vice Pres*
Swee Khim, *CTO*
Jerry Kirby, *VP Sales*
Jinesh Desai, *Manager*
EMP: 100 **Privately Held**
WEB: www.adaptivecircuits.com
SIC: 3674 Semiconductors & related devices
HQ: Integra Technologies Silicon Valley Llc
1635 Mccarthy Blvd
Milpitas CA 95035

(P-18906)
INTEGRATED DEVICE TECH INC (PA)
Also Called: I D T
6024 Silver Creek Vly Rd, San Jose
(95138-1011)
P.O. Box 67071, Scotts Valley (95067-7071)
PHONE....................408 284-8200
Gregory L Waters, *President*
Ken Kannappan, *Ch of Bd*
Brian C White, *CFO*
Norman Taffe, *Bd of Directors*
Matthew D Brandalise,
▲ EMP: 277
SQ FT: 263,000
SALES: 842.7MM **Publicly Held**
WEB: www.idt.com
SIC: 3674 Integrated circuits, semiconductor networks, etc.

(P-18907)
INTEGRATED DEVICE TECH INC
Purchase Office
6024 Silver Creek Vly, San Jose
(95138-1011)
PHONE....................408 284-1433
Regi John, *Vice Pres*
EMP: 291
SALES (corp-wide): 842.7MM **Publicly Held**
WEB: www.idt.com
SIC: 3674 Semiconductors & related devices
PA: Integrated Device Technology, Inc.
6024 Silver Creek Vly Rd
San Jose CA 95138
408 284-8200

(P-18908)
INTEGRATED MATERIALS INC
Also Called: IMI
135 Nicholson Ln, San Jose (95134-1359)
PHONE....................408 964-7700
Daniel Rubin, *President*
Kirk Johnson, *CFO*
Sang In Lee, *CTO*
▲ EMP: 20
SQ FT: 12,000
SALES (est): 2MM
SALES (corp-wide): 850.3MM **Privately Held**
WEB: www.integratedmaterials.com
SIC: 3674 Semiconductors & related devices
HQ: Ferrotec (Usa) Corporation
33 Constitution Dr
Bedford NH 03110
603 472-6800

(P-18909)
INTEGRTED SILICON SOLUTION INC (PA)
1623 Buckeye Dr, Milpitas (95035-7423)
PHONE....................408 969-6600
Jimmy Lee, *CEO*
KY Han, *Vice Chairman*
Scott Howarth, *President*
Sanjiv Asthana, *Vice Pres*
Allen Chang, *Vice Pres*
▲ EMP: 57
SQ FT: 55,612
SALES (est): 215.8MM **Privately Held**
WEB: www.issi.com
SIC: 3674 Semiconductors & related devices

(P-18910)
INTEL AMERICAS INC (HQ)
2200 Mission College Blvd, Santa Clara
(95054-1549)
PHONE....................408 765-8080
Craig R Barrett, *CEO*
▲ EMP: 47
SALES (est): 11.5MM
SALES (corp-wide): 62.7B **Publicly Held**
SIC: 3674 Semiconductors & related devices
PA: Intel Corporation
2200 Mission College Blvd
Santa Clara CA 95054
408 765-8080

(P-18911)
INTEL CORPORATION
1200 Creekside Dr, Folsom (95630-3431)
PHONE....................916 943-6809
Thomas Lyda, *Design Engr*
Georgna Gonzalez-Hall, *Technology*
Sheng Huang, *Senior Engr*
Joe Li, *Senior Engr*
Brent Chartrand, *Manager*
EMP: 58
SALES (corp-wide): 62.7B **Publicly Held**
SIC: 3674 Microprocessors
PA: Intel Corporation
2200 Mission College Blvd
Santa Clara CA 95054
408 765-8080

(P-18912)
INTEL CORPORATION
111 Theory Ste 100, Irvine (92617-3020)
PHONE....................408 765-8080
Van Truong, *Design Engr*
Elvyn Donawerth, *Engineer*
EMP: 11

P R O D U C T S & S V C S

SALES (corp-wide): 62.7B Publicly Held
SIC: 3674 Microprocessors
PA: Intel Corporation
2200 Mission College Blvd
Santa Clara CA 95054
408 765-8080

(P-18913)
INTEL CORPORATION
2300 Mission College Blvd, Santa Clara
(95054-1531)
PHONE.................................408 425-8398
Ziya MA, *Manager*
EMP: 200
SALES (corp-wide): 62.7B Publicly Held
SIC: 3674 Semiconductors & related devices
PA: Intel Corporation
2200 Mission College Blvd
Santa Clara CA 95054
408 765-8080

(P-18914)
INTEL CORPORATION
44235 Nobel Dr, Fremont (94538-3178)
PHONE.................................510 651-9841
Mike Ricci, *General Mgr*
Doug Gambetta, *Engineer*
EMP: 35
SALES (corp-wide): 62.7B Publicly Held
WEB: www.intel.com
SIC: 3674 Microprocessors
PA: Intel Corporation
2200 Mission College Blvd
Santa Clara CA 95054
408 765-8080

(P-18915)
INTEL CORPORATION
1900 Prairie City Rd, Folsom (95630-9599)
PHONE.................................916 356-8080
Conrad Wiederhold, *Manager*
Dan Lecam, *President*
Suzanne Listar, *President*
Gregorio Martinez, *President*
Alan Bumgarner, *Program Mgr*
EMP: 57
SALES (corp-wide): 62.7B Publicly Held
WEB: www.intel.com
SIC: 3674 3572 3577 Microprocessors;
computer storage devices; computer peripheral equipment
PA: Intel Corporation
2200 Mission College Blvd
Santa Clara CA 95054
408 765-8080

(P-18916)
INTEL FEDERAL LLC
2200 Mission College Blvd, Santa Clara
(95054-1549)
PHONE.................................302 644-3756
David Patterson,
Ron Dickel, *Vice Pres*
Ravi Jacob, *Vice Pres*
Steve Lund, *Vice Pres*
EMP: 20
SALES (est): 2MM
SALES (corp-wide): 62.7B Publicly Held
SIC: 3674 Semiconductors & related devices
PA: Intel Corporation
2200 Mission College Blvd
Santa Clara CA 95054
408 765-8080

(P-18917)
INTEL INTERNATIONAL LIMITED (HQ)
2200 Mission College Blvd, Santa Clara
(95054-1549)
PHONE.................................408 765-8080
Lee Johnny, *Principal*
EMP: 15
SALES (est): 2.9MM
SALES (corp-wide): 62.7B Publicly Held
SIC: 3674 3571 Memories, solid state; microprocessors; computers, digital, analog
or hybrid
PA: Intel Corporation
2200 Mission College Blvd
Santa Clara CA 95054
408 765-8080

(P-18918)
INTEL NETWORK SYSTEMS INC
3600 Juliette Ln, Santa Clara (95054-1540)
PHONE.................................408 765-8080
Urvi Desai, *Software Engr*
Sang I Lee, *Software Engr*
Milind Bhat, *Engineer*
Rufo De Francisco, *Engineer*
Joel Medlock, *Engineer*
EMP: 26
SALES (corp-wide): 62.7B Publicly Held
SIC: 3674 Semiconductors & related devices
HQ: Intel Network Systems Inc
77 Reed Rd
Hudson MA 01749
978 553-4000

(P-18919)
INTEL PUERTO RICO INC
2200 Mission College Blvd, Santa Clara
(95054-1549)
PHONE.................................408 765-8080
Craig Barrett, *President*
Patrick Terranova,
EMP: 50
SALES (est): 4.6MM
SALES (corp-wide): 62.7B Publicly Held
WEB: www.intel.com
SIC: 3674 3571 Memories, solid state; microprocessors; computers, digital, analog
or hybrid
PA: Intel Corporation
2200 Mission College Blvd
Santa Clara CA 95054
408 765-8080

(P-18920)
INTERCONNECT SYSTEMS INC (DH)
Also Called: I S I
741 Flynn Rd, Camarillo (93012-8056)
PHONE.................................805 482-2870
William P Miller, *President*
Louis Buldain, *Vice Pres*
Glen Griswold, *Vice Pres*
▲ EMP: 90
SQ FT: 48,000
SALES (est): 50.9MM
SALES (corp-wide): 42.9B Privately Held
WEB: www.isipkg.com
SIC: 3674 Computer logic modules
HQ: Molex, Llc
2222 Wellington Ct
Lisle IL 60532
630 969-4550

(P-18921)
INTERMOLECULAR INC (PA)
3011 N 1st St, San Jose (95134-2004)
PHONE.................................408 582-5700
Chris Kramer, *President*
Bruce M McWilliams, *Ch of Bd*
C Richard Neely, *CFO*
Bill Roeschlein, *CFO*
Marvin D Burkett, *Bd of Directors*
EMP: 175
SQ FT: 146,000
SALES: 37.2MM Publicly Held
WEB: www.intermolecular.com
SIC: 3674 Integrated circuits, semiconductor networks, etc.

(P-18922)
INTERNATIONAL RECTIFIER CORP (PA)
17885 Von Karman Ave # 100, Irvine
(92614-5256)
PHONE.................................949 453-1008
Fax: 949 453-8748
EMP: 23
SQ FT: 6,000
SALES (est): 3.9MM Privately Held
SIC: 3674 3672

(P-18923)
INTERNATIONAL RECTIFIER HIREL
2520 Junction Ave, San Jose (95134-1902)
PHONE.................................408 944-0239
Granville C Rains, *Manager*
Ilan Daskal, *CFO*
Rene Figueroa, *Engineer*
Sadiki Jordan, *Engineer*
Adam Winterstrom, *Engineer*

EMP: 110
SALES (corp-wide): 8.3B Privately Held
WEB: www.irf.com
SIC: 3674 Semiconductors & related devices
HQ: International Rectifier Hirel Products, Inc.
2520 Junction Ave
San Jose CA

(P-18924)
INTERNTIONAL SEMICDTR TECH INC
3099 Alexis Dr, Palo Alto (94304-1304)
PHONE.................................650 941-7096
Raman K Rau, *President*
EMP: 22
SQ FT: 2,000
SALES (est): 1.4MM Privately Held
SIC: 3674 Semiconductor circuit networks

(P-18925)
INTEST CORPORATION
47777 Warm Springs Blvd, Fremont
(94539-7470)
PHONE.................................408 678-9123
Dale Christman, *Manager*
Deborah Cook, *Controller*
Rick Baze, *Manager*
EMP: 45
SALES (corp-wide): 66.8MM Publicly Held
WEB: www.intest.com
SIC: 3674 Semiconductors & related devices
PA: Intest Corporation
804 E Gate Dr Ste 200
Mount Laurel NJ 08054
856 505-8800

(P-18926)
INTEST SILICON VALLEY CORP
47777 Warm Springs Blvd, Fremont
(94539-7470)
PHONE.................................408 678-9123
Dale Christman, *General Mgr*
Hugh Tregan Jr, *CFO*
Leonard Torres, *Manager*
EMP: 45
SALES (est): 6.1MM
SALES (corp-wide): 66.8MM Publicly Held
SIC: 3674 Semiconductors & related devices
PA: Intest Corporation
804 E Gate Dr Ste 200
Mount Laurel NJ 08054
856 505-8800

(P-18927)
INVECAS INC
2901 Tasman Dr Ste 111, Santa Clara
(95054-1137)
PHONE.................................408 758-5636
Dasaradha Gude, *CEO*
Prasad Chalasani, *President*
Khanh Le, *President*
Jayanta Lahiri, *Vice Pres*
Ian Williams, *Vice Pres*
EMP: 25
SQ FT: 8,536
SALES (est): 3.3MM Privately Held
SIC: 3674 Semiconductors & related devices

(P-18928)
INVENLUX CORPORATION
168 Mason Way Ste B5, City of Industry
(91746-2339)
PHONE.................................626 277-4163
Chunhui Yan, *President*
EMP: 29
SQ FT: 18,000
SALES (est): 4.4MM Privately Held
SIC: 3674 Light emitting diodes

(P-18929)
INVENSAS CORPORATION
3025 Orchard Pkwy, San Jose
(95134-2017)
PHONE.................................408 324-5100
Craig Mitchell, *President*
Javier Delacruz, *President*
Kazumi Allen, *Vice Pres*
Scott F McGrath, *Engineer*

Kevin Chen, *Director*
EMP: 33
SALES (est): 7.3MM
SALES (corp-wide): 373.7MM Publicly Held
SIC: 3674 Integrated circuits, semiconductor networks, etc.
HQ: Tessera Technologies, Inc.
3025 Orchard Pkwy
San Jose CA 95134
408 321-6000

(P-18930)
IOG PRODUCTS LLC
1025 N Brand Blvd Ste 301, Glendale
(91202-3634)
PHONE.................................818 350-5070
Mark Newgreen, *CFO*
Brandon Collier, *Sales Staff*
EMP: 15
SALES (est): 2.5MM Privately Held
SIC: 3674 3669 Radiation sensors; visual
communication systems

(P-18931)
IQ-ANALOG CORPORATION
12348 High Bluff Dr # 110, San Diego
(92130-3547)
PHONE.................................858 200-0388
Michael S Kappes, *President*
Randy Wayland, *Vice Pres*
Nitin Nidhi, *Engineer*
Felicia Kappes, *Persnl Mgr*
EMP: 25
SALES (est): 3.4MM Privately Held
SIC: 3674 Semiconductors & related devices

(P-18932)
IRVINE SENSORS CORPORATION
3001 Red Hill Ave 3-105, Costa Mesa
(92626-4506)
PHONE.................................714 444-8700
John C Carson, *President*
James Justice, *Admin Sec*
EMP: 43 EST: 2013
SALES (est): 4MM Privately Held
SIC: 3674 8731 Semiconductors & related
devices; electronic research

(P-18933)
IWATT INC (DH)
Also Called: Dialog Semiconductor
675 Campbell Tech Pkwy # 150, Campbell
(95008-5053)
PHONE.................................408 374-4200
Ronald P Edgerton, *CEO*
James V McCanna, *CFO*
Alex Sinar, *Vice Pres*
Kaj Den Daas, *Principal*
Brian McDonald, *Principal*
▲ EMP: 45
SQ FT: 26,000
SALES: 50MM
SALES (corp-wide): 1.3B Privately Held
WEB: www.iwatt.com
SIC: 3674 Semiconductors & related devices
HQ: Dialog Semiconductor Gmbh
Neue Str. 95
Kirchheim Unter Teck 73230
702 180-50

(P-18934)
IXYS LLC (HQ)
1590 Buckeye Dr, Milpitas (95035-7418)
PHONE.................................408 457-9000
Nathan Zommer, *CEO*
Uzi Sasson, *President*
Dat Huynh, *Technology*
EMP: 94
SQ FT: 51,000
SALES: 322.1MM
SALES (corp-wide): 1.2B Publicly Held
WEB: www.ixys.com
SIC: 3674 Integrated circuits, semiconductor networks, etc.
PA: Littelfuse, Inc.
8755 W Higgins Rd Ste 500
Chicago IL 60631
773 628-1000

▲ = Import ▼=Export
◆ =Import/Export

(P-18935)
IXYS INTGRTD CRCTS DIV AV INC
145 Columbia, Aliso Viejo (92656-1413)
PHONE..............................949 831-4622
Nathan Zommer, *Ch of Bd*
Uzi Sasson, *CFO*
Bret Howe, *Design Engr*
Bret Burns, *Engineer*
EMP: 26
SQ FT: 28,000
SALES (est): 4.4MM
SALES (corp-wide): 1.2B **Publicly Held**
WEB: www.ixys.com
SIC: 3674 7389 Microcircuits, integrated (semiconductor); design services
HQ: Ixys, Llc
  1590 Buckeye Dr
  Milpitas CA 95035
  408 457-9000

(P-18936)
IXYS LONG BEACH INC (DH)
2500 Mira Mar Ave, Long Beach (90815-1758)
PHONE..............................562 296-6584
Nathan Zommer, *CEO*
Arnold Agbayani, *CFO*
▲ EMP: 25
SQ FT: 20,000
SALES (est): 4.4MM
SALES (corp-wide): 1.2B **Publicly Held**
SIC: 3674 5065 Semiconductors & related devices; electronic parts & equipment
HQ: Ixys, Llc
  1590 Buckeye Dr
  Milpitas CA 95035
  408 457-9000

(P-18937)
JA SOLAR USA INC
2570 N 1st St Ste 360, San Jose (95131-1029)
PHONE..............................408 586-0000
Jian Xie, *CEO*
Anthea Chung, *CFO*
Ming Yang, *Vice Pres*
▲ EMP: 10
SQ FT: 6,527
SALES (est): 4MM **Privately Held**
SIC: 3674 Solar cells

(P-18938)
JAZZ SEMICONDUCTOR INC (DH)
Also Called: Towerjazz
4321 Jamboree Rd, Newport Beach (92660-3007)
PHONE..............................949 435-8000
Amir Elstein, *Ch of Bd*
Itzhak Edrei, *President*
Rafi Mor, *COO*
Oren Shirazi, *CFO*
Ilan Rabinovich, *Vice Pres*
▲ EMP: 700
SQ FT: 300,000
SALES (est): 221.4MM
SALES (corp-wide): 1.3B **Privately Held**
WEB: www.jazzsemi.com
SIC: 3674 Wafers (semiconductor devices)

(P-18939)
JINKOSOLAR (US) INC
595 Market St Ste 2200, San Francisco (94105-2834)
PHONE..............................415 402-0502
Duan Yang Chen, *Accounts Mgr*
◆ EMP: 13
SALES (est): 16.3MM
SALES (corp-wide): 16.7MM **Privately Held**
SIC: 3674 Semiconductors & related devices
PA: Jinkosolar (U.S.) Holding Inc.
  595 Market St Ste 2200
  San Francisco CA 94105
  415 402-0502

(P-18940)
K LIVE
Also Called: Bulb Star
300 W Valley Blvd 33, Alhambra (91803-3338)
PHONE..............................626 289-2885
Ken Lively, *CEO*

▲ EMP: 10
SALES: 2MM **Privately Held**
WEB: www.bulbstar.com
SIC: 3674 Light emitting diodes

(P-18941)
KEYSSA INC (PA)
655 Campbell Technology P, Campbell (95008-5060)
PHONE..............................408 637-2300
Tony Fadell, *CEO*
Gordon Almquist, *Vice Pres*
Nick Antonopoulos, *Vice Pres*
Srikanth Gondi, *Vice Pres*
Roger Isaac, *Vice Pres*
EMP: 37
SALES (est): 9.5MM **Privately Held**
SIC: 3674 3577 Semiconductors & related devices; computer peripheral equipment

(P-18942)
KISCO CONFORMAL COATING LLC (PA)
6292 San Ignacio Ave C, San Jose (95119-1385)
PHONE..............................408 224-6533
Yoshiya Wasa, *Mng Member*
Takatoshi Masuda, *Mng Member*
▲ EMP: 10
SALES (est): 1.3MM **Privately Held**
SIC: 3674 Light emitting diodes

(P-18943)
KLA-TENCOR ASIA-PAC DIST CORP
1 Technology Dr, Milpitas (95035-7916)
PHONE..............................408 875-4144
Mark Nordstrom, *Principal*
▲ EMP: 32
SALES (est): 3.8MM
SALES (corp-wide): 4B **Publicly Held**
WEB: www.tencor.com
SIC: 3674 Semiconductors & related devices
PA: Kla-Tencor Corporation
  1 Technology Dr
  Milpitas CA 95035
  408 875-3000

(P-18944)
KOPIN CORPORATION
501 Tevis Trl, Hollister (95023-9367)
PHONE..............................831 636-5556
Jeff Jacobson, *Manager*
EMP: 45
SALES (corp-wide): 27.8MM **Publicly Held**
WEB: www.kopin.com
SIC: 3674 Semiconductors & related devices
PA: Kopin Corporation
  125 North Dr
  Westborough MA 01581
  508 870-5959

(P-18945)
KSM CORP
1959 Concourse Dr, San Jose (95131-1708)
PHONE..............................408 514-2400
Jooswan Kim, *CEO*
Harvinder P Singh, *President*
EMP: 500
SQ FT: 18,000
SALES: 100MM
SALES (corp-wide): 78.5MM **Privately Held**
SIC: 3674 Semiconductors & related devices
PA: Ksm Component Co., Ltd.
  90 Wolha-Ro 589beon-Gil, Haseong-Myeon
  Gimpo 10011
  319 800-181

(P-18946)
KYOCERA INTERNATIONAL INC (HQ)
8611 Balboa Ave, San Diego (92123-1580)
PHONE..............................858 492-1456
Robert Whisler, *President*
William Edwards, *Vice Pres*
George Woodworth, *Vice Pres*
Eric Klein, *Admin Sec*
◆ EMP: 150

SQ FT: 16,000
SALES (est): 73.9MM
SALES (corp-wide): 14.8B **Publicly Held**
SIC: 3674 Semiconductors & related devices
PA: Kyocera Corporation
  6, Tobadonocho, Takeda, Fushimi-Ku
  Kyoto KYO 612-8
  756 043-500

(P-18947)
KYOCERA INTERNATIONAL INC
8611 Balboa Ave, San Diego (92123-1580)
PHONE..............................858 614-2581
Robert Eklund, *Branch Mgr*
EMP: 80
SALES (corp-wide): 14.8B **Publicly Held**
SIC: 3674 Integrated circuits, semiconductor networks, etc.
HQ: Kyocera International, Inc.
  8611 Balboa Ave
  San Diego CA 92123
  858 492-1456

(P-18948)
L & M ELECTRONICS
541 Taylor Way Ste 10, San Carlos (94070-6254)
PHONE..............................650 341-1608
Ed Luzzi, *President*
EMP: 15
SQ FT: 1,800
SALES: 300K **Privately Held**
SIC: 3674 8731 Solid state electronic devices; commercial physical research

(P-18949)
LAM RESEARCH CORPORATION
3590 N 1st St Ste 200, San Jose (95134-1808)
PHONE..............................408 434-6109
John Newman, *Principal*
Denis Syomin, *Engineer*
EMP: 45
SALES (corp-wide): 11B **Publicly Held**
WEB: www.lamrc.com
SIC: 3674 Semiconductors & related devices
PA: Lam Research Corporation
  4650 Cushing Pkwy
  Fremont CA 94538
  510 572-0200

(P-18950)
LAM RESEARCH CORPORATION (PA)
4650 Cushing Pkwy, Fremont (94538-6401)
PHONE..............................510 572-0200
Martin B Anstice, *CEO*
Stephen G Newberry, *Ch of Bd*
Timothy M Archer, *President*
Douglas R Bettinger, *CFO*
Sarah A O'Dowd,
EMP: 100
SALES: 11B **Publicly Held**
WEB: www.lamrc.com
SIC: 3674 Wafers (semiconductor devices)

(P-18951)
LAM RESEARCH CORPORATION
1 Portola Ave, Livermore (94551-7647)
PHONE..............................510 572-8400
EMP: 25
SALES (corp-wide): 11B **Publicly Held**
SIC: 3674 Semiconductors & related devices
PA: Lam Research Corporation
  4650 Cushing Pkwy
  Fremont CA 94538
  510 572-0200

(P-18952)
LAM RESEARCH CORPORATION
4400 Cushing Pkwy, Fremont (94538-6429)
PHONE..............................510 572-0200
Robin Mancuso Grady, *Branch Mgr*
Iqbal Shareef, *Engineer*
Helen Zhu, *Engineer*
EMP: 86
SALES (corp-wide): 11B **Publicly Held**
WEB: www.lamrc.com
SIC: 3674 Semiconductors & related devices

PA: Lam Research Corporation
  4650 Cushing Pkwy
  Fremont CA 94538
  510 572-0200

(P-18953)
LANTIQ NORTH AMERICA INC
2880 Zanker Rd Ste 100, San Jose (95134-2121)
PHONE..............................408 503-8700
Richard Walther, *CEO*
John Knoll, *President*
EMP: 13
SALES (est): 1.9MM **Privately Held**
SIC: 3674 Transistors

(P-18954)
LASER OPERATIONS LLC
Also Called: Qpc Laser
15632 Roxford St, Sylmar (91342-1265)
PHONE..............................818 986-0000
Morris Lichtenstein, *CEO*
Mikhail Leibov, *President*
Robert Lammert, *Vice Pres*
Kulya Ponek, *General Mgr*
Jeffrey Ungar, *CTO*
EMP: 27
SQ FT: 40,320
SALES (est): 6.2MM **Privately Held**
SIC: 3674 Semiconductors & related devices

(P-18955)
LATTICE SEMICONDUCTOR CORP
2115 Onel Dr, San Jose (95131-2032)
PHONE..............................408 826-6000
Al Chan, *Manager*
Srinivas Perisetty, *Engineer*
Gordon Hands, *Sls & Mktg Exec*
EMP: 300
SALES (corp-wide): 385.9MM **Publicly Held**
WEB: www.latticesemi.com
SIC: 3674 Integrated circuits, semiconductor networks, etc.
PA: Lattice Semiconductor Corp
  111 Sw 5th Ave Ste 700
  Portland OR 97204
  503 268-8000

(P-18956)
LED ONE DISTRIBUTION INC (PA)
45885 Hotchkiss St, Fremont (94539-7004)
PHONE..............................510 770-1189
Jonathan Chu, *CEO*
Ivan Chu, *General Mgr*
Shen Jen WA Ng, *Admin Sec*
Sheila Hsiao, *Opers Mgr*
Susan Miller, *Marketing Mgr*
EMP: 20
SQ FT: 17,000
SALES (est): 3.5MM **Privately Held**
SIC: 3674 Light emitting diodes

(P-18957)
LEDCONN CORP
301 Thor Pl, Brea (92821-4133)
PHONE..............................714 256-2111
Tsanyu Wang, *President*
Wan Ting Huang, *CFO*
Denise Torres, *Office Admin*
Dave Rodas, *Natl Sales Mgr*
Tina Yee, *Sales Mgr*
▲ EMP: 15
SQ FT: 2,000
SALES (est): 4MM **Privately Held**
SIC: 3674 Light emitting diodes

(P-18958)
LEDENGIN INC (PA)
651 River Oaks Pkwy, San Jose (95134-1907)
PHONE..............................408 922-7200
David Tahmassebi, *President*
Seth Halio, *CFO*
Xiantao Yan, *CTO*
Kr Subramanian, *VP Opers*
▲ EMP: 35
SQ FT: 15,037
SALES (est): 8.8MM **Privately Held**
WEB: www.ledengin.com
SIC: 3674 Light emitting diodes

PRODUCTS & SVCS

(P-18959)
LEDTRONICS INC
23105 Kashiwa Ct, Torrance (90505-4026)
PHONE..................................310 534-1505
Pervaiz Lodhie, *President*
Almas Lodhie, *Vice Pres*
Eugene Enriquez, *Engineer*
Simon Song, *Engineer*
Stanley Bouchereau, *Materials Mgr*
▲ EMP: 130
SQ FT: 60,000
SALES: 13.8MM **Privately Held**
WEB: www.led.net
SIC: 3674 3825 3641 Light emitting
diodes; instruments to measure electric-
ity; electric lamps

(P-18960)
LEVEL 5 NETWORKS INC
840 W California Ave, Sunnyvale
(94086-4828)
PHONE..................................408 245-9300
Ashfaq Munshi, *CEO*
Steve Pope, *CTO*
EMP: 50
SQ FT: 12,759
SALES (est): 5MM **Privately Held**
SIC: 3674 Semiconductor diodes & recti-
fiers

(P-18961)
**LINEAR INTEGRATED SYSTEMS
INC**
4042 Clipper Ct, Fremont (94538-6540)
PHONE..................................510 490-9160
Cindy Cook Johnson, *CEO*
Tim McCune, *President*
Timothy McCune, *President*
Michael Ansberry, *Vice Pres*
Jaime Cook, *Sales Staff*
EMP: 17
SQ FT: 5,000
SALES (est): 2.8MM **Privately Held**
SIC: 3674 Integrated circuits, semiconduc-
tor networks, etc.

(P-18962)
**LINEAR TECHNOLOGY
CORPORATION**
Also Called: Linear Express
720 Sycamore Dr, Milpitas (95035-7406)
PHONE..................................408 428-2050
Quang Ndyem, *Branch Mgr*
Keith Bennett, *Engineer*
Ryan Huff, *Engineer*
Rick Bowdoin, *Purch Mgr*
David S Lee, *Director*
EMP: 14
SALES (corp-wide): 5.1B **Publicly Held**
SIC: 3674 Integrated circuits, semiconduc-
tor networks, etc.
HQ: Linear Technology Llc
1630 Mccarthy Blvd
Milpitas CA 95035
408 432-1900

(P-18963)
**LINEAR TECHNOLOGY
CORPORATION**
1530 Buckeye Dr, Milpitas (95035-7418)
PHONE..................................408 434-6237
EMP: 54
SALES (corp-wide): 5.1B **Publicly Held**
SIC: 3674 Integrated circuits, semiconduc-
tor networks, etc.
HQ: Linear Technology Llc
1630 Mccarthy Blvd
Milpitas CA 95035
408 432-1900

(P-18964)
LINEAR TECHNOLOGY LLC (HQ)
1630 Mccarthy Blvd, Milpitas (95035-7417)
PHONE..................................408 432-1900
Lothar Maier, *CEO*
Vicki A Hembree, *President*
Alexander R McCann, *COO*
Donald P Zerio, *CFO*
Robert C Dobkin, *Vice Pres*
▲ EMP: 900
SQ FT: 430,000

SALES: 1.4B
SALES (corp-wide): 5.1B **Publicly Held**
WEB: www.linear.com
SIC: 3674 Integrated circuits, semiconduc-
tor networks, etc.
PA: Analog Devices, Inc.
1 Technology Way
Norwood MA 02062
781 329-4700

(P-18965)
LINEAR TECHNOLOGY LLC
911 Olive St, Santa Barbara (93101-1406)
PHONE..................................805 965-6400
Robert Swanson, *CEO*
Kaung Htoo, *Engineer*
EMP: 54
SALES (corp-wide): 5.1B **Publicly Held**
SIC: 3674 Integrated circuits, semiconduc-
tor networks, etc.
HQ: Linear Technology Llc
1630 Mccarthy Blvd
Milpitas CA 95035
408 432-1900

(P-18966)
LINEAR TECHNOLOGY LLC
5465 Morehouse Dr Ste 155, San Diego
(92121-4713)
PHONE..................................408 432-1900
Ralf Butz, *Manager*
Kirk Albrektsen, *Sales Engr*
EMP: 54
SALES (corp-wide): 5.1B **Publicly Held**
SIC: 3674 Integrated circuits, semiconduc-
tor networks, etc.
HQ: Linear Technology Llc
1630 Mccarthy Blvd
Milpitas CA 95035
408 432-1900

(P-18967)
LION SEMICONDUCTOR INC
332 Townsend St, San Francisco
(94107-1607)
PHONE..................................415 462-4933
Wonyoung Kim, *CEO*
John Crossley, *Vice Pres*
Thomas LI, *Engineer*
Hans Meyvaert, *Engineer*
Sehyung Jeon, *Marketing Staff*
EMP: 13 EST: 2012
SALES (est): 132.9K **Privately Held**
SIC: 3674 Microcircuits, integrated (semi-
conductor)

(P-18968)
LSI CORPORATION (DH)
Also Called: Broadcom
1320 Ridder Park Dr, San Jose
(95131-2313)
PHONE..................................408 433-8000
Abhijit Y Talwalkar, *President*
D Jeffrey Richardson, *COO*
Bryon Look, *CFO*
Jean F Rankin, *Exec VP*
Gautam Srivastava, *Senior VP*
▲ EMP: 2400
SQ FT: 240,000
SALES (est): 2.5B
SALES (corp-wide): 17.6B **Publicly Held**
WEB: www.lsi.com
SIC: 3674 Microcircuits, integrated (semi-
conductor)
HQ: Avago Technologies Wireless (U.S.A.)
Manufacturing Llc
4380 Ziegler Rd
Fort Collins CO 80525
970 288-2575

(P-18969)
LSI CORPORATION
9745 Prospect Ave, Santee (92071-6209)
PHONE..................................619 312-0903
EMP: 49
SALES (corp-wide): 4.2B **Privately Held**
SIC: 3674
HQ: Lsi Corporation
1320 Ridder Park Dr
San Jose CA 95131
408 433-8000

(P-18970)
LSI CORPORATION
Also Called: LSI Logic
2 Park Plz Ste 440, Irvine (92614-2535)
PHONE..................................800 372-2447
Al Di Cicco, *Branch Mgr*
EMP: 20
SALES (corp-wide): 17.6B **Publicly Held**
SIC: 3674 Semiconductors & related de-
vices
HQ: Lsi Corporation
1320 Ridder Park Dr
San Jose CA 95131
408 433-8000

(P-18971)
LSI CORPORATION
1310 Ridder Park Dr, San Jose
(95131-2313)
PHONE..................................408 436-8379
Kay Framan, *Branch Mgr*
Trinh Tran, *Director*
EMP: 16
SALES (corp-wide): 17.6B **Publicly Held**
SIC: 3674 Semiconductors & related de-
vices
HQ: Lsi Corporation
1320 Ridder Park Dr
San Jose CA 95131
408 433-8000

(P-18972)
LUMENETIX INC
4742 Scotts Valley Dr, Scotts Valley
(95066-4231)
PHONE..................................877 805-7284
James Kingman, *CEO*
Sanjoy Ghose, *Vice Pres*
Kellie Mages, *Principal*
Herman Ferrier, *Electrical Engi*
Tom Poliquin, *Electrical Engi*
▲ EMP: 34
SALES (est): 9.8MM **Privately Held**
SIC: 3674 Light emitting diodes

(P-18973)
LUMIO INC
6355 Topanga Canyon Blvd # 335, Wood-
land Hills (91367-2102)
PHONE..................................586 861-2408
Freddy Raitan, *CEO*
Mario Neves, *Senior VP*
Dan Gunders, *Vice Pres*
EMP: 12
SALES (est): 2.3MM **Privately Held**
SIC: 3674 Radiation sensors

(P-18974)
LUXTERA INC
2320 Camino Vida Roble # 100, Carlsbad
(92011-1562)
PHONE..................................760 448-3520
Greg Young, *President*
Tom Foody, *CFO*
Edward P Holtaway, *Senior VP*
Joseph Balardeta, *Vice Pres*
Bradley Byk, *Vice Pres*
EMP: 105
SALES (est): 3.3MM **Privately Held**
WEB: www.luxtera.com
SIC: 3674 Semiconductors & related de-
vices

(P-18975)
M-PULSE MICROWAVE INC
576 Charcot Ave, San Jose (95131-2201)
PHONE..................................408 432-1480
Billy Long, *President*
Wendell Sanders, *Shareholder*
Hector Flores, *Admin Sec*
Pam Long, *Sales Staff*
EMP: 25
SQ FT: 24,000
SALES (est): 3.5MM **Privately Held**
WEB: www.mpulsemw.com
SIC: 3674 Integrated circuits, semiconduc-
tor networks, etc.

(P-18976)
**MACKENZIE LABORATORIES
INC**
1163 Nicole Ct, Glendora (91740-5387)
P.O. Box 1416 (91740-1416)
PHONE..................................909 394-9007
Nagy Khattar, *President*
Joe Coussa, *Vice Pres*

Bob Satchell, *Research*
Robert Satchell, *Research*
Chantel Najera, *Personnel*
▲ EMP: 25
SQ FT: 20,000
SALES (est): 4.4MM **Privately Held**
WEB: www.macklabs.com
SIC: 3674 3663 Semiconductors & related
devices; radio & TV communications
equipment

(P-18977)
MACQUARIE ELECTRONICS INC
2153 Otoole Ave Ste 20, San Jose
(95131-1331)
PHONE..................................408 965-3860
Paul Jasmine, *President*
Jana Daley, *Manager*
▲ EMP: 12
SALES (est): 1.7MM **Privately Held**
SIC: 3674 Semiconductors & related de-
vices

(P-18978)
**MAGNUM SEMICONDUCTOR
INC**
6024 Silver Creek Vly Rd, San Jose
(95138-1011)
PHONE..................................408 934-3700
Gopal Solanki, *President*
Terry Griffin, *CFO*
Tao He, *Software Engr*
Fure-Ching Jeng, *Software Engr*
Josh Kim, *Software Engr*
▲ EMP: 233
SQ FT: 45,000
SALES (est): 29.6MM
SALES (corp-wide): 842.7MM **Publicly
Held**
WEB: www.magnumsemi.com
SIC: 3674 Integrated circuits, semiconduc-
tor networks, etc.
HQ: Gigpeak, Inc.
6024 Silver Creek Vly Rd
San Jose CA 95138

(P-18979)
MAGTEK INC
20725 Annalee Ave, Carson (90746-3572)
PHONE..................................562 631-8602
James Niu, *Engineer*
Wayne Mrezek, *Purch Agent*
Louis Sturett, *Sales Executive*
EMP: 16
SALES (corp-wide): 57.4MM **Privately
Held**
SIC: 3674 Semiconductors & related de-
vices
PA: Magtek, Inc.
1710 Apollo Ct
Seal Beach CA 90740
562 546-6400

(P-18980)
**MARTEQ PROCESS SOLUTIONS
INC**
1721 S Grand Ave, Santa Ana
(92705-4808)
PHONE..................................714 495-4275
Danny L Richter, *President*
Charles Edwards, *Surgery Dir*
Kevin Jacobs, *VP Finance*
▼ EMP: 10
SQ FT: 7,000
SALES (est): 1.1MM **Privately Held**
WEB: www.marteqpro.com
SIC: 3674 Semiconductors & related de-
vices

(P-18981)
**MARVELL SEMICONDUCTOR
INC (HQ)**
5488 Marvell Ln, Santa Clara
(95054-3606)
PHONE..................................408 222-2500
Matt Murphy, *CEO*
David Chen, *President*
Jean Hu, *CFO*
Juergen Gromer, *Bd of Directors*
Neil Kim, *Exec VP*
◆ EMP: 900
SALES (est): 545.2MM **Privately Held**
WEB: www.marvel.com
SIC: 3674 Semiconductors & related de-
vices

2019 California
Manufacturers Register

▲ = Import ▼=Export
◆ =Import/Export

(P-18982)
MARVELL TECHNOLOGY GROUP LTD (HQ)
5488 Marvell Ln, Santa Clara (95054-3606)
PHONE..................408 222-2500
Richard S Hill, *Ch of Bd*
George A De Urioste, *CFO*
Clyde R Hosein, *CFO*
James Shih, *Vice Pres*
Pantas Sutardja, *Vice Pres*
▲ EMP: 36
SALES (est): 85.9MM Privately Held
WEB: www.marvelltechnologygroup.com
SIC: 3674 Semiconductors & related devices

(P-18983)
MASIMO SEMICONDUCTOR INC
40 Parker, Irvine (92618-1604)
PHONE..................603 595-8900
Mark P De Raad, *President*
Gerry Hammarth, *Treasurer*
Hugh Ferguson, *Accounts Mgr*
EMP: 20
SQ FT: 90,000
SALES (est): 2.2MM Publicly Held
SIC: 3674 Light emitting diodes
PA: Masimo Corporation
52 Discovery
Irvine CA 92618

(P-18984)
MAXIM INTEGRATED PRODUCTS INC (PA)
160 Rio Robles, San Jose (95134-1813)
PHONE..................408 601-1000
Tunc Doluca, *President*
William P Sullivan, *Ch of Bd*
Bruce E Kiddoo, *CFO*
Vivek Jain, *Senior VP*
Edwin B Medlin, *Senior VP*
EMP: 956
SQ FT: 435,000
SALES: 2.4B Publicly Held
WEB: www.maxim-ic.com
SIC: 3674 Microcircuits, integrated (semiconductor)

(P-18985)
MAXIM-DALLAS DIRECT INC
120 San Gabriel Dr, Sunnyvale (94086-5125)
PHONE..................800 659-5909
Tunc Doluca, *President*
EMP: 14
SALES (est): 1.2MM Privately Held
SIC: 3674 Semiconductors & related devices

(P-18986)
MAXLINEAR INC (PA)
5966 La Place Ct Ste 100, Carlsbad (92008-8830)
PHONE..................760 692-0711
Kishore Seendripu, *Ch of Bd*
Steven G Litchfield, *CFO*
Michael Bollesen, *Vice Pres*
Michael J Lachance, *Vice Pres*
James Lougheed, *Vice Pres*
▲ EMP: 45
SQ FT: 68,000
SALES: 420.3MM Publicly Held
WEB: www.maxlinear.com
SIC: 3674 Semiconductors & related devices

(P-18987)
MDC VACUUM PRODUCTS LLC (PA)
30962 Santana St, Hayward (94544-7058)
P.O. Box 398436, San Francisco (94139-8436)
PHONE..................510 265-3500
Roger Cockroft, *CEO*
Tim Lima, *CFO*
Timothy Lima, *CFO*
Rob Holoboff, *General Mgr*
Andre Thomas, *Technical Staff*
▲ EMP: 100 EST: 1976
SQ FT: 45,000
SALES: 41MM Privately Held
WEB: www.mdcvacuum.com
SIC: 3674 3491 Wafers (semiconductor devices); pressure valves & regulators, industrial

(P-18988)
MEGACHIPS TECHNOLOGY AMER CORP (HQ)
Also Called: Kawasaki Micro Elec Amer
2755 Orchard Pkwy, San Jose (95134-2008)
PHONE..................408 570-0555
Koichi Akeyama, *CEO*
Koji Takano, *CFO*
Tommy Aizawa, *Vice Pres*
Joel Silverman, *Vice Pres*
Hima Gadupudi, *Info Tech Mgr*
▲ EMP: 40
SQ FT: 16,000
SALES (est): 13.4MM
SALES (corp-wide): 835.6MM Privately Held
WEB: www.klsi.com
SIC: 3674 Integrated circuits, semiconductor networks, etc.
PA: Megachips Corporation
1-1-1, Miyahara, Yodogawa-Ku
Osaka OSK 532-0
663 992-884

(P-18989)
MEIVAC INCORPORATED
5830 Hellyer Ave, San Jose (95138-1004)
PHONE..................408 362-1000
Richard Meidinger, *CEO*
David Meidinger, *President*
Todd Johnson, *Manager*
EMP: 30
SQ FT: 27,000
SALES (est): 8.9MM Privately Held
WEB: www.meivac.com
SIC: 3674 Semiconductors & related devices

(P-18990)
MELLANOX TECHNOLOGIES INC
Also Called: Accounts Payable
350 Oakmead Pkwy Ste 100, Sunnyvale (94085-5423)
P.O. Box 67143, Scotts Valley (95067-7143)
PHONE..................408 970-3400
Eyal Waldman, *CEO*
Thomas Riordan, *Bd of Directors*
Yann Malinge, *Electrical Engi*
Hong Liang, *Engineer*
Bhavin Bijlani, *Senior Engr*
EMP: 31
SALES (corp-wide): 857.5MM Privately Held
SIC: 3674 Semiconductors & related devices
HQ: Mellanox Technologies, Inc.
350 Oakmead Pkwy
Sunnyvale CA 94085
408 970-3400

(P-18991)
MELLANOX TECHNOLOGIES INC (HQ)
350 Oakmead Pkwy, Sunnyvale (94085-5400)
PHONE..................408 970-3400
Eyal Waldman, *Ch of Bd*
Chris Shea, *President*
Alon Webman, *President*
Shai Cohen, *COO*
Michael Gray, *CFO*
EMP: 250
SQ FT: 39,000
SALES: 863.8MM
SALES (corp-wide): 857.5MM Privately Held
SIC: 3674 Integrated circuits, semiconductor networks, etc.
PA: Mellanox Technologies, Ltd.
26 Hakidma
Upper Yokneam 20692
747 237-200

(P-18992)
MENLO MICROSYSTEMS INC
49 Discovery Ste 150, Irvine (92618-6710)
PHONE..................949 903-2369

Russ Garcia, *CEO*
EMP: 23
SALES: 3MM Privately Held
SIC: 3674 Semiconductors & related devices

(P-18993)
MERLIN SOLAR TECHNOLOGIES INC
5891 Rue Ferrari, San Jose (95138-1857)
PHONE..................678 650-8892
Venkatesan Murali, *CEO*
Gopal Prahbu, *Principal*
Abe Subramanian, *Principal*
EMP: 32
SALES (est): 1.5MM
SALES (corp-wide): 2MM Privately Held
SIC: 3674 Solar cells
PA: Aci Solar Holdings Na Inc
303 Twin Dolphin Dr # 600
Redwood City CA 94065
650 227-3271

(P-18994)
MIASOLE
2590 Walsh Ave, Santa Clara (95051-1315)
PHONE..................408 919-5700
Jeff Zhou, *CEO*
Merle McClendon, *CFO*
Atiye Bayman, *CTO*
Subrata Ghosh, *Director*
Tom Hecht, *Director*
▲ EMP: 315
SALES (est): 57.5MM Privately Held
WEB: www.miasole.com
SIC: 3674 Solar cells

(P-18995)
MIASOLE HI-TECH CORP (DH)
2590 Walsh Ave, Santa Clara (95051-1315)
PHONE..................408 919-5700
Jeffrey X Zhou, *CEO*
Merle McClendon, *CFO*
Steven Berry, *Vice Pres*
Jason Corneille, *Vice Pres*
Dave Pearce, *Executive*
EMP: 135
SALES (est): 30.4MM Privately Held
SIC: 3674 5074 Solar cells; heating equipment & panels, solar
HQ: Hanergy Holding (America) Llc
1350 Bayshore Hwy
Burlingame CA 94010
650 288-3722

(P-18996)
MICREL LLC
2180 Fortune Dr, San Jose (95131-1815)
PHONE..................408 944-0800
Raymond Zinn, *CEO*
Tina Wong, *Executive Asst*
Peter Stavish, *Info Tech Mgr*
Abdennour Mezerreg, *Engineer*
Jenny Sun, *Engineer*
EMP: 728
SALES (corp-wide): 3.9B Publicly Held
SIC: 3674 Integrated circuits, semiconductor networks, etc.
HQ: Micrel, Llc
2355 W Chandler Blvd
Chandler AZ 85224
480 792-7200

(P-18997)
MICREL LLC
Also Called: Micrel Semiconductor
1849 Fortune Dr, San Jose (95131-1724)
PHONE..................408 944-0800
Mark Lunsford, *Branch Mgr*
Karen Jakabcin, *Technical Staff*
Desislava Andreeva, *Marketing Staff*
Ben Dowlat, *Director*
Marissa Magcase, *Manager*
EMP: 250
SALES (corp-wide): 3.9B Publicly Held
WEB: www.micrel.com
SIC: 3674 Semiconductors & related devices
HQ: Micrel, Llc
2355 W Chandler Blvd
Chandler AZ 85224
480 792-7200

(P-18998)
MICREL LLC
1931 Fortune Dr, San Jose (95131-1724)
PHONE..................408 944-0800
Jung-Chen Lin, *Branch Mgr*
Satoshi Ibuki, *Design Engr*
Gene Wang, *Engineer*
EMP: 250
SALES (corp-wide): 3.9B Publicly Held
WEB: www.micrel.com
SIC: 3674 Semiconductors & related devices
HQ: Micrel, Llc
2355 W Chandler Blvd
Chandler AZ 85224
480 792-7200

(P-18999)
MICRO GAGE INC
9537 Telstar Ave Ste 131, El Monte (91731-2912)
PHONE..................626 443-1741
Bruce Talmo, *President*
Martin Chinn, *Vice Pres*
EMP: 35 EST: 1972
SQ FT: 9,000
SALES (est): 5.4MM Privately Held
SIC: 3674 Semiconductors & related devices

(P-19000)
MICRO SEMICDTR RESEARCHES LLC
805 Aldo Ave Ste 101, Santa Clara (95054-2200)
PHONE..................408 492-1369
Seiji Yamashita, *Branch Mgr*
EMP: 25
SALES (corp-wide): 1.7MM Privately Held
SIC: 3674 8748 Semiconductors & related devices; test development & evaluation service
PA: Micro Semiconductor Researches, Llc
310 W 52nd St Apt 12b
New York NY 10019
646 863-6070

(P-19001)
MICROCHIP TECHNOLOGY INC
450 Holger Way, San Jose (95134-1368)
PHONE..................408 735-9110
Greg Winner, *CEO*
Vuong Hau, *Software Engr*
Thuan Vu, *Design Engr*
Michael Huynh, *Engineer*
Jin-Ho Kim, *Engineer*
EMP: 166
SALES (corp-wide): 3.9B Publicly Held
SIC: 3674 Integrated circuits, semiconductor networks, etc.
PA: Microchip Technology Inc
2355 W Chandler Blvd
Chandler AZ 85224
480 792-7200

(P-19002)
MICROFLEX TECHNOLOGIES LLC
430 W Collins Ave, Orange (92867-5508)
PHONE..................714 937-1507
Micheal Doyle, *Mng Member*
EMP: 11
SALES (est): 2.3MM Privately Held
WEB: www.microflexseals.com
SIC: 3674 Semiconductors & related devices

(P-19003)
MICRON TECHNOLOGY INC
570 Alder Dr Bldg 2, Milpitas (95035-7443)
PHONE..................408 855-4000
Dana Krelle, *Vice Pres*
Jennifer Glenday, *Program Mgr*
David Knuth, *Technology*
Layne Ng, *Engineer*
Ghislain Provost, *Engineer*
EMP: 48
SALES (corp-wide): 30.3B Publicly Held
WEB: www.micron.com
SIC: 3674 Random access memory (RAM)
PA: Micron Technology, Inc.
8000 S Federal Way
Boise ID 83716
208 368-4000

(P-19004)
MICRON TECHNOLOGY INC
2235 Iron Point Rd, Folsom (95630-8765)
PHONE.................................916 458-3003
Glen Hawk, *Branch Mgr*
John Buza, *Engineer*
Donald Inouye, *Engineer*
Sharon Caudill, *Analyst*
Andrew Gafken, *Director*
EMP: 512
SALES (corp-wide): 30.3B **Publicly Held**
SIC: 3674 Integrated circuits, semiconductor networks, etc.
PA: Micron Technology, Inc.
8000 S Federal Way
Boise ID 83716
208 368-4000

(P-19005)
MICROPLEX INC
1070 Ortega Way, Placentia (92870-7124)
PHONE.................................714 630-8220
Clay Kucenas, *President*
Catherine A Kucenas, *Executive*
EMP: 15
SQ FT: 10,500
SALES: 2MM **Privately Held**
WEB: www.microplexinc.com
SIC: 3674 Semiconductors & related devices

(P-19006)
MICROSEMI COMMUNICATIONS INC
4721 Calle Carga, Camarillo (93012-8541)
PHONE.................................805 388-3700
Martin S McDermut, *Principal*
EMP: 30
SALES (corp-wide): 3.9B **Publicly Held**
WEB: www.cicada-semi.com
SIC: 3674 Semiconductors & related devices
HQ: Microsemi Communications, Inc.
4721 Calle Carga
Camarillo CA 93012
805 388-3700

(P-19007)
MICROSEMI COMMUNICATIONS INC (DH)
Also Called: Catawba County Schools
4721 Calle Carga, Camarillo (93012-8541)
PHONE.................................805 388-3700
Christopher R Gardner, *President*
Martin S McDermut, *CFO*
Jacob Nielsen, *CIO*
EMP: 105
SQ FT: 111,000
SALES (est): 84.3MM
SALES (corp-wide): 3.9B **Publicly Held**
WEB: www.vitesse.com
SIC: 3674 Semiconductors & related devices
HQ: Microsemi Corporation
1 Enterprise
Aliso Viejo CA 92656
949 380-6100

(P-19008)
MICROSEMI CORP - PWR PRDTS GRP
3000 Oakmead Village Dr, Santa Clara (95051-0819)
PHONE.................................408 986-8031
Cindy Matts, *Vice Pres*
EMP: 15
SALES (corp-wide): 3.9B **Publicly Held**
WEB: www.advancedpower.com
SIC: 3674 Transistors
HQ: Microsemi Corp. - Power Products Group
405 Sw Columbia St
Bend OR 97702
541 382-8028

(P-19009)
MICROSEMI CORP - RF POWER PDTS
3000 Oakmead Village Dr, Santa Clara (95051-0819)
PHONE.................................408 986-8031
Michael Mallinger, *Principal*
EMP: 54
SALES (corp-wide): 3.9B **Publicly Held**
SIC: 3674 Transistors

HQ: Microsemi Corp. - Rf Power Products
3000 Oakmead Village Dr
Santa Clara CA
408 986-8031

(P-19010)
MICROSEMI CORP- RF INTEGRATED (DH)
Also Called: Microsemi Rfis
105 Lake Forest Way, Folsom (95630-4708)
PHONE.................................916 850-8640
James J Peterson, *President*
Ralph Brandi, *COO*
John W Hohener, *CFO*
David H Hall, *Vice Pres*
▲ EMP: 115
SALES (est): 8.7MM
SALES (corp-wide): 3.9B **Publicly Held**
SIC: 3674 Semiconductors & related devices
HQ: Microsemi Corporation
1 Enterprise
Aliso Viejo CA 92656
949 380-6100

(P-19011)
MICROSEMI CORP-ANALOG (DH)
Also Called: Linfinity Microelectronics
11861 Western Ave, Garden Grove (92841-2119)
PHONE.................................714 898-8121
James Peterson, *CEO*
Paul Pickle, *COO*
John Hohener, *CFO*
Russ Garcia, *Exec VP*
Steve Litchfield, *Security Dir*
EMP: 74
SALES (est): 157.6MM
SALES (corp-wide): 3.9B **Publicly Held**
SIC: 3674 Semiconductor circuit networks
HQ: Microsemi Corporation
1 Enterprise
Aliso Viejo CA 92656
949 380-6100

(P-19012)
MICROSEMI CORPORATION
Also Called: Microsemi Corp - Santa Ana
11861 Western Ave, Garden Grove (92841-2119)
PHONE.................................714 898-7112
Lane Jorgensen, *Manager*
EMP: 350
SQ FT: 93,000
SALES (corp-wide): 3.9B **Publicly Held**
SIC: 3674 Semiconductors & related devices
HQ: Microsemi Corporation
1 Enterprise
Aliso Viejo CA 92656
949 380-6100

(P-19013)
MICROSEMI CORPORATION (HQ)
1 Enterprise, Aliso Viejo (92656-2606)
PHONE.................................949 380-6100
James J Peterson, *CEO*
Paul H Pickle, *President*
John W Hohener, *CFO*
Thomas Anderson, *Bd of Directors*
Richard Beyer, *Bd of Directors*
EMP: 50
SALES: 1.8B
SALES (corp-wide): 3.9B **Publicly Held**
SIC: 3674 Integrated circuits, semiconductor networks, etc.; rectifiers, solid state; Zener diodes; diodes, solid state (germanium, silicon, etc.)
PA: Microchip Technology Inc
2355 W Chandler Blvd
Chandler AZ 85224
480 792-7200

(P-19014)
MICROSEMI CORPORATION
3843 Brickway Blvd # 100, Santa Rosa (95403-9060)
PHONE.................................707 568-5900
Amanda Lando, *President*
EMP: 121
SALES (corp-wide): 3.9B **Publicly Held**
SIC: 3674 Semiconductors & related devices

HQ: Microsemi Corporation
1 Enterprise
Aliso Viejo CA 92656
949 380-6100

(P-19015)
MICROSEMI CORPORATION
3850 N 1st St, San Jose (95134-1702)
PHONE.................................408 643-6000
Jim Peterson, *CEO*
EMP: 10
SALES (corp-wide): 3.9B **Publicly Held**
SIC: 3674 Semiconductors & related devices
HQ: Microsemi Corporation
1 Enterprise
Aliso Viejo CA 92656
949 380-6100

(P-19016)
MICROSEMI SOC CORP (DH)
3870 N 1st St, San Jose (95134-1702)
PHONE.................................408 643-6000
James J Peterson, *CEO*
John W Hohener, *CFO*
Esmat Z Hamdy, *Senior VP*
Fares N Mubarak, *Senior VP*
David L Van De Hey, *Vice Pres*
▲ EMP: 119
SQ FT: 158,000
SALES (est): 163.2MM
SALES (corp-wide): 3.9B **Publicly Held**
WEB: www.actel.com
SIC: 3674 7371 Microcircuits, integrated (semiconductor); computer software development
HQ: Microsemi Corporation
1 Enterprise
Aliso Viejo CA 92656
949 380-6100

(P-19017)
MICROSEMI SOC CORP
2051 Stierlin Ct, Mountain View (94043-4655)
PHONE.................................650 318-4200
Mary Segura, *Manager*
EMP: 31
SALES (corp-wide): 3.9B **Publicly Held**
SIC: 3674 Microcircuits, integrated (semiconductor)
HQ: Microsemi Soc Corp.
3870 N 1st St
San Jose CA 95134
408 643-6000

(P-19018)
MICROSEMI STOR SOLUTIONS INC (DH)
1380 Bordeaux Dr, Sunnyvale (94089-1005)
PHONE.................................408 239-8000
Paul Pickle, *President*
Adhir Mattu, *President*
John W Hohener, *CFO*
EMP: 99
SQ FT: 85,000
SALES (est): 299.4MM
SALES (corp-wide): 3.9B **Publicly Held**
SIC: 3674 Modules, solid state
HQ: Microsemi Corporation
1 Enterprise
Aliso Viejo CA 92656
949 380-6100

(P-19019)
MINDSPEED TECHNOLOGIES INC (HQ)
Also Called: Macom
4000 Macarthur Blvd, Newport Beach (92660-2558)
PHONE.................................949 579-3000
Raouf Y Halim, *CEO*
Stephen N Ananias, *CFO*
Abdelnaser M Adas, *Senior VP*
Najabat H Bajwa, *Senior VP*
Gerald J Hamilton, *Senior VP*
EMP: 76 EST: 2002
SQ FT: 97,000
SALES (est): 67.8MM **Publicly Held**
WEB: www.mindspeed.com
SIC: 3674 Semiconductors & related devices

(P-19020)
MINUS K TECHNOLOGY INC
460 Hindry Ave Ste C, Inglewood (90301-2044)
PHONE.................................310 348-9656
David L Platus, *President*
Nancee Schwartz, *Admin Sec*
EMP: 110
SQ FT: 2,500
SALES (est): 13.8MM **Privately Held**
WEB: www.minusk.com
SIC: 3674 Optical isolators

(P-19021)
MIPS TECH INC (HQ)
3201 Scott Blvd, Santa Clara (95054-3008)
PHONE.................................408 530-5000
Sandeep Vij, *President*
Krishna Raghavan, *COO*
William Slater, *CFO*
Ravikrishna Cherukuri, *Vice Pres*
Brad Holtzinger, *Vice Pres*
▲ EMP: 99
SQ FT: 36,013
SALES (est): 29.3MM **Privately Held**
WEB: www.mips.com
SIC: 3674 Microprocessors
PA: Wave Computing, Inc.
42 W Campbell Ave Ste 301
Campbell CA 95008
408 412-8645

(P-19022)
MOBIVEIL INC
890 Hillview Ct Ste 250, Milpitas (95035-4574)
PHONE.................................408 791-2977
Ravikumar R Thummarukudy, *CEO*
Dale Olstinske, *Vice Pres*
Amit Saxena, *Vice Pres*
D Srinivasan, *Principal*
Gopa Periyadan, *Council Mbr*
EMP: 13 EST: 2011
SALES (est): 1.9MM **Privately Held**
SIC: 3674 Semiconductors & related devices

(P-19023)
MONOLITHIC POWER SYSTEMS INC (PA)
79 Great Oaks Blvd, San Jose (95119-1311)
PHONE.................................408 826-0600
Michael R Hsing, *Ch of Bd*
Deming Xiao, *President*
Bernie Blegen, *CFO*
Maurice Sciammas, *Senior VP*
Saria Tseng, *Vice Pres*
EMP: 133
SQ FT: 106,000
SALES: 470.9MM **Publicly Held**
WEB: www.monolithicpower.com
SIC: 3674 8711 Semiconductors & related devices; engineering services

(P-19024)
MONTAGE TECHNOLOGY INC
101 Metro Dr Ste 500, San Jose (95110-1342)
PHONE.................................408 982-2788
Howard Yang, *Principal*
Leechung Yiu, *CTO*
Kenneth Chew, *VP Opers*
Lee Khem, *Sales Staff*
Robert Jin, *Manager*
EMP: 16
SALES (est): 2.9MM **Privately Held**
SIC: 3674 Semiconductors & related devices

(P-19025)
MOSYS INC (PA)
2309 Bering Dr, San Jose (95131-1125)
PHONE.................................408 418-7500
Thomas Riordan, *COO*
James W Sullivan, *CFO*
Stephen Domenik, *Bd of Directors*
Victor Lee, *Bd of Directors*
James Sullivan, *Vice Pres*
EMP: 68
SQ FT: 47,000
SALES: 8.8MM **Publicly Held**
WEB: www.mosysinc.com
SIC: 3674 Integrated circuits, semiconductor networks, etc.

▲ = Import ▼=Export
◆ =Import/Export

(P-19026)
MOTOROLA SOLUTIONS INC
9665 Chesapeake Dr # 220, San Diego
(92123-1367)
PHONE..................................858 541-2163
Amanda Hornik, *Manager*
EMP: 17
SALES (corp-wide): 6.3B **Publicly Held**
WEB: www.motorola.com
SIC: 3674 Semiconductors & related devices
PA: Motorola Solutions, Inc.
500 W Monroe St Ste 4400
Chicago IL 60661
847 576-5000

(P-19027)
MPS INTERNATIONAL LTD
79 Great Oaks Blvd, San Jose
(95119-1311)
PHONE..................................408 826-0600
Michael R Hsing, *CEO*
▼ EMP: 1000 EST: 1997
SQ FT: 100,000
SALES: 388.6MM **Publicly Held**
SIC: 3674 Semiconductors & related devices
PA: Monolithic Power Systems, inc.
79 Great Oaks Blvd
San Jose CA 95119

(P-19028)
MRV COMMUNICATIONS INC (PA)
20520 Nordhoff St, Chatsworth
(91311-6113)
PHONE..................................818 773-0900
Mark J Bonney, *President*
Kenneth H Traub, *Ch of Bd*
Robert M Pons, *Vice Chairman*
Stephen Krulik, *CFO*
Koby Bergman, *Vice Pres*
▲ EMP: 130
SALES: 80.3MM **Privately Held**
SIC: 3674 Integrated circuits, semiconductor networks, etc.

(P-19029)
NANOSILICON INC
2461 Autumnvale Dr, San Jose
(95131-1802)
PHONE..................................408 263-7341
Lincoln Bejan, *President*
Jackie Bejan, *CFO*
Michelle Piffero-Alberaw, *Business Mgr*
John Ayala, *VP Opers*
EMP: 22
SQ FT: 30,000
SALES: 3.5MM **Privately Held**
SIC: 3674 Semiconductors & related devices

(P-19030)
NANOSYS INC
233 S Hillview Dr, Milpitas (95035-5417)
PHONE..................................408 240-6700
Jason Hartlove, *CEO*
Martin Devenney, *COO*
Noland Granberry, *Exec VP*
John Hanlow, *Senior VP*
Russell Kempt, *Vice Pres*
EMP: 113
SQ FT: 32,000
SALES (est): 36.5MM **Privately Held**
WEB: www.nanosysinc.com
SIC: 3674 Semiconductors & related devices

(P-19031)
NATEL ENGINEERING COMPANY INC (PA)
Also Called: Neotech
9340 Owensmouth Ave, Chatsworth
(91311-6915)
PHONE..................................818 734-6523
Sudesh K Arora, *President*
Kunal Sharma, *COO*
Laura Siegal, *CFO*
John Lowrey, *Officer*
James Howe, *Vice Pres*
▲ EMP: 210
SQ FT: 200,000

SALES (est): 1.2B **Privately Held**
WEB: www.natelengr.com
SIC: 3674 3679 Semiconductors & related devices; antennas, receiving

(P-19032)
NATIONAL SEMICONDUCTOR CORP (HQ)
2900 Semiconductor Dr, Santa Clara
(95051-0695)
PHONE..................................408 721-5000
Ellen L Barker, *CEO*
Lewis Chew, *CFO*
Todd M Duchene, *Senior VP*
Edward J Sweeney, *Senior VP*
Jamie E Samath, *Vice Pres*
▲ EMP: 1700
SALES (est): 334.7MM
SALES (corp-wide): 14.9B **Publicly Held**
WEB: www.national.com
SIC: 3674 Microprocessors
PA: Texas Instruments Incorporated
12500 Ti Blvd
Dallas TX 75243
214 479-3773

(P-19033)
NDSP DELAWARE INC
Also Called: Ndsp Crp
224 Airport Pkwy Ste 400, San Jose
(95110-1095)
PHONE..................................408 626-1640
Ven L Lee, *President*
Leonard Liu, *Chairman*
Hongmin Zhang, *CTO*
EMP: 51
SQ FT: 9,285
SALES (est): 2.6MM
SALES (corp-wide): 80.6MM **Publicly Held**
WEB: www.pixelworks.com
SIC: 3674 Integrated circuits, semiconductor networks, etc.
PA: Pixelworks, Inc.
224 Airport Pkwy Ste 400
San Jose CA 95110
408 200-9200

(P-19034)
NEOCONIX INC
4020 Moorpark Ave Ste 108, San Jose
(95117-1845)
PHONE..................................408 530-9393
Asuri Raghavan, *President*
Jim Witham, *CEO*
Dirk Brown, *Exec VP*
Phil Damberg, *Vice Pres*
Dinesh Kalakkad, *Vice Pres*
EMP: 40
SQ FT: 5,000
SALES (est): 6.3MM **Privately Held**
SIC: 3674 Semiconductors & related devices

(P-19035)
NEOPHOTONICS CORPORATION
40931 Encyclopedia Cir, Fremont
(94538-2436)
PHONE..................................510 933-4100
Stephen Rishton, *Director*
EMP: 12
SALES (est): 1.4MM **Privately Held**
SIC: 3674 Semiconductors & related devices

(P-19036)
NEOPHOTONICS CORPORATION (PA)
2911 Zanker Rd, San Jose (95134-2125)
PHONE..................................408 232-9200
Timothy S Jenks, *Ch of Bd*
CHI Yue Cheung, *COO*
Elizabeth EBY, *CFO*
Benjamin L Sitler, *Senior VP*
Wupen Yuen, *Senior VP*
EMP: 291
SQ FT: 103,314
SALES: 292.8MM **Publicly Held**
WEB: www.neophotonics.com
SIC: 3674 Semiconductors & related devices

(P-19037)
NETHRA IMAGING INC (PA)
2855 Bowers Ave, Santa Clara
(95051-0917)
PHONE..................................408 257-5880
Ramesh Singh, *President*
EMP: 13
SALES (est): 3.6MM **Privately Held**
WEB: www.nethra-imaging.com
SIC: 3674 Semiconductors & related devices

(P-19038)
NETLIST INC (PA)
175 Technology Dr Ste 150, Irvine
(92618-2479)
PHONE..................................949 435-0025
Chun K Hong, *Ch of Bd*
Gail Sasaki, *CFO*
Jeffrey Benck, *Bd of Directors*
Jun Cho, *Bd of Directors*
Blake Welcher, *Bd of Directors*
EMP: 95
SQ FT: 8,200
SALES: 38.3MM **Publicly Held**
WEB: www.netlistinc.com
SIC: 3674 Random access memory (RAM)

(P-19039)
NETLOGIC MICROSYSTEMS LLC
Also Called: Broadcom
3975 Freedom Cir Ste 900, Santa Clara
(95054-1255)
PHONE..................................408 454-3000
Ronald S Jankov, *CEO*
Scott A McGregor, *President*
Michael Tate, *CFO*
Behrooz Abdi, *Exec VP*
Eric K Brandt, *Exec VP*
EMP: 645
SQ FT: 105,930
SALES (est): 71.9MM
SALES (corp-wide): 17.6B **Publicly Held**
WEB: www.netlogicmicro.com
SIC: 3674 Integrated circuits, semiconductor networks, etc.
HQ: Broadcom Corporation
1320 Ridder Park Dr
San Jose CA 95131

(P-19040)
NEWPORT FAB LLC
Also Called: Jazz Semiconductor
4321 Jamboree Rd, Newport Beach
(92660-3007)
PHONE..................................949 435-8000
Susanna Bennette,
Rex Edwards, *General Mgr*
Anna Acker, *Human Res Dir*
EMP: 99
SALES (est): 1,000K
SALES (corp-wide): 1.3B **Privately Held**
SIC: 3674 Wafers (semiconductor devices)
HQ: Jazz Semiconductor, Inc.
4321 Jamboree Rd
Newport Beach CA 92660
949 435-8000

(P-19041)
NEXGEN POWER SYSTEMS INC
2010 El Camino Real, Santa Clara
(95050-4051)
PHONE..................................408 230-7698
Dinesh Ramanathan, *President*
Narayanan Karu, *CFO*
EMP: 30 EST: 2017
SQ FT: 3,400
SALES (est): 111.7K **Privately Held**
SIC: 3674 Semiconductor circuit networks

(P-19042)
NGCODEC INC
440 N Wolfe Rd Ste 2187, Sunnyvale
(94085-3869)
PHONE..................................408 766-4382
Oliver Gunasekara, *CEO*
Alberto Duenas, *Chairman*
Neel Mani, *Sr Software Eng*
EMP: 20 EST: 2012
SALES (est): 892.3K **Privately Held**
SIC: 3674 Semiconductors & related devices

(P-19043)
NVIDIA CORPORATION (PA)
2788 San Tomas Expy, Santa Clara
(95051-0952)
PHONE..................................408 486-2000
Jen-Hsun Huang, *President*
Colette M Kress, *CFO*
David Shannon, *Officer*
Ajay K Puri, *Exec VP*
Debora Shoquist, *Exec VP*
▲ EMP: 458
SALES: 9.7B **Publicly Held**
WEB: www.nvidia.com
SIC: 3674 Semiconductors & related devices

(P-19044)
NVIDIA CORPORATION
2001 Walsh Ave, Santa Clara
(95050-2522)
PHONE..................................408 566-5364
Marvin D Burkett, *President*
Michael Griffith, *Info Tech Dir*
Jeff Berry, *Info Tech Mgr*
Subhash Gutti, *Software Engr*
Vishwanath Kadam, *Software Engr*
EMP: 17 **Publicly Held**
SIC: 3674 Semiconductors & related devices
PA: Nvidia Corporation
2788 San Tomas Expy
Santa Clara CA 95051

(P-19045)
NVIDIA DEVELOPMENT INC
2701 San Tomas Expy, Santa Clara
(95050-2519)
PHONE..................................408 486-2000
EMP: 27
SALES (est): 5.8MM **Publicly Held**
SIC: 3674 Semiconductors & related devices
PA: Nvidia Corporation
2788 San Tomas Expy
Santa Clara CA 95051

(P-19046)
NXP USA INC
2680 Zanker Rd Ste 200, San Jose
(95134-2144)
PHONE..................................408 518-5500
Rob Shane, *Branch Mgr*
Ruediger Stroh, *Exec VP*
Kwame Adwere, *Counsel*
EMP: 75
SALES (corp-wide): 9.2B **Privately Held**
SIC: 3674 Semiconductors & related devices
HQ: Nxp Usa, Inc.
6501 W William Cannon Dr
Austin TX 78735
512 933-8214

(P-19047)
NXP USA INC
411 E Plumeria Dr, San Jose (95134-1924)
PHONE..................................408 518-5500
EMP: 500
SALES (corp-wide): 9.2B **Privately Held**
SIC: 3674 Integrated circuits, semiconductor networks, etc.
HQ: Nxp Usa, Inc.
6501 W William Cannon Dr
Austin TX 78735
512 933-8214

(P-19048)
NXP USA INC
Also Called: Philips Semiconductors
690 E Arques Ave, Sunnyvale
(94085-3829)
PHONE..................................408 991-2700
Susie Ostrega, *Manager*
EMP: 39
SALES (corp-wide): 9.2B **Privately Held**
WEB: www.philipslogic.com
SIC: 3674 Integrated circuits, semiconductor networks, etc.
HQ: Nxp Usa, Inc.
6501 W William Cannon Dr
Austin TX 78735
512 933-8214

PRODUCTS & SVCS

(P-19049)
NXP USA INC
440 N Wolfe Rd, Sunnyvale (94085-3869)
PHONE..................................408 991-2000
Scott McGregor, *President*
EMP: 39
SALES (corp-wide): 9.2B **Privately Held**
WEB: www.philipslogic.com
SIC: 3674 Integrated circuits, semiconductor networks, etc.
HQ: Nxp Usa, Inc.
   6501 W William Cannon Dr
   Austin TX 78735
   512 933-8214

(P-19050)
NXP USA INC
9 Cushing Ste 100, Irvine (92618-4225)
PHONE..................................949 399-4000
Roger Schalk, *Branch Mgr*
EMP: 16
SALES (corp-wide): 9.2B **Privately Held**
WEB: www.freescale.com
SIC: 3674 Integrated circuits, semiconductor networks, etc.
HQ: Nxp Usa, Inc.
   6501 W William Cannon Dr
   Austin TX 78735
   512 933-8214

(P-19051)
OCLARO INC (PA)
225 Charcot Ave, San Jose (95131-1107)
PHONE..................................408 383-1400
Greg Dougherty, *CEO*
Marissa Peterson, *Ch of Bd*
Craig Cocchi, *COO*
Pete Mangan, *CFO*
Adam Carter, *Ch Credit Ofcr*
EMP: 83
SQ FT: 27,000
SALES (est): 543.1MM **Publicly Held**
SIC: 3674 3826 3827 Light emitting diodes; laser scientific & engineering instruments; optical instruments & apparatus

(P-19052)
OCLARO FIBER OPTICS INC (HQ)
Also Called: Opnext, Inc.
225 Charcot Ave, San Jose (95131-1107)
PHONE..................................408 383-1400
Harry L Bosco, *President*
Robert J Nobile, *CFO*
Atsushi Horiuchi, *Senior VP*
Justin J O'Neill, *Senior VP*
Justin J O Neill, *General Counsel*
EMP: 45 **EST:** 2000
SQ FT: 30,574
SALES (est): 52.9MM
SALES (corp-wide): 543.1MM **Publicly Held**
WEB: www.opnext.com
SIC: 3674 Photoconductive cells; photoelectric cells, solid state (electronic eye)
PA: Oclaro, Inc.
   225 Charcot Ave
   San Jose CA 95131
   408 383-1400

(P-19053)
OEPIC SEMICONDUCTORS INC
1231 Bordeaux Dr, Sunnyvale (94089-1203)
PHONE..................................408 747-0388
Yi-Ching Pao, *President*
EMP: 35 **EST:** 2000
SQ FT: 18,000
SALES (est): 7.7MM **Privately Held**
SIC: 3674 Semiconductors & related devices

(P-19054)
OFF GRID LABS INC
555 De Haro St Ste 220, San Francisco (94107-2399)
PHONE..................................415 344-0953
Xavier Helgesen, *Co-CEO*
Guido Frantzen, *CFO*
William Lenihan, *Co-CEO*
EMP: 25 **EST:** 2015
SQ FT: 2,500
SALES: 5MM **Privately Held**
SIC: 3674 Solar cells

PA: Off Grid Electric Ltd
   C/O: Estera Trust (Cayman) Limited
   Grand Cayman GR CAYMAN

(P-19055)
OKAMOTO CORPORATION
Also Called: Semiconductor Equipment Div
7175 Via Corona, San Jose (95139-1135)
PHONE..................................408 654-8400
Bob Pinto, *Manager*
EMP: 16
SALES (corp-wide): 208.9MM **Privately Held**
WEB: www.okamotocorp.com
SIC: 3674 Integrated circuits, semiconductor networks, etc.
HQ: Okamoto Corporation
   370 Corporate Woods Pkwy
   Vernon Hills IL 60061
   847 235-3500

(P-19056)
OMNISIL
5401 Everglades St, Ventura (93003-6523)
PHONE..................................805 644-2514
David Clark, *President*
Karin Clark, *Corp Secy*
Dennis Strang, *Vice Pres*
▲ **EMP:** 21
SQ FT: 9,800
SALES (est): 4.5MM **Privately Held**
WEB: www.omnisil.com
SIC: 3674 Silicon wafers, chemically doped

(P-19057)
OMNIVISION TECHNOLOGIES INC (HQ)
4275 Burton Dr, Santa Clara (95054-1512)
PHONE..................................408 567-3000
Shaw Hong, *CEO*
Raymond Wu, *President*
Henry Yang, *COO*
Anson Chan, *CFO*
Lindsay Grant, *Vice Pres*
EMP: 119
SQ FT: 207,000
SALES (est): 1.3B **Privately Held**
WEB: www.ovt.com
SIC: 3674 Semiconductors & related devices

(P-19058)
OMTEK INC
3722 Calle Cita, Santa Barbara (93105-2411)
PHONE..................................805 687-9629
Robert Webb, *President*
EMP: 23
SQ FT: 15,000
SALES (est): 1.3MM **Privately Held**
SIC: 3674

(P-19059)
ONE RESONANCE SENSORS LLC
8291 Aero Pl Ste 120, San Diego (92123-2037)
PHONE..................................407 637-0771
Pablo Prado, *CEO*
Gregory Holifield,
Will McEllen,
EMP: 10
SALES (est): 1.5MM **Privately Held**
SIC: 3674 Semiconductors & related devices

(P-19060)
ONESUN LLC
27 Gate 5 Rd, Sausalito (94965-1401)
PHONE..................................415 230-4277
Paul Hawken,
EMP: 10
SALES (est): 1.3MM **Privately Held**
SIC: 3674 Semiconductors & related devices

(P-19061)
ONSPEC TECHNOLOGY PARTNERS INC
Also Called: Bi Cmos Foundry
975 Comstock St, Santa Clara (95054-3407)
PHONE..................................408 654-7627

Peter Liljegren, *Vice Pres*
Wayne Lammer, *Manager*
EMP: 20
SALES (est): 3MM **Privately Held**
SIC: 3674 Wafers (semiconductor devices)

(P-19062)
OPTASENSE INC
3350 Scott Blvd Bldg 1, Santa Clara (95054-3107)
PHONE..................................408 970-3500
Lew Stolpner, *Vice Pres*
EMP: 11
SALES (corp-wide): 1.1B **Privately Held**
SIC: 3674 Semiconductors & related devices
HQ: Optasense, Inc.
   12709 Haynes Rd
   Houston TX 77066
   713 493-0348

(P-19063)
OPTO DIODE CORPORATION
1260 Calle Suerte, Camarillo (93012-8053)
PHONE..................................805 465-8700
Mary Hagerty-Goldberg, *Principal*
EMP: 28
SALES (est): 4.9MM **Privately Held**
SIC: 3674 Semiconductors & related devices

(P-19064)
OPTOELECTRONIX INC (PA)
111 W Saint John St # 588, San Jose (95113-1105)
PHONE..................................408 437-9488
Chuck Berghoff, *President*
Tom Thayer, *COO*
Dato Yap Peng Hooi, *Vice Pres*
Robert Kow, *Vice Pres*
EMP: 18 **EST:** 2008
SALES (est): 2.5MM **Privately Held**
SIC: 3674 Light emitting diodes

(P-19065)
ORBOTECH LT SOLAR LLC
Also Called: Olt Solar
5970 Optical Ct, San Jose (95138-1400)
PHONE..................................408 414-3777
Georg Bremer, *Mng Member*
Kam Law,
Matt Toshima,
Michael Butler, *Director*
EMP: 20
SALES (est): 3.8MM **Privately Held**
SIC: 3674 Integrated circuits, semiconductor networks, etc.

(P-19066)
ORTEL A DIVISION EMCORE CO (HQ)
2015 Chestnut St, Alhambra (91803-1542)
PHONE..................................626 293-3400
Mary E Ortel, *President*
EMP: 15
SALES (est): 1MM
SALES (corp-wide): 122.9MM **Publicly Held**
WEB: www.forceinc.com
SIC: 3674 3559 Integrated circuits, semiconductor networks, etc.; semiconductor manufacturing machinery
PA: Emcore Corporation
   2015 Chestnut St
   Alhambra CA 91803
   626 293-3400

(P-19067)
OSE USA INC (HQ)
1737 N 1st St Ste 350, San Jose (95112-4523)
PHONE..................................408 452-9080
Edmond Tseng, *President*
Adonai Mack, *Analyst*
EMP: 12
SALES: 4.5MM
SALES (corp-wide): 461.3MM **Privately Held**
WEB: www.ose.com.tw
SIC: 3674 Integrated circuits, semiconductor networks, etc.
PA: Orient Semiconductor Electronics Limited
   9, Central 3rd St.,
   Kaohsiung City 81170
   736 131-31

(P-19068)
OSI OPTOELECTRONICS INC
Also Called: Advanced Photonix
1240 Avenida Acaso, Camarillo (93012-8754)
PHONE..................................805 987-0146
Jean-Pierre Maufras, *General Mgr*
EMP: 50
SALES (corp-wide): 1B **Publicly Held**
SIC: 3674 Semiconductors & related devices
HQ: Osi Optoelectronics, Inc.
   12525 Chadron Ave
   Hawthorne CA 90250
   310 978-0516

(P-19069)
OSI SYSTEMS INC (PA)
12525 Chadron Ave, Hawthorne (90250-4807)
PHONE..................................310 978-0516
Deepak Chopra, *Ch of Bd*
Alan Edrick, *CFO*
Rick Merritt, *Officer*
Ajay Mehra, *Exec VP*
Victor Sze, *Exec VP*
EMP: 325
SQ FT: 88,000
SALES: 1B **Publicly Held**
WEB: www.osi-systems.com
SIC: 3674 3845 Integrated circuits, semiconductor networks, etc.; photoconductive cells; photoelectric cells, solid state (electronic eye); electromedical equipment; ultrasonic scanning devices, medical

(P-19070)
PAC TECH USA PACKG TECH INC
328 Martin Ave, Santa Clara (95050-3112)
PHONE..................................408 588-1925
Heinrich Ldeke, *CEO*
Thorsten Teutsch, *President*
Bernd Otto, *Engineer*
Axel Scheffler, *Engineer*
Richard McKee, *Business Mgr*
EMP: 14 **EST:** 2001
SALES: 12.7MM
SALES (corp-wide): 27.3MM **Privately Held**
SIC: 3674 Wafers (semiconductor devices)
PA: Pac Tech - Packaging Technologies Gmbh
   Am Schlangenhorst 7-9
   Nauen 14641
   332 144-9510

(P-19071)
PANTRONIX CORPORATION
2710 Lakeview Ct, Fremont (94538-6534)
PHONE..................................510 656-5898
Stanley Wang, *President*
Bret Buckler, *President*
Franny Wang, *Corp Secy*
Dave Toledo, *Data Proc Staff*
Susan Bristow, *Human Res Mgr*
▲ **EMP:** 250
SQ FT: 82,000
SALES (est): 37.7MM **Privately Held**
WEB: www.pantronix.com
SIC: 3674 8734 Integrated circuits, semiconductor networks, etc.; testing laboratories

(P-19072)
PATRIOT MEMORY LLC (PA)
47027 Benicia St, Fremont (94538-7331)
PHONE..................................510 979-1021
Paul Jones, *Mng Member*
Doug Diggs,
Keevin Hameen, *Manager*
▲ **EMP:** 125
SALES (est): 22.7MM **Privately Held**
WEB: www.patriotmem.com
SIC: 3674 5045 Semiconductors & related devices; computers

(P-19073)
PAYTON TECHNOLOGY CORPORATION
17665 Newhope St Ste B, Fountain Valley (92708-8209)
PHONE..................................714 885-8000
John Tu, *President*

▲ = Import ▼=Export
◆ =Import/Export

David Sun, *Admin Sec*
▲ EMP: 161
SALES (est): 15.8MM **Privately Held**
SIC: **3674** Semiconductors & related devices

(P-19074)
PERFECTVIPS INC
2099 Gateway Pl Ste 240, San Jose
(95110-1017)
PHONE....................................408 912-2316
Prasana Kumari, *Principal*
Abira Das, *Human Resources*
Sandeep Mohankumar, *Sales Staff*
Kartiki Parekh, *Manager*
EMP: 15
SALES (est): 1.2MM **Privately Held**
SIC: **3674** Semiconductors & related devices

(P-19075)
PIEZO-METRICS INC (PA)
Also Called: Micron Instruments
4509 Runway St, Simi Valley (93063-3479)
PHONE....................................805 522-4676
Herbert Chelner, *President*
Sharon Chelner, *Vice Pres*
EMP: 35
SQ FT: 9,000
SALES (est): 6.6MM **Privately Held**
WEB: www.microninstruments.com
SIC: **3674** 3829 Strain gages, solid state; pressure transducers

(P-19076)
PIXELWORKS INC (PA)
224 Airport Pkwy Ste 400, San Jose
(95110-1095)
PHONE....................................408 200-9200
Todd A Debonis, *President*
Richard L Sanquini, *Ch of Bd*
Steven L Moore, *CFO*
Charles Gibson, *Bd of Directors*
Daniel Heneghan, *Bd of Directors*
EMP: 60
SQ FT: 19,000
SALES: 80.6MM **Publicly Held**
WEB: www.pixelworks.com
SIC: **3674** 7372 Semiconductors & related devices; prepackaged software; utility computer software

(P-19077)
PMC-SIERRA US INC
1380 Bordeaux Dr, Sunnyvale
(94089-1005)
PHONE....................................408 239-8000
Steve Geiser, *CEO*
EMP: 10
SALES (est): 1.4MM
SALES (corp-wide): 3.9B **Publicly Held**
SIC: **3674** Microprocessors
HQ: Microsemi Storage Solutions, Inc.
1380 Bordeaux Dr
Sunnyvale CA 94089
408 239-8000

(P-19078)
PNY TECHNOLOGIES INC
2099 Gateway Pl Ste 220, San Jose
(95110-1017)
PHONE....................................408 392-4100
Clint Rosenthal, *Director*
EMP: 20
SALES (corp-wide): 157.9MM **Privately Held**
SIC: **3674** 5045 Memories, solid state; computers, peripherals & software
PA: Pny Technologies, Inc.
100 Jefferson Rd
Parsippany NJ 07054
973 515-9700

(P-19079)
POINT NINE TECHNOLOGIES INC (PA)
2697 Lavery Ct Ste 8, Newbury Park
(91320-1585)
PHONE....................................805 375-6600
Fred Quigg, *Ch of Bd*
Dixie Quigg, *President*
Laura Vega, *CFO*
EMP: 15
SQ FT: 7,000

SALES: 7MM **Privately Held**
WEB: www.rfmosfet.com
SIC: **3674** Transistors

(P-19080)
POLISHING CORPORATION AMERICA
Also Called: PCA
442 Martin Ave, Santa Clara (95050-2911)
PHONE....................................888 892-3377
Stuart Becker, *CEO*
▲ EMP: 26
SQ FT: 10,000
SALES (est): 2.1MM **Privately Held**
WEB: www.pcasilicon.com
SIC: **3674** Silicon wafers, chemically doped

(P-19081)
POLYFET RF DEVICES INC
1110 Avenida Acaso, Camarillo
(93012-8725)
PHONE....................................805 484-9582
S K Leong, *President*
EMP: 25
SQ FT: 7,500
SALES (est): 4.5MM **Privately Held**
WEB: www.polyfet.com
SIC: **3674** Transistors

(P-19082)
POLYSTAK INC
1159 Sonora Ct 109, Sunnyvale
(94086-5384)
PHONE....................................408 441-1400
Kyung Suk Kang, *President*
Christina Kim, *Administration*
EMP: 18 EST: 1999
SQ FT: 4,300
SALES (est): 2.1MM **Privately Held**
WEB: www.polystak.com
SIC: **3674** Modules, solid state

(P-19083)
POWER INTEGRATIONS INC (PA)
5245 Hellyer Ave, San Jose (95138-1002)
PHONE....................................408 414-9200
Balu Balakrishnan, *President*
E Floyd Kvamme, *Ch of Bd*
Sandeep Nayyar, *CFO*
Richard Francis, *Officer*
Radu Barsan, *Vice Pres*
EMP: 269
SALES: 431.7MM **Publicly Held**
WEB: www.powerint.com
SIC: **3674** Integrated circuits, semiconductor networks, etc.

(P-19084)
PRECISE TECHNOLOGY INC
33 Hammond Ste 210, Irvine (92618-1637)
PHONE....................................949 453-1997
Kambiz Parhami, *CEO*
EMP: 10
SALES (est): 195.6K **Privately Held**
SIC: **3674** Memories, solid state

(P-19085)
PRIME SOLUTIONS INC
4261 Business Center Dr, Fremont
(94538-6357)
PHONE....................................510 490-2255
Harry H Moroyan, *President*
Vera Moroyan, *Admin Sec*
EMP: 17
SQ FT: 1,200
SALES (est): 2.4MM **Privately Held**
WEB: www.primesol.com
SIC: **3674** Integrated circuits, semiconductor networks, etc.

(P-19086)
PRINTEC HT ELECTRONICS LLC
501 Sally Pl, Fullerton (92831-5014)
PHONE....................................714 484-7597
Nancy Cheng,
Greg Morton, *Manager*
▲ EMP: 50
SQ FT: 12,000
SALES: 10MM **Privately Held**
SIC: **3674** 3629 Modules, solid state; electronic generation equipment

PA: Printec H. T. Electronics Corp.
No. 38, Liyan St.,
New Taipei City
282 277-899

(P-19087)
PROMEX INDUSTRIES INCORPORATED
Also Called: Quik-Pak
10987 Via Frontera, San Diego
(92127-1703)
PHONE....................................858 674-4676
Steve Swendrowski, *General Mgr*
EMP: 28
SALES (corp-wide): 20.7MM **Privately Held**
SIC: **3674** Integrated circuits, semiconductor networks, etc.
PA: Promex Industries, Incorporated
3075 Oakmead Village Dr
Santa Clara CA 95051
408 496-0222

(P-19088)
PROMEX INDUSTRIES INCORPORATED (PA)
3075 Oakmead Village Dr, Santa Clara
(95051-0811)
PHONE....................................408 496-0222
Richard F Otte, *CEO*
Chris Pugh, *Vice Pres*
Dr Edward Binkley, *Principal*
Luna Abouelkhir, *Materials Mgr*
▲ EMP: 65 EST: 1999
SQ FT: 30,000
SALES (est): 20.7MM **Privately Held**
SIC: **3674** Modules, solid state; hybrid integrated circuits; integrated circuits, semiconductor networks, etc.

(P-19089)
PROTONEX LLC
2331 Circadian Way, Santa Rosa
(95407-5437)
PHONE....................................707 566-2260
Eric Walters,
Becky OH,
EMP: 18
SALES (est): 797.1K **Privately Held**
SIC: **3674** Radiation sensors

(P-19090)
PSEMI CORPORATION (DH)
9369 Carroll Park Dr, San Diego
(92121-3264)
PHONE....................................858 731-9400
James S Cable, *Ch of Bd*
Takaki Muratajay C Biskupski, *CFO*
Takaki Murata, *Vice Pres*
Ronald Reedy, *Vice Pres*
Anil Tata, *Vice Pres*
▲ EMP: 70
SQ FT: 96,384
SALES (est): 110.1MM
SALES (corp-wide): 12.8B **Privately Held**
WEB: www.psemi.com
SIC: **3674** Silicon wafers, chemically doped
HQ: Murata Electronics North America, Inc.
2200 Lake Park Dr Se
Smyrna GA 30080
770 436-1300

(P-19091)
PSIBER DATA SYSTEMS INC
7075 Mission Gorge Rd K, San Diego
(92120-2454)
PHONE....................................619 287-9970
Darrell J Johnson, *President*
Brandon Mueller, *Design Engr*
Cameron Fedeli, *Mfg Mgr*
▲ EMP: 10
SQ FT: 3,000
SALES (est): 1.6MM **Privately Held**
SIC: **3674** Semiconductors & related devices

(P-19092)
PYRAMID SEMICONDUCTOR CORP
1249 Reamwood Ave, Sunnyvale
(94089-2226)
PHONE....................................408 542-9430
Joe Rothstein, *President*
Douglas Beaubien, *Vice Pres*

Dr Jagtar Sandhu, *Vice Pres*
EMP: 11
SQ FT: 8,400
SALES (est): 2.1MM **Privately Held**
WEB: www.pyramidsemiconductor.com
SIC: **3674** Integrated circuits, semiconductor networks, etc.

(P-19093)
QLOGIC LLC (DH)
15485 Sand Canyon Ave, Irvine
(92618-3154)
PHONE....................................949 389-6000
Syed Ali,
Connie Williams, *IT Executive*
Todd Owens, *Marketing Staff*
Arthur Chadwick,
M Raghib Hussain,
▲ EMP: 138
SQ FT: 161,000
SALES (est): 458.9MM **Privately Held**
WEB: www.qlogic.com
SIC: **3674** Integrated circuits, semiconductor networks, etc.

(P-19094)
QMAT INC
Also Called: Quenta Material
2424 Walsh Ave, Santa Clara
(95051-1303)
PHONE....................................498 228-5858
Francois Henley, *Principal*
Kristine Ryan, *Admin Sec*
EMP: 26 EST: 2012
SALES (est): 4.7MM **Privately Held**
SIC: **3674** Wafers (semiconductor devices)

(P-19095)
QORVO US INC
3099 Orchard Dr, San Jose (95134-2005)
PHONE....................................408 493-4304
Timothy R Richardson, *Manager*
EMP: 43
SALES (corp-wide): 2.9B **Publicly Held**
WEB: www.rfmd.com
SIC: **3674** Integrated circuits, semiconductor networks, etc.
HQ: Qorvo Us, Inc.
7628 Thorndike Rd
Greensboro NC 27409
336 664-1233

(P-19096)
QORVO US INC
3099 Orchard Dr, San Jose (95134-2005)
PHONE....................................408 577-6200
Bruce Diamond, *CEO*
Eric Palsgaard, *Engineer*
EMP: 374
SALES (corp-wide): 2.9B **Publicly Held**
SIC: **3674** Microcircuits, integrated (semiconductor)
HQ: Qorvo Us, Inc.
7628 Thorndike Rd
Greensboro NC 27409
336 664-1233

(P-19097)
QUALCOMM ATHEROS INC (HQ)
1700 Technology Dr, San Jose
(95110-1383)
PHONE....................................408 773-5200
Steve Mollenkopf, *CEO*
Richard Bahr, *Vice Pres*
Kerry Jett, *Executive*
Lilia Munoz, *Executive*
Gary Szilagyi, *General Mgr*
▲ EMP: 600
SALES (est): 219.8MM
SALES (corp-wide): 22.2B **Publicly Held**
WEB: www.airvia.com
SIC: **3674** 4899 Integrated circuits, semiconductor networks, etc.; communication signal enhancement network system
PA: Qualcomm Incorporated
5775 Morehouse Dr
San Diego CA 92121
858 587-1121

(P-19098)
QUALCOMM DATACENTER TECH INC (HQ)
5775 Morehouse Dr, San Diego
(92121-1714)
PHONE....................................858 567-1121
Dileep Bhandarkar, *Vice Pres*

Anand Chandrasekher, *General Mgr*
EMP: 99
SALES (est): 4.3MM
SALES (corp-wide): 22.2B **Publicly Held**
SIC: 3674 Integrated circuits, semiconductor networks, etc.
PA: Qualcomm Incorporated
5775 Morehouse Dr
San Diego CA 92121
858 587-1121

(P-19099)
QUALCOMM INCORPORATED
2016 Palomar Airport Rd # 100, Carlsbad
(92011-4400)
PHONE................................858 651-8481
David Lieber, *Principal*
EMP: 350
SALES (corp-wide): 22.2B **Publicly Held**
SIC: 3674 Integrated circuits, semiconductor networks, etc.
PA: Qualcomm Incorporated
5775 Morehouse Dr
San Diego CA 92121
858 587-1121

(P-19100)
QUALCOMM INCORPORATED
3135 Kifer Rd, Santa Clara (95051-0804)
PHONE................................408 216-6797
Vincent Jones, *Branch Mgr*
EMP: 350
SALES (corp-wide): 22.2B **Publicly Held**
SIC: 3674 Integrated circuits, semiconductor networks, etc.
PA: Qualcomm Incorporated
5775 Morehouse Dr
San Diego CA 92121
858 587-1121

(P-19101)
QUALCOMM INCORPORATED
3165 Kifer Rd, Santa Clara (95051-0804)
PHONE................................858 587-1121
Stephen Zee, *Branch Mgr*
Je W Kim, *Vice Pres*
Naveen Rawat, *Sr Software Eng*
Kefeng Tan, *Sr Software Eng*
Nicole Gross, *Info Tech Dir*
EMP: 14
SALES (corp-wide): 22.2B **Publicly Held**
WEB: www.qualcomm.com
SIC: 3674 Integrated circuits, semiconductor networks, etc.
PA: Qualcomm Incorporated
5775 Morehouse Dr
San Diego CA 92121
858 587-1121

(P-19102)
QUALCOMM INCORPORATED
5751 Pacific Center Blvd, San Diego
(92121-4252)
PHONE................................858 909-0316
Margaret L Johnson, *Branch Mgr*
Krishna Mendu, *Info Tech Mgr*
Kapil Tuteja, *Technology*
Vitaly Drapkin, *Engineer*
Harry Dang, *Senior Engr*
EMP: 350
SALES (corp-wide): 22.2B **Publicly Held**
WEB: www.qualcomm.com
SIC: 3674 Integrated circuits, semiconductor networks, etc.
PA: Qualcomm Incorporated
5775 Morehouse Dr
San Diego CA 92121
858 587-1121

(P-19103)
QUALCOMM INCORPORATED
9393 Waples St Ste 150, San Diego
(92121-3931)
PHONE................................858 587-1121
EMP: 350
SALES (corp-wide): 22.2B **Publicly Held**
WEB: www.qualcomm.com
SIC: 3674 7372 Integrated circuits, semiconductor networks, etc.; prepackaged software
PA: Qualcomm Incorporated
5775 Morehouse Dr
San Diego CA 92121
858 587-1121

(P-19104)
QUALCOMM INCORPORATED
10160 Pacific Mesa Blvd # 100, San Diego
(92121-4390)
PHONE................................858 587-1121
Marinko Karanovic, *Director*
EMP: 350
SALES (corp-wide): 22.2B **Publicly Held**
SIC: 3674 7372 6794 Integrated circuits, semiconductor networks, etc.; business oriented computer software; patent buying, licensing, leasing
PA: Qualcomm Incorporated
5775 Morehouse Dr
San Diego CA 92121
858 587-1121

(P-19105)
QUALCOMM LIMITED PARTNER INC
5775 Morehouse Dr, San Diego
(92121-1714)
PHONE................................858 587-1121
Anthony Thornley, *President*
Richard Sulpivil, *President*
EMP: 25
SALES (est): 1.6MM
SALES (corp-wide): 22.2B **Publicly Held**
SIC: 3674 Semiconductors & related devices
PA: Qualcomm Incorporated
5775 Morehouse Dr
San Diego CA 92121
858 587-1121

(P-19106)
QUALCOMM TECHNOLOGIES INC (HQ)
5525 Morehouse Dr, San Diego
(92121-1710)
PHONE................................858 587-1121
Steve Mollenkopf, *CEO*
Cristiano Amon, *President*
Dileep Bhandarkar, *Vice Pres*
Joe Glynn, *Vice Pres*
Mike Refermat, *Vice Pres*
▲ **EMP:** 140
SALES (est): 2.5B
SALES (corp-wide): 22.2B **Publicly Held**
SIC: 3674 7372 6794 Integrated circuits, semiconductor networks, etc.; business oriented computer software; patent buying, licensing, leasing
PA: Qualcomm Incorporated
5775 Morehouse Dr
San Diego CA 92121
858 587-1121

(P-19107)
QUANTENNA COMMUNICATIONS INC (PA)
1704 Automation Pkwy, San Jose
(95131-1873)
PHONE................................669 209-5500
Sam Heidari, *Ch of Bd*
Sean Sobers, *CFO*
Edward Frank, *Bd of Directors*
Harold Hughes, *Bd of Directors*
Jack Lazar, *Bd of Directors*
EMP: 28
SQ FT: 84,000
SALES: 176.3MM **Publicly Held**
SIC: 3674 Semiconductors & related devices

(P-19108)
QUANTUM 3D HEADQUARTERS
6330 San Ignacio Ave, San Jose
(95119-1209)
PHONE................................408 361-9999
Gordon Campbell, *Principal*
▲ **EMP:** 11
SALES (est): 691.1K **Privately Held**
SIC: 3674 Semiconductors & related devices

(P-19109)
QUANTUM SOLAR INC
6 Endeavor Dr, Corte Madera
(94925-2024)
PHONE................................415 924-8140
Tom Faust, *CEO*
EMP: 10

SALES (est): 800.3K **Privately Held**
SIC: 3674 Semiconductors & related devices

(P-19110)
QUANTUMSCAPE CORPORATION
1730 Technology Dr, San Jose
(95110-1331)
PHONE................................408 452-2000
Jagdeep Singh, *President*
Vanessa Ann Truong, *Controller*
EMP: 121
SALES (est): 576.7K **Privately Held**
SIC: 3674 Semiconductors & related devices

(P-19111)
QUELLAN INC
Also Called: Intersil Quellan
1001 Murphy Ranch Rd, Milpitas
(95035-7912)
PHONE................................408 546-3487
Tony Stelliga, *CEO*
Donald Macleod, *Ch of Bd*
James Diller, *CEO*
Guy Anthony, *CFO*
Joy Laskar, *CTO*
EMP: 27
SALES (est): 1.3MM
SALES (corp-wide): 4.5B **Privately Held**
SIC: 3674 Semiconductors & related devices
HQ: Renesas Electronics America Inc.
1001 Murphy Ranch Rd
Milpitas CA 95035
408 432-8888

(P-19112)
QUORUM SYSTEMS INC
5960 Cornerstone Ct W # 200, San Diego
(92121-3780)
PHONE................................858 546-0895
Bernard Xavier PHD, *President*
EMP: 10
SALES (est): 1.2MM **Privately Held**
WEB: www.quorumsystems.com
SIC: 3674 Semiconductors & related devices

(P-19113)
R2 SEMICONDUCTOR INC
1196 Borregas Ave Ste 201, Sunnyvale
(94089-1340)
PHONE................................408 745-7400
David Fisher, *President*
Frank Sasselli, *Vice Pres*
Larry Burns, *Principal*
Andrew Hartland, *Principal*
Ravi Ramachandran, *Principal*
EMP: 20
SALES (est): 3.4MM **Privately Held**
SIC: 3674 Integrated circuits, semiconductor networks, etc.

(P-19114)
RAMBUS INC
1050 Entp Way Ste 700, Sunnyvale
(94089)
PHONE................................440 397-2549
Becky Saldivar, *Branch Mgr*
EMP: 20
SALES (corp-wide): 393.1MM **Publicly Held**
SIC: 3674 Semiconductors & related devices
PA: Rambus Inc.
1050 Entp Way Ste 700
Sunnyvale CA 94089
408 462-8000

(P-19115)
RAMBUS INC (PA)
1050 Entp Way Ste 700, Sunnyvale
(94089)
PHONE................................408 462-8000
Luc Seraphin, *President*
Eric Stang, *Ch of Bd*
Rahul Mathur, *CFO*
Ellis Fisher, *Bd of Directors*
Penelope Herscher, *Bd of Directors*
◆ **EMP:** 277

SALES: 393.1MM **Publicly Held**
WEB: www.rambus.com
SIC: 3674 6794 Integrated circuits, semiconductor networks, etc.; patent owners & lessors

(P-19116)
RAMBUS INC
Lighting Technology Division
1050 Enterprise Way # 700, Sunnyvale
(94089-1417)
PHONE................................408 462-8000
Jeff Parker, *Senior VP*
Samira Naraghi, *Director*
EMP: 12
SALES (corp-wide): 393.1MM **Publicly Held**
SIC: 3674 Semiconductors & related devices
PA: Rambus Inc.
1050 Entp Way Ste 700
Sunnyvale CA 94089
408 462-8000

(P-19117)
REACTION TECHNOLOGY INC (PA)
3400 Bassett St, Santa Clara (95054-2703)
PHONE................................408 970-9601
Uzi Sasson, *CEO*
James Jacobson, *President*
David Sallous, *Vice Pres*
Janice Baker, *Office Mgr*
EMP: 21
SQ FT: 10,800
SALES (est): 3.6MM **Privately Held**
WEB: www.reactiontechnology.com
SIC: 3674 Integrated circuits, semiconductor networks, etc.

(P-19118)
REDPINE SIGNALS INC (PA)
2107 N 1st St Ste 540, San Jose
(95131-2028)
PHONE................................408 748-3385
Venkat Mattela, *CEO*
Kalpana Atluri, *President*
Nvenkatesh Venkatesh, *Senior VP*
David Casey, *Vice Pres*
Narasimha Nookala, *Vice Pres*
EMP: 27
SALES (est): 19MM **Privately Held**
SIC: 3674 Integrated circuits, semiconductor networks, etc.

(P-19119)
REFLEX PHOTONICS INC
1250 Oakmead Pkwy, Sunnyvale
(94085-4027)
PHONE................................408 501-8886
Ken Ahmad, *CEO*
Thomas Mino, *President*
David R Rolston PH D, *CTO*
EMP: 30
SALES (est): 1.8MM **Privately Held**
WEB: www.reflexphotonics.com
SIC: 3674

(P-19120)
RELIANCE COMPUTER CORP
2451 Mission College Blvd, Santa Clara
(95054-1214)
PHONE................................408 492-1915
▲ **EMP:** 115
SALES (est): 6MM
SALES (corp-wide): 4.2B **Publicly Held**
SIC: 3674 3672
HQ: Broadcom Corporation
5300 California Ave
Irvine CA 95131
949 926-5000

(P-19121)
RENESAS ELECTRONICS AMER INC
205 Llagas Rd, Morgan Hill (95037-3079)
PHONE................................408 546-3434
Kevin Ellis, *Principal*
EMP: 600
SALES (corp-wide): 4.5B **Privately Held**
SIC: 3674 Semiconductors & related devices
HQ: Renesas Electronics America Inc.
1001 Murphy Ranch Rd
Milpitas CA 95035
408 432-8888

▲ = Import ▼=Export
◆ =Import/Export

(P-19122)
RENESAS ELECTRONICS AMER INC
Also Called: Intersil Techwell
1541 Rollins Rd, Burlingame (94010-2305)
PHONE......................408 588-6750
Richard Turner, *Director*
EMP: 600
SALES (corp-wide): 4.5B **Privately Held**
SIC: 3674 Semiconductors & related devices
HQ: Renesas Electronics America Inc.
1001 Murphy Ranch Rd
Milpitas CA 95035
408 432-8888

(P-19123)
RENESAS ELECTRONICS AMER INC
Also Called: Intersil Design Center
10865 Rancho Bernardo Rd, San Diego
(92127-2113)
PHONE......................858 451-7240
Steve Trunkett, *Branch Mgr*
EMP: 600
SALES (corp-wide): 4.5B **Privately Held**
SIC: 3674 Semiconductors & related devices
HQ: Renesas Electronics America Inc.
1001 Murphy Ranch Rd
Milpitas CA 95035
408 432-8888

(P-19124)
RESONANT INC (PA)
110 Castilian Dr Ste 100, Goleta
(93117-3028)
PHONE......................805 308-9803
George B Holmes, *President*
John Major, *Ch of Bd*
Neal Fenzi, *COO*
Jeff Killian, *CFO*
Janet Cooper, *Bd of Directors*
EMP: 37
SQ FT: 9,000
SALES: 653K **Publicly Held**
SIC: 3674 Semiconductors & related devices

(P-19125)
REVOLUTION LIGHTING TECH INC
2280 Ward Ave, Simi Valley (93065-1859)
PHONE......................248 969-3800
EMP: 15
SALES (corp-wide): 152.3MM **Publicly Held**
SIC: 3674 Light emitting diodes
PA: Revolution Lighting Technologies, Inc.
177 Broad St Fl 12
Stamford CT 06901
203 504-1111

(P-19126)
RF DIGITAL CORPORATION
1601 Pcf Cast Hwy Ste 290, Hermosa
Beach (90254)
PHONE......................949 610-0008
Armen Kazanchian, *President*
Rod Landers, *COO*
Julie Stahl, *Office Mgr*
EMP: 105
SQ FT: 5,000
SALES (est): 17.9MM
SALES (corp-wide): 581.5MM **Privately Held**
SIC: 3674 Modules, solid state
HQ: Heptagon Usa, Inc.
465 N Whisman Rd Ste 200
Mountain View CA 94043
650 336-7990

(P-19127)
RIDGELINE POWER LLC
12100 Wilshire Blvd 805, Los Angeles
(90025-7120)
PHONE......................800 504-5844
H David Ramm, *CEO*
Tod Erich Fromlath, *COO*
Ganna Halvorsen, *Chairman*
EMP: 23
SALES (est): 1.7MM **Privately Held**
SIC: 3674 1711 Solar cells; solar energy
contractor

(P-19128)
RKD ENGINEERING CORP INC
316 S Navarra Dr, Scotts Valley
(95066-3622)
PHONE......................831 430-9464
Kirk Martin, *President*
Daniel Kaschala, *Vice Pres*
EMP: 10
SALES (est): 770K **Privately Held**
SIC: 3674 Semiconductor circuit networks

(P-19129)
ROBERTSON PRECISION INC
2971 Spring St, Redwood City
(94063-3935)
PHONE......................650 363-2212
Bernadette Robertson, *CEO*
William B Robertson, *President*
Eric Paulsen, *General Mgr*
EMP: 13
SALES (est): 1.6MM **Privately Held**
WEB: www.robertsonprecision.com
SIC: 3674 3842 3829 Wafers (semiconductor devices); implants, surgical; measuring & controlling devices

(P-19130)
RTG INC
4030 Spencer St Ste 108, Torrance
(90503-2463)
P.O. Box 3986 (90510-3986)
PHONE......................310 534-3016
Kurt Rasmussen, *President*
Mojca Rasmussen, *Corp Secy*
EMP: 10
SQ FT: 5,000
SALES (est): 1.3MM **Privately Held**
WEB: www.rtg.com
SIC: 3674 8731 Integrated circuits, semiconductor networks, etc.; electronic research

(P-19131)
S-ENERGY AMERICA INC (HQ)
18022 Cowan Ste 260, Irvine (92614-1600)
PHONE......................949 281-7897
David Kim, *President*
EMP: 12
SALES (est): 2.8MM
SALES (corp-wide): 181.6MM **Privately Held**
SIC: 3674 Solar cells
PA: S-Energy Co., Ltd.
3/F Mirae Asset Tower
Seongnam 13494
704 339-7100

(P-19132)
S3 GRAPHICS INC
940 Mission Ct, Fremont (94539-8202)
PHONE......................510 687-4900
Wenchih Chen, *President*
Iming Pai, *Vice Pres*
Michael Shiuan, *Vice Pres*
Joyce Cheng, *Engineer*
Allen Law, *Engineer*
EMP: 129
SALES (est): 14.8MM **Privately Held**
WEB: www.s3graphics.com
SIC: 3674 Semiconductors & related devices
PA: S3 Graphics Co., Ltd
C/O: Card Corporate Services Ltd
George Town GR CAYMAN
-

(P-19133)
SAAZ MICRO INC
94 W Cochran St Ste A, Simi Valley
(93065-0948)
PHONE......................805 405-0700
Atul Joshi, *CEO*
EMP: 10
SALES (est): 512.7K **Privately Held**
SIC: 3674 Semiconductors & related devices

(P-19134)
SAC-TEC LABS INC (PA)
24301 Wilmington Ave, Carson
(90745-6139)
PHONE......................310 375-5295
Robert Kunesh, *President*
Marylin Hafermalz, *Shareholder*
Manouk Ohanesyan, *Officer*
Bruce Kaufman, *Executive*

Kelley Owen, *Train & Dev Mgr*
EMP: 28
SQ FT: 10,000
SALES (est): 3.5MM **Privately Held**
SIC: 3674 Semiconductors & related devices

(P-19135)
SAMIL POWER US LTD
3478 Buskirk Ave Ste 1000, Pleasant Hill
(94523-4378)
PHONE......................925 930-3924
Peter Peiju Cui, *CEO*
▲ EMP: 600
SQ FT: 2,000
SALES (est): 24.7MM
SALES (corp-wide): 81.6K **Privately Held**
SIC: 3674 Solar cells
PA: Wuxi Samil Power Co., Ltd.
No.52, Huigu Venture Park, Zhenghe
Boulevard, Huishan District
Wuxi 21417
510 835-9313

(P-19136)
SANTIER INC
10103 Carroll Canyon Rd, San Diego
(92131-1109)
PHONE......................858 271-1993
Kevin Cotner, *CEO*
Warren Bartholomew, *CFO*
▼ EMP: 64
SQ FT: 23,000
SALES: 10MM
SALES (corp-wide): 18.5MM **Privately Held**
SIC: 3674 Semiconductors & related devices
HQ: Egide (Usa), Llc
4 Washington St
Cambridge MD 21613
410 901-6100

(P-19137)
SCALABLE SYSTEMS RES LABS INC
544 Monterey Rd, Pacifica (94044-2016)
PHONE......................650 322-6507
Axel K Kloth, *President*
EMP: 28
SALES: 3MM **Privately Held**
SIC: 3674 7371 7373 8731 Semiconductors & related devices; computer software development; computer integrated systems design; electronic research

(P-19138)
SCINTERA NETWORKS INC
160 Rio Robles, San Jose (95134-1813)
PHONE......................408 636-2600
Davin Lee, *CEO*
Scott M Gibson, *CFO*
Steffen Hahn, *Vice Pres*
Bob Koupal, *Vice Pres*
Rajeev Krishnamoorthy, *Vice Pres*
EMP: 30
SQ FT: 20,000
SALES (est): 5.5MM **Privately Held**
WEB: www.scintera.com
SIC: 3674 Semiconductors & related devices

(P-19139)
SEMI AUTOMATION & TECH INC
Also Called: Noel Technologies
1510 Dell Ave Ste C, Campbell
(95008-6917)
PHONE......................408 374-9549
Kristin Boyce, *President*
Brenda Hill, *Vice Pres*
Marianne Getreu, *Admin Asst*
Thelma Kamuchey, *Engineer*
▲ EMP: 42
SQ FT: 7,500
SALES (est): 7.5MM **Privately Held**
WEB: www.noeltech.com
SIC: 3674 Semiconductors & related devices

(P-19140)
SEMICNDCTOR CMPONENTS INDS LLC
2975 Stender Way, Santa Clara
(95054-3214)
PHONE......................408 542-1000
Gelu Voicu, *Manager*

EMP: 250
SALES (corp-wide): 5.5B **Publicly Held**
SIC: 3674 Semiconductors & related devices
HQ: Semiconductor Components Industries, Llc
5005 E Mcdowell Rd
Phoenix AZ 85008
800 282-9855

(P-19141)
SEMICOA CORPORATION
333 Mccormick Ave, Costa Mesa
(92626-3479)
PHONE......................714 979-1900
Thomas E Epley, *CEO*
Ramesh Ramchandani, *President*
Perry Denning, *COO*
Gary B Joyce, *CFO*
▲ EMP: 60
SALES (est): 13MM **Privately Held**
SIC: 3674 Semiconductors & related devices

(P-19142)
SEMICONDUCTOR COMPONENTS INC
Also Called: SCI
1353 E Edinger Ave, Santa Ana
(92705-4430)
PHONE......................714 547-6059
Archie L Brainard, *President*
EMP: 20 EST: 1959
SQ FT: 2,500
SALES (est): 2.4MM **Privately Held**
WEB: www.semiconductorcomponents.com
SIC: 3674 Semiconductor circuit networks

(P-19143)
SEMICONDUCTOR LOGISTICS CORP
14409 Iseli Rd, Santa Fe Springs
(90670-5205)
PHONE......................562 921-0399
Clarine Reed, *Manager*
EMP: 11
SALES (est): 785.8K **Privately Held**
WEB: www.slc-semiconductors.com
SIC: 3674 Semiconductors & related devices

(P-19144)
SEMICONIX CORP (PA)
2968 Scott Blvd, Santa Clara (95054-3322)
PHONE......................408 986-8026
Serban Porumbescu, *President*
Mihaela Porumbescu, *CFO*
Thuan Lai, *Vice Pres*
EMP: 12
SALES: 2.5MM **Privately Held**
WEB: www.semiconix.com
SIC: 3674 Semiconductors & related devices

(P-19145)
SEMINET INC
150 Great Oaks Blvd, San Jose
(95119-1347)
PHONE......................408 754-8537
Humayun Kabir, *Principal*
Greg Krikorian, *Principal*
EMP: 10
SALES (est): 1.2MM **Privately Held**
WEB: www.seminet.com
SIC: 3674 Semiconductors & related devices

(P-19146)
SEMTECH CORPORATION (PA)
200 Flynn Rd, Camarillo (93012-8790)
PHONE......................805 498-2111
Mohan R Maheswaran, *President*
Rockell N Hankin, *Ch of Bd*
Emeka N Chukwu, *CFO*
James P Burra, *Vice Ch Bd*
Charles B Ammann, *Exec VP*
▲ EMP: 180 EST: 1960
SQ FT: 87,600
SALES: 587.8MM **Publicly Held**
WEB: www.semtech.com
SIC: 3674 Semiconductors & related devices

(P-19147)
SEMTECH SAN DIEGO CORPORATION
10021 Willow Creek Rd, San Diego (92131-1657)
PHONE..................858 695-1808
Mark Drucker, *President*
Sharon Faltemier, *Vice Pres*
Matt Peter, *Engineer*
Tom Pimental, *Buyer*
EMP: 46
SQ FT: 25,000
SALES (est): 4.5MM
SALES (corp-wide): 587.8MM **Publicly Held**
WEB: www.semtech.com
SIC: 3674 Integrated circuits, semiconductor networks, etc.
PA: Semtech Corporation
200 Flynn Rd
Camarillo CA 93012
805 498-2111

(P-19148)
SENSORONIX INC
16181 Scientific, Irvine (92618-4325)
PHONE..................949 528-0906
Sid M Gomman, *President*
Mina Gomnam, *Controller*
EMP: 12
SALES (est): 1.7MM **Privately Held**
WEB: www.sensoronix.com
SIC: 3674 Infrared sensors, solid state

(P-19149)
SII SEMICONDUCTOR USA CORP
21221 S Wstn Ave Ste 250, Torrance (90501)
PHONE..................310 517-7771
James Schlumpberger, *Vice Pres*
EMP: 11
SALES (est): 577.7K **Privately Held**
SIC: 3674 Semiconductors & related devices

(P-19150)
SILICON GENESIS CORPORATION
Also Called: Sigen
145 Baytech Dr, San Jose (95134-2303)
PHONE..................408 228-5858
Theodore E Fong, *CEO*
Francois J Henley, *President*
Theodore Fong, *CEO*
Philip J Ong, *Vice Pres*
Brad Dutton, *Info Tech Mgr*
▲ EMP: 70
SALES (est): 14.2MM **Privately Held**
WEB: www.sigen.com
SIC: 3674 8731 Semiconductors & related devices; commercial physical research

(P-19151)
SILICON IMAGE INC (HQ)
2115 Onel Dr, San Jose (95131-2032)
PHONE..................408 616-4000
Joe Bedewi, *CFO*
Kurt Thielen, *President*
Byron Milstead, *Vice Pres*
David L Rutledge, *CTO*
Victor Da Costa, *Engng Exec*
▲ EMP: 63
SQ FT: 128,154
SALES (est): 77.1MM
SALES (corp-wide): 385.9MM **Publicly Held**
WEB: www.siimage.com
SIC: 3674 7371 Semiconductors & related devices; computer software development & applications
PA: Lattice Semiconductor Corp
111 Sw 5th Ave Ste 700
Portland OR 97204
503 268-8000

(P-19152)
SILICON LABS INTEGRATION INC (HQ)
Also Called: Silicon Laboratories
940 Stewart Dr, Sunnyvale (94085-3912)
PHONE..................408 702-1400
Jean Luc Nauleau, *President*
Pierre Lamond, *Chairman*
Eric Radza, *Engineer*

Jim Parker, *Manager*
EMP: 19
SALES (est): 3.1MM **Publicly Held**
WEB: www.integration.com
SIC: 3674 Semiconductors & related devices

(P-19153)
SILICON LIGHT MACHINES CORP (DH)
820 Kifer Rd, Sunnyvale (94086-5200)
PHONE..................408 240-4700
Lars Eng, *CEO*
Ken Fukui, *Senior VP*
EMP: 11
SQ FT: 18,000
SALES (est): 2.3MM
SALES (corp-wide): 3.1B **Privately Held**
WEB: www.siliconlight.com
SIC: 3674 Semiconductors & related devices
HQ: Screen North America Holdings, Inc.
5110 Tollview Dr
Rolling Meadows IL 60008
847 870-7400

(P-19154)
SILICON MOTION INC
690 N Mccarthy Blvd # 200, Milpitas (95035-5134)
PHONE..................408 501-5300
Wallace Kou, *President*
Jason Chiang, *CFO*
Richard Chang, *Vice Pres*
Bernadette Aguilon, *Admin Asst*
Robert Abutan, *Software Engr*
EMP: 60
SQ FT: 12,000
SALES (est): 11.9MM **Privately Held**
WEB: www.siliconmotion.com
SIC: 3674 Integrated circuits, semiconductor networks, etc.
HQ: Silicon Motion, Inc.
8f-1, 36, Tai Yuan St.,
Chupei City HSI 30265
355 268-88

(P-19155)
SILICON SPECIALISTS INC
2487 Industrial Pkwy W, Hayward (94545-5007)
PHONE..................510 732-9796
Wayne Cheung, *President*
Kimberly Nguyen, *Vice Pres*
EMP: 10
SQ FT: 8,000
SALES (est): 1MM **Privately Held**
SIC: 3674 Wafers (semiconductor devices)

(P-19156)
SILICON SPREAD CORP
19925 S Creek Blvd 100, Cupertino (95014)
PHONE..................855 446-7634
Tao Jing, *CEO*
Dat Dinh, *Manager*
EMP: 70
SALES (est): 3.2MM **Privately Held**
SIC: 3674 Integrated circuits, semiconductor networks, etc.

(P-19157)
SILICON STANDARD CORP
Also Called: SSC
4701 Patrick Henry Dr # 16, Santa Clara (95054-1863)
PHONE..................408 234-6964
EMP: 20
SALES (est): 2.2MM **Privately Held**
WEB: www.siliconstandard.com
SIC: 3674

(P-19158)
SILICON TURNKEY SOLUTIONS INC (HQ)
1804 Mccarthy Blvd, Milpitas (95035-7410)
PHONE..................408 904-0200
Richard Kingdon, *President*
Michael Rooney, *CFO*
Mado Dhouni, *Vice Pres*
Virginia Benguerel, *Executive*
Dave Sinofsky, *Business Dir*
EMP: 17
SQ FT: 35,000

SALES (est): 16.8MM
SALES (corp-wide): 87.1MM **Privately Held**
WEB: www.siliconturnkey.com
SIC: 3674 5065 Microcircuits, integrated (semiconductor); semiconductor devices
PA: Micross Components, Inc.
7725 N Orange Blossom Trl
Orlando FL 32810
407 298-7100

(P-19159)
SILICON VLY MCRELECTRONICS INC
Also Called: S V M
2985 Kifer Rd, Santa Clara (95051-0802)
PHONE..................408 844-7100
Patrick Callinan, *President*
Helen Tsai, *Vice Pres*
Nathan Barnes, *Technology*
Jon Broenen, *Sr Project Mgr*
◆ EMP: 30
SQ FT: 30,000
SALES (est): 7.3MM **Privately Held**
WEB: www.svmi.com
SIC: 3674 Semiconductors & related devices

(P-19160)
SILICONCORE TECHNOLOGY INC
890 Hillview Ct Ste 120, Milpitas (95035-4573)
PHONE..................408 946-8185
Eric LI, *President*
Sonny Tang, *President*
Robert Young, *President*
Heng Liu, *Officer*
Nicos Syrimis, *Senior VP*
▲ EMP: 23
SQ FT: 6,000
SALES (est): 27MM **Privately Held**
WEB: www.silicon-core.com
SIC: 3674 Integrated circuits, semiconductor networks, etc.

(P-19161)
SILICONIX INCORPORATED (HQ)
2585 Junction Ave, San Jose (95134-1923)
PHONE..................408 988-8000
Serge Jaunay, *CEO*
King Owyang, *President*
Nick Bacile, *COO*
▲ EMP: 610
SQ FT: 220,100
SALES (est): 319.4MM
SALES (corp-wide): 2.6B **Publicly Held**
SIC: 3674 Transistors
PA: Vishay Intertechnology, Inc.
63 Lancaster Ave
Malvern PA 19355
610 644-1300

(P-19162)
SILVER PEAK SYSTEMS INC (PA)
2860 De La Cruz Blvd # 100, Santa Clara (95050-2635)
PHONE..................408 935-1800
David Hughes, *CEO*
Eric Yeaman, *CFO*
John Vincenzo, *Chief Mktg Ofcr*
Nick Applegarth, *Vice Pres*
Derek Granath, *Vice Pres*
EMP: 120
SQ FT: 29,000
SALES (est): 31.8MM **Privately Held**
WEB: www.silver-peak.com
SIC: 3674 Integrated circuits, semiconductor networks, etc.

(P-19163)
SIMMITRI INC
Also Called: Simmitri Energy Efficiency
1999 S Bascom Ave Ste 700, Campbell (95008-2205)
PHONE..................408 779-3333
EMP: 45
SALES (est): 1.5MM **Privately Held**
SIC: 3674 Solar cells

(P-19164)
SIPEX CORPORATION (DH)
48720 Kato Rd, Fremont (94538-7312)
PHONE..................510 668-7000

Ralph Schmitt, *CEO*
Clyde R Wallin, *CFO*
Lee Cleveland, *Senior VP*
Khem Chhabra, *Engineer*
Cs Mitter, *Manager*
EMP: 140
SQ FT: 95,700
SALES (est): 13.2MM
SALES (corp-wide): 420.3MM **Publicly Held**
WEB: www.sipex.com
SIC: 3674 Integrated circuits, semiconductor networks, etc.; monolithic integrated circuits (solid state)
HQ: Exar Corporation
1060 Rincon Cir
San Jose CA 95131
669 265-6100

(P-19165)
SIRF TECHNOLOGY HOLDINGS INC (DH)
1060 Rincon Cir, San Jose (95131-1325)
PHONE..................408 523-6500
Diosdado B Banatao, *Ch of Bd*
Diosdado P Banatao, *Ch of Bd*
Dennis Bencala, *CFO*
Geoffrey Ribar, *CFO*
Kanwar Chadha, *Vice Pres*
EMP: 75
SQ FT: 48,000
SALES (est): 30.9MM
SALES (corp-wide): 22.2B **Publicly Held**
WEB: www.sirf.com
SIC: 3674 3663 Semiconductors & related devices;

(P-19166)
SITEK PROCESS SOLUTIONS
233 Technology Way Ste 3, Rocklin (95765-1208)
PHONE..................916 797-9000
James Mullany, *President*
Terri Mullany, *Vice Pres*
Tyler Israel, *Manager*
▲ EMP: 13
SQ FT: 8,000
SALES (est): 2.5MM **Privately Held**
WEB: www.sitekprocess.com
SIC: 3674 Semiconductors & related devices

(P-19167)
SITIME CORPORATION (HQ)
5451 Patrick Henry Dr, Santa Clara (95054-1167)
PHONE..................408 328-4400
Rajesh Vashist, *CEO*
Kurt Peterson, *Shareholder*
Mark Lunsford, *President*
Craig Garber, *CFO*
Piyush Sevalia, *Exec VP*
EMP: 70
SQ FT: 32,000
SALES (est): 18.7MM
SALES (corp-wide): 835.6MM **Privately Held**
WEB: www.sitime.com
SIC: 3674 5065 Semiconductors & related devices; semiconductor devices
PA: Megachips Corporation
1-1-1, Miyahara, Yodogawa-Ku
Osaka OSK 532-0
663 992-884

(P-19168)
SJT TECH INDUSTRIES INC
1400 Coleman Ave Ste E28, Santa Clara (95050-4358)
PHONE..................408 980-9547
Jake Rhee, *Principal*
EMP: 10
SALES (est): 1MM **Privately Held**
SIC: 3674 Semiconductors & related devices

(P-19169)
SK HYNIX MEMORY SOLUTIONS INC (HQ)
3103 N 1st St, San Jose (95134-1934)
PHONE..................408 514-3500
Tony Yoon, *CEO*
Sang SOO Son, *CFO*
Chee Hoe Chu, *Vice Pres*
Amos Kim, *Admin Asst*
Scott Owen, *Administration*

▲ = Import ▼=Export
◆ =Import/Export

EMP: 22
SALES (est): 35.9MM
SALES (corp-wide): 27.1B **Privately Held**
SIC: 3674 Semiconductors & related devices
PA: Sk Hynix Inc.
2091 Gyeongchung-Daero, Bubal-Eup
Icheon 17336
823 163-0411

(P-19170)
SKYWORKS SOLUTIONS INC
2427 W Hillcrest Dr, Newbury Park
(91320-2202)
PHONE..................805 480-4400
Michael Gooch, *Manager*
Terry Pope, *COO*
Frank S Lee, *Info Tech Dir*
Lam Luu, *Engineer*
Alireza Kheirkhahi, *Senior Mgr*
EMP: 56
SALES (corp-wide): 3.8B **Publicly Held**
WEB: www.alphaind.com
SIC: 3674 Semiconductors & related devices
PA: Skyworks Solutions, Inc.
20 Sylvan Rd
Woburn MA 01801
781 376-3000

(P-19171)
SKYWORKS SOLUTIONS INC
730 Lawrence Dr, Newbury Park
(91320-2207)
PHONE..................805 480-4227
Xiao-Ping LI, *Engineer*
EMP: 56
SALES (corp-wide): 3.8B **Publicly Held**
SIC: 3674 Semiconductors & related devices
PA: Skyworks Solutions, Inc.
20 Sylvan Rd
Woburn MA 01801
781 376-3000

(P-19172)
SMART GLOBAL HOLDINGS INC (PA)
39870 Eureka Dr, Newark (94560-4809)
PHONE..................510 623-1231
Ajay Shah, *Ch of Bd*
Iain Mackenzie, *President*
Jack Pacheco, *COO*
Sandeep Nayyar, *Bd of Directors*
Mukesh Patel, *Bd of Directors*
EMP: 11 EST: 1988
SQ FT: 79,480
SALES: 1.2B **Publicly Held**
SIC: 3674 Semiconductors & related devices

(P-19173)
SMART MODULAR TECH DE INC (HQ)
45800 Northport Loop W, Fremont
(94538-6413)
PHONE..................510 623-1231
Jack Pacheco, *CEO*
EMP: 175
SALES (est): 166.5MM
SALES (corp-wide): 1.2B **Publicly Held**
SIC: 3674 Semiconductors & related devices
PA: Smart Global Holdings, Inc.
39870 Eureka Dr
Newark CA 94560
510 623-1231

(P-19174)
SMART MODULAR TECHNOLOGIES INC
15635 Alton Pkwy Ste 155, Irvine
(92618-7326)
PHONE..................949 753-0117
Wayne Eisenberg, *Manager*
Denise Pomeroy, *Executive*
EMP: 23
SALES (corp-wide): 1.2B **Publicly Held**
WEB: www.smartm.com
SIC: 3674 Semiconductors & related devices
HQ: Smart Modular Technologies Inc.
39870 Eureka Dr
Newark CA 94560

(P-19175)
SMT ELECTRONICS MFG INC
2630 S Shannon St, Santa Ana
(92704-5230)
PHONE..................714 751-8894
Henry T Tran, *CEO*
Huy Pham, *General Mgr*
EMP: 35
SQ FT: 12,104
SALES (est): 4.6MM **Privately Held**
WEB: www.smtelectronics.com
SIC: 3674 3672 Integrated circuits, semiconductor networks, etc.; printed circuit boards

(P-19176)
SOLAICX
600 Clipper Dr, Belmont (94002-4119)
PHONE..................408 988-5000
David Ranhoff, *President*
Guy Anthony, *CFO*
John T Sedgwick, *Founder*
Peter Bostock PHD, *Vice Pres*
Peter Schwartz, *Vice Pres*
▲ **EMP:** 83
SQ FT: 36,000
SALES (est): 8.9MM
SALES (corp-wide): 2.4B **Privately Held**
WEB: www.solaicx.com
SIC: 3674 Silicon wafers, chemically doped
PA: Sunedison, Inc.
13736 Riverport Dr
Maryland Heights MO 63043
314 770-7300

(P-19177)
SOLARTECH POWER INC
901 E Cedar St, Ontario (91761-5572)
PHONE..................909 673-0178
Sherry Fu, *President*
Maribel Rivera, *Sales Staff*
EMP: 10 EST: 2005
SALES (est): 1.4MM **Privately Held**
SIC: 3674 Solar cells

(P-19178)
SOLERA LABORATORIES INC
3940 Freedom Cir, Santa Clara
(95054-1204)
PHONE..................408 200-3131
John O'Neill, *President*
Saad Al Kenany, *CEO*
Larry Lessler, *CFO*
EMP: 12
SALES (est): 1.1MM **Privately Held**
SIC: 3674 Solar cells

(P-19179)
SOLID STATE DEVICES INC
Also Called: Ssdi
14701 Firestone Blvd, La Mirada
(90638-5918)
PHONE..................562 404-4474
Arnold N Applebaum, *President*
Mike Faucher, *COO*
David Franz, *CFO*
Beatrice Candelaria, *Info Tech Mgr*
Eli Dexter, *Design Engr*
▲ **EMP:** 110
SQ FT: 32,000
SALES (est): 21.9MM **Privately Held**
WEB: www.ssdi-power.com
SIC: 3674 Diodes, solid state (germanium, silicon, etc.)

(P-19180)
SONIC TECHNOLOGY PRODUCTS INC
108 Boulder St, Nevada City (95959-2610)
P.O. Box 539, Grass Valley (95945-0539)
PHONE..................530 272-4607
Melanie Sullivan, *CEO*
Justin Reinholz, *President*
Craig Ashcraft, *Vice Pres*
Jo Alsing, *Finance Mgr*
▲ **EMP:** 29
SQ FT: 2,000
SALES (est): 7.6MM **Privately Held**
SIC: 3674 3651 Semiconductors & related devices; household audio & video equipment

(P-19181)
SORAA INC (PA)
6500 Kaiser Dr Ste 110, Fremont
(94555-3662)
PHONE..................510 456-2200
Jeffery Parker, *CEO*
George Stringer, *Senior VP*
Nahid Afshar, *Vice Pres*
Todd Antes, *Vice Pres*
Mark D'Evelyn, *Vice Pres*
◆ **EMP:** 90
SQ FT: 50,000
SALES (est): 27.3MM **Privately Held**
SIC: 3674 3641 Semiconductors & related devices; electric lamps; electric lamp (bulb) parts

(P-19182)
SOURCE PHOTONICS USA INC (HQ)
8521 Fllbrook Ave Ste 200, Canoga Park
(91304)
PHONE..................818 773-9044
Noah Lotan, *Ch of Bd*
Aaron Levy, *President*
Gordon LI, *Vice Pres*
Jan Yu, *Vice Pres*
Mark Heimbuch, *CTO*
EMP: 249
SALES (est): 40.1MM
SALES (corp-wide): 80.3MM **Privately Held**
WEB: www.luminentinc.com
SIC: 3674 Semiconductors & related devices
PA: Mrv Communications, Inc.
20520 Nordhoff St
Chatsworth CA 91311
818 773-0900

(P-19183)
SPANSION INC (HQ)
198 Champion Ct, San Jose (95134-1709)
P.O. Box 3453, Sunnyvale (94088-3453)
PHONE..................408 962-2500
John H Kispert, *President*
Akinori Kobayashi, *President*
Gary Wang, *President*
Randy W Furr, *CFO*
Glenda Dorchak, *Exec VP*
▲ **EMP:** 10
SALES (est): 1B
SALES (corp-wide): 2.3B **Publicly Held**
WEB: www.spansion.com
SIC: 3674 Integrated circuits, semiconductor networks, etc.
PA: Cypress Semiconductor Corporation
198 Champion Ct
San Jose CA 95134
408 943-2600

(P-19184)
SPANSION LLC (HQ)
198 Champion Ct, San Jose (95134-1709)
P.O. Box 3453, Sunnyvale (94088-3453)
PHONE..................512 691-8500
Tom Moon, *Opers Staff*
Thad Trent, *President*
Eugene Spevakov, *Treasurer*
▲ **EMP:** 81
SALES (est): 80.4MM
SALES (corp-wide): 2.3B **Publicly Held**
SIC: 3674 Semiconductors & related devices
PA: Cypress Semiconductor Corporation
198 Champion Ct
San Jose CA 95134
408 943-2600

(P-19185)
SPATIAL PHOTONICS INC
930 Hamlin Ct, Sunnyvale (94089-1401)
PHONE..................408 940-8800
Wald Siskens, *President*
Shaoher Pan, *CTO*
EMP: 40
SALES (est): 5.3MM **Privately Held**
SIC: 3674 Semiconductors & related devices

(P-19186)
SPECTROLAB INC
12500 Gladstone Ave, Sylmar
(91342-5373)
P.O. Box 9209 (91392-9209)
PHONE..................818 365-4611
David Lillington, *President*
Paul Ballew, *CFO*
Nasser Karam, *Vice Pres*
Jeff Peacock, *Vice Pres*
Edward Ringo, *Vice Pres*
EMP: 400
SQ FT: 50,000
SALES (est): 89.8MM
SALES (corp-wide): 93.3B **Publicly Held**
WEB: www.spectrolab.com
SIC: 3674 3679 Solar cells; power supplies, all types: static
HQ: Boeing Satellite Systems, Inc.
900 N Pacific Coast Hwy
El Segundo CA 90245

(P-19187)
STATS CHIPPAC INC (DH)
46429 Landing Pkwy, Fremont
(94538-6496)
PHONE..................510 979-8000
Tan Lay Koon, *President*
Wan Choong Hoe, *Exec VP*
Han Byung Joon, *Exec VP*
John Lau Tai Chong, *Senior VP*
Janet Taylor, *Senior VP*
▲ **EMP:** 50
SQ FT: 190,000
SALES (est): 13.9MM **Privately Held**
WEB: www.statschippac.com
SIC: 3674 Integrated circuits, semiconductor networks, etc.
HQ: Stats Chippac Pte. Ltd.
10 Ang Mo Kio Street 65
Singapore 56905
682 477-77

(P-19188)
STATS CHIPPAC TEST SVCS INC
Also Called: Fastramp
9710 Scranton Rd Ste 360, San Diego
(92121-1711)
PHONE..................858 228-4084
Louis Benton, *Manager*
EMP: 25 **Privately Held**
SIC: 3674 Semiconductors & related devices
HQ: Stats Chippac Test Services, Inc.
46429 Landing Pkwy
Fremont CA 94538

(P-19189)
STATS CHIPPAC TEST SVCS INC (DH)
Also Called: Fastramp
46429 Landing Pkwy, Fremont
(94538-6496)
PHONE..................510 979-8000
Tan Lay Koon, *President*
David Goldberg, *Admin Sec*
EMP: 15
SALES (est): 3.4MM **Privately Held**
SIC: 3674 Semiconductors & related devices
HQ: Stats Chippac Pte. Ltd.
10 Ang Mo Kio Street 65
Singapore 56905
682 477-77

(P-19190)
STION CORPORATION (PA)
333 S Grand Ave Ste 4070, Los Angeles
(90071-1544)
PHONE..................408 284-7200
Chet Farris, *CEO*
Daniel Teo, *CFO*
Isabelle Roch-Jeune, *Regl Sales Mgr*
EMP: 100
SALES (est): 75.9MM **Privately Held**
SIC: 3674 Semiconductors & related devices

(P-19191)
STMICROELECTRONICS INC
85 Enterprise Ste 300, Aliso Viejo
(92656-2614)
PHONE..................949 347-0717
EMP: 34
SALES (corp-wide): 7.4B **Privately Held**
SIC: 3674
HQ: Stmicroelectronics, Inc
750 Canyon Dr Ste 300
Coppell TX 75019
972 466-6000

PRODUCTS & SVCS

(P-19192)
STMICROELECTRONICS INC
2755 Great America Way, Santa Clara
(95054-1166)
PHONE.............................408 919-8400
Elias Antoun, *Branch Mgr*
Davide Crespi, *Design Engr*
Jeffrey Fedison, *Technology*
Ashish Bhargava, *Engineer*
John Kvam, *Engineer*
EMP: 26
SALES (corp-wide): 8.3B **Privately Held**
WEB: www.st.com
SIC: 3674 Semiconductors & related devices
HQ: Stmicroelectronics, Inc
   750 Canyon Dr Ste 300
   Coppell TX 75019
   972 466-6000

(P-19193)
STRATAMET INC
46009 Hotchkiss St, Fremont (94539-7081)
PHONE.............................510 651-7176
Mark A Capalongan, *CEO*
Mark Wesson, *President*
▲ EMP: 25
SQ FT: 13,000
SALES (est): 2.2MM **Privately Held**
WEB: www.stratamet.com
SIC: 3674 3671 3699 3264 Semiconductors & related devices; electron tubes; electrical equipment & supplies; porcelain electrical supplies

(P-19194)
STRATEDGE CORPORATION
Also Called: Strat Edge
9424 Abraham Way Ste A, Santee
(92071-5640)
PHONE.............................866 424-4962
Tim Going, *President*
Josie Santos, *CFO*
Casey Krawiec, *Vice Pres*
Donald Pehle, *QA Dir*
Tisha Soto, *Recruiter*
EMP: 40
SALES (est): 7.6MM **Privately Held**
WEB: www.stratedge.com
SIC: 3674 Semiconductors & related devices

(P-19195)
STRETCH INC
48720 Kato Rd, Fremont (94538-7312)
PHONE.............................408 543-2700
Craig Lytle, *President*
Bob Beachler, *Vice Pres*
Wayne P Heideman, *Vice Pres*
Elena Gonzalez, *Executive Asst*
Albert Wang, *CTO*
EMP: 65
SALES (est): 6.7MM
SALES (corp-wide): 420.3MM **Publicly Held**
WEB: www.stretchinc.com
SIC: 3674 Integrated circuits, semiconductor networks, etc.
HQ: Exar Corporation
   1060 Rincon Cir
   San Jose CA 95131
   669 265-6100

(P-19196)
SUMCO PHOENIX CORPORATION
2099 Gateway Pl Ste 400, San Jose
(95110-1017)
PHONE.............................408 352-3880
Abate Drar, *Technical Staff*
EMP: 67
SALES (corp-wide): 2.3B **Privately Held**
SIC: 3674 Silicon wafers, chemically doped
HQ: Sumco Phoenix Corporation
   19801 N Tatum Blvd
   Phoenix AZ 85050
   480 473-6000

(P-19197)
SUMMIT MICROELECTRONICS INC (HQ)
757 N Mary Ave, Sunnyvale (94085-2909)
PHONE.............................408 523-1000
Patrick Brockett, *President*

Rich Palm, *President*
Larry Clifford, *Vice Pres*
EMP: 21
SQ FT: 25,000
SALES (est): 3.1MM
SALES (corp-wide): 22.2B **Publicly Held**
SIC: 3674
PA: Qualcomm Incorporated
   5775 Morehouse Dr
   San Diego CA 92121
   858 587-1121

(P-19198)
SUMMIT WIRELESS TECH INC
6840 Via Del Oro Ste 280, San Jose
(95119-1380)
PHONE.............................408 627-4716
Brett Moyer, *Ch of Bd*
Gary Williams, *CFO*
EMP: 49
SQ FT: 1,500
SALES: 1.1MM **Privately Held**
SIC: 3674 Semiconductors & related devices

(P-19199)
SUNCORE INC
3200 El Camino Real # 100, Irvine
(92602-1378)
PHONE.............................949 450-0054
Steven Brimmer, *President*
Donald A Nevins, *Treasurer*
Michael Swan, *Vice Pres*
Jennifer Mansoor, *Executive Asst*
Richard Sanett, *Director*
▲ EMP: 20
SQ FT: 5,000
SALES (est): 2.4MM **Privately Held**
SIC: 3674 5063 5065 Solar cells; batteries; electronic parts & equipment

(P-19200)
SUNLINE ENERGY INC
7546 Trade St, San Diego (92121-2412)
PHONE.............................858 997-2408
Matthew Margolin, *CEO*
Justin Jeffries, *Opers Mgr*
EMP: 48
SQ FT: 5,000
SALES (est): 483.1K **Privately Held**
SIC: 3674 3829 Solar cells; solarimeters

(P-19201)
SUNLINK CORPORATION (PA)
2 Belvedere Pl Ste 210, Mill Valley
(94941-2486)
PHONE.............................415 925-9650
Michael Maulick, *President*
Martin Lynch, *COO*
Ken Schwarz, *CFO*
John Eastwood, *Chairman*
Katherine Reid Sherwood, *Senior VP*
EMP: 11
SQ FT: 3,000
SALES: 56.5MM **Privately Held**
WEB: www.sunlinkllc.com
SIC: 3674 Stud bases or mounts for semiconductor devices

(P-19202)
SUNPOWER CORPORATION (DH)
77 Rio Robles, San Jose (95134-1859)
PHONE.............................408 240-5500
Thomas H Werner, *Ch of Bd*
Charles D Boynton, *CFO*
Kenneth J Mahaffey, *Exec VP*
William P Mulligan III, *Exec VP*
Douglas J Richards, *Exec VP*
▲ EMP: 600
SQ FT: 129,000
SALES: 1.8B
SALES (corp-wide): 8.3B **Publicly Held**
WEB: www.sunpowercorp.com
SIC: 3674 3679 Solar cells; photoelectric cells, solid state (electronic eye); power supplies, all types: static
HQ: Total Energies Nouvelles Activites Usa
   La Defense
   Courbevoie 92400
   147 444-546

(P-19203)
SUNPREME INC
615 Palomar Ave, Sunnyvale (94085-2913)
PHONE.............................408 245-1112

Ashok K Sinha, *CEO*
Mike Wanebo, *President*
Ratson Morad, *COO*
Surinder S Bedi, *Exec VP*
Homi Fateni, *Senior VP*
◆ EMP: 30 EST: 2009
SALES (est): 8.2MM **Privately Held**
SIC: 3674 Solar cells

(P-19204)
SUNSIL INC (PA)
3174 Danville Blvd Ste 1, Alamo
(94507-1919)
P.O. Box 220 (94507-0220)
PHONE.............................925 648-7779
Seth Alavi, *President*
▲ EMP: 10 EST: 1999
SALES (est): 8.1MM **Privately Held**
WEB: www.sunsil.com
SIC: 3674 Semiconductors & related devices

(P-19205)
SUNSYSTEM TECHNOLOGY LLC
Also Called: Next Phase Solar
2802 10th St, Berkeley (94710-2711)
PHONE.............................510 984-2027
Adam Burstein, *Branch Mgr*
EMP: 375
SALES (est): 31.6MM
SALES (corp-wide): 52.2MM **Privately Held**
SIC: 3674 Photovoltaic devices, solid state
PA: Sunsystem Technology Llc
   2731 Citrus Rd Ste D
   Rancho Cordova CA 95742
   916 671-3351

(P-19206)
SUNWORKS INC (PA)
1030 Winding Creek Rd # 100, Roseville
(95678-7046)
PHONE.............................916 409-6900
Charles Cargile, *CEO*
Joshua Schechter, *Ch of Bd*
Philip Radmilovic, *CFO*
Paul C McDonnel, *Treasurer*
EMP: 92
SALES: 77.4MM **Publicly Held**
WEB: www.machinetalker.com
SIC: 3674 Integrated circuits, semiconductor networks, etc.

(P-19207)
SUPERTEX INC (HQ)
1235 Bordeaux Dr, Sunnyvale
(94089-1203)
PHONE.............................408 222-8888
Henry C Pao PH D, *President*
Benedict C K Choy, *Senior VP*
Mike Yeh, *Design Engr Mgr*
Miguel Salcedo, *Research*
John Billingsley, *Technology*
▲ EMP: 62
SQ FT: 42,000
SALES (est): 51.2MM
SALES (corp-wide): 3.9B **Publicly Held**
SIC: 3674 Integrated circuits, semiconductor networks, etc.; light emitting diodes; semiconductor circuit networks; monolithic integrated circuits (solid state)
PA: Microchip Technology Inc
   2355 W Chandler Blvd
   Chandler AZ 85224
   480 792-7200

(P-19208)
SURFACE ART ENGINEERING INC
81 Bonaventura Dr, San Jose
(95134-2105)
PHONE.............................408 433-4700
Jennifer Lee, *CEO*
Richard Kundert, *President*
Angela Choi, *Program Mgr*
Paul Edwards, *Engineer*
Jimmy Chung, *Purchasing*
▲ EMP: 50
SQ FT: 24,000
SALES (est): 12.3MM **Privately Held**
WEB: www.surface-art.com
SIC: 3674 Computer logic modules

(P-19209)
SYMMETRY ELECTRONICS LLC (DH)
Also Called: Semiconductorstore.com
5400 W Rosecrans Ave, Hawthorne
(90250-6682)
PHONE.............................310 536-6190
Joe Caravana, *Co-Founder*
Scott Wing, *President*
Gil Zaharoni, *Co-Founder*
▲ EMP: 35
SQ FT: 15,000
SALES (est): 9.6MM
SALES (corp-wide): 242.1B **Publicly Held**
WEB: www.semiconductorstore.com
SIC: 3674 Semiconductors & related devices
HQ: Tti, Inc.
   2441 Northeast Pkwy
   Fort Worth TX 76106
   817 740-9000

(P-19210)
T-RAM SEMICONDUCTOR INC
2109 Landings Dr, Mountain View
(94043-0839)
PHONE.............................408 597-3670
Dado Banatao, *Ch of Bd*
Sam R Nakib, *President*
Scott Robins, *Vice Pres*
EMP: 21
SQ FT: 28,000
SALES (est): 2.8MM **Privately Held**
WEB: www.t-ram.com
SIC: 3674 Semiconductors & related devices

(P-19211)
TAHOE RF SEMICONDUCTOR INC
12834 Earhart Ave, Auburn (95602-9027)
PHONE.............................530 823-9786
Irshad A Rasheed, *CEO*
Christopher Saint, *Vice Pres*
EMP: 15
SQ FT: 6,000
SALES (est): 2.6MM **Privately Held**
WEB: www.tahoerf.com
SIC: 3674 8711 Semiconductors & related devices; engineering services

(P-19212)
TAKEX AMERICA INC
151 San Zeno Way, Sunnyvale
(94086-5307)
PHONE.............................877 371-2727
Yuji Egawa, *President*
▲ EMP: 23
SALES (est): 3.4MM **Privately Held**
SIC: 3674 Infrared sensors, solid state

(P-19213)
TECH-SEMI INC
2355 Paragon Dr Ste A, San Jose
(95131-1334)
PHONE.............................408 451-9588
Jintu Wang, *Administration*
◆ EMP: 10
SALES (est): 1MM **Privately Held**
SIC: 3674 Semiconductors & related devices

(P-19214)
TECHNOPROBE AMERICA INC
2526 Qume Dr Ste 27, San Jose
(95131-1870)
PHONE.............................408 573-9911
Stefano Felici, *President*
Stefano Lazzari, *Bd of Directors*
Reina Perez, *General Mgr*
Hugh Obyrne, *Engineer*
Aberash Tefera, *Human Resources*
EMP: 25
SQ FT: 800
SALES: 450K **Privately Held**
SIC: 3674 Semiconductors & related devices

▲ = Import ▼=Export
◆ =Import/Export

(P-19215)
TECK ADVANCED MATERIALS INC (DH)
Also Called: Cominco Advanced Material
13670 Danielson St Ste H, Poway
(92064-6890)
PHONE...............................858 391-2935
Donald R Lindsay, *CEO*
Norman B Keevil, *Ch of Bd*
Mike Martin, *President*
▲ EMP: 17
SALES (est): 3.1MM
SALES (corp-wide): 9.4B **Privately Held**
SIC: 3674 Semiconductors & related devices
HQ: Teck American Incorporated
501 N Riverpoint Blvd # 300
Spokane WA 99202
509 747-6111

(P-19216)
TELA INNOVATIONS INC
475 Alberto Way Ste 120, Los Gatos
(95032-5480)
PHONE...............................408 558-6300
Scott Becker, *CEO*
Carney Becker, *President*
Peter Calverley, *CFO*
Liz Stewart, *Vice Pres*
EMP: 45
SALES (est): 5.2MM **Privately Held**
SIC: 3674 Integrated circuits, semiconductor networks, etc.

(P-19217)
TELEDYNE DEFENSE ELEC LLC
Also Called: Teledyne Hirel Electronics
765 Sycamore Dr, Milpitas (95035-7465)
PHONE...............................408 737-0992
EMP: 105
SALES (corp-wide): 2.6B **Publicly Held**
SIC: 3674 Semiconductors & related devices
HQ: Teledyne Defense Electronics, Llc
1274 Terra Bella Ave
Mountain View CA 94043
650 691-9800

(P-19218)
TELEDYNE E2V, INC.
Also Called: Teledyne Hirel Electronics
765 Sycamore Dr, Milpitas (95035-7465)
PHONE...............................408 737-0992
EMP: 44
SQ FT: 67,000
SALES (est): 20.4MM
SALES (corp-wide): 2.6B **Publicly Held**
WEB: www.e2v.com/aero
SIC: 3674 Semiconductors & related devices
HQ: E2v Holdings Inc.
660 White Plains Rd # 525
Tarrytown NY 10591
415 987-2211

(P-19219)
TELEDYNE INSTRUMENTS INC
9855 Carroll Canyon Rd, San Diego
(92131-1103)
PHONE...............................858 842-3127
Mark Page, *Manager*
EMP: 20
SALES (corp-wide): 2.6B **Publicly Held**
WEB: www.teledynesolutions.com
SIC: 3674 3678 3613 3423 Semiconductors & related devices; electronic connectors; switchgear & switchboard apparatus; hand & edge tools
HQ: Teledyne Instruments, Inc.
1049 Camino Dos Rios
Thousand Oaks CA 91360
805 373-4545

(P-19220)
TELEDYNE TECHNOLOGIES INC
Also Called: Teledyne Cougar
290 Santa Ana Ct, Sunnyvale
(94085-4512)
PHONE...............................408 773-8814
Sheila Pugatch, *Branch Mgr*
EMP: 305
SALES (corp-wide): 2.6B **Publicly Held**
WEB: www.teledyne.com
SIC: 3674 Semiconductors & related devices

PA: Teledyne Technologies Inc
1049 Camino Dos Rios
Thousand Oaks CA 91360
805 373-4545

(P-19221)
TELEGENT SYSTEMS USA INC
10180 Telesis Ct Ste 500, San Diego
(92121-2787)
PHONE...............................408 523-2800
Ford Tamer, *CEO*
Weijie Yun, *Ch of Bd*
Samuel Sheng, *CTO*
EMP: 25
SQ FT: 6,437
SALES (est): 2.2MM **Privately Held**
WEB: www.telegentsystems.com
SIC: 3674 Microcircuits, integrated (semiconductor)
HQ: Spreadtrum Communications (Shanghai) Co., Ltd.
Building 1, Exhibition Center, 2288,
Zuchongzhi Road, China (Sha
Shanghai 20120
212 036-0600

(P-19222)
TENSORCOM INC
3530 John Hopkins Ct, San Diego
(92121-1121)
PHONE...............................760 496-3264
Patrick Soon-Shiong, *CEO*
Zaw Soe, *Exec VP*
Rosalie McDonnough, *Admin Asst*
Stephen J How, *Administration*
Steve Truong, *Software Engr*
◆ EMP: 32
SQ FT: 5,000
SALES (est): 1.3MM **Privately Held**
SIC: 3674 Microcircuits, integrated (semiconductor)

(P-19223)
TERIDIAN SEMICONDUCTOR CORP (DH)
6440 Oak Cyn Ste 100, Irvine
(92618-5208)
PHONE...............................714 508-8800
Mark Casper, *CEO*
John Silk, *Vice Pres*
Pete Todd, *Vice Pres*
David Gruetter, *CTO*
EMP: 90
SALES (est): 5.7MM
SALES (corp-wide): 2.4B **Publicly Held**
WEB: www.teridian.com
SIC: 3674 Semiconductors & related devices

(P-19224)
TESSERA INC (DH)
3025 Orchard Pkwy, San Jose
(95134-2017)
PHONE...............................408 321-6000
Richard Chernicoff, *President*
Simon McElrea, *President*
Tudor Brown, *Bd of Directors*
Christopher Seams, *Bd of Directors*
Donald Stout, *Bd of Directors*
EMP: 12
SQ FT: 51,000
SALES (est): 10.2MM
SALES (corp-wide): 373.7MM **Publicly Held**
WEB: www.tessera.com
SIC: 3674 8999 Integrated circuits, semiconductor networks, etc.; inventor
HQ: Tessera Technologies, Inc.
3025 Orchard Pkwy
San Jose CA 95134
408 321-6000

(P-19225)
TESSERA INTELLECTUAL PRPTS INC
3025 Orchard Pkwy, San Jose
(95134-2017)
PHONE...............................408 321-6000
Tom Lacey, *Principal*
EMP: 68 **EST:** 2012
SALES (est): 383.3K
SALES (corp-wide): 373.7MM **Publicly Held**
SIC: 3674 Integrated circuits, semiconductor networks, etc.

HQ: Tessera, Inc.
3025 Orchard Pkwy
San Jose CA 95134

(P-19226)
TESSERA INTLLCTUAL PRPRTY CORP
3025 Orchard Pkwy, San Jose
(95134-2017)
PHONE...............................408 321-6000
Tom Lacey, *CEO*
Murali Dharan, *President*
Robert A Young PHD, *President*
Robert Andersen, *CFO*
EMP: 40 **EST:** 2011
SALES (est): 4.4MM
SALES (corp-wide): 373.7MM **Publicly Held**
SIC: 3674 Microcircuits, integrated (semiconductor)
HQ: Tessera Technologies, Inc.
3025 Orchard Pkwy
San Jose CA 95134
408 321-6000

(P-19227)
TESSERA TECHNOLOGIES INC (HQ)
3025 Orchard Pkwy, San Jose
(95134-2017)
PHONE...............................408 321-6000
Tom Lacey, *CEO*
Jon E Kirchner, *President*
Robert Andersen, *CFO*
Peter Van Deventer, *Chief Mktg Ofcr*
Kevin Doohan, *Officer*
▲ EMP: 37
SALES: 273.3MM
SALES (corp-wide): 373.7MM **Publicly Held**
WEB: www.tessera.com
SIC: 3674 6794 Integrated circuits, semiconductor networks, etc.; memories, solid state; patent buying, licensing, leasing
PA: Xperi Corporation
3025 Orchard Pkwy
San Jose CA 95134
408 321-6000

(P-19228)
TEXAS INSTRUMENTS INCORPORATED
165 Gibraltar Ct, Sunnyvale (94089-1301)
PHONE...............................408 541-9900
Al Wagner, *Manager*
Bjoy Santos, *Technology*
Stu Chambers, *Accounts Exec*
Rajni Dharmarajan, *Associate*
EMP: 27
SALES (corp-wide): 14.9B **Publicly Held**
WEB: www.ti.com
SIC: 3674 Microprocessors
PA: Texas Instruments Incorporated
12500 Ti Blvd
Dallas TX 75243
214 479-3773

(P-19229)
TEXAS INSTRUMENTS INCORPORATED
2900 Semiconductor Dr, Santa Clara
(95051-0606)
PHONE...............................669 721-5000
Lisa Kennedy, *Program Mgr*
Justin Prayogo, *Design Engr*
Michael Hinh, *Technology*
Brani Dubocanin, *Engineer*
Khalid Jakoush, *Engineer*
EMP: 27
SALES (corp-wide): 14.9B **Publicly Held**
SIC: 3674 3613 3822 3578 Microprocessors; microcircuits, integrated (semiconductor); computer logic modules; memories, solid state; power circuit breakers; thermostats & other environmental sensors; calculators & adding machines
PA: Texas Instruments Incorporated
12500 Ti Blvd
Dallas TX 75243
214 479-3773

(P-19230)
TEXAS INSTRUMENTS INCORPORATED
14351 Myford Rd, Tustin (92780-7074)
PHONE...............................714 731-7110
EMP: 190
SALES (corp-wide): 12.2B **Publicly Held**
SIC: 3674
PA: Texas Instruments Incorporated
12500 Ti Blvd
Dallas TX 75243
214 479-3773

(P-19231)
TEXTRON INC
Textron Defense Systems
1309 Dynamic St, Petaluma (94954-1420)
PHONE...............................707 763-8855
Bill Doherty, *Manager*
EMP: 97
SQ FT: 30,000
SALES (corp-wide): 14.2B **Publicly Held**
WEB: www.textron.com
SIC: 3674 Infrared sensors, solid state
PA: Textron Inc.
40 Westminster St
Providence RI 02903
401 421-2800

(P-19232)
TOUCHDOWN TECHNOLOGIES INC
5188 Commerce Dr, Baldwin Park
(91706-1450)
PHONE...............................626 472-6732
Haruo Matsuno, *President*
Patrick Flynn, *President*
Raffi Garabedian, *Vice Pres*
Brian Flowers, *Admin Sec*
▼ EMP: 103
SQ FT: 30,000
SALES (est): 17.2MM **Privately Held**
SIC: 3674 Semiconductor diodes & rectifiers

(P-19233)
TOWER SEMICONDUCTOR USA INC
2570 N 1st St Ste 480, San Jose
(95131-1018)
PHONE...............................408 770-1320
Doron Simon, *President*
Steve Ransom, *Info Tech Dir*
Julie Akina, *Human Resources*
Oren Shirazi, *Director*
EMP: 15
SQ FT: 4,100
SALES (est): 2.9MM
SALES (corp-wide): 1.3B **Privately Held**
SIC: 3674 Semiconductors & related devices
PA: Tower Semiconductor Ltd
20 Shaul Amor Blvd
Migdal Haemek 23530
465 066-11

(P-19234)
TRANSMETA CORP
3940 Freedom Cir, Santa Clara
(95054-1204)
PHONE...............................408 327-9831
Ralph J Harms, *Principal*
Daniel L Hillman, *President*
EMP: 50 **EST:** 2010
SALES (est): 5.8MM **Privately Held**
SIC: 3674 Semiconductors & related devices

(P-19235)
TRINA SOLAR (US) INC
100 Century Center Ct # 501, San Jose
(95112-4535)
PHONE...............................800 696-7114
Jifan Gao, *CEO*
Rongfang Yin, *President*
Teresa Tan, *CFO*
Merry Xu, *CFO*
Colin Yang, *Officer*
◆ EMP: 41
SQ FT: 7,000
SALES (est): 16.4MM
SALES (corp-wide): 582.1MM **Privately Held**
WEB: www.trinasolar.com
SIC: 3674 Solar cells

PA: Trina Solar Co.,Ltd
No.2, Tianhe Road, Trina Pv Industrial
Park, Xinbei Dist.
Changzhou 21303
519 851-7602

(P-19236)
TROPIAN INC
20813 Stevens Creek Blvd, Cupertino
(95014-2185)
PHONE..................................408 865-1300
Tim Unger, *President*
Earl Mc Cune, *CTO*
▲ EMP: 60
SQ FT: 26,000
SALES (est): 4.4MM **Privately Held**
SIC: 3674 Semiconductors & related devices

(P-19237)
TSI TECH DEVMNT &
COMMERCIALIZ
7501 Foothills Blvd, Roseville
(95747-6504)
PHONE..................................916 786-3900
Matthew Nadeau,
EMP: 10
SALES (est): 598.3K **Privately Held**
SIC: 3674 Integrated circuits, semiconductor networks, etc.

(P-19238)
TSMC TECHNOLOGY INC
2585 Junction Ave, San Jose (95134-1923)
PHONE..................................408 382-8052
Lora Ho, *President*
Dick Thurston, *President*
Wendell Huang, *Treasurer*
Richard L Thurston, *Admin Sec*
Alex Kalnitsky, *Director*
EMP: 57
SALES (est): 10.3MM
SALES (corp-wide): 32.4B **Privately Held**
SIC: 3674 Semiconductor circuit networks
HQ: Tsmc Partners Ltd.
C/O: Portcullis Trusnet (Bvi) Limited
Road Town

(P-19239)
TWILIGHT TECHNOLOGY INC
(PA)
325 N Shepard St, Anaheim (92806-2832)
P.O. Box 1149, Placentia (92871-1149)
PHONE..................................714 257-2257
Randy Greene, *President*
James Donaghy, *Vice Pres*
Gale Greene, *Admin Sec*
Scott Teson, *Sales Mgr*
Kathy Gibson, *Manager*
EMP: 20 EST: 1997
SQ FT: 12,000
SALES (est): 2.9MM **Privately Held**
WEB: www.forcetechnologies.co.uk
SIC: 3674 Integrated circuits, semiconductor networks, etc.

(P-19240)
TWIN CREEKS TECHNOLOGIES
INC (PA)
3930 N 1st St Ste 10, San Jose (95134-1501)
P.O. Box 1476, Los Gatos (95031-1476)
PHONE..................................408 368-3733
Srinivasan Sivaram, *President*
EMP: 14
SALES (est): 2.6MM **Privately Held**
WEB: www.twincreekstechnologies.com
SIC: 3674 Semiconductors & related devices

(P-19241)
TWO PORE GUYS INC
2161 Delaware Ave Ste B, Santa Cruz
(95060-5790)
PHONE..................................831 515-8515
Dan Heller, *CEO*
Cherry Zhao, *Research*
Eric Thorne, *Engineer*
Yanan Zhao, *Engineer*
Kim Smith, *Opers Staff*
EMP: 19
SQ FT: 12,000

SALES (est): 746.9K **Privately Held**
SIC: 3674 Semiconductors & related devices

(P-19242)
UBICOM INC
195 Baypointe Pkwy, San Jose
(95134-1697)
PHONE..................................408 433-3330
Gangesh Ganesan, *CEO*
Douglas C Spreng, *Ch of Bd*
Alain Martinez, *CFO*
Josiane Valverde, *Vice Pres*
Linda Fu, *Accountant*
EMP: 75
SQ FT: 15,000
SALES (est): 6.6MM **Privately Held**
WEB: www.ubicom.com
SIC: 3674 Integrated circuits, semiconductor networks, etc.

(P-19243)
UHV SPUTTERING INC
275 Digital Dr, Morgan Hill (95037-2878)
PHONE..................................408 779-2826
Rick Wooden, *President*
Linda Wooden, *CFO*
John Cavanaugh, *QC Mgr*
EMP: 19
SQ FT: 10,000
SALES (est): 3.8MM **Privately Held**
SIC: 3674 3471 Thin film circuits; electroplating & plating

(P-19244)
ULTRASIL CORP
3527 Breakwater Ave, Hayward
(94545-3610)
PHONE..................................510 266-3700
John Dancovich, *President*
EMP: 20
SQ FT: 5,000
SALES (est): 3.4MM **Privately Held**
WEB: www.ultrasil.com
SIC: 3674 Integrated circuits, semiconductor networks, etc.

(P-19245)
UMC GROUP(USA)
488 De Guigne Dr, Sunnyvale
(94085-3903)
PHONE..................................408 523-7800
Robert Tsao, *Chairman*
Peter Chang, *Vice Chairman*
Ing-Dar Liu, *Vice Chairman*
Fu Tai Liou, *President*
Jason S Wang, *CEO*
▲ EMP: 75 EST: 1997
SQ FT: 40,000
SALES (est): 14.4MM
SALES (corp-wide): 4.9B **Privately Held**
WEB: www.hope-umc.com
SIC: 3674 5065 Wafers (semiconductor devices); electronic parts & equipment
PA: United Microelectronics Corp.
3, Li Hsin 2nd Rd., Science-Based Industrial Park,
Hsinchu City 30077
357 822-58

(P-19246)
UNIREX CORP
Also Called: Unirex Technology
2288 E 27th St, Vernon (90058-1131)
PHONE..................................323 589-4000
Bijan Neman, *President*
Behzad Neman, *Admin Sec*
Farzad Neman, *VP Human Res*
Richard Engler, *VP Sales*
Herlinda F Garcia, *Sales Staff*
▲ EMP: 13
SQ FT: 33,000
SALES (est): 2.5MM **Privately Held**
WEB: www.unirex.net
SIC: 3674 3572 Magnetic bubble memory device; computer storage devices

(P-19247)
UNISEM (SUNNVALE) INC (PA)
2241 Calle De Luna, Santa Clara
(95054-1002)
PHONE..................................408 734-3222
Marita Erickson, *President*
James K Cook, *CFO*
Gil Chiu, *Vice Pres*
EMP: 14

SQ FT: 5,798
SALES (est): 3.5MM **Privately Held**
SIC: 3674 Integrated circuits, semiconductor networks, etc.

(P-19248)
UNITED PRO FAB MFG INC
Also Called: Pro Fab Manufacturing
45300 Industrial Pl Ste 5, Fremont
(94538-6453)
PHONE..................................510 651-5570
Rajesh Gupta, *President*
Seema Gupta, *Vice Pres*
▲ EMP: 10
SQ FT: 5,000
SALES (est): 1.6MM **Privately Held**
WEB: www.pfmfg.com
SIC: 3674 Semiconductors & related devices

(P-19249)
US SENSOR CORP
1832 W Collins Ave, Orange (92867-5425)
PHONE..................................714 639-1000
Roger W Dankert, *CEO*
Dan Dankert, *President*
Huan Nguyen, *Vice Pres*
Denny Nguyen, *VP Mfg*
EMP: 100
SQ FT: 30,000
SALES (est): 20.9MM
SALES (corp-wide): 1.2B **Publicly Held**
WEB: www.ussensor.com
SIC: 3674 3676 Semiconductors & related devices; thermistors, except temperature sensors
PA: Littelfuse, Inc.
8755 W Higgins Rd Ste 500
Chicago IL 60631
773 628-1000

(P-19250)
V-SILICON INC
47467 Fremont Blvd, Fremont
(94538-6504)
PHONE..................................510 897-0168
Thinh Tran, *CEO*
EMP: 10
SALES (est): 398.2K **Privately Held**
SIC: 3674 Semiconductors & related devices

(P-19251)
VEECO INSTRUMENTS INC
Also Called: Veeco C V C
3100 Laurelview Ct, Santa Clara (95054)
PHONE..................................510 657-8523
EMP: 28
SALES (corp-wide): 392.8MM **Publicly Held**
SIC: 3674 5065
PA: Veeco Instruments Inc.
Terminal Dr
Plainview NY 11803
516 677-0200

(P-19252)
VENTURA TECHNOLOGY
GROUP
855 E Easy St Ste 104, Simi Valley
(93065-1825)
PHONE..................................805 581-0800
Douglas E Lafountaine, *President*
EMP: 47
SQ FT: 7,400
SALES (est): 12.5MM **Privately Held**
WEB: www.venturatech.com
SIC: 3674 Random access memory (RAM); read-only memory (ROM)

(P-19253)
VERISILICON INC (HQ)
2150 Gold St Ste 200, San Jose
(95002-3702)
P.O. Box 1090 (95108-1090)
PHONE..................................408 844-8560
Wayne WEI Ming Dai, *President*
Prasad Kalluri, *President*
Robert Brown, *CFO*
David Jarmon, *Vice Pres*
Shanghung Lin, *Vice Pres*
▲ EMP: 17
SQ FT: 55,000

SALES (est): 6.7MM **Privately Held**
WEB: www.verisilicon.com
SIC: 3674 Semiconductors & related devices

(P-19254)
VESTA TECHNOLOGY INC
3973 Soutirage Ln, San Jose (95135-1735)
PHONE..................................408 519-5800
Karl W Markert, *CEO*
Sang-In Lee, *Vice Pres*
EMP: 10
SALES (est): 930K **Privately Held**
SIC: 3674 Semiconductors & related devices

(P-19255)
VIA TELECOM INC
3390 Carmel Mountain Rd # 100, San
Diego (92121-1053)
PHONE..................................858 350-5560
Ker Zhang, *CEO*
Chenwei Yan, *COO*
Mark Davis, *Vice Pres*
▲ EMP: 107
SALES (est): 14.3MM **Privately Held**
WEB: www.viatelecom.com
SIC: 3674 Semiconductors & related devices
PA: Jingrui Science And Technology (Beijing) Limited Company
Via Building, Tsinghua Science Park
Building 7, No.1 Zhongguancu
Beijing
105 985-2288

(P-19256)
VIAVI SOLUTIONS INC
80 Rose Orchard Way, San Jose
(95134-1356)
PHONE..................................408 577-1478
Sergei Pacht, *Branch Mgr*
Jimmy Tai, *Administration*
Danny Lau, *Engineer*
Mark Tashima, *Engineer*
Yanyan Xiong, *Engineer*
EMP: 129
SALES (corp-wide): 811.4MM **Publicly Held**
SIC: 3674 Optical isolators
PA: Viavi Solutions Inc.
6001 America Center Dr # 6
San Jose CA 95002
408 404-3600

(P-19257)
VIAVI SOLUTIONS INC (PA)
6001 America Center Dr # 6, San Jose
(95002-2562)
PHONE..................................408 404-3600
Oleg Khaykin, *President*
Richard E Belluzzo, *Ch of Bd*
Amar Maletira, *CFO*
Paul McNab, *Chief Mktg Ofcr*
Ralph Rondinone, *Senior VP*
◆ EMP: 320
SQ FT: 37,000
SALES: 880.4MM **Publicly Held**
WEB: www.jdsuniphase.com
SIC: 3674 3826 Analytical instruments; laser scientific & engineering instruments; optical isolators

(P-19258)
VIAVI SOLUTIONS INC
430 N Mccarthy Blvd, Milpitas
(95035-5112)
PHONE..................................408 546-5000
Craig Cocchi, *Senior VP*
Kim Quillin, *Vice Pres*
Julie Young, *Executive*
Enzo Di Luigi, *General Mgr*
John Kassin, *Admin Asst*
EMP: 191
SALES (corp-wide): 811.4MM **Publicly Held**
SIC: 3674 3826 Analytical instruments; optical isolators
PA: Viavi Solutions Inc.
6001 America Center Dr # 6
San Jose CA 95002
408 404-3600

▲ = Import ▼=Export
◆ =Import/Export

(P-19259)
VIOLIN MMORY FDRAL SYSTEMS INC
4555 Great America Pkwy, Santa Clara (95054-1243)
PHONE..................................650 396-1500
John Kapitula, *President*
EMP: 10
SQ FT: 1,000
SALES (est): 753.8K
SALES (corp-wide): 50.8MM **Privately Held**
SIC: 3674 7389 Semiconductors & related devices;
PA: Violin Memory, Inc.
4555 Great America Pkwy # 150
Santa Clara CA 95054
650 396-1500

(P-19260)
VIRAGE LOGIC CORPORATION (HQ)
700 E Middlefield Rd, Mountain View (94043-4024)
PHONE..................................650 584-5000
Alexander Shubat, *President*
Brian Sereda, *CFO*
Andreas Kuehlmann, *Vice Pres*
Karl Mathern, *Admin Asst*
Joanne Sukow, *Administration*
EMP: 354
SQ FT: 61,500
SALES (est): 39.8MM
SALES (corp-wide): 2.7B **Publicly Held**
WEB: www.viragelogic.com
SIC: 3674 Integrated circuits, semiconductor networks, etc.
PA: Synopsys, Inc.
690 E Middlefield Rd
Mountain View CA 94043
650 584-5000

(P-19261)
VISHAY THIN FILM LLC
Also Called: Vishay Spectoral Electronics
4051 Greystone Dr, Ontario (91761-3100)
PHONE..................................909 923-3313
Robert Leon, *Mng Member*
Sheila Rigg, *Principal*
EMP: 70
SALES: 950K **Privately Held**
SIC: 3674 Thin film circuits

(P-19262)
VISHAY TRANSDUCERS LTD
2930 Inland Empire Blvd # 100, Ontario (91764-4802)
PHONE..................................626 363-7500
Dubi Zandman, *CEO*
Philx Zanman, *General Ptnr*
▲ EMP: 50
SALES (est): 6MM
SALES (corp-wide): 254.3MM **Publicly Held**
SIC: 3674 Semiconductors & related devices
PA: Vishay Precision Group, Inc.
3 Great Valley Pkwy # 150
Malvern PA 19355
484 321-5300

(P-19263)
VISIONARY ELECTRONICS INC
141 Parker Ave, San Francisco (94118-2607)
PHONE..................................415 751-8811
Brad Mc Millan, *President*
Roger Peterson, *Shareholder*
Jeff Fearn, *Treasurer*
EMP: 73 EST: 1974
SALES (est): 8.6MM **Privately Held**
WEB: www.viselect.com
SIC: 3674 3679 Microprocessors; recording & playback heads, magnetic

(P-19264)
VITESSE MANUFACTURING & DEV
Also Called: Vitesse Semiconductor
4721 Calle Carga, Camarillo (93012-8541)
PHONE..................................805 388-3700
Chris Gardner, *President*
EMP: 200

SALES (est): 24.6MM
SALES (corp-wide): 3.9B **Publicly Held**
WEB: www.vitesse.com
SIC: 3674 Microcircuits, integrated (semiconductor)
HQ: Microsemi Communications, Inc.
4721 Calle Carga
Camarillo CA 93012
805 388-3700

(P-19265)
VOLTAGE MULTIPLIERS INC (PA)
Also Called: V M I
8711 W Roosevelt Ave, Visalia (93291-9458)
PHONE..................................559 651-1402
Dennis J Kemp, *President*
John Yakura, *Corp Secy*
Kenneth Hage, *Vice Pres*
Robbie Hodgkins, *Engineer*
EMP: 176
SQ FT: 24,000
SALES (est): 23.2MM **Privately Held**
WEB: www.voltagemultipliers.com
SIC: 3674 Diodes, solid state (germanium, silicon, etc.)

(P-19266)
VOLTERRA SEMICONDUCTOR LLC (HQ)
Also Called: Volterra Semiconductor Corp
160 Rio Robles, San Jose (95134-1813)
PHONE..................................408 601-1000
Mark Casper, *President*
Christopher Paisley, *Ch of Bd*
Craig Teuscher, *COO*
Mike Burns, *CFO*
William Numann, *Senior VP*
EMP: 32 EST: 1996
SQ FT: 73,000
SALES (est): 12.2MM
SALES (corp-wide): 2.4B **Publicly Held**
WEB: www.volterra.com
SIC: 3674 3612 Semiconductors & related devices; voltage regulators, transmission & distribution
PA: Maxim Integrated Products, Inc.
160 Rio Robles
San Jose CA 95134
408 601-1000

(P-19267)
W G HOLT INC
Also Called: Holt Integrated Circuits
23351 Madero, Mission Viejo (92691-2730)
PHONE..................................949 859-8800
David Mead, *CEO*
Paul Phangsavanh, *Technician*
William Soto, *Technology*
Estelle Taylor, *Human Res Mgr*
Scott Paladichuk, *QC Dir*
EMP: 65
SQ FT: 17,000
SALES (est): 12.7MM **Privately Held**
WEB: www.holtic.com
SIC: 3674 Integrated circuits, semiconductor networks, etc.

(P-19268)
W2 OPTRONICS INC
39523 Pardee Ct, Fremont (94538-1250)
PHONE..................................510 220-2796
Xinshi Xu, *Branch Mgr*
Dana Wu, *President*
EMP: 11
SALES (corp-wide): 1.6MM **Privately Held**
SIC: 3674 Microprocessors
PA: W2 Optronics Inc.
5500 Stewart Ave
Fremont CA 94538
510 207-8320

(P-19269)
WAFER RECLAIM SERVICES LLC (PA)
Also Called: Wrs Materials
2240 Ringwood Ave, San Jose (95131-1716)
PHONE..................................408 945-8112
Richard Mee, *President*
Dave Griffeth, *CFO*
Lazaro Reyes, *General Mgr*
David Liang, *Software Dev*
Ted Hoffman, *Technology*
▲ EMP: 182

SQ FT: 12,000
SALES (est): 37.7MM **Privately Held**
WEB: www.waferreclaim.com
SIC: 3674 8742 Integrated circuits, semiconductor networks, etc.; financial consultant

(P-19270)
WAFERNET INC
2142 Paragon Dr, San Jose (95131-1305)
PHONE..................................408 437-9747
Lori L Vann, *President*
Dave Mewes, *Vice Pres*
Jon Mewes, *Vice Pres*
Paul Piligian, *Accounts Mgr*
▲ EMP: 17
SALES (est): 4MM **Privately Held**
WEB: www.wafernet.com
SIC: 3674 Semiconductors & related devices

(P-19271)
WAVEXING INC
3200 Scott Blvd, Santa Clara (95054-3007)
PHONE..................................408 896-1982
EMP: 10
SALES: 500K **Privately Held**
SIC: 3674

(P-19272)
WELDEX CORPORATION (PA)
6751 Katella Ave, Cypress (90630-5105)
PHONE..................................714 761-2100
G W Goddard, *CEO*
William Jung, *President*
Nicole Donovan, *Accounts Mgr*
June Hwang, *Accounts Mgr*
Jeffrey Powell, *Accounts Mgr*
▲ EMP: 32
SQ FT: 15,000
SALES (est): 23.4MM **Privately Held**
WEB: www.weldex.com
SIC: 3674 3663 Light emitting diodes; television closed circuit equipment

(P-19273)
WINSLOW AUTOMATION INC
Also Called: Six Sigma
905 Montague Expy, Milpitas (95035-6817)
PHONE..................................408 262-9004
Russell Winslow, *CEO*
Daryl Sawtelle, *CFO*
Scott Pon, *Technology*
Tisha Wolf, *Opers Mgr*
Rachel Chen, *Sales Mgr*
EMP: 58
SQ FT: 24,784
SALES (est): 12.4MM **Privately Held**
WEB: www.solderquik.com
SIC: 3674 Semiconductors & related devices

(P-19274)
WINWAY USA INC
1800 Wyatt Dr Ste 2, Santa Clara (95054-1527)
PHONE..................................203 775-9311
Mark Wang, *CEO*
Stephen A Evans, *President*
Robert Bollo, *CFO*
EMP: 45
SQ FT: 5,000
SALES: 10MM **Privately Held**
SIC: 3674 Semiconductors & related devices
PA: Winway Technology Co., Ltd.
68, Chuangyi S. Rd.,
Kaohsiung City
736 109-99

(P-19275)
WORLDWIDE ENERGY & MFG USA INC (PA)
1675 Rollins Rd Ste F, Burlingame (94010-2320)
PHONE..................................650 692-7788
John Ballard, *Ch of Bd*
Tiffany Margaret Shum, *Director*
▲ EMP: 25
SQ FT: 9,680
SALES: 28MM **Privately Held**
WEB: www.wwmusa.com
SIC: 3674 Semiconductors & related devices

(P-19276)
XEL USA INC
Also Called: XEL Group
66 Argonaut Ste 170, Aliso Viejo (92656-4124)
PHONE..................................949 425-8686
Paul Kuszka, *CEO*
Wendy Luttrell, *Info Tech Mgr*
EMP: 25
SALES (est): 5.2MM **Privately Held**
SIC: 3674 Magnetic bubble memory device

(P-19277)
XILINX INC
42063 Benbow Dr, Fremont (94539-5002)
PHONE..................................510 770-9449
David Liu, *Principal*
EMP: 62
SALES (corp-wide): 2.5B **Publicly Held**
SIC: 3674 Microcircuits, integrated (semiconductor)
PA: Xilinx, Inc.
2100 All Programable
San Jose CA 95124
408 559-7778

(P-19278)
XILINX INC
2050 All Programable # 4, San Jose (95124-4355)
PHONE..................................408 879-6563
Kung Demi, *Manager*
EMP: 10
SALES (corp-wide): 2.5B **Publicly Held**
WEB: www.xilinx.com
SIC: 3674 Microcircuits, integrated (semiconductor)
PA: Xilinx, Inc.
2100 All Programable
San Jose CA 95124
408 559-7778

(P-19279)
XILINX DEVELOPMENT CORPORATION (HQ)
2100 All Programable, San Jose (95124-4355)
PHONE..................................408 559-7778
Jon A Olson, *CEO*
EMP: 10
SALES (est): 724.9K
SALES (corp-wide): 2.5B **Publicly Held**
SIC: 3674 Semiconductors & related devices
PA: Xilinx, Inc.
2100 All Programable
San Jose CA 95124
408 559-7778

(P-19280)
YADAV TECHNOLOGY INC
48371 Fremont Blvd # 101, Fremont (94538-6554)
PHONE..................................510 438-0148
Petro Estakhri, *CEO*
Rani Ranjan, *Principal*
EMP: 11
SALES (est): 947.3K **Privately Held**
SIC: 3674 Semiconductors & related devices

(P-19281)
YIELD ENGINEERING SYSTEMS INC
203 Lawrence Dr Ste A, Livermore (94551-5152)
PHONE..................................925 373-8353
Ken Macwilliams, *CEO*
Dan Dunkly, *President*
Fred Garcy, *CFO*
William A Moffat, *Founder*
Zia Karim, *Chief Mktg Ofcr*
EMP: 36
SQ FT: 20,000
SALES (est): 7MM **Privately Held**
WEB: www.yieldengineering.com
SIC: 3674 Semiconductors & related devices

(P-19282)
YIELD ENHANCEMENT SERVICES INC
Also Called: Yes-Tek
364 Sunpark Ct, San Jose (95136-2145)
PHONE..................................408 410-5825

Rick Torres, *President*
Efren Q Ebreo, *CFO*
EMP: 10
SQ FT: 7,000
SALES (est): 968.7K **Privately Held**
SIC: 3674 Semiconductors & related devices

(P-19283)
ZENVERGE INC
2680 Zanker Rd Ste 200, San Jose
(95134-2144)
PHONE..............................408 350-5052
Amir Mobini, *CEO*
Tony Masterson, *COO*
Vincent A McCord, *CFO*
Raghu RAO, *Vice Pres*
EMP: 70
SALES (est): 13.4MM **Privately Held**
SIC: 3674 Semiconductors & related devices

(P-19284)
ZEP SOLAR LLC (DH)
161 Mitchell Blvd Ste 104, San Rafael
(94903-2085)
PHONE..............................415 479-6900
Michael John Miskovsky, *CEO*
Peter David, *CFO*
Christina Manansala, *Vice Pres*
Jack West, *CTO*
Bryan Vo, *Engineer*
▲ **EMP:** 28
SQ FT: 8,200
SALES (est): 11MM
SALES (corp-wide): 11.7B **Publicly Held**
SIC: 3674 Photovoltaic devices, solid state

(P-19285)
ZEST LABS INC (HQ)
2349 Bering Dr, San Jose (95131-1125)
PHONE..............................408 200-6500
Peter Mehring, *CEO*
Scott Durgin, *CTO*
EMP: 34
SQ FT: 8,000
SALES (est): 1.5MM **Publicly Held**
WEB: www.intelleflex.com
SIC: 3674 Semiconductors & related devices

(P-19286)
ZILOG INC (DH)
1590 Buckeye Dr, Milpitas (95035-7418)
PHONE..............................408 513-1500
Darin G Billerbeck, *President*
Mike Speckman, *President*
Perry J Grace, *CFO*
Steve Darrough, *Vice Pres*
Dan Eaton, *Vice Pres*
EMP: 29
SQ FT: 42,000
SALES (est): 18.3MM
SALES (corp-wide): 1.2B **Publicly Held**
WEB: www.zilog.com
SIC: 3674 Microcircuits, integrated (semiconductor)
HQ: Ixys, Llc
　　1590 Buckeye Dr
　　Milpitas CA 95035
　　408 457-9000

(P-19287)
ZORAN CORPORATION (DH)
1060 Rincon Cir, San Jose (95131-1325)
PHONE..............................972 673-1600
Daniel Willard Gardiner, *CEO*
Mustafa Ozgen, *President*
Karl Schneider, *CFO*
Isaac Shenberg PHD, *Senior VP*
Robert Kirk, *Vice Pres*
▲ **EMP:** 50
SQ FT: 89,000
SALES (est): 110.7MM
SALES (corp-wide): 22.2B **Publicly Held**
WEB: www.zoran.com
SIC: 3674 Integrated circuits, semiconductor networks, etc.

(P-19288)
ZT PLUS
1321 Mountain View Cir, Azusa
(91702-1649)
PHONE..............................626 208-3440
Sandy Grouf, *Principal*
▲ **EMP:** 12

SALES (est): 839.5K **Privately Held**
SIC: 3674 Thermoelectric devices, solid state

3675 Electronic Capacitors

(P-19289)
ADVANCED MNLYTHIC CERAMICS INC
Also Called: AMC
15191 Bledsoe St, Sylmar (91342-2710)
PHONE..............................818 364-9800
N Eric Johanson, *Ch of Bd*
Phu Luu, *President*
Steve Makl, *Principal*
▲ **EMP:** 130
SQ FT: 35,000
SALES (est): 12.8MM **Privately Held**
WEB: www.amccaps.com
SIC: 3675 Electronic capacitors
HQ: Johanson Dielectrics, Inc.
　　15191 Bledsoe St
　　Sylmar CA 91342
　　818 364-9800

(P-19290)
AMERICAN CAPACITOR CORPORATION
5367 3rd St, Irwindale (91706-2085)
PHONE..............................626 814-4444
Joseph Latourelle, *President*
EMP: 25 **EST:** 1979
SQ FT: 14,200
SALES (est): 3.1MM **Privately Held**
WEB: www.americancapacitor.com
SIC: 3675 5065 Electronic capacitors; electronic parts & equipment

(P-19291)
BESTRONICS HOLDINGS INC (PA)
2090 Fortune Dr, San Jose (95131-1823)
PHONE..............................408 385-7777
Nat Mani, *CEO*
Steve Yetso, *Vice Pres*
Ron Menigoz, *CTO*
EMP: 47
SQ FT: 73,000
SALES (est): 65MM **Privately Held**
SIC: 3675 Electronic capacitors

(P-19292)
BISHOP ELECTRONICS CORPORATION
3729 Sn Gabril Rvr Pkwy A, Pico Rivera
(90660-1457)
P.O. Box 6491 (90661-6491)
PHONE..............................562 695-0446
William Bishop, *President*
James Bowman, *Vice Pres*
Paco Sarmiento, *Engineer*
Dolly Tuttle, *Director*
▲ **EMP:** 42 **EST:** 1977
SQ FT: 13,000
SALES (est): 6.8MM **Privately Held**
WEB: www.bishopelectronics.com
SIC: 3675 Electronic capacitors

(P-19293)
CSI TECHNOLOGIES INC
2540 Fortune Way, Vista (92081-8441)
PHONE..............................760 682-2222
Gary W Greiser, *President*
Perry Sheth, *Shareholder*
Narendra C Soni, *Shareholder*
▲ **EMP:** 18
SQ FT: 18,000
SALES (est): 3.3MM **Privately Held**
SIC: 3675 Electronic capacitors

(P-19294)
I M B ELECTRONIC PRODUCTS
1800 E Via Burton, Anaheim (92806-1213)
PHONE..............................714 523-2110
Steve Binnix, *President*
EMP: 55
SQ FT: 18,000
SALES (est): 3.6MM
SALES (corp-wide): 88.3MM **Publicly Held**
WEB: www.selas.com
SIC: 3675 Electronic capacitors

PA: Intricon Corporation
　　1260 Red Fox Rd
　　Arden Hills MN 55112
　　651 636-9770

(P-19295)
INCA ONE CORPORATION
1648 W 134th St, Gardena (90249-2014)
PHONE..............................310 808-0001
Adriana Roberts, *President*
Tupac Roberts, *Vice Pres*
▲ **EMP:** 35 **EST:** 1971
SQ FT: 17,000
SALES (est): 6.8MM **Privately Held**
WEB: www.inca-tvlifts.com
SIC: 3675 Electronic capacitors

(P-19296)
INTEGER HOLDINGS CORPORATION
Also Called: Greatbatch Medical
8830 Siempre Viva Rd # 100, San Diego
(92154-6272)
PHONE..............................619 498-9448
Raul Mata, *Branch Mgr*
EMP: 17
SALES (corp-wide): 1.4B **Publicly Held**
WEB: www.greatbatch.com
SIC: 3675 Electronic capacitors
PA: Integer Holdings Corporation
　　5830 Gran Pkwy Ste 1150
　　Plano TX 75024
　　214 618-5243

(P-19297)
JENNINGS TECHNOLOGY CO LLC (DH)
970 Mclaughlin Ave, San Jose
(95122-2611)
PHONE..............................408 292-4025
W David Smith,
Kurt Gallo, *Vice Pres*
Jamie Horton, *Vice Pres*
Roderick Mosely, *Director*
▲ **EMP:** 70
SALES (est): 14.8MM
SALES (corp-wide): 34.3B **Privately Held**
WEB: www.jenningstech.com
SIC: 3675 3679 3625 Electronic capacitors; electronic circuits; relays, for electronic use
HQ: Abb Installation Products Inc.
　　860 Ridge Lake Blvd
　　Memphis TN 38120
　　901 252-5000

(P-19298)
JOHANSON DIELECTRICS INC (HQ)
15191 Bledsoe St, Sylmar (91342-2700)
PHONE..............................818 364-9800
N Eric Johanson, *CEO*
Justin Greene, *CFO*
Yibo Zhang, *Senior Engr*
John Mayhew, *Analyst*
Dan Ward, *Manager*
▲ **EMP:** 163
SALES (est): 26.4MM **Privately Held**
WEB: www.johansondielectrics.com
SIC: 3675 Electronic capacitors

(P-19299)
JOHANSON TECHNOLOGY INC
4001 Calle Tecate, Camarillo (93012-5087)
PHONE..............................805 389-1166
John Petrinec, *CEO*
D Ick Crawford, *Plant Mgr*
▲ **EMP:** 159
SQ FT: 30,000
SALES (est): 21MM **Privately Held**
WEB: www.johansontechnology.com
SIC: 3675 5065 3674 Electronic capacitors; electronic parts & equipment; semiconductors & related devices
PA: Johanson Ventures, Inc.
　　15191 Bledsoe St
　　Sylmar CA 91342

(P-19300)
NEMCO ELECTRONICS CORP
40 Roan Pl, Woodside (94062-4249)
PHONE..............................650 571-1234
Eugene J Porto, *Chairman*
John Nolan, *President*

James Rapoport, *Exec VP*
Ann Nolan, *Admin Sec*
EMP: 150
SQ FT: 10,000
SALES (est): 23MM **Privately Held**
WEB: www.nemcocaps.com
SIC: 3675 Electronic capacitors

(P-19301)
NOVACAP LLC
25111 Anza Dr, Valencia (91355-3478)
PHONE..............................661 295-5920
Mark Skoog, *CEO*
Carlos Valenzuela, *QA Dir*
Shelley Mears, *Info Tech Mgr*
Shuping Lin, *Engineer*
Ted Valentine, *Engineer*
▲ **EMP:** 280
SQ FT: 38,000
SALES (est): 76.7MM
SALES (corp-wide): 744.2MM **Publicly Held**
WEB: www.novacap.com
SIC: 3675 Electronic capacitors
PA: Knowles Corporation
　　1151 Maplewood Dr
　　Itasca IL 60143
　　630 250-5100

(P-19302)
PACIFIC CAPACITOR CO
288 Digital Dr, Morgan Hill (95037-2877)
PHONE..............................408 778-6670
Steven Francis, *President*
Harold Francis, *President*
EMP: 12
SQ FT: 10,000
SALES (est): 1.5MM **Privately Held**
SIC: 3675 Electronic capacitors

(P-19303)
TRIGON COMPONENTS INC
939 Mariner St, Brea (92821-3827)
PHONE..............................714 990-1367
Yeankai Chorng, *CEO*
Maria Chorng, *Office Mgr*
▲ **EMP:** 20
SQ FT: 10,000
SALES (est): 3.2MM **Privately Held**
WEB: www.trigoncomp.com
SIC: 3675 5065 Condensers, electronic; electronic parts & equipment

(P-19304)
UNION TECHNOLOGY CORP
718 Monterey Pass Rd, Monterey Park
(91754-3607)
PHONE..............................323 266-6603
Laurie Lou, *Branch Mgr*
EMP: 45
SALES (est): 1.7MM **Privately Held**
WEB: www.uniontechcorp.com
SIC: 3675 Electronic capacitors
PA: Union Technology Corp.
　　718 Monterey Pass Rd
　　Monterey Park CA 91754

(P-19305)
VIRGIL WALKER INC
Also Called: Auton Motorized Systems
29102 Hancock Pkwy, Valencia
(91355-1066)
PHONE..............................661 294-9142
Fax: 310 295-5639
◆ **EMP:** 32
SQ FT: 15,000
SALES (est): 4.6MM **Privately Held**
WEB: www.auton.com
SIC: 3675

(P-19306)
WRIGHT CAPACITORS INC
Also Called: WCI
2610 Oak St, Santa Ana (92707-3720)
PHONE..............................714 546-2490
Casey Crandall, *President*
Pendra Lafee, *CFO*
Bev Woods, *Bookkeeper*
▲ **EMP:** 15 **EST:** 1977
SQ FT: 6,500
SALES (est): 2.6MM **Privately Held**
WEB: www.wrightcap.com
SIC: 3675 Electronic capacitors

▲ = Import ▼=Export
◆ =Import/Export

3676 Electronic Resistors

(P-19307)
CALIFORNIA MICRO DEVICES CORP (HQ)
3001 Stender Way, Santa Clara (95054-3216)
PHONE..................408 542-1051
Robert V Dickinson, *President*
John Jorgensen, *President*
Kevin J Berry, *CFO*
Kyle D Baker, *Vice Pres*
Daniel Hauck, *Vice Pres*
▲ EMP: 19
SQ FT: 26,800
SALES (est): 7MM
SALES (corp-wide): 5.5B **Publicly Held**
WEB: www.calmicro.com
SIC: 3676 3675 3672 3674 Electronic resistors; electronic capacitors; printed circuit boards; microcircuits, integrated (semiconductor)
PA: On Semiconductor Corporation
5005 E Mcdowell Rd
Phoenix AZ 85008
602 244-6600

(P-19308)
MICRO-OHM CORPORATION
1088 Hamilton Rd, Duarte (91010-2742)
PHONE..................626 357-5377
Byron Ritchey, *CEO*
Charles Schwab, *President*
Barbette Bowers, *Corp Secy*
Mark Craven, *Vice Pres*
▲ EMP: 26 EST: 1961
SQ FT: 10,000
SALES (est): 3.4MM **Privately Held**
WEB: www.micro-ohm.com
SIC: 3676 Electronic resistors

(P-19309)
RIEDON INC (PA)
300 Cypress Ave, Alhambra (91801-3001)
PHONE..................626 284-9901
Michael A Zoeller, *President*
Duane Ebbert, *Vice Pres*
Greg Wood, *Vice Pres*
Oscar Coroy, *Technology*
Becky Hinojosa, *Technology*
▲ EMP: 150
SQ FT: 12,000
SALES (est): 18.7MM **Privately Held**
WEB: www.riedon.com
SIC: 3676 Electronic resistors

(P-19310)
VISHAY INTERTECHNOLOGY INC
677 Arrow Grand Cir, Covina (91722-2146)
PHONE..................626 331-0502
EMP: 15
SALES (corp-wide): 2.6B **Publicly Held**
WEB: www.vishay.com
SIC: 3676 Electronic resistors
PA: Vishay Intertechnology, Inc.
63 Lancaster Ave
Malvern PA 19355
610 644-1300

(P-19311)
VISHAY THIN FILM LLC
Also Called: Vishay Spectrol
4051 Greystone Dr, Ontario (91761-3100)
PHONE..................909 923-3313
▲ EMP: 50
SALES (est): 6.4MM **Privately Held**
SIC: 3676 3861 3577 Electronic resistors; photographic equipment & supplies; computer peripheral equipment

(P-19312)
YAGEO AMERICA CORPORATION
2550 N 1st St Ste 480, San Jose (95131-1038)
PHONE..................408 240-6200
CHI Wen Chang, *President*
John Blackerby, *Regl Sales Mgr*
Dean Rambo, *Regl Sales Mgr*
Lisa Ramirez, *Sales Associate*
Andrew Skelly, *Sales Staff*
▲ EMP: 20
SALES (est): 2.5MM
SALES (corp-wide): 1B **Privately Held**
SIC: 3676 Electronic resistors
PA: Yageo Corporation
3f, 233-1, 233-2, Baoqiao Rd.,
New Taipei City 23145
266 299-999

3677 Electronic Coils & Transformers

(P-19313)
ADTEC TECHNOLOGY INC
48625 Warm Springs Blvd, Fremont (94539-7782)
PHONE..................510 226-5766
Shuitsu Fujii, *President*
Jor Amster, *President*
Nobuyuki Horita, *Exec Dir*
Junko Szymanski, *Admin Sec*
EMP: 13
SQ FT: 6,703
SALES (est): 6.2MM
SALES (corp-wide): 64.6MM **Privately Held**
WEB: www.adtecusa.com
SIC: 3677 Electronic coils, transformers & other inductors
PA: Adtec Plasma Technology Co.,Ltd.
5-6-10, Hikinocho
Fukuyama HIR 721-0
849 451-359

(P-19314)
ADVANCED CHIP MAGNETICS INC
4225 Spencer St, Torrance (90503-2421)
PHONE..................310 370-8188
Denise Nguyen, *CEO*
Steven Nguyen, *Admin Sec*
Benjamin Nguyen, *Manager*
Steve Nguyen, *Consultant*
EMP: 10
SQ FT: 10,000
SALES (est): 1.3MM **Privately Held**
SIC: 3677 Electronic coils, transformers & other inductors

(P-19315)
AEM ELECTRONICS (USA) INC
6610 Cobra Way, San Diego (92121-4107)
PHONE..................858 481-0210
Daniel H Chang, *CEO*
EMP: 32
SALES (est): 9MM **Privately Held**
SIC: 3677 3613 8742 3559 Inductors, electronic; fuses, electric; planning consultant; electronic component making machinery; metal powders, pastes & flakes; chemical preparations

(P-19316)
AHN ENTERPRISES LLC
Also Called: Santronics
1240 Birchwood Dr Ste 2, Sunnyvale (94089-2205)
PHONE..................408 734-1878
Raymond Ahn,
Joan Song, *Vice Pres*
Joanna Abes,
Garrick Ahn,
Grant Ahn,
▲ EMP: 19
SQ FT: 5,000
SALES (est): 1.4MM **Privately Held**
WEB: www.santronics-usa.com
SIC: 3677 Electronic transformers

(P-19317)
ALLIED COMPONENTS INTL
19671 Descartes, Foothill Ranch (92610-2609)
PHONE..................949 356-1780
Neal McDonald, *President*
Ruben Ramirez, *CFO*
▲ EMP: 25
SQ FT: 9,000
SALES (est): 5.4MM **Privately Held**
WEB: www.alliedcomponents.com
SIC: 3677 Electronic coils, transformers & other inductors

(P-19318)
AMI/COAST MAGNETICS INC
5333 W Washington Blvd, Los Angeles (90016-1191)
PHONE..................323 936-6188
Satya Dosaj, *CEO*
Phillis Dosaj, *Shareholder*
Dev Dosaj, *President*
Rajan Dosaj, *Accounts Mgr*
EMP: 49 EST: 1965
SQ FT: 25,000
SALES (est): 8.5MM **Privately Held**
WEB: www.coastmagnetics.com
SIC: 3677 3549 Electronic transformers; coil winding machines for springs

(P-19319)
ARAS POWER TECHNOLOGIES (PA)
371 Fairview Way, Milpitas (95035-3024)
PHONE..................408 935-8877
Fariborz RAD, *President*
▲ EMP: 15
SQ FT: 5,000
SALES (est): 1.9MM **Privately Held**
WEB: www.arastech.com
SIC: 3677 3679 Transformers power supply, electronic type; static power supply converters for electronic applications

(P-19320)
ASTRON CORPORATION
9 Autry, Irvine (92618-2768)
PHONE..................949 458-7277
Loren Pochirowski, *President*
William Pochirowski, *Officer*
Fred Sanchez, *Engineer*
▲ EMP: 40
SQ FT: 18,000
SALES (est): 7.9MM **Privately Held**
WEB: www.astroncorp.com
SIC: 3677 3679 Transformers power supply, electronic type; electronic circuits

(P-19321)
BECKER SPECIALTY CORPORATION
15310 Arrow Blvd, Fontana (92335-3249)
PHONE..................909 356-1095
Jack McGrew, *Branch Mgr*
EMP: 12
SALES (corp-wide): 886.4MM **Privately Held**
WEB: www.beckers-bic.com
SIC: 3677 Electronic coils, transformers & other inductors
HQ: Becker Specialty Corporation
2526 Delta Ln
Elk Grove Village IL 60007

(P-19322)
BEL POWER SOLUTIONS INC
Also Called: Power One
2390 Walsh Ave, Santa Clara (95051-1301)
PHONE..................866 513-2839
Dennis Ackerman, *President*
Colin Dunn, *VP Finance*
Steve Dawson, *Director*
▲ EMP: 2000
SALES (est): 8MM
SALES (corp-wide): 491.6MM **Publicly Held**
SIC: 3677 Electronic coils, transformers & other inductors
PA: Bel Fuse Inc.
206 Van Vorst St
Jersey City NJ 07302
201 432-0463

(P-19323)
BOURNS INC (PA)
1200 Columbia Ave, Riverside (92507-2129)
PHONE..................951 781-5500
Gordon L Bourns, *CEO*
Erik Meijer, *President*
James Heiken, *CFO*
Gregg Gibbons, *Exec VP*
Roy Alvarez, *Administration*
◆ EMP: 171
SQ FT: 205,000
SALES (est): 500MM **Privately Held**
WEB: www.bourns.com
SIC: 3677 3676 3661 3639 Electronic transformers; electronic resistors; telephone & telegraph apparatus; major kitchen appliances, except refrigerators & stoves; electronic circuits; connectors & terminals for electrical devices

(P-19324)
CAL COIL MAGNETICS INC
2523 Seaman Ave, El Monte (91733-1927)
PHONE..................626 455-0011
Scott Alvarado, *President*
Lisa Alvarado, *Admin Sec*
▲ EMP: 30 EST: 1954
SQ FT: 7,000
SALES (est): 4.2MM **Privately Held**
WEB: www.calcoilmagnetics.com
SIC: 3677 3612 Transformers power supply, electronic type; coil windings, electronic; transformers, except electric

(P-19325)
COAST/DVNCED CHIP MGNETICS INC
Also Called: Coast/A C M
4225 Spencer St, Torrance (90503-2421)
PHONE..................310 370-8188
Benjamin Nguyen, *CEO*
Allen Adams, *President*
Ben Nguyen, *CEO*
Karlis Lossing, *Info Tech Mgr*
EMP: 19 EST: 1952
SQ FT: 3,000
SALES (est): 4.5MM **Privately Held**
WEB: www.coastacm.com
SIC: 3677 Electronic coils, transformers & other inductors

(P-19326)
COIL WINDING SPECIALIST INC
Also Called: Cws
353 W Grove Ave, Orange (92865-3205)
PHONE..................714 279-9010
James Lau, *President*
Kian Chow, *VP Opers*
◆ EMP: 15
SQ FT: 1,000
SALES (est): 4.9MM **Privately Held**
SIC: 3677 Inductors, electronic

(P-19327)
COILTECH INCORPORATED
3545 Cadillac Ave Ste B, Costa Mesa (92626-1452)
PHONE..................714 708-8715
Mark Stoner, *President*
EMP: 15
SALES (est): 1.3MM **Privately Held**
WEB: www.coiltechinc.com
SIC: 3677 Electronic coils, transformers & other inductors

(P-19328)
COMPONETICS INC
2492 Turquoise Cir, Newbury Park (91320-1209)
PHONE..................805 498-0939
Oscar Maldonado, *President*
EMP: 11
SQ FT: 6,275
SALES (est): 2.1MM **Privately Held**
WEB: www.componeticsinc.com
SIC: 3677 Coil windings, electronic

(P-19329)
CORONA MAGNETICS INC
Also Called: C M I
201 Corporate Terrace St, Corona (92879-6000)
P.O. Box 1355 (92878-1355)
PHONE..................951 735-7558
Jay Paasch, *CEO*
Cory Villa, *COO*
Heike Paasch, *Vice Pres*
John McMillin, *Administration*
Erick Bechtel, *Engineer*
EMP: 120 EST: 1968
SQ FT: 17,000
SALES (est): 21.6MM **Privately Held**
WEB: www.corona-magnetics.com
SIC: 3677 3679 Transformers power supply, electronic type; electronic circuits

PRODUCTS & SVCS

(P-19330)
CUSTOM COILS INC
4000 Industrial Way, Benicia (94510-1242)
PHONE..................................707 752-8633
Tom Quinn, *President*
John Quinn, *CEO*
Brian Quinn, *Vice Pres*
EMP: 15
SQ FT: 7,200
SALES (est): 3.4MM **Privately Held**
WEB: www.ccoils.com
SIC: 3677 Electronic coils, transformers & other inductors

(P-19331)
CYPRESS MAGNETICS INC
8753 Industrial Ln, Rancho Cucamonga (91730-4527)
PHONE..................................909 987-3570
Suresh Mahajan, *President*
EMP: 10
SALES (est): 438K **Privately Held**
SIC: 3677 Electronic coils, transformers & other inductors

(P-19332)
DSPM INC
Also Called: Digital Signal Power Mfg
1921 S Quaker Ridge Pl, Ontario (91761-8041)
PHONE..................................714 970-2304
Milton Hanson, *President*
Maureen Hanson, *Vice Pres*
Carey Neill, *Controller*
Pedro Esparza, *Sales Associate*
▲ **EMP:** 20
SQ FT: 30,000
SALES (est): 6MM **Privately Held**
WEB: www.dspm.com
SIC: 3677 Transformers power supply, electronic type

(P-19333)
DUCOMMUN INCORPORATED
Dbp Microwave Div
1321 Mountain View Cir, Azusa (91702-1649)
P.O. Box 1062, Rancho Santa Fe (92067-1062)
PHONE..................................626 812-9666
EMP: 35
SALES (corp-wide): 550.6MM **Publicly Held**
SIC: 3677 3674 3625 3613
PA: Ducommun Incorporated
200 Sandpointe Ave # 700
Santa Ana CA 92707
657 335-3665

(P-19334)
FILTER CONCEPTS INCORPORATED
22895 Eastpark Dr, Yorba Linda (92887-4653)
PHONE..................................714 545-7003
Peter Murphy, *President*
Lester Edelberg, *President*
EMP: 38
SQ FT: 15,000
SALES (est): 5.2MM **Privately Held**
WEB: www.audiopower.com
SIC: 3677 Filtration devices, electronic
PA: Astrodyne Corporation
36 Newburgh Rd
Hackettstown NJ 07840

(P-19335)
FILTRATION DEVELOPMENT CO LLC
Also Called: Fdc Aerofilter
3920 Sandstone Dr, El Dorado Hills (95762-9652)
PHONE..................................415 884-0555
Andrew Rowen,
EMP: 19 **EST:** 1998
SQ FT: 3,000
SALES (est): 10MM **Privately Held**
WEB: www.fdcaerofilter.com
SIC: 3677 Filtration devices, electronic

(P-19336)
FRONTIER ELECTRONICS CORP
667 Cochran St, Simi Valley (93065-1939)
PHONE..................................805 522-9998
Jeannie Gu, *President*
Winston Gu, *Vice Pres*
Sandra Chang, *Office Mgr*
Jean Pope, *Controller*
Jay Valguno, *Safety Mgr*
▲ **EMP:** 18
SQ FT: 15,246
SALES: 5MM **Privately Held**
WEB: www.frontierusa.com
SIC: 3677 3674 Inductors, electronic; transformers power supply, electronic type; semiconductors & related devices

(P-19337)
FROST MAGNETICS INCORPORATED
49643 Hartwell Rd, Oakhurst (93644-8522)
PHONE..................................559 642-2536
Michael E Frost, *President*
Anita Frost, *Vice Pres*
▲ **EMP:** 30 **EST:** 1964
SQ FT: 16,200
SALES (est): 6.4MM **Privately Held**
WEB: www.frostmagnetics.com
SIC: 3677 Electronic transformers

(P-19338)
FSP GROUP USA CORP
14284 Albers Way, Chino (91710-6940)
PHONE..................................909 606-0960
Joseph Huang, *President*
Ana Brady, *Accounts Exec*
John Chen, *Accounts Exec*
▲ **EMP:** 10
SALES (est): 1.9MM
SALES (corp-wide): 478.9MM **Privately Held**
SIC: 3677 Transformers power supply, electronic type
PA: Fsp Technology Inc.
22, Jianguo E. Rd.,
Taoyuan City TAY 33068
337 598-88

(P-19339)
H B R INDUSTRIES INC
2261 Fortune Dr Ste B, San Jose (95131-1861)
PHONE..................................408 988-0800
Henk Ryssemus, *Owner*
Teresa Ryssemus, *Admin Sec*
▲ **EMP:** 10 **EST:** 1979
SQ FT: 5,000
SALES (est): 1.7MM **Privately Held**
SIC: 3677 3679 3555 5065 Electronic transformers; cores, magnetic; printing trades machinery; electronic parts & equipment

(P-19340)
INDUCTOR SUPPLY INC
Also Called: ISI
11542 Knott St Ste 3, Garden Grove (92841-1826)
PHONE..................................714 894-9050
Diana Klimek, *President*
Steve Andrews, *Business Mgr*
▲ **EMP:** 10 **EST:** 1979
SQ FT: 5,000
SALES (est): 1.6MM **Privately Held**
WEB: www.inductorsupply.com
SIC: 3677 Electronic coils, transformers & other inductors

(P-19341)
INTELLIPOWER INC
1746 N Saint Thomas Cir, Orange (92865-4247)
PHONE..................................714 921-1580
G W Bill Shipman, *CEO*
Dana Helmes, *CFO*
Dan Johnson, *CFO*
Gary Krig, *Hum Res Coord*
Jerrold Hornstein, *VP Sales*
EMP: 100
SQ FT: 22,000
SALES (est): 21.3MM **Privately Held**
SIC: 3677 Transformers power supply, electronic type

(P-19342)
JAMES L HALL CO INCORPORATED
Also Called: Jetronics Company
218 Roberts Ave, Santa Rosa (95401-6146)
P.O. Box U (95402-0280)
PHONE..................................707 544-2436
Stephen Vallarino, *Mng Member*
EMP: 55
SALES (est): 9.7MM
SALES (corp-wide): 8.2MM **Privately Held**
SIC: 3677 3679 Electronic coils, transformers & other inductors; electronic circuits
PA: James L. Hall Co., Incorporated
360 Tesconi Cir Ste B
Santa Rosa CA 95401
707 547-0775

(P-19343)
MAGNETIC COILS INC
150 San Hedrin Cir, Willits (95490-8753)
PHONE..................................707 459-5994
Don Setzco, *Manager*
EMP: 35
SALES (corp-wide): 5.2MM **Privately Held**
WEB: www.mcitransformer.com
SIC: 3677 Electronic coils, transformers & other inductors
PA: Magnetic Coils Inc.
411 Manhattan Ave
West Babylon NY
631 587-0510

(P-19344)
MAGNOTEK MANUFACTURING INC
6510 Box Springs Blvd, Riverside (92507-0740)
PHONE..................................951 653-8461
Donald K Furness, *CEO*
▲ **EMP:** 80
SQ FT: 500
SALES (est): 9.6MM **Privately Held**
SIC: 3677 Electronic transformers

(P-19345)
MAGTECH & POWER CONVERSION INC
Also Called: Speciality Labs
1146 E Ash Ave, Fullerton (92831-5018)
PHONE..................................714 451-0106
Viet Pho, *President*
Linh Pho, *Vice Pres*
Tien Tran, *Engineer*
Heidi Pham, *Manager*
EMP: 40
SQ FT: 9,000
SALES: 1MM **Privately Held**
WEB: www.magtechpower.com
SIC: 3677 Electronic transformers

(P-19346)
MERCURY MAGNETICS INC
Also Called: Gulf Enterprises
10050 Remmet Ave, Chatsworth (91311-3854)
PHONE..................................818 998-7791
Sergio Hamernik, *President*
Susan Hamernik, *Vice Pres*
▲ **EMP:** 20
SQ FT: 21,000
SALES (est): 5.1MM **Privately Held**
WEB: www.mercurymagnetics.com
SIC: 3677 Electronic transformers

(P-19347)
MIL-SPEC MAGNETICS INC
169 Pacific St, Pomona (91768-3215)
PHONE..................................909 598-8116
Shelton Gunewardena, *CEO*
Tony Gunewardena, *President*
Andrew Gunewardena, *Principal*
Eksath Weerekoon, *Director*
EMP: 30
SQ FT: 6,000
SALES: 2.8MM **Privately Held**
SIC: 3677 3675 Electronic transformers; inductors, electronic; electronic capacitors

(P-19348)
NATIONAL CERTIFIED FABRICATORS
Also Called: Griswold Water Systems
1525 E 6th St, Corona (92879-1716)
PHONE..................................951 278-8992
David E Griswold, *President*
EMP: 10
SQ FT: 21,000
SALES (est): 1.8MM **Privately Held**
WEB: www.griswoldfiltration.com
SIC: 3677 3585 Filtration devices, electronic; parts for heating, cooling & refrigerating equipment

(P-19349)
NATIONAL CNSTR RENTALS INC
Also Called: Storage and Sanitation
11029 Beech Ave, Fontana (92337-7268)
PHONE..................................909 574-1400
Robert Bisty, *Manager*
EMP: 25
SALES (corp-wide): 123.3MM **Privately Held**
WEB: www.rentnational.com
SIC: 3677 Transformers power supply, electronic type
HQ: National Construction Rentals, Inc.
15319 Chatsworth St
Mission Hills CA 91345
818 221-6000

(P-19350)
PAYNE MAGNETICS INC
854 W Front St, Covina (91722-3614)
PHONE..................................626 332-6207
George Payne, *Chairman*
Jon S Payne, *President*
Scott Kolb, *Division Mgr*
Bernadette Lopez, *Bookkeeper*
▲ **EMP:** 100
SQ FT: 6,600
SALES (est): 15.1MM **Privately Held**
WEB: www.payne-magnetics.com
SIC: 3677 3699 Electronic transformers; inductors, electronic; electrical equipment & supplies

(P-19351)
PCA ELECTRONICS INC
16799 Schoenborn St, North Hills (91343-6194)
PHONE..................................818 892-0761
Morris Weinberg, *President*
Benjamin Weinberg, *Vice Pres*
Ben Weinberg, *General Mgr*
Ira Goldstein, *Technology*
Bruce Luisi, *Sales Mgr*
EMP: 44
SQ FT: 30,000
SALES (est): 7.7MM **Privately Held**
WEB: www.pcainc.com
SIC: 3677 Electronic transformers

(P-19352)
PEARSON ELECTRONICS INC
4009 Transport St, Palo Alto (94303-4914)
PHONE..................................650 494-6444
Paul A Pearson, *President*
Patricia Pearson, *Vice Pres*
Cathy Breton, *Sales Staff*
EMP: 18
SQ FT: 14,400
SALES: 3MM **Privately Held**
WEB: www.pearsonelectronics.com
SIC: 3677 Electronic transformers

(P-19353)
POWER DISTRIBUTION INC
4011 W Carriage Dr, Santa Ana (92704-6301)
PHONE..................................714 513-1500
David Hensley, *President*
EMP: 10 **Privately Held**
SIC: 3677 3612 3613 Electronic coils, transformers & other inductors; transformers, except electric; switchgear & switchboard apparatus
HQ: Power Distribution, Inc.
4200 Oakleys Ln
Richmond VA 23223
804 737-9880

▲ = Import ▼=Export
◆ =Import/Export

(P-19354)
PREMIER MAGNETICS INC
20381 Barents Sea Cir, Lake Forest
(92630-8807)
PHONE...................................949 452-0511
James Earley, *President*
▲ EMP: 30
SALES (est): 5.8MM **Privately Held**
WEB: www.premiermag.com
SIC: 3677 3612 Electronic coils, trans-
formers & other inductors; specialty trans-
formers

(P-19355)
PUROFLUX CORPORATION
2121 Union Pl, Simi Valley (93065-1661)
PHONE...................................805 579-0216
Henry Nmi Greenberg, *President*
Kevin Carter, *Engineer*
Santos Lopez, *Purchasing*
Richard Lajoie, *Sales Associate*
▼ EMP: 17
SQ FT: 25,000
SALES (est): 3.7MM **Privately Held**
SIC: 3677 3613 Filtration devices, elec-
tronic; control panels, electric

(P-19356)
R & M COILS
27547 Terrytown Rd, Sun City
(92586-3217)
PHONE...................................951 672-9855
Rudolph Hesse, *Owner*
EMP: 12
SALES: 260K **Privately Held**
SIC: 3677 Electronic coils, transformers &
other inductors

(P-19357)
R H BARDEN INC
Also Called: Lodestone Pacific
4769 E Wesley Dr, Anaheim (92807-1941)
PHONE...................................714 970-0900
Richard H Barden III, *President*
Rich Damico, *COO*
Susan Barden, *Mktg Coord*
Jennifer Dinh, *Manager*
▲ EMP: 15
SQ FT: 12,000
SALES (est): 2.8MM **Privately Held**
WEB: www.lodestonepacific.com
SIC: 3677 Electronic coils, transformers &
other inductors

(P-19358)
RAYCO ELECTRONIC MFG INC
1220 W 130th St, Gardena (90247-1502)
PHONE...................................310 329-2660
Mahendra P Patel, *CEO*
Steve Mardani, *Vice Pres*
Mayan Patel, *Vice Pres*
EMP: 50 EST: 1941
SQ FT: 20,000
SALES (est): 11.9MM **Privately Held**
WEB: www.raycoelectronics.com
SIC: 3677 3612 3621 Electronic trans-
formers; filtration devices, electronic;
transformers, except electric; motors &
generators

(P-19359)
ROBERT M HADLEY COMPANY INC
4054 Transport St Ste B, Ventura
(93003-8325)
PHONE...................................805 658-7286
James A Hadley, *CEO*
Jim Hadley, *President*
Christopher Waian, *Vice Pres*
E C Waian, *Vice Pres*
Chris Waian, *General Mgr*
EMP: 90
SQ FT: 28,000
SALES: 4.7MM **Privately Held**
WEB: www.rmhco.com
SIC: 3677 Transformers power supply,
electronic type

(P-19360)
RODON PRODUCTS INC
15481 Electronic Ln Ste A, Huntington
Beach (92649-1355)
PHONE...................................714 898-3528
Robert W Bertels Jr, *President*
Sandra Bertels, *Vice Pres*
Steve Freeman, *Vice Pres*

EMP: 25
SALES (est): 3.4MM **Privately Held**
WEB: www.rodonproducts.com
SIC: 3677 3679 Electronic coils, trans-
formers & other inductors; electronic cir-
cuits

(P-19361)
SCOTTS VALLEY MAGNETICS INC
300 El Pueblo Rd Ste 107, Scotts Valley
(95066-4238)
P.O. Box 66575 (95067-6575)
PHONE...................................831 438-3600
Norma Humphries, *President*
Karina Humphries, *Treasurer*
Jerry Humphries, *Vice Pres*
John F Humphries, *Admin Sec*
Michelle Richmond, *Sales Staff*
▲ EMP: 24
SQ FT: 15,000
SALES (est): 4.5MM **Privately Held**
WEB: www.svmagnetics.com
SIC: 3677 3679 3829 Filtration devices,
electronic; electronic transformers; induc-
tors, electronic; transformers power sup-
ply, electronic type; power supplies, all
types: static; measuring & controlling de-
vices

(P-19362)
SI MANUFACTURING INC
1440 S Allec St, Anaheim (92805-6305)
PHONE...................................714 956-7110
James R Reed, *President*
Ataollah Shafizadeh, *Exec VP*
Ata Shafizadeh, *Vice Pres*
▲ EMP: 50
SALES (est): 9.5MM **Privately Held**
WEB: www.simfg.com
SIC: 3677 3612 3679 3613 Electronic
coils, transformers & other inductors;
transformers, except electric; electronic
loads & power supplies; switchgear &
switchboard apparatus; engineering serv-
ices

(P-19363)
SMART WIRES INC (PA)
Also Called: S W G
3292 Whipple Rd, Union City (94587-1217)
PHONE...................................415 800-5555
Jim Davis, *CEO*
Neal Dikeman, *CFO*
Allan Rosenberg, *Principal*
Jane Linder, *Admin Sec*
Deniz Gundogdu, *Mfg Staff*
EMP: 15
SALES (est): 4.4MM **Privately Held**
SIC: 3677 Electronic coils, transformers &
other inductors

(P-19364)
SONOMA PHOTONICS INC
1750 Northpoint Pkwy C, Santa Rosa
(95407-7597)
PHONE...................................707 568-1202
Mark A Caylor, *President*
Wesley G Bush, *President*
Craig Witt, *Design Engr*
Jason Keller, *Engineer*
Annie Lee, *Controller*
EMP: 50 EST: 2000
SQ FT: 30,000
SALES (est): 8.8MM **Publicly Held**
WEB: www.sonomaphotonics.com
SIC: 3677 3827 Filtration devices, elec-
tronic; optical instruments & lenses
HQ: Northrop Grumman Systems Corpora-
tion
2980 Fairview Park Dr
Falls Church VA 22042
703 280-2900

(P-19365)
STANGENES INDUSTRIES INC (PA)
1052 E Meadow Cir, Palo Alto
(94303-4271)
PHONE...................................650 855-9926
Magne Stangenes, *CEO*
Kari Stangenes, *CFO*
▲ EMP: 113 EST: 1974
SQ FT: 15,500

SALES (est): 19.3MM **Privately Held**
WEB: www.stangenes.com
SIC: 3677 Electronic transformers

(P-19366)
SUEZ WTS SERVICES USA INC
Also Called: GE
1800 Thibodo Rd Ste 210, Vista
(92081-7515)
PHONE...................................760 598-1800
Don Von Gruenigen, *Branch Mgr*
EMP: 14
SALES (corp-wide): 86.1MM **Privately Held**
WEB: www.geosmonics.com
SIC: 3677 Electronic coils, transformers &
other inductors
HQ: Suez Wts Services Usa, Inc.
4545 Patent Rd
Norfolk VA 23502
757 855-9000

(P-19367)
SYNDER INC (PA)
Also Called: Synder Filtration
4941 Allison Pkwy, Vacaville (95688-8795)
PHONE...................................707 451-6060
Edward Yeh, *CEO*
Joseph Y Wang, *President*
Y C Jao PHD, *Vice Pres*
▲ EMP: 33
SQ FT: 26,000
SALES (est): 8.1MM **Privately Held**
WEB: www.synderfiltration.com
SIC: 3677 8748 8742 Filtration devices,
electronic; systems analysis or design; in-
dustry specialist consultants

(P-19368)
TUR-BO JET PRODUCTS CO INC
5025 Earle Ave, Rosemead (91770-1197)
PHONE...................................626 285-1294
Richard Bloom, *President*
Richard L Bloom, *Vice Pres*
Michael Bloom, *Engineer*
Negwa Brownfield, *Accounting Mgr*
Tamara Graeber, *Human Res Mgr*
▲ EMP: 95 EST: 1945
SQ FT: 27,000
SALES (est): 20.9MM **Privately Held**
WEB: www.turbojetproducts.com
SIC: 3677 Coil windings, electronic

(P-19369)
TURBO COIL MANUFACTURING INC
1740 Evergreen St, Duarte (91010-2845)
PHONE...................................626 599-7777
Hector Delgadillo, *CEO*
EMP: 33 EST: 2010
SALES (est): 4.9MM **Privately Held**
SIC: 3677 Electronic coils, transformers &
other inductors

(P-19370)
WJLP COMPANY INC
Also Called: West Coast Magnetics
4848 Frontier Way Ste 100, Stockton
(95215-9670)
P.O. Box 31330 (95213-1330)
PHONE...................................800 628-1123
Weyman Lundquist, *President*
Vivien Yang, *Engineer*
Maria Larios, *Human Resources*
Toni Jimenez, *Purch Mgr*
Lisa Reyes, *Prdtn Mgr*
▲ EMP: 100
SQ FT: 8,000
SALES: 5MM **Privately Held**
WEB: www.wcmagnetics.com
SIC: 3677 3357 Electronic transformers;
inductors, electronic; coaxial cable, non-
ferrous

3678 Electronic Connectors

(P-19371)
ADVANCED GLOBAL TECH GROUP
8015 E Treeview Ct, Anaheim
(92808-1553)
PHONE...................................714 281-8020
Brian Hayes, *President*
Mary Hayes, *Corp Secy*

Tom Marcello, *Director*
▲ EMP: 21
SALES: 2.5MM **Privately Held**
SIC: 3678 3652 4813 0191

(P-19372)
ALPHA PRODUCTS INC
351 Irving Dr, Oxnard (93030-5173)
PHONE...................................805 981-8666
Tony Gulrajani, *President*
▲ EMP: 27
SQ FT: 12,000
SALES (est): 4.9MM **Privately Held**
SIC: 3678 5065 Electronic connectors;
electronic parts & equipment

(P-19373)
AMPHENOL CORPORATION
Amphenol Rf
5069 Maureen Ln Ste B, Moorpark
(93021-7149)
PHONE...................................805 378-6464
Mike Comer, *Manager*
EMP: 11
SALES (corp-wide): 7B **Publicly Held**
SIC: 3678 Electronic connectors
PA: Amphenol Corporation
358 Hall Ave
Wallingford CT 06492
203 265-8900

(P-19374)
BRANTNER AND ASSOCIATES INC (DH)
Also Called: Sea Con
1700 Gillespie Way, El Cajon (92020-1874)
PHONE...................................619 562-7070
Patrick G Simar, *President*
Denton Seilhan, *Exec VP*
▲ EMP: 142
SQ FT: 35,000
SALES (est): 28.6MM
SALES (corp-wide): 13.1B **Privately Held**
SIC: 3678 3643 Electronic connectors;
current-carrying wiring devices
HQ: Brantner Holding Company
501 Oakside Ave
Redwood City CA 94063
650 361-5292

(P-19375)
CHINA LOCO SZHOU PRECISE INDUS
4125 Business Center Dr, Fremont
(94538-6355)
PHONE...................................510 429-3700
Alex Wang, *Branch Mgr*
EMP: 20
SALES (corp-wide): 24MM **Privately Held**
WEB: www.leoco.net
SIC: 3678 Electronic connectors
PA: Leoco (Suzhou) Precise Industrial Co.,
Ltd.
No.300, Liuxu Rd., Economic And
Technological Development Zone,
Wujiang 21520
512 634-5546

(P-19376)
CIRCUIT ASSEMBLY CORP (PA)
3 Vanderbilt Ste A, Irvine (92618-2777)
PHONE...................................949 855-7887
Andrew Lang, *President*
Lili Su, *President*
Robert Brinckman, *Vice Pres*
Terri Lang, *Vice Pres*
Shami Ramdial, *Sales Mgr*
▲ EMP: 30 EST: 1969
SQ FT: 62,000
SALES (est): 4.1MM **Privately Held**
WEB: www.circuitassembly.com
SIC: 3678 Electronic connectors

(P-19377)
COMPONENT EQUIPMENT COINC
Also Called: Ceco
3050 Camino Del Sol, Oxnard
(93030-7275)
PHONE...................................805 988-8004
Bill Rigby, *President*
Thomas Conway, *Vice Pres*
Tom Conway, *Vice Pres*
Sheila Richmond, *Human Res Dir*

EMP: 75
SQ FT: 32,000
SALES (est): 10.4MM Privately Held
WEB: www.ceco-inc.com
SIC: 3678 Electronic connectors

(P-19378)
CONESYS INC (PA)
2280 W 208th St, Torrance (90501-1452)
PHONE...................310 618-3737
Walter Neubauer Jr, CEO
John Vinke, CFO
Andrew Dawson, Vice Pres
Andres Murillo, General Mgr
Dave Dierickx, Design Engr
EMP: 78
SQ FT: 95,000
SALES (est): 27.9MM Privately Held
WEB: www.conesys.com
SIC: 3678 Electronic connectors

(P-19379)
CONESYS INC
548 Amapola Ave, Torrance (90501-1472)
PHONE...................310 212-0065
Teresa Lynn De Foreest, Administration
Karim Louanchi, General Mgr
Mark Edwards, CIO
Laurent Gonin, Technology
Scott Stewart, Opers Staff
EMP: 12
SALES (est): 1.9MM
SALES (corp-wide): 27.9MM Privately
Held
SIC: 3678 Electronic connectors
PA: Conesys, Inc.
2280 W 208th St
Torrance CA 90501
310 618-3737

(P-19380)
CONNECTOR KINGS CORPORATION
Also Called: Connectorkings.com
2110 Mcallister St, Riverside (92503-6704)
P.O. Box 2084, Redlands (92373-0661)
PHONE...................951 710-1180
William B Furlong, President
EMP: 13
SALES (est): 2.2MM Privately Held
SIC: 3678 Electronic connectors

(P-19381)
COOPER CROUSE-HINDS LLC
Also Called: General Connector
750 W Ventura Blvd, Camarillo
(93010-8382)
PHONE...................805 484-0543
Alexander M Cutler, CEO
Robert Sierra, Principal
EMP: 135 Privately Held
SIC: 3678 3663 3451 Electronic connec-
tors; radio & TV communications equip-
ment; screw machine products
HQ: Cooper Crouse-Hinds, Llc
1201 Wolf St
Syracuse NY 13208
315 477-7000

(P-19382)
COOPER INTERCONNECT INC
750 W Ventura Blvd, Camarillo
(93010-8382)
PHONE...................805 553-9632
EMP: 100 Privately Held
SIC: 3678 3643 Electronic connectors;
current-carrying wiring devices
HQ: Cooper Interconnect, Inc.
750 W Ventura Blvd
Camarillo CA 93010
805 484-0543

(P-19383)
CORSAIR ELEC CONNECTORS INC
17100 Murphy Ave, Irvine (92614-5916)
PHONE...................949 833-0273
Amir Saket, President
Margot Rodelli, Administration
Brian Pace, Engineer
Steven Simmons, Finance
Steve Simmons, Controller
EMP: 140
SQ FT: 34,554
SALES (est): 20.6MM Privately Held
SIC: 3678 Electronic connectors

(P-19384)
CRISTEK INTERCONNECTS INC (PA)
5395 E Hunter Ave, Anaheim (92807-2054)
PHONE...................888 265-9162
Cristi Cristich, President
Julie Barker, CFO
John B Pollock, Vice Pres
EMP: 135
SALES (est): 28.5MM Privately Held
WEB: www.cristek.com
SIC: 3678 Electronic connectors

(P-19385)
CS MANFACTURING INDUS SVCS INC (PA)
619 Paulin Ave Ste 105, Calexico
(92231-2671)
P.O. Box 2914 (92232-2914)
PHONE...................760 890-7746
Cesar Samaniego Silva, President
EMP: 15
SQ FT: 1,000
SALES (est): 1.4MM Privately Held
SIC: 3678 Electronic connectors

(P-19386)
DETORONICS CORP
13071 Rosecrans Ave, Santa Fe Springs
(90670-4930)
PHONE...................626 579-7130
Kenneth S Clark, CEO
Marcia Baroda, CFO
Jamie Saltos, General Mgr
Mayren Mendoza, Production
Nancy Chavez, Sales Mgr
EMP: 37
SQ FT: 20,000
SALES (est): 7.5MM Privately Held
WEB: www.detoronics.com
SIC: 3678 Electronic connectors

(P-19387)
DS CYPRESS MAGNETICS INC
8753 Industrial Ln, Rancho Cucamonga
(91730-4527)
PHONE...................909 987-3570
Suresh S Mahajan, President
Dan Reimders, Vice Pres
▲ EMP: 10 EST: 2005
SALES (est): 1.5MM Privately Held
SIC: 3678 8742 Electronic connectors;
management consulting services

(P-19388)
DUEL SYSTEMS INC
2025 Galeway Pl Ste 235, San Jose
(95110)
PHONE...................408 453-9500
Don Duda, President
▲ EMP: 25
SQ FT: 34,000
SALES (est): 3.4MM
SALES (corp-wide): 908.3MM Publicly
Held
WEB: www.methode.com
SIC: 3678 Electronic connectors
PA: Methode Electronics, Inc
7401 W Wilson Ave
Chicago IL 60706
708 867-6777

(P-19389)
EVENSPHERE INCORPORATION
1249 S Diamond Bar Blvd, Diamond Bar
(91765-4122)
PHONE...................909 247-3030
Jeng H Yuh, President
EMP: 50
SALES (est): 3.8MM Privately Held
SIC: 3678 3229 3357 Electronic connec-
tors; fiber optics strands; fiber optic cable
(insulated)

(P-19390)
FEI EFA INC (DH)
Also Called: Dcg Systems
3400 W Warren Ave, Fremont
(94538-6425)
PHONE...................510 897-6800
Israel Niv, CEO
Ronen Benzion, President
Bob Conners, CFO
Tameyasu Anayama, Vice Pres
Jeff Block, Business Dir

EMP: 95
SQ FT: 45,000
SALES (est): 72.1MM
SALES (corp-wide): 20.9B Publicly Held
SIC: 3678 Electronic connectors
HQ: Fei Company
5350 Ne Dawson Creek Dr
Hillsboro OR 97124
503 726-7500

(P-19391)
FLEXIBLE MANUFACTURING LLC
Also Called: F M I
1719 S Grand Ave, Santa Ana
(92705-4808)
PHONE...................714 259-7996
Frank Meza,
Tom Rendina, CFO
Ross Silberfarb, Vice Pres
Bart Pacetti, Program Mgr
Dave Silberfarb, Opers Mgr
▲ EMP: 100
SQ FT: 15,000
SALES (est): 20.8MM Privately Held
WEB: www.flexiblemanufacturing.com
SIC: 3678 Electronic connectors

(P-19392)
GLEN-MAC SWISS CO
12848 Weber Way, Hawthorne
(90250-5537)
PHONE...................310 978-4555
Torkom Postajian, President
Armen Postajian, Corp Secy
▲ EMP: 15
SQ FT: 12,676
SALES: 1.2MM Privately Held
SIC: 3678 3429 3451 3599 Electronic
connectors; manufactured hardware (gen-
eral); screw machine products; machine
shop, jobbing & repair

(P-19393)
HCC INDUSTRIES INC (HQ)
4232 Temple City Blvd, Rosemead
(91770-1552)
PHONE...................626 443-8933
Richard Ferraid, President
EMP: 15
SQ FT: 36,000
SALES (est): 148.6MM
SALES (corp-wide): 4.3B Publicly Held
WEB: www.hccmachining.com
SIC: 3678 Electronic connectors
PA: Ametek, Inc.
1100 Cassatt Rd
Berwyn PA 19312
610 647-2121

(P-19394)
HIGH CONNECTION DENSITY INC
820 Kifer Rd Ste A, Sunnyvale
(94086-5200)
PHONE...................408 743-9700
Tsuyoshi Taira, President
Charlie Stevenson, COO
EMP: 25
SALES (est): 2.7MM Privately Held
WEB: www.hcdcorp.com
SIC: 3678 8734 Electronic connectors;
testing laboratories

(P-19395)
I O INTERCONNECT LTD (PA)
Also Called: I/O Interconnect
1202 E Wakeham Ave, Santa Ana
(92705-4145)
PHONE...................714 564-1111
Gary Kung, CEO
Karen Young, VP Human Res
Roland Balusek, Sales Dir
Maurice Kopstein, Director
▲ EMP: 50
SQ FT: 38,000
SALES (est): 222MM Privately Held
WEB: www.iointerconnect.com
SIC: 3678 3679 Electronic connectors;
harness assemblies for electronic use:
wire or cable

(P-19396)
ICONN INC
Also Called: Iconn Technologies
8909 Irvine Center Dr, Irvine (92618-4249)
PHONE...................949 297-8448
Rob Tondreault, President
Turker Hidirlar, COO
▲ EMP: 39
SQ FT: 9,920
SALES (est): 6.1MM Privately Held
SIC: 3678 3643 5063 3613 Electronic
connectors; connectors & terminals for
electrical devices; connectors, electric
cord; lugs & connectors, electrical; power
connectors, electric; booster (jump-start)
cables, automotive

(P-19397)
INFINITE ELECTRONICS INTL INC (DH)
17792 Fitch, Irvine (92614-6020)
PHONE...................949 261-1920
Terry G Jarnigan, CEO
Jim Dauw, COO
Scott Rosner, CFO
David Quinn, Exec VP
Penny Cotner, Vice Pres
▲ EMP: 164
SQ FT: 40,000
SALES (est): 300MM Privately Held
WEB: www.pasternack.com
SIC: 3678 3357 3651 3643 Electronic
connectors; coaxial cable, nonferrous;
household audio & video equipment; cur-
rent-carrying wiring devices
HQ: Infinite Electronics, Inc.
17792 Fitch
Irvine CA 92614
949 261-1920

(P-19398)
J-T E C H
548 Amapola Ave, Torrance (90501-1472)
PHONE...................310 533-6700
Walter Naubauer Jr, CEO
EMP: 136
SALES (est): 5.9MM Privately Held
SIC: 3678 Electronic connectors

(P-19399)
JOSLYN SUNBANK COMPANY LLC
1740 Commerce Way, Paso Robles
(93446-3620)
PHONE...................805 238-2840
Angel Cruz, Principal
Nayan Patel, Program Mgr
Mike Norman, Plant Mgr
Eric Lardiere,
Marlo Oliver,
EMP: 500 EST: 1997
SQ FT: 80,000
SALES (est): 115.7MM
SALES (corp-wide): 2B Publicly Held
WEB: www.sunbankcorp.com
SIC: 3678 3643 5065 Electronic connec-
tors; connectors & terminals for electrical
devices; connectors, electronic
PA: Esterline Technologies Corp
500 108th Ave Ne Ste 1500
Bellevue WA 98004
425 453-9400

(P-19400)
L & M MACHINING CORPORATION
550 S Melrose St, Placentia (92870-6327)
PHONE...................714 414-0923
Mike MAI, President
Lynn MAI, Human Resources
Troy Ferreira, Opers Mgr
Janice MAI, Internal Med
Moon Tran, Manager
EMP: 55
SQ FT: 31,000
SALES: 3MM Privately Held
WEB: www.lmcnc.com
SIC: 3678 Electronic connectors

(P-19401)
MIN-E-CON LLC
17312 Eastman, Irvine (92614-5522)
PHONE...................949 250-0087
Wendell Jacob, Mng Member
Jack Michael, Personnel

▲ = Import ▼=Export
◆ =Import/Export

Gary Schneider, *QC Mgr*
John M Brown,
Wendell P Jacob,
▼ **EMP:** 60 **EST:** 1974
SALES (est): 9.5MM **Privately Held**
WEB: www.min-e-con.com
SIC: 3678 Electronic connectors

(P-19402)
MOLEX LLC
Also Called: Custom Goods Warehouse
12200 Arrow Rte, Rancho Cucamonga
(91739-9682)
PHONE....................909 803-1362
John Franco, *Branch Mgr*
EMP: 26
SALES (corp-wide): 42.9B **Privately Held**
SIC: 3678 3643 3357 3679 Electronic
connectors; connectors & terminals for
electrical devices; communication wire;
fiber optic cable (insulated); electronic circuits
HQ: Molex, Llc
2222 Wellington Ct
Lisle IL 60532
630 969-4550

(P-19403)
NEA ELECTRONICS INC
14370 White Sage Rd, Moorpark
(93021-8720)
PHONE....................805 292-4010
Steven Perkins, *President*
EMP: 24
SQ FT: 20,000
SALES (est): 5.8MM **Privately Held**
WEB: www.neaelectronics.com
SIC: 3678 3629 3592 Electronic connec-
tors; battery chargers, rectifying or nonro-
tating; valves

(P-19404)
NMC CORPORATION
2427 Bonniebrook Dr, Stockton
(95207-1562)
PHONE....................209 986-0899
Joshua Benjestorf, *CEO*
EMP: 20
SALES (est): 1.5MM **Privately Held**
SIC: 3678 Electronic connectors

(P-19405)
NOVA MOBILE SYSTEMS INC
2888 Loker Ave E Ste 311, Carlsbad
(92010-6686)
PHONE....................800 734-9885
George Ecker, *President*
John Mannion, *COO*
Trevin Sandison, *Engineer*
EMP: 10
SALES (est): 1.3MM **Privately Held**
SIC: 3678 Electronic connectors

(P-19406)
ONANON INC
720 S Milpitas Blvd, Milpitas (95035-5449)
PHONE....................408 262-8990
Dennis Joel Johnson, *CEO*
Thomas R Sahakian, *CFO*
Robert Bejarano, *General Mgr*
Suzanne Figueroa, *Office Mgr*
Katie Hoose, *Design Engr*
EMP: 49
SQ FT: 25,000
SALES (est): 10.4MM **Privately Held**
WEB: www.onanon.com
SIC: 3678 3089 Electronic connectors;
laminating of plastic

(P-19407)
P W WIRING SYSTEMS LLC
Also Called: Pw Wiring Systems
9415 Kruse Rd, Pico Rivera (90660-1430)
PHONE....................562 463-9055
Steven Koundouriotis,
EMP: 36
SALES (est): 5.2MM **Privately Held**
WEB: www.pwwiringsystems.com
SIC: 3678 Electronic connectors

(P-19408)
QCEPT TECHNOLOGIES INC
Also Called: Qcept Technologies California
47354 Fremont Blvd, Fremont
(94538-6501)
PHONE....................510 490-1120

Bret Bergman, *CEO*
EMP: 25
SALES (corp-wide): 4.5MM **Privately
Held**
SIC: 3678 Electronic connectors
PA: Qcept Technologies Inc.
1201 Peachtree St Ne # 500
Atlanta GA
-

(P-19409)
R KERN ENGINEERING & MFG CORP
13912 Mountain Ave, Chino (91710-9018)
PHONE....................909 664-2440
Richard Kern, *CEO*
Roland A Kern, *Ch of Bd*
Helga Kern, *Treasurer*
Jose Nunez, *Vice Pres*
Jay Nunez, *IT/INT Sup*
▲ **EMP:** 54
SQ FT: 34,000
SALES (est): 15.3MM **Privately Held**
WEB: www.kerneng.com
SIC: 3678 3599 Electronic connectors;
machine shop, jobbing & repair

(P-19410)
RAYCON TECHNOLOGY INC (PA)
5252 Mcfadden Ave, Huntington Beach
(92649-1237)
PHONE....................714 799-4100
Raymond Smith, *President*
▲ **EMP:** 10
SQ FT: 20,000
SALES (est): 1.4MM **Privately Held**
WEB: www.raycontech.com
SIC: 3678 Electronic connectors

(P-19411)
RF INDUSTRIES LTD (PA)
7610 Miramar Rd Ste 6000, San Diego
(92126-4238)
PHONE....................858 549-6340
Robert D Dawson, *President*
Mark Turfler, *CFO*
EMP: 86
SQ FT: 21,908
SALES: 30.9MM **Publicly Held**
WEB: www.rfindustries.com
SIC: 3678 3643 3663 Electronic connec-
tors; electric connectors; connectors &
terminals for electrical devices; transmit-
ter-receivers, radio

(P-19412)
TE CONNECTIVITY
5733 W Whittier Ave, Hemet (92545-9030)
PHONE....................951 765-2200
EMP: 17 **EST:** 2013
SALES (est): 5.7MM **Privately Held**
SIC: 3678 Electronic connectors

(P-19413)
TE CONNECTIVITY CORPORATION
305 Constitution Dr, Menlo Park
(94025-1110)
PHONE....................650 361-3333
Christine Brown, *Branch Mgr*
EMP: 34
SALES (corp-wide): 13.1B **Privately Held**
WEB: www.raychem.com
SIC: 3678 Electronic connectors
HQ: Te Connectivity Corporation
1050 Westlakes Dr
Berwyn PA 19312
610 893-9800

(P-19414)
TE CONNECTIVITY CORPORATION
305 Constitution Dr, Menlo Park
(94025-1110)
PHONE....................650 361-3333
Jeff Harrison, *Branch Mgr*
EMP: 350
SALES (corp-wide): 13.1B **Privately Held**
WEB: www.raychem.com
SIC: 3678 Electronic connectors
HQ: Te Connectivity Corporation
1050 Westlakes Dr
Berwyn PA 19312
610 893-9800

(P-19415)
TE CONNECTIVITY CORPORATION
Also Called: Deutstch Industrial Products
700 S Hathaway St, Banning (92220-5904)
PHONE....................951 929-3323
Teri Elrod, *Manager*
EMP: 476
SALES (corp-wide): 13.1B **Privately Held**
WEB: www.deutschecd.com
SIC: 3678 3643 Electronic connectors;
current-carrying wiring devices
HQ: Te Connectivity Corporation
1050 Westlakes Dr
Berwyn PA 19312
610 893-9800

(P-19416)
TE CONNECTIVITY CORPORATION
5733 W Whittier Ave, Hemet (92545-9030)
PHONE....................951 765-2250
EMP: 98
SALES (corp-wide): 13.1B **Privately Held**
WEB: www.deutschecd.com
SIC: 3678 Electronic connectors
HQ: Te Connectivity Corporation
1050 Westlakes Dr
Berwyn PA 19312
610 893-9800

(P-19417)
TE CONNECTIVITY CORPORATION
Defense Aerospace Operations
250 Eddie Jones Way, Oceanside
(92058-1200)
P.O. Box 2630 (92051-2630)
PHONE....................760 757-7500
Richard Niemi, *Branch Mgr*
EMP: 501
SALES (corp-wide): 13.1B **Privately Held**
WEB: www.deutschecd.com
SIC: 3678 Electronic connectors
HQ: Te Connectivity Corporation
1050 Westlakes Dr
Berwyn PA 19312
610 893-9800

(P-19418)
TE CONNECTIVITY CORPORATION
1455 Adams Dr, Menlo Park (94025-1438)
PHONE....................650 361-3302
Dwayne Goodwin, *Manager*
EMP: 150
SALES (corp-wide): 13.1B **Privately Held**
WEB: www.raychem.com
SIC: 3678 Electronic connectors
HQ: Te Connectivity Corporation
1050 Westlakes Dr
Berwyn PA 19312
610 893-9800

(P-19419)
TE CONNECTIVITY CORPORATION
Also Called: Wireless Systems Segment
5300 Hellyer Ave, San Jose (95138-1003)
PHONE....................408 624-3000
Robert Tavares, *Vice Pres*
EMP: 307
SALES (corp-wide): 13.1B **Privately Held**
WEB: www.raychem.com
SIC: 3678 Electronic connectors
HQ: Te Connectivity Corporation
1050 Westlakes Dr
Berwyn PA 19312
610 893-9800

(P-19420)
TE CONNECTIVITY CORPORATION
Also Called: Tyco Electronics
9543 Henrich Dr Ste 7, San Diego (92154)
PHONE....................619 454-5176
Enrique Aristi, *Office Mgr*
EMP: 20
SALES (corp-wide): 13.1B **Privately Held**
SIC: 3678 3643 Electronic connectors;
current-carrying wiring devices; connec-
tors & terminals for electrical devices

HQ: Te Connectivity Corporation
1050 Westlakes Dr
Berwyn PA 19312
610 893-9800

(P-19421)
TE CONNECTIVITY CORPORATION
Also Called: Deutsch Dao
5733 W Whittier Ave, Hemet (92545-9030)
PHONE....................760 757-7500
EMP: 297
SALES (corp-wide): 13.1B **Privately Held**
SIC: 3678 Electronic connectors
HQ: Te Connectivity Corporation
1050 Westlakes Dr
Berwyn PA 19312
610 893-9800

(P-19422)
TE CONNECTIVITY CORPORATION
6900 Paseo Padre Pkwy, Fremont
(94555-3641)
PHONE....................650 361-3615
Thomas J Lynch, *CEO*
EMP: 600
SALES (corp-wide): 13.1B **Privately Held**
SIC: 3678 Electronic connectors
HQ: Te Connectivity Corporation
1050 Westlakes Dr
Berwyn PA 19312
610 893-9800

(P-19423)
TE CONNECTIVITY CORPORATION
Defense Aerospace Operations
5733 W Whittier Ave, Hemet (92545-9030)
PHONE....................951 765-2200
Richard Niemi, *Director*
EMP: 297
SALES (corp-wide): 13.1B **Privately Held**
WEB: www.deutschecd.com
SIC: 3678 3643 3577 Electronic connec-
tors; current-carrying wiring devices; com-
puter peripheral equipment
HQ: Te Connectivity Corporation
1050 Westlakes Dr
Berwyn PA 19312
610 893-9800

(P-19424)
TEKTEST INC
Also Called: E-Z-Hook Test Products Div
225 N 2nd Ave, Arcadia (91006-3286)
P.O. Box 660729 (91066-0729)
PHONE....................626 446-6175
Phelps M Wood, *President*
Beverly Wood, *Vice Pres*
EMP: 20 **EST:** 1970
SQ FT: 24,000
SALES: 2.7MM **Privately Held**
WEB: www.e-z-hook.com
SIC: 3678 Electronic connectors

(P-19425)
TIMCO/CAL RF INC
3910 Royal Ave Ste A, Simi Valley
(93063-3270)
PHONE....................805 582-1777
James V Clarizio Jr, *President*
EMP: 20
SQ FT: 13,000
SALES (est): 2.5MM **Privately Held**
SIC: 3678 Electronic connectors

(P-19426)
ULTI-MATE CONNECTOR INC
1872 N Case St, Orange (92865-4233)
PHONE....................714 637-7099
Bruce I Billington, *CEO*
Thierry Pombart, *Vice Pres*
Jacky Lin, *Engineer*
Isabel Mendoza, *Purchasing*
Yolanda Abraham, *VP Sales*
▲ **EMP:** 45
SQ FT: 11,000
SALES: 8MM **Privately Held**
WEB: www.umi-c.com
SIC: 3678 Electronic connectors

PRODUCTS & SVCS

(P-19427)
UNIT INDUSTRIES INC (PA)
3122 Maple St, Santa Ana (92707-4408)
PHONE..........................714 871-4161
Anthony Codet, *President*
J W Abouchar, *CEO*
Lizabeth Mulligan Codet, *Admin Sec*
EMP: 35
SQ FT: 16,000
SALES (est): 8.9MM Privately Held
WEB: www.unitindustries.com
SIC: 3678 Electronic connectors

3679 Electronic Components, NEC

(P-19428)
2 S 2 INC
Also Called: Display Integration Tech
1357 Rocky Point Dr, Oceanside
(92056-5864)
PHONE..........................760 599-9225
Benjamin G Chapman, *President*
Stephen Bolus, *Marketing Mgr*
Robert Hover, *Sales Mgr*
EMP: 10 Privately Held
SIC: 3679 Liquid crystal displays (LCD)
PA: 2 S 2, Inc.
    1702 A St Ste C
    Sparks NV 89431

(P-19429)
3Y POWER TECHNOLOGY INC
80 Bunsen, Irvine (92618-4210)
PHONE..........................949 450-0152
Yuan Yu, *President*
▲ EMP: 17
SQ FT: 13,800
SALES (est): 3.1MM Privately Held
WEB: www.3ypower.com
SIC: 3679 Power supplies, all types: static;
electronic circuits

(P-19430)
A R ELECTRONICS INC
Also Called: Audiolink
31290 Plantation Dr, Thousand Palms
(92276-6604)
PHONE..........................760 343-1200
Larry N Rich, *President*
Larry Rich, *President*
Cheryl Rich, *Admin Sec*
EMP: 25
SQ FT: 10,000
SALES (est): 3.6MM Privately Held
SIC: 3679 5065 Electronic circuits; electronic parts & equipment

(P-19431)
ABC ASSEMBLY INC
43006 Osgood Rd, Fremont (94539-5629)
PHONE..........................408 293-3560
Tim Suleymanov, *CEO*
Mike Suleymanov, *Chairman*
Tofik Kasumov, *Purch Mgr*
Lora Suleymanova, *Prdtn Mgr*
EMP: 12
SQ FT: 9,000
SALES (est): 3.2MM Privately Held
WEB: www.abcassembly.com
SIC: 3679 Electronic circuits

(P-19432)
ACCRATRONICS SEALS CORPORATION
Also Called: A T S
2211 Kenmere Ave, Burbank (91504-3493)
PHONE..........................818 843-1500
William Fisch, *CEO*
Corby Jones, *President*
Delbert Jones, *Vice Pres*
Troy Jones, *Vice Pres*
Deken Jones, *Admin Sec*
EMP: 72
SQ FT: 10,000
SALES (est): 6MM Privately Held
WEB: www.accratronics.com
SIC: 3679 Hermetic seals for electronic equipment

(P-19433)
ACCU-GLASS PRODUCTS INC
25047 Anza Dr, Valencia (91355-3414)
PHONE..........................818 365-4215
Charles Miltenberger, *President*
Jamie Faulconer, *COO*
EMP: 10
SQ FT: 4,000
SALES (est): 1.9MM Privately Held
WEB: www.accuglassproducts.com
SIC: 3679 Electronic circuits

(P-19434)
ADCO PRODUCTS INC
23091 Mill Creek Dr, Laguna Hills
(92653-1258)
PHONE..........................937 339-6267
George Adkins, *President*
Randy Adkins, *Vice Pres*
EMP: 60
SQ FT: 12,500
SALES (est): 10.1MM Privately Held
SIC: 3679 2499 Electronic circuits; harness assemblies for electronic use: wire or cable; surveyors' stakes, wood

(P-19435)
ADVANCED MICROWAVE INC
333 Moffett Park Dr, Sunnyvale
(94089-1208)
PHONE..........................408 739-4214
Mike Ghandehari, *President*
Susan Ghandehari, *Corp Secy*
EMP: 12
SQ FT: 5,000
SALES (est): 1.3MM Privately Held
WEB: www.advmic.com
SIC: 3679 Microwave components

(P-19436)
AEI ELECTECH CORP
Also Called: Sunpower USA
33485 Western Ave, Union City
(94587-3201)
PHONE..........................510 489-5088
David Shu, *President*
▲ EMP: 15
SALES (est): 2.1MM Privately Held
WEB: www.sunpower-usa.com
SIC: 3679 Power supplies, all types: static

(P-19437)
AHEAD MAGNETICS INC
Also Called: Aheadtek
6410 Via Del Oro, San Jose (95119-1208)
PHONE..........................408 226-9800
Tim Higgins, *Principal*
Ed Soldani, *CFO*
Patrick Johnston, *Vice Pres*
Yolanda Verdugo, *Executive*
Kenny Kern, *Engineer*
▲ EMP: 78
SQ FT: 32,000
SALES (est): 13.3MM Privately Held
WEB: www.aheadtek.com
SIC: 3679 Recording & playback heads, magnetic
PA: Huritga International Holding (S) Pte.
    Ltd.
    10 Anson Road
    Singapore

(P-19438)
AIH LLC (DH)
Also Called: Astec International Holding
5810 Van Allen Way, Carlsbad
(92008-7300)
PHONE..........................760 930-4600
Jay Geldmacher, *CEO*
Tom Rosenast, *CFO*
EMP: 22
SALES (est): 1.2B Privately Held
SIC: 3679 3629 3621 Power supplies, all types: static; power conversion units, a.c. to d.c.: static-electric; power generators
HQ: Artesyn Embedded Technologies, Inc.
    2900 S Diablo Way Ste 190
    Tempe AZ 85282
    800 759-1107

(P-19439)
ALPHA SCIENTIFIC ELEC INC
2727 Boeing Way, Stockton (95206-3983)
PHONE..........................510 782-4747
Ron H Rumrill, *President*

Ila Rumrill, *Corp Secy*
Ken Rumrill, *Vice Pres*
EMP: 12
SQ FT: 10,000
SALES (est): 2.2MM Privately Held
WEB: www.alphascientific.com
SIC: 3679 Power supplies, all types: static

(P-19440)
ALYN INDUSTRIES INC
Also Called: Electronic Source Company
16028 Arminta St, Van Nuys (91406-1808)
PHONE..........................818 988-7696
Scott J Alyn, *CEO*
Christine Young, *Program Mgr*
Ana Gomez, *Buyer*
Maria De Jesus, *Manager*
▼ EMP: 100
SQ FT: 11,500
SALES (est): 18.5MM Privately Held
SIC: 3679 Electronic circuits

(P-19441)
AMERICAN AUDIO COMPONENT INC
Also Called: AAC
20 Fairbanks Ste 198, Irvine (92618-1673)
PHONE..........................909 596-3788
David Plekenpol, *CEO*
Richard Monk, *CFO*
Willie Maglonso, *Info Tech Dir*
▲ EMP: 26
SALES: 3MM Privately Held
WEB: www.american-audio.com
SIC: 3679 Transducers, electrical
HQ: Aac Acoustic Technologies (Shenzhen)
    Co., Ltd.
    F/6-10, Block A,Nanjing University
    Production And Research Base,
    Shenzhen
    755 339-7201

(P-19442)
AMERICAN INDUS SYSTEMS INC
Also Called: A I S
1768 Mcgaw Ave, Irvine (92614-5732)
PHONE..........................888 485-6688
Nelson Tsay, *CEO*
Joe Fijak, *COO*
▲ EMP: 30
SQ FT: 25,000
SALES (est): 5.9MM
SALES (corp-wide): 1.1B Privately Held
WEB: www.aispro.com
SIC: 3679 Liquid crystal displays (LCD)
PA: Ennoconn Corporation
    3-6f, 10, Jiankang Rd.,
    New Taipei City 23586
    255 908-050

(P-19443)
AMETEK PROGRAMMABLE POWER INC (HQ)
9250 Brown Deer Rd, San Diego
(92121-2267)
PHONE..........................858 450-0085
Timothy F Croal, *CEO*
John Molinelli, *CFO*
Shawn Smith, *Vice Pres*
Joellen Atkins, *Program Mgr*
Dylan Mora, *Program Mgr*
▲ EMP: 231 EST: 2006
SQ FT: 110,000
SALES (est): 96.7MM
SALES (corp-wide): 4.3B Publicly Held
WEB: www.elgar.com
SIC: 3679 Power supplies, all types: static
PA: Ametek, Inc.
    1100 Cassatt Rd
    Berwyn PA 19312
    610 647-2121

(P-19444)
AMSCO US INC
15341 Texaco Ave, Paramount
(90723-3946)
PHONE..........................562 630-0333
Mike Yazdi, *President*
Victor Yazdi, *Vice Pres*
Karina Vega, *Purch Dir*
Tarane Yazdi, *VP Opers*
Liset Morando, *Accounts Mgr*
EMP: 110

SALES (est): 20.6MM Privately Held
WEB: www.amscous.com
SIC: 3679 Harness assemblies for electronic use: wire or cable

(P-19445)
APEM INC
Also Called: Ch Products
970 Park Center Dr, Vista (92081-8312)
PHONE..........................760 598-2518
Peter Brouilette, *President*
EMP: 81
SALES (corp-wide): 561.1MM Privately
Held
SIC: 3679 3577 Electronic switches; computer peripheral equipment
HQ: Apem, Inc.
    63 Neck Rd
    Haverhill MA 01835

(P-19446)
APPLIED THIN-FILM PRODUCTS (PA)
Also Called: Atp
3620 Yale Way, Fremont (94538-6182)
PHONE..........................510 661-4287
David J Adams, *CEO*
Russ Alm, *President*
Ryan Nguyen, *COO*
Steven Cheung, *Bd of Directors*
Franco Pietroforte, *Vice Pres*
EMP: 112
SQ FT: 18,000
SALES: 25MM Privately Held
WEB: www.thinfilm.com
SIC: 3679 Microwave components

(P-19447)
APPLIED THIN-FILM PRODUCTS
3439 Edison Way, Fremont (94538-6179)
PHONE..........................510 661-4287
David Adams, *Branch Mgr*
EMP: 16 Privately Held
SIC: 3679 Microwave components
PA: Applied Thin-Film Products
    3620 Yale Way
    Fremont CA 94538

(P-19448)
ARTECH INDUSTRIES INC
1966 Keats Dr, Riverside (92501-1747)
PHONE..........................951 276-3331
Mansukh R Bera, *President*
Girish Bera, *CFO*
Madan Bera, *Vice Pres*
▲ EMP: 36
SQ FT: 24,500
SALES (est): 5.4MM Privately Held
WEB: www.artech-loadcell.com
SIC: 3679 Loads, electronic

(P-19449)
ASEA POWER SYSTEMS
15272 Newsboy Cir, Huntington Beach
(92649-1202)
PHONE..........................714 896-9695
Mark A Woodward, *President*
Russ Engle, *Exec VP*
◆ EMP: 30
SQ FT: 6,100
SALES (est): 5.8MM Privately Held
WEB: www.aseapower.com
SIC: 3679 Static power supply converters for electronic applications

(P-19450)
ASTRO SEAL INC
827 Palmyrita Ave Ste B, Riverside
(92507-1820)
PHONE..........................951 787-6670
Michael Hammer, *President*
Karen Upfold, *Opers Mgr*
Roger Hammer, *Director*
Van Watt, *Supervisor*
▲ EMP: 34 EST: 1964
SQ FT: 42,000
SALES (est): 6.4MM Privately Held
WEB: www.astroseal.com
SIC: 3679 3678 Hermetic seals for electronic equipment; electronic connectors

(P-19451)
ASTRODYNE CORPORATION
Also Called: Astrodynetdi
22895 Eastpark Dr, Yorba Linda
(92887-4653)
PHONE....................................714 289-0055
Bob Singh, *CEO*
▲ EMP: 45
SALES (est): 2.4MM **Privately Held**
SIC: 3679 Electronic circuits

(P-19452)
ATLAS MAGNETICS INC
1121 N Kraemer Pl, Anaheim (92806-1923)
PHONE....................................714 632-9718
Maurice Brear, *CEO*
Tim Pagano, *QC Mgr*
EMP: 15
SALES (est): 1.5MM **Privately Held**
SIC: 3679 3592 Solenoids for electronic
applications; valves, aircraft

(P-19453)
AVI
431 Janemar Rd, Fallbrook (92028-2631)
PHONE....................................760 451-9379
Dien Nhu Do, *President*
Thai-Hoa Nguyen, *Treasurer*
EMP: 17
SQ FT: 8,000
SALES (est): 1.7MM **Privately Held**
SIC: 3679

(P-19454)
AZ DISPLAYS INC
75 Columbia, Aliso Viejo (92656-1498)
PHONE....................................949 831-5000
Reiner Moegling, *President*
▲ EMP: 50
SALES (est): 7.5MM **Privately Held**
WEB: www.azettler.com
SIC: 3679 Liquid crystal displays (LCD)
HQ: American Zettler Inc.
75 Columbia
Aliso Viejo CA 92656
949 360-5830

(P-19455)
B & G ELECTRONIC ASSEMBLY INC
10350 Regis Ct, Rancho Cucamonga
(91730-3055)
PHONE....................................909 608-2077
Robert M Odell, *CEO*
Lillian Odell, *Vice Pres*
Lorraine Arvizo, *Admin Sec*
EMP: 18
SQ FT: 8,900
SALES (est): 4.2MM **Privately Held**
WEB: www.bgelectronic.com
SIC: 3679 Harness assemblies for elec-
tronic use: wire or cable

(P-19456)
B T E DELTEC INC (DH)
Also Called: Powerware
2727 Kurtz St, San Diego (92110-3109)
PHONE....................................619 291-4211
Dan Jackson, *President*
Chris Peavey, *VP Finance*
EMP: 250
SQ FT: 80,000
SALES (est): 9.6MM **Privately Held**
SIC: 3679 Electronic circuits; power sup-
plies, all types: static
HQ: Eaton Corporation
1000 Eaton Blvd
Cleveland OH 44122
440 523-5000

(P-19457)
BAE SYSTEMS INFO & ELEC SYS
1930 S Vnyrd Ave M S 1102 Ms, Ontario
(91761)
PHONE....................................603 885-4321
EMP: 62
SALES (corp-wide): 24.2B **Privately Held**
WEB: www.iesi.na.baesystems.com
SIC: 3679 3769 Electronic circuits; guided
missile & space vehicle parts & auxiliary
equipment

HQ: Bae Systems Information And Electronic Systems Integration Inc.
65 Spit Brook Rd
Nashua NH 03060
603 885-4321

(P-19458)
BANH AN BINH
1965 Stonewood Ln, San Jose
(95132-1354)
PHONE....................................408 935-8950
A Banh, *Principal*
EMP: 20
SALES (est): 1.9MM **Privately Held**
SIC: 3679

(P-19459)
BARTOLINI GUITARS
Also Called: Bartolini Pickups
2133 Research Dr Ste 16, Livermore
(94550-3854)
PHONE....................................386 517-6823
William Bartolini, *Partner*
EMP: 16
SALES (est): 1.5MM **Privately Held**
WEB: www.bartolini.net
SIC: 3679 Recording & playback appara-
tus, including phonograph

(P-19460)
BASIC ELECTRONICS INC
11371 Monarch St, Garden Grove
(92841-1406)
PHONE....................................714 530-2400
Nancy Balzano, *President*
Al Balzano, *Vice Pres*
Aurora Medina, *Info Tech Dir*
EMP: 30
SQ FT: 20,000
SALES (est): 4.9MM **Privately Held**
WEB: www.basicinc.com
SIC: 3679 3672 3613 Electronic circuits;
power supplies, all types: static; printed
circuit boards; switchgear & switchboard
apparatus

(P-19461)
BEATS ELECTRONICS LLC (PA)
Also Called: Beats By Dr. Dre
8600 Hayden Pl, Culver City (90232-2902)
PHONE....................................424 268-3055
EMP: 13 EST: 2010
SALES (est): 6.1MM **Privately Held**
SIC: 3679 3651

(P-19462)
BEI NORTH AMERICA LLC (HQ)
1461 Lawrence Dr, Thousand Oaks
(91320-1303)
PHONE....................................805 716-0642
Martha Sullivan, *President*
Jeffrey Cote, *Vice Pres*
Alison Roelke, *Vice Pres*
EMP: 10
SALES: 54MM
SALES (corp-wide): 746MM **Privately
Held**
SIC: 3679 Electronic circuits
PA: Custom Sensors & Technologies, Inc.
1461 Lawrence Dr
Thousand Oaks CA 91320
805 716-0322

(P-19463)
BEMA ELECTRONIC MFG INC
4545 Cushing Pkwy, Fremont
(94538-6466)
PHONE....................................510 490-7770
Helen Kwong, *President*
Suju Kwong, *CFO*
Charles Evans, *Program Mgr*
Nancy Lo, *Program Mgr*
Wayne Yu, *General Mgr*
▲ EMP: 79
SQ FT: 26,205
SALES (est): 24MM **Privately Held**
WEB: www.bemaelectronics.com
SIC: 3679 Electronic circuits

(P-19464)
BENCHMARK ELEC MFG SOL MOORPK
200 Science Dr, Moorpark (93021-2003)
PHONE....................................805 532-2800
Bill Lehr, *Director*
EMP: 523

SALES (est): 66.1MM
SALES (corp-wide): 2.4B **Publicly Held**
WEB: www.smtek.com
SIC: 3679 Electronic circuits
HQ: Benchmark Electronics Manufacturing
Solutions Inc.
5550 Hellyer Ave
San Jose CA 95138
408 754-9800

(P-19465)
BENTEK CORPORATION
Also Called: Bentek Solar
1991 Senter Rd, San Jose (95112-2631)
PHONE....................................408 954-9600
Mitchell Schoch, *President*
Lou Marzano, *President*
Mel Pagdanganan, *Info Tech Mgr*
Raul Samson, *Business Anlyst*
Jamie Aimonetti, *Human Res Dir*
▲ EMP: 100
SALES (est): 39.8MM **Privately Held**
SIC: 3679 Electronic circuits

(P-19466)
BERKELEY SCIENTIFIC
21 Westminster Ave, Kensington
(94708-1036)
PHONE....................................510 525-1945
Lee Donaghey, *President*
EMP: 10
SQ FT: 2,000
SALES (est): 656.5K **Privately Held**
WEB: www.berkeleyscientific.com
SIC: 3679 8999 Electronic circuits; inven-
tor

(P-19467)
BI TECHNOLOGIES CORPORATION
413 Rood Rd Ste 7, Calexico (92231-9765)
PHONE....................................714 447-2402
EMP: 17
SALES (corp-wide): 475.6MM **Privately
Held**
WEB: www.bitechnologies.com
SIC: 3679 Electronic circuits
HQ: Bi Technologies Corporation
4200 Bonita Pl
Fullerton CA 92835
714 447-2300

(P-19468)
BI-SEARCH INTERNATIONAL INC
17550 Gillette Ave, Irvine (92614-5610)
PHONE....................................714 258-4500
Kevin Y Kim, *President*
Yong Su Kim, *CFO*
Jennifer Kwak, *Controller*
Ken Cho, *Purchasing*
◆ EMP: 43
SQ FT: 45,000
SALES (est): 23.6MM **Privately Held**
WEB: www.bisearch.com
SIC: 3679 Liquid crystal displays (LCD)

(P-19469)
BIVAR INC
4 Thomas, Irvine (92618-2593)
PHONE....................................949 951-8808
Thomas Silber, *CEO*
Reid Rice, *VP Finance*
▲ EMP: 40
SQ FT: 26,040
SALES (est): 7.8MM **Privately Held**
WEB: www.bivar.com
SIC: 3679 Electronic circuits

(P-19470)
BRANDT ELECTRONICS INC
1971 Tarob Ct, Milpitas (95035-6825)
PHONE....................................408 240-0014
Phillip D Duvall, *CEO*
Steve Hall, *Vice Pres*
Luis Caroza, *General Mgr*
David Alvarado, *Electrical Engi*
Rogelio Jose, *Engineer*
EMP: 40
SQ FT: 12,000
SALES (est): 7.3MM **Privately Held**
WEB: www.brandtelectronics.com
SIC: 3679 Power supplies, all types: static

(P-19471)
C & A TRANSDUCERS INC
14329 Commerce Dr, Garden Grove
(92843-4949)
PHONE....................................714 554-9188
Daniel Toledo, *President*
EMP: 25
SQ FT: 6,000
SALES: 2.5MM **Privately Held**
WEB: www.ca-transducers.com
SIC: 3679 3677 3674 Transducers, elec-
trical; electronic coils, transformers &
other inductors; semiconductors & related
devices

(P-19472)
C & S ASSEMBLY INC
1150 N Armando St, Anaheim
(92806-2609)
PHONE....................................866 779-8939
Sandra A Foley, *President*
Chris Foley, *Vice Pres*
Christopher Foley, *Vice Pres*
Loretta Baldwin, *Office Mgr*
EMP: 15
SQ FT: 12,000
SALES (est): 2.4MM **Privately Held**
WEB: www.cnsassembly.com
SIC: 3679 5063 Harness assemblies for
electronic use: wire or cable; electronic
wire & cable

(P-19473)
C D INTERNATIONAL TECH INC
695 Pinnacle Pl, Livermore (94550-9705)
PHONE....................................408 986-0725
Zhong Cao, *President*
▲ EMP: 15
SQ FT: 10,000
SALES (est): 2.3MM **Privately Held**
WEB: www.cdint.com
SIC: 3679 Transducers, electrical

(P-19474)
CABLE HARNESS SYSTEMS INC
7462 Talbert Ave, Huntington Beach
(92648-1239)
PHONE....................................714 841-9650
Mike Fuchs, *President*
Chris Cortez, *Purchasing*
EMP: 30
SALES (est): 5MM **Privately Held**
WEB: www.cableharness.com
SIC: 3679 Harness assemblies for elec-
tronic use: wire or cable

(P-19475)
CAC INC
20322 Windrow Dr Ste 100, Lake Forest
(92630-8150)
PHONE....................................949 587-3328
Patrick Redfern, *President*
▲ EMP: 12
SALES (est): 1.8MM **Privately Held**
WEB: www.cacproducts.com
SIC: 3679 Electronic circuits

(P-19476)
CAL SOUTHERN BRAIDING INC
Also Called: Scb Division
7450 Scout Ave, Bell Gardens
(90201-4932)
PHONE....................................562 927-5531
Neal Castleman, *President*
EMP: 60
SQ FT: 38,000
SALES (est): 10.9MM
SALES (corp-wide): 145.3MM **Privately
Held**
WEB: www.socalbraid.com
SIC: 3679 Harness assemblies for elec-
tronic use: wire or cable
PA: Dcx-Chol Enterprises, Inc.
12831 S Figueroa St
Los Angeles CA 90061
310 516-1692

(P-19477)
CALEX MFG CO INC
2401 Stanwell Dr Frnt, Concord
(94520-4872)
PHONE....................................925 687-4411
Paul S Cuff, *CEO*
Katherine Patti, *General Mgr*
Ed Wong, *Senior Engr*

PRODUCTS & SVCS

Robert Zorovic, *Buyer*
Kathy Waldron, *Mfg Staff*
▲ EMP: 45
SALES (est): 11.4MM **Privately Held**
WEB: www.calex.com
SIC: 3679 Static power supply converters for electronic applications; power supplies, all types: static

(P-19478)
CARDIGAN ROAD PRODUCTIONS
1999 Ave Of The Sts 110, Los Angeles (90067)
PHONE..................................310 289-1442
Marc Friedland, *President*
EMP: 38 EST: 2001
SALES (est): 2.1MM **Privately Held**
SIC: 3679 Electronic circuits

(P-19479)
CARROS SENSORS SYSTEMS CO LLC
Also Called: Systron Donner Inertial
355 Lennon Ln, Walnut Creek (94598-2475)
PHONE..................................925 979-4400
Victor Dragotti, *Design Engr*
David Hoyh, *Sales Dir*
Mark Chamberlain, *Marketing Staff*
Harry Angus, *Manager*
Mike Souza, *Supervisor*
EMP: 125
SALES (corp-wide): 2.7MM **Privately Held**
SIC: 3679 Electronic circuits
HQ: Carros Sensors & Systems Company, Llc
1461 Lawrence Dr
Thousand Oaks CA 91320

(P-19480)
CARROS SENSORS SYSTEMS CO LLC (DH)
Also Called: BEI Industrial Encoders
1461 Lawrence Dr, Thousand Oaks (91320-1303)
PHONE..................................805 968-0782
Eric Pilaud, *CEO*
Jean-Yves Mouttet, *Treasurer*
Victor Copeland, *Admin Sec*
Jean-Yves Vo, *CTO*
Mohamed Choukri, *Technical Staff*
▲ EMP: 125
SALES (est): 100.9MM
SALES (corp-wide): 2.7MM **Privately Held**
SIC: 3679 Electronic circuits
HQ: Sensata Technologies, Inc.
529 Pleasant St
Attleboro MA 02703
508 236-3800

(P-19481)
CCM ASSEMBLY & MFG INC
2275 Michael Faraday Dr # 6, San Diego (92154-7927)
PHONE..................................760 560-1310
Erika Marcela Murillo, *CEO*
Sergio Murillo, *President*
John Savage, *Vice Pres*
John Gjata, *Project Mgr*
Esthela Mena, *Purchasing*
▲ EMP: 50 EST: 1997
SQ FT: 10,000
SALES (est): 9MM **Privately Held**
WEB: www.ccmassembly.com
SIC: 3679 3441 Harness assemblies for electronic use: wire or cable; fabricated structural metal

(P-19482)
CELESCO TRANSDUCER PRODUCTS
20630 Plummer St, Chatsworth (91311-5111)
PHONE..................................818 701-2701
Hernan Cortez, *Principal*
▲ EMP: 13
SALES (est): 1.8MM **Privately Held**
SIC: 3679 1541 Transducers, electrical; industrial buildings & warehouses

(P-19483)
CELESTICA LLC
Also Called: D&H Manufacturing
49235 Milmont Dr, Fremont (94538-7349)
PHONE..................................510 770-5100
Mark Morris, *Branch Mgr*
EMP: 200
SALES (corp-wide): 24.5B **Privately Held**
SIC: 3679 Electronic circuits
HQ: Celestica Llc
11 Continental Blvd # 103
Merrimack NH 03054

(P-19484)
CELLTRON INC
19860 Plummer St, Chatsworth (91311-5652)
P.O. Box 98, Galena KS (66739-0098)
PHONE..................................620 783-1333
Stacey Williams, *CFO*
EMP: 10
SALES (est): 398.2K **Privately Held**
SIC: 3679 Harness assemblies for electronic use: wire or cable

(P-19485)
CENTERLINE MANUFACTURING INC
Also Called: Centerline Engineering
1234 E Ash Ave Ste D, Fullerton (92831-5013)
PHONE..................................714 525-9890
David Khoe, *President*
Jack Antes, *Ch of Bd*
Randolph Scott, *President*
▲ EMP: 10
SQ FT: 6,000
SALES: 50K **Privately Held**
WEB: www.centerline-engineering.com
SIC: 3679 Harness assemblies for electronic use: wire or cable

(P-19486)
CERNEX INC
1710 Zanker Rd Ste 103, San Jose (95112-4219)
PHONE..................................408 541-9226
Chanh Huynh, *President*
▲ EMP: 25
SQ FT: 5,200
SALES (est): 5.5MM **Privately Held**
WEB: www.cernex.com
SIC: 3679 Microwave components

(P-19487)
CIAO WIRELESS INC
4000 Via Pescador, Camarillo (93012-5044)
PHONE..................................805 389-3224
Glen Wasylewski, *President*
Glen Wasyleuski, *VP Sales*
Etzon Garcia, *Sales Staff*
Justin Harrison, *Manager*
Felipe Roque, *Assistant*
▼ EMP: 55
SQ FT: 42,000
SALES (est): 12MM **Privately Held**
WEB: www.ciaowireless.com
SIC: 3679 3699 Microwave components; pulse amplifiers

(P-19488)
CICON ENGINEERING INC
8345 Canoga Ave, Canoga Park (91304-2605)
PHONE..................................818 909-6060
Eric Lopez, *Manager*
EMP: 20
SALES (est): 990.1K
SALES (corp-wide): 49.6MM **Privately Held**
SIC: 3679 Harness assemblies for electronic use: wire or cable
PA: Cicon Engineering, Inc.
6633 Odessa Ave
Van Nuys CA 91406
818 909-6060

(P-19489)
CICON ENGINEERING INC
21421 Schoenborn St, Canoga Park (91304-2630)
PHONE..................................818 882-6508
Richard McKee, *Manager*
EMP: 10

SALES (est): 619.8K
SALES (corp-wide): 49.6MM **Privately Held**
WEB: www.cicon.com
SIC: 3679 Harness assemblies for electronic use: wire or cable
PA: Cicon Engineering, Inc.
6633 Odessa Ave
Van Nuys CA 91406
818 909-6060

(P-19490)
CICON ENGINEERING INC (PA)
6633 Odessa Ave, Van Nuys (91406-5746)
PHONE..................................818 909-6060
Ali Kolahi, *President*
Farah Kolahi, *Shareholder*
Brian Rash, *CFO*
Abdi Kolahi, *Vice Pres*
Laurie Kertenian, *Executive*
EMP: 181
SQ FT: 50,000
SALES (est): 49.6MM **Privately Held**
WEB: www.cicon.com
SIC: 3679 Harness assemblies for electronic use: wire or cable

(P-19491)
CINEMAG INC
4487 Ish Dr, Simi Valley (93063-7665)
PHONE..................................818 993-4644
David Garen, *President*
Thomas Reichenbach, *President*
EMP: 12
SALES (est): 1.6MM **Privately Held**
SIC: 3679 Antennas, receiving

(P-19492)
CIRCUIT AUTOMATION INC
5292 System Dr, Huntington Beach (92649-1527)
PHONE..................................714 763-4180
Thomas Meeker, *President*
Yuki Kojima, *President*
Sherlene Meeker, *CFO*
Masayuki Kojima, *Vice Pres*
Larry Lindland, *Manager*
◆ EMP: 18
SQ FT: 15,000
SALES: 2MM **Privately Held**
WEB: www.circuitautomation.com
SIC: 3679 Electronic circuits

(P-19493)
CKS SOLUTION INCORPORATED
556 Vanguard Way Ste C, Brea (92821-3929)
PHONE..................................714 292-6307
Patrick Park, *Manager*
EMP: 25
SALES (corp-wide): 6.3MM **Privately Held**
SIC: 3679 Liquid crystal displays (LCD)
PA: Cks Solution Incorporated
4293 Muhlhauser Rd
Fairfield OH 45014
513 947-1277

(P-19494)
CLARY CORPORATION
150 E Huntington Dr, Monrovia (91016-3415)
PHONE..................................626 359-4486
John G Clary, *Ch of Bd*
Donald Ash, *CFO*
Donald G Ash, *Treasurer*
Estella Gonzalez, *Project Mgr*
Leo Tran, *QC Mgr*
EMP: 40
SQ FT: 26,000
SALES (est): 9.7MM **Privately Held**
WEB: www.clary.com
SIC: 3679 5063 3612 Electronic loads & power supplies; power supplies, all types: static; electrical apparatus & equipment; transformers, except electric

(P-19495)
COASTAL COMPONENT INDS INC
Also Called: C C I
133 E Bristol Ln, Orange (92865-2749)
PHONE..................................714 685-6677
Ronna Coe, *Chairman*
Mark Coe, *President*

Donald B Coe, *CEO*
Donald Coe, *CEO*
Diana Romero, *Vice Pres*
EMP: 20
SQ FT: 6,027
SALES (est): 3.9MM **Privately Held**
WEB: www.ccicoastal.com
SIC: 3679 5065 3643 3678 Electronic circuits; electronic parts & equipment; electric connectors; electronic connectors; relays & industrial controls; manufactured hardware (general)

(P-19496)
COHERENT ASIA INC
5100 Patrick Henry Dr, Santa Clara (95054-1112)
PHONE..................................408 764-4000
John R Ambroseo, *President*
John Ambroseo, *President*
Helene Simonet, *Exec VP*
EMP: 98
SALES (est): 11.2MM
SALES (corp-wide): 1.7B **Publicly Held**
SIC: 3679 3827 Electronic crystals; optical instruments & lenses
PA: Coherent, Inc.
5100 Patrick Henry Dr
Santa Clara CA 95054
408 764-4000

(P-19497)
COMMUNICATIONS & PWR INDS LLC
CPI
6385 San Ignacio Ave, San Jose (95119-1206)
PHONE..................................650 846-2900
Gordon Ballantyne, *Branch Mgr*
EMP: 130 **Privately Held**
SIC: 3679 3699 3671 3663 Microwave components; electrical equipment & supplies; vacuum tubes; radio & TV communications equipment
HQ: Communications & Power Industries Llc
607 Hansen Way
Palo Alto CA 94304

(P-19498)
COMPASS COMPONENTS INC (PA)
Also Called: Compass Manufacturing Service
48133 Warm Springs Blvd, Fremont (94539-7498)
PHONE..................................510 656-4700
Jack Maxwell, *CEO*
Bob Duplantier, *President*
Irene Madrid, *Associate Dir*
Sabrina Toste, *Administration*
Wasiq Shirazi, *Technology*
EMP: 110 EST: 1979
SQ FT: 36,000
SALES: 51.9MM **Privately Held**
WEB: www.ccicms.com
SIC: 3679 5065 Harness assemblies for electronic use: wire or cable; electronic parts

(P-19499)
COMPSERV INC
42 Golf Rd, Pleasanton (94566-9752)
PHONE..................................415 331-4571
Michael J Maslana, *President*
Christopher Alessio, *Vice Pres*
Robert Boguski, *Vice Pres*
EMP: 19
SQ FT: 9,000
SALES (est): 1.8MM **Privately Held**
WEB: www.compserv-inc.com
SIC: 3679 Electronic circuits

(P-19500)
CPI INTERNATIONAL HOLDING CORP
811 Hansen Way, Palo Alto (94304-1031)
PHONE..................................650 846-2900
O Joe Caldarelli, *CEO*
Robert A Fickett, *President*
John R Beighley, *Vice Pres*
John Overstreet, *Vice Pres*
Andrew E Tafler, *Vice Pres*
EMP: 17
SALES (est): 494.6MM **Privately Held**
SIC: 3679 Electronic circuits

PA: Cpi International Holding Llc
811 Hansen Way
Palo Alto CA 94304
-

(P-19501)
CRANE CO
Also Called: Crane Valves Services Division
3948 Teal Ct, Benicia (94510-1202)
PHONE..................707 748-7166
Evan Russell, *Manager*
EMP: 11
SALES (corp-wide): 2.7B **Publicly Held**
WEB: www.stellarinteractivesolutions.com
SIC: 3679 Oscillators
PA: Crane Co.
100 1st Stamford Pl # 300
Stamford CT 06902
203 363-7300

(P-19502)
CRUCIAL POWER PRODUCTS
14000 S Broadway, Los Angeles
(90061-1018)
PHONE..................323 721-5017
Abbie Gougerchian, *Principal*
Alan Stone, *Vice Pres*
Martin Corral, *Manager*
EMP: 12
SALES (est): 1.1MM **Privately Held**
WEB: www.crucialpower.com
SIC: 3679 Electronic circuits

(P-19503)
CRYSTAL CAL LAB INC
3981 E Miraloma Ave, Anaheim
(92806-6201)
PHONE..................714 991-1580
Michele Anderson, *President*
Joe Maddock, *Research*
EMP: 26
SQ FT: 7,600
SALES (est): 3MM **Privately Held**
SIC: 3679 3825

(P-19504)
CSR TECHNOLOGY INC (DH)
1060 Rincon Cir, San Jose (95131-1325)
PHONE..................408 523-6500
Brett Gladden, *CEO*
Ron Mackintosh, *Chairman*
Chris Ladas, *Exec VP*
David Gittens, *Info Tech Mgr*
ADI Leshem, *Technical Staff*
▲ **EMP:** 133
SALES (est): 59.6MM
SALES (corp-wide): 22.2B **Publicly Held**
SIC: 3679 3812 3674 Electronic circuits;
search & navigation equipment; semicon-
ductors & related devices
HQ: Qualcomm Technologies International,
Ltd.
Northern Ireland Science Park,
Queen's Road, Queen's Island
Belfast BT3 9
289 046-3140

(P-19505)
CURTIS TECHNOLOGY INC
11391 Sorrento Valley Rd, San Diego
(92121-1303)
PHONE..................858 453-5797
Alex Jvirblis, *President*
Daksha Dave, *Corp Secy*
EMP: 15 **EST:** 1959
SQ FT: 18,000
SALES (est): 2.3MM **Privately Held**
WEB: www.curtistechnology.com
SIC: 3679 8711 3229 Electronic circuits;
consulting engineer; pressed & blown
glass

(P-19506)
CUSTOM MICROWAVE
COMPONENTS
44249 Old Warm Sprng Blvd, Fremont
(94538-6168)
PHONE..................510 651-3434
Gregory Mau, *President*
EMP: 10
SQ FT: 12,000
SALES (est): 1.5MM **Privately Held**
WEB: www.customwave.com
SIC: 3679 Microwave components

(P-19507)
CUSTOM SENSORS & TECH INC
(PA)
Also Called: C S T
1461 Lawrence Dr, Thousand Oaks
(91320-1303)
PHONE..................805 716-0322
Martha Sullivan, *CEO*
Lori Appel, *Comms Dir*
Remi Chazalmartin, *General Mgr*
Elizabeth Lewis, *Executive Asst*
Lawrence Hutton, *Info Tech Mgr*
▲ **EMP:** 77
SALES (est): 722.3MM **Privately Held**
WEB: www.cst.schneider-electric.com
SIC: 3679 Electronic circuits

(P-19508)
DAWN VME PRODUCTS
47915 Westinghouse Dr, Fremont
(94539-7483)
PHONE..................510 657-4444
Barry W Burnsides, *CEO*
Cheryl A Burnsides, *Vice Pres*
Tim Collins, *Program Mgr*
Abe Exmundo, *Financial Exec*
Sharnjit Sekhon, *QC Mgr*
▲ **EMP:** 45
SQ FT: 20,000
SALES (est): 9.7MM **Privately Held**
WEB: www.dawnvme.com
SIC: 3679 Electronic circuits

(P-19509)
DCX-CHOL ENTERPRISES INC
Also Called: Scb Division of Dcx-Chol
7450 Scout Ave, Bell (90201-4932)
PHONE..................562 927-5531
Ben Dose, *Branch Mgr*
EMP: 60
SALES (corp-wide): 145.3MM **Privately
Held**
SIC: 3679 Harness assemblies for elec-
tronic use: wire or cable
PA: Dcx-Chol Enterprises, Inc.
12831 S Figueroa St
Los Angeles CA 90061
310 516-1692

(P-19510)
DE ANZA MANUFACTURING
SVCS INC
1271 Reamwood Ave, Sunnyvale
(94089-2275)
PHONE..................408 734-2020
Art Takahara, *President*
Michael Takahara, *Vice Pres*
Dale Walker, *Engineer*
Sarah Walker, *Marketing Staff*
▼ **EMP:** 60
SQ FT: 24,000
SALES (est): 11.3MM **Privately Held**
WEB: www.deanzamfg.com
SIC: 3679 3643 Harness assemblies for
electronic use: wire or cable; current-car-
rying wiring devices

(P-19511)
DELTA GROUP ELECTRONICS
INC
10180 Scripps Ranch Blvd, San Diego
(92131-1234)
PHONE..................858 569-1681
Bill West, *Manager*
EMP: 55
SALES (corp-wide): 149.2MM **Privately
Held**
WEB: www.deltagroupinc.com
SIC: 3679 3577 3672 Electronic circuits;
computer peripheral equipment; printed
circuit boards
PA: Delta Group Electronics, Inc.
4521a Osuna Rd Ne
Albuquerque NM 87109
505 883-7674

(P-19512)
DICON FIBEROPTICS INC (PA)
1689 Regatta Blvd Bldg W1, Richmond
(94804-7438)
PHONE..................510 620-5000
Ho-Shang Lee, *President*
Dr Gilles Corcos, *Ch of Bd*
Robert Schleicher, *Vice Pres*
Ana Lowe, *Executive*

Hoffman Cheung, *QA Dir*
▲ **EMP:** 119
SQ FT: 202,000
SALES (est): 81.1MM **Privately Held**
WEB: www.diconfiber.com
SIC: 3679 3827 Electronic switches; opti-
cal instruments & lenses

(P-19513)
DIGITAL POWER CORPORATION
(HQ)
48430 Lakeview Blvd, Fremont
(94538-6532)
PHONE..................510 657-2635
Amos Kohn, *Officer*
Milton C Ault III, *Ch of Bd*
William B Horne, *CFO*
Moti Rosenberg, *Bd of Directors*
Don Ashton, *Engineer*
▲ **EMP:** 26 **EST:** 1969
SQ FT: 12,396
SALES: 10.1MM **Publicly Held**
WEB: www.digipwr.com
SIC: 3679 Electronic switches
PA: Dpw Holdings, Inc.
201 Shipyard Way
Newport Beach CA 92663
510 657-2635

(P-19514)
DIGITAL VIEW INC
18440 Tech Dr Ste 130, Morgan Hill
(95037)
PHONE..................408 782-7773
Neil Wood, *President*
Rob Warren, *Engineer*
Ericka Ramirez, *Opers Mgr*
Nayan Patel, *Prdtn Mgr*
Dusty Perryman, *Mktg Dir*
◆ **EMP:** 10
SQ FT: 6,000
SALES (est): 2.2MM
SALES (corp-wide): 9.1MM **Privately
Held**
WEB: www.digitalview.com
SIC: 3679 7313 Liquid crystal displays
(LCD); electronic media advertising repre-
sentatives
HQ: Digital View Limited
Rm 705-708 7/F Texwood Plz
Kwun Tong KLN
286 136-15

(P-19515)
DIVERSFIED TCHNCAL
SYSTEMS INC (PA)
1720 Apollo Ct, Seal Beach (90740-5617)
PHONE..................562 493-0158
Stephen D Pruitt, *CEO*
Steve Pruitt, *President*
Kirsten Larsen, *CFO*
George M Beckage, *Vice Pres*
Tim Kippen, *Vice Pres*
▲ **EMP:** 29
SQ FT: 55,000
SALES (est): 15MM **Privately Held**
WEB: www.dtsweb.com
SIC: 3679 3825 Electronic circuits; ana-
log-digital converters, electronic instru-
mentation type

(P-19516)
DJ GREY COMPANY INC
455 Allan Ct, Healdsburg (95448-4802)
PHONE..................707 431-2779
Marla J Grey, *President*
Michele Perry, *Vice Pres*
EMP: 15
SQ FT: 4,500
SALES (est): 2.3MM **Privately Held**
WEB: www.djgreycompany.com
SIC: 3679 Electronic circuits

(P-19517)
DREAMCTCHERS
EMPWERMENT NETWRK
2201 Tuolumne St, Vallejo (94589-2524)
PHONE..................707 558-1775
George Lytal, *Ch of Bd*
EMP: 25
SALES (est): 368.5K **Privately Held**
SIC: 3679 Voice controls

(P-19518)
DUCOMMUN INCORPORATED
(PA)
200 Sandpointe Ave # 700, Santa Ana
(92707-5759)
PHONE..................657 335-3665
Stephen G Oswald, *President*
Douglas L Groves, *CFO*
Rosalie F Rogers, *Officer*
Jerry L Redondo, *Senior VP*
Christopher D Wampler, *Vice Pres*
▲ **EMP:** 174 **EST:** 1849
SALES: 558.1MM **Publicly Held**
SIC: 3679 3728 Microwave components;
aircraft body & wing assemblies & parts

(P-19519)
DYNALLOY INC
1562 Reynolds Ave, Irvine (92614-5612)
PHONE..................714 436-1206
Wayne Brown, *CEO*
Jess Brown, *Vice Pres*
EMP: 20
SQ FT: 8,000
SALES (est): 4.8MM **Privately Held**
WEB: www.dynalloy.com
SIC: 3679 3357 5065 Electronic circuits;
nonferrous wiredrawing & insulating; elec-
tronic parts

(P-19520)
DYTRAN INSTRUMENTS INC
21592 Marilla St, Chatsworth (91311-4137)
PHONE..................818 700-7818
Nicholas D Change II, *President*
Michael Change, *Vice Pres*
Anne Hackney, *Vice Pres*
Michael R Change, *General Mgr*
Vanessa Villasenor, *Administration*
EMP: 160
SQ FT: 8,000
SALES (est): 35.9MM **Privately Held**
WEB: www.dytran.com
SIC: 3679 3829 Transducers, electrical;
measuring & controlling devices

(P-19521)
E M EMERGENCY POWER
SUPPLIES
1133 Mission St, South Pasadena
(91030-3211)
P.O. Box 189 (91031-0189)
PHONE..................626 799-3549
Peter Kingston Jr, *President*
Linda Kingston, *Vice Pres*
EMP: 25
SQ FT: 10,000
SALES (est): 1.8MM **Privately Held**
WEB: www.day-ray.com
SIC: 3679 Power supplies, all types: static

(P-19522)
EASY NETWORKS CABLING
3538 Shelley Way, Riverside (92503-4332)
PHONE..................951 742-8119
Geraldo Morales, *Owner*
EMP: 10
SALES (est): 1.3MM **Privately Held**
SIC: 3679 General electrical contractor

(P-19523)
ECLIPSE MICROWAVE INC
2095 Ringwood Ave Ste 60, San Jose
(95131-1786)
PHONE..................408 526-1100
Jeffrey P Rapadas, *President*
EMP: 14
SALES (est): 2MM **Privately Held**
WEB: www.eclipsemicrowave.com
SIC: 3679 Microwave components

(P-19524)
ELCON INC
1009 Timothy Dr, San Jose (95133-1043)
PHONE..................408 292-7800
Anthony J Barraco, *CEO*
Timothy Dyer, *Vice Pres*
Steve Loveless, *Principal*
Vish Sarkar, *Engineer*
Trinh Tran,
EMP: 50
SQ FT: 31,000
SALES (est): 8.4MM **Privately Held**
WEB: www.elcon-inc.com
SIC: 3679 Commutators, electronic

PRODUCTS & SVCS

(P-19525)
ELECTRO SWITCH CORP
Also Called: Arga Controls A Unit
10410 Trademark St, Rancho Cucamonga
(91730-5826)
PHONE..................................909 581-0855
Kathy Brown, *Branch Mgr*
EMP: 15
SALES (corp-wide): 90.3MM **Privately Held**
SIC: 3679 Transducers, electrical
HQ: Electro Switch Corp.
775 Pleasant St Ste 1
Weymouth MA 02189
781 335-1195

(P-19526)
ELECTRO-SUPPORT SYSTEMS CORP
Also Called: IMS-Ess
27449 Colt Ct, Temecula (92590-3674)
P.O. Box 50067, Irvine (92619-0067)
PHONE..................................951 676-2751
Richard Olson, *President*
Mark Bridgeford, *Admin Sec*
EMP: 20 EST: 1977
SQ FT: 12,500
SALES (est): 3.3MM **Privately Held**
WEB: www.ims-ess.com
SIC: 3679 3845 3728 Electronic circuits; electromedical equipment; military aircraft equipment & armament

(P-19527)
ELECTRO-TECH PRODUCTS INC
2001 E Gladstone St Ste A, Glendora
(91740-5381)
PHONE..................................909 592-1434
Ramzi Bader, *President*
Suzane Bader, *CFO*
▲ EMP: 30
SQ FT: 11,000
SALES (est): 6.1MM **Privately Held**
WEB: www.etp-inc.com
SIC: 3679 Electronic circuits; power supplies, all types: static

(P-19528)
ELECTROCUBE INC (PA)
Also Called: Southern Electronics
3366 Pomona Blvd, Pomona (91768-3234)
PHONE..................................909 595-1821
Langdon Clay Parrill, *President*
Donald Duquette, *Vice Pres*
Scott Wieland, *Principal*
◆ EMP: 62
SQ FT: 27,000
SALES (est): 9.2MM **Privately Held**
WEB: www.electrocube.com
SIC: 3679 3675 Electronic circuits; electronic capacitors

(P-19529)
ELECTROFAB INC
Also Called: Qual-Tronix
18611 Maude Ave, Saratoga (95070-6215)
P.O. Box 807, Tahoe City (96145-0807)
PHONE..................................408 943-9380
Frank Casale, *President*
▲ EMP: 40
SALES (est): 3.5MM **Privately Held**
SIC: 3679 Harness assemblies for electronic use: wire or cable

(P-19530)
ELMECH INC
195 San Pedro Ave Ste E15, Morgan Hill
(95037-5140)
P.O. Box 2606 (95038-2606)
PHONE..................................408 782-2990
Paul Balog, *President*
Mathew Schreyer, *Supervisor*
EMP: 12
SQ FT: 4,400
SALES (est): 2.5MM **Privately Held**
WEB: www.elmechinc.com
SIC: 3679 Harness assemblies for electronic use: wire or cable

(P-19531)
EMAC ASSEMBLY CORP
21615 Parthenia St, Canoga Park
(91304-1517)
PHONE..................................818 882-2999
Lupe Garcia, *President*
EMP: 15
SALES (est): 1.6MM **Privately Held**
SIC: 3679 3469 Electronic circuits; stamping metal for the trade

(P-19532)
EMI SOLUTIONS INC
13805 Alton Pkwy Ste B, Irvine
(92618-1690)
PHONE..................................949 206-9960
Julie Ydens, *Ch of Bd*
Bob Ydens, *President*
Sue Lester, *Office Mgr*
▼ EMP: 18
SQ FT: 6,500
SALES (est): 1.7MM **Privately Held**
WEB: www.4emi.com
SIC: 3679 Electronic circuits

(P-19533)
EMLINQ LLC
Also Called: Electronic Mfg Leaders & Qulty
2125 N Madera Rd Ste C, Simi Valley
(93065-7711)
PHONE..................................805 409-4807
Tamara Bitticks, *Mng Member*
Michael Raj, *Vice Pres*
Linda Hana, *Program Mgr*
Mallory Simonoff, *Program Mgr*
Henok Tadesse, *Engineer*
▲ EMP: 52
SALES (est): 24.4MM **Privately Held**
SIC: 3679 Electronic circuits

(P-19534)
ENERGY RECOVERY PRODUCTS INC (HQ)
893 Patriot Dr Ste E, Moorpark
(93021-3357)
PHONE..................................805 499-4090
Abdul Sher-Jan, *President*
Jeanne Archer, *Accountant*
EMP: 12
SQ FT: 3,000
SALES (est): 2.1MM
SALES (corp-wide): 6.6MM **Privately Held**
SIC: 3679 Power supplies, all types: static
PA: Erp Power, Llc
893 Patriot Dr Ste E
Moorpark CA 93021
805 517-1300

(P-19535)
ENFORA INC
9645 Scranton Rd Ste 205, San Diego
(92121-1764)
PHONE..................................972 234-1689
Mark Weinzierl, *President*
Kenneth Leddon, *Senior VP*
Catherine F Ratcliffe, *Senior VP*
Slim S Souissi, *Senior VP*
▲ EMP: 100
SQ FT: 27,000
SALES (est): 13.7MM
SALES (corp-wide): 219.3MM **Publicly Held**
SIC: 3679 Commutators, electronic
HQ: Novatel Wireless, Inc.
9605 Scranton Rd Ste 300
San Diego CA 92121
858 812-3400

(P-19536)
ESP CORP
1175 W Victoria St, Compton (90220-5813)
PHONE..................................310 639-2535
Bayasouk Ounthaung, *President*
Joseph Acosta, *QC Dir*
EMP: 20
SALES (est): 1.8MM **Privately Held**
SIC: 3679 Electronic components

(P-19537)
EXPRESS MANUFACTURING INC (PA)
3519 W Warner Ave, Santa Ana
(92704-5214)
PHONE..................................714 979-2228
Chauk Pan Chin, *President*
Catherine Lee Chin, *Treasurer*
C M Chin, *Vice Pres*
Stana Marko, *Vice Pres*
Tony Chin, *Admin Sec*
▲ EMP: 204

SQ FT: 96,000
SALES (est): 153.9MM **Privately Held**
WEB: www.eminc.com
SIC: 3679 3672 Electronic circuits; printed circuit boards

(P-19538)
FABRI-TECH COMPONENTS INC
49038 Milmont Dr, Fremont (94538-7301)
PHONE..................................510 249-2000
Terry Anest, *President*
Teo Seow Phong, *CEO*
Tami Cayton, *Manager*
Gerald Lim, *Manager*
EMP: 15
SQ FT: 7,000
SALES (est): 3.8MM **Privately Held**
WEB: www.fabritech.net
SIC: 3679 Electronic circuits
PA: Fabri-Tech Components (S) Pte Ltd
3 Tuas Basin Link
Singapore
686 282-22

(P-19539)
FABRICAST INC (PA)
2517 Seaman Ave, South El Monte
(91733-1927)
P.O. Box 3176 (91733-0176)
PHONE..................................626 443-3247
H Phelps Wood III, *President*
Phelps Wood, *CIO*
EMP: 25 EST: 1960
SQ FT: 6,250
SALES (est): 2.4MM **Privately Held**
WEB: www.fabricast.com
SIC: 3679 3621 Electronic circuits; motors & generators

(P-19540)
FASTRAK MANUFACTURING SVCS INC
1275 Alma Ct, San Jose (95112-5943)
PHONE..................................408 298-6414
Phillip Guzman, *CEO*
Michelle Hilty, *President*
Michael Corriveau, *Sales Staff*
EMP: 20
SALES (est): 3.7MM **Privately Held**
SIC: 3679 8711 Harness assemblies for electronic use: wire or cable; electronic circuits; electrical or electronic engineering

(P-19541)
FEDERAL CUSTOM CABLE LLC
1891 Alton Pkwy Ste A, Irvine
(92606-4985)
PHONE..................................949 851-3114
Juliette Khamis, *Admin Asst*
Jabra Khamis, *Admin Asst*
Violet Kamis, *Human Res Mgr*
Jan Deckert, *Purch Agent*
Abe Kamis, *Safety Mgr*
EMP: 50
SALES: 9.8MM **Privately Held**
WEB: www.fccable.com
SIC: 3679 Electronic circuits

(P-19542)
FEMA ELECTRONICS CORPORATION
22 Corporate Park, Irvine (92606-3112)
PHONE..................................714 825-0140
Bob Cheng, *CEO*
Chinyun Cheng, *Treasurer*
▲ EMP: 30
SQ FT: 3,000
SALES (est): 5.9MM **Privately Held**
WEB: www.femacorp.com
SIC: 3679 Electronic crystals

(P-19543)
FERRARI INTRCNNECT SLTIONS INC
4385 E Lowell St Ste A, Ontario
(91761-2228)
PHONE..................................951 684-8034
David Ferrari, *President*
EMP: 10
SQ FT: 2,700
SALES (est): 760.3K **Privately Held**
SIC: 3679 Electronic circuits

(P-19544)
FLEX INTERCONNECT TECH INC
1603 Watson Ct, Milpitas (95035-6806)
PHONE..................................408 956-8204
Chetan Shah, *CEO*
Dean Matsuo, *Corp Secy*
Nitin Desai, *Engineer*
Yaqub Obaidi, *Engineer*
Banu Laxman, *Accountant*
EMP: 41
SQ FT: 15,000
SALES (est): 9.6MM **Privately Held**
WEB: www.fit4flex.com
SIC: 3679 Electronic circuits

(P-19545)
FLEXTRONICS CORPORATION (DH)
6201 America Center Dr, Alviso
(95002-2563)
PHONE..................................803 936-5200
Marc A Onetto, *President*
Martin McEnroe, *President*
Christian Bauwens, *Vice Pres*
Marcin FIC, *Vice Pres*
Scott Graybeal, *Vice Pres*
▲ EMP: 277
SQ FT: 350,000
SALES (est): 177.8MM
SALES (corp-wide): 25.4B **Privately Held**
SIC: 3679 3577 3571 Electronic circuits; computer peripheral equipment; electronic computers

(P-19546)
FREQUENCY MANAGEMENT INTL (PA)
15302 Bolsa Chica St, Huntington Beach
(92649-1245)
PHONE..................................714 373-8100
Kouros Sariri, *President*
Daniel Huss, *Senior Engr*
Kevin Panizza, *Mktg Dir*
EMP: 13
SQ FT: 16,000
SALES (est): 2.6MM **Privately Held**
WEB: www.frequencymanagement.com
SIC: 3679 Antennas, receiving

(P-19547)
FUELBOX INC
201 W Montecito St, Santa Barbara
(93101-3824)
PHONE..................................919 949-9179
Robert Herr, *CEO*
Ryan Heinberg, *CFO*
Dan Friedman, *Chief Mktg Ofcr*
EMP: 11
SQ FT: 900
SALES: 450K **Privately Held**
SIC: 3679 Antennas, receiving

(P-19548)
GAR ENTERPRISES
Also Called: K.G.S.electronics Inc.
1396 W 9th St, Upland (91786-5724)
PHONE..................................909 985-4575
Alex Morales, *Mfg Staff*
Wanda Tally, *Manager*
EMP: 20
SALES (est): 874K
SALES (corp-wide): 34.4MM **Privately Held**
WEB: www.kgselectronics.com
SIC: 3679 3621 3577 Electronic loads & power supplies; motors & generators; computer peripheral equipment
PA: Gar Enterprises
418 E Live Oak Ave
Arcadia CA 91006
626 574-1175

(P-19549)
GAVIAL HOLDINGS INC (PA)
Also Called: Gavial Engineering & Mfg
1435 W Mccoy Ln, Santa Maria
(93455-1002)
PHONE..................................805 614-0060
Morgan Maxwell Connor, *CEO*
Dennis Levinski, *Engineer*
EMP: 15
SQ FT: 24,500

▲ = Import ▼ =Export
◆ =Import/Export

SALES (est): 79.4MM **Privately Held**
WEB: www.gavial.com
SIC: **3679** Electronic circuits; electric services; investors

(P-19550)

GAVIAL HOLDINGS INC
Also Called: Arrow Industries
139 Industrial Way, Buellton (93427-9592)
P.O. Box 198 (93427-0198)
PHONE.................................805 688-6734
Dave Watkins, *Branch Mgr*
EMP: 33
SALES (corp-wide): 79.4MM **Privately Held**
WEB: www.gavial.com
SIC: **3679** 3545 Electronic circuits; machine tool accessories
PA: Gavial Holdings, Inc.
    1435 W Mccoy Ln
    Santa Maria CA 93455
    805 614-0060

(P-19551)

GAVIAL ITC LLC
869 Ward Dr, Santa Barbara (93111-2920)
PHONE.................................805 614-0060
Morgan Connor, *President*
EMP: 99
SQ FT: 30,000
SALES (est): 2.7MM **Privately Held**
SIC: **3679** Transducers, electrical

(P-19552)

GES US (NEW ENGLAND) INC
1051 S East St, Anaheim (92805-5749)
PHONE.................................978 459-4434
Riachard Pelletier, *General Mgr*
EMP: 150
SQ FT: 70,000
SALES (est): 12.7MM
SALES (corp-wide): 2.9B **Privately Held**
WEB: www.ges-us.com
SIC: **3679** 3672 Electronic circuits; printed circuit boards
HQ: Ges Investment Pte. Ltd.
    28 Marsiling Lane
    Singapore 73915
    673 298-98

(P-19553)

GLIMMERGLASS NETWORKS INC
3945 Freedom Cir Ste 560, Santa Clara (95054-1269)
PHONE.................................510 780-1800
Robert Lundy, *President*
Joon Choi, *Vice Pres*
Chusak Siripocanont, *Vice Pres*
Salman Qamar, *Sr Software Eng*
Vay Lo, *Software Dev*
EMP: 40
SQ FT: 15,000
SALES (est): 8.5MM **Privately Held**
WEB: www.glimmerglass.com
SIC: **3679** Electronic loads & power supplies

(P-19554)

GM ASSOCIATES INC
9824 Kitty Ln, Oakland (94603-1070)
PHONE.................................510 430-0806
Melvyn Nutter, *President*
Karen E Beato, *CEO*
Terri Hartman, *Vice Pres*
Mark Lowe, *Technical Staff*
Sue Hogan, *Human Res Dir*
▲ EMP: 58
SQ FT: 8,000
SALES (est): 8.7MM **Privately Held**
WEB: www.gmassoc.com
SIC: **3679** 3229 Quartz crystals, for electronic application; scientific glassware

(P-19555)

GOOCH & HOUSEGO PALO ALTO LLC (HQ)
Also Called: Crystal Technology
44247 Nobel Dr, Fremont (94538-3178)
PHONE.................................650 856-7911
Jon Fowler, *President*
Mark Batzdorf, *CFO*
Peter Bordui, *Bd of Directors*
Denise Delange, *Info Tech Mgr*
▲ EMP: 65
SQ FT: 25,000

SALES (est): 10.7MM
SALES (corp-wide): 143.7MM **Privately Held**
WEB: www.crystaltechnology.com
SIC: **3679** Electronic crystals
PA: Gooch & Housego Plc
    Dowlish Ford
    Ilminster TA19
    146 025-6440

(P-19556)

GREEN CIRCUITS INC
1130 Ringwood Ct, San Jose (95131-1726)
PHONE.................................408 526-1700
Ted Park, *CEO*
Michael Nguyen, *President*
Kary Coleman, *Program Mgr*
Collin Vo, *Program Mgr*
Tim Wang, *Program Mgr*
▲ EMP: 68
SALES (est): 28.7MM **Privately Held**
SIC: **3679** Electronic circuits

(P-19557)

GROWTHSTOCK INC
2921 Daimler St, Santa Ana (92705-5810)
PHONE.................................949 660-9473
John T Sandberg, *Ch of Bd*
Michele Sandberg, *Vice Pres*
EMP: 200
SALES: 15MM **Privately Held**
WEB: www.sandberg.com
SIC: **3679** 3825 8711 5999 Electronic circuits; test equipment for electronic & electrical circuits; consulting engineer; telephone equipment & systems

(P-19558)

GTRAN INC (PA)
829 Flynn Rd, Camarillo (93012-8702)
PHONE.................................805 445-4500
Ray Yu, *President*
Deepak Mehrotra, *CEO*
Douglas Holmes, *Vice Pres*
▲ EMP: 48
SQ FT: 226,000
SALES (est): 6.2MM **Privately Held**
WEB: www.gtran.com
SIC: **3679** Electronic circuits

(P-19559)

HANA MICROELECTRONICS INC
3100 De La Cruz Blvd # 204, Santa Clara (95054-2438)
PHONE.................................408 452-7474
Sanjay Mitra, *President*
EMP: 13
SQ FT: 2,500
SALES (est): 1.3MM
SALES (corp-wide): 656.3MM **Privately Held**
WEB: www.hanaus.com
SIC: **3679** Electronic circuits
HQ: Hana Semiconductor (Bkk) Company Limited
    65/98 Soi Vibhavadi Rangsit 64 Yeak 2
    Lak Si
    252 149-35

(P-19560)

HARBOR ELECTRONICS INC (PA)
3021 Kenneth St, Santa Clara (95054-3416)
PHONE.................................408 988-6544
Michael Brannan, *President*
Paul Diehl, *Vice Pres*
Tracy Tang, *Controller*
EMP: 190
SQ FT: 50,000
SALES (est): 45MM **Privately Held**
WEB: www.harbor-electronics.com
SIC: **3679** 3672 Harness assemblies for electronic use: wire or cable; printed circuit boards

(P-19561)

HARPER & TWO INC (PA)
2937 Cherry Ave, Signal Hill (90755-1910)
PHONE.................................562 424-3030
Dan Kilstofte, *President*
Jim Quilty, *Admin Sec*
EMP: 18
SALES (est): 2.7MM **Privately Held**
WEB: www.harperandtwo.com
SIC: **3679** Electronic circuits

(P-19562)

HART ELECTRONIC ASSEMBLY INC
21726 Lassen St, Chatsworth (91311-3623)
PHONE.................................818 709-2761
Lanell Allen, *Owner*
EMP: 100
SQ FT: 10,000
SALES (est): 12.5MM **Privately Held**
WEB: www.hartelectronic.com
SIC: **3679** 3672 3441 Electronic circuits; printed circuit boards; fabricated structural metal

(P-19563)

HARWIL PRECISION PRODUCTS
541 Kinetic Dr, Oxnard (93030-7923)
PHONE.................................805 988-6800
Geoffrey Strand, *President*
Teresa Bowmar, *Treasurer*
Bruce Bowmar, *Vice Pres*
Cynthia Strand, *Admin Sec*
Ellis Anderson, *Opers Staff*
EMP: 30
SQ FT: 33,000
SALES (est): 5.9MM **Privately Held**
WEB: www.harwil.com
SIC: **3679** 3625 3823 Electronic circuits; flow actuated electrical switches; industrial instrmnts msrmnt display/control process variable

(P-19564)

HELIOVOLT CORPORATION
3945 Freedom Cir Ste 560, Santa Clara (95054-1269)
PHONE.................................512 767-6079
Dong S Kim, *President*
Billy J Stanbery, *President*
John Prater, *Vice Pres*
Steve Darnell, *Principal*
Louay Eldada, *CTO*
▲ EMP: 98
SALES (est): 13.6MM **Privately Held**
WEB: www.heliovolt.com
SIC: **3679** Power supplies, all types: static

(P-19565)

HERLEY INDUSTRIES INC
4820 Estgate Mall Ste 200, San Diego (92121)
PHONE.................................858 812-7300
Tonya West, *Purch Agent*
EMP: 65
SALES (corp-wide): 1B **Privately Held**
SIC: **3679** Microwave components
HQ: Herley Industries, Inc.
    3061 Industry Dr
    Lancaster PA 17603
    717 397-2777

(P-19566)

HERMETIC SEAL CORPORATION (DH)
Also Called: Ametek HCC
4232 Temple City Blvd, Rosemead (91770-1592)
PHONE.................................626 443-8931
Andrew Goldfarb, *President*
George McCormack, *Sales Mgr*
Rene Ayala, *Warehouse Mgr*
Peter Billante, *Director*
Mark Turunen, *Manager*
EMP: 200
SQ FT: 36,000
SALES (est): 76.6MM
SALES (corp-wide): 4.3B **Publicly Held**
SIC: **3679** 3469 Hermetic seals for electronic equipment; metal stampings
HQ: Hcc Industries Inc.
    4232 Temple City Blvd
    Rosemead CA 91770
    626 443-8933

(P-19567)

HILLTRON CORPORATION
2528 Qume Dr Ste 4, San Jose (95131-1836)
PHONE.................................408 597-4424
Tanya Ahmed, *President*
EMP: 13
SALES (est): 1.8MM **Privately Held**
SIC: **3679** Electronic circuits

(P-19568)

HTI TURNKEY MANUFACTURING SVCS
2200 Zanker Rd Ste A, San Jose (95131-1111)
PHONE.................................408 955-0807
MAI Linh Tran, *CEO*
Thanah MAI Tran, *Admin Sec*
Vic Tinio, *Consultant*
EMP: 25
SQ FT: 10,000
SALES: 2MM **Privately Held**
WEB: www.hti9001.com
SIC: **3679** Harness assemblies for electronic use: wire or cable

(P-19569)

HUNTER TECHNOLOGY CORPORATION (HQ)
1940 Milmont Dr, Milpitas (95035-2578)
PHONE.................................408 957-1300
Joseph F O'Neil, *President*
Mark Evans, *COO*
▲ EMP: 167 EST: 1987
SQ FT: 62,500
SALES (est): 45.7MM
SALES (corp-wide): 374.9MM **Publicly Held**
WEB: www.hunterpcb.com
SIC: **3679** Microwave components
PA: Sparton Corporation
    425 N Martingale Rd
    Schaumburg IL 60173
    847 762-5800

(P-19570)

HWA IN AMERICA INC (PA)
Also Called: Orange Pack Solution
1541 Santiago Ridge Way, San Diego (92154-7704)
PHONE.................................619 567-4539
Sun Duk Kim, *President*
Ji Lee, *Principal*
▲ EMP: 12 EST: 1997
SALES: 6.4MM **Privately Held**
SIC: **3679** 5199 Static power supply converters for electronic applications; packaging materials

(P-19571)

I J RESEARCH INC
2919 Tech Ctr, Santa Ana (92705-5657)
PHONE.................................714 546-8522
Rick Yoon, *President*
Kevin Danh, *COO*
Sandy Yoon, *CFO*
Herbert Ludowieg, *Vice Pres*
An Tran, *Engineer*
▲ EMP: 35
SQ FT: 12,500
SALES (est): 6.7MM **Privately Held**
WEB: www.ijresearch.com
SIC: **3679** Hermetic seals for electronic equipment

(P-19572)

I SOURCE TECHNICAL SVCS INC
575 Rancho Cir, Irvine (92618)
PHONE.................................949 453-1500
Irene Horvath, *Branch Mgr*
EMP: 10 **Privately Held**
SIC: **3679** Electronic circuits
PA: I Source Technical Services, Inc.
    5 Rancho Cir
    Lake Forest CA 92630

(P-19573)

I SOURCE TECHNICAL SVCS INC (PA)
5 Rancho Cir, Lake Forest (92630-8324)
PHONE.................................949 453-1500
Irene Horvath, *President*
Mik Horvath, *Vice Pres*
David Tuza, *General Mgr*
EMP: 17
SALES (est): 1.8MM **Privately Held**
WEB: www.i-source.com
SIC: **3679** Electronic circuits

P R O D U C T S & S V C S

(P-19574)
IMERGY POWER SYSTEMS INC
3945 Freedom Cir Ste 560, Santa Clara
(95054-1269)
PHONE..................510 668-1485
William D Watkins, *CEO*
Kelly Truman, *President*
Jack Jenkins-Stark, *CFO*
Viraj Patel, *CFO*
Gilles Champagne, *Vice Pres*
▲ EMP: 40
SQ FT: 35,000
SALES (est): 9MM **Privately Held**
WEB: www.deeyaenergy.com
SIC: 3679 Electronic loads & power supplies

(P-19575)
IMPACT LLC
22521 Avenida Empresa # 107, Rcho STA
Marg (92688-2041)
PHONE..................714 546-6000
Phil Laney,
Tim Scanlon, *VP Sales*
EMP: 28
SALES (est): 3.3MM **Privately Held**
WEB: www.impactllc.com
SIC: 3679 3829 Electronic circuits; measuring & controlling devices

(P-19576)
INFINITE ELECTRONICS INC
(HQ)
17792 Fitch, Irvine (92614-6020)
PHONE..................949 261-1920
Penny Cotner, *President*
Krishnan Iyer, *Vice Pres*
EMP: 36
SQ FT: 40,000
SALES (est): 300MM **Privately Held**
SIC: 3679 Electronic circuits

(P-19577)
INFORCE COMPUTING INC (PA)
48820 Kato Rd Ste 600b, Fremont
(94538-7335)
PHONE..................510 683-9999
Jagat R Acharya, *President*
Akhil Xavier, *Software Engr*
EMP: 10 EST: 2007
SALES (est): 3.9MM **Privately Held**
SIC: 3679 Electronic circuits

(P-19578)
INNOVISTA SENSORS AMERICAS INC (PA)
2945 Townsgate Rd Ste 200, Westlake Village (91361-5866)
PHONE..................805 267-7176
Eric Pilaud, *President*
Ben Watt, *CFO*
EMP: 29 EST: 2015
SALES (est): 20.7MM **Privately Held**
SIC: 3679 3577 Electronic circuits; encoders, computer peripheral equipment

(P-19579)
INSTRUMENT DESIGN ENG ASSOC I
Also Called: Idea
2923 Saturn St Ste F, Brea (92821-6260)
PHONE..................714 525-3302
Sabrina Lu, *President*
EMP: 20
SALES (est): 2.7MM **Privately Held**
WEB: www.ledidea.com
SIC: 3679 3674 Electronic circuits; semiconductors & related devices

(P-19580)
INTEGRATED MICROWAVE CORP
Also Called: Imcsd
11353 Sorrento Valley Rd, San Diego
(92121-1303)
PHONE..................858 259-2600
Mary Ellen Clark, *CEO*
David Bodmer, *CFO*
Terry Curella, *Vice Pres*
Steve Porter, *Vice Pres*
Steven Porter, *Vice Pres*
◆ EMP: 85 EST: 1982
SQ FT: 24,142

SALES (est): 17.6MM **Privately Held**
WEB: www.imcsd.com
SIC: 3679 Microwave components

(P-19581)
INTEGRITY TECHNOLOGY CORP
2505 Technology Dr, Hayward
(94545-4869)
PHONE..................270 812-8867
J P Young, *President*
J Garcia, *Manager*
J Jefferson, *Manager*
EMP: 40
SQ FT: 4,000
SALES (est): 2.5MM **Privately Held**
WEB: www.integritytechnology.net
SIC: 3679 3677 Electronic circuits; electronic coils, transformers & other inductors

(P-19582)
INTERCTIVE DSPLAY SLUTIONS INC
490 Wald, Irvine (92618-4638)
PHONE..................949 727-9493
Brian Chung, *President*
Rudy Rodriguez, *President*
Paul Kitzerow, *Senior VP*
Son Park, *Vice Pres*
Danny Lee, *Opers Staff*
▲ EMP: 12
SALES (est): 8.8MM **Privately Held**
WEB: www.pvdisplay.com
SIC: 3679 Liquid crystal displays (LCD)

(P-19583)
INTERFACE MASTERS TECH INC
150 E Brokaw Rd, San Jose (95112-4203)
PHONE..................408 441-9341
Benjamin Askarinam, *CEO*
Sima Askarinam, *President*
Kevin Yan, *Engineer*
Casey Trinh, *Accountant*
Ly Bui, *Purchasing*
EMP: 50
SQ FT: 3,000
SALES (est): 13.8MM **Privately Held**
SIC: 3679 Electronic switches

(P-19584)
INTERLOG CORPORATION
Also Called: Interlog Construction
1295 N Knollwood Cir, Anaheim
(92801-1310)
PHONE..................714 529-7808
Justin H Kwon, *CEO*
Paul Kim, *Executive*
Sami Lee, *Admin Asst*
Nathanael Kim, *Info Tech Mgr*
Sunny Yim, *Manager*
▲ EMP: 20
SALES (est): 8MM **Privately Held**
SIC: 3679 Electronic circuits

(P-19585)
INTERNATIONAL ELECTRONIC DESIG (PA)
Also Called: Ied Group
2630 S Shannon St, Santa Ana
(92704-5230)
PHONE..................714 662-1018
Eben Benade, *CEO*
Eben Denade, *President*
▲ EMP: 10
SQ FT: 16,000
SALES (est): 4MM **Privately Held**
SIC: 3679 Electronic circuits

(P-19586)
INTERNTNAL PWR DC PWR SUPS INC
900 Graves Ave, Oxnard (93030-7284)
PHONE..................805 981-1188
Craig Johnson, *President*
Ronald E Ostlund, *Ch of Bd*
EMP: 26
SQ FT: 14,000
SALES (est): 3.6MM **Privately Held**
SIC: 3679 Power supplies, all types: static

(P-19587)
ISOLINK INC
880 Yosemite Way, Milpitas (95035-6360)
PHONE..................408 946-1968
David Aldrich, *CEO*

Jorge Rosario, *Treasurer*
Stephan Ching, *Vice Pres*
Manor Narayanan, *General Mgr*
Bill Cantarini, *Engineer*
▲ EMP: 32
SQ FT: 16,600
SALES (est): 5.3MM **Privately Held**
WEB: www.isolink.com
SIC: 3679 3827 Electronic circuits; optical instruments & lenses

(P-19588)
J & L DIGITAL PRECISION INC
551 Taylor Way Ste 15, San Carlos
(94070-6252)
PHONE..................650 592-0170
John L Obertelli, *President*
Loretta Obertelli, *Corp Secy*
Gail Firpo, *Vice Pres*
Louis Firpo, *Vice Pres*
Jeff Obertelli, *Vice Pres*
EMP: 11
SALES (est): 2MM **Privately Held**
WEB: www.jldigital.com
SIC: 3679 Electronic circuits

(P-19589)
J L COOPER ELECTRONICS INC
Also Called: Jlcooper
142 Arena St, El Segundo (90245-3901)
PHONE..................310 322-9990
James Loren Cooper, *President*
Mark Van Kirk, *Director*
▲ EMP: 25
SALES (est): 4.1MM **Privately Held**
WEB: www.jlcooper.com
SIC: 3679 Recording & playback apparatus, including phonograph

(P-19590)
J R V PRODUCTS INC
1314 N Harbor Blvd # 302, Santa Ana
(92703-1300)
P.O. Box 5645, Orange (92863-5645)
PHONE..................714 259-9772
Curt Shoup, *President*
John Beckingham, *President*
▲ EMP: 13
SQ FT: 6,000
SALES (est): 990K **Privately Held**
WEB: www.jrvproductsinc.com
SIC: 3679 Electronic switches; electronic circuits; electronic loads & power supplies

(P-19591)
J&M MANUFACTURING INC
430 Aaron St, Cotati (94931-3016)
P.O. Box 2435, Rohnert Park (94927-2435)
PHONE..................707 795-8223
James O Judd Jr, *Owner*
Paul L Matthias, *CFO*
▲ EMP: 34
SQ FT: 25,000
SALES (est): 7.1MM **Privately Held**
WEB: www.jmmfg.com
SIC: 3679 3444 Electronic circuits; metal housings, enclosures, casings & other containers

(P-19592)
JAMES L HALL CO INCORPORATED (PA)
360 Tesconi Cir Ste B, Santa Rosa
(95401-4677)
P.O. Box 309 (95402-0309)
PHONE..................707 547-0775
Steve Vallarino, *President*
Morey Serpa, *CFO*
Linda Beyce, *Corp Secy*
EMP: 55 EST: 1919
SQ FT: 1,400
SALES (est): 8.2MM **Privately Held**
WEB: www.jetronics.com
SIC: 3679 Electronic circuits

(P-19593)
JASPER ELECTRONICS
1580 N Kellogg Dr, Anaheim (92807-1902)
PHONE..................714 917-0749
Robert Nishimoto, *CEO*
Hiroshi Tango, *Chairman*
Bill Galey, *Project Mgr*
Mike Cline, *Manager*
▲ EMP: 30
SQ FT: 17,000

SALES (est): 6.2MM **Privately Held**
WEB: www.jasperelectronics.com
SIC: 3679 Electronic loads & power supplies; power supplies, all types: static

(P-19594)
JAVAD EMS INC
900 Rock Ave, San Jose (95131-1615)
PHONE..................408 770-1700
Javad Ashjaee, *President*
Gary Walker, *Vice Pres*
Linda Bezoni, *Principal*
Pam Walke, *Principal*
▲ EMP: 95
SALES (est): 20MM **Privately Held**
SIC: 3679 Electronic circuits

(P-19595)
JAXX MANUFACTURING INC
Also Called: Craig Kackert Design Tech
1912 Angus Ave, Simi Valley (93063-3494)
PHONE..................805 526-4979
Greg Liu, *President*
Robert Barr, *Program Mgr*
Veronica Liu, *General Mgr*
Dan Smith, *CIO*
EMP: 45
SALES (est): 8.6MM **Privately Held**
SIC: 3679 Electronic circuits

(P-19596)
JAYCO INTERFACE TECHNOLOGY INC
1351 Pico St, Corona (92881-3373)
PHONE..................951 738-2000
Hemant Mistry, *President*
Shaila RAO, *Treasurer*
EMP: 40
SQ FT: 23,000
SALES (est): 8.1MM **Privately Held**
WEB: www.jaycopanels.com
SIC: 3679 5065 Electronic circuits; electronic parts & equipment

(P-19597)
JAYCO MMI INC
1351 Pico St, Corona (92881-3373)
PHONE..................951 738-2000
Shaila Mistry, *President*
Hemant Mistry, *Vice Pres*
Shaila RAO, *Vice Pres*
EMP: 42
SQ FT: 24,000
SALES (est): 5.3MM **Privately Held**
SIC: 3679 5065 3577 2759 Electronic circuits; electronic parts & equipment; computer peripheral equipment; commercial printing; engineering services

(P-19598)
JDI DISPLAY AMERICA INC (PA)
1740 Tech Dr Ste 460, San Jose (95110)
PHONE..................408 501-3720
Atsuhiko Tokinosu, *President*
Shuichi Odsuka, *CEO*
Koichiro Taniyama, *CFO*
Robert Bogdanoff, *District Mgr*
EMP: 20
SALES (est): 3.2MM **Privately Held**
SIC: 3679 7374 Liquid crystal displays (LCD); computer processing services

(P-19599)
JDS TECHNOLOGIES
12200 Thatcher Ct, Poway (92064-6876)
PHONE..................858 486-8787
Jeff Stein, *Owner*
EMP: 14
SQ FT: 7,000
SALES (est): 1MM **Privately Held**
SIC: 3679 Electronic circuits

(P-19600)
JIC INDUSTRIAL CO INC
978 Hanson Ct, Milpitas (95035-3165)
PHONE..................408 935-9880
Frank Yen, *President*
▲ EMP: 15
SALES (est): 1.7MM **Privately Held**
WEB: www.jicusa.com
SIC: 3679 3678 3357 Electronic circuits; electronic connectors; nonferrous wire-drawing & insulating

(P-19601)
JLAB LLC
Also Called: Jlab Audio
2281 Las Palmas Dr # 101, Carlsbad
(92011-1527)
PHONE.............................405 445-7219
Win Cramer, *President*
▲ EMP: 20
SQ FT: 5,000
SALES (est): 13.1MM Privately Held
SIC: 3679 Headphones, radio

(P-19602)
JOLO INDUSTRIES INC
10432 Brightwood Dr, Santa Ana
(92705-1591)
PHONE.............................714 554-6840
James S Giampiccolo, *President*
Theresa Giampiccolo, *Corp Secy*
Chip Giampiccolo, *Vice Pres*
Louise Matamoros, *Mfg Staff*
EMP: 20
SQ FT: 8,000
SALES (est): 1.8MM Privately Held
SIC: 3679 3678 Electronic circuits; electronic connectors

(P-19603)
JOMAR MACHINING INC
180 Constitution Dr Ste 8, Menlo Park
(94025-1137)
PHONE.............................650 324-2143
Joe Bencsik, *President*
Margaret Bencsik, *Corp Secy*
EMP: 14
SQ FT: 3,600
SALES (est): 1.5MM Privately Held
SIC: 3679 Antennas, receiving; antennas, satellite: household use; cores, magnetic; cryogenic cooling devices for infrared detectors, masers

(P-19604)
K S EQUIPMENT INC
17 Hangar Way, Watsonville (95076-2454)
PHONE.............................831 722-7173
Jeff Kidwell, *President*
Margaret Kidwell, *Corp Secy*
▲ EMP: 10
SQ FT: 13,000
SALES (est): 770K Privately Held
WEB: www.ksequipment.com
SIC: 3679 Switches, stepping

(P-19605)
KAMA INTERCONNECT INC
8030 Remmet Ave Ste 3, Canoga Park
(91304-6411)
PHONE.............................818 713-9810
Amir Behzadi, *President*
Abbas Ghasemi, *Corp Secy*
Ali Kolahi, *Vice Pres*
Ruberto Domanis, *Manager*
EMP: 10
SQ FT: 5,000
SALES (est): 1.6MM Privately Held
SIC: 3679 Electronic circuits; harness assemblies for electronic use: wire or cable

(P-19606)
KATOLEC DEVELOPMENT INC
6120 Business Center Ct, San Diego
(92154)
PHONE.............................619 710-0075
Eisuke Kato, *President*
▲ EMP: 20
SALES (est): 6.8MM
SALES (corp-wide): 315.1MM Privately Held
SIC: 3679 Electronic circuits
PA: Katolec Corporation
2-8-7, Edagawa
Koto-Ku TKY 135-0
356 837-000

(P-19607)
KAVLICO CORPORATION (HQ)
1461 Lawrence Dr, Thousand Oaks
(91320-1303)
PHONE.............................805 523-2000
Martha Sullivan, *President*
Nicolas Cortes, *Engineer*
Hamid Pasha, *Engineer*
Jeffrey Cote, *Director*
Jeff Stanton, *Manager*
▲ EMP: 1390

SQ FT: 284,000
SALES (est): 396.6MM
SALES (corp-wide): 722.3MM Privately Held
SIC: 3679 3829 3823 Transducers, electrical; measuring & controlling devices; industrial instrmnts msrmnt display/control process variable
PA: Custom Sensors & Technologies, Inc.
1461 Lawrence Dr
Thousand Oaks CA 91320
805 716-0322

(P-19608)
KAVLICO CORPORATION
2475 Pseo De Las Americas, San Diego
(92154-7255)
PHONE.............................805 523-2000
EMP: 33
SALES (corp-wide): 722.3MM Privately Held
SIC: 3679 3829 Transducers, electrical; measuring & controlling devices
HQ: Kavlico Corporation
1461 Lawrence Dr
Thousand Oaks CA 91320
805 523-2000

(P-19609)
KELYTECH CORPORATION
1482 Gladding Ct, Milpitas (95035-6831)
PHONE.............................408 935-0888
K C Wong, *President*
Stanley Chiu, *Vice Pres*
Katie Wong, *Executive*
Kevin Wong, *Office Mgr*
Irene Wong, *Admin Sec*
EMP: 40
SQ FT: 8,500
SALES: 2MM Privately Held
WEB: www.kelytech.com
SIC: 3679 Electronic circuits

(P-19610)
KG TECHNOLOGIES INC
6028 State Farm Dr, Rohnert Park
(94928-2133)
P.O. Box 7089, Cotati (94931-7089)
PHONE.............................888 513-1874
Philipp Gruner, *President*
Timothy Wells, *President*
Thomas Gruner, *Treasurer*
Steve Layton, *Vice Pres*
Massimo Perucchini, *VP Opers*
▲ EMP: 12
SQ FT: 5,600
SALES (est): 2.1MM
SALES (corp-wide): 668.6MM Privately Held
WEB: www.kgtechnologies.net
SIC: 3679 Electronic circuits
HQ: Clodi L.L.C.
429 E Cotati Ave
Cotati CA 94931
707 664-5006

(P-19611)
KMW USA INC (HQ)
Also Called: KMW Communications
1818 E Orangethorpe Ave, Fullerton
(92831-5324)
PHONE.............................714 515-1100
Duk Y Kim, *President*
Burton Calloway, *Vice Pres*
Yeong Kim, *Vice Pres*
▲ EMP: 27
SQ FT: 4,500
SALES (est): 6.3MM
SALES (corp-wide): 133.2MM Privately Held
WEB: www.kmwinc.com
SIC: 3679 5063 Electronic circuits; electrical apparatus & equipment; control & signal wire & cable, including coaxial
PA: Kmw.Inc
183-19 Yeongcheon-Ro
Hwaseong 18462
823 137-0860

(P-19612)
KRITECH CORPORATION (PA)
333 W 131st St, Los Angeles (90061-1103)
PHONE.............................310 538-9940
Louis Riberio, *President*
EMP: 15
SQ FT: 6,000

SALES (est): 1.3MM Privately Held
SIC: 3679 3053 Electronic circuits; gaskets, packing & sealing devices

(P-19613)
KRYTAR INC
1288 Anvilwood Ave, Sunnyvale (94089)
PHONE.............................408 734-5999
Nancy Russell, *Ch of Bd*
Douglas Hagan, *President*
Amy Renwald, *Admin Asst*
Michael Romero, *Engineer*
Hilda Clayton, *Purchasing*
EMP: 20
SALES (est): 3.8MM Privately Held
WEB: www.krytar.com
SIC: 3679 Microwave components; electronic circuits

(P-19614)
L P GLASSBLOWING INC
2322 Calle Del Mundo, Santa Clara
(95054-1007)
PHONE.............................408 988-7561
Leopold Pivk, *President*
Hilda Pivk, *Vice Pres*
Dana Prodanovic, *General Mgr*
EMP: 30
SQ FT: 6,700
SALES (est): 4.5MM Privately Held
WEB: www.lpglassblowing.com
SIC: 3679 3229 Quartz crystals, for electronic application; pressed & blown glass

(P-19615)
LABWORKS INC
2950 Airway Ave Ste A16, Costa Mesa
(92626-6019)
PHONE.............................714 549-1981
Gary Curtis Butts, *CEO*
Nick Lus, *Vice Pres*
EMP: 10
SQ FT: 5,000
SALES (est): 1.5MM Privately Held
WEB: www.labworks-inc.com
SIC: 3679 3812 Electronic circuits; search & navigation equipment

(P-19616)
LANDMARK LCDS INC
12453 Blue Meadow Ct, Saratoga
(95070-3820)
PHONE.............................408 386-4257
Richard Kim, *President*
EMP: 10 EST: 2015
SALES (est): 512.7K Privately Held
SIC: 3679 Liquid crystal displays (LCD)

(P-19617)
LANDMARK TECHNOLOGY INC
1660 Mckee Rd, San Jose (95116-1263)
PHONE.............................408 435-8890
Sun Lu, *President*
Jean Lu, *CFO*
Fanny Yip, *Admin Asst*
▲ EMP: 22
SQ FT: 13,000
SALES (est): 3MM Privately Held
WEB: www.landmarktek.com
SIC: 3679 3674 Liquid crystal displays (LCD); semiconductors & related devices

(P-19618)
LE VU
4234 54th St, McClellan (95652-2100)
PHONE.............................916 231-1594
Fred Frasier, *Chief*
EMP: 50
SALES (est): 3.2MM Privately Held
SIC: 3679 Electronic components

(P-19619)
LEACH INTERNATIONAL CORP (HQ)
Also Called: Esterline Power Systems
6900 Orangethorpe Ave, Buena Park
(90620-1390)
P.O. Box 5032 (90622-5032)
PHONE.............................714 736-7537
Richard Brad Lawrence, *CEO*
Mark Thek, *President*
John Danley, *COO*
Alain Durand, *Vice Pres*
Imtiaz Khan, *Project Engr*
EMP: 500 EST: 1919

SALES (est): 226.6MM
SALES (corp-wide): 2B Publicly Held
SIC: 3679 Electronic circuits
PA: Esterline Technologies Corp
500 108th Ave Ne Ste 1500
Bellevue WA 98004
425 453-9400

(P-19620)
LG INNOTEK USA INC (HQ)
2540 N 1st St Ste 400, San Jose
(95131-1016)
PHONE.............................408 955-0364
Sung IL Yang, *President*
Harry Kang, *Marketing Mgr*
▲ EMP: 19
SQ FT: 71,168
SALES (est): 18MM
SALES (corp-wide): 6.5B Privately Held
SIC: 3679 Antennas, receiving
PA: Lg Innotek Co., Ltd.
98 Huam-Ro, Jung-Gu
Seoul 04637
822 377-7111

(P-19621)
LHV POWER CORPORATION (PA)
10221 Buena Vista Ave A, Santee
(92071-4484)
PHONE.............................619 258-7700
James Gevarges, *President*
Ladge Leitner, *Technology*
Marylou Barrios, *Opers Staff*
▲ EMP: 25
SQ FT: 20,000
SALES (est): 3.5MM Privately Held
WEB: www.hitekpower.com
SIC: 3679 Power supplies, all types: static

(P-19622)
LIBRA CABLE TECHNOLOGIES INC
Monterey Business Park 27, Torrance
(90503)
PHONE.............................310 618-8182
Palle Gravesen Jensen, *CEO*
Liza L Jensen, *Project Mgr*
EMP: 12
SALES (est): 1.7MM
SALES (corp-wide): 4.2MM Privately Held
SIC: 3679 Harness assemblies for electronic use: wire or cable
PA: Electronic House Uab
Dariaus Ir Gireno G. 99
Vilnius
523 067-51

(P-19623)
LIEDER DEVELOPMENT INC
1839 S Lake Pl, Ontario (91761-5789)
PHONE.............................909 947-7722
Kimball Chase, *CEO*
Paul Caraway, *President*
Beth Thomas, *Office Mgr*
EMP: 15
SQ FT: 7,200
SALES: 2.4MM Privately Held
WEB: www.liederdev.com
SIC: 3679 Microwave components

(P-19624)
LIGHTCROSS INC
2630 Corporate Pl, Monterey Park
(91754-7645)
PHONE.............................626 236-4500
Robert Barron, *President*
Daniel Kim, *Corp Secy*
Tom Smith, *Vice Pres*
EMP: 34 EST: 2000
SQ FT: 23,000
SALES (est): 3.2MM Privately Held
WEB: www.lightcross.com
SIC: 3679 Electronic circuits

(P-19625)
LIGHTECH FIBEROPTIC INC
1987 Adams Ave, San Leandro
(94577-1005)
PHONE.............................510 567-8700
Tracy Scott, *COO*
Jimmy Ko, *President*
Teresa Chan, *Human Res Dir*
EMP: 40
SQ FT: 11,000

SALES (est): 4.8MM **Privately Held**
WEB: www.lightech.net
SIC: **3679** 3229 Electronic switches;
pressed & blown glass

(P-19626)
LITHIUMSTART INC
865 Hinckley Rd, Burlingame (94010-1502)
PHONE.................................800 520-8864
James Voss, *Principal*
Manavendra Sial, *Principal*
Edward Yocum, *Principal*
▲ EMP: 20
SQ FT: 20,000
SALES: 3.7MM **Privately Held**
SIC: **3679** Electronic loads & power sup-
plies
PA: Eaglepicher Technologies, Llc
C & Porter St
Joplin MO 64801

(P-19627)
LOGITECH STREAMING MEDIA INC
7600 Gateway Blvd, Newark (94560-1159)
PHONE.................................510 795-8500
Bracken Darrell, *CEO*
Joseph Sullivan, *Senior VP*
Michele Hermann, *Vice Pres*
Jolanda Pas, *Office Mgr*
Jeff Eisenman, *Sr Ntwrk Engine*
▲ EMP: 24
SQ FT: 18,000
SALES (est): 2.5MM
SALES (corp-wide): 2.2B **Privately Held**
WEB: www.slimdevices.com
SIC: **3679** Electronic circuits
PA: Logitech International S.A.
Les Chatagnis
Apples VD
218 635-111

(P-19628)
LUCERO CABLES INC
193 Stauffer Blvd, San Jose (95125-1042)
PHONE.................................408 536-0340
Madeline Eliasnia, *CEO*
Surendra Gupta, *President*
Art Eliasnia, *Chairman*
Iraj Pessian, *Treasurer*
Serjik Avanes, *Vice Pres*
▲ EMP: 110 EST: 1978
SQ FT: 50,000
SALES (est): 17.6MM **Privately Held**
WEB: www.luceromfg.com
SIC: **3679** 3571 Harness assemblies for
electronic use: wire or cable; electronic
computers

(P-19629)
LUCIX CORPORATION (HQ)
800 Avenida Acaso Ste E, Camarillo
(93012-8758)
PHONE.................................805 987-6645
Mark Shahriary, *President*
Cheryl Johnson, *CFO*
D Ick Fanucchi, *Vice Pres*
▲ EMP: 83
SQ FT: 48,000
SALES: 31.5MM **Publicly Held**
WEB: www.lucix.com
SIC: **3679** 8731 Microwave components;
commercial physical research

(P-19630)
M R F TECHNIQUES INC
Also Called: Rf Techniques
2245b Fortune Dr Ste B, San Jose
(95131-1806)
PHONE.................................408 433-1941
Sara Mathew, *President*
Moni Mathew, *Admin Sec*
EMP: 11
SQ FT: 3,000
SALES (est): 1.3MM **Privately Held**
WEB: www.rftechniques.com
SIC: **3679** 3676 3674 3672 Electronic cir-
cuits; electronic resistors; integrated cir-
cuits, semiconductor networks, etc.;
semiconductor circuit networks; thin film
circuits; printed circuit boards

(P-19631)
M WAVE DESIGN CORPORATION
94 W Cochran St Ste B, Simi Valley
(93065-0948)
PHONE.................................805 499-8825
Ken Boswell, *CEO*
Bonnie Murray, *Admin Sec*
EMP: 10
SQ FT: 6,600
SALES (est): 1.5MM **Privately Held**
SIC: **3679** 5065 Microwave components;
electronic parts & equipment

(P-19632)
M2 ANTENNA SYSTEMS INC
Also Called: Msquared
4402 N Selland Ave, Fresno (93722-4191)
PHONE.................................559 221-2271
Myrna Staal, *President*
Mike Staal, *Vice Pres*
EMP: 15
SQ FT: 10,000
SALES (est): 3MM **Privately Held**
WEB: www.m2inc.com
SIC: **3679** 5999 3625 Antennas, receiv-
ing; mobile telephones & equipment; posi-
tioning controls, electric

(P-19633)
MAGNETIC CIRCUIT ELEMENTS INC
Also Called: M C E
1540 Moffett St, Salinas (93905-3351)
PHONE.................................831 757-8752
John S Conklin, *CEO*
Lisa Battaglia, *Executive*
Bruce Armour, *Administration*
Stacey Callahan, *Administration*
EMP: 49
SQ FT: 11,000
SALES (est): 7.8MM **Privately Held**
WEB: www.mcemagnetics.com
SIC: **3679** 3677 Electronic circuits; elec-
tronic coils, transformers & other induc-
tors

(P-19634)
MAGNETIC DESIGN LABS INC
1636 E Edinger Ave Ste H, Santa Ana
(92705-5020)
PHONE.................................714 558-3355
ABI Kazem, *Principal*
Judith Kazem, *President*
Judith A Kazem, *CEO*
Kamran Kazem, *Vice Pres*
Virginia Montoya, *Purch Mgr*
EMP: 15
SQ FT: 6,000
SALES (est): 1.3MM **Privately Held**
WEB: www.magneticdesign.com
SIC: **3679** 5065 Power supplies, all types:
static; electronic parts & equipment

(P-19635)
MAGNETIC SENSORS CORP
1365 N Mccan St, Anaheim (92806-1316)
PHONE.................................714 630-8380
Charles Boudakian, *President*
Don Payne, *Vice Pres*
Brenda Crain, *Office Mgr*
Frank Cegelski, *Technology*
Mario Gregory, *Electrical Engi*
EMP: 43
SQ FT: 15,000
SALES (est): 9.2MM **Privately Held**
WEB: www.magsensors.com
SIC: **3679** 3677 Transducers, electrical;
coil windings, electronic

(P-19636)
MAGNITUDE ELECTRONICS LLC
926 Bransten Rd, San Carlos
(94070-4029)
PHONE.................................650 551-1850
Hal White, *Mng Member*
Gilles Grosgurin,
Staci Arndt, *Manager*
Sam Hesselgren, *Manager*
Carla White, *Manager*
▲ EMP: 12
SQ FT: 2,500
SALES (est): 5MM **Privately Held**
WEB: www.magnitude-electronics.com
SIC: **3679** Electronic circuits

(P-19637)
MANUTRONICS INC
736 S Hillview Dr, Milpitas (95035-5455)
PHONE.................................408 262-6579
Cuong Tran, *CEO*
EMP: 14
SALES (est): 2.3MM **Privately Held**
SIC: **3679** Electronic circuits

(P-19638)
MARKI MICROWAVE INC
215 Vineyard Ct, Morgan Hill (95037-7121)
PHONE.................................408 778-4200
Ferenc A Marki, *President*
Christine Marki, *CFO*
Christopher Marki, *Opers Staff*
EMP: 45
SQ FT: 9,800
SALES (est): 10.8MM **Privately Held**
WEB: www.markimicrowave.com
SIC: **3679** Microwave components

(P-19639)
MASK TECHNOLOGY INC
2601 Oak St, Santa Ana (92707-3720)
PHONE.................................714 557-3383
Andrew Holzmann, *President*
Joanne Deblis, *Director*
EMP: 25
SQ FT: 9,800
SALES (est): 3.1MM **Privately Held**
WEB: www.masktek.com
SIC: **3679** Electronic circuits

(P-19640)
MAURY MICROWAVE INC
2900 Inland Empire Blvd, Ontario
(91764-4804)
PHONE.................................909 987-4715
Gregory M Maury, *CEO*
Marc A Maury, *President*
Ted Lewis, *Vice Pres*
Jane Cary, *General Mgr*
Grace Sun, *Admin Asst*
▲ EMP: 115
SQ FT: 6,000
SALES (est): 37.5MM **Privately Held**
WEB: www.maurymw.com
SIC: **3679** Microwave components

(P-19641)
MAXTROL CORPORATION
1701 E Edinger Ave Ste B6, Santa Ana
(92705-5010)
PHONE.................................714 245-0506
Uri Ranon, *President*
Leo Pardo, *Vice Pres*
EMP: 40
SQ FT: 5,000
SALES (est): 3.3MM **Privately Held**
WEB: www.maxtrol.com
SIC: **3679** Electronic circuits

(P-19642)
MC ELECTRONICS LLC
1891 Airway Dr, Hollister (95023-9099)
PHONE.................................831 637-1651
Jan Kreminski,
Timothy Michael, *Technology*
Crystal Herrera, *Accounting Mgr*
Bishop McElvaney, *Mfg Mgr*
EMP: 399
SQ FT: 6,000
SALES (est): 81.8MM
SALES (corp-wide): 322.3MM **Privately Held**
WEB: www.mcelectronics.com
SIC: **3679** Harness assemblies for elec-
tronic use: wire or cable
PA: Volex Plc
Holbrook House
Richmond TW10
203 370-8830

(P-19643)
MEAN WELL USA INC
44030 Fremont Blvd, Fremont
(94538-6042)
PHONE.................................510 683-8886
Shiao Ta Tung, *CEO*
David Tung, *President*
Benny Cheung, *Technology*
Candy Lee, *Accountant*
Mandy U Yang, *Human Resources*
▲ EMP: 19
SQ FT: 13,500

SALES (est): 4.4MM **Privately Held**
WEB: www.meanwellusa.com
SIC: **3679** Static power supply converters
for electronic applications
PA: Mean Well Enterprises Co., Ltd.
No. 28, Wu Chuan 3rd Rd.,
New Taipei City
222 996-100

(P-19644)
MEMBRANE SWITCH AND PANEL INC
3198 Arprt Loop Dr Ste K, Costa Mesa
(92626)
PHONE.................................714 957-6905
John B Corzine, *President*
EMP: 16
SQ FT: 5,000
SALES (est): 2.1MM **Privately Held**
WEB: www.membraneusa.com
SIC: **3679** Antennas, receiving

(P-19645)
MEMRY CORPORATION
4065 Campbell Ave, Menlo Park
(94025-1006)
PHONE.................................650 463-3400
Dean Tulumaris, *Manager*
EMP: 120
SALES (corp-wide): 62.1MM **Privately Held**
WEB: www.memry.com
SIC: **3679** 3841 3769 3714 Harness assemblies for electronic use: wire or cable;
surgical & medical instruments; guided
missile & space vehicle parts & auxiliary
equipment; motor vehicle parts & accessories
HQ: Memry Corporation
3 Berkshire Blvd
Bethel CT 06801
203 739-1100

(P-19646)
MERCURY UNITED ELECTRONICS INC
Also Called: Global Electronics Intl
9804 Cres Ctr Dr Ste 603, Rancho Cuca-
monga (91730-5782)
PHONE.................................909 466-0427
Chih-Hsun Yen, *CEO*
Jason Yen, *President*
Jean Hsi, *Corp Secy*
Jyh Yaw Yen, *Vice Pres*
EMP: 25
SQ FT: 8,460
SALES (est): 3MM **Privately Held**
SIC: **3679** 5065 Quartz crystals, for elec-
tronic application; paging & signaling
equipment

(P-19647)
MICRO CHIPS OF AMERICA INC
5302 Comercio Ln Apt 1, Woodland Hills
(91364-2049)
PHONE.................................818 577-9543
Sara Baires, *President*
Steve Levy, *CEO*
David Levy, *Treasurer*
Erets Levy, *Vice Pres*
EMP: 25
SQ FT: 3,000
SALES: 2MM **Privately Held**
SIC: **3679** 3674 Electronic circuits; semi-
conductors & related devices

(P-19648)
MICRO LAMBDA WIRELESS INC
46515 Landing Pkwy, Fremont
(94538-6421)
PHONE.................................510 770-9221
John Nguyen, *President*
David Suddarth, *Vice Pres*
Myra Verret, *Administration*
Susan Sun, *Info Tech Mgr*
MAI Lam, *Accountant*
EMP: 39
SQ FT: 19,000
SALES (est): 8MM **Privately Held**
WEB: www.microlambdawireless.com
SIC: **3679** 5065 3663 Microwave compo-
nents; electronic parts & equipment; radio
& TV communications equipment

(P-19649)
MICROFABRICA INC
7911 Haskell Ave, Van Nuys (91406-1909)
PHONE..................................888 964-2763
Eric Miller, *Principal*
Uri Frodis, *Senior VP*
Richard Chen, *Vice Pres*
Greg Schmitz, *Vice Pres*
Nina Levy, *Admin Asst*
EMP: 50
SQ FT: 39,000
SALES (est): 13.6MM **Privately Held**
WEB: www.microfabrica.com
SIC: 3679 Electronic circuits

(P-19650)
MICROMETALS INC (PA)
5615 E La Palma Ave, Anaheim
(92807-2109)
PHONE..................................714 970-9400
Richard H Barden, *CEO*
Chris Oliver, *Admin Mgr*
Pedro Lopez, *QA Dir*
Rosa Massie, *Purch Mgr*
Teresa Longridge, *Purch Agent*
▲ **EMP:** 90 **EST:** 1951
SQ FT: 50,000
SALES (est): 34MM **Privately Held**
WEB: www.micrometals.com
SIC: 3679 Cores, magnetic

(P-19651)
MICROMETALS/TEXAS INC
5615 E La Palma Ave, Anaheim
(92807-2109)
PHONE..................................325 677-8753
Richard H Barden, *President*
Ken Gist, *Manager*
◆ **EMP:** 250
SQ FT: 20,000
SALES (est): 32MM
SALES (corp-wide): 34MM **Privately
Held**
WEB: www.micrometals.com
SIC: 3679 Cores, magnetic
PA: Micrometals, Inc.
5615 E La Palma Ave
Anaheim CA 92807
714 970-9400

(P-19652)
MICROSEMI SEMICONDUCTOR US INC
3843 Brickway Blvd # 100, Santa Rosa
(95403-9059)
PHONE..................................707 568-5900
Julio Perdomo, *CEO*
Hiroshi Kondoh, *COO*
Jerome C Nathan, *CFO*
Jeff Meyer, *CTO*
Stephanie Pannell, *Purchasing*
▼ **EMP:** 72
SQ FT: 26,000
SALES (est): 9.5MM
SALES (corp-wide): 3.9B **Publicly Held**
WEB: www.centellax.com
SIC: 3679 Microwave components
HQ: Cnt Acquisition Corp.
1 Enterprise
Aliso Viejo CA 92656
949 380-6100

(P-19653)
MICROWAVE TECHNOLOGY INC (DH)
4268 Solar Way, Fremont (94538-6335)
PHONE..................................510 651-6700
Nathan Zommer, *CEO*
Zong Cai, *Engineer*
Shawn Smith, *Engineer*
Quin Manor, *Purch Mgr*
Hanh Nguyen, *QC Mgr*
EMP: 45
SQ FT: 30,800
SALES (corp-wide): 1.2B **Publicly Held**
WEB: www.mwtinc.com
SIC: 3679 3663 Commutators, electronic;
amplifiers, RF power & IF
HQ: Ixys, Llc
1590 Buckeye Dr
Milpitas CA 95035
408 457-9000

(P-19654)
MINATRONIC INC
1139 13th St, Paso Robles (93446-2644)
PHONE..................................805 239-8864
Max Clinger, *President*
EMP: 19
SALES (est): 2MM **Privately Held**
SIC: 3679 5065 Electronic circuits; electronic parts & equipment

(P-19655)
MITSUBISHI ELECTRIC VISUAL
Also Called: Mevsa
10833 Valley View St # 300, Cypress
(90630-5046)
PHONE..................................800 553-7278
Tadashi Hiraoka, *CEO*
Kenichiro Yamanishi, *Chairman*
Perry Pappous, *Admin Sec*
Matthew Eakin, *Info Tech Mgr*
Susie Delgado, *Assistant*
▲ **EMP:** 150
SALES (est): 56.8MM
SALES (corp-wide): 41.5B **Privately Held**
SIC: 3679 Liquid crystal displays (LCD)
PA: Mitsubishi Electric Corporation
2-7-3, Marunouchi
Chiyoda-Ku TKY 100-0
332 182-111

(P-19656)
MULTIMEDIA LED INC (PA)
4225 Prado Rd Ste 108, Corona
(92880-7443)
PHONE..................................951 280-7500
Steven Craig, *CEO*
Alex Birner, *President*
▲ **EMP:** 14
SALES: 1.6MM **Privately Held**
SIC: 3679 Electronic circuits

(P-19657)
MUSTARD SEED TECHNOLOGIES INC
Also Called: P K C
3000 W Warner Ave, Santa Ana
(92704-5311)
PHONE..................................714 556-7007
Bruce T McCleave Sr, *President*
Roger Litz, *Vice Pres*
James R Seiler Jr, *Admin Sec*
Paul Kaplin, *Info Tech Dir*
Joel Longoria, *Natl Sales Mgr*
▲ **EMP:** 134
SQ FT: 26,000
SALES (est): 41MM **Privately Held**
WEB: www.4pkc.com
SIC: 3679 5065 Harness assemblies for
electronic use: wire or cable; electronic
parts & equipment

(P-19658)
NEW VISION DISPLAY INC (HQ)
1430 Blue Oaks Blvd # 100, Roseville
(95747-5156)
PHONE..................................916 786-8111
Jeff Olyniec, *CEO*
Owen Chen, *Ch of Bd*
Alan M Lefko, *CFO*
◆ **EMP:** 28
SQ FT: 4,200
SALES: 113MM **Privately Held**
SIC: 3679 Liquid crystal displays (LCD)
PA: New Vision Display (Shenzhen) Co.,
Ltd.
No.102, Lijia Rd., Henggang Town,
Longgang Dist.
Shenzhen 51810
755 286-2088

(P-19659)
NEWAYS INC
28202 Cabot Rd Ste 100, Laguna Niguel
(92677-1247)
PHONE..................................949 264-1542
EMP: 38
SALES (est): 1.9MM **Privately Held**
SIC: 3679

(P-19660)
NEXSUN ELECTRONICS INC
Also Called: Nemco
142 Technology Dr Ste 150, Irvine
(92618-2429)
PHONE..................................949 680-4725
Casey Conlan, *President*

▲ **EMP:** 25
SQ FT: 14,000
SALES (est): 7.4MM **Privately Held**
WEB: www.suntsunc.com
SIC: 3679 Electronic circuits; recording &
playback apparatus, including phonograph

(P-19661)
NEXYN CORPORATION
1287 Forgewood Ave, Sunnyvale
(94089-2216)
PHONE..................................408 962-0895
Joyce Benton, *CEO*
LI Benton, *Ch of Bd*
Robert Benton, *President*
Jim Chen, *CFO*
EMP: 10
SQ FT: 5,000
SALES (est): 1.5MM **Privately Held**
WEB: www.nexyn.com
SIC: 3679 Oscillators

(P-19662)
NORTRA CABLES INC
570 Gibraltar Dr, Milpitas (95035-6315)
PHONE..................................408 942-1106
Jim Love, *President*
Lyn Hickey, *Shareholder*
Andy O'Brien, *Programmer Anys*
Ron Huynh, *Technology*
Michelle Lateur, *Manager*
EMP: 60
SQ FT: 14,000
SALES (est): 14.8MM **Privately Held**
WEB: www.nortra-cables.com
SIC: 3679 Harness assemblies for electronic use: wire or cable

(P-19663)
NOVANTA CORPORATION
4575 Cushing Pkwy, Fremont
(94538-6466)
PHONE..................................510 770-1417
John A Roush, *Branch Mgr*
EMP: 20 **Publicly Held**
SIC: 3679 3825 8711 Liquid crystal displays (LCD); digital test equipment, electronic & electrical circuits; engineering
services
HQ: Novanta Corporation
125 Middlesex Tpke
Bedford MA 01730
781 266-5700

(P-19664)
NOVANTA CORPORATION
Also Called: Reach Technology
5750 Hellyer Ave, San Jose (95138-1000)
PHONE..................................408 754-4176
Kariem Khadr, *Branch Mgr*
Chris Messineo, *Software Engr*
Dan Neumann, *Opers Staff*
Sarah Harrington, *Marketing Staff*
Debbie Gronski, *Manager*
EMP: 20 **Publicly Held**
SIC: 3679 Liquid crystal displays (LCD)
HQ: Novanta Corporation
125 Middlesex Tpke
Bedford MA 01730
781 266-5700

(P-19665)
NRC MANUFACTURING INC
47690 Westinghouse Dr, Fremont
(94539-7473)
PHONE..................................510 438-9400
Rata Chea, *President*
David Hang, *CFO*
Curtis Myrick, *Project Mgr*
Savuth Bun, *Prdtn Mgr*
Michael Ornelas, *Manager*
EMP: 18
SQ FT: 16,000
SALES: 3MM **Privately Held**
SIC: 3679 Electronic circuits

(P-19666)
O M JONES INC
Also Called: Micro-Tronics
18897 Microtronics Way, Sonora
(95370-9288)
P.O. Box 4375 (95370-1375)
PHONE..................................209 532-1008
Lawrence Jones, *President*
Olga Jones, *CFO*

Kevin Jones, *Vice Pres*
Mark Knowles, *Vice Pres*
Gina Prock, *Vice Pres*
EMP: 23
SQ FT: 7,300
SALES (est): 2.4MM **Privately Held**
WEB: www.micro-tronics.net
SIC: 3679 Microwave components

(P-19667)
OASIS MATERIALS COMPANY LP
12131 Community Rd Ste D, Poway
(92064-8893)
PHONE..................................858 486-8846
Frank Polese, *President*
Christopher Bateman, *Partner*
Stephen Nootens, *Partner*
Ryan Dutcher, *Graphic Designe*
Jonathan Ayor, *Engineer*
EMP: 35
SQ FT: 22,000
SALES (est): 7.9MM **Privately Held**
SIC: 3679 Electronic circuits; hermetic
seals for electronic equipment

(P-19668)
OBERON CO
7216 Via Colina, San Jose (95139-1130)
PHONE..................................408 227-3730
Inez Termerson, *President*
Ian Temerson, *Manager*
EMP: 85
SALES (est): 5.2MM **Privately Held**
WEB: www.oberon.net
SIC: 3679 Electronic circuits

(P-19669)
OCG INC
17952 Lyons Cir, Huntington Beach
(92647-7167)
PHONE..................................714 375-4024
Jocelyn Lucas-Skarzenski, *President*
▲ **EMP:** 75
SALES (est): 10.5MM **Privately Held**
WEB: www.ocgconnect.com
SIC: 3679 Harness assemblies for electronic use: wire or cable

(P-19670)
OMEGA LEADS INC
Also Called: Wire Harness & Cable Assembly
1509 Colorado Ave, Santa Monica
(90404-3316)
PHONE..................................310 394-6786
Jeff Sweet Sr, *President*
Carole Faxon, *Technology*
Cynthia Gonzalez, *Technology*
EMP: 20
SQ FT: 7,200
SALES (est): 4.6MM **Privately Held**
WEB: www.omegaleads.com
SIC: 3679 Harness assemblies for electronic use: wire or cable

(P-19671)
OMNI CONNECTION INTL INC
126 Via Trevizio, Corona (92879-1772)
PHONE..................................951 898-6232
Henry Cheng, *President*
Phyllis Ting, *Vice Pres*
▲ **EMP:** 410
SQ FT: 65,000
SALES (est): 77.7MM **Privately Held**
WEB: www.omni-conn.com
SIC: 3679 Harness assemblies for electronic use: wire or cable

(P-19672)
OMNIYIG INC
3350 Scott Blvd Bldg 66, Santa Clara
(95054-3174)
PHONE..................................408 988-0843
William Capogeannis, *Ch of Bd*
Cathleen Capogeannis, *Treasurer*
Maria Rosales, *Office Mgr*
Michaela Nieblas, *Admin Asst*
EMP: 26
SQ FT: 12,000
SALES (est): 4.4MM **Privately Held**
WEB: www.omniyig.com
SIC: 3679 Microwave components

(P-19673)
ONSHORE TECHNOLOGIES INC
2771 Plaza Dl Amo 802-8, Torrance
(90503)
PHONE..................................310 533-4888
Max Van Orden, *President*
EMP: 25
SALES (est): 5.9MM **Privately Held**
SIC: 3679 Harness assemblies for electronic use: wire or cable

(P-19674)
OPTIMUM DESIGN ASSOCIATES INC (PA)
1075 Serpentine Ln Ste A, Pleasanton
(94566-4809)
PHONE..................................925 401-2004
Nick A Barbin, *CEO*
Roger Hileman, *CFO*
Harold Carpenter, *Vice Pres*
Everett Frank, *General Mgr*
Clinton Gann, *Engineer*
◆ EMP: 76
SQ FT: 22,000
SALES (est): 20MM **Privately Held**
WEB: www.optimumdesign.com
SIC: 3679 3577 8711 Electronic circuits;
computer peripheral equipment; engineering services

(P-19675)
OPTO 22
43044 Business Park Dr, Temecula
(92590-3614)
PHONE..................................951 695-3000
Mark Engman, *President*
Kathleen Roe, *Corp Secy*
Benson Hougland, *Vice Pres*
Bob Sheffres, *Vice Pres*
Jonathan Fischer, *Software Dev*
◆ EMP: 200 EST: 1974
SQ FT: 135,000
SALES (est): 54.8MM **Privately Held**
WEB: www.opto22.com
SIC: 3679 3823 3625 Electronic switches;
industrial instrmnts msrmnt display/control process variable; relays & industrial controls

(P-19676)
ORBITAL SCIENCES CORPORATION
Also Called: Space Systems Group
20 Ryan Ranch Rd Ste 214, Monterey
(93940-6439)
PHONE..................................703 406-5000
Steven Mumma, *Director*
EMP: 99 EST: 1990
SALES (est): 5.7MM **Privately Held**
SIC: 3679 Antennas, satellite: household use

(P-19677)
ORMET CIRCUITS INC
6555 Nncy Rdge Dr Ste 200, San Diego
(92121)
PHONE..................................858 831-0010
Till Langner, *CEO*
◆ EMP: 22
SQ FT: 18,000
SALES (est): 1.6MM
SALES (corp-wide): 18B **Privately Held**
SIC: 3679 Electronic circuits
HQ: Emd Performance Materials Corp.
1200 Intrepid Ave Ste 3
Philadelphia PA 19112
888 367-3275

(P-19678)
OXFORD INSTRUMENTS X-RAY TECH
Also Called: X-Ray Technology Group
360 El Pueblo Rd, Scotts Valley
(95066-4228)
PHONE..................................831 439-9729
Bernard Scanlan, *CEO*
Barbara Cabico, *Finance*
▲ EMP: 69
SQ FT: 6,600
SALES (est): 14.9MM
SALES (corp-wide): 415.9MM **Privately Held**
WEB: www.oxfordxtg.com
SIC: 3679 3844 Power supplies, all types: static; X-ray apparatus & tubes

HQ: Oxford Instruments Holdings, Inc.
600 Milik St
Carteret NJ 07008
732 541-1300

(P-19679)
PACMAG INC
Also Called: Pacific Magnetics
87 Georgina St, Chula Vista (91910-6121)
PHONE..................................619 872-0343
Mary Hill, *President*
Francisco Perez, *Engineer*
▲ EMP: 17
SALES (est): 2.8MM **Privately Held**
SIC: 3679 Electronic circuits

(P-19680)
PALOMAR DISPLAY PRODUCTS INC
5803 Newton Dr Ste C, Carlsbad
(92008-7380)
PHONE..................................760 931-3200
Paul Bell, *President*
Bill Barnard, *Info Tech Mgr*
John Gutz, *Engineer*
Amy Russo, *Human Res Dir*
EMP: 32 EST: 1997
SQ FT: 10,500
SALES (est): 7.1MM **Privately Held**
WEB: www.palomardisplays.com
SIC: 3679 Electronic switches

(P-19681)
PARTSEARCH TECHNOLOGIES INC (DH)
Also Called: Andrews Electronics
27460 Avenue Scott D, Valencia
(91355-3472)
PHONE..................................800 289-0300
Hubert Joly, *CEO*
EMP: 23
SQ FT: 10,000
SALES (est): 4.9MM
SALES (corp-wide): 42.1B **Publicly Held**
WEB: www.partsearch.com
SIC: 3679 Commutators, electronic

(P-19682)
PCH INTERNATIONAL USA INC (PA)
Also Called: Pch Lime Lab
135 Mississippi St Fl 1, San Francisco
(94107-2536)
PHONE..................................415 643-5463
William Casey, *CEO*
Sean Peters, *VP Bus Dvlpt*
Wayne Ford, *IT/INT Sup*
EMP: 22
SALES (est): 9.6MM **Privately Held**
SIC: 3679 Antennas, receiving

(P-19683)
PEAG LLC
Also Called: Jlab Audio
2281 Las Palmas Dr Rm 101, Carlsbad
(92011-1527)
PHONE..................................520 349-9371
Win Cramer, *Branch Mgr*
EMP: 10
SQ FT: 5,000
SALES (est): 1.4MM
SALES (corp-wide): 20MM **Privately Held**
SIC: 3679 Headphones, radio
PA: Peag, Llc
17950 Preston Rd Ste 360
Dallas TX 75252
858 683-3634

(P-19684)
PENUMBRA BRANDS INC
1010 S Coast Highway 101, Encinitas
(92024-5002)
PHONE..................................385 336-6120
Gentry Jensen, *CEO*
EMP: 18
SALES (est): 3.4MM **Privately Held**
SIC: 3679 Antennas, receiving

(P-19685)
PLANAR MONOLITHICS INDS INC
4921 Robert J Mathews, El Dorado Hills
(95762-5772)
PHONE..................................916 542-1401

Ashok Gorwara, *President*
EMP: 40
SQ FT: 40,000
SALES (est): 3.1MM **Privately Held**
SIC: 3679 3677 Attenuators; electronic circuits; electronic switches; oscillators; filtration devices, electronic
PA: Planar Monolithics Industries, Inc.
7311 Grove Rd Ste F
Frederick MD 21704

(P-19686)
POLARA ENGINEERING INC
9153 Stellar Ct, Corona (92883-4924)
PHONE..................................951 547-5500
John F McGaffey, *CEO*
Brian Beckwith, *CIO*
Mike Gonzales, *Engineer*
Stephen Jones, *Engineer*
Reed McKissick, *Engineer*
▲ EMP: 65 EST: 1963
SQ FT: 35,000
SALES (est): 16.3MM **Privately Held**
WEB: www.polara.com
SIC: 3679 3677 Electronic circuits; electronic coils, transformers & other inductors

(P-19687)
PPST INC (PA)
17692 Fitch, Irvine (92614-6022)
PHONE..................................800 421-1921
Kevin J Voelcker, *President*
▲ EMP: 35
SALES (est): 17.3MM **Privately Held**
SIC: 3679 Power supplies, all types: static

(P-19688)
PRB LOGICS CORP
1901 Newport Blvd Ste 350, Costa Mesa
(92627-2299)
PHONE..................................951 255-8963
Alicio Martinez, *President*
Roger Vasquez, *Sales Staff*
EMP: 17
SALES (est): 2.4MM **Privately Held**
SIC: 3679 Electronic circuits

(P-19689)
PRECISION ENGINEERING INDS
Also Called: Precision Engineering Industry
11627 Cantara St, North Hollywood
(91605-1604)
PHONE..................................818 767-8590
Greg Kellzi, *President*
▲ EMP: 15
SQ FT: 23,975
SALES (est): 1.8MM **Privately Held**
SIC: 3679 5063 Electronic circuits; burglar alarm systems

(P-19690)
PRECISION HERMETIC TECH INC
1940 W Park Ave, Redlands (92373-8042)
PHONE..................................909 381-6011
Daniel B Schachtel, *President*
Sari Schachtel, *CFO*
Ventura Mejia, *QA Dir*
Jim Padilla, *Senior Engr*
Steve Schnieder, *Human Resources*
EMP: 77
SQ FT: 25,000
SALES (est): 13.5MM **Privately Held**
WEB: www.pht.net
SIC: 3679 Hermetic seals for electronic equipment

(P-19691)
PRED TECHNOLOGIES USA INC
7855 Fay Ave Ste 310, La Jolla
(92037-4280)
PHONE..................................858 999-2114
Charles Speidel, *CEO*
EMP: 70 EST: 2016
SALES (est): 162.8K **Privately Held**
SIC: 3679 Headphones, radio

(P-19692)
PSC CIRCUITS INC
5160 Rivergrade Rd, Baldwin Park
(91706-1406)
PHONE..................................626 373-1728
Pashih Oliver Su, *President*
EMP: 30 EST: 2000

SALES (est): 2.8MM **Privately Held**
WEB: www.psccircuits.com
SIC: 3679 Electronic circuits

(P-19693)
PULSE ELECTRONICS CORPORATION (HQ)
15255 Innovation Dr # 100, San Diego
(92128-3410)
PHONE..................................858 674-8100
Mark C J Twaalfhoven, *CEO*
Ronald Fleck, *Technician*
Alan Wong, *Technology*
Amber Grove, *Marketing Mgr*
Bruce Elliott, *Sales Mgr*
▲ EMP: 65 EST: 1947
SQ FT: 50,000
SALES: 343.5MM
SALES (corp-wide): 652.7MM **Privately Held**
WEB: www.pulseelectronics.com
SIC: 3679 3612 3663 Electronic circuits;
transformers, except electric; antennas, transmitting & communications
PA: Ocm Pe Holdings, L.P.
333 S Grand Ave Fl 28
Los Angeles CA 90071
213 830-6213

(P-19694)
Q MICROWAVE INC
1591 Pioneer Way, El Cajon (92020-1637)
PHONE..................................619 258-7322
Eric Maat, *CEO*
Craig Higginson, *President*
Craig Shauan, *Vice Pres*
Rory Shauan, *Engineer*
Leah Diehl, *Purch Agent*
EMP: 65
SQ FT: 18,000
SALES (est): 10.9MM **Privately Held**
WEB: www.qmicrowave.com
SIC: 3679 5065 Microwave components;
electronic parts & equipment

(P-19695)
Q TECH CORPORATION
10150 Jefferson Blvd, Culver City
(90232-3502)
PHONE..................................310 836-7900
Kouros Sariri, *President*
Rosa Menendez, *President*
Sally Phillips, *President*
Richard Taylor, *Vice Pres*
Minh Dao, *Program Mgr*
EMP: 200
SQ FT: 21,000
SALES (est): 54.1MM **Privately Held**
WEB: www.q-tech.com
SIC: 3679 Oscillators

(P-19696)
Q-VIO LLC
10211 Pacific Mesa Blvd, San Diego
(92121-4327)
PHONE..................................858 777-8299
Ray Pronko, *Mng Member*
Joel Zettl, *CFO*
Kirk Frederick,
EMP: 15
SQ FT: 7,700
SALES: 4.5MM **Privately Held**
SIC: 3679 Liquid crystal displays (LCD)

(P-19697)
QORVO CALIFORNIA INC
Also Called: Qorvo US
950 Lawrence Dr, Newbury Park
(91320-1522)
PHONE..................................805 480-5050
Charles J Abronson, *Ch of Bd*
Mark Lampenfeld, *President*
Paul O Daughenbaugh, *CEO*
Ralph G Quinsey, *Chairman*
Susan Liles, *Treasurer*
EMP: 49 EST: 1996
SQ FT: 11,000
SALES (est): 9.7MM
SALES (corp-wide): 2.9B **Publicly Held**
WEB: www.capwireless.com
SIC: 3679 Electronic circuits
HQ: Qorvo Us, Inc.
7628 Thorndike Rd
Greensboro NC 27409
336 664-1233

▲ = Import ▼=Export
◆ =Import/Export

(P-19698)
QORVO US INC
950 Lawrence Dr, Newbury Park
(91320-1522)
PHONE..............................805 480-5099
Paul Daughenbaugh, *Branch Mgr*
EMP: 49
SALES (corp-wide): 2.9B **Publicly Held**
SIC: 3679 Electronic circuits
HQ: Qorvo Us, Inc.
7628 Thorndike Rd
Greensboro NC 27409
336 664-1233

(P-19699)
**QUALITY QUARTZ
ENGINEERING INC (PA)**
8484 Central Ave, Newark (94560-3430)
PHONE..............................510 791-1013
Scott Moseley, *CEO*
Kevin Cordia, *Exec VP*
Geri Roberts, *Purchasing*
Mike Mathewson, *Manager*
Melissa Richards, *Accounts Mgr*
▲ EMP: 24
SQ FT: 20,000
SALES (est): 10.7MM **Privately Held**
WEB: www.qqe.com
SIC: 3679 Quartz crystals, for electronic
application

(P-19700)
**QUANTUM DIGITAL
TECHNOLOGY INC**
1525 W Alton Ave, Santa Ana
(92704-7219)
PHONE..............................310 325-4949
Kaveh Ayria, *CEO*
EMP: 15
SQ FT: 3,000
SALES (est): 2.5MM **Privately Held**
WEB: www.quantumdigitaltechnology.com
SIC: 3679 Electronic crystals

(P-19701)
RADARSONICS INC
1190 N Grove St, Anaheim (92806-2109)
PHONE..............................714 630-7288
Deborah Rhea, *President*
▲ EMP: 15
SQ FT: 12,000
SALES (est): 2.3MM **Privately Held**
SIC: 3679 5099 Transducers, electrical;
firearms & ammunition, except sporting

(P-19702)
**RANTEC MICROWAVE SYSTEMS
INC**
Microwave Specialty Company
2066 Wineridge Pl, Escondido
(92029-1930)
PHONE..............................760 744-1544
Ben Walpole, *President*
Eric Robyn, *Prdtn Mgr*
EMP: 27
SALES (corp-wide): 16.6MM **Privately
Held**
SIC: 3679 Antennas, receiving; microwave
components
PA: Rantec Microwave Systems, Inc.
31186 La Baya Dr
Westlake Village CA 91362
818 223-5000

(P-19703)
RANTEC POWER SYSTEMS INC
1173 Los Olivos Ave, Los Osos
(93402-3230)
PHONE..............................805 596-6000
Michael C Bickel, *President*
Frank Janku, *CFO*
Sam Poland, *Technician*
Alan Garton, *Design Engr*
Kevin Aban, *Engineer*
EMP: 98
SQ FT: 40,000
SALES: 35.5MM
SALES (corp-wide): 33.3MM **Privately
Held**
WEB: www.rantec.com
SIC: 3679 Power supplies, all types: static
PA: Rps Holdings, Inc.
1173 Los Olivos Ave
Los Osos CA 93402
805 596-6000

(P-19704)
REEDEX INC
15526 Commerce Ln, Huntington Beach
(92649-1602)
PHONE..............................714 894-0311
Dan Reed, *President*
Ted Reed, *Vice Pres*
▲ EMP: 49
SALES (est): 9.4MM **Privately Held**
WEB: www.reedex.com
SIC: 3679 Harness assemblies for elec-
tronic use: wire or cable

(P-19705)
REGAL ELECTRONICS INC (PA)
2029 Otoole Ave, San Jose (95131-1301)
P.O. Box 60008, Sunnyvale (94088-0008)
PHONE..............................408 988-2288
Tony Lee, *President*
Madeleine Lee, *CEO*
Dr William Kunz, *Exec VP*
▲ EMP: 23
SQ FT: 26,000
SALES (est): 2.3MM **Privately Held**
WEB: www.regalusa.com
SIC: 3679 3678 3612 Electronic circuits;
electronic connectors; transformers, ex-
cept electric

(P-19706)
RELCOMM INC
4868 Highway 4 Ste G, Angels Camp
(95222)
PHONE..............................209 736-0421
Robert Henkel, *Ch of Bd*
Carolyn A Henkel, *Admin Sec*
EMP: 12
SQ FT: 8,000
SALES (est): 1.9MM **Privately Held**
SIC: 3679 Commutators, electronic

(P-19707)
**RENESAS ELECTRONICS AMER
INC (DH)**
1001 Murphy Ranch Rd, Milpitas
(95035-7912)
PHONE..............................408 432-8888
Necip Sayiner, *President*
Richard Crowley, *CFO*
Malcolm Cambra, *Bd of Directors*
Ryan Roderick, *Exec VP*
Terry Brophy, *Vice Pres*
▲ EMP: 277
SQ FT: 126,000
SALES: 542.1MM
SALES (corp-wide): 4.5B **Privately Held**
SIC: 3679 3674 Electronic circuits; inte-
grated circuits, semiconductor networks,
etc.
HQ: Renesas Electronics Corporation
3-2-24, Toyosu
Koto-Ku TKY 135-0
367 733-000

(P-19708)
RJA INDUSTRIES INC
Also Called: Automation Electronics
9640 Topanga Canyon Pl J, Chatsworth
(91311-0880)
PHONE..............................818 998-5124
Robert Aiani, *President*
Lynn Aiani, *Corp Secy*
Chris Aiani, *Vice Pres*
Sandra Acnason, *Controller*
EMP: 20 EST: 1974
SQ FT: 10,000
SALES (est): 4MM **Privately Held**
SIC: 3679 Harness assemblies for elec-
tronic use: wire or cable; electronic cir-
cuits

(P-19709)
ROCKER SOLENOID COMPANY
Also Called: Rocker Industries
1500 240th St, Harbor City (90710-1309)
PHONE..............................310 534-5660
Francis E Goodyear, *CEO*
Raymond Hatashita, *Chairman*
Milton A Mather, *Vice Pres*
Doug Clayton, *Information Mgr*
Berlyn Perry, *Contract Mgr*
▼ EMP: 70 EST: 1954
SQ FT: 23,000

SALES (est): 18.1MM **Privately Held**
WEB: www.rockerindustries.com
SIC: 3679 Solenoids for electronic applica-
tions

(P-19710)
ROGAR MANUFACTURING INC
Also Called: Ro Gar Mfg
866 E Ross Ave, El Centro (92243-9652)
PHONE..............................760 335-3700
Pat Lewis, *Principal*
EMP: 126
SALES (corp-wide): 17.6MM **Privately
Held**
SIC: 3679 Electronic circuits
PA: Rogar Manufacturing Incorporated
1520 Montague Expy
San Jose CA 95131
408 894-9800

(P-19711)
ROMAN KRUCHOWHY
6486 Palomino Cir, Somis (93066-9740)
PHONE..............................805 386-7939
Roman Kruchowy, *Principal*
EMP: 10
SALES: 120K **Privately Held**
SIC: 3679 Electronic components

(P-19712)
ROTECH ENGINEERING INC
1020 S Melrose St Ste A, Placentia
(92870-7169)
PHONE..............................714 632-0532
Ralph Ono, *President*
EMP: 20
SQ FT: 10,000
SALES (est): 5.6MM **Privately Held**
WEB: www.rotech-busbar.com
SIC: 3679 Electronic circuits

(P-19713)
RTIE HOLDINGS LLC
1800 E Via Burton, Anaheim (92806-1213)
PHONE..............................714 765-8200
Mark Schelbert,
Jonathan Smith,
EMP: 80
SALES (est): 7.2MM **Privately Held**
SIC: 3679 Electronic circuits

(P-19714)
S & C PRECISION INC
5045 Calmview Ave, Baldwin Park
(91706-1802)
PHONE..............................626 338-7149
Jose Sanchez, *President*
EMP: 10
SQ FT: 3,000
SALES: 1,000K **Privately Held**
SIC: 3679 3721 3599 Microwave compo-
nents; aircraft; machine shop, jobbing &
repair

(P-19715)
SAFE ENVIRONMENT ENGRG LP
28474 Westinghouse Pl, Valencia
(91355-0929)
PHONE..............................661 295-5500
David Lamensdorf, *Managing Prtnr*
Jack Boone, *Vice Pres*
Sue Springer, *VP Mktg*
EMP: 10
SQ FT: 3,000
SALES (est): 1.8MM **Privately Held**
WEB: www.safeenv.com
SIC: 3679 7629 5084 Electronic circuits;
electrical repair shops; safety equipment

(P-19716)
**SAGER ELECTRICAL SUPPLY
CO INC**
Sager Power System
2390 Owen St, Santa Clara (95054-3210)
PHONE..............................408 588-1750
Paul Christiansen, *Production*
EMP: 15
SALES (corp-wide): 242.1B **Publicly
Held**
SIC: 3679 Power supplies, all types: static
HQ: Sager Electrical Supply Company Inc.
19 Leona Dr
Middleboro MA 02346
508 923-6600

(P-19717)
**SANDBERG INDUSTRIES INC
(PA)**
Also Called: E M S
2921 Daimler St, Santa Ana (92705-5810)
PHONE..............................949 660-9473
J Sandberg, *CEO*
Steve Walker, *President*
John T Sandberg, *Treasurer*
Leo Boarts, *Vice Pres*
Becky Tamblyn, *Admin Sec*
EMP: 52
SQ FT: 30,000
SALES (est): 13.4MM **Privately Held**
SIC: 3679 3825 3672 3643 Electronic cir-
cuits; test equipment for electronic & elec-
trical circuits; printed circuit boards;
current-carrying wiring devices

(P-19718)
SAS MANUFACTURING INC
405 N Smith Ave, Corona (92880-6905)
PHONE..............................951 734-1808
Theo F Smit Jr, *CEO*
Sharon Smit, *Vice Pres*
Harold E Welsh, *Purchasing*
EMP: 45
SQ FT: 24,000
SALES (est): 8.5MM **Privately Held**
WEB: www.sasmanufacturing.com
SIC: 3679 Harness assemblies for elec-
tronic use: wire or cable

(P-19719)
SCEPTRE INC
Also Called: E-Scepter
16800 Gale Ave, City of Industry
(91745-1804)
PHONE..............................626 369-3698
Stephen Liu, *CEO*
Kieu Dao, *Marketing Mgr*
▲ EMP: 50
SALES (est): 11.6MM **Privately Held**
WEB: www.sceptre.com
SIC: 3679 Liquid crystal displays (LCD)

(P-19720)
SCHNEIDER ELECTRIC IT USA
Also Called: APC By Scheineder Electric
1660 Scenic Ave, Costa Mesa
(92626-1410)
PHONE..............................714 513-7313
Alex Aguilar, *Branch Mgr*
Tai Lam, *CIO*
Mike Habibi, *Technology*
Paul Marchand, *Technical Staff*
Rodolfo Reyna, *Engineer*
EMP: 450
SALES (corp-wide): 200.4K **Privately
Held**
SIC: 3679 Power supplies, all types: static
HQ: Schneider Electric It Usa, Inc.
132 Fairgrounds Rd
West Kingston RI 02892

(P-19721)
SEASONIC ELECTRONICS INC
301 Aerojet Ave, Azusa (91702)
PHONE..............................626 969-9966
Hsiu-Cheng Chang, *CEO*
Vincent Chang, *Principal*
Annie Chang, *Accountant*
Zoe Liu, *Accounts Mgr*
▲ EMP: 14
SALES (est): 2.2MM **Privately Held**
WEB: www.seasonic.com
SIC: 3679 Electronic loads & power sup-
plies

(P-19722)
SECURITY PEOPLE INC
Also Called: Digilock
9 Willowbrook Ct, Petaluma (94954-6507)
PHONE..............................707 766-6000
Asil Gokcebay, *CEO*
Bill Gordon, *President*
Stephanie Becker, *Marketing Staff*
▲ EMP: 30
SALES (est): 11.9MM **Privately Held**
WEB: www.digilock.com
SIC: 3679 Electronic circuits

PRODUCTS & SVCS

(P-19723)
SENSATA TECHNOLOGIES INC
Also Called: BEI Duncan
1461 Lawrence Dr, Thousand Oaks
(91320-1303)
PHONE..............805 968-0782
Philippe Roux, *Branch Mgr*
EMP: 125
SALES (corp-wide): 2.7MM **Privately Held**
SIC: 3679 Electronic circuits; quartz crystals, for electronic application; transducers, electrical
HQ: Sensata Technologies, Inc.
529 Pleasant St
Attleboro MA 02703
508 236-3800

(P-19724)
SIGNATURE TECH GROUP INC
Also Called: A & A Electronic Assembly
11960 Borden Ave, San Fernando
(91340-1808)
PHONE..............818 890-7611
Victor Castro, *Owner*
EMP: 20
SQ FT: 10,000
SALES (est): 2.4MM **Privately Held**
SIC: 3679 3672 Electronic circuits; printed circuit boards

(P-19725)
SINKPAD LLC
511 Princeland Ct, Corona (92879-1383)
PHONE..............714 660-2944
Kris K Vasoya, *President*
Kris Vasoya, *Officer*
Tushar Patel, *Exec VP*
Abdul Aslami, *Sales Staff*
Sam Bhayani,
EMP: 10
SQ FT: 11,500
SALES: 3.2MM **Privately Held**
SIC: 3679 Antennas, receiving

(P-19726)
SKYWORKS SOLUTIONS INC
5221 California Ave, Irvine (92617-3073)
PHONE..............949 231-3000
Bruce Raymond, *Manager*
Mike Cuenco, *Info Tech Mgr*
Jeremy Goodrich, *Design Engr*
Jeffrey Moffett, *Engng Exec*
EMP: 100
SALES (corp-wide): 3.8B **Publicly Held**
WEB: www.alphaind.com
SIC: 3679 3674 3663 3264 Microwave components; antennas, receiving; semiconductor diodes & rectifiers; diodes, solid state (germanium, silicon, etc.); transistors; wafers (semiconductor devices); microwave communication equipment; antennas, transmitting & communications; mobile communication equipment; ferrite & ferrite parts; filtering media, pottery
PA: Skyworks Solutions, Inc.
20 Sylvan Rd
Woburn MA 01801
781 376-3000

(P-19727)
SL POWER ELECTRONICS CORP (PA)
6050 King Dr Ste A, Ventura (93003-7176)
PHONE..............800 235-5929
Jim Taylor, *President*
Ken Owens, *CEO*
Karim Alhusseini, *Vice Pres*
Steven Miller, *Vice Pres*
Donald Baldwin, *Technology*
▲ EMP: 65 EST: 1978
SQ FT: 36,480
SALES (est): 167.6MM **Privately Held**
SIC: 3679 Power supplies, all types: static

(P-19728)
SMITHS INTRCNNECT AMERICAS INC
1550 Scenic Ave, Costa Mesa
(92626-1420)
PHONE..............714 371-1100
Dom Matos, *President*
Sandra Mariscal, *Project Mgr*
Shannon Durr, *Marketing Staff*
EMP: 300

SALES (corp-wide): 4.1B **Privately Held**
SIC: 3679 Microwave components
HQ: Smiths Interconnect Americas, Inc.
5101 Richland Ave
Kansas City KS 66106
913 342-5544

(P-19729)
SMT MFG INCORPORATAED
970 S Loyola Dr, Anaheim (92807-5111)
PHONE..............714 738-9999
Abid Ali Mirza, *CEO*
EMP: 20
SALES (est): 2.3MM **Privately Held**
WEB: www.smtmfg.com
SIC: 3679 Electronic circuits

(P-19730)
SO-CAL VALUE ADDED LLC
809 Calle Plano, Camarillo (93012-8516)
PHONE..............805 389-5335
Marco Muniz Day, *Vice Pres*
EMP: 35
SALES: 4MM **Privately Held**
SIC: 3679 3643 Harness assemblies for electronic use: wire or cable; current-carrying wiring devices

(P-19731)
SORA POWER INC (PA)
1141 Olympic Dr, Corona (92881-3391)
PHONE..............951 479-9880
Ramesh Patel, *CEO*
Remy Lacroix, *Vice Pres*
▲ EMP: 10 EST: 1956
SALES: 5MM **Privately Held**
WEB: www.sorapower.com
SIC: 3679 Electronic circuits

(P-19732)
SOUTH BAY CIRCUITS INC
210 Hillsdale Ave, San Jose (95136-1392)
PHONE..............408 978-8992
EMP: 164
SALES (corp-wide): 70.7MM **Privately Held**
SIC: 3679
PA: South Bay Circuits, Inc.
99 N Mckemy Ave
Chandler AZ 85226
480 940-3125

(P-19733)
SPARTON IRVINE LLC
Also Called: Electronic Manufacturing Tech
2802 Kelvin Ave Ste 100, Irvine
(92614-5897)
PHONE..............949 855-6625
Michael Wayne Leedom, *President*
Leah Dupre, *Vice Pres*
Rodger Lee, *Vice Pres*
Samuel Varela, *Engineer*
EMP: 75
SQ FT: 30,000
SALES (est): 30.5MM
SALES (corp-wide): 374.9MM **Publicly Held**
WEB: www.emtllc.com
SIC: 3679 Harness assemblies for electronic use: wire or cable
HQ: Sparton Emt, Llc
425 N Martingale Rd Ste 2
Schaumburg IL 60173
800 772-7866

(P-19734)
STANDARD CRYSTAL CORP
17626 Barber Ave, Artesia (90701-3832)
PHONE..............626 443-2121
James Zhang, *President*
EMP: 10
SQ FT: 12,300
SALES (est): 1.3MM **Privately Held**
WEB: www.standardcrystalcorp.com
SIC: 3679 5065 Oscillators; electronic crystals; electronic parts & equipment

(P-19735)
STARLED INC
2059 E Del Amo Blvd, Rancho Dominguez
(90220-6131)
PHONE..............310 603-0403
Andres Alvarez, *President*
David Cheselske, *Treasurer*
Luis Lemus, *Sales Engr*
Joseph Mikolli, *Sales Staff*

Alma Mejia, *Advisor*
EMP: 18
SQ FT: 4,500
SALES (est): 2.7MM **Privately Held**
WEB: www.starled.com
SIC: 3679 Electronic circuits

(P-19736)
STATEK CORPORATION (HQ)
512 N Main St, Orange (92868-1182)
PHONE..............714 639-7810
Brian McCarthy, *President*
Michael Dastmalchian, *Co-President*
Gary Engel, *Admin Asst*
Patricia Ramsey, *Administration*
Dr Shih S Chuang, *CTO*
▲ EMP: 52 EST: 1970
SQ FT: 71,000
SALES (est): 30.3MM
SALES (corp-wide): 75.8MM **Privately Held**
WEB: www.statek.com
SIC: 3679 Electronic circuits; quartz crystals, for electronic application; oscillators
PA: Technicorp International Ii, Inc.
512 N Main St
Orange CA 92868
714 639-7810

(P-19737)
STEWART AUDIO (HQ)
100 W El Camino Real # 72, Mountain View
(94040-2664)
PHONE..............209 588-8111
Richard Otte, *President*
Tom Kritzer, *President*
Brian McCormick, *Chief Mktg Ofcr*
Chris Pugh, *Vice Pres*
Kevin Stone, *General Mgr*
▲ EMP: 14
SQ FT: 3,000
SALES (est): 7.6MM
SALES (corp-wide): 20.7MM **Privately Held**
WEB: www.stewartaudio.com
SIC: 3679 8711 3651 Recording & playback apparatus, including phonograph; designing: ship, boat, machine & product; household audio & video equipment
PA: Promex Industries, Incorporated
3075 Oakmead Village Dr
Santa Clara CA 95051
408 496-0222

(P-19738)
STRIKE TECHNOLOGY INC
Also Called: Wilorco
24311 Wilmington Ave, Carson
(90745-6139)
PHONE..............562 437-3428
Robert Kunesh, *Ch of Bd*
John Hofland, *General Mgr*
Raul Vera, *Engineer*
Manuk Hilda, *Opers Mgr*
John Cardall, *Sales Staff*
EMP: 25 EST: 2001
SQ FT: 9,800
SALES (est): 5.1MM **Privately Held**
WEB: www.striketechnology.com
SIC: 3679 Static power supply converters for electronic applications

(P-19739)
SUPPORT SYSTEMS INTL CORP
Also Called: Fiber Optic Cable Shop
136 S 2nd St Dept B, Richmond
(94804-2110)
PHONE..............510 234-9090
Ben G Parsons, *President*
Richard St John, *Vice Pres*
▼ EMP: 65
SQ FT: 15,000
SALES (est): 7.3MM **Privately Held**
WEB: www.support-systems-intl.com
SIC: 3679 Harness assemblies for electronic use: wire or cable

(P-19740)
SURE POWER INC
Also Called: Martek Power
1111 Knox St, Torrance (90502-1034)
PHONE..............310 542-8561
Maricela Sanchez, *Branch Mgr*
Michael Ibanez, *General Mgr*
Rene San Pedro, *MIS Mgr*
Adam Shapley, *Controller*

Bob Duarte, *Natl Sales Mgr*
EMP: 44 **Privately Held**
WEB: www.martekpower.com
SIC: 3679 Power supplies, all types: static
HQ: Sure Power, Inc.
10955 Sw Avery St
Tualatin OR 97062
503 692-5360

(P-19741)
SYSTRON DONNER INERTIAL INC
2700 Systron Dr, Concord (94518-1399)
PHONE..............925 979-4400
Eric Pilaud, *President*
Mark Collins, *Technology*
Lawrence Pizzella, *Electrical Engi*
Tony Rios, *Engineer*
Shi Tien, *Engineer*
EMP: 117
SALES (est): 4.1MM
SALES (corp-wide): 20.7MM **Privately Held**
SIC: 3679 3829 Electronic circuits; accelerometers
PA: Innovista Sensors Americas, Inc.
2945 Townsgate Rd Ste 200
Westlake Village CA 91361
805 267-7176

(P-19742)
T S MANUFACTURING INC
24926 State Highway 108, Mi Wuk Village
(95346-9714)
PHONE..............209 586-1025
Janice Sue Olson, *President*
EMP: 75
SALES (est): 4.2MM **Privately Held**
SIC: 3679 3672 Static power supply converters for electronic applications; printed circuit boards

(P-19743)
TANGO SYSTEMS INC
1980 Concourse Dr, San Jose
(95131-1719)
PHONE..............408 526-2330
Ravi Mullapudi, *CEO*
EMP: 52
SQ FT: 15,000
SALES (est): 14MM **Privately Held**
SIC: 3679 3641 Attenuators; lamps, vapor

(P-19744)
TDK ELECTRONICS INC
11770 Bernardo Plaza Ct, San Diego
(92128-2422)
PHONE..............858 485-4640
Cliff Zatz, *Principal*
EMP: 10
SALES (corp-wide): 11.9B **Privately Held**
SIC: 3679 5065 3546 Electronic crystals; diskettes, computer; power-driven handtools; grinders, portable: electric or pneumatic
HQ: Tdk Electronics Inc.
485b Us Highway 1 S # 200
Iselin NJ 08830
732 906-4300

(P-19745)
TDK-LAMBDA AMERICAS INC
401 Mile Of Cars Way # 325, National City
(91950-6614)
PHONE..............619 575-4400
Pascal Shauson, *CEO*
Vinod Bapat, *President*
George Bees, *President*
Ian Pawloski, *Program Mgr*
David Gutierrez, *Senior Mgr*
EMP: 200
SALES (corp-wide): 11.9B **Privately Held**
WEB: www.lambdapower.com
SIC: 3679 Power supplies, all types: static
HQ: Tdk-Lambda Americas Inc.
405 Essex Rd
Tinton Falls NJ 07753
732 922-9300

(P-19746)
TE CONNECTIVITY LTD
Also Called: Te Circuit Protection
305 Constitution Dr, Menlo Park
(94025-1110)
PHONE..............650 361-4923
Thomas J Lynch, *CEO*

Terrence Curtin, *President*
Joe Donahue, *COO*
Mario Calastri, *CFO*
John Jenkins, *Exec VP*
EMP: 47
SALES (est): 8.6MM
SALES (corp-wide): 1.2B **Publicly Held**
SIC: 3679 Electronic circuits
PA: Littelfuse, Inc.
8755 W Higgins Rd Ste 500
Chicago IL 60631
773 628-1000

(P-19747)
TECH ELECTRONIC SYSTEMS INC
592 E State St, Ontario (91761-1727)
PHONE................909 986-4395
Robert B Contreras, *CEO*
Jack Merrick, *Opers Mgr*
EMP: 15
SQ FT: 14,000
SALES (est): 2.9MM **Privately Held**
WEB: www.techelectronicsys.com
SIC: 3679 3499 Liquid crystal displays (LCD); locks, safe & vault: metal

(P-19748)
TEK ENTERPRISES INC
7730 Airport Bus Pkwy, Van Nuys (91406)
PHONE................818 785-5971
Tek T Tjia, *President*
Amy Tjia, *COO*
Anthony Fredrick, *Vice Pres*
EMP: 31
SALES (est): 2.7MM **Privately Held**
SIC: 3679 3621 Harness assemblies for electronic use: wire or cable; coils, for electric motors or generators

(P-19749)
TELEDYNE DEFENSE ELEC LLC
Teledyne Relays
12525 Daphne Ave, Hawthorne (90250-3308)
PHONE................323 777-0077
Hamid Emami, *Manager*
An Trinh, *Research*
Kien Trinh, *Research*
John Jouwsma, *Engineer*
Jack Shropshire, *Engineer*
EMP: 107
SQ FT: 86,000
SALES (corp-wide): 2.6B **Publicly Held**
WEB: www.teledyne.com
SIC: 3679 Microwave components
HQ: Teledyne Defense Electronics, Llc
1274 Terra Bella Ave
Mountain View CA 94043
650 691-9800

(P-19750)
TELEDYNE DEFENSE ELEC LLC
Also Called: Teledyne Reynolds
1001 Knox St, Torrance (90502-1030)
PHONE................310 823-5491
Jim McCosky, *Manager*
Tacko Sakho, *Engineer*
Dianna German, *Manager*
EMP: 14
SQ FT: 4,500
SALES (corp-wide): 2.6B **Publicly Held**
WEB: www.teledynereynolds.com
SIC: 3679 Microwave components
HQ: Teledyne Defense Electronics, Llc
1274 Terra Bella Ave
Mountain View CA 94043
650 691-9800

(P-19751)
TELEDYNE DEFENSE ELEC LLC
Also Called: Teledyne Microwave Solutions
11361 Sunrise Park Dr, Rancho Cordova (95742-6587)
PHONE................916 638-3344
Bob Dipple, *Branch Mgr*
David A Zavadil, *Vice Pres*
Russell Shaller, *General Mgr*
Pete Hradecky, *Info Tech Mgr*
Mary Mason, *Technology*
EMP: 200

SALES (corp-wide): 2.6B **Publicly Held**
SIC: 3679 3672 3663 3651 Microwave components; printed circuit boards; radio & TV communications equipment; household audio & video equipment; traveling wave tubes
HQ: Teledyne Defense Electronics, Llc
1274 Terra Bella Ave
Mountain View CA 94043
650 691-9800

(P-19752)
TELEDYNE DEFENSE ELEC LLC (HQ)
Also Called: Teledyne Microwave Solutions
1274 Terra Bella Ave, Mountain View (94043-1820)
PHONE................650 691-9800
Richard Palilonis, *CEO*
Dana Fogle, *Info Tech Mgr*
Brandi Cannon, *Human Res Dir*
Patti Goldsmith, *Buyer*
Val Terry, *Mfg Staff*
▲ **EMP:** 25
SALES: 104MM
SALES (corp-wide): 2.6B **Publicly Held**
SIC: 3679 Microwave components
PA: Teledyne Technologies Inc
1049 Camino Dos Rios
Thousand Oaks CA 91360
805 373-4545

(P-19753)
TELEDYNE TECHNOLOGIES INC
Also Called: Teledyne Controls
501 Continental Blvd, El Segundo (90245-5036)
PHONE................310 765-3600
Masood Hassan, *Vice Pres*
Joe Allen, *President*
Sherrel Smith, *Admin Asst*
Marybell Moreno, *Administration*
Wanda Bose, *Info Tech Mgr*
EMP: 300
SALES (corp-wide): 2.6B **Publicly Held**
WEB: www.teledyne.com
SIC: 3679 8731 3812 3519 Electronic circuits; commercial physical research; search & navigation equipment; internal combustion engines
PA: Teledyne Technologies Inc
1049 Camino Dos Rios
Thousand Oaks CA 91360
805 373-4545

(P-19754)
TELEDYNE TECHNOLOGIES INC
3350 Moore St, Los Angeles (90066-1704)
P.O. Box 25964 (90025-0964)
PHONE................310 820-4616
Kim Rosol, *Branch Mgr*
Jody Glasser, *President*
EMP: 300
SALES (corp-wide): 2.6B **Publicly Held**
SIC: 3679 Electronic circuits
PA: Teledyne Technologies Inc
1049 Camino Dos Rios
Thousand Oaks CA 91360
805 373-4545

(P-19755)
TELEDYNE TECHNOLOGIES INC (PA)
1049 Camino Dos Rios, Thousand Oaks (91360-2362)
PHONE................805 373-4545
Robert Mehrabian, *Ch of Bd*
George C Bobb III, *President*
Janice L Hess, *President*
Aldo Pichelli, *President*
Michael Read, *President*
EMP: 250
SALES: 2.6B **Publicly Held**
WEB: www.teledyne.com
SIC: 3679 3761 3519 3724 Electronic circuits; guided missiles & space vehicles; internal combustion engines; gasoline engines; engines, diesel & semi-diesel or dual-fuel; aircraft engines & engine parts; research & development on aircraft engines & parts; aircraft control systems, electronic; navigational systems & instruments; semiconductors & related devices

(P-19756)
TELEDYNE TECHNOLOGIES INC
12964 Panama St, Los Angeles (90066)
PHONE................310 822-8229
Bruce Gecks, *Manager*
Matthew Bakker, *President*
Sam Calvillo, *President*
Jody Glasser, *President*
Carl Adams, *Vice Pres*
EMP: 360
SALES (corp-wide): 2.6B **Publicly Held**
WEB: www.teledyne.com
SIC: 3679 Electronic circuits
PA: Teledyne Technologies Inc
1049 Camino Dos Rios
Thousand Oaks CA 91360
805 373-4545

(P-19757)
TELEDYNE WIRELESS LLC
Also Called: Teledyne Microwave Solutions
1274 Terra Bella Ave, Mountain View (94043-1820)
PHONE................650 691-9800
Daniel Cheadle Sr, *Branch Mgr*
EMP: 107
SALES (corp-wide): 2.6B **Publicly Held**
SIC: 3679 Microwave components
HQ: Teledyne Defense Electronics, Llc
1274 Terra Bella Ave
Mountain View CA 94043
650 691-9800

(P-19758)
TELEDYNE WIRELESS LLC
11361 Sunrise Park Dr, Rancho Cordova (95742-6587)
PHONE................916 638-3344
EMP: 111
SALES (corp-wide): 2.3B **Publicly Held**
SIC: 3679
HQ: Teledyne Wireless, Llc
1274 Terra Bella Ave
Mountain View CA 94043
650 691-9800

(P-19759)
TEMPO AUTOMATION INC
2460 Alameda St, San Francisco (94103)
PHONE................415 320-1261
Jeffrey McAlvay, *CEO*
Jesse Koenig, *COO*
Daniel Radler, *Opers Staff*
Christine Pearsall, *VP Mktg*
EMP: 35
SQ FT: 2,000
SALES (est): 1.4MM **Privately Held**
SIC: 3679 Electronic circuits

(P-19760)
TERADYNE INC
30701 Agoura Rd, Agoura Hills (91301-5928)
PHONE................818 991-2900
Greg Beecher, *Manager*
Hoa Phan, *Exec VP*
Lori Dunn, *Executive*
Joel Justin, *Info Tech Mgr*
Alan Hussey, *Design Engr*
EMP: 290
SALES (corp-wide): 2.1B **Publicly Held**
WEB: www.teradyne.com
SIC: 3679 Electronic circuits
PA: Teradyne, Inc.
600 Riverpark Dr
North Reading MA 01864
978 370-2700

(P-19761)
THERMAL ELECTRONICS INC
403 W Minthorn St, Lake Elsinore (92530-2801)
P.O. Box 5000 (92531-5000)
PHONE................951 674-3555
David Zackerson, *CEO*
Gerald Barnes, *Shareholder*
James Mikesell, *President*
Butch Noll, *President*
David McCullagh, *CFO*
EMP: 15 **EST:** 1977
SQ FT: 10,000
SALES (est): 4.2MM **Privately Held**
WEB: www.thermalelectronics.com
SIC: 3679 Electronic circuits

(P-19762)
THIN FILM ELECTRONICS INC
Also Called: NFC Innovation Center
2581 Junction Ave, San Jose (95134-1923)
PHONE................408 503-7300
Peter Fischer, *CEO*
EMP: 70 **EST:** 2011
SQ FT: 61,000
SALES: 18.6MM
SALES (corp-wide): 5.9MM **Privately Held**
SIC: 3679 Electronic circuits
PA: Thin Film Electronics Asa
Henrik Ibsens Gate 100
Oslo 0255
232 751-59

(P-19763)
THOMPSON MAGNETICS INC
Also Called: Auto Doctor
42255 Baldaray Cir Ste C, Temecula (92590-3632)
P.O. Box 2019 (92593-2019)
PHONE................951 676-0243
Howard M Thompson Sr, *Ch of Bd*
Betty J Thompson, *Corp Secy*
David Thompson, *Vice Pres*
Howard M Thompson Jr, *Vice Pres*
EMP: 14 **EST:** 1969
SQ FT: 16,000
SALES: 2.7MM **Privately Held**
SIC: 3679 7538 Cores, magnetic; general automotive repair shops

(P-19764)
TNP INSTRUMENTS INC
119 Star Of India Ln, Carson (90746-1415)
PHONE................310 532-2222
Vu Tran, *President*
EMP: 14
SQ FT: 5,000
SALES: 1.4MM **Privately Held**
WEB: www.tnpinstruments.com
SIC: 3679 5065 Liquid crystal displays (LCD); electronic parts & equipment

(P-19765)
TOSHIBA AMERICA ELECTRONIC
2610 Orchard Pkwy, San Jose (95134-2020)
PHONE................408 526-2400
Larry Jordon, *Principal*
EMP: 50
SALES (corp-wide): 37B **Privately Held**
SIC: 3679 8731 3674 Electronic circuits; commercial physical research; semiconductors & related devices
HQ: Toshiba America Electronic Components Inc
5231 California Ave
Irvine CA 92617
949 462-7700

(P-19766)
TOWERJAZZ TEXAS INC (PA)
4321 Jamboree Rd, Newport Beach (92660-3007)
PHONE................949 435-8000
Rex Edwards, *Principal*
EMP: 68 **EST:** 2015
SALES (est): 34.4MM **Privately Held**
SIC: 3679 Electronic circuits

(P-19767)
TRAK MICROWAVE CORPORATION
Also Called: Channel Microwave
375 Conejo Ridge Ave, Thousand Oaks (91361-4928)
PHONE................805 267-0100
Ken Boswell, *Manager*
Serge Taylor, *President*
EMP: 14
SALES (corp-wide): 4.1B **Privately Held**
SIC: 3679 Microwave components
HQ: Trak Microwave Corporation
4726 Eisenhower Blvd
Tampa FL 33634
813 901-7200

(P-19768)
TRANSDUCER TECHNIQUES LLC
42480 Rio Nedo, Temecula (92590-3734)
PHONE..................................951 719-3965
Randy A Baker, *Mng Member*
Gary Mann, *Systems Mgr*
EMP: 37
SQ FT: 27,000
SALES (est): 8.8MM **Privately Held**
WEB: www.ttloadcells.com
SIC: 3679 Electronic circuits; transducers, electrical; loads, electronic

(P-19769)
TRANSKO ELECTRONICS INC
3981 E Miraloma Ave, Anaheim (92806-6201)
PHONE..................................714 528-8000
Ae Duk Chun, *CEO*
Jimmy Tim, *Opers Mgr*
▲ **EMP:** 12
SQ FT: 7,000
SALES (est): 2.2MM **Privately Held**
WEB: www.transko.com
SIC: 3679 Electronic loads & power supplies; oscillators; electronic crystals

(P-19770)
TRI TEK ELECTRONICS INC
25358 Avenue Stanford, Valencia (91355-1214)
PHONE..................................661 295-0020
James Gillson, *President*
Josie Gillson, *CFO*
Anthony Lopez, *Principal*
Joe Fattrusso, *Purch Mgr*
EMP: 40
SQ FT: 22,000
SALES (est): 8.1MM **Privately Held**
WEB: www.tri-tekelectronics.com
SIC: 3679 Harness assemblies for electronic use: wire or cable; electronic circuits

(P-19771)
TRI-MAG INC
1601 Clancy Ct, Visalia (93291-9253)
Rural Route 4079 (93278)
PHONE..................................559 651-2222
Jia Ming LI, *Ch of Bd*
▲ **EMP:** 27
SQ FT: 27,000
SALES (est): 3.8MM **Privately Held**
WEB: www.tri-mag.com
SIC: 3679 3677 Electronic switches; filtration devices, electronic

(P-19772)
TRUE CIRCUITS INC
4300 El Camino Real # 200, Los Altos (94022-1090)
PHONE..................................650 949-3400
Stephen Maneatis, *CEO*
EMP: 10
SALES (est): 1.5MM **Privately Held**
WEB: www.truecircuits.com
SIC: 3679 8711 Electronic circuits; engineering services

(P-19773)
TRUE VISION DISPLAYS INC
16402 Berwyn Rd, Cerritos (90703-2440)
PHONE..................................562 407-0630
Steven H Yu, *CEO*
▲ **EMP:** 12
SQ FT: 30,460
SALES (est): 2MM **Privately Held**
SIC: 3679 Liquid crystal displays (LCD)

(P-19774)
TURTLE BEACH CORPORATION (PA)
11011 Via Frontera Ste A, San Diego (92127-1752)
PHONE..................................914 345-2255
Juergen Stark, *President*
Ronald Doornink, *Ch of Bd*
John T Hanson, *CFO*
Andrew Wolfe, *Bd of Directors*
Rodney Schutt, *Senior VP*
▲ **EMP:** 221
SQ FT: 30,000
SALES: 149.1MM **Publicly Held**
SIC: 3679 Parametric amplifiers

(P-19775)
TXC TECHNOLOGY INC (HQ)
451 W Lambert Rd Ste 201, Brea (92821-3920)
PHONE..................................714 990-5510
Peter Wan Shing Lin, *President*
Lou Lee, *CEO*
Jennifer Tsai, *Administration*
EMP: 12
SQ FT: 1,900
SALES (est): 1.2MM
SALES (corp-wide): 291.7MM **Privately Held**
SIC: 3679 Electronic circuits
PA: Txc Corporation
      4 F, No. 16, Sec. 2, Zhongyang S. Rd.,
      Taipei City TAP 11270
      228 941-202

(P-19776)
U S CIRCUIT INC
2071 Wineridge Pl, Escondido (92029-1931)
PHONE..................................760 489-1413
Michael Fariba, *President*
Mukesh Patel, *Vice Pres*
T J Sojitra, *Vice Pres*
Rupal Sojitra, *General Mgr*
Connie Wolff, *Human Resources*
EMP: 80
SQ FT: 40,000
SALES (est): 14.4MM **Privately Held**
WEB: www.uscircuit.com
SIC: 3679 3672 Electronic circuits; printed circuit boards

(P-19777)
UNIQUIFY INC
2030 Fortune Dr Ste 200, San Jose (95131-1835)
PHONE..................................408 235-8810
Josh Lee, *CEO*
Kevin Lau, *President*
Jung Ho Lee, *President*
Sam Kim, *COO*
Ras R Sheffield, *CFO*
EMP: 50
SALES (est): 9.2MM **Privately Held**
SIC: 3679 Electronic circuits

(P-19778)
US ETA INC
Also Called: Eta USA
16170 Vineyard Blvd # 180, Morgan Hill (95037-5498)
PHONE..................................408 778-5875
Hiroshi Kitagawa, *CEO*
Amir Safakish, *President*
Sahar Safakish, *Engineer*
Keon Safakish, *Opers Mgr*
▲ **EMP:** 12
SQ FT: 8,000
SALES: 3MM
SALES (corp-wide): 25.9MM **Privately Held**
WEB: www.eta-usa.com
SIC: 3679 5063 Electronic switches; transformers & transmission equipment
PA: Eta Electric Industry Co., Ltd.
      2-16-10, Honhaneda
      Ota-Ku TKY 144-0
      337 457-771

(P-19779)
VANDER-BEND MANUFACTURING INC
2701 Orchard Pkwy, San Jose (95134-2008)
PHONE..................................408 245-5150
Greg Biggs, *President*
Jill De Dios, *Admin Sec*
Weng Wong, *Technology*
Mark Hoag, *Mfg Staff*
Steve Wolf, *Manager*
▲ **EMP:** 510
SQ FT: 207,000
SALES (est): 170.9MM **Privately Held**
WEB: www.vander-bend.com
SIC: 3679 3444 3549 Harness assemblies for electronic use: wire or cable; sheet metalwork; metalworking machinery

(P-19780)
VAS ENGINEERING INC
4750 Viewridge Ave, San Diego (92123-1640)
PHONE..................................858 569-1601
Rohak Vora, *CEO*
T J Sojitra, *Shareholder*
Greg Atzmiller, *Vice Pres*
Kris Yoder, *HR Admin*
▲ **EMP:** 50
SQ FT: 19,200
SALES (est): 14.3MM **Privately Held**
WEB: www.vasengineering.com
SIC: 3679 3823 Electronic circuits; harness assemblies for electronic use: wire or cable; temperature measurement instruments, industrial

(P-19781)
VASTCIRCUITS & MFG LLC
2226 Goodyear Ave Unit B, Ventura (93003-7746)
PHONE..................................805 421-4299
Erica Gonzalez-Preciado, *President*
EMP: 10
SALES (est): 398.2K **Privately Held**
SIC: 3679 Electronic circuits

(P-19782)
VERTEX LCD INC
600 S Jefferson St Ste K, Placentia (92870-6634)
P.O. Box 206 (92871-0206)
PHONE..................................714 223-7111
Gene Huh, *President*
Andy Tseng, *CFO*
Brian Yi, *Electrical Engi*
Joshua Kim, *Finance*
Mark Kim,
EMP: 35
SQ FT: 5,000
SALES (est): 6.2MM **Privately Held**
SIC: 3679 Liquid crystal displays (LCD)

(P-19783)
VICTOR WIETESKI
Also Called: Vic Company
9427 Santa Fe Springs Rd, Santa Fe Springs (90670-2622)
PHONE..................................562 946-9715
Wieteski Victor, *Owner*
Victor Wieteski, *Owner*
EMP: 15
SALES (est): 680.3K **Privately Held**
SIC: 3679 Electronic circuits

(P-19784)
VOICE ASSIST INC
Also Called: (A DEVELOPMENT STAGE COMPANY)
15 Enterprise Ste 350, Aliso Viejo (92656-2655)
PHONE..................................949 655-1611
Michael Metcalf, *Ch of Bd*
EMP: 16
SALES (est): 564.6K **Privately Held**
SIC: 3679 Voice controls

(P-19785)
WAIN INDUSTRIES
1567 Shadowglen Ct, Westlake Village (91361-1435)
PHONE..................................805 581-5900
Michael Wainess, *President*
Ellen Wainess, *Corp Secy*
EMP: 14
SQ FT: 3,500
SALES (est): 1MM **Privately Held**
WEB: www.wainindustries.com
SIC: 3679 Harness assemblies for electronic use: wire or cable

(P-19786)
WAVE CIRCUITS
1260 Avenida Acaso Ste H, Camarillo (93012-8746)
PHONE..................................805 987-3008
Douglas Neuhalfen, *President*
Susan Neuhalfen, *Vice Pres*
EMP: 20
SQ FT: 14,000
SALES (est): 1.8MM **Privately Held**
SIC: 3679 3699 3672 Electronic circuits; electrical equipment & supplies; printed circuit boards

(P-19787)
WAVESTREAM CORPORATION (HQ)
545 W Terrace Dr, San Dimas (91773-2915)
PHONE..................................909 599-9080
Robert Huffman, *CEO*
Nimrod Itach, *CFO*
Francis Auricchio, *Exec VP*
Klaus Beecker, *Vice Pres*
Suzanne Martin, *Vice Pres*
EMP: 103
SQ FT: 33,000
SALES (est): 30.5MM
SALES (corp-wide): 279.5MM **Privately Held**
WEB: www.wavestream.com
SIC: 3679 8731 Microwave components; commercial physical research
PA: Gilat Satellite Networks Ltd.
      21 Yegia Kapaim
      Petah Tikva 49130
      392 520-00

(P-19788)
WELLEX CORPORATION (PA)
551 Brown Rd, Fremont (94539-7003)
PHONE..................................510 743-1818
Tzu Tai Tsai, *CEO*
Richard Fitzgerald, *President*
Jack Chen, *COO*
Edward Lin, *COO*
Jackson Wang, *Chairman*
▲ **EMP:** 108
SQ FT: 88,516
SALES (est): 38.9MM **Privately Held**
WEB: www.wellex.com
SIC: 3679 3672 Harness assemblies for electronic use: wire or cable; printed circuit boards

(P-19789)
WRIGHT TECHNOLOGIES INC
1352 Blue Oaks Blvd # 140, Roseville (95678-7028)
PHONE..................................916 773-4424
Janice Wright, *President*
Chuck Allen, *CEO*
EMP: 10
SALES (est): 950K **Privately Held**
SIC: 3679 Microwave components; radio frequency measuring equipment; electrical or electronic engineering

(P-19790)
WYVERN TECHNOLOGIES INC
1205 E Warner Ave, Santa Ana (92705-5431)
PHONE..................................714 966-0710
James J Weber, *President*
Jim Hunt, *Program Mgr*
Jim Weber, *General Mgr*
Debbie Hansen, *Office Mgr*
Carole Gordon, *Controller*
EMP: 30
SQ FT: 10,000
SALES (est): 3.7MM **Privately Held**
WEB: www.wyverncorp.com
SIC: 3679 Microwave components

(P-19791)
XCEIVE CORPORATION
3900 Freedom Cir Ste 200, Santa Clara (95054-1222)
PHONE..................................408 486-5610
Jean-Louis Bories, *President*
Alain-Serge Porret, *President*
Meryl Rains, *CFO*
George Fang, *Vice Pres*
Peter Cohn, *Admin Sec*
EMP: 45
SQ FT: 3,500
SALES (est): 6.4MM **Privately Held**
WEB: www.xceive.com
SIC: 3679 Electronic circuits

(P-19792)
XP POWER LLC (DH)
990 Benecia Ave, Sunnyvale (94085-2804)
PHONE..................................408 732-7777
Mike Laver, *Mng Member*
Frank Bidwell, *President*
Roger Bartlett, *Exec Dir*
Ngoc Vo, *Executive Asst*
Dawn Nussle, *Admin Asst*
▲ **EMP:** 60

▲ = Import ▼=Export
◆ =Import/Export

SQ FT: 58,000
SALES (est): 56.8MM **Privately Held**
SIC: **3679** Electronic loads & power supplies
HQ: Xp Power Plc
16 Horseshoe Park
Reading BERKS RG8 7
118 984-5515

(P-19793)
Z-COMMUNICATIONS INC
6779 Mesa Ridge Rd # 150, San Diego (92121-2932)
PHONE.................................858 621-2700
Zdravko Divjak, *President*
EMP: 15
SALES (corp-wide): 2.7MM **Privately Held**
SIC: **3679** Oscillators
PA: Z-Communications, Inc.
4909 Nautilus Ct N # 201
Boulder CO 80301
858 621-2700

(P-19794)
Z-TRONIX INC
6327 Alondra Blvd, Paramount (90723-3750)
PHONE.................................562 808-0800
Kamran Jahangard-Mahboob, *CEO*
Roy R Jahangard, *President*
▲ EMP: 20
SQ FT: 18,000
SALES (est): 5.3MM **Privately Held**
WEB: www.z-tronix.com
SIC: **3679** 5063 5065 Harness assemblies for electronic use: wire or cable; wire & cable; connectors, electronic

(P-19795)
ZENTEC GROUP
26190 Entp Way Ste 200, Lake Forest (92630)
PHONE.................................949 586-3609
Giles Denning, *President*
Mary Gentile, *CFO*
EMP: 10
SALES (est): 940K **Privately Held**
WEB: www.pectelusa.com
SIC: **3679** Harness assemblies for electronic use: wire or cable

---
3691 Storage Batteries

(P-19796)
AA PORTABLE POWER CORPORATION
825 S 19th St, Richmond (94804-3808)
PHONE.................................510 525-2328
Xiao Ping Jiang, *President*
Reiko Aso, *Admin Sec*
▲ EMP: 35
SQ FT: 15,000
SALES (est): 6.1MM **Privately Held**
WEB: www.aaportablepower.com
SIC: **3691** Storage batteries

(P-19797)
ADARA POWER INC
15466 Los Gatos Blvd # 109351, Los Gatos (95032-2542)
PHONE.................................844 223-2969
Neil Maguire, *CEO*
Greg Maguire, *Vice Pres*
◆ EMP: 11
SQ FT: 5,000
SALES: 320K **Privately Held**
SIC: **3691** Storage batteries

(P-19798)
BATTERY TECHNOLOGY INC (PA)
Also Called: B T I
16651 E Johnson Dr, City of Industry (91745-2413)
PHONE.................................626 336-6878
Christopher Chu, *President*
Andy Tong, *Vice Pres*
Scott Carlson, *CTO*
Banry Chu, *Manager*
Andy Leung, *Consultant*
▲ EMP: 62
SQ FT: 20,000

SALES (est): 7.5MM **Privately Held**
WEB: www.batterytech.com
SIC: **3691** Storage batteries

(P-19799)
CALEB TECHNOLOGY CORPORATION
2905 Lomita Blvd, Torrance (90505-5106)
PHONE.................................310 257-4780
Thomas S Lin, *President*
Lily W Lin, *Treasurer*
EMP: 20
SQ FT: 14,000
SALES (est): 279.9K **Privately Held**
WEB: www.caleb-battery.com
SIC: **3691** Batteries, rechargeable

(P-19800)
COMPONENT CONCEPTS LLC
1732 Ord Way, Oceanside (92056-1501)
PHONE.................................760 722-9559
Chuck Eshom, *CEO*
Dan Perry, *Accounts Exec*
▲ EMP: 14
SALES (est): 3.3MM **Privately Held**
WEB: www.componentconcepts.com
SIC: **3691** Batteries, rechargeable

(P-19801)
EAST PENN MANUFACTURING CO
2920 Ramco St, West Sacramento (95691-6404)
PHONE.................................916 374-9965
EMP: 14
SALES (corp-wide): 2.5B **Privately Held**
SIC: **3691** Storage batteries
PA: East Penn Manufacturing Co.
102 Deka Rd
Lyon Station PA 19536
610 682-6361

(P-19802)
ENERGY SALES LLC (PA)
2030 Ringwood Ave, San Jose (95131-1728)
PHONE.................................503 690-9000
Kathryn Wilke, *President*
Valerie Franco, *Vice Pres*
▲ EMP: 36 EST: 1972
SQ FT: 8,100
SALES (est): 6.4MM **Privately Held**
WEB: www.energy-sales.com
SIC: **3691** 5063 5065 Storage batteries; batteries; electronic parts & equipment

(P-19803)
ENERSYS
30069 Ahern Ave, Union City (94587-1234)
PHONE.................................510 887-8080
Tom Larkin, *Branch Mgr*
EMP: 15
SALES (corp-wide): 2.5B **Publicly Held**
SIC: **3691** Lead acid batteries (storage batteries)
PA: Enersys
2366 Bernville Rd
Reading PA 19605
610 208-1991

(P-19804)
ENERSYS
5580 Edison Ave, Chino (91710-6936)
PHONE.................................909 464-8251
Ken Hill, *Branch Mgr*
EMP: 88
SALES (corp-wide): 2.5B **Publicly Held**
SIC: **3691** Lead acid batteries (storage batteries)
PA: Enersys
2366 Bernville Rd
Reading PA 19605
610 208-1991

(P-19805)
ENERVAULT CORPORATION
1100 La Avenida St Ste A, Mountain View (94043-1453)
PHONE.................................408 636-7519
Ron Mosso, *CEO*
Denis Giorno, *Ch of Bd*
Thomas E Colson, *COO*
Thomas Jahn, *CFO*
Craig Horne, *Officer*
▲ EMP: 14

SALES (est): 3MM **Privately Held**
SIC: **3691** Storage batteries

(P-19806)
ENEVATE CORPORATION
101 Theory Ste 200, Irvine (92617-3089)
PHONE.................................949 243-0399
Robert A Rango, *President*
John B Kennedy, *CFO*
Sameer V RAO, *CFO*
Heidi Houghton, *Officer*
Jarvis Tou, *Exec VP*
▲ EMP: 43
SQ FT: 17,000
SALES (est): 9.8MM **Privately Held**
SIC: **3691** Storage batteries

(P-19807)
EXIDE TECHNOLOGIES
345 Cessna Cir Ste 101, Corona (92880-2519)
PHONE.................................951 520-0677
Adam Sicre, *Manager*
EMP: 25
SALES (corp-wide): 2.6B **Privately Held**
WEB: www.exideworld.com
SIC: **3691** Storage batteries
PA: Exide Technologies
13000 Deerfield Pkwy # 200
Milton GA 30004
678 566-9000

(P-19808)
FIRST LITHIUM LLC
17244 S Main St, Carson (90749)
PHONE.................................310 489-6266
Dazhe Wong, *Mng Member*
EMP: 10
SALES (est): 308.9K **Privately Held**
SIC: **3691** Storage batteries

(P-19809)
FLUX POWER HOLDINGS INC (PA)
985 Poinsettia Ave Ste A, Vista (92081-8416)
PHONE.................................877 505-3589
Ronald F Dutt, *President*
Christopher L Anthony, *Ch of Bd*
EMP: 29
SQ FT: 22,054
SALES: 4.1MM **Publicly Held**
SIC: **3691** 5063 Storage batteries; batteries, rechargeable; storage batteries, industrial

(P-19810)
GOLD PEAK INDS N AMER INC
Also Called: GP Batteries
11245 W Bernardo Ct # 104, San Diego (92127-1676)
PHONE.................................858 674-6099
Edward Lam, *CEO*
Cindy Huth, *CFO*
Harold Decker, *Opers Mgr*
Vincent Cheung, *Marketing Mgr*
Larry Allen, *Sales Mgr*
▲ EMP: 40 EST: 2000
SALES (est): 6.9MM
SALES (corp-wide): 813.3MM **Privately Held**
WEB: www.gpina.com
SIC: **3691**
HQ: Gold Peak Industries (Taiwan) Ltd.
211, Chung Cheng Rd., Sec. 2,
Hukou Hsiang HSI
359 927-11

(P-19811)
INDUSTRIAL BATTERY ENGRG INC
Also Called: I B E
9121 De Garmo Ave, Sun Valley (91352-2697)
PHONE.................................818 767-7067
Birger Holmquist, *CEO*
Michael Sloan, *President*
Javier Sanchez, *Corp Secy*
Ralph Holanov, *Vice Pres*
Derek Sloan, *Vice Pres*
EMP: 30
SQ FT: 20,000
SALES (est): 5.9MM **Privately Held**
WEB: www.ibe-inc.com
SIC: **3691** 3629 Storage batteries; electronic generation equipment

(P-19812)
M B S INC
Also Called: Accu Rack
18514 Yorba Linda Blvd, Yorba Linda (92886-4179)
PHONE.................................714 693-9952
EMP: 13
SALES (corp-wide): 1.7MM **Privately Held**
SIC: **3691** Storage batteries
PA: M B S Inc
1961 E Miraloma Ave Ste D
Placentia CA 92870
714 693-9952

(P-19813)
POWERSTORM HOLDINGS INC
Also Called: Powerstorm Ess
31244 Palos Verdes Dr W # 245, Rancho Palos Verdes (90275-5370)
PHONE.................................424 327-2991
Michel J Freni, *Ch of Bd*
Shailesh Upreti, *Vice Pres*
Wendy Ito, *Executive Asst*
EMP: 12
SQ FT: 2,000
SALES: 128.9K **Privately Held**
SIC: **3691** 4911 5063 Storage batteries; ; ; storage batteries, industrial

(P-19814)
SEEO INC
3906 Trust Way, Hayward (94545-3716)
PHONE.................................510 782-7336
Hal Zarem, *President*
Hany Eitouni, *Vice Pres*
▲ EMP: 17
SALES (est): 4.7MM
SALES (corp-wide): 261.7MM **Privately Held**
SIC: **3691** Storage batteries
HQ: Robert Bosch Llc
2800 S 25th Ave
Broadview IL 60155
248 876-1000

(P-19815)
SIMPLIPHI POWER INC
420 Bryant Cir Ste A-B, Ojai (93023-4209)
PHONE.................................805 640-6700
Catherine Von Burg, *CEO*
Edwin F Moore, *President*
Bill Sechrest, *CFO*
Stuart Lennox, *Officer*
▲ EMP: 12
SQ FT: 5,300
SALES (est): 3MM **Privately Held**
SIC: **3691** Storage batteries

(P-19816)
TELEDYNE TECHNOLOGIES INC
Also Called: Teledyne Battery Products
840 W Brockton Ave, Redlands (92374-2902)
P.O. Box 7950 (92375-1150)
PHONE.................................909 793-3131
Greg Donahey, *Branch Mgr*
Amanda Haines, *Admin Asst*
Jerri Lorsbach, *Admin Asst*
Barbara Cathey, *Administration*
Judy Taylor, *Administration*
EMP: 58
SALES (corp-wide): 2.6B **Publicly Held**
WEB: www.teledyne.com
SIC: **3691** 3692 Storage batteries; primary batteries, dry & wet
PA: Teledyne Technologies Inc
1049 Camino Dos Rios
Thousand Oaks CA 91360
805 373-4545

(P-19817)
TENERGY CORPORATION
Also Called: All-Battery.com
436 Kato Ter, Fremont (94539-8332)
PHONE.................................510 687-0388
Xiangbing LI, *CEO*
Ling Ch Liang, *Admin Sec*
Lydia Del Real, *Accounts Mgr*
▲ EMP: 90
SALES (est): 18.7MM **Privately Held**
SIC: **3691** 5063 Alkaline cell storage batteries; batteries

---

(P-19818)
VYCON INC
16323 Shoemaker Ave # 600, Cerritos (90703-2244)
PHONE..................562 282-5500
Vatche Artinian, *CEO*
Frank Delattre, *President*
Ken Demirjian, *COO*
Patrick T McMullen, *CTO*
▲ EMP: 52
SQ FT: 38,000
SALES (est): 10.5MM
SALES (corp-wide): 22MM **Privately Held**
SIC: 3691 Storage batteries
PA: Calnetix, Inc.
16323 Shoemaker Ave
Cerritos CA 90703
562 293-1660

(P-19819)
ZEROBASE ENERGY LLC
Also Called: Zero Base
46609 Fremont Blvd, Fremont (94538-6410)
PHONE..................888 530-9376
Steve Hogge, *President*
Roger Rose, *Vice Pres*
Nancy Kuncaitis, *Opers Mgr*
Wayne Labrie, *Production*
Mark Lucas, *Sales Staff*
EMP: 22
SALES: 5.5MM **Privately Held**
SIC: 3691 3699 4911 Storage batteries; generators, ultrasonic;

3692 Primary Batteries: Dry & Wet

(P-19820)
B & B BATTERY (USA) INC (PA)
6415 Randolph St, Commerce (90040-3511)
PHONE..................323 278-1900
Jack Liu, *President*
George Liu, *Vice Pres*
Byron Close, *Sales Staff*
David Liu, *Manager*
▲ EMP: 20
SQ FT: 20,000
SALES (est): 15.3MM **Privately Held**
WEB: www.bb-battery.com
SIC: 3692 Primary batteries, dry & wet

(P-19821)
CONCORDE BATTERY CORP (PA)
2009 W San Bernardino Rd, West Covina (91790-1006)
PHONE..................626 813-1234
Donald W Godber, *President*
Glenn Hollett, *Vice Pres*
Coral Ferguson, *General Mgr*
Greg Gomez, *Info Tech Mgr*
Anthony Tapia, *Info Tech Mgr*
▲ EMP: 27
SQ FT: 36,000
SALES (est): 23MM **Privately Held**
WEB: www.concordebattery.com
SIC: 3692 Dry cell batteries, single or multiple cell

(P-19822)
PRIMUS POWER CORPORATION
3967 Trust Way, Hayward (94545-3723)
PHONE..................510 342-7600
Thomas Stepien, *CEO*
Jorg Heinemann, *Officer*
Richard Winter, *CTO*
Ken Balish, *Engineer*
Mark Collins, *Opers Staff*
EMP: 50
SALES (est): 14.7MM **Privately Held**
SIC: 3692 Primary batteries, dry & wet

(P-19823)
QUALLION LLC
12744 San Fernando Rd # 100, Sylmar (91342-3854)
PHONE..................818 833-2000
Alfred E Mann,
Jackie York, *CFO*
▲ EMP: 155
SALES (est): 40.1MM
SALES (corp-wide): 2.5B **Publicly Held**
WEB: www.quallion.com
SIC: 3692 Primary batteries, dry & wet
PA: Enersys
2366 Bernville Rd
Reading PA 19605
610 208-1991

(P-19824)
SHORAI INC
16020 Caputo Dr 100, Morgan Hill (95037-5521)
PHONE..................408 720-8821
David Radford, *Ch of Bd*
James McCormick, *President*
Phuc Lam, *Exec VP*
Kevin Riley, *Exec VP*
Marianne Guarena, *Cust Mgr*
▲ EMP: 15
SQ FT: 10,000
SALES: 10MM **Privately Held**
SIC: 3692 Primary batteries, dry & wet

(P-19825)
TROJAN BATTERY COMPANY LLC (PA)
10375 Slusher Dr, Santa Fe Springs (90670-3748)
PHONE..................800 423-6569
Neil Thomas, *President*
John Beering, *COO*
Edward Dunlap, *CFO*
Dave Godber, *Exec VP*
Mike Everett, *Senior VP*
◆ EMP: 365 EST: 1925
SQ FT: 160,000
SALES (est): 207.9MM **Privately Held**
WEB: www.trojan-battery.com
SIC: 3692 3691 Primary batteries, dry & wet; lead acid batteries (storage batteries)

3694 Electrical Eqpt For Internal Combustion Engines

(P-19826)
ALTERNATORS STARTERS ETC
Also Called: Auto Lectrics
1360 White Oaks Rd Ste H, Campbell (95008-6749)
PHONE..................408 559-3540
Muhammed Osman, *President*
EMP: 12
SQ FT: 2,500
SALES (est): 1.9MM **Privately Held**
WEB: www.autolectrics.com
SIC: 3694 Automotive electrical equipment

(P-19827)
AST POWER LLC
54 Coral Reef, Newport Coast (92657-1904)
PHONE..................949 226-2275
Ali Navid, *Mng Member*
◆ EMP: 20
SQ FT: 2,500
SALES (est): 1.7MM **Privately Held**
SIC: 3694 2834 3841 2086 Engine electrical equipment; pharmaceutical preparations; surgical & medical instruments; mineral water, carbonated: packaged in cans, bottles, etc.; computer software development & applications

(P-19828)
BARRETT ENGINEERING INC
Also Called: Racemate Alternators
1725 Burton St, San Diego (92111-7001)
PHONE..................858 256-9194
John Barrett, *President*
Kay Barrett, *Corp Secy*
EMP: 15
SQ FT: 4,000
SALES: 300K **Privately Held**
WEB: www.racemate.com
SIC: 3694 5531 Alternators, automotive; speed shops, including race car supplies

(P-19829)
BATTERY-BIZ INC
Also Called: Ebatts.com
1380 Flynn Rd, Camarillo (93012-8016)
PHONE..................805 437-7777
Ophir Marish, *CEO*
Yossi Jakubovits, *Admin Sec*
▲ EMP: 63
SQ FT: 60,000
SALES (est): 14.1MM **Privately Held**
WEB: www.batterybiz.net
SIC: 3694 Battery charging generators, automobile & aircraft

(P-19830)
DSM&T CO INC
10609 Business Dr, Fontana (92337-8212)
PHONE..................909 357-7960
Sergio Corona, *CEO*
Marco Granados, *Engineer*
▲ EMP: 170 EST: 1982
SQ FT: 41,000
SALES (est): 45.9MM **Privately Held**
WEB: www.dsmt.com
SIC: 3694 3357 3634 3643 Harness wiring sets, internal combustion engines; nonferrous wiredrawing & insulating; heating pads, electric; connectors, electric cord

(P-19831)
ELECTRICAL REBUILDERS SLS INC (PA)
Also Called: Vapex-Genex-Precision
1559 W 134th St, Gardena (90249-2215)
PHONE..................323 249-7545
Mike Klapper, *President*
Mary Ann Klapper, *Corp Secy*
David Klapper, *Vice Pres*
▲ EMP: 75
SQ FT: 90,000
SALES (est): 7.2MM **Privately Held**
SIC: 3694 3592 3714 Distributors, motor vehicle engine; carburetors; motor vehicle brake systems & parts

(P-19832)
ENGINE ELECTRONICS INC
Also Called: Compu-Fire
12155 Pangborn Ave, Downey (90241-5624)
P.O. Box 189, La Verne (91750-0189)
PHONE..................562 803-1700
Lewis Hemphill, *President*
EMP: 10
SQ FT: 17,000
SALES: 2.6MM **Privately Held**
WEB: www.compufire.com
SIC: 3694 Engine electrical equipment

(P-19833)
GENER8 LLC
500 Mercury Dr, Sunnyvale (94085-4018)
PHONE..................650 940-9898
David Louis Klein, *CEO*
William Bischel, *General Mgr*
Julie Dupre, *Office Mgr*
James Quigley, *Software Engr*
Daniel Chandler, *VP Engrg*
▲ EMP: 130
SQ FT: 16,000
SALES (est): 23.3MM **Privately Held**
WEB: www.gener8.net
SIC: 3694 7389 Engine electrical equipment; personal service agents, brokers & bureaus

(P-19834)
HTK AUTOMOTIVE USA CORP
Also Called: Decoded USA
5218 Rivergrade Rd, Irwindale (91706-1336)
PHONE..................888 998-9366
Karim Boumajdi, *President*
EMP: 18
SQ FT: 21,000
SALES: 41.7MM **Privately Held**
SIC: 3694 Automotive electrical equipment

(P-19835)
INTERNATIONAL RES DEV CORP NEV (PA)
Also Called: IRD
5212 Chelsea St, La Jolla (92037-7910)
PHONE..................858 488-9900
Robert E Kane, *President*
Anthony Renda, *Vice Pres*
▲ EMP: 15
SALES (est): 1.5MM **Privately Held**
SIC: 3694 Automotive electrical equipment

(P-19836)
JAPAN ENGINE INC
1951 Williams St, San Leandro (94577-2303)
PHONE..................510 532-7878
Yu Feng Lin, *CEO*
Michael Yi, *Principal*
◆ EMP: 20
SALES (est): 4.3MM **Privately Held**
SIC: 3694 Engine electrical equipment

(P-19837)
JET PERFORMANCE PRODUCTS INC
Also Called: Jet Transmission
17491 Apex Cir, Huntington Beach (92647-5728)
PHONE..................714 848-5500
Bryant Seller, *President*
Dan Nicholas, *Mktg Dir*
Dannette Rayburn,
EMP: 25
SQ FT: 8,500
SALES (est): 4.1MM **Privately Held**
WEB: www.jetchip.com
SIC: 3694 3714 Automotive electrical equipment; motor vehicle parts & accessories

(P-19838)
MAXWELL TECHNOLOGIES INC (PA)
3888 Calle Fortunada, San Diego (92123-1825)
PHONE..................858 503-3300
Franz Fink, *President*
Steven Bilodeau, *Ch of Bd*
David Lyle, *CFO*
Everett Wiggins, *Vice Pres*
EMP: 277
SQ FT: 30,500
SALES: 130.3MM **Publicly Held**
WEB: www.maxwell.com
SIC: 3694 3629 Engine electrical equipment; capacitors & condensers; capacitors, a.c., for motors or fluorescent lamp ballasts; capacitors, fixed or variable; power conversion units, a.c. to d.c.: static-electric

(P-19839)
MITSUBISHI ELC AUTO AMER INC
5800 Skylab Rd, Huntington Beach (92647-2054)
PHONE..................714 902-1900
Ted Katashima, *General Mgr*
Gregory Kimmons, *Opers Mgr*
Michael Burk, *QC Mgr*
EMP: 45
SALES (corp-wide): 41.5B **Privately Held**
SIC: 3694 Automotive electrical equipment; alternators, automotive
HQ: Mitsubishi Electric Automotive America, Inc.
4773 Bethany Rd
Mason OH 45040
513 573-6614

(P-19840)
NGK SPARK PLUGS (USA) INC
68 Fairbanks, Irvine (92618-1602)
P.O. Box 30745, Los Angeles (90030-0745)
PHONE..................949 580-2639
Mark Pratt, *Branch Mgr*
EMP: 25
SALES (corp-wide): 3.8B **Privately Held**
SIC: 3694 Ignition apparatus & distributors
HQ: Ngk Spark Plugs (U.S.A.), Inc.
46929 Magellan
Wixom MI 48393
248 926-6900

(P-19841)
NRG EVGO
11390 W Olympic Blvd Fl 2, Los Angeles (90064-1607)
PHONE..................310 268-8017
EMP: 16 EST: 2013

SALES (est): 3.6MM **Privately Held**
SIC: **3694** Battery charging generators, automobile & aircraft

(P-19842)
ORIGINAL DISTRIBUTOR EXCHANGE
2538 E 52nd St, Huntington Park (90255-2501)
PHONE..................................323 583-8707
Jose Luis Veloz, *Owner*
EMP: 12 EST: 1975
SQ FT: 3,000
SALES (est): 1.2MM **Privately Held**
SIC: **3694** 3621 Automotive electrical equipment; generators, automotive & aircraft; distributors, motor vehicle engine; starters, for motors

(P-19843)
PARTS OUT INC (PA)
Also Called: Ats International
1875 Century Park E # 2200, Los Angeles (90067-2337)
PHONE..................................626 560-1540
Siong Tan, *President*
▲ EMP: 15 EST: 2001
SQ FT: 100,000
SALES: 6MM **Privately Held**
SIC: **3694** Distributors, motor vehicle engine

(P-19844)
PERTRONIX INC
Also Called: Patriot Products
15601 Cypress Ave Unit B, Irwindale (91706-2120)
PHONE..................................909 599-5955
Jack Porter, *Manager*
EMP: 40
SALES (corp-wide): 13.8MM **Privately Held**
WEB: www.pertronix.com
SIC: **3694** 5013 Ignition apparatus, internal combustion engines; automotive supplies & parts
PA: Pertronix, Inc.
440 E Arrow Hwy
San Dimas CA 91773
909 599-5955

(P-19845)
PRECO AIRCRAFT MOTORS INC
1133 Mission St, South Pasadena (91030-3211)
P.O. Box 189 (91031-0189)
PHONE..................................626 799-3549
Peter Kingston Jr, *President*
Peter Kingston Sr, *Chairman*
Linda D Kingston, *Vice Pres*
EMP: 29
SQ FT: 10,000
SALES (est): 3.3MM **Privately Held**
SIC: **3694** Motors, starting: automotive & aircraft

(P-19846)
TELEMETRIA TELEPHONY TECH INC
2635 N 1st St Ste 205, San Jose (95134-2032)
PHONE..................................408 428-0101
Allen Nejah, *President*
Mike Wallach, *CFO*
EMP: 10
SALES (est): 1.1MM **Privately Held**
SIC: **3694** Engine electrical equipment

(P-19847)
TRADEMARK CONSTRUCTION CO INC (PA)
Also Called: Jmw Truss and Components
15916 Bernardo Center Dr, San Diego (92127-1828)
PHONE..................................760 489-5647
Richard D Wilson, *President*
Nancy Wilson, *Corp Secy*
John Cao, *Vice Pres*
EMP: 100
SQ FT: 12,000
SALES (est): 19.5MM **Privately Held**
WEB: www.jmwtruss.com
SIC: **3694** Engine electrical equipment

(P-19848)
TRAFFIC SENSOR CORPORATION
3205 Pomona Blvd, Pomona (91768-3233)
PHONE..................................909 468-4625
Bruce Howard, *President*
EMP: 11
SQ FT: 20,000
SALES: 1MM **Privately Held**
WEB: www.tscorp1.com
SIC: **3694** Harness wiring sets, internal combustion engines

(P-19849)
URIMAN INC (HQ)
650 N Puente St, Brea (92821-2880)
PHONE..................................714 257-2080
Kyeong Ho Lee, *CEO*
Kyung Hoon Park, *COO*
Young Hak Yun, *CFO*
◆ EMP: 122
SQ FT: 42,144
SALES (est): 26.2MM
SALES (corp-wide): 1.3B **Privately Held**
WEB: www.uriman.com
SIC: **3694** 3625 3714 Alternators, automotive; starter, electric motor; power steering equipment, motor vehicle
PA: Halla Corporation
289 Olympic-Ro, Songpa-Gu
Seoul 05510
223 434-5114

(P-19850)
VANTAGE VEHICLE INTL INC
Also Called: Vantage Vehicle Group
1740 N Delilah St, Corona (92879-1893)
PHONE..................................951 735-1200
Michael Pak, *President*
Brian Swan, *Technical Staff*
▲ EMP: 30
SQ FT: 50,000
SALES (est): 5.6MM **Privately Held**
WEB: www.vantagevehicle.com
SIC: **3694** Distributors, motor vehicle engine

(P-19851)
VEONEER US INC
Also Called: Veoneer Santa Barbara
420 S Fairview Ave, Goleta (93117-3627)
PHONE..................................805 571-1777
EMP: 47
SALES (corp-wide): 770MM **Publicly Held**
SIC: **3694** 8731 Automotive electrical equipment; electronic research
HQ: Veoneer Us, Inc.
26545 American Dr
Southfield MI 48034
248 223-8074

(P-19852)
WAN LI INDUSTRIAL DEV INC
141 Mercury Cir, Pomona (91768-3211)
PHONE..................................909 594-1818
Yanlin Zhang, *President*
▲ EMP: 10 EST: 1992
SALES (est): 1.7MM **Privately Held**
SIC: **3694** Alternators, automotive

(P-19853)
WELLS MFG USA INC
9698 Telstar Ave Ste 312, El Monte (91731-3010)
PHONE..................................626 575-2886
Jackson You, *President*
▲ EMP: 10
SQ FT: 4,000
SALES (est): 1.4MM
SALES (corp-wide): 64.1MM **Privately Held**
SIC: **3694** Engine electrical equipment
PA: Hong Kong Wells Limited
Rm 3-4 10/F Hermes Coml Ctr
Tsim Sha Tsui KLN
237 712-67

3695 Recording Media

(P-19854)
3DCD
3233 Mission Oaks Blvd, Camarillo (93012-5138)
PHONE..................................805 383-3837
John Town, *Principal*
Tim Belcher, *VP Opers*
EMP: 17
SALES: 950K **Privately Held**
SIC: **3695** Magnetic & optical recording media

(P-19855)
ALPHALOGIX INC
5811 Mcfadden Ave, Huntington Beach (92649-1323)
PHONE..................................714 901-1456
Robert D McCandless, *CEO*
EMP: 52
SALES (est): 5.1MM **Privately Held**
SIC: **3695** Computer software tape & disks: blank, rigid & floppy

(P-19856)
BERKLEY INTEGRATED AUDIO SOFTW
Also Called: B I A S
121 H St, Petaluma (94952-5125)
PHONE..................................707 782-1866
Steve Berkley, *President*
Christine Anuszkiewicz, *CFO*
Christine Berkley, *Vice Pres*
EMP: 20
SALES (est): 2.2MM **Privately Held**
WEB: www.bias-inc.com
SIC: **3695** Computer software tape & disks: blank, rigid & floppy

(P-19857)
CAMSOFT CORPORATION
32295 Mission Trl Ste 8, Lake Elsinore (92530-2305)
PHONE..................................951 674-8100
Gary J Corey, *President*
Diane Corey, *Vice Pres*
Ruben Ordonez, *Technology*
EMP: 20
SQ FT: 3,000
SALES (est): 1.5MM **Privately Held**
WEB: www.camsoftcorp.com
SIC: **3695** Computer software tape & disks: blank, rigid & floppy

(P-19858)
CD VIDEO MANUFACTURING INC
Also Called: C D Video
12650 Westminster Ave, Santa Ana (92706-2139)
PHONE..................................714 265-0770
Minh T Nguyen, *President*
Dave Nickelson, *Office Mgr*
Carmen Janusewski, *Opers Mgr*
Joe Brunatti, *Sales Staff*
Veronica Castaneda, *Sales Staff*
▲ EMP: 60
SQ FT: 11,000
SALES (est): 24MM **Privately Held**
WEB: www.cdvideomfg.com
SIC: **3695** 3652 7819 Video recording tape, blank; compact laser discs, prerecorded; services allied to motion pictures

(P-19859)
CVC AUDIO & VIDEO SUPPLY INC
425 Cheyenne Pl, Placentia (92870-1525)
PHONE..................................714 526-5725
Frank Childs, *President*
Roger Childs, *Treasurer*
Carling H Childs, *Vice Pres*
EMP: 12
SQ FT: 6,300
SALES (est): 2MM **Privately Held**
WEB: www.cvcaudiovideo.com
SIC: **3695** Audio range tape, blank; video recording tape, blank

(P-19860)
ECLIPSE DATA TECHNOLOGIES INC
5139 Johnson Dr, Pleasanton (94588-3343)
PHONE..................................925 224-8880
Kevin McDonnell, *President*
Johan De Meulder, *Vice Pres*
Carol Din, *Admin Asst*
Johnathan Dacquisto, *Engineer*
Bob Edmonds, *VP Sales*
▲ EMP: 10
SQ FT: 1,500
SALES (est): 1.5MM **Privately Held**
WEB: www.eclipsedata.com
SIC: **3695** 7371 Computer software tape & disks: blank, rigid & floppy; custom computer programming services

(P-19861)
ELECTRONIC ARTS REDWOOD INC (HQ)
Also Called: Ea Sports
209 Redwood Shores Pkwy, Redwood City (94065-1175)
PHONE..................................650 628-1500
Larry Probst, *CEO*
Daryl Holt, *Vice Pres*
EMP: 69
SALES: 2.9MM
SALES (corp-wide): 5.1B **Publicly Held**
SIC: **3695** Video recording tape, blank
PA: Electronic Arts Inc.
209 Redwood Shores Pkwy
Redwood City CA 94065
650 628-1500

(P-19862)
ELM SYSTEM INC
11622 El Carmino Real 1, San Diego (92130)
PHONE..................................408 694-2750
Ingyeom Kim, *CEO*
EMP: 18
SALES (est): 4MM **Privately Held**
SIC: **3695** Computer software tape & disks: blank, rigid & floppy

(P-19863)
ERISS
1124 Glen Ellen Pl 201, San Marcos (92078-1029)
PHONE..................................858 722-2177
Barbara Nyegaard, *Principal*
EMP: 10
SQ FT: 12,000
SALES (est): 1.4MM **Privately Held**
WEB: www.eriss.com
SIC: **3695** Computer software tape & disks: blank, rigid & floppy

(P-19864)
FARSTONE TECHNOLOGY INC
184 Technology Dr Ste 205, Irvine (92618-2435)
PHONE..................................949 336-4321
Thomas Lin, *President*
Mary Chuang, *Exec VP*
Tom Fedro, *Exec VP*
EMP: 110
SALES (est): 3.1MM
SALES (corp-wide): 208.7MM **Privately Held**
WEB: www.farstone.com
SIC: **3695** Computer software tape & disks: blank, rigid & floppy
PA: Solartech Energy Corp.
16, Guangfu N. Rd.,
Hukou Hsiang HSI 30351
352 768-88

(P-19865)
HOFFMAN MAGNETICS INC
19528 Ventura Blvd, Tarzana (91356-2917)
PHONE..................................818 717-5095
Leslie Hoffman, *CEO*
Irina Atlasmsn, *CFO*
EMP: 20
SALES (est): 1.7MM **Privately Held**
SIC: **3695**

(P-19866)
INTERMAG INC
1650 Santa Ana Ave, Sacramento
(95838-1752)
PHONE...............................916 568-6744
T C Lin, *President*
CM Chen, *CFO*
EMP: 222
SQ FT: 117,288
SALES (est): 18MM **Privately Held**
SIC: 3695 Computer software tape &
disks: blank, rigid & floppy

(P-19867)
JULY SYSTEMS INC (PA)
533 Airport Blvd Ste 395, Burlingame
(94010-2012)
PHONE...............................650 685-2460
BJ Arun, *CEO*
Rajash Reddy, *President*
Ashook Narasimhan, *Principal*
Vivek Menon, *VP Sales*
Deann Swanson, *Consultant*
EMP: 16
SALES (est): 9.5MM **Privately Held**
WEB: www.julysystems.com
SIC: 3695 Computer software tape &
disks: blank, rigid & floppy

(P-19868)
KEYIN INC
Also Called: Acca Recording Products
511 S Harbor Blvd Ste C, La Habra
(90631-9376)
P.O. Box 90533, City of Industry (91715-
0533)
PHONE...............................562 690-3888
Fax: 562 690-8788
▲ EMP: 12
SQ FT: 12,000
SALES (est): 1.9MM **Privately Held**
SIC: 3695

(P-19869)
MEDIOSTREAM INC
4962 El Camino Real # 120, Los Altos
(94022-1454)
PHONE...............................650 625-8900
Ian Xie, *Ch of Bd*
Philip F Otto, *President*
EMP: 25
SQ FT: 10,000
SALES (est): 1.9MM **Privately Held**
WEB: www.mediostream.com
SIC: 3695 Computer software tape &
disks: blank, rigid & floppy

(P-19870)
MICROTECH SYSTEMS INC
5617 Scotts Valley Dr # 100, Scotts Valley
(95066-3482)
PHONE...............................650 596-1900
Corwin Nichols, *CEO*
Michael Fallavollita, *Vice Pres*
Lance Danbe, *Executive*
Crowin Nichols, *Executive*
Victoria Nichols, *Admin Sec*
EMP: 15
SALES (est): 3.6MM **Privately Held**
WEB: www.rotech.com
SIC: 3695 Optical disks & tape, blank

(P-19871)
MONTEREY DESIGN SYSTEMS INC
2171 Landings Dr, Mountain View
(94043-0837)
PHONE...............................408 747-7370
Jacques Benkoski, *President*
Aidan Cullen, *CFO*
James Koford, *Chairman*
▲ EMP: 128 EST: 1996
SALES (est): 12.1MM **Privately Held**
SIC: 3695 5045 3675 Computer software
tape & disks: blank, rigid & floppy; com-
puter software; electronic capacitors

(P-19872)
MOTA GROUP INC (PA)
Also Called: Unorth
60 S Market St Ste 1100, San Jose
(95113-2366)
P.O. Box 1116, Campbell (95009-1116)
PHONE...............................408 370-1248
Michael Faro, *CEO*
Jeffrey L Garon, *CFO*

Lily Q Ju, *Admin Sec*
◆ EMP: 25
SALES (est): 4.7MM **Privately Held**
SIC: 3695 Computer software tape &
disks: blank, rigid & floppy

(P-19873)
MSE MEDIA SOLUTIONS
Also Called: M S E Media Solutions
6013 Scott Way, Commerce (90040-3515)
PHONE...............................323 721-1656
Michelle Cardinale, *Owner*
Francisco Arevalo, *Associate*
▲ EMP: 24
SQ FT: 14,100
SALES (est): 2MM **Privately Held**
WEB: www.msemedia.com
SIC: 3695 Video recording tape, blank

(P-19874)
NEURAL ID LLC
203 Redwood Shr Pkwy # 250, Redwood
City (94065-6103)
PHONE...............................650 394-8800
Tim Carruthers, *CEO*
Will Frederick, *CFO*
Jon Myers, *Founder*
Mike Kelly, *Engineer*
EMP: 11
SQ FT: 2,500
SALES (est): 1.5MM **Privately Held**
WEB: www.neuralid.com
SIC: 3695

(P-19875)
NORDSON CALIFORNIA INC
Also Called: Nordson Asymtek
2747 Loker Ave W, Carlsbad (92010-6601)
PHONE...............................760 918-8490
Michael F Hilton, *CEO*
Hector Pulido, *Senior VP*
Gregory A Thaxton, *Senior VP*
Robert E Veillette, *Vice Pres*
Joy Ladner, *Executive Asst*
◆ EMP: 94
SALES (est): 53.8MM
SALES (corp-wide): 2B **Publicly Held**
SIC: 3695 3561 Computer software tape &
disks: blank, rigid & floppy; pump jacks &
other pumping equipment
PA: Nordson Corporation
28601 Clemens Rd
Westlake OH 44145
440 892-1580

(P-19876)
PARALLOCITY INC
440 N Wolfe Rd, Sunnyvale (94085-3869)
PHONE...............................408 524-1530
Shekhar Ambe, *President*
David Cowan, *VP Sales*
EMP: 25 EST: 2007
SALES (est): 1.8MM **Privately Held**
SIC: 3695 Computer software tape &
disks: blank, rigid & floppy

(P-19877)
PROCESSEXCHANGE INC
25876 The Old Rd 159, Santa Clarita
(91381-1711)
PHONE...............................661 799-2548
Jeff Cohen, *President*
EMP: 20
SALES (est): 1.2MM **Privately Held**
WEB: www.process-exchange.com
SIC: 3695 Computer software tape &
disks: blank, rigid & floppy

(P-19878)
QUARTIC WEST TECHNOLOGIES
425 W 235th St, Carson (90745-5116)
PHONE...............................909 202-7038
Manny Mendoza, *Partner*
EMP: 12
SALES: 100K **Privately Held**
SIC: 3695 Instrumentation type tape, blank

(P-19879)
RECOMMIND INC (HQ)
550 Kearny St Ste 700, San Francisco
(94108-2589)
PHONE...............................415 394-7899
Steve King, *CEO*
Bernard Huger, *CFO*
David Baskin, *Vice Pres*

Keith Bernstein, *Vice Pres*
Steve Kennedy, *Vice Pres*
EMP: 100
SQ FT: 15,000
SALES: 55.2MM
SALES (corp-wide): 2.2B **Privately Held**
WEB: www.recommind.com
SIC: 3695 Computer software tape &
disks: blank, rigid & floppy
PA: Open Text Corporation
275 Frank Tompa Dr
Waterloo ON N2L 0
519 888-7111

(P-19880)
REEL PICTURE PRODUCTIONS LLC
5330 Eastgate Mall, San Diego
(92121-2804)
PHONE...............................858 587-0301
Michael Ishayik, *Mng Member*
David Smiljkovich, *CFO*
▲ EMP: 75
SQ FT: 45,000
SALES (est): 17.3MM **Privately Held**
SIC: 3695 Optical disks & tape, blank

(P-19881)
SCENEWISE INC
Also Called: Comchoice
2201 Park Pl Ste 100, El Segundo
(90245-4909)
PHONE...............................310 466-7692
Bob D Hively, *Ch of Bd*
Duncan Wain, *President*
Leslie Hively, *Corp Secy*
EMP: 70
SQ FT: 19,000
SALES (est): 6.6MM **Privately Held**
SIC: 3695 0971 Magnetic tape; game
services

(P-19882)
SONY DADC US INC
4499 Glencoe Ave, Marina Del Rey
(90292-6357)
PHONE...............................310 760-8500
Geoff Cambel, *Branch Mgr*
EMP: 30
SALES (corp-wide): 80.1B **Privately Held**
SIC: 3695 Audio range tape, blank
HQ: Sony Dadc Us Inc.
1800 N Fruitridge Ave
Terre Haute IN 47804
812 462-8100

(P-19883)
SUSTAIN TECHNOLOGIES INC (PA)
915 E 1st St, Los Angeles (90012-4050)
PHONE...............................213 229-5300
Jerry Salzman, *President*
EMP: 10
SALES: 3MM **Privately Held**
SIC: 3695 Computer software tape &
disks: blank, rigid & floppy

(P-19884)
TARGET TECHNOLOGY COMPANY LLC (PA)
564 Wald, Irvine (92618-4637)
PHONE...............................949 788-0909
Han H Nee
Stephene Nguyen, *Accountant*
Paul Maye, *Marketing Staff*
EMP: 18 EST: 2000
SALES (est): 4.4MM **Privately Held**
WEB: www.targettechnology.com
SIC: 3695 Magnetic & optical recording
media

(P-19885)
TECHNICOLOR DISC SERVICES CORP (PA)
3233 Mission Oaks Blvd, Camarillo
(93012-5097)
PHONE...............................805 445-1122
Mary Fialkowski, *President*
O F Raimondo, *Executive*
▲ EMP: 200
SQ FT: 62,000

SALES (est): 30.9MM **Privately Held**
SIC: 3695 7361 Computer software tape &
disks: blank, rigid & floppy; audio range
tape, blank; video recording tape, blank;
employment agencies

(P-19886)
THINKWAVE INC
7959 Covert Ln, Sebastopol (95472-2757)
P.O. Box 2418 (95473-2418)
PHONE...............................707 824-6200
Jim Kiriakis, *CEO*
EMP: 15
SALES (est): 1.6MM **Privately Held**
WEB: www.thinkwave.com
SIC: 3695 7371 Computer software tape &
disks: blank, rigid & floppy; custom com-
puter programming services

(P-19887)
UNITED AUDIO VIDEO GROUP INC
6855 Vineland Ave, North Hollywood
(91605-6410)
PHONE...............................818 980-6700
Miriam Newman, *President*
Lauri Newman, *Corp Secy*
Steven Newman, *Vice Pres*
Larry Schwartz, *General Mgr*
▲ EMP: 25
SQ FT: 11,500
SALES (est): 4.4MM **Privately Held**
WEB: www.unitedavg.com
SIC: 3695 5065 Audio range tape, blank;
video recording tape, blank; tapes, audio
& video recording

(P-19888)
VIDA CORPORATION
17807 Maclaren St Ste A, City of Industry
(91744-5700)
PHONE...............................626 839-4912
Eva Chang Hsu, *President*
Tony Hsu, *Vice Pres*
EMP: 30
SQ FT: 40,000
SALES (est): 314.8K **Privately Held**
SIC: 3695 5099 Magnetic tape; video
recording tape, blank; video cassettes,
accessories & supplies

(P-19889)
WD MEDIA LLC
1710 Automation Pkwy, San Jose
(95131-1873)
PHONE...............................408 576-2000
Timothy D Harris, *CEO*
Kathleen A Bayless, *CFO*
Mr Jan Schwartz, *Treasurer*
Richard A Kashnow, *Bd of Directors*
Peter S Norris, *Exec VP*
▲ EMP: 426
SQ FT: 188,000
SALES (est): 73.3MM
SALES (corp-wide): 20.6B **Publicly Held**
WEB: www.komag.com
SIC: 3695 Magnetic & optical recording
media
PA: Western Digital Corporation
5601 Great Oaks Pkwy
San Jose CA 95119
408 717-6000

(P-19890)
WEBALO INC
1990 S Bundy Dr Ste 350, Los Angeles
(90025-5257)
PHONE...............................310 828-7335
Peter Price, *CEO*
Ashish Agarwal, *Vice Pres*
Michael Berlin, *Office Mgr*
Seth Bruder, *CTO*
Pelin Ersavas, *Analyst*
EMP: 12
SQ FT: 500
SALES (est): 1.1MM **Privately Held**
SIC: 3695 Computer software tape &
disks: blank, rigid & floppy

(P-19891)
WEFEA INC
4695 Chabot Dr Ste 200, Pleasanton
(94588-2756)
PHONE...............................925 218-1839
Jay K Patel, *President*
EMP: 25

▲ = Import ▼=Export
◆ =Import/Export

SQ FT: 900
SALES: 10MM **Privately Held**
SIC: **3695** Computer software tape & disks: blank, rigid & floppy

---

3699 Electrical Machinery, Eqpt & Splys, NEC

(P-19892)
3D ROBOTICS INC (PA)
Also Called: Diy Drones
1608 4th St Ste 410, Berkeley (94710-1749)
PHONE..................................415 599-1404
Chris Anderson, *CEO*
Kailey Griffith, *Partner*
Jordi Munoz, *President*
Andy Jensen, *COO*
John Cherbini, *Vice Pres*
▲ EMP: 70 EST: 2009
SALES (est): 11.7MM **Privately Held**
SIC: **3699** Electrical equipment & supplies

(P-19893)
A T PARKER INC (PA)
Also Called: Solar Electronics Company
10866 Chandler Blvd, North Hollywood (91601-2945)
PHONE..................................818 755-1700
Tom A Parker, *President*
Jo Ann Dennis, *Vice Pres*
Sue Parker, *Asst Sec*
▼ EMP: 22
SQ FT: 7,500
SALES (est): 3.1MM **Privately Held**
WEB: www.parker-inc.com
SIC: **3699** Electrical equipment & supplies

(P-19894)
A&P CALIBRATIONS INC
6920 Koll Center Pkwy # 223, Pleasanton (94566-3156)
PHONE..................................925 417-6608
Douglas Willoughby, *President*
Chin Chu Willoughby, *Vice Pres*
EMP: 14
SALES: 1.6MM **Privately Held**
SIC: **3699** Electrical equipment & supplies

(P-19895)
AAMP OF AMERICA
2500 E Francis St, Ontario (91761-7730)
PHONE..................................805 338-6800
Dennis Hill, *Owner*
▲ EMP: 11
SALES (est): 2.1MM **Privately Held**
SIC: **3699** Electrical equipment & supplies

(P-19896)
ABB ENTERPRISES INC
Also Called: Access Security
4740 Northgate Blvd # 165, Sacramento (95834-1150)
PHONE..................................916 649-3800
Robert Hammer, *President*
Pheron Blossom, *Vice Pres*
EMP: 10
SQ FT: 2,000
SALES: 5K **Privately Held**
SIC: **3699** Security control equipment & systems

(P-19897)
ABECO ELECTRIC SERVICE INC
357 E Arrow Hwy Ste 207, San Dimas (91773-3366)
PHONE..................................909 599-7755
Jose Gerardo Arroyo, *CEO*
EMP: 22
SALES (est): 4MM **Privately Held**
SIC: **3699** Electrical equipment & supplies

(P-19898)
ACCSYS TECHNOLOGY INC
1177 Quarry Ln, Pleasanton (94566-4787)
PHONE..................................925 462-6949
Hirofumi Hiro Seki, *CEO*
Takao Kuboniwa, *President*
Glenn James, *Electrical Engi*
Steve Domingo, *Engineer*
Keenan Moore, *Engineer*
▲ EMP: 26
SQ FT: 15,400

SALES (est): 7.3MM
SALES (corp-wide): 87.9B **Privately Held**
WEB: www.linacs.com
SIC: **3699 8731 3663** Linear accelerators; commercial physical research; amplifiers, RF power & IF
PA: Hitachi, Ltd.
1-6-6, Marunouchi
Chiyoda-Ku TKY 100-0
332 581-111

(P-19899)
ADVANCED MANUFACTURING TECH
3140a E Coronado St, Anaheim (92806-1914)
PHONE..................................714 238-1488
Tom Lee, *Director*
Craig M Riedel, *CFO*
Wayne Wilson, *General Mgr*
EMP: 120
SQ FT: 54,000
SALES (est): 11.4MM
SALES (corp-wide): 2.3B **Privately Held**
WEB: www.mflex.com
SIC: **3699** Electrical equipment & supplies
HQ: Multi-Fineline Electronix, Inc.
101 Academy Ste 250
Irvine CA 92617
949 453-6800

(P-19900)
AGENTS WEST INC
Also Called: Electrical Products Rep
6 Hughes Ste 210, Irvine (92618-2063)
PHONE..................................949 614-0293
Aldo Pellicciotti, *President*
Clyde Collins, *Treasurer*
Stephen Benshoof, *Vice Pres*
Robert Rathburn, *Admin Sec*
Cherie Childers, *Marketing Mgr*
EMP: 23 EST: 1978
SQ FT: 30,000
SALES (est): 3MM **Privately Held**
SIC: **3699 5063** Electrical equipment & supplies; electrical apparatus & equipment; electrical supplies

(P-19901)
AIRPATROL CORPORATION
17 E Sir F Drake Blvd 1, Larkspur (94939)
PHONE..................................410 794-1214
Cleve Adams, *CEO*
Sage Osterfeld, *Chief Mktg Ofcr*
Barbara Bell, *Office Mgr*
Guy Levy-Yurista, *CTO*
EMP: 11
SQ FT: 2,984
SALES (est): 1.9MM
SALES (corp-wide): 45.1MM **Publicly Held**
SIC: **3699 5065** Security control equipment & systems; security devices; security control equipment & systems
PA: Inpixon
2479 E Byshore Rd Ste 195
Palo Alto CA 94303
408 702-2167

(P-19902)
AITECH DEFENSE SYSTEMS INC
19756 Prairie St, Chatsworth (91311-6531)
PHONE..................................818 700-2000
Moshe Tal, *CEO*
Erez Konfino, *CFO*
Karine Echighian, *Administration*
Richard Layne, *Technology*
Norman Butler, *Engineer*
◆ EMP: 48
SQ FT: 22,000
SALES: 15.7MM **Privately Held**
WEB: www.rugged.com
SIC: **3699** Electrical equipment & supplies
PA: Aitech Rugged Group, Inc.
19756 Prairie St
Chatsworth CA 91311

(P-19903)
AITECH RUGGED GROUP INC (PA)
19756 Prairie St, Chatsworth (91311-6531)
PHONE..................................818 700-2000
Moshe Tal, *CEO*
Erez Konfino, *CFO*
EMP: 50

SALES: 29.9MM **Privately Held**
SIC: **3699** Electrical equipment & supplies

(P-19904)
AKT AMERICA INC (HQ)
3101 Scott Blvd Bldg 91, Santa Clara (95054-3318)
PHONE..................................408 563-5455
In Doo Kang, *Vice Pres*
William Kuo, *Vice Pres*
Abhijit Chakraborty, *Software Engr*
Abhishek Mishra, *Software Engr*
Monika Taneja, *Software Engr*
▲ EMP: 400
SQ FT: 200,000
SALES: 8B
SALES (corp-wide): 14.5B **Publicly Held**
WEB: www.appliedmaterials.com
SIC: **3699** Electrical equipment & supplies
PA: Applied Materials, Inc.
3050 Bowers Ave
Santa Clara CA 95054
408 727-5555

(P-19905)
ALERTENTERPRISE INC
4350 Starboard Dr, Fremont (94538-6434)
PHONE..................................510 440-0840
Jasvir Gill, *CEO*
Kaval Kaur, *COO*
Lance Holloway, *Business Dir*
Subrat Singh, *Director*
EMP: 140
SQ FT: 24,000
SALES (est): 25.3MM **Privately Held**
SIC: **3699** Security devices

(P-19906)
ALPHA LASER
302 Elizabeth Ln, Corona (92880-2504)
PHONE..................................951 582-0285
Kaan Cakmak, *President*
Sule Cakmak, *Office Mgr*
EMP: 13
SALES (est): 1.1MM **Privately Held**
SIC: **3699** Laser welding, drilling & cutting equipment

(P-19907)
ALTA PROPERTIES INC
Also Called: Sonatech Division
879 Ward Dr, Santa Barbara (93111-2920)
PHONE..................................805 683-1431
Karen Vaughn, *Administration*
EMP: 475
SALES (corp-wide): 197.5MM **Privately Held**
WEB: www.sonatech.com
SIC: **3699** Electrical equipment & supplies
PA: Alta Properties, Inc.
879 Ward Dr
Santa Barbara CA 93111
805 967-0171

(P-19908)
ALTA PROPERTIES INC
Sonatech
879 Ward Dr, Santa Barbara (93111-2920)
PHONE..................................805 690-5382
Mark Shaw, *Vice Pres*
EMP: 475
SALES (corp-wide): 197.5MM **Privately Held**
SIC: **3699** Underwater sound equipment
PA: Alta Properties, Inc.
879 Ward Dr
Santa Barbara CA 93111
805 967-0171

(P-19909)
AMREX-ZETRON INC
Also Called: Amrex Electrotherapy Equipment
7034 Jackson St, Paramount (90723-4835)
PHONE..................................310 527-6868
George Bell, *President*
Carina Bassett, *Manager*
▲ EMP: 35
SQ FT: 20,000
SALES (est): 5.7MM **Privately Held**
WEB: www.amrex-zetron.com
SIC: **3699 3845** High-energy particle physics equipment; electromedical equipment

(P-19910)
AOPTIX TECHNOLOGIES INC
695 Campbell Tech Pkwy # 100, Campbell (95008-5076)
PHONE..................................408 558-3300
Michael Klayko, *CEO*
Dean Senner, *Ch of Bd*
Anthony Mazzarella, *President*
Earl C Charles, *CFO*
Chandrasekhar Pusarla, *Senior VP*
EMP: 65 EST: 2000
SQ FT: 12,000
SALES (est): 1.2MM **Privately Held**
WEB: www.aoptix.com
SIC: **3699** Laser systems & equipment

(P-19911)
AREESYS CORPORATION
4055 Clipper Ct, Fremont (94538-6540)
PHONE..................................510 979-9601
Kai-An Wang, *CEO*
Ning Zhao, *CFO*
EMP: 40
SALES (est): 5.5MM **Privately Held**
SIC: **3699** Electrical equipment & supplies

(P-19912)
ARM ELECTRONICS INC
8860 Industrial Ave # 140, Roseville (95678-6204)
P.O. Box 1388 (95678-8388)
PHONE..................................916 787-1100
Mark Haney, *CEO*
▲ EMP: 44
SQ FT: 45,000
SALES (est): 5MM **Privately Held**
WEB: www.armelectronics.com
SIC: **3699** Security control equipment & systems

(P-19913)
ASSA ABLOY ENTRANCE SYS US INC
Also Called: Besam Entrance Solutions
9733 Kent St 100, Elk Grove (95624-8800)
PHONE..................................916 686-4116
Jim Dill, *Branch Mgr*
EMP: 18
SALES (corp-wide): 9B **Privately Held**
SIC: **3699 1796 3442** Door opening & closing devices, electrical; installing building equipment; metal doors
HQ: Assa Abloy Entrance Systems Us Inc.
1900 Airport Rd
Monroe NC 28110
704 290-5520

(P-19914)
ASSA ABLOY ENTRANCE SYSTEMS US
Also Called: Besam Entrance Solutions
1520 S Sinclair St, Anaheim (92806-5933)
PHONE..................................714 578-0526
Erik Huber, *Branch Mgr*
EMP: 53
SALES (corp-wide): 9B **Privately Held**
SIC: **3699 1796 3442** Door opening & closing devices, electrical; installing building equipment; metal doors
HQ: Assa Abloy Entrance Systems Us Inc.
1900 Airport Rd
Monroe NC 28110
704 290-5520

(P-19915)
AVAAK INC
2200 Faraday Ave Ste 150, Carlsbad (92008-7224)
PHONE..................................858 453-9866
Gregory Drew, *CEO*
EMP: 45
SQ FT: 10,000
SALES: 1.9MM **Publicly Held**
SIC: **3699** Security control equipment & systems
PA: Netgear, Inc.
350 E Plumeria Dr
San Jose CA 95134

(P-19916)
AVIVA BIOSCIENCES CORPORATION
6330 Nncy Rdge Dr Ste 103, San Diego (92121)
PHONE....................................858 552-0888
Norrie Russell, *President*
Lei Wu PHD, *COO*
Lei Wu, *COO*
Peter Wilding, *Chairman*
Xiaobo Wang, *Surgery Dir*
EMP: 26 **EST:** 1999
SQ FT: 15,000
SALES (est): 5.8MM **Privately Held**
WEB: www.avivabio.com
SIC: 3699 Electrical equipment & supplies

(P-19917)
AXIAL INC
26022 Pala, Mission Viejo (92691-2787)
PHONE....................................949 334-6008
Jeff Johns, *President*
Ronak Jani, *Managing Dir*
George Ferris, *Mng Member*
EMP: 10
SALES (est): 1.3MM
SALES (corp-wide): 320.5MM **Privately Held**
SIC: 3699 Electric sound equipment
PA: Hobbico, Inc.
1608 Interstate Dr
Champaign IL 61822
217 398-3630

(P-19918)
AZTECH PRODUCTS INTERNATIONAL
326 10th St, Del Mar (92014-2825)
PHONE....................................858 481-8412
Chris Underhill, *President*
▲ **EMP:** 27
SALES: 2.5MM **Privately Held**
SIC: 3699 Electrical equipment & supplies

(P-19919)
BLISSLIGHTS INC
100 E San Marcos Blvd # 308, San Marcos (92069-2989)
PHONE....................................888 868-4603
Alan Lee, *President*
▲ **EMP:** 45
SALES (est): 27.7MM **Privately Held**
SIC: 3699 Laser systems & equipment

(P-19920)
BOLIDE TECHNOLOGY GROUP INC
Also Called: Bolide International
468 S San Dimas Ave, San Dimas (91773-4045)
PHONE....................................909 305-8889
David Liu, *President*
Angela Wang, *Office Mgr*
Nancy Garcilazo, *Graphic Designe*
Fiona Du, *Accountant*
Camilo Avila, *Sales Mgr*
◆ **EMP:** 70
SQ FT: 16,000
SALES (est): 11.1MM **Privately Held**
WEB: www.bolideco.com
SIC: 3699 Security devices

(P-19921)
BYRUM TECHNOLOGIES INC
550 S Pacific St Ste 100, San Marcos (92078-4058)
PHONE....................................760 744-6692
James E Byrum, *President*
Kathleen J Byrum, *Admin Sec*
EMP: 28
SQ FT: 12,000
SALES (est): 2.8MM **Privately Held**
SIC: 3699 7692 Laser welding, drilling & cutting equipment; welding repair

(P-19922)
C C T LASER SERVICES INC
25421 S Schulte Rd, Tracy (95377-9709)
PHONE....................................209 833-1110
Roger Underwood, *President*
EMP: 10
SQ FT: 10,000

SALES (est): 1.4MM **Privately Held**
WEB: www.cctlaser.com
SIC: 3699 Laser welding, drilling & cutting equipment

(P-19923)
CAL STAR SYSTEMS GROUP INC
Also Called: Quikstor
6613 Valjean Ave, Van Nuys (91406-5817)
PHONE....................................818 922-2000
Dennis Levitt, *President*
Tony Gardner, *Opers Mgr*
Shaina Cossairt, *Sales Staff*
▲ **EMP:** 22
SALES (est): 3.4MM **Privately Held**
WEB: www.quikstor.com
SIC: 3699 7371 Security devices; computer software development

(P-19924)
CARTTRONICS LLC (HQ)
8 Studebaker, Irvine (92618-2012)
PHONE....................................888 696-2278
John R French,
Donald Testa, *Vice Pres*
Rebecca Lawton, *Accountant*
Theresa Weaver, *Accountant*
▲ **EMP:** 27
SQ FT: 14,000
SALES (est): 3.4MM
SALES (corp-wide): 18.8MM **Privately Held**
WEB: www.carttronics.com
SIC: 3699 7382 5065 Security devices; security systems services; security control equipment & systems
PA: Gatekeeper Systems, Inc.
90 Icon
Foothill Ranch CA 92610
949 268-1414

(P-19925)
CED ANAHEIM 018
Also Called: California Electric Supply
1304 S Allec St, Anaheim (92805-6303)
PHONE....................................714 956-5156
Steve Richardson, *Manager*
Tom A Catullo, *Manager*
EMP: 14
SALES (est): 2.5MM **Privately Held**
SIC: 3699 5063 Electrical equipment & supplies; electrical apparatus & equipment

(P-19926)
CENTRAL TECH INC
2271 Ringwood Ave, San Jose (95131-1717)
PHONE....................................408 955-0919
EMP: 13
SALES (est): 2.7MM **Privately Held**
SIC: 3699 Electronic training devices

(P-19927)
CLEAN AMERICA INC
Also Called: EDM Performance Accessories
1400 Pioneer St, Brea (92821-3720)
PHONE....................................562 694-5990
Jim E Swartzbaugh, *President*
Tom Adams, *Vice Pres*
Anna Dominick, *Vice Pres*
Anthony Gonzalez, *Vice Pres*
Dave Liukkonen, *Sales Mgr*
▲ **EMP:** 15
SQ FT: 14,000
SALES (est): 3.8MM **Privately Held**
WEB: www.cleanup-america.com
SIC: 3699 Electrical equipment & supplies

(P-19928)
CLEAR PATH TECHNOLOGIES INC
561 W Rincon St, Corona (92880-2019)
P.O. Box 1996 (92878-1996)
PHONE....................................951 278-3520
William Nitze, *President*
Roger Spillmann, *CEO*
Andy Tabag, *Vice Pres*
EMP: 10
SALES (est): 1.4MM **Privately Held**
SIC: 3699 Fire control or bombing equipment, electronic

(P-19929)
CODA ENERGY HOLDINGS LLC
111 N Artsakh St 300, Glendale (91206-4093)
PHONE....................................626 775-3900
Paul Detering, *CEO*
Peter Nortman, *COO*
John Bryan, *Vice Pres*
Davnette Librando,
Edward Solar,
▲ **EMP:** 43
SALES (est): 8.3MM **Privately Held**
SIC: 3699 Household electrical equipment

(P-19930)
COHERENT INC
Also Called: Coherent Auburn Group, The
5100 Patrick Henry Dr, Santa Clara (95054-1112)
PHONE....................................408 764-4000
Robin Henderson, *General Mgr*
EMP: 700
SALES (corp-wide): 1.7B **Publicly Held**
SIC: 3699 3827 3674 Laser systems & equipment; optical instruments & lenses; semiconductors & related devices
PA: Coherent, Inc.
5100 Patrick Henry Dr
Santa Clara CA 95054
408 764-4000

(P-19931)
CONSTRUCTION INNOVATIONS LLC
Also Called: Ci
10630 Mather Blvd Ste 200, Mather (95655-4125)
PHONE....................................855 725-9555
Larry A Devore, *President*
James B Littlejohn, *CFO*
EMP: 150
SQ FT: 17,000
SALES: 160MM **Privately Held**
SIC: 3699 8711 Electrical equipment & supplies; consulting engineer
PA: Bdg Innovations, Llc
6001 Outfall Cir
Sacramento CA 95828
855 725-9555

(P-19932)
CONTROLLED ENTRANCES INC
27525 Valley Center Rd A, Valley Center (92082-6528)
PHONE....................................760 749-1212
Bruce Clark, *President*
Shaun Clark, *Manager*
EMP: 15
SQ FT: 6,000
SALES (est): 2.2MM **Privately Held**
WEB: www.controlledentrancesinc.com
SIC: 3699 1799 5211 Security devices; fence construction; fencing

(P-19933)
CONVERGINT TECHNOLOGIES LLC
1667 N Batavia St, Orange (92867-3508)
PHONE....................................714 546-2780
Mike Mathis, *Branch Mgr*
Alyssa Mathes, *Admin Asst*
Justin Neuberger, *Sales Engr*
EMP: 20
SALES (corp-wide): 469.1MM **Privately Held**
WEB: www.convergint.com
SIC: 3699 Security devices
PA: Convergint Technologies Llc
1 Commerce Dr
Schaumburg IL 60173
847 620-5000

(P-19934)
COZZIA USA LLC
861 S Oak Park Rd, Covina (91724-3624)
PHONE....................................626 667-2272
Mark Holmes, *COO*
Jimmy Lo, *CFO*
Loann Luu, *Accounts Mgr*
▲ **EMP:** 20
SQ FT: 5,500
SALES: 21MM
SALES (corp-wide): 648MM **Privately Held**
SIC: 3699 Electrical equipment & supplies

PA: Xiamen Comfort Science&Technology
Group Co., Ltd
No. 168 Qianpu Road, Siming District
Xiamen 36100
592 331-5392

(P-19935)
CUBIC DEFENSE APPLICATIONS INC
CMS Secure Comms
9333 Balboa Ave, San Diego (92123-1515)
PHONE....................................858 505-2870
Jerry Madigan, *Vice Pres*
EMP: 200
SALES (corp-wide): 1.4B **Publicly Held**
SIC: 3699 7382 Security devices; security systems services
HQ: Cubic Defense Applications, Inc.
9333 Balboa Ave
San Diego CA 92123
858 277-6780

(P-19936)
CUBIC DEFENSE APPLICATIONS INC (HQ)
9333 Balboa Ave, San Diego (92123-1515)
P.O. Box 85587 (92186-5587)
PHONE....................................858 277-6780
William J Toti, *CEO*
John D Thomas, *CFO*
James R Edwards, *Senior VP*
Mark A Harrison, *Senior VP*
Norman R Bishop, *Vice Pres*
▼ **EMP:** 589
SQ FT: 130,000
SALES (est): 1.3B
SALES (corp-wide): 1.4B **Publicly Held**
SIC: 3699 3663 3812 Flight simulators (training aids); electronic; radio & TV communications equipment; aircraft/aerospace flight instruments & guidance systems; navigational systems & instruments; defense systems & equipment; search & detection systems & instruments
PA: Cubic Corporation
9333 Balboa Ave
San Diego CA 92123
858 277-6780

(P-19937)
CXC SIMULATIONS LLC
3160 W El Segundo Blvd, Hawthorne (90250-4842)
PHONE....................................888 918-2010
Chris Considine,
Jochen Repolust,
EMP: 11
SALES (est): 1.3MM **Privately Held**
SIC: 3699 Flight simulators (training aids), electronic

(P-19938)
CYBER SWITCHING INC
2050 Ringwood Ave Frnt, San Jose (95131-1783)
PHONE....................................408 595-3670
Charles H Reynolds, *President*
Shelly Paiva, *CFO*
Richard Yeadon, *Vice Pres*
EMP: 25
SQ FT: 25,000
SALES (est): 4.5MM **Privately Held**
WEB: www.cyberswitching.com
SIC: 3699 Electrical equipment & supplies

(P-19939)
CYBERSWITCHINGPATENTS LLC
1921 Ringwood Ave, San Jose (95131-1721)
PHONE....................................408 436-9830
Chuck Reynolds, *Mng Member*
EMP: 13
SALES (est): 2MM **Privately Held**
SIC: 3699 Electrical equipment & supplies

(P-19940)
CYMER LLC (HQ)
Also Called: Asml Usa
17075 Thornmint Ct, San Diego (92127-2413)
PHONE....................................858 385-7300
Joost Stienen, *CEO*
Robert P Akins, *Senior VP*

▲ = Import ▼ =Export
◆ =Import/Export

Richard L Sandstrom, *Senior VP*
Geert Beullens, *Vice Pres*
Pamela Schock, *Surgery Dir*
▲ **EMP:** 555
SALES: 571MM
SALES (corp-wide): 10.6B **Privately Held**
SIC: 3699 3827 Laser systems & equipment; lens mounts
PA: Asml Holding N.V.
De Run 6501
Veldhoven 5504
402 683-000

(P-19941)
D & D SECURITY RESOURCES INC (PA)
Also Called: D&D Security Enterprises
716 Richfield Rd, Placentia (92870-6760)
PHONE..........................714 985-9409
Dean Smith, *President*
Queen Quiocho, *Executive Asst*
Aldrin Martinez, *Sales Mgr*
Jeff Rogers, *Sales Staff*
Randy Clarke, *Accounts Mgr*
▲ **EMP:** 20
SQ FT: 4,500
SALES (est): 8.5MM **Privately Held**
WEB: www.ddsecurity.com
SIC: 3699 5712 Security devices; office furniture

(P-19942)
DATA STORM INC
Also Called: Mytek America
2001 Manistee Dr, La Canada Flintridge (91011-1209)
PHONE..........................818 352-4994
Byung Woo Min, *President*
Chunghee Min, *Admin Sec*
▲ **EMP:** 13
SQ FT: 8,000
SALES (est): 1.9MM **Privately Held**
WEB: www.mytekalarms.com
SIC: 3699 5999 Security control equipment & systems; alarm signal systems

(P-19943)
DELTA TURNSTILES LLC
Also Called: Delta Turnstile Controls
1011 Detroit Ave, Concord (94518-2410)
P.O. Box 3664, Santa Clara (95055-3664)
PHONE..........................925 969-1498
Thomas Howell, *Mng Member*
Vanessa Howell, *Project Mgr*
EMP: 10
SALES (est): 1.3MM **Privately Held**
WEB: www.deltaturnstile.com
SIC: 3699 Security devices

(P-19944)
DESIGNER SOUND SEC SYSTEMS
13547 Ventura Blvd # 338, Sherman Oaks (91423-3825)
PHONE..........................818 981-9249
Anthony Stampfer, *President*
EMP: 12
SALES (est): 1.7MM **Privately Held**
SIC: 3699 7382 1731 Security control equipment & systems; security systems services; safety & security specialization

(P-19945)
DISTRIBUTION ELECTRNICS VLUED
Also Called: Deva
2651 Dow Ave, Tustin (92780-7207)
PHONE..........................714 368-1717
Rodger Dale Baker, *CEO*
Ken Plock, *Vice Pres*
▲ **EMP:** 23 **EST:** 1974
SQ FT: 13,800
SALES (est): 6MM **Privately Held**
SIC: 3699 5065 Electrical equipment & supplies; electronic parts & equipment
HQ: Deva, Inc.
450 W 15th St Ste 501
New York NY 10011
212 223-2466

(P-19946)
DIY CO
3360 20th St, San Francisco (94110-2655)
PHONE..........................844 564-6349
Zach Klein, *CEO*

EMP: 16
SALES (est): 1.6MM **Privately Held**
SIC: 3699 Teaching machines & aids, electronic
PA: Littlebits Electronics Inc.
601 W 26th St Rm M274
New York NY 10001
-

(P-19947)
DOORKING INC (PA)
120 S Glasgow Ave, Inglewood (90301-1502)
PHONE..........................310 645-0023
Thomas Richmond, *President*
Leo Montegrande, *CFO*
Pat Kochie, *Vice Pres*
Susan Richmond, *Admin Sec*
Bill Jones, *Info Tech Mgr*
◆ **EMP:** 185 **EST:** 1948
SQ FT: 16,000
SALES: 55MM **Privately Held**
WEB: www.dkaccess.com
SIC: 3699 5065 3829 Security control equipment & systems; security control equipment & systems; measuring & controlling devices

(P-19948)
DPSS LASERS INC
2525 Walsh Ave, Santa Clara (95051-1316)
PHONE..........................408 988-4300
Alex Laymon, *President*
Thomas Hogan, *CEO*
Malinna Tian, *Accounting Mgr*
Karen Wheeler, *Human Res Mgr*
Oscar Varela, *Manager*
EMP: 30
SQ FT: 25,000
SALES (est): 6.2MM **Privately Held**
WEB: www.dpss-lasers.com
SIC: 3699 Laser systems & equipment

(P-19949)
DUNAN SENSING LLC
1953 Concourse Dr, San Jose (95131-1708)
PHONE..........................408 613-1015
Tom Nguyen, *Principal*
Annie Tran, *Manager*
EMP: 14
SQ FT: 15,000
SALES: 2MM **Privately Held**
SIC: 3699 Laser welding, drilling & cutting equipment

(P-19950)
DUTEK INCORPORATED
2228 Oak Ridge Way, Vista (92081-8341)
PHONE..........................760 599-0171
David Du, *CEO*
Bill Marsh, *Vice Pres*
Dee Trabert, *Financial Exec*
Eugene Galati, *Senior Buyer*
Michael Du, *Purch Agent*
EMP: 50
SQ FT: 4,500
SALES: 9.8MM **Privately Held**
SIC: 3699 3629 3643 Electrical equipment & supplies; electronic generation equipment; current-carrying wiring devices

(P-19951)
DYNAMIC FABRICATION INC
2615 S Hickory St, Santa Ana (92707-3713)
PHONE..........................714 662-2440
Andrew Crook, *President*
Olga Garcia Crook, *Corp Secy*
EMP: 15
SQ FT: 22,000
SALES (est): 4.7MM **Privately Held**
WEB: www.dynamicfab.com
SIC: 3699 3728 3764 3761 Laser welding, drilling & cutting equipment; aircraft parts & equipment; engines & engine parts, guided missile; guided missiles & space vehicles

(P-19952)
E E SYSTEMS GROUP INC
12346 Valley Blvd Unit A, El Monte (91732-3682)
PHONE..........................626 452-8988

Randall Wang, *President*
▲ **EMP:** 12
SALES (est): 1.2MM **Privately Held**
SIC: 3699 Security devices

(P-19953)
E-FUEL CORPORATION
15466 Los Gatos Blvd 37, Los Gatos (95032-2542)
PHONE..........................408 267-2667
Thomas J Quinn, *President*
Floyd Butterfield, *Vice Pres*
Bruce Padula, *Vice Pres*
David Swanson, *Project Mgr*
Mike Mathews, *Engineer*
EMP: 32
SALES (est): 3MM **Privately Held**
SIC: 3699

(P-19954)
EASTERNCCTV (USA) LLC
110 N California Ave, City of Industry (91744-4321)
PHONE..........................626 961-8810
Xianjie Xiong, *Mng Member*
EMP: 78
SALES (corp-wide): 10.7MM **Privately Held**
SIC: 3699 Security devices
PA: Easterncctv (Usa), Llc
50 Commercial St
Plainview NY 11803
516 870-3779

(P-19955)
ECOLINK
2055 Corte Del Miguel, Carlsbad (92008)
PHONE..........................760 431-8804
Michael Lamb, *CEO*
Quinto Petrucci, *Vice Pres*
Anna Poltoratska, *Project Mgr*
Brandon Gruber, *Engineer*
▲ **EMP:** 15 **EST:** 2009
SALES (est): 1.2MM **Privately Held**
SIC: 3699 Security devices

(P-19956)
ELECTRIC GATE STORE INC (PA)
421 Park Ave, San Fernando (91340-2525)
PHONE..........................818 504-2300
Jorge Nunez, *President*
Karla Nunez, *Vice Pres*
▲ **EMP:** 150
SQ FT: 4,725
SALES (est): 18.9MM **Privately Held**
WEB: www.gatestore.com
SIC: 3699 Security devices

(P-19957)
ELECTRIC GATE STORE INC
15342 Chatsworth St, Mission Hills (91345-2041)
PHONE..........................818 361-6872
Jorge Nunez, *Branch Mgr*
EMP: 150
SALES (corp-wide): 18.9MM **Privately Held**
SIC: 3699 Security devices
PA: Electric Gate Store, Inc.
421 Park Ave
San Fernando CA 91340
818 504-2300

(P-19958)
ELECTRONIC INTERFACE CO INC
Also Called: Applied Engineering
6341 San Ignacio Ave # 10, San Jose (95119-1202)
PHONE..........................408 286-2134
Jack Yao, *President*
Katherine Nguyen, *Controller*
EMP: 75
SALES (est): 17.3MM **Privately Held**
SIC: 3699 7694 Electrical equipment & supplies; armature rewinding shops

(P-19959)
ELECTROWAVE ULTRASONICS CORP
27932 Valley Center Rd, Valley Center (92082-6546)
PHONE..........................858 695-2227
John Cottle, *General Mgr*

EMP: 27
SALES (est): 2.8MM **Privately Held**
SIC: 3699 Cleaning equipment, ultrasonic, except medical & dental

(P-19960)
ELSON ELECTRIC
3440 Vincent Rd Ste C, Pleasant Hill (94523-4380)
PHONE..........................925 464-7461
Rachel Moreno, *Principal*
EMP: 11
SALES (est): 2.7MM **Privately Held**
SIC: 3699 Electrical equipment & supplies

(P-19961)
ENVIA SYSTEMS INC
7979 Gateway Blvd Ste 101, Newark (94560-1157)
P.O. Box 14142, Fremont (94539-1342)
PHONE..........................510 509-1367
Sujeet Kumar, *President*
Michael Sinkula, *Director*
▲ **EMP:** 50 **EST:** 2007
SALES (est): 9.2MM **Privately Held**
SIC: 3699 Electrical equipment & supplies

(P-19962)
EOPLEX INC
1321 Ridder Park Dr 10, San Jose (95131-2306)
PHONE..........................408 638-5100
Arthur L Chait, *CEO*
EMP: 13
SALES (est): 1.6MM **Privately Held**
SIC: 3699 Electrical equipment & supplies

(P-19963)
EOPLEX TECHNOLOGIES INC
2940 N 1st St, San Jose (95134-2021)
PHONE..........................408 638-5100
Arthur Chait, *President*
Charles Taylor, *Founder*
Philip E Rogren, *VP Mktg*
Sean Foote, *Director*
Michio Fujimura, *Director*
▲ **EMP:** 15
SALES (est): 3MM **Privately Held**
WEB: www.eoplex.com
SIC: 3699 Electrical equipment & supplies

(P-19964)
ETON CORPORATION
1015 Corporation Way, Palo Alto (94303-4305)
PHONE..........................650 903-3866
Esmail Amid-Hozour, *President*
John Smith, *Senior VP*
Skip Orvis, *Engineer*
Winston Wang, *Engineer*
Elena Hui, *Business Mgr*
▲ **EMP:** 45
SQ FT: 10,400
SALES (est): 11.9MM **Privately Held**
WEB: www.etoncorp.com
SIC: 3699 Electrical equipment & supplies

(P-19965)
FAAC
357 S Acacia Ave Unit 357 # 357, Fullerton (92831-4748)
PHONE..........................800 221-8278
Andrea Marcellan, *Branch Mgr*
Matt Rupard, *Technician*
EMP: 10
SALES (corp-wide): 3.7MM **Privately Held**
SIC: 3699 Door opening & closing devices, electrical
PA: Faac
3160 Murrell Rd
Rockledge FL

(P-19966)
FEITIAN TECHNOLOGIES US INC
4677 Old Ironsides Dr # 312, Santa Clara (95054-1857)
PHONE..........................408 352-5553
Yu Huang, *CEO*
EMP: 10
SALES (est): 739K **Privately Held**
SIC: 3699 Security devices

(P-19967)
FLYTHISSIM TECHNOLOGIES INC
3534 Empleo St Ste B, San Luis Obispo (93401-7333)
PHONE..................................844 746-2846
Roland Nissim, *Director*
Carl Suttle, *Director*
EMP: 10
SALES (est): 714.1K **Privately Held**
SIC: 3699 Flight simulators (training aids), electronic

(P-19968)
FORMAX TECHNOLOGIES INC
Also Called: Fti
305 S Soderquist Rd, Turlock (95380-5130)
PHONE..................................209 668-1001
Ryan Lindsay, *President*
T Ryan Lindsay, *President*
Timothy D Lindsay, *CEO*
Melody Wright, *Cust Svc Dir*
▲ EMP: 35
SQ FT: 66,000
SALES (est): 5.4MM **Privately Held**
SIC: 3699 Electrical equipment & supplies

(P-19969)
FREEDOM PHOTONICS LLC
41 Aero Camino, Goleta (93117-3104)
PHONE..................................805 967-4900
Milan Mashanovitch,
Daniel Renner, *Vice Pres*
Rebekah Norris, *Admin Asst*
Brian Ehrsam, *Engineer*
Henry Garrett, *Senior Engr*
EMP: 33
SQ FT: 14,500
SALES (est): 7.3MM **Privately Held**
WEB: www.freedomphotonics.com
SIC: 3699 3827 3674 Laser systems & equipment; optical test & inspection equipment; light sensitive devices

(P-19970)
FULLER MANUFACTURING INC
130 Ridge Rd, Sutter Creek (95685)
P.O. Box 999 (95685-0999)
PHONE..................................209 267-5071
Christopher Fuller, *President*
Shirley Fuller, *Corp Secy*
EMP: 15
SQ FT: 5,000
SALES (est): 1.4MM **Privately Held**
SIC: 3699 3694 3679 Electrical equipment & supplies; automotive electrical equipment; electronic circuits

(P-19971)
FUTURE FIBRE TECH US INC (HQ)
800 W El Cam, Mountain View (94040)
PHONE..................................650 903-2222
Eric Reynolds, *Vice Pres*
Leigh Davis, *CFO*
Ricardo Abreu, *Manager*
Erick Reynolds, *Manager*
EMP: 14
SALES (est): 4MM
SALES (corp-wide): 9.6MM **Privately Held**
SIC: 3699 Security control equipment & systems
PA: Ava Risk Group Limited
10 Hartnett Cl
Mulgrave VIC 3170
395 903-100

(P-19972)
GATEKEEPER SYSTEMS INC (PA)
90 Icon, Foothill Ranch (92610-3000)
PHONE..................................949 268-1414
Michael Lawler, *CEO*
Stephen Hannah, *President*
Erik Paulson, *President*
R J Brandes, *Vice Pres*
James Auyang, *General Mgr*
◆ EMP: 35
SQ FT: 15,000
SALES (est): 18.8MM **Privately Held**
WEB: www.gatekeepersystems.com
SIC: 3699 Security devices

(P-19973)
GEFEN LLC
1800 S Mcdowell Blvd Ext, Petaluma (94954-6962)
PHONE..................................818 772-9100
Hagai Gefen, *CEO*
Tony Dowzall, *President*
Jill Gefen, *Vice Pres*
Aaron Hernandez, *Director*
Robert Lemer, *Director*
▲ EMP: 42
SQ FT: 8,000
SALES: 44MM
SALES (corp-wide): 2.7B **Privately Held**
WEB: www.gefen.com
SIC: 3699 High-energy particle physics equipment
HQ: Nortek Security & Control Llc
5919 Sea Otter Pl Ste 100
Carlsbad CA 92010
800 472-5555

(P-19974)
GEMFIRE CORPORATION
2570 N 1st St Ste 440, San Jose (95131-1018)
PHONE..................................408 519-6015
Rick Tompane, *CEO*
Carl Yordan, *CFO*
William Bischel, *Vice Pres*
EMP: 85
SQ FT: 50,000
SALES (est): 11.2MM **Privately Held**
SIC: 3699 8731 Laser systems & equipment; commercial physical research

(P-19975)
GLOBAL CUSTOM SECURITY INC
755 Lakefield Rd Ste B, Westlake Village (91361-2646)
PHONE..................................818 889-6900
Delaney Broussard, *President*
Carla Broussard, *Corp Secy*
Lisa Pickens, *Manager*
EMP: 12
SQ FT: 2,400
SALES (est): 2.4MM **Privately Held**
WEB: www.globalcustom.com
SIC: 3699 1731 Security devices; electrical work

(P-19976)
GORES RADIO HOLDINGS LLC
10877 Wilshire Blvd # 1805, Los Angeles (90024-4341)
PHONE..................................310 209-3010
Alex Gores, *President*
EMP: 1501
SALES (est): 58MM
SALES (corp-wide): 4.5B **Privately Held**
SIC: 3699 7382 Security devices; security systems services
PA: The Gores Group Llc
9800 Wilshire Blvd
Beverly Hills CA 90212
310 209-3010

(P-19977)
HALO NEURO INC
735 Market St Fl 4, San Francisco (94103-2034)
PHONE..................................650 784-0881
Daniel S Chao, *CEO*
Brett Wingeier, *CTO*
Kane Russell, *Marketing Staff*
EMP: 14
SALES (est): 910.3K **Privately Held**
SIC: 3699 Electrical equipment & supplies

(P-19978)
HESS PRECISION LASER INC
4747 Stratos Way Ste D, Modesto (95356-8893)
P.O. Box 747, Denair (95316-0747)
PHONE..................................209 575-1634
Randall R Hess, *President*
Belinda M Hess, *CFO*
Weston Hess, *Opers Mgr*
EMP: 10
SQ FT: 7,200
SALES (est): 2.1MM **Privately Held**
WEB: www.hessprecisionlaser.com
SIC: 3699 Laser systems & equipment

(P-19979)
IAMPLUS LLC
809 N Cahuenga Blvd, Los Angeles (90038-3703)
PHONE..................................323 210-3852
Phil Molyneux, *President*
Rosemary Peschken, *CFO*
Will Adams, *Founder*
Chandrasekar Rathakrishnan, *Director*
EMP: 40 EST: 2012
SQ FT: 3,900
SALES: 4.8MM
SALES (corp-wide): 19.5MM **Privately Held**
SIC: 3699 Electronic generation equipment
PA: I.Am.Plus Electronics, Inc.
809 N Cahuenga Blvd
Los Angeles CA 90038
323 210-3852

(P-19980)
IJK & CO INC
Also Called: Bayshore Lights
225 Industrial St, San Francisco (94124-1928)
PHONE..................................415 826-8899
Michael Tseng, *CEO*
Jun Tan, *Store Mgr*
EMP: 50
SALES: 20MM **Privately Held**
SIC: 3699 5063 Electrical equipment & supplies; electrical supplies; plumbing, heating, air-conditioning contractors; lighting maintenance service

(P-19981)
IMPEVA LABS INC (PA)
2570 W El Cam, Mountain View (94040)
PHONE..................................650 559-0103
Bradley H Feldman, *President*
Gregory L Tanner, *Treasurer*
Randall L Shepard, *Senior VP*
Thomas A Echols, *Vice Pres*
William L Hoese, *Vice Pres*
EMP: 13
SQ FT: 3,400
SALES (est): 3.1MM **Privately Held**
WEB: www.impeva.com
SIC: 3699 Security devices

(P-19982)
INNOVATIVETEK INC
1271 W 9th St, Upland (91786-5706)
PHONE..................................909 981-3401
Sandy Samudrala, *President*
Teresa Romero, *Exec VP*
Theresa Romero, *Exec VP*
Paul Trinh, *Vice Pres*
Ashley McBride, *Clerk*
EMP: 23
SALES: 3MM **Privately Held**
SIC: 3699 Electronic training devices

(P-19983)
INTEGRITY SECURITY SVCS INC
7585 Irvine Center Dr, Irvine (92618-2969)
PHONE..................................949 756-0690
Jeffrey R Hazarian, *President*
Gregory Powell, *Vice Pres*
Michael Zaturensky, *Sr Software Eng*
Cameron Durham, *Software Engr*
Jason Isaacs, *General Counsel*
EMP: 14
SQ FT: 4,400
SALES (est): 2.4MM
SALES (corp-wide): 76.5MM **Privately Held**
WEB: www.valicore.com
SIC: 3699 7371 Security control equipment & systems; custom computer programming services; computer software systems analysis & design, custom; computer software development
PA: Green Hills Software, Inc.
30 W Sola St
Santa Barbara CA 93101
805 965-6044

(P-19984)
INTELLIGENCE SUPPORT GROUP LTD
Also Called: I S G
7100 Monache Mtn, Inyokern (93527)
PHONE..................................800 504-3341
Richard Disabatino, *CEO*
William Alden, *President*

Richard Di Sabatino, *Manager*
EMP: 20
SQ FT: 20,000
SALES (est): 2.4MM **Privately Held**
WEB: www.isghq.com
SIC: 3699 Security control equipment & systems

(P-19985)
INTERGEN INC
1145 Tasman Dr, Sunnyvale (94089-2228)
PHONE..................................408 245-2737
Kris Madeyski, *President*
John Horn, *Admin Sec*
EMP: 11
SQ FT: 7,000
SALES (est): 1.3MM **Privately Held**
SIC: 3699 7371 Laser systems & equipment; computer software development & applications

(P-19986)
IONETIX CORPORATION (PA)
1 Ferry Building Ste 255, San Francisco (94111-4243)
PHONE..................................415 944-1440
Kevin Cameron, *CEO*
John Vincent, *President*
Carrie Busch, *VP Finance*
Carrie Stewart, *Purchasing*
Mark Leuschner, *VP Opers*
EMP: 35
SALES (est): 6.6MM **Privately Held**
SIC: 3699 Cyclotrons

(P-19987)
IRONWOOD ELECTRIC INC
1239 N Tustin Ave, Anaheim (92807-1603)
PHONE..................................714 630-2350
Raymond Chafe, *Principal*
Luis Villalobos, *Project Mgr*
Anders Howmann, *Technology*
EMP: 28 EST: 2011
SALES (est): 6.6MM **Privately Held**
SIC: 3699 1731 Electrical equipment & supplies; electrical work

(P-19988)
IWERKS ENTERTAINMENT INC
Also Called: Simex-Iwerks
27509 Avenue Hopkins, Santa Clarita (91355-3910)
PHONE..................................661 678-1800
Gary Matus, *CEO*
Donald Stults, *COO*
Jeff Dahl, *CFO*
Mark Cornell, *Senior VP*
Susan Schloeder, *Director*
EMP: 75
SQ FT: 23,000
SALES (est): 1.4MM **Privately Held**
WEB: www.iwerks.com
SIC: 3699 7819 Electrical equipment & supplies; developing & printing of commercial motion picture film
PA: Simex Inc
600-210 King St E
Toronto ON M5A 1
416 597-1585

(P-19989)
JACK J ENGEL MANUFACTURING INC
Also Called: Creative Automation
11641 Pendleton St, Sun Valley (91352-2502)
PHONE..................................818 767-6220
Jack Engel, *President*
Jack J Engel, *President*
Ilene Rosen, *CFO*
Ilene Engel, *Corp Secy*
Gary Helmers, *Sales Executive*
EMP: 34
SQ FT: 15,000
SALES (est): 6.4MM **Privately Held**
WEB: www.creativedispensing.com
SIC: 3699 5063 Electrical equipment & supplies; electrical supplies

(P-19990)
JANTEK ELECTRONICS INC
4820 Arden Dr, Temple City (91780-4001)
PHONE..................................626 350-4198
Danny Jan, *Vice Pres*
Joe Jan, *Exec VP*
Zon Jan, *Project Leader*

▲ = Import ▼=Export
◆ =Import/Export

Shirley Jan, *Controller*
◆ **EMP:** 15
SQ FT: 5,700
SALES (est): 1.5MM **Privately Held**
WEB: www.jantek.com
SIC: 3699 8748 5063 Security control
equipment & systems; communications
consulting; electric alarms & signaling
equipment

(P-19991)
JBB INC
Also Called: Precision Waterjet
880 W Crowther Ave, Placentia
(92870-6348)
PHONE....................888 538-9287
Jack Budd, *President*
EMP: 25
SQ FT: 17,000
SALES (est): 5.1MM **Privately Held**
WEB: www.h20jet.com
SIC: 3699 Laser welding, drilling & cutting
equipment

(P-19992)
JDSU PHOTONIC POWER (HQ)
1768 Automation Pkwy, San Jose
(95131-1873)
PHONE....................408 546-5000
Kevin Kennedy, *Owner*
▲ **EMP:** 10
SALES (est): 2MM
SALES (corp-wide): 811.4MM **Publicly
Held**
SIC: 3699 Laser systems & equipment
PA: Viavi Solutions Inc.
6001 America Center Dr # 6
San Jose CA 95002
408 404-3600

(P-19993)
JEICO SECURITY INC
Also Called: Camtron US
1525 N Endeavor Ln Ste Q, Anaheim
(92801-1156)
EMP: 10
SQ FT: 3,000
SALES (est): 83.7K **Privately Held**
SIC: 3699

(P-19994)
JELUZ ELECTRIC LTD LLC
Also Called: Fbs Floor Box Systems
25060 Hancock Ave, Murrieta
(92562-5930)
PHONE....................800 216-8307
Cecilia Quenardelle,
Jorge Luis Muttoni Jr,
EMP: 20
SQ FT: 10,000
SALES (est): 2MM **Privately Held**
SIC: 3699 Pulse amplifiers

(P-19995)
KANEX
3 Pointe Dr Ste 300, Brea (92821-7623)
PHONE....................888 975-1368
Kelvin Yan, *CEO*
▲ **EMP:** 25
SQ FT: 20,000
SALES (est): 6.2MM **Privately Held**
WEB: www.apogeeinc.net
SIC: 3699 5065 Electrical equipment &
supplies; electronic parts & equipment

(P-19996)
KELLY PNEUMATICS INC
711 W 17th St Ste F8, Costa Mesa
(92627-4346)
PHONE....................949 278-5721
Ed Kelly, *President*
Dyann Kelly, *Vice Pres*
▲ **EMP:** 15
SQ FT: 1,350
SALES (est): 2.1MM **Privately Held**
WEB: www.kpiwebsite.com
SIC: 3699 Electrical equipment & supplies

(P-19997)
KERI SYSTEMS INC (PA)
302 Enzo Dr, San Jose (95138-1860)
PHONE....................408 435-8400
Ted Geiszler, *President*
Ken Geiszler, *President*
Peter Moreno, *Technical Staff*
Vince Deiuliis, *Marketing Mgr*

Elisabeth Morton, *Sales Staff*
▲ **EMP:** 53
SQ FT: 20,000
SALES (est): 10.2MM **Privately Held**
WEB: www.entraguard.com
SIC: 3699 3829 Security control equip-
ment & systems; measuring & controlling
devices

(P-19998)
**KINETIC ELECTRIC
CORPORATION**
944 Industrial Blvd 946, Chula Vista
(91911-1608)
PHONE....................619 654-1157
Camilo Sanchez Fernandez, *President*
Luz Fernandez, *CFO*
EMP: 50
SALES (est): 3.3MM **Privately Held**
SIC: 3699 Electrical equipment & supplies

(P-19999)
KNIGHTSCOPE INC
1070 Terra Bella Ave, Mountain View
(94043-1830)
PHONE....................650 924-1025
William Santana Li, *CEO*
Jack Schenk, *President*
Marina Hardof, *CFO*
EMP: 10 **EST:** 2013
SALES (est): 579.2K **Privately Held**
SIC: 3699 Security devices

(P-20000)
**KULICKE SFFA WEDGE
BONDING INC**
Also Called: Kulicke & Soffa Industries
1821 E Dyer Rd Ste 200, Santa Ana
(92705-5700)
PHONE....................949 660-0440
Scott Kulicke, *President*
Lester Wong, *Senior VP*
Tom Naves, *Information Mgr*
Jason Fu, *Technology*
Dang Tran, *Electrical Engi*
▲ **EMP:** 200
SALES (est): 36.6MM
SALES (corp-wide): 809MM **Publicly
Held**
WEB: www.kns.com
SIC: 3699 Electrical equipment & supplies
PA: Kulicke And Soffa Industries, Inc.
1005 Virginia Dr
Fort Washington PA 19034
215 784-6000

(P-20001)
L T SEROGE INC
Also Called: Laser Tech
7400 Jurupa Ave, Riverside (92504-1030)
PHONE....................951 354-7141
Anthony Di Guglielmo, *CEO*
Chuck Markley, *Manager*
EMP: 15
SQ FT: 50,000
SALES: 3.6MM **Privately Held**
WEB: www.lasertech911.com
SIC: 3699 Laser welding, drilling & cutting
equipment

(P-20002)
L3 COMMUNICATIONS LINK
210 Franklin Blvd, Lemoore (93245)
PHONE....................559 998-5295
Charlie Werner, *President*
EMP: 40
SALES (est): 2.7MM **Privately Held**
SIC: 3699 Flight simulators (training aids),
electronic

(P-20003)
LASEROD TECHNOLOGIES LLC
20312 Gramercy Pl, Torrance
(90501-1511)
PHONE....................310 328-5869
Charles T Moffitt, *Mng Member*
David V Adams Jr, *Mng Member*
▼ **EMP:** 20
SQ FT: 8,000
SALES (est): 3.7MM **Privately Held**
SIC: 3699 Laser systems & equipment;
laser welding, drilling & cutting equipment

(P-20004)
LGPHILIPS LCD AMER FIN CORP
150 E Brokaw Rd, San Jose (95112-4203)
PHONE....................408 350-7600
Kyoung Park, *Principal*
Davis Lee, *Vice Pres*
▲ **EMP:** 26
SALES (est): 3.3MM **Privately Held**
SIC: 3699 3651 3634 Electrical equip-
ment & supplies; household audio & video
equipment; electric housewares & fans

(P-20005)
LIFELINE SEC & AUTOMTN INC
2081 Arena Blvd Ste 260, Sacramento
(95834-2309)
PHONE....................916 285-9078
Gordon Johnson, *President*
EMP: 48
SALES (est): 2MM **Privately Held**
SIC: 3699 Security devices
PA: Ghs Interactive Security Llc
21031 Warner Center Ln D
Woodland Hills CA 91367
-

(P-20006)
LINTELLE ENGINEERING INC
380 El Pueblo Rd Ste 105, Scotts Valley
(95066-4212)
PHONE....................831 439-8400
Levon Billuts, *President*
Clara Diane, *Shareholder*
William L Turne, *Shareholder*
EMP: 30
SQ FT: 32,000
SALES (est): 5MM
SALES (corp-wide): 85.8MM **Privately
Held**
WEB: www.lintelle.com/corp-profile.html
SIC: 3699 Electrical equipment & supplies
PA: Creo Capital Partners Llc
12400 Walsh Ave Ste 1100
Los Angeles CA 90066
310 230-8600

(P-20007)
LORENZ INC
Also Called: Karel Manufacturing
280 Campillo St Ste G, Calexico
(92231-3200)
PHONE....................760 356-1019
Zaven Arakelian, *President*
Sergio Chao-Bushoven, *Info Tech Dir*
Isabel Garcia, *Info Tech Mgr*
▲ **EMP:** 400
SQ FT: 73,000
SALES (est): 94.7MM **Privately Held**
SIC: 3699 Electrical equipment & supplies

(P-20008)
**LOW VOLTAGE ARCHITECTURE
INC**
11715 San Vicente Blvd, Los Angeles
(90049-6628)
P.O. Box 1182, Malibu (90265-1182)
PHONE....................310 573-7588
Matthew Denos, *President*
EMP: 22
SALES: 5MM **Privately Held**
SIC: 3699 8712 Security control equip-
ment & systems; architectural services

(P-20009)
LT SECURITY INC (PA)
Also Called: L T S
18738 San Jose Ave, City of Industry
(91748-1323)
PHONE....................626 435-2838
Tzu Ping Ho, *CEO*
Grant Long, *President*
Yifan Chen, *Admin Asst*
Jason Lim, *Sales Mgr*
Grace Chen, *Marketing Staff*
▲ **EMP:** 32
SALES (est): 8MM **Privately Held**
SIC: 3699 Security devices

(P-20010)
MAAS-ROWE CARILLONS INC
2255 Meyers Ave, Escondido (92029-1007)
P.O. Box 462366 (92046-2366)
PHONE....................760 743-1311
Paul H Rowe, *President*
Elaine Rowe, *Vice Pres*
▲ **EMP:** 25 **EST:** 1958

SQ FT: 10,500
SALES (est): 4.2MM **Privately Held**
WEB: www.maasrowe.com
SIC: 3699 Bells, electric

(P-20011)
MACON INDUSTRIES INC
Also Called: Lightwave Laser
3186 Coffey Ln, Santa Rosa (95403-2555)
PHONE....................707 566-2116
Jhon Macon, *President*
EMP: 10
SQ FT: 5,000
SALES (est): 1.3MM **Privately Held**
WEB: www.lightwavelaser.com
SIC: 3699 Laser welding, drilling & cutting
equipment

(P-20012)
**MARTRONIC ENGINEERING INC
(PA)**
874 Patriot Dr Unit D, Moorpark
(93021-3605)
PHONE....................805 583-0808
Richard Marsh, *President*
Ellen Marsh, *Corp Secy*
Matt Marsh, *Purchasing*
EMP: 11 **EST:** 1975
SQ FT: 6,700
SALES: 1.7MM **Privately Held**
WEB: www.meilaser.com
SIC: 3699 Laser systems & equipment

(P-20013)
MEDIA KING INC
140 W Valley Blvd 201a, San Gabriel
(91776-3760)
PHONE....................626 288-4558
Tsai Shih Yang, *CEO*
Julie Ye, *President*
▲ **EMP:** 22
SALES (est): 2.5MM **Privately Held**
SIC: 3699

(P-20014)
MEGAVISION INC
5765 Thornwood Dr, Goleta (93117-3830)
P.O. Box 60158, Santa Barbara (93160-
0158)
PHONE....................805 964-1400
Ken Boydston, *President*
Lynn Watson, *Admin Sec*
EMP: 13
SQ FT: 4,000
SALES (est): 1.8MM **Privately Held**
SIC: 3699 3861 3577 Electrical equip-
ment & supplies; photographic equipment
& supplies; computer peripheral equip-
ment

(P-20015)
**MEGGITT SAFETY SYSTEMS
INC (HQ)**
Also Called: Meggitt Control Systems
1785 Voyager Ave, Simi Valley
(93063-3363)
PHONE....................805 584-4100
Dennis Hutton, *President*
Dolores Watai, *Vice Pres*
Scott Richards, *Program Mgr*
Sandy Russo, *Admin Mgr*
Mila Calderon, *Admin Asst*
▲ **EMP:** 210
SQ FT: 180,000
SALES (est): 123.2MM
SALES (corp-wide): 2.6B **Privately Held**
WEB: www.meggittsafety.com
SIC: 3699 3724 3728 Betatrons; exhaust
systems, aircraft; engine heaters, aircraft;
aircraft parts & equipment
PA: Meggitt Plc
Atlantic House, Aviation Park West
Christchurch BH23
120 259-7597

(P-20016)
**MERCURY SECURITY
PRODUCTS LLC**
2355 Mira Mar Ave, Long Beach
(90815-1755)
PHONE....................562 986-9105
Joseph Grillo, *CEO*
Michael Serafin, *President*
Hing Hung, *Exec VP*
▲ **EMP:** 19

SQ FT: 12,000
SALES (est): 4.4MM
SALES (corp-wide): 9B **Privately Held**
WEB: www.mercury-security.com
SIC: 3699 8742 Security control equipment & systems; industry specialist consultants
HQ: Hid Global Corporation
611 Center Ridge Dr
Austin TX 78753
800 237-7769

(P-20017)
MICROLUX INC
1065 Asbury St, San Jose (95126-1855)
P.O. Box 4095, Santa Clara (95056-4095)
PHONE...................408 435-1700
Edic Sliva, *President*
EMP: 12
SQ FT: 20,000
SALES (est): 1.7MM **Privately Held**
WEB: www.microlux.com
SIC: 3699 Laser welding, drilling & cutting equipment

(P-20018)
MOBIUS PHOTONICS INC
110 Pioneer Way Ste A, Mountain View (94041-1519)
PHONE...................408 496-1084
Robert L Mortensen, *CEO*
Robert L Byer, *Ch of Bd*
Kiyomi Monro, *CEO*
Mark Byer, *COO*
Manuel Leonardo, *CTO*
EMP: 10
SQ FT: 500
SALES (est): 1.1MM
SALES (corp-wide): 1.4B **Publicly Held**
WEB: www.mobiusphotonics.com
SIC: 3699 Laser systems & equipment
PA: Ipg Photonics Corporation
50 Old Webster Rd
Oxford MA 01540
508 373-1100

(P-20019)
MOTICONT
6901 Woodley Ave, Van Nuys (91406-4844)
PHONE...................818 785-1800
Joseph Hank, *Partner*
Aaron Eghbal, *Partner*
EMP: 22
SALES (est): 3.4MM **Privately Held**
SIC: 3699 Linear accelerators; electron linear accelerators

(P-20020)
MULTI POWER PRODUCTS INC
47931 Westinghouse Dr, Fremont (94539-7483)
PHONE...................415 883-6300
Paul Chait, *President*
EMP: 13
SALES (corp-wide): 2.4MM **Privately Held**
WEB: www.power-products.com
SIC: 3699 Electrical equipment & supplies
PA: Multi Power Products, Inc.
2901 Tasman Dr Ste 111
Santa Clara CA
415 354-5688

(P-20021)
MYE TECHNOLOGIES INC
28460 Westinghouse Pl, Valencia (91355-0929)
PHONE...................661 964-0217
Anthony Garcia, *President*
Virg Kasputis, *General Mgr*
Terry Miller, *Controller*
Ken Hanks, *Natl Sales Mgr*
▲ EMP: 45
SQ FT: 5,000
SALES (est): 8.6MM **Privately Held**
WEB: www.myeclubtv.com
SIC: 3699 Electric sound equipment

(P-20022)
NANOTRONICS IMAGING INC
Also Called: Nanotronics Automation
777 Flynn Rd, Hollister (95023-9558)
PHONE...................831 630-0700
Randy Griffith, *Branch Mgr*
EMP: 15

SALES (corp-wide): 2.4MM **Privately Held**
SIC: 3699 Electronic training devices
PA: Nanotronics Imaging, Inc.
2251 Front St Ste 109-111
Cuyahoga Falls OH 44221
330 926-9809

(P-20023)
NELSON & SONS ELECTRIC INC
401 N Walnut Rd, Turlock (95380-9426)
PHONE...................209 667-4343
Keith Nelson, *President*
Shelly Nelson, *Treasurer*
David Nelson, *Vice Pres*
Travis Nelson, *Vice Pres*
EMP: 50
SALES (est): 14.6MM **Privately Held**
SIC: 3699 Electrical equipment & supplies

(P-20024)
NEOCATENA NETWORKS INC
6300 Old School Rd, Pleasanton (94588-9409)
PHONE...................650 200-7340
John Lima, *President*
Boris Wolf, *COO*
Tony Newman, *Vice Pres*
Lukas Grunwald, *CTO*
◆ EMP: 10
SALES (est): 948.5K **Privately Held**
SIC: 3699 7382 Security devices; security systems services

(P-20025)
NETWORK CHEMISTRY INC
1804 Embarcadero Rd # 201, Palo Alto (94303-3341)
PHONE...................650 858-3120
Lou Ryan, *Ch of Bd*
Robert Mirkovich, *CEO*
EMP: 14
SQ FT: 2,700
SALES (est): 1.8MM **Privately Held**
WEB: www.networkchemistry.com
SIC: 3699 Security devices

(P-20026)
NETWORKED ENERGY SERVICES CORP (HQ)
Also Called: Grid Modernization Division
5215 Hellyer Ave Ste 150, San Jose (95138-1089)
PHONE...................408 622-9900
Michael Anderson, *CEO*
Will Mathieson, *CFO*
Fremont Bainbridge, *Sr Software Eng*
Mike Bucsa, *Director*
Haoqing Sun, *Manager*
▲ EMP: 33
SALES (est): 8.9MM
SALES (corp-wide): 1B **Privately Held**
SIC: 3699 Grids, electric
PA: S&T Ag
Industriezeile 35
Linz 4021
732 766-40

(P-20027)
NEW WAVE RESEARCH INCORPORATED (HQ)
48660 Kato Rd, Fremont (94538-7339)
PHONE...................510 249-1550
Pei Hsien Fang, *Chairman*
Rick Wong, *CFO*
▲ EMP: 110
SQ FT: 65,000
SALES (est): 7.9MM
SALES (corp-wide): 367.8MM **Publicly Held**
WEB: www.new-wave.com
SIC: 3699 3674 Laser systems & equipment; semiconductors & related devices
PA: Electro Scientific Industries, Inc.
13900 Nw Science Park Dr
Portland OR 97229
503 641-4141

(P-20028)
NEWAGE PAVILIONS LLC
9360 Penfield Ave, Chatsworth (91311-6550)
PHONE...................818 701-9600
Ron Hay, *President*
▲ EMP: 12
SQ FT: 29,000

SALES (est): 1.2MM **Privately Held**
SIC: 3699 Electrical equipment & supplies

(P-20029)
NEWPORT CORPORATION
Also Called: Spectra-Physics Laser Div
3635 Peterson Way, Santa Clara (95054-2809)
P.O. Box 7013, Mountain View (94039)
PHONE...................408 980-4300
Sergey Mayzemberg, *Prgrmr*
Elgin Bravo, *Engineer*
Jenny Liu, *Engineer*
Jeri Loman, *Engineer*
Eric McPhee, *Mfg Staff*
EMP: 800
SALES (corp-wide): 1.9B **Publicly Held**
SIC: 3699 5049 Laser systems & equipment; scientific instruments
HQ: Newport Corporation
1791 Deere Ave
Irvine CA 92606
949 863-3144

(P-20030)
NM LASER PRODUCTS INC
337 Piercy Rd, San Jose (95138-1403)
PHONE...................408 227-8299
David Woodruff, *President*
EMP: 10
SQ FT: 3,000
SALES (est): 1.2MM **Privately Held**
SIC: 3699 Laser systems & equipment

(P-20031)
NOARK ELECTRIC (USA) INC
2188 Pomona Blvd, Pomona (91768-3332)
PHONE...................626 330-7007
Er Nan, *CEO*
Sulayman Usman, *Regional Mgr*
Benjamin Nan, *General Mgr*
Chris Jarrell, *Director*
▲ EMP: 16
SALES (est): 2.6MM **Privately Held**
SIC: 3699 Electrical equipment & supplies

(P-20032)
NORTEK SECURITY & CONTROL LLC
12471 Riverside Dr, Eastvale (91752-1007)
PHONE...................760 438-7000
John West, *Principal*
EMP: 10
SALES (corp-wide): 2.7B **Privately Held**
SIC: 3699 Security control equipment & systems
HQ: Nortek Security & Control Llc
5919 Sea Otter Pl Ste 100
Carlsbad CA 92010
800 472-5555

(P-20033)
NOVASENTIS INC
25 Edwards Ct Ste 17, Burlingame (94010-2429)
PHONE...................814 238-7400
Francois Jeanneau, *President*
Ralph Russo, *Ch of Bd*
Michael Vestel, *CTO*
EMP: 26
SALES (est): 3.9MM **Privately Held**
SIC: 3699 Electrical equipment & supplies

(P-20034)
NUPHOTON TECHNOLOGIES INC
41610 Corning Pl, Murrieta (92562-7023)
PHONE...................951 696-8366
Ramadas Pillai, *CEO*
Dan Vera, *COO*
Vish Govindan, *CFO*
Norm Nelson, *Vice Pres*
Sindu Pillai, *Vice Pres*
EMP: 16
SQ FT: 12,000
SALES (est): 5.3MM **Privately Held**
WEB: www.nuphoton.com
SIC: 3699 Laser systems & equipment

(P-20035)
O & S CALIFORNIA INC
Also Called: Osca-Arcosa
9731 Siempre Viva Rd E, San Diego (92154-7200)
PHONE...................619 661-1800
Kazuo Murata, *President*

Jos Luis Furlong, *Vice Pres*
Arturo Urrea, *Info Tech Mgr*
Faustino Gomez, *Technology*
Satoshi Imamasa, *Accounting Mgr*
▲ EMP: 400
SQ FT: 4,676
SALES (est): 164.7MM
SALES (corp-wide): 325.1MM **Privately Held**
WEB: www.osca-arcosa.com
SIC: 3699 Electrical equipment & supplies
PA: Onamba Co., Ltd.
3-1-27, Fukaekita, Higashinari-Ku
Osaka OSK 537-0
669 766-101

(P-20036)
OBSERVABLES INC
117 N Milpas St, Santa Barbara (93103-3345)
PHONE...................805 272-9255
Abraham Schryer, *President*
EMP: 12
SALES (est): 487.8K **Privately Held**
SIC: 3699 Security control equipment & systems

(P-20037)
OSI SUBSIDIARY INC
12525 Chadron Ave, Hawthorne (90250-4807)
PHONE...................310 978-0516
Deepak Chopra, *CEO*
Ajay Mehra, *President*
Alan Edrick, *CFO*
Lou Campana, *Vice Pres*
Narayan Taneja, *Vice Pres*
EMP: 400
SALES (est): 64.4MM
SALES (corp-wide): 1B **Publicly Held**
WEB: www.osioptoelectronics.com
SIC: 3699 Laser systems & equipment
PA: Osi Systems, Inc.
12525 Chadron Ave
Hawthorne CA 90250
310 978-0516

(P-20038)
PACIFIC CONTROLS INC
Also Called: Pacific Controls E D M
4949 Newcastle Ave, Encino (91316-4210)
PHONE...................818 345-1970
George Jariabek, *President*
Tamara G Jariabek, *Treasurer*
EMP: 19
SQ FT: 5,000
SALES (est): 1.6MM **Privately Held**
WEB: www.pacificcontrols.com
SIC: 3699 Electrical equipment & supplies

(P-20039)
PEC MANUFACTURING INC
2110 Ringwood Ave, San Jose (95131-1715)
PHONE...................408 577-1839
Eric Truong, *President*
EMP: 10
SALES (est): 2.1MM **Privately Held**
WEB: www.pecmfg.com
SIC: 3699 Extension cords

(P-20040)
PHASE-A-MATIC INC
39360 3rd St E Ste C301, Palmdale (93550-3257)
PHONE...................661 947-8485
Colin G Johnstone, *President*
Juan Ochoa, *Technician*
Donna Johnstone, *Engineer*
Monica Varelas, *Accounting Mgr*
Mike Jones, *Controller*
▲ EMP: 12 EST: 1965
SQ FT: 10,000
SALES (est): 2.3MM **Privately Held**
WEB: www.phase-a-matic.com
SIC: 3699 Electrical equipment & supplies

(P-20041)
PHILATRON INTERNATIONAL (PA)
Also Called: Santa Fe Supply Company
15315 Cornet St, Santa Fe Springs (90670-5531)
PHONE...................562 802-0452
Phillip M Ramos Jr, *CEO*
Phillip M Ramos Sr, *Exec VP*

▲ = Import ▼=Export
◆ =Import/Export

Isela Cid, *Executive*
Juan Lomeli, *Technical Mgr*
Joel Jarquin, *Technician*
EMP: 140 **EST:** 1978
SQ FT: 100,000
SALES (est): 29.9MM **Privately Held**
WEB: www.philatron.com
SIC: 3699 3694 3357 Electrical equipment & supplies; engine electrical equipment; communication wire

(P-20042)
PINE GROVE GROUP INC
25500 State Highway 88, Pioneer (95666-9647)
PHONE...................209 295-7733
Dan Nolting, *CEO*
Alicia Mullarney, *Production*
EMP: 30
SQ FT: 8,000
SALES (est): 5.3MM **Privately Held**
WEB: www.pinegrovegroup.com
SIC: 3699 Electrical equipment & supplies

(P-20043)
POWER PARAGON INC
Also Called: Power Systems Group
901 E Ball Rd, Anaheim (92805-5916)
PHONE...................714 956-9200
Harvey Cohen, *Manager*
EMP: 350
SALES (corp-wide): 9.5B **Publicly Held**
WEB: www.powerparagon.com
SIC: 3699 8721 8741 3612 Electrical equipment & supplies; accounting, auditing & bookkeeping; management services; personnel management; transformers, except electric
HQ: Power Paragon, Inc.
901 E Ball Rd
Anaheim CA 92805
714 956-9200

(P-20044)
POWERFLARE CORPORATION
37 Ringwood Ave, Atherton (94027-2231)
P.O. Box 7615, Menlo Park (94026-7615)
PHONE...................650 208-2580
Kenneth Dueker, *CEO*
EMP: 11
SALES (est): 1.2MM **Privately Held**
SIC: 3699 Electrical equipment & supplies

(P-20045)
PRECISION FLIGHT CONTROLS
2747 Merc Dr Ste 100, Rancho Cordova (95742)
PHONE...................916 414-1310
Mike Altman, *President*
Bart Altman, *Vice Pres*
April Obrien, *Office Mgr*
Terry Altman, *Human Resources*
Tracy Cook, *Marketing Staff*
EMP: 13
SQ FT: 11,000
SALES (est): 3.1MM **Privately Held**
WEB: www.flypfc.com
SIC: 3699 Flight simulators (training aids), electronic

(P-20046)
PRIORITY TECH SYSTEMS INC
Also Called: Pts Security
14040 Runnymede St, Van Nuys (91405-2511)
PHONE...................818 756-5413
Mauricio Navarro, *President*
EMP: 15
SALES (est): 1.7MM **Privately Held**
SIC: 3699 1731 Security devices; fire detection & burglar alarm systems specialization

(P-20047)
PRO SYSTEMS FABRICATORS INC (PA)
14643 Hawthorne Ave, Fontana (92335-2544)
PHONE...................909 350-9147
Edith Sugarman, *President*
Lynn Sugarman, *Treasurer*
Trina Jackson, *Admin Sec*
▲ **EMP:** 15
SQ FT: 11,000

SALES (est): 1.3MM **Privately Held**
SIC: 3699 3677 3564 Electrical equipment & supplies; filtration devices, electronic; blowers & fans

(P-20048)
PRO-SPOT INTERNATIONAL INC
5932 Sea Otter Pl, Carlsbad (92010-6630)
PHONE...................760 407-1414
Joran Olsson, *President*
Lee Stout, *Business Dir*
Wendy Olsson, *Admin Sec*
Manisha Aravala, *Design Engr*
Steve Clark, *Engineer*
▲ **EMP:** 17
SALES (est): 5.8MM **Privately Held**
WEB: www.prospot.com
SIC: 3699 Electrical welding equipment

(P-20049)
PROTOTYPE EXPRESS LLC
3506 W Lake Center Dr D, Santa Ana (92704-6985)
PHONE...................714 751-3533
Bob Tavi, *Mng Member*
EMP: 15 **EST:** 1995
SQ FT: 7,000
SALES (est): 2.7MM **Privately Held**
WEB: www.prototypexpress.com
SIC: 3699 Electrical equipment & supplies

(P-20050)
QED SYSTEMS INC
1330 30th St Ste C, San Diego (92154-3471)
PHONE...................619 424-3225
EMP: 30
SALES (corp-wide): 167MM **Privately Held**
SIC: 3699
PA: Qed Systems, Inc.
4646 N Witchduck Rd
Virginia Beach VA 23455
757 490-5000

(P-20051)
QUARTON USA INC
3230 Fallow Field Dr, Diamond Bar (91765-3479)
PHONE...................888 532-2221
Chao-CHI Huang, *President*
Cindy Lin, *Controller*
▲ **EMP:** 15
SALES (est): 2MM **Privately Held**
WEB: www.quarton.com
SIC: 3699 Laser systems & equipment

(P-20052)
R J R TECHNOLOGIES INC (PA)
7875 Edgewater Dr, Oakland (94621-2001)
PHONE...................510 638-5901
Wil Salhuana, *President*
Tony Bregante, *CFO*
Richard J Ross, *Principal*
Janet Cunningham, *QC Mgr*
Jose Badillo, *Cust Mgr*
EMP: 105
SQ FT: 50,000
SALES (est): 25MM **Privately Held**
WEB: www.rjrpolymers.com
SIC: 3699 Cleaning equipment, ultrasonic, except medical & dental

(P-20053)
RACHE CORPORATION
1160 Avenida Acaso, Camarillo (93012-8719)
PHONE...................805 389-6868
Steven Wisuri, *President*
Steve Garcia, *Project Engr*
Kevin Millar, *Engineer*
Andy Varahamurthy, *Mktg Dir*
EMP: 10
SQ FT: 8,500
SALES (est): 1MM **Privately Held**
WEB: www.rache.com
SIC: 3699 7389 Laser welding, drilling & cutting equipment; metal cutting services

(P-20054)
RACO MANUFACTURING & ENGRG CO
1400 62nd St, Emeryville (94608-2099)
PHONE...................510 658-6713
Constance Brown, *President*
Connie Brown, *Vice Pres*

James Brown, *Vice Pres*
Gene Cottom, *Sales Mgr*
James Garnett, *Director*
EMP: 14 **EST:** 1947
SQ FT: 5,500
SALES (est): 3.3MM **Privately Held**
WEB: www.racoman.com
SIC: 3699 3823 Electrical equipment & supplies; temperature instruments: industrial process type

(P-20055)
RAYTHEON COMPANY
6380 Hollister Ave, Goleta (93117-3114)
PHONE...................805 967-5511
Jack Gressingh, *General Mgr*
Randy Brown, *President*
Brian Hatt, *President*
Carl Jelinex, *Principal*
Adolph Schulbach, *Principal*
EMP: 200
SQ FT: 102,570
SALES (corp-wide): 25.3B **Publicly Held**
SIC: 3699 3812 Countermeasure simulators, electric; search & navigation equipment
PA: Raytheon Company
870 Winter St
Waltham MA 02451
781 522-3000

(P-20056)
RELDOM CORPORATION
3241 Industry Dr, Signal Hill (90755-4013)
PHONE...................562 498-3346
Peter Modler, *CEO*
EMP: 20
SALES (est): 4.4MM **Privately Held**
WEB: www.reldom.com
SIC: 3699 Security devices

(P-20057)
RGBLASE LLC
3984 Washington Blvd # 306, Fremont (94538-4954)
PHONE...................510 585-8449
Pan MA, *Mng Member*
EMP: 12
SALES (est): 993.2K **Privately Held**
WEB: www.rgblase.com
SIC: 3699 Laser systems & equipment

(P-20058)
RHUBCOMMUNICATIONS INC
4340 Stevens Creek Blvd, San Jose (95129-1102)
PHONE...................408 899-2830
Larry Dorie, *President*
John Mao, *CTO*
EMP: 13
SQ FT: 1,000
SALES (est): 605K **Privately Held**
SIC: 3699 Electrical equipment & supplies

(P-20059)
RIGOLI ENTERPRISES INC
Also Called: Rignoli Pacific
1983 Potrero Grande Dr, Monterey Park (91755-7420)
PHONE...................626 573-0242
Arthur R Rigoli, *President*
Adam Rigoli, *Vice Pres*
EMP: 14
SALES (est): 1.3MM **Privately Held**
WEB: www.mindpik.com
SIC: 3699 Fire control or bombing equipment, electronic

(P-20060)
RKS INC (HQ)
1955 Cordell Ct Ste 104, El Cajon (92020-0901)
PHONE...................858 571-4444
Russell Leonard Scheppmann, *CEO*
Allen Thomas, *COO*
Scott Skillman, *CFO*
Mike McMinn, *Vice Pres*
Brian Shultz, *Vice Pres*
EMP: 18
SQ FT: 7,747
SALES: 4.4MM
SALES (corp-wide): 34.3B **Privately Held**
WEB: www.aps-technology.com
SIC: 3699 Door opening & closing devices, electrical; security devices; security control equipment & systems

PA: Abb Ltd
Affolternstrasse 44
ZUrich ZH 8050
433 177-111

(P-20061)
ROMEO SYSTEMS INC
Also Called: Romeo Power
4380 Ayers Ave, Vernon (90058-4306)
PHONE...................323 675-2180
Michael Patterson, *CEO*
Erik Fleming, *COO*
Porter Harris, *CTO*
◆ **EMP:** 202
SQ FT: 114,000
SALES (est): 80.5K **Privately Held**
SIC: 3699 8731 High-energy particle physics equipment; energy research

(P-20062)
SACO
Also Called: S A C O Your Manufacturing Co
3525 Old Conejo Rd # 107, Newbury Park (91320-2154)
PHONE...................805 499-7788
Samuel Bernstein, *Owner*
Phil Bernstein, *Owner*
EMP: 20
SALES (est): 250K **Privately Held**
SIC: 3699 3651 Electrical equipment & supplies; household audio & video equipment

(P-20063)
SCHNEIDER ELECTRIC USA INC
1660 Scenic Ln, Costa Mesa (92626-1410)
PHONE...................714 662-4432
Jimmy Russel, *Manager*
Richard Demeule, *Software Engr*
Evandro Marchi, *Manager*
Juan Ponce, *Manager*
EMP: 20
SALES (corp-wide): 200.4K **Privately Held**
WEB: www.squared.com
SIC: 3699 Electrical equipment & supplies
HQ: Schneider Electric Usa, Inc.
800 Federal St
Andover MA 01810
978 975-9600

(P-20064)
SEA BREEZE TECHNOLOGY INC
Also Called: Tech 22
1160 Joshua Way, Vista (92081-7836)
PHONE...................760 727-6366
Thomas Skarvada, *President*
EMP: 17
SQ FT: 3,000
SALES (est): 2.1MM **Privately Held**
SIC: 3699 Electrical equipment & supplies

(P-20065)
SERRA LASER AND WATERJET INC
1740 N Orangethorpe Park, Anaheim (92801-1138)
PHONE...................714 680-6211
Glenn Kline, *CEO*
EMP: 30
SALES (est): 1.6MM **Privately Held**
SIC: 3699 Laser welding, drilling & cutting equipment

(P-20066)
SIDUS SOLUTIONS LLC (PA)
7352 Trade St, San Diego (92121-2422)
P.O. Box 420698 (92142-0698)
PHONE...................619 275-5533
Leonard Pool, *Mng Member*
EMP: 12 **EST:** 2000
SQ FT: 1,000
SALES: 1.5MM **Privately Held**
WEB: www.sidus-solutions.com
SIC: 3699 Security devices

(P-20067)
SIENNA CORPORATION INC
41350 Christy St, Fremont (94538-3115)
PHONE...................510 440-0200
EMP: 21 **EST:** 1995
SALES (est): 3.2MM **Privately Held**
SIC: 3699

(P-20068)
SIERRA NEVADA CORPORATION
145 Parkshore Dr, Folsom (95630-4726)
PHONE..................................916 985-8799
Carolyn Cain, *Branch Mgr*
Matthew Main, *Manager*
EMP: 30
SALES (corp-wide): 1.5B **Privately Held**
WEB: www.sncorp.com
SIC: 3699 Countermeasure simulators,
electric
PA: Sierra Nevada Corporation
444 Salomon Cir
Sparks NV 89434
775 331-0222

(P-20069)
SIGMA 6 ELECTRONICS INC
Also Called: Litus Global Solutions
7030 Alamitos Ave Ste E, San Diego
(92154-4764)
P.O. Box 711094 (92171-1094)
PHONE..................................858 279-4300
Scott Housman, *President*
Samanth Kelley, *General Mgr*
EMP: 11
SALES (est): 2.9MM **Privately Held**
SIC: 3699 Electrical equipment & supplies

(P-20070)
SKYGUARD LLC
2945 Townsgate Rd Ste 200, Westlake Vil-
lage (91361-5866)
PHONE..................................703 262-0500
David Power, *CEO*
Wendy Collins, *Controller*
EMP: 25
SALES (est): 2.5MM **Privately Held**
SIC: 3699

(P-20071)
SMTC CORPORATION
431 Kato Ter, Fremont (94539-8333)
PHONE..................................510 737-0700
John Caldwell, *CEO*
David Sandberg, *Bd of Directors*
Joe Bustos, *Vice Pres*
Seth Choi, *Vice Pres*
Chris Christiani, *Vice Pres*
▲ EMP: 100 EST: 1994
SALES (est): 22.4MM
SALES (corp-wide): 139.2MM **Privately
Held**
SIC: 3699 Electrical equipment & supplies
PA: Smtc Corporation
7050 Woodbine Ave Suite 300
Markham ON L3R 4
905 479-1810

(P-20072)
SOLIANT ENERGY INC
1100 La Avenida St Ste A, Mountain View
(94043-1453)
PHONE..................................626 396-9500
Terry Bailey, *President*
Michael Deck, *CFO*
▲ EMP: 47
SQ FT: 4,500
SALES (est): 5.5MM **Privately Held**
WEB: www.practicalinstruments.com
SIC: 3699 Electrical equipment & supplies

(P-20073)
SONNET TECHNOLOGIES INC
8 Autry, Irvine (92618-2708)
PHONE..................................949 587-3500
Robert Farnsworth, *President*
Robert Rich, *Admin Sec*
Martin Wagner, *Engineer*
Martin Muggee, *Marketing Mgr*
Angelia Farnsworth Magill, *Director*
▲ EMP: 27
SQ FT: 17,000
SALES (est): 6.4MM **Privately Held**
WEB: www.sonnettech.com
SIC: 3699 Electrical equipment & supplies

(P-20074)
SONY BIOTECHNOLOGY INC
1730 N 1st St Fl 2, San Jose (95112-4508)
PHONE..................................800 275-5963
Allen Poirson, *President*
Narayan Prabhu, *CFO*
EMP: 65

SALES (est): 12.8MM
SALES (corp-wide): 80.1B **Privately Held**
WEB: www.i-cyt.com
SIC: 3699 7372 Laser systems & equip-
ment; prepackaged software
HQ: Sony Corporation Of America
25 Madison Ave Fl 27
New York NY 10010
212 833-8000

(P-20075)
SORAA LASER DIODE INC (PA)
Also Called: Sld Laser
485 Pine Ave, Goleta (93117-3709)
PHONE..................................805 696-6999
Steven Denbaars, *CEO*
James Raring, *President*
Eric B Kim, *CEO*
Thomas Caulfield, *COO*
George Stringer, *Senior VP*
EMP: 40 EST: 2013
SQ FT: 3,000
SALES (est): 16.3MM **Privately Held**
SIC: 3699 Laser systems & equipment

(P-20076)
SORAA LASER DIODE INC
6500 Kaiser Dr, Fremont (94555-3661)
PHONE..................................805 696-6999
Steven Denbaars, *CEO*
EMP: 40
SALES (corp-wide): 16.3MM **Privately
Held**
SIC: 3699 Laser systems & equipment
PA: Soraa Laser Diode, Inc.
485 Pine Ave
Goleta CA 93117
805 696-6999

(P-20077)
SOUNDCRAFT INC
Also Called: Secura Key
20301 Nordhoff St, Chatsworth
(91311-6128)
PHONE..................................818 882-0020
Joel Smulson, *President*
Randy Watkins, *President*
Martin Casden, *Vice Pres*
Wayne Dow, *Technology*
Rene Aldaya, *Controller*
◆ EMP: 35
SQ FT: 12,000
SALES (est): 8.7MM **Privately Held**
WEB: www.securakey.com
SIC: 3699 1731 3829 Security control
equipment & systems; safety & security
specialization; measuring & controlling
devices

(P-20078)
SPECTRA-PHYSICS INC
Also Called: Laser Division
3635 Peterson Way, Santa Clara
(95054-2809)
P.O. Box 19607, Irvine (92623-9607)
PHONE..................................650 961-2550
Robert J Phillippy, *CEO*
Long Ngo, *Technician*
ADI Diner, *Project Mgr*
Timothy Cheng, *Engineer*
Mark Feldman, *Engineer*
▼ EMP: 800
SQ FT: 19,500
SALES (est): 104.7MM
SALES (corp-wide): 1.9B **Publicly Held**
WEB: www.spectraphysics.com
SIC: 3699 8731 Laser systems & equip-
ment; commercial physical research
HQ: Newport Corporation
1791 Deere Ave
Irvine CA 92606
949 863-3144

(P-20079)
SSG ALLIANCE LLC (PA)
2550 Smrsville Rd Unit 55, Brentwood
(94513)
PHONE..................................925 526-6050
Mohammed J Khan, *President*
EMP: 11 EST: 2015
SALES: 300K **Privately Held**
SIC: 3699 Security devices

(P-20080)
STERIS CORPORATION
9020 Activity Rd Ste D, San Diego
(92126-4454)
PHONE..................................858 586-1166
Walt Rosebrough, *Manager*
EMP: 60
SALES (corp-wide): 2.6B **Privately Held**
SIC: 3699 Electrical equipment & supplies
HQ: Steris Corporation
5960 Heisley Rd
Mentor OH 44060
440 354-2600

(P-20081)
STIR
2210 Lincoln Ave, Pasadena (91103)
PHONE..................................626 657-0918
Jean-Paul Labrosse, *CEO*
Warren Horton, *Engineer*
EMP: 15
SALES (est): 1.5MM **Privately Held**
SIC: 3699 Electrical equipment & supplies

(P-20082)
STRACON INC
1672 Kaiser Ave Ste 1, Irvine (92614-5700)
PHONE..................................949 851-2288
Son Pham, *President*
Lisette Nguyen, *Financial Exec*
EMP: 17
SQ FT: 10,000
SALES (est): 4.1MM **Privately Held**
WEB: www.straconinc.com
SIC: 3699 Electrical equipment & supplies

(P-20083)
SUMMIT ELECTRIC & DATA INC
28338 Constellation Rd # 920, Valencia
(91355-5098)
PHONE..................................661 775-9901
Ray Vasquez, *President*
EMP: 24 EST: 2010
SALES (est): 4.5MM **Privately Held**
SIC: 3699 1731 Electrical equipment &
supplies; electrical work

(P-20084)
**SUSS MCRTEC PHTNIC
SYSTEMS INC**
220 Klug Cir, Corona (92880-5409)
PHONE..................................951 817-3700
Courtney T Sheets, *CEO*
Debbie Blanchard, *CFO*
Debbie Brown, *CFO*
Stephen Thompson, *Officer*
Kerry Schuster, *Program Mgr*
EMP: 90 EST: 1966
SALES (est): 20MM
SALES (corp-wide): 196.3MM **Privately
Held**
WEB: www.tamsci.com
SIC: 3699 7389 Electrical equipment &
supplies;
PA: SUss Microtec Se
SchleiBheimer Str. 90
Garching B. Munchen 85748
893 200-70

(P-20085)
TASCENT INC
475 Alberto Way Ste 200, Los Gatos
(95032-5480)
PHONE..................................650 799-4611
Dean Senner, *CEO*
Scott Clark, *Vice Pres*
Alastair Partington, *Vice Pres*
Joey Pritikin, *Vice Pres*
Ed Costello, *Engineer*
EMP: 16 EST: 2015
SALES (est): 2.5MM **Privately Held**
SIC: 3699 Security devices

(P-20086)
TECHKO INC
27301 Calle De La Rosa, San Juan Capis-
trano (92675-1875)
PHONE..................................949 486-0678
Joseph Y Ko, *CEO*
Rosemary Borne, *Vice Pres*
▲ EMP: 1000
SQ FT: 18,000
SALES (est): 80MM **Privately Held**
WEB: www.techkousa.com
SIC: 3699 3589 Security devices; shred-
ders, industrial & commercial

(P-20087)
TEKLINK SECURITY INC
Also Called: Securityman
4601 E Airport Dr, Ontario (91761-7869)
PHONE..................................909 230-6668
Sam Hsien Jung Yu, *President*
Mike Chen, *Vice Pres*
▲ EMP: 50
SALES (est): 4.9MM **Privately Held**
SIC: 3699 Security control equipment &
systems

(P-20088)
TELEDYNE INSTRUMENTS INC
Also Called: Teledyne Blueview
14020 Stowe Dr, Poway (92064-6846)
PHONE..................................425 492-7400
James Volz, *Branch Mgr*
EMP: 26
SALES (corp-wide): 2.6B **Publicly Held**
SIC: 3699 Electrical equipment & supplies
HQ: Teledyne Instruments, Inc.
1049 Camino Dos Rios
Thousand Oaks CA 91360
805 373-4545

(P-20089)
TR MANUFACTURING LLC (HQ)
33210 Central Ave, Union City
(94587-2010)
PHONE..................................510 657-3850
Dom Tran, *CEO*
Jack Cho, *COO*
EMP: 250
SQ FT: 52,000
SALES (est): 108MM
SALES (corp-wide): 10.1B **Publicly Held**
WEB: www.trmfginc.com
SIC: 3699 Extension cords
PA: Corning Incorporated
1 Riverfront Plz
Corning NY 14831
607 974-9000

(P-20090)
TRI POWER ELECTRIC INC
1211 N La Loma Cir, Anaheim
(92806-1802)
PHONE..................................714 630-6445
Ronald Staley, *Owner*
Anita Staley, *CFO*
Mike Diaz, *Purch Mgr*
EMP: 13
SALES (est): 2.4MM **Privately Held**
SIC: 3699 1731 Electrical equipment &
supplies; electrical work

(P-20091)
TRIGON ELECTRONICS INC
22765 Savi Ranch Pkwy C, Yorba Linda
(92887-4620)
PHONE..................................714 633-7442
Milton L Sneller, *CEO*
Lorna R Sneller, *President*
EMP: 14
SQ FT: 18,000
SALES (est): 3.4MM **Privately Held**
WEB: www.trigonelectronics.com
SIC: 3699 Security control equipment &
systems

(P-20092)
**TURNER DESIGNS
HYDROCARBON INS**
2027 N Gateway Blvd # 109, Fresno
(93727-1648)
PHONE..................................559 253-1414
Gary Bartman, *President*
Mark Fletcher, *Corp Secy*
EMP: 43
SQ FT: 17,000
SALES (est): 8.3MM **Privately Held**
WEB: www.oilinwatermonitors.com
SIC: 3699 Electrical equipment & supplies

(P-20093)
ULTRA-STEREO LABS INC
Also Called: U S L
181 Bonetti Dr, San Luis Obispo
(93401-7397)
PHONE..................................805 549-0161
James A Cashin, *President*
Jack Cashin, *President*
Linda Wilhelmi, *Executive*
Dj Layland, *Info Tech Mgr*
Larry Hildenbrand, *Engrg Dir*

▲ = Import ▼=Export
◆ =Import/Export

▲ **EMP:** 48
SQ FT: 15,000
SALES (est): 11.5MM
SALES (corp-wide): 91.4MM **Privately Held**
WEB: www.uslinc.com
SIC: 3699 Electric sound equipment
PA: Qsc, Llc
 1675 Macarthur Blvd
 Costa Mesa CA 92626
 714 754-6175

(P-20094)
UNDERSEA SYSTEMS INTL INC
Also Called: Ocean Technology Systems
3133 W Harvard St, Santa Ana
(92704-3912)
PHONE.................................714 754-7848
Michael R Pelissier, *President*
Jerry Peck, *Chairman*
◆ **EMP:** 62
SQ FT: 18,000
SALES (est): 13.3MM **Privately Held**
WEB: www.oceantechnologysystems.com
SIC: 3699 8711 Underwater sound equipment; acoustical engineering; electrical or electronic engineering

(P-20095)
UNITED SECURITY PRODUCTS INC
Also Called: Amtek
13250 Gregg St Ste B, Poway
(92064-7164)
P.O. Box 785 (92074-0785)
PHONE.................................800 227-1592
Ted R Greene, *President*
Linda Ulrich, *Supervisor*
▲ **EMP:** 32
SQ FT: 16,000
SALES (est): 6.5MM **Privately Held**
WEB: www.unitedsecurity.com
SIC: 3699 5999 Security devices; alarm signal systems; safety supplies & equipment

(P-20096)
USA TOPDON LLC
18351 Colima Rd Unit 255, Rowland Heights (91748-2791)
PHONE.................................833 233-5535
Ke Lou,
EMP: 10
SALES (est): 350K **Privately Held**
SIC: 3699 Automotive driving simulators (training aids), electronic

(P-20097)
USA VISION SYSTEMS INC (HQ)
9301 Irvine Blvd, Irvine (92618-1669)
PHONE.................................949 583-1519
Kuang Cheng Tai, *President*
Mike Liu, *General Mgr*
▲ **EMP:** 40
SALES (est): 14.4MM
SALES (corp-wide): 52.7MM **Privately Held**
WEB: www.usavisionsys.com
SIC: 3699 Security control equipment & systems
PA: Geovision Inc.
 9f, 246, Nei Hu Rd., Sec. 1,
 Taipei City TAP 11493
 287 978-377

(P-20098)
VIAVI SOLUTIONS INC
Also Called: Jsdu
2789 Northpoint Pkwy, Santa Rosa
(95407-7350)
PHONE.................................707 545-6440
Toni McWilliamns, *Principal*
Fred Van Milligen, *General Mgr*
Leland Black, *Design Engr*
Prasad Kunigiri, *Technology*
John Olson, *Train & Dev Mgr*
EMP: 200
SALES (corp-wide): 811.4MM **Publicly Held**
WEB: www.jdsuniphase.com
SIC: 3699 Laser systems & equipment
PA: Viavi Solutions Inc.
 6001 America Center Dr # 6
 San Jose CA 95002
 408 404-3600

(P-20099)
VIAVI SOLUTIONS INC
Also Called: Jdsu
1750 Automation Pkwy, San Jose
(95131-1873)
PHONE.................................408 546-5000
Garry Ronco, *Manager*
Paul McNab, *Exec VP*
Ralph Rondione, *Senior VP*
Don O' Connor, *Vice Pres*
Kevin Siebert, *Vice Pres*
EMP: 200
SALES (corp-wide): 880.4MM **Publicly Held**
WEB: www.jdsuniphase.com
SIC: 3699 Electrical equipment & supplies
PA: Viavi Solutions Inc.
 6001 America Center Dr # 6
 San Jose CA 95002
 408 404-3600

(P-20100)
VIDEO SIMPLEX INC
5160 Mercury Pt Ste C, San Diego
(92111-1225)
PHONE.................................858 467-9762
Richard Hinckley, *President*
Larry Dodds, *Data Proc Exec*
EMP: 15
SALES (est): 1.6MM **Privately Held**
WEB: www.videosimplex.com
SIC: 3699 Electrical equipment & supplies

(P-20101)
VIGITRON INC
7810 Trade St 100, San Diego
(92121-2445)
PHONE.................................858 484-5209
Ali Eghbal, *President*
Neil Heller, *VP Bus Dvlpt*
Jeff Wood, *General Mgr*
Gabriela Mendoza, *Accountant*
Loi Thai, *Buyer*
▲ **EMP:** 10
SALES (est): 2.3MM **Privately Held**
WEB: www.vigitron.com
SIC: 3699 3669 Security devices; visual communication systems

(P-20102)
VIKING ACCESS SYSTEMS LLC
631 Wald, Irvine (92618-4628)
PHONE.................................949 753-1280
Ali Tehranchi, *Mng Member*
Cesar Delgado, *Technical Staff*
Daniel Perez, *Opers Mgr*
Chris Mazzuckis, *Natl Sales Mgr*
Gio Carrillo, *Regl Sales Mgr*
▲ **EMP:** 23
SALES (est): 4.6MM **Privately Held**
SIC: 3699 3625 Security control equipment & systems; relays & industrial controls; control equipment, electric

(P-20103)
VISIONARY SOLUTIONS INC
2060 Alameda Padre Serra, Santa Barbara
(93103-1713)
PHONE.................................805 845-8900
Jordan Christoff, *President*
William Bakewell, *Vice Pres*
Scott Freshman, *Vice Pres*
EMP: 11
SQ FT: 3,600
SALES (est): 4.5MM **Privately Held**
WEB: www.vsicam.com
SIC: 3699 8731 Electrical equipment & supplies; electronic research

(P-20104)
VMANOO INC
480 Rosemarie Dr, Arcadia (91007-8316)
PHONE.................................626 662-1342
Zhifeng Xiao, *CEO*
EMP: 10
SALES (est): 419K **Privately Held**
SIC: 3699 Christmas tree lighting sets, electric

(P-20105)
VORTRAN LASER TECHNOLOGY INC
21 Golden Land Ct Ste 200, Sacramento
(95834-2426)
PHONE.................................916 283-8208
Doug Wilner, *CEO*

Gordon Wong, *President*
James Lee, *Exec VP*
EMP: 10
SALES: 684.8K
SALES (corp-wide): 3.8MM **Privately Held**
SIC: 3699 Laser systems & equipment
PA: Vortran Medical Technology 1, Inc
 21 Golden Land Ct Ste 100
 Sacramento CA 95834
 916 648-8460

(P-20106)
VTI INSTRUMENTS CORPORATION (HQ)
2031 Main St, Irvine (92614-6509)
PHONE.................................949 955-1894
Paul Dhillon, *CEO*
Jasdeep Dhillon, *President*
▲ **EMP:** 38
SQ FT: 11,500
SALES (est): 11.3MM
SALES (corp-wide): 4.3B **Publicly Held**
WEB: www.vxitech.com
SIC: 3699 Electrical equipment & supplies
PA: Ametek, Inc.
 1100 Cassatt Rd
 Berwyn PA 19312
 610 647-2121

(P-20107)
WECKWORTH ELECTRIC GROUP INC
1261 Hawks Flight Ct A, El Dorado Hills
(95762-9684)
PHONE.................................916 933-3066
Jeffrey T Baggaley, *CEO*
EMP: 13
SALES (est): 1.8MM **Privately Held**
SIC: 3699 Electrical equipment & supplies

(P-20108)
WEIN PRODUCTS INC
880 W 1st St Apt 315, Los Angeles
(90012-2430)
PHONE.................................213 749-6250
Stan Weinberg, *President*
Christine Weinberg, *Vice Pres*
Laurel Calfee, *Office Mgr*
▲ **EMP:** 25
SQ FT: 7,000
SALES (est): 4.3MM **Privately Held**
SIC: 3699 3634 3861 3564 Photographic control systems, electronic; humidifiers, electric: household; photographic equipment & supplies; blowers & fans

(P-20109)
WEST COAST CHAIN MFG CO
Also Called: Key-Bak
4245 Pacific Privado, Ontario
(91761-1588)
P.O. Box 9088 (91762-9088)
PHONE.................................909 923-7800
Boake Paugh, *President*
Mike Winegar, *Vice Pres*
▲ **EMP:** 50 **EST:** 1948
SQ FT: 31,000
SALES (est): 10.9MM **Privately Held**
WEB: www.keybak.com
SIC: 3699 Security devices

(P-20110)
WESTERN DNING - SCHNEIDER CAFE
3500 Pelco Way, Clovis (93612-5620)
PHONE.................................559 292-1981
Matthew Bates, *Database Admin*
Brian Mahaffey, *Network Tech*
Marcel Mendes, *QC Mgr*
J K Carpenter, *Senior Mgr*
Jensen Roy, *Senior Mgr*
▲ **EMP:** 28
SALES (est): 6.6MM **Privately Held**
SIC: 3699 Electrical equipment & supplies

(P-20111)
WESTGATE MFG INC
2462 E 28th St, Vernon (90058-1402)
PHONE.................................877 805-2252
Eryeh Hadjian, *President*
AVI Hadjian, *CFO*
▲ **EMP:** 11
SALES (est): 2.5MM **Privately Held**
SIC: 3699 Electrical equipment & supplies

(P-20112)
WESTPAK USA INC
1235 N Red Gum St, Anaheim
(92806-1821)
PHONE.................................714 530-6995
Steven Tyler, *President*
Linh Cao, *COO*
Julie Bui, *CFO*
▲ **EMP:** 10
SQ FT: 1,900
SALES (est): 1MM **Privately Held**
WEB: www.westpakusa.com
SIC: 3699 8711 Cleaning equipment, ultrasonic, except medical & dental; engineering services

(P-20113)
WG SECURITY PRODUCTS INC
2105 S Bascom Ave Ste 316, Campbell
(95008-3295)
PHONE.................................408 241-8000
Xiao Hui Yang, *CEO*
Ed Wolfe, *President*
Graham Handyside, *Vice Pres*
Tonya Williams, *Administration*
Sean Vuong, *IT/INT Sup*
▲ **EMP:** 40
SALES (est): 7.3MM **Privately Held**
WEB: www.wgspi.com
SIC: 3699 5065 Security devices; security control equipment & systems

(P-20114)
WHISTLE LABS INC
1355 Market St Fl 2, San Francisco
(94103-1307)
PHONE.................................415 692-0200
Benjamin Jacobs, *CEO*
Steven Eidelman, *COO*
Scott Neuberger, *CFO*
Kathryn Rose, *CFO*
Heather Wajer, *Chief Mktg Ofcr*
EMP: 30
SQ FT: 3,000
SALES (est): 4.8MM **Privately Held**
SIC: 3699 3824 Electrical equipment & supplies; totalizing meters, consumption registering

(P-20115)
XENONICS INC
3186 Lionshead Ave # 100, Carlsbad
(92010-4700)
PHONE.................................760 477-8900
Alan Magerman, *Ch of Bd*
Jeff Kennedy, *President*
Rick Kay, *CFO*
EMP: 10
SQ FT: 10,000
SALES (est): 2.4MM **Privately Held**
WEB: www.xenonics.com
SIC: 3699 High-energy particle physics equipment

(P-20116)
XIRGO TECHNOLOGIES LLC
188 Camino Ruiz Fl 2, Camarillo
(93012-6700)
PHONE.................................805 319-4079
Roberto Piolanti, *CEO*
Mark Grout, *CFO*
Shawn Aleman, *Chief Mktg Ofcr*
Nader Barakat Sr, *Principal*
Don Bosch Sr, *Principal*
EMP: 30
SALES (est): 7.3MM **Privately Held**
SIC: 3699 Electronic training devices

(P-20117)
YASKAWA AMERICA INC
47215 Lakeview Blvd, Fremont
(94538-6530)
PHONE.................................510 651-5204
Noel Sarmiento, *Branch Mgr*
EMP: 25
SALES (corp-wide): 4B **Privately Held**
WEB: www.methodsmachine.com
SIC: 3699 Electrical equipment & supplies
HQ: Yaskawa America, Inc.
 2121 Norman Dr
 Waukegan IL 60085
 847 887-7000

P
R
O
D
U
C
T
S

&

S
V
C
S

(P-20118)
ZECO SYSTEMS INC (HQ)
Also Called: Greenlots
925 N La Brea Ave, West Hollywood
(90038-2321)
PHONE..................................888 751-8560
Brett Hauser, *CEO*
Lin-Dhuang Khoo, *Senior VP*
Harmeet Singh, *CTO*
Ron Mahabir, *Director*
EMP: 20 **EST:** 2012
SQ FT: 2,000
SALES: 2MM **Privately Held**
SIC: 3699 Accelerating waveguide structures
PA: Zeco Systems Pte. Ltd.
52a Amoy Street
Singapore
622 759-40

3711 Motor Vehicles & Car Bodies

(P-20119)
AB SUPPLY
45461 Fremont Blvd Ste 8, Fremont
(94538-6330)
PHONE..................................510 651-1914
Steven J Tamer, *Owner*
▲ **EMP:** 15
SQ FT: 900
SALES (est): 2.1MM **Privately Held**
SIC: 3711 Automobile bodies, passenger car, not including engine, etc.

(P-20120)
ACME MOTOR CORPORATION
Also Called: Full Potential Motor Sports
20701 Cereal St, Lake Elsinore
(92530-9650)
PHONE..................................949 370-0441
Karl Gulledge, *CEO*
EMP: 10
SALES (est): 591.7K **Privately Held**
SIC: 3711 Motor vehicles & car bodies

(P-20121)
AFTERMARKET PARTS COMPANY LLC
10293 Birtcher Dr, Mira Loma
(91752-1827)
PHONE..................................951 681-2751
Bill Coryell, *Branch Mgr*
EMP: 302
SALES (corp-wide): 2.3B **Privately Held**
SIC: 3711 Motor vehicles & car bodies
HQ: The Aftermarket Parts Company Llc
3229 Sawmill Pkwy
Delaware OH 43015
740 369-1056

(P-20122)
ALAN JOHNSON PRFMCE ENGRG INC
Also Called: Johnson Racing
1097 Foxen Canyon Rd, Santa Maria
(93454-9146)
PHONE..................................805 922-1202
Alan P Johnson, *President*
Chris Barker, *Manager*
▲ **EMP:** 24
SQ FT: 25,000
SALES (est): 3.7MM **Privately Held**
SIC: 3711 Motor vehicles & car bodies

(P-20123)
ALEPH GROUP INC
1900 E Alessandro Blvd # 105, Riverside
(92508-2311)
PHONE..................................951 213-4815
Jales Mello, *CEO*
▼ **EMP:** 26 **EST:** 2012
SALES: 4.5MM **Privately Held**
SIC: 3711 Motor vehicles & car bodies

(P-20124)
AMERICAN CARRIER SYSTEMS
2285 E Date Ave, Fresno (93706-5426)
PHONE..................................559 442-1500
Philip Sweet, *President*
David Sweet, *Admin Sec*
▲ **EMP:** 90
SQ FT: 36,552

SALES (est): 9.9MM **Privately Held**
SIC: 3711 Motor vehicles & car bodies

(P-20125)
AMERICAN CUSTOM GOLF CARS INC
15740 El Prado Rd, Chino (91710-9105)
PHONE..................................909 597-2885
Reinier Hoogenraad, *President*
Dan Hoogenraad, *Vice Pres*
Marco Hoogenraad, *Vice Pres*
Ray Hoogenradd, *Marketing Staff*
◆ **EMP:** 15
SQ FT: 9,000
SALES: 5MM **Privately Held**
WEB: www.acgcars.com
SIC: 3711 Automobile assembly, including specialty automobiles

(P-20126)
AMERICAN HX AUTO TRADE INC
Also Called: U.S. Specialty Vehicles
9373 Hyssop Dr, Rancho Cucamonga
(91730-6104)
PHONE..................................909 484-1010
Amy Lin, *Mng Member*
▲ **EMP:** 72
SALES (est): 504.6K **Privately Held**
SIC: 3711 Automobile bodies, passenger car, not including engine, etc.

(P-20127)
ATIEVA USA INC
Also Called: Lucid Motors, Inc
7500 Gateway Blvd, Newark (94560)
PHONE..................................510 648-3553
Jeffery Jia, *CEO*
Derek Jenkins, *Vice Pres*
Henry LI, *Vice Pres*
Mark Thorogood, *Program Mgr*
Vince Kim, *Sr Software Eng*
▲ **EMP:** 320 **EST:** 2007
SQ FT: 65,000
SALES (est): 112.7MM **Privately Held**
SIC: 3711 8711 Motor vehicles & car bodies; engineering services
PA: Atieva Inc
C/O: Maples Corporate Services Limited
George Town GR CAYMAN
-

(P-20128)
AUTOANYTHING INC
6602 Convoy Ct Ste 200, San Diego
(92111-1009)
PHONE..................................858 569-8111
Brandon Proctor, *President*
EMP: 132
SALES (est): 3.7MM **Privately Held**
SIC: 3711 Motor vehicles & car bodies

(P-20129)
BAATZ ENTERPRISES INC
Also Called: Tow Industries
2910 Allesandro St, Los Angeles
(90039-3407)
PHONE..................................323 660-4866
Mark Ormonde Baatz, *CEO*
John O Baatz, *President*
Helen Baatz, *Treasurer*
Juan Calvillo, *General Mgr*
Jessica Tow, *Admin Asst*
▼ **EMP:** 17
SQ FT: 12,200
SALES: 20MM **Privately Held**
SIC: 3711 5013 7538 Motor vehicles & car bodies; truck parts & accessories; truck engine repair, except industrial

(P-20130)
BECKER AUTOMOTIVE DESIGNS INC
Also Called: Becker Automotive Design USA
1711 Ives Ave, Oxnard (93033-1866)
PHONE..................................805 487-5227
Howard Bernard Becker, *CEO*
Debra Becker, *Corp Secy*
◆ **EMP:** 39
SQ FT: 35,000
SALES (est): 7.5MM **Privately Held**
SIC: 3711 Cars, armored, assembly of

(P-20131)
BESPOKE COACHWORKS INC
7641 Burnet Ave, Van Nuys (91405-1006)
PHONE..................................818 571-9900
Gabi Mashal, *CEO*
Elie Rothstein, *Vice Pres*
EMP: 12
SALES (est): 2.4MM **Privately Held**
SIC: 3711 3713 5511 Motor vehicles & car bodies; van bodies; vans, new & used

(P-20132)
CENTRIC PARTS INC
14528 Bonelli St, City of Industry
(91746-3022)
PHONE..................................626 961-5775
Dino Crescentini, *CEO*
Dan Lelchuk, *CEO*
Greg Woo, *Vice Pres*
Peter Chen, *Engineer*
Stacy Widner, *Credit Mgr*
▲ **EMP:** 87
SALES (est): 25.8MM **Privately Held**
SIC: 3711 Automobile assembly, including specialty automobiles

(P-20133)
COACHWORKS HOLDINGS INC
1863 Service Ct, Riverside (92507-2341)
PHONE..................................951 684-9585
Dale Carson, *President*
Terri L Carson, *Admin Sec*
EMP: 300
SALES (est): 30.4MM
SALES (corp-wide): 57.1MM **Privately Held**
SIC: 3711 Motor buses, except trackless trolleys, assembly of
PA: D/T Carson Enterprises, Inc.
42882 Ivy St
Murrieta CA 92562
951 684-9585

(P-20134)
DEINY AUTOMOTIVE INC
13040 Bradley Ave, Sylmar (91342-3831)
PHONE..................................818 362-5865
Ken Sapper, *President*
Diana Deiny, *Vice Pres*
Frank Deiny Jr, *Vice Pres*
Joan Sapper, *Admin Sec*
▼ **EMP:** 19
SQ FT: 14,000
SALES: 2.4MM **Privately Held**
WEB: www.1speedway.com
SIC: 3711 Chassis, motor vehicle

(P-20135)
DIME RESEARCH AND DEVELOPMENT
Also Called: Dime Racing
5542 Research Dr, Huntington Beach
(92649-1614)
PHONE..................................714 969-7879
Jonathan Kennedy, *Principal*
EMP: 50
SALES: 52MM **Privately Held**
SIC: 3711 Automobile assembly, including specialty automobiles

(P-20136)
DIMORA ENTERPRISES
3475 N Indian Canyon Dr, Palm Springs
(92262-1611)
PHONE..................................760 832-9070
Alfred Dimora, *Principal*
EMP: 15
SALES: 950K **Privately Held**
SIC: 3711 Motor vehicles & car bodies

(P-20137)
ELDORADO NATIONAL CAL INC (HQ)
9670 Galena St, Riverside (92509-3089)
PHONE..................................951 727-9300
Peter Orthwein, *CEO*
◆ **EMP:** 350
SQ FT: 62,000
SALES (est): 94.7MM **Publicly Held**
WEB: www.enconline.com
SIC: 3711 Buses, all types, assembly of

(P-20138)
ELECTRIC VEHICLES INTL LLC (PA)
1627 Army Ct Ste 1, Stockton
(95206-4100)
PHONE..................................209 939-0405
Ricky Hanna,
Carl Berg,
William H Hardacre,
Balwinder Samra,
▲ **EMP:** 47 **EST:** 1997
SQ FT: 90,000
SALES (est): 8.5MM **Privately Held**
WEB: www.evi-usa.com
SIC: 3711 Buses, all types, assembly of

(P-20139)
EVELOZCITY INC
19951 Mariner Ave Ste 150, Torrance
(90503-1738)
PHONE..................................318 849-6327
Stefan Krause, *President*
Rasmus Vandercolff, *CFO*
Richard Kim, *Vice Pres*
Ulrich Kranz, *Vice Pres*
Karl-Thomas Neumann, *Vice Pres*
EMP: 230
SQ FT: 90,000
SALES (est): 13.1MM **Privately Held**
SIC: 3711 Motor vehicles & car bodies

(P-20140)
FEDERAL SIGNAL CORPORATION
1108 E Raymond Way, Anaheim
(92801-1119)
PHONE..................................714 871-3336
EMP: 25
SALES (corp-wide): 707.9MM **Publicly Held**
SIC: 3711
PA: Federal Signal Corporation
1415 W 22nd St Ste 1100
Oak Brook IL 60523
630 954-2000

(P-20141)
FISKER AUTO & TECH GROUP LLC
3080 Airway Ave, Costa Mesa
(92626-6034)
PHONE..................................714 723-3247
EMP: 233
SALES: 300K **Privately Held**
SIC: 3711

(P-20142)
FLYER DEFENSE LLC
151 W 135th St, Los Angeles (90061-1645)
PHONE..................................310 674-5030
Gerald M Friedman, *CEO*
David Katz, *Technology*
▲ **EMP:** 20 **EST:** 2000
SALES: 3MM
SALES (corp-wide): 222.7MM **Privately Held**
SIC: 3711 3714 Military motor vehicle assembly; motor vehicle parts & accessories
PA: Marvin Engineering Co., Inc.
261 W Beach Ave
Inglewood CA 90302
310 674-5030

(P-20143)
FORD MOTOR COMPANY
1 Glen Bell Way, Irvine (92618-3344)
PHONE..................................949 453-9891
Mark Hutchins, *President*
EMP: 200
SALES (corp-wide): 156.7B **Publicly Held**
WEB: www.ford.com
SIC: 3711 Motor vehicles & car bodies
PA: Ford Motor Company
1 American Rd
Dearborn MI 48126
313 322-3000

(P-20144)
GILLIG LLC
451 Discovery Dr, Livermore (94551-9534)
PHONE..................................510 785-1500
Dennis Howard, *President*
EMP: 500

SALES (corp-wide): 1.5B **Privately Held**
SIC: 3711 Buses, all types, assembly of
HQ: Gillig Llc
451 Discovery Dr
Livermore CA 94551
510 785-1500

(P-20145)
GLOBAL ENVIRONMENTAL PDTS INC
Also Called: Global Sweeping Solutions
5405 Industrial Pkwy, San Bernardino
(92407-1803)
PHONE...................909 713-1600
Walter Pusic, *Principal*
Sebastian Mentelski, *President*
Bashkim Abdulla, *Electrical Engi*
Naomi Thompson, *Opers Mgr*
Manuel Hernandez, *Manager*
▲ **EMP:** 67
SQ FT: 104,000
SALES (est): 25.1MM **Privately Held**
SIC: 3711 Street sprinklers & sweepers (motor vehicles), assembly of

(P-20146)
GREENKRAFT INC (PA)
2530 S Birch St, Santa Ana (92707-3444)
PHONE...................714 545-7777
George Gemayel, *Ch of Bd*
George Patrick, *COO*
Sosi Bardakjian, *CFO*
Frank Ziegler, *Sales Staff*
EMP: 18
SQ FT: 51,942
SALES: 1.1MM **Privately Held**
SIC: 3711 3519 Motor vehicles & car bodies; internal combustion engines

(P-20147)
GREENKRAFT INC
2530 S Birch St, Santa Ana (92707-3444)
PHONE...................714 545-7777
George Gemayel, *CEO*
▲ **EMP:** 18
SALES (est): 846.9K **Privately Held**
SIC: 3711 Motor vehicles & car bodies
PA: Greenkraft, Inc.
2530 S Birch St
Santa Ana CA 92707

(P-20148)
HALCORE GROUP INC
Leader Industries
10941 Weaver Ave, South El Monte
(91733-2752)
PHONE...................626 575-0880
Gary Hunter, *Manager*
Garry Hunter, *Manager*
EMP: 100 **Publicly Held**
WEB: www.hortonambulance.com
SIC: 3711 Motor vehicles & car bodies
HQ: Halcore Group, Inc.
3800 Mcdowell Rd
Grove City OH 43123
614 539-8181

(P-20149)
HCHD
1175 S Grove Ave Ste 104, Ontario
(91761-3470)
PHONE...................909 923-8889
Hui Luo, *President*
EMP: 13
SALES (est): 1.4MM
SALES (corp-wide): 447.6MM **Privately Held**
SIC: 3711 Automobile assembly, including specialty automobiles
PA: Huachangda Intelligent Equipment Group Co., Ltd.
No.9, Dongyi Avenue
Shiyan 44201
719 876-7909

(P-20150)
HONDA NORTH AMERICA INC (HQ)
700 Van Ness Ave, Torrance (90501-1486)
P.O. Box 2206 (90509-2206)
PHONE...................310 781-4961
Takuji Yamada, *President*
Tetsuo Iwamura, *President*
Hiroshi Soda, *Vice Pres*
Bob Fegan, *General Mgr*

Mary Sanchez, *Administration*
EMP: 500
SQ FT: 7,000
SALES (est): 7.8B
SALES (corp-wide): 144.1B **Privately Held**
SIC: 3711 8748 Automobile assembly, including specialty automobiles; business consulting
PA: Honda Motor Co., Ltd.
2-1-1, Minamiaoyama
Minato-Ku TKY 107-0
334 231-111

(P-20151)
HYBRID KINETIC MOTORS CORP
800 E Colo Blvd Ste 880, Pasadena
(91101)
PHONE...................626 683-7330
Chuantao Wang, *CEO*
Yung Yeung, *President*
Sijun He, *Director*
Rosemary Yoo, *Receptionist*
EMP: 10
SALES (est): 1.3MM **Privately Held**
SIC: 3711 Automobile assembly, including specialty automobiles

(P-20152)
JAPANESE TRUCK DISMANTLING
940 Alameda St, Wilmington (90744-3841)
PHONE...................310 835-3100
Don Mahrin, *President*
▲ **EMP:** 15
SQ FT: 20,000
SALES: 1.2MM **Privately Held**
SIC: 3711 5015 Automobile assembly, including specialty automobiles; automotive parts & supplies, used

(P-20153)
KANDI USA INC
738 Epperson Dr, City of Industry
(91748-1336)
PHONE...................909 941-4588
Wangyuan Hu, *CEO*
Timothy Pei, *General Mgr*
▲ **EMP:** 10
SALES: 1.5MM
SALES (corp-wide): 41.6MM **Privately Held**
SIC: 3711 Motor vehicles & car bodies
PA: Zhejiang Kandi Vehicles Co., Ltd.
Inside Of Kangdi Automobile City, Industrial Park
Jinhua 32101
579 822-3988

(P-20154)
KARMA AUTOMOTIVE LLC (DH)
9950 Jeronimo Rd, Irvine (92618-2014)
PHONE...................714 723-3247
Liang Zhou, *CEO*
John Wilson, *Officer*
Joost Devries, *Vice Pres*
Mikael Elley, *Vice Pres*
Rod Hanks, *Vice Pres*
EMP: 277
SQ FT: 262,463
SALES (est): 107.9MM
SALES (corp-wide): 2.9B **Privately Held**
SIC: 3711 Motor vehicles & car bodies

(P-20155)
LIPPERT COMPONENTS INC
168 S Spruce Ave, Rialto (92376-9005)
PHONE...................909 873-0061
Andrew Zanschoick, *Manager*
EMP: 70
SALES (corp-wide): 2.1B **Publicly Held**
WEB: www.lci1.com
SIC: 3711 3469 3444 3714 Chassis, motor vehicle; stamping metal for the trade; metal roofing & roof drainage equipment; motor vehicle parts & accessories; welding on site
HQ: Lippert Components, Inc.
3501 County Road 6 E
Elkhart IN 46514
574 312-7480

(P-20156)
MARS MEDICAL RIDE CORP
23702 Main St, Carson (90745-5744)
PHONE...................310 518-1024
Ernie Soriano, *President*
Flordeliza Soriano, *Vice Pres*
EMP: 10
SQ FT: 900
SALES (est): 1MM **Privately Held**
SIC: 3711 4119 Ambulances (motor vehicles), assembly of; ambulance service

(P-20157)
MARVIN LAND SYSTEMS INC
Also Called: Marvin Group The
261 W Beach Ave, Inglewood
(90302-2904)
PHONE...................310 674-5030
Gerald M Friedman, *President*
Leon Tsimmerman, *CFO*
Shahar Rafalovitz, *Design Engr*
Maheep Singh, *Project Engr*
Andy Garba, *Warehouse Mgr*
▲ **EMP:** 44
SQ FT: 200,000
SALES (est): 15.3MM
SALES (corp-wide): 222.7MM **Privately Held**
WEB: www.marvineng.com
SIC: 3711 Military motor vehicle assembly
PA: Marvin Engineering Co., Inc.
261 W Beach Ave
Inglewood CA 90302
310 674-5030

(P-20158)
MILLENWORKS
1361 Valencia Ave, Tustin (92780-6459)
PHONE...................714 426-5500
Ellen M Lord, *CEO*
Dean Banks, *President*
Rod Millen, *CEO*
▲ **EMP:** 75
SQ FT: 76,000
SALES (est): 13.1MM
SALES (corp-wide): 14.2B **Publicly Held**
WEB: www.millenworks.com
SIC: 3711 5012 7549 8731 Military motor vehicle assembly; commercial vehicles; automotive customizing services, non-factory basis; electronic research
HQ: Textron Systems Corporation
201 Lowell St
Wilmington MA 01887
978 657-5111

(P-20159)
MODA ENTERPRISES INC
Also Called: Southern California Tow Eqp
1334 N Knollwood Cir, Anaheim
(92801-1311)
PHONE...................714 484-0076
Kamy Modarres, *President*
Hector Rivas, *General Mgr*
EMP: 11
SQ FT: 9,000
SALES: 7MM **Privately Held**
WEB: www.towequipments.com
SIC: 3711 Wreckers (tow truck), assembly of

(P-20160)
MULLEN TECHNOLOGIES INC (PA)
1405 Pioneer St, Brea (92821-3721)
PHONE...................714 613-1900
David Michery, *CEO*
Jerry Alvan, *CFO*
William Johnston, *Exec VP*
Francis McMahon, *CTO*
EMP: 11
SQ FT: 24,730
SALES (est): 4.8MM **Privately Held**
SIC: 3711 5013 Motor vehicles & car bodies; motor vehicle supplies & new parts

(P-20161)
NAVISTAR INC
14651 Ventura Blvd, Sherman Oaks
(91403-3617)
PHONE...................818 907-0129
EMP: 60
SALES (corp-wide): 8.5B **Publicly Held**
SIC: 3711 Truck & tractor truck assembly

HQ: Navistar, Inc.
2701 Navistar Dr
Lisle IL 60532
331 332-5000

(P-20162)
NEWFIELD TECHNOLOGY CORP (PA)
4230 E Airport Dr Ste 105, Ontario
(91761-3702)
P.O. Box 1290, Upland (91785-1290)
PHONE...................909 931-4405
Minoru Nitta, *President*
▲ **EMP:** 40
SALES (est): 4.1MM **Privately Held**
SIC: 3711 Motor vehicles & car bodies

(P-20163)
PHOENIX CARS LLC
Also Called: Phoenix Motorcars
401 S Doubleday Ave, Ontario
(91761-1501)
PHONE...................909 987-0815
Alexander Lee, *CEO*
Yasmin Fallah, *Info Tech Mgr*
▲ **EMP:** 16
SQ FT: 40,000
SALES (est): 4.5MM **Privately Held**
SIC: 3711 Cars, electric, assembly of
HQ: Al Yousuf Motors (L.L.C.)
Between 2nd And 3rd Interchange,
Next To Noor Bank Metro Sta Al
Dubai
433 910-50

(P-20164)
PROTERRA INC (PA)
1815 Rollins Rd, Burlingame (94010-2204)
PHONE...................864 438-0000
Ryan Popple, *President*
Josh Ensign, *COO*
Amy Ard, *CFO*
Matt Horton, *Ch Credit Ofcr*
Joann Covington, *Officer*
▲ **EMP:** 110
SQ FT: 14,000
SALES (est): 46.1MM **Privately Held**
WEB: www.proterra.com
SIC: 3711 Bus & other large specialty vehicle assembly

(P-20165)
RACEPAK LLC
Also Called: Race Pak
30402 Esperanza, Rcho STA Marg
(92688-2144)
PHONE...................888 429-4709
Fax: 949 709-5556
▲ **EMP:** 29
SQ FT: 6,000
SALES (est): 5.5MM **Privately Held**
WEB: www.csisensors.com
SIC: 3711

(P-20166)
RAMON LOPEZ
Also Called: Prestige Limousine
4752 Ijams Rd, Stockton (95210-3605)
PHONE...................209 478-9500
Ramon R Lopez, *Owner*
EMP: 10
SALES: 1MM **Privately Held**
WEB: www.prestigelimos.com
SIC: 3711 4119 Automobile assembly, including specialty automobiles; limousine rental, with driver

(P-20167)
RAYTHEON COMPANY
9400 Santa Fe Springs Rd, Santa Fe
Springs (90670-2623)
PHONE...................310 884-1825
Lisa Nguyen, *Manager*
EMP: 200
SALES (corp-wide): 25.3B **Publicly Held**
SIC: 3711 8711 Motor vehicles & car bodies; engineering services
PA: Raytheon Company
870 Winter St
Waltham MA 02451
781 522-3000

P R O D U C T S & S V C S

(P-20168)
RIPON VOLUNTEER FIREMANS ASSN
142 S Stockton Ave, Ripon (95366-2759)
PHONE..................................209 599-4209
Dennis Ditters, *Chief*
EMP: 18
SALES: 27K **Privately Held**
SIC: 3711 Ambulances (motor vehicles), assembly of; fire department vehicles (motor vehicles), assembly of

(P-20169)
SABA MOTORS INC
521 Charcot Ave Ste 165, San Jose (95131-1152)
PHONE..................................408 219-8675
Simon Saba, *President*
EMP: 10 **EST:** 2009
SALES (est): 753.3K **Privately Held**
SIC: 3711 Motor vehicles & car bodies

(P-20170)
SALEEN INCORPORATED (PA)
2735 Wardlow Rd, Corona (92882-2869)
PHONE..................................714 400-2121
Paul Wilbur, *President*
Stephen Saleen, *CEO*
Brian Walsh, *Senior VP*
Michael Simmons, *Sales Staff*
EMP: 500
SALES (est): 73.7MM **Privately Held**
SIC: 3711 Automobile assembly, including specialty automobiles; motor trucks, except off-highway, assembly of

(P-20171)
SHELBY CARROLL INTL INC (PA)
19021 S Figueroa St, Gardena (90248-4510)
PHONE..................................310 538-2914
Carroll Shelby, *Principal*
Mike Lambert, *Relations*
EMP: 28
SALES (est): 9.3MM **Privately Held**
SIC: 3711 Motor vehicles & car bodies

(P-20172)
TCI ENGINEERING INC
Also Called: Total Cost Involved
1416 Brooks St, Ontario (91762-3613)
PHONE..................................909 984-1773
Edward Moss, *President*
Sherly Prakarsa, *CFO*
EMP: 54
SQ FT: 25,000
SALES (est): 12.4MM **Privately Held**
WEB: www.totalcostinvolved.com
SIC: 3711 5531 3714 Chassis, motor vehicle; automotive & home supply stores; motor vehicle parts & accessories

(P-20173)
TESLA INC
18260 S Harlan Rd, Lathrop (95330-8757)
PHONE..................................209 647-7037
Julio Sanclemente, *Manager*
EMP: 18
SALES (corp-wide): 11.7B **Publicly Held**
SIC: 3711 Motor vehicles & car bodies
PA: Tesla, Inc.
     3500 Deer Creek Rd
     Palo Alto CA 94304
     650 681-5000

(P-20174)
TESLA INC
38503 Cherry St Ste I, Newark (94560-4717)
PHONE..................................510 896-6400
EMP: 663
SALES (corp-wide): 11.7B **Publicly Held**
SIC: 3711 Motor vehicles & car bodies
PA: Tesla, Inc.
     3500 Deer Creek Rd
     Palo Alto CA 94304
     650 681-5000

(P-20175)
TESLA INC
1055 Page Ave, Fremont (94538-7341)
PHONE..................................707 373-4035
EMP: 22

SALES (est): 5.5MM
SALES (corp-wide): 11.7B **Publicly Held**
SIC: 3711 Motor vehicles & car bodies
PA: Tesla, Inc.
     3500 Deer Creek Rd
     Palo Alto CA 94304
     650 681-5000

(P-20176)
TESLA INC (PA)
3500 Deer Creek Rd, Palo Alto (94304-1317)
PHONE..................................650 681-5000
Elon Musk, *CEO*
Robyn Denholm, *Ch of Bd*
Deepak Ahuja, *CFO*
Bradley Buss, *Bd of Directors*
Doug Field, *Senior VP*
▲ **EMP:** 225
SQ FT: 350,000
SALES (est): 11.7B **Publicly Held**
WEB: www.teslamotors.com
SIC: 3711 3714 3674 Automobile assembly, including specialty automobiles; cars, electric, assembly of; motor vehicle parts & accessories; solar cells

(P-20177)
TESLA MOTORS STORE SANTANA ROW
333 Santana Row, San Jose (95128-2000)
PHONE..................................408 249-2815
Alex Frank, *Manager*
EMP: 10
SALES (est): 1MM **Privately Held**
SIC: 3711 Motor vehicles & car bodies

(P-20178)
TIFFANY COACHWORKS INC
1771 N Delilah St, Corona (92879-1865)
PHONE..................................951 657-2680
William Auden, *CEO*
James Powel, *CEO*
▲ **EMP:** 115
SQ FT: 57,000
SALES (est): 11.2MM **Privately Held**
SIC: 3711 Motor vehicles & car bodies

(P-20179)
TOYOTA MOTOR ENGINEERING & MAN
6375 N Paramount Blvd, Lakewood (90805-3301)
PHONE..................................562 428-3604
Dom Berardesco, *Branch Mgr*
Jim Ecklund, *Purch Agent*
EMP: 86
SALES (corp-wide): 275.7B **Privately Held**
WEB: www.ttc-usa.com
SIC: 3711 3713 Motor vehicles & car bodies; truck & bus bodies
HQ: Toyota Motor Engineering & Manufacturing North America, Inc.
     25 Atlantic Ave
     Erlanger KY 41018

(P-20180)
UNDERCAR EXPRESS INC
57 N Altadena Dr, Pasadena (91107-3331)
PHONE..................................626 683-2787
Shahe Kalaydjian, *CEO*
EMP: 10 **EST:** 1995
SALES (est): 1.4MM **Privately Held**
SIC: 3711 Automobile assembly, including specialty automobiles
PA: Undercar Plus Inc.
     4100 Goodwin Ave
     Los Angeles CA 90039

(P-20181)
VALLEY MOTOR CENTER INC
Also Called: Star Racecars
10639 Glenoaks Blvd, Pacoima (91331-1613)
PHONE..................................818 686-3350
Gary E Rodrigues, *President*
▲ **EMP:** 10
SQ FT: 30,000
SALES (est): 1.4MM **Privately Held**
WEB: www.valleymotorcenter.com
SIC: 3711

(P-20182)
WARLOCK INDUSTRIES
Also Called: Tiffany Coach Builders
23129 Cajalco Rd Ste A, Perris (92570-7298)
PHONE..................................951 657-2680
Carter J Read, *CEO*
Mike Sears, *Finance Mgr*
David Perry, *Controller*
▼ **EMP:** 46 **EST:** 2009
SQ FT: 118,600
SALES (est): 7.9MM **Privately Held**
SIC: 3711 Motor vehicles & car bodies

(P-20183)
WEST COAST UNLIMITED
Also Called: West Coast Airlines
11161 Pierce St, Riverside (92505-2713)
PHONE..................................951 352-1234
H J Manning, *Manager*
L K Manning, *President*
EMP: 11
SQ FT: 6,000
SALES (est): 1MM **Privately Held**
SIC: 3711 7699 Fire department vehicles (motor vehicles), assembly of; fire control (military) equipment repair

(P-20184)
WIDE OPEN INDUSTRIES LLC
21088 Bake Pkwy Ste 100, Lake Forest (92630-2165)
PHONE..................................949 635-2292
Christian Hammarskjold, *Mng Member*
Andrew Grimshaw, *Production*
Darrin Graham, *Consultant*
EMP: 20
SALES: 950K **Privately Held**
SIC: 3711 3714 5012 Motor vehicles & car bodies; motor vehicle parts & accessories; automobiles & other motor vehicles

(P-20185)
ZOOX INC (PA)
Also Called: Zoox Labs
1149 Chess Dr, Foster City (94404-1102)
PHONE..................................650 733-9669
Carl Bass, *Chairman*
Ashu Rege, *Vice Pres*
Jesse Levinson, *CTO*
Ryan McMichael, *Technical Staff*
Paul Mueller, *Engineer*
EMP: 197
SALES (est): 120MM **Privately Held**
SIC: 3711 Automobile assembly, including specialty automobiles

---

3713 Truck & Bus Bodies

(P-20186)
ACCESS MFG INC
Also Called: Tradesman Trucktops
1805 Railroad Ave, Winters (95694-2011)
P.O. Box 519 (95694-0519)
PHONE..................................530 795-0720
John Neil, *CEO*
EMP: 11
SQ FT: 20,000
SALES (est): 1.8MM **Privately Held**
WEB: www.accessmfg.com
SIC: 3713 Truck tops

(P-20187)
ALTEC INDUSTRIES INC
1450 N 1st St, Dixon (95620-9798)
PHONE..................................707 678-0800
Adam Baxandall, *Branch Mgr*
Nicholas Franklin, *Engineer*
Mark Quiambao, *Sales Staff*
Nathan Bacchus, *Facilities Mgr*
Glenn Maier, *Manager*
EMP: 14
SALES (corp-wide): 766.2MM **Privately Held**
SIC: 3713 Truck & bus bodies
HQ: Altec Industries, Inc.
     210 Inverness Center Dr
     Birmingham AL 35242
     205 991-7733

(P-20188)
AMERICAN CUSTOM COACH INC
1255 W Colton Ave, Redlands (92374-2861)
PHONE..................................909 796-4747
Jales Mello, *President*
EMP: 14
SQ FT: 10,000
SALES (est): 2.1MM **Privately Held**
WEB: www.americancc.com
SIC: 3713 Specialty motor vehicle bodies

(P-20189)
AMERICAN TRCK TRLR BDY CO INC (PA)
100 W Valpico Rd Ste D, Tracy (95376-8198)
PHONE..................................209 836-8985
Clint Garner, *President*
Michael A Garner, *President*
Toni Ageno, *CFO*
Adam Garner, *Treasurer*
Dallas Dodson, *Vice Pres*
EMP: 42
SQ FT: 40,000
SALES (est): 8.6MM **Privately Held**
WEB: www.attbcinc.com
SIC: 3713 Truck bodies (motor vehicles)

(P-20190)
AMREP INC (PA)
1555 S Cucamonga Ave, Ontario (91761-4512)
PHONE..................................909 923-0430
Gabriel Ghibaudo, *CEO*
Steve Ford, *President*
Eric Mattson, *Vice Pres*
Eric Barnhart, *General Mgr*
Wesley Shearer, *General Mgr*
EMP: 109
SQ FT: 40,000
SALES (est): 40MM **Privately Held**
WEB: www.amrepinc.com
SIC: 3713 Truck bodies (motor vehicles)

(P-20191)
ARMENCO CATRG TRCK MFG CO INC
11819 Vose St, North Hollywood (91605-5748)
PHONE..................................818 768-0400
Gerhayr Djahani, *President*
Yres Mardros, *Vice Pres*
Arthur Djahani, *General Mgr*
EMP: 12
SQ FT: 6,000
SALES: 1.7MM **Privately Held**
WEB: www.cateringtruck.com
SIC: 3713 Truck bodies (motor vehicles)

(P-20192)
ARROW TRUCK BODIES & EQUIPMENT
1639 S Campus Ave, Ontario (91761-4364)
P.O. Box 6328, Whittier (90609-6328)
PHONE..................................909 947-3991
Raymond A Glaze, *President*
Keith Wysocki, *President*
Richard Rubio, *Corp Secy*
EMP: 27
SQ FT: 33,980
SALES: 2.5MM **Privately Held**
WEB: www.arrowtruckbodies.com
SIC: 3713 Truck bodies (motor vehicles)

(P-20193)
ARROW TRUCK SALES INCORPORATED
10175 Cherry Ave, Fontana (92335-5217)
PHONE..................................909 829-2365
Corey Garland, *Manager*
Jorge Moreno, *Administration*
Jaime Morgutia, *Sales Staff*
EMP: 11
SALES (corp-wide): 39.6B **Privately Held**
WEB: www.arrowtruckatlanta.com
SIC: 3713 Truck bodies & parts
HQ: Arrow Truck Sales Incorporated
     3200 Manchester Trfy L-70
     Kansas City MO 64129
     816 923-5000

(P-20194)
BETTS COMPANY
2867 S Maple Ave, Fresno (93725-2217)
PHONE..................................559 498-8624
Carlos Holdin, *Branch Mgr*
EMP: 46
SQ FT: 56,672
SALES (corp-wide): 70.1MM **Privately Held**
WEB: www.bettspring.com
SIC: 3713 3495 3452 3493 Truck & bus bodies; wire springs; bolts, nuts, rivets & washers; automobile springs
PA: Betts Company
2843 S Maple Ave
Fresno CA 93725
559 498-3304

(P-20195)
CALIFORNIA SUPERTRUCKS INC
14385 Veterans Way, Moreno Valley (92553-9059)
PHONE..................................951 656-2903
Chris Robinson, *President*
Tim Clark, *Vice Pres*
Bradley Myers, *Vice Pres*
EMP: 27 **EST:** 1996
SQ FT: 20,000
SALES (est): 4.6MM **Privately Held**
WEB: www.californiasupertrucks.com
SIC: 3713 3011 5014 5013 Truck bodies & parts; inner tubes, all types; pneumatic tires, all types; truck tires & tubes; truck parts & accessories

(P-20196)
COMMERCIAL MINI FREIGHTERS INC
Also Called: CMF
1524 W 15th St, Long Beach (90813-1207)
P.O. Box 9272 (90810-0272)
PHONE..................................562 437-2166
Larry Sackrison, *President*
EMP: 20
SQ FT: 20,000
SALES (est): 2.9MM **Privately Held**
WEB: www.jack-frost.com
SIC: 3713 Truck bodies (motor vehicles)

(P-20197)
COMMERCIAL TRUCK EQP CO LLC
Also Called: California Truck Equipment
12351 Bellflower Blvd, Downey (90242-2829)
PHONE..................................562 803-4466
Mark Pearlman, *President*
Jose Franco, *Engineer*
Jeff Guisto, *Marketing Staff*
EMP: 50
SALES (est): 9.7MM **Privately Held**
WEB: www.ctec-truckbody.com
SIC: 3713 Truck bodies (motor vehicles)

(P-20198)
COOKS TRUCK BODY MFG INC
9600 Del Rd, Roseville (95747-9108)
PHONE..................................916 784-3220
Jerry Cook Jr, *President*
Brian Diamond, *Treasurer*
Cindy Diamond, *Vice Pres*
EMP: 13
SQ FT: 11,400
SALES (est): 2.3MM **Privately Held**
WEB: www.cookstruckbody.com
SIC: 3713 Truck bodies (motor vehicles)

(P-20199)
DELTA STAG MANUFACTURING
Also Called: Delta-Stag Truck Body
1818 E Rosslynn Ave, Fullerton (92831-5140)
PHONE..................................562 904-6444
George Cashman Sr, *President*
EMP: 60
SQ FT: 100,000
SALES (est): 9.8MM **Privately Held**
WEB: www.deltastag.com
SIC: 3713 7549 Truck bodies (motor vehicles); specialty motor vehicle bodies; automotive maintenance services

(P-20200)
DENBESTE MANUFACTURING INC
810 Den Beste Ct Ste 107, Windsor (95492-6843)
PHONE..................................707 838-1407
Lori Denbeste, *President*
EMP: 11
SALES (est): 1.7MM **Privately Held**
SIC: 3713 Tank truck bodies

(P-20201)
DIAMOND TRUCK BODY MFG INC
1908 E Fremont St, Stockton (95205-4523)
PHONE..................................209 943-1655
Tony Teresi, *President*
Frances Teresi, *Treasurer*
EMP: 14 **EST:** 1978
SQ FT: 11,250
SALES (est): 2.7MM **Privately Held**
WEB: www.diamondtruckbody.com
SIC: 3713 Truck bodies (motor vehicles)

(P-20202)
DOUGLASS TRUCK BODIES INC
231 21st St, Bakersfield (93301-4138)
PHONE..................................661 327-0258
Rick Douglass, *President*
Jean Raley, *Corp Secy*
Deborah Douglass, *Vice Pres*
Rey Mesa, *Mfg Staff*
Jacob Araiza, *Foreman/Supr*
EMP: 24
SQ FT: 5,000
SALES (est): 5.8MM **Privately Held**
WEB: www.douglasstruckbodies.com
SIC: 3713 Truck bodies (motor vehicles)

(P-20203)
DYNAFLEX PRODUCTS (PA)
Also Called: Exhaust Tech
6466 Gayhart St, Commerce (90040-2506)
PHONE..................................323 724-1555
Robert L McGovern, *Principal*
Gil Contreras, *Vice Pres*
Rich Schevis, *Engineer*
Peter Jensen, *Maint Spvr*
Andy Ulloa, *Manager*
EMP: 75
SQ FT: 64,000
SALES (est): 20.1MM **Privately Held**
WEB: www.dynaflexproducts.com
SIC: 3713 3498 3714 Truck & bus bodies; fabricated pipe & fittings; exhaust systems & parts, motor vehicle

(P-20204)
EBUS INC
9250 Washburn Rd, Downey (90242-2909)
PHONE..................................562 904-3474
Anders B Eklov, *Ch of Bd*
Jon Switalski, *President*
Christopher Martin, *Office Admin*
Chris Mejia, *Engineer*
Lou Ellen Pruden, *Controller*
EMP: 45
SALES (est): 6MM **Privately Held**
WEB: www.ebus.com
SIC: 3713 Bus bodies (motor vehicles)

(P-20205)
FLEMING METAL FABRICATORS
2810 Tanager Ave, Commerce (90040-2716)
PHONE..................................323 723-8203
Wade M Fleming, *President*
Marc Fleming, *Vice Pres*
Mark Miles, *Engineer*
EMP: 30
SQ FT: 36,000
SALES (est): 6.4MM **Privately Held**
WEB: www.flemingmetal.com
SIC: 3713 3441 3714 3577 Truck bodies & parts; fabricated structural metal; motor vehicle parts & accessories; computer peripheral equipment; electronic computers

(P-20206)
GAYLORDS INC (PA)
13538 Excelsior Dr, Santa Fe Springs (90670-5616)
PHONE..................................562 529-7543
William G Lunney IL, *President*
Jose Escudero, *Purchasing*

EMP: 12
SQ FT: 4,800
SALES (est): 9.3MM **Privately Held**
SIC: 3713 Truck tops

(P-20207)
GENERAL TRUCK BODY INC
1130 S Vail Ave, Montebello (90640-6021)
PHONE..................................323 276-1933
Kam C Law, *President*
Peter Lee, *Treasurer*
Dana Pearce, *General Mgr*
Miles Olsen, *Manager*
Roland Tercero, *Manager*
▲ **EMP:** 99
SQ FT: 43,000
SALES (est): 13.9MM **Privately Held**
SIC: 3713 Truck bodies (motor vehicles)

(P-20208)
GILLIG LLC (HQ)
451 Discovery Dr, Livermore (94551-9534)
PHONE..................................510 785-1500
Derek Maunus, *President*
Jerry Sheehan, *Vice Pres*
Laura Hernandez, *Admin Asst*
Chuck Smith, *MIS Dir*
Bill Bear, *Info Tech Mgr*
▲ **EMP:** 277
SQ FT: 150,000
SALES (est): 230.7MM
SALES (corp-wide): 1.5B **Privately Held**
WEB: www.gillig.com
SIC: 3713 Truck & bus bodies
PA: Henry Crown And Company
222 N La Salle St # 2000
Chicago IL 60601
312 236-6300

(P-20209)
HARBOR TRUCK BODIES INC
Also Called: Harbor Truck Body
255 Voyager Ave, Brea (92821-6223)
PHONE..................................714 996-0411
Ken Lindt, *President*
Doug Anderson, *Info Tech Dir*
John Houng, *Engineer*
Randy Dickerson, *Human Res Dir*
Warren Mason, *Sales Dir*
EMP: 79
SQ FT: 50,000
SALES (est): 22.3MM **Privately Held**
WEB: www.harbortruck.com
SIC: 3713 7532 Truck bodies (motor vehicles); body shop, automotive

(P-20210)
HARDWARE IMPORTS INC
Also Called: Western Hardware Company
161 Commerce Way, Walnut (91789-2719)
PHONE..................................909 595-6201
Gayle Pacheco, *President*
Robert Pacheco, *CFO*
▲ **EMP:** 15
SQ FT: 6,000
SALES (est): 2.8MM **Privately Held**
SIC: 3713 3429 Truck & bus bodies; furniture hardware

(P-20211)
JJS TRUCK EQUIPMENT LLC
Also Called: D & H Trucking Equipment
9685 Via Excelencia # 200, San Diego (92126-7500)
PHONE..................................858 566-1155
James Coffman,
James Aland,
EMP: 25
SQ FT: 45,000
SALES (est): 402.1K **Privately Held**
SIC: 3713 7538 5013 Truck bodies (motor vehicles); truck engine repair, except industrial; truck parts & accessories

(P-20212)
LEE BROTHERS TRUCK BODY INC
18915 Roselle Ave, Torrance (90504-5618)
PHONE..................................310 532-7980
Richard Lee, *President*
Ron Lee, *Vice Pres*
EMP: 10
SQ FT: 1,800

SALES: 1.5MM **Privately Held**
WEB: www.leebrostruck.com
SIC: 3713 7532 5531 Truck bodies & parts; body shop, trucks; truck equipment & parts

(P-20213)
LIMOS BY TIFFANY INC
Also Called: Tiffany Coachworks
23129 Cajalco Rd, Perris (92570-7298)
P.O. Box 46 (92572-0046)
PHONE..................................951 657-2680
William Auden, *President*
Carter Read, *Corp Secy*
EMP: 35
SQ FT: 56,000
SALES (est): 6.5MM **Privately Held**
SIC: 3713 Specialty motor vehicle bodies

(P-20214)
MASTER BODY WORKS INC
9824 Atlantic Ave, South Gate (90280-5219)
PHONE..................................323 564-6901
James Coates, *President*
Mary R Coates, *Corp Secy*
William Hare, *Exec VP*
EMP: 25 **EST:** 1952
SQ FT: 90,000
SALES (est): 3.7MM **Privately Held**
WEB: www.masterbody.com
SIC: 3713 3714 Truck bodies (motor vehicles); motor vehicle parts & accessories

(P-20215)
MCLELLAN EQUIPMENT INC (PA)
251 Shaw Rd, South San Francisco (94080-6605)
PHONE..................................650 873-8100
Molly Mausser, *CEO*
Kristi Parres, *Corp Secy*
Scott McLellan, *Vice Pres*
Annette De Maria, *Executive Asst*
▲ **EMP:** 80
SQ FT: 12,000
SALES (est): 10.2MM **Privately Held**
SIC: 3713 3532 7532 3312 Truck bodies (motor vehicles); truck beds; mining machinery; tops (canvas or plastic), installation or repair: automotive; blast furnaces & steel mills

(P-20216)
MCLELLAN EQUIPMENT INC
13221 Crown Ave, Hanford (93230-9508)
PHONE..................................559 582-8100
Scott McLellan, *Vice Pres*
Chris Epperson, *Info Tech Dir*
EMP: 70
SALES (est): 10.9MM
SALES (corp-wide): 9.8MM **Privately Held**
SIC: 3713 3532 7532 3312 Truck bodies (motor vehicles); truck beds; mining machinery; tops (canvas or plastic), installation or repair: automotive; blast furnaces & steel mills
PA: Mclellan Equipment, Inc.
251 Shaw Rd
South San Francisco CA 94080
650 873-8100

(P-20217)
MCLELLAN INDUSTRIES INC
13221 Crown Ave, Hanford (93230-9508)
PHONE..................................650 873-8100
Victor Resendez, *Manager*
Ranae Agurrie, *Sales Mgr*
EMP: 80
SALES (corp-wide): 23.2MM **Privately Held**
WEB: www.mclellanindustries.com
SIC: 3713 Truck bodies (motor vehicles)
PA: Mclellan Industries, Inc.
251 Shaw Rd
South San Francisco CA 94080
650 873-8100

(P-20218)
MCNEILUS TRUCK AND MFG INC
401 N Pepper Ave, Colton (92324-1817)
P.O. Box 1588 (92324-0849)
PHONE..................................909 370-2100
Liza Langley, *Branch Mgr*

EMP: 33
SALES (corp-wide): 6.8B **Publicly Held**
WEB: www.mcneiluscompanies.com
SIC: 3713 5511 3711 3531 Cement mixer bodies; pickups, new & used; truck & tractor truck assembly; construction machinery
HQ: Mcneilus Truck And Manufacturing, Inc.
524 County Rd 34 E
Dodge Center MN 55927
614 868-0760

(P-20219)
METRO TRUCK BODY INCORPORATED
1201 W Jon St, Torrance (90502-1288)
PHONE..................................310 532-5570
Vincent Rigali, *CEO*
Vincint X Rigali, *President*
Philip W Rigali, *CEO*
Sid Halushka, *Corp Secy*
Virginia Rigali, *Vice Pres*
▲ **EMP:** 47
SQ FT: 20,000
SALES (est): 8.3MM **Privately Held**
WEB: www.metrotruckbody.com
SIC: 3713 7532 5012 5531 Truck bodies (motor vehicles); body shop, automotive; truck bodies; truck equipment & parts

(P-20220)
MORGAN TRUCK BODY LLC
Morgan Truck Body Div
7888 Lincoln Ave, Riverside (92504-4443)
PHONE..................................951 689-0800
Barry Price, *Manager*
EMP: 90
SALES (corp-wide): 1.2B **Privately Held**
WEB: www.morgancorp.com
SIC: 3713 Truck bodies (motor vehicles)
HQ: Morgan Truck Body, Llc
111 Morgan Way
Morgantown PA 19543
610 286-5025

(P-20221)
NORCAL WASTE EQUIPMENT CO
299 Park St, San Leandro (94577-1501)
PHONE..................................510 568-8336
Otto C Ganter, *President*
EMP: 20
SQ FT: 10,000
SALES (est): 3.4MM **Privately Held**
SIC: 3713 Truck bodies (motor vehicles)

(P-20222)
PACIFIC TRUCK EQUIPMENT INC
11655 Washington Blvd, Whittier (90606-2424)
PHONE..................................562 464-9674
Julie Hargrave, *CEO*
John Hargrave, *President*
EMP: 73
SALES (est): 18.4MM **Privately Held**
WEB: www.pacifictruckequipment.com
SIC: 3713 Truck bodies (motor vehicles)

(P-20223)
PACIFIC TRUCK TANK INC
7029 Florin Perkins Rd A, Sacramento (95828-2656)
PHONE..................................916 379-9280
Kirby Fleming, *President*
Jerry Jones, *Vice Pres*
EMP: 20
SQ FT: 22,000
SALES (est): 4.3MM **Privately Held**
WEB: www.pacifictrucktank.com
SIC: 3713 Truck beds

(P-20224)
PHENIX ENTERPRISES INC (PA)
Also Called: Phenix Truck Bodies and Eqp
1785 Mount Vernon Ave, Pomona (91768-3330)
PHONE..................................909 469-0411
Benjamin Albertini, *Chairman*
Norma E Albertini, *President*
Rick Albertini, *CEO*
Paul Albertini, *Corp Secy*
Maria Anderson, *Sales Staff*
EMP: 40

SQ FT: 100,000
SALES (est): 7.6MM **Privately Held**
WEB: www.phenixent.com
SIC: 3713 3711 Truck bodies (motor vehicles); motor vehicles & car bodies

(P-20225)
RUSSIAN RIVER UTILITY INC
7131 Mirabel Rd, Forestville (95436-9555)
P.O. Box 730 (95436-0730)
PHONE..................................707 887-7735
Hal Wood, *President*
Jamie Dunton, *Shareholder*
Cindy Kilass, *Admin Sec*
EMP: 10
SQ FT: 1,700
SALES (est): 3.6MM **Privately Held**
WEB: www.rruwater.com
SIC: 3713 Utility truck bodies

(P-20226)
RYANGMW INC
13861 Dry Creek Rd, Auburn (95602-8482)
PHONE..................................530 305-2499
Ryan Gangemi, *Principal*
EMP: 13 **EST:** 2008
SALES (est): 1.3MM **Privately Held**
SIC: 3713 Automobile wrecker truck bodies

(P-20227)
SAF-T-CAB INC (PA)
3241 S Parkway Dr, Fresno (93725-2319)
P.O. Box 2587 (93745-2587)
PHONE..................................559 268-5541
Fred Mattern, *President*
Dan Lockie, *Corp Secy*
▲ **EMP:** 54
SQ FT: 12,000
SALES (est): 9.7MM **Privately Held**
WEB: www.saftcab.com
SIC: 3713 3532 Truck cabs for motor vehicles; truck beds; mining machinery

(P-20228)
SKAUG TRUCK BODY WORKS
1404 1st St, San Fernando (91340-2795)
PHONE..................................818 365-9123
George L Skaug, *President*
William Reeves, *Vice Pres*
EMP: 18
SQ FT: 3,200
SALES (est): 3.2MM **Privately Held**
SIC: 3713 Truck bodies (motor vehicles)

(P-20229)
SOUTHLAND MIXER SERVICE
12231 Hibiscus Rd, Adelanto (92301-1702)
PHONE..................................760 246-6080
Esteban Castilleja, *Owner*
EMP: 11
SQ FT: 15,220
SALES (est): 1.7MM **Privately Held**
SIC: 3713 Truck bodies & parts

(P-20230)
SPARTAN TRUCK COMPANY INC
12266 Branford St, Sun Valley (91352-1009)
PHONE..................................818 899-1111
Myan Spaccarelli, *President*
Ana Alfaro, *Office Mgr*
Joe Capistran, *Opers Spvr*
Dan Spaccarelli, *Sales Mgr*
EMP: 35
SQ FT: 25,000
SALES (est): 7.3MM **Privately Held**
SIC: 3713 7532 3537 Garbage, refuse truck bodies; top & body repair & paint shops; industrial trucks & tractors

(P-20231)
SPECIALTY EQUIPMENT CO
1921 E Pomona St, Santa Ana (92705-5119)
PHONE..................................714 258-1622
Richard Page, *President*
EMP: 25
SALES (est): 4.9MM **Privately Held**
SIC: 3713 3711 Truck bodies & parts; motor vehicles & car bodies

(P-20232)
SUPREME CORPORATION
Also Called: Supreme Truck Body
22135 Alessandro Blvd, Moreno Valley (92553-8215)
PHONE..................................951 656-6101
Mike Oium, *General Mgr*
Coral Ortega, *VP Human Res*
Cindy Fuller, *Purchasing*
Jon Buchholz, *Plant Mgr*
Jon Uchholz, *Plant Mgr*
EMP: 115
SALES (corp-wide): 1.7B **Publicly Held**
SIC: 3713 Truck bodies (motor vehicles)
HQ: Supreme Corporation
2581 Kercher Rd
Goshen IN 46528
574 642-4888

(P-20233)
VAHE ENTERPRISES INC
Also Called: Aa Leasing
750 E Slauson Ave, Los Angeles (90011-5236)
PHONE..................................323 235-6657
Vahe Karapetian, *CEO*
Clarence Stokes, *Asst Controller*
▲ **EMP:** 90
SQ FT: 60,000
SALES (est): 17.5MM **Privately Held**
WEB: www.aacatertruck.com
SIC: 3713 7513 Truck bodies (motor vehicles); truck leasing, without drivers

---

3714 Motor Vehicle Parts & Access

(P-20234)
6F RESOLUTION INC
5100 W Goldleaf Cir, Los Angeles (90056-1658)
PHONE..................................209 467-0490
Pete Warinne, *Manager*
EMP: 80
SALES (corp-wide): 12.3MM **Privately Held**
SIC: 3714 Motor vehicle parts & accessories
PA: 6f Resolution, Inc.
5100 W Goldleaf Cir # 215
Los Angeles CA 90056
323 292-6644

(P-20235)
A TERRYCABLE CALIFORNIA CORP
17376 Eucalyptus St, Hesperia (92345-5118)
PHONE..................................760 244-9351
Terry P Davis, *President*
EMP: 21
SQ FT: 10,000
SALES (est): 1.5MM **Privately Held**
WEB: www.terrycable.com
SIC: 3714 Motor vehicle parts & accessories

(P-20236)
AA PRODUCTS INTERNATIONAL INC (PA)
500 Balboa St A, San Francisco (94118-3823)
PHONE..................................415 752-2075
Thomas Lee, *President*
Lily Liu, *Admin Sec*
▲ **EMP:** 19
SALES (est): 1.4MM **Privately Held**
SIC: 3714 Motor vehicle parts & accessories

(P-20237)
ACME HEADLINING CO
Also Called: Acme Auto Headlining
550 W 16th St, Long Beach (90813-1510)
P.O. Box 847 (90801-0847)
PHONE..................................562 432-0281
Bob Westmoreland, *Vice Pres*
Don Young, *Director*
▲ **EMP:** 75
SQ FT: 18,000
SALES: 7.2MM **Privately Held**
SIC: 3714 Tops, motor vehicle

(P-20238)
ACSCO PRODUCTS INC
313 N Lake St, Burbank (91502-1816)
PHONE..................................818 953-2240
Thomas W Mc Intyre, *President*
EMP: 20
SQ FT: 4,000
SALES (est): 4.4MM **Privately Held**
WEB: www.acsco.net
SIC: 3714 Motor vehicle parts & accessories

(P-20239)
ADOMANI INC
4740 Green River Rd, Corona (92880-9185)
PHONE..................................951 407-9860
James L Reynolds, *Ch of Bd*
Richard A Eckert, *COO*
Michael K Menerey, *CFO*
Kevin G Kanning, *Vice Pres*
Robert E Williams, *Vice Pres*
EMP: 11
SALES (est): 425K **Privately Held**
SIC: 3714 Motor vehicle parts & accessories

(P-20240)
ADVANCE ADAPTERS INC
4320 Aerotech Center Way, Paso Robles (93446-8529)
P.O. Box 247 (93447-0247)
PHONE..................................805 238-7000
Mike Partridge, *President*
John Partridge, *Vice Pres*
Mario Darg, *Purchasing*
Dustin Bellew, *Opers Mgr*
Steve Roberts, *Sales Mgr*
▲ **EMP:** 44
SQ FT: 44,000
SALES (est): 10.1MM **Privately Held**
WEB: www.advanceadapters.com
SIC: 3714 Transmission housings or parts, motor vehicle

(P-20241)
ADVANCED CLUTCH TECHNOLOGY INC
206 E Avenue K4, Lancaster (93535-4685)
PHONE..................................661 940-7555
Tracy Nunez, *CEO*
Dirk Starksen, *President*
Daniel Starksen, *Officer*
Danette Starksen, *Admin Sec*
Rich Barsamian, *VP Sales*
▲ **EMP:** 30
SQ FT: 18,000
SALES (est): 6.9MM **Privately Held**
WEB: www.advancedclutch.com
SIC: 3714 Clutches, motor vehicle

(P-20242)
ADVANCED ENGINE MANAGEMENT INC (PA)
Also Called: A E M
2205 W 126th St Ste A, Hawthorne (90250-3367)
PHONE..................................310 484-2322
Gregory David Neuwirth, *President*
Wilson Tam, *CFO*
Peter Neuwirth, *Chairman*
Andrew Zheng, *Bd of Directors*
Cynthia Isom, *General Mgr*
▲ **EMP:** 115
SQ FT: 78,000
SALES (est): 39.1MM **Privately Held**
SIC: 3714 Motor vehicle engines & parts

(P-20243)
ADVANCED FLOW ENGINEERING INC (PA)
Also Called: Afe Power
252 Granite St, Corona (92879-1283)
PHONE..................................951 493-7155
Shahriar Nick Niakan, *President*
David Howey, *CFO*
Chris Barron, *Vice Pres*
Eric Griffith, *Vice Pres*
Stuart Miyagishima, *Vice Pres*
▲ **EMP:** 90
SQ FT: 60,000
SALES (est): 19.2MM **Privately Held**
WEB: www.afefilters.com
SIC: 3714 Motor vehicle engines & parts

(P-20244)
ADVANCED STRUCTURAL TECH INC
Also Called: Asa
950 Richmond Ave, Oxnard (93030-7212)
PHONE..................................805 204-9133
Robert Melsness, *President*
Douglas Jones, *Treasurer*
Kevin Black, *Engineer*
April Pence, *Engineer*
Albert Betkouchar, *Controller*
▼ EMP: 135
SALES (est): 30MM **Privately Held**
SIC: 3714 Wheel rims, motor vehicle

(P-20245)
ADVANTI RACING USA LLC (DH)
10721 Business Dr Ste 1, Fontana
(92337-8252)
PHONE..................................951 272-5930
Raymond Chan, *Principal*
EMP: 20
SALES (est): 2.5MM
SALES (corp-wide): 326.3MM **Privately Held**
SIC: 3714 Wheel rims, motor vehicle
HQ: Yhi Corporation (Singapore) Pte Ltd
2 Pandan Road
Singapore 60925
626 421-55

(P-20246)
AEC GROUP INC
Also Called: Advantage Engrg & Chemistry
3600 W Carriage Dr, Santa Ana
(92704-6416)
PHONE..................................714 444-1395
Mike Lau, *President*
Erik Waelput, *Vice Pres*
Steve Duck, *Sales Staff*
EMP: 15
SQ FT: 12,000
SALES (est): 3.5MM **Privately Held**
WEB: www.aecgroup.net
SIC: 3714 Lubrication systems & parts, motor vehicle

(P-20247)
AEP-CALIFORNIA LLC
10729 Wheatlands Ave C, Santee
(92071-2887)
PHONE..................................619 596-1925
Melvin Sheldon, *Principal*
EMP: 12
SALES (est): 2.1MM **Privately Held**
SIC: 3714 Sanders, motor vehicle safety

(P-20248)
AGILITY FUEL SYSTEMS LLC (DH)
3335 Susan St Ste 100, Costa Mesa
(92626-1647)
PHONE..................................949 236-5520
Kathleen Ligocki, *CEO*
Ron Eickeleman, *President*
William Nowicke, *COO*
Tom Russell, *CFO*
Joe Pike, *Vice Pres*
▲ EMP: 238
SALES (est): 113.9MM
SALES (corp-wide): 175.1MM **Privately Held**
SIC: 3714 Fuel systems & parts, motor vehicle
HQ: Agility Fuel Solutions Llc
3335 Susan St Ste 100
Costa Mesa CA 92626
949 236-5520

(P-20249)
AIR FLOW RESEARCH HEADS INC
28611 Industry Dr, Valencia (91355-5413)
PHONE..................................661 257-8124
Rick Sperling, *President*
Chris Sperling, *Technician*
Chris Paul, *Plant Mgr*
Jess Ulloa, *Prdtn Mgr*
Steve Arent, *Natl Sales Mgr*
▲ EMP: 40
SQ FT: 14,000
SALES (est): 8.9MM **Privately Held**
WEB: www.airflowresearch.com
SIC: 3714 Cylinder heads, motor vehicle

(P-20250)
ALL SALES MANUFACTURING INC
Also Called: AMI
5121 Hillsdale Cir, El Dorado Hills
(95762-5708)
PHONE..................................916 933-0236
Steve Dringenberg, *President*
Joanne Dringenberg, *Vice Pres*
Heath Dringenberg, *Opers Mgr*
▲ EMP: 50
SQ FT: 1,200
SALES (est): 3.8MM **Privately Held**
WEB: www.allsalesmfg.com
SIC: 3714 Motor vehicle parts & accessories

(P-20251)
AMCOR INDUSTRIES INC
Also Called: Gorilla Automotive Products
2011 E 49th St, Vernon (90058-2801)
PHONE..................................323 585-2852
Peter J Schermer, *President*
◆ EMP: 25
SQ FT: 30,000
SALES (est): 4.7MM **Privately Held**
SIC: 3714 3429 Motor vehicle wheels & parts; manufactured hardware (general)
PA: Wheel Pros, Llc
5347 S Valentia Way # 200
Greenwood Village CO 80111
-

(P-20252)
AMERICAN CYLINDER HEAD INC
499 Lesser St, Oakland (94601-4916)
PHONE..................................510 261-1590
Arvid Elbeck, *CEO*
Einer Elbeck, *Corp Secy*
David Smith, *Sales Staff*
EMP: 10
SALES (est): 2.4MM **Privately Held**
SIC: 3714 Motor vehicle parts & accessories

(P-20253)
AMERICAN CYLNDR HD RPR/EXCG
499 Lesser St, Oakland (94601-4916)
PHONE..................................510 536-1764
Arvid E Elbeck, *President*
Einer Elbeck, *Vice Pres*
EMP: 14
SQ FT: 17,000
SALES (est): 1.9MM **Privately Held**
SIC: 3714 Cylinder heads, motor vehicle

(P-20254)
AMERICAN FABRICATION CORP (PA)
Also Called: American Best Car Parts
2891 E Via Martens, Anaheim
(92806-1751)
PHONE..................................714 632-1709
Greg Knox, *President*
Jodee Jensen Smith, *Vice Pres*
Teresa Piepgrass, *Executive*
▲ EMP: 175
SALES (est): 25.1MM **Privately Held**
WEB: www.teamxenon.com
SIC: 3714 Motor vehicle parts & accessories

(P-20255)
AMERICAN RIM SUPPLY INC
1955 Kellogg Ave, Carlsbad (92008-6582)
PHONE..................................760 431-3666
Robert D Ward, *President*
Aj Ward, *Prdtn Mgr*
▼ EMP: 40
SQ FT: 20,000
SALES (est): 10.1MM **Privately Held**
SIC: 3714 Wheel rims, motor vehicle

(P-20256)
ANGELUS PLATING WORKS
1713 W 134th St, Gardena (90249-2083)
PHONE..................................310 516-1883
Gerald Bozajian, *President*
EMP: 10
SQ FT: 10,000

SALES (est): 1.5MM **Privately Held**
WEB: www.angelusplating.com
SIC: 3714 3471 Exhaust systems & parts, motor vehicle; plating & polishing

(P-20257)
APEX PRECISION TECH INC
23622 Calabasas Rd # 323, Calabasas
(91302-1594)
PHONE..................................317 821-1000
Robert Oswald, *Ch of Bd*
Jerry Jackson, *President*
Bryson Ocker, *President*
EMP: 45
SQ FT: 40,000
SALES (est): 11.7MM **Privately Held**
WEB: www.apexprecision.com
SIC: 3714 3586 3498 3462 Motor vehicle parts & accessories; measuring & dispensing pumps; fabricated pipe & fittings; iron & steel forgings

(P-20258)
APTIV SERVICES 3 (US) LLC (HQ)
30 Corporate Park Ste 303, Irvine
(92606-5133)
P.O. Box 439018, San Diego (92143-9018)
PHONE..................................949 458-3100
Kevin Clark, *Ch of Bd*
▲ EMP: 12
SALES (est): 88.5MM
SALES (corp-wide): 16.6B **Privately Held**
SIC: 3714 Motor vehicle parts & accessories
PA: Aptiv Plc
Queensway House Hilgrove Street
Jersey JE1 1
163 422-4000

(P-20259)
ARIAS INDUSTRIES INC
Also Called: Arias Pistons
275 Roswell Ave, Long Beach
(90803-1538)
PHONE..................................310 532-9737
Nicholas Arias Jr, *President*
Carmen Arias, *Vice Pres*
Neza Berri, *Managing Dir*
EMP: 20
SQ FT: 20,000
SALES (est): 3.3MM **Privately Held**
WEB: www.ariaspistons.com
SIC: 3714 Motor vehicle engines & parts

(P-20260)
AUTO TECH ENGINEERING INC
Also Called: Auto Tech Engineering Company
3870 Garner Rd, Riverside (92501-1066)
PHONE..................................909 428-9072
Katigha Wongthaweesap, *President*
Jim De Francisco, *General Mgr*
▼ EMP: 25
SALES (est): 152.4K **Privately Held**
SIC: 3714 Axles, motor vehicle

(P-20261)
AUTOLIV ASP INC
Also Called: Autoliv Seatbelt Facility
9355 Airway Rd Ste 3, San Diego
(92154-7931)
PHONE..................................619 661-9347
Alberto Garcia, *Branch Mgr*
EMP: 155
SALES (corp-wide): 10.3B **Publicly Held**
SIC: 3714 Motor vehicle parts & accessories
HQ: Autoliv Asp, Inc.
1320 Pacific Dr
Auburn Hills MI 84401
248 475-9000

(P-20262)
AUTOMOCO LLC
Also Called: B & M Racing & Prfmce Pdts
9142 Independence Ave, Chatsworth
(91311-5902)
PHONE..................................707 544-4761
Brian Applegate, *President*
EMP: 80
SALES (est): 6.3MM **Privately Held**
SIC: 3714 Transmission housings or parts, motor vehicle

(P-20263)
AUTOMOTIVE EXCH & SUP OF CAL (PA)
Also Called: AES
4354 Twain Ave Ste G, San Diego
(92120-3419)
PHONE..................................619 282-3207
John Matheson, *CEO*
Mark James Matheson, *President*
EMP: 25
SQ FT: 6,000
SALES (est): 1.5MM **Privately Held**
SIC: 3714 Motor vehicle engines & parts

(P-20264)
AZUSA ENGINEERING INC
1542 W Industrial Park St, Covina
(91722-3487)
PHONE..................................626 966-4071
James M Patronite, *CEO*
Tom Patronite, *President*
James Patronite, *Vice Pres*
Janice M Patronite, *Admin Sec*
▲ EMP: 17
SQ FT: 17,000
SALES (est): 2.7MM **Privately Held**
WEB: www.azusaeng.com
SIC: 3714 Transmission housings or parts, motor vehicle

(P-20265)
B & I FENDER TRIMS INC
1401 Air Wing Rd, San Diego
(92154-7705)
PHONE..................................718 326-4323
Albert Sasson, *President*
Yzhak Faigenblat, *Vice Pres*
Dylan Mc Cue, *Manager*
▲ EMP: 90
SQ FT: 80,000
SALES (est): 11.9MM **Privately Held**
SIC: 3714 Motor vehicle body components & frame; motor vehicle wheels & parts

(P-20266)
BAB STEERING HYDRAULICS (PA)
Also Called: Bab Hydraulics
14554 Whittram Ave, Fontana
(92335-3108)
PHONE..................................208 573-4502
William Carlson, *President*
▲ EMP: 20
SQ FT: 15,000
SALES (est): 4.9MM **Privately Held**
WEB: www.babsteering.com
SIC: 3714 3713 5084 Hydraulic fluid power pumps for auto steering mechanism; truck & bus bodies; hydraulic systems equipment & supplies

(P-20267)
BEKO RADIATOR CORES INC
2322 Bates Ave Ste A, Concord
(94520-8565)
PHONE..................................925 671-2975
John Bekakis, *President*
Bernice Bekakis, *Treasurer*
Maria Bekakis, *Admin Sec*
EMP: 20
SQ FT: 8,000
SALES (est): 2.7MM **Privately Held**
WEB: www.bekoradiator.com
SIC: 3714 Radiators & radiator shells & cores, motor vehicle

(P-20268)
BESTOP BAJA LLC
Also Called: Baja Designs
185 Bosstick Blvd, San Marcos
(92069-5932)
PHONE..................................760 560-2252
Deanne Moore, *CEO*
Pauline Salazar, *Admin Asst*
Trent Kirby, *Mktg Dir*
Diego Land, *Sales Staff*
▲ EMP: 24
SQ FT: 14,000
SALES: 5MM
SALES (corp-wide): 38.9B **Privately Held**
WEB: www.bajadesigns.com
SIC: 3714 5013 5571 Motor vehicle electrical equipment; motorcycle parts; motorcycle parts & accessories

PRODUCTS & SVCS

HQ: Bestop, Inc.
333 Centennial Pkwy Ste B
Louisville CO 80027
800 845-3567

(P-20269)
BIG GUN INC
Also Called: Big Gun Exhaust
190 Business Center Dr B, Corona
(92880-1713)
PHONE..................714 970-0423
Larry Riggs, *President*
▲ EMP: 10
SALES (est): 1.2MM **Privately Held**
SIC: 3714 Exhaust systems & parts, motor
vehicle

(P-20270)
BLOWER DRIVE SERVICE CO
Also Called: BDS
1280 W Lambert Rd Ste B, Brea
(92821-2820)
PHONE..................562 693-4302
Craig Railsback, *Partner*
Lance Railsback, *Partner*
Lance E Railsback, *Vice Pres*
EMP: 20 EST: 1969
SQ FT: 11,000
SALES (est): 3.2MM **Privately Held**
WEB: www.blowerdriveservice.com
SIC: 3714 Motor vehicle engines & parts

(P-20271)
BLUETONE MUFFLER MFG CO
9366 Klingerman St, South El Monte
(91733-2545)
PHONE..................626 442-1073
Yuki Mashiro, *Owner*
Yuki Yamashiro, *President*
Aurelia Yamashiro, *Admin Sec*
EMP: 20
SALES (est): 1.8MM **Privately Held**
SIC: 3714 Mufflers (exhaust), motor vehi-
cle

(P-20272)
BNP ENTERPRISES LLC
22902 Roebuck St, Lake Forest
(92630-2952)
PHONE..................949 770-5438
William Paulson,
EMP: 10
SALES: 100K **Privately Held**
SIC: 3714 Motor vehicle parts & acces-
sories

(P-20273)
BOSCH AUTO SVC SOLUTIONS INC (PA)
2030 Alameda Padre Serra, Santa Barbara
(93103-1704)
PHONE..................805 966-2000
Robert Jennings, *President*
EMP: 12 EST: 2012
SALES (est): 3MM **Privately Held**
SIC: 3714 3829 Motor vehicle parts & ac-
cessories; aircraft & motor vehicle meas-
urement equipment

(P-20274)
BSST LLC
5462 Irwindale Ave Ste A, Irwindale
(91706-2074)
PHONE..................626 593-4500
Lon Bell,
Sandy Grouf, *CFO*
Maurice Gunderson,
▲ EMP: 17
SQ FT: 12,000
SALES: 5MM
SALES (corp-wide): 985.6MM **Publicly Held**
WEB: www.bsst.com
SIC: 3714 Heaters, motor vehicle; air con-
ditioner parts, motor vehicle; cleaners, air,
motor vehicle
PA: Gentherm Incorporated
21680 Haggerty Rd Ste 101
Northville MI 48167
248 504-0500

(P-20275)
BULLS-EYE MARKETING INC
Also Called: GTC Manufacturing
6610 Goodyear Rd, Benicia (94510-1250)
P.O. Box 5466, Walnut Creek (94596-1466)
PHONE..................707 745-5278
Al Benaroya, *CEO*
Mario Benaroya, *Admin Sec*
EMP: 10
SALES (est): 619.7K **Privately Held**
SIC: 3714 3566 Clutches, motor vehicle;
torque converters, except automotive

(P-20276)
BUNKER CORP (PA)
Also Called: Energy Suspension
1131 Via Callejon, San Clemente
(92673-6230)
PHONE..................949 361-3935
Donald Bunker, *CEO*
Heather Mills, *HR Admin*
Mark Kranz, *Purchasing*
Kevin Taeger, *Marketing Mgr*
Boni Cambel, *Manager*
▼ EMP: 100
SQ FT: 78,000
SALES (est): 18.3MM **Privately Held**
WEB: www.energysuspension.com
SIC: 3714 Motor vehicle body components
& frame

(P-20277)
BURNS STAINLESS LLC
1041 W 18th St Ste B104, Costa Mesa
(92627-4583)
PHONE..................949 631-5120
Jack Burns,
Rick Popovits,
EMP: 10
SQ FT: 6,200
SALES (est): 118.4K **Privately Held**
WEB: www.burnsstainless.com
SIC: 3714 Exhaust systems & parts, motor
vehicle

(P-20278)
BUS SERVICES CORPORATION
Also Called: Trams International
6801 Suva St, Bell Gardens (90201-1937)
PHONE..................562 231-1770
Don Duffy, *President*
Linda Duffy, *Corp Secy*
Newton Montano, *General Mgr*
Herman Montano, *Engineer*
▼ EMP: 35
SQ FT: 70,000
SALES (est): 7.7MM **Privately Held**
SIC: 3714 Motor vehicle body components
& frame

(P-20279)
BYD MOTORS LLC (HQ)
1800 S Figueroa St, Los Angeles
(90015-3422)
PHONE..................213 748-3980
Stella LI, *CEO*
Ke LI, *President*
Michael Auftin, *Vice Pres*
Sandra Itkoff, *Vice Pres*
Fred Ni, *Vice Pres*
▲ EMP: 39
SALES (est): 2.5MM
SALES (corp-wide): 2.4MM **Privately Held**
SIC: 3714 Motor vehicle electrical equip-
ment
PA: Byd Us Holding Inc.
1800 S Figueroa St
Los Angeles CA 90015
213 748-3980

(P-20280)
C F MANUFACTURING
11867 Sheldon St, Sun Valley
(91352-1508)
PHONE..................818 504-9899
Angela Fluke, *President*
EMP: 10
SALES (est): 1.5MM **Privately Held**
SIC: 3714 Wheels, motor vehicle

(P-20281)
CALIFORNIA MINI TRUCK INC
Also Called: Full-Traction Suspension
12539 Jomani Dr, Bakersfield
(93312-3456)
PHONE..................661 398-9585
Steven D Kramer, *President*
Randall Kramer, *Vice Pres*
EMP: 10
SALES (est): 1.1MM **Privately Held**
WEB: www.full-traction.com
SIC: 3714 Motor vehicle parts & acces-
sories

(P-20282)
CALMINI PRODUCTS INC
6951 Mcdivitt Dr, Bakersfield (93313-2020)
PHONE..................661 398-9500
Randy Kramer, *President*
Steven D Kramer, *Vice Pres*
David Kampa, *Info Tech Dir*
▲ EMP: 10
SQ FT: 12,000
SALES (est): 1.8MM **Privately Held**
WEB: www.calmini.com
SIC: 3714 5961 Motor vehicle engines &
parts; automotive supplies & equipment,
mail order

(P-20283)
CAR SOUND EXHAUST SYSTEM INC
Magnaflow Performance Exhaust
1901 Corporate Ctr, Oceanside
(92056-5831)
PHONE..................949 858-5900
Don Priestley, *Sales Staff*
EMP: 51
SALES (corp-wide): 97.1MM **Privately Held**
SIC: 3714 Mufflers (exhaust), motor vehi-
cle
PA: Car Sound Exhaust System, Inc.
1901 Corporate Ctr
Oceanside CA 92056
949 858-5900

(P-20284)
CAR SOUND EXHAUST SYSTEM INC (PA)
Also Called: Magnaflow
1901 Corporate Ctr, Oceanside
(92056-5831)
PHONE..................949 858-5900
Jerry Paolone, *CEO*
Dan Paolone, *President*
Stephen Kasprisin, *CFO*
Andrea Gigliotti, *Vice Pres*
George Latos, *Vice Pres*
▲ EMP: 20
SQ FT: 45,000
SALES (est): 97.1MM **Privately Held**
SIC: 3714 Exhaust systems & parts, motor
vehicle

(P-20285)
CAR SOUND EXHAUST SYSTEM INC
Also Called: Magnaslow
30142 Ave De Las Bndra, Rcho STA Marg
(92688-2116)
PHONE..................949 858-5900
Don Billings, *Manager*
Richard Waitas, *Engineer*
EMP: 84
SALES (corp-wide): 97.1MM **Privately Held**
SIC: 3714 Exhaust systems & parts, motor
vehicle
PA: Car Sound Exhaust System, Inc.
1901 Corporate Ctr
Oceanside CA 92056
949 858-5900

(P-20286)
CAR SOUND EXHAUST SYSTEM INC
23201 Antonio Pkwy, Rcho STA Marg
(92688-2653)
PHONE..................949 858-5900
Jerry Paolone, *Branch Mgr*
EMP: 20
SALES (corp-wide): 97.1MM **Privately Held**
SIC: 3714 Exhaust systems & parts, motor
vehicle
PA: Car Sound Exhaust System, Inc.
1901 Corporate Ctr
Oceanside CA 92056
949 858-5900

(P-20287)
CENERGY SOLUTIONS INC
40967 Albrae St, Fremont (94538-2486)
PHONE..................510 474-7593
Gary Fanger, *President*
Michael Maxey, *Admin Sec*
Greg Fanger, *Director*
EMP: 10 EST: 2012
SQ FT: 2,945
SALES: 300K **Privately Held**
SIC: 3714 Propane conversion equipment,
motor vehicle

(P-20288)
CENTER LINE WHEEL CORPORATION
Also Called: Center Line Performance
Wheels
19451 Surf Dr, Huntington Beach
(92648-5598)
PHONE..................562 921-9637
Ray Lipper, *President*
▲ EMP: 100
SQ FT: 42,000
SALES (est): 17.6MM **Privately Held**
WEB: www.centerlinewheels.com
SIC: 3714 Wheels, motor vehicle

(P-20289)
CHAMPION LABORATORIES INC
740 Palmyrita Ave Ste A, Riverside
(92507-1826)
PHONE..................951 275-0715
Genaro Iniguez, *Branch Mgr*
EMP: 11
SALES (corp-wide): 753.3MM **Privately Held**
SIC: 3714 Filters: oil, fuel & air, motor vehi-
cle
HQ: Champion Laboratories, Inc.
200 S 4th St
Albion IL 62806
618 445-6011

(P-20290)
CIRCLE RACING WHEELS INC (PA)
14955 Don Julian Rd, City of Industry
(91746-3112)
PHONE..................800 959-2100
Michael Stallings, *President*
Bob Strickland, *CFO*
Sherrie Stallings, *Corp Secy*
EMP: 15
SQ FT: 45,000
SALES (est): 1.9MM **Privately Held**
WEB: www.wheelvintiques.com
SIC: 3714 5013 Wheel rims, motor vehi-
cle; wheels, motor vehicle

(P-20291)
COATES INCORPORATED
Also Called: Les Schwab
73816 S Delleker Rd, Portola
(96122-6401)
PHONE..................530 832-1533
Stoages Bill, *President*
EMP: 13
SALES (corp-wide): 1MM **Privately Held**
SIC: 3714 7534 Motor vehicle brake sys-
tems & parts; tire retreading & repair
shops
PA: Coates Incorporated
73816 S Delleker Rd
Portola CA 96122
530 832-1533

(P-20292)
COBRA ENGINEERING INC
23801 La Palma Ave, Yorba Linda
(92887-5540)
PHONE..................714 692-8180
Timothy D McCool, *Principal*
Tim Mc Cool, *President*
Linda Mc Cool, *Admin Sec*

Ken Boyko, *Technical Staff*
▲ EMP: 70
SQ FT: 33,000
SALES (est): 14.2MM **Privately Held**
SIC: **3714** Exhaust systems & parts, motor vehicle

(P-20293)
CODA AUTOMOTIVE INC
4250 Stevens Creek Blvd, San Jose
(95129-1336)
PHONE..................408 763-4071
EMP: 48 **Privately Held**
SIC: **3714** Motor vehicle parts & accessories
PA: Coda Automotive Inc
2340 S Fairfax Ave
Los Angeles CA 90016

(P-20294)
CODA AUTOMOTIVE INC
12101 W Olympic Blvd, Los Angeles
(90064-1017)
PHONE..................310 820-3611
Phil Murtaugh, *CEO*
EMP: 48 **Privately Held**
SIC: **3714** Motor vehicle parts & accessories
PA: Coda Automotive Inc
2340 S Fairfax Ave
Los Angeles CA 90016

(P-20295)
CODA AUTOMOTIVE INC
1441 Camino Del Rio S, San Diego
(92108-3521)
PHONE..................619 291-2040
EMP: 48 **Privately Held**
SIC: **3714** Motor vehicle parts & accessories
PA: Coda Automotive Inc
2340 S Fairfax Ave
Los Angeles CA 90016

(P-20296)
CODA AUTOMOTIVE INC
14 Auto Center Dr, Irvine (92618-2802)
PHONE..................949 830-7000
EMP: 48 **Privately Held**
SIC: **3714** Motor vehicle parts & accessories
PA: Coda Automotive Inc
2340 S Fairfax Ave
Los Angeles CA 90016

(P-20297)
CONE ENGINEERING INC
10883 Portal Dr, Los Alamitos
(90720-2508)
PHONE..................714 828-4861
Craig M Stenberg, *President*
Pauline Stenberg, *Chairman*
Edwin Stenberg, *Vice Pres*
▲ EMP: 13 **EST:** 1970
SQ FT: 22,000
SALES (est): 2.5MM **Privately Held**
WEB: www.coneeng.com
SIC: **3714** Exhaust systems & parts, motor vehicle

(P-20298)
COUNTERPART AUTOMOTIVE INC
419 W Brenna Ln, Orange (92867-5637)
PHONE..................714 771-1732
Walter T Froemke, *President*
Eric Froemke, *CFO*
Daniel Bowers, *Vice Pres*
▲ EMP: 10
SQ FT: 8,000
SALES (est): 1.3MM **Privately Held**
SIC: **3714** Motor vehicle parts & accessories

(P-20299)
CR LAURENCE CO INC (HQ)
Also Called: Cr Laurence
2503 E Vernon Ave, Vernon (90058-1826)
P.O. Box 58923, Los Angeles (90058-0923)
PHONE..................323 588-1281
Donald E Friese, *CEO*
Greg Rewers, *Vice Pres*

Gary Byrum, *Executive*
Jane Hanna, *Branch Mgr*
Doug Monroe, *Branch Mgr*
◆ EMP: 180
SQ FT: 170,000
SALES (est): 436MM
SALES (corp-wide): 29.7B **Privately Held**
WEB: www.crlaurence.com
SIC: **3714** 5072 5039 Sun roofs, motor vehicle; hand tools; glass construction materials
PA: Crh Public Limited Company
Stonemasons Way
Dublin 14
140 410-00

(P-20300)
CRAIG MANUFACTURING COMPANY (PA)
8129 Slauson Ave, Montebello
(90640-6621)
PHONE..................323 726-7355
Craig Taslitt, *President*
Julie Taslitt Gross, *Vice Pres*
EMP: 60 **EST:** 1976
SQ FT: 16,000
SALES (est): 5.9MM **Privately Held**
WEB: www.craigmanufacturing.com
SIC: **3714** Radiators & radiator shells & cores, motor vehicle

(P-20301)
CROWER ENGRG & SLS CO INC
Also Called: Crower Cams
6180 Business Center Ct, San Diego
(92154-5604)
PHONE..................619 690-7810
Doug Evans, *President*
H Bruce Crower, *CEO*
Loren Harris, *Vice Pres*
▲ EMP: 150
SQ FT: 40,000
SALES (est): 31MM **Privately Held**
WEB: www.crower.com
SIC: **3714** Camshafts, motor vehicle; fuel systems & parts, motor vehicle; clutches, motor vehicle

(P-20302)
CUMMINS ELECTRIFIED POWER NA
1181 Cadillac Ct, Milpitas (95035-3055)
PHONE..................408 624-1231
Joerg Ferchau, *CEO*
Andrew Frank, *CTO*
James Delarosa, *Technician*
Dana Morton, *Human Resources*
Kristal Ferchau, *Marketing Staff*
EMP: 11
SALES (est): 3.3MM
SALES (corp-wide): 20.4B **Publicly Held**
SIC: **3714** Motor vehicle electrical equipment
PA: Cummins Inc.
500 Jackson St
Columbus IN 47201
812 377-5000

(P-20303)
CURRIE ENTERPRISES
382 N Smith Ave, Corona (92880-6971)
PHONE..................714 528-6957
Raymond Currie, *President*
Charles Currie, *Vice Pres*
John Currie, *Admin Sec*
Lorraine Currie, *Manager*
▲ EMP: 50
SQ FT: 13,000
SALES (est): 13.8MM **Privately Held**
WEB: www.new9inch.com
SIC: **3714** 3599 Differentials & parts, motor vehicle; gears, motor vehicle; machine shop, jobbing & repair

(P-20304)
CUSTOM WHEELS AND ACC INC
41710 Reagan Way, Murrieta
(92562-6934)
PHONE..................714 827-5200
Connie Buck, *President*
▲ EMP: 10
SQ FT: 18,000
SALES (est): 5MM **Privately Held**
WEB: www.cwausa.com
SIC: **3714** Motor vehicle wheels & parts

(P-20305)
CYLINDER HEAD EXCHANGE INC
12677 San Fernando Rd, Sylmar
(91342-3727)
PHONE..................818 364-2371
Dennis Woolsey, *President*
Wayne Heinis, *Sales Executive*
EMP: 12
SQ FT: 8,000
SALES (est): 2MM **Privately Held**
SIC: **3714** Cylinder heads, motor vehicle

(P-20306)
D & S CUSTOM PLATING INC
11552 Anabel Ave, Garden Grove
(92843-3707)
PHONE..................714 537-5411
Fax: 714 537-5413
EMP: 13
SQ FT: 1,500
SALES (est): 1.3MM **Privately Held**
SIC: **3714**

(P-20307)
DAA DRAEXLMAIER AUTO AMER LLC
801 Challenger St, Livermore
(94551-9536)
PHONE..................864 485-1000
Andrew Bailey, *Branch Mgr*
EMP: 100 **Privately Held**
SIC: **3714** Motor vehicle parts & accessories
HQ: Daa Draexlmaier Automotive Of America Llc
1751 E Main St
Duncan SC 29334

(P-20308)
DAICEL SAFETY SYSTEMS (DH)
Also Called: Dssa AZ
2655 1st St Ste 300, Simi Valley
(93065-1580)
PHONE..................805 387-1000
Satoshi Sakamoto, *President*
Nick Bruge, *COO*
Harry Rector, *CFO*
▲ EMP: 13
SALES (est): 3.4MM
SALES (corp-wide): 4.3B **Privately Held**
SIC: **3714** Sanders, motor vehicle safety
HQ: Daicel America Holdings, Inc.
1 Parker Plz
Fort Lee NJ 07024
201 461-4466

(P-20309)
DALE C SANNIPOLI
Also Called: Hauler Racks
27616 Tyler Ave, Sun City (92585-9242)
PHONE..................760 347-2033
Dale C Sannipoli, *Owner*
EMP: 15
SQ FT: 17,000
SALES (est): 1.5MM **Privately Held**
WEB: www.haulerracks.com
SIC: **3714** Motor vehicle parts & accessories

(P-20310)
DANCHUK MANUFACTURING INC
3201 S Standard Ave, Santa Ana
(92705-5640)
PHONE..................714 540-4363
Arthur Danchuk, *President*
Daniel Danchuk, *CEO*
Tricia Sousa, *COO*
Steve Brown, *CFO*
Danny Danchuk, *Vice Pres*
▲ EMP: 71
SQ FT: 33,000
SALES (est): 13.6MM **Privately Held**
WEB: www.danchuk.com
SIC: **3714** 3465 Motor vehicle parts & accessories; automotive stampings

(P-20311)
DEE ENGINEERING INC (PA)
1600 Sierra Madre Cir, Placentia
(92870-6626)
PHONE..................714 979-4990
Edward C Fulton, *President*

Gary T Fulton, *Vice Pres*
Rick Sadler, *Vice Pres*
Gloria Martinez, *Office Mgr*
▲ EMP: 35
SQ FT: 43,000
SALES (est): 8.1MM **Privately Held**
WEB: www.deeeng.com
SIC: **3714** Motor vehicle parts & accessories

(P-20312)
DEL WEST ENGINEERING INC (PA)
Also Called: Del West USA
28128 Livingston Ave, Valencia
(91355-4115)
PHONE..................661 295-5700
Al Sommer, *Chairman*
Mark Sommer, *President*
Rosemarie Chegwin, *Vice Pres*
Guido Keijzers, *Vice Pres*
EMP: 135
SQ FT: 50,000
SALES: 22.6MM **Privately Held**
WEB: www.delwestusa.com
SIC: **3714** Motor vehicle parts & accessories

(P-20313)
DELPHI CONNECTION SYSTEMS LLC
8662 Siempre Viva Rd, San Diego
(92154-6211)
PHONE..................949 458-3155
EMP: 15 **Privately Held**
SIC: **3714**
HQ: Delphi Connection Systems, Llc
30 Corporate Park Ste 303
Irvine CA 92606

(P-20314)
DENSO INTERNATIONAL AMER INC
Also Called: Dwam
3252 Business Park Dr, Vista (92081-8525)
PHONE..................760 597-7400
Loraine Graves, *Principal*
Kazuaki Nanmo, *Vice Pres*
George Poole, *Technician*
EMP: 12
SALES (corp-wide): 47.9B **Privately Held**
SIC: **3714** Motor vehicle parts & accessories
HQ: Denso International America, Inc.
24777 Denso Dr
Southfield MI 48033
248 350-7500

(P-20315)
DENSO PDTS & SVCS AMERICAS INC
41673 Corning Pl, Murrieta (92562-7023)
PHONE..................951 698-3379
Yoshihiko Yamada, *President*
Keiko Asada, *Enginr/R&D Asst*
Jean-Michel Henchoz, *Engineer*
William Coffelt, *Senior Buyer*
Gordon Lyons, *Production*
EMP: 150
SALES (corp-wide): 47.9B **Privately Held**
SIC: **3714** Motor vehicle parts & accessories
HQ: Denso Products And Services Americas, Inc.
3900 Via Oro Ave
Long Beach CA 90810
310 834-6352

(P-20316)
DONALDSON COMPANY INC
26235 Technology Dr, Valencia
(91355-1147)
PHONE..................661 295-0800
Paul Akian, *President*
EMP: 99
SALES (corp-wide): 2.7B **Publicly Held**
WEB: www.donaldson.com
SIC: **3714** Mufflers (exhaust), motor vehicle
PA: Donaldson Company, Inc.
1400 W 94th St
Minneapolis MN 55431
952 887-3131

(P-20317)
DONOVAN ENGINEERING CORP
Also Called: Donovan Aluminum Racing Engine
2305 Border Ave, Torrance (90501-3614)
PHONE...................310 320-3772
Kathleen Donovan, *President*
Norman Woodruff, *Vice Pres*
EMP: 12
SQ FT: 15,000
SALES (est): 1.7MM **Privately Held**
WEB: www.donovanengineering.com
SIC: 3714 Motor vehicle engines & parts

(P-20318)
DOUGLAS TECHNOLOGIES GROUP INC (PA)
Also Called: Douglas Wheel
1340 N Melrose Dr, Vista (92083-2916)
PHONE...................760 758-5560
Johnny Leach, *President*
Steve Millwee, *Production*
Matthew Maringola, *Advt Staff*
▲ EMP: 40
SQ FT: 60,000
SALES (est): 11.8MM **Privately Held**
WEB: www.douglaswheel.com
SIC: 3714 Wheel rims, motor vehicle

(P-20319)
DUKES RESEARCH AND MFG INC
9060 Winnetka Ave, Northridge (91324-3293)
PHONE...................818 998-9811
Patricia Huffman, *President*
EMP: 40
SALES (est): 3.2MM **Privately Held**
SIC: 3714 Fuel pumps, motor vehicle

(P-20320)
DYNATRAC PRODUCTS CO INC
7392 Count Cir, Huntington Beach (92647-4551)
PHONE...................714 596-4461
Jim McGean, *President*
Scott Frary, *Marketing Staff*
Rob Brewer, *Manager*
Peter Le, *Manager*
EMP: 15
SQ FT: 1,600
SALES (est): 4MM **Privately Held**
WEB: www.dynatrac.com
SIC: 3714 5013 5531 Motor vehicle transmissions, drive assemblies & parts; motor vehicle supplies & new parts; truck equipment & parts

(P-20321)
EAGLE ENTERPRISES INC
Also Called: Webers Auto Parts
604 W Whittier Blvd, Montebello (90640-5236)
P.O. Box 1579 (90640-7579)
PHONE...................323 721-4741
Steve Weber, *Owner*
EMP: 23
SQ FT: 1,824
SALES (est): 2.5MM
SALES (corp-wide): 6MM **Privately Held**
SIC: 3714 5531 Automotive wiring harness sets; automotive parts
PA: Eagle Enterprises, Inc.
604 W Whittier Blvd
Montebello CA 90640
323 721-4741

(P-20322)
EDELBROCK HOLDINGS INC
2301 Dominguez Way, Torrance (90501-6200)
PHONE...................310 781-2290
Jeff Paige, *Manager*
EMP: 117 **Privately Held**
SIC: 3714 Motor vehicle parts & accessories
PA: Edelbrock Holdings, Inc.
2700 California St
Torrance CA 90503

(P-20323)
EDELBROCK HOLDINGS INC
1380 S Buena Vista St, San Jacinto (92583-4665)
PHONE...................951 654-6677
EMP: 204 **Privately Held**
SIC: 3714 Motor vehicle parts & accessories
PA: Edelbrock Holdings, Inc.
2700 California St
Torrance CA 90503

(P-20324)
EFI TECHNOLOGY INC
4025 Spencer St Ste 102, Torrance (90503-2499)
PHONE...................310 793-2505
Graham Western, *President*
Marc Nunley, *Engineer*
Josie Ross, *Purchasing*
EMP: 20
SQ FT: 3,750
SALES (est): 1.9MM **Privately Held**
WEB: www.efitechnology.com
SIC: 3714 8748 8731 Fuel systems & parts, motor vehicle; communications consulting; electronic research

(P-20325)
EGR INCORPORATED (DH)
4000 Greystone Dr, Ontario (91761-3101)
PHONE...................909 923-7075
David Camerlengo, *President*
Rod Horwill, *CEO*
▲ EMP: 110
SQ FT: 70,000
SALES (est): 21.8MM **Privately Held**
WEB: www.egrinc.com
SIC: 3714 Motor vehicle parts & accessories

(P-20326)
ENDERLE FUEL INJECTION
1830 Voyager Ave, Simi Valley (93063-3348)
PHONE...................805 526-3838
Kent H Enderle, *President*
Joan C Enderle, *Corp Secy*
Jim Rehfeld, *Vice Pres*
EMP: 20
SQ FT: 18,000
SALES (est): 4.2MM **Privately Held**
SIC: 3714 Fuel systems & parts, motor vehicle

(P-20327)
ENGINE WORLD LLC
1487 67th St, Emeryville (94608-1015)
PHONE...................510 653-4444
Parviz Jabbari,
Said Saffari,
▲ EMP: 25
SQ FT: 60,000
SALES (est): 5.6MM **Privately Held**
SIC: 3714 Rebuilding engines & transmissions, factory basis

(P-20328)
EVANS WALKER ENTERPRISES
Also Called: Evans, Walker Racing
2304 Fleetwood Dr, Riverside (92509-2409)
P.O. Box 2469 (92516-2469)
PHONE...................951 784-7223
Walker Evans, *President*
Phyllis Evans, *Corp Secy*
Randall Anderson, *Vice Pres*
Reid Nordin, *Manager*
John Umber, *Assistant*
▲ EMP: 20
SQ FT: 20,000
SALES (est): 11.5MM **Privately Held**
WEB: www.walkerevansracing.com
SIC: 3714 Motor vehicle parts & accessories

(P-20329)
EXHAUST GAS TECHNOLOGIES INC
15642 Dupont Ave Ste B, Chino (91710-7615)
PHONE...................909 548-8100
Dennis Lawler, *President*
Maria Lawler, *Vice Pres*
EMP: 12

SQ FT: 5,000
SALES (est): 1.9MM **Privately Held**
WEB: www.exhaustgas.com
SIC: 3714 3829 Exhaust systems & parts, motor vehicle; thermocouples

(P-20330)
FABCO HOLDINGS INC
151 Lawrence Dr, Livermore (94551-5126)
PHONE...................925 454-9500
Gerard Giucidi, *CEO*
Allen Sunderland, *President*
David Doden, *Vice Pres*
Michael Chapman, *Controller*
▲ EMP: 2635
SALES (est): 228.8MM **Privately Held**
SIC: 3714 Axles, motor vehicle

(P-20331)
FACTORY REPRODUCTIONS
13353 Benson Ave, Chino (91710-5246)
PHONE...................909 590-5252
David Deberry, *President*
Suzy Nelson, *Chief Mktg Ofcr*
Doug Heideman, *Vice Pres*
Mike Deberry, *Manager*
▲ EMP: 10
SQ FT: 18,000
SALES (est): 1.9MM **Privately Held**
WEB: www.factoryreproductions.com
SIC: 3714 Wheels, motor vehicle

(P-20332)
FASTER FASTER INC
Also Called: Alta Motors
185 Valley Dr, Brisbane (94005-1340)
PHONE...................415 230-0755
Marc Daniel Fenigstein, *CEO*
Derek Dorresteyn, *Officer*
Jeff Sand, *Officer*
Victor Pritzker, *Vice Pres*
Brandon Dawson, *Engineer*
▲ EMP: 42
SQ FT: 24,000
SALES (est): 7.8MM **Privately Held**
SIC: 3714 Power transmission equipment, motor vehicle; motor vehicle electrical equipment

(P-20333)
FAT PERFORMANCE INC
1558 N Case St, Orange (92867-3635)
PHONE...................714 637-2889
Ronald Fleming, *President*
J Greg Aronson, *Vice Pres*
EMP: 10 EST: 1975
SQ FT: 6,600
SALES (est): 1.3MM **Privately Held**
WEB: www.fatperformance.com
SIC: 3714 5961 7538 Motor vehicle engines & parts; automotive supplies & equipment, mail order; general automotive repair shops

(P-20334)
FCA US LLC
Also Called: Chrysler West Coast Bus Ctr
7700 Irvine Center Dr # 400, Irvine (92618-2923)
PHONE...................949 450-5111
Chris Chandler, *Manager*
EMP: 30
SALES (corp-wide): 130.8B **Privately Held**
SIC: 3714 3711 Automobile assembly, including specialty automobiles; truck & tractor truck assembly; bus & other large specialty vehicle assembly; motor vehicle engines & parts
HQ: Fca Us Llc
1000 Chrysler Dr
Auburn Hills MI 48326

(P-20335)
FLOWMASTER INC
1500 Overland Ct, West Sacramento (95691-3490)
PHONE...................916 371-2345
Bill Rider, *Branch Mgr*
EMP: 150
SALES (corp-wide): 139.7MM **Privately Held**
SIC: 3714 Mufflers (exhaust), motor vehicle

HQ: Flowmaster, Inc.
100 Stony Point Rd # 125
Santa Rosa CA 95401
707 544-4761

(P-20336)
FLOWMASTER INC (HQ)
100 Stony Point Rd # 125, Santa Rosa (95401-4131)
PHONE...................707 544-4761
Brian Appelgate, *President*
Ross Mignoli, *Treasurer*
Thomas J Caracciolo, *Admin Sec*
▲ EMP: 50
SQ FT: 160,000
SALES (est): 25.8MM
SALES (corp-wide): 139.7MM **Privately Held**
SIC: 3714 Mufflers (exhaust), motor vehicle
PA: Driven Performance Brands, Inc.
100 Stony Point Rd # 125
Santa Rosa CA 95401
707 544-4761

(P-20337)
FOOTE AXLE & FORGE LLC
3954 Whiteside St, Los Angeles (90063-1615)
PHONE...................323 268-4151
Michael F Denton Sr, *Mng Member*
Sergio Rebollo, *Technical Staff*
Rene Ramos, *Engineer*
Merrie N Denton,
▲ EMP: 32
SQ FT: 66,000
SALES: 3MM **Privately Held**
WEB: www.footeaxle.com
SIC: 3714 Differentials & parts, motor vehicle

(P-20338)
FORGIATO INC
11915 Wicks St, Sun Valley (91352-1908)
PHONE...................818 771-9779
Nisan G Celik, *CEO*
Gary Tegeleci, *Mktg Dir*
Jack Steven, *Manager*
▲ EMP: 62
SQ FT: 60,000
SALES (est): 13.5MM **Privately Held**
WEB: www.forgiato.com
SIC: 3714 Motor vehicle wheels & parts

(P-20339)
FOX FACTORY INC
Also Called: Fox Racing Shox
750 Vernon Way, El Cajon (92020-1979)
PHONE...................619 768-1800
Tim King, *Manager*
EMP: 10 EST: 2013
SALES (est): 1.6MM **Privately Held**
SIC: 3714 Motor vehicle parts & accessories

(P-20340)
FOX FACTORY INC (HQ)
Also Called: Fox Racing Shox
130 Hangar Way, Watsonville (95076-2406)
PHONE...................831 274-6500
Larry L Enterline, *CEO*
Robert C Fox Jr, *President*
Mario Galasso, *President*
Mark Jordan, *Marketing Staff*
◆ EMP: 143
SQ FT: 86,000
SALES (est): 70.7MM
SALES (corp-wide): 475.6MM **Publicly Held**
WEB: www.foxracingshox.com
SIC: 3714 Shock absorbers, motor vehicle
PA: Fox Factory Holding Corp.
915 Disc Dr
Scotts Valley CA 95066
831 274-6500

(P-20341)
FRIEDL CORPORATION
Also Called: Axles Now
1291 N Patt St, Anaheim (92801-2550)
P.O. Box 3233, Orange (92857-0233)
PHONE...................714 443-0122
Daniel Friedl, *CEO*
EMP: 15 EST: 2014
SQ FT: 5,000

SALES: 1.2MM **Privately Held**
SIC: 3714 Axles, motor vehicle

(P-20342)
FTG INC (PA)
Also Called: Filtration Technology Group
12750 Center Court Dr S # 280, Cerritos
(90703-8593)
PHONE..............................562 865-9200
Pino Pathak, *President*
Zion Dunn, *Opers Mgr*
▲ EMP: 20
SQ FT: 2,000
SALES: 4MM **Privately Held**
WEB: www.ftginc.com
SIC: 3714 5085 3069 3053 Filters: oil,
fuel & air, motor vehicle; industrial sup-
plies; bushings, rubber; castings, rubber;
grommets, rubber; packing, rubber

(P-20343)
FUEL INJECTION
CORPORATION
2246 N Macarthur Dr, Tracy (95376-2823)
PHONE..............................925 371-6551
Robert B White, *President*
Bob White, *CFO*
Janet White, *Treasurer*
Kathy White, *Admin Sec*
Tony Hart, *Engineer*
▲ EMP: 15
SQ FT: 10,000
SALES: 2MM **Privately Held**
WEB: www.fuelinjectioncorp.com
SIC: 3714 Motor vehicle parts & acces-
sories

(P-20344)
FUEL INJECTION ENGINEERING
CO
Also Called: Hilborn Fuel Injection Company
22892 Glenwood Dr, Aliso Viejo
(92656-1520)
PHONE..............................949 360-0909
Duane Hilborn, *President*
Edrias Snipes, *Vice Pres*
EMP: 12 EST: 1948
SALES (est): 1.7MM **Privately Held**
SIC: 3714 Motor vehicle parts & acces-
sories

(P-20345)
GAHH LLC (HQ)
11128 Gault St, North Hollywood
(91605-6305)
PHONE..............................800 722-2292
Rodney Wells, *CEO*
Bryan Auney, *President*
Brian Aune, *Vice Pres*
Jack Dekirmendjian, *Vice Pres*
John R Benefield,
▲ EMP: 10
SQ FT: 7,000
SALES: 1.9MM
SALES (corp-wide): 807.5K **Privately
Held**
WEB: www.gahhinc.com
SIC: 3714 7532 Motor vehicle parts &
cessories; upholstery & trim shop, auto-
motive
PA: Topdown, Inc.
633 Chestnut St Ste 1640
Chattanooga TN 37450
423 755-0888

(P-20346)
GARY SCHROEDER
ENTERPRISES
2080 Floyd St, Burbank (91504-3408)
PHONE..............................818 565-1133
Gary Schroeder, *CEO*
EMP: 10
SQ FT: 2,000
SALES (est): 1.1MM **Privately Held**
SIC: 3714 Motor vehicle parts & acces-
sories

(P-20347)
GEAR VENDORS INC
1717 N Magnolia Ave, El Cajon
(92020-1243)
PHONE..............................619 562-0060
Ken R Johnson, *CEO*
Rick Johnson, *President*
Dennis Good, *Mfg Staff*

▲ EMP: 35 EST: 1981
SQ FT: 35,000
SALES (est): 6.8MM **Privately Held**
WEB: www.gearvendors.com
SIC: 3714 Transmissions, motor vehicle

(P-20348)
GENERAL MOTORS LLC
3050 Lomita Blvd, Torrance (90505-5103)
PHONE..............................313 556-5000
Nicholas Herron, *Branch Mgr*
Mark Abent, *Manager*
EMP: 819 **Publicly Held**
SIC: 3714 3711 Motor vehicle parts & ac-
cessories; automobile assembly, including
specialty automobiles; truck & tractor
truck assembly; military motor vehicle as-
sembly
HQ: General Motors Llc
300 Renaissance Ctr L1
Detroit MI 48243

(P-20349)
GENTHERM INCORPORATED
5462 Irwindale Ave Ste A, Irwindale
(91706-2074)
PHONE..............................626 593-4500
EMP: 10
SALES (corp-wide): 985.6MM **Publicly
Held**
SIC: 3714 Motor vehicle parts & acces-
sories
PA: Gentherm Incorporated
21680 Haggerty Rd Ste 101
Northville MI 48167
248 504-0500

(P-20350)
GERHARDT GEAR CO INC
133 E Santa Anita Ave, Burbank
(91502-1926)
PHONE..............................818 842-6700
Ronald J Gerhardt, *CEO*
Mitch Gerhardt, *President*
Kurht Gerhardt, *Vice Pres*
John Kim, *General Mgr*
EMP: 46
SQ FT: 30,000
SALES: 8.8MM **Privately Held**
WEB: www.gerhardtgear.com
SIC: 3714 3728 3769 3462 Gears, motor
vehicle; gears, aircraft power transmis-
sion; guided missile & space vehicle parts
& auxiliary equipment; iron & steel forg-
ings

(P-20351)
GERMANEX IMPORTS INC
19015 Parthenia St, Northridge
(91324-3727)
PHONE..............................818 700-0441
Agop Tarpinian, *President*
EMP: 12 EST: 1987
SALES (est): 1.8MM **Privately Held**
SIC: 3714 Tops, motor vehicle

(P-20352)
GIBSON PERFORMANCE
CORPORATION
Also Called: Gibson Exhaust Systems
1270 Webb Cir, Corona (92879-5760)
PHONE..............................951 372-1220
Ronald Gibson, *President*
Julie Gibson, *CFO*
▲ EMP: 75
SQ FT: 50,000
SALES (est): 15.7MM **Privately Held**
WEB: www.gibsonperformance.com
SIC: 3714 5013 Exhaust systems & parts,
motor vehicle; motor vehicle supplies &
new parts

(P-20353)
GITS MANUFACTURING
COMPANY INC
9250 Sepulveda Blvd # 202, North Hills
(91343-3901)
PHONE..............................641 782-2105
Daryl Lilly, *President*
Michael Taylor, *Vice Pres*
▲ EMP: 114
SQ FT: 75,000

SALES (est): 20.5MM
SALES (corp-wide): 1.1B **Publicly Held**
WEB: www.gitsmfg.com
SIC: 3714 3625 3469 Lubrication systems
& parts, motor vehicle; actuators, indus-
trial; metal stampings
PA: Actuant Corporation
N86w12500 Westbrook Xing
Menomonee Falls WI 53051
262 293-1500

(P-20354)
GRANATELLI MOTOR SPORTS
INC
1000 Yarnell Pl, Oxnard (93033-2454)
PHONE..............................805 486-6644
Joseph R Granatelli, *President*
Jassper Esteban, *Info Tech Mgr*
▲ EMP: 31
SQ FT: 49,000
SALES (est): 5.4MM **Privately Held**
WEB: www.granatellimotorsports.com
SIC: 3714 Fuel systems & parts, motor ve-
hicle

(P-20355)
GROVER PRODUCTS CO (PA)
3424 E Olympic Blvd, Los Angeles
(90023-3000)
P.O. Box 23966 (90023-0966)
PHONE..............................323 263-9981
John Adam Roesch Jr, *CEO*
▲ EMP: 40
SQ FT: 60,000
SALES (est): 12.2MM **Privately Held**
WEB: www.airhorns.com
SIC: 3714 3494 5999 Motor vehicle brake
systems & parts; valves & pipe fittings;
plumbing & heating supplies

(P-20356)
GROVER PRODUCTS CO
3424 E Olympic Blvd, Los Angeles
(90023-3000)
PHONE..............................323 263-9981
John Adam Roesch Jr, *Branch Mgr*
EMP: 95
SALES (corp-wide): 12.4MM **Privately
Held**
WEB: www.airhorns.com
SIC: 3714 Motor vehicle parts & acces-
sories
PA: Grover Products Co.
3424 E Olympic Blvd
Los Angeles CA 90023
323 263-9981

(P-20357)
HALDEX BRAKE PRODUCTS
CORP
291 Kettering Dr, Ontario (91761-8132)
PHONE..............................909 974-1200
EMP: 14
SALES (corp-wide): 528.7MM **Privately
Held**
SIC: 3714 Motor vehicle parts & acces-
sories
HQ: Haldex Brake Products Corporation
10930 N Pomona Ave
Kansas City MO 64153
816 891-2470

(P-20358)
HANNEMANN FIBERGLASS INC
1132 W Kirkwall Rd, Azusa (91702-5128)
PHONE..............................626 969-7317
Harold H Hannemann, *President*
EMP: 12
SQ FT: 9,000
SALES (est): 2.1MM **Privately Held**
WEB: www.hannemannfiberglass.com
SIC: 3714 Motor vehicle parts & acces-
sories

(P-20359)
HEDMAN MANUFACTURING (PA)
Also Called: Hedman Hedders
12438 Putnam St, Whittier (90602-1002)
PHONE..............................562 204-1031
Robert Bandergriff, *President*
Ron Funfar, *Vice Pres*
Lee Robinson, *Natl Sales Mgr*
David Barlow, *Sales Staff*
▲ EMP: 45 EST: 1978

SALES (est): 13.2MM **Privately Held**
WEB: www.hedman.com
SIC: 3714 Exhaust systems & parts, motor
vehicle

(P-20360)
HELLWIG PRODUCTS COMPANY
INC
16237 Avenue 296, Visalia (93292-9675)
PHONE..............................559 734-7451
Donald Hellwig, *Ch of Bd*
Mark Hellwig, *President*
▲ EMP: 30 EST: 1946
SQ FT: 37,000
SALES (est): 10.6MM **Privately Held**
WEB: www.hellwigproducts.com
SIC: 3714 3493 Motor vehicle parts
& accessories; automobile springs; stabi-
lizing bars (cargo), metal

(P-20361)
HILBORN MANUFACTURING
CORP
Also Called: Fuel Injection Engineering
22892 Glenwood Dr, Aliso Viejo
(92656-1520)
PHONE..............................949 360-0909
Stuart Hilborn, *Director*
Duane Hilborn, *President*
Kathy Hilborn, *Treasurer*
Virgina Hilborn, *Corp Secy*
Edris Snipes, *Vice Pres*
EMP: 13 EST: 1954
SQ FT: 17,000
SALES (est): 1.7MM **Privately Held**
WEB: www.hilborninjection.com
SIC: 3714 Fuel systems & parts, motor ve-
hicle

(P-20362)
HONDA ACCESSORY AMERICA
(DH)
1900 Harpers Way, Torrance (90501-1521)
PHONE..............................310 781-5300
Hirofumi Nishikawa, *Ch of Bd*
Tatsuya Kubo, *CEO*
▲ EMP: 24
SQ FT: 20,000
SALES (est): 5.1MM
SALES (corp-wide): 144.1B **Privately
Held**
SIC: 3714 5013 Motor vehicle parts & ac-
cessories; motor vehicle supplies & new
parts
HQ: Honda North America, Inc.
700 Van Ness Ave
Torrance CA 90501
310 781-4961

(P-20363)
HONEYWELL INTERNATIONAL
INC
510 W Aten Rd, Imperial (92251-9718)
PHONE..............................760 355-3420
Mike Billasenor, *Manager*
EMP: 24
SALES (corp-wide): 40.5B **Publicly Held**
WEB: www.honeywell.com
SIC: 3714 Motor vehicle parts & acces-
sories
PA: Honeywell International Inc.
115 Tabor Rd
Morris Plains NJ 07950
973 455-2000

(P-20364)
HORSTMAN MANUFACTURING
CO INC
2371 La Mirada Dr, Vista (92081-7863)
PHONE..............................760 598-2100
Allen Bourgeois, *President*
Gary Gebhart, *COO*
▲ EMP: 30 EST: 1963
SQ FT: 13,140
SALES (est): 3.8MM **Privately Held**
WEB: www.horstmanclutches.com
SIC: 3714 3944 Motor vehicle engines &
parts; games, toys & children's vehicles

(P-20365)
HOWCO INC
Also Called: C N C
1221 W Morena Blvd, San Diego
(92110-3837)
PHONE..............................619 275-1663

(PA)=Parent Co (HQ)=Headquarters (DH)=Div Headquarters
✿ = New Business established in last 2 years

Charles H Neal, *President*
Delores Neal, *Vice Pres*
EMP: 16
SQ FT: 5,000
SALES (est): 2.5MM **Privately Held**
SIC: 3714 Motor vehicle brake systems & parts

(P-20366)
HT MULTINATIONAL INC
Also Called: Unisun Multinational
12851 Reservoir St Apt A, Chino
(91710-2908)
PHONE....................626 964-2686
Chunli Zhao, *CEO*
▲ **EMP:** 21
SALES (est): 8.7MM
SALES (corp-wide): 614.4K **Privately Held**
SIC: 3714 3429 5072 Motor vehicle brake systems & parts; filters: oil, fuel & air, motor vehicle; manufactured hardware (general); hardware
HQ: Sinatex, S.A. De C.V.
Industriales No. 1188 Pte.
Cajeme SON. 85210

(P-20367)
IDDEA CALIFORNIA LLC
Also Called: Go Rhino
589 Apollo St, Brea (92821-3127)
PHONE....................714 257-7389
Manuel Alvarez, *Mng Member*
Peter Taylor, *General Mgr*
Ron Storer,
Lilly Castillo, *Cust Mgr*
▲ **EMP:** 14
SQ FT: 50,000
SALES (est): 3.6MM **Privately Held**
WEB: www.gorhino.com
SIC: 3714 Motor vehicle parts & accessories

(P-20368)
IDRIVE INC
249 N Turnpike Rd, Santa Barbara
(93111-1928)
PHONE....................805 308-6094
Sean O'Neil, *President*
Curt Andrews, *Vice Pres*
Lucian Dragomir, *Principal*
Al Bilotti, *Technical Staff*
EMP: 17
SQ FT: 1,500
SALES (est): 3.3MM **Privately Held**
SIC: 3714 Motor vehicle parts & accessories

(P-20369)
IMPCO TECHNOLOGIES INC (HQ)
3030 S Susan St, Santa Ana (92704-6435)
PHONE....................714 656-1200
Massimo Fracchia, *General Mgr*
Ro Blackwood, *Vice Pres*
Peter Chase, *Principal*
Bert Feddeck, *Engineer*
Anthony Jordan, *Engineer*
◆ **EMP:** 160
SQ FT: 108,000
SALES (est): 116.9MM
SALES (corp-wide): 240.3MM **Privately Held**
WEB: www.impcotechnologies.com
SIC: 3714 3592 7363 Fuel systems & parts, motor vehicle; carburetors; engineering help service
PA: Westport Fuel Systems Inc
1750 75th Ave W Suite 101
Vancouver BC
604 718-2000

(P-20370)
INDIAN HEAD INDUSTRIES INC
Also Called: MGM Brakes
1184 S Cloverdale Blvd, Cloverdale
(95425-4412)
P.O. Box 249 (95425-0249)
PHONE....................707 894-3333
Bob Stutsman, *Manager*
EMP: 75

SALES (corp-wide): 64.3MM **Privately Held**
WEB: www.indianheadindustries.com
SIC: 3714 Motor vehicle brake systems & parts
PA: Indian Head Industries, Inc.
6200 Hars Tech Blvd
Charlotte NC 28269
704 547-7411

(P-20371)
INLAND EMPIRE DRIVE LINE SVC (PA)
4035 E Guasti Rd Ste 301, Ontario
(91761-1532)
PHONE....................909 390-3030
Gregory Frick, *President*
Carolyn Frick, *Corp Secy*
Jeff Gilroy, *Vice Pres*
EMP: 16
SQ FT: 7,500
SALES (est): 2MM **Privately Held**
WEB: www.iedls.com
SIC: 3714 7539 Drive shafts, motor vehicle; automotive repair shops; powertrain components repair services

(P-20372)
INNOVA ELECTRONICS CORPORATION
Also Called: Equipment & Tool Institute
17352 Von Karman Ave, Irvine
(92614-6204)
PHONE....................714 241-6800
Ieon C Chenn, *President*
Hector Guillen, *Technician*
Phuong Pham, *Engineer*
Bob Caser, *Sales Staff*
Marina Weinhold, *Sales Staff*
EMP: 29
SQ FT: 12,000
SALES (est): 14.5MM **Privately Held**
WEB: www.iequus.com
SIC: 3714 Motor vehicle electrical equipment

(P-20373)
INTERNATIONAL MERCANTILE
6102 Avenida Encinas, Carlsbad
(92011-1005)
PHONE....................760 438-2205
Terry Morehouse, *Owner*
▲ **EMP:** 10
SQ FT: 4,000
SALES (est): 835.7K **Privately Held**
WEB: www.im356-911.com
SIC: 3714 Motor vehicle parts & accessories

(P-20374)
J C S VOLKS MACHINE
Also Called: Jcs
15626 Cypress Ave, Irwindale
(91706-2119)
PHONE....................626 338-6003
Jeff Jarosz, *Partner*
Jorge Contreras, *Partner*
Brad Jarosz, *Partner*
Dave Jarosz, *Partner*
EMP: 19
SQ FT: 7,000
SALES: 700K **Privately Held**
WEB: www.jcsvwparts.com
SIC: 3714 Rebuilding engines & transmissions, factory basis

(P-20375)
JASPER ENGINE EXCHANGE INC
1477 E Cedar St Ste D, Ontario
(91761-8330)
PHONE....................800 827-7455
Roger Brenner, *Manager*
EMP: 14
SALES (corp-wide): 501.9MM **Privately Held**
SIC: 3714 4225 Rebuilding engines & transmissions, factory basis; fuel systems & parts, motor vehicle; gears, motor vehicle; general warehousing & storage
PA: Jasper Engine Exchange, Inc.
815 Wernsing Rd
Jasper IN 47546
812 482-1041

(P-20376)
JOHN BOYD ENTERPRISES INC
Also Called: JB Radiator Specialties
8441 Specialty Cir, Sacramento
(95828-2523)
PHONE....................916 504-3622
Phillip King, *Branch Mgr*
EMP: 109
SALES (corp-wide): 54.6MM **Privately Held**
SIC: 3714 Motor vehicle parts & accessories
PA: John Boyd Enterprises, Inc.
8401 Specialty Cir
Sacramento CA 95828
916 381-4790

(P-20377)
JOHN BOYD ENTERPRISES INC (PA)
Also Called: J B Enterprises
8401 Specialty Cir, Sacramento
(95828-2523)
P.O. Box 292460 (95829-2460)
PHONE....................916 381-4790
Donna Boyd, *Treasurer*
Lisa McKnight, *Executive Asst*
▲ **EMP:** 119
SQ FT: 14,000
SALES (est): 54.6MM **Privately Held**
SIC: 3714 3433 Radiators & radiator shells & cores, motor vehicle; heating equipment, except electric

(P-20378)
JOHNSON CONTROLS INC
6383 Las Positas Rd, Livermore
(94551-5103)
PHONE....................925 447-9200
Carol Skelly, *Branch Mgr*
EMP: 345 **Privately Held**
SIC: 3714 Motor vehicle body components & frame
HQ: Johnson Controls, Inc.
5757 N Green Bay Ave
Milwaukee WI 53209
414 524-1200

(P-20379)
KAMM INDUSTRIES INC
Also Called: Prp Seats
27555 Commerce Center Dr, Temecula
(92590-2519)
PHONE....................800 317-6253
Aaron Wedeking, *CEO*
Mike Doherty, *Co-Owner*
Jason Dearmond, *Sales Staff*
Scott Royce, *Sales Staff*
▲ **EMP:** 43
SALES: 6.4MM **Privately Held**
SIC: 3714 Motor vehicle parts & accessories

(P-20380)
KARBZ INC
Also Called: SSC Racing
77806 Flora Rd Ste E, Palm Desert
(92211-4108)
PHONE....................760 567-9953
Joe Ramos, *President*
Jim Boltz, *Vice Pres*
▲ **EMP:** 15 **EST:** 1994
SQ FT: 40,000
SALES (est): 1.1MM **Privately Held**
WEB: www.sscracing.com
SIC: 3714 Motor vehicle parts & accessories

(P-20381)
KENNEDY ENGINEERED PRODUCTS
38830 17th St E, Palmdale (93550-3915)
PHONE....................661 272-1147
Hobert Kennedy, *Owner*
▲ **EMP:** 14
SQ FT: 5,900
SALES: 2MM **Privately Held**
WEB: www.kennedyeng.com
SIC: 3714 Motor vehicle parts & accessories

(P-20382)
KF FIBERGLASS INC (PA)
8247 Phlox St, Downey (90241-4841)
PHONE....................562 869-1536

Ron Belk, *President*
David Ruiz, *Vice Pres*
EMP: 25
SQ FT: 35,000
SALES (est): 3.8MM **Privately Held**
SIC: 3714 Motor vehicle parts & accessories

(P-20383)
KING SHOCK TECHNOLOGY INC
12472 Edison Way, Garden Grove
(92841-2821)
PHONE....................714 530-8701
Lance King, *President*
Brett King, *Vice Pres*
Ross King, *Vice Pres*
Sharon King, *Vice Pres*
Rick Koutzoukis, *Engineer*
◆ **EMP:** 45
SQ FT: 18,000
SALES (est): 14.7MM **Privately Held**
WEB: www.kingshocks.com
SIC: 3714 Motor vehicle body components & frame

(P-20384)
KW AUTOMOTIVE NORTH AMER INC
300 W Pontiac Way, Clovis (93612-5606)
PHONE....................800 445-3767
Klaus M Wohlfarth, *President*
Darrell Edwards, *General Mgr*
Julie Sliger, *Office Mgr*
Freddie Breine, *Purch Mgr*
Robert Schuetz, *Director*
▲ **EMP:** 40
SQ FT: 115,000
SALES (est): 9MM
SALES (corp-wide): 31.8MM **Privately Held**
SIC: 3714 Motor vehicle parts & accessories
PA: Kw Automotive Gmbh
Aspachweg 14
Fichtenberg 74427
797 196-300

(P-20385)
LAPCO WEST LLC
Also Called: L A P C O
6901 Marlin Cir, La Palma (90623-1018)
PHONE....................714 773-1380
Graem Elliot, *CEO*
EMP: 20
SALES (est): 1.6MM
SALES (corp-wide): 5.6MM **Privately Held**
SIC: 3714 Motor vehicle brake systems & parts
PA: Spektrum Brakes, Llc
13140 Midway Pl
Cerritos CA 90703
714 777-2323

(P-20386)
LIQUID ROBOTICS INC (HQ)
1329 Moffett Park Dr, Sunnyvale
(94089-1134)
PHONE....................408 636-4200
Gary Gysin, *President*
Graham Hine, *Partner*
Caryn Nightengale, *CFO*
Daniel J Middleton, *Exec VP*
Mark Bindon, *Vice Pres*
▲ **EMP:** 100
SQ FT: 5,000
SALES (est): 19.5MM
SALES (corp-wide): 93.3B **Publicly Held**
WEB: www.liquidr.com
SIC: 3714 Hydraulic fluid power pumps for auto steering mechanism
PA: The Boeing Company
100 N Riverside Plz
Chicago IL 60606
312 544-2000

(P-20387)
LOGICAL TRADING CO
Also Called: Logical Clean Air Solutions
3625 E Thousand Oaks Blvd, Westlake Village (91362-3626)
PHONE....................805 230-0099
Saeid Ladjevardi, *CEO*
EMP: 10 **EST:** 2006

SALES (est): 2.1MM **Privately Held**
SIC: 3714 Exhaust systems & parts, motor vehicle

(P-20388)
LOS ANGELES SLEEVE CO INC
Also Called: La Sleeve
12051 Rivera Rd, Santa Fe Springs (90670-2211)
PHONE..................562 945-7578
Nick G Metchkoff, *President*
Sarah Metchkoff, *Shareholder*
James G Metchkoff, *Treasurer*
David Metchkoff, *Vice Pres*
Dave Lasco, *Managing Dir*
▲ EMP: 29
SQ FT: 33,000
SALES (est): 5.5MM **Privately Held**
WEB: www.lasleeve.com
SIC: 3714 Exhaust systems & parts, motor vehicle

(P-20389)
LSI PRODUCTS INC
12885 Wildflower Ln, Riverside (92503-9772)
PHONE..................951 343-9270
Alex Danze, *CEO*
▲ EMP: 70
SALES (est): 14.1MM **Privately Held**
SIC: 3714 Motor vehicle parts & accessories

(P-20390)
LUND MOTION PRODUCTS INC
Also Called: AMP Research
15651 Mosher Ave, Tustin (92780-6426)
PHONE..................949 221-0023
Mitch Fogle, *President*
Chris Schumacher, *Engineer*
Eric Bajza, *Associate*
EMP: 35 **Privately Held**
SIC: 3714 Motor vehicle parts & accessories
HQ: Lund Motion Products, Inc.
4325 Hamilton Mill Rd
Buford GA 30518
678 804-3767

(P-20391)
M C O INC
13925 Benson Ave, Chino (91710-7024)
PHONE..................909 627-3574
Leon O Martin, *President*
Vicki Martin, *Corp Secy*
EMP: 15
SQ FT: 10,000
SALES (est): 2.2MM **Privately Held**
SIC: 3714 Frames, motor vehicle

(P-20392)
M E D INC
14001 Marquardt Ave, Santa Fe Springs (90670-5088)
PHONE..................562 921-0464
Steven Moore, *CEO*
Susan Lowe, *CFO*
Joel Moore, *General Mgr*
Lydia Zuniga, *Office Mgr*
Mike Medici, *Buyer*
EMP: 70 EST: 1974
SQ FT: 40,000
SALES (est): 16MM **Privately Held**
WEB: www.dmeexpansionjoints.com
SIC: 3714 3429 Exhaust systems & parts, motor vehicle; clamps, couplings, nozzles & other metal hose fittings

(P-20393)
MAGNUSON PRODUCTS LLC
Also Called: Magnuson Superchargers
1990 Knoll Dr Ste A, Ventura (93003-7309)
PHONE..................805 642-8833
Kim Pendergast, *CEO*
Tim Krauskopf, *President*
Owen Peterson, *Project Mgr*
Tom Amick, *Engineer*
Dan Bronsten, *Engineer*
EMP: 49
SQ FT: 45,600
SALES (est): 20.9MM **Privately Held**
WEB: www.magnusonproducts.com
SIC: 3714 Motor vehicle parts & accessories

(P-20394)
MAIER RACING ENTERPRISES INC
22215 Meekland Ave, Hayward (94541-3855)
PHONE..................510 581-7600
William G Maier, *President*
Shirley J Maier, *Corp Secy*
Margaret H Maier, *Vice Pres*
EMP: 11 EST: 1969
SQ FT: 14,200
SALES (est): 1.5MM **Privately Held**
WEB: www.maierracing.com
SIC: 3714 5531 Motor vehicle parts & accessories; automotive & home supply stores

(P-20395)
MANUFACTURING & PROD SVCS CORP
Also Called: M P S
2222 Enterprise St, Escondido (92029-2015)
PHONE..................760 796-4300
Michael McGowen, *President*
EMP: 10
SQ FT: 5,400
SALES (est): 1.5MM **Privately Held**
SIC: 3714 Motor vehicle parts & accessories

(P-20396)
MARGUS AUTOMOTIVE ELC EXCH
165 E Jefferson Blvd, Los Angeles (90011-2330)
PHONE..................323 232-5281
Donald Lopez, *President*
Carolyn Lopez, *CFO*
EMP: 61
SQ FT: 28,570
SALES (est): 6.2MM **Privately Held**
SIC: 3714 3694 3621 3568 Motor vehicle parts & accessories; motor generator sets, automotive; motors, starting: automotive & aircraft; motors & generators; power transmission equipment

(P-20397)
MAXON INDUSTRIES INC
11921 Slauson Ave, Santa Fe Springs (90670-2221)
P.O. Box 3434, Los Angeles (90078-3434)
PHONE..................562 464-0099
Murray Lugash, *President*
Larry Lugash, *Exec VP*
Brenda Leung, *Vice Pres*
Lorena Baltazar, *Comms Mgr*
EMP: 75 EST: 1957
SQ FT: 250,000
SALES (est): 13.5MM **Privately Held**
SIC: 3714 Motor vehicle parts & accessories

(P-20398)
MCLEOD RACING LLC
1570 Lakeview Loop, Anaheim (92807-1819)
PHONE..................714 630-2764
Paul Lee, *President*
Lana Chrisman, *Vice Pres*
EMP: 10
SQ FT: 17,500
SALES (est): 2.1MM **Privately Held**
SIC: 3714 Clutches, motor vehicle

(P-20399)
MERITOR SPECIALTY PRODUCTS LLC (HQ)
151 Lawrence Dr, Livermore (94551-5126)
PHONE..................248 435-1000
Carl D Anderson II,
Nicholas Kahmke, *Design Engr*
Henry Sicat, *Engineer*
Michael Chapman, *Controller*
Steve Montano, *Senior Buyer*
▲ EMP: 19
SQ FT: 85,000
SALES (est): 304.2MM **Publicly Held**
WEB: www.fabcoautomotive.com
SIC: 3714 Axles, motor vehicle; gears, motor vehicle; transmission housings or parts, motor vehicle; transmissions, motor vehicle

(P-20400)
METRA ELECTRONICS CORPORATION
Also Called: Antenna Works
3201 E 59th St, Long Beach (90805-4501)
PHONE..................562 470-6601
Steve Hertel, *Manager*
EMP: 15
SALES (corp-wide): 164.1MM **Privately Held**
WEB: www.metraonline.com
SIC: 3714 Motor vehicle body components & frame
PA: Metra Electronics Corporation
460 Walker St
Holly Hill FL 32117
386 257-1186

(P-20401)
MGM BRAKES
1184 S Cloverdale Blvd, Cloverdale (95425-4412)
P.O. Box 249 (95425-0249)
PHONE..................707 894-3333
Ron Parker, *Owner*
Bob Stutsman, *Plant Mgr*
Kim Jones, *Sales Staff*
◆ EMP: 65 EST: 2015
SALES (est): 284.4K **Privately Held**
SIC: 3714 3625 Air brakes, motor vehicle; brakes, electromagnetic

(P-20402)
MID-WEST FABRICATING CO
Also Called: West Bent Bolt Division
8623 Dice Rd, Santa Fe Springs (90670-2511)
PHONE..................562 698-9615
Steve Petersen, *Manager*
Stephen Petersen, *Vice Pres*
EMP: 40
SQ FT: 40,000
SALES (corp-wide): 25.5MM **Privately Held**
WEB: www.midwestfab.com
SIC: 3714 3452 3316 3312 Tie rods, motor vehicle; bolts, nuts, rivets & washers; cold finishing of steel shapes; wire products, steel or iron
PA: Mid-West Fabricating Co.
313 N Johns St
Amanda OH 43102
740 969-4411

(P-20403)
MILODON INCORPORATED
2250 Agate Ct, Simi Valley (93065-1842)
PHONE..................805 577-5950
Steve Morrison, *President*
▲ EMP: 40 EST: 1957
SQ FT: 32,000
SALES (est): 7.4MM **Privately Held**
WEB: www.milodon.com
SIC: 3714 Motor vehicle engines & parts

(P-20404)
MOBIS PARTS AMERICA LLC
10550 Talbert Ave 4, Fountain Valley (92708-6031)
PHONE..................949 450-0014
H S Lee,
EMP: 270
SALES (corp-wide): 17.7B **Privately Held**
SIC: 3714 Motor vehicle body components & frame
HQ: Mobis Parts America, Llc
10550 Talbert Ave Fl 4
Fountain Valley CA 92708
786 515-1101

(P-20405)
MORENO INDUSTRIES INC
Also Called: Intro Designs
1225 N Knollwood Cir, Anaheim (92801-1310)
PHONE..................714 229-9696
Jose L Moreno, *President*
Victor Moreno, *Vice Pres*
▲ EMP: 10
SQ FT: 1,400
SALES (est): 1.8MM **Privately Held**
WEB: www.introwheels.com
SIC: 3714 Wheels, motor vehicle

(P-20406)
MOTORCAR PARTS OF AMERICA INC (PA)
Also Called: MPA
2929 California St, Torrance (90503-3914)
PHONE..................310 212-7910
Selwyn Joffe, *Ch of Bd*
David Lee, *CFO*
Timothy Vargo, *Bd of Directors*
Barbara Whittaker, *Bd of Directors*
Kevin Daly, *Officer*
◆ EMP: 833
SQ FT: 231,000
SALES: 428MM **Publicly Held**
WEB: www.motorcarparts.com
SIC: 3714 3694 3625 5013 Motor vehicle parts & accessories; alternators, automotive; starter, electric motor; motor vehicle supplies & new parts

(P-20407)
MUSCLE ROAD INC
Also Called: Classic Soft Trim Central Cal
28838 Ave 15 One Half, Madera (93638)
P.O. Box 1013 (93639-1013)
PHONE..................559 499-6888
Dennis Patterson, *President*
EMP: 10
SQ FT: 15,000
SALES (est): 1.4MM **Privately Held**
SIC: 3714 Automotive wiring harness sets

(P-20408)
MYGRANT GLASS COMPANY INC
10220 Camino Santa Fe, San Diego (92121-3105)
PHONE..................858 455-8022
Tom Andia, *President*
EMP: 20
SQ FT: 32,185
SALES (corp-wide): 178.4MM **Privately Held**
SIC: 3714 5013 Motor vehicle parts & accessories; motor vehicle supplies & new parts
PA: Mygrant Glass Company, Inc.
3271 Arden Rd
Hayward CA 94545
510 785-4360

(P-20409)
NEW CENTURY INDUSTRIES INC
7231 Rosecrans Ave, Paramount (90723-2501)
P.O. Box 1845 (90723-1845)
PHONE..................562 634-9551
Michael Mason, *CEO*
EMP: 50
SQ FT: 32,000
SALES (est): 9.3MM **Privately Held**
SIC: 3714 3465 3469 Wheels, motor vehicle; automotive stampings; stamping metal for the trade

(P-20410)
NOLOGY ENGINEERING INC
1333 Keystone Way, Vista (92081-8311)
PHONE..................760 591-0888
Werner Funk, *President*
Jan Quigley, *CFO*
EMP: 14
SQ FT: 11,000
SALES: 1.1MM **Privately Held**
WEB: www.nology.com
SIC: 3714 Motor vehicle parts & accessories

(P-20411)
OCTILLION POWER SYSTEMS INC
721 Sandoval Way, Hayward (94544-7112)
PHONE..................510 397-5952
Peng Zhou, *CEO*
Paul Beach, *President*
▲ EMP: 14 EST: 2010
SALES (est): 1.9MM **Privately Held**
SIC: 3714 Transmissions, motor vehicle

(P-20412)
OFFENHAUSER SALES CORP
5300 Alhambra Ave, Los Angeles (90032-3405)
PHONE..................323 225-1307

PRODUCTS & SVCS

Fred C Offenhauser Jr, *President*
EMP: 13
SQ FT: 15,000
SALES (est): 2MM **Privately Held**
SIC: 3714 Motor vehicle parts & accessories

(P-20413)
OMNITEK ENGINEERING CORP (PA)
1333 Keystone Way Ste 101, Vista (92081-8311)
PHONE..................760 591-0089
Werner Funk, *President*
Richard Miller, *CFO*
Janice M Quigley, *Vice Pres*
▲ **EMP:** 12
SQ FT: 25,000
SALES: 1MM **Publicly Held**
WEB: www.omnitekcorp.com
SIC: 3714 Motor vehicle parts & accessories

(P-20414)
ONKI CORP
294 Hegenberger Rd, Oakland (94621-1436)
PHONE..................510 567-8875
Daren On, *President*
▲ **EMP:** 10
SALES (est): 830K **Privately Held**
WEB: www.onkicorp.com
SIC: 3714 5013 Motor vehicle parts & accessories; truck parts & accessories

(P-20415)
ORGAN-O-SIL FIBER CO INC
Also Called: Organosil Fiber Co
17616 Gothard St Ste B, Huntington Beach (92647-6215)
P.O. Box 86 (92648-0086)
PHONE..................714 847-8310
Ruby Riggs, *President*
Margaret Riggs, *President*
EMP: 27
SQ FT: 3,000
SALES: 2MM **Privately Held**
SIC: 3714 Mufflers (exhaust), motor vehicle

(P-20416)
P & S SALES INC
20943 Cabot Blvd, Hayward (94545-1155)
PHONE..................510 732-2628
Robert Phillips, *President*
Diane Phillips, *Treasurer*
David Phillips, *Vice Pres*
Edwin Morrison, *Manager*
EMP: 12
SQ FT: 40,000
SALES (est): 3.5MM **Privately Held**
SIC: 3714 5013 Motor vehicle parts & accessories; automotive supplies

(P-20417)
PANA-PACIFIC CORPORATION
838 N Laverne Ave, Fresno (93727-6868)
PHONE..................559 457-4700
Kristina Reed, *President*
Harrison Brix, *COO*
▲ **EMP:** 150 EST: 2004
SALES (est): 17.2MM
SALES (corp-wide): 143.4MM **Privately Held**
WEB: www.brixcom.com
SIC: 3714 Motor vehicle parts & accessories
PA: The Brix Group Inc
838 N Laverne Ave
Fresno CA 93727
559 457-4700

(P-20418)
PARTS EXPEDITING AND DIST CO
Also Called: Pedco
10805 Artesia Blvd # 112, Cerritos (90703-2699)
PHONE..................562 944-3199
Virgil Cooley, *President*
Rachel Cooley, *Vice Pres*
EMP: 40 EST: 1975
SQ FT: 32,000

SALES (est): 5.5MM **Privately Held**
WEB: www.pedco.net
SIC: 3714 3519 Rebuilding engines & transmissions, factory basis; internal combustion engines

(P-20419)
PC VAUGHAN MFG CORP (PA)
1278 Mercantile St, Oxnard (93030-7522)
PHONE..................805 278-2555
Jeff Starin, *President*
Jerry Ryan, *Vice Pres*
▲ **EMP:** 14
SQ FT: 12,000
SALES (est): 3.2MM **Privately Held**
WEB: www.pcvaughan.com
SIC: 3714 Motor vehicle parts & accessories

(P-20420)
PILOT INC (PA)
Also Called: Pilot Automotive
13000 Temple Ave, City of Industry (91746-1416)
PHONE..................626 937-6988
Scott Webb, *President*
Michael Du, *CFO*
▲ **EMP:** 100
SQ FT: 407,000
SALES (est): 1.3MM **Privately Held**
WEB: www.pilotautomotive.com
SIC: 3714 5015 Motor vehicle parts & accessories; automotive accessories, used

(P-20421)
POWER BRAKE EXCHANGE INC
6853 Suva St, Bell (90201-1937)
PHONE..................562 806-6661
Charles Pitts, *President*
EMP: 15
SALES (corp-wide): 4.2MM **Privately Held**
WEB: www.power-brake-exchange.com
SIC: 3714 Motor vehicle brake systems & parts
PA: Power Brake Exchange, Inc.
45 Affonso Dr
Carson City NV 89706
408 292-1305

(P-20422)
POWER PROS RACG EXHUST SYSTEMS
Also Called: Power Pros Exhaust Systems
817 S Lakeview Ave Ste J, Placentia (92870-6718)
PHONE..................714 777-3278
Don Kistler, *President*
Thomas Kistler, *CEO*
EMP: 12
SQ FT: 7,000
SALES: 1.2MM **Privately Held**
WEB: www.thepowerpros.com
SIC: 3714 5013 Exhaust systems & parts, motor vehicle; motorcycle parts

(P-20423)
PRECISION DIE CUTTING INC
Also Called: Precision Film & Tape
150 Doolittle Dr, San Leandro (94577-1014)
PHONE..................510 636-9654
Glenn Yamagata, *CEO*
Arthur N Aronsen, *President*
Joan Yamagata, *CEO*
EMP: 33
SQ FT: 25,000
SALES (est): 3.7MM **Privately Held**
SIC: 3714 2675 Motor vehicle parts & accessories; die-cut paper & board
PA: Aronsen & Company
150 Doolittle Dr
San Leandro CA
510 636-9654

(P-20424)
PRIME WHEEL CORPORATION
23920 Vermont Ave, Harbor City (90710-1602)
PHONE..................310 326-5080
Eddie Chen, *Manager*
Ramon Limon, *Opers Spvr*
EMP: 500
SQ FT: 200,000

SALES (corp-wide): 329MM **Privately Held**
WEB: www.primewheel.com
SIC: 3714 3471 5013 Motor vehicle wheels & parts; plating & polishing; automotive supplies & parts
PA: Prime Wheel Corporation
17705 S Main St
Gardena CA 90248
310 516-9126

(P-20425)
PRIME WHEEL CORPORATION
250 W Apra St, Compton (90220-5521)
PHONE..................310 516-9126
Lynn Biscocho, *Branch Mgr*
EMP: 20
SALES (corp-wide): 329MM **Privately Held**
SIC: 3714 Motor vehicle parts & accessories
PA: Prime Wheel Corporation
17705 S Main St
Gardena CA 90248
310 516-9126

(P-20426)
PRIME WHEEL CORPORATION (PA)
17705 S Main St, Gardena (90248-3516)
PHONE..................310 516-9126
Henry Chen, *CEO*
Tony Fan, *Shareholder*
Webb Carter, *Vice Chairman*
Philip Chen, *President*
Mitchell M Tung, *President*
◆ **EMP:** 600
SQ FT: 320,000
SALES (est): 329MM **Privately Held**
WEB: www.primewheel.com
SIC: 3714 Wheels, motor vehicle

(P-20427)
PRO PRODUCTS INC
2967 Avenida De Autlan, Ontario (91764)
PHONE..................909 605-0545
Ed Neumann, *President*
Kathleen M Neuman, *Treasurer*
▲ **EMP:** 30
SQ FT: 25,000
SALES (est): 1.7MM **Privately Held**
SIC: 3714 Motor vehicle parts & accessories

(P-20428)
PROGRESS GROUP
1600 E Miraloma Ave, Placentia (92870-6622)
PHONE..................714 630-9017
Jeff Cheechov, *President*
▲ **EMP:** 14 EST: 2009
SALES (est): 2.9MM **Privately Held**
SIC: 3714 Motor vehicle parts & accessories

(P-20429)
PROGRESSIVE HOUSING INC
Also Called: Happy Daze Rv's
5605 Southfront Rd, Livermore (94551-9513)
PHONE..................916 920-8255
EMP: 15
SALES (corp-wide): 19.4MM **Privately Held**
SIC: 3714 Motor vehicle parts & accessories
PA: Progressive Housing Inc
1199 El Camino Ave
Sacramento CA 95815
916 920-8255

(P-20430)
PURE FORGE
13011 Kirkham Way, Poway (92064-7112)
PHONE..................760 201-0951
Nathan K Meckel, *President*
EMP: 11
SALES (est): 867.9K **Privately Held**
SIC: 3714 Motor vehicle parts & accessories

(P-20431)
QF LIQUIDATION INC
25242 Arctic Ocean Dr, Lake Forest (92630-8821)
PHONE..................949 399-4500

Brian Olson, *CFO*
EMP: 35 **Privately Held**
SIC: 3714 8731 Fuel systems & parts, motor vehicle; commercial physical research
PA: Qf Liquidation, Inc.
25242 Arctic Ocean Dr
Lake Forest CA 92630

(P-20432)
QF LIQUIDATION INC (PA)
Also Called: Quantum Technologies
25242 Arctic Ocean Dr, Lake Forest (92630-8821)
PHONE..................949 930-3400
W Brian Olson, *President*
Bradley J Timon, *CFO*
Mark Arold, *Vice Pres*
Kenneth R Lombardo, *Vice Pres*
David M Mazaika, *Exec Dir*
◆ **EMP:** 172
SQ FT: 156,000
SALES (est): 37.5MM **Privately Held**
SIC: 3714 3764 8711 Motor vehicle parts & accessories; guided missile & space vehicle propulsion unit parts; engineering services

(P-20433)
R F P & WELDING
310 E Easy St Ste E, Simi Valley (93065-7531)
P.O. Box 940370 (93094-0370)
PHONE..................805 526-3425
Randy Miller, *Owner*
EMP: 10
SQ FT: 1,500
SALES (est): 1.1MM **Privately Held**
WEB: www.rfpwelding.com
SIC: 3714 7692 Exhaust systems & parts, motor vehicle; welding repair

(P-20434)
RACE TECHNOLOGIES LLC
17422 Murphy Ave, Irvine (92614-5922)
PHONE..................714 438-1118
Jaime Trimble,
▲ **EMP:** 14
SALES (est): 3MM **Privately Held**
WEB: www.racetechnologies.com
SIC: 3714 5013 Motor vehicle brake systems & parts; automotive brakes

(P-20435)
RACEPAK LLC
30402 Esperanza, Rcho STA Marg (92688-2144)
PHONE..................949 709-5555
Tom Tomlinson, *President*
Jeff Greene, *Vice Pres*
Brian Woodard, *Creative Dir*
Mary House, *CTO*
Olischefski Kelly, *Project Engr*
EMP: 28 EST: 2014
SALES: 8.9MM
SALES (corp-wide): 109.9MM **Privately Held**
SIC: 3714 Motor vehicle parts & accessories
PA: Holley Performance Products Inc.
1801 Russellville Rd
Bowling Green KY 42101
270 782-2900

(P-20436)
RADFLO SUSPENSION TECHNOLOGY
11233 Condor Ave, Fountain Valley (92708-6105)
PHONE..................714 965-7828
Glenn Classen, *CEO*
▲ **EMP:** 11
SQ FT: 5,000
SALES (est): 1.6MM **Privately Held**
WEB: www.radflo.com
SIC: 3714 Shock absorbers, motor vehicle

(P-20437)
RAM OFF ROAD ACCESSORIES INC
3901 Medford St, Los Angeles (90063-1608)
PHONE..................323 266-3850
Chris Foterek, *President*
William Longo, *Vice Pres*

EMP: 30
SQ FT: 103,000
SALES (est): 4.8MM **Privately Held**
SIC: 3714 Motor vehicle body components & frame

(P-20438)
RB RACING
1234 W 134th St, Gardena (90247-1903)
PHONE..................310 515-5720
Lynn Hilkemeyer Behn, *Owner*
EMP: 15
SQ FT: 2,500
SALES (est): 1.7MM **Privately Held**
WEB: www.rbracing-rsr.com
SIC: 3714 Motor vehicle parts & accessories

(P-20439)
RICH PRODUCTS
1041 Broadway Ave, San Pablo (94806-2260)
PHONE..................510 234-7547
Donald Rich, *Partner*
Mary Rich, *Partner*
EMP: 10
SQ FT: 3,000
SALES (est): 1.2MM **Privately Held**
WEB: www.richproductsco.com
SIC: 3714 Exhaust systems & parts, motor vehicle

(P-20440)
RK SPORT INC
26900 Jefferson Ave, Murrieta (92562-9112)
PHONE..................951 894-7883
Mike Lozano, *President*
Robert Smith, *President*
Julie Lozano, *Vice Pres*
EMP: 20
SQ FT: 15,000
SALES: 2MM **Privately Held**
WEB: www.rksport.com
SIC: 3714 5531 5013 Motor vehicle parts & accessories; automotive parts; automotive supplies & parts

(P-20441)
RLV TUNED EXHAUST PRODUCTS
2351 Thompson Way Bldg A, Santa Maria (93455-1041)
PHONE..................805 925-5461
Rodney L Verlengiere, *President*
Arthur R Verlengiere, *Corp Secy*
Art Verlengiere, *Vice Pres*
▲ **EMP:** 23 **EST:** 1978
SQ FT: 5,000
SALES (est): 4.5MM **Privately Held**
SIC: 3714 Exhaust systems & parts, motor vehicle

(P-20442)
ROADSTER WHEELS INC
14955 Don Julian Rd, City of Industry (91746-3112)
PHONE..................626 333-3007
Yvette Marchisset, *Vice Pres*
EMP: 14
SQ FT: 52,000
SALES (est): 1.1MM **Privately Held**
SIC: 3714 Wheels, motor vehicle

(P-20443)
S&B FILTERS INC
15461 Slover Ave Ste A, Fontana (92337-1306)
PHONE..................909 947-0015
Berry Carter, *President*
Sandra Rivera, *Office Mgr*
Pilun Chen, *Design Engr*
Rosa Madrigal, *Purch Mgr*
Gabriel Lopez, *Prdtn Mgr*
▲ **EMP:** 58
SALES: 11.4MM **Privately Held**
WEB: www.sbfilters.com
SIC: 3714 3564 Filters: oil, fuel & air, motor vehicle; filters, air: furnaces, air conditioning equipment, etc.

(P-20444)
SANKO ELECTRONICS AMERICA INC (HQ)
20700 Denker Ave Ste A, Torrance (90501-6415)
PHONE..................310 618-1677
Hironori Saigusa, *CEO*
Akio Saigusa, *President*
Toshiaki Yamashita, *President*
Bryant Pham, *Purchasing*
▲ **EMP:** 19
SQ FT: 35,000
SALES (est): 3.9MM
SALES (corp-wide): 94.3MM **Privately Held**
SIC: 3714 Motor vehicle parts & accessories
PA: Sanko Electric Co.,Ltd.
7-23, Tamanoicho, Atsuta-Ku
Nagoya AIC 456-0
526 826-711

(P-20445)
SEDENQUIST-FRASER ENTPS INC
Also Called: Leisure Components
16730 Gridley Rd, Cerritos (90703-1730)
PHONE..................562 924-5763
Jitu Patel, *President*
Veary N Im, *Manager*
EMP: 20 **EST:** 1974
SQ FT: 22,000
SALES (est): 3.1MM **Privately Held**
WEB: www.sftech.com
SIC: 3714 3089 3544 Motor vehicle parts & accessories; plastic processing; special dies, tools, jigs & fixtures

(P-20446)
SHIFT MANAGEMENT INC
Also Called: SMI
1060 National Dr Ste 3, Sacramento (95834-2972)
PHONE..................916 381-4700
Ervin Kral, *President*
▲ **EMP:** 16
SQ FT: 18,000
SALES (est): 3MM **Privately Held**
SIC: 3714 Rebuilding engines & transmissions, factory basis

(P-20447)
SHRIN CORPORATION
Also Called: Cover King
900 E Arlee Pl, Anaheim (92805-5645)
P.O. Box 9860 (92812-7860)
PHONE..................714 850-0303
Narendra K Gupta, *President*
Robby Gupta, *Vice Pres*
Natrajan Sreebharan, *Technology*
Natarajan Sreedharan, *Technology*
Aaron Loterina, *Graphic Designe*
◆ **EMP:** 150
SQ FT: 90,000
SALES (est): 34.1MM **Privately Held**
WEB: www.coverking.com
SIC: 3714 5013 Motor vehicle parts & accessories; automotive supplies & parts

(P-20448)
SIMWON AMERICA CORP
400 Darcy Pkwy, Lathrop (95330-9796)
PHONE..................925 276-3412
Yong Joon Bae, *CEO*
EMP: 15
SALES (est): 6.7MM **Privately Held**
SIC: 3714 Acceleration equipment, motor vehicle

(P-20449)
SINISTER MFG COMPANY INC
Also Called: Mkm Customs
2025 Opportunity Dr Ste 7, Roseville (95678-3010)
PHONE..................916 772-9253
Brian P George, *President*
Mike Mitchell, *CFO*
Robert McCrickard, *General Mgr*
CJ Whitehead, *Project Mgr*
Rosa Gutierrez, *Manager*
▲ **EMP:** 45
SQ FT: 11,000
SALES: 20MM **Privately Held**
SIC: 3714 Motor vehicle parts & accessories

(P-20450)
SLAM SPECIALTIES LLC (PA)
5845 E Terrace Ave, Fresno (93727-1398)
PHONE..................559 348-9038
Harry Solakian, *Mng Member*
Tim Garcia, *Sales Executive*
Nick Solakian,
Sheryl Solakian,
▼ **EMP:** 16
SQ FT: 10,000
SALES (est): 2.3MM **Privately Held**
WEB: www.slamspecialties.com
SIC: 3714 Motor vehicle engines & parts

(P-20451)
SOUTHLAND CLUTCH INC
Also Called: Clutches New or Rebuilt
101 E 18th St, National City (91950-4529)
PHONE..................619 477-2105
Dan Levine, *President*
Colleen Llanos, *Office Mgr*
EMP: 11 **EST:** 1970
SQ FT: 8,000
SALES: 2MM **Privately Held**
WEB: www.southlandclutch.com
SIC: 3714 Clutches, motor vehicle

(P-20452)
SPECIAL DEVICES INCORPORATED (HQ)
Also Called: Sdi
2655 1st St Ste 300, Simi Valley (93065-1580)
PHONE..................805 387-1000
Yasuhiro Sakaki, *CEO*
Mike Mendonca, *COO*
Harry Rector, *CFO*
Nicholas J Bruge, *Ch Credit Ofcr*
Jim Coppinger, *Controller*
▲ **EMP:** 400
SQ FT: 170,000
SALES (est): 120.8MM
SALES (corp-wide): 4.3B **Privately Held**
WEB: www.specialdevices.com
SIC: 3714 Motor vehicle parts & accessories
PA: Daicel Corporation
3-1, Ofukacho, Kita-Ku
Osaka OSK 530-0
676 397-171

(P-20453)
SPECIALTY PRODUCTS DESIGN INC
11252 Sunco Dr, Rancho Cordova (95742-6515)
PHONE..................916 635-8108
Chris Hill, *President*
Carol Hill, *Corp Secy*
EMP: 11 **EST:** 1970
SQ FT: 22,000
SALES (est): 2.2MM **Privately Held**
WEB: www.spdexhaust.com
SIC: 3714 Exhaust systems & parts, motor vehicle

(P-20454)
SPECTRUM ACCESSORY DISTRS
9770 Carroll Centre Rd, San Diego (92126-6504)
PHONE..................858 653-6470
C Dwight Anderson, *President*
EMP: 115
SALES (est): 8.5MM **Privately Held**
SIC: 3714 5013 Motor vehicle body components & frame; motor vehicle supplies & new parts

(P-20455)
SUNNY AMERICA & GLOBAL AUTOTEC
2681 Dow Ave Ste A, Tustin (92780-7244)
PHONE..................714 544-0400
Alex Han, *Owner*
▲ **EMP:** 65
SALES (est): 5.7MM **Privately Held**
SIC: 3714 Motor vehicle engines & parts

(P-20456)
SUPERIOR INDS INTL HLDINGS LLC (HQ)
7800 Woodley Ave, Van Nuys (91406-1722)
PHONE..................818 781-4973
Steven J Borick, *Ch of Bd*
Emory Brown, *Vice Pres*
Parveen Kakar, *Vice Pres*
Shawn Pallagi, *Vice Pres*
James Sistek, *Vice Pres*
▲ **EMP:** 31
SALES (est): 1.6MM
SALES (corp-wide): 1.1B **Publicly Held**
SIC: 3714 Motor vehicle wheels & parts
PA: Superior Industries International, Inc.
26600 Telg Rd Ste 400
Southfield MI 48033
248 352-7300

(P-20457)
SUSPENSION TECHNOLOGIES INC
1075 North Ave, Sanger (93657-3539)
PHONE..................559 875-8883
James Fairweather, *CEO*
Rick Hedrick, *President*
Glenn Cox, *Vice Pres*
EMP: 15
SALES (est): 1.7MM **Privately Held**
WEB: www.suspensiontechnologies.com
SIC: 3714 Motor vehicle parts & accessories

(P-20458)
TABC INC (DH)
6375 N Paramount Blvd, Long Beach (90805-3301)
PHONE..................562 984-3305
Michael Bafan, *CEO*
Yoshiaki Nishino, *Treasurer*
Don Loomis, *Finance Mgr*
◆ **EMP:** 117
SQ FT: 8,820
SALES (est): 133.4MM
SALES (corp-wide): 275.7B **Privately Held**
SIC: 3714 3713 3469 Motor vehicle parts & accessories; truck beds; metal stampings

(P-20459)
TAP MANUFACTURING LLC
Also Called: Pro Comp
2360 Boswell Rd, Chula Vista (91914-3510)
PHONE..................619 216-1444
Darren M Salvin, *Principal*
▲ **EMP:** 18
SALES (est): 4.1MM **Privately Held**
SIC: 3714 Motor vehicle parts & accessories

(P-20460)
TASKER METAL PRODUCTS INC
1823 S Hope St, Los Angeles (90015-4197)
P.O. Box 15368 (90015-0368)
PHONE..................213 765-5400
Eugene L Golling, *President*
Rudi Verstegen, *Vice Pres*
Rudy Verstegen, *Vice Pres*
▲ **EMP:** 15
SQ FT: 12,000
SALES (est): 550K **Privately Held**
WEB: www.taskermetalproducts.com
SIC: 3714 Motor vehicle body components & frame; hoods, motor vehicle

(P-20461)
TEECO PRODUCTS INC
Paca
7471 Reese Rd, Sacramento (95828-3721)
PHONE..................916 688-3535
Tom Valvered, *Manager*
EMP: 30
SALES (est): 3.8MM
SALES (corp-wide): 19.4MM **Privately Held**
WEB: www.teecoproducts.com
SIC: 3714 5084 3443 Propane conversion equipment, motor vehicle; propane conversion equipment; fabricated plate work (boiler shop)

PRODUCTS & SVCS

PA: Teeco Products Inc.
16881 Armstrong Ave
Irvine CA 92606
949 261-6295

(P-20462)
TENNECO AUTOMOTIVE OPER CO INC
6925 Atlantic Ave, Long Beach (90805-1415)
PHONE..................562 630-0700
Danny Walker, *Manager*
EMP: 65
SALES (corp-wide): 9.2B **Publicly Held**
WEB: www.tenneco-automotive.com
SIC: 3714 3713 Motor vehicle parts & accessories; truck & bus bodies
HQ: Tenneco Automotive Operating Company, Inc.
500 N Field Dr
Lake Forest IL 60045
847 482-5000

(P-20463)
TESLA INC
3203 Jack Northrop Ave, Hawthorne (90250-4424)
PHONE..................310 219-4652
EMP: 13
SALES (corp-wide): 11.7B **Publicly Held**
SIC: 3714 3711 Motor vehicle parts & accessories; cars, electric, assembly of
PA: Tesla, Inc.
3500 Deer Creek Rd
Palo Alto CA 94304
650 681-5000

(P-20464)
THERMAL SOLUTIONS MFG INC
Also Called: THERMAL SOLUTIONS MANUFACTURING INC.
1390 S Tippecanoe Ave B, San Bernardino (92408-2998)
PHONE..................909 796-0754
Maureen Baker, *Branch Mgr*
EMP: 34
SALES (corp-wide): 30.1MM **Privately Held**
WEB: www.mytinytiger.com
SIC: 3714 Radiators & radiator shells & cores, motor vehicle
PA: Thermal Solutions Manufacturing, Inc.
15 Century Blvd Ste 102
Nashville TN 37214
800 359-9186

(P-20465)
THYSSENKRUPP BILSTEIN AMER INC
14102 Stowe Dr, Poway (92064-7147)
PHONE..................858 386-5900
Doug Robertson, *Vice Pres*
Regis Finn, *Marketing Mgr*
Alireza Mohammadi, *Sr Project Mgr*
Janet Diato, *Manager*
EMP: 42
SALES (corp-wide): 48.7B **Privately Held**
SIC: 3714 5013 Motor vehicle parts & accessories; motor vehicle supplies & new parts
HQ: Thyssenkrupp Bilstein Of America, Inc.
8685 Bilstein Blvd
Hamilton OH 45015
888 461-7600

(P-20466)
TILTON ENGINEERING INC
25 Easy St, Buellton (93427-9566)
P.O. Box 1787 (93427-1787)
PHONE..................805 688-2353
Jason Wahl, *President*
Todd Cooper, *Vice Pres*
Kirk Skaufel, *Vice Pres*
Patty Madden, *Office Mgr*
Casey Lund, *Chief Engr*
▲ EMP: 50 EST: 1972
SQ FT: 15,000
SALES (est): 10.8MM **Privately Held**
WEB: www.tiltonracing.com
SIC: 3714 Motor vehicle parts & accessories

(P-20467)
TRANSGO
Also Called: Transco
2621 Merced Ave, El Monte (91733-1905)
PHONE..................626 443-7456
Gilbert W Younger, *Principal*
Sema Reyes, *Admin Sec*
EMP: 25
SQ FT: 4,560
SALES (est): 4.2MM **Privately Held**
SIC: 3714 Motor vehicle parts & accessories

(P-20468)
TRANSPORTATION POWER INC
Also Called: Transpower
2415 Auto Park Way, Escondido (92029-1222)
PHONE..................858 248-4255
Michael C Simon, *President*
Paul Scott, *Vice Pres*
James Burns, *Chief*
EMP: 45
SALES (est): 10.1MM **Privately Held**
WEB: www.transpowerusa.com
SIC: 3714 Motor vehicle parts & accessories

(P-20469)
TRISTAR GLOBAL INC
Also Called: Pinnacle
526 Coralridge Pl, La Puente (91746-3000)
PHONE..................626 363-6978
Benjamin Chau, *President*
▼ EMP: 10
SALES (est): 1.4MM **Privately Held**
WEB: www.tristarglobal.com
SIC: 3714 Motor vehicle parts & accessories

(P-20470)
TUBE TECHNOLOGIES INC
Also Called: TTI Performance Exhaust
1555 Consumer Cir, Corona (92880-1726)
PHONE..................951 371-4878
Sam Davis, *President*
Trini Respico, *Corp Secy*
Tom Nakawatase, *Vice Pres*
Raul Rodriguez, *Vice Pres*
▲ EMP: 30
SQ FT: 18,400
SALES (est): 4.7MM **Privately Held**
WEB: www.ttiexhaust.com
SIC: 3714 3498 Exhaust systems & parts, motor vehicle; tube fabricating (contract bending & shaping)

(P-20471)
TURBONETICS HOLDINGS INC
14399 Princeton Ave, Moorpark (93021-1481)
PHONE..................805 581-0333
Brad Lewis, *Vice Pres*
Greg Papp, *Finance Dir*
Gary Monina, *Sales Dir*
▲ EMP: 49
SQ FT: 50,000
SALES (est): 9.3MM
SALES (corp-wide): 3.8B **Publicly Held**
SIC: 3714 Motor vehicle parts & accessories
PA: Westinghouse Air Brake Technologies Corporation
1001 Airbrake Ave
Wilmerding PA 15148
412 825-1000

(P-20472)
U S WHEEL CORPORATION
Also Called: US Wheel
15702 Producer Ln, Huntington Beach (92649-1303)
PHONE..................714 892-0021
Eliot Mason, *President*
Kristie Boerum, *Executive*
Larry Es, *General Mgr*
Jason Johnson, *Sales Staff*
Mike Campos, *Manager*
▲ EMP: 45
SQ FT: 135,000
SALES (est): 16.2MM **Privately Held**
WEB: www.uswheel.com
SIC: 3714 Wheels, motor vehicle

(P-20473)
UFO DESIGNS
Also Called: S F Technology
16730 Gridley Rd, Cerritos (90703-1730)
PHONE..................562 924-5763
Jitu Patel, *President*
EMP: 22
SALES (corp-wide): 3.8MM **Privately Held**
WEB: www.ufodesign.com
SIC: 3714 3089 Motor vehicle parts & accessories; plastic processing
PA: U.F.O. Designs
5812 Machine Dr
Huntington Beach CA 92649
714 892-4420

(P-20474)
ULTIMATE RAIL EQUIPMENT INC
30914 San Antonio St, Hayward (94544-7110)
PHONE..................510 324-5000
Geoff Nelson, *President*
Roger Tsai, *Prdtn Mgr*
▲ EMP: 10
SALES (est): 1.7MM **Privately Held**
SIC: 3714 Motor vehicle parts & accessories

(P-20475)
UNI FILTER INC
1468 Manhattan Ave, Fullerton (92831-5222)
PHONE..................714 535-6933
Lanny R Mitchell, *President*
Kenneth E Mitchell, *Shareholder*
Robert A Nichols, *Shareholder*
Kathi Perry, *Corp Secy*
Tom Gross, *Vice Pres*
EMP: 60 EST: 1971
SQ FT: 26,000
SALES (est): 3MM **Privately Held**
WEB: www.unifilter.com
SIC: 3714 Filters: oil, fuel & air, motor vehicle

(P-20476)
UNITED RESEARCH & MFG
Also Called: U R M
2630 Progress St, Vista (92081-8412)
PHONE..................760 727-4320
Danny Horrell, *President*
▲ EMP: 10
SQ FT: 15,000
SALES (est): 730K **Privately Held**
SIC: 3714 3599 Motor vehicle brake systems & parts; machine shop, jobbing & repair

(P-20477)
US HYBRID CORPORATION (PA)
445 Maple Ave, Torrance (90503-3807)
PHONE..................310 212-1200
Abas Goodarzi, *CEO*
Don C Kang, *President*
Daniel Orlowski, *Program Mgr*
Michael Harrington, *Chief Engr*
Ed Jones, *Manager*
▲ EMP: 42
SQ FT: 18,000
SALES (est): 7.1MM **Privately Held**
WEB: www.ushybrid.com
SIC: 3714 Motor vehicle engines & parts

(P-20478)
US MOTOR WORKS LLC (PA)
14722 Anson Ave, Santa Fe Springs (90670-5306)
PHONE..................562 404-0488
Gil Benjaman,
Doron Goren, *Executive*
Avram Ben-Yehuda,
◆ EMP: 104
SQ FT: 37,000
SALES (est): 21.5MM **Privately Held**
WEB: www.usmotorworks.com
SIC: 3714 Water pump, motor vehicle

(P-20479)
US RADIATOR CORPORATION (PA)
4423 District Blvd, Vernon (90058-3111)
PHONE..................323 826-0965
Donald Armstrong, *President*

William Zimmerman, *Treasurer*
Tim Armstrong, *Vice Pres*
▲ EMP: 29
SQ FT: 35,000
SALES (est): 3.6MM **Privately Held**
WEB: www.usradiator.com
SIC: 3714 Radiators & radiator shells & cores, motor vehicle

(P-20480)
VIGILANT MARINE SYSTEMS LLC
2045 S Baker Ave, Ontario (91761-8027)
PHONE..................909 597-9508
Craig Mason,
▲ EMP: 11 EST: 2002
SALES (est): 1.6MM **Privately Held**
SIC: 3714 Filters: oil, fuel & air, motor vehicle

(P-20481)
VINTIQUE INC
1828 W Sequoia Ave, Orange (92868-1018)
PHONE..................714 634-1932
Chad Looney, *President*
Judy Looney, *Treasurer*
Denise Looney, *Vice Pres*
▲ EMP: 23
SQ FT: 17,000
SALES (est): 4MM **Privately Held**
WEB: www.vintique.com
SIC: 3714 Motor vehicle parts & accessories

(P-20482)
WAH HUNG GROUP INC (PA)
1000 E Garvey Ave, Monterey Park (91755-3031)
PHONE..................626 571-8700
Man Kwong Ng, *CEO*
EMP: 20
SALES (est): 4MM **Privately Held**
SIC: 3714 Wheel rims, motor vehicle

(P-20483)
WAH HUNG GROUP INC
283 E Garvey Ave, Monterey Park (91755-1811)
PHONE..................626 571-8700
EMP: 26
SALES (corp-wide): 4MM **Privately Held**
SIC: 3714 Wheel rims, motor vehicle
PA: Wah Hung Group, Inc.
1000 E Garvey Ave
Monterey Park CA 91755
626 571-8700

(P-20484)
WALKER PRODUCTS (PA)
14291 Commerce Dr, Garden Grove (92843-4944)
PHONE..................714 554-5151
Michael Gerard Weaver, *President*
Grant Kitching, *Vice Pres*
Timothy A Weaver, *Admin Sec*
Garth McKee, *Engineer*
Ronda Bowen, *Finance Dir*
▲ EMP: 25
SQ FT: 125,000
SALES (est): 53.3MM **Privately Held**
WEB: www.walkerproducts.com
SIC: 3714 Motor vehicle parts & accessories

(P-20485)
WEB CAM INC
Also Called: Web CAM
1815 Massachusetts Ave, Riverside (92507-2616)
PHONE..................951 341-0112
Steve Story, *President*
Lori Dunlap, *Vice Pres*
EMP: 13
SQ FT: 6,000
SALES (est): 2MM **Privately Held**
WEB: www.webcaminc.net
SIC: 3714 Camshafts, motor vehicle

(P-20486)
WILWOOD ENGINEERING
4700 Calle Bolero, Camarillo (93012-8561)
PHONE..................805 388-1188
William H Wood, *President*
Steve Cornelius, *General Mgr*
Larry Wolff, *General Mgr*

▲ = Import ▼=Export
◆ =Import/Export

Roger Hayes, *Engineer*
Roman Spandrio, *Engineer*
▲ EMP: 120 EST: 1977
SALES (est): 32.1MM **Privately Held**
WEB: www.wilwood.com
SIC: 3714 Motor vehicle parts & accessories

(P-20487)
WINDSHIELD PROS INCORPORATED
4501 E Airport Dr, Ontario (91761-7877)
PHONE..................................951 272-2867
Michael Fox, *Principal*
EMP: 27
SALES (est): 2.1MM **Privately Held**
WEB: www.windshieldpros.com
SIC: 3714 Windshield frames, motor vehicle

(P-20488)
WORKS PERFORMANCE PRODUCTS INC
21045 Osborne St, Canoga Park (91304-1744)
PHONE..................................818 701-1010
Gilles Vaillancourt, *President*
Douglas Yerkes, *Vice Pres*
Randall Randa, *Info Tech Mgr*
Seth Mottel, *Technology*
EMP: 43
SQ FT: 14,700
SALES (est): 9MM **Privately Held**
WEB: www.worksperformance.com
SIC: 3714 Shock absorbers, motor vehicle

(P-20489)
WSW CORP (PA)
Also Called: Waag
16000 Strathern St, Van Nuys (91406-1316)
PHONE..................................818 989-5008
Gary Waagenaar, *CEO*
Mike Calka, *President*
Jennifer Waagenaar, *Vice Pres*
▲ EMP: 45
SQ FT: 55,000
SALES: 1.2MM **Privately Held**
WEB: www.waag.com
SIC: 3714 5712 Motor vehicle parts & accessories; beds & accessories; bedding & bedsprings

(P-20490)
YINLUN TDI LLC
Also Called: Thermal Dynamics
4850 E Airport Dr, Ontario (91761-7818)
PHONE..................................909 390-3944
Thomas Thielen, *CEO*
EMP: 257
SQ FT: 85,000
SALES (est): 20.3MM
SALES (corp-wide): 652.5MM **Privately Held**
SIC: 3714 Motor vehicle engines & parts
PA: Zhejiang Yinlun Machinery Co., Ltd.
No.8, East Shifeng Road, Fuxi District
Tiantai County 31720
576 839-3839

(P-20491)
ZOOPS PRODUCTS INC
931 E Lincoln St Ste A, Banning (92220-6241)
P.O. Box 3282, Bakersfield (93385-3282)
PHONE..................................951 922-2396
Frank Zupan Jr, *CEO*
Lance Ablin, *President*
Frank Zupan Sr, *CFO*
▲ EMP: 11
SQ FT: 20,000
SALES (est): 1.4MM **Privately Held**
SIC: 3714 Motor vehicle parts & accessories

3715 Truck Trailers

(P-20492)
ACE TRAILER CO
Also Called: American Carrier Equipment
2285 E Date Ave, Fresno (93706-5477)
PHONE..................................559 442-1500
Phillip Sweet, *President*
David Sweet, *Corp Secy*

Darlene Reece, *Purch Agent*
EMP: 40
SALES: 6.9MM **Privately Held**
SIC: 3715 Truck trailers

(P-20493)
ANDERSEN INDUSTRIES INC
17079 Muskrat Ave, Adelanto (92301-2259)
PHONE..................................760 246-8766
Steven Andersen, *CEO*
Neil Andersen, *Vice Pres*
Wayne Andersen, *Vice Pres*
Judy McCalmon, *Admin Asst*
Dave Andersen, *Mfg Dir*
EMP: 25
SQ FT: 110,000
SALES (est): 7.2MM **Privately Held**
WEB: www.andersenmp.com
SIC: 3715 3441 3444 Truck trailers; fabricated structural metal; hoppers, sheet metal

(P-20494)
CALIFORNIA CART BUILDER LLC
29375 Hunco Way, Lake Elsinore (92530-2756)
PHONE..................................951 245-1114
Elma M Eaton, *Mng Member*
Rodney Eaton,
EMP: 10
SALES (est): 1.8MM **Privately Held**
SIC: 3715 Trailer bodies

(P-20495)
CALIFORNIA FLEET SERVICES INC (PA)
1044 Madruga Rd, Lathrop (95330-9779)
P.O. Box 364, Lemont IL (60439-0364)
PHONE..................................209 858-0283
Randy C Schwoeble, *President*
Jim Farej, *Chairman*
EMP: 15 EST: 2009
SQ FT: 1,400
SALES (est): 1.8MM **Privately Held**
SIC: 3715 Truck trailers

(P-20496)
CIMC INTERMODAL EQUIPMENT LLC (HQ)
10533 Sessler St, South Gate (90280-7251)
PHONE..................................562 904-8600
Frank Sonzela, *CEO*
Missy Pinksaw, *Executive*
Robert Horton, *Chief Engr*
Silvia Arellano, *Accounting Mgr*
Maria Munoz, *Human Res Dir*
▲ EMP: 70
SQ FT: 180,000
SALES: 56MM
SALES (corp-wide): 11.5B **Privately Held**
SIC: 3715 7539 Truck trailer chassis; trailer repair
PA: China International Marine Containers (Group) Co., Ltd.
Cimc R&D Center, No.2 Gangwan Avenue,Shekou Industrial Zone,Nans Shenzhen 51806
755 268-0263

(P-20497)
CONCEPT VEHICLE TECHNOLOGIES
Also Called: Concept Transporters
2695 S Cherry Ave Ste 120, Fresno (93706-5488)
PHONE..................................559 233-1313
Bruce Canepa, *President*
Jeff Gardner, *Vice Pres*
EMP: 12
SALES (est): 1.5MM **Privately Held**
SIC: 3715 7539 3711 Truck trailers; trailer repair; motor trucks, except off-highway, assembly of

(P-20498)
COZAD TRAILER SALES LLC
4907 E Waterloo Rd, Stockton (95215-2096)
PHONE..................................209 931-3000
Tom G Pistacchio,
Randy Askins, *Purch Agent*
Delores Pistacchio,

▲ EMP: 92 EST: 1953
SQ FT: 78,000
SALES (est): 28.2MM **Privately Held**
WEB: www.cozadtrailers.com
SIC: 3715 7539 Trailer bodies; trailer repair

(P-20499)
DART WAREHOUSE CORPORATION (HQ)
1430 S Eastman Ave Ste 1, Commerce (90023-4091)
P.O. Box 23931, Los Angeles (90023-0931)
PHONE..................................323 981-8205
Robert Anthony Santich, *CEO*
Raoul Dedeaux, *President*
Ashok Agarwal, *Treasurer*
Steve Roskelley, *Exec VP*
Don Brown, *Vice Pres*
▲ EMP: 255 EST: 1938
SQ FT: 1,200,000
SALES (est): 65.9MM
SALES (corp-wide): 101.2MM **Privately Held**
WEB: www.dartentities.com
SIC: 3715 Truck trailers
PA: Dart Transportation Service, A Corporation
1430 S Eastman Ave Ste 1
Commerce CA 90023
323 981-8205

(P-20500)
DEXTER AXLE COMPANY
Also Called: Unique Functional Products
135 Sunshine Ln, San Marcos (92069-1733)
PHONE..................................760 744-1610
Steve Moore, *Director*
Fred Wang, *Engineer*
Penny Calfo, *Accounting Mgr*
John Goethals, *Prdtn Mgr*
Damian Sullivan, *Sales Mgr*
EMP: 125
SALES (corp-wide): 245.3MM **Privately Held**
SIC: 3715 3714 Trailer bodies; motor vehicle parts & accessories
HQ: Dexter Axle Company
2900 Industrial Pkwy
Elkhart IN 46516

(P-20501)
ERMM CORPORATION
Also Called: J & L Tank Co
5415 Martin Luther King, Lynwood (90262-3961)
PHONE..................................310 635-0524
Norma Ritterbush, *President*
Michael Ritterbush, *Vice Pres*
EMP: 23 EST: 1968
SQ FT: 450,000
SALES (est): 4.2MM **Privately Held**
SIC: 3715 3795 5561 7538 Truck trailers; tanks & tank components; recreational vehicle dealers; general automotive repair shops; motor vehicle parts & accessories

(P-20502)
GLENN ENGINEERING INC
9850 3rd St, Delhi (95315-9624)
PHONE..................................209 667-4555
Thomas Glenn, *President*
Mary Glenn, *Treasurer*
EMP: 10
SQ FT: 7,000
SALES (est): 1.5MM **Privately Held**
SIC: 3715 Truck trailers

(P-20503)
HARLEY MURRAY INC
Also Called: Murray Trailers
1754 E Mariposa Rd, Stockton (95205-7790)
PHONE..................................209 466-0266
Douglas G Murray, *President*
EMP: 55 EST: 1946
SQ FT: 41,000
SALES: 4.5MM **Privately Held**
WEB: www.murraytrailer.com
SIC: 3715 7539 Semitrailers for truck tractors; trailer repair

(P-20504)
IRON WORKS ENTERPRISES INC
801 S 7th St, Modesto (95351-3903)
PHONE..................................209 572-7450
Larry Buehner, *Treasurer*
EMP: 20
SALES (est): 1.8MM **Privately Held**
SIC: 3715

(P-20505)
JACOBSEN TRAILER INC
1128 E South Ave, Fowler (93625-9798)
PHONE..................................559 834-5971
Eugene Jacobsen, *President*
Joetta Jacobsen, *Corp Secy*
EMP: 23
SQ FT: 9,400
SALES (est): 4.4MM **Privately Held**
WEB: www.jacobsentrailers.com
SIC: 3715 5013 7519 5084 Truck trailers; trailer parts & accessories; trailer rental; trailers, industrial

(P-20506)
MCQUAIDE BROTHERS CORPORATION
Also Called: F E Trailers
11919 Woodside Ave, Lakeside (92040-2913)
PHONE..................................619 444-9932
John McQuaide, *President*
Alan McQuaide, *Vice Pres*
EMP: 10
SQ FT: 13,000
SALES (est): 1.2MM **Privately Held**
WEB: www.fetrailers.com
SIC: 3715 7539 5599 Truck trailers; trailer repair; utility trailers

(P-20507)
OWEN TRAILERS INC
9020 Jurupa Rd, Riverside (92509-3106)
PHONE..................................951 361-4557
Loren Owen Jr, *President*
Angela P Owen, *Corp Secy*
Jeff Owen, *General Mgr*
EMP: 25
SQ FT: 34,000
SALES: 3MM **Privately Held**
WEB: www.owentrailers.com
SIC: 3715 Truck trailers

(P-20508)
PERFORMANCE TRAILERS INC
2901 Falcon Dr, Madera (93637-9287)
PHONE..................................559 673-6300
Kevin D Gerhardt Sr, *President*
Kevin Gerhardt, *President*
EMP: 25
SQ FT: 24,000
SALES: 1.5MM **Privately Held**
WEB: www.perftrlrs.com
SIC: 3715 Trailer bodies

(P-20509)
PERFORMANCE TRUCK AND TRLR LLC
500 Etiwanda Ave, Ontario (91761-8634)
PHONE..................................909 605-0323
Bryan Kobus, *CFO*
EMP: 12
SALES (est): 1.7MM **Privately Held**
SIC: 3715 Truck trailers

(P-20510)
R A PHILLIPS INDUSTRIES INC
Phillips Coml Vhcl Pdts Div
12070 Burke St, Santa Fe Springs (90670-2676)
PHONE..................................562 781-2100
Bob Phillips, *President*
EMP: 300
SALES (corp-wide): 85.8MM **Privately Held**
SIC: 3715 3713 Truck trailers; truck & bus bodies
PA: R. A. Phillips Industries, Inc.
12012 Burke St
Santa Fe Springs CA 90670
562 781-2121

P R O D U C T S & S V C S

(P-20511)
R V GAMBLER
6966 Saxon Rd Spc 14, Adelanto
(92301-9513)
PHONE...........................928 927-5966
Russel Peralta, *Owner*
EMP: 16
SALES (est): 1.3MM **Privately Held**
SIC: 3715 Truck trailers

(P-20512)
SUNWAY MECHANICAL & ELEC TECH
1650 S Grove Ave Ste A, Ontario
(91761-4018)
PHONE...........................909 673-7959
Zili Xu, *President*
WEI Liu, *CFO*
Yan Guo, *Admin Sec*
EMP: 11
SALES (est): 1.3MM **Privately Held**
SIC: 3715 Truck trailers

(P-20513)
TRU-TRAILERS INC
Also Called: Tru-Trailers Manufacturing
4444 E Lincoln Ave, Fresno (93725-9709)
PHONE...........................559 251-7591
Judy A True, *Vice Pres*
Tom M True, *President*
Terry True, *Admin Sec*
EMP: 13
SQ FT: 4,000
SALES (est): 3.3MM **Privately Held**
SIC: 3715 7699 5013 Trailers or vans for transporting horses; trailer bodies; tractor repair; trailer parts & accessories

(P-20514)
TUFF BOY HOLDING INC
Also Called: Tuff Boy Trailers
5151 Almondwood Rd, Manteca
(95337-8868)
PHONE...........................209 239-1361
Martin Harris, *President*
John Cambra, *Vice Pres*
EMP: 44
SQ FT: 1,500
SALES (est): 5.1MM **Privately Held**
SIC: 3715 Semitrailers for truck tractors

(P-20515)
UNITED STATES LOGISTICS GROUP
Also Called: US Logistics
2700 Rose Ave Ste A, Signal Hill
(90755-1929)
P.O. Box 10129, Glendale (91209-3129)
PHONE...........................562 989-9555
Khachatur Khudikyan, *CEO*
Chester Whisenant, *Manager*
EMP: 32
SALES (est): 5.7MM **Privately Held**
SIC: 3715 Truck trailers

(P-20516)
UNLIMITED TRCK TRLR MAINT INC
825 S Maple Ave Ste D, Montebello
(90640-5400)
PHONE...........................323 727-2500
Yoan Leon, *President*
EMP: 25
SALES (est): 3.1MM **Privately Held**
SIC: 3715 Truck trailers

(P-20517)
UTILITY TRAILER MFG CO (PA)
17295 Railroad St Ste A, City of Industry
(91748-1043)
PHONE...........................626 964-7319
Paul F Bennett, *Ch of Bd*
Harold C Bennett, *President*
Craig M Bennett, *Senior VP*
Jeffrey J Bennett, *Vice Pres*
Stephen F Bennett, *Vice Pres*
◆ **EMP:** 300
SQ FT: 50,000
SALES (est): 964.8MM **Privately Held**
WEB: www.utm.com
SIC: 3715 Semitrailers for truck tractors

(P-20518)
UTILITY TRAILER MFG CO
Tautliner Division
301 Paseo Tesoro, Walnut (91789-2726)
PHONE...........................909 594-6026
Linda Baker, *Manager*
EMP: 315
SALES (corp-wide): 964.8MM **Privately Held**
WEB: www.utm.com
SIC: 3715 5199 Truck trailers; tarpaulins
PA: Utility Trailer Manufacturing Company
17295 Railroad St Ste A
City Of Industry CA 91748
626 964-7319

(P-20519)
UTILITY TRAILER MFG CO
Also Called: Utility Trlr Sls Southern Cal
15567 Valley Blvd, Fontana (92335-6351)
PHONE...........................909 428-8300
Thayne Stanger, *Branch Mgr*
EMP: 45
SALES (corp-wide): 964.8MM **Privately Held**
SIC: 3715 Semitrailers for truck tractors
PA: Utility Trailer Manufacturing Company
17295 Railroad St Ste A
City Of Industry CA 91748
626 964-7319

(P-20520)
VINTAGE TRANSPORT INC
161 Fair Ln, Placerville (95667-3929)
PHONE...........................530 622-3046
Lisa Nadeau, *President*
James Nadeau, *Vice Pres*
EMP: 11
SALES (est): 1.3MM **Privately Held**
WEB: www.vintagetransport.com
SIC: 3715 Demountable cargo containers

3716 Motor Homes

(P-20521)
B & B R V INC
3750 Auto Mall Dr, Anderson (96007-4929)
PHONE...........................530 365-7043
Charles Barnes, *CEO*
EMP: 20
SALES (est): 3.8MM **Privately Held**
SIC: 3716 Recreational van conversion (self-propelled), factory basis

(P-20522)
CT COACHWORKS LLC
9700 Indiana Ave, Riverside (92503-5563)
PHONE...........................951 343-8787
Steven Thomas, *Principal*
Susan Thomas,
▲ **EMP:** 11
SALES (est): 2.4MM **Privately Held**
SIC: 3716 Recreational van conversion (self-propelled), factory basis

(P-20523)
FLEETWOOD MOTOR HOMES-CALIFINC (DH)
Also Called: Fleetwood Homes
3125 Myers St, Riverside (92503-5527)
P.O. Box 7638 (92513-7638)
PHONE...........................951 354-3000
Edward B Caudill, *CEO*
Elden L Smith, *President*
Boyd R Plowman, *CFO*
Lyle N Larkin, *Treasurer*
Christopher J Braun, *Senior VP*
▲ **EMP:** 37
SQ FT: 262,900
SALES (est): 91.2MM
SALES (corp-wide): 2.3B **Privately Held**
SIC: 3716 Motor homes
HQ: Fleetwood Enterprises, Inc.
1351 Pomona Rd Ste 230
Corona CA 92882
951 354-3000

(P-20524)
LAZY DAZE INC
4303 Mission Blvd, Montclair (91763-6052)
PHONE...........................909 627-1103
H Edward Newton, *President*
Steve Newton, *Vice Pres*
▼ **EMP:** 20

SQ FT: 30,000
SALES (est): 3.2MM **Privately Held**
WEB: www.lazydaze.com
SIC: 3716 Motor homes

(P-20525)
REXHALL INDUSTRIES INC
26857 Tannahill Ave, Canyon Country
(91387-3969)
PHONE...........................661 726-5470
William Jonathan Rex, *Ch of Bd*
James C Rex, *Vice Pres*
Cheryl Rex, *Admin Sec*
▲ **EMP:** 46
SQ FT: 120,000
SALES (est): 7.5MM **Privately Held**
WEB: www.rexhall.com
SIC: 3716 Motor homes

(P-20526)
UNIVERSAL SPECIALTY VEHICLES
7879 Pine Crest Dr, Riverside
(92506-5401)
PHONE...........................951 943-7747
Andrew Hall, *President*
Mary Hall, *Vice Pres*
Chrystal Montes, *Admin Asst*
Evelyn Castillo, *Technology*
EMP: 16
SQ FT: 14,000
SALES (est): 3.2MM **Privately Held**
WEB: www.usv1.com
SIC: 3716 Motor homes

3721 Aircraft

(P-20527)
ACRA AEROSPACE LLC
2121 E Via Burton, Anaheim (92806-1220)
PHONE...........................714 778-1900
Chris Jones, *CFO*
Patrice Maree, *Sales Executive*
EMP: 28
SALES (est): 5.7MM **Privately Held**
SIC: 3721 Aircraft

(P-20528)
ADVANCED TACTICS INC
3339 Airport Dr, Torrance (90505-6152)
PHONE...........................310 701-3659
Don Shaw, *President*
Lori K Tang, *Marketing Staff*
Rustom Jehangir, *Manager*
EMP: 12
SALES (est): 1.7MM **Privately Held**
SIC: 3721 Aircraft

(P-20529)
AERCAP US GLOBAL AVIATION LLC (HQ)
Also Called: Aercap Los Angeles
10250 Constellation Blvd, Los Angeles
(90067-6200)
PHONE...........................310 788-1999
Sean Sullivan,
Keith Helming, *CFO*
Alex Khatibi, *Executive*
Howard Watts,
EMP: 23
SALES (est): 259.4MM
SALES (corp-wide): 1B **Privately Held**
SIC: 3721 4581 6159 Aircraft; airport leasing, if operating airport; equipment & vehicle finance leasing companies
PA: Aercap Holdings N.V.
Unknown Dutch Address

353 163-6065

(P-20530)
AERO CORPORATION
3061 Quail Run Rd, Los Alamitos
(90720-2901)
PHONE...........................562 598-2281
J Strom, *President*
EMP: 20 **EST:** 2010
SALES (est): 1.3MM **Privately Held**
SIC: 3721 Aircraft

(P-20531)
AEROSYSNG INC
Also Called: Aerosystems Engineering
1112 W Barkley Ave, Orange (92868-1213)
PHONE...........................714 633-1901
Minna Chae, *Partner*
EMP: 10
SALES (est): 1.2MM **Privately Held**
SIC: 3721 Aircraft

(P-20532)
AEROVIRONMENT INC
1610 S Magnolia Ave, Monrovia
(91016-4547)
PHONE...........................626 357-9983
Ken Craig, *Vice Pres*
Peter Holbert, *Engineer*
Mark Nelson, *Engineer*
Jason Levine, *Analyst*
Jamie Wagner, *Production*
EMP: 61
SALES (corp-wide): 271MM **Publicly Held**
SIC: 3721 Aircraft
PA: Aerovironment, Inc.
800 Royal Oaks Dr Ste 210
Monrovia CA 91016
626 357-9983

(P-20533)
AEROVIRONMENT INC (PA)
800 Royal Oaks Dr Ste 210, Monrovia
(91016-6364)
P.O. Box 5031 (91017-7131)
PHONE...........................626 357-9983
Wahid Nawabi, *President*
Timothy E Conver, *Ch of Bd*
Teresa Covington, *CFO*
Charles Burbage, *Bd of Directors*
Catharine Merigold, *Bd of Directors*
▲ **EMP:** 60
SQ FT: 36,000
SALES: 271MM **Publicly Held**
WEB: www.avinc.com
SIC: 3721 Gliders (aircraft)

(P-20534)
AEROVIRONMENT INC
1725 Peck Rd, Monrovia (91016-4531)
PHONE...........................626 357-9983
Tim Conver, *Ch of Bd*
EMP: 21
SALES (corp-wide): 271MM **Publicly Held**
SIC: 3721 8711 Aircraft; engineering services
PA: Aerovironment, Inc.
800 Royal Oaks Dr Ste 210
Monrovia CA 91016
626 357-9983

(P-20535)
AEROVIRONMENT INC
222 E Huntington Dr # 118, Monrovia
(91016-8014)
PHONE...........................626 357-9983
EMP: 23
SALES (corp-wide): 271MM **Publicly Held**
SIC: 3721 Aircraft
PA: Aerovironment, Inc.
800 Royal Oaks Dr Ste 210
Monrovia CA 91016
626 357-9983

(P-20536)
AEROVIRONMENT INC
2290 Agate Ct, Simi Valley (93065-1935)
PHONE...........................626 357-9983
David Villa, *Manager*
Joseph O'Connor, *Admin Sec*
EMP: 10
SALES (corp-wide): 271MM **Publicly Held**
SIC: 3721 1541 Aircraft; industrial buildings & warehouses
PA: Aerovironment, Inc.
800 Royal Oaks Dr Ste 210
Monrovia CA 91016
626 357-9983

(P-20537)
AEROVIRONMENT INC
825 S Myrtle Ave, Monrovia (91016-3424)
PHONE...........................626 357-9983
Stewart Hindle, *Manager*

Jon Ross, *Program Mgr*
Ronald Norton, *Engineer*
EMP: 20
SALES (corp-wide): 271MM **Publicly Held**
WEB: www.avinc.com
SIC: 3721 Aircraft
PA: Aerovironment, Inc.
800 Royal Oaks Dr Ste 210
Monrovia CA 91016
626 357-9983

(P-20538)
AMERICAN SCENCE TECH AS T CORP (PA)
50 California St Fl 21, San Francisco (94111-4624)
P.O. Box 9148, Laguna Beach (92652-7142)
PHONE.....................415 251-2800
James Johnson, *President*
Jake Soujah, *President*
EMP: 135
SQ FT: 12,000
SALES: 348MM **Privately Held**
SIC: 3721 3724 3761 3764 Aircraft; aircraft engines & engine parts; guided missiles & space vehicles; guided missile & space vehicle propulsion unit parts; guided missile & space vehicle parts & auxiliary equipment

(P-20539)
AMERICAN SCENCE TECH AS T CORP
2372 Morse Ave Ste 571, Irvine (92614-6234)
PHONE.....................310 773-1978
Kinda Assouad, *Branch Mgr*
EMP: 85
SALES (corp-wide): 348MM **Privately Held**
SIC: 3721 3724 3761 3764 Aircraft; aircraft engines & engine parts; guided missiles & space vehicles; guided missile & space vehicle propulsion unit parts; guided missile & space vehicle parts & auxiliary equipment
PA: American Science & Technology (As&T) Corporation
50 California St Fl 21
San Francisco CA 94111
415 251-2800

(P-20540)
ANAHEIM PRECISION SHTMTL MFG (HQ)
Also Called: ANAHEIM PRECISION MFG
1738 N Neville St, Orange (92865-4214)
PHONE.....................714 453-0100
Anthony Puccio, *CEO*
Joe Puccio, *COO*
Gilles Madelmont, *CFO*
EMP: 150
SQ FT: 57,000
SALES: 9.5MM
SALES (corp-wide): 14.7MM **Privately Held**
WEB: www.anaheimprecision.com
SIC: 3721 3444 3728 3479 Motorized aircraft; culverts, flumes & pipes; aircraft body & wing assemblies & parts; aircraft landing assemblies & brakes; aircraft assemblies, subassemblies & parts; etching & engraving; machine & other job shop work
PA: Manufacturing Solutions, Inc.
1738 N Neville St
Orange CA 92865
714 453-0100

(P-20541)
ARCTIC SLOPE WORLD SVCS INC
225 Bishop Rd Bldg 23, Vandenberg Afb (93437)
PHONE.....................805 605-7560
Andrew Gallegos, *President*
EMP: 585
SALES: 950K **Privately Held**
SIC: 3721 Aircraft

(P-20542)
ASTRAEUS AEROSPACE LLC
16255 Ventura Blvd # 625, Encino (91436-2302)
PHONE.....................310 907-9205
David Wagreich, *CEO*
Sariah Dorbin,
EMP: 12
SALES (est): 487.7K **Privately Held**
SIC: 3721 Research & development on aircraft by the manufacturer

(P-20543)
BOEING COMPANY
Lemoore Nval Base Hnger 1, Lemoore (93245)
P.O. Box 1160 (93245-1160)
PHONE.....................559 998-8260
George Baldwin, *Manager*
EMP: 50
SALES (corp-wide): 93.3B **Publicly Held**
SIC: 3721 Aircraft
PA: The Boeing Company
100 N Riverside Plz
Chicago IL 60606
312 544-2000

(P-20544)
BOEING COMPANY
22308 Harbor Ridge Ln, Torrance (90502-2451)
PHONE.....................310 662-7286
EMP: 1005
SALES (corp-wide): 93.3B **Publicly Held**
SIC: 3721 Airplanes, fixed or rotary wing; helicopters; research & development on aircraft by the manufacturer
PA: The Boeing Company
100 N Riverside Plz
Chicago IL 60606
312 544-2000

(P-20545)
BOEING COMPANY
2201 Seal Beach Blvd, Seal Beach (90740-5603)
PHONE.....................562 797-5831
James Albaugh, *Branch Mgr*
EMP: 1000
SALES (corp-wide): 93.3B **Publicly Held**
SIC: 3721 Aircraft
PA: The Boeing Company
100 N Riverside Plz
Chicago IL 60606
312 544-2000

(P-20546)
BOEING COMPANY
5463 Plumeria Ln, Cypress (90630-7912)
PHONE.....................714 952-1509
EMP: 895
SALES (corp-wide): 93.3B **Publicly Held**
SIC: 3721 Airplanes, fixed or rotary wing
PA: The Boeing Company
100 N Riverside Plz
Chicago IL 60606
312 544-2000

(P-20547)
BOEING COMPANY
24172 Via Madrugada, Mission Viejo (92692-1907)
PHONE.....................949 452-0259
EMP: 895
SALES (corp-wide): 93.3B **Publicly Held**
SIC: 3721 Airplanes, fixed or rotary wing
PA: The Boeing Company
100 N Riverside Plz
Chicago IL 60606
312 544-2000

(P-20548)
BOEING COMPANY
122 E Jones Rd Bldg 151, Edwards (93524-8202)
PHONE.....................661 810-4686
Kenneth R Westman, *CEO*
EMP: 1005
SALES (corp-wide): 93.3B **Publicly Held**
SIC: 3721 Airplanes, fixed or rotary wing; helicopters; research & development on aircraft by the manufacturer
PA: The Boeing Company
100 N Riverside Plz
Chicago IL 60606
312 544-2000

(P-20549)
BOEING COMPANY
3521 E Spring St, Long Beach (90806-2431)
PHONE.....................714 317-1070
EMP: 996
SALES (corp-wide): 93.3B **Publicly Held**
SIC: 3721 Airplanes, fixed or rotary wing
PA: The Boeing Company
100 N Riverside Plz
Chicago IL 60606
312 544-2000

(P-20550)
BOEING COMPANY
2400 E Wardlow Rd, Long Beach (90807-5310)
PHONE.....................562 593-6668
EMP: 996
SALES (corp-wide): 93.3B **Publicly Held**
SIC: 3721 Airplanes, fixed or rotary wing
PA: The Boeing Company
100 N Riverside Plz
Chicago IL 60606
312 544-2000

(P-20551)
BOEING COMPANY
12203 Hillwood Dr, Whittier (90604-3109)
PHONE.....................562 944-6583
EMP: 895
SALES (corp-wide): 93.3B **Publicly Held**
SIC: 3721 Airplanes, fixed or rotary wing
PA: The Boeing Company
100 N Riverside Plz
Chicago IL 60606
312 544-2000

(P-20552)
BOEING COMPANY
3460 Cherry Ave Bldg 56, Long Beach (90807-4912)
PHONE.....................562 425-3613
EMP: 996
SALES (corp-wide): 93.3B **Publicly Held**
SIC: 3721 Airplanes, fixed or rotary wing
PA: The Boeing Company
100 N Riverside Plz
Chicago IL 60606
312 544-2000

(P-20553)
BOEING COMPANY
18310 Readiness St, Victorville (92394-7911)
PHONE.....................760 246-0273
Ray Rich, *Manager*
EMP: 996
SALES (corp-wide): 93.3B **Publicly Held**
SIC: 3721 Airplanes, fixed or rotary wing
PA: The Boeing Company
100 N Riverside Plz
Chicago IL 60606
312 544-2000

(P-20554)
BOEING COMPANY
15400 Graham St Ste 101, Huntington Beach (92649-1257)
PHONE.....................714 934-9801
Ray Murillo, *Branch Mgr*
Terry Majerski, *Consultant*
EMP: 996
SALES (corp-wide): 93.3B **Publicly Held**
SIC: 3721 Airplanes, fixed or rotary wing
PA: The Boeing Company
100 N Riverside Plz
Chicago IL 60606
312 544-2000

(P-20555)
BOEING COMPANY
222 N Pacific Coast Hwy # 2050, El Segundo (90245-5660)
PHONE.....................310 426-4100
Barry Waldman, *Manager*
Bonnie Lindley, *Engineer*
EMP: 100
SALES (corp-wide): 93.3B **Publicly Held**
SIC: 3721 Airplanes, fixed or rotary wing
PA: The Boeing Company
100 N Riverside Plz
Chicago IL 60606
312 544-2000

(P-20556)
BOEING COMPANY
5301 Bolsa Ave, Huntington Beach (92647-2048)
PHONE.....................714 896-3311
Jim Albaugh, *Branch Mgr*
EMP: 996
SALES (corp-wide): 93.3B **Publicly Held**
SIC: 3721 3761 Airplanes, fixed or rotary wing; guided missiles & space vehicles
PA: The Boeing Company
100 N Riverside Plz
Chicago IL 60606
312 544-2000

(P-20557)
BOEING COMPANY
3855 N Lakewood Blvd D35-0072, Long Beach (90846-0001)
PHONE.....................562 593-5511
Marcia Solomon, *Branch Mgr*
Mike Matthews, *Principal*
Sean Frankel, *Administration*
Sanober Khan, *Network Enginr*
Jerry Baccari, *Prgrmr*
EMP: 30
SALES (corp-wide): 93.3B **Publicly Held**
SIC: 3721 Aircraft
PA: The Boeing Company
100 N Riverside Plz
Chicago IL 60606
312 544-2000

(P-20558)
BOEING COMPANY
2401 E Wardlow Rd, Long Beach (90807-5309)
PHONE.....................562 496-1000
Nan Bouchard, *Vice Pres*
EMP: 2000
SALES (corp-wide): 93.3B **Publicly Held**
SIC: 3721 Airplanes, fixed or rotary wing
PA: The Boeing Company
100 N Riverside Plz
Chicago IL 60606
312 544-2000

(P-20559)
BOEING COMPANY
5301 Bolsa Ave, Huntington Beach (92647-2048)
PHONE.....................714 896-1301
Dave Bullock, *CFO*
EMP: 559
SALES (corp-wide): 93.3B **Publicly Held**
SIC: 3721 Aircraft
PA: The Boeing Company
100 N Riverside Plz
Chicago IL 60606
312 544-2000

(P-20560)
BOEING COMPANY
2401 E Wardlow Rd, Long Beach (90807-5309)
P.O. Box 200 (90801-0200)
PHONE.....................562 593-5511
Linda Van Reeden, *Manager*
Carola Najera, *Office Admin*
Wael Elaref, *Project Mgr*
Kimberly De La Torre, *Technical Staff*
Sanford Fleishman, *Engineer*
EMP: 1400
SALES (corp-wide): 93.3B **Publicly Held**
SIC: 3721 Airplanes, fixed or rotary wing
PA: The Boeing Company
100 N Riverside Plz
Chicago IL 60606
312 544-2000

(P-20561)
BOEING COMPANY
14441 Astronautics Ln, Huntington Beach (92647-2080)
PHONE.....................714 896-1670
EMP: 996
SALES (corp-wide): 93.3B **Publicly Held**
SIC: 3721 Airplanes, fixed or rotary wing
PA: The Boeing Company
100 N Riverside Plz
Chicago IL 60606
312 544-2000

PRODUCTS & SVCS

(P-20562)
BOEING COMPANY
451 1st St, Travis Afb (94535-2186)
P.O. Box 1415 (94535-0415)
PHONE..............................707 437-8574
Steve Andrews, *Branch Mgr*
EMP: 996
SALES (corp-wide): 93.3B **Publicly Held**
SIC: 3721 Airplanes, fixed or rotary wing
PA: The Boeing Company
100 N Riverside Plz
Chicago IL 60606
312 544-2000

(P-20563)
BOEING COMPANY
5301 Bolsa Ave, Huntington Beach
(92647-2048)
PHONE..............................714 896-1839
John Vaswani, *Vice Pres*
EMP: 3500
SALES (corp-wide): 93.3B **Publicly Held**
SIC: 3721 Aircraft
PA: The Boeing Company
100 N Riverside Plz
Chicago IL 60606
312 544-2000

(P-20564)
BOEING COMPANY
5222 Rancho Rd, Huntington Beach
(92647-2052)
PHONE..............................714 896-3311
Paula Hutt, *Branch Mgr*
EMP: 30
SALES (corp-wide): 93.3B **Publicly Held**
SIC: 3721 Aircraft
PA: The Boeing Company
100 N Riverside Plz
Chicago IL 60606
312 544-2000

(P-20565)
BOEING COMPANY
1700 E Imperial Ave, El Segundo
(90245-2646)
PHONE..............................310 416-9319
Joe Buford, *Principal*
Ron Martyn, *Admin Asst*
Dillard Leslie, *Manager*
EMP: 996
SALES (corp-wide): 93.3B **Publicly Held**
SIC: 3721 Airplanes, fixed or rotary wing
PA: The Boeing Company
100 N Riverside Plz
Chicago IL 60606
312 544-2000

(P-20566)
BOEING COMPANY
8900 De Soto Ave, Canoga Park
(91304-1967)
PHONE..............................818 428-1154
Archi Burds, *Principal*
EMP: 1005
SALES (corp-wide): 93.3B **Publicly Held**
SIC: 3721 Airplanes, fixed or rotary wing
PA: The Boeing Company
100 N Riverside Plz
Chicago IL 60606
312 544-2000

(P-20567)
BOEING COMPANY
5250 Tanker Way, March ARB
(92518-1748)
PHONE..............................951 571-0122
EMP: 996
SALES (corp-wide): 93.3B **Publicly Held**
SIC: 3721 Airplanes, fixed or rotary wing
PA: The Boeing Company
100 N Riverside Plz
Chicago IL 60606
312 544-2000

(P-20568)
BOEING INTELLECTUAL
3501 Bolsa Ave, Huntington Beach (92647)
PHONE..............................562 797-2020
Martin Bentrott, *Vice Pres*
Russell Kuchynka, *Vice Pres*
Eric Muehle, *General Mgr*
Daniela Nau, *Administration*
Robert Maclean, *Info Tech Dir*
EMP: 28

SALES (est): 3.2MM
SALES (corp-wide): 93.3B **Publicly Held**
SIC: 3721 Airplanes, fixed or rotary wing;
helicopters; research & development on
aircraft by the manufacturer
PA: The Boeing Company
100 N Riverside Plz
Chicago IL 60606
312 544-2000

(P-20569)
BOEING SATELLITE SYSTEMS INC
2300 E Imperial Hwy, El Segundo
(90245-2813)
P.O. Box 92919, Los Angeles (90009-2919)
PHONE..............................310 568-2735
Steve Tsukamoto, *Manager*
Pamela Campadonia, *Purch Mgr*
Jesse Arroyo, *Manager*
Irina Dubovitsky, *Manager*
EMP: 10
SALES (corp-wide): 93.3B **Publicly Held**
SIC: 3721 Aircraft
HQ: Boeing Satellite Systems, Inc.
900 N Pacific Coast Hwy
El Segundo CA 90245

(P-20570)
BOEING SATELLITE SYSTEMS INC
1950 E Imperial Hwy, El Segundo
(90245-2701)
PHONE..............................310 364-6444
Patrick Bailleul, *Manager*
Dj Gowanlock, *Software Engr*
Michael Bohman, *Design Engr*
Kim Levine, *Engineer*
Jerry Macfarlane, *Engineer*
EMP: 22
SQ FT: 36,220
SALES (corp-wide): 93.3B **Publicly Held**
SIC: 3721 Aircraft
HQ: Boeing Satellite Systems, Inc.
900 N Pacific Coast Hwy
El Segundo CA 90245

(P-20571)
CALIFORNIA BLIMPS
738 W 17th St Ste D, Costa Mesa
(92627-4340)
PHONE..............................949 650-1183
Paul Pacelli, *Owner*
EMP: 10
SQ FT: 1,900
SALES (est): 420K **Privately Held**
WEB: www.californiablimps.com
SIC: 3721 Blimps

(P-20572)
CHIPTON-ROSS INC
420 Culver Blvd, Playa Del Rey
(90293-7706)
PHONE..............................310 414-7800
Judith Hinkley, *President*
Carla Bernal, *Administration*
Angela Malachowski, *Administration*
Emmanuel Morgan, *Administration*
Juan Saldarriaga, *Administration*
EMP: 100
SQ FT: 6,000
SALES: 9MM **Privately Held**
SIC: 3721 3731 8731 Motorized aircraft;
military ships, building & repairing; com-
mercial physical research

(P-20573)
CLEAN WAVE MANAGEMENT INC
Also Called: Impact Bearing
1291 Puerta Del Sol, San Clemente
(92673-6310)
PHONE..............................949 488-2922
Fax: 949 488-2923
▲ **EMP:** 15
SALES (est): 2.1MM **Privately Held**
WEB: www.aircraftbearing.com
SIC: 3721

(P-20574)
CNS AVIATION INC
1240 N Simon Cir, Anaheim (92806-1814)
PHONE..............................714 901-7072

Scott David Dantuono, *President*
EMP: 10
SALES (est): 2.1MM **Privately Held**
SIC: 3721 Aircraft

(P-20575)
COMAC AMERICA CORPORATION
4350 Von Karman Ave # 400, Newport
Beach (92660-2007)
PHONE..............................760 616-9614
WEI Ye, *CEO*
EMP: 13
SALES (est): 1.2MM **Privately Held**
SIC: 3721 Aircraft
HQ: State-Owned Assets Supervision And
Administration Commission Of The
State Council
No.26, Xuanwumen (W) Ave.
Beijing
106 319-2000

(P-20576)
DAYTON SUPERIOR CORPORATION
10780 Mulberry Ave, Fontana
(92337-7062)
PHONE..............................909 957-7271
EMP: 30 **Publicly Held**
SIC: 3721 Aircraft
HQ: Dayton Superior Corporation
1125 Byers Rd
Miamisburg OH 45342
937 866-0711

(P-20577)
EXPERIMENTAL AIRCRAFT ASSN
7026 Lasaine Ave, Van Nuys (91406-3544)
PHONE..............................818 705-2744
Charles Ducat, *President*
EMP: 12
SALES (est): 871.5K **Privately Held**
SIC: 3721 Aircraft

(P-20578)
GDAS-LINCOLN INC
Also Called: Gulfstream California
1501 Aviation Blvd, Lincoln (95648-9388)
PHONE..............................916 645-8961
David Pearman, *General Mgr*
James Kratz, *General Mgr*
Gentry Caulder, *Human Res Mgr*
EMP: 53
SALES (est): 7.9MM **Privately Held**
SIC: 3721 Aircraft

(P-20579)
GENERAL ATOMIC AERON
14040 Danielson St, Poway (92064-6857)
PHONE..............................858 455-4560
EMP: 15 **Privately Held**
SIC: 3721 Aircraft
HQ: General Atomics Aeronautical Sys-
tems, Inc.
14200 Kirkham Way
Poway CA 92064

(P-20580)
GENERAL ATOMIC AERON
13330 Evening Creek Dr N, San Diego
(92128-4110)
PHONE..............................858 964-6700
Neal Blue, *President*
Jesus Padilla, *Info Tech Mgr*
Doug Seybert, *Engineer*
Theressa Brown, *Opers Staff*
Roland Hogue, *Opers Staff*
EMP: 500 **Privately Held**
SIC: 3721 Aircraft
HQ: General Atomics Aeronautical Sys-
tems, Inc.
14200 Kirkham Way
Poway CA 92064

(P-20581)
GENERAL ATOMIC AERON
9779 Yucca Rd, Adelanto (92301-2265)
PHONE..............................760 246-3660
Jim Machin, *Manager*
EMP: 135 **Privately Held**
WEB: www.ga-asi.com
SIC: 3721 Aircraft

HQ: General Atomics Aeronautical Systems, Inc.
14200 Kirkham Way
Poway CA 92064

(P-20582)
GENERAL ATOMIC AERON
3550 General Atomics Ct, San Diego
(92121-1122)
PHONE..............................858 455-2810
Victoria Freed, *Administration*
Bruce Trumbo, *Info Tech Mgr*
Shaun Donovan, *Technical Staff*
Gregory Chapelle, *Engineer*
Mark Chung, *Engineer*
EMP: 500 **Privately Held**
SIC: 3721 Aircraft
HQ: General Atomics Aeronautical Sys-
tems, Inc.
14200 Kirkham Way
Poway CA 92064

(P-20583)
GENERAL ATOMIC AERON
Mission Systems
16761 Via Del Campo Ct, San Diego
(92127-1713)
PHONE..............................858 455-4309
Cyndra Flanagen, *Director*
Michael Neale, *President*
Edward Lebla, *Program Mgr*
Jay Stoneburner, *Program Mgr*
Jean Valentine, *Program Mgr*
EMP: 500 **Privately Held**
WEB: www.ga-asi.com
SIC: 3721 Aircraft
HQ: General Atomics Aeronautical Sys-
tems, Inc.
14200 Kirkham Way
Poway CA 92064

(P-20584)
GENERAL ATOMIC AERON
73 El Mirage Airport Rd B, Adelanto
(92301-9540)
PHONE..............................760 388-8208
Gary Bener, *Branch Mgr*
Michael Stroup, *Engineer*
Lonnie Fishter, *Manager*
EMP: 200
SQ FT: 34,425 **Privately Held**
WEB: www.generalatomics.com
SIC: 3721 Aircraft
HQ: General Atomics Aeronautical Sys-
tems, Inc.
14200 Kirkham Way
Poway CA 92064

(P-20585)
GENERAL ATOMIC AERON (DH)
Also Called: US Gov GA Aeronautical Uav
14200 Kirkham Way, Poway (92064-7103)
PHONE..............................858 312-2810
Neal Blue, *President*
Tony Navarra, *Treasurer*
Brad Clark, *Vice Pres*
Stacy Jakuttis, *Vice Pres*
Stephen Bell, *Program Mgr*
▲ **EMP:** 500
SQ FT: 900,000
SALES (est): 1.5B **Privately Held**
WEB: www.ga-asi.com
SIC: 3721 Aircraft

(P-20586)
GENERAL ATOMIC AERON
14115 Stowe Dr, Poway (92064-7145)
PHONE..............................858 312-2543
Deborah Mettas, *Contractor*
James Cole, *Administration*
Elsa Kleinfieldt, *Buyer*
EMP: 500 **Privately Held**
SIC: 3721 Aircraft
HQ: General Atomics Aeronautical Sys-
tems, Inc.
14200 Kirkham Way
Poway CA 92064

▲ = Import ▼=Export
◆ =Import/Export

(P-20587)
GENERAL ATOMICS INTL SVCS CORP
3483 Dunhill St, San Diego (92121-1200)
PHONE..................................858 455-4141
EMP: 37 **Privately Held**
SIC: 3721 Aircraft
HQ: General Atomics International Services
Corporation
3550 General Atomics Ct
San Diego CA 92121

(P-20588)
GENERAL ELECTRIC COMPANY
18000 Phantom St, Victorville
(92394-7913)
PHONE..................................760 530-5200
John Hardell, *Principal*
Mark Solorio, *Engineer*
Dave Kiehl, *Opers Mgr*
Noah Demerly, *Maintence Staff*
Tamrat Antenyistegn, *Senior Mgr*
EMP: 50
SALES (corp-wide): 122B **Publicly Held**
SIC: 3721 Aircraft
PA: General Electric Company
41 Farnsworth St
Boston MA 02210
617 443-3000

(P-20589)
GULF STREAMS
4150 E Donald Douglas Dr, Long Beach
(90808-1725)
PHONE..................................562 420-1818
Mike Kambourian, *Owner*
Scott Horner, *Info Tech Mgr*
Mike Anderson, *Buyer*
Jim Curby, *Safety Mgr*
Carlos Garcia, *Manager*
▲ EMP: 19
SALES (est): 3.5MM **Privately Held**
SIC: 3721 Aircraft

(P-20590)
GULFSTREAM AEROSPACE CORP GA
9818 Mina Ave, Whittier (90605-3035)
PHONE..................................562 907-9300
EMP: 1189
SALES (corp-wide): 30.9B **Publicly Held**
SIC: 3721 Airplanes, fixed or rotary wing
HQ: Gulfstream Aerospace Corporation
(Georgia)
500 Gulfstream Rd
Savannah GA 31408
912 965-3000

(P-20591)
HILLER AIRCRAFT CORPORATION
925 M St, Firebaugh (93622-2234)
P.O. Box 246 (93622-0246)
PHONE..................................559 659-5959
Steven Palm, *General Mgr*
EMP: 30
SQ FT: 100,000
SALES (est): 4.6MM **Privately Held**
SIC: 3721 Helicopters

(P-20592)
IMPOSSIBLE AEROSPACE CORP
1118 Elko Dr, Sunnyvale (94089-2207)
PHONE..................................707 293-9367
Albert Spencer Gore, *CEO*
EMP: 15
SALES (est): 2.6MM **Privately Held**
SIC: 3721 Aircraft

(P-20593)
JETEFFECT INC (PA)
3250 Airflite Way Fl 3, Long Beach
(90807-5312)
PHONE..................................562 989-8800
Bryan Comstock, *President*
EMP: 10 EST: 2001
SALES (est): 1.4MM **Privately Held**
WEB: www.jeteffect.com
SIC: 3721 Aircraft

(P-20594)
JVR SHEETMETAL FABRICATION INC
Also Called: TALSCO
7101 Patterson Dr, Garden Grove
(92841-1415)
PHONE..................................714 841-2464
Jose Castaneda, *CEO*
EMP: 33
SQ FT: 1,000
SALES: 3.8MM **Privately Held**
SIC: 3721 Aircraft

(P-20595)
KAY AND ASSOCIATES INC
300 Reeves Blvd, Lemoore (93246-7400)
PHONE..................................559 410-0917
Gregory Kay, *President*
Dianna Chinn Heinz, *CFO*
EMP: 40
SALES (est): 1.8MM **Privately Held**
SIC: 3721 Aircraft

(P-20596)
KITTY HAWK CORPORATION (PA)
2700 Broderick Way, Mountain View
(94043-1108)
PHONE..................................650 641-0076
Sebastian Thrun, *CEO*
Curtis Conaway, *Technician*
Robert Moore, *Engineer*
Nihal Murthy, *Engineer*
Eric Von Herbulis, *Engineer*
EMP: 110
SQ FT: 30,000
SALES (est): 27.6MM **Privately Held**
SIC: 3721 Aircraft

(P-20597)
KOREA AEROSPACE INDUSTRIES LTD
16700 Valley View Ave # 205, La Mirada
(90638-5852)
PHONE..................................714 868-8560
Jy Moon, *Branch Mgr*
EMP: 11
SALES (corp-wide): 1.9B **Privately Held**
WEB: www.samsungamerica.com
SIC: 3721 Aircraft
PA: Korea Aerospace Industries, Ltd
41 Gongdan 1-Ro, Sanam-Myeon
Sacheon 52529
825 585-1100

(P-20598)
LOCKHEED MARTIN (HQ)
1111 Lockheed Martin Way, Sunnyvale
(94089-1212)
PHONE..................................408 834-9741
Dave Turkington, *Principal*
EMP: 33
SALES (est): 8.5MM **Publicly Held**
SIC: 3721 Aircraft

(P-20599)
LOCKHEED MARTIN CORPORATION
2655 S Macarthur Dr, Tracy (95376-8188)
PHONE..................................408 756-3008
EMP: 430
SALES (corp-wide): 45.3B **Publicly Held**
SIC: 3721
PA: Lockheed Martin Corporation
6801 Rockledge Dr
Bethesda MD 20817
301 897-6000

(P-20600)
LOCKHEED MARTIN CORPORATION
1374 Holland Ct, San Jose (95118-3423)
PHONE..................................408 742-5219
EMP: 430
SALES (corp-wide): 47.1B **Publicly Held**
SIC: 3721
PA: Lockheed Martin Corporation
6801 Rockledge Dr
Bethesda MD 20817
301 897-6000

(P-20601)
LOCKHEED MARTIN CORPORATION
1330 30th St Ste A, San Diego
(92154-3471)
PHONE..................................619 298-8453
EMP: 435
SALES (corp-wide): 46.1B **Publicly Held**
SIC: 3721
PA: Lockheed Martin Corporation
6801 Rockledge Dr
Bethesda MD 20817
301 897-6000

(P-20602)
MISSION RESEARCH CORPORATION (DH)
Also Called: Atk Mission Research
6750 Navigator Way # 200, Goleta
(93117-3657)
PHONE..................................805 690-2447
Kevin Vogel, *Principal*
Jeff Vosburgh, *Vice Pres*
Patrick Figge, *Senior Mgr*
EMP: 10
SQ FT: 40,000
SALES (est): 15.8MM **Publicly Held**
WEB: www.mrcla.com
SIC: 3721 Research & development on aircraft by the manufacturer
HQ: Northrop Grumman Innovation Systems, Inc.
45101 Warp Dr
Dulles VA 20166
703 406-5000

(P-20603)
MOLLER INTERNATIONAL INC
1855 N 1st St Unit C, Dixon (95620-9758)
PHONE..................................530 756-5086
Paul S Moller, *President*
Jim Toreson, *Chairman*
Faulkner White, *Corp Secy*
EMP: 12
SQ FT: 13,000
SALES: 500K **Privately Held**
SIC: 3721 3724 Aircraft; aircraft engines & engine parts; research & development on aircraft engines & parts

(P-20604)
NORTHROP GRUMMAN SYSTEMS CORP
Also Called: Electronic Systems Co Esco
401 E Hendy Ave, Sunnyvale (94086-5100)
P.O. Box 3499 (94088-3499)
PHONE..................................408 735-2241
William Pitts, *Branch Mgr*
Carol Pace, *Executive*
Matt Mason, *Design Engr*
Emmanuel Aivaliotis, *Engineer*
Edwin Constantino, *Engineer*
EMP: 305 **Publicly Held**
WEB: www.sperry.ngc.com
SIC: 3721 Motorized aircraft; research & development on aircraft by the manufacturer
HQ: Northrop Grumman Systems Corporation
2980 Fairview Park Dr
Falls Church VA 22042
703 280-2900

(P-20605)
NORTHROP GRUMMAN SYSTEMS CORP
Also Called: Litton Navigation Systems Div
21240 Burbank Blvd Ms29, Woodland Hills
(91367-6680)
PHONE..................................818 715-4040
Bill Allison, *Division Pres*
James McHugh, *Program Mgr*
Patricia White, *Program Mgr*
Cammy Reynoso, *Executive Asst*
Jim Kemp, *Admin Asst*
EMP: 1000 **Publicly Held**
WEB: www.sperry.ngc.com
SIC: 3721 Airplanes, fixed or rotary wing
HQ: Northrop Grumman Systems Corporation
2980 Fairview Park Dr
Falls Church VA 22042
703 280-2900

(P-20606)
NORTHROP GRUMMAN SYSTEMS CORP
1 Hornet Way Dept Mt00w5, El Segundo
(90245-2804)
PHONE..................................310 632-1846
Richard A Lautzenheiser, *Manager*
Kenneth L Bedingfield, *Vice Pres*
Randy Agura, *General Mgr*
Leticia Razo, *General Mgr*
Mark Gebert, *Senior Engr*
EMP: 317 **Publicly Held**
SIC: 3721 Airplanes, fixed or rotary wing
HQ: Northrop Grumman Systems Corporation
2980 Fairview Park Dr
Falls Church VA 22042
703 280-2900

(P-20607)
NORTHROP GRUMMAN SYSTEMS CORP
Also Called: Air Combat Systems
3520 E Avenue M, Palmdale (93550-7401)
PHONE..................................661 272-7000
David G Hogarth, *Manager*
Alan Muller, *Program Mgr*
Patricia Helke, *Admin Asst*
William Ekstrand, *Engineer*
Hubie Figueiredo, *Engineer*
EMP: 300 **Publicly Held**
WEB: www.sperry.ngc.com
SIC: 3721 3812 3761 Aircraft; search & navigation equipment; guided missiles & space vehicles
HQ: Northrop Grumman Systems Corporation
2980 Fairview Park Dr
Falls Church VA 22042
703 280-2900

(P-20608)
NORTHROP GRUMMAN SYSTEMS CORP
9112 Spectrum Center Blvd, San Diego
(92123-1439)
PHONE..................................858 514-9020
EMP: 11 **Publicly Held**
SIC: 3721 Airplanes, fixed or rotary wing
HQ: Northrop Grumman Systems Corporation
2980 Fairview Park Dr
Falls Church VA 22042
703 280-2900

(P-20609)
NORTHROP GRUMMAN SYSTEMS CORP
Western Region
3520 E Avenue M, Palmdale (93550-7401)
PHONE..................................661 540-0446
Jim Pace, *Branch Mgr*
EMP: 305 **Publicly Held**
WEB: www.sperry.ngc.com
SIC: 3721
HQ: Northrop Grumman Systems Corporation
2980 Fairview Park Dr
Falls Church VA 22042
703 280-2900

(P-20610)
NORTHROP GRUMMAN SYSTEMS CORP
2477 Manhattan Beach Blvd, Redondo
Beach (90278-1544)
PHONE..................................310 812-4321
Bruce R Gerding, *Vice Pres*
EMP: 305 **Publicly Held**
WEB: www.sperry.ngc.com
SIC: 3721 Airplanes, fixed or rotary wing
HQ: Northrop Grumman Systems Corporation
2980 Fairview Park Dr
Falls Church VA 22042
703 280-2900

(P-20611)
NORTHROP GRUMMAN SYSTEMS CORP
1111 W 3rd St, Azusa (91702-3328)
PHONE..................................626 812-1464
Michael Clayton, *Manager*
Mark Miller, *Engineer*

Ben Arredondo, *Manager*
Michael Doshim, *Manager*
EMP: 305 **Publicly Held**
WEB: www.sperry.ngc.com
SIC: 3721 Airplanes, fixed or rotary wing
HQ: Northrop Grumman Systems Corporation
2980 Fairview Park Dr
Falls Church VA 22042
703 280-2900

(P-20612)
NORTHROP GRUMMAN SYSTEMS CORP
1 Hornet Way, El Segundo (90245-2804)
PHONE.....................................310 332-1000
Kevin Witherell, *Principal*
Mike Garland, *Network Enginr*
Dan Kumamoto, *Manager*
EMP: 200 **Publicly Held**
WEB: www.sperry.ngc.com
SIC: 3721 Aircraft
HQ: Northrop Grumman Systems Corporation
2980 Fairview Park Dr
Falls Church VA 22042
703 280-2900

(P-20613)
NORTHROP GRUMMAN SYSTEMS CORP
Also Called: Northrop Grumman Mar Systems
401 E Hendy Ave Ms33-3, Sunnyvale (94086-5100)
P.O. Box 3499 (94088-3499)
PHONE.....................................408 735-3011
J Hupton, *Branch Mgr*
Sifredo Vences, *Administration*
Eryka Black, *Engineer*
David Fursh, *Engineer*
Nandor Horvath, *Engineer*
EMP: 1000 **Publicly Held**
WEB: www.sperry.ngc.com
SIC: 3721 3519 3511 Aircraft; internal combustion engines; turbines & turbine generator sets
HQ: Northrop Grumman Systems Corporation
2980 Fairview Park Dr
Falls Church VA 22042
703 280-2900

(P-20614)
NORTHROP GRUMMAN SYSTEMS CORP
Also Called: Aerospace Systems
1 Space Park Blvd, Redondo Beach (90278-1071)
PHONE.....................................310 812-1089
Gary Ervin, *Branch Mgr*
Martin Roden, *Engineer*
EMP: 305 **Publicly Held**
SIC: 3721 3761 3728 3812 Airplanes, fixed or rotary wing; research & development on aircraft by the manufacturer; guided missiles, complete; guided missiles & space vehicles, research & development; fuselage assembly, aircraft; wing assemblies & parts, aircraft; research & dev by manuf., aircraft parts & auxiliary equip; inertial guidance systems; gyroscopes; warfare counter-measure equipment; search & detection systems & instruments; test equipment for electronic & electrical circuits; aircraft servicing & repairing
HQ: Northrop Grumman Systems Corporation
2980 Fairview Park Dr
Falls Church VA 22042
703 280-2900

(P-20615)
NORTHROP GRUMMAN SYSTEMS CORP
1 Space Park Blvd D, Redondo Beach (90278-1071)
PHONE.....................................310 812-4321
Bruce Gaines, *Principal*
Jeffrey D Grant, *President*
John Price, *Vice Pres*
David Thornhill, *Program Mgr*
Maria Sanchez, *Admin Mgr*
EMP: 305 **Publicly Held**

SIC: 3721 3761 3728 Airplanes, fixed or rotary wing; research & development on aircraft by the manufacturer; guided missiles, complete; guided missiles & space vehicles, research & development; fuselage assembly, aircraft; wing assemblies & parts, aircraft; research & dev by manuf., aircraft parts & auxiliary equip
HQ: Northrop Grumman Systems Corporation
2980 Fairview Park Dr
Falls Church VA 22042
703 280-2900

(P-20616)
NORTHROP GRUMMAN SYSTEMS CORP
Also Called: Northrop Grumman Info Systems
5441 Luce Ave, McClellan (95652-2417)
PHONE.....................................408 531-2524
Michael O'Brien, *Manager*
EMP: 550 **Publicly Held**
SIC: 3721 Airplanes, fixed or rotary wing; research & development on aircraft by the manufacturer
HQ: Northrop Grumman Systems Corporation
2980 Fairview Park Dr
Falls Church VA 22042
703 280-2900

(P-20617)
PDQ ENGINEERING INC
1199 Avenida Acaso Ste F, Camarillo (93012-8739)
PHONE.....................................805 482-1334
Shannon Clark, *President*
Elmer Clark, *Vice Pres*
Richard Mellett, *Director*
Scott Jenkins, *Manager*
EMP: 28
SQ FT: 10,000
SALES: 3.3MM **Privately Held**
WEB: www.pdqeng.com
SIC: 3721 Airplanes, fixed or rotary wing

(P-20618)
POSITEX INC
2569 Mccabe Way Ste 210, Irvine (92614-5220)
PHONE.....................................307 201-0601
Mark Azzarito, *Principal*
EMP: 11 EST: 2016
SALES (est): 453.6K **Privately Held**
SIC: 3721 Aircraft

(P-20619)
QUALITY TECH MFG INC
170 W Mindanao St, Bloomington (92316-2946)
PHONE.....................................909 465-9565
Rudolph A Gutierrez, *President*
Camilio Gutierrez, *Vice Pres*
Chris Gutierrez, *Engineer*
Yvette Gutierrez, *Financial Exec*
Hernan Delgado, *Buyer*
EMP: 37
SQ FT: 18,000
SALES (est): 6.9MM **Privately Held**
WEB: www.qualitytechmfg.com
SIC: 3721 Aircraft

(P-20620)
QUICKSILVER AERONAUTICS LLC
40084 Villa Venecia, Temecula (92591-1667)
PHONE.....................................951 506-0061
Guillermo F Escutia Nunez,
Daniel Perez Munoz,
EMP: 10
SALES (est): 1.6MM **Privately Held**
WEB: www.quicksilveraircraft.com
SIC: 3721 Aircraft

(P-20621)
RALC INC
Also Called: Cnc Manufacturing
42158 Sarah Way, Temecula (92590-3401)
PHONE.....................................951 693-0098
Lydia Cruz, *President*
Refugio Cruz, *Vice Pres*
Rich Cruz, *General Mgr*
George Marshall, *Prdtn Mgr*
EMP: 12 EST: 1996
SQ FT: 6,800

SALES (est): 1.5MM **Privately Held**
SIC: 3721 Aircraft

(P-20622)
ROBERT GROVE
Also Called: Grove Aircraft Co
1860 Joe Crosson Dr, El Cajon (92020-1227)
PHONE.....................................619 562-1268
Robert Grove, *Owner*
▲ **EMP:** 12
SALES (est): 650K **Privately Held**
WEB: www.groveaircraft.com
SIC: 3721 8748 Aircraft; test development & evaluation service

(P-20623)
ROBINSON HELICOPTER CO INC
2901 Airport Dr, Torrance (90505-6115)
PHONE.....................................310 539-0508
Kurt L Robinson, *CEO*
Frank Robinson, *President*
Tim Goetz, *CFO*
Mario Moraga, *Buyer*
P Wayne Walden, *VP Mfg*
◆ **EMP:** 970 EST: 1973
SQ FT: 260,000
SALES (est): 222.6MM **Privately Held**
WEB: www.robinsonheli.com
SIC: 3721 Helicopters

(P-20624)
SAN-JOAQUIN HELICOPTERS INC
Also Called: S J Helicopter Service
1408 S Lexington St, Delano (93215-9783)
PHONE.....................................661 725-6603
Jim Josephson, *Branch Mgr*
EMP: 10
SALES (corp-wide): 39.2MM **Privately Held**
WEB: www.sjhelicopters.com
SIC: 3721 Helicopters
PA: San-Joaquin Helicopters Inc.
1408 S Lexington St
Delano CA 93215
661 725-1898

(P-20625)
SCALED COMPOSITES LLC
1624 Flight Line, Mojave (93501-1663)
PHONE.....................................661 824-4541
Kevin Mickey, *President*
Mark Taylor, *CFO*
Cory Bird, *Vice Pres*
Ben Diachun, *Vice Pres*
Jason Kelley, *Vice Pres*
EMP: 500
SQ FT: 160,000
SALES (est): 228.1MM **Publicly Held**
WEB: www.scaled.com
SIC: 3721 3999 8711 Aircraft; models, except toy; aviation &/or aeronautical engineering
HQ: Northrop Grumman Systems Corporation
2980 Fairview Park Dr
Falls Church VA 22042
703 280-2900

(P-20626)
SILICON VALLEY EXPRESS
1250 Aviation Ave Ste 105, San Jose (95110-1133)
PHONE.....................................408 292-0677
Doug Bensing, *Owner*
EMP: 15
SALES (est): 2.1MM **Privately Held**
WEB: www.siliconvalleyexpress.com
SIC: 3721 Aircraft

(P-20627)
SOARING AMERICA CORPORATION
Also Called: Mooney International
8354 Kimball Ave F360, Chino (91708-9267)
P.O. Box 2937, Chino Hills (91709-0098)
PHONE.....................................909 270-2628
Cheng-Yuan Jerry Chen, *CEO*
Albert LI, *CFO*
EMP: 45

SALES (est): 9.7MM **Privately Held**
SIC: 3721 3728 Research & development on aircraft by the manufacturer; motorized aircraft; research & dev by manuf., aircraft parts & auxiliary equip

(P-20628)
SPORT KITES INC
Also Called: Wills Wing
500 W Blueridge Ave, Orange (92865-4206)
PHONE.....................................714 998-6359
Steven Pearson, *President*
Michael Meier, *Vice Pres*
Linda Meier, *Admin Sec*
▲ **EMP:** 18
SQ FT: 16,000
SALES: 3.5MM **Privately Held**
SIC: 3721 Hang gliders

(P-20629)
TDL AERO ENTERPRISES
44 Macready Dr, Merced (95341-6405)
P.O. Box 249, Hilmar (95324-0249)
PHONE.....................................209 722-7300
Tom Lopez, *President*
EMP: 19
SALES (est): 2.2MM **Privately Held**
SIC: 3721 5088 7389 Airplanes, fixed or rotary wing; transportation equipment & supplies;

(P-20630)
TELEXCA INC
13463 Nomwaket Rd, Apple Valley (92308-6591)
PHONE.....................................760 247-4277
Roberto Brand, *President*
Elba Brand, *Vice Pres*
EMP: 16
SALES (est): 2.8MM **Privately Held**
SIC: 3721 Aircraft

(P-20631)
TRI MODELS INC
5191 Oceanus Dr, Huntington Beach (92649-1026)
PHONE.....................................714 896-0823
Prince A Herzog Sr, *CEO*
Jeff Herzog, *President*
P Prince, *Vice Pres*
Todd Lisk, *QC Mgr*
▲ **EMP:** 80
SALES (est): 17.4MM **Privately Held**
SIC: 3721 Airplanes, fixed or rotary wing

(P-20632)
TRIUMPH AEROSTRUCTURES LLC
3901 Jack Northrop Ave, Hawthorne (90250-4442)
PHONE.....................................310 322-1000
Marty Jones, *Branch Mgr*
EMP: 680 **Publicly Held**
WEB: www.voughtaircraft.com
SIC: 3721 Aircraft
HQ: Triumph Aerostructures, Llc
300 Austin Blvd
Red Oak TX 75154

(P-20633)
UNMANNED INNOVATION INC (PA)
Also Called: Airware
460 Bryant St Ste 200, San Francisco (94107-1303)
PHONE.....................................877 714-4828
Yvonne Wassenaar, *CEO*
David Milanes, *President*
Bill Aker, *Vice Pres*
Emmanuel De Maistre, *Vice Pres*
Sasha Pesic, *Vice Pres*
EMP: 56
SQ FT: 23,770
SALES (est): 12.4MM **Privately Held**
SIC: 3721 Aircraft

(P-20634)
WEST E CMNTY ACCESS NETWRK INC
Also Called: We Can Foundation
646 W 60th St, Los Angeles (90044-6331)
PHONE.....................................323 967-0520
Michael McLaughlin, *Exec Dir*

▲ = Import ▼=Export
◆ =Import/Export

EMP: 100
SALES (est): 774K **Privately Held**
SIC: 3721 Research & development on aircraft by the manufacturer

(P-20635)
WORLDWIDE AEROS CORP
1734 Aeros Way, Montebello (90640-6504)
PHONE..................................818 344-3999
Igor Pasternak, *President*
Carrie Cass, *CFO*
Anatoliy Pasternak, *Manager*
▲ EMP: 82
SALES (est): 16.9MM **Privately Held**
WEB: www.aerosml.com
SIC: 3721 8711 Airships; aviation &/or aeronautical engineering

(P-20636)
ZODIAC AEROSPACE
11340 Jersey Blvd, Rancho Cucamonga (91730-4919)
PHONE..................................909 652-9700
Robert Tom, *COO*
Tanya Dias, *Program Mgr*
Mark Seman, *Program Mgr*
Margarita Vazquez, *Program Mgr*
Jeff Hurst, *Project Engr*
EMP: 13
SALES (est): 1MM **Privately Held**
SIC: 3721 Aircraft

3724 Aircraft Engines & Engine Parts

(P-20637)
3-D PRECISION MACHINE INC
42132 Remington Ave, Temecula (92590-2547)
PHONE..................................951 296-5449
Linda Luoma, *President*
Roy Luoma, *Founder*
EMP: 25
SQ FT: 14,000
SALES: 3.5MM **Privately Held**
SIC: 3724 Research & development on aircraft engines & parts

(P-20638)
A F B SYSTEMS INC
Also Called: Sierra Tech
20400 Prairie St Unit B, Chatsworth (91311-8129)
PHONE..................................818 775-0151
Frank Carbone, *Principal*
Norberto A Cusiuato, *President*
Jose A Nicosis, *Admin Sec*
Jeinny Urrego, *Sls & Mktg Exec*
EMP: 10
SQ FT: 20,719
SALES (est): 720K **Privately Held**
SIC: 3724 Aircraft engines & engine parts

(P-20639)
AC&A ENTERPRISES LLC (HQ)
25692 Atlantic Ocean Dr, Lake Forest (92630-8800)
PHONE..................................949 716-3511
Justin Uchida, *CEO*
Justin Schultz,
▲ EMP: 85
SALES (est): 39.1MM
SALES (corp-wide): 30.3MM **Privately Held**
SIC: 3724 3511 Aircraft engines & engine parts; turbines & turbine generator sets
PA: Ac&A Enterprises Holdings, Llc
25692 Atlantic Ocean Dr
Lake Forest CA 92630
949 716-3511

(P-20640)
ACCURATE GRINDING AND MFG CORP
807 E Parkridge Ave, Corona (92879-6609)
PHONE..................................951 479-0909
Douglas Nilsen, *CEO*
Hans J Nilsen, *President*
David Nilsen, *Admin Sec*
Jose Castillo, *Facilities Mgr*
▲ EMP: 35
SQ FT: 15,000

SALES (est): 8.9MM **Privately Held**
WEB: www.accurategrindingmfg.com
SIC: 3724 3812 Aircraft engines & engine parts; search & navigation equipment

(P-20641)
ADVANCED GROUND SYSTEMS (HQ)
Also Called: Agse
10805 Painter Ave, Santa Fe Springs (90670-4526)
PHONE..................................562 906-9300
Diane Henderson, *CEO*
David Chetwood, *CFO*
Frank Judge, *General Mgr*
Tony Romero, *General Mgr*
Roy Stone, *General Mgr*
▲ EMP: 40
SALES (est): 14MM
SALES (corp-wide): 23.6MM **Privately Held**
WEB: www.westmont.com
SIC: 3724 Aircraft engines & engine parts
PA: Westmont Industries
10805 Painter Ave Uppr
Santa Fe Springs CA 90670
562 944-6137

(P-20642)
AERO TURBINE INC
6800 Lindbergh St, Stockton (95206-3934)
PHONE..................................209 983-1112
Douglas R Clayton, *President*
C W Dinsley, *Treasurer*
David Mattson, *Exec VP*
▲ EMP: 60
SQ FT: 51,000
SALES: 14.8MM **Privately Held**
WEB: www.aeroturbine.aero
SIC: 3724 Aircraft engines & engine parts

(P-20643)
AEROMAX INDUSTRIES INC
9027 Canoga Ave Unit Hi, Canoga Park (91304-1541)
PHONE..................................818 701-9500
Thomas Brizes, *CEO*
Thelma Martinez, *Principal*
Martha Wilson, *Manager*
EMP: 10
SQ FT: 7,000
SALES: 6.4MM **Privately Held**
WEB: www.aeromax.com
SIC: 3724 5088 Aircraft engines & engine parts; aircraft & space vehicle supplies & parts

(P-20644)
APPROVED TURBO COMPONENTS
1545 E Acequia Ave, Visalia (93292-6652)
PHONE..................................559 627-3600
Michael Rogers, *President*
▲ EMP: 10 EST: 1998
SALES (est): 1.1MM **Privately Held**
SIC: 3724 Turbo-superchargers, aircraft

(P-20645)
ASSOCIATED AROSPC ACTIVITIES
600 California St Fl 6, San Francisco (94108-2733)
PHONE..................................510 483-9020
Marian A Johnson, *Ch of Bd*
Douglass E Johnson Jr, *President*
Rebecca Mc Dougal, *Admin Sec*
EMP: 32
SQ FT: 55,000
SALES (est): 6.4MM **Privately Held**
WEB: www.aaai.com
SIC: 3724 3599 Machine shop, jobbing & repair; turbines, aircraft type

(P-20646)
DUCOMMUN AEROSTRUCTURES INC (HQ)
268 E Gardena Blvd, Gardena (90248-2814)
PHONE..................................310 380-5390
Anthony J Reardon, *CEO*
◆ EMP: 450
SQ FT: 300,000

SALES (est): 279MM
SALES (corp-wide): 558.1MM **Publicly Held**
SIC: 3724 3812 3728 Aircraft engines & engine parts; search & navigation equipment; aircraft parts & equipment
PA: Ducommun Incorporated
200 Sandpointe Ave # 700
Santa Ana CA 92707
657 335-3665

(P-20647)
DUCOMMUN AEROSTRUCTURES INC
1885 N Batavia St, Orange (92865-4105)
PHONE..................................714 637-4401
Kent T Christensen, *Branch Mgr*
EMP: 18
SALES (corp-wide): 558.1MM **Publicly Held**
SIC: 3724 3812 3728 Aircraft engines & engine parts; search & navigation equipment; aircraft parts & equipment
HQ: Ducommun Aerostructures, Inc.
268 E Gardena Blvd
Gardena CA 90248
310 380-5390

(P-20648)
DUCOMMUN AEROSTRUCTURES INC
23301 Wilmington Ave, Carson (90745-6209)
PHONE..................................310 513-7200
Eugene Conese Jr, *Director*
EMP: 39
SALES (corp-wide): 558.1MM **Publicly Held**
SIC: 3724 Aircraft engines & engine parts
HQ: Ducommun Aerostructures, Inc.
268 E Gardena Blvd
Gardena CA 90248
310 380-5390

(P-20649)
ENCORE INTERNATIONAL
5511 Skylab Rd, Huntington Beach (92647-2068)
PHONE..................................949 559-0930
Antonio Perez, *President*
Mike Melancon, *CFO*
▲ EMP: 50 EST: 2015
SQ FT: 80,000
SALES: 218K **Privately Held**
SIC: 3724 Aircraft engines & engine parts

(P-20650)
GKN AEROSPACE CHEM-TRONICS INC
1148 Bert Acosta St, El Cajon (92020-1101)
P.O. Box 1604 (92022-1604)
PHONE..................................619 258-5012
Mike Worthen, *Branch Mgr*
EMP: 18
SALES (corp-wide): 12.7B **Privately Held**
SIC: 3724 Aircraft engines & engine parts
HQ: Gkn Aerospace Chem-Tronics Inc.
1150 W Bradley Ave
El Cajon CA 92020
619 448-2320

(P-20651)
GKN AEROSPACE CHEM-TRONICS INC (HQ)
1150 W Bradley Ave, El Cajon (92020-1504)
P.O. Box 1604 (92022-1604)
PHONE..................................619 448-2320
Marcus J Bryson, *CEO*
Michael A Beck, *President*
Les Emanuel, *CFO*
Stacey Clapp, *Vice Pres*
Jason Langteau, *Network Mgr*
▲ EMP: 648 EST: 1953
SQ FT: 400,000
SALES (est): 240.2MM
SALES (corp-wide): 12.7B **Privately Held**
WEB: www.chem-tronics.com
SIC: 3724 7699 Aircraft engines & engine parts; aircraft & heavy equipment repair services

PA: Gkn Limited
Po Box 55
Redditch WORCS B98 0
152 751-7715

(P-20652)
HONEYWELL INTERNATIONAL INC
6452 Morion Cir, Huntington Beach (92647-6532)
PHONE..................................310 512-4237
EMP: 556
SALES (corp-wide): 40.5B **Publicly Held**
WEB: www.honeywell.com
SIC: 3724 Aircraft engines & engine parts
PA: Honeywell International Inc.
115 Tabor Rd
Morris Plains NJ 07950
973 455-2000

(P-20653)
HONEYWELL INTERNATIONAL INC
12800 Brookprinter Pl, Poway (92064-6812)
PHONE..................................858 513-1223
Mark Okeefe, *Manager*
EMP: 15
SALES (corp-wide): 40.5B **Publicly Held**
WEB: www.honeywell.com
SIC: 3724 Aircraft engines & engine parts
PA: Honeywell International Inc.
115 Tabor Rd
Morris Plains NJ 07950
973 455-2000

(P-20654)
HONEYWELL INTERNATIONAL INC
2525 W 190th St, Torrance (90504-6002)
PHONE..................................310 323-9500
Ken Defusco, *Branch Mgr*
EMP: 1000
SALES (corp-wide): 40.5B **Publicly Held**
WEB: www.honeywell.com
SIC: 3724 Aircraft engines & engine parts
PA: Honeywell International Inc.
115 Tabor Rd
Morris Plains NJ 07950
973 455-2000

(P-20655)
HONEYWELL INTERNATIONAL INC
3105 Prince Valiant Ln, Modesto (95350-1414)
PHONE..................................951 500-6086
EMP: 694
SALES (corp-wide): 40.5B **Publicly Held**
SIC: 3724 Aircraft engines & engine parts
PA: Honeywell International Inc.
115 Tabor Rd
Morris Plains NJ 07950
973 455-2000

(P-20656)
HONEYWELL INTERNATIONAL INC
27831 Abadejo, Mission Viejo (92692-2521)
PHONE..................................949 425-3992
EMP: 694
SALES (corp-wide): 40.5B **Publicly Held**
SIC: 3724 Aircraft engines & engine parts
PA: Honeywell International Inc.
115 Tabor Rd
Morris Plains NJ 07950
973 455-2000

(P-20657)
HONEYWELL INTERNATIONAL INC
25 S Stockton St Ste C, Lodi (95240-2978)
PHONE..................................209 323-8520
EMP: 673
SALES (corp-wide): 40.5B **Publicly Held**
SIC: 3724 Aircraft engines & engine parts
PA: Honeywell International Inc.
115 Tabor Rd
Morris Plains NJ 07950
973 455-2000

(P-20658)
HONEYWELL INTERNATIONAL INC
6201 W Imperial Hwy, Los Angeles (90045-6306)
PHONE....................310 410-9605
Harvey Ticlo, *Manager*
EMP: 300
SQ FT: 145,000
SALES (corp-wide): 40.5B **Publicly Held**
WEB: www.honeywell.com
SIC: 3724 Research & development on aircraft engines & parts
PA: Honeywell International Inc.
115 Tabor Rd
Morris Plains NJ 07950
973 455-2000

(P-20659)
HONEYWELL INTERNATIONAL INC
233 Paulin Ave 8500, Calexico (92231-2615)
PHONE....................760 312-5300
William Bouscher, *Principal*
EMP: 657
SALES (corp-wide): 40.5B **Publicly Held**
WEB: www.honeywell.com
SIC: 3724 Aircraft engines & engine parts
PA: Honeywell International Inc.
115 Tabor Rd
Morris Plains NJ 07950
973 455-2000

(P-20660)
HONEYWELL INTERNATIONAL INC
13475 Danielson St # 130, Poway (92064-8858)
PHONE....................858 848-3187
Scott Covey, *Branch Mgr*
EMP: 668
SALES (corp-wide): 40.5B **Publicly Held**
SIC: 3724 Aircraft engines & engine parts
PA: Honeywell International Inc.
115 Tabor Rd
Morris Plains NJ 07950
973 455-2000

(P-20661)
HONEYWELL INTERNATIONAL INC
13475 Danielson St # 130, Poway (92064-8858)
PHONE....................858 679-4140
Jeffrey Goodrich, *Branch Mgr*
EMP: 68
SALES (corp-wide): 40.5B **Publicly Held**
SIC: 3724 Aircraft engines & engine parts
PA: Honeywell International Inc.
115 Tabor Rd
Morris Plains NJ 07950
973 455-2000

(P-20662)
HONEYWELL INTERNATIONAL INC
13475 Danielson St # 130, Poway (92064-8858)
PHONE....................858 513-6391
Jeffrey Goodrich, *President*
EMP: 49
SALES (corp-wide): 40.5B **Publicly Held**
SIC: 3724 Aircraft engines & engine parts
PA: Honeywell International Inc.
115 Tabor Rd
Morris Plains NJ 07950
973 455-2000

(P-20663)
INFINITY AEROSPACE INC (PA)
9060 Winnetka Ave, Northridge (91324-3235)
PHONE....................818 998-9811
Chet Huffman, *CEO*
R Lloyd Huffman, *Ch of Bd*
Steve Lonngren, *President*
Pat Patrick, *President*
Don Petote, *Buyer*
EMP: 67
SQ FT: 30,000
SALES (est): 11.5MM **Privately Held**
WEB: www.dukesinc.com
SIC: 3724 Pumps, aircraft engine

(P-20664)
INTERNATIONAL WIND INC (PA)
137 N Joy St, Corona (92879-1321)
PHONE....................562 240-3963
Cory Arendt, *President*
EMP: 49
SALES: 7MM **Privately Held**
SIC: 3724 8711 8742 Turbines, aircraft type; engineering services; aviation &/or aeronautical engineering; consulting engineer; management consulting services; maintenance management consultant

(P-20665)
JAMES HUNKINS
Also Called: Hunkins Enterprises
601 Lairport St, El Segundo (90245-5005)
PHONE....................310 640-8243
James Hunkins, *Owner*
EMP: 14
SALES (est): 979.3K **Privately Held**
WEB: www.jdh-stech.com
SIC: 3724 Aircraft engines & engine parts

(P-20666)
JET/BRELLA INC
6849 Hayvenhurst Ave, Van Nuys (91406-4718)
PHONE....................818 786-5480
William Onasch, *President*
Eddie Ester, *QC Mgr*
Ty Carson, *Manager*
Edwin Juarez, *Manager*
EMP: 30
SQ FT: 18,000
SALES: 500K **Privately Held**
WEB: www.jetbrella.com
SIC: 3724 3728 5088 Aircraft engines & engine parts; aircraft parts & equipment; aircraft & parts

(P-20667)
KINGS CRATING INC (PA)
Also Called: Reyes Machining
1364 Pioneer Way, El Cajon (92020-1626)
PHONE....................619 590-1664
Manuel Reyes, *President*
Sheila Reyes, *CFO*
Lynn Mason, *Admin Sec*
EMP: 20
SQ FT: 25,000
SALES (est): 3.2MM **Privately Held**
SIC: 3724 Aircraft engines & engine parts

(P-20668)
LOGISTICAL SUPPORT LLC
Also Called: RTC Aerospace
20409 Prairie St, Chatsworth (91311-6029)
PHONE....................818 341-3344
Jerry Hill,
EMP: 125
SQ FT: 14,600
SALES (est): 11MM **Privately Held**
WEB: www.logisticalsupport.com
SIC: 3724 Aircraft engines & engine parts

(P-20669)
MAPE ENGINEERING INC
Also Called: America Manufacturing
9840 6th St, Rancho Cucamonga (91730-5714)
PHONE....................626 338-7964
Manny Perales, *CEO*
Iraida Andrade, *President*
EMP: 10
SALES: 350K **Privately Held**
SIC: 3724 Research & development on aircraft engines & parts

(P-20670)
MARTON PRECISION MFG LLC
1365 S Acacia Ave, Fullerton (92831-5315)
PHONE....................714 808-6523
Daniel J Marton, *President*
Mary Marton, *CFO*
Peter Greenthal, *General Mgr*
Joe Marton, *VP Opers*
Crystal Torres, *Manager*
EMP: 47
SQ FT: 20,000
SALES: 7.5MM **Privately Held**
WEB: www.martoninc.com
SIC: 3724 3599 3827 Aircraft engines & engine parts; machine & other job shop work; optical instruments & apparatus

(P-20671)
PACIFIC AERODYNAMIC INC
889 N Main St, Orange (92868-1107)
PHONE....................714 450-9140
George Kassaseya, *President*
EMP: 12
SALES: 1.5MM **Privately Held**
SIC: 3724 Aircraft engines & engine parts

(P-20672)
PARAGON PRECISION INC
25620 Rye Canyon Rd Ste A, Valencia (91355-1139)
PHONE....................661 257-1380
Allan Smith, *President*
Mike Keithley, *CFO*
EMP: 35
SQ FT: 14,000
SALES: 3.2MM **Privately Held**
WEB: www.paragon-precision.com
SIC: 3724 Aircraft engines & engine parts

(P-20673)
PARKER-HANNIFIN CORPORATION
Fluid Systems Division
16666 Von Karman Ave, Irvine (92606-4997)
PHONE....................949 833-3000
Matthew Stafford, *Manager*
Catherine Beegan, *Office Admin*
WEI Chiu, *Software Engr*
Eddie Ramos, *Research*
Jeremy Schumacher, *Project Engr*
EMP: 400
SALES (corp-wide): 12B **Publicly Held**
WEB: www.parker.com
SIC: 3724 3728 Aircraft engines & engine parts; aircraft parts & equipment
PA: Parker-Hannifin Corporation
6035 Parkland Blvd
Cleveland OH 44124
216 896-3000

(P-20674)
PRATT
6633 Canoga Ave, Canoga Park (91303-2703)
P.O. Box 7922 (91309-7922)
PHONE....................818 586-1000
Jerry Jackson, *Principal*
EMP: 23 EST: 2011
SALES (est): 6.6MM **Privately Held**
SIC: 3724 Aircraft engines & engine parts

(P-20675)
QUALITY AEROSTRUCTURES COMPANY
10291 Trademark St Ste A, Rancho Cucamonga (91730-5847)
PHONE....................909 987-4888
Fred Quinones, *President*
Michael Cabral, *Senior VP*
Rosa Rios, *Accountant*
EMP: 15
SQ FT: 15,000
SALES (est): 1.2MM **Privately Held**
SIC: 3724 Aircraft engines & engine parts

(P-20676)
ROLLS-ROYCE CORPORATION
7200 Earhart Rd, Oakland (94621-4511)
PHONE....................510 635-1500
Marion C Blakey, *President*
Jennifer Clark, *General Mgr*
Jeff Craig, *IT/INT Sup*
Barbara Britt, *VP Human Res*
Rolls Royce, *Human Resources*
EMP: 500
SALES (corp-wide): 21.5B **Privately Held**
SIC: 3724 3519 Aircraft engines & engine parts; jet propulsion engines; marine engines
HQ: Rolls-Royce Corporation
450 S Meridian St
Indianapolis IN 46225

(P-20677)
S & R CNC MACHINING
13183 Kelowna St, Pacoima (91331-4061)
PHONE....................818 767-5200
Salvador Ramirez, *Owner*
EMP: 19
SQ FT: 2,700
SALES (est): 3.2MM **Privately Held**
WEB: www.srcncmachining.com
SIC: 3724 3714

(P-20678)
SAFRAN PWR UNITS SAN DIEGO LLC
4255 Ruffin Rd Ste 100, San Diego (92123-1247)
PHONE....................858 223-2228
Rick Elgin, *Vice Pres*
EMP: 70 EST: 2015
SQ FT: 22,000
SALES (est): 6.8MM
SALES (corp-wide): 650.9MM **Privately Held**
SIC: 3724 Research & development on aircraft engines & parts
HQ: Safran Power Units
8 Chemin Du Pont De Rupe
Toulouse 31200
561 375-500

(P-20679)
SENIOR AEROSPACE JET PDTS CORP (HQ)
9106 Balboa Ave, San Diego (92123-1512)
PHONE....................858 278-8400
Willis H Fletcher, *Ch of Bd*
Ronald R Blair, *President*
John Shepherd, *COO*
Damon Evans, *Executive*
Steven Konold, *Admin Sec*
EMP: 142 EST: 1965
SQ FT: 125,000
SALES (est): 47.1MM
SALES (corp-wide): 1.3B **Privately Held**
WEB: www.jetproducts.com
SIC: 3724 3462 3444 Aircraft engines & engine parts; iron & steel forgings; sheet metalwork

(P-20680)
SIERRA AEROSPACE LLC
2263 Ward Ave, Simi Valley (93065-1863)
PHONE....................805 526-8669
Wayne R Hay, *President*
Brad Johnson, *Vice Pres*
Dave Wilson, *Vice Pres*
EMP: 16
SQ FT: 7,500
SALES: 2.6MM **Privately Held**
SIC: 3724

(P-20681)
TELEDYNE RISI INC
Also Called: Teledyne Elctronic Safety Pdts
19735 Dearborn St, Chatsworth (91311-6510)
PHONE....................818 718-6640
Mike Summer, *Branch Mgr*
EMP: 12
SALES (corp-wide): 2.6B **Publicly Held**
WEB: www.teledyne.com
SIC: 3724 Aircraft engines & engine parts
HQ: Teledyne Risi, Inc.
32727 W Corral Hollow Rd
Tracy CA 95376
925 456-9700

(P-20682)
THERMAL STRUCTURES INC (DH)
2362 Railroad St, Corona (92880-5421)
PHONE....................951 736-9911
Vaughn Barnes, *President*
Mark Diederich, *Executive*
Mike Lesher, *Executive*
Rocky Branum, *MIS Dir*
Jeff Smith, *Info Tech Dir*
▲ EMP: 270
SQ FT: 175,000
SALES (est): 94.1MM **Publicly Held**
WEB: www.thermalstructures.com
SIC: 3724 Aircraft engines & engine parts
HQ: Heico Aerospace Holdings Corp.
3000 Taft St
Hollywood FL 33021
954 987-4000

▲ = Import ▼=Export
◆ =Import/Export

(P-20683)
THOMPSON AEROSPACE INC (PA)
8687 Research Dr Ste 250, Irvine
(92618-4290)
PHONE..................................949 264-1600
Mark Thompson, *President*
Trevor Coolidge, *President*
Heiko Wiedmann, *CFO*
Fred Esch, *Vice Pres*
Craig Jones, *Vice Pres*
EMP: 10
SALES (est): 1.2MM **Privately Held**
SIC: 3724 3728 Aircraft engines & engine
parts; aircraft parts & equipment

(P-20684)
THRUN MFG INC
31947 Corydon St Ste 170, Lake Elsinore
(92530-8531)
PHONE..................................949 677-2461
Christine N Thrun, *President*
Scott Gordon, *Vice Pres*
EMP: 23
SQ FT: 25,000
SALES: 21MM **Privately Held**
WEB: www.thrun.com
SIC: 3724 3769 Aircraft engines & engine
parts; guided missile & space vehicle
parts & auxiliary equipment

(P-20685)
TMJ PRODUCTS INC
515 S Palm Ave Ste 6, Alhambra
(91803-1430)
PHONE..................................626 576-4063
Jones Tsui, *President*
S L Tsui, *Vice Pres*
▲ EMP: 14
SQ FT: 1,600
SALES (est): 2.1MM **Privately Held**
SIC: 3724 Aircraft engines & engine parts

(P-20686)
TURBINE COMPONENTS INC
Also Called: T C I
8985 Crestmar Pt, San Diego
(92121-3222)
PHONE..................................858 678-8568
Raffee Esmailians, *President*
Tom Hughes, *Vice Pres*
EMP: 48
SQ FT: 55,000
SALES: 5MM
SALES (corp-wide): 674.9MM **Publicly Held**
WEB: www.turbinecomponents.com
SIC: 3724 Turbines, aircraft type
PA: Rbc Bearings Incorporated
102 Willenbrock Rd
Oxford CT 06478
203 267-7001

(P-20687)
UNITED TECHNOLOGIES CORP
Also Called: Chemical Systems Div
600 Metcalf Rd, San Jose (95138-9601)
PHONE..................................408 779-9121
Greg Fatobic, *Branch Mgr*
EMP: 660
SALES (corp-wide): 59.8B **Publicly Held**
WEB: www.utc.com
SIC: 3724 3769 3489 Rocket motors, air-
craft; guided missile & space vehicle parts
& auxiliary equipment; ordnance & acces-
sories
PA: United Technologies Corporation
10 Farm Springs Rd
Farmington CT 06032
860 728-7000

(P-20688)
UNITED TECHNOLOGIES CORP
Also Called: Space Propulsions Div
600 Metcalf Rd, San Jose (95138-9601)
P.O. Box 109600, West Palm Beach FL
(33410-9600)
PHONE..................................408 779-9121
Mark Mounsey, *Manager*
EMP: 750

SALES (corp-wide): 59.8B **Publicly Held**
WEB: www.utc.com
SIC: 3724 3585 3534 3721 Aircraft engines & engine parts; refrigeration & heating equipment; elevators & moving
stairways; aircraft; surgical appliances &
supplies; motor vehicle parts & accessories
PA: United Technologies Corporation
10 Farm Springs Rd
Farmington CT 06032
860 728-7000

(P-20689)
UNITED TECHNOLOGIES CORP
4384 Enterprise Pl, Fremont (94538-6365)
PHONE..................................510 438-1300
Richard Haswell, *Branch Mgr*
EMP: 255
SALES (corp-wide): 59.8B **Publicly Held**
SIC: 3724 Aircraft engines & engine parts
PA: United Technologies Corporation
10 Farm Springs Rd
Farmington CT 06032
860 728-7000

(P-20690)
VIP MANUFACTURING & ENGRG CORP
Also Called: VIP Mfg & Engr
1084 Martin Ave, Santa Clara
(95050-2609)
PHONE..................................408 727-6545
L A Vargo Jr, *President*
Emma Vargo, *CFO*
EMP: 14
SQ FT: 10,500
SALES: 1.7MM **Privately Held**
WEB: www.vip10.com
SIC: 3724 3451 3599 Aircraft engines &
engine parts; screw machine products;
machine shop, jobbing & repair

(P-20691)
WESTERN PRECISION AERO LLC
11600 Monarch St, Garden Grove
(92841-1817)
PHONE..................................714 893-7999
Ed McKenna, *Mng Member*
Norma Davis, *CFO*
EMP: 37
SQ FT: 16,000
SALES (est): 6.1MM
SALES (corp-wide): 674.9MM **Publicly Held**
SIC: 3724 Aircraft engines & engine parts
PA: Rbc Bearings Incorporated
102 Willenbrock Rd
Oxford CT 06478
203 267-7001

(P-20692)
WKF (FRIEDMAN ENTERPRISES INC (PA)
Also Called: Eff Aero
2334 Stagecoach Rd Ste B, Stockton
(95215-7939)
PHONE..................................925 673-9100
Wayne Friedman, *President*
EMP: 19
SALES (est): 1.3MM **Privately Held**
SIC: 3724 Aircraft engines & engine parts

(P-20693)
ZURICH ENGINEERING INC
Also Called: Vf Engineering USA
1365 N Dynamics St Ste E, Anaheim
(92806-1904)
PHONE..................................714 528-0066
Nikhil Saran, *President*
▲ EMP: 10
SQ FT: 4,000
SALES (est): 1.4MM **Privately Held**
SIC: 3724 Turbo-superchargers, aircraft

3728 Aircraft Parts & Eqpt, NEC

(P-20694)
A & A AEROSPACE INC
1442 Hayes Ave, Long Beach
(90813-1124)
PHONE..................................562 901-6803
Arnie Puentes, *President*
EMP: 17
SALES (corp-wide): 5MM **Privately Held**
SIC: 3728 Aircraft parts & equipment
PA: A & A Aerospace, Inc.
13649 Pumice St
Santa Fe Springs CA 90670
562 901-6803

(P-20695)
A & A AEROSPACE INC
1987 W 16th St, Long Beach (90813-1136)
PHONE..................................562 901-6803
Arnie Puentes, *President*
EMP: 12
SALES (corp-wide): 5MM **Privately Held**
SIC: 3728 Aircraft parts & equipment
PA: A & A Aerospace, Inc.
13649 Pumice St
Santa Fe Springs CA 90670
562 901-6803

(P-20696)
A-INFO INC
60 Tesla, Irvine (92618-4603)
PHONE..................................949 346-7326
Linda Williams, *Asst Mgr*
EMP: 35
SALES (est): 1.3MM **Privately Held**
SIC: 3728 3812 5049 Aircraft parts &
equipment; antennas, radar or communications; analytical instruments; scientific
instruments; scientific recording equipment

(P-20697)
AAA AIR SUPPORT
13723 Harvard Pl, Gardena (90249-2527)
PHONE..................................310 538-1377
Matthew D Kerster, *President*
Joan Robinson- Berry, *Vice Pres*
Kent Fisher, *Vice Pres*
Jack House, *Vice Pres*
Matthew Kerster, *Vice Pres*
EMP: 12
SQ FT: 15,000
SALES: 3.6MM **Privately Held**
SIC: 3728 5088 Aircraft parts & equip-
ment; aircraft & space vehicle supplies &
parts

(P-20698)
ACE AIR MANUFACTURING
1430 W 135th St, Gardena (90249-2218)
PHONE..................................310 323-7246
Roger Brandt, *President*
EMP: 17
SQ FT: 12,000
SALES: 2MM **Privately Held**
SIC: 3728 Aircraft parts & equipment

(P-20699)
ACE AVIATION SERVICE INC
3239 Roymar Rd Ste B, Oceanside
(92058-1342)
PHONE..................................760 721-2804
Donald Nicolai, *President*
EMP: 12
SQ FT: 2,000
SALES (est): 1.3MM **Privately Held**
SIC: 3728 3714 Aircraft assemblies, sub-
assemblies & parts; motor vehicle parts &
accessories

(P-20700)
ACE CLEARWATER ENTERPRISES INC (PA)
19815 Magellan Dr, Torrance (90502-1107)
PHONE..................................310 323-2140
James D Dodson, *President*
Kellie Johnson, *CEO*
Agustin Gonzalez, *Officer*
Sal Chavez, *Engineer*
Irina Kleyman, *Engineer*
EMP: 100 EST: 1961

SALES (est): 42.8MM **Privately Held**
WEB: www.aceclearwater.com
SIC: 3728 3544 7692 3812 Aircraft parts
& equipment; special dies, tools, jigs &
fixtures; welding repair; search & navigation equipment; sheet metalwork

(P-20701)
ACROMIL LLC
18421 Railroad St, City of Industry
(91748-1233)
PHONE..................................626 964-2522
John T Cave II,
Jon Konheim,
Gerald A Niznick,
EMP: 99 EST: 2015
SQ FT: 96,000
SALES (est): 10.5MM **Privately Held**
SIC: 3728 Aircraft body & wing assemblies
& parts

(P-20702)
ACROMIL CORPORATION (PA)
18421 Railroad St, City of Industry
(91748-1281)
PHONE..................................626 964-2522
Gerald A Niznick, *President*
John Stock, *President*
Jon Konheim, *COO*
Jeane Aguilera, *CFO*
Jeanne Aguilera, *CFO*
◆ EMP: 100
SQ FT: 100,000
SALES (est): 24.9MM **Privately Held**
WEB: www.acromil.com
SIC: 3728 Aircraft body & wing assemblies
& parts

(P-20703)
ACUFAST AIRCRAFT PRODUCTS INC
12445 Gladstone Ave, Sylmar
(91342-5321)
PHONE..................................818 365-7077
Art Dovlatian, *President*
Jaime Salazar, *Vice Pres*
EMP: 40
SALES: 6MM **Privately Held**
SIC: 3728 Aircraft parts & equipment

(P-20704)
ADAMS RITE AEROSPACE INC (DH)
4141 N Palm St, Fullerton (92835-1025)
PHONE..................................714 278-6500
John Schaefer, *President*
Aleem Shaikh, *Business Dir*
Ivonne Saldana, *Admin Asst*
Jennifer Aniag, *Administration*
Kevin Tang, *Design Engr*
EMP: 149
SQ FT: 100,000
SALES (est): 42.8MM
SALES (corp-wide): 3.5B **Publicly Held**
WEB: www.ar-aero.com
SIC: 3728 Aircraft parts & equipment

(P-20705)
ADAPTIVE AEROSPACE CORPORATION
20304 W Valley Blvd Ste H, Tehachapi
(93561-8697)
PHONE..................................661 822-2850
Bill McCune, *CEO*
Duana Pera, *Controller*
EMP: 15
SQ FT: 4,000
SALES: 3MM **Privately Held**
WEB: www.adaptaero.com
SIC: 3728 Aircraft parts & equipment

(P-20706)
ADVANCED MTLS JOINING CORP (PA)
Also Called: Advanced Technology Co
2858 E Walnut St, Pasadena (91107-3755)
PHONE..................................626 449-2696
Jean L De Silvestri, *President*
Mohammed Islam, *President*
EMP: 41
SQ FT: 23,000
SALES (est): 7.8MM **Privately Held**
WEB: www.at-co.com
SIC: 3728 3724 Aircraft parts & equip-
ment; aircraft engines & engine parts

PRODUCTS & SVCS

(P-20707)
AEG INDUSTRIES INC
1219 Briggs Ave, Santa Rosa
(95401-4761)
PHONE..................707 575-0697
Peggy McIlnay-Moe, *President*
Peg McIlnay-Moe, *President*
William Pottorff, *President*
Dennis McIlnay Moe, *Vice Pres*
EMP: 20
SQ FT: 6,500
SALES: 3MM **Privately Held**
WEB: www.aegindustries.com
SIC: 3728 Aircraft parts & equipment

(P-20708)
AERO DYNAMIC MACHINING INC
11791 Monarch St, Garden Grove
(92841-1818)
PHONE..................714 379-1073
David Nguyen, *President*
Wendy Nguyen, *CFO*
Kevin Tran, *Vice Pres*
John Fairris, *Technical Staff*
David Niino, *Mktg Dir*
▲ **EMP:** 60 **EST:** 1998
SQ FT: 30,000
SALES (est): 22.4MM **Privately Held**
WEB: www.aerodynamicinc.com
SIC: 3728 Aircraft parts & equipment

(P-20709)
AERO ENGINEERING & MFG CO CAL
28217 Avenue Crocker, Valencia
(91355-1249)
PHONE..................661 295-0875
Dennis L Junker, *CEO*
Lance R Junker, *President*
Richard Jucksch, *Vice Pres*
Rick Jucksch, *General Mgr*
Lance Junker, *VP Sales*
▼ **EMP:** 49
SQ FT: 21,000
SALES (est): 14MM **Privately Held**
WEB: www.aeroeng.com
SIC: 3728 5088 Aircraft assemblies, sub-assemblies & parts; aircraft & parts

(P-20710)
AERO PACIFIC CORPORATION (PA)
Also Called: Merco Manufacturing Co
588 Porter Way, Placentia (92870-6453)
PHONE..................714 961-9200
Mark Heasley, *President*
Angelica Sosa, *Vice Pres*
Ashley Nicholls, *VP Engrg*
Matt Heasley, *Business Mgr*
EMP: 80
SQ FT: 60,000
SALES: 15MM **Privately Held**
WEB: www.mercomfg.com
SIC: 3728 Aircraft parts & equipment

(P-20711)
AERO PACIFIC CORPORATION
Aero Pacific Mfg
588 Porter Way, Placentia (92870-6453)
PHONE..................714 961-9200
Mark Heasley, *Branch Mgr*
EMP: 50
SALES (corp-wide): 15MM **Privately Held**
SIC: 3728 Aircraft parts & equipment
PA: Aero Pacific Corporation
588 Porter Way
Placentia CA 92870
714 961-9200

(P-20712)
AERO PRECISION INDUSTRIES LLC (PA)
201 Lindbergh Ave, Livermore
(94551-7667)
PHONE..................925 455-9900
Richard Archer, *President*
Ertugrul Turhal, *President*
Angel Flores, *Senior VP*
Ryann Ness, *Office Admin*
Carol Knepper, *Admin Asst*
▼ **EMP:** 128
SQ FT: 45,000

SALES: 150MM **Privately Held**
WEB: www.apiinc.net
SIC: 3728 Aircraft parts & equipment

(P-20713)
AERO SENSE INC
26074 Avenue Hall Ste 18, Valencia
(91355-3445)
PHONE..................661 257-1608
Sohail Tabrizi, *President*
Ro Missaghian, *CFO*
▲ **EMP:** 15
SALES (est): 3MM **Privately Held**
SIC: 3728 Aircraft parts & equipment

(P-20714)
AERO-CRAFT HYDRAULICS INC
392 N Smith Ave, Corona (92880-6971)
PHONE..................951 736-4690
Rod Guzman Sr, *President*
Jim Venneau, *President*
Stephen Olson, *CFO*
Brad Davidson, *Vice Pres*
Tom Venneau, *Vice Pres*
EMP: 43
SQ FT: 16,500
SALES (est): 10.3MM **Privately Held**
WEB: www.aero-craft.com
SIC: 3728 5084 7699 Aircraft body & wing assemblies & parts; hydraulic systems equipment & supplies; aircraft & heavy equipment repair services

(P-20715)
AEROJET ROCKETDYNE INC (HQ)
2001 Aerojet Rd, Rancho Cordova
(95742-6418)
P.O. Box 13222, Sacramento (95813-3222)
PHONE..................916 355-4000
Warren M Boley Jr, *CEO*
Kathleen E Redd, *CFO*
John Joy, *Treasurer*
Steve Warren, *Ch Credit Ofcr*
Mohammed A Khan, *Senior VP*
▲ **EMP:** 1400
SALES (est): 926.8MM
SALES (corp-wide): 1.8B **Publicly Held**
SIC: 3728 3764 3769 3761 Aircraft body & wing assemblies & parts; propulsion units for guided missiles & space vehicles; guided missile & space vehicle parts & auxiliary equipment; guided missiles & space vehicles
PA: Aerojet Rocketdyne Holdings, Inc.
222 N Pacific Coast Hwy
El Segundo CA 90245
310 252-8100

(P-20716)
AEROJET ROCKETDYNE INC
Also Called: Rocket Shop
1180 Iron Point Rd # 350, Folsom
(95630-8321)
PHONE..................916 355-4000
Craig Halterman, *Vice Pres*
Hal Martin, *Vice Pres*
Bob Shenton, *Vice Pres*
Warren Yasuhara, *Vice Pres*
Timothy Murphy, *Comms Dir*
EMP: 14
SALES (corp-wide): 1.8B **Publicly Held**
SIC: 3728 Aircraft body & wing assemblies & parts
HQ: Aerojet Rocketdyne, Inc.
2001 Aerojet Rd
Rancho Cordova CA 95742
916 355-4000

(P-20717)
AEROLIANT MANUFACTURING INC
Also Called: Fordon Grind Industries
1613 Lockness Pl, Torrance (90501-5119)
PHONE..................310 257-1903
Patricia A Wiacek, *President*
Greg Wiacek, *Vice Pres*
EMP: 20 **EST:** 2009
SQ FT: 7,200
SALES: 2.5MM **Privately Held**
SIC: 3728 Aircraft parts & equipment

(P-20718)
AEROMETALS INC (PA)
3920 Sandstone Dr, El Dorado Hills
(95762-9652)
PHONE..................916 939-6888
Rex Kamphefner, *President*
Fred Blodgett, *Associate Dir*
Tony Bohm, *Program Mgr*
David Postema, *General Mgr*
Michele Howell, *Administration*
◆ **EMP:** 152
SQ FT: 70,000
SALES: 39.6MM **Privately Held**
SIC: 3728 Aircraft parts & equipment

(P-20719)
AEROSHEAR AVIATION SVCS INC (PA)
7701 Woodley Ave 200, Van Nuys
(91406-1732)
PHONE..................818 779-1650
Lonnie Paschal, *CEO*
Christine Paschal, *CFO*
Ryan Hogan,
EMP: 44
SQ FT: 42,000
SALES (est): 7.4MM **Privately Held**
WEB: www.aeroshearaviation.com
SIC: 3728 3599 1799 Aircraft parts & equipment; machine shop, jobbing & repair; welding on site

(P-20720)
AEROSPACE COMPOSITE PRODUCTS (PA)
Also Called: Acp Composites
78 Lindbergh Ave, Livermore (94551-9503)
PHONE..................925 443-5900
George William Sparr, *President*
Jessica Sparr, *Vice Pres*
Barbara Sparr, *Admin Mgr*
Connie Austin, *Human Res Mgr*
Amanda Caulder, *Marketing Mgr*
EMP: 20
SALES (est): 7.9MM **Privately Held**
WEB: www.acp-composites.com
SIC: 3728 5961 3624 Aircraft assemblies, subassemblies & parts; mail order house; carbon & graphite products

(P-20721)
AEROSPACE DYNAMICS INTL INC
Also Called: ADI
25540 Rye Canyon Rd, Valencia
(91355-1169)
PHONE..................661 257-3535
Joseph I Snowden, *CEO*
▲ **EMP:** 450
SQ FT: 250,000
SALES (est): 180.5MM
SALES (corp-wide): 242.1B **Publicly Held**
WEB: www.adi-aero.com
SIC: 3728 Aircraft parts & equipment
HQ: Precision Castparts Corp.
4650 Sw Mcdam Ave Ste 300
Portland OR 97239
503 946-4800

(P-20722)
AEROSPACE ENGINEERING CORP
2632 Saturn St, Brea (92821-6701)
PHONE..................714 996-8178
Trevor Burdge, *President*
Blake Breiner, *Engineer*
Arnold Cobos, *Engineer*
EMP: 70
SALES: 9.1MM **Privately Held**
SIC: 3728 3541 Aircraft parts & equipment; numerically controlled metal cutting machine tools

(P-20723)
AEROSPACE PARTS HOLDINGS INC
Also Called: Cadence Aerospace
3150 E Miraloma Ave, Anaheim
(92806-1906)
PHONE..................949 877-3630
Ron Case, *CEO*
Mike Coburn, *COO*
Don Devore, *CFO*
EMP: 1175

SALES: 301MM **Privately Held**
SIC: 3728 Aircraft parts & equipment

(P-20724)
AHF-DUCOMMUN INCORPORATED (HQ)
Also Called: Ducommun Arostructures-Gardena
268 E Gardena Blvd, Gardena
(90248-2814)
P.O. Box 2310 (90247-0310)
PHONE..................310 380-5390
Joseph C Berenato, *Principal*
◆ **EMP:** 250
SQ FT: 105,000
SALES: 279MM
SALES (corp-wide): 558.1MM **Publicly Held**
SIC: 3728 3812 3769 3469 Aircraft body & wing assemblies & parts; search & navigation equipment; guided missile & space vehicle parts & auxiliary equipment; metal stampings
PA: Ducommun Incorporated
200 Sandpointe Ave # 700
Santa Ana CA 92707
657 335-3665

(P-20725)
AIRBORNE TECHNOLOGIES INC
999 Avenida Acaso, Camarillo
(93012-8700)
P.O. Box 2210 (93011-2210)
PHONE..................805 389-3700
Peter Wollons, *CEO*
Gary Ferris, *President*
EMP: 67
SQ FT: 40,000
SALES: 15.1MM **Privately Held**
SIC: 3728 5088 7699 3812 Aircraft parts & equipment; aircraft equipment & supplies; aircraft & heavy equipment repair services; search & navigation equipment

(P-20726)
AIRCRAFT HINGE INC
24930 Avenue Tibbitts, Valencia
(91355-3426)
PHONE..................661 257-3434
Doug Silva, *President*
Robbie Johnson, *President*
Brianne Dautel, *Office Mgr*
Terrina Arroyo, *Finance Dir*
Rob Helfrich, *Opers Staff*
▲ **EMP:** 20
SQ FT: 11,000
SALES (est): 4.5MM **Privately Held**
WEB: www.aircrafthinge.com
SIC: 3728 Aircraft parts & equipment

(P-20727)
AIRPARTS EXPRESS INC
3420 W Macarthur Blvd G, Santa Ana
(92704-6853)
PHONE..................714 308-2764
Mike Sweney, *CEO*
Thomas J Murphy, *President*
Shaun Murphy, *CFO*
Hardy Blackman, *Vice Pres*
Jeff Parker, *Admin Sec*
▲ **EMP:** 54
SQ FT: 2,000
SALES (est): 5.7MM **Privately Held**
WEB: www.airpartsexpress.net
SIC: 3728 Aircraft parts & equipment

(P-20728)
AIRTECH INTERNATIONAL INC (PA)
Also Called: Airtech Advanced Mtls Group
5700 Skylab Rd, Huntington Beach
(92647-2055)
PHONE..................714 899-8100
Jeff Dahlgren, *President*
◆ **EMP:** 130
SQ FT: 150,000
SALES (est): 60.6MM **Privately Held**
WEB: www.airtechintl.com
SIC: 3728 3081 5088 2673 Aircraft parts & equipment; unsupported plastics film & sheet; aeronautical equipment & supplies; bags: plastic, laminated & coated; coated & laminated paper; packaging paper & plastics film, coated & laminated

▲ = Import ▼=Export
◆ =Import/Export

(P-20729)
ALATUS AEROSYSTEMS (PA)
Also Called: F.K.a Trmph Strctrs-Los Angles
17055 Gale Ave, City of Industry
(91745-1808)
PHONE.....................................610 251-1000
Scott Holland, *CEO*
Mark Peterman, *COO*
Richard Yang, *CFO*
Rich Oak, *Exec VP*
Pete Perry, *General Mgr*
◆ EMP: 184
SQ FT: 350,000
SALES (est) 70.9MM **Privately Held**
WEB: www.triumphgroup.com
SIC: 3728 3489 Aircraft parts & equipment; wing assemblies & parts, aircraft; alighting (landing gear) assemblies, aircraft; artillery or artillery parts, over 30 mm.

(P-20730)
ALATUS AEROSYSTEMS
Also Called: Triumph Structures - Brea
423 Berry Way, Brea (92821-3115)
PHONE.....................................714 732-0559
Manny Chacon, *Manager*
Ron Stuart, *Info Tech Mgr*
Melanie Carter, *Train & Dev Mgr*
Edward Defraene, *Maintence Staff*
EMP: 100
SALES (corp-wide) 70.9MM **Privately Held**
WEB: www.voughtaircraft.com
SIC: 3728 3489 Aircraft parts & equipment; wing assemblies & parts, aircraft; alighting (landing gear) assemblies, aircraft; artillery or artillery parts, over 30 mm.
PA: Alatus Aerosystems
17055 Gale Ave
City Of Industry CA 91745
610 251-1000

(P-20731)
ALATUS AEROSYSTEMS
9301 Mason Ave, Chatsworth
(91311-5202)
PHONE.....................................626 498-7376
Richard Oak, *Manager*
Sancho Sy, *Info Tech Mgr*
Hector Zaldivar, *Maint Spvr*
Alice Calzada, *Director*
Greg Rogozinski, *Manager*
EMP: 80
SALES (corp-wide) 70.9MM **Privately Held**
WEB: www.triumphgroup.com
SIC: 3728 3489 Aircraft parts & equipment; wing assemblies & parts, aircraft; alighting (landing gear) assemblies, aircraft; artillery or artillery parts, over 30 mm.
PA: Alatus Aerosystems
17055 Gale Ave
City Of Industry CA 91745
610 251-1000

(P-20732)
ALIGN AEROSPACE LLC (DH)
9401 De Soto Ave, Chatsworth
(91311-4920)
PHONE.....................................818 727-7800
Ian Cohen,
Matt Connor, *Vice Pres*
Cecille Hayes, *Vice Pres*
Loyce Wilson, *Program Mgr*
Dan Fitch, *General Mgr*
EMP: 218
SQ FT: 73,000
SALES (est) 114.7MM **Privately Held**
SIC: 3728 Aircraft parts & equipment

(P-20733)
AMG TORRANCE LLC (DH)
Also Called: Metric Precision
5401 Business Dr, Huntington Beach
(92649-1225)
PHONE.....................................310 515-2584
Omar Khan, *CEO*
Angelique Flores, *Controller*
EMP: 69
SQ FT: 37,800
SALES (est) 15.9MM **Privately Held**
SIC: 3728 Ailerons, aircraft

HQ: Aerospace Manufacturing Group Inc
5401 Business Dr
Huntington Beach CA 92649
714 373-4300

(P-20734)
AMRO FABRICATING CORPORATION
17101 Heacock St, Moreno Valley
(92551-9560)
PHONE.....................................951 842-6140
EMP: 49
SALES (corp-wide) 53.6MM **Privately Held**
SIC: 3728
PA: Amro Fabricating Corporation
1430 Adelia Ave
South El Monte CA 91733
626 579-2200

(P-20735)
AMRO FABRICATING CORPORATION (PA)
1430 Adelia Ave, South El Monte
(91733-3003)
PHONE.....................................626 579-2200
John Hammond, *President*
Michael Riley, *CEO*
Joe Bianchi, *Program Mgr*
Sam Rosa, *Program Mgr*
Maria Robles, *Admin Asst*
EMP: 250
SQ FT: 150,000
SALES (est) 78.7MM **Privately Held**
WEB: www.amrofab.com
SIC: 3728 3769 3544 Aircraft parts & equipment; guided missile & space vehicle parts & auxiliary equipment; special dies, tools, jigs & fixtures

(P-20736)
AMRON MANUFACTURING INC
Also Called: Amron Urethane Products
635 Gregory Cir, Corona (92881-3596)
PHONE.....................................714 278-9204
Daniel Horvath, *President*
Irene Munoz, *Office Mgr*
Norma Horvath, *Admin Sec*
EMP: 12
SQ FT: 15,000
SALES (est) 1.1MM **Privately Held**
SIC: 3728 Aircraft parts & equipment

(P-20737)
ANMAR PRECISION COMPONENTS
7424 Greenbush Ave, North Hollywood
(91605-4005)
PHONE.....................................818 764-0901
Bruno Mudy, *President*
Teresa Mudy, *Corp Secy*
Anthony Mudy, *Vice Pres*
EMP: 18
SQ FT: 10,000
SALES (est) 1.6MM **Privately Held**
SIC: 3728 Aircraft parts & equipment

(P-20738)
APPLIED AROSPC STRUCTURES CORP (PA)
Also Called: Aasc
3437 S Airport Way, Stockton
(95206-3853)
P.O. Box 6189 (95206-0189)
PHONE.....................................209 982-0160
John E Rule, *President*
Rhonda Ward, *Corp Secy*
Burton Weil, *Admin Sec*
Allen Stephens, *Design Engr*
Gary Van Waters, *Business Mgr*
▲ EMP: 230
SQ FT: 100,000
SALES (est) 44.7MM **Privately Held**
WEB: www.aascworld.com
SIC: 3728 Aircraft parts & equipment

(P-20739)
APPLIED CMPSITE STRUCTURES INC (HQ)
1195 Columbia St, Brea (92821-2922)
PHONE.....................................714 990-6300
David Horner, *CEO*
Jorge Garcia, *CFO*
Michael Rowan, *Vice Pres*
Justin Uchida, *Principal*

Gary Beasley, *Technology*
EMP: 116 EST: 1975
SQ FT: 100,000
SALES (est) 54.7MM
SALES (corp-wide) 30.3MM **Privately Held**
WEB: www.bradleyspareparts.com
SIC: 3728 Aircraft parts & equipment
PA: Ac&A Enterprises Holdings, Llc
25692 Atlantic Ocean Dr
Lake Forest CA 92630
949 716-3511

(P-20740)
APPROVED AERONAUTICS LLC
1240 Graphite Dr, Corona (92881-3308)
PHONE.....................................951 200-3730
David A Janes Jr,
EMP: 10
SQ FT: 3,000
SALES (est) 2.1MM **Privately Held**
WEB: www.approvedaeronautics.com
SIC: 3728 Aircraft parts & equipment

(P-20741)
ARDEN ENGINEERING INC (DH)
3130 E Miraloma Ave, Anaheim
(92806-1906)
PHONE.....................................714 998-6410
John R Meisenbach Sr, *CEO*
Michael J Stow, *President*
▲ EMP: 21
SQ FT: 25,000
SALES (est) 36.1MM
SALES (corp-wide) 195.8MM **Privately Held**
WEB: www.arden-engr.com
SIC: 3728 Aircraft body assemblies & parts
HQ: Arden Engineering Holdings, Inc.
1878 N Main St
Orange CA 92865
714 998-6410

(P-20742)
ARDEN ENGINEERING INC
1878 N Main St, Orange (92865-4117)
Rural Route 3130, Anaheim (92806)
PHONE.....................................714 998-6410
Thorin Southworth, *Director*
EMP: 20
SALES (corp-wide) 195.8MM **Privately Held**
SIC: 3728 Aircraft body assemblies & parts
HQ: Arden Engineering, Inc.
3130 E Miraloma Ave
Anaheim CA 92806
714 998-6410

(P-20743)
ARMORSTRUXX LLC
Also Called: Novastruxx Composite Materials
130 Calle Iglesia, San Clemente
(92672-7535)
PHONE.....................................949 366-1300
Scott Mack, *Branch Mgr*
EMP: 14 **Privately Held**
WEB: www.armorstruxx.com
SIC: 3728 Military aircraft equipment & armament
PA: Armorstruxx, Llc
850 Thurman St
Lodi CA 95240

(P-20744)
ARMORSTRUXX LLC (PA)
850 Thurman St, Lodi (95240-8228)
PHONE.....................................209 365-9400
Scott Mack,
Aaron Starkovich, *Director*
EMP: 100
SQ FT: 100,000
SALES (est) 32.1MM **Privately Held**
WEB: www.armorstruxx.com
SIC: 3728 Military aircraft equipment & armament

(P-20745)
ARROWHEAD PRODUCTS CORPORATION
4411 Katella Ave, Los Alamitos
(90720-3599)
PHONE.....................................714 828-7770
Andrew Whelan, *President*
Leslie Fernandes, *President*
Bill Gardner, *Vice Pres*

Jared Goodfriend, *Vice Pres*
Peter Rowe, *Vice Pres*
▲ EMP: 640
SQ FT: 250,000
SALES (est) 184.8MM
SALES (corp-wide) 507.2MM **Privately Held**
WEB: www.arrowheadproducts.net
SIC: 3728 Aircraft parts & equipment
HQ: Industrial Manufacturing Company Llc
8223 Brecksville Rd Ste 1
Brecksville OH 44141
440 838-4700

(P-20746)
ASTRO-TEK INDUSTRIES LLC
1198 N Kraemer Blvd, Anaheim
(92806-1916)
PHONE.....................................714 238-0022
Terry Smith, *Vice Pres*
Jack Wright II, *Manager*
EMP: 80
SQ FT: 50,000
SALES (est) 21.3MM **Privately Held**
WEB: www.astro-tek.com
SIC: 3728 3599 3548 3449 Aircraft parts & equipment; electrical discharge machining (EDM); welding apparatus; miscellaneous metalwork

(P-20747)
ASTURIES MANUFACTURING CO INC
310 Cessna Cir, Corona (92880-2509)
PHONE.....................................951 270-1766
Manuel Perez, *President*
Luis Perez, *Vice Pres*
Chadd Creed, *QC Dir*
Larry Raines, *Opers Mgr*
EMP: 25
SQ FT: 50,850
SALES (est) 6.1MM **Privately Held**
SIC: 3728 3559 Aircraft parts & equipment; semiconductor manufacturing machinery

(P-20748)
AVALON MACHINE PRODUCTS INC
419 Main St Ste A, Huntington Beach
(92648-8100)
PHONE.....................................323 979-8656
Jack Gingrich, *President*
Debbie Gingrich, *Corp Secy*
EMP: 15
SQ FT: 12,000
SALES (est) 1.7MM **Privately Held**
SIC: 3728 3451 Aircraft assemblies, subassemblies & parts; screw machine products

(P-20749)
AVCORP CMPSITE FABRICATION INC
1600 W 135th St, Gardena (90249-2506)
P.O. Box 1007 (90249-0007)
PHONE.....................................310 970-5658
Marcus Maria Van Rooij, *President*
Hardeep Sidhu, *Info Tech Mgr*
EMP: 400 EST: 2015
SQ FT: 350,000
SALES: 75MM
SALES (corp-wide) 117MM **Privately Held**
SIC: 3728 Aircraft parts & equipment
PA: Avcorp Industries Inc
10025 River Way
Delta BC V4G 1
604 582-1137

(P-20750)
AVCORP CMPSTES FABRICATION INC
1551 W 139th St, Gardena (90249-2603)
PHONE.....................................310 527-0700
EMP: 12 EST: 2017
SALES (est) 2.1MM **Privately Held**
SIC: 3728 Aircraft parts & equipment

(P-20751)
AVIATOR SYSTEMS INC
37440 Calle De Lobo, Murrieta
(92562-7109)
PHONE.....................................949 677-2461
Scott Gordon, *President*

(PA)=Parent Co (HQ)=Headquarters (DH)=Div Headquarters
✪ = New Business established in last 2 years

2019 California
Manufacturers Register

847

PRODUCTS & SVCS

EMP: 10 EST: 2014
SALES (est): 624.7K **Privately Held**
SIC: 3728 Aircraft parts & equipment

(P-20752)
AVIBANK MFG INC (DH)
11500 Sherman Way, North Hollywood
(91605-5827)
P.O. Box 9909 (91609-1909)
PHONE.................................818 392-2100
Dan Welter, *President*
John Duran, *Vice Pres*
▲ EMP: 115 EST: 1945
SALES (est): 92.7MM
SALES (corp-wide): 242.1B **Publicly Held**
SIC: 3728 Aircraft parts & equipment
HQ: Sps Technologies, Llc
301 Highland Ave
Jenkintown PA 19046
215 572-3000

(P-20753)
B & E MANUFACTURING CO INC
12151 Monarch St, Garden Grove
(92841-2927)
PHONE.................................714 898-2269
Larry Solinger, *President*
Ann Lee Solinger, *Corp Secy*
Randy Solinger, *Vice Pres*
Michael Howlett, *General Mgr*
Tim Rusk, *QC Dir*
EMP: 45
SQ FT: 26,000
SALES (est): 11MM **Privately Held**
WEB: www.bandemfg.com
SIC: 3728 Aircraft parts & equipment

(P-20754)
B/E AEROSPACE INC
Also Called: Teklam
350 W Rincon St, Corona (92880-2004)
PHONE.................................951 278-4563
Bob Simmons, *Vice Pres*
EMP: 219 **Publicly Held**
SIC: 3728 Aircraft parts & equipment
HQ: B/E Aerospace, Inc.
1400 Corporate Center Way
Wellington FL 33414
561 791-5000

(P-20755)
B/E AEROSPACE INC
7155 Fenwick Ln, Westminster
(92683-5218)
PHONE.................................714 896-9001
Jim Melrose, *Manager*
EMP: 250 **Publicly Held**
WEB: www.beaerospace.com
SIC: 3728 3647 Aircraft parts & equipment; aircraft lighting fixtures
HQ: B/E Aerospace, Inc.
1400 Corporate Center Way
Wellington FL 33414
561 791-5000

(P-20756)
B/E AEROSPACE INC
Advanced Thermal Sciences
3355 E La Palma Ave, Anaheim
(92806-2815)
PHONE.................................714 688-4200
Bruce Thayer, *General Mgr*
Bill Godecker, *President*
Grant West, *Vice Pres*
Kevin Lehnert, *Executive*
Masashi Iwao, *General Mgr*
EMP: 300 **Publicly Held**
WEB: www.beaerospace.com
SIC: 3728 3585 Aircraft parts & equipment; refrigeration & heating equipment
HQ: B/E Aerospace, Inc.
1400 Corporate Center Way
Wellington FL 33414
561 791-5000

(P-20757)
BAI INC
21 Airport Blvd Ste B, South San Francisco
(94080-6518)
PHONE.................................650 872-1700
Thomas Lawrence Dolan, *President*
George Jue, *Treasurer*
EMP: 19
SQ FT: 9,000

SALES: 18.5MM **Privately Held**
WEB: www.bai-inc.com
SIC: 3728 Aircraft parts & equipment

(P-20758)
BAILEY INDUSTRIES INC
25256 Terreno Dr, Mission Viejo
(92691-5528)
PHONE.................................949 461-0807
Nonny Bailey, *President*
EMP: 12
SALES (est): 1.1MM **Privately Held**
WEB: www.baileyindustries.com
SIC: 3728 4783 2679 5088 Aircraft parts & equipment; packing & crating; labels, paper: made from purchased material; aircraft equipment & supplies

(P-20759)
BANDY MANUFACTURING LLC
3420 N San Fernando Blvd, Burbank
(91504-2532)
P.O. Box 7716 (91510-7716)
PHONE.................................818 846-9020
Tom Fulton, *President*
Kevin L Cummings, *CEO*
Tom Hoffa, *Design Engr*
Sal Ortiz, *Engineer*
Jean Decastro, *Human Res Mgr*
EMP: 93 EST: 1952
SQ FT: 60,000
SALES (est): 22.5MM **Privately Held**
SIC: 3728 Aircraft parts & equipment

(P-20760)
BERANEK INC
2340 W 205th St, Torrance (90501-1436)
PHONE.................................310 328-9094
George Beranek, *CEO*
Douglas Beranek, *President*
Hector D Beranek, *Exec VP*
Vilma N Beranek, *Admin Sec*
EMP: 22
SQ FT: 20,000
SALES (est): 8.8MM **Privately Held**
WEB: www.beranekinc.com
SIC: 3728 Aircraft parts & equipment

(P-20761)
BRICE MANUFACTURING CO INC
Also Called: Haeco Americas Cabin Solutions
10262 Norris Ave, Pacoima (91331-2217)
PHONE.................................818 896-2938
Richard Kendall, *CEO*
Mark Peterman, *President*
Lee Fox, *CFO*
▲ EMP: 25
SQ FT: 60,000
SALES (est): 13.2MM
SALES (corp-wide): 10.2B **Privately Held**
WEB: www.bricemfg.com
SIC: 3728 7641 Aircraft parts & equipment; furniture repair & maintenance
HQ: Haeco Americas, Inc.
623 Radar Rd
Greensboro NC 27410
336 668-4410

(P-20762)
C & H HYDRAULICS INC
Also Called: Acme Divac Industries
1585 Monrovia Ave, Newport Beach
(92663-2806)
PHONE.................................949 646-6230
James F Andreae Jr, *CEO*
Cindy Bender, *Purchasing*
EMP: 17
SQ FT: 8,000
SALES (est): 2.9MM **Privately Held**
SIC: 3728 8734 3769 3812 Aircraft parts & equipment; testing laboratories; guided missile & space vehicle parts & auxiliary equipment; search & navigation equipment; current-carrying wiring devices; hydraulic equipment repair

(P-20763)
C&D ZODIAC INC
Also Called: 4 Flight
8595 Milliken Ave Ste 101, Rancho Cucamonga (91730-4942)
PHONE.................................909 652-9700
Tom McFarland, *CEO*
EMP: 200

SALES (corp-wide): 650.9MM **Privately Held**
SIC: 3728 Aircraft parts & equipment
HQ: C&D Zodiac, Inc.
5701 Bolsa Ave
Huntington Beach CA 92647
714 934-0000

(P-20764)
C&D ZODIAC INC
12472 Industry St, Garden Grove
(92841-2819)
PHONE.................................714 901-2672
Mike Boyd, *Branch Mgr*
EMP: 250
SALES (corp-wide): 650.9MM **Privately Held**
SIC: 3728 Aircraft parts & equipment
HQ: C&D Zodiac, Inc.
5701 Bolsa Ave
Huntington Beach CA 92647
714 934-0000

(P-20765)
C&D ZODIAC INC (DH)
Also Called: Zodiac Aerospace
5701 Bolsa Ave, Huntington Beach
(92647-2063)
PHONE.................................714 934-0000
Christophe Bernardini, *CEO*
Norman Jordan, *CEO*
Jeff Henry, *CFO*
Scott Savian, *Exec VP*
Aurimar Debrito, *Vice Pres*
▲ EMP: 500
SQ FT: 150,000
SALES (est): 1B
SALES (corp-wide): 650.9MM **Privately Held**
WEB: www.zodiac.com
SIC: 3728 Aircraft assemblies, subassemblies & parts
HQ: Zodiac Us Corporation
1747 State Route 34
Wall Township NJ 07727
732 681-3527

(P-20766)
C&D ZODIAC INC
2850 Skyway Dr, Santa Maria
(93455-1410)
PHONE.................................805 922-3013
Jude F Dozor, *Branch Mgr*
EMP: 15
SALES (corp-wide): 650.9MM **Privately Held**
SIC: 3728 Aircraft parts & equipment
HQ: C&D Zodiac, Inc.
5701 Bolsa Ave
Huntington Beach CA 92647
714 934-0000

(P-20767)
C&D ZODIAC INC
11240 Warland Dr, Cypress (90630-5035)
PHONE.................................562 344-4780
Gary Reese, *Branch Mgr*
EMP: 248
SALES (corp-wide): 650.9MM **Privately Held**
SIC: 3728 Aircraft assemblies, subassemblies & parts
HQ: C&D Zodiac, Inc.
5701 Bolsa Ave
Huntington Beach CA 92647
714 934-0000

(P-20768)
C&D ZODIAC INC
Also Called: C & D Aerospace
7330 Lincoln Way, Garden Grove
(92841-1427)
PHONE.................................714 891-1906
Alec Azarian, *Branch Mgr*
EMP: 330
SALES (corp-wide): 650.9MM **Privately Held**
SIC: 3728 3443 Aircraft assemblies, subassemblies & parts; fabricated plate work (boiler shop)
HQ: C&D Zodiac, Inc.
5701 Bolsa Ave
Huntington Beach CA 92647
714 934-0000

(P-20769)
C&D ZODIAC INC
Also Called: C&D Zodiac Aerodesign
6754 Calle De Linea # 111, San Diego
(92154-8021)
PHONE.................................619 671-0430
Jose Martinez, *Manager*
EMP: 223
SALES (corp-wide): 650.9MM **Privately Held**
SIC: 3728 Aircraft parts & equipment
HQ: C&D Zodiac, Inc.
5701 Bolsa Ave
Huntington Beach CA 92647
714 934-0000

(P-20770)
C&D ZODIAC INC
1945 S Grove Ave, Ontario (91761-5616)
PHONE.................................909 947-2725
Danny Martin, *Branch Mgr*
Angelina Alaniz, *Human Res Mgr*
EMP: 300
SALES (corp-wide): 650.9MM **Privately Held**
SIC: 3728 Aircraft assemblies, subassemblies & parts
HQ: C&D Zodiac, Inc.
5701 Bolsa Ave
Huntington Beach CA 92647
714 934-0000

(P-20771)
CAD MANUFACTURING INC
7320 Adams St, Paramount (90723-4008)
PHONE.................................562 408-1113
John Mburu, *President*
Harry Samat, *Vice Pres*
EMP: 10
SQ FT: 8,000
SALES (est): 1.5MM **Privately Held**
WEB: www.cadmanufacturing.com
SIC: 3728 3544 Aircraft parts & equipment; special dies, tools, jigs & fixtures

(P-20772)
CADENCE AEROSPACE LLC (PA)
3150 E Miraloma Ave, Anaheim
(92806-1906)
PHONE.................................949 877-3630
Ron Case, *Mng Member*
Lanny Shirk, *President*
Joyce Pae, *CFO*
Don Devore, *Exec VP*
Robert J Saia, *Senior VP*
EMP: 41 EST: 2010
SQ FT: 5,000
SALES (est): 195.8MM **Privately Held**
SIC: 3728 Aircraft body assemblies & parts

(P-20773)
CAL TECH PRECISION INC
1830 N Lemon St, Anaheim (92801-1000)
PHONE.................................714 992-4130
Guy W Haarlammert, *President*
▲ EMP: 99
SALES (est): 11.1MM **Privately Held**
WEB: www.caltechprecision.com
SIC: 3728 Aircraft parts & equipment

(P-20774)
CALIFORNIA COMPOSITES MGT INC
1935 E Occidental St, Santa Ana
(92705-5115)
PHONE.................................714 258-0405
Fred Good, *Ch of Bd*
EMP: 25
SQ FT: 30,000
SALES (est): 4.2MM **Privately Held**
WEB: www.ccdicomposites.com
SIC: 3728 3812 3624 Aircraft parts & equipment; search & navigation equipment; carbon & graphite products

(P-20775)
CANYON COMPOSITES INCORPORATED
1548 N Gemini Pl, Anaheim (92801-1152)
PHONE.................................714 991-8181
BJ Rutkoski, *President*
Eric Collins, *Treasurer*
Robert Gray, *Vice Pres*
Van H Pat, *Senior Engr*

EMP: 40
SQ FT: 31,500
SALES (est): 11.3MM **Privately Held**
WEB: www.canyoncomposites.com
SIC: 3728 8711 Aircraft parts & equipment; engineering services

(P-20776)
CANYON ENGINEERING PDTS INC
28909 Avenue Williams, Valencia (91355-4183)
PHONE..................661 294-0084
Todd Strickland, *President*
Paul Knerr, *Vice Pres*
EMP: 88
SQ FT: 70,000
SALES (est): 11.6MM
SALES (corp-wide): 685.7MM **Publicly Held**
WEB: www.canyonengineering.com
SIC: 3728 Aircraft assemblies, subassemblies & parts
PA: Esco Technologies Inc.
9900 Clayton Rd Ste A
Saint Louis MO 63124
314 213-7200

(P-20777)
CARBON BY DESIGN LLC
4128 Avenida De La Plata A, Oceanside (92056-6026)
PHONE..................760 643-1300
Dominick Consalvi,
Patrick Daugherty, *Opers Mgr*
EMP: 75
SQ FT: 25,000
SALES: 4.7MM **Publicly Held**
WEB: www.carbonbydesign.com
SIC: 3728 3761 Airframe assemblies, except for guided missiles; guided missiles & space vehicles; guided missiles & space vehicles, research & development
HQ: Flight Support Group Inc
161 Turnberry Cir
New Smyrna FL 32168
954 987-4000

(P-20778)
CARDONA MANUFACTURING CORP
1869 N Victory Pl, Burbank (91504-3476)
PHONE (818) 841-8358
Louis Cardona, *President*
Jo Ann Cardona, *Corp Secy*
Cindy Mayberry, *Vice Pres*
Joe Martinez, *Info Tech Mgr*
Cathy Martinez, *Purchasing*
EMP: 26
SQ FT: 10,000
SALES (est): 3.9MM **Privately Held**
WEB: www.cardonamfg.com
SIC: 3728 3812 Aircraft parts & equipment; search & navigation equipment

(P-20779)
CAVOTEC DABICO US INC
5665 Corporate Ave, Cypress (90630-4727)
PHONE..................714 947-0005
Gary Matthews, *President*
Christian Bernadotte, *Admin Sec*
Chris Clayton, *Accountant*
Dorothy Chen, *Controller*
▲ **EMP:** 36
SALES (est): 9.4MM **Privately Held**
SIC: 3728 Aircraft parts & equipment

(P-20780)
CHOL ENTERPRISES INC
12831 S Figueroa St, Los Angeles (90061-1157)
PHONE..................310 516-1328
Neal Castleman, *President*
Brian Gamberg, *Vice Pres*
EMP: 26
SQ FT: 25,000
SALES (est): 3.1MM **Privately Held**
SIC: 3728 3769 3678 3357 Aircraft assemblies, subassemblies & parts; guided missile & space vehicle parts & auxiliary equipment; electronic connectors; nonferrous wiredrawing & insulating

(P-20781)
CIRCOR AEROSPACE INC
2301 Wardlow Cir, Corona (92880-2801)
PHONE..................951 270-6200
Christopher R Celtruda, *General Mgr*
Bill Asmus, *Principal*
▲ **EMP:** 315
SQ FT: 80,000
SALES (est): 44.2MM
SALES (corp-wide): 661.7MM **Publicly Held**
WEB: www.circor.com
SIC: 3728 3625 Alighting (landing gear) assemblies, aircraft; actuators, industrial
PA: Circor International, Inc.
30 Corporate Dr Ste 200
Burlington MA 01803
781 270-1200

(P-20782)
COATING SPECIALTIES INC
Also Called: Aero Products Co.
815 E Rosecrans Ave, Los Angeles (90059-3510)
PHONE..................310 639-6900
Martha Taylor, *Admin Sec*
EMP: 14
SQ FT: 31,000
SALES: 3MM **Privately Held**
WEB: www.aeroproductsco.com
SIC: 3728 3812 Aircraft assemblies, subassemblies & parts; search & navigation equipment

(P-20783)
COI CERAMICS INC
Also Called: Coic
7130 Miramar Rd Ste 100b, San Diego (92121-2340)
PHONE..................858 621-5700
David A Shanahan, *CEO*
Steve Atmur, *Director*
Andy Szweda, *Director*
EMP: 41
SQ FT: 3,000
SALES (est): 12.9MM **Publicly Held**
WEB: www.coi-world.com
SIC: 3728 Aircraft parts & equipment
HQ: Northrop Grumman Innovation Systems, Inc.
45101 Warp Dr
Dulles VA 20166
703 406-5000

(P-20784)
COMPOSITES HORIZONS LLC (HQ)
1601 W Industrial Park St, Covina (91722-3418)
PHONE..................626 331-0861
Jeff Hynes, *President*
Renee Fahmy, *Vice Pres*
Tom Schulz, *Administration*
▲ **EMP:** 140
SQ FT: 25,000
SALES (est): 25.1MM
SALES (corp-wide): 385.4MM **Privately Held**
WEB: www.chi-covina.com
SIC: 3728 3844 2821 Aircraft parts & equipment; X-ray apparatus & tubes; nuclear irradiation equipment; plastics materials & resins
PA: Ascent Aerospace Holdings Llc
16445 23 Mile Rd
Macomb MI 48042
212 916-8142

(P-20785)
COMPUCRAFT INDUSTRIES INC
Also Called: Cii
8787 Olive Ln, Santee (92071-4137)
P.O. Box 712529 (92072-2529)
PHONE..................619 448-0787
Maurice Brear, *President*
Margarita Brear, *CFO*
EMP: 50
SQ FT: 85,000
SALES: 6MM **Privately Held**
WEB: www.ccind.com
SIC: 3728 Aircraft assemblies, subassemblies & parts

(P-20786)
CONDOR PACIFIC INDS CAL INC
905 Rancho Conejo Blvd, Newbury Park (91320-1716)
PHONE..................818 889-2150
Sidney Meltzner, *President*
Cher Gibson, *Program Mgr*
Charles Shuman, *Financial Exec*
EMP: 20
SALES: 3MM **Privately Held**
SIC: 3728 Aircraft parts & equipment

(P-20787)
CORONADO MANUFACTURING INC
8991 Glenoaks Blvd, Sun Valley (91352-2038)
PHONE..................818 768-5010
Allen F Gowing, *President*
Phillip Belmonte, *Vice Pres*
Scott Wilke, *Managing Dir*
Mylinn Dasalla, *Mktg Dir*
▼ **EMP:** 50
SQ FT: 19,000
SALES (est): 9MM **Privately Held**
WEB: www.coronadomfg.com
SIC: 3728 5084 Military aircraft equipment & armament; aircraft assemblies, subassemblies & parts; industrial machine parts

(P-20788)
CUSTOM AIRCRAFT INTERIORS INC
3701 Industry Ave, Lakewood (90712-4113)
PHONE..................562 426-5098
William Erwin, *CEO*
Kurt Erwin, *Vice Pres*
Julie Manley, *Sales Staff*
EMP: 10
SQ FT: 11,000
SALES (est): 1.8MM **Privately Held**
SIC: 3728 Aircraft parts & equipment

(P-20789)
CYNTHIA GARCIA
Also Called: Aero Space Composites
11782 Western Ave Ste 7, Stanton (90680-3458)
PHONE..................714 897-4654
Cynthia Garcia, *Owner*
EMP: 10
SQ FT: 6,000
SALES: 800K **Privately Held**
SIC: 3728 3812 8711 Aircraft parts & equipment; search & navigation equipment; aviation &/or aeronautical engineering

(P-20790)
D & D GEAR INCORPORATED
Also Called: Absolute Technologies
4890 E La Palma Ave, Anaheim (92807-1911)
PHONE..................714 692-6570
Bill Beverage, *President*
Tom Davis, *General Mgr*
Leonard Dye, *Technology*
Dusty Hill, *Technology*
Jason Praditbatuga, *Engineer*
▲ **EMP:** 210
SQ FT: 82,500
SALES (est): 59.8MM **Privately Held**
WEB: www.absolutetechnologies.com
SIC: 3728 Aircraft parts & equipment

(P-20791)
D & S INDUSTRIES INC
4515 E Eisenhower Cir, Anaheim (92807-1852)
PHONE..................714 779-8074
David Pierce Jr, *President*
Lisa Wilson, *Manager*
EMP: 13
SQ FT: 8,000
SALES (est): 3MM **Privately Held**
SIC: 3728 Aircraft parts & equipment

(P-20792)
DASCO ENGINEERING CORP
24747 Crenshaw Blvd, Torrance (90505-5308)
PHONE..................310 326-2277
Ward Olson, *President*

John Karle, *Vice Pres*
Glen Olson, *Vice Pres*
◆ **EMP:** 105 **EST:** 1964
SQ FT: 50,000
SALES (est): 22.9MM **Privately Held**
WEB: www.dascoeng.com
SIC: 3728 Aircraft body & wing assemblies & parts

(P-20793)
DATUM PRECISION INC
345 Crown Point Cir # 800, Grass Valley (95945-9526)
PHONE..................530 272-8415
John T Jans III, *President*
EMP: 10
SQ FT: 3,000
SALES (est): 1.4MM **Privately Held**
SIC: 3728 3599 Aircraft assemblies, subassemblies & parts; machine shop, jobbing & repair

(P-20794)
DIAGNOSTIC SOLUTIONS INTL LLC
2580 E Philadelphia St C, Ontario (91761-8093)
PHONE..................909 930-3600
Brian Hatcher, *Mng Member*
Gino Ela, *Opers Mgr*
Elena Buckley,
EMP: 16
SQ FT: 5,000
SALES (est): 3.2MM **Privately Held**
SIC: 3728 Aircraft parts & equipment

(P-20795)
DJI SERVICE LLC
17301 Edwards Rd, Cerritos (90703-2427)
PHONE..................818 235-0788
Hao Shen,
EMP: 15
SALES (est): 4.9MM **Privately Held**
SIC: 3728 Aircraft parts & equipment

(P-20796)
DMEA MSC
5584 Patrol Rd Bldg 1069, McClellan (95652-2200)
PHONE..................916 568-4087
Tamara Sullivan, *Principal*
EMP: 22
SALES (est): 3.2MM **Privately Held**
SIC: 3728 Military aircraft equipment & armament

(P-20797)
DOWNEY MANUFACTURING INC
11421 Downey Ave, Downey (90241-4934)
PHONE..................562 862-3311
Bill Read, *President*
EMP: 10
SQ FT: 15,000
SALES: 750K **Privately Held**
WEB: www.downeymfg.com
SIC: 3728 Alighting (landing gear) assemblies, aircraft; aircraft flight instrument repair

(P-20798)
DPI LABS INC
1350 Arrow Hwy, La Verne (91750-5218)
PHONE..................909 392-5777
Vicki Brown, *CEO*
Al Snow, *CFO*
Pam Archibald, *Vice Pres*
Greg Desmet, *Vice Pres*
EMP: 35
SALES (est): 8MM **Privately Held**
WEB: www.dpilabs.com
SIC: 3728 Aircraft parts & equipment

(P-20799)
DRETLOH AIRCRAFT SUPPLY INC (PA)
2830 E La Cresta Ave, Anaheim (92806-1816)
PHONE..................714 632-6982
Eugene Holte, *President*
Freda Holte, *Corp Secy*
Randy Holte, *Vice Pres*
Mark Holte, *General Mgr*
Carol Snyder, *Office Mgr*
▲ **EMP:** 15
SQ FT: 10,000

PRODUCTS & SVCS

SALES (est): 2.3MM **Privately Held**
SIC: 3728 5199 Aircraft parts & equipment; foam rubber

(P-20800)
DRIESSEN AIRCRAFT INTERIOR
Also Called: Zodiac Electrical Inserts USA
14505 Astronautics Ln, Huntington Beach (92647-2067)
PHONE...................................714 861-7300
Richard Braun, *General Mgr*
EMP: 50
SALES (corp-wide): 650.9MM **Privately Held**
SIC: 3728 Aircraft parts & equipment
HQ: Driessen Aircraft Interior Systems, Inc.
17311 Nichols Ln
Huntington Beach CA 92647
714 861-7300

(P-20801)
DRIESSEN AIRCRAFT INTERIOR (DH)
Also Called: Driessen Galleys USA
17311 Nichols Ln, Huntington Beach (92647-5721)
PHONE...................................714 861-7300
Matt Stafford, *General Mgr*
Boris Gorelik, *CFO*
Stephen Jones, *Info Tech Mgr*
Tuoi Nguyen, *Accountant*
Jerry Hall, *Director*
▲ EMP: 236
SQ FT: 90,000
SALES (est): 170.1MM
SALES (corp-wide): 650.9MM **Privately Held**
WEB: www.driessenusa.com
SIC: 3728 Aircraft parts & equipment
HQ: Driessen Aerospace Group N.V.
Toermalijnstraat 16
Alkmaar 1812
883 743-773

(P-20802)
DUCOMMUN AEROSTRUCTURES INC
801 Royal Oaks Dr, Monrovia (91016-3630)
PHONE...................................626 358-3211
Maurice Harris, *General Mgr*
EMP: 30
SALES (corp-wide): 558.1MM **Publicly Held**
SIC: 3728 Aircraft parts & equipment
HQ: Ducommun Aerostructures, Inc.
268 E Gardena Blvd
Gardena CA 90248
310 380-5390

(P-20803)
DUCOMMUN LABARGE TECH INC (HQ)
Also Called: American Electronics
23301 Wilmington Ave, Carson (90745-6209)
PHONE...................................310 513-7200
Stephen G Oswald, *CEO*
Douglas L Groves, *CFO*
Amy M Paul, *Admin Sec*
▲ EMP: 180 EST: 1958
SQ FT: 117,000
SALES (est): 54.7MM
SALES (corp-wide): 558.1MM **Publicly Held**
WEB: www.ductech.com
SIC: 3728 3769 5065 3812 Aircraft parts & equipment; guided missile & space vehicle parts & auxiliary equipment; electronic parts & equipment; search & navigation equipment; current-carrying wiring devices; relays & industrial controls
PA: Ducommun Incorporated
200 Sandpointe Ave # 700
Santa Ana CA 92707
657 335-3665

(P-20804)
DYNAMATION RESEARCH INC
2301 Pontius Ave, Los Angeles (90064-1809)
PHONE...................................909 864-2310
Gal Lipkin, *President*
Margalit Dorel, *Financial Exec*
George Ghorbani, *Sales Staff*
EMP: 15

SQ FT: 5,500
SALES (est): 3MM **Privately Held**
SIC: 3728 3812 Aircraft parts & equipment; search & navigation equipment

(P-20805)
EATON INDUSTRIAL CORPORATION
Also Called: Ground Fueling
9650 Jeronimo Rd, Irvine (92618-2024)
PHONE...................................949 425-9700
Keith Mayer, *Branch Mgr*
Debby Reynolds, *General Mgr*
EMP: 300 **Privately Held**
SIC: 3728 3594 3561 3492 Aircraft parts & equipment; fluid power pumps & motors; pumps & pumping equipment; fluid power valves & hose fittings
HQ: Eaton Industrial Corporation
23555 Euclid Ave
Cleveland OH 44117
216 523-4205

(P-20806)
ENCORE INTERIORS INC (PA)
Also Called: Lift By Encore
5511 Skylab Rd Ste 101, Huntington Beach (92647-2071)
PHONE...................................949 559-0930
Thomas McFarland, *President*
Karl Jonson, *CFO*
Aram Krikorian, *Vice Pres*
Jennifer Simmons, *Graphic Designe*
▲ EMP: 130
SQ FT: 42,000
SALES (est): 45.8MM **Privately Held**
WEB: www.compositesunlimited.com
SIC: 3728 1799 Aircraft parts & equipment; renovation of aircraft interiors

(P-20807)
ENCORE SEATS INC (PA)
Also Called: Lift By Encore
5511 Skylab Rd, Huntington Beach (92647-2068)
PHONE...................................949 559-0930
Thomas McFarland, *CEO*
Mike Melancon, *CFO*
Aram Krikorian, *Vice Pres*
EMP: 10 EST: 2015
SQ FT: 80,000
SALES (est): 5.9MM **Privately Held**
SIC: 3728 Aircraft assemblies, subassemblies & parts; seat ejector devices, aircraft

(P-20808)
ENCORE SEATS INC
Lift By Encore
5511 Skylab Rd, Huntington Beach (92647-2068)
PHONE...................................949 559-0930
EMP: 37
SALES (corp-wide): 5.9MM **Privately Held**
SIC: 3728 Aircraft parts & equipment
PA: Encore Seats Inc.
5511 Skylab Rd
Huntington Beach CA 92647
949 559-0930

(P-20809)
ENGINEERING JK AEROSPACE & DEF
23231 La Palma Ave, Yorba Linda (92887-4768)
PHONE...................................714 414-6722
Jonathan Crisan, *President*
EMP: 15 EST: 2017
SALES (est): 587.5K **Privately Held**
SIC: 3728 Aircraft parts & equipment

(P-20810)
F & L TOOLS CORPORATION
Also Called: F & L Tls Precision Machining
245 Jason Ct, Corona (92879-6199)
PHONE...................................951 279-1555
Tracey Pratt, *President*
Larry Pratt, *President*
Daryl Pratt, *General Mgr*
Albert Cruz, *Prdtn Mgr*
Shawn Wolfe, *Sales Staff*
EMP: 18
SQ FT: 8,100
SALES (est): 3.9MM **Privately Held**
WEB: www.fltcorp.com
SIC: 3728 Aircraft parts & equipment

(P-20811)
FARRAR GRINDING COMPANY
347 E Beach Ave, Inglewood (90302-3191)
PHONE...................................323 678-4879
Clarke Farrar, *President*
EMP: 14 EST: 1957
SQ FT: 6,000
SALES: 774.3K **Privately Held**
WEB: www.farrar-grinding.com
SIC: 3728 3599 Aircraft parts & equipment; machine shop, jobbing & repair

(P-20812)
FEDERAL AVIATION ADM
Also Called: Flight Standards District Off
2250 E Imperial Hwy # 140, El Segundo (90245-3543)
PHONE...................................310 640-9640
Richard Falcon, *Manager*
EMP: 40 **Publicly Held**
WEB: www.faa.gov
SIC: 3728 Airplane brake expanders; aircraft armament, except guns
HQ: Federal Aviation Administration
800 Independence Ave Sw
Washington DC 20591
-

(P-20813)
FLARE GROUP
Also Called: Aviation Equipment Processing
1571 Macarthur Blvd, Costa Mesa (92626-1407)
PHONE...................................714 850-2080
Dennis Heider, *President*
Steve Osorio, *Vice Pres*
Daryl Silva, *Principal*
Eric Trainor, *Principal*
Jim Vinyard, *Principal*
EMP: 25
SALES (est): 6.1MM **Privately Held**
SIC: 3728 Aircraft parts & equipment; aircraft body assemblies & parts

(P-20814)
FLEXCO INC
6855 Suva St, Bell Gardens (90201-1999)
PHONE...................................562 927-2525
Erik Moller, *President*
EMP: 36
SQ FT: 14,000
SALES: 3MM **Privately Held**
WEB: www.flexcoinc.com
SIC: 3728 3496 Aircraft parts & equipment; miscellaneous fabricated wire products

(P-20815)
FLIGHT ENVIRONMENTS INC
570 Linne Rd Ste 100, Paso Robles (93446-9460)
P.O. Box 3169 (93447-3169)
PHONE...................................805 226-2912
Eamon F Halpin, *CEO*
Colin Judge, *COO*
Viviana Gutierrez, *Executive Asst*
Sergio Flores, *Prdtn Mgr*
EMP: 25
SQ FT: 11,000
SALES (est): 3.1MM **Privately Held**
WEB: www.flightenvironments.com
SIC: 3728 Aircraft parts & equipment

(P-20816)
FMH AEROSPACE CORP
Also Called: F M H
17072 Daimler St, Irvine (92614-5548)
PHONE...................................714 751-1000
Rick Busch, *CEO*
Valerie Gorman, *CFO*
David Difranco, *Admin Sec*
Sheryl McNicol, *HR Admin*
▲ EMP: 100
SQ FT: 15,000
SALES: 28.2MM
SALES (corp-wide): 4.3B **Publicly Held**
WEB: www.flexiblemetalhose.com
SIC: 3728 Aircraft parts & equipment
PA: Ametek, Inc.
1100 Cassatt Rd
Berwyn PA 19312
610 647-2121

(P-20817)
FORMING SPECIALTIES INC
1309 W Walnut Pkwy, Compton (90220-5030)
PHONE...................................310 639-1122
Darrell E Madole, *President*
Kevin Herbert, *Vice Pres*
Shannon Madole, *General Mgr*
EMP: 33
SQ FT: 40,000
SALES (est): 4.9MM **Privately Held**
WEB: www.formingspecialties.com
SIC: 3728 3444 Aircraft parts & equipment; sheet metalwork

(P-20818)
FORREST MACHINING INC
Also Called: FORRESTMACHINING.COM
27756 Avenue Mentry, Valencia (91355-3453)
PHONE...................................661 257-0231
Joanne Butler, *CEO*
George Lodwick, *CFO*
Joe Velazquez, *Executive*
Tony Montoya, *Program Mgr*
Steve Wooten, *General Mgr*
▲ EMP: 200 EST: 1977
SALES (est): 45.1MM **Privately Held**
WEB: www.forrestmachining.com
SIC: 3728 Aircraft parts & equipment

(P-20819)
FORTNER ENG & MFG INC
918 Thompson Ave, Glendale (91201-2079)
PHONE...................................818 240-7740
David W Fortner, *President*
Robert S Fortner, *General Mgr*
Mike Malone, *Info Tech Mgr*
Jon Benoit, *Engineer*
Gary M Fortner, *Engineer*
EMP: 53 EST: 1952
SQ FT: 24,000
SALES (est): 11.6MM
SALES (corp-wide): 467.7MM **Privately Held**
WEB: www.fortnereng.com
SIC: 3728 Aircraft parts & equipment
PA: Wencor Group, Llc
416 Dividend Dr
Peachtree City GA 30269
678 490-0140

(P-20820)
FRAZIER AVIATION INC
445 N Fox St, San Fernando (91340-2501)
PHONE...................................818 898-1998
Robert L Frazier, *CEO*
Robert Frazier III, *President*
Marcia Cooper, *Vice Pres*
Charles E Ricard, *Vice Pres*
Pamela Gay, *Controller*
EMP: 42 EST: 1956
SQ FT: 44,000
SALES (est): 9.9MM **Privately Held**
WEB: www.frazieraviation.com
SIC: 3728 5088 Aircraft body assemblies & parts; transportation equipment & supplies

(P-20821)
GALI CORPORATION
Also Called: Dynamation Research
2301 Pontius Ave, Los Angeles (90064-1809)
PHONE...................................310 477-1224
Gal Lipkin, *CEO*
EMP: 14
SALES (est): 2.2MM **Privately Held**
WEB: www.dynamation.com
SIC: 3728 3812 Aircraft parts & equipment; aircraft control instruments

(P-20822)
GE AVIATION SYSTEMS LLC
Also Called: Mechancal Systm-Rial Refueling
23695 Via Del Rio, Yorba Linda (92887-2715)
PHONE...................................714 692-0200
Mary Normand, *Controller*
EMP: 250
SALES (corp-wide): 122B **Publicly Held**
SIC: 3728 Aircraft assemblies, subassemblies & parts

▲ = Import ▼=Export
◆ =Import/Export

HQ: Ge Aviation Systems Llc
1 Neumann Way
Cincinnati OH 45215
937 898-9600

(P-20823)
GEAR MANUFACTURING INC
Also Called: G M I
3701 E Miraloma Ave, Anaheim
(92806-2123)
PHONE...............................714 792-2895
Gary M Smith, *CEO*
Aaron Smith, *Info Tech Mgr*
Dave Mackley, *QC Mgr*
George Abbascia, *Sales Staff*
EMP: 50
SQ FT: 26,500
SALES (est): 11.7MM **Privately Held**
WEB: www.gearmfg.com
SIC: 3728 3714 3566 3568 Gears, air-
craft power transmission; bearings, motor
vehicle; speed changers, drives & gears;
power transmission equipment; motorcy-
cles, bicycles & parts

(P-20824)
GFMI AEROSPACE & DEFENSE INC
17375 Mount Herrmann St, Fountain Valley
(92708-4103)
PHONE...............................714 361-4444
George Gaffoglio, *CEO*
Ruben Gaffoglio, *President*
Mike Alexander, *COO*
EMP: 30 EST: 2011
SALES (est): 2.6MM **Privately Held**
WEB: www.gfmiaero.com
SIC: 3728 8711

(P-20825)
GLEDHILL/LYONS INC
Also Called: Accurate Technology
1521 N Placentia Ave, Anaheim
(92806-1236)
PHONE...............................714 502-0274
David M Lyons, *President*
EMP: 43 EST: 2000
SQ FT: 31,200
SALES (est): 13.5MM **Privately Held**
WEB: www.accuratetechnology.net
SIC: 3728 Aircraft parts & equipment

(P-20826)
GLOBAL AEROSPACE TECH CORP
25109 Rye Canyon Loop, Valencia
(91355-5004)
PHONE...............................818 407-5600
Steve Cormier, *CEO*
Don Spengler, *CFO*
EMP: 22
SQ FT: 40,000
SALES (est): 5.2MM **Privately Held**
WEB: www.globalatcorp.com
SIC: 3728 Aircraft parts & equipment

(P-20827)
GLOBAL AEROSTRUCTURES
10291 Trademark St Ste C, Rancho Cuca-
monga (91730-5847)
PHONE...............................909 987-4888
EMP: 15
SALES: 2MM **Privately Held**
SIC: 3728

(P-20828)
GME MFG INC
10641 Pullman Ct, Rancho Cucamonga
(91730-4847)
PHONE...............................909 989-4478
Leo Garcia, *President*
Olivia Gutierrez, *Admin Sec*
EMP: 10
SQ FT: 8,000
SALES (est): 2MM **Privately Held**
SIC: 3728 Accumulators, aircraft propeller

(P-20829)
GOODRICH CORPORATION
Goodrich Super Temp Division
11120 Norwalk Blvd, Santa Fe Springs
(90670-3830)
PHONE...............................562 906-7372
Michael Grundelsky, *Manager*
Ronnie Wilson, *Research*
EMP: 10

SALES (corp-wide): 59.8B **Publicly Held**
WEB: www.bfgoodrich.com
SIC: 3728 Aircraft parts & equipment
HQ: Goodrich Corporation
2730 W Tyvola Rd
Charlotte NC 28217
704 423-7000

(P-20830)
GOODRICH CORPORATION
Also Called: Goodrich Aerostructures
850 Lagoon Dr, Chula Vista (91910-2001)
PHONE...............................619 691-4111
David Gitlin, *President*
Jared Hippe, *Vice Pres*
Beth Garrison, *Administration*
Jeff Fryhling, *Info Tech Mgr*
Deven Hansen, *Info Tech Mgr*
▲ EMP: 84
SALES (est): 32MM **Privately Held**
SIC: 3728 Aircraft parts & equipment

(P-20831)
GOODRICH CORPORATION
2727 E Imperial Hwy, Brea (92821-6713)
PHONE...............................714 984-1461
Rob Gibbs, *General Mgr*
Lydia Kirk, *General Mgr*
John Morse, *Engng Exec*
David Lopes, *Project Engr*
Tedd Wong, *Engineer*
EMP: 140
SALES (corp-wide): 59.8B **Publicly Held**
WEB: www.bfgoodrich.com
SIC: 3728 Aircraft parts & equipment
HQ: Goodrich Corporation
2730 W Tyvola Rd
Charlotte NC 28217
704 423-7000

(P-20832)
GOODRICH CORPORATION
Goodrich Wheel and Brake Svcs
9920 Freeman Ave, Santa Fe Springs
(90670-3421)
PHONE...............................562 944-4441
Hosrow Bordbar, *Manager*
Rudy Delarosa, *Officer*
Mark Posada, *Purch Dir*
EMP: 55
SALES (corp-wide): 59.8B **Publicly Held**
WEB: www.bfgoodrich.com
SIC: 3728 Aircraft parts & equipment
HQ: Goodrich Corporation
2730 W Tyvola Rd
Charlotte NC 28217
704 423-7000

(P-20833)
GST INDUSTRIES INC
9060 Winnetka Ave, Northridge
(91324-3235)
PHONE...............................818 350-1900
EMP: 24
SQ FT: 9,700
SALES: 2.3MM
SALES (corp-wide): 8.4MM **Privately Held**
WEB: www.gstindustries.net
SIC: 3728
PA: Infinity Aerospace, Inc.
9060 Winnetka Ave
Northridge CA 91324
818 998-9811

(P-20834)
H & R AEROSPACE INC
1025 N Tustin St Apt 505, Orange
(92867-5954)
PHONE...............................714 893-1737
Richard Chae, *President*
Hien Nguyen, *Shareholder*
EMP: 15 EST: 2010
SQ FT: 7,000
SALES (est): 2MM **Privately Held**
SIC: 3728 Aircraft parts & equipment

(P-20835)
HAGER MFG INC
14610 Industry Cir, La Mirada
(90638-5815)
PHONE...............................714 522-8870
Donald L Bowley, *President*
Patricia Bowley, *CFO*
EMP: 25 EST: 1969
SQ FT: 10,800

SALES (est): 3.8MM **Privately Held**
SIC: 3728 3599 Aircraft assemblies, subassemblies & parts; machine shop, jobbing & repair

(P-20836)
HELICOPTER TECH CO LTD PARTNR
12902 S Broadway, Los Angeles
(90061-1118)
PHONE...............................310 523-2750
Frank Palminteri, *President*
Gary Burdorf, *Vice Pres*
James Fackler, *VP Opers*
◆ EMP: 24
SQ FT: 197,000
SALES (est): 5.8MM **Privately Held**
SIC: 3728 3721 Aircraft parts & equip-
ment; helicopters

(P-20837)
HQ MACHINE TECH LLC
6900 8th St, Buena Park (90620-1036)
PHONE...............................714 956-3388
Robert Groner, *President*
EMP: 35 EST: 2017
SALES (est): 1.9MM **Privately Held**
SIC: 3728 Aircraft parts & equipment

(P-20838)
HUGO ENGINEERING CO INC
837 Van Ness Ave, Torrance (90501-2230)
PHONE...............................310 320-0288
Loreto Gonzalez, *President*
Angie Gonzalez, *Vice Pres*
EMP: 10 EST: 1979
SQ FT: 5,500
SALES: 1.9MM **Privately Held**
SIC: 3728 Aircraft parts & equipment

(P-20839)
HUTCHINSON AROSPC & INDUST INC
Also Called: ARS
4510 W Vanowen St, Burbank
(91505-1135)
PHONE...............................818 843-1000
Shano Cristilli, *Branch Mgr*
Niel O'Hara, *General Mgr*
Gigi Tran, *General Mgr*
Armando Perez, *Design Engr*
Jose Navarro, *Project Engr*
EMP: 165
SALES (corp-wide): 8.3B **Publicly Held**
SIC: 3728 Aircraft parts & equipment
HQ: Hutchinson Aerospace & Industry, Inc.
82 South St
Hopkinton MA 01748
508 417-7000

(P-20840)
HYDRAULICS INTERNATIONAL INC (PA)
9201 Independence Ave, Chatsworth
(91311-5905)
PHONE...............................818 998-1231
Nicky Ghaemmaghami, *CEO*
Shah Banifazl, *CFO*
Linda Ghaemmaghami, *Vice Pres*
Beth Wynn, *General Mgr*
Anahit Baghdasaryan, *Engineer*
◆ EMP: 277
SQ FT: 78,000
SALES: 105.6MM **Privately Held**
WEB: www.hiifsu.com
SIC: 3728 Aircraft parts & equipment

(P-20841)
HYDRAULICS INTERNATIONAL INC
9000 Mason Ave, Chatsworth
(91311-6178)
PHONE...............................818 998-1236
Chuck Sherman, *Branch Mgr*
Jeffrey Riley, *Vice Pres*
Angel Gomez, *Engineer*
EMP: 62
SALES (corp-wide): 105.6MM **Privately Held**
WEB: www.hiifsu.com
SIC: 3728 Aircraft parts & equipment
PA: Hydraulics International, Inc.
9201 Independence Ave
Chatsworth CA 91311
818 998-1231

(P-20842)
HYDRO-AIRE INC (DH)
3000 Winona Ave, Burbank (91504-2540)
PHONE...............................818 526-2600
Brendan J Curran, *CEO*
Tazewell Rowe, *Treasurer*
Ermine Adzhemyan, *Administration*
Stuart Johnson, *Planning*
Herman Yih, *Software Engr*
▲ EMP: 43
SQ FT: 173,000
SALES (est): 123.1MM
SALES (corp-wide): 2.7B **Publicly Held**
WEB: www.craneco.com
SIC: 3728 Aircraft parts & equipment

(P-20843)
HYDROFORM USA INCORPORATED
2848 E 208th St, Carson (90810-1101)
PHONE...............................310 632-6353
Chester K Jablonski, *CEO*
Mauricio Salazar, *CFO*
Patrick Tang, *CFO*
Steven Stansbury, *Info Tech Dir*
Stephen Hsu, *Info Tech Mgr*
▼ EMP: 154
SQ FT: 95,000
SALES: 35MM **Privately Held**
WEB: www.hydroformusa.com
SIC: 3728 Aircraft parts & equipment

(P-20844)
ICON AIRCRAFT INC (PA)
2141 Icon Way, Vacaville (95688-8766)
PHONE...............................707 564-4000
Kirk Hawkins, *CEO*
Thomas Wieners, *COO*
Rich Bridge, *Vice Pres*
Vicky Schoennagel, *Program Mgr*
Ashley Freyer, *Executive Asst*
EMP: 74
SALES (est): 25.7MM **Privately Held**
SIC: 3728 Aircraft parts & equipment

(P-20845)
IKHANA GROUP INC
Also Called: Ikhana Aircraft Services
37260 Sky Canyon Dr # 20, Murrieta
(92563-2680)
PHONE...............................951 600-0009
John A Zublin, *President*
Marcos M Carvalhal, *CFO*
Marcos Carvalhal, *CFO*
Stanley R Fisher, *Exec VP*
Marilyn Meyer, *Executive Asst*
▲ EMP: 120 EST: 2007
SALES (est): 21MM **Privately Held**
SIC: 3728 Flaps, aircraft wing

(P-20846)
IMPRESA AEROSPACE LLC (PA)
344 W 157th St, Gardena (90248-2135)
PHONE...............................310 354-1200
Scott Smith, *CEO*
Dennis Fitzgerald, *Vice Pres*
David Hirsch, *Vice Pres*
Jose Banuelos, *General Mgr*
Toaale Mulitauaopele, *Info Tech Mgr*
EMP: 16
SQ FT: 26,000
SALES (est): 48MM **Privately Held**
WEB: www.ventureaircraft.com
SIC: 3728 3444 Aircraft parts & equip-
ment; sheet metalwork

(P-20847)
IMPRESA AEROSPACE LLC
344 W 157th St, Gardena (90248-2135)
PHONE...............................843 553-2021
Charles Vangraan, *Manager*
Scott Smith, *CEO*
EMP: 16
SALES (corp-wide): 48MM **Privately Held**
SIC: 3728 3444 Aircraft parts & equip-
ment; sheet metalwork
PA: Impresa Aerospace, Llc
344 W 157th St
Gardena CA 90248
310 354-1200

(P-20848)
INFLIGHT WARNING SYSTEMS INC
Also Called: Iws Predictive Technologies
3910 Prospect Ave Unit P, Yorba Linda
(92886-1746)
PHONE..................................714 993-9394
Joseph Barclay, *President*
Dirk Fichtner, *President*
Ehrick Steve, *COO*
Jeff Bulkin, *CFO*
George Orff, *Admin Sec*
EMP: 19
SQ FT: 6,000
SALES (est): 1.6MM **Privately Held**
WEB: www.iws-llc.com
SIC: 3728 Aircraft assemblies, subassemblies & parts

(P-20849)
INTERTRADE AVIATION CORP
5722 Buckingham Dr, Huntington Beach
(92649-1130)
PHONE..................................714 895-3335
Ted Newfield, *President*
▲ EMP: 45 EST: 1980
SQ FT: 65,000
SALES (est): 7.4MM **Privately Held**
SIC: 3728 5088 Aircraft assemblies, sub-assemblies & parts; transportation equipment & supplies

(P-20850)
ITT AEROSPACE CONTROLS LLC (HQ)
28150 Industry Dr, Valencia (91355-4101)
PHONE..................................315 568-7258
Philip Bordages,
Becky Petersen, *Admin Asst*
Steven Giuliano,
▲ EMP: 44 EST: 2011
SALES (est): 56.3MM
SALES (corp-wide): 2.5B **Publicly Held**
SIC: 3728 Aircraft parts & equipment
PA: Itt Inc.
    1133 Westchester Ave N-100
    White Plains NY 10604
    914 641-2000

(P-20851)
ITT AEROSPACE CONTROLS LLC
ITT Aerospace Controls Unit S
28150 Industry Dr, Valencia (91355-4101)
PHONE..................................661 295-4000
Robert Briggs, *Manager*
Farrokh Batliwala, *President*
Reggie Gardner, *Regional Mgr*
Mostafa Donyanavard, *Engineer*
Lee Hutchins, *Engineer*
EMP: 300
SALES (corp-wide): 2.5B **Publicly Held**
WEB: www.ittind.com
SIC: 3728 Aircraft parts & equipment
HQ: Itt Aerospace Controls Llc
    28150 Industry Dr
    Valencia CA 91355
    315 568-7258

(P-20852)
ITT AEROSPACE CONTROLS LLC
28150 Industry Dr, Valencia (91355-4101)
PHONE..................................661 295-4000
Jim Dauw, *President*
Art E Lewis, *Manager*
EMP: 27
SALES (corp-wide): 2.5B **Publicly Held**
SIC: 3728 Aircraft parts & equipment
HQ: Itt Aerospace Controls Llc
    28150 Industry Dr
    Valencia CA 91355
    315 568-7258

(P-20853)
IVOPROP CORPORATION
15903 Lakewood Blvd # 103, Bellflower
(90706-4300)
PHONE..................................562 602-1451
Ivo Zdarskty, *President*
EMP: 12
SALES (est): 1.4MM **Privately Held**
WEB: www.ivoprop.com
SIC: 3728 Aircraft propellers & associated equipment

(P-20854)
JCM ENGINEERING CORP
2690 E Cedar St, Ontario (91761-8533)
PHONE..................................909 923-3730
Carlo A Moyano, *President*
William Durante, *President*
Yvonne Moyano, *Vice Pres*
Gregory E Marsella, *Admin Sec*
Nancy Ong, *Technology*
EMP: 85
SQ FT: 140,000
SALES (est): 16.2MM **Privately Held**
WEB: www.jcmcorp.com
SIC: 3728 Aircraft body & wing assemblies & parts

(P-20855)
JENNY SAMMON
Also Called: Aerofutures
600 Anton Blvd Ste 1100, Costa Mesa
(92626-7100)
PHONE..................................951 926-4326
Jenny Sammon, *President*
Michael Metheny, *Principal*
EMP: 10 EST: 2016
SQ FT: 2,500
SALES (est): 311.4K **Privately Held**
SIC: 3728 Aircraft parts & equipment

(P-20856)
JET AIR FBO LLC
681 Kenney St, El Cajon (92020-1278)
PHONE..................................619 448-5991
Dan Gayet,
Liz Nunery, *Manager*
Wafaa Stele, *Manager*
EMP: 30
SQ FT: 250,000
SALES (est): 2.2MM **Privately Held**
SIC: 3728 Refueling equipment for use in flight, airplane

(P-20857)
JETSTREAM TRADING CO
1005 E Las Tunas Dr U356, San Gabriel
(91776-1614)
PHONE..................................818 921-7158
Jimmy Xiao Zhu, *CEO*
Jie Zhu, *President*
EMP: 10
SQ FT: 500
SALES (est): 1.1MM **Privately Held**
SIC: 3728 Aircraft parts & equipment

(P-20858)
JOHNSON CALDRAUL INC
Also Called: Cal-Draulics
220 N Delilah St Ste 101, Corona
(92879-1883)
PHONE..................................951 340-1067
Douglas Johnson, *President*
Kenneth W Johnson, *Vice Pres*
EMP: 30
SQ FT: 12,000
SALES: 3MM **Privately Held**
WEB: www.caldraulics.com
SIC: 3728 3593 Aircraft parts & equipment; fluid power cylinders & actuators

(P-20859)
K & E INC
Also Called: Micro Space Products
3906 W 139th St, Hawthorne (90250-7497)
PHONE..................................310 675-3309
Cathy Riegler, *CEO*
Rudi Riegler, *President*
Rina Marquez, *Controller*
◆ EMP: 12
SQ FT: 10,000
SALES: 1MM **Privately Held**
SIC: 3728 Aircraft parts & equipment

(P-20860)
KLUNE INDUSTRIES INC (DH)
7323 Coldwater Canyon Ave, North Hollywood (91605-4206)
PHONE..................................818 503-8100
Joseph I Snowden, *CEO*
Kenneth Ward, *CFO*
Ian Davis, *Program Mgr*
Brad Jackson, *Purchasing*
Scott Gregory, *Manager*
▲ EMP: 358
SQ FT: 125,000

SALES (est): 131.1MM
SALES (corp-wide): 242.1B **Publicly Held**
SIC: 3728 Aircraft parts & equipment

(P-20861)
KOITO AVIATION LLC
25011 Avenue Stanford D, Valencia
(91355-4771)
PHONE..................................661 257-2878
Robet Ayvazian,
Chitoshi Fujii,
▲ EMP: 10
SALES (est): 1MM **Privately Held**
SIC: 3728 Aircraft parts & equipment

(P-20862)
KS ENGINEERING INC
14948 Shoemaker Ave, Santa Fe Springs
(90670-5552)
PHONE..................................562 483-7788
Clifford Yu, *President*
Kap Yu, *Manager*
EMP: 10
SQ FT: 14,000
SALES (est): 1.5MM **Privately Held**
SIC: 3728 Aircraft body & wing assemblies & parts

(P-20863)
LAMSCO WEST INC
Also Called: Shimtech US
29101 The Old Rd, Santa Clarita
(91355-1014)
PHONE..................................661 295-8620
Steve Griffith, *President*
Rick Casillas, *COO*
Scott Wilkinson, *CFO*
Favian Arellano, *Administration*
Frank Cortez, *Planning*
EMP: 150
SQ FT: 31,280
SALES: 39.5MM
SALES (corp-wide): 97.1MM **Privately Held**
WEB: www.lamscowest.com
SIC: 3728 Aircraft parts & equipment
HQ: Shimtech Industries Limited
    7a/B Millington Road
    Hayes MIDDX UB3 4
    208 571-0055

(P-20864)
LANIC ENGINEERING INC (PA)
Also Called: Lanic Aerospace
12144 6th St, Rancho Cucamonga
(91730-6111)
PHONE..................................877 763-0411
S Robert Leaming, *CEO*
Shaun Arnold, *President*
EMP: 36
SQ FT: 30,000
SALES: 2.5MM **Privately Held**
WEB: www.lanicengineering.com
SIC: 3728 3721 Aircraft parts & equipment; aircraft

(P-20865)
LAVI SYSTEMS INC
13731 Saticoy St, Van Nuys (91402-6517)
PHONE..................................818 373-5400
Leonard Gross, *Chairman*
Ray Lavi, *President*
Bernard Shapiro, *Vice Pres*
Leonard Shapiro, *Admin Sec*
EMP: 18
SQ FT: 11,500
SALES (est): 636.7K
SALES (corp-wide): 72.3MM **Privately Held**
WEB: www.lavisystems.com
SIC: 3728 Aircraft parts & equipment
PA: Shapco Inc.
    1666 20th St Ste 100
    Santa Monica CA 90404
    310 264-1666

(P-20866)
LEE AEROSPACE PRODUCTS INC
90 W Easy St Ste 5, Simi Valley
(93065-6206)
PHONE..................................805 527-1811
Darrell Lee, *President*
Estelle Lee, *Treasurer*
EMP: 10

SQ FT: 25,000
SALES (est): 1.3MM **Privately Held**
WEB: www.leeaerospace-ca.com
SIC: 3728 Aircraft parts & equipment

(P-20867)
LLAMAS PLASTICS INC
12970 Bradley Ave, Sylmar (91342-3851)
PHONE..................................818 362-0371
Ricardo M Llamas, *CEO*
Oswald Llamas, *President*
Jeff Mabry, *Corp Secy*
EMP: 105
SQ FT: 37,000
SALES (est): 30.7MM **Privately Held**
WEB: www.llamasplastics.com
SIC: 3728 3089 3083 Aircraft parts & equipment; plastic containers, except foam; laminated plastics plate & sheet

(P-20868)
LMI AEROSPACE INC
1351 Specialty Dr, Vista (92081-8521)
PHONE..................................760 597-7066
EMP: 170
SALES (corp-wide): 1MM **Privately Held**
SIC: 3728 Aircraft parts & equipment
HQ: Lmi Aerospace, Inc.
    411 Fountain Lakes Blvd
    Saint Charles MO 63301
    636 946-6525

(P-20869)
LPJ AEROSPACE LLC
741 E 223rd St, Carson (90745-4111)
PHONE..................................310 834-5700
Louie Labadie,
EMP: 15
SALES (est): 1.5MM **Privately Held**
SIC: 3728 Aircraft parts & equipment

(P-20870)
LUXFER INC (DH)
Also Called: Luxfer Gas Cylinder
3016 Kansas Ave Bldg 1, Riverside
(92507-3445)
PHONE..................................336 578-4515
John Rhodes, *President*
Anthony Barnes, *President*
Micheal Edwards, *Vice Pres*
Richard Lintin, *Info Tech Mgr*
Susan Packler, *VP Human Res*
◆ EMP: 70
SQ FT: 120,000
SALES (est): 139.1MM
SALES (corp-wide): 441.3MM **Privately Held**
WEB: www.luxfer-ecare.com
SIC: 3728 3354 Aircraft parts & equipment; shapes, extruded aluminum

(P-20871)
MACHINETEK LLC
1985 Palomar Oaks Way, Carlsbad
(92011-1307)
PHONE..................................760 438-6644
Kevin S Darroch, *President*
Donald Firm, *COO*
David Humphreys, *Engineer*
Doug Rupert, *QC Mgr*
Hanns O Lindberg,
EMP: 18
SQ FT: 21,000
SALES: 2.5MM **Privately Held**
WEB: www.machinetek.com
SIC: 3728 Aircraft assemblies, subassemblies & parts

(P-20872)
MANEY AIRCRAFT INC
1305 S Wanamaker Ave, Ontario
(91761-2237)
PHONE..................................909 390-2500
Martin T Bright, *CEO*
David A Ederer, *Shareholder*
Michael Neely, *Shareholder*
Candace Gonzalez, *Admin Asst*
EMP: 30
SQ FT: 14,700

▲ = Import ▼=Export
◆ =Import/Export

SALES (est): 7.1MM **Privately Held**
WEB: www.maneyaircraft.com
SIC: **3728** 5088 3829 3812 Aircraft assemblies, subassemblies & parts; aircraft & parts; aircraft & motor vehicle measurement equipment; search & navigation equipment; guided missile & space vehicle parts & auxiliary equipment; aircraft, self-propelled

(P-20873)
MARINO ENTERPRISES INC
Also Called: Gear Technology
10671 Civic Center Dr, Rancho Cucamonga (91730-3804)
PHONE....................909 476-0343
Thomas Marino, *President*
Sharon Nevius, *Human Res Mgr*
Tom Cruse, *Prdtn Mgr*
Fernando Aleman, *QC Mgr*
EMP: 35
SQ FT: 16,320
SALES (est): 7.2MM **Privately Held**
SIC: **3728** 3769 Gears, aircraft power transmission; guided missile & space vehicle parts & auxiliary equipment

(P-20874)
MARVIN ENGINEERING CO INC (PA)
Also Called: Marvin Group, The
261 W Beach Ave, Inglewood (90302-2904)
PHONE....................310 674-5030
Gerald M Friedman, *CEO*
Howard Gussman, *President*
Leon Tsimmerman, *CFO*
Carrie Ignacia, *Vice Pres*
Seth Silverstein, *Vice Pres*
▲ EMP: 580
SQ FT: 300,000
SALES (est): 222.7MM **Privately Held**
WEB: www.marvineng.com
SIC: **3728** Aircraft parts & equipment

(P-20875)
MASON ELECTRIC CO
13955 Balboa Blvd, Sylmar (91342-1084)
PHONE....................818 361-3366
Steven Brune, *Vice Pres*
Ricardo Lakandula, *Program Mgr*
Joe Fielding, *Design Engr*
Andrew Steier, *Technology*
Arturo Goche, *Project Engr*
EMP: 350
SQ FT: 105,000
SALES (est): 58.8MM
SALES (corp-wide): 2B **Publicly Held**
WEB: www.mason-electric.com
SIC: **3728** Aircraft parts & equipment
PA: Esterline Technologies Corp
500 108th Ave Ne Ste 1500
Bellevue WA 98004
425 453-9400

(P-20876)
MASTER RESEARCH & MFG INC
13528 Pumice St, Norwalk (90650-5249)
PHONE....................562 483-8789
Enrique Viano, *Vice Pres*
Adriana Viano, *President*
EMP: 53 EST: 1977
SQ FT: 18,000
SALES (est): 13MM **Privately Held**
WEB: www.master-research.com
SIC: **3728** Aircraft body assemblies & parts

(P-20877)
MATTERNET INC
3511 Edison Way, Menlo Park (94025-1815)
PHONE....................650 260-2727
Andreas Ratopoulos, *CEO*
Josephine Driscoll, *Opers Staff*
EMP: 28
SALES (est): 4.8MM **Privately Held**
SIC: **3728** Target drones

(P-20878)
MAVERICK AEROSPACE INC
3718 Capitol Ave, City of Industry (90601-1731)
PHONE....................714 578-1700
David Feltch, *CEO*
George Ono, *President*
Nigel Young, *Vice Pres*

Laurie Chavez, *Office Mgr*
Tina Ruth, *Office Mgr*
EMP: 16
SQ FT: 12,000
SALES (est): 3MM **Privately Held**
WEB: www.kjackaero.com
SIC: **3728** Aircraft assemblies, subassemblies & parts

(P-20879)
MAVERICK AEROSPACE LLC
3718 Capitol Ave, City of Industry (90601-1731)
PHONE....................714 578-1700
EMP: 10
SALES (est): 360.4K **Privately Held**
SIC: **3728** Aircraft parts & equipment

(P-20880)
MAVERICK AEROSPACE LLC
3718 Capitol Ave, City of Industry (90601-1731)
PHONE....................714 578-1700
Steve Crisanti, *CEO*
Val Darie, *Vice Pres*
George Ono, *Vice Pres*
EMP: 44
SQ FT: 40,000
SALES (est): 781.9K **Privately Held**
SIC: **3728** 3544 3761 3441 Aircraft parts & equipment; special dies, tools, jigs & fixtures; guided missiles & space vehicles; fabricated structural metal; guided missile & space vehicle parts & auxiliary equipment; machine shop, jobbing & repair

(P-20881)
MEGGITT
1785 Voyager Ave Ste 100, Simi Valley (93063-3365)
PHONE....................877 666-0712
Diane Bird, *President*
Doug Webb, *CFO*
Brian Bondarenko, *Senior VP*
Phyllis Pearce, *Senior VP*
Steve Fackler, *Vice Pres*
EMP: 107
SALES (est): 13.8MM **Privately Held**
SIC: **3728** Aircraft parts & equipment

(P-20882)
MEGGITT (SAN DIEGO) INC (DH)
Also Called: Meggitt Polymers & Composites
6650 Top Gun St, San Diego (92121-4112)
PHONE....................858 824-8976
Michael Louderback, *General Mgr*
Richard Ramirez, *Treasurer*
Gary Hatchett, *Officer*
Tom Little, *Senior VP*
Eric Lardiere, *Vice Pres*
EMP: 120
SQ FT: 120,000
SALES (est): 40.9MM
SALES (corp-wide): 2.6B **Privately Held**
SIC: **3728** Roto-blades for helicopters
HQ: Meggitt-Usa, Inc.
1955 Surveyor Ave
Simi Valley CA 93063
805 526-5700

(P-20883)
MEGGITT DEFENSE SYSTEMS INC
9801 Muirlands Blvd, Irvine (92618-2521)
PHONE....................949 465-7700
Roger Brum, *President*
Greg Brostek, *CFO*
Christine Gunning, *Info Tech Mgr*
Brian Schroeder, *Info Tech Mgr*
David Dorr, *Engineer*
EMP: 220 EST: 1998
SQ FT: 50,000
SALES (est): 82.7MM
SALES (corp-wide): 2.6B **Privately Held**
WEB: www.wd.com
SIC: **3728** Military aircraft equipment & armament
PA: Meggitt Plc
Atlantic House, Aviation Park West
Christchurch BH23
120 259-7597

(P-20884)
MEGGITT-USA INC (HQ)
Also Called: Meggitt Polymers & Composites
1955 Surveyor Ave, Simi Valley (93063-3369)
PHONE....................805 526-5700
Eric Lardiere, *President*
Peter Stammers, *President*
Robert W Soukup, *Treasurer*
Barney Rosenberg, *Vice Pres*
Jennifer Limon, *Admin Asst*
▲ EMP: 271
SQ FT: 3,000
SALES (est): 401.4MM
SALES (corp-wide): 2.6B **Privately Held**
SIC: **3728** 3829 3679 Aircraft parts & equipment; vibration meters, analyzers & calibrators; electronic switches
PA: Meggitt Plc
Atlantic House, Aviation Park West
Christchurch BH23
120 259-7597

(P-20885)
MENCHES TOOL & DIE INC
30995 San Benito St, Hayward (94544-7936)
PHONE....................650 592-2328
John Menches Jr, *CEO*
Rosa Menches, *Admin Sec*
Uwe Brinkmann, *Manager*
Darla Stevenson, *Manager*
EMP: 20
SQ FT: 22,400
SALES (est): 3.7MM **Privately Held**
WEB: www.menches.com
SIC: **3728** Aircraft parts & equipment

(P-20886)
MGB INDUSTRIES INC
679 Anita St Ste B, Chula Vista (91911-4662)
PHONE....................619 247-9284
EMP: 16
SALES (est): 200K **Privately Held**
SIC: **3728** 5949

(P-20887)
MIKELSON MACHINE SHOP INC
2546 Merced Ave, South El Monte (91733-1924)
PHONE....................626 448-3920
James Michaelson, *President*
James M Mikelson, *President*
▼ EMP: 23 EST: 1967
SQ FT: 14,000
SALES (est): 5.4MM **Privately Held**
SIC: **3728** Aircraft parts & equipment

(P-20888)
MILCOMM INC
10291 Trademark St Ste C, Rancho Cucamonga (91730-5847)
PHONE....................626 523-8305
Candy Benevides, *CEO*
Michael Cabral, *President*
EMP: 13
SQ FT: 13,603
SALES: 900K **Privately Held**
SIC: **3728** Aircraft assemblies, subassemblies & parts

(P-20889)
MISSION CRTICAL COMPOSITES LLC
15400 Graham St Ste 102, Huntington Beach (92649-1257)
PHONE....................714 831-2100
Robert Hartman, *Mng Member*
EMP: 22 EST: 2012
SALES: 3.4MM **Privately Held**
SIC: **3728** 3721 3724 3761 Aircraft assemblies, subassemblies & parts; aircraft; aircraft engines & engine parts; guided missiles & space vehicles; guided missile & space vehicle propulsion unit parts; airframe assemblies, guided missiles

(P-20890)
MONAERO ENGINEERING INC
17011 Industry Pl, La Mirada (90638-5819)
PHONE....................714 994-5463
Harish Bhutani, *President*
Stephen Russo, *Design Engr*
Ajay Pall, *Engineer*
Gloria Contreras, *Purch Mgr*

Jerry Claustor, *QC Mgr*
▲ EMP: 10
SQ FT: 8,750
SALES (est): 1.5MM **Privately Held**
WEB: www.monaero.com
SIC: **3728** Aircraft parts & equipment

(P-20891)
MONOGRAM SYSTEMS
Also Called: Zodiac Aerospace
1500 Glenn Curtiss St, Carson (90746-4012)
PHONE....................801 400-7944
Perrie Weiner, *Manager*
Dawn Garrett, *Program Mgr*
Oscar Lopez, *Design Engr*
Kristian Orozco, *Design Engr*
Joel Montiel, *Project Engr*
EMP: 18
SALES (est): 3.4MM **Privately Held**
SIC: **3728** Aircraft parts & equipment

(P-20892)
MS AEROSPACE MATERIALS LLC
180 Erma Ct Ste 160, Chico (95928-6996)
PHONE....................323 813-4105
Mike Sealey,
EMP: 10 EST: 2013
SQ FT: 1,000
SALES: 750K **Privately Held**
SIC: **3728** Aircraft parts & equipment

(P-20893)
MULGREW ARCFT COMPONENTS INC
1810 S Shamrock Ave, Monrovia (91016-4251)
PHONE....................626 256-1375
Mike Houshiar, *CEO*
Adrian Velasquez, *Program Mgr*
Sevak Piry, *Engineer*
EMP: 58
SQ FT: 45,000
SALES (est): 8.2MM **Privately Held**
WEB: www.mulgrewaircraft.com
SIC: **3728** Aircraft assemblies, subassemblies & parts

(P-20894)
N2 DEVELOPMENT INC
Also Called: N2 Aero
1819 Dana St Ste A, Glendale (91201-2007)
PHONE....................323 210-3251
Gregory Nelson, *President*
Olen Nelson, *Vice Pres*
EMP: 15
SQ FT: 4,000
SALES (est): 600K **Privately Held**
SIC: **3728** Aircraft parts & equipment

(P-20895)
NASCO AIRCRAFT BRAKE INC
Also Called: Meggitt Arcft Braking Systems
13300 Estrella Ave, Gardena (90248-1519)
PHONE....................310 532-4430
Daniel Aron, *CEO*
Phil Friedman, *Corp Secy*
Terry Jones, *Business Dir*
Leah Garcia, *General Mgr*
Milan Pantic, *Engineer*
EMP: 100
SQ FT: 25,000
SALES (est): 20.8MM
SALES (corp-wide): 2.6B **Privately Held**
WEB: www.nascoaircraft.com
SIC: **3728** Brakes, aircraft
HQ: Meggitt Aircraft Braking Systems Corporation
1204 Massillon Rd
Akron OH 44306
330 796-4400

(P-20896)
NC DYNAMICS INCORPORATED
Also Called: Ncdi
6925 Downey Ave, Long Beach (90805-1823)
PHONE....................562 634-7392
Kevin Minter, *CEO*
Randall L Bazz, *President*
Vince Braun, *President*
Mike Perrin, *Program Mgr*
Joe Canale, *Prgrmr*
▲ EMP: 151

PRODUCTS & SVCS

SALES (est): 49.6MM
SALES (corp-wide): 118.6MM **Privately Held**
WEB: www.ncdynamics.com
SIC: 3728 Aircraft parts & equipment
PA: Harlow Aerostructures Llc
1501 S Mclean Blvd
Wichita KS 67213
316 265-5268

(P-20897)
NEILL AIRCRAFT CO
1260 W 15th St, Long Beach (90813-1390)
PHONE..............................562 432-7981
Judith L Carpenter, *President*
Robert Alvarez, *President*
Eddie Enriquez, *CFO*
Brad Barnett, *General Mgr*
Jesus Vejar, *Design Engr*
EMP: 275 **EST:** 1956
SQ FT: 150,000
SALES (est): 52.2MM **Privately Held**
WEB: www.neillaircraft.com
SIC: 3728 Aircraft body & wing assemblies
& parts

(P-20898)
ORCON AEROSPACE
2600 Central Ave Ste E, Union City
(94587-3187)
P.O. Box 2936, Douglas GA (31534-2936)
PHONE..............................510 489-8100
Hollis Bascom, *President*
Dennis Murray, *Vice Pres*
EMP: 150
SQ FT: 200,000
SALES (est): 13MM **Privately Held**
WEB: www.orcon.com
SIC: 3728 Aircraft parts & equipment

(P-20899)
OTTO INSTRUMENT SERVICE
INC (PA)
1441 Valencia Pl, Ontario (91761-7639)
PHONE..............................909 930-5800
William R Otto Jr, *President*
Elizabeth Otto, *Treasurer*
Ben Rosenthal, *Exec VP*
Richard Delman, *Vice Pres*
Lynnae Otto, *Vice Pres*
EMP: 135
SQ FT: 36,800
SALES (est): 29.5MM **Privately Held**
SIC: 3728 5088 7699 Aircraft parts &
equipment; aircraft equipment & supplies;
aircraft flight instrument repair

(P-20900)
PACIFIC AERO COMPONENTS
INC (PA)
Also Called: Aero Component Engineering
28887 Industry Dr, Valencia (91355-5419)
PHONE..............................818 841-9258
David Bill, *President*
Carmody Tom, *Marketing Staff*
EMP: 10
SQ FT: 4,000
SALES (est): 869.2K **Privately Held**
WEB: www.aerocomponent.com
SIC: 3728 3492 Aircraft assemblies, sub-
assemblies & parts; hose & tube fittings &
assemblies, hydraulic/pneumatic

(P-20901)
PACIFIC AIR INDUSTRIES INC
9650 De Soto Ave, Chatsworth
(91311-5012)
PHONE..............................310 829-4345
Paul H Ridley-Tree, *CEO*
Fred Gaunt, *President*
Sally Van Arnam, *Vice Pres*
Ron Munzlinger, *Purch Dir*
Tom Nolet, *VP Mktg*
▲ **EMP:** 45
SQ FT: 45,000
SALES (est): 5.6MM **Privately Held**
WEB: www.pac-air.com
SIC: 3728 Aircraft parts & equipment

(P-20902)
PACIFIC SKY SUPPLY INC
8230 San Fernando Rd, Sun Valley
(91352-3218)
PHONE..............................818 768-3700
Emilio B Perez, *CEO*
Emilio Perez, *President*

Valorie Stromer, *Executive*
Kelly Anderson, *Admin Sec*
Patrick Brocato, *Engineer*
EMP: 59
SQ FT: 27,000
SALES (est): 15.8MM **Privately Held**
WEB: www.pacsky.com
SIC: 3728 3724 5088 Aircraft parts &
equipment; aircraft engines & engine
parts; transportation equipment & sup-
plies

(P-20903)
PARAMOUNT PANELS INC
Also Called: California Plasteck
1531 E Cedar St, Ontario (91761-5762)
PHONE..............................909 947-5168
John Thorne, *Vice Pres*
Arthur Thorne, *President*
EMP: 30
SALES (corp-wide): 6.8MM **Privately
Held**
SIC: 3728 Aircraft parts & equipment
PA: Paramount Panels, Inc.
1531 E Cedar St
Ontario CA 91761
909 947-8008

(P-20904)
PARKER-HANNIFIN
CORPORATION
Also Called: Fluid Systems Division
16666 Von Karman Ave, Irvine
(92606-4997)
PHONE..............................216 896-2663
Greg Crowe, *General Mgr*
Robert Wells, *Engineer*
EMP: 100
SALES (corp-wide): 12B **Publicly Held**
WEB: www.parker.com
SIC: 3728 3724 Aircraft parts & equip-
ment; aircraft engines & engine parts
PA: Parker-Hannifin Corporation
6035 Parkland Blvd
Cleveland OH 44124
216 896-3000

(P-20905)
PARKER-HANNIFIN
CORPORATION
Also Called: Parker Aerospace
14300 Alton Pkwy, Irvine (92618-1898)
PHONE..............................949 833-3000
Robert Bond, *Branch Mgr*
James Beverly, *Executive*
Debbie Arizobal, *Program Mgr*
Scott Bierman, *Program Mgr*
Carl Kubat, *Program Mgr*
EMP: 101
SQ FT: 180,000
SALES (corp-wide): 14.3B **Publicly Held**
SIC: 3728 Aircraft assemblies, subassem-
blies & parts
PA: Parker-Hannifin Corporation
6035 Parkland Blvd
Cleveland OH 44124
216 896-3000

(P-20906)
PARKER-HANNIFIN
CORPORATION
Control Systems Division
14300 Alton Pkwy, Irvine (92618-1898)
PHONE..............................949 833-3000
Carl Moffitt, *General Mgr*
Michael Villa, *Design Engr*
William Bishop, *Engineer*
Steve Friend, *Engineer*
Jonathan Zolp, *Engineer*
EMP: 700
SALES (corp-wide): 12B **Publicly Held**
WEB: www.parker.com
SIC: 3728 Aircraft body & wing assemblies
& parts
PA: Parker-Hannifin Corporation
6035 Parkland Blvd
Cleveland OH 44124
216 896-3000

(P-20907)
PARKER-HANNIFIN
CORPORATION
Also Called: Stratoflex Product Division
3800 Calle Tecate, Camarillo (93012-5070)
PHONE..............................805 419-7000

William Cartmill, *Opers Mgr*
Philip Berg, *Engineer*
Ricardo Garcia, *Engineer*
Suzanne Schmitz, *Purch Dir*
Ronald Stone, *Senior Mgr*
EMP: 150
SALES (corp-wide): 14.3B **Publicly Held**
WEB: www.parker.com
SIC: 3728 3769 3568 Aircraft parts &
equipment; guided missile & space vehi-
cle parts & auxiliary equipment; power
transmission equipment
PA: Parker-Hannifin Corporation
6035 Parkland Blvd
Cleveland OH 44124
216 896-3000

(P-20908)
PCA AEROSPACE INC (PA)
17800 Gothard St, Huntington Beach
(92647-6217)
PHONE..............................714 841-1750
Brian Murray, *CEO*
Gregory Ruffalo, *COO*
▲ **EMP:** 71 **EST:** 1963
SQ FT: 58,000
SALES (est): 19MM **Privately Held**
WEB: www.pcaaerospace.com
SIC: 3728 3599 Aircraft parts & equip-
ment; machine shop, jobbing & repair

(P-20909)
PERFORMANCE PLASTICS INC
7919 Saint Andrews Ave, San Diego
(92154-8224)
PHONE..............................619 482-5031
Lance Brean, *President*
Karash Turpin, *COO*
Jeremiah Barrera, *Technology*
Rumiko Bemis, *Controller*
EMP: 140
SQ FT: 50,000
SALES (est): 27.5MM **Privately Held**
SIC: 3728 Aircraft parts & equipment

(P-20910)
PIEDRAS MACHINE
CORPORATION
15154 Downey Ave Ste B, Paramount
(90723-4595)
PHONE..............................562 602-1500
Salvador Piedra, *President*
Ruben Piedra, *CFO*
Monica Piedra, *Executive Asst*
Lucia Piedra, *Admin Sec*
EMP: 19
SALES: 1.2MM **Privately Held**
SIC: 3728 Aircraft parts & equipment

(P-20911)
PMC INC (HQ)
12243 Branford St, Sun Valley
(91352-1010)
PHONE..............................818 896-1101
Christopher Lette, *President*
Rick Wolfe, *General Mgr*
EMP: 36 **EST:** 1962
SALES (est): 542.7MM
SALES (corp-wide): 2.5B **Privately Held**
WEB: www.pmcwichita.com
SIC: 3728 3724 Bodies, aircraft; engine
mount parts, aircraft
PA: Pmc Global, Inc.
12243 Branford St
Sun Valley CA 91352
818 896-1101

(P-20912)
PRECISE AERO PRODUCTS INC
4120 Indus Way, Riverside (92503-4847)
PHONE..............................951 340-4554
Bud Andrews, *President*
Catherine Andrews, *Admin Sec*
EMP: 10
SQ FT: 5,414
SALES: 850K **Privately Held**
WEB: www.preciseaero.com
SIC: 3728 3599 Aircraft parts & equip-
ment; machine shop, jobbing & repair

(P-20913)
PRECISION AEROSPACE CORP
11155 Jersey Blvd Ste A, Rancho Cuca-
monga (91730-5148)
PHONE..............................909 945-9604
Jim Hudson, *President*

EMP: 70
SQ FT: 50,000
SALES (est): 15.1MM **Privately Held**
WEB: www.pac.cc
SIC: 3728 Aircraft assemblies, subassem-
blies & parts

(P-20914)
PRECISION TUBE BENDING
13626 Talc St, Santa Fe Springs
(90670-5173)
PHONE..............................562 921-6723
Diane M Williams, *CEO*
Harry Rowe, *General Mgr*
Lisa Gomez, *Admin Asst*
Bonnie Lazzareschi, *VP Finance*
Charles Thomas, *Mfg Staff*
EMP: 98
SQ FT: 60,000
SALES (est): 27.7MM **Privately Held**
WEB: www.precision-tube-bending.com
SIC: 3728 Aircraft parts & equipment

(P-20915)
PRISM MFG
3057 12th St, Riverside (92507)
PHONE..............................310 538-3857
Eng Tan, *CEO*
Teng Tan, *Vice Pres*
Jeff Gove, *General Mgr*
EMP: 25
SQ FT: 135,000
SALES: 3MM **Privately Held**
SIC: 3728 Aircraft body assemblies & parts

(P-20916)
PROGRAMMED COMPOSITES
INC
250 Klug Cir, Corona (92880-5409)
PHONE..............................951 520-7300
Fax: 951 520-7300
EMP: 250
SALES: 20MM
SALES (corp-wide): 3.1B **Publicly Held**
SIC: 3728 3769
PA: Orbital Atk, Inc.
45101 Warp Dr
Dulles VA 20166
703 406-5000

(P-20917)
PTI TECHNOLOGIES INC (DH)
501 Del Norte Blvd, Oxnard (93030-7983)
PHONE..............................805 604-3700
Sam Chapetta, *President*
Kanwar Suri, *Senior VP*
Beth Kozlowski, *Vice Pres*
Jim Martin, *Vice Pres*
Laura Aguilar, *Admin Asst*
▲ **EMP:** 212
SQ FT: 225,000
SALES (est): 29.8MM
SALES (corp-wide): 685.7MM **Publicly
Held**
WEB: www.ptitechnologies.com
SIC: 3728 Aircraft parts & equipment
HQ: Esco Technologies Holding Llc
9900 Clayton Rd Ste A
Saint Louis MO 63124
314 213-7200

(P-20918)
Q1 TEST INC
1100 S Grove Ave Ste B2, Ontario
(91761-4574)
PHONE..............................909 390-9718
Allen Riley, *CEO*
Jason Riley, *President*
EMP: 21
SQ FT: 10,500
SALES (est): 2.5MM **Privately Held**
SIC: 3728 Turret test fixtures, aircraft

(P-20919)
QUALITY FORMING LLC
Also Called: Qfi Prv Aerospace
22906 Frampton Ave, Torrance
(90501-5035)
PHONE..............................310 539-2855
Mark Severns, *President*
▲ **EMP:** 100

▲ = Import ▼=Export
◆ =Import/Export

SALES (est): 22.2MM
SALES (corp-wide): 195.8MM **Privately Held**
WEB: www.qfinc.com
SIC: **3728** Aircraft assemblies, subassemblies & parts
HQ: Qpi Holdings, Inc.
22906 Frampton Ave
Torrance CA 90501
310 539-2855

(P-20920)
RAM AEROSPACE INC
4010 N Palm St Ste 101, Fullerton (92835-1030)
PHONE..................................714 853-1703
Rajen Rathod, *CEO*
Ravin Rathod, *President*
EMP: 10
SQ FT: 8,000
SALES (est): 1.1MM **Privately Held**
WEB: www.rjproductsllc.com
SIC: **3728** 3599 3769 Aircraft parts & equipment; machine shop, jobbing & repair; guided missile & space vehicle parts & auxiliary equipment

(P-20921)
ROGERS HOLDING COMPANY INC
Also Called: V & M Precision Grinding Co.
1130 Columbia St, Brea (92821-2921)
PHONE..................................714 257-4850
Aldo Devile, *Principal*
Maynard Hallman, *Partner*
Tom Rogers, *Vice Pres*
Carlos Gonzalez, *Program Mgr*
William Fickling 1111, *Program Mgr*
EMP: 30 EST: 1946
SQ FT: 65,000
SALES: 5MM **Privately Held**
WEB: www.vm-machining.com
SIC: **3728** Alighting (landing gear) assemblies, aircraft

(P-20922)
ROHR INC (HQ)
Also Called: UTC Aerospace Systems Company
850 Lagoon Dr, Chula Vista (91910-2001)
PHONE..................................619 691-4111
Greg Peters, *President*
Curtis Reusser, *President*
Laurence A Chapman, *CFO*
Brian Broderick, *Vice Pres*
Robert A Gustafson, *Vice Pres*
▲ EMP: 2100
SQ FT: 2,770,000
SALES (est): 989.9MM
SALES (corp-wide): 59.8B **Publicly Held**
SIC: **3728** Nacelles, aircraft
PA: United Technologies Corporation
10 Farm Springs Rd
Farmington CT 06032
860 728-7000

(P-20923)
RSA ENGINEERED PRODUCTS LLC
110 W Cochran St Ste A, Simi Valley (93065-6228)
PHONE..................................805 584-4150
Ray Scarcello, *President*
Leslie Fernandes, *President*
Scott Leeds, *CFO*
John Yi, *Program Mgr*
Cindy Estrada, *Administration*
◆ EMP: 90
SQ FT: 43,000
SALES: 25MM **Privately Held**
SIC: **3728** Aircraft parts & equipment

(P-20924)
SANDERS COMPOSITES INC (DH)
Also Called: Sanders Composites Industries
4075 Ruffin Rd, San Diego (92123-1817)
PHONE..................................858 571-5220
Larry O'Toole, *CEO*
Larry O'Toole, *CEO*
Melissa Rainey, *Financial Analy*
EMP: 44
SQ FT: 44,400

SALES (est): 9.4MM
SALES (corp-wide): 182.4MM **Privately Held**
WEB: www.sanderscomposites.com
SIC: **3728** Aircraft assemblies, subassemblies & parts
HQ: Sanders Industries
3701 E Conant St
Long Beach CA 90808
562 354-2920

(P-20925)
SANTA MONICA PROPELLER SVC INC
3135 Dnald Douglas Loop S, Santa Monica (90405-3210)
PHONE..................................310 390-6233
Leonid Polyakov, *CEO*
Edward Polyakov, *Administration*
▲ EMP: 15
SQ FT: 11,000
SALES (est): 2.1MM **Privately Held**
WEB: www.santamonicapropeller.com
SIC: **3728** 5088 Aircraft propellers & associated equipment; aircraft assemblies, subassemblies & parts; aircraft & parts

(P-20926)
SANTOS PRECISION INC
2220 S Anne St, Santa Ana (92704-4411)
PHONE..................................714 957-0299
Francisco Santos, *President*
Evelyn Santos, *Corp Secy*
Richard Santos, *Vice Pres*
EMP: 34 EST: 1979
SQ FT: 14,800
SALES (est): 8.5MM **Privately Held**
WEB: www.santosprecision.com
SIC: **3728** Aircraft parts & equipment

(P-20927)
SEAMAN PRODUCTS OF CALIFORNIA
12329 Gladstone Ave, Sylmar (91342-5319)
PHONE..................................818 361-2012
Carol Haisten, *President*
EMP: 17
SQ FT: 13,000
SALES (est): 2.3MM **Privately Held**
SIC: **3728** Aircraft assemblies, subassemblies & parts

(P-20928)
SEHANSON INC
2121 E Via Burton, Anaheim (92806-1220)
PHONE..................................714 778-1900
Stanley E Hanson, *President*
Sergio Rodriguez, *COO*
Christopher J Jones, *CFO*
Judy Trumbull, *Executive*
Marty Michael, *General Mgr*
EMP: 40 EST: 2000
SQ FT: 18,000
SALES (est): 6.9MM **Privately Held**
WEB: www.acraaerospace.com
SIC: **3728** 3429 Aircraft parts & equipment; manufactured hardware (general)

(P-20929)
SENIOR OPERATIONS LLC
Senior Aerospace SSP
2980 N San Fernando Blvd, Burbank (91504-2522)
PHONE..................................818 260-2900
Launie Flemning, *Manager*
Halston Howard, *Program Mgr*
Aurora Mendoza, *Administration*
Stephenie Hill, *Info Tech Mgr*
Antonio Rojas, *Info Tech Mgr*
EMP: 380
SALES (corp-wide): 1.3B **Privately Held**
SIC: **3728** 3599 Aircraft parts & equipment; bellows, industrial: metal
HQ: Senior Operations Llc
300 E Devon Ave
Bartlett IL 60103
630 837-1811

(P-20930)
SHIM-IT CORPORATION
1691 California Ave, Corona (92881-3375)
PHONE..................................562 467-8600
Jeff Johnson, *President*
Joe Carrillo, *Vice Pres*
Diane Hesson, *Vice Pres*

Rosa Aleman, *General Mgr*
Heidi Stout, *General Mgr*
EMP: 13 EST: 1961
SQ FT: 8,500
SALES (est): 1.3MM **Privately Held**
SIC: **3728** 3542 Aircraft parts & equipment; machine tools, metal forming type

(P-20931)
SHIMTECH INDUSTRIES US INC
29101 The Old Rd, Valencia (91355-1014)
PHONE..................................661 295-8620
Scott Wilkinson, *CFO*
EMP: 99
SQ FT: 75,000
SALES (est): 2.8MM **Privately Held**
SIC: **3728** Aircraft parts & equipment

(P-20932)
SIMCARDZ4U INC
818 W 7th St Fl 6, Los Angeles (90017-3407)
PHONE..................................213 359-0602
Noah Benchimol, *CEO*
EMP: 10
SALES (est): 490.5K **Privately Held**
SIC: **3728** Target drones

(P-20933)
SKYLOCK INDUSTRIES
1290 W Optical Dr, Azusa (91702-3249)
PHONE..................................626 334-2391
Jeff Creoiserat, *Ch of Bd*
Jim Pease, *President*
Candy Perez, *Office Mgr*
Bruce Shih, *Info Tech Mgr*
Bill Phillips, *Project Engr*
EMP: 70
SQ FT: 14,000
SALES (est): 16.2MM **Privately Held**
WEB: www.skylock.com
SIC: **3728** Aircraft parts & equipment

(P-20934)
SOUTHWEST MACHINE & PLASTIC CO
Also Called: Southwest Plastics Co
620 W Foothill Blvd, Glendora (91741-2403)
PHONE..................................626 963-6919
W Thomas Jorgensen, *President*
Alfred D Jorgensen, *Vice Pres*
▲ EMP: 30 EST: 1937
SALES (est): 4.5MM **Privately Held**
SIC: **3728** 3089 3544 Aircraft parts & equipment; injection molding of plastics; special dies, tools, jigs & fixtures

(P-20935)
SPACE-LOK INC
13306 Halldale Ave, Gardena (90249-2204)
P.O. Box 2919 (90247-1119)
PHONE..................................310 527-6150
Scott F Wade, *President*
Jeffrey Wade, *CFO*
EMP: 138 EST: 1962
SALES (est): 12.3MM
SALES (corp-wide): 163.1MM **Privately Held**
WEB: www.space-lok.com
SIC: **3728** 3542 3812 3452 Aircraft assemblies, subassemblies & parts; machine tools, metal forming type; search & navigation equipment; bolts, nuts, rivets & washers
HQ: Novaria Fastening Systems, Llc
6300 Ridglea Pl Ste 800
Fort Worth TX 76116
817 381-3810

(P-20936)
SPACEAGE CONTROL INC
4001 Inglewood Ave # 101, Redondo Beach (90278-1121)
PHONE..................................661 206-6666
Thomas M Anderson III, *General Mgr*
Thomas Anderson, *Vice Pres*
Jeff Simpson, *Marketing Mgr*
Tom Anderson, *Manager*
EMP: 25 EST: 1968
SQ FT: 5,000

SALES (est): 3.5MM **Privately Held**
SIC: **3728** 3679 3829 3825 Aircraft parts & equipment; electronic circuits; aircraft & motor vehicle measurement equipment; instruments to measure electricity; conveyors & conveying equipment

(P-20937)
STEECON INC
5362 Indl Dr, Huntington Beach (92649)
PHONE..................................714 895-5313
Charles Steel, *CEO*
Chris Steel, *CEO*
Linda Steel, *Project Mgr*
Matt Hanson, *Engineer*
Aaron Casanova, *Purch Mgr*
EMP: 11
SQ FT: 12,000
SALES (est): 3MM **Privately Held**
WEB: www.steecon.com
SIC: **3728** Aircraft body assemblies & parts

(P-20938)
STOCKTON PROPELLER INC
2478 Wilcox Rd, Stockton (95215-2319)
PHONE..................................209 982-4000
Robert C Hake, *President*
EMP: 10
SQ FT: 8,000
SALES (est): 1.2MM **Privately Held**
WEB: www.stocktonpropeller.com
SIC: **3728** Aircraft propellers & associated equipment

(P-20939)
STRATOFLIGHT (DH)
Also Called: Western Methods
25540 Rye Canyon Rd, Valencia (91355-1109)
PHONE..................................949 622-0700
Joseph I Snowden, *CEO*
▲ EMP: 81
SALES (est): 30MM
SALES (corp-wide): 242.1B **Publicly Held**
WEB: www.stratoflightcorp.com
SIC: **3728** Aircraft parts & equipment
HQ: Precision Castparts Corp.
4650 Sw Mcdam Ave Ste 300
Portland OR 97239
503 946-4800

(P-20940)
SUNGEAR INC
8535 Arjons Dr Ste G, San Diego (92126-4360)
PHONE..................................858 549-3166
Don Brown, *President*
Randall Palinski, *Vice Pres*
EMP: 42
SQ FT: 16,000
SALES (est): 8.5MM
SALES (corp-wide): 50.5MM **Privately Held**
WEB: www.sungearinc.com
SIC: **3728** Gears, aircraft power transmission
PA: H-D Advanced Manufacturing Company
2200 Georgetown Dr # 300
Sewickley PA 15143
724 759-2850

(P-20941)
SUNVAIR OVERHAUL INC
Also Called: A H Plating
29145 The Old Rd, Valencia (91355-1015)
PHONE..................................661 257-6123
John Waschak, *CEO*
Robert Waschak, *Officer*
Timothy Waschak, *Officer*
EMP: 45
SQ FT: 35,000
SALES (est): 5.5MM **Privately Held**
SIC: **3728** 5088 Alighting (landing gear) assemblies, aircraft; aircraft & parts

(P-20942)
SYMBOLIC DISPLAYS INC
1917 E Saint Andrew Pl, Santa Ana (92705-5143)
PHONE..................................714 258-2811
Candy Suits, *CEO*
▼ EMP: 76 EST: 1964
SQ FT: 15,860

SALES: 10.6MM **Privately Held**
WEB: www.symbolicdisplays.com
SIC: **3728** 3812 3577 Aircraft parts & equipment; search & navigation equipment; computer peripheral equipment

(P-20943)
T & F SHEET METALS FAB
15607 New Century Dr, Gardena (90248-2128)
PHONE..................................310 516-8548
Thomas Medina, *President*
Hector Medina, *Vice Pres*
EMP: 32
SQ FT: 9,800
SALES: 3.5MM **Privately Held**
SIC: **3728** Aircraft parts & equipment

(P-20944)
T M W ENGINEERING INC
14810 S San Pedro St, Gardena (90248-2000)
PHONE..................................310 768-8211
Bernard Welsch, *President*
EMP: 10
SQ FT: 5,552
SALES (est): 800K **Privately Held**
WEB: www.tmwengineering.com
SIC: **3728** 8711 3599 Aircraft parts & equipment; industrial engineers; machine shop, jobbing & repair

(P-20945)
TCA PRECISION PRODUCTS LLC
Also Called: V&M Prcsion Machining Grinding
1130 Columbia St, Brea (92821-2921)
PHONE..................................714 257-4850
Gregory Felix,
Alyce Schreiber,
EMP: 14
SALES (est): 671.1K **Privately Held**
SIC: **3728** Aircraft parts & equipment

(P-20946)
TDG AEROSPACE INC
545 Corporate Dr, Escondido (92029-1500)
PHONE..................................760 466-1040
Virginia Richard, *Ch of Bd*
Gerry Bench, *President*
Fred Bond, *CFO*
EMP: 18
SQ FT: 13,000
SALES (est): 4MM **Privately Held**
WEB: www.tdgaerospace.com
SIC: **3728** Aircraft parts & equipment

(P-20947)
TDK MACHINING
10772 Capital Ave Ste 7n, Garden Grove (92843-4969)
PHONE..................................714 554-4166
Kenney Nguyen, *President*
EMP: 10 EST: 1998
SALES (est): 1.7MM **Privately Held**
SIC: **3728** Aircraft parts & equipment

(P-20948)
THALES AVIONICS
48 Discovery, Irvine (92618-3151)
PHONE..................................949 381-3033
Dominique Giannoni, *Owner*
EMP: 15 EST: 2017
SALES (est): 1.6MM **Privately Held**
SIC: **3728** Aircraft parts & equipment

(P-20949)
THALES AVIONICS INC
Also Called: Inflight Entrmt & Connectivity
51 Discovery, Irvine (92618-3119)
PHONE..................................949 790-2500
Brad Foreman, *Manager*
Andy White, *Project Engr*
Richard Lopez, *Manager*
EMP: 225
SALES (corp-wide): 305.4MM **Privately Held**
SIC: **3728** 3663 Aircraft parts & equipment; radio & TV communications equipment
HQ: Thales Avionics, Inc.
140 Centennial Ave
Piscataway NJ 08854
732 242-6300

(P-20950)
THOMPSON INDUSTRIES LTD
Also Called: Thompson ADB Industries
7155 Fenwick Ln, Westminster (92683-5218)
PHONE..................................310 679-9193
Werner Lieberherr, *CEO*
EMP: 21
SQ FT: 52,000
SALES (est): 8MM **Publicly Held**
WEB: www.thompsonindustriesltd.com
SIC: **3728** Aircraft parts & equipment
HQ: B/E Aerospace, Inc.
1400 Corporate Center Way
Wellington FL 33414
561 791-5000

(P-20951)
TMC AEROSPACE INC
2865 Pullman St, Santa Ana (92705-5713)
PHONE..................................949 250-4999
Scott Holland, *President*
Bob Yari, *President*
William Gresher, *CFO*
Jean White, *Info Tech Mgr*
EMP: 40
SALES (est): 323.1K **Privately Held**
SIC: **3728** Aircraft parts & equipment

(P-20952)
TMW CORPORATION (PA)
Also Called: Crown Discount Tools
15148 Bledsoe St, Sylmar (91342-3807)
PHONE..................................818 362-5665
William Windette, *President*
Gary Berger, *Vice Pres*
EMP: 110 EST: 1973
SQ FT: 115,000
SALES (est): 10.5MM **Privately Held**
SIC: **3728** Aircraft landing assemblies & brakes

(P-20953)
TOPNOTCH QUALITY WORKS INC
12455 Branford St Ste 8, Pacoima (91331-3461)
PHONE..................................818 897-7679
Eric Wong, *Vice Pres*
Veerayakit Patcsaranaparat, *President*
EMP: 10
SALES: 800K **Privately Held**
SIC: **3728** Aircraft parts & equipment

(P-20954)
TRANSDIGM INC
Also Called: Adel Wiggins Group
5000 Triggs St, Commerce (90022-4833)
P.O. Box 14088, Newark NJ (07198-0088)
PHONE..................................323 269-9181
Brady Fitzpatrick, *Branch Mgr*
Katrina Ureno, *Administration*
Ken Ong, *Info Tech Mgr*
Chris Quang, *Design Engr*
Darryl Sparks, *Engineer*
EMP: 50
SALES (corp-wide): 3.5B **Publicly Held**
WEB: www.electromotion.com
SIC: **3728** Aircraft parts & equipment
HQ: Transdigm, Inc.
4223 Monticello Blvd
Cleveland OH 44121

(P-20955)
TRANSDIGM INC
Adel Wiggins Grp-Commercial Div
5000 Triggs St, Commerce (90022-4833)
P.O. Box 22228, Los Angeles (90022-0228)
PHONE..................................323 269-9181
Cindy Terakawa, *Branch Mgr*
EMP: 163
SALES (corp-wide): 3.5B **Publicly Held**
WEB: www.electromotion.com
SIC: **3728** 3365 Aircraft parts & equipment; aerospace castings, aluminum
HQ: Transdigm, Inc.
4223 Monticello Blvd
Cleveland OH 44121

(P-20956)
TRANSDIGM INC
Adel Wggins Grup- Military Div
5000 Triggs St, Commerce (90022-4833)
P.O. Box 22228, Los Angeles (90022-0228)
PHONE..................................323 269-9181
Brady Fitzpatrick, *Branch Mgr*
EMP: 163
SALES (corp-wide): 3.5B **Publicly Held**
WEB: www.electromotion.com
SIC: **3728** 3365 Aircraft parts & equipment; aerospace castings, aluminum
HQ: Transdigm, Inc.
4223 Monticello Blvd
Cleveland OH 44121

(P-20957)
TRI-FITTING MFG COMPANY
10414 Rush St, South El Monte (91733-3344)
PHONE..................................626 442-2000
Ralph Bernal, *President*
EMP: 15 EST: 1977
SQ FT: 13,000
SALES (est): 2.6MM **Privately Held**
SIC: **3728** 3494 3492 Aircraft assemblies, subassemblies & parts; valves & pipe fittings; fluid power valves & hose fittings

(P-20958)
TRI-TECH PRECISION INC
1863 N Case St, Orange (92865-4234)
PHONE..................................714 970-1363
Ernie Husted, *President*
EMP: 17
SALES (est): 2.9MM **Privately Held**
SIC: **3728** 3544 Aircraft parts & equipment; special dies, tools, jigs & fixtures

(P-20959)
TRIO MANUFACTURING INC
601 Lairport St, El Segundo (90245-5005)
PHONE..................................310 640-6123
Michael Hunkins, *President*
Brian Hunkins, *Vice Pres*
▲ EMP: 60
SALES (est): 18.8MM **Privately Held**
WEB: www.triomanufacturing.com
SIC: **3728** 3829 3812 3663 Aircraft parts & equipment; measuring & controlling devices; search & navigation equipment; radio & TV communications equipment

(P-20960)
TRIUMPH ACTUATION SYSTMS-VALEN
28150 Harrison Pkwy, Valencia (91355-4109)
PHONE..................................661 295-1015
Daniel J Crowley, *President*
Jim McCabe, *CFO*
Lance Turner, *Senior VP*
John B Wright II, *Senior VP*
Gary Tenison, *Vice Pres*
EMP: 250
SALES (est): 76.6MM **Publicly Held**
WEB: www.efs-calif.com
SIC: **3728** Aircraft parts & equipment
PA: Triumph Group, Inc.
899 Cassatt Rd Ste 210
Berwyn PA 19312

(P-20961)
TRIUMPH EQUIPMENT INC
13434 S Ontario Ave, Ontario (91761-7956)
PHONE..................................909 947-5983
Brigitte A De Laura, *President*
EMP: 35
SQ FT: 2,700
SALES (est): 2.3MM **Privately Held**
SIC: **3728** Aircraft parts & equipment

(P-20962)
TRIUMPH FABRICATIONS
Also Called: Triumph Fbrication - San Diego
203 N Johnson Ave, El Cajon (92020-3111)
PHONE..................................619 440-2504
Richard C III, *CEO*
Mark Gobin, *President*
Nancy Ravy, *Buyer*
Bob Vildibill, *Director*
EMP: 160

SALES (est): 39.2MM **Publicly Held**
WEB: www.triumphgrp.com
SIC: **3728** Aircraft body & wing assemblies & parts
PA: Triumph Group, Inc.
899 Cassatt Rd Ste 210
Berwyn PA 19312

(P-20963)
TRIUMPH INSULATION SYSTEMS
2401 Portico Blvd, Calexico (92231-9604)
PHONE..................................760 768-1700
Manuel Estrada, *Manager*
▲ EMP: 13
SALES (est): 3.2MM **Privately Held**
SIC: **3728** Aircraft parts & equipment

(P-20964)
TRIYAR CAPITAL CALIFORNIA LLC (PA)
10850 Wilshire Blvd, Los Angeles (90024-4305)
PHONE..................................310 441-5654
Steven Yari, *Mng Member*
Bob Yari, *Mng Member*
EMP: 10
SALES (est): 1.2MM **Privately Held**
SIC: **3728** 6719 Aircraft parts & equipment; investment holding companies, except banks

(P-20965)
UNITED STATES DEPT OF NAVY
Also Called: Naval Maint Training Group
672 13th St Ste 1, Port Hueneme (93042-5011)
PHONE..................................805 989-5402
Dave Atkins, *Branch Mgr*
EMP: 30 **Publicly Held**
SIC: **3728** 9711 Aircraft training equipment; Navy
HQ: United States Department Of The Navy
1200 Navy Pentagon
Washington DC 20350

(P-20966)
UNITED TECHNOLOGIES CORP
Also Called: UTC Aerospace Systems
11120 Norwalk Blvd, Santa Fe Springs (90670-3830)
PHONE..................................562 944-6244
Louis R Chenevert, *CEO*
Andrew Szumlas, *General Mgr*
EMP: 20
SALES (est): 2.9MM **Privately Held**
SIC: **3728** 3312 Brakes, aircraft; wheels

(P-20967)
UNITED TECHNOLOGIES CORP
Also Called: UTC Aerospace Systems
8200 Arlington Ave, Riverside (92503-0428)
PHONE..................................951 351-5400
Leland Walley, *Vice Pres*
Shirin Folsom, *General Mgr*
Brian Rock, *Programmer Anys*
Dave Craghead, *Research*
Richard Pekarske, *Research*
EMP: 33
SALES (corp-wide): 59.8B **Publicly Held**
WEB: www.bfgoodrich.com
SIC: **3728** 8711 3724 Aviation &/or aeronautical engineering; aircraft engines & engine parts; aircraft landing assemblies & brakes
PA: United Technologies Corporation
10 Farm Springs Rd
Farmington CT 06032
860 728-7000

(P-20968)
VANTAGE ASSOCIATES INC
Also Called: Vantage Master Machine Company
900 Civic Center Dr, National City (91950-1013)
PHONE..................................619 477-6940
Paul Roy, *Branch Mgr*
EMP: 40
SALES (corp-wide): 63.6MM **Privately Held**
SIC: **3728** Aircraft assemblies, subassemblies & parts

▲ = Import ▼=Export
◆ =Import/Export

PA: Vantage Associates Inc.
900 Civic Center Dr
National City CA 91950
619 477-6940

(P-20969)
VENTURA AEROSPACE INC
31355 Agoura Rd, Westlake Village
(91361-4610)
PHONE.....................818 540-3130
Mark L Snow, *CEO*
Michael Snow, *Vice Pres*
EMP: 16
SQ FT: 2,000
SALES (est): 4.2MM Privately Held
WEB: www.venturaaerospace.com
SIC: 3728 Aircraft parts & equipment

(P-20970)
WESANCO INC
14870 Desman Rd, La Mirada
(90638-5746)
PHONE.....................714 739-4989
Andrew D Shyer, *President*
Sean Mackenzie, *Vice Pres*
Karen Allison, *Office Mgr*
Sandra Alford, *Financial Exec*
▲ EMP: 30
SQ FT: 30,000
SALES: 12MM
SALES (corp-wide): 82.9MM Privately Held
WEB: www.wesanco.com
SIC: 3728 Oleo struts, aircraft
HQ: Zsi-Foster, Inc.
45065 Michigan Ave
Canton MI 48188

(P-20971)
WESTERN METHODS MACHINERY CORP
2344 Pullman St, Santa Ana (92705-5507)
PHONE.....................949 252-6600
Mark Heasley, *President*
EMP: 120 EST: 1977
SALES (est): 15MM Privately Held
WEB: www.compassaerospace.com
SIC: 3728 3769 Aircraft parts & equipment; guided missile & space vehicle parts & auxiliary equipment

(P-20972)
WHITTAKER CORPORATION
1955 Surveyor Ave Fl 2, Simi Valley
(93063-3369)
PHONE.....................805 526-5700
Erick Lardiere, *President*
▲ EMP: 40
SQ FT: 276,000
SALES (est): 12.4MM
SALES (corp-wide): 2.6B Privately Held
WEB: www.whittakercorporation.com
SIC: 3728 3669 7373 Aircraft parts & equipment; fire detection systems, electric; smoke detectors; systems integration services
PA: Meggitt Plc
Atlantic House, Aviation Park West
Christchurch BH23
120 259-7597

(P-20973)
WILLIAMS AEROSPACE & MFG INC
2820 Via Orange Way Ste G, Spring Valley
(91978-1742)
PHONE.....................619 660-6220
William L Cary, *President*
Shane Nonthavet, *Vice Pres*
Allison Sauer,
EMP: 23
SQ FT: 16,000
SALES: 6MM Privately Held
SIC: 3728 Aircraft parts & equipment

(P-20974)
WOODWARD HRT INC
1700 Business Center Dr, Duarte
(91010-2859)
PHONE.....................626 359-9211
Brian Langan, *Branch Mgr*
Carol Borchers, *General Mgr*
Oshin Eskandarian, *Technology*
Tom Lio, *Engineer*
Anthony McClarnon, *Engineer*

EMP: 400
SALES (corp-wide): 2.3B Publicly Held
SIC: 3728 3492 Aircraft assemblies, sub-assemblies & parts; electrohydraulic servo valves, metal
HQ: Woodward Hrt, Inc.
25200 Rye Canyon Rd
Santa Clarita CA 91355
661 294-6000

(P-20975)
WOODWARD HRT INC
Also Called: Woodward Duarte
1700 Business Center Dr, Duarte
(91010-2859)
PHONE.....................626 359-9211
Don Grimes, *Manager*
Dennis Cain, *Engineer*
EMP: 250
SALES (corp-wide): 2.3B Publicly Held
SIC: 3728 5084 Aircraft parts & equipment; hydraulic systems equipment & supplies
HQ: Woodward Hrt, Inc.
25200 Rye Canyon Rd
Santa Clarita CA 91355
661 294-6000

(P-20976)
YEAGER MANUFACTURING CORP (PA)
Also Called: Cummins Aerospace
2200 E Orangethorpe Ave, Anaheim
(92806-1229)
PHONE.....................714 879-2800
William B Cummins, *CEO*
Sean Cummins, *President*
Nieves Medina, *Train & Dev Mgr*
Rebecca Morehead, *Pediatrics*
EMP: 40
SQ FT: 35,000
SALES (est): 5.7MM Privately Held
WEB: www.cumminsaerospace.com
SIC: 3728 3812 3519 Aircraft parts & equipment; search & navigation equipment; internal combustion engines

(P-20977)
ZENITH MANUFACTURING INC
Also Called: Zipco
11129 Dora St, Sun Valley (91352-3339)
PHONE.....................818 767-2106
James Phoung, *President*
EMP: 25
SQ FT: 47,000
SALES: 3MM Privately Held
SIC: 3728 Aircraft parts & equipment

(P-20978)
ZODIAC AEROSPACE
7330 Lincoln Way, Garden Grove
(92841-1427)
PHONE.....................714 891-0683
David Ronnenburg, *President*
Tuyen Bui, *Design Engr*
Tracy Doan, *Engineer*
Enguerrand Guilloux, *Buyer*
Rusty Canevari, *Opers Mgr*
EMP: 15
SALES (corp-wide): 650.9MM Privately Held
SIC: 3728 Aircraft parts & equipment
HQ: Zodiac Aerospace
Cs20001
Plaisir 78370
161 342-323

(P-20979)
ZODIAC CABIN & STRUCTURES
1945 S Grove Ave, Ontario (91761-5616)
PHONE.....................909 947-4115
Lek Makpaiboon, *General Mgr*
Yolly Leyva, *Clerk*
EMP: 13
SALES (est): 1.9MM
SALES (corp-wide): 650.9MM Privately Held
SIC: 3728 Aircraft parts & equipment
HQ: Zodiac Aerospace
Cs20001
Plaisir 78370
161 342-323

(P-20980)
ZODIAC SEAT SHELLS US LLC
2641 Airpark Dr, Santa Maria (93455-1415)
PHONE.....................805 922-5995
Klaus Koester, *CEO*
Manolito Corpuz, *Engineer*
EMP: 650
SALES (est): 143.3MM
SALES (corp-wide): 650.9MM Privately Held
SIC: 3728 Aircraft parts & equipment
HQ: Zodiac Seats Us Llc
2000 Weber Dr
Gainesville TX 76240
940 668-4825

(P-20981)
ZODIAC WATER&WASTE AERO SYSTEM
Also Called: Monogram Systems
1500 Glenn Curtiss St, Carson
(90746-4012)
PHONE.....................310 884-7000
David Conrad, *Vice Pres*
Edward Gloss, *Engineer*
EMP: 39 EST: 1958
SALES (est): 10.9MM
SALES (corp-wide): 650.9MM Privately Held
SIC: 3728 Aircraft parts & equipment
HQ: Zodiac Aerospace
Cs20001
Plaisir 78370
161 342-323

(P-20982)
ZODIAK SERVICES AMERICA
6734 Valjean Ave, Van Nuys (91406-5818)
PHONE.....................310 884-7200
Lou Pedonne, *President*
EMP: 56 EST: 2000
SQ FT: 10,000
SALES (est): 5.2MM
SALES (corp-wide): 650.9MM Privately Held
WEB: www.aircruisers.com
SIC: 3728 5088 Oxygen systems, aircraft; transportation equipment & supplies
HQ: Air Cruisers Company, Llc
1747 State Route 34
Wall Township NJ 07727
732 681-3527

3731 Shipbuilding & Repairing

(P-20983)
ALLIANCE TECHNICAL SVCS INC
1785 Utah Ave, Lompoc (93437-6020)
PHONE.....................805 606-3020
EMP: 12
SQ FT: 5,734
SALES (corp-wide): 10.2MM Privately Held
SIC: 3731
PA: Alliance Technical Services, Inc.
400 W 24th St
Norfolk VA 23517
757 628-9500

(P-20984)
APR ENGINEERING INC
Also Called: Oceanwide Repairs
1812 W 9th St, Long Beach (90813-2614)
P.O. Box 9100 (90810-0100)
PHONE.....................562 983-3800
Roy Herington, *President*
Trina Young, *Treasurer*
Nicholas Berry, *Purchasing*
Trina Caracoza, *Manager*
▲ EMP: 33
SALES (est): 6.8MM Privately Held
WEB: www.oceanwiderepair.com
SIC: 3731 Shipbuilding & repairing

(P-20985)
BAE SYSTEMS SAN DIEGO (DH)
2205 Belt St, San Diego (92113-3634)
P.O. Box 13308 (92170-3308)
PHONE.....................619 238-1000
Erwin Bieber, *President*
James M Blue, *Vice Pres*

Alice M Eldridge, *Vice Pres*
Karen Odermatt, *Executive Asst*
David Dekkers, *Admin Sec*
◆ EMP: 166 EST: 1976
SALES (est): 225.7MM
SALES (corp-wide): 24.2B Privately Held
WEB: www.baesystems-sandiego-shiprepair.com
SIC: 3731 Shipbuilding & repairing; barges, building & repairing; lighters, marine: building & repairing; ferryboats, building & repairing
HQ: Bae Systems Ship Repair Inc.
750 W Berkley Ave
Norfolk VA 23523
757 494-4000

(P-20986)
BAE SYSTEMS SAN DIEGO
7330 Engineer Rd Ste A, San Diego
(92111-1434)
P.O. Box 13308 (92170-3308)
PHONE.....................619 238-1000
EMP: 370
SALES (corp-wide): 24.2B Privately Held
SIC: 3731 Barges, building & repairing
HQ: Bae Systems San Diego Ship Repair Inc.
2205 Belt St
San Diego CA 92113
619 238-1000

(P-20987)
BAY CITY MARINE INC
1625 Cleveland Ave, National City
(91950-4212)
PHONE.....................619 477-3991
Fred Hays, *Manager*
EMP: 25
SALES (corp-wide): 4.8MM Privately Held
WEB: www.baycitymarine.com
SIC: 3731 Military ships, building & repairing
PA: Bay City Marine, Inc.
1625 Cleveland Ave
National City CA 91950
619 477-3991

(P-20988)
BAY SHIP & YACHT CO (PA)
2900 Main St Ste 2100, Alameda
(94501-7739)
PHONE.....................510 337-9122
William Elliott, *CEO*
Bill Elliott, *President*
Vicki Elliott, *Treasurer*
Alan Cameron, *Vice Pres*
Gerona Goethe, *Principal*
▲ EMP: 210
SQ FT: 20,000
SALES (est): 85.1MM Privately Held
WEB: www.bay-ship.com
SIC: 3731 3732 Commercial cargo ships, building & repairing; combat vessels, building & repairing; barges, building & repairing; yachts, building & repairing

(P-20989)
COASTAL DECKING INC
2050 Wilson Ave Ste A, National City
(91950-6500)
PHONE.....................619 477-0567
Frank Safely, *President*
EMP: 24
SQ FT: 3,000
SALES (est): 2.6MM Privately Held
SIC: 3731 Shipbuilding & repairing

(P-20990)
COASTAL MARINE MAINT CO LLC (PA)
Also Called: Cmmc
250 W Wardlow Rd, Long Beach
(90807-4429)
PHONE.....................562 432-8066
Joe Gregorio,
Gary Beale,
Erick Garcia,
▲ EMP: 13
SQ FT: 6,626
SALES (est): 949K Privately Held
SIC: 3731 Cargo vessels, building & repairing

(P-20991)
COLONNAS SHIPYARD WEST LLC
105 S 31st St, San Diego (92113-1403)
PHONE................................619 557-8373
Robert Boyd, *Principal*
EMP: 30
SALES (est): 2.9MM **Privately Held**
SIC: 3731 Shipbuilding & repairing

(P-20992)
CONTINENTAL MARITIME INDS INC
1995 Bay Front St, San Diego (92113-2122)
PHONE................................619 234-8851
David H Mc Queary, *President*
Lee E Wilson, *Vice Pres*
Maryanne Davis, *Human Res Mgr*
Raquel Sherman, *Purchasing*
Stewie Youngerman, *Manager*
EMP: 429
SQ FT: 90,000
SALES (est): 84MM **Publicly Held**
SIC: 3731 Shipbuilding & repairing
PA: Huntington Ingalls Industries, Inc.
4101 Washington Ave
Newport News VA 23607

(P-20993)
CRAFT LABOR & SUPPORT SVCS LLC
1545 Tidelands Ave Ste C, National City (91950-4240)
PHONE................................619 336-9977
Michael Greene, *Branch Mgr*
Jackie Vazquez, *Manager*
EMP: 100
SALES (corp-wide): 10.3MM **Privately Held**
SIC: 3731 Shipbuilding & repairing
PA: Craft Labor And Support Services, Llc
7636 230th St Sw Apt B
Edmonds WA 98026
206 304-4543

(P-20994)
DEEPFLIGHT
1150 Brickyard Cove Rd, Point Richmond (94801-4181)
PHONE................................510 236-3422
Adam Wright, *CEO*
Robert Chamberlain, *COO*
Karen Hawkes, *Vice Pres*
Edwin Chiu, *Electrical Engi*
EMP: 12 EST: 1996
SALES (est): 2.6MM **Privately Held**
SIC: 3731 Submarines, building & repairing

(P-20995)
GENERAL DYNAMICS CORPORATION
General Dynamics Nassco
2798 Harbor Dr, San Diego (92113-3650)
PHONE................................619 544-3400
Steven Strobel, *Vice Pres*
Michael Askew, *President*
Christopher Barnes, *President*
Erin Eastman, *Area Mgr*
Mark Holmes, *Area Mgr*
EMP: 42
SALES (corp-wide): 30.9B **Publicly Held**
SIC: 3731 Shipbuilding & repairing
PA: General Dynamics Corporation
2941 Frview Pk Dr Ste 100
Falls Church VA 22042
703 876-3000

(P-20996)
HII SAN DIEGO SHIPYARD INC
1995 Bay Front St, San Diego (92113-2122)
PHONE................................619 234-8851
Christopher Joseph Miner, *CEO*
Ronald Sugar, *President*
Carl Vancio, *Chief Mktg Ofcr*
Bryan Herring, *Vice Pres*
Lee Wilson, *Vice Pres*
EMP: 325
SQ FT: 90,000

SALES (est): 63.6MM **Publicly Held**
WEB: www.cmsd.net
SIC: 3731 Military ships, building & repairing
PA: Huntington Ingalls Industries, Inc.
4101 Washington Ave
Newport News VA 23607

(P-20997)
INTEGRATED MARINE SERVICES INC
Also Called: IMS
2320 Main St, Chula Vista (91911-4610)
PHONE................................619 429-0300
L'arry Samano, *President*
EMP: 55
SALES: 11MM **Privately Held**
SIC: 3731 Shipbuilding & repairing

(P-20998)
LARSON AL BOAT SHOP
1046 S Seaside Ave, San Pedro (90731-7334)
PHONE................................310 514-4100
Jack Wall, *CEO*
George Wall, *Vice Pres*
Gloria Wall, *Vice Pres*
Mary Rodriguez, *Executive*
Kelly Wall, *Asst Controller*
▲ EMP: 70
SQ FT: 65,000
SALES (est): 17MM **Privately Held**
WEB: www.larsonboat.com
SIC: 3731 Military ships, building & repairing; commercial cargo ships, building & repairing; marinas

(P-20999)
MARE ISLAND DRY DOCK LLC
1180 Nimitz Ave, Vallejo (94592-1053)
PHONE................................707 652-7356
Stephen Dileo, *Mng Member*
Harry Nicholsen, *CFO*
William Dunbar, *Vice Pres*
Dale Lacey, *Vice Pres*
Paul Gates, *Program Mgr*
EMP: 60 EST: 2012
SALES: 32.4MM **Privately Held**
SIC: 3731 Shipbuilding & repairing

(P-21000)
MARINE GROUP BOAT WORKS LLC
997 G St, Chula Vista (91910-3414)
PHONE................................619 427-6767
Herb Engel,
Laura Machado, *CFO*
Arthur E Engel, *Chairman*
Leah Yam, *Comms Dir*
Brooks Detchon, *Project Mgr*
▲ EMP: 115
SALES (est): 46.9MM **Privately Held**
WEB: www.marinegroupbw.com
SIC: 3731 Shipbuilding & repairing

(P-21001)
MAXON CRS LLC
5400 W Rosecrans Ave # 105, Hawthorne (90250-6682)
PHONE................................424 236-4660
Isaac Zaharoni, *President*
Tom Carmody,
Letty Mercado,
EMP: 21
SQ FT: 9,411
SALES (est): 855.5K **Privately Held**
SIC: 3731 Shipbuilding & repairing

(P-21002)
MILLER MARINE
2275 Manya St, San Diego (92154-4713)
PHONE................................619 791-1500
Pauline Senter, *CEO*
Edward Senter, *President*
Miller Marine, *Admin Sec*
Denise Patron, *Manager*
EMP: 45
SQ FT: 13,500
SALES (est): 10.7MM **Privately Held**
WEB: www.millermarine.us
SIC: 3731 7389 Shipbuilding & repairing; grinding, precision: commercial or industrial; metal slitting & shearing

(P-21003)
MORRISON MAR & INTERMODAL INC
753 Tunbridge Rd Ste A150, Danville (94526-4319)
PHONE................................925 362-4599
Scott Morrison, *President*
Dave Burns, *General Mgr*
Laura Forslund, *Opers Mgr*
▲ EMP: 25
SQ FT: 1,500
SALES: 1MM **Privately Held**
WEB: www.morrisonmarine.com
SIC: 3731 4789 Cargo vessels, building & repairing; cargo loading & unloading services

(P-21004)
NATIONAL STL & SHIPBUILDING CO (HQ)
Also Called: Nassco
2798 Harbor Dr, San Diego (92113-3650)
P.O. Box 85278 (92186-5278)
PHONE................................619 544-3400
Frederick J Harris, *President*
Michael Toner, *Ch of Bd*
Kevin Graney, *President*
D H Fogg, *Treasurer*
John Keane, *Bd of Directors*
▲ EMP: 277
SQ FT: 100,000
SALES (est): 510.1MM
SALES (corp-wide): 30.9B **Publicly Held**
WEB: www.nassco.com
SIC: 3731 Military ships, building & repairing; commercial cargo ships, building & repairing
PA: General Dynamics Corporation
2941 Frview Pk Dr Ste 100
Falls Church VA 22042
703 876-3000

(P-21005)
NAVIGATIONAL SERVICES INC
34 E 17th St Ste C, National City (91950-4501)
P.O. Box 2444 (91951-2444)
PHONE................................619 409-6992
Frank Soto Sr, *President*
Don Fritz, *CFO*
Lupita Lopez, *Manager*
EMP: 12
SQ FT: 3,800
SALES (est): 2.1MM **Privately Held**
SIC: 3731 Commercial passenger ships, building & repairing

(P-21006)
OC FLEET SERVICE INC
8270 Monroe Ave, Stanton (90680-2612)
PHONE................................714 460-8069
Russell Loud, *President*
Evell Stanley, *Vice Pres*
EMP: 15
SQ FT: 150,000
SALES (est): 2MM **Privately Held**
SIC: 3731 Shipbuilding & repairing

(P-21007)
PACIFIC SHIP REPR FBRCTION INC (PA)
1625 Rigel St, San Diego (92113-3887)
P.O. Box 13428 (92170-3428)
PHONE................................619 232-3200
David J Moore, *CEO*
Marvin Cannegieter, *Program Mgr*
Mark Sickert, *Program Mgr*
Nancy Gurley, *Office Mgr*
Charlie Jenkins, *Administration*
EMP: 287
SQ FT: 136,000
SALES: 45.1MM **Privately Held**
WEB: www.pacship.com
SIC: 3731 3444 Combat vessels, building & repairing; sheet metalwork

(P-21008)
PACORD INC
Also Called: L-3 Pacord
240 W 30th St, National City (91950-7204)
PHONE................................619 336-2200
Russell J Pearce, *Branch Mgr*
EMP: 50

SALES (corp-wide): 9.5B **Publicly Held**
SIC: 3731 1731 Shipbuilding & repairing; electrical work
HQ: Pacord Inc
3835 E Princess Anne Rd
Norfolk VA 23502
757 855-8037

(P-21009)
PAIGE SITTA & ASSOCIATES INC (PA)
Also Called: PAIGE FLOOR COVERING SPECIALIS
2050 Wilson Ave Ste B, National City (91950-6500)
PHONE................................619 233-5912
Scott Nicholson, *President*
Peter Sitta, *Vice Pres*
Alex Cervantes, *Office Mgr*
Debbie Kelley, *Controller*
EMP: 35
SQ FT: 9,000
SALES (est): 4.3MM **Privately Held**
WEB: www.paigefc.com
SIC: 3731 1752 Shipbuilding & repairing; floor laying & floor work

(P-21010)
PATRIOT MRITIME COMPLIANCE LLC
1320 Willow Pass Rd # 485, Concord (94520-7940)
PHONE................................925 296-2000
Richard Naccara, *Mng Member*
Judy Collins,
Timothy Gill,
Jordan Truchan,
EMP: 13
SALES (est): 1.4MM **Privately Held**
SIC: 3731 Shipbuilding & repairing

(P-21011)
PYR PRESERVATION SERVICES
2393 Newton Ave Ste B, San Diego (92113-3666)
PHONE................................619 338-8395
Daniel R Cummins, *CEO*
EMP: 30
SQ FT: 12,500
SALES (est): 1.1MM **Privately Held**
SIC: 3731 3589 3479 2851 Commercial cargo ships, building & repairing; sandblasting equipment; etching & engraving; epoxy coatings

(P-21012)
ROBERT E BLAKE INC
Also Called: General Engrg & Mch Works
135 Clara St, San Francisco (94107-1120)
PHONE................................415 391-2255
Peter J Blake, *President*
Robert Blake, *President*
EMP: 15 EST: 1967
SQ FT: 11,000
SALES (est): 1.5MM **Privately Held**
SIC: 3731 3599 3519 3444 Shipbuilding & repairing; machine shop, jobbing & repair; engines, diesel & semi-diesel or dual-fuel; sheet metalwork

(P-21013)
SEA TEK SPARS & RIGGING INC
508 E E St Ste B, Wilmington (90744-6059)
PHONE................................310 549-1800
Maria Almazan, *President*
EMP: 11
SALES (est): 1.2MM **Privately Held**
SIC: 3731 Marine rigging

(P-21014)
SOUTHERN CALIFORNIA INSULATION
Also Called: SCI
2050 Wilson Ave Ste C, National City (91950-6500)
PHONE................................619 477-1303
Mitch Spenst, *President*
EMP: 20
SALES (est): 2.2MM **Privately Held**
SIC: 3731 1742 Shipbuilding & repairing; plastering, drywall & insulation

▲ = Import ▼=Export
◆ =Import/Export

(P-21015) TECNICO CORPORATION
1670 Brandywine Ave Ste D, Chula Vista (91911-6071)
PHONE 619 426-7385
Jerald Steen, Manager
EMP: 45 Privately Held
SIC: 3731 Shipbuilding & repairing
HQ: Tecnico Corporation
831 Industrial Ave
Chesapeake VA 23324
757 545-4013

(P-21016) WALASHEK INDUSTRIAL & MAR INC
2826 Eighth St, Berkeley (94710-2707)
PHONE 206 624-2880
Frank Welashek, Manager
EMP: 11
SALES (corp-wide): 29.3MM Privately Held
WEB: www.walashek.com
SIC: 3731 Shipbuilding & repairing
HQ: Walashek Industrial & Marine, Inc.
3411 Amherst St
Norfolk VA 23513

(P-21017) WALASHEK INDUSTRIAL & MAR INC
1428 Mckinley Ave, National City (91950-4217)
PHONE 619 498-1711
Frank Walashek, Manager
EMP: 43
SALES (corp-wide): 29.3MM Privately Held
WEB: www.walashek.com
SIC: 3731 Shipbuilding & repairing
HQ: Walashek Industrial & Marine, Inc.
3411 Amherst St
Norfolk VA 23513

(P-21018) WALKER DESIGN INC
Also Called: Walker Engineering Enterprises
9255 San Fernando Rd, Sun Valley (91352-1416)
PHONE 818 252-7788
Robert A Walker Jr, CEO
Shari Goodgame, Corp Secy
Michael Delillo, Vice Pres
Ken Sacks, VP Sales
Blaine Tornow, Consultant
▲ EMP: 33
SQ FT: 29,800
SALES (est): 7.4MM Privately Held
WEB: www.walkerairsep.com
SIC: 3731 Lighters, marine: building & repairing

3732 Boat Building & Repairing

(P-21019) ADEPT PROCESS SERVICES INC
Also Called: APS Marine
1505 Cleveland Ave, National City (91950-4210)
P.O. Box 2130, Imperial Beach (91933-2130)
PHONE 619 434-3194
Gary Southerland, President
Andrea Southerland, Administration
EMP: 34
SQ FT: 30,000
SALES (est): 4.2MM Privately Held
WEB: www.adeptworks.net
SIC: 3732 4493 7699 Boat building & repairing; boat yards, storage & incidental repair; boat repair

(P-21020) AIR & GAS TECH INC
3191 Commercial St, San Diego (92113-1426)
PHONE 619 557-8373
Anthony Greenwell, President
EMP: 25
SQ FT: 18,000
SALES (est): 5.9MM Privately Held
WEB: www.cemcorp.net
SIC: 3732 Boat building & repairing

(P-21021) ANACAPA MARINE SERVICES (PA)
Also Called: Anacapa Boatyard
151 Shipyard Way Ste 5, Newport Beach (92663-4460)
PHONE 805 985-1818
Richard Fairchild, President
Jj Marine Acquisition, Principal
EMP: 17
SQ FT: 8,000
SALES (est): 3.1MM Privately Held
WEB: www.amsboatyard.com
SIC: 3732 5088 Boat building & repairing; marine supplies

(P-21022) BASIN MARINE INC
Also Called: Basin Marine Shipyard
829 Harbor Island Dr A, Newport Beach (92660-7235)
PHONE 949 673-0360
Paul Smith, President
▲ EMP: 18
SQ FT: 44,000
SALES (est): 4.7MM Privately Held
SIC: 3732 5551 Boat building & repairing; marine supplies

(P-21023) BAY MARINE BOATWORKS INC
310 W Cutting Blvd, Richmond (94804-2018)
PHONE 510 237-0140
Erik Mattson, President
William Elliott, Principal
▲ EMP: 36
SQ FT: 500
SALES (est): 7.4MM
SALES (corp-wide): 85.1MM Privately Held
WEB: www.bay-ship.com
SIC: 3732 Boat building & repairing
PA: Bay Ship & Yacht Co.
2900 Main St Ste 2100
Alameda CA 94501
510 337-9122

(P-21024) BOATWORKS
2251 Townsgate Rd, Westlake Village (91361-2404)
PHONE 805 374-9455
Alex Toller, Owner
EMP: 10
SALES (est): 815.9K Privately Held
SIC: 3732 Boat building & repairing

(P-21025) CATALINA YACHTS INC (PA)
Also Called: Morgan Marine
21200 Victory Blvd, Woodland Hills (91367-2582)
PHONE 818 884-7700
Frank W Butler, President
Sharon Day, Corp Secy
◆ EMP: 200
SQ FT: 200,000
SALES (est): 52.2MM Privately Held
WEB: www.catalinayachts.com
SIC: 3732 5551 Sailboats, building & repairing; boat dealers

(P-21026) COBRA PERFORMANCE BOATS INC
5109 Holt Blvd, Montclair (91763-4820)
PHONE 909 482-0047
Jeff Bohn, President
EMP: 10
SQ FT: 18,000
SALES (est): 1.3MM Privately Held
SIC: 3732 5551 7699 Boat building & repairing; boat dealers; boat repair

(P-21027) CRYSTALINER CORP
1626 Placentia Ave, Costa Mesa (92627-4385)
PHONE 949 548-0292
Jerry Norek, President
Jack L Norek Jr, Treasurer
Dorothy La Rose, Admin Sec
EMP: 20
SQ FT: 9,000
SALES (est): 2.5MM Privately Held
SIC: 3732 5551 5088 Boat building & repairing; marine supplies; marine supplies

(P-21028) DAVIS BOATS
2601 Engine Ave, Paso Robles (93446)
PHONE 805 227-1170
Harold Davis, President
Ardith Davis, Corp Secy
Larry Davis, Vice Pres
EMP: 10
SQ FT: 4,000
SALES (est): 1.3MM Privately Held
WEB: www.davisboats.com
SIC: 3732 5551 Motorboats, inboard or outboard: building & repairing; motor boat dealers

(P-21029) DEEP OCEAN ENGINEERING INC
2403 Qume Dr, San Jose (95131-1821)
PHONE 408 436-1102
Fang LI, CEO
EMP: 15
SALES (est): 3MM Privately Held
SIC: 3732 Boat building & repairing

(P-21030) DR RADON BOATBUILDING INC (PA)
67 Depot Rd, Goleta (93117-3430)
PHONE 805 692-2170
Donald Rae Radon, CEO
Linda Radon, Corp Secy
EMP: 13
SQ FT: 20,000
SALES (est): 1.4MM Privately Held
WEB: www.radonboats.com
SIC: 3732 Fishing boats: lobster, crab, oyster, etc.: small

(P-21031) DRISCOLL INC
Also Called: Driscoll Boat Works
2500 Shelter Island Dr, San Diego (92106-3114)
PHONE 619 226-2500
Thomas Driscoll, President
John Gerald Driscoll, Ch of Bd
Mary-Carol Driscoll, Corp Secy
Joseph E Driscoll, Vice Pres
▲ EMP: 50 EST: 1947
SQ FT: 2,400
SALES (est): 9.8MM Privately Held
WEB: www.driscollinc.com
SIC: 3732 Yachts, building & repairing

(P-21032) DRISCOLL MISSION BAY LLC
1500 Quivira Way Ste 2, San Diego (92109-8300)
PHONE 619 223-5191
Mary Carol Driscoll,
▲ EMP: 13
SQ FT: 1,000
SALES (est): 2.4MM Privately Held
WEB: www.driscoll-boats.com
SIC: 3732 Boat building & repairing

(P-21033) DUFFIELD MARINE INC (PA)
Also Called: Duffield Electric Boat Company
670 W 17th St Ste E7, Costa Mesa (92627-3664)
PHONE 760 246-1211
Marshall Duffield, President
Raul Sanchez, Manager
EMP: 25
SALES (est): 10.9MM Privately Held
WEB: www.duffyboats.com
SIC: 3732 Boat building & repairing

(P-21034) DUFFIELD MARINE INC
Also Called: Duffy Electric Boat
2001 W Coast Hwy, Newport Beach (92663-4713)
PHONE 949 645-6812
Karl Tahti, Manager
EMP: 25
SALES (corp-wide): 10.9MM Privately Held
WEB: www.duffyboats.com
SIC: 3732 Boat building & repairing
PA: Duffield Marine Inc.
670 W 17th St Ste E7
Costa Mesa CA 92627
760 246-1211

(P-21035) EPIC BOATS LLC (PA)
2755 Dos Aarons Way Ste A, Vista (92081-8359)
PHONE 760 542-6060
Chris Anthony,
Karen Callow,
EMP: 14
SQ FT: 30,000
SALES (est): 2.3MM Privately Held
WEB: www.epicboats.com
SIC: 3732 Boats, fiberglass: building & repairing

(P-21036) FANTASEA ENTERPRISES INC
Also Called: Pacific Avalon Yacht Charters
2901 W Coast Hwy Ste 160, Newport Beach (92663-4030)
PHONE 949 673-8545
John Gueola, President
Roy King, President
EMP: 10 EST: 1994
SQ FT: 3,000
SALES (est): 910K Privately Held
WEB: www.pacificavalon.com
SIC: 3732 Yachts, building & repairing

(P-21037) FASHION BLACKSMITH INC
121 Starfish Way, Crescent City (95531-4447)
PHONE 707 464-9219
Dale Long, President
EMP: 10
SQ FT: 9,000
SALES: 980K Privately Held
SIC: 3732 Boat building & repairing

(P-21038) FINELINE INDUSTRIES INC (PA)
Also Called: Centurion
2047 Grogan Ave, Merced (95341-6440)
PHONE 209 384-0255
Richard D Lee, President
Clark Bird, CFO
Pamela Lee, Corp Secy
Jeffrey Polan, Vice Pres
▼ EMP: 121
SQ FT: 38,000
SALES (est): 36.8MM Privately Held
WEB: www.centurionboats.com
SIC: 3732 Boats, fiberglass: building & repairing

(P-21039) GAMBOL INDUSTRIES INC
1825 W Pier D St, Long Beach (90802-1033)
PHONE 562 901-2470
Robert A Stein, President
John Bridwell, Vice Pres
▲ EMP: 45
SALES (est): 8.9MM Privately Held
WEB: www.gambolindustries.com
SIC: 3732 7699 4493 Yachts, building & repairing; boat repair; boat yards, storage & incidental repair

(P-21040) GREGOR INC
Also Called: Gregor Boat Co
3565 N Hazel Ave, Fresno (93722-4913)
PHONE 559 441-7703
Wilton W Gregory, President
EMP: 10 EST: 1964
SQ FT: 70,000
SALES (est): 825K Privately Held
WEB: www.gregorboats.com
SIC: 3732 5551 Fishing boats: lobster, crab, oyster, etc.: small; boat dealers

(P-21041) HALLETT BOATS
180 S Irwindale Ave, Azusa (91702-3211)
PHONE 626 969-8844
Nick Barron, President

Shirley Barron, *Corp Secy*
EMP: 25
SQ FT: 21,000
SALES (est): 3.9MM **Privately Held**
WEB: www.hallettboats.com
SIC: 3732 5091 Motorboats, inboard or outboard: building & repairing; boats, canoes, watercrafts & equipment

(P-21042)
HENDERSON SERVICES INC
Also Called: Valco Boats
6722 N Stonebridge Dr, Fresno (93711-1194)
PHONE...............................559 435-8874
Donald L Henderson, *President*
Linda Henderson, *Treasurer*
EMP: 25
SQ FT: 22,000
SALES (est): 2MM **Privately Held**
SIC: 3732 Motorboats, inboard or outboard: building & repairing

(P-21043)
HOBIE CAT COMPANY
4925 Oceanside Blvd, Oceanside (92056-3099)
PHONE...............................760 758-9100
Richard Rogers, *CEO*
Doug Skidmore, *President*
Bill Baldwin, *CFO*
Philip Dow, *Design Engr*
Jason Kardas, *Engineer*
◆ **EMP:** 150 EST: 1995
SQ FT: 60,000
SALES (est): 34.8MM **Privately Held**
WEB: www.hobiecat.com
SIC: 3732 Sailboats, building & repairing

(P-21044)
INDEL ENGINEERING INC
Also Called: Marina Shipyard
6400 E Marina Dr, Long Beach (90803-4618)
PHONE...............................562 594-0995
D E Bud Tretter, *President*
D E Tretter, *President*
Kurt Tretter, *Corp Secy*
Jerry Tretter, *Vice Pres*
EMP: 35
SQ FT: 3,000
SALES (est): 6.3MM **Privately Held**
WEB: www.marinashipyard.com
SIC: 3732 Houseboats, building & repairing; motorboats, inboard or outboard: building & repairing

(P-21045)
INNESPACE PRODUCTIONS
20172 Charlanne Dr, Redding (96002-9222)
PHONE...............................530 241-2800
Robert Innes, *President*
Dan Tazza, *Vice Pres*
▼ **EMP:** 12 EST: 2010
SALES (est): 1.7MM **Privately Held**
SIC: 3732 Boat building & repairing

(P-21046)
INTERNATIONAL INBOARD MAR INC
2556 W 16th St, Merced (95348-4355)
PHONE...............................209 384-2566
Roger Cruser, *President*
Robert Jessen, *Vice Pres*
EMP: 32
SQ FT: 6,000
SALES (est): 5.1MM **Privately Held**
WEB: www.calabriaboats.com
SIC: 3732 Motorboats, inboard or outboard: building & repairing

(P-21047)
JAMES BETTS ENTERPRISES INC
100 Sierra Terrace Rd, Tahoe City (96145)
P.O. Box 991, Friday Harbor WA (98250-0991)
PHONE...............................530 581-1331
James Betts, *President*
Janis Betts, *Corp Secy*
EMP: 20
SQ FT: 22,000
SALES (est): 2.5MM **Privately Held**
SIC: 3732 Yachts, building & repairing

(P-21048)
KAYE SANDY ENTERPRISES INC
Also Called: Porta-Bote International
1074 Independence Ave, Mountain View (94043-1602)
PHONE...............................650 961-5334
Alex R Kaye, *President*
Frances Kaye, *Corp Secy*
▼ **EMP:** 35
SQ FT: 4,000
SALES (est): 6.1MM **Privately Held**
WEB: www.porta-bote.com
SIC: 3732 5551 Boat building & repairing; boat dealers

(P-21049)
LAVEY CRAFT PRFMCE BOATS INC
175 Vander St, Corona (92880-6972)
PHONE...............................951 273-9690
Jeff A Camire, *CEO*
Jeff Camire, *CEO*
Chris Camire, *Admin Sec*
EMP: 13
SQ FT: 4,500
SALES (est): 1.4MM **Privately Held**
WEB: www.laveycraft.com
SIC: 3732 Boats, fiberglass: building & repairing

(P-21050)
LEAR BAYLOR INC
7215 Garden Grove Blvd C, Garden Grove (92841-4221)
PHONE...............................714 799-9396
Shanda Lear-Baylor, *President*
Mary Lou, *Manager*
EMP: 25
SALES: 3MM **Privately Held**
WEB: www.learbaylor.com
SIC: 3732 Boats, fiberglass: building & repairing

(P-21051)
M V OUTER LIMITS
Also Called: Outer Limits Sports Fishing
11464 Eastridge Pl, San Diego (92131-3547)
PHONE...............................858 689-1828
Ken Franke, *Owner*
EMP: 10
SALES: 470K **Privately Held**
SIC: 3732 Fishing boats: lobster, crab, oyster, etc.: small

(P-21052)
MACGREGOR YACHT CORPORATION
1631 Placentia Ave, Costa Mesa (92627-4311)
PHONE...............................310 621-2206
Roger Mac Gregor, *President*
Mary Lou Mac Gregor, *Corp Secy*
EMP: 74 EST: 1963
SQ FT: 10,000
SALES (est): 9.5MM **Privately Held**
SIC: 3732 5551 Sailboats, building & repairing; boat dealers

(P-21053)
MARINE TECH
1500 Quivira Way Ste 1, San Diego (92109-8300)
PHONE...............................619 225-0448
Ezobrio Netto, *Owner*
Carla Kralagodri, *Principal*
EMP: 16
SALES (est): 989.7K **Privately Held**
SIC: 3732 Boat building & repairing

(P-21054)
MARITIME SOLUTIONS LLC
1616 Newton Ave, San Diego (92113-1013)
PHONE...............................619 234-2676
Kim M Zeledon, *EMP:* 30
EMP: 30
SQ FT: 4,000
SALES (est): 5.6MM **Privately Held**
SIC: 3732 3731 8711 Boat building & repairing; shipbuilding & repairing; engineering services

(P-21055)
MAURER MARINE INC
873 W 17th St, Costa Mesa (92627-4308)
PHONE...............................949 645-7673
Craig Maurer, *President*
Jay S Maurer, *Vice Pres*
Garrett Maurer, *Parts Mgr*
EMP: 18
SALES (est): 4MM **Privately Held**
WEB: www.maurermarine.com
SIC: 3732 7389 Yachts, building & repairing; yacht brokers

(P-21056)
MB SPORTS INC
280 Airpark Rd, Atwater (95301-9535)
PHONE...............................209 357-4153
Myung Bo Hong, *CEO*
▲ **EMP:** 40
SQ FT: 16,000
SALES (est): 9.8MM **Privately Held**
WEB: www.mbsports.net
SIC: 3732 5551 5091 Motorboats, inboard or outboard: building & repairing; boat dealers; boats, canoes, watercrafts & equipment

(P-21057)
MOOSE BOATS INC
1175 Nimitz Ave Ste 115, Vallejo (94592-1003)
PHONE...............................707 778-9828
Christian Lind, *CEO*
Aaron Lind, *Treasurer*
Roger N Fleck, *Exec VP*
Stephen Dirkes, *General Mgr*
Mark Stott, *Sales Engr*
EMP: 16
SQ FT: 20,000
SALES (est): 3.4MM **Privately Held**
WEB: www.mooseboats.com
SIC: 3732 Boat building & repairing

(P-21058)
NAVIGATOR YACHTS AND PDTS INC
364 Malbert St, Perris (92570-8336)
PHONE...............................951 657-2117
Xia Wang, *CEO*
Jule Marshall, *Principal*
EMP: 150
SQ FT: 30,000
SALES (est): 16.1MM **Privately Held**
SIC: 3732 Yachts, building & repairing

(P-21059)
OCEAN PROTECTA INCORPORATED
10743 Progress Way, Cypress (90630-4714)
PHONE...............................714 891-2628
Edgar Chong Tan, *CEO*
Myron Reyes, *President*
EMP: 50
SALES (est): 5.8MM **Privately Held**
SIC: 3732 Boat building & repairing

(P-21060)
OCEANSIDE MARINE CENTER INC (PA)
1550 Harbor Dr N, Oceanside (92054-1031)
PHONE...............................760 722-1833
John Tyrell, *President*
Myrtle Tyrell, *Vice Pres*
EMP: 10 EST: 1964
SQ FT: 5,000
SALES (est): 918.9K **Privately Held**
SIC: 3732 Boat building & repairing

(P-21061)
PACIFIC YACHT TOWERS
165 Balboa St Ste C10, San Marcos (92069-1347)
PHONE...............................760 744-4831
Tom Newton, *President*
EMP: 10
SQ FT: 5,000
SALES (est): 1.3MM **Privately Held**
WEB: www.pacificyachttowers.com
SIC: 3732 5091 Motorized boat, building & repairing; boat accessories & parts

(P-21062)
R & D RACING PRODUCTS USA INC
12983 Los Nietos Rd, Santa Fe Springs (90670-3011)
PHONE...............................562 906-1190
Glenn Dickinson, *President*
Bill Chapin, *Vice Pres*
▲ **EMP:** 15
SQ FT: 5,000
SALES (est): 2.3MM **Privately Held**
WEB: www.rd-performance.com
SIC: 3732 Boat building & repairing

(P-21063)
SHELTER ISLAND YACHTWAYS LTD
Also Called: Shelter Island Boatyard
2330 Shelter Island Dr # 1, San Diego (92106-3126)
PHONE...............................619 222-0481
William Roberts, *General Ptnr*
Steven Giordano, *Executive*
▲ **EMP:** 30 EST: 1953
SQ FT: 20,000
SALES (est): 5.4MM **Privately Held**
SIC: 3732 6512 Boat building & repairing; lessors of piers, docks, associated buildings & facilities

(P-21064)
STONE BOAT YARD INC
2517 Blanding Ave, Alameda (94501-1599)
PHONE...............................510 523-3030
David Olson, *President*
EMP: 15
SQ FT: 47,250
SALES (est): 1.7MM **Privately Held**
SIC: 3732 3731 Boat building & repairing; shipbuilding & repairing

(P-21065)
TBYCI LLC
Also Called: Boatyard-Channel Islands, The
3615 Victoria Ave, Oxnard (93035-4360)
PHONE...............................805 985-6800
Gregory Schem,
Craig Campbell, *General Mgr*
EMP: 16 EST: 2013
SQ FT: 7,500
SALES (est): 682K **Privately Held**
SIC: 3732 3731 Motorized boat, building & repairing; motorboats, inboard or outboard: building & repairing; sailboats, building & repairing; patrol boats, building & repairing; crew boats, building & repairing

(P-21066)
VENTURA HARBOR BOATYARD INC
1415 Spinnaker Dr, Ventura (93001-4339)
PHONE...............................805 654-1433
Robert Bartosh, *President*
Dale Morris, *CFO*
Kim Morris, *Vice Pres*
Stephen James, *Admin Sec*
Peggy Nielsen, *VP Sales*
EMP: 35
SQ FT: 2,000
SALES: 4.8MM **Privately Held**
SIC: 3732 4493 Boat building & repairing; boat yards, storage & incidental repair

(P-21067)
VINTAGE AERO ENGINES
1582 Goodrick Dr Ste 8a, Tehachapi (93561-1672)
PHONE...............................661 822-4107
Michael Nixon, *Owner*
EMP: 16
SALES (est): 1.4MM **Privately Held**
SIC: 3732 Tenders (small motor craft), building & repairing

(P-21068)
W D SCHOCK CORP
364 Malbert St, Perris (92570-8336)
P.O. Box 79184, Corona (92877-0172)
PHONE...............................951 277-3377
Alexander Vucelic, *President*
▼ **EMP:** 30 EST: 1946
SQ FT: 30,000

▲ = Import ▼=Export
◆ =Import/Export

SALES (est): 4.9MM **Privately Held**
WEB: www.wdschock.com
SIC: 3732 Sailboats, building & repairing

(P-21069)
WESTERLY MARINE INC
3535 W Garry Ave, Santa Ana
(92704-6422)
PHONE..............................714 966-8550
Lynn Bowser, *President*
Steven Lee, *Vice Pres*
Skip Gronier, *Purch Agent*
▲ EMP: 26 EST: 1970
SQ FT: 18,000
SALES (est): 6.1MM **Privately Held**
WEB: www.westerly-marine.com
SIC: 3732 Boat building & repairing

(P-21070)
WHEELS MAGAZINE INC
1409 Centinela Ave, Inglewood
(90302-1141)
P.O. Box 2617, Gardena (90247-0617)
PHONE..............................310 402-9013
Terry Taylor, *Principal*
EMP: 50
SALES (est): 1.9MM **Privately Held**
SIC: 3732 Non-motorized boat, building &
repairing

(P-21071)
WILLARD MARINE INC
1250 N Grove St, Anaheim (92806-2130)
PHONE..............................714 630-4018
George L Angle, *Chairman*
Ulrich Gottschling, *President*
Jojo Nery, *President*
Gabriella M Carrera, *CFO*
Dave Gutierrez, *Vice Pres*
▲ EMP: 55
SQ FT: 45,000
SALES (est): 17.2MM **Privately Held**
WEB: www.willardmarine.com
SIC: 3732 Boats, fiberglass: building & re-
pairing

(P-21072)
WINDWARD YACHT & REPAIR INC
Also Called: Windward Yacht Center
13645 Fiji Way, Venice (90292-6986)
PHONE..............................310 823-4581
Jacob Wood, *President*
Arlen Wood, *Vice Pres*
Susan Santora, *Accountant*
Simon Landt, *Manager*
Chris Waid, *Manager*
▲ EMP: 14
SQ FT: 5,000
SALES (est): 1.9MM **Privately Held**
SIC: 3732 Boat building & repairing

3743 Railroad Eqpt

(P-21073)
BOMBARDIER TRANSPORTATION
1555 N San Fernando Rd, Los Angeles
(90065-1261)
PHONE..............................323 224-3461
Robert Young, *Manager*
EMP: 100
SALES (corp-wide): 16.2B **Privately Held**
SIC: 3743 Railroad equipment
HQ: Bombardier Transportation (Holdings)
Usa Inc
1501 Lebanon Church Rd
Pittsburgh PA 15236
412 655-5700

(P-21074)
CABLE CAR CLASSICS INC
3239 Rio Lindo Ave, Healdsburg
(95448-9495)
PHONE..............................707 433-6810
Matthew Etchell, *President*
Robert Etchell Sr, *Admin Sec*
Michelle Buchignani, *Purchasing*
Rick Ward, *Sales Staff*
Greg Etchell, *Manager*
▲ EMP: 10
SQ FT: 10,000

SALES (est): 940K **Privately Held**
WEB: www.cablecarclassics.com
SIC: 3743 Interurban cars & car equip-
ment; streetcars & car equipment

(P-21075)
EAGLE SYSTEMS INC
1601 Atlas Rd, Richmond (94806-1101)
PHONE..............................510 231-2686
EMP: 10 **Privately Held**
SIC: 3743 Railway motor cars
HQ: Eagle Systems, Inc.
230 Grant Rd Ste A1
East Wenatchee WA 98802
509 884-7575

(P-21076)
GUNDERSON RAIL SERVICES LLC
Also Called: Greenbrier Rail Services
1475 Cooley Ct, San Bernardino
(92408-2830)
P.O. Box 1715 (92402-1715)
PHONE..............................909 478-0541
Kevin Johnson, *Controller*
EMP: 30
SQ FT: 64,248
SALES (corp-wide): 2.5B **Publicly Held**
SIC: 3743 Railroad equipment
HQ: Gunderson Rail Services Llc
1 Centerpointe Dr Ste 200
Lake Oswego OR 97035
503 684-7000

(P-21077)
HITACHI RAIL USA INC (PA)
101 The Embarcadero # 210, San Fran-
cisco (94105-1222)
PHONE..............................415 397-7010
Giancarlo Fantappie, *President*
▲ EMP: 14
SQ FT: 5,000
SALES (est): 25.7MM **Privately Held**
SIC: 3743 Train cars & equipment, freight
or passenger

(P-21078)
KINKISHARYO INTERNATIONAL LLC (DH)
300 N Cntntl Blvd Ste 300, El Segundo
(90245)
PHONE..............................424 276-1803
Masaya Wakuda, *Mng Member*
Grace Adahikari,
Donald Boss,
Keji Tanin,
▲ EMP: 19 EST: 1999
SQ FT: 6,000
SALES (est): 25.6MM
SALES (corp-wide): 578.9MM **Privately
Held**
WEB: www.kinkisharyo-usa.com
SIC: 3743 3321 Train cars & equipment,
freight or passenger; railroad car wheels
& brake shoes; cast iron

(P-21079)
KNORR BRAKE COMPANY LLC
29471 Kohoutek Way, Union City
(94587-1237)
PHONE..............................510 475-0770
Paul Akins, *Branch Mgr*
EMP: 10 **Privately Held**
WEB: www.knorrbrakecorp.com
SIC: 3743 Railroad equipment
HQ: Knorr Brake Company Llc
1 Arthur Peck Dr
Westminster MD 21157
410 875-0900

(P-21080)
LEVAC SPECIALTIES INC
2305 Cemo Cir, Gold River (95670-4424)
PHONE..............................916 362-3795
Leo Levac, *President*
EMP: 14 EST: 1999
SQ FT: 6,000
SALES (est): 2.4MM **Privately Held**
SIC: 3743 Rapid transit cars & equipment

(P-21081)
MBF TRANSPORTATION LLC
13610 Imperial Hwy Ste 6, Santa Fe
Springs (90670-4875)
PHONE..............................562 282-0540
Michael Marchica,

EMP: 10 EST: 2014
SALES (est): 886.3K **Privately Held**
SIC: 3743 Freight cars & equipment

(P-21082)
PACIFIC GREEN TRUCKING INC
512 E C St, Wilmington (90744-6618)
PHONE..............................310 830-4528
Adrian Zarate, *CEO*
EMP: 11 EST: 2009
SALES (est): 1.3MM **Privately Held**
SIC: 3743 Freight cars & equipment

(P-21083)
PARAGON PRODUCTS LLC (PA)
4475 Golden Foothill Pkwy, El Dorado Hills
(95762-9638)
PHONE..............................916 941-9717
Ted Keefer, *President*
Renee Lajou, *CFO*
Tim Chris, *Opers Staff*
Paul Davies,
◆ EMP: 40
SQ FT: 12,000
SALES (est): 13.2MM **Privately Held**
WEB: www.paragonproducts.net
SIC: 3743 Railroad locomotives & parts,
electric or nonelectric; locomotives &
parts

(P-21084)
UNION TANK CAR COMPANY
175 W Jackson Blvd, Bakersfield (93311)
PHONE..............................312 431-3111
Bill Constantino, *Director*
EMP: 153
SALES (corp-wide): 242.1B **Publicly
Held**
SIC: 3743 Train cars & equipment, freight
or passenger
HQ: Union Tank Car Company
175 W Jackson Blvd # 2100
Chicago IL 60604
312 431-3111

(P-21085)
WOOJIN IS AMERICA INC
5108 Azusa Canyon Rd, Irwindale
(91706-1846)
PHONE..............................626 386-0101
Ted Ogawa, *CEO*
Sharon Peck, *CFO*
Rich Lee, *Administration*
▲ EMP: 10
SALES (est): 1.6MM
SALES (corp-wide): 3.5MM **Privately
Held**
SIC: 3743 4789 Railroad equipment; rail-
road maintenance & repair services
HQ: Woojin Industrial Systems Co., Ltd.
95 Sari-Ro, Sari-Myeon
Goesan 28046
824 382-0414

**3751 Motorcycles, Bicycles
& Parts**

(P-21086)
ACCELL NORTH AMERICA
2685 Park Center Dr Ste C, Simi Valley
(93065-6211)
PHONE..............................805 915-4900
Larry Pizzi, *President*
Allan Klein, *CFO*
◆ EMP: 45
SQ FT: 51,000
SALES (est): 6.5MM **Privately Held**
WEB: www.currietech.com
SIC: 3751 5571 Bicycles & related parts;
motorcycles

(P-21087)
ALL AMERICAN RACERS INC
Also Called: Dan Gurneys All Amercn Racers
2334 S Broadway, Santa Ana
(92707-3250)
P.O. Box 2186 (92707-0186)
PHONE..............................714 557-2116
Daniel S Gurney, *CEO*
Justin B Gurney, *CEO*
Kathy Weida, *Vice Pres*
Ellen La Bond, *Accountant*
EMP: 162
SQ FT: 25,000

SALES (est): 36.2MM **Privately Held**
WEB: www.allamericanracers.com
SIC: 3751 Motorcycles & related parts

(P-21088)
AMERICAN PERFORMANCE ENGI
7347 W Rosamond Blvd, Rosamond
(93560-7284)
PHONE..............................661 256-7309
Jay Eshbach, *Owner*
EMP: 11
SALES (est): 1.6MM **Privately Held**
SIC: 3751 5013 Motorcycles & related
parts; motorcycle parts

(P-21089)
B & E ENTERPRISES
1380 N Mccan St, Anaheim (92806-1316)
PHONE..............................714 630-3731
Michael Banister, *President*
Edward Miller, *Vice Pres*
EMP: 13
SQ FT: 9,100
SALES (est): 2.3MM **Privately Held**
WEB: www.tubebender.com
SIC: 3751 3714 3599 Frames, motorcycle
& bicycle; motor vehicle parts & acces-
sories; machine shop, jobbing & repair

(P-21090)
BARNETT TOOL & ENGINEERING
Also Called: Barnett Performance Products
2238 Palma Dr, Ventura (93003-8068)
PHONE..............................805 642-9435
Michael Taylor, *President*
Colleen Taylor, *CFO*
EMP: 60
SQ FT: 43,000
SALES (est): 12.2MM **Privately Held**
SIC: 3751 Motorcycle accessories; motor-
cycles & related parts

(P-21091)
BELT DRIVES LTD
Also Called: B D L
505 W Lambert Rd, Brea (92821-3909)
PHONE..............................714 693-1313
Steve R Yetzke, *CEO*
Kathy Yetzke, *Shareholder*
EMP: 21
SQ FT: 30,000
SALES (est): 5.3MM **Privately Held**
WEB: www.beltdrives.com
SIC: 3751 Motorcycles & related parts

(P-21092)
BILLS PIPES INC
226 N Maple St, Corona (92880-6913)
PHONE..............................951 371-1329
William Cervera, *President*
EMP: 15
SQ FT: 4,500
SALES (est): 2.1MM **Privately Held**
WEB: www.billspipes.com
SIC: 3751 Motorcycle accessories; motor-
cycles & related parts

(P-21093)
BROOKSHIRE INNOVATIONS LLC
502 Giuseppe Ct Ste 7, Roseville
(95678-6306)
PHONE..............................916 786-7601
Kelly Nippear,
▲ EMP: 35
SQ FT: 60,000
SALES (est): 3.7MM **Privately Held**
SIC: 3751 Motorcycle accessories

(P-21094)
BUCHANANS SPOKE & RIM
805 W 8th St, Azusa (91702-2247)
PHONE..............................626 969-4655
Robert Buchanan, *CEO*
Kenny Buchanan, *Vice Pres*
▲ EMP: 21
SQ FT: 21,000
SALES (est): 2.9MM **Privately Held**
WEB: www.buchananspokes.com
SIC: 3751 Motorcycles & related parts

(P-21095)
C C PRODUCTS
Also Called: San Jose BMW
1990 W San Carlos St, San Jose
(95128-1812)
PHONE...................................408 295-0205
Chris Hodgson, *Owner*
EMP: 11
SQ FT: 5,200
SALES: 3MM **Privately Held**
WEB: www.ccproducts.com
SIC: 3751 7699 Motorcycles & related parts; motorcycle repair service

(P-21096)
CAL MOTO
2490 Old Middlefield Way, Mountain View
(94043-2317)
PHONE...................................650 966-1183
Kari W Prager, *President*
▲ **EMP:** 18
SALES (est): 7.2MM **Privately Held**
SIC: 3751 Bicycles & related parts

(P-21097)
CEE BAILEYS AIRCRAFT PLAS INC
6900 W Acco St, Montebello (90640-5435)
P.O. Box 1028 (90640-1028)
PHONE...................................323 721-4900
Jeff Johnston, *CEO*
Bryan Elliot, *Controller*
EMP: 24
SQ FT: 5,000
SALES: 3MM **Privately Held**
SIC: 3751 3728 3089 Motorcycle accessories; aircraft parts & equipment; windows, plastic

(P-21098)
CORBIN PACIFIC INC
11445 Commercial Pkwy, Castroville
(95012-3201)
PHONE...................................408 633-2500
EMP: 35
SALES (corp-wide): 11.9MM **Privately Held**
SIC: 3751 Saddles & seat posts, motorcycle & bicycle
PA: Corbin Pacific, Inc.
2360 Technology Pkwy
Hollister CA 95023
831 634-1100

(P-21099)
CORBIN PACIFIC INC (PA)
2360 Technology Pkwy, Hollister
(95023-2512)
PHONE...................................831 634-1100
Michael W Hanagan, *CEO*
Beverly Hanagan, *Admin Sec*
▲ **EMP:** 64
SQ FT: 80,000
SALES (est): 11.9MM **Privately Held**
SIC: 3751 Saddles & seat posts, motorcycle & bicycle

(P-21100)
CRITERION COMPOSITES INC
14349 Commerce Dr, Garden Grove
(92843-4949)
PHONE...................................714 554-2717
Don Guichard, *President*
EMP: 13 **EST:** 2008
SALES (est): 1.8MM **Privately Held**
SIC: 3751 3624 Bicycles & related parts; carbon & graphite products

(P-21101)
CULT CVLT
1555 E Saint Gertrude Pl, Santa Ana
(92705-5309)
PHONE...................................714 435-2858
Robert Morales, *Principal*
▲ **EMP:** 12
SALES (est): 1.7MM **Privately Held**
SIC: 3751 Motorcycles, bicycles & parts

(P-21102)
CUSTOM CHROME MANUFACTURING
155 E Main Ave Ste 150, Morgan Hill
(95037-7521)
PHONE...................................408 825-5000
Dan Cook, *Principal*

Bill Prescott, *VP Admin*
Sharon Dela Cruz, *Marketing Staff*
Bill McClure, *Manager*
▲ **EMP:** 206
SALES (est): 41.1MM
SALES (corp-wide): 332.7MM **Privately Held**
WEB: www.customchrome.com
SIC: 3751 Motorcycle accessories; frames, motorcycle & bicycle
HQ: Dae-Il Usa, Inc.
155 E Main Ave Ste 150
Morgan Hill CA 95037
-

(P-21103)
CYCLE SHACK INC
816 Murchison Dr, Millbrae (94030-3026)
PHONE...................................650 583-7014
Homer H Dyer, *President*
Buzz Dyer, *President*
Grove Hoover II, *Vice Pres*
Steve Reedy, *Admin Sec*
EMP: 59
SQ FT: 35,000
SALES (est): 9.9MM **Privately Held**
WEB: www.cycle-shack.com
SIC: 3751 Motorcycles & related parts; motorcycle accessories

(P-21104)
D & D MOTORCYCLE SERVICE INC
10401 Alameda St, Lynwood (90262-1758)
PHONE...................................323 567-9480
Ken Harold, *President*
EMP: 25
SQ FT: 17,000
SALES (est): 2.8MM **Privately Held**
WEB: www.danddservicesinc.com
SIC: 3751 Motorcycles & related parts

(P-21105)
DAYTEC CENTER LLC
Also Called: Jpm Finishing Company
17469 Lemon St, Hesperia (92345-5151)
P.O. Box 401328 (92340-1328)
PHONE...................................760 995-3515
Phil Day,
▲ **EMP:** 24
SQ FT: 40,000
SALES (est): 3.7MM **Privately Held**
SIC: 3751 3479 Frames, motorcycle & bicycle; coating of metals with plastic or resins

(P-21106)
EDELBROCK LLC (HQ)
2700 California St, Torrance (90503-3907)
PHONE...................................310 781-2222
Don Barry, *President*
Wayne Murray, *President*
John Colaianne, *CEO*
Steve Zitkus, *CFO*
Danny Castillo, *Vice Pres*
▲ **EMP:** 300
SQ FT: 290,000
SALES (est): 117.1MM **Privately Held**
WEB: www.edelbrock.com
SIC: 3751 3714 Motorcycle accessories; manifolds, motor vehicle

(P-21107)
ELECTRIC BIKE COMPANY LLC
519 Superior Ave, Newport Beach
(92663-3630)
PHONE...................................949 264-4080
Sean Lupton-Smith, *Mng Member*
Kim King, *Office Mgr*
Cristina Salvador, *Assistant*
EMP: 10
SALES (est): 1MM **Privately Held**
SIC: 3751 Motorcycles, bicycles & parts

(P-21108)
ENDURANCE PTC
8 Madrona St, Mill Valley (94941-1812)
PHONE...................................415 445-9155
Andrea Kennedy, *CEO*
Tim Fleming, *Manager*
Tammy Scott, *Manager*
EMP: 10
SALES (est): 1.3MM **Privately Held**
SIC: 3751 Motorcycles & related parts; motorcycle accessories; brakes, friction clutch & other; bicycle

(P-21109)
FMF RACING
Also Called: Flying Machine Factory
18033 S Santa Fe Ave, Compton
(90221-5514)
PHONE...................................310 631-4363
Don Emler, *CEO*
Eric Van Tichelin, *Managing Dir*
Richard King, *MIS Dir*
Erik Mattson, *Design Engr*
Daniel Beck, *Human Res Mgr*
▲ **EMP:** 150
SALES (est): 25.5MM **Privately Held**
WEB: www.fmfracing.com
SIC: 3751 5571 Motorcycle accessories; motorcycle parts & accessories

(P-21110)
FOX FACTORY HOLDING CORP (PA)
915 Disc Dr, Scotts Valley (95066-4543)
PHONE...................................831 274-6500
Larry L Enterline, *CEO*
Dudley Mendenhall, *Ch of Bd*
Elizabeth Fetter, *Bd of Directors*
Carl Nichols, *Bd of Directors*
Ted Waitman, *Bd of Directors*
EMP: 31
SALES: 475.6MM **Publicly Held**
SIC: 3751 Motorcycles, bicycles & parts

(P-21111)
FOX FACTORY INC (HQ)
Also Called: Fox Racing Shox
915 Disc Dr, Scotts Valley (95066-4543)
PHONE...................................831 274-6500
Larry Enterline, *CEO*
Bob Fox, *President*
Susie Geiss, *Engineer*
Evan Fetty, *Sales Staff*
Bruce Mallory, *Supervisor*
EMP: 90 **EST:** 1978
SALES (est): 29.5MM **Publicly Held**
SIC: 3751 Bicycles & related parts

(P-21112)
GLOBAL MOTORSPORT PARTS INC
155 E Main Ave Ste 150, Morgan Hill
(95037-7521)
PHONE...................................408 778-0500
Joseph F Keenan, *Ch of Bd*
Seth Murdock, *CFO*
◆ **EMP:** 102
SQ FT: 13,000
SALES (est): 9MM
SALES (corp-wide): 332.7MM **Privately Held**
SIC: 3751 5013 Motorcycle accessories; motorcycle parts
HQ: Dae-Il Usa, Inc.
155 E Main Ave Ste 150
Morgan Hill CA 95037

(P-21113)
GPR STABILIZER LLC
8715 Dead Stick Rd, San Diego
(92154-7710)
PHONE...................................619 661-0101
Randy Norman,
EMP: 10
SALES (est): 1.4MM **Privately Held**
SIC: 3751 Motorcycles & related parts

(P-21114)
HEADWINDS
Also Called: Tradewinds
221 W Maple Ave, Monrovia (91016-3329)
PHONE...................................626 359-8044
Joel Felty, *Owner*
Julie Felty, *Co-Owner*
EMP: 13
SQ FT: 10,000
SALES (est): 1.5MM **Privately Held**
WEB: www.headwinds.com
SIC: 3751 3599 Motorcycle accessories; machine shop, jobbing & repair

(P-21115)
HIGH END SEATING SOLUTIONS LLC
1919 E Occidental St, Santa Ana
(92705-5115)
PHONE...................................714 259-0177

Lars Roulund, *CEO*
EMP: 35 **EST:** 1998
SQ FT: 23,000
SALES (est): 5.1MM **Privately Held**
WEB: www.highendseats.com
SIC: 3751 Saddles & seat posts, motorcycle & bicycle

(P-21116)
HIGHWAY TWO
1 Columbia Ste 200, Aliso Viejo
(92656-1473)
PHONE...................................877 395-8088
EMP: 11
SALES (est): 2.3MM **Privately Held**
SIC: 3751 Bicycles & related parts
PA: Highway Two
1909 Miller Dr
Olney IL 62450
-

(P-21117)
IMS PRODUCTS INC
6240 Box Springs Blvd E, Riverside
(92507-0748)
PHONE...................................951 653-7720
C H Wheat, *President*
EMP: 16 **EST:** 1976
SQ FT: 10,000
SALES (est): 2.3MM **Privately Held**
WEB: www.imsproducts.com
SIC: 3751 5571 Motorcycles & related parts; motorcycle accessories; motorcycle dealers

(P-21118)
INTENSE CYCLES INC
42380 Rio Nedo, Temecula (92590-3708)
PHONE...................................951 296-9596
Jeff Steber, *President*
Chad Peterson, *COO*
Eelco Niermeijer, *CFO*
Marvin Strand, *Vice Pres*
Robert Warren, *Opers Staff*
▲ **EMP:** 32
SQ FT: 12,000
SALES (est): 7.2MM **Privately Held**
WEB: www.intensecycles.com
SIC: 3751 Frames, motorcycle & bicycle

(P-21119)
K & N ENGINEERING INC (PA)
1455 Citrus St, Riverside (92507-1603)
P.O. Box 1329 (92502-1329)
PHONE...................................951 826-4000
Jerry E Mall, *Chairman*
Thomas McGann, *CEO*
Steven J Rogers, *CEO*
▲ **EMP:** 565
SQ FT: 270,000
SALES (est): 124.1MM **Privately Held**
WEB: www.kandn.org
SIC: 3751 3599 3714 Handle bars, motorcycle & bicycle; air intake filters, internal combustion engine, except auto; filters: oil, fuel & air, motor vehicle

(P-21120)
KDF INC
Also Called: PRO-CISION MACHINING
15875 Concord Cir, Morgan Hill
(95037-5448)
PHONE...................................408 779-3731
Ken Fredenburg, *President*
EMP: 30
SQ FT: 20,000
SALES: 3MM **Privately Held**
SIC: 3751 3599 Bicycles & related parts; machine & other job shop work; electrical discharge machining (EDM)

(P-21121)
KIBBLWHITE PRECISION MACHINING
580 Crespi Dr Ste H, Pacifica
(94044-3426)
PHONE...................................650 359-4704
Will Kibblewhite, *President*
▲ **EMP:** 23
SQ FT: 3,000
SALES (est): 4.1MM **Privately Held**
WEB: www.blackdiamondvalves.com
SIC: 3751 3599 Motorcycles & related parts; machine shop, jobbing & repair

(P-21122)
KRAFT TECH INC
661 Arroyo St, San Fernando
(91340-2219)
PHONE..............................818 837-3520
Javier Mendoza, *President*
▲ EMP: 13 EST: 1990
SQ FT: 40,000
SALES (est): 3MM **Privately Held**
WEB: www.krafttech.com
SIC: 3751 Motorcycle accessories

(P-21123)
LEPERA ENTERPRISES INC
8207 Lankershim Blvd, North Hollywood
(91605-1614)
PHONE..............................818 767-5110
Robert Lepera, *President*
Robert Le Pera, *President*
Christine Le Pera, *Admin Sec*
Christine Lepera, *Admin Sec*
EMP: 26
SQ FT: 7,000
SALES (est): 2.8MM **Privately Held**
WEB: www.lepera.com
SIC: 3751 Saddles & seat posts, motorcycle & bicycle

(P-21124)
LOADED BOARDS INC
10575 Virginia Ave, Culver City
(90232-3520)
PHONE..............................310 839-1800
Don Tashman, *CEO*
Don Cashman, *Info Tech Mgr*
Maria Alarcon, *Accounting Mgr*
Brian Dolen, *Mktg Dir*
Dan Briggs, *Sales Mgr*
▲ EMP: 17
SQ FT: 5,500
SALES (est): 3.8MM **Privately Held**
WEB: www.loadedboards.com
SIC: 3751 Bicycles & related parts; frames, motorcycle & bicycle

(P-21125)
MAHINDRA TRACTOR ASSEMBLY INC (DH)
Also Called: Mahindra Genze
2901 Bayview Dr, Fremont (94538-6520)
PHONE..............................650 779-5180
Vish Palekar, *CEO*
Deven Kataria, *COO*
Sangeeta Laud, *Treasurer*
Shabbir Boxwala, *Administration*
Tim Navarrette, *Marketing Staff*
▲ EMP: 30
SQ FT: 1,600
SALES (est): 9.6MM
SALES (corp-wide): 7.4B **Privately Held**
SIC: 3751 Motor scooters & parts

(P-21126)
MAIER MANUFACTURING INC
416 Crown Point Cir Ste 1, Grass Valley
(95945-9558)
PHONE..............................530 272-9036
Charles A Maier, *President*
George Maier, *Vice Pres*
Mark Maier, *Vice Pres*
▲ EMP: 45
SQ FT: 79,000
SALES (est): 6.7MM **Privately Held**
WEB: www.maier-mfg.com
SIC: 3751 3082 Motorcycle accessories; unsupported plastics profile shapes

(P-21127)
MARKLAND INDUSTRIES INC (PA)
1111 E Mcfadden Ave, Santa Ana
(92705-4103)
PHONE..............................714 245-2850
Donald R Markland, *President*
▲ EMP: 74
SQ FT: 100,000
SALES (est): 32.2MM **Privately Held**
WEB: www.marklandindustries.com
SIC: 3751 Motorcycle accessories

(P-21128)
MATRIX CONCEPTS LLC
28010 Industry Dr, Valencia (91355-4191)
PHONE..............................661 253-1592
Cameron Cole, *Mng Member*

Rick Smith, *Vice Pres*
Chadd Cole, *Mng Member*
▲ EMP: 12
SQ FT: 12,000
SALES (est): 2.1MM **Privately Held**
SIC: 3751 Motorcycle accessories

(P-21129)
MEGACYCLE ENGINEERING INC
Also Called: Megacycle Cams
90 Mitchell Blvd, San Rafael (94903-2039)
PHONE..............................415 472-3195
James H Dour, *President*
Barbara Dour, *Treasurer*
Lisa Dour, *Office Mgr*
EMP: 14
SQ FT: 7,500
SALES (est): 2MM **Privately Held**
WEB: www.megacyclecams.com
SIC: 3751 3714 5013 Motorcycles & related parts; camshafts, motor vehicle; automotive supplies & parts; motorcycle parts

(P-21130)
MOTORSPORT AFTRMRKET GROUP INC (DH)
17771 Mitchell N Ste A, Irvine
(92614-6028)
PHONE..............................949 440-5500
Andrew Graves, *CEO*
Brian Etter, *President*
J A Lacy, *CEO*
Scott Christman, *Admin Sec*
Michael Moore, *Admin Sec*
EMP: 13
SALES (est): 344.4MM **Privately Held**
WEB: www.maggroup.com
SIC: 3751 Motorcycle accessories

(P-21131)
MOVEMENT PRODUCTS INC
22365 El Toro Rd Ste 295, Lake Forest
(92630-5053)
PHONE..............................949 206-0000
James K Miansian, *President*
EMP: 10 EST: 2012
SALES (est): 250K **Privately Held**
SIC: 3751 5013 Motorcycles, bicycles & parts; automotive supplies & parts

(P-21132)
PRO CIRCUIT PRODUCTS INC
2388 Railroad St, Corona (92880-5410)
PHONE..............................951 734-3320
Randy Fleisher, *Manager*
EMP: 15
SALES (corp-wide): 8.9MM **Privately Held**
WEB: www.procircuit.com
SIC: 3751 Motorcycles & related parts
PA: Pro Circuit Products, Inc.
2771 Wardlow Rd
Corona CA 92882
951 738-8050

(P-21133)
REDLANDS CCI INC
721 Nevada St Ste 308, Redlands
(92373-8053)
P.O. Box 365 (92373-0121)
PHONE..............................909 307-6500
Michael E Lyon, *President*
Michael Lyon, *President*
Robert Lyon, *Vice Pres*
EMP: 25
SALES (est): 3.7MM **Privately Held**
SIC: 3751 5091 Bicycles & related parts; bicycle equipment & supplies

(P-21134)
RICHES INTERNATIONAL INC
Also Called: Airtech Streamlining
2530 Fortune Way, Vista (92081-8441)
PHONE..............................760 598-3366
Kent Riches, *President*
EMP: 15
SQ FT: 10,000
SALES (est): 1.5MM **Privately Held**
WEB: www.airtech-streamlining.com
SIC: 3751 Motorcycle accessories

(P-21135)
RITCHEY DESIGN INC (PA)
236 N Santa Cruz Ave # 238, Los Gatos
(95030-7262)
PHONE..............................650 368-4018
Thomas W Ritchey, *President*
Maris Adamovics, *Manager*
Eric Breedy, *Manager*
▲ EMP: 17
SQ FT: 10,000
SALES (est): 2.3MM **Privately Held**
WEB: www.ritcheylogic.com
SIC: 3751

(P-21136)
SANTA CRUZ BICYCLES LLC
Also Called: Santa Cruz Bikes
2841 Mission St, Santa Cruz (95060-5705)
PHONE..............................831 459-7560
Rob Roskopp,
Niki Woodward, *Planning*
Andre Nagel, *Technology*
Peter Mueller-Wille, *Engineer*
Mike Woods, *Engineer*
▲ EMP: 70
SQ FT: 70,000
SALES (est): 19.1MM
SALES (corp-wide): 7.3B **Privately Held**
WEB: www.santacruzmtb.com
SIC: 3751 Bicycles & related parts
PA: Pon Holdings B.V.
Rondebeltweg 31
Almere
886 060-100

(P-21137)
SPINERGY INC
1914 Palomar Oaks Way # 100, Carlsbad
(92008-6515)
PHONE..............................760 496-2121
Martin Connolly, *President*
Henry Mathers, *CFO*
Ryan Webb, *Info Tech Mgr*
Will Cloake, *VP Opers*
Ryan Baker, *Sales Mgr*
▲ EMP: 80
SQ FT: 63,000
SALES (est): 14.7MM **Privately Held**
WEB: www.spinergy.com
SIC: 3751 3949 7389 Bicycles & related parts; exercise equipment; design services

(P-21138)
SPYKE INC
12155 Pangborn Ave, Downey
(90241-5624)
PHONE..............................562 803-1700
Steve Campbell, *President*
▲ EMP: 23 EST: 1996
SQ FT: 15,000
SALES (est): 4.1MM **Privately Held**
WEB: www.spyke1.com
SIC: 3751 Motorcycles, bicycles & parts

(P-21139)
SUPREME PTA INVESTMENTS CORP
Also Called: Supreme Legends USA
221 N Loara St, Anaheim (92801-5535)
PHONE..............................949 707-0288
Paul Appel, *CEO*
Tom Thornton, *CFO*
EMP: 14 EST: 2000
SQ FT: 12,000
SALES (est): 1.5MM **Privately Held**
SIC: 3751 Motorcycle accessories

(P-21140)
SUZUKI MOTOR OF AMERICA INC (HQ)
Also Called: Suzuki USA
3251 E Imperial Hwy, Brea (92821-6795)
P.O. Box 1100 (92822-1100)
PHONE..............................714 996-7040
Takeshi Hayasaki, *President*
Suzanne Miller, *COO*
Robert Alsip, *Trustee*
Takuya Sato, *Exec VP*
Ed Sedeno, *Vice Pres*
◆ EMP: 250

SALES (est): 114.6MM
SALES (corp-wide): 35.2B **Privately Held**
SIC: 3751 3519 3799 Motorcycles & related parts; outboard motors; recreational vehicles
PA: Suzuki Motor Corporation
300, Takatsukacho, Minami-Ku
Hamamatsu SZO 432-8
534 402-061

(P-21141)
T3M INC
3403 10th St Ste 709, Riverside
(92501-3641)
PHONE..............................909 464-1535
Noel Cherowbrier, *CEO*
MI Zhang, *Ch of Bd*
Doug Rodgers, *Vice Pres*
Jennifer Dao, *Opers Staff*
Cesar Alcantara, *Production*
▲ EMP: 37
SALES (est): 5.4MM **Privately Held**
WEB: www.t3motion.com
SIC: 3751 Motorcycles, bicycles & parts

(P-21142)
TOLEMAR INC
Also Called: Tolemar Manufacturing
5221 Oceanus Dr, Huntington Beach
(92649-1028)
PHONE..............................714 362-8166
Steve Ramelot, *CEO*
▲ EMP: 45
SQ FT: 25,000
SALES (est): 8MM **Privately Held**
WEB: www.tolemar.com
SIC: 3751 Motorcycles & related parts; motorcycle accessories

(P-21143)
TOOMEY RACING USA
5050 Wing Way, Paso Robles
(93446-9528)
PHONE..............................805 239-8870
Stuart Toomey, *Owner*
▼ EMP: 10
SQ FT: 5,000
SALES (est): 440K **Privately Held**
WEB: www.toomey.com
SIC: 3751 5012 5571 Motorcycles & related parts; motorcycles; motorcycle parts & accessories

(P-21144)
TORCANO INDUSTRIES INC
20381 Lk Frest Dr Ste B10, Lake Forest
(92630)
PHONE..............................855 359-3339
John Denson, *CEO*
EMP: 40 EST: 2013
SALES (est): 3MM **Privately Held**
SIC: 3751 Bicycles & related parts

(P-21145)
TRICO SPORTS INC
13541 Desmond St, Pacoima
(91331-2301)
PHONE..............................818 899-7705
Paul Yates, *President*
George R Yates, *Vice Pres*
▲ EMP: 90
SQ FT: 60,000
SALES (est): 9.5MM **Privately Held**
SIC: 3751 Bicycles & related parts; saddles & seat posts, motorcycle & bicycle

(P-21146)
TRY ALL 3 SPORTS
Also Called: Tri All
931 Calle Negocio Ste O, San Clemente
(92673-6224)
PHONE..............................949 492-2255
Bill Langford, *Owner*
Eric Tothan, *Manager*
EMP: 12
SALES: 500K **Privately Held**
WEB: www.triall3sports.com
SIC: 3751 5091 Bicycles & related parts; bicycle equipment & supplies

(P-21147)
TWO BROTHERS RACING INC
401 S Grand Ave, Santa Ana (92705-4102)
PHONE..............................714 550-6070
Craig A Erion, *President*
James Saechao, *Sales Staff*

◆ **EMP**: 18
SQ FT: 50,000
SALES (est): 4.3MM **Privately Held**
SIC: 3751 5013 Motorcycles & related parts; motorcycle parts

(P-21148)
V&H PERFORMANCE LLC
Also Called: Vance & Hines
13861 Rosecrans Ave, Santa Fe Springs (90670-5207)
PHONE..............................562 921-7461
Andrew Graves, *CEO*
Byron Hines, *Shareholder*
Lonnie Harrison, *Ch of Bd*
Brian Etter, *President*
Ken Draper, *Vice Pres*
▼ **EMP**: 65
SQ FT: 12,000
SALES (est): 24.2MM **Privately Held**
WEB: www.maggroup.com
SIC: 3751 5013 Motorcycles, bicycles & parts; motorcycle parts
HQ: Motorsport Aftermarket Group, Inc.
17771 Mitchell N Ste A
Irvine CA 92614
949 440-5500

(P-21149)
WESTERN MFG & DISTRG LLC
Also Called: I.V. League Medical
835 Flynn Rd, Camarillo (93012-8702)
P.O. Box 7192, Rancho Santa Fe (92067-7192)
PHONE..............................805 988-1010
Bill Nichols,
Donnell Nichols, *CFO*
Teri Yates, *General Mgr*
EMP: 40
SQ FT: 25,000
SALES (est): 6.5MM **Privately Held**
WEB: www.mcenterprisesusa.com
SIC: 3751 3841 3599 Motorcycles & related parts; motorcycle accessories; surgical & medical instruments; machine shop, jobbing & repair

(P-21150)
WILDERNESS TRAIL BIKES INC (PA)
475 Miller Ave, Mill Valley (94941-2941)
PHONE..............................415 389-5040
Patrick Seidler, *President*
Charlie Cunningham, *Vice Pres*
Stephen M Potts, *Vice Pres*
Mark J Slate, *Vice Pres*
Susan Weaber, *Principal*
▲ **EMP**: 15
SQ FT: 2,000
SALES (est): 1.7MM **Privately Held**
SIC: 3751 5941 Bicycles & related parts; bicycle & bicycle parts

(P-21151)
WORKS CONNECTION
4130 Product Dr, Cameron Park (95682-8459)
PHONE..............................530 642-9488
Eric Phipps, *Owner*
▲ **EMP**: 11
SQ FT: 2,800
SALES (est): 1.7MM **Privately Held**
WEB: www.worksconnection.com
SIC: 3751 Motorcycles & related parts

(P-21152)
YUKON TRAIL INC
1175 Woodlawn St, Ontario (91761-4559)
PHONE..............................909 218-5286
Michael Du, *CEO*
Jun Wu Liu, *President*
▲ **EMP**: 12 **EST**: 2010
SALES (est): 1.5MM **Privately Held**
SIC: 3751 Motorcycles, bicycles & parts

(P-21153)
ZERO GRAVITY CORPORATION
Also Called: Zero Gravity Group
912 Pancho Rd Ste A, Camarillo (93012-8597)
PHONE..............................805 388-8803
Glenn Cook, *President*
◆ **EMP**: 35
SQ FT: 2,800

SALES (est): 5.7MM **Privately Held**
WEB: www.zerogravity-racing.com
SIC: 3751 Motorcycle accessories

(P-21154)
ZING RACING PRODUCTS
27430 Bostik Ct Ste 101, Temecula (92590-5511)
PHONE..............................760 219-4700
Bob Zingg, *Partner*
Dr Calvin Spoolstra, *Partner*
EMP: 10 **EST**: 1997
SQ FT: 8,000
SALES (est): 820K **Privately Held**
WEB: www.zingracing.com
SIC: 3751 Motorcycles, bicycles & parts

3761 Guided Missiles & Space Vehicles

(P-21155)
ARCTURUS UAV INC
539 Martin Ave, Rohnert Park (94928-2048)
PHONE..............................707 206-9372
D'Milo Hallerberg,
Dmilo Hallerberg, *General Mgr*
Eric Folkestad, *Technology*
Philip Mahill, *Marketing Staff*
Chase Hallerberg, *Manager*
EMP: 10
SQ FT: 23,000
SALES (est): 1.8MM **Privately Held**
SIC: 3761 3728 Guided missiles & space vehicles; military aircraft equipment & armament

(P-21156)
BOEING COMPANY
5301 Bolsa Ave, Huntington Beach (92647-2048)
PHONE..............................714 896-3311
James McNerney, *Branch Mgr*
R Gale Schluter, *Vice Pres*
Will Trafton, *Vice Pres*
Brad Logan, *Design Engr*
Clarissa Jones, *Technology*
EMP: 368
SQ FT: 2,200,000
SALES (corp-wide): 93.3B **Publicly Held**
SIC: 3761 3769 Guided missiles & space vehicles; guided missile & space vehicle parts & auxiliary equipment
PA: The Boeing Company
100 N Riverside Plz
Chicago IL 60606
312 544-2000

(P-21157)
CENIC NTWRK OPERATIONS WEBSITE
5757 Plaza Dr Ste 205, Cypress (90630-5048)
PHONE..............................714 220-3494
Bill Clebsch, *Principal*
Thomas West, *Exec Dir*
Christine Goodheart, *Consultant*
Julia Staats, *Associate*
EMP: 11 **EST**: 2010
SALES (est): 1.2MM **Privately Held**
SIC: 3761 Guided missiles & space vehicles, research & development

(P-21158)
CLIFFDALE LLC
20409 Prairie St, Chatsworth (91311-6029)
PHONE..............................818 885-0300
William Hart,
EMP: 16
SQ FT: 24,000
SALES (est): 2MM **Privately Held**
SIC: 3761 Guided missiles & space vehicles

(P-21159)
JACOBS TECHNOLOGY INC
8 Draco Dr Bldg 8350, Edwards (93524-7200)
PHONE..............................661 275-6100
Frank Costanza, *Manager*
EMP: 20
SALES (corp-wide): 10B **Publicly Held**
SIC: 3761 Rockets, space & military, complete

HQ: Jacobs Technology Inc.
600 William Northern Blvd
Tullahoma TN 37388
931 455-6400

(P-21160)
LOCKHEED MARTIN CORPORATION
16020 Empire Grade, Santa Cruz (95060-9628)
PHONE..............................831 425-6000
Joane Meguior, *Manager*
David Barauna, *Controller*
Joshua Ceccarelli, *Human Res Mgr*
Byron Ravenscraft, *Manager*
Bill Rose, *Manager*
EMP: 85 **Publicly Held**
WEB: www.lockheedmartin.com
SIC: 3761 8734 8731 Guided missiles & space vehicles, research & development; space vehicles, complete; testing laboratories; commercial physical research
PA: Lockheed Martin Corporation
6801 Rockledge Dr
Bethesda MD 20817

(P-21161)
LOCKHEED MARTIN CORPORATION
Lockheed Martin Metrology Svcs
1111 Lockheed Martin Way, Sunnyvale (94089-1212)
PHONE..............................408 756-5751
Joe Eder, *Program Mgr*
Neil Etling, *Program Mgr*
Stu Lowenthal, *Program Mgr*
Todd Mortensen, *General Mgr*
Brent Frisky, *Administration*
EMP: 64 **Publicly Held**
SIC: 3761 Space vehicles, complete; guided missiles, complete; ballistic missiles, complete; guided missiles & space vehicles, research & development
PA: Lockheed Martin Corporation
6801 Rockledge Dr
Bethesda MD 20817

(P-21162)
LOCKHEED MARTIN CORPORATION
160 E Tasman Dr, San Jose (95134-1619)
P.O. Box 3504, Sunnyvale (94088-3504)
PHONE..............................408 747-2626
John Limdquist, *Manager*
Barbara Rave, *President*
Michael Massa, *Senior Engr*
EMP: 400 **Publicly Held**
WEB: www.lockheedmartin.com
SIC: 3761 3663 Guided missiles & space vehicles; radio & TV communications equipment
PA: Lockheed Martin Corporation
6801 Rockledge Dr
Bethesda MD 20817

(P-21163)
LOCKHEED MARTIN CORPORATION
1111 Lockheed Martin Way, Sunnyvale (94089-1212)
P.O. Box 3504 (94088-3504)
PHONE..............................408 742-4321
Christin Kulinski, *CEO*
David Blevins, *Engineer*
Kevin Chiu, *Engineer*
John Gibb, *Engineer*
Beomhee Lee, *Engineer*
EMP: 584 **Publicly Held**
WEB: www.lockheedmartin.com
SIC: 3761 3663 Radio & TV communications equipment; ballistic missiles, complete
PA: Lockheed Martin Corporation
6801 Rockledge Dr
Bethesda MD 20817

(P-21164)
MASTEN SPACE SYSTEMS INC
1570 Sabovich St 25, Mojave (93501-1681)
PHONE..............................661 824-3423

Joel Scotkin, *CEO*
Shawn Mahoney, *COO*
David Masten, *CTO*
Sean Mahoney, *Info Tech Mgr*
Matthew Kuhns, *Chief Engr*
EMP: 14
SQ FT: 6,000
SALES (est): 3.3MM **Privately Held**
WEB: www.masten-space.com
SIC: 3761 Guided missiles & space vehicles

(P-21165)
NANOSTELLAR INC
3696 Haven Ave Ste B, Redwood City (94063-4604)
PHONE..............................650 368-1010
Pankaj Dhingra, *CEO*
Samuel D Hires, *President*
Mark D Muenchow, *CFO*
▼ **EMP**: 33
SQ FT: 23,000
SALES (est): 4.3MM **Privately Held**
SIC: 3761 Guided missiles & space vehicles, research & development

(P-21166)
ORBITAL SCIENCES CORPORATION
Talo Rd Bldg 1555, Lompoc (93437)
PHONE..............................805 734-5400
Eric Denbrook, *Manager*
Jonathan Chan, *Electrical Engi*
Philip Kasavan, *Electrical Engi*
EMP: 100 **Publicly Held**
WEB: www.orbital.com
SIC: 3761 Space vehicles, complete
HQ: Orbital Sciences Corporation
45101 Warp Dr
Dulles VA 20166
703 406-5000

(P-21167)
PACIFIC BULLETPROOF CO
4985 E Landon Dr, Anaheim (92807-1972)
P.O. Box 536, Yorba Linda (92885-0536)
PHONE..............................714 630-5447
James L McCarthy, *CEO*
◆ **EMP**: 11 **EST**: 1993
SQ FT: 6,000
SALES (est): 3.9MM **Privately Held**
WEB: www.pacificbulletproof.com
SIC: 3761

(P-21168)
PARABILIS SPACE TECH INC
1195 Linda Vista Dr Ste F, San Marcos (92078-3824)
PHONE..............................855 727-2245
David J Streich, *CEO*
Richard Slansky, *Exec VP*
Christopher Grainger, *Vice Pres*
Frank Macklin, *Chief Engr*
EMP: 10 **EST**: 2014
SQ FT: 3,242
SALES (est): 809.4K **Privately Held**
SIC: 3761 Guided missiles & space vehicles, research & development

(P-21169)
SPACE EXPLORATION TECH CORP (PA)
Also Called: Spacex
1 Rocket Rd, Hawthorne (90250-6844)
PHONE..............................310 363-6000
Elon R Musk, *CEO*
Gwynne Shotwell, *President*
Bret Johnsen, *CFO*
Hans Koenigsmann, *Vice Pres*
Bob Reagan, *Vice Pres*
◆ **EMP**: 1500
SQ FT: 964,000
SALES (est): 1B **Privately Held**
WEB: www.spacex.com
SIC: 3761 Rockets, space & military, complete

(P-21170)
STELLAR EXPLORATION INC
835 Airport Dr, San Luis Obispo (93401-8370)
P.O. Box 1, Moffett Field (94035-0001)
PHONE..............................805 459-1425
Tomas Svitek, *President*
Iva Svitek, *Admin Sec*
EMP: 12

▲ = Import ▼=Export
◆ =Import/Export

SQ FT: 3,000
SALES: 1.3MM **Privately Held**
SIC: 3761 Space vehicles, complete

(P-21171)
TAYCO ENGINEERING INC
10874 Hope St, Cypress (90630-5214)
P.O. Box 6034 (90630-0034)
PHONE..............................714 952-2240
Jay Chung, *President*
Lisa Taylor, *President*
Ann Taylor, *COO*
Sheri T Nikolakopulos, *CFO*
Brent Taylor, *Vice Pres*
EMP: 130
SQ FT: 55,600
SALES: 16.2MM **Privately Held**
WEB: www.taycoeng.com
SIC: 3761 Guided missiles & space vehicles

(P-21172)
TERRAN ORBITAL
CORPORATION (PA)
15330 Barranca Pkwy, Irvine (92618-2215)
PHONE..............................212 496-2300
Anthony Previte, *CEO*
Jordi Puig-Suari, *Admin Sec*
EMP: 30
SALES (est): 6.6MM **Privately Held**
SIC: 3761 3764 Space vehicles, complete; guided missiles & space vehicles, research & development; guided missile & space vehicle engines, research & devel.

(P-21173)
TSC LLC
Also Called: Spaceship Company, The
16555 Spcship Landing Way, Mojave (93501-1534)
PHONE..............................661 824-6600
George Whitesides,
Adam King, *Officer*
Enrico Palermo, *Vice Pres*
Dale Tutt, *Vice Pres*
Megan Schneider, *Admin Asst*
EMP: 850
SQ FT: 200,000
SALES (est): 70MM **Privately Held**
SIC: 3761 Rockets, space & military, complete
HQ: Virgin Galactic, Llc
16555 Spcship Landing Way
Mojave CA 93501

(P-21174)
TYVAK NN-SATELLITE SYSTEMS
INC
15330 Barranca Pkwy, Irvine (92618-2215)
PHONE..............................949 753-1020
Anthony Previte, *CEO*
Marco Villa, *Treasurer*
Ehson Mosleh, *Vice Pres*
Austin Williams, *Vice Pres*
Roland Coelho, *General Mgr*
EMP: 75
SALES (est): 6.3MM
SALES (corp-wide): 6.6MM **Privately Held**
WEB: www.tyvak.com
SIC: 3761 3764 Space vehicles, complete; guided missiles & space vehicles, research & development; guided missile & space vehicle propulsion unit parts; guided missile & space vehicle engines, research & devel.
PA: Terran Orbital Corporation
15330 Barranca Pkwy
Irvine CA 92618
212 496-2300

(P-21175)
UNITED LAUNCH ALLIANCE
LLC
1579 Utah Ave Bldg 7525, Vandenberg Afb (93437)
PHONE..............................303 269-5876
Deborah Settit, *Principal*
EMP: 100
SALES (corp-wide): 1.2B **Privately Held**
SIC: 3761 Guided missiles & space vehicles

PA: United Launch Alliance, L.L.C.
9501 E Panorama Cir
Centennial CO 80112
720 922-7100

(P-21176)
US ROCKETS
Munsey Rd Mile 11, Cantil (93519)
P.O. Box 1242, Claremont (91711-1242)
PHONE..............................707 267-3393
Jerry Irvine, *Owner*
EMP: 14
SQ FT: 6,000
SALES (est): 648.3K **Privately Held**
SIC: 3761 Rockets, space & military, complete

```
3764 Guided Missile/Space
Vehicle Propulsion Units &
parts
```

(P-21177)
INTERNET SCIENCE
EDUCATION PRJ
805 Chestnut St, San Francisco (94133-2245)
PHONE..............................415 806-3156
Jack Sarfatti, *President*
EMP: 10 EST: 1995
SALES: 172.6K **Privately Held**
SIC: 3764 3812 8731 Guided missile & space vehicle engines, research & devel.; defense systems & equipment; commercial physical research; energy research

(P-21178)
MICROCOSM INC
3111 Lomita Blvd, Torrance (90505-5108)
PHONE..............................310 219-2700
James Wertz, *President*
Alice Wertz, *Corp Secy*
Dr Robert E Conger, *Vice Pres*
EMP: 40
SQ FT: 50,000
SALES (est): 7.9MM **Privately Held**
WEB: www.smad.com
SIC: 3764 2731 3769 Guided missile & space vehicle propulsion unit parts; book publishing; guided missile & space vehicle parts & auxiliary equipment

(P-21179)
NORTHROP GRUMMAN
INNOVATION
Also Called: Ca75 Atk
9617 Distribution Ave, San Diego (92121-2307)
PHONE..............................858 621-5700
David W Thompson, *President*
Ed Boyce, *Program Mgr*
Steve Connell, *Senior Engr*
Matthew Anderson, *Finance Dir*
EMP: 300 **Publicly Held**
SIC: 3764 Guided missile & space vehicle propulsion unit parts
HQ: Northrop Grumman Innovation Systems, Inc.
45101 Warp Dr
Dulles VA 20166
703 406-5000

(P-21180)
NORTHROP GRUMMAN
INNOVATION
250 Klug Cir, Corona (92880-5409)
PHONE..............................951 520-7300
Dave Shanahan, *Branch Mgr*
EMP: 63 **Publicly Held**
WEB: www.mrcwdc.com
SIC: 3764 Guided missile & space vehicle propulsion unit parts
HQ: Northrop Grumman Innovation Systems, Inc.
45101 Warp Dr
Dulles VA 20166
703 406-5000

(P-21181)
NORTHROP GRUMMAN
INNOVATION
6750 Navigator Way # 200, Goleta (93117-3657)
PHONE..............................805 961-8600
John Nisbet, *Branch Mgr*
EMP: 63 **Publicly Held**
WEB: www.mrcwdc.com
SIC: 3764 Guided missile & space vehicle propulsion unit parts
HQ: Northrop Grumman Innovation Systems, Inc.
45101 Warp Dr
Dulles VA 20166
703 406-5000

(P-21182)
THALES ALENIA SPACE NORTH
AMER
20400 Stevens Creek Blvd # 245, Cupertino (95014-2217)
PHONE..............................408 973-9845
Luciano Saccani, *CEO*
EMP: 11
SQ FT: 1,200
SALES: 2MM
SALES (corp-wide): 305.4MM **Privately Held**
SIC: 3764 3769 3761
HQ: Thales Alenia Space Italia Spa
Via Saccomuro 24
Roma RM 00131
064 151-1

(P-21183)
WASK ENGINEERING INC
3905 Dividend Dr, Cameron Park (95682-7214)
PHONE..............................530 672-2795
Wendel Burkhardt, *President*
Kim Burkhardt, *CFO*
John Crapuchettes, *Chief Engr*
EMP: 11
SQ FT: 3,500
SALES: 1.6MM **Privately Held**
WEB: www.waskengr.com
SIC: 3764 Engines & engine parts, guided missile

```
3769 Guided Missile/Space
Vehicle Parts & Eqpt, NEC
```

(P-21184)
AEROWIND CORPORATION
1959 John Towers Ave, El Cajon (92020-1117)
PHONE..............................619 569-1960
William L Kousens, *CEO*
Tam Nguyen, *Engineer*
EMP: 15
SQ FT: 20,000
SALES (est): 3.9MM **Privately Held**
WEB: www.aerowind.com
SIC: 3769 3469 Guided missile & space vehicle parts & aux eqpt, rsch & dev; machine parts, stamped or pressed metal

(P-21185)
AMERICAN AUTOMATED
ENGRG INC
Also Called: A A E Aerospace & Coml Tech
5382 Argosy Ave, Huntington Beach (92649-1037)
PHONE..............................714 898-9951
Kenneth Christensen, *President*
EMP: 85
SQ FT: 48,000
SALES: 26MM **Privately Held**
WEB: www.aaeaerospace.com
SIC: 3769 Guided missile & space vehicle parts & auxiliary equipment

(P-21186)
ATK SPACE SYSTEMS INC
600 Pine Ave, Goleta (93117-3831)
PHONE..............................805 685-2262
Blake Larson, *CEO*
EMP: 100 **Publicly Held**
WEB: www.mrcwdc.com

SIC: 3769 Guided missile & space vehicle parts & auxiliary equipment
HQ: Atk Space Systems Inc.
6033 Bandini Blvd
Commerce CA 90040
323 722-0222

(P-21187)
CHEMRING ENERGETIC
DEVICES
24205 Garnier St, Torrance (90505-5323)
PHONE..............................310 784-2100
David K Shingledecker, *President*
Jan L Hauhe, *CFO*
Mike Kearns, *Opers Mgr*
EMP: 130
SQ FT: 76,000
SALES (est): 24.9MM
SALES (corp-wide): 734.6MM **Privately Held**
WEB: www.hstc.com
SIC: 3769 Guided missile & space vehicle parts & aux eqpt, rsch & dev
PA: Chemring Group Plc
Roke Manor
Romsey HANTS SO51

(P-21188)
CLIFFDALE MANUFACTURING
LLC
Also Called: RTC Aerospace
20409 Prairie St, Chatsworth (91311-6029)
PHONE..............................818 341-3344
Jason Darley, *CEO*
Jerry Koger, *President*
EMP: 130 EST: 1943
SQ FT: 42,000
SALES (est): 17MM **Privately Held**
WEB: www.robertstool.net
SIC: 3769 3599 Guided missile & space vehicle parts & auxiliary equipment; machine shop, jobbing & repair

(P-21189)
COMPOSITE OPTICS
INCORPORATED
Also Called: Atk
7130 Miramar Rd Ste 100b, San Diego (92121-2340)
PHONE..............................937 490-4145
James P Gormican, *Principal*
Barbara McVeigh, *Principal*
Gary Van Gorder, *General Mgr*
James Barnhill, *Engineer*
John Marks, *VP Mktg*
EMP: 800
SQ FT: 257,400
SALES (est): 253MM **Publicly Held**
WEB: www.coiceramics.com
SIC: 3769 Guided missile & space vehicle parts & auxiliary equipment
HQ: Northrop Grumman Innovation Systems, Inc.
45101 Warp Dr
Dulles VA 20166
703 406-5000

(P-21190)
DATA DEVICE CORPORATION
13000 Gregg St Ste C, Poway (92064-7151)
PHONE..............................631 567-5600
David French, *President*
Dr Kevin M Stein, *CEO*
EMP: 37 EST: 2016
SALES (est): 1.4MM **Privately Held**
SIC: 3769 Guided missile & space vehicle parts & aux eqpt, rsch & dev

(P-21191)
DATA DEVICE CORPORATION
13000 Gregg St Ste C, Poway (92064-7151)
PHONE..............................858 503-3300
Dan Veenstra, *Branch Mgr*
EMP: 35
SALES (est): 1.1MM
SALES (corp-wide): 3.5B **Publicly Held**
SIC: 3769 Guided missile & space vehicle parts & aux eqpt, rsch & dev
HQ: Data Device Corporation
105 Wilbur Pl
Bohemia NY 11716
631 567-5600

P R O D U C T S & S V C S

(P-21192)
GOODRICH CORPORATION
Also Called: UTC Aerospace Systems
3530 Branscombe Rd, Fairfield (94533)
P.O. Box Kk (94533-0659)
PHONE.................707 422-1880
Aaron Bennetts, *Manager*
Dave Coolidge, *Prdtn Mgr*
EMP: 25
SALES (corp-wide): 59.8B Publicly Held
SIC: 3769 Guided missile & space vehicle
  parts & auxiliary equipment
HQ: Goodrich Corporation
    2730 W Tyvola Rd
    Charlotte NC 28217
    704 423-7000

(P-21193)
HYDROMACH INC
20400 Prairie St, Chatsworth (91311-8129)
PHONE.................818 341-0915
Norberto A Cusinato, *CEO*
Jose Nicosia, *Vice Pres*
Anna M Cusinato, *Admin Sec*
Rinku Bhamber, *Purchasing*
Damian Causarano, *Buyer*
EMP: 40
SQ FT: 23,000
SALES (est): 8.2MM Privately Held
SIC: 3769 3599 Guided missile & space
  vehicle parts & auxiliary equipment; ma-
  chine shop, jobbing & repair

(P-21194)
**KDL PRECISION MOLDING
CORP**
Also Called: Custom Silicone Technologies
11381 Bradley Ave, Pacoima (91331-2358)
PHONE.................818 896-9899
David Wyckoff, *President*
Lee Brown, *CFO*
Ben Bensal, *Vice Pres*
EMP: 70
SQ FT: 10,000
SALES (est): 13.9MM Privately Held
WEB: www.kdlprecision.com
SIC: 3769 2822 3061 Guided missile &
  space vehicle parts & auxiliary equip-
  ment; silicone rubbers; oil & gas field ma-
  chinery rubber goods (mechanical)

(P-21195)
LEDA CORPORATION
7080 Kearny Dr, Huntington Beach
(92648-6254)
PHONE.................714 841-7821
Joseph K Tung, *President*
David Tung, *Vice Pres*
Dorothy Tung, *Vice Pres*
EMP: 30
SQ FT: 15,000
SALES: 4.1MM Privately Held
WEB: www.ledacorp.net
SIC: 3769 Guided missile & space vehicle
  parts & aux eqpt, rsch & dev

(P-21196)
MICRO STEEL INC
7850 Alabama Ave, Canoga Park
(91304-4905)
PHONE.................818 348-8701
Lazar Hersko, *President*
Claudia Sceelo, *Vice Pres*
Tova Hersko, *Admin Sec*
Ophir Lipski, *Purch Mgr*
EMP: 25
SQ FT: 14,500
SALES: 3.7MM Privately Held
WEB: www.microsteel.com
SIC: 3769 Guided missile & space vehicle
  parts & auxiliary equipment

(P-21197)
STANFORD MU CORPORATION
Also Called: Airborne Components
20725 Annalee Ave, Carson (90746-3503)
PHONE.................310 605-2888
Stanford Mu, *President*
Robert Friend, *Exec VP*
Lynn Price, *Vice Pres*
Robert Ching, *Finance*
EMP: 40

SALES (est): 8MM Privately Held
WEB: www.stanfordmu.com
SIC: 3769 3764 7699 Guided missile &
  space vehicle parts & auxiliary equipment; guided missile & space vehicle
  propulsion unit parts; propulsion units for
  guided missiles & space vehicles; aircraft
  & heavy equipment repair services

(P-21198)
VANTAGE ASSOCIATES INC (PA)
900 Civic Center Dr, National City
(91950-1013)
PHONE.................619 477-6940
Paul Roy, *CEO*
Eric Clack, *President*
Andrea Alpinieri Glover, *CFO*
Maggie Ambrose, *Admin Asst*
Edgar Flores, *Director*
EMP: 35
SQ FT: 15,000
SALES (est): 63.6MM Privately Held
WEB: www.vantagemmc.com
SIC: 3769 2821 3728 3083 Guided mis-
  sile & space vehicle parts & auxiliary
  equipment; plastics materials & resins;
  aircraft parts & equipment; laminated
  plastics plate & sheet

```
3792 Travel Trailers &
Campers
```

(P-21199)
**COMPOSITE PLASTIC SYSTEMS
INC**
1701a River Rock Rd, Santa Maria
(93454-2581)
PHONE.................805 354-1391
Rienk Ayers, *Regional Mgr*
EMP: 17 EST: 2013
SALES (est): 1.3MM Privately Held
SIC: 3792 1623 3728 House trailers, ex-
  cept as permanent dwellings; transmitting
  tower (telecommunication) construction;
  research & dev by manuf., aircraft parts &
  auxiliary equip

(P-21200)
CUSTOM FIBREGLASS MFG CO
Also Called: Custom Hardtops
1711 Harbor Ave, Long Beach
(90813-1300)
PHONE.................562 432-5454
Hartmut W Schroeder, *President*
Joel Thiefburg, *CFO*
Robert L Edwards, *Senior VP*
▲ EMP: 165 EST: 1966
SQ FT: 135,000
SALES: 48.5MM
SALES (corp-wide): 1.2B Privately Held
WEB: www.snugtop.com
SIC: 3792 Pickup covers, canopies or caps
HQ: Truck Accessories Group, Llc
    28858 Ventura Dr
    Elkhart IN 46517
    574 522-5337

(P-21201)
**FLEETWOOD TRAVEL TRLRS
IND INC (DH)**
3125 Myers St, Riverside (92503-5527)
P.O. Box 7638 (92513-7638)
PHONE.................951 354-3000
Edward B Caudill, *President*
Boyd R Plowman, *CFO*
Lyle N Larkin, *Treasurer*
Christopher J Braun, *Senior VP*
Forrest D Theobald, *Senior VP*
EMP: 14 EST: 1971
SQ FT: 262,900
SALES: 9.3MM
SALES (corp-wide): 2.3B Privately Held
SIC: 3792 Travel trailers & campers
HQ: Fleetwood Enterprises, Inc.
    1351 Pomona Rd Ste 230
    Corona CA 92882
    951 354-3000

(P-21202)
FOREST RIVER INC
255 S Pepper Ave, Rialto (92376-6721)
PHONE.................909 873-3777
Ty Miller, *Owner*
EMP: 20

SALES (corp-wide): 242.1B Publicly
Held
WEB: www.forestriverinc.com
SIC: 3792 Tent-type camping trailers
HQ: Forest River, Inc.
    900 County Road 1 N
    Elkhart IN 46514

(P-21203)
FOUR WHEEL CAMPERS INC
109 Pioneer Ave, Woodland (95776-6123)
PHONE.................530 666-1442
Tom Hanagan, *President*
Sonam Chand, *Admin Asst*
Brandon Gonzales, *Purchasing*
Stan Kennedy, *Sales Executive*
▲ EMP: 25
SQ FT: 24,000
SALES (est): 5.6MM Privately Held
SIC: 3792 5561 Travel trailers & campers;
  recreational vehicle dealers

(P-21204)
GOLDEN OFFICE TRAILERS INC
18257 Grand Ave, Lake Elsinore
(92530-6159)
P.O. Box 669, Wildomar (92595-0669)
PHONE.................951 678-2177
Hal D Woods, *President*
EMP: 25
SALES (est): 4.6MM Privately Held
SIC: 3792 5271 Travel trailers & campers;
  mobile homes

(P-21205)
LIFETIME CAMPER SHELLS INC
1375 N E St, San Bernardino (92405-4506)
PHONE.................909 885-2814
Joe Malotte, *President*
Gwen Malotte, *Corp Secy*
EMP: 20 EST: 1980
SQ FT: 1,000
SALES (est): 3.2MM Privately Held
SIC: 3792 Campers, for mounting on
  trucks

(P-21206)
LIN CONSULTING LLC
Also Called: Airstream of Orange County
15086 Beach Blvd, Midway City
(92655-1414)
PHONE.................714 650-8595
Margaret Bayston, *CEO*
Ira Cohen, *Principal*
Ken Kaiden, *Principal*
EMP: 11
SALES (est): 202.9K Privately Held
SIC: 3792 4725 Travel trailers & campers;
  tour operators

(P-21207)
MVP RV INC
40 E Verdugo Ave, Burbank (91502-1931)
PHONE.................951 848-4288
Brad Williams, *President*
Pablo Carmona, *COO*
Roger Humeston, *CFO*
▲ EMP: 50
SALES (est): 6.5MM Privately Held
SIC: 3792 Travel trailer chassis

(P-21208)
PACIFIC COACHWORKS INC
3411 N Perris Blvd Bldg 1, Perris
(92571-3100)
PHONE.................951 686-7294
Brett Bashaw, *CEO*
Michael Rhodes, *Admin Sec*
Isabel Pacheco, *Manager*
EMP: 155
SALES (est): 48MM Privately Held
WEB: www.pacificcoachworks.com
SIC: 3792 Travel trailers & campers

(P-21209)
PROTO HOMES LLC
917 W 17th St, Los Angeles (90015-3317)
PHONE.................310 271-7544
Frank Vafaee,
EMP: 40
SQ FT: 8,000
SALES: 9MM Privately Held
SIC: 3792 House trailers, except as per-
  manent dwellings

(P-21210)
SHADOW INDUSTRIES INC
Also Called: Shadow Trailers
8941 Electric St, Cypress (90630-2240)
PHONE.................714 995-4353
Fritz Stanley Owner, *President*
EMP: 14
SQ FT: 2,804
SALES: 1,000K Privately Held
WEB: www.shadowtrailers.com
SIC: 3792 5599 Travel trailers & campers;
  utility trailers

(P-21211)
SIX PAC CAMPERS INC
109 Pioneer Ave, Woodland (95776-6123)
PHONE.................800 242-1442
Tom Hanagan, *President*
EMP: 10
SQ FT: 20,000
SALES: 6MM Privately Held
WEB: www.fourwh.com
SIC: 3792 Truck campers (slide-in)

(P-21212)
TAILGATER INC
Also Called: Versarack
881 Vertin Ave, Salinas (93901-4524)
P.O. Box 629 (93902-0629)
PHONE.................831 424-7710
Warren P Landon, *President*
Barbara Landon, *Treasurer*
Barbara H Landon, *Corp Secy*
Dick Renard, *Vice Pres*
Robbie Hohstadt, *Office Mgr*
EMP: 15
SALES (est): 1.4MM Privately Held
WEB: www.tailgater.net
SIC: 3792 3713 Pickup covers, canopies
  or caps; truck & bus bodies

(P-21213)
**TRUCK ACCESSORIES GROUP
LLC**
Leer West
1686 E Beamer St, Woodland
(95776-6219)
PHONE.................530 666-0176
Dave Madison, *Manager*
Stephen Magee, *Admin Sec*
Chris Lewey, *Info Tech Mgr*
EMP: 115
SALES (corp-wide): 1.2B Privately Held
WEB: www.leer.com
SIC: 3792 3713 Pickup covers, canopies
  or caps; truck & bus bodies
HQ: Truck Accessories Group, Llc
    28858 Ventura Dr
    Elkhart IN 46517
    574 522-5337

```
3795 Tanks & Tank
Components
```

(P-21214)
**BAE SYSTEMS LAND
ARMAMENTS LP**
6331 San Ignacio Ave, San Jose
(95119-1202)
PHONE.................408 289-0111
Dan Richard, *Manager*
Cary Murakami, *Principal*
Thomas Schroeder, *Principal*
EMP: 60
SALES (corp-wide): 24.2B Privately Held
WEB: www.bradleyspareparts.com
SIC: 3795 Tanks & tank components
HQ: Bae Systems Land & Armaments L.P.
    2000 15th Nw Fl 11 Flr 11
    Arlington VA 22201
    703 907-8250

(P-21215)
DN TANKS INC (PA)
351 Cypress Ln, El Cajon (92020-1603)
PHONE.................619 440-8181
Charles Crowley, *CEO*
Bill Hendrickson, *Co-CEO*
Bill Crowley, *Exec VP*
Dave Gourley, *Exec VP*
Shelly Anderson, *Vice Pres*
▼ EMP: 152

▲ = Import ▼=Export
◆ =Import/Export

SALES (est): 80MM **Privately Held**
SIC: 3795 8711 1542 Tanks & tank components; engineering services; nonresidential construction

(P-21216)
DYK INCORPORATED (HQ)
Also Called: Dyk Prestressed Tanks
351 Cypress Ln, El Cajon (92020-1603)
P.O. Box 696 (92022-0696)
PHONE..............................619 440-8181
Charles Crowley, CEO
Max R Dykmans, President
Don Paula, CFO
Danish Ihsan, Officer
David Gourley, Exec VP
▲ EMP: 25
SALES (est): 4.8MM **Privately Held**
WEB: www.dyk.com
SIC: 3795 8711 1542 Tanks & tank components; engineering services; nonresidential construction

(P-21217)
PREMIER TANK SERVICE INC
34933 Imperial St, Bakersfield (93308)
PHONE..............................661 833-2960
Lupe Lopez, President
EMP: 40 EST: 2007
SQ FT: 5,000
SALES (est): 3.5MM **Privately Held**
SIC: 3795 7699 Tanks & tank components; tank repair

(P-21218)
SANTA ROSA STAIN
1400 Airport Blvd, Santa Rosa (95403-1023)
P.O. Box 518 (95402-0518)
PHONE..............................707 544-7777
Mark Ferronato, President
Michele Cotta, Corp Secy
Rod Ferronato, Vice Pres
EMP: 45
SQ FT: 12,000
SALES (est): 17.2MM **Privately Held**
WEB: www.srss.com
SIC: 3795 Tanks & tank components

(P-21219)
TIGER TANKS INC
3397 Edison Hwy, Bakersfield (93307-2234)
PHONE..............................661 363-8335
Toll Free:................................888 -
Robert E Bimat, Ch of Bd
Darryck Selk, President
Bryan Lewis, CFO
Roger Burns, Vice Pres
Carol Bimat, Admin Sec
EMP: 30
SQ FT: 55,000
SALES (est): 6.2MM **Privately Held**
WEB: www.tigertanksinc.com
SIC: 3795 3443 Tanks & tank components; fabricated plate work (boiler shop)

3799 Transportation Eqpt, NEC

(P-21220)
ADVANCED DISPLAY SYSTEMS INC
8614 Central Ave, Stanton (90680-2720)
PHONE..............................714 995-2200
Roger J Nichols, President
EMP: 11
SQ FT: 12,000
SALES (est): 1MM **Privately Held**
WEB: www.advanceddisplaysystems.com
SIC: 3799 Golf carts, powered; trailers & trailer equipment; pushcarts & wheelbarrows

(P-21221)
ADVANCED TRANSIT DYNAMICS INC
Also Called: Atdynamics
3150 Corporate Pl, Hayward (94545-3916)
PHONE..............................510 619-8245
Andrew Smith, CEO
Mitch Slomiak, CFO
Kyle Houston, Vice Pres
EMP: 57

SQ FT: 25,000
SALES (est): 9.4MM
SALES (corp-wide): 1.3B **Publicly Held**
SIC: 3799 Trailers & trailer equipment
HQ: Stemco Products, Inc.
300 Industrial Dr
Longview TX 75602
800 527-8492

(P-21222)
ASSAULT INDUSTRIES INC
12691 Monarch St, Garden Grove (92841-3918)
PHONE..............................714 799-6711
Marcelo Danze, President
▲ EMP: 10
SALES (est): 469.3K **Privately Held**
SIC: 3799 All terrain vehicles (ATV)

(P-21223)
CLR ANALYTICS INC
25 Mauchly Ste 315, Irvine (92618-2361)
PHONE..............................949 864-6696
Lianyu Chu, President
Meng Zhang, Assistant
◆ EMP: 10
SALES (est): 758.3K **Privately Held**
SIC: 3799 Trailers & trailer equipment

(P-21224)
CLUB CAR LLC
Also Called: Engersall
1203 Hall Ave, Riverside (92509-2214)
PHONE..............................951 735-4675
Adam Burke, Manager
EMP: 30 **Privately Held**
WEB: www.clubcar.com
SIC: 3799 5088 Golf carts, powered; golf carts
HQ: Club Car, Llc
4125 Washington Rd
Evans GA 30809
706 863-3000

(P-21225)
DG PERFORMANCE SPC INC
4100 E La Palma Ave, Anaheim (92807-1814)
PHONE..............................714 961-8850
Mark W Dooley, President
William J Dooley, Ch of Bd
Joan K Dooley, Corp Secy
Mike Turret, Plant Mgr
EMP: 100
SQ FT: 25,000
SALES (est): 16.4MM **Privately Held**
WEB: www.dgperf.com
SIC: 3799 3751 5012 5961 Recreational vehicles; motorcycles & related parts; recreation vehicles, all-terrain; fitness & sporting goods, mail order; motor vehicle parts & accessories; carburetors, pistons, rings, valves

(P-21226)
DHM ENTERPRISES INC
7609 Wilbur Way, Sacramento (95828-4927)
PHONE..............................916 688-7767
George Backovich, President
John Pennell, Treasurer
Bruce Pennell, Vice Pres
EMP: 25
SALES (est): 3.1MM **Privately Held**
WEB: www.dhmenterprises.com
SIC: 3799 5551 Boat trailers; boat dealers

(P-21227)
EKKO MATERIAL HDLG EQP MFG INC
1761 W Holt Ave, Pomona (91768-3315)
PHONE..............................909 212-1962
Xiaobo Liu, CEO
Don Hwang, Director
EMP: 10
SQ FT: 9,000
SALES: 500K **Privately Held**
SIC: 3799 Towing bars & systems

(P-21228)
FLEETWOOD ENTERPRISES INC (DH)
1351 Pomona Rd Ste 230, Corona (92882-7165)
PHONE..............................951 354-3000
Nelson Potter, President

Christopher J Braun, Exec VP
Paul C Eskritt, Exec VP
Charley Lott, Exec VP
Todd L Inlander, Senior VP
EMP: 237 EST: 1950
SALES (est): 1.9B
SALES (corp-wide): 2.3B **Privately Held**
WEB: www.fleetwood.com
SIC: 3799 2451 5561 Recreational vehicles; mobile homes; recreational vehicle parts & accessories

(P-21229)
G & F HORSE TRAILER REPAIR
Also Called: G & F White Wedding Carriages
2175 S Willow Ave, Bloomington (92316-2970)
PHONE..............................909 820-4600
George E Liblin, Owner
EMP: 15 EST: 1979
SQ FT: 15,000
SALES (est): 750K **Privately Held**
SIC: 3799 7539 4789 Horse trailers, except fifth-wheel type; trailer repair; horse drawn transportation services

(P-21230)
GENESIS SUPREME RV INC
23129 Cajalco Rd, Perris (92570-7298)
PHONE..............................951 337-0254
Pablo Carmona, CEO
EMP: 28
SALES (est): 6.3MM **Privately Held**
SIC: 3799 Recreational vehicles

(P-21231)
HALL ASSOCIATES RACG PDTS INC
23104 Normandie Ave, Torrance (90502-2619)
PHONE..............................310 326-4111
Ammie Armstrong, CEO
Kennith C Hall, President
EMP: 17
SQ FT: 7,000
SALES (est): 3.5MM **Privately Held**
WEB: www.hallassociatesmachine.com
SIC: 3799 8733 3699 Recreational vehicles; research institute; security devices

(P-21232)
HUA RONG INTERNATIONAL CORP
Also Called: Excalibur Motorsports
14020 Cent Ave Ste 530, Chino (91710)
PHONE..............................909 591-8800
Wade W Liu, CEO
Jin Lee, Vice Pres
▲ EMP: 11
SQ FT: 10,000
SALES (est): 1.4MM **Privately Held**
WEB: www.atv4usa.com
SIC: 3799 5013 All terrain vehicles (ATV); wheels, motor vehicle

(P-21233)
IPC INDUSTRIES INC (PA)
Also Called: Innovative Products Co
27230 Madison Ave Ste C2, Temecula (92590-5690)
PHONE..............................951 695-2720
Michael P Highsmith, CEO
Doug Highsmith, Vice Pres
Stacy Hammond, Office Mgr
EMP: 14 EST: 1995
SQ FT: 11,000
SALES (est): 2.6MM **Privately Held**
SIC: 3799 Trailers & trailer equipment

(P-21234)
LIQUIDSPRING TECHNOLOGIES INC
10400 Pioneer Blvd Ste 1, Santa Fe Springs (90670-3728)
PHONE..............................562 941-4344
Richard J Meyer, President
Carl Harr, Marketing Staff
▼ EMP: 11 EST: 1982
SQ FT: 6,000
SALES (est): 1.2MM **Privately Held**
SIC: 3799 3714 Automobile trailer chassis; universal joints, motor vehicle

(P-21235)
MIGHTY MOVER TRAILERS INC
224 N Sherman Ave, Corona (92882-1843)
P.O. Box 2887 (92878-2887)
PHONE..............................951 736-0225
Rex Burgus, President
Andy Bui, Corp Secy
John Lee, Vice Pres
EMP: 35
SQ FT: 30,000
SALES (est): 4MM **Privately Held**
WEB: www.mightymovertrailers.com
SIC: 3799 5599 Trailers & trailer equipment; utility trailers

(P-21236)
NATIONAL SIGNAL INC
2440 Artesia Ave, Fullerton (92833-2543)
PHONE..............................714 441-7707
Marcos Fernandez, President
Lupe Martinez, President
Lupe Mertinez, Vice Pres
Margie Fernandez, Controller
Luis Jonas, Purch Mgr
◆ EMP: 50
SQ FT: 55,000
SALES (est): 14.2MM **Privately Held**
SIC: 3799 Trailers & trailer equipment

(P-21237)
OMF PERFORMANCE PRODUCTS
Also Called: Orchard's Metal Fabrication
8199 Mar Vista Ct, Riverside (92504-4372)
PHONE..............................951 354-8272
Tim Orchard, Owner
EMP: 10
SQ FT: 2,000
SALES (est): 1.3MM **Privately Held**
WEB: www.omfperformance.com
SIC: 3799 All terrain vehicles (ATV)

(P-21238)
PACIFIC BOAT TRAILERS INC (PA)
13643 5th St, Chino (91710-5168)
PHONE..............................909 902-0094
Roger Treichler, President
Vicky Treichler, Vice Pres
EMP: 20
SQ FT: 30,000
SALES (est): 1MM **Privately Held**
WEB: www.pacifictrailers.com
SIC: 3799 Boat trailers

(P-21239)
PREMIER TRAILER MANUFACTURING
30517 Ivy Rd, Visalia (93291-9553)
P.O. Box 191 (93279-0191)
PHONE..............................559 651-2212
Gene A Cuelho Jr, President
Sally Cuelho, Admin Sec
EMP: 50
SALES (est): 14.1MM **Privately Held**
SIC: 3799 Trailers & trailer equipment

(P-21240)
S&S INVESTMENT CLUB (PA)
5340 Gateway Plaza Dr, Benicia (94510-2123)
PHONE..............................707 747-5508
Michael Combest, CFO
Scott Murphy, President
Cathy Felix, Office Mgr
EMP: 14
SQ FT: 10,200
SALES (est): 2.7MM **Privately Held**
WEB: www.nicksgolfcarts.com
SIC: 3799 5012 5599 Golf carts, powered; recreational vehicles, motor homes & trailers; golf services & professionals; golf cart, powered

(P-21241)
SPORT BOAT TRAILERS INC
430 C St, Patterson (95363-2724)
P.O. Box 1686 (95363-1686)
PHONE..............................209 892-5388
Robert J Kehl, President
EMP: 12
SQ FT: 3,700
SALES (est): 5MM **Privately Held**
SIC: 3799 7539 Boat trailers; trailer repair

(P-21242)
STIERS RV CENTERS LLC
Also Called: American Rv
25410 The Old Rd, Santa Clarita
(91381-1704)
PHONE..............................661 254-6000
Nancy Houck, *Manager*
EMP: 14
SALES (corp-wide): 4.2B **Publicly Held**
SIC: 3799 Recreational vehicles; automobile trailer chassis; carriages, horse drawn
HQ: Stier's Rv Centers, Llc
　　5500 Wible Rd
　　Bakersfield CA 93313
　　661 323-8000

(P-21243)
SUPERIOR ON SITE SERVICE INC
237 S Bent Ave, San Marcos (92078-1226)
PHONE..............................760 744-4420
Brian Rott, *CEO*
Jenny Wang-Berman, *VP Finance*
EMP: 10
SALES (est): 672K **Privately Held**
SIC: 3799 Golf carts, powered

(P-21244)
UNIVERSAL TRAILERS INC
2750 Mulberry St, Riverside (92501-2531)
PHONE..............................951 784-0543
Nghiem Nguyen, *Principal*
Thuan Nguyen, *Principal*
EMP: 15
SQ FT: 22,000
SALES (est): 1.3MM **Privately Held**
SIC: 3799 5599 Trailers & trailer equipment; utility trailers

(P-21245)
VM CUSTOM BOAT TRAILERS
5200 S Peach Ave, Fresno (93725-9708)
PHONE..............................559 486-0410
Dennis E Enochs, *Partner*
David E Enochs, *Partner*
EMP: 21 **EST:** 1967
SQ FT: 3,000
SALES (est): 3.6MM **Privately Held**
WEB: www.recdealers.com
SIC: 3799 Boat trailers

(P-21246)
WAGONMASTERS CORPORATION
Also Called: Joe's Trailer Repair
11060 Cherry Ave, Fontana (92337-7119)
PHONE..............................909 823-6188
Joseph M Burt, *President*
EMP: 10
SQ FT: 10,200
SALES (est): 930K **Privately Held**
WEB: www.trailerrepairusa.com
SIC: 3799 Trailers & trailer equipment

(P-21247)
WHILL INC (PA)
285 Old County Rd Ste 6, San Carlos (94070-6316)
PHONE..............................844 699-4455
Satoshi Sugie, *CEO*
Kenji Goho, *CFO*
Grace Chuang, *Opers Staff*
Navneet Chagger, *Sales Engr*
EMP: 10
SALES: 1.3MM **Privately Held**
SIC: 3799 Off-road automobiles, except recreational vehicles

3812 Search, Detection, Navigation & Guidance Systs & Instrs

(P-21248)
3H COMMUNICATION SYSTEMS INC
4000 Barranca Pkwy # 250, Irvine (92604-4710)
PHONE..............................949 529-1583
Purna Subedi, *CEO*
Michael Giarratano, *President*
Luis Wong, *Principal*
EMP: 48 **EST:** 2014
SALES (est): 6.3MM **Privately Held**
SIC: 3812 4813 4812 3663 Search & navigation equipment; voice telephone communications; radio telephone communication; radio & TV communications equipment; rockets, space & military, complete

(P-21249)
ABL SPACE SYSTEMS COMPANY
224 Oregon St, El Segundo (90245-4214)
P.O. Box 1608 (90245-6608)
PHONE..............................650 996-8214
Harrison O'Hanley, *CEO*
Daniel Piemont, *CFO*
Darin V Pelt, *Admin Sec*
EMP: 10 **EST:** 2017
SALES (est): 671.9K **Privately Held**
SIC: 3812 Acceleration indicators & systems components, aerospace

(P-21250)
ACCUTURN CORPORATION
7189 Old 215 Frontage Rd, Moreno Valley (92553-7903)
PHONE..............................951 656-6621
Ignatius C Araujo, *CEO*
Henri Rahmon, *Shareholder*
Mark Sayegh, *Shareholder*
Iggy Araujo, *President*
Tammy Ryder, *QC Mgr*
EMP: 26 **EST:** 1974
SQ FT: 15,000
SALES (est): 3.8MM **Privately Held**
WEB: www.accuturncorp.com
SIC: 3812 3089 3599 Acceleration indicators & systems components, aerospace; automotive parts, plastic; machine shop, jobbing & repair

(P-21251)
AERO CHIP INTGRTED SYSTEMS INC
13565 Freeway Dr, Santa Fe Springs (90670-5633)
PHONE..............................310 329-8600
Solomon M Gavrila, *President*
Liviu Pribac, *Vice Pres*
EMP: 13
SQ FT: 50,000
SALES (est): 3.4MM **Privately Held**
WEB: www.AeroChip.com
SIC: 3812 Acceleration indicators & systems components, aerospace

(P-21252)
AEROANTENNA TECHNOLOGY INC
20732 Lassen St, Chatsworth (91311-4507)
PHONE..............................818 993-3842
Yosef Klein, *President*
Joe Klein, *President*
Carmela Klein, *Admin Sec*
Jenny Borenstein, *Accounts Mgr*
▲ **EMP:** 140
SALES (est): 35.6MM **Publicly Held**
WEB: www.aeroantenna.com
SIC: 3812 3663 Antennas, radar or communications; antennas, transmitting & communications
HQ: Heico Electronic Technologies Corp.
　　3000 Taft St
　　Hollywood FL 33021
　　954 987-6101

(P-21253)
AEROJET RCKETDYNE HOLDINGS INC (PA)
222 N Pacific Coast Hwy, El Segundo (90245-5648)
P.O. Box 537012, Sacramento (95853-7012)
PHONE..............................310 252-8100
Eileen Drake, *President*
Warren G Lichtenstein, *Ch of Bd*
Mark Tucker, *COO*
Paul R Lundstrom, *CFO*
Gregory A Jones, *Senior VP*
EMP: 75 **EST:** 1915

SALES: 1.8B **Publicly Held**
WEB: www.gencorp.com
SIC: 3812 3764 3769 6552 Defense systems & equipment; propulsion units for guided missiles & space vehicles; guided missile & space vehicle parts & auxiliary equipment; subdividers & developers; real property lessors

(P-21254)
AEROSPACE LGACY FOUNDATION INC
12214 Lakewood Blvd, Downey (90242-2662)
P.O. Box 40684 (90239-1684)
PHONE..............................562 922-8068
Gerald Blackburn, *President*
EMP: 15 **EST:** 2008
SALES (est): 1MM **Privately Held**
SIC: 3812 Aircraft/aerospace flight instruments & guidance systems

(P-21255)
AMETEK AMERON LLC
4750 Littlejohn St, Baldwin Park (91706-2274)
PHONE..............................626 337-4640
EMP: 35
SALES (corp-wide): 3.5B **Publicly Held**
SIC: 3812
HQ: Ametek Ameron, Llc
　　4750 Littlejohn St
　　Baldwin Park CA 91706
　　626 337-4640

(P-21256)
AO SKY CORPORATION
4989 Pedro Hill Rd, Pilot Hill (95664-9610)
PHONE..............................415 717-9901
Craig Miller, *President*
EMP: 11
SALES (est): 1.7MM **Privately Held**
SIC: 3812 Aircraft/aerospace flight instruments & guidance systems

(P-21257)
APEX TECHNOLOGY HOLDINGS INC
Also Called: Apex Design Technology
2850 E Coronado St, Anaheim (92806-2503)
PHONE..............................714 688-7188
Lance Schroeder, *President*
EMP: 120
SQ FT: 80,000
SALES (est): 19MM **Privately Held**
SIC: 3812 Acceleration indicators & systems components, aerospace

(P-21258)
ARMTEC COUNTERMEASURES CO (DH)
85901 Avenue 53, Coachella (92236-2607)
PHONE..............................760 398-0143
Paul Heidenreich, *Vice Pres*
Freeman Swank, *Vice Pres*
Veronica Ramos, *Admin Asst*
Blanca Villagomez, *Admin Asst*
Miguel Ortega, *Design Engr*
◆ **EMP:** 12
SQ FT: 100,000
SALES (est): 67MM
SALES (corp-wide): 2B **Publicly Held**
WEB: www.armtecdefense.com
SIC: 3812 Defense systems & equipment
HQ: Armtec Defense Products Co.
　　85901 Avenue 53
　　Coachella CA 92236
　　760 398-0143

(P-21259)
ARX PAX LABS INC
20 S Santa Cruz Ave # 102, Los Gatos (95030-6800)
PHONE..............................408 335-7630
Greg Henderson, *Principal*
Scott Santandrea, *Vice Pres*
Marilyn Parks, *Principal*
EMP: 16
SALES (est): 1.7MM **Privately Held**
SIC: 3812 Search & navigation equipment

(P-21260)
ASCENT TOOLING GROUP LLC
1395 S Lyon St, Santa Ana (92705-4608)
PHONE..............................949 455-0665
Brian Williams, *CEO*
Paul Walsh, *COO*
Steve Littauer, *CFO*
Ray Kauffmann, *Vice Pres*
EMP: 1108
SALES (est): 67MM
SALES (corp-wide): 385.4MM **Privately Held**
SIC: 3812 Acceleration indicators & systems components, aerospace
PA: Ascent Aerospace Holdings Llc
　　16445 23 Mile Rd
　　Macomb MI 48042
　　212 916-8142

(P-21261)
ASRC AEROSPACE CORP
Nasa Ames Research Ctr, Mountain View (94035)
PHONE..............................650 604-5946
Ted Price, *Manager*
EMP: 50
SALES (corp-wide): 2.8B **Privately Held**
WEB: www.asrcaerospace.com
SIC: 3812 7371 7373 5088 Search & navigation equipment; custom computer programming services; computer integrated systems design; transportation equipment & supplies
HQ: Asrc Aerospace Corp
　　7000 Muirkirk Meadows Dr # 100
　　Beltsville MD 20705
　　301 837-5500

(P-21262)
ASTRO AEROSPACE
6384 Via Real, Carpinteria (93013-2928)
PHONE..............................805 684-6641
Albert F Myers, *CEO*
Richard Nelson, *President*
John Alvarez, *General Mgr*
Danny Chae, *Project Mgr*
Mark Foster, *Engineer*
EMP: 110
SQ FT: 70,000
SALES (est): 42MM **Publicly Held**
WEB: www.trw.com
SIC: 3812 Search & navigation equipment
HQ: Northrop Grumman Systems Corporation
　　2980 Fairview Park Dr
　　Falls Church VA 22042
　　703 280-2900

(P-21263)
ATK SPACE SYSTEMS INC
1960 E Grand Ave Ste 1150, El Segundo (90245-5061)
PHONE..............................310 343-3799
Dale Woolheater, *Director*
EMP: 600 **Publicly Held**
SIC: 3812 Search & navigation equipment
HQ: Atk Space Systems Inc.
　　11310 Frederick Ave
　　Beltsville MD 20705
　　301 595-5500

(P-21264)
BAE SYSTEMS LAND ARMAMENTS LP
6331 San Ignacio Ave, San Jose (95119-1202)
P.O. Box 5300958 (95153-5398)
PHONE..............................408 289-0111
Mark Pedrazzi, *Manager*
Ted Kimes, *Program Mgr*
Loren Van Huystee, *Program Mgr*
Vicki Modad, *Executive Asst*
Monica Miller, *Admin Sec*
EMP: 1000
SALES (corp-wide): 24.2B **Privately Held**
WEB: www.udlp.com
SIC: 3812 Search & navigation equipment
HQ: Bae Systems Land & Armaments L.P.
　　2000 15th Nw Fl 11 Flr 11
　　Arlington VA 22201
　　703 907-8250

▲ = Import ▼ =Export
◆ =Import/Export

(P-21265)
BENMAR MARINE ELECTRONICS INC
2225 S Huron Dr, Santa Ana (92704-4941)
PHONE..................714 540-5120
Norton W Lazarus, *President*
Ronald J Klammer, *Ch of Bd*
Calvin King, *Human Res Dir*
EMP: 10
SQ FT: 3,000
SALES: 10MM **Privately Held**
SIC: 3812 Navigational systems & instruments

(P-21266)
BIOSPHERICAL INSTRUMENTS INC
5340 Riley St, San Diego (92110-2621)
PHONE..................619 686-1888
Charles Booth, *CEO*
Dr John Morrow, *President*
Randy Lind, *Engineer*
EMP: 14
SQ FT: 7,000
SALES (est): 3MM **Privately Held**
WEB: www.biospherical.com
SIC: 3812 8733 3826 Light or heat emission operating apparatus; research institute; photometers

(P-21267)
BOEING COMPANY
210 Reeves Blvd Bldg 210 # 210, Lemoore (93246-7200)
PHONE..................559 998-8214
Steven Bruce, *Branch Mgr*
EMP: 20
SALES (corp-wide): 93.3B **Publicly Held**
SIC: 3812 Acceleration indicators & systems components, aerospace
PA: The Boeing Company
100 N Riverside Plz
Chicago IL 60606
312 544-2000

(P-21268)
BOEING COMPANY
1500 E Avenue M, Palmdale (93550-1501)
PHONE..................661 212-0024
Dan Brown, *Manager*
Kimberly Robidoux, *Engineer*
Ofelia Chavez, *Financial Analy*
EMP: 342
SALES (corp-wide): 93.3B **Publicly Held**
SIC: 3812 Space vehicle guidance systems & equipment; missile guidance systems & equipment
PA: The Boeing Company
100 N Riverside Plz
Chicago IL 60606
312 544-2000

(P-21269)
BOEING SATELLITE SYSTEMS
2060 E Imperial Hwy Fl 1, El Segundo (90245-3507)
PHONE..................310 364-5088
EMP: 54
SALES (corp-wide): 96.1B **Publicly Held**
SIC: 3812
HQ: Boeing Satellite Systems International, Inc.
2260 E Imperial Hwy
El Segundo CA 90245
310 364-4000

(P-21270)
CAL-SENSORS INC (PA)
1260 Calle Suerte, Camarillo (93012-8053)
PHONE..................707 303-3837
Craig A Hindman, *CEO*
Jane Howard, *General Mgr*
EMP: 38
SQ FT: 14,800
SALES (est): 2.7MM **Privately Held**
WEB: www.calsensors.com
SIC: 3812 3674 Infrared object detection equipment; semiconductors & related devices

(P-21271)
COBHAM ADV ELEC SOL INC
9404 Chesapeake Dr, San Diego (92123-1303)
PHONE..................858 560-1301

Vincent Trnka, *Branch Mgr*
Raymond Duarte, *Administration*
Dave Brooks, *Engineer*
Kevin Beaver, *Controller*
Eric Hangartner, *Manager*
EMP: 208
SALES (corp-wide): 2.7B **Privately Held**
SIC: 3812 Search & navigation equipment
HQ: Cobham Advanced Electronic Solutions Inc.
305 Richardson Rd
Lansdale PA 19446

(P-21272)
COBHAM ADV ELEC SOL INC
5300 Hellyer Ave, San Jose (95138-1003)
PHONE..................408 624-3000
Charles Stuff, *President*
Merrill McFarland, *Design Engr Mgr*
Michael Pors, *Electrical Engi*
Andrew Berg, *Engineer*
Derek Lew, *Engineer*
EMP: 316
SALES (corp-wide): 2.7B **Privately Held**
SIC: 3812 3679 Search & navigation equipment; microwave components
HQ: Cobham Advanced Electronic Solutions Inc.
305 Richardson Rd
Lansdale PA 19446

(P-21273)
CODAR OCEAN SENSORS LTD (PA)
1914 Plymouth St, Mountain View (94043-1796)
PHONE..................408 773-8240
Donald E Barrick, *President*
Peter M Lilleboe, *Treasurer*
Belinda J Lipa, *Vice Pres*
James Isaacson, *Admin Sec*
Janice Tran, *Admin Asst*
EMP: 14
SQ FT: 2,000
SALES (est): 2.2MM **Privately Held**
WEB: www.codaros.com
SIC: 3812 7629 Antennas, radar or communications; electrical repair shops

(P-21274)
COMPUTATIONAL SENSORS CORP
1042 Via Los Padres, Santa Barbara (93111-1345)
PHONE..................805 962-1175
John D Langan, *President*
EMP: 22 EST: 1999
SQ FT: 5,500
SALES: 3MM **Privately Held**
SIC: 3812

(P-21275)
CONNECTED HOLDINGS LLC
4740 Von Karman Ave # 120, Newport Beach (92660-8109)
PHONE..................714 907-6371
Brian Boling, *President*
Aaron Lujan, *CFO*
EMP: 11
SALES (est): 776.7K **Privately Held**
SIC: 3812 Navigational systems & instruments

(P-21276)
CONSOLIDATED AEROSPACE MFG LLC (PA)
Also Called: CAM
1425 S Acacia Ave, Fullerton (92831-5317)
PHONE..................714 989-2797
Dave Werner, *Mng Member*
Jordan Law,
EMP: 18
SALES (est): 167.6MM **Privately Held**
SIC: 3812 Search & navigation equipment

(P-21277)
CPP IND
16800 Chestnut St, City of Industry (91748-1017)
PHONE..................909 595-2252
Alan Hill, *President*
EMP: 12

SALES (est): 1.4MM **Privately Held**
SIC: 3812 Acceleration indicators & systems components, aerospace

(P-21278)
CRANE AEROSPACE INC
Crane Aerospace & Electronics
3000 Winona Ave, Burbank (91504-2540)
PHONE..................818 526-2600
Brendan Curran, *President*
Bob Tavares, *President*
Gregg Robison, *Vice Pres*
Jeff Campbell, *Program Mgr*
Michael Rohona, *Program Mgr*
EMP: 61
SALES (corp-wide): 2.7B **Publicly Held**
SIC: 3812 Defense systems & equipment
HQ: Crane Aerospace, Inc.
100 Stamford Pl
Stamford CT 06902

(P-21279)
CREATIVE ELECTRON INC
201 Trade St, San Marcos (92078-4373)
PHONE..................760 752-1192
Guilherme Cardoso, *President*
Bill Cardoso, *President*
Glen Thomas, *Vice Pres*
Brian Wagner, *Vice Pres*
Tom Gasaway, *Software Dev*
▲ EMP: 11
SQ FT: 10,000
SALES (est): 3MM **Privately Held**
SIC: 3812 3826 Detection apparatus: electronic/magnetic field, light/heat; electron paramagnetic spin type apparatus

(P-21280)
CUBIC CORPORATION (PA)
9333 Balboa Ave, San Diego (92123-1589)
PHONE..................858 277-6780
Walter C Zable, *Ch of Bd*
Bradley H Feldmann, *Ch of Bd*
Michael Knowles, *President*
Elena Forest, *COO*
Anshooman AGA, *CFO*
EMP: 1243
SQ FT: 500,000
SALES: 1.4B **Publicly Held**
WEB: www.cubic.com
SIC: 3812 3699 7372 Defense systems & equipment; flight simulators (training aids), electronic; application computer software

(P-21281)
CUBIC DEFENSE APPLICATIONS INC
2055 Dublin Dr Ste 200, San Diego (92154-8202)
PHONE..................619 661-1010
David Buss, *President*
Cera Connaughy, *Associate*
EMP: 75 EST: 1956
SALES (est): 2.3MM **Privately Held**
SIC: 3812 7389 Search & navigation equipment; business services

(P-21282)
DAVIS INSTRUMENTS CORPORATION
3465 Diablo Ave, Hayward (94545-2778)
PHONE..................510 732-9229
James S Acquistapace, *Ch of Bd*
Robert W Selig Jr, *President*
Kevin McCarthy, *COO*
Susan Tatum, *CFO*
◆ EMP: 100
SQ FT: 77,000
SALES (est): 25.4MM **Privately Held**
WEB: www.davisnet.com
SIC: 3812 3429 3829 3823 Navigational systems & instruments; marine hardware; measuring & controlling devices; industrial instrmnts msrmnt display/control process variable; farm machinery & equipment

(P-21283)
DAVTRON
427 Hillcrest Way, Emerald Hills (94062-4012)
PHONE..................650 369-1188
Betty Torresdal, *Ch of Bd*
Kevin Torresdal, *President*

Brock Torresdal, *CFO*
▼ EMP: 14
SALES (est): 2.5MM **Privately Held**
WEB: www.davtron.com
SIC: 3812 Aircraft flight instruments

(P-21284)
DECA INTERNATIONAL CORP
Also Called: Golf Buddy
10700 Norwalk Blvd, Santa Fe Springs (90670-3824)
PHONE..................714 367-5900
Seung Wook Jung, *CEO*
Jason Kim, *Info Tech Mgr*
▲ EMP: 28
SQ FT: 3,000
SALES (est): 12MM **Privately Held**
SIC: 3812 Navigational systems & instruments

(P-21285)
DECATUR ELECTRONICS INC (HQ)
15890 Bernardo Center Dr, San Diego (92127-2320)
PHONE..................888 428-4315
Brian Brown, *CEO*
Luisa Nechodom, *Treasurer*
Jean Farmer, *Regl Sales Mgr*
Donnie Hendrickson, *Regl Sales Mgr*
Robert Watson, *Regl Sales Mgr*
◆ EMP: 70
SQ FT: 10,000
SALES (est): 9.1MM **Privately Held**
WEB: www.decaturradar.com
SIC: 3812 Radar systems & equipment

(P-21286)
DECATUR ELECTRONICS INC
Also Called: Thunderworks Division
10729 Wheatlands Ave C, Santee (92071-2887)
PHONE..................619 596-1925
Kevin Mitchell, *Manager*
EMP: 35 **Privately Held**
WEB: www.decaturradar.com
SIC: 3812 Radar systems & equipment
HQ: Decatur Electronics, Inc.
15890 Bernardo Center Dr
San Diego CA 92127
888 428-4315

(P-21287)
DG ENGINEERING CORP (PA)
Also Called: Schulz Engineering
13326 Ralston Ave, Sylmar (91342-7608)
PHONE..................818 364-9024
Gary Gilmore, *Ch of Bd*
Aret Demiral, *President*
▲ EMP: 26
SQ FT: 7,000
SALES (est): 3.4MM **Privately Held**
WEB: www.dge-corp.com
SIC: 3812 3845 Aircraft control systems, electronic; electromedical equipment

(P-21288)
EATON AEROSPACE LLC
E E M C O Div
2905 Winona Ave, Burbank (91504-2539)
PHONE..................818 550-4200
John H Morris, *Branch Mgr*
EMP: 35 **Privately Held**
SIC: 3812 3621 Acceleration indicators & systems components, aerospace; motors, electric
HQ: Eaton Aerospace Llc
1000 Eaton Blvd
Cleveland OH 44122
216 523-5000

(P-21289)
EATON AEROSPACE LLC
9650 Jeronimo Rd, Irvine (92618-2024)
PHONE..................949 452-9500
Lily Bridenbaker, *Manager*
EMP: 25 **Privately Held**
SIC: 3812 3365 Acceleration indicators & systems components, aerospace; aerospace castings, aluminum
HQ: Eaton Aerospace Llc
1000 Eaton Blvd
Cleveland OH 44122
216 523-5000

(P-21290)
ECTEC INC
Also Called: Electrnic Cmbat Test Evluation
632 E Rancho Vista Blvd A, Palmdale
(93550-3001)
P.O. Box 902287 (93590-2287)
PHONE....................................661 451-1098
Nancy Fitzhugh, *President*
William Fitzhugh, *Vice Pres*
EMP: 11
SQ FT: 4,000
SALES (est): 1.4MM **Privately Held**
WEB: www.ectecinc.com
SIC: 3812 8748 8731 Search & naviga-
tion equipment; communications consult-
ing; electronic research

(P-21291)
ELITE AVIATION PRODUCTS INC
1641 Reynolds Ave, Irvine (92614-5709)
PHONE....................................949 536-7199
Zeeshawn Zia, *CEO*
Essam Mohamed, *General Mgr*
Robert Pecanic, *Opers Staff*
Steve Miller, *Consultant*
EMP: 50 **EST:** 2013
SALES (est): 1.8MM
SALES (corp-wide): 7MM **Privately Held**
SIC: 3812
PA: Elite Aerospace Group, Inc.
15773 Gateway Cir
Tustin CA 92780
949 536-7199

(P-21292)
ENSIGN-BICKFORD AROSPC DEF CO
14370 White Sage Rd, Moorpark
(93021-8720)
P.O. Box 429 (93020-0429)
PHONE....................................805 292-4000
Brendan Walsh, *Vice Pres*
EMP: 23
SALES (corp-wide): 185.7MM **Privately Held**
SIC: 3812 Search & navigation equipment
HQ: Ensign-Bickford Aerospace & Defense Co
640 Hopmeadow St
Simsbury CT 06070
860 843-2289

(P-21293)
FIBCO COMPOSITES INC
1220 Hearthside Ct, Fullerton
(92831-1070)
PHONE....................................714 269-1118
Anthony J Rivera, *President*
EMP: 12
SQ FT: 16,544
SALES (est): 890K **Privately Held**
SIC: 3812 3728 Radar systems & equip-
ment; aircraft body assemblies & parts

(P-21294)
FIRAN TECH GROUP USA CORP (HQ)
20750 Marilla St, Chatsworth (91311-4407)
PHONE....................................818 407-4024
Brad Bourne, *President*
EMP: 11
SALES (est): 52.1MM
SALES (corp-wide): 74.8MM **Privately Held**
SIC: 3812 Aircraft control systems, elec-
tronic
PA: Firan Technology Group Corporation
250 Finchdene Sq
Scarborough ON M1X 1
416 299-4000

(P-21295)
FLIGHT METALS LLC
879 W 190th St Ste 400, Gardena
(90248-4223)
PHONE....................................800 838-9047
Jay Sheehan, *Principal*
EMP: 11
SALES (est): 1.3MM **Privately Held**
SIC: 3812 Aircraft/aerospace flight instru-
ments & guidance systems

(P-21296)
FLIR SYSTEMS INC
6769 Hollister Ave # 100, Goleta
(93117-5572)
PHONE....................................805 964-9797
James Woolaway, *CEO*
Andres P Moreno, *Info Tech Dir*
Stephanie Marasciullo, *Software Engr*
Greg Carlson, *Project Mgr*
Hanspeter Adam, *Engineer*
EMP: 40
SALES (corp-wide): 1.8B **Publicly Held**
SIC: 3812 Aircraft/aerospace flight instru-
ments & guidance systems
PA: Flir Systems, Inc.
27700 Sw Parkway Ave
Wilsonville OR 97070
503 498-3547

(P-21297)
GARNER PRODUCTS INC
10620 Industrial Ave # 100, Roseville
(95678-6241)
PHONE....................................916 784-0200
Ronald Stofan, *CEO*
Michelle M Stofan, *Admin Sec*
EMP: 15
SQ FT: 24,000
SALES (est): 3.3MM **Privately Held**
SIC: 3812 3663 7389 Degaussing equip-
ment; radio broadcasting & communica-
tions equipment; document & office
record destruction

(P-21298)
GENESIS ENGINEERING INC
6053 Wellfleet Way, San Jose
(95129-4763)
PHONE....................................408 249-5034
Steve Hayes, *President*
EMP: 10
SALES (est): 1MM **Privately Held**
SIC: 3812 3669 Electronic detection systems (aeronautical); burglar alarm apparatus, electric; fire alarm apparatus,
electric; fire detection systems, electric;
intercommunication systems, electric

(P-21299)
GEODETICS INC
2649 Ariane Dr, San Diego (92117-3422)
PHONE....................................858 729-0872
Lydia Bock, *President*
Hondo Geodetics, *Vice Pres*
Jeffrey Fayaman, *General Mgr*
Christina Mainland, *Controller*
Guadalupe Gonzalez, *Production*
EMP: 30 **EST:** 1999
SQ FT: 2,500
SALES (est): 6.7MM **Privately Held**
WEB: www.geodetics.com
SIC: 3812 Search & navigation equipment

(P-21300)
GLOBAL TECH INSTRUMENTS INC
18380 Enterprise Ln, Huntington Beach
(92648-1201)
PHONE....................................714 375-1811
John Frampton, *President*
EMP: 12
SALES (est): 1.5MM **Privately Held**
WEB: www.globaltechinstruments.com
SIC: 3812 Search & navigation equipment

(P-21301)
GOLDAK INC
15835 Monte St Ste 104, Sylmar
(91342-7674)
PHONE....................................818 240-2666
Dan Mulcahey, *President*
Jeanie Mulcahey, *CFO*
Thomas Mulcahey, *CFO*
Butch Mulcahey, *Vice Pres*
Chris Sanford, *General Mgr*
EMP: 25
SQ FT: 3,000
SALES (est): 4.5MM **Privately Held**
WEB: www.goldak.com
SIC: 3812 Detection apparatus: elec-
tronic/magnetic field, light/heat

(P-21302)
GRAMERCY AEROSPACE MFG LLC
17224 Gramercy Pl, Gardena
(90247-5211)
PHONE....................................310 515-0576
Edward Navarro, *President*
Frank Peckham, *Vice Pres*
▼ **EMP:** 11
SALES: 1.5MM **Privately Held**
SIC: 3812 Acceleration indicators & sys-
tems components, aerospace

(P-21303)
HARRIS CORPORATION
Also Called: Surveillance Solutions
7821 Orion Ave, Van Nuys (91406-2029)
P.O. Box 7713 (91409-7713)
PHONE....................................818 901-2523
Chris Bernhardt, *President*
J Malloy, *Vice Pres*
EMP: 350
SALES (corp-wide): 6.1B **Publicly Held**
WEB: www.ittind.com
SIC: 3812 Search & navigation equipment
PA: Harris Corporation
1025 W Nasa Blvd
Melbourne FL 32919
321 727-9100

(P-21304)
HARRIS CORPORATION
Also Called: Edo Rcnnssnce Srvllnce Sys-
tems
7821 Orion Ave, Van Nuys (91406-2029)
PHONE....................................408 201-8000
EMP: 325
SALES (corp-wide): 6.1B **Publicly Held**
SIC: 3812 Defense systems & equipment
PA: Harris Corporation
1025 W Nasa Blvd
Melbourne FL 32919
321 727-9100

(P-21305)
HARRIS CORPORATION
Also Called: Rf Communiactions
9201 Spectrum Center Blvd # 105, San
Diego (92123-1407)
PHONE....................................619 684-7511
Bill Bry, *Manager*
EMP: 25
SALES (corp-wide): 6.1B **Publicly Held**
SIC: 3812 Search & navigation equipment
PA: Harris Corporation
1025 W Nasa Blvd
Melbourne FL 32919
321 727-9100

(P-21306)
HONEYWELL INTERNATIONAL INC
2525 W 190th St, Torrance (90504-6002)
PHONE....................................734 392-5525
Allen Voorheef, *Branch Mgr*
EMP: 453
SALES (corp-wide): 40.5B **Publicly Held**
WEB: www.honeywell.com
SIC: 3812 Missile guidance systems &
equipment
PA: Honeywell International Inc.
115 Tabor Rd
Morris Plains NJ 07950
973 455-2000

(P-21307)
HOYA CORPORATION USA
680 N Mccarthy Blvd # 120, Milpitas
(95035-5120)
PHONE....................................408 654-2200
Hiroshi Suzuki, *President*
Robert Gusello, *Vice Pres*
Hiromichi Okutsu, *Director*
Lynn Brown, *Manager*
EMP: 10
SALES (corp-wide): 5B **Privately Held**
WEB: www.hoyaoptics.com
SIC: 3812 3211 Search & navigation
equipment; flat glass
HQ: Hoya Corporation Usa
680 N Mccarthy Blvd # 120
Milpitas CA 95035

(P-21308)
INTEROCEAN INDUSTRIES INC
Also Called: Interocean Systems
3738 Ruffin Rd, San Diego (92123-1812)
PHONE....................................858 292-0808
Michael Pearlman, *CEO*
Stephen Pearlman, *Admin Sec*
▼ **EMP:** 31 **EST:** 1945
SQ FT: 65,000
SALES (est): 7.3MM **Privately Held**
WEB: www.interoceansystems.com
SIC: 3812 3699 3826 3531 Search &
navigation equipment; underwater sound
equipment; environmental testing equip-
ment; marine related equipment; indus-
trial flow & liquid measuring instruments;
geophysical & meteorological testing
equipment

(P-21309)
INTEROCEAN SYSTEMS LLC
Also Called: Interocean Systems, Inc.
3738 Ruffin Rd, San Diego (92123-1812)
PHONE....................................858 565-8400
Michael D Pearlman, *President*
EMP: 35
SALES: 2.5MM
SALES (corp-wide): 125.5MM **Privately Held**
SIC: 3812 3699 Search & navigation
equipment; underwater sound equipment
PA: Delmar Systems, Inc.
8114 Highway 90 E
Broussard LA 70518
337 365-0180

(P-21310)
INVENSENSE INC (HQ)
1745 Tech Dr Ste 200, San Jose (95110)
PHONE....................................408 501-2200
Behrooz Abdi, *President*
Amit Shah, *Ch of Bd*
Mark Dentinger, *CFO*
Daniel Goehl, *Vice Pres*
MO Maghsoudnia, *Vice Pres*
EMP: 115
SQ FT: 159,000
SALES: 418.4MM
SALES (corp-wide): 11.9B **Privately Held**
WEB: www.invensense.com
SIC: 3812 Gyroscopes
PA: Tdk Corporation
3-9-1, Shibaura
Minato-Ku TKY 108-0
368 527-300

(P-21311)
JARIET TECHNOLOGIES INC
103 W Torrance Blvd, Redondo Beach
(90277-3633)
PHONE....................................310 698-1001
Charles Harper, *CEO*
David Clark, *Vice Pres*
Monica Gilbert, *Vice Pres*
Matthew Hoppe, *Vice Pres*
Craig Hornbuckle, *Principal*
EMP: 35
SQ FT: 20,000
SALES (est): 3.5MM **Privately Held**
SIC: 3812 Search & navigation equipment

(P-21312)
JENNINGS AERONAUTICS INC
3183 Duncan Ln Ste C, San Luis Obispo
(93401-6781)
PHONE....................................805 544-0932
Gordon Jennings, *President*
EMP: 39
SQ FT: 19,000
SALES: 12MM **Privately Held**
SIC: 3812 7371 Electronic detection systems (aeronautical); aircraft control systems, electronic; defense systems &
equipment; computer software development & applications; computer software
development

(P-21313)
JOHNSTON AIRCRAFT SERVICE INC
6679 Dale Fry Rd, Tulare (93274-9078)
P.O. Box 1457 (93275-1457)
PHONE....................................559 686-1795
David R Johnston, *President*
◆ **EMP:** 15

SALES (est): 1.6MM **Privately Held**
SIC: 3812 Aircraft/aerospace flight instruments & guidance systems

(P-21314)
KAP MANUFACTURING INC
327 W Allen Ave, San Dimas (91773-1441)
PHONE.................................909 599-2525
Michael D' Amato, *CFO*
Kathleen D Amato, *President*
Michael D Amato, *CEO*
Bryan D'Amato, *Vice Pres*
Bryan Damato, *Vice Pres*
EMP: 27
SQ FT: 6,000
SALES (est): 5.9MM **Privately Held**
WEB: www.kapmfg.com
SIC: 3812 Acceleration indicators & systems components, aerospace

(P-21315)
L-3 COMMUNICATIONS WESCAM
428 Aviation Blvd Ste 3l, Santa Rosa (95403-1069)
PHONE.................................707 568-3000
Dan Heibel, *President*
EMP: 33
SALES (est): 7.8MM
SALES (corp-wide): 9.5B **Publicly Held**
SIC: 3812 3861 Search & navigation equipment; photographic equipment & supplies
PA: L3 Technologies, Inc.
600 3rd Ave Fl 34
New York NY 10016
212 697-1111

(P-21316)
L3 TECHNOLOGIES INC
Ocean Systems Division
15825 Roxford St, Sylmar (91342-3537)
PHONE.................................818 833-2500
Alex Miseirvitch, *Vice Pres*
Frank Cipolla, *Vice Pres*
Refugio Alfaro, *Senior Buyer*
EMP: 200
SALES (corp-wide): 9.5B **Publicly Held**
SIC: 3812 Search & navigation equipment
PA: L3 Technologies, Inc.
600 3rd Ave Fl 34
New York NY 10016
212 697-1111

(P-21317)
LAIRD R & F PRODUCTS INC (DH)
2091 Rutherford Rd, Carlsbad (92008-7320)
PHONE.................................760 916-9410
Scott Griffiths, *President*
▲ **EMP:** 50
SQ FT: 62,000
SALES (est): 8.9MM
SALES (corp-wide): 1.2B **Privately Held**
WEB: www.randf.com
SIC: 3812 Radar systems & equipment
HQ: Laird Technologies, Inc.
16401 Swingley
Chesterfield MO 63017
636 898-6000

(P-21318)
LITE MACHINES CORPORATION
2222 Faraday Ave, Carlsbad (92008-7235)
PHONE.................................765 463-0959
Paul Arlton, *President*
David Arlton, *Vice Pres*
Donna Arlton, *Assistant VP*
EMP: 12
SQ FT: 8,000
SALES (est): 2.1MM **Privately Held**
WEB: www.litemachines.com
SIC: 3812 3721 Aircraft control systems, electronic; automatic pilots, aircraft; aircraft; research & development on aircraft by the manufacturer

(P-21319)
LOCKHEED MARTIN CORPORATION
4203 Smith Grade, Santa Cruz (95060-9705)
P.O. Box 3504 (95063-3504)
PHONE.................................831 425-6000

Dave Murphey, *Branch Mgr*
Fred Rust, *Safety Mgr*
EMP: 4536 **Publicly Held**
WEB: www.lockheedmartin.com
SIC: 3812 Search & navigation equipment
PA: Lockheed Martin Corporation
6801 Rockledge Dr
Bethesda MD 20817

(P-21320)
LOCKHEED MARTIN CORPORATION
1523 Crom St, Manteca (95337-6507)
PHONE.................................408 756-1400
Gari Young, *Mfg Mgr*
EMP: 473 **Publicly Held**
SIC: 3812 Search & navigation equipment
PA: Lockheed Martin Corporation
6801 Rockledge Dr
Bethesda MD 20817

(P-21321)
LOCKHEED MARTIN CORPORATION
2770 De La Cruz Blvd, Santa Clara (95050-2624)
PHONE.................................408 734-4980
Ed Novak, *Director*
Carol Crose, *Director*
EMP: 1018 **Publicly Held**
WEB: www.lockheedmartin.com
SIC: 3812 Search & navigation equipment
PA: Lockheed Martin Corporation
6801 Rockledge Dr
Bethesda MD 20817

(P-21322)
LOCKHEED MARTIN CORPORATION
4524 Chancery Ln, Dublin (94568-1314)
PHONE.................................925 756-4594
S Larson, *Principal*
EMP: 473 **Publicly Held**
SIC: 3812 Search & navigation equipment
PA: Lockheed Martin Corporation
6801 Rockledge Dr
Bethesda MD 20817

(P-21323)
LOCKHEED MARTIN CORPORATION
1105 Remington Ct, Sunnyvale (94087-2072)
PHONE.................................408 756-1868
Mark Ellson, *Principal*
EMP: 473 **Publicly Held**
SIC: 3812 Search & navigation equipment
PA: Lockheed Martin Corporation
6801 Rockledge Dr
Bethesda MD 20817

(P-21324)
LOCKHEED MARTIN CORPORATION
Also Called: Buellton Advanced Materials
153 Industrial Way, Buellton (93427-9592)
PHONE.................................805 686-4069
EMP: 491 **Publicly Held**
SIC: 3812 Search & navigation equipment
PA: Lockheed Martin Corporation
6801 Rockledge Dr
Bethesda MD 20817

(P-21325)
LOCKHEED MARTIN CORPORATION
3251 Hanover St, Palo Alto (94304-1121)
PHONE.................................650 424-2000
Aram Mica, *Vice Pres*
Marillyn Lewson, *President*
Caroline Markus, *Research*
Eric Roth, *Research*
Scott Smith, *Research*
EMP: 625
SQ FT: 350,000 **Publicly Held**
WEB: www.lockheedmartin.com
SIC: 3812 Search & navigation equipment

PA: Lockheed Martin Corporation
6801 Rockledge Dr
Bethesda MD 20817

(P-21326)
LOCKHEED MARTIN CORPORATION
266 Caspian Dr, Sunnyvale (94089-1014)
PHONE.................................408 781-8570
Robert Butler III, *Manager*
Joseph A Rich, *Engineer*
William G Conrad Jr, *Manager*
Dave Shinety, *Manager*
EMP: 17 **Publicly Held**
WEB: www.lockheedmartin.com
SIC: 3812 Search & navigation equipment
PA: Lockheed Martin Corporation
6801 Rockledge Dr
Bethesda MD 20817

(P-21327)
LOCKHEED MARTIN CORPORATION
Also Called: Lockheed Martin Space Systems
3251 Hanover St C, Palo Alto (94304-1121)
P.O. Box 179, Denver CO (80201-0179)
PHONE.................................650 424-2000
Vance Coffman, *Manager*
Marillyn Hewson, *CEO*
Mike Boothroyd, *Project Mgr*
Ben Hertz, *Senior Engr*
EMP: 13 **Publicly Held**
WEB: www.lockheedmartin.com
SIC: 3812 Search & navigation equipment
PA: Lockheed Martin Corporation
6801 Rockledge Dr
Bethesda MD 20817

(P-21328)
LOCKHEED MARTIN CORPORATION
3100 Zanker Rd, San Jose (95134-1965)
PHONE.................................408 473-7498
David Turkington, *Branch Mgr*
EMP: 3000 **Publicly Held**
WEB: www.lockheedmartin.com
SIC: 3812 3761 Search & navigation equipment; guided missiles & space vehicles
PA: Lockheed Martin Corporation
6801 Rockledge Dr
Bethesda MD 20817

(P-21329)
LOCKHEED MARTIN CORPORATION
3201 Airpark Dr Ste 204, Santa Maria (93455-1833)
PHONE.................................805 614-3671
Mike Berdeguez, *Principal*
Matt Glenn, *Opers Staff*
EMP: 3000 **Publicly Held**
WEB: www.lockheedmartin.com
SIC: 3812 3761 Search & navigation equipment; guided missiles & space vehicles
PA: Lockheed Martin Corporation
6801 Rockledge Dr
Bethesda MD 20817

(P-21330)
LOCKHEED MARTIN CORPORATION
Also Called: Lockheed Martin Aeronautics Co
225 N Flightline Rd, Edwards (93524-0001)
PHONE.................................661 277-0691
Brian Larson, *Manager*
EMP: 1539 **Publicly Held**
WEB: www.lockheedmartin.com
SIC: 3812 Search & navigation equipment
PA: Lockheed Martin Corporation
6801 Rockledge Dr
Bethesda MD 20817

(P-21331)
LOCKHEED MARTIN CORPORATION
1111 Lockheed Martin Way, Sunnyvale (94089-1212)
P.O. Box 3504 (94088-3504)
PHONE.................................408 742-6688
B H Rogers, *Branch Mgr*
Sandy Weber, *Executive*
Esau Martinez, *Administration*
Jack Han, *MIS Dir*
Doug Chapman, *Research*
EMP: 25 **Publicly Held**
WEB: www.lockheedmartin.com
SIC: 3812 Search & navigation equipment
PA: Lockheed Martin Corporation
6801 Rockledge Dr
Bethesda MD 20817

(P-21332)
LOCKHEED MARTIN CORPORATION
10325 Meanley Dr, San Diego (92131-3011)
PHONE.................................858 740-5100
Mike Berdeguez, *Manager*
Ginger Floyd, *Engineer*
EMP: 250 **Publicly Held**
WEB: www.lockheedmartin.com
SIC: 3812 Search & navigation equipment
PA: Lockheed Martin Corporation
6801 Rockledge Dr
Bethesda MD 20817

(P-21333)
LOCKHEED MARTIN CORPORATION
2895 Golf Course Dr, Ventura (93003-7610)
PHONE.................................805 650-4600
Ben Egerton, *General Mgr*
EMP: 26 **Publicly Held**
WEB: www.lockheedmartin.com
SIC: 3812 Search & navigation equipment
PA: Lockheed Martin Corporation
6801 Rockledge Dr
Bethesda MD 20817

(P-21334)
LOCKHEED MARTIN CORPORATION
Also Called: Lockheed Martin Aeronautics Co
1011 Lockheed Way, Palmdale (93599-0001)
PHONE.................................661 572-7428
Rick Baker, *Vice Pres*
Steve Cox, *Program Mgr*
Donald Parry, *Program Mgr*
James Jones, *General Mgr*
Michael Gowetski, *Administration*
EMP: 4000 **Publicly Held**
WEB: www.lockheedmartin.com
SIC: 3812 Search & navigation equipment
PA: Lockheed Martin Corporation
6801 Rockledge Dr
Bethesda MD 20817

(P-21335)
LOCKHEED MARTIN CORPORATION
Also Called: Lockheed Martin Space Sys
16020 Empire Grade, Santa Cruz (95060-9628)
PHONE.................................831 425-6375
Byron Ravenscraft, *Manager*
EMP: 85 **Publicly Held**
WEB: www.lockheedmartin.com
SIC: 3812 Search & navigation equipment
PA: Lockheed Martin Corporation
6801 Rockledge Dr
Bethesda MD 20817

(P-21336)
LOCKHEED MARTIN CORPORATION
Santa Barbara Focal Plane
346 Bollay Dr, Goleta (93117-5550)
PHONE.................................805 571-2346
Bryan Butler, *Manager*

Mary Mendoza, *Manager*
EMP: 100
SQ FT: 8,500 **Publicly Held**
WEB: www.lockheedmartin.com
SIC: 3812 Infrared object detection equipment
PA: Lockheed Martin Corporation
6801 Rockledge Dr
Bethesda MD 20817

(P-21337)
LOCKHEED MARTIN CORPORATION
1111 Lockheed Martin Way, Sunnyvale (94089-1212)
PHONE....................................408 756-5836
Paul Johnson, *Manager*
EMP: 1261 **Publicly Held**
WEB: www.lockheedmartin.com
SIC: 3812 7371 Nautical instruments; custom computer programming services
PA: Lockheed Martin Corporation
6801 Rockledge Dr
Bethesda MD 20817

(P-21338)
LOCKHEED MARTIN CORPORATION
10325 Meanley Dr, San Diego (92131-3011)
PHONE....................................858 740-5100
Jeff Zeimantz, *Manager*
Chris Andert, *Principal*
EMP: 250 **Publicly Held**
WEB: www.lockheedmartin.com
SIC: 3812 Search & navigation equipment
PA: Lockheed Martin Corporation
6801 Rockledge Dr
Bethesda MD 20817
-

(P-21339)
LOCKHEED MARTIN CORPORATION
22630 Aguadero Pl, Santa Clarita (91350-1301)
PHONE....................................661 572-7363
Robert Scobie, *Manager*
EMP: 430 **Publicly Held**
SIC: 3812 Search & navigation equipment
PA: Lockheed Martin Corporation
6801 Rockledge Dr
Bethesda MD 20817
-

(P-21340)
LOCKHEED MARTIN CORPORATION
1643 Kitchener Dr, Sunnyvale (94087-4133)
PHONE....................................408 756-4386
Martha Steiner, *Branch Mgr*
EMP: 430 **Publicly Held**
SIC: 3812 Search & navigation equipment
PA: Lockheed Martin Corporation
6801 Rockledge Dr
Bethesda MD 20817
-

(P-21341)
LOCKHEED MARTIN CORPORATION
1111 Lockheed Martin Way, Sunnyvale (94089-1212)
PHONE....................................408 742-4321
Jim Harrington, *Manager*
Robert Ivanco, *Engineer*
Melina Snider, *Export Mgr*
Bill Henninger, *Manager*
EMP: 10 **Publicly Held**
WEB: www.lockheedmartin.com
SIC: 3812 Search & navigation equipment
PA: Lockheed Martin Corporation
6801 Rockledge Dr
Bethesda MD 20817
-

(P-21342)
LOCKHEED MARTIN CORPORATION
Also Called: Lockheed Martin Naval
1121 W Reeves Ave, Ridgecrest (93555-2313)
PHONE....................................760 446-1700
John Polak, *Branch Mgr*
EMP: 232 **Publicly Held**
SIC: 3812 Search & navigation equipment
PA: Lockheed Martin Corporation
6801 Rockledge Dr
Bethesda MD 20817

(P-21343)
LOCKHEED MARTIN SKUNK WORKS
1001 Lockheed Way, Palmdale (93599-0001)
PHONE....................................661 572-2974
Robert J Stevens, *CEO*
Mark Towle, *Engineer*
EMP: 14 **EST:** 2008
SALES (est): 1.5MM **Privately Held**
SIC: 3812 Search & navigation equipment

(P-21344)
LYTX INC (PA)
9785 Towne Centre Dr, San Diego (92121-1968)
PHONE....................................858 430-4000
Brandon Nixon, *CEO*
Dave Riordan, *COO*
David Riordan, *COO*
Steve Lifshatz, *CFO*
Paul J Pucino, *CFO*
EMP: 300
SQ FT: 100,000
SALES (est): 130.4MM **Privately Held**
WEB: www.drivecam.com
SIC: 3812 Search & detection systems & instruments

(P-21345)
MEGGITT (ORANGE COUNTY) INC
Also Called: Meggitt Aerospace
355 N Pastoria Ave, Sunnyvale (94085-4110)
PHONE....................................408 739-3533
Joseph Fragala, *Principal*
EMP: 15
SALES (corp-wide): 2.6B **Privately Held**
SIC: 3812 8731 3829 Search & navigation equipment; commercial physical research; measuring & controlling devices
HQ: Meggitt (Orange County), Inc.
14600 Myford Rd
Irvine CA 92606

(P-21346)
MEGGITT SAFETY SYSTEMS INC
Meggitt Control Systems
1785 Voyager Ave Ste 100, Simi Valley (93063-3365)
PHONE....................................805 584-4100
Jim Healy, *Director*
EMP: 200
SALES (corp-wide): 2.6B **Privately Held**
SIC: 3812 Aircraft control systems, electronic
HQ: Meggitt Safety Systems, Inc.
1785 Voyager Ave
Simi Valley CA 93063
805 584-4100

(P-21347)
METROTECH CORPORATION (PA)
Also Called: Vivax-Metrotech
3251 Olcott St, Santa Clara (95054-3006)
PHONE....................................408 734-3880
Christian Stolz, *CEO*
Andrew Hoare, *President*
Mark Royle, *President*
Mark Drew, *Vice Pres*
Dee Hoare, *General Mgr*
▲ **EMP:** 78 **EST:** 1976
SQ FT: 65,000

SALES (est): 17.1MM **Privately Held**
WEB: www.metrotech.com
SIC: 3812 Search & navigation equipment detection apparatus: electronic/magnetic field, light/heat; water leak detectors; measuring & controlling devices

(P-21348)
MILLENNIUM SPACE SYSTEMS INC (HQ)
2265 E El Segundo Blvd, El Segundo (90245-4608)
PHONE....................................310 683-5840
Stan Dubyn, *CEO*
Tiffany Guthrie, *COO*
Laura White, *CFO*
Gregg Owens, *Comp Spec*
Angela Kroboth, *Database Admin*
EMP: 32
SQ FT: 10,000
SALES (est): 10.9MM
SALES (corp-wide): 93.3B **Publicly Held**
WEB: www.millennium-space.com
SIC: 3812 Search & navigation equipment
PA: The Boeing Company
100 N Riverside Plz
Chicago IL 60606
312 544-2000

(P-21349)
MOBILE CROSSING INC
Also Called: Everything Mobile
1230 Oakmead Pkwy Ste 304, Sunnyvale (94085-4017)
PHONE....................................916 485-2773
Raymond Hou, *President*
Chris Stocker, *Vice Pres*
▲ **EMP:** 12
SQ FT: 1,500
SALES: 1.5MM **Privately Held**
SIC: 3812 Navigational systems & instruments

(P-21350)
MOOG INC
21339 Nordhoff St, Chatsworth (91311-5819)
PHONE....................................818 341-5156
Ruben Nalbandian, *Sales Mgr*
David Schindler, *Administration*
John Holzinger, *Design Engr*
Steve Zhao, *Design Engr*
Phil Scott, *Technology*
EMP: 150
SALES (corp-wide): 2.7B **Publicly Held**
WEB: www.moog.com
SIC: 3812 Aircraft control systems, electronic
PA: Moog Inc.
400 Jamison Rd
Elma NY 14059
716 652-2000

(P-21351)
MOOG INC
7406 Hollister Ave, Goleta (93117-2583)
PHONE....................................805 618-3900
Robert W Urban, *General Mgr*
Robert Urban, *Manager*
EMP: 300
SALES (corp-wide): 2.7B **Publicly Held**
SIC: 3812 3492 3625 3769 Aircraft control systems, electronic; electrohydraulic servo valves, metal; relays & industrial controls; actuators, industrial; guided missile & space vehicle parts & auxiliary equipment; airframe assemblies, guided missiles; aircraft parts & equipment; motors & generators
PA: Moog Inc.
400 Jamison Rd
Elma NY 14059
716 652-2000

(P-21352)
MOOG INC
Also Called: Moog Aircraft Group
20263 S Western Ave, Torrance (90501-1310)
PHONE....................................310 533-1178
Alberto Bilalon, *Manager*
Michael Keene, *Administration*
Jennifer Morrison, *Administration*
Andrew Dippel, *Software Engr*
Jeffrey Matsuda, *Technical Staff*
EMP: 450

SALES (corp-wide): 2.7B **Publicly Held**
WEB: www.moog.com
SIC: 3812 Search & navigation equipment
PA: Moog Inc.
400 Jamison Rd
Elma NY 14059
716 652-2000

(P-21353)
MOUNTAIN LAKE LABS
Also Called: Mlabs
2675 Lands End Dr, Lakeport (95453-9605)
PHONE....................................707 331-3297
Stanley Snow, *Principal*
EMP: 10 **EST:** 2015
SALES (est): 581.8K **Privately Held**
SIC: 3812 3761 3764 3769 Aircraft/aerospace flight instruments & guidance systems; guided missiles & space vehicles, research & development; guided missile & space vehicle engines, research & devel.; airframe assemblies, guided missiles; nose cones, guided missiles;

(P-21354)
MTI DE BAJA INC
42941 Madio St Ste 2, Indio (92201-1978)
PHONE....................................951 654-2333
Monty Merkin, *CEO*
Mike Merkin, *Vice Pres*
EMP: 28
SALES (est): 1.9MM **Privately Held**
SIC: 3812 Acceleration indicators & systems components, aerospace

(P-21355)
NAVCOM DEFENSE ELECTRONICS INC (PA)
9129 Stellar Ct, Corona (92883-4924)
PHONE....................................951 268-9205
Clifford C Christ, *President*
David Eliasson, *CFO*
EMP: 52
SQ FT: 61,000
SALES (est): 9.6MM **Privately Held**
WEB: www.navcom.com
SIC: 3812 Navigational systems & instruments

(P-21356)
NEVWEST INC
1225 S Expo Way Ste 140, San Diego (92154)
PHONE....................................619 420-8100
Alfredo Liburd, *President*
Virginia Burd, *Vice Pres*
EMP: 30
SALES (est): 7.1MM **Privately Held**
SIC: 3812 Warfare counter-measure equipment

(P-21357)
NORTHROP GRUMMAN CORPORATION
14099 Champlain Ct, Fontana (92336-3506)
PHONE....................................626 812-2842
Eugene Kanechika, *Branch Mgr*
Michael Miracle, *Purch Agent*
John St Rock, *Manager*
EMP: 735 **Publicly Held**
SIC: 3812 Aircraft/aerospace flight instruments & guidance systems
PA: Northrop Grumman Corporation
2980 Fairview Park Dr
Falls Church VA 22042
-

(P-21358)
NORTHROP GRUMMAN CORPORATION
9736 Trigger Pl, Chatsworth (91311-2655)
PHONE....................................818 715-3264
Kevin Kern, *Branch Mgr*
EMP: 735 **Publicly Held**
SIC: 3812 Aircraft/aerospace flight instruments & guidance systems
PA: Northrop Grumman Corporation
2980 Fairview Park Dr
Falls Church VA 22042
-

(P-21359)
NORTHROP GRUMMAN CORPORATION
Northrop Grumman Aviation
1 Hornet Way, El Segundo (90245-2804)
PHONE..............................310 332-1000
Ray Pollok, *Manager*
Badar Farooquee, *Officer*
Keith Nobuhara, *Department Mgr*
Peggy Polite, *Administration*
Amitav Chaki, *Info Tech Mgr*
EMP: 200 Publicly Held
SIC: 3812 Search & navigation equipment
PA: Northrop Grumman Corporation
2980 Fairview Park Dr
Falls Church VA 22042

(P-21360)
NORTHROP GRUMMAN CORPORATION
18701 Caminito Pasadero, San Diego
(92128-6162)
PHONE..............................858 967-1221
Dagnall Barry, *Branch Mgr*
EMP: 735 Publicly Held
SIC: 3812 Search & detection systems & instruments
PA: Northrop Grumman Corporation
2980 Fairview Park Dr
Falls Church VA 22042

(P-21361)
NORTHROP GRUMMAN CORPORATION
28063 Liana Ln, Valencia (91354-1483)
PHONE..............................310 332-0412
Ed Huey, *Branch Mgr*
EMP: 735 Publicly Held
SIC: 3812 Search & navigation equipment
PA: Northrop Grumman Corporation
2980 Fairview Park Dr
Falls Church VA 22042

(P-21362)
NORTHROP GRUMMAN CORPORATION
17311 Santa Barbara St, Fountain Valley
(92708-3321)
PHONE..............................310 332-6653
EMP: 735 Publicly Held
SIC: 3812 Aircraft/aerospace flight instruments & guidance systems
PA: Northrop Grumman Corporation
2980 Fairview Park Dr
Falls Church VA 22042

(P-21363)
NORTHROP GRUMMAN CORPORATION
18701 Wilmington Ave, Carson
(90746-2819)
PHONE..............................310 764-3000
Howard Rosenthal, *Branch Mgr*
April Miramontes, *Administration*
Priscilla Bustos, *Analyst*
Bonnie Luhrs, *Manager*
EMP: 735 Publicly Held
SIC: 3812 Search & navigation equipment
PA: Northrop Grumman Corporation
2980 Fairview Park Dr
Falls Church VA 22042

(P-21364)
NORTHROP GRUMMAN CORPORATION
10806 Willow Ct, San Diego (92127-2428)
PHONE..............................858 618-7617
Jeff Machler, *Branch Mgr*
EMP: 735 Publicly Held
SIC: 3812 Aircraft/aerospace flight instruments & guidance systems
PA: Northrop Grumman Corporation
2980 Fairview Park Dr
Falls Church VA 22042

(P-21365)
NORTHROP GRUMMAN CORPORATION
4010 Sorrento Valley Blvd, San Diego
(92121-1432)
PHONE..............................858 514-9259
Thomas Adam, *Principal*
Don Kane, *Project Engr*
EMP: 735 Publicly Held
SIC: 3812 Aircraft/aerospace flight instruments & guidance systems
PA: Northrop Grumman Corporation
2980 Fairview Park Dr
Falls Church VA 22042

(P-21366)
NORTHROP GRUMMAN CORPORATION
4020 Redondo Beach Ave, Redondo Beach
(90278-1109)
PHONE..............................310 812-4321
Lac Tran, *Design Engr*
Todd Jameson, *Engineer*
EMP: 17
SALES (est): 2.2MM Privately Held
SIC: 3812 Search & navigation equipment

(P-21367)
NORTHROP GRUMMAN INNOVATION
9401 Corvin Ave, Woodland Hills (91367)
PHONE..............................818 887-8100
Ron Hill, *Branch Mgr*
EMP: 500 Publicly Held
SIC: 3812 Aircraft/aerospace flight instruments & guidance systems
HQ: Northrop Grumman Innovation Systems, Inc.
45101 Warp Dr
Dulles VA 20166
703 406-5000

(P-21368)
NORTHROP GRUMMAN INTL TRDG INC
21240 Burbank Blvd, Woodland Hills
(91367-6680)
PHONE..............................818 715-3607
Tina Davis, *Administration*
EMP: 958 EST: 2014
SALES: 24MM Publicly Held
SIC: 3812 Search & navigation equipment
HQ: Northrop Grumman International, Inc.
2980 Fairview Park Dr
Falls Church VA 22042

(P-21369)
NORTHROP GRUMMAN SYSTEMS CORP
2700 Camino Del Sol, Oxnard
(93030-7967)
PHONE..............................805 278-2074
Pierre Courduroux, *Branch Mgr*
EMP: 508 Publicly Held
SIC: 3812 Aircraft/aerospace flight instruments & guidance systems
HQ: Northrop Grumman Systems Corporation
2980 Fairview Park Dr
Falls Church VA 22042
703 280-2900

(P-21370)
NORTHROP GRUMMAN SYSTEMS CORP
California Microwave Systems
21200 Burbank Blvd, Woodland Hills
(91367-6675)
PHONE..............................818 715-2597
Roy Medlin, *Opers Mgr*
Joan Kirk, *Administration*
Lisle Sherwin, *Engineer*
EMP: 50 Publicly Held
WEB: www.sperry.ngc.com
SIC: 3812 Search & navigation equipment
HQ: Northrop Grumman Systems Corporation
2980 Fairview Park Dr
Falls Church VA 22042
703 280-2900

(P-21371)
NORTHROP GRUMMAN SYSTEMS CORP
17066 Goldentop Rd, San Diego
(92127-2412)
PHONE..............................858 618-4349
Gerald Dufresne, *Manager*
EMP: 2000 Publicly Held
SIC: 3812 3761 7373 3721 Search & detection systems & instruments; radar systems & equipment; defense systems & equipment; warfare counter-measure equipment; guided missiles, complete; guided missiles & space vehicles, research & development; computer integrated systems design; airplanes, fixed or rotary wing; research & development on aircraft by the manufacturer; aircraft servicing & repairing; ordnance & accessories
HQ: Northrop Grumman Systems Corporation
2980 Fairview Park Dr
Falls Church VA 22042
703 280-2900

(P-21372)
NORTHROP GRUMMAN SYSTEMS CORP
1100 W Hollyvale St, Azusa (91702-3305)
P.O. Box 296 (91702-0296)
PHONE..............................626 812-1000
Carl Fischer, *Manager*
Larry Tiller, *General Mgr*
James Lott, *Sr Ntwrk Engine*
Mike Pettey, *Comp Lab Dir*
Marc Lavertu, *Network Mgr*
EMP: 210 Publicly Held
WEB: www.sperry.ngc.com
SIC: 3812 Search & navigation equipment
HQ: Northrop Grumman Systems Corporation
2980 Fairview Park Dr
Falls Church VA 22042
703 280-2900

(P-21373)
NORTHROP GRUMMAN SYSTEMS CORP
Northrop Grumman Info Systems
5441 Luce Ave, McClellan (95652-2417)
PHONE..............................916 570-4454
John Dydiw, *Manager*
Rob Pierson, *Engineer*
EMP: 25 Publicly Held
WEB: www.trw.com
SIC: 3812 Search & navigation equipment
HQ: Northrop Grumman Systems Corporation
2980 Fairview Park Dr
Falls Church VA 22042
703 280-2900

(P-21374)
NORTHROP GRUMMAN SYSTEMS CORP
Also Called: Northrop Grumman Space
9326 Spectrum Center Blvd, San Diego
(92123-1443)
PHONE..............................858 514-9000
Mike Twyman, *Branch Mgr*
Larry Stullich, *Program Mgr*
Sam Yacoub, *Technology*
Ted Batha, *Manager*
EMP: 220 Publicly Held
WEB: www.trw.com
SIC: 3812 Search & navigation equipment
HQ: Northrop Grumman Systems Corporation
2980 Fairview Park Dr
Falls Church VA 22042
703 280-2900

(P-21375)
NORWICH AERO PRODUCTS INC (HQ)
6900 Orangethorpe Ave B, Buena Park
(90620-1390)
P.O. Box 109, Norwich NY (13815-0109)
PHONE..............................607 336-7636
Curtis Reusser, *CEO*
Roger Alan Ross, *President*
Robert D George, *CFO*
Christoper Ainsworth, *VP Opers*
EMP: 64
SQ FT: 56,000
SALES (est): 12.8MM
SALES (corp-wide): 2B Publicly Held
WEB: www.norwichaero.com
SIC: 3812 3829 3823 Search & navigation equipment; measuring & controlling devices; temperature instruments: industrial process type
PA: Esterline Technologies Corp
500 108th Ave Ne Ste 1500
Bellevue WA 98004
425 453-9400

(P-21376)
OCEAN AERO INC
10350 Sorrento Valley Rd, San Diego
(92121-1642)
PHONE..............................858 945-3768
Eric Patten, *CEO*
EMP: 30
SALES (est): 330K Privately Held
SIC: 3812 Search & detection systems & instruments

(P-21377)
PACIFIC DESIGN TECH INC
Also Called: PDT
6300 Lindmar Dr, Goleta (93117-3112)
PHONE..............................805 961-9110
Richard M Fisher, *President*
George Nagy, *Executive*
Larry Taggart, *Business Dir*
Ed Sweeney, *District Mgr*
Larry Theriault, *Admin Sec*
EMP: 28
SQ FT: 19,000
SALES (est): 9.9MM Privately Held
WEB: www.pd-tech.com
SIC: 3812 Acceleration indicators & systems components, aerospace

(P-21378)
PACIFIC SCIENTIFIC COMPANY (DH)
Also Called: Electro Kinetics Division
1785 Voyager Ave, Simi Valley
(93063-3363)
PHONE..............................805 526-5700
James Simpkins, *Principal*
James Healey, *General Mgr*
David Penner, *Finance Dir*
◆ EMP: 23
SALES (est): 79.7MM
SALES (corp-wide): 2.6B Privately Held
WEB: www.pacsci.com
SIC: 3812 3669 3621 3694 Aircraft control systems, electronic; fire detection systems, electric; generators & sets, electric; motors, electric; servomotors, electric; alternators, automotive; water quality monitoring & control systems; control equipment, electric
HQ: Meggitt-Usa, Inc.
1955 Surveyor Ave
Simi Valley CA 93063
805 526-5700

(P-21379)
PANEL PRODUCTS INC
21818 S Wilmington Ave # 411, Long Beach
(90810-1642)
PHONE..............................310 830-3331
Nabil Abdou, *CEO*
Sherine Attia, *Vice Pres*
Jeffrey Fliehler, *Project Engr*
Gerges Khalil, *Engineer*
Ken Patton, *Engineer*
EMP: 20
SALES: 5MM Privately Held
SIC: 3812 Aircraft control instruments

(P-21380)
PAPAGO INC
376 Lemon Creek Dr Ste E, Walnut
(91789-2667)
PHONE..............................909 595-6896
Chan Hsi-Chung, *Administration*
Janet Liao, *Business Dir*
EMP: 13
SALES (est): 1.7MM Privately Held
SIC: 3812 Navigational systems & instruments

(P-21381)
PNEUDRAULICS INC
8575 Helms Ave, Rancho Cucamonga
(91730-4591)
PHONE....................................909 980-5366
Michael Saville, *CEO*
Dain Miller, *President*
Michael Schober, *Vice Pres*
Kimberly Karsting, *Administration*
Bryan Akioka, *Project Engr*
▼ **EMP:** 275
SQ FT: 48,000
SALES (est): 52.4MM
SALES (corp-wide): 3.5B **Publicly Held**
WEB: www.pneudraulics.com
SIC: 3812 Acceleration indicators & systems components, aerospace
PA: Transdigm Group Incorporated
1301 E 9th St Ste 3000
Cleveland OH 44114
216 706-2960

(P-21382)
PRENAV INC
121 Beech St, Redwood City (94063-2135)
PHONE....................................650 264-7279
Nathan Schuett, *CEO*
Nick Rossi, *President*
Marc Ausman, *COO*
Asa Hammond, *Chief Engr*
Elsa Zhang, *Opers Staff*
EMP: 15
SQ FT: 11,000
SALES (est): 1MM **Privately Held**
SIC: 3812 Aircraft/aerospace flight instruments & guidance systems

(P-21383)
QUANERGY SYSTEMS INC (PA)
482 Mercury Dr, Sunnyvale (94085-4706)
PHONE....................................408 245-9500
Louay Eldada, *President*
Axel Fuchs, *President*
Mike Healy, *CFO*
John Novak, *Vice Pres*
Bruce Shibuya, *Vice Pres*
EMP: 77
SALES (est): 10.4MM **Privately Held**
SIC: 3812 Infrared object detection equipment

(P-21384)
QUANTUM3D INC (PA)
1759 Mccarthy Blvd, Milpitas (95035-7416)
PHONE....................................408 600-2500
Clayton Conrad, *President*
Murat Kose, *CFO*
◆ **EMP:** 19
SQ FT: 20,000
SALES (est): 14.8MM **Privately Held**
SIC: 3812 Aircraft control instruments

(P-21385)
RADTEC ENGINEERING INC
1780 La Costa Meadows Dr # 102, San
Marcos (92078-9101)
PHONE....................................760 510-2715
Mohammad Haq, *Manager*
EMP: 12 **Privately Held**
WEB: www.radar-sales.com
SIC: 3812 5065 Radar systems & equipment; radar detectors
PA: Radtec Engineering, Inc.
2150 W 6th Ave Ste F
Broomfield CO 80020

(P-21386)
RANTEC MICROWAVE SYSTEMS INC (PA)
31186 La Baya Dr, Westlake Village
(91362-4003)
PHONE....................................818 223-5000
Carl Grindle, *CEO*
Carl E Grindle, *CEO*
Steven Chegwin, *CFO*
Steven B Chegwin, *Treasurer*
Graham R Wilson, *Admin Sec*
EMP: 55
SQ FT: 35,000
SALES (est): 16.6MM **Privately Held**
WEB: www.rantecmdm.com
SIC: 3812 Antennas, radar or communications

(P-21387)
RAYTHEON COMPANY
14471 Danes Cir, Huntington Beach
(92647-2223)
PHONE....................................310 334-0430
Steve Chu,
EMP: 15
SALES (corp-wide): 25.3B **Publicly Held**
SIC: 3812 8711 3663 3674 Defense systems & equipment; engineering services; radio & TV communications equipment; semiconductors & related devices
PA: Raytheon Company
870 Winter St
Waltham MA 02451
781 522-3000

(P-21388)
RAYTHEON COMPANY
1921 Mariposa St, El Segundo (90245)
PHONE....................................310 647-1000
David Wajsgras, *Branch Mgr*
Mike Vanbiezen, *Program Mgr*
EMP: 100
SALES (corp-wide): 25.3B **Publicly Held**
SIC: 3812 4899 Sonar systems & equipment; satellite earth stations
PA: Raytheon Company
870 Winter St
Waltham MA 02451
781 522-3000

(P-21389)
RAYTHEON COMPANY
16035 E Bridger St, Covina (91722-3323)
PHONE....................................626 675-2584
EMP: 170
SALES (corp-wide): 25.3B **Publicly Held**
SIC: 3812 Defense systems & equipment
PA: Raytheon Company
870 Winter St
Waltham MA 02451
781 522-3000

(P-21390)
RAYTHEON COMPANY
1801 Hughes Dr, Fullerton (92833-2200)
P.O. Box 902, El Segundo (90245-0902)
PHONE....................................714 446-2584
John Coarse, *Branch Mgr*
Robert Eland, *Program Mgr*
David Heine, *Info Tech Mgr*
Brett Robblee, *Info Tech Mgr*
Gerald Plunk, *Project Mgr*
EMP: 15
SALES (corp-wide): 25.3B **Publicly Held**
SIC: 3812 Sonar systems & equipment
PA: Raytheon Company
870 Winter St
Waltham MA 02451
781 522-3000

(P-21391)
RAYTHEON COMPANY
1801 Hughes Dr, Fullerton (92833-2200)
P.O. Box 3310 (92834-3310)
PHONE....................................714 446-3513
Jeff Leiter, *Principal*
Richard Ascheri, *Sr Ntwrk Engine*
Amber Suh, *Software Engr*
Kyle Sanders, *Technical Staff*
James Carr, *Electrical Engi*
EMP: 99
SALES (corp-wide): 25.3B **Publicly Held**
SIC: 3812 8711 Defense systems & equipment; engineering services
PA: Raytheon Company
870 Winter St
Waltham MA 02451
781 522-3000

(P-21392)
RAYTHEON COMPANY
350 E Ridgecrest Blvd # 202, Ridgecrest
(93555-3928)
PHONE....................................760 384-3295
Jim Lemon, *Manager*
EMP: 25
SALES (corp-wide): 25.3B **Publicly Held**
SIC: 3812 Sonar systems & equipment
PA: Raytheon Company
870 Winter St
Waltham MA 02451
781 522-3000

(P-21393)
RAYTHEON COMPANY
8650 Balboa Ave, San Diego (92123-1502)
PHONE....................................619 628-3345
Tom Harwell, *Program Mgr*
Calvin Trinh, *Admin Sec*
Lou Grein, *Senior Engr*
EMP: 250
SALES (corp-wide): 25.3B **Publicly Held**
SIC: 3812 Sonar systems & equipment
PA: Raytheon Company
870 Winter St
Waltham MA 02451
781 522-3000

(P-21394)
RAYTHEON COMPANY
1801 Hughes Dr, Fullerton (92833-2200)
P.O. Box 3310 (92834-3310)
PHONE....................................714 732-0119
Barry Bolton, *Contract Mgr*
Kelly Allison, *Principal*
EMP: 132
SALES (corp-wide): 25.3B **Publicly Held**
SIC: 3812 7371 Sonar systems & equipment; computer software development & applications
PA: Raytheon Company
870 Winter St
Waltham MA 02451
781 522-3000

(P-21395)
RAYTHEON COMPANY
2000 E El Segundo Blvd, El Segundo
(90245-4501)
PHONE....................................310 647-1000
John Jones, *Manager*
Travis Slocumb, *Vice Pres*
Bill Balcer, *Program Mgr*
Thomas Traylor, *Planning Mgr*
Debby Yamane, *Executive Asst*
EMP: 500
SALES (corp-wide): 25.3B **Publicly Held**
SIC: 3812 Defense systems & equipment
PA: Raytheon Company
870 Winter St
Waltham MA 02451
781 522-3000

(P-21396)
RAYTHEON COMPANY
2000 Elsegundo Blvd, El Segundo (90245)
PHONE....................................310 647-8334
Pam Nullmayer, *Branch Mgr*
EMP: 400
SALES (corp-wide): 25.3B **Publicly Held**
SIC: 3812 Radar systems & equipment
PA: Raytheon Company
870 Winter St
Waltham MA 02451
781 522-3000

(P-21397)
RAYTHEON COMPANY
Bldg 471 North End, Port Hueneme
(93043-0001)
PHONE....................................805 985-6851
Jackie Samuel, *Manager*
EMP: 16
SALES (corp-wide): 25.3B **Publicly Held**
SIC: 3812 Sonar systems & equipment
PA: Raytheon Company
870 Winter St
Waltham MA 02451
781 522-3000

(P-21398)
RAYTHEON COMPANY
2200 E Imperial Hwy, El Segundo
(90245-3504)
PHONE....................................310 334-2050
Katherine Auld, *Principal*
EMP: 15
SALES (corp-wide): 25.3B **Publicly Held**
SIC: 3812 Radar systems & equipment
PA: Raytheon Company
870 Winter St
Waltham MA 02451
781 522-3000

(P-21399)
RAYTHEON COMPANY
6150 W Century Blvd, Los Angeles
(90045-5325)
P.O. Box 7651, Van Nuys (91409-7651)
PHONE....................................310 338-1324
Mike Rabens, *Sales/Mktg Mgr*
Manwai Szeto, *Finance Mgr*
Diana Villanueva, *Manager*
EMP: 75
SALES (corp-wide): 25.3B **Publicly Held**
SIC: 3812 Sonar systems & equipment
PA: Raytheon Company
870 Winter St
Waltham MA 02451
781 522-3000

(P-21400)
RAYTHEON COMPANY
2000 E El Segundo Blvd, El Segundo
(90245-4501)
PHONE....................................310 647-9438
Donna McCullough, *Branch Mgr*
EMP: 1000
SALES (corp-wide): 25.3B **Publicly Held**
SIC: 3812 3663 3761 3231 Defense systems & equipment; space satellite communications equipment; airborne radio communications equipment; guided missiles & space vehicles, research & development; rockets, space & military, complete; scientific & technical glassware: from purchased glass; integrated circuits, semiconductor networks, etc.; semiconductor circuit networks
PA: Raytheon Company
870 Winter St
Waltham MA 02451
781 522-3000

(P-21401)
RAYTHEON COMPANY
2000 E El Segundo Blvd, El Segundo
(90245-4501)
P.O. Box 902 (90245-0902)
PHONE....................................310 647-1000
Christine Combs, *Manager*
Hon Tran, *Technology*
EMP: 500
SALES (corp-wide): 25.3B **Publicly Held**
SIC: 3812 Search & navigation equipment
PA: Raytheon Company
870 Winter St
Waltham MA 02451
781 522-3000

(P-21402)
RAYTHEON COMPANY
2000 E El Segundo Blvd, El Segundo
(90245-4501)
PHONE....................................310 647-1000
William Swanson, *Principal*
EMP: 50
SALES (corp-wide): 25.3B **Publicly Held**
SIC: 3812 Radar systems & equipment
PA: Raytheon Company
870 Winter St
Waltham MA 02451
781 522-3000

(P-21403)
RAYTHEON COMPANY
75 Coromar Dr, Goleta (93117-3088)
PHONE....................................805 562-4611
Mike E Allgeier, *Branch Mgr*
EMP: 100
SALES (corp-wide): 25.3B **Publicly Held**
SIC: 3812 8731 3845 3825 Sonar systems & equipment; commercial research laboratory; electronic research; electromedical equipment; instruments to measure electricity
PA: Raytheon Company
870 Winter St
Waltham MA 02451
781 522-3000

(P-21404)
RAYTHEON COMPANY
1901 W Malvern Ave 618, Fullerton
(92833-2177)
PHONE....................................714 446-3232
Dan Buranham, *President*
Tiep Tran, *Sr Software Eng*
EMP: 400

SALES (corp-wide): 25.3B **Publicly Held**
SIC: **3812** 3829 Defense systems & equipment; aircraft & motor vehicle measurement equipment
PA: Raytheon Company
870 Winter St
Waltham MA 02451
781 522-3000

(P-21405)
RAYTHEON COMPANY
10606 7th St, Rancho Cucamonga (91730-5438)
PHONE................................909 483-4040
Raul Mendoza, *Manager*
EMP: 75
SALES (corp-wide): 25.3B **Publicly Held**
SIC: **3812** Sonar systems & equipment
PA: Raytheon Company
870 Winter St
Waltham MA 02451
781 522-3000

(P-21406)
RAYTHEON COMPANY
2175 Park Pl, El Segundo (90245-4705)
PHONE................................310 334-7675
Raymond T Wheeler, *Manager*
EMP: 50
SALES (corp-wide): 25.3B **Publicly Held**
SIC: **3812** Sonar systems & equipment
PA: Raytheon Company
870 Winter St
Waltham MA 02451
781 522-3000

(P-21407)
RAYTHEON COMPANY
75 Coromar Dr, Goleta (93117-3088)
PHONE................................805 562-4611
Mike E Allgeier, *Manager*
David Page, *Program Mgr*
Stefan Baur, *Info Tech Dir*
Samantha Caballero, *Info Tech Mgr*
Bill Rogoza, *Info Tech Mgr*
EMP: 100
SALES (corp-wide): 25.3B **Publicly Held**
SIC: **3812** 8731 3845 3825 Sonar systems & equipment; commercial research laboratory; electronic research; electromedical equipment; instruments to measure electricity
PA: Raytheon Company
870 Winter St
Waltham MA 02451
781 522-3000

(P-21408)
RAYTHEON COMPANY
2000 E El Segundo Blvd, El Segundo (90245-4501)
P.O. Box 902 (90245-0902)
PHONE................................310 647-9438
Rick Yuse, *Branch Mgr*
EMP: 10000
SALES (corp-wide): 25.3B **Publicly Held**
SIC: **3812** Defense systems & equipment
PA: Raytheon Company
870 Winter St
Waltham MA 02451
781 522-3000

(P-21409)
RAYTHEON COMPANY
8650 Balboa Ave, San Diego (92123-1502)
PHONE................................858 571-6598
Gary Michell, *Program Mgr*
Kimberly Teague, *Project Mgr*
Darth Veynar, *Engineer*
Stephanie Love-Payne, *Human Res Mgr*
Susie Mingle, *Human Resources*
EMP: 80
SALES (corp-wide): 25.3B **Publicly Held**
SIC: **3812** Sonar systems & equipment
PA: Raytheon Company
870 Winter St
Waltham MA 02451
781 522-3000

(P-21410)
RAYTHEON COMPANY
63 Hollister St, Goleta (93117)
PHONE................................805 967-5511
Randy Brown, *President*
John Thornburg, *General Mgr*
Karen Steinfeld, *Engineer*

Paul Gardner, *Director*
EMP: 131
SALES (corp-wide): 25.3B **Publicly Held**
SIC: **3812** Defense systems & equipment
PA: Raytheon Company
870 Winter St
Waltham MA 02451
781 522-3000

(P-21411)
RAYTHEON DGITAL FORCE TECH LLC
6779 Mesa Ridge Rd # 150, San Diego (92121-2996)
PHONE................................858 546-1244
Brett Balazs, *Program Mgr*
EMP: 40
SQ FT: 14,500
SALES (est): 8MM
SALES (corp-wide): 25.3B **Publicly Held**
WEB: www.digitalforcetech.com
SIC: **3812** 8711 Defense systems & equipment; engineering services
HQ: Raytheon Bbn Technologies Corp.
10 Moulton St
Cambridge MA 02138
617 873-8000

(P-21412)
REMCOR TECHNICAL INDUSTRIES
7025 Alamitos Ave, San Diego (92154-4709)
PHONE................................619 424-8878
Ron Mueller, *President*
Ellie Mueller, *Admin Sec*
▲ EMP: 25
SQ FT: 6,000
SALES (est): 2MM **Privately Held**
WEB: www.remcortech.com
SIC: **3812** Detection apparatus: electronic/magnetic field, light/heat

(P-21413)
REVEAL IMAGING TECH INC
10260 Campus Point Dr # 6133, San Diego (92121-1522)
PHONE................................858 826-9909
Joseph S Secker, *CEO*
Bill Aitkenhead PHD, *President*
James Buckley, *President*
Carol Raymond, *President*
David Reissfelder, *CFO*
▲ EMP: 65
SQ FT: 2,000
SALES (est): 7.7MM
SALES (corp-wide): 10.1B **Publicly Held**
WEB: www.revealimaging.com
SIC: **3812** 7372 Search & detection systems & instruments; application computer software
HQ: Leidos, Inc.
11951 Freedom Dr Ste 500
Reston VA 20190
571 526-6000

(P-21414)
ROCKWELL COLLINS INC
4553 Glencoe Ave Ste 100, Marina Del Rey (90292-7917)
PHONE................................310 751-3298
EMP: 120 **Publicly Held**
SIC: **3812** Search & navigation equipment
PA: Rockwell Collins, Inc.
400 Collins Rd Ne
Cedar Rapids IA 52498

(P-21415)
ROCKWELL COLLINS INC
1733 Alton Pkwy, Irvine (92606-4901)
PHONE................................714 929-3000
EMP: 99 **Publicly Held**
WEB: www.kaiserelectronics.com
SIC: **3812** Search & navigation equipment
PA: Rockwell Collins, Inc.
400 Collins Rd Ne
Cedar Rapids IA 52498

(P-21416)
ROCKWELL COLLINS INC
1757 Carr Rd, Calexico (92231-9781)
PHONE................................760 540-2232
Victor Romero, *Manager*
Karla Meza, *Engineer*

Priscilla Lara, *Buyer*
Nestor Ramirez, *Manager*
Nick Trent, *Manager*
EMP: 25 **Publicly Held**
WEB: www.keo.com
SIC: **3812** Search & navigation equipment
PA: Rockwell Collins, Inc.
400 Collins Rd Ne
Cedar Rapids IA 52498

(P-21417)
ROCKWELL COLLINS OPTRONICS INC
2752 Loker Ave W, Carlsbad (92010-6603)
PHONE................................319 295-1000
Melissa Ospby, *Branch Mgr*
Charles Micka, *Engineer*
EMP: 13 **Publicly Held**
WEB: www.keo.com
SIC: **3812** Search & navigation equipment
HQ: Rockwell Collins Optronics, Inc.
400 Collins Rd Ne
Cedar Rapids IA 52498

(P-21418)
ROGERSON AIRCRAFT CORPORATION (PA)
2201 Alton Pkwy, Irvine (92606-5033)
PHONE................................949 660-0666
Michael J Rogerson, *President*
Gordon Neil, *President*
Jonathan C Smith, *CFO*
Milton R Pizinger, *Vice Pres*
EMP: 180 EST: 1975
SQ FT: 50,000
SALES (est): 42.7MM **Privately Held**
WEB: www.rogerson.com
SIC: **3812** 3545 3492 3728 Aircraft flight instruments; machine tool accessories; fluid power valves & hose fittings; fuel tanks, aircraft

(P-21419)
ROGERSON KRATOS
403 S Raymond Ave, Pasadena (91105-2609)
PHONE................................626 449-3090
Lawrence Smith, *CEO*
Cannon Mathews, *CFO*
Michael Rogerson, *Chairman*
Milton R Pizinger, *Vice Pres*
EMP: 160
SQ FT: 28,000
SALES (est): 42.2MM
SALES (corp-wide): 42.7MM **Privately Held**
WEB: www.rogersonkratos.com
SIC: **3812** 3825 3699 Aircraft flight instruments; instruments to measure electricity; electrical equipment & supplies
PA: Rogerson Aircraft Corporation
2201 Alton Pkwy
Irvine CA 92606
949 660-0666

(P-21420)
ROZENDAL ASSOCIATES INC
9530 Pathway St Ste 101, Santee (92071-4171)
PHONE................................619 562-5596
Tim Rozendal, *President*
Jean Rozendal, *Vice Pres*
EMP: 10
SQ FT: 5,500
SALES: 1MM **Privately Held**
WEB: www.rozendalassociates.com
SIC: **3812** 3663 8711 Radar systems & equipment; antennas, transmitting & communications; engineering services

(P-21421)
SAFRAN ELEC DEF AVNICS USA LLC
3184 Pullman St, Costa Mesa (92626-3319)
PHONE................................949 642-2427
Parice Smith, *CEO*
Jeffrey J Krolopp, *Vice Pres*
Kelly Bristol, *Program Mgr*
Pamela Gray, *General Mgr*
Patti Hager, *General Mgr*
EMP: 170
SQ FT: 56,000

SALES (corp-wide): 650.9MM **Privately Held**
WEB: www.eaton.com
SIC: **3812** Aircraft/aerospace flight instruments & guidance systems
HQ: Safran Electronics & Defense, Avionics Usa, Llc
2802 Safran Dr
Grand Prairie TX 75052
972 314-3600

(P-21422)
SAGO SYSTEMS INC
10455 Pacific Center Ct, San Diego (92121-4339)
PHONE................................858 646-5300
John Lovberg, *President*
EMP: 10
SQ FT: 5,000
SALES: 1.1MM **Privately Held**
WEB: www.sagosystems.com
SIC: **3812** Search & navigation equipment

(P-21423)
SANDEL AVIONICS INC
2405 Dogwood Way, Vista (92081-8409)
PHONE................................760 727-4900
Gerald Block, *Branch Mgr*
EMP: 169
SALES (corp-wide): 90MM **Privately Held**
SIC: **3812** Aircraft control instruments; aircraft flight instruments; air traffic control systems & equipment, electronic; antennas, radar or communications
PA: Sandel Avionics, Inc.
2401 Dogwood Way
Vista CA 92081
760 727-4900

(P-21424)
SANDEL AVIONICS INC (PA)
2401 Dogwood Way, Vista (92081-8409)
PHONE................................760 727-4900
Gerald Block, *President*
Grant Miller, *CFO*
Javed Khan, *Vice Pres*
Charla Parks, *Admin Asst*
Mark Krause, *Sr Software Eng*
EMP: 31
SQ FT: 16,000
SALES: 90MM **Privately Held**
WEB: www.sandel.com
SIC: **3812** Aircraft control instruments; aircraft flight instruments; air traffic control systems & equipment, electronic; antennas, radar or communications

(P-21425)
SANDERS AIRCRAFT INC
Also Called: Sanders Aircraft Technologies
17149 Lambert Rd, Ione (95640-9527)
P.O. Box 1088 (95640-1088)
PHONE................................209 274-2955
Ruth Sanders, *President*
Brian Sanders, *Vice Pres*
EMP: 10
SQ FT: 18,000
SALES: 1MM **Privately Held**
WEB: www.sandersaircraft.com
SIC: **3812** Aircraft/aerospace flight instruments & guidance systems

(P-21426)
SATCOM SOLUTIONS CORPORATION
31119 Via Colinas Ste 501, Westlake Village (91362-3933)
PHONE................................818 991-9794
Fred Joubert, *President*
Ellie Bahadori, *Office Mgr*
▼ EMP: 10
SQ FT: 7,500
SALES: 2MM **Privately Held**
SIC: **3812** 3669 Navigational systems & instruments; intercommunication systems, electric

(P-21427)
SCIENTIFIC-ATLANTA LLC
Scientific Atlanta
13112 Evening Creek Dr S, San Diego (92128-4108)
PHONE................................619 679-6000
Richard Lapointe, *Controller*
EMP: 350

SALES (corp-wide): 48B **Publicly Held**
WEB: www.scientific-atlanta.com
SIC: 3812 Navigational systems & instruments
HQ: Scientific-Atlanta Llc
5030 Sugarloaf Pkwy
Lawrenceville GA 30044
678 277-1000

(P-21428)
SENSOR CONCEPTS INCORPORATED
7950 National Dr, Livermore (94550-8811)
P.O. Box 2657 (94551-2657)
PHONE..................925 443-9001
Michael Sanders, *President*
John Ashton, *Vice Pres*
George Blenis, *Pharmacy Dir*
Matthew Bogdanov, *Info Tech Mgr*
Gabriel Hojman, *Software Engr*
EMP: 55
SALES (est): 5.2MM **Privately Held**
WEB: www.sensorconcepts.com
SIC: 3812 8711 Radar systems & equipment; engineering services

(P-21429)
SENSOR SYSTEMS INC
8929 Fullbright Ave, Chatsworth (91311-6179)
PHONE..................818 341-5366
Mary E Bazar, *CEO*
Rafael Melero, *Vice Pres*
Si Robin, *Vice Pres*
Dennis E Bazar, *Admin Sec*
Rajah Castillo, *Engineer*
EMP: 258
SQ FT: 60,000
SALES (est): 48.6MM **Privately Held**
WEB: www.sensorantennas.com
SIC: 3812 Aircraft flight instruments

(P-21430)
SIERRA MONOLITHICS INC
5141 California Ave # 150, Irvine (92617-3060)
PHONE..................949 269-4400
Emeka Chukwu, *Owner*
EMP: 11
SALES (corp-wide): 587.8MM **Publicly Held**
SIC: 3812 Search & navigation equipment
HQ: Sierra Monolithics, Inc.
103 W Torrance Blvd
Redondo Beach CA 90277
310 698-1000

(P-21431)
SIEVA NETWORKS INC (PA)
281 Countrybrook Loop, San Ramon (94583-4476)
PHONE..................408 475-1953
Vijay Pillai, *President*
EMP: 10
SQ FT: 2,000
SALES (est): 1.6MM **Privately Held**
SIC: 3812 Search & navigation equipment

(P-21432)
SKYDIO INC
114 Hazel Ave, Redwood City (94061-3112)
PHONE..................408 203-8497
Adam P Bry, *CEO*
Abraham Bachrach, *CTO*
Hayk Martirosyan, *Software Dev*
EMP: 18
SQ FT: 15,000
SALES (est): 961.6K **Privately Held**
SIC: 3812 Acceleration indicators & systems components, aerospace

(P-21433)
SNAPTRACS INC
5775 Morehouse Dr, San Diego (92121-1714)
PHONE..................858 587-1121
Scott L Neuberger, *CEO*
EMP: 14 EST: 2012
SALES (est): 2.8MM **Privately Held**
SIC: 3812 Search & navigation equipment

(P-21434)
SONCELL NORTH AMERICA INC (HQ)
Also Called: AEP Cali
10729 Whelt Lands Ave C, San Diego (92107)
PHONE..................619 795-4600
Luisa Nechodom, *CEO*
Jessica Faustino, *Controller*
Mike Lanctot, *Accounts Mgr*
EMP: 23 EST: 2011
SALES (est): 10.6MM
SALES (corp-wide): 1.2B **Privately Held**
SIC: 3812 Radar systems & equipment
PA: Bowmer And Kirkland Limited
High Edge Court
Belper DE56
177 385-2636

(P-21435)
SPACE INFORMATION LABS LLC
Also Called: Sil
2260 Meredith Ln Ste A, Santa Maria (93455-1117)
PHONE..................805 925-9010
Edmund Burke, *CEO*
Denise Burke, *CFO*
Shaun Luther, *Engineer*
Michelle Buhring, *Purch Agent*
Jim Hammond, *QC Mgr*
EMP: 15
SALES (est): 3.1MM **Privately Held**
SIC: 3812 Search & navigation equipment

(P-21436)
SPEC TOOL COMPANY
Also Called: Alice G Fink-Painter
11805 Wakeman St, Santa Fe Springs (90670-2130)
P.O. Box 1056, Pico Rivera (90660-1056)
PHONE..................323 723-9533
Alice G Fink-Painter, *President*
D B Fink, *CEO*
Albert G Fink Jr, *Vice Pres*
EMP: 50 EST: 1954
SALES (est): 8.7MM **Privately Held**
SIC: 3812 Aircraft control systems, electronic

(P-21437)
TECNOVA ADVANCED SYSTEMS INC
Also Called: Tecnadyne
9770 Carroll Centre Rd, San Diego (92126-6504)
P.O. Box 676086, Rancho Santa Fe (92067-6086)
PHONE..................858 586-9660
Andrew Bazeley, *President*
Ute Pelzer, *CFO*
EMP: 20
SQ FT: 17,150
SALES (est): 4.5MM **Privately Held**
WEB: www.tecnadyne.com
SIC: 3812 Search & navigation equipment

(P-21438)
TELEDYNE CONTROLS LLC
501 Continental Blvd, El Segundo (90245-5036)
P.O. Box 1026 (90245-1026)
PHONE..................310 765-3600
Aldo Pichelli, *CEO*
Robert Mehrabian, *Ch of Bd*
Masood Hassan, *President*
Susan L Main, *CFO*
George C Bobb III, *Ch Credit Ofcr*
EMP: 616
SALES (est): 92.7MM
SALES (corp-wide): 2.6B **Publicly Held**
SIC: 3812 Search & navigation equipment
PA: Teledyne Technologies Inc
1049 Camino Dos Rios
Thousand Oaks CA 91360
805 373-4545

(P-21439)
TELEDYNE INSTRUMENTS INC
Also Called: Teledyne Rd Instruments
14020 Stowe Dr, Poway (92064-6846)
PHONE..................858 842-2600
Dennis Klahn, *Branch Mgr*
Jeff McNicholl, *Info Tech Dir*
Gregg Lougeay, *Info Tech Mgr*
Joe Michniewicz, *Software Engr*

Robert Abirgas, *Design Engr*
EMP: 140
SALES (corp-wide): 2.6B **Publicly Held**
SIC: 3812 3829 Search & navigation equipment; measuring & controlling devices
HQ: Teledyne Instruments, Inc.
1049 Camino Dos Rios
Thousand Oaks CA 91360
805 373-4545

(P-21440)
TELEDYNE TECHNOLOGIES INC
12870 Panama St, Los Angeles (90066-6532)
PHONE..................310 893-1600
Bruce Gecks, *Branch Mgr*
John Kuelbs, *Vice Pres*
John Villa, *Manager*
EMP: 12
SQ FT: 19,102
SALES (corp-wide): 2.6B **Publicly Held**
WEB: www.teledyne.com
SIC: 3812 3674 3519 3724 Aircraft control systems, electronic; navigational systems & instruments; semiconductors & related devices; internal combustion engines; gasoline engines; engines, diesel & semi-diesel or dual-fuel; research & development on aircraft engines & parts
PA: Teledyne Technologies Inc
1049 Camino Dos Rios
Thousand Oaks CA 91360
805 373-4545

(P-21441)
TELENAV INC (PA)
4655 Great America Pkwy # 300, Santa Clara (95054-1236)
PHONE..................408 245-3800
H P Jin, *Ch of Bd*
Salman Dhanani, *President*
Hassan Wahla, *President*
Michael Strambi, *CFO*
Samuel Chen, *Bd of Directors*
EMP: 156
SQ FT: 55,000
SALES: 106.1MM **Publicly Held**
WEB: www.telenav.com
SIC: 3812 Navigational systems & instruments

(P-21442)
TINKER & RASOR INC
791 S Waterman Ave, San Bernardino (92408-2331)
P.O. Box 1667 (92402-1667)
PHONE..................909 890-0700
Theodore Byerley, *President*
Mary Butcher, *Admin Sec*
Denise Byerley, *Admin Sec*
▲ EMP: 23 EST: 1948
SQ FT: 15,000
SALES (est): 4.3MM **Privately Held**
WEB: www.tinker-rasor.com
SIC: 3812 3829 Detection apparatus: electronic/magnetic field, light/heat; measuring & controlling devices

(P-21443)
TMC ICE PROTECTION SYSTEMS LLC
Also Called: TMC Aero
25775 Jefferson Ave, Murrieta (92562-6903)
PHONE..................951 677-6934
Edward Rigney, *COO*
EMP: 20
SALES (corp-wide): 3MM **Privately Held**
SIC: 3812 8711 Aircraft/aerospace flight instruments & guidance systems; aviation &/or aeronautical engineering
PA: Tmc Ice Protection Systems Llc
10850 Wilshire Blvd # 1250
Los Angeles CA 90024
760 672-0559

(P-21444)
TOWER MECHANICAL PRODUCTS INC
Also Called: Allied Mechanical Products
1720 S Bon View Ave, Ontario (91761-4411)
PHONE..................714 947-2723
Richard B Slater, *President*
Susan J Hardy, *Corp Secy*

James W Longcrier, *Vice Pres*
EMP: 126
SQ FT: 148,000
SALES (est): 13.3MM
SALES (corp-wide): 34.2MM **Privately Held**
SIC: 3812 Acceleration indicators & systems components, aerospace
PA: Tower Industries, Inc.
1518 N Endeavor Ln Ste C
Anaheim CA 92801
714 630-8145

(P-21445)
TRIMBLE INC
945 Stewart Dr Ste 100, Sunnyvale (94085-3913)
PHONE..................408 481-8490
Paul Montgomery, *Director*
Brian Jackman, *Manager*
EMP: 11
SALES (corp-wide): 2.6B **Publicly Held**
SIC: 3812 Navigational systems & instruments
PA: Trimble Inc.
935 Stewart Dr
Sunnyvale CA 94085
408 481-8000

(P-21446)
TRIMBLE INC (PA)
935 Stewart Dr, Sunnyvale (94085-3913)
PHONE..................408 481-8000
Ulf J Johansson, *Ch of Bd*
Steven W Berglund, *President*
Robert G Painter, *CFO*
Nickolas W Vande Steeg, *Vice Ch Bd*
James A Kirkland, *Senior VP*
EMP: 750 EST: 1978
SQ FT: 167,000
SALES: 2.6B **Publicly Held**
WEB: www.trimble.com
SIC: 3812 3829 Navigational systems & instruments; measuring & controlling devices

(P-21447)
TRIMBLE INC
1720 Prairie City Rd, Folsom (95630-4043)
PHONE..................916 294-2000
EMP: 40
SALES (corp-wide): 2.6B **Publicly Held**
SIC: 3812 Navigational systems & instruments
PA: Trimble Inc.
935 Stewart Dr
Sunnyvale CA 94085
408 481-8000

(P-21448)
TRIMBLE INC
510 Deguigne Dr, Sunnyvale (94085)
PHONE..................408 481-8000
EMP: 11
SALES (corp-wide): 2.6B **Publicly Held**
WEB: www.trimble.com
SIC: 3812 3829 5049 Navigational systems & instruments; measuring & controlling devices; surveyors' instruments
PA: Trimble Inc.
935 Stewart Dr
Sunnyvale CA 94085
408 481-8000

(P-21449)
TRIMBLE MILITARY & ADVNCED SYS
510 De Guigne Dr, Sunnyvale (94085-3920)
P.O. Box 3642 (94088-3642)
PHONE..................408 481-8000
Ron Smith, *President*
Su Law, *Info Tech Mgr*
▼ EMP: 55
SQ FT: 22,000
SALES (est): 4MM
SALES (corp-wide): 2.6B **Publicly Held**
WEB: www.trimble.com
SIC: 3812 3829 Search & navigation equipment; measuring & controlling devices
PA: Trimble Inc.
935 Stewart Dr
Sunnyvale CA 94085
408 481-8000

▲ = Import ▼=Export
◆ =Import/Export

(P-21450)
TUFFER MANUFACTURING CO INC
163 E Liberty Ave, Anaheim (92801-1012)
PHONE................................714 526-3077
Cathy Kim, *President*
Edward Yang, *COO*
Ken Kim, *Vice Pres*
David Walters, *Vice Pres*
Ryan Hamilton, *Project Mgr*
EMP: 39 **EST:** 1977
SQ FT: 12,000
SALES (est): 6.6MM **Privately Held**
WEB: www.tuffermfg.com
SIC: 3812 3599 Search & navigation equipment; machine shop, jobbing & repair

(P-21451)
UVIFY INC
1 Market Spear Twr Fl 36, San Francisco (94105)
PHONE................................628 200-4469
Hyon Lim, *Mng Member*
EMP: 13
SALES (est): 491.5K **Privately Held**
SIC: 3812 Electronic detection systems (aeronautical)

(P-21452)
VALENCE SURFACE TECH LLC
Valence San Carlos
1000 Commercial St, San Carlos (94070-4024)
PHONE................................323 770-0240
John Garin, *Manager*
EMP: 50
SALES (corp-wide): 103MM **Privately Held**
SIC: 3812 Aircraft/aerospace flight instruments & guidance systems
PA: Valence Surface Technologies Llc
1790 Hughes Landing Blvd
The Woodlands TX 77380
888 540-0878

(P-21453)
VELODYNE LIDAR INC
345 Digital Dr, Morgan Hill (95037-2878)
PHONE................................408 465-2800
Jaime Gonzalez, *Manager*
EMP: 300
SALES (corp-wide): 33.2MM **Privately Held**
SIC: 3812 5731 Altimeters, standard & sensitive; radio, television & electronic stores
PA: Velodyne Lidar, Inc.
5521 Hellyer Ave
San Jose CA 95138
408 465-2800

(P-21454)
VIASAT INC
Also Called: Enerdyne Division
1935 Cordell Ct, El Cajon (92020-0911)
PHONE................................619 438-6000
Brandon Nixon, *President*
Ron Wangerin, *CFO*
Mike Kulinski, *Vice Pres*
Steve Gardner, *CTO*
Jeremy Johnson, *Technology*
EMP: 60
SQ FT: 20,000
SALES (est): 9.2MM
SALES (corp-wide): 1.5B **Publicly Held**
WEB: www.enerdyne.com
SIC: 3812 Search & navigation equipment
PA: Viasat, Inc.
6155 El Camino Real
Carlsbad CA 92009
760 476-2200

(P-21455)
VOTAW PRECISION TECH INC
13153 Lakeland Rd, Santa Fe Springs (90670-4520)
P.O. Box 314, Seal Beach (90740-0314)
PHONE................................562 944-0661
Steve Lamb, *CEO*
David Takes, *President*
Jonathan Miller, *CFO*
Steve Crisanti, *Exec VP*
Tamara Williams, *Principal*
EMP: 10 **EST:** 1964
SQ FT: 240,000

SALES: 40MM
SALES (corp-wide): 121.3MM **Privately Held**
WEB: www.votaw.com
SIC: 3812 Acceleration indicators & systems components, aerospace; aircraft/aerospace flight instruments & guidance systems; navigational systems & instruments
PA: Burtek Holdings Inc.
50325 Patricia St
Chesterfield MI
-

(P-21456)
WESCAM USA INC (HQ)
424 Aviation Blvd, Santa Rosa (95403-1069)
PHONE................................707 236-1077
Michael T Strianese, *CEO*
John Dehne, *President*
EMP: 11
SALES (est): 1.8MM
SALES (corp-wide): 9.5B **Publicly Held**
SIC: 3812 Search & navigation equipment
PA: L3 Technologies, Inc.
600 3rd Ave Fl 34
New York NY 10016
212 697-1111

3821 Laboratory Apparatus & Furniture

(P-21457)
ADVANCE ENGINEERING & TECH CO
Also Called: Advance Lab Instr & Sups
717 W Temple St Ste 203, Los Angeles (90012-2616)
PHONE................................213 250-8338
EMP: 12
SQ FT: 3,000
SALES: 500K **Privately Held**
SIC: 3821 Laboratory equipment: fume hoods, distillation racks, etc.

(P-21458)
BERLIN FOOD & LAB EQUIPMENT CO
43 S Linden Ave, South San Francisco (94080-6407)
PHONE................................650 589-4231
Michael F Ulrich, *President*
Mark Cottonaro, *COO*
Michael Ulrich, *COO*
Jackie McClymond, *Admin Asst*
Donna Coates, *Controller*
EMP: 23 **EST:** 1947
SQ FT: 50,000
SALES (est): 5.7MM **Privately Held**
WEB: www.berlinusa.com
SIC: 3821 1799 Laboratory apparatus & furniture; home/office interiors finishing, furnishing & remodeling; food service equipment installation

(P-21459)
BICO INC
Also Called: Bico-Braun International
3116 W Valhalla Dr, Burbank (91505-1296)
P.O. Box 6339 (91510-6339)
PHONE................................818 842-7179
Robert De Palma, *Principal*
Margaret De Palma, *Vice Pres*
Eddie Simmons, *Purchasing*
EMP: 10 **EST:** 1888
SQ FT: 15,453
SALES (est): 2.6MM **Privately Held**
WEB: www.bicoinc.com
SIC: 3821 Laboratory apparatus, except heating & measuring

(P-21460)
CERA INC
14180 Live Oak Ave Ste I, Baldwin Park (91706-1350)
P.O. Box 1608 (91706-7608)
PHONE................................626 814-2688
Philip Dimson, *Owner*
◆ **EMP:** 21
SQ FT: 2,000
SALES (est): 4.8MM **Privately Held**
SIC: 3821 Chemical laboratory apparatus

(P-21461)
CESCA THERAPEUTICS INC (PA)
2711 Citrus Rd, Rancho Cordova (95742-6228)
PHONE................................916 858-5100
Xiaochun Xu, *Ch of Bd*
Jeff Cauble, *CFO*
Chuck Novak, *CFO*
Mahendra RAO, *Bd of Directors*
Philip Coelho, *Officer*
EMP: 84
SQ FT: 28,000
SALES: 14.5MM **Publicly Held**
WEB: www.thermogenesis.com
SIC: 3821 Freezers, laboratory

(P-21462)
CHEMAT TECHNOLOGY INC
Also Called: Chemat Vision
9036 Winnetka Ave, Northridge (91324-3235)
PHONE................................818 727-9786
Haixing Zheng, *CEO*
Syed Haider, *Electrical Engi*
Ana Sintop, *Accounting Mgr*
Haixing Zhou, *Sls & Mktg Exec*
Vivian LI, *Manager*
▲ **EMP:** 32
SQ FT: 30,000
SALES (est): 6.6MM **Privately Held**
WEB: www.chemat.com
SIC: 3821 3827 Chemical laboratory apparatus; optical test & inspection equipment

(P-21463)
CHROMACODE INC
2330 Faraday Ave Ste 100, Carlsbad (92008-7244)
PHONE................................442 244-4369
Alex Dickinson, *Bd of Directors*
Gregory Gosch, *CEO*
Lynne Rollins, *CFO*
EMP: 27 **EST:** 2014
SALES (est): 394.1K **Privately Held**
SIC: 3821 Clinical laboratory instruments, except medical & dental

(P-21464)
CLEATECH LLC
2106 N Glassell St Orange, Orange (92865)
PHONE................................714 754-6668
Sam Kashanchi,
Elizabeth Villa, *HR Admin*
Karen Ledbetter, *Manager*
Angelica Rosales, *Representative*
EMP: 27
SALES: 3MM **Privately Held**
WEB: www.cleatech.com
SIC: 3821 Laboratory apparatus & furniture

(P-21465)
COUNTY OF SAN BERNARDINO
Also Called: Arrow Head Regional Med Ctr
400 N Pepper Ave, Colton (92324-1801)
PHONE................................909 580-0015
Carolyn Leech, *Director*
Adrian Martinez, *Nursing Mgr*
Susan Peterson, *Human Res Dir*
Martha L Melendez, *Family Practiti*
Jamie Aochi, *Obstetrician*
EMP: 50 **Privately Held**
SIC: 3821 8071 Clinical laboratory instruments, except medical & dental; blood analysis laboratory
PA: County Of San Bernardino
385 N Arrowhead Ave
San Bernardino CA 92415
909 387-3841

(P-21466)
COVALENT METROLOGY SVCS LLC
921 Thompson Pl, Sunnyvale (94085-4518)
PHONE................................408 498-4611
James C Hunter, *Mng Member*
EMP: 10
SQ FT: 3,500
SALES: 500K **Privately Held**
SIC: 3821 Laboratory apparatus & furniture

(P-21467)
DICKINSON CORPORATION
31 Commercial Blvd Ste G, Novato (94949-6114)
PHONE................................415 883-7147
Matthew Bishop, *CEO*
Jon Myers, *CEO*
Steve Tanner, *Chairman*
Wayne Dickinson, *Chief Engr*
Matt Bishop, *Director*
EMP: 12
SQ FT: 7,400
SALES: 500K **Privately Held**
SIC: 3821 Physics laboratory apparatus

(P-21468)
DUKE SCIENTIFIC CORPORATION
46360 Fremont Blvd, Fremont (94538-6406)
PHONE................................650 424-1177
Stanley D Duke, *CEO*
Philip Warren, *President*
Ellen Layendecker, *Treasurer*
Heather Vail, *Admin Sec*
EMP: 26 **EST:** 1970
SQ FT: 14,000
SALES: 5MM
SALES (corp-wide): 20.9B **Publicly Held**
WEB: www.dukescientific.com
SIC: 3821 Laboratory apparatus & furniture
PA: Thermo Fisher Scientific Inc.
168 3rd Ave
Waltham MA 02451
781 622-1000

(P-21469)
ENDRESS+HOUSER CONDUCTA
4123 E La Palma Ave # 200, Anaheim (92807-1867)
PHONE................................714 577-5600
Wolfgang Bable, *President*
Stephen Johnson, *Engineer*
EMP: 14
SALES (est): 2.1MM **Privately Held**
SIC: 3821 Laboratory measuring apparatus

(P-21470)
ENDRUN TECHNOLOGIES LLC
2270 Northpoint Pkwy, Santa Rosa (95407-7398)
PHONE................................707 573-8633
Bruce Penrod, *Vice Pres*
Georgia Johnson, *CFO*
Dan Paine, *General Mgr*
Debbie Mossberg, *Materials Mgr*
Ron Holm, *Marketing Mgr*
EMP: 13
SQ FT: 7,400
SALES (est): 3.8MM **Privately Held**
WEB: www.endruntechnologies.com
SIC: 3821 3825 Time interval measuring equipment, electric (lab type); frequency meters: electrical, mechanical & electronic

(P-21471)
EVERGREEN INDUSTRIES INC (DH)
Also Called: Evergreen Scientific
2254 E 49th St, Vernon (90058-2823)
P.O. Box 58248, Los Angeles (90058-0248)
PHONE................................323 583-1331
Gregory Wong, *CEO*
Jean Wong, *Vice Pres*
◆ **EMP:** 38
SQ FT: 122,100
SALES (est): 11.7MM
SALES (corp-wide): 2.9B **Privately Held**
WEB: www.evergreensci.com
SIC: 3821 Laboratory equipment: fume hoods, distillation racks, etc.
HQ: Protective Industries, Inc.
2150 Elmwood Ave
Buffalo NY 14207
716 876-9951

(P-21472)
GARDNER SYSTEMS INC
3321 S Yale St, Santa Ana (92704-6446)
PHONE................................714 668-9018
Joe Gardner, *President*
Claudia Gardner, *Corp Secy*
Richard Reeves, *Vice Pres*

Oscar Carbajal, *Opers Mgr*
▲ **EMP:** 15
SQ FT: 8,000
SALES (est): 3MM **Privately Held**
WEB: www.gardner-systems.com
SIC: 3821 Laboratory apparatus & furniture

(P-21473)
GENETRONICS INC
11494 Sorrento Valley Rd A, San Diego
(92121-1318)
PHONE..............................858 597-6006
James Heppell, *Chairman*
Avtar Dhillon, *President*
Peter Kies, *CFO*
Babak Nemati PH, *Vice Pres*
Douglas Murdock, *Admin Sec*
EMP: 26
SQ FT: 25,000
SALES (est): 5.8MM **Publicly Held**
WEB: www.genetronics.com
SIC: 3821 8731 3826 Laboratory appara-
tus, except heating & measuring; biotech-
nical research, commercial; analytical
instruments
PA: Inovio Pharmaceuticals, Inc.
660 W Germantown Pike
Plymouth Meeting PA 19462

(P-21474)
HANSON LAB FURNITURE INC
747 Calle Plano, Camarillo (93012-8556)
PHONE..............................805 498-3121
Mike Hanson, *President*
Joseph F Matta, *COO*
Joe Matta, *Vice Pres*
▲ **EMP:** 30
SQ FT: 40,000
SALES (est): 7.9MM **Privately Held**
WEB: www.hansonlab.com
SIC: 3821 Laboratory furniture

(P-21475)
HITACHI CHEM DIAGNOSTICS INC
630 Clyde Ct, Mountain View (94043-2239)
PHONE..............................650 961-5501
Takashi Miyamoto, *CEO*
Kazuyoshi Tsunoda, *President*
Keiichi Takeda, *CFO*
Rob Stephens, *Exec Dir*
Cinda Curley, *Admin Asst*
EMP: 190
SQ FT: 31,000
SALES (est): 33.8MM
SALES (corp-wide): 87.9B **Privately Held**
WEB: www.hcdiagnostics.com
SIC: 3821 2835 8071 Laboratory measur-
ing apparatus; in vitro diagnostics; med-
ical laboratories
HQ: Hitachi Chemical Company, Ltd.
1-9-2, Marunouchi
Chiyoda-Ku TKY 100-0
355 337-000

(P-21476)
IDEX HEALTH & SCIENCE LLC (HQ)
600 Park Ct, Rohnert Park (94928-7906)
PHONE..............................707 588-2000
Jeff Cannon, *President*
Travis Winslow, *Info Tech Mgr*
Richard Felton, *Engineer*
William French, *Engineer*
Kurt Pickle, *Engineer*
▲ **EMP:** 87
SQ FT: 70,000
SALES (est): 186.3MM
SALES (corp-wide): 2.2B **Publicly Held**
SIC: 3821 3829 3826 3823 Laboratory
apparatus & furniture; measuring & con-
trolling devices; analytical instruments; in-
dustrial instrmnts msrmnt display/control
process variable; valves & pipe fittings
PA: Idex Corporation
1925 W Field Ct Ste 200
Lake Forest IL 60045
847 498-7070

(P-21477)
INTEGENX INC (HQ)
5720 Stoneridge Dr # 300, Pleasanton
(94588-2739)
PHONE 925 701-3400
Robert A Schueren, *CEO*

David V Smith, *COO*
David King, *Exec VP*
▲ **EMP:** 69
SQ FT: 10,000
SALES (est): 13.7MM
SALES (est): 20.9B **Publicly Held**
WEB: www.microchipbiotech.com
SIC: 3821 Sample preparation apparatus
PA: Thermo Fisher Scientific Inc.
168 3rd Ave
Waltham MA 02451
781 622-1000

(P-21478)
ISEC INCORPORATED
5735 Krny Vlla Rd Ste 105, San Diego
(92123)
PHONE..............................858 279-9085
Don Shaw, *Branch Mgr*
EMP: 248
SALES (corp-wide): 295.9MM **Privately
Held**
SIC: 3821 Laboratory apparatus & furniture
PA: Isec, Incorporated
6000 Greenwood Plaza Blvd # 200
Greenwood Village CO 80111
410 381-6049

(P-21479)
LASER REFERENCE INC
151 Martinvale Ln, San Jose (95119-1454)
PHONE..............................408 361-0220
Lee Robson, *President*
Christopher Middleton, *Treasurer*
Mike Middleton, *Admin Sec*
▲ **EMP:** 35
SQ FT: 9,500
SALES (est): 6.1MM **Privately Held**
WEB: www.proshotlaser.com
SIC: 3821 3829 3699 Laser beam align-
ment devices; measuring & controlling de-
vices; electrical equipment & supplies

(P-21480)
MARVAC SCIENTIFIC MFG CO
3231 Monument Way Ste I, Concord
(94518-2444)
PHONE..............................925 825-4636
George Marin, *President*
Steve Marin, *Treasurer*
Douglas Marin, *Vice Pres*
EMP: 18
SQ FT: 20,000
SALES (est): 4MM **Privately Held**
WEB: www.marvacscientific.com
SIC: 3821 Vacuum pumps, laboratory

(P-21481)
MYC DIRECT INC
19977 Harrison Ave, Walnut (91789-2848)
PHONE..............................909 287-9919
Michael Chen, *Owner*
▲ **EMP:** 10
SQ FT: 20,000
SALES (est): 1.2MM **Privately Held**
SIC: 3821 Laboratory apparatus & furniture

(P-21482)
NEWPORT CORPORATION (HQ)
1791 Deere Ave, Irvine (92606-4814)
P.O. Box 19607 (92623-9607)
PHONE..............................949 863-3144
Seth Bagshaw, *President*
Derek D'Antilio, *Treasurer*
Jeff Parker, *Vice Pres*
Kathleen Burke, *Admin Sec*
Greg Reischlein, *CIO*
◆ **EMP:** 277 **EST:** 1938
SALES (est): 625.7MM
SALES (corp-wide): 1.9B **Publicly Held**
WEB: www.newport.com
SIC: 3821 3699 3827 3826 Worktables,
laboratory; laser systems & equipment;
optical instruments & lenses; mirrors, opti-
cal; prisms, optical; analytical optical in-
struments; laser scientific & engineering
instruments
PA: Mks Instruments, Inc.
2 Tech Dr Ste 201
Andover MA 01810
978 645-5500

(P-21483)
NORTHRDGE TR-MDLITY IMGING INC
Also Called: Trifoil Imaging
9457 De Soto Ave, Chatsworth
(91311-4920)
PHONE..............................818 709-2468
Kevin Parnham, *President*
Ryan Weirich, *CFO*
EMP: 15 **EST:** 2013
SQ FT: 11,000
SALES (est): 3.8MM **Privately Held**
SIC: 3821 7699 Clinical laboratory instru-
ments, except medical & dental; medical
equipment repair, non-electric

(P-21484)
PARTER MEDICAL PRODUCTS INC
17015 Kingsview Ave, Carson
(90746-1220)
PHONE..............................310 327-4417
Hormonz Foroughi, *President*
Parviz Hassanzadeh, *Shareholder*
▲ **EMP:** 160
SQ FT: 40,000
SALES (est): 46.9MM **Privately Held**
WEB: www.partermedical.com
SIC: 3821 Sterilizers

(P-21485)
PASADENA BIO CLLBRTIVE INCBTOR
Also Called: Pasadena Bscence Colloborative
2265 E Foothill Blvd, Pasadena
(91107-3658)
PHONE..............................626 507-8487
Robert Bishop, *President*
Bruce Blonstrom, *President*
EMP: 12
SALES: 554.3K **Privately Held**
SIC: 3821 Incubators, laboratory

(P-21486)
PERFORMANCE PLUS LABORATORIES
3609 Vista Mercado, Camarillo
(93012-8055)
P.O. Box 2690 (93011-2690)
PHONE..............................805 383-7871
Anthony J Von Teuber, *President*
Dr Tim Barber, *COO*
EMP: 112
SQ FT: 25,000
SALES (est): 1.1MM **Privately Held**
SIC: 3821 Laboratory apparatus, except
heating & measuring

(P-21487)
QUALIGEN INC (PA)
2042 Corte Del Nogal A, Carlsbad
(92011-1438)
PHONE..............................760 918-9165
Paul A Rosinack, *CEO*
Christopher L Lotz, *CFO*
Christopher Lotz, *CFO*
Craig Fecker, *Exec VP*
Michael S Poirier, *Senior VP*
EMP: 45
SQ FT: 23,000
SALES (est): 8.5MM **Privately Held**
WEB: www.qualigeninc.com
SIC: 3821 3841 Laboratory apparatus &
furniture; surgical & medical instruments

(P-21488)
RYSS LAB INC
29540 Kohoutek Way, Union City
(94587-1221)
PHONE..............................510 477-9570
Ming Lee, *CEO*
Diana Lee, *Executive Asst*
EMP: 13
SQ FT: 1,000
SALES (est): 2.3MM **Privately Held**
WEB: www.ryss.com
SIC: 3821 Chemical laboratory apparatus

(P-21489)
SAN DIEGO INSTRUMENTS INC
9155 Brown Deer Rd Ste 8, San Diego
(92121-2260)
PHONE..............................858 530-2600
Carl Lischer, *President*
Dr Richard Butcher, *Vice Pres*

Kenneth Fite, *Vice Pres*
Mark A Geyer, *Vice Pres*
James Lischer, *Purchasing*
EMP: 10
SQ FT: 5,000
SALES (est): 2.3MM **Privately Held**
WEB: www.sandiegoinstruments.com
SIC: 3821 Laboratory equipment: fume
hoods, distillation racks, etc.

(P-21490)
SEPOR INC
718 N Fries Ave, Wilmington (90744-5403)
PHONE..............................310 830-6601
Tim Lee Miller, *CEO*
Drew Willis, *COO*
Charles Kubach, *Engineer*
Bud Metcalf, *Engineer*
Lucy Ortiz, *Manager*
◆ **EMP:** 11
SQ FT: 6,000
SALES (est): 2.7MM **Privately Held**
WEB: www.sepor.com
SIC: 3821 Sample preparation apparatus;
laboratory heating apparatus; crushing &
grinding apparatus, laboratory; furnaces,
laboratory

(P-21491)
SHALON VENTURES
155 Island Dr, Palo Alto (94301-3127)
PHONE..............................650 324-9090
Tadmor Shalon, *President*
John Desilva, *Info Tech Mgr*
▲ **EMP:** 14
SALES (est): 2.2MM **Privately Held**
WEB: www.shalon.com
SIC: 3821 Clinical laboratory instruments,
except medical & dental

(P-21492)
TECAN SYSTEMS INC
2450 Zanker Rd, San Jose (95131-1126)
PHONE..............................408 953-3100
David Martyr, *CEO*
Rudolf Eugster, *CFO*
Martin Brusdeilins, *Exec VP*
Michael Winniman, *Regional Mgr*
Sean Leu, *Software Engr*
▲ **EMP:** 100 **EST:** 1972
SQ FT: 23,400
SALES (est): 28.2MM
SALES (corp-wide): 554.6MM **Privately
Held**
WEB: www.tecansystems.com
SIC: 3821 3829 3561 3494 Laboratory
apparatus, except heating & measuring;
measuring & controlling devices; pumps &
pumping equipment; valves & pipe fit-
tings; unsupported plastics profile shapes;
commercial physical research
HQ: Tecan U.S. Group, Inc.
9401 Globe Center Dr # 140
Morrisville NC 27560
919 361-5200

(P-21493)
THERAPAK LLC
651 Wharton Dr, Claremont (91711-4819)
PHONE..............................626 357-5900
Randy Hawk, *Branch Mgr*
EMP: 150 **Privately Held**
WEB: www.therapak.com
SIC: 3821 Clinical laboratory instruments,
except medical & dental
HQ: Therapak Llc
651 Wharton Dr
Claremont CA 91711
909 267-2000

(P-21494)
TLI ENTERPRISES INC (PA)
23950 Clawiter Rd, Hayward (94545-1811)
P.O. Box 3711 (94540-3711)
PHONE..............................510 538-3304
John Mark Trujillo, *Principal*
EMP: 30 **EST:** 1937
SQ FT: 18,000
SALES: 12MM **Privately Held**
WEB: www.thermionicscorp.com
SIC: 3821 3471 Vacuum pumps, labora-
tory; cleaning, polishing & finishing

▲ = Import ▼=Export
◆ =Import/Export

(P-21495)
TORREY PINES SCIENTIFIC INC
2713 Loker Ave W, Carlsbad (92010-6601)
PHONE..................................760 930-9400
Michael Cassiano, *CEO*
Caroline Cassiano, *President*
Anthony Cassiano, *Chairman*
▲ **EMP:** 10
SALES (est): 4MM **Privately Held**
WEB: www.torreypinesscientific.com
SIC: 3821 Laboratory equipment: fume
hoods, distillation racks, etc.

(P-21496)
**TOTAL SOURCE
MANUFACTURING**
Also Called: Total Source Manufacturing Co
1445 Engineer St, Vista (92081-8846)
PHONE..................................760 598-2146
Stacy Camp, *President*
Saied Sardarian, *President*
▲ **EMP:** 1800
SALES (est): 146.6MM **Privately Held**
WEB: www.tsmfg.com
SIC: 3821 Laboratory equipment: fume
hoods, distillation racks, etc.

**3822 Automatic
Temperature Controls**

(P-21497)
AIR DRY CO OF AMERICA LLC
1740 Commerce Way, Paso Robles
(93446-3620)
PHONE..................................805 227-0434
Jeff Watson, *President*
Richard Tudor, *Engineer*
Veronica Contreras, *Human Resources*
Christine Schmitt, *Assistant*
EMP: 20
SQ FT: 20,000
SALES (est): 3.1MM **Privately Held**
SIC: 3822 Auto controls regulating residntl
& coml environmt & applncs

(P-21498)
**AIR MONITOR CORPORATION
(PA)**
1050 Hopper Ave, Santa Rosa
(95403-1695)
P.O. Box 6358 (95406-0358)
PHONE..................................707 544-2706
Dean De Baun, *CEO*
Sharon Hughes, *CFO*
Chris De Baun, *Admin Sec*
EMP: 70 **EST:** 1967
SQ FT: 50,000
SALES (est): 12.5MM **Privately Held**
WEB: www.airmonitor.com
SIC: 3822 Air flow controllers, air condition-
ing & refrigeration

(P-21499)
AROMYX CORPORATION
605 Tasman Dr Apt 1101, Sunnyvale
(94089-1871)
PHONE..................................650 430-8100
Chris Hanson, *President*
Luke Schneider, *Bd of Directors*
Ed Costello, *Vice Pres*
Victor Cushman, *VP Sls/Mktg*
EMP: 10
SALES: 2MM **Privately Held**
WEB: www.pervasivebiosensors.com
SIC: 3822 Auto controls regulating residntl
& coml environmt & applncs

(P-21500)
AVC SPECIALISTS INC
5146 N Commerce Ave Ste G, Moorpark
(93021-7138)
PHONE..................................513 458-2600
Tom Shideler, *President*
Barbara Shideler, *Admin Sec*
▼ **EMP:** 20 **EST:** 1977
SQ FT: 5,000
SALES (est): 4MM
SALES (corp-wide): 345MM **Publicly
Held**
WEB: www.avcspecialists.com
SIC: 3822 Electric air cleaner controls, au-
tomatic

PA: Ceco Environmental Corp.
14651 Dallas Pkwy
Dallas TX 75254
513 458-2600

(P-21501)
C3-ILEX LLC (PA)
46609 Fremont Blvd, Fremont
(94538-6410)
P.O. Box 3224, Los Altos (94024-0224)
PHONE..................................510 659-8300
Sue Schwee, *President*
John Klimaszewski, *Vice Pres*
EMP: 21
SQ FT: 15,000
SALES (est): 4.9MM **Privately Held**
WEB: www.c3ilex.com
SIC: 3822 Auto controls regulating residntl
& coml environmt & applncs

(P-21502)
**CATALYTIC SOLUTIONS INC
(HQ)**
1700 Fiske Pl, Oxnard (93033-1863)
PHONE..................................805 486-4649
David Gann, *CEO*
Charlie Karl, *CEO*
Kevin McDonnell, *CFO*
Dan McGuire, *Vice Pres*
Steven Golden, *CTO*
▲ **EMP:** 68
SQ FT: 75,000
SALES (est): 22.5MM **Publicly Held**
WEB: www.catsoln.com
SIC: 3822 Auto controls regulating residntl
& coml environmt & applncs

(P-21503)
CHEVRON USA INC
345 California St Fl 18, San Francisco
(94104-2650)
PHONE..................................415 733-0063
John S Watson, *CEO*
EMP: 300
SALES (corp-wide): 141.7B **Publicly
Held**
SIC: 3822 6531 3823 3691 Energy cutoff
controls, residential or commercial types;
buying agent, real estate; industrial instrmnts msrmnt display/control process
variable; storage batteries; semiconductors & related devices; electrical equipment & supplies
HQ: Chevron U.S.A. Inc.
6001 Bollinger Canyon Rd D1248
San Ramon CA 94583
925 842-1000

(P-21504)
**CHRONOMITE LABORATORIES
INC**
17451 Hurley St, City of Industry
(91744-5106)
P.O. Box 3527 (91744-0527)
PHONE..................................310 534-2300
Donald E Morris, *CEO*
Suzanne Jayroe, *Technical Staff*
Cathy Milostan, *Sales Staff*
▲ **EMP:** 34
SALES: 6.5MM
SALES (corp-wide): 85MM **Privately
Held**
WEB: www.chronomite.com
SIC: 3822 8731 3432 Water heater con-
trols; commercial physical research;
plumbing fixture fittings & trim
PA: Acorn Engineering Company
15125 Proctor Ave
City Of Industry CA 91746
800 488-8999

(P-21505)
CLEAR SKIES SOLUTIONS INC
2345 Mirada Ct, Tracy (95377-0217)
PHONE..................................925 570-4471
Scott Vaughn, *CEO*
EMP: 12
SALES: 950K **Privately Held**
SIC: 3822 Auto controls regulating residntl
& coml environmt & applncs

(P-21506)
COMPAC ENGINEERING INC
1111 Noffsinger Ln, Paradise (95969-6323)
P.O. Box 9 (95967-0009)
PHONE..................................530 872-2042

James W Jones, *President*
Greg Jones, *Vice Pres*
EMP: 12
SQ FT: 5,000
SALES (est): 1.2MM **Privately Held**
SIC: 3822 Liquid level controls, residential
or commercial heating

(P-21507)
**CONTRCTOR CMPLIANCE
MONITORING**
2343 Donnington Way, San Diego
(92139-2927)
PHONE..................................619 472-9065
Deborah Wilder, *Branch Mgr*
Jessica Finau, *Opers Mgr*
Heather Faulkner, *Manager*
EMP: 22
SALES (corp-wide): 2.5MM **Privately
Held**
SIC: 3822 5082 Building services monitor-
ing controls, automatic; general construc-
tion machinery & equipment
PA: Contractor Compliance & Monitoring
Inc
635 Mariners Island Blvd 200b
San Mateo CA 94404
650 522-4403

(P-21508)
CRGSYNERGY
21 Commercial Blvd Ste 14, Novato
(94949-6109)
PHONE..................................415 497-0182
Eli Cohen, *Ch of Bd*
EMP: 20
SQ FT: 20,000
SALES (est): 1.5MM **Privately Held**
SIC: 3822 Building services monitoring
controls, automatic

(P-21509)
**EARTHSAVERS EROSION CTRL
LLC**
12972 County Road 102, Woodland
(95776-9119)
P.O. Box 2083 (95776-2083)
PHONE..................................530 662-7700
Darrell Hinz, *Mng Member*
Doug Bailey,
Greg Baker,
EMP: 13 **EST:** 2009
SALES (est): 4.8MM **Privately Held**
SIC: 3822 5039 Auto controls regulating
residntl & coml environmt & applncs; soil
erosion control fabrics

(P-21510)
ECO GLOBAL SOLUTIONS INC
221 Gateway Rd W Ste 403, NAPA
(94558-6623)
PHONE..................................707 254-9844
Joseph Chuang, *CEO*
Delia Otero, *Admin Mgr*
EMP: 10
SALES (est): 1.2MM **Privately Held**
SIC: 3822 3826 Auto controls regulating
residntl & coml environmt & applncs; envi-
ronmental testing equipment

(P-21511)
ELECTRASEM CORP
372 Elizabeth Ln, Corona (92880-2528)
PHONE..................................951 371-6140
Don S Edwards, *President*
▲ **EMP:** 17
SALES (est): 3MM
SALES (corp-wide): 1.2B **Publicly Held**
WEB: www.generalmonitors.com
SIC: 3822 Electric heat proportioning con-
trols, modulating controls
HQ: General Monitors, Inc.
26776 Simpatica Cir
Lake Forest CA 92630
949 581-4464

(P-21512)
**FIRST AMERICAN BUILDING
SVCS**
6 Commodore Dr Unit 530, Emeryville
(94608-1639)
PHONE..................................415 299-7597
Justin Sina Moayed, *President*
EMP: 10 **EST:** 2017

SALES (est): 542.6K **Privately Held**
SIC: 3822 Building services monitoring
controls, automatic

(P-21513)
**GEM MOBILE TREATMENT SVCS
INC (HQ)**
2525 Cherry Ave Ste 105, Signal Hill
(90755-2054)
PHONE..................................562 595-7075
Paul Anderson, *COO*
Shane Whittington, *CFO*
Pam Patterson, *Manager*
Chris Ripley, *Accounts Mgr*
EMP: 22
SALES (est): 24.3MM **Privately Held**
SIC: 3822 1629 Vapor heating controls;
waste water & sewage treatment plant
construction

(P-21514)
**HONEYWELL INTERNATIONAL
INC**
2055 Dublin Dr, San Diego (92154-8203)
PHONE..................................619 671-5612
Virgel McCormick, *Manager*
Enrique Del Villar, *Design Engr*
EMP: 110
SALES (corp-wide): 40.5B **Publicly Held**
WEB: www.honeywell.com
SIC: 3822 3494 Auto controls regulating
residntl & coml environmt & applncs;
valves & pipe fittings
PA: Honeywell International Inc.
115 Tabor Rd
Morris Plains NJ 07950
973 455-2000

(P-21515)
LINK4 CORPORATION
175 E Freedom Ave, Anaheim
(92801-1006)
PHONE..................................714 524-0004
Yen Pham, *President*
Fred Kaifer, *Vice Pres*
▲ **EMP:** 11
SALES (est): 2.6MM **Privately Held**
WEB: www.link4corp.com
SIC: 3822 Auto controls regulating residntl
& coml environmt & applncs

(P-21516)
**MICRO GROW GREENHOUSE
SYSTEMS**
42065 Zevo Dr Ste B1, Temecula
(92590-3746)
PHONE..................................951 296-3340
Thomas Piini, *President*
Hunter Weeks, *Software Dev*
Randy Cox, *Technician*
▲ **EMP:** 10
SQ FT: 4,000
SALES (est): 2.3MM **Privately Held**
WEB: www.microgrow.com
SIC: 3822 Controls, combination limit & fan

(P-21517)
MOLEKULE INC (PA)
1184 Harrison St, San Francisco
(94103-4524)
PHONE..................................352 871-3803
Lovely Goswami, *President*
Dilip Goswami, *CEO*
Jaya RAO, *COO*
Peter Riering-Czekalla, *Chief Mktg Ofcr*
Gaurav Agarwal, *Vice Pres*
EMP: 10
SALES (est): 2.9MM **Privately Held**
SIC: 3822 3829 Air flow controllers, air
conditioning & refrigeration; measuring &
controlling devices

(P-21518)
**NEWMATIC ENGINEERING INC
(PA)**
355 Goddard Ste 250, Irvine (92618-4644)
PHONE..................................415 824-2664
Richard Yardley, *President*
Sydney Kwan, *Treasurer*
EMP: 12
SQ FT: 21,000
SALES (est): 3.1MM **Privately Held**
WEB: www.newmatic.net
SIC: 3822 Air flow controllers, air condition-
ing & refrigeration

(P-21519)
NVENT THERMAL LLC (DH)
899 Broadway St, Redwood City
(94063-3104)
PHONE..................................650 474-7414
Brad Faulconer, *President*
Spencer Leslie, *Director*
◆ EMP: 300 EST: 2000
SQ FT: 65,000
SALES: 750MM
SALES (corp-wide): 352.2K **Privately Held**
WEB: www.tycothermal.com
SIC: 3822 1711 Auto controls regulating residntl & coml environmt & applncs; heating & air conditioning contractors
HQ: Nvent Management Company
1665 Utica Ave S Ste 700
Saint Louis Park MN 55416
763 204-7700

(P-21520)
OLS CONTROLS
15215 Old Ranch Rd, Los Gatos
(95033-8329)
PHONE..................................408 353-6564
Joseph Ols, *Principal*
EMP: 10
SALES: 500K **Privately Held**
SIC: 3822 Auto controls regulating residntl & coml environmt & applncs

(P-21521)
PARAGON CONTROLS INCORPORATED
Also Called: PCI
2371 Circadian Way, Santa Rosa
(95407-5439)
P.O. Box 99, Forestville (95436-0099)
PHONE..................................707 579-1424
Richard Thomas Reis, *President*
Cheryl Reis, *Treasurer*
Larry E Winterbourne, *Vice Pres*
Dennis Reis, *Admin Sec*
▲ EMP: 15
SQ FT: 8,200
SALES (est): 3.7MM **Privately Held**
WEB: www.paragoncontrols.com
SIC: 3822 3823 Air flow controllers, air conditioning & refrigeration; fan control, temperature responsive; pressure controllers, air-conditioning system type; primary elements for process flow measurement

(P-21522)
PERTRONIX INC (PA)
440 E Arrow Hwy, San Dimas
(91773-3340)
PHONE..................................909 599-5955
Thomas A Reh, *CEO*
Thomas Reh, *CFO*
Joh R Sherer, *Vice Pres*
Anthony Sinatra, *Technology*
▲ EMP: 40
SQ FT: 22,000
SALES (est): 13.8MM **Privately Held**
WEB: www.pertronix.com
SIC: 3822 3694 Auto controls regulating residntl & coml environmt & applncs; ignition apparatus, internal combustion engines

(P-21523)
REC SOLAR COMMERCIAL CORP
3450 Broad St Ste 105, San Luis Obispo
(93401-7214)
PHONE..................................844 732-7652
Matt Walz, *CEO*
Gary Morris, *CFO*
EMP: 120 EST: 2013
SQ FT: 15,000
SALES (est): 633.4K
SALES (corp-wide): 23.5B **Publicly Held**
SIC: 3822 Energy cutoff controls, residential or commercial types
PA: Duke Energy Corporation
550 S Tryon St
Charlotte NC 28202
704 382-3853

(P-21524)
RED MOUNTAIN INC
Also Called: J&B Mountain Holding
17767 Mitchell N, Irvine (92614-6028)
PHONE..................................949 595-4475
Brian Slezak, *President*
Jay Murata, *CFO*
▼ EMP: 12
SALES (est): 990K **Privately Held**
WEB: www.redmtnengr.com
SIC: 3822 Auto controls regulating residntl & coml environmt & applncs

(P-21525)
RESIDENTIAL CTRL SYSTEMS INC
Also Called: R C S
11481 Sunrise Gold Cir # 1, Rancho Cordova (95742-6545)
PHONE..................................916 635-6784
Michael Kuhlmann, *President*
Mike Hoffman, *Vice Pres*
James Bunton, *Purch Mgr*
Gene Goodell, *VP Mktg*
EMP: 25
SALES: 2MM **Privately Held**
SIC: 3822 Damper operators: pneumatic, thermostatic, electric; pneumatic relays, air-conditioning type; energy cutoff controls, residential or commercial types

(P-21526)
SALUS NORTH AMERICA INC
Also Called: Salus Enterprises of N Amer
850 Main St, Redwood City (94063-1902)
PHONE..................................888 387-2587
Shen Owyang, *President*
Janine M Kinney, *Admin Sec*
EMP: 13
SALES (est): 4.1MM **Privately Held**
SIC: 3822 Thermostats & other environmental sensors
HQ: Computime Group Limited
6/F Hong Kong Science Park Bldg 20e
Ph 3
Sha Tin NT
226 003-00

(P-21527)
SENSIT INC
1652 Plum Ln Ste 106, Redlands
(92374-4594)
PHONE..................................909 793-5816
Shudong Zhou, *President*
Huiling Chen, *Admin Sec*
▲ EMP: 14
SALES (est): 1.4MM **Privately Held**
SIC: 3822 Thermostats & other environmental sensors

(P-21528)
SFC COMMUNICATIONS INC
65 Post Ste 1000, Irvine (92618-5216)
PHONE..................................949 553-8566
Saundra Jacobs, *President*
EMP: 10 EST: 2010
SALES (est): 1.4MM **Privately Held**
SIC: 3822 Auto controls regulating residntl & coml environmt & applncs

(P-21529)
SIEMENS INDUSTRY INC
6 Journey Ste 200, Aliso Viejo
(92656-5321)
PHONE..................................949 448-0600
Linda Wang, *Principal*
EMP: 97
SALES (corp-wide): 97.7B **Privately Held**
SIC: 3822 Air conditioning & refrigeration controls
HQ: Siemens Industry, Inc.
100 Technology Dr
Alpharetta GA 30005
770 740-300C

(P-21530)
SIEMENS INDUSTRY INC
2775 Goodrick Ave, Richmond
(94801-1109)
PHONE..................................510 237-2325
Stefan Kraemer, *Manager*
EMP: 81
SALES (corp-wide): 97.7B **Privately Held**
SIC: 3822 Air conditioning & refrigeration controls

HQ: Siemens Industry, Inc.
100 Technology Dr
Alpharetta GA 30005
770 740-3000

(P-21531)
SIEMENS INDUSTRY INC
3650 Industrial Blvd # 100, West Sacramento (95691-6512)
PHONE..................................916 553-4444
Rick Glaser, *Principal*
David Howe, *Project Mgr*
Sanjin Tufekcic, *Engineer*
Sebastian Ziegler, *Finance*
EMP: 13
SALES (corp-wide): 97.7B **Privately Held**
WEB: www.sibt.com
SIC: 3822 Thermostats & other environmental sensors
HQ: Siemens Industry, Inc.
100 Technology Dr
Alpharetta GA 30005
770 740-3000

(P-21532)
SIEMENS INDUSTRY INC
7464 French Rd, Sacramento
(95828-4600)
PHONE..................................916 681-3000
Oliver Hauck, *Branch Mgr*
Chris Maynard, *IT/INT Sup*
Tien Pham, *Project Mgr*
Vasiliy Karamalak, *Electrical Engi*
Lennart Bergstrom, *Engineer*
EMP: 200
SALES (corp-wide): 97.7B **Privately Held**
SIC: 3822 5063 3669 1731 Air conditioning & refrigeration controls; thermostats & other environmental sensors; electric alarms & signaling equipment; emergency alarms; safety & security specialization; security systems services; relays & industrial controls
HQ: Siemens Industry, Inc.
100 Technology Dr
Alpharetta GA 30005
770 740-3000

(P-21533)
T&L AIR CONDITIONING INC
164 W Live Oak Ave, Arcadia (91007-8562)
PHONE..................................626 294-9888
Shinn Liu, *President*
EMP: 15
SQ FT: 2,928
SALES (est): 2.8MM **Privately Held**
SIC: 3822 Air flow controllers, air conditioning & refrigeration

(P-21534)
TRANSFIRST CORPORATION
900 E Blanco Rd, Salinas (93901-4419)
P.O. Box 1788 (93902-1788)
PHONE..................................831 424-2911
James Lugg, *President*
Richard Macleod, *Vice Pres*
Teresa Scattini, *Vice Pres*
Cathy Kuehl, *Controller*
Michael Parachini, *Opers Staff*
▲ EMP: 27
SALES (est): 7.8MM **Privately Held**
WEB: www.transfresh.com
SIC: 3822 Air conditioning & refrigeration controls

(P-21535)
TRUE FRESH HPP LLC
6535 Caballero Blvd B, Buena Park
(90620-8106)
PHONE..................................949 531-6519
Paul Harrison, *Opers Staff*
Ashley Shafer, *Marketing Staff*
Ashley Collins, *Director*
Shalene Davis, *Director*
Patrick Jacobi, *Director*
EMP: 14 EST: 2015
SALES (est): 3.2MM **Privately Held**
SIC: 3822 Refrigeration controls (pressure)

(P-21536)
VERMILLIONS ENVIRONMENTAL
Also Called: Envirnmental Pdts Applications
78900 Avenue 47 Ste 106, La Quinta
(92253-2070)
PHONE..................................760 777-8035
John Vermillion, *President*

EMP: 20
SALES (est): 5.6MM **Privately Held**
SIC: 3822 Auto controls regulating residntl & coml environmt & applncs

(P-21537)
VIGILENT CORPORATION (PA)
1111 Broadway Fl 3, Oakland
(94607-4139)
PHONE..................................888 305-4451
David Hudson, *CEO*
Dave Lynch, *CFO*
Dave Hudson, *Officer*
Andy Gordon, *Vice Pres*
Jeff Rauenhorst, *Vice Pres*
EMP: 33
SALES (est): 4.4MM **Privately Held**
SIC: 3822 Auto controls regulating residntl & coml environmt & applncs

(P-21538)
X CONTROLS INC
6640 Lusk Blvd Ste A101, San Diego
(92121-2771)
PHONE..................................858 717-0004
Tom Karpecki, *President*
Boris Batiyenko, *Vice Pres*
EMP: 12
SALES (est): 1MM **Privately Held**
SIC: 3822 3699 1731 7382 Building services monitoring controls, automatic; security control equipment & systems; computerized controls installation; security systems services; auditing services

---

3823 Indl Instruments For Meas, Display & Control

(P-21539)
3D INSTRUMENTS LP (DH)
Also Called: Sierra Precision
4990 E Hunter Ave, Anaheim (92807-2057)
PHONE..................................714 399-9200
Felix Brockmeyer, *VP Opers*
Michael Gerster, *President*
Garey Cooper, *Vice Pres*
Agus Kusumadi, *Engineer*
Sheila Ivy, *Purchasing*
EMP: 41
SQ FT: 22,500
SALES (est): 13.1MM
SALES (corp-wide): 429.2MM **Privately Held**
WEB: www.3dhb.com
SIC: 3823 Pressure gauges, dial & digital
HQ: Wika Holding, L P
1000 Wiegand Blvd
Lawrenceville GA 30043
770 513-8200

(P-21540)
ACCU-GAGE & THREAD GRINDING CO
40 S San Gabriel Blvd, Pasadena
(91107-3750)
PHONE..................................626 568-2932
Conrad A Vios, *President*
EMP: 10
SQ FT: 4,000
SALES: 1MM **Privately Held**
WEB: www.accugageandthread.com
SIC: 3823 Pressure measurement instruments, industrial

(P-21541)
ADS LLC
Also Called: A D S Environmental Srvs
15205 Springdale St, Huntington Beach
(92649-1156)
PHONE..................................714 379-9778
Paul Mitchell, *Manager*
EMP: 25
SALES (corp-wide): 2.2B **Publicly Held**
SIC: 3823 8748 Flow instruments, industrial process type; environmental consultant
HQ: Ads Llc
340 The Bridge St Ste 204
Huntsville AL 35806
256 430-3366

▲ = Import ▼ = Export
◆ = Import/Export

(P-21542)
ADVANCED ELECTROMAGNETICS INC
Also Called: Aemi
1320 Air Wing Rd Ste 101, San Diego (92154-7707)
PHONE...................619 449-9492
Per Iversen, *President*
Monica Jaramillo, *Controller*
Eder Marengo, *Production*
Ruben Padilla, *Manager*
◆ EMP: 37 EST: 1980
SQ FT: 16,000
SALES (est): 9.5MM
SALES (corp-wide): 16.5MM **Privately Held**
SIC: 3823 3825 Absorption analyzers: infrared, X-ray, etc.: industrial; instruments to measure electricity
HQ: Orbit/Fr, Inc.
650 Louis Dr Ste 100
Warminster PA 18974

(P-21543)
ADVANCED PRESSURE TECHNOLOGY
Also Called: AP Tech
687 Technology Way, NAPA (94558-7512)
PHONE...................707 259-0102
Rene Zakhour, *President*
Kathy Wright, *CFO*
Barbara Cornelius, *Admin Asst*
Roman Sheykhet, *Project Engr*
Hugh Bohan, *Engineer*
▲ EMP: 95
SALES (est): 32.8MM **Privately Held**
WEB: www.aptech-online.com
SIC: 3823 Pressure gauges, dial & digital

(P-21544)
AIR INSTRMNTS MEASUREMENTS LLC
Also Called: Aim Mail Centers
3579 E Foothill Blvd, Pasadena (91107-3119)
PHONE...................626 791-1912
Harry C Lord, *President*
EMP: 10
SQ FT: 5,000
SALES (est): 951.5K **Privately Held**
WEB: www.aimanalysis.com
SIC: 3823 On-stream gas/liquid analysis instruments, industrial

(P-21545)
ALPHA SENSORS INC
Also Called: Alpha Technics
125 S Tremont St Ste 100, Oceanside (92054-3028)
PHONE...................949 250-6578
Daniel M O'Brien, *CEO*
Lisa Marie Ryan, *President*
Joe Barbosa, *Engineer*
Linda Lee, *Accountant*
EMP: 24
SALES (est): 5.4MM **Privately Held**
WEB: www.alphatechnics.com
SIC: 3823 Temperature measurement instruments, industrial

(P-21546)
AMETEK AMERON LLC (HQ)
Also Called: Mass Systems
4750 Littlejohn St, Baldwin Park (91706-2274)
PHONE...................626 337-4640
Keith Marsicola, *Mng Member*
Larry Collings, *General Mgr*
Ramy Ghebrial, *General Mgr*
Jeremy Kang, *Software Engr*
Michael Mallari, *Engineer*
EMP: 55
SQ FT: 2,600
SALES (est): 19.2MM
SALES (corp-wide): 4.3B **Publicly Held**
SIC: 3823 3999 3728 8711 Pressure gauges, dial & digital; fire extinguishers, portable; aircraft parts & equipment; industrial engineers; clothing, fire resistant & protective
PA: Ametek, Inc.
1100 Cassatt Rd
Berwyn PA 19312
610 647-2121

(P-21547)
AMOBEE INC
10201 Wtridge Cir Ste 200, San Diego (92121)
PHONE...................858 638-1515
Alice Dickey, *Accounts Mgr*
EMP: 12
SALES (corp-wide): 13.3B **Privately Held**
SIC: 3823 Digital displays of process variables
HQ: Amobee, Inc.
901 Marshall St 200
Redwood City CA 94063

(P-21548)
ANALYTICAL INDUSTRIES INC
Also Called: Advanced Instruments
2855 Metropolitan Pl, Pomona (91767-1853)
PHONE...................909 392-6900
Frank S Gregus, *President*
Patrick J Prindible, *Vice Pres*
Mohammad Razaq, *Vice Pres*
Mark Gregus, *VP Opers*
Fernando Murillo, *Sales Staff*
EMP: 45
SQ FT: 15,000
SALES (est): 9.3MM **Privately Held**
WEB: www.aii1.com
SIC: 3823 On-stream gas/liquid analysis instruments, industrial

(P-21549)
ARGA CONTROLS INC
10410 Trademark St, Rancho Cucamonga (91730-5826)
PHONE...................626 799-3314
Bob Pineau, *President*
Linda Halsey, *President*
EMP: 18
SALES (est): 3.5MM **Privately Held**
WEB: www.arizonasunsales.com
SIC: 3823 3829 3625 3613 Industrial instrmnts msrmnt display/control process variable; measuring & controlling devices; relays & industrial controls; switchgear & switchboard apparatus

(P-21550)
AUTOFLOW PRODUCTS CO
15915 S San Pedro St, Gardena (90248-2555)
PHONE...................310 515-2866
Richard E Hughes, *President*
Jeri M Hughes, *CFO*
Miranda King, *Data Proc Staff*
EMP: 15
SQ FT: 6,500
SALES (est): 1.5MM **Privately Held**
WEB: www.autoflowproducts.com
SIC: 3823 3491

(P-21551)
BAMBECK SYSTEMS INC (PA)
1921 Carnegie Ave Ste 3a, Santa Ana (92705-5510)
PHONE...................949 250-3100
Robert J Bambeck, *President*
Robert Deweerd, *Vice Pres*
Melinda Yoshida, *Finance*
Delano McKenzie, *Purchasing*
EMP: 19
SQ FT: 6,100
SALES (est): 3.2MM **Privately Held**
WEB: www.bambecksystems.com
SIC: 3823 Boiler controls: industrial, power & marine type

(P-21552)
BESTEST INTERNATIONAL
Also Called: Bestest Medical
181 W Orangethorpe Ave C, Placentia (92870-6931)
PHONE...................714 974-8837
Pamela Bogart, *President*
John Bogart, *CFO*
EMP: 15
SQ FT: 9,200
SALES: 5MM **Privately Held**
SIC: 3823 3841 Industrial instrmnts msrmnt display/control process variable; surgical & medical instruments

(P-21553)
BIODOT INC (PA)
2852 Alton Pkwy, Irvine (92606-5104)
PHONE...................949 440-3685
Thomas C Tisone, *CEO*
David Gracie, *CFO*
Barbara McIntosh, *Vice Pres*
Anthony Lemmo, *General Mgr*
Trish Morley, *Office Mgr*
EMP: 30
SQ FT: 24,000
SALES (est): 4.6MM **Privately Held**
WEB: www.biodot.com
SIC: 3823 3826 Industrial instrmnts msrmnt display/control process variable; analytical instruments

(P-21554)
BRILLIANT INSTRUMENTS INC
1622 W Campbell Ave 107, Campbell (95008-1535)
PHONE...................408 866-0426
Shalom Kattan, *CEO*
EMP: 12
SALES (est): 1.8MM **Privately Held**
SIC: 3823 Industrial process control instruments

(P-21555)
BROADLEY-JAMES-CORPORATION
19 Thomas, Irvine (92618-2704)
PHONE...................949 829-5555
Leighton S Broadley, *CFO*
George S Moyer, *Business Dir*
Dan Folwell, *General Mgr*
Catherine A Broadley, *Admin Sec*
Joseph Cracchiolo, *Info Tech Dir*
EMP: 65
SQ FT: 24,000
SALES (est): 19.1MM **Privately Held**
WEB: www.broadleyjames.com
SIC: 3823 3822 Electrodes used in industrial process measurement; auto controls regulating resdntl & coml environmt & applncs

(P-21556)
CAMERON TECHNOLOGIES US INC
Also Called: Cameron's Measurement Systems
4040 Capitol Ave, Whittier (90601-1735)
PHONE...................562 222-8440
Victor Hart, *Plant Mgr*
EMP: 100 **Publicly Held**
SIC: 3823 Industrial flow & liquid measuring instruments
HQ: Cameron Technologies Us, Inc.
1000 Mcclaren Woods Dr
Coraopolis PA 15108
724 695-3798

(P-21557)
CANNALINK INC
110 W C St Ste 1300, San Diego (92101-3978)
PHONE...................310 921-1955
Robert Plomgren, *CEO*
Robert Malasek, *CFO*
James Truher, *Chairman*
Ed Hart, *Vice Pres*
Robert L McCauley, *CTO*
EMP: 10 EST: 1997
SQ FT: 37,000
SALES (est): 1.4MM **Privately Held**
SIC: 3823 4899 4841 Computer interface equipment for industrial process control; data communication services; cable & other pay television services

(P-21558)
CARMEL INSTRUMENTS LLC
1622 W Campbell Ave, Campbell (95008-1535)
PHONE...................408 866-0426
Shulamit Sofge, *General Mgr*
EMP: 10
SQ FT: 5,000
SALES (est): 591.5K **Privately Held**
SIC: 3823 Industrial process control instruments

(P-21559)
CBRITE INC
421 Pine Ave, Goleta (93117-3709)
PHONE...................805 722-1121
Boo Nilsson, *President*
Henning Stauss, *Vice Pres*
Mary Nirenberg, *Admin Asst*
Gang Yu, *CTO*
Alan Gomez, *Engineer*
EMP: 17
SALES (est): 4.3MM **Privately Held**
SIC: 3823 8731 Industrial instrmnts msrmnt display/control process variable; electronic research

(P-21560)
CDS DIRECT INC
24583 Avenida Musico, Murrieta (92562-3921)
P.O. Box 683, Gardnerville NV (89410-0683)
PHONE...................760 747-2734
Rick Ford, *President*
Wendy Ford, *CFO*
▲ EMP: 12
SQ FT: 10,000
SALES (est): 2MM **Privately Held**
WEB: www.cdsdirectinc.com
SIC: 3823 Computer interface equipment for industrial process control

(P-21561)
CELAMARK CORP
8 Digital Dr Ste 100, Novato (94949-5759)
P.O. Box 2333 (94948-2333)
PHONE...................415 883-3386
Charles Ray, *President*
▲ EMP: 25
SALES (est): 3.2MM **Privately Held**
WEB: www.celamark.com
SIC: 3823 2389 3822 2671 Controllers for process variables, all types; disposable garments & accessories; auto controls regulating resdntl & coml environmt & applncs; packaging paper & plastics film, coated & laminated

(P-21562)
CK TECHNOLOGIES INC (PA)
Also Called: Ckt
3629 Vista Mercado, Camarillo (93012-8055)
PHONE...................805 987-4801
Karl F Zimmermann, *President*
Heidi Zimmermann, *Info Tech Mgr*
Lisa Kohrt, *Technology*
Paul Nowlin, *Purch Agent*
Hassan Kamal, *Production*
EMP: 33
SQ FT: 34,000
SALES (est): 10.1MM **Privately Held**
WEB: www.ckt.com
SIC: 3823 3825 5065 Water quality monitoring & control systems; instruments to measure electricity; electronic parts & equipment

(P-21563)
CLEAR BLUE ENERGY CORP
17150 Via Del Ca, San Diego (92127)
PHONE...................858 451-1549
Paul Santina, *CEO*
Jim Kelly, *President*
EMP: 12
SALES (est): 3.6MM **Privately Held**
SIC: 3823 Water quality monitoring & control systems

(P-21564)
CONDOR ELECTRONICS INC
990 San Antonio Rd, Palo Alto (94303-4917)
PHONE...................408 745-7141
Christian Dorward, *President*
▲ EMP: 30
SQ FT: 7,300
SALES: 11MM **Privately Held**
WEB: www.condorelectronics.net
SIC: 3823 5065 Panelboard indicators, recorders & controllers: receiver; electronic parts & equipment

P
R
O
D
U
C
T
S

&

S
V
C
S

(P-21565)
CONTINENTAL CONTROLS CORP
7720 Kenamar Ct C, San Diego (92121-2425)
PHONE................................858 638-1709
Carlyn Ross Fisher, *CEO*
Ross Fisher, *President*
David Fisher, *Vice Pres*
Richard Fisher, *Vice Pres*
JC Richardson, *Regional Mgr*
▲ EMP: 30
SQ FT: 17,000
SALES (est): 8.3MM **Privately Held**
WEB: www.continentalcontrols.com
SIC: 3823 Industrial instrmnts msrmnt display/control process variable

(P-21566)
COUNTY OF NAPA
Also Called: Flood Ctrl Wtr Cnservation Dst
804 1st St, NAPA (94559-2623)
PHONE................................707 259-8620
Robert Peterson, *Director*
Gallegos Teresa, *Officer*
Tina Spencer, *Admin Sec*
Stephanie Sifuentes, *Analyst*
Richard Thomasser, *Controller*
EMP: 15 **Privately Held**
WEB: www.billkeller.com
SIC: 3823 Water quality monitoring & control systems
PA: County Of Napa
1195 Third St Ste 310
Napa CA 94559
707 253-4421

(P-21567)
CRYSTAL ENGINEERING CORP
708 Fiero Ln Ste 9, San Luis Obispo (93401-7945)
P.O. Box 3033 (93403-3033)
PHONE................................805 595-5477
David Porter, *President*
Patrick Cullen, *Technician*
Janine White, *Manager*
▲ EMP: 38
SALES (est): 9.8MM
SALES (corp-wide): 4.3B **Publicly Held**
WEB: www.crystalengineering.net
SIC: 3823 Pressure gauges, dial & digital; industrial process measurement equipment
PA: Ametek, Inc.
1100 Cassatt Rd
Berwyn PA 19312
610 647-2121

(P-21568)
CYBERWARE LABORATORY INC
12835 Corte Cordillera, Salinas (93908-8964)
PHONE................................831 484-1064
David Addleman, *President*
Lloyd Addleman, *Treasurer*
Stephen Addleman, *Vice Pres*
Sue Addleman, *Vice Pres*
Pat Addleman, *Admin Sec*
EMP: 16
SQ FT: 12,000
SALES (est): 1.6MM **Privately Held**
WEB: www.cyberware.com
SIC: 3823 Digital displays of process variables

(P-21569)
DELPHI CONTROL SYSTEMS INC
2806 Metropolitan Pl, Pomona (91767-1854)
PHONE................................909 593-8099
Beth A Barbonc, *President*
Scott Crail, *Vice Pres*
EMP: 15
SQ FT: 11,000
SALES (est): 3MM **Privately Held**
WEB: www.delphicontrolsystems.com
SIC: 3823 3613 Industrial process control instruments; control panels, electric

(P-21570)
DESERT MICROSYSTEMS INC
3387 Chicago Ave, Riverside (92507-6815)
PHONE................................951 682-3867
Albert Johnson, *President*
EMP: 25
SALES (est): 2.9MM **Privately Held**
WEB: www.desertmicrosys.com
SIC: 3823 3577 3571 Computer interface equipment for industrial process control; computer peripheral equipment; electronic computers

(P-21571)
DIGITAL DYNAMICS INC
5 Victor Sq, Scotts Valley (95066-3531)
PHONE................................831 438-4444
Jerde, *President*
William P Ledeen, *Ch of Bd*
Carolyn Jerde, *Admin Sec*
Robert Ankeney, *Sr Software Eng*
William Waggoner, *Info Tech Mgr*
EMP: 45
SQ FT: 18,000
SALES (est): 12.3MM **Privately Held**
WEB: www.digitaldynamics.com
SIC: 3823 Industrial instrmnts msrmnt display/control process variable

(P-21572)
DIGIVISION INC
9830 Summers Ridge Rd, San Diego (92121-3083)
PHONE................................858 530-0100
Randy Millar, *Exec VP*
Richard Hier, *Vice Pres*
EMP: 13
SQ FT: 10,000
SALES (est): 1.4MM **Privately Held**
WEB: www.digivision.com
SIC: 3823 8731 Digital displays of process variables; commercial physical research

(P-21573)
DONNASHI ENTERPRISES INC
43644 Parkway Esplanade W, La Quinta (92253-4097)
PHONE................................760 200-3402
Jill Ames, *General Mgr*
Basheva Macpherson, *Exec VP*
EMP: 30 EST: 2011
SALES (est): 2.2MM **Privately Held**
SIC: 3823 Water quality monitoring & control systems

(P-21574)
DURO-SENSE CORP
869 Sandhill Ave, Carson (90746-1210)
PHONE................................310 533-6877
Jay Waterman, *President*
Roger S Waterman, *Ch of Bd*
EMP: 15
SQ FT: 8,000
SALES (est): 3.5MM **Privately Held**
WEB: www.duro-sense.com
SIC: 3823 Temperature instruments: industrial process type

(P-21575)
DUSOUTH INDUSTRIES
Also Called: Dst Controls
651 Stone Rd, Benicia (94510-1141)
PHONE................................707 745-5117
William P Southard, *President*
Read Hayward, *Vice Pres*
EMP: 30
SQ FT: 14,000
SALES (est): 10.9MM **Privately Held**
SIC: 3823 Industrial instrmnts msrmnt display/control process variable

(P-21576)
EAGLE TECH MANUFACTURING INC
841 Walker St, Watsonville (95076-4116)
PHONE................................831 768-7467
Alfredo Madrigal, *President*
Hector Madrigal, *Vice Pres*
Bertha Guerrero, *Bookkeeper*
Jesus Navarro, *Buyer*
Enrique Hernandez, *Marketing Staff*
▲ EMP: 35
SQ FT: 5,000
SALES (est): 7.3MM **Privately Held**
WEB: www.eagletechman.com
SIC: 3823 Electrolytic conductivity instruments, industrial process

(P-21577)
EDC-BIOSYSTEMS INC
49090 Milmont Dr, Fremont (94538-7301)
PHONE................................510 257-1500
Roger Williams, *CEO*
Greg Stephens, *President*
Chuck Reichel, *Vice Pres*
Linna Lee, *Purchasing*
◆ EMP: 25
SQ FT: 18,600
SALES (est): 5.6MM **Privately Held**
WEB: www.edcbiosystems.com
SIC: 3823 Industrial process measurement equipment

(P-21578)
ELDRIDGE PRODUCTS INC
465 Reservation Rd, Marina (93933-3430)
PHONE................................831 648-7777
Mark F Eldridge, *President*
Barbara Regan, *Controller*
Joseph Limon, *Purchasing*
David Garello, *Marketing Staff*
Richard Taylor, *Manager*
▼ EMP: 20
SQ FT: 8,500
SALES (est): 4.9MM **Privately Held**
WEB: www.epiflow.com
SIC: 3823 3824 Flow instruments, industrial process type; fluid meters & counting devices

(P-21579)
EMBEDDED DESIGNS INC
Also Called: K I C
16120 W Bernardo Dr Ste A, San Diego (92127-1875)
PHONE................................858 673-6050
Casey Kazmierowicz, *Chairman*
Bjorn Dahle, *President*
Henryk J Kazmier, *CFO*
Miles Moreau, *Vice Pres*
Phil Kazmierowicz, *Admin Sec*
EMP: 32
SQ FT: 9,500
SALES (est): 6.7MM **Privately Held**
WEB: www.kicthermal.com
SIC: 3823 Temperature measurement instruments, industrial

(P-21580)
EMCO FLUID SYSTEMS INC
28150 Harrison Pkwy, Valencia (91355-4109)
PHONE................................661 295-1015
Richard W Fritch, *President*
EMP: 183
SALES (est): 17.7MM **Privately Held**
SIC: 3823 Industrial instrmnts msrmnt display/control process variable

(P-21581)
EMERSON PROCESS MANAGEMENT
5466 Complex St Ste 203, San Diego (92123-1124)
PHONE................................858 492-1069
Ron Buchholz, *Manager*
Daniel Masso, *Senior Engr*
EMP: 20
SALES (corp-wide): 15.2B **Publicly Held**
WEB:
www.emersonprocesspowerwater.com
SIC: 3823 Industrial instrmnts msrmnt display/control process variable
HQ: Emerson Process Management Power & Water Solutions, Inc.
200 Beta Dr
Pittsburgh PA 15238
412 963-4000

(P-21582)
ESYS ENERGY CONTROL COMPANY
12881 Knott St Ste 227, Garden Grove (92841-3947)
PHONE................................714 372-3322
Abio Russeniello, *Owner*
Tyler Adkins, *Manager*
EMP: 25
SALES (est): 1.7MM **Privately Held**
SIC: 3823 Combustion control instruments

(P-21583)
FLOWMETRICS INC
9201 Independence Ave, Chatsworth (91311-5905)
PHONE................................818 407-3420
Hormoz Ghaemmaghami, *President*
Irfan Ahmad, *Purch Dir*
EMP: 22
SQ FT: 4,000
SALES (est): 4MM **Privately Held**
WEB: www.flowmetrics.com
SIC: 3823 Industrial flow & liquid measuring instruments

(P-21584)
FLUID COMPONENTS INTL LLC (PA)
Also Called: F C I
1755 La Costa Meadows Dr A, San Marcos (92078-5187)
PHONE................................760 744-6950
Dan McQueen, *CEO*
Daniel M McQueen, *President*
Barbara Succetti, *CFO*
Jim Delee, *Regional Mgr*
Ron Ogle, *Administration*
▲ EMP: 187
SQ FT: 49,000
SALES (est): 41.4MM **Privately Held**
WEB: www.fluidcomponents.com
SIC: 3823 Industrial instrmnts msrmnt display/control process variable

(P-21585)
FLUID POWER CTRL SYSTEMS INC
1400 E Valencia Dr, Fullerton (92831-4733)
PHONE................................714 525-3727
Harsoyo Lukito, *President*
EMP: 21
SALES (est): 3.4MM **Privately Held**
SIC: 3823 Fluidic devices, circuits & systems for process control

(P-21586)
FLUID RESEARCH CORPORATION
30281 Esperanza, Rcho STA Marg (92688-2130)
PHONE................................714 258-2350
Paul Ellsworth, *Principal*
Marilyn Fisher, *Sales Staff*
EMP: 21
SQ FT: 15,000
SALES (est): 6.1MM **Privately Held**
WEB: www.fluidresearch.com
SIC: 3823 Industrial instrmnts msrmnt display/control process variable

(P-21587)
FORTREND ENGINEERING CORP
2220 Otoole Ave, San Jose (95131-1326)
PHONE................................408 734-9311
Chris Wu PHD, *CEO*
Joseph MA PHD, *Chairman*
Richard Morgan, *Vice Pres*
Harriet West, *Executive*
Leonid Rakhamimov, *Engineer*
EMP: 41 EST: 1979
SQ FT: 20,000
SALES (est): 8.9MM **Privately Held**
WEB: www.fortrend.com
SIC: 3823 Industrial instrmnts msrmnt display/control process variable

(P-21588)
FRONTLINE ENVIRONMENTAL TEC
Also Called: Frontline Technologies
3195 Park Rd Ste C, Benicia (94510-1185)
P.O. Box 426 (94510-0426)
PHONE................................707 745-1116
Randall L Sherwood, *President*
Kelly Weaver, *Sales Engr*
Lynne Trammell, *Manager*
EMP: 15
SQ FT: 5,000
SALES (est): 3MM **Privately Held**
WEB: www.frontlineworldwide.com
SIC: 3823 1731 Industrial instrmnts msrmnt display/control process variable; environmental system control installation

▲ = Import ▼=Export
◆ =Import/Export

(P-21589)
FUNDAMENTAL TECH INTL INC
Also Called: F T I
2900 E 29th St, Long Beach (90806-2315)
PHONE..................................562 595-0661
Maarten Propper, *CEO*
John Jacobson, *President*
▼ EMP: 21
SQ FT: 20,000
SALES (est): 3.5MM Privately Held
SIC: 3823 Liquid analysis instruments, industrial process type

(P-21590)
FUNKTION TECHNOLOGIES INC
2110 Artesia Blvd B202, Redondo Beach (90278-3073)
PHONE..................................310 937-7335
Danish Qureshi, *CEO*
EMP: 10
SALES (est): 577K Privately Held
SIC: 3823 Industrial process measurement equipment

(P-21591)
FUTEK ADVANCED SENSOR TECH INC
10 Thomas, Irvine (92618-2702)
PHONE..................................949 465-0900
Javad Mokhberi, *CEO*
Javad Mokhbery, *CEO*
Dan Solomon, *CFO*
Javad Von Mokhbery, *Info Tech Dir*
Blake McKenna, *Engineer*
EMP: 140
SQ FT: 23,000
SALES (est): 30MM Privately Held
WEB: www.futek.com
SIC: 3823 8711 Industrial instrmnts msrmnt display/control process variable; engineering services

(P-21592)
GALIL MOTION CONTROL INC
270 Technology Way, Rocklin (95765-1228)
PHONE..................................800 377-6329
Jacob Tal, *Principal*
Wayne Baron, *President*
Brian Kambe, *Vice Pres*
Kaushal Shah, *Vice Pres*
John Thompson, *Vice Pres*
EMP: 36
SQ FT: 30,000
SALES (est): 9.2MM Privately Held
WEB: www.galilmc.com
SIC: 3823 Industrial instrmnts msrmnt display/control process variable

(P-21593)
GATEWORKS CORPORATION
3026 S Higuera St, San Luis Obispo (93401-6606)
PHONE..................................805 781-2000
Gordon Edmonds, *President*
Doug Hollingsworth, *Vice Pres*
Ron Eisworth, *Admin Sec*
EMP: 12 EST: 1995
SQ FT: 2,100
SALES (est): 3.8MM Privately Held
WEB: www.gateworks.com
SIC: 3823 Computer interface equipment for industrial process control

(P-21594)
GEORG FISCHER SIGNET LLC
3401 Aero Jet Ave, El Monte (91731-2801)
PHONE..................................626 571-2770
Charlotte Hill, *Mng Member*
Thad Snowden, *Maintence Staff*
▲ EMP: 90 EST: 1953
SQ FT: 27,000
SALES (est): 20.1MM
SALES (corp-wide): 4.2B Privately Held
WEB: www.gfsignet.com
SIC: 3823 Industrial process control instruments
HQ: Georg Fischer Spa
    Via Sondrio 1
    Cernusco Sul Naviglio MI 20063
    029 218-61

(P-21595)
GET ENGINEERING CORP
9350 Bond Ave, El Cajon (92021-2850)
PHONE..................................619 443-8295

L Adams, *CEO*
Guille Tuttle, *Shareholder*
Rodney Tuttle, *Shareholder*
Leslie Adams, *CEO*
David Shaw, *COO*
EMP: 20
SQ FT: 14,500
SALES (est): 5MM Privately Held
WEB: www.getntds.com
SIC: 3823 7373 3812 3679 Computer interface equipment for industrial process control; computer integrated systems design; search & navigation equipment; electronic circuits

(P-21596)
GRAPHTEC AMERICA INC (DH)
17462 Armstrong Ave, Irvine (92614-5724)
PHONE..................................949 770-6010
Yasutaka Arakawa, *CEO*
Kenichi Sahara, *CFO*
Renee Kunkle, *Credit Mgr*
Chuck Reitzell, *VP Sales*
Dominick Bizzari, *Sales Mgr*
◆ EMP: 50
SQ FT: 35,000
SALES (est): 6.7MM
SALES (corp-wide): 447.4MM Privately Held
WEB: www.graphtecusa.com
SIC: 3823 5064 Industrial instrmnts msrmnt display/control process variable; video cassette recorders & accessories
HQ: Graphtec Corp.
    503-10, Shinanocho, Totsuka-Ku
    Yokohama KNG 244-0
    458 256-200

(P-21597)
HARDY PROCESS SOLUTIONS
9440 Carroll Park Dr # 150, San Diego (92121-5201)
PHONE..................................858 278-2900
Eric Schellenberger, *President*
Steve Hanes, *CFO*
Jim Ephraim, *General Mgr*
Chris Prazak, *General Mgr*
Jeanne Singer, *Technical Staff*
◆ EMP: 50 EST: 1980
SQ FT: 63,000
SALES (est): 13MM
SALES (corp-wide): 4.6B Publicly Held
WEB: www.hardyinst.com
SIC: 3823 3829 3596 Industrial instrmnts msrmnt display/control process variable; measuring & controlling devices; scales & balances, except laboratory
HQ: Dynamic Instruments, Inc.
    10737 Lexington Dr
    Knoxville TN 37932
    858 278-4900

(P-21598)
HARRIS CORPORATION
Also Called: Exelis
591 Camno De La Reina 5, San Diego (92108)
PHONE..................................619 296-6900
Jim Wantrobski, *Principal*
EMP: 195
SALES (corp-wide): 6.1B Publicly Held
SIC: 3823 3812 Industrial instrmnts msrmnt display/control process variable; search & navigation equipment
PA: Harris Corporation
    1025 W Nasa Blvd
    Melbourne FL 32919
    321 727-9100

(P-21599)
HEWITT INDUSTRIES LOS ANGELES
5492 Bolsa Ave, Huntington Beach (92649-1021)
PHONE..................................714 891-9300
John T Hewitt, *President*
▲ EMP: 45 EST: 1955
SQ FT: 42,000
SALES (est): 7.2MM Privately Held
WEB: www.hewittindustries.com
SIC: 3823 3714 3625 Pyrometers, industrial process type; temperature instruments: industrial process type; motor vehicle parts & accessories; relays & industrial controls

(P-21600)
I DES INC
864 Saint Francis Way, Rio Vista (94571-1250)
PHONE..................................707 374-7500
Dan Simpson, *President*
▲ EMP: 35
SALES (est): 4.7MM Privately Held
SIC: 3823 Hydrometers, industrial process type

(P-21601)
I T I ELECTRO-OPTIC CORP (PA)
Also Called: Ccd
11500 W Olympic Blvd, Los Angeles (90064-1524)
PHONE..................................310 445-8900
MEI Shi, *Ch of Bd*
Robert Nevins, *President*
Henry Hong, *Executive*
James Wang, *VP Finance*
John Sun, *Analyst*
▲ EMP: 40
SQ FT: 5,000
SALES (est): 4.8MM Privately Held
SIC: 3823 Infrared instruments, industrial process type

(P-21602)
I T I ELECTRO-OPTIC CORP
1500 E Olympic Blvd # 400, Los Angeles (90021-1900)
PHONE..................................310 312-4526
John Sun, *Manager*
EMP: 20
SALES (corp-wide): 4.8MM Privately Held
SIC: 3823 Infrared instruments, industrial process type
PA: I T I Electro-Optic Corporation
    11500 W Olympic Blvd
    Los Angeles CA 90064
    310 445-8900

(P-21603)
I/O SELECT INC
9835 Carroll Centre Rd # 100, San Diego (92126-6507)
PHONE..................................858 537-2060
Rob Henley, *President*
Julie A Henley, *Exec VP*
Julie Henley, *Exec VP*
H Philip White, *Vice Pres*
EMP: 15
SQ FT: 6,100
SALES: 3MM Privately Held
SIC: 3823 Industrial process measurement equipment

(P-21604)
INNOVATIVE INTEGRATION INC
741 Flynn Rd, Camarillo (93012-8056)
PHONE..................................805 520-3300
Jim Henderson, *President*
Dan McLane, *Vice Pres*
▲ EMP: 30
SQ FT: 11,000
SALES (est): 8.9MM Privately Held
WEB: www.innovative-dsp.com
SIC: 3823 3571 Industrial instrmnts msrmnt display/control process variable; electronic computers

(P-21605)
INSTRUMENT & VALVE SERVICES CO
531 Getty Ct Ste D, Benicia (94510-1180)
PHONE..................................707 745-4664
George Noland, *Manager*
EMP: 11
SALES (corp-wide): 15.2B Publicly Held
WEB: www.instrm3nt.com
SIC: 3823 Industrial instrmnts msrmnt display/control process variable
HQ: Instrument & Valve Services Company
    205 S Center St
    Marshalltown IA 50158

(P-21606)
JR3 INC
22 Harter Ave Ste 1, Woodland (95776-5901)
PHONE..................................530 661-3677
John E Ramming, *President*
Joe Coehlo, *Engineer*

EMP: 11
SQ FT: 7,500
SALES (est): 877.7K Privately Held
WEB: www.jr3.com
SIC: 3823 Industrial instrmnts msrmnt display/control process variable

(P-21607)
KASHIYAMA USA INC
41432 Christy St, Fremont (94538-5105)
PHONE..................................510 979-0070
Take Hirabayashi, *President*
Take Hiraboyashi, *President*
Koichi Miura, *Controller*
Tommy Yamamoto, *Accounts Mgr*
▲ EMP: 10
SALES (est): 1.3MM Privately Held
WEB: www.kashiyama.com
SIC: 3823 3826 Thermal conductivity instruments, industrial process type; electrolytic conductivity instruments

(P-21608)
KERN WATER BANK AUTHORITY
1620 Mill Rock Way # 500, Bakersfield (93311-1343)
PHONE..................................661 398-4900
Jon Parker, *Manager*
Jonathan Parker, *General Mgr*
Cheryl Harding, *Administration*
Danelle Brooks, *Technology*
EMP: 13
SALES (est): 2.2MM Privately Held
SIC: 3823 Water quality monitoring & control systems

(P-21609)
KING INSTRUMENT COMPANY INC
12700 Pala Dr, Garden Grove (92841-3924)
PHONE..................................714 891-0008
Clyde F King, *President*
EMP: 50
SQ FT: 46,000
SALES (est): 12.8MM Privately Held
WEB: www.kinginstrumentco.com
SIC: 3823 Flow instruments, industrial process type

(P-21610)
KING NUTRONICS CORPORATION
6421 Independence Ave, Woodland Hills (91367-2608)
PHONE..................................818 887-5460
J Robert King, *President*
Leslie King, *Admin Sec*
Amir Gnessin, *Engineer*
Terry Lew, *Engineer*
Mohammad Houman, *QC Mgr*
EMP: 20
SQ FT: 21,000
SALES (est): 5.1MM Privately Held
WEB: www.kingnutronics.com
SIC: 3823 3825 Pressure measurement instruments, industrial; temperature instruments: industrial process type; instruments to measure electricity

(P-21611)
KOCO MOTION US LLC
335 Cochrane Cir, Morgan Hill (95037-2831)
PHONE..................................408 612-4970
Max Wietharn, *Principal*
▲ EMP: 13 EST: 2011
SALES (est): 2.2MM Privately Held
SIC: 3823 Industrial process control instruments

(P-21612)
LAIRD TECHNOLOGIES INC
2040 Fortune Dr Ste 102, San Jose (95131-1850)
PHONE..................................408 544-9500
Troy Hodges, *Owner*
EMP: 50
SALES (corp-wide): 1.2B Privately Held
SIC: 3823 Absorption analyzers: infrared, X-ray, etc.: industrial

P
R
O
D
U
C
T
S
&
S
V
C
S

HQ: Laird Technologies, Inc.
16401 Swingley
Chesterfield MO 63017
636 898-6000

(P-21613)
LINDAHL ENTERPRISES LTD INC
936 N Oaks Ave, Ontario (91762-2046)
PHONE..................................909 391-7052
Dwight L Lindahl, *President*
EMP: 20
SQ FT: 2,000
SALES: 100K Privately Held
SIC: 3823 Controllers for process variables, all types

(P-21614)
LOGIC BEACH INC (PA)
8363 Center Dr Ste 6f, La Mesa
(91942-2942)
PHONE..................................619 698-3300
David Parks, *President*
Martha Osterling, *Vice Pres*
EMP: 10
SQ FT: 2,000
SALES (est): 2MM Privately Held
WEB: www.logicbeach.com
SIC: 3823 3825 Data loggers, industrial process type; battery testers, electrical

(P-21615)
MANNING HOLOFF CO INC
15610 Moorpark St Apt 3, Encino
(91436-1639)
PHONE..................................818 407-2500
Geraldine Holoff, *President*
Susan Holoff, *Vice Pres*
James Krasne, *Admin Sec*
Sue Holoff, *VP Finance*
EMP: 25
SALES: 2.1MM Privately Held
WEB: www.magna-lite.com
SIC: 3823 3648 Industrial instrmnts msrmnt display/control process variable; lighting equipment

(P-21616)
MARINESYNC CORPORATION
3235 Hancock St, San Diego (92110-4419)
P.O. Box 80174 (92138-0174)
PHONE..................................619 578-2953
Austin Bleier, *CEO*
EMP: 10
SALES (est): 1.5MM Privately Held
SIC: 3823 Telemetering instruments, industrial process type

(P-21617)
MICRO LITHOGRAPHY INC
1247 Elko Dr, Sunnyvale (94089-2211)
PHONE..................................408 747-1769
Yung-Tsai Yen, *CEO*
Chris Yen, *President*
Sandy Yen, *Exec VP*
John T Liu, *General Mgr*
David Wang, *Administration*
▲ EMP: 225
SQ FT: 100,000
SALES (est): 58.1MM Privately Held
WEB: www.mliusa.com
SIC: 3823 3674 Industrial instrmnts msrmnt display/control process variable; semiconductors & related devices

(P-21618)
MICROCOOL
72216 Northshore St # 103, Thousand
Palms (92276-2325)
PHONE..................................760 322-1111
Mike Lemche, *President*
Christopher Stanley, *Vice Pres*
James Murphy, *Admin Sec*
▲ EMP: 15
SQ FT: 5,800
SALES (est): 3.4MM Privately Held
WEB: www.microcool.com
SIC: 3823 Humidity instruments, industrial process type

(P-21619)
MODUTEK CORP
6387 San Ignacio Ave, San Jose
(95119-1206)
PHONE..................................408 362-2000
Douglas G Wagner, *President*
Robert Brody, *Vice Pres*

Joanne Turley, *Finance Dir*
EMP: 21
SQ FT: 21,000
SALES (est): 5.4MM Privately Held
WEB: www.modutek.com
SIC: 3823 7373 Temperature instruments: industrial process type; systems integration services

(P-21620)
MOTION INDUSTRIES INC
Also Called: Numatic Engineering
7915 Ajay Dr, Sun Valley (91352-5315)
PHONE..................................818 768-1200
EMP: 38
SALES (corp-wide): 16.3B Publicly Held
SIC: 3823 Temperature measurement instruments, industrial
HQ: Motion Industries, Inc.
1605 Alton Rd
Birmingham AL 35210
205 956-1122

(P-21621)
MOUNTZ INC (PA)
Also Called: Dg Mountz Associates
1080 N 11th St, San Jose (95112-2927)
PHONE..................................408 292-2214
Brad Mountz, *President*
David Aviles, *CFO*
Lorna U Mountz, *Treasurer*
Sanjar Chakamian, *Bd of Directors*
Rob Stewart, *General Mgr*
▲ EMP: 43
SQ FT: 30,000
SALES: 15MM Privately Held
SIC: 3823 5085 Industrial instrmnts msrmnt display/control process variable; fasteners & fastening equipment

(P-21622)
MYRON L COMPANY
2450 Impala Dr, Carlsbad (92010-7226)
PHONE..................................760 438-2021
Gary O Robinson, *President*
Jerry Adams, *Vice Pres*
Suzanne Schultz, *Executive*
◆ EMP: 80
SQ FT: 43,000
SALES (est): 24.5MM Privately Held
WEB: www.myronl.com
SIC: 3823 3825 3613 Electrodes used in industrial process measurement; instruments to measure electricity; switchgear & switchboard apparatus

(P-21623)
N A SUEZ
Also Called: West Bsin Wtr Rclamation Plant
1935 S Hughes Way, El Segundo
(90245-4729)
PHONE..................................310 414-0183
Reza Nabegh, *Manager*
Henry Phan, *Buyer*
Joe Diaz, *Maintence Staff*
Temitayo Abegunde, *Manager*
EMP: 45
SALES (corp-wide): 86.1MM Privately
Held
WEB: www.unitedwaterservices.com
SIC: 3823 Water quality monitoring & control systems
HQ: N A Suez
461 From Rd Ste F
Paramus NJ 07652
201 767-9300

(P-21624)
NON-LINEAR SYSTEMS
Also Called: Nls
4561 Mission Gorge Pl F, San Diego
(92120-4113)
PHONE..................................619 521-2161
Pamela Finley, *Owner*
Jesse L Finley, *Co-Owner*
▼ EMP: 10
SQ FT: 6,000
SALES (est): 986.5K Privately Held
WEB: www.nonlinearsystems.com
SIC: 3823 3825 Temperature instruments: industrial process type; test equipment for electronic & electric measurement; current measuring equipment; oscillographs & oscilloscopes; volt meters

(P-21625)
NORDSON ASYMTEK INC
2475 Ash St, Vista (92081-8424)
PHONE..................................760 727-2880
Dave Padgett, *Branch Mgr*
Juan Villagomez, *Supervisor*
EMP: 15
SALES (corp-wide): 2B Publicly Held
SIC: 3823 Industrial instrmnts msrmnt display/control process variable
HQ: Nordson Asymtek, Inc.
2747 Loker Ave W
Carlsbad CA 92010
760 431-1919

(P-21626)
NORDSON ASYMTEK INC (HQ)
2747 Loker Ave W, Carlsbad (92010-6601)
PHONE..................................760 431-1919
Peter Bierhuis, *CEO*
Erik Fiske, *Principal*
Bernard McHugh, *General Mgr*
Kyle Canales, *Info Tech Dir*
Andrew Austin, *Technical Staff*
▲ EMP: 200
SQ FT: 100,000
SALES (est): 60.1MM
SALES (corp-wide): 2B Publicly Held
WEB: www.asymtek.com
SIC: 3823 Industrial flow & liquid measuring instruments
PA: Nordson Corporation
28601 Clemens Rd
Westlake OH 44145
440 892-1580

(P-21627)
OLEUMTECH CORPORATION
19762 Pauling, Foothill Ranch
(92610-2611)
PHONE..................................949 305-9009
Paul Gregory, *CEO*
Vrej ISA, *COO*
Brent McAdams, *Vice Pres*
Colin Miller, *Software Dev*
Ryan Osterhoudt, *Accountant*
EMP: 43
SQ FT: 55,000
SALES: 15MM Privately Held
WEB: www.oleumtech.com
SIC: 3823 Industrial instrmnts msrmnt display/control process variable

(P-21628)
OMRON SCIENTIFIC TECH INC (DH)
Also Called: Optical Sensor Division
6550 Dumbarton Cir, Fremont
(94555-3605)
PHONE..................................510 608-3400
Joseph J Lazzara, *President*
James A Ashford, *Senior VP*
James A Lazzara, *Senior VP*
Grace Eblacas, *General Mgr*
Naoya Ochi, *General Mgr*
◆ EMP: 250 EST: 1979
SQ FT: 95,700
SALES (est): 50.6MM
SALES (corp-wide): 8B Privately Held
SIC: 3823 3827 Industrial instrmnts msrmnt display/control process variable; optical instruments & lenses
HQ: Omron Management Center Of America, Inc.
2895 Greenspoint Pkwy # 100
Hoffman Estates IL 60169
224 520-7650

(P-21629)
PAC 21
11888 Western Ave, Stanton (90680-3438)
PHONE..................................714 891-7000
Will G Durant, *President*
George Lindsley, *Shareholder*
Will Durant, *President*
Ariel Durant, *Admin Sec*
EMP: 10
SQ FT: 9,000
SALES (est): 1.3MM Privately Held
WEB: www.pac21.com
SIC: 3823 Industrial process control instruments

(P-21630)
PARKER-HANNIFIN CORPORATION
Veriflo Division
250 Canal Blvd, Richmond (94804-2002)
PHONE..................................510 235-9590
Pera Horne, *General Mgr*
Fergus Bourke, *Engineer*
Dan Morgan, *Engineer*
Anil Raina, *Engineer*
Dave Alden, *Controller*
EMP: 100
SALES (corp-wide): 12B Publicly Held
WEB: www.parker.com
SIC: 3823 3842 3841 3625 Industrial process control instruments; respirators; surgical & medical instruments; relays & industrial controls; industrial valves
PA: Parker-Hannifin Corporation
6035 Parkland Blvd
Cleveland OH 44124
216 896-3000

(P-21631)
PATTEN SYSTEMS INC
15598 Producer Ln, Huntington Beach
(92649-1308)
PHONE..................................714 799-5656
John Capitano, *Principal*
Jason Neves, *Sales Associate*
John Raia, *Sales Associate*
EMP: 17
SALES (est): 3MM Privately Held
SIC: 3823 Analyzers, industrial process type

(P-21632)
PHOTON INC
1671 Dell Ave Ste 208, Campbell
(95008-6900)
PHONE..................................408 226-1000
John Fleisher, *President*
Judith Fleisher, *Corp Secy*
Jeffrey Guttman, *Chief Engr*
Derrick Peterman, *Sales Staff*
EMP: 17
SQ FT: 10,000
SALES (est): 3.6MM Privately Held
SIC: 3823 8711 Industrial instrmnts msrmnt display/control process variable; consulting engineer

(P-21633)
PHYN LLC
1855 Del Amo Blvd, Torrance (90501-1302)
PHONE..................................310 400-4001
Ryan Kim, *CEO*
Chester J Pipkin, *President*
EMP: 10 EST: 2016
SALES (est): 1.4MM
SALES (corp-wide): 60.3B Privately Held
SIC: 3823 Water quality monitoring & control systems
HQ: Belkin International, Inc.
12045 Waterfront Dr
Playa Vista CA 90094
310 751-5100

(P-21634)
PRESSURE PROFILE SYSTEMS INC
5757 W Century Blvd # 600, Los Angeles
(90045-6429)
PHONE..................................310 641-8100
Denis A O'Connor, *CEO*
Jae S Son, *CEO*
Steven Sanchez, *Treasurer*
Wing Young, *Vice Pres*
David Ables, *Admin Sec*
EMP: 17
SALES (est): 3.9MM Privately Held
WEB: www.pressureprofile.com
SIC: 3823 Industrial instrmnts msrmnt display/control process variable

(P-21635)
PRIME MEASUREMENT PRODUCTS LLC (PA)
Also Called: Barton Sales
900 Turnbull Canyon Rd, City of Industry
(91745-1404)
PHONE..................................626 961-2547
Jeff Warren, *Mng Member*
Ferlie San Antonio, *Controller*
James Warren,

▲ = Import ▼=Export
◆ =Import/Export

▲ **EMP:** 325 **EST:** 1925
SQ FT: 217,000
SALES (est): 37.9MM **Privately Held**
WEB: www.prime-measurement.com
SIC: 3823 3625 Liquid level instruments, industrial process type; relays & industrial controls

(P-21636)
PROCESS SOLUTIONS INC
Also Called: PSI
1077 Dell Ave Ste A, Campbell (95008-6628)
PHONE.................................408 370-6540
Brent Simmons, *CEO*
Gunnar Thortarson, *Vice Pres*
Christian Kucera, *Technology*
Gunnar Thordarson, *Human Res Mgr*
Gary Turner, *Director*
▲ **EMP:** 32
SALES (est): 11.2MM **Privately Held**
WEB: www.4psi.net
SIC: 3823 Water quality monitoring & control systems

(P-21637)
PROTEUS INDUSTRIES INC
340 Pioneer Way, Mountain View (94041-1577)
PHONE.................................650 964-4163
Jon Heiner, *CEO*
Mark Nicewonger, *Vice Pres*
Rene Truong, *Engineer*
Tommy Yiu, *Engineer*
Patty Quinata, *Buyer*
▲ **EMP:** 50
SQ FT: 40,000
SALES (est): 12.6MM **Privately Held**
WEB: www.proteusind.com
SIC: 3823 3829 3826 3824 Industrial instrmnts msrmnt display/control process variable; measuring & controlling devices; analytical instruments; fluid meters & counting devices; relays & industrial controls

(P-21638)
Q-MARK MANUFACTURING INC
Also Called: Quality Components Co
30051 Comercio, Rcho STA Marg (92688-2106)
PHONE.................................949 457-1913
Mark Osterstock, *President*
EMP: 14
SQ FT: 5,120
SALES: 2.7MM **Privately Held**
WEB: www.cmms.com
SIC: 3823 3599 Industrial instrmnts msrmnt display/control process variable; machine shop, jobbing & repair

(P-21639)
QED INC
2920 Halladay St, Santa Ana (92705-5623)
PHONE.................................714 546-6010
Erik K Moller, *CEO*
Randy Heartfield, *President*
Mary C Heartfield, *Admin Sec*
Lizbeth Santibanez, *Info Tech Mgr*
Chris Barr, *Engineer*
▲ **EMP:** 43
SQ FT: 13,000
SALES: 5.6MM **Privately Held**
WEB: www.qedinstruments.com
SIC: 3823 3829 3812 Pressure gauges, dial & digital; accelerometers; pressure & vacuum indicators, aircraft engine; aircraft/aerospace flight instruments & guidance systems; aircraft flight instruments; aircraft control systems, electronic

(P-21640)
QUANTUM-DYNAMICS CO INC
6414 Independence Ave, Woodland Hills (91367-2607)
PHONE.................................818 719-0142
Arnold F Liu, *President*
Frederick F Liu, *President*
Lily Liu, *Corp Secy*
Arnold Liu, *Vice Pres*
EMP: 18
SQ FT: 25,000
SALES: 1.5MM **Privately Held**
SIC: 3823 8731 Flow instruments, industrial process type; engineering laboratory, except testing

(P-21641)
QUICKLOGIC CORPORATION
1277 Orleans Dr, Sunnyvale (94089-1138)
PHONE.................................408 990-4000
Brian C Faith, *President*
E Thomas Hart, *Ch of Bd*
Sue Cheung, *CFO*
Arturo Krueger, *Bd of Directors*
Christine Russell, *Bd of Directors*
EMP: 91
SQ FT: 42,600
SALES (est): 12.1MM **Privately Held**
WEB: www.quicklogic.com
SIC: 3823 3674 Programmers, process type; integrated circuits, semiconductor networks, etc.

(P-21642)
R G HANSEN ASSOCIATES (PA)
5951 Encina Rd Ste 106, Goleta (93117-6251)
P.O. Box 160 (93116-0160)
PHONE.................................805 564-3388
Ian Wood, *President*
EMP: 12
SQ FT: 10,000
SALES (est): 1.1MM **Privately Held**
WEB: www.cryostat.com
SIC: 3823 Industrial instrmnts msrmnt display/control process variable

(P-21643)
RAIN MSTR IRRGTION SYSTEMS INC
5825 Jasmine St, Riverside (92504-1144)
P.O. Box 489 (92502-0489)
PHONE.................................805 527-4498
Jim Sieminski, *President*
John Torosiani, *Admin Sec*
Jeff Clarke, *Sales Mgr*
Samantha Larson, *Sales Staff*
Dan Salvatori, *Manager*
EMP: 32
SQ FT: 13,000
SALES (est): 4.7MM
SALES (corp-wide): 2.5B **Publicly Held**
WEB: www.toro.com
SIC: 3823 Industrial instrmnts msrmnt display/control process variable
PA: The Toro Company
8111 Lyndale Ave S
Bloomington MN 55420
952 888-8801

(P-21644)
RENAU CORPORATION
Also Called: Renau Electronic Laboratories
9309 Deering Ave, Chatsworth (91311-5858)
PHONE.................................818 341-1994
Karol Renau, *CEO*
Christine Renau, *Admin Sec*
Jackie Renau, *Technology*
Ryan Hoang, *Engineer*
Roman Pyrzynski, *Engineer*
▲ **EMP:** 20
SQ FT: 10,000
SALES (est): 6.4MM **Privately Held**
WEB: www.renau.com
SIC: 3823 Controllers for process variables, all types; time cycle & program controllers, industrial process type

(P-21645)
ROHRBACK COSASCO SYSTEMS INC (DH)
11841 Smith Ave, Santa Fe Springs (90670-3226)
PHONE.................................562 949-0123
Bryan Sanderlin, *CEO*
Stan Zupan, *Data Proc Staff*
David Price, *Technology*
Ryan Epstein, *Project Engr*
Alex Calleros, *Credit Mgr*
▼ **EMP:** 71
SQ FT: 37,000
SALES (est): 17.3MM
SALES (corp-wide): 1.5B **Privately Held**
WEB: www.rohrbackcosasco.com
SIC: 3823 8742 Industrial instrmnts msrmnt display/control process variable; industry specialist consultants
HQ: Halma Investment Holdings Limited
Misbourne Court Rectory Way
Amersham BUCKS
149 472-1111

(P-21646)
RONAN ENGINEERING COMPANY (PA)
Also Called: Ronan Engnrng/Rnan Msrment Div
28209 Avenue Stanford, Valencia (91355-3984)
P.O. Box 129, Castaic (91310-0129)
PHONE.................................661 702-1344
John A Hewitson, *CEO*
▼ **EMP:** 56
SQ FT: 50,000
SALES (est): 15.7MM **Privately Held**
WEB: www.ronanmeasure.com
SIC: 3823 3825 Industrial instrmnts msrmnt display/control process variable; measuring instruments & meters, electric

(P-21647)
SABIA INCORPORATED (PA)
10915 Technology Pl, San Diego (92127-1811)
PHONE.................................858 217-2200
Steve Foster, *CEO*
Craig Belnap, *President*
Clinton L Lingren, *President*
James Miller, *Vice Pres*
Edward Nunn, *Vice Pres*
EMP: 27
SQ FT: 17,260
SALES (est): 6.3MM **Privately Held**
WEB: www.sabiainc.com
SIC: 3823 Industrial instrmnts msrmnt display/control process variable

(P-21648)
SANTA BARBARA CONTROL SYSTEMS
Also Called: Chemtrol
5375 Overpass Rd, Santa Barbara (93111-3015)
PHONE.................................805 683-8833
Pablo Navarro, *President*
Jacques Steininger, *CEO*
Karen Grigsby, *Office Mgr*
Nader Swich, *Info Tech Dir*
Joe Osuna, *Accountant*
EMP: 19
SQ FT: 8,000
SALES: 6.1MM **Privately Held**
WEB: www.sbcontrol.com
SIC: 3823 3589 7699 Water quality monitoring & control systems; swimming pool filter & water conditioning systems; cash register repair

(P-21649)
SCHNEIDER ELC SYSTEMS USA INC
Also Called: Triconex
26561 Rancho Pkwy S, Lake Forest (92630-8301)
PHONE.................................949 885-0700
Morgan England, *Branch Mgr*
Brian Urban, *Network Analyst*
Quang Vu, *Design Engr*
Paul Groner, *Engineer*
Lynne Duren, *Controller*
EMP: 10
SALES (corp-wide): 200.4K **Privately Held**
WEB: www.foxboro.com
SIC: 3823 Controllers for process variables, all types
HQ: Schneider Electric Systems Usa, Inc.
38 Neponset Ave
Foxboro MA 02035
508 543-8750

(P-21650)
SCIENTIFIC REPAIR INC
Also Called: SRI Instruments
20720 Earl St Ste 2, Torrance (90503-3034)
PHONE.................................310 214-5092
Hugh Goldsmith, *President*
EMP: 12
SQ FT: 5,000
SALES: 6MM **Privately Held**
WEB: www.srigc.com
SIC: 3823 Chromatographs, industrial process type

(P-21651)
SEMIFAB INC
150 Great Oaks Blvd, San Jose (95119-1347)
PHONE.................................408 414-5928
Hauynium Kabir, *President*
Greg Krikorian, *CFO*
Gerry Reynolds, *VP Sales*
◆ **EMP:** 60 **EST:** 1978
SQ FT: 55,000
SALES (est): 10.1MM **Privately Held**
WEB: www.semifab.com
SIC: 3823 3822 Industrial instrmnts msrmnt display/control process variable; temperature instruments: industrial process type; temperature controls, automatic

(P-21652)
SENDX MEDICAL INC (DH)
1945 Palomar Oaks Way # 100, Carlsbad (92011-1300)
PHONE.................................760 930-6300
Todd Fletcher, *President*
Doreen Milford, *President*
Matt Leader, *Vice Pres*
John Worley, *Vice Pres*
▲ **EMP:** 116 **EST:** 1998
SQ FT: 35,000
SALES (est): 32MM
SALES (corp-wide): 18.3B **Publicly Held**
WEB: www.danaher-dps.com
SIC: 3823 Industrial instrmnts msrmnt display/control process variable
HQ: Danrad Holding Aps
Akandevej 21
BrOnshOj 2700
382 738-27

(P-21653)
SENSORTECH SYSTEMS INC
Also Called: Sensor Engineering
341 Bernoulli Cir, Oxnard (93030-5164)
PHONE.................................805 981-3735
Colin Hanson, *President*
Roger Carlson, *Shareholder*
John Fordham, *Admin Sec*
▲ **EMP:** 12
SQ FT: 4,000
SALES (est): 3MM **Privately Held**
WEB: www.sensortech.com
SIC: 3823 3826 3829 Digital displays of process variables; analytical instruments; measuring & controlling devices

(P-21654)
SENSOSCIENTIFIC INC
685 Cochran St Ste 200, Simi Valley (93065-1921)
PHONE.................................800 279-3101
Ramin Rostami, *CEO*
Mike Zarei, *Vice Pres*
Isabelle Diep, *Finance Dir*
Seth Goldstein, *Regl Sales Mgr*
Jorge Marroquin, *Regl Sales Mgr*
▲ **EMP:** 25
SQ FT: 4,000
SALES: 5MM **Privately Held**
SIC: 3823 Industrial instrmnts msrmnt display/control process variable

(P-21655)
SILENX CORPORATION
10606 Shoemaker Ave Ste A, Santa Fe Springs (90670-4071)
PHONE.................................562 941-4200
Peter Kim, *President*
Chris Kim, *Treasurer*
Annie Kim, *Accounts Mgr*
▲ **EMP:** 15
SQ FT: 10,000
SALES: 1MM **Privately Held**
WEB: www.silenx.com
SIC: 3823 Computer interface equipment for industrial process control

(P-21656)
SJCONTROLS INC
2248 Obispo Ave Ste 203, Long Beach (90755-4026)
PHONE.................................562 494-1400
David J Olszewski, *President*
Frederick D Hesley Jr, *Chairman*
Stephen Czaus, *Vice Pres*
Jazmin Jones, *Office Mgr*
Yiotis Papadopoulos, *Info Tech Dir*

PRODUCTS & SVCS

(PA)=Parent Co (HQ)=Headquarters (DH)=Div Headquarters
✪ = New Business established in last 2 years

2019 California
Manufacturers Register

885

EMP: 11
SQ FT: 8,000
SALES (est): 2.8MM **Privately Held**
WEB: www.sjcontrols.com
SIC: 3823 5084 3824 Industrial instrmnts msrmnt display/control process variable; controlling instruments & accessories; fluid meters & counting devices

(P-21657)
SOUND WAVES INSULLATION INC
1406 Ritchey St Ste D, Santa Ana (92705-4735)
PHONE..................................714 556-2110
Todd Terray, *President*
Wally Fisk, *Vice Pres*
EMP: 20
SALES: 1.5MM **Privately Held**
SIC: 3823 Thermal conductivity instruments, industrial process type

(P-21658)
SPARLING INSTRUMENTS LLC
4097 Temple City Blvd, El Monte (91731-1046)
PHONE..................................626 444-0571
Yosufi Tyebkhan, *Mng Member*
▲ EMP: 25
SQ FT: 56,000
SALES (est): 6.5MM **Privately Held**
WEB: www.sparlinginstruments.com
SIC: 3823 5084 3824 Fluid meters & counting devices; industrial instrmnts msrmnt display/control process variable; industrial machinery & equipment

(P-21659)
SST TECHNOLOGIES
Also Called: Sst International
9801 Everest St, Downey (90242-3113)
PHONE..................................562 803-3361
Anthony Wilson, *President*
Ralph Burroughs, *CFO*
Aj Wilson, *General Mgr*
Dan Ross, *Engineer*
Estela Torres, *Accountant*
◆ EMP: 24
SQ FT: 20,000
SALES (est): 6.3MM **Privately Held**
WEB: www.edmsupply.com
SIC: 3823 Thermal conductivity instruments, industrial process type
PA: Palomar Technologies, Inc.
    2728 Loker Ave W
    Carlsbad CA 92010

(P-21660)
STAR-LUCK ENTERPRISE INC
11807 Harrington St, Bakersfield (93311-9278)
PHONE..................................661 665-9999
Xiaodong Zhou, *President*
Stephen Thompson, *Senior VP*
David Johnson, *Vice Pres*
▲ EMP: 12
SQ FT: 11,800
SALES: 4MM **Privately Held**
SIC: 3823 Pressure measurement instruments, industrial

(P-21661)
SUPERFISH INC
2595 E Byshore Rd Ste 150, Palo Alto (94303)
PHONE..................................650 752-6564
Shaul Gal-Oz, *President*
EMP: 18 EST: 2008
SALES (est): 3.8MM **Privately Held**
SIC: 3823 Analyzers, industrial process type

(P-21662)
TELEDYNE ADVANCED POLLUTION
9970 Carroll Canyon Rd, San Diego (92131-1106)
PHONE..................................858 657-9800
Robert Mehrabian, *President*
Jeff Franks, *General Mgr*
Mary Perlaki Neely, *Administration*
Larry Dana, *Info Tech Mgr*
Daryl Goodwin, *Technician*
EMP: 35

SALES (est): 7.9MM **Privately Held**
SIC: 3823 Industrial instrmnts msrmnt display/control process variable

(P-21663)
TELEDYNE INSTRUMENTS INC
Also Called: Teledyne Analytical Instrs
16830 Chestnut St, City of Industry (91748-1017)
PHONE..................................626 934-1500
Tom Compas, *Branch Mgr*
Thomas Compas, *General Mgr*
Steve Krechmery, *Info Tech Mgr*
Tony Ho, *Technology*
Connie Favela, *Engineer*
EMP: 170
SQ FT: 70,000
SALES (corp-wide): 2.6B **Publicly Held**
SIC: 3823 Industrial instrmnts msrmnt display/control process variable
HQ: Teledyne Instruments, Inc.
    1049 Camino Dos Rios
    Thousand Oaks CA 91360
    805 373-4545

(P-21664)
TELEDYNE INSTRUMENTS INC
Also Called: Teledyne Oceanscience
14020 Stowe Dr, Poway (92064-6846)
PHONE..................................760 754-2400
Dennis Klahn, *Principal*
Ed Tyburski, *President*
Harold Maxfield, *Vice Pres*
Brant Stewart, *Administration*
Jim Volz, *Info Tech Mgr*
EMP: 21
SALES (corp-wide): 2.6B **Publicly Held**
SIC: 3823 Buoyancy instruments, industrial process type
HQ: Teledyne Instruments, Inc.
    1049 Camino Dos Rios
    Thousand Oaks CA 91360
    805 373-4545

(P-21665)
TERN DESIGN LTD
Also Called: Oceanscience
14020 Stowe Dr, Poway (92064-6846)
PHONE..................................760 754-2400
Ronald George, *President*
Adrian McDonald, *Executive*
Darryl Symonds, *Manager*
EMP: 25
SQ FT: 4,800
SALES (est): 6.2MM **Privately Held**
WEB: www.oceanscience.com
SIC: 3823 Buoyancy instruments, industrial process type

(P-21666)
TERRY B LOWE
Also Called: Data Scale
42430 Blacow Rd, Fremont (94539-5621)
PHONE..................................510 651-7350
Terry B Lowe, *Owner*
▲ EMP: 10 EST: 1974
SQ FT: 6,000
SALES (est): 1.7MM **Privately Held**
WEB: www.datascale.com
SIC: 3823 Industrial process control instruments

(P-21667)
TEST ENTERPRISES INC (PA)
Also Called: Thermonics
1288 Reamwood Ave, Sunnyvale (94089-2233)
PHONE..................................408 542-5900
James C Kufis, *CEO*
▲ EMP: 32
SQ FT: 22,000
SALES (est): 6MM **Privately Held**
WEB: www.thermonics.com
SIC: 3823 3825 Temperature measurement instruments, industrial; semiconductor test equipment

(P-21668)
THERMOMETRICS CORPORATION (PA)
18714 Parthenia St, Northridge (91324-3813)
PHONE..................................818 886-3755
Jorge Hernandez, *President*
Robert Hernandez, *Vice Pres*
Steve Stapol, *Technology*

Tyler Lawson, *Engineer*
Victoria Dukes, *Controller*
EMP: 30
SQ FT: 16,897
SALES (est): 7.1MM **Privately Held**
WEB: www.thermometricscorp.com
SIC: 3823 Industrial instrmnts msrmnt display/control process variable

(P-21669)
THERMX TEMPERATURE TECH
Also Called: Thermx Southwest
7370 Opportunity Rd Ste S, San Diego (92111-2245)
PHONE..................................858 573-0983
John Bowman, *President*
Karen Bowman, *CFO*
Sheri Bernal, *Info Tech Mgr*
EMP: 11
SQ FT: 1,500
SALES (est): 2.4MM **Privately Held**
WEB: www.thermx.com
SIC: 3823 Industrial instrmnts msrmnt display/control process variable

(P-21670)
TRANSLOGIC INCORPORATED
5641 Engineer Dr, Huntington Beach (92649-1123)
PHONE..................................714 890-0058
Donald Ross, *CEO*
Gregory Ross, *Admin Sec*
EMP: 41
SALES (est): 7.7MM **Privately Held**
WEB: www.translogicinc.com
SIC: 3823 3829 Temperature instruments: industrial process type; thermocouples, industrial process type; measuring & controlling devices

(P-21671)
U S AIR FILTRATION INC (PA)
23811 Washington Ave C110176, Murrieta (92562-2275)
PHONE..................................951 491-7282
James H Perkins, *President*
EMP: 15
SQ FT: 3,900
SALES (est): 2.7MM **Privately Held**
WEB: www.usairfiltration.com
SIC: 3823 1796 Industrial process control instruments; pollution control equipment installation

(P-21672)
ULTRA CLEAN TECHNOLOGY SYSTEMS (HQ)
Also Called: Uct
26462 Corporate Ave, Hayward (94545-3914)
PHONE..................................510 576-4400
Jim Skullhammer, *CEO*
Leonard Mezhvinsky, *President*
Casey Eichler, *CFO*
Deborah Hayward, *Senior VP*
Lavi Lev, *Senior VP*
▲ EMP: 120
SQ FT: 12,000
SALES (est): 135.5MM
SALES (corp-wide): 924.3MM **Publicly Held**
SIC: 3823 Industrial instrmnts msrmnt display/control process variable
PA: Ultra Clean Holdings, Inc.
    26462 Corporate Ave
    Hayward CA 94545
    510 576-4400

(P-21673)
VALLEY CONTROLS INC
583 E Dinuba Ave, Reedley (93654-3531)
P.O. Box 1205 (93654-1205)
PHONE..................................559 638-5115
Verl A Tyler, *President*
Robin Tyler, *Treasurer*
Doyle Anderson, *Vice Pres*
EMP: 14 EST: 1978
SQ FT: 14,500
SALES (est): 1.4MM **Privately Held**
WEB: www.valleycontrols.com
SIC: 3823 1731 Industrial instrmnts msrmnt display/control process variable; electrical work

(P-21674)
VEEX INC
2827 Lakeview Ct, Fremont (94538-6534)
PHONE..................................510 651-0500
Cyrille Morelle, *President*
Carl Goldschmidt, *General Mgr*
Kun Shi, *General Mgr*
Simon Suh, *Sr Software Eng*
Mike Venter, *VP Sls/Mktg*
EMP: 19
SQ FT: 8,000
SALES (est): 5.9MM **Privately Held**
SIC: 3823 Programmers, process type

(P-21675)
VERTIV CORPORATION
35 Parker, Irvine (92618-1605)
PHONE..................................949 457-3600
Anita Golden, *Branch Mgr*
Rj Miller, *Marketing Staff*
Mark Asgarian, *Accounts Exec*
EMP: 50
SALES (corp-wide): 322.9MM **Privately Held**
SIC: 3823 Industrial instrmnts msrmnt display/control process variable
HQ: Vertiv Corporation
    1050 Dearborn Dr
    Columbus OH 43085
    614 888-0246

(P-21676)
WATER RESOURCES CAL DEPT
901 P St Lbby, Sacramento (95814-6424)
PHONE..................................916 651-9203
Mark Cowin, *Branch Mgr*
EMP: 99 **Privately Held**
SIC: 3823 Water quality monitoring & control systems
HQ: California Department Of Water Resources
    1416 9th St
    Sacramento CA 95814
    916 653-9394

(P-21677)
WORLDWIDE ENVMTL PDTS INC (PA)
Also Called: Imperials Sand Dunes
1100 Beacon St, Brea (92821-2936)
PHONE..................................714 990-2700
William Oscar Delaney, *CEO*
Benjamin Rico, *President*
Garrett Delaney, *Chief Mktg Ofcr*
Steven Alford, *Info Tech Mgr*
Brian Ho, *Prgrmr*
EMP: 90
SQ FT: 23,000
SALES: 18.6MM **Privately Held**
WEB: www.wep-inc.com
SIC: 3823 3694 Industrial instrmnts msrmnt display/control process variable; automotive electrical equipment

(P-21678)
XIRRUS INC
2101 Corporate Center Dr A, Thousand Oaks (91320-1419)
PHONE..................................805 262-1600
Shane Buckley, *CEO*
Steve Degennaro, *CFO*
Jillian Mansolf, *Chief Mktg Ofcr*
Sam Bass, *Vice Pres*
Shari Brantley, *Vice Pres*
◆ EMP: 200
SQ FT: 25,000
SALES (est): 48.3MM **Privately Held**
WEB: www.xirrus.com
SIC: 3823 Computer interface equipment for industrial process control

(P-21679)
YOUNG ENGINEERING & MFG INC (PA)
560 W Terrace Dr, San Dimas (91773-2914)
P.O. Box 3984 (91773-7984)
PHONE..................................909 394-3225
Winston Young, *President*
Joanne Young, *Vice Pres*
Carrie Garcia, *Info Tech Mgr*
Heidi Berger, *Marketing Staff*
Minlu Zhang, *Manager*
◆ EMP: 32
SQ FT: 55,000

SALES (est): 4.5MM **Privately Held**
WEB: www.youngeng.com
SIC: **3823** 5084 8711 5074 Industrial instrmnts msrmnt display/control process
variable; industrial machinery & equipment; consulting engineer; water purification equipment

3824 Fluid Meters & Counters

(P-21680)
BLUE-WHITE INDUSTRIES LTD (PA)
5300 Business Dr, Huntington Beach
(92649-1224)
PHONE...............................714 893-8529
Robert E Gledhill, *President*
Cindy Henderson, *Corp Secy*
Robert E Gledhill III, *Vice Pres*
Jeanne Hendrickson, *Vice Pres*
Daniel Estrada, *General Mgr*
▲ EMP: 71 EST: 1957
SQ FT: 48,000
SALES: 20MM **Privately Held**
WEB: www.bluwhite.com
SIC: **3824** 3561 3589 Water meters; in-
dustrial pumps & parts; sewage & water
treatment equipment

(P-21681)
BRITELAB
6341 San Ignacio Ave, San Jose
(95119-1202)
PHONE...............................650 961-0671
Robert De Neve, *CEO*
Paul Rogan, *CFO*
Jae Jung, *Officer*
Kris Correa, *Program Mgr*
Saeed Seyed, *CTO*
▲ EMP: 65
SQ FT: 52,000
SALES (est): 29.9MM **Privately Held**
SIC: **3824** 8741 8742 Mechanical &
electromechanical counters & devices;
management services; management con-
sulting services

(P-21682)
COUNTY OF ALAMEDA
Also Called: Registrar of Voters Office
1225 Fallon St Ste G1, Oakland
(94612-4229)
PHONE...............................510 272-6964
Bradley Clark, *Principal*
Gerald Veras, *Manager*
EMP: 30 **Privately Held**
WEB: www.co.alameda.ca.us
SIC: **3824** 9199 Registers, linear tallying;
general government administration;
PA: County Of Alameda
1221 Oak St Ste 555
Oakland CA 94612
510 272-6691

(P-21683)
CURTIS INSTRUMENTS INC
Also Called: Curtis PMC
235 E Airway Blvd, Livermore
(94551-7664)
PHONE...............................925 961-1088
Steven Post, *Branch Mgr*
Steve Post, *General Mgr*
Andrea Mokros, *Administration*
Larry Piggins, *Software Engr*
Mike Bachman, *Project Dir*
EMP: 70
SALES (corp-wide): 301.5MM **Privately
Held**
SIC: **3824** 3829 3825 3629 Speed indi-
cators & recorders, vehicle; aircraft &
motor vehicle measurement equipment;
elapsed time meters, electronic; elec-
tronic generation equipment; relays & in-
dustrial controls; motors & generators
PA: Curtis Instruments, Inc.
200 Kisco Ave
Mount Kisco NY 10549
914 666-2971

(P-21684)
DANAHER CORPORATION
Ketema Division
3255 W Stetson Ave, Hemet (92545-7763)
PHONE...............................951 652-6811
James Pugh, *Branch Mgr*
Steve Sheere, *Info Tech Mgr*
EMP: 220
SALES (corp-wide): 18.3B **Publicly Held**
SIC: **3824** 5084 3613 Water meters; in-
dustrial machinery & equipment;
switchgear & switchboard apparatus
PA: Danaher Corporation
2200 Penn Ave Nw Ste 800w
Washington DC 20037
202 828-0850

(P-21685)
DEXERIALS AMERICA CORPORATION
2001 Gateway Pl Ste 455e, San Jose
(95110-1044)
PHONE...............................408 441-0846
Nelly Soudakova, *Owner*
Jennie Liu, *Sales Staff*
EMP: 10
SALES (corp-wide): 657.7MM **Privately
Held**
SIC: **3824** Magnetic counters
HQ: Dexerials America Corporation
215 Satellite Blvd Ne # 400
Suwanee GA 30024
770 945-3845

(P-21686)
EMCOR GROUP INC
2 Cromwell, Irvine (92618-1816)
PHONE...............................949 475-6020
Henry Magdaleno, *Principal*
Frank Ledda, *President*
Joel Sakamoto, *Branch Mgr*
Jeff Figueroa, *Director*
Richard Jerry, *Manager*
EMP: 29
SALES (est): 12MM **Privately Held**
SIC: **3824** Fluid meters & counting devices

(P-21687)
EMITCON INC
Also Called: Airex
1175 N Van Horne Way, Anaheim
(92806-2506)
PHONE...............................714 632-8595
Jack M Preston, *President*
EMP: 35
SQ FT: 45,000
SALES (est): 5.3MM **Privately Held**
SIC: **3824** Integrating & totalizing meters
for gas & liquids

(P-21688)
EXELIXIS INC
Division 1
1851 Harbor Bay Pkwy, Alameda
(94502-3010)
PHONE...............................650 837-7000
Michael M Morrissey, *President*
EMP: 371 **Publicly Held**
SIC: **3824** 8731 Fluid meters & counting
devices; commercial physical research;
biological research
PA: Exelixis, Inc.
1851 Harbor Bay Pkwy
Alameda CA 94502

(P-21689)
INTERSCAN CORPORATION
4590 Ish Dr Ste 110, Simi Valley
(93063-7682)
PHONE...............................805 823-8301
Richard Shaw, *President*
Lorienne Shaw, *Treasurer*
Michael Shaw, *Vice Pres*
Jordan Shaw, *Technical Staff*
Sharon Evans, *Manager*
EMP: 23
SQ FT: 10,000
SALES (est): 5.9MM **Privately Held**
WEB: www.gasdetection.com
SIC: **3824** 3829 Gas meters, domestic &
large capacity: industrial; measuring &
controlling devices

(P-21690)
LIQUA-TECH CORPORATION
Also Called: L T C
3501 N State St, Ukiah (95482-3008)
PHONE...............................800 659-3556
Marta J Sligh, *President*
Rick Tindall, *Office Mgr*
Edward L Bruce, *Director*
EMP: 14
SQ FT: 17,000
SALES (est): 3.2MM **Privately Held**
WEB: www.liqua-tech.com
SIC: **3824** Liquid meters

(P-21691)
MCCROMETER INC
3255 W Stetson Ave, Hemet (92545-7763)
PHONE...............................951 652-6811
Stephen Bell, *President*
Ian Rule, *Vice Pres*
Mohammad Daraghma, *Regl Sales Mgr*
◆ EMP: 230
SQ FT: 9,090
SALES (est): 64.3MM
SALES (corp-wide): 18.3B **Publicly Held**
WEB: www.mccrometer.com
SIC: **3824** Water meters
PA: Danaher Corporation
2200 Penn Ave Nw Ste 800w
Washington DC 20037
202 828-0850

(P-21692)
MINDRUM PRECISION INC
Also Called: Mindrum Precision Products
10000 4th St, Rancho Cucamonga
(91730-5793)
PHONE...............................909 989-1728
Diane Mindrum, *CEO*
Anthony Pinder, *President*
Daniel P Mindrum, *Corp Secy*
Scot Howell, *Vice Pres*
Adam Pohl, *Vice Pres*
EMP: 49 EST: 1956
SQ FT: 30,000
SALES (est): 10.4MM **Privately Held**
WEB: www.mindrum.com
SIC: **3824** 3827 3823 3264 Fluid meters
& counting devices; optical instruments &
lenses; industrial instrmnts msrmnt dis-
play/control process variable; porcelain
electrical supplies; products of purchased
glass

(P-21693)
PACIFIC UTILITY PRODUCTS INC
2950 E Philadelphia St, Ontario
(91761-8545)
PHONE...............................909 923-1800
Diana Grootonk, *CEO*
EMP: 18 EST: 2013
SALES (est): 4MM **Privately Held**
SIC: **3824** Fluid meters & counting devices

(P-21694)
STEM CONSULTANTS INC
645 Chestnut Ave Apt 202, Long Beach
(90802-1271)
PHONE...............................612 987-8008
Tiroshen Fonseka, *CEO*
EMP: 10 EST: 2016
SALES (est): 573.3K **Privately Held**
SIC: **3824** 8748 8711 7389 Mechanical &
electromechanical counters & devices;
systems analysis & engineering consulting services; mechanical engineering;
structural engineering;

(P-21695)
THERMO GAMMA-METRICS LLC (HQ)
10010 Mesa Rim Rd, San Diego
(92121-2912)
PHONE...............................858 450-9811
Ken Berger, *President*
Sandra Lambert, *Admin Sec*
▲ EMP: 20
SQ FT: 45,000
SALES (est): 7.5MM
SALES (corp-wide): 20.9B **Publicly Held**
WEB: www.gammametrics.com
SIC: **3824** 3826 3812 3823 Controls, rev-
olution & timing instruments; environmen-
tal testing equipment; search & detection
systems & instruments; industrial instrm-
nts msrmnt display/control process vari-
able
PA: Thermo Fisher Scientific Inc.
168 3rd Ave
Waltham MA 02451
781 622-1000

(P-21696)
TRI-CONTINENT SCIENTIFIC INC
12740 Earhart Ave, Auburn (95602-9027)
PHONE...............................530 273-8888
Lee Carter, *CEO*
Brenton Hanlon, *President*
Sandra Zoch, *Treasurer*
Ross Waring, *Technician*
Leeann Smith, *Engineer*
▲ EMP: 85
SQ FT: 34,000
SALES (est): 17.7MM
SALES (corp-wide): 2.3B **Publicly Held**
WEB: www.tricontinent.com
SIC: **3824** 3829 3821 3561 Integrating &
totalizing meters for gas & liquids; totaliz-
ing meters, consumption registering;
measuring & controlling devices; labora-
tory apparatus & furniture; pumps &
pumping equipment
HQ: Gardner Denver, Inc.
222 E Erie St Ste 500
Milwaukee WI 53202

(P-21697)
ZENNER PERFORMANCE METERS INC
1910 E Westward Ave, Banning
(92220-6366)
P.O. Box 895 (92220-0019)
PHONE...............................951 849-8822
Ron Gallon, *CEO*
▲ EMP: 23
SALES (est): 5.4MM **Privately Held**
SIC: **3824** Water meters

3825 Instrs For Measuring & Testing Electricity

(P-21698)
2M MACHINING & MFG CO
8630 Santa Fe Ave, South Gate
(90280-2601)
PHONE...............................323 564-9388
Kwok Lee, *President*
EMP: 15 EST: 1973
SQ FT: 11,000
SALES (est): 2MM **Privately Held**
SIC: **3825** Electrical power measuring
equipment

(P-21699)
A H SYSTEMS INC
9710 Cozycroft Ave, Chatsworth
(91311-4401)
PHONE...............................818 998-0223
Arthur C Cohen, *President*
Jodi Henderson, *Treasurer*
Michael Cohen, *Vice Pres*
Lori Weiss, *Admin Sec*
▲ EMP: 10
SQ FT: 5,300
SALES (est): 2MM **Privately Held**
WEB: www.ahsystems.com
SIC: **3825** Test equipment for electronic &
electric measurement

(P-21700)
ACCEL-RF CORPORATION
4380 Viewridge Ave Ste D, San Diego
(92123-1678)
PHONE...............................858 278-2074
Roland Shaw, *President*
Tucker Weaver, *CFO*
David Sanderlin, *Vice Pres*
Ellen Williams, *Principal*
Hannah Going, *General Mgr*
▲ EMP: 12

SALES (est): 4.2MM **Privately Held**
WEB: www.accelrf.com
SIC: **3825** Electron tube test equipment

(P-21701)
ADVANCED MICROTECHNOLOGY INC
480 Vista Way, Milpitas (95035-5406)
PHONE..............................408 945-9191
Eugene R Wertz, *President*
Ray Franciscus, *VP Mfg*
EMP: 15
SQ FT: 5,000
SALES (est): 2.2MM **Privately Held**
WEB: www.advancedmicrotech.com
SIC: **3825** 8711 Test equipment for electronic & electrical circuits; engineering services

(P-21702)
ADVANCED SAFETY DEVICES LLC
Also Called: Asd
21430 Strathern St Unit M, Canoga Park (91304-4188)
PHONE..............................818 701-9200
Nima Parto, *General Mgr*
Mort Parto, *Sls & Mktg Exec*
▲ EMP: 10
SALES: 950K **Privately Held**
SIC: **3825** Instruments to measure electricity

(P-21703)
AEA TECHNOLOGY INC
5933 Sea Lion Pl Ste 112, Carlsbad (92010-6625)
PHONE..............................760 931-8979
George Naber, *President*
Ed Stevenson, *Vice Pres*
EMP: 10
SALES (est): 1.4MM **Privately Held**
SIC: **3825** Instruments to measure electricity

(P-21704)
AEHR TEST SYSTEMS (PA)
400 Kato Ter, Fremont (94539-8332)
PHONE..............................510 623-9400
Gayn Erickson, *President*
Rhea J Posedel, *Ch of Bd*
Kunio Sano, *President*
Kenneth B Spink, *CFO*
Vernon Rogers, *Exec VP*
▲ EMP: 79 EST: 1977
SQ FT: 51,289
SALES: 29.5MM **Publicly Held**
WEB: www.aehr.com
SIC: **3825** Test equipment for electronic & electrical circuits

(P-21705)
AGILENT TECH WORLD TRADE INC (HQ)
5301 Stevens Creek Blvd, Santa Clara (95051-7201)
PHONE..............................408 345-8886
Adrian Dillon, *CEO*
D Craig Norlund, *Treasurer*
Marie O Huber, *Asst Sec*
EMP: 16
SALES (est): 86.6MM
SALES (corp-wide): 4.4B **Publicly Held**
SIC: **3825** Instruments to measure electricity
PA: Agilent Technologies, Inc.
5301 Stevens Creek Blvd
Santa Clara CA 95051
408 345-8886

(P-21706)
AGILENT TECHNOLOGIES INC
39201 Cherry St, Newark (94560-4967)
PHONE..............................510 794-1234
Cheol H Han, *Principal*
EMP: 350
SALES (corp-wide): 4.4B **Publicly Held**
WEB: www.agilent.com
SIC: **3825** Instruments to measure electricity
PA: Agilent Technologies, Inc.
5301 Stevens Creek Blvd
Santa Clara CA 95051
408 345-8886

(P-21707)
AGILENT TECHNOLOGIES INC
91 Blue Ravine Rd, Folsom (95630-4720)
PHONE..............................916 985-7888
James T Olsen, *Branch Mgr*
EMP: 250
SALES (corp-wide): 4.4B **Publicly Held**
WEB: www.agilent.com
SIC: **3825** Instruments to measure electricity
PA: Agilent Technologies, Inc.
5301 Stevens Creek Blvd
Santa Clara CA 95051
408 345-8886

(P-21708)
AGILENT TECHNOLOGIES INC
1170 Mark Ave, Carpinteria (93013-2918)
PHONE..............................805 566-6655
Britt Meelby Jensen, *General Mgr*
Charlotte Halsgaard, *Administration*
Jason Henry, *Administration*
Lynette Girvin, *Info Tech Dir*
Frederic Jougla, *Info Tech Dir*
EMP: 17
SALES (corp-wide): 4.4B **Publicly Held**
SIC: **3825** Instruments to measure electricity
PA: Agilent Technologies, Inc.
5301 Stevens Creek Blvd
Santa Clara CA 95051
408 345-8886

(P-21709)
AGILENT TECHNOLOGIES INC
5301 Stevens Creek Blvd, Santa Clara (95051-7201)
P.O. Box 58059 (95052-8059)
PHONE..............................408 345-8886
Bill Sullivan, *CEO*
EMP: 2000
SALES (corp-wide): 4.4B **Publicly Held**
WEB: www.agilent.com
SIC: **3825** Instruments to measure electricity
PA: Agilent Technologies, Inc.
5301 Stevens Creek Blvd
Santa Clara CA 95051
408 345-8886

(P-21710)
AGILENT TECHNOLOGIES INC
11011 N Torrey Pines Rd, La Jolla (92037-1007)
PHONE..............................858 373-6300
Janet King, *Principal*
EMP: 453
SALES (corp-wide): 4.4B **Publicly Held**
SIC: **3825** Instruments to measure electricity
PA: Agilent Technologies, Inc.
5301 Stevens Creek Blvd
Santa Clara CA 95051
408 345-8886

(P-21711)
AGILENT TECHNOLOGIES INC
10054 Foothills Blvd, Roseville (95747-7102)
PHONE..............................916 785-1000
Larry Hermone, *Branch Mgr*
EMP: 12
SALES (corp-wide): 4.4B **Publicly Held**
SIC: **3825** Instruments to measure electricity
PA: Agilent Technologies, Inc.
5301 Stevens Creek Blvd
Santa Clara CA 95051
408 345-8886

(P-21712)
AGILENT TECHNOLOGIES INC (PA)
5301 Stevens Creek Blvd, Santa Clara (95051-7201)
P.O. Box 58059 (95052-8059)
PHONE..............................408 345-8886
Michael R McMullen, *President*
James G Cullen, *Ch of Bd*
Mark Doak, *President*
Sam Raha, *President*
Jacob Thaysen, *President*
▲ EMP: 277

(P-21713)
AGILENT TECHNOLOGIES INC
5301 Stevens Creek Blvd, Santa Clara (95051-7201)
PHONE..............................408 345-8886
Gail Jacobs, *Branch Mgr*
Hewlett E Melton Jr, *Principal*
EMP: 3275
SALES (corp-wide): 4.4B **Publicly Held**
WEB: www.agilent.com
SIC: **3825** Instruments to measure electricity
PA: Agilent Technologies, Inc.
5301 Stevens Creek Blvd
Santa Clara CA 95051
408 345-8886

(P-21714)
AGILENT TECHNOLOGIES INC
3175 Bowers Ave, Santa Clara (95054-3225)
P.O. Box 58059 (95052-8059)
PHONE..............................408 553-7777
Paul Sedlewicz, *Branch Mgr*
EMP: 3275
SALES (corp-wide): 4.4B **Publicly Held**
WEB: www.agilent.com
SIC: **3825** Instruments to measure electricity
PA: Agilent Technologies, Inc.
5301 Stevens Creek Blvd
Santa Clara CA 95051
408 345-8886

(P-21715)
AGILENT TECHNOLOGIES INC
30721 Russell Ranch Rd, Westlake Village (91362-7382)
PHONE..............................408 345-8886
Alice Liu, *Principal*
EMP: 3275
SALES (corp-wide): 4.4B **Publicly Held**
WEB: www.agilent.com
SIC: **3825** Instruments to measure electricity
PA: Agilent Technologies, Inc.
5301 Stevens Creek Blvd
Santa Clara CA 95051
408 345-8886

(P-21716)
AGILENT TECHNOLOGIES INC
11011 N Torrey Pines Rd, La Jolla (92037-1007)
PHONE..............................858 373-6300
EMP: 453
SALES (corp-wide): 4B **Publicly Held**
SIC: **3825**
PA: Agilent Technologies, Inc.
5301 Stevens Creek Blvd
Santa Clara CA 95051
408 345-8886

(P-21717)
ALTA PROPERTIES INC
International Transducer
869 Ward Dr, Santa Barbara (93111-2920)
PHONE..............................805 683-2575
Brian Dolan, *Director*
EMP: 475
SALES (corp-wide): 197.5MM **Privately Held**
SIC: **3825** 3812 Transducers for volts, amperes, watts, vars, frequency, etc.; search & navigation equipment
PA: Alta Properties, Inc.
879 Ward Dr
Santa Barbara CA 93111
805 967-0171

(P-21718)
ALTA SOLUTIONS INC
12580 Stowe Dr, Poway (92064-6804)
PHONE..............................858 668-5200
Robert B Mihata, *President*
Julia K Mihata, *COO*
David S Baggest, *Vice Pres*
Dave Baggest, *Engineer*

Robert Diplock, *Mfg Staff*
EMP: 14
SQ FT: 12,000
SALES (est): 3.8MM **Privately Held**
WEB: www.altasol.com
SIC: **3825** Instruments to measure electricity

(P-21719)
AMERICAN PROBE & TECH INC
1795 Grogan Ave, Merced (95341-6455)
PHONE..............................408 263-3356
Kenneth M Chabraya, *President*
Kim Merrill, *Vice Pres*
EMP: 11
SQ FT: 4,300
SALES: 1MM **Privately Held**
WEB: www.americanprobe.com
SIC: **3825** Test equipment for electronic & electric measurement

(P-21720)
ANRITSU US HOLDING INC (HQ)
Also Called: Anritsu Company
490 Jarvis Dr, Morgan Hill (95037-2834)
PHONE..............................408 778-2000
Wade Hulon, *President*
▲ EMP: 500
SQ FT: 244,000
SALES: 323.5MM
SALES (corp-wide): 806.8MM **Privately Held**
SIC: **3825** 3663 5065 Test equipment for electronic & electric measurement; radio & TV communications equipment; electronic parts & equipment
PA: Anritsu Corporation
5-1-1, Onna
Atsugi KNG 243-0
462 231-111

(P-21721)
APPLIED MICROSTRUCTURES INC
2381 Bering Dr, San Jose (95131-1125)
PHONE..............................408 907-2885
Jeffrey Chinn, *CEO*
Fred Helmrich, *Vice Pres*
Mike Khosla, *VP Engrg*
Kathy Parsons, *Controller*
Al Leyva, *Opers Staff*
EMP: 17
SQ FT: 3,500
SALES (est): 3.2MM **Privately Held**
SIC: **3825** Digital panel meters, electricity measuring

(P-21722)
APRIL INSTRUMENT
1401 Fallen Leaf Ln, Los Altos (94024-5810)
P.O. Box 62046, Sunnyvale (94088-2046)
PHONE..............................650 964-8379
Bill Chan, *Owner*
EMP: 10
SALES: 2MM **Privately Held**
WEB: www.aprilinstrument.com
SIC: **3825** Microwave test equipment

(P-21723)
ARBITER SYSTEMS INCORPORATED (PA)
1324 Vendels Cir Ste 121, Paso Robles (93446-3806)
PHONE..............................805 237-3831
Craig Armstrong, *President*
Bruce Roeder, *CFO*
EMP: 30 EST: 1973
SQ FT: 15,000
SALES (est): 3.6MM **Privately Held**
WEB: www.arbiter.com
SIC: **3825** 3829 3663 Test equipment for electronic & electric measurement; measuring & controlling devices; radio & TV communications equipment

(P-21724)
ASSET EQUITY HOLDINGS LLC
34413 Cleveland Ave, San Diego (92163)
PHONE..............................925 339-5440
Diego Del Rio,
EMP: 10
SALES (est): 679.6K **Privately Held**
SIC: **3825** 7389 Standards & calibration equipment for electrical measuring;

SALES (est): 1.9MM **Privately Held**
WEB: www.infoscantech.com
SIC: 3825 Test equipment for electronic & electrical circuits

(P-21773)
INGRASYS TECHNOLOGY USA INC
2025 Gateway Pl Ste 190, San Jose (95110-1052)
PHONE..................863 271-8266
Taiyu Chou, *CEO*
Kelly Chen, *Sales Staff*
▲ **EMP:** 20 **EST:** 2009
SALES (est): 11MM **Privately Held**
SIC: 3825 4899 Network analyzers; communication signal enhancement network system
PA: Ingrasys Technology Inc.
21f, 207, Fu Hsing Rd.,
Taoyuan City TAY
333 626-88

(P-21774)
INNOTECH ENERGY INC
1200 Business Center Dr, San Leandro (94577-2241)
PHONE..................510 639-9197
Jason Yuhe Ji, *Owner*
Xue Wang, *Senior Mgr*
EMP: 11 **EST:** 2012
SALES: 686.5K **Privately Held**
SIC: 3825 8731 Energy measuring equipment, electrical; energy research

(P-21775)
INTELLIGENT CMPT SOLUTIONS INC (PA)
8968 Fullbright Ave, Chatsworth (91311-6123)
PHONE..................818 998-5805
Uzi Kohavi, *President*
Gonen Ravid, *CEO*
▲ **EMP:** 25
SQ FT: 21,000
SALES (est): 4.9MM **Privately Held**
SIC: 3825 3577 3572 Test equipment for electronic & electrical circuits; computer peripheral equipment; computer storage devices

(P-21776)
INTEPRO AMERICA LP (PA)
14662 Franklin Ave Ste E, Tustin (92780-7224)
PHONE..................714 953-2686
Gary Halmbacher,
Joe Engler,
Joseph Engler,
▲ **EMP:** 25
SALES (est): 3.6MM **Privately Held**
WEB: www.inteproate.com
SIC: 3825 Frequency meters: electrical, mechanical & electronic

(P-21777)
INTERNATIONAL TRANDUCER CORP
Also Called: Channel Technologies Group
869 Ward Dr, Santa Barbara (93111-2920)
PHONE..................805 683-2575
R M Callahan, *Co-COB*
Kevin Ruelas, *President*
Robert F Carlson, *Co-COB*
Brian Dolan, *Director*
EMP: 160 **EST:** 1966
SALES (est): 50.7MM
SALES (corp-wide): 79.4MM **Privately Held**
WEB: www.itc-transducers.com
SIC: 3825 3812 Transducers for volts, amperes, watts, vars, frequency, etc.; search & navigation equipment
PA: Gavial Holdings, Inc.
1435 W Mccoy Ln
Santa Maria CA 93455
805 614-0060

(P-21778)
INTERSTATE ELECTRONICS CORP (HQ)
Also Called: L-3 Interstate Electronics
602 E Vermont Ave, Anaheim (92805-5607)
P.O. Box 3117 (92803-3117)
PHONE..................714 758-0500
Thomas L Walsh, *President*
Carol Grogg, *Vice Pres*
Candace Lee, *Admin Sec*
EMP: 275
SQ FT: 235,700
SALES (est): 168.7MM
SALES (corp-wide): 9.5B **Publicly Held**
WEB: www.iechome.com
SIC: 3825 3812 3679 Test equipment for electronic & electric measurement; navigational systems & instruments; liquid crystal displays (LCD)
PA: L3 Technologies, Inc.
600 3rd Ave Fl 34
New York NY 10016
212 697-1111

(P-21779)
IXIA (HQ)
26601 Agoura Rd, Calabasas (91302-1959)
PHONE..................818 871-1800
Neil Dougherty, *President*
Jason Kary, *CFO*
Jeffrey LI, *Treasurer*
Matthew S Alexander, *Senior VP*
Curt Crosby, *Vice Pres*
EMP: 277
SQ FT: 116,000
SALES (est): 484.8MM
SALES (corp-wide): 3.1B **Publicly Held**
SIC: 3825 7371 Network analyzers; custom computer programming services; software programming applications
PA: Keysight Technologies, Inc.
1400 Fountaingrove Pkwy
Santa Rosa CA 95403
800 829-4444

(P-21780)
IXIA
Also Called: Ixia Communications
26701 Agoura Rd, Calabasas (91302-1960)
PHONE..................818 871-1800
EMP: 13
SALES (corp-wide): 3.1B **Publicly Held**
SIC: 3825 Network analyzers
HQ: Ixia
26601 Agoura Rd
Calabasas CA 91302
818 871-1800

(P-21781)
JEFF J POLICH INC
Also Called: All American Electric
281 E San Bernardino Rd, Covina (91723-1625)
PHONE..................626 339-3070
Jeff J Polich, *CEO*
EMP: 10
SALES: 350K **Privately Held**
SIC: 3825 Integrating electricity meters

(P-21782)
JEM AMERICA CORP
3000 Laurelview Ct, Fremont (94538-6575)
PHONE..................510 683-9234
Kazumasa Okubo, *Owner*
Eddie Kazama, *President*
Phil MAI, *Vice Pres*
Trisha Quach, *Technician*
Hirotaka Inoue, *Technology*
EMP: 50
SQ FT: 17,000
SALES (est): 5MM
SALES (corp-wide): 109.8MM **Privately Held**
WEB: www.jemam.com
SIC: 3825 Test equipment for electronic & electric measurement
PA: Japan Electronic Materials Corporation
2-5-13, Nishinagasucho
Amagasaki HYO 660-0
664 822-007

(P-21783)
KELLY NETWORK SOLUTIONS INC
473 Sapena Ct Ste 24, Santa Clara (95054-2427)
PHONE..................650 364-7201
Roland Valtierra, *President*
EMP: 21
SALES (est): 4MM **Privately Held**
SIC: 3825 Network analyzers

(P-21784)
KEYSIGHT TECHNOLOGIES INC (PA)
1400 Fountaingrove Pkwy, Santa Rosa (95403-1738)
P.O. Box 4026, Englewood CO (80155-4026)
PHONE..................800 829-4444
Ronald S Nersesian, *President*
Paul N Clark, *Ch of Bd*
Mark Pierpoint, *President*
Neil Dougherty, *CFO*
Marie Hattar, *Chief Mktg Ofcr*
EMP: 277 **EST:** 1939
SALES: 3.1B **Publicly Held**
SIC: 3825 Industrial instrmnts msrmnt display/control process variable; measuring & controlling devices; electronic equipment repair

(P-21785)
KEYSIGHT TECHNOLOGIES INC
700 Lairport St, El Segundo (90245-5006)
PHONE..................310 524-4600
Eric Taylor, *Vice Pres*
EMP: 21
SQ FT: 13,000
SALES (corp-wide): 3.1B **Publicly Held**
SIC: 3825 Instruments to measure electricity
PA: Keysight Technologies, Inc.
1400 Fountaingrove Pkwy
Santa Rosa CA 95403
800 829-4444

(P-21786)
KEYSIGHT TECHNOLOGIES INC
5301 Stevens Creek Blvd, Santa Clara (95051-7201)
PHONE..................408 553-3290
Nunes Luisa, *Executive Asst*
Monica Ward, *Project Mgr*
Richard Kinder, *Research*
Paul Corredoura, *Engineer*
Joshua Sarris, *Engineer*
EMP: 28
SALES (corp-wide): 3.1B **Publicly Held**
SIC: 3825 Instruments to measure electricity
PA: Keysight Technologies, Inc.
1400 Fountaingrove Pkwy
Santa Rosa CA 95403
800 829-4444

(P-21787)
KIMBALL ELECTRONICS INDIANA
5215 Hellyer Ave Ste 130, San Jose (95138-1090)
PHONE..................669 234-1110
Christopher Thyen, *Vice Pres*
EMP: 40
SALES (est): 7.8MM
SALES (corp-wide): 1B **Publicly Held**
SIC: 3825 Instruments to measure electricity
PA: Kimball Electronics, Inc.
1205 Kimball Blvd
Jasper IN 47546
812 634-4000

(P-21788)
KLA-TENCOR CORPORATION (PA)
1 Technology Dr, Milpitas (95035-7916)
PHONE..................408 875-3000
Richard P Wallace, *President*
Edward W Barnholt, *Ch of Bd*
Bren D Higgins, *CFO*
Vishal Pathak, *Treasurer*
Teri A Little,
◆ **EMP:** 300 **EST:** 1975
SQ FT: 727,302

SALES: 4B **Publicly Held**
WEB: www.tencor.com
SIC: 3825 7699 7629 3827 Semiconductor test equipment; optical instrument repair; electronic equipment repair; optical test & inspection equipment

(P-21789)
KLA-TENCOR CORPORATION
3530 Bassett St, Santa Clara (95054-2704)
PHONE..................408 496-2055
EMP: 55
SALES (corp-wide): 4B **Publicly Held**
SIC: 3825 Instruments to measure electricity
PA: Kla-Tencor Corporation
1 Technology Dr
Milpitas CA 95035
408 875-3000

(P-21790)
KLA-TENCOR CORPORATION
850 Auburn Ct, Fremont (94538-7306)
PHONE..................510 456-2490
Kathryn Cross, *Director*
EMP: 55
SALES (corp-wide): 4B **Publicly Held**
WEB: www.tencor.com
SIC: 3825 Semiconductor test equipment
PA: Kla-Tencor Corporation
1 Technology Dr
Milpitas CA 95035
408 875-3000

(P-21791)
LIQUID ROBOTICS FEDERAL INC
1329 Moffett Park Dr, Sunnyvale (94089-1134)
PHONE..................408 636-4200
Sandra McVey, *Principal*
Bill Vass, *CEO*
Steven R Springsteel, *COO*
Gary Gysin, *Exec VP*
Graham Hine, *Senior VP*
EMP: 11
SALES (est): 1.3MM **Privately Held**
SIC: 3825 Waveform measuring and/or analyzing equipment

(P-21792)
LITEL INSTRUMENTS INC
10650 Scripps Ranch Blvd # 105, San Diego (92131-2471)
PHONE..................858 546-3788
Robert O Hunter Jr, *President*
Brent Gill, *Opers Staff*
EMP: 29
SALES (est): 4.5MM **Privately Held**
SIC: 3825 Instruments to measure electricity

(P-21793)
LIVEWIRE TEST LABS INC
Also Called: Livewire Innovation
808 Calle Plano, Camarillo (93012-8557)
PHONE..................801 293-8300
Ron Vogel, *CEO*
Cynthia Furse, *Ch of Bd*
Lucas Thomson, *Electrical Engi*
Brent Waddoups, *Engineer*
Marji Ketaily, *Opers Staff*
EMP: 10
SQ FT: 7,900
SALES (est): 1.6MM **Privately Held**
WEB: www.livewiretest.com
SIC: 3825 Test equipment for electronic & electrical circuits; engine electrical test equipment

(P-21794)
LUCAS/SIGNATONE CORPORATION (PA)
Also Called: Lucas Labs
393 Tomkins Ct Ste J, Gilroy (95020-3632)
PHONE..................408 848-2851
L Brent Dickson, *President*
Dennis Dickson, *CFO*
Phillip Shen, *Sr Software Eng*
Brian Dickson, *Human Res Dir*
Loren Dickson, *VP Sls/Mktg*
EMP: 30

P R O D U C T S & S V C S

SALES (est): 4.9MM **Privately Held**
WEB: www.lucaslabs.com
SIC: **3825** 3559 Semiconductor test equipment; semiconductor manufacturing machinery

(P-21795)
LUMILEDS LLC (HQ)
370 W Trimble Rd, San Jose (95131-1008)
PHONE......................408 964-2900
Mark Adams, *CEO*
Ilan Daskal, *CFO*
Cheree McAlpine, *Senior VP*
Steve Barlow, *General Mgr*
Jy Bhardwaj, *CTO*
▲ EMP: 21
SALES (est): 156.2MM **Publicly Held**
WEB: www.luxeon.com
SIC: **3825** Instruments to measure electricity

(P-21796)
MACHINE CONTROL TECH INC
210 Crouse Dr, Corona (92879-8093)
PHONE......................951 808-0973
Samuel Yu, *President*
▲ EMP: 10
SALES (est): 1.7MM **Privately Held**
SIC: **3825** 7389 Test equipment for electronic & electrical circuits;

(P-21797)
MAGNEBIT HOLDING CORPORATION (PA)
9590 Chesapeake Dr Ste 5, San Diego (92123-1348)
PHONE......................858 573-0727
Catherine Jacobson, *President*
Peter Jacobson, *Ch of Bd*
EMP: 25
SQ FT: 8,000
SALES (est): 2.2MM **Privately Held**
WEB: www.magnebit.com
SIC: **3825** 3471 Instruments to measure electricity; plating & polishing

(P-21798)
MAGNETIC RCRDING SOLUTIONS INC
3080 Oakmead Village Dr, Santa Clara (95051-0808)
PHONE......................408 970-8266
Vladimir Pogrebinsky, *President*
Wayne Erickson, *Exec VP*
EMP: 35
SQ FT: 6,000
SALES (est): 5.1MM **Privately Held**
WEB: www.mrs-usa.com
SIC: **3825** Test equipment for electronic & electrical circuits

(P-21799)
MARVELL SEMICONDUCTOR INC
5450 Bayfront Plz, Santa Clara (95054-3600)
PHONE......................408 855-8839
EMP: 31 **Privately Held**
SIC: **3825**
HQ: Marvell Semiconductor, Inc.
5488 Marvell Ln
Santa Clara CA 95054

(P-21800)
MARVIN TEST SOLUTIONS INC
1770 Kettering, Irvine (92614-5616)
PHONE......................949 263-2222
Loofie Gutterman, *President*
Leon Tsimmerman, *CFO*
Gerald Friedman, *Treasurer*
EMP: 70
SQ FT: 31,000
SALES: 21.6MM
SALES (corp-wide): 222.7MM **Privately Held**
WEB: www.geotestinc.com
SIC: **3825** Instruments to measure electricity
PA: Marvin Engineering Co., Inc.
261 W Beach Ave
Inglewood CA 90302
310 674-5030

(P-21801)
MATERIALS DEVELOPMENT CORP (PA)
21541 Nordhoff St Ste B, Chatsworth (91311-6982)
PHONE......................818 700-8290
Barton Gordon, *President*
Dr Robert S Harp, *Corp Secy*
Robert Harp, *Admin Sec*
EMP: 10
SQ FT: 6,000
SALES (est): 1.5MM **Privately Held**
WEB: www.mdc4cv.com
SIC: **3825** Semiconductor test equipment

(P-21802)
MAURICE LANDSTRASS
1667 Rosita Rd, Pacifica (94044-4433)
PHONE......................650 355-5532
Maurice Landstrass, *Owner*
EMP: 20
SALES (est): 2MM **Privately Held**
SIC: **3825** Semiconductor test equipment

(P-21803)
MEASUREMENT SPECIALTIES INC
Also Called: Te Connectivity
424 Crown Point Cir, Grass Valley (95945-9089)
PHONE......................530 273-4608
Frank Guidone, *CEO*
EMP: 60
SALES (corp-wide): 13.1B **Privately Held**
SIC: **3825** 3676 Instruments to measure electricity; electronic resistors
HQ: Measurement Specialties, Inc.
1000 Lucas Way
Hampton VA 23666
757 766-1500

(P-21804)
MEREX INC
1283 Flynn Rd, Camarillo (93012-8013)
P.O. Box 3474, Chatsworth (91313-3474)
PHONE......................805 446-2700
Chester J Dopler, *CEO*
Ahmad Shams, *President*
Nathan Skop, *Exec VP*
EMP: 12
SALES (est): 1.7MM **Privately Held**
SIC: **3825** Instruments to measure electricity

(P-21805)
MICRO-PROBE INCORPORATED (HQ)
Also Called: M P I
617 River Oaks Pkwy, San Jose (95134-1907)
PHONE......................408 457-3900
Mike Slessor, *CEO*
Todd Swart, *President*
Patrick Kuhn, *Vice Pres*
Teresa Williams, *Info Tech Mgr*
Ricardo Davila, *Engineer*
▲ EMP: 95
SQ FT: 43,000
SALES (est): 30.3MM **Publicly Held**
WEB: www.microprobe.com
SIC: **3825** Test equipment for electronic & electrical circuits

(P-21806)
MICROSOURCE INC
5990 Gleason Dr, Dublin (94568-7644)
PHONE......................925 328-4650
John R Regazzi, *CEO*
Suresh Nair, *CEO*
Temi Oduozor, *Controller*
Jim Taber, *VP Sales*
EMP: 55 EST: 1981
SQ FT: 24,000
SALES: 16MM
SALES (corp-wide): 9.8MM **Publicly Held**
WEB: www.microsource-inc.com
SIC: **3825** Instruments to measure electricity
PA: Giga-Tronics Incorporated
5990 Gleason Dr
Dublin CA 94568
925 328-4650

(P-21807)
MITCHELL INSTRUMENTS CO INC
1570 Cherokee St, San Marcos (92078-2433)
PHONE......................760 744-2690
James Desportes, *CEO*
◆ EMP: 15
SQ FT: 8,000
SALES (est): 4.4MM **Privately Held**
WEB: www.mitchellinstrument.net
SIC: **3825** Instruments to measure electricity

(P-21808)
MRV SYSTEMS LLC
6370 Lusk Blvd Ste F100, San Diego (92121-2754)
PHONE......................800 645-7114
Fredric Maas, *Mng Member*
Michael Letchinger,
EMP: 20
SALES (est): 2.2MM **Privately Held**
WEB: www.mrvsys.com
SIC: **3825** 3823 Instruments to measure electricity; temperature measurement instruments, industrial

(P-21809)
MULTITEST ELCTRNIC SYSTEMS INC (DH)
3021 Kenneth St, Santa Clara (95054-3416)
PHONE......................408 988-6544
Dave Tacelli, *CEO*
Joy Marquez, *Administration*
Marcel Hartwig, *Project Engr*
Ferry Bunjamin, *Engineer*
Patrick Joyal, *Engineer*
▲ EMP: 280
SQ FT: 40,000
SALES (est): 52.6MM
SALES (corp-wide): 352.7MM **Publicly Held**
WEB: www.multitest.com
SIC: **3825** 3674 3624 Semiconductor test equipment; semiconductors & related devices; brushes & brush stock contacts, electric
HQ: Xcerra Corporation
825 University Ave
Norwood MA 02062
781 461-1000

(P-21810)
N H RESEARCH INCORPORATED
16601 Hale Ave, Irvine (92606-5049)
PHONE......................949 474-3900
Peter Swartz, *President*
Tom Fairburn, *Design Engr*
Kamran Firooz, *Technical Staff*
▲ EMP: 75
SQ FT: 29,000
SALES (est): 17.9MM **Privately Held**
WEB: www.nhresearch.com
SIC: **3825** 3829 Test equipment for electronic & electrical circuits; measuring & controlling devices

(P-21811)
NAPTECH TEST EQUIPMENT INC
11270 Clayton Creek Rd, Lower Lake (95457-9440)
PHONE......................707 995-7145
Roger Briggs, *President*
Donald Dyne, *Electrical Engi*
◆ EMP: 15
SQ FT: 12,000
SALES: 2.3MM **Privately Held**
WEB: www.naptech.com
SIC: **3825** Instruments to measure electricity

(P-21812)
NATIONAL INSTRUMENTS CORP
Also Called: Ni Microwave Components
4600 Patrick Henry Dr, Santa Clara (95054-1817)
PHONE......................408 610-6800
Dirk De Mol, *Branch Mgr*
EMP: 338

SALES (corp-wide): 1.2B **Publicly Held**
SIC: **3825** Instruments to measure electricity
PA: National Instruments Corporation
11500 N Mopac Expy
Austin TX 78759
512 338-9119

(P-21813)
NEARFIELD SYSTEMS INC
19730 Magellan Dr, Torrance (90502-1104)
PHONE......................310 525-7000
Greg Hindman, *President*
Dan Slater, *Vice Pres*
▼ EMP: 62
SALES (est): 18.8MM
SALES (corp-wide): 44.8MM **Privately Held**
WEB: www.nearfield.com
SIC: **3825** 3829 Test equipment for electronic & electric measurement; measuring & controlling devices
PA: Nsi-Mi Technologies, Llc
1125 Satellite Blvd Nw # 100
Suwanee GA 30024
678 475-8300

(P-21814)
NEOLOGY INC (HQ)
13520 Evening Creek Dr N # 460, San Diego (92128-8105)
PHONE......................858 391-0260
Francisco Martinez De Vela, *CEO*
Francisco Martinez, *CEO*
Joan Finley, *CFO*
Manuel Moreno, *Vice Pres*
Sheshi Nyalamadugu, *Vice Pres*
◆ EMP: 37
SQ FT: 23,050
SALES (est): 8MM
SALES (corp-wide): 131.6MM **Privately Held**
WEB: www.neology-rfid.com
SIC: **3825** Integrated circuit testers
PA: Smartrac N.V.
Strawinskylaan 851
Amsterdam
203 050-150

(P-21815)
NEOSEM TECHNOLOGY INC (DH)
Also Called: Flexstar Technology, Inc
1965 Concourse Dr, San Jose (95131-1708)
PHONE......................408 643-7000
DH Yeom, *President*
Michael Bellon, *President*
Fred Hendrix, *President*
Mike Rogowski, *COO*
Andrew Warner, *CFO*
▲ EMP: 20
SQ FT: 18,000
SALES (est): 16.6MM
SALES (corp-wide): 37.3MM **Privately Held**
WEB: www.flexstar.com
SIC: **3825** Test equipment for electronic & electrical circuits
HQ: Neosem Holdings, Inc.
11001 Lakeline Blvd # 150
Austin TX 78717
512 257-5018

(P-21816)
NEXTEST SYSTEMS CORPORATION
Also Called: Nextest Systems Teradyne Co
875 Embedded Way, San Jose (95138-1030)
PHONE......................408 960-2400
Mark Jadiela, *CEO*
Tim F Moriarty, *President*
James P Moniz, *CFO*
Robin Adler, *Bd of Directors*
Paul Barics, *Vice Pres*
▲ EMP: 125
SQ FT: 33,200
SALES (est): 39.9MM
SALES (corp-wide): 2.1B **Publicly Held**
WEB: www.nextest.com
SIC: **3825** Instruments to measure electricity

▲ = import ▼=Export
◆ =Import/Export

PA: Teradyne, Inc.
600 Riverpark Dr
North Reading MA 01864
978 370-2700

(P-21817)
NIKON RESEARCH CORP AMERICA
1399 Shoreway Rd, Belmont (94002-4107)
PHONE....................800 446-4566
W Thomas Novak, *CEO*
Donis Flagello, *President*
Hamid Zarringhalam, *Exec VP*
Mitsuaki Yonekawa, *Senior VP*
Mohamad Zarringhalam, *Senior VP*
EMP: 40
SQ FT: 15,000
SALES (est): 12.2MM
SALES (corp-wide): 6.7B **Privately Held**
WEB: www.nikonrca.com
SIC: 3825 Semiconductor test equipment
HQ: Nikon Americas Inc.
1300 Walt Whitman Rd Fl 2
Melville NY 11747

(P-21818)
NOVA MEASURING INSTRUMENTS INC (HQ)
3090 Oakmead Village Dr, Santa Clara (95051-0808)
PHONE....................408 200-4344
May Su, *President*
Dror David, *Officer*
EMP: 24
SQ FT: 3,355
SALES (est): 3.5MM
SALES (corp-wide): 163.9MM **Privately Held**
SIC: 3825 Semiconductor test equipment
PA: Nova Measuring Instruments Ltd
Ness Ziona
Ness Ziona 76100
893 875-05

(P-21819)
NOVA MEASURING INSTRUMENTS INC
1270 Oakmead Pkwy Ste 215, Sunnyvale (94085-4041)
PHONE....................408 746-9921
Mauri Marcan, *President*
EMP: 10
SALES (corp-wide): 163.9MM **Privately Held**
SIC: 3825 Semiconductor test equipment
HQ: Nova Measuring Instruments, Inc.
3090 Oakmead Village Dr
Santa Clara CA 95051
408 200-4344

(P-21820)
NOVTEK INC
Also Called: Novtek Test Systems
7018 Mariposa St, Santee (92071-5648)
PHONE....................408 441-9934
Douglas E Eastman III, *President*
James Harper, *COO*
Ruth Eastman, *Vice Pres*
Joe Raynak, *Vice Pres*
EMP: 11
SQ FT: 13,000
SALES (est): 1.8MM **Privately Held**
WEB: www.novtek.com
SIC: 3825 8999 Integrated circuit testers; scientific consulting

(P-21821)
NOVX CORPORATION
1750 N Loop Rd Ste 100, Alameda (94502-8011)
PHONE....................408 998-5555
Steve Heymann, *President*
Lem Hollins, *Vice Pres*
Lyle Nelsen, *Vice Pres*
◆ EMP: 25
SQ FT: 6,000
SALES: 3MM **Privately Held**
SIC: 3825 Electrical energy measuring equipment

(P-21822)
OML INC
300 Digital Dr, Morgan Hill (95037-2896)
PHONE....................408 779-2698
Charles Oleson, *President*
Yuenie Lau, *Vice Pres*
Mitzi Chow, *General Mgr*
Jackie Lau, *Marketing Mgr*
EMP: 10
SQ FT: 2,450
SALES (est): 1.9MM **Privately Held**
WEB: www.omlinc.com
SIC: 3825 Microwave test equipment

(P-21823)
PACIFIC WESTERN SYSTEMS INC (PA)
505 E Evelyn Ave, Mountain View (94041-1613)
PHONE....................650 961-8855
Daniel A Worsham, *Ch of Bd*
Becky Worsham, *Corp Secy*
EMP: 20
SQ FT: 40,000
SALES (est): 2.3MM **Privately Held**
WEB: www.pacificwesternsystems.com
SIC: 3825 3567 Semiconductor test equipment; industrial furnaces & ovens

(P-21824)
PERICOM SEMICONDUCTOR CORP (HQ)
1545 Barber Ln, Milpitas (95035-7409)
PHONE....................408 232-9100
Alex Chiming Hui, *President*
Kevin S Bauer, *CFO*
James Boyd, *CFO*
Angela Chen, *Senior VP*
CHI-Hung Hui, *Senior VP*
◆ EMP: 23
SQ FT: 85,040
SALES: 128.8MM
SALES (corp-wide): 1B **Publicly Held**
WEB: www.pericom.com
SIC: 3825 3674 Instruments to measure electricity; frequency synthesizers; integrated circuits; semiconductor networks, etc.
PA: Diodes Incorporated
4949 Hedgcoxe Rd Ste 200
Plano TX 75024
972 987-3900

(P-21825)
PHASE MATRIX INC
Also Called: Ni Microwave Components
4600 Patrick Henry Dr, Santa Clara (95054-1817)
PHONE....................408 610-6810
Pete Pragastis, *President*
Eric Starkloff, *CEO*
George Clark, *CFO*
Charanbir Mahal, *Vice Pres*
Natasha Kaushal, *Accountant*
EMP: 50
SQ FT: 24,000
SALES (est): 21.7MM
SALES (corp-wide): 1.2B **Publicly Held**
WEB: www.phasematrix.com
SIC: 3825 Test equipment for electronic & electric measurement
PA: National Instruments Corporation
11500 N Mopac Expy
Austin TX 78759
512 338-9119

(P-21826)
PHOENIX MARINE CORPORATION (PA)
700 Larkspur Landing Cir # 175, Larkspur (94939-1754)
PHONE....................415 464-8116
David Brining, *President*
EMP: 73
SALES (est): 8.4MM **Privately Held**
SIC: 3825 3643 Synchroscopes; connectors, electric cord

(P-21827)
PHOTON DYNAMICS INC (HQ)
5970 Optical Ct, San Jose (95138-1400)
PHONE....................408 226-9900
Malcolm J Thompson PHD, *Ch of Bd*
Amichai Steinberg, *President*
Errol Moore, *CEO*
James P Moniz, *CFO*
Dr Abraham Gross, *Exec VP*
◆ EMP: 112
SQ FT: 128,520

SALES: 82.7MM
SALES (corp-wide): 900.8MM **Privately Held**
WEB: www.photondynamics.com
SIC: 3825 3829 Test equipment for electronic & electrical circuits; measuring & controlling devices
PA: Orbotech Ltd.
7 Hasanhedrin Blvd.
Yavne 81215
894 235-33

(P-21828)
POWER STANDARDS LAB INC
980 Atlantic Ave Ste 100, Alameda (94501-1098)
PHONE....................510 522-4400
Alex McEachern, *President*
Barry Tangney, *COO*
Andreas Eberhard, *Vice Pres*
Asmar Farooq, *Engineer*
Thomas Pua, *Engineer*
EMP: 32
SQ FT: 12,000
SALES (est): 8.6MM **Privately Held**
WEB: www.powerstandards.com
SIC: 3825 8734 Power measuring equipment, electrical; testing laboratories
PA: Equipements Power Survey Ltee, Les 7880 Rte Transcanadienne
Saint-Laurent QC H4T 1
514 333-8392

(P-21829)
PROBE-RITE CORP
600 Mission St, Santa Clara (95050-6041)
P.O. Box 242 (95052-0242)
PHONE....................408 727-0100
Frank Ardezzone, *President*
EMP: 27
SQ FT: 3,000
SALES (est): 1.1MM **Privately Held**
SIC: 3825 3569 3491 3535 Semiconductor test equipment; robots, assembly line: industrial & commercial; automatic regulating & control valves; robotic conveyors; hybrid integrated circuits

(P-21830)
PROGRAM DATA INCORPORATED
Also Called: Pdi
16291 Jackson Ranch Rd, Silverado (92676-9706)
PHONE....................714 649-2122
Allen Aksu, *President*
Seyyal Aksu, *Treasurer*
EMP: 17 EST: 1969
SQ FT: 25,000
SALES (est): 1.1MM **Privately Held**
WEB: www.programdata.com
SIC: 3825 3643 Test equipment for electronic & electric measurement; current-carrying wiring devices

(P-21831)
PRONK TECHNOLOGIES INC (PA)
8933 Lankershim Blvd, Sun Valley (91352-1916)
PHONE....................818 768-5600
Karl Ruiter, *President*
Christine Chee Ruiter, *Vice Pres*
Denize Machit, *Admin Sec*
▼ EMP: 12
SQ FT: 4,000
SALES (est): 1MM **Privately Held**
WEB: www.pronktech.com
SIC: 3825 Test equipment for electronic & electric measurement

(P-21832)
PULSE INSTRUMENTS
1234 Francisco St, Torrance (90502-1200)
PHONE....................310 515-5330
Sylvia Kan, *President*
David Kan, *Vice Pres*
Steven Kan, *Vice Pres*
Michael Woi, *Info Tech Dir*
EMP: 23
SQ FT: 15,000

SALES (est): 5MM **Privately Held**
WEB: www.pulseinstruments.com
SIC: 3825 3823 3621 Instruments to measure electricity; industrial instrmnts msrmnt display/control process variable; motors & generators

(P-21833)
QUALECTRON SYSTEMS CORPORATION
321 E Brokaw Rd, San Jose (95112-4208)
PHONE....................408 986-1686
Ricky MA, *President*
▲ EMP: 10
SQ FT: 10,000
SALES (est): 1.3MM **Privately Held**
WEB: www.qualectron.com
SIC: 3825 Test equipment for electronic & electric measurement

(P-21834)
QUALITAU INCORPORATED (PA)
830 Maude Ave, Mountain View (94043-4022)
PHONE....................650 282-6226
Gadi Krieger, *CEO*
Jacob Herschmann, *President*
Nava Ben-Yehuda, *Vice Pres*
Tony Chavez, *Principal*
Peter Y Cuevas, *Principal*
EMP: 55
SQ FT: 16,000
SALES (est): 12.9MM **Privately Held**
SIC: 3825 Semiconductor test equipment

(P-21835)
QUANTUM FOCUS INSTRUMENTS CORP
2385 La Mirada Dr, Vista (92081-7863)
PHONE....................760 599-1122
Grant Albright, *President*
Victoria Albright, *Admin Sec*
▼ EMP: 13
SQ FT: 7,500
SALES (est): 3.3MM **Privately Held**
SIC: 3825 Instruments to measure electricity

(P-21836)
QXQ INC
44113 S Grimmer Blvd, Fremont (94538-6350)
PHONE....................510 252-1522
Roger Quan, *President*
Weili Aguilar, *COO*
Kelly Nguyen, *CFO*
Jack Jenkins, *Admin Sec*
George Quan, *Opers Mgr*
▲ EMP: 33
SQ FT: 2,600
SALES (est): 7.5MM **Privately Held**
WEB: www.qxq.com
SIC: 3825 Instruments to measure electricity

(P-21837)
RADIO FREQUENCY SIMULATION
25371 Diana Cir, Mission Viejo (92691-4514)
PHONE....................714 974-7377
Richard C Damon, *President*
Diane Langius, *Administration*
EMP: 29
SALES (est): 1.6MM **Privately Held**
SIC: 3825 Radio frequency measuring equipment

(P-21838)
RADX TECHNOLOGIES INC
10650 Scripps Ranch Blvd # 100, San Diego (92131-2470)
PHONE....................619 677-1849
Cristina B Matthews, *Finance*
Ross Smith, *CEO*
Thomas Kais, *CFO*
EMP: 16
SALES (est): 2.7MM **Privately Held**
SIC: 3825 3663 7372 Instruments to measure electricity; radio & TV communications equipment; prepackaged software

---

(P-21839)
RIEDON INC
13065 Tom White Way Ste F, Norwalk
(90650-8935)
PHONE....................562 926-2304
Greg Wood, *Branch Mgr*
EMP: 10 **Privately Held**
SIC: 3825 3679 Shunts, electrical; power supplies, all types: static
PA: Riedon, Inc.
　　300 Cypress Ave
　　Alhambra CA 91801

(P-21840)
ROD L ELECTRONICS INC (PA)
935 Sierra Vista Ave F, Mountain View
(94043-1759)
P.O. Box 52158, Palo Alto (94303-0754)
PHONE....................650 322-0711
Roy Clay Sr, *Owner*
Roy Clay, *Owner*
▲ **EMP:** 14
SALES (est): 2.1MM **Privately Held**
SIC: 3825 Test equipment for electronic & electrical circuits

(P-21841)
ROOS INSTRUMENTS INC
Also Called: RI
2285 Martin Ave, Santa Clara
(95050-2715)
PHONE....................408 748-8589
Mark D Roos, *President*
Catherine Roos, *COO*
Esther Chen, *Sr Software Eng*
John Ward, *Data Proc Dir*
Ray Beers, *Engineer*
EMP: 21
SQ FT: 22,000
SALES (est): 5.6MM **Privately Held**
WEB: www.roos.com
SIC: 3825 Semiconductor test equipment

(P-21842)
SAGE INSTRUMENTS INC
240 Airport Blvd, Freedom (95019-2636)
PHONE....................831 761-1000
Dave McIntosh, *CEO*
Brett M Mackinnon, *President*
Ray Levasseur, *CFO*
Renshou Dai, *Officer*
Steven Glassman, *Sales Staff*
EMP: 90
SQ FT: 20,000
SALES (est): 17.5MM **Privately Held**
SIC: 3825 Test equipment for electronic & electric measurement

(P-21843)
SANGFOR TECHNOLOGIES INC
46721 Fremont Blvd, Fremont
(94538-6539)
PHONE....................408 520-7898
Darwin Ceng, *CEO*
EMP: 900
SALES (est): 61.3MM **Privately Held**
SIC: 3825 Network analyzers

(P-21844)
SATELLITE TELEWORK CENTERS INC (PA)
6265 Highway 9, Felton (95018-9710)
PHONE....................831 222-2100
Barbara Sprenger, *President*
EMP: 11
SALES (est): 3.3MM **Privately Held**
SIC: 3825 7389 Network analyzers; office facilities & secretarial service rental

(P-21845)
SEAGULL SOLUTIONS INC
15105 Concord Cir Ste 100, Morgan Hill
(95037-5487)
PHONE....................408 778-1127
Carol Lawless, *CFO*
Donald L Ekhoff, *CTO*
EMP: 13
SQ FT: 8,717
SALES (est): 2MM **Privately Held**
WEB: www.seagullsolutions.net
SIC: 3825 Instruments to measure electricity

(P-21846)
SEMPREX CORPORATION
782 Camden Ave, Campbell (95008-4102)
PHONE....................408 379-3230
Karl Volk, *President*
Chris Cox, *Prdtn Mgr*
EMP: 13
SQ FT: 12,500
SALES (est): 2.2MM **Privately Held**
WEB: www.semprex.com
SIC: 3825 Semiconductor test equipment

(P-21847)
SENTIENT ENERGY INC (PA)
880 Mitten Rd Ste 105, Burlingame
(94010-1309)
PHONE....................650 523-6680
James A Keener, *CEO*
Michael Bauer, *President*
EMP: 12
SQ FT: 15,000
SALES (est): 5.4MM **Privately Held**
SIC: 3825 Instruments to measure electricity

(P-21848)
SHB INSTRUMENTS INC
19215 Parthenia St Ste A, Northridge
(91324-5168)
PHONE....................818 773-2000
Barry Megdal, *President*
▲ **EMP:** 10
SQ FT: 2,500
SALES (est): 2MM **Privately Held**
SIC: 3825 Test equipment for electronic & electrical circuits

(P-21849)
SIGNUM SYSTEMS CORPORATION
1211 Flynn Rd Unit 104, Camarillo
(93012-6208)
PHONE....................805 383-3682
Jerry Lewandowski, *President*
Robert Chyla, *Vice Pres*
◆ **EMP:** 17
SQ FT: 6,000
SALES (est): 3MM
SALES (corp-wide): 40.8MM **Privately Held**
WEB: www.signum.com
SIC: 3825 3577 Test equipment for electronic & electrical circuits; computer peripheral equipment
PA: I.A.R. Systems Group Ab
　　Strandbodgatan 11tr
　　Uppsala 753 2
　　841 092-000

(P-21850)
SOF-TEK INTEGRATORS INC
Also Called: Op-Test
4712 Mtn Lakes Blvd # 200, Redding
(96003-1479)
PHONE....................530 242-0527
Daniel C Morrow, *President*
Meredith Morrow, *CFO*
S Curt Dodds, *Vice Pres*
Daniel Morrow, *Executive*
Annmary Morrow, *Admin Sec*
EMP: 16
SQ FT: 5,000
SALES (est): 800K **Privately Held**
WEB: www.op-test.com
SIC: 3825 8711 Instruments to measure electricity; engineering services

(P-21851)
SOLARIUS DEVELOPMENT INC
2390 Bering Dr, San Jose (95131-1121)
PHONE....................408 541-0151
Peter Joshua, *President*
Marco Negrete, *General Mgr*
Amy Zullo, *Office Mgr*
Hitendra Mistry, *Project Mgr*
Zhitong Luo, *Technology*
EMP: 10
SQ FT: 3,600
SALES (est): 2.8MM **Privately Held**
SIC: 3825 Electrical energy measuring equipment

(P-21852)
SOTCHER MEASUREMENT INC
115 Phelan Ave Ste 10, San Jose
(95112-6122)
PHONE....................408 574-0112
Marc Sotcher, *President*
EMP: 12
SQ FT: 9,000
SALES: 1.5MM **Privately Held**
WEB: www.sotcher.com
SIC: 3825 Test equipment for electronic & electrical circuits

(P-21853)
SPECTRUM INSTRUMENTS INC
570 E Arrow Hwy Ste D, San Dimas
(91773-3347)
PHONE....................909 971-9710
Thomas Verseput, *President*
Jeffrey Grous, *Director*
Donald REA, *Director*
EMP: 15
SALES: 830K **Privately Held**
WEB: www.spectruminstruments.com
SIC: 3825 Frequency synthesizers; time code generators

(P-21854)
STEM INC
100 Rollins Rd, Millbrae (94030-3115)
PHONE....................415 937-7836
John Carrington, *CEO*
David Erhart, *President*
Bill Bush, *CFO*
William Bush, *CFO*
Karen Butterfield, *Officer*
◆ **EMP:** 110
SQ FT: 20,000
SALES (est): 36MM **Privately Held**
SIC: 3825 Electrical power measuring equipment

(P-21855)
STRUCTURAL DIAGNOSTICS INC
Also Called: S D I
650 Via Alondra, Camarillo (93012-8733)
PHONE....................805 987-7755
Paul R Teagle, *President*
EMP: 28
SQ FT: 30,000
SALES (est): 5.8MM **Privately Held**
WEB: www.sdindt.com
SIC: 3825 Instruments to measure electricity

(P-21856)
STS INSTRUMENTS INC
17711 Mitchell N, Irvine (92614-6028)
P.O. Box 1805, Ardmore OK (73402-1805)
PHONE....................580 223-4773
Kevin Voelcker, *President*
William D Long, *Treasurer*
Barbara J Stinnett, *Admin Sec*
▲ **EMP:** 18
SQ FT: 20,000
SALES (est): 3MM
SALES (corp-wide): 17.3MM **Privately Held**
WEB: www.sltrco.com
SIC: 3825 Test equipment for electronic & electrical circuits
PA: Ppst, Inc.
　　17692 Fitch
　　Irvine CA 92614
　　800 421-1921

(P-21857)
SURFACE OPTICS CORP
11555 Rancho Bernardo Rd, San Diego
(92127-1441)
PHONE....................858 675-7404
Jonathan Dummer, *CEO*
James Jafolla, *President*
James C Jafolla, *President*
Marian Geremia, *CFO*
Marian K Geremia, *CFO*
EMP: 50
SQ FT: 18,000
SALES (est): 12.6MM **Privately Held**
WEB: www.surfaceoptics.com
SIC: 3825 8748 3829 8731 Instruments to measure electricity; business consulting; measuring & controlling devices; commercial physical research

(P-21858)
SV PROBE INC
6680 Via Del Oro, San Jose (95119-1392)
PHONE....................480 635-4700
Kevin Kurtz, *Principal*
EMP: 100
SALES (corp-wide): 13.9B **Privately Held**
SIC: 3825 Test equipment for electronic & electrical circuits
HQ: Sv Probe, Inc.
　　7810 S Hardy Dr Ste 109
　　Tempe AZ 85284
　　-

(P-21859)
SV PROBE INC
535 E Brokaw Rd, San Jose (95112-1004)
PHONE....................408 653-2387
Trong Pham, *President*
EMP: 10
SALES (corp-wide): 13.9B **Privately Held**
SIC: 3825 Semiconductor test equipment
HQ: Sv Probe, Inc.
　　7810 S Hardy Dr Ste 109
　　Tempe AZ 85284
　　-

(P-21860)
SV PROBE INC
535 E Brokaw Rd, San Jose (95112-1004)
PHONE....................408 727-6341
Gary Luu, *Branch Mgr*
EMP: 200
SALES (corp-wide): 13.9B **Privately Held**
WEB: www.svprobe.com
SIC: 3825 Semiconductor test equipment
HQ: Sv Probe, Inc.
　　7810 S Hardy Dr Ste 109
　　Tempe AZ 85284

(P-21861)
SYNTHESYS RESEARCH INC (DH)
4250 Burton Dr, Santa Clara (95054-1551)
PHONE....................408 753-1630
Lutz Henckels, *CEO*
James Waschura, *President*
Thomas Waschura, *CTO*
EMP: 60
SQ FT: 8,000
SALES (est): 5MM
SALES (corp-wide): 6.6B **Publicly Held**
WEB: www.synthesysresearch.com
SIC: 3825 Test equipment for electronic & electrical measurement
HQ: Tektronix, Inc.
　　14150 Sw Karl Braun Dr
　　Beaverton OR 97005
　　800 833-9200

(P-21862)
TASEON INC
515 S Flower St Fl 25, Los Angeles
(90071-2228)
PHONE....................408 240-7800
Albert Wong, *CEO*
Sue Whitsett, *Administration*
Rachel Wang, *Technical Staff*
▲ **EMP:** 65
SQ FT: 21,000
SALES (est): 7.4MM **Privately Held**
SIC: 3825 Network analyzers

(P-21863)
TECHNOLOGY FOR ENERGY CORP
Also Called: Dynamic Instruments
9440 Carroll Park Dr # 150, San Diego
(92121-5201)
PHONE....................858 278-4900
Paul Whitten Sr, *Vice Pres*
EMP: 10
SALES (est): 168.9K **Privately Held**
SIC: 3825 Analog-digital converters, electronic instrumentation type

(P-21864)
TEKTRONIX INC
2368 Walsh Ave, Santa Clara
(95051-1323)
PHONE....................408 496-0800
Douglas Shafer, *Branch Mgr*
EMP: 22

▲ = Import ▼=Export
◆ =Import/Export

SALES (corp-wide): 6.6B **Publicly Held**
WEB: www.tek.com
SIC: 3825 Instruments to measure electricity
HQ: Tektronix, Inc.
14150 Sw Karl Braun Dr
Beaverton OR 97005
800 833-9200

(P-21865)
TELEDYNE LECROY INC
Also Called: Lecroy Prtocol Solutions Group
765 Sycamore Dr, Milpitas (95035-7465)
PHONE............................408 727-6600
James Allen, *Technical Staff*
Roy Chestnut, *Technical Staff*
Amit Bakshi, *Engineer*
Gordon Getty, *Engineer*
Matthew Hall, *Director*
EMP: 22
SALES (corp-wide): 2.6B **Publicly Held**
WEB: www.lecroy.com
SIC: 3825 3829 Test equipment for electronic & electrical circuits; oscillographs & oscilloscopes; measuring & controlling devices
HQ: Teledyne Lecroy, Inc.
700 Chestnut Ridge Rd
Chestnut Ridge NY 10977
845 425-2000

(P-21866)
TELSOR CORPORATION
42181 Avenida Alvarado B, Temecula (92590-3429)
PHONE............................951 296-3066
Frank Simon, *Ch of Bd*
EMP: 10
SQ FT: 1,775
SALES (est): 800K **Privately Held**
SIC: 3825 Radio frequency measuring equipment

(P-21867)
TERADYNE INC
30801 Agoura Rd, Agoura Hills (91301-2054)
PHONE............................818 991-9700
Wayne Hardenberg, *Principal*
David Evans, *CTO*
Paul Hatmaker, *Info Tech Dir*
Garnik Abrahamian, *Info Tech Mgr*
Chris Vosse, *Technology*
EMP: 140
SALES (corp-wide): 2.1B **Publicly Held**
SIC: 3825 Semiconductor test equipment
PA: Teradyne, Inc.
600 Riverpark Dr
North Reading MA 01864
978 370-2700

(P-21868)
TERADYNE INC
Also Called: Circuit Bd Test & Insptn Sls
5251 California Ave # 100, Irvine (92617-3075)
PHONE............................949 453-0900
Ken Ovens, *Branch Mgr*
EMP: 55
SALES (corp-wide): 2.1B **Publicly Held**
WEB: www.teradyne.com
SIC: 3825 Semiconductor test equipment
PA: Teradyne, Inc.
600 Riverpark Dr
North Reading MA 01864
978 370-2700

(P-21869)
TERADYNE INC
875 Embedded Way, San Jose (95138-1030)
PHONE............................408 960-2400
Ron Butler, *General Mgr*
EMP: 225
SALES (corp-wide): 2.1B **Publicly Held**
WEB: www.teradyne.com
SIC: 3825 Test equipment for electronic & electric measurement
PA: Teradyne, Inc.
600 Riverpark Dr
North Reading MA 01864
978 370-2700

(P-21870)
TESEDA CORPORATION
160 Rio Robles Bldg D, San Jose (95134-1813)
PHONE............................650 320-8188
Jack Chen, *Branch Mgr*
EMP: 10
SALES (corp-wide): 1.9MM **Privately Held**
WEB: www.teseda.com
SIC: 3825 Test equipment for electronic & electric measurement
PA: Teseda Corporation
6915 Sw Mcdam Ave Ste 245
Portland OR 97219
503 223-3315

(P-21871)
TEST CONNECTIONS INC
1146 W 9th St, Upland (91786-5728)
PHONE............................909 981-1810
Michael A Curtis, *President*
Patrica Jones, *CFO*
Patricia Jones, *Treasurer*
Brian Jones, *Engineer*
EMP: 10
SQ FT: 5,000
SALES (est): 1.5MM **Privately Held**
WEB: www.tciinfo.com
SIC: 3825 3679 Test equipment for electronic & electrical circuits; electronic circuits

(P-21872)
TEST ELECTRONICS
821 Smith Rd, Watsonville (95076-9798)
PHONE............................831 763-2000
Ed Armstrong, *Owner*
EMP: 42
SALES (est): 2.9MM **Privately Held**
WEB: www.testelectronics.com
SIC: 3825 Test equipment for electronic & electrical circuits

(P-21873)
TEST ENTERPRISES INC
Fet-Test
1288 Reamwood Ave, Sunnyvale (94089-2233)
PHONE............................408 778-0234
Gary Wolfe, *Principal*
EMP: 24
SQ FT: 13,777
SALES (corp-wide): 6MM **Privately Held**
WEB: www.thermonics.com
SIC: 3825 Semiconductor test equipment
PA: Test Enterprises, Inc.
1288 Reamwood Ave
Sunnyvale CA 94089
408 542-5900

(P-21874)
TEST-UM INC
430 N Mccarthy Blvd, Milpitas (95035-5112)
PHONE............................818 464-5021
David Vellequette, *CEO*
▲ EMP: 18
SQ FT: 8,000
SALES (est): 2.7MM
SALES (corp-wide): 811.4MM **Publicly Held**
WEB: www.test-um.com
SIC: 3825 Test equipment for electronic & electric measurement
PA: Viavi Solutions Inc.
6001 America Center Dr # 6
San Jose CA 95002
408 404-3600

(P-21875)
TESTMETRIX INC
426 S Hillview Dr, Milpitas (95035-5464)
PHONE............................408 730-5511
Christian Cojocneanu, *President*
Stephanie Haag, *CFO*
Mike Bulat, *Director*
EMP: 24
SQ FT: 10,000
SALES (est): 4.7MM **Privately Held**
WEB: www.testmetrix.com
SIC: 3825 3674 Test equipment for electronic & electric measurement; semiconductors & related devices

(P-21876)
TESTRONIC LABORATORIES INC
111 N First St Ste 304, Burbank (91502-1854)
PHONE............................818 845-3223
Neil Goodall, *President*
EMP: 30
SALES (est): 3.6MM **Privately Held**
SIC: 3825 Digital test equipment, electronic & electrical circuits

(P-21877)
THIRD MLLENNIUM TEST SOLUTIONS
Also Called: 3 MTS
3101 Alexis Dr, Palo Alto (94304-1306)
PHONE............................650 949-1120
Wilmer R Bottoms, *Branch Mgr*
EMP: 10
SALES (corp-wide): 2.1MM **Privately Held**
WEB: www.3mts.com
SIC: 3825 Semiconductor test equipment
PA: Third Millennium Test Solutions, Inc
3003 Bunker Hill Ln # 106
Santa Clara CA

(P-21878)
TIGER JET NETWORK INC
50 Airport Pkwy Ofc, San Jose (95110)
PHONE............................408 437-7727
Y W Sing, *Ch of Bd*
Julia Chow, *CFO*
Stanley Lo, *Vice Pres*
David Lewis, *Marketing Staff*
▲ EMP: 10
SQ FT: 5,000
SALES (est): 1.2MM
SALES (corp-wide): 97.4MM **Privately Held**
WEB: www.tjnet.com
SIC: 3825 Network analyzers
HQ: Ymax Corporation
222 Lakeview Ave Ste 1600
West Palm Beach FL 33401

(P-21879)
TRANSLARITY INC
46575 Fremont Blvd, Fremont (94538-6409)
PHONE............................510 371-7900
Laura Oliphant, *CEO*
Mark Gardiner, *COO*
Garry Crossland, *Vice Pres*
Curt Ward, *Vice Pres*
Chuck Wiley,
EMP: 19
SQ FT: 20,000
SALES (est): 4.6MM **Privately Held**
WEB: www.octsci.com
SIC: 3825 Semiconductor test equipment

(P-21880)
TRENDPOINT SYSTEMS INC
283 Winfield Cir, Corona (92880-6943)
PHONE............................925 855-0600
Lisa Mandell, *CEO*
Donna Carter, *Admin Sec*
Jonathon Trout, *CTO*
EMP: 10
SALES (est): 3.1MM **Privately Held**
WEB: www.trendpoint.com
SIC: 3825 Instruments to measure electricity

(P-21881)
TRI-NET INC
14721 Hilton Dr, Fontana (92336-4013)
PHONE............................909 483-3555
Rosemarie V Hall, *President*
Rex Arnold, *Engineer*
EMP: 15
SQ FT: 7,500
SALES (est): 3.3MM **Privately Held**
SIC: 3825 Test equipment for electronic & electric measurement

(P-21882)
TRT BSNESS NTWRK SOLUTIONS INC
15551 Red Hill Ave Ste A, Tustin (92780-7325)
PHONE............................714 380-3888
Julia Swen, *President*
▲ EMP: 13
SALES (est): 1.3MM **Privately Held**
WEB: www.trtinfo.com
SIC: 3825 Network analyzers

(P-21883)
VALDOR FIBER OPTICS INC (PA)
1838 D St, Hayward (94541-4435)
PHONE............................510 293-1212
Las Yabut, *President*
Kandra Kalanick, *Controller*
EMP: 29
SQ FT: 12,000
SALES (est): 3.8MM **Privately Held**
SIC: 3825 Measuring instruments & meters, electric

(P-21884)
VERTOX COMPANY
11752 Garden Grove Blvd # 113, Garden Grove (92843-1423)
PHONE............................714 530-4541
Steven L Hacker, *Owner*
▲ EMP: 12
SQ FT: 1,000
SALES (est): 838.1K **Privately Held**
WEB: www.vertox.org
SIC: 3825 Meters: electric, pocket, portable, panelboard, etc.

(P-21885)
VITREK LLC
12169 Kirkham Rd Ste C, Poway (92064-8835)
PHONE............................858 689-2755
Kevin P Clark, *President*
Chad Clark, *Sales Mgr*
Bryan Withers, *Manager*
▲ EMP: 15
SQ FT: 4,000
SALES (est): 3.8MM **Privately Held**
WEB: www.vitrek.com
SIC: 3825 Test equipment for electronic & electric measurement

(P-21886)
VLSI STANDARDS INC
5 Technology Dr, Milpitas (95035-7916)
PHONE............................408 428-1800
Ian Smith, *President*
EMP: 34
SQ FT: 17,500
SALES (est): 5.4MM
SALES (corp-wide): 4B **Publicly Held**
WEB: www.vlsistandards.com
SIC: 3825 Standards & calibration equipment for electrical measuring
PA: Kla-Tencor Corporation
1 Technology Dr
Milpitas CA 95035
408 875-3000

(P-21887)
W J KEENAN
408 Sunrise Ave, Roseville (95661-4123)
PHONE............................916 783-5201
W J Keenan, *Owner*
EMP: 25
SALES (est): 1.9MM **Privately Held**
SIC: 3825 Standards & calibrating equipment, laboratory

(P-21888)
XANDEX INC
1360 Redwood Way Ste A, Petaluma (94954-1104)
PHONE............................707 763-7799
Kamran Shamsavari, *President*
Nariman Manoochehri, *CEO*
▲ EMP: 93
SQ FT: 20,000
SALES (est): 20.6MM **Privately Held**
WEB: www.xandex.com
SIC: 3825 3674 Instruments to measure electricity; wafers (semiconductor devices)

P R O D U C T S & S V C S

(P-21889)
Z K CELLTEST INC
2310 Walsh Ave, Santa Clara
(95051-1301)
PHONE.....................408 541-2620
Richard Miletic, *President*
Bruce Morley, *President*
▲ EMP: 15
SALES (est): 3.1MM **Privately Held**
WEB: www.zk.com
SIC: 3825 Test equipment for electronic &
electrical circuits

3826 Analytical Instruments

(P-21890)
AB SCIEX LLC (HQ)
1201 Radio Rd, Redwood City
(94065-1217)
PHONE.....................877 740-2129
Rainer Blair, *Mng Member*
Thomas Covey, *Vice Pres*
Marian Cadiz, *Executive Asst*
John Gordon, *CIO*
Angelika Khazan, *Info Tech Mgr*
EMP: 100
SALES (est): 44.3MM
SALES (corp-wide): 18.3B **Publicly Held**
SIC: 3826 Analytical instruments
PA: Danaher Corporation
    2200 Penn Ave Nw Ste 800w
    Washington DC 20037
    202 828-0850

(P-21891)
ACCESS SYSTEMS INC
4947 Hillsdale Cir, El Dorado Hills
(95762-5707)
PHONE.....................916 941-8099
Michael Herd, *President*
Barbara Ponce, *Office Mgr*
Barbara Bonner, *Info Tech Mgr*
Greg Johnston, *Opers Mgr*
EMP: 11
SQ FT: 3,000
SALES (est): 2.8MM **Privately Held**
WEB: www.accesssystems.us
SIC: 3826 3699 Integrators (mathematical
instruments); security control equipment
& systems

(P-21892)
ACELLS CORP
Also Called: Amcells
1351 Dist Way Ste 1, Vista (92081)
PHONE.....................760 727-6666
Jenny Zhang, *President*
David Allen, *Vice Pres*
▲ EMP: 10
SQ FT: 10,000
SALES (est): 1.5MM **Privately Held**
WEB: www.amcells.com
SIC: 3826 Analytical instruments

(P-21893)
**ADVANCED MICRO
INSTRUMENTS INC**
Also Called: AMI
225 Paularino Ave, Costa Mesa
(92626-3313)
PHONE.....................714 848-5533
Steve Kirchnavy, *President*
W William Layton, *CFO*
EMP: 23
SQ FT: 2,500
SALES (est): 4.8MM **Privately Held**
WEB: www.amio2.com
SIC: 3826 Analytical instruments

(P-21894)
AFFYMETRIX INC
3380 Central Expy, Santa Clara
(95051-0704)
PHONE.....................408 731-5000
George Beers, *Branch Mgr*
EMP: 54
SALES (corp-wide): 20.9B **Publicly Held**
SIC: 3826 Analytical instruments
HQ: Affymetrix, Inc.
    3380 Central Expy
    Santa Clara CA 95051

(P-21895)
AFFYMETRIX INC
3450 Central Expy, Santa Clara
(95051-0703)
PHONE.....................408 731-5000
Mirasol Abriam, *Branch Mgr*
EMP: 74
SALES (corp-wide): 20.9B **Publicly Held**
WEB: www.affymetrix.com
SIC: 3826 2835 Analytical instruments; in
vitro & in vivo diagnostic substances
HQ: Affymetrix, Inc.
    3380 Central Expy
    Santa Clara CA 95051
　-

(P-21896)
AFFYMETRIX INC (HQ)
3380 Central Expy, Santa Clara
(95051-0704)
PHONE.....................408 731-5000
Seth H Hoogasian, *President*
Gary McMaster, *Officer*
Siang Chin, *Vice Pres*
John Dangelo, *Vice Pres*
Doug Farrell, *Vice Pres*
EMP: 277
SALES (est): 291.4MM
SALES (corp-wide): 20.9B **Publicly Held**
WEB: www.affymetrix.com
SIC: 3826 Analytical instruments
PA: Thermo Fisher Scientific Inc.
    168 3rd Ave
    Waltham MA 02451
    781 622-1000

(P-21897)
AFFYMETRIX ANATRACE
3380 Central Expy, Santa Clara
(95051-0704)
P.O. Box 178 (95052-0178)
PHONE.....................408 731-5756
EMP: 14
SALES (est): 3.2MM **Privately Held**
SIC: 3826

(P-21898)
AGILONE INC (PA)
771 Vaqueros Ave, Sunnyvale
(94085-3527)
PHONE.....................877 769-3047
Omer Artun, *CEO*
Steve McDermott, *Vice Pres*
Dan Moore, *Vice Pres*
Mark Vashon, *Vice Pres*
Peter Godfrey, *Principal*
EMP: 53 EST: 2011
SQ FT: 6,000
SALES (est): 13.5MM **Privately Held**
SIC: 3826 Analytical instruments

(P-21899)
ALZA CORPORATION
1010 Joaquin Rd, Mountain View
(94043-1242)
PHONE.....................650 564-5000
Duane Frise, *Branch Mgr*
EMP: 725
SALES (corp-wide): 76.4B **Publicly Held**
WEB: www.alza.com
SIC: 3826 Analytical instruments
HQ: Alza Corporation
    700 Eubanks Dr
    Vacaville CA 95688
    707 453-6400

(P-21900)
ALZA CORPORATION
700 Eubanks Dr, Vacaville (95688-9470)
PHONE.....................707 453-6400
David Danks, *Vice Pres*
EMP: 650
SQ FT: 23,040
SALES (corp-wide): 76.4B **Publicly Held**
WEB: www.alza.com
SIC: 3826 Analytical instruments
HQ: Alza Corporation
    700 Eubanks Dr
    Vacaville CA 95688
    707 453-6400

(P-21901)
AMBIOS TECHNOLOGY INC (PA)
1 Technology Dr, Milpitas (95035-7916)
PHONE.....................831 427-1160
Patrick O'Hara, *President*

▲ EMP: 22
SQ FT: 5,800
SALES: 6.2MM **Privately Held**
WEB: www.ambiostech.com
SIC: 3826 Laser scientific & engineering
instruments

(P-21902)
**ANALYTCAL SCENTIFIC INSTRS
INC**
Also Called: A S I
3023 Research Dr, San Pablo
(94806-5206)
PHONE.....................510 669-2250
Stephen H Graham, *President*
Yasu Graham, *Vice Pres*
EMP: 30
SQ FT: 12,000
SALES (est): 8.3MM **Privately Held**
WEB: www.hplc-asi.com
SIC: 3826 3494 Analytical instruments;
valves & pipe fittings

(P-21903)
ANALYTIK JENA US LLC (DH)
Also Called: Uvp, LLC
2066 W 11th St, Upland (91786-3509)
P.O. Box 5015 (91785-5015)
PHONE.....................909 946-3197
Chris Griffith, *CEO*
Laura Rentschler, *Technology*
Luis Moreno, *Accounting Mgr*
Ivan Wong, *Accountant*
Brian Vigil, *Senior Buyer*
◆ EMP: 97
SQ FT: 42,000
SALES (est): 16.5MM
SALES (corp-wide): 2.6B **Privately Held**
SIC: 3826 3641 Analytical instruments; ul-
traviolet lamps
HQ: Analytik Jena Ag
    Konrad-Zuse-Str. 1
    Jena 07745
    364 177-70

(P-21904)
**APPLIED INSTRUMENT TECH
INC**
2121 Aviation Dr, Upland (91786-2195)
PHONE.....................909 204-3700
Joseph Laconte, *President*
EMP: 40
SALES (est): 10.6MM
SALES (corp-wide): 200.4K **Privately
Held**
SIC: 3826 Analytical instruments
HQ: Schneider Electric Usa, Inc.
    800 Federal St
    Andover MA 01810
    978 975-9600

(P-21905)
APTON BIOSYSTEMS INC
24245 Elise Ct, Los Altos Hills
(94024-5117)
PHONE.....................650 284-6992
Bryan Staker, *Chief Engr*
Bart Staker, *Development*
EMP: 10
SALES (est): 713.8K **Privately Held**
SIC: 3826 Protein analyzers, laboratory
type

(P-21906)
ASA CORPORATION
3111 Sunset Blvd Ste V, Rocklin
(95677-3090)
PHONE.....................530 305-3720
John Mehlhaff, *President*
EMP: 15
SALES (est): 5MM **Privately Held**
SIC: 3826 Surface area analyzers

(P-21907)
ATE MICROGRAPHICS INC
3101 Whipple Rd Ste 22, Union City
(94587-1223)
PHONE.....................510 475-5882
Edmund Monberg, *President*
Debra Rosen, *General Mgr*
EMP: 10
SQ FT: 20,000
SALES (est): 1MM **Privately Held**
WEB: www.lasermotion.com
SIC: 3826 8742 Photomicrographic appa-
ratus; management consulting services

(P-21908)
BECKMAN COULTER INC
15989 Cypress Ave, Chino (91708-9100)
PHONE.....................909 597-3967
EMP: 82
SALES (corp-wide): 18.3B **Publicly Held**
SIC: 3826 3821 3841
HQ: Beckman Coulter, Inc.
    250 S Kraemer Blvd
    Brea CA 92821
    714 993-5321

(P-21909)
BECKMAN COULTER INC
167 W Poplar Ave, Porterville (93257-5311)
PHONE.....................559 784-0800
Marshall Black, *Opers-Prdtn-Mfg*
George Garza, *Engineer*
Blaine Willis, *Mfg Mgr*
EMP: 200
SQ FT: 36,000
SALES (corp-wide): 18.3B **Publicly Held**
WEB: www.beckman.com
SIC: 3826 Analytical instruments
HQ: Beckman Coulter, Inc.
    250 S Kraemer Blvd
    Brea CA 92821
    714 993-5321

(P-21910)
BECKMAN COULTER INC
2470 Faraday Ave, Carlsbad (92010-7224)
PHONE.....................760 438-9151
Claire O'Donadan, *Opers-Prdtn-Mfg*
EMP: 200
SALES (corp-wide): 18.3B **Publicly Held**
WEB: www.beckman.com
SIC: 3826 Analytical instruments
HQ: Beckman Coulter, Inc.
    250 S Kraemer Blvd
    Brea CA 92821
    714 993-5321

(P-21911)
BECKMAN COULTER INC
2040 Enterprise Blvd, West Sacramento
(95691-5045)
PHONE.....................916 374-3511
EMP: 77
SALES (corp-wide): 18.3B **Publicly Held**
SIC: 3826 Analytical instruments
HQ: Beckman Coulter, Inc.
    250 S Kraemer Blvd
    Brea CA 92821
    714 993-5321

(P-21912)
BEMCO INC (PA)
2255 Union Pl, Simi Valley (93065-1661)
PHONE.....................805 583-4970
Randy Jean Bruskrud, *President*
Brian Bruskrud, *Admin Sec*
Richard Behrendt, *Sales Engr*
EMP: 25 EST: 1951
SQ FT: 50,000
SALES (est): 5.9MM **Privately Held**
WEB: www.bemcoinc.com
SIC: 3826 Environmental testing equip-
ment

(P-21913)
BIO RAD LABORATORIES
2000 Alfred Nobel Dr, Hercules
(94547-1804)
PHONE.....................510 741-1000
Lincoln Fong, *Principal*
Rob McConnell, *Sales Staff*
EMP: 85
SALES (est): 30.6MM **Privately Held**
SIC: 3826 Analytical instruments

(P-21914)
**BIO-RAD LABORATORIES INC
(PA)**
1000 Alfred Nobel Dr, Hercules
(94547-1898)
PHONE.....................510 724-7000
Norman Schwartz, *Ch of Bd*
John Hertia, *President*
Annette Tumolo, *President*
Christine A Tsingos, *CFO*
Ronald W Hutton, *Treasurer*
◆ EMP: 277

SALES: 2.1B **Publicly Held**
WEB: www.bio-rad.com
SIC: **3826** 3845 2835 Electromedical
equipment; in vitro & in vivo diagnostic
substances; electrophoresis equipment

(P-21915)
BIO-RAD LABORATORIES INC
Also Called: Finance Department
225 Linus Pauling Dr, Hercules
(94547-1816)
PHONE.................................510 741-6916
Lanette Ewing, *Branch Mgr*
Michael Crowley, *Exec VP*
Shannon Hall, *General Mgr*
Andrew Rieger, *Admin Asst*
Tanya Wang, *Admin Asst*
EMP: 1500
SALES (corp-wide): 2.1B **Publicly Held**
SIC: **3826** Electrophoresis equipment
PA: Bio-Rad Laboratories, Inc.
1000 Alfred Nobel Dr
Hercules CA 94547
510 724-7000

(P-21916)
BIO-RAD LABORATORIES INC
21 Technology Dr, Irvine (92618-2335)
PHONE.................................949 789-0685
EMP: 473
SALES (corp-wide): 2.1B **Publicly Held**
SIC: **3826** Analytical instruments
PA: Bio-Rad Laboratories, Inc.
1000 Alfred Nobel Dr
Hercules CA 94547
510 724-7000

(P-21917)
BIO-RAD LABORATORIES INC
Bio-RAD U S S D
2000 Alfred Nobel Dr, Hercules
(94547-1804)
PHONE.................................510 741-1000
EMP: 125
SQ FT: 95,850
SALES (corp-wide): 2.1B **Publicly Held**
WEB: www.bio-rad.com
SIC: **3826** Analytical instruments
PA: Bio-Rad Laboratories, Inc.
1000 Alfred Nobel Dr
Hercules CA 94547
510 724-7000

(P-21918)
BIO-RAD LABORATORIES INC
Bio-RAD Clinical Systems Div
4000 Alfred Nobel Dr, Hercules
(94547-1810)
PHONE.................................510 741-6709
EMP: 125
SQ FT: 87,750
SALES (corp-wide): 2.1B **Publicly Held**
WEB: www.bio-rad.com
SIC: **3826** Analytical instruments
PA: Bio-Rad Laboratories, Inc.
1000 Alfred Nobel Dr
Hercules CA 94547
510 724-7000

(P-21919)
BIO-RAD LABORATORIES INC
2000 Alfred Nobel Dr, Hercules
(94547-1804)
PHONE.................................510 232-7000
Norman Swartz, *CEO*
Yuri Arseniev, *Manager*
EMP: 1500
SALES (corp-wide): 2.1B **Publicly Held**
WEB: www.bio-rad.com
SIC: **3826** Analytical instruments
PA: Bio-Rad Laboratories, Inc.
1000 Alfred Nobel Dr
Hercules CA 94547
510 724-7000

(P-21920)
BIO-RAD LABORATORIES INC
6000 James Watson Dr, Hercules (94547)
PHONE.................................510 741-6715
Bill Radcliff, *Manager*
EMP: 473
SALES (corp-wide): 2.1B **Publicly Held**
WEB: www.bio-rad.com
SIC: **3826** 3841 3825 Analytical instru-
ments; surgical & medical instruments; in-
struments to measure electricity

PA: Bio-Rad Laboratories, Inc.
1000 Alfred Nobel Dr
Hercules CA 94547
510 724-7000

(P-21921)
BIO-RAD LABORATORIES INC
Also Called: Lifescience
2000 Alfred Nobel Dr, Hercules
(94547-1804)
PHONE.................................510 741-6999
Burt Zabin, *Manager*
EMP: 300
SALES (corp-wide): 2.1B **Publicly Held**
WEB: www.bio-rad.com
SIC: **3826** 3841 3829 Analytical instru-
ments; surgical & medical instruments;
measuring & controlling devices
PA: Bio-Rad Laboratories, Inc.
1000 Alfred Nobel Dr
Hercules CA 94547
510 724-7000

(P-21922)
BIO-RAD LABORATORIES INC
Also Called: Bio-RAD Labs
2000 Alfred Nobel Dr, Hercules
(94547-1804)
PHONE.................................510 232-7000
Paul Bouchard, *Branch Mgr*
EMP: 473
SQ FT: 6,880
SALES (corp-wide): 2.1B **Publicly Held**
WEB: www.bio-rad.com
SIC: **3826** Electrophoresis equipment
PA: Bio-Rad Laboratories, Inc.
1000 Alfred Nobel Dr
Hercules CA 94547
510 724-7000

(P-21923)
BIO-RAD LABORATORIES INC
5400 E 2nd St, Benicia (94510-1059)
PHONE.................................510 741-5790
Bruce Bartholomew, *Manager*
Michael Chern, *Software Dev*
Rajesh RAO, *Analyst*
Esther Rios, *Accountant*
Roda Reed, *Buyer*
EMP: 20
SALES (corp-wide): 2.1B **Publicly Held**
WEB: www.bio-rad.com
SIC: **3826** Analytical instruments
PA: Bio-Rad Laboratories, Inc.
1000 Alfred Nobel Dr
Hercules CA 94547
510 724-7000

(P-21924)
BIO-RAD LABORATORIES INC
2500 Atlas Rd, Richmond (94806-1170)
PHONE.................................510 724-7000
EMP: 473
SALES (corp-wide): 2.1B **Publicly Held**
SIC: **3826** Electrophoresis equipment
PA: Bio-Rad Laboratories, Inc.
1000 Alfred Nobel Dr
Hercules CA 94547
510 724-7000

(P-21925)
BIOLOG INC
21124 Cabot Blvd, Hayward (94545-1130)
PHONE.................................510 785-2564
Barry R Bochner, *President*
Edwin Fineman, *Vice Pres*
Doug Rife, *Vice Pres*
EMP: 40
SQ FT: 25,000
SALES (est): 10.5MM **Privately Held**
WEB: www.biolog.com
SIC: **3826** Analytical instruments

(P-21926)
BIONANO GENOMICS INC (PA)
9640 Twne Cntre Dr 100, San Diego
(92121)
PHONE.................................858 888-7600
R Erik Holmlin, *President*
David L Barker, *Ch of Bd*
Mark Borodkin, *COO*
Mike Ward, *CFO*
Warren Robinson, *Ch Credit Ofcr*
EMP: 65
SQ FT: 33,128

PA: Bio-Rad Laboratories, Inc.
1000 Alfred Nobel Dr
Hercules CA 94547
510 724-7000

SALES: 9.5MM **Publicly Held**
WEB: www.bionanogenomics.com
SIC: **3826** 5049 8071 Analytical instruments; analytical instruments; biological
laboratory

(P-21927)
BIOPAC SYSTEMS INC
42 Aero Camino, Goleta (93117-3105)
PHONE.................................805 685-0066
Alan Macy, *CEO*
Marc Wester, *CFO*
William McMullen, *Vice Pres*
Steven Matsumura, *Executive*
EMP: 40
SQ FT: 16,000
SALES (est): 10.6MM **Privately Held**
WEB: www.biopac.com
SIC: **3826** Analytical instruments

(P-21928)
BIORAD INC
9500 Jeronimo Rd, Irvine (92618-2017)
PHONE.................................949 598-1200
Alex Alzona, *General Mgr*
Ankit Ghai, *Administration*
Zdravko Bradic, *Research*
Raksha Inamdar, *Research*
Charles Weir, *Research*
EMP: 33
SALES (est): 4.8MM **Privately Held**
SIC: **3826** Analytical instruments

(P-21929)
**BRUKER BIOSPIN
CORPORATION**
Also Called: Bruker Biosciences Cad
61 Daggett Dr, San Jose (95134-2109)
PHONE.................................510 683-4300
Malcolm Bramwell, *Sales/Mktg Mgr*
Scott Ireland, *Sales Staff*
EMP: 25
SALES (corp-wide): 1.7B **Publicly Held**
WEB: www.brukerbiospin.com
SIC: **3826** Analytical instruments
HQ: Bruker Biospin Corporation
15 Fortune Dr
Billerica MA 01821
978 667-9580

(P-21930)
**CALIFRNIA ANLYTICAL INSTRS
INC**
1312 W Grove Ave, Orange (92865-4136)
PHONE.................................714 974-5560
R Pete Furton, *President*
Loren T Mathews, *Corp Secy*
Harold J Peper, *Exec VP*
Jim Mabe, *Design Engr*
Brenda Woods, *Purch Mgr*
EMP: 55
SQ FT: 26,400
SALES (est): 14.3MM **Privately Held**
WEB: www.gasanalyzers.com
SIC: **3826** Gas analyzers instruments

(P-21931)
CENTER HEALTH SERVICES
Also Called: San Diego Lgbt Community Ctr
2313 El Cajon Blvd, San Diego
(92104-1105)
P.O. Box 3357 (92163-1357)
PHONE.................................619 692-2077
Deborah Stern-Ellis, *Director*
Ian Johnson, *Director*
EMP: 10
SALES (est): 1.7MM **Privately Held**
SIC: **3826** 8742 Blood testing apparatus;
hospital & health services consultant

(P-21932)
CEPHEID
904 E Caribbean Dr, Sunnyvale
(94089-1189)
PHONE.................................408 541-4191
EMP: 14
SALES (corp-wide): 18.3B **Publicly Held**
SIC: **3826**
HQ: Cepheid
904 E Caribbean Dr
Sunnyvale CA 94089

(P-21933)
CEPHEID (HQ)
904 E Caribbean Dr, Sunnyvale
(94089-1189)
PHONE.................................408 541-4191
Warren Kocmond, *President*
Daniel E Madden, *CFO*
William E Murray,
Michael Fitzgerald, *Exec VP*
David H Persing, *Exec VP*
◆ EMP: 277
SALES: 538.5MM
SALES (corp-wide): 18.3B **Publicly Held**
WEB: www.cepheid.com
SIC: **3826** 3841 Analytical instruments;
surgical & medical instruments
PA: Danaher Corporation
2200 Penn Ave Nw Ste 800w
Washington DC 20037
202 828-0850

(P-21934)
CITY OF SAN DIEGO
Also Called: Public Utilites Emts
2392 Kincaid Rd, San Diego (92101-0811)
PHONE.................................619 758-2310
Steve Meyer, *Manager*
EMP: 38
SQ FT: 92,782 **Privately Held**
WEB: www.eayo.com
SIC: **3826** Sewage testing apparatus
PA: City Of San Diego
202 C St
San Diego CA 92101
619 236-6330

(P-21935)
COHERENT INC (PA)
5100 Patrick Henry Dr, Santa Clara
(95054-1112)
PHONE.................................408 764-4000
John R Ambroseo, *President*
Garry W Rogerson, *Ch of Bd*
Kevin Palatnik, *CFO*
Nicki May, *Bd of Directors*
Bret M Dimarco, *Exec VP*
EMP: 1082
SQ FT: 200,000
SALES: 1.7B **Publicly Held**
WEB: www.coherent.com
SIC: **3826** 3845 3699 Laser scientific &
engineering instruments; laser systems &
equipment, medical; laser systems &
equipment

(P-21936)
**COMBIMATRIX CORPORATION
(HQ)**
310 Goddard Ste 150, Irvine (92618-4617)
PHONE.................................949 753-0624
Mark McDonough, *Officer*
R Judd Jessup, *Ch of Bd*
Scott R Burell, *CFO*
Kim Leroux, *Vice Pres*
Jason Brooks, *Executive*
EMP: 30
SQ FT: 12,200
SALES: 12.8MM **Publicly Held**
WEB: www.combimatrix.com
SIC: **3826** 8731 Analytical instruments;
biotechnical research, commercial

(P-21937)
CONNECTEDYARD INC
Also Called: Phin
1841 Zanker Rd Ste 10, San Jose
(95112-4223)
PHONE.................................415 699-8844
Justin Miller, *CEO*
Mark Janes, *COO*
EMP: 25 EST: 2014
SALES (est): 3MM
SALES (corp-wide): 545.5MM **Privately
Held**
SIC: **3826** 7371 Water testing apparatus;
computer software development & appli-
cations
PA: Hayward Industries, Inc.
620 Division St
Elizabeth NJ 07201
908 351-5400

(P-21938)
CONTINUUM ELECTRO-OPTICS INC
140 Baytech Dr, San Jose (95134-2302)
PHONE.................................408 727-3240
Robert Buckley, *CEO*
Larry Cramer, *President*
Frank Romero, *Treasurer*
Curt Frederickson, *Vice Pres*
Scott Rinner, *Vice Pres*
◆ **EMP:** 75
SQ FT: 44,000
SALES (est): 26.2MM
SALES (corp-wide): 23.7MM **Privately Held**
WEB: www.continuumlasers.com
SIC: 3826 Laser scientific & engineering instruments
PA: Amplitude Technologies
Espace Du Bois Chaland 2a4
Lisses 91090
169 112-790

(P-21939)
CORETEST SYSTEMS INC
400 Woodview Ave, Morgan Hill (95037-2827)
PHONE.................................408 778-3771
Jared M Potter, *CEO*
Avid Lynch, *President*
EMP: 15
SQ FT: 7,000
SALES (est): 3.7MM **Privately Held**
WEB: www.coretest.com
SIC: 3826 Analytical instruments

(P-21940)
CRAIC TECHNOLOGIES INC
948 N Amelia Ave, San Dimas (91773-1401)
PHONE.................................310 573-8180
Paul Martin, *President*
Jumi Lee, *Vice Pres*
Arlene Adolfo, *Manager*
EMP: 12
SQ FT: 3,500
SALES (est): 2.7MM **Privately Held**
WEB: www.microspectra.com
SIC: 3826 Analytical instruments

(P-21941)
CUPERTRONIX INC
2946 Via Torino, Santa Clara (95051-6084)
PHONE.................................408 887-5455
Larry L Shi, *CEO*
Larry Shi, *CEO*
EMP: 10 **EST:** 2015
SALES (est): 732K **Privately Held**
SIC: 3826 3661 Analytical optical instruments; fiber optics communications equipment

(P-21942)
CYBORTRONICS INCORPORATED
440 Nibus, Brea (92821-3204)
PHONE.................................949 855-2814
Brian Supplee, *President*
Eric Luebben, *Vice Pres*
EMP: 12
SQ FT: 6,500
SALES (est): 5.8MM **Privately Held**
WEB: www.cybortronics.com
SIC: 3826 3825 Environmental testing equipment; test equipment for electronic & electric measurement

(P-21943)
CYTEK DEVELOPMENT INC
4059 Clipper Ct, Fremont (94538-6540)
PHONE.................................510 657-0102
▲ **EMP:** 13
SQ FT: 3,000
SALES (est): 3.8MM **Privately Held**
SIC: 3826

(P-21944)
DATARAY INCORPORATED
1675 Market St, Redding (96001-1022)
PHONE.................................530 472-1717
Steven Garvey, *President*
Kevin Garvey, *COO*
Joy Garvey, *Corp Secy*
EMP: 10

SALES (est): 2.2MM **Privately Held**
WEB: www.dataray.com
SIC: 3826 Laser scientific & engineering instruments

(P-21945)
DIONEX CORPORATION (HQ)
1228 Titan Way Ste 1002, Sunnyvale (94085-4074)
P.O. Box 3603 (94088-3603)
PHONE.................................408 737-0700
Mark Casper, *President*
Craig A McCollam, *CFO*
Bruce Barton, *Exec VP*
Jasmine Gruia Gray PHD, *Vice Pres*
Bill Baker, *Regional Mgr*
EMP: 400
SQ FT: 252,000
SALES (est): 290.3MM
SALES (corp-wide): 20.9B **Publicly Held**
WEB: www.dionex.com
SIC: 3826 2819 3087 3841 Chromatographic equipment, laboratory type; chemicals, reagent grade: refined from technical grade; custom compound purchased resins; surgical & medical instruments
PA: Thermo Fisher Scientific Inc.
168 3rd Ave
Waltham MA 02451
781 622-1000

(P-21946)
DIONEX CORPORATION
Also Called: Thermo Fisher
501 Mercury Dr, Sunnyvale (94085-4019)
P.O. Box 3603 (94088-3603)
PHONE.................................408 737-0700
Lucis Brancil, *Manager*
EMP: 100
SALES (corp-wide): 20.9B **Publicly Held**
WEB: www.dionex.com
SIC: 3826 Analytical instruments
HQ: Dionex Corporation
1228 Titan Way Ste 1002
Sunnyvale CA 94085
408 737-0700

(P-21947)
DOW PHRMACEUTICAL SCIENCES INC
Also Called: Solano Clinical Research
1330 Redwood Way Ste C, Petaluma (94954-7122)
PHONE.................................707 793-2600
Weldon Ryan, *CEO*
Bhaskar Chaudhuri, *President*
Raymond W Anderson, *CFO*
Karen Yu, *General Mgr*
Gordon J Dow, *CTO*
EMP: 140
SQ FT: 42,000
SALES (est): 25.3MM
SALES (corp-wide): 8.7B **Privately Held**
WEB: www.dowpharm.com
SIC: 3826 Analytical instruments
HQ: Valeant Pharmaceuticals International
400 Somerset Corp Blvd
Bridgewater NJ 08807
908 927-1400

(P-21948)
DRY VAC ENVIRONMENTAL INC (PA)
864 Saint Francis Way, Rio Vista (94571-1250)
PHONE.................................707 374-7500
Dan Simpson, *President*
Greg Crocco, *Shareholder*
EMP: 25
SQ FT: 50,000
SALES (est): 2.4MM **Privately Held**
SIC: 3826 3531 Liquid testing apparatus; construction machinery

(P-21949)
DVS SCIENCES INC
7000 Shoreline Ct Ste 100, South San Francisco (94080-7603)
PHONE.................................408 900-7205
Joseph J Victor, *President*
Mark Tebneoer, *CFO*
Scott Tanner, *Founder*
EMP: 50

SALES (est): 6.8MM
SALES (corp-wide): 101.9MM **Publicly Held**
SIC: 3826 2819 Analytical instruments; chemicals, reagent grade: refined from technical grade
PA: Fluidigm Corporation
7000 Shoreline Ct Ste 100
South San Francisco CA 94080
650 266-6000

(P-21950)
ELECTRON IMAGING INCORPORATED
14260 Garden Rd Ste A12, Poway (92064-4973)
PHONE.................................858 679-1569
Ken Arnold, *Principal*
EMP: 10
SALES (est): 960K **Privately Held**
WEB: www.hte.com
SIC: 3826 Analytical instruments

(P-21951)
ELECTRONIC SENSOR TECH INC
1125 Bsneca Ctr Cir Ste B, Newbury Park (91320)
PHONE.................................805 480-1994
William Wittmeyer, *CEO*
Ifty Talib, *Marketing Staff*
Kelly Dang,
EMP: 10
SQ FT: 12,700
SALES: 420K **Publicly Held**
WEB: www.estcal.com
SIC: 3826 3829 Gas chromatographic instruments; measuring & controlling devices
PA: Halfmoon Bay Capital Limited
C/O Trident Trust Company (B.V.I) Limited
Road Town

(P-21952)
EMD MILLIPORE CORPORATION
25801 Industrial Blvd B, Hayward (94545-2223)
PHONE.................................510 576-1367
Lawrence F Bruder, *CEO*
Karen Abercrombia, *Office Admin*
Lissie Boyle, *VP Sales*
EMP: 180
SALES (corp-wide): 18B **Privately Held**
SIC: 3826 Analytical instruments
HQ: Emd Millipore Corporation
400 Summit Dr
Burlington MA 01803
781 533-6000

(P-21953)
EMD MILLIPORE CORPORATION
26578 Old Julian Hwy, Ramona (92065-6733)
PHONE.................................760 788-9692
Haizhen Liu, *Manager*
EMP: 10
SQ FT: 9,694
SALES (corp-wide): 18B **Privately Held**
SIC: 3826 Analytical instruments
HQ: Emd Millipore Corporation
400 Summit Dr
Burlington MA 01803
781 533-6000

(P-21954)
EMD MILLIPORE CORPORATION
28835 Single Oak Dr, Temecula (92590-5501)
PHONE.................................951 676-8080
Patrick Schneider, *Manager*
EMP: 180
SALES (corp-wide): 18B **Privately Held**
SIC: 3826 Analytical instruments
HQ: Emd Millipore Corporation
400 Summit Dr
Burlington MA 01803
781 533-6000

(P-21955)
EMD MILLIPORE CORPORATION
Also Called: Bioscience Research Reagents
28820 Single Oak Dr, Temecula (92590-3607)
PHONE.................................951 676-8080

John Ambroziak, *Manager*
EMP: 180
SALES (corp-wide): 18B **Privately Held**
WEB: www.millipore.com
SIC: 3826 2836 2835 Biological products, except diagnostic; vaccines; in vitro & in vivo diagnostic substances; liquid testing apparatus
HQ: Emd Millipore Corporation
400 Summit Dr
Burlington MA 01803
781 533-6000

(P-21956)
ENDRESS & HAUSER CONDUCTA INC
Also Called: Endresshauser Conducta
4123 E La Palma Ave, Anaheim (92807-1867)
PHONE.................................800 835-5474
Manfred A Jagiella, *CEO*
Claude Genswein, *CFO*
Steve Anderson, *Senior VP*
Joachin Hartmyer, *General Mgr*
Steve Ruff, *General Mgr*
EMP: 50 **EST:** 1976
SQ FT: 31,000
SALES (est): 12.5MM
SALES (corp-wide): 2.6B **Privately Held**
WEB: www.conducta.endress.com
SIC: 3826 3823 Water testing apparatus; industrial instrmnts msrmnt display/control process variable
HQ: Endress+Hauser Conducta Gmbh+Co. Kg
Dieselstr. 24
Gerlingen 70839
715 620-90

(P-21957)
ENTECH INSTRUMENTS INC
2207 Agate Ct, Simi Valley (93065-1839)
PHONE.................................805 527-5939
Daniel B Cardin, *CEO*
Edward Kocharyan, *QA Dir*
Tasha McKay, *Marketing Staff*
Jared Bossart, *Director*
▲ **EMP:** 55
SQ FT: 25,000
SALES (est): 14.3MM **Privately Held**
WEB: www.entechinst.com
SIC: 3826 Environmental testing equipment

(P-21958)
EUV TECH INC
2840 Howe Rd Ste A, Martinez (94553-4035)
PHONE.................................925 229-4388
Rupert Perera, *President*
Dave Houser, *President*
Chami Perera, *VP Opers*
Derek Yegian, *Director*
EMP: 15 **EST:** 1996
SQ FT: 6,000
SALES (est): 3.8MM **Privately Held**
WEB: www.euvl.com
SIC: 3826 Laser scientific & engineering instruments

(P-21959)
FILMETRICS INC (PA)
10655 Roselle St Ste 200, San Diego (92121-1557)
PHONE.................................858 573-9300
Scott Chalmers, *President*
Aaron Glabman, *Software Engr*
Menno Bouman, *Technology*
Charles Chen, *Technology*
John Coleman, *Technology*
EMP: 20
SQ FT: 2,691
SALES (est): 4.8MM **Privately Held**
WEB: www.filmetrix.com
SIC: 3826 Analytical optical instruments

(P-21960)
FLIR EOC LLC
Also Called: Flir Elctr-Ptcal Comp Bus Unit
2223 Eastman Ave Ste B, Ventura (93003-8050)
P.O. Box 6217 (93006-6217)
PHONE.................................805 642-4645
John Baumann, *General Mgr*
EMP: 30
SQ FT: 7,264

▲ = Import ▼=Export
◆ =Import/Export

SALES (est): 5.8MM
SALES (corp-wide): 1.8B **Publicly Held**
WEB: www.aeriusphotonics.com
SIC: **3826** Laser scientific & engineering instruments
PA: Flir Systems, Inc.
27700 Sw Parkway Ave
Wilsonville OR 97070
503 498-3547

(P-21961)
FULL SPECTRUM ANALYTICS INC (PA)
Also Called: FSA
1252 Quarry Ln, Pleasanton (94566-4756)
PHONE....................925 485-9000
Tom S Fider, *President*
Alan Chan, *CFO*
John Martin, *Treasurer*
Bill Bressan, *Regional Mgr*
Leslie Castillo, *Admin Asst*
EMP: 10
SQ FT: 5,000
SALES (est): 7.8MM **Privately Held**
WEB: www.fullspectrum-inc.com
SIC: **3826** Analytical instruments

(P-21962)
GENETIX USA INC
120 Baytech Dr, San Jose (95134-2302)
P.O. Box 528, Richmond IL (60071-0528)
PHONE....................408 719-6400
Mark Reid, *President*
Shenny Braemer, *Sales Executive*
▲ EMP: 18
SQ FT: 5,500
SALES (est): 2.9MM
SALES (corp-wide): 342.6K **Privately Held**
WEB: www.genetix.com
SIC: **3826** Analytical instruments
HQ: Launchchange Limited
19 Jessops Riverside
Sheffield
-

(P-21963)
HAMAX AMERICA INC (PA)
660 Baker St Ste 405s, Costa Mesa (92626-4411)
P.O. Box 3613, Laguna Hills (92654-3613)
PHONE....................714 641-7528
Takahira Hamada, *CEO*
▲ EMP: 10
SALES (est): 2.5MM **Privately Held**
SIC: **3826** 3452 Laser scientific & engineering instruments; bolts, nuts, rivets & washers

(P-21964)
HAMILTON SUNDSTRAND CORP
Applied Science Operation
2771 N Garey Ave, Pomona (91767-1809)
P.O. Box 2801 (91769-2801)
PHONE....................909 593-3581
Bob Hertel, *Branch Mgr*
Cory Hannegan, *Engineer*
Joel Harris, *Engineer*
Dr Robt Hertel, *Engineer*
Pie Ngov, *Engineer*
EMP: 240
SALES (corp-wide): 59.8B **Publicly Held**
WEB: www.hamilton-standard.com
SIC: **3826** 3861 3812 Spectrometers; cameras, still & motion picture (all types); search & navigation equipment
HQ: Hamilton Sundstrand Corporation
1 Hamilton Rd
Windsor Locks CT 06096
860 654-6000

(P-21965)
HI-Q ENVIRONMENTAL PDTS CO INC
7386 Trade St, San Diego (92121-2422)
PHONE....................858 549-2818
Marc A Held, *CEO*
Sherry Williams, *Office Mgr*
Nagaraj Ramakrishna, *Engineer*
▲ EMP: 12 EST: 1973
SQ FT: 5,000
SALES (est): 3MM **Privately Held**
WEB: www.hi-q.net
SIC: **3826** Analytical instruments

(P-21966)
HIGH SIERRA ELECTRONICS INC
155 Spring Hill Dr # 106, Grass Valley (95945-5929)
PHONE....................530 273-2080
James Logan, *CEO*
Ilse Gayl, *President*
Brian Loflin, *CFO*
EMP: 26
SQ FT: 9,100
SALES (est): 1MM **Privately Held**
SIC: **3826** 8748 8731 Environmental testing equipment; communications consulting; electronic research

(P-21967)
HITACHI HIGH-TECHNOLOGIES
20770 Nordhoff St, Chatsworth (91311-5900)
PHONE....................818 280-0745
Mark Kawamura, *CEO*
Mike Takahashi, *President*
Shaul Balkan, *Senior VP*
Peter Lee, *Info Tech Mgr*
Arlyn Ramirez, *Finance*
EMP: 17
SQ FT: 900
SALES (est): 4MM
SALES (corp-wide): 87.9B **Privately Held**
WEB: www.siintusa.com
SIC: **3826** Analytical instruments
HQ: Hitachi High-Tech Science Corporation
1-24-14, Nishishimbashi
Minato-Ku TKY 105-0
335 043-966

(P-21968)
HOEFER INC
760 National Ct, Richmond (94804-2008)
PHONE....................415 282-2307
Hugh Douglas, *COO*
Ron Miller, *Accounting Mgr*
John Kelly, *Prdtn Mgr*
▲ EMP: 30 EST: 1967
SQ FT: 30,000
SALES (est): 5.5MM **Publicly Held**
WEB: www.hoeferinc.com
SIC: **3826** Electrophoresis equipment
PA: Harvard Bioscience, Inc.
84 October Hill Rd Ste 10
Holliston MA 01746

(P-21969)
HORIBA INSTRUMENTS INC (DH)
Also Called: Horiba Automotive Test Systems
9755 Research Dr, Irvine (92618-4626)
PHONE....................949 250-4811
Jai Hakhu, *Ch of Bd*
Toshiya Higashino, *President*
▲ EMP: 195 EST: 1998
SQ FT: 80,000
SALES (est): 136.3MM
SALES (corp-wide): 1.7B **Privately Held**
WEB: www.horibalab.com
SIC: **3826** 3829 3511 3825 Analytical instruments; measuring & controlling devices; turbines & turbine generator sets; instruments to measure electricity; diagnostic equipment, medical; medical laboratory equipment; hospital equipment & supplies; physician equipment & supplies; industrial process measurement equipment
HQ: Horiba International Corp
9755 Research Dr
Irvine CA 92618
949 250-4811

(P-21970)
HYDROLYNX SYSTEMS INC
950 Riverside Pkwy Ste 10, West Sacramento (95605-1501)
PHONE....................916 374-1800
Kimberly A Blair, *President*
David Leader, *Vice Pres*
EMP: 10 EST: 1998
SQ FT: 7,000
SALES (est): 1.9MM **Privately Held**
WEB: www.hydrolynx.com
SIC: **3826** Environmental testing equipment

(P-21971)
ILLUMINA INC (PA)
5200 Illumina Way, San Diego (92122-4616)
PHONE....................858 202-4500
Francis A Desouza, *President*
Jay T Flatley, *Ch of Bd*
Sam A Samad, *CFO*
Aimee Hoyt, *Officer*
Mark Van Oene, *Officer*
▲ EMP: 277
SQ FT: 1,218,000
SALES (est): 2.7B **Publicly Held**
WEB: www.illumina.com
SIC: **3826** 3821 Analytical instruments; clinical laboratory instruments, except medical & dental

(P-21972)
ILLUMINA INC
200 Lincoln Centre Dr, Foster City (94404-1122)
PHONE....................510 670-9300
Mary Schramke, *Principal*
Susan Knowles, *Associate Dir*
Peter Lundberg, *CTO*
Abraham Mansir, *Technician*
Fiona Kaper, *Research*
EMP: 24
SALES (corp-wide): 2.7B **Publicly Held**
SIC: **3826** Analytical instruments
PA: Illumina, Inc.
5200 Illumina Way
San Diego CA 92122
858 202-4500

(P-21973)
ILLUMINA INC
9440 Carroll Park Dr # 100, San Diego (92121-5201)
PHONE....................858 202-4500
EMP: 216 EST: 2010
SALES (est): 25.6MM **Privately Held**
SIC: **3826** Analytical instruments

(P-21974)
ILLUMINA INC
9885 Towne Centre Dr, San Diego (92121-1975)
PHONE....................800 809-4566
William Rastetter, *Chairman*
Jeff Eidel, *Vice Pres*
Frank Lynch, *Associate Dir*
Kathleen Pierce, *Associate Dir*
Stacie Young, *Associate Dir*
EMP: 335
SALES (est): 30.1MM **Privately Held**
SIC: **3826** Analytical instruments

(P-21975)
INFRARED INDUSTRIES INC
25590 Seaboard Ln, Hayward (94545-3210)
PHONE....................510 782-8100
Mark Russell, *President*
Martha Rykala, *CFO*
▲ EMP: 10
SQ FT: 10,000
SALES (est): 1.8MM **Privately Held**
WEB: www.infraredindustries.com
SIC: **3826** Gas analyzing equipment

(P-21976)
INFRASTRUCTUREWORLD LLC
1001 Bayhill Dr Ste 200, San Bruno (94066-5902)
PHONE....................650 871-3950
Barbara L Treat, *Mng Member*
Cordell Hull,
EMP: 20
SALES (est): 1.6MM **Privately Held**
WEB: www.infrastructureworld.com
SIC: **3826**

(P-21977)
INTERGLOBAL WASTE MANAGEMENT
820 Calle Plano, Camarillo (93012-8557)
PHONE....................805 388-1588
Harold Katersky, *Ch of Bd*
Thomas Williams, *Shareholder*
Clay Causey, *Sales Staff*
Dwight Norris, *Sales Staff*
Tim O'Connell, *Sales Staff*
EMP: 80

SALES (est): 867.1K **Privately Held**
SIC: **3826** Analytical instruments

(P-21978)
INTERNTIONAL THERMAL INSTR INC
4511 Sun Valley Rd, Del Mar (92014-4114)
P.O. Box 309 (92014-0309)
PHONE....................858 755-4436
Norman D Greene, *General Mgr*
Derek Greene, *CEO*
Derek Loren, *Engineer*
EMP: 10
SQ FT: 5,000
SALES (est): 1.2MM **Privately Held**
WEB: www.iticompany.com
SIC: **3826** 5084 Instruments measuring thermal properties; instruments & control equipment

(P-21979)
J&M ANALYTIK AG
141 California St Apt G, Arcadia (91006-6528)
PHONE....................626 297-2930
Biplab Bhawal, *Sales Staff*
EMP: 26
SALES (est): 2.1MM **Privately Held**
SIC: **3826** Spectroscopic & other optical properties measuring equipment

(P-21980)
KETT
Also Called: Kett U S
9581 Featherhill Dr, Villa Park (92861-2633)
PHONE....................714 974-8837
John Bogart, *Managing Dir*
Mike Ragole, *Manager*
EMP: 12 EST: 1988
SQ FT: 10,000
SALES (est): 1.2MM **Privately Held**
WEB: www.kett.com
SIC: **3826** Analytical instruments

(P-21981)
LAB VISION CORPORATION (DH)
Also Called: Thermo Fisher Scientific
46500 Kato Rd, Fremont (94538-7310)
PHONE....................510 979-5000
Seth H Hoogasian, *CEO*
David Bespalko, *President*
Parisa Khosropour, *Vice Pres*
Jeremy Carter, *Research*
Puneet Suri, *Director*
▲ EMP: 10
SQ FT: 12,163
SALES (est): 733K
SALES (corp-wide): 20.9B **Publicly Held**
WEB: www.labvision.com
SIC: **3826** 3841 5122 Analytical instruments; diagnostic apparatus, medical; biologicals & allied products

(P-21982)
LAMBDA RESEARCH OPTICS INC
1695 Macarthur Blvd, Costa Mesa (92626-1440)
PHONE....................714 327-0600
Mark W Youn, *President*
Gina Youn, *Manager*
▲ EMP: 65
SQ FT: 3,500
SALES (est): 14MM **Privately Held**
SIC: **3826** 3827 3229 Laser scientific & engineering instruments; optical instruments & lenses; pressed & blown glass

(P-21983)
LIFE TECHNOLOGIES CORPORATION
500 Lincoln Centre Dr, Foster City (94404-1158)
PHONE....................760 603-7200
EMP: 115
SALES (corp-wide): 20.9B **Publicly Held**
SIC: **3826** Analytical instruments
HQ: Life Technologies Corporation
5781 Van Allen Way
Carlsbad CA 92008
760 603-7200

P R O D U C T S & S V C S

(P-21984)
MAGNETIC INSIGHT INC
980 Atlantic Ave Ste 102, Alameda
(94501-1098)
PHONE................................510 291-1200
Anna Christensen, *CEO*
Daniel Hensley, *Partner*
Patrick Goodwill, *CTO*
Justin Konkle, *Research*
Christopher Reed, *Business Mgr*
EMP: 14 EST: 2012
SALES (est): 3.3MM **Privately Held**
SIC: 3826 Analytical instruments

(P-21985)
MAKO INDUSTRIES SC INC
1280 N Red Gum St, Anaheim
(92806-1820)
PHONE................................714 632-1400
John Tittelfitz, *CEO*
Gia Moy, *Administration*
▲ EMP: 39 EST: 2007
SALES (est): 9.4MM **Privately Held**
WEB: www.makoindustries.com
SIC: 3826 Environmental testing equipment

(P-21986)
MANTA INSTRUMENTS
6370 Lusk Blvd Ste F208, San Diego
(92121-2755)
PHONE................................858 449-5801
EMP: 10
SALES (est): 1.6MM **Privately Held**
SIC: 3826 Analytical instruments

(P-21987)
MARBIL INDUSTRIES INC
2201 N Glassell St, Orange (92865-2701)
PHONE................................714 974-4032
Allan V Thompson, *President*
William B Thomson Jr, *Shareholder*
EMP: 20
SQ FT: 10,000
SALES (est): 1.6MM **Privately Held**
SIC: 3826 Mass spectrometers

(P-21988)
**MARINE SPILL RESPONSE
CORP**
990 W Waterfront Dr, Eureka (95501-0173)
PHONE................................707 442-6087
EMP: 30
SALES (corp-wide): 113.9MM **Privately
Held**
SIC: 3826 Environmental testing equipment
PA: Marine Spill Response Corporation
220 Spring St Ste 500
Herndon VA 20170
703 326-5600

(P-21989)
MARKES INTERNATIONAL INC
Also Called: Alms Company
2355 Gold Meadow Way # 120, Gold River
(95670-6365)
PHONE................................513 745-0241
Elizabeth Woolfenden, *Director*
Alun Cole, *Director*
EMP: 100
SALES: 1MM **Privately Held**
SIC: 3826 Analytical instruments

(P-21990)
MEANS ENGINEERING INC
5927 Geiger Ct, Carlsbad (92008-7305)
PHONE................................760 931-9452
David William Means, *CEO*
Richard Howard, *Partner*
Lisa Means, *Exec VP*
Rick Crook, *Program Mgr*
Jamey Korff, *Manager*
EMP: 70
SQ FT: 34,000
SALES (est): 19.6MM **Privately Held**
WEB: www.meanseng.com
SIC: 3826 3699 3559 Analytical instruments; electrical equipment & supplies; semiconductor manufacturing machinery

(P-21991)
**MESOTECH INTERNATIONAL
INC**
4531 Harlin Dr, Sacramento (95826-9716)
PHONE................................916 368-2020
Michael Lydon, *President*
Christopher Swinehart, *Program Mgr*
Johnathan Walters, *Project Engr*
Adrian Vidrio, *Electrical Engi*
Craig Daniel, *Engineer*
EMP: 14
SALES (est): 3.3MM **Privately Held**
WEB: www.mesotech.com
SIC: 3826 Analytical instruments

(P-21992)
METAL ETCH SERVICES INC
1165 Linda Vista Dr # 106, San Marcos
(92078-3821)
PHONE................................760 510-9476
Elias Malfavor Jr, *President*
Carlos Dugay, *Natl Sales Mgr*
EMP: 20
SALES (est): 3.5MM **Privately Held**
WEB: metaletchservices.com
SIC: 3826 3951 3479 Laser scientific & engineering instruments; pens & mechanical pencils; etching on metals

(P-21993)
METROLASER INC
22941 Mill Creek Dr, Laguna Hills
(92653-1215)
PHONE................................949 553-0688
Cecil Hess, *Founder*
Thomas Jenkins, *President*
Cecil F Hess, *CEO*
James Trolinger, *Vice Pres*
Regis Morgan, *Technician*
EMP: 10
SQ FT: 8,157
SALES: 2.9MM **Privately Held**
WEB: www.metrolaserinc.com
SIC: 3826 8731 Laser scientific & engineering instruments; commercial physical research

(P-21994)
MICRO-TECH SCIENTIFIC INC
Also Called: Microtech Scientific
3059 Palm Hill Dr, Vista (92084-6555)
PHONE................................760 597-9088
Frank J Yang, *President*
May Yang, *CFO*
Calvin Yang, *Enginr/R&D Mgr*
Jason Campbell, *Sales/Mktg Dir*
Yi-Yeah Tseng, *Director*
▲ EMP: 16
SQ FT: 21,100
SALES (est): 3MM **Privately Held**
WEB: www.micro-tech.us
SIC: 3826 3841

(P-21995)
MK DIGITAL DIRECT INC
Also Called: or Technology
861 Harold Pl Ste 209, Chula Vista
(91914-4555)
PHONE................................619 661-0628
◆ EMP: 10
SQ FT: 5,600
SALES (est): 2MM **Privately Held**
SIC: 3826

(P-21996)
**MOLECULAR DEVICES LLC
(HQ)**
3860 N 1st St, San Jose (95134-1702)
PHONE................................408 747-1700
Kevin Chance, *President*
Jim Duff, *COO*
Susan Murphy, *Vice Pres*
Poonam Taneja, *Vice Pres*
Shawn Laymon, *General Mgr*
▲ EMP: 125
SALES (est): 149.2MM
SALES (corp-wide): 18.3B **Publicly Held**
WEB: www.moleculardevices.com
SIC: 3826 3841 Analytical instruments; surgical & medical instruments
PA: Danaher Corporation
2200 Penn Ave Nw Ste 800w
Washington DC 20037
202 828-0850

(P-21997)
MOTIONLOFT INC
550 15th St Ste 29, San Francisco
(94103-5032)
PHONE................................415 580-7671
Joyce Reitman, *CEO*
Dan Daogaru, *President*
Chris Garrison, *VP Sales*
Dan Flynn, *Sales Associate*
Daniel Malak, *Sales Associate*
EMP: 39
SALES (est): 8.7MM **Privately Held**
SIC: 3826 7372 Analytical instruments; application computer software; business oriented computer software

(P-21998)
NANOIMAGING SERVICES INC
4940 Carroll Canyon Rd # 115, San Diego
(92121-1735)
PHONE................................888 675-8261
Clinton S Potter, *President*
EMP: 14
SALES (est): 1MM **Privately Held**
SIC: 3826 Microscopes, electron & proton

(P-21999)
NANOVEA INC (PA)
6 Morgan Ste 156, Irvine (92618-1922)
PHONE................................949 461-9292
Pierre Leroux, *President*
Marina Wessa, *Office Admin*
Jeff Tomita, *Info Tech Mgr*
Tim Palermo, *Engineer*
Tim Van Lingen, *Opers Mgr*
EMP: 14
SALES (est): 2.6MM **Privately Held**
SIC: 3826 Analytical instruments

(P-22000)
NEONODE INC (PA)
2880 Zanker Rd, San Jose (95134-2117)
PHONE................................408 496-6722
Thomas Eriksson, *President*
Per Bystedt, *Ch of Bd*
Ulf Martensson, *COO*
Lars Lindqvist, *CFO*
Andreas Bunge, *Bd of Directors*
EMP: 60
SQ FT: 6,508
SALES: 10.2MM **Publicly Held**
SIC: 3826 Infrared analytical instruments

(P-22001)
**OXFORD INSTRS ASYLUM RES
INC (HQ)**
6310 Hollister Ave, Santa Barbara
(93117-3115)
PHONE................................805 696-6466
Jason Cleveland, *CEO*
John Green, *President*
Roger Proksch, *President*
Richard Clark, *CFO*
Dick Clark, *Exec VP*
EMP: 55
SALES (est): 8.6MM
SALES (corp-wide): 415.9MM **Privately
Held**
SIC: 3826 Analytical instruments
PA: Oxford Instruments Plc
Tubney Woods
Abingdon OXON OX13
186 539-3200

(P-22002)
**PACIFIC BIOSCIENCES CAL INC
(PA)**
1305 Obrien Dr, Menlo Park (94025-1445)
PHONE................................650 521-8000
Michael Hunkapiller, *CEO*
Susan K Barnes, *CFO*
Kathy Ordonez, *Ch Credit Ofcr*
David Botstein, *Bd of Directors*
Brook H Byers, *Bd of Directors*
EMP: 268
SQ FT: 186,000
SALES: 93.4MM **Publicly Held**
WEB: www.nanofluidics.com
SIC: 3826 Analytical instruments

(P-22003)
PHENOMENEX INC (HQ)
411 Madrid Ave, Torrance (90501-1430)
PHONE................................310 212-0555
Farshad Mahjoor, *President*

Frank T McFaden, *CFO*
Lars Torstensson, *Business Dir*
Alex Gharagozlow, *Exec Dir*
Luke Steece, *District Mgr*
▲ EMP: 250
SQ FT: 100,000
SALES (est): 120.1MM
SALES (corp-wide): 18.3B **Publicly Held**
WEB: www.phenomenex.com
SIC: 3826 Analytical instruments
PA: Danaher Corporation
2200 Penn Ave Nw Ste 800w
Washington DC 20037
202 828-0850

(P-22004)
PHYNEXUS INC
3670 Charter Park Dr B, San Jose
(95136-1396)
PHONE................................408 267-7214
Douglas Gjerde, *CEO*
Sue Kalman, *Owner*
Tiffany Nguyen, *Vice Pres*
JAS Stout, *Administration*
Jonathan Grambow, *Research*
EMP: 10
SQ FT: 10,000
SALES (est): 2.3MM **Privately Held**
WEB: www.phynexus.com
SIC: 3826 Analytical instruments

(P-22005)
PICARRO INC (PA)
3105 Patrick Henry Dr, Santa Clara
(95054-1815)
PHONE................................408 962-3900
Alex Balkanski, *President*
Laura Perrone, *CFO*
Brenda Glaze, *Senior VP*
Jan Willem Poelmann, *Senior VP*
Jean Berthold, *Vice Pres*
EMP: 24
SQ FT: 15,250
SALES (est): 8.6MM **Privately Held**
WEB: www.picarro.com
SIC: 3826 Analytical instruments

(P-22006)
PIXON IMAGING INC
Also Called: Pixonimaging
4930 Longford St, San Diego (92117-2156)
PHONE................................858 352-0100
Chiyoko Lord, *Vice Pres*
EMP: 25
SALES: 950K **Privately Held**
SIC: 3826 Magnetic resonance imaging apparatus

(P-22007)
**PROFESSIONAL IMAGING SVCS
INC**
Also Called: Pro Imaging
1548 Jayken Way Ste C, Chula Vista
(91911-7142)
PHONE................................858 565-4217
Steven Richard Ford, *President*
Anne Ford, *Shareholder*
EMP: 10
SQ FT: 4,000
SALES: 1.2MM **Privately Held**
WEB: www.proimagingservices.com
SIC: 3826 8742 Magnetic resonance imaging apparatus; hospital & health services consultant

(P-22008)
Q CORPORATION
4880 Adohr Ln, Camarillo (93012-8508)
PHONE................................805 383-8998
Margaret Negri, *President*
James Topp, *CEO*
Wayne Hopkins, *CFO*
Stanton Ens, *Admin Sec*
Stephanie Blood, *Manager*
▲ EMP: 48
SQ FT: 22,000
SALES (est): 17MM **Privately Held**
WEB: www.theqcorporation.net
SIC: 3826 Environmental testing equipment

(P-22009)
QUANTUM DESIGN INC (PA)
Also Called: Quantum Design International
10307 Pacific Center Ct, San Diego
(92121-4340)
PHONE..................................858 481-4400
Greg Degeller, *President*
Martin Kugler, *COO*
David Schultz, *CFO*
Michael B Simmonds, *Vice Pres*
▲ EMP: 217
SQ FT: 118,000
SALES (est): 41.5MM **Privately Held**
WEB: www.qdusa.com
SIC: 3826 Laser scientific & engineering
instruments

(P-22010)
QUEST DIAGNOSTICS NICHOLS INST (HQ)
33608 Ortega Hwy, San Juan Capistrano
(92675-2042)
PHONE..................................949 728-4000
Catherine T Doherty, *CEO*
Nicholas Conti, *Vice Pres*
Timothy Sharpe, *Vice Pres*
Dan Haemmerle, *Exec Dir*
Michael Caulfield, *Research*
EMP: 1000
SQ FT: 240,000
SALES (est): 218.9MM
SALES (corp-wide): 7.7B **Publicly Held**
WEB: www.nicholsinstitute.com
SIC: 3826 8071 Analytical instruments;
testing laboratories
PA: Quest Diagnostics Incorporated
500 Plaza Dr Ste G
Secaucus NJ 07094
973 520-2700

(P-22011)
RS TECHNICAL SERVICES INC (PA)
1327 Clegg St, Petaluma (94954-1126)
P.O. Box 750579 (94975-0579)
PHONE..................................707 778-1974
Michael Sutliff, *Principal*
Michael W Sutliff, *CEO*
Kathey Sutliff, *Admin Sec*
Kyle Chandler, *Opers Staff*
EMP: 88
SQ FT: 15,000
SALES (est): 13.2MM **Privately Held**
WEB: www.rstechserv.com
SIC: 3826 3823 Sewage testing apparatus; industrial instrmnts msrmnt
display/control process variable

(P-22012)
RTEC-INSTRUMENTS INC
1810 Oakland Rd Ste B, San Jose
(95131-2316)
PHONE..................................408 456-0801
Vishal Khosla, *CEO*
Gautam Char, *Vice Pres*
Nick DOE, *Vice Pres*
Jun Xiao, *Vice Pres*
Ming Chan, *Engineer*
EMP: 25
SQ FT: 3,000
SALES (est): 6.5MM **Privately Held**
SIC: 3826 Analytical instruments

(P-22013)
SAGE METERING INC
8 Harris Ct Ste D1, Monterey (93940-5716)
PHONE..................................831 242-2030
Robert Steinberg, *President*
David Huey, *CFO*
Myrna Hartnett, *Office Mgr*
Jorge Morales, *Engineer*
Gary Russell, *Engineer*
▲ EMP: 10
SQ FT: 2,400
SALES (est): 2.3MM **Privately Held**
WEB: www.sagemetering.com
SIC: 3826 Instruments measuring thermal
properties

(P-22014)
SCI INSTRUMENTS INC (PA)
6355 Corte Del Abeto C105, Carlsbad
(92011-1443)
PHONE..................................760 634-3822
Emad S Zawaideh, *President*

EMP: 12
SQ FT: 4,000
SALES: 10MM **Privately Held**
WEB: www.sci-soft.com
SIC: 3826 Laser scientific & engineering
instruments

(P-22015)
SCREENING SYSTEMS INC (PA)
36 Blackbird Ln, Aliso Viejo (92656-1765)
P.O. Box 3931, Laguna Hills (92654-3931)
PHONE..................................949 855-1751
Susan L Baker, *President*
Susan Baker, *CFO*
Peter Baker, *Consultant*
EMP: 25
SQ FT: 34,000
SALES (est): 3.6MM **Privately Held**
WEB: www.scrsys.com
SIC: 3826 3829 Environmental testing
equipment; measuring & controlling devices

(P-22016)
SE-IR CORPORATION
87 Santa Felicia Dr, Goleta (93117-2804)
P.O. Box 60656, Santa Barbara (93160-0656)
PHONE..................................805 571-6800
Gregory Pierce, *CEO*
Susan Stegall, *Treasurer*
EMP: 10
SQ FT: 4,500
SALES: 1,000K **Privately Held**
WEB: www.seir.com
SIC: 3826 7699 Infrared analytical instruments; industrial equipment services

(P-22017)
SEPRAGEN CORPORATION
1205 San Luis Obispo St, Hayward
(94544-7915)
PHONE..................................510 475-0650
Vinit Saxena, *Ch of Bd*
Henry N Edmunds, *CFO*
EMP: 28
SQ FT: 23,000
SALES (est): 5.9MM **Privately Held**
WEB: www.sepragen.com
SIC: 3826 Liquid chromatographic instruments

(P-22018)
SHORE WESTERN MANUFACTURING
225 W Duarte Rd, Monrovia (91016-4545)
PHONE..................................626 357-3251
Donald Schroeder, *President*
Alice Schroeder, *Corp Secy*
Joe Schroeder, *Vice Pres*
Belinda Frederick, *IT/INT Sup*
Matthew Schroeder, *Engineer*
▲ EMP: 34 EST: 1967
SQ FT: 16,000
SALES: 5MM **Privately Held**
WEB: www.shorewestern.com
SIC: 3826 Environmental testing equipment

(P-22019)
SMITHS DETECTION LLC
1251 E Dyer Rd Ste 140, Santa Ana
(92705-5677)
PHONE..................................714 258-4400
Karen Bomba, *CEO*
Chris Le, *General Mgr*
George Syage, *Technician*
Chris McBee, *Manager*
EMP: 609
SALES (corp-wide): 650.9MM **Privately Held**
SIC: 3826 3812 Magnetic resonance imaging apparatus; search & navigation
equipment
HQ: Smiths Detection, Llc
7151 Gateway Blvd
Newark CA 94560
510 739-2400

(P-22020)
SPECTRASENSORS INC
11027 Arrow Rte, Rancho Cucamonga
(91730-4866)
PHONE..................................909 980-4238
Jeffrey Immelt, *CFO*
EMP: 24

SALES (corp-wide): 2.6B **Privately Held**
SIC: 3826 Analytical instruments
HQ: Spectrasensors, Inc.
4333 W Sam Houston Pkwy N
Houston TX 77043
713 466-3172

(P-22021)
SPRITE INDUSTRIES INCORPORATED
Also Called: Sprite Showers
1791 Railroad St, Corona (92880-2511)
PHONE..................................951 735-1015
David K Farley, *President*
Kathleen Farley, *Vice Pres*
Doris Farley, *Admin Sec*
Kathy Farley, *Human Res Mgr*
Sherry Farley, *VP Sales*
▲ EMP: 20 EST: 1974
SQ FT: 25,000
SALES (est): 3.9MM **Privately Held**
WEB: www.spritewater.com
SIC: 3826 3589 Water testing apparatus;
water filters & softeners, household type

(P-22022)
STANFORD RESEARCH SYSTEMS INC
Also Called: SRS
1290 Reamwood Ave Ste D, Sunnyvale
(94089-2279)
PHONE..................................408 744-9040
William R Green, *President*
John Willison, *Vice Pres*
Dave Ames, *Executive*
Alex Chen, *Design Engr*
Matt Kowitt, *Project Mgr*
EMP: 140
SQ FT: 20,000
SALES (est): 49.9MM **Privately Held**
WEB: www.srsys.com
SIC: 3826 Analytical instruments

(P-22023)
SYAGEN TECHNOLOGY LLC
1251 E Dyer Rd Ste 140, Santa Ana
(92705-5677)
PHONE..................................714 258-4400
Karen Bomba,
EMP: 20
SQ FT: 5,000
SALES (est): 3.9MM
SALES (corp-wide): 650.9MM **Privately Held**
WEB: www.syagen.com
SIC: 3826 Analytical instruments
HQ: Smiths Detection, Llc
7151 Gateway Blvd
Newark CA 94560
510 739-2400

(P-22024)
TALIS BIOMEDICAL CORPORATION
230 Constitution Dr, Menlo Park
(94025-1109)
PHONE..................................650 433-3000
Martin Goldberg, *Branch Mgr*
EMP: 48 **Privately Held**
SIC: 3826 Analytical instruments
PA: Talis Biomedical Corporation
125 S Clark St Fl 17
Chicago IL 60603

(P-22025)
TEAM CHINA CALIFORNIA LLC
3138 Madeira Ave, Costa Mesa
(92626-2324)
PHONE..................................714 424-9999
Patrick Mulcahy,
EMP: 12
SALES: 2MM **Privately Held**
WEB: www.teamchinausa.com
SIC: 3826 8731 Environmental testing
equipment; environmental research

(P-22026)
TECHCOMP (USA) INC
Also Called: Scion Instruments
3500 W Warren Ave, Fremont
(94538-6499)
PHONE..................................510 683-4300
Chris O'Connor, *CEO*
James O'Connor, *Principal*

EMP: 24
SQ FT: 17,000
SALES (est): 4.1MM **Privately Held**
SIC: 3826 7371 Analytical instruments;
computer software development & applications
PA: Techcomp (Europe) Limited
Lake House Market Hill
Royston HERTS
-

(P-22027)
TELEDYNE INSTRUMENTS INC
Teledyne Hanson Research
9810 Variel Ave, Chatsworth (91311-4316)
PHONE..................................818 882-7266
Thomas Reslewic, *Branch Mgr*
EMP: 31
SALES (corp-wide): 2.6B **Publicly Held**
SIC: 3826 Analytical instruments
HQ: Teledyne Instruments, Inc.
1049 Camino Dos Rios
Thousand Oaks CA 91360
805 373-4545

(P-22028)
TERUMO AMERICAS HOLDING INC
Also Called: Cardiovascular Systems
1311 Valencia Ave, Tustin (92780-6447)
PHONE..................................714 258-8001
Kevin Hoffman, *Branch Mgr*
Charlie Noel, *Vice Pres*
Sean Hylton, *Sales Staff*
EMP: 117
SALES (corp-wide): 5.5B **Privately Held**
WEB: www.terumomedical.com
SIC: 3826 Hemoglobinometers; gas analyzing equipment
HQ: Terumo Americas Holding, Inc.
2101 Cottontail Ln
Somerset NJ 08873
732 302-4900

(P-22029)
TETRA TECH EC INC
17885 Von Karman Ave # 500, Irvine
(92614-5227)
PHONE..................................949 809-5000
Andrew Brack, *Branch Mgr*
EMP: 49
SALES (corp-wide): 2.7B **Publicly Held**
SIC: 3826 Environmental testing equipment
HQ: Tetra Tech Ec, Inc.
6 Century Dr Ste 3
Parsippany NJ 07054
973 630-8000

(P-22030)
THERMO FINNIGAN LLC (HQ)
355 River Oaks Pkwy, San Jose
(95134-1908)
PHONE..................................408 965-6000
Anthony H Smith, *Mng Member*
Jonathan C Wilk,
▲ EMP: 500
SALES (est): 82.1MM
SALES (corp-wide): 20.9B **Publicly Held**
SIC: 3826 Analytical instruments
PA: Thermo Fisher Scientific Inc.
168 3rd Ave
Waltham MA 02451
781 622-1000

(P-22031)
THERMO FISCHER SCIENTIFIC INC
22801 Roscoe Blvd, West Hills
(91304-3200)
PHONE..................................747 494-1413
EMP: 11
SALES (est): 1.7MM **Privately Held**
SIC: 3826 Analytical instruments

(P-22032)
THERMO FISHER SCIENTIFIC
3380 Central Expy, Santa Clara
(95051-0704)
PHONE..................................408 731-5056
Jake Chen, *Info Tech Dir*
James Dubey, *Info Tech Dir*
Surapaneni Padmaja, *Info Tech Dir*
Tina Chen, *Research*
Vicky Huynh, *Research*
EMP: 29

SALES (est): 2.2MM **Privately Held**
SIC: 3826 Analytical instruments

(P-22033)
THERMO FISHER SCIENTIFIC
Also Called: Thermofinnegan
355 River Oaks Pkwy, San Jose
(95134-1908)
P.O. Box 49031 (95161)
PHONE..................408 894-9835
Ian Jardin, *Branch Mgr*
King Poon, *President*
Kenneth Apicerno, *Vice Pres*
Herb Kenny, *Vice Pres*
Viatcheslav Kovtoun, *Research*
EMP: 400
SALES (corp-wide): 20.9B **Publicly Held**
WEB: www.thermo.com
SIC: 3826 Analytical instruments
HQ: Thermo Fisher Scientific (Ashville) Llc
28 Schenck Pkwy Ste 400
Asheville NC 28803
828 658-2711

(P-22034)
THERMO FISHER SCIENTIFIC INC
15982 San Antonio Ave, Chino (91710)
PHONE..................909 393-3205
Claudia Groebner, *Branch Mgr*
EMP: 307
SALES (corp-wide): 20.9B **Publicly Held**
SIC: 3826 Thermal analysis instruments, laboratory type
PA: Thermo Fisher Scientific Inc.
168 3rd Ave
Waltham MA 02451
781 622-1000

(P-22035)
THERMO FISHER SCIENTIFIC INC
422 Aldo Ave, Santa Clara (95054-2301)
PHONE..................408 988-1103
Jessie Hernandez, *Principal*
Dave Sparling, *President*
▲ **EMP:** 14 **EST:** 2010
SALES (est): 4.6MM **Privately Held**
SIC: 3826 Analytical instruments

(P-22036)
THERMO FISHER SCIENTIFIC INC
675 S Sierra Ave, Solana Beach (92075-3200)
PHONE..................858 481-6386
Wes Woll, *Principal*
EMP: 307
SALES (corp-wide): 20.9B **Publicly Held**
SIC: 3826 Analytical instruments
PA: Thermo Fisher Scientific Inc.
168 3rd Ave
Waltham MA 02451
781 622-1000

(P-22037)
THERMO FISHER SCIENTIFIC INC
200 Oyster Point Blvd, South San Francisco (94080-1911)
PHONE..................650 876-1949
Ernest Hardy, *Branch Mgr*
EMP: 54
SALES (corp-wide): 20.9B **Publicly Held**
SIC: 3826 Analytical instruments
PA: Thermo Fisher Scientific Inc.
168 3rd Ave
Waltham MA 02451
781 622-1000

(P-22038)
THERMO FISHER SCIENTIFIC INC
46500 Kato Rd, Fremont (94538-7310)
PHONE..................510 979-5000
EMP: 22
SALES (corp-wide): 20.9B **Publicly Held**
SIC: 3826 Analytical instruments
PA: Thermo Fisher Scientific Inc.
168 3rd Ave
Waltham MA 02451
781 622-1000

(P-22039)
THERMO FISHER SCIENTIFIC INC
180 Oyster Point Blvd, South San Francisco (94080-1909)
PHONE..................650 246-5265
Kelly LI, *Research*
Darryl Len, *Director*
Andrew Velasquez, *Manager*
EMP: 17
SALES (corp-wide): 20.9B **Publicly Held**
SIC: 3826 Environmental testing equipment
PA: Thermo Fisher Scientific Inc.
168 3rd Ave
Waltham MA 02451
781 622-1000

(P-22040)
THERMO FISHER SCIENTIFIC INC
9389 Waples St, San Diego (92121-3903)
PHONE..................858 453-7551
Cesar Ramiriz, *Manager*
EMP: 10
SALES (corp-wide): 20.9B **Publicly Held**
SIC: 3826 Analytical instruments
PA: Thermo Fisher Scientific Inc.
168 3rd Ave
Waltham MA 02451
781 622-1000

(P-22041)
THERMO FISHER SCIENTIFIC INC
7000 Shoreline Ct, South San Francisco (94080-1945)
PHONE..................650 638-6409
EMP: 250
SALES (corp-wide): 20.9B **Publicly Held**
SIC: 3826 3845 3823 Analytical instruments; electromedical equipment; industrial instrmnts msrmnt display/control process variable
PA: Thermo Fisher Scientific Inc.
168 3rd Ave
Waltham MA 02451
781 622-1000

(P-22042)
THERMO FISHER SCIENTIFIC INC
46500 Kato Rd, Fremont (94538-7310)
PHONE..................317 490-5809
EMP: 17
SALES (corp-wide): 20.9B **Publicly Held**
SIC: 3826 Environmental testing equipment
PA: Thermo Fisher Scientific Inc.
168 3rd Ave
Waltham MA 02451
781 622-1000

(P-22043)
THERMO FISHER SCIENTIFIC INC
10010 Mesa Rim Rd, San Diego (92121-2912)
PHONE..................858 882-1286
Anand Shirur, *Branch Mgr*
Richard Leathers, *Info Tech Mgr*
Eric Empey, *Manager*
EMP: 14
SALES (corp-wide): 20.9B **Publicly Held**
WEB: www.thermo.com
SIC: 3826 Analytical instruments
PA: Thermo Fisher Scientific Inc.
168 3rd Ave
Waltham MA 02451
781 622-1000

(P-22044)
THERMOQUEST CORPORATION
355 River Oaks Pkwy, San Jose (95134-1908)
P.O. Box 49031 (95161-9031)
PHONE..................408 965-6000
EMP: 1215
SALES: 431.8MM
SALES (corp-wide): 16.9B **Publicly Held**
SIC: 3826 3823
PA: Thermo Fisher Scientific Inc.
168 3rd Ave
Waltham MA 02451
781 622-1000

(P-22045)
TURNER DESIGNS INC
1995 N 1st St, San Jose (95112-4220)
PHONE..................408 749-0994
Jim Crawford, *President*
EMP: 45 **EST:** 1972
SQ FT: 20,000
SALES (est): 10.6MM **Privately Held**
WEB: www.turnerdesigns.com
SIC: 3826 Analytical instruments

(P-22046)
UNITED STATES THERMOELECTRIC
Also Called: Ustc
13267 Contractors Dr, Chico (95973-8851)
PHONE..................530 345-8000
James M Kerner, *President*
▲ **EMP:** 30
SALES (est): 5.8MM **Privately Held**
WEB: www.ustechcon.com
SIC: 3826 3823 Thermal analysis instruments, laboratory type; industrial instrmnts msrmnt display/control process variable

(P-22047)
VEECO PROCESS EQUIPMENT INC
Also Called: Digital Instruments Div
112 Robin Hill Rd, Goleta (93117-3107)
PHONE..................805 967-1400
Don Kenia, *CEO*
Brent Nelson, *Executive*
Jojo Daof, *Manager*
Dan Shatynski, *Manager*
EMP: 190
SALES (corp-wide): 484.7MM **Publicly Held**
SIC: 3826 3827 Microscopes, electron & proton; optical instruments & lenses
HQ: Veeco Process Equipment Inc.
1 Terminal Dr
Plainview NY 11803

(P-22048)
W R GRACE & CO - CONN
Also Called: Grace Dvson Discovery Sciences
17434 Mojave St, Hesperia (92345-7611)
PHONE..................760 244-6107
Fred Festa, *Branch Mgr*
EMP: 100
SALES (corp-wide): 1.7B **Publicly Held**
WEB: www.chromatography.com
SIC: 3826 Chromatographic equipment, laboratory type
HQ: W. R. Grace & Co.-Conn.
7500 Grace Dr
Columbia MD 21044
410 531-4000

(P-22049)
WATERS TECHNOLOGIES CORP
18271 Mcdurmott St, Irvine (92614)
PHONE..................949 474-4320
Bobette Frye, *Branch Mgr*
EMP: 10 **Publicly Held**
SIC: 3826 3829 7371 7372 Chromatographic equipment, laboratory type; spectrometers, liquid scintillation & nuclear; computer software systems analysis & design, custom; computer software development; prepackaged software
HQ: Waters Technologies Corporation,
34 Maple St
Milford MA 01757
508 478-2000

(P-22050)
WYATT TECHNOLOGY CORPORATION (PA)
6330 Hollister Ave, Goleta (93117-3115)
PHONE..................805 681-9009
Philip J Wyatt, *CEO*
Clifford D Wyatt, *President*
Geofrey K Wyatt, *President*
Carolyn Walton, *CFO*
EMP: 120
SQ FT: 30,000
SALES (est): 33.6MM **Privately Held**
WEB: www.mals.com
SIC: 3826 Laser scientific & engineering instruments

(P-22051)
XIA LLC
31057 Genstar Rd, Hayward (94544-7831)
PHONE..................510 494-9020
William K Warburton,
Karl Meyer, *General Mgr*
Nicole Thomas, *Admin Asst*
Brendan McNally, *Engineer*
Mark Walby, *Senior Engr*
EMP: 18
SQ FT: 8,000
SALES (est): 3.3MM **Privately Held**
WEB: www.xia.com
SIC: 3826 Analytical instruments

(P-22052)
YSI INCORPORATED
Also Called: Yellow Springs Instruments
9940 Summers Ridge Rd, San Diego (92121-2997)
PHONE..................858 546-8327
Chris Ward, *Branch Mgr*
Zhivko Grozev, *Engineer*
EMP: 50 **Publicly Held**
WEB: www.sontek.com
SIC: 3826 3823 3841 Water testing apparatus; industrial instrmnts msrmnt display/control process variable; temperature measurement instruments, industrial; diagnostic apparatus, medical
HQ: Ysi Incorporated
1700 Brannum Ln 1725
Yellow Springs OH 45387
937 767-7241

(P-22053)
ZINSSER NA INC
19145 Parthenia St Ste C, Northridge (91324-5108)
PHONE..................818 341-2906
Clifford Olson, *President*
EMP: 10
SQ FT: 5,000
SALES (est): 1.6MM
SALES (corp-wide): 8.2MM **Privately Held**
WEB: www.zinsserna.com
SIC: 3826 Mass spectroscopy instrumentation
HQ: Zinsser Analytic Gesellschaft Mit Beschrankter Haftung
Schwalbacher Str. 62
Eschborn 65760
697 891-060

(P-22054)
ZYGO CORPORATION
1971 Milmont Dr, Milpitas (95035-2577)
PHONE..................408 434-1000
Robert Plozl, *Manager*
EMP: 30
SALES (corp-wide): 4.3B **Publicly Held**
WEB: www.zygo.com
SIC: 3826 3829 3827 Microscopes, electron & proton; measuring & controlling devices; optical instruments & lenses
HQ: Zygo Corporation
21 Laurel Brook Rd
Middlefield CT 06455
860 347-8506

3827 Optical Instruments

(P-22055)
AAREN SCIENTIFIC INC (DH)
Also Called: Carl Zeiss Meditec,
1040 S Vintage Ave Ste A, Ontario (91761-3631)
PHONE..................909 937-1033
Hans-Joachim Miesner, *President*
Stevens Chevillotte, *Treasurer*
Victor Garcia, *Vice Pres*
James Thornton, *Admin Sec*
Jan Willem De Cler, *Director*
▲ **EMP:** 70
SQ FT: 15,000
SALES (est): 26.7MM **Privately Held**
SIC: 3827 3851 Optical instruments & lenses; ophthalmic goods
HQ: Carl Zeiss Meditec, Inc.
5160 Hacienda Dr
Dublin CA 94568
925 557-4100

▲ = Import ▼=Export
◆ =Import/Export

(P-22056)
ABRISA TECHNOLOGIES
200 Hallock Dr, Santa Paula (93060-9646)
P.O. Box 489 (93061-0489)
PHONE....................805 525-4902
Blake Fennell, CEO
Maarten Oostendorp, CFO
Maartin Ostendorp, CFO
Susan Hirst, Vice Pres
Nathan Chambers, Program Mgr
EMP: 20
SALES (est): 3.2MM Privately Held
SIC: 3827 Optical instruments & lenses

(P-22057)
ADTECH PHOTONICS INC
Also Called: Adtech Optics
18007 Cortney Ct, City of Industry
(91748-1203)
PHONE....................626 956-1000
Mary Fong, CEO
Ed Ho, Vice Pres
Marvin Lee, Administration
Mary Quach, Administration
Ulisses Gamboa, Engineer
EMP: 25
SALES (est): 4.5MM Privately Held
SIC: 3827 Optical instruments & lenses

(P-22058)
ALLUXA INC
3660 N Laughlin Rd, Santa Rosa
(95403-1027)
PHONE....................707 284-1040
Mike Scobey, President
Jeff Johansen, Engineer
EMP: 36
SALES (est): 8.1MM Privately Held
SIC: 3827 Optical instruments & lenses

(P-22059)
APOLLO INSTRUMENTS INC
55 Peters Canyon Rd, Irvine (92606-1402)
PHONE....................949 756-3111
Alice Z Gheen, President
Peter Wang, Vice Pres
▲ EMP: 21
SALES (est): 3.5MM Privately Held
WEB: www.apolloinstruments.com
SIC: 3827 3822 Optical instruments &
lenses; auto controls regulating residntl &
coml environmt & applncs

(P-22060)
**BLUE SKY RESEARCH
INCORPORATED (PA)**
510 Alder Dr, Milpitas (95035-7443)
PHONE....................408 941-6068
Christopher Gladding, President
Sandip Basu, CFO
Joe Kulakofsky, Vice Pres
Charles Mackrodt, Sales Staff
Cara Prunty, Accounts Exec
EMP: 49
SQ FT: 21,000
SALES (est): 5.3MM Privately Held
SIC: 3827 3674 Lenses, optical: all types
except ophthalmic; semiconductors & re-
lated devices

(P-22061)
CARL ZEISS INC
Humphrey Systems
5160 Hacienda Dr, Dublin (94568-7315)
P.O. Box 8111, Pleasanton (94588-8711)
PHONE....................925 557-4100
Kieth Hunt, Manager
Kenny Patterson, Vice Pres
Derek Mernagh, General Mgr
Kathryn Benapfl, Executive Asst
David Swaw, Admin Asst
EMP: 40 Privately Held
SIC: 3827 3851 3845 3841 Optical test &
inspection equipment; ophthalmic goods;
electromedical equipment; surgical &
medical instruments
HQ: Carl Zeiss, Inc.
1 Zeiss Dr
Thornwood NY 10594
914 747-1800

(P-22062)
CARL ZEISS MEDITEC INC (DH)
5160 Hacienda Dr, Dublin (94568-7562)
P.O. Box 100372, Pasadena (91189-0003)
PHONE....................925 557-4100

James V Mazzo, President
Roberto Deger, CFO
Christine Randle, Chief Mktg Ofcr
Thomas Simmerer, Officer
Tom Fry, Vice Pres
▲ EMP: 277
SALES (est): 211.8MM Privately Held
SIC: 3827 Optical instruments & apparatus
HQ: Carl Zeiss Meditec Ag
Goschwitzer Str. 51-52
Jena 07745
364 122-00

(P-22063)
CARL ZEISS MEDITEC INC
5160 Hacienda Dr, Dublin (94568-7562)
PHONE....................858 716-0661
Carl Zeiss, Manager
EMP: 28 Privately Held
SIC: 3827 Optical instruments & lenses
HQ: Carl Zeiss Meditec, Inc.
5160 Hacienda Dr
Dublin CA 94568
925 557-4100

(P-22064)
**CASCADE OPTICAL COATING
INC**
1225 E Hunter Ave, Santa Ana
(92705-4131)
PHONE....................714 543-9777
Ken Romo, Vice Pres
Lawrence D Hundsdoerfer, President
Claudia J Hundsdoerfer, Corp Secy
EMP: 13
SQ FT: 8,500
SALES: 2.8MM Privately Held
WEB: www.c-optical.com
SIC: 3827 Lens coating equipment

(P-22065)
CELESTRON ACQUISITION LLC
2835 Columbia St, Torrance (90503-3877)
PHONE....................310 328-9560
Dave Anderson, CEO
Paul Roth, CFO
Corey Lee, Vice Pres
Sylvia Shen, Mng Member
▲ EMP: 77
SALES (est): 80MM Privately Held
WEB: www.celestron.com
SIC: 3827 Telescopes: elbow, panoramic,
sighting, fire control, etc.; lenses, optical:
all types except ophthalmic
HQ: Sw Technology Corporation
2835 Columbia St
Torrance CA 90503
310 328-9560

(P-22066)
CELESTRON LLC
2835 Columbia St, Torrance (90503-3877)
PHONE....................310 328-9560
Alan Hale, Chairman
EMP: 50 EST: 2014
SALES (est): 12.2MM Privately Held
SIC: 3827 Telescopes: elbow, panoramic,
sighting, fire control, etc.; lenses, optical:
all types except ophthalmic

(P-22067)
**CHEMICAL & MATERIAL
TECHNOLOGY**
Also Called: Cmt
229 Creekside Village Dr, Los Gatos
(95032-7351)
P.O. Box 2351 (95031-2351)
PHONE....................408 354-2656
William R Kraus, President
T W Ireland, Vice Pres
Joseph R Spaziani, Vice Pres
EMP: 25
SQ FT: 2,000
SALES (est): 2MM Privately Held
SIC: 3827 8741 3674 8742 Lenses, opti-
cal: all types except ophthalmic; manage-
ment services; semiconductors & related
devices; management consulting services

(P-22068)
CI SYSTEMS INC
759 Cochran St Ste A, Simi Valley
(93065-1978)
PHONE....................805 520-2233
Robert Buckwald, President
Dario Cabib, Vice Pres

Debbi Hwett, Admin Sec
Kim Browne, Administration
Garrick Matheson, Marketing Staff
▲ EMP: 10
SQ FT: 3,500
SALES (est): 2.1MM Privately Held
WEB: www.ci-systems.com
SIC: 3827 Optical test & inspection equip-
ment

(P-22069)
COLLIMATED HOLES INC
460 Division St, Campbell (95008-6923)
PHONE....................408 374-5080
Richard Mead, President
Dan Dickerson, Executive
EMP: 20
SQ FT: 11,600
SALES (est): 2.9MM Privately Held
WEB: www.collimatedholes.com
SIC: 3827 Optical instruments & appara-
tus; optical elements & assemblies, ex-
cept ophthalmic

(P-22070)
COMCORE TECHNOLOGIES INC
Also Called: Comcore Opcital Communication
48834 Kato Rd Ste 108a, Fremont
(94538-7368)
PHONE....................510 498-8858
Yong Huang, President
Heather Hu, Sales Mgr
EMP: 20
SQ FT: 22,000
SALES: 4MM Privately Held
SIC: 3827 Optical instruments & apparatus

(P-22071)
DELTRONIC CORPORATION
Also Called: Hi-Precision Grinding
3900 W Segerstrom Ave, Santa Ana
(92704-6312)
PHONE....................714 545-5800
Robert C Larzelere, President
Sterling Sander, CFO
Diane Larzelere, Admin Sec
▼ EMP: 73
SQ FT: 40,000
SALES (est): 16.1MM Privately Held
WEB: www.deltronic.com
SIC: 3827 3545 Optical comparators;
gauges (machine tool accessories)

(P-22072)
DI MAXX TECHNOLOGIES LLC
11838 Kemper Rd, Auburn (95603-9531)
P.O. Box 21810, Eugene OR (97402-0412)
PHONE....................530 888-1942
Leonard Mott,
Gary Debell,
Tony Louderback,
Ron Haynes, Manager
EMP: 16 EST: 2000
SALES (est): 2.9MM Privately Held
WEB: www.dimax.com
SIC: 3827 Optical instruments & lenses

(P-22073)
**DIELECTRIC COATING
INDUSTRIES**
Also Called: DCI
30997 Huntwood Ave # 104, Hayward
(94544-7041)
PHONE....................510 487-5980
Carmen Bischer Jr, President
Carmen Bischer Sr, Vice Pres
▲ EMP: 10
SQ FT: 8,000
SALES (est): 1.9MM Privately Held
SIC: 3827 Reflectors, optical

(P-22074)
DIGILENS INC
1288 Hammerwood Ave, Sunnyvale
(94089-2232)
PHONE....................408 734-0219
Christopher Pickett, CEO
Ratson Morad, COO
Michael Angel, CFO
Jonathan David Waldern, Chairman
Rick Santos, Vice Pres
EMP: 40
SQ FT: 15,000
SALES: 4MM Privately Held
SIC: 3827 Optical instruments & lenses

(P-22075)
ELECTRO OPTICAL INDUSTRIES
320 Storke Rd Ste 100, Goleta
(93117-2992)
PHONE....................805 964-6701
Stephen Scopatz, General Mgr
Thierry Campos, President
Maegan Piccolo, Admin Asst
Randy Trent, Design Engr
Mike Moschitto, Opers Mgr
EMP: 21
SALES (corp-wide): 4.9MM Privately
Held
SIC: 3827 Optical instruments & apparatus
PA: Electro Optical Industries, Inc
50 Milk St Fl 16
Boston MA 02109
617 401-2196

(P-22076)
FLEX PRODUCTS INC
1402 Mariner Way, Santa Rosa
(95407-7370)
PHONE....................707 525-6866
Michael B Sullivan, President
Joseph Zils, President
Mary Ellen King, IT/INT Sup
Dave New, Technician
Larry Mathis, Engineer
EMP: 225
SQ FT: 70,000
SALES (est): 30.8MM
SALES (corp-wide): 880.4MM Publicly
Held
WEB: www.flexrest.com
SIC: 3827 3081 Lens coating equipment;
unsupported plastics film & sheet
HQ: Optical Coating Laboratory, Llc
2789 Northpoint Pkwy
Santa Rosa CA 95407
707 545-6440

(P-22077)
FOREAL SPECTRUM INC
2370 Qume Dr Ste A, San Jose
(95131-1842)
PHONE....................408 923-1675
Anmin Zheng, CEO
Liang Zhou, President
Ronggui Shen, Vice Pres
Dan Cifelli, VP Sales
▲ EMP: 25
SALES (est): 5MM Privately Held
WEB: www.forealspectrum.com
SIC: 3827 Optical instruments & lenses

(P-22078)
GMTO CORPORATION
Also Called: Giant Mgllan Tlscope Orgnztnal
465 N Halstead St Ste 250, Pasadena
(91107-3226)
PHONE....................626 204-0500
Patrick McCarthy, President
Dr Robert N Shelton, President
Alan Gordon, CFO
Amy Honbo, Controller
▲ EMP: 70 EST: 2007
SQ FT: 40,000
SALES: 5.4MM Privately Held
WEB: www.gmto.org
SIC: 3827 Telescopes: elbow, panoramic,
sighting, fire control, etc.

(P-22079)
**GOOCH AND HOUSEGO CAL
LLC**
5390 Kazuko Ct, Moorpark (93021-1790)
PHONE....................805 529-3324
Kenneth Neczypor, Mng Member
Ken Kistner, QC Mgr
Kathy Sarna, Cust Mgr
Adam Morrow, Associate
EMP: 80
SALES (est): 13.7MM
SALES (corp-wide): 143.7MM Privately
Held
SIC: 3827 3823 Optical instruments &
lenses; industrial instrmnts msrmnt dis-
play/control process variable
PA: Gooch & Housego Plc
Dowlish Ford
Ilminster TA19
146 025-6440

(P-22080)
GUIDED WAVE INC
3033 Gold Canal Dr, Rancho Cordova
(95670-6129)
PHONE..................................916 638-4944
Susan Foulk, *CEO*
Don Goldman, *Vice Pres*
William Grooms, *Vice Pres*
Debra Hall, *Vice Pres*
James Low, *Info Tech Mgr*
EMP: 32
SQ FT: 15,000
SALES (est): 6.6MM **Privately Held**
WEB: www.guided-wave.com
SIC: 3827 Optical instruments & apparatus

(P-22081)
H SILANI & ASSOCIATES INC
Also Called: Supervision Eyewear Suppliers
210 S Robertson Blvd, Beverly Hills
(90211-2811)
PHONE..................................310 623-4848
Hossein Silani, *President*
EMP: 10
SQ FT: 1,300
SALES (est): 550K **Privately Held**
SIC: 3827 5995 Optical instruments &
lenses; optical goods stores; contact
lenses, prescription; eyeglasses, prescrip-
tion

(P-22082)
HOYA CORPORATION USA (DH)
680 N Mccarthy Blvd # 120, Milpitas
(95035-5120)
PHONE..................................408 492-1069
Hiroshi Suzuki, *Principal*
▲ EMP: 10
SQ FT: 1,000
SALES (est): 2.6MM
SALES (corp-wide): 5B **Privately Held**
WEB: www.hoyaoptics.com
SIC: 3827 Optical instruments & lenses
HQ: Hoya Holdings, Inc.
680 N Mccarthy Blvd # 120
Milpitas CA 95035
408 654-2300

(P-22083)
HOYA HOLDINGS INC
Hoya Corporation USA
425 E Huntington Dr, Monrovia
(91016-3632)
PHONE..................................626 739-5200
Al Benzoni, *Vice Pres*
EMP: 63
SALES (corp-wide): 5B **Privately Held**
WEB: www.hoyaholdings.com
SIC: 3827 Optical instruments & lenses
HQ: Hoya Holdings, Inc.
680 N Mccarthy Blvd # 120
Milpitas CA 95035
408 654-2300

(P-22084)
I-COAT COMPANY LLC
12020 Mora Dr Ste 2, Santa Fe Springs
(90670-6082)
PHONE..................................800 832-2628
Jack J Jue, *Mng Member*
Frances Peck, *Controller*
Allison Igawa, *Opers Staff*
Tom Pfeiffer, *Natl Sales Mgr*
Tim Stephen,
▲ EMP: 50
SQ FT: 6,000
SALES (est): 11.4MM **Privately Held**
WEB: www.icoatcompany.com
SIC: 3827 Optical instruments & lenses

(P-22085)
IDEX HEALTH & SCIENCE LLC
2051 Palomar Airpt Rd # 200, Carlsbad
(92011-1461)
PHONE..................................760 438-2131
Blake Fennell, *Branch Mgr*
Elizabeth Hernandez, *General Mgr*
Bill Butterfield, *Engineer*
Bill Papworth, *Engineer*
Jeanine Lopresti, *VP Human Res*
EMP: 184
SALES (corp-wide): 2.2B **Publicly Held**
SIC: 3827 3699 Optical instruments &
lenses; laser systems & equipment

HQ: Idex Health & Science Llc
600 Park Ct
Rohnert Park CA 94928
707 588-2000

(P-22086)
II-VI OPTICAL SYSTEMS INC
14192 Chambers Rd, Tustin (92780-6908)
PHONE..................................714 247-7100
Mark Maiberger, *General Mgr*
Scott Fleming, *Planning*
Tom Lange, *Business Anlyst*
David Hejny, *Project Engr*
Kent Weed, *Engineer*
EMP: 60
SALES (corp-wide): 1.1B **Publicly Held**
SIC: 3827 7389 8748 Optical instruments
& apparatus; design services; business
consulting
HQ: Ii-Vi Optical Systems, Inc.
36570 Briggs Rd
Murrieta CA 92563
951 926-2994

(P-22087)
INFINITE OPTICS INC
1712 Newport Cir Ste F, Santa Ana
(92705-5118)
PHONE..................................714 557-2299
Geza Keller, *President*
Daniel Houston, *Vice Pres*
Denise Banionis, *Principal*
Steven Crawford, *Principal*
Joseph Goodhand, *Principal*
EMP: 24
SQ FT: 12,860
SALES (est): 5MM **Privately Held**
WEB: www.infiniteoptics.com
SIC: 3827 Lens coating & grinding equip-
ment

(P-22088)
INNEOS LLC
5700 Stoneridge Dr # 200, Pleasanton
(94588-2897)
PHONE..................................925 226-0138
Brian C Peters, *CEO*
Eric Grann, *Vice Pres*
Stephannie Elliott, *Office Mgr*
Tony Woodward, *Design Engr*
Logan Stowe, *Electrical Engi*
EMP: 27
SALES (est): 8.9MM **Privately Held**
SIC: 3827 Optical elements & assemblies,
except ophthalmic

(P-22089)
INSCOPIX INC
2462 Embarcadero Way, Palo Alto
(94303-3313)
PHONE..................................650 600-3886
Kunal Ghosh, *President*
Shung Chieh, *Vice Pres*
Glenn Powell, *Vice Pres*
Michael Wycisk, *Engineer*
Leonila Gamboa, *Purchasing*
EMP: 15
SQ FT: 6,041
SALES (est): 4.5MM **Privately Held**
SIC: 3827 Microscopes, except electron,
proton & corneal

(P-22090)
INTEVAC PHOTONICS INC (HQ)
3560 Bassett St, Santa Clara (95054-2704)
PHONE..................................408 986-9888
Joseph Pietras III, *President*
Timothy Justyn, *Exec VP*
Albert Zecher, *General Mgr*
EMP: 17
SALES (est): 10.5MM
SALES (corp-wide): 112.8MM **Publicly
Held**
SIC: 3827 Optical instruments & lenses
PA: Intevac, Inc.
3560 Bassett St
Santa Clara CA 95054
408 986-9888

(P-22091)
INTEVAC PHOTONICS INC
Also Called: Intevac Vision Systems
5909 Sea Lion Pl Ste A, Carlsbad
(92010-6634)
PHONE..................................760 476-0339
Jerome Carollo, *General Mgr*

Michael Hoppe, *Info Tech Mgr*
EMP: 22
SALES (corp-wide): 112.8MM **Publicly
Held**
SIC: 3827 Optical instruments & lenses
HQ: Intevac Photonics, Inc.
3560 Bassett St
Santa Clara CA 95054

(P-22092)
IRCAMERA LLC
30 S Calle Cesar Chavez, Santa Barbara
(93103-5652)
PHONE..................................805 965-9650
Steve McHugh, *Mng Member*
Clareesa Stehmeier, *Controller*
Len Kamlet, *Manager*
EMP: 20
SALES (est): 4.7MM **Publicly Held**
SIC: 3827 3812 Optical test & inspection
equipment; infrared object detection
equipment
HQ: Santa Barbara Infrared, Inc.
30 S Calle Cesar Chavez D
Santa Barbara CA 93103
805 965-3669

(P-22093)
IT CONCEPTS LLC
1244 Quarry Ln Ste B, Pleasanton
(94566-4767)
PHONE..................................925 401-0010
Naum Pinkhasik, *Mng Member*
Sergey Perunov, *Mfg Staff*
Alla Balashov,
Inna Boyanzhu,
▼ EMP: 12
SQ FT: 9,000
SALES (est): 6.3MM **Privately Held**
SIC: 3827 Optical instruments & apparatus
PA: International Technology Concepts, Inc.
1244 Quarry Ln Ste B
Pleasanton CA 94566

(P-22094)
JIMS OPTICAL
Also Called: Jim & Lees Optical
5253 Jerusalem Ct Ste G, Modesto
(95356-9238)
PHONE..................................209 549-2517
Jim Lima, *Owner*
EMP: 11
SQ FT: 550
SALES (est): 1.2MM **Privately Held**
SIC: 3827 Optical instruments & lenses

(P-22095)
JOHNSON & JOHNSON
2501 Pullman St, Santa Ana (92705-5515)
PHONE..................................714 247-8200
James V Mazzo, *President*
Kathy Schiller, *Executive Asst*
Daniel Lang, *Engineer*
Robert Mijares, *Engineer*
An Nguyen, *Sales Staff*
EMP: 38
SALES (corp-wide): 76.4B **Publicly Held**
SIC: 3827 Optical instruments & lenses
HQ: Johnson & Johnson Surgical Vision,
Inc.
1700 E Saint Andrew Pl
Santa Ana CA 92705
714 247-8200

(P-22096)
KAMA-TECH CORPORATION
3451 Main St Ste 109, Chula Vista
(91911-5894)
PHONE..................................619 421-7858
Ichiro Kamakura, *President*
▲ EMP: 15
SALES (est): 5.1MM **Privately Held**
WEB: www.kazmisakata.com
SIC: 3827 Binoculars

(P-22097)
LENS TECHNOLOGY I LLC
Also Called: LTI
45 Parker Ste 100, Irvine (92618-1658)
PHONE..................................714 690-6470
John Quinn, *President*
Sung Tark, *Vice Pres*
John W Quinn III, *General Mgr*
Chandravad Patel, *Research*

Darren Crosby, *Engineer*
EMP: 16
SQ FT: 11,500
SALES (est): 4.6MM **Privately Held**
WEB: www.lenstech.com
SIC: 3827 5049 Lens coating equipment;
optical goods

(P-22098)
LIGHT LABS INC
636 Ramona St, Palo Alto (94301-2545)
PHONE..................................650 272-6942
Dave Grannan, *CEO*
Bradley Lautenbach, *Senior VP*
Prashant Velagaleti, *Vice Pres*
Rajiv Laroia, *CTO*
EMP: 78
SQ FT: 5,000
SALES (est): 27MM **Privately Held**
SIC: 3827 Optical instruments & lenses

(P-22099)
LIQWIZ LLC
5375 Black Ave Apt 1, Pleasanton
(94566-5962)
P.O. Box 1804 (94566-0180)
PHONE..................................925 285-3100
Mark Koziol, *Partner*
Ivan D Maleev,
EMP: 10
SALES (est): 567.6K **Privately Held**
SIC: 3827 Optical instruments & apparatus

(P-22100)
LUMENTUM OPERATIONS LLC
1750 Automation Pkwy # 400, San Jose
(95131-1873)
PHONE..................................408 546-5483
EMP: 19
SALES (corp-wide): 1.2B **Publicly Held**
SIC: 3827 5995 Optical instruments &
lenses; optical goods stores
HQ: Lumentum Operations Llc
400 N Mccarthy Blvd
Milpitas CA 95035
408 546-5483

(P-22101)
LUMINIT LLC
1850 W 205th St, Torrance (90501-1526)
PHONE..................................310 320-1066
Engin Arik,
Seth Coe-Sullivan, *President*
Ed Kaiser, *Vice Pres*
Leo Katsenelenson, *Vice Pres*
Karma Burns, *Executive Asst*
▲ EMP: 42
SALES (est): 11.7MM **Privately Held**
WEB: www.luminit.com
SIC: 3827 Optical instruments & lenses

(P-22102)
**MACHINE VISION PRODUCTS
INC (PA)**
3270 Corporate Vw Ste D, Vista
(92081-8570)
PHONE..................................760 438-1138
George T Ayoub, *CEO*
▲ EMP: 73
SQ FT: 60,000
SALES (est): 15.5MM **Privately Held**
WEB: www.machinevisionproducts.com
SIC: 3827 7371 3229 Optical instruments
& lenses; custom computer programming
services; pressed & blown glass

(P-22103)
MARK OPTICS INC
1424 E Saint Gertrude Pl, Santa Ana
(92705-5271)
PHONE..................................714 545-6684
Julie A Houser, *President*
Judy A Chapman, *CFO*
Chris Svarczkopf, *General Counsel*
▲ EMP: 20
SALES (est): 4.1MM **Privately Held**
WEB: www.markoptics.com
SIC: 3827 Optical elements & assemblies,
except ophthalmic

(P-22104)
MCBAIN INSTRUMENTS INC
1650 Voyager Ave Ste B, Simi Valley
(93063-3392)
PHONE..................................805 581-6800
Michael Crump, *CEO*

▲ = Import ▼=Export
◆ =Import/Export

Al Guadagno, *CFO*
EMP: 19
SALES (est): 2.3MM **Privately Held**
SIC: 3827 7699 Microscopes, except electron, proton & corneal; professional instrument repair services

(P-22105)
MEADE INSTRUMENTS CORP
27 Hubble, Irvine (92618-4209)
PHONE..................................949 451-1450
Wenjun Ni, *CEO*
Victor Aniceto, *President*
Hector Martinez, *Controller*
April Bihum, *Marketing Staff*
Jimmy Nguyen, *Sales Staff*
▲ **EMP:** 92 **EST:** 1972
SQ FT: 25,000
SALES (est): 21.2MM **Privately Held**
WEB: www.meade.com
SIC: 3827 Telescopes: elbow, panoramic, sighting, fire control, etc.

(P-22106)
MELLES GRIOT INC
2072 Corte Del Nogal, Carlsbad (92011-1427)
PHONE..................................760 438-2131
Marcus Barber, *Manager*
EMP: 10
SALES (est): 236.6K **Privately Held**
SIC: 3827 Optical instruments & lenses

(P-22107)
METAMATERIAL TECH USA INC
5880 W Las Positas Blvd, Pleasanton (94588-8552)
PHONE..................................650 993-9223
Boris Kobrin, *CTO*
EMP: 10
SQ FT: 5,000
SALES (est): 621.1K **Privately Held**
SIC: 3827 Optical instruments & lenses

(P-22108)
MICRO-VU CORP CALIFORNIA (PA)
7909 Conde Ln, Windsor (95492-9779)
PHONE..................................707 838-6272
Edward P Amormino, *President*
Virginia Amormino, *Corp Secy*
Jordan Reese, *Administration*
Dick Henke, *Software Engr*
Terry Alexander, *Engineer*
▲ **EMP:** 80
SQ FT: 60,000
SALES (est): 17.6MM **Privately Held**
WEB: www.microvu.com
SIC: 3827 Optical comparators

(P-22109)
NEWPORT GLASS WORKS LTD
10564 Fern Ave, Stanton (90680-2648)
P.O. Box 127 (90680-0127)
PHONE..................................714 484-8100
Ray Larsen, *Director*
EMP: 13 **EST:** 1978
SQ FT: 40,000
SALES (est): 1MM
SALES (corp-wide): 2.2MM **Privately Held**
SIC: 3827 Lenses, optical: all types except ophthalmic
PA: Newport Optical Industries Ltd
10564 Fern Ave
Stanton CA 90680
714 484-8100

(P-22110)
NEWPORT OPTICAL INDUSTRIES (PA)
Also Called: Newport Glassworks
10564 Fern Ave, Stanton (90680-2648)
P.O. Box 127 (90680-0127)
PHONE..................................714 484-8100
Ray Larsen, *President*
▲ **EMP:** 20
SQ FT: 12,000
SALES (est): 2.2MM **Privately Held**
SIC: 3827 5049 Lenses, optical: all types except ophthalmic; optical goods

(P-22111)
NORDSON YESTECH INC
2747 Loker Ave W, Carlsbad (92010-6601)
PHONE..................................949 361-2714

Don Miller, *President*
Christine Schwarzmann, *CFO*
Robert E Veillette, *Admin Sec*
EMP: 32
SQ FT: 10,000
SALES: 25MM
SALES (corp-wide): 2B **Publicly Held**
WEB: www.nordson.com
SIC: 3827 Optical test & inspection equipment
PA: Nordson Corporation
28601 Clemens Rd
Westlake OH 44145
440 892-1580

(P-22112)
OCLARO PHOTONICS INC (DH)
225 Charcot Ave, San Jose (95131-1107)
PHONE..................................408 383-1400
Ken Ibbs, *President*
Andrew Davidson, *Project Mgr*
Pamela Hemphill, *Manager*
▲ **EMP:** 100
SQ FT: 130,000
SALES (est): 12.1MM
SALES (corp-wide): 1.9B **Publicly Held**
WEB: www.newfocus.com
SIC: 3827 3699 3229 Optical instruments & lenses; electrical equipment & supplies; pressed & blown glass
HQ: Newport Corporation
1791 Deere Ave
Irvine CA 92606
949 863-3144

(P-22113)
ONDAX INC
850 E Duarte Rd, Monrovia (91016-4275)
PHONE..................................626 357-9600
Randy Heyler, *CEO*
Christophe Moser, *President*
Eric Maye, *Engineer*
Jorge Perez, *Engineer*
Dawn Ebertowski, *Sales Staff*
EMP: 15 **EST:** 2000
SQ FT: 60,000
SALES (est): 3.4MM **Privately Held**
WEB: www.ondax.com
SIC: 3827 Optical instruments & apparatus

(P-22114)
ONYX OPTICS INC
6551 Sierra Ln, Dublin (94568-2798)
PHONE..................................925 833-1969
Helmuthe Meissner, *Ch of Bd*
David Meissner, *President*
Stephanie Meissner, *CEO*
EMP: 15
SQ FT: 8,500
SALES (est): 5MM **Privately Held**
WEB: www.onyxoptics.com
SIC: 3827 Optical instruments & lenses

(P-22115)
OPTICAL PHYSICS COMPANY
4133 Guardian St G, Simi Valley (93063-3382)
PHONE..................................818 880-2907
Richard A Hutchin, *CEO*
Marc Jacoby, *President*
A Thomas Stanley, *Vice Pres*
EMP: 15
SQ FT: 12,000
SALES: 5.1MM **Privately Held**
SIC: 3827 Optical instruments & apparatus

(P-22116)
OPTISCAN LTD
48290 Vista Calico Ste A, La Quinta (92253-8409)
PHONE..................................760 777-9595
Daniel Sherman, *President*
Howard Gurock, *Vice Pres*
EMP: 11
SQ FT: 3,000
SALES: 14MM **Privately Held**
WEB: www.opticscan.com
SIC: 3827 5049 Sighting & fire control equipment, optical; periscopes; optical test & inspection equipment; optical goods

(P-22117)
OPTOSIGMA CORPORATION
3210 S Croddy Way, Santa Ana (92704-6348)
PHONE..................................949 851-5881
Yosuke Kondo, *CEO*
Takayoshi Tafaka, *President*
Roger Matsunaga, *Senior VP*
Steve McNamee, *Vice Pres*
Laury Hoganson, *Admin Asst*
EMP: 25
SQ FT: 13,000
SALES (est): 4.9MM
SALES (corp-wide): 82.4MM **Privately Held**
WEB: www.optosigma.com
SIC: 3827 Optical instruments & lenses
PA: Sigma Koki Co., Ltd.
1-19-9, Midori
Sumida-Ku TKY 130-0
356 386-551

(P-22118)
PACIFIC COAST OPTICS INC
10604 Industrial Ave # 100, Roseville (95678-6226)
PHONE..................................916 789-0111
Shannon Rogers, *President*
Phillip Sharp, *Manager*
▼ **EMP:** 20
SQ FT: 14,000
SALES (est): 732K **Privately Held**
WEB: www.pcoptics.com
SIC: 3827 Optical instruments & apparatus

(P-22119)
PACIFIC LINK CORP
Also Called: Extra Lite
15865 Chemical Ln, Huntington Beach (92649-1510)
PHONE..................................714 897-3525
Frank Lyn, *President*
Ken Lin, *Vice Pres*
Olive Lin, *Vice Pres*
▲ **EMP:** 10
SQ FT: 3,500
SALES (est): 885.7K **Privately Held**
WEB: www.extralite.com
SIC: 3827 3851 Lenses, optical: all types except ophthalmic; ophthalmic goods

(P-22120)
PACIFIC QUARTZ INC
1404 E Saint Gertrude Pl, Santa Ana (92705-5215)
PHONE..................................714 546-8133
Greg Dickson, *CEO*
E Roy Dickson, *President*
Julio Nunez, *Vice Pres*
Alex Meza, *QC Mgr*
Julie Austin, *Manager*
EMP: 30
SQ FT: 14,000
SALES: 3.5MM **Privately Held**
WEB: www.pacificquartz.com
SIC: 3827 Optical elements & assemblies, except ophthalmic

(P-22121)
PARKS OPTICAL INC
80 W Easy St Ste 3, Simi Valley (93065-1665)
P.O. Box 1859 (93062-1859)
PHONE..................................805 522-6722
Maurice Sweiss, *President*
▲ **EMP:** 28
SQ FT: 25,000
SALES (est): 4.9MM **Privately Held**
WEB: www.parksoptical.com
SIC: 3827 5999 Binoculars; telescopes: elbow, panoramic, sighting, fire control, etc.; telescopes

(P-22122)
PHILIPS ELEC N AMER CORP
13700 Live Oak Ave, Baldwin Park (91706-1319)
PHONE..................................626 480-0755
EMP: 150
SALES (corp-wide): 26B **Privately Held**
SIC: 3827 3641
HQ: Philips Electronics North America Corporation
3000 Minuteman Rd Ms1203
Andover MA 01810
978 687-1501

(P-22123)
PHOENIX TECHNOLOGY GROUP INC
Also Called: Phoenix Research Labs
6630 Owens Dr, Pleasanton (94588-3334)
PHONE..................................925 485-1100
Norbert Massie, *President*
Stephan Hoffmann, *Engineer*
Annamarie Jegers, *Finance Dir*
Scott Johnston, *Director*
EMP: 17
SQ FT: 9,000
SALES (est): 4.9MM **Privately Held**
SIC: 3827 Optical instruments & apparatus

(P-22124)
PIONEER MATERIALS INC
548 Trinidad Ln, Foster City (94404-3725)
PHONE..................................650 357-7130
Leon Chiu, *President*
EMP: 20
SALES (est): 2.2MM **Privately Held**
WEB: www.pioneer-materials.com
SIC: 3827 Optical instruments & lenses

(P-22125)
PVP ADVANCED EO SYSTEMS INC
14312 Franklin Ave # 100, Tustin (92780-7011)
PHONE..................................714 508-2740
Bruce E Ferguson, *CEO*
John Le Blanc, *CFO*
Russell Hammett, *Engineer*
Geoff Miller, *Engineer*
Timothy Montgomery, *Senior Engr*
▲ **EMP:** 50
SQ FT: 21,000
SALES (est): 13.3MM **Privately Held**
WEB: www.pvpaeo.com
SIC: 3827 Optical instruments & apparatus

(P-22126)
REDFERN INTEGRATED OPTICS INC
3350 Scott Blvd Bldg 1, Santa Clara (95054-3107)
PHONE..................................408 970-3500
Larry Marshall, *CEO*
EMP: 20
SALES (est): 3.2MM
SALES (corp-wide): 1.1B **Privately Held**
WEB: www.rio1.com
SIC: 3827 Optical elements & assemblies, except ophthalmic
HQ: Optasense Holdings Limited
Cody Technology Park Ively Road
Farnborough HANTS GU14

(P-22127)
REYNARD CORPORATION
1020 Calle Sombra, San Clemente (92673-6227)
PHONE..................................949 366-8866
Forrest Reynard, *President*
Chris Sousoures, *CFO*
Jean Reynard, *Vice Pres*
Randy Reynard, *Vice Pres*
Renee Hooper, *Sales Staff*
EMP: 32
SQ FT: 28,000
SALES (est): 10.7MM **Privately Held**
WEB: www.reynardcorp.com
SIC: 3827 Mirrors, optical; lenses, optical: all types except ophthalmic; prisms, optical

(P-22128)
RRDS INC (PA)
12 Goodyear Ste 100, Irvine (92618-3764)
PHONE..................................949 284-6239
Troy Barnes, *CEO*
Celeste Barnes, *Accountant*
▲ **EMP:** 17
SALES: 210K **Privately Held**
SIC: 3827 5012 3949 5045 Optical instruments & lenses; automobiles & other motor vehicles; sporting & athletic goods; computers, peripherals & software; tanks & tank components

P R O D U C T S & S V C S

(P-22129)
RVISION INC (HQ)
2365 Paragon Dr Ste D, San Jose
(95131-1335)
PHONE.....................619 233-1403
Brian M Kelly, *President*
Ryan Wald, *President*
Robb Warwick, *Treasurer*
Daniel Spradling, *Admin Sec*
Lance Rosenzweig, *Director*
EMP: 18
SQ FT: 11,000
SALES: 3.6MM **Privately Held**
WEB: www.rvisionusa.com
SIC: 3827 3861 1731 5063 Optical in-
struments & lenses; cameras & related
equipment; electrical work; electrical ap-
paratus & equipment

(P-22130)
SCIENTIFIC IMAGING CORPORATION (PA)
Also Called: Scientific Instrument Company
262 E Hamilton Ave Ste H, Campbell
(95008-0238)
PHONE.....................408 374-7300
Fred Lustig, *Ch of Bd*
Costa Tsobanakis, *President*
EMP: 25
SQ FT: 15,000
SALES: 13MM **Privately Held**
WEB: www.simicroscopes.com
SIC: 3827 Microscopes, except electron,
proton & corneal

(P-22131)
SCIENTIFIC IMAGING INC
Also Called: Scientific Instrument Company
262 E Hamilton Ave Ste H, Campbell
(95008-0238)
PHONE.....................408 374-7300
Costa Tsobanakis, *Principal*
Kristia Catron, *Principal*
EMP: 10
SALES: 950K **Privately Held**
SIC: 3827 Optical instruments & lenses

(P-22132)
SCOPE CITY (PA)
2978 Topaz Ave, Simi Valley (93063-2168)
P.O. Box 1630 (93062-1630)
PHONE.....................805 522-6646
Maurice Sweiss, *CEO*
▲ **EMP:** 35
SQ FT: 35,000
SALES (est): 2.8MM **Privately Held**
WEB: www.scopecity.com
SIC: 3827 Optical instruments & lenses

(P-22133)
SDO COMMUNICATIONS CORP
47365 Galindo Dr, Fremont (94539-7235)
PHONE.....................408 979-0289
CHI Hao Liu, *Principal*
CHI-Sho Liu, *Treasurer*
Wuei-Fang Ko, *Director*
EMP: 52
SQ FT: 27,000
SALES (est): 5.9MM **Privately Held**
WEB: www.sdocorp.com
SIC: 3827 3229 Optical instruments & ap-
paratus; pressed & blown glass

(P-22134)
SELLERS OPTICAL INC
Also Called: Precision Optical
320 Kalmus Dr, Costa Mesa (92626-6013)
PHONE.....................949 631-6800
Alan Mixon Lambert, *Ch of Bd*
Rod Randolph, *President*
Paul Dimeck, *Vice Pres*
Alan Lambert Jr, *Vice Pres*
Nick Lambert, *Vice Pres*
EMP: 57 **EST:** 1981
SQ FT: 17,000
SALES (est): 8MM **Privately Held**
WEB: www.precisionoptical.com
SIC: 3827 Optical instruments & apparatus

(P-22135)
SHEERVISION INC (PA)
4030 Palos Verdes Dr N # 104, Rllng HLS
Est (90274-2559)
PHONE.....................310 265-8918
Suzanne Lewsadder, *CEO*
Patrick Adams, *CFO*

Gordon Stover, *Sales Executive*
John F Guhl, *Regl Sales Mgr*
Myra Straussman, *Sales Staff*
EMP: 14 **EST:** 1986
SQ FT: 3,090
SALES (est): 1.2MM **Publicly Held**
WEB: www.sheervision.com
SIC: 3827 Optical instruments & lenses

(P-22136)
SIERRA PRECISION OPTICS INC
12830 Earhart Ave, Auburn (95602-9027)
PHONE.....................530 885-6979
Michael Dorich, *CEO*
Eloise Dorich, *Admin Sec*
EMP: 25
SQ FT: 15,000
SALES: 4MM **Privately Held**
WEB: www.sierraoptics.com
SIC: 3827 Optical instruments & apparatus

(P-22137)
SPECTRUM SCIENTIFIC INC
16692 Hale Ave Ste A, Irvine (92606-5052)
PHONE.....................949 260-9900
Daphnie Chakran, *President*
Dave Erickson, *CTO*
Steve Dandrea, *Prdtn Mgr*
EMP: 12
SALES (est): 2.5MM **Privately Held**
WEB: www.ssioptics.com
SIC: 3827 Optical instruments & lenses

(P-22138)
STELLARVUE
11820 Kemper Rd, Auburn (95603-9500)
PHONE.....................530 823-7796
Vic Maris, *Partner*
▲ **EMP:** 10
SALES (est): 1MM **Privately Held**
WEB: www.stellarvue.com
SIC: 3827 Telescopes: elbow, panoramic,
sighting, fire control, etc.

(P-22139)
SUNEX INC (PA)
3160 Lionshead Ave Ste 2, Carlsbad
(92010-4705)
PHONE.....................760 597-2966
Alex Ning, *President*
EMP: 10
SALES (est): 1.4MM **Privately Held**
WEB: www.optics-online.com
SIC: 3827 Optical instruments & apparatus

(P-22140)
SVETWHEEL LLC
121 Arundel Rd, San Carlos (94070-1905)
PHONE.....................650 245-6080
Victor Faybishenko,
Vladimir Solodovnikov,
EMP: 12
SALES (est): 1.5MM **Privately Held**
SIC: 3827 Lenses, optical: all types except
ophthalmic; optical alignment & display in-
struments

(P-22141)
TFD INCORPORATED
Also Called: Thin Film Devices
1180 N Tustin Ave, Anaheim (92807-1732)
PHONE.....................714 630-7127
Saleem Shaikh, *CEO*
Joy Shaikh, *CFO*
▲ **EMP:** 25
SQ FT: 20,000
SALES (est): 5.8MM **Privately Held**
SIC: 3827 Optical instruments & lenses

(P-22142)
TM MICROSCOPES VCO METRLGY GRP
112 Robin Hill Rd, Goleta (93117-3107)
PHONE.....................805 967-2700
Gary Aden, *President*
Bill Muller, *Vice Pres*
Brent Nelson, *Financial Exec*
▲ **EMP:** 80
SQ FT: 25,000
SALES (est): 9.6MM **Privately Held**
SIC: 3827 Microscopes, except electron,
proton & corneal

(P-22143)
TWIN COAST METROLOGY INC (PA)
333 Wshngton Blvd Ste 362, Marina Del
Rey (90292)
PHONE.....................310 709-2308
Eric Stone, *President*
Jason Remillard, *Treasurer*
Amy Remillard, *Admin Sec*
EMP: 15
SQ FT: 1,200
SALES (est): 1.8MM **Privately Held**
SIC: 3827 Optical instruments & lenses

(P-22144)
V-A OPTICAL COMPANY INC
60 Red Hill Ave, San Anselmo
(94960-2424)
PHONE.....................415 459-1919
Michael Valliant, *President*
EMP: 10
SQ FT: 6,000
SALES: 1MM **Privately Held**
WEB: www.vaoptical.com
SIC: 3827 Optical elements & assemblies,
except ophthalmic

(P-22145)
VSP LABS INC (PA)
Also Called: Vspone
3333 Quality Dr, Rancho Cordova
(95670-7985)
PHONE.....................866 569-8800
Donald E Oakley, *President*
Don Ball, *CFO*
EMP: 39
SALES (est): 33.8MM **Privately Held**
SIC: 3827 5049 Optical instruments &
lenses; optical goods

(P-22146)
WAVE PRECISION INC
5390 Kazuko Ct, Moorpark (93021-1790)
PHONE.....................805 529-3324
Kenneth L Scribner, *President*
Dennis B Hotchkiss, *Vice Pres*
EMP: 75 **EST:** 1974
SQ FT: 16,000
SALES (est): 7.1MM **Privately Held**
WEB: www.generaloptics.com
SIC: 3827 Optical instruments & apparatus

(P-22147)
WESTWOOD GROUP
Also Called: Telic Company
28478 Westinghouse Pl, Valencia
(91355-0929)
PHONE.....................661 702-8603
Arthur Kennedy, *President*
Candie Kennedy, *Finance*
EMP: 15
SQ FT: 6,000
SALES (est): 2.6MM **Privately Held**
WEB: www.telicco.com
SIC: 3827 Optical instruments & lenses

(P-22148)
WINT CORPORATION
5686 Country Club Pkwy, San Jose
(95138-2220)
PHONE.....................408 532-8356
Frank Wang, *President*
EMP: 200
SQ FT: 3,000
SALES (est): 15.1MM **Privately Held**
SIC: 3827 Optical instruments & lenses

(P-22149)
WINTRISS ENGINEERING CORP
9010 Kenamar Dr Ste 101, San Diego
(92121-3437)
PHONE.....................858 550-7300
Andrew W Ash, *CEO*
Vic Wintriss, *President*
Chris Kiraly, *CTO*
Jerry Rose, *Regl Sales Mgr*
Pete Burggren, *Sales Staff*
▲ **EMP:** 23
SQ FT: 11,576
SALES (est): 6.3MM **Privately Held**
WEB: www.weco.com
SIC: 3827 Optical test & inspection equip-
ment

(P-22150)
WSGLASS HOLDINGS INC
Also Called: Western States Glass
180 Main Ave, Sacramento (95838-2015)
PHONE.....................916 388-5885
Curt Colgan, *Branch Mgr*
EMP: 17 **Privately Held**
WEB: www.westernstatesglass.com
SIC: 3827 Glasses, field or opera
HQ: Wsglass Holdings, Inc.
3241 Darby Cmn
Fremont CA 94539
510 623-5000

(P-22151)
Z C & R COATING FOR OPTICS INC
1401 Abalone Ave, Torrance (90501-2889)
PHONE.....................310 381-3060
Celso Cabrera, *President*
Robert Cabrera, *General Mgr*
Fred Praudisch, *VP Opers*
Vincent Gutierrez, *QC Mgr*
Daniel Duarte, *Sls & Mktg Exec*
EMP: 43
SQ FT: 21,781
SALES (est): 8.6MM
SALES (corp-wide): 251.3MM **Privately Held**
WEB: www.zcrcoatings.com
SIC: 3827 Lens coating equipment
HQ: Abrisa Industrial Glass, Inc.
200 Hallock Dr
Santa Paula CA 93060
805 525-4902

(P-22152)
ZYGO CORPORATION
Also Called: Zygo Optical Systems
2031 Main St, Irvine (92614-6509)
PHONE.....................714 918-7433
Eric D'Lppolito, *Manager*
EMP: 22
SALES (corp-wide): 4.3B **Publicly Held**
WEB: www.zygo.com
SIC: 3827 Optical instruments & lenses
HQ: Zygo Corporation
21 Laurel Brook Rd
Middlefield CT 06455
860 347-8506

(P-22153)
ZYGO EPO
3900 Lakeside Dr, Richmond (94806-1963)
PHONE.....................510 243-7592
EMP: 11
SALES (est): 2MM **Privately Held**
SIC: 3827 Optical instruments & lenses

3829 Measuring & Controlling Devices, NEC

(P-22154)
ABAXIS INC (HQ)
3240 Whipple Rd, Union City (94587-1217)
PHONE.....................510 675-6500
Clinton H Severson, *CEO*
Donald P Wood, *President*
Ross Taylor, *CFO*
Sigrid Rose, *Exec VP*
Bill Roberts, *Vice Pres*
◆ **EMP:** 180
SQ FT: 158,378
SALES: 244.7MM
SALES (corp-wide): 5.3B **Publicly Held**
WEB: www.abaxis.com
SIC: 3829 2835 Medical diagnostic sys-
tems, nuclear; in vitro & in vivo diagnostic
substances; veterinary diagnostic sub-
stances
PA: Zoetis Inc.
10 Sylvan Way Ste 105
Parsippany NJ 07054
973 822-7000

(P-22155)
ACLARA BIOSCIENCES INC
Also Called: A Company In Development
Stage
345 Oyster Point Blvd, South San Fran-
cisco (94080-1913)
PHONE.....................800 297-2728
Thomas G Klopack, *CEO*
Thomas J Baruch, *Ch of Bd*

EMP: 62
SQ FT: 44,000
SALES (est): 7.4MM **Privately Held**
WEB: www.virologic.om
SIC: 3829 8731 3826 3821 Measuring & controlling devices; commercial physical research; analytical instruments; laboratory apparatus & furniture; chemical preparations

(P-22156)
ACO PACIFIC INC
2604 Read Ave, Belmont (94002-1520)
PHONE..............................650 595-8588
Noland Lewis, *President*
EMP: 10
SQ FT: 25,000
SALES: 870K **Privately Held**
WEB: www.acopacific.com
SIC: 3829 Measuring & controlling devices

(P-22157)
ACTSOLAR INC
2900 Semiconductor Dr, Santa Clara (95051-0606)
PHONE..............................408 721-5000
Andrew Foss, *President*
Brian Dupin, *Vice Pres*
EMP: 15
SQ FT: 3,000
SALES (est): 95.1K
SALES (corp-wide): 14.9B **Publicly Held**
WEB: www.national.com
SIC: 3829 Measuring & controlling devices
HQ: National Semiconductor Corporation
　2900 Semiconductor Dr
　Santa Clara CA 95051
　408 721-5000

(P-22158)
ALL WEATHER INC
Also Called: AWI
1065 National Dr Ste 1, Sacramento (95834-2037)
PHONE..............................916 928-1000
Jason Hall, *President*
Bob Perrin, *Exec VP*
Steve Vansanten, *Vice Pres*
Neal Dillman, *CTO*
Bartlomiej Klusek, *Software Engr*
◆ **EMP:** 65
SQ FT: 50,000
SALES (est): 21.9MM **Privately Held**
WEB: www.allweather.com
SIC: 3829 8999 3674 Weather tracking equipment; weather related services; radiation sensors

(P-22159)
ALPHA TECHNICS INC
125 S Tremont St Ste 100, Oceanside (92054-3028)
PHONE..............................949 250-6578
Lisa Marie Ryan, *President*
EMP: 200 **EST:** 2011
SQ FT: 6,000
SALES (est): 29.1MM **Privately Held**
SIC: 3829 Thermometers & temperature sensors

(P-22160)
ALVARADO MANUFACTURING CO INC
12660 Colony Ct, Chino (91710-2975)
PHONE..............................909 591-8431
Bret Armatas, *CEO*
▲ **EMP:** 71
SQ FT: 69,000
SALES (est): 22.3MM **Privately Held**
WEB: www.alvaradomfg.com
SIC: 3829 Turnstiles, equipped with counting mechanisms

(P-22161)
APICAL INSTRUMENTS INC
2971 Spring St, Redwood City (94063-3935)
PHONE..............................650 967-1030
Bruno Strul PHD, *CEO*
EMP: 14
SQ FT: 15,000
SALES (est): 3.7MM **Privately Held**
WEB: www.apicalinstr.com
SIC: 3829 8742 3841 Measuring & controlling devices; industry specialist consultants; surgical & medical instruments

(P-22162)
APPLIED PHYSICS SYSTEMS INC (PA)
Also Called: 2-G Enterprises
425 Clyde Ave, Mountain View (94043-2209)
PHONE..............................650 965-0500
William Goodman, *President*
Robert Goodman, *Vice Pres*
Dwayne Bakaas, *General Mgr*
Christine Goodman, *Admin Sec*
Toni Shuma, *Software Engr*
EMP: 112
SALES (est): 28.4MM **Privately Held**
WEB: www.appliedphysics.com
SIC: 3829 8711 Magnetometers; consulting engineer

(P-22163)
APPLIED TECHNOLOGIES ASSOC INC (HQ)
Also Called: A T A
3025 Buena Vista Dr, Paso Robles (93446-8555)
PHONE..............................805 239-9100
William B Wade, *President*
Chris Barker, *Owner*
George Walker, *Vice Pres*
Matt Schirle, *Software Engr*
Dennis Buckley, *Engng Exec*
▲ **EMP:** 127
SALES (est): 20.8MM **Privately Held**
WEB: www.ata-sd.com
SIC: 3829 1381 Surveying instruments & accessories; drilling oil & gas wells
PA: Scientific Drilling International, Inc.
　16071 Greenspoint Park
　Houston TX 77060
　281 443-3300

(P-22164)
AQUA MEASURE INSTRUMENT CO
Also Called: Moisture Register Products
9567 Arrow Rte Ste E, Rancho Cucamonga (91730-4550)
PHONE..............................909 941-7776
John W Lundstrom, *Principal*
Dean Curd, *Principal*
Arthur B Schultz, *Principal*
▲ **EMP:** 13
SQ FT: 13,500
SALES (est): 3MM **Privately Held**
WEB: www.moistureregisterproducts.com
SIC: 3829 3826 Moisture density meters; analytical instruments

(P-22165)
ASTRO HAVEN ENTERPRISES INC
555 Anton Blvd Ste 150, Costa Mesa (92626-7036)
P.O. Box 3637, San Clemente (92674-3637)
PHONE..............................949 215-3777
Priscilla Brotherston, *President*
▼ **EMP:** 12
SALES (est): 573.8K **Privately Held**
SIC: 3829 Measuring & controlling devices

(P-22166)
ATMOS ENGINEERING INC
443 Dearborn Park Rd, Pescadero (94060-9706)
P.O. Box 807 (94060-0807)
PHONE..............................650 879-1674
Rodger Reinhart, *President*
EMP: 12
SALES (est): 1.7MM **Privately Held**
WEB: www.atmos.com
SIC: 3829 Temperature sensors, except industrial process & aircraft

(P-22167)
AUTOMATIC CONTROL ENGRG CORP
Also Called: Johnson Contrls Authorized Dlr
20788 Corsair Blvd, Hayward (94545-1010)
PHONE..............................510 293-6040
Robert Crowder, *CEO*
Stephen Crowder, *Vice Pres*
EMP: 46
SQ FT: 15,000

SALES (est): 14.8MM **Privately Held**
SIC: 3829 5084 5075 Measuring & controlling devices; instruments & control equipment; warm air heating & air conditioning

(P-22168)
AXCELIS TECHNOLOGIES INC
1360 Reynolds Ave Ste 106, Irvine (92614-5535)
PHONE..............................949 477-5160
EMP: 400
SALES (corp-wide): 410.5MM **Publicly Held**
SIC: 3829 Ion chambers
PA: Axcelis Technologies, Inc.
　108 Cherry Hill Dr
　Beverly MA 01915
　978 787-4000

(P-22169)
AXCELIS TECHNOLOGIES INC
5673 W Las Positas Blvd # 205, Pleasanton (94588-4077)
PHONE..............................510 979-1970
Ali Moghadam, *Manager*
EMP: 400
SALES (corp-wide): 410.5MM **Publicly Held**
SIC: 3829 Ion chambers
PA: Axcelis Technologies, Inc.
　108 Cherry Hill Dr
　Beverly MA 01915
　978 787-4000

(P-22170)
BARKSDALE INC (DH)
3211 Fruitland Ave, Vernon (90058-3717)
P.O. Box 58843, Los Angeles (90058-0843)
PHONE..............................323 583-6243
C Ian Dodd, *President*
Vivian Fahy, *Vice Pres*
Ralf Fuehr, *Vice Pres*
Doug Holland, *Vice Pres*
Tarun Shivlani, *Vice Pres*
▲ **EMP:** 149
SQ FT: 115,000
SALES (est): 25.7MM
SALES (corp-wide): 2.7B **Publicly Held**
WEB: www.barksdale.net
SIC: 3829 3491 3823 3643 Measuring & controlling devices; industrial valves; industrial instrmnts msrmnt display/control process variable; current-carrying wiring devices

(P-22171)
BECHLER CAMS INC
1313 S State College Pkwy, Anaheim (92806-5298)
PHONE..............................714 774-5150
Daniel Lennert, *President*
Laura Stearman, *Corp Secy*
Jim Humphrey, *Mfg Staff*
EMP: 16 **EST:** 1957
SQ FT: 11,500
SALES: 2.3MM **Privately Held**
WEB: www.bechlercams.com
SIC: 3829 Measuring & controlling devices

(P-22172)
BRENNER-FIEDLER & ASSOCIATES (PA)
Also Called: B F
4059 Flat Rock Dr, Riverside (92505-5859)
PHONE..............................562 404-2721
James Kloman, *CEO*
Debbie McKinley, *Info Tech Mgr*
Chris Roome, *Info Tech Mgr*
Rocio Hernandez, *Technical Staff*
Humam Qaqish, *Engineer*
EMP: 39
SQ FT: 28,669
SALES (est): 15.7MM **Privately Held**
WEB: www.brenner-fiedler.com
SIC: 3829 5085 Accelerometers; pistons & valves; valves & fittings

(P-22173)
C&C BUILDING AUTOMATION CO INC
390 Swift Ave Ste 22, South San Francisco (94080-6221)
PHONE..............................650 292-7450
Chuck Chavez, *Principal*
Lynn Meneguzzi, *Administration*

Francisco Jauregui, *Design Engr*
Cliff McIntire, *Engineer*
EMP: 25
SQ FT: 6,000
SALES (est): 5.6MM **Privately Held**
WEB: www.ccbac.com
SIC: 3829 Measuring & controlling devices

(P-22174)
CALIFORNIA DYNAMICS CORP (PA)
Also Called: Caldyn
5572 Alhambra Ave, Los Angeles (90032-3195)
PHONE..............................323 223-3882
Donald Benkert, *President*
Adell Benkert, *President*
Tim Benkert, *Sales Mgr*
Dustin Jordan, *Sales Engr*
Scott Sween, *Sales Staff*
▲ **EMP:** 25
SQ FT: 30,000
SALES (est): 3MM **Privately Held**
WEB: www.caldyn.com
SIC: 3829 Vibration meters, analyzers & calibrators

(P-22175)
CALIFORNIA SENSOR CORPORATION
2075 Corte Del Nogal P, Carlsbad (92011-1413)
PHONE..............................760 438-0525
Ralph Miller, *CEO*
David L Byma, *President*
Richard Wilkinson, *Treasurer*
Robert Destremps, *Vice Pres*
EMP: 30
SQ FT: 6,000
SALES: 8.1MM **Privately Held**
WEB: www.calsense.com
SIC: 3829 5083 Measuring & controlling devices; irrigation equipment

(P-22176)
CARGO DATA CORPORATION
1502 Eastman Ave Ste A, Ventura (93003-8020)
P.O. Box 6553 (93006-6553)
PHONE..............................805 650-5922
Bud Pohle, *President*
Becky Wallet, *Administration*
Roger Niebolt, *Sales Mgr*
Tammy Wylie, *Sales Mgr*
▲ **EMP:** 10
SALES (est): 840K **Privately Held**
SIC: 3829 Temperature sensors, except industrial process & aircraft

(P-22177)
CARTURNER INC (PA)
929 Poinsettia Ave # 104, Vista (92081-8459)
PHONE..............................760 598-7448
Bill Schwenker, *President*
Eugene J Polley, *Accountant*
EMP: 13
SALES (est): 2.7MM **Privately Held**
SIC: 3829 3444 Turntable indicator testers; sheet metalwork

(P-22178)
CBS SCIENTIFIC CO INC (PA)
10805 Vista Sorrento Pkwy # 100, San Diego (92121-2701)
P.O. Box 856, Del Mar (92014-0856)
PHONE..............................858 755-4959
▲ **EMP:** 40
SQ FT: 25,000
SALES (est): 3.6MM **Privately Held**
WEB: www.cbsscientific.com
SIC: 3829 3821

(P-22179)
CERCACOR LABORATORIES INC
40 Parker, Irvine (92618-1604)
PHONE..............................949 679-6100
Joe E Kiani, *President*
Brenda Montgomery, *Vice Pres*
Sean Merritt, *Research*
Sean Machida, *Engineer*
Jonathan Rosario, *Engineer*
EMP: 11

P R O D U C T S & S V C S

SALES (est): 1.7MM **Privately Held**
SIC: 3829 Pulse analyzers, nuclear monitoring

(P-22180)
COMET TECHNOLOGIES USA INC
Also Called: Plasma Control Technologies
2370 Bering Dr, San Jose (95131-1121)
PHONE..................408 325-8770
Paul Smith, *Manager*
Conor O'Mahony, *Vice Pres*
Robert Jardim, *Administration*
Knut Mehr, *Engineer*
Jeffrey Waters, *Engineer*
EMP: 50
SALES (corp-wide): 443.3MM **Privately Held**
WEB: www.cometna.com
SIC: 3829 Measuring & controlling devices
HQ: Comet Technologies Usa Inc.
100 Trap Falls Road Ext
Shelton CT 06484
203 447-3200

(P-22181)
COMPUTATIONAL SYSTEMS INC
4301 Resnik Ct, Bakersfield (93313-4852)
PHONE..................661 832-5306
Shannon Romine, *Branch Mgr*
EMP: 50
SALES (corp-wide): 15.2B **Publicly Held**
SIC: 3829 Stress, strain & flaw detecting/measuring equipment
HQ: Computational Systems, Incorporated
8000 West Florissant Ave
Saint Louis MO 63136
314 553-2000

(P-22182)
CUBIC TRNSP SYSTEMS INC (HQ)
5650 Kearny Mesa Rd, San Diego (92111-1305)
P.O. Box 85587 (92186-5587)
PHONE..................858 268-3100
Stephen O Shewmaker, *CEO*
Walter C Zable, *Ch of Bd*
Steve Purcell, *Senior VP*
Rasheed Behrooznia, *Vice Pres*
Raymond De Kozan, *Vice Pres*
◆ **EMP:** 550
SALES (est): 172.6MM
SALES (corp-wide): 1.4B **Publicly Held**
SIC: 3829 1731 Fare registers for street cars, buses, etc.; toll booths, automatic; telephone & telephone equipment installation
PA: Cubic Corporation
9333 Balboa Ave
San Diego CA 92123
858 277-6780

(P-22183)
CUBIC TRNSP SYSTEMS INC
1800 Sutter St Ste 900, Concord (94520-2536)
PHONE..................925 348-9163
Derrick Benoit, *Manager*
EMP: 175
SALES (corp-wide): 1.4B **Publicly Held**
SIC: 3829 Fare registers for street cars, buses, etc.
HQ: Cubic Transportation Systems, Inc.
5650 Kearny Mesa Rd
San Diego CA 92111
858 268-3100

(P-22184)
DAKOTA ULTRASONICS CORPORATION
1500 Green Hills Rd # 107, Scotts Valley (95066-4945)
PHONE..................831 431-9722
Teresa Engel, *COO*
Jaime Rico, *COO*
Rich Engel, *Data Proc Staff*
Laurie Gudhal, *CPA*
EMP: 13
SQ FT: 4,500
SALES (est): 3MM **Privately Held**
WEB: www.dakotainst.com
SIC: 3829 Gauging instruments, thickness ultrasonic

(P-22185)
DAVIDSON OPTRONICS INC
Also Called: Doi Venture
9087 Arrow Rte Ste 180, Rancho Cucamonga (91730-4451)
P.O. Box 1560, West Covina (91793-1560)
PHONE..................626 962-5181
Eugene Dumitrascu, *Ch of Bd*
Dan State, *President*
Debra Richards, *Admin Sec*
EMP: 22
SQ FT: 40,000
SALES (est): 4.2MM
SALES (corp-wide): 31.2MM **Privately Held**
WEB: www.davidsonoptronics.com
SIC: 3829 3827 Measuring & controlling devices; optical instruments & apparatus
HQ: Trioptics, Inc.
9087 Arrow Rte Ste 180
Rancho Cucamonga CA 91730
626 962-5181

(P-22186)
DELTATRAK INC
1236 Doker Dr, Modesto (95351-1587)
PHONE..................209 579-5343
Allen Hui, *Manager*
EMP: 50
SQ FT: 25,468
SALES (corp-wide): 15.5MM **Privately Held**
WEB: www.deltatrak.com
SIC: 3829 Temperature sensors, except industrial process & aircraft
PA: Deltatrak, Inc.
6140 Stoneridge Mall Rd # 180
Pleasanton CA 94588
925 249-2250

(P-22187)
DELTATRAK INC (PA)
6140 Stoneridge Mall Rd # 180, Pleasanton (94588-3288)
P.O. Box 398 (94566-0039)
PHONE..................925 249-2250
Frederick L Wu, *CEO*
Elizabeth Garcia, *Vice Pres*
Jeanne Solis, *Administration*
Charles Langbehn, *Engineer*
Michelle Alvino, *Business Mgr*
▲ **EMP:** 25
SQ FT: 7,500
SALES (est): 15.5MM **Privately Held**
WEB: www.deltatrak.com
SIC: 3829 3823 3822 Temperature sensors, except industrial process & aircraft; industrial instrmnts msrmnt display/control process variable; auto controls regulating residntl & coml environmt & applncs

(P-22188)
DYNAMIC SOLUTIONS
631 W Rosecrans Ave # 23, Gardena (90248-1516)
P.O. Box 7963, Northridge (91327-7963)
PHONE..................253 273-7936
Aimmee Hagler, *Partner*
Steven Wood, *Partner*
EMP: 12
SQ FT: 10,000
SALES (est): 1.5MM **Privately Held**
WEB: www.dynsolusa.com
SIC: 3829 Vibration meters, analyzers & calibrators

(P-22189)
EAGLEMETRIC CORP
98 Discovery, Irvine (92618-3105)
PHONE..................949 288-3363
Patrick Lee, *President*
EMP: 12 **EST:** 2010
SALES (est): 974.8K **Privately Held**
SIC: 3829 Measuring & controlling devices

(P-22190)
ECKERT ZEGLER ISOTOPE PDTS INC
1800 N Keystone St, Burbank (91504-3417)
PHONE..................661 309-1010
Karl Amlauer, *Branch Mgr*
EMP: 30

SALES (corp-wide): 163.4MM **Privately Held**
WEB: www.isotopeproducts.com
SIC: 3829 Nuclear radiation & testing apparatus
HQ: Eckert & Ziegler Isotope Products, Inc.
24937 Avenue Tibbitts
Valencia CA 91355
661 309-1010

(P-22191)
ECKERT ZEGLER ISOTOPE PDTS INC (HQ)
Also Called: Isotope Products Lab
24937 Avenue Tibbitts, Valencia (91355-3427)
PHONE..................661 309-1010
Frank Yeager, *CEO*
Joe Hathcock, *President*
Karen Haskins, *Treasurer*
Benny Crowell, *Manager*
EMP: 45
SQ FT: 40,000
SALES: 44.6MM
SALES (corp-wide): 163.4MM **Privately Held**
WEB: www.isotopeproducts.com
SIC: 3829 Nuclear radiation & testing apparatus
PA: Eckert & Ziegler Strahlen- Und Medizintechnik Ag
Robert-Rossle-Str. 10
Berlin 13125
309 410-840

(P-22192)
ECKERT ZEGLER ISOTOPE PDTS INC
1800 N Keystone St, Burbank (91504-3417)
PHONE..................661 309-1010
EMP: 30
SALES (corp-wide): 158.2MM **Privately Held**
SIC: 3829
HQ: Eckert & Ziegler Isotope Products, Inc.
24937 Avenue Tibbitts
Valencia CA 91355
661 309-1010

(P-22193)
EMISSION METHODS INC
Also Called: Webber EMI
1307 S Wanamaker Ave, Ontario (91761-2237)
PHONE..................909 605-6800
Kenneth Parker, *President*
Betty Wysocki, *Office Mgr*
EMP: 20
SQ FT: 14,100
SALES (est): 4.4MM **Privately Held**
WEB: www.webberemi.com
SIC: 3829 3499 3599 Dynamometer instruments; aircraft & motor vehicle measurement equipment; novelties & specialties, metal; carnival machines & equipment, amusement park

(P-22194)
ET WATER SYSTEMS LLC
384 Bel Marin Keys Blvd # 145, Novato (94949-5366)
PHONE..................415 945-9383
Bruce J Cardinal,
Mark Coppersmith, *Managing Dir*
David Curtis,
▲ **EMP:** 14
SALES (est): 1.4MM **Privately Held**
SIC: 3829 Measuring & controlling devices

(P-22195)
EXCELITAS TECHNOLOGIES CORP
1330 E Cypress St, Covina (91724-2103)
PHONE..................626 967-6021
Patrick O'Shaunessey, *Branch Mgr*
Kate Bates, *General Mgr*
Chau Chan, *Engineer*
Maria Rodriguez, *Engineer*
EMP: 120 **Privately Held**
SIC: 3829 3679 Thermometers & temperature sensors; electronic circuits
HQ: Excelitas Technologies Corp.
200 West St
Waltham MA 02451

(P-22196)
EXCESS TRADING INC
Also Called: Precision Designed Products
12350 Montague St Ste L, Pacoima (91331-2201)
PHONE..................310 212-0020
Mark L Silberberg, *President*
EMP: 25
SALES (est): 3.2MM **Privately Held**
WEB: www.excesstrading.com
SIC: 3829 Levels & tapes, surveying

(P-22197)
EXP COMPUTER
Also Called: Xeltek
1296 Kifer Rd Ste 605, Sunnyvale (94086-5318)
PHONE..................408 530-8080
Soonam Kim, *President*
Juok Kim, *Treasurer*
Robert Parente, *Admin Sec*
Amina Sheraaz, *Sales Staff*
▲ **EMP:** 10
SQ FT: 3,500
SALES (est): 1.6MM **Privately Held**
WEB: www.xeltek.com
SIC: 3829 5065 Measuring & controlling devices; electronic parts & equipment

(P-22198)
F & D FLORES ENTERPRISES INC
Also Called: Hardware Specialties
761 E Francis St, Ontario (91761-5514)
PHONE..................909 975-4853
Frank Flores, *President*
▲ **EMP:** 11
SQ FT: 20,000
SALES (est): 1.4MM **Privately Held**
WEB: www.sentryturnstiles.com
SIC: 3829 5031 3446 Automatic turnstiles & related apparatus; lumber, plywood & millwork; architectural metalwork

(P-22199)
FAR WEST TECHNOLOGY INC
330 S Kellogg Ave, Goleta (93117-3814)
PHONE..................805 964-3615
John D Rickey, *CEO*
John Handloser Jr, *Exec VP*
Scot Larson, *Manager*
▲ **EMP:** 17 **EST:** 1971
SQ FT: 6,100
SALES (est): 3.6MM **Privately Held**
WEB: www.fwt.com
SIC: 3829 Nuclear radiation & testing apparatus

(P-22200)
FITBIT INC (PA)
199 Fremont St Fl 14, San Francisco (94105-2253)
PHONE..................415 513-1000
James Park, *Ch of Bd*
Ronald Kisling, *CFO*
Tim Rosa, *Chief Mktg Ofcr*
Jeff Devine, *Exec VP*
Andy Missan, *Exec VP*
EMP: 277
SQ FT: 366,000
SALES: 1.6B **Publicly Held**
SIC: 3829 Measuring & controlling devices

(P-22201)
FLOWLINE INC
Also Called: Flowline Liquid Intelligence
10500 Humbolt St, Los Alamitos (90720-2439)
PHONE..................562 598-3015
Stephen E Olson, *Ch of Bd*
Scott Olson, *President*
Mike Ehlert, *Engineer*
Mike Rafferty, *Engineer*
Joe Tran, *Engineer*
EMP: 25
SQ FT: 8,000
SALES (est): 4.5MM **Privately Held**
WEB: www.flowline.com
SIC: 3829 5084 Measuring & controlling devices; industrial machinery & equipment

(P-22202)
FOOTHILL INSTRUMENTS LLC
5011 Jarvis Ave, La Canada (91011-1640)
PHONE..................818 952-5600

Glenn Houser, *Partner*
Leslie Miller, *Partner*
EMP: 10 **EST:** 1999
SALES (est): 1.1MM **Privately Held**
WEB: www.foothill-instruments.com
SIC: 3829 Measuring & controlling devices

(P-22203)
FOUR D IMAGING
808 Gilman St, Berkeley (94710-1422)
PHONE..................510 290-3533
Glen Stevick, *President*
Tyler Worden, *Managing Prtnr*
EMP: 12
SALES (est): 1.3MM **Privately Held**
SIC: 3829 Measuring & controlling devices

(P-22204)
FRONTLINE INSTRS & CONTRLS
Also Called: Frontline Technologies
3195 Park Rd Ste C, Benicia (94510-1185)
PHONE..................707 747-9766
Lee Sherwood, *President*
EMP: 10
SALES: 200K **Privately Held**
SIC: 3829 Measuring & controlling devices

(P-22205)
GAMMA SCIENTIFIC INC
Also Called: Road Vista
9925 Carroll Canyon Rd, San Diego
(92131-1105)
PHONE..................858 635-9008
Kong G Loh, *COO*
▲ **EMP:** 48
SQ FT: 20,000
SALES: 11.9MM **Privately Held**
WEB: www.gamma-sci.com
SIC: 3829 3648 3821 Measuring & con-
trolling devices; reflectors for lighting
equipment: metal; calibration tapes for
physical testing machines

(P-22206)
GENERAL NUCLEONICS INC
2807 Metropolitan Pl, Pomona
(91767-1853)
PHONE..................909 593-4985
Sam Dominey, *President*
Donald Blincow, *Vice Pres*
Teresa Estrella, *Office Mgr*
Anice Dusseldorf, *Accounting Mgr*
John Mahoney, *VP Opers*
EMP: 10
SQ FT: 14,000
SALES (est): 1.6MM **Privately Held**
WEB: www.generalnucleonics.com
SIC: 3829 Stress, strain & flaw
detecting/measuring equipment; gauging
instruments, thickness ultrasonic

(P-22207)
GEOMETRICS INC
2190 Fortune Dr, San Jose (95131-1815)
PHONE..................408 428-4244
Mark Prouty, *President*
Rod Bravo, *CFO*
Bart Hoekstra, *Vice Pres*
Craig Lippus, *Vice Pres*
Ron Royal, *Vice Pres*
EMP: 80
SALES: 26.6MM
SALES (corp-wide): 410.1MM **Privately Held**
WEB: www.geometrics.com
SIC: 3829 Geophysical or meteorological
electronic equipment
HQ: Oyo Corporation U.S.A.
245 N Carmelo Ave Ste 101
Pasadena CA 91107

(P-22208)
GUNNEBO ENTRANCE CONTROL INC (HQ)
Also Called: Omega Turnstiles
535 Getty Ct Ste F, Benicia (94510-1179)
PHONE..................707 748-0885
John Haining, *CEO*
Jenifer Babbitt, *Admin Sec*
Doug Lenzo, *Regl Sales Mgr*
▲ **EMP:** 18
SQ FT: 20,000

SALES (est): 1.5MM
SALES (corp-wide): 709.9MM **Privately Held**
WEB: www.gunneboentrance.us
SIC: 3829 Automatic turnstiles & related
apparatus
PA: Gunnebo Ab
Johan Pa Gardas Gata 7
Goteborg 412 5
102 095-000

(P-22209)
H2SCAN CORPORATION
27215 Turnberry Ln Unit A, Valencia
(91355-1068)
PHONE..................661 775-9575
Michael Allman, *CEO*
Dennis W Reid, *President*
Phil Lachina, *COO*
Kevin D Ayers, *CFO*
Vikas Lakhotia, *Vice Pres*
EMP: 25
SQ FT: 10,000
SALES (est): 7.9MM **Privately Held**
SIC: 3829 Hydrometers, except industrial
process type

(P-22210)
HAMILTON SUNDSTRAND SPC SYSTMS
Also Called: Hsssi
2771 N Garey Ave, Pomona (91767-1809)
PHONE..................909 593-3581
Edward Francis, *Exec Dir*
Lawrence R McNamara, *President*
Eugene Dougherty, *Treasurer*
Clinton Gardiner, *Vice Pres*
Daniel C Lee, *General Mgr*
EMP: 76
SQ FT: 134,000
SALES (est): 9.5MM
SALES (corp-wide): 59.8B **Publicly Held**
WEB: www.hsssi.com
SIC: 3829 Measuring & controlling devices
HQ: Goodrich Corporation
2730 W Tyvola Rd
Charlotte NC 28217
704 423-7000

(P-22211)
HEXAGON METROLOGY INC
Romer Cimcore
3536 Seagate Way, Oceanside
(92056-2672)
PHONE..................760 994-1401
Steve Ilmrud, *General Mgr*
EMP: 60
SALES (corp-wide): 18.8MM **Privately Held**
SIC: 3829 Measuring & controlling devices
HQ: Hexagon Metrology, Inc.
250 Circuit Dr
North Kingstown RI 02852
401 886-2000

(P-22212)
HIGHLAND TECHNOLOGY
650 Potrero Ave, San Francisco
(94110-2117)
PHONE..................415 551-1700
John Larkin, *President*
Denise Thiry, *Shareholder*
Hugh Callahan, *Vice Pres*
Rebecca McKee, *Admin Sec*
Claudia Deveze, *Design Engr*
EMP: 20
SQ FT: 6,000
SALES (est): 4.9MM **Privately Held**
WEB: www.highlandtechnology.com
SIC: 3829 Measuring & controlling devices

(P-22213)
HILZ CABLE ASSEMBLIES INC
31889 Corydon St Ste 110, Lake Elsinore
(92530-8509)
PHONE..................951 245-0499
Darlene Hilz, *President*
▲ **EMP:** 15
SALES: 1MM **Privately Held**
SIC: 3829 Cable testing machines

(P-22214)
HORIBA INSTRUMENTS INC
430 Indio Way, Sunnyvale (94085-4202)
PHONE..................408 730-4772
Margarita Trujillo, *Opers Mgr*

EMP: 75
SALES (corp-wide): 1.7B **Privately Held**
SIC: 3829 Measuring & controlling devices
HQ: Horiba Instruments Incorporated
9755 Research Dr
Irvine CA 92618
949 250-4811

(P-22215)
HORIBA INTERNATIONAL CORP (HQ)
9755 Research Dr, Irvine (92618-4626)
PHONE..................949 250-4811
Atsushi Horiba, *Ch of Bd*
Masayuki Adachi, *President*
Jai Hakhu, *CEO*
Richard Marting, *Vice Pres*
Sunao Kikkawa, *Admin Sec*
▲ **EMP:** 100
SQ FT: 40,000
SALES (est): 161.3MM
SALES (corp-wide): 1.7B **Privately Held**
SIC: 3829 Measuring & controlling devices
PA: Horiba,Ltd.
2, Miyanohigashicho, Kisshoin, Mi-
nami-Ku
Kyoto KYO 601-8
753 138-121

(P-22216)
IMDEX TECHNOLOGY USA LLC
3474 Empresa Dr Ste 150, San Luis Obispo
(93401-7391)
PHONE..................805 540-2017
George Vu,
Tim Price,
EMP: 20 **EST:** 2011
SQ FT: 3,500
SALES (est): 4.1MM **Privately Held**
SIC: 3829 8711 Surveying instruments &
accessories; engineering services
PA: Imdex Ltd
216 Balcatta Rd
Balcatta WA 6021

(P-22217)
INTELLIGENT BARCODE SYSTEMS
2190 Sherwood Rd, San Marino
(91108-2849)
PHONE..................626 576-8938
Vincent Chang, *President*
Karen Lee, *Treasurer*
EMP: 10
SQ FT: 2,400
SALES (est): 1.1MM **Privately Held**
WEB: www.barcodesystems.com
SIC: 3829 Measuring & controlling devices

(P-22218)
INTERNATIONAL SENSOR TECH INC
3 Whatney Ste 100, Irvine (92618-2836)
PHONE..................949 452-9000
Tommy Chou, *President*
Jack Chou, *Shareholder*
Doris Chou, *Corp Secy*
▲ **EMP:** 27
SQ FT: 20,000
SALES (est): 4.4MM **Privately Held**
WEB: www.intlsensor.com
SIC: 3829 Gas detectors

(P-22219)
IRROMETER COMPANY INC
Also Called: Watermark
1425 Palmyrita Ave, Riverside
(92507-1600)
P.O. Box 2424 (92516-2424)
PHONE..................951 689-1701
Thomas C Penning, *President*
Joseph Legget, *Treasurer*
Alfred J Hawkins, *Vice Pres*
Tom Penning, *General Mgr*
Linda Sciortino, *General Mgr*
EMP: 18 **EST:** 1951
SQ FT: 9,000
SALES (est): 4.7MM **Privately Held**
WEB: www.irrometer.com
SIC: 3829 Measuring & controlling devices

(P-22220)
J L SHEPHERD AND ASSOCIATES
1010 Arroyo St, San Fernando
(91340-1822)
PHONE..................818 898-2361
Joseph L Shepherd, *President*
Dorothy Shepherd, *Corp Secy*
Diana Shepherd, *Vice Pres*
Mary Shepherd, *Vice Pres*
▲ **EMP:** 27 **EST:** 1967
SQ FT: 15,000
SALES (est): 7.8MM **Privately Held**
WEB: www.jlshepherd.com
SIC: 3829 3844 Nuclear radiation & test-
ing apparatus; irradiation equipment

(P-22221)
JOHANSON INNOVATIONS INC
2975 Hawk Hill Ln, San Luis Obispo
(93405-8328)
PHONE..................805 544-4697
Michael Belingheri, *President*
EMP: 10
SALES (est): 890K **Privately Held**
SIC: 3829 Measuring & controlling devices

(P-22222)
KALILA MEDICAL INC
1400 Dell Ave Ste C, Campbell
(95008-6620)
PHONE..................408 819-5175
Joshua Hagerman, *Surgery Dir*
EMP: 25
SQ FT: 12,536
SALES: 900K
SALES (corp-wide): 5.5B **Privately Held**
SIC: 3829 Thermometers, including digital:
clinical
HQ: Terumo Americas Holding, Inc.
2101 Cottontail Ln
Somerset NJ 08873
732 302-4900

(P-22223)
KAP MEDICAL
1395 Pico St, Corona (92881-3373)
PHONE..................951 340-4360
Raj K Gowda, *President*
Dave Lewis, *Vice Pres*
Dan Rosenmayer, *Vice Pres*
Carlos Prado, *Human Resources*
▲ **EMP:** 35
SQ FT: 20,000
SALES (est): 13.9MM **Privately Held**
SIC: 3829 8711 Medical diagnostic sys-
tems, nuclear; consulting engineer

(P-22224)
KARL STORZ IMAGING INC (HQ)
Also Called: Optronics
1 S Los Carneros Rd, Goleta (93117-5506)
PHONE..................805 968-5563
Emery Skraupa, *General Mgr*
Jim Fish, *Vice Pres*
Gail Lobdell, *Executive Asst*
Barbara Meehan, *Admin Asst*
Yesenia Vasquez, *Info Tech Mgr*
EMP: 344
SQ FT: 105,000
SALES (est): 141.2MM
SALES (corp-wide): 1.6B **Privately Held**
SIC: 3829 3841 Measuring & controlling
devices; surgical & medical instruments
PA: Karl Storz Se & Co. Kg
Dr.-Karl-Storz-StraBe 34
Tuttlingen 78532
746 170-80

(P-22225)
KHN SOLUTIONS INC
Also Called: Bactrack
300 Broadway Ste 26, San Francisco
(94133-4529)
PHONE..................877 334-6876
Keith Nothacker, *CEO*
Pauline Basaran, *Vice Pres*
Stacey Sachs, *Vice Pres*
Shawn Casey, *Marketing Staff*
Jason Farrara, *Accounts Mgr*
◆ **EMP:** 12
SQ FT: 4,000
SALES: 50MM **Privately Held**
SIC: 3829 Breathalyzers

P R O D U C T S & S V C S

(P-22226)
KWJ ENGINEERING INC (PA)
Also Called: Eco Sensors
8430 Central Ave Ste C, Newark
(94560-3457)
PHONE......................510 794-4296
Joseph R Stetter, *President*
Edward F Stetter, *CFO*
Erin Springsteen, *Admin Asst*
Joseph Stetter, *CTO*
Bennett Meulendyk, *Senior Engr*
EMP: 25
SQ FT: 10,000
SALES (est): 5.3MM Privately Held
WEB: www.kwjengineering.com
SIC: 3829 5084 Gas detectors; instruments & control equipment

(P-22227)
LEX PRODUCTS LLC
11847 Sheldon St, Sun Valley
(91352-1508)
PHONE......................818 768-4474
Bob Luther, *President*
Elizabeth Luther, *President*
Patrick Legler, *Sales Associate*
EMP: 14
SALES (est): 1.9MM Privately Held
SIC: 3829 3315 3643 3613 Measuring & controlling devices; cable, steel: insulated or armored; current-carrying wiring devices; switchboards & parts, power
PA: Lex Products Llc
15 Progress Dr
Shelton CT 06484

(P-22228)
LOIS A VALESKIE
Also Called: Municon Consultants
2200 Jerrold Ave Ste K, San Francisco
(94124-1034)
PHONE......................415 641-2570
Lois A Valeskie, *Owner*
EMP: 10
SQ FT: 4,200
SALES (est): 1,000K Privately Held
WEB: www.municon.net
SIC: 3829 8711 Vibration meters, analyzers & calibrators; consulting engineer

(P-22229)
LUFFT USA INC
1110 Eugenia Pl Ste 200, Carpinteria
(93013-2081)
PHONE......................805 335-8500
Michael Corbett, *Branch Mgr*
Ann Pattison, *CEO*
Erik Wright, *Office Mgr*
EMP: 14
SALES (est): 2.4MM Privately Held
SIC: 3829 Weather tracking equipment
PA: Lufft Usa, Inc.
420 Boardwalk Dr
Youngsville NC 27596

(P-22230)
MARATHON PRODUCTS INCORPORATED
627 Mccormick St, San Leandro
(94577-1109)
P.O. Box 21579, Piedmont (94620-1579)
PHONE......................510 562-6450
Jon Nakagawa, *President*
Kevin Flynn, *Vice Pres*
Michael Cordero, *Administration*
Mikkel Ridley, *Network Tech*
Sandra Holt, *Manager*
▲ EMP: 12
SALES (est): 2.4MM Privately Held
SIC: 3829 Temperature sensors, except industrial process & aircraft

(P-22231)
MEASUREMENT SPECIALTIES INC
20630 Plummer St, Chatsworth
(91311-5111)
PHONE......................818 701-2750
Robert Simon, *Branch Mgr*
James Bishop, *Manager*
EMP: 98
SALES (corp-wide): 13.1B Privately Held
SIC: 3829 Measuring & controlling devices

HQ: Measurement Specialties, Inc.
1000 Lucas Way
Hampton VA 23666
757 766-1500

(P-22232)
MECHANIZED SCIENCE SEALS INC
Also Called: Ms Bellows
5322 Mcfadden Ave, Huntington Beach
(92649-1239)
PHONE......................714 898-5602
Jon Hamren, *President*
Victoria Hamren, *Treasurer*
Robin Hamren, *Admin Sec*
Linda Welsh, *Manager*
EMP: 20 EST: 1964
SQ FT: 10,000
SALES (est): 4MM Privately Held
WEB: www.msbellows.com
SIC: 3829 Measuring & controlling devices

(P-22233)
MEGGITT (ORANGE COUNTY) INC (HQ)
Also Called: Meggitt Sensing Systems
14600 Myford Rd, Irvine (92606-1005)
PHONE......................949 493-8181
Mel Hilderbrand, *President*
Veronica Reyes, *Treasurer*
Sara Kruse, *Vice Pres*
Cheryl Tindle, *General Mgr*
Jim Henderson, *Sr Software Eng*
▲ EMP: 266
SQ FT: 125,000
SALES (est): 86.6MM
SALES (corp-wide): 2.6B Privately Held
SIC: 3829 Vibration meters, analyzers & calibrators
PA: Meggitt Plc
Atlantic House, Aviation Park West
Christchurch BH23
120 259-7597

(P-22234)
MEPS REAL-TIME INC
6451 El Camino Real Ste C, Carlsbad
(92009-2800)
PHONE......................760 448-9500
Gordon Krass, *CEO*
Jim Caputo, *Vice Pres*
Paul Elizondo, *Vice Pres*
Jay Williams, *Vice Pres*
Shariq Hussain, *CTO*
EMP: 50
SALES (est): 12.8MM Privately Held
SIC: 3829 Accelerometers

(P-22235)
METTLER-TOLEDO RAININ LLC (HQ)
7500 Edgewater Dr, Oakland (94621-3027)
P.O. Box 2160 (94621-0060)
PHONE......................510 564-1600
Gerhard Keller, *General Mgr*
Olivier Filliol, *CEO*
Henri Chahine, *COO*
Shawn Vadala, *CFO*
Kathryn Savage, *Regional Mgr*
▲ EMP: 120
SQ FT: 55,000
SALES (est): 108.5MM
SALES (corp-wide): 2.7B Publicly Held
WEB: www.rainin.com
SIC: 3829 3821 Measuring & controlling devices; pipettes, hemocytometer
PA: Mettler-Toledo International Inc.
1900 Polaris Pkwy Fl 6
Columbus OH 43240
614 438-4511

(P-22236)
MICRO-METRIC INC
1050 Commercial St, San Jose
(95112-1419)
PHONE......................408 452-8505
Fax: 408 452-8412
EMP: 15
SQ FT: 6,500
SALES (est): 3.2MM Privately Held
WEB: www.micro-metric.com
SIC: 3829 7699 8734

(P-22237)
MIRION TECHNOLOGIES INC (PA)
3000 Executive Pkwy # 518, San Ramon
(94583-4355)
PHONE......................925 543-0800
Thomas Logan, *CEO*
Anthony Rabb, *CFO*
Mike Brumbaugh, *Exec VP*
Seth Rosen, *Exec VP*
Kip Bennett, *Vice Pres*
EMP: 158
SQ FT: 10,300
SALES (est): 285.7MM Privately Held
WEB: www.mirion.com
SIC: 3829 Measuring & controlling devices

(P-22238)
MISTRAS GROUP INC
3551 Voyager St Ste 104, Torrance
(90503-1674)
PHONE......................310 793-7173
Colm Walsh, *Branch Mgr*
EMP: 20 Publicly Held
SIC: 3829 Measuring & controlling devices
PA: Mistras Group, Inc.
195 Clarksville Rd Ste 2
Princeton Junction NJ 08550

(P-22239)
MITCHELL TEST & SAFETY INC
Also Called: Mitchell Instruments
1570 Cherokee St, San Marcos
(92078-2433)
PHONE......................760 744-2690
Sherwin Desportes, *President*
Michael Macvie, *Principal*
EMP: 12
SALES (est): 1.2MM Privately Held
SIC: 3829 Measuring & controlling devices

(P-22240)
NDT SYSTEMS INC
5542 Buckingham Dr Ste A, Huntington Beach (92649-1158)
PHONE......................714 893-2438
Grant Johnston, *CEO*
Gregory Smith, *President*
Ray Riebeling, *Executive*
Martin Leyba, *General Mgr*
Stephen Pastore, *Senior Engr*
EMP: 22
SALES (est): 4.4MM Privately Held
WEB: www.ndtsystems.com
SIC: 3829 Ultrasonic testing equipment

(P-22241)
OMNI OPTICAL PRODUCTS INC (PA)
17282 Eastman, Irvine (92614)
PHONE......................714 634-5700
Ken Panique, *President*
Jeferrey Frank, *Manager*
Cindy Von Hershman, *Manager*
▲ EMP: 22
SALES (est): 4.8MM Privately Held
WEB: www.omnisurvey.com
SIC: 3829 Surveying instruments & accessories

(P-22242)
OPTIVUS PROTON THERAPY INC
1475 Victoria Ct, San Bernardino
(92408-2831)
P.O. Box 608, Loma Linda (92354-0608)
PHONE......................909 799-8300
Jon W Slater, *CEO*
Daryl L Anderson, *CFO*
Matt Livingston, *Administration*
Raymond Terry, *Administration*
Dan Lafuze, *Sr Software Eng*
EMP: 75
SQ FT: 35,000
SALES (est): 17.6MM Privately Held
WEB: www.optivus.com
SIC: 3829 7371 8742 3699 Nuclear radiation & testing apparatus; custom computer programming services; maintenance management consultant; electrical equipment & supplies

(P-22243)
OPTRON SCIENTIFIC COMPANY INC
Also Called: Technical Associates
7051 Eton Ave, Canoga Park (91303-2112)
PHONE......................818 883-6103
Robert Goldstein, *President*
Kimberly Hallowell, *Train & Dev Mgr*
EMP: 15
SQ FT: 10,000
SALES (est): 3.1MM Privately Held
WEB: www.tech-associates.com
SIC: 3829 Nuclear radiation & testing apparatus

(P-22244)
OTSUKA AMERICA INC (DH)
1 Embarcadero Ctr # 2020, San Francisco
(94111-3750)
PHONE......................415 986-5300
Hiromi Yoshikawa, *Ch of Bd*
Shun Uchida, *President*
William Mc Hale, *Vice Pres*
Robert Sedor, *Vice Pres*
Sandy Hanneke, *Information Mgr*
◆ EMP: 10
SALES (est): 488.2MM
SALES (corp-wide): 11B Privately Held
SIC: 3829 3499 5122 2833 Spectrometers, liquid scintillation & nuclear; magnets, permanent: metallic; pharmaceuticals; vitamins, natural or synthetic: bulk, uncompounded; wines; mineral water, carbonated: packaged in cans, bottles, etc.
HQ: Otsuka Pharmaceutical Co., Ltd.
2-16-4, Konan
Minato-Ku TKY 108-0
367 171-400

(P-22245)
OUSTER INC
350 Treat Ave, San Francisco
(94110-1941)
PHONE......................415 949-0108
Charles Pacala, *CEO*
Mark Frichtl, *COO*
EMP: 60 EST: 2015
SALES (est): 288.4K Privately Held
SIC: 3829 Surveying instruments & accessories

(P-22246)
PACIFIC DIVERSIFIED CAPITAL CO
101 Ash St, San Diego (92101-3017)
PHONE......................619 696-2000
Steve Baum, *Ch of Bd*
Thomas Page, *Ch of Bd*
Henry Huta, *President*
Michael Lowell, *Vice Pres*
EMP: 800
SALES (est): 49.1MM
SALES (corp-wide): 11.2B Publicly Held
SIC: 3829 Measuring & controlling devices
HQ: San Diego Gas & Electric Company
8326 Century Park Ct
San Diego CA 92123
619 696-2000

(P-22247)
PACIFIC INSTRUMENTS INC
4080 Pike Ln, Concord (94520-1227)
PHONE......................925 827-9010
John Hueckel, *President*
Norm Hueckel, *Vice Pres*
Timothy Pellegrini, *Engineer*
Alice Forsyth, *Human Res Mgr*
Lee Hueckel, *Opers Staff*
▲ EMP: 21
SQ FT: 18,000
SALES (est): 6.2MM Privately Held
WEB: www.pacificinstruments.com
SIC: 3829 Measuring & controlling devices
PA: Vishay Precision Israel Ltd
26 Harokmim, Entrance
Holon
355 708-88

(P-22248)
PACIFIC PRECISION LABS INC
Also Called: J M A R Precision Systems
9430 Lurline Ave, Chatsworth
(91311-6003)
PHONE......................818 700-8977

▲ = Import ▼=Export
◆ =Import/Export

Chandu Vanjani, *President*
Ed Laiche, *Director*
▲ EMP: 25
SQ FT: 10,000
SALES (est): 4.7MM **Privately Held**
SIC: 3829 Measuring & controlling devices

(P-22249)
PAVILION INTEGRATION CORP
2528 Qume Dr Ste 1, San Jose
(95131-1836)
PHONE..................................408 453-8801
Ningyi Luo, *President*
Beningyi Luo, *President*
Jason Cao, *Vice Pres*
Dieter Gebhard, *Director*
EMP: 11
SQ FT: 3,000
SALES (est): 617.9K **Privately Held**
SIC: 3829 Instrumentation for reactor controls, auxiliary

(P-22250)
PHOENIX AERIAL SYSTEMS INC
10131 National Blvd, Los Angeles
(90034-3804)
PHONE..................................323 577-3366
Grayson Omans, *President*
Raymond Akol, *Sales Associate*
EMP: 15
SQ FT: 1,500
SALES: 500K **Privately Held**
SIC: 3829 Surveying instruments & accessories

(P-22251)
PROMEGA BSYSTEMS SUNNYVALE INC
3945 Freedom Cir Ste 200, Santa Clara
(95054-1264)
PHONE..................................408 636-2400
William A Linton, *Principal*
Ivan Ivanov, *Manager*
EMP: 35
SQ FT: 20,000
SALES (est): 6.5MM
SALES (corp-wide): 420.8MM **Privately Held**
WEB: www.turnerbiosystems.com
SIC: 3829 Measuring & controlling devices
PA: Promega Corporation
2800 Woods Hollow Rd
Fitchburg WI 53711
608 274-4330

(P-22252)
PROPRIETARY CONTROLS SYSTEMS
Also Called: P C S C
3541 Challenger St, Torrance
(90503-1641)
PHONE..................................310 303-3600
Masami Kosaka, *President*
Robert K Takahashi, *Vice Pres*
Al Portal, *Director*
EMP: 45
SQ FT: 29,000
SALES (est): 8MM
SALES (corp-wide): 5.1MM **Privately Held**
WEB: www. 1pcsc.com
SIC: 3829 3669 Measuring & controlling devices; burglar alarm apparatus, electric
PA: Ttik Inc
3541 Challenger St
Torrance CA 90503
310 303-3600

(P-22253)
QUALITY CONTROL SOLUTIONS INC
43339 Bus Pk Dr Ste 101, Temecula
(92590-3636)
PHONE..................................951 676-1616
Louis Todd, *President*
Denise Todd, *Admin Sec*
EMP: 25
SQ FT: 7,500
SALES (est): 4.5MM **Privately Held**
WEB: www.qc-solutions.com
SIC: 3829 5084 Measuring & controlling devices; instruments & control equipment

(P-22254)
QUANTUM GROUP INC
6827 Nancy Ridge Dr, San Diego
(92121-2233)
PHONE..................................858 566-9959
Mark K Goldstein, *President*
Ivan Nelson, *Shareholder*
Robert Banach, *Vice Pres*
▲ EMP: 100
SALES (est): 18.7MM **Privately Held**
SIC: 3829 8732 7389 Fire detector systems, non-electric; research services, except laboratory; fire protection service other than forestry or public

(P-22255)
QUINT MEASURING SYSTEMS INC
Also Called: Quint Graphics
2922 Saklan Indian Dr, Walnut Creek
(94595-3911)
PHONE..................................510 351-9405
Carol Quint, *President*
Richard Quint, *Chairman*
▲ EMP: 10
SQ FT: 5,000
SALES: 2MM **Privately Held**
WEB: www.quintmeasuring.com
SIC: 3829 3552 Measuring & controlling devices; silk screens for textile industry

(P-22256)
RADCAL PARTNERS IA CALIFORNIA
426 W Duarte Rd, Monrovia (91016-4591)
PHONE..................................626 359-4575
J Howard Marshall III, *Chairman*
Paul B Sunde, *President*
John Crawford, *Treasurer*
Timothy Harrington, *Vice Pres*
John Lumsden, *Admin Sec*
EMP: 48
SQ FT: 10,000
SALES (est): 6.4MM
SALES (corp-wide): 6.7MM **Privately Held**
WEB: www.radcal.com
SIC: 3829 Nuclear radiation & testing apparatus
PA: Radcal Corporation
426 W Duarte Rd
Monrovia CA 91016
626 359-4575

(P-22257)
RADIANT DETECTOR TECH LLC
19355 Bus Center Dr Ste 8, Northridge
(91324-3576)
PHONE..................................818 709-2468
Jan S Iwanczyk, *President*
Peter Lee, *Vice Pres*
EMP: 11
SQ FT: 15,000
SALES: 190K **Privately Held**
WEB: www.radiantdetectors.com
SIC: 3829 Nuclear radiation & testing apparatus

(P-22258)
RAE SYSTEMS INC (DH)
1349 Moffett Park Dr, Sunnyvale
(94089-1134)
PHONE..................................408 952-8200
Robert Chen, *President*
Christopher Toney, *COO*
Michael Hansen, *CFO*
Ming Tang PHD, *Exec VP*
Thomas N Gre, *Vice Pres*
▲ EMP: 104
SQ FT: 67,000
SALES (est): 98.7MM
SALES (corp-wide): 40.5B **Publicly Held**
WEB: www.raesystems.com
SIC: 3829 3812 3699 Gas detectors; search & detection systems & instruments; security control equipment & systems
HQ: Honeywell Analytics Inc.
405 Barclay Blvd
Lincolnshire IL 60069
847 955-8200

(P-22259)
RAYTHEON COMPANY
1801 Hughes Dr Dd311, Fullerton
(92833-2200)
PHONE..................................714 446-2287
John Coarse, *President*
Kelly Allison, *Principal*
EMP: 80
SALES (corp-wide): 25.3B **Publicly Held**
SIC: 3829 7371 3578 Toll booths, automatic; custom computer programming services; calculating & accounting equipment
PA: Raytheon Company
870 Winter St
Waltham MA 02451
781 522-3000

(P-22260)
RHEOSENSE INC
2420 Camino Ramon Ste 240, San Ramon
(94583-4319)
PHONE..................................925 866-3801
Seong-Gi Baek, *CEO*
Dennis Kong, *Electrical Engi*
Hua Han, *Manager*
EMP: 14
SQ FT: 1,400
SALES (est): 3.5MM **Privately Held**
WEB: www.rheosense.com
SIC: 3829 Breathalyzers

(P-22261)
SANTA CLARA IMAGING
Also Called: SCI
1825 Civic Center Dr # 1, Santa Clara
(95050-7302)
PHONE..................................408 296-5555
Reza Hashemieh, *Principal*
EMP: 40
SALES (est): 4.6MM **Privately Held**
SIC: 3829 8099 Measuring & controlling devices; blood related health services

(P-22262)
SECO MANUFACTURING COMPANY INC
4155 Oasis Rd, Redding (96003-0859)
P.O. Box 493592 (96049-3592)
PHONE..................................530 225-8155
Steven W Berglund, *CEO*
Mike Dahl, *General Mgr*
Eric Sabourin, *Research*
Joshua Dugo, *Engineer*
Daniel Moller, *Engineer*
▲ EMP: 120
SQ FT: 73,400
SALES (est): 29.6MM
SALES (corp-wide): 2.6B **Publicly Held**
WEB: www.surveying.com
SIC: 3829 Surveying instruments & accessories
PA: Trimble Inc.
935 Stewart Dr
Sunnyvale CA 94085
408 481-8000

(P-22263)
SEMCO
1495 S Gage St, San Bernardino
(92408-2835)
PHONE..................................909 799-9666
Shawn Martin, *Owner*
▲ EMP: 25
SQ FT: 5,400
SALES: 2MM **Privately Held**
SIC: 3829 3599 Physical property testing equipment; machine shop, jobbing & repair

(P-22264)
SEMCO INSTRUMENTS INC (DH)
25700 Rye Canyon Rd, Valencia
(91355-1148)
PHONE..................................661 257-2000
Michael G Moore, *President*
Vincent Sandoval, *CEO*
EMP: 177
SQ FT: 38,000
SALES (est): 82.8MM
SALES (corp-wide): 3.5B **Publicly Held**
WEB: www.semcoinstruments.com
SIC: 3829 Thermometers & temperature sensors

(P-22265)
SENSO-METRICS INC
4584 Runway St, Simi Valley (93063-3449)
PHONE..................................805 527-3640
Gary Johnson, *President*
Joan P Evans, *Corp Secy*
John Smith, *Exec VP*
EMP: 16
SQ FT: 16,288
SALES: 4.5MM **Privately Held**
WEB: www.senso-metrics.com
SIC: 3829 5084 Measuring & controlling devices; industrial machinery & equipment

(P-22266)
SENSONETICS INC
11164 Young River Ave, Fountain Valley
(92708-4109)
PHONE..................................714 799-1616
Gary Sahagen, *CEO*
Laurie Childress, *Business Mgr*
◆ EMP: 17 EST: 1998
SQ FT: 8,000
SALES (est): 3.5MM **Privately Held**
WEB: www.sensonetics.com
SIC: 3829 Pressure transducers

(P-22267)
SENTINEL HYDROSOLUTIONS LLC
1223 Pacific Oaks Pl # 104, Escondido
(92029-2913)
PHONE..................................866 410-1134
Scott Pallais, *Chairman*
EMP: 12
SQ FT: 3,500
SALES: 1.1MM **Privately Held**
SIC: 3829 Liquid leak detection equipment

(P-22268)
SENTRAN L L C (PA)
4355 E Lowell St Ste F, Ontario
(91761-2225)
PHONE..................................888 545-8988
Ken Kramer, *CEO*
Carlos Valdes, *COO*
Jorge Valdes, *Persnl Dir*
Tim Petersen, *QC Mgr*
Chad Brown, *Sales Mgr*
▲ EMP: 19
SQ FT: 5,000
SALES (est): 4MM **Privately Held**
WEB: www.sentranllc.com
SIC: 3829 Measuring & controlling devices

(P-22269)
SIERRA MONITOR CORPORATION (PA)
1991 Tarob Ct, Milpitas (95035-6840)
PHONE..................................408 262-6611
Jeffrey S Brown, *President*
Gordon R Arnold, *Ch of Bd*
Tamara S Allen, *CFO*
Michael C Farr, *Vice Pres*
▲ EMP: 56
SQ FT: 28,000
SALES: 19.7MM **Publicly Held**
WEB: www.sierramonitor.com
SIC: 3829 3822 Measuring & controlling devices; auto controls regulating residntl & coml environmt & applncs

(P-22270)
SIMON HARRISON
Also Called: Mri
551 5th St Ste A, San Fernando
(91340-2268)
PHONE..................................818 898-1036
Simon Harrison, *Owner*
EMP: 30
SALES (est): 1.9MM **Privately Held**
WEB: www.simonharrison.com
SIC: 3829 Torsion testing equipment

(P-22271)
SIMPA NETWORKS INC
2595 Mission St Ste 300, San Francisco
(94110-2574)
PHONE..................................415 216-3204
Michael Macharg, *Director*
EMP: 10
SALES (est): 600K **Privately Held**
SIC: 3829 Measuring & controlling devices

(P-22272)
SKF CONDITION MONITORING INC (DH)
Also Called: SKF Aptitude Exchange
9444 Balboa Ave Ste 150, San Diego (92123-4377)
PHONE..................................858 496-3400
Mark McGinn, *CEO*
Robert Kaufman, *Manager*
Kirk Tisdale, *Manager*
EMP: 120
SQ FT: 31,000
SALES (est): 17.9MM
SALES (corp-wide): 9.2B **Privately Held**
WEB: www.skfcm.com
SIC: 3829 Vibration meters, analyzers & calibrators
HQ: Skf Usa Inc.
    890 Forty Foot Rd
    Lansdale PA 19446
    267 436-6000

(P-22273)
SOBERLINK HEALTHCARE LLC
16787 Beach Blvd 211, Huntington Beach (92647-4848)
PHONE..................................714 975-7200
Brad Keays, *CEO*
EMP: 13
SALES (est): 1.1MM **Privately Held**
SIC: 3829 Breathalyzers

(P-22274)
SOILMOISTURE EQUIPMENT CORP
801 S Kellogg Ave, Goleta (93117-3886)
P.O. Box 30025, Santa Barbara (93130-0025)
PHONE..................................805 964-3525
Whitney Skaling, *CEO*
Kenneth Macaulay, *CFO*
Percy E Skaling, *Principal*
Jan Skaling, *Admin Sec*
Ken Macaulay, *Info Tech Mgr*
▲ **EMP:** 23 **EST:** 1950
SQ FT: 14,000
SALES (est): 5.5MM **Privately Held**
WEB: www.soilmoisture.com
SIC: 3829 Measuring & controlling devices

(P-22275)
SOLANO DIAGNOSTICS IMAGING
1101 B Gale Wilson Blvd # 100, Fairfield (94533-3771)
PHONE..................................707 646-4646
Adrian Ritts, *Manager*
Laverna Hubbard, *Administration*
Melody Rodriguez, *Supervisor*
EMP: 15
SQ FT: 4,000
SALES (est): 2.8MM **Privately Held**
SIC: 3829 8071 8011 Medical diagnostic systems, nuclear; medical laboratories; radiologist

(P-22276)
SOLMETRIC CORPORATION
Also Called: Suneye
117 Morris St Ste 100, Sebastopol (95472-3846)
PHONE..................................707 823-4600
Macdonald Willand, *President*
Mark Galli, *Vice Pres*
Keith Rose, *Vice Pres*
Phil Frantz, *Office Admin*
Bernie Burke, *Info Tech Mgr*
▲ **EMP:** 26
SALES: 3.6MM
SALES (corp-wide): 268MM **Publicly Held**
SIC: 3829 Solarimeters
HQ: Vivint Solar, Inc.
    1800 W Ashton Blvd
    Lehi UT 84043
    877 404-4129

(P-22277)
SPECTRAL DYNAMICS INC (PA)
2199 Zanker Rd, San Jose (95131-2109)
PHONE..................................760 761-0440
Stewart J Slykhous, *CEO*
James D Tucker, *CFO*
Deepak Jariwala, *Regional Mgr*
John Arbuckle, *General Mgr*
Russ Ayres, *Engineer*
▲ **EMP:** 20
SQ FT: 12,000
SALES (est): 8.2MM **Privately Held**
WEB: www.spectraldynamics.com
SIC: 3829 Measuring & controlling devices

(P-22278)
SPECTRAL LABS INCORPORATED
15920 Bernardo Center Dr, San Diego (92127-1828)
PHONE..................................858 451-0540
James H Winso, *President*
John Rolando, *Shareholder*
Eric Ackermann, *Vice Pres*
James Adams, *Project Mgr*
EMP: 20
SQ FT: 2,000
SALES: 400K **Privately Held**
SIC: 3829 Measuring & controlling devices

(P-22279)
SPIRACLE TECHNOLOGY LLC
10601 Calle Lee Ste 190, Los Alamitos (90720-6788)
PHONE..................................714 418-1091
Michael Farne, *Mng Member*
Sam Lim, *Engineer*
▲ **EMP:** 10
SQ FT: 7,000
SALES (est): 1.5MM **Privately Held**
SIC: 3829 Measuring & controlling devices

(P-22280)
SYSTEMS INTEGRATED LLC
2200 N Glassell St Ste A, Orange (92865-2771)
PHONE..................................714 998-0900
Susan Corrales-Diaz, *Manager*
John Holbrook, *Director*
EMP: 41
SQ FT: 7,000
SALES (est): 7.2MM **Privately Held**
SIC: 3829 Measuring & controlling devices

(P-22281)
SYSTEMS L C WOMACK
1615 Yeager Ave, La Verne (91750-5854)
PHONE..................................909 593-7304
Mike Rowlett, *President*
EMP: 10
SALES (corp-wide): 85.3MM **Privately Held**
SIC: 3829 7373 3594 Aircraft & motor vehicle measurement equipment; systems integration services; pumps, hydraulic power transfer
HQ: Womack Systems, L.C.
    13835 Senlac Dr
    Farmers Branch TX 75234
    214 357-3871

(P-22282)
TEK84 ENGINEERING GROUP LLC
13230 Evening Creek Dr S # 202, San Diego (92128-4106)
PHONE..................................858 676-5382
Steven W Smith, *Mng Member*
Barbara Hatfield,
EMP: 10
SALES (est): 750K **Privately Held**
SIC: 3829 Measuring & controlling devices

(P-22283)
TEKVISIONS INC (PA)
40970 Anza Rd, Temecula (92592-9368)
PHONE..................................951 506-9709
Tom Cramer, *President*
Nicholas Christie, *Corp Secy*
Doug Bowe, *Vice Pres*
Elizabeth Blythe, *Credit Mgr*
▲ **EMP:** 10
SQ FT: 1,880
SALES (est): 4.1MM **Privately Held**
WEB: www.tekvisions.com
SIC: 3829 5045 Measuring & controlling devices; computer peripheral equipment

(P-22284)
TELATEMP CORPORATION
2910 E La Palma Ave Ste C, Anaheim (92806-2618)
PHONE..................................714 414-0343
Daniel Stack, *President*
Evelyn Darringer, *Vice Pres*
EMP: 12
SQ FT: 3,200
SALES: 3MM **Privately Held**
WEB: www.telatemp.com
SIC: 3829 Thermometers & temperature sensors

(P-22285)
TELEDYNE DGITAL IMAGING US INC
Also Called: Teledyne RAD-Icon Imaging
765 Sycamore Dr, Milpitas (95035-7465)
PHONE..................................408 736-6000
EMP: 15
SALES (corp-wide): 2.6B **Publicly Held**
SIC: 3829 3674 Measuring & controlling devices; semiconductors & related devices
HQ: Teledyne Digital Imaging Us, Inc.
    700 Technology Park Dr # 2
    Billerica MA 01821
    978 670-2000

(P-22286)
TELEDYNE INSTRUMENTS INC
Also Called: Teledyne API
9970 Carroll Canyon Rd A, San Diego (92131-1106)
PHONE..................................619 239-5959
Jeff Franks, *Branch Mgr*
Larry Dana, *Technology*
Michael Parker, *Technology*
Patrick King, *Project Engr*
Cristina Decker, *Engineer*
EMP: 100
SALES (corp-wide): 2.6B **Publicly Held**
WEB: www.teledynesolutions.com
SIC: 3829 3823 Measuring & controlling devices; industrial instrmnts msrmnt display/control process variable
HQ: Teledyne Instruments, Inc.
    1049 Camino Dos Rios
    Thousand Oaks CA 91360
    805 373-4545

(P-22287)
TEMPTRON ENGINEERING INC
7823 Deering Ave, Canoga Park (91304-5006)
PHONE..................................818 346-4900
Edward Skei, *President*
Beverly Skei, *Treasurer*
Anna Vartanian, *Accountant*
Pablo Cruz, *Prdtn Mgr*
EMP: 35 **EST:** 1971
SQ FT: 13,000
SALES (est): 6.9MM **Privately Held**
SIC: 3829 3769 3823 Measuring & controlling devices; guided missile & space vehicle parts & auxiliary equipment; temperature instruments: industrial process type

(P-22288)
THERM-X OF CALIFORNIA INC (PA)
3200 Investment Blvd, Hayward (94545-3807)
P.O. Box 768, Alamo (94507-0768)
PHONE..................................510 441-7566
Dan Trujillo, *CEO*
Skip Johnson, *President*
Phil Quinton, *President*
Linda Trujillo, *Corp Secy*
Dorita Castillano, *Planning*
EMP: 177
SQ FT: 74,300
SALES (est): 37.8MM **Privately Held**
WEB: www.therm-x.com
SIC: 3829 Measuring & controlling devices

(P-22289)
TOPCON POSITIONING SYSTEMS INC (DH)
7400 National Dr, Livermore (94550-7340)
PHONE..................................925 245-8300
Raymond O'Connor, *President*
David Mudrick, *CFO*
M Yamazaki, *Exec VP*
Mark S Bittner, *Senior VP*
Joe Brabec, *Senior VP*
◆ **EMP:** 122
SQ FT: 80,000
SALES (est): 108.5MM
SALES (corp-wide): 1.3B **Privately Held**
WEB: www.topconlaser.com
SIC: 3829 3625 3823 3699 Surveying instruments & accessories; relays & industrial controls; industrial instrmnts msrmnt display/control process variable; electrical equipment & supplies; surveying services; excavation work
HQ: Topcon America Corporation
    111 Bauer Dr
    Oakland NJ 07436
    201 599-5100

(P-22290)
TRI ELECTRONICS INC
4667 Mission Gorge Pl B, San Diego (92120-4148)
PHONE..................................858 571-4881
Leonid Radomyshelsky, *President*
Michael Radomyshelsky, *Corp Secy*
▲ **EMP:** 10
SQ FT: 2,500
SALES (est): 1.6MM **Privately Held**
WEB: www.trielectronics.com
SIC: 3829 Measuring & controlling devices

(P-22291)
TRUTOUCH TECHNOLOGIES INC
2020 Iowa Ave Ste 102, Riverside (92507-2417)
PHONE..................................909 703-5963
Benjamin Ver Steeg, *CEO*
Oscar Lazaro, *Partner*
David Desrochers, *CFO*
Gerald Grafe, *Admin Sec*
Ries Robinson, *Director*
EMP: 14
SQ FT: 5,000
SALES (est): 2.3MM **Privately Held**
WEB: www.trutouchtechnologies.com
SIC: 3829 Measuring & controlling devices

(P-22292)
UNITED TESTING SYSTEMS INC
1375 S Acacia Ave Ste A, Fullerton (92831-5311)
PHONE..................................714 638-2322
Carol M Watson, *President*
Thomas D Settimi, *Vice Pres*
Syed Ahmed, *Managing Dir*
Jeffrey M Routley, *Admin Sec*
Andrew Nguyen, *Engineer*
▲ **EMP:** 52 **EST:** 1964
SQ FT: 40,000
SALES: 7.9MM **Privately Held**
SIC: 3829 8734 5084 Hardness testing equipment; tensile strength testing equipment; calibration & certification; industrial machinery & equipment

(P-22293)
US NUCLEAR CORP (PA)
7051 Eton Ave, Canoga Park (91303-2112)
PHONE..................................818 296-0746
Robert Goldstein, *CEO*
Darian Andersen, *CFO*
Rachel Boulds, *CFO*
EMP: 16
SALES (est): 1.3MM **Privately Held**
SIC: 3829 Nuclear radiation & testing apparatus

(P-22294)
VANTARI MEDICAL LLC
15440 Laguna Canyon Rd, Irvine (92618-2138)
PHONE..................................949 783-5300
Nick Arroyo, *CEO*
Phil Lamb, *CFO*
Brooke Hambleton, *Senior VP*
EMP: 17
SALES (est): 5.3MM **Privately Held**
SIC: 3829 Medical diagnostic systems, nuclear

(P-22295)
VENA ENGINEERING CORP
7 Hangar Way, Watsonville (95076-2450)
P.O. Box 628, Freedom (95019-0628)
PHONE..................................831 724-5738
Martin Greatorex, *President*
Jeff Greatorex, *Vice Pres*
EMP: 10
SQ FT: 7,000

SALES (est): 1.5MM **Privately Held**
WEB: www.vena.com
SIC: **3829** Measuring & controlling devices

(P-22296)
VTI-VALTRONICS INC
3463 Double Springs Rd, Valley Springs
(95252-9275)
PHONE...................................209 754-0707
Irvin G Burough, *President*
Melissa K Powers, *CFO*
Ruby L Burough, *Vice Pres*
Melinda Janovro, *Manager*
▼ EMP: 19
SQ FT: 9,600
SALES (est): 2.8MM **Privately Held**
WEB: www.val-tronics.com
SIC: **3829** Measuring & controlling devices

(P-22297)
WELLBORE NAVIGATION INC (PA)
Also Called: Welnav
1240 N Jefferson St Ste M, Anaheim
(92807-1632)
PHONE...................................714 259-7760
Charles Ron Adams, *President*
Sandy Adams, *Admin Sec*
EMP: 15 EST: 1981
SQ FT: 7,000
SALES (est): 2MM **Privately Held**
WEB: www.welnavinc.com
SIC: **3829 1381 7371** Surveying instruments & accessories; directional drilling oil & gas wells; computer software development

(P-22298)
YS CONTROLS LLC
3041 S Shannon St, Santa Ana
(92704-6320)
PHONE...................................714 641-0727
John Sapone, *President*
Tony Johnson, *President*
▲ EMP: 28
SQ FT: 10,080
SALES (est): 3.8MM
SALES (corp-wide): 4.3MM **Privately Held**
WEB: www.yscontrols.com
SIC: **3829** Measuring & controlling devices
PA: Maul Mfg., Inc.
3041 S Shannon St
Santa Ana CA 92704
714 641-0727

3841 Surgical & Medical Instrs & Apparatus

(P-22299)
3 GEN INC
31521 Rancho Viejo Rd # 104, San Juan
Capistrano (92675-1868)
PHONE...................................949 481-6384
John Bottjer, *President*
Nizar Mullani,
Thorsten Trotzenberg,
EMP: 13
SQ FT: 3,000
SALES (est): 1.8MM **Privately Held**
WEB: www.epifluoroscope.com
SIC: **3841** Surgical & medical instruments

(P-22300)
5 I SCIENCES INC
16885 Via Del Campo Ct # 130, San Diego
(92127-1744)
PHONE...................................858 943-4566
Richard M Rose MD, *CEO*
Jerome Aarestad, *Director*
EMP: 15
SALES (est): 133.1K **Privately Held**
SIC: **3841** Surgical & medical instruments

(P-22301)
AB MEDICAL TECHNOLOGIES INC
20272 Skypark Dr, Redding (96002-9250)
PHONE...................................530 605-2522
Tammy Blanton, *CEO*
Dwight Abbott, *President*
Ken Brown, *President*
EMP: 10
SQ FT: 7,000

SALES (est): 1.4MM **Privately Held**
SIC: **3841** Surgical & medical instruments

(P-22302)
ABBOTT LABORATORIES
Also Called: Abbott Diagnostics Division
4551 Great America Pkwy, Santa Clara
(95054-1208)
PHONE...................................408 330-0057
Jim Janik, *Branch Mgr*
Cindy Kelly, *Executive*
Lorilee Adams, *Project Dir*
Manijeh Hosseini, *Project Mgr*
Jose Ochoa, *Project Mgr*
EMP: 450
SQ FT: 117,500
SALES (corp-wide): 27.3B **Publicly Held**
WEB: www.abbott.com
SIC: **3841** Medical instruments & equipment, blood & bone work
PA: Abbott Laboratories
100 Abbott Park Rd
Abbott Park IL 60064
224 667-6100

(P-22303)
ABBOTT LABORATORIES
Also Called: Abbott Vascular
3200 Lakeside Dr, Santa Clara
(95054-2807)
P.O. Box 58167 (95052-8167)
PHONE...................................408 845-3000
Jean Reyda, *Branch Mgr*
EMP: 750
SALES (corp-wide): 27.3B **Publicly Held**
WEB: www.abbott.com
SIC: **3841 8731** Surgical & medical instruments; commercial physical research
PA: Abbott Laboratories
100 Abbott Park Rd
Abbott Park IL 60064
224 667-6100

(P-22304)
ABBOTT VASCULAR INC
42301 Zevo Dr Ste D, Temecula
(92590-3731)
P.O. Box 9018 (92589-9018)
PHONE...................................951 914-2400
Rhonda Reddick, *Manager*
EMP: 31
SALES (corp-wide): 27.3B **Publicly Held**
WEB: www.abbottvascular.com
SIC: **3841** Catheters
HQ: Abbott Vascular Inc.
3200 Lakeside Dr
Santa Clara CA 95054
408 845-3000

(P-22305)
ABBOTT VASCULAR INC
30590 Cochise Cir, Murrieta (92563-2501)
P.O. Box 3020, North Chicago IL (60064-9320)
PHONE...................................408 845-3186
EMP: 200
SALES (corp-wide): 27.3B **Publicly Held**
WEB: www.abbottvascular.com
SIC: **3841** Surgical instruments & apparatus
HQ: Abbott Vascular Inc.
3200 Lakeside Dr
Santa Clara CA 95054
408 845-3000

(P-22306)
ABBOTT VASCULAR INC
Also Called: Advanced Cardiovascular System
3200 Lakeside Dr, Santa Clara
(95054-2807)
P.O. Box 58167 (95052-8167)
PHONE...................................408 845-3000
Chip Hance, *President*
EMP: 49
SALES (corp-wide): 27.3B **Publicly Held**
SIC: **3841** Surgical instruments & apparatus
HQ: Abbott Vascular Inc.
3200 Lakeside Dr
Santa Clara CA 95054
408 845-3000

(P-22307)
ACCESS CLOSURE INC
5452 Betsy Ross Dr, Santa Clara
(95054-1101)
PHONE...................................408 610-6500
Gregory D Casciaro, *President*
John J Buckley, *CFO*
Susan Aloyan, *Exec VP*
Stephen Mackinnon, *Vice Pres*
Ariel Sutton, *Vice Pres*
EMP: 344
SQ FT: 40,000
SALES (est): 56.4MM
SALES (corp-wide): 136.8B **Publicly Held**
WEB: www.accessclosure.com
SIC: **3841** Surgical & medical instruments
PA: Cardinal Health, Inc.
7000 Cardinal Pl
Dublin OH 43017
614 757-5000

(P-22308)
ACCESS SCIENTIFIC INC
1042 N El Camino Real, Encinitas
(92024-1322)
PHONE...................................858 354-8761
Steve Bierman, *CEO*
Bill Bold, *President*
Albert M Misajon, *Officer*
Rick Pluth, *Vice Pres*
EMP: 34
SQ FT: 2,700
SALES (est): 5.4MM **Privately Held**
SIC: **3841** Surgical & medical instruments

(P-22309)
ACCESS SCIENTIFIC LLC
3910 Sorrento Valley Blvd # 200, San Diego
(92121-1419)
PHONE...................................858 259-8333
Paul Jazwin,
Glen Lakin, *Treasurer*
Richard Delgado, *Opers Staff*
Christina Ray, *Manager*
EMP: 25 EST: 2012
SALES (est): 3.5MM **Privately Held**
SIC: **3841** Surgical & medical instruments

(P-22310)
ACCLARENT INC
33 Technology Dr, Irvine (92618-2346)
PHONE...................................650 687-5888
David Shepherd, *President*
Heather Wozniak, *Regional Mgr*
Crystal Sein-Lwin, *Technician*
Cristina Todasco, *Director*
Matt Schoger, *Consultant*
EMP: 400
SALES (est): 112.6MM
SALES (corp-wide): 76.4B **Publicly Held**
WEB: www.acclarent.com
SIC: **3841** Surgical & medical instruments
HQ: Ethicon Inc.
Us Route 22
Somerville NJ 08876
732 524-0400

(P-22311)
ACCRIVA DGNOSTICS HOLDINGS INC (DH)
Also Called: Itc Nexus Holding Company
6260 Sequence Dr, San Diego
(92121-4358)
PHONE...................................858 404-8203
Scott Cramer, *CEO*
Greg Tibbitts, *CFO*
Frank Laduca, *Officer*
Matt Bastardi, *Vice Pres*
Mickie Henshall, *Vice Pres*
EMP: 350
SALES (est): 107MM
SALES (corp-wide): 157.1MM **Privately Held**
SIC: **3841 2835 6719** Diagnostic apparatus, medical; blood derivative diagnostic agents; hemotology diagnostic agents; investment holding companies, except banks
HQ: Instrumentation Laboratory Company
180 Hartwell Rd
Bedford MA 01730
781 861-0710

(P-22312)
ACCURAY INCORPORATED (PA)
1310 Chesapeake Ter, Sunnyvale
(94089-1100)
PHONE...................................408 716-4600
Louis J Lavigne Jr, *Ch of Bd*
Elizabeth Davila, *Vice Chairman*
Joshua H Levine, *President*
Andy Kirkpatrick, *COO*
Kevin Waters, *CFO*
EMP: 117
SQ FT: 164,000
SALES: 404.9MM **Publicly Held**
WEB: www.accuray.com
SIC: **3841** Surgical instruments & apparatus

(P-22313)
ACCUTECH LLC
2641 La Mirada Dr, Vista (92081-8435)
PHONE...................................760 599-6555
Terrence Lee,
Todd Patrie, *Regl Sales Mgr*
Paul Grenier, *Sales Mgr*
Anna Proussalis, *Accounts Mgr*
Lawrence O'neil, *Representative*
EMP: 30
SALES (est): 4.4MM **Privately Held**
WEB: www.cholestrak.com
SIC: **3841** Diagnostic apparatus, medical

(P-22314)
ADEPT MED INTERNATIONAL INC (PA)
665 Pleasant Valley Rd, Diamond Springs
(95619-9241)
PHONE...................................530 621-1220
Tim Quigley, *President*
Christine Quigley, *Vice Pres*
EMP: 10
SQ FT: 6,500
SALES (est): 2MM **Privately Held**
WEB: www.adeptmed.com
SIC: **3841** Diagnostic apparatus, medical

(P-22315)
ADVANCED OXYGEN THERAPY INC (HQ)
3512 Seagate Way Ste 100, Oceanside
(92056-2688)
PHONE...................................760 431-4700
Mike Griffiths, *CEO*
EMP: 19
SALES (est): 3MM **Privately Held**
SIC: **3841** Diagnostic apparatus, medical
PA: Aoti, Inc.
3512 Seagate Way Ste 100
Oceanside CA 92056
760 431-4700

(P-22316)
ADVANCED REFRACTIVE TECH
12518 Cavallo St, San Diego (92130-2740)
PHONE...................................949 940-1300
Randal Bailey, *President*
Laurence M Schreiber, *COO*
EMP: 15 EST: 1999
SQ FT: 10,000
SALES (est): 1.2MM **Privately Held**
WEB: www.advancedrefractive.com
SIC: **3841** Surgical & medical instruments

(P-22317)
ADVANCED STERLIZATION (DH)
Also Called: A S P
33 Technology Dr, Irvine (92618-2346)
PHONE...................................800 595-0200
Bernard Zovighian, *CEO*
Matthew Murawski, *Director*
Michelle Gray, *Manager*
EMP: 50
SALES (est): 22.1MM
SALES (corp-wide): 76.4B **Publicly Held**
SIC: **3841** Surgical & medical instruments
HQ: Ethicon Us Llc
4545 Creek Rd 3
Blue Ash OH 45242
513 337-7000

(P-22318)
ADVANCEDCATH TECHNOLOGIES LLC (HQ)
176 Component Dr, San Jose
(95131-1119)
PHONE...................................408 433-9505

Randall Sword, *CEO*
Suresh Sainath, *President*
Lucian Bejinariu, *Vice Pres*
Ken Koen, *Vice Pres*
Tim Maes, *Vice Pres*
EMP: 32
SALES (est): 19.1MM
SALES (corp-wide): 13.1B **Privately Held**
WEB: www.advancedcath.com
SIC: 3841 Catheters
PA: Te Connectivity Ltd.
Rheinstrasse 20
Schaffhausen SH 8200
526 336-677

(P-22319)
AIRXPANDERS INC (PA)
3047 Orchard Pkwy, San Jose
(95134-2024)
PHONE..................................650 964-1437
Frank Grillo, *President*
Scott Dodson, *President*
Ryan Han, *Engineer*
Daisy Lu, *Controller*
Jenny Timpany, *Buyer*
EMP: 64
SALES: 3.9MM **Privately Held**
SIC: 3841 Medical instruments & equipment, blood & bone work

(P-22320)
ALCON LABORATORIES INC
Also Called: Alcon Surgical
15800 Alton Pkwy, Irvine (92618-3818)
P.O. Box 19587 (92623-9587)
PHONE..................................949 753-6488
Kenneth Lickel, *Manager*
Steve Ambrose, *Associate Dir*
Julie Hornung, *Admin Asst*
Jim Garwood, *Info Tech Mgr*
Daryush Agahi, *Design Engr*
EMP: 600
SQ FT: 32,000
SALES (corp-wide): 49.1B **Privately Held**
WEB: www.alconlabs.com
SIC: 3841 3851 5049 Surgical & medical instruments; ophthalmic goods; optical goods
HQ: Alcon Laboratories, Inc.
6201 South Fwy
Fort Worth TX 76134
817 293-0450

(P-22321)
ALCON LENSX INC (DH)
15800 Alton Pkwy, Irvine (92618-3818)
PHONE..................................949 753-1393
Kevin J Buehler, *CEO*
Elaine Whitbeck,
Robert Nguyen, *Software Engr*
Simin Shoari, *Software Engr*
Sumit Yadav, *Software Engr*
EMP: 99 EST: 2006
SQ FT: 20,000
SALES (est): 22.7MM
SALES (corp-wide): 49.1B **Privately Held**
SIC: 3841 Surgical lasers
HQ: Alcon Laboratories Holding Corporation
6201 South Fwy
Fort Worth TX 76134
817 293-0450

(P-22322)
ALCON RESEARCH LTD
15800 Alton Pkwy, Irvine (92618-3818)
PHONE..................................949 387-2142
Ed Richards, *Owner*
Charles Barbe, *Senior Buyer*
EMP: 29
SALES (corp-wide): 49.1B **Privately Held**
SIC: 3841 Surgical instruments & apparatus
HQ: Alcon Research, Ltd.
6201 South Fwy
Fort Worth TX 76134
817 551-4555

(P-22323)
ALCOTREVI INC
1133 S Central Ave 1, Glendale
(91204-2212)
PHONE..................................818 244-0400
Fredrik Der-Hacopian, *Director*
Dr Samvel Hmayakyan, *Bd of Directors*
EMP: 10

SALES (est): 680K **Privately Held**
SIC: 3841 Surgical & medical instruments

(P-22324)
ALEPH GROUP INC
Also Called: A G I
6920 Sycamore Canyon Blvd, Riverside
(92507-0781)
PHONE..................................951 213-4815
EMP: 14
SALES: 3MM **Privately Held**
SIC: 3841 3843 8099

(P-22325)
ALL MANUFACTURERS INC
Also Called: Allied Harbor Aerospace Fas
2900 Palisades Dr, Corona (92880-9429)
PHONE..................................951 280-4200
Jon R Gerwin, *CEO*
Ron Gerwin, *President*
EMP: 42
SQ FT: 30,000
SALES: 30MM **Privately Held**
WEB: www.allied1.com
SIC: 3841 3694 Surgical & medical instruments; motors, starting: automotive & aircraft

(P-22326)
ALLEZ SPINE LLC (PA)
Also Called: Phygen
2301 Dupont Dr Ste 510, Irvine
(92612-7518)
PHONE..................................949 752-7885
Souhail Toubia,
Kelvin Nguyen, *Design Engr*
Allyson Lodwick, *Legal Staff*
Brett Menmuir, *Consultant*
EMP: 19
SALES (est): 2.5MM **Privately Held**
SIC: 3841 Diagnostic apparatus, medical

(P-22327)
ALLIANCE MEDICAL PRODUCTS INC
Also Called: Siegfried Irvine
9342 9292 Jeronimo Rd, Irvine (92618)
PHONE..................................949 768-4690
Darrin Schellin, *CEO*
Brian Jones, *COO*
Dan Moore, *CFO*
Tom Lucas, *Vice Pres*
Peter Mead, *Lab Dir*
▲ **EMP:** 130
SQ FT: 55,000
SALES (est): 98.7MM
SALES (corp-wide): 759MM **Privately Held**
SIC: 3841 7819 Medical instruments & equipment, blood & bone work; laboratory service, motion picture
HQ: Siegfried Usa Holding , Inc.
33 Industrial Park Rd
Pennsville NJ 08070
856 678-3601

(P-22328)
ALPHATEC HOLDINGS INC (PA)
5818 El Camino Real, Carlsbad
(92008-8816)
PHONE..................................760 431-9286
Terry M Rich, *CEO*
Mortimer Berkowitz III, *Ch of Bd*
Michael Plunkett, *President*
Patrick Miles, *Chairman*
Quentin Blackford, *Bd of Directors*
EMP: 30
SQ FT: 76,693
SALES: 101.7MM **Publicly Held**
SIC: 3841 Surgical & medical instruments

(P-22329)
ALPINE BIOMED CORP
1501 Industrial Rd, San Carlos
(94070-4111)
PHONE..................................650 802-0400
James B Hawkins, *President*
Lori Lazarescu, *Manager*
EMP: 120
SQ FT: 1,460
SALES (est): 6.4MM
SALES (corp-wide): 500.9MM **Publicly Held**
WEB: www.alpinebiomed.com
SIC: 3841 Catheters

PA: Natus Medical Incorporated
6701 Koll Center Pkwy # 120
Pleasanton CA 94566
925 223-6700

(P-22330)
ALTHEA AJINOMOTO INC
11040 Roselle St, San Diego (92121-1205)
PHONE..................................858 882-0123
J David Enloe Jr, *President*
Martha J Demski, *CFO*
Ej Brandreth, *Senior VP*
Chris Duffy, *Senior VP*
Bert Barbosa, *Vice Pres*
EMP: 164
SQ FT: 85,000
SALES (est): 66.3MM
SALES (corp-wide): 10.8B **Privately Held**
WEB: www.altheatech.com
SIC: 3841 2836 Hypodermic needles & syringes; coagulation products
PA: Ajinomoto Co., Inc.
1-15-1, Kyobashi
Chuo-Ku TKY 104-0
352 508-111

(P-22331)
AMADA MIYACHI AMERICA INC
245 E El Norte St, Monrovia (91016-4828)
PHONE..................................626 303-5676
Susan Gu, *Manager*
EMP: 20
SALES (corp-wide): 2.8B **Privately Held**
SIC: 3841 Surgical & medical instruments
HQ: Amada Miyachi America, Inc.
1820 S Myrtle Ave
Monrovia CA 91016
-

(P-22332)
AMEDICA BIOTECH INC
28301 Industrial Blvd K, Hayward
(94545-4429)
PHONE..................................510 785-5980
Jian Feng Chen, *President*
Shaofang You, *CFO*
Leo Yang, *Admin Sec*
▲ **EMP:** 17
SALES (est): 1.7MM
SALES (corp-wide): 27.3B **Publicly Held**
WEB: www.amedicabiotech.com
SIC: 3841 8731
HQ: Alere Inc.
51 Sawyer Rd Ste 200
Waltham MA 02453
781 647-3900

(P-22333)
AMEDITECH INC
9940 Mesa Rim Rd, San Diego
(92121-2910)
PHONE..................................858 535-1968
Robert Joel, *Principal*
▲ **EMP:** 118 EST: 1999
SQ FT: 47,000
SALES (est): 22.1MM
SALES (corp-wide): 27.3B **Publicly Held**
WEB: www.ameditech.com
SIC: 3841 Medical instruments & equipment, blood & bone work
HQ: Alere Inc.
51 Sawyer Rd Ste 200
Waltham MA 02453
781 647-3900

(P-22334)
AMERICAN MSTR TECH SCNTFIC INC
Also Called: American Histology Reagent Co
1330 Thurman St, Lodi (95240-3145)
P.O. Box 2539 (95241-2539)
PHONE..................................209 368-4031
Brandon B Jones, *President*
▲ **EMP:** 26
SQ FT: 25,000
SALES (est): 5MM
SALES (corp-wide): 27MM **Privately Held**
WEB: www.americanmastertech.com
SIC: 3841 2835 Medical instruments & equipment, blood & bone work; cytology & histology diagnostic agents
PA: Slmp, Llc
2090 Commerce Dr
Mckinney TX 75069
972 436-1010

(P-22335)
AMO USA INC
1700 E Saint Andrew Pl, Santa Ana
(92705-4933)
PHONE..................................714 247-8200
Tom Frinzi, *President*
Pat Holloway, *Opers Staff*
Karen Huckvale, *Manager*
EMP: 200
SQ FT: 100,000
SALES: 1.1B
SALES (corp-wide): 76.4B **Publicly Held**
WEB: www.visx.com
SIC: 3841 3845 Surgical & medical instruments; laser systems & equipment, medical
HQ: Johnson & Johnson Surgical Vision, Inc.
1700 E Saint Andrew Pl
Santa Ana CA 92705
714 247-8200

(P-22336)
ANSELL HEALTHCARE PRODUCTS LLC
9301 Oakdale Ave Ste 300, Chatsworth
(91311-6539)
PHONE..................................205 423-8770
Maurice Davis, *Mng Member*
EMP: 30
SALES (est): 3.1MM **Privately Held**
SIC: 3841 Surgical & medical instruments

(P-22337)
APAMA MEDICAL INC
745 Camden Ave Ste A, Campbell
(95008-4146)
PHONE..................................408 903-4094
AMR Salahieh, *President*
John Buckley, *CFO*
Pj Iranitalab, *Development*
EMP: 15
SQ FT: 7,000
SALES (est): 3.3MM
SALES (corp-wide): 9B **Publicly Held**
SIC: 3841 Diagnostic apparatus, medical
PA: Boston Scientific Corporation
300 Boston Scientific Way
Marlborough MA 01752
508 683-4000

(P-22338)
APPLIED CARDIAC SYSTEMS INC
1 Hughes Ste A, Irvine (92618-2064)
PHONE..................................949 855-9366
Loren A Manera, *CEO*
Tricia Meads, *CFO*
Shannon Koerber, *Vice Pres*
Susan Marcus, *Vice Pres*
Tim Heinemeyer, *Executive*
▲ **EMP:** 64 EST: 1981
SQ FT: 18,000
SALES (est): 11.8MM **Privately Held**
WEB: www.acsholter.com
SIC: 3841 Diagnostic apparatus, medical

(P-22339)
APPLIED MANUFACTURING LLC
22872 Avenida Empresa, Rcho STA Marg
(92688-2650)
PHONE..................................949 713-8000
Tom Wachli, *President*
EMP: 1200
SALES (est): 30MM
SALES (corp-wide): 576MM **Privately Held**
SIC: 3841 Surgical & medical instruments
HQ: Applied Medical Resources Corporation
22872 Avenida Empresa
Rcho Sta Marg CA 92688
949 713-8000

(P-22340)
APPLIED MEDICAL CORPORATION (PA)
22872 Avenida Empresa, Rcho STA Marg
(92688-2650)
PHONE..................................949 713-8000
Said Hilal, *CEO*
Ray Frame, *Vice Pres*
Chris Myers, *Vice Pres*
Matt Petrime, *Vice Pres*

Mary Stegwell, *Vice Pres*
EMP: 113 **EST:** 1987
SALES (est): 576MM Privately Held
SIC: 3841 Surgical & medical instruments

(P-22341)
APPLIED MEDICAL RESOURCES CORP (HQ)
Also Called: Applied Medical Distribution
22872 Avenida Empresa, Rcho STA Marg
(92688-2650)
PHONE....................949 713-8000
Said S Hilal, *President*
Nabil Hilal, *President*
Gary Johnson, *President*
Stephen E Stanley, *President*
Michael Vaughn, *President*
▲ **EMP:** 277
SQ FT: 800,000
SALES: 485.1MM
SALES (corp-wide): 576MM **Privately Held**
WEB: www.acucise.com
SIC: 3841 Surgical & medical instruments
PA: Applied Medical Corporation
22872 Avenida Empresa
Rcho Sta Marg CA 92688
949 713-8000

(P-22342)
APPLIED SCIENCE INC
983 Golden Gate Ter, Grass Valley
(95945-5938)
PHONE....................530 273-8299
Jonathan G Morgan, *President*
Dale Richardson, *VP Sales*
▲ **EMP:** 17
SQ FT: 6,200
SALES (est): 2MM **Privately Held**
WEB: www.hemoflow.com
SIC: 3841 Surgical & medical instruments

(P-22343)
APRICOT DESIGNS INC
677 Arrow Grand Cir, Covina (91722-2146)
PHONE....................626 966-3299
Felix Yiu, *CEO*
Tedd Wong, *CFO*
Justin Liu, *Design Engr*
Xiao Duan, *Engineer*
Andrea Esparza, *Purchasing*
▲ **EMP:** 38
SQ FT: 6,200
SALES (est): 7.8MM **Privately Held**
WEB: www.apricotdesign.com
SIC: 3841 Surgical & medical instruments

(P-22344)
ARDIAN INC
1380 Shorebird Way, Mountain View
(94043-1338)
PHONE....................650 417-6500
EMP: 11
SALES (est): 1.2MM **Publicly Held**
SIC: 3841
HQ: Medtronic, Inc.
710 Medtronic Pkwy
Minneapolis MN 55432
763 514-4000

(P-22345)
ARKAL MEDICAL INC
46575 Fremont Blvd, Fremont
(94538-6409)
PHONE....................510 933-1950
EMP: 33
SALES (est): 4.7MM **Privately Held**
SIC: 3841

(P-22346)
ARTHREX INC
460 Ward Dr Ste C, Santa Barbara
(93111-2351)
PHONE....................805 964-8104
Paul Waters, *Engineer*
EMP: 76
SALES (corp-wide): 424.1MM **Privately Held**
SIC: 3841 Diagnostic apparatus, medical
PA: Arthrex, Inc.
1370 Creekside Blvd
Naples FL 34108
239 643-5553

(P-22347)
ASTHMATX INC
888 Ross Dr Ste 100, Sunnyvale
(94089-1406)
PHONE....................408 419-0100
Glen French, *President*
Debbie Brown, *Vice Pres*
Fearthal Hennessi, *Vice Pres*
Bill Wizeman, *Vice Pres*
Karen Passafaro, *VP Mktg*
EMP: 60
SQ FT: 22,000
SALES (est): 6MM
SALES (corp-wide): 9B **Publicly Held**
WEB: www.asthmatx.com
SIC: 3841 Surgical & medical instruments
PA: Boston Scientific Corporation
300 Boston Scientific Way
Marlborough MA 01752
508 683-4000

(P-22348)
ASTURA MEDICAL
Also Called: Hyghte Holdings
3186 Lionshead Ave # 100, Carlsbad
(92010-4700)
PHONE....................760 814-8047
Joel Gandrall, *President*
Megan Henley, *Principal*
EMP: 10
SQ FT: 4,500
SALES (est): 690.6K **Privately Held**
SIC: 3841 Surgical & medical instruments

(P-22349)
AURIS HEALTH INC (PA)
150 Shoreline Dr, Redwood City
(94065-1400)
PHONE....................650 610-0750
Frederic Moll, *Chairman*
Jeffery B Alvarez, *Admin Sec*
EMP: 130 **EST:** 2007
SALES (est): 36.4MM **Privately Held**
SIC: 3841 Surgical & medical instruments

(P-22350)
AVANTEC VASCULAR CORPORATION
870 Hermosa Ave, Sunnyvale
(94085-4104)
PHONE....................408 329-5400
Kiminori Toda, *CEO*
Motasim Sirhan, *President*
Jim Shy, *Vice Pres*
Nat Bowditch, *Principal*
Cynthia Wu, *Accountant*
▲ **EMP:** 35
SALES (est): 122K **Privately Held**
WEB: www.avantecvascular.com
SIC: 3841 Medical instruments & equipment, blood & bone work

(P-22351)
AVINGER INC
400 Chesapeake Dr, Redwood City
(94063-4739)
PHONE....................650 241-7900
Jeffrey M Soinski, *President*
James G Cullen, *Ch of Bd*
Mark Weinswig, *CFO*
Himanshu N Patel, *CTO*
EMP: 65
SQ FT: 44,200
SALES (est): 9.9MM **Privately Held**
SIC: 3841 Catheters

(P-22352)
B BRAUN MEDICAL INC
1151 Mildred St Ste B, Ontario
(91761-3504)
PHONE....................909 906-7575
EMP: 1300 **Privately Held**
SIC: 3841 Surgical & medical instruments
HQ: B. Braun Medical Inc.
824 12th Ave
Bethlehem PA 18018
610 691-5400

(P-22353)
B BRAUN MEDICAL INC
2525 Mcgaw Ave, Irvine (92614-5841)
PHONE....................610 691-5400
Keith Klaes, *Manager*
Caroll Neubauer, *Bd of Directors*
Rose Radocha, *Admin Asst*
Nadine Nguyen, *Sr Ntwrk Engine*

Cheri Emmons, *QA Dir*
EMP: 1300 **Privately Held**
SIC: 3841 Catheters
HQ: B. Braun Medical Inc.
824 12th Ave
Bethlehem PA 18018
610 691-5400

(P-22354)
BARRX MEDICAL INC
Also Called: Covidien
540 Oakmead Pkwy, Sunnyvale
(94085-4022)
PHONE....................408 328-7300
Vafa Jamali, *Vice Pres*
Richard Short, *President*
Kevin Cordell, *Vice Pres*
Robert Haggerty, *Vice Pres*
Rhonda Veloni, *Executive Asst*
EMP: 94
SQ FT: 19,000
SALES (est): 16.7MM **Privately Held**
WEB: www.barrx.com
SIC: 3841 Surgical & medical instruments
HQ: Covidien Limited
20 Lower Hatch Street
Dublin 2
-

(P-22355)
BAXALTA US INC
1700 Rancho Conejo Blvd, Thousand Oaks
(91320-1424)
PHONE....................805 498-8664
Paul Marshall, *Manager*
Kevin Westbrook, *Info Tech Mgr*
Alix Rucinski, *Manager*
EMP: 500
SALES (corp-wide): 15.1B **Privately Held**
SIC: 3841 2835 2389 3842 Surgical & medical instruments; catheters; medical instruments & equipment, blood & bone work; surgical instruments & apparatus; blood derivative diagnostic agents; hospital gowns; surgical appliances & supplies; medical laboratory equipment; intravenous solutions
HQ: Baxalta Us Inc.
1200 Lakeside Dr
Bannockburn IL 60015
224 948-2000

(P-22356)
BAXTER HEALTHCARE CORPORATION
Also Called: Baxter Medication Delivery
17511 Armstrong Ave, Irvine (92614-5725)
PHONE....................949 474-6301
Michael Mussallem, *Manager*
Charles Mooney, *Research*
Leticia Molina, *Human Res Mgr*
Javier Pereira, *Mfg Dir*
Vinny Marchionni, *Plant Mgr*
EMP: 250
SALES (corp-wide): 10.5B **Publicly Held**
SIC: 3841 Surgical & medical instruments
HQ: Baxter Healthcare Corporation
1 Baxter Pkwy
Deerfield IL 60015
224 948-2000

(P-22357)
BAXTER HEALTHCARE CORPORATION
Baxter Bentley
1402 Alton Pkwy, Irvine (92606-4838)
P.O. Box 11150, Santa Ana (92711-1150)
PHONE....................949 250-2500
Mike Musalem, *President*
John McGrath, *Vice Pres*
EMP: 75
SQ FT: 72,000
SALES (corp-wide): 10.5B **Publicly Held**
SIC: 3841 Surgical & medical instruments
HQ: Baxter Healthcare Corporation
1 Baxter Pkwy
Deerfield IL 60015
224 948-2000

(P-22358)
BAXTER HEALTHCARE CORPORATION
700 Vaughn Rd, Dixon (95620-9226)
PHONE....................503 285-0212
Robert Fretwell, *Branch Mgr*
EMP: 72

SALES (corp-wide): 10.5B **Publicly Held**
SIC: 3841 Surgical & medical instruments
HQ: Baxter Healthcare Corporation
1 Baxter Pkwy
Deerfield IL 60015
224 948-2000

(P-22359)
BAYER CORPORATION
Pharmaceutical Division
820 Parker St, Berkeley (94710-2440)
P.O. Box 1986 (94701-1986)
PHONE....................510 705-5000
Wolfgang Plischke, *President*
Roger Dehaven, *Senior VP*
Bruce Rhodes, *Technician*
Anthony Hsieh, *Project Mgr*
Nasir Hassan, *Engineer*
EMP: 500
SALES (corp-wide): 41.2B **Privately Held**
SIC: 3841 2834 Surgical & medical instruments; pharmaceutical preparations
HQ: Bayer Corporation
100 Bayer Rd Bldg 14
Pittsburgh PA 15205
412 777-2000

(P-22360)
BECKMAN COULTER INC
Beckman Coulter Diagnostics
250 S Kraemer Blvd, Brea (92821-6232)
P.O. Box 8000 (92822-8000)
PHONE....................818 970-2161
Albert Ziegler, *Manager*
Felicia Moreno, *Senior Mgr*
EMP: 200
SALES (corp-wide): 18.3B **Publicly Held**
WEB: www.beckman.com
SIC: 3841 3821 Surgical & medical instruments; clinical laboratory instruments, except medical & dental
HQ: Beckman Coulter, Inc.
250 S Kraemer Blvd
Brea CA 92821
714 993-5321

(P-22361)
BECTON DICKINSON AND COMPANY
10975 Torreyana Rd, San Diego
(92121-1106)
PHONE....................858 812-8800
Roger McFadden, *Branch Mgr*
EMP: 429
SALES (corp-wide): 12B **Publicly Held**
SIC: 3841 Hypodermic needles & syringes
PA: Becton, Dickinson And Company
1 Becton Dr
Franklin Lakes NJ 07417
201 847-6800

(P-22362)
BECTON DICKINSON AND COMPANY
Bd Biosciences
2350 Qume Dr, San Jose (95131-1812)
PHONE....................408 432-9475
William Rhodes, *Principal*
Donna Boles, *Vice Pres*
Jeff Ezell, *Corp Comm Staff*
Dinesh Gandhi, *Manager*
Larry Tom, *Manager*
EMP: 332
SALES (corp-wide): 12B **Publicly Held**
SIC: 3841 3826 2899 2835 Surgical & medical instruments; analytical instruments; chemical preparations; in vitro & in vivo diagnostic substances
PA: Becton, Dickinson And Company
1 Becton Dr
Franklin Lakes NJ 07417
201 847-6800

(P-22363)
BENTEC MEDICAL OPCO LLC
1380 E Beamer St, Woodland
(95776-6003)
PHONE....................530 406-3333
Scott Christensen, *CEO*
Krishna Niraula, *Finance*
EMP: 50 **EST:** 2016
SALES: 10MM **Privately Held**
SIC: 3841 Surgical & medical instruments

P R O D U C T S & S V C S

(P-22364)
BENTEC SCIENTIFIC LLC
1380 E Beamer St, Woodland
(95776-6003)
PHONE................................530 406-3333
Briant Benson,
EMP: 40
SQ FT: 17,000
SALES (est): 6.7MM **Privately Held**
SIC: 3841 Surgical & medical instruments

(P-22365)
BIO-MEDICAL DEVICES INC
Also Called: Maxair Systems
17171 Daimler St, Irvine (92614-5508)
PHONE................................949 752-9642
Nick Herbert, *President*
Alan Davidner, *Shareholder*
Harry N Herbert, *CEO*
Ray Sadeghi, *General Mgr*
Tim Klink, *Engineer*
▲ EMP: 37
SQ FT: 40,000
SALES (est): 10.2MM **Privately Held**
WEB: www.bmdi.com
SIC: 3841 2353 Surgical & medical instruments; hats, caps & millinery

(P-22366)
BIO-MEDICAL DEVICES INTL INC
17171 Daimler St, Irvine (92614-5508)
PHONE................................800 443-3842
Nicholas Herbert, *President*
Vince Gonzalez, *Sales Dir*
Corey Wick, *Marketing Mgr*
Allan Schultz, *Marketing Staff*
Michelle Chu, *Sales Staff*
EMP: 11
SALES (est): 1.9MM **Privately Held**
SIC: 3841 2353 Surgical & medical instruments; hats, caps & millinery

(P-22367)
BIOCARE MEDICAL LLC
60 Berry Dr, Pacheco (94553-5601)
PHONE................................925 603-8000
Roy Yih,
Hien Hoang, *Mfg Staff*
Gene Castagnini,
Michelle Diehl, *Accounts Exec*
▼ EMP: 154
SQ FT: 51,000
SALES (est): 35.9MM **Privately Held**
WEB: www.biocare.net
SIC: 3841 2835 5047 Diagnostic apparatus, medical; in vitro & in vivo diagnostic substances; diagnostic equipment, medical

(P-22368)
BIOCHECK INC
Also Called: Bio Check, Inc.
425 Eccles Ave, South San Francisco (94080-1902)
PHONE................................650 573-1968
John Chen, *CEO*
EMP: 22
SQ FT: 7,000
SALES (est): 3.9MM **Privately Held**
WEB: www.biocheckinc.com
SIC: 3841 5047 Diagnostic apparatus, medical; diagnostic equipment, medical
PA: Origene Technologies, Inc.
9620 Med Ctr Dr Ste 200
Rockville MD 20850

(P-22369)
BIOFILM INC
3225 Executive Rdg, Vista (92081-8527)
PHONE................................760 727-9030
Lisa A O'Carroll, *CEO*
Daniel Wray, *Ch of Bd*
Mike Adams, *COO*
Lois Wray, *Admin Sec*
Nicole Chia, *Research*
EMP: 54
SQ FT: 61,000
SALES (est): 13.9MM **Privately Held**
WEB: www.biofilm.com
SIC: 3841 Surgical & medical instruments

(P-22370)
BIOGENERAL INC
9925 Mesa Rim Rd, San Diego (92121-2911)
PHONE................................858 453-4451
Victor Wild, *President*
Carlos Alvarez, *Supervisor*
▲ EMP: 15
SALES (est): 3.9MM **Privately Held**
WEB: www.biogeneral.com
SIC: 3841 Surgical & medical instruments

(P-22371)
BIOGENEX LABORATORIES (PA)
49026 Milmont Dr, Fremont (94538-7301)
PHONE................................510 824-1400
Krishan L Kalra, *CEO*
Satya Kalra, *Admin Sec*
Ajay Kumar, *Finance*
◆ EMP: 35
SQ FT: 31,000
SALES: 8.5MM **Privately Held**
WEB: www.biogenex.com
SIC: 3841 2835 8731 2819 Diagnostic apparatus, medical; cytology & histology diagnostic agents; commercial physical research; chemicals, reagent grade: refined from technical grade

(P-22372)
BIOINITIATIVES INC
7641 Galilee Rd Ste 110, Roseville (95678-7212)
PHONE................................916 780-9100
Mark Sienkiewicz, *President*
Matthaus Dengler, *Vice Pres*
EMP: 36
SALES (est): 17.8MM **Privately Held**
SIC: 3841 Surgical & medical instruments

(P-22373)
BIOJECT INC
6769 Mesa Ridge Rd Ste 99, San Diego (92121-2995)
PHONE................................503 692-8001
Mark Logomasini, *President*
Christine Farrell, *Vice Pres*
Richard R Stout MD, *Vice Pres*
EMP: 20
SALES (est): 3.2MM **Publicly Held**
SIC: 3841 Surgical instruments & apparatus
HQ: Bioject Medical Technologies Inc.
7180 Sw Sandburg St
Tigard OR 97223

(P-22374)
BIOMERICA INC (PA)
17571 Von Karman Ave, Irvine (92614-6207)
PHONE................................949 645-2111
Zackary Irani, *Ch of Bd*
Janet Moore, *CFO*
Francis Cano, *Bd of Directors*
Mark Sirgo, *Bd of Directors*
Elisabeth Laderman, *Vice Pres*
▲ EMP: 49 EST: 1971
SQ FT: 22,000
SALES: 5.5MM **Publicly Held**
WEB: www.biomerica.com
SIC: 3841 Diagnostic apparatus, medical

(P-22375)
BIOSEAL
167 W Orangethorpe Ave, Placentia (92870-6922)
PHONE................................714 528-4695
Bill Runion, *President*
Robert C Kopple, *Corp Secy*
Jeff Myers, *Controller*
Lauren Martin, *Human Resources*
John Benitez, *Sales Associate*
▲ EMP: 40
SQ FT: 8,500
SALES (est): 9MM **Privately Held**
WEB: www.biosealnet.com
SIC: 3841 5047 Surgical & medical instruments; hospital equipment & furniture

(P-22376)
BIT GROUP USA INC (PA)
Also Called: Bit Medtech
15870 Bernardo Center Dr, San Diego (92127-2320)
PHONE................................858 613-1200

Marius Balger, *CEO*
Susanne Gottschalk, *CFO*
▲ EMP: 70 EST: 1998
SQ FT: 35,000
SALES (est): 17.1MM **Privately Held**
WEB: www.bit-companies.com/bit-medtech
SIC: 3841 8711 Surgical & medical instruments; engineering services

(P-22377)
BOSTON SCIENTIFIC CORPORATION
28460 Avenue Stanford, Valencia (91355-4856)
PHONE................................661 645-6668
Erin Fuller, *Principal*
EMP: 285
SALES (corp-wide): 9B **Publicly Held**
SIC: 3841 Surgical & medical instruments
PA: Boston Scientific Corporation
300 Boston Scientific Way
Marlborough MA 01752
508 683-4000

(P-22378)
BOSTON SCIENTIFIC CORPORATION
150 Baytech Dr, San Jose (95134-2302)
PHONE................................408 935-3400
Tom Flemming, *Manager*
Daniel Teran, *Engineer*
Zhen Wallis, *Engineer*
Brendan Crowley, *Controller*
Daljit Kaur, *QC Mgr*
EMP: 125
SALES (corp-wide): 9B **Publicly Held**
WEB: www.bsci.com
SIC: 3841 3842 Surgical appliances & supplies; grafts, artificial: for surgery; diagnostic apparatus, medical
PA: Boston Scientific Corporation
300 Boston Scientific Way
Marlborough MA 01752
508 683-4000

(P-22379)
BOSTON SCIENTIFIC CORPORATION
Also Called: Boston Scientific - Valencia
25155 Rye Canyon Loop, Valencia (91355-5004)
PHONE................................800 678-2575
Phill Tarves, *Manager*
Rafael Carbunaru, *Vice Pres*
Lisa Welker-Finney, *Vice Pres*
Tom Robinson, *VP Bus Dvlpt*
Manahan Mylene, *Administration*
EMP: 45
SALES (corp-wide): 9B **Publicly Held**
WEB: www.bsci.com
SIC: 3841 Surgical & medical instruments
PA: Boston Scientific Corporation
300 Boston Scientific Way
Marlborough MA 01752
508 683-4000

(P-22380)
BOSTON SCIENTIFIC CORPORATION
150 Baytech Dr, San Jose (95134-2302)
PHONE................................408 935-3400
Ven Vegesna, *Branch Mgr*
EMP: 285
SALES (corp-wide): 9B **Publicly Held**
SIC: 3841 Surgical & medical instruments
PA: Boston Scientific Corporation
300 Boston Scientific Way
Marlborough MA 01752
508 683-4000

(P-22381)
BRANAN MEDICAL CORPORATION (PA)
9940 Mesa Rim Rd, San Diego (92121-2910)
PHONE................................949 598-7166
Cindy Horton, *CEO*
Raphael Wong, *President*
Beckie Chien, *Vice Pres*
Anthony Wong, *Technology*
Vinh MAI, *Director*
▲ EMP: 30
SQ FT: 8,400

SALES (est): 4MM **Privately Held**
WEB: www.brananmedical.com
SIC: 3841 Diagnostic apparatus, medical

(P-22382)
BREG INC (HQ)
2885 Loker Ave E, Carlsbad (92010-6626)
PHONE................................760 599-3000
Brad Lee, *President*
Stuart M Essig, *Ch of Bd*
Aarti Gautam, *President*
Geoff Siegel, *President*
Aaron Heisler, *CFO*
▲ EMP: 200
SQ FT: 104,000
SALES: 24K
SALES (corp-wide): 478.8MM **Privately Held**
WEB: www.breg.com
SIC: 3841 Surgical & medical instruments
PA: Water Street Healthcare Partners Llc
444 W Lake St Ste 1800
Chicago IL 60606
312 506-2900

(P-22383)
BRIGHTWATER MEDICAL INC
42580 Rio Nedo, Temecula (92590-3727)
P.O. Box 1286, Murrieta (92564-1286)
PHONE................................951 290-3410
Bob Smouse, *CEO*
Kent Stalker, *Vice Pres*
Guillermo Hoffman, *Controller*
EMP: 15 EST: 2014
SQ FT: 5,000
SALES: 500K **Privately Held**
SIC: 3841 Surgical & medical instruments

(P-22384)
CALBIOTECH INC
1935 Cordell Ct, El Cajon (92020-0911)
PHONE................................619 660-6162
Noori Barka, *President*
Ann Barka, *Manager*
▼ EMP: 38
SQ FT: 22,500
SALES: 4MM
SALES (corp-wide): 105.6MM **Publicly Held**
WEB: www.calbiotech.com
SIC: 3841 8731 8071 Diagnostic apparatus, medical; medical research, commercial; medical laboratories
HQ: Erba Diagnostics Mannheim Gmbh
Mallaustr. 69-73
Mannheim 68219

(P-22385)
CALDERA MEDICAL INC
5171 Clareton Dr, Agoura Hills (91301-4523)
PHONE................................818 879-6555
Bryon L Merade, *Ch of Bd*
Jeff Hubauer, *COO*
David Hochman, *CFO*
Dan Keeffe, *Vice Pres*
Pat Kothari, *Info Tech Mgr*
EMP: 70
SQ FT: 25,000
SALES (est): 2.6MM **Privately Held**
WEB: www.calderamedical.com
SIC: 3841 Surgical & medical instruments

(P-22386)
CAMINO NEUROCARE
5955 Pacific Center Blvd, San Diego (92121-4309)
PHONE................................858 455-1115
Tony Andrasfay, *Manager*
Bill Chiklakis, *Sales Staff*
EMP: 100
SQ FT: 35,000
SALES (est): 9.5MM **Publicly Held**
WEB: www.integra-ls.com
SIC: 3841 Diagnostic apparatus, medical; blood pressure apparatus
PA: Integra Lifesciences Holdings Corporation
311 Enterprise Dr
Plainsboro NJ 08536

▲ = Import ▼=Export
◆ =Import/Export

(P-22387)
CAPISTRANO LABS INC
150 Calle Iglesia Ste B, San Clemente
(92672-7550)
PHONE..................949 492-0390
Paul Meyers, *President*
Matt Stabley, *Treasurer*
EMP: 20
SQ FT: 8,000
SALES (est): 3.2MM **Privately Held**
WEB: www.capolabs.com
SIC: 3841 Diagnostic apparatus, medical

(P-22388)
CARDIVA MEDICAL INC
2900 Lakeside Dr Ste 160, Santa Clara
(95054-2817)
PHONE..................408 470-7100
John Russell, *President*
Rick Anderson, *Ch of Bd*
Glenn Foy, *President*
Justin Ballotta, *COO*
Malcolm Farnsworth, *CFO*
EMP: 135
SALES (est): 26.5MM **Privately Held**
WEB: www.cardivamedical.com
SIC: 3841 Surgical & medical instruments

(P-22389)
CARE FUSION
10020 Pacific Mesa Blvd, San Diego
(92121-4386)
PHONE..................858 617-2000
EMP: 704
SALES (est): 175.8MM **Privately Held**
SIC: 3841

(P-22390)
CAREFUSION 207 INC
1100 Bird Center Dr, Palm Springs
(92262-8000)
PHONE..................760 778-7200
Edward Borkowski, *CFO*
Carol Zilm, *President*
Amarendra Duvvur, *Treasurer*
Mark Stauffer, *Officer*
Cathy Cooney, *Exec VP*
▲ EMP: 327
SALES (est): 31.7MM
SALES (corp-wide): 113.7MM **Privately Held**
SIC: 3841 8741 Surgical & medical instruments; nursing & personal care facility management
PA: Vyaire Holding Company
26125 N Riverwoods Blvd
Mettawa IL 60045
872 757-0114

(P-22391)
CAREFUSION 211 INC
22745 Savi Ranch Pkwy, Yorba Linda
(92887-4668)
PHONE..................714 283-2228
David Mowry, *President*
David Stafford, *CFO*
Kevin Klemz, *Admin Sec*
EMP: 638
SALES (est): 866K
SALES (corp-wide): 113.7MM **Privately Held**
SIC: 3841 Surgical & medical instruments
HQ: Vyaire Medical, Inc.
26125 N Riverwoods Blvd # 1
Mettawa IL 60045
833 327-3284

(P-22392)
CAREFUSION 213 LLC (DH)
3750 Torrey View Ct, San Diego
(92130-2622)
PHONE..................800 523-0502
David L Schlotterbeck, *CEO*
Dwight Windstead, *COO*
Edward Borkowski, *CFO*
◆ EMP: 450
SALES (est): 165MM
SALES (corp-wide): 12B **Publicly Held**
SIC: 3841 Surgical & medical instruments

(P-22393)
CAREFUSION CORPORATION
Also Called: Care Fusion Products
3750 Torrey View Ct, San Diego
(92130-2622)
PHONE..................888 876-4287

David Scott, *Officer*
Mike Riddle, *Vice Pres*
Eleonora Kaziyeva, *Engineer*
Carlos Ramos-Rocha, *Engineer*
Rogina White, *Engineer*
EMP: 12
SALES (corp-wide): 12B **Publicly Held**
SIC: 3841 Medical instruments & equipment, blood & bone work
HQ: Carefusion Corporation
3750 Torrey View Ct
San Diego CA 92130

(P-22394)
CAREFUSION CORPORATION
22745 Savi Ranch Pkwy, Yorba Linda
(92887-4668)
PHONE..................800 231-2466
Bill Ross, *Branch Mgr*
Jim Farvour, *Program Mgr*
Thomas McCollum, *Electrical Engi*
Michael Cegielski, *Engineer*
Terry Lowe, *Engineer*
EMP: 34
SALES (corp-wide): 12B **Publicly Held**
SIC: 3841 Surgical & medical instruments
HQ: Carefusion Corporation
3750 Torrey View Ct
San Diego CA 92130

(P-22395)
CARL ZEISS MEDITEC PROD LLC
1040 S Vintage Ave Ste A, Ontario
(91761-3631)
PHONE..................877 644-4657
Hans-Joachim Miesner, *President*
Paul Yun, *Treasurer*
James Thornton, *Admin Sec*
EMP: 99
SQ FT: 67,000
SALES (est): 2.9MM **Privately Held**
SIC: 3841 Surgical & medical instruments
HQ: Carl Zeiss Meditec, Inc.
5160 Hacienda Dr
Dublin CA 94568
925 557-4100

(P-22396)
CARL ZEISS OPHTHALMIC SYSTEMS
5160 Hacienda Dr, Dublin (94568-7562)
PHONE..................925 557-4100
Lothar Coob, *President*
Henriette Meyer, *Shareholder*
EMP: 230 EST: 2000
SALES (est): 12.4MM **Privately Held**
SIC: 3841 Medical instruments & equipment, blood & bone work

(P-22397)
CAROLINA LQUID CHMISTRIES CORP
510 W Central Ave Ste C, Brea
(92821-3032)
P.O. Box 92249 (92822)
PHONE..................336 722-8910
Phil Shugart, *Branch Mgr*
Renato Pena, *Vice Pres*
Felix Soto, *Engineer*
EMP: 12
SALES (est): 1.5MM **Privately Held**
SIC: 3841 Surgical & medical instruments
PA: Carolina Liquid Chemistries Corporation
313 Gallimore Dairy Rd
Greensboro NC 27409

(P-22398)
CATHERA INC
627 National Ave, Mountain View
(94043-2221)
PHONE..................650 388-5088
Aaron Berez, *CEO*
EMP: 15
SALES (est): 816.5K **Privately Held**
SIC: 3841 Surgical & medical instruments

(P-22399)
CELERUS DIAGNOSTICS INC
100 N Hill Dr Ste 32, Brisbane
(94005-1012)
PHONE..................805 684-0854
Rusty Reed, *CEO*
EMP: 25
SQ FT: 11,000
SALES (est): 2.8MM **Privately Held**
SIC: 3841 Surgical & medical instruments

(P-22400)
CEREBROTECH MEDICAL SYSTEMS (PA)
1048 Serpentine Ln # 301, Pleasanton
(94566-4734)
PHONE..................925 399-5392
Mitchell Levinson, *CEO*
Michell Levinson, *CEO*
EMP: 18
SALES (est): 3.7MM **Privately Held**
SIC: 3841 Diagnostic apparatus, medical

(P-22401)
CERUS CORPORATION (PA)
2550 Stanwell Dr Ste 300, Concord
(94520-4813)
PHONE..................925 288-6000
William M Greenman, *President*
Daniel N Swisher Jr, *Ch of Bd*
Kevin D Green, *CFO*
Timothy Anderson, *Bd of Directors*
Bruce Cozadd, *Bd of Directors*
▲ EMP: 175
SQ FT: 36,029
SALES (est): 43.5MM **Publicly Held**
WEB: www.cerus.com
SIC: 3841 Blood transfusion equipment

(P-22402)
CETERIX ORTHOPAEDICS INC
6500 Kaiser Dr Ste 120, Fremont
(94555-3662)
PHONE..................650 316-8660
John McCutcheon, *CEO*
Michael Hendricksen, *Vice Pres*
EMP: 28 EST: 2010
SALES (est): 5.1MM **Privately Held**
SIC: 3841 Surgical instruments & apparatus

(P-22403)
CHEN-TECH INDUSTRIES INC (DH)
Also Called: ATI Forged Products
9 Wrigley, Irvine (92618-2711)
PHONE..................949 855-6716
Richard Harshman, *CEO*
Shannon Ko, *President*
Cat Ton, *Accountant*
EMP: 38
SQ FT: 18,000
SALES (est): 13.7MM **Publicly Held**
WEB: www.aeroforge-tech.com
SIC: 3841 3769 3724 3463 Surgical & medical instruments; guided missile & space vehicle parts & auxiliary equipment; aircraft engines & engine parts; aluminum forgings
HQ: Ati Ladish Llc
5481 S Packard Ave
Cudahy WI 53110
414 747-2611

(P-22404)
CHROMOLOGIC LLC
1225 S Shamrock Ave, Monrovia
(91016-4244)
PHONE..................626 381-9974
Naresh Menon, *Mng Member*
Tiffany Moreno, *Admin Asst*
Justin Eng, *Software Engr*
Andrea Maleki, *Marketing Staff*
Claude Rogers, *Manager*
EMP: 28
SALES (est): 4.8MM **Privately Held**
WEB: www.chromologic.com
SIC: 3841 Diagnostic apparatus, medical

(P-22405)
CIRTEC MEDICAL LLC
101b Cooper Ct, Los Gatos (95032-7604)
PHONE..................408 395-0443
Michael Forman, *Branch Mgr*
Erik Morgan, *Info Tech Dir*

EMP: 60
SALES (corp-wide): 57.8MM **Privately Held**
WEB: www.cirtecmed.com
SIC: 3841 Surgical & medical instruments
PA: Cirtec Medical, Llc
99 Print Shop Rd
Enfield CT 06082
413 525-5700

(P-22406)
COALIGN INNOVATIONS INC
2684 Middlefield Rd Ste A, Redwood City
(94063-3479)
PHONE..................888 714-4440
Paul Goeld, *CEO*
John Ashley, *Exec VP*
John Barrett, *Exec VP*
Joe Loy, *Vice Pres*
EMP: 20
SALES (est): 2.4MM **Privately Held**
SIC: 3841 5999 Medical instruments & equipment, blood & bone work; medical apparatus & supplies

(P-22407)
COMPOSITE MANUFACTURING INC
Also Called: CMI
970 Calle Amanecer Ste D, San Clemente
(92673-6250)
PHONE..................949 361-7580
Roger Malcolm, *President*
Tim Salter, *CEO*
Linda Perkovich, *CFO*
Kimberly Bobb, *Info Tech Mgr*
Rob Kelly, *Manager*
EMP: 36
SQ FT: 16,000
SALES (est): 7MM **Privately Held**
WEB: www.carbonfiber.com
SIC: 3841 3624 Operating tables; carbon & graphite products

(P-22408)
CONCENTRIC MEDICAL INC
47900 Bayside Pkwy, Fremont
(94538-6515)
PHONE..................650 938-2100
Maria Sainz, *President*
Brett Hale, *CFO*
EMP: 40
SQ FT: 22,000
SALES (est): 7.8MM
SALES (corp-wide): 12.4B **Publicly Held**
WEB: www.concentric-medical.com
SIC: 3841 Surgical & medical instruments
PA: Stryker Corporation
2825 Airview Blvd
Portage MI 49002
269 385-2600

(P-22409)
CONFLUENT MEDICAL TECH INC (PA)
47533 Westinghouse Dr, Fremont
(94539-7463)
PHONE..................510 683-2000
Dean Schauer, *CEO*
Tom Duerig, *President*
Doug Hutchison, *Officer*
Craig Bonsignore, *Vice Pres*
John Dicello, *Vice Pres*
◆ EMP: 300
SQ FT: 90,000
SALES (est): 202.7MM **Privately Held**
SIC: 3841 5047 Surgical & medical instruments; medical & hospital equipment

(P-22410)
COVIDIEN HOLDING INC
2101 Faraday Ave, Carlsbad (92008-7205)
PHONE..................760 603-5020
Rohit Vij, *Manager*
EMP: 19 **Privately Held**
SIC: 3841 Surgical & medical instruments
HQ: Covidien Holding Inc.
710 Medtronic Pkwy
Minneapolis MN 55432

PRODUCTS & SVCS

(P-22411)
COVIDIEN HOLDING INC
Also Called: Covidien Kenmex
2475 Paseo De Las Amrcs A, San Diego
(92154-7255)
PHONE...................................619 690-8500
Javira Gonzales, *Manager*
EMP: 1900 **Privately Held**
SIC: 3841 Surgical & medical instruments
HQ: Covidien Holding Inc.
710 Medtronic Pkwy
Minneapolis MN 55432

(P-22412)
COVIDIEN LP
Also Called: Vascular Therapies
9775 Toledo Way, Irvine (92618-1811)
PHONE...................................949 837-3700
Hal Hurwitz, *CFO*
Jessica Varela, *Admin Asst*
Ricky Villarreal, *Research*
Greg Hamel, *Engineer*
Junwei LI, *Engineer*
EMP: 500 **Privately Held**
SIC: 3841 Surgical & medical instruments
HQ: Covidien Lp
15 Hampshire St
Mansfield MA 02048
508 261-8000

(P-22413)
CREGANNA MEDICAL DEVICES INC (DH)
Also Called: Creganna-Tactx Medical
1353 Dell Ave, Campbell (95008-6609)
PHONE...................................408 364-7100
Robert Bell Hance, *CEO*
Helen Ryan, *President*
Padraic Clarke, *CFO*
Richard Leyden, *Admin Sec*
Dwayne Burke, *Technology*
EMP: 40
SALES (est): 53.7MM
SALES (corp-wide): 13.1B **Privately Held**
SIC: 3841 Surgical & medical instruments

(P-22414)
CURAPHARM INC
10054 Prospect Ave Ste A, Santee
(92071-4328)
PHONE...................................619 449-7388
Thomas Hnat, *CEO*
Alot Nigam, *President*
EMP: 10
SALES (est): 950.4K **Privately Held**
SIC: 3841 5047 Surgical & medical instruments; medical & hospital equipment

(P-22415)
CURE MEDICAL LLC (PA)
3471 Via Lido Ste 211, Newport Beach
(92663-3929)
PHONE...................................800 570-1778
John Anderson, *CEO*
Ann E Kenowsky, *President*
Timothy Palmer, *COO*
Loren McFarland, *CFO*
▲ EMP: 12
SALES (est): 2.4MM **Privately Held**
SIC: 3841 Catheters

(P-22416)
CYTORI THERAPEUTICS INC (PA)
3020 Callan Rd, San Diego (92121-1109)
PHONE...................................858 458-0900
Marc H Hedrick, *President*
David M Rickey, *Ch of Bd*
Tiago Girao, *CFO*
Jeremy Hayden, *Ch Credit Ofcr*
Gary Lyons, *Bd of Directors*
EMP: 65
SQ FT: 77,585
SALES: 6.4MM **Publicly Held**
WEB: www.macropore.com
SIC: 3841 8731 Surgical & medical instruments; biological research

(P-22417)
DA VITA TUSTIN DIALYSIS CTR
Also Called: Devita Dialysis
2090 N Tustin Ave Ste 100, Santa Ana
(92705-7869)
PHONE...................................714 835-2450

Kelly Seigler, *Administration*
EMP: 30
SALES (est): 2MM **Privately Held**
SIC: 3841 8092 Hemodialysis apparatus; kidney dialysis centers

(P-22418)
DAVID KOPF INSTRUMENTS
7324 Elmo St, Tujunga (91042-2205)
P.O. Box 636 (91043-0636)
PHONE...................................818 352-3274
Carl Koph, *CEO*
J David Kopf, *President*
Carol Kopf, *Treasurer*
Kathy Carlough, *Technology*
Knarik Terteryan, *Assistant*
EMP: 28
SQ FT: 13,836
SALES (est): 4.9MM **Privately Held**
WEB: www.kopfinstruments.net
SIC: 3841 Veterinarians' instruments & apparatus

(P-22419)
DEPUY SYNTHES PRODUCTS INC
130 Knowles Dr Ste E, Los Gatos
(95032-1832)
PHONE...................................408 246-4300
EMP: 15
SALES (corp-wide): 76.4B **Publicly Held**
SIC: 3841 Diagnostic apparatus, medical
HQ: Depuy Synthes Products, Inc.
325 Paramount Dr
Raynham MA 02767
508 880-8100

(P-22420)
DERMANEW LLC
Also Called: Dermanew Institute
9461 Santa Monica Blvd, Beverly Hills
(90210-4620)
PHONE...................................310 276-0457
Amby Longhofer, *Branch Mgr*
EMP: 10
SALES (corp-wide): 907.2K **Privately Held**
WEB: www.dermanew.com
SIC: 3841 7231 Skin grafting equipment; facial salons
PA: Dermanew, Llc
436 Smithwood Dr
Beverly Hills CA 90212
626 442-2813

(P-22421)
DEXCOM INC (PA)
6340 Sequence Dr, San Diego
(92121-4356)
PHONE...................................858 200-0200
Kevin Sayer, *President*
Terrance H Gregg, *Ch of Bd*
Kevin Sun, *CFO*
Claudia Graham, *Chief Mktg Ofcr*
Andrew K Balo, *Exec VP*
EMP: 277
SALES: 718.5MM **Publicly Held**
WEB: www.dexcom.com
SIC: 3841 Diagnostic apparatus, medical

(P-22422)
DFINE INC (HQ)
3047 Orchard Pkwy, San Jose
(95134-2024)
PHONE...................................408 321-9999
Greg Barrett, *President*
Rick Short, *CFO*
Bob Poser, *Vice Pres*
Cindee Van Vleck, *Vice Pres*
John Szukalski, *Regl Sales Mgr*
▲ EMP: 69
SQ FT: 18,000
SALES (est): 16.7MM
SALES (corp-wide): 727.8MM **Publicly Held**
SIC: 3841 Surgical & medical instruments
PA: Merit Medical Systems, Inc.
1600 W Merit Pkwy
South Jordan UT 84095
801 253-1600

(P-22423)
DIAGNOSTIXX CALIFORNIA CORP
Also Called: Immunalysis
829 Towne Center Dr, Pomona
(91767-5901)
PHONE...................................909 482-0840
James R Soares PHD, *President*
Michael Vincent, *Vice Pres*
Dayana D Duarte, *Controller*
Mark Villoria, *Director*
Guohong Wang, *Manager*
▲ EMP: 22
SQ FT: 11,000
SALES (est): 5.8MM **Privately Held**
WEB: www.immunalysis.com
SIC: 3841 2835 Diagnostic apparatus, medical; in vitro & in vivo diagnostic substances

(P-22424)
DIAMICS INC
6 Hamilton Landing # 200, Novato
(94949-8270)
PHONE...................................415 883-0414
EMP: 12
SQ FT: 2,000
SALES (est): 97K **Privately Held**
WEB: www.diamics.com
SIC: 3841

(P-22425)
DIASOL INC (PA)
Also Called: Discount Medical Supply
1110 Arroyo St, San Fernando
(91340-1824)
PHONE...................................818 838-7077
Monica Abeles, *President*
Mary Castillo, *Vice Pres*
EMP: 16
SALES (est): 10.3MM **Privately Held**
SIC: 3841 Surgical & medical instruments

(P-22426)
DIASSESS INC
1412 62nd St, Emeryville (94608-2036)
PHONE...................................510 350-8071
John Waldeisen, *CEO*
Frankie Myers, *Engineer*
EMP: 15
SALES (est): 364.6K **Privately Held**
SIC: 3841 Surgical & medical instruments

(P-22427)
DITEC CO
Also Called: Ditec Mfg.
1019 Mark Ave, Carpinteria (93013-2912)
PHONE...................................805 566-7800
Don L Cooper, *President*
Scott Cooper, *Vice Pres*
EMP: 13
SQ FT: 10,000
SALES (est): 1.8MM **Privately Held**
WEB: www.ditecmfg.com
SIC: 3841 3843 3545 Surgical instruments & apparatus; burs, dental; diamond cutting tools for turning, boring, burnishing, etc.

(P-22428)
DUKE EMPIRICAL INC
2829 Mission St, Santa Cruz (95060-5755)
PHONE...................................831 420-1104
Robert C Laduca, *CEO*
Jennifer Ramirez, *Office Mgr*
EMP: 60
SQ FT: 9,000
SALES (est): 15.4MM **Privately Held**
WEB: www.dukeempirical.com
SIC: 3841 Diagnostic apparatus, medical

(P-22429)
DUPACO INC
4144 Avenda De La Plata, Oceanside
(92056)
PHONE...................................760 758-4550
Gregory Jordan, *President*
Kyle Wiese, *Engineer*
July Butler, *Manager*
EMP: 43
SQ FT: 30,000
SALES (est): 10.1MM **Privately Held**
WEB: www.dupacoinc.com
SIC: 3841 3845 Medical instruments & equipment, blood & bone work; electromedical equipment

(P-22430)
EASYDIAL INC (PA)
181 Technology Dr Ste 150, Irvine
(92618-2484)
PHONE...................................949 916-5851
Philippe Faurie, *CEO*
Imelda Dela Torre, *Assistant*
EMP: 57
SALES (est): 12.9MM **Privately Held**
SIC: 3841 Hemodialysis apparatus

(P-22431)
ECA MEDICAL INSTRUMENTS (DH)
1107 Tourmaline Dr, Newbury Park
(91320-1208)
PHONE...................................805 376-2509
John J Nino, *President*
James Schultz, *Exec VP*
William Hsu, *Engng Exec*
Clint Elsemore, *VP Finance*
Ron Zisman, *Controller*
EMP: 22
SQ FT: 14,982
SALES (est): 5.8MM **Publicly Held**
WEB: www.ecamedical.com
SIC: 3841 Surgical & medical instruments
HQ: Acas, Llc
2 Bethesda Metro Ctr # 1200
Bethesda MD 20814
301 951-6122

(P-22432)
ECA MEDICAL INSTRUMENTS
Also Called: Electro Component Assembly
21615 Parthenia St, Canoga Park
(91304-1517)
PHONE...................................818 998-7284
Yvonne Hairston, *Principal*
EMP: 20 **Publicly Held**
WEB: www.ecamedical.com
SIC: 3841 Surgical & medical instruments
HQ: Eca Medical Instruments
1107 Tourmaline Dr
Newbury Park CA 91320
805 376-2509

(P-22433)
EDWARDS LFSCIENCES CARDIAQ LLC
Also Called: Cardiaq Valve Technologies Inc
2 Jenner Ste 100, Irvine (92618-3832)
PHONE...................................949 387-2615
Robrecht Michiels, *CEO*
J Brent Ratz, *President*
EMP: 12
SALES (est): 1.8MM
SALES (corp-wide): 3.4B **Publicly Held**
SIC: 3841 Surgical & medical instruments
PA: Edwards Lifesciences Corp
1 Edwards Way
Irvine CA 92614
949 250-2500

(P-22434)
EDWARDS LIFESCIENCES
17192 Daimler St, Irvine (92614-5509)
PHONE...................................949 250-3783
EMP: 11
SALES (est): 962.2K **Privately Held**
SIC: 3841 Surgical & medical instruments

(P-22435)
EKLIN MEDICAL SYSTEMS INC
6359 Paseo Del Lago, Carlsbad
(92011-1317)
PHONE...................................760 918-9626
Robert Antin, *President*
EMP: 92
SQ FT: 16,000
SALES (est): 5.9MM
SALES (corp-wide): 2.5B **Privately Held**
WEB: www.eklin.com
SIC: 3841 5047 Medical instruments & equipment, blood & bone work; medical & hospital equipment
HQ: Vca Inc.
12401 W Olympic Blvd
Los Angeles CA 90064
310 571-6500

▲ = Import ▼=Export
◆ =Import/Export

(P-22436)
ELECTRONIC WAVEFORM LAB INC
5702 Bolsa Ave, Huntington Beach (92649-1128)
PHONE..............................714 843-0463
Ryan Haney, *President*
William Heaney, *President*
Patricia Heaney, *Corp Secy*
Tamara Ebert, *Regional Mgr*
Jonathan Christy, *Administration*
EMP: 25
SALES (est): 5.5MM Privately Held
WEB: www.h-wave.com
SIC: 3841 Anesthesia apparatus

(P-22437)
ELIXIR MEDICAL CORPORATION (PA)
920 N Mccarthy Blvd, Milpitas (95035-5128)
PHONE..............................408 636-2000
Motasim Sirhan, *CEO*
Bruce Barclay, *Vice Pres*
Vinayak Bhat, *Vice Pres*
Lynn Morrison, *Vice Pres*
Jesika Fiedler, *Admin Asst*
EMP: 15
SQ FT: 15,000
SALES (est): 3.5MM Privately Held
SIC: 3841 Surgical & medical instruments

(P-22438)
EMBOLX INC
530 Lakeside Dr Ste 200, Sunnyvale (94085-4063)
PHONE..............................408 990-2949
Michael Allen, *CEO*
EMP: 12 EST: 2013
SALES (est): 983K Privately Held
SIC: 3841 Catheters

(P-22439)
ENDOLOGIX INC (PA)
2 Musick, Irvine (92618-1631)
PHONE..............................949 595-7200
John Onopchenko, *CEO*
Dan Lemaitre, *Ch of Bd*
Robert D Mitchell, *President*
Jeffrey S Brown, *COO*
Vaseem Mahboob, *CFO*
▲ EMP: 265
SALES: 181.1MM Publicly Held
WEB: www.endologix.com
SIC: 3841 Catheters

(P-22440)
ENTRA HEALTH SYSTEMS LLC
1300 N Johnson Ave # 100, El Cajon (92020-1653)
PHONE..............................877 458-2646
Richard C Strobridge, *CEO*
Bruce Ahern, *Chief Mktg Ofcr*
Larry Mahar, *CTO*
Matthew Weisensee, *VP Sales*
EMP: 25
SQ FT: 11,000
SALES: 10MM Privately Held
SIC: 3841 Surgical & medical instruments
HQ: Crf Inc.
4000 Chemical Rd Ste 400
Plymouth Meeting PA 19462
267 498-2300

(P-22441)
ENTROPY ENTERPRISES LLC
170 Seacliff Dr, Pismo Beach (93449-1715)
PHONE..............................805 305-1400
Kourosh Bagheri, *Principal*
EMP: 10 EST: 2013
SALES (est): 558.6K Privately Held
SIC: 3841 Surgical & medical instruments

(P-22442)
EPICA MEDICAL INNOVATIONS LLC
2753 Camino Capistrano, San Clemente (92672-5823)
PHONE..............................949 238-6323
Greg Stoutenburgh, *Founder*
Ron Tibett, *Vice Pres*
Jason Grace, *Project Mgr*
▲ EMP: 15 EST: 2012
SQ FT: 4,441

SALES: 4.5MM
SALES (corp-wide): 18.3MM Privately Held
SIC: 3841 5047 Surgical & medical instruments; medical equipment & supplies
PA: Epica International, Inc.
2753 Camino Capistrano
San Clemente CA 92672
949 238-6323

(P-22443)
EPINEX DIAGNOSTICS INC
14351 Myford Rd Ste J, Tustin (92780-7038)
PHONE..............................949 660-7770
Asad R Zaidi, *President*
Omar Ali, *Bd of Directors*
Jeff Byrd, *Vice Pres*
David Trasoff, *Comms Dir*
Henry J Smith, *CTO*
EMP: 30
SQ FT: 3,400
SALES (est): 5.4MM Privately Held
WEB: www.epinex.com
SIC: 3841 Diagnostic apparatus, medical

(P-22444)
EVALVE INC
4045 Campbell Ave, Menlo Park (94025-1006)
PHONE..............................650 330-8100
Ferolyn T Powell, *President*
Doug Hughes, *CFO*
Sean Cleary, *Senior VP*
Bunty Banerjee, *Vice Pres*
Jonathan D Feuchtwang, *Vice Pres*
EMP: 91
SQ FT: 38,000
SALES (est): 11.1MM
SALES (corp-wide): 27.3B Publicly Held
WEB: www.evalveinc.com
SIC: 3841 Surgical & medical instruments
PA: Abbott Laboratories
100 Abbott Park Rd
Abbott Park IL 60064
224 667-6100

(P-22445)
EVOFEM INC
12400 High Bluff Dr # 600, San Diego (92130-3077)
PHONE..............................858 550-1900
Saundra Pelletier, *CEO*
Justin Jay File, *CFO*
Kelly Culwell, *Chief Mktg Ofcr*
David Friend, *Senior VP*
Russell Barrans, *Vice Pres*
▼ EMP: 12
SQ FT: 5,453
SALES (est): 4.6MM Privately Held
SIC: 3841 5047 8731 Surgical & medical instruments; medical equipment & supplies; biotechnical research, commercial

(P-22446)
EVOLVE MANUFACTURING TECH INC
47300 Bayside Pkwy, Fremont (94538-6516)
PHONE..............................650 968-9292
Noreen King, *President*
Dave Devine, *President*
Tim Wraith, *Admin Asst*
Sarvar Samia, *Human Res Mgr*
Juliea Chu, *Purch Mgr*
▲ EMP: 65
SQ FT: 45,000
SALES (est): 14.9MM Privately Held
WEB: www.evolvemfg.com
SIC: 3841 3674 8731 Ultrasonic medical cleaning equipment; semiconductors & related devices; biotechnical research, commercial

(P-22447)
EYE MEDICAL GROUP SANTA CRUZ
515 Soquel Ave, Santa Cruz (95062-2378)
PHONE..............................831 426-2550
Laurie Marquez, *General Mgr*
EMP: 12
SALES (est): 1MM Privately Held
SIC: 3841 Optometers

(P-22448)
FC GLOBAL REALTY INCORPORATED
2375 Camino Vida Roble B, Carlsbad (92011-1506)
PHONE..............................760 602-3300
Jeff O'Donnel, *CEO*
EMP: 25
SALES (corp-wide): 31.1MM Privately Held
WEB: www.photomedex.com
SIC: 3841 Surgical lasers
PA: Fc Global Realty Incorporated
40 Ramland Rd S Ste 200
Orangeburg NY 10962
215 619-3600

(P-22449)
FIBERLITE CENTRIFUGE LLC
Also Called: Thermo Fisher Scientific
422 Aldo Ave, Santa Clara (95054-2301)
PHONE..............................408 492-1109
Al Piramoon, *Mng Member*
Tim Overstreet, *Administration*
Tim Sgroi, *Sr Project Mgr*
Kim Vong, *Senior Mgr*
Markus Affolter, *Manager*
▲ EMP: 70
SQ FT: 18,000
SALES (est): 8.6MM
SALES (corp-wide): 20.9B Publicly Held
WEB: www.piramoon.com
SIC: 3841 Instruments, microsurgical: except electromedical
PA: Thermo Fisher Scientific Inc.
168 3rd Ave
Waltham MA 02451
781 622-1000

(P-22450)
FIRST CHOICE INTERNATIONAL
1201 W Artesia Blvd, Compton (90220-5305)
PHONE..............................310 537-1500
Mike Shah, *CEO*
Lidia Morales, *Sales Mgr*
EMP: 12
SALES: 250K Privately Held
SIC: 3841 Surgical & medical instruments

(P-22451)
FLUID LINE TECHNOLOGY CORP
9362 Eton Ave Ste A, Chatsworth (91311-5888)
P.O. Box 3116 (91313-3116)
PHONE..............................818 998-8848
Joseph Marcilese, *President*
Phillip Jaramilla, *Vice Pres*
▼ EMP: 25
SQ FT: 17,000
SALES (est): 4.7MM Privately Held
WEB: www.fluidlinetech.com
SIC: 3841 2833 Surgical & medical instruments; medicinals & botanicals

(P-22452)
FLUXION BIOSCIENCES INC (PA)
1600 Harbor Bay Pkwy # 150, Alameda (94502-3011)
PHONE..............................650 241-4777
Jeff Jenson, *CEO*
Jody Beecher, *Vice Pres*
Niall Murphy, *Vice Pres*
Cristian Ionescu Zanetti, *CTO*
Bryan Haines, *Technical Staff*
▲ EMP: 30
SQ FT: 10,000
SALES (est): 3.6MM Privately Held
WEB: www.fluxionbio.com
SIC: 3841 Diagnostic apparatus, medical

(P-22453)
FORSYTHE TECH WORLDWIDE
23924 Victory Blvd, Woodland Hills (91367-1253)
PHONE..............................818 710-8694
Thomas Delahanty, *President*
EMP: 10
SALES (est): 1.1MM Privately Held
WEB: www.forsythetechnologies.com
SIC: 3841 Diagnostic apparatus, medical

(P-22454)
FOUNDRY MED INNOVATIONS INC
Also Called: Toolbox Medical Innovations
1630 Faraday Ave Ste 102, Carlsbad (92008-7313)
PHONE..............................888 445-2333
John K Zeis, *President*
Jenn S Zeis, *Vice Pres*
Daniele Narelli, *Technician*
Afton Anderson, *Research*
Colleen Monaco, *Research*
EMP: 17
SALES (est): 1.7MM Privately Held
SIC: 3841 Diagnostic apparatus, medical

(P-22455)
FRANS MANUFACTURING INC
126 N Vinewood St, Escondido (92029-1332)
PHONE..............................760 741-9135
Frans Ketelaars, *President*
Michael Wibier, *Vice Pres*
EMP: 13
SQ FT: 3,900
SALES (est): 2.1MM Privately Held
SIC: 3841 Surgical & medical instruments

(P-22456)
FREEDOM MEDITECH INC
5090 Shoreham Pl Ste 109, San Diego (92122-5934)
PHONE..............................858 638-1433
John Gerace, *CEO*
Daniel M Bradbury, *Ch of Bd*
Craig Misrach, *President*
Sharad Mishra, *Info Tech Mgr*
Emily Arsenault, *Manager*
EMP: 20
SALES (est): 2.8MM Privately Held
SIC: 3841 Surgical & medical instruments

(P-22457)
FZIOMED INC (PA)
231 Bonetti Dr, San Luis Obispo (93401-7376)
PHONE..............................805 546-0610
John S Krelle, *President*
Ronald F Haynes, *Ch of Bd*
Vanessa Fruit, *QA Dir*
Kane Assemi, *Info Tech Mgr*
Mark Miller, *Engineer*
EMP: 40
SQ FT: 36,000
SALES (est): 4.8MM Privately Held
WEB: www.fzio.com
SIC: 3841 Surgical & medical instruments

(P-22458)
GALEN ROBOTICS INC
541 Jefferson Ave Ste 100, Redwood City (94063-1700)
PHONE..............................408 502-5960
Bruce Lichorowic, *President*
Lori Munog, *CFO*
Feimo Shen, *Vice Pres*
David Sunders, *CTO*
EMP: 15 EST: 2016
SQ FT: 15,000
SALES (est): 528.8K Privately Held
SIC: 3841 Surgical instruments & apparatus

(P-22459)
GE VENTURES INC
2882 Sand Hill Rd Ste 240, Menlo Park (94025-7057)
PHONE..............................650 233-3900
Sue Siegal, *CEO*
EMP: 30 EST: 2015
SALES (est): 2.9MM Privately Held
SIC: 3841 Surgical & medical instruments

(P-22460)
GENALYTE INC
10520 Wateridge Cir, San Diego (92121-5782)
PHONE..............................858 956-1200
Cary Gunn, *CEO*
Kevin Lo, *President*
Todd Ritter, *President*
Kevin McGee, *Officer*
Martin Gleeson, *Vice Pres*
EMP: 18
SQ FT: 4,035

SALES (est): 5.1MM **Privately Held**
WEB: www.genalyte.com
SIC: 3841 Diagnostic apparatus, medical

(P-22461)
GLAUKOS CORPORATION (PA)
229 Avenida Fabricante, San Clemente
(92672-7531)
PHONE..........................949 367-9600
Thomas W Burns, *President*
William J Link, *Ch of Bd*
Chris M Calcaterra, *COO*
Joseph E Gilliam, *CFO*
EMP: 206
SALES: 159.2MM **Publicly Held**
WEB: www.glaukos.com
SIC: 3841 Eye examining instruments &
apparatus

(P-22462)
GRIFFIN LABORATORIES
43379 Bus Pk Dr Ste 300, Temecula
(92590-3687)
PHONE..........................951 695-6727
Clifford J Griffin, *President*
Karen Griffin, *Vice Pres*
Julie Hess, *Purch Agent*
Eric Howell, *Sales Staff*
EMP: 10 EST: 1994
SQ FT: 5,000
SALES (est): 1.9MM **Privately Held**
WEB: www.griffinlab.com
SIC: 3841 Surgical & medical instruments

(P-22463)
GUIDANT SALES LLC
825 E Middlefield Rd, Mountain View
(94043-4025)
PHONE..........................650 965-2634
EMP: 35
SALES (corp-wide): 9B **Publicly Held**
WEB: www.guidant.com
SIC: 3841 Surgical & medical instruments
HQ: Guidant Sales Llc
4100 Hamline Ave N
Saint Paul MN 55112

(P-22464)
HAEMONETICS CORPORATION
95 Declaration Dr Ste 3, Chico
(95973-4916)
PHONE..........................530 774-2081
EMP: 317
SALES (corp-wide): 903.9MM **Publicly
Held**
SIC: 3841 Medical instruments & equip-
ment, blood & bone work
PA: Haemonetics Corporation
400 Wood Rd
Braintree MA 02184
781 848-7100

(P-22465)
HAEMONETICS
MANUFACTURING INC (HQ)
1684 W Industrial Park St, Covina
(91722-3419)
PHONE..........................626 339-7388
Neil Ryding, *CEO*
▲ EMP: 31
SQ FT: 61,313
SALES (est): 32.2MM
SALES (corp-wide): 903.9MM **Publicly
Held**
SIC: 3841 Surgical & medical instruments
PA: Haemonetics Corporation
400 Wood Rd
Braintree MA 02184
781 848-7100

(P-22466)
HANSEN MEDICAL INC
800 E Middlefield Rd, Mountain View
(94043-4030)
PHONE..........................650 404-5800
Cary Vance, *President*
Michael L Eagle, *Ch of Bd*
Cary G Vance, *President*
Christopher P Lowe, *CFO*
Robert Cathcart, *Senior VP*
EMP: 130
SQ FT: 63,000

SALES: 16MM
SALES (corp-wide): 36.4MM **Privately
Held**
WEB: www.hansenmedical.com
SIC: 3841 Catheters
PA: Auris Health, Inc.
150 Shoreline Dr
Redwood City CA 94065
650 610-0750

(P-22467)
HANTEL TECHNOLOGIES INC
3496 Breakwater Ct, Hayward
(94545-3613)
PHONE..........................510 400-1164
Mary M Pascual Gallup, *CEO*
David Gallup, *President*
Dennis Mello, *Manager*
▲ EMP: 40 EST: 1998
SQ FT: 18,000
SALES (est): 7.6MM **Privately Held**
WEB: www.hanteltech.com
SIC: 3841 Surgical & medical instruments

(P-22468)
HARBOR MEDTECH INC
4 Jenner Ste 190, Irvine (92618-3831)
PHONE..........................949 679-4800
Jerry Mezger, *President*
Jim Jungwirth, *CFO*
Jon Zalk, *Officer*
EMP: 12
SALES (est): 1.8MM **Privately Held**
SIC: 3841 Surgical & medical instruments

(P-22469)
HEMODIALYSIS INC
Also Called: Hunnington Dialysis Center
806 S Fair Oaks Ave, Pasadena
(91105-2601)
PHONE..........................626 792-0548
Susan Burkhart, *Manager*
EMP: 50
SALES (corp-wide): 10.4MM **Privately
Held**
SIC: 3841 8011 Hemodialysis apparatus;
hematologist
PA: Hemodialysis, Inc.
710 W Wilson Ave
Glendale CA 91203
818 500-8736

(P-22470)
HOWMEDICA OSTEONICS CORP
1947 W Collins Ave, Orange (92867-5426)
PHONE..........................714 557-5010
Lynn Wagnor, *Branch Mgr*
EMP: 27
SALES (corp-wide): 12.4B **Publicly Held**
SIC: 3841 Surgical & medical instruments
HQ: Howmedica Osteonics Corp.
325 Corporate Dr
Mahwah NJ 07430
201 831-5000

(P-22471)
HOYA SURGICAL OPTICS INC
15335 Fairfield Ranch Rd # 250, Chino Hills
(91709-8841)
PHONE..........................909 680-3900
Yasuro Mori, *CFO*
Bruno Chermette, *President*
EMP: 20
SALES (est): 2.7MM **Privately Held**
SIC: 3841 Surgical & medical instruments

(P-22472)
HYCOR BIOMEDICAL LLC
7272 Chapman Ave Ste A, Garden Grove
(92841-2103)
PHONE..........................714 933-3000
Dick Aderman, *President*
Eric Whitters, *COO*
Phil Crusco, *Vice Pres*
Richard Hockins, *Vice Pres*
Kim Walker, *Vice Pres*
▲ EMP: 120 EST: 1985
SQ FT: 76,000
SALES (est): 6.5MM
SALES (corp-wide): 98MM **Privately
Held**
WEB: www.hycorbiomedical.com
SIC: 3841 2835 Surgical & medical instru-
ments; in vitro & in vivo diagnostic sub-
stances

PA: Linden, Llc
111 S Wacker Dr Ste 3350
Chicago IL 60606
312 506-5657

(P-22473)
I-FLOW LLC
43 Discovery Ste 100, Irvine (92618-3773)
PHONE..........................800 448-3569
Donald Earhart, *President*
James J Dal Porto, *COO*
James R Talevich, *CFO*
EMP: 1100
SQ FT: 66,675
SALES (est): 126.5MM
SALES (corp-wide): 18.2B **Publicly Held**
WEB: www.iflo.com
SIC: 3841 Surgical instruments & appara-
tus
PA: Kimberly-Clark Corporation
351 Phelps Dr
Irving TX 75038
972 281-1200

(P-22474)
ICU MEDICAL INC (PA)
951 Calle Amanecer, San Clemente
(92673-6212)
PHONE..........................949 366-2183
Vivek Jain, *Ch of Bd*
Christian B Voigtlander, *COO*
Scott E Lamb, *CFO*
Scott Lamb, *CFO*
Alison D Burcar, *Vice Pres*
▲ EMP: 277
SQ FT: 39,000
SALES: 1.2B **Publicly Held**
SIC: 3841 3845 IV transfusion apparatus;
catheters; pacemaker, cardiac

(P-22475)
ICU MEDICAL SALES INC (HQ)
951 Calle Amanecer, San Clemente
(92673-6212)
PHONE..........................949 366-2183
Vivek Jain, *CEO*
EMP: 10
SQ FT: 39,000
SALES (est): 2.2MM
SALES (corp-wide): 1.2B **Publicly Held**
SIC: 3841 IV transfusion apparatus;
catheters
PA: Icu Medical, Inc.
951 Calle Amanecer
San Clemente CA 92673
949 366-2183

(P-22476)
IMMUNO CONCEPTS INC
9825 Goethe Rd Ste 350, Sacramento
(95827-3571)
PHONE..........................916 363-2649
Robert Boyes, *Branch Mgr*
Bob Boyes, *General Mgr*
Natalie Zelenov, *QC Mgr*
EMP: 45
SALES (corp-wide): 8.8MM **Privately
Held**
WEB: www.immunoconcepts.com
SIC: 3841 2835 Diagnostic apparatus,
medical; in vitro & in vivo diagnostic sub-
stances
PA: Immuno Concepts Inc
2280 Springlake Rd # 106
Dallas TX 75234
972 919-1780

(P-22477)
IMPEDIMED INC (HQ)
Also Called: Xitron Technologies
5900 Pasteur Ct Ste 125, Carlsbad
(92008-7334)
PHONE..........................760 585-2100
Richard Carreon, *CEO*
Don Myll, *CFO*
Steve St Amand, *Technology*
EMP: 20
SQ FT: 15,000
SALES (est): 4.2MM **Privately Held**
SIC: 3841 Surgical & medical instruments

(P-22478)
INARI MEDICAL INC
9272 Jeronimo Rd Ste 124, Irvine
(92618-1914)
PHONE..........................949 600-8433

Bill Hoffman, *CEO*
Eben Gordon, *Vice Pres*
Paul Lubock, *Vice Pres*
Janet Byk, *CPA*
Tara Dunn, *VP Mktg*
EMP: 22
SALES (est): 3.2MM **Privately Held**
SIC: 3841 Catheters

(P-22479)
INCELLDX INC
1541 Industrial Rd, San Carlos
(94070-4111)
PHONE..........................650 777-7630
Bruce Patterson, *CEO*
Eric Hass, *COO*
Chris Meda, *Officer*
Carol Penfold-Patters, *Vice Pres*
Daren Abe, *Office Mgr*
EMP: 13
SQ FT: 3,500
SALES (est): 2.9MM **Privately Held**
SIC: 3841 Diagnostic apparatus, medical

(P-22480)
INOGEN INC (PA)
326 Bollay Dr, Goleta (93117-5550)
PHONE..........................805 562-0500
Scott Wilkinson, *President*
Heath Lukatch, *Ch of Bd*
Alison Bauerlein, *CFO*
Benjamin Anderson-Ray, *Bd of Directors*
Byron Myers, *Exec VP*
◆ EMP: 208
SQ FT: 39,000
SALES: 249.4MM **Publicly Held**
WEB: www.inogen.net
SIC: 3841 3842 Surgical & medical instru-
ments; surgical appliances & supplies

(P-22481)
INTEGRA LFSCNCES HOLDINGS
CORP
5955 Pacific Center Blvd, San Diego
(92121-4309)
PHONE..........................609 529-9748
Peter Arduini, *CEO*
Sharon Fisher, *Partner*
Daniel Elser, *Executive*
Elizabeth Ormaza, *Program Mgr*
Brett Trimble, *Info Tech Dir*
EMP: 25 **Publicly Held**
SIC: 3841 3845 Surgical & medical instru-
ments; electromedical equipment
PA: Integra Lifesciences Holdings Corpora-
tion
311 Enterprise Dr
Plainsboro NJ 08536

(P-22482)
INTELLA INTERVENTIONAL
SYSTEMS
Also Called: Iwi
605 W California Ave, Sunnyvale
(94086-4831)
PHONE..........................650 269-1375
EMP: 62
SQ FT: 14,500
SALES (est): 7.3MM **Privately Held**
WEB: www.i-s-i.com
SIC: 3841

(P-22483)
INTERFACE ASSOCIATES INC
(HQ)
Also Called: Interface Catheter Solutions
27721 La Paz Rd, Laguna Niguel
(92677-3948)
PHONE..........................949 448-7056
Gary D Curtis, *President*
Matt Tonge, *President*
Gayle L Arnold, *CFO*
Mark Geiger, *Vice Pres*
Joe Stupecky, *CTO*
EMP: 104
SQ FT: 40,000
SALES (est): 35MM **Privately Held**
WEB: www.elcaminohospital.org
SIC: 3841 5047 Surgical & medical instru-
ments; hospital equipment & furniture

(P-22484)
INTERNATIONAL TECHNIDYNE CORP (DH)
Also Called: Accriva Diagnostics
6260 Sequence Dr, San Diego (92121-4358)
PHONE.....................858 263-2300
Scott Cramer, *President*
Tom Whalen, *COO*
Greg Tibbitts, *CFO*
Matt Bastardi, *Senior VP*
Kimberly Ballard, *Vice Pres*
EMP: 250 **EST:** 1969
SQ FT: 130,000
SALES (est): 104.5MM
SALES (corp-wide): 157.1MM **Privately Held**
WEB: www.itcmed.com
SIC: 3841 3829 Diagnostic apparatus, medical; medical diagnostic systems, nuclear
HQ: Accriva Diagnostics Holdings, Inc.
6260 Sequence Dr
San Diego CA 92121
858 404-8203

(P-22485)
INTERSECT ENT INC (PA)
1555 Adams Dr, Menlo Park (94025-1439)
PHONE.....................650 641-2100
Lisa D Earnhardt, *President*
Christine Kowalski, *COO*
Jeryl L Hilleman, *CFO*
Rob Binney, *Vice Pres*
Dan Castro, *Vice Pres*
EMP: 275
SQ FT: 50,400
SALES: 96.3MM **Publicly Held**
SIC: 3841 Surgical & medical instruments

(P-22486)
INTERVENTIONAL SPINE INC
13844 Alton Pkwy Ste 131, Irvine (92618-1689)
PHONE.....................949 472-0006
Walter Ceuvas, *CEO*
Michael Henson, *Ch of Bd*
Joseph Darling, *COO*
Stephen T Colaiezzi, *Senior VP*
EMP: 15
SQ FT: 7,500
SALES (est): 2.7MM **Privately Held**
WEB: www.triagemed.com
SIC: 3841 Surgical & medical instruments

(P-22487)
INTUBRITE LLC
2460 Coral St, Vista (92081-8430)
PHONE.....................760 727-1900
John Hicks, *Mng Member*
Leslie Tanger, *Mng Member*
James Tenger, *Mng Member*
▲ **EMP:** 10
SALES (est): 2MM **Privately Held**
SIC: 3841 Medical instruments & equipment, blood & bone work

(P-22488)
INTUITIVE SRGCAL OPRATIONS INC
1266 Kifer Rd, Sunnyvale (94086-5304)
PHONE.....................408 523-2100
Gary S Guthart, *CEO*
EMP: 45 **EST:** 2009
SALES (est): 9.3MM **Publicly Held**
SIC: 3841 Surgical & medical instruments
PA: Intuitive Surgical, Inc.
1020 Kifer Rd
Sunnyvale CA 94086

(P-22489)
INTUITIVE SURGICAL INC
1250 Kifer Rd, Sunnyvale (94086-5304)
PHONE.....................408 523-7314
Mark Brosius, *Vice Pres*
John Wagner, *Vice Pres*
Lidia Bernardo, *Executive Asst*
Benjamin Velazquez, *Planning*
Patrick Jiang, *IT/INT Sup*
EMP: 21 **Publicly Held**
SIC: 3841 Surgical & medical instruments

PA: Intuitive Surgical, Inc.
1020 Kifer Rd
Sunnyvale CA 94086

(P-22490)
INTUITIVE SURGICAL INC (PA)
1020 Kifer Rd, Sunnyvale (94086-5301)
PHONE.....................408 523-2100
Gary S Guthart, *President*
Lonnie M Smith, *Ch of Bd*
Marshall L Mohr, *CFO*
David J Rosa, *Ch Credit Ofcr*
Myriam J Curet, *Chief Mktg Ofcr*
▲ **EMP:** 183
SQ FT: 927,000
SALES: 3.1B **Publicly Held**
WEB: www.intusurg.com
SIC: 3841 Surgical & medical instruments

(P-22491)
INTUITY MEDICAL INC
Also Called: Rosedale Medical
3500 W Warren Ave, Fremont (94538-6499)
PHONE.....................408 530-1700
Emory Anderson, *President*
Emory V Anderson III, *President*
Robb Hesley, *Vice Pres*
Kelley Lipman, *Vice Pres*
Joni Furlong, *Administration*
EMP: 64
SQ FT: 18,000
SALES (est): 11.9MM **Privately Held**
SIC: 3841 Medical instruments & equipment, blood & bone work

(P-22492)
INVENIO IMAGING INC
2310 Walsh Ave, Santa Clara (95051-1301)
PHONE.....................408 753-9147
Jay Trautman, *President*
Jonathan Ross, *CFO*
◆ **EMP:** 10
SQ FT: 2,000
SALES (est): 1.3MM **Privately Held**
SIC: 3841 Surgical & medical instruments

(P-22493)
INVUITY INC
Also Called: Intelligent Photonics
444 De Haro St Ste 100, San Francisco (94107-2350)
PHONE.....................415 665-2100
Scott Flora, *CEO*
James H Mackaness, *CFO*
Andrew Sale, *Senior VP*
Paul Davison, *Vice Pres*
Joseph Guido, *Vice Pres*
EMP: 172
SQ FT: 38,135
SALES: 39.6MM
SALES (corp-wide): 12.4B **Publicly Held**
SIC: 3841 5047 Surgical instruments & apparatus; surgical equipment & supplies
PA: Stryker Corporation
2825 Airview Blvd
Portage MI 49002
269 385-2600

(P-22494)
IOWA APPROACH INC
3715 Haven Ave Ste 110, Menlo Park (94025-1047)
PHONE.....................650 422-3633
Allan Zingeler, *CEO*
EMP: 13
SALES (est): 2.1MM **Privately Held**
SIC: 3841 Surgical instruments & apparatus

(P-22495)
IRIDEX CORPORATION (PA)
1212 Terra Bella Ave, Mountain View (94043-1824)
PHONE.....................650 940-4700
William M Moore, *Ch of Bd*
Atabak Mokari, *CFO*
Scott Shuda, *Bd of Directors*
Romeo R Dizon, *Vice Pres*
EMP: 108
SQ FT: 37,166
SALES: 41.5MM **Publicly Held**
SIC: 3841 Surgical & medical instruments

(P-22496)
ISCIENCE INTERVENTIONAL CORP
41316 Christy St, Fremont (94538-3115)
PHONE.....................650 421-2700
Michael Nash, *President*
Matt Franklin, *CFO*
Stan Conston, *Vice Pres*
Ernie Edwards, *Vice Pres*
Mark Hayward, *Vice Pres*
EMP: 60
SALES (est): 7.2MM **Privately Held**
WEB: www.isciencesurgical.com
SIC: 3841 Instruments, microsurgical: except electromedical

(P-22497)
ITECH MEDICAL INC
17011 Beach Blvd Ste 900, Huntington Beach (92647-5998)
PHONE.....................714 841-2670
Warren G Baker, *Ch of Bd*
Wayne Cockburn, *CFO*
Karl R Wolcott, *VP Sls/Mktg*
EMP: 10
SALES (est): 647.6K **Privately Held**
SIC: 3841 Surgical & medical instruments

(P-22498)
IVERA MEDICAL LLC
Also Called: Ivera Medical Corporation
10805 Rancho Bernardo Rd # 100, San Diego (92127-5702)
PHONE.....................888 861-8228
Bobby E Rogers, *President*
Jack Saladow, *Marketing Staff*
EMP: 60
SALES (est): 6.6MM
SALES (corp-wide): 31.6B **Publicly Held**
SIC: 3841 IV transfusion apparatus
PA: 3m Company
3m Center
Saint Paul MN 55144
651 733-1110

(P-22499)
J F FONG INC
Also Called: American Imex
16520 Aston, Irvine (92606-4805)
PHONE.....................949 553-8885
Joan F Fong, *President*
Joseph Fong, *Vice Pres*
▲ **EMP:** 15
SQ FT: 8,000
SALES (est): 3.3MM **Privately Held**
WEB: www.americanimex.com
SIC: 3841 5047 Surgical & medical instruments; medical equipment & supplies

(P-22500)
JOHNSON & JOHNSON
Also Called: Johnson & Johnson Vision
510 Cottonwood Dr, Milpitas (95035-7403)
PHONE.....................408 273-4100
Murthy Simhambhatla, *Branch Mgr*
Kelly Decoria, *Electrical Engi*
Charles Galleano, *Senior Mgr*
EMP: 32
SALES (corp-wide): 76.4B **Publicly Held**
SIC: 3841 Ophthalmic instruments & apparatus
HQ: Johnson & Johnson Surgical Vision, Inc.
1700 E Saint Andrew Pl
Santa Ana CA 92705
714 247-8200

(P-22501)
KARL STORZ ENDSCPY-AMERICA INC
2151 E Grand Ave Ste 100, El Segundo (90245-2838)
PHONE.....................508 248-9011
Marsha Hunter, *Branch Mgr*
David Chatenever, *Vice Pres*
Mylene Paysan-Hilario, *Comms Mgr*
Marc Amling, *Exec Dir*
Cory Alcala, *General Mgr*
EMP: 20
SALES (corp-wide): 1.6B **Privately Held**
WEB: www.ksela.com
SIC: 3841 Surgical & medical instruments

HQ: Karl Storz Endoscopy-America, Inc.
2151 E Grand Ave
El Segundo CA 90245
424 218-8100

(P-22502)
KARL STORZ ENDSCPY-AMERICA INC (HQ)
2151 E Grand Ave, El Segundo (90245-5017)
PHONE.....................424 218-8100
Charles Wilhelm, *CEO*
Sken Huang, *CFO*
Mark Green, *Vice Pres*
Jean L Hopper, *Vice Pres*
Claire Stevens, *Executive*
▲ **EMP:** 277
SQ FT: 90,000
SALES (est): 278MM
SALES (corp-wide): 1.6B **Privately Held**
WEB: www.ksela.com
SIC: 3841 5047 Surgical & medical instruments; medical equipment & supplies
PA: Karl Storz Se & Co. Kg
Dr.-Karl-Storz-StraBe 34
Tuttlingen 78532
746 170-80

(P-22503)
KENLOR INDUSTRIES INC
1560 E Edinger Ave Ste A1, Santa Ana (92705-4913)
PHONE.....................714 647-0770
Kamales Som PHD, *President*
Sudeep Banerjee, *Vice Pres*
EMP: 12
SQ FT: 5,000
SALES (est): 1.5MM **Privately Held**
WEB: www.kenlor.com
SIC: 3841 2834 Surgical & medical instruments; pharmaceutical preparations

(P-22504)
KINEMATIC AUTOMATION INC
21085 Longeway Rd, Sonora (95370-8968)
P.O. Box 69, Twain Harte (95383-0069)
PHONE.....................209 532-3200
David Carlberg, *President*
Ted Meigs, *Vice Pres*
EMP: 55
SQ FT: 19,000
SALES (est): 13.2MM **Privately Held**
WEB: www.kinematic.com
SIC: 3841 7389 Diagnostic apparatus, medical; design, commercial & industrial

(P-22505)
KONG VETERINARY PRODUCTS
Also Called: KVP
16018 Adelante St Ste C, Irwindale (91702-3236)
PHONE.....................626 633-0077
Nancy Klinkhart, *President*
Herman Klinkhart, *Vice Pres*
Roger Klinkhart, *Vice Pres*
Kristi Pray, *Buyer*
Adam Holstein, *Sales Staff*
EMP: 15 **EST:** 1960
SQ FT: 8,000
SALES (est): 1.4MM **Privately Held**
SIC: 3841 3842 Surgical & medical instruments; surgical appliances & supplies

(P-22506)
KOROS USA INC
610 Flinn Ave, Moorpark (93021-2008)
PHONE.....................805 529-0825
Tibor Koros, *President*
Alexander Leparulo, *Sales Staff*
▲ **EMP:** 25 **EST:** 1974
SQ FT: 12,000
SALES (est): 4.9MM **Privately Held**
WEB: www.korosusa.com
SIC: 3841 Diagnostic apparatus, medical

(P-22507)
LEICA BIOSYSTEMS IMAGING INC
Also Called: Aperio
1360 Park Center Dr, Vista (92081-8300)
PHONE.....................760 539-1100
James F O'Reilly, *Vice Pres*
Keith B Hagen, *COO*
Jared N Schwartz, *Officer*
Greg Crandall, *Vice Pres*

P
R
O
D
U
C
T
S

&

S
V
C
S

Steven V Russell, *Vice Pres*
EMP: 182
SQ FT: 37,000
SALES (est): 33.9MM **Privately Held**
SIC: 3841 Surgical & medical instruments

(P-22508)
LIFE SCIENCE OUTSOURCING INC
Also Called: Medical Device Manufacturing
830 Challenger St, Brea (92821-2946)
PHONE..................................714 672-1090
Barry Kazemi, *President*
Charlie Ricci, *Vice Pres*
▲ **EMP:** 80
SQ FT: 56,000
SALES (est): 18.3MM **Privately Held**
WEB: www.lso-inc.com
SIC: 3841 Surgical instruments & apparatus

(P-22509)
LIFEMED OF CALIFORNIA
13948 Mountain Ave, Chino (91710-9018)
P.O. Box 787 (91708-0787)
PHONE..................................800 543-3633
Thomas Hamon, *President*
Pat Brinker, *Vice Pres*
EMP: 21
SQ FT: 10,000
SALES (est): 2.4MM **Privately Held**
WEB: www.lifemedinc.com
SIC: 3841 Hemodialysis apparatus; medical instruments & equipment, blood & bone work

(P-22510)
LIFESCAN PRODUCTS LLC (HQ)
1000 Gibraltar Dr, Milpitas (95035-6312)
PHONE..................................408 719-8443
Eric Milledge, *Ch of Bd*
Louis Caro, *CFO*
Sonia Rodriguez, *Buyer*
Natasha Shaw, *Mktg Dir*
Praveen Sharma, *Sr Project Mgr*
EMP: 65
SALES (est): 52.6MM
SALES (corp-wide): 76.4B **Publicly Held**
SIC: 3841 3845 Surgical & medical instruments; ultrasonic scanning devices, medical
PA: Johnson & Johnson
   1 Johnson And Johnson Plz
   New Brunswick NJ 08933
   732 524-0400

(P-22511)
LINKS MEDICAL PRODUCTS INC (PA)
9247 Research Dr, Irvine (92618-4286)
PHONE..................................949 753-0001
Thomas L Buckley, *CEO*
Patrick Buckley, *President*
Sandy Campbell, *Office Mgr*
Chad Muhr, *Mktg Dir*
Joe Greco, *Sales Dir*
▲ **EMP:** 28
SQ FT: 8,800
SALES (est): 4.4MM **Privately Held**
WEB: www.linksmed.com
SIC: 3841 Medical instruments & equipment, blood & bone work

(P-22512)
LINVATEC CORPORATION
Also Called: Envision Medical
26 Castilian Dr Ste B, Goleta (93117-5565)
PHONE..................................805 571-8100
Bruce Smears, *Manager*
EMP: 80
SALES (corp-wide): 796.3MM **Publicly Held**
WEB: www.hallsurgical.com
SIC: 3841 3861 Surgical & medical instruments; photographic equipment & supplies
HQ: Linvatec Corporation
   11311 Concept Blvd
   Largo FL 33773
   727 392-6464

(P-22513)
LOMA VISTA MEDICAL INC
863a Mitten Rd Ste 100a, Burlingame (94010-1303)
PHONE..................................650 490-4747

Alex Tilson, *CEO*
Mark Scheeff, *Vice Pres*
EMP: 15
SQ FT: 4,500
SALES (est): 2.2MM **Privately Held**
SIC: 3841 Surgical & medical instruments

(P-22514)
LOMBARD MEDICAL TECH INC (HQ)
6440 Oak Cyn Ste 200, Irvine (92618-5209)
PHONE..................................949 379-3750
Kurt Lemvigh, *CEO*
Simon Hubbert, *CEO*
William Kullback, *CFO*
Michael Carrel, *Bd of Directors*
Timothy Haines, *Bd of Directors*
EMP: 20
SQ FT: 17,000
SALES: 13.2MM
SALES (corp-wide): 112.2K **Privately Held**
SIC: 3841 Surgical & medical instruments
PA: Lombard Medical Technologies Limited
   Lombard Medical House
   Didcot OXON
   123 575-0800

(P-22515)
LUMENIS INC (DH)
2077 Gateway Pl Ste 300, San Jose (95110-1149)
PHONE..................................408 764-3000
Tzipi Ozer Armon, *CEO*
Harel Beit-On, *Ch of Bd*
Abner Ray, *President*
Shlomi Cohen, *CFO*
Kevin Morano, *CFO*
▲ **EMP:** 150
SALES (est): 217.3MM **Privately Held**
SIC: 3841 Surgical & medical instruments
HQ: Lumenis Ltd.
   6 Hakidma
   Upper Yokneam 20692
   495 990-00

(P-22516)
MAGNABIOSCIENCES LLC
6325 Lusk Blvd, San Diego (92121-3733)
PHONE..................................858 481-4400
Ron Sager,
Dave Cox,
Gerald D Daviessnager,
Greg Degeller,
Ronald E Sager,
EMP: 100
SQ FT: 2,200
SALES (est): 12.4MM
SALES (corp-wide): 41.5MM **Privately Held**
WEB: www.qdusa.com
SIC: 3841 5047 5999 Diagnostic apparatus, medical; diagnostic equipment, medical; medical apparatus & supplies
PA: Quantum Design, Inc.
   10307 Pacific Center Ct
   San Diego CA 92121
   858 481-4400

(P-22517)
MAGNAMOSIS INC
953 Indiana St Rm 212, San Francisco (94107-3007)
PHONE..................................707 484-8774
Michael Harrison, *President*
Michael Danty, *COO*
EMP: 10 EST: 2012
SALES (est): 456.3K **Privately Held**
SIC: 3841 Surgical & medical instruments

(P-22518)
MALLINCKRODT INC
3298 Morning Ridge Ave, Thousand Oaks (91362-1195)
PHONE..................................805 553-9303
Mark Thom, *President*
EMP: 13
SALES (est): 1MM **Privately Held**
SIC: 3841 Ultrasonic medical cleaning equipment

(P-22519)
MARLEE MANUFACTURING INC
4711 E Guasti Rd, Ontario (91761-8106)
PHONE..................................909 390-3222

Russell Wells, *President*
Shawn Cory, *President*
Patricia Wells, *Vice Pres*
Leeanne Ledgerwood, *Accountant*
Larry Pettit, *QC Dir*
EMP: 39
SQ FT: 41,000
SALES (est): 7.5MM **Privately Held**
WEB: www.marleemanufacturing.com
SIC: 3841 3599 Surgical & medical instruments; machine shop, jobbing & repair

(P-22520)
MATTHEY JOHNSON INC
Also Called: Shape Memory Applications
1070 Coml St Ste 110, San Jose (95112)
PHONE..................................408 727-2221
Brian Woodward, *Branch Mgr*
Bill Burton, *Engineer*
Jose Hurtado, *Engineer*
Jennifer Brierly, *Manager*
EMP: 50
SALES (corp-wide): 15B **Privately Held**
SIC: 3841 3496 3356 3357 Surgical & medical instruments; miscellaneous fabricated wire products; nonferrous rolling & drawing; nonferrous wiredrawing & insulating; steel wire & related products
HQ: Matthey Johnson Inc
   435 Devon Park Dr Ste 600
   Wayne PA 19087
   610 971-3000

(P-22521)
MCCASH MANUFACTURING INC
1256 Washoe Dr, San Jose (95120-4005)
PHONE..................................408 748-8991
Jason McCash, *President*
EMP: 25 EST: 1999
SQ FT: 1,200
SALES (est): 2.7MM **Privately Held**
WEB: www.mccashmfg.com
SIC: 3841 Surgical & medical instruments

(P-22522)
MED-SAFE SYSTEMS INC
10975 Torreyana Rd, San Diego (92121-1106)
PHONE..................................855 236-2772
Joseph Taylor, *General Mgr*
◆ **EMP:** 200
SQ FT: 90,000
SALES (est): 11.4MM
SALES (corp-wide): 12B **Publicly Held**
WEB: www.becton.com
SIC: 3841 Surgical instruments & apparatus
PA: Becton, Dickinson And Company
   1 Becton Dr
   Franklin Lakes NJ 07417
   201 847-6800

(P-22523)
MEDEDGE INC
11965 Venice Blvd Ste 407, Los Angeles (90066-3982)
P.O. Box 3028, Venice (90294-3028)
PHONE..................................310 745-2290
EMP: 16
SQ FT: 2,000
SALES (est): 1.2MM **Privately Held**
WEB: www.mededge-inc.com
SIC: 3841

(P-22524)
MEDICAL AESTHETICS MENLO PARK
885 Oak Grove Ave Ste 101, Menlo Park (94025-4400)
PHONE..................................650 336-3358
EMP: 10
SALES (est): 825K **Privately Held**
SIC: 3841 7991 Surgical lasers; spas

(P-22525)
MEDICAL DEVICE RESOURCE CORP
Also Called: M D Resource
5981 Graham Ct, Livermore (94550-9710)
PHONE..................................510 732-9950
Melbourne Kimsey II, *President*
Ken Morgan, *Opers Staff*
Karla Simmons, *Consultant*
▼ **EMP:** 10

SALES (est): 2MM **Privately Held**
WEB: www.mdresource.com
SIC: 3841 Surgical instruments & apparatus; medical instruments & equipment, blood & bone work; suction therapy apparatus

(P-22526)
MEDICAL INSTR DEV LABS INC
Also Called: Mid Labs
557 Mccormick St, San Leandro (94577-1107)
PHONE..................................510 357-3952
Dr Rob Peabody Sr, *CEO*
David Chen, *President*
Carl Wang, *President*
Brenda Balletto, *Vice Pres*
Rong Wang, *Vice Pres*
EMP: 35
SQ FT: 17,000
SALES (est): 7.5MM **Privately Held**
WEB: www.midlabs.com
SIC: 3841 Ophthalmic instruments & apparatus

(P-22527)
MEDICAL TACTILE INC
5757 W Century Blvd # 600, Los Angeles (90045-6401)
PHONE..................................310 641-8228
Jae Son, *Chairman*
Denis O'Connor, *CEO*
Eric Carver, *General Mgr*
Steven Sanchez, *Admin Sec*
John Blazek, *Director*
▼ **EMP:** 12
SQ FT: 10,000
SALES (est): 1.2MM **Privately Held**
SIC: 3841 Diagnostic apparatus, medical

(P-22528)
MEDICOOL INC
20460 Gramercy Pl, Torrance (90501-1513)
PHONE..................................310 782-2200
Steve Yeager, *Principal*
▲ **EMP:** 17
SQ FT: 15,000
SALES (est): 1.7MM **Privately Held**
WEB: www.medicool.com
SIC: 3841 Inhalators, surgical & medical

(P-22529)
MEDIKA THERAPEUTICS INC
Also Called: Medika Health Care
4046 Clipper Ct, Fremont (94538-6540)
PHONE..................................510 377-0898
Roy Chin, *Chairman*
EMP: 10
SALES (est): 919.7K **Privately Held**
SIC: 3841 5999 7389 Surgical & medical instruments; medical apparatus & supplies; design services

(P-22530)
MEDINA MEDICAL INC
39684 Eureka Dr, Newark (94560-4805)
PHONE..................................650 396-7756
Erik T Engelson, *CEO*
EMP: 10
SALES (est): 1.8MM **Privately Held**
SIC: 3841 Surgical & medical instruments
HQ: Medtronic, Inc.
   710 Medtronic Pkwy
   Minneapolis MN 55432
   763 514-4000

(P-22531)
MEDTRONIC INC
5345 Skyllane Blvd, Santa Rosa (95403)
PHONE..................................707 541-3144
Eric Kunz, *Branch Mgr*
EMP: 30 **Privately Held**
SIC: 3841 5047 5999 Surgical & medical instruments; medical equipment & supplies; medical apparatus & supplies
HQ: Medtronic, Inc.
   710 Medtronic Pkwy
   Minneapolis MN 55432
   763 514-4000

(P-22532)
MEDTRONIC ATS MEDICAL INC
1851 E Deere Ave, Santa Ana (92705-5720)
PHONE..................................949 380-9333

Walter Cuevas, *Branch Mgr*
EMP: 40 **Privately Held**
WEB: www.atsmedical.com
SIC: 3841 Surgical instruments & apparatus
HQ: Medtronic Ats Medical, Inc.
3800 Annapolis Ln N # 175
Minneapolis MN 55447
763 553-7736

(P-22533)
MEDTRONIC PS MEDICAL INC (DH)
125 Cremona Dr, Goleta (93117-5503)
PHONE................805 571-3769
Austin Noll, *General Mgr*
Megan Trobridge, *Project Mgr*
Nick Rizzi, *Engineer*
Scott Sharp, *Engineer*
Chris Larson, *Business Mgr*
◆ **EMP:** 200
SQ FT: 82,000
SALES (est): 28.1MM **Privately Held**
SIC: 3841 Surgical & medical instruments
HQ: Medtronic, Inc.
710 Medtronic Pkwy
Minneapolis MN 55432
763 514-4000

(P-22534)
MEDTRONIC SPINE LLC (DH)
1221 Crossman Ave, Sunnyvale (94089-1103)
PHONE................408 548-6500
Bill Hawkins, *President*
Karen D Talmadge, *Vice Pres*
EMP: 229 **EST:** 2008
SQ FT: 151,000
SALES (est): 71.1MM **Privately Held**
WEB: www.kyphon.com
SIC: 3841 Surgical & medical instruments
HQ: Medtronic, Inc.
710 Medtronic Pkwy
Minneapolis MN 55432
763 514-4000

(P-22535)
MEDWAVES INC (PA)
16760 W Bernardo Dr, San Diego (92127-1904)
PHONE................858 946-0015
Theodore Ormsby, *President*
George Leung, *Officer*
Daniel Yeh, *QC Dir*
York Chen, *Manager*
Ted Ormsbuy, *Manager*
EMP: 18
SALES (est): 2.6MM **Privately Held**
WEB: www.medwaves.com
SIC: 3841 Surgical & medical instruments

(P-22536)
MELCO ENGINEERING CORPORATION
3605 Avenida Cumbre, Calabasas (91302-3034)
P.O. Box 8907 (91372-8907)
PHONE................818 591-1000
Henry B David, *President*
EMP: 10
SALES (est): 1.1MM **Privately Held**
WEB: www.melcowire.com
SIC: 3841 Surgical & medical instruments

(P-22537)
MERIT CABLES INCORPORATED
830 N Poinsettia St, Santa Ana (92701-3853)
PHONE................714 547-3054
Ted Hendrickson, *Principal*
Ruben Mauricio, *CFO*
David Greenwald, *Vice Pres*
Rich McHugh, *Director*
▼ **EMP:** 25
SQ FT: 8,000
SALES (est): 4MM **Privately Held**
WEB: www.meritcables.com
SIC: 3841 Surgical & medical instruments

(P-22538)
METTLER ELECTRONICS CORP
1333 S Claudina St, Anaheim (92805-6266)
PHONE................714 533-2221
Stephen C Mettler, *CEO*
Mark Mettler, *President*

Matthew Ferrari, *CFO*
Suzanne Kowahl, *Executive*
Donna Mettler, *Admin Sec*
▲ **EMP:** 42 **EST:** 1957
SQ FT: 22,500
SALES (est): 7MM **Privately Held**
WEB: www.mettlerelec.com
SIC: 3841 Surgical & medical instruments

(P-22539)
MICRO THERAPEUTICS INC (HQ)
Also Called: Ev3 Neurovascular
9775 Toledo Way, Irvine (92618-1811)
PHONE................949 837-3700
Thomas C Wilder III, *President*
Thomas Berryman, *CFO*
Eileen Lynch, *Marketing Staff*
Seth Else, *Sales Staff*
EMP: 17
SQ FT: 43,000
SALES (est): 11.2MM **Privately Held**
SIC: 3841 Surgical & medical instruments

(P-22540)
MICROVENTION INC (DH)
Also Called: Microvention Terumo
35 Enterprise, Aliso Viejo (92656-2601)
PHONE................714 258-8000
Richard Cappetta, *President*
Bill Hughes, *COO*
Matt Fitz, *Senior VP*
Bruce Canter, *Vice Pres*
Thierry De Bosson, *Vice Pres*
▲ **EMP:** 268 **EST:** 1997
SQ FT: 35,000
SALES (est): 269.3MM
SALES (corp-wide): 5.5B **Privately Held**
WEB: www.microvention.com
SIC: 3841 Surgical & medical instruments
HQ: Terumo Americas Holding, Inc.
2101 Cottontail Ln
Somerset NJ 08873
732 302-4900

(P-22541)
MICRUS ENDOVASCULAR LLC (HQ)
821 Fox Ln, San Jose (95131-1601)
PHONE................408 433-1400
P Laxminarain, *President*
Robert A Stern, *President*
John T Kilcoyne, *CEO*
Gordon T Sangster, *CFO*
Edward F Ruppel Jr, *Ch Credit Ofcr*
EMP: 139
SQ FT: 42,000
SALES (est): 32.9MM
SALES (corp-wide): 76.4B **Publicly Held**
WEB: www.micruscorp.com
SIC: 3841 Surgical instruments & apparatus
PA: Johnson & Johnson
1 Johnson And Johnson Plz
New Brunswick NJ 08933
732 524-0400

(P-22542)
MIKROSCAN TECHNOLOGIES INC
2764 Gateway Rd 100, Carlsbad (92009-1730)
PHONE................760 893-8095
Robert Goerlitz, *CEO*
Kim Mahon, *Admin Asst*
James Crowe, *Sr Software Eng*
Victor Casas, *CTO*
Cooper Nelson, *Technician*
EMP: 10
SALES (est): 3MM **Privately Held**
SIC: 3841 Surgical & medical instruments

(P-22543)
MINERVA SURGICAL INC
101 Saginaw Dr, Redwood City (94063-4717)
PHONE................650 399-1770
David Clapper, *CEO*
Ryan Zimmer, *Manager*
▲ **EMP:** 14
SQ FT: 2,000
SALES (est): 3.5MM **Privately Held**
SIC: 3841 Surgical & medical instruments

(P-22544)
MINITOUCH INC
47853 Warm Springs Blvd, Fremont (94539-7400)
PHONE................510 651-5000
Dinesh Mody, *President*
Sadna Kumbhani, *Vice Pres*
EMP: 11
SQ FT: 10,000
SALES (est): 655.9K **Privately Held**
SIC: 3841 Surgical & medical instruments

(P-22545)
MIZUHO ORTHOPEDIC SYSTEMS INC (HQ)
Also Called: Mizuho OSI
30031 Ahern Ave, Union City (94587-1234)
P.O. Box 1468 (94587-6468)
PHONE................510 429-1500
Takashi Nemoto, *CEO*
Steve Lamb, *President*
Yosup Kim, *Treasurer*
Patrick Rimroth, *General Mgr*
Carlos Sanchez, *Director*
◆ **EMP:** 272
SQ FT: 111,100
SALES (est): 57.5MM
SALES (corp-wide): 114.2MM **Privately Held**
WEB: www.osiosi.com
SIC: 3841 Operating tables
PA: Mizuho Co., Ltd.
3-30-13, Hongo
Bunkyo-Ku TKY 113-0
338 153-191

(P-22546)
MODERN METALS INDUSTRIES INC
14000 S Broadway, Los Angeles (90061-1018)
P.O. Box 701, El Segundo (90245-0701)
PHONE................800 437-6633
Lee Sherrill, *President*
Andrew Sherrill, *President*
Nick Bell, *Regl Sales Mgr*
Jeff Timmer, *Regl Sales Mgr*
▲ **EMP:** 40
SQ FT: 40,000
SALES (est): 4.3MM **Privately Held**
WEB: www.mmimedcarts.com
SIC: 3841 Surgical & medical instruments

(P-22547)
MONOBIND INC (PA)
100 N Pointe Dr, Lake Forest (92630-2270)
PHONE................949 951-2665
Frederick Jerome, *President*
Dr Jay Singh, *Vice Pres*
Veronica Landa, *Administration*
Anthony Shatola, *QA Dir*
Tony Shatola, *QC Dir*
▲ **EMP:** 37 **EST:** 1977
SQ FT: 18,000
SALES (est): 6.2MM **Privately Held**
WEB: www.monobind.com
SIC: 3841 Diagnostic apparatus, medical

(P-22548)
MORGAN MEDESIGN INC
7700 Bell Rd Ste B, Windsor (95492-8559)
PHONE................707 568-2929
Jim Whitman, *CEO*
EMP: 11
SQ FT: 10,000
SALES: 3.6MM **Privately Held**
WEB: www.morganmedesign.com
SIC: 3841 Diagnostic apparatus, medical

(P-22549)
MPS MEDICAL INC
830 Challenger St Ste 200, Brea (92821-2946)
PHONE................714 672-1090
Ryan B Kazemi, *Opers Mgr*
EMP: 27 **EST:** 2014
SALES (est): 2MM **Privately Held**
SIC: 3841 Surgical & medical instruments

(P-22550)
MRI INTERVENTIONS INC
5 Musick, Irvine (92618-1638)
PHONE................949 900-6833
Francis P Grillo, *President*
Kimble L Jenkins, *Ch of Bd*

Peter G Piferi, *COO*
Peter Piferi, *COO*
Harold A Hurwitz, *CFO*
EMP: 33
SQ FT: 7,400
SALES: 7.3MM **Privately Held**
SIC: 3841 Surgical & medical instruments

(P-22551)
NEOMEND INC
60 Technology Dr, Irvine (92618-2301)
PHONE................949 783-3300
David Renzi, *President*
Erik Reese, *President*
Ken Watson, *President*
Kevin Cousins, *CFO*
Pete Davis, *Vice Pres*
▼ **EMP:** 90
SQ FT: 21,000
SALES (est): 17.1MM
SALES (corp-wide): 12B **Publicly Held**
SIC: 3841 Surgical & medical instruments
HQ: C. R. Bard, Inc.
730 Central Ave
New Providence NJ 07974
908 277-8000

(P-22552)
NEOTRACT INC (DH)
Also Called: Urolift
4473 Willow Rd Ste 100, Pleasanton (94588-8570)
PHONE................925 401-0700
David R Amerson, *President*
Doug Hughes, *CFO*
Ted Bender, *Vice Pres*
Theodore M Bender, *Vice Pres*
Lisa E Campbell, *Vice Pres*
EMP: 12
SQ FT: 200
SALES (est): 4MM
SALES (corp-wide): 2.1B **Publicly Held**
SIC: 3841 8733 8011 Medical instruments & equipment, blood & bone work; medical research; urologist

(P-22553)
NEURAL ANALYTICS INC
2440 S Sepulveda Blvd # 115, Los Angeles (90064-1744)
PHONE................818 317-4999
Leo Petrossian, *CEO*
Mark Hattendorf, *CFO*
Neil A Martin, *Chief Mktg Ofcr*
Robert Hamilton, *Vice Pres*
Dan Henchey, *Vice Pres*
EMP: 14
SQ FT: 3,000
SALES (est): 1.7MM **Privately Held**
SIC: 3841 3845 Diagnostic apparatus, medical; ultrasonic scanning devices, medical

(P-22554)
NEUROPTICS INC
23041 Ave D L Carlota 1, Laguna Hills (92653)
PHONE................949 250-9792
Kamran Siminou, *CEO*
William Worthen, *President*
▲ **EMP:** 18
SALES (est): 3.6MM **Privately Held**
WEB: www.neuroptics.com
SIC: 3841 Surgical & medical instruments

(P-22555)
NEVRO CORP
1800 Bridge Pkwy, Redwood City (94065-1164)
PHONE................650 251-0005
Rami Elghandour, *President*
Michael Demane, *Ch of Bd*
Andrew H Galligan, *CFO*
David Caraway, *Chief Mktg Ofcr*
Doug Alleavitch, *Vice Pres*
EMP: 308
SQ FT: 50,000
SALES: 326.6MM **Privately Held**
SIC: 3841 Surgical & medical instruments

(P-22556)
NEW WORLD MEDICAL INCORPORATED
10763 Edison Ct, Rancho Cucamonga (91730-4844)
PHONE................909 466-4304

PRODUCTS & SVCS

A Mateen Ahmed, *President*
Suhail Abdullah, *Officer*
Omar Ahmed, *Vice Pres*
Xavier Ocon, *Sales Mgr*
EMP: 17
SQ FT: 10,000
SALES: 15.9MM **Privately Held**
WEB: www.ahmedvalve.com
SIC: 3841 Ophthalmic instruments & apparatus

(P-22557)
NEWPORT MEDICAL INSTRS INC
Also Called: Covidien
1620 Sunflower Ave, Costa Mesa
(92626-1513)
PHONE.....................949 642-3910
Philippe Negre, *President*
Craig Dorsman, *Admin Sec*
Patti Gunter, *Info Tech Mgr*
Robert Dugan, *Engineer*
Anna Hoang, *Engineer*
▲ **EMP:** 95
SQ FT: 33,328
SALES (est): 20.8MM **Privately Held**
WEB: www.newportnmi.com
SIC: 3841 3842 3845 Surgical & medical instruments; respirators; electromedical equipment
HQ: Covidien Limited
20 Lower Hatch Street
Dublin 2

(P-22558)
NEXUS DX INC
6759 Mesa Ridge Rd, San Diego
(92121-4902)
PHONE.....................858 410-4600
Nam Shin, *CEO*
Joseph M Nemmers Jr, *President*
Jim P McMenamy, *Vice Pres*
Gordon Sangster, *Vice Pres*
Dan Johnson, *Associate Dir*
▲ **EMP:** 480
SQ FT: 25,000
SALES (est): 60.8MM
SALES (corp-wide): 148.1B **Privately Held**
SIC: 3841 Diagnostic apparatus, medical
PA: Samsung Electronics Co., Ltd.
129 Samseong-Ro, Yeongtong-Gu
Suwon 16677
822 200-9544

(P-22559)
NORDSON MEDICAL (CA) LLC
7612 Woodwind Dr, Huntington Beach
(92647-7164)
PHONE.....................657 215-4200
David Zgonc, *Mng Member*
Robert Foster,
John Pickett, *Director*
Delfin Rojas, *Manager*
EMP: 51
SQ FT: 40,000
SALES (est): 21.6MM **Privately Held**
WEB: www.avalonlabs.com
SIC: 3841 Surgical & medical instruments

(P-22560)
NUMOTECH INC
9420 Reseda Blvd Ste 504, Northridge
(91324-2932)
PHONE.....................818 772-1579
Robert Felton, *President*
EMP: 100
SALES (est): 6.7MM **Privately Held**
WEB: www.numotech.com
SIC: 3841 Medical instruments & equipment, blood & bone work

(P-22561)
NUVASIVE INC (PA)
7475 Lusk Blvd, San Diego (92121-5707)
PHONE.....................858 909-1800
Gregory T Lucier, *Ch of Bd*
Patrick Miles, *Vice Chairman*
Jason M Hannon, *President*
Matthew W Link, *President*
Edmund J Roschak, *CEO*
▲ **EMP:** 75
SQ FT: 154,000

SALES: 1B **Publicly Held**
WEB: www.nuvasive.com
SIC: 3841 Surgical & medical instruments

(P-22562)
NUVASIVE SPCLZED ORTHPDICS INC
101 Enterprise Ste 100, Aliso Viejo
(92656-2604)
PHONE.....................949 837-3600
Edmund Roschak, *CEO*
Robert Krist, *CFO*
Jeff Rydin, *Security Dir*
Gary Hague, *Engineer*
Toby Jacobs, *Engineer*
EMP: 100
SQ FT: 52,741
SALES (est): 3.3MM
SALES (corp-wide): 1B **Publicly Held**
SIC: 3841 Inhalation therapy equipment
PA: Nuvasive, Inc.
7475 Lusk Blvd
San Diego CA 92121
858 909-1800

(P-22563)
NYPRO HEALTHCARE BAJA INC
Also Called: Nypro Precision Assemblies
2195 Britannia Blvd # 107, San Diego
(92154-6290)
PHONE.....................619 498-9250
Joe Borden, *Chairman*
Courtney Ryan, *President*
Thomas J Flannery, *Treasurer*
▲ **EMP:** 600
SQ FT: 60,000
SALES (est): 164.3MM
SALES (corp-wide): 22.1B **Publicly Held**
SIC: 3841 3679 Surgical & medical instruments; electronic circuits
HQ: Nypro Inc.
101 Union St
Clinton MA 01510
978 365-8100

(P-22564)
OBALON THERAPEUTICS INC
5421 Avd Encinas Ste F, Carlsbad
(92008-4410)
PHONE.....................760 795-6558
Andrew Rasdal, *President*
Kim Kamdar, *Ch of Bd*
Kelly Huang, *President*
William Plovanic, *CFO*
Neil Drake, *Vice Pres*
EMP: 113
SQ FT: 20,200
SALES: 9.9MM **Privately Held**
SIC: 3841 Surgical & medical instruments

(P-22565)
OCT MEDICAL IMAGING INC
1002 Health Sciences Rd, Irvine
(92617-3010)
PHONE.....................949 701-6656
Tirunelveli Ramalingam, *CFO*
EMP: 10
SALES (est): 1.5MM **Privately Held**
SIC: 3841 Diagnostic apparatus, medical

(P-22566)
OCULEVE INC
4410 Rosewood Dr, Pleasanton
(94588-3050)
PHONE.....................415 745-3784
Michael D Ackermann, *President*
EMP: 15
SALES (est): 3.9MM **Privately Held**
SIC: 3841 Eye examining instruments & apparatus
PA: Allergan Public Limited Company
Euro House
Cork

(P-22567)
OHADI MANAGEMENT CORPORATION
11088 Elm Ave, Rancho Cucamonga
(91730-7676)
PHONE.....................909 625-2000
Camiar Ohadi, *President*
EMP: 12 **EST:** 2008
SALES (est): 621.1K **Privately Held**
SIC: 3841 Diagnostic apparatus, medical

(P-22568)
OLYMPUS AMERICA INC
Also Called: OLYMPUS AMERICA INC.
2400 Ringwood Ave, San Jose
(95131-1700)
PHONE.....................408 935-5000
Mark Gumz, *President*
EMP: 400
SALES (corp-wide): 7.3B **Privately Held**
SIC: 3841 Diagnostic apparatus, medical
HQ: Olympus America Inc
3500 Corporate Pkwy
Center Valley PA 18034
484 896-5000

(P-22569)
ONCOGENESIS INC
Also Called: Medical Devices Manufacturer
385 Woodview Ave Ste 150, Morgan Hill
(95037-8121)
PHONE.....................408 636-7725
Peter Gombrich, *Chairman*
Wayne Kay, *CEO*
Wendell Jones, *Finance*
EMP: 10 **EST:** 2008
SALES (est): 1.4MM **Privately Held**
SIC: 3841 Diagnostic apparatus, medical

(P-22570)
ONSET MEDICAL CORPORATION
13900 Alton Pkwy Ste 120, Irvine
(92618-1621)
PHONE.....................949 716-1100
Joseph Bishop, *President*
David Richard, *CFO*
▲ **EMP:** 20
SALES (est): 2.6MM
SALES (corp-wide): 5.5B **Privately Held**
SIC: 3841 Surgical & medical instruments
HQ: Terumo Americas Holding, Inc.
2101 Cottontail Ln
Somerset NJ 08873
732 302-4900

(P-22571)
OPTIMEDICA CORPORATION
510 Cottonwood Dr, Milpitas (95035-7403)
PHONE.....................408 850-8600
Miles White, *CEO*
Mark J Forchette, *President*
Mark A Murray, *CFO*
EMP: 140
SALES (est): 37.2MM **Privately Held**
WEB: www.optimedica.com
SIC: 3841 Eye examining instruments & apparatus

(P-22572)
OPTISCAN BIOMEDICAL CORP
24590 Clawiter Rd, Hayward (94545-2222)
PHONE.....................510 342-5800
Cary G Vance, *President*
Peter Rule, *Ch of Bd*
Donald Webber, *COO*
Patrick Nugent, *CFO*
Jim Causey, *Vice Pres*
EMP: 50
SQ FT: 10,000
SALES (est): 10.6MM **Privately Held**
WEB: www.farir.com
SIC: 3841 Diagnostic apparatus, medical

(P-22573)
OPTOVUE INC (PA)
2800 Bayview Dr, Fremont (94538-6518)
PHONE.....................510 623-8868
Jay WEI, *CEO*
John Hawley, *President*
David Voris, *President*
Paul Kealey, *Senior VP*
Tony Ko, *Vice Pres*
▲ **EMP:** 86
SQ FT: 12,400
SALES (est): 33.9MM **Privately Held**
WEB: www.optovue.com
SIC: 3841 5048 Surgical & medical instruments; ophthalmic goods

(P-22574)
ORANGE CNTY CSTL PHYSCIANS INC
Also Called: Coastal Medical Supply
4879 E La Palma Ave, Anaheim
(92807-1956)
P.O. Box 25606 (92825-5606)
PHONE.....................808 545-2500
Stephen Seink, *CEO*
Shilpa Deshmukh, *CFO*
EMP: 11
SALES (est): 1.3MM **Privately Held**
SIC: 3841 Surgical & medical instruments

(P-22575)
ORAYA THERAPEUTICS INC
3 Twin Dolphin Dr Ste 175, Redwood City
(94065-5160)
P.O. Box 5122, Belmont (94002-5122)
PHONE.....................510 456-3700
Jim Taylor, *President*
Michael Gertner, *Shareholder*
Mark Arnoldussen, *Senior Mgr*
▲ **EMP:** 27
SALES (est): 5MM **Privately Held**
SIC: 3841 Medical instruments & equipment, blood & bone work

(P-22576)
OSSEON LLC
2301 Circadian Way # 300, Santa Rosa
(95407-5461)
PHONE.....................707 636-5940
Ronald Clough, *CEO*
Spencer Hill,
EMP: 19
SQ FT: 10,000
SALES (est): 2.4MM **Privately Held**
SIC: 3841 Surgical & medical instruments

(P-22577)
P K ENGINEERING & MFG CO INC
200 E Shell Rd 2b, Ventura (93001-1261)
PHONE.....................805 628-9556
William Kilbury, *President*
Robert Kilbury, *Vice Pres*
EMP: 15
SQ FT: 8,700
SALES (est): 1.3MM **Privately Held**
SIC: 3841 Surgical instruments & apparatus; saws, surgical

(P-22578)
PACIFIC INTEGRATED MFG INC
4364 Bonita Rd Ste 454, Bonita
(91902-1421)
PHONE.....................619 921-3464
Stephen F Keane, *CEO*
Charles Peinado, *President*
EMP: 200
SALES (est): 6.6MM **Privately Held**
SIC: 3841 Diagnostic apparatus, medical

(P-22579)
PAN PROBE BIOTECH INC
7396 Trade St, San Diego (92121-2422)
PHONE.....................858 689-9936
Shujie Cui, *CEO*
Alice Yu, *Vice Pres*
▲ **EMP:** 18
SQ FT: 5,246
SALES (est): 2.1MM **Privately Held**
WEB: www.panprobebiotech.com
SIC: 3841 Diagnostic apparatus, medical

(P-22580)
PARAMIT CORPORATION (PA)
Also Called: Lathrop Engineering
18735 Madrone Pkwy, Morgan Hill
(95037-2876)
PHONE.....................408 782-5600
Balbir Rataul, *President*
Balbir S Rataul, *President*
Tom La Rose, *CFO*
▲ **EMP:** 287 **EST:** 1990
SQ FT: 150,000
SALES (est): 128.1MM **Privately Held**
WEB: www.paramit.com
SIC: 3841 Tonometers, medical

(P-22581)
PENUMBRA INC (PA)
1 Penumbra, Alameda (94502-7676)
PHONE.....................510 748-3200

▲ = Import ▼=Export
◆ =Import/Export

Adam Elsesser, *Ch of Bd*
Daniel Davis, *President*
James Pray, *President*
SRI Kosaraju, *CFO*
Robert Evans, *Exec VP*
EMP: 256
SQ FT: 295,000
SALES: 333.7MM **Publicly Held**
WEB: www.penumbrainc.com
SIC: 3841 Surgical & medical instruments

(P-22582)
PHARMACO-KINESIS CORPORATION
6053 W Century Blvd # 600, Los Angeles (90045-6400)
PHONE.................310 641-2700
Frank Adell, *Principal*
Thomas Chen, *Principal*
Peter Hirshfield, *Principal*
John Muthew, *Principal*
EMP: 26
SALES (est): 5.6MM **Privately Held**
WEB: www.pharmaco-kinesis.com
SIC: 3841 Surgical & medical instruments

(P-22583)
PHILIPS MEDICAL SYSTEMS CLEVEL
5290 Overpass Rd Ste 209, Santa Barbara (93111-2050)
PHONE.................805 681-0463
Charles Carder, *Principal*
EMP: 12
SALES (corp-wide): 20.9B **Privately Held**
SIC: 3841 Surgical & medical instruments
HQ: Philips Medical Systems (Cleveland), Inc.
595 Miner Rd
Cleveland OH 44143
440 247-2652

(P-22584)
PHILLIPS-MEDISIZE
Also Called: Affinity Medical Tech LLC
3545 Harbor Blvd, Costa Mesa (92626-1406)
PHONE.................949 477-9495
Bob Frank, *General Mgr*
Hank Mancini, *Business Mgr*
EMP: 240
SQ FT: 45,000
SALES (est): 42.9MM
SALES (corp-wide): 42.9B **Privately Held**
WEB: www.affinitymed.com
SIC: 3841 Surgical & medical instruments
HQ: Molex, Llc
2222 Wellington Ct
Lisle IL 60532
630 969-4550

(P-22585)
PNEUMRX INC
4255 Burton Dr, Santa Clara (95054-1512)
PHONE.................650 625-4440
Erin McGurk, *CEO*
Olivier Delporte, *Senior VP*
Lauren Selmeier, *Vice Pres*
Steve Fermin, *Executive Asst*
Shawna Pillado, *Executive Asst*
EMP: 35
SALES (est): 8MM **Privately Held**
WEB: www.pneumrx.com
SIC: 3841 Surgical & medical instruments

(P-22586)
POST-SRGCAL RHAB SPCALISTS LLC
12774 Florence Ave, Santa Fe Springs (90670-3906)
P.O. Box 2886 (90670-0886)
PHONE.................562 236-5600
Steven Howser, *Mng Member*
EMP: 15 **EST:** 2005
SALES (est): 1.9MM **Privately Held**
SIC: 3841 Surgical & medical instruments

(P-22587)
PRANALYTICA INC
1101 Colorado Ave, Santa Monica (90401-3009)
PHONE.................310 458-3345
C Kumar N Patel, *President*
Shantanu Kulkarni, *Engineer*
Francis McGuire, *VP Finance*

EMP: 15
SQ FT: 7,350
SALES: 3MM **Privately Held**
SIC: 3841 3826 Surgical & medical instruments; laser scientific & engineering instruments

(P-22588)
PRO-DEX INC (PA)
2361 Mcgaw Ave, Irvine (92614-5831)
PHONE.................949 769-3200
Richard L Van Kirk, *President*
Nicholas J Swenson, *Ch of Bd*
Richard Van Kirk, *COO*
Alisha K Charlton, *CFO*
Raymond Cabillot, *Bd of Directors*
EMP: 70
SQ FT: 28,180
SALES: 22.4MM **Publicly Held**
WEB: www.pro-dex.com
SIC: 3841 3843 7372 3594 Surgical & medical instruments; dental equipment; business oriented computer software; motors, pneumatic; business consulting

(P-22589)
PROSURG INC
Also Called: Ximed Medical Systems
2195 Trade Zone Blvd, San Jose (95131-1743)
PHONE.................408 945-4040
Ashvin H Desai, *President*
EMP: 40
SQ FT: 14,800
SALES: 4MM **Privately Held**
WEB: www.prosurg.com
SIC: 3841 3823 Surgical & medical instruments; industrial instrmnts msrmnt display/control process variable

(P-22590)
PROVASIS THERAPEUTICS INC
9177 Sky Park Ct B, San Diego (92123-4341)
PHONE.................858 712-2101
Terrance Bruggeman, *Ch of Bd*
John W Cardosa, *CFO*
Bruce E Bennett Jr, *Vice Pres*
Laura E Dipietro, *Vice Pres*
Gary L Loomis PHD, *Vice Pres*
EMP: 36 **EST:** 1995
SQ FT: 20,400
SALES (est): 2.9MM **Privately Held**
WEB: www.provasis.com
SIC: 3841 8011 Surgical instruments & apparatus; physical medicine, physician/surgeon

(P-22591)
PRYOR PRODUCTS
1819 Peacock Blvd, Oceanside (92056-3578)
PHONE.................760 724-8244
Jeffrey Pryor, *CEO*
Jon Willmschen, *COO*
Krista Finney, *Vice Pres*
Paul Pryor, *Vice Pres*
▲ **EMP:** 50
SQ FT: 29,000
SALES (est): 10.9MM **Privately Held**
WEB: www.pryorproducts.com
SIC: 3841 IV transfusion apparatus

(P-22592)
PULMONX CORPORATION (PA)
700 Chesapeake Dr, Redwood City (94063-4731)
PHONE.................650 364-0400
Glen French, *President*
Rodney C Perkins, *CEO*
Peter Soltesz, *COO*
Beran Rose, *Vice Pres*
Narinder Shargill, *Vice Pres*
▲ **EMP:** 49
SQ FT: 6,950
SALES (est): 9.2MM **Privately Held**
WEB: www.pulmonx.com
SIC: 3841 Medical instruments & equipment, blood & bone work

(P-22593)
PULSAR VASCULAR INC
130 Knowles Dr Ste E, Los Gatos (95032-1832)
PHONE.................408 246-4300
Robert M Abrams, *President*

Chas Roue, *Vice Pres*
EMP: 15
SQ FT: 4,500
SALES (est): 2.8MM
SALES (corp-wide): 76.4B **Publicly Held**
SIC: 3841 Diagnostic apparatus, medical
HQ: Depuy Synthes Products, Inc.
325 Paramount Dr
Raynham MA 02767
508 880-8100

(P-22594)
PULSE METRIC INC
2100 Hawley Dr, Vista (92084-2615)
PHONE.................760 842-8224
Shiu-Shin Chio PHD, *Ch of Bd*
EMP: 12
SALES (est): 1.3MM **Privately Held**
WEB: www.pulsemetric.com
SIC: 3841 Blood pressure apparatus

(P-22595)
RA MEDICAL SYSTEMS INC
2070 Las Palmas Dr, Carlsbad (92011-1518)
PHONE.................760 804-1648
Dean Irwin, *Ch of Bd*
Jeffrey Kraws, *President*
Andrew Jackson, *COO*
Melissa Burstein, *Exec VP*
▼ **EMP:** 75
SQ FT: 32,000
SALES: 5.8MM **Privately Held**
WEB: www.ramed.com
SIC: 3841 3845 Surgical lasers; laser systems & equipment, medical

(P-22596)
RADIOLOGY SUPPORT DEVICES
1904 E Dominguez St, Long Beach (90810-1002)
PHONE.................310 518-0527
Matthew Alderson, *CEO*
EMP: 29
SQ FT: 16,000
SALES (est): 5.7MM **Privately Held**
WEB: www.rsdphantoms.com
SIC: 3841 3844 Diagnostic apparatus, medical; X-ray apparatus & tubes

(P-22597)
RAPID DIAGNOSTICS INC
Also Called: Mp Biomedical
1429 Rollins Rd, Burlingame (94010-2316)
PHONE.................650 558-0395
Huanjie Wang, *CEO*
Tom Stankovich, *CFO*
▲ **EMP:** 26 **EST:** 1981
SALES (est): 2.7MM
SALES (corp-wide): 370.7MM **Privately Held**
SIC: 3841 Diagnostic apparatus, medical
HQ: Mp Biomedicals, Llc
3 Hutton Centre Dr # 100
Santa Ana CA 92707
949 833-2500

(P-22598)
RECOR MEDICAL INC (PA)
1049 Elwell Ct, Palo Alto (94303-4308)
PHONE.................631 676-2730
Andrew Weiss, *CEO*
Antoine Papiernik, *President*
Mano Iyer, *COO*
Matthew Franklin, *CFO*
Leslie Coleman, *Vice Pres*
EMP: 11
SQ FT: 1,500
SALES (est): 1.8MM **Privately Held**
SIC: 3841 Surgical & medical instruments

(P-22599)
REPLENISH INC
73 N Vinedo Ave, Pasadena (91107-3759)
PHONE.................626 219-7867
Sean Caffey, *Chairman*
Mark Humayun, *President*
Yu-Chong Tai, *Co-Founder*
Aileen Sumida, *Accounting Mgr*
Rosa Balbuena, *Recruiter*
EMP: 10
SALES (est): 1.8MM **Privately Held**
SIC: 3841 Medical instruments & equipment, blood & bone work

(P-22600)
RES MED INC
9001 Spectrum Center Blvd, San Diego (92123-1438)
PHONE.................858 746-2400
Christopher Bartlett, *Exec Dir*
David Pendarvis, *Senior VP*
Klaus Schindhelm, *Senior VP*
Gil Bendov, *Vice Pres*
David D'Cruz, *Vice Pres*
EMP: 35
SALES (est): 3.1MM **Privately Held**
SIC: 3841 Surgical & medical instruments

(P-22601)
RESMED INC (PA)
9001 Spectrum Center Blvd, San Diego (92123-1438)
PHONE.................858 836-5000
Michael Farrell, *CEO*
Peter Farrell, *Ch of Bd*
Rob Douglas, *President*
Robert Douglas, *COO*
Brett Sandercock, *CFO*
EMP: 277
SQ FT: 230,000
SALES: 2.3B **Publicly Held**
WEB: www.resmed.com
SIC: 3841 Diagnostic apparatus, medical

(P-22602)
RESPIRATORY SUPPORT PRODUCTS
9255 Customhouse Plz N, San Diego (92154-7636)
PHONE.................619 710-1000
Anthony V Beran, *President*
▲ **EMP:** 29 **EST:** 1975
SQ FT: 35,000
SALES (est): 2.6MM **Privately Held**
WEB: www.rspace.com
SIC: 3841 3845 Surgical instruments & apparatus; medical instruments & equipment, blood & bone work; electromedical equipment

(P-22603)
RESTORATION ROBOTICS INC (PA)
128 Baytech Dr, San Jose (95134-2302)
PHONE.................408 883-6888
Ryan Rhodes, *President*
Frederic Moll, *Ch of Bd*
Gabriele Zingaretti, *COO*
Mark Hair, *CFO*
Shelley Thunen, *Bd of Directors*
EMP: 87
SQ FT: 23,000
SALES: 21.3MM **Publicly Held**
SIC: 3841 5047 Surgical & medical instruments; electro-medical equipment

(P-22604)
REVERSE MEDICAL CORPORATION
13700 Alton Pkwy Ste 167, Irvine (92618-1618)
PHONE.................949 215-0660
Jeffrey Valko, *President*
Brian Strauss, *CTO*
EMP: 15
SALES (est): 2.7MM **Privately Held**
SIC: 3841 Surgical & medical instruments
HQ: Covidien Limited
20 Lower Hatch Street
Dublin 2

(P-22605)
RF SURGICAL SYSTEMS LLC
5927 Landau Ct, Carlsbad (92008-8803)
PHONE.................855 522-7027
John Buhler, *President*
Ron Wangerin, *CFO*
William Blair, *CTO*
John Barnhill, *VP Mktg*
▲ **EMP:** 55
SQ FT: 24,000
SALES (est): 19.4MM **Privately Held**
WEB: www.rfsurg.com
SIC: 3841 Surgical & medical instruments
HQ: Medtronic, Inc.
710 Medtronic Pkwy
Minneapolis MN 55432
763 514-4000

(P-22606)
RH USA INC
Also Called: Lumenis
455 N Canyons Pkwy Ste B, Livermore
(94551-7682)
PHONE..................925 245-7900
Jeannette Trujillo, *Vice Pres*
Brian Guscott, *Vice Pres*
Joshua Miller, *Electrical Engi*
Bob Schultz, *Engineer*
Miranda Yee, *Finance Mgr*
▲ EMP: 42
SQ FT: 40,000
SALES (est): 9.4MM **Privately Held**
SIC: 3841 Surgical & medical instruments
PA: R.H. Technologies Ltd
5 Hatzoref
Nazareth Illit
460 890-00

(P-22607)
ROBERT BOSCH LLC
Also Called: Bosch Diagnostics
2030 Alameda Padre Serra, Santa Barbara
(93103-1704)
PHONE..................805 966-2000
Andreas Huber, *Branch Mgr*
EMP: 30
SALES (corp-wide): 261.7MM **Privately Held**
SIC: 3841 Diagnostic apparatus, medical
HQ: Robert Bosch Llc
2800 S 25th Ave
Broadview IL 60155
248 876-1000

(P-22608)
ROBERT P VON ZABERN
4121 Tigris Way, Riverside (92503-4844)
PHONE..................951 734-7215
Robert P Von Zabern, *Owner*
EMP: 13
SQ FT: 1,500
SALES (est): 1.1MM **Privately Held**
WEB: www.vzs.net
SIC: 3841 Surgical instruments & apparatus

(P-22609)
ROXWOOD MEDICAL INC
400 Seaport Ct Ste 103, Redwood City
(94063-2799)
PHONE..................650 779-4555
Mehrdad Farhangnia, *CEO*
John Miller, *Vice Pres*
Helen Song, *Vice Pres*
Veronica Thompson, *Senior Mgr*
Kegan Centala, *Associate*
EMP: 15
SQ FT: 3,000
SALES (est): 2.3MM **Privately Held**
SIC: 3841 Surgical & medical instruments
PA: Btg Plc
5 Fleet Place
London EC4M

(P-22610)
RUXCO ENGINEERING INC
6051 Entp Dr Ste 105, Diamond Springs
(95619)
PHONE..................530 622-4122
Michael Ruck, *President*
Silvia Ruck, *CFO*
EMP: 13
SQ FT: 10,000
SALES (est): 1.4MM **Privately Held**
SIC: 3841 3812 Medical instruments & equipment, blood & bone work; acceleration indicators & systems components, aerospace

(P-22611)
SADRA MEDICAL INC
160 Knowles Dr, Los Gatos (95032-1828)
PHONE..................408 370-1550
Michael F Mahoney, *President*
Ken Martin, *President*
Jon Bohane, *CFO*
Robert Chang, *Exec VP*
Dave Paul, *Vice Pres*
EMP: 20
SALES (est): 3.7MM
SALES (corp-wide): 9B **Publicly Held**
WEB: www.sadramedical.com
SIC: 3841 Surgical medical instruments

PA: Boston Scientific Corporation
300 Boston Scientific Way
Marlborough MA 01752
508 683-4000

(P-22612)
SANARUS MEDICAL INCORPORATED
7068 Koll Center Pkwy # 425, Pleasanton
(94566-3111)
PHONE..................925 460-6080
John Howe, *President*
Israel Madera, *Vice Pres*
George Matlock, *Design Engr*
Roseanne Driscoll, *Manager*
BJ Hardman, *Manager*
EMP: 12
SQ FT: 12,000
SALES (est): 1.7MM **Privately Held**
WEB: www.sanarus.com
SIC: 3841 Surgical & medical instruments
PA: Sanarus Technologies, Inc.
1249 Quarry Ln Ste 150
Pleasanton CA 94566

(P-22613)
SANGSTAT MEDICAL CORP (DH)
6300 Dumbarton Cir, Fremont
(94555-3644)
PHONE..................510 789-4300
Jean-Jacques Bienaim, *CEO*
EMP: 11
SALES (est): 4.7MM
SALES (corp-wide): 609.6MM **Privately Held**
SIC: 3841 Surgical instruments & apparatus
HQ: Genzyme Corporation
50 Binney St
Cambridge MA 02142
617 252-7500

(P-22614)
SANOVAS INC
2597 Kerner Blvd, San Rafael
(94901-5571)
PHONE..................415 729-9391
Lawrence Gerrans, *President*
Robert Farrell, *CFO*
Steve Budill, *Vice Pres*
Mike Humason, *Vice Pres*
Roy Morgan, *Vice Pres*
EMP: 36
SALES (est): 6.7MM **Privately Held**
SIC: 3841 Surgical & medical instruments

(P-22615)
SCHOLTEN SURGICAL INSTRS INC
170 Commerce St Ste 101, Lodi
(95240-0871)
PHONE..................209 365-1393
Arie Scholten, *President*
Jim Van Andel, *COO*
EMP: 15
SALES (est): 1.6MM **Privately Held**
WEB: www.bioptome.com
SIC: 3841 Surgical & medical instruments

(P-22616)
SCIGENE CORPORATION
1287 Reamwood Ave, Sunnyvale
(94089-2234)
PHONE..................408 733-7337
James Stanchfield, *President*
EMP: 12
SQ FT: 12,000
SALES: 2.2MM **Privately Held**
WEB: www.scigene.com
SIC: 3841 Surgical & medical instruments

(P-22617)
SCITON INC
925 Commercial St, Palo Alto
(94303-4908)
PHONE..................650 493-9155
James Hobart, *CEO*
Ariel Weaver, *Partner*
Daniel Negus, *President*
Jay Patel, *Vice Pres*
Dan Negus, *Executive*
▼ EMP: 74
SQ FT: 15,000

SALES (est): 18.2MM **Privately Held**
WEB: www.sciton.com
SIC: 3841 Surgical lasers

(P-22618)
SECHRIST INDUSTRIES INC
4225 E La Palma Ave, Anaheim
(92807-1844)
PHONE..................714 579-8400
Edward Pulwer, *CEO*
John Razzano, *CFO*
Lou Becovitz, *General Mgr*
Sean Terry, *QA Dir*
Eric Mouness, *Technical Mgr*
▲ EMP: 88
SQ FT: 74,000
SALES (est): 815.2K
SALES (corp-wide): 21.3MM **Privately Held**
WEB: www.sechristind.com
SIC: 3841 Surgical & medical instruments
HQ: Wound Care Holdings, Llc
5220 Belfort Rd Ste 130
Jacksonville FL 32256
800 379-9774

(P-22619)
SECOND SIGHT MEDICAL PDTS INC (PA)
12744 San Fernando Rd, Sylmar
(91342-3853)
PHONE..................818 833-5000
Jonathan Will McGuire, *President*
Robert J Greenberg, *Ch of Bd*
Pat Ryan, *COO*
John T Blake, *CFO*
Gregg William, *Chairman*
EMP: 110
SQ FT: 45,351
SALES: 7.9MM **Publicly Held**
WEB: www.2-sight.com
SIC: 3841 Ophthalmic instruments & apparatus

(P-22620)
SEMLER SCIENTIFIC INC
911 Bern Ct Ste 110, San Jose
(95112-1242)
PHONE..................877 774-4211
Douglas Murphy-Chutorian, *CEO*
Herbert J Semler, *Ch of Bd*
Daniel E Conger, *CFO*
EMP: 29
SALES: 12.4MM **Privately Held**
SIC: 3841 Surgical & medical instruments

(P-22621)
SEQUENT MEDICAL INC
11 Columbia Ste A, Aliso Viejo
(92656-1427)
PHONE..................949 830-9600
Thomas C Wilder, *President*
Kevin J Cousins, *CFO*
Andrew J Hykes, *Vice Pres*
Andrew Hykes, *Vice Pres*
Paul G Krell, *Vice Pres*
EMP: 65
SALES (est): 11.9MM
SALES (corp-wide): 5.5B **Privately Held**
WEB: www.sequentmedical.com
SIC: 3841 Surgical & medical instruments
HQ: Microvention, Inc.
35 Enterprise
Aliso Viejo CA 92656
714 258-8000

(P-22622)
SHEATHING TECHNOLOGIES INC
675 Jarvis Dr Ste A, Morgan Hill
(95037-2830)
PHONE..................408 782-2720
Larry Polayes, *President*
▲ EMP: 46
SQ FT: 10,000
SALES (est): 9.4MM **Privately Held**
WEB: www.sheathes.com
SIC: 3841 Diagnostic apparatus, medical

(P-22623)
SHOCKWAVE MEDICAL INC
48501 Warm Springs Blvd, Fremont
(94539-7750)
PHONE..................510 279-4262
Doug Godshall, *President*
Beaux Alexander, *Vice Pres*

Nora Hadding, *Vice Pres*
Kirti Kamdar, *Vice Pres*
Alexis Brash, *Research*
EMP: 10
SALES (est): 2.3MM **Privately Held**
SIC: 3841 Diagnostic apparatus, medical

(P-22624)
SIMPLAY LABS LLC
1140 E Arques Ave, Sunnyvale
(94085-4602)
PHONE..................408 616-4000
Joseph Lias,
▲ EMP: 31
SALES (est): 3.2MM **Privately Held**
SIC: 3841 Surgical & medical instruments

(P-22625)
SMITHS MEDICAL ASD INC
2231 Rutherford Rd, Carlsbad
(92008-8811)
PHONE..................760 602-4400
Donald Cornwall, *Manager*
EMP: 108
SALES (corp-wide): 4.1B **Privately Held**
SIC: 3841 IV transfusion apparatus
HQ: Smiths Medical Asd, Inc.
6000 Nathan Ln N Ste 100
Plymouth MN 55442
763 383-3000

(P-22626)
SONOMA ORTHOPEDIC PRODUCTS INC
2735 Sand Hill Rd Ste 205, Menlo Park
(94025-7130)
PHONE..................847 807-4378
Charles Nelson, *CEO*
Matt Jerome, *President*
Rick Epstein, *CEO*
Kyle Lappin, *Vice Pres*
Alex Winber, *Vice Pres*
EMP: 13
SQ FT: 5,000
SALES (est): 2.2MM **Privately Held**
SIC: 3841 Surgical & medical instruments

(P-22627)
SOURCE SCIENTIFIC LLC
2144 Michelson Dr, Irvine (92612-1304)
PHONE..................949 231-5096
Richard Henson,
Bruce Sargeant,
▲ EMP: 39
SQ FT: 27,464
SALES (est): 5.4MM
SALES (corp-wide): 661.3MM **Privately Held**
WEB: www.sourcescientific.com
SIC: 3841 8711 Surgical & medical instruments; engineering services
HQ: Bit Analytical Instruments Gmbh
Am Kronberger Hang 3
Schwalbach Am Taunus 65824
619 680-6100

(P-22628)
SOURCE SURGICAL INC
3130 20th St Ste 200, San Francisco
(94110-2789)
PHONE..................415 861-7040
Craig Sparks, *President*
Todd Marinchak, *CFO*
Kevin Miller, *Managing Dir*
Mike Powers, *Area Mgr*
Debra Cash, *Office Mgr*
EMP: 18
SQ FT: 2,300
SALES (est): 1.5MM **Privately Held**
WEB: www.sourcesurgical.com
SIC: 3841 Surgical instruments & apparatus

(P-22629)
SPECIALTEAM MEDICAL SVC INC
22445 La Palma Ave Ste F, Yorba Linda
(92887-3811)
PHONE..................714 694-0348
Terry Bagwell, *President*
Erick Bickett, *CFO*
Billy Teeple, *Vice Pres*
EMP: 15
SQ FT: 7,000

SALES (est): 2.2MM **Privately Held**
WEB: www.specialteam.com
SIC: **3841** Surgical & medical instruments

(P-22630)
SPECTRANETICS CORPORATION
5055 Brandin Ct, Fremont (94538-3140)
PHONE...................................510 933-7964
Gil Paet, *Principal*
EMP: 80
SALES (est): 2.1MM **Privately Held**
SIC: **3841** 5047 5999 Surgical & medical instruments; medical equipment & supplies; medical apparatus & supplies

(P-22631)
SPINALMOTION INC
201 San Antonio Cir # 115, Mountain View (94040-1252)
PHONE...................................650 947-3472
Christine Hanni, *CFO*
EMP: 11
SALES (est): 1.4MM **Privately Held**
WEB: www.spinalmotion.com
SIC: **3841** Diagnostic apparatus, medical

(P-22632)
SPINE VIEW INC
3167 Skyway Ct, Fremont (94539-5910)
PHONE...................................510 490-1753
Roy Chin, *CEO*
Sam Park, *COO*
Susan Stretesky, *Officer*
Al Mirel, *Project Mgr*
Sean Farrell, *Research*
EMP: 56
SQ FT: 24,500
SALES (est): 8.1MM **Privately Held**
SIC: **3841** Surgical & medical instruments

(P-22633)
SPINEEX INC
4046 Clipper Ct, Fremont (94538-6540)
PHONE...................................510 573-1093
Roy Chin, *Ch of Bd*
Andrew Rogers, *President*
Christie Wang, *President*
George Oliva, *CFO*
Eric Blossey, *Ch Credit Ofcr*
EMP: 14 EST: 2017
SALES (est): 2MM **Privately Held**
SIC: **3841** 5047 Surgical & medical instruments; medical equipment & supplies

(P-22634)
SPIRACUR INC (PA)
Also Called: Snap
1180 Bordeaux Dr, Sunnyvale (94089-1209)
PHONE...................................650 364-1544
Chris Fashek, *Chairman*
Moshe Pinto, *Exec VP*
Lawrence Hu, *Vice Pres*
Linda Lamagna, *Vice Pres*
Yousuf Mazhar, *Vice Pres*
EMP: 58
SALES: 7MM **Privately Held**
SIC: **3841** Surgical & medical instruments

(P-22635)
SSCOR INC
11064 Randall St, Sun Valley (91352-2621)
PHONE...................................818 504-4054
Samuel D Say, *President*
Raju Thomas, *President*
Jonathan Kim, *Vice Pres*
Suzette George, *Office Mgr*
Betty Say, *Admin Sec*
▲ EMP: 16
SQ FT: 12,000
SALES (est): 3.5MM **Privately Held**
WEB: www.sscor.com
SIC: **3841** Suction therapy apparatus

(P-22636)
ST JUDE MEDICAL LLC
Also Called: Abbott
645 Almanor Ave, Sunnyvale (94085-2927)
PHONE...................................408 738-4883
Ron Matricaria, *Principal*
Nathan Harold, *Program Mgr*
Jose Claudio, *MIS Dir*
Fahfu Ho, *Software Engr*
Cathy Bortolin, *IT/INT Sup*
EMP: 275

SALES (corp-wide): 27.3B **Publicly Held**
WEB: www.sjm.com
SIC: **3841** Medical instruments & equipment, blood & bone work
HQ: St. Jude Medical, Llc
1 Saint Jude Medical Dr
Saint Paul MN 55117
651 756-2000

(P-22637)
STRYKER CORPORATION
Also Called: Stryker Neurovascular
47900 Bayside Pkwy, Fremont (94538-6515)
PHONE...................................510 413-2500
EMP: 38
SALES (corp-wide): 12.4B **Publicly Held**
SIC: **3841** Surgical & medical instruments
PA: Stryker Corporation
2825 Airview Blvd
Portage MI 49002
269 385-2600

(P-22638)
STRYKER CORPORATION
3407 E La Palma Ave, Anaheim (92806-2021)
PHONE...................................714 764-1700
Lynn Wagnor, *Branch Mgr*
EMP: 38
SALES (corp-wide): 12.4B **Publicly Held**
SIC: **3841** Surgical & medical instruments
PA: Stryker Corporation
2825 Airview Blvd
Portage MI 49002
269 385-2600

(P-22639)
SURGISTAR INC (PA)
Also Called: Sabel
2310 La Mirada Dr, Vista (92081-7862)
PHONE...................................760 598-2480
Jonathan Woodward, *President*
Hema Chaudhary, *Vice Pres*
▲ EMP: 35
SQ FT: 12,000
SALES: 9MM **Privately Held**
SIC: **3841** Surgical & medical instruments

(P-22640)
SYNVASIVE TECHNOLOGY INC
4925 R J Mathews Park 1, El Dorado Hills (95762)
PHONE...................................916 939-3913
Kelly Fisher, *Principal*
EMP: 23
SALES (corp-wide): 7.8B **Publicly Held**
SIC: **3841** Surgical knife blades & handles
HQ: Synvasive Technology, Inc.
8690 Technology Way
Reno NV 89521
775 332-2726

(P-22641)
TACSENSE INC
10 N East St Ste 108, Woodland (95776-5921)
PHONE...................................530 797-0008
William Aldrich, *CEO*
Tingrui Pan, *President*
Hong Ye,
Suzanne Papamichail,
EMP: 10 EST: 2015
SQ FT: 4,000
SALES: 250K **Privately Held**
SIC: **3841** Blood pressure apparatus

(P-22642)
TACTX MEDICAL INC (DH)
Also Called: Creganna - Tactx Medical
1353 Dell Ave, Campbell (95008-6609)
PHONE...................................408 364-7100
Robert Bell Hance, *CEO*
Nitin Matani, *President*
Helen Ryan, *President*
Jeff Kraus, *Vice Pres*
Doug Wilkins, *Vice Pres*
▼ EMP: 115
SQ FT: 12,000
SALES (est): 23.6MM
SALES (corp-wide): 13.1B **Privately Held**
WEB: www.tactxmed.com
SIC: **3841** Surgical stapling devices

(P-22643)
TANDEM DIABETES CARE INC (PA)
11075 Roselle St, San Diego (92121-1204)
PHONE...................................858 366-6900
Kim D Blickenstaff, *President*
Dick P Allen, *Ch of Bd*
John F Sheridan, *COO*
Leigh Vosseller, *CFO*
Brian B Hansen, *Ch Credit Ofcr*
EMP: 210
SQ FT: 108,000
SALES: 84.2MM **Publicly Held**
SIC: **3841** 2833 Surgical & medical instruments; insulin: bulk, uncompounded

(P-22644)
TEARLAB CORPORATION (PA)
150 La Terraza Blvd # 101, Escondido (92025-3877)
PHONE...................................858 455-6006
Joseph Jensen, *CEO*
Elias Vamvakas, *Ch of Bd*
Michael Marquez, *CFO*
Adrienne Graves, *Bd of Directors*
Paul Karpecki, *Bd of Directors*
EMP: 10
SQ FT: 14,700
SALES: 27.1MM **Publicly Held**
SIC: **3841** 3851 Eye examining instruments & apparatus; ophthalmic instruments & apparatus; ophthalmic goods

(P-22645)
TECOMET INC
503 S Vincent Ave, Azusa (91702-5131)
PHONE...................................626 334-1519
EMP: 506
SALES (corp-wide): 871.2MM **Privately Held**
SIC: **3841** 3444 Diagnostic apparatus, medical; surgical instruments & apparatus; medical instruments & equipment, blood & bone work; sheet metalwork
PA: Tecomet Inc.
115 Eames St
Wilmington MA 01887
978 642-2400

(P-22646)
TENACORE HOLDINGS INC
1525 E Edinger Ave, Santa Ana (92705-4907)
PHONE...................................714 444-4643
Peter Bonin III, *President*
Brand R Caso, *Vice Pres*
David Pak, *Info Tech Dir*
Francis Perez, *Project Mgr*
Andres Arcos, *Technical Staff*
▲ EMP: 100
SQ FT: 35,000
SALES: 15MM **Privately Held**
WEB: www.tenacore.com
SIC: **3841** 7699 Surgical instruments & apparatus; surgical instrument repair

(P-22647)
TENEX HEALTH INC
26902 Vista Ter, Lake Forest (92630-8123)
PHONE...................................949 454-7500
William Maya, *President*
Ivan Mijatovic, *CFO*
Jagi Gill, *Officer*
Bernard Morrey, *Officer*
▲ EMP: 70
SQ FT: 15,000
SALES: 8MM **Privately Held**
SIC: **3841** Surgical & medical instruments

(P-22648)
THERANOS INC (PA)
7373 Gateway Blvd, Newark (94560-1149)
PHONE...................................650 838-9292
David Taylor, *CEO*
Patrick O'Neill, *Ch Credit Ofcr*
Tim Cooper, *Vice Pres*
Alan Grose, *Vice Pres*
Ross Cartwright, *Network Enginr*
EMP: 100
SALES (est): 34.8MM **Privately Held**
WEB: www.theranos.com
SIC: **3841** 8748 Diagnostic apparatus, medical; testing services

(P-22649)
THERAPEUTIC INDUSTRIES INC
72096 Dunham Way Ste E, Thousand Palms (92276-3320)
P.O. Box 92 (92276-0092)
PHONE...................................760 343-2502
Chris Lehude, *President*
Merideth Laureno, *Bd of Directors*
EMP: 15 EST: 2014
SALES (est): 1.7MM **Privately Held**
SIC: **3841** Surgical & medical instruments

(P-22650)
THERASENSE INC
1360 S Loop Rd, Alameda (94502-7000)
PHONE...................................510 749-5400
W Mark Lortz, *CEO*
EMP: 11
SALES (est): 682.4K
SALES (corp-wide): 27.3B **Publicly Held**
WEB: www.abbott.com
SIC: **3841** Surgical & medical instruments
PA: Abbott Laboratories
100 Abbott Park Rd
Abbott Park IL 60064
224 667-6100

(P-22651)
TITAN MEDICAL DME INC
803 Camarillo Springs Rd A, Camarillo (93012-9459)
P.O. Box 7746, Thousand Oaks (91359-7746)
PHONE...................................818 889-9998
Ted Nordblum, *President*
▲ EMP: 11
SQ FT: 2,800
SALES (est): 850K **Privately Held**
SIC: **3841** Muscle exercise apparatus, ophthalmic

(P-22652)
TOP QUEST INC
13872 Magnolia Ave, Chino (91710-7027)
PHONE...................................626 839-8618
Shaoching Sung, *CEO*
EMP: 17
SALES (est): 2.7MM **Privately Held**
SIC: **3841** 7699 Surgical knife blades & handles; knife, saw & tool sharpening & repair

(P-22653)
TOP SHELF MANUFACTURING LLC
1851 Paradise Rd Ste B, Tracy (95304-8524)
PHONE...................................209 834-8185
Mark Hirsch,
Jeff Leonard,
▲ EMP: 15
SALES (est): 3.9MM **Privately Held**
WEB: www.topshelfmfg.com
SIC: **3841** Diagnostic apparatus, medical

(P-22654)
TRANSCEND MEDICAL INC
127 Independence Dr, Menlo Park (94025-1112)
PHONE...................................650 325-2050
Fax: 650 325-2815
EMP: 10
SALES (est): 1.8MM
SALES (corp-wide): 49.1B **Privately Held**
SIC: **3841**
PA: Novartis Ag
Lichtstrasse 35
Basel BS 4056
613 241-111

(P-22655)
TRELLEBORG SEALING SOLUTIONS (DH)
Also Called: Issac
2761 Walnut Ave, Tustin (92780-7051)
PHONE...................................714 415-0280
William Reising, *CEO*
Ron Fraleigh, *President*
Don Borje, *COO*
Tom Mazelin, *Vice Pres*
Sean McPherson, *Business Mgr*
EMP: 150
SQ FT: 1,600

(PA)=Parent Co (HQ)=Headquarters (DH)=Div Headquarters
✿ = New Business established in last 2 years

SALES (est): 35.7MM
SALES (corp-wide): 3.7B **Privately Held**
SIC: 3841 Surgical & medical instruments
HQ: Trelleborg Corporation
200 Veterans Blvd Ste 3
South Haven MI 49090
269 639-9891

(P-22656)
TRIREME MEDICAL LLC
7060 Koll Center Pkwy, Pleasanton
(94566-3106)
PHONE.............................925 931-1300
Eitan Konstantino, *President*
EMP: 70
SQ FT: 15,000
SALES: 10.6MM **Privately Held**
SIC: 3841 Suction therapy apparatus

(P-22657)
TRIVASCULAR INC (DH)
3910 Brickway Blvd, Santa Rosa
(95403-1070)
PHONE.............................707 543-8800
Christopher G Chavez, *CEO*
Michael Chobotov, *Officer*
Robert Whirley, *Vice Pres*
EMP: 40
SALES (est): 6.2MM **Publicly Held**
SIC: 3841 Surgical & medical instruments
HQ: Trivascular Technologies, Inc.
3910 Brickway Blvd
Santa Rosa CA 95403
707 543-8800

(P-22658)
TRIVASCULAR TECHNOLOGIES INC (HQ)
3910 Brickway Blvd, Santa Rosa
(95403-1070)
PHONE.............................707 543-8800
Christopher G Chavez, *President*
Michael R Kramer, *CFO*
Michael V Chobotov, *CTO*
Robert G Whirley, *Development*
EMP: 14
SQ FT: 110,000
SALES (est): 31.8MM **Publicly Held**
SIC: 3841 Surgical & medical instruments

(P-22659)
TRUER MEDICAL INC
1050 N Batavia St Ste C, Orange
(92867-5542)
PHONE.............................714 628-9785
Timothy Truitt, *CEO*
Gerry Kritner, *Admin Sec*
EMP: 12 EST: 2008
SQ FT: 7,000
SALES (est): 562.6K **Privately Held**
SIC: 3841 Anesthesia apparatus

(P-22660)
TRUEVISION SYSTEMS INC
Also Called: Truevision 3d Surgical
315 Bollay Dr Ste 101, Goleta
(93117-2948)
PHONE.............................805 963-9700
A Burton Tripathi, *CEO*
Robert Reali, *Vice Pres*
Begonia Bacigalupe, *QA Dir*
Wendy McHugh, *QA Dir*
Michael Reimer, *Technical Staff*
▲ EMP: 36
SQ FT: 10,549
SALES: 4MM **Privately Held**
WEB: www.truevisionsys.com
SIC: 3841 Surgical & medical instruments

(P-22661)
U S MEDICAL INSTRUMENTS INC (PA)
888 Prospect St Ste 100, La Jolla
(92037-8200)
P.O. Box 928439, San Diego (92192-8439)
PHONE.............................619 661-5500
Matthew Mazur, *CEO*
Carlos H Manjarrez, *Vice Pres*
George A Schapiro, *Admin Sec*
Eldridge Fridge, *Director*
William Maloney, *Director*
EMP: 27
SQ FT: 60,000
SALES (est): 6.2MM **Privately Held**
WEB: www.eusmi.com
SIC: 3841 Surgical & medical instruments

(P-22662)
UNITED ORTHOPEDIC GROUP LLC
2885 Loker Ave E, Carlsbad (92010-6626)
PHONE.............................760 729-8585
Brad Lee, *President*
EMP: 12
SALES (est): 2.3MM
SALES (corp-wide): 478.8MM **Privately Held**
SIC: 3841 Surgical & medical instruments
HQ: Breg, Inc.
2885 Loker Ave E
Carlsbad CA 92010
760 599-3000

(P-22663)
VACUMETRICS INC
Also Called: Vacumed
4538 Wstnghouse St Unit A, Ventura
(93003)
PHONE.............................805 644-7461
John J Hoppe, *President*
▲ EMP: 12
SQ FT: 6,000
SALES (est): 2.9MM **Privately Held**
WEB: www.vacumed.com
SIC: 3841 Surgical & medical instruments

(P-22664)
VARIAN ASSOCIATES LIMITED
3100 Hansen Way, Palo Alto (94304-1038)
PHONE.............................650 493-4000
Timothy E Guertin, *President*
Elisha W Finney, *Vice Pres*
Tai Yun Chen, *Controller*
EMP: 32
SALES (est): 5MM
SALES (corp-wide): 2.6B **Publicly Held**
SIC: 3841 3829 Diagnostic apparatus, medical; medical diagnostic systems, nuclear
PA: Varian Medical Systems, Inc.
3100 Hansen Way
Palo Alto CA 94304
650 493-4000

(P-22665)
VARIAN MEDICAL SYSTEMS INC
3120 Hansen Way, Palo Alto (94304-1030)
PHONE.............................408 321-4468
George Zdasiuk, *Vice Pres*
Boris Nepo, *Design Engr*
EMP: 45
SALES (corp-wide): 2.6B **Publicly Held**
WEB: www.varian.com
SIC: 3841 Surgical & medical instruments
PA: Varian Medical Systems, Inc.
3100 Hansen Way
Palo Alto CA 94304
650 493-4000

(P-22666)
VARIAN MEDICAL SYSTEMS INC
660 N Mccarthy Blvd, Milpitas
(95035-5113)
PHONE.............................408 321-9400
Viki Sparks, *Branch Mgr*
EMP: 200
SALES (corp-wide): 2.6B **Publicly Held**
WEB: www.varian.com
SIC: 3841 Surgical & medical instruments
PA: Varian Medical Systems, Inc.
3100 Hansen Way
Palo Alto CA 94304
650 493-4000

(P-22667)
VARIAN MEDICAL SYSTEMS INC
3045 Hanover St, Palo Alto (94304-1129)
P.O. Box 10022 (94303-0922)
PHONE.............................650 493-4000
Sharon Rylander, *Branch Mgr*
EMP: 118
SALES (corp-wide): 2.6B **Publicly Held**
WEB: www.varian.com
SIC: 3841 Surgical & medical instruments
PA: Varian Medical Systems, Inc.
3100 Hansen Way
Palo Alto CA 94304
650 493-4000

(P-22668)
VASCULAR IMAGING PROFESSIONALS (PA)
1340 N Dynamics St Ste A, Anaheim
(92806-1902)
PHONE.............................949 278-5622
Matthew Lieberman, *Principal*
EMP: 10 EST: 2011
SALES (est): 3.7MM **Privately Held**
SIC: 3841 Diagnostic apparatus, medical

(P-22669)
VENTA MEDICAL INC
1971 Milmont Dr, Milpitas (95035-2577)
PHONE.............................510 429-9300
Bill Northum, *General Mgr*
Joseph S Coel, *COO*
Michael W Wimmer, *CFO*
EMP: 40
SALES: 7MM
SALES (corp-wide): 4.3B **Publicly Held**
SIC: 3841 3449 Inhalation therapy equipment; curtain wall, metal
HQ: Ltc Holdings, Inc.
3021 N Delany Rd
Waukegan IL 60087
847 249-5900

(P-22670)
VENTION MED DESIGN & DEV INC
Also Called: Tdc Medical California
610 Palomar Ave, Sunnyvale (94085-2912)
PHONE.............................603 707-8753
Gary Boseck, *Branch Mgr*
Matthew Davis, *Program Mgr*
Graham Garvin, *Design Engr*
Audrey Larson, *Research*
Stacy Patch, *Engineer*
EMP: 18
SALES (corp-wide): 2B **Publicly Held**
SIC: 3841 Surgical & medical instruments
HQ: Vention Medical Design And Development Inc.
261 Cedar Hill St Ste 1
Marlborough MA 01752
508 481-6233

(P-22671)
VENTUS MEDICAL INC
1100 La Avenida St Ste A, Mountain View
(94043-1453)
PHONE.............................408 200-5299
Peter Wyles, *President*
Sandra Gardiner, *CFO*
Mike Favet, *Senior VP*
John Fraboni, *Vice Pres*
Glenn Johnson, *Vice Pres*
EMP: 25
SQ FT: 14,000
SALES (est): 6.9MM **Privately Held**
SIC: 3841 Surgical & medical instruments

(P-22672)
VERSATILE POWER INC
743 Camden Ave B, Campbell
(95008-4101)
PHONE.............................408 341-4600
Jerry Price, *CEO*
Gerald Price, *President*
Hugo Torres, *Engineer*
Shad Schidel, *QC Mgr*
▲ EMP: 12
SALES (est): 1.9MM **Privately Held**
WEB: www.versatilepower.com
SIC: 3841 3825 Medical instruments & equipment, blood & bone work; semiconductor test equipment

(P-22673)
VERTOS MEDICAL INC
95 Enterprise Ste 325, Aliso Viejo
(92656-2612)
PHONE.............................949 349-0008
James M Corbett, *CEO*
Rebecca Colbert, *CFO*
EMP: 62 EST: 2005
SQ FT: 25,000
SALES (est): 7.2MM **Privately Held**
SIC: 3841 3842 Medical instruments & equipment, blood & bone work; surgical appliances & supplies

(P-22674)
VESTA MEDICAL LLC
Also Called: Vestara
3750 Torrey View Ct, San Diego
(92130-2622)
PHONE.............................949 660-8648
Alan Davidner, *Mng Member*
Gary Brookshire, *CFO*
EMP: 10
SALES (est): 1.3MM
SALES (corp-wide): 12B **Publicly Held**
SIC: 3841 Medical instruments & equipment, blood & bone work
HQ: Carefusion Corporation
3750 Torrey View Ct
San Diego CA 92130

(P-22675)
VIASYS RESPIRATORY CARE INC
Also Called: Biosys Healthcare
22745 Savi Ranch Pkwy, Yorba Linda
(92887-4668)
PHONE.............................714 283-2228
William B Ross, *President*
EMP: 230
SQ FT: 120,000
SALES (est): 22.4MM
SALES (corp-wide): 12B **Publicly Held**
WEB: www.sensormedics.com
SIC: 3841 Diagnostic apparatus, medical
HQ: Carefusion Corporation
3750 Torrey View Ct
San Diego CA 92130

(P-22676)
VNUS MEDICAL TECHNOLOGIES INC
5799 Fontanoso Way, San Jose
(95138-1015)
PHONE.............................408 360-7200
Brian E Farley, *President*
Peter Osborne, *CFO*
Kirti Kamdar, *Senior VP*
John W Kapples, *Vice Pres*
Mark S Saxton, *Vice Pres*
EMP: 231
SQ FT: 93,650
SALES (est): 26.7MM **Privately Held**
WEB: www.vnus.com
SIC: 3841 Catheters
HQ: Covidien Lp
15 Hampshire St
Mansfield MA 02048
508 261-8000

(P-22677)
VORTRAN MEDICAL TECHNOLOGY 1 (PA)
21 Golden Land Ct Ste 100, Sacramento
(95834-2427)
PHONE.............................916 648-8460
Gordon Wong MD, *President*
Diana Cha, *Admin Asst*
EMP: 28
SALES (est): 3.8MM **Privately Held**
WEB: www.vortran.com
SIC: 3841 Inhalators, surgical & medical

(P-22678)
VOYAGE MEDICAL INC
610 Galveston Dr, Redwood City
(94063-4721)
PHONE.............................650 503-7500
Vahid Saadat, *President*
Allan Zingeler, *President*
Michael Wiley, *CFO*
John Allison, *Vice Pres*
Douglas M Bruce, *Vice Pres*
EMP: 35
SALES (est): 3.6MM **Privately Held**
SIC: 3841 Surgical & medical instruments

(P-22679)
W L GORE & ASSOCIATES INC
2890 De La Cruz Blvd, Santa Clara
(95050-2619)
PHONE.............................928 864-2705
Mohan Sancheti, *Branch Mgr*
EMP: 184
SALES (corp-wide): 3.4B **Privately Held**
SIC: 3841 Surgical & medical instruments

PA: W. L. Gore & Associates, Inc.
555 Paper Mill Rd
Newark DE 19711
302 738-4880

(P-22680)
WANG NMR INC
550 N Canyons Pkwy, Livermore
(94551-9472)
PHONE.........................925 443-0212
Sou-Tien Wang, *CEO*
Bert Wang, *President*
Henry Chen, *Vice Pres*
Clyde Taylor, *Vice Pres*
▲ **EMP:** 25
SQ FT: 36,000
SALES (est): 4.2MM **Privately Held**
WEB: www.wangnmr.com
SIC: 3841 Diagnostic apparatus, medical

(P-22681)
WAVE 80 BIOSCIENCES INC
1100 26th St, San Francisco (94107-3527)
PHONE.........................415 487-7976
Daniel Laser, *President*
Richard A Goozh, *CFO*
EMP: 18
SALES (est): 3.3MM **Privately Held**
WEB: www.wave80.com
SIC: 3841 Diagnostic apparatus, medical

(P-22682)
WORKMAN HOLDINGS INC
Also Called: Tabco Precision
525 Industrial Way, Fallbrook (92028-2244)
PHONE.........................760 723-5283
Kyle Workman, *President*
Robyn Menossi, *Office Mgr*
EMP: 10
SALES (est): 1.5MM **Privately Held**
SIC: 3841 3851 Surgical & medical instruments; frames & parts, eyeglass & spectacle

(P-22683)
ZELTIQ AESTHETICS INC
Also Called: Coolsculpting
6723 Sierra Ct, Dublin (94568-2699)
PHONE.........................925 474-2519
Patrick Williams, *Principal*
EMP: 10 **Privately Held**
SIC: 3841 Surgical & medical instruments
HQ: Zeltiq Aesthetics, Inc.
4410 Rosewood Dr
Pleasanton CA 94588

(P-22684)
ZELTIQ AESTHETICS INC (DH)
Also Called: Coolsculpting
4410 Rosewood Dr, Pleasanton
(94588-3050)
PHONE.........................925 474-2500
Mark J Foley, *President*
Todd E Zavodnick, *President*
Taylor Harris, *CFO*
Sergio Garcia, *Senior VP*
Brad Hauser, *Vice Pres*
▲ **EMP:** 277
SQ FT: 71,670
SALES (est): 354.2MM **Privately Held**
WEB: www.zeltiq.com
SIC: 3841 Surgical & medical instruments
HQ: Allergan Holdco Us, Inc.
400 Interpace Pkwy Ste D
Parsippany NJ 07054
862 261-7000

(P-22685)
ZIPLINE MEDICAL INC
747 Camden Ave Ste A, Campbell
(95008-4147)
PHONE.........................408 412-7228
John R Tighe, *President*
Amir Belson, *Founder*
Bauback Safa, *Officer*
Trish Howell, *Vice Pres*
Eric Storne, *Vice Pres*
EMP: 19
SALES (est): 3MM **Privately Held**
SIC: 3841 7389 Surgical & medical instruments;

(P-22686)
ZMK MEDICAL TECHNOLOGIES INC
Also Called: Eigen
13366 Grass Valley Ave A, Grass Valley
(95945-9549)
PHONE.........................530 274-1240
Mahtab Damda,
EMP: 30
SALES (est): 3.2MM **Privately Held**
SIC: 3841 Surgical & medical instruments

3842 Orthopedic, Prosthetic & Surgical Appliances/Splys

(P-22687)
ACUTUS MEDICAL INC
2210 Faraday Ave Ste 100, Carlsbad
(92008-7225)
PHONE.........................858 673-1621
Randy Werneth, *CEO*
John Dahldorf, *CFO*
Graydon Beatty, *CTO*
EMP: 13
SALES (est): 4MM **Privately Held**
SIC: 3842 Abdominal supporters, braces & trusses

(P-22688)
ADENNA INC
201 S Milliken Ave, Ontario (91761-7832)
PHONE.........................909 510-6999
Thomas Friedl, *CEO*
Patrick Fitzmaurice, *CFO*
Jesilyn Duke, *Vice Pres*
Janice Adkins, *Credit Mgr*
▲ **EMP:** 13 **EST:** 1997
SQ FT: 13,000
SALES (est): 3.2MM **Privately Held**
WEB: www.adenna.com
SIC: 3842 Surgical appliances & supplies

(P-22689)
ADEX MEDICAL INC
6101 Quail Valley Ct D, Riverside
(92507-0764)
P.O. Box 97, Temecula (92593-0097)
PHONE.........................951 653-9122
Michael M Ghafouri, *President*
EMP: 25 **EST:** 1996
SQ FT: 15,000
SALES (est): 3MM **Privately Held**
WEB: www.adexmed.com
SIC: 3842 3843 5999 5047 Surgical appliances & supplies; dental equipment & supplies; medical apparatus & supplies; medical & hospital equipment; industrial supplies

(P-22690)
ADVANCED ARM DYNAMICS (PA)
123 W Torrance Blvd # 203, Redondo
Beach (90277-3614)
PHONE.........................310 372-3050
John Miguelez, *President*
Misty Carver, *Principal*
Dan Conyers, *Principal*
Carol Sorrels, *Principal*
Tiffany Ryan, *Director*
EMP: 44
SALES (est): 10.7MM **Privately Held**
SIC: 3842 Prosthetic appliances

(P-22691)
ADVANCED BIONICS LLC
Also Called: A B
28515 Westinghouse Pl, Valencia
(91355-4833)
PHONE.........................661 362-1400
Rainer Platz, *CEO*
Laura Benesh, *Admin Asst*
Delilah Garcia, *Admin Asst*
Alexander Gutierrez, *QA Dir*
Steven Becker, *Software Engr*
EMP: 500
SALES (est): 67.8MM
SALES (corp-wide): 2.8B **Privately Held**
SIC: 3842 Hearing aids

PA: Sonova Holding Ag
Laubisrutistrasse 28
StAfa ZH 8712
589 280-101

(P-22692)
ADVANCED BIONICS CORPORATION (HQ)
28515 Westinghouse Pl, Valencia
(91355-4833)
PHONE.........................661 362-1400
Rainer Platz, *CEO*
Michael Sundler, *Managing Prtnr*
Jeffrey Goldberg, *Senior VP*
Robert Gulock, *Vice Pres*
Cedric Navarro, *Vice Pres*
▲ **EMP:** 214
SALES (est): 130MM
SALES (corp-wide): 2.8B **Privately Held**
SIC: 3842 Hearing aids
PA: Sonova Holding Ag
Laubisrutistrasse 28
StAfa ZH 8712
589 280-101

(P-22693)
ADVANCED ORTHOTIC DESIGNS
9351 Narnia Dr, Riverside (92503-5634)
PHONE.........................951 710-1640
Mark Latham, *CEO*
EMP: 11
SQ FT: 1,500
SALES (est): 675.4K
SALES (corp-wide): 1.3MM **Privately Held**
WEB: www.advancedorthoticdesigns.com
SIC: 3842 Braces, orthopedic; orthopedic appliances
PA: New Day, Inc.
8026 Sitio Caucho
Carlsbad CA

(P-22694)
ADVANCED PROSTHETICS LLC
7015 N Chestnut Ave # 103, Fresno
(93720-0349)
PHONE.........................559 298-0321
Glen Ellis, *CEO*
Jason Schott,
EMP: 10
SQ FT: 4,000
SALES (est): 701.5K **Privately Held**
SIC: 3842 Orthopedic appliances

(P-22695)
ALPHATEC SPINE INC (HQ)
5818 El Camino Real, Carlsbad
(92008-8816)
PHONE.........................760 494-6610
James M Corbett, *CEO*
Patrick Ryan, *President*
Michael Plunkett, *COO*
M Ross Simmonds, *COO*
Jeffrey G Black, *CFO*
▲ **EMP:** 250
SALES (est): 89.2MM
SALES (corp-wide): 101.7MM **Publicly Held**
WEB: www.alphatecspine.com
SIC: 3842 8711 5047 Surgical appliances & supplies; engineering services; medical equipment & supplies
PA: Alphatec Holdings, Inc.
5818 El Camino Real
Carlsbad CA 92008
760 431-9286

(P-22696)
ALPHATEC SPINE INC
2150 Palomar Airport Rd, Carlsbad
(92011-4406)
PHONE.........................760 431-9286
Mitsuo Asai, *Principal*
Dave Keizer, *Director*
EMP: 12
SALES (est): 1.2MM **Privately Held**
SIC: 3842 Surgical appliances & supplies

(P-22697)
AMERICAN CERAMIC TECHNOLOGY (PA)
12909 Lomas Verdes Dr, Poway
(92064-1250)
P.O. Box 461479, Escondido (92046-1479)
PHONE.........................619 992-3104
Richard Vaughn Culbertson, *CEO*
Tafi Martell, *Info Tech Mgr*
Scott McCall, *Engineer*
Sean Forehand, *Business Mgr*
EMP: 15 **EST:** 2008
SALES (est): 3.5MM **Privately Held**
SIC: 3842 3443 Radiation shielding aprons, gloves, sheeting, etc.; nuclear shielding, metal plate

(P-22698)
AMERICAN METAL ENTERPRISES INC
15855 Chemical Ln, Huntington Beach
(92649-1510)
PHONE.........................714 894-6810
Scott B Edwards, *CEO*
EMP: 10 **EST:** 2012
SALES (est): 414.8K **Privately Held**
SIC: 3842 Braces, elastic

(P-22699)
AMERICH CORPORATION (PA)
13212 Saticoy St, North Hollywood
(91605-3404)
PHONE.........................818 982-1711
Edward Richmond, *President*
Dino Pacifici, *Vice Pres*
Greg Richmond, *Vice Pres*
Lauren Timberlake, *Graphic Designe*
Chantal Difrancesca, *Accountant*
▲ **EMP:** 120
SQ FT: 145,000
SALES (est): 32.5MM **Privately Held**
WEB: www.americh.com
SIC: 3842 3432 3431 3261 Whirlpool baths, hydrotherapy equipment; plumbing fixture fittings & trim; metal sanitary ware; vitreous plumbing fixtures

(P-22700)
ANSELL SNDEL MED SOLUTIONS LLC
9301 Oakdale Ave Ste 300, Chatsworth
(91311-6539)
PHONE.........................818 534-2500
Anthony B Lopez, *President*
Wendell Franke, *Associate Dir*
Stephanie Barth, *Principal*
▲ **EMP:** 32
SQ FT: 14,600
SALES (est): 6.3MM
SALES (corp-wide): 1.3B **Privately Held**
WEB: www.sandelmedical.com
SIC: 3842 Surgical appliances & supplies
PA: Ansell Limited
L3 678 Victoria St
Richmond VIC 3121
392 707-270

(P-22701)
ARS ENTERPRISES (PA)
15554 Minnesota Ave, Paramount
(90723-4119)
PHONE.........................562 946-3505
Ben Hom, *Mng Member*
Michael D Dunn, *Ch of Bd*
Glenn Caster, *President*
Alan Silverstein, *Sales Engr*
Marshall Geller, *Mng Member*
EMP: 14
SQ FT: 11,000
SALES (est): 2MM **Privately Held**
WEB: www.rely-ars.com
SIC: 3842 5074 Autoclaves, hospital & surgical; boilers, steam

(P-22702)
ASPEN MEDICAL PRODUCTS
6481 Oak Cyn, Irvine (92618-5202)
P.O. Box 22116, Pasadena (91185-0001)
PHONE.........................949 681-0200
Daniel J Williamson, *CEO*
Randy Barbera, *CFO*
Scott Hampson, *Vice Pres*
Andrew Purner, *Vice Pres*
Ben Mascardo, *Administration*
▲ **EMP:** 70

P
R
O
D
U
C
T
S

&

S
V
C
S

SQ FT: 52,000
SALES (est): 19.7MM **Privately Held**
WEB: www.aspenmp.com
SIC: 3842 Cervical collars

(P-22703)
AXIOM INDUSTRIES INC
Also Called: Prime Engineering
4202 W Sierra Madre Ave, Fresno
(93722-3932)
PHONE..............................559 276-1310
Mary Wilson Boegel, *President*
Bruce Boegel, *CFO*
Mark Allen, *Vice Pres*
Robert Rego, *Engineer*
◆ **EMP:** 26
SALES (est): 4.5MM **Privately Held**
WEB: www.primeengineering.com
SIC: 3842 Technical aids for the handicapped

(P-22704)
BAUERS & COLLINS
Also Called: Community Vision
6765 Lankershim Blvd, North Hollywood
(91606-1614)
PHONE..............................818 983-1281
Robert F Collins, *Owner*
EMP: 15 **EST:** 1999
SALES (est): 1.6MM **Privately Held**
WEB: www.communityvisions.org
SIC: 3842 Prosthetic appliances

(P-22705)
BIO CYBERNETICS INTERNATIONAL
Also Called: Cybertech
2701 Kimball Ave, Pomona (91767-2268)
PHONE..............................909 447-7050
Matthew Waidelich, *President*
Charles Hughes, *Vice Pres*
Dick Prendergast, *Vice Pres*
Richard Prendergast, *Vice Pres*
SC Chan, *Mfg Dir*
▲ **EMP:** 15
SQ FT: 10,000
SALES (est): 2MM **Privately Held**
WEB: www.cybertechmedical.com
SIC: 3842

(P-22706)
BIOMECHANICAL ANALYSIS &
Also Called: Biomechanical Services
20509 Earlgate St, Walnut (91789-2909)
PHONE..............................714 990-5932
Greg Wolfe, *President*
Kevin Hasegawa, *Shareholder*
Brian Killeen, *Shareholder*
Dr William Sniechowski, *Shareholder*
Scott De Francisco, *Vice Pres*
EMP: 45
SQ FT: 13,000
SALES (est): 5.9MM **Privately Held**
WEB: www.biomechanical.com
SIC: 3842 5999 Orthopedic appliances; orthopedic & prosthesis applications

(P-22707)
BIOMET SAN DIEGO LLC
1540 Rubenstein Ave, Cardiff By The Sea
(92007-2436)
PHONE..............................760 942-2786
Trude Jackson, *President*
EMP: 10
SQ FT: 2,200
SALES: 4.7MM **Privately Held**
SIC: 3842 Implants, surgical

(P-22708)
BIONICSOUND INC
Also Called: Bionikear.com
390 Spar Ave Ste 104, San Jose
(95117-1643)
PHONE..............................714 300-4809
Asela Jayampathy, *CEO*
EMP: 14
SQ FT: 5,000
SALES: 15MM **Privately Held**
SIC: 3842 Hearing aids

(P-22709)
BOSTON SCNTFIC NRMDLATION CORP
25129 Rye Canyon Loop, Valencia
(91355-5004)
PHONE..............................661 949-4869

Jeff Greiner, *President*
EMP: 10
SALES (corp-wide): 9B **Publicly Held**
SIC: 3842 3841 Hearing aids; surgical instruments & apparatus
HQ: Boston Scientific Neuromodulation Corporation
25155 Rye Canyon Loop
Valencia CA 91355
-

(P-22710)
BOSTON SCNTFIC NRMDLATION CORP (HQ)
25155 Rye Canyon Loop, Valencia
(91355-5004)
PHONE..............................661 949-4310
Michael F Mahoney, *CEO*
Supratim Bose, *Exec VP*
Jeffrey D Capello, *Exec VP*
Kevin Ballinger, *Senior VP*
Wendy Carruthers, *Senior VP*
▲ **EMP:** 450
SQ FT: 26,000
SALES (est): 92.7MM
SALES (corp-wide): 9B **Publicly Held**
SIC: 3842 3841 5047 Hearing aids; surgical & medical instruments; metabolism apparatus; surgical instruments & apparatus; medical & hospital equipment; hearing aids
PA: Boston Scientific Corporation
300 Boston Scientific Way
Marlborough MA 01752
508 683-4000

(P-22711)
BREATHE TECHNOLOGIES INC
175 Technology Dr Ste 100, Irvine
(92618-2473)
PHONE..............................949 988-7700
Lawrence A Mastrovich, *President*
John L Miclot, *Ch of Bd*
Rebecca Mabry, *Senior VP*
Samir S Ahmad, *Vice Pres*
William C Arsenault, *Vice Pres*
EMP: 39
SALES (est): 12.2MM **Privately Held**
WEB: www.breathetechnologies.com
SIC: 3842 Respirators; respiratory protection equipment, personal

(P-22712)
CASTLE HILL HOLDINGS INC
Also Called: Collier O & P
3161 Putnam Blvd, Pleasant Hill
(94523-4650)
PHONE..............................925 943-1119
Richard Todd, *President*
Leslie Wells, *CEO*
George Villarruel, *Director*
EMP: 10
SALES (est): 1.3MM **Privately Held**
SIC: 3842 Braces, orthopedic; canes, orthopedic; foot appliances, orthopedic

(P-22713)
CHASSIS UNLIMITED
3573 1st St Ste B, Livermore (94551-4920)
PHONE..............................925 339-6035
William Ivie, *Principal*
EMP: 10
SALES (est): 1.4MM **Privately Held**
SIC: 3842 Welders' hoods

(P-22714)
CONVAID PRODUCTS INC
2830 California St, Torrance (90503-3908)
P.O. Box 4209, Pls Vrds Pnsl (90274-9571)
PHONE..............................310 618-0111
Chris Braun, *CEO*
Mervyn M Watkins, *CEO*
Ro Octave, *CFO*
Sheryl Vargas, *Analyst*
Christy Harp, *Human Res Mgr*
◆ **EMP:** 89
SALES (est): 21.6MM **Privately Held**
WEB: www.convaid.com
SIC: 3842 Wheelchairs

(P-22715)
CURTISS-WRIGHT CONTROLS
Also Called: Penny & Giles Drive Technology
210 Ranger Ave, Brea (92821-6215)
PHONE..............................714 982-1860
John Camp, *President*

Stephen Eccleston, *General Mgr*
EMP: 25
SALES (corp-wide): 2.2B **Publicly Held**
WEB: www.autronics.com
SIC: 3842 Braces, elastic
HQ: Curtiss-Wright Controls Integrated Sensing, Inc.
28965 Avenue Penn
Valencia CA 91355
626 851-3100

(P-22716)
DJ ORTHOPEDICS LLC
3151 Scott St, Vista (92081-8365)
PHONE..............................760 727-1280
Andi Donner, *Principal*
Paul Van Langen, *Vice Pres*
Tabitha Skoglund, *Credit Mgr*
Thomas Sillman, *Sales Staff*
Jill Cook, *Director*
EMP: 18
SALES (est): 3MM **Privately Held**
SIC: 3842 Surgical appliances & supplies

(P-22717)
DJO GLOBAL INC (DH)
1430 Decision St, Vista (92081-8553)
PHONE..............................760 727-1280
Brady Shirley, *President*
Kenneth W Davidson, *Ch of Bd*
Vickie L Capps, *CFO*
Tom Capizzi, *Exec VP*
Jeanine Kestler, *Exec VP*
◆ **EMP:** 550
SQ FT: 70,000
SALES (est): 1.9B
SALES (corp-wide): 7.1B **Publicly Held**
WEB: www.encoremed.com
SIC: 3842 Surgical appliances & supplies; implants, surgical

(P-22718)
DONN & DOFF INC
Also Called: Tegerstrand Orthtics Prsthtics
2102 Civic Center Dr, Redding
(96001-2704)
PHONE..............................530 241-4040
Dona Tegerstrand, *President*
Sue Mc Gaity, *Office Mgr*
EMP: 15
SQ FT: 3,000
SALES (est): 2.2MM **Privately Held**
WEB: www.donnanddoff.com
SIC: 3842 Limbs, artificial; braces, orthopedic

(P-22719)
DYNAMICS ORTHOTICS & PROSTHETI
Also Called: Dynamics O&P
1830 W Olympic Blvd # 123, Los Angeles
(90006-3734)
PHONE..............................213 383-9212
Peter J Sean, *CEO*
Sharon Sean, *Mktg Dir*
Sharon Cho, *Manager*
EMP: 30
SQ FT: 20,662
SALES (est): 4.9MM **Privately Held**
SIC: 3842 Orthopedic appliances; limbs, artificial

(P-22720)
EARGO INC (PA)
1600 Technology Dr Fl 6, San Jose
(95110-1382)
PHONE..............................650 996-9508
Christian Gormsen, *CEO*
Bill Browney, *Ch Credit Ofcr*
Jurgen Pauquet, *Ch Credit Ofcr*
Daniel Shen, *Ch Credit Ofcr*
Brownie William, *Officer*
EMP: 80
SQ FT: 20,000
SALES (est): 11.3MM **Privately Held**
SIC: 3842 5047 7371 Hearing aids; hearing aids; computer software development & applications

(P-22721)
EARLENS CORPORATION
4045a Campbell Ave, Menlo Park
(94025-1006)
PHONE..............................650 366-9000
William M Facteau, *President*
Mark Bishop, *COO*

George Harter, *CFO*
Rodney Perkins, *Chief Mktg Ofcr*
Jill Hannemann, *Executive Asst*
EMP: 14
SALES (est): 4.1MM **Privately Held**
SIC: 3842 Hearing aids

(P-22722)
EDWARDS LIFESCIENCES CORP
1402 Alton Pkwy, Irvine (92606-4838)
PHONE..............................949 250-3522
Diane Nguyen, *Branch Mgr*
Maribelle Aguinaldo, *Manager*
Nancy Cohen, *Manager*
Beverly Tanaka, *Manager*
EMP: 13
SALES (corp-wide): 3.4B **Publicly Held**
SIC: 3842 Surgical appliances & supplies
PA: Edwards Lifesciences Corp
1 Edwards Way
Irvine CA 92614
949 250-2500

(P-22723)
EDWARDS LIFESCIENCES CORP (PA)
1 Edwards Way, Irvine (92614-5688)
PHONE..............................949 250-2500
Michael A Mussallem, *Ch of Bd*
Scott B Ullem, *CFO*
Scott Beggins, *Vice Pres*
Donald E Bobo Jr, *Vice Pres*
Denise E Botticelli, *Vice Pres*
EMP: 1600
SALES: 3.4B **Publicly Held**
WEB: www.edwards.com
SIC: 3842 Surgical appliances & supplies

(P-22724)
EDWARDS LIFESCIENCES CORP
1212 Alton Pkwy, Irvine (92606-4837)
PHONE..............................949 553-0611
Rita Hernandez, *Branch Mgr*
EMP: 21
SALES (corp-wide): 3.4B **Publicly Held**
WEB: www.edwards.com
SIC: 3842 Surgical appliances & supplies
PA: Edwards Lifesciences Corp
1 Edwards Way
Irvine CA 92614
949 250-2500

(P-22725)
EKSO BIONICS HOLDINGS INC
1414 Harbour Way S # 1201, Richmond
(94804-3628)
PHONE..............................510 984-1761
Jack Peurach, *President*
Steven Sherman, *Ch of Bd*
Russell Delonzor, *COO*
John Glenn, *CFO*
Maximilian Scheder-Bieschi, *CFO*
EMP: 108
SQ FT: 45,000
SALES: 14.2MM **Privately Held**
SIC: 3842 5999 Crutches & walkers; walkers; canes, orthopedic; medical apparatus & supplies

(P-22726)
EMERGENT GROUP INC (DH)
10939 Pendleton St, Sun Valley
(91352-1522)
PHONE..............................818 394-2800
Bruce J Haber, *CEO*
Louis Buther, *President*
William M McKay, *CFO*
EMP: 55
SQ FT: 13,000
SALES (est): 7.8MM **Privately Held**
WEB: www.primedical.net
SIC: 3842 7352 Surgical appliances & supplies; medical equipment rental
HQ: Universal Hospital Services, Inc.
6625 W 78th St Ste 300
Minneapolis MN 55439
952 893-3200

(P-22727)
ENDOSEE CORPORATION
4546 El Camino Real, Los Altos
(94022-1099)
PHONE..............................650 383-5156
Xiaolong Bruce Ouyang, *CEO*
EMP: 10

▲ = Import ▼=Export
◆ =Import/Export

SALES (est): 2.7MM
SALES (corp-wide): 2.1B **Publicly Held**
SIC: 3842 Gynecological supplies & appliances
HQ: Coopersurgical, Inc.
95 Corporate Dr
Trumbull CT 06611

(P-22728)
ENDOTEC INC
14525 Valley View Ave H, Santa Fe Springs (90670-5237)
PHONE....................714 681-6306
Young B Shim, *CEO*
EMP: 12
SQ FT: 5,900
SALES (est): 1.9MM **Privately Held**
SIC: 3842 Orthopedic appliances

(P-22729)
ESP SAFETY INC
555 N 1st St, San Jose (95112-5314)
PHONE....................408 886-9746
Ivan Lukisa, *President*
Anna Trofimova, *Vice Pres*
Fabian Martinez, *Technology*
EMP: 10
SQ FT: 8,000
SALES (est): 2.1MM **Privately Held**
WEB: www.esp-corporation.com
SIC: 3842 Personal safety equipment

(P-22730)
ETHICON INC
Advanced Sterilization Pdts
33 Technology Dr, Irvine (92618-2346)
PHONE....................949 581-5799
Charles Austin, *Branch Mgr*
Saheed Alam, *Engineer*
EMP: 300
SALES (corp-wide): 76.4B **Publicly Held**
WEB: www.ethiconinc.com
SIC: 3842 Sutures, absorbable & non-absorbable
HQ: Ethicon Inc.
Us Route 22
Somerville NJ 08876
732 524-0400

(P-22731)
FOOT IN MOTION INC
Also Called: Kevin Orthopedic
2022 Broadway Ste A, Santa Monica (90404-2971)
PHONE....................312 752-0990
Kevin Rosenbloom, *President*
Jacob Karp, *Business Dir*
◆ EMP: 15
SALES (est): 1.6MM **Privately Held**
SIC: 3842 Foot appliances, orthopedic

(P-22732)
FRANK STUBBS CO INC
1830 Eastman Ave, Oxnard (93030-8935)
PHONE....................805 278-4300
Glenn Soensker, *CFO*
David Paul Pearson, *President*
Glenn Alan Slensker, *CFO*
Dan Betkhoodu, *Purch Mgr*
EMP: 49
SQ FT: 50,100
SALES (est): 6.3MM **Privately Held**
WEB: www.fstubbs.com
SIC: 3842 Supports: abdominal, ankle, arch, kneecap, etc.; personal safety equipment

(P-22733)
FREEDOM DESIGNS INC
2241 N Madera Rd, Simi Valley (93065-1762)
PHONE....................805 582-0077
Gerald B Blouch, *CEO*
Robert Gardner, *General Mgr*
◆ EMP: 120 EST: 1981
SQ FT: 40,000
SALES (est): 21.6MM
SALES (corp-wide): 966.5MM **Publicly Held**
WEB: www.freedomdesigns.com
SIC: 3842 Wheelchairs
PA: Invacare Corporation
1 Invacare Way
Elyria OH 44035
440 329-6000

(P-22734)
FREEDOM INNOVATIONS LLC (HQ)
3 Morgan, Irvine (92618-1917)
PHONE....................949 672-0032
Maynard Carkhuff,
Robert Glidden, *Engineer*
Lee Kim,
Brent Wallace,
◆ EMP: 20
SQ FT: 6,800
SALES (est): 18MM **Privately Held**
SIC: 3842 Foot appliances, orthopedic

(P-22735)
FREUDENBERG MEDICAL LLC
5050 Rivergrade Rd, Baldwin Park (91706-1405)
PHONE....................626 814-9684
Coburn Pharr, *Manager*
EMP: 149
SALES (corp-wide): 8.3B **Privately Held**
SIC: 3842 Prosthetic appliances
HQ: Freudenberg Medical, Llc
1110 Mark Ave
Carpinteria CA 93013
805 684-3304

(P-22736)
FREUDENBERG MEDICAL LLC (DH)
Also Called: Helix Medical
1110 Mark Ave, Carpinteria (93013-2918)
PHONE....................805 684-3304
Jorg Schneewind, *CEO*
Thomas Vassalo, *President*
Deanna Caballero, *Vice Pres*
Steve Lents, *Vice Pres*
Ward Sokoloski, *Vice Pres*
◆ EMP: 267
SQ FT: 66,000
SALES (est): 157.6MM
SALES (corp-wide): 8.3B **Privately Held**
WEB: www.helixmed.com
SIC: 3842 Prosthetic appliances

(P-22737)
GLOBAL ORTHOPEDIC INC
6540 Lusk Blvd Ste C255, San Diego (92121-5795)
PHONE....................480 861-5122
Eric Kohler, *Principal*
EMP: 10
SALES: 800K **Privately Held**
SIC: 3842 Surgical appliances & supplies

(P-22738)
GUARDIAN SURVIVAL GEAR INC
1401 S Hicks Ave, Commerce (90023-3240)
PHONE....................760 519-5643
Daniel Kunz, *President*
▲ EMP: 15
SQ FT: 15,000
SALES: 1.5MM **Privately Held**
SIC: 3842 First aid, snake bite & burn kits

(P-22739)
HAND BIOMECHANICS LAB INC
77 Scripps Dr Ste 104, Sacramento (95825-6209)
PHONE....................916 923-5073
John Agee MD, *President*
Paul Sullivan, *Assistant*
Jesse Wallace, *Assistant*
EMP: 16
SQ FT: 2,600
SALES (est): 2.3MM **Privately Held**
WEB: www.handbiolab.com
SIC: 3842 Orthopedic appliances

(P-22740)
HANGER
6099 Malburg Way, Vernon (90058-3947)
PHONE....................323 238-7738
EMP: 15 EST: 2005
SALES (est): 1.9MM **Privately Held**
SIC: 3842 Surgical appliances & supplies

(P-22741)
HANGER INC
Also Called: Hanger P&O
24 Antelope Blvd, Red Bluff (96080-2807)
PHONE....................530 528-1795

EMP: 12
SALES (corp-wide): 1B **Publicly Held**
SIC: 3842 Surgical appliances & supplies
PA: Hanger, Inc.
10910 Domain Dr Ste 300
Austin TX 78758
512 777-3800

(P-22742)
HANGER PROSTHETICS & ORTHO
Also Called: Hanger Clinic
6300 Wilshire Blvd # 150, Los Angeles (90048-5211)
PHONE....................323 866-2555
Sam Liang, *President*
Vinit Asar, *Ch of Bd*
EMP: 99
SQ FT: 1,500
SALES (est): 4.1MM **Privately Held**
SIC: 3842 Prosthetic appliances

(P-22743)
HANGER PRSTHETCS & ORTHO INC
7700 Imperial Hwy Ste E2, Downey (90242-3466)
PHONE....................562 803-3322
Phil Conley, *Manager*
EMP: 13
SALES (corp-wide): 1B **Publicly Held**
SIC: 3842 Surgical appliances & supplies
HQ: Hanger Prosthetics & Orthotics, Inc.
10910 Domain Dr Ste 300
Austin TX 78758
512 777-3800

(P-22744)
HANGER PRSTHETCS & ORTHO INC
Also Called: Hanger Clinic
18022 Cowan Ste 285, Irvine (92614-6814)
PHONE....................949 863-1951
EMP: 86
SALES (corp-wide): 762.8MM **Publicly Held**
SIC: 3842
HQ: Hanger Prosthetics & Orthotics, Inc.
10910 Main Dr
Austin TX 78758
512 777-3800

(P-22745)
HANGER PRSTHETCS & ORTHO INC
Also Called: Nova Care Orthtics Prosthetics
15725 Pomerado Rd, Poway (92064-2068)
PHONE....................858 487-4516
Dhruval Shah, *Branch Mgr*
EMP: 19
SALES (corp-wide): 1B **Publicly Held**
SIC: 3842 5999 Prosthetic appliances; orthopedic & prosthesis applications
HQ: Hanger Prosthetics & Orthotics, Inc.
10910 Domain Dr Ste 300
Austin TX 78758
512 777-3800

(P-22746)
HANGER PRSTHETCS & ORTHO INC
4659 Las Positas Rd Ste A, Livermore (94551-9631)
PHONE....................925 371-5081
Regina Lnd, *Branch Mgr*
EMP: 14
SALES (corp-wide): 1B **Publicly Held**
SIC: 3842 Orthopedic appliances
HQ: Hanger Prosthetics & Orthotics, Inc.
10910 Domain Dr Ste 300
Austin TX 78758
512 777-3800

(P-22747)
HONEYWELL SAFETY PDTS USA INC
7828 Waterville Rd, San Diego (92154-8205)
PHONE....................619 661-8383
Dave M Cote, *CEO*
EMP: 150
SALES (corp-wide): 40.5B **Publicly Held**
SIC: 3842 Ear plugs

HQ: Honeywell Safety Products Usa, Inc.
2711 Centerville Rd
Wilmington DE 19808
302 636-5401

(P-22748)
IMPERATIVE CARE INC
1359 Dell Ave, Campbell (95008-6609)
PHONE....................650 274-3882
Farhad Khosravi, *President*
EMP: 25
SQ FT: 7,000
SALES (est): 126.9K **Privately Held**
SIC: 3842 Surgical appliances & supplies

(P-22749)
IMPLANT DIRECT SYBRON MFG LLC
3050 E Hillcrest Dr, Westlake Village (91362-3171)
PHONE....................818 444-3300
Gerald A Niznick,
Jay Choi, *Vice Pres*
Tom Stratton, *Executive*
Gisella Zimmermann, *Administration*
Allison E Jean, *Technical Mgr*
EMP: 200
SQ FT: 45,622
SALES (est): 30.6MM
SALES (corp-wide): 18.3B **Publicly Held**
WEB: www.implantdirect.com
SIC: 3842 Implants, surgical
PA: Danaher Corporation
2200 Penn Ave Nw Ste 800w
Washington DC 20037
202 828-0850

(P-22750)
IMPLANTECH ASSOCIATES INC
Also Called: Allied Bio Medical
6025 Nicolle St Ste B, Ventura (93003-7602)
PHONE....................805 289-1665
William Binder, *President*
Lillie Cranfill, *Admin Mgr*
Liliana Castillo, *Info Tech Mgr*
Andrew Leicht, *Engineer*
Tina Post, *Engineer*
EMP: 30
SQ FT: 11,000
SALES (est): 5.6MM **Privately Held**
WEB: www.implantech.com
SIC: 3842 Implants, surgical

(P-22751)
INFAB CORPORATION
1040 Avenida Acaso, Camarillo (93012-8712)
PHONE....................805 987-5255
Donald J Cusick, *President*
Brittany Lepley, *Mktg Dir*
▲ EMP: 57
SQ FT: 40,000
SALES: 12.3MM **Privately Held**
WEB: www.infabcorp.com
SiC: 3842 Radiation shielding aprons, gloves, sheeting, etc.

(P-22752)
INHEALTH TECHNOLOGIES
1110 Mark Ave, Carpinteria (93013-2918)
PHONE....................800 477-5969
Ed Munoz, *Principal*
Constantine Davlantes, *Vice Pres*
Deanna Caballero, *Human Res Dir*
Rachel Peterson, *Human Res Mgr*
Anthony Serna, *Marketing Mgr*
EMP: 16
SALES (est): 2.2MM **Privately Held**
WEB: www.inhealth.com
SIC: 3842 Surgical appliances & supplies

(P-22753)
INLAND ARTFL LIMB & BRACE INC (PA)
680 Parkridge Ave, Norco (92860-3124)
PHONE....................951 734-1835
Guy Savidan CP, *President*
EMP: 17
SALES (est): 2.3MM **Privately Held**
SIC: 3842 5999 Limbs, artificial; artificial limbs

(P-22754)
INTERPORE CROSS INTL INC (DH)
181 Technology Dr, Irvine (92618-2484)
PHONE..................................949 453-3200
Dan Hann, *President*
Greg Hartman, *CFO*
▲ EMP: 58
SALES (est): 17.4MM
SALES (corp-wide): 7.8B **Publicly Held**
WEB: www.interpore.com
SIC: 3842 3843 Orthopedic appliances;
surgical appliances & supplies; dental
equipment & supplies
HQ: Biomet, Inc.
345 E Main St
Warsaw IN 46580
574 267-6639

(P-22755)
IX MEDICAL (PA)
725 W Anaheim St, Long Beach
(90813-2819)
PHONE..................................877 902-6446
Kerry Brady, *President*
EMP: 10
SQ FT: 4,000
SALES: 3.5MM **Privately Held**
SIC: 3842 Radiation shielding aprons,
gloves, sheeting, etc.

(P-22756)
J & K ORTHOPEDICS INC
320 E Bonita Ave, Pomona (91767-1926)
PHONE..................................909 621-1180
George Boyer, *President*
EMP: 13
SQ FT: 5,000
SALES (est): 1.7MM **Privately Held**
SIC: 3842 Orthopedic appliances

(P-22757)
JACUZZI BRANDS LLC (PA)
Also Called: Jacuzzi Group Worldwide
13925 City Center Dr # 200, Chino Hills
(91709-5437)
PHONE..................................909 606-1416
Robert Rowen, *CEO*
Alex P Marini, *President*
Peter Munk, *President*
Robert I Rowan, *President*
David Broadbent, *CFO*
▲ EMP: 50
SQ FT: 15,134
SALES (est): 1.6B **Privately Held**
SIC: 3842 Whirlpool baths, hydrotherapy
equipment

(P-22758)
JOA CORPORATION (PA)
Also Called: Johnsons Orthopedic
7254 Magnolia Ave, Riverside
(92504-3829)
PHONE..................................951 785-4411
William Kearney, *President*
Lesli Kearney, *CFO*
EMP: 34
SQ FT: 6,000
SALES (est): 4.2MM **Privately Held**
WEB: www.johnsonsorthopedic.com
SIC: 3842 5999 8011 Braces, orthopedic;
limbs, artificial; orthopedic & prosthesis
applications; orthopedic physician

(P-22759)
JOHNSON & JOHNSON
15715 Arrow Hwy, Irwindale (91706-2006)
PHONE..................................909 839-8650
Cathy Somalis, *Manager*
EMP: 300
SALES (corp-wide): 76.4B **Publicly Held**
WEB: www.jnj.com
SIC: 3842 Dressings, surgical
PA: Johnson & Johnson
1 Johnson And Johnson Plz
New Brunswick NJ 08933
732 524-0400

(P-22760)
JOHNSON & JOHNSON
5110 Commerce Dr, Baldwin Park
(91706-1450)
PHONE..................................909 839-8690
Thad Condon, *Branch Mgr*
EMP: 27

SALES (corp-wide): 76.4B **Publicly Held**
WEB: www.jnj.com
SIC: 3842 Dressings, surgical
PA: Johnson & Johnson
1 Johnson And Johnson Plz
New Brunswick NJ 08933
732 524-0400

(P-22761)
JOHNSON WILSHIRE INC
17343 Freedom Way, City of Industry
(91748-1001)
PHONE..................................562 777-0088
David W Pang, *President*
EMP: 30
SQ FT: 120,000
SALES (est): 2MM **Privately Held**
SIC: 3842 Personal safety equipment;
gloves, safety; linemen's safety belts

(P-22762)
KAISE PERMA SAN FRANC MEDIC CE
2425 Geary Blvd, San Francisco
(94115-3358)
PHONE..................................415 833-2000
Michael Alexander, *Senior VP*
Harhindar Chima, *Lab Dir*
EMP: 23
SALES (est): 4.1MM **Privately Held**
SIC: 3842 Autoclaves, hospital & surgical

(P-22763)
KINAMED INC
820 Flynn Rd, Camarillo (93012-8701)
PHONE..................................805 384-2748
Clyde R Pratt, *President*
Vineet Sarin, *President*
Lorraine Willis, *CFO*
Bob Bruce, *Vice Pres*
Kathy Considine, *Director*
EMP: 26
SQ FT: 28,828
SALES (est): 520K **Privately Held**
WEB: www.kinamed.com
SIC: 3842 Implants, surgical
PA: Vme Acquisition Corp.
820 Flynn Rd
Camarillo CA 93012

(P-22764)
KINGSLEY MFG CO (PA)
1984 Placentia Ave, Costa Mesa
(92627-3421)
P.O. Box 5010 (92628-5010)
PHONE..................................949 645-4401
Jeffry Kingsley, *President*
Jane Kingsley, *Treasurer*
Denise Kingsley, *Admin Sec*
EMP: 10
SQ FT: 6,000
SALES: 1MM **Privately Held**
SIC: 3842 Orthopedic appliances

(P-22765)
KVP INTERNATIONAL INC
13775 Ramona Ave, Chino (91710-5405)
PHONE..................................888 411-7387
John Nelson, *CEO*
Ken Bowman, *COO*
Mary Ann Gehring, *CFO*
Alan McCool, *Purch Mgr*
Manny Becerra, *Sales Mgr*
▲ EMP: 41
SALES (est): 12.5MM **Privately Held**
SIC: 3842 5047 Abdominal supporters,
braces & trusses; veterinarians' equip-
ment & supplies

(P-22766)
MAST BIOSURGERY USA INC
6749 Top Gun St Ste 108, San Diego
(92121-4151)
PHONE..................................858 550-8050
Thomas Brooas, *President*
Thoms Brooas, *President*
EMP: 30
SQ FT: 10,000
SALES (est): 5.1MM **Privately Held**
WEB: www.mastbio.com
SIC: 3842 Implants, surgical

(P-22767)
MBK ENTERPRISES INC
Also Called: MBK Tape Solutions
9959 Canoga Ave, Chatsworth
(91311-3002)
PHONE..................................818 998-1477
Jeffrey Kaminski, *President*
Marcella B Kaminski, *Corp Secy*
Steve Gilbert, *Marketing Staff*
▲ EMP: 40
SQ FT: 14,000
SALES (est): 12.2MM **Privately Held**
WEB: www.mbk1.com
SIC: 3842 Adhesive tape & plasters, med-
icated or non-medicated

(P-22768)
MEDI KID COMPANY
448 S Palm Ave Ste A, Hemet
(92543-4819)
P.O. Box 5398 (92544-0398)
PHONE..................................951 925-8800
Melinda Siwek, *CEO*
EMP: 10
SALES (est): 790K **Privately Held**
WEB: www.medi-kid.com
SIC: 3842 Restraints, patient

(P-22769)
MEDICAL PACKAGING CORPORATION
Also Called: Hygenia
941 Avenida Acaso, Camarillo
(93012-8755)
PHONE..................................805 388-2383
Frederic L Nason, *President*
Susan J Nason, *Corp Secy*
EMP: 100
SQ FT: 45,000
SALES (est): 19.4MM **Privately Held**
SIC: 3842 2835 Surgical appliances &
supplies; in vitro & in vivo diagnostic sub-
stances

(P-22770)
MEDLINE INDUSTRIES INC
Also Called: Medline Industries
42500 Winchester Rd, Temecula
(92590-2570)
PHONE..................................951 296-2600
EMP: 11
SALES (corp-wide): 5.6B **Privately Held**
SIC: 3842 Surgical appliances & supplies
PA: Medline Industries, Inc.
3 Lakes Dr
Northfield IL 60093
847 949-5500

(P-22771)
MEDTRONIC INC
3576 Unocal Pl Bldg B, Santa Rosa
(95403-1774)
PHONE..................................707 541-3281
Omar Ishrak, *CEO*
Chris Hadland, *Vice Pres*
Suzy Ortmann, *Executive Asst*
Ann Gilster, *Administration*
Leigh L Meyer, *Info Tech Mgr*
EMP: 63 **Privately Held**
SIC: 3842 3841 3845 Surgical appliances
& supplies; implants; surgical & medical
medical instruments; blood transfusion
equipment; catheters; medical instru-
ments & equipment, blood & bone work;
pacemaker, cardiac
HQ: Medtronic, Inc.
710 Medtronic Pkwy
Minneapolis MN 55432
763 514-4000

(P-22772)
MENTOR WORLDWIDE LLC (DH)
33 Technology Dr, Irvine (92618-2346)
PHONE..................................800 636-8678
David Shepherd, *President*
Dean Freed, *President*
Robert Hum, *President*
Warren Foust, *Vice Pres*
Flavia Pease,
▲ EMP: 250

SALES (est): 275.6MM
SALES (corp-wide): 76.4B **Publicly Held**
WEB: www.mentordirect.com
SIC: 3842 3845 3841 Surgical appliances
& supplies; prosthetic appliances; implants, surgical; cosmetic restorations; ultrasonic medical equipment, except
cleaning; medical instruments & equipment, blood & bone work
HQ: Ethicon Inc.
Us Route 22
Somerville NJ 08876
732 524-0400

(P-22773)
MIRAMAR LABS INC
2790 Walsh Ave, Santa Clara
(95051-0963)
PHONE..................................408 940-8700
R Michael Kleine, *President*
Brigid A Makes, *CFO*
Steven W Kim, *CTO*
Steven M Higa, *Mfg Staff*
Robert Ellis, *Marketing Staff*
EMP: 24 EST: 2006
SALES (est): 6MM
SALES (corp-wide): 36.5MM **Publicly Held**
SIC: 3842 Surgical appliances & supplies
PA: Sientra, Inc.
420 S Fairview Ave # 200
Santa Barbara CA 93117
805 562-3500

(P-22774)
MOLDEX-METRIC INC
10111 Jefferson Blvd, Culver City
(90232-3509)
PHONE..................................310 837-6500
Mark Magidson, *CEO*
Debra Magidson, *Admin Sec*
◆ EMP: 500 EST: 1960
SQ FT: 80,000
SALES (est): 136.1MM **Privately Held**
WEB: www.moldex.com
SIC: 3842 Personal safety equipment; ear
plugs

(P-22775)
MULLER COMPANY
3366 N Torrey Pines Ct # 140, La Jolla
(92037-1025)
PHONE..................................858 587-9955
Stephen Muller, *Branch Mgr*
EMP: 12
SALES (corp-wide): 27.8MM **Privately Held**
SIC: 3842 Hearing aids
PA: The Muller Company
18881 Von Karman Ave # 400
Irvine CA 92612
949 476-9800

(P-22776)
MY TRUE IMAGE MFG INC
Also Called: Design Veronique
999 Marina Way S, Richmond
(94804-3738)
PHONE..................................510 970-7990
Veronica C Smith, *President*
Manuel Espinoza, *General Mgr*
Macarthur Alfaro, *Prdtn Mgr*
Jose Rodriguez, *Production*
▲ EMP: 80
SQ FT: 30,000
SALES (est): 13.4MM **Privately Held**
SIC: 3842 Surgical appliances & supplies

(P-22777)
NEUROSTRUCTURES INC
199 Technology Dr Ste 110, Irvine
(92618-2447)
PHONE..................................800 352-6103
Moti Altarc, *Principal*
EMP: 13
SALES (est): 1.7MM **Privately Held**
SIC: 3842 Braces, orthopedic

(P-22778)
NOBBE ORTHOPEDICS INC
3010 State St, Santa Barbara
(93105-3304)
PHONE..................................805 687-7508
Ralph W Nobbe, *President*
Bret Laurent, *President*
Erwin Nobbe, *Vice Pres*

▲ = Import ▼=Export
◆ =Import/Export

Rolf Schiefel, *Vice Pres*
EMP: 11
SQ FT: 2,850
SALES (est): 1.6MM **Privately Held**
WEB: www.nobbeorthopedics.com
SIC: 3842 2342 Cosmetic restorations; braces, orthopedic; trusses, orthopedic & surgical; supports: abdominal, ankle, arch, kneecap, etc.; corsets & allied garments

(P-22779)
NORELL PRSTHTICS ORTHOTICS INC (PA)
Also Called: Synergy Prosthetics
48521 Warm Sprnigs 305, Fremont (94539)
PHONE..................510 770-9010
Louis Cosenza, *CEO*
Robert Fagnani, *President*
EMP: 12
SQ FT: 4,000
SALES (est): 2.6MM **Privately Held**
SIC: 3842 Limbs, artificial; braces, orthopedic

(P-22780)
NU-HOPE LABORATORIES INC
12640 Branford St, Pacoima (91331-3451)
P.O. Box 331150 (91333-1150)
PHONE..................818 899-7711
Bradley J Galindo, *CEO*
Estelle Galindo, *CFO*
▲ **EMP:** 38
SQ FT: 25,000
SALES (est): 7.2MM **Privately Held**
WEB: www.nu-hope.com
SIC: 3842 Colostomy appliances

(P-22781)
NUPRODX INC
161 S Vasco Rd Ste G, Livermore (94551-5131)
PHONE..................925 292-0866
David Gaskell, *President*
EMP: 15
SALES (corp-wide): 2.4MM **Privately Held**
SIC: 3842 3999 Wheelchairs; wheelchair lifts
PA: Nuprodx, Inc.
889 Hayes St
Sonoma CA 95476
415 472-1699

(P-22782)
OCEAN HEAT INC
13610 Imperial Hwy Ste 4, Santa Fe Springs (90670-4873)
PHONE..................951 208-1923
Jason Johnson, *CEO*
EMP: 15
SQ FT: 29,000
SALES (est): 1.1MM **Privately Held**
SIC: 3842 Hydrotherapy equipment

(P-22783)
OMNICAL INC
557 Jessie St, San Fernando (91340-2542)
PHONE..................818 837-7531
Ron Tinero, *President*
Ellen Tinero, *Admin Sec*
EMP: 12
SQ FT: 9,100
SALES (est): 1MM **Privately Held**
WEB: www.omnical.com
SIC: 3842 5047 Surgical appliances & supplies; medical & hospital equipment

(P-22784)
ORTHO ENGINEERING INC (PA)
5759 Uplander Way, Culver City (90230-6605)
PHONE..................310 559-5996
George Ashkharikian, *President*
Gevorg Ashkharikyan, *Info Tech Mgr*
Avo Ashkharhikian, *Director*
Minas Ashkharikian, *Manager*
EMP: 24
SQ FT: 4,000
SALES: 3MM **Privately Held**
WEB: www.orthoengineering.com
SIC: 3842 Braces, orthopedic; prosthetic appliances

(P-22785)
ORTHOR ENGINEERING INC
3737 Martin Luther King J, Lynwood (90262-3513)
PHONE..................310 604-0000
Reza Aszali, *President*
EMP: 60
SALES (est): 3MM **Privately Held**
SIC: 3842 Prosthetic appliances

(P-22786)
OSSUR AMERICAS INC (DH)
27051 Towne Centre Dr, Foothill Ranch (92610-2819)
PHONE..................949 362-3883
Mahesh Mansukhani, *CEO*
Avanindra Chaturvedi, *CFO*
▲ **EMP:** 261
SQ FT: 12,000
SALES (est): 123.3MM **Privately Held**
SIC: 3842 Braces, orthopedic; orthopedic appliances
HQ: Ossur Hf.
Grjothalsi 5
Reykjavik 110
425 340-0

(P-22787)
OSSUR AMERICAS INC
27051 Towne Centre Dr, Foothill Ranch (92610-2819)
PHONE..................949 382-3883
Edward Castillo, *Branch Mgr*
EMP: 13 **Privately Held**
SIC: 3842 Prosthetic appliances
HQ: Ossur Americas, Inc.
27051 Towne Centre Dr
Foothill Ranch CA 92610
949 362-3883

(P-22788)
OSSUR AMERICAS INC
Also Called: Ossur North America
742 Pancho Rd, Camarillo (93012-8576)
P.O. Box 5194, Los Angeles (90055-0194)
PHONE..................805 484-2600
Cathy McAnn, *Branch Mgr*
EMP: 32 **Privately Held**
SIC: 3842 Prosthetic appliances; limbs, artificial
HQ: Ossur Americas, Inc.
27051 Towne Centre Dr
Foothill Ranch CA 92610
949 362-3883

(P-22789)
PACIFIC COAST LABORATORIES
Also Called: PCL Communications
1031 San Leandro Blvd, San Leandro (94577-1534)
PHONE..................510 351-2770
Monte Martinez, *President*
EMP: 15
SQ FT: 60,000
SALES (est): 2.6MM **Privately Held**
WEB: www.pcl-cfa.com
SIC: 3842 Hearing aids; ear plugs; noise protectors, personal

(P-22790)
PASSY-MUIR INC
1212 Mcgaw Ave, Irvine (92614-5537)
PHONE..................949 833-8255
Joseph Agra, *Principal*
EMP: 10
SALES (corp-wide): 6.7MM **Privately Held**
SIC: 3842 Surgical appliances & supplies
PA: Passy-Muir, Inc.
17992 Mitchell S Ste 200
Irvine CA 92614
949 833-8255

(P-22791)
PASSY-MUIR INC (PA)
17992 Mitchell S Ste 200, Irvine (92614-6813)
PHONE..................949 833-8255
Cameron Jolly, *President*
Ryan Williams, *COO*
Mary Sarris, *General Mgr*
Ashley Cataline, *Executive Asst*
Bert Magelo, *Info Tech Mgr*
EMP: 40
SQ FT: 1,200

SALES (est): 6.7MM **Privately Held**
WEB: www.passy-muir.com
SIC: 3842 Orthopedic appliances

(P-22792)
PAULSON MANUFACTURING CORP (PA)
46752 Rainbow Canyon Rd, Temecula (92592-5984)
PHONE..................951 676-2451
Roy Paulson, *President*
Joyce Paulson, *Corp Secy*
Thomas V Paulson, *Vice Pres*
Miriam Mesina, *Human Res Mgr*
John Wojcik, *Purch Mgr*
▲ **EMP:** 100
SQ FT: 42,000
SALES: 15.3MM **Privately Held**
WEB: www.paulsonmfg.com
SIC: 3842 Personal safety equipment

(P-22793)
PHOENIX IMPROVING LIFE LLC
Also Called: Readysmart
148 Farley St, Mountain View (94043-4418)
PHONE..................650 248-0655
Tracy Ferea,
EMP: 15
SALES (est): 1.2MM **Privately Held**
SIC: 3842 Surgical appliances & supplies

(P-22794)
PHONAK LLC
47257 Fremont Blvd, Fremont (94538-6502)
PHONE..................510 743-3939
Debbie Toroba, *Mfg Staff*
EMP: 10
SALES (corp-wide): 2.8B **Privately Held**
SIC: 3842 Hearing aids
HQ: Phonak, Llc
4520 Weaver Pkwy Ste 1
Warrenville IL 60555
630 821-5000

(P-22795)
PONG RESEARCH CORPORATION
1010 S Coast Highway 101 # 105, Encinitas (92024-5069)
PHONE..................858 914-5299
David Pinn, *Principal*
EMP: 13 **EST:** 2014
SALES (est): 1.7MM **Privately Held**
SIC: 3842 3674 Radiation shielding aprons, gloves, sheeting, etc.; radiation sensors

(P-22796)
POSEY PRODUCTS LLC (HQ)
Also Called: Posey Co
5635 Peck Rd, Arcadia (91006-5851)
PHONE..................626 443-3143
Kevin McNamara, *President*
Bonnie Bishop, *Vice Pres*
Alfredo Martinez, *Vice Pres*
John Waller, *District Mgr*
Tracey Bertolina, *General Mgr*
▲ **EMP:** 143
SQ FT: 24,000
SALES: 100MM
SALES (corp-wide): 180.7MM **Privately Held**
SIC: 3842 5047 Medical & hospital equipment; belts: surgical, sanitary & corrective
PA: Tidi Products, Llc
570 Enterprise Dr
Neenah WI 54956
920 751-4300

(P-22797)
PROSTAT FIRST AID LLC
24922 Anza Dr Ste A, Valencia (91355-1232)
PHONE..................661 705-1256
Karla Vasquez, *Sales Mgr*
▲ **EMP:** 11
SALES (est): 1.2MM **Privately Held**
SIC: 3842 5199 Bandages & dressings; first aid supplies

(P-22798)
PROSTHETIC AND ORTHOTIC GROUP (PA)
2669 Myrtle Ave Ste 101, Signal Hill (90755-2746)
PHONE..................562 595-6445
Glenn Matsushima, *President*
Sonia Marlow, *General Mgr*
Larry Wong, *Admin Sec*
Sonia Enriquez, *Opers Staff*
EMP: 12
SQ FT: 2,700
SALES (est): 1.6MM **Privately Held**
WEB: www.p-o-group.com
SIC: 3842 Braces, orthopedic; limbs, artificial

(P-22799)
PULSE SYSTEMS LLC
4090 Nelson Ave, Concord (94520-8513)
PHONE..................925 798-4080
Herb Bellucci,
Scott Summers, *Office Admin*
Wen Ho, *Engineer*
Brett Poole, *Opers Staff*
Bob Lamson, *Sales Dir*
EMP: 45
SQ FT: 12,600
SALES (est): 13.5MM
SALES (corp-wide): 8.4MM **Publicly Held**
WEB: www.pulsesystemscorp.com
SIC: 3842 3841 Surgical appliances & supplies; surgical & medical instruments
PA: United American Healthcare Corporation
303 E Wacker Dr Ste 1040
Chicago IL 60601
313 393-4571

(P-22800)
QUINN MEDICAL INC
1000 Calle Cor-fillera, San Clemente (92673-6235)
PHONE..................949 784-0310
Thierry Arguin, *President*
Lori Weekley, *Controller*
▲ **EMP:** 19 **EST:** 2008
SQ FT: 12,000
SALES (est): 2.6MM
SALES (corp-wide): 3.6MM **Privately Held**
SIC: 3842 5047 Braces, orthopedic; canes, orthopedic; foot appliances, orthopedic; medical equipment & supplies
HQ: Thuasne
118 Rue Marius Aufan
Levallois Perret 92300
141 059-292

(P-22801)
RACING PLUS INC
Also Called: Parker Pumper Helmet Co
3834 Wacker Dr, Mira Loma (91752-1147)
PHONE..................951 360-5906
Harold Nicks, *President*
EMP: 11
SQ FT: 9,200
SALES (est): 1.4MM **Privately Held**
SIC: 3842 Helmets, space

(P-22802)
RAY-BAR ENGINEERING CORP
697 W Foothill Blvd, Azusa (91702-2346)
P.O. Box 415 (91702-0415)
PHONE..................626 969-1818
Toll Free:..................877 -
Joyce Vicky Wohler, *President*
Shirley Saldarriaga, *Admin Asst*
◆ **EMP:** 12
SQ FT: 15,000
SALES (est): 1.2MM **Privately Held**
WEB: www.raybar.net
SIC: 3842 Radiation shielding aprons, gloves, sheeting, etc.

(P-22803)
RESPIRONICS INC
14101 Rosecrans Ave Ste F, La Mirada (90638-3551)
PHONE..................562 483-6805
Jimmy Gibbs, *Manager*
EMP: 13

PRODUCTS & SVCS

SALES (corp-wide): 20.9B **Privately Held**
WEB: www.respironics.com
SIC: **3842** 7699 Surgical appliances &
supplies; medical equipment repair, nonelectric
HQ: Respironics, Inc.
1001 Murry Ridge Ln
Murrysville PA 15668
724 387-5200

(P-22804)
REVA MEDICAL INC
Also Called: (A DEVELOPMENT STAGE
COMPANY)
5751 Copley Dr Ste B, San Diego
(92111-7912)
PHONE..............................858 966-3000
Robert B Stockman, *CEO*
Ray Larkin Jr, *Ch of Bd*
Robert K Schultz, *President*
Katrina L Thompson, *CFO*
Jeffrey A Anderson, *Senior VP*
EMP: 46
SQ FT: 37,000
SALES: 45K **Privately Held**
WEB: www.teamreva.com
SIC: **3842** Surgical appliances & supplies

(P-22805)
RICHARD J TREVINO MD
Also Called: Sonus-USA
175 N Jackson Ave Ste 200, San Jose
(95116-1909)
PHONE..............................408 926-5300
Ricardo J Trevino MD, *President*
EMP: 10
SQ FT: 2,400
SALES (est): 1.8MM **Privately Held**
SIC: **3842** Hearing aids

(P-22806)
**SAN JOAQUIN ORTHTICS &
PRSTHTC**
2211 N California St, Stockton
(95204-5503)
PHONE..............................209 932-0170
Matthew Shane Evans, *CEO*
Mike Beck, *Principal*
EMP: 11
SALES (est): 957.1K **Privately Held**
SIC: **3842** Orthopedic appliances

(P-22807)
SAS SAFETY CORPORATION
3031 Gardenia Ave, Long Beach
(90807-5215)
PHONE..............................562 427-2775
Patrick Larmon, *CEO*
James McCool, *Treasurer*
Daniel Lett, *Admin Sec*
Nick Mlouk, *Info Tech Mgr*
Theresa Pachejo, *Credit Mgr*
▲ EMP: 60
SQ FT: 90,000
SALES (est): 36MM
SALES (corp-wide): 11.3B **Privately Held**
WEB: www.sassafety.com
SIC: **3842** Personal safety equipment
HQ: Bunzl Usa Holdings Llc
1 Cityplace Dr Ste 200
Saint Louis MO 63141

(P-22808)
SEASPINE INC
Also Called: Integra Lifesciences
5770 Armada Dr, Carlsbad (92008-4608)
PHONE..............................760 727-8399
Keith Valentine, *CEO*
Keith Bradley, *Bd of Directors*
Ruth Fleming, *Director*
EMP: 80
SQ FT: 22,000
SALES (est): 5.5MM
SALES (corp-wide): 131.8MM **Publicly
Held**
WEB: www.seaspine.com
SIC: **3842** 5999 Orthopedic appliances;
orthopedic & prosthesis applications
HQ: Seaspine Orthopedics Corporation
5770 Armada Dr
Carlsbad CA 92008
866 942-8698

(P-22809)
**SEASPINE ORTHOPEDICS CORP
(HQ)**
5770 Armada Dr, Carlsbad (92008-4608)
PHONE..............................866 942-8698
Keith Valentine, *CEO*
EMP: 20
SALES (est): 15.3MM
SALES (corp-wide): 131.8MM **Publicly
Held**
SIC: **3842** 5999 Orthopedic appliances;
orthopedic & prosthesis applications
PA: Seaspine Holdings Corporation
5770 Armada Dr
Carlsbad CA 92008
760 727-8399

(P-22810)
SECURITY PRO USA
10530 Venice Blvd Ste 200, Culver City
(90232-3308)
PHONE..............................310 841-5845
Al Even, *Owner*
Nelson Miranda, *Purch Mgr*
◆ EMP: 14
SALES (est): 2.7MM **Privately Held**
SIC: **3842** Clothing, fire resistant & protec-
tive

(P-22811)
**SHAMROCK MARKETING CO
INC (HQ)**
Also Called: Shamrock Manufacturing
5445 Daniels St, Chino (91710-9009)
PHONE..............................909 591-8855
Hansen Jap, *CEO*
Hanson Lawrence, *President*
Jeremy Sligh, *Technology*
Julia Ku, *Natl Sales Mgr*
Angela Yiu, *Sales Mgr*
▲ EMP: 15 EST: 1997
SQ FT: 28,000
SALES (est): 2.2MM **Privately Held**
WEB: www.smcgloves.com
SIC: **3842** Gloves, safety
PA: Shamrock Manufacturing Corpora, Pt
11 Jl. Pemuda
Medan
614 558-888

(P-22812)
SHAPE MEMORY MEDICAL INC
807 Aldo Ave Ste 109, Santa Clara
(95054-2254)
PHONE..............................979 599-5201
Ted Ruppel, *President*
Scott Kraus, *VP Sales*
Carolyn Bruguera, *General Counsel*
EMP: 10 EST: 2009
SALES (est): 589.3K **Privately Held**
SIC: **3842** Surgical appliances & supplies

(P-22813)
SIENTRA INC (PA)
420 S Fairview Ave # 200, Santa Barbara
(93117-3654)
PHONE..............................805 562-3500
Jeffrey M Nugent, *Ch of Bd*
Charles Huiner, *COO*
Patrick F Williams, *CFO*
EMP: 103
SQ FT: 20,000
SALES: 36.5MM **Publicly Held**
SIC: **3842** Surgical appliances & supplies

(P-22814)
**SIMPSON PERFORMANCE PDTS
INC**
Also Called: Team Simpson Racing
1407 240th St, Harbor City (90710-1306)
PHONE..............................310 325-6035
Dave Nelson, *Executive*
Kevin Falk, *Manager*
EMP: 100 **Privately Held**
WEB: www.simpsonraceproducts.com
SIC: **3842** 2326 Surgical appliances &
supplies; men's & boys' work clothing
HQ: Simpson Performance Products, Inc.
328 Fm 306
New Braunfels TX 78130
830 214-0034

(P-22815)
SMITH & NEPHEW INC
4085 Nelson Ave Ste E, Concord
(94520-1257)
PHONE..............................925 681-3300
Martin Myers, *Principal*
EMP: 50
SALES (corp-wide): 4.7B **Privately Held**
SIC: **3842** Surgical appliances & supplies
HQ: Smith & Nephew, Inc.
1450 E Brooks Rd
Memphis TN 38116
901 396-2121

(P-22816)
SMITHS MEDICAL ASD INC
9255 Customhouse Plz N, San Diego
(92154-7636)
PHONE..............................619 710-1000
Aldo Soto, *Branch Mgr*
Nadfe Guerrero, *Engineer*
Juan Duran, *Supervisor*
EMP: 20
SALES (corp-wide): 4.1B **Privately Held**
WEB: www.smith-medical.com
SIC: **3842** Surgical appliances & supplies
HQ: Smiths Medical Asd, Inc.
6000 Nathan Ln N Ste 100
Plymouth MN 55442
763 383-3000

(P-22817)
**SPECTRUM
PROSTHETICS/ORTHOTICS**
1844 South St, Redding (96001-1809)
PHONE..............................530 243-4500
Forest Sexton, *President*
Jeff Zeller, *Admin Sec*
Kristen Dittmar, *Manager*
EMP: 11
SALES: 1.5MM **Privately Held**
SIC: **3842** Prosthetic appliances

(P-22818)
**SPINAL AND ORTHOPEDIC
DEVICES**
5920 Noble Ave, Van Nuys (91411-3025)
PHONE..............................818 908-9000
Frank McMurray, *President*
Steven McMurray, *Vice Pres*
Hal White, *General Mgr*
EMP: 13
SQ FT: 1,500
SALES: 2.5MM **Privately Held**
SIC: **3842** Implants, surgical

(P-22819)
STEMRAD INC
228 Hamilton Ave Fl 3, Palo Alto
(94301-2583)
PHONE..............................650 933-3377
Daniel Levitt, *CEO*
EMP: 12
SALES (est): 682.3K **Privately Held**
SIC: **3842** Clothing, fire resistant & protec-
tive

(P-22820)
STERIS CORPORATION
Also Called: Vts Medical Systems
324 Martin Ave, Santa Clara (95050-3102)
PHONE..............................800 614-6789
Mark Craig, *Manager*
EMP: 10
SALES (corp-wide): 2.6B **Privately Held**
SIC: **3842** Surgical appliances & supplies
HQ: Steris Corporation
5960 Heisley Rd
Mentor OH 44060
440 354-2600

(P-22821)
STINGRAY SHIELDS CORP
Stingray Shields 16870 W, San Diego
(92127)
PHONE..............................619 325-9003
Erin Finegold, *President*
EMP: 10
SALES (est): 816.5K **Privately Held**
SIC: **3842** Radiation shielding aprons,
gloves, sheeting, etc.

(P-22822)
STJ ORTHOTIC SERVICES INC
225 Benjamin Dr Ste 103, Corona
(92879-8080)
PHONE..............................951 279-5650
Michael Connor, *Manager*
EMP: 50 **Privately Held**
WEB: www.stjorthotic.com
SIC: **3842** 5999 3131 Orthopedic appli-
ances; orthopedic & prosthesis applica-
tions; footwear cut stock
PA: Stj Orthotic Services Inc
920 Wellwood Ave Ste B
Lindenhurst NY 11757

(P-22823)
STRENUMED INC
4864 Market St Ste D, Ventura
(93003-5786)
PHONE..............................805 477-1000
Brenda Acosta, *CEO*
Doug Walker, *President*
▲ EMP: 10
SALES (est): 1.3MM **Privately Held**
WEB: www.strenumed.com
SIC: **3842** Surgical appliances & supplies

(P-22824)
SUNRISE MEDICAL (US) LLC
2842 N Business Park Ave, Fresno
(93727-1328)
PHONE..............................559 292-2171
Thomas Rossnagel, *CEO*
▲ EMP: 99
SALES (est): 23.8MM **Privately Held**
SIC: **3842** Wheelchairs

(P-22825)
SUNRISE MEDICAL INC
2382 Faraday Ave Ste 200, Carlsbad
(92008-7220)
PHONE..............................619 930-1500
Thomas Rossnagel, *CEO*
Peter Riley, *CFO*
Randi Binstock, *Vice Pres*
EMP: 42 EST: 1983
SALES (est): 5MM **Privately Held**
SIC: **3842** Orthopedic appliances

(P-22826)
**SUPERIOR SOUND
TECHNOLOGY LLC**
707 Vintage Ave, Suisun City (94534-7418)
PHONE..............................707 863-7431
Claudia Pordes, *President*
EMP: 11
SALES (est): 1.3MM **Privately Held**
SIC: **3842** 5049 5099 5999 Personal
safety equipment; ear plugs; law enforce-
ment equipment & supplies; machine
guns; safety equipment & supplies; safety
supplies & equipment

(P-22827)
SUREFIRE LLC (PA)
18300 Mount Baldy Cir, Fountain Valley
(92708-6122)
PHONE..............................714 545-9444
John W Matthews, *President*
Sean Vo, *CFO*
Joel Smith,
Paul Lopez, *Research*
Daniel Fischer, *Production*
◆ EMP: 490 EST: 2000
SQ FT: 45,000
SALES (est): 199.5MM **Privately Held**
SIC: **3842** 3484 3648 Ear plugs; guns
(firearms) or gun parts, 30 mm. & below;
flashlights

(P-22828)
SUTURA INC
17080 Newhope St, Fountain Valley
(92708-4206)
PHONE..............................714 427-0398
Anthony Nobles, *CEO*
David Kernan, *COO*
EMP: 28
SQ FT: 20,000
SALES (est): 3.1MM
SALES (corp-wide): 27.8MM **Privately
Held**
WEB: www.whitebox-advisors.com
SIC: **3842** Surgical appliances & supplies;
sutures, absorbable & non-absorbable

PA: Whitebox Advisors Llc
3033 Excelsior Blvd # 300
Minneapolis MN 55416
612 253-6001

(P-22829)
SYMPHONIX DEVICES INC
1735 N 1st St, San Jose (95112-4529)
PHONE..................................408 323-8218
Kirk B Davis, *President*
William Arthur, *Ch of Bd*
Terence J Griffin, *CFO*
Geoffrey R Ball, *Vice Pres*
Patrick J Rimroth, *VP Opers*
EMP: 10
SALES (est): 1.3MM **Privately Held**
SIC: 3842 Hearing aids

(P-22830)
TECHNIGLOVE INTERNATIONAL INC
3750 Pierce St, Riverside (92503)
PHONE..................................951 582-0890
Janine Gass, *CEO*
Darcy Maskrey, *Opers Staff*
▲ **EMP:** 10
SALES (est): 1.4MM **Privately Held**
WEB: www.techniglove.com
SIC: 3842 Gloves, safety

(P-22831)
TENDER CORPORATION
Also Called: Adventure Medical Kits
1141 Harbor Bay Pkwy # 103, Alameda
(94502-2219)
PHONE..................................510 261-7414
Jason Cartwright,
Kyle Peter, *Sales Mgr*
Erik Amborn, *Sales Staff*
Jonathan Greer, *Sales Staff*
EMP: 20
SALES (est): 2.1MM
SALES (corp-wide): 31.1MM **Privately Held**
SIC: 3842 First aid, snake bite & burn kits
PA: Tender Corporation
944 Industrial Park Rd
Littleton NH 03561
603 444-5464

(P-22832)
THINK SURGICAL INC
47201 Lakeview Blvd, Fremont
(94538-6530)
PHONE..................................510 249-2300
In K Mun, *CEO*
Hyunmo Ku, *CFO*
Amit Sandhu, *Design Engr*
Daniel Bonny, *Research*
Nathan Netravali, *Research*
EMP: 160
SQ FT: 70,000
SALES (est): 31.6MM **Privately Held**
SIC: 3842 Surgical appliances & supplies

(P-22833)
TMJ SOLUTIONS INC
Also Called: TMJ Concepts
2233 Knoll Dr, Ventura (93003-7398)
PHONE..................................805 650-3391
David Samson, *President*
William Anspach, *Shareholder*
Erik Rinde, *Engineer*
Irasema Estrada, *Controller*
Russ Milligan, *Opers Staff*
EMP: 15
SQ FT: 7,280
SALES (est): 1.3MM **Privately Held**
WEB: www.tmjconcepts.com
SIC: 3842 Prosthetic appliances

(P-22834)
TOTAL RESOURCES INTL INC (PA)
420 S Lemon Ave, Walnut (91789-2956)
PHONE..................................909 594-1220
George Rivera, *CEO*
Gregg Rivera, *President*
Merlyn Rivera, *Vice Pres*
▲ **EMP:** 80
SQ FT: 115,000
SALES (est): 12MM **Privately Held**
WEB: www.totalresourcesintl.com
SIC: 3842 First aid, snake bite & burn kits

(P-22835)
TRI QUALITY INC
Also Called: Nutec Rehab
5840 S Watt Ave Ste A, Sacramento
(95829-9352)
PHONE..................................916 388-5939
Otmar H Weber, *President*
James Lindquist, *Vice Pres*
Dagmar Weber, *Admin Sec*
▲ **EMP:** 28
SQ FT: 10,000
SALES (est): 3.8MM **Privately Held**
WEB: www.triquality.com
SIC: 3842 Wheelchairs

(P-22836)
ULTIMATE EARS CONSUMER LLC
3 Jenner Ste 180, Irvine (92618-3835)
PHONE..................................949 502-8340
Mindy Harvey, *Owner*
Jenine Civil, *Marketing Mgr*
Jeanette Coffey, *Sales Mgr*
Jen Colacchio, *Sales Staff*
Melinda Harvey,
▲ **EMP:** 24
SALES (est): 4.1MM
SALES (corp-wide): 2.2B **Privately Held**
SIC: 3842 Hearing aids
HQ: Logitech Inc.
7700 Gateway Blvd
Newark CA 94560
510 795-8500

(P-22837)
US ARMOR CORPORATION
10715 Bloomfield Ave, Santa Fe Springs
(90670-3913)
PHONE..................................562 207-4240
Stephen Armellino, *President*
Susan L Armellino, *Corp Secy*
David Miller, *Engineer*
Victoria Rios, *Purch Mgr*
Cecelia Stack, *Opers Mgr*
▲ **EMP:** 45
SQ FT: 14,000
SALES (est): 11.3MM **Privately Held**
WEB: www.usarmor.com
SIC: 3842 2326 5999 Bulletproof vests;
men's & boys' work clothing; safety supplies & equipment

(P-22838)
VCP MOBILITY INC
2842 N Business Park Ave, Fresno
(93727-1328)
PHONE..................................559 292-2171
Thomas Rossnagel, *Branch Mgr*
Randi Binstock, *President*
EMP: 400
SALES (corp-wide): 396.7MM **Privately Held**
SIC: 3842 Surgical appliances & supplies
HQ: Vcp Mobility, Inc.
6899 Winchester Cir # 200
Boulder CO 80301
303 218-4500

(P-22839)
VCP MOBILITY HOLDINGS INC
Also Called: Sunrise Med HM Hlth Care Group
745 Design Ct Ste 602, Chula Vista
(91911-6165)
PHONE..................................619 213-6500
Steve Winston, *Manager*
EMP: 320
SALES (corp-wide): 402.8MM **Privately Held**
WEB: www.sleepcompliance.com
SIC: 3842 Wheelchairs
HQ: Vcp Mobility Holdings, Inc.
7477 Dry Creek Pkwy
Niwot CO 80503
303 218-4600

(P-22840)
VCP MOBILITY HOLDINGS INC
Also Called: Quickie Designs
2842 N Business Park Ave, Fresno
(93727-1328)
PHONE..................................303 218-4500
Adtar Kooner, *Manager*
Mitzi Harper, *Info Tech Mgr*
Son Le, *Design Engr*
Daniel Silveira, *Design Engr*

Dana Tacescu, *Design Engr*
EMP: 350
SALES (corp-wide): 402.8MM **Privately Held**
WEB: www.sleepcompliance.com
SIC: 3842 Surgical appliances & supplies
HQ: Vcp Mobility Holdings, Inc.
7477 Dry Creek Pkwy
Niwot CO 80503
303 218-4600

(P-22841)
VISALIA CTR 4 AMBLTRY MED & SV
Also Called: Visalia Cams
842 S Akers St, Visalia (93277-8309)
PHONE..................................559 740-4094
Burton Redd, *Partner*
EMP: 30
SQ FT: 5,000
SALES (est): 5MM **Privately Held**
SIC: 3842 Trusses, orthopedic & surgical

(P-22842)
VISION QUEST INDUSTRIES INC (PA)
Also Called: V Q Orthocare
18011 Mitchell S Ste A, Irvine
(92614-6863)
PHONE..................................949 261-6382
James W Knape, *CEO*
Kevin Lunau, *COO*
Bob Blachford, *CFO*
▲ **EMP:** 100
SQ FT: 35,500
SALES (est): 18.3MM **Privately Held**
WEB: www.vqorthocare.com
SIC: 3842 5999 Braces, orthopedic; medical apparatus & supplies

(P-22843)
VISION QUEST INDUSTRIES INC
Also Called: Vq Orthocare
1390 Decision St Ste A, Vista
(92081-8578)
PHONE..................................760 734-1550
Kevin Lunau, *Branch Mgr*
James W Knape, *CEO*
EMP: 75
SALES (corp-wide): 18.3MM **Privately Held**
WEB: www.vqorthocare.com
SIC: 3842 5999 Braces, orthopedic; medical apparatus & supplies
PA: Vision Quest Industries Incorporated
18011 Mitchell S Ste A
Irvine CA 92614
949 261-6382

(P-22844)
VME ACQUISITION CORP (PA)
Also Called: Kinamad
820 Flynn Rd, Camarillo (93012-8701)
PHONE..................................805 384-2748
Clyde R Pratt, *President*
Lorraine Willis, *CFO*
EMP: 30
SQ FT: 14,000
SALES: 600K **Privately Held**
SIC: 3842 7342 Surgical appliances & supplies; disinfecting & pest control services

(P-22845)
WALKER CREATIONS
907 Vista Del Rio, Santa Maria
(93458-8238)
PHONE..................................805 349-0755
EMP: 12
SALES (est): 879.9K **Privately Held**
SIC: 3842

(P-22846)
WEBER ORTHOPEDIC INC (PA)
Also Called: Hely & Weber Orthopedic
1185 E Main St, Santa Paula (93060-2954)
P.O. Box 832 (93061-0832)
PHONE..................................805 525-8474
Jim Weber, *President*
Lou Ruggiero, *Officer*
John P Hely, *Vice Pres*
Dave Cormier, *General Mgr*
Mark Vo, *Engineer*
▲ **EMP:** 40
SQ FT: 28,000

SALES (est): 5.9MM **Privately Held**
WEB: www.helyweber.net
SIC: 3842 5047 Braces, orthopedic; orthopedic equipment & supplies

(P-22847)
WEST COAST ORTHOTIC/PROSTHETIC
3215 N California St # 2, Stockton
(95204-3433)
PHONE..................................209 942-4166
Dave Vera, *Principal*
EMP: 12
SALES (est): 2.2MM **Privately Held**
WEB: www.wcop.com
SIC: 3842 Braces, orthopedic

(P-22848)
WESTERN GLOVE MANUFACTURING
10747 Norwalk Blvd, Santa Fe Springs
(90670-3823)
P.O. Box 558, Paramount (90723-0558)
PHONE..................................562 634-3720
C Edward Chu, *President*
Hong Brian Choi, *Vice Pres*
EMP: 60
SALES (est): 4.4MM **Privately Held**
SIC: 3842 3151 2326

(P-22849)
WHITEHALL MANUFACTURING INC
Also Called: A Division Acorn Engrg Co
15125 Proctor Ave, City of Industry
(91746-3327)
P.O. Box 3527 (91744-0527)
PHONE..................................626 336-4561
Donald E Morris, *President*
Kathryn L Morris, *Corp Secy*
William D Morris, *Vice Pres*
Steve Stormes, *Vice Pres*
EMP: 750
SQ FT: 2,000
SALES (est): 18.1MM
SALES (corp-wide): 85MM **Privately Held**
WEB: www.whitehallmfg.com
SIC: 3842 Whirlpool baths, hydrotherapy equipment
PA: Acorn Engineering Company
15125 Proctor Ave
City Of Industry CA 91746
800 488-8999

(P-22850)
XR LLC
15251 Pipeline Ln, Huntington Beach
(92649-1135)
PHONE..................................714 847-9292
ARI Suss,
Kelly Eberhard Allen,
▲ **EMP:** 27
SQ FT: 68,000
SALES (est): 4.4MM **Privately Held**
WEB: www.extremerestraints.com
SIC: 3842 Personal safety equipment

(P-22851)
ZIMMER INTERMED INC
1647 Yeager Ave, La Verne (91750-5854)
PHONE..................................909 392-0882
Kelly Liebhart, *President*
EMP: 50
SALES (est): 6MM **Privately Held**
SIC: 3842 Prosthetic appliances

3843 Dental Eqpt & Splys

(P-22852)
3M COMPANY
2111 Mcgaw Ave, Irvine (92614-0908)
PHONE..................................949 863-1360
David Goldinger, *Branch Mgr*
Dena Robertson, *Executive*
David Yrigoyen, *Design Engr*
Joshua Cheng, *Engineer*
Joel Knott, *Engineer*
EMP: 10
SQ FT: 77,656
SALES (corp-wide): 31.6B **Publicly Held**
WEB: www.mmm.com
SIC: 3843 5047 Dental equipment & supplies; dental equipment & supplies

PA: 3m Company
3m Center
Saint Paul MN 55144
651 733-1110

(P-22853)
3M UNITEK CORPORATION
2724 Peck Rd, Monrovia (91016-5097)
PHONE......................626 445-7960
Mary Jo Abler, *CEO*
Fred Palensky, *Vice Pres*
James Pang, *Info Tech Mgr*
Side Guerrero, *Engineer*
Erasmo Robles, *Engineer*
▲ **EMP:** 480
SQ FT: 249,000
SALES (est): 88.6MM
SALES (corp-wide): 31.6B **Publicly Held**
WEB: www.mmm.com
SIC: 3843 Orthodontic appliances; dental
hand instruments; dental laboratory
equipment
PA: 3m Company
3m Center
Saint Paul MN 55144
651 733-1110

(P-22854)
ALIGN TECHNOLOGY INC (PA)
Also Called: Invisalign
2820 Orchard Pkwy, San Jose
(95134-2019)
PHONE......................408 470-1000
Joseph M Hogan, *President*
C Raymond Larkin Jr, *Ch of Bd*
John F Morici, *CFO*
Simon Beard, *Senior VP*
Roger E George, *Senior VP*
▲ **EMP:** 277
SALES: 1.4B **Publicly Held**
WEB: www.invisalign.com
SIC: 3843 Orthodontic appliances

(P-22855)
ALPHA DENTAL OF UTAH INC
12898 Towne Center Dr, Cerritos
(90703-8546)
PHONE......................562 467-7759
Anthony S Barth, *Principal*
Teresa Lanta, *Treasurer*
Shahab Haghnazari, *Systs Prg Mgr*
James Sogar, *Technology*
Tina Byers, *Manager*
EMP: 21
SALES (est): 1.9MM **Privately Held**
SIC: 3843 Dental equipment & supplies

(P-22856)
AMERICAN TOOTH INDUSTRIES
1200 Stellar Dr, Oxnard (93033-2404)
PHONE......................805 487-9868
Emilio Pozzi, *CEO*
Angela Fontenot, *President*
Bruno Pozzi, *President*
Victoria Pozzi, *Exec VP*
Roberto Trada, *Exec VP*
▲ **EMP:** 98
SQ FT: 28,000
SALES (est): 15.6MM **Privately Held**
SIC: 3843 Teeth, artificial (not made in
dental laboratories)

(P-22857)
ARGEN CORPORATION
8515 Miralani Dr, San Diego (92126-4352)
PHONE......................858 455-7900
Anton Woolf, *CEO*
Neil Wainstein, *Technology*
EMP: 17
SALES (est): 4.4MM **Privately Held**
SIC: 3843 Dental equipment & supplies

(P-22858)
AURIDENT INC
610 S State College Blvd, Fullerton
(92831-5138)
P.O. Box 7200 (92834-7200)
PHONE......................714 870-1851
Howard M Hoffman, *President*
Fredelle G Hoffman, *Corp Secy*
David H Fell, *Vice Pres*
My Nguyen, *Finance Mgr*
Janet Eastman, *Accountant*
EMP: 30
SQ FT: 2,700

SALES (est): 5MM **Privately Held**
WEB: www.aurident.com
SIC: 3843 Dental alloys for amalgams

(P-22859)
BELPORT COMPANY INC (PA)
Also Called: Gingi Pak
4825 Calle Alto, Camarillo (93012-8530)
P.O. Box 240 (93011-0240)
PHONE......................805 484-1051
Jo Pennington, *President*
Lupe Becerra, *Cust Mgr*
Nicole Cali, *Manager*
EMP: 19
SQ FT: 22,000
SALES (est): 2.6MM **Privately Held**
SIC: 3843 Dental hand instruments; com-
pounds, dental; impression material, den-
tal

(P-22860)
BIEN AIR USA INC
5 Corporate Park Ste 160, Irvine
(92606-5167)
PHONE......................949 477-6050
Arthur Mateen, *Vice Pres*
Jean Claude Maeier, *President*
EMP: 12
SALES (est): 1MM **Privately Held**
WEB: www.bienair.com
SIC: 3843 7699 5047 Dental equipment;
dental instrument repair; hospital equip-
ment & furniture

(P-22861)
BIOLASE INC (PA)
4 Cromwell, Irvine (92618-1816)
PHONE......................949 361-1200
Todd Norbe, *CEO*
Jonathan T Lord, *Ch of Bd*
John R Beaver, *CFO*
Richard Lanman, *Bd of Directors*
Frederic Moll, *Bd of Directors*
EMP: 195
SQ FT: 57,000
SALES: 46.9MM **Publicly Held**
WEB: www.biolase.com
SIC: 3843 3841 Dental equipment & sup-
plies; dental equipment; dental hand in-
struments; dental laboratory equipment;
surgical lasers

(P-22862)
CONAMCO SA DE CV
3008 Palm Hill Dr, Vista (92084-6555)
PHONE......................760 586-4356
Jane Mitchell, *Vice Pres*
Alfredo Mobarak, *Ch of Bd*
EMP: 75
SQ FT: 20,000
SALES (est): 2MM **Privately Held**
SIC: 3843 Cement, dental

(P-22863)
CROSSTEX INTERNATIONAL INC
14059 Stage Rd, Santa Fe Springs
(90670-5225)
PHONE......................562 921-3343
Alan Sammartano, *Branch Mgr*
EMP: 10
SALES (corp-wide): 871.9MM **Publicly Held**
WEB: www.crosstex.com
SIC: 3843 Dental equipment & supplies
HQ: Crosstex International, Inc.
10 Ranick Rd
Hauppauge NY 11788
631 582-6777

(P-22864)
CYBER MEDICAL IMAGING INC
Also Called: Xdr Radiology
11300 W Olympic Blvd # 710, Los Angeles
(90064-1637)
PHONE......................888 937-9729
Douglas Yoon, *CEO*
Joel Karafin, *Officer*
Adam Chen, *Senior VP*
EMP: 25
SQ FT: 2,800
SALES: 6.1MM **Privately Held**
SIC: 3843 Dental equipment & supplies

(P-22865)
DANVILLE MATERIALS LLC
4020 E Leaverton Ct, Anaheim
(92807-1610)
PHONE......................714 399-0334
Greg Dorsman, *Manager*
Caroline Franklin, *Admin Asst*
EMP: 20
SALES (corp-wide): 21.6MM **Privately Held**
SIC: 3843 Dental materials
HQ: Danville Materials, Llc
2875 Loker Ave E
Carlsbad CA 92010
760 743-7744

(P-22866)
DANVILLE MATERIALS LLC (HQ)
2875 Loker Ave E, Carlsbad (92010-6626)
PHONE......................760 743-7744
Steve Schiess, *President*
Caroline Dorsman, *Admin Asst*
Sean Chen, *Director*
▲ **EMP:** 36
SALES (est): 6.1MM
SALES (corp-wide): 21.6MM **Privately Held**
SIC: 3843 Dental equipment & supplies
PA: Zest Anchors, Inc.
2875 Loker Ave E
Carlsbad CA 92010
760 743-7744

(P-22867)
DEN-MAT HOLDINGS LLC (HQ)
1017 W Central Ave, Lompoc
(93436-2701)
PHONE......................805 346-3700
Steven J Semmelmayer, *CEO*
Robert Cartagena, *COO*
Trevor Roots, *CFO*
Todd J Tiberi, *Principal*
Carol Newberry, *Admin Asst*
▲ **EMP:** 10
SALES (est): 168.8MM **Privately Held**
SIC: 3843 Dental materials
PA: Cp Dental Llc
2727 Skyway Dr
Santa Maria CA 93455
800 433-6628

(P-22868)
DENOVO DENTAL INC
5130 Commerce Dr, Baldwin Park
(91706-1450)
P.O. Box 548 (91706-0548)
PHONE......................626 480-0182
Richard R Parker, *President*
Joseph Parker, *Vice Pres*
Jeanette Parker, *Admin Sec*
▼ **EMP:** 20
SQ FT: 10,000
SALES (est): 5.4MM **Privately Held**
WEB: www.denovodental.com
SIC: 3843 5047 Dental equipment & sup-
plies; dental equipment & supplies

(P-22869)
DENTIUM USA (HQ)
Also Called: Implantium
6731 Katella Ave, Cypress (90630-5105)
PHONE......................714 226-0229
Sung Min Chung, *President*
S Ghildyal, *CEO*
Eun Kyung Son, *Vice Pres*
Martin Zamora, *CIO*
Justine Yi, *Controller*
▲ **EMP:** 12
SQ FT: 5,500
SALES (est): 3MM
SALES (corp-wide): 112.1MM **Privately Held**
SIC: 3843 Dental equipment
PA: Dentium Co., Ltd.
440 Teheran-Ro 87-Gil, Gangnam-Gu
Seoul 06169
824 222-1842

(P-22870)
DENTSPLY SIRONA INC
13553 Calimesa Blvd, Yucaipa
(92399-2303)
PHONE......................909 795-2080
Vernon Goodwalt, *Branch Mgr*
Mark Pimentel, *Regl Sales Mgr*

EMP: 80
SALES (corp-wide): 3.9B **Publicly Held**
WEB: www.dentsply.com
SIC: 3843 5047 Dental equipment & sup-
plies; dentists' professional supplies
PA: Dentsply Sirona Inc.
221 W Philadelphia St
York PA 17401
717 845-7511

(P-22871)
DENTTIO INC
116 N Maryland Ave # 125, Glendale
(91206-4291)
PHONE......................323 254-1000
Young Han, *CEO*
EMP: 16
SALES: 2.2MM **Privately Held**
SIC: 3843 Dental equipment & supplies

(P-22872)
DEXTA CORPORATION
962 Kaiser Rd, NAPA (94558-6298)
PHONE......................707 255-2454
Mark M Rusin, *President*
Paul Rusin, *Vice Pres*
EMP: 52
SQ FT: 19,000
SALES (est): 9.4MM **Privately Held**
WEB: www.dexta.com
SIC: 3843 Dental chairs; dental equipment

(P-22873)
DIAMODENT INC
1577 N Harmony Cir, Anaheim
(92807-6003)
PHONE......................888 281-8850
Kazem Jeff Rassoli, *President*
EMP: 15
SQ FT: 3,000
SALES (est): 2.4MM **Privately Held**
WEB: www.diamodent.com
SIC: 3843 Dental equipment & supplies

(P-22874)
DOCKUM RESEARCH LABORATORY
844 E Mariposa St, Altadena (91001-2421)
PHONE......................626 794-1821
Greta Dockum, *President*
EMP: 12
SQ FT: 5,000
SALES: 424.4K **Privately Held**
SIC: 3843 Dental equipment & supplies

(P-22875)
ECONOTEK INC (PA)
Also Called: Eti Empire Direct
2895 E Blue Star St, Anaheim
(92806-2508)
P.O. Box 6972, Orange (92863-6972)
PHONE......................714 238-1131
Robert Wilcken, *President*
Phil Miller, *Vice Pres*
Denise Quackenbush, *Admin Asst*
Valerie Poon, *Sales Staff*
EMP: 10
SQ FT: 5,000
SALES (est): 3.4MM **Privately Held**
WEB: www.econotek.com
SIC: 3843 Plaster, dental

(P-22876)
EMDIN INTERNATIONAL CORP
15841 Business Center Dr, Irwindale
(91706-2053)
P.O. Box 660901, Arcadia (91066-0901)
PHONE......................626 813-3740
Dinesh C Tandon, *President*
Tandon Marianne, *Exec VP*
Maryann Tandon, *Vice Pres*
EMP: 10
SQ FT: 10,000
SALES: 800K **Privately Held**
WEB: www.emdin.com
SIC: 3843 Dental equipment & supplies

(P-22877)
ENDODENT INC
851 Meridian St, Duarte (91010-3588)
PHONE......................626 359-5715
Jerry Sullivan, *President*
Nicolas M Lenz, *General Mgr*
EMP: 34
SQ FT: 10,000

▲ = Import ▼=Export
◆ =Import/Export

SALES (est): 3MM **Privately Held**
WEB: www.endodent.com
SIC: 3843

(P-22878)
EVERBRANDS INC
10547 W Pico Blvd, Los Angeles
(90064-2319)
PHONE...................855 595-2999
Michael Florman, *CEO*
Joshua Wallace, *President*
EMP: 15
SQ FT: 6,000
SALES: 775.5K **Privately Held**
SIC: 3843 5999 2844 Oral preparations;
cosmetic preparations

(P-22879)
**EVOLVE DENTAL
TECHNOLOGIES INC**
5 Vanderbilt, Irvine (92618-2011)
PHONE...................949 713-0909
Rodger Kurthy, *CEO*
Sharon Kurthy, *President*
EMP: 14
SALES (est): 1.5MM **Privately Held**
SIC: 3843 Dental equipment & supplies

(P-22880)
G HARTZELL & SON INC
2372 Stanwell Cir, Concord (94520-4807)
PHONE...................925 798-2206
Andy Hartzell, *President*
Andrew McIver, *Owner*
EMP: 30
SQ FT: 20,000
SALES (est): 3.2MM **Privately Held**
WEB: www.ghartzellandson.com
SIC: 3843 3842 Dental equipment & sup-
plies; surgical appliances & supplies

(P-22881)
**GOLDEN EMPIRE DENTAL LAB
INC**
929 21st St, Bakersfield (93301-4706)
PHONE...................661 327-1888
Chuck Kim, *President*
EMP: 10
SQ FT: 2,100
SALES (est): 1.1MM **Privately Held**
WEB: www.gedentallab.com
SIC: 3843 Dental laboratory equipment

(P-22882)
**HAND PIECE PARTS AND
PRODUCTS**
707 W Angus Ave, Orange (92868-1305)
PHONE...................714 997-4331
Steve Bowen, *President*
Lyla Bowen, *Vice Pres*
EMP: 30
SQ FT: 18,000
SALES (est): 3MM **Privately Held**
WEB: www.handpieceparts.com
SIC: 3843 Dental materials

(P-22883)
HENRY J PEREZ DDS
Also Called: G & P Dntl Care Former Partnr
132 S A St Ste B, Oxnard (93030-5690)
PHONE...................805 983-6768
Henry J Perez Jr DDS, *Owner*
Rose Kravagna, *Manager*
EMP: 10
SALES (est): 839.9K **Privately Held**
SIC: 3843 Orthodontic appliances

(P-22884)
JAZZ IMAGING LLC
800 Chartot Ave Ste 100, San Jose
(95131)
PHONE...................567 234-5299
Todd Miller, *Info Tech Mgr*
Kumar Joshi, *VP Opers*
EMP: 10 EST: 2014
SALES: 1MM **Privately Held**
SIC: 3843 5047 Dental equipment & sup-
plies; dental equipment & supplies

(P-22885)
**JENERIC/PENTRON
INCORPORATED (HQ)**
1717 W Collins Ave, Orange (92867-5422)
PHONE...................203 265-7397
Gordon Cohen, *President*

Martin Schulman, *Exec VP*
EMP: 200
SQ FT: 46,000
SALES (est): 10MM
SALES (corp-wide): 18.1MM **Privately
Held**
WEB: www.pentron.com
SIC: 3843 Dental equipment
PA: Pentron Corporation
53 N Plains Industrial Rd
Wallingford CT 06492
203 265-7397

(P-22886)
JMU DENTAL INC
16273 Gale Ave, City of Industry
(91745-1719)
PHONE...................909 676-0000
Jianmin Yu, *CEO*
EMP: 10
SQ FT: 10,000
SALES (est): 377.1K **Privately Held**
SIC: 3843 Dental equipment & supplies

(P-22887)
**KAINOS DENTAL
TECHNOLOGIES LLC (PA)**
1844 San Miguel Dr 308b, Walnut Creek
(94596-8604)
PHONE...................800 331-4834
William Gianni, *CEO*
Andrew Nam, *COO*
Michael Finke, *CTO*
EMP: 24
SQ FT: 3,000
SALES (est): 3.4MM **Privately Held**
SIC: 3843 3841 Dental equipment & sup-
plies; surgical & medical instruments

(P-22888)
KERR CORPORATION (DH)
1717 W Collins Ave, Orange (92867-5422)
P.O. Box 14247 (92863-1447)
PHONE...................714 516-7400
Damien McDonald, *CEO*
Philip Read, *President*
Steve Semmelmayer, *President*
Alexander Wallstein, *President*
Steve Dunkerken, *Treasurer*
◆ EMP: 218
SQ FT: 105,000
SALES (est): 347MM
SALES (corp-wide): 18.3B **Publicly Held**
WEB: www.kerrdental.com
SIC: 3843 Dental materials; dental labora-
tory equipment; impression material, den-
tal; dental hand instruments

(P-22889)
LACLEDE INC
Also Called: Laclede Research Center
2103 E University Dr, Rancho Dominguez
(90220-6413)
PHONE...................310 605-4280
Michael Pellico, *President*
Stephen Pellico, *Vice Pres*
▲ EMP: 35
SQ FT: 25,000
SALES (est): 9.6MM **Privately Held**
WEB: www.laclede.com
SIC: 3843 Dental equipment

(P-22890)
**LANCER ORTHODONTICS INC
(PA)**
1493 Poinsettia Ave # 143, Vista
(92081-8544)
PHONE...................760 744-5585
Giorgio Beretta, *CEO*
Lisa LI, *CFO*
Janet Moore, *Admin Sec*
▲ EMP: 20
SQ FT: 9,240
SALES (est): 14.3MM **Privately Held**
WEB: www.lancerortho.com
SIC: 3843 5047 Orthodontic appliances;
dental equipment & supplies

(P-22891)
LARES RESEARCH
295 Lockheed Ave, Chico (95973-9026)
PHONE...................530 345-1767
Craig J Lares, *President*
Christian Godoy, *Exec Dir*
Bruce Holderbein, *Engineer*
Larry McCulloch, *Engineer*

Jason Orgain, *Engineer*
EMP: 39 EST: 1956
SQ FT: 30,000
SALES (est): 9.5MM **Privately Held**
WEB: www.laresdental.com
SIC: 3843 Hand pieces & parts, dental

(P-22892)
LIGHT MOBILE INC
Also Called: Danso Dental Lab
7968 Arjons Dr Ste D, San Diego
(92126-6362)
PHONE...................858 278-1750
Mal H Park, *Principal*
Daniel Park, *President*
EMP: 17 EST: 2008
SQ FT: 6,500
SALES (est): 1.5MM **Privately Held**
SIC: 3843 8072 Teeth, artificial (not made
in dental laboratories); artificial teeth pro-
duction

(P-22893)
MICROTECH LLC
17260 Newhope St, Fountain Valley
(92708-4210)
PHONE...................714 966-1645
Reed Payne, *Owner*
Tuan Nuygen,
Lance Payne,
EMP: 22
SQ FT: 1,600
SALES (est): 3.3MM **Privately Held**
SIC: 3843 Dental equipment & supplies

(P-22894)
NEIGHBORING LLC
2427 Sentinel Ln, San Marcos
(92078-2138)
PHONE...................818 271-0640
Xiaohong Liu, *President*
Sean Gelt, *Manager*
EMP: 11
SQ FT: 2,400
SALES (est): 133.1K **Privately Held**
SIC: 3843 Dental equipment & supplies

(P-22895)
NOBEL BIOCARE USA LLC
22715 Savi Ranch Pkwy, Yorba Linda
(92887-4609)
PHONE...................714 282-4800
Thomas Olsen, *President*
Frederick Walther, *Treasurer*
Kristof Verbiest, *District Mgr*
Anne Gonzales, *General Mgr*
Corinne Lozano, *General Mgr*
▲ EMP: 500
SQ FT: 150,000
SALES (est): 290MM
SALES (corp-wide): 18.3B **Publicly Held**
SIC: 3843 Dental equipment
HQ: Nobel Biocare Ab
Kungsgatan 15
Goteborg 411 1
318 188-00

(P-22896)
ORMCO CORPORATION (DH)
Also Called: Sybron Endo
1717 W Collins Ave, Orange (92867-5422)
PHONE...................714 516-7400
Patrik Eriksson, *CEO*
Vicente Reynal, *President*
Jason R Davis, *Vice Pres*
Randy Knuckles, *Vice Pres*
Ryan Alexander, *District Mgr*
◆ EMP: 100
SQ FT: 104,000
SALES (est): 152.8MM
SALES (corp-wide): 18.3B **Publicly Held**
WEB: www.ormco.com
SIC: 3843 Orthodontic appliances

(P-22897)
ORTHO ORGANIZERS INC
1822 Aston Ave, Carlsbad (92008-7306)
PHONE...................760 448-8600
David Parker, *Chairman*
Russell J Bonafede, *President*
Alison Weber, *CFO*
Ted Dreifuss, *Vice Pres*
Robert Riley, *Vice Pres*
▲ EMP: 226
SQ FT: 65,000

SALES (est): 33.7MM
SALES (corp-wide): 12.4B **Publicly Held**
WEB: www.orthoorganizers.com
SIC: 3843 5047 Orthodontic appliances;
dental equipment & supplies
PA: Henry Schein, Inc.
135 Duryea Rd
Melville NY 11747
631 843-5500

(P-22898)
**ORTHODENTAL
INTERNATIONAL INC**
280 Campillo St Ste J, Calexico
(92231-3200)
PHONE...................760 357-8070
Armando Lozano, *President*
▲ EMP: 57
SALES (est): 7.4MM
SALES (corp-wide): 3.9B **Publicly Held**
SIC: 3843 Orthodontic appliances
PA: Dentsply Sirona Inc.
221 W Philadelphia St
York PA 17401
717 845-7511

(P-22899)
PANADENT CORPORATION
580 S Rancho Ave, Colton (92324-3252)
PHONE...................909 783-1841
Arlene Lee, *Ch of Bd*
Thomas E Lee, *President*
Brian Richardson, *Sales Associate*
Robert Sarabia, *Sales Staff*
EMP: 20
SQ FT: 1,200
SALES: 3.5MM **Privately Held**
WEB: www.panadent.com
SIC: 3843 Dental hand instruments

(P-22900)
**PAR ORTHODONTIC
LABORATORY**
23141 La Cadena Dr Ste K, Laguna Hills
(92653-1423)
P.O. Box 30010, Laguna Niguel (92607-
0010)
PHONE...................949 472-4788
Ronald N Rogowski, *President*
Patricia A Rogowski, *Corp Secy*
EMP: 20
SQ FT: 3,000
SALES: 900K **Privately Held**
WEB: www.parortho.com
SIC: 3843 Orthodontic appliances

(P-22901)
PRECISION ONE MEDICAL INC
3923 Oceanic Dr Ste 200, Oceanside
(92056-5866)
PHONE...................760 945-7966
John Tyszka, *CEO*
Steve Patterson, *President*
Chip Prescott, *CFO*
EMP: 80
SQ FT: 10,000
SALES (est): 12.7MM **Privately Held**
SIC: 3843 Dental equipment & supplies

(P-22902)
PROMA INC
730 Kingshill Pl, Carson (90746-1219)
PHONE...................310 327-0035
Raymond Tai, *CEO*
Harold Tai, *Ch of Bd*
▲ EMP: 40 EST: 1967
SQ FT: 37,000
SALES (est): 7MM **Privately Held**
SIC: 3843 Dental equipment & supplies

(P-22903)
PURELIFE DENTAL
201 Santa Monica Blvd # 400, Santa Mon-
ica (90401-2212)
PHONE...................310 587-0783
April Strong, *Project Mgr*
EMP: 11
SALES (est): 1.9MM **Privately Held**
SIC: 3843 Dental equipment & supplies

(P-22904)
PURELINE ORALCARE INC
804 Estates Dr Ste 104, Aptos
(95003-3571)
P.O. Box 1070, Capitola (95010-1070)
PHONE...................831 662-9500

Jack Conrey, *President*
EMP: 11
SQ FT: 8,500
SALES (est): 1.3MM **Privately Held**
WEB: www.purelineoralcare.com
SIC: 3843 5047 Dental equipment; dental
equipment & supplies

(P-22905)
RAY FOSTER DENTAL EQUIPMENT
5421 Commercial Dr, Huntington Beach
(92649-1231)
PHONE..............................714 897-7795
John Foster, *President*
Muriel Foster, *Corp Secy*
Mark Foster, *Vice Pres*
▲ **EMP:** 15
SQ FT: 12,000
SALES (est): 2.3MM **Privately Held**
WEB: www.fosterdental.com
SIC: 3843 Dental equipment

(P-22906)
REPLACEMENT PARTS INDS INC
Also Called: RPI
625 Cochran St, Simi Valley (93065-1939)
P.O. Box 940250 (93094-0250)
PHONE..............................818 882-8611
Ira Lapides, *President*
Albert M Lapides, *Chairman*
Sherry Lapides, *Corp Secy*
Joan Woodlock, *Vice Pres*
Phillip Grauel, *Telecomm Mgr*
▲ **EMP:** 25 **EST:** 1972
SQ FT: 15,000
SALES (est): 5.5MM **Privately Held**
WEB: www.rpiparts.com
SIC: 3843 3841 3821 Dental equipment;
surgical & medical instruments; laboratory
apparatus, except heating & measuring

(P-22907)
SAESHIN AMERICA INC
216 Technology Dr Ste F, Irvine
(92618-2416)
PHONE..............................949 825-6925
Richard Ryu, *General Mgr*
EMP: 23 **EST:** 2016
SALES (est): 3.2MM
SALES (corp-wide): 25.1MM **Privately Held**
SIC: 3843 Dental equipment & supplies
PA: Saeshin Precision Co., Ltd.
52 Secheon-Ro 1-Gil, Dasa-Eup
Dalseong-Gun
Daegu 42921
825 358-7237

(P-22908)
SANDERS ORTHODONTIC LAB INC
5653 Stoneridge Dr # 107, Pleasanton
(94588-8543)
PHONE..............................925 251-0019
Tom Asai, *President*
Ida Asai, *Vice Pres*
EMP: 11 **EST:** 1964
SQ FT: 1,000
SALES (est): 300K **Privately Held**
WEB: www.sanderslab.com
SIC: 3843 Orthodontic appliances

(P-22909)
SELANE PRODUCTS INC (PA)
Also Called: Sml Space Maintainers Labs
9129 Lurline Ave, Chatsworth
(91311-5922)
P.O. Box 4184, Van Nuys (91409-4184)
PHONE..............................818 998-7460
Rob Veis, *CEO*
Anna McNaught, *Graphic Designe*
Eric Evans, *Sales Staff*
Wendy Kayne, *Manager*
Scott Veis, *Manager*
▲ **EMP:** 60
SQ FT: 12,000
SALES (est): 10.5MM **Privately Held**
WEB: www.smldent.com
SIC: 3843 8072 Orthodontic appliances;
dental laboratories

(P-22910)
SONENDO INC (PA)
26061 Merit Cir Ste 102, Laguna Hills
(92653-7010)
PHONE..............................949 766-3636
Michael Watts, *CFO*
Bob Anthony, *Vice Pres*
Chris Rabbitt, *Principal*
Thomas Bravek, *Administration*
Roy Chen, *CTO*
EMP: 39
SALES (est): 5MM **Privately Held**
SIC: 3843 Dental equipment & supplies

(P-22911)
SWIFT HEALTH SYSTEMS INC
111 Academy Ste 150, Irvine (92617-3053)
PHONE..............................877 258-8677
Philong Pham, *CEO*
Kenneth Chang, *CFO*
Lawrence McCorkle, *Controller*
EMP: 35
SALES (est): 329.4K **Privately Held**
SIC: 3843 Orthodontic appliances

(P-22912)
SYBRON DENTAL SPECIALTIES INC
824 Cowan Rd, Burlingame (94010-1205)
PHONE..............................650 340-0393
Karen Hedman, *Opers Mgr*
EMP: 550
SALES (corp-wide): 18.3B **Publicly Held**
SIC: 3843 Dental laboratory equipment
HQ: Sybron Dental Specialties, Inc.
1717 W Collins Ave
Orange CA 92867

(P-22913)
SYBRON DENTAL SPECIALTIES INC
1332 S Lone Hill Ave, Glendora
(91740-5339)
PHONE..............................909 596-0276
Andy Astadurian, *Branch Mgr*
Lars Gehlbach, *Vice Pres*
Yexenia Torres, *Planning*
Gerardo Lara, *Design Engr*
Janna Parsonage, *Project Mgr*
EMP: 550
SALES (corp-wide): 18.3B **Publicly Held**
WEB: www.sybrondentalspecialties.com
SIC: 3843 Dental equipment & supplies
HQ: Sybron Dental Specialties, Inc.
1717 W Collins Ave
Orange CA 92867

(P-22914)
SYBRON DENTAL SPECIALTIES INC (HQ)
Also Called: Analytic Endodontics
1717 W Collins Ave, Orange (92867-5422)
PHONE..............................949 255-8700
Dan Even, *CEO*
Steven Semmelmayer, *President*
Henricus A M Van Duijnhoven, *CEO*
Mike Beaudoin, *Vice Pres*
Mark C Yorba, *Vice Pres*
◆ **EMP:** 250
SQ FT: 16,000
SALES (est): 1.1B
SALES (corp-wide): 18.3B **Publicly Held**
WEB: www.sybrondentalspecialties.com
SIC: 3843 2834 Dental laboratory equip-
ment; orthodontic appliances; pharma-
ceutical preparations
PA: Danaher Corporation
2200 Penn Ave Nw Ste 800w
Washington DC 20037
202 828-0850

(P-22915)
TALLADIUM INC (PA)
27360 Muirfield Ln, Valencia (91355-1010)
PHONE..............................661 295-0900
Eddie Harms-, *CEO*
Geoff Harms, *CFO*
Steve Brennan, *Sales Mgr*
Jason Smith, *Sales Staff*
◆ **EMP:** 41
SQ FT: 9,000

SALES: 12MM **Privately Held**
WEB: www.talladium.com
SIC: 3843 3541 5047 Investment material, dental; milling machines; dental
equipment & supplies

(P-22916)
TECH WEST VACUUM INC
2625 N Argyle Ave, Fresno (93727-1304)
PHONE..............................559 291-1650
John Napier, *President*
▲ **EMP:** 40
SQ FT: 30,000
SALES (est): 9.5MM **Privately Held**
WEB: www.tech-west.com
SIC: 3843 Dental equipment

(P-22917)
TPC ADVANCE TECHNOLOGY INC
18519 Gale Ave, City of Industry
(91748-1321)
PHONE..............................626 810-4337
Chung Liang Want, *President*
Scott Beckley, *Vice Pres*
▲ **EMP:** 10
SALES (est): 850K **Privately Held**
WEB: www.tpcdental.com
SIC: 3843 Dental equipment & supplies

(P-22918)
TRI DENTAL INNOVATORS CORP
13902 West St, Garden Grove
(92843-3915)
PHONE..............................714 554-1170
▲ **EMP:** 12
SALES (est): 1.1MM **Privately Held**
SIC: 3843

(P-22919)
TRUABUTMENT INC
17742 Cowan, Irvine (92614-6012)
PHONE..............................714 956-1488
Hyungick Kim, *CEO*
Sangho Yoo, *CFO*
EMP: 59
SQ FT: 1,800
SALES: 12MM **Privately Held**
SIC: 3843 Dental equipment & supplies

(P-22920)
US DENTAL INC
Also Called: Young Dental
13043 166th St, Cerritos (90703-2201)
PHONE..............................562 404-3500
Young Hoon Park, *CEO*
EMP: 20
SALES (est): 1.1MM **Privately Held**
SIC: 3843 Dental equipment & supplies

(P-22921)
VAN R DENTAL PRODUCTS INC
600 E Hueneme Rd, Oxnard (93033-8600)
PHONE..............................805 488-1122
Don D Porteous, *President*
Joan Porteous, *Treasurer*
Russell W Porteous Jr, *Vice Pres*
▲ **EMP:** 10
SQ FT: 4,500
SALES (est): 1.5MM **Privately Held**
SIC: 3843 Dental equipment & supplies

(P-22922)
VIADE PRODUCTS INC
354 Dawson Dr, Camarillo (93012-8008)
PHONE..............................805 484-2114
Keith Zinser, *President*
Sandra Zinser, *Corp Secy*
John Menzie, *Vice Pres*
EMP: 20 **EST:** 1968
SQ FT: 8,000
SALES: 1.5MM **Privately Held**
WEB: www.viade.com
SIC: 3843 5047 5999 Dental laboratory
equipment; dental materials; dental labo-
ratory equipment; medical apparatus &
supplies

(P-22923)
VMC INTERNATIONAL LLC
Also Called: Vaniman Manufacturing
140 N Brandon Rd Ste C, Fallbrook
(92028-2338)
P.O. Box 74 (92088-0074)
PHONE..............................760 723-1498
Don Vaniman, *General Mgr*

Sandra Vaniman, *Consultant*
EMP: 16
SQ FT: 7,000
SALES: 1.8MM **Privately Held**
WEB: www.vaniman.com
SIC: 3843 Dental equipment

(P-22924)
WELLS DENTAL INC
Also Called: Wells Precision Machining
5860 Flynn Creek Rd, Comptche (95427)
PHONE..............................707 937-0521
Richard B Wells, *President*
Marvin Wells, *Corp Secy*
Ginger Wells, *Exec VP*
Anita Wells, *Office Mgr*
EMP: 15
SQ FT: 15,000
SALES (est): 2.6MM **Privately Held**
WEB: www.wellsdental.com
SIC: 3843 Dental laboratory equipment

(P-22925)
WESTSIDE RESOURCES INC
2967 Michelson Dr Ste G, Irvine
(92612-8801)
PHONE..............................800 944-3939
Donovan Berkely, *CEO*
Derek Jenkins, *Vice Pres*
▲ **EMP:** 40
SQ FT: 18,000
SALES (est): 6.8MM **Privately Held**
SIC: 3843 5047 Dental equipment & sup-
plies; medical & hospital equipment

3844 X-ray Apparatus & Tubes

(P-22926)
AMERICAN MEDICAL SALES INC
218 Bronwood Ave, Los Angeles
(90049-3104)
PHONE..............................310 471-8900
Daniel Giesberg, *President*
Carol Lifland, *Vice Pres*
Richard Giesberg, *Admin Sec*
EMP: 30 **EST:** 1955
SQ FT: 20,000
SALES (est): 4.4MM **Privately Held**
WEB: www.ams4illuminators.com
SIC: 3844 Lamps, X-ray

(P-22927)
ASHTEL STUDIOS INC
Also Called: Ashtel Dental
1610 E Philadelphia St, Ontario
(91761-5759)
PHONE..............................909 434-0911
Anish Patel, *President*
Andy Chandra, *President*
Jessica Reza, *Director*
▲ **EMP:** 25
SQ FT: 40,000
SALES: 30.5MM **Privately Held**
WEB: www.ashteldental.com
SIC: 3844 X-ray apparatus & tubes

(P-22928)
ASTROPHYSICS INC (PA)
21481 Ferrero, City of Industry
(91789-5233)
PHONE..............................909 598-5488
Francois Zayek, *President*
Mark Zayek, *COO*
John Pan, *CFO*
Phillip Wascher, *Vice Pres*
John Whelan, *Vice Pres*
◆ **EMP:** 134
SQ FT: 65,376
SALES (est): 47.3MM **Privately Held**
SIC: 3844 X-ray apparatus & tubes

(P-22929)
CARL ZISS X-RAY MICROSCOPY INC
4385 Hopyard Rd Ste 100, Pleasanton
(94588-2758)
PHONE..............................925 701-3600
Bobby Blair, *CEO*
Peter Jackson, *President*
Timothy Hart, *Corp Secy*
Jin Yoon, *Principal*
EMP: 66 **EST:** 2000

SALES (est): 19.2MM **Privately Held**
SIC: **3844** 5047 X-ray apparatus & tubes;
X-ray machines & tubes
HQ: Carl Zeiss Microscopy Gmbh
Carl-Zeiss-Promenade 10
Jena 07745
364 164-0

(P-22930)
CARR CORPORATION (PA)
1547 11th St, Santa Monica (90401-2999)
PHONE...................................310 587-1113
John Carr, *President*
Paul Carr, *Exec VP*
Reese Carr, *Vice Pres*
EMP: 25 **EST:** 1946
SQ FT: 25,000
SALES (est): 6.4MM **Privately Held**
WEB: www.carrcorporation.com
SIC: **3844** 3861 3842 X-ray apparatus &
tubes; processing equipment, photo-
graphic; surgical appliances & supplies

(P-22931)
CURA MEDICAL
TECHNOLOGIES LLC
1365 S Acacia Ave, Fullerton (92831-5315)
PHONE...................................949 939-4406
Tyler Bengard,
EMP: 10
SALES (est): 650K **Privately Held**
SIC: **3844** X-ray apparatus & tubes

(P-22932)
EFFECTOR THERAPEUTICS INC
11180 Roselle St Ste A, San Diego
(92121-1211)
PHONE...................................858 546-3997
Steve Worland, *CEO*
Alana McNulty, *CFO*
Jeremy Barton, *Chief Mktg Ofcr*
Kevin Webster, *Senior VP*
Annette Matthies, *Vice Pres*
EMP: 24 **EST:** 2013
SALES (est): 4.1MM **Privately Held**
SIC: **3844**

(P-22933)
HOLOGIC INC
1240 Elko Dr, Sunnyvale (94089-2212)
PHONE...................................408 745-0975
EMP: 195
SALES (corp-wide): 3B **Publicly Held**
SIC: **3844** X-ray apparatus & tubes
PA: Hologic, Inc.
250 Campus Dr
Marlborough MA 01752
508 263-2900

(P-22934)
IMMPORT THERAPEUTICS INC
Also Called: Antigen Discovery Inc.
1 Technology Dr Ste E309, Irvine
(92618-2343)
PHONE...................................949 679-4068
Philip Felgner, *President*
Joseph Campo, *Project Mgr*
Angela Yee, *Controller*
Jiin Felgner, *Mfg Staff*
EMP: 13
SALES (est): 2.3MM **Privately Held**
WEB: www.immport-inc.com
SIC: **3844** Therapeutic X-ray apparatus &
tubes

(P-22935)
LYNCEAN TECHNOLOGIES INC
44755 S Grimmer Blvd B, Fremont
(94538-7603)
PHONE...................................650 320-8300
Ronald Ruth, *CEO*
Rod Loewen, *Shareholder*
Jeff Rifkin, *Vice Pres*
Jack Kasahara, *VP Bus Dvlpt*
Oleg Lipkind, *Electrical Engi*
EMP: 17
SQ FT: 13,000
SALES (est): 2.7MM **Privately Held**
WEB: www.lynceantech.com
SIC: **3844** X-ray generators

(P-22936)
MATSUSADA PRECISION INC
299 Harbor Way, South San Francisco
(94080-6811)
PHONE...................................650 877-0151

Sadayoshi Matsuda, *President*
EMP: 10
SALES (est): 820.7K **Privately Held**
SIC: **3844** X-ray generators

(P-22937)
NORDSON DAGE INC
2747 Loker Ave W, Carlsbad (92010-6601)
PHONE...................................440 985-4496
John J Keane, *CEO*
Phil Vere, *CFO*
Robert E Veillette, *Admin Sec*
Efren Jimenez, *Technical Staff*
▲ **EMP:** 30 **EST:** 1977
SQ FT: 6,000
SALES (est): 9.7MM
SALES (corp-wide): 2B **Publicly Held**
WEB: www.dageinc.com
SIC: **3844** 3544 5065 3823 X-ray appa-
ratus & tubes; special dies, tools, jigs &
fixtures; electronic parts; industrial instrm-
nts msrmnt display/control process vari-
able; instruments to measure electricity;
analytical instruments
HQ: Dage Holdings Limited
25 Faraday Road
Aylesbury BUCKS
129 631-7800

(P-22938)
NORTHERN CAL PET IMAGING
CTR
3195 Folsom Blvd, Sacramento
(95816-5233)
PHONE...................................916 737-3211
Ruth Tesar, *Exec Dir*
Richard Isip, *Radiology*
EMP: 10
SALES (est): 7.1MM **Privately Held**
WEB: www.ncpic.com
SIC: **3844** Radiographic X-ray apparatus &
tubes

(P-22939)
NOVARAY MEDICAL INC
39655 Eureka Dr, Newark (94560-4806)
PHONE...................................510 619-9200
Marc C Whyte, *President*
EMP: 11
SALES (est): 1.2MM **Privately Held**
SIC: **3844** X-ray apparatus & tubes

(P-22940)
RAPISCAN LABORATORIES INC
(HQ)
3793 Spinnaker Ct, Fremont (94538-6537)
PHONE...................................408 961-9700
Shiva Kumar, *President*
Martin Kennemer, *Info Tech Mgr*
Mala Sivakumar, *Software Dev*
▲ **EMP:** 60 **EST:** 1997
SQ FT: 36,000
SALES (est): 19.3MM
SALES (corp-wide): 1B **Publicly Held**
WEB: www.rapiscansystems.com
SIC: **3844** X-ray apparatus & tubes
PA: Osi Systems, Inc.
12525 Chadron Ave
Hawthorne CA 90250
310 978-0516

(P-22941)
RAPISCAN SYSTEMS INC (HQ)
2805 Columbia St, Torrance (90503-3804)
PHONE...................................310 978-1457
Deepak Chopra, *CEO*
Ajay Mehra, *President*
Andy Kotowski, *COO*
Eric Luiz, *CFO*
Ted Alston, *Vice Pres*
◆ **EMP:** 201
SQ FT: 93,000
SALES (est): 139.7MM
SALES (corp-wide): 1B **Publicly Held**
WEB: www.rapiscan.com
SIC: **3844** X-ray apparatus & tubes
PA: Osi Systems, Inc.
12525 Chadron Ave
Hawthorne CA 90250
310 978-0516

(P-22942)
STRATEGIC MEDICAL
VENTURES LLC (PA)
280 Newport Center Dr, Newport Beach
(92660-7526)
PHONE...................................949 355-5212
Antony Clarke, *Mng Member*
Michael McKinnon,
EMP: 20 **EST:** 2010
SALES (est): 2.6MM **Privately Held**
SIC: **3844** X-ray apparatus & tubes

(P-22943)
TRUFOCUS CORPORATION
468 Westridge Dr, Watsonville
(95076-4159)
PHONE...................................831 761-9981
George G Howard, *President*
Kevin Bedolla, *Admin Sec*
Dianne Moody, *Exec Sec*
EMP: 16
SQ FT: 12,500
SALES: 2MM **Privately Held**
WEB: www.trufocus.com
SIC: **3844** X-ray apparatus & tubes

(P-22944)
VARIAN MEDICAL SYSTEMS
INC (PA)
3100 Hansen Way, Palo Alto (94304-1030)
PHONE...................................650 493-4000
R Andrew Eckert, *Ch of Bd*
Timothy E Guertin, *Vice Chairman*
Kolleen T Kennedy, *President*
Chris Toth, *President*
Dow R Wilson, *President*
EMP: 1710
SQ FT: 481,000
SALES: 2.6B **Publicly Held**
WEB: www.varian.com
SIC: **3844** 7372 3845 Therapeutic X-ray
apparatus & tubes; radiographic X-ray ap-
paratus & tubes; irradiation equipment;
prepackaged software; electromedical ap-
paratus

(P-22945)
WILLICK ENGINEERING CO INC
12516 Lakeland Rd, Santa Fe Springs
(90670-3940)
PHONE...................................562 946-4242
Dan Guerrero, *President*
Gus Guerrero, *Mfg Mgr*
Lori Guerrero, *Manager*
◆ **EMP:** 16 **EST:** 1983
SQ FT: 10,673
SALES (est): 3.3MM **Privately Held**
WEB: www.willick.com
SIC: **3844** 3612 7629 X-ray apparatus &
tubes; specialty transformers; electrical
equipment repair, high voltage

(P-22946)
ZIEHM INSTRUMENTARIUM
4181 Latham St, Riverside (92501-1729)
PHONE...................................407 615-8560
Wolfram Klawitter, *President*
Richard Westrick, *Treasurer*
Lars Nillson, *Vice Pres*
Stan Talaba, *Vice Pres*
EMP: 22
SQ FT: 11,000
SALES: 1.2MM **Privately Held**
SIC: **3844** X-ray apparatus & tubes

3845 Electromedical &
Electrotherapeutic
Apparatus

(P-22947)
ABBOTT VASCULAR INC (HQ)
3200 Lakeside Dr, Santa Clara
(95054-2807)
PHONE...................................408 845-3000
John M Capek, *President*
Charles D Foltz, *CEO*
Mark Murray, *CFO*
▲ **EMP:** 277
SQ FT: 370,000

SALES (est): 634.5MM
SALES (corp-wide): 27.3B **Publicly Held**
WEB: www.abbottvascular.com
SIC: **3845** Ultrasonic scanning devices,
medical
PA: Abbott Laboratories
100 Abbott Park Rd
Abbott Park IL 60064
224 667-6100

(P-22948)
ALERE CONNECT LLC
9975 Summers Ridge Rd, San Diego
(92121-2997)
PHONE...................................888 876-3327
Kent E Dicks, *CEO*
Lyle Scritsmier, *CFO*
David Teitel, *Treasurer*
Ellen Chiniars, *Admin Sec*
EMP: 22
SALES (est): 3.7MM **Privately Held**
WEB: www.medapps.com
SIC: **3845** Electromedical equipment

(P-22949)
AVANTIS MEDICAL SYSTEMS
INC
2367 Bering Dr, San Jose (95131-1125)
PHONE...................................408 733-1901
Matt Frushell, *President*
Anthony Ditonno, *Ch of Bd*
Scott Dodson, *President*
Larry Tannenbaum, *CFO*
Salmaan Hameed, *Vice Pres*
EMP: 38
SQ FT: 4,700
SALES (est): 6.1MM **Privately Held**
WEB: www.avantismedical.com
SIC: **3845** Endoscopic equipment, elec-
tromedical

(P-22950)
AXELGAARD MANUFACTURING
CO LTD (PA)
520 Industrial Way, Fallbrook (92028-2244)
PHONE...................................760 723-7554
Jens Axelgaard, *CEO*
Dan Jeffery, *President*
Gil Thomson, *Vice Pres*
Emily Adam, *Info Tech Mgr*
Ken Wertz, *Design Engr*
▲ **EMP:** 92
SQ FT: 33,000
SALES (est): 29MM **Privately Held**
SIC: **3845** Electromedical equipment

(P-22951)
AXELGAARD MANUFACTURING
CO LTD
329 W Aviation Rd, Fallbrook (92028-3201)
PHONE...................................760 723-7554
Yen Axelgaard, *Manager*
Alma Gutierrez, *Administration*
Nancy Liddle, *Finance*
Janice Williams, *Controller*
Judy Phillips, *Human Res Dir*
EMP: 35
SALES (corp-wide): 29MM **Privately**
Held
SIC: **3845** Electromedical equipment
PA: Axelgaard Manufacturing Co., Ltd.
520 Industrial Way
Fallbrook CA 92028
760 723-7554

(P-22952)
BIOMED INSTRUMENTS INC
1511 Alto Ln, Fullerton (92831-2007)
PHONE...................................714 459-5716
Rashad A Zeineh, *President*
Julie Zeineh, *Vice Pres*
EMP: 18
SQ FT: 3,200
SALES (est): 987.4K **Privately Held**
WEB: www.biomedinstruments.com
SIC: **3845**

(P-22953)
BIONESS INC
25103 Rye Canyon Loop, Valencia
(91355-5004)
PHONE...................................661 362-4850
Todd Cushman, *President*
Jim McHargue, *COO*
Dan Lutz, *CFO*

PRODUCTS & SVCS

Alfred E Mann, *Chairman*
Eric Grigsby, *Chief Mktg Ofcr*
▲ **EMP:** 190
SQ FT: 29,000
SALES (est): 37.2MM **Privately Held**
WEB: www.bioness.com
SIC: 3845 5047 Transcutaneous electrical nerve stimulators (TENS); medical & hospital equipment; medical equipment & supplies

(P-22954)
BIOSENSE WEBSTER INC (HQ)
33 Technology Dr, Irvine (92618-2346)
PHONE...............................909 839-8500
Shlomi Nachman, *CEO*
David Shepherd, *President*
Mary Rex, *CFO*
Tom Turley, *Vice Pres*
Lori Chehade, *Empl Benefits*
▲ **EMP:** 150
SALES (est): 180.7MM
SALES (corp-wide): 76.4B **Publicly Held**
WEB: www.biosensewebster.com
SIC: 3845 3841 Electromedical apparatus; surgical & medical instruments
PA: Johnson & Johnson
1 Johnson And Johnson Plz
New Brunswick NJ 08933
732 524-0400

(P-22955)
BIOSENSE WEBSTER INC
15715 Arrow Hwy, Baldwin Park (91706-2006)
PHONE...............................909 839-7752
Corin Chavez, *Production*
Joel Jenkins, *Manager*
EMP: 34
SALES (corp-wide): 76.4B **Publicly Held**
SIC: 3845 Electromedical apparatus
HQ: Biosense Webster Inc
33 Technology Dr
Irvine CA 92618
909 839-8500

(P-22956)
BRADEN PARTNERS LP A CALIF
Also Called: Med Mart
619 Mccormick St, San Leandro (94577-1109)
PHONE...............................510 562-5501
Kate Dougherty, *Branch Mgr*
EMP: 13
SALES (corp-wide): 68.9MM **Privately Held**
SIC: 3845 Respiratory analysis equipment, electromedical
HQ: Braden Partners, L.P., A California Limited Partnership
1304 Sthpint Blvd Ste 130
Petaluma CA 94954

(P-22957)
CARE INNOVATIONS LLC
950 Iron Point Rd Ste 160, Folsom (95630-9304)
PHONE...............................800 450-0970
Randy Swanson, *CEO*
Marcus Grindstaff, *COO*
Bruce Pruden, *CFO*
EMP: 50
SALES (est): 7.1MM **Privately Held**
SIC: 3845 3641 Electromedical apparatus; electrotherapeutic lamp units

(P-22958)
CAREFUSION CORPORATION (HQ)
3750 Torrey View Ct, San Diego (92130-2622)
PHONE...............................858 617-2000
Thomas E Polen Jr, *President*
Christopher R Reidy, *CFO*
Don Abbey, *Exec VP*
Donovan Delmare, *Vice Pres*
Joseph Diprima, *Vice Pres*
▲ **EMP:** 277

SALES (est): 4.3B
SALES (corp-wide): 12B **Publicly Held**
SIC: 3845 8742 3841 Electromedical equipment; respiratory analysis equipment, electromedical; hospital & health services consultant; surgical instruments & apparatus
PA: Becton, Dickinson And Company
1 Becton Dr
Franklin Lakes NJ 07417
201 847-6800

(P-22959)
CHALGREN ENTERPRISES
Also Called: Jari Electro Supply
380 Tomkins Ct, Gilroy (95020-3631)
PHONE...............................408 847-3994
Richard Kaiser, *President*
Michael Kaiser, *Vice Pres*
Rebecca Kaiser, *Vice Pres*
EMP: 15 **EST:** 1965
SQ FT: 4,200
SALES: 2.1MM **Privately Held**
SIC: 3845 Electromedical equipment

(P-22960)
CLARIFY MEDICAL INC
401 W A St Ste 950, San Diego (92101-7998)
PHONE...............................877 738-6041
George W Mahaffey, *CEO*
David Hale, *Chairman*
Sharlene Kakimoto, *Chief Mktg Ofcr*
Andre Gamelin, *Vice Pres*
Lisa Christy, *Manager*
EMP: 20
SQ FT: 800
SALES (est): 398.5K **Privately Held**
SIC: 3845 Laser systems & equipment, medical

(P-22961)
CLI LIQUIDATING CORPORATION
47266 Benicia St, Fremont (94538-7330)
PHONE...............................510 354-0300
Fax: 510 657-4476
EMP: 81
SQ FT: 29,000
SALES (est): 11MM **Privately Held**
WEB: www.cardima.com
SIC: 3845

(P-22962)
CLINICLOUD INC
350 Townsend St Ste 758, San Francisco (94107-1693)
PHONE...............................415 801-3283
Andrew Lin, *CEO*
Hon Weng Chong, *CTO*
EMP: 51
SQ FT: 5,000
SALES: 61.8K **Privately Held**
SIC: 3845 Electromedical equipment

(P-22963)
CNC MACHINING SOLUTIONS INC
12155 Magnolia Ave 10c, Riverside (92503-4905)
PHONE...............................951 688-4267
Theresa Taylor, *CEO*
Dale Caldwell, *CFO*
Michael Taylor, *Exec VP*
Ronda Caldwell, *Admin Sec*
EMP: 10
SQ FT: 6,500
SALES: 650K **Privately Held**
SIC: 3845 Medical cleaning equipment, ultrasonic

(P-22964)
COASTLINE INTERNATIONAL
1207 Bangor St, San Diego (92106-2407)
PHONE...............................888 748-7177
Larry Angione, *President*
Jose Vargas, *Plant Mgr*
Brett South, *Director*
▲ **EMP:** 250
SQ FT: 32,000
SALES (est): 4.6MM **Privately Held**
WEB: www.coastlineintl.com
SIC: 3845 3841 Electromedical equipment; surgical & medical instruments

(P-22965)
CONVERSION DEVICES INC
15481 Electronic Ln Ste D, Huntington Beach (92649-1355)
PHONE...............................714 898-6551
Roland Roth, *President*
Harish Khatter, *Engineer*
EMP: 25
SQ FT: 11,000
SALES (est): 3.5MM **Privately Held**
WEB: www.cdipower.com
SIC: 3845 3577 Electromedical apparatus; computer peripheral equipment

(P-22966)
COOLSYSTEMS INC (HQ)
Also Called: Game Ready
1800 Sutter St Ste 500, Concord (94520-2587)
PHONE...............................888 426-3732
John Tushar, *President*
Steven Voskuil, *CFO*
Matt Bouza, *Senior VP*
Cindy Kumar, *VP Finance*
▲ **EMP:** 104
SQ FT: 18,298
SALES: 27MM
SALES (corp-wide): 611.6MM **Publicly Held**
WEB: www.gameready.com
SIC: 3845 Laser systems & equipment, medical
PA: Avanos Medical, Inc.
5405 Windward Pkwy
Alpharetta GA 30004
678 425-9273

(P-22967)
COOLTOUCH CORPORATION
Also Called: Cool Touch
9085 Foothills Blvd, Roseville (95747-7130)
PHONE...............................916 677-1975
Nina Davis, *President*
EMP: 18 **EST:** 1996
SALES (est): 2.1MM **Privately Held**
WEB: www.cooltouch.com
SIC: 3845 Laser systems & equipment, medical

(P-22968)
CUTERA INC (PA)
3240 Bayshore Blvd, Brisbane (94005-1021)
PHONE...............................415 657-5500
James A Reinstein, *President*
J Daniel Plants, *Ch of Bd*
R Jason Richey, *COO*
Sandra A Gardiner, *CFO*
Clinton Severson, *Bd of Directors*
EMP: 230
SQ FT: 66,000
SALES: 151.4MM **Publicly Held**
SIC: 3845 Laser systems & equipment, medical

(P-22969)
CYTEK BIOSCIENCES INC
46107 Landing Pkwy, Fremont (94538-6407)
PHONE...............................510 657-0110
Wendin Kiang, *CEO*
Patrik S Jeanmonod, *CFO*
Steve Ziganti, *Vice Pres*
Ming Yan, *CTO*
EMP: 11 **EST:** 2014
SALES (est): 235.8K **Privately Held**
SIC: 3845 3841 Laser systems & equipment, medical; diagnostic apparatus, medical

(P-22970)
DAYLIGHT DEFENSE LLC
Also Called: Drs Daylight Solutions Inc.
15378 Ave Of Science, San Diego (92128-3451)
PHONE...............................858 432-7500
Timothy Day,
EMP: 175
SALES (est): 2.2MM
SALES (corp-wide): 9.2B **Privately Held**
SIC: 3845 Laser systems & equipment, medical

HQ: Daylight Solutions, Inc.
15378 Ave Of Science # 200
San Diego CA 92128
858 432-7500

(P-22971)
DECISION SCIENCES MED CO LLC
Also Called: Decision Medical
12345 First American Way # 100, Poway (92064-6828)
PHONE...............................858 602-1600
Stanton Sloane, *President*
George R Creel, *Managing Prtnr*
Paul Bartholomew, *CFO*
Jim Hayes, *Chief Engr*
EMP: 20
SALES (est): 2.6MM **Privately Held**
SIC: 3845 3841 Electromedical equipment; surgical & medical instruments

(P-22972)
DOLPHIN MEDICAL INC (HQ)
12525 Chadron Ave, Hawthorne (90250-4807)
PHONE...............................800 448-6506
Deepak Chopra, *President*
Thomas Scharf, *Vice Pres*
▲ **EMP:** 100
SALES (est): 48.3MM
SALES (corp-wide): 1B **Publicly Held**
WEB: www.dolphinmedical.com
SIC: 3845 Ultrasonic medical equipment, except cleaning
PA: Osi Systems, Inc.
12525 Chadron Ave
Hawthorne CA 90250
310 978-0516

(P-22973)
EBR SYSTEMS INC
480 Oakmead Pkwy, Sunnyvale (94085-4708)
PHONE...............................408 720-1906
Allan Will, *Ch of Bd*
Mark Cowan, *President*
Stephen Oconnor, *President*
Mark Schwartz, *President*
Andrew Shute, *President*
EMP: 23
SQ FT: 8,500
SALES (est): 4.1MM **Privately Held**
WEB: www.ebrsystemsinc.com
SIC: 3845 Cardiographs

(P-22974)
EDWARDS LIFESCIENCES US INC
1 Edwards Way, Irvine (92614-5688)
PHONE...............................949 250-2500
Michael A Mussallem, *CEO*
Dirksen J Lehman, *Vice Pres*
Jean-Luc Lemercier, *Vice Pres*
Christine Z McCauley, *Vice Pres*
Stanton J Rowe, *Vice Pres*
EMP: 26 **EST:** 2011
SALES (est): 4.6MM
SALES (corp-wide): 3.4B **Publicly Held**
SIC: 3845 Patient monitoring apparatus; pacemaker, cardiac
PA: Edwards Lifesciences Corp
1 Edwards Way
Irvine CA 92614
949 250-2500

(P-22975)
EKO DEVICES INC
2600 10th St Ste 260, Berkeley (94710-2597)
PHONE...............................844 356-3384
Connor Landgraf, *CEO*
Jason Bellet, *COO*
Craig Bagby, *Vice Pres*
Nicole Gaskari, *Business Anlyst*
Tanay Nandgaonkar, *Research*
EMP: 10
SALES (est): 1.3MM **Privately Held**
SIC: 3845 Electromedical equipment

(P-22976)
EXAM ROOM SUPPLY LLC
2419 Hrbour Blvd Unit 126, Ventura (93001)
PHONE...............................805 298-3631
Charles Solomon, *Mng Member*
M Wash, *Mng Member*

EMP: 15
SALES (est): 1MM **Privately Held**
SIC: 3845 3841 5047 5999 Electromedical apparatus; diagnostic apparatus, medical; medical & hospital equipment; medical apparatus & supplies

(P-22977)
EXO SYSTEMS INC
333 Pali Ct, Oakland (94611-1855)
PHONE.....................510 655-5033
Sandeep Akkaraju, *President*
Janusz Bryzek, *CEO*
Yusuf Haque, *Vice Pres*
EMP: 22
SALES (est): 1.2MM **Privately Held**
SIC: 3845 Ultrasonic medical equipment, except cleaning

(P-22978)
EXPLORAMED NC7 INC
201 San Antonio Cir # 172, Mountain View (94040-1255)
PHONE.....................650 559-5805
Naomi Kelman, *CEO*
EMP: 28
SQ FT: 5,175
SALES (est): 4.3MM **Privately Held**
SIC: 3845 Electromedical apparatus

(P-22979)
GAMING FUND GROUP
1940 Embarcadero, Oakland (94606-5213)
PHONE.....................510 532-8881
David Chau, *President*
Susan Williams, *Executive Asst*
Emerald Fung, *Software Dev*
EMP: 10
SALES (est): 1.2MM **Privately Held**
SIC: 3845 Pacemaker, cardiac

(P-22980)
GARFIELD IMAGING CENTER INC
555 N Garfield Ave, Monterey Park (91754-1202)
PHONE.....................626 572-0912
Clark Gardner MD, *President*
Yolanda Odell, *Exec Dir*
EMP: 14
SQ FT: 3,000
SALES (est): 2.1MM
SALES (corp-wide): 52.7MM **Privately Held**
SIC: 3845 Magnetic resonance imaging device, nuclear
HQ: Insight Health Services Corp.
   5775 Wayzata Blvd Ste 400
   Minneapolis MN 55416

(P-22981)
GIVEN IMAGING LOS ANGELES LLC
Also Called: Sierra Scientific Instrs LLC
5860 Uplander Way, Culver City (90230-6608)
PHONE.....................310 641-8492
Tom Parks PHD, *President*
Ron McIntyre, *CFO*
Eric Finkelman, *Vice Pres*
Jeffrey Sawyer, *Marketing Staff*
Gary Carruthers, *Manager*
◆ **EMP:** 175
SALES (est): 22MM **Privately Held**
WEB: www.sierrainst.com
SIC: 3845 Electromedical equipment
PA: Given Imaging Ltd.
   2 Hacarmel
   Upper Yokneam
   490 977-77

(P-22982)
HALO NEURO INC
Also Called: Halo Neuroscience
735 Market St Fl 4, San Francisco (94103-2034)
PHONE.....................415 851-3338
Daniel Chao, *CEO*
Mark Mastlier, *Chief Mktg Ofcr*
Brett Wingeier, *CTO*
Alex Cates, *Research*
Kane Russell, *Marketing Staff*
EMP: 17
SQ FT: 8,000

SALES (est): 792.8K **Privately Held**
SIC: 3845 Electrotherapeutic apparatus

(P-22983)
HEMOSENSE INC
9975 Summers Ridge Rd, San Diego (92121-2997)
PHONE.....................408 719-1393
James D Merselis, *President*
Gordon Sangster, *CFO*
Timothy I Still, *Exec VP*
William H Dippel, *Vice Pres*
David L Phillips, *Vice Pres*
EMP: 79
SQ FT: 15,250
SALES (est): 5.3MM
SALES (corp-wide): 27.3B **Publicly Held**
WEB: www.hemosense.com
SIC: 3845 Automated blood & body fluid analyzers, except laboratory
HQ: Alere Inc.
   51 Sawyer Rd Ste 200
   Waltham MA 02453
   781 647-3900

(P-22984)
HOLOGIC INC
10210 Genetic Center Dr, San Diego (92121-4362)
PHONE.....................858 410-8000
Gonzalo Martinez, *Branch Mgr*
Jorgine Ellerbrock, *Senior VP*
Brad Blake, *Vice Pres*
Raj Iyer, *Associate Dir*
Tom Shimei, *Associate Dir*
EMP: 36
SALES (corp-wide): 3B **Publicly Held**
SIC: 3845 Ultrasonic medical equipment, except cleaning
PA: Hologic, Inc.
   250 Campus Dr
   Marlborough MA 01752
   508 263-2900

(P-22985)
HOSPITAL SYSTEMS INC
750 Garcia Ave, Pittsburg (94565-5012)
PHONE.....................925 427-7800
Jennifer M Miller, *Ch of Bd*
David H Miller, *President*
Rebecca Miller, *President*
Kathie Campbell, *VP Opers*
Seye Louie, *Prdtn Mgr*
EMP: 72
SQ FT: 20,000
SALES (est): 11.5MM **Privately Held**
WEB: www.hospitalsystems.com
SIC: 3845 Electromedical equipment

(P-22986)
HYGEIA II MEDICAL GROUP INC
6241 Yarrow Dr Ste A, Carlsbad (92011-1541)
PHONE.....................714 515-7571
Mark Engler, *CEO*
Brett Nakfoor, *President*
▲ **EMP:** 40
SALES (est): 4.5MM **Privately Held**
SIC: 3845 Electromedical equipment

(P-22987)
HYGEIA II MEDICAL GROUP INC
6241 Yarrow Dr Ste A, Carlsbad (92011-1541)
PHONE.....................714 515-7571
Mark Engler, *CEO*
Brett Nakfoor, *President*
EMP: 40
SALES (est): 1.6MM **Privately Held**
SIC: 3845 Electromedical equipment

(P-22988)
HYPERBARIC TECHNOLOGIES INC
3224 Hoover Ave, National City (91950-7224)
PHONE.....................619 336-2022
W T Gurnee, *President*
Julie Vaickus, *Controller*
EMP: 80
SQ FT: 15,000

SALES: 2.5MM **Privately Held**
WEB: www.oxyheal.com
SIC: 3845 3841 7352 3443 Electromedical equipment; medical instruments & equipment, blood & bone work; medical equipment rental; fabricated plate work (boiler shop)

(P-22989)
ICRCO INC
26 Coromar Dr, Goleta (93117-3024)
PHONE.....................310 921-9559
Stephen Neushul, *Branch Mgr*
EMP: 10
SALES (corp-wide): 25.7MM **Privately Held**
SIC: 3845 Laser systems & equipment, medical
PA: Icrco, Inc.
   26 Coromar Dr
   Goleta CA 93117
   310 921-9559

(P-22990)
ICRCO INC (PA)
Also Called: Image Capture Review
26 Coromar Dr, Goleta (93117-3024)
PHONE.....................310 921-9559
Stephen Neushul, *CEO*
Linda Pahl, *CFO*
MO Duwaik, *Lab Dir*
Abhinav Singh, *Technical Mgr*
Shelton Johnson, *Web Dvlpr*
▲ **EMP:** 50
SQ FT: 11,000
SALES (est): 25.7MM **Privately Held**
WEB: www.icrcompany.com
SIC: 3845 Laser systems & equipment, medical

(P-22991)
INTERSON CORP
7150 Koll Center Pkwy, Pleasanton (94566-3164)
PHONE.....................925 462-4948
Monica Solak, *Director*
EMP: 22 **EST:** 2015
SALES (est): 284.7K **Privately Held**
SIC: 3845 Electromedical apparatus

(P-22992)
IOGYN INC
150 Baytech Dr, San Jose (95134-2302)
PHONE.....................408 996-2517
Csaba Truckai, *Exec Dir*
John Shadduck, *Exec Dir*
David Clapper, *Director*
Rodney Perkins, *Director*
Bruno Strul, *Director*
EMP: 13 **EST:** 2010
SALES (est): 2.2MM
SALES (corp-wide): 9B **Publicly Held**
SIC: 3845 Ultrasonic scanning devices, medical
PA: Boston Scientific Corporation
   300 Boston Scientific Way
   Marlborough MA 01752
   508 683-4000

(P-22993)
IRHYTHM TECHNOLOGIES INC (PA)
650 Townsend St Ste 500, San Francisco (94103-6227)
PHONE.....................415 632-5700
Abhijit Y Talwalkar, *Ch of Bd*
Kevin M King, *President*
Matthew C Garrett, *CFO*
Bruce Bodaken, *Bd of Directors*
Ralph Snyderman, *Bd of Directors*
EMP: 30
SQ FT: 60,873
SALES: 98.5MM **Publicly Held**
WEB: www.irhythmtech.com
SIC: 3845 3841 Electrocardiographs; diagnostic apparatus, medical

(P-22994)
IRIS MEDICAL INSTRUMENTS INC
Also Called: Iridex
1212 Terra Bella Ave, Mountain View (94043-1824)
PHONE.....................650 940-4700
Ted Boutacoff, *CEO*
EMP: 130

SALES (est): 7.3MM
SALES (corp-wide): 41.5MM **Publicly Held**
WEB: www.iridex.com
SIC: 3845 Laser systems & equipment, medical
PA: Iridex Corporation
   1212 Terra Bella Ave
   Mountain View CA 94043
   650 940-4700

(P-22995)
JENAVALVE TECHNOLOGY INC
7545 Irvine Center Dr, Irvine (92618-2932)
PHONE.....................949 396-7555
Victoria Carr Brendel, *CEO*
Helmut J Straubinger, *President*
John F Migliazza, *COO*
John Migliazza, *COO*
Stephan Wehselau, *CFO*
EMP: 38
SALES (est): 6.4MM **Privately Held**
SIC: 3845 Ultrasonic medical equipment, except cleaning

(P-22996)
JOHNSON & JOHNSON (HQ)
Also Called: Abbott Medical Optics Inc.
1700 E Saint Andrew Pl, Santa Ana (92705-4933)
P.O. Box 25929 (92799-5929)
PHONE.....................714 247-8200
Thomas Frinzi, *President*
Victor Chang, *President*
Catherine Mazzacco, *Vice Pres*
Colleen Hulshof, *Executive Asst*
Robin Kerr, *Systems Dir*
▲ **EMP:** 300
SALES (est): 1.2B
SALES (corp-wide): 76.4B **Publicly Held**
WEB: www.amo-inc.com
SIC: 3845 3841 Laser systems & equipment, medical; ophthalmic instruments & apparatus
PA: Johnson & Johnson
   1 Johnson And Johnson Plz
   New Brunswick NJ 08933
   732 524-0400

(P-22997)
LEAF HEALTHCARE INC
5994 W Las Positas Blvd # 217, Pleasanton (94588-8509)
PHONE.....................925 621-1800
Mark Weckwerth, *CEO*
Mark Smith, *President*
Weckwerth Mark, *COO*
Daniel Shen, *Ch Credit Ofcr*
▼ **EMP:** 10
SQ FT: 4,400
SALES (est): 1.6MM **Privately Held**
SIC: 3845 Patient monitoring apparatus

(P-22998)
LIFESCIENCE PLUS INC
2520 Wyandotte St Ste A, Mountain View (94043-2381)
P.O. Box 60783, Palo Alto (94306-0783)
PHONE.....................650 565-8172
Vicky Feng, *President*
Lason Magallones, *Vice Pres*
Sally Pennington, *General Mgr*
Audrey Vitale, *Director*
▲ **EMP:** 10
SQ FT: 3,000
SALES (est): 780K **Privately Held**
WEB: www.lifescienceplus.com
SIC: 3845 Ultrasonic scanning devices, medical

(P-22999)
LIFETRAK INCORPORATED
8371 Central Ave Ste A, Newark (94560-3473)
PHONE.....................510 413-9030
Mike Tsai, *CEO*
▲ **EMP:** 10
SALES: 5MM **Privately Held**
SIC: 3845
PA: Salutron Incorporated
   8371 Central Ave Ste A
   Newark CA 94560

PRODUCTS & SVCS

(P-23000)
LOBUE LASER & EYE MEDICAL CTRS
40740 California Oaks Rd, Murrieta (92562-5727)
PHONE...............................951 696-1135
EMP: 29
SALES (corp-wide): 3.8MM **Privately Held**
SIC: 3845 Laser systems & equipment, medical
PA: Lobue Laser & Eye Medical Ctrs Inc
40700 California Oaks Rd
Murrieta CA 92562
951 696-1135

(P-23001)
LUMASENSE TECH HOLDINGS INC (HQ)
3301 Leonard Ct, Santa Clara (95054-2054)
PHONE...............................408 727-1600
Steve Abely, *CEO*
Vivek Joshi, *President*
Steve Uhlir, *President*
Jose Ysaguirre, *President*
Brandt Mark, *Vice Pres*
EMP: 80
SQ FT: 62,000
SALES (est): 103.2MM
SALES (corp-wide): 671MM **Publicly Held**
WEB: www.lumasenseinc.com
SIC: 3845 3829 3825 3823 Electromedical equipment; measuring & controlling devices; instruments to measure electricity; temperature instruments: industrial process type
PA: Advanced Energy Industries, Inc.
1625 Sharp Point Dr
Fort Collins CO 80525
970 221-4670

(P-23002)
MAQUET MEDICAL SYSTEMS USA LLC
120 Baytech Dr, San Jose (95134-2302)
PHONE...............................408 635-3900
Heribert Ballhaus, *CEO*
Heinz Jacqui, *Exec VP*
Reinhard Mayer, *Vice Pres*
Hilde Van Der Westhuizen, *Vice Pres*
EMP: 525
SQ FT: 75,000
SALES (est): 77.9MM
SALES (corp-wide): 2.6B **Privately Held**
SIC: 3845 Ultrasonic scanning devices, medical
HQ: Maquet Gmbh
Kehler Str. 31
Rastatt 76437
722 293-20

(P-23003)
MASIMO CORPORATION
40 Parker, Irvine (92618-1604)
PHONE...............................949 297-7000
Paul Jansen, *Exec VP*
Ron Coverston, *Vice Pres*
Vaughn Eldstrom, *Vice Pres*
Steve Jensen, *Vice Pres*
Mathew Jimenez, *Vice Pres*
EMP: 50 **Publicly Held**
SIC: 3845 Electromedical equipment
PA: Masimo Corporation
52 Discovery
Irvine CA 92618

(P-23004)
MASIMO CORPORATION
9600 Jeronimo Rd, Irvine (92618-2024)
PHONE...............................949 297-7000
Joe Kiani, *Branch Mgr*
EMP: 50 **Publicly Held**
SIC: 3845 Electromedical equipment
PA: Masimo Corporation
52 Discovery
Irvine CA 92618

(P-23005)
MASIMO CORPORATION (PA)
52 Discovery, Irvine (92618-3105)
PHONE...............................949 297-7000

Joe Kiani, *Ch of Bd*
Jon Coleman, *President*
Rick Fishel, *President*
Anand Sampath, *COO*
Micah Young, *CFO*
EMP: 350
SQ FT: 213,400
SALES: 798.1MM **Publicly Held**
WEB: www.masimo.com
SIC: 3845 Patient monitoring apparatus; phonocardiographs

(P-23006)
MAUI IMAGING INC
256 Gibraltar Dr Ste 110, Sunnyvale (94089-1337)
PHONE...............................408 744-1127
David J Specht, *CEO*
EMP: 10
SALES (est): 1.3MM **Privately Held**
SIC: 3845 Electromedical equipment

(P-23007)
MC LIQUIDATION INC
Also Called: Intraop Medical Services
570 Del Rey Ave, Sunnyvale (94085-3528)
PHONE...............................408 636-1020
John Powers, *President*
J K Hullett, *CFO*
Richard A Belford, *Vice Pres*
Winfield Jones, *VP Sales*
EMP: 28
SQ FT: 14,419
SALES (est): 3.7MM **Privately Held**
SIC: 3845 Electromedical equipment

(P-23008)
MEDIVISION INC
Also Called: Medivision Optics
4883 E La Palma Ave # 503, Anaheim (92807-1957)
PHONE...............................714 563-2772
Kevin May, *President*
EMP: 15
SQ FT: 6,000
SALES (est): 1.5MM **Privately Held**
WEB: www.medivisionusa.com
SIC: 3845 7699 5047 Endoscopic equipment, electromedical; scientific equipment repair service; physician equipment & supplies

(P-23009)
MEDTRONIC INC
1659 Gailes Blvd, San Diego (92154-8230)
PHONE...............................949 798-3934
Araceli Rodriguez, *Branch Mgr*
Emily Miller, *Manager*
EMP: 300 **Privately Held**
SIC: 3845 Electromedical equipment
HQ: Medtronic, Inc.
710 Medtronic Pkwy
Minneapolis MN 55432
763 514-4000

(P-23010)
MEDTRONIC INC
2200 Powell St, Emeryville (94608-1809)
PHONE...............................510 985-9670
Reggie Dupee, *Sales Staff*
EMP: 192 **Privately Held**
SIC: 3845 Electromedical equipment
HQ: Medtronic, Inc.
710 Medtronic Pkwy
Minneapolis MN 55432
763 514-4000

(P-23011)
MEDTRONIC INC
125 Cremona Dr, Goleta (93117-5503)
PHONE...............................805 571-3769
EMP: 16 **Privately Held**
SIC: 3845 3842 3841 Electromedical equipment; implants, surgical; blood transfusion equipment
HQ: Medtronic, Inc.
710 Medtronic Pkwy
Minneapolis MN 55432
763 514-4000

(P-23012)
MEDTRONIC INC
18000 Devonshire St, Northridge (91325-1219)
PHONE...............................300 646-4633
EMP: 204 **Privately Held**

SIC: 3845 Electromedical equipment
HQ: Medtronic, Inc.
710 Medtronic Pkwy
Minneapolis MN 55432
763 514-4000

(P-23013)
MEDTRONIC INC
9 Parker, Irvine (92618-1653)
PHONE...............................949 486-9973
EMP: 12 **Privately Held**
SIC: 3845 Electromedical equipment
HQ: Medtronic, Inc.
710 Medtronic Pkwy
Minneapolis MN 55432
763 514-4000

(P-23014)
MEDTRONIC INC
9775 Toledo Way, Irvine (92618-1811)
PHONE...............................949 837-3700
Lisa Greenwood, *Executive Asst*
Catherine Fogel, *Director*
Scott Koehler, *Director*
Laura Heaton, *Manager*
Kevin Schreiner, *Manager*
EMP: 24
SALES (est): 3.2MM **Privately Held**
SIC: 3845 Electromedical equipment

(P-23015)
MEDTRONIC INC
1851 E Deere Ave, Santa Ana (92705-5720)
PHONE...............................949 474-3943
Walter Cuevas, *Manager*
Donna Saito, *Admin Sec*
Mario Anaya, *Technician*
Monique Poon, *Technician*
Carol Eberhardt, *Engrg Mgr*
EMP: 59
SQ FT: 47,000 **Privately Held**
WEB: www.medtronic.com
SIC: 3845 Electromedical equipment
HQ: Medtronic, Inc.
710 Medtronic Pkwy
Minneapolis MN 55432
763 514-4000

(P-23016)
MEDTRONIC INC
1860 Barber Ln, Milpitas (95035-7422)
PHONE...............................408 548-6618
Richard Mott, *CEO*
Giovanni Napoli, *Vice Pres*
Jim Adzema, *Info Tech Dir*
Silvio Martinez, *Opers Staff*
Abiram Quinonez, *Sales Staff*
EMP: 20 **Privately Held**
WEB: www.medtronic.com
SIC: 3845 Electromedical equipment
HQ: Medtronic, Inc.
710 Medtronic Pkwy
Minneapolis MN 55432
763 514-4000

(P-23017)
MEDTRONIC INC
11811 Landon Dr, Mira Loma (91752-4002)
PHONE...............................951 332-3600
EMP: 21 **Privately Held**
SIC: 3845 Electromedical equipment
HQ: Medtronic, Inc.
710 Medtronic Pkwy
Minneapolis MN 55432
763 514-4000

(P-23018)
MEDTRONIC MINIMED INC (DH)
18000 Devonshire St, Northridge (91325-1219)
PHONE...............................800 646-4633
Catherine Szyman, *President*
Eric P Geismar, *Vice Pres*
Ron Lund, *Vice Pres*
Greg Meehan, *Vice Pres*
George J Montague, *Vice Pres*
▲ **EMP:** 1200
SQ FT: 250,000
SALES (est): 859.1MM **Privately Held**
WEB: www.minimed.com
SIC: 3845 Electromedical equipment
HQ: Medtronic, Inc.
710 Medtronic Pkwy
Minneapolis MN 55432
763 514-4000

(P-23019)
MENTZER ELECTRONICS
858 Stanton Rd, Burlingame (94010-1404)
P.O. Box 610, Barrington IL (60011-0610)
PHONE...............................650 697-2642
Fax: 650 697-2405
EMP: 24
SQ FT: 14,000
SALES (est): 2.1MM **Privately Held**
WEB: www.mentzerelectronics.com
SIC: 3845 3672

(P-23020)
NANOSTIM INC
776 Palomar Ave, Sunnyvale (94085-2914)
PHONE...............................408 530-0700
Drew Hoffmann, *CEO*
EMP: 17
SALES (est): 2.9MM
SALES (corp-wide): 27.3B **Publicly Held**
SIC: 3845 Pacemaker, cardiac
HQ: St. Jude Medical, Llc
1 Saint Jude Medical Dr
Saint Paul MN 55117
651 756-2000

(P-23021)
NATUS INC
Also Called: Ecogear-Products
19 Suffolk Ave Ste C, Sierra Madre (91024-2570)
PHONE...............................626 355-3746
Jimmy Chen, *President*
▲ **EMP:** 10
SALES (est): 734.5K **Privately Held**
SIC: 3845 Electromedical equipment

(P-23022)
NATUS MEDICAL INCORPORATED
1501 Industrial Rd, San Carlos (94070-4111)
PHONE...............................303 962-1800
James B Hawkins, *CEO*
David Doan, *CFO*
Christopher Chung, *Vice Pres*
Marybeth Smith, *Vice Pres*
Dale Isacks, *Regional Dir*
EMP: 34
SALES (corp-wide): 500.9MM **Publicly Held**
SIC: 3845 Electromedical equipment
PA: Natus Medical Incorporated
6701 Koll Center Pkwy # 120
Pleasanton CA 94566
925 223-6700

(P-23023)
NATUS MEDICAL INCORPORATED
5955 Pacific Center Blvd, San Diego (92121-4309)
PHONE...............................858 260-2590
Stephen Dirocco, *Director*
EMP: 71
SALES (corp-wide): 500.9MM **Publicly Held**
SIC: 3845 3841 Electromedical equipment; electrotherapeutic apparatus; surgical instruments & apparatus
PA: Natus Medical Incorporated
6701 Koll Center Pkwy # 120
Pleasanton CA 94566
925 223-6700

(P-23024)
NATUS MEDICAL INCORPORATED (PA)
6701 Koll Center Pkwy # 120, Pleasanton (94566-8061)
PHONE...............................925 223-6700
Robert A Gunst, *Ch of Bd*
James B Hawkins, *President*
Jonathan Kennedy, *CFO*
Doris Engibous, *Bd of Directors*
Barbara Paul, *Bd of Directors*
EMP: 277
SQ FT: 8,200
SALES: 500.9MM **Publicly Held**
WEB: www.natus.com
SIC: 3845 Electromedical equipment

(P-23025)
NEW SOURCE TECHNOLOGY LLC
6678 Owens Dr Ste 105, Pleasanton
(94588-3324)
PHONE....................925 462-6888
Gregory A Pon, *President*
Jenny Jiang, *Business Mgr*
Hong Yin, *Manager*
EMP: 15
SALES (est): 297.2K Privately Held
WEB: www.newsourcetechnology.com
SIC: 3845 Laser systems & equipment, medical

(P-23026)
NEW STAR LASERS INC
Also Called: Cooltouch
8331 Sierra College Blvd # 204, Roseville
(95661-9412)
PHONE....................916 677-1900
Ilan Ben-David, *CEO*
Nina Davis, *President*
David R Hennings, *President*
Ruben Florez, *Vice Pres*
Mike Jaynes, *Administration*
EMP: 41
SQ FT: 20,000
SALES (est): 8.2MM Privately Held
WEB: www.newstarlasers.com
SIC: 3845 Laser systems & equipment, medical

(P-23027)
NIHON KOHDEN ORANGEMED INC
15375 Barranca Pkwy C109, Irvine
(92618-2206)
PHONE....................949 502-6448
Hong-Lin Du, *CEO*
EMP: 12
SALES (est): 707.1K Privately Held
SIC: 3845 Electromedical equipment

(P-23028)
NORCAL RESPIRATORY INC
3075 Crossroads Dr Ste A, Redding
(96003-8018)
PHONE....................530 246-1200
Jim Rahmann, *President*
EMP: 21
SALES (est): 3.6MM Privately Held
SIC: 3845 Respiratory analysis equipment, electromedical

(P-23029)
OPOTEK INC
2233 Faraday Ave Ste E, Carlsbad
(92008-7214)
PHONE....................760 929-0770
Eli Margalith, *President*
Larry Bay, *Vice Pres*
Renee Robinson, *Office Mgr*
Lamoine Baker, *Human Res Dir*
EMP: 14
SQ FT: 4,000
SALES (est): 1.6MM Privately Held
WEB: www.opotek.com
SIC: 3845 Laser systems & equipment, medical

(P-23030)
OPTEK GROUP INC
23 Corporate Plaza Dr # 150, Newport
Beach (92660-7911)
PHONE....................949 629-2558
Allan Hsieh, *President*
Perry Hsieh, *Admin Sec*
EMP: 25
SQ FT: 3,000
SALES: 3MM Privately Held
SIC: 3845 5084 Electromedical equipment; chemical process equipment

(P-23031)
ORATEC INTERVENTIONS INC (DH)
3696 Haven Ave, Redwood City
(94063-4604)
PHONE....................901 396-2121
Ron Sparks, *CEO*
Mark Frost, *Treasurer*
Jerry Goodman, *Vice Pres*
Reuben Rosales, *Vice Pres*
James Ralston, *Admin Sec*

EMP: 10
SQ FT: 37,000
SALES (est): 9.7MM
SALES (corp-wide): 4.7B Privately Held
WEB: www.oratec.com
SIC: 3845 8011 3841 Electromedical equipment; offices & clinics of medical doctors; surgical & medical instruments
HQ: Smith & Nephew, Inc.
1450 E Brooks Rd
Memphis TN 38116
901 396-2121

(P-23032)
PACESETTER INC (DH)
Also Called: Ventritex
15900 Valley View Ct, Sylmar
(91342-3585)
P.O. Box 9221 (91392-9221)
PHONE....................818 362-6822
Eric S Fain, *CEO*
Ronald A Matricaria, *President*
Ron Thompson, *Vice Pres*
Ed Ferrier, *Executive*
Jeff Chateau, *Purch Agent*
▲ EMP: 725
SALES (est): 321.9MM
SALES (corp-wide): 27.3B Publicly Held
SIC: 3845 Defibrillator
HQ: St. Jude Medical, Llc
1 Saint Jude Medical Dr
Saint Paul MN 55117
651 756-2000

(P-23033)
PALYON MEDICAL CORPORATION
28432 Constellation Rd, Valencia
(91355-5081)
P.O. Box 2091, Tubac AZ (85646-2091)
PHONE....................661 705-5601
Luis Malave, *CEO*
EMP: 25
SALES (est): 4.3MM Privately Held
SIC: 3845 Ultrasonic scanning devices, medical

(P-23034)
PARACOR MEDICAL INC
19200 Stevns Crk Blvd # 200, Cupertino
(95014-2530)
PHONE....................408 207-1050
William Mavity, *President*
Pooja Joshipura, *Supervisor*
EMP: 30
SQ FT: 12,000
SALES (est): 3.7MM Privately Held
WEB: www.paracormedical.com
SIC: 3845 Ultrasonic scanning devices, medical

(P-23035)
PART HANDLING ENGRG & DEV CORP
42175 Zevo Dr, Temecula (92590-2503)
PHONE....................951 308-4450
Bassam A Poullath, *President*
Basil Poullath, *Vice Pres*
Brittany Poullath, *Bookkeeper*
EMP: 10
SQ FT: 8,200
SALES (est): 1.5MM Privately Held
SIC: 3845 3535 5084 Electromedical equipment; robotic conveyors; conveyor systems

(P-23036)
QPC LASERS INC
15632 Roxford St, Sylmar (91342-1265)
PHONE....................818 986-0000
Hao Zhao, *CEO*
EMP: 13
SALES (est): 469.3K Privately Held
SIC: 3845 Laser systems & equipment, medical

(P-23037)
R & D NOVA INC
833 Marlborough Ave 200, Riverside
(92507-2133)
PHONE....................951 781-7332
Scott Snyder, *President*
Martin Clajus, *General Mgr*
Frank Walker, *Manager*
EMP: 15
SQ FT: 4,000

SALES (est): 2.4MM
SALES (corp-wide): 16.6MM Privately Held
WEB: www.novarad.com
SIC: 3845 3812 Magnetic resonance imaging device, nuclear; search & detection systems & instruments
PA: Kromek Group Plc
Thomas Wright Way
Stockton-On-Tees TS21
174 062-6050

(P-23038)
RADLINK INC
815 N Nash St, El Segundo (90245-2824)
PHONE....................310 643-6900
Thomas T Hacking, *Ch of Bd*
Brian Kordich, *QC Mgr*
Michelle Iafigliola, *Sales Staff*
Dani Miller, *Sales Staff*
Mehrshad Pezeshki, *Sales Staff*
EMP: 30 EST: 1999
SQ FT: 25,000
SALES (est): 6.5MM Privately Held
SIC: 3845 Ultrasonic scanning devices, medical

(P-23039)
REAL-TIME RADIOGRAPHY INC
3825 Hopyard Rd Ste 220, Pleasanton
(94588-2786)
PHONE....................925 416-1903
Shaul Dukeman, *President*
EMP: 24
SQ FT: 1,800
SALES (est): 1.5MM Privately Held
WEB: www.realtimeradiography.com
SIC: 3845 Cardiographs; pacemaker, cardiac

(P-23040)
REFLEXION MEDICAL INC
25821 Industrial Blvd # 200, Hayward
(94545-2919)
PHONE....................650 239-9070
Samuel R Mazin, *President*
Todd Powell, *President*
Martyn Webster, *CFO*
David Q Larkin, *Vice Pres*
Partha Ray, *Vice Pres*
EMP: 37
SALES (est): 5.9MM Privately Held
SIC: 3845 Electromedical equipment

(P-23041)
RESONANCE TECHNOLOGY INC
18121 Parthenia St Ste A, Northridge
(91325-3351)
PHONE....................818 882-1997
Mokhtar Ziarati, *CEO*
Susanna Ziarati, *Shareholder*
Montero Jaime, *Technician*
Parisa Ziarati, *Project Mgr*
Benjamin Montero, *Technical Staff*
▲ EMP: 11
SALES (est): 1.9MM Privately Held
WEB: www.fmri.net
SIC: 3845 Magnetic resonance imaging device, nuclear

(P-23042)
RFA MEDICAL SOLUTIONS
40874 Calido Pl, Fremont (94539-3633)
PHONE....................510 583-9500
EMP: 10
SALES: 800K Privately Held
SIC: 3845

(P-23043)
RITA MEDICAL SYSTEMS INC (HQ)
46421 Landing Pkwy, Fremont
(94538-6496)
PHONE....................510 771-0400
Michael D Angel, *CFO*
Jelle W Kylstra, *Vice Pres*
Juan Soto, *Vice Pres*
Mario Martinez, *General Mgr*
Darrin Uecker, *CTO*
EMP: 77
SQ FT: 14,500

SALES (est): 13.1MM
SALES (corp-wide): 344.2MM Publicly Held
SIC: 3845 3841 Electromedical equipment; surgical & medical instruments; catheters
PA: Angiodynamics, Inc.
14 Plaza Dr
Latham NY 12110
518 795-1400

(P-23044)
ROX MEDICAL INC (PA)
150 Calle Iglesia Ste A, San Clemente
(92672-7550)
PHONE....................949 276-8968
Mike Mackinnon, *CEO*
Keegan Harper, *Ch of Bd*
Paul A Sobotka, *Officer*
Suzan Hughes, *Office Mgr*
Beth Hughes, *Controller*
EMP: 20
SQ FT: 3,500
SALES (est): 3.6MM Privately Held
SIC: 3845 Ultrasonic scanning devices, medical

(P-23045)
SALUTRON INCORPORATED (PA)
8371 Central Ave Ste A, Newark
(94560-3473)
PHONE....................510 795-2876
Mike Tsai, *CEO*
Yong Jin Lee, *CTO*
Christine Han, *Controller*
▲ EMP: 30
SQ FT: 11,000
SALES (est): 60MM Privately Held
WEB: www.salutron.com
SIC: 3845 Patient monitoring apparatus

(P-23046)
SENSOR DYNAMICS INC
4568 Enterprise St, Fremont (94538-6315)
PHONE....................510 623-1459
Wun Yann Liao, *President*
▲ EMP: 15
SQ FT: 10,000
SALES (est): 2.1MM Privately Held
WEB: www.sensordynamics.com
SIC: 3845 Electromedical apparatus
PA: Direction Technology Co., Ltd.
88-7, Kuang Fu Rd., Sec. 1,
New Taipei City
229 953-081

(P-23047)
SIEMENS MED SOLUTIONS USA INC
Also Called: Oncology Care Systems Group
4040 Nelson Ave, Concord (94520-1200)
PHONE....................925 246-8200
Ajit Singh, *President*
Naeemah Johnson-Mcquill, *Administration*
EMP: 450
SALES (corp-wide): 97.7B Privately Held
WEB: www.siemensmedical.com
SIC: 3845 3842 5047 Electromedical equipment; surgical appliances & supplies; hospital equipment & furniture
HQ: Siemens Medical Solutions Usa, Inc.
40 Liberty Blvd
Malvern PA 19355
888 826-9702

(P-23048)
SIUI AMERICA INC
780 Montague Expy Ste 608, San Jose
(95131-1320)
PHONE....................408 432-8881
James MA, *President*
▲ EMP: 10
SALES: 3MM Privately Held
WEB: www.siuiamerica.com
SIC: 3845 Ultrasonic scanning devices, medical

(P-23049)
SMART CAREGIVER CORPORATION
1229 N Mcdowell Blvd, Petaluma
(94954-1112)
PHONE....................707 781-7450
Timothy Long, *President*

P
R
O
D
U
C
T
S

&

S
V
C
S

Lauren Long, *Admin Sec*
Lena Winterboer, *Admin Sec*
▲ EMP: 25
SQ FT: 4,200
SALES (est): 10MM **Privately Held**
WEB: www.smartcaregivercorp.com
SIC: 3845 Electromedical equipment

(P-23050)
SOLTA MEDICAL INC (DH)
7031 Koll Center Pkwy # 260, Pleasanton
(94566-3134)
PHONE.................................510 786-6946
J Michael Pearson, *President*
Howard B Schiller, *Treasurer*
Robert Chai-Onn, *Admin Sec*
Doug Fett, *Director*
▲ EMP: 12
SQ FT: 88,000
SALES (est): 77.8MM
SALES (corp-wide): 8.7B **Privately Held**
WEB: www.thermage.com
SIC: 3845 Laser systems & equipment,
medical
HQ: Valeant Pharmaceuticals International
400 Somerset Corp Blvd
Bridgewater NJ 08807
908 927-1400

(P-23051)
SOLTA MEDICAL INC
25901 Industrial Blvd, Hayward
(94545-2995)
PHONE.................................510 782-2286
Doug Heigo, *Branch Mgr*
Lisa Parr, *Vice Pres*
Katherine Grant, *Managing Dir*
Jack Ham, *Engineer*
Mark Spaw, *Engineer*
EMP: 150
SALES (corp-wide): 8.7B **Privately Held**
SIC: 3845 Electromedical equipment
HQ: Solta Medical, Inc.
7031 Koll Center Pkwy # 260
Pleasanton CA 94566
510 786-6946

(P-23052)
SOTERA WIRELESS INC
10020 Huennekens St, San Diego
(92121-2966)
PHONE.................................858 427-4620
Thomas Watlington, *CEO*
Charlie Alvarez, *President*
Tom Watlington, *CEO*
Mark Spring, *CFO*
Benjamin Kanter, *Chief Mktg Ofcr*
EMP: 104
SQ FT: 29,928
SALES (est): 26.6MM **Privately Held**
SIC: 3845 Electromedical equipment

(P-23053)
SOUND IMAGING INC
7580 Trade St Ste A, San Diego
(92121-2479)
PHONE.................................858 622-0082
Sunny Tabrizi, *CFO*
Daniel Rubalcaba, *Engineer*
EMP: 19
SQ FT: 5,800
SALES (est): 3.3MM **Privately Held**
WEB: www.soundimaging.com
SIC: 3845 5047 5999 Laser systems &
equipment, medical; medical equipment &
supplies; medical apparatus & supplies

(P-23054)
SPECTRANETICS
6531 Dumbarton Cir, Fremont
(94555-3619)
PHONE.................................408 592-2111
EMP: 11 EST: 2015
SALES (est): 1.4MM **Privately Held**
SIC: 3845 Electromedical equipment

(P-23055)
STRAND PRODUCTS INC (PA)
725 E Yanonali St, Santa Barbara
(93103-3235)
P.O. Box 4610 (93140-4610)
PHONE.................................805 568-0304
James Wilson, *President*
Wesley Pruncke, *Vice Pres*
Lourdes Madrigal, *Buyer*
▲ EMP: 22

SQ FT: 6,000
SALES (est): 4MM **Privately Held**
WEB: www.strandproducts.com
SIC: 3845 5063 Ultrasonic scanning de-
vices, medical; wire & cable

(P-23056)
SYNERON INC (DH)
Also Called: Syneron Candela
3 Goodyear Ste A, Irvine (92618-2050)
PHONE.................................866 259-6661
Shimon Eckhouse, *Ch of Bd*
Christine Mignanelli, *Partner*
Doron Gerstel, *President*
Shimon Eckhouse, *CEO*
Asaf Alperovitz, *CFO*
EMP: 53
SALES (est): 96.6MM **Privately Held**
SIC: 3845 Laser systems & equipment,
medical
HQ: Syneron Medical Ltd
Upper Yokneam
Upper Yokneam
732 442-200

(P-23057)
TAE LIFE SCIENCES LLC
19641 Da Vinci, Foothill Ranch
(92610-2603)
PHONE.................................949 830-2117
Bruce Bauer,
EMP: 10
SALES (est): 577.8K
SALES (corp-wide): 50.3MM **Privately
Held**
SIC: 3845 2834 Laser systems & equip-
ment, medical; pharmaceutical prepara-
tions
PA: Tae Technologies, Inc.
19631 Pauling
Foothill Ranch CA 92610
949 830-2117

(P-23058)
TENSYS MEDICAL INC
12625 High Bluff Dr # 213, San Diego
(92130-2052)
PHONE.................................858 552-1941
Stuart Gallant, *CEO*
Denise Pacenpo, *Administration*
Ceasar Avalos, *Info Tech Mgr*
Andrew Katayama, *Engineer*
Russ Hempstead, *Senior Engr*
EMP: 32
SQ FT: 25,370
SALES (est): 6.4MM **Privately Held**
WEB: www.tensysmedical.com
SIC: 3845 3841 Ultrasonic scanning de-
vices, medical; surgical & medical instru-
ments

(P-23059)
THORATEC CORPORATION (DH)
6035 Stoneridge Dr, Pleasanton
(94588-3270)
PHONE.................................925 847-8600
D Keith Grossman, *President*
Taylor C Harris, *CFO*
Jason Amaral, *Vice Pres*
Laxmi Peri, *Vice Pres*
Lisa Powell, *Vice Pres*
▲ EMP: 193
SQ FT: 66,000
SALES (est): 477.5MM
SALES (corp-wide): 27.3B **Publicly Held**
WEB: www.thoratec.com
SIC: 3845 3841 Electromedical equip-
ment; surgical & medical instruments; di-
agnostic apparatus, medical
HQ: St. Jude Medical, Llc
1 Saint Jude Medical Dr
Saint Paul MN 55117
651 756-2000

(P-23060)
TOPCON MED LASER SYSTEMS INC
606 Enterprise Ct, Livermore (94550-5200)
PHONE.................................888 760-8657
Dean Scotch, *Vice Pres*
Rob Orsino, *President*
Hideharu Suzuki, *President*
Dan Van Buskirk, *Program Mgr*
Bobbie Heap, *Area Mgr*
▲ EMP: 45

SALES (est): 8.4MM
SALES (corp-wide): 1.3B **Privately Held**
SIC: 3845 Laser systems & equipment,
medical
HQ: Topcon America Corporation
111 Bauer Dr
Oakland NJ 07436
201 599-5100

(P-23061)
TRI-STAR TECHNOLOGIES INC
2201 Rosecrans Ave, El Segundo
(90245-4910)
PHONE.................................310 536-0444
Alex Kerner, *President*
EMP: 12
SQ FT: 80,000
SALES: 4.4MM
SALES (corp-wide): 4B **Publicly Held**
WEB: www.tri-star-technologies.com
SIC: 3845 2836 3542 Laser systems &
equipment, medical; plasmas; crimping
machinery, metal
PA: Carlisle Companies Incorporated
16430 N Scottsdale Rd # 400
Scottsdale AZ 85254
704 501-1100

(P-23062)
TRIA BEAUTY INC
7999 Gateway Blvd Ste 100, Newark
(94560-1144)
PHONE.................................925 701-2500
Kevin J Appelbaum, *CEO*
Michelle Ritchie, *President*
Peter S Wyles, *President*
Michael R Lopez, *COO*
Sandra Gardiner, *CFO*
▲ EMP: 100
SQ FT: 30,000
SALES (est): 20.7MM **Privately Held**
WEB: www.spectragenics.com
SIC: 3845 Electromedical equipment

(P-23063)
TRIMEDYNE INC (PA)
5 Holland Ste 223, Irvine (92618-2579)
PHONE.................................949 951-3800
Glenn D Yeik, *President*
Marvin P Loeb, *Ch of Bd*
L Dean Crawford, *Vice Pres*
Brian T Kenney, *Vice Pres*
EMP: 43
SQ FT: 9,215
SALES (est): 5.3MM **Publicly Held**
WEB: www.trimedyne.com
SIC: 3845 7352 Laser systems & equip-
ment, medical; medical equipment rental

(P-23064)
VAVE HEALTH INC
2955 Campus Dr Ste 110, San Mateo
(94403-2563)
PHONE.................................650 387-7059
Amin Nikoozadeh, *CEO*
EMP: 15
SALES (est): 989.1K **Privately Held**
SIC: 3845 Ultrasonic medical equipment,
except cleaning

(P-23065)
VERTIFLEX INC
2714 Loker Ave W Ste 100, Carlsbad
(92010-6640)
PHONE.................................442 325-5900
Earl R Fender, *CEO*
William H Duffell, *Vice Pres*
Michel E Hughes, *Vice Pres*
Kyle Hayes, *Research*
EMP: 40 EST: 2004
SQ FT: 25,000
SALES (est): 7.8MM **Privately Held**
SIC: 3845 Ultrasonic scanning devices,
medical

(P-23066)
VIBRYNT INC
2570 W El Camino Real # 310, Mountain
View (94040-1306)
PHONE.................................650 362-6100
Beverly A Huss, *President*
Theodore M Bender, *Vice Pres*
Laurie Hook, *Vice Pres*
EMP: 30
SQ FT: 4,121

SALES (est): 3.1MM **Privately Held**
SIC: 3845

(P-23067)
VITAL CONNECT INC
224 Airport Pkwy Ste 300, San Jose
(95110-1022)
PHONE.................................408 963-4600
Nersi Nazari, *President*
Michael Dillhyon, *President*
Martin Webster, *CFO*
EMP: 50
SALES (est): 9.4MM **Privately Held**
SIC: 3845 Ultrasonic scanning devices,
medical

(P-23068)
VIVOMETRICS INC
16030 Ventura Blvd # 470, Encino
(91436-2731)
PHONE.................................805 667-2225
Howard R Baker, *President*
EMP: 35 EST: 1999
SQ FT: 8,220
SALES (est): 3.5MM **Privately Held**
WEB: www.vivometrics.com
SIC: 3845 3842 Patient monitoring appa-
ratus; surgical appliances & supplies

(P-23069)
VOLCANO CORPORATION (DH)
3721 Vly Cntre Dr Ste 500, San Diego
(92130)
PHONE.................................800 228-4728
R Scott Huennekens, *President*
Ronald A Matricaria, *Ch of Bd*
John T Dahldorf, *CFO*
Darin M Lippoldt, *Exec VP*
John Onopchenko, *Exec VP*
▲ EMP: 300
SQ FT: 92,602
SALES: 393.6MM
SALES (corp-wide): 20.9B **Privately Held**
WEB: www.volcanocorp.com
SIC: 3845 Ultrasonic medical equipment,
except cleaning

(P-23070)
VOLCANO CORPORATION
Also Called: Volcano Therapeutics
2451 Merc Dr Ste 200, Rancho Cordova
(95742)
PHONE.................................916 281-2932
Saul Salayandia, *Manager*
EMP: 280
SALES (corp-wide): 20.9B **Privately Held**
SIC: 3845 Electromedical equipment
HQ: Volcano Corporation
3721 Vly Cntre Dr Ste 500
San Diego CA 92130
800 228-4728

(P-23071)
VOLCANO CORPORATION
1931 Old Middlefield Way, Mountain View
(94043-2557)
PHONE.................................650 938-5300
R Scott Huennekens, *President*
EMP: 280
SALES (corp-wide): 20.9B **Privately Held**
SIC: 3845 Electromedical equipment
HQ: Volcano Corporation
3721 Vly Cntre Dr Ste 500
San Diego CA 92130
800 228-4728

(P-23072)
VOLCANO CORPORATION
2870 Kilgore Rd, Rancho Cordova
(95670-6133)
PHONE.................................916 638-8008
Scott Huennekens, *CEO*
Scott Williams, *CIO*
Emmanuel De Maere, *Human Res Mgr*
Gary N Shelp, *Buyer*
Justin Caranfa, *Consultant*
EMP: 280
SALES (corp-wide): 20.9B **Privately Held**
WEB: www.volcanocorp.com
SIC: 3845 Ultrasonic scanning devices,
medical
HQ: Volcano Corporation
3721 Vly Cntre Dr Ste 500
San Diego CA 92130
800 228-4728

(P-23073)
XINTEC CORPORATION (PA)
Also Called: Convergent Laser Technologies
1660 S Loop Rd, Alameda (94502-7091)
PHONE..................................510 832-2130
Mark H K Chim, *President*
Marilyn M Chou, *Exec VP*
Marilyn Chou, *Exec VP*
Jennifer Mok, *General Mgr*
Jenny Ha, *Purchasing*
▲ EMP: 20
SQ FT: 20,000
SALES (est): 3.3MM **Privately Held**
WEB: www.convergentlaser.com
SIC: 3845 Laser systems & equipment, medical

(P-23074)
ZOLL CIRCULATION INC
2000 Ringwood Ave, San Jose
(95131-1728)
PHONE..................................408 541-2140
Richard A Packer, *CEO*
James Palabzolo, *President*
Rick Helkowski, *Vice Pres*
Kenneth E Ludlum, *Principal*
Jonathan A Rennert, *Principal*
▲ EMP: 130
SALES (est): 39.9MM
SALES (corp-wide): 19.1B **Privately Held**
WEB: www.revivant.com
SIC: 3845 3841 Electromedical equipment; surgical & medical instruments
HQ: Zoll Medical Corporation
269 Mill Rd
Chelmsford MA 01824
978 421-9655

(P-23075)
ZOLL MEDICAL CORPORATION
2000 Ringwood Ave, San Jose
(95131-1728)
PHONE..................................408 419-2929
Beth Barredo, *Manager*
Dean Severns, *Electrical Engi*
Jim Mazzone, *Engineer*
EMP: 15
SALES (corp-wide): 19.1B **Privately Held**
SIC: 3845 Defibrillator
HQ: Zoll Medical Corporation
269 Mill Rd
Chelmsford MA 01824
978 421-9655

3851 Ophthalmic Goods

(P-23076)
ABBS VISION SYSTEMS INC
Also Called: Guard-Dogs
4848 Colt St Ste 14, Ventura (93003-7732)
PHONE..................................805 642-0499
Susan Lindahl, *President*
Arthur Lindahl, *Vice Pres*
▲ EMP: 10
SQ FT: 1,200
SALES (est): 1.4MM **Privately Held**
WEB: www.guard-dogs.com
SIC: 3851 Protective eyeware

(P-23077)
ADVANCED VISION SCIENCE INC
5743 Thornwood Dr, Goleta (93117-3801)
PHONE..................................805 683-3851
Khalid Mentak, *Ch of Bd*
EMP: 40
SQ FT: 30,000
SALES (est): 9.2MM
SALES (corp-wide): 2.1B **Privately Held**
WEB: www.advancedvisionscience.com
SIC: 3851 3841 8011 Intraocular lenses; surgical & medical instruments; offices & clinics of medical doctors
PA: Santen Pharmaceutical Co., Ltd.
4-20, Ofukacho, Kita-Ku
Osaka OSK 530-0
663 217-000

(P-23078)
AMERON INTERNATIONAL CORP
Ameron Protective Linings
201 N Berry St, Brea (92821-3931)
P.O. Box 1629 (92822-1629)
PHONE..................................714 256-7755
Micheal Carruth, *Branch Mgr*
EMP: 30
SALES (corp-wide): 7.3B **Publicly Held**
WEB: www.ameron.com
SIC: 3851 3081 Ophthalmic goods; unsupported plastics film & sheet
HQ: Ameron International Corporation
7909 Parkwood Circle Dr
Houston TX 77036
713 375-3700

(P-23079)
B-LITE OPTICAL INC
18314 Ward St, Fountain Valley
(92708-6853)
PHONE..................................714 964-8450
Richard Dang, *CEO*
Han Dang, *President*
EMP: 10 EST: 1977
SQ FT: 4,500
SALES (est): 563.6K **Privately Held**
SIC: 3851 Lenses, ophthalmic

(P-23080)
BARTON PERREIRA LLC (PA)
459 Wald, Irvine (92618-4639)
PHONE..................................949 305-5360
William G Barton,
Dwight Chiles, *Partner*
Mike Niewald, *Managing Prtnr*
Jennifer Soho, *General Mgr*
Robert Fiddler, *CIO*
▲ EMP: 25 EST: 2006
SALES (est): 4.2MM **Privately Held**
SIC: 3851 Protective eyeware

(P-23081)
BAUSCH & LOMB INCORPORATED
50 Technology Dr, Irvine (92618-2301)
PHONE..................................949 788-6000
Ron Zarella, *Branch Mgr*
James Leblanc, *Info Tech Dir*
Edward Kennedy, *Director*
David Diehl, *Manager*
EMP: 200
SALES (corp-wide): 8.7B **Privately Held**
WEB: www.bausch.com
SIC: 3851 Ophthalmic goods
HQ: Bausch & Lomb Incorporated
1400 N Goodman St
Rochester NY 14609
585 338-6000

(P-23082)
BROTHERS OPTICAL LABORATORY
870 N Eckhoff St, Orange (92868-1008)
PHONE..................................714 639-9852
John Ragazzo, *President*
Joseph Ragazzo, *Corp Secy*
Peter Comoglio, *Vice Pres*
▲ EMP: 90 EST: 1973
SQ FT: 19,000
SALES (est): 12.8MM **Privately Held**
SIC: 3851 5048 Lenses, ophthalmic; ophthalmic goods

(P-23083)
CALIFORNIA COATING LAB
670 Mccormick St, San Leandro
(94577-1110)
PHONE..................................510 357-1800
William Lee, *Owner*
Angie Lewis-Stuber, *Admin Asst*
EMP: 20
SALES (est): 2.1MM **Privately Held**
WEB: www.californiacoatinglab.com
SIC: 3851 Lens coating, ophthalmic

(P-23084)
CARL ZEISS VISION INC (DH)
12121 Scripps Summit Dr, San Diego
(92131-4608)
PHONE..................................858 790-7700
Jens Boy, *President*
Carmen Sarracco, *VP Finance*
Paul Green, *Finance*

Donna Poole, *Finance*
Meredith Feldman, *Marketing Mgr*
▲ EMP: 80
SQ FT: 9,000
SALES (est): 280MM **Privately Held**
WEB: www.zeiss.com/us
SIC: 3851 3827 Lenses, ophthalmic; lenses, optical: all types except ophthalmic
HQ: Carl Zeiss Vision International Gmbh
Turnstr. 27
Aalen 73430
736 159-10

(P-23085)
CONTEX INC
Also Called: Contex Inc Contact Lenses
4505 Van Nuys Blvd, Van Nuys
(91403-2914)
PHONE..................................818 788-5836
Nick Stoyan, *President*
Ann Stoyan, *Vice Pres*
Gary Stoyan, *Vice Pres*
EMP: 15
SQ FT: 5,000
SALES (est): 3.4MM **Privately Held**
WEB: www.oklens.com
SIC: 3851 8011 Contact lenses; offices & clinics of medical doctors

(P-23086)
COOPER COMPANIES INC (PA)
6140 Stoneridge Mall Rd # 590, Pleasanton
(94588-3772)
PHONE..................................925 460-3600
Albert G White III, *President*
A Thomas Bender, *Ch of Bd*
Daniel G McBride, *COO*
Brian Andrews, *CFO*
Allan E Rubenstein, *Vice Ch Bd*
EMP: 142
SQ FT: 103,990
SALES (est): 2.1B **Publicly Held**
WEB: www.coopercos.com
SIC: 3851 3842 Contact lenses; surgical appliances & supplies; gynecological supplies & appliances

(P-23087)
COOPERVISION INC
6150 Stoneridge Mall Rd # 370, Pleasanton
(94588-3241)
PHONE..................................925 251-6600
Stephen Fanning, *CEO*
Amy Appleton, *Accountant*
Sarah Cooley, *Human Res Mgr*
Susan Malone, *Director*
Ye Hong, *Manager*
EMP: 100
SALES (corp-wide): 2.1B **Publicly Held**
SIC: 3851 Contact lenses
HQ: Coopervision, Inc.
209 High Point Dr Ste 100
Victor NY 14564

(P-23088)
DITA INC (PA)
Also Called: Dita Eyewear
1 Columbia Ste 130, Aliso Viejo
(92656-1473)
PHONE..................................949 599-2700
Sukhmeet Dhillon, *President*
Shahid Ghani, *Treasurer*
Shahid Ghant, *Director*
Jeffrey J Solorio, *Director*
▲ EMP: 33
SQ FT: 3,000
SALES (est): 4.2MM **Privately Held**
WEB: www.ditaeyewear.com
SIC: 3851 5995 Ophthalmic goods; optical goods stores

(P-23089)
DRAGON ALLIANCE INC
971 Calle Amanecer, San Clemente
(92673-4228)
PHONE..................................760 931-4900
William H Howard, *President*
James Flanagan, *Vice Pres*
Ryan Vance, *Admin Sec*
Westley Grant, *Administration*
▲ EMP: 45
SQ FT: 3,500

SALES (est): 8MM
SALES (corp-wide): 3.2B **Privately Held**
WEB: www.dragonoptical.com
SIC: 3851 Glasses, sun or glare
HQ: Marchon Eyewear, Inc.
201 Old Country Rd Fl 3
Melville NY 11747
631 756-8530

(P-23090)
EAGLE LABORATORIES LLC
Also Called: Eagle Labs
10201a Trademark St Ste A, Rancho Cucamonga (91730-5849)
PHONE..................................909 481-0011
Dennis M Decamp, *President*
Michael Decamp, *Vice Pres*
Richard Decamp, *Vice Pres*
EMP: 65
SQ FT: 30,000
SALES (est): 5.3MM **Privately Held**
SIC: 3851 Frames, lenses & parts, eyeglass & spectacle
PA: Innovia Medical
815 Northwest Pkwy # 100
Saint Paul MN 55121
651 789-3939

(P-23091)
ELECTRIC VISUAL EVOLUTION LLC (PA)
950 Calle Amanecer # 101, San Clemente
(92673-4231)
PHONE..................................949 940-9125
Eric Crane, *CEO*
Billy Benda, *Finance*
Scott Morris, *Controller*
Steve Hurst, *VP Opers*
Derek Bradley, *Sales Dir*
▲ EMP: 28 EST: 1999
SQ FT: 2,000
SALES (est): 5.3MM **Privately Held**
SIC: 3851 5094 5136 Glasses, sun or glare; watchcases; apparel belts, men's & boys'

(P-23092)
EMPIRE OPTICAL OF CALIFORNIA
7633 Varna Ave, North Hollywood
(91605-1748)
PHONE..................................818 997-6474
Noel Diaz, *Principal*
Neil Grossman, *President*
Joanne Grossman, *Corp Secy*
Jessica Gomez, *Sales Associate*
Charles Thomas, *Marketing Staff*
EMP: 45
SQ FT: 5,000
SALES (est): 7.1MM **Privately Held**
SIC: 3851 Lens grinding, except prescription: ophthalmic
HQ: Essilor Laboratories Of America, Inc.
13515 N Stemmons Fwy
Dallas TX 75234
972 241-4141

(P-23093)
ENHANCED VISION SYSTEMS INC (HQ)
5882 Machine Dr Ste A, Huntington Beach
(92649-5710)
PHONE..................................714 374-1829
Tom Tiernan, *CEO*
Scott Drake, *Vice Pres*
Jesse Perez, *Vice Pres*
Ronald Roeten, *Managing Dir*
Kamran Siminou, *CTO*
◆ EMP: 21
SALES (est): 11.9MM
SALES (corp-wide): 17.6MM **Privately Held**
WEB: www.enhancedvision.com
SIC: 3851 Ophthalmic goods
PA: Freedom Scientific Blv Group, Llc
17757 Us Highway 19 N # 560
Clearwater FL 33764
727 803-8000

(P-23094)
ESSILOR LABORATORIES AMER INC
801 N Burke St, Visalia (93292-3822)
PHONE..................................800 624-6672
Real Goulet, *Principal*

P R O D U C T S & S V C S

Eric Dennewitz, *General Mgr*
EMP: 50 **Privately Held**
SIC: 3851 Eyeglasses, lenses & frames
HQ: Essilor Laboratories Of America, Inc.
13515 N Stemmons Fwy
Dallas TX 75234
972 241-4141

(P-23095)
ESSILOR LABORATORIES AMER INC
Also Called: Elite Optical
1450 W Walnut St, Compton (90220-5013)
PHONE..........................310 604-8668
Real Goulet, *Principal*
EMP: 50 **Privately Held**
SIC: 3851 Eyeglasses, lenses & frames
HQ: Essilor Laboratories Of America, Inc.
13515 N Stemmons Fwy
Dallas TX 75234
972 241-4141

(P-23096)
EXPRESS LENS LAB INC
17150 Newhope St Ste 305, Fountain Valley (92708-4251)
PHONE..........................714 545-1024
Brian Goldstone, *President*
EMP: 30
SQ FT: 5,000
SALES (est): 3MM **Privately Held**
SIC: 3851 8011 5049 Ophthalmic goods; offices & clinics of medical doctors; optical goods

(P-23097)
EYEBRAIN MEDICAL INC
Also Called: Neurolenses
3184 Airway Ave Ste C, Costa Mesa (92626-4619)
PHONE..........................949 339-5157
Corley Davis, *President*
Danny Perales, *COO*
Thomas J Chirillo, *Ch Credit Ofcr*
▲ EMP: 16
SQ FT: 6,000
SALES: 392K **Privately Held**
SIC: 3851 Eyeglasses, lenses & frames

(P-23098)
EYEFLUENCE INC
1600 Amphitheatre Pkwy, Mountain View (94043-1351)
PHONE..........................408 586-8632
Jim Marggraff, *CEO*
Peter Milford, *CTO*
Gurmeet Kalra, *Software Engr*
EMP: 29
SALES (est): 3.7MM **Privately Held**
SIC: 3851

(P-23099)
EYEONICS INC
Also Called: Bausch & Lomb Surgical Div
50 Technology Dr, Irvine (92618-2301)
PHONE..........................949 788-6000
Joseph F Gordon, *CEO*
Steven Silverman, *Vice Pres*
Lori Gembka, *MIS Mgr*
Ed Martin, *Technology*
EMP: 18
SQ FT: 5,000
SALES (est): 3.8MM
SALES (corp-wide): 8.7B **Privately Held**
SIC: 3851 Ophthalmic goods
HQ: Bausch & Lomb Incorporated
1400 N Goodman St
Rochester NY 14609
585 338-6000

(P-23100)
HOYA OPTICAL INC (PA)
1400 Carpenter Ln, Modesto (95351-1102)
P.O. Box 580870 (95358-0016)
PHONE..........................209 579-7739
Fred Fink, *CEO*
Lester Thornburg, *Regional Mgr*
Steve Weidman, *General Mgr*
Maria Bennett, *Director*
EMP: 90
SQ FT: 17,700
SALES (est): 7.6MM **Privately Held**
SIC: 3851 8011 5995 5048 Ophthalmic goods; offices & clinics of medical doctors; optical goods stores; ophthalmic goods

(P-23101)
INITIUM EYEWEAR INC
412 Olive Ave Ste 218, Huntington Beach (92648-5142)
PHONE..........................714 444-0866
Jason Kazmer, *Principal*
EMP: 11
SALES (est): 149.1K **Privately Held**
SIC: 3851 Eyeglasses, lenses & frames

(P-23102)
IRD ACQUISITIONS LLC
Also Called: Ir Hunter
12810 Earhart Ave, Auburn (95602-9027)
PHONE..........................530 210-2966
Stephen Bindon, *CEO*
EMP: 12
SQ FT: 7,500
SALES (est): 2.4MM
SALES (corp-wide): 26.7MM **Privately Held**
SIC: 3851 3949 3827 Goggles: sun, safety, industrial, underwater, etc.; target shooting equipment; telescopes: elbow, panoramic, sighting, fire control, etc.
PA: Trijicon, Inc.
49385 Shafer Ct
Wixom MI 48393
248 960-7700

(P-23103)
J G HERNANDEZ COMPANY
Also Called: Collard Rose Optical Lab
12402 Philadelphia St, Whittier (90601-3932)
PHONE..........................562 698-2286
J G Hernandez, *President*
Robby J Hernandez, *President*
David Milan, *Vice Pres*
EMP: 47 EST: 1948
SQ FT: 2,400
SALES: 10MM **Privately Held**
SIC: 3851 Lenses, ophthalmic
HQ: Essilor Laboratories Of America, Inc.
13515 N Stemmons Fwy
Dallas TX 75234
972 241-4141

(P-23104)
KATZ & KLEIN
9901 Horn Rd Ste D, Sacramento (95827-1944)
PHONE..........................916 444-2024
Corrine Hood, *President*
Candy Corcoran, *Treasurer*
Mike Francesconi, *Vice Pres*
Magic Munson -Cs, *Manager*
EMP: 33
SQ FT: 7,500
SALES (est): 3.3MM **Privately Held**
WEB: www.katzandklein.com
SIC: 3851 5049 Ophthalmic goods; optical goods

(P-23105)
LENS C-C INC (PA)
Also Called: Con-Cise Contact Lens Co
1750 N Loop Rd Ste 150, Alameda (94502-8013)
PHONE..........................800 772-3911
Carl Moore, *President*
Lynda Baker, *Vice Pres*
Dan Davis, *Vice Pres*
Shelley Farley, *Accounts Exec*
EMP: 100 EST: 1949
SQ FT: 34,000
SALES (est): 7.6MM **Privately Held**
WEB: www.con-cise.com
SIC: 3851 Contact lenses

(P-23106)
LENSVECTOR INC
6203 San Ignacio Ave, San Jose (95119-1371)
PHONE..........................408 542-0300
Howard Earhart, *CEO*
Mark Gemello, *CFO*
EMP: 70
SALES (est): 11.5MM **Privately Held**
SIC: 3851 Ophthalmic goods

(P-23107)
LUXE LABORATORY
7052 Orangewood Ave Ste 8, Garden Grove (92841-1419)
PHONE..........................714 221-2330

Richard Wilhelm, *President*
EMP: 10 EST: 2012
SQ FT: 5,000
SALES: 1.5MM **Privately Held**
SIC: 3851 Ophthalmic goods

(P-23108)
MARCH VISION CARE INC
6701 Center Dr W Ste 790, Los Angeles (90045-1563)
PHONE..........................310 665-0975
Glen A March Jr, *President*
Shawn Shahzad, *President*
Gavin Galimi, *CFO*
Christos Poulios, *CFO*
Gavin G Galimi, *Exec VP*
EMP: 42
SALES (est): 8.2MM **Privately Held**
SIC: 3851 Frames, lenses & parts, eyeglass & spectacle
PA: March Holdings, Inc.
6701 Center Dr W Ste 790
Los Angeles CA 90045
-

(P-23109)
MEDENNIUM INC (PA)
9 Parker Ste 150, Irvine (92618-1691)
PHONE..........................949 789-9000
Jacob Feldman, *President*
James R Zullo, *CFO*
Loi Diep, *Manager*
EMP: 38
SQ FT: 20,000
SALES (est): 4.6MM **Privately Held**
WEB: www.medennium.com
SIC: 3851 Intraocular lenses

(P-23110)
NITINOL DEVELOPMENT CORP
Also Called: Nitinol Devices & Components
47533 Westinghouse Dr, Fremont (94539-7463)
PHONE..........................510 683-2000
Tom Duerig, *President*
Mark Lemma, *CFO*
Chun Tam, *CFO*
Chuck Faris, *Vice Pres*
David Johnston, *Vice Pres*
EMP: 600
SQ FT: 30,000
SALES (est): 18.7MM **Privately Held**
SIC: 3851 3496 Frames & parts, eyeglass & spectacle; miscellaneous fabricated wire products

(P-23111)
NVISION LASER EYE CENTERS INC
Also Called: Meister Eye & Laser
5959 Greenback Ln Ste 310, Citrus Heights (95621-4700)
PHONE..........................916 723-7400
Richard Meister, *Branch Mgr*
EMP: 15
SALES (corp-wide): 6.2MM **Privately Held**
SIC: 3851 Frames, lenses & parts, eyeglass & spectacle
PA: Nvision Laser Eye Centers Inc.
3155d Sedona Ct 100
Ontario CA 91764
909 605-1975

(P-23112)
OAKLEY INC
20081 Ellipse, Foothill Ranch (92610-3001)
PHONE..........................949 672-6849
EMP: 52 **Privately Held**
SIC: 3851 Ophthalmic goods
HQ: Oakley, Inc.
1 Icon
Foothill Ranch CA 92610
949 951-0991

(P-23113)
OAKLEY SALES CORP
1 Icon, El Toro (92610-3000)
PHONE..........................949 951-0991
Link Newcomb, *President*
Derek Baker, *Vice Pres*
◆ EMP: 18
SQ FT: 400,000

SALES (est): 3.3MM **Privately Held**
WEB: www.oakley.com
SIC: 3851 Glasses, sun or glare
HQ: Oakley, Inc.
1 Icon
Foothill Ranch CA 92610
949 951-0991

(P-23114)
OASIS MEDICAL INC (PA)
510-528 S Vermont Ave, Glendora (91741)
P.O. Box 1137 (91740-1137)
PHONE..........................909 305-5400
Norman Delgado, *Ch of Bd*
Craig Delgado, *President*
Arlene Delgado, *Corp Secy*
Maria Lacayo-Zuniga, *Engineer*
Richard Quach, *Engineer*
▲ EMP: 55
SQ FT: 14,000
SALES (est): 13.6MM **Privately Held**
WEB: www.oasismedical.com
SIC: 3851 5048 Ophthalmic goods; ophthalmic goods

(P-23115)
OPHTHONIX INC
900 Glenneyre St, Laguna Beach (92651-2707)
PHONE..........................760 842-5600
Stephen J Osbaldeston, *CEO*
Jim Bergmark, *Finance Dir*
▲ EMP: 60
SQ FT: 50,000
SALES (est): 7.4MM **Privately Held**
WEB: www.ophthonix.com
SIC: 3851 Eyes, glass & plastic

(P-23116)
OPTI LITE OPTICAL
5552 W Adams Blvd, Los Angeles (90016-2542)
PHONE..........................323 932-6828
Howard Mochayoff, *Owner*
EMP: 20
SQ FT: 5,512
SALES (est): 2.1MM **Privately Held**
SIC: 3851 Lens grinding, except prescription: ophthalmic

(P-23117)
PRESBIBIO LLC
Also Called: Presbia
8845 Irvine Center Dr, Irvine (92618-4247)
PHONE..........................949 502-7010
Todd Cooper,
Jarett Fenton, *CFO*
Neal Gonzales, *Vice Pres*
John Strobel, *Vice Pres*
Michelle McLachlan, *Office Admin*
EMP: 45
SALES (est): 5.1MM **Privately Held**
SIC: 3851 Frames, lenses & parts, eyeglass & spectacle

(P-23118)
RAFI SYSTEMS INC
23453 Golden Springs Dr, Diamond Bar (91765-2030)
PHONE..........................909 861-6574
Mohamed Rafiuzzaman, *President*
Mrs Kusum Rafiquzza, *CEO*
EMP: 95
SQ FT: 5,000
SALES (est): 8.9MM **Privately Held**
WEB: www.rafisystems.com
SIC: 3851 3843 5047 5048 Frames, lenses & parts, eyeglass & spectacle; dental equipment; dental equipment & supplies; ophthalmic goods

(P-23119)
RICHMOND OPTICAL CO
923 Berryessa Rd, San Jose (95133-1002)
PHONE..........................510 783-1420
Ronald Furr, *President*
Ken Furr, *Vice Pres*
EMP: 12
SQ FT: 1,800
SALES (est): 1.1MM **Privately Held**
SIC: 3851 5048 Ophthalmic goods; frames, ophthalmic

(P-23120)
SAFETY AMERICA INC
2766 Via Orange Way Ste D, Spring Valley
(91978-1753)
PHONE................................619 660-6968
EMP: 12
SQ FT: 2,000
SALES: 1.2MM **Privately Held**
WEB: www.safetyamerica.com
SIC: 3851 7389

(P-23121)
SAM VAZIRI VANCE INC (PA)
Also Called: Sama Eyewear
15120 Keswick St, Van Nuys (91405-1134)
PHONE................................323 822-3955
Sheila Vance, *President*
Hossein Kazemi, *Vice Pres*
▲ **EMP:** 20
SQ FT: 3,400
SALES (est): 4.6MM **Privately Held**
WEB: www.samaeyewear.net
SIC: 3851 Protective eyeware

(P-23122)
SIGNATURE EYEWEAR INC (PA)
317 Isis Ave Ste 207, Inglewood
(90301-2030)
PHONE................................310 330-2700
Michael Prince, *CEO*
Richard M Torre, *Ch of Bd*
Jill Gardner, *Senior VP*
Raul Khantzis, *Senior VP*
Kevin D Seifert, *Senior VP*
▲ **EMP:** 105
SQ FT: 64,000
SALES (est): 13.2MM **Privately Held**
WEB: www.signatureeyewear.com
SIC: 3851 Eyeglasses, lenses & frames

(P-23123)
SPELLBOUND DEVELOPMENT GROUP
Also Called: Spellbound Entertainment
17192 Gillette Ave, Irvine (92614-5603)
PHONE................................949 474-8577
Earl Votolato, *President*
Bobbie Simmons, *General Mgr*
▲ **EMP:** 10
SALES (est): 1.7MM **Privately Held**
WEB: www.spellboundinc.com
SIC: 3851 7812 5099 Goggles: sun,
safety, industrial, underwater, etc.; video
production; safety equipment & supplies

(P-23124)
SPORTRX INC
5076 Santa Fe St Ste A, San Diego
(92109-1634)
PHONE................................858 571-0240
Gabby Bloch, *CEO*
Nigel Bloch, *Vice Pres*
Shelby Staab, *Manager*
▲ **EMP:** 20
SQ FT: 5,000
SALES (est): 4.3MM **Privately Held**
WEB: www.sportrx.com
SIC: 3851 Eyeglasses, lenses & frames

(P-23125)
SPY INC (PA)
1896 Rutherford Rd, Carlsbad
(92008-7326)
PHONE................................760 804-8420
Seth Hamot, *Ch of Bd*
Barry Buchholtz, *President*
James McGinty, *CFO*
Jim Sepanek, *Exec VP*
▲ **EMP:** 94
SQ FT: 32,551
SALES (est): 38.1MM **Publicly Held**
WEB: www.orangetwentyone.com
SIC: 3851 5099 Glasses, sun or glare;
sunglasses

(P-23126)
STAAR SURGICAL COMPANY (PA)
1911 Walker Ave, Monrovia (91016-4846)
PHONE................................626 303-7902
Caren Mason, *President*
Louis E Silverman, *Ch of Bd*
Deborah Andrews, *CFO*
Samuel Gesten,
Hans-Martin Blickensdoerfer, *Senior VP*

▲ **EMP:** 245 **EST:** 1982
SALES: 90.6MM **Publicly Held**
WEB: www.staar.com
SIC: 3851 Ophthalmic goods

(P-23127)
STAAR SURGICAL COMPANY
15102 Redhiill Ave, Tustin (92780)
PHONE................................626 303-7902
Keith Holiday, *Branch Mgr*
EMP: 16
SALES (corp-wide): 90.6MM **Publicly Held**
SIC: 3851 Ophthalmic goods
PA: Staar Surgical Company
1911 Walker Ave
Monrovia CA 91016
626 303-7902

(P-23128)
SYNERGEYES INC (PA)
2232 Rutherford Rd, Carlsbad
(92008-8814)
PHONE................................760 476-9410
James K Kirchner, *President*
Thomas M Crews, *President*
James Gorechner, *CEO*
Paul K Kammann, *CFO*
David Voris, *CFO*
▲ **EMP:** 78
SALES (est): 10.6MM **Privately Held**
SIC: 3851 Contact lenses

(P-23129)
TEKIA INC
17 Hammond Ste 414, Irvine (92618-1635)
PHONE................................949 699-1300
Gene Currie, *President*
Larry Blake, *VP Engrg*
Rachael MAI, *Manager*
EMP: 20
SQ FT: 5,000
SALES: 2MM **Privately Held**
WEB: www.tekia.com
SIC: 3851 8742 Intraocular lenses; hospi-
tal & health services consultant

(P-23130)
VISIONARY INC
2940 E Miraloma Ave, Anaheim
(92806-1811)
PHONE................................714 237-1900
Richard Belliveau, *President*
Cindy Belliveau, *Treasurer*
EMP: 30
SQ FT: 16,000
SALES: 2.5MM **Privately Held**
SIC: 3851 5048 Contact lenses; contact
lenses

(P-23131)
WHEELER OPTICAL LAB
8200 Katella Ave Ste A, Stanton
(90680-3262)
PHONE................................714 891-2016
Alex Aguilar, *Owner*
EMP: 10
SQ FT: 1,700
SALES (est): 862.6K **Privately Held**
SIC: 3851 Lenses, ophthalmic

(P-23132)
X WILEY INC (PA)
Also Called: Wiley X Eyewear
7800 Patterson Pass Rd, Livermore
(94550-9544)
PHONE................................925 243-9810
Myles R Freeman Sr, *CEO*
Myles J Freeman Jr, *President*
Steve Gerlovich, *Vice Pres*
Teresa Araujo, *Human Res Mgr*
Renee Engberson, *Sales Staff*
▲ **EMP:** 75
SQ FT: 35,000
SALES (est): 18.9MM **Privately Held**
WEB: www.wileyx.com
SIC: 3851 5048 2381 2339 Frames,
lenses & parts, eyeglass & spectacle;
ophthalmic goods; gloves, work: woven or
knit, made from purchased materials;
women's & misses' athletic clothing &
sportswear

(P-23133)
YOUNGER MFG CO (PA)
Also Called: Younger Optics
2925 California St, Torrance (90503-3914)
PHONE................................310 783-1533
Joseph David Rips, *CEO*
Tom Balch, *President*
Roshan Seresinhe, *CFO*
David Ambler, *Vice Pres*
Nancy Yamasaki, *Admin Sec*
▲ **EMP:** 280
SQ FT: 130,000
SALES (est): 246.4MM **Privately Held**
WEB: www.youngeroptics.com
SIC: 3851 Lenses, ophthalmic

(P-23134)
ZEROUV
16792 Burke Ln, Huntington Beach
(92647-4559)
PHONE................................714 584-0015
Viet Tran, *Principal*
EMP: 12
SALES (est): 904K **Privately Held**
SIC: 3851 Eyeglasses, lenses & frames

3861 Photographic Eqpt & Splys

(P-23135)
3ALITY DIGITAL LLC
Also Called: 3ality Technica
55 E Orange Grove Ave, Burbank
(91502-1827)
PHONE................................818 333-3000
Steve Schklair, *CEO*
EMP: 12 **Privately Held**
SIC: 3861 Cameras & related equipment
PA: 3ality Digital Llc
895 N Todd Ave
Azusa CA 91702

(P-23136)
AB MANUFACTURING INC
115 Red River Way, San Jose
(95136-3352)
PHONE................................408 972-5085
Dan Maurer, *President*
Anhvu Vu, *Treasurer*
Corinne Avila, *Office Mgr*
EMP: 10
SQ FT: 2,200
SALES (est): 970K **Privately Held**
WEB: www.abmfg.com
SIC: 3861 7699 Photographic equipment
& supplies; photographic equipment re-
pair

(P-23137)
AFTERMASTER INC (PA)
6671 W Sunset Blvd # 1520, Hollywood
(90028-7175)
PHONE................................310 657-4886
Lawrence G Ryckman, *Ch of Bd*
Mirella Chavez, *CFO*
Mark Depew, *Senior VP*
Aaron Ryckman, *Senior VP*
Sheldon Yakus, *Senior VP*
EMP: 11
SALES: 879.9K **Publicly Held**
SIC: 3861 Sound recording & reproducing
equipment, motion picture

(P-23138)
ALTIA SYSTEMS INC
10020 N De Anza Blvd # 200, Cupertino
(95014-2213)
PHONE................................408 996-9710
Aurangzeb Khan, *CEO*
Naveed Alam, *Vice Pres*
Osman Ahmed, *Software Engr*
Yashket Gupta, *Project Leader*
Priya Krishnan, *Marketing Mgr*
▲ **EMP:** 19
SALES (est): 3.3MM **Privately Held**
SIC: 3861 Cameras & related equipment

(P-23139)
ANSCHUTZ FILM GROUP LLC (HQ)
1888 Century Park E # 1400, Los Angeles
(90067-1718)
PHONE................................310 887-1000

Michael Bostick, *CEO*
▲ **EMP:** 30
SALES (est): 2.5MM **Privately Held**
SIC: 3861 Motion picture film

(P-23140)
AUTOCUE INC
Also Called: O'Connor Engineering Labs
2701 N Ontario St, Burbank (91504-2517)
PHONE................................213 627-4570
Joel Johnson, *General Mgr*
Cary Clayton, *Vice Pres*
George Baffa, *Agent*
EMP: 31
SALES (corp-wide): 5.4MM **Privately Held**
SIC: 3861 Photographic equipment & sup-
plies
PA: Autocue, Inc.
122 W 30th St Rm 312
New York NY 10001
212 929-7755

(P-23141)
AVID TECHNOLOGY INC
2600 10th St Ste 100, Berkeley
(94710-2512)
PHONE................................510 486-8302
EMP: 462
SALES (corp-wide): 419MM **Publicly Held**
SIC: 3861 Photographic equipment & sup-
plies
PA: Avid Technology, Inc.
75 Network Dr
Burlington MA 01803
978 640-6789

(P-23142)
AVID TECHNOLOGY INC
101 S 1st St Ste 200, Burbank
(91502-1938)
PHONE................................818 557-2520
Kristin Bedient, *Manager*
EMP: 20
SALES (corp-wide): 419MM **Publicly Held**
WEB: www.avid.com
SIC: 3861 Editing equipment, motion pic-
ture: viewers, splicers, etc.
PA: Avid Technology, Inc.
75 Network Dr
Burlington MA 01803
978 640-6789

(P-23143)
AVID TECHNOLOGY INC
14007 Runnymede St, Van Nuys
(91405-2510)
PHONE................................818 779-7860
EMP: 215
SALES (corp-wide): 677.9MM **Publicly Held**
SIC: 3861
PA: Avid Technology, Inc.
75 Network Dr
Burlington MA 01803
978 640-6789

(P-23144)
CHRISTIE DIGITAL SYSTEMS INC (HQ)
10550 Camden Dr, Cypress (90630-4600)
PHONE................................714 236-8610
Rex Balz, *President*
EMP: 17
SALES (est): 123.8MM
SALES (corp-wide): 1.6B **Privately Held**
SIC: 3861 6719 Projectors, still or motion
picture, silent or sound; investment hold-
ing companies, except banks
PA: Ushio Inc.
1-6-5, Marunouchi
Chiyoda-Ku TKY 100-0
356 571-000

(P-23145)
CINE MECHANICS INC
20610 Plummer St, Chatsworth
(91311-5111)
PHONE................................818 701-7944
Albert Beck Jr, *President*
EMP: 14
SQ FT: 11,000
SALES: 1MM **Privately Held**
SIC: 3861 Cameras & related equipment

(P-23146)
COMPUTER PROMPTING SERVICE
617 S Victory Blvd, Burbank (91502-2424)
PHONE..................................818 563-3465
Bron Galleran, *President*
EMP: 12 **EST:** 1983
SALES: 200K **Privately Held**
WEB: www.computerprompting.com
SIC: 3861 Blueprint reproduction machines & equipment

(P-23147)
CONTINUOUS CARTRIDGE
Also Called: Acuprint.com
5973 Avenida Encinas # 140, Carlsbad (92008-4476)
PHONE..................................760 929-4808
EMP: 30
SALES (est): 1.9MM
SALES (corp-wide): 7.4MM **Privately Held**
WEB: www.ebanklink.com
SIC: 3861
PA: Acuprint, Inc.
  5973 Avenida Encinas
  Carlsbad CA 92008
  760 929-4808

(P-23148)
CRASHCAM INDUSTRIES CORP
19627 Vision Dr, Topanga (90290-3116)
PHONE..................................310 283-5379
Ed Gutentag, *President*
EMP: 10
SQ FT: 1,500
SALES (est): 1.1MM **Privately Held**
SIC: 3861 Cameras, still & motion picture (all types)

(P-23149)
DION ROSTAMIAN
Also Called: Pic Flick
1146 N Central Ave 227, Glendale (91202-2506)
PHONE..................................877 633-0293
EMP: 12 **EST:** 2012
SALES (est): 670K **Privately Held**
SIC: 3861

(P-23150)
DJI TECHNOLOGY INC
201 S Victory Blvd, Burbank (91502-2349)
PHONE..................................818 235-0789
Jie Shen, *CEO*
EMP: 22 **EST:** 2015
SALES (est): 4.7MM **Privately Held**
SIC: 3861 Aerial cameras; cameras & related equipment

(P-23151)
DOREMI CINEMA LLC
1020 Chestnut St, Burbank (91506-1623)
PHONE..................................818 562-1101
Camille Rizko,
Safar Ghazal,
Emil Rizko,
EMP: 45
SQ FT: 20,000
SALES: 10MM **Privately Held**
SIC: 3861 Motion picture apparatus & equipment

(P-23152)
DURA IMAGING GROUP
1596 S Anaheim Blvd Ste A, Anaheim (92805-6229)
P.O. Box 1584, Garden Grove (92842-1584)
PHONE..................................714 254-1400
Sang Kim, *President*
Edward Wang, *CFO*
EMP: 10
SQ FT: 5,000
SALES: 1.2MM **Privately Held**
SIC: 3861 Toners, prepared photographic (not made in chemical plants)

(P-23153)
DXG TECHNOLOGY USA INC
Also Called: Dxg USA
330 Turnbull Canyon Rd, City of Industry (91745-1009)
PHONE..................................626 820-0687
Jackson Tzu-Chiang Yu, *President*

Tien-Ta Chih, *Shareholder*
Yung-Hsi Chen, *Shareholder*
Aaron Chen, *President*
Chih WEI Shih, *General Mgr*
◆ **EMP:** 26
SQ FT: 28,255
SALES: 36MM **Privately Held**
SIC: 3861 Cameras & related equipment

(P-23154)
E PHOCUS INC
10455 Pacific Center Ct, San Diego (92121-4339)
PHONE..................................858 646-5462
Tzuchiang Hsieh, *President*
Tzu-Chiang Hsieh, *President*
EMP: 13
SALES (est): 1MM **Privately Held**
SIC: 3861 Photographic equipment & supplies

(P-23155)
EASTMAN KODAK COMPANY
3 Santa Elena, Rcho STA Marg (92688-2409)
PHONE..................................949 306-9034
James Saavedra, *Sales Staff*
EMP: 65
SALES (corp-wide): 1.5B **Publicly Held**
SIC: 3861 Photographic equipment & supplies
PA: Eastman Kodak Company
  343 State St
  Rochester NY 14650
  585 724-4000

(P-23156)
ELEMENT TECHNICA LLC
4617 W Jefferson Blvd, Los Angeles (90016-4006)
PHONE..................................323 993-5329
Hector Ortega,
EMP: 12
SALES (est): 12MM **Privately Held**
WEB: www.slscine.com
SIC: 3861 Cameras & related equipment

(P-23157)
ELEPHANT FILMZ & MUSIC INC
3943 Irvine Blvd Ste 430, Irvine (92602-2400)
PHONE..................................310 925-8712
Aj Jamal, *CEO*
Abiola Lawal, *CFO*
EMP: 10
SQ FT: 800
SALES: 100K **Privately Held**
SIC: 3861 Motion picture film

(P-23158)
EPS-CINEWORKS LLC
3330 Chnga Blvd W Ste 200, Los Angeles (90068-1354)
PHONE..................................818 766-5000
Steven Balvanz, *Exec VP*
Adam Bergeron, *Administration*
Jed Unrot, *CTO*
Jerry Sawyer, *Technician*
Anthony Alas, *Accounting Mgr*
EMP: 13
SALES (est): 1.9MM **Privately Held**
SIC: 3861 Photographic equipment & supplies

(P-23159)
ESSENCE IMAGING INC
20651 Golden Springs Dr, Walnut (91789-3866)
PHONE..................................909 979-2116
Eliza Un, *CEO*
▲ **EMP:** 30 **EST:** 2006
SALES (est): 2.8MM **Privately Held**
SIC: 3861 Printing equipment, photographic

(P-23160)
FASTEC IMAGING CORPORATION
17150 Via DI Cmpo 301, San Diego (92127)
PHONE..................................858 592-2342
Stephen W Ferrell, *President*
Charles Mrdjenovich, *President*
Tony Montiel, *Vice Pres*
EMP: 25

SALES: 1,000K **Privately Held**
SIC: 3861 Cameras & related equipment

(P-23161)
GOPRO INC (PA)
3000 Clearview Way, San Mateo (94402-3710)
PHONE..................................650 332-7600
Nicholas Woodman, *Ch of Bd*
Brian McGee, *CFO*
Stephen Baumer, *Officer*
Fabrice Barbier, *Vice Pres*
Jonathan Harris, *Vice Pres*
EMP: 495
SQ FT: 311,000
SALES: 1.1B **Publicly Held**
WEB: www.gopro.com
SIC: 3861 7372 Cameras & related equipment; prepackaged software

(P-23162)
HF GROUP INC (PA)
Also Called: Houston Fearless 76
203 W Artesia Blvd, Compton (90220-5517)
PHONE..................................310 605-0755
Myung S Lee, *Ch of Bd*
James H Lee, *President*
Virginia C Clark, *CFO*
Sarah Lettiere, *CFO*
Gary Colby, *Vice Pres*
EMP: 47
SQ FT: 45,000
SALES (est): 9.9MM **Privately Held**
WEB: www.houstonfearless.com
SIC: 3861 Processing equipment, photographic; cameras, still & motion picture (all types); sensitized film, cloth & paper

(P-23163)
HITI DIGITAL AMERICA INC
675 Brea Canyon Rd Ste 7, Walnut (91789-3065)
PHONE..................................909 594-0099
Kuo-Hua Liang, *CEO*
Kevin Linton, *Sales Staff*
◆ **EMP:** 22
SALES (est): 4.4MM **Privately Held**
SIC: 3861 7384 Printing equipment, photographic; photographic services

(P-23164)
HOLLYWOOD FILM COMPANY
Also Called: Hav Holdings & Subsidiaries
9265 Borden Ave, Sun Valley (91352-2034)
PHONE..................................818 683-1130
Vincent Carabello, *President*
Antonia L Carabello, *Director*
▲ **EMP:** 100
SQ FT: 79,000
SALES (est): 15.9MM **Privately Held**
WEB: www.hollywoodfilmco.com
SIC: 3861 7819 Editing equipment, motion picture: viewers, splicers, etc.; services allied to motion pictures

(P-23165)
HOYA HOLDINGS INC (HQ)
680 N Mccarthy Blvd # 120, Milpitas (95035-5120)
PHONE..................................408 654-2300
Hiroshi Suzuki, *CEO*
Eiichiro Ikeda, *COO*
Ryo Hirooka, *CFO*
▲ **EMP:** 180
SALES (est): 129.9MM
SALES (corp-wide): 5B **Privately Held**
WEB: www.hoyaholdings.com
SIC: 3861 3825 3827 Photographic sensitized goods; test equipment for electronic & electric measurement; optical instruments & lenses
PA: Hoya Corporation
  6-10-1, Nishishinjuku
  Shinjuku-Ku TKY 160-0
  369 114-811

(P-23166)
IDEAS IN MOTION
1435 Eolus Ave, Encinitas (92024-1733)
PHONE..................................760 635-1181
Jake Barto, *President*
EMP: 10
SALES (est): 720K **Privately Held**
WEB: www.ideasinmotion.com
SIC: 3861 Motion picture film

(P-23167)
INDUSTRIAL SEC ALLIANC PTNRS
Also Called: Isap
3033 5th Ave Ste 400, San Diego (92103-5873)
PHONE..................................619 232-7041
Brian Kelly, *President*
Howard Landa, *Ch of Bd*
Michael Lumpkin, *CEO*
EMP: 10 **EST:** 1997
SQ FT: 1,400
SALES (est): 1.2MM **Privately Held**
WEB: www.isapusa.com
SIC: 3861 Cameras & related equipment

(P-23168)
INTEGRATED DESIGN TOOLS INC (PA)
Also Called: I D T
1 W Mountain St Unit 3, Pasadena (91103-3070)
P.O. Box 16488, Tallahassee FL (32317-6488)
PHONE..................................850 222-5939
Luiz M Lourenco, *President*
Maria Pinos, *Production*
Rick Sutherland, *Sales Mgr*
EMP: 11 **EST:** 1997
SALES (est): 3.7MM **Privately Held**
WEB: www.idtvision.com
SIC: 3861 5043 Cameras & related equipment; cameras & photographic equipment

(P-23169)
IQINVISION INC
27127 Calle Arroyo # 1920, San Juan Capistrano (92675-2765)
PHONE..................................949 369-8100
Charles Chestnutt, *President*
Rob Ledenko, *Exec VP*
▲ **EMP:** 65
SQ FT: 2,000
SALES: 12.6MM
SALES (corp-wide): 26.6MM **Privately Held**
WEB: www.iqeye.com
SIC: 3861 5946 Lens shades, camera; camera & photographic supply stores
PA: Vicon Industries, Inc.
  135 Fell Ct
  Hauppauge NY 11788
  631 952-2288

(P-23170)
ITERIS INC (PA)
1700 Carnegie Ave Ste 100, Santa Ana (92705-5551)
PHONE..................................949 270-9400
J Joseph Bergera, *President*
Andrew Schmidt, *CFO*
Joseph Boissy, *Chief Mktg Ofcr*
Tiger Harris, *Assoc VP*
Duane Hartmann, *Assoc VP*
▲ **EMP:** 146
SQ FT: 41,000
SALES: 103.7MM **Publicly Held**
WEB: www.iteris.com
SIC: 3861 8742 3699 Cameras & related equipment; driers, photographic; printing equipment, photographic; densitometers; transportation consultant; security control equipment & systems

(P-23171)
J L FISHER INC
1000 W Isabel St, Burbank (91506-1404)
PHONE..................................818 846-8366
James L Fisher, *President*
Cary Clayton, *Vice Pres*
Mark Gregory, *Technician*
Dan Rood, *Research*
Frank Kay, *Mktg Dir*
▲ **EMP:** 60
SALES (est): 10.2MM **Privately Held**
WEB: www.jlfisher.com
SIC: 3861 3663 7359 Motion picture apparatus & equipment; radio & TV communications equipment; equipment rental & leasing

▲ = Import ▼ =Export
◆ =Import/Export

(P-23172)
KALTEC ELECTRONICS INC (PA)
Also Called: Kaltec Enterprises
16220 Bloomfield Ave, Cerritos (90703-2113)
PHONE............................813 888-9555
Hee K Lee, *CEO*
Wade Thomas, *COO*
▲ EMP: 14
SQ FT: 13,000
SALES: 45MM **Privately Held**
WEB: www.kaltech.net
SIC: **3861** Cameras & related equipment

(P-23173)
KEY ITEMS SALES INC
Also Called: Memory Makers Photo ACC
21037 Superior St, Chatsworth (91311-4322)
PHONE............................818 885-0586
Jay Lewis, *Manager*
EMP: 19
SALES (corp-wide): 12.7MM **Privately Held**
SIC: **3861** Photographic equipment & supplies
PA: Key Items Sales Inc
    1307 Superior St
    Chatsworth CA
    818 885-5070

(P-23174)
KK AUDIO INC
12620 Raymer St, North Hollywood (91605-4307)
P.O. Box 16346 (91615-6346)
PHONE............................818 765-2921
Kurt Koesler, *President*
EMP: 12
SQ FT: 12,500
SALES (est): 1.6MM **Privately Held**
WEB: www.kkaudio.com
SIC: **3861** 2517 Sound recording & reproducing equipment, motion picture; wood television & radio cabinets

(P-23175)
L-3 CMMNICATIONS SONOMA EO INC
Also Called: Wescam Sonoma Operations
428 Aviation Blvd, Santa Rosa (95403-1069)
PHONE............................707 568-3000
Andy Fordham, *General Mgr*
Dennis Wood, *Info Tech Mgr*
John Dennison, *Director*
EMP: 200
SQ FT: 20,000
SALES (est): 35.8MM
SALES (corp-wide): 9.5B **Publicly Held**
SIC: **3861** 3812 Photographic equipment & supplies; heads-up display systems (HUD), aeronautical
PA: L3 Technologies, Inc.
    600 3rd Ave Fl 34
    New York NY 10016
    212 697-1111

(P-23176)
LUMENS INTEGRATION INC
4116 Clipper Ct, Fremont (94538-6514)
PHONE............................510 657-8367
Andy Chang, *President*
Christopher Skaggs, *Manager*
▲ EMP: 14
SQ FT: 5,200
SALES (est): 2.6MM **Privately Held**
WEB: www.mylumens.com
SIC: **3861** 5043 Projectors, still or motion picture, silent or sound; projection apparatus, motion picture & slide
PA: Lumens Digital Optics Inc.
    5f-1, 20, Taiyuan St.,
    Chupei City HSI
    355 262-55

(P-23177)
MATTHEWS STUDIO EQUIPMENT INC
Also Called: M S E
4520 W Valerio St, Burbank (91505-1046)
PHONE............................818 843-6715
Edward Phillips III, *President*
▲ EMP: 45

SALES (est): 9.7MM **Privately Held**
WEB: www.msegrip.com
SIC: **3861** Motion picture apparatus & equipment; stands, camera & projector; tripods, camera & projector

(P-23178)
ME & ME COSTUMES INC
1117 N Formosa Ave, West Hollywood (90046-5808)
PHONE............................323 876-4432
Mary Ellen Fields, *President*
EMP: 10
SALES (est): 550.1K **Privately Held**
SIC: **3861** Motion picture film

(P-23179)
MODERN STUDIO EQUIPMENT INC
7414 Bellaire Ave, North Hollywood (91605-4303)
PHONE............................818 764-8574
Seno Mousally, *President*
Rina Mousally, *Vice Pres*
Rosy Valencia, *Accounts Exec*
EMP: 19
SQ FT: 22,000
SALES (est): 3.7MM **Privately Held**
SIC: **3861** Motion picture apparatus & equipment

(P-23180)
MOVING IMAGE TECHNOLOGIES LLC
17760 Newhope St Ste B, Fountain Valley (92708-5442)
PHONE............................714 751-7998
Glenn Sherman, *President*
Frank Tees, *Vice Pres*
Brandon Shaffer, *Engineer*
Thuha Nguyen, *Controller*
Debra Walker, *Purch Dir*
▲ EMP: 46
SQ FT: 18,000
SALES (est): 9.4MM **Privately Held**
WEB: www.movingimagetech.com
SIC: **3861** Motion picture apparatus & equipment

(P-23181)
MPO VIDEOTRONICS INC (PA)
5069 Maureen Ln, Moorpark (93021-7148)
PHONE............................805 499-8513
Larry Kaiser, *President*
Julius Barron, *Vice Pres*
Don Gaston, *Director*
EMP: 75 EST: 1947
SALES (est): 9.6MM **Privately Held**
WEB: www.mpo-video.com
SIC: **3861** 5065 7819 3823 Motion picture apparatus & equipment; video equipment, electronic; equipment rental, motion picture; industrial instrmnts msrmnt display/control process variable; household audio & video equipment

(P-23182)
MVM PRODUCTS LLC
946 Calle Amanecer Ste E, San Clemente (92673-6221)
PHONE............................949 366-1470
Daniel W Loyer,
Steve L Boden,
EMP: 81
SQ FT: 76,000
SALES (est): 10.7MM **Privately Held**
SIC: **3861** Toners, prepared photographic (not made in chemical plants)

(P-23183)
OPTOMA TECHNOLOGY INC
47697 Westinghouse Dr # 100, Fremont (94539-7401)
PHONE............................510 897-8600
Robert Sterzing, *Principal*
Hans Wang, *Exec VP*
Genevieve Page, *Admin Asst*
Marty Medina, *Technical Staff*
Sindy Yip, *Controller*
▲ EMP: 120
SQ FT: 34,000
SALES (est): 23.1MM
SALES (corp-wide): 1.7B **Privately Held**
WEB: www.optomausa.com
SIC: **3861** Projectors, still or motion picture, silent or sound

HQ: Optoma Corporation
    12f, 213, Sec. 3, Beixin Rd.,
    New Taipei City 23143
    289 118-600

(P-23184)
PANAVISION INC
Also Called: Panavision Hollywood
6735 Selma Ave, Los Angeles (90028-6134)
PHONE............................323 464-3800
Lisa Harp, *Vice Pres*
EMP: 55 **Privately Held**
WEB: www.panastore.com
SIC: **3861** Photographic equipment & supplies
PA: Panavision Inc.
    6101 Variel Ave
    Woodland Hills CA 91367

(P-23185)
PANAVISION INTERNATIONAL LP (HQ)
6101 Variel Ave, Woodland Hills (91367-3722)
P.O. Box 4360 (91365-4360)
PHONE............................818 316-1080
Robert Beitcher, *President*
Ross Landfbuam, *CFO*
▲ EMP: 380
SQ FT: 150,000
SALES (est): 124.6MM **Privately Held**
WEB: www.panavision.com
SIC: **3861** Cameras & related equipment

(P-23186)
PHASESPACE INC (PA)
1937 Oak Park Blvd Ste A, Pleasant Hill (94523-4660)
PHONE............................925 945-6533
Tracy McSheery, *CEO*
Charles Luther, *CFO*
Dennis Gates, *Director*
▲ EMP: 14
SQ FT: 6,000
SALES (est): 2.9MM **Privately Held**
SIC: **3861** Motion picture apparatus & equipment

(P-23187)
PHOTOFLEX INC
1800 Green Hills Rd # 104, Scotts Valley (95066-4984)
PHONE............................831 786-1370
Eugene Kester, *President*
Renee Chamberlain, *Sales Staff*
▲ EMP: 18
SQ FT: 18,835
SALES (est): 4.9MM **Privately Held**
WEB: www.photoflex.com
SIC: **3861** 5043 Photographic equipment & supplies; photographic equipment & supplies; cameras & photographic equipment

(P-23188)
PHOTRONICS INC (DH)
Also Called: Photronics California
2428 N Ontario St, Burbank (91504-3119)
PHONE............................203 740-5653
James Mac Donald Jr, *Ch of Bd*
Constantine Maristos, *CEO*
Corinne Adkins, *Accounts Mgr*
EMP: 280 EST: 1970
SQ FT: 30,000
SALES (est): 29.2MM
SALES (corp-wide): 450.6MM **Publicly Held**
SIC: **3861** Photographic equipment & supplies

(P-23189)
PRESTON CINEMA SYSTEMS INC
1659 11th St Ste 100, Santa Monica (90404-3739)
PHONE............................310 453-1852
Howard Preston, *President*
Paul Davi, *Administration*
Alanna Berkson, *Technical Staff*
Roque Muna, *Electrical Engi*
Mirko Kovacevic, *Engineer*
EMP: 11

SALES (est): 1.9MM **Privately Held**
WEB: www.prestoncinema.com
SIC: **3861** 7359 Motion picture apparatus & equipment; audio-visual equipment & supply rental

(P-23190)
PRINTER CARTRIDGE USA
14276 Barrymore St, San Diego (92129-3304)
PHONE............................858 538-7630
Brad Belland, *Owner*
EMP: 10 EST: 2009
SALES (est): 176.9K **Privately Held**
SIC: **3861** Photographic equipment & supplies

(P-23191)
RADEX STEREO CO INC
13228 Crenshaw Blvd, Gardena (90249-1546)
PHONE............................310 516-9015
Steven Bracker, *President*
Nina Bracker, *Vice Pres*
Shannon O'Donnell, *Manager*
▲ EMP: 10
SQ FT: 6,500
SALES (est): 1.6MM **Privately Held**
WEB: www.radexinc.com
SIC: **3861** Photographic equipment & supplies

(P-23192)
REDCOM LLC (HQ)
Also Called: Red Digital Cinema Camera Co
34 Parker, Irvine (92618-1609)
PHONE............................949 206-7900
James H Jannard, *CEO*
Vince Hassel, *CFO*
Kevin Cabrera, *Officer*
Rusty Bennett, *Vice Pres*
Mike D Executive, *Vice Pres*
▲ EMP: 61
SALES (est): 150.2MM
SALES (corp-wide): 1.7MM **Privately Held**
SIC: **3861** Motion picture apparatus & equipment
PA: Red Europe Limited
    Pinewood Road
    Iver BUCKS SL0 0
    175 378-5454

(P-23193)
RICOH ELECTRONICS INC (DH)
Also Called: Ricoh Development California
1100 Valencia Ave, Tustin (92780-6450)
PHONE............................714 566-2500
Jeffrey A Briwick, *President*
Yoshinori Yamashita, *CEO*
Howard Suzuki, *CFO*
Cuong Doan, *Division Mgr*
Eiko Risch, *Division Mgr*
◆ EMP: 300
SQ FT: 146,000
SALES (est): 443MM
SALES (corp-wide): 19.3B **Privately Held**
WEB: www.ricohelectronicsinc.com
SIC: **3861** 3695 Photocopy machines; toners, prepared photographic (not made in chemical plants); magnetic & optical recording media
HQ: Ricoh Usa, Inc.
    70 Valley Stream Pkwy
    Malvern PA 19355
    610 296-8000

(P-23194)
ROSCO LABORATORIES INC
9420 Chivers Ave, Sun Valley (91352-2654)
PHONE............................800 767-2652
Maria Szots, *Manager*
Valeria Moncada, *Admin Asst*
Huey Davis, *Traffic Mgr*
Bogdan Nicolescu, *Production*
Jim Meyer, *Manager*
EMP: 12 **Privately Held**
SIC: **3861** Photographic equipment & supplies
HQ: Rosco Laboratories, Inc.
    52 Harbor View Ave
    Stamford CT 06902
    203 708-8900

P R O D U C T S & S V C S

(P-23195)
SA HARTMAN & ASSOCIATES INC
Also Called: S A Hartman Productions
14570 Benefit St, Sherman Oaks
(91403-5508)
PHONE..................818 907-9681
Steve A Hartman, *President*
EMP: 25
SALES: 500K **Privately Held**
SIC: **3861** 6211 Motion picture film; investment firm, general brokerage

(P-23196)
SPYGLASS ENTRMT GROUP LLC
245 N Beverly Dr, Beverly Hills
(90210-5319)
PHONE..................310 443-5800
Gary Barber, *Chairman*
Jose Gutierrez, *CEO*
Roger Birnbaum,
EMP: 14
SALES (est): 1.7MM **Privately Held**
SIC: **3861** Motion picture film; motion picture apparatus & equipment

(P-23197)
STEWART FILMSCREEN CORP (PA)
1161 Sepulveda Blvd, Torrance
(90502-2797)
PHONE..................310 326-1422
Grant W Stewart, *CEO*
Patrick H Stewart, *CEO*
Todd Eddy, *Vice Pres*
Donald R Stewart, *Vice Pres*
Thomas E Stewart, *Vice Pres*
▲ EMP: 160 EST: 1947
SQ FT: 43,000
SALES (est): 28.5MM **Privately Held**
SIC: **3861** Screens, projection

(P-23198)
SUNRISE IMAGING INC
1813 E Dyer Rd Ste 410, Santa Ana
(92705-5731)
PHONE..................949 252-3003
Dennis Childs, *Admin Sec*
Jain Ash, *Vice Pres*
Robert Lasnik, *Vice Pres*
EMP: 10
SQ FT: 6,000
SALES (est): 1.3MM **Privately Held**
WEB: www.sunriseimaging.com
SIC: **3861** Cameras, microfilm; microfilm equipment: cameras, projectors, readers, etc.

(P-23199)
SUSS MCRTEC PRCISION PHOTOMASK
Also Called: Image Technology
821 San Antonio Rd, Palo Alto
(94303-4618)
PHONE..................415 494-3113
Frank Averdung, *CEO*
Alex Naderi, *President*
Patricia Christiansen, *CFO*
EMP: 25
SQ FT: 10,000
SALES (est): 3.3MM
SALES (corp-wide): 196.3MM **Privately Held**
WEB: www.sussphotomask.com
SIC: **3861** Photographic equipment & supplies
HQ: Suss Microtec Inc.
220 Klug Cir
Corona CA 92880
408 940-0300

(P-23200)
SWENSON GROUP INC
Also Called: Swenson Group Inc Xerox
1620 S Amphlett Blvd, San Mateo
(94402-2521)
PHONE..................650 655-4990
Dean Swenson, *President*
Danielle Addis, *Office Mgr*
EMP: 15 **Privately Held**
WEB: www.theswensongroup.com
SIC: **3861** Photographic equipment & supplies

PA: The Swenson Group
207 Boeing Ct
Livermore CA 94551

(P-23201)
TECHNICAL FILM SYSTEMS INC
Also Called: T F S
4650 Calle Quetzal, Camarillo
(93012-8558)
PHONE..................805 384-9470
Manfred G Michelson, *President*
Markus Michelson, *Vice Pres*
EMP: 14
SQ FT: 1,800
SALES: 1MM **Privately Held**
WEB: www.techfilmsystems.com
SIC: **3861** Printing equipment, photographic

(P-23202)
TETRACAM INC
21601 Devonshire St # 310, Chatsworth
(91311-8423)
PHONE..................818 718-2119
George Ismael, *President*
John Edling, *Treasurer*
Steve Heinold, *Exec VP*
Dean Shen, *Vice Pres*
Gerry King, *General Mgr*
▲ EMP: 16
SQ FT: 4,200
SALES: 1.6MM **Privately Held**
WEB: www.tetracam.com
SIC: **3861** Microfilm equipment: cameras, projectors, readers, etc.

(P-23203)
THERMAPRINT CORP
11 Autry Ste B, Irvine (92618-2766)
PHONE..................949 583-0800
Natalie J Hochner, *President*
Gary Larsen, *CEO*
▲ EMP: 25
SQ FT: 14,500
SALES (est): 3.9MM **Privately Held**
WEB: www.fiberopticdesign.com
SIC: **3861** 3443 3585 2759 Graphic arts plates, sensitized; fabricated plate work (boiler shop); parts for heating, cooling & refrigerating equipment; screen printing

(P-23204)
TRIPRISM INC
15950 Bernardo Center Dr B, San Diego
(92127-1829)
PHONE..................858 675-7552
Tim Justice, *President*
Steve Chua, *CEO*
Serge Caleca, *Admin Sec*
Audrey Lin, *Web Dvlpr*
EMP: 10
SQ FT: 3,800
SALES (est): 1.3MM **Privately Held**
WEB: www.triprism.com
SIC: **3861** Photographic equipment & supplies

(P-23205)
TWO THIRTY TWO PRODUCTINS INC
7108 Katella Ave Ste 440, Stanton
(90680-2803)
PHONE..................714 317-5317
Paul Dillon, *President*
Anna Dillon, *Exec VP*
EMP: 25
SQ FT: 6,500
SALES (est): 1.6MM **Privately Held**
SIC: **3861** Motion picture film

(P-23206)
UNIQ VISION INC
2924 Scott Blvd, Santa Clara (95054-3312)
PHONE..................408 330-0818
Chuck Woo, *President*
Minh Lam, *Vice Pres*
Rex Siu, *Vice Pres*
▲ EMP: 110
SALES (est): 10MM **Privately Held**
WEB: www.uniqvision.com
SIC: **3861** Cameras & related equipment

(P-23207)
UNITY SALES INTERNATIONAL INC
Also Called: Unity Digital
2950 Airway Ave Ste A12, Costa Mesa
(92626-6019)
PHONE..................714 800-1700
Timothy McCanna, *President*
Kathy Prickett, *Manager*
EMP: 15
SQ FT: 4,000
SALES (est): 2MM **Privately Held**
WEB: www.unitydigital.com
SIC: **3861** Cameras & related equipment

(P-23208)
VELOCITY IMAGING PRODUCTS INC
8139 Center St, La Mesa (91942-2915)
PHONE..................619 433-8000
Linda Stavola, *CEO*
EMP: 15
SALES (est): 2.1MM **Privately Held**
WEB: www.velocityimagingproducts.com
SIC: **3861** Photocopy machines

(P-23209)
VICTORY STUDIO
1840 Victory Blvd, Glendale (91201-2558)
PHONE..................818 972-0737
John Ankwicz, *Office Mgr*
John Smith, *Owner*
Angela Bravo, *Executive*
EMP: 10
SALES (est): 1.3MM **Privately Held**
SIC: **3861** Motion picture film

(P-23210)
VITEK INDUS VIDEO PDTS INC
28492 Constellation Rd, Valencia
(91355-5081)
PHONE..................661 294-8043
Greg Bier, *CEO*
Vic Korhonian, *CEO*
▲ EMP: 20 EST: 1998
SQ FT: 9,200
SALES (est): 4MM **Privately Held**
WEB: www.vitekcctv.com
SIC: **3861** 5099 Cameras & related equipment; video & audio equipment

(P-23211)
VONNIC INC
16610 Gale Ave, City of Industry
(91745-1801)
PHONE..................626 964-2345
Kim Por Lin, *CEO*
Kitty Lam, *CFO*
▲ EMP: 23
SALES (est): 7.8MM **Privately Held**
SIC: **3861** Cameras & related equipment

(P-23212)
WINDOW SOLUTIONS
Also Called: Solar Art
9301 Research Dr, Irvine (92618-4288)
PHONE..................650 349-2499
Paul Murphy, *Principal*
Bernardo Bramante, *President*
EMP: 15
SALES (est): 1.9MM **Privately Held**
WEB: www.windowsolutions.com
SIC: **3861** 5719 Film, sensitized motion picture, X-ray, still camera, etc.; window shades

(P-23213)
XEROX CORPORATION
2980 Inland Empire Blvd # 105, Ontario
(91764-6567)
PHONE..................909 605-7900
John Palmer, *Manager*
EMP: 10
SALES (corp-wide): 10.2B **Publicly Held**
WEB: www.xerox.com
SIC: **3861** Photographic equipment & supplies
PA: Xerox Corporation
201 Merritt 7
Norwalk CT 06851
203 968-3000

(P-23214)
XEROX CORPORATION
1851 E 1st St Ste 200, Santa Ana
(92705-4072)
PHONE..................714 565-1200
Linda Avila, *Manager*
Pam Holsen, *Marketing Mgr*
Michael Alexandor, *Marketing Staff*
Carol Sarkesian, *Marketing Staff*
Denise Devlin, *Manager*
EMP: 150
SALES (corp-wide): 10.2B **Publicly Held**
WEB: www.xerox.com
SIC: **3861** 3577 7629 7378 Photocopy machines; computer peripheral equipment; business machine repair, electric; computer peripheral equipment repair & maintenance
PA: Xerox Corporation
201 Merritt 7
Norwalk CT 06851
203 968-3000

3873 Watch & Clock Devices & Parts

(P-23215)
ACCUSPLIT (PA)
7901 Stoneridge Dr # 350, Pleasanton
(94588-4531)
PHONE..................925 290-1900
W Ron Sutton, *President*
Byron Dana Lindstrom, *Exec VP*
Steve Simmons, *Vice Pres*
Barbara Jacobs, *Office Mgr*
Joey Sutton, *Sales Staff*
▲ EMP: 17
SALES (est): 3MM **Privately Held**
WEB: www.pedometer.com
SIC: **3873** 3824 Watches & parts, except crystals & jewels; controls; revolution & timing instruments; pedometers

(P-23216)
AMG EMPLOYEE MANAGEMENT INC
Also Called: Time Masters
3235 N San Fernando Rd 1d, Los Angeles
(90065-1443)
PHONE..................323 254-7448
Tigran Galstyan, *President*
Larry Taylor, *Director*
▲ EMP: 17
SALES (est): 2.3MM **Privately Held**
SIC: **3873** 7371 7372 3579 Timers for industrial use, clockwork mechanism only; computer software development; business oriented computer software; time clocks & time recording devices

(P-23217)
BLOCKS WEARABLES INC
1800 Century Park E Fl 10, Los Angeles
(90067-1513)
PHONE..................650 307-9557
Alireza Tahmasebzadeh, *Director*
EMP: 10
SALES (est): 398.3K **Privately Held**
SIC: **3873** Watchcases

(P-23218)
CALIFORNIA CLOCK CO (PA)
Also Called: Youngs Evergreen Nursery Co
16060 Abajo Cir, Fountain Valley
(92708-1312)
P.O. Box 9901 (92728-0901)
PHONE..................714 545-4321
Woody Young, *Owner*
EMP: 10 EST: 1964
SALES (est): 1.4MM **Privately Held**
WEB: www.californiaclock.com
SIC: **3873** 2731 5193 Clocks, assembly of; books: publishing only; nursery stock

(P-23219)
CHASE-DURER LTD (PA)
8455 Ftn Ave Unit 515, West Hollywood
(90069)
PHONE..................310 550-7280
Brandon Chase, *President*
Fred Goode, *Manager*
▲ EMP: 19 EST: 1997

SALES (est): 1.2MM **Privately Held**
WEB: www.chasedurer.com
SIC: 3873 Watches, clocks, watchcases & parts

(P-23220)
CLUB DONATELLO OWNERS ASSN
501 Post St, San Francisco (94102-1228)
PHONE..............................415 474-7333
Daryl Clark, *President*
Sherwin David, *Opers Staff*
▲ EMP: 21
SALES (est): 1.9MM **Privately Held**
SIC: 3873 Timers for industrial use, clock-work mechanism only

(P-23221)
MOD ELECTRONICS INC
Also Called: Ese
142 Sierra St, El Segundo (90245-4117)
PHONE..............................310 322-2136
William Kaiser, *President*
Brian Way, *Vice Pres*
Bill Rajaniemi, *Technical Staff*
Fernando Vallin, *Sales Staff*
▲ EMP: 26
SQ FT: 7,500
SALES (est): 4.6MM **Privately Held**
WEB: www.ese-web.com
SIC: 3873 3663 3651 3625 Clocks, as-sembly of; radio & TV communications equipment; household audio & video equipment; relays & industrial controls

(P-23222)
OLIO DEVICES INC
1100 La Avenida St Ste A, Mountain View (94043-1453)
PHONE..............................650 918-6546
Steven Jacobs, *CEO*
EMP: 27
SALES (est): 3.2MM **Privately Held**
SIC: 3873 Watchcases

(P-23223)
PEBBLE TECHNOLOGY CORP
900 Middlefield Rd Ste 5, Redwood City (94063-1681)
PHONE..............................888 224-5820
EMP: 44
SALES (est): 18.9MM **Privately Held**
SIC: 3873

(P-23224)
SUNBURST PRODUCTS INC
Also Called: Freestyle
1570 Corporate Dr Ste F, Costa Mesa (92626-1428)
PHONE..............................949 722-0158
EMP: 40
SQ FT: 12,000
SALES (est): 3.3MM
SALES (corp-wide): 98.7K **Privately Held**
WEB: www.freestyleusa.com
SIC: 3873 3172 3845
HQ: Awc Liquidating Co.
  1407 Broadway Rm 400
  New York NY 10018
  212 221-1177

(P-23225)
TAKANE USA INC (HQ)
369 Van Ness Way Ste 715, Torrance (90501-6249)
PHONE..............................310 212-1411
Kenji Hanaoka, *President*
▲ EMP: 21
SQ FT: 47,000
SALES (est): 13.1MM
SALES (corp-wide): 3.6MM **Privately Held**
SIC: 3873 Movements, watch or clock
PA: Takane Co., Ltd.
  3465, Kaminohara, Tamagawa
  Chino NAG 391-0
  266 726-111

(P-23226)
VITALE HOME DESIGNS INC
Also Called: Fancy Schmancy Art Frames
24425 Woolsey Canyon Rd # 46, Canoga Park (91304-1131)
PHONE..............................818 888-2481
Toni Vitale, *President*
EMP: 15

SALES: 96K **Privately Held**
SIC: 3873 Watches, clocks, watchcases & parts

3911 Jewelry: Precious Metal

(P-23227)
ACE HOLDINGS INC
650 S Hill St Ste 510, Los Angeles (90014-1753)
PHONE..............................213 972-2100
John Arzoian, *CEO*
Linda Fass, *President*
EMP: 200
SQ FT: 65,000
SALES (est): 18MM **Privately Held**
SIC: 3911 Jewelry, precious metal

(P-23228)
ADRIENNE DESIGNS LLC (PA)
Also Called: A/D Enterprises
17150 Newhope St Ste 514, Fountain Valley (92708-4253)
PHONE..............................714 558-1209
Clifford E Johnston, *President*
▲ EMP: 13
SQ FT: 10,000
SALES (est): 2.1MM **Privately Held**
SIC: 3911 Necklaces, precious metal

(P-23229)
ADRIENNE DESIGNS LLC
17150 Newhope St Ste 514, Fountain Valley (92708-4253)
PHONE..............................800 621-5632
Sumit Shah, *Branch Mgr*
EMP: 18
SALES (corp-wide): 2.1MM **Privately Held**
SIC: 3911 Jewelry, precious metal
PA: Adrienne Designs Llc
  17150 Newhope St Ste 514
  Fountain Valley CA 92708
  714 558-1209

(P-23230)
ALEX VELVET INC
3334 Eagle Rock Blvd, Los Angeles (90065-2843)
PHONE..............................323 255-6900
Krikor Alexanian, *President*
Berj Alexanian, *CFO*
▲ EMP: 35
SQ FT: 15,000
SALES (est): 1.2MM **Privately Held**
WEB: www.alexvelvetdisplays.com
SIC: 3911 7319 5046 Jewelry mountings & trimmings; display advertising service; store fixtures & display equipment

(P-23231)
ALLISON-KAUFMAN CO
7640 Haskell Ave, Van Nuys (91406-2005)
PHONE..............................818 373-5100
Bart Kaufman, *President*
Jay A Kaufman, *Vice Pres*
Victoria Sober, *Regl Sales Mgr*
▲ EMP: 72 EST: 1946
SQ FT: 21,000
SALES (est): 9.8MM **Privately Held**
WEB: www.allison-kaufman.com
SIC: 3911 Jewelry, precious metal

(P-23232)
ALOR INTERNATIONAL LTD
Also Called: Philippe Charriol USA
4330 La Jolla Village Dr # 100, San Diego (92122-6201)
PHONE..............................858 454-0011
Jack Zemer, *CEO*
Sandy Zemer, *President*
Tal Zemer, *Officer*
Ori Zemer, *Vice Pres*
▲ EMP: 45
SQ FT: 10,000
SALES (est): 8.8MM **Privately Held**
WEB: www.charriol-usa.com
SIC: 3911 3172 3915 Vanity cases, pre-cious metal; personal leather goods; jewel preparing: instruments, tools, watches & jewelry

(P-23233)
ALUMA USA INC
435 Tesconi Cir, Santa Rosa (95401-4619)
PHONE..............................707 545-9344
Doron Sharfman, *President*
▲ EMP: 22
SQ FT: 8,867
SALES: 15MM **Privately Held**
WEB: www.alumausa.net
SIC: 3911 Jewelry, precious metal

(P-23234)
AMERICAS GOLD INC
Also Called: Americas Gold - Amrcas Da-monds
650 S Hill St Ste 224, Los Angeles (90014-1769)
PHONE..............................213 688-4904
Rafi M Siddiqui, *President*
Samina Siddiqui, *Vice Pres*
EMP: 30
SQ FT: 4,500
SALES (est): 5.4MM **Privately Held**
WEB: www.americasgold.com
SIC: 3911 Jewelry, precious metal

(P-23235)
AMINCO INTERNATIONAL USA INC (PA)
Also Called: California Premium Incentives
20571 Crescent Bay Dr, Lake Forest (92630-8825)
PHONE..............................949 457-3261
William Wu, *President*
Ann Wu, *Treasurer*
▲ EMP: 50 EST: 1978
SQ FT: 35,000
SALES (est): 6.8MM **Privately Held**
WEB: www.amincousa.com
SIC: 3911 5099 Jewelry, precious metal; brass goods

(P-23236)
ANATOMETAL INC
411 Ingalls St, Santa Cruz (95060-5836)
PHONE..............................831 454-9880
Barry Blanchard, *President*
EMP: 40
SQ FT: 8,000
SALES (est): 6.8MM **Privately Held**
WEB: www.anatometal.com
SIC: 3911 Jewelry, precious metal

(P-23237)
AR CASTING INC
7240 Coldwater Canyon Ave B, North Hollywood (91605-4246)
PHONE..............................818 765-1202
Abel Rojas, *President*
EMP: 16
SALES (est): 1.3MM **Privately Held**
WEB: www.aandrcasting.com
SIC: 3911 Jewelry, precious metal

(P-23238)
ARTS ELEGANCE INC
154 W Bellevue Dr, Pasadena (91105-2504)
PHONE..............................626 793-4794
Arutiun Mikaelian, *President*
EMP: 45
SALES (corp-wide): 13.4MM **Privately Held**
SIC: 3911 Jewelry, precious metal
PA: Art's Elegance, Inc.
  739 E Walnut St Ste 200
  Pasadena CA 91101
  626 405-1522

(P-23239)
ARZY COMPANY INC
Also Called: Arzy Company Fine Jewelry
650 S Hill St Ste 915, Los Angeles (90014-1752)
PHONE..............................213 627-7344
Hossein Arzy, *President*
EMP: 10
SALES (est): 1.3MM **Privately Held**
SIC: 3911 3961 Bracelets, precious metal; costume jewelry, ex. precious metal & semiprecious stones

(P-23240)
ASK GOLD COMPANY INC
716 S Olive St Fl 3, Los Angeles (90014-2602)
PHONE..............................213 622-4005
Sarkis Ashikian, *President*
EMP: 25
SALES (est): 1.2MM **Privately Held**
SIC: 3911 Jewelry apparel

(P-23241)
ASTOURIAN JEWELRY MFG INC
635 S Hill St Ste 407, Los Angeles (90014-1819)
PHONE..............................213 683-0436
Viken Astourian, *President*
▲ EMP: 13
SQ FT: 1,200
SALES (est): 3.5MM **Privately Held**
SIC: 3911 Jewelry, precious metal

(P-23242)
AVE JEWELRY INC
Also Called: Ave Jewelry Design Mfg
13127 Ebell St, North Hollywood (91605-1006)
PHONE..............................213 488-0097
Greg Avetisian, *President*
Anaid Melkonian, *Vice Pres*
EMP: 15
SQ FT: 12,300
SALES (est): 1.3MM **Privately Held**
SIC: 3911

(P-23243)
BARGUEIRAS RENE INC
Also Called: R B I
621 S Victory Blvd, Burbank (91502-2424)
PHONE..............................818 500-8288
Rene Bargueiras, *President*
Sena Bargueiras, *Vice Pres*
Angie Vaca, *Controller*
EMP: 12
SQ FT: 1,300
SALES (est): 1.1MM **Privately Held**
WEB: www.rb-inc.com
SIC: 3911 5094 Jewelry apparel; bracelets, precious metal; earrings, pre-cious metal; rings, finger: precious metal; jewelry & precious stones

(P-23244)
BARKEVS INC
707 S Broadway Ste 415, Los Angeles (90014-2858)
PHONE..............................800 227-7321
Barkev Meserlian, *President*
Vatche Meserlian, *Office Mgr*
Seta Ratevosian, *Accountant*
Marina Kurian, *Mktg Dir*
EMP: 10
SALES (est): 991.4K **Privately Held**
WEB: www.barkevs.com
SIC: 3911 5944 Jewelry, precious metal; jewelry, precious stones & precious met-als

(P-23245)
BASHOURA INC
539 S Glenwood Ave, Glendora (91741-3514)
PHONE..............................626 963-7600
Jean Bashoura, *President*
Moussa Bashoura, *Treasurer*
Tony Bashoura, *Vice Pres*
Tania Bashoura, *Admin Sec*
▲ EMP: 11
SQ FT: 5,760
SALES (est): 1.2MM **Privately Held**
WEB: www.bashoura.com
SIC: 3911 Jewelry, precious metal

(P-23246)
BEZ AMBAR INC
611 Wilshire Blvd Ste 607, Los Angeles (90017-2912)
PHONE..............................213 629-9191
Betzalael Ambar, *President*
Alex Fuentes, *Opers Mgr*
▲ EMP: 40
SQ FT: 5,200
SALES: 4.1MM **Privately Held**
SIC: 3911 Jewelry, precious metal

(P-23247)
C GONSHOR FINE JEWELRY INC
640 S Hill St Ste 546a, Los Angeles
(90014-4745)
PHONE..................213 629-1075
Chain Gonshor, *President*
Misha Kottler, *Vice Pres*
EMP: 10
SQ FT: 2,500
SALES (est): 1.2MM **Privately Held**
SIC: 3911 5094 Jewelry apparel; jewelry

(P-23248)
CARETTA INC
Also Called: Spiegel's Jewelry Factory
13400 Saticoy St Ste 1, North Hollywood
(91605-7600)
PHONE..................818 781-9486
Bruce Spiegel, *CEO*
Etta Spiegel, *Vice Pres*
Zeda Spiegel, *Manager*
EMP: 11
SALES (est): 1.5MM **Privately Held**
WEB: www.jewelryfactory.com
SIC: 3911 Jewelry, precious metal

(P-23249)
CHAIN & CHARM INC
Also Called: Chain & Charm Jewelry Mfg
817 San Julian St Ph 1, Los Angeles
(90014-2400)
PHONE..................213 683-1039
Cheo K Chia, *President*
Meang K Chia, *Vice Pres*
EMP: 75
SQ FT: 26,000
SALES (est): 9.5MM **Privately Held**
WEB: www.chainandcharm.com
SIC: 3911 Jewelry, precious metal

(P-23250)
CHAIN SMITH INC
5009 Walnut Grove Ave, San Gabriel
(91776-2023)
PHONE..................626 287-3666
Joseph Win, *President*
Paulina Chu, *Shareholder*
Theresa Win, *Shareholder*
Magdalena Shu, *Treasurer*
Lawrence Win, *Vice Pres*
EMP: 50
SQ FT: 16,000
SALES (est): 4.5MM **Privately Held**
SIC: 3911 3544 Jewelry, precious metal; special dies, tools, jigs & fixtures

(P-23251)
CHARLES LIGETI CO
611 Wilshire Blvd Ste 801, Los Angeles
(90017-2925)
PHONE..................213 612-0831
Charles Ligeti, *Owner*
Marie Rose Cabrera, *Vice Pres*
Lulu Tupas, *Admin Sec*
EMP: 30 **EST:** 1957
SQ FT: 1,500
SALES (est): 3.1MM **Privately Held**
WEB: www.charlesligeti.com
SIC: 3911 Rings, finger: precious metal

(P-23252)
CONNERS ORO-CAL MFG CO
1720 Bird St, Oroville (95965-4806)
PHONE..................530 533-5065
David J Conner, *President*
Susan Y Conner, *Admin Sec*
EMP: 18
SQ FT: 2,850
SALES (est): 10.1MM **Privately Held**
SIC: 3911 3873 5094 Jewelry, precious metal; watches, clocks, watchcases & parts; jewelry & precious stones; clocks, watches & parts

(P-23253)
CPS GEM CORPORATION
Also Called: C.P.s Fine Gems Jwly Collectn
1327 S Myrtle Ave, Monrovia (91016-4150)
PHONE..................213 627-4019
Allan Pung, *CEO*
Tina Pung, *President*
EMP: 10
SALES (est): 1.2MM **Privately Held**
WEB: www.cpsgems.com
SIC: 3911 5944 Jewelry, precious metal; jewelry stores

(P-23254)
CUBIC ZEE JEWELRY INC
728 S Hill St Ste 900, Los Angeles
(90014-2731)
P.O. Box 811695 (90081-0012)
PHONE..................213 614-9800
Sarkis Ulikyan, *President*
Ovakim Ulikyan, *Vice Pres*
EMP: 11 **EST:** 2010
SALES (est): 2.2MM **Privately Held**
SIC: 3911 Jewelry, precious metal

(P-23255)
DESIGNED BY SCORPIO INC
550 S Hill St Ste 1605, Los Angeles
(90013-2494)
PHONE..................213 612-4440
Kirkor Yerganyan, *Partner*
Lena Yerganyan, *Partner*
EMP: 18
SQ FT: 3,000
SALES (est): 1.9MM **Privately Held**
WEB: www.designedbyscorpio.com
SIC: 3911 Jewelry mountings & trimmings

(P-23256)
DIARING INC
550 S Hill St Ste 990, Los Angeles
(90013-2466)
PHONE..................213 489-3894
Sarju Vora, *President*
Devang Vora, *Vice Pres*
EMP: 10
SQ FT: 1,500
SALES (est): 1MM **Privately Held**
WEB: www.diaring.com
SIC: 3911 5094 Jewelry, precious metal; jewelry; jewelry, precious stones & precious metals

(P-23257)
DOVES JEWELRY CORPORATION
2860 N Naomi St, Burbank (91504-2023)
PHONE..................818 955-8886
Egine Artinian, *President*
Helen Adji-Artinian, *Admin Sec*
EMP: 20
SQ FT: 3,000
SALES (est): 1.3MM **Privately Held**
SIC: 3911 5094 Jewelry, precious metal; jewelry

(P-23258)
EAR CHARMS INC
Also Called: Ear Gear
1855 Laguna Canyon Rd, Laguna Beach
(92651-1121)
P.O. Box 4289 (92652-4289)
PHONE..................949 494-4147
Sandra Callisto, *President*
Mike Callisto, *Vice Pres*
George Reynolds, *Director*
EMP: 12
SALES (est): 1.1MM **Privately Held**
WEB: www.earcuff.net
SIC: 3911 5944 Earrings, precious metal; jewelry, precious stones & precious metals

(P-23259)
EJ DIAMONDS INC
631 S Olive St Ste 201, Los Angeles
(90014-3656)
PHONE..................213 623-2329
Albert Can, *President*
EMP: 10
SALES (est): 694.3K **Privately Held**
SIC: 3911 Jewelry apparel

(P-23260)
ELBA JEWELRY INC
Also Called: Elba Company
910 N Amelia Ave, San Dimas
(91773-1401)
PHONE..................909 394-5803
Edouard Bachoura, *President*
Raymonda Duzich, *CFO*
Mary B Pimpare, *Cust Mgr*
EMP: 19
SQ FT: 10,000
SALES (est): 2.4MM **Privately Held**
WEB: www.elbainc.com
SIC: 3911 Jewelry, precious metal

(P-23261)
ELEMENTS
20314a Gramercy Pl, Torrance (90501)
PHONE..................310 781-1384
Derrick Obatake, *Owner*
EMP: 25
SALES (est): 1.6MM **Privately Held**
SIC: 3911 Jewelry, precious metal

(P-23262)
F CONRAD FURLONG INC
Also Called: Furlong, Conrad
550 S Hill St Ste 1620, Los Angeles
(90013-2452)
PHONE..................213 623-4191
Franklin Conrad Furlong, *President*
Irene Furlong, *Vice Pres*
EMP: 13
SQ FT: 1,600
SALES (est): 1.4MM **Privately Held**
SIC: 3911 Jewelry apparel

(P-23263)
FAITH KNIGHT INC
2340 Mountain Ave, La Crescenta
(91214-3134)
PHONE..................213 488-1569
Faith Knight, *President*
Raul Banuelos, *Vice Pres*
EMP: 10
SALES (est): 200K **Privately Held**
SIC: 3911 Jewelry apparel

(P-23264)
FARSI JEWELRY MFG CO INC
631 Suth Olive St Ste 565, Los Angeles
(90014)
PHONE..................213 624-0043
Yousef Eshaghzadeh, *President*
Masoud Eshaghzadeh, *Treasurer*
Saied Eshaghzadeh, *Admin Sec*
EMP: 13
SALES (est): 2.3MM **Privately Held**
SIC: 3911 Jewelry, precious metal

(P-23265)
G W MANUFACTURING JEWELERS
Also Called: Golden West Jewelers
861 6th Ave Ste 800, San Diego
(92101-6318)
PHONE..................619 234-5850
Joseph Carini, *President*
Steven Herczeg, *Vice Pres*
EMP: 32
SQ FT: 3,900
SALES (est): 4.3MM **Privately Held**
WEB: www.gold-west.com
SIC: 3911 Jewelry, precious metal

(P-23266)
GGCO INC
Also Called: Eccentric Jewelry
18380 Ventura Blvd, Tarzana (91356-4219)
PHONE..................213 623-3636
Ghzaros Ghazarossian, *President*
EMP: 20
SQ FT: 2,400
SALES (est): 1.9MM **Privately Held**
SIC: 3911 Jewelry, precious metal

(P-23267)
GINA DESIGNS
870 Sanitarium Rd, Angwin (94576-9707)
PHONE..................707 967-1041
EMP: 10 **EST:** 1991
SALES (est): 563.3K **Privately Held**
SIC: 3911

(P-23268)
GIVING KEYS INC
836 Traction Ave, Los Angeles
(90013-1816)
PHONE..................213 935-8791
Caitlin Crosby, *CEO*
Brit Gilmore, *President*
Nikki Sloan, *Production*
Ashley Castro, *Marketing Mgr*
Tyler Maisha, *Sales Mgr*
▲ **EMP:** 55 **EST:** 2012
SQ FT: 8,000
SALES: 7.5MM **Privately Held**
SIC: 3911 Jewelry, precious metal

(P-23269)
GOLD COUTURE 22 K
6406 Kinglet Way, Carlsbad (92011-2700)
PHONE..................760 602-0690
Himgauri Kulkarni, *Partner*
Raju Katari, *Partner*
EMP: 10
SQ FT: 2,200
SALES: 2MM **Privately Held**
SIC: 3911 5094 Jewel settings & mountings, precious metal; jewelry

(P-23270)
GOLD CRAFT JEWELRY CORP (PA)
Also Called: Gcj
640 S Hill St Ste 650, Los Angeles
(90014-4701)
PHONE..................213 623-5460
Vahi Urun, *President*
EMP: 17
SQ FT: 12,000
SALES (est): 2.7MM **Privately Held**
WEB: www.goldcraftco.co
SIC: 3911 5094 Earrings, precious metal; jewelry

(P-23271)
GOLD CRAFT JEWELRY CORP
Also Called: Jewelry Manufacturing
640 S Hill St Ste 650, Los Angeles
(90014-4701)
PHONE..................213 623-8673
Nuran Urun, *Opers-Prdtn-Mfg*
EMP: 40
SALES (corp-wide): 2.7MM **Privately Held**
WEB: www.goldcraftco.com
SIC: 3911 3599 Earrings, precious metal; machine shop, jobbing & repair
PA: Gold Craft Jewelry Corp.
640 S Hill St Ste 650
Los Angeles CA 90014
213 623-5460

(P-23272)
HARTEN JEWELRY CO INC
8213 Villaverde Dr, Whittier (90605-1339)
PHONE..................562 652-5006
Ofer Harten, *President*
Bessy Harten, *Vice Pres*
EMP: 20
SQ FT: 4,000
SALES (est): 1.8MM **Privately Held**
WEB: www.harten.com
SIC: 3911 5094 Jewelry apparel; jewelry

(P-23273)
HERFF JONES LLC
14321 Goose St, Corona (92880-0922)
PHONE..................951 541-3938
EMP: 15
SALES (corp-wide): 1.1B **Privately Held**
SIC: 3911 Rings, finger: precious metal
HQ: Herff Jones, Llc
4501 W 62nd St
Indianapolis IN 46268
800 419-5462

(P-23274)
HOLLY YASHI INC
1300 9th St, Arcata (95521-5703)
PHONE..................707 822-0389
Paul S Lubitz, *President*
Holly A Hosterman, *Vice Pres*
Trevor Shirk, *Research*
Danielle Demartini, *Graphic Designe*
Robin Weburg, *Accountant*
▲ **EMP:** 54
SQ FT: 4,800
SALES (est): 11.4MM **Privately Held**
WEB: www.hollyyashi.com
SIC: 3911 Earrings, precious metal; necklaces, precious metal

(P-23275)
HUMIDTECH INC
1241 Johnson Ave Ste 345, San Luis Obispo (93401-3306)
PHONE..................805 541-9500
Robin Marks, *President*
EMP: 10 **EST:** 1996
SQ FT: 6,000
SALES: 750K **Privately Held**
WEB: www.humidtech.com
SIC: 3911 Cigar & cigarette accessories

(P-23276)
ISHARYA INC
4340 Stevens Creek Blvd, San Jose
(95129-1102)
PHONE..................................415 462-6294
Radhika Tandon, *President*
Vikas Singh, *Executive*
Jay Panjwani, *Prdtn Mgr*
Nisha Khiani, *Pub Rel Staff*
Manisha Chincholia, *Manager*
EMP: 25
SQ FT: 10,000
SALES (est): 2.3MM **Privately Held**
SIC: 3911 Jewelry, precious metal

(P-23277)
J GOOD IN INC
576 Explorer St, Brea (92821-3108)
PHONE..................................714 257-9391
Jenny Cheng, *Principal*
▲ EMP: 18
SALES (est): 2.1MM **Privately Held**
SIC: 3911 Jewelry, precious metal

(P-23278)
JEWELRY CLUB HOUSE INC
606 S Olive St Ste 2000, Los Angeles
(90014-1656)
PHONE..................................213 362-7888
Lo Huang, *President*
Victor Han, *CEO*
John Han, *CFO*
▲ EMP: 15
SALES (est): 904.2K **Privately Held**
SIC: 3911 Jewelry, precious metal

(P-23279)
JEWELS BY ANGELO INC
9221 Rives Ave, Downey (90240-2658)
PHONE..................................562 862-6293
Angelo R Cardono, *President*
EMP: 15
SQ FT: 10,180
SALES (est): 2.1MM **Privately Held**
WEB: www.jewelsbyangelo.com
SIC: 3911 Jewelry, precious metal

(P-23280)
JOSTENS INC
Also Called: Jostens Printing & Publishing
231 S Kelsey St, Visalia (93291-7973)
P.O. Box 991 (93279-0991)
PHONE..................................559 622-5200
Bruce Mortan, *Branch Mgr*
EMP: 180
SQ FT: 10,000
SALES (corp-wide): 14.7B **Publicly Held**
WEB: www.jostens.com
SIC: 3911 Rings, finger: precious metal
HQ: Jostens, Inc.
7760 France Ave S Ste 400
Minneapolis MN 55435
952 830-3300

(P-23281)
KESMOR ASSOCIATES
Also Called: American Designs
610 S Broadway Ste 717, Los Angeles
(90014-1814)
PHONE..................................213 629-2300
Joseph Keshoyan, *President*
Hasmik Keshoyan, *Vice Pres*
EMP: 20
SQ FT: 6,000
SALES (est): 2.1MM **Privately Held**
SIC: 3911 Jewelry, precious metal

(P-23282)
KITSCH LLC (PA)
307 N New Hampshire Ave, Los Angeles
(90004-3408)
PHONE..................................424 240-5551
Cassandra Morales Thurswell, *CEO*
Jeremy Thurswell, *President*
▲ EMP: 12
SQ FT: 5,000
SALES (est): 1.3MM **Privately Held**
SIC: 3911 5131 5094 Jewelry, precious
metal; hair accessories; jewelry

(P-23283)
KOBI KATZ INC
Also Called: Baguette World
801 S Flower St Fl 3, Los Angeles
(90017-4617)
PHONE..................................213 689-0076

Kobi Katz, *President*
Eli Sandberg, *Treasurer*
EMP: 62 EST: 1981
SQ FT: 14,000
SALES (est): 9.4MM **Privately Held**
SIC: 3911 5094 Jewelry apparel; dia-
monds (gems)

(P-23284)
LA GEM AND JWLY DESIGN INC
Also Called: La Rocks
659 S Broadway Fl 7, Los Angeles
(90014-2291)
PHONE..................................213 488-1290
Joseph W Behney, *CEO*
Ashish Arora, *CFO*
Elsa Behney, *Admin Sec*
▲ EMP: 100
SQ FT: 10,000
SALES (est): 39.2MM **Privately Held**
SIC: 3911 5094 Jewelry, precious metal;
jewelry

(P-23285)
LEGACY BANDS INC
13261 Paxton St, Pacoima (91331-2357)
PHONE..................................818 890-2527
Aram Naobandain, *President*
▲ EMP: 10
SALES (est): 500K **Privately Held**
WEB: www.legacybands.com
SIC: 3911 Jewelry apparel

(P-23286)
LEONARD CRAFT CO LLC
3501 W Segerstrom Ave, Santa Ana
(92704-6449)
PHONE..................................714 549-0678
Stephen D Leonard, *Mng Member*
EMP: 95
SALES (est): 10.6MM **Privately Held**
SIC: 3911 5947 Jewelry, precious metal;
gift shop

(P-23287)
LINX BRACELETS INC
Also Called: Linx & More
23147 Ventura Blvd # 250, Woodland Hills
(91364-1112)
PHONE..................................818 224-4050
Gina Eckstein, *CEO*
Ivette Helfend, *President*
Cheryl Bloxberg, *COO*
Alexandra Legaspi, *Cust Mgr*
EMP: 12
SQ FT: 2,400
SALES (est): 1.4MM **Privately Held**
WEB: www.linxandmore.com
SIC: 3911 5094 Jewelry, precious metal;
jewelry & precious stones

(P-23288)
LIVINGSTONE JEWELRY CO INC
631 S Olive St Ste 340, Los Angeles
(90014-3656)
PHONE..................................213 683-1040
Jim Shaw, *President*
EMP: 10
SQ FT: 800
SALES (est): 1.1MM **Privately Held**
WEB: www.livingstonejewelry.com
SIC: 3911 5944 Jewelry, precious metal;
jewelry stores

(P-23289)
LUCIOUS JEWELS
10 Via Dulcinea, Palm Desert
(92260-3122)
PHONE..................................760 779-1304
Linda Heller, *Owner*
EMP: 10
SALES (est): 592.6K **Privately Held**
SIC: 3911 Jewelry, precious metal

(P-23290)
LUMINAR CREATIONS
420 N Moss St, Burbank (91502-1726)
PHONE..................................818 843-0010
Joseph Toobi, *President*
Daniel Toobi, *Corp Secy*
Jonathan Toobi, *Accounts Exec*
EMP: 30
SQ FT: 8,000
SALES (est): 3.8MM **Privately Held**
SIC: 3911 Jewelry, precious metal

(P-23291)
M & H CREATIVE DESIGN INC
550 S Hill St Ste 1030, Los Angeles
(90013-1881)
PHONE..................................213 627-8881
Fax: 213 627-5999
EMP: 10
SQ FT: 1,000
SALES (est): 800K **Privately Held**
SIC: 3911

(P-23292)
MAKSE INC
Also Called: K&M Jewellery
52 E Santa Anita Ave, Burbank
(91502-1923)
PHONE..................................213 622-5030
Karapet Naapatyan, *President*
EMP: 16
SQ FT: 3,500
SALES (est): 2.5MM **Privately Held**
SIC: 3911 5094 Jewelry, precious metal;
jewelry

(P-23293)
MALCOLM DEMILLE INC
650 S Frontage Rd, Nipomo (93444-9148)
PHONE..................................805 929-4353
Malcolm Demille, *President*
Janet Demille, *CFO*
Phil Scorsone, *Purchasing*
Stephan Hodges, *Sales Associate*
EMP: 15
SALES (est): 1.9MM **Privately Held**
WEB: www.mdemille.com
SIC: 3911 Jewelry mountings & trimmings

(P-23294)
**MANUFACTURING USA
ENTERPRISES**
632 Irving Ave, Glendale (91201-2029)
PHONE..................................818 409-3070
Manuel Galachyan, *President*
Naira Galachyan, *Admin Sec*
EMP: 28
SQ FT: 3,000
SALES: 4.5MM **Privately Held**
SIC: 3911 Jewel settings & mountings, pre-
cious metal

(P-23295)
**MARJORIE BAER
ACCESSORIES**
1389 Lowrie Ave, South San Francisco
(94080-6403)
PHONE..................................650 872-2272
Marjorie Baer, *President*
▲ EMP: 39
SALES (est): 4.3MM **Privately Held**
WEB: www.mbaer.com
SIC: 3911 Jewelry, precious metal

(P-23296)
MASTINI DESIGNS
9454 Wilshire Blvd # 600, Beverly Hills
(90212-2931)
PHONE..................................800 979-4848
Shahrad Tabibzadeh, *President*
Farokh Tabibzadeh, *Corp Secy*
Mahasti Tabibzadeh, *Vice Pres*
EMP: 10
SQ FT: 1,000
SALES (est): 1.3MM **Privately Held**
WEB: www.mastini.com
SIC: 3911 5094 Jewelry apparel; dia-
monds (gems); precious stones (gems)

(P-23297)
**MERIDIAN JEWELRY & DESIGN
INC**
3814 La Cresta Ave, Oakland
(94602-1727)
PHONE..................................510 428-2095
Lynn B Olander, *CEO*
Lynn Olander, *President*
Brad Olander, *CEO*
EMP: 17
SALES (est): 1.5MM **Privately Held**
SIC: 3911 Jewelry, precious metal

(P-23298)
MODERN GOLD DESIGN INC
Also Called: Aaagolddesigns
650 S Hill St Ste 509, Los Angeles
(90014-1753)
PHONE..................................213 614-1818
Movses Khayoyan, *President*
EMP: 20
SQ FT: 5,000
SALES (est): 2.2MM **Privately Held**
WEB: www.aaagolddesigns.com
SIC: 3911 5944 Jewelry, precious metal;
jewelry stores

(P-23299)
**MONTBLANC NORTH AMERICA
LLC**
Also Called: Montblanc Santa Clara
2855 Stevens Creek Blvd, Santa Clara
(95050-6709)
PHONE..................................408 241-5188
Cindy Lawler, *Branch Mgr*
EMP: 12
SALES (corp-wide): 13.6B **Privately Held**
SIC: 3911 Mountings, gold or silver: pens,
leather goods, etc.
HQ: Montblanc North America, Llc
645 5th Ave Fl 6
New York NY 10022

(P-23300)
NAREG JEWELRY INC
640 S Hill St Ste 542a, Los Angeles
(90014-4704)
PHONE..................................213 683-1660
Greg Iskanian, *President*
EMP: 30
SQ FT: 5,000
SALES (est): 2.6MM **Privately Held**
SIC: 3911 Jewelry, precious metal

(P-23301)
**NATIONWIDE JEWELRY MFRS
INC**
Also Called: B & B Jewelry Mfg
631 S Olive St Ste 790, Los Angeles
(90014-3607)
PHONE..................................213 489-1215
Ben Behnam, *CEO*
Behrooz Behnam, *Vice Pres*
Parviz Behnam, *Vice Pres*
▲ EMP: 16
SQ FT: 4,000
SALES (est): 3MM **Privately Held**
SIC: 3911 5094 Jewelry, precious metal;
jewelry

(P-23302)
NEW CENTURY GOLD LLC
6303 Owensmouth Ave Fl 10, Woodland
Hills (91367-2262)
PHONE..................................818 936-2676
Derek Lee, *Mng Member*
EMP: 10
SALES (est): 845.4K **Privately Held**
SIC: 3911 Jewelry, precious metal

(P-23303)
**NEW GOLD MANUFACTURING
INC**
2150 N Lincoln St, Burbank (91504-3337)
PHONE..................................818 847-1020
Mesrop Samvelian, *CEO*
▲ EMP: 60
SALES (est): 5.8MM **Privately Held**
SIC: 3911 Jewelry, precious metal

(P-23304)
OBATAKE INC
Also Called: Lucy Ann
20309 Gramercy Pl Ste A, Torrance
(90501-1531)
PHONE..................................310 782-2730
Derrick Obatake, *President*
Jennifer Seiler, *Sales Executive*
EMP: 20
SALES: 5MM **Privately Held**
WEB: www.lucyann.com
SIC: 3911 5084 Jewelry, precious metal;
industrial machinery & equipment

(P-23305)
PADILLA JEWELERS INC
6118 Venice Blvd Fl 2, Los Angeles
(90034-2227)
PHONE....................................323 931-1678
Manuel Padilla Jr, *President*
EMP: 14
SALES (est): 2.5MM **Privately Held**
SIC: 3911 Jewelry, precious metal; jewelry
apparel

(P-23306)
QJM CORP
606 S Olive St Ste 2170, Los Angeles
(90014-1695)
PHONE....................................213 622-0264
Meenu Agarwal, *President*
Rajiv Agarwal, *Vice Pres*
EMP: 12
SALES (est): 930K **Privately Held**
WEB: www.qjmcorp.com
SIC: 3911 Jewelry, precious metal

(P-23307)
QUAD R TECH
521 W Rosecrans Ave, Gardena
(90248-1514)
PHONE....................................310 851-6161
Vlademmer Reil, *President*
EMP: 150
SALES (est): 13.2MM **Privately Held**
SIC: 3911 Earrings, precious metal

(P-23308)
RICHLINE GROUP INC
455 N Moss St, Burbank (91502-1727)
PHONE....................................818 848-5555
Bob Wagner, *Principal*
EMP: 198
SALES (corp-wide): 242.1B **Publicly
Held**
WEB: www.aurafin.net
SIC: 3911 Necklaces, precious metal
HQ: Richline Group, Inc.
1385 Broadway Fl 12
New York NY 10018

(P-23309)
RICHLINE GROUP INC
Also Called: Aurafin Oroamerica
443 N Varney St, Burbank (91502-1733)
P.O. Box 7340 (91510-7340)
PHONE....................................818 848-5555
Guy Benhamou, *Branch Mgr*
EMP: 198
SALES (corp-wide): 242.1B **Publicly
Held**
SIC: 3911 Necklaces, precious metal
HQ: Richline Group, Inc.
1385 Broadway Fl 12
New York NY 10018

(P-23310)
RJ JEWELRY INC
Also Called: Rubens Jewelry Mfg
650 S Hill St Ste 414, Los Angeles
(90014-1773)
PHONE....................................213 627-9936
Gevork Karapetian, *President*
Diana Karapetian, *Vice Pres*
Ruben Karapetian, *Vice Pres*
EMP: 14
SQ FT: 3,000
SALES: 923.2K **Privately Held**
SIC: 3911 5094 Jewelry, precious metal;
precious metals

(P-23311)
ROBERTO MARTINEZ INC
1050 Calle Cordillera # 103, San Clemente
(92673-6240)
PHONE....................................800 257-6462
Roberto Martinez, *CEO*
Elsa Martinez-Phillips, *President*
▲ EMP: 15
SQ FT: 6,000
SALES (est): 2.3MM **Privately Held**
WEB: www.rminc.ws
SIC: 3911 5094 Jewelry apparel; jewelry

(P-23312)
SAGE GODDESS INC
3830 Del Amo Blvd Ste 102, Torrance
(90503-2119)
PHONE....................................650 733-6639
Athena I Perrakis, *CEO*
David Maeizlik, *COO*
EMP: 42
SQ FT: 12,000
SALES (est): 2.4MM **Privately Held**
SIC: 3911 5944 5999 Jewelry apparel;
jewelry, precious stones & precious met-
als; perfumes & colognes

(P-23313)
SAGE MACHADO INC
133 N Gramercy Pl, Los Angeles
(90004-4013)
PHONE....................................323 931-0595
Sage Machado, *President*
EMP: 12
SQ FT: 2,600
SALES (est): 1.3MM **Privately Held**
WEB: www.sagejewelry.com
SIC: 3911 5944 5999 5621 Jewelry, pre-
cious metal; jewelry stores; perfumes &
colognes; boutiques

(P-23314)
SAKS STYLING INCORPORATED
Also Called: Charm America
641 W Harvard St, Glendale (91204-1107)
PHONE....................................818 244-0540
Sarkis Andreasian, *President*
Adrian Andreasian, *Admin Sec*
EMP: 30
SQ FT: 10,000
SALES: 5MM **Privately Held**
SIC: 3911 Jewelry, precious metal

(P-23315)
SAUSALITO CRAFTWORKS INC
Also Called: Omnirax
2342 Marinship Way, Sausalito
(94965-1463)
P.O. Box 1792 (94966-1792)
PHONE....................................415 331-4031
David Holland, *Branch Mgr*
EMP: 12
SALES (est): 1MM
SALES (corp-wide): 1.7MM **Privately
Held**
WEB: www.sausalitocraft.com
SIC: 3911 2522 Jewelry, precious metal;
office furniture, except wood
PA: Sausalito Craftworks, Inc.
2330 Marinship Way # 160
Sausalito CA
415 332-3392

(P-23316)
**SCHNEIDERS DEISGN STUDIO
INC**
Also Called: Dave Schneider's Fine Jewelry
245 The Promenade N Fl 2, Long Beach
(90802-3179)
PHONE....................................562 437-0448
Mark Schneider, *President*
▲ EMP: 16 EST: 1946
SQ FT: 5,000
SALES (est): 2.3MM **Privately Held**
SIC: 3911 5094 Jewelry, precious metal;
jewelry

(P-23317)
SGB HOLDINGS LLC
Also Called: Secured Gold Buyers
16 Cape Woodbury, Newport Beach
(92660-8405)
PHONE....................................949 722-1149
Ryan Knott, *Mng Member*
EMP: 41 EST: 2008
SQ FT: 1,800
SALES (est): 3.8MM **Privately Held**
SIC: 3911 Jewelry, precious metal

(P-23318)
SOLID 21 INCORPORATED
Also Called: 2 Awesome International
22287 Mulholland Hwy # 82, Calabasas
(91302-5157)
PHONE....................................213 688-0900
Christopher Aire, *President*
EMP: 16

SALES: 10MM **Privately Held**
SIC: 3911 5944 7631 Jewelry, precious
metal; jewelry, precious stones & precious
metals; watch, clock & jewelry repair

(P-23319)
STAR RING INC
Also Called: Romance Ring
4429 Summerglen Ct, Moorpark
(93021-2744)
PHONE....................................818 773-4900
Kenneth Harrison, *President*
Gay Murdock, *Controller*
▲ EMP: 60
SQ FT: 10,000
SALES (est): 14.7MM **Privately Held**
WEB: www.starringinc.com
SIC: 3911 Jewelry, precious metal

(P-23320)
STATUS COLLECTION & CO INC
8383 Wilshire Blvd # 112, Beverly Hills
(90211-2404)
PHONE....................................310 432-7788
Jeremiah Spielman, *President*
EMP: 10
SQ FT: 2,100
SALES (est): 1.2MM **Privately Held**
SIC: 3911 Jewelry, precious metal

(P-23321)
STUDIO 311 INC
466 Primero Ct Ste E, Cotati (94931-3036)
PHONE....................................707 795-6599
Katherine Aberle, *President*
EMP: 12
SALES (est): 1.4MM **Privately Held**
SIC: 3911 Jewelry, precious metal

(P-23322)
SUNRISE JEWELRY MFG CORP
4425 Convoy St Ste 226, San Diego
(92111-3731)
PHONE....................................619 270-5624
Sol Levy, *President*
EMP: 329
SALES (est): 22MM **Privately Held**
SIC: 3911 Jewelry, precious metal

(P-23323)
**TARINA TARANTINO DESIGNS
LLC**
910 S Broadway Fl 6, Los Angeles
(90015-1610)
PHONE....................................213 533-8070
Alfonso Campos, *General Mgr*
▲ EMP: 10 EST: 1996
SQ FT: 2,200
SALES (est): 1.9MM **Privately Held**
WEB: www.tarinatarantino.com
SIC: 3911 Jewelry, precious metal

(P-23324)
TERRYBERRY COMPANY LLC
25600 Rye Canyon Rd # 109, Santa Clarita
(91355-1166)
PHONE....................................661 257-9971
EMP: 60
SALES (corp-wide): 42.2MM **Privately
Held**
SIC: 3911 Jewelry, precious metal
PA: Terryberry Company, Llc
2033 Oak Industrial Dr Ne
Grand Rapids MI 49505
616 458-1391

(P-23325)
THREE SISTERS DESIGN INC
Also Called: Three Sisters Jewelry Design
967 S Coast Highway 101 # 109, Encinitas
(92024-4443)
PHONE....................................760 230-2813
Zoe Mohler, *CEO*
EMP: 15
SQ FT: 1,600
SALES (est): 1.1MM **Privately Held**
SIC: 3911 Jewelry apparel

(P-23326)
TK AND COMPANY WATCHES
5827 W Pico Blvd, Los Angeles
(90019-3714)
PHONE....................................213 545-1971
EMP: 15
SALES (est): 656.6K **Privately Held**
SIC: 3911

(P-23327)
US GOLD TRADING INC
117 E Providencia Ave, Burbank
(91502-1922)
PHONE....................................818 558-7766
Sarkis Adamian, *CEO*
EMP: 18
SQ FT: 25,000
SALES (est): 2.7MM **Privately Held**
SIC: 3911 Jewelry, precious metal

(P-23328)
VAN CRAEYNEST INC
27 E State St, Redlands (92373-4753)
PHONE....................................415 362-1025
Larry Van Craeynest, *President*
Roger Van Craeynest Jr, *Corp Secy*
EMP: 15
SQ FT: 2,200
SALES (est): 1.6MM **Privately Held**
WEB: www.vancraeynest.com
SIC: 3911 Rings, finger: precious metal

(P-23329)
VAPOR CLEANERS (PA)
Also Called: Vapor Cleaners & Shirt Laundry
285 Water St, Santa Cruz (95060-4055)
PHONE....................................831 423-4646
Thomas Lee, *Owner*
EMP: 18
SALES (est): 400K **Privately Held**
SIC: 3911 Cigar & cigarette accessories

(P-23330)
VOGT WESTERN SILVER LTD
1210 Commerce Ave Ste 1, Woodland
(95776-5927)
P.O. Box 1129 (95776-1129)
PHONE....................................530 669-6840
Chester N Vogt, *President*
Casey Vogt, *Vice Pres*
Linda Baldwin, *Production*
EMP: 10 EST: 1970
SQ FT: 5,000
SALES (est): 1.6MM **Privately Held**
WEB: www.vogtsilversmiths.com
SIC: 3911 3199 Jewelry, precious metal;
leather belting & strapping

(P-23331)
**WESTERN IMPERIAL TRADING
INC**
Also Called: Imperial Designs
13946 Ventura Blvd, Sherman Oaks
(91423-3530)
PHONE....................................818 907-0768
Jacob Killedjian, *President*
EMP: 10 EST: 1975
SQ FT: 1,500
SALES (est): 1MM **Privately Held**
SIC: 3911 Jewelry, precious metal

(P-23332)
Y Y K INC
Also Called: Kim's Jewelry Manufacturer
411 W 7th St Ste 710, Los Angeles
(90014-3615)
PHONE....................................213 622-0741
Yun Bu Kim, *President*
Young Ye Kim, *Admin Sec*
▼ EMP: 15
SQ FT: 1,500
SALES (est): 1.7MM **Privately Held**
SIC: 3911 Jewelry, precious metal

(P-23333)
YERMA JEWELRY MFG INC
671 W Broadway, Glendale (91204-1007)
PHONE....................................818 551-0690
Hagob Yermanez, *President*
EMP: 50
SALES (est): 3.8MM **Privately Held**
SIC: 3911 Bracelets, precious metal

(P-23334)
**ZALEMARK HOLDING COMPANY
INC**
15260 Vntr Blvd St 1200, Sherman Oaks
(91403)
P.O. Box 280725, Northridge (91328-0725)
PHONE....................................888 682-6885
Ernest Martel, *CEO*
Charels Baron, *CFO*
Caren Currier, *CFO*
Steven Zale, *Corp Secy*

EMP: 11
SQ FT: 1,000
SALES (est): 1MM **Privately Held**
SIC: 3911 5094 Jewelry, precious metal;
jewelry

3914 Silverware, Plated & Stainless Steel Ware

(P-23335)
CAL SIMBA INC (PA)
1680 Universe Cir, Oxnard (93033-2441)
PHONE..............................805 240-1177
Jay Schechter, *CEO*
John Stout, *Corp Secy*
Stuart Seeler, *Vice Pres*
▲ EMP: 38
SQ FT: 18,000
SALES (est): 8.7MM **Privately Held**
SIC: 3914 2672 3452 2821 Trophies,
plated (all metals); labels (unprinted),
gummed: made from purchased materi-
als; pins; polyurethane resins; silk screen
design

(P-23336)
DYLN LIFESTYLE LLC
Also Called: Dyln Inspired
18242 Mcdurmott W Ste A, Irvine
(92614-4771)
PHONE..............................949 209-9401
Dorian Ayres,
▲ EMP: 15 EST: 2011
SALES (est): 1.9MM **Privately Held**
SIC: 3914 Stainless steel ware

(P-23337)
STEELCRAFT WEST
14575 Yorba Ave, Chino (91710-5710)
P.O. Box 981268, El Paso TX (79998-
1268)
PHONE..............................909 548-2696
Dwight White, *General Mgr*
EMP: 13
SALES (est): 1.8MM **Privately Held**
SIC: 3914 Holloware, stainless steel

(P-23338)
STREIVOR INC
Also Called: Streivor Air Systems
2150 Kitty Hawk Rd, Livermore
(94551-9522)
PHONE..............................925 960-9090
Jeffrey S Lambertson, *CEO*
EMP: 18
SQ FT: 35,250
SALES (est): 4.3MM **Privately Held**
SIC: 3914 Stainless steel ware

3915 Jewelers Findings & Lapidary Work

(P-23339)
BEAUDRY INTERNATIONAL LLC
3835 E Thousand Oaks Blvd, Westlake Vil-
lage (91362-3637)
PHONE..............................213 623-5025
Frank Lucero, *Mng Member*
EMP: 10
SALES (est): 1.3MM **Privately Held**
SIC: 3915 Diamond cutting & polishing

(P-23340)
BELAIR GOLD DESIGN INC
Also Called: Angie's Jewelry
650 S Hill St Ste 914, Los Angeles
(90014-1752)
PHONE..............................213 891-0152
Jack Tutungian, *President*
Angie Tutungian, *Vice Pres*
EMP: 22
SQ FT: 2,200
SALES (est): 1.9MM **Privately Held**
SIC: 3915 5094 3911 Lapidary work & di-
amond cutting & polishing; jewelry & pre-
cious stones; jewelry, precious metal

(P-23341)
CGM INC
Also Called: Cgm Findings
19611 Ventura Blvd # 211, Tarzana
(91356-2907)
PHONE..............................818 609-7088
Devinder Bindra, *CEO*
▲ EMP: 25
SQ FT: 12,000
SALES (est): 3.5MM **Privately Held**
WEB: www.cgmfindings.com
SIC: 3915 5094 Jewelers' materials & lap-
idary work; precious metals; precious
stones (gems); precious stones & metals

(P-23342)
FRESNO GEM & MINERAL SOCIETY
340 W Olive Ave, Fresno (93728-2927)
P.O. Box 9608 (93793-9608)
PHONE..............................559 486-7280
Newman Gill, *President*
EMP: 12
SALES: 74.5K **Privately Held**
SIC: 3915 Lapidary work, contract or other

(P-23343)
HING WA LEE INC
19811 Colima Rd, Walnut (91789-3421)
PHONE..............................909 595-3500
David Lee, *CEO*
EMP: 20
SALES (corp-wide): 4.3MM **Privately Held**
SIC: 3915 Jewelers' materials & lapidary work
PA: Hing Wa Lee, Inc.
19345 San Jose Ave
City Of Industry CA 91748
909 869-0900

(P-23344)
KIM SENG JEWELRY INC
818 N Broadway Ste 202, Los Angeles
(90012-2342)
PHONE..............................213 628-8566
Minh Chang, *President*
▲ EMP: 15
SQ FT: 1,400
SALES (est): 1.4MM **Privately Held**
SIC: 3915 Jewel cutting, drilling, polishing,
recutting or setting

(P-23345)
NELSON JEWELLERY (USA) INC
631 S Olive St Ste 300, Los Angeles
(90014-3637)
PHONE..............................213 489-3323
Eddie Chung, *President*
Roger Kou, *Senior VP*
▲ EMP: 18
SALES (est): 2.3MM **Privately Held**
SIC: 3915 Jewelers' materials & lapidary
work

(P-23346)
RAMONA MINING & MANUFACTURING
Also Called: Craftstones
505 Elm St, Ramona (92065-1913)
P.O. Box 847 (92065-0847)
PHONE..............................760 789-1620
Herbert Walters, *President*
Stephen Walters, *Vice Pres*
Mary Walters, *Admin Sec*
◆ EMP: 18 EST: 1953
SQ FT: 12,500
SALES (est): 2.2MM **Privately Held**
WEB: www.craftstones.com
SIC: 3915 Jewelers' materials & lapidary
work

(P-23347)
ROBERT SNELL CAST SPECIALIST
110 Spring Hill Dr Ste 20, Grass Valley
(95945-5928)
PHONE..............................530 273-8958
Robert Snell, *Owner*
Debra Snell, *Co-Owner*
EMP: 12
SALES (est): 760K **Privately Held**
SIC: 3915 Jewelers' castings

(P-23348)
STARDUST DIAMOND CORP
Also Called: Diamonds By Design
550 S Hill St Ste 1420, Los Angeles
(90013-2415)
PHONE..............................213 239-9999
Gall Raiman, *President*
Albert Gad, *Shareholder*
Janet Guttmann, *CFO*
EMP: 15
SQ FT: 3,600
SALES (est): 1.7MM **Privately Held**
WEB: www.stardustdiamonds.com
SIC: 3915 5094 Jewelers' findings & mate-
rials; diamond cutting & polishing; dia-
monds (gems)

(P-23349)
STEINHAUSEN INC
28478 Westinghouse Pl, Valencia
(91355-0929)
PHONE..............................661 702-1400
▲ EMP: 12
SALES (est): 1.2MM **Privately Held**
WEB: www.steinhauseninc.com
SIC: 3915

(P-23350)
THAT CASTING PLACE INC
6229 Outlook Ave, Los Angeles (90042-
3531)
PHONE..............................323 258-5691
Antonio Campopiano, *President*
Isabella Campopiano, *Vice Pres*
EMP: 10
SQ FT: 3,000
SALES (est): 560K **Privately Held**
SIC: 3915 Jewelers' castings

3931 Musical Instruments

(P-23351)
AGOURA MUSIC
625 N Sycamore Ave # 313, Los Angeles
(90036-2043)
PHONE..............................818 991-8316
Nima Azizi, *President*
EMP: 15
SALES (est): 1.6MM **Privately Held**
WEB: www.agouramusic.com
SIC: 3931 8299 Musical instruments; mu-
sical instrument lessons

(P-23352)
ALEMBIC INC
3005 Wiljan Ct Ste A, Santa Rosa
(95407-5702)
PHONE..............................707 523-2611
Susan L Wickersham, *President*
Ron Wickersham, *Treasurer*
Mary Nelson, *Purchasing*
EMP: 15 EST: 1969
SQ FT: 12,472
SALES (est): 2.1MM **Privately Held**
WEB: www.alembic.com
SIC: 3931 5736 Guitars & parts, electric &
nonelectric; musical instrument stores

(P-23353)
AQUARIAN ACCESSORIES CORP
Also Called: Aquarian Drumheads
1140 N Tustin Ave, Anaheim (92807-1735)
PHONE..............................714 632-0230
Ronald Marquez, *President*
Dave Donahue, *Treasurer*
Ray Burns, *Vice Pres*
Rose Marquez, *Admin Sec*
Gabe Diaz, *Sales Mgr*
EMP: 20
SQ FT: 20,000
SALES (est): 3.3MM **Privately Held**
SIC: 3931 Percussion instruments & parts

(P-23354)
AUDIO IMPRESSIONS INC
6592 Oak Springs Dr, Oak Park
(91377-3828)
PHONE..............................818 532-7360
Christopher L Stone, *President*
Leslie Stone, *Treasurer*
EMP: 13

SALES (est): 1.1MM **Privately Held**
WEB: www.audioimpressions.com
SIC: 3931 Musical instruments, electric &
electronic

(P-23355)
AXL MUSICAL INSTRUMENTS LTD
31067 San Clemente St, Hayward
(94544-7813)
P.O. Box 808, Brisbane (94005-0808)
PHONE..............................415 508-1398
Liu WEI Guo, *Branch Mgr*
Vesna Tomic, *Director*
EMP: 155
SALES (corp-wide): 2.3MM **Privately Held**
WEB: www.axlusa.com
SIC: 3931 5736 Musical instruments; mu-
sical instrument stores
PA: Shanghai Chaobo Industrial Co., Ltd.
No.2411, Xinjian No.1 Rd., Xuhang
Town, Jiading Dist.
Shanghai 20180
215 955-6047

(P-23356)
BBE SOUND INC (PA)
Also Called: G & L Musical Instruments
2548 Fender Ave Ste D, Fullerton
(92831-4439)
PHONE..............................714 897-6766
John C McLaren, *CEO*
John T Davey, *CFO*
Trang Nguyen, *Treasurer*
David C McLaren, *Exec VP*
Paul Gagon, *Vice Pres*
▲ EMP: 22
SQ FT: 10,000
SALES (est): 5.5MM **Privately Held**
SIC: 3931 3651 Guitars & parts, electric &
nonelectric; amplifiers: radio, public ad-
dress or musical instrument; microphones

(P-23357)
BLACK RUBY VENTURES LLC
Also Called: Suzuki Music USA
9323 Stevens Rd Ste A, Santee
(92071-7122)
P.O. Box 710459 (92072-0459)
PHONE..............................619 873-2000
Howard Feldman,
▲ EMP: 10
SALES (est): 1.2MM **Privately Held**
SIC: 3931 Musical instruments, electric &
electronic

(P-23358)
BOULDER CREEK GUITARS INC
5810 Obata Way Ste 1, Gilroy
(95020-7039)
PHONE..............................408 842-0222
Jeffrey Paul Strametz, *CEO*
EMP: 14 EST: 2014
SQ FT: 6,700
SALES (est): 1.9MM **Privately Held**
SIC: 3931 5099 Guitars & parts, electric &
nonelectric; musical instruments

(P-23359)
CRAVIOTTO DRUM CO
Also Called: Craviotto, John Custom Drums
81 Hangar Way Ste 8, Watsonville
(95076-2481)
PHONE..............................831 763-0855
John Craviotto, *President*
David Victor, *General Mgr*
▲ EMP: 15
SALES (est): 1.7MM **Privately Held**
WEB: www.craviottodrums.com
SIC: 3931 Guitars & parts, electric & non-
electric

(P-23360)
DEERING BANJO COMPANY INC
3733 Kenora Dr, Spring Valley
(91971-1206)
PHONE..............................619 464-8252
Charles Greg Deering, *President*
Janet Deering, *Corp Secy*
▲ EMP: 40
SQ FT: 18,000
SALES (est): 6.5MM **Privately Held**
WEB: www.deeringbanjos.com
SIC: 3931 Banjos & parts

PRODUCTS & SVCS

(P-23361)
DIGITAL MUSIC CORPORATION
3165 Coffey Ln, Santa Rosa (95403-2502)
PHONE..............................707 545-0600
Joshua C Fiden, *President*
▲ EMP: 12
SQ FT: 2,400
SALES (est): 940K **Privately Held**
WEB: www.voodoolab.com
SIC: 3931 Musical instruments, electric & electronic

(P-23362)
DRUM WORKSHOP INC (PA)
Also Called: Dw Drum
3450 Lunar Ct, Oxnard (93030-8976)
PHONE..............................805 485-6999
Christopher D Lombardi, *CEO*
Don Lombardi, *President*
John Good, *Vice Pres*
◆ EMP: 60
SQ FT: 17,000
SALES (est): 21.4MM **Privately Held**
WEB: www.dwdrums.com
SIC: 3931 Drums, parts & accessories (musical instruments)

(P-23363)
DUNCAN CARTER CORPORATION (PA)
Also Called: Seymour Duncan
5427 Hollister Ave, Santa Barbara (93111-2307)
PHONE..............................805 964-9749
Seymour Duncan, *Chairman*
Cathy Carter Duncan, *CEO*
▲ EMP: 96 EST: 1976
SQ FT: 20,000
SALES (est): 18.1MM **Privately Held**
WEB: www.seymourduncan.com
SIC: 3931 5736 3674 3651 Guitars & parts, electric & nonelectric; musical instrument stores; semiconductors & related devices; household audio & video equipment

(P-23364)
DUNLOP MANUFACTURING INC (PA)
150 Industrial Way, Benicia (94510-1112)
P.O. Box 846 (94510-0846)
PHONE..............................707 745-2722
James Andrew Dunlop, *CEO*
Jasmin Powell, *Vice Pres*
Joey Tosi, *Creative Dir*
Sally Balmaceda, *Info Tech Mgr*
Jim Silva, *Info Tech Mgr*
◆ EMP: 100 EST: 1977
SQ FT: 40,000
SALES (est): 16.2MM **Privately Held**
WEB: www.jimdunlop.com
SIC: 3931 Guitars & parts, electric & nonelectric

(P-23365)
DUNLOP MANUFACTURING INC
649 Industrial Way, Benicia (94510-1163)
PHONE..............................707 745-2709
Jasmin Powell, *Branch Mgr*
EMP: 45
SALES (corp-wide): 16.2MM **Privately Held**
SIC: 3931 Musical instruments
PA: Dunlop Manufacturing, Inc.
150 Industrial Way
Benicia CA 94510
707 745-2722

(P-23366)
E M G INC
675 Aviation Blvd Ste B, Santa Rosa (95403-1025)
P.O. Box 4394 (95402-4394)
PHONE..............................707 525-9941
Robert A Turner, *President*
Andy Gravelle, *COO*
Gary Rush, *General Mgr*
EMP: 81
SQ FT: 10,000
SALES (est): 14.5MM **Privately Held**
WEB: www.emgpickups.com
SIC: 3931 5736 Guitars & parts, electric & nonelectric; musical instrument stores

(P-23367)
ERNIE BALL INC (PA)
4117 Earthwood Ln, San Luis Obispo (93401-7541)
PHONE..............................805 544-7726
Roland S Ball, *President*
Sterling C Ball, *Vice Pres*
Sean Murphy, *Marketing Staff*
▲ EMP: 96
SQ FT: 50,000
SALES (est): 17.8MM **Privately Held**
WEB: www.ernieball.com
SIC: 3931 Guitars & parts, electric & nonelectric

(P-23368)
ERNIE BALL INC
53973 Polk St, Coachella (92236-3816)
PHONE..............................800 543-2255
Sterling C Ball, *Manager*
EMP: 54
SALES (corp-wide): 17.8MM **Privately Held**
SIC: 3931 Guitars & parts, electric & nonelectric
PA: Ernie Ball, Inc.
4117 Earthwood Ln
San Luis Obispo CA 93401
805 544-7726

(P-23369)
FENDER MUSICAL INSTRS CORP
1295 E Central Ave, San Bernardino (92408-2602)
PHONE..............................909 773-1200
EMP: 62
SALES (corp-wide): 816.3MM **Privately Held**
SIC: 3931 Musical instruments
PA: Fender Musical Instruments Corporation
17600 N Perimeter Dr # 100
Scottsdale AZ 85255
480 596-9690

(P-23370)
FENDER MUSICAL INSTRS CORP
301 Cessna Cir, Corona (92880-2521)
PHONE..............................480 596-9690
Al Guzman, *Principal*
Mike Born, *Technology*
Javier Torres, *Engineer*
Kurt Wynboom, *Finance Dir*
Lillian Guillen, *Human Res Mgr*
EMP: 600
SALES (corp-wide): 816.3MM **Privately Held**
WEB: www.fender.com
SIC: 3931 Guitars & parts, electric & nonelectric
PA: Fender Musical Instruments Corporation
17600 N Perimeter Dr # 100
Scottsdale AZ 85255
480 596-9690

(P-23371)
FULLTONE MUSICAL PRODUCTS INC
11018 Washington Blvd, Culver City (90232-3901)
PHONE..............................310 204-0155
Michael Fuller, *President*
▲ EMP: 15
SQ FT: 3,595
SALES (est): 4.3MM **Privately Held**
WEB: www.fulltone.com
SIC: 3931 5099 Musical instruments; musical instruments

(P-23372)
GIBSON BRANDS INC
Also Called: Entertainment Relations
9350 Civic Center Dr # 130, Beverly Hills (90210-3629)
PHONE..............................310 300-2369
Jennifer Feeney, *Manager*
EMP: 114
SALES (corp-wide): 568.4MM **Privately Held**
WEB: www.gibson.com
SIC: 3931 Guitars & parts, electric & nonelectric

PA: Gibson Brands, Inc.
309 Plus Park Blvd
Nashville TN 37217
615 871-4500

(P-23373)
GOODALL GUITARS INC
541 S Franklin St, Fort Bragg (95437-5101)
PHONE..............................707 962-1620
James Goodall, *President*
Jean Goodall, *Vice Pres*
EMP: 14
SQ FT: 7,200
SALES (est): 1.5MM **Privately Held**
WEB: www.goodallguitars.com
SIC: 3931 5099 Guitars & parts, electric & nonelectric; musical instruments

(P-23374)
GULBRANSEN INC
Also Called: Piano Exchange
2102 Hancock St, San Diego (92110-2083)
PHONE..............................619 296-5760
Curtis Rex Carter Jr, *CEO*
Robert L Hill, *President*
David Starky, *Senior VP*
EMP: 10
SQ FT: 6,500
SALES (est): 660K **Privately Held**
SIC: 3931 5099 Keyboard instruments & parts; pianos, all types: vertical, grand, spinet, player, etc.; musical instruments; pianos

(P-23375)
HARRIS ORGANS INC
Also Called: Harris' Precision Products
7047 Comstock Ave, Whittier (90602-1399)
PHONE..............................562 693-3442
David C Harris, *President*
EMP: 21
SQ FT: 12,000
SALES (est): 2.5MM **Privately Held**
WEB: www.harrisorgans.com
SIC: 3931 3599 Pipes, organ; machine shop, jobbing & repair

(P-23376)
HPF CORPORATION (PA)
Also Called: Suzuki Musical Instruments
9920 Prospect Ave Ste 102, Santee (92071-4349)
PHONE..............................858 566-9710
▲ EMP: 18
SQ FT: 40,000
SALES (est): 5.3MM **Privately Held**
WEB: www.suzukicorp.com
SIC: 3931 Musical instruments

(P-23377)
HUPALO REPASKY PIPE ORGANS LLC
2450 Alvarado St, San Leandro (94577-4316)
PHONE..............................510 483-6905
John Hupalo,
Steve Repasky,
▲ EMP: 15
SQ FT: 3,400
SALES (est): 239K **Privately Held**
WEB: www.hupalorepasky.com
SIC: 3931 Musical instruments

(P-23378)
KANSTUL MUSICAL INSTRS INC (PA)
Also Called: K M I
1332 S Claudina St, Anaheim (92805-6234)
PHONE..............................714 563-1000
Zigmant J Kanstul, *President*
Jack Kanstul, *Sales Staff*
EMP: 40
SQ FT: 27,000
SALES (est): 4.4MM **Privately Held**
WEB: www.kanstul.net
SIC: 3931 Brass instruments & parts

(P-23379)
LR BAGGS CORPORATION
483 N Frontage Rd, Nipomo (93444-9596)
PHONE..............................805 929-3545
Lloyd R Baggs, *CEO*
Bo Lrbaggs, *General Mgr*
Caleb Elling, *Technology*

Ed Herlihy, *Technology*
Justin Rucker, *Electrical Engi*
▲ EMP: 25
SALES (est): 4.3MM **Privately Held**
SIC: 3931 3825 3651 Guitars & parts, electric & nonelectric; transducers for volts, amperes, watts, vars, frequency, etc.; household audio & video equipment

(P-23380)
MANZANITA
Also Called: Lsl Instruments
26559 Ruether Ave, Santa Clarita (91350-2622)
PHONE..............................818 785-1111
Lisa Lerman, *CEO*
Lance Lerman, *President*
EMP: 10 EST: 2010
SALES (est): 1MM **Privately Held**
SIC: 3931 Musical instruments

(P-23381)
PALADAR MFG INC
53973 Polk St, Coachella (92236-3816)
P.O. Box 4117, San Luis Obispo (93403-4117)
PHONE..............................760 775-4222
Sterling C Ball, *President*
Roland S Ball, *Vice Pres*
▲ EMP: 52
SQ FT: 6,000
SALES (est): 8.2MM **Privately Held**
SIC: 3931 Strings, musical instrument

(P-23382)
QUILTER LABORATORIES LLC
1700 Sunflower Ave, Costa Mesa (92626-1505)
PHONE..............................714 519-6114
Patrick H Quilter, *Principal*
Nicole Cheshire, *Office Mgr*
Peter Melton, *Sales Mgr*
▲ EMP: 11 EST: 2011
SALES (est): 1.6MM **Privately Held**
SIC: 3931 Guitars & parts, electric & nonelectric

(P-23383)
REMO INC (PA)
28101 Industry Dr, Valencia (91355-4113)
PHONE..............................661 294-5600
Remo D Belli, *President*
Yolanda Davis, *COO*
Douglas Sink, *CFO*
Yerby Robert, *Vice Pres*
Fredy Shen, *Vice Pres*
◆ EMP: 300
SQ FT: 216,000
SALES (est): 47.7MM **Privately Held**
WEB: www.remo.com
SIC: 3931 Heads, drum; drums, parts & accessories (musical instruments)

(P-23384)
RICO CORPORATION (HQ)
Also Called: Rico Products
8484 San Fernando Rd, Sun Valley (91352-3227)
PHONE..............................818 394-2700
James D Addario, *CEO*
▲ EMP: 45
SALES (est): 22.8MM
SALES (corp-wide): 193.1MM **Privately Held**
WEB: www.ricoreeds.com
SIC: 3931 5099 Reeds for musical instruments; musical instruments
PA: D'addario & Company, Inc.
595 Smith St
Farmingdale NY 11735
631 439-3300

(P-23385)
RICO HOLDINGS INC
8484 San Fernando Rd, Sun Valley (91352-3227)
PHONE..............................818 394-2700
William Carpenter, *President*
Stewart Townson, *Controller*
Ruth Thresher, *Purchasing*
John Mill,
EMP: 240
SQ FT: 17,000
SALES (est): 13.3MM **Privately Held**
SIC: 3931 5099 Reeds for musical instruments; musical instruments

(P-23386)
SANTA CRUZ GUITAR CORPORATION
151 Harvey West Blvd C, Santa Cruz
(95060-2172)
PHONE..............................831 425-0999
Richard Hoover, *President*
John Anderson, *CFO*
Nathan Arrison, *Engineer*
▲ **EMP:** 22
SQ FT: 6,800
SALES (est): 3.3MM **Privately Held**
WEB: www.santacruzguitar.com
SIC: 3931 5736 Guitars & parts, electric & nonelectric; musical instrument stores

(P-23387)
SCHOENSTEIN & CO
4001 Industrial Way, Benicia (94510-1241)
PHONE..............................707 747-5858
Jack M Bethards, *President*
Louis Patterson, *Vice Pres*
Diane Delu, *Admin Sec*
EMP: 25
SQ FT: 10,000
SALES (est): 3.6MM **Privately Held**
WEB: www.schoenstein.com
SIC: 3931 7699 Pipes, organ; organ tuning & repair

(P-23388)
SHUBB CAPOS
14471 Hwy 1, Valley Ford (94972)
P.O. Box 550 (94972-0550)
PHONE..............................707 876-3001
Rick Shubb, *Partner*
Dave Coontz, *Partner*
Ruth Powers, *Executive*
▲ **EMP:** 22
SQ FT: 1,000
SALES (est): 2.4MM **Privately Held**
WEB: www.shubb.com
SIC: 3931 Guitars & parts, electric & non-electric

(P-23389)
SONGBIRD OCARINAS LLC
2751 E 11th St, Los Angeles (90023-3403)
PHONE..............................323 269-2524
Darren Steinberg, *Mng Member*
Barbara James, *Admin Sec*
Tatyana Dubashinskaya, *Internal Med*
▲ **EMP:** 11
SQ FT: 10,000
SALES (est): 1MM **Privately Held**
WEB: www.songbirdocarina.com
SIC: 3931 Ocarinas

(P-23390)
TAYLOR-LISTUG INC (PA)
Also Called: Taylor Guitars
1980 Gillespie Way, El Cajon (92020-1096)
PHONE..............................619 258-6957
Kurt Listug, *CEO*
Robert Taylor, *President*
Keith Brawley, *Vice Pres*
Brian Swerdfeger, *Vice Pres*
Chris Wellons, *Vice Pres*
▲ **EMP:** 277
SQ FT: 86,000
SALES (est): 119.9MM **Privately Held**
SIC: 3931 Guitars & parts, electric & non-electric

(P-23391)
THUNDER PRODUCTS INC
Also Called: Players Music Accessories
2469 Klein Rd, San Jose (95148-1800)
P.O. Box H (95151-0008)
PHONE..............................408 270-7800
Tony Lalonde, *CEO*
Tony La Londe, *President*
EMP: 16
SQ FT: 6,000
SALES: 750K **Privately Held**
SIC: 3931 Musical instruments

(P-23392)
TRIPLETT HARPS
220 Suburban Rd Ste C, San Luis Obispo
(93401-7526)
PHONE..............................805 544-2777
Steven Triplett, *Owner*
Debbie Triplett, *General Mgr*
▼ **EMP:** 14
SQ FT: 7,000

SALES: 800K **Privately Held**
WEB: www.triplettharps.com
SIC: 3931 5736 Harps & parts; musical instrument stores

(P-23393)
YAMAHA GUITAR GROUP INC (HQ)
Also Called: Line 6, Inc
26580 Agoura Rd, Calabasas
(91302-1921)
PHONE..............................818 575-3600
Paul Foeckler, *President*
Mary Ellen Broganer, *CFO*
Steve De Furia, *Vice Pres*
Susan Wolf, *Vice Pres*
Michel Doidic, *CTO*
◆ **EMP:** 120
SQ FT: 20,000
SALES (est): 45.5MM
SALES (corp-wide): 4B **Privately Held**
WEB: www.line6.com
SIC: 3931 Musical instruments; guitars & parts, electric & nonelectric
PA: Yamaha Corporation
10-1, Nakazawacho, Naka-Ku
Hamamatsu SZO 430-0
534 601-111

3942 Dolls & Stuffed Toys

(P-23394)
CUDDLY TOYS
1833 N Eastern Ave, Los Angeles
(90032-4115)
P.O. Box 41281 (90041-0281)
PHONE..............................323 980-0572
Leo Ramdwar, *President*
EMP: 12
SQ FT: 30,000
SALES (est): 1MM **Privately Held**
WEB: www.cuddlytoys.com
SIC: 3942 Stuffed toys, including animals

(P-23395)
DEFINE TOYS INC
Also Called: Hugfun International
1255 Bixby Dr, City of Industry
(91745-1708)
PHONE..............................626 330-8800
Ling He, *President*
Helen Wang, *Vice Pres*
▲ **EMP:** 15 **EST:** 2001
SQ FT: 15,000
SALES (est): 1.1MM **Privately Held**
SIC: 3942 Dolls & stuffed toys

(P-23396)
DREAM INTERNATIONAL USA INC
Also Called: Caltoy
7001 Village Dr Ste 280, Buena Park
(90621-2397)
PHONE..............................714 521-6007
Chul Hong Min, *CEO*
James Wang, *Exec VP*
Amy E Cho, *Managing Dir*
Suzette Lee, *General Mgr*
▲ **EMP:** 10
SALES (est): 1.4MM
SALES (corp-wide): 5.4K **Privately Held**
WEB: www.caltoy.com
SIC: 3942 5092 Stuffed toys, including animals; toys & games
PA: C&H Co., Ltd.
65 Sinbong 3-Gil
Sangju
825 453-6234

(P-23397)
KOTO INC
Also Called: Koto Bukiya
22857 Lockness Ave, Torrance
(90501-5103)
PHONE..............................310 327-7359
Jeffrey Kashida, *President*
Kazuyuki Shimizu, *President*
Hiroyo Shimizu, *COO*
May Okabe, *COO*
Aiko Shoji, *Vice Pres*
▲ **EMP:** 10
SQ FT: 5,000

SALES (est): 2MM **Privately Held**
SIC: 3942 5092 Dolls & stuffed toys; toy novelties & amusements; toys

(P-23398)
MAHAR MANUFACTURING CORP (PA)
Also Called: Fiesta Concession
2834 E 46th St, Vernon (90058-2404)
PHONE..............................323 581-9988
Michael Lauber, *CEO*
▲ **EMP:** 39
SQ FT: 100,000
SALES (est): 14.1MM **Privately Held**
WEB: www.fiestatoy.com
SIC: 3942 Stuffed toys, including animals

(P-23399)
ONE AT A TIME
3518 El Camino Real 195, Atascadero
(93422-2531)
PHONE..............................805 461-1784
Barbara Fritch, *Partner*
Bob Fritch, *Partner*
EMP: 11
SQ FT: 2,000
SALES: 39.8K **Privately Held**
SIC: 3942 5947 Dolls & stuffed toys; gift shop

(P-23400)
PHOENIX CUSTOM PROMOTIONS
Also Called: Petite Porcelain By Barbara
2005 Casa Grande Ct, Modesto
(95355-5101)
PHONE..............................209 579-1557
Abraham Angel, *President*
Barbara Angel, *Admin Sec*
▲ **EMP:** 10
SQ FT: 1,000
SALES (est): 1.2MM **Privately Held**
WEB: www.petiteporcelain.com
SIC: 3942 Dolls & stuffed toys

(P-23401)
RAYKORVAY INC
Also Called: Giant Teddy
1070 N Kraemer Pl, Anaheim
(92806-2610)
PHONE..............................714 632-8680
Reza Khosravi, *CEO*
▲ **EMP:** 16
SQ FT: 10,000
SALES (est): 2.2MM **Privately Held**
SIC: 3942 5961 Stuffed toys, including animals; toys & games (including dolls & models), mail order

(P-23402)
SNAP CREATIVE MANUFACTURING
3760 Calle Tecate Ste B, Camarillo
(93012-5061)
PHONE..............................818 735-3830
William Peter Howard Jr, *CEO*
▲ **EMP:** 12
SQ FT: 4,000
SALES: 20MM **Privately Held**
SIC: 3942 3069 Dolls & stuffed toys; toys, rubber

(P-23403)
UPD INC
Also Called: United Pacific Designs
4507 S Maywood Ave, Vernon
(90058-2610)
PHONE..............................323 588-8811
Shahin Dardashty, *President*
Ben Hooshim, *COO*
Benjamin Hooshim, *COO*
PHI Fozo, *CFO*
Fred Dardashty, *Vice Pres*
◆ **EMP:** 60
SQ FT: 140,000
SALES (est): 19.7MM **Privately Held**
SIC: 3942 5112 3944 Dolls & stuffed toys; pens &/or pencils; puzzles

---

3944 Games, Toys & Children's Vehicles

(P-23404)
ADOLF GOLDFARB
Also Called: Goldfarb & Associates
1434 6th St Ste 10, Santa Monica
(90401-2541)
PHONE..............................310 451-1211
Adolf E Goldfarb, *Owner*
EMP: 10
SQ FT: 13,000
SALES (est): 488.7K **Privately Held**
SIC: 3944 Children's vehicles, except bicycles

(P-23405)
ANKI INC (PA)
55 2nd St Ste 1500, San Francisco
(94105-3499)
PHONE..............................877 721-2654
Boris Sofman, *CEO*
Hanns Tappeiner, *President*
Dominic Ruso, *CFO*
Mark Palatucci,
Patrick De Neale, *Vice Pres*
▲ **EMP:** 21
SQ FT: 20,000
SALES (est): 10.9MM **Privately Held**
SIC: 3944 Toy trains, airplanes & automobiles

(P-23406)
ARTIFACT PUZZLES
180 Constitution Dr Ste 6, Menlo Park
(94025-1137)
PHONE..............................650 283-0589
Maya Gupta, *Mng Member*
EMP: 10
SALES: 1MM **Privately Held**
SIC: 3944 Puzzles

(P-23407)
ASSOCIATED ELECTRICS INC
26021 Commercentre Dr, Lake Forest
(92630-8853)
PHONE..............................949 544-7500
Gary Titus, *CEO*
Chung L Lai, *President*
Clifton Lett, *Vice Pres*
▲ **EMP:** 46 **EST:** 1965
SALES (est): 6.3MM **Privately Held**
WEB: www.rc10.com
SIC: 3944 Automobile & truck models, toy & hobby

(P-23408)
B DAZZLE INC
Also Called: Www.b-dazzle.com
500 Meyer Ln, Redondo Beach
(90278-5208)
PHONE..............................310 374-3000
Kathleen A Gavin, *President*
▲ **EMP:** 12
SQ FT: 5,500
SALES (est): 1.8MM **Privately Held**
WEB: www.b-dazzle.com
SIC: 3944 5092 Board games, puzzles & models, except electronic; puzzles; toys & games; puzzles; toys

(P-23409)
BANDAI AMERICA INCORPORATED (DH)
2120 Park Pl Ste 120, El Segundo
(90245-4824)
P.O. Box 6054, Cypress (90630-0054)
PHONE..............................714 816-9751
Atsushi Takeuchi, *Principal*
Katsushi Murakami, *Ch of Bd*
Takeshi Nojima, *President*
Masayuki Matsuo, *CEO*
Brian Goldner, *COO*
▲ **EMP:** 55
SQ FT: 75,000
SALES (est): 17.3MM
SALES (corp-wide): 6.3B **Privately Held**
WEB: www.bandai.com
SIC: 3944 Games, toys & children's vehicles

(P-23410)
BEEJAY LLC (PA)
Also Called: Spinner Toys & Gifts
3450 Kurtz St Ste C, San Diego
(92110-4451)
P.O. Box 81983 (92138-1983)
PHONE....................................619 220-8697
Lynda Willis, *Partner*
Jon Willis, *Vice Pres*
Richard Freeman, *Opers Staff*
Toya Davis, *Manager*
EMP: 10
SQ FT: 6,000
SALES: 1MM Privately Held
WEB: www.spinnertoys.com
SIC: 3944 5092 5199 Toy trains, airplanes
& automobiles; toys & hobby goods &
supplies; gifts & novelties

(P-23411)
BOTTELSEN DART CO INC
Also Called: American Dart Lines
945 W Mccoy Ln, Santa Maria
(93455-1109)
PHONE....................................805 922-4519
Walter Bottelsen, *President*
Aj Norrie, *General Mgr*
Susette Bottelsen, *Admin Sec*
Theresa Balderama, *Sales Mgr*
Jeff Bryan, *Director*
▲ EMP: 10
SQ FT: 10,250
SALES (est): 3.5MM Privately Held
SIC: 3944 Darts & dart games

(P-23412)
BRAINSTORMPRODUCTS LLC
1011 S Andreasen Dr # 100, Escondido
(92029-1962)
PHONE....................................760 871-1135
Randal W Joe,
Brian Tawa, *Exec VP*
Rich Brady, *Vice Pres*
Tom Mrowka, *Sales Staff*
▲ EMP: 10
SQ FT: 4,000
SALES (est): 2MM Privately Held
SIC: 3944 Kites

(P-23413)
BROKEN TOKEN
541 N Quince St Ste 1, Escondido
(92025-2570)
PHONE....................................760 294-1923
Gregory Spence, *President*
EMP: 10 EST: 2016
SALES (est): 1.1MM Privately Held
SIC: 3944 Games, toys & children's vehi-
cles

(P-23414)
BUMBLERIDE INC
2245 Kettner Blvd, San Diego (92101)
PHONE....................................619 615-0475
Matthew Reichardt, *President*
Emily Reichardt, *Vice Pres*
Sarah McKindlay-Boina, *Marketing Mgr*
▲ EMP: 10
SQ FT: 3,500
SALES: 1.9MM Privately Held
WEB: www.bumbleride.com
SIC: 3944 Strollers, baby (vehicle)

(P-23415)
CAPERON DESIGNS INC
Also Called: Beco Baby Carrier
1733 Monrovia Ave Ste N, Costa Mesa
(92627-4421)
PHONE....................................714 552-3201
Gabriela Caperon, *President*
Andrew Caperon, *Vice Pres*
▲ EMP: 15
SQ FT: 3,000
SALES (est): 2MM Privately Held
SIC: 3944 Baby carriages & restraint seats

(P-23416)
CRAFTERS COMPANION
2750 E Regal Park Dr, Anaheim
(92806-2417)
PHONE....................................714 630-2444
▲ EMP: 20 EST: 2012
SQ FT: 8,197
SALES (est): 1.9MM Privately Held
SIC: 3944

(P-23417)
CRYPTIC STUDIOS INC
980 University Ave, Los Gatos
(95032-7620)
PHONE....................................408 399-1969
Jack Emmert, *CEO*
Michael C Lewis, *President*
EMP: 100
SALES (est): 14.9MM Privately Held
WEB: www.crypticstudios.com
SIC: 3944 Video game machines, except
coin-operated
HQ: Perfect World Co., Ltd.
Rm 701-14,Building 5,No.1,Shangdi
East Road,
Beijing 10010
105 780-5623

(P-23418)
DREAMGEAR LLC
20001 S Western Ave, Torrance
(90501-1306)
PHONE....................................310 222-5522
Yahya Ahdout, *CEO*
Doris Johann, *Executive Asst*
Agustin Hernandez, *Technology*
Oliver Tesoro, *Engineer*
Moe Katouzian, *Controller*
◆ EMP: 49
SQ FT: 60,000
SALES (est): 10.7MM Privately Held
WEB: www.dreamgear.com
SIC: 3944 5023 Electronic games & toys;
electronic game machines, except coin-
operated; decorative home furnishings &
supplies

(P-23419)
**DT MATTSON ENTERPRISES
INC**
Also Called: Proline Manufacturing
201 W Lincoln St, Banning (92220-4933)
P.O. Box 456, Beaumont (92223-0456)
PHONE....................................951 849-9781
Todd Mattson, *CEO*
Cindy Cross, *Accountant*
David Hannaford, *Production*
▲ EMP: 40
SQ FT: 20,000
SALES (est): 6.1MM Privately Held
WEB: www.prolineracing.com
SIC: 3944 5521 Games, toys & children's
vehicles; trucks, tractors & trailers: used

(P-23420)
**EGGTOOTH ORIGINALS
CONSULTING**
13502 Graveyard Gulch Rd, Fort Jones
(96032-9743)
PHONE....................................530 468-5131
John West, *Owner*
Karen West, *Co-Owner*
EMP: 12
SALES (est): 852.2K Privately Held
SIC: 3944 Craft & hobby kits & sets

(P-23421)
ERGO BABY CARRIER INC (HQ)
617 W 7th St Fl 10, Los Angeles
(90017-3879)
PHONE....................................213 283-2090
Bill Chiasson, *CEO*
Karin A Frost, *President*
Elias Sabo, *President*
Svea Frost, *Vice Pres*
Vanessa Van Bui, *Vice Pres*
▲ EMP: 22
SALES: 67.3MM Publicly Held
WEB: www.ergobabycarrier.com
SIC: 3944 Baby carriages & restraint seats

(P-23422)
**EXCELLIGENCE LEARNING
CORP (PA)**
20 Ryan Ranch Rd Ste 200, Monterey
(93940-6439)
PHONE....................................831 333-2000
Kelly Crampton, *CEO*
Dipak Golechha, *President*
Judith McGuinn, *COO*
Carrie Lindsey, *Officer*
Mimi Stokes, *Officer*
▲ EMP: 50
SQ FT: 27,000

SALES (est): 241.7MM Privately Held
WEB: www.excelligencelearning.com
SIC: 3944 5999 Education aids, devices &
supplies; craft & hobby kits & sets

(P-23423)
EXPLODING KITTENS LLC
100 N Crescent Dr, Beverly Hills
(90210-5408)
PHONE....................................310 788-8699
Elan Lee,
Jackie Yu, *Accountant*
Matthew Inman,
EMP: 10
SALES (est): 10MM Privately Held
SIC: 3944 7371 Board games, children's &
adults'; computer software development &
applications

(P-23424)
EXTRON CONTRACT MFG INC
Also Called: Extron Contract Packaging
496 S Abbott Ave, Milpitas (95035-5258)
PHONE....................................510 353-0177
Andy Nguyen, *President*
EMP: 125
SQ FT: 200,000
SALES (est): 12.5MM Privately Held
SIC: 3944 3672 Electronic games & toys;
printed circuit boards

(P-23425)
**GAMES PRODUCTION
COMPANY LLC**
Also Called: Galaxy Pest Control
21323 Pacific Coast Hwy, Malibu
(90265-5202)
PHONE....................................310 456-0099
Jamie Ottilie, *CEO*
Matt Hockman, *Prgrmr*
EMP: 15 EST: 2007
SALES (est): 999.4K Privately Held
SIC: 3944 7371 7372 Electronic games &
toys; computer software development &
applications; home entertainment com-
puter software

(P-23426)
**HARDCORE RACING
COMPONENTS LLC**
27717 Avenue Scott, Valencia
(91355-1219)
PHONE....................................661 294-5032
Fax: 661 294-0770
EMP: 16 EST: 2000
SALES (est): 1.2MM Privately Held
SIC: 3944

(P-23427)
HARVEST ASIA INC
Also Called: 2 Impact Group
7888 Cherry Ave Ste G, Fontana
(92336-4273)
PHONE....................................888 800-3133
Derek Ro, *President*
Tina Kim, *Controller*
▲ EMP: 10
SQ FT: 5,000
SALES (est): 1.3MM Privately Held
SIC: 3944 3751 Children's vehicles, ex-
cept bicycles; motorcycles, bicycles &
parts

(P-23428)
HASBRO INC
16047 Mountain Ave, Chino (91708-9131)
PHONE....................................909 393-3248
Jeffrey Brown, *Manager*
EMP: 407
SALES (corp-wide): 5.2B Publicly Held
SIC: 3944 Games, toys & children's vehi-
cles
PA: Hasbro, Inc.
1027 Newport Ave
Pawtucket RI 02861
401 431-8697

(P-23429)
HORIZON HOBBY LLC
4710 E Guasti Rd Ste A, Ontario
(91761-8121)
PHONE....................................909 390-9595
Yolanda Perry, *Branch Mgr*
▲ EMP: 50
SQ FT: 27,000

SALES (corp-wide): 71.8MM Privately
Held
WEB: www.hangar-9.com
SIC: 3944 5092 Automobile & truck mod-
els, toy & hobby; hobby goods
PA: Horizon Hobby, Llc
4105 Fieldstone Rd
Champaign IL 61822
217 352-1913

(P-23430)
IMPERIAL TOY LLC (PA)
16641 Roscoe Pl, North Hills (91343-6104)
PHONE....................................818 536-6500
Peter Tiger, *Mng Member*
Arthur Hirsch,
▲ EMP: 115
SQ FT: 400,000
SALES (est): 214.9MM Privately Held
WEB: www.imperialtoy.com
SIC: 3944 Games, toys & children's vehi-
cles

(P-23431)
INSOMNIAC GAMES INC (PA)
2255 N Ontario St Ste 550, Burbank
(91504-3197)
PHONE....................................818 729-2400
Theodore C Price, *President*
Alex Hastings, *Vice Pres*
Brian Hastings, *Admin Sec*
EMP: 52 EST: 1994
SALES (est): 22.7MM Privately Held
WEB: www.insomniacgames.com
SIC: 3944 Electronic games & toys

(P-23432)
**INTERACTIVE ENTERTAINMENT
INC**
Also Called: Database Dynamics
1800 E Saint Andrew Pl, Santa Ana
(92705-5043)
PHONE....................................714 460-2343
Wayne S Schonfeld, *CEO*
Rick Odekirk, *President*
Andi Kendall, *Admin Sec*
Randy Copperman, *CIO*
Wayne Schonfeld, *VP Sls/Mktg*
EMP: 17
SQ FT: 2,500
SALES (est): 1.8MM Privately Held
WEB: www.databasedynamics.net
SIC: 3944 Electronic games & toys

(P-23433)
JADA GROUP INC
Also Called: Jada Toys
938 Hatcher Ave, City of Industry
(91748-1035)
PHONE....................................626 810-8382
Jack Chieh LI, *CEO*
May LI, *President*
Harvey Luong, *CFO*
Wai Vo, *Vice Pres*
Steven Sandler, *Vice Pres*
◆ EMP: 70
SQ FT: 45,000
SALES (est): 14.4MM Privately Held
WEB: www.jadatoys.com
SIC: 3944 Games, toys & children's vehi-
cles

(P-23434)
JAKKS PACIFIC INC
Also Called: Flying Colors
21749 Baker Pkwy, Walnut (91789-5234)
PHONE....................................909 594-7771
Michelle Tromp, *Branch Mgr*
EMP: 30 Publicly Held
SIC: 3944 5092 Games, toys & children's
vehicles; toys
PA: Jakks Pacific, Inc.
2951 28th St Ste 51
Santa Monica CA 90405

(P-23435)
JAKKS PACIFIC INC (PA)
2951 28th St Ste 51, Santa Monica
(90405-2961)
PHONE....................................424 268-9444
Stephen G Berman, *President*
John J McGrath, *COO*
Joel M Bennett, *CFO*
Brent Novak, *CFO*
Michael Gross, *Bd of Directors*

▲ = Import ▼=Export
◆ =Import/Export

EMP: 271
SALES: 613.1MM **Publicly Held**
SIC: 3944 Games, toys & children's vehicles

(P-23436)
JOHN N HANSEN CO INC (PA)
369 Adrian Rd, Millbrae (94030-3104)
PHONE..................................650 652-9833
Mary J Hansen, *Ch of Bd*
Lars Larsen, *President*
John Henson Jr, *COO*
◆ EMP: 10
SQ FT: 46,000
SALES (est): 2.3MM **Privately Held**
WEB: www.johnhansenco.com
SIC: 3944 5092 Games, toys & children's vehicles; toys & hobby goods & supplies

(P-23437)
LEAPFROG ENTERPRISES INC (HQ)
6401 Hollis St Ste 100, Emeryville
(94608-1463)
PHONE..................................510 420-5000
Nick Delany, *CEO*
William To, *President*
Alec Anderson, *CFO*
Paul Bennett, *Vice Pres*
Eugene Faulkner, *Vice Pres*
▲ EMP: 357
SALES (est): 305.2MM **Privately Held**
WEB: www.leapfrog.com
SIC: 3944 Games, toys & children's vehicles

(P-23438)
MAKERPLACE INC
684 Margarita Ave, Coronado
(92118-2321)
PHONE..................................619 435-1279
Steven Herrick, *President*
EMP: 15
SALES: 1MM **Privately Held**
SIC: 3944 Craft & hobby kits & sets

(P-23439)
MAKERSKIT LLC
Also Called: Makerskit.com
7600 Melrose Ave Ste E, Los Angeles
(90046-7451)
PHONE..................................213 973-7019
Michael Kim, *President*
John McQuade, *COO*
Michele Kee, *Director*
EMP: 20
SQ FT: 2,000
SALES (est): 2.7MM **Privately Held**
SIC: 3944 3999 5092 Craft & hobby kits & sets; novelties, bric-a-brac & hobby kits; arts & crafts equipment & supplies

(P-23440)
MATTEL INC (PA)
333 Continental Blvd, El Segundo
(90245-5032)
PHONE..................................310 252-2000
Ynon Kreiz, *Ch of Bd*
Richard Dickson, *President*
Joseph J Euteneuer, *CFO*
Robert Normile,
Amanda J Thompson,
◆ EMP: 1700 EST: 1945
SQ FT: 335,000
SALES: 4.8B **Publicly Held**
WEB: www.mattel.com
SIC: 3944 3942 Games, toys & children's vehicles; dolls & stuffed toys; dolls, except stuffed toy animals; stuffed toys, including animals

(P-23441)
MATTEL INC
2043 E Mariposa Ave, El Segundo
(90245-5001)
PHONE..................................310 252-6434
Caroline Collins, *Director*
EMP: 15
SALES (corp-wide): 4.8B **Publicly Held**
SIC: 3944 Games, toys & children's vehicles
PA: Mattel, Inc.
    333 Continental Blvd
    El Segundo CA 90245
    310 252-2000

(P-23442)
MATTEL INC
333 Continental Blvd, El Segundo
(90245-5032)
PHONE..................................310 252-3384
EMP: 29
SALES (corp-wide): 4.8B **Publicly Held**
SIC: 3944 Automobile & truck models, toy & hobby
PA: Mattel, Inc.
    333 Continental Blvd
    El Segundo CA 90245
    310 252-2000

(P-23443)
MATTEL INC
1456 E Harry Shepard Blvd, San Bernardino (92408-0137)
PHONE..................................909 382-3780
Ron Headrick, *Manager*
Scott Butterbaugh, *Plant Mgr*
EMP: 15
SALES (corp-wide): 4.8B **Publicly Held**
WEB: www.mattel.com
SIC: 3944 Games, toys & children's vehicles
PA: Mattel, Inc.
    333 Continental Blvd
    El Segundo CA 90245
    310 252-2000

(P-23444)
MATTEL DIRECT IMPORT INC (HQ)
333 Continental Blvd, El Segundo
(90245-5032)
PHONE..................................310 252-2000
Kevin Farr, *CEO*
Bryan G Stockton, *President*
Anne Ego, *Marketing Staff*
Ingrid Pettersson, *Manager*
EMP: 11
SALES (est): 4.9MM
SALES (corp-wide): 4.8B **Publicly Held**
WEB: www.mattel.com
SIC: 3944 3942 3949 Games, toys & children's vehicles; dolls, except stuffed toy animals; stuffed toys, including animals; sporting & athletic goods
PA: Mattel, Inc.
    333 Continental Blvd
    El Segundo CA 90245
    310 252-2000

(P-23445)
MEDIUM ENTERTAINMENT INC
501 Folsom St Fl 1, San Francisco
(94105-3175)
PHONE..................................469 951-2688
Andy Yang, *President*
Raymond Lau, *CEO*
Erik Yao, *Ch Credit Ofcr*
EMP: 20
SALES (est): 3.2MM **Privately Held**
SIC: 3944 Electronic games & toys

(P-23446)
MEGA BRANDS AMERICA INC (HQ)
Also Called: Rose Art Industries
3 Ada Ste 200, Irvine (92618-2322)
PHONE..................................949 727-9009
Marc Bertrand, *CEO*
Vic Bertrand, *CFO*
Cora McCoy, *Accounts Mgr*
◆ EMP: 80
SALES (est): 168.2MM **Privately Held**
WEB: www.roseart.com
SIC: 3944 Blocks, toy
PA: Mega Brands Inc
    4505 Rue Hickmore
    Saint-Laurent QC H4T 1
    514 333-5555

(P-23447)
MINDJOLT
144 2nd St Fl 4, San Francisco
(94105-3721)
PHONE..................................415 543-7800
Richard Fields, *Manager*
Jon Stegall, *Info Tech Mgr*
Christopher Glass, *Software Engr*
Stephanie Liaw, *Graphic Designe*
Shai Oren, *Senior Engr*
EMP: 16

SALES (est): 878.8K **Privately Held**
SIC: 3944 Games, toys & children's vehicles

(P-23448)
MOORES IDEAL PRODUCTS LLC
Also Called: M I P
830 W Golden Grove Way, Covina
(91722-3257)
PHONE..................................626 339-9007
Eustace Moore Jr, *Mng Member*
Rico Tututi, *Design Engr*
Alycia Moore, *Manager*
EMP: 11
SQ FT: 8,600
SALES (est): 2.2MM **Privately Held**
SIC: 3944 Automobile & truck models, toy & hobby

(P-23449)
NEKO WORLD INC
21041 S Wstn Ave Ste 200, Torrance
(90501)
PHONE..................................301 649-1188
Mike INA, *Principal*
EMP: 40 EST: 2014
SQ FT: 4,000
SALES: 15MM **Privately Held**
SIC: 3944 5092 Games, toys & children's vehicles; toys & hobby goods & supplies

(P-23450)
NEUROSMITH LLC
1000 N Studebaker Rd # 3, Long Beach
(90815-4957)
PHONE..................................562 296-1100
EMP: 23
SQ FT: 7,200
SALES (est): 2.6MM **Privately Held**
SIC: 3944

(P-23451)
NEW YORK TOY EXCHANGE INC
11955 Jack Benny Dr Ste 1, Rancho Cucamonga (91739-9230)
PHONE..................................626 327-4547
Lucy Patterson, *CEO*
James McMullin, *President*
EMP: 12
SALES: 125K **Privately Held**
SIC: 3944 Games, toys & children's vehicles

(P-23452)
NINJA JUMP INC
3221 N San Fernando Rd, Los Angeles
(90065-1414)
PHONE..................................323 255-5418
Rouben Gourchounian, *President*
Bridgette Garcia, *Executive*
Jack Chaparyan, *Manager*
Adrian Jauregui, *Accounts Exec*
Arman Muradyan, *Accounts Exec*
◆ EMP: 75
SQ FT: 35,000
SALES (est): 14.6MM **Privately Held**
WEB: www.ninjajump.com
SIC: 3944 Games, toys & children's vehicles

(P-23453)
NKOK INC
5354 Irwindale Ave Ste A, Irwindale
(91706-2068)
PHONE..................................626 330-1988
Shun Yun Chiu, *President*
Kohsche Koh, *Vice Pres*
Andy Tanaka, *Natl Sales Mgr*
Lanny Halim, *Manager*
◆ EMP: 10 EST: 1998
SQ FT: 30,000
SALES (est): 2MM **Privately Held**
WEB: www.nkok.com
SIC: 3944 Games, toys & children's vehicles

(P-23454)
PACIFIC GAMING
1975 Adams Ave, San Leandro
(94577-1005)
PHONE..................................510 562-8900
Lee Fried, *Principal*
Jason Salt, *Technical Mgr*
Steve Rockwell, *VP Sales*

EMP: 20
SALES (est): 2.9MM **Privately Held**
SIC: 3944 Bingo boards (games)

(P-23455)
PLAYHUT INC
18560 San Jose Ave, City of Industry
(91748-1365)
PHONE..................................909 869-8083
Yu Zheng, *CEO*
Iris Jamie, *Human Resources*
Theresa Deredin, *Manager*
▲ EMP: 20
SALES (est): 12.2MM **Privately Held**
SIC: 3944 Games, toys & children's vehicles
PA: Basic Fun, Inc
    301 E Yamato Rd Ste 4200
    Boca Raton FL 33431

(P-23456)
POCKET GEMS INC
220 Montgomery St Ste 750, San Francisco
(94104-3479)
PHONE..................................415 371-1333
Ben Liu, *CEO*
Arjun Dayal, *Vice Pres*
Helen Hsu, *Vice Pres*
Brian Andersen, *Office Mgr*
Matthew Koontz, *Software Engr*
EMP: 196
SALES (est): 11.2MM **Privately Held**
SIC: 3944 Electronic games & toys

(P-23457)
POOLMASTER INC
770 Del Paso Rd, Sacramento
(95834-1117)
P.O. Box 340308 (95834-0308)
PHONE..................................916 567-9800
Leon H Tager, *President*
Carol Tager, *Corp Secy*
Nora Davis, *Vice Pres*
Scheri Adams, *Human Res Dir*
Gina Dewees, *Human Resources*
◆ EMP: 55
SQ FT: 100,000
SALES (est): 12.4MM **Privately Held**
WEB: www.poolmaster.net
SIC: 3944 5091 Games, toys & children's vehicles; sporting & recreation goods

(P-23458)
PRIMARY CONCEPTS INC
1338 7th St, Berkeley (94710-1410)
P.O. Box 640, Lafayette OR (97127-0640)
PHONE..................................510 559-5545
Reid Calcott, *CEO*
Jim Whitney, *President*
▲ EMP: 17
SALES (est): 2.2MM **Privately Held**
WEB: www.primaryconcepts.com
SIC: 3944 Games, toys & children's vehicles

(P-23459)
RED ROBOT LABS INC
1935 Landings Dr, Mountain View
(94043-0808)
P.O. Box 61017, Palo Alto (94306-6017)
PHONE..................................650 762-8058
Mike Ouye, *CEO*
Felix Hu, *Vice Pres*
EMP: 19
SALES (est): 1.5MM **Privately Held**
SIC: 3944 Electronic game machines, except coin-operated

(P-23460)
ROAD CHAMPS INC (HQ)
22619 Pacific Coast Hwy, Malibu
(90265-5054)
PHONE..................................310 456-7799
Stephen Berman, *President*
EMP: 22
SQ FT: 51,000
SALES (est): 6.5MM **Publicly Held**
WEB: www.jakkspacific.com
SIC: 3944 Automobiles & trucks, toy

(P-23461)
RUMBLE ENTERTAINMENT INC
Also Called: Rumble Games
2121 S El Cmino Real C1, San Mateo
(94403)
PHONE..................................650 316-8819
Greg Richardson, *CEO*
Theresa Bottenhorn, *Human Resources*
EMP: 45
SALES (est): 6.8MM **Privately Held**
SIC: 3944 Electronic games & toys

(P-23462)
S M L INDUSTRIES INC
10965 Hartley Rd Ste P, Santee
(92071-2893)
PHONE..................................619 258-7941
Mark R Linder, *President*
EMP: 10
SQ FT: 1,500
SALES (est): 1.2MM **Privately Held**
WEB: www.smlind.com
SIC: 3944 Craft & hobby kits & sets

(P-23463)
SHELCORE INC (PA)
Also Called: Shelcore Toys
7811 Lemona Ave, Van Nuys (91405-1139)
PHONE..................................818 883-2400
Arnold Rubin, *President*
▼ EMP: 13
SQ FT: 20,000
SALES: 61.1MM **Privately Held**
WEB: www.shelcore.com
SIC: 3944 Blocks, toy; structural toy sets

(P-23464)
SIPI COMPANY INC
34734 Williams Way, Union City
(94587-5578)
PHONE..................................650 201-1169
Vincent Tong, *Ch of Bd*
EMP: 10
SALES (est): 770K **Privately Held**
SIC: 3944 7372 Electronic games & toys;
educational computer software; home entertainment computer software

(P-23465)
SKULLDUGGERY INC
5433 E La Palma Ave, Anaheim
(92807-2022)
PHONE..................................714 777-6425
Peter Koehl Sr, *CEO*
Steven Koehl, *President*
Emmaline Koehl, *Vice Pres*
▲ EMP: 14
SQ FT: 4,426
SALES: 2MM **Privately Held**
WEB: www.skullduggery.com
SIC: 3944 5961 Science kits: microscopes, chemistry sets, etc.; mail order house

(P-23466)
SONOMA INTERNATIONAL INC
Also Called: Dowling Magnets
462 W Napa St Fl 2, Sonoma
(95476-6556)
PHONE..................................707 935-0710
Niels A Chow, *President*
◆ EMP: 35
SALES (est): 4.3MM **Privately Held**
SIC: 3944 3499 Games, toys & children's vehicles; magnets, permanent: metallic

(P-23467)
STREAK TECHNOLOGY INC
43575 Mission Blvd 614, Fremont
(94539-5831)
PHONE..................................408 206-2373
Robert B Stewart, *President*
Shelley Stratton, *Vice Pres*
EMP: 12
SQ FT: 10,000
SALES: 14MM **Privately Held**
WEB: www.streaktechnology.com
SIC: 3944 Video game machines, except coin-operated

(P-23468)
SUN-MATE CORP
19730 Ventura Blvd Ste 18, Woodland Hills
(91364-6304)
PHONE..................................818 700-0572
Rami Ben-Moshe, *President*

▲ EMP: 18
SQ FT: 5,000
SALES (est): 2.8MM **Privately Held**
SIC: 3944 Electronic games & toys

(P-23469)
SUNS OUT INC
2915 Red Hill Ave A210c, Costa Mesa
(92626-5916)
PHONE..................................714 556-2314
Diane J Skilling, *President*
Carolyn Miller, *VP Mktg*
EMP: 10
SQ FT: 2,000
SALES (est): 673.1K **Privately Held**
WEB: www.sunsout.com
SIC: 3944 5092 Puzzles; toys & games

(P-23470)
TANGLE INC
385 Oyster Point Blvd 8b, South San Francisco (94080-1934)
PHONE..................................650 616-7900
Richard Zawitz, *President*
Nicholas Zawitz, *Treasurer*
Geoff McKee, *Vice Pres*
Beverly Nobleza, *Vice Pres*
Jennifer Volz, *Natl Sales Mgr*
▲ EMP: 26
SQ FT: 5,000
SALES (est): 12.9MM **Privately Held**
WEB: www.tangletoys.com
SIC: 3944 Games, toys & children's vehicles

(P-23471)
TELECHEM INTERNATIONAL INC (HQ)
927 Thompson Pl, Sunnyvale
(94085-4518)
PHONE..................................408 744-1331
Rene Schena, *Ch of Bd*
Mark Schena PHD, *President*
William L Sklar, *CFO*
Todd J Martinsky, *Senior VP*
Paul K Haje, *VP Sales*
▲ EMP: 47
SQ FT: 8,280
SALES (est): 1.9MM **Publicly Held**
WEB: www.arrayit.com
SIC: 3944 Science kits: microscopes, chemistry sets, etc.

(P-23472)
TITAN GAMING
1351 4th St Fl 4, Santa Monica
(90401-1358)
PHONE..................................310 869-3326
Brock Pierce, *CEO*
Damian Greco, *CFO*
Michael Steuer, *Chief Engr*
EMP: 15
SALES (est): 1.1MM **Privately Held**
SIC: 3944 Video game machines, except coin-operated

(P-23473)
TORRENCE TRADING INC
21041 S Wstn Ave Ste 200, Torrance
(90501)
PHONE..................................310 649-1188
EMP: 40 EST: 2014
SQ FT: 4,000
SALES (est): 2.1MM **Privately Held**
SIC: 3944 5092

(P-23474)
UNDERGROUND GAMES INC
2356 253rd St, Lomita (90717-2010)
P.O. Box 1214, Redondo Beach (90278-0214)
PHONE..................................310 379-0100
Leroy Sawyer Jr, *CEO*
Adriane Sawyer, *CFO*
EMP: 10
SQ FT: 1,000
SALES (est): 1MM **Privately Held**
SIC: 3944 Board games, puzzles & models, except electronic

(P-23475)
USAOPOLY INC
5607 Palmer Way, Carlsbad (92010-7242)
PHONE..................................760 431-5910
Dane Chapin, *CEO*
Tom Nirschel, *CFO*

Robert Dragan, *Info Tech Dir*
Erica Dennis, *Controller*
Maggie Matthews, *VP Mktg*
▲ EMP: 32
SQ FT: 10,000
SALES (est): 13.4MM **Privately Held**
SIC: 3944 Board games, puzzles & models, except electronic

(P-23476)
VISION PLASTICS MFG INC
9888 Waples St Ste B, San Diego
(92121-2921)
PHONE..................................855 476-2767
Jonathan Kemmer, *Director*
Robert Miller, *Director*
Stephen Rhoads, *Director*
Christian Sorensen, *Director*
EMP: 10
SQ FT: 8,000
SALES (est): 1.1MM **Privately Held**
SIC: 3944 Blocks, toy

(P-23477)
WESTAMERICA
4550 Mangels Blvd, Fairfield (94534-4082)
P.O. Box 1240, Suisun City (94585-1240)
PHONE..................................707 863-6000
David Payne, *CEO*
Debbie Friesen, *Vice Pres*
Claudia Rodriguez, *Info Tech Dir*
Charles Esping, *Assistant VP*
Susan Myer, *Assistant VP*
▲ EMP: 13
SALES (est): 2.1MM **Privately Held**
SIC: 3944 Banks, toy

(P-23478)
WHAT KIDS WANT INC
19428 Londelius St, Northridge
(91324-3511)
PHONE..................................818 775-0375
Jordon Kort, *CEO*
Tony Najjar, *Vice Pres*
Steven Kort, *Principal*
▲ EMP: 14 EST: 1999
SQ FT: 2,000
SALES (est): 2.6MM **Privately Held**
WEB: www.whatkidswant.net
SIC: 3944 Games, toys & children's vehicles

(P-23479)
WILLIAM MCCLUNG
Also Called: Red Caboose of Colorado
987 Keller Ave, Crescent City
(95531-2520)
PHONE..................................970 535-4601
EMP: 10
SQ FT: 5,000
SALES (est): 320K **Privately Held**
SIC: 3944

(P-23480)
WORLDWIDE GAMING SYSTEMS CORP
9205 Alabama Ave Ste E, Chatsworth
(91311-5847)
PHONE..................................818 678-9150
Peter Khai, *President*
Shannon Lewis, *Technician*
Robert Engel, *Accountant*
Robert Emert, *Sales Staff*
Roel Dulduleo, *Manager*
EMP: 25
SALES (est): 2.5MM **Privately Held**
SIC: 3944 Video game machines, except coin-operated

3949 Sporting & Athletic Goods, NEC

(P-23481)
5150 FITNESS LLC
Also Called: Made In L.A. Fitness
6741 Hollywood Blvd, Los Angeles
(90028-4604)
P.O. Box 1202 (90078-1202)
PHONE..................................323 461-1990
Andrea Lawont, *Mng Member*
EMP: 20
SQ FT: 3,400
SALES: 650K **Privately Held**
SIC: 3949 Gymnasium equipment

(P-23482)
800TOTAL GYM COMMERCIAL LLC
5225 Avd Encinas Ste C, Carlsbad
(92008-4367)
PHONE..................................858 586-6080
Jesse Campanaro, *Manager*
▲ EMP: 18
SALES (est): 830.8K **Privately Held**
SIC: 3949 Exercise equipment

(P-23483)
ABSOLUTE BOARD CO INC
4040 Calle Platino # 102, Oceanside
(92056-5833)
P.O. Box 4098 (92052-4098)
PHONE..................................760 295-2201
Matt Logan, *CEO*
▲ EMP: 23
SALES (est): 3MM **Privately Held**
SIC: 3949 Skateboards

(P-23484)
ACTIVA GLOBAL SPT & ENTRMT LLC
30950 Rncho Viejo Rd 125, San Juan
Capistrano (92675)
PHONE..................................949 265-8260
Raymond Taccolini, *Mng Member*
▲ EMP: 20
SQ FT: 2,700
SALES (est): 1.2MM **Privately Held**
SIC: 3949 Sporting & athletic goods

(P-23485)
ACTIVE SPT LIFESTYLE USA LLC
Also Called: Active Right Shop
13920 Cy Ctr Dr Ste 4025, Chino Hills
(91709)
PHONE..................................909 203-4640
Tyler Strawn, *Branch Mgr*
EMP: 30 **Privately Held**
SIC: 3949 Sporting & athletic goods
PA: Active Sports Lifestyle Usa, Llc
12178 4th St
Rancho Cucamonga CA 91730

(P-23486)
ACUSHNET COMPANY
Also Called: Titleist
2819 Loker Ave E, Carlsbad (92010-6626)
PHONE..................................760 804-6500
John Worster, *Branch Mgr*
Bilal Aljanabi, *Admin Asst*
Cesar Lopez, *Admin Asst*
Joel Avila, *Administration*
Joyce Higgins, *Info Tech Mgr*
EMP: 300
SALES (corp-wide): 313.3MM **Publicly Held**
WEB: www.titleist.com
SIC: 3949 Shafts, golf club
HQ: Acushnet Company
333 Bridge St
Fairhaven MA 02719
508 979-2000

(P-23487)
ADLER POOL TABLES INC
3155 W El Segundo Blvd A, Hawthorne
(90250-4804)
PHONE..................................310 676-5331
Bob Gillerman, *President*
▲ EMP: 25
SALES (est): 2.2MM **Privately Held**
SIC: 3949 Bridges, billiard & pool

(P-23488)
ADVANTAGE ENGINEERING CORP
Also Called: Valley Sailboards
301 Bernoulli Cir, Oxnard (93030-5164)
PHONE..................................805 216-9920
Alan K Pittman, *President*
EMP: 20
SALES (est): 1.9MM **Privately Held**
WEB: www.skirope.com
SIC: 3949 5941 2298 Water skiing equipment & supplies, except skis; sporting goods & bicycle shops; cordage & twine

▲ = Import ▼=Export
◆ =Import/Export

(P-23489)
AFTCO MFG CO INC
Also Called: Bluewater Wear
2400 S Garnsey St, Santa Ana
(92707-3335)
PHONE...................................949 660-8757
Bill Shedd, *President*
William D Shedd, *CEO*
Peggie Shedd, *Treasurer*
Jill Shedd, *General Mgr*
Nicholas Patopoff, *Prdtn Mgr*
◆ **EMP:** 71 **EST:** 1958
SQ FT: 24,000
SALES (est): 17.4MM **Privately Held**
WEB: www.aftco.com
SIC: 3949 2329 2339 Fishing tackle, general; men's & boys' leather, wool & down-filled outerwear; women's & misses' outerwear

(P-23490)
AIRSOFT ZONE CORPORATION (PA)
Also Called: Airsoft Megastore
138 E Longden Ave, Arcadia (91006-5242)
PHONE...................................818 495-6502
Mike Chan, *Owner*
George Cohen, *CFO*
Ross Collins, *Marketing Staff*
Rommel Narvasa, *Warehouse Mgr*
▲ **EMP:** 20 **EST:** 2009
SALES (est): 3.4MM **Privately Held**
SIC: 3949 Sporting & athletic goods

(P-23491)
AIRSOFT ZONE CORPORATION
Also Called: Airsoft Megastore
138 E Longden Ave, Arcadia (91006-5242)
PHONE...................................818 495-6502
George Cohen, *Branch Mgr*
EMP: 50
SALES (corp-wide): 3.4MM **Privately Held**
SIC: 3949 Sporting & athletic goods
PA: Airsoft Zone Corporation
138 E Longden Ave
Arcadia CA 91006
818 495-6502

(P-23492)
ALBANY SWIMMING POOL
Also Called: Albanay Aquatic Center
1311 Portland Ave, Albany (94706-1445)
PHONE...................................510 559-6640
William Wong, *Superintendent*
Stephen Dunkle, *Director*
EMP: 25
SALES (est): 1MM **Privately Held**
SIC: 3949 Swimming pools, except plastic

(P-23493)
ALDILA INC (HQ)
1945 Kellogg Ave, Carlsbad (92008-6582)
PHONE...................................858 513-1801
Peter R Mathewson, *Ch of Bd*
Peter H Kamin, *Shareholder*
Scott M Bier, *CFO*
John Vannoy, *IT/INT Sup*
Deborah Dutra, *Payroll Mgr*
▲ **EMP:** 56
SQ FT: 125,000
SALES (est): 139.3MM
SALES (corp-wide): 34.9B **Privately Held**
SIC: 3949 3297 Shafts, golf club; graphite refractories: carbon bond or ceramic bond
PA: Mitsubishi Chemical Holdings Corporation
1-1-1, Marunouchi
Chiyoda-Ku TKY 100-0
367 487-200

(P-23494)
ALDILA INC
Also Called: Aldila De Poway
13450 Stowe Dr, Poway (92064-6860)
PHONE...................................858 513-1801
Greg Donaldson, *Manager*
Laura Mallec, *Info Tech Dir*
Tom Pendarvis, *Facilities Dir*
Laura Naranjo, *Manager*
EMP: 200
SALES (corp-wide): 34.9B **Privately Held**
SIC: 3949 3624 5091 Shafts, golf club; carbon & graphite products; golf equipment

HQ: Aldila, Inc.
1945 Kellogg Ave
Carlsbad CA 92008
858 513-1801

(P-23495)
ALDILA GOLF CORP
13450 Stowe Dr, Poway (92064-6860)
PHONE...................................858 513-1801
EMP: 104
SALES (corp-wide): 34.9B **Privately Held**
SIC: 3949 Shafts, golf club
HQ: Aldila Golf Corp.
1945 Kellogg Ave
Carlsbad CA 92008

(P-23496)
ALDILA GOLF CORP (DH)
1945 Kellogg Ave, Carlsbad (92008-6582)
PHONE...................................858 513-1801
Peter R Mathewson, *CEO*
Scott Bier, *CFO*
Sue-WEI Yeh, *Controller*
▲ **EMP:** 78
SQ FT: 52,156
SALES (est): 15.4MM
SALES (corp-wide): 34.9B **Privately Held**
WEB: www.aldilagolf.com
SIC: 3949 Shafts, golf club
HQ: Aldila, Inc.
1945 Kellogg Ave
Carlsbad CA 92008
858 513-1801

(P-23497)
ALTERG INC
48368 Milmont Dr, Fremont (94538-7324)
PHONE...................................510 270-5900
Sanjay Gupta, *CEO*
Kevin Davidge, *CFO*
Dev Mishra, *Chief Mktg Ofcr*
Gabriel Griego, *Vice Pres*
Clement Leung, *Vice Pres*
▲ **EMP:** 60
SQ FT: 15,247
SALES (est): 12.3MM **Privately Held**
WEB: www.alter-g.com
SIC: 3949 Lacrosse equipment & supplies, general

(P-23498)
AMERICAN MAPLE INC
14020 S Western Ave, Gardena (90249-3008)
PHONE...................................310 515-8881
Ben Hong, *President*
◆ **EMP:** 13
SQ FT: 24,000
SALES (est): 4.4MM **Privately Held**
SIC: 3949 Fishing tackle, general

(P-23499)
AMERICAN PREMIER CORP
1531 S Carlos Ave, Ontario (91761-7661)
PHONE...................................909 923-7070
Michael Wu, *President*
Ric Heat, *General Mgr*
▲ **EMP:** 48
SQ FT: 15,000
SALES: 2.5MM **Privately Held**
WEB: www.americanpremiercorp.com
SIC: 3949 Reels, fishing; rods & rod parts, fishing; fishing equipment

(P-23500)
AMERICAN UNDERWATER PRODUCTS (HQ)
Also Called: Oceanic
2002 Davis St, San Leandro (94577-1211)
PHONE...................................800 435-3483
Robert R Hollis, *CEO*
Paul Elsinga, *COO*
◆ **EMP:** 93 **EST:** 1973
SQ FT: 74,000
SALES (est): 35.3MM **Privately Held**
WEB: www.pro-a.com
SIC: 3949 5941 Sporting & athletic goods; skin diving, scuba equipment & supplies

(P-23501)
AMERICANA SPORTS INC
422 S Vermont Ave, Glendora (91741-6256)
PHONE...................................626 914-0238
Chris Wellington, *President*

John Yeh, *Chairman*
▲ **EMP:** 25
SALES (est): 2.1MM **Privately Held**
SIC: 3949 Surfboards

(P-23502)
AMRON INTERNATIONAL INC (PA)
1380 Aspen Way, Vista (92081-8349)
PHONE...................................760 208-6500
Debra L Ritchie, *CEO*
Barbara Holden, *Purch Mgr*
Micaela Hernandez, *Purchasing*
Joe Esparza, *Marketing Mgr*
Mike Malone, *Marketing Staff*
◆ **EMP:** 75
SQ FT: 40,000
SALES (est): 12.9MM **Privately Held**
WEB: www.amronintl.com
SIC: 3949 5091 Skin diving equipment, scuba type; diving equipment & supplies

(P-23503)
ANDERSON BAT COMPANY LLC
236 E Orangethorpe Ave, Placentia (92870-6442)
PHONE...................................714 524-7500
Steve Anderson,
Carol Marshall, *Office Mgr*
Maria Louis, *Info Tech Mgr*
Amanda Oshiro, *Accounting Mgr*
Hector Cano, *Prdtn Mgr*
▲ **EMP:** 53
SQ FT: 5,300
SALES (est): 538.7K **Privately Held**
WEB: www.andersonbat.com
SIC: 3949

(P-23504)
ANTHONY JONES
Also Called: Coral Reef Dive Center
14161 Beach Blvd, Westminster (92683-4451)
PHONE...................................714 894-3483
Anthony Jones, *Owner*
Elizabeth Trujillo, *Office Mgr*
▲ **EMP:** 15
SALES (est): 1.1MM **Privately Held**
WEB: www.coralreefusa.com
SIC: 3949 5941 5091 Water sports equipment; water sport equipment; diving equipment & supplies

(P-23505)
AQUA-LUNG AMERICA INC (PA)
Also Called: Aqua Sphere
2340 Cousteau Ct, Vista (92081-8346)
PHONE...................................760 597-5000
Don Rockwell, *CEO*
Jean-Noel Picard, *CFO*
Craig Villines, *Executive*
Richard Vaughn, *Division Mgr*
Mark Kane, *General Mgr*
◆ **EMP:** 150
SQ FT: 135,000
SALES (est): 65.5MM **Privately Held**
WEB: www.sea-quest.com
SIC: 3949 5091 Skin diving equipment, scuba type; watersports equipment & supplies

(P-23506)
ARBOR SNOWBOARDS INC
102 Washington Blvd, Marina Del Rey (90292-5126)
PHONE...................................310 577-1120
Robert Carlson, *President*
Chris Jensen, *Vice Pres*
Nate Shute, *Engineer*
Cody Crist, *Opers Mgr*
Tina Goff, *Opers Mgr*
▲ **EMP:** 20
SQ FT: 2,400
SALES (est): 2.4MM **Privately Held**
WEB: www.arborsports.com
SIC: 3949 Winter sports equipment

(P-23507)
ASPHALT FABRIC AND ENGRG INC
2683 Lime Ave, Signal Hill (90755-2709)
PHONE...................................562 997-4129
Bill Goldsmith, *President*
Joe Salamone, *CFO*
Doug Coulter, *Vice Pres*
EMP: 90

SQ FT: 5,000
SALES (est): 13.7MM **Privately Held**
SIC: 3949 Sporting & athletic goods

(P-23508)
ATOMIC AQUATICS INC (PA)
3585 Cadillac Ave Ste A, Costa Mesa (92626-1495)
PHONE...................................714 375-1433
Dean Garraffa, *President*
Doug Toth, *Admin Sec*
▲ **EMP:** 10
SQ FT: 6,000
SALES (est): 1.4MM **Privately Held**
WEB: www.atomicaquatics.com
SIC: 3949 Water sports equipment

(P-23509)
AVET INDUSTRIES INC
Also Called: Avet Reels
9687 Topanga Canyon Pl, Chatsworth (91311-4118)
PHONE...................................818 576-9895
Aruttyun Alajajyan, *President*
Sarkis Alajajyan, *Vice Pres*
EMP: 15
SQ FT: 19,200
SALES (est): 1.9MM **Privately Held**
WEB: www.avetreels.com
SIC: 3949 Reels, fishing

(P-23510)
AZA INDUSTRIES INC (PA)
1410 Vantage Ct, Vista (92081-8509)
PHONE...................................760 560-0440
David H Brown, *President*
Jim Passamonte, *Treasurer*
Bill Pierce, *Vice Pres*
▲ **EMP:** 40
SQ FT: 27,000
SALES (est): 10.5MM **Privately Held**
WEB: www.syndromedist.com
SIC: 3949 Skateboards

(P-23511)
AZTECA SOCCER
3022 Durfee Ave Ste E, El Monte (91732-3582)
PHONE...................................626 768-2704
EMP: 11
SALES (corp-wide): 2.8MM **Privately Held**
SIC: 3949 Soccer equipment & supplies
PA: Azteca Soccer
11853 Valley Blvd
El Monte CA 91732
626 444-1608

(P-23512)
BAHNE AND COMPANY INC
Also Called: Bahne Single Ski
585 Westlake St Ste A, Encinitas (92024-3764)
P.O. Box 230326 (92023-0326)
PHONE...................................760 753-8847
William L Bahne, *President*
Robert Bahne, *Vice Pres*
▲ **EMP:** 10 **EST:** 1964
SQ FT: 6,000
SALES: 2MM **Privately Held**
WEB: www.finsunlimited.com
SIC: 3949 Water skis

(P-23513)
BASE HOCKEY LP (PA)
581 Calle Arroyo, Thousand Oaks (91360-2506)
PHONE...................................805 405-3650
Ronald Kunisaki, *Partner*
EMP: 10
SALES (est): 2.8MM **Privately Held**
WEB: www.basehockey.ca
SIC: 3949 7389 Fencing equipment (sporting goods);

(P-23514)
BBS MANUFACTURING INC
1905 Diamond St Ste A, San Marcos (92078-5185)
PHONE...................................760 798-8011
Grant Burns, *CEO*
Angela Diaz, *Office Mgr*
Roger Orange, *Manager*
◆ **EMP:** 16
SQ FT: 13,000

SALES: 3MM **Privately Held**
SIC: 3949 Skateboards

(P-23515)
BECHHOLD & SON FLASHER & LURE
616 Keller St, Petaluma (94952-2808)
P.O. Box 967, Foresthill (95631-0967)
PHONE..................................530 367-6650
Jery Bechhold, *Partner*
Roy Bechhold, *Partner*
EMP: 10
SQ FT: 5,000
SALES: 1MM **Privately Held**
WEB: www.fishcatcher.com
SIC: 3949 Fishing tackle, general

(P-23516)
BECKER SURFBOARDS INC
301 Pier Ave, Hermosa Beach
(90254-3616)
PHONE..................................310 372-6554
John Leninger, *Branch Mgr*
EMP: 10
SALES (corp-wide): 7.1MM **Privately Held**
WEB: www.beckersurf.com
SIC: 3949 Surfboards; archery equipment, general
PA: Becker Surfboards, Inc
121 Waterworks Way # 101
Irvine CA 92618
888 673-0225

(P-23517)
BELL FOUNDRY CO (PA)
5310 Southern Ave, South Gate
(90280-3690)
P.O. Box 1070 (90280-1070)
PHONE..................................323 564-5701
Cesar Capallini, *President*
Dimitry Rabyy, *CFO*
Wanda De Wald, *Treasurer*
Carlos Marquez, *Sales Engr*
▲ EMP: 60 EST: 1924
SQ FT: 140,000
SALES (est): 7.3MM **Privately Held**
WEB: www.bfco.com
SIC: 3949 3321 Dumbbells & other weightlifting equipment; gray & ductile iron foundries

(P-23518)
BELL SPORTS INC (HQ)
Also Called: Easton Bell Sports
5550 Scotts Valley Dr, Scotts Valley
(95066-3438)
PHONE..................................469 417-6600
Dan Arment, *President*
▲ EMP: 75
SQ FT: 27,197
SALES (est): 136.6MM
SALES (corp-wide): 2.3B **Publicly Held**
WEB: www.bellsports.com
SIC: 3949 3751 Helmets, athletic; bicycles & related parts
PA: Vista Outdoor Inc.
262 N University Ave
Farmington UT 84025
801 447-3000

(P-23519)
BEYNON SPORTS SURFACES INC
4668 N Sonora Ave Ste 101, Fresno
(93722-3970)
PHONE..................................559 237-2590
John T Beynon, *Branch Mgr*
EMP: 33
SALES (est): 1.7MM
SALES (corp-wide): 17.8MM **Privately Held**
SIC: 3949 1629 Track & field athletic equipment; athletic field construction
PA: Beynon Sports Surfaces, Inc.
16 Alt Rd
Hunt Valley MD 21030
410 527-0386

(P-23520)
BIJANS PROTECTIVE EQUIPMENT
3255 Santa Rosa Ave, Santa Rosa
(95407-7951)
PHONE..................................707 528-4647

Fereshteh Kia Bijan, *CEO*
Turadj Bijan, *President*
Feri Bijan, *Admin Sec*
▲ EMP: 60
SQ FT: 15,000
SALES (est): 6.7MM **Privately Held**
SIC: 3949 Protective sporting equipment; pads: football, basketball, soccer, lacrosse, etc.; guards: football, basketball, soccer, lacrosse, etc.

(P-23521)
BILLY BEEZ USA LLC
24201 Valencia Blvd, Santa Clarita
(91355-1861)
PHONE..................................661 383-0050
EMP: 13
SALES (corp-wide): 15.6MM **Privately Held**
SIC: 3949 5137 7999 Playground equipment; women's & children's dresses, suits, skirts & blouses; amusement ride
PA: Billy Beez Usa, Llc
3 W 35th St Fl 3 # 3
New York NY 10001
646 606-2249

(P-23522)
BILLY BEEZ USA LLC
925 Blossom Hill Rd # 1397, San Jose
(95123-1230)
PHONE..................................408 300-9547
EMP: 20
SALES (corp-wide): 15.6MM **Privately Held**
SIC: 3949 5137 7999 Playground equipment; women's & children's dresses, suits, skirts & blouses; amusement ride
PA: Billy Beez Usa, Llc
3 W 35th St Fl 3 # 3
New York NY 10001
646 606-2249

(P-23523)
BLACK BOX DISTRIBUTION LLC
371 2nd St Ste 1, Encinitas (92024-3524)
PHONE..................................760 268-1174
Frank Messmann, *CEO*
James Thomas, *President*
Michelle Wenner,
▲ EMP: 70
SALES (est): 6.4MM **Privately Held**
WEB: www.blackboxdist.com
SIC: 3949 Skateboards

(P-23524)
BLOCK ALTERNATIVES
604 W Avenue L Ste 101, Lancaster
(93534-7148)
PHONE..................................661 729-2800
Richard Bartlett, *Owner*
EMP: 11
SQ FT: 6,500
SALES (est): 817.5K **Privately Held**
WEB: www.blockalternatives.com
SIC: 3949 2262 2759 Sporting & athletic goods; screen printing: manmade fiber & silk broadwoven fabrics; screen printing

(P-23525)
BOARDS ON NORD INC
14822 Meridian Meadows Ln, Chico
(95973-9255)
PHONE..................................530 513-3922
Josh Morrow, *President*
▲ EMP: 10
SALES (est): 643.2K **Privately Held**
SIC: 3949 7389 Skateboards;

(P-23526)
BODY FLEX SPORTS INC (PA)
21717 Ferrero, Walnut (91789-5209)
PHONE..................................909 598-9876
Bob Hsiung, *President*
Evan Chin, *Bookkeeper*
▲ EMP: 12
SQ FT: 10,000
SALES (est): 2.9MM **Privately Held**
WEB: www.bodyflex.com
SIC: 3949 Exercise equipment

(P-23527)
BOOSTED INC (PA)
Also Called: Boosted Boards
915 Linda Vista Ave, Mountain View
(94043-1902)
PHONE..................................650 549-4169
Sanjay Dastoor, *CEO*
John Ulmen, *CTO*
Jason Bluhm, *Engineer*
Julian Farnam, *Engineer*
Ngoc Nguyen, *Engineer*
EMP: 26
SALES (est): 4.9MM **Privately Held**
SIC: 3949 Skateboards

(P-23528)
BRAVO SPORTS
Also Called: Sector9
4370 Jutland Dr, San Diego (92117-3642)
PHONE..................................858 408-0083
Derek Oneill, *CEO*
EMP: 50
SALES (corp-wide): 22.4MM **Privately Held**
SIC: 3949 Skateboards
HQ: Bravo Sports
12801 Carmenita Rd
Santa Fe Springs CA 90670
562 484-5100

(P-23529)
BRAVO SPORTS (HQ)
12801 Carmenita Rd, Santa Fe Springs
(90670-4805)
PHONE..................................562 484-5100
Leonardo Pais, *President*
Drew Brassard, *COO*
Steve Segvich, *CFO*
Ken Edlauer, *Accounting Dir*
Steven Finney, *Controller*
▲ EMP: 80
SALES (est): 22.4MM
SALES (corp-wide): 22.4MM **Privately Held**
SIC: 3949 Sporting & athletic goods
PA: Transom Bravo Holdings Corp.
12801 Carmenita Rd
Santa Fe Springs CA 90670
562 484-5100

(P-23530)
BUILD AT HOME LLC
273 N Benson Ave, Upland (91786-5614)
PHONE..................................909 949-1601
Joseph Ciaglia,
EMP: 10 EST: 2015
SALES (est): 441.1K **Privately Held**
SIC: 3949 Skateboards

(P-23531)
CALLAWAY GOLF COMPANY
5858 Dryden Pl, Carlsbad (92008-6503)
PHONE..................................760 804-4502
Pascual Luna, *Principal*
EMP: 1000
SALES (corp-wide): 1B **Publicly Held**
SIC: 3949 Sporting & athletic goods
PA: Callaway Golf Company
2180 Rutherford Rd
Carlsbad CA 92008
760 931-1771

(P-23532)
CALLAWAY GOLF COMPANY
44500 Indian Wells Ln, Indian Wells
(92210-8746)
PHONE..................................760 345-4653
Mike Pease, *Director*
EMP: 1000
SALES (corp-wide): 1B **Publicly Held**
SIC: 3949 Shafts, golf club
PA: Callaway Golf Company
2180 Rutherford Rd
Carlsbad CA 92008
760 931-1771

(P-23533)
CALLAWAY GOLF COMPANY (PA)
2180 Rutherford Rd, Carlsbad
(92008-7328)
PHONE..................................760 931-1771
Oliver G Brewer III, *President*
Ronald S Beard, *Ch of Bd*
Alex M Boezeman, *President*
Brian P Lynch, *CFO*

Richard H Arnett, *Senior VP*
◆ EMP: 277
SQ FT: 269,000
SALES: 1B **Publicly Held**
WEB: www.callawaygolf.com
SIC: 3949 2329 2339 6794 Golf equipment; shafts, golf club; balls: baseball, football, basketball, etc.; bags, golf; men's & boys' sportswear & athletic clothing; athletic (warmup, sweat & jogging) suits: men's & boys'; women's & misses' athletic clothing & sportswear; athletic clothing: women's, misses' & juniors'; women's & misses' accessories; patent buying, licensing, leasing

(P-23534)
CAMELBAK ACQUISITION CORP
2000 S Mcdowell Blvd, Petaluma
(94954-6901)
PHONE..................................707 792-9700
EMP: 101
SALES (est): 5.2MM
SALES (corp-wide): 2.3B **Publicly Held**
SIC: 3949 Camping equipment & supplies
PA: Vista Outdoor Inc.
262 N University Ave
Farmington UT 84025
801 447-3000

(P-23535)
CAMELBAK PRODUCTS LLC (HQ)
2000 S Mcdowell Blvd, Petaluma
(94954-6901)
PHONE..................................707 792-9700
Scott D Chaplin, *Mng Member*
Jody Brunner,
Glenn Gross,
Stephen M Nolan,
J Marty O'Donohue,
◆ EMP: 100
SQ FT: 50,000
SALES (est): 23.7MM
SALES (corp-wide): 2.3B **Publicly Held**
SIC: 3949 Camping equipment & supplies
PA: Vista Outdoor Inc.
262 N University Ave
Farmington UT 84025
801 447-3000

(P-23536)
CASA DE HERMANDAD (PA)
Also Called: WEST AREA OPPORTUNITY CENTER
11750 W Pico Blvd, Los Angeles
(90064-1309)
PHONE..................................310 477-8272
David Abelar, *President*
EMP: 30
SQ FT: 4,500
SALES: 59K **Privately Held**
SIC: 3949 Driving ranges, golf, electronic

(P-23537)
CHAMPION DISCS INCORPORATED
Also Called: Innova Champion Discs
950 S Dupont Ave, Ontario (91761-1525)
PHONE..................................800 408-8449
David B Dunipace, *President*
Charles Duvall, *Treasurer*
Harold G Duvall, *Vice Pres*
Greg Muir, *Vice Pres*
Tim Selinske, *Admin Sec*
▲ EMP: 11
SQ FT: 22,000
SALES (est): 2.2MM **Privately Held**
WEB: www.innovadiscs.com
SIC: 3949 Sporting & athletic goods

(P-23538)
CHANNEL ISLANDS SURFBOARDS INC
1115 Mark Ave, Carpinteria (93013-2917)
PHONE..................................805 745-2823
Al Merrik, *Manager*
EMP: 10
SALES (corp-wide): 149.4MM **Privately Held**
SIC: 3949 Surfboards
HQ: Channel Islands Surfboards Inc.
36 Anacapa St
Santa Barbara CA 93101
805 966-7213

▲ = Import ▼=Export
◆ =Import/Export

(P-23539)
CHAPMN-WLTERS INTRCOASTAL CORP
Also Called: Cwic
141 Via Lampara, Rcho STA Marg
(92688-2954)
PHONE...................949 448-9940
Andrew De Camara, *Receiver*
Cindi A Walters, *President*
◆ EMP: 40
SQ FT: 103,000
SALES (est): 4.3MM **Privately Held**
WEB: www.cwicfluid.com
SIC: 3949 Sporting & athletic goods

(P-23540)
CITY OF SANTA FE SPRINGS
Also Called: Santafe Spg PKS&rec Lake Cntr
11641 Florence Ave, Santa Fe Springs
(90670-4353)
PHONE...................562 868-8761
Manuel Cantu, *Director*
EMP: 10 **Privately Held**
WEB: www.santafesprings.org
SIC: 3949 Track & field athletic equipment
PA: City Of Santa Fe Springs
11710 Telegraph Rd
Santa Fe Springs CA 90670
562 409-7500

(P-23541)
CLEANWORLD
2330 Gold Meadow Way, Gold River
(95670-4471)
PHONE...................916 635-7300
Michele Wong, *CEO*
Daniela Calvitti, *CFO*
Terry Carlone, *Officer*
Joshua Rapport, *Vice Pres*
Amy Tucker, *Info Tech Mgr*
EMP: 13
SALES (est): 2MM **Privately Held**
SIC: 3949 Exercise equipment

(P-23542)
CONDOR OUTDOOR PRODUCTS INC
5268 Rivergrade Rd, Baldwin Park
(91706-1336)
PHONE...................626 358-3270
Spencer Tien, *President*
Jennifer Saavedra, *Executive*
Nell Chen, *General Mgr*
Steve Law, *Info Tech Mgr*
David Le, *Director*
▲ EMP: 37
SQ FT: 11,000
SALES (est): 5.2MM **Privately Held**
WEB: www.condoroutdoor.com
SIC: 3949 Sporting & athletic goods

(P-23543)
CONTINENTAL FIBERGLASS INC (PA)
17031 Muskrat Ave, Adelanto
(92301-2259)
PHONE...................760 246-6480
William Lohman, *President*
Joe Sica, *Sales Dir*
Del Hardwick, *Facilities Mgr*
▼ EMP: 10
SQ FT: 25,000
SALES (est): 1.8MM **Privately Held**
SIC: 3949 Swimming pools, except plastic

(P-23544)
CORE INDUSTRIES INC
Also Called: Star Trac
14410 Myford Rd, Irvine (92606-1001)
PHONE...................800 228-6635
Michael Bruno, *CEO*
Dustin Grosz, *President*
◆ EMP: 360
SALES (est): 31.4MM
SALES (corp-wide): 267.3MM **Privately Held**
SIC: 3949 Sporting & athletic goods
HQ: Core Industries Llc
4400 Ne 77th Ave Ste 300
Vancouver WA 98662
360 326-4090

(P-23545)
CRAZY INDUSTRIES
8675 Avenida Costa Norte, San Diego
(92154-6253)
PHONE...................619 270-9090
Brian Kelly, *Controller*
EMP: 40
SALES (corp-wide): 3.8MM **Privately Held**
SIC: 3949 Sporting & athletic goods
PA: Crazy Industries
9840 Prospect Ave
Santee CA 92071
619 270-9090

(P-23546)
CYCLE HOUSE LLC
8511 Melrose Ave, West Hollywood
(90069-5114)
PHONE...................310 358-0888
Adam Gillman, *Mng Member*
Julien Crochet,
Lara Gillman,
▲ EMP: 35
SALES (est): 226.5K **Privately Held**
SIC: 3949 Exercising cycles

(P-23547)
D HAUPTMAN CO INC
Also Called: Fold-A-Goal
4856 W Jefferson Blvd, Los Angeles
(90016-3921)
PHONE...................323 734-2507
David Hauptman, *President*
Amy Schaub, *Treasurer*
Aaron Hauptman, *Vice Pres*
Diana Hauptman, *Admin Sec*
Merlyn Cruz, *Manager*
◆ EMP: 23
SQ FT: 11,000
SALES (est): 3.3MM **Privately Held**
WEB: www.fold-a-goal.com
SIC: 3949 Soccer equipment & supplies

(P-23548)
DGB LLC
Also Called: Rusty Surfboards
8495 Commerce Ave, San Diego
(92121-2608)
PHONE...................858 578-0414
Rusty Preisendorfer, *President*
EMP: 20
SALES (est): 892.1K **Privately Held**
SIC: 3949 Surfboards

(P-23549)
DIAMOND BASEBALL COMPANY INC
Also Called: Diamond Sports
1880 E Saint Andrew Pl, Santa Ana
(92705-5043)
PHONE...................800 366-2999
Jay Hicks, *CEO*
Andrea Jackson, *President*
Robert W Ezell, *Vice Pres*
Monte Robertson, *Marketing Staff*
Janet Carlton, *Cust Mgr*
▲ EMP: 23
SQ FT: 120,000
SALES (est): 3.3MM **Privately Held**
WEB: www.diamond-sports.com
SIC: 3949 5091 Baseball equipment & supplies, general; athletic goods

(P-23550)
DIVING UNLIMITED INTERNATIONAL
1148 Delevan Dr, San Diego (92102-2499)
PHONE...................619 236-1203
Susan Long, *CEO*
Richard Long, *President*
Robin Jacoway, *General Mgr*
Dan Drake, *Engineer*
Shahram Homayounfar, *Controller*
◆ EMP: 75
SQ FT: 14,500
SALES (est): 9.7MM **Privately Held**
WEB: www.dui-online.com
SIC: 3949 Skin diving equipment, scuba type

(P-23551)
DYNA-KING INC
Also Called: Abby Precision Mfg
597 Santana Dr Ste A, Cloverdale
(95425-4250)
PHONE...................707 894-5566
Lenora Abby, *President*
Shannon Langevin, *CFO*
Ron Abby, *Officer*
EMP: 12
SQ FT: 5,000
SALES: 800K **Privately Held**
WEB: www.dyna-king.com
SIC: 3949 5941 5091 Fishing equipment; sporting goods & bicycle shops; sporting & recreation goods

(P-23552)
DYNAFLEX INTERNATIONAL
Also Called: Dynabee USA
1144 N Grove St, Anaheim (92806-2109)
PHONE...................714 630-0909
▲ EMP: 20
SQ FT: 5,000
SALES (est): 2MM **Privately Held**
WEB: www.dynaflexpro.com
SIC: 3949

(P-23553)
EAI-JR286 INC
20100 S Vermont Ave, Torrance
(90502-1361)
PHONE...................310 297-6400
Jonathan Hirshberg, *Principal*
EMP: 12
SALES (est): 287K **Privately Held**
SIC: 3949 Baseball equipment & supplies, general

(P-23554)
EASTON HOCKEY INC (DH)
Also Called: Eastern Sports
3500 Willow Ln, Thousand Oaks
(91361-4921)
PHONE...................818 782-6445
Mary George, *CEO*
Anthony Palma, *President*
Paul E Harrington, *Principal*
Jessica Green, *Marketing Mgr*
Nina Groat, *Legal Staff*
◆ EMP: 500
SQ FT: 30,000
SALES (est): 123.2MM **Privately Held**
WEB: www.eastonbike.com
SIC: 3949 Sporting & athletic goods
HQ: Brg Sports, Inc.
1700 E Higgins Rd Ste 500
Des Plaines IL 60018
224 585-5200

(P-23555)
EF COMPOSITE TECHNOLOGIES LP
2151 Las Palmas Dr Ste D, Carlsbad
(92011-1575)
PHONE...................800 433-6723
Ronald A Grimes, *Partner*
▲ EMP: 10 EST: 1994
SALES (est): 880.4K **Privately Held**
SIC: 3949 Sporting & athletic goods

(P-23556)
EFGP INC
Also Called: E. Force Sports
2080 Las Palmas Dr # 102, Carlsbad
(92011-1570)
PHONE...................760 692-3900
Ronald A Grimes, *President*
▲ EMP: 15
SALES (est): 1.3MM **Privately Held**
WEB: www.eforce.com
SIC: 3949 Racket sports equipment

(P-23557)
ERMICO ENTERPRISES INC
1111 17th St Ste B, San Francisco
(94107-2406)
P.O. Box 885403 (94188-5403)
PHONE...................415 822-6776
Rebekah Engel, *President*
Linda Decay, *Corp Secy*
Gwynned Vitello, *Vice Pres*
▲ EMP: 100
SQ FT: 19,000
SALES (est): 12.4MM **Privately Held**
SIC: 3949 3599 3365 3366 Skateboards; machine shop, jobbing & repair; aluminum foundries; brass foundry

(P-23558)
EXACTACATOR INC (PA)
2237 Stagecoach Rd, Stockton
(95215-7915)
P.O. Box 8501 (95208-0501)
PHONE...................209 464-8979
James G Nesbitt, *President*
Shelley Holcomb, *Treasurer*
John Nakashima, *Vice Pres*
Barbara Nesbitt, *Admin Sec*
Melissa Ping, *Admin Sec*
▲ EMP: 25
SQ FT: 21,000
SALES (est): 2.4MM **Privately Held**
WEB: www.viseinserts.com
SIC: 3949 Bowling equipment & supplies; bows, archery

(P-23559)
FAIRWAY IMPORT-EXPORT INC
Also Called: Lantic USA
2130 E Gladwick St, Rancho Dominguez
(90220-6203)
PHONE...................310 637-6162
Guido Rietdyk, *President*
Kevin Hinyub, *Admin Sec*
▲ EMP: 35
SQ FT: 17,000
SALES (est): 5.3MM **Privately Held**
SIC: 3949 Protective sporting equipment

(P-23560)
FIELD TIME TARGET TRAINING LLC
8230 Electric Ave, Stanton (90680-2640)
PHONE...................714 677-2841
Michael R Kaplan,
Lee Pratt, *Principal*
EMP: 14 EST: 2011
SALES (est): 1.7MM **Privately Held**
SIC: 3949 Targets, archery & rifle shooting

(P-23561)
FINIS INC (PA)
Also Called: Finis USA
7085 Las Positas Rd Ste E, Livermore
(94551-5116)
PHONE...................925 454-0111
John Mix, *CEO*
Bob Bowe, *CFO*
Vicki Espiritu, *Comms Mgr*
Plamen Nikolov, *General Mgr*
Clarke Dolliver, *Graphic Designe*
◆ EMP: 25
SQ FT: 20,000
SALES (est): 3.4MM **Privately Held**
WEB: www.finisinc.com
SIC: 3949 Surfboards

(P-23562)
FITNESS WAREHOUSE LLC (PA)
Also Called: Hoist Fitness Systems
9990 Alesmith Ct Ste 130, San Diego
(92126-4200)
PHONE...................858 578-7676
Jeffrey Partrick, *Partner*
Jeremy Miller, *COO*
Jody Paulsen, *Executive*
Ozgur Gorur, *Opers Staff*
Jenna Novotny, *Marketing Staff*
◆ EMP: 30
SALES (est): 2.5MM **Privately Held**
SIC: 3949 Sporting & athletic goods

(P-23563)
FLOW SPORTS INC (PA)
1011 Calle Sombra Ste 220, San Clemente
(92673-4206)
PHONE...................949 361-5260
Anthony Scaturro, *CEO*
Anthony D Scaturro, *President*
◆ EMP: 23
SALES (est): 3.5MM **Privately Held**
WEB: www.flow.com
SIC: 3949 Snow skiing equipment & supplies, except skis

(P-23564)
FLYDIVE INC (PA)
3209 Midway Dr Unit 203, San Diego
(92110-4517)
PHONE..............................844 359-3483
James Plante, *CEO*
▲ EMP: 16
SQ FT: 12,000
SALES (est): 1.4MM **Privately Held**
SIC: 3949 Water sports equipment

(P-23565)
FORESIGHT SPORTS LLC
9825 Businesspark Ave, San Diego
(92131-1101)
PHONE..............................858 880-0179
Jon Watters, *CEO*
Scott Wilson, *Vice Pres*
Chris Kiraly, *CTO*
Anthony Mucciolo, *Electrical Engi*
John Young, *Senior Buyer*
▲ EMP: 30
SALES (est): 8MM **Privately Held**
SIC: 3949 Golf equipment

(P-23566)
**FUJIKURA COMPOSITE
AMERICA INC**
Also Called: Fujikuria Composits
1483 Poinsettia Ave # 103, Vista
(92081-8536)
PHONE..............................760 598-6060
Peter Sanchez, *President*
Kenji Morita, *CFO*
▲ EMP: 20
SQ FT: 8,000
SALES (est): 2.6MM
SALES (corp-wide): 278.2MM **Privately
Held**
WEB: www.fujikuragolf.com
SIC: 3949 Shafts, golf club
PA: Fujikura Rubber Ltd.
3-5-7, Ariake
Koto-Ku TKY 135-0
335 278-111

(P-23567)
G PUCCI & SONS INC
460 Valley Dr, Brisbane (94005-1210)
PHONE..............................415 468-0452
John Pucci, *Owner*
Stefano Pucci, *President*
Angelo Pucci, *CFO*
◆ EMP: 10
SQ FT: 50,050
SALES (est): 1.4MM **Privately Held**
WEB: www.p-line.com
SIC: 3949 Fishing tackle, general

(P-23568)
GENTRY GOLF MAINTENANCE
14893 Ball Rd, Anaheim (92806-5048)
PHONE..............................714 630-3541
Dave Graff, *Partner*
EMP: 20
SALES (est): 987.1K **Privately Held**
SIC: 3949 5941 Driving ranges, golf, elec-
tronic; golf goods & equipment

(P-23569)
GERALD GENTELLALLI
Also Called: Rancho Safari
19360 Camino Vista Rd, Ramona
(92065-6770)
P.O. Box 691 (92065-0691)
PHONE..............................760 789-2094
Gerald Gentellalli, *President*
EMP: 15
SQ FT: 5,000
SALES (est): 1.3MM **Privately Held**
SIC: 3949 5961 Hunting equipment;
archery equipment, general; fishing, hunt-
ing & camping equipment & supplies: mail
order

(P-23570)
GLB INVESTMENT INC
Also Called: Central Coast Yamaha
2004 Preisker Ln Ste B, Santa Maria
(93454-1156)
PHONE..............................805 925-1971
Gary Betts, *President*
Leann Betts, *Treasurer*
EMP: 10
SQ FT: 11,500
SALES (est): 1.2MM **Privately Held**
WEB: www.centralcoastyamaha.com
SIC: 3949 5571 Water sports equipment;
motorcycles

(P-23571)
GLIMMER GEAR
4337 Alabama St, San Diego (92104-1023)
PHONE..............................619 399-9211
Kali Hussain, *Owner*
EMP: 10
SALES: 97K **Privately Held**
SIC: 3949 7389 5961 Sporting & athletic
goods; ; catalog & mail-order houses

(P-23572)
GLOBAL BILLIARD MFG CO INC
1141 Sandhill Ave, Carson (90746-1314)
PHONE..............................310 764-5000
Torben W Gramstrup, *President*
Solveig M Gramstrup, *Admin Sec*
◆ EMP: 20
SQ FT: 30,000
SALES: 1.3MM **Privately Held**
WEB: www.globalbilliard.com
SIC: 3949 Billiard & pool equipment & sup-
plies, general

(P-23573)
GOLF DESIGN INC
Also Called: Golf Design USA
10523 Humbolt St, Los Alamitos
(90720-5401)
PHONE..............................714 899-4040
John Tate, *President*
Patricia Tate, *VP Finance*
Michael Cheek, *Sales Staff*
▲ EMP: 70
SQ FT: 18,000
SALES (est): 10.8MM **Privately Held**
SIC: 3949 Golf equipment

(P-23574)
GOOMBY LLC
Also Called: Goomby Skateboarding
8350 Wilshire Blvd # 200, Beverly Hills
(90211-2327)
PHONE..............................323 556-0637
John Pyle,
Dave Pyle,
◆ EMP: 13 EST: 2007
SQ FT: 2,000
SALES (est): 753.4K **Privately Held**
SIC: 3949 Skateboards

(P-23575)
GP INDUSTRIES INC
3230 Rvrsid Ave Ste 110, Paso Robles
(93446)
PHONE..............................805 227-6565
Phil Patti, *CEO*
Arthur Gutierrez, *Corp Secy*
▲ EMP: 15 EST: 1999
SALES (est): 2.6MM **Privately Held**
WEB: www.gpindinc.com
SIC: 3949 Sporting & athletic goods

(P-23576)
**GRAVITY BOARDING COMPANY
INC**
Also Called: Skateboard
2211 S Hcnda Blvd Ste 201, Hacienda
Heights (91745)
PHONE..............................760 591-4144
Michael Bream, *President*
Mary Bream, *Shareholder*
Chris Taylor, *Shareholder*
EMP: 12
SQ FT: 5,000
SALES (est): 1.3MM **Privately Held**
SIC: 3949 5941 Skateboards; skateboard-
ing equipment

(P-23577)
**GREENFIELDS OUTDOOR
FITNES INC**
2617 W Woodland Dr, Anaheim
(92801-2627)
PHONE..............................888 315-9037
Samuel Mendelsohn, *CEO*
Aviv Avivshay, *Shareholder*
Allison Abel, *Marketing Mgr*
◆ EMP: 15
SALES: 4MM **Privately Held**
SIC: 3949 Gymnasium equipment

(P-23578)
GSI CAPITAL PARTNERS LLC
888 Rancheros Dr Ste A, San Marcos
(92069-3044)
PHONE..............................760 745-1768
Mario F Garcia, *President*
Michael MA, *Vice Pres*
Andrew H Tarlow, *Mng Member*
▲ EMP: 13
SQ FT: 11,000
SALES (est): 1.2MM **Privately Held**
SIC: 3949 Golf equipment

(P-23579)
GUISEPPE INC
Also Called: Guiseppe Custom Cue Cases
6920 Knott Ave Ste H, Buena Park
(90621-4645)
PHONE..............................714 670-7700
Joe D Angeletti, *President*
▲ EMP: 16
SALES (est): 1.1MM **Privately Held**
SIC: 3949 Billiard & pool equipment & sup-
plies, general

(P-23580)
**HAMPTON FITNESS PRODUCTS
LTD**
1913 Portola Rd, Ventura (93003-8030)
PHONE..............................805 339-9733
Zagngang Guo, *Ch of Bd*
Shirley Jay, *CFO*
Robert Hornbuckle, *Vice Pres*
▲ EMP: 14
SQ FT: 30,000
SALES: 7MM **Privately Held**
WEB: www.hamptonfit.com
SIC: 3949 Exercise equipment

(P-23581)
HATCH OUTDOORS INC
961 Park Center Dr, Vista (92081-8312)
PHONE..............................760 734-4343
John Torok, *President*
Danny Ashcraft, *Vice Pres*
▲ EMP: 11
SALES (est): 1.3MM **Privately Held**
SIC: 3949 Fishing equipment; bait, artifi-
cial: fishing; fishing tackle, general;
hooks, fishing

(P-23582)
HAYDENSHAPES SURFBOARDS
122 Arena St Unit B, El Segundo
(90245-3901)
PHONE..............................310 648-8268
Hayden Cox, *Owner*
Katrina Grange, *Manager*
◆ EMP: 11
SALES (est): 1.3MM **Privately Held**
SIC: 3949 Surfboards

(P-23583)
HEART RATE INC
Also Called: Versaclimber
1411 E Wilshire Ave, Santa Ana
(92705-4422)
PHONE..............................714 850-9716
Richard D Charnitski, *President*
Dan Charnitski, *Admin Sec*
Peri Fetsch, *Controller*
Brett Collins, *Sales Staff*
▲ EMP: 38
SQ FT: 18,000
SALES (est): 5.7MM **Privately Held**
WEB: www.heartrateinc.com
SIC: 3949 Exercise equipment

(P-23584)
HILLERICH & BRADSBY CO
Also Called: R & B Research & Development
5960 Jetton Ln, Loomis (95650-9594)
PHONE..............................916 652-4267
George Berger, *Branch Mgr*
EMP: 20
SALES (corp-wide): 87.6MM **Privately
Held**
WEB: www.slugger.com
SIC: 3949 Baseball equipment & supplies,
general; golf equipment; sticks: hockey,
lacrosse, etc.
PA: Hillerich & Bradsby Co.
800 W Main St
Louisville KY 40202
502 585-5226

(P-23585)
HILLERICH & BRADSBY CO
Also Called: H & B Sports Products Div
1800 S Archibald Ave, Ontario
(91761-7647)
PHONE..............................800 282-2287
Tom R Harris, *Branch Mgr*
EMP: 100
SALES (corp-wide): 96.3MM **Privately
Held**
WEB: www.slugger.com
SIC: 3949 3354 Baseball equipment &
supplies, general; aluminum extruded
products
PA: Hillerich & Bradsby Co.
800 W Main St
Louisville KY 40202
502 585-5226

(P-23586)
HOIST FITNESS SYSTEMS INC
11900 Community Rd, Poway
(92064-7143)
PHONE..............................858 578-7676
Jeff Partrick, *CEO*
Lisa Shouse, *Accounting Mgr*
Diane Anderson, *Human Res Mgr*
Natalie Mendoza, *Sales Mgr*
Karen Kirch, *Sales Associate*
◆ EMP: 65
SQ FT: 105,000
SALES (est): 9.9MM **Privately Held**
WEB: www.hoistfitness.com
SIC: 3949 5941 Exercise equipment; exer-
cise equipment

(P-23587)
HUPA INTERNATIONAL INC
Also Called: Body Flex Sports
21717 Ferrero, Walnut (91789-5209)
PHONE..............................909 598-9876
Bob Hsiung, *President*
Yvonne Hsiung, *Facilities Mgr*
▲ EMP: 21
SQ FT: 30,000
SALES (est): 1.9MM **Privately Held**
WEB: www.bodychamp.com
SIC: 3949 Exercise equipment

(P-23588)
**I & I SPORTS SUPPLY COMPANY
(PA)**
19751 Figueroa St, Carson (90745-1004)
PHONE..............................310 715-6800
Alan Iba, *President*
▲ EMP: 20
SALES (est): 4.4MM **Privately Held**
WEB: www.ilsports.com
SIC: 3949 5091 5941 Sporting & athletic
goods; sporting & recreation goods; mar-
tial arts equipment & supplies

(P-23589)
IGOLPING INC
43583 Greenhills Way, Fremont
(94539-5916)
PHONE..............................866 507-4440
Doug Sumaraga, *Principal*
EMP: 10
SQ FT: 2,000
SALES (est): 680K **Privately Held**
SIC: 3949 Driving ranges, golf, electronic

(P-23590)
**ILLAH SPORTS INC A
CORPORATION**
Also Called: Belding Golf Bag Company, The
1610 Fiske Pl, Oxnard (93033-1849)
PHONE..............................805 240-7790
Brien Patermo, *CEO*
Steve Perrin, *President*
Jackie Perrin, *Vice Pres*
▲ EMP: 50
SALES (est): 5.8MM **Privately Held**
SIC: 3949 Bags, golf

(P-23591)
INNOVATIVE EARTH PRODUCTS
232 Avenida Fabricante, San Clemente
(92672-7555)
PHONE..............................888 588-5955
Steve Yates, *President*
▲ EMP: 10
SQ FT: 4,100

SALES: 100K **Privately Held**
SIC: **3949** Camping equipment & supplies

(P-23592)
INSIDE PARK
2353 S Azusa Ave, West Covina
(91792-1532)
PHONE..............................626 964-1800
Bobby Cao, *Mng Member*
EMP: 15
SALES (est): 1.6MM **Privately Held**
SIC: **3949** Sporting & athletic goods

(P-23593)
INTERNATIONAL SALES INC
Also Called: ISI
3210 Production Ave Ste B, Oceanside
(92058-1306)
PHONE..............................760 722-1455
Linda Prettyman, *President*
Ed Mroz, *Vice Pres*
▲ EMP: 20
SQ FT: 11,000
SALES (est): 1.5MM **Privately Held**
SIC: **3949** 2321 3751 Skateboards; men's
& boys' furnishings; bicycles & related
parts

(P-23594)
**INTERNTNAL INDIAN TRATY
CUNCIL**
2940 16th St Ste 305, San Francisco
(94103-3688)
PHONE..............................415 641-4482
Andrea Carmen, *Exec Dir*
Francisco Cali, *President*
Bill Means, *Bd of Directors*
EMP: 13
SALES: 563.3K **Privately Held**
WEB: www.treatycouncil.org
SIC: **3949** Indian clubs

(P-23595)
**IRON GRIP BARBELL COMPANY
INC**
4012 W Garry Ave, Santa Ana
(92704-6300)
PHONE..............................714 850-6900
Scott Frasco, *CEO*
Michael Rojas, *President*
Irma Ramirez, *General Mgr*
Chuck Brown, *Controller*
Robert Lowe, *Opers Mgr*
▼ EMP: 85
SQ FT: 63,000
SALES (est): 18.2MM **Privately Held**
WEB: www.irongrip.com
SIC: **3949** Exercise equipment

(P-23596)
IZORLINE INTERNATIONAL INC
6725 Somerset Blvd, Paramount
(90723-3706)
PHONE..............................562 531-6000
Steve Ichinokuchi, *Owner*
▲ EMP: 10
SQ FT: 3,515
SALES (est): 1MM **Privately Held**
WEB: www.izorline.com
SIC: **3949** 5091 Fishing tackle, general;
fishing equipment & supplies

(P-23597)
J B L ENTERPRISES INC
3219 Roymar Rd, Oceanside (92058-1311)
P.O. Box 1105, Orange (92856-0105)
PHONE..............................760 754-2727
Guy Skinner, *President*
▲ EMP: 13
SQ FT: 10,000
SALES (est): 1.8MM **Privately Held**
SIC: **3949** Fishing equipment; spears &
spearguns, fishing

(P-23598)
J F CHRISTOPHER INC
Also Called: Bonehead Composites
3110 Indian Ave Ste D, Perris
(92571-3271)
PHONE..............................951 943-1166
Chris Frisella, *President*
EMP: 15
SALES (est): 1.2MM **Privately Held**
WEB: www.boneheadcomposites.com
SIC: **3949** Helmets, athletic

(P-23599)
JOHNSON OUTDOORS INC
Scuba Pro
1166 Fesler St Ste A, El Cajon
(92020-1813)
PHONE..............................619 402-1023
Joe Stella, *Branch Mgr*
John Richardson, *Technician*
Jill Maucere, *Human Resources*
Alda Rivera, *Buyer*
EMP: 45
SALES (corp-wide): 490.5MM **Publicly
Held**
SIC: **3949** 5091 Skin diving equipment,
scuba type; diving equipment & supplies
PA: Johnson Outdoors Inc.
555 Main St
Racine WI 53403
262 631-6600

(P-23600)
KAREEM CORPORATION
Also Called: Kareem Cart Commissary & Mfg
4423 S Vermont Ave, Los Angeles
(90037-2413)
PHONE..............................323 234-0724
Mona Abdul Jawwad, *President*
Magdy Mahpa, *Admin Sec*
EMP: 10
SALES (est): 1.2MM **Privately Held**
WEB: www.kareemcarts.com
SIC: **3949** Carts, caddy

(P-23601)
KAYO CORP (PA)
Also Called: Kayo Store, The
6351 Yarrow Dr Ste D, Carlsbad
(92011-1545)
PHONE..............................760 918-0405
Troy Morgan, *President*
Leila Morgan, *Admin Sec*
▲ EMP: 11
SALES (est): 2.5MM **Privately Held**
WEB: www.thekayocorp.com
SIC: **3949** Skateboards

(P-23602)
KEISER CORPORATION (PA)
Also Called: Keiser Sports Health Equipment
2470 S Cherry Ave, Fresno (93706-5004)
PHONE..............................559 256-8000
Dennis L Keiser, *CEO*
Portlinn Pangburn, *CFO*
Kathy Keiser, *Treasurer*
Randy Keiser, *Vice Pres*
Gyl Keiser, *Admin Sec*
◆ EMP: 100 EST: 1977
SQ FT: 100,000
SALES (est): 22.8MM **Privately Held**
WEB: www.keiser.com
SIC: **3949** Exercise equipment

(P-23603)
KENNY GIANNINI PUTTERS LLC
74755 N Cove Dr, Indian Wells
(92210-7142)
P.O. Box 2400, Palm Desert (92261-2400)
PHONE..............................760 851-9475
EMP: 12
SALES (est): 1MM **Privately Held**
SIC: **3949**

(P-23604)
**L A STEEL CRAFT PRODUCTS
(PA)**
1975 Lincoln Ave, Pasadena (91103-1321)
P.O. Box 90365 (91109-0365)
PHONE..............................626 798-7401
Beverly Holt, *President*
John C Gaudesi, *COO*
Joy Smith, *Accountant*
Eugene Bourgeault, *Manager*
▲ EMP: 23 EST: 1951
SQ FT: 200,000
SALES (est): 3.2MM **Privately Held**
WEB: www.lasteelcraft.com
SIC: **3949** Playground equipment

(P-23605)
LAB SURF COMPANY
3205 Production Ave Ste G, Oceanside
(92058-1304)
PHONE..............................760 757-1975
Ivan Mendoza, *President*
EMP: 11

SALES (est): 790K **Privately Held**
SIC: **3949** Surfboards

(P-23606)
LEADMASTERS
17229 Lemon St Ste E11, Hesperia
(92345-5188)
PHONE..............................760 949-6566
Jim Pearce, *Owner*
▲ EMP: 10
SQ FT: 5,800
SALES (est): 738.6K **Privately Held**
SIC: **3949** 5091 Fishing tackle, general;
fishing tackle

(P-23607)
LIQUID FORCE WAKEBOARDS
Also Called: Free Motion Wakeboards
364 2nd St Ste 7, Encinitas (92024-3557)
PHONE..............................760 943-8364
Tony Finn, *Owner*
Jessica O'Leary, *Project Mgr*
▼ EMP: 50
SALES (est): 3.1MM **Privately Held**
WEB: www.liquidforce.com
SIC: **3949** Water sports equipment

(P-23608)
LOB-STER INC (PA)
Also Called: Lobster Sports
7340 Fulton Ave, North Hollywood
(91605-4113)
PHONE..............................818 764-6000
Tony Potter, *President*
Melissa Bush, *Finance Mgr*
Curtis Toney, *Sales Staff*
◆ EMP: 13
SQ FT: 8,000
SALES (est): 1.6MM **Privately Held**
WEB: www.lobstersports.com
SIC: **3949** Tennis equipment & supplies

(P-23609)
LOUD MOUTH INC
3840 Edna Pl Apt 1, San Diego
(92116-3778)
PHONE..............................619 743-0370
Dasean Cunningham, *CEO*
Kevin Gniadek, *CFO*
EMP: 22
SALES (est): 932.9K **Privately Held**
SIC: **3949** Fencing equipment (sporting
goods)

(P-23610)
**LUCKY STRIKE
ENTERTAINMENT INC (PA)**
15260 Ventura Blvd # 1110, Sherman Oaks
(91403-5346)
PHONE..............................818 933-3752
Steven Foster, *President*
Joseph Carini, *General Mgr*
Andrew Keys, *General Mgr*
Tim Killeen, *General Mgr*
Bryan Reis, *General Mgr*
EMP: 50
SALES (est): 264.4MM **Privately Held**
SIC: **3949** 5812 5813 Bowling alleys &
accessories; American restaurant; bar
(drinking places)

(P-23611)
MARPO KINETICS INC
1306 Stealth St, Livermore (94551-9356)
PHONE..............................925 606-6919
Marius Popescu, *President*
Mike Jeffrey, *Sales Staff*
▲ EMP: 10
SALES (est): 1MM **Privately Held**
WEB: www.marpokinetics.com
SIC: **3949** Sporting & athletic goods

(P-23612)
MARTIN SPORTS INC (PA)
Also Called: Martin Archery
1100 Glendon Ave Ste 920, Los Angeles
(90024-3513)
PHONE..............................509 529-2554
Rich Weatherford, *Principal*
Tracy Reiff, *President*
Richard Weatherford, *CEO*
Tim Larkin, *CFO*
Kevin MA, *Vice Pres*
▲ EMP: 31
SQ FT: 28,000

SALES (est): 5.5MM **Privately Held**
SIC: **3949** Sporting & athletic goods

(P-23613)
MASTER INDUSTRIES INC
1001 S Linwood Ave, Santa Ana
(92705-4323)
PHONE..............................949 660-0644
Bill Norman, *President*
Steve Norman, *COO*
Helen Norman, *Corp Secy*
Steven Norman, *General Mgr*
▲ EMP: 48
SQ FT: 55,000
SALES (est): 4.4MM **Privately Held**
WEB: www.masterindustries.com
SIC: **3949** Bowling equipment & supplies

(P-23614)
MATRIX SHAFTS
4992 E Hunter Ave, Anaheim (92807-2057)
PHONE..............................714 970-9977
Hoyt McGarity, *Managing Prtnr*
Daniel You, *COO*
Tara Smith, *Admin Mgr*
Evan Choi, *Manager*
Chris Elson, *Manager*
▲ EMP: 25
SALES (est): 1.5MM **Privately Held**
SIC: **3949** Golf equipment

(P-23615)
MAUI TOYS
2951 28th St Ste 1000, Santa Monica
(90405-2993)
PHONE..............................330 747-4333
Brian D Kessler, *President*
Cynthia Kessler, *Principal*
◆ EMP: 38
SQ FT: 17,000
SALES (est): 6.1MM **Privately Held**
SIC: **3949** 3944 Exercise equipment;
games, toys & children's vehicles

(P-23616)
MED-FIT SYSTEMS INC
3553 Rosa Way, Fallbrook (92028-2663)
PHONE..............................760 723-3618
Dean Sbragia, *President*
Juergen Kopf, *Vice Pres*
Alex Sbragia, *Admin Sec*
▲ EMP: 128
SQ FT: 1,500
SALES (est): 20.7MM **Privately Held**
SIC: **3949** 5047 Exercise equipment; ther-
apy equipment

(P-23617)
MEL & ASSOCIATES INC (PA)
Also Called: Freeline Design Surfboards
821 41st Ave, Santa Cruz (95062-4420)
PHONE..............................831 476-2950
John Mel, *President*
Brittney Barrios, *Buyer*
EMP: 10
SALES (est): 1.2MM **Privately Held**
WEB: www.freelinesurf.com
SIC: **3949** 5941 Surfboards; surfing equip-
ment & supplies

(P-23618)
MICHAEL HAGAN
Also Called: Racehorse Supply
17858 Laurel Dr, Fontana (92336-2835)
PHONE..............................909 213-5916
Sofia Sandoval, *Principal*
Mike Hagan, *Manager*
EMP: 22
SALES: 270K **Privately Held**
SIC: **3949** Sporting & athletic goods

(P-23619)
**MIRAGE SPRTFSHNG &
COMMRCL**
1810 Kapalua Dr, Oxnard (93036-7745)
PHONE..............................805 983-0975
Joe Villareal, *CEO*
Erin Villareal, *CFO*
EMP: 12
SALES (est): 1.1MM **Privately Held**
SIC: **3949** Reels, fishing

(P-23620)
MISSION HOCKEY COMPANY (PA)
12 Goodyear Ste 100, Irvine (92618-3764)
PHONE..............................949 585-9390
Michael Whan, *CEO*
Christopher Lynch, *CFO*
▲ EMP: 13
SQ FT: 10,000
SALES (est): 2MM **Privately Held**
WEB: www.missionitech.com
SIC: 3949 Hockey equipment & supplies, general

(P-23621)
MURREY INTERNATIONAL INC
25701 Weston Dr, Laguna Niguel (92677-1482)
PHONE..............................310 532-6091
Patrick Murrey, *President*
Ron Murrey, *Corp Secy*
Rosemary Murrey, *Corp Secy*
Larry Murrey, *Vice Pres*
Ted Murrey, *Vice Pres*
▲ EMP: 25
SQ FT: 40,000
SALES (est): 3.1MM **Privately Held**
WEB: www.murreyintl.com
SIC: 3949 1542 Bowling alleys & accessories; custom builders, non-residential

(P-23622)
MUSCLE DYNAMICS CORPORATION
14133 Freeway Dr, Santa Fe Springs (90670-5813)
P.O. Box 3752 (90670-1752)
PHONE..............................562 926-3232
Fax: 310 323-7608
▲ EMP: 12
SQ FT: 24,000
SALES (est): 910K **Privately Held**
WEB: www.muscledynamics.com
SIC: 3949 5941

(P-23623)
MV EXCEL
2838 Garrison St, San Diego (92106-2720)
PHONE..............................619 223-7493
William E Poole, *Owner*
EMP: 12
SALES (est): 647.7K **Privately Held**
SIC: 3949 Fishing equipment

(P-23624)
NHS INC
Also Called: Santa Cruz Skateboards
104 Bronson St Ste 9, Santa Cruz (95062-3487)
P.O. Box 2718 (95063-2718)
PHONE..............................831 459-7800
Robert A Denike, *CEO*
Bob Denike, *President*
Caylin Tardif, *CFO*
Richard H Novak, *Chairman*
Jeff Kendall, *Vice Pres*
▲ EMP: 92
SQ FT: 50,000
SALES (est): 21MM **Privately Held**
WEB: www.nhs-inc.com
SIC: 3949 2329 Skateboards; winter sports equipment; athletic (warmup, sweat & jogging) suits: men's & boys'

(P-23625)
NORBERTS ATHLETIC PRODUCTS
354 W Gardena Blvd, Gardena (90248-2739)
P.O. Box 1890, San Pedro (90733-1890)
PHONE..............................310 830-6672
Loren Dill, *President*
▲ EMP: 19
SQ FT: 4,000
SALES (est): 3.2MM **Privately Held**
WEB: www.norberts.net
SIC: 3949 Sporting & athletic goods

(P-23626)
ORCA ARMS LLC
9825 Carroll Centre Rd # 100, San Diego (92126-6508)
PHONE..............................858 586-0503
Hamid R Ray Akhavan, *Mng Member*
Ardeshir Akhavan,

▲ EMP: 68 EST: 2012
SQ FT: 5,500
SALES: 1MM **Privately Held**
SIC: 3949 5099 Sporting & athletic goods; firearms & ammunition, except sporting

(P-23627)
PACIFIC FLYWAY DECOY ASSN
300 Marble Dr, Antioch (94509-6221)
PHONE..............................925 754-4978
Terry Avila, *President*
Donna Burcio, *Treasurer*
EMP: 11
SALES: 67.1K **Privately Held**
SIC: 3949 2395 Decoys, duck & other game birds; art goods for embroidering, stamped: purchased materials

(P-23628)
PARAGON TACTICAL INC
Also Called: S T I
1580 Commerce St, Corona (92880-1729)
PHONE..............................951 736-9440
Art Fransen, *CEO*
Ed Fransen, *Senior VP*
Arthur Fransen, *Executive*
EMP: 12
SQ FT: 10,100
SALES (est): 2.2MM **Privately Held**
WEB: www.supertrap.com
SIC: 3949 Shooting equipment & supplies, general

(P-23629)
PRECISION SPORTS INC
Also Called: Labeda Inline Wheels & Frames
29910 Ohana Cir, Lake Elsinore (92532-2413)
PHONE..............................951 674-1665
Curt Labeda, *President*
Shelly Labeda, *Treasurer*
Sherri Labeda, *Admin Sec*
▲ EMP: 90
SQ FT: 9,500
SALES (est): 13.7MM **Privately Held**
WEB: www.labeda.com
SIC: 3949 Skates & parts, roller

(P-23630)
PROSERIES LLC
3400 Airport Ave Bldg E, Santa Monica (90405-6132)
PHONE..............................213 533-6400
Shaun Sheikh, *Mng Member*
EMP: 15
SQ FT: 2,000
SALES: 300K **Privately Held**
SIC: 3949 Team sports equipment

(P-23631)
RAINBOW FIN COMPANY INC
677 Beach Dr, Watsonville (95076-1904)
PHONE..............................831 728-2998
Glen Dewitt, *Principal*
Kathleen Dewitt, *Principal*
Shawd Dewitt, *Principal*
▲ EMP: 20
SQ FT: 4,000
SALES (est): 1.7MM **Privately Held**
WEB: www.rainbowfins.com
SIC: 3949 Windsurfing boards (sailboards) & equipment; surfboards

(P-23632)
RAP4
7700 Arroyo Cir, Gilroy (95020-7312)
PHONE..............................408 434-0434
Kt Tran, *President*
EMP: 20
SALES (est): 930.5K **Privately Held**
SIC: 3949 Shooting equipment & supplies, general

(P-23633)
RBG HOLDINGS CORP (PA)
7855 Haskell Ave Ste 350, Van Nuys (91406-1936)
PHONE..............................818 782-6445
Paul Harrington, *Principal*
EMP: 18
SALES (est): 40.4MM **Privately Held**
SIC: 3949 5091 3751 Sporting & athletic goods; sporting & recreation goods; motorcycles, bicycles & parts

(P-23634)
REAL ACTION PAINTBALL INC
Also Called: Modern Combat Solutions
7700 Arroyo Cir, Gilroy (95020-7312)
PHONE..............................408 848-2846
Nicole Nguyen, *Partner*
Kt Tran, *President*
Loc Pham, *CIO*
Mike Lovato, *Opers Mgr*
◆ EMP: 12
SQ FT: 15,000
SALES: 2.5MM **Privately Held**
WEB: www.rap4.com
SIC: 3949 Sporting & athletic goods

(P-23635)
REVOLUTION ENTERPRISES INC
12170 Dearborn Pl, Poway (92064-7110)
PHONE..............................858 679-5785
Joseph Hadzicki, *President*
David Hadzicki, *Vice Pres*
▲ EMP: 12
SALES: 1MM **Privately Held**
WEB: www.revolutionenterprises.net
SIC: 3949 Sporting & athletic goods

(P-23636)
RIP CURL INC (DH)
Also Called: Rip Curl USA
3030 Airway Ave, Costa Mesa (92626-6010)
PHONE..............................714 422-3600
Kelly Gibson, *CEO*
Matt Szot, *CFO*
Paul Harvey, *Vice Pres*
Kerry Joubert, *General Mgr*
Richard Fisher, *Info Tech Mgr*
◆ EMP: 60
SQ FT: 25,000
SALES (est): 48.4MM **Privately Held**
WEB: www.ripcurl.com
SIC: 3949 Surfboards; shuffleboards & shuffleboard equipment

(P-23637)
ROBOWORM INC
764 Calle Plano, Camarillo (93012-8555)
PHONE..............................805 389-1636
Greg Stump, *President*
EMP: 13
SALES (est): 1MM **Privately Held**
WEB: www.roboworm.com
SIC: 3949 Lures, fishing: artificial

(P-23638)
ROGER CLEVELAND GOLF CO INC (PA)
Also Called: Cleveland Golf-Srixon
5601 Skylab Rd, Huntington Beach (92647-2064)
PHONE..............................714 889-1300
Greg Hopkins, *CEO*
Michael Kline, *Owner*
Todd Harman, *President*
William Bird, *CFO*
Mark Perfetti, *Vice Pres*
▲ EMP: 165
SQ FT: 140,000
SALES (est): 38MM **Privately Held**
SIC: 3949 Golf equipment

(P-23639)
ROGUE RIVER RIFLEWORKS INC
Also Called: Rogue River Super Scopes
570 Linne Rd Ste 110, Paso Robles (93446-9460)
PHONE..............................805 227-4611
Geoff Miller, *President*
Craig Boddington, *COO*
Judy Sonne, *CFO*
EMP: 10
SQ FT: 5,000
SALES: 1.5MM **Privately Held**
SIC: 3949 Hunting equipment

(P-23640)
ROSEN & ROSEN INDUSTRIES INC
Also Called: R & R Industries
204 Avenida Fabricante, San Clemente (92672-7538)
PHONE..............................949 361-9238
Richard Rosen, *President*

Daniel Rosen, *Vice Pres*
▲ EMP: 80
SQ FT: 22,500
SALES (est): 8.1MM **Privately Held**
WEB: www.rrind.com
SIC: 3949 7389 Sporting & athletic goods; embroidering of advertising on shirts, etc.

(P-23641)
ROYAL ROBBINS LLC
Royal Robbins Div
1524 Princeton Ave, Modesto (95350-5728)
PHONE..............................209 529-6913
EMP: 30
SALES (corp-wide): 816K **Privately Held**
SIC: 3949 5136 2339 Sporting & athletic goods; sportswear, men's & boys'; women's & misses' outerwear
HQ: Royal Robbins, Llc
1524 Princeton Ave
Modesto CA 95350
209 529-6913

(P-23642)
RPSZ CONSTRUCTION LLC
1201 W 5th St Ste T340, Los Angeles (90017-1489)
PHONE..............................314 677-5831
Rick Platt, *Mng Member*
EMP: 30 EST: 2008
SQ FT: 3,500
SALES (est): 6.5MM
SALES (corp-wide): 1.6MM **Privately Held**
SIC: 3949 Trampolines & equipment
HQ: Sky Zone, Llc
1201 W 5th St Ste T340
Los Angeles CA 90017
310 734-0300

(P-23643)
RTG INVESTMENT GROUP INC
Also Called: Gym Parts Depot
149 S Barrington Ave, Los Angeles (90049-3310)
PHONE..............................310 444-5554
Roy Greenberg, *CEO*
Tania Cobb, *CFO*
EMP: 12
SALES (est): 1.2MM **Privately Held**
WEB: www.motususa.com
SIC: 3949 Gymnasium equipment

(P-23644)
RUSTY SURFBOARDS INC (PA)
8495 Commerce Ave, San Diego (92121-2608)
PHONE..............................858 578-0414
Angela Preidendorfer, *President*
Angela Preisendorfer, *President*
◆ EMP: 24
SALES (est): 2.9MM **Privately Held**
WEB: www.rustysurfboards.com
SIC: 3949 5941 Surfboards; surfing equipment & supplies

(P-23645)
RUSTY SURFBOARDS INC
2170 Avenida De La Playa, La Jolla (92037-3214)
PHONE..............................858 551-0262
Eric Graftman, *Manager*
EMP: 10
SALES (est): 695.9K
SALES (corp-wide): 2.9MM **Privately Held**
WEB: www.rustysurfboards.com
SIC: 3949 Surfboards
PA: Rusty Surfboards Inc
8495 Commerce Ave
San Diego CA 92121
858 578-0414

(P-23646)
S/R INDUSTRIES INC (HQ)
Also Called: Marksman Products
10652 Bloomfield Ave, Santa Fe Springs (90670-3912)
PHONE..............................562 968-5800
Yu Zhisong, *President*
Peter Hernandez, *Manager*
▲ EMP: 12
SQ FT: 25,000

SALES (est): 1.8MM
SALES (corp-wide): 5.4MM **Privately Held**
WEB: www.marksman.com
SIC: 3949 Sporting & athletic goods
PA: Shanghai Gongzi Machinery Manufacturing Co., Ltd.
No.60, Hongtu Rd., Fengcheng Town
Shanghai 20000
215 717-5190

(P-23647)
SAMIS SPORTS
5215 1/2 W Adams Blvd, Los Angeles (90016-2646)
PHONE..................323 965-8093
Alida Lopez, *Principal*
EMP: 10
SALES: 250K **Privately Held**
SIC: 3949 Sporting & athletic goods

(P-23648)
SCAPE GOAT IND
6901 Quail Pl Unit E, Carlsbad (92009-4120)
PHONE..................760 931-1802
EMP: 10
SALES (est): 460.9K **Privately Held**
SIC: 3949

(P-23649)
SCARLET SAINTS SOFTBALL
304 Grande Ave, Davis (95616-0212)
PHONE..................530 613-1443
John Sleuter, *Principal*
EMP: 12
SALES: 2K **Privately Held**
SIC: 3949 8641 8661 Softball equipment & supplies; social associations; churches, temples & shrines

(P-23650)
SEIRUS INNOVATIVE ACC INC
13975 Danielson St, Poway (92064-6889)
PHONE..................858 513-1212
Michael Carey, *President*
Joseph H Edwards, *Treasurer*
Wendy Carey, *Vice Pres*
▲ EMP: 20
SQ FT: 11,000
SALES (est): 4MM **Privately Held**
WEB: www.seirus.com
SIC: 3949 Sporting & athletic goods

(P-23651)
SKATE ONE CORP
Also Called: Roller Bones
30 S La Patera Ln Ste 9, Santa Barbara (93117-3253)
PHONE..................805 964-1330
George Powell, *President*
Mike Mete, *Design Engr*
Robert August, *Technology*
Deville Nunes, *Technology*
Steve Sherlock, *Graphic Designe*
▲ EMP: 80
SQ FT: 67,000
SALES (est): 13MM **Privately Held**
WEB: www.skateone.com
SIC: 3949 Skateboards; skates & parts, roller

(P-23652)
SLIVNIK MACHINING INC
1070 Linda Vista Dr Ste A, San Marcos (92078-2653)
PHONE..................760 744-8692
Leo Slivnik, *President*
Monica Slivnik, *CFO*
Adela Slivnik, *Vice Pres*
August Slivnik, *Vice Pres*
Christina Slivnik, *Admin Sec*
EMP: 35
SQ FT: 22,000
SALES (est): 3.1MM **Privately Held**
WEB: www.sli-bos.com
SIC: 3949 3599 Shafts, golf club; machine shop, jobbing & repair

(P-23653)
SMOOTH OPERATOR LLC
3388 Main St, San Diego (92113-3831)
P.O. Box 13250 (92170-3250)
PHONE..................619 233-8177
Tod Swank,
Tonie Morehead, *Administration*

▲ EMP: 20 EST: 1977
SQ FT: 26,500
SALES (est): 1.7MM **Privately Held**
WEB: www.watsonlaminates.com
SIC: 3949 Skateboards

(P-23654)
SOCAL SKATESHOP
24002 Via Fabricante # 205, Mission Viejo (92691-3901)
PHONE..................949 305-5321
Mike Hirsh, *Owner*
EMP: 10
SALES (est): 944.3K **Privately Held**
SIC: 3949 Skateboards

(P-23655)
SOCCER 90
1235 Veterans Blvd, Redwood City (94063-2608)
PHONE..................650 599-9900
Will Clark, *Office Mgr*
EMP: 10
SALES (est): 521.7K **Privately Held**
SIC: 3949 Sporting & athletic goods

(P-23656)
SOUTH STREET INC
Also Called: Twelve Strike
2231 E Curry St, Long Beach (90805-3209)
PHONE..................562 984-6240
Ron W Richmond, *CEO*
Susiy Richmond, *Treasurer*
Darryl Seals, *Technician*
▲ EMP: 10
SQ FT: 21,600
SALES (est): 1.6MM **Privately Held**
WEB: www.twelvestrike.com
SIC: 3949 Bowling equipment & supplies

(P-23657)
SPEEDPLAY INC
10151 Pacific Mesa Blvd # 107, San Diego (92121-4329)
PHONE..................858 453-4707
Richard Bryne, *CEO*
Sharon Worman, *President*
Rachel Barnes, *Controller*
Bryan Hite, *Sales Mgr*
Bobby Schultze, *Sales Staff*
▲ EMP: 25
SQ FT: 5,600
SALES (est): 2.5MM **Privately Held**
WEB: www.speedplay.com
SIC: 3949 Sporting & athletic goods

(P-23658)
SPEEDSKINS INC
Also Called: Atm Skateboards
2919 San Luis Rey Rd, Oceanside (92058-1219)
PHONE..................760 439-3119
John Falahee, *President*
Leah Falahee, *Vice Pres*
▲ EMP: 16
SQ FT: 7,000
SALES (est): 1.7MM **Privately Held**
SIC: 3949 5136 Skateboards; men's & boys' clothing

(P-23659)
SPN INVESTMENTS INC
Also Called: Einflatables
6481 Orangethorpe Ave # 12, Buena Park (90620-1376)
PHONE..................562 777-1140
Steven Nero, *CEO*
Victor Favela, *Accounts Exec*
Luis Ramirez, *Accounts Exec*
EMP: 45 EST: 2011
SALES (est): 6.6MM **Privately Held**
SIC: 3949 Playground equipment

(P-23660)
SPORT ROCK INTERNATIONAL INC
Also Called: Park Pets and Boulders
450 Marquita Ave, Paso Robles (93446-5910)
P.O. Box 32, Pismo Beach (93448-0032)
PHONE..................805 434-5474
Mike English, *President*
Kathy English, *Admin Sec*
EMP: 10
SQ FT: 13,000

SALES: 700K **Privately Held**
WEB: www.sportrockintl.com
SIC: 3949 Sporting & athletic goods

(P-23661)
SPORTS HOOP INC
12669 Beryl Way, Jurupa Valley (92509-1213)
PHONE..................626 387-6027
Kun Yuan Lin, *President*
Mie Lee, *CFO*
▲ EMP: 16
SALES (est): 1.4MM **Privately Held**
WEB: www.fitnessports.com
SIC: 3949 Sporting & athletic goods

(P-23662)
STA-SLIM PRODUCTS INC
600 N Pacific Ave, San Pedro (90731-2024)
P.O. Box 1470 (90733-1470)
PHONE..................310 514-1155
Tom Lincir, *President*
Diane Lincir, *Vice Pres*
Chet Groskreutz, *VP Sales*
EMP: 17
SQ FT: 40,000
SALES (est): 1.2MM **Privately Held**
WEB: www.ivankobarbell.com
SIC: 3949 Exercising cycles

(P-23663)
STX INC
Also Called: Alta Industries
418 Aviation Blvd, Santa Rosa (95403-1074)
P.O. Box 4407, Petaluma (94955-4407)
PHONE..................707 284-3549
William S Anderson, *President*
▲ EMP: 50 EST: 1978
SQ FT: 48,000
SALES (est): 5.4MM **Privately Held**
WEB: www.altaindustries.com
SIC: 3949 Protective sporting equipment

(P-23664)
STYLE UP AMERICA INC
2600 E 8th St, Los Angeles (90023-2104)
PHONE..................213 553-1134
Neil Miller, *President*
▲ EMP: 10
SQ FT: 22,000
SALES: 850K **Privately Held**
SIC: 3949 Sporting & athletic goods

(P-23665)
SUBMERSIBLE SYSTEMS INC
7413 Slater Ave, Huntington Beach (92647-6228)
PHONE..................714 842-6566
Anthony Buban, *President*
Christine Buban, *Corp Secy*
Larry Tram, *Opers Staff*
Shannon Bermudez, *Mktg Dir*
Vincent Santoianni, *Manager*
▲ EMP: 15
SQ FT: 12,000
SALES (est): 2.1MM **Privately Held**
WEB: www.submersiblesystems.com
SIC: 3949 Skin diving equipment, scuba type

(P-23666)
SUPERIOR FOAM PRODUCTS INC
Also Called: Custom X Body Boards
394 Via El Centro, Oceanside (92058-1237)
PHONE..................760 722-1585
Ronald M Noric, *President*
David Cunniff, *Shareholder*
Debbie Colwell, *President*
◆ EMP: 10
SQ FT: 4,400
SALES (est): 1MM **Privately Held**
SIC: 3949 Surfboards

(P-23667)
SUREGRIP INTERNATIONAL CO
5519 Rawlings Ave, South Gate (90280-7495)
PHONE..................562 923-0724
James Ball, *Vice Pres*
Ione L Ball, *President*
Sharon Plewinski, *Accountant*
▲ EMP: 60 EST: 1937

SQ FT: 30,000
SALES (est): 7.4MM **Privately Held**
WEB: www.suregrip.com
SIC: 3949 Skates & parts, roller

(P-23668)
SURF MORE PRODUCTS INC
250 Calle Pintoresco, San Clemente (92672-7504)
PHONE..................949 492-0753
Robert B Nealy, *President*
Sara Nealy, *Vice Pres*
Luis Benito, *Accounts Mgr*
▲ EMP: 25
SQ FT: 5,200
SALES (est): 2.8MM **Privately Held**
WEB: www.surfmorexm.com
SIC: 3949 Surfboards

(P-23669)
SURF TO SUMMIT INC
7234 Hollister Ave, Goleta (93117-2807)
PHONE..................805 964-1896
Eric States, *President*
Julie States, *Vice Pres*
Brandon Nebbling, *Sales Executive*
▲ EMP: 18
SALES (est): 1.9MM **Privately Held**
WEB: www.surftosummit.com
SIC: 3949 Sporting & athletic goods

(P-23670)
SURFY SURFY
974 N Coast Highway 101, Encinitas (92024-2051)
PHONE..................760 452-7687
Jean Paul St Pierre, *Principal*
EMP: 13
SALES (est): 1.5MM **Privately Held**
SIC: 3949 Surfboards

(P-23671)
TAYLOR MADE GOLF COMPANY INC
5545 Fermi Ct, Carlsbad (92008-7324)
PHONE..................760 918-6000
Dave Brownie, *Vice Pres*
John Gonsalves, *Vice Pres*
Chuck Presto, *Vice Pres*
Bill Reimus, *Vice Pres*
Keith Sbarbaro, *Vice Pres*
EMP: 109
SALES (est): 18.1MM **Privately Held**
SIC: 3949 Golf equipment

(P-23672)
TAYLORMADE GOLF COMPANY INC (HQ)
5545 Fermi Ct, Carlsbad (92008-7324)
PHONE..................877 860-8624
Mark King, *President*
Ben Sharpe, *CEO*
Melissa Claassen, *CFO*
John Kawaja, *Exec VP*
Sean Toulon, *Exec VP*
◆ EMP: 495 EST: 1979
SALES (est): 285.8MM
SALES (corp-wide): 2.1B **Privately Held**
WEB: www.taylormade-golf.com
SIC: 3949 Shafts, golf club
PA: Kps Capital Partners, Lp
485 Lexington Ave Fl 31
New York NY 10017
212 338-5100

(P-23673)
TONY HAWK INC
1161-A S Melrose Dr 362, Vista (92081)
PHONE..................760 477-2477
Steve Hawk, *Principal*
Pat Hawk, *COO*
Sandy Dusablon, *Bd of Directors*
EMP: 10
SALES: 822.8K **Privately Held**
SIC: 3949 Skateboards

(P-23674)
TORERO SPECIALTY PRODUCTS LLC
Also Called: Newport Vessels
222 E Huntington Dr # 225, Monrovia (91016-8006)
PHONE..................415 520-3481
Patrick Dean, *President*
Robert E Dean,

William L Shepherd IV,
▲ **EMP:** 12
SALES: 5MM **Privately Held**
SIC: 3949 3999 2392 Sporting & athletic
goods; advertising display products; boat
cushions

(P-23675)
TRIACTIVE AMERICA INC
1244 Trail View Pl, Nipomo (93444-6663)
PHONE..................805 595-1005
Jim Sargen, *President*
Marc Sargen, *CFO*
▲ **EMP:** 10
SQ FT: 1,600
SALES: 900K **Privately Held**
WEB: www.triactiveamerica.com
SIC: 3949 Sporting & athletic goods

(P-23676)
TRIDENT DIVING EQUIPMENT
9616 Owensmouth Ave, Chatsworth
(91311-4803)
PHONE..................818 998-7518
Lowell Dreyfuss, *President*
Tom Bird, *CFO*
Maria Navarro, *Office Mgr*
Barry Douglas, *Sales Staff*
◆ **EMP:** 22
SQ FT: 12,000
SALES (est): 2.5MM **Privately Held**
WEB: www.tridentdive.com
SIC: 3949 Skin diving equipment, scuba
type

(P-23677)
TRUE TEMPER SPORTS INC
9401 Waples St Ste 140, San Diego
(92121-3929)
PHONE..................858 404-0405
Scott Hennessy, *President*
▲ **EMP:** 24
SQ FT: 17,885
SALES (est): 3.2MM **Privately Held**
SIC: 3949 Shafts, golf club

(P-23678)
TUFFSTUFF FITNESS INTL INC
13971 Norton Ave, Chino (91710-5473)
PHONE..................909 629-1600
Cammie Grider, *President*
Pete Asistin, *Vice Pres*
Monida Grider, *Vice Pres*
Donny Penado, *General Mgr*
Lois Rodriguez, *Controller*
▲ **EMP:** 180
SQ FT: 150,000
SALES (est): 23.6MM **Privately Held**
SIC: 3949 Exercise equipment

(P-23679)
TWIN PEAK INDUSTRIES INC
Also Called: Jungle Jumps
12420 Montague St Ste E, Pacoima
(91331-2140)
PHONE..................800 259-5906
Edmond K Keshishian, *President*
Raffi Sepanian, *Principal*
EMP: 32
SALES (est): 3.8MM **Privately Held**
WEB: www.twinpeakindustries.com
SIC: 3949 3069 Playground equipment;
air-supported rubber structures

(P-23680)
U S BOWLING CORPORATION
5480 Schaefer Ave, Chino (91710-6901)
PHONE..................909 548-0644
David Frewing, *President*
Dolores Frewing, *Corp Secy*
Janet Frewing, *Officer*
Daroll L Frewing, *Principal*
Brent Pfluger, *Comp Spec*
▲ **EMP:** 15
SQ FT: 50,000
SALES (est): 2.7MM **Privately Held**
SIC: 3949 1799 Bowling alleys & acces-
sories; bowling alley installation

(P-23681)
U S DIVERS CO INC
2340 Cousteau Ct, Vista (92081-8346)
PHONE..................760 597-5000
Don Rockwell, *President*
Stephen Murnane, *CFO*
Kristen Silver, *General Mgr*

EMP: 126 **EST:** 1947
SALES: 40MM **Privately Held**
SIC: 3949 Water sports equipment; skin
diving equipment, scuba type
HQ: Aqualung International
Ere Avenue
Carros 06510

(P-23682)
UNITY CLOTHING INC
Also Called: Unity Clothing Company
3788 Rockwell Ave, El Monte (91731-2384)
PHONE..................626 579-5588
Raymond Hwang, *President*
▲ **EMP:** 12
SQ FT: 4,000
SALES: 600K **Privately Held**
SIC: 3949 Sporting & athletic goods

(P-23683)
US FIBERGLASS INC
17031 Muskrat Ave, Adelanto
(92301-2259)
PHONE..................760 246-3822
William H Lohman, *President*
EMP: 12
SQ FT: 52,000
SALES (est): 1.1MM **Privately Held**
SIC: 3949 Swimming pools, except plastic

(P-23684)
VF OUTDOOR LLC
Also Called: North Face, The
180 Post St, San Francisco (94108-4703)
PHONE..................415 433-3223
David Garcia, *Manager*
EMP: 43
SALES (corp-wide): 11.8B **Publicly Held**
WEB: www.thenorthface.com
SIC: 3949 Sporting & athletic goods
HQ: Vf Outdoor, Llc
2701 Harbor Bay Pkwy
Alameda CA 94502
510 618-3500

(P-23685)
VICTORIA SKIMBOARDS
2955 Laguna Canyon Rd # 1, Laguna
Beach (92651-1194)
PHONE..................949 494-0059
Charles Haines III, *President*
▲ **EMP:** 25
SQ FT: 4,500
SALES (est): 2.3MM **Privately Held**
WEB: www.vicskim.com
SIC: 3949 5941 Surfboards; surfing equip-
ment & supplies

(P-23686)
VISION AQUATICS INC
4542 Skidmore Ct, Moorpark (93021-2234)
PHONE..................818 749-2178
Peter J Gillette, *President*
Patricia Gillette, *Treasurer*
EMP: 10
SALES: 3.7MM **Privately Held**
WEB: www.visionaquatics.com
SIC: 3949 Swimming pools, plastic

(P-23687)
VISTA OUTDOOR INC
Also Called: Brg Sports
5550 Scotts Valley Dr, Scotts Valley
(95066-3438)
PHONE..................831 461-7500
Mark Teixeira, *Branch Mgr*
Craig Phillips, *Sales Staff*
Alex Alexander, *Director*
Ken Faber, *Director*
Brad Bishop, *Manager*
EMP: 20
SALES (corp-wide): 2.3B **Publicly Held**
SIC: 3949 Bags, rosin
PA: Vista Outdoor Inc.
262 N University Ave
Farmington UT 84025
801 447-3000

(P-23688)
WATERMANS GUILD
260 E Dyer Rd Ste L, Santa Ana
(92707-3753)
PHONE..................714 751-0603
Gregory Martz, *Owner*
EMP: 10

SQ FT: 3,200
SALES (est): 390K **Privately Held**
SIC: 3949 Surfboards

(P-23689)
WEST COAST TRENDS INC
Also Called: Train Reaction
17811 Jamestown Ln, Huntington Beach
(92647-7136)
PHONE..................714 843-9288
Jeffrey C Herold, *CEO*
Vivienne Herold, *CFO*
Amanda Hamel, *Executive Asst*
Jim Jamison, *Technology*
Beth Hoagland, *Accounting Mgr*
◆ **EMP:** 50
SQ FT: 26,000
SALES (est): 5.9MM **Privately Held**
WEB: www.clubglove.com
SIC: 3949 Golf equipment

(P-23690)
WESTERN GOLF INC
1340 N Jefferson St, Anaheim
(92807-1614)
PHONE..................800 448-4409
Robert B Wagner Jr, *CEO*
◆ **EMP:** 14
SQ FT: 15,500
SALES (est): 1.7MM **Privately Held**
WEB: www.westerngolf.com
SIC: 3949 5091

(P-23691)
WESTERN GOLF CAR MFG INC
Also Called: Western Golf Car Sales Co
69391 Dillon Rd, Desert Hot Springs
(92241-8433)
PHONE..................760 671-6691
Scott Stevens, *President*
Robert W Thomas, *Vice Pres*
Robert Evans, *Controller*
EMP: 55
SQ FT: 60,000
SALES (est): 35.5K **Privately Held**
SIC: 3949 3799 Sporting & athletic goods;
golf carts, powered

(P-23692)
WILLIAM GETZ CORP
539 W Walnut Ave, Orange (92868-2232)
PHONE..................714 516-2050
Michael Paulsen, *President*
▲ **EMP:** 27
SQ FT: 10,000
SALES (est): 2.4MM **Privately Held**
SIC: 3949 Sporting & athletic goods

(P-23693)
XS SCUBA INC (PA)
4040 W Chandler Ave, Santa Ana
(92704-5202)
PHONE..................714 424-0434
Daniel F Babcock, *President*
◆ **EMP:** 25
SALES (est): 3MM **Privately Held**
WEB: www.xsscuba.com
SIC: 3949 5091 Skin diving equipment,
scuba type; diving equipment & supplies

(P-23694)
YELLOW INC
Also Called: Rollin Industries
9350 Trade Pl Ste C, San Diego
(92126-6334)
PHONE..................858 689-4851
▲ **EMP:** 50
SALES (est): 451.7K **Privately Held**
WEB: www.pony-ex.com
SIC: 3949

(P-23695)
ZEPP LABS INC
75 E Santa Clara St # 93, San Jose
(95113-1826)
PHONE..................314 662-2145
Jason Fass, *CEO*
Bruce McAllister, *CFO*
Robin Han, *Senior Mgr*
▲ **EMP:** 50
SQ FT: 4,000
SALES (est): 4.7MM **Privately Held**
SIC: 3949 4832 Sporting & athletic goods;
sports

(P-23696)
ZONSON COMPANY INC
3197 Lionshead Ave, Carlsbad
(92010-4702)
PHONE..................760 597-0338
Jeff Yearours, *Vice Pres*
Ronnie Shaw, *Manager*
▲ **EMP:** 26
SALES (est): 2.2MM **Privately Held**
SIC: 3949 Bags, golf

3951 Pens & Mechanical Pencils

(P-23697)
AMITY RUBBERIZED PEN COMPANY
612 N Commercial Ave, Covina
(91723-1309)
PHONE..................626 969-0863
Robert Oroumieh, *President*
▲ **EMP:** 22
SALES (est): 1.3MM **Privately Held**
SIC: 3951 Ball point pens & parts

(P-23698)
ANOTO INCORPORATED
7677 Oakport St Ste 1200, Oakland
(94621-1975)
PHONE..................510 777-0071
Jim Marggraff, *CEO*
EMP: 18
SALES (est): 1.6MM **Privately Held**
SIC: 3951 Pens & mechanical pencils

(P-23699)
HARTLEY COMPANY
Also Called: Hartley-Racon
1987 Placentia Ave, Costa Mesa
(92627-6265)
P.O. Box 10999 (92627-0999)
PHONE..................949 646-9643
Ed Kuder, *President*
Mike Quinley, *Vice Pres*
▲ **EMP:** 22
SQ FT: 75,000
SALES (est): 3.7MM **Privately Held**
SIC: 3951 Cartridges, refill: ball point pens

(P-23700)
NATIONAL PEN CO LLC (DH)
12121 Scripps Summit Dr # 200, San Diego
(92131-4609)
P.O. Box 847203, Dallas TX (75284-7203)
PHONE..................866 388-9850
Peter Kelly, *CEO*
David Thompson, *Ch of Bd*
Richard N Obrigawitch, *COO*
Kathy McDermott, *Sr Corp Ofcr*
Wayne Palmer, *CTO*
◆ **EMP:** 150
SQ FT: 40,000
SALES: 327.2MM
SALES (corp-wide): 2.1B **Privately Held**
SIC: 3951 3993 Pens & mechanical pen-
cils; advertising novelties
HQ: Cimpress Usa Incorporated
275 Wyman St Ste 100
Waltham MA 02451
866 614-8002

(P-23701)
RTL ELECTRONICS
1972 Del Amo Blvd Ste D, Torrance
(90501-1334)
PHONE..................310 320-0451
Eiji Kanno, *Owner*
EMP: 10
SALES (est): 800K **Privately Held**
SIC: 3951 Pens & mechanical pencils

(P-23702)
TOLERANCE TECHNOLOGY INC
1756 Junction Ave Ste C, San Jose
(95112-1045)
PHONE..................408 586-8811
Ke Qian, *CEO*
EMP: 10
SALES (est): 968.2K **Privately Held**
SIC: 3951 5084 Pens & mechanical pen-
cils; industrial machinery & equipment

▲ = Import ▼=Export
◆ =Import/Export

3952 Lead Pencils, Crayons & Artist's Mtrls

(P-23703)
AARDVARK CLAY & SUPPLIES INC (PA)
1400 E Pomona St, Santa Ana (92705-4858)
PHONE.....................714 541-4157
George Johnston, *President*
K Douglas Mac Pherson, *Corp Secy*
Daniel T Carreon, *Vice Pres*
Richard Mac Pherson, *Vice Pres*
Lynne Urquiza, *Manager*
▲ EMP: 30
SQ FT: 25,000
SALES (est): 4.2MM **Privately Held**
WEB: www.aardvarkclay.com
SIC: **3952** 5945 Modeling clay; arts & crafts supplies

(P-23704)
ALLIED PRESSROOM PRODUCTS INC
Also Called: Allied Litho Products
3546 Emery St, Los Angeles (90023-3908)
PHONE.....................323 266-6250
Mark Rios, *Manager*
EMP: 12
SALES (est): 2MM
SALES (corp-wide): 9.3MM **Privately Held**
SIC: **3952** 5199 Lead pencils & art goods; art goods & supplies
PA: Allied Pressroom Products, Inc.
4814 Persimmon Ct
Monroe NC 28110
954 920-0909

(P-23705)
AR-CE INC
Also Called: Stretch Art
141 E 162nd St, Gardena (90248-2801)
PHONE.....................310 771-1960
Sarkis Cetinyan, *President*
Herman Artinian, *Vice Pres*
EMP: 15
SQ FT: 6,000
SALES (est): 1.1MM **Privately Held**
WEB: www.stretch-art.com
SIC: **3952** Lead pencils & art goods

(P-23706)
CONVERSION TECHNOLOGY CO INC (PA)
5360 N Commerce Ave, Moorpark (93021-1762)
PHONE.....................805 378-0033
Jim Newkirk, *President*
Russell Greenhouse, *COO*
Ray Salinas, *Branch Mgr*
Terrill Newkirk, *Office Mgr*
▲ EMP: 50
SQ FT: 28,000
SALES (est): 7.5MM **Privately Held**
WEB: www.fluidink.com
SIC: **3952** 2893 2899 Ink, drawing: black & colored; printing ink; ink or writing fluids

(P-23707)
DOSTAL STUDIO
898 Lincoln Ave, San Rafael (94901-3330)
PHONE.....................415 721-7080
Frank Dostal, *Owner*
EMP: 15
SQ FT: 4,000
SALES: 600K **Privately Held**
WEB: www.dostalstudio.com
SIC: **3952** Frames for artists' canvases

(P-23708)
J F MCCAUGHIN CO
2628 River Ave, Rosemead (91770-3302)
PHONE.....................626 573-3000
Jim Mallory, *Branch Mgr*
EMP: 30
SALES (corp-wide): 667.6MM **Privately Held**
WEB: www.argueso.com
SIC: **3952** Wax, artists'

HQ: J. F. Mccaughin Co.
2817 Mccracken St
Norton Shores MI 49441
231 759-7304

(P-23709)
MANSOOR AMARNA CORP
16923 Kinzie St, Northridge (91343-1715)
PHONE.....................818 894-8937
Henry Mansoor, *President*
EMP: 12
SALES (est): 982.6K **Privately Held**
SIC: **3952** Artists' equipment

(P-23710)
SALIS INTERNATIONAL INC
3921 Oceanic Dr Ste 802, Oceanside (92056-5857)
PHONE.....................303 384-3588
Lawrence R Salis, *President*
▲ EMP: 38
SQ FT: 10,000
SALES (est): 5.2MM **Privately Held**
WEB: www.salisinternational.com
SIC: **3952** Water colors, artists'

(P-23711)
SIENA DECOR INC
1250 Philadelphia St, Pomona (91766-5535)
PHONE.....................909 895-8585
Duc Do, *CEO*
▲ EMP: 10 EST: 2012
SQ FT: 60,000
SALES (est): 308.7K **Privately Held**
SIC: **3952** Colors, artists': water & oxide ceramic glass

(P-23712)
TARA MATERIALS INC
7615 Siempre Viva Rd, San Diego (92154-6217)
P.O. Box 406, Cottonwood (96022-0406)
PHONE.....................619 671-1018
John I Benator, *Owner*
EMP: 20
SALES (corp-wide): 66MM **Privately Held**
WEB: www.taramaterials.com
SIC: **3952** Lead pencils & art goods
PA: Tara Materials, Inc.
322 Industrial Park Dr
Lawrenceville GA 30046
770 963-5256

(P-23713)
TREKELL & CO INC
17459 Lilac St Ste B, Hesperia (92345-5106)
PHONE.....................800 378-3867
Brian Trekell, *President*
▲ EMP: 11
SALES (est): 1.2MM **Privately Held**
SIC: **3952** Brushes, air, artists'

3953 Marking Devices

(P-23714)
BRANDNEW INDUSTRIES INC
375 Pine Ave Ste 22, Santa Barbara (93117-3725)
PHONE.....................805 964-8251
Sean David Clayton, *President*
Lisa Frey, *Partner*
Tim Sisneros, *Sales Staff*
EMP: 15 EST: 1991
SQ FT: 2,000
SALES: 1MM **Privately Held**
SIC: **3953** Irons, marking or branding

(P-23715)
GENERAL METAL ENGRAVING INC
Also Called: Kumjian Enterprises
9254 Garvey Ave, South El Monte (91733-1020)
P.O. Box 762, San Gabriel (91778-0762)
PHONE.....................626 443-8961
Sarkis Kumjian, *President*
EMP: 30

SALES (est): 4.2MM **Privately Held**
WEB: www.generalmetalengraving.com
SIC: **3953** 3544 Printing dies, rubber or plastic, for marking machines; special dies, tools, jigs & fixtures

(P-23716)
GREEN LAKE INVESTORS LLC
Also Called: Laser Excel
3310 Coffey Ln, Santa Rosa (95403-1917)
PHONE.....................707 577-1301
Ron Macken, *Manager*
EMP: 25
SALES (est): 1.7MM
SALES (corp-wide): 14.5MM **Privately Held**
WEB: www.laserexcel.com
SIC: **3953** 2759 3699 Stencils, painting & marking; screen printing; electrical equipment & supplies
PA: Green Lake Investors Llc
620 Cardinal Ln
Hartland WI 53029
262 369-5000

(P-23717)
HERO ARTS RUBBER STAMPS INC
1200 Hrbour Way S Ste 201, Richmond (94804)
PHONE.....................510 232-4200
Aaron Leventhal, *CEO*
Jacqueline Leventhal, *President*
Sheena Douglas, *Webmaster*
Tami Hartley, *Legal Staff*
▲ EMP: 59 EST: 1974
SQ FT: 70,000
SALES: 6.4MM **Privately Held**
SIC: **3953** Marking devices

(P-23718)
JOY PRODUCTS CALIFORNIA INC
Also Called: Coastal Enterprises
17281 Mount Wynne Cir, Fountain Valley (92708-4107)
PHONE.....................714 437-7250
Shayne Perkins, *President*
Jay Kollins, *Office Mgr*
▲ EMP: 15
SQ FT: 12,000
SALES (est): 3MM **Privately Held**
WEB: www.coastalsportswear.com
SIC: **3953** 2759 Screens, textile printing; screen printing

(P-23719)
KLJ MOBILE NOTARY INC
9502 Oak St Apt D, Bellflower (90706-5201)
PHONE.....................562 852-8253
Karen Jackson, *CEO*
EMP: 15
SALES: 500K **Privately Held**
SIC: **3953** Marking devices

(P-23720)
NOVA TOOL CO
Also Called: Wilbur Manufacturing
27736 Industrial Blvd, Hayward (94545-4047)
PHONE.....................925 828-7172
Frank D Aerni, *President*
Nancy Aerni, *Vice Pres*
▲ EMP: 10
SQ FT: 80,000
SALES (est): 1.4MM **Privately Held**
WEB: www.novatoolco.com
SIC: **3953** Irons, marking or branding

(P-23721)
ON-LINE STAMPCO INC
Also Called: California Stamp Company
3341 Hancock St, San Diego (92110-4302)
PHONE.....................800 373-5614
Donna Wright, *CEO*
Neal Wright, *President*
Sean Lazar, *Vice Pres*
Gina Guerra, *Production*
EMP: 11
SQ FT: 6,000
SALES (est): 1.5MM **Privately Held**
WEB: www.olstamp.com
SIC: **3953** 2759 Embossing seals & hand stamps; engraving

(P-23722)
STENCIL MASTER INC
780 Charcot Ave, San Jose (95131-2224)
PHONE.....................408 428-9695
Sang M Yu, *President*
Grace Song, *Sls & Mktg Exec*
EMP: 17 EST: 1997
SQ FT: 9,000
SALES (est): 2.4MM **Privately Held**
WEB: www.stencilmaster.net
SIC: **3953** Cancelling stamps, hand: rubber or metal

(P-23723)
UNITED CEREBRAL PALSY ASSN SAN
Also Called: Ready Stamps
10405 Sn Dgo Mssn Rd 10, San Diego (92108)
PHONE.....................619 282-8790
Jim Elliott, *Manager*
Barbara Cox, *Manager*
EMP: 18
SALES (corp-wide): 3.3MM **Privately Held**
WEB: www.readystamps.com
SIC: **3953** 5945 Marking devices; hobby, toy & game shops
PA: United Cerebral Palsy Association Of San Diego County
8525 Gibbs Dr Ste 209
San Diego CA 92123
858 495-3155

3955 Carbon Paper & Inked Ribbons

(P-23724)
ACI SUPPLIES LLC
425 N Berry St, Brea (92821-3105)
PHONE.....................714 989-1821
Carlos Adeva,
Benny Adeva, *Opers Mgr*
▲ EMP: 15
SALES: 11MM **Privately Held**
SIC: **3955** Print cartridges for laser & other computer printers

(P-23725)
BUSHNELL RIBBON CORPORATION
300 W Brookdale Pl, Fullerton (92832-1465)
P.O. Box 2543, Santa Fe Springs (90670-0543)
PHONE.....................562 948-1410
Jim Kinmartin, *President*
Mary Alice Milward, *Treasurer*
James C Kinmartin, *Vice Pres*
Paul C Kinmartin, *Vice Pres*
EMP: 70
SQ FT: 24,000
SALES (est): 8.4MM **Privately Held**
WEB: www.bushnellribbon.com
SIC: **3955** Ribbons, inked: typewriter, adding machine, register, etc.

(P-23726)
CALIFORNIA RIBBON CARBN CO INC
10914 Thienes Ave, South El Monte (91733-3404)
PHONE.....................323 724-9100
Robert J Picou, *President*
Louis Titus, *Corp Secy*
Clara Picou, *Vice Pres*
John Bank, *Natl Sales Mgr*
▲ EMP: 100 EST: 1939
SQ FT: 12,000
SALES (est): 13.4MM **Privately Held**
WEB: www.californiaribbon.com
SIC: **3955** Ribbons, inked: typewriter, adding machine, register, etc.

(P-23727)
E ALKO INC
Also Called: Laser Imaging International
8201 Woodley Ave, Van Nuys (91406-1231)
PHONE.....................818 587-9700
Eyal Alkoby, *CEO*
Beth Alkoby, *Principal*
▲ EMP: 190

SQ FT: 45,000
SALES (est): 17.3MM **Privately Held**
SIC: 3955 3861 Print cartridges for laser & other computer printers; photographic equipment & supplies

(P-23728)
ECMM SERVICES INC
500 S Kraemer Blvd # 100, Brea
(92821-6763)
PHONE....................714 988-9388
Vincent Yang, *President*
Donald Sung, *Principal*
EMP: 250
SALES (est): 25.9MM
SALES (corp-wide): 60.3B **Privately Held**
SIC: 3955 5045 Print cartridges for laser & other computer printers; printers, computer
PA: Hon Hai Precision Industry Co., Ltd.
66, Zhongshan Rd.,
New Taipei City 23680
222 683-477

(P-23729)
GENERAL RIBBON CORP
Also Called: G R C
5775 E Ls Angls Ave Ste 2, Chatsworth
(91311)
PHONE....................818 709-1234
Stephen R Morgan, *President*
Robert W Daggs, *Ch of Bd*
▲ **EMP:** 500 **EST:** 1946
SQ FT: 110,000
SALES (est): 46.5MM **Privately Held**
WEB: www.printgrc.com
SIC: 3955 3861 Ribbons, inked: typewriter, adding machine, register, etc.; photographic equipment & supplies

(P-23730)
HYDRO FLOW FILTRATION SYS LLC
42074 Remington Ave, Temecula
(92590-2551)
PHONE....................951 296-0904
Charles Lacy, *Mng Member*
Michael T Baird,
Mounir S Ibrahim,
▲ **EMP:** 15
SQ FT: 5,200
SALES: 1MM **Privately Held**
SIC: 3955 Carbon paper & inked ribbons

(P-23731)
LASER RECHARGE INC (PA)
Also Called: Encompass
9935 Horn Rd Ste A, Sacramento
(95827-1954)
PHONE....................916 737-6360
Michael Mooney, *CEO*
Dave Michon, *President*
Shannon Mooney, *CFO*
Vickie Morgan, *Manager*
EMP: 24
SQ FT: 10,000
SALES (est): 4.6MM **Privately Held**
WEB: www.laserrecharge.net
SIC: 3955 7699 5943 Print cartridges for laser & other computer printers; office equipment & accessory customizing; office forms & supplies

(P-23732)
LASER TONER & COMPUTER SUPPLY
940 Enchanted Way Ste 106, Simi Valley
(93065-0907)
P.O. Box 239, Moorpark (93020-0239)
PHONE....................805 529-3300
Richard Bradbury, *President*
Jodie Bradbury, *Admin Sec*
EMP: 10
SQ FT: 8,000
SALES: 2MM **Privately Held**
SIC: 3955 7378 5943 5112 Print cartridges for laser & other computer printers; computer peripheral equipment repair & maintenance; office forms & supplies; computer & photocopying supplies

(P-23733)
LASERCARE TECHNOLOGIES INC (PA)
3375 Robertson Pl, Los Angeles
(90034-3311)
PHONE....................310 202-4200
Paul Wilhelm, *President*
Marissa McFarland, *Accounts Exec*
EMP: 34
SQ FT: 12,000
SALES (est): 4.5MM **Privately Held**
WEB: www.lasercare.com
SIC: 3955 7378 5734 Print cartridges for laser & other computer printers; computer peripheral equipment repair & maintenance; printers & plotters: computers

(P-23734)
MAGNUM DATA INC
28130 Avenue Crocker # 303, Valencia
(91355-3421)
PHONE....................800 869-2589
Mike Mahfouz, *CEO*
EMP: 10
SQ FT: 2,500
SALES (est): 510K **Privately Held**
SIC: 3955 Print cartridges for laser & other computer printers

(P-23735)
PACIFIC COMPUTER PRODUCTS INC
2210 S Huron Dr, Santa Ana (92704-4947)
PHONE....................714 549-7535
Bernard R Loper, *President*
Patty Vacher, *Treasurer*
Timothy Buckley, *Vice Pres*
EMP: 25
SQ FT: 12,000
SALES (est): 1.6MM **Privately Held**
SIC: 3955 5045

(P-23736)
PLANET GREEN CARTRIDGES INC
20724 Lassen St, Chatsworth
(91311-4507)
PHONE....................818 725-2596
Sean Levi, *President*
Natalya Levi, *Treasurer*
◆ **EMP:** 84
SQ FT: 29,699
SALES (est): 13.8MM **Privately Held**
WEB: www.pginkjets.com
SIC: 3955 5093 Print cartridges for laser & other computer printers; plastics scrap

(P-23737)
RAYZIST PHOTOMASK INC (PA)
Also Called: Honor Life
955 Park Center Dr, Vista (92081-8312)
PHONE....................760 727-8561
Randy S Willis, *CEO*
Jim Kemp, *CFO*
James Myers, *Prdtn Mgr*
Mark Heddy, *Sales Mgr*
▲ **EMP:** 54
SQ FT: 28,000
SALES (est): 10.1MM **Privately Held**
WEB: www.rayzist.com
SIC: 3955 3281 3589 Stencil paper, gelatin or spirit process; cut stone & stone products; sandblasting equipment

(P-23738)
SERCOMP LLC (PA)
5401 Tech Cir Ste 200, Moorpark
(93021-1713)
P.O. Box 92728, City of Industry (91715-2728)
PHONE....................805 299-0020
Mike Goodman,
EMP: 89 **EST:** 2003
SQ FT: 67,000
SALES (est): 5.6MM **Privately Held**
WEB: www.sercomp.com
SIC: 3955 3577 Print cartridges for laser & other computer printers; computer peripheral equipment

(P-23739)
UNIVERSAL IMAGING TECH INC
4733 Torrance Blvd 997, Torrance
(90503-4100)
PHONE....................310 961-2098

Shad Applegate, *President*
EMP: 16
SQ FT: 4,000
SALES: 1.6MM **Privately Held**
SIC: 3955 Print cartridges for laser & other computer printers

(P-23740)
US PRINT & TONER INC
Also Called: National Copy Cartridge
1990 Friendship Dr, El Cajon (92020-1128)
PHONE....................619 562-6995
James Meyers, *President*
Steven Giannetta, *Sales Staff*
▲ **EMP:** 22
SQ FT: 6,500
SALES (est): 3.4MM **Privately Held**
WEB: www.nationalcopycartridge.com
SIC: 3955 Print cartridges for laser & other computer printers

(P-23741)
VISION IMAGING SUPPLIES INC
7920 Deering Ave, Canoga Park
(91304-5007)
PHONE....................818 710-7200
Benard Khachi, *CEO*
Raymond Khachi, *Vice Pres*
▲ **EMP:** 50
SQ FT: 4,000
SALES (est): 8MM **Privately Held**
WEB: www.vis-llc.com
SIC: 3955 Print cartridges for laser & other computer printers

---

3961 Costume Jewelry & Novelties

(P-23742)
A G ARTWEAR INC
Also Called: Frederic Duclos
15564 Producer Ln, Huntington Beach
(92649-1308)
P.O. Box 2460 (92647-0460)
PHONE....................714 898-3636
Karen M Duclos, *President*
Frederic Duclos, *Vice Pres*
EMP: 10
SQ FT: 2,100
SALES (est): 1.3MM **Privately Held**
WEB: www.fredericduclos.com
SIC: 3961 Costume jewelry

(P-23743)
B & R ACCESSORIES INC
7508 Deering Ave Ste D, Canoga Park
(91303-1436)
PHONE....................213 688-8727
Brijinder S Ahluwalia, *President*
▲ **EMP:** 10
SALES (est): 1.1MM **Privately Held**
SIC: 3961 Costume jewelry

(P-23744)
COLORON JEWELRY INC
Also Called: Coloron Jewelry Manufacturing
7242 Valjean Ave, Van Nuys (91406-3412)
PHONE....................818 565-1100
Ilan Lavian, *President*
Olivia Rodriguez, *Sales Mgr*
Staci Allen, *Merchandising*
EMP: 14 **EST:** 2000
SQ FT: 2,000
SALES (est): 2.2MM **Privately Held**
SIC: 3961 Costume jewelry

(P-23745)
DOGEARED INC
6053 Bristol Pkwy, Culver City
(90230-6601)
PHONE....................310 846-4444
Marcia Maizel-Clarke, *President*
Cynthia Helsley, *COO*
Douglas Clarke, *Treasurer*
Chad Berryhill, *CTO*
Francine Campos, *Human Res Mgr*
EMP: 76
SALES (est): 17.5MM **Privately Held**
WEB: www.dogearedjewelry.com
SIC: 3961 Costume jewelry

(P-23746)
EDGY SOUL
22337 Pacific Coast Hwy # 143, Malibu
(90265-5030)
PHONE....................310 800-2861
Lori Roberts, *COO*
EMP: 12
SQ FT: 1,100
SALES (est): 824.6K **Privately Held**
SIC: 3961 Costume jewelry

(P-23747)
FML INC
Also Called: Dynasty Import Co
2765 16th St, San Francisco (94103-4215)
PHONE....................415 864-5084
Fred Lane, *President*
Mayling Lane, *Vice Pres*
Anyta Lane, *Opers Staff*
◆ **EMP:** 11 **EST:** 1950
SQ FT: 40,000
SALES (est): 2.2MM **Privately Held**
SIC: 3961 5094 Costume jewelry, ex. precious metal & semiprecious stones; jewelry

(P-23748)
JAM DESIGN INC
5415 Cleon Ave, North Hollywood
(91601-2834)
PHONE....................818 505-1680
Marie Van Demark, *President*
EMP: 12
SQ FT: 1,500
SALES (est): 870K **Privately Held**
SIC: 3961 Jewelry apparel, non-precious metals

(P-23749)
JMGJ GROUP INC
10120 Wexted Way, Elk Grove
(95757-5501)
PHONE....................866 293-2872
Jacque Ojadidi, *CEO*
EMP: 10 **EST:** 2017
SQ FT: 3,900
SALES: 500K **Privately Held**
SIC: 3961 5944 5094 Costume jewelry, ex. precious metal & semiprecious stones; jewelry stores; jewelry

(P-23750)
KEY ITEM SALES INC
21037 Superior St, Chatsworth
(91311-4322)
PHONE....................818 885-0928
EMP: 10 **EST:** 2013
SALES (est): 1MM **Privately Held**
SIC: 3961

(P-23751)
KULAYFUL SILICONE BRACELETS
2267 Joshua Tree Way, West Covina
(91791-4331)
PHONE....................626 610-3816
Chris Angeles, *President*
EMP: 20 **EST:** 2013
SALES (est): 838.5K **Privately Held**
SIC: 3961 Bracelets, except precious metal

(P-23752)
LIZ PALACIOS DESIGNS LTD
1 Stanton Way, Mill Valley (94941-1421)
PHONE....................415 626-4630
Liz Palacios, *President*
Mingyu Fang, *Office Mgr*
EMP: 29
SQ FT: 7,500
SALES (est): 3.9MM **Privately Held**
WEB: www.lizpalacios.com
SIC: 3961

(P-23753)
LOUNGEFLY LLC
Also Called: Lounge Fly
20310 Plummer St, Chatsworth
(91311-5371)
PHONE....................818 718-5600
Trevor Schultz,
Candice Lee, *Graphic Designe*
Jason Hoffman, *Opers Staff*
Dale Schultz, *Natl Sales Mgr*
Tess Aquino, *Sales Staff*

▲ **EMP:** 25
SQ FT: 2,500
SALES (est): 5.6MM **Privately Held**
WEB: www.loungefly.com
SIC: 3961 Costume jewelry

(P-23754)
NEW ORIGINS ACCESSORIES INC (PA)
Also Called: Charming Hawaii
3980 Valley Blvd Ste D, Walnut
(91789-1530)
PHONE..............................909 869-7559
Vinod Kumar, *President*
Manju Kumar, *Admin Sec*
▲ **EMP:** 12
SQ FT: 2,400
SALES (est): 1.4MM **Privately Held**
SIC: 3961 Costume jewelry, ex. precious metal & semiprecious stones

(P-23755)
NOVELA DESIGNS INC
643 S Olive St Ste 421, Los Angeles
(90014-3608)
PHONE..............................213 505-4092
Alejandro Fuentes, *President*
EMP: 10
SQ FT: 1,200
SALES: 500K **Privately Held**
SIC: 3961 Costume jewelry

(P-23756)
PEARL ROVE INC
9570 Ridgehaven Ct Ste B, San Diego
(92123-1667)
PHONE..............................858 869-1827
Pnina Gruver, *Admin Sec*
EMP: 12
SQ FT: 2,300
SALES (est): 603.9K **Privately Held**
SIC: 3961 5632 Costume jewelry, ex. precious metal & semiprecious stones; costume jewelry

(P-23757)
PIN CRAFT INC
Also Called: Pin Concepts
7933 Ajay Dr, Sun Valley (91352-5315)
PHONE..............................818 248-0077
Vahe Asatourian, *President*
◆ **EMP:** 27
SALES (est): 647.6K **Privately Held**
WEB: www.pincraft.com
SIC: 3961 Pins (jewelry), except precious metal

(P-23758)
SAMS TRADE DEVELOPMENT CORP
818 S Main St, Los Angeles (90014-2002)
PHONE..............................213 225-0188
Sam Chu, *President*
▲ **EMP:** 24
SALES (est): 2.4MM **Privately Held**
SIC: 3961 Costume jewelry, ex. precious metal & semiprecious stones

(P-23759)
SPORT PINS INTERNATIONAL INC
888 Berry Ct Ste A, Upland (91786-8445)
PHONE..............................909 985-4549
Connie Bivens, *President*
John Bivens, *CFO*
Michael Bivens, *Treasurer*
Mike Bivens, *Vice Pres*
Jeff Bivens, *Admin Sec*
◆ **EMP:** 14
SQ FT: 2,300
SALES (est): 2.4MM **Privately Held**
WEB: www.sportpins.net
SIC: 3961 2395 3499 Pins (jewelry), except precious metal; emblems, embroidered; novelties & giftware, including trophies

(P-23760)
V & V MANUFACTURING INC
15320 Proctor Ave, City of Industry
(91745-1023)
PHONE..............................626 330-0641
Everett C Visk, *President*
Everett Visk, *President*
Steve Visk, *Vice Pres*

EMP: 12
SQ FT: 3,500
SALES: 800K **Privately Held**
SIC: 3961 Costume jewelry, ex. precious metal & semiprecious stones

---

3965 Fasteners, Buttons, Needles & Pins

(P-23761)
BECKMAN INDUSTRIES
701 Del Nrte Blvd Ste 205, Oxnard (93030)
P.O. Box 2307, Agoura Hills (91376-2307)
PHONE..............................805 375-3003
Robert Becker, *President*
Danny Becker, *Vice Pres*
Bob Becker, *Purchasing*
EMP: 16
SQ FT: 19,248
SALES (est): 3.4MM **Privately Held**
WEB: www.beckmanindustries.com
SIC: 3965 5072 Fasteners; hardware

(P-23762)
BRAXTON CARIBBEAN MFG CO INC
2641 Walnut Ave, Tustin (92780-7005)
PHONE..............................714 508-3570
Thomas Ordway, *President*
Robert Dionne, *Principal*
Joesph Triano, *Principal*
EMP: 62
SALES (est): 8.7MM **Privately Held**
WEB: www.braxtonca.com
SIC: 3965 Fasteners, buttons, needles & pins

(P-23763)
CATAME INC (PA)
Also Called: Ucan Zippers
1930 Long Beach Ave, Los Angeles
(90058-1020)
PHONE..............................213 749-2610
Liz H Lai, *CEO*
Paul Lai, *CFO*
Hyrum Lai, *General Mgr*
Floyd Lai, *Admin Sec*
▲ **EMP:** 26
SQ FT: 50,000
SALES (est): 4.7MM **Privately Held**
WEB: www.catameinc.com
SIC: 3965 5131 Zipper; zippers

(P-23764)
ENGINEERING MATERIALS CO INC
2055 W Cowles St, Long Beach
(90813-1087)
PHONE..............................562 436-0063
Edward Rickter, *President*
Susan J Brackett, *Treasurer*
Cynthia Ann Russell, *Admin Sec*
EMP: 20 **EST:** 1951
SQ FT: 24,000
SALES (est): 1.9MM **Privately Held**
SIC: 3965 Fasteners

(P-23765)
FASTENER TECHNOLOGY CORP
7415 Fulton Ave, North Hollywood
(91605-4116)
PHONE..............................818 764-6467
B Gulistan, *CEO*
Anna Stayer, *Vice Pres*
Puppy Carellon, *Info Tech Mgr*
Margarita Szabo, *Human Res Mgr*
Dave Prakash, *Plant Mgr*
EMP: 89 **EST:** 1979
SQ FT: 24,000
SALES (est): 11.8MM **Privately Held**
WEB: www.ftc-usa.com
SIC: 3965 3452 Fasteners; bolts, nuts, rivets & washers

(P-23766)
GIST INC
Also Called: Gist Silversmiths
4385 Pleasant Valley Rd, Placerville
(95667-8430)
PHONE..............................530 644-8000
Gary Gist, *President*
Jennifer Folsom, *Vice Pres*
Wende Heinen, *Sales Staff*
▲ **EMP:** 85

SQ FT: 15,000
SALES (est): 12.9MM **Privately Held**
WEB: www.gistsilversmiths.com
SIC: 3965 3911 Buckles & buckle parts; jewelry apparel

(P-23767)
HENWAY INC
Also Called: Anatase Products
1314 Goodrick Dr, Tehachapi (93561-1508)
PHONE..............................661 822-6873
David Benhan, *Vice Pres*
Scott Baker, *Treasurer*
Scott D Baker, *Corp Secy*
EMP: 18
SQ FT: 18,500
SALES (est): 2MM **Privately Held**
WEB: www.aircraftbolts.com
SIC: 3965 3452 Fasteners; bolts, nuts, rivets & washers

(P-23768)
L & P BUTTON & TRIMMING CO
2477 Ridgeway Rd, San Marino
(91108-2118)
PHONE..............................626 796-0903
Patty P Chan, *President*
Leon Tsay, *Vice Pres*
▲ **EMP:** 10
SALES (est): 1.3MM **Privately Held**
SIC: 3965 Buttons & parts

(P-23769)
LABELTEX MILLS INC (PA)
6100 Wilmington Ave, Los Angeles
(90001-1826)
PHONE..............................323 582-0228
Torag Pourshamtobi, *CEO*
Shahrokh Shamtobi, *President*
Ben Younessi, *Vice Pres*
Rebecca Cocco, *Executive*
Rima Anvarovaite, *General Mgr*
◆ **EMP:** 200
SQ FT: 135,000
SALES (est): 27.5MM **Privately Held**
WEB: www.labeltexmills.com
SIC: 3965 2253 2241 Fasteners, buttons, needles & pins; collar & cuff sets, knit; labels, woven

(P-23770)
MORTON GRINDING INC
Also Called: Morton Manufacturing
201 E Avenue K15, Lancaster
(93535-4572)
PHONE..............................661 298-0895
Yolanda A Morton, *Ch of Bd*
Frank Morton, *President*
Wallace Morton, *President*
Patrick Dansby, *Corp Secy*
John Morton, *Vice Pres*
EMP: 110
SQ FT: 45,000
SALES (est): 26.7MM **Privately Held**
SIC: 3965 3769 3452 Fasteners; guided missile & space vehicle parts & auxiliary equipment; bolts, nuts, rivets & washers

(P-23771)
PAIHO NORTH AMERICA CORP
16051 El Prado Rd, Chino (91708-9144)
PHONE..............................661 257-6611
Yi Ming Lin, *President*
Shu-Ching Hsieh, *CFO*
▲ **EMP:** 22
SQ FT: 52,000
SALES (est): 8.3MM **Privately Held**
SIC: 3965 Fasteners, hooks & eyes

(P-23772)
SHORELINE PRODUCTS INC
Also Called: Sola Products
120 Calle Iglesia Ste A, San Clemente
(92672-7543)
PHONE..............................949 388-1919
Cassandra House, *Owner*
Steven House, *Director*
▲ **EMP:** 10
SALES (est): 1.6MM **Privately Held**
SIC: 3965 3949 Fasteners; surfboards

(P-23773)
SPS TECHNOLOGIES LLC
Also Called: Aerospace Fasteners Group
1224 E Warner Ave, Santa Ana
(92705-5414)
PHONE..............................714 545-9311
Mike Kleene, *Branch Mgr*
Sebastian Bordron, *Technology*
Debbie Lupascu, *Technology*
Bruno Cuevas, *Human Res Mgr*
Karen Alexander, *Sales Mgr*
EMP: 500
SQ FT: 40,000
SALES (corp-wide): 242.1B **Publicly Held**
WEB: www.spst.com
SIC: 3965 3728 3452 3714 Fasteners; aircraft parts & equipment; bolts, nuts, rivets & washers; motor vehicle parts & accessories; machine tool accessories; iron & steel forgings
HQ: Sps Technologies, Llc
301 Highland Ave
Jenkintown PA 19046
215 572-3000

(P-23774)
SPS TECHNOLOGIES LLC
Cherry Aerospace Div
1224 E Warner Ave, Santa Ana
(92705-5414)
PHONE..............................714 371-1925
Michael Harhen, *Branch Mgr*
Amy Salgado, *Human Resources*
EMP: 500
SALES (corp-wide): 242.1B **Publicly Held**
WEB: www.spst.com
SIC: 3965 3452 Fasteners; bolts, nuts, rivets & washers
HQ: Sps Technologies, Llc
301 Highland Ave
Jenkintown PA 19046
215 572-3000

(P-23775)
TOLEETO FASTENER INTERNATIONAL
1580 Jayken Way, Chula Vista
(91911-4644)
PHONE..............................619 662-1355
David Deavenport, *President*
Tom V Oss, *Vice Pres*
Sara Davenport, *Principal*
Carol McKay, *Sales Staff*
EMP: 26
SQ FT: 10,000
SALES: 1.8MM **Privately Held**
WEB: www.toleeto.com
SIC: 3965 Fasteners, buttons, needles & pins

(P-23776)
TOMARCO CONTRACTOR SPC INC
Also Called: Tamarco Contractor Specialties
9372 Cabot Dr, San Diego (92126-4311)
PHONE..............................858 547-0700
Patrick Armstrong, *Manager*
EMP: 10
SALES (corp-wide): 66MM **Privately Held**
WEB: www.tomarco.com
SIC: 3965 Fasteners; eyelets, metal: clothing, fabrics, boots or shoes; buckles & buckle parts
PA: Tomarco Contractor Specialties, Inc.
14848 Northam St
La Mirada CA 90638
714 523-1771

(P-23777)
TOTAL CONCEPT ENTERPRISES INC
3745 E Jensen Ave, Fresno (93725)
PHONE..............................559 485-8413
Liz Limoune, *President*
Carol Jacobs, *Vice Pres*
EMP: 17
SQ FT: 18,000
SALES: 4MM **Privately Held**
SIC: 3965 5085 3842 Fasteners; fasteners & fastening equipment; abdominal supporters, braces & trusses

P R O D U C T S & S V C S

(P-23778)
TVS DISTRIBUTORS INC (PA)
Also Called: Tts Products
2822 E Olympic Blvd, Los Angeles
(90023-3412)
PHONE..................................323 268-1347
Vera Sapp, *President*
▲ **EMP:** 12
SQ FT: 8,000
SALES (est): 1.9MM **Privately Held**
SIC: 3965 Fasteners

(P-23779)
TWO LADS INC (PA)
5001 Hampton St, Vernon (90058-2133)
P.O. Box 58572, Los Angeles (90058-0572)
PHONE..................................323 584-0064
Lee R Adams, *President*
David Scharf, *Corp Secy*
Linda Gold, *Sales Mgr*
▼ **EMP:** 30
SQ FT: 6,300
SALES (est): 3.4MM **Privately Held**
SIC: 3965 5131 2241 Buttons & parts;
buttons; narrow fabric mills

(P-23780)
WCBM COMPANY (PA)
Also Called: West Coast Button Mfg Co
1812 W 135th St, Gardena (90249-2520)
PHONE..................................323 262-3274
Keith Tanabe, *CEO*
Grace Kadoya, *CFO*
▲ **EMP:** 32
SQ FT: 19,000
SALES (est): 2.2MM **Privately Held**
SIC: 3965 Buttons & parts

(P-23781)
WEST COAST AEROSPACE INC
(PA)
220 W E St, Wilmington (90744-5502)
PHONE..................................310 518-3167
Kenneth L Wagner Jr, *President*
Thomas Lieb, *Vice Pres*
Jeannie Vassor, *Administration*
Tom Nyikos, *Engineer*
Ryan Wagner, *Human Res Dir*
▲ **EMP:** 90
SQ FT: 7,200
SALES (est): 18.1MM **Privately Held**
WEB: www.westcoastaerospace.com
SIC: 3965 3452 Fasteners; bolts, nuts, riv-
ets & washers

(P-23782)
WEST COAST AEROSPACE INC
3017 E Las Hermanas St, Compton
(90221)
PHONE..................................310 632-2064
Chris Brumby, *Manager*
EMP: 10
SALES (corp-wide): 18.1MM **Privately
Held**
WEB: www.westcoastaerospace.com
SIC: 3965 Fasteners
PA: West Coast Aerospace, Inc.
220 W E St
Wilmington CA 90744
310 518-3167

(P-23783)
YKK (USA) INC
Also Called: Y K K U S A
5001 E La Palma Ave, Anaheim
(92807-1926)
PHONE..................................714 701-1200
Mike Blunt, *Manager*
Lynne Mostajo, *Accounting Mgr*
Christine Austria, *Personnel*
EMP: 150
SALES (corp-wide): 7B **Privately Held**
SIC: 3965 5131 Fasteners; hooks, cro-
chet; zipper; fasteners, hooks & eyes; zip-
pers
HQ: Ykk (U.S.A.), Inc.
1300 Cobb Industrial Dr
Marietta GA 30066
770 427-5521

3991 Brooms & Brushes

(P-23784)
A & B BRUSH MFG CORP
1150 3 Ranch Rd, Duarte (91010-2751)
PHONE..................................626 303-8856
Donn Anawalt Jr, *President*
Tom Derto, *Manager*
▲ **EMP:** 15
SQ FT: 26,500
SALES (est): 2.4MM **Privately Held**
SIC: 3991 Brushes, household or industrial

(P-23785)
AMERICAN ROTARY BROOM CO
INC (PA)
181 Pawnee St Ste B, San Marcos
(92078-2555)
PHONE..................................760 591-4025
James Wagner, *President*
Mary M Wagner, *Corp Secy*
Joe Baeskens, *Vice Pres*
EMP: 10 **EST:** 1955
SQ FT: 9,720
SALES (est): 2MM **Privately Held**
WEB: www.americanrotarybroom.com
SIC: 3991 Street sweeping brooms, hand
or machine

(P-23786)
AMERICAN ROTARY BROOM CO
INC
688 New York Dr, Pomona (91768-3311)
PHONE..................................909 629-9117
Joe Baeskens, *Vice Pres*
Clayton Trejo, *Sales Executive*
EMP: 26
SALES (corp-wide): 2MM **Privately Held**
WEB: www.americanrotarybroom.com
SIC: 3991 3711 4959 Brooms; motor ve-
hicles & car bodies; sweeping service:
road, airport, parking lot, etc.
PA: American Rotary Broom Co., Inc.
181 Pawnee St Ste B
San Marcos CA 92078
760 591-4025

(P-23787)
BRUSH RESEARCH MFG CO
Also Called: BRM MANUFACTURING
4642 Floral Dr, Los Angeles (90022-1288)
PHONE..................................323 261-2193
Tara L Rands, *CEO*
Grant Fowlie, *President*
Heather Jones, *Treasurer*
Mary Rands, *Treasurer*
Robert Fowlie, *Officer*
▲ **EMP:** 130 **EST:** 1962
SALES (est): 21.8MM **Privately Held**
WEB: www.brushresearch.com
SIC: 3991 Brushes, household or industrial

(P-23788)
BUTLER HOME PRODUCTS LLC
9409 Buffalo Ave, Rancho Cucamonga
(91730-6012)
PHONE..................................909 476-3884
Paul Anton, *Branch Mgr*
EMP: 13 **Privately Held**
WEB: www.mrcleantools.com
SIC: 3991 2392 Brooms; brushes, house-
hold or industrial; mops, floor & dust
HQ: Butler Home Products, Llc
2 Cabot Rd Ste 1
Hudson MA 01749
508 597-8000

(P-23789)
CT OLDENKAMP LLC
Also Called: Martin Sweeping
78380 Clarke Ct, La Quinta (92253-2213)
PHONE..................................760 200-9510
Curtis Oldenkamp, *Principal*
EMP: 10
SALES (est): 1.3MM **Privately Held**
SIC: 3991 Street sweeping brooms, hand
or machine

(P-23790)
ENVIRO-COMMERCIAL
SWEEPING
210 San Jose Ave Ste 5, Chico (95927)
PHONE..................................408 920-0274

Michael P Delucchi, *President*
Romy Salgado, *Treasurer*
Rebecca Rossi, *Admin Sec*
EMP: 15
SALES (est): 1.4MM **Privately Held**
WEB: www.envirocommercial.com
SIC: 3991 7538 Street sweeping brooms,
hand or machine; general automotive re-
pair shops

(P-23791)
FOAMPRO MFG INC
Also Called: Foampro Manufacturing
1781 Langley Ave, Irvine (92614-5621)
P.O. Box 18888 (92623-8888)
PHONE..................................949 252-0112
Gregory Isaac, *Ch of Bd*
Chad Coil, *Vice Pres*
▲ **EMP:** 80 **EST:** 1952
SQ FT: 25,000
SALES (est): 11.6MM **Privately Held**
WEB: www.foampromfg.com
SIC: 3991 Paint rollers; paint brushes

(P-23792)
GORDON BRUSH MFG CO INC
(PA)
3737 Capitol Ave, City of Industry
(90601-1732)
PHONE..................................323 724-7777
Kenneth L Rakusin, *President*
William E Loitz, *Vice Pres*
Denis Valentine, *Design Engr*
Brian Greer, *Technology*
Bill Loitz, *Engineer*
▲ **EMP:** 60 **EST:** 1951
SQ FT: 51,600
SALES (est): 15MM **Privately Held**
WEB: www.gordenbrush.net
SIC: 3991 Brushes, household or industrial

(P-23793)
KINGSOLVER INC
Also Called: Supreme Enterprise
8417 Secura Way, Santa Fe Springs
(90670-2215)
P.O. Box 3106 (90670-0106)
PHONE..................................562 945-7590
Keith Kingsolver, *President*
Christina Kingsolver, *Admin Sec*
▲ **EMP:** 19
SQ FT: 22,000
SALES (est): 2.7MM **Privately Held**
WEB: www.kingsolver.com
SIC: 3991 5199 Brooms; broom, mop &
paint handles

(P-23794)
LAKIM INDUSTRIES
INCORPORATED (PA)
Also Called: Quali-Tech Manufacturing
389 Rood Rd, Calexico (92231-9763)
PHONE..................................310 637-8900
Song B Kim, *CEO*
Juhyun Kim, *VP Finance*
Hector Herrera, *Opers Staff*
▲ **EMP:** 30
SALES (est): 4.8MM **Privately Held**
WEB: www.quali-techmfg.com
SIC: 3991 Paint rollers; paint brushes

(P-23795)
NORTHWESTERN CONVERTING
CO
Also Called: Premier Mop & Broom
2395 Railroad St, Corona (92880-5411)
PHONE..................................800 959-3402
Tom Buckles, *President*
Thomas M Buckles, *President*
▲ **EMP:** 100
SALES (est): 13.8MM **Privately Held**
WEB: www.premiermop.com
SIC: 3991 Brooms & brushes

(P-23796)
PASCO INDUSTRIES INC
2040 Redondo Pl, Fullerton (92835-3306)
PHONE..................................714 992-2051
Carl G Cantonis, *CEO*
George Cantonis, *President*
Cynthia C Cantonis-Finn, *Vice Pres*
Anne Cantonis, *Admin Sec*
EMP: 15 **EST:** 1951
SQ FT: 28,000

SALES: 900K **Privately Held**
SIC: 3991 5199 Paint rollers; paint
brushes; sponges (animal); chamois
leather

(P-23797)
UNITED ROTARY BRUSH CORP
688 New York Dr, Pomona (91768-3311)
PHONE..................................909 629-9117
Joe Baeskens, *Branch Mgr*
EMP: 37
SALES (corp-wide): 47.1MM **Privately
Held**
SIC: 3991 Brushes, household or industrial
PA: United Rotary Brush Corporation
15607 W 100th Ter
Lenexa KS 66219
913 888-8450

(P-23798)
UNITED ROTARY BRUSH CORP
160 Enterprise Ct Ste B, Galt (95632-8179)
PHONE..................................913 888-8450
Jim Olvera, *Manager*
EMP: 25
SALES (corp-wide): 47.1MM **Privately
Held**
WEB: www.united-rotary.com
SIC: 3991 Brushes, household or industrial
PA: United Rotary Brush Corporation
15607 W 100th Ter
Lenexa KS 66219
913 888-8450

(P-23799)
WESTCOAST BRUSH MFG INC
1330 Philadelphia St, Pomona
(91766-5563)
PHONE..................................909 627-7170
Heriberto Guerrero, *President*
Concepcion Guerrero, *Vice Pres*
Eddie Guerrero, *Executive*
▲ **EMP:** 22
SQ FT: 20,000
SALES (est): 3.3MM **Privately Held**
WEB: www.westcoastbrush.com
SIC: 3991 Brushes, household or industrial

(P-23800)
WORLD TREND INC (PA)
1920 W Holt Ave, Pomona (91768-3351)
PHONE..................................909 620-9945
Barnabas C Chen, *President*
▲ **EMP:** 15
SQ FT: 22,000
SALES (est): 1.4MM **Privately Held**
WEB: www.worldtrend.com
SIC: 3991 Toothbrushes, except electric;
brushes, except paint & varnish

3993 Signs & Advertising
Displays

(P-23801)
A GOOD SIGN & GRAPHICS CO
2110 S Susan St, Santa Ana (92704-4417)
PHONE..................................714 444-4466
Babak Richard Abedi, *CEO*
Mike Scott, *General Mgr*
Ted Howard, *Project Mgr*
Gene Long, *Project Mgr*
Ruben Bengoa, *Prdtn Mgr*
EMP: 18 **EST:** 2008
SALES (est): 2.3MM **Privately Held**
WEB: www.agoodsign.com
SIC: 3993 Signs, not made in custom sign
painting shops

(P-23802)
A PLUS SIGNS INC
4270 N Brawley Ave, Fresno (93722-3979)
PHONE..................................559 275-0700
Chris Pacheco, *President*
Jeff Ashlock, *Vice Pres*
Lauren Gibson, *Project Mgr*
Joaquin Federico, *Sales Mgr*
EMP: 47
SQ FT: 12,000
SALES (est): 4MM **Privately Held**
WEB: www.a-plussigns.com
SIC: 3993 7389 2399 Electric signs;
signs, not made in custom sign painting
shops; sign painting & lettering shop; ban-
ners, pennants & flags

(P-23803)
AAHS ENTERPRISES INC
Also Called: Aahs Graphics Signs & Engrv
6600 Telegraph Rd, Commerce
(90040-3210)
PHONE..................................323 838-9130
Gurmeet Sawhney, *President*
Mandeep Singh, *Info Tech Mgr*
EMP: 16
SALES: 1.8MM **Privately Held**
SIC: 3993 Signs & advertising specialties

(P-23804)
AARONS SIGNS & PRINTING
3770 Van Buren Blvd, Riverside
(92503-4250)
PHONE..................................951 352-7303
Gary Kerrington, *Principal*
EMP: 30
SALES (est): 1.8MM **Privately Held**
WEB: www.aaronssigns.com
SIC: 3993 Signs & advertising specialties

(P-23805)
ABIS SIGNS INC
14240 Don Julian Rd Ste E, City of Industry
(91746-3040)
PHONE..................................626 818-4329
Eddie Takahashi, *Principal*
EMP: 14
SALES (corp-wide): 729.2K **Privately
Held**
SIC: 3993 Neon signs
PA: Abis Signs Inc
12223 Highland Ave 106-21
Rancho Cucamonga CA 91739
626 818-4303

(P-23806)
ABSOLUTE SIGN INC
10655 Humbolt St, Los Alamitos
(90720-2447)
PHONE..................................562 592-5838
Patricia Scialampo, *President*
Gregory Benedict, *Vice Pres*
EMP: 15
SALES (est): 1.9MM **Privately Held**
WEB: www.absolutesign.com
SIC: 3993 Electric signs; neon signs

(P-23807)
ACT NOW INSTANT SIGNS INC
Also Called: Act Now Signs
550 W Cienega Ave Ste B, San Dimas
(91773-2977)
PHONE..................................909 394-7818
James R Kuhlman, *President*
Kathy Kuhlman, *Vice Pres*
EMP: 10
SQ FT: 5,000
SALES (est): 952.7K **Privately Held**
SIC: 3993 Signs, not made in custom sign
painting shops

(P-23808)
AD ART INC (PA)
Also Called: Ad Art Sign Company
150 Executive Park Blvd # 2100, San Fran-
cisco (94134-3364)
PHONE..................................415 869-6460
Terry J Long, *CEO*
Robert Kiereczyk, *President*
Doug Head, *Exec VP*
Duane Contento, *Senior VP*
David Esajian, *Vice Pres*
▲ **EMP:** 70
SQ FT: 4,000
SALES: 27MM **Privately Held**
WEB: www.adart.com
SIC: 3993 Electric signs

(P-23809)
ADTEK MEDIA INC
Also Called: Pumptop TV
13841 West St, Garden Grove
(92843-3912)
PHONE..................................949 680-4200
Richard Paulsen, *President*
Mitchell Phan, *CFO*
Richard Nelson, *Vice Pres*
Roy Reeves, *Vice Pres*
EMP: 30
SQ FT: 10,000
SALES: 5MM **Privately Held**
SIC: 3993 Signs & advertising specialties

(P-23810)
ADTI MEDIA LLC
Also Called: Advanced Digital Tech Intl
1257 Simpson Way, Escondido
(92029-1403)
PHONE..................................951 795-4446
James P Martingale,
Joe Milkovits, *Vice Pres*
Brian Reed, *Production*
Rick Baldacci,
Lawrence F De George,
▲ **EMP:** 30
SALES (est): 5.3MM **Privately Held**
SIC: 3993 Signs & advertising specialties

(P-23811)
AHR SIGNS INCORPORATED
Also Called: Ampersand Contract Signing Grp
3400 N San Fernando Rd, Los Angeles
(90065-1419)
PHONE..................................323 255-1102
Rouben Varozian, *President*
Ray Reynolds, *Associate*
EMP: 13
SQ FT: 15,000
SALES (est): 1.7MM **Privately Held**
WEB: www.ampersandsigns.com
SIC: 3993 Signs, not made in custom sign
painting shops

(P-23812)
AINOR SIGNS INC
5443 Stationers Way, Sacramento
(95842-1900)
PHONE..................................916 348-4370
Joseph Ainor, *President*
Catherine Bettencourt, *Admin Sec*
Christie Lawrence, *Controller*
EMP: 12 **EST:** 2006
SQ FT: 1,500
SALES (est): 2.2MM **Privately Held**
SIC: 3993 Signs, not made in custom sign
painting shops

(P-23813)
ALPHA SIGNS INC
8565 23rd Ave, Sacramento (95826-4901)
PHONE..................................916 379-0225
Jason Lane, *President*
EMP: 15
SALES (est): 1.4MM **Privately Held**
SIC: 3993 Electric signs

(P-23814)
**AMERICAN ACRYLIC DISPLAY
INC**
1061 S Leslie St, La Habra (90631-6843)
PHONE..................................714 738-7990
Mario Herrera, *President*
Francisco Rivera, *Vice Pres*
EMP: 11
SQ FT: 7,000
SALES (est): 1.4MM **Privately Held**
WEB: www.acrylicdisplayinc.com
SIC: 3993 3089 Displays & cutouts, win-
dow & lobby; plastic processing

(P-23815)
**AMERICAN FLEET & RET
GRAPHICS**
Also Called: Amgraph
2091 Del Rio Way, Ontario (91761-8038)
PHONE..................................909 937-7570
Kristin Stewart, *CEO*
Brian Stewart, *President*
Kenny Kim, *Prdtn Mgr*
Valerie Fleischman, *Accounts Mgr*
EMP: 37
SALES (est): 6.9MM **Privately Held**
SIC: 3993 Signs & advertising specialties

(P-23816)
ANDERSON SIGNS
Also Called: Anderson's Signs & Crane
1240 N Filbert St, Stockton (95205-3813)
P.O. Box 336, Victor (95253-0336)
PHONE..................................209 367-0120
Steve Anderson, *Owner*
EMP: 10
SALES (est): 760.3K **Privately Held**
WEB: www.thelouisvillechannel.com
SIC: 3993 Signs & advertising specialties

(P-23817)
APEX UNIVERSAL INC (PA)
11033 Forest Pl, Santa Fe Springs
(90670-3935)
PHONE..................................562 944-8878
Frank Fei, *President*
Janet Yang, *General Mgr*
Melody Aguilar, *Sales Mgr*
▲ **EMP:** 14
SQ FT: 7,500
SALES (est): 2.1MM **Privately Held**
WEB: www.apexuniversal.net
SIC: 3993 3669 Signs & advertising spe-
cialties; transportation signaling devices

(P-23818)
**ARCHITECTURAL DESIGN
SIGNS INC (PA)**
Also Called: Ad/S Companies
1160 Railroad St, Corona (92882-1835)
PHONE..................................951 278-0680
Sean L Solomon, *President*
Roberto Soltero III, *Vice Pres*
EMP: 95
SQ FT: 630,000
SALES (est): 25.6MM **Privately Held**
WEB: www.ad-s.com
SIC: 3993 Signs & advertising specialties

(P-23819)
ARCHITECTURAL S WEIDNER
Also Called: WEIDNERCA
5001 24th St, Sacramento (95822-2201)
PHONE..................................800 561-7446
Mark Douglas Copeland, *CEO*
Edwin F Weidner III, *President*
Edwin F Weidner Jr, *Chairman*
Kathy Weidner, *Treasurer*
Arie Korver, *Vice Pres*
EMP: 47
SQ FT: 20,450
SALES: 10.1MM **Privately Held**
WEB: www.weidnersignage.com
SIC: 3993 2759 7389 Signs & advertising
specialties; screen printing; sign painting
& lettering shop

(P-23820)
ARROW SIGN CO (PA)
Also Called: Arrow Sign Company
1051 46th Ave, Oakland (94601-4436)
PHONE..................................209 931-5522
Charles Sterne, *President*
Jeremy Blackburn, *Project Mgr*
Dan Jetke, *Project Mgr*
Michael Bennett, *Engineer*
Tina Mowdy, *Credit Mgr*
EMP: 48 **EST:** 1958
SQ FT: 119,375
SALES (est): 12.3MM **Privately Held**
WEB: www.arrowsigncompany.com
SIC: 3993 Electric signs

(P-23821)
ARROW SIGN CO
3133 N Ad Art Rd, Stockton (95215-2217)
PHONE..................................209 931-7852
Chuck Sterne, *Branch Mgr*
EMP: 27
SALES (corp-wide): 12.3MM **Privately
Held**
WEB: www.arrowsigncompany.com
SIC: 3993 Electric signs
PA: Arrow Sign Co.
1051 46th Ave
Oakland CA 94601
209 931-5522

(P-23822)
ART & SIGN PRODUCTION INC
3651 E Chevy Chase Dr, Glendale
(91206-1211)
PHONE..................................818 245-6945
Chris Ghantous, *President*
Armand Ghantous, *Treasurer*
Gill Ghantous, *Vice Pres*
Gisele Ghantous, *Admin Sec*
EMP: 10
SQ FT: 15,000
SALES (est): 1.3MM **Privately Held**
WEB: www.artandsign.com
SIC: 3993 7374 Signs & advertising spe-
cialties; computer graphics service

(P-23823)
ART SIGNWORKS INC
41785 Elm St Ste 302, Murrieta
(92562-9276)
PHONE..................................951 698-8484
Paul Williamson, *President*
Enrique Valenzuela, *Vice Pres*
Cheryl Burnette, *Principal*
Christie Valenzuela, *Principal*
Kevin Cohn, *Production*
EMP: 10
SQ FT: 5,000
SALES: 700K **Privately Held**
SIC: 3993 Signs & advertising specialties

(P-23824)
ASTRO DISPLAY COMPANY INC
4247 E Airport Dr, Ontario (91761-7640)
PHONE..................................909 605-2875
Thomas Andric, *Ch of Bd*
EMP: 20
SQ FT: 16,000
SALES: 1.5MM **Privately Held**
SIC: 3993 7319 3089 Displays & cutouts,
window & lobby; display advertising serv-
ice; plastic processing

(P-23825)
B & H SIGNS INC
926 S Primrose Ave, Monrovia
(91016-3440)
PHONE..................................626 359-6643
William Henry, *President*
David Salse, *Chiropractor*
EMP: 56
SQ FT: 7,000
SALES (est): 6.8MM **Privately Held**
SIC: 3993 Signs, not made in custom sign
painting shops

(P-23826)
BEELINE GROUP LLC
31023 Huntwood Ave, Hayward
(94544-7007)
P.O. Box 757, Carthage MO (64836-0757)
PHONE..................................510 477-5400
Josh Roberts, *CEO*
Wayne Kimball, *CFO*
Phil Green, *Vice Pres*
Julie Stier, *Exec Dir*
Susan Nilsen, *Area Mgr*
EMP: 57
SQ FT: 27,000
SALES (est): 17MM **Privately Held**
SIC: 3993 Signs & advertising specialties

(P-23827)
BIG 10 PRODUCTIONS INC
6006 Washington Blvd, Culver City
(90232-7422)
PHONE..................................310 280-1610
Dan Levine, *President*
EMP: 90
SQ FT: 40,000
SALES (est): 5.1MM **Privately Held**
WEB: www.big10.com
SIC: 3993 5112 Advertising novelties;
marking devices

(P-23828)
BK SIGNS INC
1028 W Kirkwall Rd, Azusa (91702-5126)
PHONE..................................626 334-5600
Brian Scott Kanner, *CEO*
EMP: 18
SQ FT: 16,000
SALES (est): 2.9MM **Privately Held**
WEB: www.bksigns.com
SIC: 3993 1731 Signs & advertising spe-
cialties; advertising artwork; general elec-
trical contractor

(P-23829)
**BLACKCOFFEE FABRICATORS
INC**
Also Called: Blackcoffee Sign Fabricators
4319 Santa Ana St Ste B, Ontario
(91761-7852)
PHONE..................................909 974-4499
Erin Foley, *President*
Dale Foley, *Vice Pres*
Jim Foley, *Vice Pres*
Maria Foley, *Admin Sec*
EMP: 14
SQ FT: 1,800

P
R
O
D
U
C
T
S

&

S
V
C
S

SALES (est): 1.1MM **Privately Held**
SIC: 3993 Signs & advertising specialties

(P-23830)
BLAKE SIGN COMPANY INC
11661 Seaboard Cir, Stanton (90680-3427)
PHONE..................................714 891-5682
John A Blake, *President*
Devin Blake, *Shareholder*
Mike Blake, *Shareholder*
Dan Blake, *Vice Pres*
Joan Blake, *Vice Pres*
EMP: 17
SQ FT: 5,400
SALES (est): 2.4MM **Privately Held**
WEB: www.blakesigns.com
SIC: 3993 Signs, not made in custom sign painting shops

(P-23831)
BLANCHARD SIGNS
6750 Central Ave Ste A, Riverside (92504-1447)
PHONE..................................951 354-5050
Ron Blanchard, *Partner*
Carol Blanchard, *Partner*
EMP: 11
SALES: 600K **Privately Held**
SIC: 3993 Signs, not made in custom sign painting shops

(P-23832)
BLAZER EXHIBITS & GRAPHICS INC
4227 Technology Dr, Fremont (94538-6339)
PHONE..................................408 263-7000
David Graham, *CEO*
Loren Ellis, *President*
Susan Graham, *Treasurer*
Vanessa Ellis, *Vice Pres*
Daniel Thomas, *Executive*
EMP: 15
SQ FT: 20,000
SALES (est): 2.1MM **Privately Held**
WEB: www.blazergraphics.com
SIC: 3993 Signs & advertising specialties

(P-23833)
BRAILLE SIGNS INC
16782 Von Karman Ave # 30, Irvine (92606-2419)
PHONE..................................949 797-1570
Steve Corum, *President*
Ruth Corum, *Vice Pres*
Jason Chuang, *Supervisor*
▲ EMP: 13
SQ FT: 3,000
SALES (est): 1.9MM **Privately Held**
WEB: www.braillesignsinc.com
SIC: 3993 Signs, not made in custom sign painting shops

(P-23834)
BRIGHTSIGN LLC
983 University Ave Bldg A, Los Gatos (95032-7637)
PHONE..................................408 852-9263
Anthony Wood,
Bryan Kennedy, *President*
Sarah Dryden, *CFO*
Carlyn Fernandez, *Admin Asst*
Keith Byres, *VP Opers*
▲ EMP: 79
SQ FT: 12,540
SALES (est): 2.2MM **Privately Held**
SIC: 3993 Signs & advertising specialties

(P-23835)
BRITE-LITE NEON CORP
5514 Satsuma Ave, North Hollywood (91601-2840)
PHONE..................................818 763-4798
Philip Mastopietro, *President*
Mark Mastopietro, *Corp Secy*
Rick Cincis, *Vice Pres*
EMP: 15
SQ FT: 10,000
SALES (est): 1.3MM **Privately Held**
WEB: www.briteliteneon.com
SIC: 3993 7629 Neon signs; electrical repair shops

(P-23836)
CAL-SIGN WHOLESALE INC
5260 Jerusalem Ct, Modesto (95356-9219)
PHONE..................................209 523-7446
Greg Johnson, *President*
Roger Johnson, *Corp Secy*
Mark Johnson, *Vice Pres*
Jerad Myers, *Prdtn Mgr*
Jared Meyers, *Manager*
EMP: 17
SQ FT: 4,050
SALES (est): 2.2MM **Privately Held**
WEB: www.calsignwholesale.com
SIC: 3993 Electric signs

(P-23837)
CALIFORNIA NEON PRODUCTS
Also Called: C N P Signs & Graphics
4530 Mission Gorge Pl, San Diego (92120-4106)
PHONE..................................619 283-2191
Peter McCarter, *CEO*
Richard McCarter, *Corp Secy*
Robert McCarter, *Vice Pres*
EMP: 70 EST: 1939
SQ FT: 40,000
SALES (est): 19MM **Privately Held**
WEB: www.cnpsigns.com
SIC: 3993 1799 Electric signs; sign installation & maintenance

(P-23838)
CALIFORNIA SIGNS INC
Also Called: CA Signs
10280 Glenoaks Blvd, Pacoima (91331-1604)
PHONE..................................818 899-1888
Matthew Miller, *President*
Maribel Santoyo, *Department Mgr*
Yvette Miller, *Admin Sec*
Jack Daghestanian, *Prdtn Mgr*
Justin Miooer, *Opers Staff*
EMP: 35
SQ FT: 21,000
SALES (est): 6.1MM **Privately Held**
WEB: www.casigns.com
SIC: 3993 Signs, not made in custom sign painting shops

(P-23839)
CANZONE AND COMPANY
Also Called: C & C Signs
1345 W Cowles St, Long Beach (90813-2734)
PHONE..................................714 537-8175
Chris Canzone, *President*
Jessica Canzone, *Treasurer*
EMP: 20
SQ FT: 4,800
SALES (est): 2.9MM **Privately Held**
SIC: 3993 Signs, not made in custom sign painting shops

(P-23840)
CAPITOL NEON
5920 Rosebud Ln Ste 1, Sacramento (95841-2980)
PHONE..................................916 349-1800
Michael L Durfee, *Partner*
Rocky Morino, *Partner*
Ron Underwood, *Partner*
Cindy Durfee, *Director*
Jennifer Sissney, *Manager*
EMP: 14
SQ FT: 16,000
SALES (est): 1.6MM **Privately Held**
WEB: www.capitolneon.com
SIC: 3993 Neon signs

(P-23841)
CARREON DEVELOPMENT INC
Also Called: South Bay Neon
4286 Powderhorn Dr, San Diego (92154-1719)
PHONE..................................619 690-4973
Isaac S Carreon, *President*
EMP: 11 EST: 1982
SQ FT: 4,000
SALES (est): 770K **Privately Held**
SIC: 3993 Electric signs

(P-23842)
CELLOTAPE INC (HQ)
39611 Eureka Dr, Newark (94560-4806)
PHONE..................................510 651-5551
Toll Free:..................................888 -

Pete Offermann, *Ch of Bd*
Eric Lomas, *Admin Sec*
Nick Testanero, *Director*
EMP: 102
SQ FT: 55,000
SALES (est): 24.6MM
SALES (corp-wide): 236.4MM **Privately Held**
SIC: 3993 2675 2672 2759 Signs & advertising specialties; die-cut paper & board; coated & laminated paper; labels & seals: printing
PA: Resource Label Group, Llc
147 Seaboard Ln
Franklin TN 37067
615 661-5900

(P-23843)
CHANDLER SIGNS LLC
3220 Executive Rdg # 250, Vista (92081-8573)
PHONE..................................760 734-1708
Chuck Riffe, *Vice Pres*
EMP: 100
SALES (corp-wide): 74MM **Privately Held**
WEB: www.chandlersigns.com
SIC: 3993 Electric signs
PA: Chandler Signs, Llc
14201 Sovereign Rd 101
Fort Worth TX 76155
214 902-2000

(P-23844)
CHIEF NEON SIGN CO INC
15027 S Maple Ave, Gardena (90248-1939)
PHONE..................................310 327-1317
Alan D Paulson, *President*
Alan M Paulson, *President*
Armeta Paulson, *Corp Secy*
Lisa Paila, *Office Mgr*
EMP: 12
SQ FT: 12,400
SALES (est): 970K **Privately Held**
WEB: www.chiefneonsign.com
SIC: 3993 Signs, not made in custom sign painting shops

(P-23845)
CLEGG INDUSTRIES INC
Also Called: Clegg Promo
19032 S Vermont Ave, Gardena (90248-4412)
PHONE..................................310 225-3800
Timothy P Clegg, *CEO*
Kevin Clegg, *President*
Michael Amar, *Senior VP*
Michael Bistocchi, *Senior VP*
Los Angeles, *Vice Pres*
▲ EMP: 175
SQ FT: 31,000
SALES (est): 25.1MM **Privately Held**
WEB: www.cleggonline.com
SIC: 3993 3648 2542 Advertising novelties; lighting equipment; partitions & fixtures, except wood

(P-23846)
COAST SIGN INCORPORATED
Also Called: Coast Sign Display
1500 W Embassy St, Anaheim (92802-1016)
PHONE..................................714 520-9144
Afshan Alemi, *CEO*
S Charlie Alemi, *President*
Michelle Hoffman, *Project Mgr*
Karrie Reiter, *Project Mgr*
Alex Vazquez, *Project Mgr*
▲ EMP: 250
SQ FT: 130,000
SALES (est): 50MM **Privately Held**
WEB: www.coastsign.com
SIC: 3993 Signs, not made in custom sign painting shops

(P-23847)
CONTINENTAL SIGNS INC
7541 Santa Rita Cir Ste D, Stanton (90680-3498)
PHONE..................................714 894-2011
Joseph Artinger, *President*
Edward Artinger, *Vice Pres*
EMP: 24
SQ FT: 7,800

SALES: 1.6MM **Privately Held**
WEB: www.continentalsigns.com
SIC: 3993 1731 Signs, not made in custom sign painting shops; general electrical contractor

(P-23848)
CORNERSTONE DISPLAY GROUP INC (PA)
28606 Livingston Ave, Valencia (91355-4186)
PHONE..................................661 705-1700
Tom Hester, *Principal*
Kip Kirkpatrick, *Partner*
Michael Morgan, *Executive*
Brent Jacobson, *Art Dir*
Sean Ounjian, *Sr Project Mgr*
▲ EMP: 45
SQ FT: 20,000
SALES (est): 8.5MM **Privately Held**
WEB: www.cornerstonedisplay.com
SIC: 3993 Advertising artwork; displays & cutouts, window & lobby

(P-23849)
CORPORATE SIGN SYSTEMS INC
2464 De La Cruz Blvd, Santa Clara (95050-2923)
PHONE..................................408 292-1600
Danny Moran, *CEO*
Phil Wyatt, *Vice Pres*
John Reagan, *Administration*
Joe Dichoso, *Project Mgr*
Aaron Froke, *Technology*
EMP: 20 EST: 1961
SQ FT: 7,000
SALES (est): 3.6MM **Privately Held**
WEB: www.corporatesigns.com
SIC: 3993 7389 Signs & advertising specialties; sign painting & lettering shop

(P-23850)
COWBOY DIRECT RESPONSE
Also Called: Synergy Direct Response
130 E Alton Ave, Santa Ana (92707-4415)
PHONE..................................714 824-3780
Cynthia Rogers, *President*
John T Rogers, *CEO*
Brenda Manos, *Business Dir*
Erin Anderson, *Executive Asst*
Norm Shepherd, *Admin Sec*
EMP: 35
SQ FT: 10,000
SALES (est): 7MM **Privately Held**
WEB: www.synergydr.com
SIC: 3993 8999 2759 Advertising artwork; advertising copy writing; promotional printing

(P-23851)
CREATIVE SIGN INC
17922 Lyons Cir, Huntington Beach (92647-7167)
PHONE..................................714 842-4343
Thomas Morrison, *President*
Patricia Morrison, *Vice Pres*
EMP: 10
SQ FT: 10,000
SALES: 900K **Privately Held**
SIC: 3993 Advertising artwork

(P-23852)
CUMMINGS RESOURCES LLC
1495 Columbia Ave, Riverside (92507-2021)
PHONE..................................951 248-1130
Jim Mole, *Plant Mgr*
EMP: 24
SQ FT: 50,000
SALES (corp-wide): 869.1MM **Privately Held**
SIC: 3993 Signs & advertising specialties
HQ: Cummings Resources Llc
15 Century Blvd Ste 200
Nashville TN 37214

(P-23853)
D N G CUMMINGS INC
Also Called: Action Sign Systems
3580 Haven Ave Ste 1, Redwood City (94063-4639)
PHONE..................................650 593-8974
Dorothy Cummings, *President*
Greg Cummings, *Vice Pres*

Richard Cummings, *Vice Pres*
Gregory Patrick, *General Mgr*
Michael Dauria, *Sales Staff*
EMP: 20
SQ FT: 9,600
SALES (est): 2.1MM **Privately Held**
SIC: 3993 Signs, not made in custom sign painting shops

(P-23854)
D3 LED LLC (PA)
Also Called: Dynamic Digital Displays
11370 Sunrise Park Dr, Rancho Cordova (95742-6542)
PHONE................................916 669-7408
George Pappas, *Mng Member*
Eric Bland, *Vice Pres*
Bob Magnus, *Vice Pres*
Frank Barnes, *Executive*
Sean Morrough, *Managing Dir*
◆ **EMP:** 20
SQ FT: 60,000
SALES (est): 13.8MM **Privately Held**
WEB: www.d3led.com
SIC: 3993 Signs & advertising specialties

(P-23855)
DEE SIGN CO
Also Called: Go Logo
16250 Stagg St, Van Nuys (91406-1715)
PHONE................................818 988-1000
Brad Hunefeld, *President*
EMP: 61
SALES (corp-wide): 8.6MM **Privately Held**
WEB: www.dee-sign.com
SIC: 3993 Signs & advertising specialties
PA: Dee Sign Co.
6163 Allen Rd
West Chester OH 45069
513 779-3333

(P-23856)
DG DISPLAYS LLC
355 Parkside Dr, San Fernando (91340-3036)
PHONE................................877 358-5976
Robert Blumenfeld,
Zachary Blumenfeld,
EMP: 30
SALES (est): 802.2K **Privately Held**
SIC: 3993 Signs & advertising specialties

(P-23857)
DUNBAR ELECTRIC SIGN COMPANY
Also Called: City Crane
4020 Rosedale Hwy, Bakersfield (93308-6131)
P.O. Box 10717 (93389-0717)
PHONE................................661 323-2600
Clayton Dunbar, *CEO*
EMP: 22
SALES (est): 2.5MM **Privately Held**
WEB: www.cityneon.com
SIC: 3993 7629 5999 1799 Electric signs; neon signs; electrical equipment repair services; banners; sign installation & maintenance

(P-23858)
DUNCAN DESIGN INC
48 Barham Ave, Santa Rosa (95407-6117)
PHONE................................707 636-2300
Greg Duncan, *President*
Michael Harmon, *CFO*
EMP: 10
SQ FT: 2,000
SALES: 700K **Privately Held**
WEB: www.duncandesigninc.com
SIC: 3993 Signs & advertising specialties

(P-23859)
DYNAMITE SIGN GROUP INC
Also Called: TNT Electric Signs Co
3080 E 29th St, Long Beach (90806-2317)
PHONE................................562 595-7725
William Henigsman, *President*
Michael Gray, *Vice Pres*
Bill Henigsman, *Marketing Staff*
EMP: 30
SQ FT: 7,500
SALES (est): 5.1MM **Privately Held**
WEB: www.tntelectricsign.com
SIC: 3993 Neon signs

(P-23860)
EAGLE SIGNS INC
1028 E Acacia St, Ontario (91761-4553)
PHONE................................909 923-3034
Robert Kneevers, *President*
Christopher Kneevers, *Partner*
Drew Solome, *Opers Mgr*
EMP: 11
SQ FT: 6,700
SALES (est): 775K **Privately Held**
WEB: www.eaglesigns.net
SIC: 3993 Signs & advertising specialties

(P-23861)
EDELMANN USA INC (DH)
Also Called: Bert-Co. of Ontario CA
2150 S Parco Ave, Ontario (91761-5768)
P.O. Box 4150 (91761-1068)
PHONE................................323 669-5700
EMP: 20
SALES (est): 216K
SALES (corp-wide): 361.2MM **Privately Held**
SIC: 3993 Signs & advertising specialties
HQ: Edelmann Gmbh
Steinheimer Str. 45
Heidenheim An Der Brenz 89518
732 134-00

(P-23862)
EGADS LLC
42191 Sarah Way, Temecula (92590-3415)
PHONE................................951 695-9050
EMP: 11
SALES (corp-wide): 42.6MM **Privately Held**
SIC: 3993
PA: E.Gads, Llc
3235 Polaris Ave
Las Vegas NV 89102
702 314-7777

(P-23863)
EGGLESTON SIGNS
Also Called: Sign Post, The
1558 Juliesse Ave Ste S, Sacramento (95815-1827)
PHONE................................916 920-1750
Jeam Basben, *Owner*
EMP: 14
SQ FT: 6,000
SALES (est): 1MM **Privately Held**
SIC: 3993 6512 Signs & advertising specialties; commercial & industrial building operation

(P-23864)
ELRO MANUFACTURING COMPANY (PA)
Also Called: Elro Sign Company
400 W Walnut St, Gardena (90248-3137)
PHONE................................310 380-7444
Max R Rhodes, *CEO*
Frank J Rhodes, *Treasurer*
Eliesha Ingram, *Human Res Mgr*
Eric Neu, *Opers Staff*
EMP: 37 **EST:** 1948
SQ FT: 18,000
SALES (est): 6.2MM **Privately Held**
WEB: www.elrosigns.com
SIC: 3993 Electric signs

(P-23865)
ENCORE IMAGE INC
303 W Main St, Ontario (91762-3843)
P.O. Box 9297 (91762-9297)
PHONE................................909 986-4632
Mark Haist, *President*
EMP: 20 **EST:** 1945
SQ FT: 30,000
SALES (est): 3.1MM
SALES (corp-wide): 29.5MM **Privately Held**
WEB: www.ontarioneon.com
SIC: 3993 1799 Electric signs; sign installation & maintenance
PA: Encore Image Group, Inc.
1445 Sepulveda Blvd
Torrance CA 90501
310 534-7500

(P-23866)
ENCORE IMAGE GROUP INC (PA)
1445 Sepulveda Blvd, Torrance (90501-5004)
PHONE................................310 534-7500
Kozell Boren, *Ch of Bd*
Tom Johnson, *President*
▲ **EMP:** 90
SQ FT: 70,000
SALES (est): 29.5MM **Privately Held**
WEB: www.gotsign.com
SIC: 3993 Electric signs

(P-23867)
ENHANCE AMERICA INC
3463 Grapevine St, Mira Loma (91752-3504)
PHONE................................951 361-3000
Jackson Ling, *President*
Jeff Hasting, *COO*
Heidi Mann, *Regl Sales Mgr*
Heather Mullen, *Regl Sales Mgr*
Ray Wong, *Manager*
◆ **EMP:** 20
SALES (est): 3.1MM **Privately Held**
SIC: 3993 Signs & advertising specialties

(P-23868)
EVANS MANUFACTURING INC (PA)
7422 Chapman Ave, Garden Grove (92841-2106)
P.O. Box 5669 (92846-0669)
PHONE................................714 379-6100
Alan Vaught, *CEO*
◆ **EMP:** 185
SQ FT: 17,000
SALES (est): 44.6MM **Privately Held**
WEB: www.evans-mfg.com
SIC: 3993 3089 Signs & advertising specialties; injection molding of plastics

(P-23869)
EVERBRITE WEST LLC
Also Called: Fluoresco Lighting & Sign
2778 Pomona Blvd, Pomona (91768-3222)
PHONE................................909 468-0861
Ladd Kleiman, *Branch Mgr*
EMP: 75
SALES (corp-wide): 244.9MM **Privately Held**
SIC: 3993 Signs & advertising specialties
HQ: Everbrite West Llc
5505 S Nogales Hwy
Tucson AZ 85706
520 623-7953

(P-23870)
EVERBRITE WEST LLC
2733 Via Orange Way, Spring Valley (91978-1717)
PHONE................................619 444-9000
Ken Christianson, *Branch Mgr*
James Subers, *Sales Staff*
EMP: 10
SALES (corp-wide): 244.9MM **Privately Held**
SIC: 3993 1731 7629 3648 Electric signs; lighting contractor; electrical repair shops; lighting equipment; commercial indusl & institutional electric lighting fixtures
HQ: Everbrite West Llc
5505 S Nogales Hwy
Tucson AZ 85706
520 623-7953

(P-23871)
EXHIBIT WORKS INC
Also Called: Ewi Worldwide
19531 Pauling, Foothill Ranch (92610-2623)
PHONE................................949 470-0850
Dominic Silvio, *Branch Mgr*
EMP: 15
SALES (corp-wide): 105.3MM **Privately Held**
SIC: 3993 7389 Displays & cutouts, window & lobby; advertising, promotional & trade show services
PA: Exhibit Works, Inc.
27777 Inkster Rd Ste 200
Farmington Hills MI 48334
734 525-9010

(P-23872)
EXPO-3 INTERNATIONAL INC
12350 Edison Way 60, Garden Grove (92841-2810)
PHONE................................714 379-8383
Daniel J Mills, *Ch of Bd*
Chris Smith, *President*
John Cooper, *Technology*
Reynaldo Acevado, *Director*
EMP: 20
SQ FT: 60,000
SALES (est): 2.4MM **Privately Held**
WEB: www.expo3.com
SIC: 3993 Signs & advertising specialties

(P-23873)
EXPRESS SIGN AND NEON
1720 W Slauson Ave, Los Angeles (90047-1119)
PHONE................................323 291-3333
Frank Bang, *Owner*
▲ **EMP:** 15
SALES (est): 1.4MM **Privately Held**
SIC: 3993 Signs, not made in custom sign painting shops

(P-23874)
FAIRMONT SIGN COMPANY
850 S Guild Ave, Lodi (95240-3170)
PHONE................................209 365-6490
Garry Seafreed, *Branch Mgr*
Garry Seefried, *Plant Mgr*
EMP: 45
SALES (corp-wide): 7.2MM **Privately Held**
SIC: 3993 Signs, not made in custom sign painting shops
PA: Fairmont Sign Company
3750 E Outer Dr
Detroit MI 48234
313 368-4000

(P-23875)
FAN FAVE INC
Also Called: Fanfave
285 S Dupont Ave Ste 104, Ontario (91761-1597)
PHONE................................909 975-4999
Gary Arnett, *CEO*
Jeff Arnett, *President*
EMP: 20
SQ FT: 17,000
SALES: 800K **Privately Held**
SIC: 3993 Advertising artwork

(P-23876)
FAST AD INC
224 S Center St, Santa Ana (92703-4302)
PHONE................................714 835-9353
Guy W Barnes, *President*
Kathleen Barnes, *Corp Secy*
EMP: 60
SQ FT: 12,000
SALES (est): 2.5MM **Privately Held**
WEB: www.fastad.com
SIC: 3993 Signs & advertising specialties

(P-23877)
FASTSIGNS
650 Harrison St, San Francisco (94107-1311)
PHONE................................415 537-6900
Jason Moline, *Owner*
Bruce Vaughn, *Vice Pres*
Richard Jongordon, *Admin Sec*
EMP: 11
SQ FT: 7,000
SALES: 1MM **Privately Held**
SIC: 3993 Signs & advertising specialties

(P-23878)
FASTSIGNS
2130 S El Camino Real, San Mateo (94403-1800)
PHONE................................650 345-0900
David Skromme, *Owner*
Linda Skromme, *Co-Owner*
EMP: 10
SQ FT: 4,000
SALES (est): 992.3K **Privately Held**
SIC: 3993 Signs & advertising specialties

PRODUCTS & SVCS

(P-23879)
FEDERAL HEATH SIGN COMPANY LLC (PA)
4602 North Ave, Oceanside (92056-3509)
PHONE....................760 941-0715
Kenneth A Hendricks, *Ch of Bd*
Kevin Stotmeiser, *President*
Ken Moultray, *COO*
James Schmidt, *CFO*
Stewart Edinger, *Senior VP*
◆ EMP: 83
SQ FT: 50,000
SALES (est): 169.1MM **Privately Held**
WEB: www.zimsign.com
SIC: 3993 Neon signs

(P-23880)
FEDERAL PRISON INDUSTRIES
Also Called: Unicor
3901 Klein Blvd, Lompoc (93436-2706)
PHONE....................805 735-2771
Steve Southall, *Manager*
EMP: 25 **Publicly Held**
SIC: 3993 2759 3315 2521 Signs & advertising specialties; commercial printing; cable, steel: insulated or armored; wood office furniture; correctional institutions; ; miscellaneous fabricated wire products
HQ: Federal Prison Industries, Inc
320 1st St Nw
Washington DC 20534
202 305-3500

(P-23881)
FLYNN SIGNS AND GRAPHICS INC
Also Called: Flynn Signs and Letters
1345 Coronado Ave, Long Beach (90804-2806)
PHONE....................562 498-6655
David Flynn, *President*
EMP: 13
SQ FT: 16,150
SALES (est): 1.8MM **Privately Held**
WEB: www.flynnsigns.com
SIC: 3993 Signs, not made in custom sign painting shops

(P-23882)
FOVELL ENTERPRISES INC
Also Called: Southwest Sign Company
1852 Pomona Rd, Corona (92880-1777)
PHONE....................951 734-6275
Jack Fovell, *CEO*
▲ EMP: 26
SQ FT: 12,500
SALES (est): 4.3MM **Privately Held**
WEB: www.southwestsign.com
SIC: 3993 Electric signs

(P-23883)
FRESNO NEON SIGN CO INC
5901 E Clinton Ave, Fresno (93727-8641)
PHONE....................559 292-2944
William Kratt, *President*
Kimberly Kratt Rutiaga, *Vice Pres*
Phyllis Kratt, *Admin Sec*
EMP: 12
SQ FT: 22,000
SALES (est): 1.6MM **Privately Held**
WEB: www.fresnoneon.com
SIC: 3993 1799 Electric signs; neon signs; scoreboards, electric; sign installation & maintenance

(P-23884)
FUSION SIGN & DESIGN INC (PA)
680 Columbia Ave, Riverside (92507-2144)
PHONE....................877 477-8777
Loren Hanson, *CEO*
Jacob Strantz, *Executive*
Brian Johnson, *Division Mgr*
Robin Tait, *Division Mgr*
Brian Figueroa, *Graphic Designe*
▲ EMP: 96
SALES (est): 25.3MM **Privately Held**
SIC: 3993 Electric signs

(P-23885)
G M P C LLC
Also Called: Econscious
2180 S Mcdowell Blvd, Petaluma (94954-6974)
PHONE....................707 766-9504

Dale Denkensohn, *Branch Mgr*
EMP: 15
SALES (corp-wide): 14.3MM **Privately Held**
SIC: 3993 7336 Advertising novelties; commercial art & graphic design
PA: Gmpc, Llc
11390 W Olym Blvd Ste 400
Los Angeles CA 90064
310 392-4070

(P-23886)
GARNETT SIGNS LLC
Also Called: Garnett Sign Studio
441 Victory Ave, South San Francisco (94080-6312)
PHONE....................650 871-9518
Stephen Savoy, *President*
Maggie Cox, *Office Mgr*
Clifford Kane, *Project Mgr*
Meral Agi, *Graphic Designe*
Masaki Kitamori, *Graphic Designe*
EMP: 15
SQ FT: 13,250
SALES: 1.5MM **Privately Held**
WEB: www.garnettsign.com
SIC: 3993 3479 Signs, not made in custom sign painting shops; name plates: engraved, etched, etc.

(P-23887)
GARYS SIGNS AND SCREEN PRTG
Also Called: Gary's Signs & Screen Printing
1620 Ackerman Dr, Lodi (95240-6334)
PHONE....................209 369-8592
Gary Markle, *President*
Robyn Markle, *Admin Sec*
EMP: 11 EST: 1972
SQ FT: 3,750
SALES (est): 880K **Privately Held**
SIC: 3993 2759 Electric signs; screen printing

(P-23888)
GEORGE P JOHNSON COMPANY
18500 Crenshaw Blvd, Torrance (90504-5055)
PHONE....................310 965-4300
John Capano, *Branch Mgr*
Patrick Santy, *Vice Pres*
Christian Anderson, *Technology*
Jim Updike, *Opers Mgr*
Sonnier Davida, *Producer*
EMP: 100
SALES (corp-wide): 273.9MM **Privately Held**
SIC: 3993 Signs & advertising specialties
HQ: George P Johnson Company
3600 Giddings Rd
Auburn Hills MI 48326
248 475-2500

(P-23889)
GMPC LLC
Also Called: Big Accessories
2180 S Mcdowell Blvd, Petaluma (94954-6974)
PHONE....................707 766-1702
Steve Wegner,
EMP: 17
SALES (corp-wide): 14.3MM **Privately Held**
SIC: 3993 7336 Advertising novelties; commercial art & graphic design
PA: Gmpc, Llc
11390 W Olym Blvd Ste 400
Los Angeles CA 90064
310 392-4070

(P-23890)
GRADE A SIGN LLC
529 N La Cienega Blvd # 300, West Hollywood (90048-2001)
PHONE....................310 652-9700
Sloan Schaffer, *Mng Member*
Scott Gorelick,
EMP: 20
SALES (est): 1.3MM **Privately Held**
SIC: 3993

(P-23891)
GREGORY M FINK
Also Called: G. Fink & Associates
23182 Alcalde Dr Ste H, Laguna Hills (92653-1450)
PHONE....................949 305-4242
Greg Fink, *Owner*
◆ EMP: 12
SALES (est): 1.2MM **Privately Held**
SIC: 3993 Electric signs

(P-23892)
HARBOR SIGNS INC
850 N Union St, Stockton (95205-4152)
PHONE....................209 463-8686
Malcolm Fortune, *President*
Laura Fortune, *Corp Secy*
Kurt Loewen, *Vice Pres*
EMP: 12
SQ FT: 10,000
SALES (est): 1.2MM **Privately Held**
WEB: www.harborsignsinc.com
SIC: 3993 Signs, not made in custom sign painting shops

(P-23893)
HERITAGE DESIGN
32382 Del Obispo St B1, San Juan Capistrano (92675-4029)
PHONE....................949 248-1300
Claudia Martinez, *President*
EMP: 10
SALES (est): 830.1K **Privately Held**
SIC: 3993 Signs & advertising specialties

(P-23894)
HUPP SIGNS & LIGHTING INC
70 Loren Ave, Chico (95928-7433)
P.O. Box 7730 (95927-7730)
PHONE....................530 345-7078
Joe Hupp,
EMP: 30
SQ FT: 18,000
SALES (est): 4.3MM **Privately Held**
WEB: www.huppneon.com
SIC: 3993 Neon signs

(P-23895)
ICON IDENTITY SOLUTIONS INC
10156 Sharon Cir, Rancho Cucamonga (91730-5300)
PHONE....................909 942-5100
EMP: 87
SALES (corp-wide): 119MM **Privately Held**
SIC: 3993 Signs & advertising specialties
PA: Icon Identity Solutions, Inc.
1701 Golf Rd Ste 1-900
Rolling Meadows IL 60008
847 364-2250

(P-23896)
ILLUMINATED CREATIONS INC
Also Called: Ellis and Ellis Sign
1111 Joellis Way, Sacramento (95815-3914)
PHONE....................916 924-1936
Bret E Ellis, *CEO*
Sydney Ellis, *President*
Brenda Mansur, *CFO*
Sharon Ellis, *Corp Secy*
Brad Edward Ellis, *Vice Pres*
EMP: 40 EST: 1975
SQ FT: 60,000
SALES (est): 6.9MM **Privately Held**
WEB: www.ellissigns.com
SIC: 3993 Signs, not made in custom sign painting shops

(P-23897)
IMAGINE THAT UNLIMITED
Also Called: Charlaine Graphics
13100 Kirkham Way Ste 211, Poway (92064-7128)
PHONE....................858 566-8868
Carol Honeysett, *President*
Susan Rudolph, *CFO*
EMP: 10
SQ FT: 3,500
SALES (est): 1.2MM **Privately Held**
SIC: 3993 Electric signs

(P-23898)
IMPACT MARKETING DISPLAYS LLC
Also Called: Impact Displays
1725 De La Cruz Blvd # 4, Santa Clara (95050-3011)
PHONE....................408 217-6850
Theodore Ridgway, *Mng Member*
▲ EMP: 13
SALES (est): 1.3MM **Privately Held**
SIC: 3993 Signs & advertising specialties

(P-23899)
INFINITY WATCH CORPORATION
Also Called: Iwcus
21078 Commerce Point Dr, Walnut (91789-3051)
PHONE....................626 289-9878
Patrick Tam, *President*
Brenda Tam, *Vice Pres*
▲ EMP: 25
SQ FT: 12,000
SALES (est): 2.8MM **Privately Held**
WEB: www.infinitywatch.com
SIC: 3993 Signs & advertising specialties

(P-23900)
INFLATABLE ADVERTISING CO INC
1600 W Olympic Blvd, Los Angeles (90015-3802)
PHONE....................213 387-6839
Susan Talesnick, *President*
Michel Rimolos, *Treasurer*
William H Neusteter, *Admin Sec*
EMP: 12
SALES (est): 890K **Privately Held**
SIC: 3993 Advertising novelties

(P-23901)
INFLATABLE DESIGN GROUP INC
Also Called: Idg
1080 W Bradley Ave Ste B, El Cajon (92020-1500)
PHONE....................619 596-6100
Shawn McEachern, *President*
▲ EMP: 16
SQ FT: 32,000
SALES (est): 1.8MM **Privately Held**
SIC: 3993 Advertising novelties

(P-23902)
INLAND SIGNS INC
10783 Bell Ct, Rancho Cucamonga (91730-4834)
PHONE....................909 581-0699
Klodian Gjoka, *President*
Filip Gjoka, *Principal*
EMP: 22 EST: 2002
SALES: 9MM **Privately Held**
WEB: www.inlandsigns.com
SIC: 3993 Electric signs

(P-23903)
INTEGRATED SIGN ASSOCIATES
1160 Pioneer Way Ste M, El Cajon (92020-1944)
PHONE....................619 579-2229
Aaron Coippinger, *President*
Genie Jackson, *Project Mgr*
Tony Asano, *Art Dir*
Curt Bauer, *Accounts Exec*
Ross Rogers, *Accounts Exec*
EMP: 30
SQ FT: 15,000
SALES (est): 4.5MM **Privately Held**
WEB: www.isasign.com
SIC: 3993 Neon signs

(P-23904)
J S HACKL ARCHI SIGNA INC
1999 Alpine Way, Hayward (94545-1701)
PHONE....................510 940-2608
John Hackley, *President*
Francine Crawford, *Accounts Mgr*
EMP: 17
SQ FT: 20,000
SALES (est): 2MM **Privately Held**
WEB: www.hackley.net
SIC: 3993 Signs & advertising specialties

(P-23905)
JACK B MARTIN
Also Called: Jack Martin Signworks
109 E 5th St, Hanford (93230-5130)
PHONE......................559 583-1175
Jack Martin, *Owner*
EMP: 10
SALES: 1.4MM **Privately Held**
SIC: 3993 Signs & advertising specialties

(P-23906)
JAR VENTURES INC
Also Called: Sign-A-Rama
1355 Hartnell Ave, Redding (96002-2227)
PHONE......................530 224-9655
John Robbins, *President*
EMP: 21
SALES (est): 2.7MM **Privately Held**
SIC: 3993 Signs & advertising specialties

(P-23907)
JEFF FRANK
Also Called: Northwest Signs
120 Encinal St, Santa Cruz (95060-2111)
PHONE......................831 469-8208
Jeff Frank, *Owner*
Nancy Burk, *Office Mgr*
Richard Priola, *Sales Staff*
EMP: 15
SQ FT: 5,000
SALES (est): 1.1MM **Privately Held**
WEB: www.cyclo-x.com
SIC: 3993 7349 Signs & advertising specialties; lighting maintenance service

(P-23908)
JOHN BISHOP DESIGN INC
Also Called: J B3d
731 N Main St, Orange (92868-1105)
PHONE......................714 744-2300
John Bishop, *President*
Lisa Bishop, *Corp Secy*
EMP: 38
SQ FT: 1,000
SALES (est): 5.6MM **Privately Held**
WEB: www.jb3d.com
SIC: 3993 Signs & advertising specialties

(P-23909)
JOHNSON UNITED INC (PA)
Also Called: United Sign Systems
5201 Pentecost Dr, Modesto (95356-9271)
PHONE......................209 543-1320
Darryl Johnson, *CEO*
Andy Soares, *Principal*
Mike Noordewier, *Admin Sec*
Robert Cain, *Project Mgr*
Shanna Sand, *Project Mgr*
▼ **EMP:** 31
SQ FT: 23,000
SALES: 7.5MM **Privately Held**
SIC: 3993 Signs & advertising specialties

(P-23910)
JSJ ELECTRICAL DISPLAY CORP
167 Grobric Ct, Fairfield (94534-1673)
PHONE......................707 747-5595
Brian Schneider, *President*
Jeff Jensen, *Managing Prtnr*
Clayton Jensen, *Vice Pres*
Shawn West, *Project Mgr*
Larry Koyle, *Art Dir*
EMP: 18
SQ FT: 20,000
SALES: 2.5MM **Privately Held**
WEB: www.jsjdisplay.com
SIC: 3993 Neon signs

(P-23911)
JUSTIPHER INC
Also Called: Fastsigns
1248 W Winton Ave, Hayward
(94545-1406)
PHONE......................510 918-6800
Linda Fong, *Branch Mgr*
EMP: 15 **Privately Held**
SIC: 3993 Signs & advertising specialties
PA: Justipher, Inc.
1901 Franklin St
Oakland CA 94612

(P-23912)
K S DESIGNS INC
Also Called: Cal West Designs
9515 Sorensen Ave, Santa Fe Springs
(90670-2650)
PHONE......................562 929-3973
Robin Shelton, *President*
EMP: 32
SQ FT: 49,000
SALES: 1.8MM **Privately Held**
SIC: 3993 Displays & cutouts, window & lobby

(P-23913)
LEDPAC LLC
9850 Siempre Viva Rd # 5, San Diego
(92154-7247)
PHONE......................760 489-8067
Jacques Dubord,
Amy Dubord,
EMP: 52
SALES (est): 585.6K **Privately Held**
SIC: 3993 3646 Signs & advertising specialties; fluorescent lighting fixtures, commercial

(P-23914)
LEOTEK ELECTRONICS USA LLC
1955 Lundy Ave, San Jose (95131-1848)
PHONE......................408 380-1788
James C Hwang, *CEO*
Chen-Ho Wu, *President*
Nora Schultz, *Regional Mgr*
Joanne Cheng, *Accountant*
Wea Huang, *Human Resources*
▲ **EMP:** 23
SQ FT: 10,000
SALES (est): 4.8MM
SALES (corp-wide): 7.1B **Privately Held**
WEB: www.leotek.com
SIC: 3993 5046 Electric signs; signs, electrical
PA: Lite-On Technology Corporation
22f, 392, Ruey Kuang Rd.,
Taipei City TAP 11492
287 982-888

(P-23915)
LIVING WAY INDUSTRIES INC
Also Called: Creative Graphic Services
20734 Centre Pointe Pkwy, Santa Clarita
(91350-2966)
PHONE......................661 298-3200
Ronald Niner, *President*
Matt Hare, *Vice Chairman*
Charlene E Niner, *Treasurer*
Grace Isherwood, *Admin Asst*
Sara Hedstrom, *Production*
EMP: 18 **EST:** 1970
SQ FT: 22,500
SALES (est): 3.6MM **Privately Held**
SIC: 3993 Signs & advertising specialties

(P-23916)
LOCAL NEON CO INC
12536 Chadron Ave, Hawthorne
(90250-4850)
PHONE......................310 978-2000
Scott Blakely, *President*
Cassius C Blakely, *Shareholder*
Jeanne Blakely, *Admin Sec*
EMP: 50 **EST:** 1953
SQ FT: 20,000
SALES (est): 4.8MM **Privately Held**
SIC: 3993 Signs & advertising specialties

(P-23917)
LOREN INDUSTRIES
Also Called: Loren Electric Sign & Lighting
12226 Coast Dr, Whittier (90601-1607)
PHONE......................562 699-1122
Daniel Marc Lorenzon, *CEO*
Michelle Lornezon, *Vice Pres*
Christopher Reiff, *Sales Staff*
EMP: 45
SQ FT: 8,000
SALES (est): 7.5MM **Privately Held**
WEB: www.luxorindustries.com
SIC: 3993 3648 1799 Electric signs; outdoor lighting equipment; street lighting fixtures; sign installation & maintenance

(P-23918)
MANERI SIGN CO INC
1928 W 135th St, Gardena (90249-2452)
PHONE......................310 327-6261
Don Nicholas, *President*
Andrew Deeter, *Manager*
Samantha Norys, *Accounts Mgr*
EMP: 35
SQ FT: 20,000
SALES: 6MM
SALES (corp-wide): 81.9MM **Privately Held**
WEB: www.manerisign.net
SIC: 3993 Signs & advertising specialties
PA: Traffic Solutions Corporation
4000 Westerly Pl Ste 100
Newport Beach CA 92660
949 553-8272

(P-23919)
MARK EASE PRODUCTS INC
132 S Aurora St, Stockton (95202-3121)
P.O. Box 607 (95201-0607)
PHONE......................209 462-8632
Karl Gassner, *President*
Laura Gassner, *Corp Secy*
EMP: 20
SQ FT: 8,000
SALES (est): 1.9MM **Privately Held**
WEB: www.markease.com
SIC: 3993 3953 Signs, not made in custom sign painting shops; marking devices

(P-23920)
MARTINELLI ENVMTL GRAPHICS
Also Called: Martinelli Envmtl Graphics
1829 Egbert Ave, San Francisco
(94124-2519)
PHONE......................415 468-4000
Jack Martinelli, *President*
Patty Martinelli, *Treasurer*
Michael Lawrence, *Project Mgr*
Jeff Osicka, *Director*
EMP: 15
SQ FT: 8,000
SALES: 1.3MM **Privately Held**
WEB: www.martinelli-graphics.com
SIC: 3993 Electric signs

(P-23921)
MAXWELL ALARM SCREEN MFG INC
Also Called: Maxwell Sign and Decal Div
20327 Nordhoff St, Chatsworth
(91311-6128)
PHONE......................818 773-5533
Michael A Kagen, *CEO*
Patty Kagen, *Treasurer*
Rita Cortes, *Office Mgr*
EMP: 28
SQ FT: 28,000
SALES (est): 4.1MM **Privately Held**
SIC: 3993 3442 Signs & advertising specialties; screens, window, metal

(P-23922)
MCHALE SIGN COMPANY INC
3707 Electro Way, Redding (96002-9346)
PHONE......................530 223-2030
Patrick Corey, *President*
Bernice Corey, *Corp Secy*
Kevin Corey, *Technology*
EMP: 12
SQ FT: 14,000
SALES: 619.8K **Privately Held**
WEB: www.mchalesign.com
SIC: 3993 Electric signs

(P-23923)
MEDIA NATION ENTERPRISES LLC (PA)
Also Called: Media Nation USA
15271 Barranca Pkwy, Irvine (92618-2201)
PHONE......................888 502-8222
Navin D Narang, *Mng Member*
Angela Meyer, *Administration*
Bradley M Barlow,
EMP: 45
SQ FT: 6,500
SALES (est): 5.3MM **Privately Held**
SIC: 3993 5699 7371 Signs & advertising specialties; customized clothing & apparel; software programming applications

(P-23924)
MEGA SIGN INC
Also Called: Mega Led Technology
6500 Flotilla St, Commerce (90040-1714)
PHONE......................888 315-7446
David Park, *President*
Joseph Kim, *Sales Staff*
▲ **EMP:** 22 **EST:** 2007
SQ FT: 30,000
SALES (est): 4.1MM **Privately Held**
SIC: 3993 Electric signs

(P-23925)
METAL ART OF CALIFORNIA INC
Also Called: Sign Mart Retail Store
640 N Cypress St, Orange (92867-6604)
PHONE......................714 532-7100
Gene S Sobel, *Manager*
EMP: 90
SALES (corp-wide): 19.5MM **Privately Held**
WEB: www.sign-mart.com
SIC: 3993 7389 2759 Signs & advertising specialties; engraving service; screen printing
PA: Metal Art Of California, Inc.
640 N Cypress St
Orange CA 92867
714 532-7100

(P-23926)
METAL ART OF CALIFORNIA INC (PA)
Also Called: Sign Mart
640 N Cypress St, Orange (92867-6604)
PHONE......................714 532-7100
Gene S Sobel, *President*
Calvin Larson, *Vice Pres*
April Flett, *Manager*
▲ **EMP:** 91 **EST:** 1974
SQ FT: 22,000
SALES: 19.5MM **Privately Held**
WEB: www.sign-mart.com
SIC: 3993 Signs & advertising specialties

(P-23927)
MINA-TREE SIGNS INCORPORATED (PA)
1233 E Ronald St, Stockton (95205-3331)
P.O. Box 8406 (95208-0406)
PHONE......................209 941-2921
Harold Leroy Minatre, *President*
EMP: 37
SALES (est): 4.6MM **Privately Held**
WEB: www.mina-treesigns.com
SIC: 3993 Electric signs; advertising novelties

(P-23928)
MONOGRAPHX INC
1052 251st St, Harbor City (90710-2418)
PHONE......................310 325-6780
Ira Thompson, *President*
Linda Bryan, *Vice Pres*
Kerry Kelly, *Manager*
EMP: 10 **EST:** 1978
SALES: 1.5MM **Privately Held**
WEB: www.monographx.com
SIC: 3993 Displays & cutouts, window & lobby

(P-23929)
MORRIS ROBERTS LLC
20251 Sw Acacia St # 120, Newport Beach
(92660-0768)
PHONE......................800 672-3974
John Morris,
EMP: 24
SALES (est): 1.2MM **Privately Held**
SIC: 3993 Signs & advertising specialties

(P-23930)
MOTIVATIONAL SYSTEMS INC
2200 Cleveland Ave, National City
(91950-6412)
PHONE......................800 748-6584
Robert Young, *Branch Mgr*
Hardy Van Wyk, *Engineer*
EMP: 25
SALES (corp-wide): 25.6MM **Privately Held**
WEB: www.motivationalsystems.com
SIC: 3993 Signs & advertising specialties

PRODUCTS & SVCS

PA: Motivational Systems, Inc.
2200 Cleveland Ave
National City CA 91950
619 474-8246

(P-23931)
MOTIVATIONAL SYSTEMS INC
11437 Sunrise Gold Cir A, Rancho Cordova
(95742-7206)
PHONE.............................916 635-0234
Debra Bennett, *Manager*
EMP: 30
SALES (corp-wide): 25.6MM **Privately
Held**
WEB: www.motivationalsystems.com
SIC: 3993 7336 Signs, not made in custom sign painting shops; commercial art & graphic design
PA: Motivational Systems, Inc.
2200 Cleveland Ave
National City CA 91950
619 474-8246

(P-23932)
NATIONAL SIGN & MARKETING CORP
13580 5th St, Chino (91710-5113)
P.O. Box 2409 (91708-2409)
PHONE.............................909 591-4742
John J Kane, *President*
Jeffrey Fredrickson, *Corp Secy*
Jim Mole, *Planning*
Rhonda Robinson, *Project Mgr*
Steve Rosenbloom, *Sales Dir*
EMP: 70
SQ FT: 46,000
SALES (est): 14MM **Privately Held**
SIC: 3993 Neon signs

(P-23933)
NATIONAL STOCK SIGN COMPANY
Also Called: Nassco
1040 El Dorado Ave, Santa Cruz
(95062-2825)
PHONE.............................831 476-2020
Lorie Kurt Patrick, *President*
Henrietta Cooper, *President*
Robert Cooper, *Corp Secy*
EMP: 10
SQ FT: 10,000
SALES (est): 1.3MM **Privately Held**
SIC: 3993 Signs, not made in custom sign painting shops

(P-23934)
NEIMAN/HOELLER INC
Also Called: Neiman & Company
6842 Valjean Ave, Van Nuys (91406-4712)
PHONE.............................818 781-8600
Harry J Neiman, *CEO*
Robert R Hoeller III, *President*
EMP: 56
SQ FT: 17,000
SALES (est): 8.1MM **Privately Held**
WEB: www.neimanandco.com
SIC: 3993 3646 Electric signs; ornamental lighting fixtures, commercial

(P-23935)
NEON IDEAS
1635 Buena Vista St, Ventura
(93001-2214)
PHONE.............................805 648-7681
Larry Gieskeing, *Owner*
EMP: 10
SALES (est): 420K **Privately Held**
SIC: 3993 Neon signs

(P-23936)
OKI DOKI SIGNS
Also Called: Od Signs
1680 W Winton Ave Ste 7, Hayward
(94545-1333)
PHONE.............................510 940-7446
Kin So, *Owner*
Thomas Ng, *Sales Mgr*
▲ **EMP:** 12
SQ FT: 1,750
SALES (est): 1.5MM **Privately Held**
WEB: www.odsigns.com
SIC: 3993 Signs & advertising specialties

(P-23937)
ORANGE CNTY NAME PLATE CO INC
13201 Arctic Cir, Santa Fe Springs
(90670-5509)
P.O. Box 2764 (90670-0764)
PHONE.............................714 522-7693
Elias Rodriguez, *President*
Sam Rodriguez, *Corp Secy*
Rod Rodriguez, *Chief Mktg Ofcr*
Ben L Rodriguez, *Vice Pres*
Angela Alaniz, *Sls & Mktg Exec*
EMP: 85
SQ FT: 31,000
SALES (est): 14.3MM **Privately Held**
WEB: www.counterman.org
SIC: 3993 Name plates: except engraved, etched, etc.: metal

(P-23938)
OUSSOREN EPPEL CORPORATION
Also Called: Gateway Marketing Concepts
12232 Thatcher Ct, Poway (92064-6876)
P.O. Box 231666, Encinitas (92023-1666)
PHONE.............................858 483-6770
Judith Oussoren Eppel, *President*
Karl Eppel, *Legal Staff*
▲ **EMP:** 10
SALES (est): 1.6MM **Privately Held**
WEB: www.qualitybadges.com
SIC: 3993 2396 2754 Signs, not made in custom sign painting shops; automotive & apparel trimmings; promotional printing, gravure

(P-23939)
OUTDOOR SIGN SYSTEM INC (PA)
22603 La Palma Ave # 309, Yorba Linda
(92887-6709)
PHONE.............................714 692-2052
Edward J Hoke, *Principal*
Nicole Stankus, *CFO*
EMP: 15
SALES (est): 2.2MM **Privately Held**
SIC: 3993 Electric signs

(P-23940)
P&P ENTERPRISES
1246 W 7th St, Los Angeles (90017-2362)
PHONE.............................213 802-0890
Carlos A Paredes, *Owner*
EMP: 10
SQ FT: 3,500
SALES: 750K **Privately Held**
SIC: 3993 Signs & advertising specialties

(P-23941)
PACIFIC NEON
2939 Academy Way, Sacramento
(95815-1802)
P.O. Box 15100 (95851-0100)
PHONE.............................916 927-0527
Oleta Lambert, *Ch of Bd*
John Drury, *President*
Brian Rath, *Sr Corp Ofcr*
Doug Sterne, *Prdtn Mgr*
Samantha Hollinger,
EMP: 40
SQ FT: 65,000
SALES (est): 8.1MM **Privately Held**
WEB: www.pacificneon.com
SIC: 3993 1799 7359 Electric signs; sign installation & maintenance; sign rental

(P-23942)
PD GROUP
Also Called: Sign-A-Rama
41945 Boardwalk Ste L, Palm Desert
(92211-9099)
PHONE.............................760 674-3028
Jeff Gracy, *President*
Terrance Flannagan, *Vice Pres*
Terry Flanagan, *Info Tech Mgr*
Ed Landen, *Marketing Staff*
Ashley Robbins, *Sales Staff*
EMP: 25
SQ FT: 11,500
SALES (est): 1.5MM **Privately Held**
SIC: 3993 7389 5999 Electric signs; sign painting & lettering shop; banners

(P-23943)
PELICAN SIGN SERVICE INC
1565 Lafayette St, Santa Clara
(95050-3978)
PHONE.............................408 246-3833
Frank Pleican, *CEO*
Frank E Pelican Jr, *President*
Merie Steinman, *Manager*
EMP: 11 **EST:** 1975
SQ FT: 6,200
SALES (est): 1.3MM **Privately Held**
WEB: www.pelicansigns.com
SIC: 3993 Signs & advertising specialties

(P-23944)
PRIMUS INC (PA)
Also Called: Western Highway Products
17901 Jamestown Ln, Huntington Beach
(92647-7138)
PHONE.............................714 527-2261
Steve Ellsworth, *President*
Timothy M Riordan, *Vice Pres*
▲ **EMP:** 60
SQ FT: 120,000
SALES (est): 13.4MM **Privately Held**
WEB: www.couchandphilippi.com
SIC: 3993 Signs, not made in custom sign painting shops

(P-23945)
PRIMUS INC
Western Highway Products
17901 Jamestown Ln, Huntington Beach
(92647-7138)
PHONE.............................714 527-2261
Steve Elsworth, *President*
EMP: 10
SALES (corp-wide): 13.4MM **Privately
Held**
WEB: www.couchandphilippi.com
SIC: 3993 3669 Signs, not made in custom sign painting shops; transportation signaling devices
PA: Primus, Inc.
17901 Jamestown Ln
Huntington Beach CA 92647
714 527-2261

(P-23946)
PRO-LITE INC
Also Called: Advanced Products
3505 Cadillac Ave Ste D, Costa Mesa
(92626-1464)
PHONE.............................714 668-9988
Kuo-Fong Kaoh, *President*
Tom Yerke, *Vice Pres*
Daravon Chanthapadith, *Executive Asst*
Linda Turner, *Sales Mgr*
Ivan Jiang, *Manager*
▲ **EMP:** 17
SQ FT: 7,200
SALES (est): 3MM **Privately Held**
WEB: www.pro-lite.com
SIC: 3993 Signs & advertising specialties

(P-23947)
QUIEL BROS ELC SIGN SVC CO INC
272 S I St, San Bernardino (92410-2408)
PHONE.............................909 885-4476
Larry R Quiel, *President*
Raymond Quiel, *Chairman*
Gary Quiel, *Vice Pres*
Jerry Quiel, *Vice Pres*
Dave Saudargas, *Manager*
▲ **EMP:** 40
SQ FT: 8,000
SALES (est): 6.3MM **Privately Held**
WEB: www.quielsigns.com
SIC: 3993 7353 1731 7629 Electric signs; cranes & aerial lift equipment, rental or leasing; general electrical contractor; electrical equipment repair, high voltage

(P-23948)
R&M DEESE INC
Also Called: Electro-Tech's
1875 Sampson Ave, Corona (92879-6009)
P.O. Box 2317 (92878-2317)
PHONE.............................951 734-7342
Raymond Deese, *President*
Mary Deese, *Corp Secy*
Ray Deese, *Executive*
▲ **EMP:** 22
SQ FT: 20,000

SALES (est): 2.8MM **Privately Held**
SIC: 3993 3679 Signs & advertising specialties; liquid crystal displays (LCD)

(P-23949)
RAGO NEON INC
235 Laurel Ave, Hayward (94541-3822)
PHONE.............................510 537-1903
Antone F Rago II, *President*
EMP: 16
SQ FT: 9,600
SALES (est): 1.8MM **Privately Held**
WEB: www.ragoneon.com
SIC: 3993 Neon signs

(P-23950)
RAPID DISPLAYS INC
33195 Lewis St, Union City (94587-2201)
PHONE.............................510 471-6955
Bruce Watson, *President*
EMP: 300
SALES (corp-wide): 130.1MM **Privately
Held**
WEB: www.rapiddisplays.com
SIC: 3993 Displays & cutouts, window & lobby
PA: Rapid Displays, Inc.
4300 W 47th St
Chicago IL 60632
773 927-5000

(P-23951)
REICHERT ENTERPRISES INC
Also Called: Reichert's Signs
2720 S Harbor Blvd, Santa Ana
(92704-5822)
PHONE.............................714 513-9199
Dan Demell, *President*
EMP: 40
SQ FT: 5,800
SALES (est): 3.8MM **Privately Held**
WEB: www.rsisigns.com
SIC: 3993 5999 Signs & advertising specialties; banners, flags, decals & posters

(P-23952)
RICHARDS NEON SHOP INC
Also Called: RNS Channel Letters
4375 Prado Rd Ste 102, Corona
(92880-7444)
PHONE.............................951 279-6767
Richard Pando, *President*
EMP: 24
SALES (est): 3.8MM **Privately Held**
WEB: www.richardsneon.com
SIC: 3993 Electric signs

(P-23953)
ROSS NAME PLATE COMPANY
2 Red Plum Cir, Monterey Park
(91755-7486)
PHONE.............................323 725-6812
Michael Ross, *President*
EMP: 37
SQ FT: 25,000
SALES (est): 5.1MM **Privately Held**
WEB: www.rossnameplate.com
SIC: 3993 2754 Name plates: except engraved, etched, etc.: metal; labels: gravure printing

(P-23954)
S2K GRAPHICS INC
Also Called: S 2 K
9255 Deering Ave, Chatsworth
(91311-5804)
PHONE.............................818 885-3900
Dan C Pulos, *CEO*
Jack Wilson, *Ch of Bd*
Dana Rosellini, *Corp Secy*
Zack Morrissette, *Graphic Designe*
Gary Lucius, *Accounting Mgr*
EMP: 35
SALES (est): 8.6MM
SALES (corp-wide): 2.9B **Privately Held**
WEB: www.s2kgraphics.com
SIC: 3993 7532 2759 Signs & advertising specialties; truck painting & lettering; screen printing
HQ: Franke Usa Holding, Inc.
1105 N Market St Ste 1300
Wilmington DE 19801

▲ = Import ▼=Export
◆ =Import/Export

(P-23955)
SAFEWAY SIGN COMPANY
9875 Yucca Rd, Adelanto (92301-2282)
PHONE.................................760 246-7070
Michael F Moore, *President*
Andrea M Gutierrez, *Vice Pres*
David C Moore, *Vice Pres*
EMP: 49 **EST:** 1948
SQ FT: 60,000
SALES (est): 13.4MM **Privately Held**
WEB: www.safewaysign.com
SIC: 3993 Signs, not made in custom sign
painting shops

(P-23956)
SALES OFFICE ACCESSORIES INC
7211 Patterson Dr, Garden Grove
(92841-1421)
PHONE.................................714 896-9600
Ken Morelli, *President*
EMP: 10
SALES (est): 1MM **Privately Held**
WEB: www.soainc.com
SIC: 3993 Signs & advertising specialties

(P-23957)
SAN DIEGO ELECTRIC SIGN INC
1890 Cordell Ct Ste 105, El Cajon
(92020-0913)
P.O. Box 103, Bonita (91908-0103)
PHONE.................................619 258-1775
Greg Ballard, *President*
Jayne Ballard, *Vice Pres*
Janie Ballard, *General Mgr*
Lelsie Crosby, *Admin Sec*
EMP: 17
SALES (est): 2.2MM **Privately Held**
SIC: 3993 Electric signs

(P-23958)
SAN PEDRO SIGN COMPANY
701 Lakme Ave, Wilmington (90744-5943)
PHONE.................................310 549-4661
Gus Navarro, *President*
EMP: 20
SQ FT: 7,000
SALES (est): 3.2MM **Privately Held**
WEB: www.spesco.com
SIC: 3993 Electric signs

(P-23959)
SCHEA HOLDINGS INC
Also Called: Signgroup/Karman
9812 Independence Ave, Chatsworth
(91311-4319)
PHONE.................................818 888-3818
Michael Schackne, *President*
Kathryn Schackne, *Vice Pres*
Kathy Schackne, *Vice Pres*
EMP: 22
SQ FT: 10,000
SALES: 2MM **Privately Held**
WEB: www.asigngroup.net
SIC: 3993 Electric signs

(P-23960)
SHYE WEST INC (PA)
Also Called: Imagine This
43 Corporate Park Ste 102, Irvine
(92606-5137)
PHONE.................................949 486-4598
Patrick Papaccio, *President*
Craig Perkins, *President*
Shawn Keep, *Vice Pres*
Michael Tabor, *Vice Pres*
Adam Bullock, *Executive*
▲ **EMP:** 27
SQ FT: 6,000
SALES (est): 9.9MM **Privately Held**
WEB: www.promogiant.com
SIC: 3993 5099 Advertising novelties; nov-
elties, durable

(P-23961)
SIGN ART CO
423 S California St, San Gabriel
(91776-2527)
PHONE.................................626 287-2512
Eddy Hsieh, *President*
EMP: 10
SQ FT: 2,800
SALES (est): 540K **Privately Held**
SIC: 3993 Electric signs

(P-23962)
SIGN DESIGNS INC
Also Called: Macdonald Screen Print
204 Campus Way, Modesto (95350-5845)
P.O. Box 4590 (95352-4590)
PHONE.................................209 524-4484
David Johnston, *President*
Pete Michelini, *Corp Secy*
Doug Smith, *Vice Pres*
Bill Heyman, *Controller*
Clay Snider, *Human Res Dir*
EMP: 44
SQ FT: 35,000
SALES (est): 6.7MM **Privately Held**
WEB: www.signdesigns.com
SIC: 3993 Electric signs

(P-23963)
SIGN EXCELLENCE LLC
8515 Telfair Ave, Sun Valley (91352-3928)
PHONE.................................818 308-1044
Jose D Gutierrez, *Mng Member*
EMP: 12
SALES (est): 1.4MM **Privately Held**
SIC: 3993 Signs & advertising specialties

(P-23964)
SIGN INDUSTRIES INC
2101 Carrillo Privado, Ontario
(91761-7600)
PHONE.................................909 930-0303
Maria Saavedra, *President*
Enrique Saavedra, *Admin Sec*
Joe Rhodes, *Human Res Dir*
▲ **EMP:** 30
SQ FT: 4,500
SALES (est): 6.8MM **Privately Held**
WEB: www.signindustries.com
SIC: 3993 Neon signs

(P-23965)
SIGN SOLUTIONS INC
Also Called: Artsigns
532 Mercury Dr, Sunnyvale (94085-4018)
PHONE.................................408 245-7133
Fax: 408 245-1389
EMP: 14
SQ FT: 7,600
SALES (est): 1.8MM **Privately Held**
WEB: www.artsigns.net
SIC: 3993

(P-23966)
SIGN SOURCE INC
Also Called: Signsource
204 W Carleton Ave Ste A, Orange
(92867-3632)
PHONE.................................714 979-9979
John Mearns, *President*
Doug O'Dwyer, *General Mgr*
EMP: 15
SQ FT: 23,000
SALES (est): 2.2MM **Privately Held**
WEB: www.signsource.net
SIC: 3993 Signs & advertising specialties

(P-23967)
SIGN SPECIALISTS CORPORATION
111 W Dyer Rd Ste F, Santa Ana
(92707-3425)
PHONE.................................714 641-0064
Garrick Batt, *CEO*
Sean Baldwin, *Sales Executive*
EMP: 22 **EST:** 2001
SALES (est): 4MM **Privately Held**
WEB: www.sign-specialists.com
SIC: 3993 Signs, not made in custom sign
painting shops

(P-23968)
SIGN TECHNOLOGY INC
Also Called: Signtech
1700 Entp Blvd Ste F, West Sacramento
(95691)
PHONE.................................916 372-1200
Michael Wilmer, *CEO*
Dan Worsley, *Sales Dir*
Dallas Dorn, *Sales Staff*
EMP: 30
SQ FT: 11,660
SALES (est): 4.5MM **Privately Held**
WEB: www.signtechnology.com
SIC: 3993 Signs, not made in custom sign
painting shops

(P-23969)
SIGNAGE SOLUTIONS CORPORATION
2231 S Dupont Dr, Anaheim (92806-6105)
PHONE.................................714 491-0299
Chris Deruyter, *CEO*
Jim Gledhill, *Vice Pres*
Jose Villanueva, *Business Dir*
Betty Austin, *Project Mgr*
Rene Camarena, *Project Mgr*
EMP: 30
SQ FT: 14,000
SALES (est): 5.5MM **Privately Held**
WEB: www.signage-solutions.com
SIC: 3993 7389 Signs & advertising spe-
cialties; sign painting & lettering shop

(P-23970)
SIGNQUEST
13040 Cerise Ave, Hawthorne
(90250-5523)
PHONE.................................310 355-0528
Ramy Nicholas, *Principal*
EMP: 20
SALES (est): 1.4MM **Privately Held**
SIC: 3993 Signs & advertising specialties

(P-23971)
SIGNS AND SERVICES COMPANY
10980 Boatman Ave, Stanton
(90680-2602)
PHONE.................................714 761-8200
Jacob Deryuyter, *CEO*
Matt De Ruyter, *President*
Henry Hu, *Controller*
Barbara Aguilar, *Manager*
EMP: 33
SQ FT: 16,000
SALES: 4.5MM **Privately Held**
SIC: 3993 Signs, not made in custom sign
painting shops

(P-23972)
SIGNS OF SUCCESS INC
2350 Skyway Dr Ste 10, Santa Maria
(93455-1532)
PHONE.................................805 925-7545
Stephen Sheppard, *President*
Glenda Sheppard, *Treasurer*
EMP: 16
SQ FT: 3,600
SALES (est): 500K **Privately Held**
WEB: www.signsofsuccess.net
SIC: 3993 7389 5999 Signs & advertising
specialties; sign painting & lettering shop;
decals

(P-23973)
SIGNTECH ELECTRICAL ADVG INC
4444 Federal Blvd, San Diego
(92102-2505)
PHONE.................................619 527-6100
Harold E Schauer Jr, *CEO*
David E Schauer, *President*
Kimra Schauer, *CFO*
Art Navarro, *Vice Pres*
Patty Soria, *Vice Pres*
EMP: 120
SQ FT: 25,000
SALES (est): 26.7MM **Privately Held**
WEB: www.signtechusa.com
SIC: 3993 1799 Electric signs; sign instal-
lation & maintenance

(P-23974)
SIGNTRONIX INC (PA)
1445 Sepulveda Blvd, Torrance
(90501-5004)
PHONE.................................310 534-7500
Tommy K Boren, *CEO*
▲ **EMP:** 59
SALES (est): 21.4MM **Privately Held**
SIC: 3993 Signs & advertising specialties

(P-23975)
SIGNWORLD AMERICA INC (PA)
12023 Arrow Rte, Rancho Cucamonga
(91739-9219)
PHONE.................................844 900-7446
Yangchi Chung, *CEO*
◆ **EMP:** 17

SALES (est): 2.5MM **Privately Held**
SIC: 3993 5199 5999 Signs & advertising
specialties; advertising specialties; banners

(P-23976)
SIMPLY SMASHING INC
Also Called: Fruehe Design
4790 W Jacquelyn Ave, Fresno
(93722-6406)
PHONE.................................559 658-2367
Tim Fruehe, *President*
EMP: 20
SALES (est): 3.1MM **Privately Held**
SIC: 3993 7336 Advertising novelties;
graphic arts & related design

(P-23977)
SKYLINE DIGITAL IMAGES INC
10420 Pioneer Blvd, Santa Fe Springs
(90670-3734)
PHONE.................................562 944-1677
Jerilyn Benson, *Manager*
▲ **EMP:** 25
SALES (est): 2.1MM **Privately Held**
SIC: 3993 Displays & cutouts, window &
lobby

(P-23978)
SOTELEO SALVADAR
Also Called: S S Sign Electric
620 Imperial St, Los Angeles (90021-1310)
PHONE.................................213 621-2040
Salvador Sotelo, *Owner*
EMP: 20
SQ FT: 10,000
SALES (est): 883.1K **Privately Held**
SIC: 3993 1731 1542 1521 Signs, not
made in custom sign painting shops; gen-
eral electrical contractor; commercial &
office building, new construction; new
construction, single-family houses; multi-
family dwelling construction

(P-23979)
SPECIALIZED GRAPHICS INC
3951 Industrial Way Ste A, Concord
(94520-8552)
PHONE.................................925 680-0265
Michael Gratton, *CEO*
Jamie Navarro, *Prdtn Mgr*
EMP: 20
SQ FT: 3,500
SALES (est): 2MM **Privately Held**
WEB: www.sgsignage.com
SIC: 3993 Electric signs

(P-23980)
STANDARDVISION LLC
3370 N San Fernando Rd # 206, Los Ange-
les (90065-1437)
PHONE.................................323 222-3630
Adrian Velicescu, *CEO*
Brad Gwinn, *Officer*
Kevin Bartanian, *Exec VP*
Grif Palmer, *Vice Pres*
Alberto Garcia, *Project Dir*
▲ **EMP:** 34
SQ FT: 25,000
SALES: 31.2MM **Privately Held**
SIC: 3993 7336 Signs & advertising spe-
cialties; commercial art & graphic design

(P-23981)
STANFORD SIGN & AWNING INC (PA)
2556 Faivre St, Chula Vista (91911-4604)
PHONE.................................619 423-6200
David Lesage, *President*
Richie Del Gatto, *Opers Staff*
Carlos Davila, *Manager*
EMP: 50
SQ FT: 35,000
SALES (est): 14.1MM **Privately Held**
WEB: www.stansign.com
SIC: 3993 2394 Electric signs; canvas
awnings & canopies

(P-23982)
STREET GRAPHICS INC
Also Called: Delta Signs
1834 W Euclid Ave, Stockton (95204-2911)
PHONE.................................209 948-1713
EMP: 20
SQ FT: 12,000

SALES (est): 2.5MM **Privately Held**
WEB: www.deltasigns.net
SIC: 3993

(P-23983)
SUPERIOR ELECTRICAL ADVG (PA)
1700 W Anaheim St, Long Beach (90813-1102)
PHONE...................................562 495-3808
Jim Sterk, *CEO*
Patti Skoglundadams, *President*
Stan Janocha, *COO*
Doug Tokeshi, *CFO*
▲ EMP: 85 EST: 1962
SQ FT: 100,000
SALES: 15.7MM **Privately Held**
SIC: 3993 7629 Electric signs; electrical equipment repair services

(P-23984)
SUPERIOR ELECTRICAL ADVG
125 Houston Ln, Lodi (95240-2422)
PHONE...................................209 334-3337
David Coberly, *Manager*
EMP: 10
SALES (est): 772.3K
SALES (corp-wide): 15.7MM **Privately Held**
SIC: 3993 7629 Electric signs; electrical equipment repair services
PA: Superior Electrical Advertising
1700 W Anaheim St
Long Beach CA 90813
562 495-3808

(P-23985)
SUPERSONIC ADS INC
17 Bluxome St, San Francisco (94107-1605)
PHONE...................................650 825-6010
Gil Shoham, *CEO*
Dock Kim, *President*
Adam David, *Vice Pres*
Damon B Marshall, *Vice Pres*
Daphne Saragosti, *Vice Pres*
EMP: 22
SALES (est): 3MM **Privately Held**
SIC: 3993 Advertising artwork

(P-23986)
T D I SIGNS
1419 Seabright Ave, Long Beach (90813-1100)
PHONE...................................562 436-5188
Arthur Rivas, *President*
EMP: 25
SQ FT: 10,000
SALES (est): 3.8MM **Privately Held**
WEB: www.tdisigns.com
SIC: 3993 Electric signs

(P-23987)
TAE GWANG INC
4922 S Figueroa St, Los Angeles (90037-3344)
PHONE...................................323 233-2882
Sammy Chu, *President*
EMP: 15
SQ FT: 3,401
SALES (est): 1.5MM **Privately Held**
WEB: www.taegwang.com
SIC: 3993 Signs & advertising specialties

(P-23988)
TFN ARCHITECTURAL SIGNAGE INC (PA)
Also Called: Third Floor North Company
3411 W Lake Center Dr, Santa Ana (92704-6925)
PHONE...................................714 556-0990
Brian L Burnett, *President*
Catherine Burnett, *Shareholder*
Jeff Burnett, *Shareholder*
Teresa Burnett, *Treasurer*
Jim Clark, *Executive*
EMP: 45
SQ FT: 8,800
SALES (est): 6.7MM **Privately Held**
SIC: 3993 Signs, not made in custom sign painting shops

(P-23989)
THOMAS-SWAN SIGN COMPANY INC
2717 Goodrick Ave, Richmond (94801-1109)
PHONE...................................415 621-1511
Allen E Thomas, *CEO*
Michael Roberts, *President*
Donna Thomas, *Treasurer*
Stacy Roberts, *Vice Pres*
EMP: 35 EST: 1877
SQ FT: 40,000
SALES (est): 7.2MM **Privately Held**
WEB: www.thomasswan.com
SIC: 3993 Electric signs; neon signs

(P-23990)
TIMLIN INDUSTRIES INC
6777 Nancy Ridge Dr, San Diego (92121-2231)
PHONE...................................541 947-6771
Tim Kloos, *President*
Kaye Warner, *Admin Sec*
EMP: 40
SQ FT: 4,800
SALES (est): 3.8MM **Privately Held**
SIC: 3993 5199 5947 Advertising novelties; advertising specialties; novelties

(P-23991)
TO INDUSTRIES INC
Also Called: Quantam Signs & Graphics
23180 Del Lago Dr, Lake Forest (92630)
PHONE...................................949 454-6078
Keith To, *President*
EMP: 12
SALES (est): 1.5MM **Privately Held**
WEB: www.quantum-signs.com
SIC: 3993 Signs, not made in custom sign painting shops

(P-23992)
TORTOLANI INC
1313 Mirasol St, Los Angeles (90023-3108)
PHONE...................................323 268-1488
Robin Tortolani, *President*
Robin Tortolani Italia, *President*
EMP: 14 EST: 1997
SALES (est): 800K **Privately Held**
WEB: www.tortolani.com
SIC: 3993 5944 Advertising novelties; jewelry stores

(P-23993)
TRADENET ENTERPRISE INC
Also Called: Vantage Led
1930 S Vineyard Ave, Ontario (91761-7706)
PHONE...................................888 595-3956
Chris MA, *President*
Christine Fierro, *General Mgr*
Steven Lopes, *Software Dev*
Brandon Saunders, *Software Dev*
Jimmy Gonzalez, *Technical Staff*
▲ EMP: 60
SQ FT: 150,000
SALES (est): 10.5MM **Privately Held**
SIC: 3993 Electric signs

(P-23994)
TRAFFIC CONTROL & SAFETY CORP
13755 Blaisdell Pl, Poway (92064-6837)
PHONE...................................858 679-7292
David Nicholas, *Regional Mgr*
Dennis Philbin, *Sales Associate*
EMP: 11 **Privately Held**
WEB: www.statewidesafety.com
SIC: 3993 5088 7359 5082 Signs, not made in custom sign painting shops; transportation equipment & supplies; work zone traffic equipment (flags, cones, barrels, etc.); contractors' materials
PA: Traffic Control And Safety Corporation
1100 Main St
Irvine CA 92614

(P-23995)
ULTRANEON SIGN CORP
Also Called: Ultraneon Sign Company
5458 Complex St Ste 401, San Diego (92123-1118)
PHONE...................................858 569-6716

Gus Hadaya, *President*
EMP: 40
SQ FT: 22,000
SALES: 5MM **Privately Held**
SIC: 3993 Neon signs; scoreboards, electric

(P-23996)
UNIVERSAL CUSTOM DISPLAY
Also Called: Universal Custom Design
9104 Elkmont Dr Ste 100, Elk Grove (95624-9724)
PHONE...................................916 714-2505
Daniel Hayes, *President*
Don Almeda, *Vice Pres*
Charles Dickenson, *Vice Pres*
Margie Joson, *Managing Dir*
Jeanne Hayes, *Admin Sec*
▲ EMP: 175
SQ FT: 120,000
SALES (est): 42.7MM **Privately Held**
WEB: www.universalcustomdisplay.com
SIC: 3993 2541 Signs & advertising specialties; display fixtures, wood

(P-23997)
UNIVERSAL MERCANTILE EXCHANGE (PA)
Also Called: Umx
21128 Commerce Point Dr, Walnut (91789-3053)
PHONE...................................909 839-0556
Hs Che Wang, *President*
William Huang, *Vice Pres*
▲ EMP: 15
SQ FT: 8,026
SALES (est): 1.3MM **Privately Held**
WEB: www.umei.com
SIC: 3993 5091 5099 Signs & advertising specialties; golf & skiing equipment & supplies; fire extinguishers

(P-23998)
VISIBLE GRAPHICS INC
9736 Eton Ave, Chatsworth (91311-4305)
PHONE...................................818 787-0477
Janine Kendall, *CEO*
Ken Kendall, *CFO*
EMP: 16 EST: 2002
SALES (est): 6.6MM **Privately Held**
WEB: www.visiblegraphics.com
SIC: 3993 Signs & advertising specialties

(P-23999)
VISIONEERED IMAGE SYSTEMS INC
444 W Ocean Blvd Ste 1400, Long Beach (90802-4522)
PHONE...................................818 613-7600
Anthony Materna, *President*
Karl Boldt, *Senior VP*
EMP: 16
SALES (est): 1.2MM **Privately Held**
SIC: 3993 Electric signs

(P-24000)
VOGUE SIGN INC
715 Commercial Ave, Oxnard (93030-7233)
PHONE...................................805 487-7222
Jack Woodruff, *President*
Christian Muldoon, *Project Mgr*
Kirk Hamilton, *Sales Mgr*
Ron Wilkinson, *Manager*
EMP: 12
SQ FT: 11,000
SALES (est): 1.9MM **Privately Held**
WEB: www.voguesigns.com
SIC: 3993 Electric signs

(P-24001)
VOMELA SPECIALTY COMPANY
Corporate Identity Systems
1342 San Mateo Ave, South San Francisco (94080-6501)
PHONE...................................650 877-8000
Robert Pietila, *Branch Mgr*
EMP: 27
SALES (corp-wide): 148.4MM **Privately Held**
SIC: 3993 2759 Signs & advertising specialties; screen printing
PA: Vomela Specialty Company
274 Fillmore Ave E
Saint Paul MN 55107
651 228-2200

(P-24002)
VPRO INC
Also Called: Sticker City
4638 Van Nuys Blvd, Sherman Oaks (91403-2915)
PHONE...................................818 905-5678
Andisne Soleimanpour, *President*
Idin Soleimanpour, *Admin Sec*
Dean Soleimani, *Sales Executive*
Alexa Solano, *Sales Staff*
EMP: 11
SALES (est): 193.4K **Privately Held**
SIC: 3993 Signs & advertising specialties

(P-24003)
WESTERN ELECTRICAL ADVG CO
Also Called: Southwest Sign Systems
853 Dogwood Ave, El Centro (92243)
P.O. Box 587 (92244-0587)
PHONE...................................760 352-0471
Dennis Berg, *President*
Vernon I Berg, *Chairman*
Glenna L Berg, *Corp Secy*
EMP: 25
SALES (est): 802K **Privately Held**
SIC: 3993 1731 Electric signs; signs, not made in custom sign painting shops; general electrical contractor

(P-24004)
WESTERN SIGN COMPANY INC
6221a Enterprise Dr Ste A, Diamond Springs (95619-9398)
PHONE...................................916 933-3765
David Brazelton, *President*
Todd Johnston, *Vice Pres*
Keith Wills, *Vice Pres*
Cindy Brazelton, *Admin Sec*
Wendie Denham, *Opers Mgr*
EMP: 20 EST: 1959
SQ FT: 12,000
SALES (est): 3.2MM **Privately Held**
WEB: www.westernsign.com
SIC: 3993 1799 Electric signs; neon signs; sign installation & maintenance

(P-24005)
WILLIAMS SIGN CO
111 S Huntington St, Pomona (91766-1436)
PHONE...................................909 622-5304
Chad Bruce, *President*
Justin M Williams, *President*
Sharon Willison, *Treasurer*
Marcelle Williams, *Vice Pres*
EMP: 10
SQ FT: 4,700
SALES (est): 1.2MM **Privately Held**
SIC: 3993 1799 Neon signs; sign installation & maintenance

(P-24006)
WOLFPACK INC
Also Called: Wolfpack Sign Group
2440 Grand Ave Ste B, Vista (92081-7829)
P.O. Box 3620 (92085-3620)
PHONE...................................760 736-4500
Carolyn Wolf, *CEO*
Peter Wolf, *Corp Secy*
Ryan Meyer, *Vice Pres*
EMP: 20
SQ FT: 15,000
SALES (est): 3.2MM **Privately Held**
WEB: www.wolfpacksigns.com
SIC: 3993 Signs, not made in custom sign painting shops

(P-24007)
Y2K PRECISION SHEETMETAL INC
3831 E La Palma Ave, Anaheim (92807-1721)
PHONE...................................714 632-3901
Hoang Ha, *President*
Paulina Ha, *Executive*
EMP: 10
SALES (est): 1.3MM **Privately Held**
WEB: www.y2ksheetmetal.com
SIC: 3993 Signs & advertising specialties

(P-24008)
YOUNG ELECTRIC SIGN COMPANY
Also Called: Yesco
875 National Dr Ste 107, Sacramento
(95834-1162)
PHONE............................916 419-8101
Rachel Williamson, *Branch Mgr*
EMP: 35
SALES (corp-wide): 364.3MM **Privately Held**
SIC: 3993 5999 1799 Electric signs; awnings; sign installation & maintenance
PA: Young Electric Sign Company Inc
2401 S Foothill Dr
Salt Lake City UT 84109
801 464-4600

(P-24009)
YOUNG ELECTRIC SIGN COMPANY
Also Called: Yesco
10235 Bellegrave Ave, Mira Loma
(91752-1919)
PHONE............................909 923-7668
Duane Wardle, *Branch Mgr*
Megan Hornsby, *Office Mgr*
Bob Mountain, *Safety Mgr*
EMP: 100
SQ FT: 8,500
SALES (corp-wide): 364.3MM **Privately Held**
SIC: 3993 1799 Electric signs; sign installation & maintenance
PA: Young Electric Sign Company Inc
2401 S Foothill Dr
Salt Lake City UT 84109
801 464-4600

(P-24010)
ZUMAR INDUSTRIES INC
9719 Santa Fe Springs Rd, Santa Fe Springs (90670-2919)
P.O. Box 2883 (90670-0883)
PHONE............................562 941-4633
Benn Limcke, *President*
Tj Thibert, *Info Tech Mgr*
EMP: 56 EST: 1947
SQ FT: 30,000
SALES (est): 5.8MM
SALES (corp-wide): 31.8MM **Privately Held**
WEB: www.zumar.com
SIC: 3993 Signs & advertising specialties
PA: Zumar Industries, Inc.
12015 Steele St S
Tacoma WA 98444
253 536-7740

3995 Burial Caskets

(P-24011)
GOLDEN STATE CASKET CO
Also Called: A B C Caskets
1705 N Indiana St, Los Angeles
(90063-2576)
PHONE............................323 268-1783
Joseph Conzevoy, *President*
Isrela Conzevoy, *Vice Pres*
EMP: 20 EST: 1933
SQ FT: 10,000
SALES (est): 2.2MM **Privately Held**
WEB: www.abettercasket.com
SIC: 3995 Burial caskets

(P-24012)
PETTIGREW & SONS CASKET CO
6151 Power Inn Rd, Sacramento
(95824-2343)
PHONE............................916 383-0777
Fay Pettigrew, *President*
Althea Pettigrew, *Treasurer*
Donald Pettigrew, *Vice Pres*
James Pettigrew, *Vice Pres*
Barbara Hart, *Admin Sec*
▼ EMP: 20
SQ FT: 25,000
SALES (est): 2.5MM **Privately Held**
WEB: www.pettigrewcaskets.com
SIC: 3995 Burial caskets

3996 Linoleum & Hard Surface Floor Coverings, NEC

(P-24013)
ALTRO USA INC
Also Called: Compass Flooring
12648 Clark St, Santa Fe Springs
(90670-3950)
PHONE............................562 944-8292
Al Boegh, *Principal*
Cy Allen, *Consultant*
EMP: 19
SALES (corp-wide): 30MM **Privately Held**
SIC: 3996 5023 Hard surface floor coverings; resilient floor coverings: tile or sheet
PA: Altro Usa, Inc.
80 Industrial Way Ste 1
Wilmington MA 01887
408 441-1700

(P-24014)
HOVEY TILE ART
1221 Opal Ave, Mentone (92359-1272)
PHONE............................909 794-3815
Dean Hovey, *Owner*
EMP: 21
SALES (est): 1.5MM **Privately Held**
SIC: 3996 Tile, floor: supported plastic

(P-24015)
RENOS FLOOR COVERING INC
61 Paul Dr, San Rafael (94903-2115)
P.O. Box 503, NAPA (94559-0503)
PHONE............................415 459-1403
Carolyn Reno, *President*
John Norman, *Vice Pres*
EMP: 16
SQ FT: 3,000
SALES (est): 3MM **Privately Held**
SIC: 3996 Asphalted-felt-base floor coverings: linoleum, carpet

(P-24016)
WILLIAM A SHUBECK
10961 Desert Lawn Dr # 102, Calimesa
(92320-2232)
PHONE............................909 795-6970
William A Shubeck, *Owner*
EMP: 20
SALES (est): 1MM **Privately Held**
SIC: 3996 Hard surface floor coverings

3999 Manufacturing Industries, NEC

(P-24017)
1254 INDUSTRIES
1444 Alpine Pl, San Marcos (92078-3801)
PHONE............................760 798-8531
▲ EMP: 13
SALES (est): 1.6MM **Privately Held**
SIC: 3999 Barber & beauty shop equipment

(P-24018)
5 STAR REDEMPTION INC
Also Called: Planet Star
8803 Shirley Ave, Northridge (91324-3412)
PHONE............................818 709-0875
William B Faith, *President*
▲ EMP: 20 EST: 1996
SALES (est): 2.1MM **Privately Held**
WEB: www.fivestarredemption.com
SIC: 3999 Coin-operated amusement machines

(P-24019)
A & A JEWELRY TOOLS FINDINGS
Also Called: A&A Jewelry Tools & Supplies
319 W 6th St, Los Angeles (90014-1703)
PHONE............................213 627-8004
Gene Adem, *Partner*
Robert Adem, *Partner*
Fouad Farah, *Partner*
Naim Farah, *Partner*
Phlip Farah, *Partner*
▲ EMP: 18

SQ FT: 3,000
SALES (est): 2MM **Privately Held**
WEB: www.aajewelry.com
SIC: 3999 5944 Atomizers, toiletry; jewelry, precious stones & precious metals

(P-24020)
A S G CORPORATION
Also Called: Smith & Company
1230 Long Beach Ave, Los Angeles
(90021-2320)
PHONE............................213 748-6361
Albert Weiss, *President*
William Weiss, *Vice Pres*
Esther Weiss, *Admin Sec*
◆ EMP: 15
SQ FT: 3,750
SALES (est): 1.8MM **Privately Held**
SIC: 3999 7929 Lamp shade frames; entertainers & entertainment groups

(P-24021)
ABOVE & BEYOND BALLOONS INC
Also Called: Above and Beyond
16661 Jamboree Rd, Irvine (92606-5118)
PHONE............................949 586-8470
Michael Chaklos, *CEO*
Karen Chaklos, *Vice Pres*
Michael Brown, *Marketing Staff*
▲ EMP: 44
SQ FT: 25,000
SALES (est): 6MM **Privately Held**
WEB: www.advertisingballons.com
SIC: 3999 Advertising display products

(P-24022)
ACCURATE GRINDING USA INC
29057 Avenue Penn, Valencia
(91355-5426)
PHONE............................818 768-4497
Ralph Sulpizio, *President*
EMP: 20
SALES (est): 504.6K **Privately Held**
SIC: 3999 Manufacturing industries

(P-24023)
ACCURATE STAGING MFG INC (PA)
13900 S Figueroa St, Los Angeles
(90061-1028)
PHONE............................310 324-1040
Alfredo Gomez, *CEO*
Jose Cantu, *President*
Carlos Alvarenga, *Mfg Staff*
EMP: 35
SQ FT: 18,000
SALES (est): 5.4MM **Privately Held**
WEB: www.accuratestaging.com
SIC: 3999 Stage hardware & equipment, except lighting

(P-24024)
ADVANCED BUILDING SYSTEMS INC
11905 Regentview Ave, Downey
(90241-5515)
PHONE............................818 652-4252
Alex Youssef, *President*
EMP: 20
SALES (est): 504.6K **Privately Held**
SIC: 3999 Manufacturing industries

(P-24025)
ADVANCED COSMETIC RES LABS INC
Also Called: Acrl
20550 Prairie St, Chatsworth (91311-6006)
PHONE............................818 709-9945
Kitty Hunter, *President*
Celeste Guillen, *Research*
Prakash Patel, *Research*
Richard Garza, *Sr Project Mgr*
Mari Medina, *Clerk*
▲ EMP: 50
SQ FT: 48,000
SALES (est): 7.3MM **Privately Held**
WEB: www.advancedcosmeticlabs.com
SIC: 3999 2844 Barber & beauty shop equipment; toilet preparations

---

(P-24026)
ADVANCED MOBILITY INC
7720 Sepulveda Blvd, Van Nuys
(91405-1018)
PHONE............................818 780-1788
Scott Deacon, *President*
Linda V Winkle, *Treasurer*
Linda Van Winkle, *Corp Secy*
Bill Deacon, *Vice Pres*
EMP: 19 EST: 1975
SQ FT: 12,000
SALES (est): 1MM **Privately Held**
SIC: 3999 5531 Wool pulling; automotive accessories

(P-24027)
AEGIS PRINCIPIA LLC
12165 Ojeda Ct, Tustin (92782-1284)
PHONE............................714 731-2283
Brando Balarezo,
EMP: 10
SALES (est): 508.1K **Privately Held**
SIC: 3999 Novelties, bric-a-brac & hobby kits

(P-24028)
AKON INCORPORATED
2135 Ringwood Ave, San Jose
(95131-1725)
PHONE............................408 432-8039
Surya Sareen, *President*
Louis Seieroe, *Business Dir*
Karl Liu, *Analyst*
Sylvia Van, *Controller*
Sandeep Sareen, *Sales Staff*
EMP: 60
SQ FT: 35,000
SALES (est): 11.8MM **Privately Held**
SIC: 3999 Slot machines

(P-24029)
ALL AMERICAN FABRICATION
1328 Burton Ave Ste B10, Salinas
(93901-4437)
PHONE............................831 676-3490
Ahumberto Abalos, *Owner*
EMP: 12
SALES (est): 51.3K **Privately Held**
SIC: 3999 Manufacturing industries

(P-24030)
ALL POWER MANUFACTURING CO
13141 Molette St, Santa Fe Springs
(90670-5500)
PHONE............................562 802-2640
Michael J Hartnett, *Principal*
Martha Lopez, *Info Tech Mgr*
Maria Salazar, *Info Tech Mgr*
Yvonne Garcia, *Business Mgr*
Karen Ford, *Controller*
EMP: 14
SALES (corp-wide): 674.9MM **Publicly Held**
SIC: 3999 Atomizers, toiletry
HQ: All Power Manufacturing Co
1 Tribiology Ctr
Oxford CT 06478
562 802-2640

(P-24031)
ALLIED FEATHER & DOWN CORP (PA)
6905 W Acco St Ste A, Montebello
(90640-5448)
PHONE............................323 581-5677
Steve Uretsky, *CEO*
Fion Huang, *Vice Pres*
Andy Perez, *Office Mgr*
Marylou Ramirez, *Admin Asst*
Jonathan Uretsky, *VP Opers*
◆ EMP: 50
SQ FT: 12,000
SALES (est): 8.3MM **Privately Held**
WEB: www.alliedfeather.com
SIC: 3999 5719 Down (feathers); bedding (sheets, blankets, spreads & pillows)

(P-24032)
ALOHA BAY
Also Called: Bright Lights Candle Company
16275 A Main St, Lower Lake (95457)
PHONE............................707 994-3267
Bernard S Burger, *CEO*
Roy Dixon, *Principal*

▲ EMP: 35
SQ FT: 1,500
SALES (est): 4MM **Privately Held**
WEB: www.brightlightscandles.com
SIC: 3999 5199 Candles; candles

(P-24033)
AMARETTO ORCHARDS LLC
Also Called: Famoso Nut
32331 Famoso Woody Rd, Mc Farland
(93250-9771)
PHONE...................................661 399-9697
Bruce Baretta,
David Delis, *Controller*
Harmeet Kaur, *Production*
Jose Jaime, *Foreman/Supr*
Laura Hernandez, *Supervisor*
▼ EMP: 20
SALES (est): 2.9MM **Privately Held**
SIC: 3999 2068 Nut shells, grinding, from
purchased nuts; salted & roasted nuts &
seeds

(P-24034)
**AMERICAN MADE MAKE BE-
LEAVES**
5311 Derry Ave Ste C, Agoura Hills
(91301-5075)
PHONE...................................800 634-1402
John A Lewis Jr, *President*
Susanne Lewis, *Corp Secy*
Jack Lewis, *Principal*
▲ EMP: 11
SQ FT: 7,000
SALES (est): 800K **Privately Held**
SIC: 3999 5992 5999 5193 Plants, artifi-
cial & preserved; florists; artificial flowers;
artificial flowers

(P-24035)
**AMERICAN STRAW COMPANY
LLC**
1697 Woods Dr, Los Angeles (90069-1633)
PHONE...................................213 304-1095
Carolyn Chen,
EMP: 15
SALES (est): 397K **Privately Held**
SIC: 3999 Straw goods

(P-24036)
AMEX MANUFACTURING INC
2307 Avenida Costa Este, San Diego
(92154-6275)
PHONE...................................619 391-7412
Yong H Kim, *CEO*
Nick Espinoza, *Purch Mgr*
Alex Kim, *Accounts Mgr*
▲ EMP: 12
SALES: 9.5MM **Privately Held**
SIC: 3999 Barber & beauty shop equip-
ment

(P-24037)
**AMGEN MANUFACTURING
LIMITED**
1 Amgen Center Dr, Newbury Park
(91320-1799)
PHONE...................................787 656-2000
Victoria H Blatter, *Principal*
Martina Rech, *Human Res Mgr*
Irma Gonzalez, *Production*
Raphael Van Eemeren, *Senior Mgr*
EMP: 12
SALES (est): 45K
SALES (corp-wide): 22.8B **Publicly Held**
SIC: 3999 Atomizers, toiletry
PA: Amgen Inc.
1 Amgen Center Dr
Thousand Oaks CA 91320
805 447-1000

(P-24038)
ANIMA INTERNATIONAL CORP
234 S 5th Ave, City of Industry
(91746-2900)
PHONE...................................626 723-4960
MEI LI, *President*
Benjamin MA, *Vice Pres*
▲ EMP: 12
SQ FT: 4,000
SALES (est): 1.3MM **Privately Held**
WEB: www.animainternational.com
SIC: 3999 Pet supplies

(P-24039)
ANIMAL LOVERS PET CENTER
4305 Gravenstein Hwy S, Sebastopol
(95472-6032)
P.O. Box 2428, Sequim WA (98382-4343)
PHONE...................................360 683-0906
Alex Sladowski, *President*
G M Sladowski, *Vice Pres*
EMP: 14
SALES (est): 1.2MM **Privately Held**
WEB: www.animallovers.com
SIC: 3999 Pet supplies

(P-24040)
ANTHONYS CHRISTMAS TREES
Also Called: Anthonys Chistmas Tree
510 Alston Rd, Santa Barbara
(93108-2304)
PHONE...................................805 966-6668
Anthony Dal Bello, *President*
Maria Dal Bello, *Admin Sec*
EMP: 50
SALES (est): 5.1MM **Privately Held**
WEB: www.anthonyschristmastrees.com
SIC: 3999 5199 Wreaths, artificial; Christ-
mas trees, including artificial; Christmas
novelties

(P-24041)
AQUIESSE
2280 Ward Ave, Simi Valley (93065-1859)
PHONE...................................805 583-4600
Michael Joseph Horn, *Principal*
▲ EMP: 13
SALES (est): 1.3MM **Privately Held**
SIC: 3999 Candles

(P-24042)
ARRIVE-AI INC
16751 Millikan Ave, Irvine (92606-5009)
PHONE...................................949 221-0166
Jose Vasquez, *President*
EMP: 10
SALES (est): 283.1K **Privately Held**
SIC: 3999 Manufacturing industries

(P-24043)
**ARTEFFEX
CONCEPTIONEERING**
911 Mayo St, Los Angeles (90042-3122)
PHONE...................................818 506-5358
Dan O'Quinn, *Owner*
EMP: 10
SALES (est): 430K **Privately Held**
SIC: 3999 Puppets & marionettes

(P-24044)
**ARTIFICIAL GRASS
LIQUIDATORS**
Also Called: Agl
28071 Diaz Rd Ste A, Temecula
(92590-3475)
PHONE...................................951 677-3377
Dillon Georgian, *President*
EMP: 30 EST: 2015
SALES (est): 1.2MM **Privately Held**
SIC: 3999 Grasses, artificial & preserved

(P-24045)
ATA BOY INC
3171 Los Feliz Blvd # 205, Los Angeles
(90039-1536)
PHONE...................................323 644-0117
Alan Cushman, *President*
Judy Albright, *CFO*
Alex Perez, *Natl Sales Mgr*
▲ EMP: 31
SQ FT: 4,000
SALES (est): 3.3MM **Privately Held**
WEB: www.ata-boy.com
SIC: 3999 5947 Novelties, bric-a-brac &
hobby kits; gift shop

(P-24046)
ATLAS MATCH LLC
1337 Limerick Dr, Placentia (92870-3410)
PHONE...................................714 993-3328
Doug Lamp, *General Mgr*
EMP: 60
SALES (est): 2.2MM **Privately Held**
SIC: 3999

(P-24047)
BADGE CO
Also Called: The Badge Company
18261 Enterprise Ln Ste D, Huntington
Beach (92648-1245)
PHONE...................................714 842-3037
David J Bowen, *President*
EMP: 17 EST: 1979
SQ FT: 6,000
SALES (est): 1.6MM **Privately Held**
WEB: www.badge.com
SIC: 3999 Badges, metal: policemen, fire-
men, etc.

(P-24048)
BART MANUFACTURING INC
3787 Spinnaker Ct, Fremont (94538-6537)
PHONE...................................408 320-4373
Dave Weissbart, *CEO*
Trevor Weissbart, *Finance Mgr*
Joel Weissbart, *Opers Mgr*
EMP: 23
SALES (est): 3MM **Privately Held**
SIC: 3999 Chairs, hydraulic, barber &
beauty shop

(P-24049)
BEAD SHOPPE
2030 Douglas Blvd Ste 42, Roseville
(95661-3857)
PHONE...................................916 782-8642
Ester Morse, *Owner*
▲ EMP: 12
SALES (est): 571K **Privately Held**
WEB: www.thebeadshoppe.com
SIC: 3999 5094 Stringing beads; beads

(P-24050)
BERG MANUFACTURING INC
408 Aldo Ave, Santa Clara (95054-2301)
PHONE...................................408 727-2374
Doug Berg, *CEO*
Jamie Berg, *President*
EMP: 10
SALES (est): 1.4MM **Privately Held**
SIC: 3999 Barber & beauty shop equip-
ment

(P-24051)
**BLUEWICK HOME & BODY CO
LLC**
1701 Edgewood Dr, Alhambra
(91803-2916)
PHONE...................................626 282-2664
Arthur Hernandez,
Yoshi Maruyama,
▲ EMP: 12
SQ FT: 19,000
SALES (est): 1.2MM **Privately Held**
SIC: 3999 Candles

(P-24052)
**BRIGHT GLOW CANDLE
COMPANY INC (PA)**
110 Erie St, Pomona (91768-3342)
PHONE...................................909 469-0119
Richard Alcedo, *President*
▲ EMP: 39
SQ FT: 64,000
SALES (est): 8.4MM **Privately Held**
WEB: www.brightglowcandle.com
SIC: 3999 Candles

(P-24053)
CA937 AFJROTC
12431 Roscoe Blvd Ste 300, Sun Valley
(91352-3723)
PHONE...................................818 394-3600
EMP: 99 EST: 2013
SALES (est): 3.1MM **Privately Held**
SIC: 3999

(P-24054)
**CAESAR HARDWARE INTL LTD
(HQ)**
1445 Huntington Dr # 205, South Pasadena
(91030-4553)
PHONE...................................800 306-3829
Chao Xu, *CEO*
EMP: 20

SALES (est): 1.8MM
SALES (corp-wide): 310.2K **Privately
Held**
SIC: 3999 3429 Atomizers, toiletry; fire-
place equipment, hardware: andirons,
grates, screens
PA: Yuyao Super Wing Foreign Trade Co.,
Ltd
Room 1401, Yangguang International
Mansion, No.55, Yuli Road
Yuyao
574 626-2691

(P-24055)
**CALIFORNIA ACRYLIC INDS INC
(HQ)**
Also Called: Cal Spas
1462 E 9th St, Pomona (91766-3833)
PHONE...................................909 623-8781
Casey Loyd, *President*
Sheba Nobel, *CFO*
Buzz Loyd, *Admin Sec*
▲ EMP: 41
SQ FT: 300,000
SALES (est): 23.8MM **Privately Held**
SIC: 3999 3949 Hot tubs; billiard & pool
equipment & supplies, general

(P-24056)
**CALIFORNIA EXOTIC NOVLT
LLC**
1455 E Francis St, Ontario (91761-8329)
P.O. Box 50400 (91761-1078)
PHONE...................................909 606-1950
Susan Colvin, *CEO*
Josh Leduff, *Chief Mktg Ofcr*
Jackie White, *Vice Pres*
Aaron Buden, *Technology*
Jennifer Jackson, *Controller*
▲ EMP: 80
SQ FT: 66,000
SALES (est): 43.7MM **Privately Held**
WEB: www.calexotics.com
SIC: 3999 5947 Novelties, bric-a-brac &
hobby kits; novelties

(P-24057)
**CALIFORNIA INDUSTIRAL MFG
LLC (PA)**
1221 Independence Pl, Gridley
(95948-9341)
P.O. Box 830, Durham (95938-0830)
PHONE...................................530 846-9960
EMP: 15
SALES (est): 3.3MM **Privately Held**
SIC: 3999 Manufacturing industries

(P-24058)
**CAMBRO MANUFACTURING
COMPANY**
21558 Ferrero, City of Industry
(91789-5216)
PHONE...................................909 354-8962
EMP: 12
SALES (corp-wide): 308.4MM **Privately
Held**
SIC: 3999 Barber & beauty shop equip-
ment
PA: Cambro Manufacturing Company Inc
5801 Skylab Rd
Huntington Beach CA 92647
714 848-1555

(P-24059)
CANDAMAR DESIGNS INC
520 E Jamie Ave, La Habra (90631-6842)
P.O. Box 325, Bonsall (92003-0325)
PHONE...................................714 871-6190
Carla E Martin, *President*
▲ EMP: 30 EST: 1970
SQ FT: 12,500
SALES (est): 1.8MM **Privately Held**
WEB: www.candamar.com
SIC: 3999 5949 Sewing kits, novelty;
sewing, needlework & piece goods

(P-24060)
CANDLEBAY CO
3440 W Warner Ave Ste Cd, Santa Ana
(92704-5320)
PHONE...................................949 307-1807
Craig Dualba, *President*
▲ EMP: 10

SALES (est): 1.1MM **Privately Held**
WEB: www.candlebay.com
SIC: **3999** Candles

(P-24061)
CANNALOGIC
5404 Whitsett Ave 219, Valley Village
(91607-1615)
PHONE..................................619 458-0775
Jasmine Savoy, *President*
EMP: 17
SALES (est): 440.7K **Privately Held**
SIC: **3999** Manufacturing industries

(P-24062)
CCL LABEL INC
21481 8th St E, Sonoma (95476-9291)
PHONE..................................707 938-7800
Michelle Clayworth, *Comptroller*
William Miller, *Technical Mgr*
John Arters, *Graphic Designe*
Brian Casey, *Engineer*
David Giffin, *Engineer*
EMP: 12
SALES (corp-wide): 3.7B **Privately Held**
SIC: **3999** Barber & beauty shop equipment
HQ: Ccl Label, Inc.
161 Worcester Rd Ste 504
Framingham MA 01701
508 872-4511

(P-24063)
CDM COMPANY INC
12 Corporate Plaza Dr # 200, Newport
Beach (92660-7986)
PHONE..................................949 644-2820
Mitch Junkins, *President*
Mia Brown, *Vice Pres*
Wendy Diehl, *Vice Pres*
Dana Pescrillo, *Project Mgr*
Tina Vollmer, *Project Mgr*
▲ EMP: 23
SQ FT: 7,000
SALES (est): 3.3MM **Privately Held**
WEB: www.thecdmco.com
SIC: **3999** 3944 8742 5112 Novelties,
bric-a-brac & hobby kits; games, toys &
children's vehicles; marketing consulting
services; pens &/or pencils

(P-24064)
CERTIFIX INC
Also Called: Certifix Live Scan
700 N Valley St Ste B, Anaheim
(92801-3824)
PHONE..................................714 496-3850
Helmy El Mangoury, *CEO*
EMP: 14 EST: 2007
SALES (est): 1,000K **Privately Held**
WEB: www.certifixlivescan.com
SIC: **3999** 7381 Fingerprint equipment;
fingerprint service

(P-24065)
CES ELECTRONICS MFG INC
14731 Franklin Ave Ste E, Tustin
(92780-7221)
PHONE..................................714 505-3441
Nicolae Stafan, *Principal*
EMP: 11
SALES (est): 1.2MM **Privately Held**
SIC: **3999** Manufacturing industries

(P-24066)
CLAMP SWING PRICING CO INC
8386 Capwell Dr, Oakland (94621-2114)
PHONE..................................510 567-1600
Benjamin Garfinkle, *President*
Wilma Garfinkle, *Ch of Bd*
Kamran Faizi, *Sales Mgr*
▲ EMP: 30
SQ FT: 47,000
SALES (est): 4.5MM **Privately Held**
WEB: www.clampswing.com
SIC: **3999** Identification plates

(P-24067)
CMTG
164 W Highland Ave, San Bernardino
(92405-4016)
PHONE..................................310 908-6687
Rick Carpentiero, *CEO*
EMP: 10

SALES: 1,000K **Privately Held**
WEB: www.cmtg.com
SIC: **3999** Manufacturing industries

(P-24068)
CONSOLIDATED TRAINING LLC
144 Holm Rd Spc 47, Watsonville
(95076-2428)
PHONE..................................831 768-8888
EMP: 22
SALES: 15MM **Privately Held**
SIC: **3999**

(P-24069)
COUNTRY FLORAL SUPPLY INC
6909 Las Positas Rd Ste F, Livermore
(94551-5113)
PHONE..................................925 960-9823
Michelle Luke, *Manager*
EMP: 53
SALES (corp-wide): 48.5MM **Privately Held**
SIC: **3999** 5193 Artificial trees & flowers;
artificial flowers
PA: Country Floral Supply, Inc.
3802 Weatherly Cir
Westlake Village CA 91361
805 520-8026

(P-24070)
CRP SPORTS LLC
3191 Red Hill Ave Ste 250, Costa Mesa
(92626-3495)
PHONE..................................949 395-7759
Steven Senft, *Chief Mktg Ofcr*
Steve Patel, *Exec VP*
John Rudow, *Sales Dir*
EMP: 10
SALES (est): 614.4K **Privately Held**
SIC: **3999** Manufacturing industries

(P-24071)
CRYOPACIFIC INCORPORATED
641 S Palm St Ste G, La Habra
(90631-5784)
P.O. Box 626 (90633-0626)
PHONE..................................562 697-7904
Randy Reynoso, *Principal*
EMP: 10
SALES (est): 990.8K **Privately Held**
SIC: **3999** Manufacturing industries

(P-24072)
D&H MANUFACTURING COMPANY
Also Called: D&H / R&D
49235 Milmont Dr, Fremont (94538-7349)
PHONE..................................510 770-5100
Marie Dunaway, *Human Res Mgr*
EMP: 15 EST: 2015
SALES (est): 1.6MM **Privately Held**
SIC: **3999** Manufacturing industries

(P-24073)
DANGEROUS COFFEE CO LLC
3644 Midway Dr, San Diego (92110-5201)
PHONE..................................619 405-8291
Quentin Sponselee,
EMP: 10
SALES (est): 364.9K **Privately Held**
SIC: **3999** Manufacturing industries

(P-24074)
DARYLS PET SHOP
208 E State St, Redlands (92373-5233)
PHONE..................................909 793-1788
Leslie Triplette, *President*
EMP: 15
SALES (est): 848K **Privately Held**
SIC: **3999** Pet supplies; boat models, except toy; models, general, except toy; railroad models, except toy

(P-24075)
DAT FARMS INC
24514 Oro Valley Rd, Auburn (95602-8229)
PHONE..................................408 848-8060
Toshio Nakashima, *President*
Dennis Milar, *Vice Pres*
EMP: 15
SQ FT: 38,800
SALES: 1.5MM **Privately Held**
WEB: www.datfarms.com
SIC: **3999** Flowers, artificial & preserved

(P-24076)
DB STUDIOS INC
17032 Murphy Ave, Irvine (92614-5914)
PHONE..................................949 833-0100
Darin Rasmussen, *President*
Mark Bense, *CFO*
Mike Mikyska, *Vice Pres*
John Riley, *Vice Pres*
Alexis Lowery, *Graphic Designe*
▲ EMP: 35
SQ FT: 22,500
SALES (est): 4.3MM
SALES (corp-wide): 1.1B **Publicly Held**
WEB: www.displayboys.com
SIC: **3999** 3993 3993 7319 Advertising
display products; signs & advertising specialties; advertising, promotional & trade
show services; display advertising service; commercial art & graphic design
PA: Innerworkings, Inc.
600 W Chicago Ave Ste 850
Chicago IL 60654
312 642-3700

(P-24077)
DESERT SHADES INC
5014 W Jefferson Blvd, Los Angeles
(90016-3925)
PHONE..................................323 731-5000
Benny Nadal, *Regional Mgr*
Marlene Nadal, *Admin Sec*
▲ EMP: 14
SQ FT: 4,400
SALES (est): 1.3MM **Privately Held**
SIC: **3999** Shades, lamp or candle

(P-24078)
DEVELOPLUS INC
1575 Magnolia Ave, Corona (92879-2073)
PHONE..................................951 738-8595
Deorao K Agrey, *CEO*
▲ EMP: 70
SQ FT: 40,000
SALES (est): 15.4MM **Privately Held**
SIC: **3999** 5087 Hair & hair-based products; beauty parlor equipment & supplies

(P-24079)
DIMENSION ONE SPAS INC (HQ)
1819 Aston Ave Ste 105, Carlsbad
(92008-7338)
PHONE..................................800 345-7727
Robert Hallam, *President*
Linda Hallam, *Ch of Bd*
Terry Hauser, *Vice Pres*
Phil Sandner, *Vice Pres*
Sam Sims, *Vice Pres*
▼ EMP: 160
SQ FT: 125,000
SALES (est): 24.9MM
SALES (corp-wide): 1.6B **Privately Held**
WEB: www.d1spas.com
SIC: **3999** 3088 Hot tubs; plastics plumbing fixtures
PA: Jacuzzi Brands Llc
13925 City Center Dr # 200
Chino Hills CA 91709
909 606-1416

(P-24080)
DKP DESIGNS INC
110 Maryland St, El Segundo (90245-4115)
PHONE..................................310 322-6000
Deborah P Koppel, *President*
Brad Koppel, *Vice Pres*
Diana Rodriguez, *Vice Pres*
Yolanda Silver, *Executive*
Trevor Koppel, *Pharmacy Dir*
▲ EMP: 15 EST: 1996
SQ FT: 4,000
SALES (est): 2.1MM **Privately Held**
WEB: www.dkpdesigns.com
SIC: **3999** Advertising display products

(P-24081)
DOGSPORT INC
Also Called: Dogsport International
244 S Palm Dr, Beverly Hills (90212-3516)
PHONE..................................323 362-6450
Hope Adams, *President*
Jarson Silvers, *CFO*
EMP: 11
SALES: 100K **Privately Held**
SIC: **3999** 7389 Pet supplies;

(P-24082)
DOLPHIN SPAS INC
701 W Foothill Blvd, Azusa (91702-2348)
PHONE..................................626 334-0099
Kareem Azizeh, *President*
EMP: 11
SQ FT: 27,000
SALES: 2MM **Privately Held**
WEB: www.dolphinspas.com
SIC: **3999** 5999 Hot tubs; spas & hot tubs

(P-24083)
E-LIQ CUBE INC (PA)
13515 Alondra Blvd, Santa Fe Springs
(90670-5602)
PHONE..................................562 537-9454
▲ EMP: 18
SALES: 1MM **Privately Held**
SIC: **3999**

(P-24084)
EATYOURMEALSCOM LLC
4418 Deer Ridge Rd, Danville
(94506-6017)
PHONE..................................925 984-5452
Michael Hughes,
EMP: 12
SALES (est): 329.6K **Privately Held**
SIC: **3999** Manufacturing industries

(P-24085)
ECO-SHELL INC
5230 Grange Rd, Corning (96021-9239)
PHONE..................................530 824-8794
Charles R Crain Jr, *CEO*
Chris Tomasetti, *Sales Dir*
◆ EMP: 22 EST: 1996
SQ FT: 60,000
SALES (est): 4.4MM **Privately Held**
WEB: www.ecoshell.com
SIC: **3999** Nut shells, grinding, from purchased nuts

(P-24086)
ECOLIGHT INC
Also Called: Stone Candles
1660 Lincoln Blvd, Santa Monica
(90404-3712)
PHONE..................................310 450-7444
Daniel Wainer, *President*
Michael Wainer, *Manager*
EMP: 13
SALES: 1.1MM **Privately Held**
SIC: **3999** 5199 5999 Candles; candles;
candle shops

(P-24087)
ED JONES COMPANY
2834 8th St, Berkeley (94710-2707)
PHONE..................................510 704-0704
Chester F Stegman, *President*
Krista Stegman, *Treasurer*
Jonathan Bloom, *Vice Pres*
Janet Johnson, *Office Mgr*
Elisabeth Rusca, *Admin Sec*
EMP: 10
SQ FT: 5,000
SALES (est): 910.7K **Privately Held**
WEB: www.edjonesco.com
SIC: **3999** 5199 Badges, metal: policemen, firemen, etc.; badges

(P-24088)
EDGATE CORRELATION SVCS LLC
5473 Krny Vlla Rd Ste 300, San Diego
(92123)
PHONE..................................858 712-9341
Sara Schiff,
Rick Wells,
EMP: 25
SALES: 950K **Privately Held**
SIC: **3999** Education aids, devices & supplies

(P-24089)
EDWARDS LIFESCIENCE FING LLC
1 Edwards Way, Irvine (92614-5688)
PHONE..................................949 250-3480
Mike Mussaollem, *President*
EMP: 13
SALES (est): 1.2MM
SALES (corp-wide): 3.4B **Publicly Held**
SIC: **3999** Advertising curtains

PA: Edwards Lifesciences Corp
1 Edwards Way
Irvine CA 92614
949 250-2500

(P-24090)
EG WEAR INC
4512 Harlin Dr Ste A, Sacramento
(95826-9719)
PHONE..................................916 361-1508
Mark Wolfgram, *Principal*
EMP: 11
SALES (est): 1.2MM Privately Held
SIC: 3999 2759 Embroidery kits; screen
printing

(P-24091)
ELAFREE INC
Also Called: Creations Salon
17779 Main St Ste F&G, Irvine
(92614-4796)
PHONE..................................949 724-9390
Aaron Gaskin, *President*
Kimberly C Gaskin, *Corp Secy*
Kimberly Gaskin, *Executive*
EMP: 12
SQ FT: 2,000
SALES: 410K Privately Held
SIC: 3999 Hair & hair-based products

(P-24092)
ETTORE PRODUCTS CO
2100 N Loop Rd, Alameda (94502-8010)
P.O. Box 2164, Oakland (94621-0064)
PHONE..................................510 748-4130
Michael A Smahlik, *Principal*
Diane Smahlik, *Corp Secy*
Rose N Bisbiglia, *Human Resources*
Chuck Chan, *QC Mgr*
John Becker, *Natl Sales Mgr*
▲ EMP: 85
SQ FT: 30,000
SALES (est): 21.2MM Privately Held
WEB: www.ettore.com
SIC: 3999 Window squeegees

(P-24093)
EVO MANUFACTURING INC
1829 W Commonwealth Ave, Fullerton
(92833-3013)
PHONE..................................714 879-8913
EMP: 10
SALES (est): 822K Privately Held
SIC: 3999 Manufacturing industries

(P-24094)
FANCY MODELS CORP
3500 Yale Way, Fremont (94538-6180)
PHONE..................................510 683-0819
Ching Yu, *President*
EMP: 10
SQ FT: 11,000
SALES (est): 879.6K Privately Held
WEB: www.fancymodels.com
SIC: 3999 3944 Models, general, except
toy; games, toys & children's vehicles

(P-24095)
FLAME & WAX INC
Also Called: Voluspa
2900 Mccabe Way, Irvine (92614-6239)
PHONE..................................949 752-4000
Troy Arntsen, *President*
Erika Roybal, *Executive Asst*
Oanh Tran, *Accountant*
Crystal Castillo, *Human Resources*
Jennifer Hicks, *Purch Mgr*
▲ EMP: 31
SALES (est): 6.5MM Privately Held
SIC: 3999 2844 Candles; toilet prepara-
tions

(P-24096)
FLAME OUT INC
Also Called: Deist Safety
2623 N San Fernando Rd, Los Angeles
(90065-1316)
PHONE..................................323 221-0000
James F Deist, *President*
▲ EMP: 20
SQ FT: 8,000
SALES (est): 1.1MM Privately Held
WEB: www.flameout.net
SIC: 3999 Fire extinguishers, portable

(P-24097)
FOIL CORE INC
5452 Mcfadden Ave, Huntington Beach
(92649-1241)
PHONE..................................714 891-1695
Vince Long, *CEO*
Lisa Long, *Vice Pres*
Anthony Longo, *Vice Pres*
Lisa Longo, *Opers Mgr*
Vince Longo, *Manager*
▲ EMP: 23 EST: 2009
SALES (est): 1.6MM Privately Held
SIC: 3999 Manufacturing industries

(P-24098)
FOLKMANIS INC
1219 Park Ave, Emeryville (94608-3607)
PHONE..................................510 658-7677
Atis Folkmanis, *President*
Dan Folkmanis, *Vice Pres*
Judy Folkmanis, *Vice Pres*
Jack Tallman, *Human Res Mgr*
Elaine Kollias, *Mktg Dir*
◆ EMP: 40
SALES (est): 4.8MM Privately Held
WEB: www.folkmanis.com
SIC: 3999 3942 Puppets & marionettes;
dolls & stuffed toys

(P-24099)
**FORRESTER EASTLAND
CORPORATION**
Also Called: Versa Stage
1320 Storm Pkwy, Torrance (90501-5041)
PHONE..................................310 784-2464
Clive Forrester, *CEO*
Erik Eastland, *President*
EMP: 27
SQ FT: 17,900
SALES (est): 6.4MM Privately Held
WEB: www.allaccessinc.com
SIC: 3999 7819 Stage hardware & equip-
ment, except lighting; equipment & prop
rental, motion picture production

(P-24100)
**FOSS LAMPSHADE STUDIOS
INC (PA)**
1357 International Blvd, Oakland
(94606-4303)
P.O. Box 1795, San Leandro (94577-0179)
PHONE..................................510 534-4133
Mark Foss, *President*
EMP: 12
SALES (est): 881.6K Privately Held
SIC: 3999 3645 Lamp shade frames; resi-
dential lighting fixtures

(P-24101)
FOUNTAINHEAD INDUSTRIES
700 N San Vicente Blvd G910, West Holly-
wood (90069-5061)
PHONE..................................310 248-2444
Hal Kline, *President*
EMP: 20
SALES (est): 536.3K Privately Held
SIC: 3999 Chairs, hydraulic, barber &
beauty shop

(P-24102)
FRINGE STUDIO LLC
17909 Fitch, Irvine (92614-6016)
P.O. Box 3663, Culver City (90231-3663)
PHONE..................................949 387-9680
Scott Kingsland, *Mng Member*
Todd Kirshner,
▲ EMP: 10
SALES (est): 4.8MM Privately Held
SIC: 3999 Candles; shades, lamp or can-
dle
PA: Punch Studio, Llc
6025 W Slauson Ave
Culver City CA 90230
-

(P-24103)
GALAXY ENTERPRISES INC
Also Called: Galaxy Medical
5411 Sheila St, Commerce (90040-2103)
PHONE..................................323 728-3980
Henry Talei, *Principal*
▲ EMP: 25 EST: 1949
SQ FT: 40,000

SALES (est): 3.3MM Privately Held
WEB: www.galaxymfg.com
SIC: 3999 3843 3841 Barber & beauty
shop equipment; dental chairs; medical
instruments & equipment, blood & bone
work

(P-24104)
GARMON CORPORATION
Also Called: Naturvet
27461 Via Industria, Temecula
(92590-3752)
PHONE..................................951 296-6308
Scott J Garmon, *President*
Joe Da Silva, *President*
Joe Dasilva, *Senior VP*
J Max Garmon, *Principal*
Brynna Macias, *Graphic Designe*
▲ EMP: 62
SQ FT: 18,500
SALES (est): 33.1K Privately Held
WEB: www.naturvet.com
SIC: 3999 Pet supplies

(P-24105)
GEMINI INDUSTRIES INC
1910 E Warner Ave Ste G, Santa Ana
(92705-5548)
PHONE..................................949 553-4255
Melissa Long, *Human Res Dir*
EMP: 11
SALES (est): 1.1MM Privately Held
SIC: 3999 Barber & beauty shop equip-
ment

(P-24106)
GENERAL WAX CO INC (PA)
Also Called: General Wax & Candle Co
6863 Beck Ave, North Hollywood
(91605-6206)
P.O. Box 9398 (91609-1398)
PHONE..................................818 765-5800
Carol Lazar, *CEO*
Mike Tapp, *President*
Colton Lazar, *Corp Secy*
Jerry Baker, *Executive*
Martha Smith, *Office Mgr*
◆ EMP: 85
SQ FT: 120,000
SALES (est): 21.4MM Privately Held
WEB: www.genwax.com
SIC: 3999 Candles

(P-24107)
**GERMAINS SEED TECHNOLOGY
INC**
8333 Swanston Ln, Gilroy (95020-4517)
PHONE..................................408 848-8120
Paul Mullan, *CEO*
Patrick Clode, *Treasurer*
Catherine Farr, *Admin Sec*
▲ EMP: 39
SALES (est): 6MM
SIC: 3999 Seeds, coated or treated, from
purchased seeds
HQ: Germain's(U.K.)Limited
Hansa Road
King's Lynn
155 377-4012

(P-24108)
GLOBAL DOLLS CORP
1903 Aviation Blvd, Lincoln (95648-9557)
PHONE..................................916 645-3000
Dieter Piwek, *President*
Laurel Piwek, *Vice Pres*
EMP: 10
SQ FT: 12,000
SALES (est): 760K Privately Held
SIC: 3999 5199 Doll wigs (hair); wigs

(P-24109)
GLOBAL ENTERPRISE MFG INC
1560 S Harris Ct, Anaheim (92806-5931)
P.O. Box 590, La Mirada (90637-0590)
PHONE..................................657 234-1150
Jacob Bahbah, *President*
Andrew J Bahbah, *Vice Pres*
EMP: 22
SALES (est): 661.1K Privately Held
SIC: 3999 Manufacturing industries

(P-24110)
GLOBAL SYN-TURF INC
6319 Chalet Dr, Commerce (90040-3705)
PHONE..................................562 928-2800
EMP: 10
SALES (est): 930.9K
SALES (corp-wide): 2.6MM Privately
Held
SIC: 3999 Atomizers, toiletry
PA: Global Syn-Turf, Inc.
5960 Inglewood Dr Ste 150
Pleasanton CA 94588
877 796-8873

(P-24111)
GLOBALUXE INC
Also Called: Candle Crafters
2280 Ward Ave, Simi Valley (93065-1859)
PHONE..................................805 583-4600
Michael Joseph Horn, *CEO*
▲ EMP: 20
SALES (est): 3.1MM Privately Held
WEB: www.globaluxe.com
SIC: 3999 5199 5999 Candles; candles;
candle shops

(P-24112)
**GOLD LEAF & METALLIC
POWDERS**
6001 Santa Monica Blvd, Los Angeles
(90038-1807)
PHONE..................................323 769-4888
Scott Holland, *Manager*
Salvador Castillo, *Purchasing*
EMP: 50
SALES (est): 1.6MM Privately Held
WEB: www.glandmp.com
SIC: 3999 3497 Manufacturing industries;
metal foil & leaf

(P-24113)
GOLDEN SUPREME INC
12304 Mccann Dr, Santa Fe Springs
(90670-3333)
PHONE..................................562 903-1063
Ross Stillwagon, *President*
Ricardo J Fischbach, *Shareholder*
Fernando Fischbach, *Treasurer*
▲ EMP: 30
SQ FT: 13,000
SALES (est): 3.3MM Privately Held
WEB: www.goldensupreme.com
SIC: 3999 5087 Hair curlers, designed for
beauty parlors; beauty parlor equipment &
supplies

(P-24114)
H & H SPECIALTIES INC
14850 Don Julian Rd Ste B, City of Industry
(91746-3122)
PHONE..................................626 575-0776
Reid Neslage, *Owner*
Mary Louise Higgins, *Principal*
EMP: 31 EST: 1967
SQ FT: 30,000
SALES (est): 4.5MM Privately Held
WEB: www.hhspecialties.com
SIC: 3999 3625 Stage hardware & equip-
ment, except lighting; relays & industrial
controls

(P-24115)
H P GROUP
5070 Lindsay Ct, Chino (91710-5746)
PHONE..................................909 364-1069
Tim Zhu, *Owner*
EMP: 10 EST: 2001
SALES (est): 509K Privately Held
SIC: 3999 Candles

(P-24116)
HAIR BY COUTURE INC
1010 W Magnolia Blvd, Burbank
(91506-1649)
PHONE..................................310 848-7676
Olga Oks, *President*
Victor Susanin, *President*
Irina Khlebopros, *CFO*
Vanessa Lopez, *CFO*
Kirill Kizyuk, *Senior VP*
◆ EMP: 12
SQ FT: 2,000
SALES (est): 81.3K Privately Held
SIC: 3999 Hair & hair-based products

(P-24117)
HIGH TECH PET PRODUCTS INC
2111 Portola Rd A, Ventura (93003-7723)
PHONE..................................805 644-1797
Nicholas Donge, *President*
Bob Schilken, *Vice Pres*
▲ EMP: 44 EST: 1980
SALES (est): 4.5MM **Privately Held**
WEB: www.hitecpet.com
SIC: 3999 Pet supplies

(P-24118)
HOGAN MFG INC (PA)
19527 Mchenry Ave, Escalon (95320-9613)
P.O. Box 398 (95320-0398)
PHONE..................................209 838-7323
Mark Hogan, *President*
John Fusco, *Vice Pres*
Jeff Hogan, *Vice Pres*
Paul Reichmuth, *Vice Pres*
Jan Consoli, *Executive*
▲ EMP: 150 EST: 1944
SQ FT: 43,000
SALES (est): 36.9MM **Privately Held**
WEB: www.hoganmfg.com
SIC: 3999 3441 3443 1791 Wheelchair lifts; fabricated structural metal; fabricated plate work (boiler shop); structural steel erection

(P-24119)
HOGAN MFG INC
Lift-U
1520 1st St, Escalon (95320-1703)
P.O. Box 398 (95320-0398)
PHONE..................................209 838-2400
Paul Riechmuth, *Admin Mgr*
Jon Durham, *Manager*
EMP: 150
SALES (corp-wide): 36.9MM **Privately Held**
WEB: www.hoganmfg.com
SIC: 3999 3842 3714 3534 Wheelchair lifts; surgical appliances & supplies; motor vehicle parts & accessories; elevators & moving stairways
PA: Hogan Mfg., Inc.
    19527 Mchenry Ave
    Escalon CA 95320
    209 838-7323

(P-24120)
HOLIDAY FOLIAGE INC
2592 Otay Center Dr, San Diego (92154-7611)
PHONE..................................619 661-9094
Kristine Vanzutphen, *CEO*
William Vanzutphen Jr, *CFO*
Juanita Keller, *Vice Pres*
Peter Vanzutphen, *Legal Staff*
Christina Contreras, *Accounts Mgr*
▲ EMP: 50
SQ FT: 18,000
SALES (est): 7.6MM **Privately Held**
WEB: www.holidayfoliage.com
SIC: 3999 Artificial trees & flowers; flowers, artificial & preserved; wreaths, artificial

(P-24121)
HOSTRUP INDUSTRIES INC
2244 Federal Ave, Los Angeles (90064-1404)
PHONE..................................310 477-6770
Kenneth Anderson, *President*
EMP: 15
SALES (est): 881.5K **Privately Held**
SIC: 3999 Manufacturing industries

(P-24122)
HSE USA INC (PA)
5832 E 61st St, Commerce (90040-3412)
PHONE..................................323 278-0888
Nelson Yip, *President*
Herman Ye, *Marketing Staff*
EMP: 10
SQ FT: 30,000
SALES (est): 3MM **Privately Held**
SIC: 3999 Candles

(P-24123)
HUDSON INDUSTRIES INC
Also Called: Hudson Construction
11107 Lake Blvd, Felton (95018-9800)
PHONE..................................831 335-4431
Nathan Hudson, *President*

EMP: 10 EST: 2011
SALES (est): 25K **Privately Held**
SIC: 3999 Manufacturing industries

(P-24124)
HUNTCO INDUSTRIES LLC
22536 La Quilla Dr, Chatsworth (91311-1221)
P.O. Box 4026 (91313-4026)
PHONE..................................818 700-1600
David C Hunt, *Principal*
EMP: 11
SALES (est): 969.3K **Privately Held**
SIC: 3999 Manufacturing industries

(P-24125)
HUNTER/GRATZNER INDUSTRIES
4107 Redwood Ave, Los Angeles (90066-5603)
PHONE..................................310 578-9929
Ian Hunter, *President*
Shannon Gans, *CFO*
Matthew Gratzner, *Admin Sec*
EMP: 10
SQ FT: 7,500
SALES (est): 2MM **Privately Held**
WEB: www.newdealstudios.com
SIC: 3999 Models, except toy

(P-24126)
HYDROFARM LLC (PA)
2249 S Mcdowell Blvd Ext, Petaluma (94954-5661)
PHONE..................................800 634-9990
Peter Wardenburg, *President*
Jeff Peterson, *Corp Secy*
◆ EMP: 38
SALES (est): 12.7MM **Privately Held**
WEB: www.hydrofarm.com
SIC: 3999 3648 Lighting equipment; hydroponic equipment

(P-24127)
ICON LINE INC
Also Called: I.C.O.N. Salon
20600 Ventura Blvd Ste C, Woodland Hills (91364-6691)
PHONE..................................818 709-4266
Chiara Scudieri, *President*
▲ EMP: 12
SQ FT: 1,800
SALES (est): 1.2MM **Privately Held**
WEB: www.iconproducts.com
SIC: 3999 5999 Hair, dressing of, for the trade; hair care products

(P-24128)
INNOVATIVE CASEWORK MFG INC
12261 Industry St, Garden Grove (92841-2815)
PHONE..................................714 890-9100
Valerie Perez, *Principal*
EMP: 25 EST: 2017
SALES (est): 607.8K **Privately Held**
SIC: 3999 Manufacturing industries

(P-24129)
INTEGRATED MFG SOLUTIONS LLC
2590 Pioneer Ave Ste C, Vista (92081-8427)
PHONE..................................760 599-4300
Baophuong Nguyen, *President*
EMP: 24 EST: 2007
SQ FT: 2,000
SALES (est): 3MM **Privately Held**
SIC: 3999

(P-24130)
INTERCONTINENTAL N MAS
Also Called: Inp
11492 Refinement Rd, Rancho Cordova (95742-7300)
PHONE..................................916 631-1674
Lana MA, *President*
John MA, *Vice Pres*
▲ EMP: 20
SALES (est): 2.2MM **Privately Held**
WEB: www.intercontinentalnail.com
SIC: 3999 Fingernails, artificial

(P-24131)
INTERNATIONAL DECORATIVES CO
Also Called: Koala Kountry Folage
27220 N Lake Wohlford Rd, Valley Center (92082-6721)
P.O. Box 2064, Grand Lake CO (80447-2064)
PHONE..................................760 749-2682
Fax: 760 749-3671
EMP: 25
SQ FT: 2,000
SALES (est): 2.4MM **Privately Held**
WEB: www.intdecco.com
SIC: 3999 5193

(P-24132)
INTERSTATE CABINET INC
Also Called: Interstate Design Industry
1631 Pomona Rd Ste B, Corona (92880-6927)
PHONE..................................951 736-0777
James L Fago, *President*
Nancy Fago-Fleer, *Admin Sec*
▲ EMP: 30 EST: 1975
SQ FT: 56,000
SALES (est): 2.8MM **Privately Held**
WEB: www.interstatedesignind.com
SIC: 3999 Barber & beauty shop equipment

(P-24133)
IRVINE & JACHENS INC
6700 Mission St, Daly City (94014-2031)
PHONE..................................650 755-4715
Richard Stegman, *President*
EMP: 10
SQ FT: 4,500
SALES (est): 739.5K **Privately Held**
WEB: www.irvineandjachensbadges.com
SIC: 3999 3429 3965 Badges, metal: policemen, firemen, etc.; saddlery hardware; buckles & buckle parts

(P-24134)
J & A JEFFERY INC
Also Called: Western Stabilization
395 Industrial Way Ste B, Dixon (95620-9787)
P.O. Box 1022 (95620-1022)
PHONE..................................707 678-0369
John Jordan, *CEO*
Judy Jeffery, *President*
Ashley Jeffery, *Vice Pres*
EMP: 50
SQ FT: 16,000
SALES (est): 12.2MM **Privately Held**
WEB: www.wstabilization.com
SIC: 3999 0711 Custom pulverizing & grinding of plastic materials; soil preparation services

(P-24135)
J C INDUSTRIES INC
3977 Camino Ranchero, Camarillo (93012-5066)
PHONE..................................805 389-4040
▼ EMP: 15
SQ FT: 12,000
SALES (est): 980K **Privately Held**
WEB: www.jcind.com
SIC: 3999

(P-24136)
JACUZZI BRANDS LLC
Also Called: Sundance Spas
13925 City Center Dr, Chino Hills (91709-5437)
P.O. Box 2900, Chino (91708-2900)
PHONE..................................909 606-1416
Diana Fox, *Manager*
EMP: 50
SALES (corp-wide): 1.6B **Privately Held**
SIC: 3999 Hot tubs
PA: Jacuzzi Brands Llc
    13925 City Center Dr # 200
    Chino Hills CA 91709
    909 606-1416

(P-24137)
JNJ OPERATIONS LLC
Also Called: Jackandjillkidscom
859 E Sepulveda Blvd, Carson (90745-6130)
PHONE..................................855 525-6545
EMP: 20

SALES (est): 504.6K **Privately Held**
SIC: 3999

(P-24138)
JOANN LAMMENS
Also Called: Gina T Interior Accents
2152 Bonita Ave, La Verne (91750-4915)
PHONE..................................909 593-8478
Joann Lammens, *Owner*
EMP: 12
SQ FT: 4,000
SALES (est): 1.3MM **Privately Held**
SIC: 3999 5193 Artificial flower arrangements; artificial flowers

(P-24139)
JOE BLASCO ENTERPRISES INC
Also Called: Joe Blasco Cosmetics
1285 N Valdivia Way A, Palm Springs (92262-5428)
PHONE..................................323 467-4949
Joseph D Blasco, *President*
▲ EMP: 52
SQ FT: 13,788
SALES (est): 3.4MM **Privately Held**
WEB: www.joeblasco.com
SIC: 3999 7231 2844 Barber & beauty shop equipment; cosmetology school; toilet preparations
PA: Joe Blasco Make-Up Center West, Inc.
    1285 N Valdivia Way A
    Palm Springs CA 92262
    323 467-4949

(P-24140)
JT MANUFACTURING INC
1122 Wrigley Way, Milpitas (95035-5418)
PHONE..................................408 674-4338
Joe V Tran, *Principal*
EMP: 12
SALES (est): 184.1K **Privately Held**
SIC: 3999 Manufacturing industries

(P-24141)
JUUL LABS INC (PA)
560 20th St, San Francisco (94107-4344)
PHONE..................................415 829-2336
Kevin Burns, *CEO*
James Thomas Monsees, *Co-Founder*
Adam Bower, *Business Mgr*
EMP: 198
SQ FT: 8,000
SALES (est): 173.2MM **Privately Held**
SIC: 3999 Cigarette & cigar products & accessories

(P-24142)
K-TOPS PLASTIC MFG INC
15051 Don Julian Rd, City of Industry (91746-3302)
PHONE..................................626 575-9679
Charles Hsieh, *President*
Bruce Hsieh, *Corp Secy*
Nancy Hsieh, *Vice Pres*
▲ EMP: 22 EST: 2005
SALES (est): 3.1MM **Privately Held**
SIC: 3999

(P-24143)
K9 BALLISTICS INC
708 Via Alondra, Camarillo (93012-8713)
PHONE..................................805 233-8103
Jenny Chickasawah, *Human Resources*
Sean Farley, *CEO*
EMP: 16
SQ FT: 20,000
SALES (est): 1.3MM **Privately Held**
SIC: 3999 Pet supplies

(P-24144)
KAHOOTS INC
6525 Bisby Lake Ave, San Diego (92119-2600)
PHONE..................................619 337-0825
EMP: 10 **Privately Held**
SIC: 3999 Pet supplies
PA: Kahoots, Inc.
    947 Main St
    Ramona CA 92065
    -

P R O D U C T S & S V C S

(P-24145)
KAYLINE ENTERPRISES INC
3400 E Airport Way, Long Beach
(90806-2412)
P.O. Box 542, Milledgeville IL (61051-0542)
PHONE....................................562 595-4515
Dorothy Reiner, *President*
EMP: 45
SQ FT: 36,000
SALES (est): 4.8MM **Privately Held**
SIC: 3999 Barber & beauty shop equipment; parasols & frames: handles, parts & trimmings

(P-24146)
KDS NAIL PRODUCTS
Also Called: Texchem Chemical
8580 Younger Creek Dr, Sacramento
(95828-1000)
PHONE....................................916 381-9358
Dat Vinh MA, *Principal*
EMP: 14
SALES (est): 1.3MM **Privately Held**
SIC: 3999 2899 Fingernails, artificial; chemical preparations; oils & essential oils

(P-24147)
KERBER INDUSTRIES INC
166 San Lorenzo St, Pomona
(91766-2334)
PHONE....................................909 319-0877
Jeff Kerber, *President*
EMP: 22
SALES (est): 1MM **Privately Held**
SIC: 3999 Atomizers, toiletry

(P-24148)
KIMBALL NELSON INC
Also Called: Heaven or Las Vegas
7740 Lemona Ave, Van Nuys (91405-1136)
PHONE....................................310 636-0081
David Kip Smith, *President*
Nina Lazutin, *Vice Pres*
EMP: 15
SQ FT: 6,000
SALES: 900K **Privately Held**
WEB: www.rentneon.com
SIC: 3999 Theatrical scenery

(P-24149)
KITANICA MANUFACTURING
867 Isabella St, Oakland (94607-3429)
PHONE....................................707 272-7286
Leonard Riccio, *Principal*
EMP: 18
SALES (est): 226.4K **Privately Held**
SIC: 3999 Manufacturing industries

(P-24150)
KNORR BEESWAX PRODUCTS INC
14906 Via De La Valle, Del Mar
(92014-4304)
PHONE....................................760 431-2007
Steven C Knorr, *President*
Susan Prickett, *Manager*
▲ **EMP:** 13
SQ FT: 5,000
SALES: 900K **Privately Held**
WEB: www.knorrbeeswax.com
SIC: 3999 Candles

(P-24151)
KNT MANUFACTURING INC
39760 Eureka Dr, Newark (94560-4808)
PHONE....................................510 896-1699
Keith Ngo, *CEO*
Javier De La Torre, *Director*
EMP: 32
SALES (est): 6.6MM **Privately Held**
SIC: 3999 Barber & beauty shop equipment

(P-24152)
KS INDUSTRIES
3160 Camino Del Rio S # 116, San Diego
(92108-8933)
PHONE....................................858 344-1146
Krystle Moore, *CEO*
EMP: 10 **EST:** 2014
SALES (est): 794.7K **Privately Held**
SIC: 3999 Manufacturing industries

(P-24153)
KURZ TRANSFER PRODUCTS LP
415 N Smith Ave, Corona (92880-6905)
PHONE....................................951 738-9521
Hastings Kurz, *Principal*
EMP: 40
SALES (corp-wide): 73.8MM **Privately Held**
SIC: 3999 Atomizers, toiletry
PA: Kurz Transfer Products, Lp
3200 Woodpark Blvd
Charlotte NC 28206
704 927-3700

(P-24154)
KYMERA INDUSTRIES INC
14735 Manzanita Dr, Fontana
(92335-2586)
PHONE....................................909 228-7194
Jennifer Hatch, *CEO*
EMP: 10
SALES (est): 214K **Privately Held**
SIC: 3999 Manufacturing industries

(P-24155)
L & B LABORATORIES INC
1660 Mabury Rd, San Jose (95133-1032)
PHONE....................................408 251-7888
Viet Le, *Principal*
Rick Edlund, *Office Mgr*
EMP: 18
SALES (est): 2.1MM **Privately Held**
SIC: 3999 Barber & beauty shop equipment

(P-24156)
LA RUTAN
Also Called: Emily's Classic Beauty Salon
6284 Long Beach Blvd, Long Beach
(90805-2160)
P.O. Box 21398 (90801-4398)
PHONE....................................310 940-7956
Emily Fields, *President*
Aleaha Fields, *Vice Pres*
▲ **EMP:** 20
SQ FT: 600
SALES (est): 1.5MM **Privately Held**
SIC: 3999 2678 2676 2842 Hair, dressing of, for the trade; wigs, including doll wigs, toupees or wiglets; memorandum books, notebooks & looseleaf filler paper; sanitary paper products; specialty cleaning preparations; beauty shops

(P-24157)
LANSING INDUSTRIES INC
12671 High Bluff Dr # 150, San Diego
(92130-3018)
PHONE....................................858 523-0719
Benjamin Weiss, *Administration*
EMP: 11
SALES (est): 1.1MM **Privately Held**
SIC: 3999 Manufacturing industries

(P-24158)
LB MANUFACTURING LLC
1403 S Coast Hwy, Oceanside
(92054-5353)
PHONE....................................413 222-2857
Eric Banach,
EMP: 10
SALES (est): 283.1K **Privately Held**
SIC: 3999 Manufacturing industries

(P-24159)
LEARNERS DIGEST INTL LLC
450 N Brand Blvd Ste 900, Glendale
(91203-2397)
PHONE....................................818 240-7500
Fred Studier, *CEO*
Brendan McLoughlin, *Chief Mktg Ofcr*
Lon Osmond, *Vice Pres*
John Paul Uva, *Vice Pres*
Brenda Freeman, *General Mgr*
▲ **EMP:** 120
SQ FT: 35,000
SALES (est): 12.6MM
SALES (corp-wide): 5.2B **Privately Held**
WEB: www.audiodigest.org
SIC: 3999 Education aids, devices & supplies
HQ: Wolters Kluwer Health, Inc.
2001 Market St Ste 5
Philadelphia PA 19103
215 521-8300

(P-24160)
LEARNING RESOURCES INC
Also Called: Educational Insights
152 W Walnut St Ste 201, Gardena
(90248-3147)
PHONE....................................800 995-4436
EMP: 20
SALES (corp-wide): 34.6MM **Privately Held**
SIC: 3999 3944 Education aids, devices & supplies; games, toys & children's vehicles
PA: Learning Resources, Inc.
380 N Fairway Dr
Vernon Hills IL 60061
847 573-9471

(P-24161)
LEXOR INC
7400 Hazard Ave, Westminster
(92683-5031)
PHONE....................................714 444-4144
Marianna Magos, *CEO*
Christopher L Long, *President*
Sonali Bandaranayake, *Graphic Designe*
Tracy Pham, *Human Res Mgr*
Lizbeth Castro, *Personnel Assit*
◆ **EMP:** 90
SALES (est): 15.5MM **Privately Held**
SIC: 3999 Chairs, hydraulic, barber & beauty shop

(P-24162)
LIN MAI INC
Also Called: Promotion West
6333 San Fernando Rd, Glendale
(91201-2413)
PHONE....................................818 890-1220
Michael Todd, *President*
Lynn Fliegelman, *Co-President*
▲ **EMP:** 30
SALES (est): 2.7MM **Privately Held**
WEB: www.prowest.net
SIC: 3999 3993 2542 2541 Advertising display products; signs & advertising specialties; partitions & fixtures, except wood; wood partitions & fixtures

(P-24163)
LINPENG INTERNATIONAL INC
1939 S Campus Ave, Ontario (91761-5410)
PHONE....................................909 923-9881
Fisher Lin, *President*
Fiona Lin, *Manager*
▲ **EMP:** 10
SQ FT: 3,000
SALES: 600K **Privately Held**
SIC: 3999 5094 Stringing beads; beads

(P-24164)
LIXIT CORPORATION (PA)
Also Called: Equitex
100 Coombs St, NAPA (94559-3941)
P.O. Box 2580 (94558-0525)
PHONE....................................800 358-8254
Linda Parks, *President*
Elizabeth Dennis, *COO*
Janette Brooks, *CFO*
Laurie Corona, *Vice Pres*
Howard Pickens, *Vice Pres*
▲ **EMP:** 95
SQ FT: 50,000
SALES (est): 16.3MM **Privately Held**
WEB: www.lixit.com
SIC: 3999 Pet supplies

(P-24165)
LOST ART LIQUIDS LLC
Also Called: Lost Art Liquids
155 W Washington Blvd, Los Angeles
(90015-3552)
PHONE....................................213 816-2988
Ryan Thomas, *CFO*
EMP: 16
SQ FT: 9,500
SALES (est): 10MM **Privately Held**
SIC: 3999 Cigarette & cigar products & accessories

(P-24166)
MA CHER (USA) INC (HQ)
1518 Abbot Kinney Blvd, Venice
(90291-3743)
PHONE....................................310 581-5222
Derek Hydon, *President*
Martin Zoland, *Vice Pres*

▲ **EMP:** 12
SQ FT: 5,000
SALES (est): 1.4MM **Privately Held**
WEB: www.macher.com
SIC: 3999 Handbag & luggage frames & handles

(P-24167)
MACS LIFT GATE INC (PA)
2801 E South St, Long Beach
(90805-3736)
PHONE....................................562 634-5962
Richard Mac Donald, *President*
Gerald J Mac Donald, *Vice Pres*
Lawrence Mac Donald, *Vice Pres*
Daniel Mac Donald, *Accountant*
EMP: 25
SALES (est): 3.1MM **Privately Held**
SIC: 3999 5013 Wheelchair lifts; motor vehicle supplies & new parts

(P-24168)
MASTER INDS WORLDWIDE LLC
1001 S Linwood Ave, Santa Ana
(92705-4323)
PHONE....................................949 660-0644
Barbara Johnson, *Mng Member*
▲ **EMP:** 11
SALES (est): 1.3MM **Privately Held**
SIC: 3999 2426 Manufacturing industries; blanks, wood: bowling pins, handles, etc.

(P-24169)
MCCALLS COUNTRY CANNING INC
41735 Cherry St, Murrieta (92562-9186)
P.O. Box 1375 (92564-1375)
PHONE....................................951 461-2277
Daniel Patrick McCall, *CEO*
Delia McCall, *Vice Pres*
EMP: 15
SQ FT: 40,000
SALES (est): 1.8MM **Privately Held**
WEB: www.mccallscandles.com
SIC: 3999 Candles

(P-24170)
MEDIC IDS
Also Called: Medic I D'S Internatl
20350 Ventura Blvd # 140, Woodland Hills
(91364-2484)
PHONE....................................818 705-0595
Michael Silverstein, *Owner*
EMP: 10
SQ FT: 2,000
SALES (est): 846.2K **Privately Held**
WEB: www.medicid.com
SIC: 3999 Identification tags, except paper

(P-24171)
MEDICAL BREAKTHROUGH MASSAGE
28016 Industry Dr, Valencia (91355-4191)
PHONE....................................408 677-7702
Max Lun, *CEO*
Patrick O'Malley, *Opers Mgr*
EMP: 21
SQ FT: 40,000
SALES (est): 12MM **Privately Held**
SIC: 3999 Massage machines, electric: barber & beauty shops

(P-24172)
MEGIDDO GLOBAL LLC
153 W Rosecrans Ave, Gardena
(90248-1829)
PHONE....................................818 267-6686
Omer Nissani,
EMP: 10
SALES (est): 342.6K **Privately Held**
SIC: 3999 Manufacturing industries

(P-24173)
MERCADO LATINO INC
Continental Candle Company
1420 W Walnut St, Compton (90220-5013)
PHONE....................................310 537-1062
Mike Howard, *Manager*
EMP: 40
SALES (corp-wide): 252.9MM **Privately Held**
WEB: www.mercadolatinoinc.com
SIC: 3999 3641 7699 3645 Candles; electric lamps; restaurant equipment repair; residential lighting fixtures

▲ = Import ▼=Export
◆ =Import/Export

PA: Mercado Latino, Inc.
245 Baldwin Park Blvd
City Of Industry CA 91746
626 333-6862

(P-24174)
MFI INC
363 San Miguel Dr Ste 200, Newport Beach
(92660-7891)
PHONE.....................................949 313-6450
Steven Bandawat, *Principal*
EMP: 12 EST: 2014
SALES (est): 1.2MM **Privately Held**
SIC: 3999 Manufacturing industries

(P-24175)
MGR DESIGN INTERNATIONAL INC
1950 Williams Dr, Oxnard (93036-2695)
PHONE.....................................805 981-6400
Michelle Bechard, *CEO*
Rony Havive, *President*
Amy Wagner, *General Mgr*
Anne Morreghan, *Director*
Sylvia Camacho, *Accounts Exec*
◆ EMP: 200
SQ FT: 80,000
SALES (est): 28.3MM **Privately Held**
SIC: 3999 Potpourri; candles

(P-24176)
MID VALLEY GRINDING CO INC
7352 Radford Ave, North Hollywood
(91605-3786)
PHONE.....................................818 764-1086
Anthony Cagno, *President*
Don Schumacher, *Vice Pres*
EMP: 12
SALES: 973.9K **Privately Held**
SIC: 3999 3469 Custom pulverizing &
grinding of plastic materials; machine
parts, stamped or pressed metal

(P-24177)
MOBILITY SPECIALIST INC
490 Capricorn St, Brea (92821-3203)
PHONE.....................................714 674-0480
Vince Fabozzi, *Branch Mgr*
EMP: 30
SALES (corp-wide): 3.7MM **Privately Held**
WEB: www.mobilityspecialists.net
SIC: 3999 Wheelchair lifts
PA: Mobility Specialist Inc
4040 Sorrento Valley Blvd L
San Diego CA 92121
858 450-9589

(P-24178)
MOSAIC BRANDS INC
Also Called: Hair ACC By Mia Minnelli
3266 Buskirk Ave, Pleasant Hill
(94523-4315)
PHONE.....................................925 322-8700
Mia Minnelli, *President*
▲ EMP: 25
SQ FT: 20,000
SALES (est): 1.4MM **Privately Held**
SIC: 3999 3069 Hair & hair-based prod-
ucts; rubber hair accessories

(P-24179)
MOTHER PLUCKER FEATHER CO INC
2511 W 3rd St Ste 102, Los Angeles
(90057-1946)
P.O. Box 57160 (90057-0160)
PHONE.....................................213 637-0411
William Zelowitz, *President*
Steven Landerth, *CEO*
Lelan Berner, *Production*
EMP: 11
SQ FT: 16,000
SALES (est): 1.4MM **Privately Held**
WEB: www.motherplucker.com
SIC: 3999 5159 Trimmings, feather; feath-
ers

(P-24180)
MULTIS INC
766 S 12th St, San Jose (95112-2304)
PHONE.....................................510 441-2653
Sean Keenan, *President*
Stan Wilkison, *Vice Pres*
EMP: 50

SALES (est): 3.2MM **Privately Held**
SIC: 3999 Atomizers, toiletry

(P-24181)
MVP TECHNOLOGY INTL INC
44911 Industrial Dr, Fremont (94538-6486)
PHONE.....................................510 651-2425
Michael Wong, *President*
EMP: 10
SALES: 1.8MM **Privately Held**
SIC: 3999 8711 Atomizers, toiletry; engi-
neering services

(P-24182)
NAILS 2000 INTERNATIONAL INC
10892 Forbes Ave Ste A2, Garden Grove
(92843-6505)
PHONE.....................................714 265-1983
MAI Vo, *President*
▲ EMP: 16
SQ FT: 11,000
SALES (est): 2MM **Privately Held**
WEB: www.nails2000.com
SIC: 3999 Fingernails, artificial

(P-24183)
NAPA INDUSTRIES INC
1379 Beckwith Ave, Los Angeles
(90049-3615)
PHONE.....................................310 293-1209
Amir A Jandaghi, *CEO*
EMP: 10
SALES (est): 1MM **Privately Held**
SIC: 3999 Atomizers, toiletry

(P-24184)
NATO LLC
38 Laurel Mountain Rd, Mammoth Lakes
(93546)
PHONE.....................................760 934-8677
Charles Byrne, *Co-Owner*
Jose Luis Andreu, *Co-Owner*
▲ EMP: 50
SQ FT: 3,000
SALES (est): 3.2MM **Privately Held**
SIC: 3999 Pet supplies

(P-24185)
NATURE ZONE PET PRODUCTS
265 Boeing Ave, Chico (95973-9003)
PHONE.....................................530 343-5199
Fern Benson, *Owner*
EMP: 23
SQ FT: 10,000
SALES (est): 500K **Privately Held**
WEB: www.naturezonepet.com
SIC: 3999 Pet supplies

(P-24186)
NATUREMAKER INC
6225 El Camino Real, Carlsbad
(92009-1604)
PHONE.....................................760 438-4244
Gary Hanick, *President*
Bennett Abrams, *Vice Pres*
EMP: 30
SQ FT: 40,000
SALES (est): 4.1MM **Privately Held**
WEB: www.naturemaker.com
SIC: 3999 Artificial trees & flowers

(P-24187)
NESTLE PURINA PETCARE COMPANY
Also Called: Nestle Purina Factory
1710 Golden Cat Rd, Maricopa (93252)
PHONE.....................................661 769-8261
Mike Ashmore, *Manager*
Dave Brown, *General Mgr*
Ruth Jared, *Administration*
Paula Harris, *Human Res Dir*
EMP: 60
SALES (corp-wide): 90.8B **Privately Held**
SIC: 3999 Pet supplies
HQ: Nestle Purina Petcare Company
901 Chouteau Ave
Saint Louis MO 63102
314 982-1000

(P-24188)
NEW METHOD FUR DRESSING CO
131 Beacon St, South San Francisco
(94080-6985)
PHONE.....................................650 583-9881

Charles Crocker, *President*
Moe Malek, *Vice Pres*
EMP: 30
SQ FT: 22,000
SALES (est): 1.9MM **Privately Held**
SIC: 3999 3111 Furs, dressed: bleached,
curried, scraped, tanned or dyed; leather
tanning & finishing

(P-24189)
NEWTEX INDUSTRIES INC
Also Called: Thermostatic Industries
9654 Hermosa Ave, Rancho Cucamonga
(91730-5812)
PHONE.....................................323 277-0900
Jerry Joliet, *Principal*
Sudhakar Dixit, *Principal*
Jerome Joliet, *Principal*
EMP: 75 EST: 2016
SALES (est): 2.1MM **Privately Held**
SIC: 3999 Manufacturing industries

(P-24190)
NFI INDUSTRIES
11888 Mission Blvd, Mira Loma
(91752-1003)
PHONE.....................................951 681-6455
EMP: 13 EST: 2017
SALES (est): 1.4MM **Privately Held**
SIC: 3999 Atomizers, toiletry

(P-24191)
NORMAL CENTRIX INC
14101 Valleyheart Dr # 104, Sherman Oaks
(91423-2885)
PHONE.....................................310 715-9977
Jay Wilder, *CEO*
EMP: 11
SQ FT: 1,200
SALES: 1.5MM **Privately Held**
SIC: 3999 Education aids, devices & sup-
plies

(P-24192)
NORTH VALLEY CANDLE MOLDS
6928 Danyeur Rd, Redding (96001-5343)
PHONE.....................................530 247-0447
Don Sletner, *Partner*
Robert Irving, *Partner*
Barbara Sletner, *Partner*
▼ EMP: 20
SQ FT: 5,000
SALES (est): 1.6MM **Privately Held**
WEB: www.moldman.com
SIC: 3999 3544 Candles; special dies,
tools, jigs & fixtures

(P-24193)
NU VISIONS DE MEXICO SA DE CV
9355 Airway Rd, San Diego (92154-7931)
PHONE.....................................619 987-0518
▲ EMP: 160
SALES (est): 9.8MM **Privately Held**
SIC: 3999

(P-24194)
OLD AN INC
17651 Armstrong Ave, Irvine (92614-5727)
PHONE.....................................949 263-1400
Tina Rocca-Lundstrom, *President*
Tina Rocca Lundstrom, *President*
Steven Lundstrom, *Vice Pres*
▼ EMP: 30
SQ FT: 15,000
SALES (est): 2.3MM **Privately Held**
WEB: www.aromanaturals.com
SIC: 3999 Candles

(P-24195)
ORIENTAL ODYSSEYS INC
Also Called: O O Campbell
14557 Griffith St, San Leandro
(94577-6703)
PHONE.....................................510 357-6100
Sylvia White, *President*
Paul Fisher, *Vice Pres*
EMP: 30
SQ FT: 10,000
SALES (est): 2.3MM **Privately Held**
WEB: www.orientalodysseys.com
SIC: 3999 Candles

(P-24196)
ORIGIN LLC (HQ)
119 E Graham Pl, Burbank (91502-2028)
PHONE.....................................818 848-1648
Craig Lutes, *CEO*
▲ EMP: 35
SQ FT: 25,000
SALES (est): 13.5MM
SALES (corp-wide): 80MM **Privately Held**
WEB: www.originpop.com
SIC: 3999 Advertising display products
PA: Ideal Box Co.
4800 S Austin Ave
Chicago IL 60638
708 594-3100

(P-24197)
ORTEGA MANUFACTURING INC
3960 Industrial Ave, Hemet (92545-9790)
PHONE.....................................951 766-9363
Tony Ortega, *President*
Cindy Ortega, *Vice Pres*
EMP: 12
SQ FT: 12,000
SALES: 800K **Privately Held**
SIC: 3999 Novelties, bric-a-brac & hobby
kits

(P-24198)
OSI INDUSTRIES LLC
1155 Mt Vernon Ave, Riverside
(92507-1830)
PHONE.....................................951 684-4500
Mary Alexander, *Plant Engr*
Susie Miller, *Assistant*
Martin Garcia, *Supervisor*
Aaron Welch, *Supervisor*
Peggy Pierson, *Clerk*
▲ EMP: 24
SALES (est): 3.5MM **Privately Held**
SIC: 3999 Atomizers, toiletry

(P-24199)
OWEN MAGIC SUPREME INC
734 N Mckeever Ave, Azusa (91702-2394)
PHONE.....................................626 969-4519
Leslie Smith, *President*
Gertrude Smith, *Corp Secy*
EMP: 19
SQ FT: 12,000
SALES: 200K **Privately Held**
WEB: www.owenmagic.com
SIC: 3999 Magic equipment, supplies &
props

(P-24200)
PACIFIC LASERTEC INC
3821 Sienna St, Oceanside (92056-7283)
PHONE.....................................760 450-4095
Lynn Strickland, *President*
EMP: 20
SALES (est): 504.6K **Privately Held**
SIC: 3999 Manufacturing industries

(P-24201)
PACIFIC SUNSHINE ENTERPRISES
857 Gray Ave Ste B, Yuba City
(95991-3652)
PHONE.....................................530 673-1888
Billie Fa-Chun Lo, *President*
Shirley Chou, *Vice Pres*
▲ EMP: 11 EST: 1974
SQ FT: 10,000
SALES (est): 1.1MM **Privately Held**
SIC: 3999 Flowers, artificial & preserved

(P-24202)
PACIFIC TESTTRONICS INC
5983 Smithway St, Commerce
(90040-1607)
PHONE.....................................323 721-1077
William Hartfield, *Principal*
Patrick Bowers, *Shareholder*
Paul Huff, *Shareholder*
James Hartfield, *Treasurer*
EMP: 10
SALES: 88K **Privately Held**
WEB: www.hkfinc.com
SIC: 3999 Barber & beauty shop equip-
ment

(PA)=Parent Co (HQ)=Headquarters (DH)=Div Headquarters
✪ = New Business established in last 2 years

2019 California
Manufacturers Register

987

P R O D U C T S & S V C S

(P-24203)
PACMIN INCORPORATED (PA)
Also Called: Pacific Miniatures
2021 Raymer Ave, Fullerton (92833-2664)
PHONE.....................................714 447-4478
Frederick Ouweleen Jr, *President*
Flora Ouweleen, *Treasurer*
Daniel Ouweleen, *Exec VP*
Jeanne Ruppelius, *Manager*
▲ EMP: 96
SQ FT: 35,400
SALES (est): 13.5MM **Privately Held**
SIC: 3999 Models, general, except toy

(P-24204)
PARADIGM CONTRACT MFG LLC
11562 Knott St Ste 13, Garden Grove (92841-1823)
PHONE.....................................714 889-7074
Scott Penin, *Partner*
Faith Stancliff, *Partner*
EMP: 15
SQ FT: 2,077
SALES: 1.5MM **Privately Held**
SIC: 3999 Atomizers, toiletry

(P-24205)
PARYLENE USA INC
23 Spectrum Pointe Dr # 201, Lake Forest (92630-2272)
PHONE.....................................949 452-0770
David Stiles, *President*
EMP: 10 EST: 2017
SALES (est): 283.1K **Privately Held**
SIC: 3999 Manufacturing industries

(P-24206)
PDMA VENTURES INC
22951 La Palma Ave, Yorba Linda (92887-6701)
PHONE.....................................714 777-8770
Charles Platt, *President*
EMP: 35
SALES: 5MM **Privately Held**
SIC: 3999 Manufacturing industries

(P-24207)
PENINSULA PACKAGING LLC (DH)
Also Called: Peninsula Packaging Company
1030 N Anderson Rd, Exeter (93221-9341)
PHONE.....................................559 594-6813
John McKernan, *CEO*
▲ EMP: 70
SALES (est): 110.8MM
SALES (corp-wide): 5B **Publicly Held**
WEB: www.penpack.net
SIC: 3999 3085 Atomizers, toiletry; plastics bottles
HQ: Sonoco Plastics, Inc.
1 N 2nd St
Hartsville SC 29550
843 383-7000

(P-24208)
PET PARTNERS INC (PA)
Also Called: North American Pet Products
450 N Sheridan St, Corona (92880-2020)
PHONE.....................................951 279-9888
Keith Bonner, *CEO*
Ronald Bonner, *President*
Gloria Bonner, *Admin Sec*
Gordan Thulemeyer, *VP Sales*
▲ EMP: 170
SQ FT: 120,000
SALES: 35MM **Privately Held**
SIC: 3999 Pet supplies

(P-24209)
PETSPORT USA INC
1160 Railroad Ave, Pittsburg (94565-2642)
PHONE.....................................925 439-9243
Eden Hass, *CEO*
Eden G Hass, *CEO*
Erick Gonzalez, *Research*
Bret Ballinger, *QC Mgr*
▲ EMP: 14 EST: 1995
SQ FT: 18,000
SALES: 6MM **Privately Held**
WEB: www.petsportusa.com
SIC: 3999 Pet supplies

(P-24210)
PHIARO INCORPORATED
9016 Research Dr, Irvine (92618-4215)
PHONE.....................................949 727-1261
Takeichiro Iwasaki, *President*
Takuya Nishimura, *Exec Dir*
▲ EMP: 32
SQ FT: 35,000
SALES: 6MM
SALES (corp-wide): 43.1MM **Privately Held**
SIC: 3999 Models, general, except toy
PA: Phiaro Corporation, Inc.
8-2-3, Nobitome
Niiza STM 352-0
484 786-187

(P-24211)
PIERCO INCORPORATED
680 Main St, Riverside (92501-1034)
PHONE.....................................909 251-7100
Erik Flemming, *CEO*
EMP: 15
SALES (est): 1.5MM **Privately Held**
SIC: 3999 3089 Beekeepers' supplies; air mattresses, plastic

(P-24212)
POMMES FRITES CANDLE CO
Also Called: Pf Candle Co
7300 E Slauson Ave, Commerce (90040-3627)
PHONE.....................................213 488-2016
Kristen Pumphrey, *CEO*
Thomas Neuberger, *General Mgr*
EMP: 30
SALES (est): 373.5K **Privately Held**
SIC: 3999 5149 5199 5999 Candles; flavourings & fragrances; candles; candle shops

(P-24213)
PRESERVED TREESCAPES INTL INC (PA)
Also Called: Preserved Treescapes Intl
180 Vallecitos De Oro, San Marcos (92069-1435)
PHONE.....................................760 631-6789
Dennis Gabrick, *President*
▲ EMP: 50
SQ FT: 40,000
SALES (est): 17.9MM **Privately Held**
WEB: www.treescapes.com
SIC: 3999

(P-24214)
PRIDE INDUSTRIES ONE INC
10030 Foothills Blvd, Roseville (95747-7102)
P.O. Box 1200, Rocklin (95677-7200)
PHONE.....................................916 788-2100
Michael Ziegler, *CEO*
Pete Berghuis, *COO*
Jeff Dern, *CFO*
EMP: 4300
SALES (est): 228.8MM
SALES (corp-wide): 290.6MM **Privately Held**
SIC: 3999 Barber & beauty shop equipment
PA: Pride Industries
10030 Foothills Blvd
Roseville CA 95747
916 788-2100

(P-24215)
PRIMARCH MANUFACTURING INC
1211 Liberty Way, Vista (92081-8307)
PHONE.....................................760 730-8572
Douglas Smith, *CEO*
EMP: 10
SALES (est): 1.5MM **Privately Held**
SIC: 3999 Boutiquing; decorating gift items with sequins, fruit, etc.

(P-24216)
PROJEX INTERNATIONAL INC
9555 Hierba Rd, Santa Clarita (91390-4564)
PHONE.....................................661 268-0999
Richard Graham, *President*
Evan Greenberg, *Principal*
EMP: 15

SALES (est): 1.3MM **Privately Held**
SIC: 3999 Theatrical scenery

(P-24217)
PRYSM INC (PA)
180 Baytech Dr Ste 200, San Jose (95134-2304)
PHONE.....................................408 586-1100
Amit Jain, *President*
Don Williams, *President*
Tushar Kothari, *Exec VP*
Tom Blenkin, *Vice Pres*
Dana Corey, *Vice Pres*
▲ EMP: 70
SQ FT: 25,000
SALES (est): 39MM **Privately Held**
SIC: 3999 Advertising display products

(P-24218)
RADA INDUSTRY
1060 S Ditman Ave, Los Angeles (90023-2405)
PHONE.....................................323 265-3727
Bassam Rada El Reda, *Principal*
EMP: 10
SALES (est): 1.4MM **Privately Held**
SIC: 3999 Manufacturing industries

(P-24219)
RAPID MANUFACTURING (PA)
9724 Eton Ave, Chatsworth (91311-4305)
PHONE.....................................818 899-4377
EMP: 13
SALES (est): 4.4MM **Privately Held**
SIC: 3999 Barber & beauty shop equipment

(P-24220)
RARE ELEMENTS HAIR CARE
Also Called: Amato Beverly Hills
8950 W Olympic Blvd 641, Beverly Hills (90211-3561)
PHONE.....................................310 277-6524
John Amato, *Owner*
EMP: 10
SALES: 300K **Privately Held**
SIC: 3999 Hair & hair-based products

(P-24221)
REEL EFX INC
5539 Riverton Ave, North Hollywood (91601-2816)
PHONE.....................................818 762-1710
Jim Gill, *President*
Rosy Romano, *CFO*
Susan Gill, *Vice Pres*
Susan Milliken, *Vice Pres*
EMP: 25
SQ FT: 34,000
SALES: 3.4MM **Privately Held**
WEB: www.reelefx.com
SIC: 3999 Stage hardware & equipment, except lighting

(P-24222)
RESQ MANUFACTURING
11365 Sunrise Park Dr # 200, Rancho Cordova (95742-6556)
PHONE.....................................916 638-6786
Martin Szegedy, *CEO*
Jesus Gonzalez, *Prdtn Mgr*
EMP: 45 EST: 2012
SALES: 4.7MM **Privately Held**
SIC: 3999 Airplane models, except toy

(P-24223)
RICHMOND ENGINEERING CO INC
Also Called: Lewis Lifetime Tools
15472 Markar Rd, San Diego (92154)
PHONE.....................................800 589-7058
Daniel Wright, *President*
Caroline Wright, *Vice Pres*
▲ EMP: 90
SQ FT: 120,000
SALES (est): 9.8MM **Privately Held**
SIC: 3999 0782 Christmas trees, artificial; lawn & garden services

(P-24224)
RICON CORP (HQ)
1135 Aviation Pl, San Fernando (91340-1460)
PHONE.....................................818 267-3000
William Baldwin, *President*
Raymond T Betler, *CEO*

Jason Moore, *General Mgr*
◆ EMP: 108 EST: 1971
SQ FT: 225,000
SALES (est): 27.4MM
SALES (corp-wide): 3.8B **Publicly Held**
WEB: www.riconcorp.com
SIC: 3999 Wheelchair lifts
PA: Westinghouse Air Brake Technologies Corporation
1001 Airbrake Ave
Wilmerding PA 15148
412 825-1000

(P-24225)
ROLENN MANUFACTURING INC
1549 Marlborough Ave, Riverside (92507-2029)
PHONE.....................................951 682-1185
Thomas Accatino, *Principal*
EMP: 20
SALES (corp-wide): 6MM **Privately Held**
SIC: 3999 Atomizers, toiletry
PA: Rolenn Manufacturing, Inc.
2065 Roberta St
Riverside CA 92507
951 682-1185

(P-24226)
RUCCI INC
6700 11th Ave, Los Angeles (90043-4730)
PHONE.....................................323 778-9000
Ramin Lavian, *President*
Elsie Lavian, *Vice Pres*
▲ EMP: 19
SQ FT: 17,000
SALES (est): 2.3MM **Privately Held**
WEB: www.rucci.com
SIC: 3999 5087 Barber & beauty shop equipment; beauty parlor equipment & supplies

(P-24227)
SAN DIEGO AFR AMRCN GNLOGY RSC
5148 Market St, San Diego (92114-2209)
P.O. Box 740240 (92174-0240)
PHONE.....................................619 231-5810
Margaret Lewis, *Principal*
Felix Green, *Principal*
EMP: 45
SALES (est): 1.3MM **Privately Held**
SIC: 3999 Education aids, devices & supplies

(P-24228)
SAUNDERS MANUFACTURING SVCS
15330 Fairfield Ranch Rd G, Chino Hills (91709-8823)
P.O. Box 10 (91709-0001)
PHONE.....................................714 961-6492
Dennis Saunders, *President*
EMP: 10
SQ FT: 10,000
SALES (est): 800K **Privately Held**
WEB: www.smsproducts.com
SIC: 3999 Advertising display products

(P-24229)
SCAFCO CORPORATION
Also Called: Scafco Steel Stud Mfg
2177 Jerrold Ave, San Francisco (94124-1009)
PHONE.....................................415 852-7974
EMP: 20
SALES (corp-wide): 158MM **Privately Held**
SIC: 3999 Barber & beauty shop equipment
PA: Scafco Corporation
2800 E Main Ave
Spokane WA 99202
509 343-9000

(P-24230)
SCAFCO CORPORATION
2525 S Airport Way, Stockton (95206-3521)
PHONE.....................................209 670-8053
Erick King, *Branch Mgr*
EMP: 39
SALES (corp-wide): 158MM **Privately Held**
SIC: 3999 Barber & beauty shop equipment

PA: Scafco Corporation
2800 E Main Ave
Spokane WA 99202
509 343-9000

(P-24231)
SCHWARZKOPF INC (DH)
600 Corporate Pointe # 400, Culver City
(90230-7681)
PHONE..................................310 641-0990
Hans C Schwarzkopf, *President*
Heinz Bieler, *President*
Paul Widjaja, *Controller*
◆ EMP: 20
SQ FT: 5,566
SALES (est): 8.3MM
SALES (corp-wide): 23.6B **Privately Held**
WEB: www.hansschwarzkopf.com
SIC: 3999 5122 Barber & beauty shop
equipment; hair preparations
HQ: Henkel Us Operations Corporation
1 Henkel Way
Rocky Hill CT 06067
860 571-5100

(P-24232)
SCOR INDUSTRIES
2321 S Willow Ave, Bloomington
(92316-2972)
PHONE..................................909 820-5046
EMP: 12
SALES (est): 1.5MM **Privately Held**
SIC: 3999 Manufacturing industries

(P-24233)
SCOTT INDUSTRIES
736 Central Ave, Santa Maria
(93454-5715)
PHONE..................................916 812-7217
EMP: 55
SALES (est): 3.1MM **Privately Held**
SIC: 3999 Manufacturing industries

(P-24234)
SCRIPTO-TOKAI CORPORATION
(DH)
2055 S Haven Ave, Ontario (91761-0736)
PHONE..................................909 930-5000
Tomoyuki Kurata, *President*
Tokiharu Murofushi, *CFO*
Fred Ashley, *Admin Sec*
▲ EMP: 80
SQ FT: 120,000
SALES (est): 9.5MM **Privately Held**
WEB: www.scriptousa.com
SIC: 3999 3951 Cigarette lighters, except
precious metal; ball point pens & parts;
fountain pens & fountain pen desk sets;
pencils & pencil parts, mechanical
HQ: Tokai Corporation
6-21-1, Nishishinjuku
Shinjuku-Ku TKY 160-0
333 447-463

(P-24235)
SEAL FOR LIFE INDUSTRIES
LLC
2290 Enrico Fermi Dr, San Diego
(92154-7228)
PHONE..................................619 671-0932
▲ EMP: 15
SALES (est): 3.2MM **Publicly Held**
SIC: 3999 Barber & beauty shop equip-
ment
HQ: Berry Global, Inc.
101 Oakley St
Evansville IN 47710
812 424-2904

(P-24236)
SECRET GARDEN (TSG 1895)
LLC
Also Called: Tsg 1895 USA
6925 Aragon Cir Ste 1, Buena Park
(90620-1168)
PHONE..................................562 716-5544
Sunny Ooi,
▲ EMP: 10
SALES (est): 570K **Privately Held**
SIC: 3999 2679 Lamp shade frames; wall-
board, decorated: made from purchased
material

(P-24237)
SEGA HOLDINGS USA INC (DH)
9737 Lurline Ave, Chatsworth
(91311-4404)
PHONE..................................415 701-6000
Naoya Tsurumi, *CEO*
Tetsu Kayama, *President*
John Cheng, *CFO*
Sue Hughes, *Vice Pres*
John Douglas, *Administration*
◆ EMP: 175
SALES (est): 182MM
SALES (corp-wide): 3B **Privately Held**
SIC: 3999 5045 Coin-operated amuse-
ment machines; computers & acces-
sories, personal & home entertainment
HQ: Sega Games Co., Ltd.
1-1-1, Nishishinagawa
Shinagawa-Ku TKY 141-0
357 367-111

(P-24238)
SEGA OF AMERICA INC (DH)
6400 Oak Cyn Ste 100, Irvine
(92618-5204)
PHONE..................................415 806-0169
Tatsuyuki Miyazaki, *CEO*
Hayao Nakayama, *Ch of Bd*
Ian Curran, *President*
Howell Ivy, *President*
Yukio Aoyama, *Senior VP*
▲ EMP: 45
SQ FT: 9,000
SALES (est): 94.7MM
SALES (corp-wide): 3B **Privately Held**
SIC: 3999 5092 Coin-operated amuse-
ment machines; video games
HQ: Sega Holdings U.S.A., Inc.
9737 Lurline Ave
Chatsworth CA 91311
415 701-6000

(P-24239)
SENTIMENTS INC (PA)
Also Called: Best Friends By Sheri
5635 Smithway St, Commerce
(90040-1545)
PHONE..................................323 843-2080
Shohreh Dadbin, *CEO*
John Dadbin, *Treasurer*
Benjamin Dadbin, *Vice Pres*
Brandon Dadbin, *Sales Staff*
▲ EMP: 15
SALES (est): 5MM **Privately Held**
SIC: 3999 Pet supplies

(P-24240)
SGPS INC
Also Called: Show Group Production Services
15823 S Main St, Gardena (90248-2548)
PHONE..................................310 538-4175
Barrie Owen, *CEO*
Mike Estill, *General Mgr*
Katy Marx, *General Mgr*
Greg Cunningham, *Project Mgr*
Andrew Laidler, *Project Mgr*
EMP: 85
SQ FT: 40,000
SALES (est): 14.5MM **Privately Held**
WEB: www.sgps.net
SIC: 3999 Theatrical scenery

(P-24241)
SHELLPRO INC
18378 Atkins Rd, Lodi (95240-9649)
P.O. Box 2680 (95241-2680)
PHONE..................................209 334-2081
Calvin Suess, *President*
Virgil Suess, *Vice Pres*
Beth McCarty, *Bookkeeper*
EMP: 30
SQ FT: 225,000
SALES (est): 347K **Privately Held**
WEB: www.shellpro.net
SIC: 3999 Nut shells, grinding, from pur-
chased nuts

(P-24242)
SILVESTRI STUDIO INC (PA)
Also Called: Silvester California
8125 Beach St, Los Angeles (90001-3426)
P.O. Box 512198 (90051-0198)
PHONE..................................323 277-4420
E Alain Levi, *CEO*
▲ EMP: 80
SQ FT: 130,000

SALES (est): 17.9MM **Privately Held**
SIC: 3999 2542 3993 Mannequins; office
& store showcases & display fixtures;
signs & advertising specialties

(P-24243)
SILVESTRI STUDIO INC
1733 Cordova St, Los Angeles
(90007-1114)
P.O. Box 512198 (90051-0198)
PHONE..................................323 735-1481
E A Levi, *Principal*
EMP: 18
SALES (corp-wide): 17.9MM **Privately
Held**
SIC: 3999 Mannequins
PA: Silvestri Studio, Inc.
8125 Beach St
Los Angeles CA 90001
323 277-4420

(P-24244)
SKY GLOBAL SERVICES INC
23 Corporate Plaza Dr # 100, Newport
Beach (92660-7942)
PHONE..................................949 291-5511
William Harrison, *CEO*
EMP: 10
SALES: 500K **Privately Held**
SIC: 3999 Manufacturing industries

(P-24245)
SMALL WNDERS HNDCRFTED
MNTURES
7033 Canoga Ave Ste 5, Canoga Park
(91303-3118)
PHONE..................................818 703-7450
Zarin Huda, *President*
Omar Huda, *Vice Pres*
EMP: 15
SALES (est): 1MM **Privately Held**
SIC: 3999 Miniatures

(P-24246)
SOCIAL BRANDS LLC
6575 Simson St, Oakland (94605-2271)
PHONE..................................415 728-1761
Benjamin Seabury,
EMP: 20
SALES (est): 544.3K **Privately Held**
SIC: 3999 Manufacturing industries

(P-24247)
SOFTUB INC (PA)
13495 Gregg St, Poway (92064-7135)
PHONE..................................858 602-1920
Edward F McGarry, *CEO*
Tom Thornbury, *Chairman*
Joe Ellard, *District Mgr*
Darrin Jasgur, *District Mgr*
Randy Moore, *District Mgr*
▲ EMP: 85
SQ FT: 55,000
SALES (est): 38.9MM **Privately Held**
WEB: www.softub.com
SIC: 3999 Hot tubs

(P-24248)
SOUTHLAND INDUSTRIES
12131 Western Ave, Garden Grove
(92841-2914)
PHONE..................................714 901-5800
Vatche Sarkoyan, *Principal*
Kevin Coghlan, *CFO*
Cameron Garnier, *Project Engr*
Andrew Stockdale, *Project Engr*
Timothy Bittinger, *Contractor*
EMP: 1094
SALES (corp-wide): 878.7MM **Privately
Held**
SIC: 3999 Barber & beauty shop equip-
ment
PA: Southland Industries
7390 Lincoln Way
Garden Grove CA 92841
800 613-6240

(P-24249)
SPA LA LA INC
Also Called: Making Scents
21430 Strathern St Unit I, Canoga Park
(91304-4183)
PHONE..................................605 321-1276
Edith Sullivan, *President*
EMP: 12
SQ FT: 1,800

SALES (est): 920K **Privately Held**
SIC: 3999 Heating pads, nonelectric

(P-24250)
SPECKS INDUSTRIES LLC
10957 Grass Valley Cir, Moreno Valley
(92557-3913)
PHONE..................................800 511-0497
Garviea Freeny, *Principal*
EMP: 28 EST: 2016
SALES (est): 548.6K **Privately Held**
SIC: 3999 Manufacturing industries

(P-24251)
SPECTRUM BRANDS INC
Also Called: United Pet Group
5144 N Commerce Ave Ste A, Moorpark
(93021-7135)
PHONE..................................805 222-3611
EMP: 107
SALES (corp-wide): 5B **Publicly Held**
SIC: 3999 Pet supplies
HQ: Spectrum Brands, Inc.
3001 Deming Way
Middleton WI 53562
608 275-3340

(P-24252)
SPRAGG INDUSTRIES INC
20049 Crestview Dr, Canyon Country
(91351-5754)
PHONE..................................661 424-9673
Melinda Spragg, *CEO*
EMP: 10
SALES (est): 1.1MM **Privately Held**
SIC: 3999 Barber & beauty shop equip-
ment

(P-24253)
STANG INDUSTRIES INC
Also Called: Stang Industrial Products
2616 Research Dr Ste B, Corona
(92882-6978)
PHONE..................................714 556-0222
Charles Ronie, *CEO*
Abdul Kashif, *CFO*
◆ EMP: 19
SQ FT: 20,000
SALES (est): 2.9MM **Privately Held**
WEB: www.stangindustrial.com
SIC: 3999 3492 3561 Fire extinguishers,
portable; control valves, aircraft: hydraulic
& pneumatic; pumps & pumping equip-
ment

(P-24254)
STEELDECK INC
3339 Exposition Pl, Los Angeles
(90018-4034)
PHONE..................................323 290-2100
Phil Parsons, *President*
Adrian Funnell, *Vice Pres*
Pete Varela, *MIS Dir*
▲ EMP: 25
SQ FT: 54,000
SALES (est): 4.5MM **Privately Held**
WEB: www.steeldeck.com
SIC: 3999 2541 2531 Stage hardware &
equipment, except lighting; partitions for
floor attachment, prefabricated: wood;
theater furniture

(P-24255)
SUN BADGE CO
2248 S Baker Ave, Ontario (91761-7710)
PHONE..................................909 930-1444
Rick Hamilton, *President*
Chris Hamilton, *Vice Pres*
Ed Killoren, *Executive*
Benjamin Dawson, *Marketing Staff*
Kurt Bazner, *Sales Staff*
▲ EMP: 35
SQ FT: 24,000
SALES (est): 3.9MM **Privately Held**
WEB: www.sunbadgeco.com
SIC: 3999 Badges, metal: policemen, fire-
men, etc.

(P-24256)
SUN VALLEY FLORAL GROUP
LLC
3160 Upper Bay Rd, Arcata (95521-9690)
PHONE..................................707 826-8700
Lane Devries, *CEO*
▲ EMP: 750

PRODUCTS & SVCS

SALES (est): 66.3MM **Privately Held**
SIC: 3999 Flowers, artificial & preserved

(P-24257)
SUNDANCE SPAS INC (HQ)
14525 Monte Vista Ave, Chino
(91710-5721)
PHONE..................................909 606-7733
Bob Rowan, *CEO*
Jonathan Clark, *Principal*
Jeff Coles, *IT/INT Sup*
Paul V Slyke, *VP Finance*
Maggy Mendoza, *Buyer*
◆ **EMP:** 60
SALES (est): 21.9MM
SALES (corp-wide): 1.6B **Privately Held**
SIC: 3999 1799 5999 Hot tubs; swimming
pool construction; spas & hot tubs
PA: Jacuzzi Brands Llc
13925 City Center Dr # 200
Chino Hills CA 91709
909 606-1416

(P-24258)
SUNSTAR SPA COVERS INC (HQ)
13495 Gregg St, Poway (92064-7135)
PHONE..................................858 602-1950
Tom Thornbury, *Ch of Bd*
Edward McGarry, *President*
▲ **EMP:** 40
SQ FT: 34,000
SALES (est): 14.8MM
SALES (corp-wide): 38.9MM **Privately Held**
WEB: www.spatop.com
SIC: 3999 Hot tub & spa covers
PA: Softub, Inc.
13495 Gregg St
Poway CA 92064
858 602-1920

(P-24259)
SUPERIOR-STUDIO SPC INC
2239 Yates Ave, Commerce (90040-1913)
PHONE..................................323 278-0100
Jean-Pierre Fournier, *President*
Greg Duncan, *Natl Sales Mgr*
Jake Greenhouse, *Sales Staff*
▲ **EMP:** 20
SQ FT: 60,000
SALES (est): 2.2MM **Privately Held**
SIC: 3999 Advertising display products

(P-24260)
SUTTONS FOREST PRODUCTS
8222 Hallwood Blvd, Marysville
(95901-9406)
P.O. Box 1250 (95901-0035)
PHONE..................................530 741-2747
Gerry Sutton, *President*
Mary Sutton, *Admin Sec*
EMP: 11
SQ FT: 2,000
SALES (est): 1.1MM **Privately Held**
SIC: 3999 Flowers, artificial & preserved

(P-24261)
SWISSDIGITAL USA CO LTD
49 S Baldwin Ave Ste D, Sierra Madre
(91024-2580)
PHONE..................................626 351-1999
Hunter LI, *CEO*
EMP: 10
SQ FT: 500
SALES: 100K **Privately Held**
SIC: 3999 5099 Handles, handbag & lug-
gage; luggage

(P-24262)
T-REX PRODUCTS INCORPORATED
7920 Airway Rd Ste A6, San Diego
(92154-8311)
PHONE..................................619 482-4424
Alan Botterman, *President*
David Hanono, *CFO*
Olivia Zuniga, *Opers Mgr*
▲ **EMP:** 15
SQ FT: 14,000
SALES: 5.9MM **Privately Held**
WEB: www.t-rexproducts.com
SIC: 3999 Pet supplies

(P-24263)
T3 MICRO INC (PA)
228 Main St Ste 12, Venice (90291-5203)
PHONE..................................310 452-2888
Kent Yu, *President*
Jennifer Parr, *Accountant*
Ming Yee, *Manager*
▲ **EMP:** 20
SALES (est): 5.8MM **Privately Held**
SIC: 3999 Hair & hair-based products

(P-24264)
TAG TOYS INC
1810 S Acacia Ave, Compton (90220-4927)
PHONE..................................310 639-4566
Lawrence Mestyanek, *CEO*
Barbara Villafana, *CFO*
Judy Mestyanek, *Vice Pres*
EMP: 65
SQ FT: 60,000
SALES (est): 6.9MM **Privately Held**
WEB: www.tagtoys.com
SIC: 3999 8351 3944 Education aids, de-
vices & supplies; child day care services;
games, toys & children's vehicles

(P-24265)
TAKT MANUFACTURING INC
1300 E Victor Rd, Lodi (95240-0800)
PHONE..................................408 250-4975
Trevor Weissbart, *Principal*
EMP: 15
SALES (est): 397K **Privately Held**
SIC: 3999 Manufacturing industries

(P-24266)
TANDEM DESIGN INC
Also Called: Tandem Exhibit
1846 W Sequoia Ave, Orange
(92868-1018)
PHONE..................................714 978-7272
Maury Bonas, *President*
Susan Bonas, *Vice Pres*
Stephan Palalay, *Accounts Exec*
EMP: 23
SQ FT: 20,000
SALES (est): 1.8MM **Privately Held**
WEB: www.tandemdesigninc.com
SIC: 3999 Preparation of slides & exhibits

(P-24267)
TECHNICAL AMERICA INC
301 N Smith Ave, Corona (92880-1742)
PHONE..................................951 272-9540
Jing Xie, *CEO*
EMP: 55
SALES (est): 1.1MM **Privately Held**
SIC: 3999 Engineering services

(P-24268)
TECHNICAL MANUFACTURING W LLC
24820 Avenue Tibbitts, Valencia
(91355-3404)
PHONE..................................661 295-7226
Brad Topper,
Johnny Valadez,
EMP: 23
SALES (est): 4MM **Privately Held**
SIC: 3999 Barber & beauty shop equip-
ment

(P-24269)
THERMOPLAQUE COMPANY INC
14928 Calvert St, Van Nuys (91411-2698)
PHONE..................................818 988-1080
Gregory Floor, *President*
C Luke Floor, *Vice Pres*
Kathleen M Floor, *Admin Sec*
EMP: 10
SQ FT: 6,300
SALES (est): 1MM **Privately Held**
SIC: 3999 Plaques, picture, laminated

(P-24270)
TIBBAN MANUFACTURING INC
12593 Highline Dr, Apple Valley
(92308-5047)
P.O. Box 2675 (92307-0051)
PHONE..................................760 961-1160
James A Tibban, *CEO*
Tony Tibban, *Principal*
◆ **EMP:** 17

SALES (est): 2.1MM **Privately Held**
SIC: 3999 Barber & beauty shop equipment

(P-24271)
TLK INDUSTRIES INC
23650 Via Del Rio, Yorba Linda
(92887-2714)
PHONE..................................714 692-9373
Timothy Rose, *Principal*
EMP: 10 EST: 2012
SALES (est): 1MM **Privately Held**
SIC: 3999 Advertising curtains

(P-24272)
TOM LEONARD INVESTMENT CO INC
Also Called: Peak Seasons
7240 Sycamore Canyon Blvd, Riverside
(92508-2331)
PHONE..................................951 351-7778
Tom Leonard, *CEO*
Greg Szuba, *Vice Pres*
Arlene Leonard, *Admin Sec*
▲ **EMP:** 40
SQ FT: 35,000
SALES (est): 5.2MM **Privately Held**
WEB: www.peakseasons.com
SIC: 3999 3399 Christmas tree orna-
ments, except electrical & glass; paste,
metal

(P-24273)
TOYKIDZ INC
100 S Doheny Dr Ph 10, Los Angeles
(90048-2998)
P.O. Box 2035, Beverly Hills (90213-2035)
PHONE..................................213 688-2999
Trith B Dadlani, *CEO*
▲ **EMP:** 15
SALES (est): 852.2K **Privately Held**
SIC: 3999 3944 Advertising display prod-
ucts; games, toys & children's vehicles

(P-24274)
TPC INDUSTRIES LLC
5920 W Birch Ave, Fresno (93722-2878)
PHONE..................................310 849-9574
Charles Powell, *Mng Member*
Kathi Feliciano, *CFO*
EMP: 20
SALES (est): 1MM **Privately Held**
SIC: 3999 Manufacturing industries

(P-24275)
TRANS FX INC
Also Called: T F X
2361 Eastman Ave, Oxnard (93030-8136)
PHONE..................................805 485-6110
Allen Pike, *President*
Rick Bordonaro, *Exec VP*
Hollis Hedrich, *Executive*
EMP: 15
SQ FT: 25,000
SALES (est): 2.7MM **Privately Held**
WEB: www.transfx.com
SIC: 3999 3711 7389 3812 Models, ex-
cept toy; automobile assembly, including
specialty automobiles; design services;
acceleration indicators & systems compo-
nents, aerospace

(P-24276)
TRAXX CORPORATION
1201 E Lexington Ave, Pomona
(91766-5520)
PHONE..................................909 623-8032
Craig Silvers, *CEO*
Jon Hall, *Chairman*
▲ **EMP:** 100
SQ FT: 52,000
SALES (est): 16.7MM **Privately Held**
SIC: 3999 Carpet tackles

(P-24277)
TREK ARMOR INCORPORATED
41795 Elm St Ste 401, Murrieta
(92562-9278)
PHONE..................................951 319-4008
Mitchell P Walk, *CEO*
EMP: 16
SALES (est): 1.7MM **Privately Held**
SIC: 3999 Manufacturing industries

(P-24278)
TRNLWB LLC
Also Called: Trinity Lighweight
17410 Lockwood Valley Rd, Frazier Park
(93225-9318)
PHONE..................................661 245-3736
EMP: 5005
SALES (corp-wide): 13.7MM **Privately Held**
SIC: 3999 Barber & beauty shop equip-
ment
PA: Trnlwb, Llc
1112 E Cpeland Rd Ste 500
Arlington TX 76011
800 581-3117

(P-24279)
USA SOLAR TECHNOLOGY INC
28381 Vincent Moraga Dr, Temecula
(92590-3653)
PHONE..................................714 356-8360
Michael Douthwaite, *Principal*
EMP: 10
SALES (est): 283.1K **Privately Held**
SIC: 3999 Manufacturing industries

(P-24280)
USCPS
Also Called: US Composite Pipe South
3009 N Laurel Ave, Rialto (92377-3725)
PHONE..................................909 434-1888
Nabil Shehade, *Principal*
EMP: 60
SALES: 950K **Privately Held**
SIC: 3999 Manufacturing industries

(P-24281)
VERNON MACHINE AND FOUNDRY
5420 S Santa Fe Ave, Vernon
(90058-3522)
PHONE..................................323 277-0550
Bob Bouse, *President*
EMP: 12
SALES: 500K **Privately Held**
SIC: 3999 Manufacturing industries

(P-24282)
VITALHUE
2036 Nevada City Hwy # 188, Grass Valley
(95945-7700)
PHONE..................................323 646-8775
Uri Egozi, *President*
EMP: 14 EST: 2017
SALES (est): 403.9K **Privately Held**
SIC: 3999 Manufacturing industries

(P-24283)
VITAVET LABS INC
Also Called: Nuvet Labs
5717 Corsa Ave, Westlake Village
(91362-4001)
PHONE..................................818 865-2600
Blake Kirschbaum, *President*
Dr Raymond Kirschbaum, *CFO*
Shannon Kennedy, *Admin Sec*
Martha Padilla, *Cust Mgr*
Donna Cannava, *Manager*
▼ **EMP:** 20 EST: 1997
SALES (est): 2.8MM **Privately Held**
WEB: www.nuvetlabs.com
SIC: 3999 Pet supplies

(P-24284)
VIVIGLO TECHNOLOGIES INC
620 Lunar Ave Ste B, Brea (92821-3131)
PHONE..................................949 933-9738
Leslie Groll, *President*
EMP: 40
SQ FT: 15,000
SALES: 10MM **Privately Held**
WEB: www.viviglo.com
SIC: 3999 Models, except toy

(P-24285)
WATKINS MANUFACTURING CORP (HQ)
Also Called: Watkins Wellness
1280 Park Center Dr, Vista (92081-8398)
PHONE..................................760 598-6464
Steve Hammock, *President*
Kim Schaefer, *Manager*
◆ **EMP:** 277
SQ FT: 430,000

▲ = Import ▼=Export
◆ =Import/Export

SALES (est): 121.8MM
SALES (corp-wide): 7.6B **Publicly Held**
WEB: www.ownaspa.com
SIC: 3999 Hot tubs
PA: Masco Corporation
17450 College Pkwy
Livonia MI 48152
313 274-7400

(P-24286)
WBT GROUP LLC
Also Called: Wbt Industries
1401 S Shamrock Ave, Monrovia
(91016-4246)
PHONE...................323 735-1201
Lisa Stanislawski,
▲ EMP: 40
SALES (est): 4MM **Privately Held**
SIC: 3999 Buttons: Red Cross, union,
identification

(P-24287)
WELLAND INDUSTRIES LLC
3860 Prospect Ave, Yorba Linda
(92886-1724)
PHONE...................714 528-9900
Yanbing Hou, *Principal*
▲ EMP: 10
SALES (est): 826.3K **Privately Held**
SIC: 3999 Manufacturing industries

(P-24288)
WEST COAST LANYARDS INC
10661 Fulton Ct, Rancho Cucamonga
(91730-4848)
PHONE...................877 447-6030
Don Westreicher, *Principal*
Nicole Westreicher, *General Mgr*
Brandon Salazar, *Sales Staff*
▲ EMP: 19 EST: 2009
SALES (est): 1.6MM **Privately Held**
SIC: 3999 Identification badges & insignia

(P-24289)
WHITEFISH ENTERPRISES INC
14557 Griffith St, San Leandro
(94577-6703)
PHONE...................510 357-6100
Sylvia T White, *President*
▲ EMP: 14
SALES (est): 1.5MM **Privately Held**
SIC: 3999 Candles

(P-24290)
WHITESTONE INDUSTRIES INC
2076 White Ln Spc 283, Bakersfield
(93304-7608)
PHONE...................888 567-2234
Carlos Corado Garcia, *Administration*
EMP: 10
SALES (est): 926.8K **Privately Held**
SIC: 3999 Manufacturing industries

(P-24291)
WOODFORD WICKS LLC
Also Called: Woodford Wicks Candle Company
302 Williams Way, Hayward (94541-4388)
PHONE...................614 554-8474
Brett Butler,
Barbara J Blake,
Lowell F Blake,
Dorene S Butler,
George L Butler,
▲ EMP: 10
SQ FT: 2,500
SALES (est): 934.3K **Privately Held**
SIC: 3999 Candles

(P-24292)
XOLAR CORPORATION
Also Called: Hot Spring Spa
1012 E Bidwell St Ste 600, Folsom
(95630-5561)
PHONE...................916 983-6301
Ellen Fredman, *Branch Mgr*
EMP: 29
SALES (corp-wide): 7.4MM **Privately Held**
SIC: 3999 Hot tubs
PA: Xolar Corporation
2200 Mercury Way
Santa Rosa CA 95407
707 526-2380

(P-24293)
ZMB INDUSTRIES LLC
Also Called: Zombie Industries
12925 Brookprinter Pl # 400, Poway
(92064-8822)
PHONE...................858 842-1000
Roger Davis, *President*
EMP: 10 EST: 2011
SQ FT: 12,500
SALES (est): 1.1MM **Privately Held**
SIC: 3999 Barber & beauty shop equipment

(P-24294)
ZYMED LABORATORIES
458 Carlton Ct, South San Francisco
(94080-2012)
PHONE...................650 952-0110
Bean Paso, *CEO*
EMP: 40
SALES (est): 1.6MM **Privately Held**
SIC: 3999 Manufacturing industries

7372 Prepackaged Software

(P-24295)
15FIVE INC
3053 Fillmore St Ste 279, San Francisco
(94123-4009)
PHONE...................208 816-4225
David Hassell, *CEO*
Stacey Hurst, *Executive Asst*
Lior Givol, *Sales Staff*
Tim Wayne, *Director*
Emily Diaz, *Manager*
EMP: 11
SALES (est): 1.1MM **Privately Held**
SIC: 7372 7389 Application computer software; business oriented computer software;

(P-24296)
1ON1 LLC
12015 Waterfront Dr # 261, Playa Vista
(90094-2536)
PHONE...................310 448-5376
Susan Josephson, *Mng Member*
Todd Cherniawsky,
Nicole David,
Lorri Goddard,
Stephane Medam,
EMP: 50
SQ FT: 5,000
SALES: 20MM **Privately Held**
SIC: 7372 Application computer software

(P-24297)
24X7SAAS INC
2307 Larkspur Canyon Dr, San Jose
(95138-2467)
PHONE...................408 391-6205
Srinivas Burli, *CEO*
EMP: 15 EST: 2012
SALES (est): 898.7K **Privately Held**
SIC: 7372 Prepackaged software

(P-24298)
3BD HOLDINGS INC (PA)
Also Called: 3blackdot Holdings
2140 E 7th Pl Apt A2n, Los Angeles
(90021-1749)
PHONE...................323 524-0541
Angelo Pullen, *CEO*
Luke Stepleton, *President*
Shelby Brown, *COO*
Vince Cortese, *CFO*
EMP: 25
SQ FT: 10,000
SALES (est): 1.6MM **Privately Held**
SIC: 7372 5699 Application computer software; home entertainment computer software; T-shirts, custom printed

(P-24299)
3BECOM INC (PA)
2400 Lincoln Ave Ste 216, Altadena
(91001-5436)
PHONE...................818 726-0007
Bob Ntoya, *President*
Brian Jones, *COO*
Brennon Neff, *CFO*
Adam Gerber, *Principal*
Simon Wise, *Principal*
EMP: 15

SALES (est): 2.1MM **Privately Held**
SIC: 7372 Prepackaged software

(P-24300)
500FRIENDS INC (DH)
Also Called: Merkle Loyalty Solutions
77 Geary St Fl 5, San Francisco
(94108-5703)
PHONE...................800 818-8356
Justin Yoshimura, *CEO*
Michael Hemsey, *President*
Matt Gilbert, *COO*
Steve Katz, *Vice Pres*
Geoffrey Smalling, *CTO*
EMP: 20
SALES (est): 62MM
SALES (corp-wide): 291MM **Privately Held**
SIC: 7372 7371 Business oriented computer software; computer software development & applications
HQ: Merkle Inc.
7001 Columbia Gateway Dr
Columbia MD 21046
443 542-4000

(P-24301)
ABAQUS INC
530 University Ave, Palo Alto (94301-1900)
PHONE...................415 496-9436
Shailendra Jain, *CEO*
Ayush Kapahi, *Partner*
Charles Yellen, *Managing Dir*
Luke Degrossi, *Finance*
Eugene Weinraub, *Analyst*
EMP: 12 EST: 2007
SALES (est): 784.2K **Privately Held**
SIC: 7372 Business oriented computer software; software; business & non-game

(P-24302)
ABB ENTERPRISE SOFTWARE INC
60 Spear St, San Francisco (94105-1506)
PHONE...................415 527-2850
Greg Dukat, *Branch Mgr*
EMP: 175
SALES (corp-wide): 34.3B **Privately Held**
WEB: www.indusinternational.com
SIC: 7372 Business oriented computer software
HQ: Abb Enterprise Software Inc.
400 Perimeter Ctr Ter 5
Atlanta GA 30346
678 830-1000

(P-24303)
ABLE HEALTH INC
1516 Folsom St, San Francisco
(94103-3721)
P.O. Box 225310 (94122-5310)
PHONE...................617 529-6264
Rachel Katz, *CEO*
Steven Daniels, *President*
EMP: 12
SQ FT: 800
SALES (est): 263.1K **Privately Held**
SIC: 7372 Business oriented computer software

(P-24304)
ACCELA INC (PA)
2633 Camino Ramon Ste 500, San Ramon
(94583-9149)
PHONE...................925 659-3200
Ed Daihl, *CEO*
Lily Cheng, *Partner*
Robin Huey, *Partner*
Mark Jung, *Ch of Bd*
Jerald Lo, *President*
EMP: 150
SALES: 80MM **Privately Held**
WEB: www.accela.com
SIC: 7372 Business oriented computer software

(P-24305)
ACCELRYS SOFTWARE INC
5005 Wtrdge Vista Dr Fl 2 Flr 2, San Diego
(92121)
PHONE...................858 799-5000
Scipio Carnecchia, *Principal*
Kevin Cronin, *Vice Pres*
Matt Hahn, *Vice Pres*
Leif Pedersen, *Vice Pres*
Brian Sung, *Regional Mgr*

EMP: 18
SALES (est): 2.6MM **Privately Held**
SIC: 7372 Prepackaged software

(P-24306)
ACCORDENT TECHNOLOGIES INC
1846 Schooldale Dr, San Jose
(95124-1136)
PHONE...................310 374-7491
EMP: 16
SALES (corp-wide): 856.9MM **Publicly Held**
SIC: 7372
HQ: Accordent Technologies, Inc.
300 N Cntntl Blvd Ste 200
El Segundo CA 90245
310 374-7491

(P-24307)
ACCOUNTMATE SOFTWARE CORP (PA)
1445 Technology Ln Ste A5, Petaluma
(94954-7613)
PHONE...................707 774-7500
David Dierke, *Principal*
David Render, *COO*
Tommy Tan, *CTO*
Bernard Omiple, *Software Dev*
Rosemarie Dasig, *Applctn Conslt*
EMP: 32
SQ FT: 8,700
SALES (est): 4.2MM **Privately Held**
WEB: www.accountmate.com
SIC: 7372 Business oriented computer software

(P-24308)
ACM STUDENT CHAPTER AT UCR
446 Winston St Vincent, Riverside (92507)
PHONE...................951 389-0713
John Tham, *President*
EMP: 15
SALES (est): 305.2K **Privately Held**
SIC: 7372 Educational computer software

(P-24309)
ACME DATA INC
2400 Camino Ramon Ste 180, San Ramon
(94583-4211)
P.O. Box 2973, Danville (94526-7973)
PHONE...................925 913-4591
Thomas Brennan, *President*
Steven Kleinmann, *Vice Pres*
EMP: 19
SALES (est): 1.2MM **Privately Held**
WEB: www.stalworth.com
SIC: 7372 Business oriented computer software

(P-24310)
ACQUIS INC
16795 Lark Ave Ste 102, Los Gatos
(95032-7691)
PHONE...................408 402-5367
Audrey McKeown, *President*
EMP: 10
SQ FT: 2,000
SALES (est): 783.1K **Privately Held**
SIC: 7372 7371 7379 Prepackaged software; custom computer programming services; computer software development; data processing consultant

(P-24311)
ACTIVISION BLIZZARD INC
4 Hamilton Landing, Novato (94949-8256)
PHONE...................415 881-9100
EMP: 209
SALES (corp-wide): 7B **Publicly Held**
SIC: 7372 Home entertainment computer software
PA: Activision Blizzard, Inc.
3100 Ocean Park Blvd
Santa Monica CA 90405
310 255-2000

(P-24312)
ACTIVISION BLIZZARD INC (PA)
3100 Ocean Park Blvd, Santa Monica
(90405-3032)
PHONE...................310 255-2000
Robert A Kotick, *CEO*
Brian G Kelly, *Ch of Bd*

Collister Johnson, *President*
Spencer Neumann, *CFO*
Kristin Binns, *Ch Credit Ofcr*
EMP: 333
SQ FT: 153,297
SALES: 7B **Publicly Held**
WEB: www.blizzard.com
SIC: 7372 Home entertainment computer software

(P-24313)
ACTIVISION BLIZZARD INC
Blizzard Entertainment
3 Blizzard, Irvine (92618-3628)
P.O. Box 18979 (92623-8979)
PHONE...............................949 955-1380
Frank Pearce, *Principal*
Mathew Smiley, *Administration*
Alex Serio, *Software Engr*
Alix Nguyen, *Graphic Designe*
Wan-Chun MA, *Engineer*
EMP: 85
SALES (corp-wide): 7B **Publicly Held**
WEB: www.blizzard.com
SIC: 7372 Prepackaged software
PA: Activision Blizzard, Inc.
   3100 Ocean Park Blvd
   Santa Monica CA 90405
   310 255-2000

(P-24314)
ACTIVISION PUBLISHING INC (HQ)
3100 Ocean Park Blvd, Santa Monica (90405-3032)
PHONE...............................310 255-2000
Michael Griffith, *President*
Ron Doornink, *Ch of Bd*
Dave Cowling, *President*
Dan Rosensweig, *President*
Colin Schiller, *President*
EMP: 1306
SALES (est): 98.4MM
SALES (corp-wide): 7B **Publicly Held**
SIC: 7372 Home entertainment computer software
PA: Activision Blizzard, Inc.
   3100 Ocean Park Blvd
   Santa Monica CA 90405
   310 255-2000

(P-24315)
ACTUATE CORPORATION (HQ)
951 Mariners Island Blvd # 7, San Mateo (94404-1561)
PHONE...............................650 645-3000
Mark J Barrenechea, *President*
John Doolittle, *CFO*
Adam Howatson, *Chief Mktg Ofcr*
Gordon A Davies, *Officer*
Gordon Davies, *Exec VP*
EMP: 14
SQ FT: 58,000
SALES: 134.5MM
SALES (corp-wide): 2.2B **Privately Held**
WEB: www.actuate.com
SIC: 7372 Prepackaged software
PA: Open Text Corporation
   275 Frank Tompa Dr
   Waterloo ON N2L 0
   519 888-7111

(P-24316)
ACUREO INC
Also Called: Propertyradar.com
12242 Bus Park Dr Ste 20, Truckee (96161-3327)
P.O. Box 837 (96160-0837)
PHONE...............................530 550-8801
Sean O'Toole, *CEO*
Susan Heninger, *Info Tech Mgr*
Kim Bennett, *Director*
Rob Lusardi, *Director*
Madeline Schnapp, *Director*
EMP: 12
SALES (est): 1.2MM **Privately Held**
SIC: 7372 Business oriented computer software

(P-24317)
AD HOC LABS INC
Also Called: Burner App
2898 Rowena Ave Ste 100, Los Angeles (90039-2020)
PHONE...............................323 800-4927
EMP: 10 EST: 2012

SQ FT: 2,000
SALES (est): 657.8K **Privately Held**
SIC: 7372

(P-24318)
ADAPTIVE INC (PA)
65 Enterprise Ste E475, Aliso Viejo (92656-2705)
P.O. Box 305, Chesterfield VA (23832-0005)
PHONE...............................888 399-4621
Jeff Goins, *President*
Rich Hatlen, *Vice Pres*
Michael Mascarenhas, *Vice Pres*
Joe Stefaniak, *Vice Pres*
Paul Koerber, *Sr Software Eng*
EMP: 17
SQ FT: 5,000
SALES (est): 4.5MM **Privately Held**
WEB: www.adaptive.com
SIC: 7372 Prepackaged software

(P-24319)
ADAPTIVE INSIGHTS INC (HQ)
3350 W Byshore Rd Ste 200, Palo Alto (94303)
PHONE...............................650 528-7500
Thomas F Bogan, *CEO*
James D Johnson, *CFO*
Connie Dewitt, *Chief Mktg Ofcr*
Frederick M Gewant, *Officer*
Bhaskar Himatsingka, *Officer*
EMP: 200
SQ FT: 30,000
SALES: 106.5MM
SALES (corp-wide): 2.1B **Publicly Held**
WEB: www.adaptiveplanning.com
SIC: 7372 Business oriented computer software
PA: Workday, Inc.
   6110 Stoneridge Mall Rd
   Pleasanton CA 94588
   925 951-9000

(P-24320)
ADDING TECHNOLOGY (PA)
27 W Anapamu St, Santa Barbara (93101-3107)
PHONE...............................805 252-6971
Natalie Browne, *Principal*
EMP: 11
SALES (est): 2.1MM **Privately Held**
SIC: 7372 Prepackaged software

(P-24321)
ADDVOCATE INC
599 3rd St Apt 103, San Francisco (94107-3800)
PHONE...............................415 797-7620
Piers Cooper, *CEO*
Abraham Williams, *Webmaster*
John Flynn, *VP Sales*
EMP: 12
SQ FT: 25,000
SALES (est): 848.8K **Privately Held**
SIC: 7372 Business oriented computer software

(P-24322)
ADEXA INC (PA)
5777 W Century Blvd # 1100, Los Angeles (90045-5643)
PHONE...............................310 642-2100
Khosrow Cyrus Hadavi, *CEO*
Kameron Hadavi, *Vice Pres*
John Hosford, *Vice Pres*
Nick Yanagibori, *Vice Pres*
William Green, *VP Business*
EMP: 50
SQ FT: 31,000
SALES (est): 20MM **Privately Held**
WEB: www.adexa.com
SIC: 7372 Business oriented computer software

(P-24323)
ADMI INC
18525 Sutter Blvd Ste 290, Morgan Hill (95037-8102)
PHONE...............................408 776-0060
Allen D Moyer, *Principal*
EMP: 22 EST: 2007
SALES (est): 2.7MM **Privately Held**
SIC: 7372 Operating systems computer software

(P-24324)
ADOBE INC (PA)
345 Park Ave, San Jose (95110-2704)
PHONE...............................408 536-6000
Shantanu Narayen, *Ch of Bd*
Rodman Likes, *President*
Mark Garrett, *CFO*
John Murphy, *CFO*
Amy Banse, *Bd of Directors*
EMP: 600
SQ FT: 391,000
SALES: 7.3B **Publicly Held**
WEB: www.adobe.com
SIC: 7372 Application computer software

(P-24325)
ADOBE MACROMEDIA SOFTWARE LLC (HQ)
601 Townsend St, San Francisco (94103-5247)
PHONE...............................415 832-2000
Bruce R Chizen, *
Murray Demo, *
Shantanu Narayen, *
EMP: 20
SQ FT: 210,000
SALES (est): 35.8MM
SALES (corp-wide): 7.3B **Publicly Held**
WEB: www.macromedia.com
SIC: 7372 Prepackaged software; publishers' computer software; educational computer software; home entertainment computer software
PA: Adobe Inc.
   345 Park Ave
   San Jose CA 95110
   408 536-6000

(P-24326)
ADOBE SYSTEMS INCORPORATED
601 And 625 Townsend St, San Francisco (94103)
PHONE...............................415 832-2000
Les Schmidt, *Vice Pres*
Eric Robeson, *Engineer*
David Rich, *Director*
EMP: 1000
SALES (corp-wide): 7.3B **Publicly Held**
SIC: 7372 Application computer software
PA: Adobe Inc.
   345 Park Ave
   San Jose CA 95110
   408 536-6000

(P-24327)
ADS SOLUTIONS
10 Commercial Blvd # 208, Novato (94949-6107)
PHONE...............................415 897-3700
Kenneth Levin, *President*
Ann Grace, *Software Dev*
Kerry Hardesty, *
EMP: 19
SALES (est): 1.8MM **Privately Held**
WEB: www.amplexus.com
SIC: 7372 Application computer software; business oriented computer software

(P-24328)
ADVANCED PUBLISHING TECH INC (PA)
123 S Victory Blvd, Burbank (91502-2347)
PHONE...............................818 557-3035
David Kraai, *President*
David Bridges, *Vice Pres*
Jeff Sie, *Vice Pres*
Rich Mattheu, *Business Mgr*
EMP: 28
SALES (est): 3.8MM **Privately Held**
WEB: www.advpubtech.com
SIC: 7372 Publishers' computer software

(P-24329)
ADVANCED TECHNOLOGIES
2001 Columbus St, Bakersfield (93305-2312)
PHONE...............................661 872-4807
Tawna Johnson, *Owner*
Ron Johnson, *Co-Owner*
EMP: 16
SQ FT: 4,000
SALES (est): 1.1MM **Privately Held**
WEB: www.atsecure.net
SIC: 7372 Prepackaged software

(P-24330)
ADVENT RESOURCES INC
235 W 7th St, San Pedro (90731-3321)
PHONE...............................310 241-1500
Ysidro Salinas, *Ch of Bd*
Timothy Gill, *CEO*
Vishal Ghelani, *Vice Pres*
Benjamin Gill, *Vice Pres*
Mitch Stahl, *Exec Dir*
EMP: 80
SQ FT: 22,000
SALES (est): 12.2MM **Privately Held**
WEB: www.adventresources.com
SIC: 7372 Prepackaged software

(P-24331)
ADVISOR SOFTWARE INC (PA)
2175 N Calif Blvd Ste 400, Walnut Creek (94596-7103)
PHONE...............................925 299-7778
Andrew Rudd, *CEO*
Neal Ringquist, *President*
Neil Osborne, *CFO*
Michelle Farmer, *Officer*
Erik Jepson, *Officer*
EMP: 25
SQ FT: 5,500
SALES (est): 7.7MM **Privately Held**
WEB: www.advisorsoftware.com
SIC: 7372 Business oriented computer software

(P-24332)
ADVISYS INC
16969 Von Karman Ave # 125, Irvine (92606-4915)
PHONE...............................949 752-4927
Kenneth Kerr, *CEO*
Richard M Kettley, *Ch of Bd*
Gregg Janes, *Vice Pres*
Dane Parker, *Vice Pres*
Sherelyn Kettley, *Admin Sec*
EMP: 28
SQ FT: 5,000
SALES (est): 4.5MM **Privately Held**
WEB: www.kettley.com
SIC: 7372 Application computer software

(P-24333)
AELLA DATA INC
4701 Patrick Henry Dr, Santa Clara (95054-1819)
PHONE...............................408 391-4430
Changming Liu, *CEO*
Paul Jespersen, *Vice Pres*
Jared Hufferd, *VP Sales*
EMP: 12 EST: 2015
SALES: 200K **Privately Held**
SIC: 7372 Business oriented computer software

(P-24334)
AFFECTLAYER INC
Also Called: Chorus.ai
333 Bush St Fl 22, San Francisco (94104-2832)
PHONE...............................650 924-1082
Roy Raanani, *CEO*
EMP: 11
SALES (est): 289.3K **Privately Held**
SIC: 7372 Application computer software

(P-24335)
AFRESH TECHNOLOGIES INC
2948 20th St Apt 302, San Francisco (94110-2870)
PHONE...............................805 551-9245
Matthew Schwartz, *CEO*
Nathan Fenner, *COO*
Volodymyr Kuleshov, *CTO*
EMP: 10
SQ FT: 1,400
SALES (est): 221.8K **Privately Held**
SIC: 7372 Business oriented computer software

(P-24336)
AGENCYCOM LLC
5353 Grosvenor Blvd, Los Angeles (90066-6913)
PHONE...............................415 817-3800
Chan Suh, *CEO*
Jordan Warren, *President*
Rob Elliott, *CFO*
EMP: 400
SQ FT: 130,000

▲ = Import ▼=Export
◆ =Import/Export

SALES (est): 22.4MM
SALES (corp-wide): 15.2B **Publicly Held**
WEB: www.agency.com
SIC: 7372 Application computer software
PA: Omnicom Group Inc.
437 Madison Ave
New York NY 10022
212 415-3600

(P-24337)
AGGRIGATOR INC
30 E San Joaquin St # 202, Salinas
(93901-2947)
PHONE...................................650 245-5117
Gerard Rego, *CEO*
Doug Peterson, *Bd of Directors*
Margarita Quihuis, *Bd of Directors*
Benjamin Warr, *Bd of Directors*
EMP: 10 EST: 2014
SALES (est): 700.3K **Privately Held**
SIC: 7372 Business oriented computer
software

(P-24338)
AGILEPOINT INC (PA)
1916 Old Middlefield Way, Mountain View
(94043-2555)
PHONE...................................650 968-6789
Jesse Shiah, *President*
EMP: 26
SQ FT: 2,000
SALES (est): 11.1MM **Privately Held**
WEB: www.ascentn.com
SIC: 7372 Business oriented computer
software

(P-24339)
AGILOFT INC
460 Seaport Ct Ste 200, Redwood City
(94063-5548)
PHONE...................................650 587-8615
Colin Earl, *CEO*
Brandon Wright, *Partner*
Tina Quema, *Admin Asst*
Jack McDonald, *Administration*
Gregory Myers, *Business Anlyst*
EMP: 46
SQ FT: 3,200
SALES (est): 6.4MM **Privately Held**
WEB: www.supportwizard.com
SIC: 7372 Business oriented computer
software

(P-24340)
AHA LABS INC
20 Gloria Cir, Menlo Park (94025-3556)
PHONE...................................650 575-1425
Brian De Haaff, *CEO*
Christopher Waters, *Director*
Melissa Hopkins, *Manager*
EMP: 10 EST: 2013
SALES (est): 604.5K **Privately Held**
SIC: 7372 Business oriented computer
software

(P-24341)
AIRA TECH CORP
4225 Executive Sq Ste 400, La Jolla
(92037-1499)
PHONE...................................858 880-4454
Suman Kanuganti, *Co-Owner*
Troy Otillio, *COO*
Anne Bohn, *CFO*
Amy Bernal, *Vice Pres*
Scott Minick, *Principal*
EMP: 20 EST: 2015
SALES: 1MM **Privately Held**
SIC: 7372 Application computer software

(P-24342)
AKAMAI TECHNOLOGIES INC
1400 Fashion Island Blvd # 15, San Mateo
(94404-2060)
PHONE...................................617 444-3000
Jerry Trash, *Branch Mgr*
Steve Sosik, *Software Dev*
Serkan Okur, *Software Engr*
Dante Delucia, *Data Proc Staff*
Parag Phadke, *Technical Staff*
EMP: 38
SALES (corp-wide): 2.5B **Publicly Held**
SIC: 7372 Prepackaged software
PA: Akamai Technologies, Inc.
150 Broadway Ste 100
Cambridge MA 02142
617 444-3000

(P-24343)
AKIMBO SYSTEMS INC
411 Borel Ave Ste 100, San Mateo
(94402-3516)
PHONE...................................650 292-3330
Thomas F Frank, *President*
Robert Hammer, *CFO*
EMP: 24 EST: 1995
SQ FT: 4,000
SALES (est): 2MM **Privately Held**
SIC: 7372 Application computer software

(P-24344)
AKTANA INC
207 Powell St Ste 800, San Francisco
(94102-2230)
PHONE...................................888 707-3125
David Ehrlich, *President*
Jack O'Holleran, *President*
Rick Van Hoesen, *CFO*
Clay Hausmann, *Chief Mktg Ofcr*
Marc Cohen, *Officer*
EMP: 20
SALES (est): 1.7MM **Privately Held**
SIC: 7372 Prepackaged software

(P-24345)
AKUPARA GAMES LLC
8301 Gloria Ave, North Hills (91343-6325)
PHONE...................................805 471-4933
David Logan, *President*
EMP: 10
SALES (est): 264K **Privately Held**
SIC: 7372 Home entertainment computer
software

(P-24346)
ALATION INC (PA)
805 Veterans Blvd Ste 307, Redwood City
(94063-1737)
P.O. Box 1216 (94064-1216)
PHONE...................................650 779-4440
Satyen Sangani, *CEO*
Max Ochoa, *CFO*
Eric Brisson, *Vice Pres*
Steve Kennedy, *Risk Mgmt Dir*
Paul Sieben, *Admin Sec*
EMP: 26
SALES (est): 8.1MM **Privately Held**
SIC: 7372 Application computer software

(P-24347)
ALEKS CORPORATION
Also Called: Aleks Educational Systems
15640 Laguna Canyon Rd, Irvine (92618)
PHONE...................................714 245-7191
R G Wilmot Lampros, *President*
Nicolas Thiery, *President*
Jean-Claude Falmagne, *Chairman*
Gildas Cadin, *Engineer*
Raymond Ramos, *Sales Staff*
EMP: 130
SQ FT: 50,000
SALES (est): 9.9MM **Privately Held**
WEB: www.aris.ss.uci.edu
SIC: 7372 Educational computer software

(P-24348)
**ALFRESCO SOFTWARE INC
(PA)**
1825 S Grant St Ste 900, San Mateo
(94402-2675)
PHONE...................................888 317-3395
Bernadette Nixon, *CEO*
Paul Holmes-Higgin, *President*
Doug Dennerline, *CEO*
Carlton Baab, *CFO*
Bob Pritchard, *Senior VP*
EMP: 80
SALES (est): 22.4MM **Privately Held**
SIC: 7372 Prepackaged software

(P-24349)
ALIENVAULT INC (HQ)
1100 Park Pl Ste 300, San Mateo
(94403-7108)
PHONE...................................650 713-3333
Barmak Meftah, *President*
Marcus Bragg, *COO*
Andy Johnson, *CFO*
Ron Dovich, *Senior VP*
Russell Spitler, *Senior VP*
EMP: 12 EST: 2012

SALES (est): 122.6MM
SALES (corp-wide): 160.5B **Publicly
Held**
SIC: 7372 Business oriented computer
software
PA: At&T Inc.
208 S Akard St
Dallas TX 75202
210 821-4105

(P-24350)
ALIENVAULT LLC (DH)
1100 Park Pl Ste 300, San Mateo
(94403-7108)
PHONE...................................650 713-3333
Barmak Meftah, *President*
J Alberto Yepez, *Ch of Bd*
Chris Murphy, *President*
Brian Robins, *CFO*
Rita Selvaggi, *Chief Mktg Ofcr*
EMP: 61
SALES (est): 42MM
SALES (corp-wide): 160.5B **Publicly
Held**
SIC: 7372 Business oriented computer
software
HQ: Alienvault, Inc.
1100 Park Pl Ste 300
San Mateo CA 94403
650 713-3333

(P-24351)
ALIVECOR INC
444 Castro St Ste 600, Mountain View
(94041-2058)
PHONE...................................650 396-8650
Frank Petterson, *President*
John Maley, *CFO*
David E Albert, *Officer*
Francis White, *Vice Pres*
Sharon Tracy, *VP Sales*
EMP: 41
SALES: 4MM **Privately Held**
SIC: 7372 Application computer software

(P-24352)
ALLDATA LLC
9650 W Taron Dr Ste 100, Elk Grove
(95757-8197)
PHONE...................................916 684-5200
Stephen Odland,
Harry L Goldsmith,
Bob Olsen,
EMP: 76
SQ FT: 35,000
SALES (est): 43.3MM
SALES (corp-wide): 11.2B **Publicly Held**
WEB: www.alldata.com
SIC: 7372 Business oriented computer
software
PA: Autozone, Inc.
123 S Front St
Memphis TN 38103
901 495-6500

(P-24353)
ALLDIGITAL HOLDINGS INC
1405 Warner Ave Ste A, Tustin
(92780-6405)
PHONE...................................949 250-7340
Michael Linos, *President*
Brad Eisenstein, *COO*
Steve Smith, *Vice Pres*
EMP: 15
SQ FT: 3,769
SALES (est): 3.8MM **Privately Held**
SIC: 7372 Prepackaged software

(P-24354)
ALTIUM LLC
4275 Executive Sq Ste 825, La Jolla
(92037-1478)
PHONE...................................800 544-4186
Aram Mirkazemi,
Martin Ive, *Treasurer*
EMP: 75
SALES (est): 2.2MM **Privately Held**
SIC: 7372 Prepackaged software

(P-24355)
ALVENTIVE INC (PA)
2790 Walsh Ave, Santa Clara
(95051-0963)
P.O. Box 584, Cupertino (95015-0584)
PHONE...................................408 969-8000
David Tiley, *Ch of Bd*

Dave Conner, *President*
EMP: 60
SQ FT: 44,895
SALES (est): 3.4MM **Privately Held**
WEB: www.alventive.com
SIC: 7372 7373 Prepackaged software;
computer-aided design (CAD) systems
service

(P-24356)
**AMERICAN ISRAEL PUBLIC
AFFAIRS**
Also Called: Aipac
1801 Century Park E # 600, Los Angeles
(90067-2302)
PHONE...................................323 937-1184
Andy Trilling, *Director*
Pedro Cavallero, *Director*
EMP: 10
SALES (corp-wide): 88.5MM **Privately
Held**
SIC: 7372 Application computer software
PA: American Israel Public Affairs Commit-
tee (Inc)
251 H St Nw
Washington DC 20001
202 639-5200

(P-24357)
**ANALYTIC AND
COMPUTATIONAL RES**
Also Called: Acri
1931 Stradella Rd, Los Angeles
(90077-2320)
PHONE...................................310 471-3023
Akshai K Runchal, *President*
Chanchal Runchal, *Treasurer*
Madhukar RAO, *Technology*
EMP: 10
SALES (est): 1MM **Privately Held**
WEB: www.acri.net
SIC: 7372 5045 8742 Prepackaged soft-
ware; computers, peripherals & software;
industry specialist consultants

(P-24358)
ANDROMEDA SOFTWARE INC
2965 Potter Ave, Thousand Oaks
(91360-6422)
PHONE...................................805 379-4109
Sumeet Pasricha, *President*
Donn Gladstone, *CEO*
EMP: 12
SALES (est): 1.1MM **Privately Held**
WEB: www.andromedasoftware.com
SIC: 7372 7371 Prepackaged software;
custom computer programming services

(P-24359)
ANGELLIST LLC
90 Gold St, San Francisco (94133-5103)
PHONE...................................415 857-0840
Naval Ravikant, *CEO*
EMP: 12
SALES (est): 608.6K **Privately Held**
SIC: 7372 Business oriented computer
software

(P-24360)
ANSYS INC
2645 Zanker Rd, San Jose (95134-2136)
PHONE...................................408 457-2000
Vic Kulkarni, *General Mgr*
Dave Logie, *Software Dev*
Khing Phan, *Software Dev*
Yujun Cao, *Technology*
Aleksandra Egelja-Maruszew, *Technical
Staff*
EMP: 12
SALES (corp-wide): 1.1B **Publicly Held**
SIC: 7372 Prepackaged software
PA: Ansys, Inc.
2600 Ansys Dr
Canonsburg PA 15317
724 746-3304

(P-24361)
**AONIX NORTH AMERICA INC
(HQ)**
5675 Ruffin Rd Ste 305, San Diego
(92123-1362)
PHONE...................................858 457-2700
Nicolas Hadjidakis, *CEO*
Pierre Ceserini, *President*
EMP: 15

SALES (est): 3.2MM **Privately Held**
WEB: www.aonix.com
SIC: 7372 7371 Prepackaged software;
custom computer programming services
PA: Parametric Technology Europe B.V.
High Tech Campus 9 K110
Eindhoven
408 519-040

(P-24362)
APEX COMMUNICATIONS INC (DH)
21700 Oxnard St Ste 1060, Woodland Hills
(91367-7571)
PHONE.....................................818 379-8400
Ben Levy, *President*
EMP: 15
SQ FT: 7,500
SALES (est): 2.7MM **Privately Held**
WEB: www.apexvoice.com
SIC: 7372 Application computer software
HQ: Dialogic Inc.
4 Gatehall Dr Ste 9
Parsippany NJ 07054
973 967-6000

(P-24363)
APPBACKR INC
2251 Yale St, Palo Alto (94306-1427)
P.O. Box 268 (94302-0268)
PHONE.....................................650 272-6129
Trevor Cornwell, *CEO*
Johanna Casao, *Corp Comm Staff*
EMP: 10
SALES (est): 792.3K **Privately Held**
WEB: www.appbackr.com
SIC: 7372 Application computer software

(P-24364)
APPDIRECT INC (PA)
650 California St Fl 25, San Francisco
(94108-2606)
PHONE.....................................415 852-3924
Nicolas Desmarais, *Ch of Bd*
Angelica Patino, *Partner*
Daniel Saks, *President*
Michael Difilippo, *CFO*
Mark Beebe, *Vice Pres*
EMP: 59
SQ FT: 10,000
SALES (est): 24.2MM **Privately Held**
SIC: 7372 7371 Application computer soft-
ware; computer software development &
applications

(P-24365)
APPDYNAMICS LLC (HQ)
Also Called: Appdynamics, Inc.
303 2nd St Fl 8, San Francisco
(94107-1366)
PHONE.....................................415 442-8400
David Wadhwani, *President*
Dev Ittycheria, *Bd of Directors*
Daniel J Wright, *Senior VP*
Jim Cavanaugh, *Vice Pres*
Jeremy Duggan, *Vice Pres*
EMP: 135
SQ FT: 83,500
SALES: 150.5MM
SALES (corp-wide): 49.3B **Publicly Held**
SIC: 7372 Prepackaged software
PA: Cisco Systems, Inc.
170 W Tasman Dr
San Jose CA 95134
408 526-4000

(P-24366)
APPERY LLC
1340 Treat Blvd Ste 375, Walnut Creek
(94597-7590)
PHONE.....................................925 602-5504
Lynne Walter, *CFO*
Dimitry Binunsky, *Vice Pres*
EMP: 60
SQ FT: 7,200
SALES: 2MM **Privately Held**
SIC: 7372 Application computer software

(P-24367)
APPETIZE TECHNOLOGIES INC
6601 Center Dr W Ste 700, Los Angeles
(90045-1545)
PHONE.....................................877 559-4225
Max Roper, *CEO*
Jason Pratts, *COO*
Dan Machock, *CFO*

Mark Eastwood, *Officer*
Kevin Anderson, *Senior VP*
EMP: 110 EST: 2011
SALES (est): 257.6K **Privately Held**
SIC: 7372 Application computer software

(P-24368)
APPFOLIO INC (PA)
50 Castilian Dr Ste 101, Santa Barbara
(93117-5578)
PHONE.....................................805 364-6093
Jason Randall, *President*
Andreas Von Blottnitz, *Ch of Bd*
Ida Kane, *CFO*
Jonathan Walker, *CTO*
EMP: 130
SQ FT: 79,200
SALES: 143.8MM **Publicly Held**
SIC: 7372 Business oriented computer
software

(P-24369)
APPFOLIO INC
Also Called: Mycase
9201 Spectrum, San Diego (92123)
PHONE.....................................866 648-1536
Troy Alford, *Engineer*
EMP: 573
SALES (corp-wide): 143.8MM **Publicly
Held**
SIC: 7372 Prepackaged software
PA: Appfolio, Inc.
50 Castilian Dr Ste 101
Santa Barbara CA 93117
805 364-6093

(P-24370)
APPFORMIX INC
Also Called: Acelio
4 N 2nd St Ste 595, San Jose
(95113-1325)
PHONE.....................................408 899-2240
Sumeet Singh, *CEO*
Jennifer Allen, *Marketing Staff*
EMP: 15
SQ FT: 4,000
SALES (est): 1MM **Privately Held**
SIC: 7372 Utility computer software

(P-24371)
APPLIED BIOSYSTEMS LLC (DH)
5791 Van Allen Way, Carlsbad
(92008-7321)
PHONE.....................................650 638-5000
David L Szekeres, *Mng Member*
Tony L White, *Ch of Bd*
Lars Holmkvist, *President*
Kathy P Ordonez, *President*
Dennis L Winger, *CFO*
▲ EMP: 120 EST: 1937
SQ FT: 51,000
SALES (est): 347.9MM
SALES (corp-wide): 20.9B **Publicly Held**
WEB: www.applera.com
SIC: 7372 3826 Prepackaged software;
gas chromatographic instruments
HQ: Life Technologies Corporation
5781 Van Allen Way
Carlsbad CA 92008
760 603-7200

(P-24372)
APPLIED BUSINESS SOFTWARE INC
Also Called: A B S
2847 Gundry Ave, Signal Hill (90755-1812)
PHONE.....................................562 426-2188
Jerry Delgado, *President*
Elizabeth Morales, *Chief Mktg Ofcr*
Eddy Delgado, *Vice Pres*
Gerardo Delgado, *Vice Pres*
Edimia Delgado, *Admin Sec*
EMP: 15
SQ FT: 7,200
SALES (est): 2.1MM **Privately Held**
WEB: www.abstmo.com
SIC: 7372 5045 5734 Prepackaged soft-
ware; computers, peripherals & software;
computer & software stores

(P-24373)
APPLIED EXPERT SYSTEMS INC
Also Called: AES
999 Commercial St Ste 209, Palo Alto
(94303-4909)
P.O. Box 50927 (94303-0673)
PHONE.....................................650 617-2400
Catherine H Liu, *President*
David Cheng, *Vice Pres*
Ed Hu, *General Mgr*
Mark Nguyen, *Sr Software Eng*
Laura Knapp, *Consultant*
EMP: 38
SQ FT: 6,000
SALES (est): 3.4MM **Privately Held**
WEB: www.aesclever.com
SIC: 7372 Business oriented computer
software

(P-24374)
APPLIED STATISTICS & MGT INC
Also Called: Md-Staff
32848 Wolf Store Rd Ste A, Temecula
(92592-8277)
P.O. Box 891329 (92589-1329)
PHONE.....................................951 699-4600
Trung Phan, *President*
Nickolaus Phan, *COO*
Danny Cairney, *Vice Pres*
Dan Anderson, *Sales Staff*
Keith Gibson, *Manager*
EMP: 45
SQ FT: 4,000
SALES (est): 5MM **Privately Held**
WEB: www.mdstaff.com
SIC: 7372 7371 Prepackaged software;
computer software systems analysis &
design, custom

(P-24375)
APPOINTY SOFTWARE INC
16 Corning Ave Ste 136, Milpitas
(95035-5343)
PHONE.....................................408 634-4141
Nemesh Singh, *President*
EMP: 25 EST: 2016
SALES (est): 552K **Privately Held**
SIC: 7372 Business oriented computer
software

(P-24376)
APPVANCE INC
1250 Oakmead Pkwy Ste 210, Sunnyvale
(94085-4035)
PHONE.....................................408 871-0122
Kevin Surace, *CEO*
John Hubinger, *Ch of Bd*
EMP: 24
SALES (est): 1.6MM **Privately Held**
SIC: 7372 Prepackaged software

(P-24377)
APPWARE INC
Also Called: Eteam Technologies
65 Enterprise, Aliso Viejo (92656-2705)
PHONE.....................................415 732-9298
Thomas Cornelius, *President*
EMP: 25
SALES (est): 480.6K **Privately Held**
SIC: 7372 Prepackaged software

(P-24378)
APTEAN INC
2361 Rosecrans Ave # 375, El Segundo
(90245-4916)
PHONE.....................................310 536-6080
Rebecca Goco, *Manager*
EMP: 10
SALES (corp-wide): 559.6MM **Privately
Held**
SIC: 7372 Prepackaged software
PA: Aptean, Inc.
4325 Alexander Dr Ste 100
Alpharetta GA 30022
770 351-9600

(P-24379)
APTELIGENT INC
1100 La Avenida St Ste A, Mountain View
(94043-1453)
PHONE.....................................415 371-1402
Pat Gelsinger, *CEO*
Scott Bajtos, *COO*
Sanjay Poonen, *COO*
Raghu Raghuram, *COO*

Rajiv Ramaswami, *COO*
EMP: 60
SALES (est): 3.8MM
SALES (corp-wide): 78.6B **Publicly Held**
SIC: 7372 Prepackaged software
HQ: Vmware, Inc.
3401 Hillview Ave
Palo Alto CA 94304
650 427-5000

(P-24380)
APTIV DIGITAL INC
2210 W Olive Ave Fl 2, Burbank
(91506-2626)
PHONE.....................................818 295-6789
Neil Jones, *President*
Christine Otto, *Director*
EMP: 85
SALES (est): 3.2MM
SALES (corp-wide): 826.4MM **Publicly
Held**
WEB: www.tvguideinc.com
SIC: 7372 Home entertainment computer
software
HQ: Rovi Guides, Inc.
2233 N Ontario St Ste 100
Burbank CA 91504

(P-24381)
ARCTIC WOLF NETWORKS INC (PA)
111 W Evelyn Ave Ste 115, Sunnyvale
(94086-6131)
PHONE.....................................408 610-3263
Brian Nesmith, *CEO*
Kim Tremblay, *Vice Pres*
Dinah Davis, *Research*
EMP: 11
SALES (est): 2.5MM **Privately Held**
SIC: 7372 7371 Business oriented com-
puter software; computer software sys-
tems analysis & design, custom

(P-24382)
ARIA SYSTEMS INC (PA)
100 Pine St Ste 2450, San Francisco
(94111-5230)
PHONE.....................................415 852-7250
Tom Dibble, *President*
Peter Worth, *Officer*
Michael Breslin, *Vice Pres*
Janice Kennealy, *Vice Pres*
Edward Popow, *Vice Pres*
▼ EMP: 62
SALES (est): 34MM **Privately Held**
WEB: www.ariasystems.com
SIC: 7372 Prepackaged software

(P-24383)
ARIBA INC (DH)
3420 Hillview Ave Bldg 3, Palo Alto
(94304-1355)
PHONE.....................................650 849-4000
Alex Atzberger, *CEO*
Marc Malone, *CFO*
Alicia Tillman, *Chief Mktg Ofcr*
Brad Brubaker, *Admin Sec*
Patrick Haines, *Human Resources*
EMP: 105
SQ FT: 86,000
SALES (est): 434.3MM
SALES (corp-wide): 27.6B **Privately Held**
WEB: www.ariba.com
SIC: 7372 Business oriented computer
software
HQ: Sap America, Inc.
3999 West Chester Pike
Newtown Square PA 19073
610 661-1000

(P-24384)
ARISTAMD INC
11099 N Torrey Pines Rd # 290, La Jolla
(92037-1029)
PHONE.....................................858 750-4777
Brooke Levasseur, *Officer*
Dereck Tatman, *President*
Adam Darkins, *Officer*
Rebecca Dofina, *Principal*
Darryl Kuhn, *CTO*
EMP: 10
SALES (est): 1MM **Privately Held**
SIC: 7372 Operating systems computer
software

(P-24385)
ARKEIA SOFTWARE INC (DH)
1808 Aston Ave Ste 235, Carlsbad
(92008-7345)
PHONE...................................760 431-1319
William Evans, *CEO*
Hubert Verstraete, *Bd of Directors*
EMP: 11
SALES (est): 3.7MM
SALES (corp-wide): 20.6B **Publicly Held**
SIC: 7372 Prepackaged software

(P-24386)
ARXIS TECHNOLOGY INC
2468 Tapo Canyon Rd, Simi Valley
(93063-2361)
PHONE...................................805 306-7890
Christopher L Hamilton, *CEO*
Christina Serian, *Marketing Mgr*
Betsy Quis, *Manager*
EMP: 32
SALES (est): 4.4MM **Privately Held**
SIC: 7372 Prepackaged software

(P-24387)
ASCERT LLC (PA)
Also Called: Softsell Business Systems
759 Bridgeway, Sausalito (94965-2102)
PHONE...................................415 339-8500
Rob Walker,
Andrew Mould,
EMP: 12
SQ FT: 3,000
SALES (est): 1.8MM **Privately Held**
WEB: www.ascert.com
SIC: 7372 7371 Prepackaged software;
computer software development & appli-
cations

(P-24388)
ASPECT SOFTWARE INC
101 Academy Ste 130, Irvine (92617-3081)
PHONE...................................408 595-5002
James Foy, *Owner*
EMP: 50 **Privately Held**
SIC: 7372 Prepackaged software
HQ: Aspect Software, Inc.
2325 E Camelback Rd # 700
Phoenix AZ 85016
978 250-7900

(P-24389)
ASSET SCIENCE LLC
17150 Via Del Campo # 200, San Diego
(92127-2110)
PHONE...................................858 255-7982
John Sheeran, *CEO*
Terence Howard, *President*
Eric Arseneau, *CTO*
EMP: 35 **EST:** 2010
SALES: 1.3MM **Privately Held**
SIC: 7372 Application computer software

(P-24390)
ASTEA INTERNATIONAL INC
8 Hughes, Irvine (92618-2072)
PHONE...................................949 784-5000
Carl Smith, *Branch Mgr*
Robert Ostoich, *Regl Sales Mgr*
EMP: 30
SALES (corp-wide): 26.3MM **Publicly
Held**
WEB: www.astea.com
SIC: 7372 Business oriented computer
software
PA: Astea International Inc.
240 Gibraltar Rd Ste 300
Horsham PA 19044
215 682-2500

(P-24391)
ASTERA SOFTWARE CORPORATION
310 N Westlake Blvd # 140, Westlake Vil-
lage (91362-7064)
PHONE...................................805 579-0004
Ibrahim Surani, *CEO*
Munira Surani, *Admin Sec*
EMP: 12
SALES (est): 1.3MM **Privately Held**
WEB: www.astera.com
SIC: 7372 Application computer software

(P-24392)
ASTORIA SOFTWARE
160 Spear St Ste 1100, San Francisco
(94105-1546)
PHONE...................................415 956-3917
Michael Rosinski, *Branch Mgr*
Eric Kuhnen, *General Mgr*
EMP: 50 **EST:** 2010
SALES (est): 1.8MM **Privately Held**
SIC: 7372 Prepackaged software

(P-24393)
ASTRO TECHNOLOGY INC
3335 Birch St, Palo Alto (94306-2808)
PHONE...................................650 533-5087
Andy Pflaum, *CEO*
EMP: 28
SQ FT: 150
SALES (est): 188.8K
SALES (corp-wide): 272.4MM **Privately
Held**
SIC: 7372 Application computer software
PA: Slack Technologies, Inc.
500 Howard St
San Francisco CA 94105
415 579-9153

(P-24394)
ATLANTIS COMPUTING INC (PA)
900 Glenneyre St, Laguna Beach
(92651-2707)
PHONE...................................650 917-9471
Jason Donahue, *CEO*
Timm Hoyt, *Partner*
David Cumberworth, *Vice Pres*
Ruben Spruijt, *CTO*
Danielle Biondi, *Manager*
EMP: 35
SQ FT: 5,000
SALES (est): 6.6MM **Privately Held**
SIC: 7372 Business oriented computer
software

(P-24395)
ATLASSIAN INC (DH)
1098 Harrison St, San Francisco
(94103-4521)
PHONE...................................415 701-1110
Scott Farquhar, *CEO*
Doug Burgum, *Ch of Bd*
Denise Romero, *President*
Jay Simons, *President*
John Bruce, *CFO*
EMP: 101
SALES (est): 43.9MM **Privately Held**
WEB: www.atlassian.com
SIC: 7372 Business oriented computer
software

(P-24396)
ATYPON SYSTEMS LLC (PA)
5201 Great America Pkwy # 510, Santa
Clara (95054-1122)
PHONE...................................408 988-1240
Georgios Papadapoulos, *CEO*
Joshua Pyle, *President*
Gordon Tibbitts, *President*
Steve Castro, *CFO*
Jonathan Hevenstone, *Senior VP*
EMP: 60
SQ FT: 6,000
SALES (est): 13.2MM **Privately Held**
WEB: www.atypon.com
SIC: 7372 Application computer software

(P-24397)
AUDATEX NORTH AMERICA INC (DH)
Also Called: Audaexplore
15030 Ave Of, San Diego (92128)
PHONE...................................858 946-1900
Tony Aquila, *CEO*
Jack Pearlstein, *CEO*
Richard Palmer, *Vice Pres*
Don Tartre, *Vice Pres*
Ryan Hager, *VP Bus Dvlpt*
EMP: 200
SQ FT: 35,000
SALES (est): 144.6MM
SALES (corp-wide): 527.1MM **Privately
Held**
SIC: 7372 Business oriented computer
software

(P-24398)
AUTODESK INC
1 Market St, San Francisco (94105-1420)
PHONE...................................415 356-0700
Chris Bradshaw, *Vice Pres*
Yvonne Cekel, *Partner*
Wes Hamerstadt, *Partner*
Yannis Daubin, *Executive*
Tom Winter, *Executive*
EMP: 61
SALES (corp-wide): 2B **Publicly Held**
WEB: www.autodesk.com
SIC: 7372 Application computer software
PA: Autodesk, Inc.
111 Mcinnis Pkwy
San Rafael CA 94903
415 507-5000

(P-24399)
AUTODESK INC (PA)
111 Mcinnis Pkwy, San Rafael
(94903-2700)
PHONE...................................415 507-5000
Andrew Anagnost, *President*
Kathe Rodd, *Partner*
Crawford W Beveridge, *Ch of Bd*
R Scott Herren, *CFO*
Kathleen Kewley, *Treasurer*
EMP: 400 **EST:** 1982
SQ FT: 220,000
SALES: 2B **Publicly Held**
WEB: www.autodesk.com
SIC: 7372 Application computer software

(P-24400)
AUTODESK INC
3950 Civic Center Dr, San Rafael
(94903-5901)
PHONE...................................415 507-5000
Kathryn Najafi-Tagol, *Manager*
Thomas Georgens, *Bd of Directors*
Alexander Nikolayev, *Software Engr*
EMP: 250
SALES (corp-wide): 2B **Publicly Held**
WEB: www.autodesk.com
SIC: 7372 Application computer software
PA: Autodesk, Inc.
111 Mcinnis Pkwy
San Rafael CA 94903
415 507-5000

(P-24401)
AVAST SOFTWARE INC (PA)
2625 Broadway St, Redwood City
(94063-1532)
PHONE...................................844 340-9251
Vincent Wayne Steckler, *CEO*
Wendy Thompson, *Treasurer*
April Marshall, *Vice Pres*
Leah Jones, *Business Dir*
Karin Holton, *Exec Dir*
EMP: 18 **EST:** 2011
SALES (est): 43MM **Privately Held**
SIC: 7372 Application computer software

(P-24402)
AVATIER CORPORATION (PA)
4733 Chabot Dr Ste 201, Pleasanton
(94588-3971)
P.O. Box 12124 (94588-2124)
PHONE...................................925 217-5170
Nelson Cicchitto, *CEO*
Nelson A Cicchitto, *CEO*
Steven Yeffa, *CFO*
Chris Arnold *Vice Pres*
Phil Ferreira, *Vice Pres*
EMP: 21
SQ FT: 5,500
SALES (est): 12.5MM **Privately Held**
WEB: www.avatier.com
SIC: 7372 7373 Business oriented com-
puter software; systems software devel-
opment services

(P-24403)
AVOLENT INC
444 De Haro St Ste 100, San Francisco
(94107-2350)
PHONE...................................415 553-6400
Doug Roberts, *CEO*
Mike Seashols, *Ch of Bd*
Bhupi Singh, *CFO*
Kevin Han, *Exec VP*
Tanya Johnson, *Vice Pres*
EMP: 80 **EST:** 1995
SQ FT: 60,000

SALES (est): 5.7MM **Privately Held**
SIC: 7372 Application computer software

(P-24404)
AXCELEON INC
1947 Overlook Rd, Fullerton (92831-1020)
PHONE...................................714 960-5200
Michael Duffy, *President*
Mary Keogh, *CEO*
EMP: 15
SALES (est): 1.5MM **Privately Held**
WEB: www.axceleon.com
SIC: 7372 Prepackaged software

(P-24405)
AXIA TECHNOLOGIES LLC
4183 State St, Santa Barbara
(93110-1817)
PHONE...................................855 376-2942
Randal Clark, *CEO*
EMP: 21 **EST:** 2016
SALES (est): 1.2MM **Privately Held**
SIC: 7372 Prepackaged software

(P-24406)
BADGER MAPS INC
539 Broadway, San Francisco
(94133-4521)
PHONE...................................415 592-5909
Steven Benson, *CEO*
Gady Pitaru, *Officer*
Eric Clapper, *Business Dir*
Tim Jernigan, *Marketing Staff*
Ellie Aldous, *Sales Staff*
EMP: 40
SQ FT: 1,000
SALES (est): 1.1MM **Privately Held**
SIC: 7372 Application computer software

(P-24407)
BADGEVILLE INC
805 Veterans Blvd Ste 307, Redwood City
(94063-1737)
P.O. Box 2367 (94064-2367)
PHONE...................................650 323-6668
Jon Shalowitz, *President*
Stephanie Vinella, *CFO*
Karen Hsu, *Vice Pres*
Andy Pederson, *Vice Pres*
Roel Stalman, *Vice Pres*
EMP: 50 **EST:** 2010
SALES (est): 10.2MM **Privately Held**
SIC: 7372 Prepackaged software

(P-24408)
BAFFLE INC
2811 Mission College Blvd, Santa Clara
(95054-1838)
PHONE...................................408 663-6737
Ameesh Divatia, *CEO*
EMP: 10 **EST:** 2015
SQ FT: 10,000
SALES (est): 324.8K **Privately Held**
SIC: 7372 Application computer software

(P-24409)
BARRA LLC (HQ)
Also Called: Barra, Inc.
2100 Milvia St, Berkeley (94704-1113)
PHONE...................................510 548-5442
Kamal Duggirala, *CEO*
Andrew Rudd, *Ch of Bd*
Aamir Sheikh, *President*
Greg Stockett, *CFO*
Susan Gledhill, *General Mgr*
EMP: 280
SQ FT: 35,000
SALES (est): 28.2MM **Publicly Held**
WEB: www.barra.com
SIC: 7372 8741 6282 Business oriented
computer software; financial management
for business; investment advisory service

(P-24410)
BARRACUDA NETWORKS INC (HQ)
3175 Winchester Blvd, Campbell
(95008-6557)
PHONE...................................408 342-5400
William D Jenkins Jr, *President*
Dustin Driggs, *CFO*
Erin Hintz, *Chief Mktg Ofcr*
Zachary Levow, *Exec VP*
Fleming Shi, *Technology*
EMP: 225
SQ FT: 61,400

SALES: 352.6MM
SALES (corp-wide): 44.7MM **Privately Held**
WEB: www.barracudanetworks.com
SIC: 7372 7373 Prepackaged software; computer integrated systems design
PA: Barracuda Holdings, Llc
3175 Winchester Blvd
Campbell CA 95008
408 342-5400

(P-24411)
BDNA CORPORATION (PA)
339 Bernardo Ave Ste 206, Mountain View (94043-5232)
PHONE.................650 625-9530
Constantin Delivanis, *CEO*
Ossama Hassanein, *Ch of Bd*
Walker White, *President*
Fred Hessabi, *CEO*
Dave Pomeroy, *CFO*
EMP: 64
SQ FT: 7,000
SALES (est): 17.5MM **Privately Held**
WEB: www.bdnacorp.com
SIC: 7372 Business oriented computer software

(P-24412)
BEATS MUSIC LLC
235 2nd St, San Francisco (94105-3124)
PHONE.................415 590-5104
Timothy Cook, *CEO*
EMP: 95
SALES (est): 8.5MM
SALES (corp-wide): 265.6B **Publicly Held**
SIC: 7372 Prepackaged software
PA: Apple Inc.
1 Apple Park Way
Cupertino CA 95014
408 996-1010

(P-24413)
BEEKEE CORP
3050 Pullman St, Costa Mesa (92626-5901)
PHONE.................949 275-5861
Thomas Markel, *CEO*
Kaveh Mahjoob, *CTO*
EMP: 10
SALES: 500K **Privately Held**
SIC: 7372 Prepackaged software

(P-24414)
BENEFIT SOFTWARE INCORPORATED
212 Cottage Grove Ave A, Santa Barbara (93101-3450)
PHONE.................805 679-6200
Larry S Dubois, *President*
EMP: 30
SQ FT: 5,105
SALES (est): 2.4MM **Privately Held**
WEB: www.benefits4us.com
SIC: 7372 Prepackaged software

(P-24415)
BENTO TECHNOLOGIES INC
Also Called: Bento Merge Enterprises
221 Main St Ste 1325, San Francisco (94105-1946)
P.O. Box 190608 (94119-0608)
PHONE.................415 887-2028
Farhan Ahmad, *CEO*
Sean Anderson, *CFO*
Jeff Pomeroy, *Vice Pres*
Renato Steinberg, *CTO*
Senam Amegashie, *Director*
EMP: 11 **EST:** 2014
SQ FT: 2,628
SALES (est): 937K **Privately Held**
SIC: 7372 Business oriented computer software

(P-24416)
BETHEBEAST INC
446 Bayview Dr, Hermosa Beach (90254-4514)
PHONE.................424 206-1081
Michael Mahoney, *President*
Barry Brault, *CFO*
EMP: 27
SALES (est): 645.2K **Privately Held**
SIC: 7372 Educational computer software

(P-24417)
BETTERCOMPANY INC
621 Sansome St, San Francisco (94111-2395)
PHONE.................415 501-9692
Thomas Williams, *CEO*
Colin Putney, *CTO*
EMP: 10
SQ FT: 2,500
SALES (est): 501.6K **Privately Held**
SIC: 7372 Business oriented computer software

(P-24418)
BETTERWORKS SYSTEMS INC
999 Main St, Redwood City (94063-1903)
PHONE.................650 656-9013
Doug Dennerline, *CEO*
Mark Lambert, *CFO*
Mathew Geist, *Software Engr*
Justin Huang, *Software Engr*
Matthew Rasmus, *Software Engr*
EMP: 75
SALES: 8MM **Privately Held**
SIC: 7372 Publishers' computer software

(P-24419)
BGL DEVELOPMENT INC
Also Called: The Bristol Group
3070 Kerner Blvd Ste H, San Rafael (94901-5419)
P.O. Box 2399 (94912-2399)
PHONE.................415 256-2525
Peter R Harris, *President*
EMP: 10
SQ FT: 2,600
SALES (est): 1MM **Privately Held**
WEB: www.bg.com
SIC: 7372 Prepackaged software

(P-24420)
BIDCHAT INC
14570 Benefit St Unit 302, Sherman Oaks (91403-5510)
PHONE.................818 631-6212
Zachary Ein, *CEO*
EMP: 10
SALES: 5MM **Privately Held**
SIC: 7372 Business oriented computer software

(P-24421)
BIG SWITCH NETWORKS INC (PA)
3111 Coronado Dr Bldg A, Santa Clara (95054-3206)
PHONE.................650 322-6510
Douglas Murray, *CEO*
Jeffrey Wang, *President*
Seamus Hennessy, *CFO*
Wendell Laidley, *CFO*
Gregg Holzrichter, *Chief Mktg Ofcr*
EMP: 53
SALES (est): 43.2MM **Privately Held**
SIC: 7372 Prepackaged software

(P-24422)
BIGTRIBE CORPORATION
89 Crescent Ave, Sausalito (94965-2315)
PHONE.................415 331-3687
Dan R Greening, *CEO*
Dan Dickson, *Director*
Andy Fyfe, *Director*
Elizabeth Sholawsky, *Director*
EMP: 13
SQ FT: 30,000
SALES (est): 729.5K **Privately Held**
WEB: www.bigtribe.com
SIC: 7372 Business oriented computer software

(P-24423)
BILLCOM INC
1810 Embarcadero Rd, Palo Alto (94303-3308)
PHONE.................650 353-3301
Rene Lacerte, *CEO*
Penny Lam, *Partner*
Yogesh Bhumralkar, *President*
Mark Orttung, *COO*
John Rettig, *CFO*
EMP: 140
SALES (est): 35.6MM **Privately Held**
SIC: 7372 Application computer software

(P-24424)
BIMARIAN INC
3350 Scott Blvd, Santa Clara (95054-3104)
PHONE.................408 520-2666
Siva Pullabhotla, *CEO*
EMP: 25 **EST:** 2012
SQ FT: 1,500
SALES (est): 796.8K **Privately Held**
SIC: 7372 Business oriented computer software

(P-24425)
BINTI INC
1999 Harrison St Ste 1575, Oakland (94612-3585)
PHONE.................844 424-6844
Felicia Curcuru, *CEO*
EMP: 30
SALES (est): 114.8K **Privately Held**
SIC: 7372 7389 Business oriented computer software;

(P-24426)
BIOTA TECHNOLOGY INC
Also Called: Uc2
11095 Flintkote Ave Ste B, San Diego (92121-1214)
PHONE.................650 888-6512
Jay Kshatriya, *CEO*
Daniel Gilbert, *Associate*
EMP: 15
SALES (est): 109K **Privately Held**
SIC: 7372 Business oriented computer software

(P-24427)
BITZER MOBILE INC
4230 Leonard Stocking Dr, Santa Clara (95054-1777)
PHONE.................866 603-8392
Naeem Zafar, *President*
Ali Ahmed, *CTO*
EMP: 40
SQ FT: 2,000
SALES (est): 2.1MM
SALES (corp-wide): 39.8B **Publicly Held**
SIC: 7372 Business oriented computer software
PA: Oracle Corporation
500 Oracle Pkwy
Redwood City CA 94065
650 506-7000

(P-24428)
BIZMATICS INC (PA)
4010 Moorpark Ave Ste 222, San Jose (95117-1843)
PHONE.................408 873-3030
Vinay Deshpande, *CEO*
Chris Ferguson, *President*
Sneha Baing, *Executive*
Suvarna Gaikwad, *Software Engr*
Shashank Joshi, *Software Engr*
EMP: 250
SQ FT: 2,000
SALES: 5.9MM **Privately Held**
SIC: 7372 Business oriented computer software

(P-24429)
BLACKLINE SYSTEMS INC (HQ)
21300 Victory Blvd Fl 12, Woodland Hills (91367-7734)
PHONE.................818 746-4700
Therese Tucker, *CEO*
Jennifer T Pottle, *Partner*
Charles Best, *CFO*
Mark Partin, *CFO*
David Downing, *Chief Mktg Ofcr*
EMP: 108
SQ FT: 66,447
SALES (est): 123MM
SALES (corp-wide): 177MM **Publicly Held**
WEB: www.blackline.com
SIC: 7372 Business oriented computer software
PA: Blackline, Inc.
21300 Victory Blvd Fl 12
Woodland Hills CA 91367
818 223-9008

(P-24430)
BLIZZARD ENTERTAINMENT INC (HQ)
1 Blizzard, Irvine (92618-3628)
P.O. Box 18979 (92623-8979)
PHONE.................949 955-1380
Mike Morhaime, *President*
J Allen Brack, *President*
Paul Sams, *President*
Frank Pearce, *Exec VP*
Chris Metzen, *Senior VP*
▲ **EMP:** 85
SALES (est): 62.1MM
SALES (corp-wide): 7B **Publicly Held**
SIC: 7372 5734 7819 Prepackaged software; software, computer games; reproduction services, motion picture production
PA: Activision Blizzard, Inc.
3100 Ocean Park Blvd
Santa Monica CA 90405
310 255-2000

(P-24431)
BLOOMBOARD INC (PA)
227 Forest Ave, Palo Alto (94301-2511)
PHONE.................650 567-5656
Jason Lange, *President*
Audie Rubin, *Partner*
Stephen Anderson, *Officer*
Laura Trigeiro, *Software Engr*
Tim Mansfield, *VP Engrg*
EMP: 14
SQ FT: 5,100
SALES (est): 3.2MM **Privately Held**
SIC: 7372 Educational computer software

(P-24432)
BLUE COAT LLC
350 Ellis St, Mountain View (94043-2202)
PHONE.................408 220-2200
Greg Clark, *CEO*
Michael Fey, *President*
Thomas Seifert, *CFO*
Fran Rosch, *Exec VP*
Scott Taylor, *Exec VP*
EMP: 1583
SALES (est): 98.4MM
SALES (corp-wide): 4.8B **Publicly Held**
SIC: 7372 Prepackaged software
PA: Symantec Corporation
350 Ellis St
Mountain View CA 94043
650 527-8000

(P-24433)
BLUE IRON NETWORK INC
5811 Mcfadden Ave, Huntington Beach (92649-1323)
PHONE.................714 901-1456
Robert McCandless, *CEO*
Cari McCandless, *CFO*
EMP: 25
SQ FT: 11,000
SALES (est): 1.7MM **Privately Held**
SIC: 7372 Business oriented computer software

(P-24434)
BLUERUN VENTURES LP
545 Middlefield Rd # 210, Menlo Park (94025-3400)
PHONE.................650 462-7250
John Malloy, *Principal*
Jennifer Yu, *Controller*
Jamu Park, *Human Res Mgr*
Jenelle Mezzetti, *Opers Staff*
Jana Trantow, *Associate*
EMP: 17
SALES (est): 2.4MM **Privately Held**
SIC: 7372 Operating systems computer software

(P-24435)
BLUESNAP INC
5201 Great America Pkwy # 320, Santa Clara (95054-1122)
PHONE.................866 475-4687
Hagai Tal, *Branch Mgr*
EMP: 25 **Privately Held**
SIC: 7372 Application computer software
PA: Bluesnap, Inc.
800 South St Ste 640
Waltham MA 02453

(P-24436)
BLUESTACK SYSTEMS INC
2105 S Bascom Ave Ste 380, Campbell
(95008-3278)
PHONE..................................408 412-9439
Rosen Sharma, *President*
Hue Harguindeguy, *CFO*
Jay Vaishnav, *Senior VP*
Julia Larson, *Software Engr*
John Gargiulo, *Marketing Staff*
EMP: 26
SALES (est): 2.4MM **Privately Held**
SIC: 7372 Application computer software

(P-24437)
BMC SOFTWARE INC
2020 Main St Ste 700, Irvine (92614-8230)
PHONE..................................949 752-7281
Ronald Knight, *Director*
EMP: 32
SALES (corp-wide): 1.3B **Privately Held**
SIC: 7372 Prepackaged software
HQ: Bmc Software, Inc.
2103 Citywest Blvd # 2100
Houston TX 77042
713 918-8800

(P-24438)
BONAFIDE MANAGEMENT SYSTEMS
241 Lombard St, Thousand Oaks
(91360-5807)
PHONE..................................805 777-7666
Larry Lai, *CEO*
Andres Baudry, *Ch of Bd*
EMP: 12
SQ FT: 4,000
SALES (est): 1.4MM **Privately Held**
WEB: www.bonafide.com
SIC: 7372 7371 Utility computer software;
custom computer programming services

(P-24439)
BONSAI AI INC
2150 Shattuck Ave # 1200, Berkeley
(94704-1357)
PHONE..................................510 900-1112
Mark Hammond, *CEO*
Dave Cahill, *COO*
Keen Browne, *Vice Pres*
Julian Ostrow, *Vice Pres*
EMP: 42
SQ FT: 1,445
SALES (est): 49.3K
SALES (corp-wide): 110.3B **Publicly Held**
SIC: 7372
PA: Microsoft Corporation
1 Microsoft Way
Redmond WA 98052
425 882-8080

(P-24440)
BOOKETTE SOFTWARE CO INC
12795 Corte Cordillera, Salinas
(93908-8942)
PHONE..................................831 484-9250
Ronald Loiacono, *President*
EMP: 14
SALES (est): 1.1MM **Privately Held**
SIC: 7372 Prepackaged software

(P-24441)
BORLAND SOFTWARE CORPORATION
951 Mariners Isl Blvd # 460, San Mateo
(94404-1558)
PHONE..................................650 286-1900
Gina Rosenberger, *Branch Mgr*
EMP: 100
SALES (corp-wide): 834.5MM **Privately Held**
WEB: www.borland.com
SIC: 7372 Business oriented computer software
HQ: Borland Software Corporation
8310 N Cpitl Of Texas Hwy
Austin TX 78731
512 340-2200

(P-24442)
BOX INC (PA)
900 Jefferson Ave, Redwood City
(94063-1837)
PHONE..................................877 729-4269
Aaron Levie, *Ch of Bd*
Stephanie Carullo, *COO*
Dylan Smith, *CFO*
Daniel Levin, *Bd of Directors*
David Leeb, *Senior VP*
EMP: 148 **EST:** 2005
SQ FT: 340,000
SALES: 506.1MM **Publicly Held**
SIC: 7372 Application computer software

(P-24443)
BPO MANAGEMENT SERVICES INC (HQ)
8175 E Kaiser Blvd 100, Anaheim
(92808-2214)
PHONE..................................714 974-2670
Patrick Dolan, *Ch of Bd*
James Cortens, *President*
Don Rutherford, *CFO*
Koushik Dutta, *CTO*
EMP: 15
SQ FT: 3,500
SALES (est): 12.9MM
SALES (corp-wide): 28.1MM **Privately Held**
WEB: www.netguru.com
SIC: 7372 7371 Prepackaged software;
custom computer programming services
PA: Bpo Management Services, Inc
8175 E Kaiser Blvd 100
Anaheim CA 92808
714 972-2670

(P-24444)
BPO SYSTEMS INC (PA)
1700 Ygnacio Valley Rd # 205, Walnut
Creek (94598-3191)
PHONE..................................925 478-4299
Rambabu V Yarlagadda, *CEO*
EMP: 38 **EST:** 2000
SQ FT: 4,000
SALES (est): 4MM **Privately Held**
WEB: www.bposystems.com
SIC: 7372 Prepackaged software

(P-24445)
BQE SOFTWARE INC
3825 Del Amo Blvd Trrance Torrance, Tor-
rance (90503)
PHONE..................................310 602-4020
Shafat Qazi, *CEO*
Sharone Strauss, *Vice Pres*
Kari Weinberger, *Marketing Staff*
Jason Burkley, *Sales Staff*
Humza Khan, *Sales Staff*
EMP: 95
SQ FT: 20,000
SALES (est): 13.1MM **Privately Held**
WEB: www.billquick.com
SIC: 7372 5734 Application computer soft-
ware; software, business & non-game

(P-24446)
BRAGSTR LLC
20250 Plummer St, Chatsworth
(91311-5449)
PHONE..................................818 917-0312
Erik Swanson, *President*
EMP: 10 **EST:** 2012
SQ FT: 10,000
SALES (est): 396.3K **Privately Held**
SIC: 7372 Application computer software

(P-24447)
BRAINCHIP INC (HQ)
65 Enterprise, Aliso Viejo (92656-2705)
PHONE..................................949 330-6750
Louis Dinardo, *CEO*
Peter Van Der Made, *CTO*
EMP: 26 **EST:** 2014
SQ FT: 2,500
SALES (est): 3.6MM **Privately Held**
SIC: 7372 Prepackaged software

(P-24448)
BRAINS OUT MEDIA INC
2629 Foothill Blvd # 111, La Crescenta
(91214-3511)
PHONE..................................818 296-1036
Fermin Iglesias, *President*
EMP: 15 **EST:** 2014
SALES: 850K **Privately Held**
SIC: 7372 7374 Application computer soft-
ware; computer graphics service

(P-24449)
BRANCH MESSENGER INC
130 W Union St, Pasadena (91103-3628)
PHONE..................................323 300-4063
Atif Siddiqi, *President*
EMP: 10 **EST:** 2014
SALES (est): 244K **Privately Held**
SIC: 7372 Application computer software

(P-24450)
BRENDAN TECHNOLOGIES INC
1947 Camino Vida Roble # 21, Carlsbad
(92008-6540)
PHONE..................................760 929-7500
John R Dunn II, *Ch of Bd*
George Dunn, *COO*
Lowell W Giffhorn, *CFO*
Ruth Melford, *Info Tech Mgr*
EMP: 20
SQ FT: 3,988
SALES (est): 521.3K **Privately Held**
WEB: www.brendan.com
SIC: 7372 Business oriented computer
software; utility computer software; appli-
cation computer software

(P-24451)
BREVITY LLC
1405 Warner Ave Ste A, Tustin
(92780-6405)
PHONE..................................949 250-0701
Leonard Wanger,
EMP: 12 **EST:** 2017
SQ FT: 1,200
SALES (est): 256K **Privately Held**
SIC: 7372 Business oriented computer
software

(P-24452)
BRIGHTIDEA INCORPORATED
255 California St # 1100, San Francisco
(94111-4927)
PHONE..................................415 814-1387
Luis Ostdiek, *Branch Mgr*
Mike Xu, *President*
EMP: 25
SALES (est): 2.2MM
SALES (corp-wide): 7.1MM **Privately Held**
SIC: 7372 Prepackaged software
PA: Brightidea Incorporated
25 Pacific Ave
San Francisco CA
415 814-3817

(P-24453)
BRILLIANT WORLDWIDE INC
15 Butte Pl, San Francisco (94104-5069)
PHONE..................................650 468-2966
Sue Khim, *CEO*
Suyeon Khim, *CEO*
EMP: 25
SALES (est): 66.5K **Privately Held**
SIC: 7372 Educational computer software

(P-24454)
BROADLY INC
1500 Broadway Ste 200, Oakland
(94612-2002)
PHONE..................................510 400-6039
Joshua Melick, *CEO*
Laura Nelson, *Marketing Staff*
Jodi Oakley, *Sales Staff*
Kim Olson, *Sales Staff*
Jamie Taggart, *Sales Staff*
EMP: 30
SALES (est): 138.6K **Privately Held**
SIC: 7372 Business oriented computer
software

(P-24455)
BROADVISION INC (PA)
460 Seaport Ct Ste 102, Redwood City
(94063-5548)
PHONE..................................650 331-1000
Pehong Chen, *Ch of Bd*
James Dixon, *Bd of Directors*
Robert Lee, *Bd of Directors*
Francois Stieger, *Bd of Directors*
Richard Hughes, *Chief Mktg Ofcr*
EMP: 86
SQ FT: 16,399
SALES: 6.3MM **Publicly Held**
WEB: www.broadvision.com
SIC: 7372 Prepackaged software

(P-24456)
BSNAP LLC
4 Hutton Centre Dr Fl 10, Santa Ana
(92707-8713)
PHONE..................................657 269-4410
Tom Noto, *Principal*
EMP: 10 **EST:** 2017
SALES (est): 229K
SALES (corp-wide): 261.6MM **Privately Held**
SIC: 7372 Application computer software
HQ: Stearns Lending, Llc
4 Hutton Centre Dr Fl 10
Santa Ana CA 92707
714 513-7777

(P-24457)
BTRADE LLC
655 N Central Ave # 1460, Glendale
(91203-1422)
PHONE..................................818 334-4433
Steve Zapata, *Mng Member*
Don Miller, *COO*
Clifton Gonsalves, *Vice Pres*
Teresa Perez, *Vice Pres*
EMP: 25
SALES: 3MM **Privately Held**
SIC: 7372 Business oriented computer
software

(P-24458)
BUILDING ROBOTICS INC
Also Called: Comfy
300 Frank H, Oakland (94612)
PHONE..................................510 761-6482
Andrew Krioukov, *CEO*
Chitra Nayak, *COO*
Nick Colburn, *CFO*
Stephen Dawson-Haggerty, *CTO*
Brian Alward, *Sales Executive*
EMP: 15
SALES (est): 616.9K **Privately Held**
SIC: 7372 Application computer software

(P-24459)
C3 IOT INC
1300 Seaport Blvd Ste 500, Redwood City
(94063-5592)
PHONE..................................650 503-2200
Thomas M Siebel, *CEO*
Ed Abbo, *President*
Rohit Sureka, *Sr Software Eng*
EMP: 125
SQ FT: 35,000
SALES (est): 24.6MM **Privately Held**
SIC: 7372 Business oriented computer
software

(P-24460)
CA INC
3965 Freedom Cir Fl 6, Santa Clara
(95054-1286)
PHONE..................................800 225-5224
Vinod Peris, *Senior VP*
Sue Moynahan, *Director*
EMP: 166
SALES (corp-wide): 17.6B **Publicly Held**
SIC: 7372 Business oriented computer
software
HQ: Ca, Inc.
520 Madison Ave Fl 22
New York NY 10022
800 225-5224

(P-24461)
CA INC
10180 Telesis Ct Ste 500, San Diego
(92121-2787)
PHONE..................................631 342-6000
Greg Fox, *Manager*
Brian Dyson, *Sr Software Eng*
EMP: 100
SALES (corp-wide): 17.6B **Publicly Held**
WEB: www.cai.com
SIC: 7372 Prepackaged software
HQ: Ca, Inc.
520 Madison Ave Fl 22
New York NY 10022
800 225-5224

(P-24462)
CA INC
3013 Douglas Blvd Ste 120, Roseville
(95661-3842)
PHONE..................................800 405-5540
Larry Lynch, *Manager*

EMP: 20
SALES (corp-wide): 17.6B **Publicly Held**
WEB: www.cai.com
SIC: 7372 Business oriented computer
software
HQ: Ca, Inc.
520 Madison Ave Fl 22
New York NY 10022
800 225-5224

(P-24463)
CADENCE DESIGN SYSTEMS INC
2655 Seely Ave, San Jose (95134-1931)
PHONE..............................408 943-1234
EMP: 45
SALES (corp-wide): 1.9B **Publicly Held**
SIC: 7372 Prepackaged software
PA: Cadence Design Systems, Inc.
2655 Seely Ave Bldg 5
San Jose CA 95134
408 943-1234

(P-24464)
CADENCE DESIGN SYSTEMS INC
7505 Irvine Center Dr # 250, Irvine
(92618-3078)
PHONE..............................949 788-6080
EMP: 34
SALES (corp-wide): 1.9B **Publicly Held**
SIC: 7372
PA: Cadence Design Systems, Inc.
2655 Seely Ave Bldg 5
San Jose CA 95134
408 943-1234

(P-24465)
CADENCE DESIGN SYSTEMS INC (PA)
2655 Seely Ave Bldg 5, San Jose
(95134-1931)
PHONE..............................408 943-1234
Lip-Bu Tan, *President*
John B Shoven, *Ch of Bd*
Anirudh Devgan, *President*
Geoffrey G Ribar, *CFO*
Thomas P Beckley, *Senior VP*
EMP: 700
SALES: 1.9B **Publicly Held**
WEB: www.cadence.com
SIC: 7372 Prepackaged software; application computer software

(P-24466)
CADENCE DESIGN SYSTEMS INC
2150 Shattuck Ave Fl 10, Berkeley
(94704-1345)
PHONE..............................510 647-2800
Ted Vucurezich, *Branch Mgr*
EMP: 18
SALES (corp-wide): 1.9B **Publicly Held**
WEB: www.cadence.com
SIC: 7372 Application computer software
PA: Cadence Design Systems, Inc.
2655 Seely Ave Bldg 5
San Jose CA 95134
408 943-1234

(P-24467)
CADENCE DESIGN SYSTEMS INC
6700 Koll Center Pkwy # 160, Pleasanton
(94566-7060)
PHONE..............................925 895-3202
Matt Depretis, *Branch Mgr*
EMP: 10
SALES (corp-wide): 1.9B **Publicly Held**
WEB: www.cadence.com
SIC: 7372 Application computer software
PA: Cadence Design Systems, Inc.
2655 Seely Ave Bldg 5
San Jose CA 95134
408 943-1234

(P-24468)
CADENCE US INC (PA)
2655 Seely Ave, San Jose (95134-1931)
PHONE..............................408 943-1234
James Lico, *Vice Pres*
Nimish Modi, *Vice Pres*
Jessica Lee, *Info Tech Dir*
Kathleen Heinze, *Info Tech Mgr*
Jay Lawrence, *Technology*

EMP: 10
SALES (est): 1.3MM **Privately Held**
SIC: 7372 Application computer software

(P-24469)
CALYPTO DESIGN SYSTEMS INC
2099 Gateway Pl Ste 550, San Jose
(95110-1051)
PHONE..............................408 850-2300
Sanjiv Kaul, *President*
Chris Mausler, *CFO*
Larry Vaughn, *CFO*
Linda Kracht, *Office Mgr*
Abhishek Ranjan, *Engineer*
EMP: 17
SALES (est): 2.2MM **Privately Held**
WEB: www.calypto.com
SIC: 7372 Business oriented computer software

(P-24470)
CARECOGNITICS LLC
530 Lytton Ave Fl 2, Palo Alto
(94301-1541)
PHONE..............................702 355-8201
Saurabh Tara, *CEO*
Vishal Agarwal, *President*
EMP: 12
SALES: 100K **Privately Held**
SIC: 7372 8099 Application computer software; health & allied services

(P-24471)
CAREVAULT CORPORATION
182 Exbourne Ave Ste 200, San Carlos
(94070-1828)
PHONE..............................714 333-0556
Avanish Sahai, *CEO*
EMP: 10 **EST:** 2011
SALES (est): 654.7K **Privately Held**
SIC: 7372 Prepackaged software

(P-24472)
CARGO CHIEF INC
10 Rollins Rd Ste 202, Millbrae
(94030-3129)
PHONE..............................650 560-5001
Russell Jones, *CEO*
Abtin Hamidi, *Vice Pres*
Cindy Du, *VP Finance*
Jon Winters,
EMP: 12
SALES: 4MM **Privately Held**
SIC: 7372 Business oriented computer software

(P-24473)
CARPARTS TECHNOLOGIES
32122 Camn Capistrano # 100, San Juan
Capistrano (92675-3734)
PHONE..............................949 488-8860
Charles Ruban, *CEO*
Cynthia Robbins, *President*
EMP: 163 **EST:** 2004
SQ FT: 1,400
SALES (est): 6.3MM **Privately Held**
WEB: www.crcs.com
SIC: 7372 Prepackaged software

(P-24474)
CASEMAKER INC
1680 Civic Center Dr Frnt, Santa Clara
(95050-4146)
PHONE..............................408 261-8265
Jui-Long Liu, *President*
Austin Lo, *Manager*
EMP: 14
SQ FT: 11,000
SALES (est): 1.8MM **Privately Held**
WEB: www.casemaker.com
SIC: 7372 7371 Application computer software; custom computer programming services

(P-24475)
CASPIAN RESEARCH & TECH LLC
1434 Westwood Blvd Ste 14, Los Angeles
(90024-4939)
PHONE..............................310 474-3244
Amir Tarighat, *Director*
EMP: 10
SALES (est): 221.8K **Privately Held**
SIC: 7372 7382 Operating systems computer software; security systems services

(P-24476)
CASPIO INC (PA)
2953 Bunker Hill Ln # 201, Santa Clara
(95054-1131)
PHONE..............................650 691-0900
Frank Zamani, *CEO*
Spring Babb, *Admin Sec*
EMP: 23 **EST:** 2000
SQ FT: 4,000
SALES (est): 3.8MM **Privately Held**
SIC: 7372 Business oriented computer software

(P-24477)
CATALYST DEVELOPMENT CORP
56925 Yucca Trl, Yucca Valley
(92284-7913)
PHONE..............................760 228-9653
Cary Harwin, *President*
Mike Stefanik, *Senior VP*
Kapil Desai, *Analyst*
EMP: 50
SALES (est): 3MM **Privately Held**
WEB: www.catalyst.com
SIC: 7372 Business oriented computer software

(P-24478)
CATAPULT COMMUNICATIONS CORP (DH)
26601 Agoura Rd, Calabasas
(91302-1959)
PHONE..............................818 871-1800
Richard A Karp, *Ch of Bd*
David Mayfield, *President*
Chris Stephenson, *CFO*
Terry Eastham, *Vice Pres*
Barbara J Fairhurst, *Vice Pres*
▲ **EMP:** 25
SQ FT: 39,000
SALES (est): 13.9MM
SALES (corp-wide): 3.1B **Publicly Held**
WEB: www.catapult.com
SIC: 7372 3661 Application computer software; telephone & telegraph apparatus
HQ: Ixia
26601 Agoura Rd
Calabasas CA 91302
818 871-1800

(P-24479)
CELIGO INC (PA)
1820 Gateway Dr Ste 260, San Mateo
(94404-4068)
PHONE..............................650 579-0210
Jan K Arendtsz, *CEO*
Mark Simon, *Vice Pres*
Jim Leney, *Practice Mgr*
Lisa Lorenz, *Office Mgr*
Alice B Lai, *Software Engr*
EMP: 47
SALES (est): 7.5MM **Privately Held**
SIC: 7372 Business oriented computer software

(P-24480)
CELLFUSION INC
1115 Lorne Way, Sunnyvale (94087-5158)
PHONE..............................650 347-4000
Kersten Ellerbrock, *Manager*
EMP: 11 **Privately Held**
SIC: 7372 Prepackaged software
PA: Cellfusion, Inc.
2033 Gateway Pl Fl 5
San Jose CA 95110

(P-24481)
CENTRL INC
257 Castro St Ste 215, Mountain View
(94041-1287)
PHONE..............................650 641-7092
Sanjeev Dheer, *CEO*
Chris Marino, *COO*
Rupali Chopra, *General Counsel*
EMP: 33
SALES (est): 329.7K **Privately Held**
SIC: 7372 Application computer software; business oriented computer software

(P-24482)
CERNER CORPORATION
Also Called: Cerner Life Sciences
9100 Wilshire Blvd 655e, Beverly Hills
(90212-3442)
PHONE..............................310 247-7700
Gloria Shulman, *Vice Pres*
EMP: 42
SALES (corp-wide): 5.1B **Publicly Held**
WEB: www.cerner.com
SIC: 7372 Business oriented computer software
PA: Cerner Corporation
2800 Rock Creek Pkwy
Kansas City MO 64117
816 201-1024

(P-24483)
CFORIA SOFTWARE INC
4333 Park Terrace Dr # 201, Westlake Village (91361-5656)
PHONE..............................818 871-9687
Dave McIntyre, *President*
Chris Caparon, *President*
EMP: 22
SQ FT: 4,000
SALES (est): 3.8MM **Privately Held**
WEB: www.cforia.com
SIC: 7372 Business oriented computer software

(P-24484)
CFS TAX SOFTWARE
Also Called: CFS Income Tax
1445 E Los Angeles Ave # 214, Simi Valley
(93065-2828)
P.O. Box 879 (93062-0879)
PHONE..............................805 522-1157
Ted Sullivan, *President*
Nolan Stacey, *Software Dev*
Juliana Caizzo, *Technology*
Roger Stock, *Technical Staff*
Juliana Caiazzo, *Sales Staff*
EMP: 60
SALES (est): 5.4MM **Privately Held**
WEB: www.taxtools.com
SIC: 7372 8721 Business oriented computer software; accounting, auditing & bookkeeping

(P-24485)
CHANGYOUCOM (US) LLC
1654 Hollenbeck Ave # 14, Sunnyvale
(94087-5474)
PHONE..............................408 889-9866
Yanjuan Chen,
EMP: 45 **EST:** 2009
SALES (est): 3.4MM **Privately Held**
SIC: 7372 Publishers' computer software

(P-24486)
CHECK POINT SOFTWARE TECH INC (HQ)
959 Skyway Rd Ste 300, San Carlos
(94070-2723)
PHONE..............................650 628-2000
John Slavitt, *CEO*
Marius Nacht, *Ch of Bd*
Rafael Alegre, *President*
Jerry Ungerman, *President*
Eyal Desheh, *CFO*
EMP: 120
SALES (est): 222.6MM
SALES (corp-wide): 1.8B **Privately Held**
WEB: www.checkpoint.com
SIC: 7372 Operating systems computer software
PA: Check Point Software Technologies Ltd.
5 Shlomo Kaplan
Tel Aviv-Jaffa 67891
375 345-55

(P-24487)
CHEMSW INC
2480 Burskirk Ste 300, Pleasant Hill
(94523)
PHONE..............................707 864-0845
Brian Stafford, *President*
Patrick Spink, *Vice Pres*
EMP: 16
SQ FT: 2,600
SALES (est): 293.7K
SALES (corp-wide): 1.7B **Privately Held**
WEB: www.chemsw.com
SIC: 7372 Prepackaged software

▲ = Import ▼=Export
◆ =Import/Export

HQ: Dassault Systemes Biovia Corp.
5005 Wateridge Vista Dr # 2
San Diego CA 92121
-

(P-24488)
CHOWNOW INC
12181 Bluff Creek Dr # 200, Playa Vista
(90094-3232)
PHONE...................................888 707-2469
Eric Jaffe, *President*
Stuart Hathaway, *CFO*
Candice Taylor, *Recruiter*
Emily Neudorf, *Mktg Dir*
Jessica Springer, *Marketing Mgr*
EMP: 100
SQ FT: 25,000
SALES (est): 2.1MM Privately Held
SIC: 7372 Business oriented computer
software

(P-24489)
CIMMARON SOFTWARE INC
16885 W Bernardo Dr # 345, San Diego
(92127-1618)
PHONE...................................858 385-1291
Richard Lidstrom, *CEO*
Goran Stijacic, *President*
EMP: 20
SQ FT: 5,000
SALES (est): 1.7MM Privately Held
WEB: www.cimmaronsoftware.com
SIC: 7372 7371 5734 Prepackaged soft-
ware; custom computer programming
services; software, business & non-game

(P-24490)
CIPHERCLOUD INC (PA)
2581 Junction Ave Ste 200, San Jose
(95134-1923)
PHONE...................................408 519-6930
Pravin Kothari, *CEO*
Glenn Cobb, *Vice Pres*
Paul Culpepper, *Vice Pres*
Dev Ghoshal, *Vice Pres*
Harnish Kanani, *Vice Pres*
EMP: 90
SQ FT: 21,800
SALES (est): 40.3MM Privately Held
SIC: 7372 Prepackaged software

(P-24491)
CIRCA 1605 INC
1475 Folsom St Ste 200, San Francisco
(94103-3761)
PHONE...................................217 899-3512
Matthew Galligan, *CEO*
Ben Huh, *Co-Owner*
Arsenio Santos, *Co-Owner*
EMP: 20
SQ FT: 3,000
SALES (est): 1.2MM Privately Held
SIC: 7372 Application computer software

(P-24492)
CIRRENT INC
2 E 3rd Ave Ste 100, San Mateo
(94401-4011)
P.O. Box 809 (94401-0809)
PHONE...................................650 569-1135
Robert Conant, *CEO*
Marcio Avillez, *Senior VP*
EMP: 10
SALES (est): 431.3K Privately Held
SIC: 7372 Application computer software

(P-24493)
CISCO IRONPORT SYSTEMS
LLC (HQ)
170 W Tasman Dr, San Jose (95134-1706)
PHONE...................................650 989-6500
Scott Weiss, *CEO*
Tom Peterson, *President*
Craig Collins, *CFO*
Bob Kavner, *Chairman*
Kelly Bodnar Battles, *Vice Pres*
EMP: 260
SALES (est): 53.8MM
SALES (corp-wide): 49.3B Publicly Held
WEB: www.ironport.com
SIC: 7372 5045 Prepackaged software;
computers, peripherals & software
PA: Cisco Systems, Inc.
170 W Tasman Dr
San Jose CA 95134
408 526-4000

(P-24494)
CITRIX ONLINE DIVISION
7414 Hollister Ave Goleta, Los Angeles
(90074-0001)
PHONE...................................800 424-8749
EMP: 17
SALES (est): 1.3MM Privately Held
SIC: 7372 Prepackaged software

(P-24495)
CLASS TWIST INC
Also Called: Classdojo
735 Tehama St, San Francisco
(94103-3822)
PHONE...................................650 646-8235
Usamah Chaudhary, *President*
Liam Don, *Vice Pres*
Elisette Weiss, *Opers Staff*
Manoj Lamba, *Marketing Staff*
Lindsay McKinley, *Corp Comm Staff*
EMP: 12
SALES (est): 880K Privately Held
SIC: 7372 Educational computer software

(P-24496)
CLASSY INC
350 10th Ave Ste 1300, San Diego
(92101-8703)
PHONE...................................619 961-1892
Scot P Chisholm, *CEO*
Adam Aarons, *President*
Todd Crutchfield, *COO*
Carilu Dietrich, *Chief Mktg Ofcr*
Neena Gupta Needel, *
EMP: 21
SALES (est): 2.2MM Privately Held
SIC: 7372 Prepackaged software

(P-24497)
CLEARSLIDE INC (DH)
45 Fremont St Fl 32, San Francisco
(94105-2258)
PHONE...................................877 360-3366
Dustin Grosse, *CEO*
Jim Benton, *Officer*
Sandra Wright, *Vice Pres*
Erin Stanwood, *Executive*
Mike Volk, *Executive*
EMP: 84
SALES (est): 27.5MM
SALES (corp-wide): 128.6MM Privately
Held
SIC: 7372 Business oriented computer
software
HQ: Corel Corporation
1600 Carling Ave Suite 100
Ottawa ON K1Z 8
613 728-8200

(P-24498)
CLEARWELL SYSTEMS INC
350 Ellis St, Mountain View (94043-2202)
PHONE...................................877 253-2793
Aaref Hilaly, *CEO*
Anup Singh, *CFO*
Venkat Rangan, *CTO*
EMP: 110
SQ FT: 17,000
SALES (est): 7.4MM
SALES (corp-wide): 4.8B Publicly Held
WEB: www.clearwellsystems.com
SIC: 7372 Business oriented computer
software
PA: Symantec Corporation
350 Ellis St
Mountain View CA 94043
650 527-8000

(P-24499)
CLIPCALL INC
645 Harrison St Ste 200, San Francisco
(94107-3624)
PHONE...................................650 285-7597
Daniel Shaked, *CEO*
Einat Har, *CFO*
EMP: 15
SALES (est): 108.8K Privately Held
SIC: 7372 Business oriented computer
software

(P-24500)
CLOCKWARE
548 Market St, San Francisco
(94104-5401)
PHONE...................................650 556-8880
Ronald Kfoury, *President*

EMP: 15
SALES (est): 1.2MM Privately Held
WEB: www.clockware.com
SIC: 7372 Application computer software

(P-24501)
CLONETAB INC
1660 W Linne Rd Ste 214, Tracy
(95377-8027)
PHONE...................................209 292-5663
Hema Meka, *CEO*
Bharathi Meka, *CFO*
Samantha Dalton, *Sls & Mktg Exec*
EMP: 39
SALES (est): 173.7K Privately Held
SIC: 7372 Prepackaged software

(P-24502)
CLOUDCAR INC
2550 Great America Way # 301, Santa
Clara (95054-1161)
PHONE...................................650 946-1236
Philipp Popov, *CEO*
Bruce Leak, *COO*
Albert Jordan, *Vice Pres*
Samson Roopkumar, *Info Tech Mgr*
Tim Yang, *Software Dev*
EMP: 30
SALES: 1MM Privately Held
SIC: 7372 Prepackaged software

(P-24503)
CLOUDNCO INC
Also Called: CLOud&co
300 Beale St Apt 613, San Francisco
(94105-2096)
PHONE...................................408 605-8755
Matthieu Dejardins, *CEO*
EMP: 16
SALES (est): 426.9K Privately Held
SIC: 7372 Application computer software;
business oriented computer software

(P-24504)
CLOUDPIC INC
19925 Stevens Creek Blvd, Cupertino
(95014-2300)
PHONE...................................408 786-1098
Richard Chuang, *CEO*
EMP: 10
SQ FT: 300
SALES (est): 590.9K Privately Held
SIC: 7372 Application computer software

(P-24505)
CLOUDSHIELD TECHNOLOGIES
LLC
212 Gibraltar Dr, Sunnyvale (94089-1324)
PHONE...................................408 331-6640
Randy Brumfield, *Senior VP*
Timothy Laehy, *CFO*
Steven Elston, *Vice Pres*
Todd Beine, *CTO*
Ken McKeithan, *VP Engrg*
EMP: 19
SQ FT: 35,000
SALES (est): 9.6MM
SALES (corp-wide): 49.5MM Privately
Held
WEB: www.cloudshield.com
SIC: 7372 8741 8742 Prepackaged soft-
ware; business management; business
consultant
PA: Lookingglass Cyber Solution, Inc.
10740 Parkridge Blvd # 200
Reston VA 20191
703 351-1000

(P-24506)
CLOUDVELOX INC
Also Called: Cloudvelocity Software
3945 Freedom Cir Ste 240, Santa Clara
(95054-1265)
PHONE...................................408 841-4800
Rajeev Chawla, *Principal*
Chris Charette, *Technology*
EMP: 17
SALES (est): 2.1MM Privately Held
SIC: 7372 Business oriented computer
software

(P-24507)
COBALT LABS INC
2403 16th St, San Francisco (94103-4210)
PHONE...................................415 651-7028
Esben Friis Jensen, *Founder*

Jacob Hansen, *CEO*
Kevin Bourne, *Manager*
EMP: 20 EST: 2017
SALES (est): 575.6K Privately Held
SIC: 7372 Prepackaged software

(P-24508)
CODEFAST INC
21170 Canyon Oak Way, Cupertino
(95014-6572)
PHONE...................................408 687-4700
Nick Barens, *President*
EMP: 11
SALES (est): 528.5K
SALES (corp-wide): 2.7B Publicly Held
WEB: www.codefast.com
SIC: 7372 Business oriented computer
software
HQ: Coverity Llc
185 Berry St Ste 6500
San Francisco CA 94107
415 321-5200

(P-24509)
COLLABRATIVE DRG
DISCOVERY INC
Also Called: Molecular Databank
1633 Bayshore Hwy Ste 342, Burlingame
(94010-1515)
PHONE...................................650 204-3084
Barry Bunin, *President*
Lixin Liu, *Accountant*
Whitney Smith, *Director*
Kellan Gregory, *Manager*
EMP: 11
SALES (est): 1MM Privately Held
SIC: 7372 Prepackaged software

(P-24510)
COLORTOKENS INC
2101 Tasman Dr Ste 201, Santa Clara
(95054-1020)
PHONE...................................408 341-6030
Rajesh Parekh, *President*
EMP: 50
SALES (est): 1.3MM Privately Held
SIC: 7372 Business oriented computer
software

(P-24511)
COMMERCE VELOCITY LLC
1 Technology Dr Ste J725, Irvine
(92618-2353)
PHONE...................................949 756-8950
Umesh Verma, *
Ajay Chopra, *
EMP: 50
SQ FT: 5,000
SALES (est): 6.8MM
SALES (corp-wide): 7.6B Publicly Held
WEB: www.cvelocity.com
SIC: 7372 Business oriented computer
software
PA: Fidelity National Financial, Inc.
601 Riverside Ave Fl 4
Jacksonville FL 32204
904 854-8100

(P-24512)
COMPATIBLE SOFTWARE
SYSTEMS
10966 Bigge St, San Leandro
(94577-1121)
PHONE...................................510 562-1172
Marvin McClendon, *Owner*
EMP: 10
SQ FT: 1,400
SALES (est): 982.9K Privately Held
WEB: www.ctswest.com
SIC: 7372 Prepackaged software

(P-24513)
COMPOSITE SOFTWARE LLC
(HQ)
755 Sycamore Dr, Milpitas (95035-7411)
PHONE...................................800 553-6387
Jim Green, *CEO*
Jon Bode, *CFO*
Marc Breissinger, *Exec VP*
Robert Eve, *Exec VP*
Che Wijesinghe, *Exec VP*
EMP: 74
SQ FT: 14,000

SALES (est): 16.7MM
SALES (corp-wide): 49.3B Publicly Held
WEB: www.compositesw.com
SIC: 7372 Prepackaged software
PA: Cisco Systems, Inc.
170 W Tasman Dr
San Jose CA 95134
408 526-4000

(P-24514)
COMPUGROUP MEDICAL INC
25 B Tech Dr Ste 200, Irvine (92618)
PHONE................................949 789-0500
John Tangredi, COO
EMP: 21
SALES (corp-wide): 45MM Privately
Held
SIC: 7372 Prepackaged software
PA: Compugroup Medical, Inc.
3838 N Central Ave # 1600
Phoenix AZ 85012
855 270-6700

(P-24515)
COMPULINK BUSINESS SYSTEMS INC
1100 Business Center Cir, Newbury Park
(91320-1129)
PHONE................................805 446-2050
Link Wilson, President
Mark Misteravich, Executive
Cole Galbraith, CTO
Cole Galbarith, Info Tech Mgr
Jose Melendez, Technology
EMP: 120
SQ FT: 15,000
SALES (est): 16.5MM Privately Held
WEB: www.compulink-software.com
SIC: 7372 Business oriented computer
software

(P-24516)
COMPULINK MANAGEMENT CTR INC
Also Called: Laserfiche Document Imaging
3545 Long Beach Blvd, Long Beach
(90807-3941)
PHONE................................562 988-1688
Nien-Ling Wacker, President
Hedy Belttary, Vice Pres
Stephen Hall, Vice Pres
Jim Haney, Vice Pres
Thomas Phelps, Vice Pres
EMP: 170
SQ FT: 30,000
SALES (est): 37.3MM Privately Held
WEB: www.laserfiche.com
SIC: 7372 Business oriented computer
software

(P-24517)
COMPUTERS AND STRUCTURES INC
Also Called: C S I
1646 N Calif Blvd Ste 600, Walnut Creek
(94596-7456)
PHONE................................510 649-2200
Ashraf Habibullah, President
Marilyn Wilkes, Vice Pres
EMP: 14
SQ FT: 4,000
SALES (est): 2.4MM Privately Held
WEB: www.csiberkeley.com
SIC: 7372 Application computer software

(P-24518)
COMPUTRUST SOFTWARE CORP (PA)
18625 Sutter Blvd Ste 500, Morgan Hill
(95037-2864)
P.O. Box 787 (95038-0787)
PHONE................................408 782-7470
Rolf Kessel, CEO
Jacqueline Kessel, Vice Pres
Cheryl Rossi, Marketing Staff
EMP: 13 EST: 1979
SQ FT: 2,000
SALES (est): 1.3MM Privately Held
SIC: 7372 Business oriented computer
software; word processing computer soft-
ware; publishers' computer software; ap-
plication computer software

(P-24519)
CONDECO SOFTWARE INC (HQ)
2105 S Bascom Ave Ste 150, Campbell
(95008-3276)
PHONE................................917 677-7600
Martin Brooker, CEO
EMP: 34
SALES (est): 8.6MM
SALES (corp-wide): 29.3MM Privately
Held
SIC: 7372 Business oriented computer
software

(P-24520)
CONFIDENT TECHNOLOGIES INC
3830 Vly Cntre Dr Ste 705, San Diego
(92130)
PHONE................................858 345-5640
William Goldbach, Exec VP
EMP: 11 EST: 2010
SQ FT: 1,600
SALES (est): 692.7K Privately Held
SIC: 7372 Business oriented computer
software

(P-24521)
CONFLUENT INC (PA)
101 University Ave # 111, Palo Alto
(94301-1679)
PHONE................................650 453-5860
Jay Kreps, CEO
Luanne Dauber, Chief Mktg Ofcr
Neha Narkhede, Vice Pres
Todd Barnett, VP Sales
EMP: 27 EST: 2014
SQ FT: 6,000
SALES (est): 7.7MM Privately Held
SIC: 7372 Application computer software;
business oriented computer software; util-
ity computer software

(P-24522)
CONSILIO - A FIRST ADVANTAGE
605 E Huntington Dr # 211, Monrovia
(91016-6352)
PHONE................................626 921-1600
EMP: 32
SALES (corp-wide): 6.9MM Privately
Held
SIC: 7372 Application computer software
PA: Consilio, Llc
1828 L St Nw Ste 1070
Washington DC 20036
202 822-6222

(P-24523)
CONTACTUAL INC
810 W Maude Ave, Sunnyvale
(94085-2910)
PHONE................................650 292-4408
Mansour Salame, CEO
David Sohm, President
David Chen, Vice Pres
Dani Shomron, Vice Pres
Richard W Southwick, Vice Pres
EMP: 50
SQ FT: 5,000
SALES (est): 3.3MM
SALES (corp-wide): 296.5MM Publicly
Held
WEB: www.contactual.com
SIC: 7372 Prepackaged software
PA: 8x8, Inc.
2125 Onel Dr
San Jose CA 95131
408 727-1885

(P-24524)
COPLEY PRESS INC
Also Called: Signon San Diego
2375 Northside Dr Ste 300, San Diego
(92108-2700)
PHONE................................619 718-5200
Ron James, Manager
EMP: 80
SALES (corp-wide): 101.8MM Privately
Held
WEB: www.copleynewspapers.com
SIC: 7372 2711 Prepackaged software;
newspapers

PA: The Copley Press Inc
7776 Ivanhoe Ave
La Jolla CA 92037
858 454-0411

(P-24525)
COPPER CRM INC
301 Howard St Ste 600, San Francisco
(94105-6600)
PHONE................................415 231-6360
Jonathan Lee, CEO
Shaun Haase, Chief Mktg Ofcr
Charles Ashworth,
Jun Hu, Vice Pres
Justin Oberbauer, Vice Pres
EMP: 20 EST: 2011
SQ FT: 15,000
SALES (est): 2.5MM Privately Held
SIC: 7372 Application computer software

(P-24526)
CORCEN DATA INTERNATIONAL INC
17341 Irvine Blvd Ste 205, Tustin
(92780-3010)
PHONE................................714 251-6110
Han OH, President
Michelle OH, General Mgr
EMP: 12
SQ FT: 21,000
SALES (est): 765.7K Privately Held
WEB: www.corcen.com
SIC: 7372 7371 5734 Business oriented
computer software; custom computer pro-
gramming services; software, business &
non-game

(P-24527)
CORNERSTONE ONDEMAND INC (PA)
1601 Cloverfield Blvd 620s, Santa Monica
(90404-4178)
PHONE................................310 752-0200
Adam L Miller, Ch of Bd
Stephen Pfeiffer, President
Kirsten Helvey, COO
Brian L Swartz, CFO
Vincent Belliveau, Exec VP
EMP: 148
SQ FT: 108,000
SALES (est): 481.9MM Publicly Held
WEB: www.cornerstoneondemand.com
SIC: 7372 Business oriented computer
software

(P-24528)
CORRUGATED TECHNOLOGIES INC
Also Called: C T I
15150 Avenue Of Science, San Diego
(92128-3405)
PHONE................................858 578-3550
EMP: 30
SALES (est): 4.4MM Privately Held
WEB: www.corrtech.com
SIC: 7372

(P-24529)
COSMI FINANCE LLC
1635 Chelsea Rd Ste A, San Marino
(91108-2456)
PHONE................................310 603-5800
Edward O Lanchantin, Mng Member
S Amos Smith,
EMP: 12
SQ FT: 2,000
SALES (est): 2MM Privately Held
SIC: 7372 Prepackaged software

(P-24530)
COUNTERPOINT SOFTWARE INC
24528 Palermo Dr, Calabasas
(91302-2501)
PHONE................................818 222-7777
James Foley, President
Anna Dow, Vice Pres
Dick Levine, Vice Pres
Darlene Hosaka, Principal
Mary Nelson, Principal
EMP: 13
SALES (est): 1.3MM Privately Held
WEB: www.counterpoint.net
SIC: 7372 Application computer software

(P-24531)
COUPA SOFTWARE INCORPORATED (PA)
1855 S Grant St, San Mateo (94402-7016)
PHONE................................650 931-3200
Robert Bernshteyn, Ch of Bd
James Dinette, Partner
Chris Murdick, Partner
David Shanteler, Partner
Mark Riggs, COO
EMP: 111
SQ FT: 69,220
SALES: 186.7MM Publicly Held
WEB: www.coupa.com
SIC: 7372 Business oriented computer
software

(P-24532)
CROSSROADS SOFTWARE INC
210 W Birch St Ste 207, Brea
(92821-4504)
PHONE................................714 990-6433
Jeff Cullen, President
EMP: 13
SQ FT: 1,000
SALES (est): 1MM Privately Held
WEB: www.crossroadssoftware.com
SIC: 7372 Prepackaged software

(P-24533)
CRUNCH LLC
1190 Saratoga Ave, San Jose
(95129-3438)
PHONE................................650 257-8000
Saeid Ghafouri, CEO
Masoud Ghafouri, Vice Pres
EMP: 20
SALES (est): 1.2MM Privately Held
SIC: 7372 Application computer software

(P-24534)
CRYSTAL DYNAMICS INC
1400a Saport Blvd Ste 300, Redwood City
(94063)
PHONE................................650 421-7600
Philip Rogers, CEO
Robert Dyer, President
John Horsley, President
John Miller, President
Kun Chen, Info Tech Mgr
EMP: 90
SQ FT: 26,000
SALES (est): 13MM
SALES (corp-wide): 2.3B Privately Held
WEB: www.crystald.com
SIC: 7372 Business oriented computer
software
HQ: Square Enix Limited
240 Blackfriars Road
London SE1 8
208 636-3000

(P-24535)
CUADRA ASSOCIATES INC (PA)
3415 S Sepulveda Blvd # 3, Los Angeles
(90034-6060)
PHONE................................310 591-2490
Phillip Green, Principal
Ron Aspe, President
Ilene Slavick, Director
EMP: 10
SQ FT: 3,500
SALES (est): 2.5MM Privately Held
WEB: www.cuadra.com
SIC: 7372 5045 Business oriented com-
puter software; computers, peripherals &
software

(P-24536)
CULTURE AMP INC (HQ)
660 Market St Ste 500, San Francisco
(94104-5021)
PHONE................................415 326-8453
Didier Raoul Elzinga, CEO
Douglas Mark English, CFO
Rodney James Hamilton, Admin Sec
EMP: 40
SALES (est): 33.5K
SALES (corp-wide): 6.1MM Privately
Held
SIC: 7372 Prepackaged software
PA: Culture Amp Pty Ltd
L10 31 Queen St
Melbourne VIC 3000
439 193-778

(P-24537)
CUMULUS NETWORKS INC (PA)
185 E Dana St, Mountain View
(94041-1507)
PHONE..................650 383-6700
Jame Rivers, *CEO*
Nolan Leake, *Co-Owner*
Reza Malekzadeh, *Vice Pres*
Shrijeet Mukherjee, *Vice Pres*
Edward Leake, *Principal*
EMP: 124
SALES (est): 27MM **Privately Held**
SIC: 7372 7371 Publishers' computer soft-
ware; computer software development

(P-24538)
CVPS INC
9514 Glenhaven Dr, Glenhaven (95443)
P.O. Box 638 (95443-0638)
PHONE..................707 998-9364
Kai Schuette, *President*
Andy Preas, *Vice Pres*
EMP: 33
SALES (est): 3.4MM **Privately Held**
WEB: www.cvps.net
SIC: 7372 Application computer software

(P-24539)
CYBER MDIA SOLUTIONS LTD LBLTY
23161 Lake Center Dr # 220, Lake Forest
(92630-6803)
PHONE..................877 480-8255
Allan Gindi, *Mng Member*
EMP: 25 **EST:** 2003
SALES (est): 1MM **Privately Held**
SIC: 7372 Business oriented computer
software

(P-24540)
CYBERLINKCOM CORP
1073 S Winchester Blvd, San Jose
(95128-3702)
PHONE..................408 217-1850
Shing Wong, *President*
John Yoo, *Business Mgr*
Cindy Lin, *Manager*
Christina Tao, *Manager*
EMP: 12
SALES (est): 1.6MM **Privately Held**
WEB: www.pixarttech.com
SIC: 7372 Application computer software

(P-24541)
CYBREX CONSULTING INC
4470 W Sunset Blvd, Los Angeles
(90027-6302)
PHONE..................513 999-2109
Steve Kerver, *President*
EMP: 100
SQ FT: 1,000
SALES (est): 2MM **Privately Held**
SIC: 7372 8742 Prepackaged software;
real estate consultant

(P-24542)
CYLANCE INC (PA)
400 Spectrum Center Dr, Irvine
(92618-4934)
PHONE..................949 375-3380
Stuart McClure, *CEO*
David Stein, *Partner*
Daniel Doimo, *President*
Felix Marquardt, *President*
Brian Robins, *CFO*
EMP: 139 **EST:** 2012
SALES (est): 180.1MM **Privately Held**
SIC: 7372 Application computer software

(P-24543)
CYMMETRIA INC
2557 Park Blvd Apt L106, Palo Alto
(94306-1937)
PHONE..................415 568-6870
Ilya Levtov, *CEO*
Jonathan Braverman,
EMP: 24 **EST:** 2014
SALES (est): 711.5K **Privately Held**
SIC: 7372 Business oriented computer
software

(P-24544)
CYTOBANK INC
3945 Freedom Cir Ste 540, Santa Clara
(95054-1225)
PHONE..................650 918-7966
Nikesh Kotecha, *CEO*
Chris Coveney, *Sr Software Eng*
David Craford, *Opers Staff*
Todd Salomon, *Sales Dir*
Angela Landrigan, *Director*
EMP: 12
SALES (est): 14.6K **Privately Held**
SIC: 7372 7371 Application computer soft-
ware; computer software systems analy-
sis & design, custom

(P-24545)
D3PUBLISHER OF AMERICA INC
Also Called: D3 Go
15910 Ventura Blvd # 800, Encino
(91436-2810)
PHONE..................310 268-0820
Yoji Takenaka, *President*
Yuji ITOH, *Ch of Bd*
Hidetaka Tachibana, *CFO*
Russell Iriye, *Opers Staff*
Arthur Kawamoto, *Manager*
EMP: 63
SQ FT: 6,129
SALES (est): 8.4MM
SALES (corp-wide): 6.3B **Privately Held**
SIC: 7372 Home entertainment computer
software
HQ: D3 Publisher Inc.
1-9-5, Dogenzaka
Shibuya-Ku TKY 150-0
354 283-455

(P-24546)
DASHER TECHNOLOGIES INC (PA)
675 Campbell Technology P, Campbell
(95008-5092)
PHONE..................408 409-2607
Laurie Dasher, *CEO*
Al Chien, *President*
John Galatea, *VP Sales*
EMP: 42
SQ FT: 16,000
SALES (est): 18.3MM **Privately Held**
WEB: www.dashertechnologies.com
SIC: 7372 Prepackaged software

(P-24547)
DASSAULT SYSTEMES BIOVIA CORP (DH)
5005 Wateridge Vista Dr # 2, San Diego
(92121-5784)
PHONE..................858 799-5000
Max Carnecchia, *CEO*
John Pecoraro, *CFO*
Michael Piraino, *CFO*
Jason Gray, *Senior VP*
Mathew Hahn, *Senior VP*
EMP: 25
SQ FT: 68,436
SALES (est): 89.4MM
SALES (corp-wide): 1.7B **Privately Held**
WEB: www.accelrys.com
SIC: 7372 Application computer software;
business oriented computer software
HQ: 3ds Acquisition Corp.
175 Wyman St
Waltham MA 02451
781 810-5011

(P-24548)
DATA ADVANTAGE GROUP INC
145 Natoma St Fl 5, San Francisco
(94105-3733)
PHONE..................415 947-0400
Geoffrey Rayner, *CEO*
Gregory Blumstein, *President*
EMP: 15
SQ FT: 2,200
SALES (est): 1.9MM **Privately Held**
WEB: www.dataag.com
SIC: 7372 Prepackaged software

(P-24549)
DATA AGENT LLC
1349 Josephine St, Berkeley (94703-1113)
PHONE..................800 772-8314
Thuyen Nguyen, *CEO*

EMP: 12
SALES (est): 1.1MM **Privately Held**
WEB: www.DataAgent.com
SIC: 7372

(P-24550)
DATA LINKAGE SOFTWARE INC
2421 W 205th St Ste D207, Torrance
(90501-1469)
PHONE..................310 781-3056
Marwan Dajani, *President*
EMP: 15
SQ FT: 1,900
SALES (est): 1.5MM **Privately Held**
SIC: 7372 Business oriented computer
software

(P-24551)
DATABASE WORKS INC
500 S Kraemer Blvd # 110, Brea
(92821-6766)
PHONE..................714 203-8800
Terry Young, *President*
EMP: 13
SQ FT: 2,500
SALES (est): 1.5MM **Privately Held**
WEB: www.dbworks.com
SIC: 7372 3577 Business oriented com-
puter software; application computer soft-
ware; optical scanning devices

(P-24552)
DATAFOX INTELLIGENCE INC
835 Howard St 2, San Francisco
(94103-3009)
PHONE..................415 969-2144
Bastiaan Janmaat, *CEO*
Michael Dorsey, *COO*
Kelly Chris, *Executive*
Elena Tatarchenko, *Software Engr*
Alden Timme, *Chief Engr*
EMP: 18
SALES (est): 2MM **Privately Held**
SIC: 7372 Business oriented computer
software

(P-24553)
DATAGENICS SOFTWARE INC
5527 Satsuma Ave, North Hollywood
(91601-2841)
PHONE..................818 487-3900
Michael Vandemore, *President*
Pamela Vandemere, *Vice Pres*
EMP: 10
SQ FT: 2,500
SALES (est): 1MM **Privately Held**
WEB: www.datagenics.com
SIC: 7372 Business oriented computer
software

(P-24554)
DAVID CORPORATION
925 Highland Pointe Dr # 180, Roseville
(95678-5423)
PHONE..................916 762-8688
H Alex Aminian, *Branch Mgr*
EMP: 10
SALES (corp-wide): 7MM **Privately Held**
SIC: 7372 5734 7373 Prepackaged soft-
ware; software, business & non-game;
value-added resellers, computer systems
PA: David Corporation
301 Edgewater Pl Ste 116
Wakefield MA 01880
781 587-3008

(P-24555)
DE NOVO SOFTWARE
400 N Brand Blvd Ste 850, Glendale
(91203-9709)
PHONE..................213 814-1240
David Novo, *President*
EMP: 10
SQ FT: 2,000
SALES (est): 1.4MM **Privately Held**
SIC: 7372 Prepackaged software

(P-24556)
DECISIONLOGIC LLC
9820 Willow Creek Rd # 310, San Diego
(92131-1112)
PHONE..................858 586-0202
David Evans, *President*
Ryley Johnson, *Opers Mgr*
Michelle Evans, *Opers Staff*
George Cashman, *Sales Staff*

EMP: 50
SALES (est): 3.3MM **Privately Held**
SIC: 7372 Business oriented computer
software

(P-24557)
DEL MAR DATATRAC INC
Also Called: Del Mar Database
10509 Vista Sorrento Pkwy # 400, San
Diego (92121-2707)
PHONE..................858 550-8810
Jeb S Spencer, *President*
EMP: 35
SALES (est): 2.6MM
SALES (corp-wide): 417MM **Publicly Held**
WEB: www.delmardb.com
SIC: 7372 Prepackaged software
PA: Ellie Mae, Inc.
4420 Rosewood Dr Ste 500
Pleasanton CA 94588
925 227-7000

(P-24558)
DELPHIX CORP (PA)
1400 Saport Blvd Ste 200a, Redwood City
(94063)
PHONE..................650 494-1645
Chris Cook, *CEO*
Eric Schrock, *President*
Stewart Grierson, *CFO*
Jedidiah Yueh, *Officer*
Mike Stewart, *Senior VP*
EMP: 50
SQ FT: 18,000
SALES (est): 26.2MM **Privately Held**
SIC: 7372 Business oriented computer
software

(P-24559)
DEMANDBASE INC (PA)
680 Folsom St Ste 400, San Francisco
(94107-2159)
PHONE..................415 683-2660
Chris Golec, *CEO*
Peter Isaacson, *Chief Mktg Ofcr*
Alan Fletcher, *Officer*
Fatima Khan, *Officer*
Don Wight, *Officer*
EMP: 86
SALES (est): 57.2MM **Privately Held**
WEB: www.demandbase.com
SIC: 7372 Business oriented computer
software

(P-24560)
DENALI SOFTWARE INC (HQ)
2655 Seely Ave, San Jose (95134-1931)
PHONE..................408 943-1234
Sanjay Srivastava, *President*
R Mark Gogolewski, *CFO*
EMP: 36
SQ FT: 10,000
SALES (est): 4.7MM
SALES (corp-wide): 1.9B **Publicly Held**
WEB: www.denali.com
SIC: 7372 Application computer software
PA: Cadence Design Systems, Inc.
2655 Seely Ave Bldg 5
San Jose CA 95134
408 943-1234

(P-24561)
DIGISIGHT TECHNOLOGIES INC
535 Mission St Ste 1929, San Francisco
(94105-2997)
PHONE..................415 215-4440
Miki Kapoor, *CEO*
Allen Jones, *Vice Pres*
EMP: 12
SQ FT: 1,500
SALES (est): 42K **Privately Held**
SIC: 7372 Prepackaged software

(P-24562)
DINCLOUD INC
27520 Hawthorne Blvd # 185, Rllng HLS
Est (90274-3576)
PHONE..................310 929-1101
Mark Briggs, *CEO*
Mike L Chase, *Exec VP*
Ali M Dincmo, *Vice Pres*
EMP: 53
SQ FT: 1,500

SALES: 4MM
SALES (corp-wide): 43.1MM **Privately Held**
SIC: 7372 Business oriented computer software
PA: Premier Bpo, Inc.
　128 N 2nd St Ste 210
　Clarksville TN 37040
　931 551-8888

(P-24563)
DISTILLERY INC
90 Heron Ct, San Quentin (94964)
PHONE.......................415 505-5446
Adrian Szwarcburg, *President*
EMP: 55
SALES (est): 1.9MM **Privately Held**
SIC: 7372 Prepackaged software

(P-24564)
DISTINCT CORPORATION
175 Bernal Rd Ste 210, San Jose
(95119-1377)
PHONE.......................408 445-3270
Tarcisio Pedrotti, *President*
EMP: 30
SALES (est): 2.8MM **Privately Held**
WEB: www.distinct.com
SIC: 7372 Business oriented computer software

(P-24565)
DM SOFTWARE INC
1842 Park Skyline Rd, Santa Ana
(92705-3120)
PHONE.......................714 953-2653
Bill Parson, *Owner*
EMP: 10
SALES (corp-wide): 1.9MM **Privately Held**
WEB: www.oxford.com.pl
SIC: 7372 Prepackaged software
PA: Dm Software Inc
　654 Jack Cir
　Stateline NV 89449
　775 589-6049

(P-24566)
DO DINE INC
Also Called: Multani Logistics
24052 Mission Blvd, Hayward
(94544-1017)
PHONE.......................510 583-7546
Bikramjit Singh, *CEO*
EMP: 15
SQ FT: 5,000
SALES: 1.4MM **Privately Held**
SIC: 7372 Business oriented computer software

(P-24567)
DOCSEND INC
351 California St # 1200, San Francisco
(94104-2416)
PHONE.......................888 258-5951
Russell Heddleston, *CEO*
Anthony Cassanego, *CFO*
David Koslow, *Admin Sec*
Ryan O'Connor, *Sales Dir*
Russ Heddleston, *Marketing Staff*
EMP: 16
SALES (est): 384.8K **Privately Held**
SIC: 7372 Business oriented computer software

(P-24568)
DOCTOR ON DEMAND INC
275 Battery St Ste 650, San Francisco
(94111-3332)
PHONE.......................415 935-4447
Adam Jackson, *CEO*
Jennifer Nuckles, *Chief Mktg Ofcr*
Heather Johnson, *Vice Pres*
Yosselyn Dupuis, *Opers Staff*
Noah Slabotsky, *Sales Dir*
EMP: 100
SALES (est): 298.7K **Privately Held**
SIC: 7372 Application computer software

(P-24569)
DOCUSIGN INC (PA)
221 Main St Ste 1000, San Francisco
(94105-1925)
PHONE.......................415 489-4940
Daniel D Springer, *President*
Keith J Krach, *Ch of Bd*

William Neil Hudspith, *President*
Kirsten O Wolberg, *COO*
Michael J Sheridan, *CFO*
EMP: 300
SQ FT: 117,231
SALES: 518.5MM **Publicly Held**
WEB: www.docusign.com
SIC: 7372 Prepackaged software

(P-24570)
DOMICO SOFTWARE
1220 Oakland Blvd Ste 300, Walnut Creek
(94596-8409)
PHONE.......................510 841-4155
Glenn Hunter, *President*
EMP: 15
SQ FT: 4,000
SALES (est): 1.6MM **Privately Held**
WEB: www.domico.com
SIC: 7372 7371 Prepackaged software; custom computer programming services

(P-24571)
DOMINO DATA LAB INC
548 4th St, San Francisco (94107-1621)
PHONE.......................415 570-2425
Nick Elprin, *CEO*
Timothy Hughes, *Sales Executive*
Lundin Kyle, *Sales Engr*
Dan Enthoven, *Sales Staff*
EMP: 10
SALES (est): 164.5K **Privately Held**
SIC: 7372 Business oriented computer software

(P-24572)
DORADO NETWORK SYSTEMS CORP
Also Called: Corelogic Dorado
555 12th St Ste 1100, Oakland
(94607-4049)
PHONE.......................650 227-7300
Dain Ehring, *CEO*
Karen Camp, *CFO*
Adam Springer, *Senior VP*
Dave Parker, *VP Bus Dvlpt*
Rob Carpenter PHD, *CTO*
EMP: 140
SQ FT: 19,000
SALES (est): 11.7MM
SALES (corp-wide): 1.8B **Publicly Held**
WEB: www.dorado.com
SIC: 7372 Application computer software
PA: Corelogic, Inc.
　40 Pacifica Ste 900
　Irvine CA 92618
　949 214-1000

(P-24573)
DOUBLE-TAKE SOFTWARE INC (HQ)
15300 Barranca Pkwy, Irvine (92618-2200)
PHONE.......................949 253-6500
Mohamad Ali, *President*
Erik Yoder, *Technical Staff*
Eva Ullmann, *Manager*
Reggie Payne, *Consultant*
EMP: 22
SALES (est): 28.3MM
SALES (corp-wide): 239.4MM **Publicly Held**
WEB: www.nsisw.com
SIC: 7372 7373 5045 7371 Prepackaged software; computer-aided system services; computer software; custom computer programming services
PA: Carbonite, Inc.
　2 Avenue De Lafayette
　Boston MA 02111
　617 587-1100

(P-24574)
DOUBLEDUTCH INC (PA)
350 Rhode Island St # 375, San Francisco
(94103-5181)
PHONE.......................800 748-9024
Bryan Parker, *CEO*
Brad Roberts, *CFO*
Emily He, *Chief Mktg Ofcr*
Lucian Beebe, *Vice Pres*
Lawrence Coburn, *Security Dir*
EMP: 65
SALES: 28MM **Privately Held**
SIC: 7372 Application computer software

(P-24575)
DOVE TREE CANYON SOFTWARE INC
707 Broadway Ste 1240, San Diego
(92101-5322)
PHONE.......................619 236-8895
Charles William Woo, *President*
Dyana Woo, *Vice Pres*
EMP: 10
SALES: 840K **Privately Held**
WEB: www.dovetree.com
SIC: 7372 Business oriented computer software

(P-24576)
DRAFTDAY FANTASY SPORTS INC
690 5th St Ste 105, San Francisco
(94107-1517)
PHONE.......................310 306-1828
Todd Greene, *CEO*
EMP: 20
SALES (corp-wide): 4.5MM **Publicly Held**
SIC: 7372 8742 Prepackaged software; marketing consulting services
PA: X Function Inc
　45 W 89th St Apt 4a
　New York NY 10024
　212 231-0092

(P-24577)
DRAFTDAY FANTASY SPORTS INC
2058 Broadway Ofc, Santa Monica
(90404-2910)
PHONE.......................310 306-1828
EMP: 21
SQ FT: 3,200
SALES (corp-wide): 4.5MM **Publicly Held**
SIC: 7372 7371 Prepackaged software; custom computer programming services
PA: X Function Inc
　45 W 89th St Apt 4a
　New York NY 10024
　212 231-0092

(P-24578)
DRIVEAI INC
365 Ravendale Dr, Mountain View
(94043-5217)
PHONE.......................650 729-0499
Sameep Tandon, *CEO*
Swati Dube, *Co-Owner*
Brody Huval, *Co-Owner*
Jeff Kinske, *Co-Owner*
Joel Pazhayampallil, *Co-Owner*
EMP: 150 EST: 2015
SALES (est): 251.4K **Privately Held**
SIC: 7372 Prepackaged software

(P-24579)
DRIVER INC
438 Shotwell St, San Francisco
(94110-1914)
PHONE.......................415 999-4960
Will Polkinghorn, *CEO*
Amy Bronstien, *Executive Asst*
Tet Matsuguchi, *Engineer*
Pete Wild, *Opers Mgr*
EMP: 85
SALES (est): 2.7MM **Privately Held**
SIC: 7372 Educational computer software

(P-24580)
DRIVESCALE INC
1230 Midas Way Ste 210, Sunnyvale
(94085-4068)
PHONE.......................408 849-4651
Gene Banman, *CEO*
Denise Shiffman, *Officer*
Alvin Eugene Banman, *Principal*
Satya Nishtala, *Principal*
Mariana Maya, *Office Mgr*
EMP: 10 EST: 2013
SALES (est): 816.1K **Privately Held**
SIC: 7372 Application computer software

(P-24581)
DROPBOX INC (PA)
333 Brannan St, San Francisco
(94107-1810)
PHONE.......................415 857-6800
Andrew W Houston, *Ch of Bd*
Dennis M Woodside, *COO*
Ajay V Vashee, *CFO*

Quentin J Clark, *Senior VP*
Rusty Pierce, *Office Mgr*
EMP: 148
SALES: 1.1B **Publicly Held**
SIC: 7372 Prepackaged software

(P-24582)
DRUVA INC (HQ)
150 Mathilda Pl Ste 450, Sunnyvale
(94086-6016)
PHONE.......................650 241-3501
Jaspreet Singh, *CEO*
Mahesh Patel, *CFO*
Sherry Lowe, *Chief Mktg Ofcr*
Wynn White, *Chief Mktg Ofcr*
Mike Palmer,
EMP: 58
SALES (est): 22.5MM **Privately Held**
SIC: 7372 Prepackaged software

(P-24583)
DUDA MOBILE INC
577 College Ave, Palo Alto (94306-1433)
PHONE.......................855 790-0003
Itia Sadan, *CEO*
Adam Ferris, *Partner*
Sarah Carpenter, *CFO*
Jason Knaut, *CFO*
Oded Ouaknine, *Vice Pres*
EMP: 35
SALES (est): 3.8MM **Privately Held**
SIC: 7372 Application computer software

(P-24584)
DWA NOVA LLC
1000 Flower St, Glendale (91201-3007)
PHONE.......................818 695-5000
Lincoln Wallen, *CEO*
Derek Chan, *COO*
EMP: 75
SQ FT: 10,000
SALES (est): 1.4MM **Privately Held**
SIC: 7372 Business oriented computer software

(P-24585)
E-FREIGHT TECHNOLOGY INC
2225 W Cromwell Ave, Alhambra (91803)
PHONE.......................626 943-8418
Chen-Hsin MA, *President*
EMP: 30
SQ FT: 2,000
SALES (est): 2.3MM **Privately Held**
WEB: www.efreightech.com
SIC: 7372 Prepackaged software

(P-24586)
E-TRANSACTIONS SOFTWARE TECH
21195 Grenola Dr, Cupertino (95014-1625)
PHONE.......................408 873-9100
Srinivasa Reddy, *President*
Vedavathi Reddy, *Director*
EMP: 18 EST: 1998
SALES: 2.5MM **Privately Held**
WEB: www.etst.com
SIC: 7372 Prepackaged software

(P-24587)
EBIX INC
Also Called: Benefits Software
212 Cottage Ave, Santa Barbara (93101)
PHONE.......................805 568-0240
William Smith, *Manager*
EMP: 20
SALES (corp-wide): 363.9MM **Publicly Held**
SIC: 7372 7371 Prepackaged software; computer software development & applications
PA: Ebix, Inc.
　1 Ebix Way Ste 100
　Duluth GA 30097
　678 281-2020

(P-24588)
ECRIO INC
19925 Stevens Creek Blvd # 100, Cupertino (95014-2300)
PHONE.......................408 973-7290
Randy Granovetter, *CEO*
Tad Bogdan, *COO*
Nagesh Challa, *Officer*
Ted Goldstein, *Officer*
Lina Martin, *Vice Pres*
EMP: 90

SALES (est): 6.1MM **Privately Held**
WEB: www.ecrio.com
SIC: **7372** Prepackaged software

(P-24589)
EDCAST INC (PA)
1901 Old Middlefield Way # 21, Mountain
View (94043-2556)
PHONE...................................650 823-3511
Karl Mehta, *CEO*
Kalpit Jain, *Vice Pres*
Jeffrey Roth, *Vice Pres*
Ramin Mahmoodi, *Engineer*
Bhamidipati Bharani, *Director*
EMP: 27
SALES (est): 3.3MM **Privately Held**
SIC: **7372** Educational computer software

(P-24590)
EDGEWAVE INC
4225 Executive Sq # 1600, La Jolla
(92037-1487)
PHONE...................................800 782-3762
Louis E Ryan, *CEO*
Steve Kelley, *President*
Thalia R Gietzen, *CFO*
John Randall, *Vice Pres*
William R Baumel, *Principal*
EMP: 100
SQ FT: 37,000
SALES (est): 16.7MM **Privately Held**
WEB: www.edgewave.com
SIC: **7372** Operating systems computer
  software

(P-24591)
EDMODO INC
1200 Park Pl Ste 400, San Mateo
(94403-1593)
PHONE...................................310 614-6868
Nic Borg, *CEO*
Ambarish Malpani, *Vice Pres*
Marianne Biskup, *Social Dir*
Ashley Rawstron, *Sr Software Eng*
Laureano Allison, *Info Tech Mgr*
EMP: 37 EST: 2009
SALES (est): 6.7MM **Privately Held**
SIC: **7372** Educational computer software

(P-24592)
EDUCATION ELEMENTS INC
999 Skyway Rd Ste 325, San Carlos
(94070-2725)
PHONE...................................650 336-0660
Anthony Kim, *CEO*
David Irwin, *Managing Prtnr*
Victoria Bernholz, *Vice Pres*
Raymond Rozycki, *Vice Pres*
Arthur Svider, *Vice Pres*
EMP: 28
SALES (est): 3.3MM **Privately Held**
SIC: **7372** Educational computer software

(P-24593)
EDUTONE CORPORATION (PA)
Also Called: Global Grid For Learning
1101 Marina Village Pkwy # 201, Alameda
(94501-6472)
PHONE...................................888 904-9773
Robert Iskander, *President*
Julian Mobbs, *CEO*
Larry Smith, *Vice Pres*
Perry Smithson, *Vice Pres*
EMP: 10
SALES: 5MM **Privately Held**
SIC: **7372** Educational computer software

(P-24594)
EEYE INC (HQ)
Also Called: Eeye Digital Security
65 Enterprise Ste 100, Aliso Viejo
(92656-2503)
PHONE...................................949 333-1900
Kevin Hickey, *CEO*
Tyler Hanson, *CFO*
Brad Hibbert, *Vice Pres*
Marc Maiffret, *CTO*
Brian Ginn, *Software Engr*
EMP: 28 EST: 1998
SALES (est): 8.3MM
SALES (corp-wide): 51.9MM **Privately
Held**
WEB: www.eeye.com
SIC: **7372** Business oriented computer
  software

PA: Beyondtrust Software, Inc.
  5090 N 40th St Ste 400
  Phoenix AZ 85018
  623 455-6499

(P-24595)
EGAIN CORPORATION (PA)
1252 Borregas Ave, Sunnyvale
(94089-1309)
PHONE...................................408 636-4500
Ashutosh Roy, *Ch of Bd*
Eric Smit, *CFO*
Promod Narang, *Senior VP*
Todd Woodstra, *Senior VP*
Simon Broadbent, *Vice Pres*
EMP: 109
SQ FT: 42,541
SALES: 61.3MM **Publicly Held**
WEB: www.egain.com
SIC: **7372 7371** Prepackaged software;
  application computer software; custom
  computer programming services

(P-24596)
EGAIN CORPORATION
455 W Maude Ave, Sunnyvale
(94085-3540)
PHONE...................................408 212-3400
Don Paulson, *CEO*
Gary Marzik, *Partner*
Chuck Jepson, *COO*
EMP: 17
SALES (corp-wide): 61.3MM **Publicly
Held**
SIC: **7372** Application computer software
PA: Egain Corporation
  1252 Borregas Ave
  Sunnyvale CA 94089
  408 636-4500

(P-24597)
EGOMOTION INC
729 Minna St, San Francisco (94103-2707)
PHONE...................................415 849-4662
Kulveer Taggar, *CEO*
EMP: 50
SALES (est): 787.2K **Privately Held**
SIC: **7372** Business oriented computer
  software

(P-24598)
EIS GROUP INC
731 Sansome St Fl 4, San Francisco
(94111-1723)
PHONE...................................415 402-2622
Alec Miloslavsky, *CEO*
Sergiy Synyanskyy, *CFO*
Nancy Kelly, *Senior VP*
Slava Kritov, *Senior VP*
Mark Binman, *Vice Pres*
EMP: 128
SQ FT: 16,803
SALES (est): 22.7MM **Privately Held**
SIC: **7372** Business oriented computer
  software

(P-24599)
EKNOWLEDGE GROUP INC
160 W Fthill Pkwy Ste 105, Corona
(92882)
PHONE...................................951 256-4076
Scott Hildebrandt, *President*
Lori Caputo, *Director*
EMP: 35
SALES (est): 1.6MM **Privately Held**
WEB: www.eknowledge.com
SIC: **7372** Educational computer software

(P-24600)
ELECTRONIC ARTS INC (PA)
Also Called: Ea
209 Redwood Shores Pkwy, Redwood City
(94065-1175)
PHONE...................................650 628-1500
Andrew Wilson, *CEO*
Lawrence F Probst III, *Ch of Bd*
Blake Jorgensen, *COO*
Vivek Paul, *Bd of Directors*
Christopher Bruzzo, *Chief Mktg Ofcr*
EMP: 475
SQ FT: 660,000
SALES: 5.1B **Publicly Held**
WEB: www.ea.com
SIC: **7372** Home entertainment computer
  software

(P-24601)
ELECTRONIC ARTS INC
Also Called: Electronic Arts Los Angeles
5510 Lincoln Blvd Ste 100, Los Angeles
(90094-2035)
PHONE...................................310 754-7000
John Batter, *Branch Mgr*
Matt Marcou, *Manager*
EMP: 10
SALES (corp-wide): 5.1B **Publicly Held**
WEB: www.ea.com
SIC: **7372** Home entertainment computer
  software
PA: Electronic Arts Inc.
  209 Redwood Shores Pkwy
  Redwood City CA 94065
  650 628-1500

(P-24602)
**ELECTRONIC CLEARING HOUSE
INC (HQ)**
730 Paseo Camarillo, Camarillo
(93010-6064)
PHONE...................................805 419-8700
Charles J Harris, *President*
Alice L Cheung, *CFO*
Karl Asplund, *Senior VP*
Rick Slater, *Vice Pres*
William Wied, *CIO*
EMP: 100
SQ FT: 32,669
SALES (est): 11.1MM
SALES (corp-wide): 5.9B **Publicly Held**
WEB: www.echo-inc.com
SIC: **7372** Business oriented computer
  software
PA: Intuit Inc.
  2700 Coast Ave
  Mountain View CA 94043
  650 944-6000

(P-24603)
ELEKTA INC
100 Mathilda Pl Fl 5, Sunnyvale
(94086-6017)
PHONE...................................408 830-8000
Barry Hyde, *Administration*
Rhonda Ludwico, *Sr Software Eng*
Sanjay Bari, *Software Dev*
Derek Lane, *Software Dev*
Joe Shao, *Software Dev*
EMP: 40
SALES (corp-wide): 1.3B **Privately Held**
SIC: **7372 7373** Business oriented com-
  puter software; computer integrated sys-
  tems design
HQ: Elekta, Inc.
  400 Perimeter Center Ter
  Atlanta GA 30346
  770 300-9725

(P-24604)
ELEVATE INC
180 Avenida La Pata, San Clemente
(92673-6300)
PHONE...................................949 276-5428
Wright W Thurston, *CEO*
Rod Place, *COO*
Bryan Ferre, *Chief Mktg Ofcr*
Alexander Chester, *Officer*
EMP: 21
SALES (est): 1.7MM **Privately Held**
SIC: **7372** Prepackaged software

(P-24605)
ELLIE MAE INC (PA)
4420 Rosewood Dr Ste 500, Pleasanton
(94588-3059)
PHONE...................................925 227-7000
Jonathan Corr, *President*
Sigmund Anderman, *Ch of Bd*
Popi Heron, *CFO*
Brian Brown, *Exec VP*
Carina Cortez, *Exec VP*
EMP: 148 EST: 1997
SQ FT: 280,680
SALES: 417MM **Publicly Held**
WEB: www.elliemae.com
SIC: **7372 7371** Prepackaged software;
  computer software systems analysis &
  design, custom; computer software devel-
  opment & applications

(P-24606)
ELLIPSIS HEALTH INC
535 Mission St Fl 25, San Francisco
(94105-3225)
PHONE...................................650 906-6117
Mainul Islam, *CEO*
EMP: 12
SALES (est): 866.5K **Privately Held**
SIC: **7372** Application computer software

(P-24607)
**EMPOWER SOFTWARE TECH
LLC**
41695 Date St Ste A, Murrieta
(92562-7047)
PHONE...................................951 672-6257
Thomas V Smith, *Partner*
Ed Power,
Jeff Power,
Julie Smith,
Guy Sawyer, *Supervisor*
EMP: 12
SQ FT: 2,500
SALES (est): 1.4MM **Privately Held**
WEB: www.storagecommander.com
SIC: **7372** Business oriented computer
  software

(P-24608)
ENABLENCE SYSTEMS INC (HQ)
Also Called: Pannaway
2933 Bayview Dr, Fremont (94538-6520)
PHONE...................................510 226-8900
Gary Davis, *President*
Robert Monaco, *COO*
Boris Grek, *Vice Pres*
EMP: 21
SALES (est): 9.6MM
SALES (corp-wide): 3.4MM **Privately
Held**
WEB: www.pannaway.com
SIC: **7372** Application computer software
PA: Enablence Technologies Inc
  390 March Rd Suite 119
  Kanata ON K2K 0
  613 656-2850

(P-24609)
ENACT SYSTEMS INC
2600 Cmino Ramon Ste 300b, San Ramon
(94583)
PHONE...................................855 503-6228
Deep Chakraborty, *CEO*
Jyoti Jain, *President*
Manasij Kar, *COO*
Thomas King, *CFO*
Matthew Cheney, *Chairman*
EMP: 25
SQ FT: 200
SALES (est): 1.1MM **Privately Held**
SIC: **7372** Business oriented computer
  software

(P-24610)
ENERGY EXEMPLAR LLC (DH)
3013 Douglas Blvd Ste 120, Roseville
(95661-3842)
PHONE...................................916 722-1484
Louise Drayton, *CFO*
Glenn Drayton, *CTO*
EMP: 10
SQ FT: 1,400
SALES: 3.5MM **Privately Held**
SIC: **7372 8748** Utility computer software;
  business consulting

(P-24611)
ENGAGIO INC
101 S San Mateo Dr Fl 4, San Mateo
(94401-3845)
PHONE...................................650 265-2264
Jon Miller, *CEO*
Heidi Bullock, *Chief Mktg Ofcr*
Cheryl Chavez, *Officer*
Scott Fehr, *Vice Pres*
Dan Gordon, *Vice Pres*
EMP: 50 EST: 2015
SALES: 531K **Privately Held**
SIC: **7372** Business oriented computer
  software

(P-24612)
ENGRADE INC
1337 3rd Street Promenade # 300, Santa
Monica (90401-1379)
PHONE...................................800 305-1367

Zach Posner, *CEO*
Sam Elhag, *Senior Mgr*
EMP: 12
SALES (est): 1.1MM **Privately Held**
SIC: 7372 Educational computer software

(P-24613)
ENMO TECHNOLOGIES INC
3561 Homestead Rd # 233, Santa Clara
(95051-5161)
PHONE..............408 475-6819
Sunil Baliga, *CEO*
EMP: 12 **EST:** 2016
SALES (est): 154.7K **Privately Held**
SIC: 7372 Application computer software

(P-24614)
ENTCO LLC (DH)
Also Called: Autonomy Interwoven
1140 Enterprise Way, Sunnyvale
(94089-1412)
PHONE..............312 580-9100
Jeremy K Cox,
John E Calonico Jr, *Senior VP*
Mercedes De Luca, *VP Info Sys*
Rishi Varma,
EMP: 400
SQ FT: 110,000
SALES (est): 54.8MM
SALES (corp-wide): 834.5MM **Privately
Held**
WEB: www.iwov.com
SIC: 7372 Business oriented computer
software
HQ: Micro Focus (Us), Inc.
700 King Farm Blvd # 125
Rockville MD 20850
301 838-5000

(P-24615)
ENTERPRISE INFORMATICS INC
10052 Mesa Ridge Ct Ste 1, San Diego
(92121-2971)
PHONE..............858 625-3000
John W Low, *CFO*
David Dorries, *President*
Pierre De Wet, *VP Opers*
Glenn Cox, *VP Mktg*
Hilmar Retief, *Manager*
EMP: 26
SQ FT: 12,192
SALES (est): 1.5MM
SALES (corp-wide): 484.7MM **Privately
Held**
WEB: www.altris.com
SIC: 7372 Prepackaged software
PA: Bentley Systems, Incorporated
685 Stockton Dr
Exton PA 19341
610 458-5000

(P-24616)
ENTERPRISE SERVICES LLC
333 N Lantana St Ste 287, Camarillo
(93010-9009)
PHONE..............805 388-8000
EMP: 10
SALES (corp-wide): 13.5B **Publicly Held**
WEB: www.eds.com
SIC: 7372 Prepackaged software
HQ: Enterprise Services Llc
5400 Legacy Dr
Plano TX 75024
703 245-9675

(P-24617)
ENTERPRISE SIGNAL INC
Also Called: Kloudgin
440 N Wolfe Rd, Sunnyvale (94085-3869)
PHONE..............877 256-8303
Vikram Takru, *CEO*
Dharnesh Sethi, *CFO*
EMP: 65
SALES (est): 155.9K **Privately Held**
SIC: 7372 Business oriented computer
software

(P-24618)
ENTIT SOFTWARE LLC (DH)
1140 Entp Way Bldg F, Sunnyvale (94089)
PHONE..............801 861-7000
Christopher P Hsu,
Joanne Chai, *Sr Software Eng*
Bill Gu, *Project Mgr*
Daniel Levin, *Technology*
Laure Hinkle, *Sales Staff*

EMP: 11 **EST:** 2007
SALES (est): 2.3MM
SALES (corp-wide): 834.5MM **Privately
Held**
SIC: 7372 Operating systems computer
software
HQ: Micro Focus (Us), Inc.
700 King Farm Blvd # 125
Rockville MD 20850
301 838-5000

(P-24619)
ENVIZIO INC
Also Called: Enviz.io
2400 Country Dr, Fremont (94536-5329)
PHONE..............650 814-4302
Youriy Drozd, *Bd of Directors*
EMP: 24
SALES (est): 1.3MM **Privately Held**
SIC: 7372 Application computer software;
operating systems computer software

(P-24620)
EOS SOFTWARE INC
900 E Hamilton Ave # 100, Campbell
(95008-0664)
PHONE..............855 900-4876
Mohit Doshi, *CEO*
EMP: 10
SQ FT: 500
SALES (est): 621.6K **Privately Held**
SIC: 7372 Business oriented computer
software

(P-24621)
**EPICOR SOFTWARE
CORPORATION**
4120 Dublin Blvd Ste 300, Dublin
(94568-7759)
PHONE..............925 361-9900
Pervez Qureshi, *Branch Mgr*
Noel Goggin, *Senior VP*
Janie West, *Vice Pres*
Dave Yusuf, *Vice Pres*
AIN Moin, *Executive*
EMP: 101 **Publicly Held**
SIC: 7372 Prepackaged software
HQ: Epicor Software Corporation
804 Las Cimas Pkwy # 200
Austin TX 78746

(P-24622)
EPIGNOSIS LLC
315 Montgomery St Fl 9, San Francisco
(94104-1858)
PHONE..............646 797-2799
Dimitrios Tsigkos,
Chris Mathiopoulos, *Accounts Mgr*
EMP: 25 **EST:** 2012
SALES (est): 1.2MM **Privately Held**
SIC: 7372 Application computer software

(P-24623)
EQ TECHNOLOGIC INC
600 Anton Blvd, Costa Mesa (92626-7221)
PHONE..............215 891-9010
Dinesh Khaladkar, *Branch Mgr*
Joseph Garay,
EMP: 20
SALES (corp-wide): 28MM **Privately
Held**
SIC: 7372 Business oriented computer
software
PA: Eq Technologic, Inc.
500 Office Center Dr # 400
Fort Washington PA 19034
215 891-9010

(P-24624)
EQUIMINE
26457 Rancho Pkwy S, Lake Forest
(92630-8326)
PHONE..............877 437-8464
Rabih Zahr, *President*
Nedal Mackarem, *Vice Pres*
Richard Borchard, *Technology*
Burton Alicando,
EMP: 15
SALES: 4MM **Privately Held**
SIC: 7372 3429 Business oriented com-
puter software; keys, locks & related
hardware

(P-24625)
**ERI ECONOMIC RESEARCH
INST INC**
111 Academy Ste 270, Irvine (92617-3049)
PHONE..............800 627-3697
Kerry Galvin, *CEO*
Steven Becker, *CFO*
Matt Skrinjar, *Manager*
EMP: 55
SALES (est): 2.2MM **Privately Held**
WEB: www.economicresearchinstitute.com
SIC: 7372 Application computer software;
business oriented computer software

(P-24626)
ERIDE INC
1 Letterman Dr Ste 310, San Francisco
(94129-1411)
PHONE..............415 848-7800
Arthur Woo, *President*
Gary L Fischer, *CFO*
W Bradley Stewart, *Vice Pres*
Paul McBurney, *CTO*
EMP: 30
SQ FT: 5,000
SALES (est): 2.2MM
SALES (corp-wide): 711.3MM **Privately
Held**
WEB: www.eride-inc.com
SIC: 7372 Business oriented computer
software
PA: Furuno Electric Co., Ltd.
9-52, Ashiharacho
Nishinomiya HYO 662-0
798 652-111

(P-24627)
ESMART SOURCE INC
Also Called: Rfid4u
5159 Commercial Cir Ste H, Concord
(94520-8503)
P.O. Box 5366 (94524-0366)
PHONE..............408 739-3500
Sanjiv Dua, *CEO*
Tony David, *Business Dir*
Dave Frenkel, *Business Dir*
Anu Dua, *Director*
EMP: 15
SALES (est): 1.9MM **Privately Held**
SIC: 7372 7373 Business oriented com-
puter software; local area network (LAN)
systems integrator

(P-24628)
**ESQ BUSINESS SERVICES INC
(PA)**
Also Called: E S Q
20660 Stevens, Cupertino (95014)
PHONE..............925 734-9800
Iqbal S Sandhu, *Director*
Joe Haggarty, *President*
Neil Butani, *Officer*
Paul Sandhu, *CTO*
Raj Dhiman, *Technology*
EMP: 95
SQ FT: 300
SALES (est): 11.4MM **Privately Held**
WEB: www.esq.com
SIC: 7372 7379 Prepackaged software;
computer related consulting services

(P-24629)
EVENT FARM INC (PA)
2448 Main St, Santa Monica (90405-3516)
PHONE..............888 444-8162
Ryan Costello, *CEO*
Brennan McReynolds, *COO*
Alexandra Gibson, *Chief Mktg Ofcr*
Chad Blaise, *Exec VP*
Stephanie Sullivan, *Executive*
EMP: 23
SALES (est): 6.4MM **Privately Held**
SIC: 7372 Business oriented computer
software

(P-24630)
EVENTURE INTERACTIVE INC
3420 Bristol St Fl 6, Costa Mesa
(92626-1996)
PHONE..............855 986-5669
Gannon Giguiere, *Ch of Bd*
Jason Harvey, *CEO*
Michael D Rountree, *CFO*
Kelle Cohen, *Director*
EMP: 13

SQ FT: 2,000
SALES (est): 923.2K **Privately Held**
SIC: 7372 Application computer software

(P-24631)
EVOLPHIN SOFTWARE INC (PA)
2410 Camino Ramon Ste 228, San Ramon
(94583-4323)
PHONE..............888 386-4114
Brian Ahearn, *CEO*
Brad Christus, *Vice Pres*
Rahul Bhargava, *CTO*
Bryan Merrill, *Sales Executive*
EMP: 15
SQ FT: 20,000
SALES (est): 3.1MM **Privately Held**
SIC: 7372 Business oriented computer
software

(P-24632)
EVOLUTION ROBOTICS INC
1055 E Colo Blvd Ste 320, Pasadena
(91106)
PHONE..............626 993-3300
Paolo Pirjanian, *CEO*
Bill Gross, *President*
Doug McPherson, *Asst Sec*
EMP: 40
SALES (est): 4.2MM **Publicly Held**
WEB: www.evolution.com
SIC: 7372 Application computer software
PA: Irobot Corporation
8 Crosby Dr
Bedford MA 01730

(P-24633)
EXACTUALS LLC
1100 Glendon Ave Fl 17, Los Angeles
(90024-3588)
PHONE..............310 689-7491
Michael Hurst, *CEO*
Bryan Walley, *COO*
Ilie Ardelean,
Jason Hiller, *CTO*
EMP: 15
SALES (est): 381.1K **Privately Held**
SIC: 7372 Prepackaged software
HQ: City National Bank
555 S Flower St Fl 21
Los Angeles CA 90071
310 888-6000

(P-24634)
EXADEL INC (PA)
1340 Treat Blvd, Walnut Creek
(94597-2101)
PHONE..............925 363-9510
Fima Katz, *President*
Lev Shur, *President*
Lynne Walter, *CFO*
Dmitry Binunsky, *Vice Pres*
Janusz Fajkowski, *General Mgr*
EMP: 51
SALES (est): 18.6MM **Privately Held**
WEB: www.exadel.com
SIC: 7372 Application computer software

(P-24635)
**EXPANDABLE SOFTWARE INC
(PA)**
900 Lafayette St Ste 400, Santa Clara
(95050-4925)
PHONE..............408 261-7880
Bob Swedroe, *CEO*
David Kearney, *Corp Secy*
Gerald Lass, *Vice Pres*
Vern Marschke, *Vice Pres*
Kuantai Chen, *Software Engr*
EMP: 40
SQ FT: 10,000
SALES (est): 6.7MM **Privately Held**
WEB: www.expandable.com
SIC: 7372 7371 Prepackaged software;
custom computer programming services

(P-24636)
EXPERT REPUTATION LLC
Also Called: Review Concierge
101 N Acacia Ave Ste 105, Solana Beach
(92075-1198)
PHONE..............866 407-6020
Eric Januszko,
David Engel,
EMP: 13
SQ FT: 1,000

SALES (est): 1MM **Privately Held**
SIC: 7372 Application computer software

(P-24637)
EYVO INC
3030 Bridgeway Ste 110, Sausalito
(94965-2895)
PHONE.................................888 237-9801
Michael Petter, *CEO*
EMP: 15
SQ FT: 1,500
SALES (est): 641K **Privately Held**
SIC: 7372 Prepackaged software

(P-24638)
EZ 2000 INC
Also Called: EZ 2000 1 Rated Dental Sftwr
1800 Century Park E # 600, Los Angeles
(90067-1501)
PHONE.................................800 273-5033
Mark Shainberg, *President*
EMP: 10
SALES (est): 876.3K **Privately Held**
SIC: 7372 Prepackaged software

(P-24639)
EZBOARD INC
Also Called: Yuku.com
607 Market St Fl 5, San Francisco
(94105-3319)
PHONE.................................415 773-0400
Robert Labatt, *President*
EMP: 14
SQ FT: 1,400
SALES (est): 1.1MM **Privately Held**
WEB: www.ezboard.com
SIC: 7372 Application computer software

(P-24640)
EZOIC INC
5870 El Camino Real, Carlsbad
(92008-8816)
PHONE.................................760 444-4995
Dwayne Lafleur, *President*
John Cole, *Ch Credit Ofcr*
Ohad Tzur, *Vice Pres*
Gavin Bechtold, *Business Dir*
Mark Evans, *Principal*
EMP: 10
SQ FT: 218
SALES (est): 922.8K **Privately Held**
SIC: 7372 Application computer software

(P-24641)
FACEFIRST INC
15821 Ventura Blvd # 425, Encino
(91436-4776)
PHONE.................................805 482-8428
Joseph Rosenkrantz, *CEO*
Michelle Tutino, *Executive Asst*
EMP: 28
SQ FT: 6,500
SALES (est): 1.2MM **Privately Held**
SIC: 7372 7371 Business oriented computer software; computer software development

(P-24642)
FACILITRON INC
485 Alberto Way Ste 210, Los Gatos
(95032-5476)
PHONE.................................800 272-2962
Jeffrey Benjamin, *Principal*
Michael Kapul, *President*
EMP: 25 EST: 2016
SQ FT: 2,000
SALES (est): 475.5K **Privately Held**
SIC: 7372 Business oriented computer software

(P-24643)
FAIR ISAAC INTERNATIONAL CORP (HQ)
200 Smith Ranch Rd, San Rafael
(94903-5551)
PHONE.................................415 446-6000
Thomas G Grudnowski, *President*
Cheryl St John, *Cust Svc Dir*
EMP: 600
SALES (est): 51.2MM
SALES (corp-wide): 932.1MM **Publicly Held**
SIC: 7372 Business oriented computer software

PA: Fair Isaac Corporation
181 Metro Dr Ste 700
San Jose CA 95110
408 535-1500

(P-24644)
FAMSOFT CORP
1762 Tech Dr Ste 108, San Jose (95110)
PHONE.................................408 452-1550
Fareeha Fahim-Rahman, *President*
Fahad Rahman, *Sales Staff*
Scott Frick, *Associate*
EMP: 10 EST: 2007
SALES (est): 1.2MM **Privately Held**
SIC: 7372 Operating systems computer software

(P-24645)
FAMSOFT CORP
44946 Osgood Rd, Fremont (94539-6110)
PHONE.................................510 683-3940
Fahim Rahman, *CEO*
Fareeha Rahman, *President*
EMP: 20
SQ FT: 2,500
SALES (est): 1.5MM **Privately Held**
WEB: www.famsoft.com
SIC: 7372 7361 8243 7373 Prepackaged software; employment agencies; data processing schools; computer integrated systems design; custom computer programming services

(P-24646)
FIELDCENTRIX INC
8 Hughes, Irvine (92618-2072)
PHONE.................................949 784-5000
Renee Labran, *President*
Helen Fuerst, *Manager*
EMP: 30 EST: 1994
SALES (est): 2.4MM **Privately Held**
WEB: www.fieldcentrix.com
SIC: 7372 Business oriented computer software

(P-24647)
FILEMAKER INC (HQ)
5201 Patrick Henry Dr, Santa Clara
(95054-1164)
PHONE.................................408 987-7000
Dominique Philippe Goupil, *President*
Bill Epling, *CFO*
John F Pinheiro, *Vice Pres*
Albert Eisenstat, *Principal*
Steven Marcek, *CTO*
EMP: 230
SQ FT: 128,000
SALES (est): 79.1MM
SALES (corp-wide): 265.6B **Publicly Held**
WEB: www.filemaker.com
SIC: 7372 Prepackaged software
PA: Apple Inc.
1 Apple Park Way
Cupertino CA 95014
408 996-1010

(P-24648)
FILETRAIL INC
1990 The Alameda, San Jose
(95126-1432)
PHONE.................................408 289-1300
Darrell Mervau, *President*
EMP: 23
SQ FT: 2,000
SALES (est): 3.8MM **Privately Held**
WEB: www.filetrail.com
SIC: 7372 Utility computer software

(P-24649)
FIORANO SOFTWARE INC
230 California Ave # 103, Palo Alto
(94306-1637)
PHONE.................................650 326-1136
Atul Saini, *CEO*
Madhav Vodnala, *President*
Anjali Saini, *CFO*
William La Forge, *Vice Pres*
EMP: 85
SALES (est): 6.7MM **Privately Held**
SIC: 7372 7371 Prepackaged software; custom computer programming services; computer software development

(P-24650)
FIREEYE INC (PA)
601 Mccarthy Blvd, Milpitas (95035-7932)
PHONE.................................408 321-6300
Kevin R Mandia, *CEO*
Enrique Salem, *Ch of Bd*
Travis M Reese, *President*
Frank E Verdecanna, *CFO*
Alexa King, *Exec VP*
EMP: 148
SQ FT: 190,000
SALES: 751MM **Publicly Held**
WEB: www.fireeye.com
SIC: 7372 Prepackaged software

(P-24651)
FIRST ADVANTAGE TALENT MANAGEM
Also Called: Findly
98 Battery St Ste 400, San Francisco
(94111-5512)
PHONE.................................415 446-3930
Rob Stubblefield, *CFO*
Denis Lowe, *Engineer*
Heidi Baugh, *Consultant*
EMP: 26 EST: 2007
SQ FT: 4,000
SALES (est): 3.1MM **Privately Held**
SIC: 7372 Prepackaged software

(P-24652)
FIVE9 INC (PA)
4000 Executive Pkwy # 400, San Ramon
(94583-4257)
PHONE.................................925 201-2000
Rowan Trollope, *CEO*
Barry Zwarenstein, *CFO*
Michael Burkland, *Chairman*
Kevin Gavin, *Chief Mktg Ofcr*
Ryan Kam, *Chief Mktg Ofcr*
EMP: 144
SQ FT: 68,000
SALES: 200.2MM **Publicly Held**
WEB: www.five9.com
SIC: 7372 7374 Prepackaged software; data processing & preparation

(P-24653)
FLASH CODE SOLUTIONS LLC
4727 Wilshire Blvd # 302, Los Angeles
(90010-3806)
PHONE.................................800 633-7467
James B Davis, *Principal*
EMP: 17
SQ FT: 2,600
SALES (est): 616.2K **Privately Held**
SIC: 7372 Application computer software

(P-24654)
FLIPAGRAM INC
916 Silver Spur Rd # 310, Rllng HLS Est
(90274-3828)
PHONE.................................415 827-8373
Farhad Mohit, *CEO*
EMP: 16
SALES (est): 1.4MM **Privately Held**
SIC: 7372 7389 Prepackaged software;

(P-24655)
FLIPCAUSE INC
283 4th St Ste 101, Oakland (94607-4320)
PHONE.................................800 523-1950
Emerson Valiao, *CEO*
EMP: 15
SQ FT: 2,000
SALES: 3.5MM **Privately Held**
SIC: 7372 Prepackaged software

(P-24656)
FLYWHEEL SOFTWARE INC
816 Hamilton St, Redwood City
(94063-1624)
P.O. Box 3837 (94064-3837)
PHONE.................................650 260-1700
Steve Humphreys, *CEO*
Sachin Kansal, *Chief Engr*
Mark Towfiq, *Chief Engr*
Anagha Dutt, *Controller*
Roxanna Betancourt, *Marketing Mgr*
EMP: 32
SALES (est): 6.4MM **Privately Held**
SIC: 7372 Application computer software

(P-24657)
FOCUS POINT OF SALE
Also Called: Focus Pos
48 Waterworks Way, Irvine (92618-3107)
PHONE.................................949 336-7500
Julie Sharpe, *Owner*
Karrie Wermes, *Owner*
EMP: 12 EST: 2013
SQ FT: 3,900
SALES (est): 991.9K **Privately Held**
SIC: 7372 7373 Application computer software; office computer automation systems integration

(P-24658)
FOOD TO YOU USA INC
1700 Tribute Rd Ste 203, Sacramento
(95815-4415)
PHONE.................................559 549-0090
Darren McAdams, *CEO*
Bill Lenihan, *Principal*
EMP: 10
SALES (est): 2.1MM **Privately Held**
WEB: www.foodtoyou.com
SIC: 7372 Application computer software

(P-24659)
FOODLINK ONLINE LLC
475 Alberto Way Ste 100, Los Gatos
(95032-5480)
PHONE.................................408 395-7280
Eric Peters, *CEO*
Vijay V Yajnik, *Ch of Bd*
EMP: 20
SQ FT: 5,000
SALES (est): 2.7MM **Privately Held**
WEB: www.foodlinkonline.com
SIC: 7372

(P-24660)
FORECROSS CORPORATION (PA)
505 Montgomery St Fl 11, San Francisco
(94111-2585)
PHONE.................................415 543-1515
Kim O Jones, *President*
Bernadette C Castello, *CFO*
EMP: 12
SALES: 5MM **Publicly Held**
WEB: www.forecross.com
SIC: 7372 Business oriented computer software

(P-24661)
FORESITE SYSTEMS LIMITED (PA)
19925 Stevens Creek Blvd, Cupertino
(95014-2300)
PHONE.................................408 855-8600
Lance Allison, *CEO*
Graham Margetson, *President*
Travis Miller, *Vice Pres*
EMP: 11 EST: 2003
SALES (est): 3.3MM **Privately Held**
SIC: 7372 7379 Prepackaged software; computer related consulting services

(P-24662)
FORGEROCK INC (PA)
201 Mission St Ste 2900, San Francisco
(94105-1858)
PHONE.................................415 599-1100
Francis C Rosch, *CEO*
Priya Sharma, *Partner*
John Fernandez, *CFO*
John P Fernandez, *CFO*
Bob Humphrey, *Chief Mktg Ofcr*
EMP: 58
SQ FT: 15,000
SALES (est): 48.5MM **Privately Held**
SIC: 7372 5045 Prepackaged software; computer software

(P-24663)
FORGEROCK US INC (HQ)
201 Mission St, San Francisco
(94105-1831)
PHONE.................................415 599-1100
John Fernandez, *CFO*
Robert Humphrey, *Chief Mktg Ofcr*
Lasse Andresen, *CTO*
EMP: 73
SQ FT: 15,744

P
R
O
D
U
C
T
S

&

S
V
C
S

SALES (est): 14MM
SALES (corp-wide): 48.5MM **Privately Held**
SIC: 7372 5045 Prepackaged software; computer software
PA: Forgerock, Inc.
201 Mission St Ste 2900
San Francisco CA 94105
415 599-1100

(P-24664)
FORMATION INC
Also Called: Formation Systems
35 Stillman St, San Francisco (94107-1361)
PHONE..................................650 257-2277
Christian Hansen, CEO
Christian Selchau-Hansen, CEO
Ammon Haggerty, Vice Pres
EMP: 87
SQ FT: 10,000
SALES (est): 1.2MM **Privately Held**
SIC: 7372 Business oriented computer software

(P-24665)
FORMTRAN INC
26501 Rancho Pkwy S # 103, Lake Forest (92630-8359)
PHONE..................................949 829-5822
Mike Stuhley, President
Randy Woodward, Technical Mgr
EMP: 10
SQ FT: 2,500
SALES (est): 1.3MM **Privately Held**
WEB: www.formtran.com
SIC: 7372 Business oriented computer software

(P-24666)
FORTINET INC (PA)
899 Kifer Rd, Sunnyvale (94086-5205)
PHONE..................................408 235-7700
Ken Xie, Ch of Bd
Michael Xie, President
Keith Jensen, CFO
John Whittle, Vice Pres
EMP: 148
SQ FT: 162,000
SALES: 1.4B **Publicly Held**
WEB: www.fortinet.com
SIC: 7372 Prepackaged software

(P-24667)
FOUNDATION 9 ENTERTAINMENT INC (PA)
30211 A De Las Bandera200, Rancho Santa Margari (92688)
PHONE..................................949 698-1500
James N Hearn, CEO
John Goldman, Ch of Bd
David Mann, President
Steve Sardegna, Exec VP
Miguel Vazquez, Finance Mgr
EMP: 200
SALES (est): 38.1MM **Privately Held**
SIC: 7372 Home entertainment computer software

(P-24668)
FOUNDSTONE INC
27201 Puerta Real Ste 400, Mission Viejo (92691-8517)
PHONE..................................949 297-5600
George Kurtz, CEO
Stuart McClure, President
Larry McIntosh, Chief Mktg Ofcr
William Chan, Vice Pres
Chris Prosise, Vice Pres
EMP: 80
SQ FT: 15,000
SALES (est): 4.9MM **Privately Held**
WEB: www.foundstone.com
SIC: 7372 Application computer software
HQ: Mcafee, Llc
2821 Mission College Blvd
Santa Clara CA 95054
888 847-8766

(P-24669)
FRAGMOB LLC
9655 Granite Ridge Dr 2f, San Diego (92123-2674)
PHONE..................................858 587-6659
Jade Charles, CEO
Jonathan Shapiro, President

Declan Balla, Info Tech Mgr
EMP: 18
SALES (est): 1.7MM **Privately Held**
SIC: 7372 Publishers' computer software

(P-24670)
FRANZ INC
2201 Broadway Ste 715, Oakland (94612-3024)
PHONE..................................510 452-2000
Jans Aasman, CEO
Kevin Layer, COO
John Foderar, Treasurer
Duane Rettig, Bd of Directors
Craig Norvell, Vice Pres
EMP: 25
SQ FT: 5,000
SALES: 4.6MM **Privately Held**
WEB: www.franz.com/
SIC: 7372 7371 Prepackaged software; computer software development

(P-24671)
FREEZE TAG INC (PA)
18062 Irvine Blvd Ste 103, Tustin (92780-3328)
PHONE..................................714 210-3850
Craig Holland, President
Mick Donahoo, COO
Tamara Sahagun, Contractor
EMP: 11
SQ FT: 900
SALES: 2.2MM **Publicly Held**
WEB: www.freezetag.com
SIC: 7372 Prepackaged software

(P-24672)
FREIGHTGATE INC
Also Called: Edi Ideas
10055 Slater Ave Ste 231, Fountain Valley (92708-4722)
PHONE..................................714 799-2833
Martin Hubert, President
Gary Chisamore, Vice Pres
EMP: 26
SALES (est): 3.2MM
SALES (corp-wide): 2.9MM **Privately Held**
WEB: www.freightgate.com
SIC: 7372 7371 Application computer software; utility computer software; computer software development & applications
PA: Edi Ideas Inc
16051 Springdale St # 111
Huntington Beach CA 92649
714 841-2833

(P-24673)
FRIENDSLEARN INC
425 Broadway St, Redwood City (94063-3126)
PHONE..................................734 678-8814
Bhargav SRI Prakash, CEO
EMP: 15 EST: 2013
SALES (est): 568.2K **Privately Held**
SIC: 7372 Educational computer software; business oriented computer software; home entertainment computer software; application computer software

(P-24674)
FRONTAPP INC
525 Brannan St Ste 300, San Francisco (94107-1632)
PHONE..................................415 680-3048
Mathilde Collin, CEO
Laurent Perrin, CTO
EMP: 71
SQ FT: 11,000
SALES: 5MM **Privately Held**
SIC: 7372 Application computer software

(P-24675)
FRONTRANGE HOLDING INC
490 N Mccarthy Blvd, Milpitas (95035-5118)
PHONE..................................408 601-2800
Jon Temple, CEO
Ian Mc Ewan, Vice Pres
Duane Russell, Info Tech Dir
David Bellandi, VP Mktg
Gene Torre, VP Mktg
EMP: 383

SALES (est): 12.6MM **Privately Held**
SIC: 7372 7371 Prepackaged software; computer software systems analysis & design, custom

(P-24676)
FRONTRANGE SOLUTIONS USA INC
490 N Mccarthy Blvd # 100, Milpitas (95035-5118)
PHONE..................................925 398-1800
Michael E Kohlsdorf, CEO
Karen Rogge, CFO
Sheik Hameed, Senior VP
Steve Lindeman, Vice Pres
Raj Patel, Vice Pres
EMP: 17
SALES (est): 1.1MM **Privately Held**
SIC: 7372 Prepackaged software

(P-24677)
FUJISOFT AMERICA INC
1710 S Amphlett Blvd # 215, San Mateo (94402-2705)
PHONE..................................650 235-9422
James Prenton, Administration
Renhong Sun, CEO
Yusuke Osada, QA Dir
EMP: 13
SQ FT: 2,700
SALES (corp-wide): 1.6B **Privately Held**
SIC: 7372 Prepackaged software
HQ: Fujisoft Service Bureau Incorporated
2-19-7, Kotobashi
Sumida-Ku TKY 130-0
356 001-731

(P-24678)
FUSION MPHC HOLDING CORP
6800 Koll Center Pkwy, Pleasanton (94566-7045)
PHONE..................................925 201-2500
Paul Millie, CFO
EMP: 106 EST: 2007
SALES (est): 1.4MM
SALES (corp-wide): 150.5MM **Publicly Held**
SIC: 7372 6719 Business oriented computer software; investment holding companies, except banks
PA: Fusion Connect, Inc.
420 Lexington Ave Rm 1718
New York NY 10170
212 201-2400

(P-24679)
FUZEBOX SOFTWARE CORPORATION (HQ)
150 Spear St Ste 900, San Francisco (94105-5118)
PHONE..................................415 692-4800
David Obrand, CEO
Charlie Newark-French, President
Mark Stubbs, CFO
Eric Davison, Sr Software Eng
Nathan Hopper, Sr Software Eng
EMP: 14
SQ FT: 16,000
SALES (est): 19.8MM
SALES (corp-wide): 110.8MM **Privately Held**
WEB: www.callwave.com
SIC: 7372 Application computer software
PA: Fuze, Inc.
2 Copley Pl Ste 700
Boston MA 02116
800 890-1553

(P-24680)
G7 PRODUCTIVITY SYSTEMS
Also Called: Versacheck
16885 W Bernardo Dr # 290, San Diego (92127-1618)
P.O. Box 270459 (92198-2459)
PHONE..................................858 675-1095
Thomas Priebus, President
Teri Pfarr, COO
Jim Danforth, CFO
EMP: 60
SQ FT: 18,000
SALES (est): 3.9MM **Privately Held**
WEB: www.g7ps.com
SIC: 7372 Prepackaged software

(P-24681)
GAMECLOUD STUDIOS INC
30111 Tech Dr Ste 110, Murrieta (92563)
PHONE..................................951 677-2345
Aaron Baker, CEO
Kat Ifa, Office Mgr
George Gaxiola, CTO
John Krikorian, Software Engr
EMP: 20 EST: 2010
SALES (est): 1.2MM **Privately Held**
SIC: 7372

(P-24682)
GAMEMINE LLC
2341 Wilson Ave, Venice (90291-4738)
PHONE..................................310 310-3105
Flaviu Rus, Mng Member
Daneil Starr,
EMP: 35 EST: 2017
SALES: 50MM **Privately Held**
SIC: 7372 Publishers' computer software

(P-24683)
GATE-OR-DOOR INC
14811 Leroy Ave, Ripon (95366-9417)
PHONE..................................209 751-4881
James Bickle, Principal
EMP: 21 EST: 2011
SALES (est): 3MM **Privately Held**
SIC: 7372 Operating systems computer software

(P-24684)
GATHERAPP INC
301 Bryant St Apt 201, San Francisco (94107-4170)
PHONE..................................415 409-9476
Abraham Shafi, CEO
EMP: 10
SALES (est): 221.8K **Privately Held**
SIC: 7372 Application computer software

(P-24685)
GE DIGITAL LLC (HQ)
2623 Camino Ramon, San Ramon (94583-9130)
PHONE..................................925 242-6200
EMP: 300
SALES (est): 121.1K
SALES (corp-wide): 122B **Publicly Held**
SIC: 7372 Business oriented computer software
PA: General Electric Company
41 Farnsworth St
Boston MA 02210
617 443-3000

(P-24686)
GENERAL ELECTRIC COMPANY
2623 Camino Ramon, San Ramon (94583-9130)
PHONE..................................925 242-6200
Holly Gilthorpe, Ch Credit Ofcr
Rebecca Lawson, Vice Pres
Jennifer Schulze, Vice Pres
Ashima Puri, Program Mgr
Jim KAO, Technical Mgr
EMP: 67
SALES (corp-wide): 122B **Publicly Held**
SIC: 7372 Business oriented computer software
PA: General Electric Company
41 Farnsworth St
Boston MA 02210
617 443-3000

(P-24687)
GENESIS GROUP SFTWR DEVELOPERS
Also Called: Ggsdi
16027 Brookhurst St Ste G, Fountain Valley (92708-1562)
PHONE..................................714 630-4297
EMP: 25
SALES (est): 2.2MM **Privately Held**
WEB: www.ggsdi.com
SIC: 7372 7371

(P-24688)
GENESYS TELECOM LABS INC (HQ)
Also Called: Genesys Telecom Labs
2001 Junipero Serra Blvd, Daly City (94014-3891)
PHONE..................................650 466-1100

▲ = Import ▼=Export
◆ =Import/Export

Paul Segre, *CEO*
Tom Eggemeier, *President*
David Sudbey, *Ch Credit Ofcr*
Reed Henry, *Chief Mktg Ofcr*
Peter Graf, *Officer*
EMP: 450
SQ FT: 156,000
SALES (est): 641.3MM
SALES (corp-wide): 69.9MM **Privately Held**
WEB: www.genesyslabs.com
SIC: 7372 Business oriented computer software
PA: Permira Advisers Llp
80 Pall Mall
London SW1Y
207 632-1000

(P-24689)
GEOGRAPHIC DATA MGT SOLUTIONS
Also Called: G D M S-Gographic Data MGT Sol
42140 10th St W, Lancaster (93534-7004)
PHONE..................................661 949-1025
Brian Glidden, *President*
Lisa Aitken, *Vice Pres*
Daniel Stanton, *Director*
EMP: 10
SALES (est): 892.9K **Privately Held**
SIC: 7372 5045 Business oriented computer software; computers, peripherals & software

(P-24690)
GET AHEAD LEARNING LLC
70 S Lake Ave Ste 1000, Pasadena
(91101-4995)
PHONE..................................626 796-8500
Walter B Rose,
EMP: 10
SALES (est): 511.5K **Privately Held**
WEB: www.getaheadlearning.com
SIC: 7372 Educational computer software

(P-24691)
GETGOING INC
610 Bridgeport Ln, Foster City
(94404-3606)
PHONE..................................415 608-7474
Alek Vernitsky, *CEO*
Alek Strygin, *COO*
Nilesh Lakhani, *Principal*
Fred Reid, *Principal*
Ilya Gluhovsky, *Chief Engr*
EMP: 18 **EST:** 2011
SALES (est): 1.9MM **Privately Held**
SIC: 7372 7371 Application computer software; business oriented computer software; computer software development

(P-24692)
GIGAMON INC (HQ)
3300 Olcott St, Santa Clara (95054-3005)
PHONE..................................408 831-4000
Paul A Hooper, *CEO*
Michelle Hodges, *Partner*
Shane Buckley, *President*
Dave Arkley, *CFO*
Kim Decarlis, *Chief Mktg Ofcr*
EMP: 126
SQ FT: 105,600
SALES (est): 310.8MM **Privately Held**
WEB: www.gigamon.com
SIC: 7372 3577 Prepackaged software; computer peripheral equipment
PA: Ginsberg Holdco, Inc.
3300 Olcott St
Santa Clara CA 95054
408 831-4000

(P-24693)
GILDEDTREE INC
251 Lafayette Cir Ste 310, Lafayette
(94549-4388)
PHONE..................................925 246-5624
Yariv Lioz, *President*
Barry Weinstein, *Vice Pres*
EMP: 15
SALES (est): 663.6K **Privately Held**
SIC: 7372 Educational computer software

(P-24694)
GITACLOUD INC
5791 Athenour Ct, Pleasanton
(94588-9678)
PHONE..................................925 519-5965
Ashutosh Bansal,
EMP: 12
SALES (est): 256K **Privately Held**
SIC: 7372 7389 Prepackaged software;

(P-24695)
GLASSLAB INC
209 Redwood Shores Pkwy, Redwood City
(94065-1175)
PHONE..................................415 244-5584
Jessica Lindl, *Exec Dir*
Granetta Blevins, *CFO*
Michael John, *Managing Dir*
Michelle Riconscente, *Managing Dir*
Elena Macomber, *Producer*
EMP: 24 **EST:** 2014
SALES (est): 4.2MM **Privately Held**
SIC: 7372 8748 Educational computer software; educational consultant

(P-24696)
GLOBAL EDGE LLC
5230 Las Virgenes Rd # 265, Calabasas
(91302-3459)
PHONE..................................888 315-2692
William ' Cherry, *President*
EMP: 30 **Privately Held**
SIC: 7372 8721
PA: Global Edge, Llc
5230 Las Virgenes Rd # 265
Calabasas CA 91302

(P-24697)
GLOBAL EDGE LLC (PA)
5230 Las Virgenes Rd # 265, Calabasas
(91302-3459)
PHONE..................................818 207-2694
Douglas Jacobsen, *CEO*
Jay Cherry, *President*
Todd Harrington, *COO*
EMP: 25
SALES (est): 4.3MM **Privately Held**
SIC: 7372 8721 Prepackaged software; auditing services

(P-24698)
GLOBAL INFOVISION INC
2290 Ardemore Dr, Fullerton (92833-4819)
PHONE..................................714 738-4465
Prem Gupta, *President*
EMP: 10
SALES (est): 940K **Privately Held**
WEB: www.globalinfovision.net
SIC: 7372 Prepackaged software

(P-24699)
GLOBAL MICRO SOLUTIONS INC
21250 Hawthorne Blvd # 540, Torrance
(90503-5513)
PHONE..................................310 218-5678
Mike Uesugi, *President*
Angela Uesugi, *Vice Pres*
EMP: 10
SQ FT: 1,500
SALES (est): 1MM **Privately Held**
SIC: 7372 7371 Prepackaged software; computer software systems analysis & design, custom

(P-24700)
GLOBAL WAVE GROUP LLC
8a Journey Ste 100, Aliso Viejo (92656)
PHONE..................................949 916-9800
Zubin Mehta, *Mng Member*
Randy M Ruckle, *COO*
Rhett Rowe, *Senior VP*
EMP: 10 **EST:** 2007
SALES (est): 938.6K **Privately Held**
SIC: 7372 Prepackaged software

(P-24701)
GLOBALEX CORPORATION
Also Called: Revo Payments
2100 Abbot Kinney Blvd A, Venice
(90291-7003)
PHONE..................................310 593-4833
Mike Corbera, *CEO*
Lolita Carrico, *Director*

EMP: 65 **EST:** 2003
SALES (est): 5.8MM **Privately Held**
SIC: 7372 Prepackaged software

(P-24702)
GOALSR INC (PA)
3139 Independence Dr, Livermore
(94551-7595)
PHONE..................................650 453-5844
Vidyadhar Handragal, *President*
Divya Krishnaswamy, *CEO*
EMP: 34
SQ FT: 1,000
SALES (est): 500K **Privately Held**
SIC: 7372 7371 Application computer software; computer software systems analysis & design, custom; computer software development; computer software development & applications

(P-24703)
GOENGINEER INC
6400 Canoga Ave Ste 121, Woodland Hills
(91367-7781)
PHONE..................................818 716-1650
Ken Coburn, *Branch Mgr*
EMP: 11
SALES (corp-wide): 54.2MM **Privately Held**
SIC: 7372 Prepackaged software
PA: Goengineer, Inc.
1787 E Fort Union Blvd # 100
Salt Lake City UT 84121
801 359-6100

(P-24704)
GOODCO INC
543 Howard St Fl 4, San Francisco
(94105-3015)
PHONE..................................415 425-1012
Samar Birwadker, *CEO*
Subbu Balakrishinan, *CTO*
EMP: 10
SALES (est): 620K **Privately Held**
SIC: 7372 Business oriented computer software

(P-24705)
GOODRX INC (PA)
233 Wilshire Blvd Ste 990, Santa Monica
(90401-1248)
PHONE..................................310 500-6544
Douglass Hirsch, *CEO*
Mark Ensley, *Vice Pres*
Neil K Ford, *Vice Pres*
Trevor Dezdek, *Principal*
Michael Jeon, *VP Finance*
EMP: 16
SALES (est): 4.4MM **Privately Held**
SIC: 7372 Application computer software

(P-24706)
GOVERNMENTJOBSCOM INC
Also Called: Neogov
300 Continental Blvd # 565, El Segundo
(90245-5042)
PHONE..................................310 426-6304
Damir Davidovic, *CEO*
Scott Letourneau, *President*
Robert Nishimuta, *Sr Software Eng*
Chris Rosenberger, *Info Tech Mgr*
Krishna Surendra, *Info Tech Mgr*
EMP: 130
SQ FT: 5,000
SALES (est): 18.9MM **Privately Held**
WEB: www.governmentjobs.com
SIC: 7372 Prepackaged software

(P-24707)
GRADESCOPE INC
2054 University Ave # 600, Berkeley
(94704-1076)
P.O. Box 11691 (94712-2691)
PHONE..................................702 985-7442
Arjun Singh, *CEO*
EMP: 10
SQ FT: 1,600
SALES (est): 267.3K
SALES (corp-wide): 23.2MM **Privately Held**
SIC: 7372 Educational computer software
HQ: Turnitin, Llc
2101 Webster St Ste 1800
Oakland CA 94612
866 816-5046

(P-24708)
GRANITE SOFTWARE INC
7590 N Glenoaks Blvd # 102, Burbank
(91504-1011)
PHONE..................................818 252-1950
Elmer Vasquez, *President*
Christopher Negron, *Prgrmr*
Ricardo Mejia, *Director*
EMP: 15 **EST:** 1999
SALES (est): 1.2MM **Privately Held**
WEB: www.iclosingsdirect.com
SIC: 7372 Prepackaged software

(P-24709)
GRAYPAY LLC
6345 Balboa Blvd Ste 115, Encino
(91316-1517)
PHONE..................................818 387-6735
Marc Geolina, *Mng Member*
Bryan Rainey,
EMP: 60 **EST:** 2015
SALES (est): 2.4MM **Privately Held**
SIC: 7372 Business oriented computer software

(P-24710)
GREAT LAKES DATA SYSTEMS INC
Also Called: G L D S
5954 Priestly Dr, Carlsbad (92008-8812)
PHONE..................................760 602-1900
Doug Ganske, *Manager*
Garrick Russell, *COO*
Saulius Vabalas, *Vice Pres*
Christine Brown, *Office Mgr*
Jeff Dew, *Info Tech Dir*
EMP: 10
SQ FT: 6,360
SALES (corp-wide): 8MM **Privately Held**
WEB: www.cablebilling.com
SIC: 7372 Prepackaged software
PA: Great Lakes Data Systems, Inc.
306 Seippel Blvd
Beaver Dam WI 53916
920 887-7651

(P-24711)
GREEN HILLS SOFTWARE INC (PA)
30 W Sola St, Santa Barbara (93101-2599)
PHONE..................................805 965-6044
Daniel O Dowd, *CEO*
Dave Kleidermacher, *President*
Michael W Liacko, *President*
Daniel O'Dowd, *CEO*
Brad Jackson, *COO*
EMP: 105
SALES (est): 76.5MM **Privately Held**
WEB: www.ghs.com
SIC: 7372 Prepackaged software

(P-24712)
GREYHELLER LLC
111 Deerwood Rd Ste 200, San Ramon
(94583-4445)
PHONE..................................925 415-5053
Hendrix Bodden, *CEO*
EMP: 12
SQ FT: 1,500
SALES (est): 1.3MM **Privately Held**
SIC: 7372 Prepackaged software

(P-24713)
GROWDIARIES LLC
8605 Santa Monica Blvd, West Hollywood
(90069-4109)
PHONE..................................626 354-8935
Egor Prilukov,
EMP: 10
SALES (est): 221.8K **Privately Held**
SIC: 7372 Application computer software

(P-24714)
GUAVUS INC (HQ)
2860 Junction Ave, San Jose (95134-1922)
PHONE..................................650 243-3400
Anukool Lakhina, *CEO*
Michael Crane, *President*
Ty Nam, *COO*
Anupam Rastogi, *CTO*
EMP: 60

PRODUCTS & SVCS

SALES (est): 39MM
SALES (corp-wide): 305.4MM Privately Held
WEB: www.guavus.com
SIC: 7372 7371 Prepackaged software; computer software development & applications
PA: Thales
Carpe Diem Esplanade Nord Tour Aig
Courbevoie 92400
157 778-000

(P-24715)
GUCK ARIBA
807 Eleventh Ave, Sunnyvale (94089-4731)
PHONE..................650 390-1445
Jennifer Sinatra, *Managing Prtnr*
Dave Johnston, *Vice Pres*
Darlene French, *Executive*
Elke Koscher, *Executive*
Tim McKee, *Executive*
EMP: 147
SALES (est): 7MM Privately Held
SIC: 7372 Business oriented computer software

(P-24716)
GUIDANCE SOFTWARE INC (HQ)
1055 E Colo Blvd Ste 400, Pasadena (91106)
PHONE..................626 229-9191
Patrick Dennis, *President*
Mandy Mueller, *Partner*
Barry Plaga, *COO*
Michael Harris, *Chief Mktg Ofcr*
Alfredo Gomez, *Senior VP*
EMP: 215 **EST:** 1997
SQ FT: 90,000
SALES: 110.5MM
SALES (corp-wide): 2.2B Privately Held
WEB: www.guidancesoftware.com
SIC: 7372 3572 Business oriented computer software; computer storage devices
PA: Open Text Corporation
275 Frank Tompa Dr
Waterloo ON N2L 0
519 888-7111

(P-24717)
GUIDEWIRE SOFTWARE INC (PA)
1001 E Hillsdale Blvd # 8, Foster City (94404-1642)
PHONE..................650 357-9100
Marcus S Ryu, *President*
Peter Gassner, *Ch of Bd*
Richard Hart, *CFO*
Ali Kheirolomoom,
Priscilla Hung, *Officer*
EMP: 148
SQ FT: 97,674
SALES: 661MM **Publicly Held**
WEB: www.guidewire.com
SIC: 7372 Business oriented computer software

(P-24718)
H2 WELLNESS INCORPORATED
11999 San Vicente Blvd, Los Angeles (90049-5131)
PHONE..................310 362-1888
Hooman Fakki, *CEO*
Houman Arasteh, *COO*
Russ Nash, *Bd of Directors*
Esfandiar Behrouz, *Director*
John Coleman, *Director*
EMP: 55
SALES (est): 3.5MM Privately Held
SIC: 7372 Application computer software

(P-24719)
HABLA INCORPORATED
Also Called: Olark
548 Market St, San Francisco (94104-5401)
PHONE..................703 867-0135
Ben Congleton, *CEO*
EMP: 30 **EST:** 2015
SALES (est): 1MM Privately Held
SIC: 7372 Business oriented computer software

(P-24720)
HAZELCAST INC (PA)
350 Cambridge Ave Ste 100, Palo Alto (94306-1546)
PHONE..................650 521-5453
Kelly Herrell, *CEO*
Kevin Cox, *Vice Pres*
Morgan Dioli, *Vice Pres*
Fuad Malikov, *Vice Pres*
Nadine Teixeira, *Vice Pres*
EMP: 23 **EST:** 2012
SQ FT: 2,000
SALES (est): 4.9MM Privately Held
SIC: 7372 7371 Publishers' computer software; computer software systems analysis & design, custom

(P-24721)
HEALTH GORILLA INC
440 N Wolfe Rd, Sunnyvale (94085-3869)
PHONE..................844 446-7455
Steven Yaskin, *CEO*
Sergio Wagner, *Vice Pres*
Andrei Zudin, *CTO*
Heena Shah, *Manager*
EMP: 25
SALES (est): 1.7MM Privately Held
SIC: 7372 Application computer software

(P-24722)
HEALTHLINE SYSTEMS LLC (HQ)
9605 Scranton Rd Ste 200, San Diego (92121-1768)
P.O. Box 420399 (92142-0399)
PHONE..................858 673-1700
Dan E Littrell, *President*
EMP: 27
SQ FT: 20,800
SALES (est): 7.5MM
SALES (corp-wide): 247.6MM Publicly Held
WEB: www.healthlinesystem.com
SIC: 7372 7371 Business oriented computer software; computer software development
PA: Healthstream, Inc.
209 10th Ave S Ste 450
Nashville TN 37203
615 301-3100

(P-24723)
HEALTHSTREAM INC
Also Called: Echo, A Heatlhstream Company
9605 Scranton Rd Ste 200, San Diego (92121-1768)
PHONE..................800 733-8737
Robert A Frist Jr, *Ch of Bd*
EMP: 306
SALES (corp-wide): 247.6MM Publicly Held
SIC: 7372 7371 Prepackaged software; custom computer programming services
PA: Healthstream, Inc.
209 10th Ave S Ste 450
Nashville TN 37203
615 301-3100

(P-24724)
HEALTHYWEALTHYHACK INC
Also Called: Fintech Platform
16979 Frank Ave, Los Gatos (95032-3453)
PHONE..................669 225-3745
Sachin Piplani, *CEO*
EMP: 12
SALES (est): 500K Privately Held
SIC: 7372 Business oriented computer software

(P-24725)
HEARSAY SOCIAL INC (PA)
185 Berry St Ste 3800, San Francisco (94107-1725)
PHONE..................888 990-3777
Clara Shih, *CEO*
Michael H Lock, *President*
William Salisbury, *CFO*
Matt Green, *Officer*
Gaurav Agarwal, *Vice Pres*
EMP: 60
SALES (est): 13.5MM Privately Held
SIC: 7372 Publishers' computer software

(P-24726)
HEAT SOFTWARE USA INC (DH)
490 N Mccarthy Blvd, Milpitas (95035-5118)
PHONE..................408 601-2800
Steve Daly, *CEO*
Robert Latham, *Vice Pres*
Tony Matthews, *Executive*
James Lee, *Info Tech Mgr*
Yamini Ayachitam, *Software Dev*
EMP: 33
SALES (est): 54.7MM
SALES (corp-wide): 24.9MM Privately Held
SIC: 7372 Prepackaged software
HQ: Ivanti, Inc.
698 W 10000 S Ste 500
South Jordan UT 84095
801 208-1500

(P-24727)
HELLO NETWORK INC
2 Mint Plz Apt 1004, San Francisco (94103-1875)
PHONE..................408 891-4727
Orkut Buyukkokten, *CEO*
John Murphy, *COO*
EMP: 10
SALES (est): 667.6K Privately Held
SIC: 7372 Application computer software

(P-24728)
HEROKU INC
1 Market St Ste 300, San Francisco (94105-1315)
PHONE..................650 704-6107
Tod Nielsen, *CEO*
Brad Gyger, *Vice Pres*
Michael Schiff, *Vice Pres*
Eric Black, *Sr Software Eng*
Harold Gimnez, *Engineer*
EMP: 30
SALES (est): 3.4MM
SALES (corp-wide): 10.4B Publicly Held
SIC: 7372 Application computer software
PA: Salesforce.Com, Inc.
1 Market Ste 300
San Francisco CA 94105
415 901-7000

(P-24729)
HEWLETT PACKARD ENTERPRISE CO
8000 Foothills Blvd, Roseville (95747-5200)
PHONE..................916 786-8000
Michael Ketcherside, *Branch Mgr*
Nick Gunn, *Vice Pres*
Cesar Sanchez, *Program Mgr*
Phong Lam, *Administration*
Kapil Gupta, *Info Tech Mgr*
EMP: 100
SQ FT: 64,000
SALES (corp-wide): 28.8B Publicly Held
SIC: 7372 Business oriented computer software
PA: Hewlett Packard Enterprise Company
3000 Hanover St
Palo Alto CA 94304
650 687-5817

(P-24730)
HEWLETT PACKARD ENTERPRISE CO
1140 Enterprise Way, Sunnyvale (94089-1412)
PHONE..................312 580-9100
Rick Smith, *President*
Zaida Himes, *Executive Asst*
Reynolds Mark, *Sr Software Eng*
Randy Van Sickle, *Network Enginr*
Stacey Esser, *Technical Staff*
EMP: 42
SALES (corp-wide): 28.8B Publicly Held
SIC: 7372 Business oriented computer software
PA: Hewlett Packard Enterprise Company
3000 Hanover St
Palo Alto CA 94304
650 687-5817

(P-24731)
HEWLETT PACKARD ENTERPRISE CO (PA)
3000 Hanover St, Palo Alto (94304-1185)
PHONE..................650 687-5817
Antonio Neri, *President*
Patricia F Russo, *Ch of Bd*
Timothy C Stonesifer, *CFO*
Kirt P Karros, *Treasurer*
John F Schultz,
EMP: 148 **EST:** 2015
SALES: 28.8B **Publicly Held**
SIC: 7372 7379 3572 Business oriented computer software; computer related maintenance services; computer storage devices

(P-24732)
HEXACORP LTD
Also Called: Orfium
201 Ocean Ave Unit 1108p, Santa Monica (90402-1452)
PHONE..................760 815-0904
Roberts Wells, *CEO*
Christopher Mohoney, *President*
Drew Delis, *COO*
EMP: 20 **EST:** 2014
SALES: 200K Privately Held
SIC: 7372 7389 Prepackaged software;

(P-24733)
HIGHER ONE PAYMENTS INC
Also Called: Cashnet
80 Swan Way Ste 200, Oakland (94621-1439)
PHONE..................510 769-9888
Dan Peterson, *President*
Chuck Haddock, *Senior VP*
EMP: 45
SQ FT: 4,500
SALES (est): 2.7MM
SALES (corp-wide): 19.3MM Privately Held
WEB: www.cashnet.com
SIC: 7372 Business oriented computer software
HQ: Higher One, Inc.
115 Munson St
New Haven CT 06511

(P-24734)
HOLLYWOOD SOFTWARE INC
5000 Van Nuys Blvd # 460, Van Nuys (91403-1854)
PHONE..................818 205-2121
Carol Dibattiste, *CEO*
Karl Anderson, *COO*
Kim Lockhart, *Senior VP*
Larry McCourt, *Senior VP*
Susan Wells, *Senior VP*
EMP: 19 **EST:** 1997
SALES (est): 2MM Privately Held
SIC: 7372 Operating systems computer software

(P-24735)
HOOJOOK
1754 Tech Dr Ste 132, San Jose (95148)
PHONE..................408 596-9427
Shauli Chaudhuri, *CEO*
Surendra Arora, *Vice Pres*
EMP: 12
SQ FT: 1,000
SALES (est): 760K Privately Held
SIC: 7372 Application computer software

(P-24736)
HOOPLA SOFTWARE INC
84 W Santa Clara St # 460, San Jose (95113-1815)
PHONE..................408 498-9600
Michael Smalls, *CEO*
Cathleen Candia, *Executive Asst*
Julie W Smalls, *Executive Asst*
Christine Hao, *Engineer*
Jessica Headley, *Director*
EMP: 38
SALES (est): 3.5MM Privately Held
SIC: 7372 Application computer software

(P-24737)
HORTONWORKS INC (PA)
5470 Great America Pkwy, Santa Clara (95054-3644)
PHONE..................408 916-4121

Robert Bearden, *Ch of Bd*
Scott Davidson, *COO*
Alan Fudge, *Risk Mgmt Dir*
Scott Reasoner,
Scott Gnau, *CTO*
EMP: 725
SQ FT: 92,000
SALES: 261.8MM **Publicly Held**
SIC: 7372 Application computer software

(P-24738)
HOST ANALYTICS INC (HQ)
555 Twin Dolphin Dr # 400, Redwood City
(94065-2132)
PHONE..................................650 249-7100
Dave Kellogg, *CEO*
Jim Eberlin, *President*
John Schmid, *President*
Ian Halifax, *CFO*
Ben Plummer, *Chief Mktg Ofcr*
EMP: 25 EST: 2000
SALES (est): 24.1MM **Privately Held**
WEB: www.hostanalytics.com
SIC: 7372 Application computer software

(P-24739)
HOWARDSOFT
7854 Ivanhoe Ave A, La Jolla (92037-4501)
P.O. Box 8432 (92038-8432)
PHONE..................................858 454-0121
James Howard, *Owner*
Maril Sowell, *General Mgr*
Suzanne Keller, *Facilities Mgr*
EMP: 10 EST: 1980
SALES (est): 844.9K **Privately Held**
WEB: www.howardsoft.com
SIC: 7372 8721 Prepackaged software;
accounting, auditing & bookkeeping

(P-24740)
HPE ENTERPRISES LLC (HQ)
3000 Hanover St, Palo Alto (94304-1112)
PHONE..................................650 857-5817
Sheena Campbell, *Partner*
Joseph Cioppa, *Partner*
Carl McGlashan, *Officer*
Scott Anderson, *Vice Pres*
Max Cuellar, *Vice Pres*
EMP: 25 EST: 2015
SALES (est): 6.9MM
SALES (corp-wide): 28.8B **Publicly Held**
SIC: 7372 7379 3572 Prepackaged soft-
ware; computer related maintenance
services; computer storage devices
PA: Hewlett Packard Enterprise Company
3000 Hanover St
Palo Alto CA 94304
650 687-5817

(P-24741)
HUMANCONCEPTS LLC
3 Harbor Dr Ste 200, Sausalito
(94965-1491)
PHONE..................................650 581-2500
Martin Sacks,
Hanif Ismail,
Kathleen Jensen,
Luis Rivera,
EMP: 40
SQ FT: 6,500
SALES (est): 2.5MM
SALES (corp-wide): 196.6MM **Privately
Held**
WEB: www.orgplus.com
SIC: 7372 Prepackaged software
PA: Saba Software, Inc.
4120 Dublin Blvd Ste 200
Dublin CA 94568
877 722-2101

(P-24742)
HYSTERICAL SOFTWARE INC
2874 Hillside Dr, Burlingame (94010-5968)
PHONE..................................415 793-5785
Donna Pribble, *President*
EMP: 10
SALES (est): 196.7K **Privately Held**
SIC: 7372 Prepackaged software

(P-24743)
HYTRUST INC (PA)
1975 W El Camino Real # 203, Mountain
View (94040-2218)
PHONE..................................650 681-8100
John De Santis, *CEO*
Sean Cahill, *Partner*

Eric Chiu, *President*
Mercy Caprara, *CFO*
Fred Kost, *Senior VP*
EMP: 44
SQ FT: 12,000
SALES: 4.4MM **Privately Held**
SIC: 7372 Educational computer software

(P-24744)
I T M SOFTWARE CORP
1030 W Maude Ave, Sunnyvale
(94085-2812)
PHONE..................................650 864-2500
Kenneth Coleman, *CEO*
Tom Niermann, *Founder*
Steve O'Conner, *Vice Pres*
Christina Ellwood, *Principal*
Jorge Helmer, *VP Finance*
EMP: 30
SQ FT: 18,600
SALES (est): 2.1MM **Privately Held**
WEB: www.itm-software.com
SIC: 7372 Prepackaged software

(P-24745)
IAC/INTERACTIVECORP
8800 W Sunset Blvd, West Hollywood
(90069-2105)
PHONE..................................212 314-7300
Phillip Marlock, *Branch Mgr*
EMP: 13
SALES (corp-wide): 3.3B **Publicly Held**
SIC: 7372 7375 5961 Prepackaged soft-
ware; information retrieval services; on-
line data base information retrieval;
catalog & mail-order houses
PA: Iac/Interactivecorp
555 W 18th St
New York NY 10011
212 314-7300

(P-24746)
**IAR SYSTEMS SOFTWARE INC
(HQ)**
1065 E Hillsdale Blvd # 420, Foster City
(94404-1615)
PHONE..................................650 287-4250
Stefan Skarin, *CEO*
Nadim Shehayed, *President*
Dannielle Burgard, *Admin Mgr*
Ashley Thompson, *Administration*
Stephanie Bellone, *Technology*
EMP: 10
SALES (est): 2.1MM
SALES (corp-wide): 40.8MM **Privately
Held**
WEB: www.iar.com
SIC: 7372 Application computer software
PA: I.A.R. Systems Group Ab
Strandbodgatan 11tr
Uppsala 753 2
841 092-000

(P-24747)
IC MANAGE INC (PA)
2105 S Bascom Ave Ste 120, Campbell
(95008-3274)
PHONE..................................408 369-9227
Dean Drako, *President*
Shiv Sikand, *Vice Pres*
Dennis Harmon, *Principal*
Roger March, *CTO*
Gary Gendel, *Info Tech Mgr*
EMP: 15
SQ FT: 2,000
SALES (est): 2.7MM **Privately Held**
WEB: www.icmanage.com
SIC: 7372 Prepackaged software

(P-24748)
ICEBREAKER HEALTH INC
Also Called: Lemonaid Health
150 Spear St Ste 350, San Francisco
(94105-1747)
PHONE..................................415 926-5818
Ian Van Every, *President*
EMP: 12
SQ FT: 1,270
SALES (est): 500.5K **Privately Held**
SIC: 7372 Business oriented computer
software

(P-24749)
IFWE INC (HQ)
848 Battery St, San Francisco
(94111-1504)
PHONE..................................415 946-1850
Dash Gopinath, *CEO*
Greg Tseng, *CEO*
Johann Schleier Smith, *CTO*
Erik Johonnessen, *Engineer*
Louis Willacy, *Marketing Staff*
EMP: 87
SQ FT: 13,000
SALES (est): 30.7MM
SALES (corp-wide): 123.7MM **Publicly
Held**
WEB: www.tagged.com
SIC: 7372 Application computer software
PA: The Meet Group Inc
100 Union Square Dr
New Hope PA 18938
215 862-1162

(P-24750)
IGRAD INC
2163 Newcastle Ave # 100, Cardiff By The
Sea (92007-1871)
PHONE..................................858 705-2917
Rob Labreche, *President*
EMP: 22
SQ FT: 2,000
SALES (est): 1.8MM **Privately Held**
SIC: 7372 Business oriented computer
software

(P-24751)
ILLUMINATE EDUCATION INC
6531 Irvine Center Dr # 100, Irvine
(92618-2145)
PHONE..................................951 739-0186
Lane Rankin, *President*
Scott Hickson, *CFO*
John Huh, *Sr Software Eng*
Chris Walker, *CTO*
Shant Mandossian, *Software Dev*
EMP: 26 EST: 2009
SALES (est): 4.5MM **Privately Held**
SIC: 7372 7389 Educational computer
software;

(P-24752)
**IMAGEWARE SYSTEMS INC
(PA)**
10815 Rncho Brnrdo Rd 3 # 310, San
Diego (92127)
PHONE..................................858 673-8600
S James Miller Jr, *Ch of Bd*
Wayne Wetherell, *CFO*
David Harding, *Vice Pres*
David Lotze, *Vice Pres*
Mike Rerick, *Vice Pres*
EMP: 67
SQ FT: 9,927
SALES: 4.2MM **Publicly Held**
WEB: www.iwsinc.com
SIC: 7372 3699 Business oriented com-
puter software; security control equipment
& systems

(P-24753)
IMAGINE THAT INC
6830 Via Del Oro Ste 230, San Jose
(95119-1390)
PHONE..................................408 365-0305
Bob Diamond, *President*
Pat Diamond, *CFO*
Kathi Hansen, *Marketing Staff*
EMP: 15
SQ FT: 45,000
SALES (est): 1.5MM **Privately Held**
WEB: www.imaginethatinc.com
SIC: 7372 Business oriented computer
software

(P-24754)
**IMPAC MEDICAL SYSTEMS INC
(HQ)**
Also Called: Elekta / Impac Medical Systems
100 Mathilda Pl Fl 5, Sunnyvale
(94086-6017)
PHONE..................................408 830-8000
Fax: 408 830-8003
EMP: 40
SQ FT: 35,000

SALES (est): 61.6MM
SALES (corp-wide): 1.3B **Privately Held**
WEB: www.impac.com
SIC: 7372 7373
PA: Elekta Ab (Publ)
Kungstensgatan 18
Stockholm 113 5
858 725-400

(P-24755)
IMPLY DATA INC
1633 Old Bayshore Hwy # 232, Burlingame
(94010-1533)
PHONE..................................415 685-8187
Fang Jin Yang, *CEO*
John Hartley, *Exec VP*
Gian Merlino, *Exec VP*
Vadim Ogievetsky, *Exec VP*
EMP: 10 EST: 2015
SQ FT: 1,000
SALES (est): 357.3K **Privately Held**
SIC: 7372 Prepackaged software

(P-24756)
IMPULSELOGIC INC
2410 Camino Ramon Ste 240, San Ramon
(94583-4278)
PHONE..................................925 275-1028
Leslie McNeill, *President*
EMP: 18
SALES (est): 1.9MM **Privately Held**
SIC: 7372 Utility computer software

(P-24757)
**IN SYNC COMPUTER
SOLUTIONS INC**
Also Called: Insync Computer Solutions
23282 Mill Creek Dr, Laguna Hills
(92653-1658)
PHONE..................................949 837-5000
Frank Halsema, *CEO*
Karen Bessette, *CFO*
EMP: 11
SQ FT: 3,000
SALES (est): 2.1MM **Privately Held**
WEB: www.insynclh.com
SIC: 7372 Prepackaged software

(P-24758)
INBENTA TECHNOLOGIES INC
1065 E Hillsdale Blvd # 425, Foster City
(94404-1639)
PHONE..................................408 213-8771
Jordi Torras, *CEO*
David Ginebra, *COO*
Greg Wookey, *CFO*
Sam Boyle, *General Mgr*
Jordi Prats, *CTO*
EMP: 22 EST: 2011
SALES: 3MM **Privately Held**
SIC: 7372 Application computer software

(P-24759)
INCANDESCENT INC
350 Sansome St, San Francisco
(94104-1304)
PHONE..................................415 464-7975
Michael De, *CEO*
EMP: 11
SALES (est): 670K **Privately Held**
SIC: 7372 Prepackaged software

(P-24760)
INDIUM SOFTWARE INC
1250 Oakmead Pkwy Ste 210, Sunnyvale
(94085-4035)
PHONE..................................408 501-8844
Harsha Nutalapati, *CEO*
Vijay Shankar Balaji, *President*
Shailesh Khanapur, *Assoc VP*
Bala S Selva, *Senior VP*
Tilak Dharmaraj, *Sales Staff*
EMP: 250
SALES (est): 12MM **Privately Held**
WEB: www.indiumsoft.com
SIC: 7372 Prepackaged software
HQ: Indium Software (India) Limited
2nd Floor Vds House,
Chennai TN 60008
-

(P-24761)
INDIVIDUAL SOFTWARE INC
2301 Armstrong St Ste 101, Livermore
(94551-9349)
PHONE..................................925 734-6767

Jo-L Hendrickson, *President*
Diane Dietzler, *Vice Pres*
EMP: 48 **EST:** 1981
SQ FT: 20,000
SALES (est): 6MM **Privately Held**
WEB: www.individualsoftware.com
SIC: 7372 7371 Prepackaged software;
custom computer programming services

(P-24762)
INDUSTRIOUS SOFTWARE SOLUTION
Also Called: Industrious Software Solutions
8901 S La Cienega Blvd # 202, Inglewood
(90301-7414)
PHONE.....................310 672-8700
Stephen Ryza, *President*
Gina Lynn Tan, *Controller*
EMP: 17
SQ FT: 10,000
SALES (est): 1.5MM **Privately Held**
SIC: 7372 5112 Business oriented com-
puter software; business forms

(P-24763)
INDUSTRY LLC (HQ)
1811 Micheltorena St, Los Angeles
(90026-1129)
PHONE.....................310 463-6157
Ted Smith,
EMP: 11
SALES (est): 1MM **Privately Held**
SIC: 7372 Home entertainment computer
software
PA: Del Farmer Llc
1811 Micheltorena St
Los Angeles CA
310 463-6157

(P-24764)
INFINISIM INC
2860 Zanker Rd Ste 202, San Jose
(95134-2133)
PHONE.....................408 934-9777
Samia Rashid, *President*
Zakir Syed, *CTO*
Amir Alborzi, *Director*
EMP: 12
SALES (est): 786.4K **Privately Held**
SIC: 7372 Business oriented computer
software

(P-24765)
INFOR (US) INC
Also Called: MAI Systems
26250 Entp Way Ste 220, Lake Forest
(92630)
PHONE.....................678 319-8000
Barbara Nolan, *President*
Marvin Perkins, *Sales Staff*
EMP: 190
SALES (corp-wide): 3.1B **Privately Held**
SIC: 7372 Business oriented computer
software
HQ: Infor (Us), Inc.
13560 Morris Rd Ste 4100
Alpharetta GA 30004
678 319-8000

(P-24766)
INFOR (US) INC
Also Called: Hansen Information Tech
11000 Olson Dr Ste 201, Rancho Cordova
(95670-5642)
PHONE.....................916 921-0883
Charles Hansen, *Manager*
EMP: 225
SALES (corp-wide): 3.1B **Privately Held**
SIC: 7372 Application computer software
HQ: Infor (Us), Inc.
13560 Morris Rd Ste 4100
Alpharetta GA 30004
678 319-8000

(P-24767)
INFORM DECISIONS
30162 Tomas 101, Rcho STA Marg
(92688-2124)
PHONE.....................949 709-5838
Dan Forester, *President*
EMP: 13
SALES (est): 1.4MM **Privately Held**
WEB: www.informdecision.com
SIC: 7372 Business oriented computer
software

(P-24768)
INFORM SOLUTION INCORPORATED
201 Mentor Dr, Santa Barbara
(93111-3337)
PHONE.....................805 879-6000
Rey Hugh, *President*
EMP: 11
SALES (est): 567.2K
SALES (corp-wide): 76.4B **Publicly Held**
WEB: www.informsolutions.com
SIC: 7372 Prepackaged software
HQ: Mentor Worldwide Llc
33 Technology Dr
Irvine CA 92618
800 636-8678

(P-24769)
INFORMATICA LLC (DH)
2100 Seaport Blvd, Redwood City
(94063-5596)
PHONE.....................650 385-5000
Anil Chakravarthy, *CEO*
Chris Cummins, *Partner*
Nick Voll, *Partner*
Sally Jenkins, *Officer*
Jo Stoner, *Officer*
EMP: 148
SQ FT: 290,000
SALES (est): 867.4MM
SALES (corp-wide): 1B **Privately Held**
WEB: www.metadataexchange.com
SIC: 7372 Prepackaged software

(P-24770)
INFORMATION INTEGRATION GROUP
457 Palm Dr Ste 200, Glendale
(91202-4339)
PHONE.....................818 956-3744
Alec Baghdasaryan, *President*
Caroline Dolikhanians, *Accountant*
Gohar Hovhannisyan, *Assistant*
EMP: 21
SALES (est): 3.4MM **Privately Held**
WEB: www.iigservices.com
SIC: 7372 7371 Prepackaged software;
computer software development

(P-24771)
INFORMATION RESOURCES INC
400 N Johnson St, Visalia (93291-6005)
PHONE.....................559 732-0324
Ken Weber, *Branch Mgr*
EMP: 30
SQ FT: 6,000
SALES (corp-wide): 420.5MM **Privately Held**
WEB: www.infores.com
SIC: 7372 8732 Prepackaged software;
market analysis or research
PA: Information Resources, Inc
150 N Clinton St
Chicago IL 60661
312 726-1221

(P-24772)
INKTOMI CORPORATION (HQ)
701 First Ave, Sunnyvale (94089-1019)
PHONE.....................650 653-2800
David Peterschmidt, *Ch of Bd*
Randy Gottfried, *CFO*
EMP: 25
SQ FT: 177,000
SALES (est): 21.9MM **Publicly Held**
WEB: www.inktomi.com
SIC: 7372 7371 Application computer soft-
ware; custom computer programming
services

(P-24773)
INLAND TEK INC
7364 Oxford Pl, Rancho Cucamonga
(91730-8282)
PHONE.....................909 900-8457
Ahammad Akbar Khan, *President*
EMP: 10
SALES (est): 221.8K **Privately Held**
SIC: 7372 Prepackaged software

(P-24774)
INMAGE SYSTEMS INC (HQ)
1065 La Avenida St, Mountain View
(94043-1421)
PHONE.....................408 200-3840
Debbie Button, *CEO*
John Ferraro, *President*
Marty Bradford, *CFO*
EMP: 26
SALES (est): 9.2MM
SALES (corp-wide): 110.3B **Publicly Held**
SIC: 7372 Business oriented computer
software
PA: Microsoft Corporation
1 Microsoft Way
Redmond WA 98052
425 882-8080

(P-24775)
INNOVYZE INC (DH)
605 E Huntington Dr # 205, Monrovia
(91016-6353)
PHONE.....................626 568-6868
Paul F Boulos, *President*
Angela R Shirrell, *Admin Sec*
EMP: 15
SALES (est): 2.4MM
SALES (corp-wide): 4B **Privately Held**
WEB: www.mwhsoftinc.com
SIC: 7372 Prepackaged software
HQ: Mwh Americas, Inc.
370 Interlocken Blvd
Broomfield CO 80021
303 410-4000

(P-24776)
INSIDESALESCOM INC
1269 Deep Creek Rd, Livermore
(94550-8640)
PHONE.....................385 207-7252
Chris Jhorgenson, *Branch Mgr*
EMP: 100
SALES (corp-wide): 85.8MM **Privately Held**
SIC: 7372 Publishers' computer software
PA: Insidesales.Com, Inc.
34 E 1700 S Ste A113
Provo UT 84606
801 754-9940

(P-24777)
INSIGHT SOLUTIONS INC
13095 Paramount Ct, Saratoga
(95070-4209)
PHONE.....................408 725-0213
Raghav Sherma, *President*
EMP: 40
SALES (est): 2.4MM **Privately Held**
WEB: www.insightsol.com
SIC: 7372 8748 Application computer soft-
ware; business consulting

(P-24778)
INSTAGIS INC
218 9th St, San Francisco (94103-3807)
PHONE.....................415 527-6636
Julian Garcia, *CEO*
Jean Coleman, *Principal*
EMP: 18
SALES (est): 454K **Privately Held**
SIC: 7372 7374 Prepackaged software;
data processing service

(P-24779)
INSTANA INC
541 Jefferson Ave Ste 100, Redwood City
(94063-1700)
PHONE.....................415 237-3245
Pete Abrams, *COO*
EMP: 30
SALES (est): 673.3K **Privately Held**
SIC: 7372 Prepackaged software

(P-24780)
INTAPP INC (PA)
200 Portage Ave, Palo Alto (94306-2242)
PHONE.....................650 852-0400
John Hall, *CEO*
Stuart Douglass, *President*
Daniel Harsell, *President*
Kelvyn Stirk, *President*
Dan Tacone, *President*
EMP: 200

SALES: 100MM **Privately Held**
WEB: www.intapp.com
SIC: 7372 Business oriented computer
software

(P-24781)
INTEGRAL DEVELOPMENT CORP (PA)
Also Called: Integral Engineering
850 Hansen Way, Palo Alto (94304-1017)
PHONE.....................650 424-4500
Harpal Sandhu, *President*
Valerie Edwards, *COO*
Albert Yau, *CFO*
Patrick Barkhordarian, *Vice Pres*
Paul Calhoun, *Vice Pres*
EMP: 200
SQ FT: 35,000
SALES (est): 35MM **Privately Held**
WEB: www.integral.com
SIC: 7372 Business oriented computer
software

(P-24782)
INTEGRATED MGT CONCEPTS INC
3355 Cochran St Ste 201, Simi Valley
(93063-2532)
PHONE.....................805 778-1629
Mark Tillema, *President*
Karen Rose, *Treasurer*
Bela Mikofalvy, *Vice Pres*
Mark Tilema, *Manager*
Bill Shiflett, *Consultant*
EMP: 25
SALES: 2.7MM **Privately Held**
WEB: www.intgconcepts.com
SIC: 7372 Application computer software

(P-24783)
INTELLITIME SYSTEMS CORP
1118 E 17th St, Santa Ana (92701-2620)
PHONE.....................714 444-3020
Dennis Peters, *President*
Alexander Chalakov, *Vice Pres*
Leslie Van Exel, *Software Dev*
EMP: 15
SQ FT: 11,000
SALES (est): 1.7MM **Privately Held**
WEB: www.intellitime.com
SIC: 7372 Prepackaged software

(P-24784)
INTERACTIVE SOLUTIONS INC (HQ)
Also Called: Web Traffic School
283 4th St Ste 301, Oakland (94607-4320)
P.O. Box 209 (94604-0209)
PHONE.....................510 214-9002
Isaak Tsifrin, *CEO*
Gary Golduber, *President*
Gary Tsifrin, *COO*
Mercy Gitau, *General Mgr*
EMP: 67
SQ FT: 14,000
SALES (est): 12.9MM
SALES (corp-wide): 18.2MM **Privately Held**
WEB: www.drivered.com
SIC: 7372 Prepackaged software
PA: Edriving Llc
283 4th St Ste 301
Oakland CA 94607
800 243-4008

(P-24785)
INTERNET STRATEGY INC
Also Called: One Park Place
10875 Rancho Bernardo Rd # 100, San
Diego (92127-2115)
PHONE.....................858 673-6022
Jill Ewing, *President*
Steve Hundley, *CEO*
EMP: 14
SQ FT: 10,000
SALES (est): 1.2MM **Privately Held**
SIC: 7372 Prepackaged software

(P-24786)
INTERNET SYSTEMS CNSORTIUM INC (PA)
950 Charter St, Redwood City
(94063-3110)
PHONE.....................650 423-1300
Jeff Osborn, *Exec Dir*

EMP: 15
SQ FT: 10,000
SALES: 175.2K **Privately Held**
SIC: 7372 Prepackaged software

(P-24787)
INTERNICHE TECHNOLOGIES INC (PA)
7065 Elmsdale Dr, San Jose (95120-3225)
PHONE..............................408 540-1160
Larry Larder, *CEO*
John Bartas, *Admin Sec*
Larry Snyder, *VP Engrg*
EMP: 10
SALES (est): 897.1K **Privately Held**
WEB: www.iniche.com
SIC: 7372 Prepackaged software

(P-24788)
INTERSHOP COMMUNICATIONS INC
461 2nd St Apt 151, San Francisco (94107-1498)
PHONE..............................415 844-1500
Jochen Moll, *CEO*
Verspuij Rene, *Partner*
Peter Mark Droste, *Ch of Bd*
Eckhard Pfeiffer, *Chairman*
Hans W Gutsch, *Treasurer*
EMP: 20
SQ FT: 2,700
SALES (est): 3.1MM
SALES (corp-wide): 42.2MM **Privately Held**
WEB: www.inter-shop.org
SIC: 7372 7375 Prepackaged software; information retrieval services
PA: Intershop Communications Ag
  Intershop Tower
  Jena 07740
  364 150-0

(P-24789)
INTERWORKING LABS INC
230 Mount Hermon Rd # 208, Scotts Valley (95066-4034)
P.O. Box 66190 (95067-6190)
PHONE..............................831 460-7010
Christine K Wellens, *President*
Bobby Olander, *COO*
Shantel Marie Jordan, *Marketing Staff*
EMP: 10
SQ FT: 20,000
SALES (est): 1MM **Privately Held**
WEB: www.iwl.com
SIC: 7372 Application computer software

(P-24790)
INTOUCH TECHNOLOGIES INC (PA)
Also Called: Intouch Health
7402 Hollister Ave, Goleta (93117-2583)
PHONE..............................805 562-8686
Yulun Wang, *CEO*
Susan Wang, *Shareholder*
David Adornetto, *COO*
Stephen L Wilson, *CFO*
James Wright, *Assoc VP*
EMP: 301
SQ FT: 1,600
SALES (est): 23.6MM **Privately Held**
WEB: www.intouchhealth.com
SIC: 7372 Business oriented computer software

(P-24791)
INTUIT INC
7535 Torrey Santa Fe Rd, San Diego (92129-5704)
PHONE..............................858 215-8726
EMP: 36
SALES (corp-wide): 4.6B **Publicly Held**
SIC: 7372
PA: Intuit Inc.
  2700 Coast Ave
  Mountain View CA 94043
  650 944-6000

(P-24792)
INTUIT INC (PA)
2700 Coast Ave, Mountain View (94043-1140)
P.O. Box 7850 (94039-7850)
PHONE..............................650 944-6000
Brad D Smith, *Ch of Bd*

Michelle M Clatterbuck, *CFO*
Scott D Cook, *Chairman*
Laura A Fennell, *Exec VP*
Sasan K Goodarzi, *Exec VP*
EMP: 70
SQ FT: 712,000
SALES: 5.9B **Publicly Held**
WEB: www.intuit.com
SIC: 7372 Business oriented computer software

(P-24793)
INTUIT INC
2700 Coast Ave Bldg 7, Mountain View (94043-1140)
PHONE..............................650 944-6000
Brad Smith, *Branch Mgr*
EMP: 128
SALES (corp-wide): 5.9B **Publicly Held**
WEB: www.intuit.com
SIC: 7372 Business oriented computer software
PA: Intuit Inc.
  2700 Coast Ave
  Mountain View CA 94043
  650 944-6000

(P-24794)
INTUIT INC
2650 Casey Ave, Mountain View (94043-1141)
P.O. Box 7850 (94039-7850)
PHONE..............................650 944-6000
Stephen Bennett, *President*
EMP: 13
SALES (corp-wide): 5.9B **Publicly Held**
SIC: 7372 Business oriented computer software
PA: Intuit Inc.
  2700 Coast Ave
  Mountain View CA 94043
  650 944-6000

(P-24795)
INTUIT INC
2535 Garcia Ave, Mountain View (94043-1111)
PHONE..............................650 944-6000
Connie Berg, *Branch Mgr*
Ed Perez, *Partner*
Kelly Page, *Executive Asst*
Thomas Freese, *Sr Ntwrk Engine*
Alison G Reilly, *Systs Prg Mgr*
EMP: 128
SALES (corp-wide): 5.9B **Publicly Held**
WEB: www.intuit.com
SIC: 7372 Business oriented computer software
PA: Intuit Inc.
  2700 Coast Ave
  Mountain View CA 94043
  650 944-6000

(P-24796)
INTUIT INC
141 Corona Way, Portola Valley (94028-7437)
PHONE..............................650 944-2840
EMP: 136
SALES (corp-wide): 5.9B **Publicly Held**
WEB: www.intuit.com
SIC: 7372 Business oriented computer software
PA: Intuit Inc.
  2700 Coast Ave
  Mountain View CA 94043
  650 944-6000

(P-24797)
INTUIT INC
180 Jefferson Dr, Menlo Park (94025-1115)
PHONE..............................650 944-6000
Brad Smith, *Branch Mgr*
Jason Yip, *Business Anlyst*
Betsy Kha, *Marketing Staff*
Sally Shepherd, *Senior Mgr*
Pablo Espinosa, *Director*
EMP: 128
SALES (corp-wide): 5.9B **Publicly Held**
WEB: www.intuit.com
SIC: 7372 Business oriented computer software
PA: Intuit Inc.
  2700 Coast Ave
  Mountain View CA 94043
  650 944-6000

(P-24798)
INTUIT INC
Also Called: Turbotax
7545 Torrey Santa Fe Rd, San Diego (92129-5704)
PHONE..............................858 215-8000
Jason Jackson, *Branch Mgr*
William Moselle, *Business Dir*
Bradford Beidler, *Administration*
Muzaffar Malik, *Sr Software Eng*
Manny Ruiz, *Sr Software Eng*
EMP: 300
SALES (corp-wide): 5.9B **Publicly Held**
WEB: www.intuit.com
SIC: 7372 Business oriented computer software
PA: Intuit Inc.
  2700 Coast Ave
  Mountain View CA 94043
  650 944-6000

(P-24799)
INVOICE2GO INC (PA)
2317 Broadway St Fl 2, Redwood City (94063-1674)
PHONE..............................650 300-5180
Gregory Waldorf, *CEO*
Mark Bartels, *CFO*
Sarah Stone, *Office Mgr*
Vanessa Canas, *Executive Asst*
Emily Barry, *Project Mgr*
EMP: 21 **EST:** 2014
SALES (est): 2.7MM **Privately Held**
SIC: 7372 Prepackaged software

(P-24800)
INVOTECH SYSTEMS INC
20951 Burbank Blvd Ste B, Woodland Hills (91367-6696)
PHONE..............................818 461-9800
Harvey Welles, *President*
Barbara Welbat, *Admin Asst*
Robert Andrews, *Technical Mgr*
Morgan Umali, *Project Mgr*
Kerri Merchan, *Manager*
EMP: 15
SQ FT: 10,000
SALES (est): 2.7MM **Privately Held**
WEB: www.invo.com
SIC: 7372 Business oriented computer software

(P-24801)
IPOLIPO INC
Also Called: Jifflenow
440 N Wolfe Rd, Sunnyvale (94085-3869)
PHONE..............................408 916-5290
Hari Shetty, *President*
Nancy Tannous, *Executive*
Traci Cummings, *Office Mgr*
Parth Mukherjee, *Mktg Dir*
Aaron Karpaty, *Sales Mgr*
EMP: 75 **EST:** 2006
SALES (est): 3.6MM **Privately Held**
SIC: 7372 Application computer software

(P-24802)
IPRESSROOM INC
13428 Maxella Ave Ste 222, Marina Del Rey (90292-5620)
PHONE..............................310 499-0544
Chris Bechtel, *President*
Tom Madden, *Chairman*
Vadim Derkach, *Director*
EMP: 20
SQ FT: 10,000
SALES (est): 1.8MM **Privately Held**
WEB: www.ipressroom.com
SIC: 7372 Application computer software

(P-24803)
IRISLOGIC INC
2336 Walsh Ave Ste D, Santa Clara (95051-1313)
PHONE..............................408 727-4940
Nathan Sundeep, *CEO*
Maria D-Cruz, *Vice Pres*
Maria Dcruz, *Vice Pres*
Anoop Trivedi, *CTO*
Priyanka Sathe, *Software Engr*
EMP: 32
SALES (est): 3.1MM **Privately Held**
WEB: www.irislogic.com
SIC: 7372 7371 Prepackaged software; custom computer programming services

(P-24804)
ISOLUTECOM INC (PA)
9 Northam Ave, Newbury Park (91320-3323)
PHONE..............................805 498-6259
Byron Nutley, *Ch of Bd*
Don Hyun, *President*
Thomas Mangle, *CFO*
Michael Brown, *CTO*
EMP: 50
SALES (est): 5.1MM **Privately Held**
WEB: www.isolute.com
SIC: 7372 Business oriented computer software

(P-24805)
IT RETAIL INC
191 W Big Springs Rd, Riverside (92507-4737)
PHONE..............................951 683-4950
Martin E Goodwin, *President*
Terry Ficklin, *Vice Pres*
Robert E Henry, *Vice Pres*
Cristobal Diaz, *Software Dev*
Tom Xu, *Software Dev*
EMP: 12
SALES: 2MM **Privately Held**
SIC: 7372 Business oriented computer software

(P-24806)
ITC SFTWARE SLUTIONS GROUP LLC (PA)
Also Called: Itcssg
201 Sandpointe Ave # 305, Santa Ana (92707-5778)
PHONE..............................877 248-2774
Ray Jandga, *President*
Guru Gurumoorthy, *Vice Pres*
EMP: 11
SQ FT: 3,000
SALES: 10MM **Privately Held**
SIC: 7372 7371 7373 Prepackaged software; computer software systems analysis & design, custom; systems software development services

(P-24807)
ITTAVI INC
Also Called: Supportpay
1631 Alhambra Blvd # 120, Sacramento (95816-7054)
PHONE..............................866 246-4408
Sheri Atwood, *CEO*
EMP: 25
SALES (est): 905.9K **Privately Held**
SIC: 7372 7373 7371 8748 Prepackaged software; systems software development services; custom computer programming services; systems engineering consultant, ex. computer or professional

(P-24808)
IVALUA INC (HQ)
805 Veterans Blvd Ste 203, Redwood City (94063-1736)
PHONE..............................650 930-9710
Daniel Olivier Amzallag, *CEO*
John McAdoo, *CFO*
Alex Saric, *Chief Mktg Ofcr*
Gary Malhotra, *VP Mktg*
Alison Madden, *Legal Staff*
EMP: 34
SQ FT: 4,000
SALES (est): 10.4MM
SALES (corp-wide): 19.6MM **Privately Held**
SIC: 7372 Business oriented computer software
PA: Ivalua
  69 Rue De Paris
  Orsay 91400
  164 865-454

(P-24809)
IVANTI INC
150 Mathilda Pl Ste 302, Sunnyvale (94086-6012)
PHONE..............................408 343-8181
Scott Arnold, *Branch Mgr*
Tej Sidhu, *Sr Software Eng*
Mike Mills, *CTO*
Katie Lynn, *Marketing Staff*
EMP: 12

PRODUCTS & SVCS

SALES (corp-wide): 24.9MM **Privately Held**
SIC: 7372 Application computer software
HQ: Ivanti, Inc.
698 W 10000 S Ste 500
South Jordan UT 84095
801 208-1500

(P-24810)
IVYDOCTORS INC
555 Bryant St, Palo Alto (94301-1704)
PHONE..............................415 890-3937
William Lard, *Principal*
EMP: 12
SALES (est): 256K **Privately Held**
SIC: 7372 Application computer software

(P-24811)
IXSYSTEMS INC (PA)
2490 Kruse Dr, San Jose (95131-1234)
PHONE..............................408 943-4100
Mike Lauth, *CEO*
Andrew Madrid, *COO*
Brett Davis, *Exec VP*
Morgan Littlewood, *Senior VP*
Jeff Kaminsky, *General Mgr*
EMP: 60
SQ FT: 20,000
SALES (est): 17.8MM **Privately Held**
WEB: www.ixsystems.com
SIC: 7372 Operating systems computer
software

(P-24812)
J F K & ASSOCIATES INC
1100 Moraga Way Ste 202, Moraga
(94556-1155)
PHONE..............................925 388-0255
Jack Keane, *President*
EMP: 20
SALES (est): 3MM **Privately Held**
WEB: www.jfkcorp.com
SIC: 7372 Prepackaged software

(P-24813)
JAMIS SOFTWARE
CORPORATION
4909 Murphy Canyon Rd # 460, San Diego
(92123-7301)
PHONE..............................858 300-5542
Don Hanson, *President*
Stephanie Jackomis, *Vice Pres*
Vannessa Raeann, *Vice Pres*
Susan Wills, *Vice Pres*
Katie Hill, *Office Mgr*
EMP: 14
SALES (est): 1.4MM
SALES (corp-wide): 4.5B **Privately Held**
SIC: 7372 Application computer software
PA: The Gores Group Llc
9800 Wilshire Blvd
Beverly Hills CA 90212
310 209-3010

(P-24814)
JAUNT INC
Also Called: Jaunt Vr
951 Mariners Island Blvd # 500, San Mateo
(94404-1589)
PHONE..............................650 618-6579
George Kliavkoff, *CEO*
Fabrice Cantou, *CFO*
David Anderman, *Officer*
Arthur Hoff, *Officer*
Simon Wynn, *Vice Pres*
EMP: 34
SALES (est): 4.7MM **Privately Held**
SIC: 7372 7371 Application computer soft-
ware; business oriented computer soft-
ware; computer software development &
applications

(P-24815)
JEMSTEP INC
5150 El Camino Real C20, Los Altos
(94022-1534)
PHONE..............................650 966-6500
Kevin Cimring, *CEO*
Simon Roy, *President*
Mark Richards, *Vice Pres*
Matthew Rennie, *Engineer*
Shannon Dwyer, *Sales Staff*
EMP: 20

SALES (est): 1.7MM
SALES (corp-wide): 5.1B **Publicly Held**
SIC: 7372 Business oriented computer
software
HQ: Invesco North American Holdings Inc
1555 Peachtree St Ne # 1800
Atlanta GA 30309
404 892-0896

(P-24816)
JESTA DIGITAL ENTRMT INC
(HQ)
15303 Ventura Blvd # 900, Sherman Oaks
(91403-3199)
PHONE..............................323 648-4200
Jason Aintabi, *CEO*
Mark Anderson, *COO*
EMP: 12
SALES (est): 2.8MM **Privately Held**
WEB: www.jestadigital.com
SIC: 7372 Prepackaged software

(P-24817)
JETLORE LLC
1528 S El Camino Real # 101, San Mateo
(94402-3067)
PHONE..............................650 485-1822
Eldar Sadikov, *CEO*
Brian Yamasaki, *President*
Montse Medina, *COO*
Thomas Lai, *Officer*
EMP: 24
SQ FT: 6,700
SALES (est): 597.7K
SALES (corp-wide): 13B **Publicly Held**
SIC: 7372 Prepackaged software
PA: Paypal Holdings, Inc.
2211 N 1st St
San Jose CA 95131
408 967-1000

(P-24818)
JTEA INC
Also Called: Zigzagzoom
1421 Valane Dr, Glendale (91208-1741)
PHONE..............................847 878-2226
Thomas Kang, *CEO*
EMP: 20
SALES (est): 1MM **Privately Held**
SIC: 7372 Home entertainment computer
software; publishers' computer software

(P-24819)
JUMIO SOFTWARE & DEV LLC
1971 Landings Dr, Mountain View
(94043-0806)
PHONE..............................650 388-0264
EMP: 30
SALES (est): 1.2MM
SALES (corp-wide): 16.9MM **Privately
Held**
SIC: 7372
PA: Jumio Inc
268 Lambert Ave
Palo Alto CA
650 424-8545

(P-24820)
JUST LIGHT TECHNOLOGY INC
46560 Fremont Blvd # 105, Fremont
(94538-6482)
PHONE..............................510 585-5652
Jerome Tang, *CEO*
Roger Chen, *Sales Staff*
EMP: 10
SALES (est): 268.4K **Privately Held**
SIC: 7372 Business oriented computer
software

(P-24821)
JUSTENOUGH SOFTWARE
CORP INC (HQ)
15440 Laguna Canyon Rd # 100, Irvine
(92618-2138)
PHONE..............................949 706-5400
Malcolm Buxton, *President*
Robert Rackleff, *CFO*
Adam Rutledge, *Vice Pres*
Wikus Van Dyk, *Development*
David Kolbas, *Technical Staff*
EMP: 30
SALES (est): 11.3MM
SALES (corp-wide): 14.2MM **Privately
Held**
SIC: 7372 Prepackaged software

PA: Mi9 Retail Inc.
12000 Biscayne Blvd # 600
North Miami FL 33181
647 849-1101

(P-24822)
K & M SOFTWARE DESIGN LLC
2828 Cochran St Ste 351, Simi Valley
(93065-2780)
PHONE..............................805 583-0403
EMP: 10 EST: 1997
SQ FT: 1,500
SALES (est): 760K **Privately Held**
SIC: 7372

(P-24823)
KAI OS TECHNOLOGIES SFTWR
INC
7310 Miramar Rd Ste 440, San Diego
(92126-4222)
PHONE..............................858 547-3940
Sebastien A J Codeville, *President*
EMP: 15
SALES (est): 500K **Privately Held**
SIC: 7372 Operating systems computer
software

(P-24824)
KANA SOFTWARE INC (HQ)
Also Called: Verint
2550 Walsh Ave Ste 120, Santa Clara
(95051-1345)
PHONE..............................650 614-8300
Mark Duffell, *CEO*
William A Bose, *President*
Brett White, *President*
Jeff Wylie, *CFO*
James Norwood, *Chief Mktg Ofcr*
EMP: 100
SQ FT: 40,000
SALES (est): 79.7MM **Publicly Held**
SIC: 7372 Application computer software

(P-24825)
KATANA SOFTWARE INC
333 W Broadway Ste 105, Long Beach
(90802-4438)
PHONE..............................562 495-1366
Robert Woodward, *President*
Uday Sawhney, *CFO*
Andy Johnstone, *Sr Software Eng*
Mark Goles, *CTO*
Sherri Clifford, *Software Engr*
EMP: 10
SALES (est): 869.7K **Privately Held**
WEB: www.katanasoftware.com
SIC: 7372 Business oriented computer
software

(P-24826)
KBA2 INC
Also Called: Crowdoptic
55 New Montgomery St # 606, San Fran-
cisco (94105-3433)
PHONE..............................415 528-5500
Jon Fisher, *CEO*
Jim Kovach, *COO*
Tony Wu, *CFO*
James Redfield, *Vice Pres*
Richard Smith, *Vice Pres*
EMP: 15
SQ FT: 2,500
SALES (est): 1.2MM **Privately Held**
SIC: 7372 Application computer software

(P-24827)
KETERA TECHNOLOGIES INC
(HQ)
3055 Olin Ave Ste 2200, San Jose
(95128-2066)
PHONE..............................408 572-9500
Steve Savignano, *CEO*
Tom Foody, *CFO*
Leslie Cedar, *Vice Pres*
Mike Gardner, *Vice Pres*
Percival Tieng, *CTO*
EMP: 30
SALES (est): 3.8MM
SALES (corp-wide): 80.7MM **Privately
Held**
WEB: www.ketera.com
SIC: 7372 Prepackaged software
PA: Deem, Inc.
642 Harrison St Fl 2
San Francisco CA 94107
415 590-8300

(P-24828)
KEY SOLUTIONS INC
2803 Lakeview Ct, Fremont (94538-6534)
PHONE..............................510 456-4500
Srinivas Kudaravalli, *CEO*
Chittaranjan Mallipeddi, *President*
EMP: 15
SQ FT: 6,253
SALES (est): 2MM **Privately Held**
WEB: www.keyusa.com
SIC: 7372 Application computer software

(P-24829)
KHAN ACADEMY INC
1200 Villa St Ste 200, Mountain View
(94041-2922)
P.O. Box 1630 (94042-1630)
PHONE..............................650 336-5426
Salman Khan, *Exec Dir*
Jen Chong, *Partner*
Shantanu Sinha, *President*
Yin Lu, *Vice Pres*
Katherine Morris, *Vice Pres*
EMP: 85
SALES (est): 27.9MM **Privately Held**
SIC: 7372 Educational computer software

(P-24830)
KIANA ANALYTICS INC
440 N Wolfe Rd W050, Sunnyvale
(94085-3869)
PHONE..............................650 575-3871
Sebastian Andreatta, *Vice Pres*
EMP: 12
SALES (est): 409.7K **Privately Held**
SIC: 7372 Business oriented computer
software

(P-24831)
KINETIC FARM INC
210 Industrial Rd Ste 102, San Carlos
(94070-2395)
PHONE..............................650 503-3279
EMP: 17 EST: 2010
SALES (est): 1.2MM **Privately Held**
SIC: 7372

(P-24832)
KINGCOM(US) LLC (HQ)
3100 Ocean Park Blvd, Santa Monica
(90405-3032)
PHONE..............................424 744-5697
EMP: 200
SALES (est): 16.9MM
SALES (corp-wide): 7B **Publicly Held**
SIC: 7372 Home entertainment computer
software
PA: Activision Blizzard, Inc.
3100 Ocean Park Blvd
Santa Monica CA 90405
310 255-2000

(P-24833)
KINTERA INC (HQ)
Also Called: Blackbaud Internet Solutions
9605 Scranton Rd Ste 200, San Diego
(92121-1768)
PHONE..............................858 795-3000
Marc E Chardon, *CEO*
Alfred R Berkeley III, *Ch of Bd*
Richard Labarbera, *President*
Richard Davidson, *CFO*
Richard R Davidson, *Treasurer*
EMP: 76
SQ FT: 38,000
SALES (est): 38MM
SALES (corp-wide): 788.3MM **Publicly
Held**
WEB: www.kintera.org
SIC: 7372 Prepackaged software
PA: Blackbaud, Inc.
2000 Daniel Island Dr
Daniel Island SC 29492
843 216-6200

(P-24834)
KLOOMA HOLDINGS INC
113 N San Vicente Blvd, Beverly Hills
(90211-2329)
PHONE..............................305 747-3315
Gary Merisier, *CEO*
EMP: 20
SALES (est): 382.7K **Privately Held**
SIC: 7372 Application computer software

▲ = Import ▼=Export
◆ =Import/Export

(P-24835)
KNO INC
2200 Mission College Blvd, Santa Clara
(95054-1537)
PHONE.....................408 844-8120
Ronald D Dickel, *CEO*
Babur Habib, *CTO*
EMP: 70
SQ FT: 35,000
SALES (est): 9MM
SALES (corp-wide): 62.7B **Publicly Held**
SIC: 7372 Educational computer software
PA: Intel Corporation
    2200 Mission College Blvd
    Santa Clara CA 95054
    408 765-8080

(P-24836)
KNOVA SOFTWARE INC (HQ)
10201 Torre Ave Ste 350, Cupertino
(95014-2131)
PHONE.....................408 863-5800
Bruce Armstrong, *President*
Kent Heyman, *Ch of Bd*
Thomar Muise, *CFO*
Andy Feit, *Officer*
Sham Chotai, *Vice Pres*
EMP: 50
SQ FT: 16,800
SALES (est): 8.6MM
SALES (corp-wide): 559.6MM **Privately Held**
WEB: www.knova.com
SIC: 7372 Business oriented computer software
PA: Aptean, Inc.
    4325 Alexander Dr Ste 100
    Alpharetta GA 30022
    770 351-9600

(P-24837)
KOFAX LIMITED (DH)
15211 Laguna Canyon Rd, Irvine
(92618-3146)
PHONE.....................949 783-1000
Reynolds C Bish, *CEO*
James Arnold Jr, *CFO*
Grant Johnson, *Chief Mktg Ofcr*
Bradford Weller, *Exec VP*
Anthony Macciola, *CTO*
EMP: 38
SQ FT: 91,000
SALES (est): 112.2MM **Privately Held**
SIC: 7372 Business oriented computer software
HQ: Lexmark International Inc.
    740 W New Circle Rd
    Lexington KY 40511
    859 232-2000

(P-24838)
KONAMI DIGITAL ENTRMT INC (DH)
2381 Rosecrans Ave # 200, El Segundo
(90245-4922)
PHONE.....................310 220-8100
Tomohiro Uesugi, *President*
Takahiro Azuma, *Vice Pres*
Chris Bartee, *Principal*
Kazumi Kitaue, *Principal*
EMP: 68
SQ FT: 53,596
SALES (est): 34.5MM
SALES (corp-wide): 2.2B **Privately Held**
SIC: 7372 Home entertainment computer software
HQ: Konami Digital Entertainment Co., Ltd.
    9-7-2, Akasaka
    Minato-Ku TKY 107-0
    357 710-573

(P-24839)
KPISOFT INC
50 California St Ste 1500, San Francisco
(94111-4612)
PHONE.....................415 439-5228
Ravee Ramamoothie, *CEO*
EMP: 80
SQ FT: 4,000
SALES (est): 2.9MM **Privately Held**
SIC: 7372 Prepackaged software

(P-24840)
KRANEM CORPORATION
560 S Winchester Blvd, San Jose
(95128-2560)
PHONE.....................650 319-6743
Ajay Batheja, *Ch of Bd*
Edward Miller, *CFO*
Luigi Caramico, *Vice Pres*
Christopher L Rasmussen, *Admin Sec*
EMP: 190
SALES: 8.3MM **Privately Held**
SIC: 7372 Business oriented computer software

(P-24841)
KRATOS TECH TRNING SLTIONS INC (HQ)
10680 Treena St Fl 6, San Diego
(92131-2487)
PHONE.....................858 812-7300
Eric M Demarco, *President*
Kenneth Reagan, *President*
Deanna H Lund, *CFO*
Laura L Siegal, *Treasurer*
Phil Carrai, *Vice Pres*
EMP: 146
SQ FT: 25,000
SALES (est): 145.4MM **Publicly Held**
WEB: www.sys.com
SIC: 7372 Business oriented computer software

(P-24842)
KRONOS INCORPORATED
240 Commerce, Irvine (92602-5004)
PHONE.....................800 580-7374
Kaylee Uribe, *Branch Mgr*
David Alling, *Sr Software Eng*
Robert Murray, *Sr Software Eng*
Karen Katz, *Web Dvlpr*
Richard Bak, *Software Engr*
EMP: 56
SALES (corp-wide): 1B **Privately Held**
SIC: 7372 Business oriented computer software
HQ: Kronos Incorporated
    900 Chelmsford St # 312
    Lowell MA 01851
    978 250-9800

(P-24843)
KWAN SOFTWARE ENGINEERING INC
Also Called: Veripic
1879 Lundy Ave Ste 286, San Jose
(95131-1884)
PHONE.....................408 496-1200
John Kwan, *President*
Ryan Ruiz, *Engineer*
EMP: 32 EST: 1997
SALES (est): 5.3MM **Privately Held**
SIC: 7372 Business oriented computer software

(P-24844)
KYRIBA CORP (HQ)
9620 Towne Cntre Dr 200, San Diego
(92121)
PHONE.....................858 210-3560
Jean-Luc Robert, *CEO*
Timothy Ray, *President*
Didier Martineau, *COO*
Fabrice Levy, *CFO*
Fabrice Lvy, *CFO*
EMP: 50
SALES (est): 51.6MM
SALES (corp-wide): 25.3MM **Privately Held**
WEB: www.kyriba.com
SIC: 7372 Prepackaged software
PA: Kyriba
    247 Les Bureaux De La Colline
    Saint Cloud 92210
    177 920-040

(P-24845)
LASERBEAM SOFTWARE LLC
1647 Willow Pass Rd, Concord
(94520-2611)
PHONE.....................925 459-2595
Patrick Durall, *CEO*
EMP: 26
SALES (est): 1.2MM **Privately Held**
WEB: www.laserbeamsoftware.com
SIC: 7372 Application computer software

(P-24846)
LASTLINE INC
6950 Hollister Ave # 101, Goleta
(93117-2896)
PHONE.....................805 456-7075
EMP: 168 **Privately Held**
SIC: 7372 Prepackaged software
PA: Lastline, Inc.
    203 Redwood Shores Pkwy
    Redwood City CA 94065

(P-24847)
LASTLINE INC (PA)
203 Redwood Shores Pkwy, Redwood City
(94065-1198)
PHONE.....................805 456-7075
John Dilullo, *CEO*
Ananth Avva, *CFO*
Christopher Kruegel, *Officer*
Bert Rankin, *Officer*
Brian Laing, *Vice Pres*
EMP: 36
SALES (est): 30.8MM **Privately Held**
SIC: 7372 Prepackaged software

(P-24848)
LATTICE DATA INC
801 El Camino Real, Menlo Park
(94025-4807)
PHONE.....................650 800-7262
Andy Jacques, *CEO*
EMP: 20
SQ FT: 5,700
SALES (est): 330.7K
SALES (corp-wide): 265.6B **Publicly Held**
SIC: 7372 Business oriented computer software
PA: Apple Inc.
    1 Apple Park Way
    Cupertino CA 95014
    408 996-1010

(P-24849)
LAVANTE INC
5225 Hellyer Ave Ste 200, San Jose
(95138-1021)
P.O. Box 41058 (95160-1058)
PHONE.....................408 754-1410
Frank Harbist, *President*
Tom Flynn, *Chief Mktg Ofcr*
Joe Flynn, *Officer*
Jason Welshonse, *Info Tech Mgr*
Vinay Ambekar, *Engineer*
EMP: 50
SALES (est): 8.4MM **Publicly Held**
WEB: www.auditsolutions.com
SIC: 7372 Business oriented computer software
HQ: Prgx Usa, Inc.
    600 Galleria Pkwy Se # 100
    Atlanta GA 30339

(P-24850)
LAWINFOCOM INC
5901 Priestly Dr Ste 200, Carlsbad
(92008-8825)
PHONE.....................760 510-3000
Gunter Enz, *President*
Cara Mae Harrison, *COO*
EMP: 68 EST: 1989
SQ FT: 10,000
SALES: 4.6MM **Privately Held**
WEB: www.lawinfo.com
SIC: 7372 8111 7375

(P-24851)
LCPTRACKER INC
117 E Chapman Ave, Orange
(92866-1401)
P.O. Box 187 (92856-6187)
PHONE.....................714 669-0052
Mark Douglas, *President*
Loren Doll, *Vice Pres*
EMP: 20
SQ FT: 1,500
SALES (est): 2.8MM **Privately Held**
SIC: 7372 Business oriented computer software

(P-24852)
LCR-DIXON CORPORATION
2048 Union St Apt 4, San Francisco
(94123-4118)
P.O. Box 812, Bel Air MD (21014-0812)
PHONE.....................404 307-1695
Suzy SOO, *CEO*
Jeffrey Bleachler, *COO*
EMP: 16
SALES (est): 503.2K **Privately Held**
SIC: 7372 Application computer software

(P-24853)
LEADCRUNCH INC (PA)
2159 India St, San Diego (92101-1766)
PHONE.....................888 708-6649
Olin Hyde, *CEO*
David Toth, *Ch of Bd*
Sanjit Singh, *COO*
EMP: 11
SALES (est): 765.4K **Privately Held**
SIC: 7372 Business oriented computer software

(P-24854)
LEADS360 LLC
207 Hindry Ave, Inglewood (90301-1519)
PHONE.....................888 843-1777
Nick Hedges, *CEO*
David Nachman, *President*
Darian Hong, *CFO*
Darian Sj Hong, *CFO*
Josh Evans, *Senior VP*
EMP: 30
SALES (est): 6.6MM **Privately Held**
WEB: www.lea-ls360.com
SIC: 7372 7371 Prepackaged software; computer software development

(P-24855)
LEARNERS GUILD LTD
492 9th St, Oakland (94607-4055)
PHONE.....................415 448-7054
Shereef Bishay, *CEO*
EMP: 13
SQ FT: 7,500
SALES (est): 363K **Privately Held**
SIC: 7372 Educational computer software

(P-24856)
LEEYO SOFTWARE INC (HQ)
2841 Junction Ave Ste 201, San Jose
(95134-1938)
PHONE.....................408 988-5800
Jagan Reddy, *CEO*
Jeffery Pickett, *Ch of Bd*
Michael Compton, *CFO*
Karthik Ramamoorthy, *Vice Pres*
Karthikeyan Ramamoorthy, *Vice Pres*
EMP: 41
SALES (est): 17.2MM **Publicly Held**
WEB: www.leeyotech.com
SIC: 7372 Business oriented computer software

(P-24857)
LEVEL LABS LP
Also Called: Unshackled
435 Hamilton Ave, Palo Alto (94301-1810)
PHONE.....................408 499-6839
Manan Mehta, *Managing Prtnr*
Nitin Pachisia, *Mng Member*
EMP: 30
SALES (est): 116.6K **Privately Held**
SIC: 7372 Application computer software

(P-24858)
LINE EURO-AMERICAS CORP
5750 Wilshire Blvd # 640, Los Angeles
(90036-3697)
PHONE.....................323 591-0380
Jeanie Han, *CEO*
Jinyeop Yoo, *Finance Mgr*
Shanna Kang, *Human Res Mgr*
EMP: 15
SQ FT: 6,000
SALES (est): 1.4MM **Privately Held**
SIC: 7372 Prepackaged software

(P-24859)
LITHIUM TECHNOLOGIES LLC (PA)
1 Pier Ste 1 # 1, San Francisco
(94111-2028)
PHONE.....................415 757-3100

Pete Hess, *CEO*
Robert Tarkoff, *President*
Jim Cox, *CFO*
Mark Culhane, *CFO*
Misha Logvinov, *Ch Credit Ofcr*
EMP: 92
SALES (est): 104.2MM **Privately Held**
WEB: www.lithium.com
SIC: 7372 Business oriented computer
software

(P-24860)
LIVEACTION INC (PA)
3500 W Bayshore Rd, Palo Alto
(94303-4228)
PHONE...................415 837-3303
Darren Kimura, *CEO*
Rodney Caines, *Partner*
Joe Hutchinson, *Partner*
R Brooks Borcherding, *President*
Dana Matsunaga, *President*
EMP: 35
SQ FT: 3,000
SALES: 5.7MM **Privately Held**
SIC: 7372 Business oriented computer
software

(P-24861)
LIVEOFFICE LLC
Also Called: Advisorsquare
900 Corporate Pointe, Culver City
(90230-7609)
PHONE...................877 253-2793
Alexander Rusich,
Matt Hardy,
Jeffrey W Hausman,
Nikhil Menta,
Matt Smith,
EMP: 77
SQ FT: 15,000
SALES (est): 5.7MM
SALES (corp-wide): 4.8B **Publicly Held**
WEB: www.advisorsquare.com
SIC: 7372 Prepackaged software
PA: Symantec Corporation
350 Ellis St
Mountain View CA 94043
650 527-8000

(P-24862)
LIVETIME SOFTWARE INC
276 Avocado St Apt C102, Costa Mesa
(92627-7302)
PHONE...................415 905-4009
Darren Williams, *President*
EMP: 50
SALES (est): 2.7MM **Privately Held**
SIC: 7372 Prepackaged software

(P-24863)
LOANHERO INC
750 B St Ste 1410, San Diego
(92101-8190)
PHONE...................888 912-4376
Zalman Vitenson, *CEO*
Derek Barclay, *President*
Steve Connolly, *COO*
Olaf Janke, *CFO*
Mikel Sides, *Exec VP*
EMP: 10
SALES (est): 221.8K
SALES (corp-wide): 1.2MM **Privately
Held**
SIC: 7372 Business oriented computer
software
PA: Lendingpoint Llc
1201 Roberts Blvd Nw # 200
Kennesaw GA 30144
678 324-6864

(P-24864)
LOGICOOL INC
1825 De La Cruz Blvd # 201, Santa Clara
(95050-3012)
PHONE...................408 907-1344
EMP: 30
SALES (est): 2.9MM **Privately Held**
SIC: 7372

(P-24865)
LOTUSFLARE INC
530 Lakeside Dr Ste 130, Sunnyvale
(94085-4055)
PHONE...................626 695-5634
Surendra Gadodia, *CEO*
Nick Thakkar, *Director*

EMP: 15 **EST:** 2012
SALES (est): 686.4K **Privately Held**
SIC: 7372 Business oriented computer
software

(P-24866)
LOYYAL CORPORATION
44 Tehama St Fl 5, San Francisco
(94105-3110)
PHONE...................415 419-9590
Gregory Simon, *CEO*
EMP: 10
SALES: 1.9MM **Privately Held**
SIC: 7372 Application computer software

(P-24867)
LPA INSURANCE AGENCY INC
Also Called: Sat
4030 Truxel Rd Ste B, Sacramento
(95834-3767)
PHONE...................916 286-7850
Michael Winkel, *President*
EMP: 56
SQ FT: 8,000
SALES (est): 3.3MM
SALES (corp-wide): 9.1B **Publicly Held**
WEB: www.sungard.com
SIC: 7372 Application computer software
HQ: Fis Data Systems Inc.
200 Campus Dr
Collegeville PA 19426
484 582-2000

(P-24868)
LUNA IMAGING INC
2702 Media Center Dr, Los Angeles
(90065-1733)
PHONE...................323 908-1400
Marlo Lee, *President*
Lori Richmeier, *Admin Mgr*
Drake Zabriskie, *CTO*
Michelle De, *Project Mgr*
Sam Juncal, *Technology*
EMP: 15
SQ FT: 6,000
SALES (est): 1.7MM **Privately Held**
WEB: www.lunaimaging.com
SIC: 7372 7373 Publishers' computer soft-
ware; computer integrated systems de-
sign

(P-24869)
**LW CONSULTING SERVICES
LLC**
13292 Rhoda Dr, Los Altos Hills
(94022-2531)
PHONE...................650 919-3001
Lung-Lon Wey,
EMP: 10
SALES: 200K **Privately Held**
SIC: 7372 7389 Prepackaged software;

(P-24870)
**LYNX SOFTWARE
TECHNOLOGIES INC (PA)**
855 Embedded Way, San Jose
(95138-1030)
PHONE...................408 979-3900
Inder Singh, *Chairman*
Gurjot Singh, *President*
Will Keegan, *CTO*
Ingrid Osborne, *Controller*
EMP: 52
SQ FT: 30,000
SALES (est): 15.6MM **Privately Held**
WEB: www.lynuxworks.com
SIC: 7372 Business oriented computer
software

(P-24871)
LYRIS INC
4 N 2nd St Fl 11, San Jose (95113-1305)
PHONE...................800 768-2929
Scott Knies, *Principal*
EMP: 35
SALES (corp-wide): 39.9MM **Privately
Held**
WEB: www.jlhalsey.com
SIC: 7372 Business oriented computer
software
HQ: Lyris, Inc.
401 Congress Ave Ste 2650
Austin TX 78701
512 201-8287

(P-24872)
M D SOFTWARE INC
Also Called: MD Software Enterprise
1226 E 42nd Pl, San Bernardino
(92404-1525)
PHONE...................909 881-7599
Ralph Mallinger, *President*
EMP: 12
SALES (est): 900K **Privately Held**
SIC: 7372 Prepackaged software

(P-24873)
M NEXON INC
Also Called: Nexon America
222 N Pacific Coast Hwy # 300, El Se-
gundo (90245-5614)
PHONE...................213 858-5930
John Robinson, *CEO*
Masae Yoshikuni, *Administration*
EMP: 30 **EST:** 2011
SALES (est): 209.3K
SALES (corp-wide): 2.1B **Privately Held**
SIC: 7372 5092 Application computer soft-
ware; video games
PA: Nexon Co.,Ltd.
1-4-5, Roppongi
Minato-Ku TKY 106-0
366 295-318

(P-24874)
M29 TECHNOLOGY AND DESIGN
133 Bridge St Ste B, Arroyo Grande
(93420-3366)
PHONE...................805 489-9402
John Herlihy, *Owner*
Corey Aufang, *Software Dev*
Jim Fennacy, *Software Engr*
Corey Knowlton, *Sales Dir*
EMP: 12
SQ FT: 1,200
SALES (est): 750K **Privately Held**
WEB: www.m29.com
SIC: 7372 7371 Prepackaged software;
custom computer programming services

(P-24875)
MADCAP SOFTWARE INC (PA)
7777 Fay Ave Ste 210, La Jolla
(92037-4325)
PHONE...................858 320-0387
Anthony Oliver, *CEO*
Taunya Conte, *CFO*
Michael Hamilton, *Vice Pres*
Francis Novak, *Vice Pres*
John Golding, *Sr Software Eng*
EMP: 18 **EST:** 2005
SALES (est): 2.5MM **Privately Held**
SIC: 7372 Prepackaged software

(P-24876)
MAGELLAN WEST LLC
1580 Oakland Rd Ste C107, San Jose
(95131-2441)
PHONE...................408 324-0620
Damien Hessian,
EMP: 30
SQ FT: 35,000
SALES (est): 2MM **Privately Held**
WEB: www.magellanworld.com
SIC: 7372 5045 7371 3695 Prepackaged
software; computers, peripherals & soft-
ware; computer software development &
applications; computer software tape &
disks: blank, rigid & floppy

(P-24877)
MAGIC TOUCH SOFTWARE INTL
330 Rancheros Dr Ste 258, San Marcos
(92069-2979)
PHONE...................800 714-6490
Gary Bagheri, *President*
George Peiov, *Vice Pres*
Jessica Sierra, *Opers Mgr*
EMP: 14 **EST:** 2007
SQ FT: 1,500
SALES: 850K **Privately Held**
SIC: 7372 Business oriented computer
software

(P-24878)
MAGNET SYSTEMS INC
2300 Geng Rd Ste 100, Palo Alto
(94303-3352)
P.O. Box 320805, Los Gatos (95032-0113)
PHONE...................650 329-5904
Alfred Chuang, *CEO*

EMP: 30
SALES (est): 5.6MM **Privately Held**
SIC: 7372 Application computer software

(P-24879)
MAKO LABS LLC
Also Called: Injekt
169 Saxony Rd Ste 107, Encinitas
(92024-6779)
P.O. Box 908, Cardiff By The Sea (92007-
0908)
PHONE...................619 786-3618
Steve Iverson, *CEO*
Matt Gurren, *Vice Pres*
EMP: 20
SALES (est): 2.8MM **Privately Held**
SIC: 7372 Application computer software

(P-24880)
MALIKCO LLC
2121 N Calif Blvd Ste 290, Walnut Creek
(94596-7351)
PHONE...................925 974-3555
Stephynie R Malik, *CEO*
Stephynie Malik, *General Mgr*
Alexandra O'Leary, *Business Mgr*
Devyn Wood, *Marketing Staff*
Dennis Dunnigan, *Director*
EMP: 50
SQ FT: 1,000
SALES (est): 4.8MM **Privately Held**
WEB: www.malikco.com
SIC: 7372 Operating systems computer
software

(P-24881)
MARBLE SECURITY INC
68 Willow Rd, Menlo Park (94025-3653)
PHONE...................408 737-4300
David Jevans, *Ch of Bd*
Stephen Ryan, *Senior VP*
John Jefferies, *Vice Pres*
EMP: 15
SQ FT: 20,000
SALES (est): 2.3MM **Privately Held**
WEB: www.ironkey.com
SIC: 7372 Prepackaged software

(P-24882)
**MARKETING PRO CONSULTING
INC**
Also Called: Mortgageplannercrm
1230 Columbia St Ste 500, San Diego
(92101-8520)
P.O. Box 3480 (92163-1480)
PHONE...................619 233-8591
Michael Gulitz, *President*
Juliana S Krijan, *Vice Pres*
EMP: 13
SALES (est): 955.1K **Privately Held**
SIC: 7372 8742 Application computer soft-
ware; marketing consulting services

(P-24883)
MARKETRON MOBILE LLC
Also Called: Msnap, Inc.
388 Market St Ste 854, San Francisco
(94111-5378)
PHONE...................415 981-0812
Timothy Favia, *CEO*
John Evans, *Partner*
Martin Kristiseter, *President*
EMP: 15
SALES (est): 643.5K
SALES (corp-wide): 30.7MM **Privately
Held**
WEB: www.msnap.com
SIC: 7372 Application computer software
PA: Marketron Broadcast Solutions, Llc
101 Empty Saddle Trl
Hailey ID 83333
208 788-6272

(P-24884)
MARKZWARE
Also Called: Markzware Software
1805 E Dyer Rd Ste 101, Santa Ana
(92705-5742)
PHONE...................949 756-5100
Patrick Marchese, *President*
Valerie Consalvi, *Info Tech Dir*
David Peterson, *Info Tech Mgr*
Doug Rosen, *Project Mgr*
Mary Marchese, *Pub Rel Dir*
EMP: 11
SQ FT: 5,000

SALES (est): 1.2MM **Privately Held**
WEB: www.markzware.com
SIC: 7372 Business oriented computer
software

(P-24885)
MATCHPOINT SOLUTIONS (PA)
6690 Amador Plaza Rd # 225, Dublin
(94568-2993)
PHONE.....................925 829-4455
Cindy Everson, *President*
Michael Turk, *Senior VP*
Pooja Kulkarni, *Technical Mgr*
Jay Maddala, *Tech Recruiter*
Megha Ananthakrishna, *Technical Staff*
EMP: 10
SALES (est): 1.9MM **Privately Held**
SIC: 7372 Educational computer software

(P-24886)
MATRIX LOGIC CORPORATION
1380 East Ave Ste 124240, Chico
(95926-7349)
PHONE.....................415 893-9897
Stephen C Page, *President*
Frank Rayner, *Sr Consultant*
EMP: 11
SQ FT: 1,500
SALES (est): 1.2MM **Privately Held**
WEB: www.matrix-logic.com
SIC: 7372 Business oriented computer
software

(P-24887)
MAXIMUS HOLDINGS INC
2475 Hanover St, Palo Alto (94304-1114)
PHONE.....................650 935-9500
Dominic Gallello, *CEO*
Jim Johnson, *CFO*
Anshul Singh, *Executive*
EMP: 1006
SALES (est): 21.9MM
SALES (corp-wide): 569.5MM **Privately
Held**
SIC: 7372 Prepackaged software
PA: Symphony Technology Group, L.L.C.
428 University Ave
Palo Alto CA 94301
650 935-9500

(P-24888)
MAXXESS SYSTEMS INC (PA)
22661 Old Canal Rd, Yorba Linda
(92887-4601)
PHONE.....................714 772-1000
Kevin Charles Daly, *CEO*
Nancy Islas, *President*
Joel Slutzky, *Chairman*
EMP: 25
SQ FT: 12,000
SALES (est): 3.4MM **Privately Held**
WEB: www.maxxesssystems.com
SIC: 7372 Business oriented computer
software

(P-24889)
MAYSOFT INC
Also Called: The Mayflower Group
1727 Santa Barbara St, Santa Barbara
(93101-1024)
PHONE.....................978 635-1700
Frank Paolino, *President*
EMP: 10
SALES (est): 1.1MM **Privately Held**
WEB: www.maysoft.com
SIC: 7372 7371 Word processing com-
puter software; computer software sys-
tems analysis & design, custom;
computer software development

(P-24890)
MCAFEE INC
6707 Barnhurst Dr, San Diego
(92117-4208)
PHONE.....................858 967-2342
EMP: 82 **Privately Held**
SIC: 7372 Prepackaged software
HQ: Mcafee, Llc
2821 Mission College Blvd
Santa Clara CA 95054
888 847-8766

(P-24891)
MCAFEE LLC (HQ)
2821 Mission College Blvd, Santa Clara
(95054-1838)
PHONE.....................888 847-8766
Christopher Young, *CEO*
Jean-Claude Broido, *President*
Tom Miglis, *President*
Michael Berry, *CFO*
Barry McPherson, *Exec VP*
▲ EMP: 148
SQ FT: 208,000
SALES (est): 1.5B **Privately Held**
WEB: www.mcafee.com
SIC: 7372 Application computer software

(P-24892)
MCAFEE FINANCE 2 LLC
2821 Mission College Blvd, Santa Clara
(95054-1838)
PHONE.....................888 847-8766
EMP: 1129
SALES (est): 10.3MM
SALES (corp-wide): 277.9MM **Privately
Held**
SIC: 7372 Prepackaged software
HQ: Mcafee Finance 1, Llc
2821 Mission College Blvd
Santa Clara CA 95054
888 847-8766

(P-24893)
MCAFEE SECURITY LLC
2821 Mission College Blvd, Santa Clara
(95054-1838)
PHONE.....................866 622-3911
Michael Decesare, *President*
Bob Kelly, *CFO*
Edward Hayden, *Senior VP*
Louis Riley, *Senior VP*
EMP: 5030 EST: 2006
SQ FT: 208,000
SALES (est): 98.4MM **Privately Held**
SIC: 7372 Application computer software
HQ: Mcafee, Llc
2821 Mission College Blvd
Santa Clara CA 95054
888 847-8766

(P-24894)
MEDALLIA INC (PA)
450 Concar Dr, San Mateo (94402-2681)
PHONE.....................650 321-3000
Leslie Stretch, *President*
Douglas Leone, *Partner*
Fred Mondragon, *President*
Aimey Presman, *President*
Frank Slootman, *President*
EMP: 145
SQ FT: 10,000
SALES (est): 507.7MM **Privately Held**
WEB: www.medallia.com
SIC: 7372 8732 Business oriented com-
puter software; market analysis, business
& economic research

(P-24895)
MEDATA INC (PA)
5 Peters Canyon Rd # 250, Irvine
(92606-1793)
PHONE.....................714 918-1310
Cy King, *CEO*
Tom Herndon, *President*
Thomas Herndon, *COO*
Bryan Lowe, *Officer*
T Don Theis, *Senior VP*
EMP: 51
SQ FT: 17,192
SALES (est): 114.3MM **Privately Held**
WEB: www.medata.com
SIC: 7372 6411 Business oriented com-
puter software; medical insurance claim
processing, contract or fee basis

(P-24896)
MEDIA GOBBLER INC
6427 W Sunset Blvd, Los Angeles
(90028-7314)
PHONE.....................323 203-3222
Chris Kantrowitz, *CEO*
Phil Kinkade, *President*
EMP: 14
SALES (est): 1.5MM **Privately Held**
SIC: 7372 Application computer software

(P-24897)
MEDICAL DATA RECOVERY INC
17310 Red Hill Ave # 270, Irvine
(92614-5637)
P.O. Box 16634 (92623-6634)
PHONE.....................949 251-0073
Michael Mackenzie, *President*
EMP: 10
SQ FT: 2,500
SALES: 2.3MM **Privately Held**
SIC: 7372 Prepackaged software

(P-24898)
MEDICAL TRANSCRIPTION BILLING
405 Kenyon St Ste 300, San Diego (92110)
PHONE.....................800 869-3700
EMP: 561
SALES (corp-wide): 31.8MM **Publicly
Held**
SIC: 7372 Prepackaged software
PA: Medical Transcription Billing, Corp.
7 Clyde Rd
Somerset NJ 08873
732 873-5133

(P-24899)
MEDITAB SOFTWARE INC
333 Hegenberger Rd # 800, Oakland
(94621-1416)
PHONE.....................510 632-2021
Mike Patel, *President*
Marvin Chavez, *Partner*
Kal Patel, *COO*
Feros Khan, *Info Tech Mgr*
Amit Limba, *Prgrmr*
EMP: 250
SQ FT: 10,000
SALES (est): 27.9MM **Privately Held**
SIC: 7372 Business oriented computer
software

(P-24900)
MEDRIO INC (PA)
345 California St Ste 325, San Francisco
(94104-2658)
PHONE.....................415 963-3700
Michael Richard Novotny, *CEO*
Nathan Weems, *CFO*
Richard H Scheller, *Exec VP*
EMP: 30
SALES: 10.6MM **Privately Held**
SIC: 7372 Business oriented computer
software

(P-24901)
MELIAN LABS INC
Also Called: Mytime
988 Market St Ste 600, San Francisco
(94102-4007)
PHONE.....................888 423-1944
Ethan Anderson, *CEO*
Alan Federman, *Vice Pres*
EMP: 16
SALES: 3MM **Privately Held**
SIC: 7372 4813 Application computer soft-
ware;

(P-24902)
MENTOR GRAPHICS CORPORATION
18301 Von Karman Ave # 760, Irvine
(92612-0137)
PHONE.....................949 790-3200
Scott Mackerras, *Manager*
Henry Nguyen, *Engineer*
EMP: 15
SALES (corp-wide): 97.7B **Privately Held**
WEB: www.mentor.com
SIC: 7372 Business oriented computer
software
HQ: Mentor Graphics Corporation
8005 Sw Boeckman Rd
Wilsonville OR 97070
503 685-7000

(P-24903)
MERCURY INTERACTIVE LLC
5000 Birch St Ste 3000, Newport Beach
(92660-2140)
PHONE.....................949 476-3780
Rick Brown, *Manager*
EMP: 20

SALES (corp-wide): 28.8B **Publicly Held**
WEB: www.svca.mercuryinteractive.com
SIC: 7372 Prepackaged software
HQ: Mercury Interactive, Llc
3000 Hanover St
Palo Alto CA 94304
650 857-1501

(P-24904)
MERCURY INTERACTIVE LLC (HQ)
3000 Hanover St, Palo Alto (94304-1112)
P.O. Box 60069, Sunnyvale (94088-0069)
PHONE.....................650 857-1501
Anthony Zingale, *President*
Nazley Davies, *Partner*
Moshe Egert, *President*
Jon E Flaxman, *Treasurer*
Jon White, *Admin Sec*
EMP: 350
SALES (est): 107MM
SALES (corp-wide): 28.8B **Publicly Held**
WEB: www.svca.mercuryinteractive.com
SIC: 7372 Prepackaged software
PA: Hewlett Packard Enterprise Company
3000 Hanover St
Palo Alto CA 94304
650 687-5817

(P-24905)
MERCURY INTERACTIVE LLC
4452 Ocean View Blvd # 200, Montrose
(91020-1287)
PHONE.....................818 957-2087
Doug Smith, *Manager*
Andy Starr, *Finance Mgr*
EMP: 20
SALES (corp-wide): 28.8B **Publicly Held**
WEB: www.svca.mercuryinteractive.com
SIC: 7372 Prepackaged software
HQ: Mercury Interactive, Llc
3000 Hanover St
Palo Alto CA 94304
650 857-1501

(P-24906)
METRICSTREAM INC (PA)
Also Called: Complianceonline
2479 E Byshore Rd Ste 260, Palo Alto
(94303)
PHONE.....................650 620-2900
Mikael Hagstroem, *CEO*
Gaurave Kapoor, *COO*
Steve Springsteel, *President*
Steven R Springsteel, *CFO*
Gunjan Sinha, *Chairman*
EMP: 150
SALES (est): 190.9MM **Privately Held**
SIC: 7372 Application computer software

(P-24907)
MICROMEGA SYSTEMS INC
2 Fifer Ave Ste 120, Corte Madera
(94925-1153)
PHONE.....................415 924-4700
Charles Bornheim, *President*
EMP: 12
SQ FT: 3,300
SALES (est): 1.2MM **Privately Held**
WEB: www.micromegasystems.com
SIC: 7372 7371 7379 Business oriented
computer software; custom computer pro-
gramming services; computer software
development; computer related consulting
services

(P-24908)
MICROSEMI FREQUENCY TIME CORP
2300 Orchard Pkwy, San Jose
(95131-1017)
P.O. Box 39000, San Francisco (94139-
0001)
PHONE.....................408 433-0910
EMP: 15
SALES (corp-wide): 3.9B **Publicly Held**
SIC: 7372 Business oriented computer
software
HQ: Microsemi Frequency And Time Corpo-
ration
3870 N 1st St
San Jose CA 95134

(P-24909)
MICROSOFT CORPORATION
75 Enterprise Ste 100, Aliso Viejo
(92656-2628)
PHONE..............................949 680-3000
Shobhit Mishra, *Branch Mgr*
Dorion Whitlock, *Technical Staff*
EMP: 35
SALES (corp-wide): 110.3B **Publicly
Held**
SIC: 7372 Prepackaged software
PA: Microsoft Corporation
    1 Microsoft Way
    Redmond WA 98052
    425 882-8080

(P-24910)
MICROSOFT CORPORATION
9255 Towne Centre Dr # 400, San Diego
(92121-3037)
PHONE..............................858 909-3800
Stephanie McCarron, *Manager*
Scott Pigman, *Technical Staff*
Dan Morwood, *Sales Staff*
Chris Calderon, *Sr Consultant*
David Chamizo, *Sr Consultant*
EMP: 40
SALES (corp-wide): 110.3B **Publicly
Held**
WEB: www.microsoft.com
SIC: 7372 Application computer software
PA: Microsoft Corporation
    1 Microsoft Way
    Redmond WA 98052
    425 882-8080

(P-24911)
MICROSOFT CORPORATION
680 Vaqueros Ave, Sunnyvale
(94085-3523)
PHONE..............................650 964-7200
Susan Peletta, *Executive*
Lori Fazeli, *Partner*
Rukmini Iyer, *Partner*
Derek Loar, *Executive*
Jennifer Lyons, *Comms Dir*
EMP: 82
SALES (corp-wide): 110.3B **Publicly
Held**
SIC: 7372 Prepackaged software
PA: Microsoft Corporation
    1 Microsoft Way
    Redmond WA 98052
    425 882-8080

(P-24912)
MICROSOFT CORPORATION
7007 Friars Rd, San Diego (92108-1148)
PHONE..............................619 849-5872
Carolyn Allen, *Manager*
Sarah Forrest, *Manager*
Kleber Santos, *Manager*
EMP: 100
SALES (corp-wide): 110.3B **Publicly
Held**
SIC: 7372 Application computer software
PA: Microsoft Corporation
    1 Microsoft Way
    Redmond WA 98052
    425 882-8080

(P-24913)
MICROSOFT CORPORATION
1415 L St Ste 200, Sacramento
(95814-3962)
PHONE..............................916 369-3600
James Waterman, *Manager*
Mitch Pierce, *Manager*
Kristi Verma, *Manager*
EMP: 20
SALES (corp-wide): 110.3B **Publicly
Held**
WEB: www.microsoft.com
SIC: 7372 Application computer software;
operating systems computer software
PA: Microsoft Corporation
    1 Microsoft Way
    Redmond WA 98052
    425 882-8080

(P-24914)
MICROSOFT CORPORATION
1020 Entp Way Bldg B, Sunnyvale (94089)
PHONE..............................650 693-1009
William H Gates III, *Branch Mgr*
EMP: 103

SALES (corp-wide): 110.3B **Publicly
Held**
SIC: 7372 Prepackaged software
PA: Microsoft Corporation
    1 Microsoft Way
    Redmond WA 98052
    425 882-8080

(P-24915)
MICROSOFT CORPORATION
3 Park Plz Ste 1800, Irvine (92614-8541)
PHONE..............................949 263-3000
Sandy Thomas, *General Mgr*
Warren Kerby, *Info Tech Mgr*
Michael Ghekiere, *Technical Staff*
Juliet Helms, *Technical Staff*
Joseph Ruedlinger, *Sr Consultant*
EMP: 125
SALES (corp-wide): 110.3B **Publicly
Held**
WEB: www.microsoft.com
SIC: 7372 Application computer software
PA: Microsoft Corporation
    1 Microsoft Way
    Redmond WA 98052
    425 882-8080

(P-24916)
MICROSOFT CORPORATION
13031 W Jefferson Blvd # 200, Playa Vista
(90094-7001)
PHONE..............................213 806-7300
Evelyn Morgan, *Opers Mgr*
Austin Ogletree, *Partner*
Stephanie Friedman, *Executive*
Dean Suzuki, *Technology*
Matt Jackson, *Technical Staff*
EMP: 100
SALES (corp-wide): 110.3B **Publicly
Held**
WEB: www.microsoft.com
SIC: 7372 Application computer software
PA: Microsoft Corporation
    1 Microsoft Way
    Redmond WA 98052
    425 882-8080

(P-24917)
MICROSOFT CORPORATION
555 California St Ste 200, San Francisco
(94104-1504)
PHONE..............................415 972-6400
Teeka Miller, *Branch Mgr*
Laura Wallace, *Vice Pres*
Fernando Alvarado, *Executive*
Chris Fasano, *Executive*
Shelton Sunday, *Executive*
EMP: 160
SALES (corp-wide): 110.3B **Publicly
Held**
WEB: www.microsoft.com
SIC: 7372 Application computer software
PA: Microsoft Corporation
    1 Microsoft Way
    Redmond WA 98052
    425 882-8080

(P-24918)
MICROSOFT CORPORATION
2045 Lafayette St, Santa Clara
(95050-2901)
PHONE..............................408 987-9608
Jim Brown, *President*
EMP: 100
SALES (corp-wide): 110.3B **Publicly
Held**
WEB: www.microsoft.com
SIC: 7372 Application computer software
PA: Microsoft Corporation
    1 Microsoft Way
    Redmond WA 98052
    425 882-8080

(P-24919)
MICROTELEMATICS INC
Also Called: Carmine
1500 Quail St Ste 280, Newport Beach
(92660-2734)
PHONE..............................888 651-7133
Reza Fategh, *President*
Miles Herrera, *Accounts Exec*
EMP: 10
SALES: 1MM **Privately Held**
SIC: 7372 Business oriented computer
software

(P-24920)
**MICROVISION DEVELOPMENT
INC**
3142 Tiger Run Ct Ste 103, Carlsbad
(92010-6693)
PHONE..............................760 438-7781
James Harley Mayall, *CEO*
John Gaby, *Vice Pres*
Pete Calkins, *Software Dev*
Robert Cabrera, *Marketing Staff*
EMP: 23
SQ FT: 5,000
SALES (est): 2.7MM **Privately Held**
WEB: www.mvd.com
SIC: 7372 Business oriented computer
software

(P-24921)
MIDRANGE SOFTWARE INC
12716 Riverside Dr, Studio City
(91607-3383)
PHONE..............................818 762-8539
Jacques Ohana, *President*
Simon Ohana, *Vice Pres*
EMP: 20
SQ FT: 10,000
SALES (est): 2.3MM **Privately Held**
WEB: www.midrangesoftware.com
SIC: 7372 Prepackaged software

(P-24922)
MINDSAI INC
101 Cooper St Ste 218, Santa Cruz
(95060-4526)
PHONE..............................831 239-4644
Sumit Sanyal, *CEO*
EMP: 12
SALES (est): 256K **Privately Held**
SIC: 7372 Business oriented computer
software

(P-24923)
MINDSNACKS INC
1479 Folsom St, San Francisco
(94103-3734)
PHONE..............................415 875-9817
Jesse Pickard, *CEO*
Bryan Schreier, *Principal*
Aydin Senkut, *Principal*
EMP: 30 EST: 2010
SQ FT: 5,250
SALES (est): 2.3MM **Privately Held**
SIC: 7372 Application computer software

(P-24924)
MINT SOFTWARE INC
280 Hope St, Mountain View (94041-1308)
P.O. Box 7850 (94039-7850)
PHONE..............................650 944-6000
Aaron T Patzer, *President*
Rob Hayes, *Partner*
David K Michaels, *President*
EMP: 12
SQ FT: 5,000
SALES (est): 1MM
SALES (corp-wide): 5.9B **Publicly Held**
SIC: 7372 Business oriented computer
software
PA: Intuit Inc.
    2700 Coast Ave
    Mountain View CA 94043
    650 944-6000

(P-24925)
MIRTH CORPORATION
611 Anton Blvd Ste 500, Costa Mesa
(92626-1934)
PHONE..............................714 389-1200
Jon Teichrow, *President*
Samuel Sippl, *CFO*
Gary Teichrow, *Vice Pres*
Andrew Thorson, *Vice Pres*
Shelly Larrimore MBA, *Sales Staff*
EMP: 35
SQ FT: 10,000
SALES (est): 4.2MM
SALES (corp-wide): 531MM **Publicly
Held**
WEB: www.webreachinc.com
SIC: 7372 Business oriented computer
software
PA: Nextgen Healthcare, Inc.
    18111 Von Karman Ave
    Irvine CA 92612
    949 255-2600

(P-24926)
MITRATECH HOLDINGS INC
5900 Wilshire Blvd # 1500, Los Angeles
(90036-5031)
PHONE..............................323 964-0000
James Wiseman, *Project Mgr*
Jeff Drury, *Opers Staff*
Andrea Collins, *Director*
EMP: 13
SALES (corp-wide): 81.2MM **Privately
Held**
SIC: 7372 Business oriented computer
software
PA: Mitratech Holdings, Inc.
    5001 Plz On
    Austin TX 78746
    512 382-7322

(P-24927)
MIXAMO INC
2415 3rd St Ste 239, San Francisco
(94107-3177)
PHONE..............................415 255-7455
EMP: 25
SALES (est): 1.6MM
SALES (corp-wide): 7.3B **Publicly Held**
SIC: 7372
PA: Adobe Systems Incorporated
    345 Park Ave
    San Jose CA 95110
    408 536-6000

(P-24928)
MJUS LLC (FKA MINDJET LLC)
275 Battery St Ste 1000, San Francisco
(94111-3333)
PHONE..............................415 229-4344
Scott Raskin, *CEO*
Steve Glass, *President*
Steve Anderson, *CFO*
Francis Procaccia, *QA Dir*
Sasha Kipervarg, *Info Tech Dir*
EMP: 81
SQ FT: 15,140
SALES (est): 30.8MM
SALES (corp-wide): 31MM **Privately
Held**
SIC: 7372 Business oriented computer
software; educational computer software
PA: Spigit Holdings Corporation
    275 Battery St Ste 1000
    San Francisco CA 94111
    415 229-4400

(P-24929)
MOBILEIRON INC (PA)
401 E Middlefield Rd, Mountain View
(94043-4005)
PHONE..............................650 919-8100
Simon Biddiscombe, *President*
Tae Hea Nahm, *Ch of Bd*
Scott D Hill, *CFO*
Sohail Parekh, *Senior VP*
Gregory Randolph, *Senior VP*
EMP: 145
SQ FT: 78,000
SALES: 176.4MM **Publicly Held**
SIC: 7372 Prepackaged software

(P-24930)
MOBILEOPS CORPORATION
1422 Wright Ave, Sunnyvale (94087-4017)
PHONE..............................408 203-0243
Rajiv Taori, *CEO*
EMP: 10 EST: 2012
SALES (est): 702.9K **Privately Held**
SIC: 7372 Business oriented computer
software

(P-24931)
MOD2 INC
Also Called: Mod 2
3317 S Broadway, Los Angeles
(90007-4114)
PHONE..............................213 747-8424
Javid Nia, *President*
Omeed Nia, *Software Dev*
Ronald Bantayan, *Manager*
EMP: 15
SQ FT: 12,000
SALES (est): 1.2MM **Privately Held**
WEB: www.mod2.com
SIC: 7372 7371 Business oriented com-
puter software; application computer soft-
ware; computer software systems
analysis & design, custom

(P-24932)
MODE ANALYTICS INC
208 Utah St Ste 400, San Francisco
(94103-4881)
PHONE..................................415 271-7599
Derek Steer, *CEO*
Thomas Van Steyn, *Sales Staff*
Ryan Fogarty, *Accounts Exec*
EMP: 12
SALES (est): 722.2K **Privately Held**
SIC: 7372 Business oriented computer
software

(P-24933)
MOKUME SOFTWARE INC
4131 Mackin Woods Ln, San Jose
(95135-1159)
PHONE..................................408 839-7000
Ajay Jain, *President*
Vikrant Ghai, *Vice Pres*
EMP: 10
SALES (est): 523.4K
SALES (corp-wide): 132.1MM **Privately
Held**
SIC: 7372 Prepackaged software
HQ: Versant Corporation
500 Arguello St Ste 200
Redwood City CA 94063
650 232-2400

(P-24934)
MONITISE INC
1 Embarcadero Ctr Ste 900, San Francisco
(94111-3754)
PHONE..................................650 286-1059
Lisa Stanton, *General Mgr*
EMP: 12
SQ FT: 1,939
SALES (est): 2MM
SALES (corp-wide): 5.7B **Publicly Held**
SIC: 7372 Prepackaged software
HQ: Monitise Group Limited
Eversheds House
Manchester M1 5E
203 657-0900

(P-24935)
MONTAVISTA SOFTWARE LLC
(DH)
2315 N 1st St Fl 4, San Jose (95131-1010)
PHONE..................................408 572-8000
Art Landro, *President*
Sanjay Uppal, *CFO*
Jason B Wacha, *Vice Pres*
James Ready, *CTO*
EMP: 150
SALES (est): 14.5MM **Privately Held**
WEB: www.mvista.com
SIC: 7372 Prepackaged software

(P-24936)
MSCSOFTWARE CORPORATION
(HQ)
4675 Macarthur Ct Ste 900, Newport Beach
(92660-1845)
PHONE..................................714 540-8900
Dominic Gallello, *President*
Eric Favre, *Vice Pres*
Michael Hoffmann, *Vice Pres*
Leo Kilfoy, *General Mgr*
Beate Funk-Klemke, *Administration*
EMP: 245 **EST:** 1963
SALES (est): 160.4MM
SALES (corp-wide): 18.8MM **Privately
Held**
WEB: www.mscsoftware.com
SIC: 7372 Business oriented computer
software
PA: Hexagon Ab
Lilla Bantorget 15
Stockholm 111 2
860 126-20

(P-24937)
MULESOFT INC
50 Fremont St Ste 300, San Francisco
(94105-2231)
PHONE..................................415 229-2009
Greg Schott, *CEO*
Nick Trombetta, *President*
Matt Langdon, *CFO*
Vidya Peters, *Chief Mktg Ofcr*
Mark Dao, *Officer*
EMP: 841
SQ FT: 41,500

SALES: 296.4MM
SALES (corp-wide): 10.4B **Publicly Held**
WEB: www.mulesource.com
SIC: 7372 7371 Prepackaged software;
computer software development
PA: Salesforce.Com, Inc.
1 Market Ste 300
San Francisco CA 94105
415 901-7000

(P-24938)
MUNKYFUN INC
415 Jackson St Fl 1, San Francisco
(94111-1629)
PHONE..................................415 281-3837
Nicholas Pavis, *CEO*
Jon Sieker, *Vice Pres*
Oren Weizman, *Vice Pres*
Tim Ramsay, *Info Tech Dir*
EMP: 44 **EST:** 2008
SALES (est): 5.4MM **Privately Held**
SIC: 7372 Application computer software

(P-24939)
MUSICMATCH INC
16935 W Bernardo Dr # 270, San Diego
(92127-1634)
PHONE..................................858 485-4300
Dennis Mudd, *CEO*
Peter Csathy, *President*
Gary Acord, *CFO*
Chris Allen, *Senior VP*
Don Leigh, *Senior VP*
EMP: 140
SQ FT: 20,000
SALES (est): 6.9MM **Publicly Held**
WEB: www.musicmatch.com
SIC: 7372 5734 Prepackaged software;
software, business & non-game
PA: Altaba Inc.
140 E 45th St Ste 15a
New York NY 10017

(P-24940)
MY EYE MEDIA LLC (DH)
2211 N Hollywood Way, Burbank
(91505-1113)
PHONE..................................818 559-7200
Michael Kadenacy, *President*
Rodd Feingold, *CFO*
Jane C Hawley, *Senior VP*
EMP: 43
SQ FT: 20,000
SALES (est): 13.2MM **Privately Held**
WEB: www.myeyemedia.com
SIC: 7372 Business oriented computer
software
HQ: Eurofins Product Testing Us Holdings,
Inc.
11720 N Creek Pkwy N # 400
Bothell WA 98011
800 383-0085

(P-24941)
MYENERSAVE INC
Also Called: Bidgely
440 N Wolfe Rd, Sunnyvale (94085-3869)
PHONE..................................408 464-6385
Abhay Gupta, *CEO*
EMP: 11
SALES (est): 635K **Privately Held**
SIC: 7372 Utility computer software

(P-24942)
MYWAY LEARNING COMPANY
INC
47 Laurel Ave, Larkspur (94939-1910)
PHONE..................................415 937-1722
John Mayerhofer, *CEO*
EMP: 10
SALES (est): 260.9K **Privately Held**
SIC: 7372 Educational computer software

(P-24943)
NANOTECH ENTERTAINMENT
INC (PA)
311 Santa Rosa Dr, Los Gatos
(95032-5714)
PHONE..................................408 414-7355
Jeff Foley, *President*
Al Stone, *COO*
Philip Foley, *Senior VP*
Phil Foley, *Vice Pres*
Jim Hernandez, *Vice Pres*
EMP: 13

SALES (est): 5.3MM **Privately Held**
SIC: 7372 4833 Application computer software; television broadcasting stations

(P-24944)
NAZCA SOLUTIONS INC
4 First American Way, Santa Ana
(92707-5913)
PHONE..................................612 279-6100
Robert Karraa, *President*
Ted Mondale, *Vice Pres*
EMP: 20
SQ FT: 45,000
SALES (est): 897.9K **Publicly Held**
WEB: www.nazcainc.com
SIC: 7372 Application computer software
PA: First American Financial Corporation
1 First American Way
Santa Ana CA 92707
-

(P-24945)
NC INTERACTIVE LLC
1900 S Norfolk St Ste 125, San Mateo
(94403-1175)
PHONE..................................650 393-2200
Songyee Yoon, *CEO*
Eric Garay, *CFO*
Janet Lin, *General Counsel*
EMP: 99 **EST:** 2016
SQ FT: 16,692
SALES (est): 1.4MM **Privately Held**
SIC: 7372 Prepackaged software

(P-24946)
NEATPOCKET LLC
8033 W Sunset Blvd, West Hollywood
(90046-2401)
PHONE..................................323 632-7440
Aidan Marus, *CEO*
EMP: 12
SALES (est): 309.8K **Privately Held**
SIC: 7372 Business oriented computer
software

(P-24947)
NEONROOTS LLC
8560 W Sunset Blvd # 500, West Holly-
wood (90069-2311)
PHONE..................................310 907-9210
Benjamin C Lee, *CEO*
EMP: 125 **EST:** 2012
SALES (est): 4.6MM **Privately Held**
SIC: 7372 Prepackaged software

(P-24948)
NET CLEARLY
Also Called: Plutoz
300 Frank H Ogawa Plz # 234, Oakland
(94612-2037)
PHONE..................................510 465-0101
Alec Ghafouri, *CEO*
EMP: 17
SALES (est): 1MM **Privately Held**
SIC: 7372 Publishers' computer software

(P-24949)
NET OPTICS INC
Also Called: Ixia
5301 Stevens Creek Blvd, Santa Clara
(95051-7201)
PHONE..................................408 737-7777
Thomas B Miller, *CEO*
Robert Shaw, *President*
Dennis Omanoff, *COO*
Burt Podbere, *CFO*
Nadine Matityahu, *Corp Secy*
EMP: 85
SQ FT: 39,000
SALES (est): 9MM
SALES (corp-wide): 3.1B **Publicly Held**
WEB: www.netoptics.com
SIC: 7372 Operating systems computer
software
HQ: Ixia
26601 Agoura Rd
Calabasas CA 91302
818 871-1800

(P-24950)
NETAPHOR SOFTWARE INC
15510 Rockfield Blvd C100, Irvine
(92618-2726)
PHONE..................................949 470-7955
Rakesh Mahajan, *CEO*
Shripathi Kamath, *CFO*

EMP: 11
SQ FT: 2,700
SALES (est): 950K **Privately Held**
WEB: www.netaphor.com
SIC: 7372 Business oriented computer
software

(P-24951)
NETCUBE SYSTEMS INC
1275 Arbor Ave, Los Altos (94024-5330)
PHONE..................................650 862-7858
Mallikarjuna Reddy, *President*
EMP: 75
SQ FT: 1,000
SALES: 35MM **Privately Held**
SIC: 7372 7379 7371 7361 Application
computer software; computer related con-
sulting services; custom computer pro-
gramming services; employment
agencies

(P-24952)
NETSARANG INC
4701 P Henry Dr 137, Santa Clara (95054)
PHONE..................................669 204-3301
Andrew Wonik Chang, *Vice Pres*
EMP: 12
SALES: 400K **Privately Held**
SIC: 7372 Prepackaged software

(P-24953)
NETSOL TECHNOLOGIES INC
(PA)
24025 Park Sorrento # 410, Calabasas
(91302-4036)
PHONE..................................818 222-9197
Najeeb Ghauri, *Ch of Bd*
Roger Almond, *CFO*
Eugen Beckert, *Bd of Directors*
Patti L W McGlasson, *Senior VP*
Rich Chala, *Vice Pres*
EMP: 38
SQ FT: 7,210
SALES: 60.9MM **Publicly Held**
WEB: www.netsoltech.com
SIC: 7372 7373 7299 Business oriented
computer software; computer integrated
systems design; personal document & in-
formation services

(P-24954)
NETSUITE INC (DH)
Also Called: Oracle
2955 Campus Dr Ste 100, San Mateo
(94403-2539)
PHONE..................................650 627-1000
Dorian Daley, *President*
Raghu Gnanasekaran, *Partner*
Erica Prado, *President*
James Dantow, *COO*
Evan Goldberg, *Exec VP*
EMP: 148
SQ FT: 165,000
SALES: 741.1MM
SALES (corp-wide): 39.8B **Publicly Held**
SIC: 7372 Business oriented computer
software
HQ: Oc Acquisition Llc
500 Oracle Pkwy
Redwood City CA 94065
650 506-7000

(P-24955)
NETWORK AUTOMATION INC
3530 Wilshire Blvd # 1800, Los Angeles
(90010-2335)
PHONE..................................213 738-1700
Dustin Snell, *CEO*
Graham Taylor, *CTO*
EMP: 50
SQ FT: 9,000
SALES: 3.9MM
SALES (corp-wide): 70.8MM **Privately
Held**
WEB: www.networkautomation.com
SIC: 7372 Business oriented computer
software
PA: Help/Systems, Llc
6455 City West Pkwy
Eden Prairie MN 55344
952 933-0609

(P-24956)
NETWORK VIGILANCE LLC
12121 Scripps Summit Dr # 320, San Diego
(92131-4609)
PHONE..................................858 695-8676
Peter Bybee,
John Hunter, *Administration*
Gayle Bybee,
EMP: 18
SQ FT: 4,000
SALES (est): 3.9MM **Privately Held**
SIC: 7372 7375 Application computer software; information retrieval services

(P-24957)
NETWRIX CORPORATION (PA)
300 Spectrum Center Dr # 200, Irvine
(92618-4925)
PHONE..................................888 638-9749
Steve Dickson, *CEO*
Brian Helwig, *CFO*
Amede Hungerford, *Vice Pres*
John Ross, *Vice Pres*
Nora Williamson, *Technology*
EMP: 33
SQ FT: 12,000
SALES (est): 4.7MM **Privately Held**
SIC: 7372 Business oriented computer software

(P-24958)
NEW BI US GAMING LLC
10920 Via Frontera # 420, San Diego
(92127-1729)
PHONE..................................858 592-2472
Ian Bonner, *CEO*
Kimberly Armstrong, *Vice Pres*
Russell Schechter, *Vice Pres*
EMP: 92 **EST:** 2012
SALES (est): 5.8MM **Privately Held**
SIC: 7372 Prepackaged software

(P-24959)
NEW CAM COMMERCE SOLUTIONS LLC
5555 Garden Grove Blvd # 100, Westminster (92683-8227)
PHONE..................................714 338-0200
Doug Roberson, *Mng Member*
EMP: 77
SQ FT: 26,000
SALES (est): 5.9MM
SALES (corp-wide): 23.1MM **Privately Held**
SIC: 7372 Business oriented computer software
PA: Celerant Technology Corp.
4830 Arthur Kill Rd Ste 3
Staten Island NY 10309
718 351-2000

(P-24960)
NEW GENERATION SOFTWARE INC
Also Called: N G S
3835 N Freeway Blvd # 200, Sacramento
(95834-1954)
PHONE..................................916 920-2200
Bernard B Gough, *CEO*
John O'Sullivan, *Executive*
Michael Dedoshka, *Programmer Anys*
Eric Bassett, *Technology*
Mary Treadwell, *Mktg Dir*
EMP: 45
SQ FT: 10,000
SALES (est): 6.2MM **Privately Held**
WEB: www.ngsi.com
SIC: 7372 Application computer software; utility computer software

(P-24961)
NEW RELIC INC (PA)
188 Spear St Ste 1200, San Francisco
(94105-1750)
PHONE..................................650 777-7600
Lewis Cirne, *CEO*
Peter Fenton, *Ch of Bd*
Mark Sachleben, *CFO*
James Gochee,
Matthew Flaming, *Vice Pres*
EMP: 148
SQ FT: 73,391
SALES: 355MM **Publicly Held**
SIC: 7372 Application computer software

(P-24962)
NEWERA SOFTWARE INC
18625 Sutter Blvd Ste 950, Morgan Hill
(95037-8122)
P.O. Box 1797 (95038-1797)
PHONE..................................408 520-7100
Glen Bagsby, *President*
EMP: 14
SQ FT: 650
SALES (est): 1.7MM **Privately Held**
SIC: 7372 Business oriented computer software

(P-24963)
NEXENTA SYSTEMS INC
2025 Gateway Pl Ste 160, San Jose
(95110-1059)
PHONE..................................408 791-3341
Tarkan Maner, *Ch of Bd*
Rick Martig, *CFO*
Tim Guleri, *Bd of Directors*
Evan Powell, *Officer*
Jon Ash, *Vice Pres*
EMP: 230
SALES (est): 35.1MM **Privately Held**
SIC: 7372 Operating systems computer software

(P-24964)
NEXTGEN HEALTHCARE INC (PA)
18111 Von Karman Ave, Irvine
(92612-0199)
PHONE..................................949 255-2600
John R Frantz, *President*
Jeffrey H Margolis, *Ch of Bd*
Craig A Barbarosh, *Vice Chairman*
Scott E Bostick, *COO*
James R Arnold, *CFO*
EMP: 148
SQ FT: 83,100
SALES: 531MM **Publicly Held**
WEB: www.qsii.com
SIC: 7372 7373 Prepackaged software; computer integrated systems design

(P-24965)
NIGHTINGALE VANTAGEMED CORP (HQ)
10670 White Rock Rd, Rancho Cordova
(95670-6095)
PHONE..................................916 638-4744
Steven Curd, *CEO*
Mark Cameron, *COO*
Liesel Loesch, *CFO*
Richard Altinger, *Vice Pres*
Jennifer Bentley, *VP Mktg*
EMP: 55
SALES (est): 10.9MM **Privately Held**
WEB: www.vantagemed.com
SIC: 7372 Business oriented computer software
PA: Nexia Health Technologies Inc
15 Allstate Prkwy 6th Fl
Markham ON L3R 5
905 415-3063

(P-24966)
NIS AMERICA INC
4 Hutton Cntre Dr Ste 650, Santa Ana
(92707)
PHONE..................................714 540-1199
Souhei Niikawa, *CEO*
Harusato Akenaga, *President*
Johanna Hirota, *CFO*
Mitsuharu Hiraoka, *Vice Pres*
Jordan Vincent, *Marketing Mgr*
EMP: 40
SQ FT: 1,000
SALES (est): 5MM **Privately Held**
WEB: www.nisamerica.com
SIC: 7372 Publishers' computer software
PA: Nipponichi K.K.
1-8-4, Nihombashihoridomecho
Chuo-Ku TKY
-

(P-24967)
NLYTE SOFTWARE AMERICAS LTD (DH)
2800 Campus Dr Ste 135, San Mateo
(94403-2554)
PHONE..................................650 561-8200
Doug Sabella, *President*
Phil Kelly, *President*

Fred Dirla, *COO*
Owen Nisbett, *CFO*
Grant Bilbow, *Vice Pres*
EMP: 130
SALES (est): 19MM
SALES (corp-wide): 30.3MM **Privately Held**
SIC: 7372 Prepackaged software
HQ: Nlyte Software Americas Limited
26 Osiers Road
London SW18
208 877-7200

(P-24968)
NOBIX INC
2682 Bishop Dr Ste 211, San Ramon
(94583-4452)
P.O. Box 3592 (94583-8592)
PHONE..................................925 659-3500
David J Warda, *President*
David A Block, *COO*
EMP: 26
SQ FT: 9,996
SALES (est): 1.8MM **Privately Held**
WEB: www.nobix.com
SIC: 7372 Operating systems computer software

(P-24969)
NOK NOK LABS INC
2100 Geng Rd Ste 105, Palo Alto
(94303-3307)
PHONE..................................650 433-1300
Phil Dunkelberger, *CEO*
Rajiv Dholakia, *Vice Pres*
Jonas Lamis, *Vice Pres*
Naga Nagarajan, *Vice Pres*
David Wiener, *Vice Pres*
EMP: 16
SQ FT: 12,000
SALES (est): 2MM **Privately Held**
SIC: 7372 Business oriented computer software

(P-24970)
NONPROFITEASY INC (PA)
1300 Valley House Dr # 100, Rohnert Park
(94928-4931)
PHONE..................................707 929-3563
Lomesh Shah, *CEO*
Mark Feinberg, *President*
Dan Wain, *Vice Pres*
Missy Singh, *Director*
EMP: 12
SALES (est): 1.2MM **Privately Held**
SIC: 7372 Application computer software

(P-24971)
NOVASTOR CORPORATION (PA)
29209 Canwood St Ste 200, Agoura Hills
(91301-1908)
PHONE..................................805 579-6700
Peter Means, *President*
Martin Albert, *Chairman*
EMP: 30
SQ FT: 7,800
SALES (est): 5.6MM **Privately Held**
WEB: www.no-panic.com
SIC: 7372 7371 5734 Business oriented computer software; custom computer programming services; software, business & non-game

(P-24972)
NPHASE INC
323 Neptune Ave, Encinitas (92024-2521)
PHONE..................................805 750-8580
Scott A Climes, *CEO*
EMP: 20 **EST:** 2014
SALES (est): 421K **Privately Held**
SIC: 7372 Business oriented computer software

(P-24973)
NTRUST INFOTECH INC
230 Commerce Ste 180, Irvine
(92602-1336)
PHONE..................................562 207-1600
Srikanth Ramachandran, *CEO*
Janakiraman Ramachandran, *COO*
Tom Scott, *Senior VP*
Ramki Krishnamoorthy, *Vice Pres*
Radha Krishnaraj, *Vice Pres*
EMP: 65 **EST:** 2003

SALES (est): 6.5MM **Privately Held**
SIC: 7372 Business oriented computer software; computer software development & applications
PA: Ntrust Infotech Private Limited
3rd Floor Ganesh Towers
Chennai TN
-

(P-24974)
NUANCE COMMUNICATIONS INC
1198 E Arques Ave, Sunnyvale
(94085-4602)
PHONE..................................781 565-5000
Charles Berger, *President*
Denise Danielson, *Program Mgr*
Katalin Vonberg, *Technology*
Bonnie Bartosik, *Purch Agent*
Regina Schmidt, *Marketing Staff*
EMP: 150
SQ FT: 60,000 **Publicly Held**
SIC: 7372 Application computer software
PA: Nuance Communications, Inc.
1 Wayside Rd
Burlington MA 01803
-

(P-24975)
NUMECENT INC
15635 Alton Pkwy Ste 100, Irvine
(92618-7321)
PHONE..................................949 833-2800
Tom Lagatta, *CEO*
Osman Kent, *Ch of Bd*
Ed Corrente, *CFO*
Hildy Shandell, *CFO*
EMP: 30
SQ FT: 5,600
SALES (est): 3.9MM **Privately Held**
SIC: 7372 Application computer software

(P-24976)
NUORDER INC
900 Hilgard Ave, Los Angeles
(90024-3009)
PHONE..................................310 954-1313
Heath Wells, *CEO*
Tracey Solanas, *Vice Pres*
Melodie Rahbar, *VP Bus Dvlpt*
Kevin Sagarchi, *Executive*
Sarah Sandberg, *Admin Sec*
EMP: 20
SQ FT: 1,800
SALES (est): 2.7MM **Privately Held**
SIC: 7372 Application computer software

(P-24977)
NURSESBOND INC
26386 Primrose Way, Moreno Valley
(92555-2239)
P.O. Box 9258 (92552-9258)
PHONE..................................951 286-8537
Chibunna Nwaobia, *CEO*
EMP: 10
SALES: 250K **Privately Held**
SIC: 7372 8299 Application computer software; educational service, nondegree granting: continuing educ.

(P-24978)
NWP SERVICES CORPORATION (HQ)
535 Anton Blvd Ste 1100, Costa Mesa
(92626-7699)
P.O. Box 19661, Irvine (92623-9661)
PHONE..................................949 253-2500
Ron Reed, *President*
Lana Reeve,
Mike Haviken, *Exec VP*
Monique Black, *Human Resources*
Bob Smolarski, *Opers Staff*
EMP: 141
SQ FT: 21,171
SALES (est): 48.8MM
SALES (corp-wide): 670.9MM **Publicly Held**
WEB: www.nwpco.com
SIC: 7372 8721 Utility computer software; billing & bookkeeping service
PA: Realpage, Inc.
2201 Lakeside Blvd
Richardson TX 75082
972 820-3000

▲ = Import ▼=Export
◆ =Import/Export

(P-24979)
NYANSA INC
430 Cowper St Ste 250, Palo Alto
(94301-1579)
PHONE..................................650 446-7818
Abe Ankumah, *CEO*
Daniel Ken, *Vice Pres*
Anand Srinivas, *CTO*
Stephanie Gurnani, *Opers Mgr*
EMP: 45
SALES: 3MM **Privately Held**
SIC: 7372 Application computer software

(P-24980)
ODDWORLD INHABITANTS INC
869 Monterey St, San Luis Obispo
(93401-3224)
PHONE..................................805 503-3000
Sherry McKenna, *CEO*
Lorne Lanning, *President*
Maurice Konkle, *COO*
EMP: 60
SQ FT: 15,000
SALES (est): 2.4MM **Privately Held**
WEB: www.oddworld.com
SIC: 7372 Application computer software

(P-24981)
OKTA INC
Also Called: Stormpath
172 Lakeshore Dr, San Mateo
(94402-3624)
PHONE..................................650 348-2620
EMP: 16
SALES (corp-wide): 259.9MM **Publicly Held**
SIC: 7372 Business oriented computer software
PA: Okta, Inc.
301 Brannan St Fl 1
San Francisco CA 94107
888 722-7871

(P-24982)
OMNITRACS MIDCO LLC (PA)
9276 Scranton Rd Ste 200, San Diego
(92121-7703)
PHONE..................................858 651-5812
EMP: 37
SALES (est): 106.6MM **Privately Held**
SIC: 7372 Business oriented computer software; utility computer software

(P-24983)
OMNIVORE TECHNOLOGIES INC
1191 B St, Hayward (94541-4201)
PHONE..................................800 293-4058
Mike Wior, *CEO*
Andrew Hyde, *CFO*
Shane Wheatland, *Chief Mktg Ofcr*
EMP: 30
SQ FT: 3,500
SALES: 150K **Privately Held**
SIC: 7372 Business oriented computer software

(P-24984)
ON24 INC (PA)
50 Beale St Ste 800, San Francisco
(94105-1863)
PHONE..................................877 202-9599
Sharat Sharan, *President*
Ian Halifax, *CFO*
Joe Hyland, *Chief Mktg Ofcr*
Mahesh Kheny, *Vice Pres*
Thomas Masotto, *Vice Pres*
EMP: 350
SQ FT: 28,353
SALES (est): 81.9MM **Privately Held**
WEB: www.on24.com
SIC: 7372 Business oriented computer software

(P-24985)
ONC HOLDINGS INC
Also Called: Gobeme
832 Folsom St Ste 1001, San Francisco
(94107-1142)
PHONE..................................415 243-3343
David Kochbeck, *CEO*
Jim Bertoldi, *CFO*
Christian Mackey, *Director*
Dominic Rotondi, *Director*
EMP: 12 EST: 2013

SALES (est): 739.4K **Privately Held**
SIC: 7372 Educational computer software

(P-24986)
OOPSTON INC
748 S Glasgow Ave, Inglewood
(90301-3012)
PHONE..................................800 881-5901
EMP: 15
SALES: 10K **Privately Held**
SIC: 7372 4789 Business oriented computer software; transportation services

(P-24987)
OPENCLOVIS SOLUTIONS INC
765 Baywood Dr Ste 336, Petaluma
(94954-5507)
PHONE..................................707 981-7120
Hong Lu, *President*
Vk Budhraja, *CEO*
EMP: 26
SALES (est): 1.9MM **Privately Held**
SIC: 7372 Prepackaged software

(P-24988)
OPENPRO INC
Also Called: Openpro Erp Software
10061 Talbert Ave Ste 228, Fountain Valley
(92708-5159)
PHONE..................................714 378-4600
James Clark, *CEO*
Thomas Vinje, *Partner*
Shannon G Clark, *CFO*
Jason Park, *Accounts Mgr*
EMP: 12
SQ FT: 2,500
SALES (est): 1.3MM **Privately Held**
WEB: www.openpro.com
SIC: 7372 Business oriented computer software

(P-24989)
OPENTV INC (DH)
Also Called: Nagra
275 Sacramento St Ste Sl1, San Francisco
(94111-3831)
PHONE..................................415 962-5000
Yves Pitton, *CEO*
Ben Bennett, *CEO*
Andr Kudelski, *CEO*
Wesley O Hoffman, *COO*
Shum Mukherjee, *CFO*
EMP: 150
SALES (est): 78.6MM
SALES (corp-wide): 1B **Privately Held**
SIC: 7372 Prepackaged software

(P-24990)
OPENWAVE MOBILITY INC (PA)
400 Seaport Ct Ste 104, Redwood City
(94063-2799)
PHONE..................................650 480-7200
Tony Condino, *Principal*
Poh Sim Gan, *CFO*
Indranil Chatterjee, *Vice Pres*
Matt Halligan, *Vice Pres*
Dean Liming, *Vice Pres*
EMP: 29
SALES (est): 9.5MM **Privately Held**
SIC: 7372 Prepackaged software

(P-24991)
OPENX TECHNOLOGIES INC
888 E Walnut St Fl 2, Pasadena
(91101-1897)
PHONE..................................626 466-1141
Vadim Telyatnikov, *Branch Mgr*
EMP: 25
SALES (corp-wide): 171.8MM **Privately Held**
SIC: 7372 Application computer software
HQ: Openx Technologies, Inc.
888 E Walnut St Fl 2
Pasadena CA 91101

(P-24992)
OPERA COMMERCE LLC
1875 S Grant St Ste 800, San Mateo
(94402-7014)
PHONE..................................650 625-1262
Sameer Merchant,
Nadine Jarrard, *Vice Pres*
Anthony Nichols, *Vice Pres*
Benjamin Kaufman, *Principal*
Laura Schott, *Office Mgr*

EMP: 10
SALES (est): 614.1K
SALES (corp-wide): 420.6MM **Privately Held**
SIC: 7372 Prepackaged software
PA: Otello Corporation Asa
Gjerdrums Vei 19
Oslo 0484
236 924-00

(P-24993)
OPERA SOFTWARE AMERICAS LLC
1875 S Grant St Ste 750, San Mateo
(94402-2670)
PHONE..................................650 625-1262
Lars Boilesen, *CEO*
John Metzger, *President*
Erik C Harrell, *CFO*
Mahi De Silva, *Exec VP*
Jon Stocco, *Vice Pres*
EMP: 13
SALES (est): 1.6MM
SALES (corp-wide): 420.6MM **Privately Held**
SIC: 7372 Prepackaged software
PA: Otello Corporation Asa
Gjerdrums Vei 19
Oslo 0484
236 924-00

(P-24994)
OPSVEDA INC
4030 Moorpark Ave Ste 107, San Jose
(95117-1848)
PHONE..................................408 628-0461
Sanjiv Gupta, *President*
Harsh Vardhan Pant, *Vice Pres*
Vikas Rajput, *Vice Pres*
Dinesh Somani, *Vice Pres*
Harsh Mishra, *Director*
EMP: 19
SALES (est): 6.5MM **Privately Held**
SIC: 7372 7371 Business oriented computer software; computer software development

(P-24995)
OPTIMIS SERVICES INC
225 Mantua Rd, Pacific Palisades
(90272-3349)
PHONE..................................310 230-2780
Alan Morelli, *President*
EMP: 22
SALES (est): 730.9K **Privately Held**
SIC: 7372 Business oriented computer software

(P-24996)
OPTIMUM SOLUTIONS GROUP LLC
419 Ponderosa Ct, Lafayette (94549-1812)
PHONE..................................415 954-7100
G John Houtary,
Lisa Massman,
EMP: 109
SQ FT: 3,300
SALES (est): 4.5MM
SALES (corp-wide): 5.1B **Privately Held**
WEB: www.optimumsolutions.com
SIC: 7372 7371 8243 7374 Prepackaged software; computer software systems analysis & design, custom; data processing schools; computer graphics service
PA: Kpmg Llp
1676 Intl Dr Ste 1200
Mclean VA 22102
703 286-8000

(P-24997)
ORACLE AMERICA INC
Also Called: Sun Microsystems
4220 Network Cir, Santa Clara
(95054-1780)
PHONE..................................408 276-4300
Mark Toliver, *President*
Jesse Hsu, *Design Engr*
Jonathan Gibbons, *Technical Staff*
Peter Lam, *Technical Staff*
Ekaterina Pavlova, *Technical Staff*
EMP: 187
SALES (corp-wide): 39.8B **Publicly Held**
SIC: 7372 Prepackaged software

HQ: Oracle America, Inc.
500 Oracle Pkwy
Redwood City CA 94065
650 506-7000

(P-24998)
ORACLE AMERICA INC
1001 Sunset Blvd, Rocklin (95765-3702)
PHONE..................................303 272-6473
Mark Kulaga, *Branch Mgr*
Mary Zirelli, *Director*
EMP: 15
SALES (corp-wide): 39.8B **Publicly Held**
SIC: 7372 Prepackaged software
HQ: Oracle America, Inc.
500 Oracle Pkwy
Redwood City CA 94065
650 506-7000

(P-24999)
ORACLE AMERICA INC
475 Sansome St Fl 15, San Francisco
(94111-3166)
PHONE..................................415 908-3609
EMP: 58
SALES (corp-wide): 39.8B **Publicly Held**
SIC: 7372 Prepackaged software
HQ: Oracle America, Inc.
500 Oracle Pkwy
Redwood City CA 94065
650 506-7000

(P-25000)
ORACLE AMERICA INC
600 Oracle Pkwy, Redwood City
(94065-1603)
PHONE..................................408 702-5945
EMP: 17
SALES (corp-wide): 39.8B **Publicly Held**
SIC: 7372 Prepackaged software
HQ: Oracle America, Inc.
500 Oracle Pkwy
Redwood City CA 94065
650 506-7000

(P-25001)
ORACLE AMERICA INC
Also Called: Sun Microsystems
5815 Owens Dr, Pleasanton (94588-3939)
PHONE..................................925 694-3314
Terri Beck, *Manager*
EMP: 75
SALES (corp-wide): 39.8B **Publicly Held**
SIC: 7372 Prepackaged software
HQ: Oracle America, Inc.
500 Oracle Pkwy
Redwood City CA 94065
650 506-7000

(P-25002)
ORACLE AMERICA INC
Also Called: Sun Microsystems
15821 Ventura Blvd # 270, Encino
(91436-2915)
PHONE..................................818 905-0200
Stephen McKenna, *Technical Staff*
Card Pregozen, *Engineer*
EMP: 21
SALES (corp-wide): 39.8B **Publicly Held**
SIC: 7372 Prepackaged software
HQ: Oracle America, Inc.
500 Oracle Pkwy
Redwood City CA 94065
650 506-7000

(P-25003)
ORACLE AMERICA INC
Also Called: Sun Microsystems
80 Railroad Ave, Milpitas (95035-4333)
PHONE..................................408 635-3072
Bruce Webbe, *Manager*
EMP: 251
SALES (corp-wide): 39.8B **Publicly Held**
SIC: 7372 Prepackaged software
HQ: Oracle America, Inc.
500 Oracle Pkwy
Redwood City CA 94065
650 506-7000

(P-25004)
ORACLE AMERICA INC
Also Called: Sun Microsystems
9540 Towne Centre Dr, San Diego
(92121-1988)
PHONE..................................858 625-5044

P
R
O
D
U
C
T
S

&

S
V
C
S

Steven Nathan, *Manager*
EMP: 77
SALES (corp-wide): 39.8B **Publicly Held**
SIC: 7372 Prepackaged software
HQ: Oracle America, Inc.
500 Oracle Pkwy
Redwood City CA 94065
650 506-7000

(P-25005)
ORACLE AMERICA INC
Also Called: Sun Microsystems
3401 Centre Lake Dr # 410, Ontario
(91761-1201)
PHONE.....................909 605-0222
Clyde Johnston, *Branch Mgr*
EMP: 15
SALES (corp-wide): 39.8B **Publicly Held**
SIC: 7372 Prepackaged software
HQ: Oracle America, Inc.
500 Oracle Pkwy
Redwood City CA 94065
650 506-7000

(P-25006)
ORACLE AMERICA INC
Also Called: Sun Microsystems
4230 Leonard Stocking Dr, Santa Clara
(95054-1777)
PHONE.....................408 276-7534
Denise Shiffman, *VP Mktg*
Larry Williams, *COO*
Joe Fuentes, *Comms Mgr*
Michael Connaughton, *General Mgr*
William H Howard, *CIO*
EMP: 250
SALES (corp-wide): 39.8B **Publicly Held**
SIC: 7372 Prepackaged software
HQ: Oracle America, Inc.
500 Oracle Pkwy
Redwood City CA 94065
650 506-7000

(P-25007)
ORACLE CORPORATION
279 Barnes Rd, Tustin (92782-3748)
PHONE.....................713 654-0919
John Czapko, *Branch Mgr*
EMP: 191
SALES (corp-wide): 39.8B **Publicly Held**
SIC: 7372 Business oriented computer
software
PA: Oracle Corporation
500 Oracle Pkwy
Redwood City CA 94065
650 506-7000

(P-25008)
ORACLE CORPORATION
475 Sansome St Fl 15, San Francisco
(94111-3166)
PHONE.....................415 834-9731
Lisa Schwarz, *Director*
Niraj Hegdekar, *Software Engr*
Peter Yap, *Technology*
Hanno Botha, *Technical Staff*
Eric Gross, *Technical Staff*
EMP: 32
SALES (corp-wide): 39.8B **Publicly Held**
SIC: 7372 Prepackaged software
PA: Oracle Corporation
500 Oracle Pkwy
Redwood City CA 94065
650 506-7000

(P-25009)
ORACLE CORPORATION
214 Clarence Ave, Sunnyvale
(94086-5907)
PHONE.....................650 607-5402
Jitendra Chinthakindi, *Principal*
EMP: 302
SALES (corp-wide): 39.8B **Publicly Held**
SIC: 7372 Business oriented computer
software
PA: Oracle Corporation
500 Oracle Pkwy
Redwood City CA 94065
650 506-7000

(P-25010)
ORACLE CORPORATION
1408 Antigua Ln, Foster City (94404-3970)
PHONE.....................650 678-3612
ARA Michaelian, *Principal*
EMP: 302

SALES (corp-wide): 39.8B **Publicly Held**
SIC: 7372 Business oriented computer
software
PA: Oracle Corporation
500 Oracle Pkwy
Redwood City CA 94065
650 506-7000

(P-25011)
ORACLE CORPORATION
1490 Newhall St, Santa Clara
(95050-6135)
PHONE.....................408 421-2890
Stephanie Camarda, *Principal*
EMP: 302
SALES (corp-wide): 39.8B **Publicly Held**
SIC: 7372 Business oriented computer
software
PA: Oracle Corporation
500 Oracle Pkwy
Redwood City CA 94065
650 506-7000

(P-25012)
ORACLE CORPORATION
231 Kerry Dr, Santa Clara (95050-6603)
PHONE.....................408 276-5552
Annie Van Dalen, *Principal*
EMP: 302
SALES (corp-wide): 39.8B **Publicly Held**
SIC: 7372 Business oriented computer
software
PA: Oracle Corporation
500 Oracle Pkwy
Redwood City CA 94065
650 506-7000

(P-25013)
ORACLE CORPORATION
3084 Thurman Dr, San Jose (95148-3143)
PHONE.....................408 276-3822
Alasdair Rendall, *Principal*
EMP: 302
SALES (corp-wide): 39.8B **Publicly Held**
SIC: 7372 Business oriented computer
software
PA: Oracle Corporation
500 Oracle Pkwy
Redwood City CA 94065
650 506-7000

(P-25014)
ORACLE CORPORATION
9515 Towne Centre Dr, San Diego
(92121-1973)
PHONE.....................858 202-0648
Michael Smith, *Technology*
Brandon Byers, *Technical Staff*
Shannon Kagey, *Manager*
EMP: 191
SALES (corp-wide): 39.8B **Publicly Held**
SIC: 7372 Business oriented computer
software
PA: Oracle Corporation
500 Oracle Pkwy
Redwood City CA 94065
650 506-7000

(P-25015)
ORACLE CORPORATION
3532 Eastin Pl, Santa Clara (95051-2600)
PHONE.....................650 506-9864
Maneesh Jain, *Principal*
Gia Nguyen, *Senior Engr*
EMP: 302
SALES (corp-wide): 39.8B **Publicly Held**
SIC: 7372 Business oriented computer
software
PA: Oracle Corporation
500 Oracle Pkwy
Redwood City CA 94065
650 506-7000

(P-25016)
ORACLE CORPORATION
372 Calero Ave, San Jose (95123-4315)
PHONE.....................408 390-8623
Aileen F Casanave, *Principal*
EMP: 302
SALES (corp-wide): 39.8B **Publicly Held**
SIC: 7372 Business oriented computer
software
PA: Oracle Corporation
500 Oracle Pkwy
Redwood City CA 94065
650 506-7000

(P-25017)
ORACLE CORPORATION
475 Sansome St Fl 15, San Francisco
(94111-3166)
PHONE.....................415 402-7200
Victor Coskey, *Principal*
Trey Parsons, *Vice Pres*
Connor Thomas, *Vice Pres*
Minho Kim, *Sr Software Eng*
Rohit Koul, *Sr Software Eng*
EMP: 191
SALES (corp-wide): 39.8B **Publicly Held**
SIC: 7372 Business oriented computer
software
PA: Oracle Corporation
500 Oracle Pkwy
Redwood City CA 94065
650 506-7000

(P-25018)
ORACLE CORPORATION
6224 Hummingbird Ln, Rocklin
(95765-5929)
P.O. Box 3442 (95677-8469)
PHONE.....................916 435-8342
Richard Gless, *Principal*
EMP: 302
SALES (corp-wide): 39.8B **Publicly Held**
SIC: 7372 Business oriented computer
software
PA: Oracle Corporation
500 Oracle Pkwy
Redwood City CA 94065
650 506-7000

(P-25019)
ORACLE CORPORATION
5805 Owens Dr, Pleasanton (94588-3939)
PHONE.....................877 767-2253
Bor R Fu, *Senior VP*
Clement Sciammas, *Vice Pres*
Sitaraman Swaminathan, *Executive*
Kevin Supan, *Info Tech Mgr*
Ricky Frost, *Software Engr*
EMP: 315
SALES (corp-wide): 39.8B **Publicly Held**
SIC: 7372 Business oriented computer
software
PA: Oracle Corporation
500 Oracle Pkwy
Redwood City CA 94065
650 506-7000

(P-25020)
ORACLE CORPORATION
3925 Emerald Isle Ln, San Jose
(95135-1708)
PHONE.....................925 694-6258
Johnson Aremu, *Principal*
EMP: 306
SALES (corp-wide): 39.8B **Publicly Held**
SIC: 7372 Business oriented computer
software
PA: Oracle Corporation
500 Oracle Pkwy
Redwood City CA 94065
650 506-7000

(P-25021)
ORACLE CORPORATION
5863 Carmel Way, Union City
(94587-5170)
PHONE.....................510 471-6971
Renzo Zagni, *Principal*
EMP: 302
SALES (corp-wide): 39.8B **Publicly Held**
SIC: 7372 Business oriented computer
software
PA: Oracle Corporation
500 Oracle Pkwy
Redwood City CA 94065
650 506-7000

(P-25022)
ORACLE CORPORATION
5750 Hannum Ave Ste 200, Culver City
(90230-6666)
PHONE.....................310 258-7500
EMP: 302
SALES (corp-wide): 39.8B **Publicly Held**
SIC: 7372 Business oriented computer
software
PA: Oracle Corporation
500 Oracle Pkwy
Redwood City CA 94065
650 506-7000

(P-25023)
ORACLE CORPORATION
200 N Pacific Coast Hwy # 400, El Se-
gundo (90245-5628)
PHONE.....................310 343-7405
EMP: 306
SALES (corp-wide): 39.8B **Publicly Held**
SIC: 7372 Business oriented computer
software
PA: Oracle Corporation
500 Oracle Pkwy
Redwood City CA 94065
650 506-7000

(P-25024)
ORACLE CORPORATION
1001 Sunset Blvd, Rocklin (95765-3702)
PHONE.....................916 315-3500
Chris Wilson, *Branch Mgr*
Nancy Peters, *VP Admin*
Nicole Stokes, *Admin Asst*
Liz Brock, *Administration*
Pavel Buenitsky, *Info Tech Dir*
EMP: 500
SALES (corp-wide): 39.8B **Publicly Held**
SIC: 7372 7371 Business oriented com-
puter software; custom computer pro-
gramming services
PA: Oracle Corporation
500 Oracle Pkwy
Redwood City CA 94065
650 506-7000

(P-25025)
ORACLE CORPORATION
475 Sansome St Fl 15, San Francisco
(94111-3166)
P.O. Box 44471 (94144-0001)
PHONE.....................650 506-7000
Eduard Glushchenko, *Vice Pres*
Josh Ulm, *Vice Pres*
Nilesh Murthy, *Associate Dir*
Mugdha Kumar, *Sr Software Eng*
Adam Paul, *Sr Software Eng*
EMP: 24
SALES (corp-wide): 39.8B **Publicly Held**
SIC: 7372 Prepackaged software
PA: Oracle Corporation
500 Oracle Pkwy
Redwood City CA 94065
650 506-7000

(P-25026)
ORACLE SYSTEMS CORPORATION
200 N Pacific Coast Hwy # 400, El Se-
gundo (90245-4340)
PHONE.....................818 817-2900
Elizabeth Deitz, *General Mgr*
EMP: 70
SALES (corp-wide): 39.8B **Publicly Held**
WEB: www.forcecapital.com
SIC: 7372 Prepackaged software
HQ: Oracle Systems Corporation
500 Oracle Pkwy
Redwood City CA 94065
650 506-7000

(P-25027)
ORACLE SYSTEMS CORPORATION
102 Santa Barbara Ave, Daly City
(94014-1045)
PHONE.....................650 506-8648
EMP: 92
SALES (corp-wide): 39.8B **Publicly Held**
WEB: www.forcecapital.com
SIC: 7372 Prepackaged software
HQ: Oracle Systems Corporation
500 Oracle Pkwy
Redwood City CA 94065
650 506-7000

(P-25028)
ORACLE SYSTEMS CORPORATION
301 Island Pkwy, Belmont (94002-4109)
PHONE.....................650 654-7606
Sameer Patkar, *Vice Pres*
Thirupathi Annadi, *Technology*
Jennifer Tsai, *Technology*
Ramakrishna Gudia, *Manager*
EMP: 304
SALES (corp-wide): 39.8B **Publicly Held**
SIC: 7372 Prepackaged software

HQ: Oracle Systems Corporation
500 Oracle Pkwy
Redwood City CA 94065
650 506-7000

(P-25029)
**ORACLE SYSTEMS
CORPORATION**
500 Oracle Pkwy, San Mateo (94403)
PHONE..............................650 506-6780
Sayekumar Arumugam, *Principal*
EMP: 108
SALES (corp-wide): 39.8B **Publicly Held**
WEB: www.forcecapital.com
SIC: 7372 Prepackaged software
HQ: Oracle Systems Corporation
500 Oracle Pkwy
Redwood City CA 94065
650 506-7000

(P-25030)
**ORACLE SYSTEMS
CORPORATION**
501 Island Pkwy, Belmont (94002-4153)
PHONE..............................650 506-5062
Michael Rocha, *Branch Mgr*
Debbie Berumen, *Administration*
Sunil Pinto, *Technical Staff*
Anjani Prathipati, *Technical Staff*
EMP: 16
SALES (corp-wide): 39.8B **Publicly Held**
WEB: www.forcecapital.com
SIC: 7372 Prepackaged software
HQ: Oracle Systems Corporation
500 Oracle Pkwy
Redwood City CA 94065
650 506-7000

(P-25031)
**ORACLE SYSTEMS
CORPORATION**
10 Twin Dolphin Dr, Redwood City
(94065-1035)
PHONE..............................650 506-0300
Richard Grogan, *Branch Mgr*
Ravi Sharma, *Technical Staff*
Yaldah Hakim, *Marketing Staff*
Richard Cardillo, *Sales Staff*
Robin Carlier, *Sales Staff*
EMP: 252
SALES (corp-wide): 39.8B **Publicly Held**
WEB: www.forcecapital.com
SIC: 7372 Prepackaged software
HQ: Oracle Systems Corporation
500 Oracle Pkwy
Redwood City CA 94065
650 506-7000

(P-25032)
**ORACLE SYSTEMS
CORPORATION**
Also Called: PeopleSoft
1840 Gateway Dr Ste 250, San Mateo
(94404-4027)
PHONE..............................650 378-1351
Martine Riente, *Manager*
EMP: 10
SALES (corp-wide): 39.8B **Publicly Held**
WEB: www.forcecapital.com
SIC: 7372 Prepackaged software
HQ: Oracle Systems Corporation
500 Oracle Pkwy
Redwood City CA 94065
650 506-7000

(P-25033)
**ORACLE SYSTEMS
CORPORATION**
300 Oracle Pkwy, Redwood City
(94065-1667)
PHONE..............................650 506-5887
Sam Mohamad, *Vice Pres*
Madhu Punuganti, *Vice Pres*
Monica Chelone, *Program Mgr*
Azeez Zackriah, *Program Mgr*
Kiran Basavaraju, *MIS Dir*
EMP: 35
SALES (corp-wide): 39.8B **Publicly Held**
WEB: www.forcecapital.com
SIC: 7372 Prepackaged software
HQ: Oracle Systems Corporation
500 Oracle Pkwy
Redwood City CA 94065
650 506-7000

(P-25034)
**ORACLE SYSTEMS
CORPORATION**
5840 Owens Dr, Pleasanton (94588-3900)
PHONE..............................925 694-3000
Apu Gupta, *Principal*
Randall Geyer, *Sr Software Eng*
Linda Tedjakusuma, *Sr Software Eng*
Matthew Taum, *Database Admin*
Dani Graham, *Director*
EMP: 252
SALES (corp-wide): 39.8B **Publicly Held**
WEB: www.forcecapital.com
SIC: 7372 5734 Prepackaged software;
software, business & non-game
HQ: Oracle Systems Corporation
500 Oracle Pkwy
Redwood City CA 94065
650 506-7000

(P-25035)
**ORACLE SYSTEMS
CORPORATION**
2010 Main St Ste 450, Irvine (92614-7260)
PHONE..............................949 224-1000
Dawn Lotez, *Manager*
EMP: 100
SALES (corp-wide): 39.8B **Publicly Held**
WEB: www.forcecapital.com
SIC: 7372 Prepackaged software
HQ: Oracle Systems Corporation
500 Oracle Pkwy
Redwood City CA 94065
650 506-7000

(P-25036)
**ORACLE SYSTEMS
CORPORATION**
17901 Von Karman Ave # 800, Irvine
(92614-6297)
PHONE..............................949 623-9460
Fran Bracey, *Manager*
Don Kime, *Engineer*
Ralph Woodley, *Assistant*
EMP: 275
SALES (corp-wide): 39.8B **Publicly Held**
WEB: www.forcecapital.com
SIC: 7372 5045 Prepackaged software;
computers, peripherals & software
HQ: Oracle Systems Corporation
500 Oracle Pkwy
Redwood City CA 94065
650 506-7000

(P-25037)
ORACLE TALEO LLC
4140 Dublin Blvd Ste 400, Dublin
(94568-7757)
PHONE..............................925 452-3000
Dorian Daley, *President*
Eric Ball, *CFO*
Guy Gauvin, *Exec VP*
Neil Hudspith, *Exec VP*
Jason Blessing, *Senior VP*
EMP: 1164
SQ FT: 47,500
SALES (est): 98.1MM
SALES (corp-wide): 39.8B **Publicly Held**
WEB: www.taleo.com
SIC: 7372 Business oriented computer
software
PA: Oracle Corporation
500 Oracle Pkwy
Redwood City CA 94065
650 506-7000

(P-25038)
ORANGEGRID LLC
145 S State College Blvd # 350, Brea
(92821-5851)
PHONE..............................657 220-1519
Todd Mobraten, *Mng Member*
Jennifer Leuenberger, *Business Anlyst*
Ryan Werts, *Chief*
Dave Garland,
Dustin Sauter,
EMP: 28 **EST:** 2014
SALES (est): 2.4MM **Privately Held**
SIC: 7372 Prepackaged software

(P-25039)
OSR ENTERPRISES INC
1910 E Stowell Rd, Santa Maria
(93454-8002)
PHONE..............................805 925-1831

James O Rice, *CEO*
Owen S Rice, *Ch of Bd*
Betty E Rice, *Vice Pres*
EMP: 45
SQ FT: 1,500
SALES (est): 8.6MM **Privately Held**
WEB: www.osrent.com
SIC: 7372 Publishers' computer software

(P-25040)
OSSIC CORPORATION
1612 Calle Plumerias, Encinitas
(92024-4801)
PHONE..............................206 227-8585
Jason Riggs, *CEO*
Drew Downie, *Director*
EMP: 13 **EST:** 2015
SALES: 8MM **Privately Held**
SIC: 7372 Application computer software

(P-25041)
OUTPUT INC
1418 N Spring St Ste 102, Los Angeles
(90012-1924)
PHONE..............................310 795-6099
Gregg Lehrmann, *President*
EMP: 18
SALES (est): 968.9K **Privately Held**
SIC: 7372 Application computer software

(P-25042)
OUTREACH CORPORATION
Also Called: Sales & Marketing
55 Union St 2, San Francisco (94111-1227)
PHONE..............................888 938-7356
EMP: 20
SALES (corp-wide): 8.7MM **Privately
Held**
SIC: 7372 Business oriented computer
software
PA: Outreach Corporation
1441 N 34th St Ste 100
Seattle WA 98103
206 235-3672

(P-25043)
OUTSYSTEMS INC
2603 Camino Ramon Ste 210, San Ramon
(94583-9136)
PHONE..............................925 804-6189
Paulo Rosado, *CEO*
EMP: 10
SALES (est): 836.4K **Privately Held**
SIC: 7372 Application computer software
HQ: Outsystems - Software Em Rede, S.A.
Rua Do Central Park, Ediflcio 2 2oa
Linda A Velha 2795-
214 153-730

(P-25044)
OWL TERRITORY INC
Also Called: Docrun
227 Broadway Ste 303, Santa Monica
(90401-3441)
PHONE..............................800 607-0677
EMP: 12 **EST:** 2011
SQ FT: 1,200
SALES (est): 820K **Privately Held**
SIC: 7372

(P-25045)
PACIOLAN LLC (HQ)
Also Called: Ticketswest
5171 California Ave # 200, Irvine
(92617-3068)
PHONE..............................949 476-2050
Dave Butler, *CEO*
Jane Kleinberger, *Ch of Bd*
Kimberly Boren, *CFO*
Steve Shaw, *CFO*
Teri Clark, *Admin Sec*
EMP: 70 **EST:** 1980
SALES (est): 29.2MM
SALES (corp-wide): 84.5B **Publicly Held**
WEB: www.paciolan.com
SIC: 7372 5045 Business oriented com-
puter software; computers
PA: Comcast Corporation
1701 Jfk Blvd
Philadelphia PA 19103
215 286-1700

(P-25046)
**PAKEDGE DEVICE & SOFTWARE
INC**
17011 Beach Blvd Ste 600, Huntington
Beach (92647-5962)
PHONE..............................714 880-4511
Dusan Jankov, *Branch Mgr*
EMP: 22
SALES (corp-wide): 244.7MM **Publicly
Held**
SIC: 7372 Application computer software
HQ: Pakedge Device & Software Inc.
11734 S Election Rd # 200
Draper UT 84020
650 385-8700

(P-25047)
**PANORAMIC SOFTWARE
CORPORATION**
Also Called: Panosoft
9650 Research Dr, Irvine (92618-4666)
PHONE..............................877 558-8526
Jeff Von Waldburg, *President*
EMP: 17
SQ FT: 1,500
SALES: 325MM **Privately Held**
SIC: 7372 7371 Prepackaged software;
custom computer programming services

(P-25048)
**PASPORT SOFTWARE
PROGRAMS INC**
Also Called: Pasport Communications
307 Bridgeway, Sausalito (94965-2451)
PHONE..............................415 331-2606
Jon Gornstei, *President*
EMP: 10
SALES (est): 548.8K **Privately Held**
SIC: 7372 8742 Prepackaged software;
marketing consulting services

(P-25049)
PATIENTPOP INC
214 Wilshire Blvd, Santa Monica
(90401-1202)
PHONE..............................844 487-8399
Travis Schneider, *CEO*
Robert Palumbo, *Partner*
Jason Gardner, *CFO*
Luke Kervin, *Co-CEO*
Jeb Burrows, *Vice Pres*
EMP: 51
SALES (est): 1.1MM **Privately Held**
SIC: 7372 Business oriented computer
software

(P-25050)
PATRON SOLUTIONS LLC
5171 California Ave # 200, Irvine
(92617-3066)
PHONE..............................949 823-1700
Steve Shaw, *Owner*
EMP: 245
SALES (est): 17.4MM **Privately Held**
SIC: 7372 Application computer software

(P-25051)
PAXATA INC
1800 Seaport Blvd Fl 3, Redwood City
(94063-5543)
PHONE..............................650 542-7897
Prakasa Nanduri, *CEO*
David Brewster, *Co-Owner*
Rik Tamm-Daniels, *President*
John Botros, *CFO*
Shankar Ganapathy, *Officer*
EMP: 90
SQ FT: 18,000
SALES (est): 8.7MM **Privately Held**
SIC: 7372 Business oriented computer
software

(P-25052)
PAYDIVVY INC
3121 Michelson Dr Ste 150, Irvine
(92612-5679)
PHONE..............................949 313-3451
Michael Melby, *CEO*
EMP: 15
SQ FT: 2,000
SALES (est): 1.5MM **Privately Held**
SIC: 7372 7374 Word processing com-
puter software; data entry service

PRODUCTS & SVCS

(P-25053)
PAYLOCITY HOLDING CORPORATION
2107 Livingston St, Oakland (94606-5218)
PHONE...................................847 956-4850
EMP: 398
SALES (corp-wide): 377.5MM **Publicly Held**
SIC: 7372 Prepackaged software
PA: Paylocity Holding Corporation
1400 American Ln
Schaumburg IL 60173
847 463-3200

(P-25054)
PEOPLE CENTER INC
Also Called: Rippling
2443 Fillmore St, San Francisco (94115-1814)
PHONE...................................781 864-1232
Parker Conrad, CEO
Persona Sankaranarayana, CTO
EMP: 50
SQ FT: 4,000
SALES: 1MM **Privately Held**
SIC: 7372 Business oriented computer software

(P-25055)
PHANTOM CYBER CORPORATION
2479 E Byshore Rd Ste 185, Palo Alto (94303)
PHONE...................................650 208-5151
Oliver Friedrichs, CEO
Tim Driscoll, CFO
Sourabh Satish, CTO
Dan Ramaswami, Engineer
Erich Baumgartner, Opers Staff
EMP: 30 EST: 2014
SALES (est): 2.4MM
SALES (corp-wide): 1.2B **Publicly Held**
SIC: 7372 7371 Prepackaged software; computer software development & applications
PA: Splunk Inc.
270 Brannan St
San Francisco CA 94107
415 848-8400

(P-25056)
PHOENIX SOFTWARE INTL INC (PA)
831 N Park View Dr, El Segundo (90245-4932)
PHONE...................................310 338-0400
Fred G Hoschett, President
Nicholas A Miller, CFO
Nancy Munoz, Office Mgr
Stuart Morgan, Software Dev
Michael Moyer, Software Dev
◆ EMP: 25
SQ FT: 13,367
SALES: 8.7MM **Privately Held**
WEB: www.vikingsoft.com
SIC: 7372 Prepackaged software

(P-25057)
PHOENIX TECHNOLOGIES LTD (HQ)
910 E Hamilton Ave # 110, Campbell (95008-0612)
PHONE...................................408 570-1000
Rich Geruson, President
Debasish N Biswas, President
Steven S Chan, President
Brian Stein, CFO
Richard Arnold, Exec VP
EMP: 200
SQ FT: 47,000
SALES: 54.9MM **Privately Held**
WEB: www.phoenix.com
SIC: 7372 6794 Prepackaged software; patent owners & lessors

(P-25058)
PHOTOBACKS LLC
40 Paseo Montecillo, Palm Desert (92260-3126)
PHONE...................................760 582-2550
Evan Aberman, Director
EMP: 10 EST: 2011
SALES (est): 289.8K **Privately Held**
SIC: 7372 Application computer software

(P-25059)
PICTRON INC
1250 Oakmead Pkwy Ste 210, Sunnyvale (94085-4035)
PHONE...................................408 725-8888
Darwin Kuan, Exec VP
EMP: 12
SQ FT: 3,000
SALES: 1.1MM **Privately Held**
WEB: www.pictron.com
SIC: 7372 Business oriented computer software

(P-25060)
PIERRY INC (PA)
557 Grand St, Redwood City (94062-2065)
PHONE...................................800 860-7953
Josh Pierry, CEO
Ben Lee, Chief Mktg Ofcr
David Buchanan, Officer
Ozzie Thoreson, Vice Pres
Russell Zermani, Vice Pres
EMP: 50 EST: 2014
SALES (est): 7.8MM **Privately Held**
SIC: 7372 7311 Prepackaged software; advertising agencies

(P-25061)
PILLAR DATA SYSTEMS INC
2840 Junction Ave, San Jose (95134-1922)
PHONE...................................408 503-4000
Michael L Workman, CEO
Nancy Holleran, President
Edward Hayes, President
Warren Webster, Treasurer
Adrian Jones, Senior VP
EMP: 409
SQ FT: 80,000
SALES (est): 29.3MM
SALES (corp-wide): 39.8B **Publicly Held**
WEB: www.pillardata.com
SIC: 7372 Prepackaged software
PA: Oracle Corporation
500 Oracle Pkwy
Redwood City CA 94065
650 506-7000

(P-25062)
PILOT SOFTWARE INC
3410 Hillview Ave, Palo Alto (94304-1395)
PHONE...................................650 230-2830
Jonathan D Becher, President
EMP: 15
SQ FT: 4,100
SALES: 3MM **Privately Held**
SIC: 7372 Business oriented computer software

(P-25063)
PIPELINER CRM
15243 La Cruz Dr Unit 492, Pacific Palisades (90272-5328)
PHONE...................................424 280-6445
Nikoluas Kimla, CEO
Gerald Toumayan, COO
Eva Balgava, Technology
EMP: 20
SALES (est): 967.8K **Privately Held**
SIC: 7372 Business oriented computer software

(P-25064)
PIPELINERSALES INC (PA)
15243 La Cruz Dr Ste 492, Marina Del Rey (90292)
PHONE...................................323 317-7426
Nikolaus Kimla, CEO
Gerald Toumayan, COO
Radoslav Ciglansky, Project Mgr
Petra Jurencakova, Graphic Designe
Hassan Khalifa, Sales Staff
EMP: 13
SALES (est): 656.5K **Privately Held**
SIC: 7372 Prepackaged software

(P-25065)
PLANGRID INC (PA)
2111 Mission St Ste 400, San Francisco (94110-6349)
PHONE...................................415 349-7440
Tracy Young, CEO
James Cook, Partner
Kevin Halter, President
David Cain, Chief Mktg Ofcr
Robert Tesler,
EMP: 47

SQ FT: 16,000
SALES: 11.2MM **Privately Held**
SIC: 7372 Application computer software

(P-25066)
PLANIT SOLUTIONS
1240 Commerce Ave, Woodland (95776-5910)
PHONE...................................530 666-6647
Jeff Welge, Manager
EMP: 15
SALES (est): 809.2K **Privately Held**
WEB: www.planitsolutions.com
SIC: 7372 Prepackaged software

(P-25067)
PLX TECHNOLOGY INC
1320 Ridder Park Dr, San Jose (95131-2313)
PHONE...................................408 435-7400
Hock Tan, President
Anthony Maslowski, CFO
Charlie Kawwas, Senior VP
Boon Chye Ooi, Senior VP
Andy Nallappan, Vice Pres
▲ EMP: 157
SQ FT: 55,000
SALES (est): 12.1MM
SALES (corp-wide): 17.6B **Publicly Held**
WEB: www.plxtech.com
SIC: 7372 3674 Business oriented computer software; integrated circuits, semiconductor networks, etc.
HQ: Avago Technologies Wireless (U.S.A.) Manufacturing Llc
4380 Ziegler Rd
Fort Collins CO 80525
970 288-2575

(P-25068)
PMS SYSTEMS CORPORATION
Also Called: Assetsmart
26707 Agoura Rd Ste 201, Calabasas (91302-3838)
P.O. Box 997, Pacific Palisades (90272-0997)
PHONE...................................310 450-2566
Phillip T Chase, Chairman
Christopher Campbell, President
Phillip Chase, COO
Judith A Chase, Treasurer
Esther Washington, Marketing Staff
EMP: 12
SQ FT: 5,100
SALES: 3MM **Privately Held**
WEB: www.assetsmart.com
SIC: 7372 7371 Prepackaged software; computer software development

(P-25069)
POLARION SOFTWARE INC
1001 Marina Village Pkwy # 403, Alameda (94501-6401)
PHONE...................................877 572-4005
Frank Schrder, CEO
George Briner, CFO
Stefano Rizzo, Senior VP
Nikolay Entin, Vice Pres
Jiri Walek, Vice Pres
EMP: 90
SALES (est): 7.2MM **Privately Held**
SIC: 7372 Prepackaged software

(P-25070)
PORT 80 SOFTWARE INC
Also Called: I I S Mechanics
2105 Garnet Ave Ste E, San Diego (92109-3670)
PHONE...................................858 274-4497
Thomas Powell, CEO
EMP: 20
SALES (est): 1.8MM **Privately Held**
WEB: www.port80software.com
SIC: 7372 Prepackaged software

(P-25071)
PORTELLUS INC
2522 Chambers Rd Ste 100, Tustin (92780-6962)
PHONE...................................949 250-9600
John Le, President
EMP: 80
SALES: 3.6MM **Privately Held**
WEB: www.portellus.com
SIC: 7372 Prepackaged software

(P-25072)
PORTWORX INC
4940 El Camino Real # 200, Los Altos (94022-1481)
PHONE...................................650 241-3222
Murli Thirumale, CEO
Gou RAO, CTO
Aditya Dani, Software Dev
Ganesh Sangle, Software Dev
Paul Theunis, Software Engr
EMP: 31
SALES (est): 81.5K **Privately Held**
SIC: 7372 Application computer software

(P-25073)
POTENTIA LABS INC
2870 4th Ave Apt 212, San Diego (92103-6272)
PHONE...................................951 603-3531
Dustin Milner, President
Eric Lenhardt, Vice Pres
EMP: 15
SALES (est): 701K **Privately Held**
SIC: 7372 Business oriented computer software

(P-25074)
POWERSCHOOL GROUP LLC (HQ)
150 Parkshore Dr, Folsom (95630-4710)
PHONE...................................916 288-1636
Hardeep Gulati, CEO
Mark Oldemeyer, CFO
Chad Dirks, Vice Pres
Varughese George, Vice Pres
Alan Taylor, Vice Pres
EMP: 146
SALES (est): 69.6MM
SALES (corp-wide): 4.4B **Privately Held**
SIC: 7372 Prepackaged software
PA: Vista Equity Partners Management, Llc
4 Embarcadero Ctr # 2000
San Francisco CA 94111
415 765-6500

(P-25075)
POWWOW INC
594 Howard St Ste 301, San Francisco (94105-3026)
PHONE...................................415 515-4947
Andrew Cohen, CEO
Kia Behnia, President
Jonathan Kaplan, Admin Sec
Prasanna Kuppumani, Software Engr
EMP: 24
SALES (est): 460.5K **Privately Held**
SIC: 7372 Business oriented computer software

(P-25076)
PPORT COM INC
1200 Crossman Ave Ste 240, Sunnyvale (94089-1106)
PHONE...................................516 393-6759
EMP: 11 EST: 2017
SALES (est): 849.5K **Privately Held**
SIC: 7372 Prepackaged software

(P-25077)
PREDII INC
2211 Park Blvd, Palo Alto (94306-1533)
PHONE...................................650 666-2524
Tilak Kasturi, President
EMP: 20
SALES: 14MM **Privately Held**
SIC: 7372 7389 Business oriented computer software;

(P-25078)
PREDPOL INC
920 41st Ave Ste D, Santa Cruz (95062-4457)
P.O. Box 2870 (95063-2870)
PHONE...................................831 331-4550
Brian Macdonald, CEO
Christine Bottomley, CFO
EMP: 10
SALES (est): 620K **Privately Held**
SIC: 7372 Application computer software

(P-25079)
PREZI INC (PA)
450 Bryant St, San Francisco (94107-1303)
PHONE...................................415 398-8012

Peter Arvai, *CEO*
Jim Szafranski, *COO*
Narayan Menon, *CFO*
Susan Setton, *Administration*
Peter Halacsy, *CTO*
EMP: 30 **EST:** 2009
SQ FT: 1,600
SALES (est): 13.5MM **Privately Held**
WEB: www.prezi.com
SIC: 7372 Business oriented computer software

(P-25080)
PRISM SOFTWARE CORPORATION
15500 Rockfield Blvd C, Irvine (92618-2700)
PHONE..................949 855-3100
Carl S Von Bibra, *Chairman*
David Ayres, *President*
Michael Cheever, *Treasurer*
Conrad Von Bibra, *Admin Sec*
EMP: 25
SALES (est): 3.7MM **Privately Held**
WEB: www.prism-software.com
SIC: 7372 Publishers' computer software; utility computer software; word processing computer software; operating systems computer software

(P-25081)
PROCEDE SOFTWARE LP
6815 Flanders Dr Ste 200, San Diego (92121-3914)
PHONE..................858 450-4800
Peter Kneale, *General Ptnr*
Phillip Mossy, *Partner*
Sandra Djordjevich, *Technical Staff*
EMP: 20
SALES (est): 3.3MM **Privately Held**
WEB: www.procedesoftware.com
SIC: 7372 Business oriented computer software

(P-25082)
PRODUCTPLAN LLC
10 E Yanonali St Ste 2a, Santa Barbara (93101-1878)
PHONE..................805 618-2975
James Semick,
Andre Theus, *Mktg Dir*
Greg Goodman,
Nick Fields, *Manager*
EMP: 20 **EST:** 2013
SALES (est): 509.4K **Privately Held**
SIC: 7372 Business oriented computer software

(P-25083)
PROJECT CLOUDKEY INC
Also Called: Keypr
600 Wilshire Blvd Ste 700, Los Angeles (90017-3219)
PHONE..................310 596-8160
Nizar Allibhoy, *CEO*
Ben Keller, *Vice Pres*
Philippe Dias, *CTO*
Quang Vu, *Software Engr*
Nevin Wong, *Technical Staff*
EMP: 10
SALES (est): 1.3MM **Privately Held**
SIC: 7372 Business oriented computer software

(P-25084)
PROJECTORIS INC
Also Called: Screenmeet.com
582 Market St Ste 1901, San Francisco (94104-5320)
PHONE..................917 972-5553
Ben Lilienthal, *President*
Eugene Abovsky, *Admin Sec*
EMP: 15
SALES (est): 652.9K **Privately Held**
SIC: 7372 Prepackaged software

(P-25085)
PROVIDENET COMMUNICATIONS CORP
20 Great Oaks Blvd, San Jose (95119-1002)
PHONE..................408 398-6335
Greg McNab, *President*
EMP: 29
SQ FT: 6,000

SALES (est): 3.8MM **Privately Held**
WEB: www.cdumail.com
SIC: 7372 4813 Prepackaged software; telephone communication, except radio

(P-25086)
PROXIMEX CORPORATION (DH)
300 Santana Row Ste 200, San Jose (95128-2443)
PHONE..................408 215-9000
Jack Smith, *CEO*
James A Barth, *CFO*
Diane M Z Robinette, *Vice Pres*
Ken Prayoon Cheng, *CTO*
EMP: 18
SALES (est): 4.3MM **Privately Held**
WEB: www.proximex.com
SIC: 7372 Business oriented computer software
HQ: Johnson Controls Security Solutions Llc
6600 Congress Ave
Boca Raton FL 33487
561 264-2071

(P-25087)
PS SUPPORT INC
800 W El Camin Real, Mountain View (94040)
PHONE..................301 351-9366
Qiang Du, *CEO*
EMP: 11
SALES: 1MM **Privately Held**
SIC: 7372 Application computer software

(P-25088)
PUBINNO INC
1040 Mariposa St, San Francisco (94107-2520)
PHONE..................669 251-6538
Can Algul, *CEO*
Emre Ilke Cosar, *COO*
Necdet Alpmen, *CTO*
EMP: 13
SALES (est): 300K **Privately Held**
SIC: 7372 Prepackaged software

(P-25089)
PULL STRING INC
133 Kearny St 400, San Francisco (94108-4805)
PHONE..................415 758-3339
Oren Jacob, *CEO*
Martin Reddy, *CTO*
Lucas Ives, *Prgrmr*
Renee Adams, *Opers Staff*
Jamie Rollins, *Director*
EMP: 38 **EST:** 2011
SALES (est): 3MM **Privately Held**
SIC: 7372 Application computer software

(P-25090)
PUSHTOTEST INC
1735 Tech Dr Ste 820, San Jose (95110)
PHONE..................408 436-8203
EMP: 10
SALES (est): 957.4K **Privately Held**
SIC: 7372

(P-25091)
QAD INC (PA)
100 Innovation Pl, Santa Barbara (93108-2268)
PHONE..................805 566-6000
Pamela M Lopker, *Ch of Bd*
Tony Yip, *President*
Daniel Lender, *CFO*
Anton Chilton, *Exec VP*
Kara Bellamy, *Senior VP*
EMP: 148
SQ FT: 120,000
SALES: 305MM **Publicly Held**
WEB: www.qad.com
SIC: 7372 7371 Business oriented computer software; custom computer programming services

(P-25092)
QED SOFTWARE LLC
Also Called: Trinium Technologies
304 Tejon Pl, Palos Verdes Estates (90274-1204)
PHONE..................310 214-3118
Michael Thomas, *CEO*
Barry Assadi, *CTO*
EMP: 27

SQ FT: 2,500
SALES (est): 4.5MM **Privately Held**
WEB: www.triniumtech.com
SIC: 7372 Business oriented computer software
PA: Wisetech Global Limited
U3a 72 Oriordan St
Alexandria NSW 2015
-

(P-25093)
QSI 2011 INC (PA)
Also Called: Questys Solutions
2302 Martin St 475, Irvine (92612-7402)
PHONE..................949 855-6885
Rodney Anderson, *President*
Michael Richard, *CFO*
Randy Weis, *Software Engr*
Laura Lechien, *Natl Sales Mgr*
Brett Barnes, *Manager*
EMP: 18 **EST:** 1980
SQ FT: 5,050
SALES (est): 2MM **Privately Held**
WEB: www.questyssolutions.com
SIC: 7372 Business oriented computer software

(P-25094)
QUADBASE SYSTEMS INC
990 Linden Dr Ste 230, Santa Clara (95050-6175)
PHONE..................408 982-0835
Fred Luk, *President*
EMP: 15
SALES (est): 1.6MM **Privately Held**
WEB: www.quadbase.com
SIC: 7372 7371 Application computer software; custom computer programming services

(P-25095)
QUALCOMM INNOVATION CENTER INC (HQ)
4365 Executive Dr # 1100, San Diego (92121-2123)
PHONE..................858 587-1121
Rob Chandhok, *President*
Ahmad Jalali, *Vice Pres*
Steven Mair, *Program Mgr*
Joonwoo Park, *Sr Software Eng*
Ben Broussard, *Info Tech Dir*
EMP: 43 **EST:** 2009
SALES (corp-wide): 6.1MM
SALES (corp-wide): 22.2B **Publicly Held**
SIC: 7372 Prepackaged software
PA: Qualcomm Incorporated
5775 Morehouse Dr
San Diego CA 92121
858 587-1121

(P-25096)
QUANTAL INTERNATIONAL INC
455 Market St Ste 1200, San Francisco (94105-2441)
PHONE..................415 644-0754
Terry Marsh, *President*
Jeff Rogers, *COO*
Paul Pfleiderer, *CFO*
Indro Fedrigo, *Vice Pres*
EMP: 26
SQ FT: 7,000
SALES (est): 2.7MM **Privately Held**
WEB: www.quantal.com
SIC: 7372 6282 Business oriented computer software; investment advisory service

(P-25097)
QUEST SOFTWARE INC
Packettrap Networks
118 2nd St Fl 6, San Francisco (94105-3620)
PHONE..................415 373-2222
Steven M Goodman, *President*
EMP: 65
SALES (corp-wide): 1.7B **Privately Held**
SIC: 7372 Prepackaged software
HQ: Quest Software, Inc.
4 Polaris Way
Aliso Viejo CA 92656
949 754-8000

(P-25098)
QUEST SOFTWARE INC
5450 Great America Pkwy, Santa Clara (95054-3644)
PHONE..................408 899-3823
EMP: 15
SALES (corp-wide): 1.7B **Privately Held**
SIC: 7372 Prepackaged software
HQ: Quest Software, Inc.
4 Polaris Way
Aliso Viejo CA 92656
949 754-8000

(P-25099)
QUEST SOFTWARE INC
Also Called: Cloud Automation Division
4 Polaris Way, Aliso Viejo (92656-5356)
PHONE..................949 754-8000
Alexa Ives, *Partner*
Brian Odonnell, *Partner*
Anne Simpson, *Partner*
Matt Vitale, *Vice Pres*
Pritesh Doshi, *Regional Mgr*
EMP: 80
SALES (corp-wide): 1.7B **Privately Held**
SIC: 7372 Prepackaged software
HQ: Quest Software, Inc.
4 Polaris Way
Aliso Viejo CA 92656
949 754-8000

(P-25100)
QUESTIVITY INC
1680 Civic Center Dr # 209, Santa Clara (95050-4660)
PHONE..................408 615-1781
Humayun Sohel, *President*
EMP: 15
SQ FT: 1,180
SALES (est): 5MM **Privately Held**
WEB: www.questivity.com
SIC: 7372 7361 Prepackaged software; employment agencies

(P-25101)
QUMU INC
1100 Grundy Ln Ste 110, San Bruno (94066-3072)
PHONE..................650 396-8530
Jim Stewart, *CFO*
Chad Sears, *Vice Pres*
Dolores Rios, *Executive Asst*
Taimur Mirza, *Sr Software Eng*
Hamid Porasl, *Software Dev*
EMP: 56
SQ FT: 13,000
SALES (est): 9.5MM
SALES (corp-wide): 28.1MM **Publicly Held**
WEB: www.mediapublisher.com
SIC: 7372 Business oriented computer software
PA: Qumu Corporation
510 1st Ave N Ste 305
Minneapolis MN 55403
612 638-9100

(P-25102)
QWILT INC (PA)
275 Shoreline Dr Ste 510, Redwood City (94065-1413)
PHONE..................866 824-8009
Alon Maor, *CEO*
Yoni Mizrahi, *CFO*
Yuval Shahar, *Chairman*
Mark Fisher, *Vice Pres*
Yoav Gressel, *Vice Pres*
EMP: 14 **EST:** 2010
SALES (est): 3.7MM **Privately Held**
SIC: 7372 Business oriented computer software

(P-25103)
RAKSHAK
2518 Alvin St, Mountain View (94043-2708)
PHONE..................404 513-5867
Rajan K Singh, *Principal*
EMP: 20
SALES (est): 869K **Privately Held**
WEB: www.rakshak.com
SIC: 7372 Prepackaged software

(P-25104)
READ CORP
16012a Flintlock Rd, Cupertino
(95014-5401)
PHONE....................408 705-2123
Ione Benford, *CEO*
Thomas Benford, *Chairman*
EMP: 35
SALES (est): 1.7MM **Privately Held**
WEB: www.read-ink.com
SIC: 7372 Operating systems computer
software

(P-25105)
READ IT LATER INC
233 Sansome St Ste 1200, San Francisco
(94104-2300)
PHONE......................415 692-6111
Nathan Weiner, *CEO*
EMP: 34
SALES: 5MM
SALES (corp-wide): 421.2MM **Privately
Held**
SIC: 7372 Application computer software
HQ: Mozilla Corporation
331 E Evelyn Ave Ste 100
Mountain View CA 94041
650 903-0800

(P-25106)
READYTECH CORPORATION
2201 Broadway Ste 725, Oakland
(94612-3024)
PHONE......................510 834-3344
John K Woodward, *President*
Sue Ray, *CFO*
Jane Tao, *Software Engr*
Candice Cheng, *Technology*
Yasha Spong, *Business Mgr*
EMP: 14
SALES (est): 2.1MM **Privately Held**
SIC: 7372 Educational computer software

(P-25107)
**REAL SOFTWARE SYSTEMS
LLC (PA)**
21255 Burbank Blvd # 220, Woodland Hills
(91367-6610)
PHONE......................818 313-8000
Kent Sahin, *Mng Member*
Jenny Gonzales, *Consultant*
EMP: 60
SALES (est): 8MM **Privately Held**
WEB: www.realsoftwaresystems.com
SIC: 7372 Business oriented computer
software

(P-25108)
**REALIZATION TECHNOLOGIES
INC**
440 N Wolfe Rd 52, Sunnyvale
(94085-3869)
PHONE......................408 271-1720
Sanjeev Gupta, *President*
Ravi Radhakrishnan, *Admin Sec*
Chris Dailey, *Project Mgr*
Deborah Busby, *Business Mgr*
Michael Hamlin, *Director*
EMP: 20
SALES (est): 2.7MM **Privately Held**
WEB: www.realization.com
SIC: 7372 Application computer software

(P-25109)
REALPAGE INC
Also Called: Ops Technology
333 3rd St, San Francisco (94107-1240)
PHONE......................415 222-6996
Tony Howard, *Branch Mgr*
EMP: 22
SALES (corp-wide): 670.9MM **Publicly
Held**
SIC: 7372 7371 Prepackaged software;
custom computer programming services
PA: Realpage, Inc.
2201 Lakeside Blvd
Richardson TX 75082
972 820-3000

(P-25110)
REALSCOUT INC
480 Ellis St Ste 203, Mountain View
(94043-2204)
PHONE......................650 397-6500
Arthur Kaneko, *CEO*

Andrew S Flanchner, *President*
Megan Keefhaver, *Office Mgr*
Sergio Lopez, *Admin Asst*
Gil Raphaelli, *Sr Software Eng*
EMP: 15
SQ FT: 500
SALES (est): 1.5MM **Privately Held**
SIC: 7372 Business oriented computer
software

(P-25111)
REALWARE INC
444 Haas Ave, San Leandro (94577-2926)
PHONE......................510 382-9045
David Bennett, *President*
EMP: 10 EST: 1998
SALES: 1MM **Privately Held**
WEB: www.realwareinc.com
SIC: 7372 Prepackaged software

(P-25112)
REALWISE INC
Also Called: Avm Technologies
28042 Avenue Stanford E, Valencia
(91355-1157)
PHONE......................661 295-9399
Steve Sturgeon, *President*
EMP: 10
SALES (est): 907.7K **Privately Held**
WEB: www.realwise.com
SIC: 7372 5734 Business oriented com-
puter software; personal computers

(P-25113)
REASON8 INC
490 Post St Ste 526, San Francisco
(94102-1406)
PHONE......................505 220-3683
Vlad Belyaev, *CEO*
EMP: 12
SALES (est): 25.2K **Privately Held**
SIC: 7372 7389 Prepackaged software;

(P-25114)
REBOL TECHNOLOGIES INC
301 S State St, Ukiah (95482-4906)
P.O. Box 1510 (95482-1510)
PHONE......................707 485-0599
Tom Coull, *President*
Cynthia Sassenrath, *COO*
Carl Sassenrath, *CTO*
EMP: 17
SALES (est): 1MM **Privately Held**
WEB: www.rebol.com
SIC: 7372 Application computer software

(P-25115)
RECEIVD INC
Also Called: Kicksend
655 Castro St Ste 2, Mountain View
(94041-2019)
PHONE......................650 336-5817
Pradeep Elankumaran, *CEO*
Brendan Lim, *Bd of Directors*
EMP: 10 EST: 2011
SALES (est): 643.3K **Privately Held**
SIC: 7372 Application computer software

(P-25116)
RED GATE SOFTWARE INC
144 W Colo Blvd Ste 200, Pasadena
(91105)
PHONE......................626 993-3949
Tom Curtis, *President*
EMP: 23
SQ FT: 5,500
SALES (est): 2.7MM
SALES (corp-wide): 52.1MM **Privately
Held**
SIC: 7372 Business oriented computer
software
HQ: Red Gate Software Limited
Newnham House
Cambridge CAMBS CB4 0
122 342-0397

(P-25117)
RED HAT INC
444 Castro St Ste 1200, Mountain View
(94041-2064)
PHONE......................650 567-9039
Alex Daly, *Manager*
Steve Hodgson, *Executive*
Rose Naftaly, *Office Mgr*
Christina Fu, *Project Mgr*
Xiu Wang, *Engineer*

EMP: 15 **Publicly Held**
WEB: www.apacheweek.com
SIC: 7372 Operating systems computer
software
PA: Red Hat, Inc.
100 E Davie St
Raleigh NC 27601
-

(P-25118)
REDACTED-STUDIOS LLC
4100 Redwood Rd, Oakland (94619-2363)
PHONE......................510 333-0030
David Robinson, *Principal*
EMP: 10 EST: 2012
SALES (est): 545.3K **Privately Held**
SIC: 7372 Home entertainment computer
software

(P-25119)
REDCORT SOFTWARE INC
619 Woodworth Ave Ste 200, Clovis
(93612-1872)
P.O. Box 25764, Fresno (93729-5764)
PHONE......................559 434-8544
Keith Delong, *CEO*
Joshua Mewborn, *Web Dvlpr*
EMP: 10
SALES (est): 1MM **Privately Held**
WEB: www.redcort.com
SIC: 7372 Business oriented computer
software

(P-25120)
REDSEAL INC
940 Stewart Dr Ste 101, Sunnyvale
(94085-3912)
PHONE......................408 641-2200
Ray Rothrock, *Ch of Bd*
Pete Sinclair, *COO*
Bob Finley, *CFO*
Julie Parrish, *Chief Mktg Ofcr*
Gordon Adams, *Officer*
EMP: 100
SQ FT: 6,500
SALES (est): 21.3MM **Privately Held**
WEB: www.redseal.net
SIC: 7372 Prepackaged software

(P-25121)
REDWOOD APPS INC
805 Veterans Blvd Ste 322, Redwood City
(94063-1737)
PHONE......................408 348-3808
Benkat Supramanian, *President*
Markus Hummel, *Vice Pres*
EMP: 10
SQ FT: 1,000
SALES (est): 268.4K **Privately Held**
SIC: 7372 Prepackaged software

(P-25122)
REFUNDS TODAY LLC
10430 Pioneer Blvd Ste 2, Santa Fe
Springs (90670-8247)
PHONE......................323 261-0240
Dan Gonzalez, *CEO*
Juan Rodriguez, *IT/INT Sup*
Lori Bonanno-Gonzalez, *Director*
Armando Gonzalez, *Director*
EMP: 26
SQ FT: 5,400
SALES (est): 3.5MM **Privately Held**
WEB: www.refundstoday.com
SIC: 7372 Application computer software

(P-25123)
RELATEIQ INC
502 Emerson St, Palo Alto (94301)
PHONE......................650 409-2336
Stephen Loughlin, *CEO*
Jason LI, *President*
Adam Evans, *Principal*
Adam Witherspoon, *Technology*
Ryan Deforest, *Marketing Staff*
EMP: 31
SALES (est): 4.9MM **Privately Held**
SIC: 7372 Business oriented computer
software

(P-25124)
RELATIONAL CENTER
2717 S Robertson Blvd # 1, Los Angeles
(90034-2451)
PHONE......................323 935-1807
Traci Bivens Davis, *Principal*

Dan Fink, *Associate Dir*
Penny Timmons, *Psychologist*
Patricia Steffy, *Associate*
EMP: 21 EST: 2008
SALES: 721.1K **Privately Held**
SIC: 7372 Prepackaged software

(P-25125)
**RELOADED TECHNOLOGIES
INC**
17011 Beach Blvd Ste 320, Huntington
Beach (92647-7420)
PHONE......................949 870-3123
Bjorn Book-Larsson, *CEO*
EMP: 10 EST: 2013
SALES (est): 415.6K **Privately Held**
SIC: 7372 Publishers' computer software

(P-25126)
**RETAIL SOLUTIONS
INCORPORATED (PA)**
201 Ravendale Dr, Mountain View
(94043-5216)
PHONE......................650 390-6100
Bert Clement, *CEO*
Peter Rieman, *COO*
Patrick U Di Chiro, *Officer*
Jonathan Golovin, *Officer*
Dr Shantala Moham, *Senior VP*
EMP: 30
SQ FT: 18,000
SALES (est): 41.2MM **Privately Held**
WEB: www.retailsolutions.com
SIC: 7372 Business oriented computer
software

(P-25127)
RETROSPECT INC
44 Westwind Rd, Lafayette (94549-2116)
PHONE......................888 376-1078
JG Heithcock, *CEO*
Alan Pabst, *Opers Staff*
Werner Walter, *Sales Staff*
Robin Mayoff, *Senior Mgr*
EMP: 20
SALES (est): 644.9K **Privately Held**
SIC: 7372 Prepackaged software

(P-25128)
REVJET
981 Industrial Rd Ste F, San Carlos
(94070-4150)
PHONE......................650 508-2215
Patrick McNenny, *Vice Pres*
Bradley McKeon, *Vice Pres*
David Mackay, *Risk Mgmt Dir*
Serge Ioffe, *CTO*
Andriy Gusyev, *Engrg Dir*
EMP: 110 EST: 2017
SALES (est): 2.3MM **Privately Held**
SIC: 7372 Application computer software

(P-25129)
RFL GLOBAL INC
732 E Jefferson Blvd, Los Angeles
(90011-2435)
PHONE......................323 235-2580
EMP: 15 EST: 2014
SALES (est): 690K **Privately Held**
SIC: 7372

(P-25130)
RIFFYN INC (PA)
360 17th St Ste 100, Oakland
(94612-3364)
PHONE......................510 542-9868
Timothy Gardner, *CEO*
Lauryl Loberg, *Sr Software Eng*
Lili Nader, *CTO*
Ram Ranganathan, *Software Engr*
Jean Calegari, *VP Opers*
EMP: 10
SALES (est): 1.4MM **Privately Held**
SIC: 7372 Business oriented computer
software

(P-25131)
RIVERMEADOW SOFTWARE INC
2107 N 1st St Ste 660, San Jose
(95131-2005)
PHONE......................408 217-6498
Richard Scannell, *Exec VP*
Denise Maher, *Executive Asst*
Emanuele Tatti, *Sr Software Eng*
Srinivasa Vegeraju, *Sr Software Eng*
Richard Buck, *CTO*

EMP: 10 **EST:** 2013
SALES (est): 831.5K **Privately Held**
SIC: 7372 Business oriented computer
software

(P-25132)
ROSE BUSINESS SOLUTIONS INC
875 Chelsea Ln, Encinitas (92024-6675)
PHONE................................858 794-9401
K Linda Rose, *President*
Glen Medwid, *CFO*
EMP: 20
SALES: 2.7MM **Privately Held**
WEB: www.rosebizinc.com
SIC: 7372 Prepackaged software

(P-25133)
RUNA INC
2 W 5th Ave Ste 300, San Mateo
(94402-2002)
PHONE................................508 253-5000
Ashok Narasimhan, *CEO*
EMP: 15
SALES (est): 854K
SALES (corp-wide): 18.2B **Privately Held**
SIC: 7372 Business oriented computer
software
HQ: Staples, Inc.
500 Staples Dr
Framingham MA 01702
508 253-5000

(P-25134)
RYPPLE
577 Howard St Fl 3, San Francisco
(94105-4635)
PHONE................................888 479-7753
EMP: 15
SALES (est): 1.1MM **Privately Held**
SIC: 7372

(P-25135)
S-MATRIX CORPORATION
1594 Myrtle Ave, Eureka (95501-1454)
PHONE................................707 441-0404
Richard Verseput, *President*
George Cooney, *Vice Pres*
Rusdiye Freedman, *Sr Software Eng*
Dave George, *Sr Software Eng*
Matthew Cook, *QC Mgr*
EMP: 14
SALES (est): 1.6MM **Privately Held**
WEB: www.s-matrix-corp.com
SIC: 7372 7371 Business oriented com-
puter software; software programming ap-
plications

(P-25136)
SABA SOFTWARE INC (PA)
4120 Dublin Blvd Ste 200, Dublin
(94568-7759)
PHONE................................877 722-2101
Phil Saunders, *President*
Pete Low, *CFO*
Debbie Shotwell,
Michelle Humphrey, *Executive*
Tina Garnaat, *Marketing Staff*
EMP: 100
SQ FT: 36,000
SALES (est): 196.6MM **Privately Held**
WEB: www.saba.com
SIC: 7372 Application computer soft-
ware; computer software development &
applications

(P-25137)
SAFETYCHAIN SOFTWARE INC (PA)
7599 Redwood Blvd Ste 205, Novato
(94945-7706)
PHONE................................415 233-9474
Walter Smith, *Principal*
Clara Gavriliuc, *Vice Pres*
Barry Maxon, *Vice Pres*
Julia Kreger, *Project Mgr*
Tom Vieira, *Project Mgr*
EMP: 21 **EST:** 2012
SALES (est): 6.4MM **Privately Held**
SIC: 7372 Business oriented computer
software

(P-25138)
SAGE SOFTWARE INC
1380 Tatan Trail Rd, Burlingame (94010)
PHONE................................650 579-3628

Mau Chung Chang, *Branch Mgr*
EMP: 245
SALES (corp-wide): 2.2B **Privately Held**
SIC: 7372 Business oriented computer
software
HQ: Sage Software International, Inc.
271 17th St Nw Ste 1100
Atlanta GA 30363
866 996-7243

(P-25139)
SAGE SOFTWARE HOLDINGS INC (HQ)
6561 Irvine Center Dr, Irvine (92618-2118)
PHONE................................866 530-7243
Stev Swenson, *CEO*
Mack Lout, *CFO*
Doug Meyer, *Vice Pres*
EMP: 400
SALES (est): 516.3MM
SALES (corp-wide): 2.2B **Privately Held**
SIC: 7372 7371 Business oriented com-
puter software; custom computer pro-
gramming services
PA: The Sage Group Plc.
North Park Avenue
Newcastle-Upon-Tyne NE13
191 294-3000

(P-25140)
SALESFORCECOM INC
50 Fremont St, San Francisco
(94105-2276)
PHONE................................415 323-8685
Charlene Kahler, *Principal*
Aseem Gupta, *Counsel*
EMP: 21
SALES (corp-wide): 10.4B **Publicly Held**
SIC: 7372 Business oriented computer
software
PA: Salesforce.Com, Inc.
1 Market Ste 300
San Francisco CA 94105
415 901-7000

(P-25141)
SALESFORCECOM INC
1 Market Ste 300, San Francisco
(94105-5188)
PHONE................................703 463-3300
John Devoe, *Administration*
Dan Burnham, *Partner*
Colin Casey, *Partner*
Laura Wilensky, *Partner*
Mark Cerniglia, *Vice Pres*
EMP: 14
SALES (corp-wide): 10.4B **Publicly Held**
SIC: 7372 7375 Business oriented com-
puter software; information retrieval serv-
ices
PA: Salesforce.Com, Inc.
1 Market Ste 300
San Francisco CA 94105
415 901-7000

(P-25142)
SALESFORCECOM INC (PA)
1 Market Ste 300, San Francisco
(94105-5188)
PHONE................................415 901-7000
Marc Benioff, *Ch of Bd*
Keith Block, *President*
Mark Hawkins, *President*
Amy Weaver, *President*
Joe Allanson, *Senior VP*
EMP: 600 **EST:** 1999
SALES: 10.4B **Publicly Held**
WEB: www.salesforce.com
SIC: 7372 7375 Business oriented com-
puter software; information retrieval serv-
ices

(P-25143)
SALESFORCECOM INC
1442 2nd St, Santa Monica (90401-2302)
PHONE................................310 752-7000
Andy Deman, *Manager*
Ethan Alexander, *Director*
EMP: 40
SALES (corp-wide): 10.4B **Publicly Held**
WEB: www.salesforce.com
SIC: 7372 Business oriented computer
software

PA: Salesforce.Com, Inc.
1 Market Ste 300
San Francisco CA 94105
415 901-7000

(P-25144)
SANTAN SOFTWARE SYSTEMS INC
19504 Ronald Ave, Torrance (90503-1239)
P.O. Box 34521, Los Angeles (90034-0521)
PHONE................................310 836-2802
Barun Bamba, *President*
Varun Bamba, *President*
Bob Varun, *President*
Samita Bamba, *Admin Sec*
EMP: 21
SALES: 6MM **Privately Held**
WEB: www.santansoftwaresystems.com
SIC: 7372 Prepackaged software

(P-25145)
SARS SOFTWARE PRODUCTS INC
2175 Francisco Blvd E, San Rafael
(94901-5510)
P.O. Box 653, Mill Valley (94942-0653)
PHONE................................415 226-0040
Joanne Fields Doty, *President*
James Doty, *Vice Pres*
EMP: 15 **EST:** 1986
SQ FT: 2,000
SALES (est): 1.2MM **Privately Held**
SIC: 7372 Prepackaged software

(P-25146)
SAS INSTITUTE INC
Also Called: Post Montgomery Center
50 Post St Ste 50 # 50, San Francisco
(94104-4552)
PHONE................................415 421-2227
Bernard Doering, *Branch Mgr*
EMP: 33
SALES (corp-wide): 3B **Privately Held**
WEB: www.sas.com
SIC: 7372 Application computer software;
business oriented computer software; ed-
ucational computer software
PA: Sas Institute Inc.
100 Sas Campus Dr
Cary NC 27513
919 677-8000

(P-25147)
SAS INSTITUTE INC
2121 N 1st St Ste 100, San Jose
(95131-2053)
PHONE................................919 677-8000
Danny Parodi, *Manager*
EMP: 15
SALES (corp-wide): 3B **Privately Held**
WEB: www.sas.com
SIC: 7372 Application computer software;
business oriented computer software; ed-
ucational computer software
PA: Sas Institute Inc.
100 Sas Campus Dr
Cary NC 27513
919 677-8000

(P-25148)
SAS INSTITUTE INC
Salesstock.com
1148 N Lemon St, Orange (92867-4701)
PHONE................................949 250-9999
Shawn Anthony Stiltz, *Vice Pres*
EMP: 56
SALES (corp-wide): 3B **Privately Held**
SIC: 7372 Application computer software;
business oriented computer software; ed-
ucational computer software
PA: Sas Institute Inc.
100 Sas Campus Dr
Cary NC 27513
919 677-8000

(P-25149)
SASS LABS INC
Also Called: Allyo
121 W Washington Ave # 212, Sunnyvale
(94086-1107)
PHONE................................404 731-7284
Ankit Somani, *President*
Sahil Sahni, *Vice Pres*
EMP: 20
SALES (est): 382.7K **Privately Held**
SIC: 7372 Application computer software

(P-25150)
SCAMSAFE INC
Also Called: Truston
402 E Gutierrez St, Santa Barbara
(93101-1709)
PHONE................................800 960-5512
Thomas F Fragala, *CEO*
EMP: 10
SALES (est): 663.2K **Privately Held**
WEB: www.trustoncorp.com
SIC: 7372 Business oriented computer
software

(P-25151)
SCENE 53 INC
800 E Charleston Rd Apt 7, Palo Alto
(94303-4627)
PHONE................................415 404-2461
Yonatan Maor, *CEO*
Hamutal Russo, *CFO*
EMP: 20
SALES (est): 993.2K **Privately Held**
SIC: 7372 Home entertainment computer
software

(P-25152)
SCHOOL INNOVATIONS ACHIEVEMENT (PA)
5200 Golden Foothill Pkwy, El Dorado Hills
(95762-9610)
PHONE................................916 933-2290
Jeffrey C Williams, *CEO*
Jenn Abresch, *Partner*
Gemma Ball, *Partner*
Susan Cook, *COO*
Edgar Lopez, *Regional Mgr*
EMP: 95
SQ FT: 25,000
SALES: 14.8MM **Privately Held**
WEB: www.sia-us.com
SIC: 7372 8742 Prepackaged software;
management consulting services

(P-25153)
SCIENTIFIC LEARNING CORP
300 Frank H Ogawa Plz # 600, Oakland
(94612-2056)
PHONE................................510 444-3500
Louise Dube, *Vice Pres*
Chris Brookhart, *Vice Pres*
Cheryl Leatherbury, *Vice Pres*
Rhonda Flores, *Social Dir*
Holly Koob, *Comms Mgr*
EMP: 25 **Publicly Held**
WEB: www.scilearn.com
SIC: 7372 7371 Prepackaged software;
computer software development
PA: Scientific Learning Corporation
1956 Webster St Ste 200
Oakland CA 94612

(P-25154)
SCM ACCELERATORS LLC
2731 California St, San Francisco
(94115-2513)
PHONE................................415 595-8091
Scott Barrett, *President*
Chris Botha, *CEO*
Dejan Ahrens, *CTO*
EMP: 14
SALES: 9.8MM **Privately Held**
SIC: 7372 Business oriented computer
software

(P-25155)
SCOPELY INC (PA)
3530 Hayden Ave Ste A, Culver City
(90232-2413)
PHONE................................323 400-6618
Walter Driver III, *President*
Eytan Elbaz, *Vice Pres*
Eric Futoran, *Vice Pres*
Mary Bloom, *Director*
Liz Liu, *Manager*
EMP: 200
SALES (est): 8.5MM **Privately Held**
SIC: 7372 Home entertainment computer
software

(P-25156)
SE SOFTWARE INC
3340 Ocean Park Blvd # 1005, Santa Monica (90405-3204)
PHONE................................888 504-9876
Greg Hermanovic, *President*

Sean Lee, *Accountant*
EMP: 15
SALES (est): 140.3K **Privately Held**
SIC: 7372 Prepackaged software

(P-25157)
SEAL SOFTWARE INC (PA)
1990 N Calif Blvd Ste 500, Walnut Creek
(94596-3743)
PHONE.....................650 938-7325
Ulf Zetterberg, *CEO*
David Gingell, *Chief Mktg Ofcr*
Rich Bohne, *Risk Mgmt Dir*
Jim Wagner, *Security Dir*
EMP: 18
SALES (est): 4.1MM **Privately Held**
SIC: 7372 Prepackaged software

(P-25158)
SECURE COMPUTING
CORPORATION (DH)
3965 Freedom Cir 4, Santa Clara
(95054-1206)
PHONE.....................408 979-2020
Daniel Ryan, *President*
Richard Scott, *Ch of Bd*
Timothy J Steinkopf, *CFO*
Atri Chatterjee, *Senior VP*
Michael J Gallagher, *Senior VP*
EMP: 40
SQ FT: 10,895
SALES (est): 100.4MM **Privately Held**
WEB: www.securecomp.com
SIC: 7372 Prepackaged software
HQ: Mcafee, Llc
    2821 Mission College Blvd
    Santa Clara CA 95054
    888 847-8766

(P-25159)
SECUREDATA INC
3255 Chnga Blvd W Ste 301, Los Angeles
(90068-1778)
PHONE.....................424 363-8529
Dmitri Kardashev, *CEO*
EMP: 12
SALES: 3.3MM **Privately Held**
SIC: 7372 Application computer software

(P-25160)
SEEK SOFTWARE INC
1645 Mission Avenida, Morgan Hill
(95037-2969)
PHONE.....................408 316-4169
Jordan Smallwood, *CEO*
EMP: 12
SALES (est): 256K **Privately Held**
SIC: 7372 7999 Application computer software; physical fitness instruction

(P-25161)
SEMOTUS INC
Also Called: Hiplink Software
718 University Ave # 110, Los Gatos
(95032-7608)
PHONE.....................408 667-2046
Anthony Lapine, *Chairman*
Pamela Lapine, *President*
Amy Lane, *Admin Asst*
Michael Henkelman, *Engineer*
Adam Terry, *Sales Mgr*
EMP: 25
SQ FT: 4,000
SALES (est): 2.2MM **Privately Held**
WEB: www.hiplink.com
SIC: 7372 7371 8243 Prepackaged software; computer software systems analysis & design, custom; operator training, computer

(P-25162)
SENETUR LLC
399 Lakeside Dr Ste 400, Oakland (94612)
PHONE.....................650 269-1023
Adrian Walker, *CEO*
EMP: 10
SQ FT: 500
SALES (est): 244K **Privately Held**
SIC: 7372 Business oriented computer software

(P-25163)
SEPASOFT INC
1264 Hawks Flight Ct, El Dorado Hills
(95762-9348)
PHONE.....................916 939-1684

Thomas Andrew Hechtman, *President*
Roxanna Hechtman, *CFO*
Byounghyun An, *Software Engr*
Mark French, *Engineer*
EMP: 15 **EST:** 2003
SQ FT: 2,955
SALES (est): 80.1K **Privately Held**
SIC: 7372 Prepackaged software

(P-25164)
SEQUENT SOFTWARE INC
4699 Old Ironsides Dr # 470, Santa Clara
(95054-1861)
PHONE.....................650 419-2713
Andrew Weinstein, *CEO*
Robb Duffield, *CEO*
Lance Johnson, *Officer*
John Kirst, *Officer*
Hans Reisgies, *Senior VP*
EMP: 17
SALES (est): 3.8MM **Privately Held**
SIC: 7372 Application computer software

(P-25165)
SERRA SYSTEMS INC (HQ)
126 Mill St, Healdsburg (95448-4438)
PHONE.....................707 433-5104
Paul Deas, *President*
Pamela Deas, *Corp Secy*
Steven Deas, *Vice Pres*
EMP: 17
SQ FT: 7,000
SALES (est): 3.4MM
SALES (corp-wide): 75.4MM **Privately Held**
WEB: www.serrasystems.com
SIC: 7372 Business oriented computer software
PA: E & M Electric And Machinery, Inc.
    126 Mill St
    Healdsburg CA 95448
    707 433-5578

(P-25166)
SESAME SOFTWARE INC
5201 Great America Pkwy # 320, Santa
Clara (95054-1122)
PHONE.....................866 474-7575
Richard D Banister, *President*
Michael Hoydic, *Accounting Mgr*
Steven Hoydic, *Sales Staff*
Louis Linfoot, *Manager*
Scott O'Dell, *Manager*
EMP: 22
SALES: 1.7MM **Privately Held**
WEB: www.sesamesoftware.com
SIC: 7372 Business oriented computer software

(P-25167)
SHAREDATA INC
Also Called: Sharedta/E Trade Bus Solutions
2465 Augustine Dr, Santa Clara (95054)
PHONE.....................408 490-2500
Laura Fay, *President*
EMP: 53
SALES (est): 1.9MM **Privately Held**
SIC: 7372 Business oriented computer software

(P-25168)
SHARPE SOFTWARE INC
925 Market St, Yuba City (95991-4210)
PHONE.....................530 671-6499
Daniel Ontiveros, *President*
Vanessa Visger, *Info Tech Mgr*
Brent Hooton, *Manager*
EMP: 10
SQ FT: 5,680
SALES (est): 1.1MM **Privately Held**
WEB: www.sharpesoft.com
SIC: 7372 Business oriented computer software

(P-25169)
SHERBIT HEALTH INC
2200 Powell St Ste 460, Emeryville
(94608-2253)
PHONE.....................925 683-8116
Alex Senemar, *CEO*
EMP: 12
SALES (est): 281.6K **Privately Held**
SIC: 7372 Business oriented computer software

(P-25170)
SHORTCUTS SOFTWARE INC
7711 Center Ave Ste 550, Huntington
Beach (92647-3075)
PHONE.....................714 622-6600
Rebecca Randall, *CEO*
Malcom Raward, *Treasurer*
Paul Tate, *Vice Pres*
Angel Gonzales, *Supervisor*
EMP: 30
SALES (est): 3.7MM
SALES (corp-wide): 147.3MM **Privately Held**
WEB: www.shortcuts.com.au
SIC: 7372 Business oriented computer software
HQ: Shortcuts Software Pty Ltd
    L 2 South Tower 10 Browning St
    South Brisbane QLD 4101

(P-25171)
SHOTSPOTTER INC
Also Called: SST
7979 Gateway Blvd Ste 210, Newark
(94560-1158)
PHONE.....................510 794-3100
Ralph A Clark, *President*
Alan R Stewart, *CFO*
Thomas Groos, *Bd of Directors*
Marc Morial, *Bd of Directors*
Paul S Ames, *Senior VP*
EMP: 76
SQ FT: 12,020
SALES: 23.7MM **Privately Held**
WEB: www.shotspotter.com
SIC: 7372 7382 Prepackaged software; security systems services

(P-25172)
SIEENA INC
Also Called: Definity First
1901 Avenue Of The Stars, Los Angeles
(90067-6001)
PHONE.....................310 455-6188
Mauricio Galvan, *President*
Fernando Gutierrez, *Vice Pres*
Christina Kaney, *Business Mgr*
EMP: 40
SALES (corp-wide): 660K **Privately Held**
SIC: 7372 Business oriented computer software
PA: Sieena, Inc
    12555 High Bluff Dr # 333
    San Diego CA 92130
    310 455-6188

(P-25173)
SIEMENS PRODUCT LIFE MGMT
SFTW
Also Called: Siemens PLM Software
2077 Gateway Pl Ste 400, San Jose
(95110-1085)
PHONE.....................408 941-4600
Lorena Mendoza, *Branch Mgr*
Tona McGean, *Administration*
Robert Lee, *Software Dev*
EMP: 49
SALES (corp-wide): 97.7B **Privately Held**
SIC: 7372 Prepackaged software
HQ: Siemens Product Lifecycle Management Software Inc.
    5800 Granite Pkwy Ste 600
    Plano TX 75024
    972 987-3000

(P-25174)
SIGHT MACHINE INC
243 Vallejo St, San Francisco (94111-1511)
PHONE.....................888 461-5739
Jon Sobel, *CEO*
John Stone, *President*
Syed Hoda, *Chief Mktg Ofcr*
Jerry Wu, *Officer*
Kurt Demaagd, *Vice Pres*
EMP: 60
SQ FT: 6,500
SALES (est): 2MM **Privately Held**
SIC: 7372 Business oriented computer software

(P-25175)
SIGHTEN INC
426 17th St Ste 600, Oakland
(94612-2849)
PHONE.....................415 965-3000

Conlan O'Leary, *CEO*
Tyler Slauson, *Associate*
EMP: 22
SALES (est): 732.7K **Privately Held**
SIC: 7372 Application computer software

(P-25176)
SIMPLEFEED INC
289 S San Antonio Rd # 2, Los Altos
(94022-3758)
PHONE.....................650 947-7445
Mark Carlson, *President*
Alik Elishberg, *Vice Pres*
Sequoia Capital, *Principal*
Yuriy Grinberg, *Chief Engr*
EMP: 15
SALES: 1.3MM **Privately Held**
SIC: 7372 Prepackaged software

(P-25177)
SIMPLELEGAL INC
488 Ellis St, Mountain View (94043-2204)
PHONE.....................415 763-5366
Nathan Wenzel, *CEO*
EMP: 11
SALES (est): 289.3K **Privately Held**
SIC: 7372 Business oriented computer software

(P-25178)
SIOS TECHNOLOGY CORP (HQ)
155 Bovet Rd Ste 476, San Mateo
(94402-3112)
PHONE.....................650 645-7000
Jerry Melnick, *President*
Kellymarie Silva, *Partner*
Celia Cattani, *Vice Pres*
Bob Williamson, *Vice Pres*
Junkyo Fujieda, *Principal*
EMP: 10
SQ FT: 4,400
SALES: 8MM
SALES (corp-wide): 111.3MM **Privately Held**
WEB: www.steeleye.com
SIC: 7372 Business oriented computer software
PA: Sios Corporation
    2-12-3, Minamiazabu
    Minato-Ku TKY 106-0
    364 015-111

(P-25179)
SKYLIGHT SOFTWARE INC
3792 Bertini Ct Apt 1, San Jose
(95117-1906)
PHONE.....................408 858-3933
Shabbir Khan, *President*
Sandhya Dalal, *Consultant*
EMP: 20
SQ FT: 1,400
SALES: 500K **Privately Held**
WEB: www.skylightsoftware.com
SIC: 7372 Prepackaged software

(P-25180)
SLACK TECHNOLOGIES INC
(PA)
500 Howard St, San Francisco
(94105-3000)
PHONE.....................415 579-9153
Daniel Stewart Butterfield, *CEO*
April Underwood, *Officer*
Ved Kodipyaka, *Info Tech Dir*
Michelle Lusen, *Recruiter*
Adams Keith, *Chief*
EMP: 148
SALES (est): 272.4MM **Privately Held**
SIC: 7372 Business oriented computer software

(P-25181)
SMART ACTION COMPANY LLC
300 Continental Blvd # 350, El Segundo
(90245-5042)
PHONE.....................310 776-9200
Tom Lewis, *CEO*
Brian Morin, *Chief Mktg Ofcr*
Michael Vanca, *Senior VP*
Louise Gold, *Vice Pres*
Peter E Voss, *Principal*
EMP: 26
SALES (est): 3.7MM **Privately Held**
SIC: 7372 Prepackaged software

(P-25182)
SMART-TEK AUTOMATED SVCS INC (HQ)
11838 Bernardo Plaza Ct # 250, San Diego (92128-2413)
PHONE....................................858 798-1644
Kelly Mowrey, *COO*
Bryan Bonar, *CEO*
EMP: 17
SQ FT: 2,000
SALES (est): 27.7MM **Publicly Held**
SIC: 7372 Business oriented computer software
PA: Trucept, Inc.
    500 La Terraza Blvd # 150
    Escondido CA 92025
    866 961-5763

(P-25183)
SMARTDRAW SOFTWARE LLC
9909 Mira Mesa Blvd, San Diego (92131-1056)
PHONE....................................858 225-3300
Paul Stannard, *CEO*
J Anthony Patterson, *COO*
Jeff Anderson, *Vice Pres*
Dan Hoffman, *Vice Pres*
Linda Kaechele, *Vice Pres*
EMP: 42
SQ FT: 14,567
SALES: 14.5MM **Privately Held**
WEB: www.smartdraw.com
SIC: 7372 Application computer software

(P-25184)
SMARTLOGIC SEMAPHORE INC
111 N Market St Ste 300, San Jose (95113-1116)
PHONE....................................408 213-9500
Rupert Bentley, *President*
EMP: 12
SALES (est): 1.2MM **Privately Held**
SIC: 7372 Business oriented computer software

(P-25185)
SMARTQED INC
421 37th Ave, San Mateo (94403-4328)
PHONE....................................925 922-4618
Rishi Mukhopadhyay, *Principal*
Julie Basu, *CEO*
EMP: 10
SALES (est): 244K **Privately Held**
SIC: 7372 7389 Business oriented computer software;

(P-25186)
SMITH MICRO SOFTWARE INC (PA)
51 Columbia, Aliso Viejo (92656-1456)
PHONE....................................949 362-5800
William W Smith Jr, *Ch of Bd*
David Blakeney, *President*
Timothy C Huffmyer, *CFO*
Thomas Campbell, *Bd of Directors*
Samuel Gulko, *Bd of Directors*
EMP: 136
SQ FT: 24,688
SALES: 22.9MM **Publicly Held**
WEB: www.smithmicro.com
SIC: 7372 Business oriented computer software

(P-25187)
SNAPLOGIC INC (PA)
1825 S Grant St Ste 550, San Mateo (94402-2119)
PHONE....................................888 494-1570
Gaurav Dhillon, *CEO*
Vaikom Krishnan, *President*
Bob Parker, *CFO*
Robert J Parker, *CFO*
David Downing, *Chief Mktg Ofcr*
EMP: 140
SALES (est): 28.8MM **Privately Held**
SIC: 7372 Business oriented computer software

(P-25188)
SNAPMD INC
121 W Lexington Dr # 412, Glendale (91203-2203)
PHONE....................................310 953-4800
Dave Skibinski, *CEO*
George Tierney, *COO*

Deric Frost, *Risk Mgmt Dir*
Douglas Campbell, *Principal*
EMP: 13
SQ FT: 2,200
SALES (est): 541.9K **Privately Held**
SIC: 7372 Business oriented computer software

(P-25189)
SO CAL SOFT-PAK INCORPORATED
Also Called: Soft Pak
8525 Gibbs Dr Ste 300, San Diego (92123-1700)
PHONE....................................619 283-2338
Brian Porter, *CEO*
Steve Belt, *Vice Pres*
Eddie Garratt, *Vice Pres*
Dawn Wittig, *Vice Pres*
Kevin Mohondro, *Prgrmr*
EMP: 31
SQ FT: 5,000
SALES (est): 4.4MM **Privately Held**
WEB: www.soft-pak.com
SIC: 7372 8742 Business oriented computer software; management consulting services

(P-25190)
SOCIALIZE INC
450 Townsend St 102, San Francisco (94107-1510)
PHONE....................................415 529-4019
Daniel R Odio, *CEO*
Sean Shadmand, *President*
Isaac Mosquera, *CTO*
EMP: 50
SALES (est): 2.8MM
SALES (corp-wide): 12MM **Privately Held**
SIC: 7372 Business oriented computer software
PA: Sharethis, Inc.
    4005 Miranda Ave Ste 100
    Palo Alto CA 94304
    650 641-0191

(P-25191)
SOFTWARE AG INC
Also Called: Software AG of Virginia
2901 Tasman Dr Ste 219, Santa Clara (95054-1138)
PHONE....................................408 490-5300
Karl-Heinz Streibich, *Branch Mgr*
Artie Alvidrez, *Senior Mgr*
EMP: 119
SALES (corp-wide): 1B **Privately Held**
SIC: 7372 Application computer software
HQ: Software Ag, Inc.
    11700 Plaza America Dr # 700
    Reston VA 20190
    703 860-5050

(P-25192)
SOFTWARE DEVELOPMENT INC
Also Called: Mi9
5000 Hopyard Rd Ste 160, Pleasanton (94588-3352)
PHONE....................................925 847-8823
Michael Burge, *President*
Jason Williams, *CFO*
Sylvia McKewon, *Office Mgr*
Willibert Pena, *Sr Software Eng*
Yamila Fleitas, *QA Dir*
EMP: 25
SQ FT: 8,400
SALES (est): 4.1MM **Privately Held**
WEB: www.sdiretail.com
SIC: 7372 7379 Prepackaged software; computer related consulting services
PA: Mi9 Business Intelligence Systems Inc
    245 Yorkland Blvd Suite 301
    North York ON M2J 4
    416 491-1483

(P-25193)
SOFTWARE LICENSING CONSULTANTS
Also Called: SLC
1001 Shannon Ct Ste B, Livermore (94550-9479)
PHONE....................................925 371-1277
Edgardo Ramirez, *Principal*
EMP: 35
SQ FT: 7,000

SALES (est): 2.9MM **Privately Held**
WEB: www.ekcos.com
SIC: 7372 5087 Prepackaged software; janitors' supplies

(P-25194)
SOFTWARE PARTNERS LLC
906 2nd St, Encinitas (92024-4410)
PHONE....................................760 944-8436
Alean Kirnak, *President*
Steve Rose, *Project Mgr*
EMP: 25
SALES (est): 1.5MM **Privately Held**
WEB: www.swpartners.com
SIC: 7372 Business oriented computer software

(P-25195)
SOLUTIONSOFT SYSTEMS INC
2350 Mission College Blvd, Santa Clara (95054-1532)
PHONE....................................408 346-1491
Paul Wang, *President*
Margaret Wang, *Principal*
EMP: 20
SALES (est): 331.9K **Privately Held**
SIC: 7372 Operating systems computer software

(P-25196)
SOLV INC
Also Called: Swinerton Builders
16798 W Bernardo Dr, San Diego (92127-1904)
PHONE....................................858 622-4040
EMP: 16
SALES (corp-wide): 27MM **Privately Held**
SIC: 7372 Prepackaged software
PA: Solv, Inc.
    260 Townsend St
    San Francisco CA
    858 622-4040

(P-25197)
SONASOFT CORP (PA)
6920 Santa Teresa Blvd # 108, San Jose (95119-1344)
PHONE....................................408 708-4000
Andy Khanna, *President*
Romesh K Japra, *Ch of Bd*
Nand Khanna, *President*
Paresh Mehta, *CFO*
Bilal Ahmed, *CTO*
EMP: 24
SALES: 771.7K **Publicly Held**
WEB: www.sonasoft.com
SIC: 7372 Prepackaged software

(P-25198)
SONIC SOLUTIONS HOLDINGS INC
2830 De La Cruz Blvd, Santa Clara (95050-2619)
PHONE....................................408 562-8400
Brian Botteri, *Manager*
EMP: 345
SALES (est): 120.6K
SALES (corp-wide): 826.4MM **Publicly Held**
SIC: 7372 Home entertainment computer software
PA: Tivo Corporation
    2160 Gold St
    San Jose CA 95002
    408 519-9100

(P-25199)
SONIC STUDIO LLC
93 Madrone Rd, Fairfax (94930-2119)
P.O. Box 238 (94978-0238)
PHONE....................................415 944-7642
Jonathan Reichbach, *President*
Madeleine Cortes, *CFO*
EMP: 11 EST: 2010
SALES (est): 704.8K **Privately Held**
SIC: 7372 7389 Home entertainment computer software;

(P-25200)
SONIC VR LLC
225 Broadway Ste 650, San Diego (92101-5039)
PHONE....................................206 227-8585
Jason Riggs, *CEO*
Jose Arjol Acebal, *COO*

Joy Lyons, *General Mgr*
David Carr, *Chief Engr*
EMP: 17
SQ FT: 6,000
SALES (est): 301.5K **Privately Held**
SIC: 7372 8731 Application computer software; commercial physical research

(P-25201)
SONOSIM INC
1738 Berkeley St Ste A, Santa Monica (90404-4105)
PHONE....................................323 473-3800
Eric Savitsky, *President*
Jay Dorman, *President*
Andres Luzio, *President*
Koren Bertolli, *COO*
Dan Katz, *Vice Pres*
EMP: 11
SQ FT: 900
SALES (est): 1.4MM **Privately Held**
SIC: 7372 7371 Educational computer software; computer software development & applications

(P-25202)
SONY INTERACTIVE ENTRMT LLC
Also Called: Snei
16535 Via Esprillo, San Diego (92127-1738)
PHONE....................................858 207-1500
Rickey Parker, *Branch Mgr*
EMP: 39
SALES (corp-wide): 80.1B **Privately Held**
SIC: 7372 Home entertainment computer software
HQ: Sony Interactive Entertainment Llc
    2207 Bridgepointe Pkwy
    Foster City CA 94404
    310 981-1500

(P-25203)
SPACE TIME INSIGHT INC
1850 Gateway Dr Ste 125, San Mateo (94404-4082)
PHONE....................................650 513-8550
Rob Schilling, *CEO*
Tony Tibshirani, *CEO*
William Tamblyn, *CFO*
Steve Lawrence, *Vice Pres*
Bryan Hughes, *Vice Pres*
EMP: 47
SALES (est): 6.6MM
SALES (corp-wide): 27.3B **Privately Held**
SIC: 7372 Business oriented computer software
PA: Nokia Oyj
    Karaportti 3
    Espoo 02610
    104 488-000

(P-25204)
SPATIAL WAVE INC
23461 S Pointe Dr Ste 300, Laguna Hills (92653-1523)
PHONE....................................949 540-6400
Ali Diba, *President*
Meade Maleki, *Vice Pres*
Jose Manaloto, *Controller*
Roger Hoang, *Associate*
EMP: 10 EST: 2008
SALES: 50K **Privately Held**
SIC: 7372 Business oriented computer software

(P-25205)
SPECIALISTS IN CSTM SFTWR INC
2574 Wellesley Ave, Los Angeles (90064-2738)
PHONE....................................310 315-9660
Helen Russell, *President*
Melissa Vance, *Treasurer*
Shawn Denning, *Project Mgr*
David Wiser, *Project Mgr*
Faith Gabriel, *Human Res Dir*
EMP: 44
SQ FT: 2,400
SALES (est): 7MM **Privately Held**
WEB: www.scs-mbs.com
SIC: 7372 Business oriented computer software

(P-25206)
SPIGIT INC
275 Battery St Ste 1000, San Francisco
(94111-3333)
PHONE...............855 774-4480
Scott Raskin, *President*
Stephen Anderson, *CFO*
Matt Chapman, *Vice Pres*
Doug Collins, *Vice Pres*
Steve Dilauro, *Vice Pres*
EMP: 99
SQ FT: 12,500
SALES (est): 13.9MM
SALES (corp-wide): 31MM **Privately Held**
SIC: 7372 Business oriented computer software
PA: Spigit Holdings Corporation
275 Battery St Ste 1000
San Francisco CA 94111
415 229-4400

(P-25207)
SPIKE CHUNSOFT INC
5000 Airport Plaza Dr # 230, Long Beach
(90815-1271)
PHONE...............562 786-5080
Mitsutoshi Sakurai, *President*
Yasuhiro Iizuka, *CFO*
Yoko Marron, *Exec Dir*
EMP: 12
SQ FT: 2,400
SALES (est): 329K
SALES (corp-wide): 1.9B **Privately Held**
SIC: 7372 7373 Home entertainment computer software; systems software development services
HQ: Spike Chunsoft Co., Ltd.
2-17-7, Akasaka
Minato-Ku TKY 107-0
355 755-670

(P-25208)
SPLUNK INC (PA)
270 Brannan St, San Francisco
(94107-2007)
PHONE...............415 848-8400
Douglas Merritt, *President*
Joe Massanova, *Partner*
Godfrey Sullivan, *Ch of Bd*
Susan St Ledger, *President*
David Conte, *CFO*
EMP: 160
SQ FT: 182,000
SALES (est): 1.2B **Publicly Held**
WEB: www.splunk.com
SIC: 7372 Business oriented computer software

(P-25209)
SPOTLITE MEDIA INC
7083 Hollywood Blvd, Los Angeles
(90028-8901)
PHONE...............650 447-9135
Ke Tang, *President*
Louie Liu, *CFO*
EMP: 20
SALES (est): 1MM **Privately Held**
SIC: 7372 Home entertainment computer software

(P-25210)
SPOTON COMPUTING INC
Also Called: Stanza
209 9th St Fl 3, San Francisco
(94103-3871)
PHONE...............650 293-7464
Smita Saxena, *CEO*
EMP: 28
SQ FT: 3,600
SALES (est): 225.6K **Privately Held**
SIC: 7372 Application computer software

(P-25211)
SQUAMTECH INC
Also Called: Shiploop
2023 22nd St, San Francisco (94107-3203)
PHONE...............415 867-8300
Marco Buhlmann, *CEO*
EMP: 10
SALES (est): 440.1K **Privately Held**
SIC: 7372 Application computer software; business oriented computer software; publishers' computer software

(P-25212)
SQUARE INC (PA)
1455 Market St Ste 600, San Francisco
(94103-1332)
PHONE...............415 375-3176
Jack Dorsey, *Ch of Bd*
Sarah Friar, *CFO*
Jim McKelvey, *Bd of Directors*
Ajmere Dale, *Officer*
David Grodsky, *Officer*
EMP: 50
SQ FT: 338,910
SALES (est): 2.2B **Publicly Held**
SIC: 7372 Prepackaged software

(P-25213)
SRA OSS INC
5201 Great America Pkwy # 419, Santa Clara (95054-1143)
PHONE...............408 855-8200
RAO Papolu, *President*
EMP: 160
SQ FT: 5,000
SALES (est): 15.6MM
SALES (corp-wide): 369.9MM **Privately Held**
WEB: www.sraoss.com
SIC: 7372 Publishers' computer software
HQ: Software Research Associates, Inc.
2-32-8, Minamiikebukuro
Toshima-Ku TKY 171-0
359 792-111

(P-25214)
SRSB INC
Also Called: Physicians Trust
5004 Cmino Escllo Ste 200, San Clemente
(92673)
PHONE...............949 234-1881
Steve Rhodes, *President*
EMP: 17
SALES (est): 1.1MM **Privately Held**
SIC: 7372 Publishers' computer software

(P-25215)
STACKLA INC
33 New Montgomery St, San Francisco
(94105-4506)
PHONE...............415 528-4910
Damien Mahoney, *CEO*
Peter Cassaidy,
EMP: 63
SALES (est): 2.4MM **Privately Held**
SIC: 7372 Application computer software

(P-25216)
STACKROX INC
700 E El Camino Real # 200, Mountain View (94040-2802)
PHONE...............650 489-6769
Kamal Shah, *President*
Yathindra Naik, *Info Tech Mgr*
Connor Gilbert, *Technical Staff*
Evan McClure, *Technical Staff*
EMP: 22
SALES (est): 416.1K **Privately Held**
SIC: 7372 Application computer software

(P-25217)
STALKER SOFTWARE INC
Also Called: Communigate Systems
125 Park Pl Ste 210, Richmond
(94801-3980)
PHONE...............415 569-2280
Vladimir Butenko, *President*
Philip Slater, *Executive*
Azdio Ballesteros, *Director*
EMP: 50
SALES (est): 5.6MM **Privately Held**
WEB: www.communigate.com
SIC: 7372 7371 Prepackaged software; custom computer programming services

(P-25218)
STANDARD COGNITION CORP
164 Townsend St Unit 9, San Francisco
(94107-1991)
PHONE...............201 707-7782
Jordan Fisher, *CEO*
Michael Suswal, *COO*
Anthony Lutz, *CFO*
EMP: 20
SALES: 2MM **Privately Held**
SIC: 7372 Business oriented computer software

(P-25219)
STARVIEW INC
2841 Junction Ave Ste 110, San Jose
(95134-1921)
P.O. Box 2294, Kalispell MT (59903-2294)
PHONE...............406 890-5910
Jerry Meerkatz, *CEO*
Steve Baunach, *Founder*
EMP: 34
SQ FT: 5,000
SALES (est): 1.7MM **Privately Held**
SIC: 7372 Business oriented computer software

(P-25220)
STAT CLINICAL SYSTEMS INC
Also Called: Stat Systems
2560 9th St Ste 317, Berkeley
(94710-2500)
PHONE...............510 705-8700
Frederick W Dietrich, *CEO*
EMP: 12
SQ FT: 2,000
SALES (est): 909.4K **Privately Held**
WEB: www.statsystems.com
SIC: 7372 Business oriented computer software

(P-25221)
STEALTH SECURITY INC
100 S Murphy Ave Ste 300, Sunnyvale
(94086-6110)
PHONE...............844 978-3258
Larry Link, *President*
Rod Beckstrom, *Ch of Bd*
Tony McIlvenna, *Vice Pres*
Ameya Talwalkar, *Vice Pres*
David Weisman, *Vice Pres*
EMP: 13
SQ FT: 5,000
SALES (est): 117K **Privately Held**
SIC: 7372 Prepackaged software

(P-25222)
STEP MOBILE INC ◆
2765 Sand Hill Rd Ste 201, Menlo Park
(94025-7098)
PHONE...............203 913-9229
CJ McDonald, *CEO*
EMP: 10 EST: 2018
SALES: 100K **Privately Held**
SIC: 7372 Application computer software

(P-25223)
STEPS MOBILE INC ◆
2035 5th St, Davis (95618-4709)
PHONE...............408 806-5178
Anthony Chang, *CEO*
Ron Yeng, *COO*
Bryan Vu, *CTO*
EMP: 10 EST: 2018
SALES: 500K **Privately Held**
SIC: 7372 7389 Application computer software;

(P-25224)
STORM8 INC
Also Called: Storm8 Entertainment
2400 Bridge Pkwy 2, Redwood City
(94065-1166)
PHONE...............650 596-8600
Perry Tam, *CEO*
Steve Parkis, *President*
Jeff Witt, *President*
Terence Fung, *Officer*
Tim Letourneau, *Officer*
EMP: 16
SALES (est): 4.3MM **Privately Held**
SIC: 7372 Prepackaged software

(P-25225)
STRATCITYCOM LLC
1317 Monterosso St, Danville
(94506-1960)
PHONE...............408 858-0006
Alfy Louis, *Mng Member*
EMP: 74
SQ FT: 3,400
SALES: 1.6MM **Privately Held**
SIC: 7372 Prepackaged software

(P-25226)
STRATEGIC INFO GROUP INC
1953 San Elijo Ave # 201, Cardiff By The Sea (92007-2348)
PHONE...............760 697-1050

Douglas Novak, *CEO*
Ray Greenwood, *Senior VP*
John Graham, *Vice Pres*
EMP: 27 EST: 1994
SALES: 4.4MM **Privately Held**
SIC: 7372 Educational computer software; application computer software; business oriented computer software

(P-25227)
STRATEGIC INSIGHTS INC
Also Called: Brightscope
9191 Towne Centre Dr # 401, San Diego
(92122-1225)
PHONE...............858 452-7500
David Gaunt, *Vice Pres*
Paul Collins, *Sr Software Eng*
Chris Ferguson, *Sr Software Eng*
Marcus Planta, *Software Dev*
Justin Siu, *Software Engr*
EMP: 65 **Privately Held**
SIC: 7372 Business oriented computer software
PA: Strategic Insights, Inc.
805 3rd Ave
New York NY 10022

(P-25228)
STRATEGY COMPANION CORP
3240 El Camino Real # 120, Irvine
(92602-1384)
PHONE...............714 460-8398
Robert Sterling, *President*
Eric Halverson, *Partner*
Grace Lin, *Office Admin*
Al Siroon, *Sales Executive*
Bill Tang, *Manager*
EMP: 70
SALES (est): 5.5MM **Privately Held**
SIC: 7372 Prepackaged software
PA: Strategy Companion Corp.
Scotia Centre 4th Floor
George Town GR CAYMAN

(P-25229)
STREAMLINE DEVELOPMENT LLC (HQ)
Also Called: Streamline Solutions
100 Smith Ranch Rd # 124, San Rafael
(94903-1900)
PHONE...............415 499-3355
Laurence Snyder, *CEO*
Walter Franz, *CFO*
EMP: 25
SQ FT: 9,000
SALES (est): 4MM
SALES (corp-wide): 993.2MM **Publicly Held**
SIC: 7372 Prepackaged software
PA: Electronics For Imaging, Inc.
6750 Dumbarton Cir
Fremont CA 94555
650 357-3500

(P-25230)
STREVUS INC
455 Market St Ste 1670, San Francisco
(94105-2472)
PHONE...............415 704-8182
Ken Hoang, *CEO*
Gregg Loos, *President*
Dmitri Korablev, *Vice Pres*
Ken Price, *Vice Pres*
Jennifer Turcotte, *Vice Pres*
EMP: 60
SALES (est): 5MM **Privately Held**
SIC: 7372 7371 Business oriented computer software; computer software development

(P-25231)
STRYDER CORP
Also Called: Handshake
225 Bush St Fl 12, San Francisco
(94104-4254)
P.O. Box 40770 (94140-0770)
PHONE...............415 981-8400
Garrett Lord, *Ch of Bd*
Ben Christensen, *Principal*
Scott Ringwelski, *Principal*
EMP: 100 EST: 2014

SALES (est): 404.2K **Privately Held**
SIC: 7372 7371 7379 Educational computer software; application computer software; business oriented computer software; computer software development & applications; computer related consulting services

(P-25232)
STUMBLEUPON INC (HQ)
535 Mission St Fl 11, San Francisco
(94105-3325)
PHONE..............................415 979-0640
Garrett Camp, *CEO*
Mark Bartels, *CFO*
Ankit Chaudhary, *Sr Software Eng*
Adrian Castaneda, *Technical Staff*
Cassady Hudson, *Accountant*
EMP: 25
SALES (est): 6MM **Privately Held**
WEB: www.STUMBLEUPON.com
SIC: 7372 Application computer software
PA: Mix Tech, Inc
   535 Mission St Fl 11
   San Francisco CA 94105
   415 940-2055

(P-25233)
SUGARSYNC INC
Also Called: Sharpcast
6922 Hollywood Blvd # 500, Los Angeles
(90028-6125)
PHONE..............................650 571-5105
Laura Yecies, *President*
Peter Chantel, *CFO*
Yihan LI, *Software Dev*
Vijaya Kumar, *Technology*
Shashidhara Vn, *Technology*
EMP: 30
SQ FT: 11,000
SALES (est): 7MM **Privately Held**
WEB: www.sugarsync.com
SIC: 7372 Business oriented computer software

(P-25234)
SUMOPTI
742 Moreno Ave, Palo Alto (94303-3617)
PHONE..............................650 331-1126
EMP: 10
SQ FT: 1,500
SALES (est): 45.8K **Privately Held**
SIC: 7372

(P-25235)
SUPER BINGE MEDIA INC
530 Bush St Ste 600, San Francisco
(94108-3634)
PHONE..............................714 688-6231
Nicholas Talarico, *President*
Yigeng Sun, *Officer*
George Zeloom, *Officer*
EMP: 13
SALES (est): 500K **Privately Held**
SIC: 7372 Application computer software
PA: Super Lucky Casino Inc.
   530 Bush St Ste 600
   San Francisco CA 94108

(P-25236)
SUPERIOR SOFTWARE INC
16055 Ventura Blvd # 650, Encino
(91436-2601)
PHONE..............................818 990-1135
EMP: 10
SQ FT: 200
SALES (est): 708.9K **Privately Held**
SIC: 7372 8111 5734

(P-25237)
SUPPORT TECHNOLOGIES INC (PA)
1939 Deere Ave, Irvine (92606-4818)
PHONE..............................949 442-2957
Tayo Daramole, *President*
Ian Yhap, *Engineer*
George Yu, *Manager*
EMP: 14
SQ FT: 2,000
SALES (est): 1.4MM **Privately Held**
WEB: www.alexusinfo.com
SIC: 7372 Prepackaged software

(P-25238)
SWIFTSTACK INC (PA)
333 Bush St Ste 1650, San Francisco
(94104-2871)
PHONE..............................415 625-0293
Don Jaworski, *CEO*
Anders Tjernlund, *COO*
Linda McClaine, *Info Tech Mgr*
Timur Alperovich, *Software Engr*
Andrew Boring, *Engineer*
EMP: 28
SALES (est): 8.3MM **Privately Held**
SIC: 7372 Business oriented computer software; application computer software

(P-25239)
SWIFTSTACK INC
1054 S De Anza Blvd, San Jose
(95129-3553)
PHONE..............................408 642-1865
Don Jaworski, *CEO*
EMP: 37
SALES (corp-wide): 8.3MM **Privately Held**
SIC: 7372 Prepackaged software
PA: Swiftstack, Inc.
   333 Bush St Ste 1650
   San Francisco CA 94104
   415 625-0293

(P-25240)
SYAPSE INC
303 2nd St Ste S650, San Francisco
(94107-2297)
PHONE..............................650 924-1461
Gary J Kurtzman MD, *CEO*
Jonathan Hirsch, *President*
Dennis Shin, *Ch Credit Ofcr*
James Lim, *Senior VP*
Andreas Heid, *Vice Pres*
EMP: 87
SALES (est): 3.2MM **Privately Held**
SIC: 7372 Prepackaged software

(P-25241)
SYMPHONY TALENT LLC
98 Battery St Ste 400, San Francisco
(94111-5512)
PHONE..............................415 968-3389
Barak Ben-Gal, *CFO*
EMP: 48
SALES (corp-wide): 50MM **Privately Held**
SIC: 7372 7361 Business oriented computer software; employment agencies
PA: Symphony Talent, Llc
   19 W 34th St Rm 1000
   New York NY 10001
   212 999-9000

(P-25242)
SYMPHONYRM INC
530 University Ave, Palo Alto (94301-1900)
PHONE..............................650 336-8430
Vipul Vyas, *Exec VP*
Blake Dong, *President*
Andy Efron, *Vice Pres*
David Gudeman, *Software Engr*
EMP: 12
SALES (est): 487.4K **Privately Held**
SIC: 7372 Business oriented computer software

(P-25243)
SYNERGEX INTERNATIONAL CORP
2330 Gold Meadow Way, Gold River
(95670-4471)
PHONE..............................916 635-7300
Michele C Wong, *CEO*
Serena Channel, *Partner*
Vigfus A Asmundson, *Shareholder*
Georgia Petersen, *Shareholder*
Thomas J Powers, *Shareholder*
EMP: 55
SQ FT: 26,000
SALES (est): 8.8MM **Privately Held**
WEB: www.synergex.com
SIC: 7372 Business oriented computer software

(P-25244)
SYNERGY GLOBAL INC
4 Embarcadero Ctr # 1400, San Francisco
(94111-4106)
PHONE..............................415 766-3540

EMP: 10 EST: 2011
SALES (est): 710K **Privately Held**
SIC: 7372

(P-25245)
SYNOPSYS INC (PA)
690 E Middlefield Rd, Mountain View
(94043-4033)
PHONE..............................650 584-5000
Aart J De Geus, *Ch of Bd*
CHI-Foon Chan, *President*
Trac Pham, *CFO*
Joseph W Logan, *Officer*
Ahsan Bootehsaz, *Vice Pres*
EMP: 500
SQ FT: 341,000
SALES (est): 2.7B **Publicly Held**
WEB: www.synopsys.com
SIC: 7372 Prepackaged software

(P-25246)
SYNOPSYS INC
199 S Los Robles Ave # 400, Pasadena
(91101-4634)
PHONE..............................626 795-9101
George Bayz, *CEO*
Jake Jacobsen, *Technical Staff*
Geoff Suzuki, *Sales Staff*
EMP: 90
SALES (corp-wide): 2.7B **Publicly Held**
SIC: 7372 8711 Application computer software; engineering services
PA: Synopsys, Inc.
   690 E Middlefield Rd
   Mountain View CA 94043
   650 584-5000

(P-25247)
SYNPLICITY INC (HQ)
690 E Middlefield Rd, Mountain View
(94043-4010)
PHONE..............................650 584-5000
Gary Meyers, *President*
Alisa Yaffa, *Ch of Bd*
Andrew Dauman, *President*
John J Hanlon, *CFO*
Andrew Haines, *Senior VP*
EMP: 160
SQ FT: 66,212
SALES (est): 17.8MM
SALES (corp-wide): 2.7B **Publicly Held**
WEB: www.synplicity.com
SIC: 7372 Prepackaged software
PA: Synopsys, Inc.
   690 E Middlefield Rd
   Mountain View CA 94043
   650 584-5000

(P-25248)
SYNTEST TECHNOLOGIES INC
4320 Stevens Creek Blvd # 100, San Jose
(95129-1285)
PHONE..............................408 720-9956
Laung-Terng Wang, *CEO*
Ravi Apte, *Senior VP*
Finney Tsai, *Vice Pres*
Ravi Atte, *Manager*
EMP: 10
SQ FT: 5,000
SALES (est): 954.5K **Privately Held**
WEB: www.syntest.com
SIC: 7372 Business oriented computer software

(P-25249)
SYSOP TOOLS INC
815 Moraga Dr, Los Angeles (90049-1633)
PHONE..............................310 598-3885
Kurt D Lewis, *President*
David Martin, *CFO*
EMP: 10
SQ FT: 2,000
SALES (est): 936.1K **Privately Held**
SIC: 7372 Business oriented computer software

(P-25250)
TAKIPI INC
797 Bryant St, San Francisco
(94107-1027)
PHONE..............................408 203-9585
Tal Weiss, *CEO*
Limor Wilks, *VP Finance*
Jon Tikh, *Business Mgr*
David Boyle, *VP Sales*
Zachary Solomon, *Sales Staff*

EMP: 10
SQ FT: 500
SALES (est): 703.8K **Privately Held**
SIC: 7372 Application computer software
PA: Takipi Ltd
   4 Rosen Pinchas
   Tel Aviv-Jaffa
   360 431-88

(P-25251)
TALISMAN SYSTEMS GROUP INC
1111 Oak St, San Francisco (94117-2216)
PHONE..............................415 357-1751
Michael Varnum, *President*
William Hatfield, *Shareholder*
Monique Knox, *Shareholder*
William Yu, *Shareholder*
EMP: 12
SALES (est): 1.7MM **Privately Held**
WEB: www.talisys.com
SIC: 7372 7371 Business oriented computer software; custom computer programming services

(P-25252)
TALIX INC
660 3rd St Ste 302, San Francisco
(94107-1921)
PHONE..............................628 220-3885
Derek Gordon, *President*
Paul Clip, *Vice Pres*
Shayan Currimbhoy, *Vice Pres*
Ashmi Shah, *Vice Pres*
Niraj Katwala, *CTO*
EMP: 70
SALES (est): 2MM **Privately Held**
SIC: 7372 8099 Application computer software; blood related health services

(P-25253)
TALKDESK INC (PA)
535 Mission St Fl 12, San Francisco
(94105-3225)
PHONE..............................888 743-3044
Ben McCarthy, *Administration*
Michael Reed, *Senior VP*
Jon Heaps, *Vice Pres*
Kristina Broughton, *Opers Mgr*
Andrew Bothwell, *VP Sales*
EMP: 34 EST: 2011
SALES (est): 8.4MM **Privately Held**
SIC: 7372 Application computer software

(P-25254)
TALLYGO INC (PA)
4133 Redwood Ave # 1015, Los Angeles
(90066-5600)
PHONE..............................510 858-1969
Thomas Scaramellino, *CEO*
Matt Triplett, *CEO*
EMP: 10
SALES (est): 819.8K **Privately Held**
SIC: 7372 Application computer software

(P-25255)
TANGOE INC
9920 Pcf Hts Blvd Ste 200, San Diego
(92121)
PHONE..............................858 452-6800
Sandy Jimenez, *Branch Mgr*
EMP: 100
SALES (corp-wide): 383.5MM **Privately Held**
SIC: 7372 Application computer software
HQ: Tangoe Us, Inc.
   169 Lackawanna Ave Ste 2b
   Parsippany NJ 07054
   973 257-0300

(P-25256)
TAPINFLUENCE INC
67 E Evelyn Ave Ste 5, Mountain View
(94041-1529)
PHONE..............................720 726-4071
Promise Phelon, *CEO*
EMP: 21 EST: 2009
SALES (est): 3.3MM **Publicly Held**
SIC: 7372 Business oriented computer software
PA: Izea Worldwide, Inc.
   480 N Orlando Ave Ste 200
   Winter Park FL 32789

(P-25257)
TAPONIX INC
Also Called: Tapclicks
5300 Stevens Creek Blvd, San Jose
(95129-1032)
PHONE................408 725-2942
Babak Hedayati, *CEO*
Syed Ahmed, *President*
Noah Jacobson, *President*
Michael Mertz, *Vice Pres*
Owen Davis, *Sr Software Eng*
EMP: 12
SQ FT: 3,192
SALES (est): 1.3MM **Privately Held**
SIC: 7372 Business oriented computer
software

(P-25258)
TDO SOFTWARE INC
6235 Lusk Blvd, San Diego (92121-2731)
PHONE................858 558-3696
Luiz Motta, *General Mgr*
Linda Matthews, *Office Mgr*
Sean Doonan, *Web Dvlpr*
Maria Medina, *Software Dev*
Darrin Sprong, *Software Engr*
EMP: 25
SQ FT: 3,600
SALES (est): 1.9MM **Privately Held**
WEB: www.tdosoftware.com
SIC: 7372 Prepackaged software
PA: Sonendo, Inc.
26061 Merit Cir Ste 102
Laguna Hills CA 92653

(P-25259)
TEACHING CHANNEL INC
2 Embarcadero Ctr Fl 8, San Francisco
(94111-3833)
PHONE................415 800-4288
George Lichter, *CEO*
EMP: 20
SQ FT: 200
SALES (est): 421K **Privately Held**
SIC: 7372 Educational computer software

(P-25260)
TEAMIFIER INC
514 Live Oak Ln, Emerald Hills
(94062-3415)
PHONE................408 591-9872
Steven Ganz, *CEO*
EMP: 10 EST: 2015
SALES (est): 38.6K **Privately Held**
SIC: 7372 7371 Application computer soft-
ware; custom computer programming
services

(P-25261)
TECH4LEARNING INC (PA)
10981 San Diego 120, San Diego (92108)
PHONE................619 283-6028
David Wagner, *President*
Dallas Jones, *CFO*
Rodger Cook, *Vice Pres*
Melinda Kolk, *Vice Pres*
Nita Seng, *Vice Pres*
EMP: 15
SQ FT: 2,839
SALES (est): 1.9MM **Privately Held**
WEB: www.tech4learning.com
SIC: 7372 Educational computer software

(P-25262)
TECHMO ENTERTAINMENT INC
3191 17 Mile Dr, Pebble Beach
(93953-3605)
P.O. Box 828 (93953-0828)
PHONE................408 309-3039
Thomas Williams, *CEO*
EMP: 12
SALES (est): 682.9K **Privately Held**
SIC: 7372 Business oriented computer
software

(P-25263)
TECHNICAL SALES INTL LLC (HQ)
910 Pleasant Grove Blvd # 120, Roseville
(95678-6193)
PHONE................866 493-6337
Tammy Ford, *CEO*
Rebecca Foletta, *Mktg Dir*
Gregory Davis,
EMP: 11

SALES (est): 2.8MM **Privately Held**
WEB: www.technicalsalesinternational.com
SIC: 7372 Application computer software

(P-25264)
TEKEVER CORPORATION
5201 Great America Pkwy, Santa Clara
(95054-1122)
PHONE................408 730-2617
Michael L Margolis, *CEO*
Andre O Oliveira, *Vice Pres*
Robert Whitehouse, *Business Dir*
EMP: 70
SALES (est): 3.3MM **Privately Held**
WEB: www.tekever.com
SIC: 7372 Prepackaged software

(P-25265)
TELESIGN HOLDINGS INC (DH)
13274 Fiji Way Ste 600, Marina Del Rey
(90292-7293)
PHONE................310 740-9700
Aled Miles, *CEO*
Philipp Gast, *CFO*
Justin Hart, *Chief Mktg Ofcr*
Tom Powledge, *Officer*
Joe Amadea, *Sales Staff*
EMP: 30 EST: 2016
SALES (est): 7.8MM **Privately Held**
SIC: 7372 Prepackaged software

(P-25266)
TELLUS SOLUTIONS INC
3350 Scott Blvd Bldg 34a, Santa Clara
(95054-3105)
PHONE................408 850-2942
Sara Jain, *President*
Jinesh Jain, *Vice Pres*
Ankush Gupta, *Tech Recruiter*
Saiteja Kothalanka, *Tech Recruiter*
Manoj Kumar, *Tech Recruiter*
EMP: 38
SALES (est): 3MM **Privately Held**
SIC: 7372 7371 7373 Prepackaged soft-
ware; custom computer programming
services; computer integrated systems
design

(P-25267)
TESELAGEN BIOTECHNOLOGY INC
1501 Mariposa St Ste 312, San Francisco
(94107-2367)
PHONE................650 387-5932
Michael John Fero, *CEO*
Tom Baruch, *Bd of Directors*
Nathan Hillson, *Security Dir*
Eduardo Abeliuk, *CTO*
Rodrigo Pavez, *Software Engr*
EMP: 10
SALES (est): 1MM **Privately Held**
SIC: 7372 Prepackaged software

(P-25268)
THEBRAIN TECHNOLOGIES LP
11522 W Washington Blvd, Los Angeles
(90066-5914)
PHONE................310 390-0100
Harlan Hugh, *General Ptnr*
Shelley Hayduk, *Partner*
EMP: 15
SQ FT: 2,850
SALES (est): 1.3MM **Privately Held**
WEB: www.thebrain.com
SIC: 7372 Business oriented computer
software; home entertainment computer
software

(P-25269)
THERMEON CORPORATION (PA)
1175 Warner Ave, Tustin (92780-6458)
PHONE................714 731-9191
Rollo S Pickford, *Ch of Bd*
Scott Sampson, *President*
Sharon Miller, *CFO*
Laura Nelson, *Vice Pres*
Terry Pearson, *Managing Dir*
EMP: 14
SQ FT: 5,000
SALES (est): 2.8MM **Privately Held**
WEB: www.thermeon.com
SIC: 7372 7373 5045 Prepackaged soft-
ware; computer systems analysis & de-
sign; computers, peripherals & software

(P-25270)
THINKSMART LLC
530 Jackson St Fl 3, San Francisco
(94133-5132)
PHONE................888 489-4284
Paul Hirner, *CEO*
Peter Cernak, *Software Dev*
Dani Dayan, *Accountant*
Dillon Knowlton, *Production*
Kelli Negro, *Marketing Staff*
EMP: 12 EST: 2013
SALES (est): 679.5K
SALES (corp-wide): 81.2MM **Privately Held**
SIC: 7372 Business oriented computer
software
PA: Mitratech Holdings, Inc.
5001 Plz On
Austin TX 78746
512 382-7322

(P-25271)
THIRDMOTION INC
795 Folsom St Fl 1, San Francisco
(94107-4226)
PHONE................415 848-2724
Roel Pieper, *CEO*
Alexander Dailey,
Randy Fish, *CTO*
EMP: 14
SALES (est): 250K **Privately Held**
SIC: 7372 Application computer software

(P-25272)
THIRDROCK SOFTWARE
7098 Chiala Ln, San Jose (95129-2856)
PHONE................408 777-2910
Subrata Dasgupta, *Owner*
EMP: 15 EST: 1995
SALES (est): 952.4K **Privately Held**
SIC: 7372 Prepackaged software

(P-25273)
THOUGHT INC
5 3rd St Ste 1030, San Francisco
(94103-3211)
PHONE................415 836-9199
Ward Mullins, *President*
Greg Baker, *CFO*
Dan Wilson, *Vice Pres*
Kevin Schroeder, *Sls & Mktg Exec*
EMP: 15
SALES (est): 1.3MM **Privately Held**
WEB: www.thoughtinc.com
SIC: 7372 Utility computer software

(P-25274)
THOUGHTSPOT INC
3000 El Camino Real, Palo Alto
(94306-2100)
PHONE................800 508-7008
Sudheesh Nair, *CEO*
Ajeet Singh, *CEO*
Anuj Gulati, *COO*
Steve Sommer, *Chief Mktg Ofcr*
David Freeman, *Senior VP*
EMP: 12
SALES (est): 3.9MM **Privately Held**
SIC: 7372 Business oriented computer
software

(P-25275)
THOUSANDEYES INC (PA)
201 Mission St Ste 1700, San Francisco
(94105-8102)
PHONE................415 513-4526
Mohit Lad, *CEO*
Mike Staiger, *CFO*
Sanjay Mehta, *Chief Mktg Ofcr*
Dave Fraleigh, *Vice Pres*
James Gibbon, *Executive*
EMP: 75
SALES (est): 17.4MM **Privately Held**
SIC: 7372 Business oriented computer
software

(P-25276)
TI LIMITED LLC (PA)
20335 Ventura Blvd, Woodland Hills
(91364-2444)
PHONE................323 877-5991
ARI Daniels,
Alberto Gamez,
EMP: 52 EST: 2016
SQ FT: 9,000

SALES: 9MM **Privately Held**
SIC: 7372 8748 Business oriented computer software; business consulting

(P-25277)
TIBCO SOFTWARE INC
575 Market St Fl 15, San Francisco
(94105-5815)
PHONE................415 344-0339
Vivek Ranadiv, *Branch Mgr*
Katherine Hatch, *Marketing Mgr*
EMP: 15
SALES (corp-wide): 4.4B **Privately Held**
SIC: 7372 Prepackaged software
HQ: Tibco Software Inc.
3307 Hillview Ave
Palo Alto CA 94304

(P-25278)
TIMELY DATA RESOURCES INC
107 Washburn Ave, Capitola (95010-3743)
PHONE................831 462-2510
Robert Weissberg, *President*
John Borgman, *Vice Pres*
Yvonne Brill, *Vice Pres*
EMP: 10
SQ FT: 2,000
SALES (est): 1.1MM **Privately Held**
WEB: www.tdrweb.com
SIC: 7372 Publishers' computer software

(P-25279)
TIMEVALUE SOFTWARE
22 Mauchly, Irvine (92618-2306)
P.O. Box 50250 (92619-0250)
PHONE................949 727-1800
Michael Applegate, *President*
Randy Fleury, *Vice Pres*
Charles Miller, *Vice Pres*
Chuck Miller, *Vice Pres*
Joshua Pacheco, *Admin Asst*
EMP: 25
SQ FT: 18,000
SALES (est): 2.5MM **Privately Held**
WEB: www.timevalue.com
SIC: 7372 7371 Prepackaged software;
computer software development

(P-25280)
TIPESTRY INC
940 Stewart Dr 203, Sunnyvale
(94085-3912)
PHONE................650 421-1344
David Davies, *CEO*
EMP: 11
SALES (est): 1MM **Privately Held**
SIC: 7372 Prepackaged software

(P-25281)
TIVIX INC (PA)
2845 California St, San Francisco
(94115-2515)
PHONE................415 680-1299
Bret Waters, *CEO*
Dariusz Fryta, *Software Engr*
Marzena Podhorska, *Opers Staff*
Bill Conneely, *Director*
EMP: 10
SALES (est): 1.4MM **Privately Held**
SIC: 7372 Application computer software

(P-25282)
TOKBOX INC
501 2nd St Ste 310, San Francisco
(94107-4191)
PHONE................415 284-4688
J Scott Lomond, *CEO*
Nidhi Gupta, *President*
Yoong Janine, *President*
Badri Rajasekar, *President*
Steve McFarlin, *Sr Software Eng*
EMP: 10
SALES (est): 2.9MM
SALES (corp-wide): 1B **Publicly Held**
SIC: 7372 Application computer software
HQ: Telefonica Digital, Inc.
501 2nd St Ste 310
San Francisco CA 94107
650 967-4357

(P-25283)
TOKY INC
530 Lytton Ave Fl 2, Palo Alto
(94301-1541)
PHONE................844 332-6433

Carlos Ruiz, *CEO*
Oscar Sanchez, *Vice Pres*
EMP: 12
SALES (est): 256K **Privately Held**
SIC: 7372 Prepackaged software

(P-25284)
TOPGUEST INC
Also Called: Ezrez Software
601 Montgomery St Fl 17, San Francisco
(94111-2621)
PHONE..................646 415-9402
Geoff Lewis, *CEO*
EMP: 20
SALES (est): 1MM **Privately Held**
SIC: 7372 Business oriented computer
software
PA: Switchfly, Inc
601 Montgomery St Fl 17
San Francisco CA 94111

(P-25285)
TOPI SYSTEMS INC
20650 4th St Apt 2, Saratoga (95070-5893)
PHONE..................408 807-5124
EMP: 10
SALES (est): 570K **Privately Held**
SIC: 7372 Prepackaged software

(P-25286)
TOPLINE GAME LABS LLC
10351 Santa Monica Blvd # 410, Los Ange-
les (90025-6937)
PHONE..................310 461-0350
David Geller, *CEO*
Elon Spar, *Ch of Bd*
Joshua Small, *COO*
EMP: 17
SQ FT: 2,500
SALES (est): 1.5MM **Privately Held**
SIC: 7372 Home entertainment computer
software

(P-25287)
TOPPAGE INC
3101 Whipple Rd Ste 28, Union City
(94587-1223)
PHONE..................510 471-6366
Frank Gabrielli, *President*
Kent Toussaint, *Manager*
EMP: 10
SALES (est): 606.3K **Privately Held**
SIC: 7372 Prepackaged software

(P-25288)
TORIAN GROUP INC
519 W Center Ave, Visalia (93291-6019)
PHONE..................559 733-1940
Tim Torian, *President*
EMP: 10
SALES (est): 1.8MM **Privately Held**
WEB: www.torian.com
SIC: 7372 Application computer software

(P-25289)
TOUCHPOINT SOLUTIONS
18426 Brookhurst St # 207, Fountain Valley
(92708-6778)
PHONE..................714 740-7242
Brett Greathouse, *President*
Mark Mortensen, *COO*
Michael Moss, *Administration*
Kory Johnson, *Accounts Exec*
EMP: 10 **EST:** 2013
SALES (est): 504.9K **Privately Held**
SIC: 7372 Application computer software

(P-25290)
TOUTAPP INC
535 Mission St Fl 14, San Francisco
(94105-3253)
PHONE..................866 548-1927
Tawheed Kader, *CEO*
David Hauser, *Engineer*
Jessica Green, *Sales Staff*
Stephanie Moon, *Manager*
EMP: 17
SALES (est): 2.2MM
SALES (corp-wide): 7.3B **Publicly Held**
SIC: 7372 Application computer software
HQ: Marketo, Inc.
901 Mariners Island Blvd
San Mateo CA 94404

(P-25291)
TRANSPLANT CONNECT INC
Also Called: I Transplant Enterprise Tech
2701 Ocean Park Blvd # 222, Santa Monica
(90405-5212)
PHONE..................310 392-1400
John Piano, *CEO*
Brian Buroker, *Partner*
Mauricio Guzman, *QA Dir*
Pamela Sabella, *QA Dir*
Lance Swegart, *QA Dir*
EMP: 28
SALES (est): 3.4MM **Privately Held**
WEB: www.transplantconnect.com
SIC: 7372 7371 Prepackaged software;
custom computer programming services

(P-25292)
**TRAVEL COMPUTER SYSTEMS
INC**
Also Called: Travcom
1990 Westwood Blvd # 310, Los Angeles
(90025-8426)
PHONE..................310 558-3130
Jack Revel, *President*
Marsha N Revel, *Admin Sec*
EMP: 16
SQ FT: 1,200
SALES: 5MM **Privately Held**
WEB: www.travcom.com
SIC: 7372 Business oriented computer
software

(P-25293)
TRAVIDIA INC (PA)
265 Airpark Blvd Ste 500, Chico
(95973-9519)
PHONE..................530 343-6400
Rand Hutchison, *CEO*
Robert Clark, *Vice Pres*
James Green, *Vice Pres*
Bob Clark, *Director*
Chris Eckland, *Director*
EMP: 150
SQ FT: 10,000
SALES (est): 7.1MM **Privately Held**
WEB: www.travidia.com
SIC: 7372 Prepackaged software

(P-25294)
TRIBEWORX LLC
4 San Joaquin Plz Ste 150, Newport Beach
(92660-5934)
PHONE..................800 949-3432
EMP: 75
SQ FT: 10,000
SALES (est): 4.9MM **Privately Held**
SIC: 7372

(P-25295)
TRILIBIS INC (PA)
Also Called: Trilibis Mobile
66 Bovet Rd Ste 285, San Mateo
(94402-3128)
P.O. Box 19170, Sacramento (95819-0170)
PHONE..................650 646-2400
Alex Panelli, *President*
Tom Burke, *CFO*
Meyyappan Alagappan, *CTO*
EMP: 12
SALES (est): 1.8MM **Privately Held**
SIC: 7372 Application computer software

(P-25296)
TRION WORLD NETWORK INC
1200 Bridge Pkwy Ste 201, Redwood City
(94065-1159)
PHONE..................650 394-1000
Jon Caneghem, *Principal*
Tara Jensen, *Senior Engr*
Andrew Sheetz, *Producer*
EMP: 12 **EST:** 2009
SALES (est): 1MM **Privately Held**
SIC: 7372 Prepackaged software

(P-25297)
TRION WORLDS, INC.
2400 Bridge Pkwy 100, Redwood City
(94065-1166)
PHONE..................650 631-9800
EMP: 294
SALES (est): 55.1MM **Privately Held**
WEB: www.trionworld.com
SIC: 7372 Home entertainment computer
software

(P-25298)
TROV INC (PA)
347 Hartz Ave, Danville (94526-3307)
PHONE..................925 478-5500
Scott Walchek, *CEO*
Mark Dowds, *Exec VP*
Michael Pearson, *Admin Sec*
Chris Desvernine, *Opers Mgr*
Athina Saravelou, *Opers Staff*
EMP: 21 **EST:** 2012
SQ FT: 4,972
SALES (est): 4MM **Privately Held**
SIC: 7372 Application computer software

(P-25299)
TSS SOFTWARE CORPORATION
200 Commerce, Irvine (92602-5000)
PHONE..................443 321-5600
Robert Miller, *CEO*
Barbara Miller, *President*
EMP: 38 **EST:** 1993
SQ FT: 3,000
SALES (est): 3MM **Privately Held**
WEB: www.titlesupport.com
SIC: 7372 7371 Prepackaged software;
custom computer programming services

(P-25300)
TUBEMOGUL INC
1250 53rd St Ste 1, Emeryville
(94608-2965)
PHONE..................510 653-0126
Brett Wilson, *President*
Derek Kruger, *Partner*
John Ratz, *Partner*
Robert Gatto, *COO*
Ron Will, *CFO*
EMP: 68
SQ FT: 49,000
SALES: 180.7MM
SALES (corp-wide): 7.3B **Publicly Held**
SIC: 7372 Application computer software
PA: Adobe Inc.
345 Park Ave
San Jose CA 95110
408 536-6000

(P-25301)
TUKKO GROUP LLC
Also Called: Tukko Labs
530 Alameda Del Prado, Novato
(94949-9810)
PHONE..................408 598-1251
Ashton B Wolfson, *CEO*
EMP: 20
SALES (est): 846.7K **Privately Held**
SIC: 7372 Prepackaged software

(P-25302)
TURBOTOOLS CORPORATION
2190 31st Ave, San Francisco
(94116-1637)
PHONE..................415 759-5599
Alex H Chernyak, *CEO*
Michael Savransky, *Vice Pres*
EMP: 15
SALES (est): 846.3K **Privately Held**
WEB: www.turbotools.com
SIC: 7372 Prepackaged software

(P-25303)
TYLER TECHNOLOGIES INC
Also Called: Tyler Camera Systems
14218 Aetna St, Van Nuys (91401-3433)
PHONE..................818 989-4420
Nelson Tyler, *Owner*
EMP: 15
SALES (corp-wide): 840.6MM **Publicly
Held**
SIC: 7372 Prepackaged software
PA: Tyler Technologies, Inc.
5101 Tennyson Pkwy
Plano TX 75024
972 713-3700

(P-25304)
TZ HOLDINGS LP
567 San Nicolas Dr # 120, Newport Beach
(92660-6513)
PHONE..................949 719-2200
Regina Paolillo, *Principal*
EMP: 2000
SALES (est): 46.9MM **Privately Held**
SIC: 7372 Prepackaged software

(P-25305)
UBER TECHNOLOGIES INC
555 Market St, San Francisco
(94105-2800)
PHONE..................415 986-2715
Margaret E Walsh, *Chairman*
EMP: 37
SALES (corp-wide): 750.5MM **Privately
Held**
SIC: 7372 Application computer software
PA: Uber Technologies, Inc.
1455 Market St Fl 4
San Francisco CA 94103

(P-25306)
**ULTIMATE SOFTWARE GROUP
INC**
5 Hutton Centre Dr # 130, Santa Ana
(92707-8738)
PHONE..................949 214-2710
John Stauffer, *Vice Pres*
Wayne Hall, *IT/INT Sup*
Tony Desabota, *Human Res Mgr*
Hrm M Patterson, *Human Resources*
Danny Pyo, *Accounts Mgr*
EMP: 44
SALES (corp-wide): 940.7MM **Publicly
Held**
SIC: 7372 Application computer software
PA: The Ultimate Software Group Inc
2000 Ultimate Way
Weston FL 33326
954 331-7000

(P-25307)
**ULTIMO SOFTWARE SOLUTIONS
INC**
33268 Central Ave 2, Union City
(94587-2010)
PHONE..................408 943-1490
Venkatasubhash Pasumarthy, *President*
Smita Pasumarthi, *CFO*
Saurabh Srivastava, *Consultant*
EMP: 127
SQ FT: 4,000
SALES (est): 10.9MM **Privately Held**
WEB: www.ultimosoft.com
SIC: 7372 Prepackaged software

(P-25308)
UNDERGROUND LABS INC
1114 Oakwood Cir, Clayton (94517-1700)
P.O. Box 982 (94517-0982)
PHONE..................925 297-5333
Jeff Annison, *CEO*
Karen Annison, *Office Mgr*
EMP: 10
SALES (est): 790K **Privately Held**
SIC: 7372 7371 Application computer soft-
ware; computer software development &
applications

(P-25309)
UNIFI SOFTWARE INC
1810 Gateway Dr Ste 380, San Mateo
(94404-4063)
PHONE..................732 614-9522
Rob Carlson, *President*
Chris Selland, *Vice Pres*
Donald Carr, *Office Mgr*
Ayush Parashar, *VP Engrg*
Andy Sheldon, *VP Mktg*
EMP: 25
SALES (est): 1.5MM **Privately Held**
SIC: 7372 Business oriented computer
software

(P-25310)
UNIFYID INC
425 2nd St Ste 201, San Francisco
(94107-1420)
PHONE..................650 887-3760
John Whaley, *CEO*
Kurt Somerville, *COO*
EMP: 10 **EST:** 2015
SQ FT: 2,900
SALES (est): 110.1K **Privately Held**
SIC: 7372 Utility computer software

(P-25311)
UNION SOLUTIONS INC
15355 Bittern Ct, San Leandro
(94579-2757)
PHONE..................510 483-1222

P R O D U C T S & S V C S

Xuan James, *Admin Sec*
Paula E Bailey, *CFO*
EMP: 14
SQ FT: 1,500
SALES (est): 560.2K **Privately Held**
WEB: www.unionsolutions.com
SIC: 7372 Prepackaged software

(P-25312)
UNISOFT CORPORATION
10 Rollins Rd Ste 118, Millbrae
(94030-3128)
PHONE.........................650 259-1290
Audrey Ruelas, *President*
Guy Hadland, *CEO*
Bernie Ruelas, *Project Mgr*
EMP: 19 **EST:** 1981
SALES (est): 2.1MM **Privately Held**
WEB: www.unisoft.com
SIC: 7372 5045 Operating systems computer software; utility computer software; computer software

(P-25313)
UNIVERSAL MCLOUD USA CORP
580 California St, San Francisco
(94104-1000)
PHONE.........................613 222-5904
Russ McMeekin, *CEO*
Michael Sicuro, *CFO*
Gino Lander, *Officer*
Darren Anderson, *Exec VP*
EMP: 15
SALES (est): 305.2K
SALES (corp-wide): 657.9K **Privately Held**
SIC: 7372 Business oriented computer software
PA: Universal Mcloud Corp
855 W Georgia St Suite 1500
Vancouver BC V6C 3
604 642-6175

(P-25314)
UNTANGLE HOLDINGS INC
100 W San Fernando St # 565, San Jose
(95113-1787)
PHONE.........................408 598-4299
Scott Devens, *CEO*
Lori Booroojian, *CFO*
Amy Abatangle, *Chief Mktg Ofcr*
Dirk Morris, *Officer*
Timur Kovalev, *CTO*
EMP: 32
SALES (est): 1MM **Privately Held**
SIC: 7372 Prepackaged software

(P-25315)
UPGUARD INC (PA)
909 San Rafael Ave, Mountain View
(94043-1925)
PHONE.........................888 882-3223
Alan Sharp-Paul, *CEO*
Mike Baukes, *CEO*
Frank Bunger, *Vice Pres*
Bill Cordero, *Vice Pres*
Alistair Pialek, *Director*
EMP: 30
SQ FT: 13,800
SALES (est): 8.9MM **Privately Held**
SIC: 7372 Business oriented computer software

(P-25316)
UPHOLD INC
301 Battery St Fl 7, San Francisco
(94111-3237)
PHONE.........................415 730-3988
Tim Parsa, *CEO*
EMP: 43
SALES (corp-wide): 7MM **Privately Held**
SIC: 7372 Application computer software
PA: Uphold, Inc.
900 Larkspur Landing Cir # 209
Larkspur CA 94939
415 528-5457

(P-25317)
UPSTANDING LLC
Also Called: Mobilityware
440 Exchange Ste 100, Irvine
(92602-1390)
PHONE.........................949 788-9900
Dave Yonamine,
Claudia Avitabile, *Office Mgr*

Carrie Collins, *Admin Asst*
Scott Hillier, *Technical Mgr*
John Libby,
EMP: 180
SQ FT: 48,000
SALES (est): 2.5MM **Privately Held**
WEB: www.upstanding.com
SIC: 7372 Business oriented computer software

(P-25318)
URBAN TRADING SOFTWARE INC
21227 Foothill Blvd, Hayward
(94541-1517)
PHONE.........................877 633-6171
Soufyan Abouahmed, *Principal*
EMP: 50
SALES (est): 1.2MM **Privately Held**
SIC: 7372 Prepackaged software

(P-25319)
VALIANTICA INC (PA)
1340 S De Anza Blvd, San Jose
(95129-4644)
PHONE.........................408 694-3803
Peiwei MI, *President*
Pramod Kumar, *Tech Recruiter*
Richard Crandall, *Human Res Mgr*
Radhika Jagtap, *Human Res Mgr*
Pooja Jadhav, *Human Resources*
EMP: 14
SALES (est): 2.1MM **Privately Held**
WEB: www.valiantica.com
SIC: 7372 Business oriented computer software

(P-25320)
VANTIQ INC
1990 N Calif Blvd Ste 400, Walnut Creek
(94596-7249)
PHONE.........................303 377-2882
Marty Sprinzen, *CEO*
Miguel Nhuch, *Risk Mgmt Dir*
Paul Butterworth, *CTO*
EMP: 13 **EST:** 2014
SQ FT: 3,500
SALES (est): 302.5K **Privately Held**
SIC: 7372 Application computer software

(P-25321)
VEEVA SYSTEMS INC (PA)
4280 Hacienda Dr, Pleasanton
(94588-2719)
PHONE.........................925 452-6500
Peter P Gassner, *CEO*
Peter Harbin, *Partner*
Gordon Ritter, *Ch of Bd*
Matthew J Wallach, *President*
Timothy S Cabral, *CFO*
EMP: 114
SALES: 685.5MM **Publicly Held**
SIC: 7372 7371 7379 Prepackaged software; software programming applications; computer related consulting services

(P-25322)
VELOS INC
42840 Christy St Ste 201, Fremont
(94538-3154)
PHONE.........................510 739-4010
John S McLlwain, *President*
Kamar Aulakh, *COO*
Amar Chahal, *Exec VP*
Umer Islah, *Project Mgr*
Stefi Panit, *Project Mgr*
EMP: 40
SQ FT: 6,117
SALES (est): 6.2MM **Privately Held**
WEB: www.velos.com
SIC: 7372 Publishers' computer software

(P-25323)
VELTI INC (HQ)
Also Called: Velti USA
150 California St Fl 10, San Francisco
(94111-4556)
PHONE.........................415 362-2077
Alex Moukas, *CEO*
Sally Rau, *President*
Wilson W Cheung, *Officer*
EMP: 35
SALES (est): 10.7MM
SALES (corp-wide): 571K **Privately Held**
WEB: www.adinfuse.com
SIC: 7372 Prepackaged software

(P-25324)
VERA SECURITY INC
318 Cambridge Ave, Palo Alto
(94306-1505)
PHONE.........................844 438-8372
Carlos Delatorre, *CEO*
Sam Wolff, *CFO*
Robin Daniels, *Chief Mktg Ofcr*
Harnish Kanani, *Officer*
Andy Zambito, *Vice Pres*
EMP: 36
SQ FT: 2,500
SALES (est): 482.6K **Privately Held**
SIC: 7372 Business oriented computer software

(P-25325)
VERBIO INC
2225 E Byshore Rd Ste 200, Palo Alto
(94303)
PHONE.........................650 862-8935
Carlos Puigjaner, *CEO*
Antonio Terradas, *Vice Pres*
EMP: 32 **EST:** 2014
SALES (est): 892.3K **Privately Held**
SIC: 7372 Business oriented computer software

(P-25326)
VERILOGIX INC
960 Knox St Bldg A, Torrance
(90502-1086)
P.O. Box 3472, Pls Vrds Pnsl (90274-9472)
PHONE.........................310 527-5100
Tom Christy, *President*
EMP: 18
SALES (est): 1.2MM **Privately Held**
WEB: www.verilogix.com
SIC: 7372 3674 Educational computer software; semiconductors & related devices

(P-25327)
VERITAS SOFTWARE GLOBAL LLC
1600 Plymouth St, Mountain View
(94043-1203)
PHONE.........................650 335-8000
EMP: 15 **EST:** 2011
SALES (est): 1.3MM **Privately Held**
SIC: 7372

(P-25328)
VEROS SOFTWARE INC
2333 N Broadway Ste 350, Santa Ana
(92706-1651)
PHONE.........................714 415-6300
Darius Bozorgi, *President*
Shirley Glowa, *President*
Jim Blust, *Vice Pres*
Farnaz Calafi, *Executive Asst*
Pramod Chaudhary, *Sr Software Eng*
EMP: 20
SALES (est): 3.9MM **Privately Held**
SIC: 7372 Application computer software

(P-25329)
VERSANT CORPORATION (HQ)
500 Arguello St Ste 200, Redwood City
(94063-1567)
PHONE.........................650 232-2400
Bernhard Woebker, *President*
Jerry Wong, *CFO*
EMP: 19
SQ FT: 6,800
SALES (est): 6.9MM
SALES (corp-wide): 132.1MM **Privately Held**
SIC: 7372 Prepackaged software
PA: Actian Corporation
2300 Geng Rd Ste 150
Palo Alto CA 94303
650 587-5500

(P-25330)
VGW US INC
442 Post St Fl 9, San Francisco
(94102-1510)
PHONE.........................415 240-0498
Derek Brinkman, *President*
EMP: 12 **EST:** 2017
SALES (est): 256K **Privately Held**
SIC: 7372 Home entertainment computer software

(P-25331)
VIDEOAMP INC (PA)
560 Mission St Ste 1379, San Francisco
(94105-2907)
PHONE.........................949 294-0351
Ross McCray, *CEO*
Jay Prasad, *Officer*
Nick Chakalos, *Senior VP*
Allison Felter, *Executive*
Dave Austria, *Business Dir*
EMP: 14
SALES (est): 5.3MM **Privately Held**
SIC: 7372 Prepackaged software

(P-25332)
VINDICIA INC
2988 Campus Dr Ste 300, San Mateo
(94403-2531)
PHONE.........................650 264-4700
Kris Nagel, *CEO*
Mark Elrod, *Exec VP*
Hurst Arthur, *Vice Pres*
Bryta Schulz, *Vice Pres*
Jason Knight, *Administration*
EMP: 135
SQ FT: 9,000
SALES (est): 15.3MM **Privately Held**
SIC: 7372 Business oriented computer software
HQ: Amdocs, Inc.
1390 Timberlake Manor Pkw
Chesterfield MO 63017
314 212-7000

(P-25333)
VIRSEC SYSTEMS INC
226 Airport Pkwy Ste 350, San Jose
(95110-1026)
PHONE.........................978 274-7260
Satya Gupta, *CTO*
Atiq Raza, *CEO*
Raymond Demeo, *COO*
Tom Miller, *Senior VP*
Saurabh Sharma, *Vice Pres*
EMP: 10
SALES (est): 927.2K **Privately Held**
WEB: www.virsec.com
SIC: 7372 Utility computer software

(P-25334)
VISAGE SOFTWARE INC
5151 California Ave # 230, Irvine
(92617-3205)
PHONE.........................949 614-0759
Jason Lankow, *CEO*
Jake Burkett, *Shareholder*
Ross Crooks, *Shareholder*
EMP: 11
SQ FT: 5,000
SALES (est): 740.2K **Privately Held**
SIC: 7372 Business oriented computer software

(P-25335)
VISIER INC (PA)
550 S Winchester Blvd, San Jose
(95128-2544)
PHONE.........................888 277-9331
John Schwarz, *CEO*
Ryan Wong, *President*
Steve Bamberger, *Officer*
Adam Binnie, *Officer*
Dave Weisbeck, *Officer*
EMP: 15
SALES (est): 3.4MM **Privately Held**
SIC: 7372 Business oriented computer software

(P-25336)
VISUALON INC
2590 N 1st St Ste 100, San Jose
(95131-1021)
PHONE.........................408 645-6618
Andy Lin, *President*
Bill Lin, *Senior VP*
Sean Torsney, *Senior VP*
EMP: 120
SALES (est): 25MM **Privately Held**
WEB: www.visualon.com
SIC: 7372 Prepackaged software

(P-25337)
VIV LABS INC
60 S Market St Ste 900, San Jose
(95113-2372)
PHONE.........................650 268-9837

▲ = Import ▼=Export
◆ =Import/Export

Dag Kittlaus, *CEO*
EMP: 17
SALES (est): 722K
SALES (corp-wide): 148.1B **Privately Held**
SIC: 7372 Utility computer software
PA: Samsung Electronics Co., Ltd.
129 Samseong-Ro, Yeongtong-Gu
Suwon 16677
822 200-9544

(P-25338)
VNOMIC INC
1250 Oakmead Pkwy, Sunnyvale
(94085-4027)
PHONE 408 890-2220
Derek Palma, *Vice Pres*
EMP: 15
SALES (est): 5.2MM **Privately Held**
SIC: 7372 Application computer software

(P-25339)
VOYANT INTERNATIONAL CORP
Also Called: Voyant Aviation Broadband
444 Castro St Ste 318, Mountain View
(94041-2059)
PHONE 800 710-6637
Dana R Waldman, *CEO*
Mark M Laisure, *Ch of Bd*
David R Wells, *CFO*
Scott Fairbairn, *CTO*
EMP: 10
SALES (est): 584.8K **Privately Held**
WEB: www.voyant.net
SIC: 7372 Business oriented computer
software

(P-25340)
WAGGL INC (PA)
3 Harbor Dr Ste 200, Sausalito
(94965-1491)
PHONE 415 399-9949
Michael Papay, *CEO*
Meghan Gehle, *Office Mgr*
Marc Campos, *Accounts Mgr*
EMP: 12 **EST:** 2014
SQ FT: 2,000
SALES (est): 309.3K **Privately Held**
SIC: 7372 Application computer software

(P-25341)
WALLABY FINANCIAL LLC
Also Called: Wallaby Financial, Inc.
680 E Colo Blvd Ste 350, Pasadena
(91101)
PHONE 626 600-2604
Matthew Goldman, *CEO*
Todd Zino, *CTO*
EMP: 35
SALES (est): 375.6K
SALES (corp-wide): 450MM **Privately
Held**
SIC: 7372 Business oriented computer
software
HQ: Baton Holding, Llc
1675 Broadway Fl 2
New York NY 10019

(P-25342)
WANADA INVESTMENTS LLC
Also Called: LLC Lindero Learning Center
5 Corporate Park Ste 110, Irvine
(92606-5165)
PHONE 818 292-8627
John Andrew Adams, *Mng Member*
EMP: 20
SALES: 205K **Privately Held**
SIC: 7372 Educational computer software

(P-25343)
WEBCLOAK LLC
2 Park Plz Ste 700, Irvine (92614-8517)
PHONE 949 417-9940
William Shopoff, *CEO*
Martin Dawson, *Officer*
EMP: 10 **EST:** 2014
SALES (est): 468.6K **Privately Held**
SIC: 7372 Application computer software

(P-25344)
WEBEDOCTOR INC
471 W Lambert Rd Ste 105, Brea
(92821-3921)
PHONE 714 990-3999
Anwer Siddiqi, *CEO*

Samar Siddiqi, *Marketing Staff*
EMP: 26
SALES (est): 2.3MM **Privately Held**
WEB: www.webedoctor.com
SIC: 7372 Application computer software

(P-25345)
WEMO MEDIA INC
550 Rose Ave, Venice (90291-2606)
PHONE 310 399-8058
Neville Spiteri, *CEO*
EMP: 10
SALES (est): 785.3K **Privately Held**
SIC: 7372 Application computer software

(P-25346)
**WEST COAST CONSULTING
LLC (PA)**
9233 Research Dr Ste 200, Irvine
(92618-4294)
PHONE 949 250-4102
Rajat Khurana,
Misty Chaudhry, *Executive*
Sagar Chand, *Tech Recruiter*
Yogesh Tomar, *Tech Recruiter*
Syed Shoaib, *Human Res Mgr*
EMP: 125
SALES (est): 14MM **Privately Held**
WEB: www.westcoastllc.com
SIC: 7372 Prepackaged software

(P-25347)
**WEST COAST CONSULTING
LLC**
9233 Research Dr Ste 200, Irvine
(92618-4294)
PHONE 949 336-7700
Rajat Khurana, *CEO*
EMP: 25
SALES (corp-wide): 14MM **Privately
Held**
SIC: 7372 Prepackaged software
PA: West Coast Consulting, Llc
9233 Research Dr Ste 200
Irvine CA 92618
949 250-4102

(P-25348)
WESTEND SOFTWARE INC (PA)
1905 Speyer Ln, Redondo Beach
(90278-4816)
PHONE 310 370-0367
Zeljko Rakocevic, *President*
EMP: 10
SALES (est): 2.4MM **Privately Held**
SIC: 7372 Prepackaged software

(P-25349)
WHAMCLOUD INC
696 San Ramon Valley Blvd, Danville
(94526-4022)
PHONE 925 452-7599
Brent Gorda, *CEO*
Eric Sackett, *Officer*
Dan Ferber, *Sales Staff*
EMP: 23
SALES (est): 1.1MM **Privately Held**
SIC: 7372 Application computer software

(P-25350)
WIND RIVER SYSTEMS INC (HQ)
500 Wind River Way, Alameda
(94501-1162)
PHONE 510 748-4100
Jim Douglas, *CEO*
Shiva Kumar, *Partner*
Scot Morrision, *President*
Barry R Mainz, *COO*
Jane Bon, *CFO*
EMP: 148
SQ FT: 273,000
SALES (est): 349.9MM **Privately Held**
WEB: www.windriver.com
SIC: 7372 7373 Application computer soft-
ware; systems software development
services

(P-25351)
WIND RIVER SYSTEMS INC
10505 Sorrento Valley Rd, San Diego
(92121-1618)
PHONE 858 824-3100
Brad Murdoch, *Vice Pres*
Arch Hughes, *Director*
EMP: 100 **Privately Held**
WEB: www.windriver.com

SIC: 7372 Prepackaged software
HQ: Wind River Systems, Inc.
500 Wind River Way
Alameda CA 94501
510 748-4100

(P-25352)
**WIRELESS GLUE NETWORKS
INC**
4185 Blackhawk Plaza Cir # 220, Danville
(94506-4622)
PHONE 925 310-4561
Peter McCabe, *President*
Matthew Dowling, *Senior VP*
Robert Fries, *Senior VP*
John Lin, *CTO*
EMP: 11
SQ FT: 2,000
SALES (est): 1MM **Privately Held**
SIC: 7372 3575 7371 Application com-
puter software; computer terminals, moni-
tors & components; computer software
development

(P-25353)
WME BI LLC
17075 Camino, San Diego (92127)
PHONE 877 592-2472
EMP: 60
SALES (est): 1.4MM **Privately Held**
SIC: 7372 Operating systems computer
software

(P-25354)
WONDERGROVE LLC
17563 Ventura Blvd Fl 1, Encino
(91316-3836)
PHONE 800 889-7249
Terrance Thoren,
Jason Richards,
Adrian Lacasse, *Editor*
EMP: 19
SALES (est): 801.6K **Privately Held**
SIC: 7372 Educational computer software

(P-25355)
WONOLO INC
535 Mission St Fl 14, San Francisco
(94105-3253)
PHONE 415 766-7692
Yong Kim, *CEO*
Asher Brustein, *COO*
Beatrice Pang, *Vice Pres*
Jeremy Burton, *CTO*
Kristy Wen, *Marketing Staff*
EMP: 39 **EST:** 2014
SQ FT: 7,500
SALES (est): 821.9K **Privately Held**
SIC: 7372 Application computer software

(P-25356)
WORDSMART CORPORATION
10025 Mesa Rim Rd, San Diego
(92121-2913)
P.O. Box 366, La Jolla (92038-0366)
PHONE 858 565-8068
David Kay, *CEO*
EMP: 70
SQ FT: 12,375
SALES (est): 9.4MM **Privately Held**
WEB: www.wordsmart.com
SIC: 7372 Educational computer software

(P-25357)
WORKSPOT INC (PA)
1601 S De Anza Blvd # 230, Cupertino
(95014-5347)
PHONE 408 533-8669
Amitabh Sinha, *President*
Maryam Alexandrian-Adams, *COO*
Ty Wang, *Vice Pres*
Puneet Chawla, *Chief Engr*
Jervis Williams, *Opers Staff*
EMP: 14
SALES (est): 3.5MM **Privately Held**
SIC: 7372 Business oriented computer
software

(P-25358)
WORLDFLASH SOFTWARE INC
3853 Marcasel Ave Ste 101, Los Angeles
(90066-4613)
PHONE 310 745-0632
Sharone Levinson, *President*
Gabrielle Frig, *CFO*
EMP: 25

SALES (est): 1.1MM **Privately Held**
WEB: www.worldflash.com
SIC: 7372 7371 Prepackaged software;
computer software development & applications

(P-25359)
WORLDLINK MEDIA
38 Keyes Ave Ste 17, San Francisco
(94129-1716)
PHONE 415 561-2141
Kirk Bergstrom, *President*
EMP: 10
SALES (est): 333.7K **Privately Held**
WEB: www.goworldlink.com
SIC: 7372 Educational computer software

(P-25360)
XAVIENT INFO SYSTEMS INC
Also Called: Xavient Digital
2125 N Madera Rd Ste B, Simi Valley
(93065-7710)
PHONE 805 955-4111
Rajeev Tandon, *CEO*
Jessica Zhou, *Partner*
Saif Ahmad, *President*
Arshad Majeed, *Exec VP*
Kurt Eltz, *Senior VP*
EMP: 1800
SALES (corp-wide): 10.4B **Privately Held**
SIC: 7372 Business oriented computer
software
HQ: Telus International (U.S) Corp.
2251 S Decatur Blvd
Las Vegas NV 89102
702 238-7900

(P-25361)
XCELMOBILITY INC
2225 E Byshore Rd Ste 200, Palo Alto
(94303)
PHONE 650 320-1728
Zhixiong WEI, *Ch of Bd*
LI Ouyang, *CFO*
Ying Yang, *Admin Sec*
EMP: 98
SALES (est): 384.5K **Privately Held**
SIC: 7372 7999 Business oriented com-
puter software; gambling & lottery serv-
ices

(P-25362)
XINET LLC (HQ)
2560 9th St Ste 312, Berkeley
(94710-2557)
PHONE 510 845-0555
Scott Seebass, *President*
Ellen Katzman, *VP Mktg*
EMP: 12
SQ FT: 9,000
SALES (est): 6.2MM **Privately Held**
WEB: www.xinet.com
SIC: 7372 7371 Prepackaged software;
custom computer programming services
PA: North Plains Systems Corp
310 Front St W Suite 600
Toronto ON M5V 3
416 345-1900

(P-25363)
XL DYNAMICS INC
18303 Gridley Rd, Cerritos (90703-5401)
P.O. Box 1052, Artesia (90702-1052)
PHONE 562 916-1402
Pavan Agarwal, *CEO*
EMP: 20
SALES (est): 1.4MM **Privately Held**
WEB: www.mortgagesoftonline.com
SIC: 7372 Prepackaged software

(P-25364)
XLSOFT CORPORATION (PA)
12 Mauchly Ste K, Irvine (92618-6304)
PHONE 949 453-2781
Mitsutoshi Watanabe, *President*
Nanako Watanabe, *CFO*
EMP: 14
SQ FT: 7,000
SALES (est): 1.9MM **Privately Held**
WEB: www.xlsoft.com
SIC: 7372 7371 Publishers' computer soft-
ware; custom computer programming
services

(P-25365)
Y-CHANGE INC
43575 Mission Blvd 416, Fremont
(94539-5831)
PHONE.................................510 573-2205
Alan Leeds, *President*
EMP: 15
SALES: 950K Privately Held
WEB: www.ychange.com
SIC: 7372 Application computer software

(P-25366)
YAYYO INC
433 N Camden Dr Ste 600, Beverly Hills
(90210-4416)
PHONE.................................310 926-2643
Ramy El-Batrawi, *CEO*
Laurie Digionanni, *COO*
Kevin F Pickard, *CFO*
EMP: 10
SALES: 235.6K
SALES (corp-wide): 762.3K Privately
Held
SIC: 7372 Prepackaged software
PA: X Llc
433 N Camden Dr Ste 600
Beverly Hills CA 90210
310 926-2643

(P-25367)
YELLOW MAGIC INCORPORATED
41571 Date St, Murrieta (92562-7086)
P.O. Box 3033, Fallbrook (92088-3033)
PHONE.................................951 506-4005
Ronald G Mintle, *CEO*
Beverly Mintle, *Corp Secy*
James Snyder, *Vice Pres*
Patrick Wallin, *Software Dev*
Paul Duffy, *Regl Sales Mgr*
EMP: 15
SALES (est): 2MM Privately Held
SIC: 7372 7389 Home entertainment computer software; educational computer software;

(P-25368)
YUJA INC
2168 Ringwood Ave, San Jose
(95131-1720)
PHONE.................................888 257-2278
Ajit Singh, *President*
Nathan Arora, *Officer*
Nannette Don, *Sales Staff*
Boudreau Kline, *Manager*
Smith Isaac, *Accounts Mgr*
EMP: 125
SALES (est): 990K Privately Held
SIC: 7372 Prepackaged software

(P-25369)
ZENDESK INC (PA)
1019 Market St, San Francisco
(94103-1612)
PHONE.................................415 418-7506
Mikkel Svane, *Ch of Bd*
Adrian McDermott, *President*
Elena Gomez, *CFO*
Inamarie Johnson,
John Geschke, *Senior VP*
EMP: 148
SQ FT: 18,000
SALES: 430.4MM Publicly Held
SIC: 7372 Business oriented computer software

(P-25370)
ZENPAYROLL INC (PA)
Also Called: Gusto
525 20th St, San Francisco (94107-4345)
PHONE.................................800 936-0383
Joshua D Reeves, *CEO*
Lauren Olson, *Partner*
Mike Dinsdale, *CFO*
Tomer London,
Lexi Reese, *Officer*
EMP: 500
SALES (est): 4.9MM Privately Held
SIC: 7372 Business oriented computer software

(P-25371)
ZENTERA SYSTEMS INC
2099 Gateway Pl Ste 420, San Jose
(95110-1017)
PHONE.................................408 436-4811

Jaushin Lee, *CEO*
Belinda Shih, *Opers Mgr*
Dhananjay Nair, *Mktg Dir*
Nancy Lam, *Accounts Exec*
EMP: 16 EST: 2012
SQ FT: 2,800
SALES (est): 1.5MM Privately Held
SIC: 7372 Business oriented computer software

(P-25372)
ZENYX INC
2870 Zanker Rd Ste 210, San Jose
(95134-2133)
PHONE.................................415 741-0170
Srikant Sharma, *CEO*
Vinay Khosla, *COO*
Scott Strother, *Officer*
Fanley Tseng, *Engineer*
Derek Pignatelli, *Director*
EMP: 10 EST: 2014
SALES (est): 494.2K Privately Held
SIC: 7372 Business oriented computer software

(P-25373)
ZINIO SYSTEMS INC
114 Sansome St Fl 4, San Francisco
(94104-3803)
PHONE.................................415 494-2700
Rusty Lewis, *CEO*
Michelle Bottomley, *President*
Richard A Maggiotto, *President*
Virendra Vase, *COO*
Tom Nofziger, *CFO*
EMP: 75
SALES (est): 8.8MM Privately Held
WEB: www.zinio.com
SIC: 7372 Publishers' computer software

(P-25374)
ZOHO CORPORATION (HQ)
4141 Hacienda Dr, Pleasanton
(94588-8566)
PHONE.................................925 924-9500
Sridhar Vembu, *CEO*
Tony Thomas, *Ch of Bd*
Sridhar Iyengar, *Vice Pres*
Rex Antony, *Technical Staff*
Rodrigo Vaca, *VP Mktg*
EMP: 14
SQ FT: 10,000
SALES (est): 171.9MM Privately Held
SIC: 7372 Application computer software

(P-25375)
ZSCALER INC (PA)
110 Rose Orchard Way, San Jose
(95134-1358)
PHONE.................................408 533-0288
Jay Chaudhry, *Ch of Bd*
Remo Canessa, *CFO*
Micheline Nijmeh, *Chief Mktg Ofcr*
Robert Schlossman,
Amit Sinha, *Exec VP*
EMP: 140
SQ FT: 56,000
SALES: 125.7MM Publicly Held
SIC: 7372 Prepackaged software

(P-25376)
ZULIP INC
185 Berry St Ste 400, San Francisco
(94107-1725)
PHONE.................................617 945-7653
Jeff Arnold, *CEO*
EMP: 12
SALES (est): 524.8K Privately Held
SIC: 7372 Prepackaged software

(P-25377)
ZUORA INC (PA)
3050 S Del St Ste 301, San Mateo (94403)
PHONE.................................800 425-1281
Tien Tzuo, *Ch of Bd*
Marc Diouane, *President*
Tyler Sloat, *CFO*
Brent R Cromley Jr, *Senior VP*
Jennifer W Pileggi, *Senior VP*
EMP: 300
SQ FT: 29,000
SALES: 167.9MM Publicly Held
SIC: 7372 Business oriented computer software

(P-25378)
ZYE LABS LLC
310 S Twin Oaks Valley Rd, San Marcos
(92078-4303)
PHONE.................................904 800-9935
John Ringgold, *CEO*
EMP: 10 EST: 2014
SQ FT: 700
SALES (est): 499.6K Privately Held
SIC: 7372 Application computer software

(P-25379)
ZYNGA INC
650 Townsend St, San Francisco
(94103-5646)
PHONE.................................415 621-2391
Zachary Zynga, *Branch Mgr*
Tami Guerrero, *Manager*
EMP: 19
SALES (corp-wide): 861.3MM Publicly
Held
SIC: 7372 Prepackaged software
PA: Zynga Inc.
699 8th St
San Francisco CA 94103
855 449-9642

(P-25380)
ZYRION INC
440 N Wolfe Rd, Sunnyvale (94085-3869)
PHONE.................................408 524-7424
EMP: 75
SQ FT: 6,000
SALES (est): 4.7MM Privately Held
SIC: 7372
PA: Kaseya Global Ireland Limited
Commerzbank House
Dublin

7692 Welding Repair

(P-25381)
A & M WELDING INC
16935 S Broadway, Gardena (90248-3111)
PHONE.................................310 329-2700
Tom A Jorgenson, *President*
Linda Jorgenson, *Vice Pres*
EMP: 18 EST: 1952
SQ FT: 25,000
SALES (est): 1.6MM Privately Held
WEB: www.ammetalforming.com
SIC: 7692 Welding repair

(P-25382)
ADAMS WELDING INC
6352 Apache Rd, Westminster
(92683-2051)
PHONE.................................714 412-7684
Gary Adams, *CEO*
Rebecca Adams, *Vice Pres*
EMP: 12
SALES: 1.5MM Privately Held
SIC: 7692 7389 Welding repair;

(P-25383)
AEROSPACE WELDING INC
2035 Granville Ave, Los Angeles
(90025-6103)
PHONE.................................310 914-0324
Edward Sutter, *President*
Craig Ittner, *Treasurer*
Gary Ittner, *Admin Sec*
Carmelita Sutter, *Controller*
EMP: 19
SQ FT: 20,000
SALES (est): 1.7MM Privately Held
WEB: www.aerospace-welding.com
SIC: 7692 Welding repair

(P-25384)
AG-WELD INC
1236 G St, Wasco (93280-2359)
P.O. Box 637 (93280-0637)
PHONE.................................661 758-3061
Jeff Mehlberg, *CEO*
Bedi Mehlberg, *Vice Pres*
Patty Mehlberg, *Controller*
▲ EMP: 15 EST: 1980
SQ FT: 20,000
SALES (est): 1.6MM Privately Held
SIC: 7692 Welding repair

(P-25385)
AGNALDOS WELDING INC
828 S Burnett Rd, Tipton (93272)
P.O. Box 154 (93272-0154)
PHONE.................................559 752-4254
Agnaldo Tamariz, *President*
Delores Tamariz, *Treasurer*
James Tamariz, *Director*
EMP: 12
SALES: 838.4K Privately Held
SIC: 7692 7699 5083 Welding repair; farm machinery repair; farm equipment parts & supplies

(P-25386)
ARCMATIC WELDING SYSTEMS INC (PA)
1175 Nimitz Ave Ste 240, Vallejo
(94592-1003)
PHONE.................................707 643-5517
William L Bong, *President*
Bill Bong, *President*
Twila Nixon, *Controller*
▲ EMP: 11
SALES (est): 1.2MM Privately Held
SIC: 7692 Welding repair

(P-25387)
B W PADILLA INC
Also Called: Brian's Welding
197 Ryland St, San Jose (95110-2241)
PHONE.................................408 275-9834
Brian Wade Padilla, *CEO*
Diana Padilla, *Vice Pres*
EMP: 24
SALES: 2.2MM Privately Held
WEB: www.brianswelding.com
SIC: 7692 Welding repair

(P-25388)
BRIGHTLIGHT WELDING & MFG INC
3395a Edward Ave, Santa Clara
(95054-2310)
PHONE.................................408 988-0418
Steve Condos, *President*
Anthony Condos, *Corp Secy*
Dan Duman, *Vice Pres*
EMP: 20
SQ FT: 8,000
SALES (est): 2.2MM Privately Held
WEB: www.brightlightwelding.com
SIC: 7692 Welding repair

(P-25389)
BROTHERS ENTERPRISES INC
Also Called: Heritage Truck Painting
7380 Mission Gorge Rd, San Diego
(92120-1224)
PHONE.................................619 229-8003
Carlos Osnaya, *President*
Victor Osnaya, *Vice Pres*
EMP: 10 EST: 2004
SQ FT: 3,000
SALES: 1.1MM Privately Held
WEB: www.heritagetruck-painting.com
SIC: 7692 7532 Automotive welding; collision shops, automotive

(P-25390)
C L P INC (PA)
Also Called: Rick's Hitches & Welding
1546 E Main St, El Cajon (92021-5901)
PHONE.................................619 444-3105
Richard Preston, *President*
Betty Preston, *Vice Pres*
EMP: 30
SQ FT: 23,500
SALES (est): 1.8MM Privately Held
SIC: 7692 7533 7699 Welding repair; muffler shop, sale or repair & installation; recreational vehicle repair services

(P-25391)
CALIFORNIA IRON DESIGN
8906 Lankershim Blvd, Sun Valley
(91352-1915)
PHONE.................................818 767-6690
Alvaro Maron, *Owner*
EMP: 12
SALES (est): 279.5K Privately Held
SIC: 7692 1799 Welding repair; special trade contractors

(P-25392)

CAMBERO METAL WORKS INC
210 Agostino Rd, San Gabriel
(91776-2503)
PHONE..............................626 309-5315
Angel Cambero, *President*
Virginia Cambero, *Vice Pres*
Nick Cambero, *Foreman/Supr*
EMP: 13 EST: 2015
SALES (est): 1.9MM Privately Held
SIC: 7692 3316 3444 Welding repair;
sheet, steel, cold-rolled; from purchased
hot-rolled; awnings, sheet metal

(P-25393)

CAMERON WELDING SUPPLY (PA)
11061 Dale Ave, Stanton (90680-3247)
P.O. Box 266 (90680-0266)
PHONE..............................714 530-9353
Elizabeth Perry, *CEO*
Joseph Churilla, *President*
Robert Rodriguez, *Branch Mgr*
Maria Mangaya, *General Mgr*
Geno Sanchez, *Store Mgr*
▲ EMP: 36
SQ FT: 4,500
SALES (est): 20MM Privately Held
WEB: www.cameronwelding.com
SIC: 7692 5999 Welding repair; welding
supplies

(P-25394)

CAMLAND INC
3152 Canopy Dr, Camarillo (93012-7763)
PHONE..............................805 485-9242
Darlene Camarillo, *CEO*
Dave Green, *Vice Pres*
EMP: 16
SQ FT: 15,000
SALES (est): 1.1MM Privately Held
WEB: www.camland.com
SIC: 7692 3713 Welding repair; truck &
bus bodies

(P-25395)

CHIAPA WELDING INC (PA)
276 E Grand Ave, Porterville (93257-2401)
PHONE..............................559 784-3400
Art Chiapa, *President*
EMP: 10
SQ FT: 3,000
SALES (est): 807.2K Privately Held
SIC: 7692 1799 1791 Welding repair;
welding on site; ornamental metal work;
iron work, structural

(P-25396)

COMPLETE CUTNG & WLDG SUPS INC
Also Called: Complete Welding Supplies
401 N Long Beach Blvd, Compton
(90221-2218)
PHONE..............................310 638-1234
G Gallardo, *Owner*
EMP: 10
SQ FT: 9,842
SALES (corp-wide): 5.7MM Privately
Held
SIC: 7692 Welding repair
PA: Complete Cutting & Welding Supplies,
Inc.
806 E Holt Ave
Pomona CA 91767
909 868-9292

(P-25397)

CW WELDING SERVICE INC (PA)
1735 Santa Fe Ave, Long Beach
(90813-1242)
PHONE..............................562 432-5421
Craig Wildvank, *President*
Jason Rodriguez, *Project Mgr*
EMP: 49
SQ FT: 22,000
SALES (est): 7.8MM Privately Held
WEB: www.cwservices.us
SIC: 7692 Welding repair

(P-25398)

DEANS CERTIFIED WELDING INC
27645 Commerce Center Dr, Temecula
(92590-2521)
PHONE..............................951 676-0242

Michael W Deam, *CEO*
EMP: 13 EST: 2015
SALES (est): 1.4MM Privately Held
SIC: 7692 Welding repair

(P-25399)

DENTONIS WELDING WORKS INC (PA)
Also Called: Dentonis Spring and Suspension
801 S Airport Way, Stockton (95205-6901)
PHONE..............................209 464-4930
David B Dentoni II, *CEO*
Donna Dentoni, *Treasurer*
Dan Dentoni, *Vice Pres*
Debbie Townley, *Human Resources*
Anthony Miranda, *Sales Mgr*
EMP: 45
SQ FT: 1,000
SALES (est): 11.4MM Privately Held
WEB: www.dentoni.com
SIC: 7692 3599 5531 7539 Welding re-
pair; machine shop, jobbing & repair; au-
tomotive parts; automotive springs,
rebuilding & repair

(P-25400)

DIP BRAZE INC
9131 De Garmo Ave, Sun Valley
(91352-2696)
PHONE..............................818 768-1555
Gail Brown, *President*
Robert Gebo, *President*
EMP: 35 EST: 1956
SQ FT: 10,500
SALES (est): 3.8MM Privately Held
WEB: www.dipbraze.com
SIC: 7692 3398 Brazing; metal heat treat-
ing

(P-25401)

DOUG DELEO WELDING INC
249 N Ashland Ave, Lindsay (93247-2430)
P.O. Box 878 (93247-0878)
PHONE..............................559 562-3700
Doug Deleo, *CEO*
Pam Deleo, *Vice Pres*
EMP: 13
SQ FT: 9,600
SALES (est): 2.4MM Privately Held
SIC: 7692 1799 Welding repair; welding
on site

(P-25402)

EDVENTURES CO INC
Also Called: Edwards Sheet Metal & Fab
1203 W Isabel St, Burbank (91506-1494)
PHONE..............................818 848-1270
Vincent A Lupo, *President*
Helene Lupo, *Vice Pres*
Jerome Flament, *Purch Mgr*
▲ EMP: 17
SQ FT: 8,000
SALES (est): 956.1K Privately Held
WEB: www.edventures.com
SIC: 7692 3444 Welding repair; sheet
metalwork

(P-25403)

ELECTRON BEAM ENGINEERING INC
1425 S Allec St, Anaheim (92805-6306)
PHONE..............................714 491-5990
Richard Trillwood, *CEO*
Grant Trillwood, *General Mgr*
Hilary Hurt, *Admin Sec*
Thomas Hurt, *Prdtn Mgr*
Patricia Trillwood, *Director*
EMP: 14
SQ FT: 17,000
SALES (est): 2.4MM Privately Held
WEB: www.ebeinc.com
SIC: 7692 3548 Welding repair; welding
apparatus

(P-25404)

GALAXY BRAZING CO INC
10015 Freeman Ave, Santa Fe Springs
(90670-3405)
PHONE..............................562 946-9039
John Mc Gee, *President*
Donna Mc Gee, *Treasurer*
EMP: 23 EST: 1961
SQ FT: 13,144

SALES (est): 2.4MM Privately Held
WEB: www.galaxybrazing.com
SIC: 7692 3398 Brazing; metal heat treat-
ing; welding on site

(P-25405)

GHAZARIAN WLDG FABRICATION INC
Also Called: Ghazarian Welding & Repair
2903 E Annadale Ave, Fresno
(93725-1944)
P.O. Box 28416 (93729-8416)
PHONE..............................559 233-1210
Ghazar Ghazarian, *Owner*
Sela Ghazarian, *Software Dev*
EMP: 10
SQ FT: 6,000
SALES (est): 1.7MM Privately Held
WEB: www.ghazarianwelding.com
SIC: 7692 Automotive welding

(P-25406)

GK WELDING INC
1150 Hensley St, Richmond (94801-2119)
PHONE..............................510 233-0133
George Kassab, *President*
EMP: 10 EST: 1996
SQ FT: 2,000
SALES (est): 266.2K Privately Held
SIC: 7692 Welding repair

(P-25407)

HAGIST WELDING
34895 Kruse Ranch Rd, Cazadero
(95421-9783)
PHONE..............................707 847-3362
Fritz Hagist, *Owner*
EMP: 12
SALES (est): 580.9K Privately Held
SIC: 7692 Cracked casting repair

(P-25408)

HANSENS WELDING INC
358 W 168th St, Gardena (90248-2733)
PHONE..............................310 329-6888
Gary D Hansen, *CEO*
Robert Hansen, *Vice Pres*
Shauna Hansen, *Admin Sec*
EMP: 25
SQ FT: 26,000
SALES (est): 5.2MM Privately Held
WEB: www.hansenswelding.com
SIC: 7692 Welding repair

(P-25409)

HAYES WELDING INC (PA)
Also Called: Valew Welding & Fabrication
12522 Violet Rd, Adelanto (92301-2704)
P.O. Box 310 (92301-0310)
PHONE..............................760 246-4878
Roger L Hayes, *CEO*
Velma D Hayes, *President*
Vernon L Hayes, *Vice Pres*
Patrick Cavanagh, *Plant Mgr*
▲ EMP: 86
SQ FT: 45,000
SALES (est): 14.5MM Privately Held
WEB: www.valew.com
SIC: 7692 3465 3714 3713 Welding re-
pair; automotive stampings; body parts,
automobile: stamped metal; fenders, au-
tomobile: stamped or pressed metal; fuel
systems & parts, motor vehicle; truck &
bus bodies; fabricated plate work (boiler
shop)

(P-25410)

HAYES WELDING INC
Also Called: Valew Welding & Fabrication
11746 Mariposa Rd Ste 100, Hesperia
(92345-1624)
PHONE..............................760 246-4878
EMP: 14
SALES (corp-wide): 14.5MM Privately
Held
SIC: 7692 Welding repair
PA: Hayes Welding, Inc.
12522 Violet Rd
Adelanto CA 92301
760 246-4878

(P-25411)

IMPACT RACING INC (PA)
Also Called: Mastercraft Safety
9335 Stevens Rd, Santee (92071-2809)
PHONE..............................619 449-9455

Robbie Pierce, *CEO*
Kelli Willmore, *Vice Pres*
▲ EMP: 20
SALES (est): 2.5MM Privately Held
WEB: www.mastercraftseats.com
SIC: 7692 2311 Welding repair; tailored
suits & formal jackets

(P-25412)

IRON WORKS & CUSTOM RACKS
15337 Illinois Ave, Paramount
(90723-4108)
PHONE..............................323 581-2222
Roberto Gonzalez, *Owner*
EMP: 12
SALES (est): 468.2K Privately Held
SIC: 7692 Welding repair

(P-25413)

IV WELDING & MECHANICAL INC
185 S 3rd St, El Centro (92243-2521)
PHONE..............................760 482-9353
Fred R Baeza, *President*
EMP: 10
SQ FT: 11,000
SALES: 650K Privately Held
SIC: 7692 Welding repair

(P-25414)

J MCDOWELL WLDG FRM MCHY INC
29820 County Road 25, Winters
(95694-9706)
P.O. Box 1210 (95694-1210)
PHONE..............................530 661-6006
Jack A McDowell, *President*
EMP: 13 EST: 2011
SALES (est): 647.2K Privately Held
SIC: 7692 7699 Welding repair; farm ma-
chinery repair

(P-25415)

JABIL SILVER CREEK INC (HQ)
Also Called: Wolfe Engineering, Inc.
5981 Optical Ct, San Jose (95138-1400)
PHONE..............................669 255-2900
John P Wolfe, *CEO*
Rita Wolfe, *Vice Pres*
Pete Leon, *Manager*
▲ EMP: 115
SQ FT: 76,000
SALES (est): 25.5MM
SALES (corp-wide): 22.1B Publicly Held
WEB: www.wolfe-engr.com
SIC: 7692 8711 3674 3317 Welding re-
pair; engineering services; semiconduc-
tors & related devices; steel pipe & tubes;
fabricated pipe & fittings
PA: Jabil Inc.
10560 Dr Martin Luther
Saint Petersburg FL 33716
727 577-9749

(P-25416)

JETI INC (PA)
Also Called: Jet I
14578 Hawthorne Ave, Fontana
(92335-2507)
PHONE..............................909 357-2966
John Lowery, *President*
Jose Gradilla, *Vice Pres*
EMP: 13
SQ FT: 10,000
SALES (est): 851.3K Privately Held
SIC: 7692 Welding repair

(P-25417)

JON STEEL ERECTORS INC
1431 S Gage St, San Bernardino
(92408-2835)
PHONE..............................909 799-0005
Octavio Arellano, *President*
EMP: 22
SALES (est): 671.4K Privately Held
SIC: 7692 5082 1791 Welding repair;
general construction machinery & equip-
ment; structural steel erection

(P-25418)

K C WELDING INC
1549 Dogwood Rd, El Centro
(92243-9605)
PHONE..............................760 352-3832

C Mostrong, *Principal*
EMP: 13
SALES (est): 1.2MM **Privately Held**
SIC: 7692 Welding repair

(P-25419)
LA HABRA WELDING INC
10819 Koontz Ave, Santa Fe Springs
(90670-4409)
PHONE..................................562 923-2229
Ira Smith, *President*
Steven Smith, *Vice Pres*
Jerry Wachel, *Admin Sec*
EMP: 12 EST: 1966
SQ FT: 30,900
SALES (est): 1.7MM **Privately Held**
WEB: www.lhwinc.com
SIC: 7692 Welding repair

(P-25420)
LAZESTAR
346 Earhart Way, Livermore (94551-9309)
PHONE..................................925 443-5293
Daniel P Schwertfeger, *President*
EMP: 25
SALES (est): 2.2MM **Privately Held**
WEB: www.lazestar.com
SIC: 7692 Welding repair

(P-25421)
MARLEON INC
Also Called: Hanley Welding
3202 W Rosecrans Ave, Hawthorne
(90250-8225)
PHONE..................................310 679-1242
Leon Hanley, *President*
EMP: 26
SQ FT: 3,000
SALES (est): 2.9MM **Privately Held**
SIC: 7692 2431 Welding repair; stair-
cases, stairs & railings

(P-25422)
**MIKES PRECISION WELDING
INC**
28073 Diaz Rd Ste D, Temecula
(92590-3464)
P.O. Box 891929 (92589-1929)
PHONE..................................951 676-4744
Michael Prunty, *President*
Jeanette Prunty, *Admin Sec*
EMP: 11
SQ FT: 3,000
SALES (est): 1.1MM **Privately Held**
SIC: 7692 Welding repair

(P-25423)
MORRIS WELDING CO INC
11210 Socrates Mine Rd, Middletown
(95461)
PHONE..................................707 987-1114
Sonnie Young, *President*
Judy Morris, *Corp Secy*
EMP: 11 EST: 1971
SQ FT: 6,000
SALES (est): 2.3MM **Privately Held**
SIC: 7692 1623 Welding repair; water,
sewer & utility lines

(P-25424)
**NEVADA HEAT TREATING INC
(PA)**
Also Called: California Brazing
37955 Central Ct Ste D, Newark
(94560-3466)
PHONE..................................510 790-2300
Richard T Penrose, *Corp Secy*
Pat McKenna, *Vice Pres*
Rosie Tullis, *Admin Asst*
Aurora Mendoza, *Senior Buyer*
Savitri Yuen, *Buyer*
◆ EMP: 37
SQ FT: 45,000
SALES (est): 13.8MM **Privately Held**
WEB: www.californiabrazing.com
SIC: 7692 3398 3599 Brazing; metal heat
treating; air intake filters, internal combus-
tion engine, except auto

(P-25425)
PERFORMANCE WELDING
2540 S Sarah St, Fresno (93706-5033)
PHONE..................................559 233-0042
Fax: 559 233-0046
EMP: 10

SALES (est): 1.1MM **Privately Held**
SIC: 7692

(P-25426)
**PHILLIPS MACHINE & WLDG CO
INC**
16125 Gale Ave, City of Industry
(91745-1709)
PHONE..................................626 855-4600
Don McKenna, *Branch Mgr*
EMP: 22
SALES (corp-wide): 12.3MM **Privately
Held**
SIC: 7692 Welding repair
PA: Phillip's Machine And Welding Com-
pany, Inc.
16125 Gale Ave
City Of Industry CA 91745
626 855-4600

(P-25427)
PT WELDING INC
1960 E Main St, Woodland (95776-6202)
PHONE..................................530 406-0267
Patrick Trafician, *CEO*
EMP: 12
SALES (est): 1.7MM **Privately Held**
SIC: 7692 Welding repair

(P-25428)
R B WELDING INC
155 E Redondo Beach Blvd, Gardena
(90248-2347)
PHONE..................................310 324-8680
Nabil Abeskharoun, *President*
EMP: 15
SQ FT: 2,500
SALES (est): 2.6MM **Privately Held**
SIC: 7692 3441 Welding repair; fabricated
structural metal

(P-25429)
**RANDY NIX CSTM WLDG & MFG
INC**
22700 Road 196, Lindsay (93247-9832)
P.O. Box 730, Strathmore (93267-0730)
PHONE..................................559 562-1958
Guy Randy Nix, *President*
Traci L Nix, *Corp Secy*
EMP: 15
SQ FT: 74,880
SALES: 1.5MM **Privately Held**
SIC: 7692 3556 Welding repair; packing
house machinery

(P-25430)
RENT ALL PARTY WORKS INC
18550 N Highway 1, Fort Bragg
(95437-8702)
PHONE..................................707 964-6661
Holly Kuchar, *President*
EMP: 14
SALES (est): 820K **Privately Held**
SIC: 7692 Welding repair

(P-25431)
RETTIG MACHINE INC
301 Kansas St, Redlands (92373-8153)
P.O. Box 7460 (92375-0460)
PHONE..................................909 793-7811
Franz A Rettig Sr, *President*
Susan L Rettig, *Corp Secy*
Franz A Rettig Jr, *Vice Pres*
Robert A Rettig, *Vice Pres*
Susan Rettig, *Executive*
EMP: 25 EST: 1952
SQ FT: 37,000
SALES: 1.6MM **Privately Held**
WEB: www.rettigmachine.com
SIC: 7692 3599 Welding repair; machine
shop, jobbing & repair

(P-25432)
**ROMEROS WELDING & MAR
SVCS INC**
519 Waterfront Ave, Vallejo (94592)
PHONE..................................925 550-0518
Jesus G Romero, *President*
Edith Romero, *Admin Sec*
EMP: 13
SQ FT: 15,000
SALES: 1.6MM **Privately Held**
SIC: 7692 7699 Welding repair; boat re-
pair

(P-25433)
SELKEN ENTERPRISES INC
Also Called: Sel-Tech
108 Boeing Ave, Chico (95973-9011)
PHONE..................................530 891-4200
Jerry Selken, *President*
Erik Rust, *General Mgr*
Jason Teixeira, *Prdtn Mgr*
EMP: 14
SQ FT: 25,000
SALES (est): 2.5MM **Privately Held**
WEB: www.sel-tech.com
SIC: 7692 3728 3721 3444 Welding re-
pair; aircraft parts & equipment; aircraft
body & wing assemblies & parts; aircraft
assemblies, subassemblies & parts; air-
craft; hoppers, sheet metal

(P-25434)
SHANNON SIDE WELDING INC
214 Shaw Rd Ste I, South San Francisco
(94080-6614)
PHONE..................................415 408-3219
Patrick M Sheedy, *CEO*
EMP: 10
SALES (est): 1.2MM **Privately Held**
SIC: 7692 Welding repair

(P-25435)
**SO CAL TRACTOR SALES CO
INC**
30517 The Old Rd, Castaic (91384-3709)
PHONE..................................818 252-1900
Utz James, *President*
EMP: 23
SQ FT: 26,000
SALES (est): 2MM **Privately Held**
SIC: 7692 7549 1799 Welding repair; high
performance auto repair & service; steam
cleaning of building exteriors

(P-25436)
**SOUTHCOAST WELDING & MFG
LLC**
2591 Faivre St Ste 1, Chula Vista
(91911-7146)
PHONE..................................619 429-1337
Patrick Shoup, *President*
Leo Mathieu, *CFO*
Jay Parast, *Vice Pres*
Elizabeth Molina, *Human Res Dir*
Frank McGhee, *Prdtn Mgr*
EMP: 270
SQ FT: 82,000
SALES (est): 30.3MM **Privately Held**
SIC: 7692 Welding repair

(P-25437)
**STAINLESS TECHNOLOGIES
LLC**
19425 W Grove Ave, Visalia (93291)
PHONE..................................559 651-0460
Robert Krikorian, *President*
Manny Hoy, *CFO*
Freddy Perales, *General Mgr*
EMP: 16 EST: 2007
SQ FT: 5,000
SALES (est): 772K **Privately Held**
SIC: 7692 Welding repair

(P-25438)
STAINLESS WORKS INC
201 E Owens Ave, Tulare (93274-5434)
PHONE..................................559 688-4310
Richard Perales, *President*
Margaret Perales, *Treasurer*
David Munoz, *Vice Pres*
Judy Munoz, *Admin Sec*
Jason Snyder, *Marketing Staff*
EMP: 12 EST: 1998
SQ FT: 2,200
SALES: 900K **Privately Held**
SIC: 7692 Welding repair

(P-25439)
**SULZER PUMP SERVICES (US)
INC**
Also Called: Sulzer Bingham Pumps
9856 Jordan Cir, Santa Fe Springs
(90670-3303)
P.O. Box 3904 (90670-1904)
PHONE..................................562 903-1000
Tim Voyles, *Manager*
EMP: 29
SQ FT: 18,968

SALES (corp-wide): 3B **Privately Held**
WEB: www.sulzerpumps.com
SIC: 7692 Welding repair
HQ: Sulzer Pump Services (Us) Inc.
101 Old Underwood Rd G
La Porte TX 77571
281 417-7110

(P-25440)
TC STEEL
464 Sonoma Mountain Rd, Petaluma
(94954-9579)
PHONE..................................707 773-2150
Tom Cleary, *President*
Kim Cleary, *CFO*
EMP: 40 EST: 1989
SALES (est): 3.9MM **Privately Held**
SIC: 7692 3449 5051 7389 Welding re-
pair; miscellaneous metalwork; structural
shapes, iron or steel; scrap steel cutting

(P-25441)
TERRI BELL
Also Called: Alpine Metals
2152 Ruth Ave Ste 4, South Lake Tahoe
(96150-4336)
PHONE..................................530 541-4180
Terri Bell, *Owner*
EMP: 12
SQ FT: 13,000
SALES (est): 700K **Privately Held**
WEB: www.alpinemetals.com
SIC: 7692 1799 Welding repair; welding
on site

(P-25442)
**THOMAS MANUFACTURING CO
LLC**
1308 W 8th Ave, Chico (95926-3002)
PHONE..................................530 893-8940
Carolyn Dauterman,
Thomas Dauterman,
▲ EMP: 25
SQ FT: 55,000
SALES (est): 2.9MM **Privately Held**
SIC: 7692 5083 3599 Welding repair;
agricultural machinery & equipment; ma-
chine shop, jobbing & repair

(P-25443)
**THOMAS WELDING & MCH SP
INC**
1308 W 8th Ave, Chico (95926-3002)
PHONE..................................530 893-8940
Thomas Danterman, *CEO*
Carolyn Sue Dauterman, *Vice Pres*
EMP: 25
SQ FT: 55,000
SALES (est): 2.5MM **Privately Held**
SIC: 7692 5083 3599 Welding repair;
agricultural machinery & equipment; ma-
chine shop, jobbing & repair

(P-25444)
TIKOS TANKS INC
Also Called: Rte Welding
14561 Hawthorne Ave, Fontana
(92335-2508)
PHONE..................................951 757-8014
Ruben Gutierrez III, *Founder*
Shana Gutierrez, *Officer*
Ruben Alonso, *Asst Mgr*
Chris Loya, *Parts Mgr*
EMP: 45
SALES (est): 7.4MM **Privately Held**
SIC: 7692 Welding repair

(P-25445)
TITAN STEEL FABRICATORS INC
1069 E Bradley Ave, El Cajon
(92021-1232)
P.O. Box 2057 (92021-0057)
PHONE..................................619 449-1271
Allan W Jones, *President*
Timothy Jackman, *Vice Pres*
EMP: 10
SALES (est): 1.7MM **Privately Held**
SIC: 7692 Welding repair

(P-25446)
TOMS METAL SPECIALISTS INC
Also Called: Toms Welding & Fabrication
1416 Wallace Ave, San Francisco
(94124-3318)
P.O. Box 24385 (94124-0385)
PHONE..................................415 822-7971

▲ = Import ▼=Export
◆ =Import/Export

Tom Chang, *CEO*
Maria Ancaja, *Accountant*
Teresa Chang, *Controller*
EMP: 33
SQ FT: 4,000
SALES (est): 6.6MM **Privately Held**
WEB: www.tomsmetal.com
SIC: 7692 Welding repair

(P-25447)
VETPOWERED LLC
2970 Main St, San Diego (92113-3730)
PHONE..................................619 269-7116
Hernan Luis Y Prado,
Rachel Luis Y Prado, *Vice Pres*
EMP: 16
SQ FT: 32,000
SALES: 2MM **Privately Held**
WEB: www.lypindustries.com
SIC: 7692 7359 3599 7699 Automotive welding; home cleaning & maintenance equipment rental services; machine shop, jobbing & repair; industrial machinery & equipment repair; commercial cooking & foodwarming equipment; ballistic missiles, complete

(P-25448)
WELDLOGIC INC
2651 Lavery Ct, Newbury Park (91320-1502)
PHONE..................................805 375-1670
Robert Elizarraz, *President*
Jack Froschauer, *Vice Pres*
Rick Heminuk, *Vice Pres*
Amil Zagheb, *Electrical Engi*
▲ **EMP:** 65
SQ FT: 25,000
SALES (est): 11.6MM **Privately Held**
WEB: www.weldlogic.com
SIC: 7692 Welding repair

(P-25449)
WEST COAST WELDING & CNSTR
390 S Del Norte Blvd, Oxnard (93030-7914)
PHONE..................................805 604-1222
Micheal Edward Barbey, *CEO*
Tamara Barbey, *CFO*
Stella Delgado, *Admin Sec*
John Bricker, *Superintendent*
EMP: 15
SALES (est): 2.2MM **Privately Held**
SIC: 7692 Welding repair

(P-25450)
WYMORE INC
697 S Dogwood Rd, El Centro (92243-9747)
P.O. Box 2618 (92244-2618)
PHONE..................................760 352-2045
Marla Wymore Stilwell, *President*
Michael Mouser, *Corp Secy*
Richard C Wymore, *Director*
Thomas A Wymore, *Director*
EMP: 30 **EST:** 1947
SQ FT: 25,200
SALES (est): 5.3MM **Privately Held**
SIC: 7692 3599 5251 5085 Welding repair; machine shop, jobbing & repair; tools; tools

---
7694 Armature Rewinding Shops

(P-25451)
ALLIED ELECTRIC MOTOR SVC INC
2635 S Sierra Vista Ave, Fresno (93725-2103)
PHONE..................................559 486-4222
Salvatore Rome, *Director*
EMP: 13
SALES (corp-wide): 43.9MM **Privately Held**
WEB: www.alliedelectric.net
SIC: 7694 Electric motor repair
PA: Allied Electric Motor Service, Inc.
4690 E Jensen Ave
Fresno CA 93725
559 486-4222

(P-25452)
ALSOP PUMP
Also Called: Alsop Electric Motor Shop
1508 Abbott St, Salinas (93901-4507)
PHONE..................................831 424-3946
Steve Allison, *Owner*
EMP: 12
SQ FT: 2,250
SALES: 389.2K **Privately Held**
SIC: 7694 5063 Electric motor repair; motors, electric

(P-25453)
ARROW ELECTRIC MOTOR SERVICE
645 Broadway St, Fresno (93721-2890)
PHONE..................................559 266-0104
Larry Kragh, *President*
Geri Kragh, *Corp Secy*
Cathy Knott, *Office Mgr*
Jeff Kragh, *Sales Staff*
Scott Kragh, *Mktg Coord*
EMP: 11
SQ FT: 25,000
SALES (est): 2MM **Privately Held**
WEB: www.arrowelectricmotor.com
SIC: 7694 Electric motor repair

(P-25454)
AUL CORP (PA)
1250 Main St Ste 300, NAPA (94559-2622)
PHONE..................................707 257-9700
Luis N Nieves, *President*
Jimmy Atkinson, *COO*
Craig Bertenshaw, *Vice Pres*
Luis Cendejas, *Admin Asst*
Matt Brady, *Business Mgr*
EMP: 40
SQ FT: 8,500
SALES (est): 3.8MM **Privately Held**
WEB: www.aulcorp.com
SIC: 7694 7549 Motor repair services; automotive maintenance services

(P-25455)
BAKERSFIELD ELC MTR REPR INC
Also Called: B E M R
121 W Sumner St, Bakersfield (93301-4137)
PHONE..................................661 327-3583
Michael Wayne Langston, *President*
Jerry Endicott, *President*
Nina Endicott, *Vice Pres*
EMP: 13 **EST:** 1949
SQ FT: 12,350
SALES: 3.6MM **Privately Held**
SIC: 7694 5063 Rewinding services; electric motor repair; motors, electric

(P-25456)
DEMARIA ELECTRIC INC
Also Called: Demaria Electric Motor Svcs
7048 Marcelle St, Paramount (90723-4839)
PHONE..................................310 549-4980
Daniel Demaria, *President*
Diane Ortiz, *Office Mgr*
Gary Demaria, *Information Mgr*
Refugio Gallegos, *Research*
EMP: 30 **EST:** 1977
SQ FT: 6,500
SALES (est): 2.4MM **Privately Held**
WEB: www.demariaelectric.com
SIC: 7694 7699 Electric motor repair; engine repair & replacement, non-automotive

(P-25457)
E & L ELECTRIC INC
12322 Los Nietos Rd, Santa Fe Springs (90670-2912)
PHONE..................................562 903-9272
Mike Fitch, *President*
EMP: 17
SQ FT: 10,000
SALES (est): 4.5MM **Privately Held**
SIC: 7694 5063 Electric motor repair; motors, electric

(P-25458)
ELECTRIC MOTOR WORKS INC
803 Inyo St, Bakersfield (93305-5127)
P.O. Box 3349 (93385-3349)
PHONE..................................661 327-4271

L B Thomasl B Thomas, *President*
Chuck Thomas, *Vice Pres*
Allan Barks, *Regl Sales Mgr*
Gordon Cantrell, *Sales Mgr*
EMP: 20
SQ FT: 7,600
SALES: 2MM **Privately Held**
SIC: 7694 5063 Electric motor repair; motors, electric

(P-25459)
EURTON ELECTRIC COMPANY INC
9920 Painter Ave, Santa Fe Springs (90670)
P.O. Box 2113 (90670-0113)
PHONE..................................562 946-4477
John Buchanan, *President*
Heather Buchanan, *Vice Pres*
▲ **EMP:** 35
SQ FT: 10,000
SALES (est): 5.1MM **Privately Held**
SIC: 7694 5063 Rewinding services; electrical supplies

(P-25460)
G POWELL ELECTRIC
Also Called: GP Electric
1020 Price Ave, Pomona (91767-5739)
PHONE..................................909 865-2291
Geepi Powell, *President*
EMP: 25
SQ FT: 19,000
SALES (est): 3MM **Privately Held**
WEB: www.gpelectric.com
SIC: 7694 5063 Electric motor repair; motors, electric

(P-25461)
GENERAL LINEAR SYSTEMS
4332 Artesia Ave, Fullerton (92833-2523)
PHONE..................................714 994-4822
Garrett Hartney, *President*
Annette Hartney, *Treasurer*
James Mynatt, *Vice Pres*
Bill Hartnet, *Sales Staff*
EMP: 16
SQ FT: 4,000
SALES (est): 1.3MM **Privately Held**
WEB: www.coilwinder.com
SIC: 7694 Coil winding service

(P-25462)
GORY ELECTRIC MOTORS INC
Also Called: C B G
2015 N San Fernando Rd, Los Angeles (90065-1288)
PHONE..................................323 221-3169
Chris Braun, *President*
Rani Braun, *Vice Pres*
EMP: 11
SQ FT: 4,000
SALES (est): 1.3MM **Privately Held**
SIC: 7694 5999 Electric motor repair; rewinding services; motors, electric

(P-25463)
GRECH MOTORS LLC (PA)
6915 Arlington Ave, Riverside (92504-1905)
PHONE..................................951 688-8347
Edward P Grech, *Mng Member*
Sue Reagan, *Executive Asst*
David Reagan, *Research*
Jocelyn Straubinger, *Accounting Mgr*
John Beck, *VP Opers*
EMP: 40
SALES (est): 6.6MM **Privately Held**
SIC: 7694 Motor repair services

(P-25464)
POWER REPS INC (PA)
Also Called: Baldor Electric Company
6480 Flotilla St, Commerce (90040-1712)
PHONE..................................323 724-6771
William Colton, *President*
Dan Clark, *Accounts Mgr*
EMP: 36
SALES (est): 4.9MM **Privately Held**
SIC: 7694 Electric motor repair

(P-25465)
R A REED ELECTRIC COMPANY (PA)
Also Called: Reed Electric & Field Service
5503 S Boyle Ave, Vernon (90058-3932)
PHONE..................................323 587-2284
John A Richard Jr, *President*
Alex Wong, *CFO*
Dorothy J Richard, *Treasurer*
Matthew Schwach, *Manager*
John Carter, *Accounts Mgr*
EMP: 29
SQ FT: 55,000
SALES (est): 6.1MM **Privately Held**
SIC: 7694 5063 Electric motor repair; motors, electric

(P-25466)
R P M ELECTRIC MOTORS
11352 Westminster Ave, Garden Grove (92843-3655)
PHONE..................................714 638-4174
Bon Pham, *Owner*
EMP: 10
SQ FT: 6,000
SALES (est): 1.6MM **Privately Held**
SIC: 7694 5063 Electric motor repair; motors, electric

(P-25467)
STANLEY ELECTRIC MOTOR CO INC
1520 E Miner Ave, Stockton (95205-4537)
PHONE..................................209 464-7321
Bradley Oneto, *President*
Sampath Jayasekara, *Engineer*
Keota Sounthone, *Purchasing*
EMP: 27
SQ FT: 92,500
SALES (est): 9.3MM **Privately Held**
WEB: www.stanleyelectric.com
SIC: 7694 5063 Electric motor repair; motors, electric

(P-25468)
SUPERIOR ELECTRIC MTR SVC INC
4622 Alcoa Ave, Vernon (90058-2416)
PHONE..................................323 583-1040
Vicky Marachelian, *President*
Art Marachelian, *Vice Pres*
EMP: 18
SQ FT: 12,000
SALES (est): 4.5MM **Privately Held**
SIC: 7694 5063 Electric motor repair; motors, electric

(P-25469)
TOM GARCIA INC
Also Called: Union Electric Motor Service
2777 Newton Ave, San Diego (92113-3713)
PHONE..................................619 232-4881
Tom Garcia Jr, *CEO*
Ben Gomez, *Data Proc Dir*
▲ **EMP:** 10
SQ FT: 18,000
SALES (est): 1.8MM **Privately Held**
WEB: www.tomgarcia.com
SIC: 7694 5999 Electric motor repair; electronic parts & equipment

(P-25470)
VALLEJO ELECTRIC MOTOR INC
925 Maine St, Vallejo (94590-6311)
PHONE..................................707 552-7488
Larry Lightman, *President*
William Cygan, *Treasurer*
Dillon Lightman, *Admin Sec*
EMP: 12
SQ FT: 7,000
SALES (est): 1.2MM **Privately Held**
SIC: 7694 Electric motor repair

(P-25471)
VINCENT ELECTRIC COMPANY (PA)
Also Called: Vincent Electic Motor Company
8383 Baldwin St, Oakland (94621-1925)
PHONE..................................510 639-4500
Ronald Vincent, *Ch of Bd*
Thomas R Marvin, *President*
Sarah Beckwich, *Treasurer*

Tom Marvin, *Officer*
Nancy Vincent Marvin, *Admin Sec*
EMP: 30
SQ FT: 27,000
SALES (est): 4.1MM **Privately Held**
WEB: www.vincentelectric.com
SIC: 7694 5063 Electric motor repair; motors, electric

(P-25472)
VISALIA ELECTRIC MOTOR SP INC
Also Called: Visalia Electric Motor Service
7515 W Sunnyview Ave, Visalia
(93291-9602)
PHONE..................................559 651-0606
Gene Quesnoy, *President*
EMP: 15
SQ FT: 30,000
SALES (est): 1.9MM **Publicly Held**
WEB: www.visaliaelectric.com
SIC: 7694 Electric motor repair
HQ: Magnetech Industrial Services, Inc.
800 Nave Rd Se
Massillon OH 44646
330 830-3500

ALPHABETIC SECTION

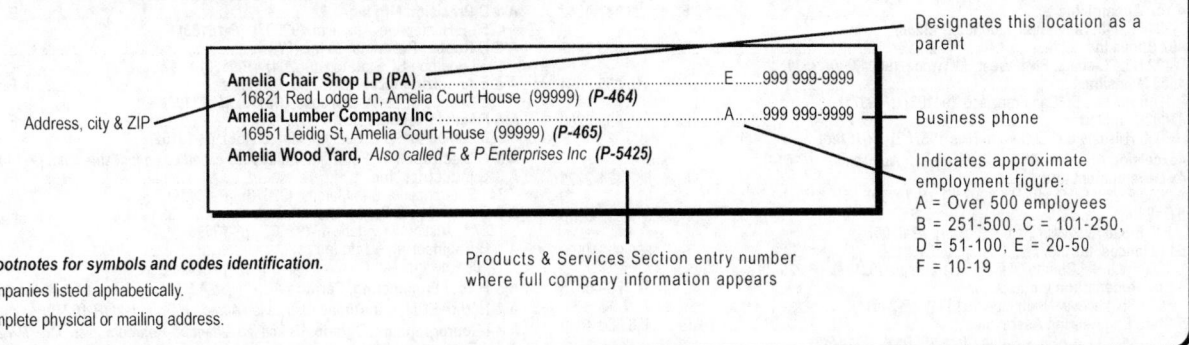

Amelia Chair Shop LP (PA) .... E........999 999-9999
   16821 Red Lodge Ln, Amelia Court House (99999) *(P-464)*
Amelia Lumber Company Inc .... A........999 999-9999
   16951 Leidig St, Amelia Court House (99999) *(P-465)*
Amelia Wood Yard, *Also called F & P Enterprises Inc (P-5425)*

Designates this location as a parent

Address, city & ZIP

Business phone

Indicates approximate
employment figure:
A = Over 500 employees
B = 251-500, C = 101-250,
D = 51-100, E = 20-50
F = 10-19

See footnotes for symbols and codes identification.
* Companies listed alphabetically.
* Complete physical or mailing address.

Products & Services Section entry number
where full company information appears

.com, Lake Elsinore *Also called Roadracing World Publishing* *(P-6248)*
101 Apparel Inc (PA) .... F.......714 454-8988
  1017 S Hathaway St Santa Ana (92705) *(P-3049)*
101 Roofing & Sheet Metal Co .... F.......415 695-0101
  1390 Wallace Ave San Francisco (94124) *(P-12446)*
101 Vertical Fabrication Inc .... E.......909 428-6000
  10255 Beech Ave Fontana (92335) *(P-12095)*
10100 Holdings Inc (PA) .... F.......310 552-0705
  10100 Santa Monica Blvd # 1050 Los Angeles (90067) *(P-4545)*
10x Genomics Inc (PA) .... F.......925 401-7300
  7068 Koll Center Pkwy # 401 Pleasanton (94566) *(P-8522)*
1254 Industries .... F.......760 798-8531
  1444 Alpine Pl San Marcos (92078) *(P-24017)*
12th Street By Cynthia Vincent, Los Angeles *Also called Green Mochi LLC (P-3312)*
15five Inc .... F.......208 816-4225
  3053 Fillmore St Ste 279 San Francisco (94123) *(P-24295)*
18 Media Inc (PA) .... F.......650 324-1818
  873 Santa Cruz Ave # 206 Menlo Park (94025) *(P-6094)*
18 Rabbits Inc (PA) .... F.......415 922-6006
  995 Market St Fl 2 San Francisco (94103) *(P-1405)*
180 Snacks (PA) .... E.......714 238-1192
  1173 N Armando St Anaheim (92806) *(P-1479)*
1891 Alton A California Co .... F.......949 261-6402
  1891 Alton Pkwy Ste A Irvine (92606) *(P-17437)*
1le California Inc .... E.......209 846-7541
  3224 Mchenry Ave Ste F Modesto (95350) *(P-17574)*
1on1 LLC .... E.......310 448-5376
  12015 Waterfront Dr # 261 Playa Vista (90094) *(P-24296)*
1st Choice Fertilizer Inc .... F.......800 504-5699
  1515 Aurora Dr San Leandro (94577) *(P-9055)*
1st Responder Fire Protection, Northridge *Also called First Responder Fire (P-15322)*
2 Awesome International, Calabasas *Also called Solid 21 Incorporated (P-23318)*
2 Impact Group, Fontana *Also called Harvest Asia Inc (P-23427)*
2 S 2 Inc .... F.......760 599-9225
  1357 Rocky Point Dr Oceanside (92056) *(P-19428)*
2 Spec Mfg, San Jose *Also called Michael T Mingione (P-5155)*
2-G Enterprises, Mountain View *Also called Applied Physics Systems Inc (P-22162)*
2.95 Guys, Poway *Also called Smoothreads Inc (P-3921)*
2016 Montgomery Inc .... F.......323 316-6886
  755 E 14th Pl Los Angeles (90021) *(P-2715)*
20th Century Spring Mfg .... E.......408 727-9100
  1282 Lorelei Ct Campbell (95008) *(P-13149)*
2100 Freedom Inc (HQ) .... D.......714 796-7000
  625 N Grand Ave Santa Ana (92701) *(P-5749)*
220 Laboratories Inc .... C.......951 683-2912
  2321 3rd St Riverside (92507) *(P-8688)*
220 Laboratories Inc (PA) .... C.......951 683-2912
  2375 3rd St Riverside (92507) *(P-8689)*
23 Bottles of Beer LLC .... E.......707 545-2337
  725 4th St Santa Rosa (95404) *(P-1556)*
24/7 Studio Equipment Inc .... D.......818 840-8247
  3111 N Kenwood St Burbank (91505) *(P-18011)*
24x7saas Inc .... F.......408 391-6205
  2307 Larkspur Canyon Dr San Jose (95138) *(P-24297)*
253 Inc .... F.......650 737-5670
  245 E Harris Ave South San Francisco (94080) *(P-12447)*
260 Resource Management LLC .... F.......866 700-1031
  100 Bayview Cir Ste 505 Newport Beach (92660) *(P-162)*
2bb Unlimited Inc .... E.......213 253-9810
  724 E 1st St Ste 300 Los Angeles (90012) *(P-3023)*
2m Machine Corporation .... F.......562 404-4225
  13171 Rosecrans Ave Santa Fe Springs (90670) *(P-16177)*
2m Machining & Mfg Co .... F.......323 564-9388
  8630 Santa Fe Ave South Gate (90280) *(P-21698)*
2nd Gen Productions Inc .... F.......800 877-6282
  400 El Sobrante Rd Corona (92879) *(P-8614)*
2nd Gen Productions Inc .... F.......951 280-9799
  400 El Sobrante Rd Corona (92879) *(P-8615)*
2xwireless Inc .... D.......877 581-8002
  1065 Marauder St Chico (95973) *(P-18012)*
3 Badge Beverage Corporation .... F.......707 343-1167
  32 Patten St Sonoma (95476) *(P-1634)*
3 Ball Co, La Mirada *Also called Twpm Inc (P-5513)*
3 D Studios .... F.......510 535-1809
  800 51st Ave Oakland (94601) *(P-12096)*

3 Gen Inc .... F.......949 481-6384
  31521 Rancho Viejo Rd # 104 San Juan Capistrano (92675) *(P-22299)*
3 Ink Productions Inc .... F.......559 275-4565
  4790 W Jacquelyn Ave Fresno (93722) *(P-2771)*
3 MTS, Palo Alto *Also called Third Millennium Test Solutions (P-21877)*
3 Point Distribution LLC .... E.......949 266-2700
  170 Technology Dr Irvine (92618) *(P-3128)*
3-D International LLC .... E.......661 250-2020
  20724 Centre Pointe Pkwy # 1 Santa Clarita (91350) *(P-8616)*
3-D Polymers .... F.......310 324-7694
  13026 S Normandie Ave Gardena (90249) *(P-9577)*
3-D Precision Machine Inc .... E.......951 296-5449
  42132 Remington Ave Temecula (92590) *(P-20637)*
3-V Fastener Co Inc .... D.......951 734-4391
  320 Reed Cir Corona (92879) *(P-13055)*
32 Bar Blues LLC .... F.......805 962-6665
  1015 Cindy Ln B Carpinteria (93013) *(P-3635)*
360 Manufacturing Solutions, Santa Clara *Also called Erb Investment Company LLC (P-16477)*
360 Systems .... F.......818 991-0360
  3281 Grande Vista Dr Newbury Park (91320) *(P-17747)*
365 Printing Inc .... F.......714 752-6990
  14747 Artesia Blvd Ste 3a La Mirada (90638) *(P-6631)*
3ality Digital LLC .... F.......818 333-3000
  55 E Orange Grove Ave Burbank (91502) *(P-23135)*
3ality Technica, Burbank *Also called 3ality Digital LLC (P-23135)*
3b Machining Co Inc .... F.......408 719-9237
  2292 Trade Zone Blvd 1a San Jose (95131) *(P-16178)*
3bd Holdings Inc (PA) .... E.......323 524-0541
  2140 E 7th Pl Apt A2n Los Angeles (90021) *(P-24298)*
3becom Inc (PA) .... F.......818 726-0007
  2400 Lincoln Ave Ste 216 Altadena (91001) *(P-24299)*
3blackdot Holdings, Los Angeles *Also called 3bd Holdings Inc (P-24298)*
3d Detailing Products For The, Santa Clarita *Also called 3-D International LLC (P-8616)*
3d Instruments LP (HQ) .... E.......714 399-9200
  4990 E Hunter Ave Anaheim (92807) *(P-21539)*
3d Machine Co Inc .... E.......714 777-8985
  4790 E Wesley Dr Anaheim (92807) *(P-16179)*
3d Remodeling Inc .... F.......925 449-5477
  111 Lindbergh Ave Ste D Livermore (94551) *(P-4265)*
3d Robotics Inc (PA) .... D.......415 599-1404
  1608 4th St Ste 410 Berkeley (94710) *(P-19892)*
3d/International Inc .... F.......661 250-2020
  20724 Centre Pointe Pkwy # 1 Santa Clarita (91350) *(P-8617)*
3dcd .... F.......805 383-3837
  3233 Mission Oaks Blvd Camarillo (93012) *(P-19854)*
3dconnexion Inc .... D.......510 713-6000
  6505 Kaiser Dr Fremont (94555) *(P-15651)*
3deo Inc .... F.......844 496-3825
  14000 Van Ness Ave Ste C Gardena (90249) *(P-14424)*
3h Communication Systems Inc .... E.......949 529-1583
  4000 Barranca Pkwy # 250 Irvine (92604) *(P-21248)*
3M Company .... C.......951 737-3441
  18750 Minnesota Rd Corona (92881) *(P-11314)*
3M Company .... F.......818 882-0606
  8357 Canoga Ave Canoga Park (91304) *(P-17127)*
3M Company .... D.......760 949-4204
  8981 Us Highway 395 Oak Hills (92344) *(P-13134)*
3M Company .... F.......714 373-2837
  7341 Anaconda Ave Garden Grove (92841) *(P-9124)*
3M Company .... F.......949 863-1360
  2111 Mcgaw Ave Irvine (92614) *(P-22852)*
3M Company .... E.......626 358-0136
  1601 S Shamrock Ave Monrovia (91016) *(P-9578)*
3M Company .... B.......818 341-1300
  19901 Nordhoff St Northridge (91324) *(P-7984)*
3M Unitek Corporation .... B.......626 445-7960
  2724 Peck Rd Monrovia (91016) *(P-22853)*
3par Inc (HQ) .... C.......510 445-1046
  4209 Technology Dr Fremont (94538) *(P-15378)*
3y Power Technology Inc .... F.......949 450-0152
  80 Bunsen Irvine (92618) *(P-19429)*
4 Flight, Rancho Cucamonga *Also called C&D Zodiac Inc (P-20763)*
4 Over LLC (HQ) .... B.......818 246-1170
  5900 San Fernando Rd D Glendale (91202) *(P-7216)*

A
L
P
H
A
B
E
T
I
C

Employee Codes: A=Over 500 employees, B=251-500
C=101-250, D=51-100, E=20-50, F=10-19

2019 California
Manfacturers Register

© Mergent Inc. 1-800-342-5647
1039

4 Over LLC F 818 246-1170
1225 Los Angeles St Glendale (91204) **(P-7217)**

4 You Apparel Inc F 323 583-4242
2944 E 44th St Vernon (90058) **(P-3288)**

402 Shoes Inc E 323 655-5437
402 N La Cienega Blvd West Hollywood (90048) **(P-3531)**

4505 Meats Inc E 415 255-3094
1246 Howard St San Francisco (94103) **(P-2371)**

478826 Limited E 916 933-5280
5050 Hillsdale Cir El Dorado Hills (95762) **(P-16180)**

4excelsior, Anaheim *Also called Excelsior Nutrition Inc* **(P-614)**

4x Development Inc F 562 424-2225
2650 E 28th St Signal Hill (90755) **(P-13150)**

5 Ball Inc F 310 830-0630
200 Broad Ave Wilmington (90744) **(P-6300)**

5 I Sciences Inc F 858 943-4566
16885 Via Del Campo Ct # 130 San Diego (92127) **(P-22300)**

5 Star Redemption Inc E 818 709-0875
8803 Shirley Ave Northridge (91324) **(P-24018)**

5-Stars Engineering Associates E 408 380-4849
3393 De La Cruz Blvd Santa Clara (95054) **(P-14746)**

500friends Inc (HQ) E 800 818-8356
77 Geary St Fl 5 San Francisco (94108) **(P-24300)**

515 W Seventh LLC F 323 278-8116
430 S Pecan St Los Angeles (90033) **(P-17575)**

5150 Fitness LLC E 323 461-1990
6741 Hollywood Blvd Los Angeles (90028) **(P-23481)**

55 Degree Wine F 323 662-5556
3111 Glendale Blvd Ste 2 Los Angeles (90039) **(P-1635)**

5800 Sunset Productions Inc F 323 460-3987
5800 W Sunset Blvd Los Angeles (90028) **(P-5750)**

5h Sheet Metal Fabrication Inc F 714 633-7544
1826 W Business Center Dr Orange (92867) **(P-12448)**

5th Axis Inc D 858 505-0432
7140 Engineer Rd San Diego (92111) **(P-13151)**

6630 Andis Wines C O Perf F 209 245-6177
11000 Shenandoah Rd Plymouth (95669) **(P-1636)**

6f Resolution Inc D 209 467-0490
5100 W Goldleaf Cir Los Angeles (90056) **(P-20234)**

7 & 8 LLC F 707 963-9425
4028 Spring Mountain Rd Saint Helena (94574) **(P-1637)**

7 For All Mankind, Los Angeles *Also called Seven For All Mankind LLC-* **(P-3088)**

7 U P RC Bottling Company D 714 974-8560
1300 W Taft Ave Orange (92865) **(P-15189)**

7 Up, Stockton *Also called Varni Brothers Corporation* **(P-2232)**

7 Up / R C Bottling Co, Vernon *Also called American Bottling Company* **(P-2089)**

7-Up, Orange *Also called 7 U P RC Bottling Company* **(P-15189)**

7x7, San Francisco *Also called Hartle Media Ventures LLC* **(P-6176)**

800total Gym Commercial LLC F 858 586-6080
5225 Avd Encinas Ste C Carlsbad (92008) **(P-23482)**

860, Shameless, Hot Wire, Los Angeles *Also called JT Design Studio Inc* **(P-3440)**

9 To 5 Seating, Hawthorne *Also called D3 Inc* **(P-4981)**

909 Magazine, Upland *Also called 909 Media Group Inc* **(P-6095)**

909 Media Group Inc F 909 608-7426
100 N Euclid Ave Ste 202 Upland (91786) **(P-6095)**

A & A Aerospace Inc F 562 901-6803
1442 Hayes Ave Long Beach (90813) **(P-20694)**

A & A Aerospace Inc F 562 901-6803
1987 W 16th St Long Beach (90813) **(P-20695)**

A & A Concrete Supply, Chico *Also called A & A Ready Mixed Concrete Inc* **(P-11026)**

A & A Custom Shutters F 818 383-1819
10465 San Fernando Rd # 8 Pacoima (91331) **(P-12286)**

A & A Electronic Assembly, San Fernando *Also called Signature Tech Group Inc* **(P-19724)**

A & A Fabrication & Polsg Corp F 562 696-0441
12031 Philadelphia St Whittier (90601) **(P-12097)**

A & A Jewelry Tools Findings F 213 627-8004
319 W 6th St Los Angeles (90014) **(P-24019)**

A & A Machine & Dev Co Inc F 310 532-7706
16625 Gramercy Pl Gardena (90247) **(P-13005)**

A & A Ready Mix Concrete, Newport Beach *Also called Lebata Inc* **(P-10948)**

A & A Ready Mixed Concrete Inc F 209 830-5070
10250 W Linne Rd Tracy (95377) **(P-11022)**

A & A Ready Mixed Concrete Inc E 310 515-0933
134 W Redondo Beach Blvd Gardena (90248) **(P-11023)**

A & A Ready Mixed Concrete Inc (PA) E 949 253-2800
4621 Teller Ave Ste 130 Newport Beach (92660) **(P-11024)**

A & A Ready Mixed Concrete Inc F 530 671-1220
1201 Market St Yuba City (95991) **(P-11025)**

A & A Ready Mixed Concrete Inc E 530 342-5989
3578 Esplanade A Chico (95973) **(P-11026)**

A & A Ready Mixed Concrete Inc E 707 399-0682
3809 Bithell Ln Suisun City (94585) **(P-11027)**

A & A Ready Mixed Concrete Inc E 209 546-1950
4035 E Mariposa Rd Stockton (95215) **(P-11028)**

A & A Ready Mixed Concrete Inc E 916 383-3756
8272 Berry Ave Sacramento (95828) **(P-11029)**

A & B Aerospace Inc E 626 334-2976
612 S Ayon Ave Azusa (91702) **(P-16181)**

A & B Brush Mfg Corp F 626 303-8856
1150 3 Ranch Rd Duarte (91010) **(P-23784)**

A & B Diecasting, Hercules *Also called Benda Tool & Model Works Inc* **(P-14485)**

A & B Sandblast Co, Los Angeles *Also called Rosenkranz Enterprises Inc* **(P-13493)**

A & C Exports & Imports, Burlingame *Also called A & C Trade Consultants Inc* **(P-12018)**

A & C Trade Consultants Inc F 650 375-7000
1 Edwards Ct Ste 101 Burlingame (94010) **(P-12018)**

A & D Plating Inc F 760 480-4580
2265 Micro Pl Ste A Escondido (92029) **(P-13299)**

A & D Precision Machining Inc E 510 657-6781
4155 Business Center Dr Fremont (94538) **(P-16182)**

A & D Precision Mfg Inc E 714 779-2714
4751 E Hunter Ave Anaheim (92807) **(P-16183)**

A & D Rubber Products Co Inc (PA) E 209 941-0100
1438 Bourbon St Stockton (95204) **(P-9513)**

A & E Anodizing Inc F 408 297-5910
652 Charles St Ste A San Jose (95112) **(P-13300)**

A & F Metal Products F 805 346-2040
520 Farnel Rd Ste L Santa Maria (93458) **(P-13152)**

A & G Electropolish, Fountain Valley *Also called Lakin Industries Inc* **(P-13443)**

A & G Industries Inc F 760 891-0323
341 Enterprise St San Marcos (92078) **(P-12449)**

A & G Instr Svc & Calibration F 714 630-7400
1227 N Tustin Ave Anaheim (92807) **(P-13698)**

A & H Engineering & Mfg Inc E 562 623-9717
17109 Edwards Rd Cerritos (90703) **(P-16184)**

A & H Tool Engineering, Cerritos *Also called A & H Engineering & Mfg Inc* **(P-16184)**

A & H Wire EDM, San Dimas *Also called Alfredo Hernandez* **(P-16249)**

A & I Reprographics, Ontario *Also called Alhambra Reprographics Inc* **(P-7226)**

A & J Enterprises Inc F 323 654-5902
7925 Santa Monica Blvd West Hollywood (90046) **(P-6632)**

A & J Industries Inc F 310 216-2170
1430 240th St Harbor City (90710) **(P-4432)**

A & J Machining Inc F 903 566-0304
16305 Vineyard Blvd Ste B Morgan Hill (95037) **(P-16185)**

A & J Manufacturing, Harbor City *Also called A & J Industries Inc* **(P-4432)**

A & J Manufacturing Company E 714 544-9570
70 Icon Foothill Ranch (92610) **(P-13153)**

A & J Precision Sheetmetal Inc D 408 885-9134
1161 N 4th St San Jose (95112) **(P-12450)**

A & L Engineering, Hawthorne *Also called Acuna Dionisio Able* **(P-16222)**

A & L Ready-Mix, Sonora *Also called L K Lehman Trucking* **(P-10947)**

A & M Electronics Inc E 661 257-3680
25018 Avenue Kearny Valencia (91355) **(P-18400)**

A & M Engineering Inc D 626 813-2020
15854 Salvatiera St Irwindale (91706) **(P-16186)**

A & M Printing, Pleasanton *Also called Leo Lam Inc* **(P-6943)**

A & M Sculpture Lighting, Los Angeles *Also called A & M Sculptured Metals LLC* **(P-12451)**

A & M Sculptured Metals LLC E 323 263-2221
1781 N Indiana St Los Angeles (90063) **(P-12451)**

A & M Welding Inc F 310 329-2700
16935 S Broadway Gardena (90248) **(P-25381)**

A & R Doors Inc F 831 637-8139
41 5th St Frnt Hollister (95023) **(P-4094)**

A & R Engineering Co Inc E 310 603-9060
1053 E Bedmar St Carson (90746) **(P-16187)**

A & R Powder Coating Inc F 714 630-0709
1198 N Grove St Ste B Anaheim (92806) **(P-13536)**

A & R Pre-Hung Door, Hollister *Also called A & R Doors Inc* **(P-4094)**

A & S Mold & Die Corp D 818 341-5393
9705 Eton Ave Chatsworth (91311) **(P-9915)**

A & V Engineering Inc F 310 637-9906
1155 W Mahalo Pl Compton (90220) **(P-16188)**

A A A Engineering & Mfg Co E 626 447-5029
2118 Huntington Dr San Marino (91108) **(P-16189)**

A A A Partitions, Los Angeles *Also called King Wire Partitions Inc* **(P-12983)**

A A A Sign & Banner Mfg Co, Los Angeles *Also called AAA Flag & Banner Mfg Co Inc* **(P-3933)**

A A Cater Truck Mfg Co Inc D 323 233-2343
750 E Slauson Ave Los Angeles (90011) **(P-4820)**

A A E Aerospace & Coml Tech, Huntington Beach *Also called American Automated Engrg Inc* **(P-21185)**

A A Label Inc (PA) E 925 803-5709
6958 Sierra Ct Dublin (94568) **(P-5692)**

A A P, Gardena *Also called American Aircraft Products Inc* **(P-12477)**

A A Prezant Discount Rbr Bands, San Mateo *Also called Prezant Company* **(P-14798)**

A A Trader, Santa Clara *Also called America Asia Trade Promotion* **(P-3705)**

A Alpha Wave Guide Co (PA) F 310 322-3487
1217 E El Segundo Blvd El Segundo (90245) **(P-2716)**

A Alpha Waveguide Tube Co, El Segundo *Also called A Alpha Wave Guide Co* **(P-2716)**

A and C Electronics F 818 886-8900
18153 Napa St Northridge (91325) **(P-18401)**

A and G Inc C 714 756-0400
1501 E Cerritos Ave Anaheim (92805) **(P-2788)**

A and G Inc (HQ) A 714 765-0400
11296 Harrel St Mira Loma (91752) **(P-3129)**

A and G News Papers, Hayward *Also called Daily Review* **(P-5825)**

A and M Ornamental Iron & Wldg F 951 734-6730
1611 Railroad St Corona (92880) **(P-12821)**

A B, Valencia *Also called Advanced Bionics LLC* **(P-22691)**

A B Boyd Co (PA) E 209 236-1111
600 S Mcclure Rd Modesto (95357) **(P-9579)**

A B C Caskets, Los Angeles *Also called Golden State Casket Co* **(P-24011)**

A B C Plastic Fabrication,, Chatsworth *Also called A B C Plastics Inc* **(P-9745)**

A B C Plastics Inc F 818 775-0065
9132 De Soto Ave Chatsworth (91311) **(P-9745)**

A B C Press, Signal Hill *Also called Floyd Dennee* **(P-7319)**

A B C Restaurant Equipment Co, South El Monte *Also called Master Enterprises Inc* **(P-12655)**

A B C-Clio Inc (PA) C 805 968-1911
130 Cremona Dr Ste C Santa Barbara (93117) **(P-6301)**

A B G Instruments & Engrg F 805 238-6262
604 30th St Paso Robles (93446) **(P-14469)**

A B S, Signal Hill *Also called Applied Business Software Inc* **(P-24372)**

A Better Trap, Fresno *Also called Better World Manufacturing Inc* **(P-9981)**

A C D, Santa Ana *Also called Acd LLC* ***(P-12357)***
A C L, Santa Clara *Also called Advanced Component Labs Inc* ***(P-18666)***
A C M, Burlingame *Also called Advanced Components Mfg* ***(P-16226)***
A C Manufacturing Inc....F....760 745-3717
3023 Mount Whitney Rd Escondido (92029) ***(P-16190)***
A C Plating, Bakersfield *Also called U M S Inc* ***(P-13525)***
A C T, La Mirada *Also called Advanced Charging Tech Inc* ***(P-17328)***
A C T, Ontario *Also called Aerospace and Coml Tooling Inc* ***(P-14356)***
A C U Precision Sheet Metal, Perris *Also called American Coffee Urn Mfg Co Inc* ***(P-12478)***
A Career Apparel, Burlingame *Also called School Apparel Inc* ***(P-3364)***
A Chemblock, Burlingame *Also called Advanced Chemblocks Inc* ***(P-8003)***
A Commom Thread, Los Angeles *Also called Dda Holdings Inc* ***(P-3403)***
A Company In Development Stage, South San Francisco *Also called Aclara Biosciences Inc* ***(P-22155)***
A D S Environmental Srvs, Huntington Beach *Also called ADS LLC* ***(P-21541)***
A D S Gold Inc....F....714 632-1888
3843 E Eagle Dr Anaheim (92807) ***(P-11542)***
A Division Acorn Engrg Co, City of Industry *Also called Whitehall Manufacturing Inc* ***(P-22849)***
A Division Continental Can Co, Santa Ana *Also called Consolidated Container Co LP* ***(P-9829)***
A Division of Metagenics, Aliso Viejo *Also called Catalina Lifesciences Inc* ***(P-8104)***
A E M, Hawthorne *Also called Advanced Engine Management Inc* ***(P-20242)***
A E T C O Inc....E....909 593-2521
2825 Metropolitan Pl Pomona (91767) ***(P-4603)***
A F B Systems Inc....F....818 775-0151
20400 Prairie St Unit B Chatsworth (91311) ***(P-20638)***
A F C Hydraulic Seals....F....323 585-9110
4926 S Boyle Ave Vernon (90058) ***(P-9514)***
A F E Industries Inc (PA)....D....562 944-6889
13233 Barton Cir Whittier (90605) ***(P-7218)***
A F M Engineering Inc....F....714 547-0194
1313 E Borchard Ave Santa Ana (92705) ***(P-16191)***
A Fab, Lake Forest *Also called American Deburring Inc* ***(P-16270)***
A G Artwear Inc....F....714 898-3636
15564 Producer Ln Huntington Beach (92649) ***(P-23742)***
A G I, Riverside *Also called Aleph Group Inc* ***(P-22324)***
A Good Sign & Graphics Co....F....714 444-4466
2110 S Susan St Santa Ana (92704) ***(P-23801)***
A H K Electronic Shtmtl Inc....E....408 778-3901
875 Jarvis Dr Ste 120 Morgan Hill (95037) ***(P-12452)***
A H Machine Inc....F....310 672-0016
214 N Cedar Ave Inglewood (90301) ***(P-16192)***
A H Plating, Valencia *Also called Sunvair Overhaul Inc* ***(P-20941)***
A H Systems Inc....F....818 998-0223
9710 Cozycroft Ave Chatsworth (91311) ***(P-21699)***
A I M, El Segundo *Also called Active Interest Media Inc* ***(P-6096)***
A I S, Irvine *Also called American Indus Systems Inc* ***(P-19442)***
A J Fasteners Inc....E....714 630-1556
2800 E Miraloma Ave Anaheim (92806) ***(P-13056)***
A K M, San Jose *Also called Akm Semiconductor Inc* ***(P-18676)***
A Lot To Say Inc....F....925 964-5079
1541 S Vineyard Ave Ontario (91761) ***(P-3931)***
A Lot To Say Inc (PA)....F....877 366-8448
4155 Blackhawk Ste 110 Danville (94506) ***(P-3932)***
A M Cabinets Inc (PA)....D....310 532-1919
239 E Gardena Blvd Gardena (90248) ***(P-4925)***
A M I, Panorama City *Also called ARC Machines Inc* ***(P-14721)***
A M T, San Jose *Also called Advance Modular Technology Inc* ***(P-15659)***
A M T Metal Fabricators Inc....E....510 236-1414
211 Parr Blvd Richmond (94801) ***(P-12098)***
A N Tool & Die Inc....F....626 795-3238
518 S Fair Oaks Ave Pasadena (91105) ***(P-16193)***
A P C, Santa Fe Springs *Also called Associated Plating Company* ***(P-13338)***
A P S, Santa Clarita *Also called Applied Polytech Systems Inc* ***(P-4568)***
A P Seedorff & Company Inc....F....714 252-5330
1338 N Knollwood Cir Anaheim (92801) ***(P-17245)***
A P Smiley & Sons Inc....E....323 937-2244
5460 W Washington Blvd Los Angeles (90016) ***(P-4757)***
A Plus Label Incorporated....E....714 229-9811
3215 W Warner Ave Santa Ana (92704) ***(P-5693)***
A Plus Signs Inc....E....559 275-0700
4270 N Brawley Ave Fresno (93722) ***(P-23802)***
A Q Pharmaceuticals Inc....E....714 903-1000
11555 Monarch St Ste C Garden Grove (92841) ***(P-7985)***
A R Electronics Inc....E....760 343-1200
31290 Plantation Dr Thousand Palms (92276) ***(P-19430)***
A R P, Ventura *Also called Automotive Racing Products Inc* ***(P-11931)***
A R P, Santa Paula *Also called Automotive Racing Products Inc* ***(P-11932)***
A R S Mechanical....F....408 288-8822
1205 N 5th St Frnt Frnt San Jose (95112) ***(P-12453)***
A Rudin Inc (PA)....D....323 589-5547
6062 Alcoa Ave Vernon (90058) ***(P-4758)***
A Rudin Designs, Vernon *Also called A Rudin Inc* ***(P-4758)***
A S A Engineering Inc....E....949 460-9911
8 Hammond Ste 105 Irvine (92618) ***(P-15379)***
A S Batle Company....F....415 864-3300
224 Mississippi St San Francisco (94107) ***(P-11343)***
A S G Corporation....F....213 748-6361
1230 Long Beach Ave Los Angeles (90021) ***(P-24020)***
A S I, North Hollywood *Also called Asi Semiconductor Inc* ***(P-18724)***
A S I, North Hollywood *Also called Advanced Semiconductor Inc* ***(P-18669)***
A S I, San Pablo *Also called Analytcal Scentific Instrs Inc* ***(P-21902)***
A S M P, Hayward *Also called Associated Screw Machine Pdts* ***(P-13013)***
A S P, Irvine *Also called Advanced Sterlization* ***(P-22317)***
A T A, Paso Robles *Also called Applied Technologies Assoc Inc* ***(P-22163)***
A T E, Oceanside *Also called Advanced Thrmlforming Entp Inc* ***(P-9930)***
A T Parker Inc (PA)....E....818 755-1700
10866 Chandler Blvd North Hollywood (91601) ***(P-19893)***
A T S, Burbank *Also called Accratronics Seals Corporation* ***(P-19432)***
A T T, Orange *Also called Air Tube Transfer Systems Inc* ***(P-14263)***
A Taste of Denmark....E....510 420-8889
3401 Telegraph Ave Oakland (94609) ***(P-1171)***
A Teichert & Son Inc....E....530 587-3811
13879 Butterfield Dr Truckee (96161) ***(P-335)***
A Teichert & Son Inc....E....209 832-4150
36314 S Bird Rd Tracy (95304) ***(P-336)***
A Teichert & Son Inc....E....530 661-4290
35030 County Road 20 Woodland (95695) ***(P-337)***
A Teichert & Son Inc....E....916 991-8170
7466 Pacific Ave Pleasant Grove (95668) ***(P-11030)***
A Teichert & Son Inc....E....209 834-8300
36314 S Bird Rd Tracy (95304) ***(P-338)***
A Teichert & Son Inc....F....530 885-4244
2601 State Highway 49 Cool (95614) ***(P-339)***
A Teichert & Son Inc....E....916 386-6920
8609 Jackson Rd Sacramento (95826) ***(P-11031)***
A Teichert & Son Inc....E....530 749-1230
3331 Walnut Ave Marysville (95901) ***(P-340)***
A Teichert & Son Inc....E....530 743-6111
4249 Hmmnton Smrtville Rd Marysville (95901) ***(P-341)***
A Teichert & Son Inc....E....916 985-0207
535 Levy Rd Folsom (95630) ***(P-11032)***
A Teichert & Son Inc....E....916 783-7132
721 Berry St Roseville (95678) ***(P-11033)***
A Teichert & Son Inc....E....916 351-0123
3417 Grant Line Rd Rancho Cordova (95742) ***(P-342)***
A Teichert & Son Inc....E....916 386-6900
8760 Kiefer Blvd Sacramento (95826) ***(P-343)***
A Terrycable California Corp....E....760 244-9351
17376 Eucalyptus St Hesperia (92345) ***(P-20235)***
A Thanks Million Inc....F....858 432-7744
8195 Mercury Ct Ste 140 San Diego (92111) ***(P-3570)***
A V Poles and Lighting Inc....E....661 945-2731
43827 Division St Lancaster (93535) ***(P-17576)***
A W Direct LLC....F....707 200-2859
980 Airway Ct Ste A Santa Rosa (95403) ***(P-1638)***
A World of Moulding....E....714 361-9308
3041 S Main St Santa Ana (92707) ***(P-4095)***
A&A Concrete Supply, Yuba City *Also called A & A Ready Mixed Concrete Inc* ***(P-11025)***
A&A Concrete Supply, Stockton *Also called A & A Ready Mixed Concrete Inc* ***(P-11028)***
A&A Concrete Supply, Sacramento *Also called A & A Ready Mixed Concrete Inc* ***(P-11029)***
A&A Engineering Inc....F....805 685-4882
158 Santa Felicia Dr Goleta (93117) ***(P-16194)***
A&A Global Imports Inc....E....323 767-5990
3359 E 50th St Vernon (90058) ***(P-9916)***
A&A Jewelry Supply, Los Angeles *Also called Adfa Incorporated* ***(P-13540)***
A&A Jewelry Tools & Supplies, Los Angeles *Also called A & A Jewelry Tools Findings* ***(P-24019)***
A&A Metal Finishing Entps LLC....E....916 442-1063
8290 Alpine Ave Sacramento (95826) ***(P-13301)***
A&A Plating, Riverside *Also called Arturo Campos* ***(P-13337)***
A&D Fire Sprinklers Inc....F....714 634-3923
2100 E Howell Ave Ste 209 Anaheim (92806) ***(P-15294)***
A&D Fire Sprinklers Inc (PA)....E....858 277-3473
7130 Convoy Ct San Diego (92111) ***(P-15295)***
A&G Machine Shop Inc....F....831 759-2261
1352 Burton Ave Ste B Salinas (93901) ***(P-16195)***
A&M Products Manufacturing Co (HQ)....E....510 271-7000
1221 Broadway Ste 51 Oakland (94612) ***(P-11315)***
A&M Timber Inc....F....530 515-1740
4002 Alta Mesa Dr Redding (96002) ***(P-3975)***
A&P Calibrations Inc....F....925 417-6608
6920 Koll Center Pkwy # 223 Pleasanton (94566) ***(P-19894)***
A&R Lighting Co....F....562 927-8617
7644 Emil Ave Bell (90201) ***(P-17667)***
A&R Tarpaulins Inc....E....909 829-3828
16246 Valley Blvd Fontana (92335) ***(P-3776)***
A&T Precision Machining....F....408 363-1198
330 Piercy Rd San Jose (95138) ***(P-16196)***
A&W Precision Machining Inc....F....310 527-7242
17907 S Figueroa St Ste C Gardena (90248) ***(P-16197)***
A-1 Engraving Co Inc....F....562 861-2216
8225 Phlox St Downey (90241) ***(P-13537)***
A-1 Estrn-Home-Made Pickle Inc....E....323 223-1141
1832 Johnston St Los Angeles (90031) ***(P-909)***
A-1 Grit Co, Riverside *Also called Newman Bros California Inc* ***(P-4200)***
A-1 Jays Machining Inc (PA)....D....408 262-1845
2228 Oakland Rd San Jose (95131) ***(P-16198)***
A-1 Machine Manufacturing Inc (PA)....C....408 727-0880
490 Gianni St Santa Clara (95054) ***(P-16199)***
A-1 Metal Products Inc....E....323 721-3334
2707 Supply Ave Commerce (90040) ***(P-12454)***
A-1 Ornamental Ironworks Inc....F....559 251-1447
4637 E White Ave Fresno (93702) ***(P-13090)***
A-1 Plastics Incorporated....F....619 444-9442
618 W Bradley Ave El Cajon (92020) ***(P-14784)***
A-Aztec Rents & Sells Inc (PA)....C....310 347-3010
2665 Columbia St Torrance (90503) ***(P-3777)***
A-H Plating Inc....D....818 845-6243
28079 Avenue Stanford Valencia (91355) ***(P-13302)***
A-I-M Plastics Inc....F....619 562-1164
9326 Abraham Way Santee (92071) ***(P-9917)***

ALPHABETIC

Employee Codes: A=Over 500 employees, B=251-500
C=101-250, D=51-100, E=20-50, F=10-19
2019 California
Manfacturers Register
© Mergent Inc. 1-800-342-5647
1041

A-Info Inc E 949 346-7326
60 Tesla Irvine (92618) *(P-20696)*
A-L-L Magnetics F 714 632-1754
2831 E Via Martens Anaheim (92806) *(P-13913)*
A-List, Commerce *Also called Just For Wraps Inc (P-3441)*
A-W Engineering Company Inc E 562 945-1041
8528 Dice Rd Santa Fe Springs (90670) *(P-13154)*
A-Z Mfg Inc E 714 444-4446
3101 W Segerstrom Ave Santa Ana (92704) *(P-13155)*
A.A.C. Forearm Forklift, Baldwin Park *Also called Above All Co Forearm Forklift (P-14305)*
A.B.S. By Allen Schwartz, Los Angeles *Also called ABs Clothing Collection Inc (P-3369)*
A.C.T., Sacramento *Also called Aluminum Coating Tech Inc (P-13326)*
A/C Folding Gates F 909 629-3026
1374 E 9th St Pomona (91766) *(P-12822)*
A/D Enterprises, Fountain Valley *Also called Adrienne Designs LLC (P-23228)*
A1 Carton Co, Los Angeles *Also called Best Box Company Inc (P-5388)*
A2, Sunnyvale *Also called Westak Inc (P-18651)*
AA Laboratory Eggs Inc (PA) F 714 893-5675
15075 Weststate St Westminster (92683) *(P-2238)*
Aa Leasing, Los Angeles *Also called Vahe Enterprises Inc (P-20233)*
AA Portable Power Corporation E 510 525-2328
825 S 19th St Richmond (94804) *(P-19796)*
AA Production Services Inc (PA) E 530 668-7525
433 2nd St Ste 103 Woodland (95695) *(P-163)*
AA Production Services Inc E 530 982-0123
8032 County Road 61 Princeton (95970) *(P-91)*
AA Products International Inc (PA) F 415 752-2075
500 Balboa St A San Francisco (94118) *(P-20236)*
AAA Air Support F 310 538-1377
13723 Harvard Pl Gardena (90249) *(P-20697)*
AAA Flag & Banner Mfg Co Inc C 310 836-3341
8966 National Blvd Los Angeles (90034) *(P-3933)*
AAA Garments & Lettering Inc F 916 363-4590
9309 La Riviera Dr Ste C Sacramento (95826) *(P-3822)*
AAA Pallet, Perris *Also called Power Pt Inc (P-14341)*
AAA Pallet Recycling & Mfg Inc E 951 681-7748
23120 Oleander Ave Perris (92570) *(P-4448)*
AAA Plating & Inspection Inc D 323 979-8930
424 E Dixon St Compton (90222) *(P-13303)*
AAA Printing By Wizard E 310 285-0505
8961 W Sunset Blvd Ste 1d West Hollywood (90069) *(P-3823)*
AAA Stamping Inc E 909 947-4151
1630 Shearwater St Ontario (91761) *(P-13156)*
Aaagolddesigns, Los Angeles *Also called Modern Gold Design Inc (P-23298)*
Aab Garage Door Inc F 310 530-3637
25333 Pennsylvania Ave Lomita (90717) *(P-4096)*
AAC, Irvine *Also called American Audio Component Inc (P-19441)*
Aaero Swiss F 714 692-0558
22347 La Palma Ave # 105 Yorba Linda (92887) *(P-16200)*
AAF Steel Structural, Lake Elsinore *Also called Afakori Inc (P-12107)*
Aahs Enterprises Inc F 323 838-9130
6600 Telegraph Rd Commerce (90040) *(P-23803)*
Aahs Graphics Signs & Engrv, Commerce *Also called Aahs Enterprises Inc (P-23803)*
Aamp of America E 805 338-6800
2500 E Francis St Ontario (91761) *(P-19895)*
Aamstamp Machine Company LLC F 661 272-0500
38960 Trade Center Dr B Palmdale (93551) *(P-13868)*
Aap Division, Inglewood *Also called Engineered Magnetics Inc (P-17340)*
Aard Industries Inc E 951 296-0844
42075 Avenida Alvarado Temecula (92590) *(P-13781)*
Aard Spring & Stamping, Temecula *Also called Aard Industries Inc (P-13781)*
Aardvark Clay & Supplies Inc (PA) E 714 541-4157
1400 E Pomona St Santa Ana (92705) *(P-23703)*
Aaren Scientific Inc (HQ) D 909 937-1033
1040 S Vintage Ave Ste A Ontario (91761) *(P-22055)*
Aaron Bennett, Santa Clara *Also called Tmk Manufacturing Inc (P-14685)*
Aaron Chang Clothing, Cardiff By The Sea *Also called Aaron Chang Photo Active Wear (P-14773)*
Aaron Chang Photo Active Wear F 760 635-0041
2611 S Coast Highway 101 Cardiff By The Sea (92007) *(P-14773)*
Aaron Corporation C 323 235-5959
1820 E 41st St Vernon (90058) *(P-3366)*
Aaron Dutt Enterprises Inc F 714 632-7035
1140 N Kraemer Blvd Ste M Anaheim (92806) *(P-13157)*
Aarons Signs & Printing F 951 352-7303
3770 Van Buren Blvd Riverside (92503) *(P-23804)*
Aasc, Stockton *Also called Applied Arospc Structures Corp (P-20738)*
Aatech E 909 854-3200
15342 Valencia Ave Fontana (92335) *(P-16004)*
AB & I Foundry, Oakland *Also called McWane Inc (P-11498)*
AB Manufacturing Inc F 408 972-5085
115 Red River Way San Jose (95136) *(P-23136)*
AB Mauri Food Inc F 562 483-4619
12604 Hiddencreek Way A Cerritos (90703) *(P-2446)*
AB Medical Technologies Inc F 530 605-2522
20272 Skypark Dr Redding (96002) *(P-22301)*
AB Sciex LLC (HQ) D 877 740-2129
1201 Radio Rd Redwood City (94065) *(P-21890)*
AB Supply F 510 651-1914
45461 Fremont Blvd Ste 8 Fremont (94538) *(P-20119)*
AB&r Inc E 323 727-0007
5849 Smithway St Commerce (90040) *(P-3367)*
Abacus Powder Coating E 626 443-7556
1829 Tyler Ave South El Monte (91733) *(P-13538)*
Abacus Printing & Graphics Inc F 818 929-6740
23806 Strathern St Canoga Park (91304) *(P-6633)*
Abacus Prtg & Digital Graphics, Canoga Park *Also called Abacus Printing & Graphics Inc (P-6633)*
Abalquiga, Los Angeles *Also called La Princesita Tortilleria (P-2568)*
Abaqus Inc F 415 496-9436
530 University Ave Palo Alto (94301) *(P-24301)*
Abaxis Inc (HQ) C 510 675-6500
3240 Whipple Rd Union City (94587) *(P-22154)*
ABB Enterprise Software Inc C 415 527-2850
60 Spear St San Francisco (94105) *(P-24302)*
ABB Enterprises Inc F 916 649-3800
4740 Northgate Blvd # 165 Sacramento (95834) *(P-19896)*
ABB Motors and Mechanical Inc F 510 785-9900
21056 Forbes Ave Hayward (94545) *(P-17174)*
Abba Roller LLC (HQ) E 909 947-1244
1351 E Philadelphia St Ontario (91761) *(P-9580)*
Abba Rubber International Inc D 909 947-1244
1351 E Philadelphia St Ontario (91761) *(P-9581)*
Abbott, Sunnyvale *Also called St Jude Medical LLC (P-22636)*
Abbott Diabetes Care Inc (HQ) C 510 749-5400
1360 S Loop Rd Alameda (94502) *(P-8454)*
Abbott Diagnostics Division, Santa Clara *Also called Abbott Laboratories (P-22302)*
Abbott Laboratories B 408 330-0057
4551 Great America Pkwy Santa Clara (95054) *(P-22302)*
Abbott Laboratories E 951 914-3000
41888 Motor Car Pkwy Temecula (92591) *(P-7986)*
Abbott Laboratories A 408 845-3000
3200 Lakeside Dr Santa Clara (95054) *(P-22303)*
Abbott Medical Optics Inc., Santa Ana *Also called Johnson & Johnson (P-22996)*
Abbott Nutrition Mfg Inc (HQ) C 707 399-1100
2351 N Watney Way Ste C Fairfield (94533) *(P-7987)*
Abbott Technologies Inc E 818 504-0644
8203 Vineland Ave Sun Valley (91352) *(P-17078)*
Abbott Vascular, Santa Clara *Also called Abbott Laboratories (P-22303)*
Abbott Vascular Inc B 951 941-2400
26531 Ynez Rd Temecula (92591) *(P-7988)*
Abbott Vascular Inc (HQ) B 408 845-3000
3200 Lakeside Dr Santa Clara (95054) *(P-22947)*
Abbott Vascular Inc E 951 914-2400
42301 Zevo Dr Ste D Temecula (92590) *(P-22304)*
Abbott Vascular Inc C 408 845-3186
30590 Cochise Cir Murrieta (92563) *(P-22305)*
Abbott Vascular Inc E 408 845-3000
3200 Lakeside Dr Santa Clara (95054) *(P-22306)*
Abbs Vision Systems Inc F 805 642-0499
4848 Colt St Ste 14 Ventura (93003) *(P-23076)*
Abby Precision Mfg, Cloverdale *Also called Dyna-King Inc (P-23551)*
ABC - Clio LLC F 800 368-6868
130 Cremona Dr Ste C Santa Barbara (93117) *(P-6302)*
ABC Assembly Inc F 408 293-3560
43006 Osgood Rd Fremont (94539) *(P-19431)*
ABC Custom Wood Shutters Inc E 949 595-0300
20561 Pascal Way Lake Forest (92630) *(P-4097)*
ABC Mechanical Inc E 619 520-4643
10521 Ironwood Ave Santee (92071) *(P-12455)*
ABC Printing Inc F 408 263-1118
1090 S Milpitas Blvd Milpitas (95035) *(P-6634)*
ABC Sheet Metal, Anaheim *Also called Steeldyne Industries (P-12771)*
ABC Sun Control LLC F 818 982-6989
7241 Ethel Ave North Hollywood (91605) *(P-3778)*
ABC-Clio, Santa Barbara *Also called A B C-Clio Inc (P-6301)*
Abco Laboratories Inc (PA) D 707 427-1818
2450 S Watney Way Fairfield (94533) *(P-7989)*
Abcron Corporation F 714 730-9988
3002 Dow Ave Ste 408 Tustin (92780) *(P-17748)*
Abd El & Larson Holdings LLC (PA) E 510 656-1600
48205 Warm Springs Blvd Fremont (94539) *(P-17128)*
Abdalian Carton, Gardena *Also called Imperial Prtg Ppr Box Mfg Inc (P-5507)*
Abeco Electric Service Inc E 909 599-7755
357 E Arrow Hwy Ste 207 San Dimas (91773) *(P-19897)*
Abekas Inc F 650 470-0900
1233 Midas Way Sunnyvale (94085) *(P-18013)*
Abel Automatics Inc E 805 484-8789
165 N Aviador St Camarillo (93010) *(P-13006)*
Abel Reels, Camarillo *Also called Abel Automatics Inc (P-13006)*
Aben Machine Products Inc F 818 673-1627
6943 Eton Ave Canoga Park (91303) *(P-16201)*
Aberdeen LLC E 562 903-1500
10420 Pioneer Blvd Santa Fe Springs (90670) *(P-15507)*
Abex Display Systems Inc (PA) C 800 537-0231
355 Parkside Dr San Fernando (91340) *(P-5381)*
Abex Exhibit Systems, San Fernando *Also called Abex Display Systems Inc (P-5381)*
ABG Communications, Mira Loma *Also called Luce Communications LLC (P-6956)*
ABG Engineering Inc F 714 282-8204
42213 Sarah Way Temecula (92590) *(P-14594)*
Abis Signs Inc F 626 818-4329
14240 Don Julian Rd Ste E City of Industry (91746) *(P-23805)*
Abisco Products Co E 562 906-9330
5925 E Washington Blvd Commerce (90040) *(P-7570)*
Abl Aero Inc E 661 257-2500
25032 Anza Dr Valencia (91355) *(P-9125)*
Abl Space Systems Company F 650 996-8214
224 Oregon St El Segundo (90245) *(P-21249)*
Able Aerospace Adhesives, Valencia *Also called Abl Aero Inc (P-9125)*
Able Card LLC E 626 969-1888
1300 W Optical Dr Ste 600 Irwindale (91702) *(P-6635)*
Able Card Corporation LLC D 626 969-1888
1300 W Optical Dr Ste 600 Irwindale (91702) *(P-7219)*
Able Design and Fabrication, Rancho Dominguez *Also called Adf Incorporated (P-12829)*

Able Health Inc ....F....617 529-6264
1516 Folsom St San Francisco (94103) ***(P-24303)***
Able Industrial Products Inc (PA) ....E....909 930-1585
2006 S Baker Ave Ontario (91761) ***(P-9515)***
Able Iron Works ....E....909 397-5300
222 Hershey St Pomona (91767) ***(P-12823)***
Able Metal Plating Inc ....E....510 569-6539
932 86th Ave Oakland (94621) ***(P-13304)***
Able Sheet Metal Inc (PA) ....E....323 269-2181
614 N Ford Blvd Los Angeles (90022) ***(P-12456)***
Able Wire EDM Inc ....F....714 255-1967
440 Atlas St Ste A Brea (92821) ***(P-16202)***
ABN Industrial Co Inc (PA) ....F....714 521-9211
5940 Dale St Buena Park (90621) ***(P-16203)***
Above & Beyond Balloons Inc ....E....949 586-8470
16661 Jamboree Rd Irvine (92606) ***(P-24021)***
Above All Co Forearm Forklift ....E....626 962-2990
14832 Arrow Hwy Baldwin Park (91706) ***(P-14305)***
Above and Beyond, Irvine *Also called Above & Beyond Balloons Inc* ***(P-24021)***
Abraham Steel Fabrication Inc ....F....805 544-8610
2741 Mcmillan Ave Ste B San Luis Obispo (93401) ***(P-12099)***
Abrams Electronics Inc ....E....831 758-6400
420 W Market St Salinas (93901) ***(P-17438)***
Abrasive Finishing Co ....E....310 323-7175
14920 S Main St Gardena (90248) ***(P-11788)***
Abrasive Wheels Inc ....F....626 935-8800
17841 E Valley Blvd City of Industry (91744) ***(P-11287)***
Abraxis Bioscience Inc ....D....310 883-1300
2730 Wilshire Blvd # 110 Santa Monica (90403) ***(P-7990)***
Abraxis Bioscience LLC (HQ) ....C....800 564-0216
11755 Wilshire Blvd Fl 20 Los Angeles (90025) ***(P-7991)***
Abrisa Glass & Coating, Santa Paula *Also called Abrisa Industrial Glass Inc* ***(P-10586)***
Abrisa Industrial Glass Inc (HQ) ....D....805 525-4902
200 Hallock Dr Santa Paula (93060) ***(P-10586)***
Abrisa Technologies ....E....805 525-4902
200 Hallock Dr Santa Paula (93060) ***(P-22056)***
ABS By Allen Schwartz, Los Angeles *Also called Aquarius Rags LLC* ***(P-3293)***
ABS By Allen Schwartz LLC (HQ) ....E....213 895-4400
1218 S Santa Fe Ave Los Angeles (90021) ***(P-3368)***
ABs Clothing Collection Inc ....F....213 895-4400
1218 S Santa Fe Ave Los Angeles (90021) ***(P-3369)***
ABS Manufacturers Inc ....F....408 295-5984
519 Horning St San Jose (95112) ***(P-12824)***
Absinthe Group Inc ....E....530 823-8527
2043 Airpark Ct Ste 30 Auburn (95602) ***(P-783)***
Absolute Aquasystems, Northridge *Also called Pure Water Centers Inc* ***(P-16093)***
Absolute Board Co Inc ....E....760 295-2201
4040 Calle Platino # 102 Oceanside (92056) ***(P-23483)***
Absolute EDM, Carlsbad *Also called Diligent Solutions Inc* ***(P-16440)***
Absolute Graphic Tech USA Inc ....E....909 597-1133
235 Jason Ct Corona (92879) ***(P-17246)***
Absolute Machine ....E....530 242-6840
5020 Mountain Lakes Blvd Redding (96003) ***(P-16204)***
Absolute Machining ....F....818 709-7367
20622 Superior St Unit 4 Chatsworth (91311) ***(P-12100)***
Absolute Screen Graphics Inc ....F....909 923-1227
2131 S Hellman Ave Ste A Ontario (91761) ***(P-3870)***
Absolute Screenprint Inc ....C....714 529-2120
333 Cliffwood Park St Brea (92821) ***(P-3871)***
Absolute Sign Inc ....F....562 592-5838
10655 Humbolt St Los Alamitos (90720) ***(P-23806)***
Absolute Technologies, Anaheim *Also called D & D Gear Incorporated* ***(P-20790)***
Absolute Turnkey Services Inc ....E....408 850-7530
555 Aldo Ave Santa Clara (95054) ***(P-18402)***
Absolute Usa Inc ....E....213 744-0044
1800 E Washington Blvd Los Angeles (90021) ***(P-17749)***
Absolute Woods Products, Goleta *Also called Madera Concepts* ***(P-4634)***
Absolution Brewing Company (PA) ....F....310 787-9563
2878 Columbia St Torrance (90503) ***(P-1557)***
Abtech Incorporated ....E....714 550-9961
3420 W Fordham Ave Santa Ana (92704) ***(P-5123)***
AC Air Technology Inc ....F....855 884-7222
13832 Magnolia Ave Chino (91710) ***(P-13135)***
AC Photonics Inc ....E....408 986-9838
2701 Northwestern Pkwy Santa Clara (95051) ***(P-14899)***
AC Products Inc ....E....714 630-7311
9930 Painter Ave Whittier (90605) ***(P-9126)***
AC Propulsion ....E....909 592-5399
446 Borrego Ct San Dimas (91773) ***(P-17175)***
AC Pumping Unit Repair Inc ....E....562 492-1300
2625 Dawson Ave Signal Hill (90755) ***(P-164)***
AC Tech, Garden Grove *Also called Advanced Chemistry & Tech Inc* ***(P-9127)***
AC&a Enterprises LLC (HQ) ....D....949 716-3511
25692 Atlantic Ocean Dr Lake Forest (92630) ***(P-20639)***
Academic Cap & Gown, Chatsworth *Also called Academic Ch Choir Gwns Mfg Inc* ***(P-3636)***
Academic Ch Choir Gwns Mfg Inc ....E....818 886-8697
20644 Superior St Chatsworth (91311) ***(P-3636)***
Academy Awning Inc ....E....800 422-9646
1501 Beach St Montebello (90640) ***(P-3824)***
Acadia Pharmaceuticals Inc (PA) ....B....858 558-2871
3611 Valley Centre Dr # 300 San Diego (92130) ***(P-7992)***
Acapulco Mexican Deli Inc ....E....323 266-0267
929 S Kern Ave Los Angeles (90022) ***(P-2372)***
ACC Precision Inc ....F....805 278-9801
321 Hearst Dr Oxnard (93030) ***(P-16205)***
Acca Recording Products, La Habra *Also called Keyin Inc* ***(P-19868)***
Accel Manufacturing Inc ....F....408 727-5883
1709 Grant St Santa Clara (95050) ***(P-14354)***
Accel-Rf Corporation ....F....858 278-2074
4380 Viewridge Ave Ste D San Diego (92123) ***(P-21700)***
Accela Inc (PA) ....C....925 659-3200
2633 Camino Ramon Ste 500 San Ramon (94583) ***(P-24304)***
Accelerated Memory Prod Inc ....E....714 460-9800
1317 E Edinger Ave Santa Ana (92705) ***(P-18660)***
Accell North America ....E....805 915-4900
2685 Park Center Dr Ste C Simi Valley (93065) ***(P-21086)***
Accelrted Mtal Fabrication LLC ....F....209 846-7998
2955 Farrar Ave Modesto (95354) ***(P-12101)***
Accelrys Software Inc ....F....858 799-5000
5005 Wtrdge Vista Dr Fl 2 Flr 2 San Diego (92121) ***(P-24305)***
Accent Awnings, Santa Ana *Also called Accent Industries Inc* ***(P-12287)***
Accent Industries Inc (PA) ....E....714 708-1389
1600 E Saint Gertrude Pl Santa Ana (92705) ***(P-12287)***
Accent Manufacturing Inc ....E....408 846-9993
105 Leavesley Rd Bldg 3d Gilroy (95020) ***(P-5217)***
Accent Plastics Inc ....D....951 273-7777
1925 Elise Cir Corona (92879) ***(P-9918)***
Accepted Co ....F....310 815-9553
2229 S Canfield Ave Los Angeles (90034) ***(P-6421)***
Acces I/O Products Inc ....E....858 550-9559
10623 Roselle St San Diego (92121) ***(P-15652)***
Access Closure Inc ....B....408 610-6500
5452 Betsy Ross Dr Santa Clara (95054) ***(P-22307)***
Access Marketing, San Luis Obispo *Also called ITW Global Tire Repair Inc* ***(P-9465)***
Access Mfg Inc ....F....530 795-0720
1805 Railroad Ave Winters (95694) ***(P-20186)***
Access Professional Inc ....F....858 571-4444
1955 Cordell Ct Ste 104 El Cajon (92020) ***(P-12825)***
Access Professional Systems, El Cajon *Also called Access Professional Inc* ***(P-12825)***
Access Scientific Inc ....E....858 354-8761
1042 N El Camino Real Encinitas (92024) ***(P-22308)***
Access Scientific LLC ....E....858 259-8333
3910 Sorrento Valley Blvd # 200 San Diego (92121) ***(P-22309)***
Access Security, Sacramento *Also called ABB Enterprises Inc* ***(P-19896)***
Access Systems Inc ....F....916 941-8099
4947 Hillsdale Cir El Dorado Hills (95762) ***(P-21891)***
Acclaim Lighting LLC ....F....323 213-4626
6122 S Eastern Ave Commerce (90040) ***(P-17577)***
Acclarent Inc ....B....650 687-5888
33 Technology Dr Irvine (92618) ***(P-22310)***
Acco Brands USA LLC ....D....650 572-2700
1500 Fashion Island Blvd # 300 San Mateo (94404) ***(P-15627)***
Acco Brands USA LLC ....E....562 941-0505
14430 Best Ave Garden Grove (92841) ***(P-9919)***
Acco Engineered Systems Inc ....F....661 631-1975
3121 N Sillect Ave # 104 Bakersfield (93308) ***(P-15931)***
Accordent Technologies Inc ....F....310 374-7491
1846 Schooldale Dr San Jose (95124) ***(P-24306)***
Accountmate Software Corp (PA) ....E....707 774-7500
1445 Technology Ln Ste A5 Petaluma (94954) ***(P-24307)***
Accounts Payable, Sunnyvale *Also called Mellanox Technologies Inc* ***(P-18990)***
Accracutt Cabinets ....F....951 685-7322
4744 Felspar St Riverside (92509) ***(P-4266)***
Accraply Inc ....E....909 605-8200
10860 6th St Rancho Cucamonga (91730) ***(P-15190)***
Accratronics Seals Corporation ....D....818 843-1500
2211 Kenmere Ave Burbank (91504) ***(P-19432)***
Accriva Dgnostics Holdings Inc (HQ) ....B....858 404-8203
6260 Sequence Dr San Diego (92121) ***(P-22311)***
Accriva Diagnostics, San Diego *Also called International Technidyne Corp* ***(P-22484)***
Accsys Technology Inc ....E....925 462-6949
1177 Quarry Ln Pleasanton (94566) ***(P-19898)***
Accu Machine Inc ....E....408 855-8835
440 Aldo Ave Santa Clara (95054) ***(P-16206)***
Accu Rack, Yorba Linda *Also called M B S Inc* ***(P-19812)***
Accu-Blend Corporation ....F....626 334-7744
1500 W Mckinley St Azusa (91702) ***(P-9319)***
Accu-Gage & Thread Grinding Co ....F....626 568-2932
40 S San Gabriel Blvd Pasadena (91107) ***(P-21540)***
Accu-Glass Products Inc ....F....818 365-4215
25047 Anza Dr Valencia (91355) ***(P-19433)***
Accu-Grinding Inc ....F....818 768-4497
8516 San Fernando Rd Sun Valley (91352) ***(P-14595)***
Accu-Seal Sencorpwhite Inc ....F....760 591-9800
225 Bingham Dr Ste B San Marcos (92069) ***(P-15191)***
Accu-Sembly Inc ....D....626 357-3447
1835 Huntington Dr Duarte (91010) ***(P-18403)***
Accu-Swiss Inc (PA) ....F....209 847-1016
544 Armstrong Way Oakdale (95361) ***(P-13007)***
Accu-Tek, Ontario *Also called Excel Industries Inc* ***(P-13204)***
Accucrome Plating Co Inc ....F....310 327-8268
115 W 154th St Gardena (90248) ***(P-13305)***
Accudyne Engineering & Eqp, Bell *Also called West Coast-Accudyne Inc* ***(P-14462)***
Accufab Inc ....F....909 930-1751
1326 E Francis St Ontario (91761) ***(P-16207)***
Accuracy, Los Angeles *Also called Q&A7 LLC* ***(P-3487)***
Accuracy Screw Machine Pdts, San Carlos *Also called Pencom Accuracy Inc* ***(P-13037)***
Accurate Always Inc ....E....650 728-9428
127 Ocean Ave Half Moon Bay (94019) ***(P-15380)***
Accurate Anodizing Inc ....F....310 637-0349
1801 W El Segundo Blvd Compton (90222) ***(P-13306)***
Accurate Circuit Engrg Inc ....D....714 546-2162
3019 Kilson Dr Santa Ana (92707) ***(P-18404)***
Accurate Dial & Nameplate Inc (PA) ....F....323 245-9181
329 Mira Loma Ave Glendale (91204) ***(P-13539)***
Accurate Double Disc Grinding, Pacoima *Also called Westcoast Grinding Corporation* ***(P-17060)***

A L P H A B E T I C

Employee Codes: A=Over 500 employees, B=251-500
C=101-250, D=51-100, E=20-50, F=10-19
2019 California
Manfacturers Register
© Mergent Inc. 1-800-342-5647
1043

Accurate Engineering Inc...E.....818 768-3919
8710 Telfair Ave Sun Valley (91352) ***(P-18405)***

Accurate Grinding and Mfg Corp...E.....951 479-0909
807 E Parkridge Ave Corona (92879) ***(P-20640)***

Accurate Grinding Usa Inc...E.....818 768-4497
29057 Avenue Penn Valencia (91355) ***(P-24022)***

Accurate Heating & Cooling Inc...E.....209 858-4125
3515 Yosemite Ave Lathrop (95330) ***(P-12457)***

Accurate Laminated Pdts Inc...E.....714 632-2773
1826 Dawns Way Fullerton (92831) ***(P-5124)***

Accurate Manufacturing Company, Glendale *Also called McCoppin Enterprises* ***(P-16727)***

Accurate Metal Products Inc...F.....951 360-3594
4276 Campbell St Riverside (92509) ***(P-12102)***

Accurate Moulding Mirror Work, Sunnyvale *Also called MRr Moulding Industries Inc* ***(P-4197)***

Accurate Plating Company...E.....323 268-8567
2811 Alcazar St Los Angeles (90033) ***(P-13307)***

Accurate Prfmce Machining Inc...E.....714 434-7811
2255 S Grand Ave Santa Ana (92705) ***(P-11505)***

Accurate Screen Processing...F.....818 957-3965
3538 Foothill Blvd La Crescenta (91214) ***(P-3872)***

Accurate Solutions Inc...F.....760 753-6524
2273 Wales Dr Cardiff By The Sea (92007) ***(P-18380)***

Accurate Staging Mfg Inc (PA)...E.....310 324-1040
13900 S Figueroa St Los Angeles (90061) ***(P-24023)***

Accurate Steel Treating Inc...E.....562 927-6528
10008 Miller Way South Gate (90280) ***(P-11789)***

Accurate Technology, Anaheim *Also called Gledhill/Lyons Inc* ***(P-20825)***

Accurate Technology Mfg Inc...D.....408 733-4344
930 Thompson Pl Sunnyvale (94085) ***(P-16208)***

Accurate Tube Bending Inc...E.....510 790-6500
37770 Timber St Newark (94560) ***(P-13872)***

Accurate Wire & Display Inc...E.....310 532-7821
3600 Oak Cliff Dr Fallbrook (92028) ***(P-13807)***

Accuray Incorporated (PA)...C.....408 716-4600
1310 Chesapeake Ter Sunnyvale (94089) ***(P-22312)***

Accuride International Inc (PA)...E.....562 903-0200
12311 Shoemaker Ave Santa Fe Springs (90670) ***(P-11923)***

Accurite Technologies Inc...F.....408 395-7100
15732 Los Gatos Blvd Los Gatos (95032) ***(P-15653)***

Accusplit (PA)...F.....925 290-1900
7901 Stoneridge Dr # 350 Pleasanton (94588) ***(P-23215)***

Accutech LLC...E.....760 599-6555
2641 La Mirada Dr Vista (92081) ***(P-22313)***

Accutech Manufacturing Inc...E.....562 903-2365
13109 Los Nietos Rd Santa Fe Springs (90670) ***(P-16209)***

Accutek Packaging Equipment Co (PA)...E.....760 734-4177
2685 S Melrose Dr Vista (92081) ***(P-15192)***

Accuturn Corporation...E.....951 656-6621
7189 Old 215 Frontage Rd Moreno Valley (92553) ***(P-21250)***

Accuvac Technology Division, Benicia *Also called Turnkey Technologies Inc* ***(P-17019)***

Acd LLC...C.....949 261-7533
2321 Pullman St Santa Ana (92705) ***(P-12357)***

Ace, Anaheim *Also called Anaheim Custom Extruders Inc* ***(P-9947)***

Ace, Santa Ana *Also called Accurate Circuit Engrg Inc* ***(P-18404)***

Ace Air Manufacturing...F.....310 323-7246
1430 W 135th St Gardena (90249) ***(P-20698)***

Ace Aviation Service Inc...F.....760 721-2804
3239 Roymar Rd Ste B Oceanside (92058) ***(P-20699)***

Ace Bindery Inc...F.....714 220-0232
10549 Dale Ave Stanton (90680) ***(P-7592)***

Ace Calendering Enterprises (PA)...F.....909 937-1901
1311 S Wanamaker Ave Ontario (91761) ***(P-9582)***

Ace Clearwater Enterprises Inc (PA)...D.....310 323-2140
19815 Magellan Dr Torrance (90502) ***(P-20700)***

Ace Clearwater Enterprises Inc...F.....310 538-5380
1614 Kona Dr Compton (90220) ***(P-14470)***

Ace Commercial Inc...E.....562 946-6664
10310 Pioneer Blvd Ste 1 Santa Fe Springs (90670) ***(P-6636)***

Ace Composites Inc...D.....530 743-1885
1394 Sky Harbor Dr Olivehurst (95961) ***(P-9920)***

Ace Graphics Inc...F.....213 746-5100
5351 Bonsai Ave Moorpark (93021) ***(P-6637)***

Ace Heaters LLC...E.....951 738-2230
130 Klug Cir Corona (92880) ***(P-15932)***

Ace Holdings Inc...C.....213 972-2100
650 S Hill St Ste 510 Los Angeles (90014) ***(P-23227)***

Ace Industries Inc...E.....619 482-2700
738 Design Ct Ste 302 Chula Vista (91911) ***(P-16210)***

Ace Iron Inc...C.....510 324-3300
929 Howard St Marina Del Rey (90292) ***(P-12826)***

Ace Machine Shop Inc...D.....310 608-2277
11200 Wright Rd Lynwood (90262) ***(P-16211)***

Ace Pleating & Stitching Inc...E.....323 582-8213
2351 E 49th St Vernon (90058) ***(P-3825)***

Ace Precision Mold Co Inc...F.....562 921-8999
14701 Carmenita Rd Norwalk (90650) ***(P-9921)***

Ace Products Enterprises Inc...E.....707 765-1500
3920 Cypress Dr Ste B Petaluma (94954) ***(P-10512)***

Ace Products Group, Petaluma *Also called Ace Products Enterprises Inc* ***(P-10512)***

Ace Sushi, Torrance *Also called Asiana Cuisine Enterprises Inc* ***(P-2458)***

Ace Trailer Co...E.....559 442-1500
2285 E Date Ave Fresno (93706) ***(P-20492)***

Acecad Inc...F.....831 655-1900
791 Foam St Ste 200 Monterey (93940) ***(P-15654)***

Acelio, San Jose *Also called Appformix Inc* ***(P-24370)***

Acells Corp...F.....760 727-6666
1351 Dist Way Ste 1 Vista (92081) ***(P-21892)***

Acelrx Pharmaceuticals Inc...E.....650 216-3500
351 Galveston Dr Redwood City (94063) ***(P-7993)***

Acer American Holdings Corp (HQ)...F.....408 533-7700
333 W San Carlos St # 1500 San Jose (95110) ***(P-15655)***

Acg Ecopack, Ontario *Also called Advanced Color Graphics* ***(P-6642)***

Achaogen Inc (PA)...C.....650 800-3636
1 Tower Pl Ste 300 South San Francisco (94080) ***(P-7994)***

Achronix Semiconductor Corp...D.....408 889-4100
2903 Bunker Hill Ln # 200 Santa Clara (95054) ***(P-18661)***

Aci Postal System...D.....562 987-2200
3245 E 59th St Long Beach (90805) ***(P-6638)***

Aci Supplies LLC...E.....714 989-1821
425 N Berry St Brea (92821) ***(P-23724)***

Acker Stone Industries Inc (HQ)...E.....951 674-0047
13296 Temescal Canyon Rd Corona (92883) ***(P-10870)***

Ackley Metal Products Inc...F.....714 979-7431
1311 E Saint Gertrude Pl B Santa Ana (92705) ***(P-16212)***

Aclara Biosciences Inc...D.....800 297-2728
345 Oyster Point Blvd South San Francisco (94080) ***(P-22155)***

Acm Machining Inc...E.....916 804-9489
240 State Highway 16 # 18 Plymouth (95669) ***(P-16213)***

Acm Machining Inc (PA)...E.....916 852-8600
11390 Gold Dredge Way Rancho Cordova (95742) ***(P-16214)***

Acm Research Inc...C.....510 445-3700
42307 Osgood Rd Ste I Fremont (94539) ***(P-16005)***

Acm Student Chapter At Ucr...F.....951 389-0713
446 Winston St Vincent Riverside (92507) ***(P-24308)***

Acme Auto Headlining, Long Beach *Also called Acme Headlining Co* ***(P-20237)***

Acme Awning & Canvas Co, San Diego *Also called Guardian Corporate Services* ***(P-3789)***

Acme Bag Co Inc (PA)...F.....530 662-6130
440 N Pioneer Ave Ste 300 Woodland (95776) ***(P-5636)***

Acme Bread Co...D.....650 938-2978
362 E Grand Ave South San Francisco (94080) ***(P-1172)***

Acme Bread Co Div II, Berkeley *Also called Doughtronics Inc* ***(P-1236)***

Acme Bread Company, Berkeley *Also called Doughtronics Inc* ***(P-1235)***

Acme Castings Inc...E.....323 583-3129
6009 Santa Fe Ave Huntington Park (90255) ***(P-11752)***

Acme Data Inc...F.....925 913-4591
2400 Camino Ramon Ste 180 San Ramon (94583) ***(P-24309)***

Acme Divac Industries, Newport Beach *Also called C & H Hydraulics Inc* ***(P-20762)***

Acme Headlining Co...D.....562 432-0281
550 W 16th St Long Beach (90813) ***(P-20237)***

Acme Machine Products, Modesto *Also called Steven Varrati* ***(P-16966)***

Acme Motor Corporation...F.....949 370-0441
20701 Cereal St Lake Elsinore (92530) ***(P-20120)***

Acme Portable Machines Inc...E.....626 610-1888
1330 Mountain View Cir Azusa (91702) ***(P-15381)***

Acme Press Inc...D.....925 682-1111
2312 Stanwell Dr Concord (94520) ***(P-6639)***

Acme Screw Products Inc...E.....323 581-8611
7950 S Alameda St Huntington Park (90255) ***(P-12970)***

Acme United Corporation...E.....714 557-2001
630 Young St Santa Ana (92705) ***(P-5271)***

Acme Vial & Glass Co...E.....805 239-2666
1601 Commerce Way Paso Robles (93446) ***(P-10614)***

Acme Wiping Materials, Los Angeles *Also called Max Fischer & Sons Inc* ***(P-3733)***

Aco Pacific Inc...F.....650 595-8588
2604 Read Ave Belmont (94002) ***(P-22156)***

Acologix Inc...E.....510 512-7200
3960 Point Eden Way Hayward (94545) ***(P-7995)***

Acom Data, Ontario *Also called Dura Micro Inc* ***(P-15531)***

Acorn Engineering Company (PA)...A.....800 488-8999
15125 Proctor Ave City of Industry (91746) ***(P-12909)***

Acorn Newspaper Inc...E.....818 706-0266
30423 Canwood St Ste 108 Agoura Hills (91301) ***(P-5751)***

Acorn Vac, Chino *Also called Acornvac Inc* ***(P-12019)***

Acorn-Gencon Plastics LLC...D.....909 591-8461
13818 Oaks Ave Chino (91710) ***(P-9922)***

Acornvac Inc...E.....909 902-1141
13818 Oaks Ave Chino (91710) ***(P-12019)***

Acosta Sheet Metal Mfg Co, San Jose *Also called Sal J Acsta Sheetmetal Mfg Inc* ***(P-12750)***

Acoustic Guitar Magazine, Richmond *Also called String Letter Publishing Inc* ***(P-6593)***

Acoustical Interiors Inc (PA)...F.....650 728-9441
123 Princeton Ave El Granada (94018) ***(P-11328)***

Acp Composites, Livermore *Also called Aerospace Composite Products* ***(P-20720)***

Acp Noxtat Inc...E.....714 547-5477
1112 E Washington Ave Santa Ana (92701) ***(P-7817)***

Acp Ventures...F.....925 297-0100
3340 Mt Diablo Blvd Ste B Lafayette (94549) ***(P-6640)***

Acpt, Huntington Beach *Also called Advanced Cmpsite Pdts Tech Inc* ***(P-9926)***

Acquis Inc...F.....408 402-5367
16795 Lark Ave Ste 102 Los Gatos (95032) ***(P-24310)***

Acra Aerospace LLC...E.....714 778-1900
2121 E Via Burton Anaheim (92806) ***(P-20527)***

Acra Enterprises Inc...F.....805 964-4757
5760 Thornwood Dr Goleta (93117) ***(P-16215)***

Acratech Inc...F.....909 392-5722
2502 Supply St Pomona (91767) ***(P-16216)***

Acri, Los Angeles *Also called Analytic and Computational Res* ***(P-24357)***

Acrl, Chatsworth *Also called Advanced Cosmetic RES Labs Inc* ***(P-24025)***

Acro-Spec Grinding Co Inc...F.....951 736-1199
4134 Indus Way Riverside (92503) ***(P-16217)***

Acroamatics Inc...E.....805 967-9909
7230 Hollister Ave Goleta (93117) ***(P-18014)***

Acrometrix Corporation...E.....707 746-8888
46500 Kato Rd Fremont (94538) ***(P-8455)***

Acromil LLC...D.....626 964-2522
18421 Railroad St City of Industry (91748) ***(P-20701)***

Acromil LLC ....D....951 808-9929
1168 Sherborn St Corona (92879) *(P-16218)*
Acromil Corporation (PA) ....D....626 964-2522
18421 Railroad St City of Industry (91748) *(P-20702)*
Acrontos Manufacturing Inc ....E....714 850-9133
1641 E Saint Gertrude Pl Santa Ana (92705) *(P-13158)*
Acroscope LLC ....F....408 727-6896
3501 Thomas Rd Ste 7 Santa Clara (95054) *(P-16219)*
Acrylic Designs Inc ....F....714 630-1370
1221 N Barsten Way Anaheim (92806) *(P-9923)*
Acrylic Distribution Corp ....D....818 767-8448
8511 Lankershim Blvd Sun Valley (91352) *(P-4903)*
Acrylicore Inc ....F....310 515-4846
15902 S Broadway Gardena (90248) *(P-9746)*
ACS, Antioch *Also called Allied Container Systems Inc (P-12913)*
ACS Co Ltd ....C....408 981-7162
6341 San Ignacio Ave San Jose (95119) *(P-14355)*
ACS Instrumentation Valves Inc ....D....510 262-1880
3065 Richmond Pkwy # 106 Richmond (94806) *(P-13699)*
Acsco Products Inc ....E....818 953-2240
313 N Lake St Burbank (91502) *(P-20238)*
Act Inc Dmand Kontrols Systems, Costa Mesa *Also called Advanced Conservation Technolo (P-12057)*
Act Now Instant Signs Inc ....F....909 394-7818
550 W Cienega Ave Ste B San Dimas (91773) *(P-23807)*
Act Now Signs, San Dimas *Also called Act Now Instant Signs Inc (P-23807)*
Actagro LLC (PA) ....E....559 369-2222
677 W Palmdon Dr Ste 108 Fresno (93704) *(P-9081)*
Actavalon Inc ....F....949 244-5684
3210 Merryfield Row San Diego (92121) *(P-7996)*
Actavis LLC ....F....951 493-5582
132 Business Center Dr Corona (92880) *(P-7997)*
Actelion Phrmaceuticals US Inc (HQ) ....E....650 624-6900
5000 Shoreline Ct Ste 200 South San Francisco (94080) *(P-7998)*
Acti Corporation Inc ....E....949 753-0352
3 Jenner Ste 160 Irvine (92618) *(P-17750)*
Actiance Inc ....E....650 631-6300
1400 Seaport Blvd Redwood City (94063) *(P-12827)*
Action Bag & Cover Inc ....D....714 965-7777
18401 Mount Langley St Fountain Valley (92708) *(P-3759)*
Action Broaching Inc ....F....949 645-8212
1717 Monrovia Ave Costa Mesa (92627) *(P-16220)*
Action Color Card, Corona *Also called Jim Perry (P-7604)*
Action Electronic Assembly Inc ....E....760 510-0003
2872 S Santa Fe Ave San Marcos (92069) *(P-18406)*
Action Embroidery Corp (PA) ....C....909 983-1359
1315 Brooks St Ontario (91762) *(P-3934)*
Action Enterprises Inc ....F....714 978-0333
1911 S Betmor Ln Anaheim (92805) *(P-9924)*
Action Gear & Broaching, Costa Mesa *Also called Action Broaching Inc (P-16220)*
Action Graphic Arts Inc ....F....626 443-3113
13065 Raintree Pl Chino (91710) *(P-7638)*
Action Innovations Inc ....E....714 978-0333
1911 S Betmor Ln Anaheim (92805) *(P-9925)*
Action Ironworks ....F....916 503-2270
1215 K St Fl 17 Sacramento (95814) *(P-12828)*
Action Laminates LLC ....F....510 259-6217
3400 Investment Blvd Hayward (94545) *(P-4926)*
Action Mold and Tool Co, Anaheim *Also called Action Innovations Inc (P-9925)*
Action Plastics, Santa Ana *Also called Smiths Action Plastic Inc (P-9911)*
Action Sign Systems, Redwood City *Also called D N G Cummings Inc (P-23853)*
Action Stamping Inc ....E....626 914-7466
517 S Glendora Ave Glendora (91741) *(P-13159)*
Actionmold, Anaheim *Also called Action Enterprises Inc (P-9924)*
Activa Global Spt & Entrmt LLC ....E....949 265-8260
30950 Rncho Viejo Rd 125 San Juan Capistrano (92675) *(P-23484)*
Active ID LLC ....F....408 782-3900
845 Embedded Way San Jose (95138) *(P-14306)*
Active Interest Media Inc (PA) ....D....310 356-4100
300 Continental Blvd # 650 El Segundo (90245) *(P-6096)*
Active Knitwear Resources Inc ....F....626 308-1328
322 S Date Ave Alhambra (91803) *(P-3208)*
Active Plating Inc ....E....714 547-0356
1411 E Pomona St Santa Ana (92705) *(P-13308)*
Active Right Shop, Chino Hills *Also called Active Spt Lifestyle USA LLC (P-23485)*
Active Spt Lifestyle USA LLC ....E....909 203-4640
13920 Cy Ctr Dr Ste 4025 Chino Hills (91709) *(P-23485)*
Active Window Products ....D....323 245-5185
5431 W San Fernando Rd Los Angeles (90039) *(P-12288)*
Activeapparel Inc (PA) ....F....951 361-0060
11076 Venture Dr Mira Loma (91752) *(P-3130)*
Activeon Inc (PA) ....F....858 798-3300
10905 Technology Pl San Diego (92127) *(P-17751)*
Activewire Inc ....F....650 465-4000
1799 Silacci Dr Campbell (95008) *(P-15656)*
Activision Blizzard Inc ....C....415 881-9100
4 Hamilton Landing Novato (94949) *(P-24311)*
Activision Blizzard Inc (PA) ....B....310 255-2000
3100 Ocean Park Blvd Santa Monica (90405) *(P-24312)*
Activision Blizzard Inc ....D....949 955-1380
3 Blizzard Irvine (92618) *(P-24313)*
Activision Publishing Inc (HQ) ....A....310 255-2000
3100 Ocean Park Blvd Santa Monica (90405) *(P-24314)*
Actodyne General Inc ....F....714 898-2776
5596 Corporate Ave Cypress (90630) *(P-17752)*
Acton Inc ....F....323 250-0685
2400 Lincoln Ave Ste 238 Altadena (91001) *(P-17176)*
Actron Manufacturing Inc ....D....951 371-0885
1841 Railroad St Corona (92880) *(P-11924)*
Actsolar Inc ....F....408 721-5000
2900 Semiconductor Dr Santa Clara (95051) *(P-22157)*
Actuate Corporation (HQ) ....F....650 645-3000
951 Mariners Island Blvd # 7 San Mateo (94404) *(P-24315)*
Acu Spec Inc ....F....408 748-8600
990 Richard Ave Ste 103 Santa Clara (95050) *(P-16221)*
Acuant Inc (HQ) ....E....213 867-2621
6080 Center Dr Ste 850 Los Angeles (90045) *(P-15657)*
Acufast Aircraft Products Inc ....E....818 365-7077
12445 Gladstone Ave Sylmar (91342) *(P-20703)*
Acuity Brands Lighting Inc ....E....818 576-9774
9144 Deering Ave Chatsworth (91311) *(P-17578)*
Acuity Brands Lighting Inc ....E....510 845-2760
2246 5th St Berkeley (94710) *(P-17579)*
Acuity Brands Lighting Inc ....E....909 395-9009
1405 Locust Ave Ontario (91761) *(P-17580)*
Aculon Inc ....F....858 350-9474
11839 Sorrento Valley Rd # 901 San Diego (92121) *(P-8967)*
Acuna Dionisio Able ....F....310 978-4741
12629 Prairie Ave Hawthorne (90250) *(P-16222)*
Acuprint, Los Angeles *Also called Ink & Color Inc (P-6881)*
Acuprint.com, Carlsbad *Also called Continuous Cartridge (P-23147)*
Acureo Inc ....F....530 550-8801
12242 Bus Park Dr Ste 20 Truckee (96161) *(P-24316)*
Acushnet Company ....B....760 804-6500
2819 Loker Ave E Carlsbad (92010) *(P-23486)*
Acutek Adhesive Specialties ....E....310 419-0190
540 N Oak St Inglewood (90302) *(P-9583)*
Acutus Medical Inc ....F....858 673-1621
2210 Faraday Ave Ste 100 Carlsbad (92008) *(P-22687)*
Acxess Spring, Colton *Also called Alfonso Jaramillo (P-13784)*
Ad Art Inc (PA) ....D....415 869-6460
150 Executive Park Blvd # 2100 San Francisco (94134) *(P-23808)*
Ad Art Company, Vernon *Also called RJ Acquisition Corp (P-7471)*
Ad Art Sign Company, San Francisco *Also called Ad Art Inc (P-23808)*
Ad Hoc Labs Inc ....F....323 800-4927
2898 Rowena Ave Ste 100 Los Angeles (90039) *(P-24317)*
Ad Industries LLC (PA) ....F....818 765-4200
14071 Peyton Dr Unit 2170 Chino Hills (91709) *(P-7571)*
Ad Review, Albany *Also called Mingo Enterprises Inc (P-6217)*
Ad Special TS EMB Screen Prtg ....F....707 452-7272
202 Bella Vista Rd Ste B Vacaville (95687) *(P-3873)*
Ad-De-Pro Inc ....F....562 862-1915
8276 Phlox St Downey (90241) *(P-13008)*
Ad/S Companies, Corona *Also called Architectural Design Signs Inc (P-23818)*
Adam Nutrition, A Division Ivc, Mira Loma *Also called International Vitamin Corp (P-8227)*
Adama Minerals, South San Francisco *Also called Zion Health Inc (P-8870)*
Adamant Enterprise Inc ....E....626 934-3399
2326 Jurado Ave Hacienda Heights (91745) *(P-5584)*
Adamas Pharmaceuticals Inc (PA) ....D....510 450-3500
1900 Powell St Ste 1000 Emeryville (94608) *(P-7999)*
Adamation, Hacienda Heights *Also called Barhena Inc (P-16018)*
Adamis Pharmaceuticals Corp (PA) ....E....858 997-2400
11682 El Camino Real # 300 San Diego (92130) *(P-8000)*
Adams and Brooks Inc ....D....213 392-8700
4345 Hallmark Pkwy San Bernardino (92407) *(P-1406)*
Adams Business Media, Palm Springs *Also called Adams Trade Press LP (P-6097)*
Adams Label Company LLC (PA) ....F....925 371-5393
6052 Industrial Way Ste G Livermore (94551) *(P-7220)*
Adams Rite Aerospace, Fullerton *Also called Zmp Aquisition Corporation (P-17327)*
Adams Rite Aerospace Inc (HQ) ....C....714 278-6500
4141 N Palm St Fullerton (92835) *(P-20704)*
Adams Trade Press LP (PA) ....E....760 318-7000
420 S Palm Canyon Dr Palm Springs (92262) *(P-6097)*
Adams Welding Inc ....F....714 412-7684
6352 Apache Rd Westminster (92683) *(P-25382)*
Adams-Campbell Company Ltd ....E....626 330-3425
15323 Proctor Ave City of Industry (91745) *(P-12458)*
Adapt Automation Inc ....E....714 662-4454
1661 Palm St Ste A Santa Ana (92701) *(P-14747)*
Adaptive Aerospace Corporation ....F....661 822-2850
20304 W Valley Blvd Ste H Tehachapi (93561) *(P-20705)*
Adaptive Digital Systems Inc ....E....949 955-3116
20322 Sw Acacia St # 200 Newport Beach (92660) *(P-18015)*
Adaptive Inc (PA) ....F....888 399-4621
65 Enterprise Ste E475 Aliso Viejo (92656) *(P-24318)*
Adaptive Insights Inc (HQ) ....C....650 528-7500
3350 W Byshore Rd Ste 200 Palo Alto (94303) *(P-24319)*
Adaptive Modular Solutions Inc ....D....310 299-7680
3025 E Dominguez St Carson (90810) *(P-12910)*
Adara Power Inc ....F....844 223-2969
15466 Los Gatos Blvd # 109351 Los Gatos (95032) *(P-19797)*
ADB Industries ....D....310 679-9193
1400 Manhattan Ave Fullerton (92831) *(P-11790)*
ADC Enterprises Inc ....F....714 538-3102
633 W Katella Ave Ste T Orange (92867) *(P-16223)*
Adco Manufacturing ....C....559 875-5563
2170 Academy Ave Sanger (93657) *(P-15193)*
Adco Products, Valencia *Also called Amzr Inc (P-3937)*
Adco Products Inc ....D....937 339-6267
23091 Mill Creek Dr Laguna Hills (92653) *(P-19434)*
Adcon Lab Inc ....E....408 531-9187
6110 Running Springs Rd San Jose (95135) *(P-14900)*
Adcotech Corporation ....D....408 943-9999
1980 Tarob Ct Milpitas (95035) *(P-14901)*
Adcraft Products Co Inc ....E....714 776-1230
1230 S Sherman St Anaheim (92805) *(P-7221)*
Add-On Computer Peripheral Inc ....D....949 546-8200
15775 Gateway Cir Tustin (92780) *(P-15658)*

A L P H A B E T I C

Employee Codes: A=Over 500 employees, B=251-500
C=101-250, D=51-100, E=20-50, F=10-19
2019 California
Manfacturers Register
© Mergent Inc. 1-800-342-5647
1045

Adding Technology (PA) ... F ... 805 252-6971
27 W Anapamu St Santa Barbara (93101) ***(P-24320)***
Addison Engineering, San Jose *Also called Addison Technology Inc* ***(P-18407)***
Addison Technology Inc ... E ... 408 749-1000
150 Nortech Pkwy San Jose (95134) ***(P-18407)***
Addition Mfg Tech CA Inc ... E ... 760 597-5220
1391 Specialty Dr Ste A Vista (92081) ***(P-14425)***
Addvocate Inc ... F ... 415 797-7620
599 3rd St Apt 103 San Francisco (94107) ***(P-24321)***
Adec, San Jose *Also called Infiniti Solutions Usa Inc* ***(P-18505)***
Adegbesan Adefemi ... E ... 310 663-0789
1525 254th St Harbor City (90710) ***(P-15382)***
Adel Wiggins Group, Commerce *Also called Transdigm Inc* ***(P-20954)***
Adelaide Marine Services LLC ... F ... 619 852-8722
100 W 35th St Unit Lm National City (91950) ***(P-9421)***
Adelanto Elementary School Dst ... E ... 760 530-7680
14350 Bellflower St Adelanto (92301) ***(P-2447)***
Adem LLC ... E ... 408 727-8955
1040 Di Giulio Ave # 160 Santa Clara (95050) ***(P-16224)***
Adenna Inc ... F ... 909 510-6999
201 S Milliken Ave Ontario (91761) ***(P-22688)***
Adept Med International Inc (PA) ... F ... 530 621-1220
665 Pleasant Valley Rd Diamond Springs (95619) ***(P-22314)***
Adept Process Services Inc ... E ... 619 434-3194
1505 Cleveland Ave National City (91950) ***(P-21019)***
Adept Technology, San Ramon *Also called Omron Adept Technologies Inc* ***(P-14280)***
Adesa International LLC ... E ... 909 321-8240
1440 S Vineyard Ave Ontario (91761) ***(P-743)***
Adesto Technologies Corp (PA) ... D ... 408 400-0578
3600 Peterson Way Santa Clara (95054) ***(P-18662)***
Adex Electronics Inc ... F ... 949 597-1772
3 Watson Irvine (92618) ***(P-18663)***
Adex Medical Inc ... E ... 951 653-9122
6101 Quail Valley Ct D Riverside (92507) ***(P-22689)***
Adexa Inc (PA) ... E ... 310 642-2100
5777 W Century Blvd # 1100 Los Angeles (90045) ***(P-24322)***
Adeza Biomedical Corporation ... C ... 408 745-6491
1240 Elko Dr Sunnyvale (94089) ***(P-8456)***
Adf Incorporated ... E ... 310 669-9700
1550 W Mahalo Pl Rancho Dominguez (90220) ***(P-12829)***
Adfa Incorporated ... E ... 213 627-8004
319 W 6th St Los Angeles (90014) ***(P-13540)***
Adhesves Sealants Coatings Div, Roseville *Also called HB Fuller Company* ***(P-9145)***
ADI, Compton *Also called American Dawn Inc* ***(P-2986)***
ADI, Valencia *Also called Aerospace Dynamics Intl Inc* ***(P-20721)***
Adiana Inc ... E ... 650 421-2900
1240 Elko Dr Sunnyvale (94089) ***(P-8001)***
Adidas North America Inc ... E ... 707 446-1070
378 Nut Tree Rd Vacaville (95687) ***(P-3131)***
Adidas Outlet Store Vacaville, Vacaville *Also called Adidas North America Inc* ***(P-3131)***
Adina For Life Inc ... E ... 415 285-9300
660 York St Ste 205 San Francisco (94110) ***(P-2239)***
Adler Pool Tables Inc ... E ... 310 676-5331
3155 W El Segundo Blvd A Hawthorne (90250) ***(P-23487)***
ADM, Colton *Also called Archer-Daniels-Midland Company* ***(P-1025)***
ADM, Los Angeles *Also called Archer-Daniels-Midland Company* ***(P-1026)***
ADM, Los Angeles *Also called Archer-Daniels-Midland Company* ***(P-1028)***
ADM, Lodi *Also called Archer-Daniels-Midland Company* ***(P-1029)***
ADM Milling Co ... D ... 530 476-2662
1603 Old Hwy 99 W Arbuckle (95912) ***(P-1023)***
ADM Works LLC ... E ... 714 245-0536
1343 E Wilshire Ave Santa Ana (92705) ***(P-11719)***
Admail West Inc ... D ... 916 554-5755
800 N 10th St Ste F Sacramento (95811) ***(P-5479)***
Admail-Express Inc ... E ... 510 471-6200
31640 Hayman St Hayward (94544) ***(P-6641)***
Admi Inc ... E ... 408 776-0060
18525 Sutter Blvd Ste 290 Morgan Hill (95037) ***(P-24323)***
Admin - Shafter Admin Office, Shafter *Also called Cemex Cnstr Mtls PCF LLC* ***(P-11074)***
Administrative Services, San Francisco *Also called City & County of San Francisco* ***(P-7272)***
Adobe Inc (PA) ... A ... 408 536-6000
345 Park Ave San Jose (95110) ***(P-24324)***
Adobe Macromedia Software LLC (HQ) ... E ... 415 832-2000
601 Townsend St San Francisco (94103) ***(P-24325)***
Adobe Systems Incorporated ... A ... 415 832-2000
601 And 625 Townsend St San Francisco (94103) ***(P-24326)***
Adolf Goldfarb ... F ... 310 451-1211
1434 6th St Ste 10 Santa Monica (90401) ***(P-23404)***
Adomani Inc ... F ... 951 407-9860
4740 Green River Rd Corona (92880) ***(P-20239)***
Adrienne Designs LLC (PA) ... F ... 714 558-1209
17150 Newhope St Ste 514 Fountain Valley (92708) ***(P-23228)***
Adrienne Designs LLC ... F ... 800 621-5632
17150 Newhope St Ste 514 Fountain Valley (92708) ***(P-23229)***
Adrienne Dresses Inc ... F ... 213 622-8557
719 S Los Angeles St # 827 Los Angeles (90014) ***(P-3289)***
ADS LLC ... E ... 714 379-9778
15205 Springdale St Huntington Beach (92649) ***(P-21541)***
ADS Solutions ... F ... 415 897-3700
10 Commercial Blvd # 208 Novato (94949) ***(P-24327)***
ADS Water Inc ... F ... 415 448-6266
12 N Altadena Dr Pasadena (91107) ***(P-16006)***
Adsantec, Torrance *Also called Advanced Science & Novel Tech* ***(P-15384)***
Adtec Technology Inc ... F ... 510 226-5766
48625 Warm Springs Blvd Fremont (94539) ***(P-19313)***
Adtech Optics, City of Industry *Also called Adtech Photonics Inc* ***(P-22057)***
Adtech Photonics Inc ... E ... 626 956-1000
18007 Cortney Ct City of Industry (91748) ***(P-22057)***
Adtech Tool Engrg Corporations ... F ... 310 515-1717
13620 Cimarron Ave Gardena (90249) ***(P-14596)***
Adtek Inc ... E ... 209 634-0300
1460 Ellerd Dr Turlock (95380) ***(P-12103)***
Adtek Media Inc ... E ... 949 680-4200
13841 West St Garden Grove (92843) ***(P-23809)***
Adti Media LLC ... E ... 951 795-4446
1257 Simpson Way Escondido (92029) ***(P-23810)***
Adult Video News, Chatsworth *Also called Avn Media Network Inc* ***(P-6310)***
Adultfriendfinder, Campbell *Also called Medleycom Incorporated* ***(P-5966)***
Adura Led Solutions LLC ... F ... 714 660-2944
511 Princeland Ct Corona (92879) ***(P-18408)***
Aduro Biotech Inc (PA) ... D ... 510 848-4400
740 Heinz Ave Berkeley (94710) ***(P-8002)***
Advance Adapters Inc ... E ... 805 238-7000
4320 Aerotech Center Way Paso Robles (93446) ***(P-20240)***
Advance Aqua Tanks, Los Angeles *Also called Alan Lem & Co Inc* ***(P-10674)***
Advance Architectural, Fountain Valley *Also called Advanced Architectural Frames* ***(P-12290)***
Advance Carbon Products Inc ... E ... 510 293-5930
2036 National Ave Hayward (94545) ***(P-17231)***
Advance Display Tech Inc ... E ... 951 757-0469
42230 Zevo Dr Temecula (92590) ***(P-18664)***
Advance Elctro Polishing, Santa Clara *Also called Process Stainless Lab Inc* ***(P-13482)***
Advance Electronic Service ... E ... 510 490-1065
44141 Fremont Blvd Fremont (94538) ***(P-18409)***
Advance Engineering & Tech Co ... F ... 213 250-8338
717 W Temple St Ste 203 Los Angeles (90012) ***(P-21457)***
Advance Engineering RES Inc ... F ... 626 354-9282
1012 W Beverly Blvd # 857 Montebello (90640) ***(P-17753)***
Advance Fabrication, Morgan Hill *Also called Barger & Associates* ***(P-9595)***
Advance Finishing ... F ... 323 754-2889
11645 S Broadway Los Angeles (90061) ***(P-13541)***
Advance Lab Instr & Sups, Los Angeles *Also called Advance Engineering & Tech Co* ***(P-21457)***
Advance Latex Products Inc ... E ... 310 559-8300
6915 Woodley Ave B Van Nuys (91406) ***(P-3532)***
Advance Modular Technology Inc ... F ... 408 453-9880
2075 Bering Dr Ste C San Jose (95131) ***(P-15659)***
Advance Overhead Door Inc ... E ... 818 781-5590
15829 Stagg St Van Nuys (91406) ***(P-12289)***
Advance Pacific Tank, Placentia *Also called Keesee Tank Company* ***(P-12393)***
Advance Paper Box Company ... C ... 323 750-2550
6100 S Gramercy Pl Los Angeles (90047) ***(P-5382)***
Advance Pipe Bending & Fabg Co, Huntington Park *Also called B F Mc Gilla Inc* ***(P-13877)***
Advance Plastics, National City *Also called B and P Plastics Inc* ***(P-9966)***
Advance Screen Graphic ... F ... 323 724-9910
5720 Union Pacific Ave Commerce (90022) ***(P-7222)***
Advance Storage Products, Huntington Beach *Also called JCM Industries Inc* ***(P-5149)***
Advanced Adbag Packaging Inc ... F ... 650 591-1625
597 Quarry Rd San Carlos (94070) ***(P-5585)***
Advanced Aerospace ... C ... 714 265-6200
10781 Forbes Ave Garden Grove (92843) ***(P-15933)***
Advanced Aircraft Seal, Riverside *Also called Sphere Alliance Inc* ***(P-7889)***
Advanced Analogic Tech Inc ... D ... 408 330-1400
2740 Zanker Rd San Jose (95134) ***(P-18665)***
Advanced Architectural Frames ... E ... 424 209-6018
17102 Newhope St Fountain Valley (92708) ***(P-12290)***
Advanced Arm Dynamics (PA) ... E ... 310 372-3050
123 W Torrance Blvd # 203 Redondo Beach (90277) ***(P-22690)***
Advanced Assemblies Inc ... F ... 408 988-1016
990 Richard Ave Ste 109 Santa Clara (95050) ***(P-18410)***
Advanced Biocatalytics Corp ... F ... 949 442-0880
18010 Sky Park Cir # 130 Irvine (92614) ***(P-8587)***
Advanced Biohealing.com, La Jolla *Also called Shire Rgenerative Medicine Inc* ***(P-8381)***
Advanced Bionics LLC ... B ... 661 362-1400
28515 Westinghouse Pl Valencia (91355) ***(P-22691)***
Advanced Bionics Corporation (HQ) ... C ... 661 362-1400
28515 Westinghouse Pl Valencia (91355) ***(P-22692)***
Advanced Building Systems Inc ... E ... 818 652-4252
11905 Regentview Ave Downey (90241) ***(P-24024)***
Advanced Cardiovascular System, Santa Clara *Also called Abbott Vascular Inc* ***(P-22306)***
Advanced Ceramic Technology ... F ... 714 538-2524
803 W Angus Ave Orange (92868) ***(P-16225)***
Advanced Charging Tech Inc ... E ... 877 228-5922
16855 Knott Ave La Mirada (90638) ***(P-17328)***
Advanced Chemblocks Inc ... F ... 650 692-2368
849 Mitten Rd Ste 101 Burlingame (94010) ***(P-8003)***
Advanced Chemical Tech Inc ... E ... 800 527-9607
8728 Utica Ave Rancho Cucamonga (91730) ***(P-7749)***
Advanced Chemistry & Tech Inc (HQ) ... E ... 714 373-8118
7341 Anaconda Ave Garden Grove (92841) ***(P-9127)***
Advanced Chip Magnetics Inc ... F ... 310 370-8188
4225 Spencer St Torrance (90503) ***(P-19314)***
Advanced Clutch Technology Inc ... E ... 661 940-7555
206 E Avenue K4 Lancaster (93535) ***(P-20241)***
Advanced Cmpsite Pdts Tech Inc ... E ... 714 895-5544
15602 Chemical Ln Huntington Beach (92649) ***(P-9926)***
Advanced Color Graphics ... D ... 909 930-1500
1921 S Business Pkwy Ontario (91761) ***(P-6642)***
Advanced Component Labs Inc ... E ... 408 327-0200
990 Richard Ave Ste 118 Santa Clara (95050) ***(P-18666)***
Advanced Components Mfg ... E ... 650 344-6272
1415 N Carolan Ave Burlingame (94010) ***(P-16226)***
Advanced Components Technology, Oakland *Also called Mills Acquisition Corporation* ***(P-12679)***
Advanced Composites Engrg, Temecula *Also called Advanced Composites Engrg LLC* ***(P-9927)***

Mergent e-mail: customerrelations@mergent.com
1046
2019 California Manufacturers Register
(P-0000) Products & Services Section entry number
(PA)=Parent Co (HQ)=Headquarters (DH)=Div Headquarters

Advanced Composites Engrg LLC ... F ... 951 694-3055
42245 Sarah Way Temecula (92590) ***(P-9927)***

Advanced Conservation Technolo ... F ... 714 668-1200
3176 Pullman St Ste 119 Costa Mesa (92626) ***(P-12057)***

Advanced Cosmetic RES Labs Inc ... E ... 818 709-9945
20550 Prairie St Chatsworth (91311) ***(P-24025)***

Advanced Cutting Tools Inc ... E ... 714 842-9376
17741 Metzler Ln Huntington Beach (92647) ***(P-11885)***

Advanced Dealer Services, Fremont *Also called Advanced Enterprises LLC* ***(P-18016)***

Advanced Design Engrg & Mfg, Santa Clara *Also called Adem LLC* ***(P-16224)***

Advanced Digital Research Inc ... F ... 949 252-1055
1813 E Dyer Rd Ste 410 Santa Ana (92705) ***(P-15628)***

Advanced Digital Tech Intl, Escondido *Also called Adti Media LLC* ***(P-23810)***

Advanced Display Systems Inc ... F ... 714 995-2200
8614 Central Ave Stanton (90680) ***(P-21220)***

Advanced Drainage Systems Inc ... E ... 559 674-4989
1025 Commerce Dr Madera (93637) ***(P-9773)***

Advanced Electromagnetics Inc ... E ... 619 449-9492
1320 Air Wing Rd Ste 101 San Diego (92154) ***(P-21542)***

Advanced Engine Management Inc (PA) ... C ... 310 484-2322
2205 W 126th St Ste A Hawthorne (90250) ***(P-20242)***

Advanced Engineering & EDM Inc ... F ... 858 679-6800
13007 Kirkham Way Ste A Poway (92064) ***(P-16227)***

Advanced Enginering and EDM ... E ... 858 679-6800
13007 Kirkham Way Ste A Poway (92064) ***(P-16228)***

Advanced Engrg Mlding Tech Inc ... E ... 951 656-6607
6510 Box Springs Blvd B Riverside (92507) ***(P-9928)***

Advanced Enterprises LLC ... F ... 408 923-5000
48511 Warm Springs Blvd # 202 Fremont (94539) ***(P-18016)***

Advanced Enviromental ... F ... 310 782-9400
2420 W Carson St Torrance (90501) ***(P-14471)***

Advanced Equipment Corporation (PA) ... E ... 714 635-5350
2401 W Commonwealth Ave Fullerton (92833) ***(P-5125)***

Advanced Fiberglass Inc ... F ... 760 433-8731
3225 Production Ave Ste A Oceanside (92058) ***(P-10629)***

Advanced Flow Engineering Inc (PA) ... D ... 951 493-7155
252 Granite St Corona (92879) ***(P-20243)***

Advanced Foam Inc ... E ... 310 515-0728
1745 W 134th St Gardena (90249) ***(P-9811)***

Advanced Global Tech Group ... E ... 714 281-8020
8015 E Treeview Ct Anaheim (92808) ***(P-19371)***

Advanced Ground Systems (HQ) ... E ... 562 906-9300
10805 Painter Ave Santa Fe Springs (90670) ***(P-20641)***

Advanced H2o, Ontario *Also called Advanced Refreshment LLC* ***(P-2080)***

Advanced Honeycomb Tech ... E ... 760 744-3200
1015 Linda Vista Dr Ste C San Marcos (92078) ***(P-13160)***

Advanced Hpc Inc ... F ... 858 716-8262
8228 Mercury Ct Ste 100 San Diego (92111) ***(P-15508)***

Advanced Indus Coatings Inc ... D ... 209 234-2700
950 Industrial Dr Stockton (95206) ***(P-13542)***

Advanced Industrial Ceramics ... E ... 408 955-9990
2449 Zanker Rd San Jose (95131) ***(P-14902)***

Advanced Industrial Services, Bakersfield *Also called CL Knox Inc* ***(P-198)***

Advanced Inst of Skin Care ... F ... 818 765-2606
7225 Fulton Ave North Hollywood (91605) ***(P-8690)***

Advanced Instruments, Pomona *Also called Analytical Industries Inc* ***(P-21548)***

Advanced Intl Tech LLC ... F ... 858 566-2945
9909 Hibert St Ste A San Diego (92131) ***(P-14903)***

Advanced Keyboard Tech Inc ... F ... 805 237-2055
2501 Golden Hill Rd # 200 Paso Robles (93446) ***(P-15383)***

Advanced Laser & Wtr Jet Cutng, Santa Clara *Also called Advanced Laser Cutting Inc* ***(P-16229)***

Advanced Laser Cutting Inc ... F ... 408 486-0700
820 Comstock St Santa Clara (95054) ***(P-16229)***

Advanced Laser Dies Inc ... F ... 562 949-0081
7647 Industry Ave Ste 200 Pico Rivera (90660) ***(P-14790)***

Advanced Lgs LLC ... F ... 818 652-4252
11905 Regentview Ave Downey (90241) ***(P-12104)***

Advanced Linear Devices Inc ... E ... 408 747-1155
415 Tasman Dr Sunnyvale (94089) ***(P-18667)***

Advanced Machine Programming, Morgan Hill *Also called AMP III LLC* ***(P-14600)***

Advanced Machining Tooling Inc ... E ... 858 486-9050
13535 Danielson St Poway (92064) ***(P-14472)***

Advanced Manufacturing Tech ... C ... 714 238-1488
3140a E Coronado St Anaheim (92806) ***(P-19899)***

Advanced Materials Inc (HQ) ... F ... 310 537-5444
20211 S Susana Rd Compton (90221) ***(P-9812)***

Advanced Materials Analysis ... F ... 650 391-4190
740 Sierra Vista Ave D Mountain View (94043) ***(P-9695)***

Advanced McHning Solutions Inc ... E ... 619 671-3055
3523 Main St Ste 606 Chula Vista (91911) ***(P-16230)***

Advanced McHning Tchniques Inc ... E ... 408 778-4500
16205 Vineyard Blvd Morgan Hill (95037) ***(P-16231)***

Advanced Metal Coatings Inc ... F ... 510 535-0185
4901 E 12th St Oakland (94601) ***(P-13543)***

Advanced Metal Forming Inc ... F ... 619 239-9437
2618 National Ave San Diego (92113) ***(P-12105)***

Advanced Metal Mfg Inc ... E ... 805 322-4161
49 Strathearn Pl Simi Valley (93065) ***(P-12459)***

Advanced Metal Works Inc ... F ... 559 237-2332
156C H St Fresno (93721) ***(P-12460)***

Advanced Mfg & Dev Inc ... C ... 707 459-9451
200 N Lenore Ave Willits (95490) ***(P-12461)***

Advanced Micro Devices Inc (PA) ... B ... 408 749-4000
2485 Augustine Dr Santa Clara (95054) ***(P-18668)***

Advanced Micro Instruments Inc ... E ... 714 848-5533
225 Paularino Ave Costa Mesa (92626) ***(P-21893)***

Advanced Microtechnology Inc ... F ... 408 945-9191
480 Vista Way Milpitas (95035) ***(P-21701)***

Advanced Microwave Inc ... F ... 408 739-4214
333 Moffett Park Dr Sunnyvale (94089) ***(P-19435)***

Advanced Mktg Print & Mail, Corona *Also called Inland Mailing Services Inc* ***(P-6887)***

Advanced Mnlythic Ceramics Inc ... C ... 818 364-9800
15191 Bledsoe St Sylmar (91342) ***(P-19289)***

Advanced Mobility Inc ... F ... 818 780-1788
7720 Sepulveda Blvd Van Nuys (91405) ***(P-24026)***

Advanced Mold Technology Inc ... F ... 714 990-0144
1560 Moonstone Brea (92821) ***(P-14473)***

Advanced Motion Controls, Camarillo *Also called Barta-Schoenewald Inc* ***(P-17181)***

Advanced Mtls Joining Corp (PA) ... E ... 626 449-2696
2858 E Walnut St Pasadena (91107) ***(P-20706)***

Advanced Orthotic Designs ... F ... 951 710-1640
9351 Narnia Dr Riverside (92503) ***(P-22693)***

Advanced Oxygen Therapy Inc (HQ) ... F ... 760 431-4700
3512 Seagate Way Ste 100 Oceanside (92056) ***(P-22315)***

Advanced Packaging & Crating ... F ... 714 892-1702
15432 Electronic Ln Huntington Beach (92649) ***(P-4515)***

Advanced Packaging Tech Amer, San Diego *Also called Apta Group Inc* ***(P-18713)***

Advanced Paper Forming LLC ... F ... 714 738-0300
541 W Rincon St Corona (92880) ***(P-9584)***

Advanced Pattern & Mold ... F ... 909 930-3444
1720 S Balboa Ave Ontario (91761) ***(P-11532)***

Advanced Photonix, Camarillo *Also called OSI Optoelectronics Inc* ***(P-19068)***

Advanced Polymer Tech LLC ... E ... 209 464-2701
3837 Imperial Way Stockton (95215) ***(P-9929)***

Advanced Power & Controls LLC ... F ... 714 540-9010
605 E Alton Ave Ste A Santa Ana (92705) ***(P-17177)***

Advanced Prcsion Machining Inc ... F ... 949 650-6113
1649 Monrovia Ave Costa Mesa (92627) ***(P-16232)***

Advanced Precision Spring ... F ... 408 436-6595
1754 Junction Ave Ste A San Jose (95112) ***(P-13782)***

Advanced Pressure Technology ... D ... 707 259-0102
687 Technology Way NAPA (94558) ***(P-21543)***

Advanced Process Services Inc ... E ... 323 278-6530
4350 E Washington Blvd Commerce (90023) ***(P-13700)***

Advanced Products, Costa Mesa *Also called Pro-Lite Inc* ***(P-23946)***

Advanced Prosthetics Llc ... F ... 559 298-0321
7015 N Chestnut Ave # 103 Fresno (93720) ***(P-22694)***

Advanced Publishing Tech Inc ... F ... 818 557-3035
1105 N Hollywood Way Burbank (91505) ***(P-6422)***

Advanced Publishing Tech Inc (PA) ... E ... 818 557-3035
123 S Victory Blvd Burbank (91502) ***(P-24328)***

Advanced Refractive Tech ... F ... 949 940-1300
12518 Cavallo St San Diego (92130) ***(P-22316)***

Advanced Refreshment LLC (HQ) ... F ... 425 746-8100
2560 E Philadelphia St Ontario (91761) ***(P-2080)***

Advanced Results Company Inc ... F ... 408 986-0123
18760 Afton Ave Saratoga (95070) ***(P-15050)***

Advanced Safety Devices LLC ... F ... 818 701-9200
21430 Strathern St Unit M Canoga Park (91304) ***(P-21702)***

Advanced Science & Novel Tech (PA) ... E ... 310 530-9400
2790 Skypark Dr Ste 104 Torrance (90505) ***(P-15384)***

Advanced Sealing (HQ) ... D ... 562 802-7782
15500 Blackburn Ave Norwalk (90650) ***(P-9516)***

Advanced Semiconductor Inc (PA) ... D ... 818 982-1200
7525 Ethel Ave Ste I North Hollywood (91605) ***(P-18669)***

Advanced Skin & Hair Inc ... F ... 310 442-9700
12121 Wilshire Blvd # 1012 Los Angeles (90025) ***(P-8691)***

Advanced Sterlization (HQ) ... E ... 800 595-0200
33 Technology Dr Irvine (92618) ***(P-22317)***

Advanced Structural Tech Inc ... C ... 805 204-9133
950 Richmond Ave Oxnard (93030) ***(P-20244)***

Advanced Surface Finishing Inc ... F ... 408 275-9718
1181 N 4th St Ste 50 San Jose (95112) ***(P-13309)***

Advanced Tactics Inc ... F ... 310 701-3659
3339 Airport Dr Torrance (90505) ***(P-20528)***

Advanced Tech Plating ... E ... 714 630-7093
1061 N Grove St Anaheim (92806) ***(P-13310)***

Advanced Technologies ... F ... 661 872-4807
2001 Columbus St Bakersfield (93305) ***(P-24329)***

Advanced Technology Co, Pasadena *Also called Advanced Mtls Joining Corp* ***(P-20706)***

Advanced Technology Machining ... F ... 661 257-2313
28210 Avenue Crocker # 301 Valencia (91355) ***(P-16233)***

Advanced Thermal Sciences ... F ... 714 688-4200
3355 E La Palma Ave Anaheim (92806) ***(P-18670)***

Advanced Thrmlforming Entp Inc ... F ... 760 722-4400
3750 Oceanic Way Oceanside (92056) ***(P-9930)***

Advanced Transit Dynamics Inc ... D ... 510 619-8245
3150 Corporate Pl Hayward (94545) ***(P-21221)***

Advanced Uv Inc ... E ... 562 407-0299
16350 Manning Way Cerritos (90703) ***(P-16007)***

Advanced Vision Science Inc ... E ... 805 683-3851
5743 Thornwood Dr Goleta (93117) ***(P-23077)***

Advanced Viticulture Inc ... F ... 707 838-3805
930 Shiloh Rd Bldg 44-E Windsor (95492) ***(P-1639)***

Advanced Vsual Image Dsign LLC ... C ... 951 279-2138
229 N Sherman Ave Irvine (92614) ***(P-7223)***

Advanced Web Offset Inc ... D ... 760 727-1700
2260 Oak Ridge Way Vista (92081) ***(P-7224)***

Advancedcath Technologies LLC (HQ) ... E ... 408 433-9505
176 Component Dr San Jose (95131) ***(P-22318)***

Advanex Americas Inc (HQ) ... D ... 714 995-4519
5780 Cerritos Ave Cypress (90630) ***(P-13783)***

ADVANING, Garden Grove *Also called Airflex5d LLC* ***(P-4821)***

Advansor Corporation ... F ... 408 228-1008
380 Fairview Way Milpitas (95035) ***(P-15385)***

Advantage Adhesives Inc ... E ... 909 204-4990
8345 White Oak Ave Rancho Cucamonga (91730) ***(P-9128)***

Employee Codes: A=Over 500 employees, B=251-500
C=101-250, D=51-100, E=20-50, F=10-19
2019 California
Manfacturers Register
© Mergent Inc. 1-800-342-5647
1047

Advantage Business Forms Inc....F....909 875-7163
102 N Riverside Ave Rialto (92376) *(P-7225)*
Advantage Custom Fixtures, Los Angeles *Also called American Furniture Systems Inc (P-4975)*
Advantage Engineering Corp....E....805 216-9920
301 Bernoulli Cir Oxnard (93030) *(P-23488)*
Advantage Engrg & Chemistry, Santa Ana *Also called AEC Group Inc (P-20246)*
Advantage Homes, Stanton *Also called Inception Homes Inc (P-4562)*
Advantage Manufacturing Inc....E....714 505-1166
616 S Santa Fe St Santa Ana (92705) *(P-17178)*
Advantage Metal Products, Livermore *Also called Segundo Metal Products Inc (P-12755)*
Advantage Pharmaceuticals....F....916 630-4960
4363 Pacific St Rocklin (95677) *(P-8004)*
Advantage Truss Company LLC....E....831 635-0377
2025 San Juan Rd Hollister (95023) *(P-4388)*
Advantec Mfs Inc....F....925 479-0625
6723 Sierra Ct Ste A Dublin (94568) *(P-15138)*
Advantest America Inc (HQ)....D....408 456-3600
3061 Zanker Rd San Jose (95134) *(P-18671)*
Advanti Racing Usa LLC (HQ)....E....951 272-5930
10721 Business Dr Ste 1 Fontana (92337) *(P-20245)*
Advenira Enterprises Inc....F....408 732-3950
320 Soquel Way Sunnyvale (94085) *(P-14904)*
Advent Resources Inc....D....310 241-1500
235 W 7th St San Pedro (90731) *(P-24330)*
Adventure Medical Kits, Alameda *Also called Tender Corporation (P-22831)*
Adventures In Personal Cmpt, Vacaville *Also called Joseph Charles Whitson (P-6509)*
Advertiser Perceptions....E....925 648-3902
3009 Deer Meadow Dr Danville (94506) *(P-5752)*
Advertiser, The, Oakdale *Also called Morris Publications (P-5981)*
Advertising Services....E....714 522-2781
7697 9th St Buena Park (90621) *(P-6643)*
Advertising Solutions, San Diego *Also called AT&T Corp (P-6438)*
Adverum Biotechnologies Inc....D....650 272-6269
1035 Obrien Dr Ste A Menlo Park (94025) *(P-8523)*
Advin Systems Inc....F....408 243-7000
11693 Vineyard Spring Ct Cupertino (95014) *(P-18672)*
Advisor Software Inc (PA)....E....925 299-7778
2175 N Calif Blvd Ste 400 Walnut Creek (94596) *(P-24331)*
Advisorsquare, Culver City *Also called Liveoffice LLC (P-24861)*
Advisys Inc....E....949 752-4927
16969 Von Karman Ave # 125 Irvine (92606) *(P-24332)*
Adwear Inc (PA)....F....213 629-2535
850 S Broadway Ste 400 Los Angeles (90014) *(P-3091)*
Adwest Technologies Inc (HQ)....E....714 632-8595
4222 E La Palma Ave Anaheim (92807) *(P-15139)*
Aea Ribbon Mics....F....626 798-9128
1029 N Allen Ave Pasadena (91104) *(P-17754)*
Aea Technology Inc....F....760 931-8979
5933 Sea Lion Pl Ste 112 Carlsbad (92010) *(P-21703)*
AEC Group Inc....F....714 444-1395
3600 W Carriage Dr Santa Ana (92704) *(P-20246)*
Aechelon Technology Inc (PA)....E....415 255-0120
888 Brannan St Ste 210 San Francisco (94103) *(P-15386)*
AEG Industries Inc....E....707 575-0697
1219 Briggs Ave Santa Rosa (95401) *(P-20707)*
Aegis Industries Inc....F....805 922-2700
2360 Thompson Way Ste A Santa Maria (93455) *(P-8873)*
Aegis Its, San Jose *Also called Team Econolite (P-18371)*
Aegis Principia LLC....F....714 731-2283
12165 Ojeda Ct Tustin (92782) *(P-24027)*
Aehr Test Systems (PA)....D....510 623-9400
400 Kato Ter Fremont (94539) *(P-21704)*
Aei Communications Corp....E....650 552-9416
1001 Broadway Ste 2d Millbrae (94030) *(P-17917)*
Aei Electech Corp....F....510 489-5088
33485 Western Ave Union City (94587) *(P-19436)*
Aei Manufacturing Inc....F....818 407-5400
9452 De Soto Ave Chatsworth (91311) *(P-17439)*
Aella Data Inc....F....408 391-4430
4701 Patrick Henry Dr Santa Clara (95054) *(P-24333)*
Aem (holdings) Inc....D....858 481-0210
6610 Cobra Way San Diego (92121) *(P-17129)*
Aem Electronics (usa) Inc....E....858 481-0210
6610 Cobra Way San Diego (92121) *(P-19315)*
Aemetis Advnced Fels Keyes Inc....E....209 632-4511
4209 Jessup Rd Ceres (95307) *(P-8968)*
Aemetis Advnced Pdts Keyes Inc....E....408 418-2415
20400 Stevens Creek Blvd Cupertino (95014) *(P-8969)*
Aemi, San Diego *Also called Advanced Electromagnetics Inc (P-21542)*
AEP Cali, San Diego *Also called Soncell North America Inc (P-21434)*
AEP Span, Fontana *Also called ASC Profiles Inc (P-12114)*
Aep-California LLC....F....619 596-1925
10729 Wheatlands Ave C Santee (92071) *(P-20247)*
Aer-Dan Precision (PA)....E....408 954-8704
1458 Seareel Pl San Jose (95131) *(P-16234)*
Aera Energy, Rio Vista *Also called Dick Brown Technical Services (P-101)*
Aera Energy LLC (HQ)....A....661 665-5000
10000 Ming Ave Bakersfield (93311) *(P-92)*
Aera Energy LLC....E....661 665-4400
59231 Main Camp Rd Mc Kittrick (93251) *(P-93)*
Aera Energy LLC....D....661 665-3200
29235 Highway 33 Maricopa (93252) *(P-94)*
Aera Energy LLC....E....559 935-7418
29010 Shell Rd Coalinga (93210) *(P-14205)*
Aera Energy South Midway, Maricopa *Also called Aera Energy LLC (P-94)*
Aercap Los Angeles, Los Angeles *Also called Aercap US Global Aviation LLC (P-20529)*
Aercap US Global Aviation LLC (HQ)....E....310 788-1999
10250 Constellation Blvd Los Angeles (90067) *(P-20529)*
Aero Bending Company....E....661 948-2363
560 Auto Center Dr Ste A Palmdale (93551) *(P-12462)*
Aero Chip Inc....E....562 404-6300
13563 Freeway Dr Santa Fe Springs (90670) *(P-16235)*
Aero Chip Intgrted Systems Inc....F....310 329-8600
13565 Freeway Dr Santa Fe Springs (90670) *(P-21251)*
Aero Chrome Plating, Panorama City *Also called TMW Corporation (P-13522)*
Aero Component Engineering, Valencia *Also called Pacific Aero Components Inc (P-20900)*
Aero Corporation....E....562 598-2281
3061 Quail Run Rd Los Alamitos (90720) *(P-20530)*
Aero Dynamic Machining Inc....D....714 379-1073
11791 Monarch St Garden Grove (92841) *(P-20708)*
Aero Engineering Inc....F....714 879-6200
1020 E Elm Ave Fullerton (92831) *(P-16236)*
Aero Engineering & Mfg Co Cal....E....661 295-0875
28217 Avenue Crocker Valencia (91355) *(P-20709)*
Aero Industries LLC....E....805 688-6734
139 Industrial Way Buellton (93427) *(P-16237)*
Aero Manufacturing & Pltg Co....E....818 241-2844
927 Thompson Ave Glendale (91201) *(P-13311)*
Aero Mechanism Precision Inc....E....818 886-1855
21700 Marilla St Chatsworth (91311) *(P-16238)*
Aero Pacific Corporation (PA)....D....714 961-9200
588 Porter Way Placentia (92870) *(P-20710)*
Aero Pacific Corporation....E....714 961-9200
588 Porter Way Placentia (92870) *(P-20711)*
Aero Powder Coating Inc....E....323 264-6405
710 Monterey Pass Rd Monterey Park (91754) *(P-13544)*
Aero Precision Engineering Inc....E....310 642-9747
11300 Hindry Ave Los Angeles (90045) *(P-12463)*
Aero Precision Industries LLC (PA)....C....925 455-9900
201 Lindbergh Ave Livermore (94551) *(P-20712)*
Aero Products Co., Los Angeles *Also called Coating Specialties Inc (P-20782)*
Aero Seating Technologies LLC (HQ)....E....626 286-1130
5795 Martin Rd Irwindale (91706) *(P-5004)*
Aero Sense Inc....F....661 257-1608
26074 Avenue Hall Ste 18 Valencia (91355) *(P-20713)*
Aero Space Composites, Stanton *Also called Cynthia Garcia (P-20789)*
Aero Turbine Inc....D....209 983-1112
6800 Lindbergh St Stockton (95206) *(P-20642)*
Aero-Clas Heat Tran Prod Inc....F....909 596-1630
1677 Curtiss Ct La Verne (91750) *(P-12358)*
Aero-Craft Hydraulics Inc....E....951 736-4690
392 N Smith Ave Corona (92880) *(P-20714)*
Aero-Electric Connector Inc....F....310 618-3737
2280 W 208th St Torrance (90501) *(P-17440)*
Aero-Electric Connector Inc (PA)....B....310 618-3737
2280 W 208th St Torrance (90501) *(P-17441)*
Aero-k Inc....E....626 350-5125
10764 Lower Azusa Rd El Monte (91731) *(P-16239)*
Aero-Mechanical Engrg Inc....F....714 891-2423
5945 Engineer Dr Huntington Beach (92649) *(P-16240)*
Aeroantenna Technology Inc....C....818 993-3842
20732 Lassen St Chatsworth (91311) *(P-21252)*
Aerocraft Heat Treating Co Inc....D....562 674-2400
15701 Minnesota Ave Paramount (90723) *(P-11791)*
Aerodynamic Engineering Inc....E....714 891-2651
15495 Graham St Huntington Beach (92649) *(P-16241)*
Aerodynamic Plating Co....D....310 329-7959
13620 S Saint Andrews Pl Gardena (90249) *(P-13312)*
Aerodyne Prcsion Machining Inc....E....714 891-1311
5471 Argosy Ave Huntington Beach (92649) *(P-16242)*
Aerofab Corporation....F....714 635-0902
4001 E Leaverton Ct Anaheim (92807) *(P-12106)*
Aerofit LLC....C....714 521-5060
1425 S Acacia Ave Fullerton (92831) *(P-13873)*
Aerofoam Industries Inc....D....951 245-4429
31855 Corydon St Lake Elsinore (92530) *(P-5005)*
Aerofutures, Costa Mesa *Also called Jenny Sammon (P-20855)*
Aerojet Rcketdyne Holdings Inc (PA)....D....310 252-8100
222 N Pacific Coast Hwy El Segundo (90245) *(P-21253)*
Aerojet Rocketdyne Inc (HQ)....A....916 355-4000
2001 Aerojet Rd Rancho Cordova (95742) *(P-20715)*
Aerojet Rocketdyne Inc....F....916 355-4000
1180 Iron Point Rd # 350 Folsom (95630) *(P-20716)*
Aerojet Rocketdyne De Inc (HQ)....C....818 586-1000
8900 De Soto Ave Canoga Park (91304) *(P-8970)*
Aerojet Rocketdyne De Inc....C....818 586-1000
9001 Lurline Ave Chatsworth (91311) *(P-8971)*
Aerol Co Inc (PA)....E....310 762-2660
19560 S Rancho Way Rancho Dominguez (90220) *(P-11720)*
Aeroliant Manufacturing Inc....E....310 257-1903
1613 Lockness Pl Torrance (90501) *(P-20717)*
Aeromax Industries Inc....F....818 701-9500
9027 Canoga Ave Unit Hi Canoga Park (91304) *(P-20643)*
Aerometals Inc (PA)....C....916 939-6888
3920 Sandstone Dr El Dorado Hills (95762) *(P-20718)*
Aeroshear Aviation Svcs Inc (PA)....E....818 779-1650
7701 Woodley Ave 200 Van Nuys (91406) *(P-20719)*
Aerospace and Coml Tooling Inc....F....909 930-5780
1866 S Lake Pl Ontario (91761) *(P-14356)*
Aerospace Composite Products (PA)....E....925 443-5900
78 Lindbergh Ave Livermore (94551) *(P-20720)*
Aerospace Dynamics Intl Inc....B....661 257-3535
25540 Rye Canyon Rd Valencia (91355) *(P-20721)*
Aerospace Engineering Corp....D....714 996-8178
2632 Saturn St Brea (92821) *(P-20722)*

Mergent e-mail: customerrelations@mergent.com
1048
2019 California
Manufacturers Register
(P-0000) Products & Services Section entry number
(PA)=Parent Co (HQ)=Headquarters (DH)=Div Headquarters

Aerospace Facilities Group Inc ....F....702 513-8336
1590 Raleys Ct Ste 30 West Sacramento (95691) ***(P-15296)***
Aerospace Fasteners Group, Santa Ana *Also called SPS Technologies LLC* ***(P-23773)***
Aerospace Lgacy Foundation Inc....F....562 922-8068
12214 Lakewood Blvd Downey (90242) ***(P-21254)***
Aerospace Parts Holdings Inc....A....949 877-3630
3150 E Miraloma Ave Anaheim (92806) ***(P-20723)***
Aerospace Seals & Gaskets....E....951 256-8380
1478 Davril Cir Ste A Corona (92880) ***(P-9517)***
Aerospace Systems, Redondo Beach *Also called Northrop Grumman Systems Corp* ***(P-20614)***
Aerospace Tool Grinding....F....562 802-3339
14020 Shoemaker Ave Norwalk (90650) ***(P-14357)***
Aerospace Welding Inc....F....310 914-0324
2035 Granville Ave Los Angeles (90025) ***(P-25383)***
Aerostar Engineering & Mfg Inc....F....310 326-5098
25514 Frampton Ave Harbor City (90710) ***(P-16243)***
Aerosysng Inc....F....714 633-1901
1112 W Barkley Ave Orange (92868) ***(P-20531)***
Aerosystems Engineering, Orange *Also called Aerosysng Inc* ***(P-20531)***
Aerotec Alloys Inc....E....562 809-1378
10632 Alondra Blvd Norwalk (90650) ***(P-11684)***
Aerotech News and Review Inc (PA)....E....520 623-9321
220 E Avenue K4 Ste 7 Lancaster (93535) ***(P-6098)***
Aerovironment Inc....D....626 357-9983
1610 S Magnolia Ave Monrovia (91016) ***(P-20532)***
Aerovironment Inc (PA)....D....626 357-9983
800 Royal Oaks Dr Ste 210 Monrovia (91016) ***(P-20533)***
Aerovironment Inc....E....626 357-9983
1725 Peck Rd Monrovia (91016) ***(P-20534)***
Aerovironment Inc....E....626 357-9983
222 E Huntington Dr # 118 Monrovia (91016) ***(P-20535)***
Aerovironment Inc....F....626 357-9983
2290 Agate Ct Simi Valley (93065) ***(P-20536)***
Aerovironment Inc....E....626 357-9983
825 S Myrtle Ave Monrovia (91016) ***(P-20537)***
Aerowind Corporation....F....619 569-1960
1959 John Towers Ave El Cajon (92020) ***(P-21184)***
AES, Palo Alto *Also called Applied Expert Systems Inc* ***(P-24373)***
AES, San Diego *Also called Automotive Exch & Sup of Cal* ***(P-20263)***
Aeswave.com, Fresno *Also called Automotive Electronics Svcs* ***(P-13811)***
Aethercomm Inc....C....760 208-6002
3205 Lionshead Ave Carlsbad (92010) ***(P-18017)***
AF Gomes Inc....E....408 453-7300
901 Commercial St Ste 140 San Jose (95112) ***(P-12464)***
AF Machine & Tool Co Inc....F....310 674-1919
950 W Hyde Park Blvd D Inglewood (90302) ***(P-16244)***
Afakori Inc....E....949 859-4277
29390 Hunco Way Lake Elsinore (92530) ***(P-12107)***
Afc Finishing Systems....E....530 533-8907
250 Airport Pkwy Oroville (95965) ***(P-12911)***
Afco, Gardena *Also called Abrasive Finishing Co* ***(P-11788)***
Afco, Alhambra *Also called Alhambra Foundry Company Ltd* ***(P-11491)***
Afco, Huntington Park *Also called Aircraft Foundry Co Inc* ***(P-11721)***
Afe Power, Corona *Also called Advanced Flow Engineering Inc* ***(P-20243)***
Affectlayer Inc....F....650 924-1082
333 Bush St Fl 22 San Francisco (94104) ***(P-24334)***
Affinity Flavors, Corona *Also called Fischler Investments Inc* ***(P-2260)***
Affinity Medical Tech LLC, Costa Mesa *Also called Phillips-Medisize* ***(P-22584)***
Affluent Living Publication, Anaheim *Also called Affluent Target Marketing Inc* ***(P-6099)***
Affluent Target Marketing Inc....E....714 446-6280
3855 E La Palma Ave # 250 Anaheim (92807) ***(P-6099)***
Affordable Goods....F....916 514-1049
131 Cognac Cir Sacramento (95835) ***(P-15387)***
Affymetrix Inc....D....408 731-5000
3380 Central Expy Santa Clara (95051) ***(P-21894)***
Affymetrix Inc....D....408 731-5000
3450 Central Expy Santa Clara (95051) ***(P-21895)***
Affymetrix Inc (HQ)....B....408 731-5000
3380 Central Expy Santa Clara (95051) ***(P-21896)***
Affymetrix Anatrace....F....408 731-5756
3380 Central Expy Santa Clara (95051) ***(P-21897)***
Afg Insulating Riverside Plant, Riverside *Also called Poma GL Specialty Windows Inc* ***(P-10605)***
Afi, Santa Clara *Also called Acu Spec Inc* ***(P-16221)***
Afn Services LLC....E....408 364-1564
368 E Campbell Ave Campbell (95008) ***(P-5218)***
AFP Advanced Food Products LLC....C....559 627-2070
1211 E Noble Ave Visalia (93292) ***(P-744)***
Afr Apparel International Inc....D....818 773-5000
19401 Business Center Dr Northridge (91324) ***(P-3533)***
Afresh Technologies Inc....F....805 551-9245
2948 20th St Apt 302 San Francisco (94110) ***(P-24335)***
Aft Corporation....E....310 576-1007
1815c Centinela Ave Santa Monica (90404) ***(P-7639)***
Aftco Mfg Co Inc....D....949 660-8757
2400 S Garnsey St Santa Ana (92707) ***(P-23489)***
After Capture, Los Angeles *Also called Rangefinder Publishing Co Inc* ***(P-6243)***
After Hours....F....562 925-5737
7310 Adams St Ste F Paramount (90723) ***(P-17755)***
Aftermarket Parts Company LLC....B....951 681-2751
10293 Birtcher Dr Mira Loma (91752) ***(P-20121)***
Aftermaster Inc (PA)....F....310 657-4886
6671 W Sunset Blvd # 1520 Hollywood (90028) ***(P-23137)***
AG Global Products LLC....E....323 334-2900
15301 Blackburn Ave Norwalk (90650) ***(P-17384)***
AG Machining Inc....D....805 531-9555
609 Science Dr Moorpark (93021) ***(P-12108)***
AG Millworks, Ventura *Also called Art Glass Etc Inc* ***(P-4106)***
AG Neovo Technology Corp....F....408 321-8210
2362 Qume Dr Ste A San Jose (95131) ***(P-15629)***
AG Ray Inc....F....209 334-1999
20400 N Kennefick Rd Acampo (95220) ***(P-14036)***
AG Spraying....F....559 698-9507
5815 S Calaveras Ave Tranquillity (93668) ***(P-13914)***
Ag-Weld Inc....F....661 758-3061
1236 G St Wasco (93280) ***(P-25384)***
AGA Precision Systems Inc....F....714 540-3163
122 E Dyer Rd Santa Ana (92707) ***(P-16245)***
Agan Woodcrafters....F....760 322-1310
175 W Radio Rd Palm Springs (92262) ***(P-4267)***
Age Incorporated....E....562 483-7300
14423 Marquardt Ave Santa Fe Springs (90670) ***(P-17130)***
Age Logistics Corporation....F....626 243-5253
426 E Duarte Rd Monrovia (91016) ***(P-14293)***
Aged Timber Co Inc....E....818 897-9663
12432 Foothill Blvd Sylmar (91342) ***(P-4072)***
Agency At All Valley, The, Hanford *Also called All Valley Printing Inc* ***(P-6648)***
Agencycom LLC....B....415 817-3800
5353 Grosvenor Blvd Los Angeles (90066) ***(P-24336)***
Agent 18, West Hollywood *Also called Sargam International Inc* ***(P-17853)***
Agents West Inc....E....949 614-0293
6 Hughes Ste 210 Irvine (92618) ***(P-19900)***
Aggregate - Cache Creek S&G, Madison *Also called Cemex Cnstr Mtls PCF LLC* ***(P-9380)***
Aggregate - Red Hill Quarry, Little Lake *Also called Kiewit Corporation* ***(P-322)***
Aggregate -Eliot Quarry, Pleasanton *Also called Cemex Cnstr Mtls PCF LLC* ***(P-11062)***
Aggregate -Patterson Quarry, Sheridan *Also called Cemex Cnstr Mtls PCF LLC* ***(P-11066)***
Aggregate -Sunol Quarry, Sunol *Also called Cemex Cnstr Mtls PCF LLC* ***(P-10751)***
Aggregate Mining Products LLC....F....951 277-1267
21780 Temescal Canyon Rd Corona (92883) ***(P-15051)***
Aggregate Products Inc (PA)....F....760 395-5312
100 Brawley Ave Thermal (92274) ***(P-324)***
Aggregate West Coast, Thermal *Also called West Coast Aggregate Supply* ***(P-391)***
Aggrigator Inc....F....650 245-5117
30 E San Joaquin St # 202 Salinas (93901) ***(P-24337)***
Aggtech Inc....E....909 795-4774
34428 Yucaipa Blvd E344 Yucaipa (92399) ***(P-344)***
Agi Publishing Inc (PA)....E....559 251-8888
1850 N Gateway Blvd # 152 Fresno (93727) ***(P-6423)***
Agi Publishing Inc....C....559 251-8888
1850 N Gateway Blvd # 152 Fresno (93727) ***(P-6424)***
Agile Technologies Inc....F....949 454-8030
2 Orion Aliso Viejo (92656) ***(P-18673)***
Agilent Tech World Trade Inc (HQ)....F....408 345-8886
5301 Stevens Creek Blvd Santa Clara (95051) ***(P-21705)***
Agilent Technologies Inc....B....510 794-1234
39201 Cherry St Newark (94560) ***(P-21706)***
Agilent Technologies Inc....C....916 985-7888
91 Blue Ravine Rd Folsom (95630) ***(P-21707)***
Agilent Technologies Inc....F....805 566-6655
1170 Mark Ave Carpinteria (93013) ***(P-21708)***
Agilent Technologies Inc....A....408 345-8886
5301 Stevens Creek Blvd Santa Clara (95051) ***(P-21709)***
Agilent Technologies Inc....B....858 373-6300
11011 N Torrey Pines Rd La Jolla (92037) ***(P-21710)***
Agilent Technologies Inc....F....916 785-1000
10054 Foothills Blvd Roseville (95747) ***(P-21711)***
Agilent Technologies Inc (PA)....B....408 345-8886
5301 Stevens Creek Blvd Santa Clara (95051) ***(P-21712)***
Agilent Technologies Inc....A....408 345-8886
5301 Stevens Creek Blvd Santa Clara (95051) ***(P-21713)***
Agilent Technologies Inc....A....408 553-7777
3175 Bowers Ave Santa Clara (95054) ***(P-21714)***
Agilent Technologies Inc....A....408 345-8886
30721 Russell Ranch Rd Westlake Village (91362) ***(P-21715)***
Agilent Technologies Inc....B....858 373-6300
11011 N Torrey Pines Rd La Jolla (92037) ***(P-21716)***
Agilepoint Inc (PA)....E....650 968-6789
1916 Old Middlefield Way Mountain View (94043) ***(P-24338)***
Agility Fuel Systems LLC (HQ)....C....949 236-5520
3335 Susan St Ste 100 Costa Mesa (92626) ***(P-20248)***
Agility Fuel Systems LLC....F....256 831-6155
3335 Susan St Ste 100 Costa Mesa (92626) ***(P-14013)***
Agiloft Inc....E....650 587-8615
460 Seaport Ct Ste 200 Redwood City (94063) ***(P-24339)***
Agilone Inc (PA)....D....877 769-3047
771 Vaqueros Ave Sunnyvale (94085) ***(P-21898)***
Agl, Temecula *Also called Artificial Grass Liquidators* ***(P-24044)***
Agnaldos Welding Inc....F....559 752-4254
828 S Burnett Rd Tipton (93272) ***(P-25385)***
Agora Natural Surfaces Inc....F....310 715-1088
339 W 168th St Gardena (90248) ***(P-11227)***
Agoura Music....F....818 991-8316
625 N Sycamore Ave # 313 Los Angeles (90036) ***(P-23351)***
Agouron Pharmaceuticals Inc (HQ)....E....858 622-3000
10777 Science Center Dr San Diego (92121) ***(P-8005)***
Agra Tech Inc....F....925 432-3342
2131 Piedmont Way Pittsburg (94565) ***(P-12912)***
Agra Trading LLC....F....530 894-1782
60 Independence Cir # 203 Chico (95973) ***(P-9056)***
Agra-Farm Foods Inc....F....626 443-2335
2223 Seaman Ave El Monte (91733) ***(P-1053)***
Agraquest Inc (HQ)....D....866 992-2937
890 Embarcadero Dr West Sacramento (95605) ***(P-9089)***
Agri Cel Inc....D....661 792-2107
401 Road 192 Delano (93215) ***(P-9813)***
Agri Service, Oceanside *Also called Mary Matava* ***(P-9106)***

Employee Codes: A=Over 500 employees, B=251-500 C=101-250, D=51-100, E=20-50, F=10-19
2019 California Manfacturers Register
© Mergent Inc. 1-800-342-5647
1049

Agri-Tech Industries LLC.....E.....619 205-9509
119 Stony Knoll Rd El Cajon (92019) ***(P-10826)***
Agribag Inc.....E.....510 533-2388
3925 Alameda Ave Oakland (94601) ***(P-2984)***
Agricultural Manufacturing.....F.....559 485-1662
4106 S Cedar Ave Fresno (93725) ***(P-14139)***
Agriculture Bag Manufacturing,, Oakland *Also called Agriculture Bag Mfg USA Inc* ***(P-2772)***
Agriculture Bag Mfg USA Inc (PA).....E.....510 632-5637
960 98th Ave Oakland (94603) ***(P-2772)***
Agrifim Irrigation Pdts Inc.....F.....559 443-6680
2855 S East Ave Fresno (93725) ***(P-14037)***
Agron Inc.....D.....310 473-7223
2440 S Sepulveda Blvd # 201 Los Angeles (90064) ***(P-3556)***
AGS Usa LLC.....C.....323 588-2200
1210 Rexford Ave Pasadena (91107) ***(P-3290)***
Agse, Santa Fe Springs *Also called Advanced Ground Systems* ***(P-20641)***
Agt, Corona *Also called Absolute Graphic Tech USA Inc* ***(P-17246)***
Agua Dulce Vineyards LLC.....E.....661 268-7402
9640 Sierra Hwy Agua Dulce (91390) ***(P-1640)***
Aguda Wilson Ramos.....F.....209 942-2446
5409 Asbury Way Stockton (95219) ***(P-18018)***
Aguilar Williams Inc.....F.....562 693-2736
7635 Baldwin Pl Whittier (90602) ***(P-13313)***
Agusa.....E.....559 924-4785
1055 S 19th Ave Lemoore (93245) ***(P-872)***
Aha Labs Inc.....F.....650 575-1425
20 Gloria Cir Menlo Park (94025) ***(P-24340)***
Ahead Magnetics Inc.....D.....408 226-9800
6410 Via Del Oro San Jose (95119) ***(P-19437)***
Aheadtek, San Jose *Also called Ahead Magnetics Inc* ***(P-19437)***
Ahf-Ducommun Incorporated (HQ).....C.....310 380-5390
268 E Gardena Blvd Gardena (90248) ***(P-20724)***
Ahlborn Structural Steel Inc.....E.....707 573-0742
1230 Century Ct Santa Rosa (95403) ***(P-12109)***
Ahn Enterprises LLC.....F.....408 734-1878
1240 Birchwood Dr Ste 2 Sunnyvale (94089) ***(P-19316)***
Ahr Signs Incorporated.....F.....323 255-1102
3400 N San Fernando Rd Los Angeles (90065) ***(P-23811)***
AI Foods Corporation.....E.....323 222-0827
1700 N Soto St Los Angeles (90033) ***(P-460)***
Ai Industries LLC (PA).....D.....650 366-4099
1725 E Byshore Rd Ste 101 Redwood City (94063) ***(P-13314)***
Aidells Sausage Company Inc.....A.....510 614-5450
2411 Baumann Ave San Lorenzo (94580) ***(P-461)***
Aih LLC (HQ).....E.....760 930-4600
5810 Van Allen Way Carlsbad (92008) ***(P-19438)***
Aii Beauty, Commerce *Also called American International Inds* ***(P-8693)***
Aim Mail Centers, Woodland *Also called American International Mfg Co* ***(P-14041)***
Aim Mail Centers, Pasadena *Also called Air Instrmnts Measurements LLC* ***(P-21544)***
Aimez Closet Inc.....F.....213 744-1222
3499 S Main St Los Angeles (90007) ***(P-3209)***
Aimmune Therapeutics Inc.....C.....650 614-5220
8000 Marina Blvd Ste 300 Brisbane (94005) ***(P-8006)***
Ainor Signs Inc.....F.....916 348-4370
5443 Stationers Way Sacramento (95842) ***(P-23812)***
Aip Aerospace Holdings, Irvine *Also called Coast Composites LLC* ***(P-16393)***
Aipac, Los Angeles *Also called American Israel Public Affairs* ***(P-24356)***
Air & Gas Tech Inc.....E.....619 557-8373
3191 Commercial St San Diego (92113) ***(P-21020)***
Air Bearing Technology, Hayward *Also called KLA Tencor* ***(P-15287)***
Air Blast Inc.....F.....626 576-0144
2050 Pepper St Alhambra (91801) ***(P-15140)***
Air Combat Systems, Palmdale *Also called Northrop Grumman Systems Corp* ***(P-20607)***
Air Craftors Engineering Inc.....F.....909 900-0635
4040 Cheyenne Ct Chino (91710) ***(P-16246)***
Air Distribution Products, San Pedro *Also called Kesclo Financial Inc* ***(P-12871)***
Air Dreams Mattresses.....F.....626 573-5733
3266 Rosemead Blvd El Monte (91731) ***(P-4849)***
Air Dry Co of America LLC.....E.....805 227-0434
1740 Commerce Way Paso Robles (93446) ***(P-21497)***
Air Electro, Chatsworth *Also called Aei Manufacturing Inc* ***(P-17439)***
Air Factors Inc.....F.....925 579-0040
4771 Arroyo Vis Ste D Livermore (94551) ***(P-15141)***
Air Filter Sales, Hayward *Also called Purolator Pdts A Filtration Co* ***(P-15171)***
Air Flow Research Heads Inc.....E.....661 257-8124
28611 Industry Dr Valencia (91355) ***(P-20249)***
Air Frame Forming Inc.....F.....562 663-1662
15717 Colorado Ave Paramount (90723) ***(P-14426)***
Air Instrmnts Measurements LLC.....F.....626 791-1912
3579 E Foothill Blvd Pasadena (91107) ***(P-21544)***
Air Link International, Anaheim *Also called D & B Supply Corp* ***(P-14271)***
Air Liquid Healthcare.....E.....909 899-4633
12460 Arrow Rte Rancho Cucamonga (91739) ***(P-7668)***
Air Liquide Electronics US LP.....E.....510 624-4338
46401 Landing Pkwy Fremont (94538) ***(P-7750)***
Air Liquide USA LLC.....E.....510 659-0162
5121 Brandin Ct Fremont (94538) ***(P-7669)***
Air Logistics Corporation (PA).....F.....626 633-0294
146 Railroad Ave Monrovia (91016) ***(P-9931)***
Air Marketing.....F.....562 208-3990
516 E 7th St Long Beach (90813) ***(P-6425)***
Air Monitor Corporation (PA).....D.....707 544-2706
1050 Hopper Ave Santa Rosa (95403) ***(P-21498)***
Air O Fan, Reedley *Also called Air-O Fan Products Corporation* ***(P-14038)***
Air Products, Vernon *Also called Evonik Corporation* ***(P-9249)***
Air Products and Chemicals Inc.....E.....408 988-2142
1515 Norman Ave Frnt Santa Clara (95054) ***(P-7670)***
Air Products and Chemicals Inc.....E.....562 944-3873
8934 Dice Rd Santa Fe Springs (90670) ***(P-7671)***
Air Products and Chemicals Inc.....F.....310 847-7300
23300 S Alameda St Carson (90810) ***(P-7672)***
Air Products and Chemicals Inc.....E.....562 437-0462
901 W 12th St Long Beach (90813) ***(P-7673)***
Air Products and Chemicals Inc.....F.....949 474-1860
400 Macarthur Blvd Newport Beach (92660) ***(P-7674)***
Air Products and Chemicals Inc.....C.....760 931-9555
1969 Palomar Oaks Way Carlsbad (92011) ***(P-7675)***
Air Products and Chemicals Inc.....E.....310 952-9172
700 N Henry Ford Ave Wilmington (90744) ***(P-7676)***
Air Solutions LLC.....F.....510 573-6474
37310 Cedar Blvd Ste J Newark (94560) ***(P-15934)***
Air Source Industries.....F.....562 426-4017
3976 Cherry Ave Long Beach (90807) ***(P-7677)***
Air Transport Manufacturing.....F.....818 504-3300
2629 Foothill Blvd La Crescenta (91214) ***(P-12465)***
Air Tube Transfer Systems Inc.....E.....714 363-0700
715 N Cypress St Orange (92867) ***(P-14263)***
Air-O Fan Products Corporation (PA).....F.....559 638-6546
507 E Dinuba Ave Reedley (93654) ***(P-14038)***
Air-Trak.....F.....858 677-9950
15090 Avenue Of Science # 103 San Diego (92128) ***(P-18019)***
Air-Vol Block Inc.....E.....805 543-1314
1 Suburban Rd San Luis Obispo (93401) ***(P-10841)***
Aira Tech Corp.....E.....858 880-4454
4225 Executive Sq Ste 400 La Jolla (92037) ***(P-24341)***
Airaya Corp.....F.....408 776-2846
18434 Technology Dr Morgan Hill (95037) ***(P-18020)***
Airbolt Industries Inc.....F.....818 767-5600
25334 Stanford Ave Unit B Valencia (91355) ***(P-11767)***
Airborne Components, Carson *Also called Stanford Mu Corporation* ***(P-21197)***
Airborne Systems N Amer CA Inc.....C.....714 662-1400
3100 W Segerstrom Ave Santa Ana (92704) ***(P-3935)***
Airborne Technologies Inc.....D.....805 389-3700
999 Avenida Acaso Camarillo (93012) ***(P-20725)***
Aircoat Inc.....F.....310 527-2258
13405 S Broadway Los Angeles (90061) ***(P-13545)***
Aircraft Covers Inc.....D.....408 738-3959
18850 Adams Ct Morgan Hill (95037) ***(P-2717)***
Aircraft Foundry Co Inc.....F.....323 587-3171
5316 Pacific Blvd Huntington Park (90255) ***(P-11721)***
Aircraft Hinge Inc.....E.....661 257-3434
24930 Avenue Tibbitts Valencia (91355) ***(P-20726)***
Aircraft Stamping Company Inc.....E.....323 283-1239
1285 Paseo Alicia San Dimas (91773) ***(P-12466)***
Aircraft Technical Publishers (PA).....D.....415 330-9500
2000 Sierra Point Pkwy # 501 Brisbane (94005) ***(P-6426)***
Airdyne Refrigeration, Cerritos *Also called Refrigerator Manufacturers LLC* ***(P-15977)***
Airdyne Refrigeration, Cerritos *Also called ARI Industries Inc* ***(P-15938)***
Airex, Anaheim *Also called Emitcon Inc* ***(P-21687)***
Airflex5d LLC.....F.....714 622-2600
12282 Knott St Garden Grove (92841) ***(P-4821)***
Airgain Inc (PA).....E.....760 579-0200
3611 Valley Centre Dr # 150 San Diego (92130) ***(P-18021)***
Airgard Inc (PA).....E.....408 573-0701
2190 Paragon Dr San Jose (95131) ***(P-15142)***
Airgas Inc.....F.....714 521-4789
15116 Canary Ave La Mirada (90638) ***(P-9057)***
Airgas Usa LLC.....F.....650 873-4212
315 Harbor Way South San Francisco (94080) ***(P-7678)***
Airgas Usa LLC.....F.....760 744-1472
1415 Grand Ave San Marcos (92078) ***(P-7679)***
Airgas Usa LLC.....E.....562 946-8394
9810 Jordan Cir Santa Fe Springs (90670) ***(P-7680)***
Airgas Usa LLC.....D.....510 429-4200
700 Decoto Rd Union City (94587) ***(P-7681)***
Airgas Usa LLC.....F.....925 969-0419
1750 Clinton Dr Concord (94521) ***(P-7682)***
Airgas Usa LLC.....E.....562 945-1383
8832 Dice Rd Santa Fe Springs (90670) ***(P-7683)***
Airgas Usa LLC.....E.....510 624-4000
46409 Landing Pkwy Fremont (94538) ***(P-7684)***
Airgas Usa LLC.....E.....562 906-8700
9756 Santa Fe Springs Rd Santa Fe Springs (90670) ***(P-7685)***
Airgas Usa LLC.....E.....661 201-8107
311 Kentucky St Bakersfield (93305) ***(P-7686)***
Airgas Usa LLC.....F.....310 329-4390
352 W 133rd St Los Angeles (90061) ***(P-7687)***
Airgas Usa LLC.....F.....909 899-4670
12550 Arrow Rte Rancho Cucamonga (91739) ***(P-7688)***
Airo Industries Company.....E.....818 838-1008
429 Jessie St San Fernando (91340) ***(P-5006)***
Airparts Express Inc.....D.....714 308-2764
3420 W Macarthur Blvd G Santa Ana (92704) ***(P-20727)***
Airpatrol Corporation.....F.....410 794-1214
17 E Sir F Drake Blvd 1 Larkspur (94939) ***(P-19901)***
Airpoint Precision Inc.....F.....530 622-0510
6221 Enterprise Dr Ste D Diamond Springs (95619) ***(P-16247)***
Airsoft Megastore, Arcadia *Also called Airsoft Zone Corporation* ***(P-23490)***
Airsoft Megastore, Arcadia *Also called Airsoft Zone Corporation* ***(P-23491)***
Airsoft Zone Corporation (PA).....E.....818 495-6502
138 E Longden Ave Arcadia (91006) ***(P-23490)***
Airsoft Zone Corporation.....E.....818 495-6502
138 E Longden Ave Arcadia (91006) ***(P-23491)***
Airspace Seal and Gasket Corp.....E.....951 256-8380
1476 Davril Cir Corona (92880) ***(P-9518)***
Airspace Systems Inc.....E.....310 704-7155
1933 Davis St Ste 229 San Leandro (94577) ***(P-17247)***

Airstream of Orange County, Midway City *Also called Lin Consulting LLC* ***(P-21206)***
Airtech Advanced Mtls Group, Huntington Beach *Also called Airtech International Inc* ***(P-20728)***
Airtech International Inc (PA).......C.......714 899-8100
5700 Skyıab Rd Huntington Beach (92647) ***(P-20728)***
Airtech Streamlining, Vista *Also called Riches International Inc* ***(P-21134)***
Airtronics Metal Products Inc (PA).......C.......408 977-7800
140 San Pedro Ave Morgan Hill (95037) ***(P-12467)***
Airware, San Francisco *Also called Unmanned Innovation Inc* ***(P-20633)***
Airxpanders Inc (PA).......D.......650 964-1437
3047 Orchard Pkwy San Jose (95134) ***(P-22319)***
Aisin Electronics Inc.......C.......209 983-4988
199 Frank West Cir Stockton (95206) ***(P-17248)***
Aisling Industries, Calexico *Also called Creation Tech Calexico Inc* ***(P-18458)***
Aitech Defense Systems Inc.......E.......818 700-2000
19756 Prairie St Chatsworth (91311) ***(P-19902)***
Aitech Rugged Group Inc (PA).......E.......818 700-2000
19756 Prairie St Chatsworth (91311) ***(P-19903)***
Aixtron Inc.......C.......669 228-3759
1700 Wyatt Dr Ste 15 Santa Clara (95054) ***(P-18674)***
Aja Video Systems Inc (PA).......E.......530 274-2048
180 Litton Dr Grass Valley (95945) ***(P-18022)***
Ajax, Union City *Also called Ichor Systems Inc* ***(P-10145)***
Ajax - Untd Pttrns & Molds Inc.......C.......510 476-8000
34585 7th St Union City (94587) ***(P-9932)***
Ajax Custom Manufacturing, Union City *Also called Ajax - Untd Pttrns & Molds Inc* ***(P-9932)***
Ajax Forge Company (PA).......E.......323 582-6307
1956 E 48th St Vernon (90058) ***(P-13091)***
Ajax Forge Company.......E.......323 582-6307
1960 E 48th St Vernon (90058) ***(P-13092)***
Ajg Inc.......E.......323 346-0171
7220 E Slauson Ave Commerce (90040) ***(P-3606)***
Ajile Systems Inc (PA).......E.......408 557-0829
920 Saratoga Ave Ste 104 San Jose (95129) ***(P-18675)***
Ajinomoto Foods North Amer Inc.......F.......510 293-1838
2395 American Ave Hayward (94545) ***(P-974)***
Ajinomoto Foods North Amer Inc.......C.......909 477-4700
4200 Concours Ste 100 Ontario (91764) ***(P-975)***
Ajinomoto Foods North Amer Inc (HQ).......D.......909 477-4700
4200 Concours Ste 100 Ontario (91764) ***(P-976)***
Ajinomoto Windsor Inc.......C.......323 277-7000
6711 S Alameda St Los Angeles (90001) ***(P-977)***
Ajinomoto Windsor, Inc., Ontario *Also called Ajinomoto Foods North Amer Inc* ***(P-976)***
AJW Construction.......E.......510 568-2300
966 81st Ave Oakland (94621) ***(P-9377)***
AK Darcy, Costa Mesa *Also called Darcy AK Corporation* ***(P-16421)***
AK Industries, Compton *Also called Allan Kidd* ***(P-17442)***
AK Mak Bakeries Division, Sanger *Also called Soojians Inc* ***(P-1381)***
Akamai Technologies Inc.......E.......617 444-3000
1400 Fashion Island Blvd # 15 San Mateo (94404) ***(P-24342)***
Akaranta Inc.......F.......909 989-9800
8661 Baseline Rd Rancho Cucamonga (91730) ***(P-8007)***
Akas Manufacturing Corporation.......E.......510 786-3200
3200 Investment Blvd Hayward (94545) ***(P-12468)***
Aker International Inc.......E.......619 423-5182
2248 Main St Ste 4 Chula Vista (91911) ***(P-10571)***
Aker Leather Products, Chula Vista *Also called Aker International Inc* ***(P-10571)***
Akido Printing Inc.......F.......510 357-0238
2096 Merced St San Leandro (94577) ***(P-6644)***
Akimbo Systems Inc.......E.......650 292-3330
411 Borel Ave Ste 100 San Mateo (94402) ***(P-24343)***
Akira Seiki U S A Inc.......F.......925 443-1200
255 Capitol St Livermore (94551) ***(P-14358)***
Akm Fire Inc.......E.......818 343-8208
18322 Oxnard St Tarzana (91356) ***(P-15297)***
Akm Semiconductor Inc.......E.......408 436-8580
1731 Tech Dr Ste 500 San Jose (95110) ***(P-18676)***
Akn Holdings LLC (PA).......F.......310 432-7100
10250 Constellation Blvd Los Angeles (90067) ***(P-6100)***
Akon Incorporated.......D.......408 432-8039
2135 Ringwood Ave San Jose (95131) ***(P-24028)***
Akra Plastic Products Inc.......E.......909 930-1999
1504 E Cedar St Ontario (91761) ***(P-9933)***
Akt, Paso Robles *Also called Advanced Keyboard Tech Inc* ***(P-15383)***
Akt America Inc (HQ).......B.......408 563-5455
3101 Scott Blvd Bldg 91 Santa Clara (95054) ***(P-19904)***
Aktana Inc.......E.......888 707-3125
207 Powell St Ste 800 San Francisco (94102) ***(P-24344)***
Akupara Games LLC.......F.......805 471-4933
8301 Gloria Ave North Hills (91343) ***(P-24345)***
Akzo Nobel Inc.......E.......909 981-6540
1338 W 9th St 40a Upland (91786) ***(P-8972)***
Akzo Nobel Inc.......E.......714 966-0934
3010 Bristol St Costa Mesa (92626) ***(P-8973)***
Akzo Nobel Inc.......E.......760 743-7374
735 N Escondido Blvd Escondido (92025) ***(P-8974)***
Al & Krla Pipe Fabricators Inc.......F.......619 448-0060
8047 Wing Ave El Cajon (92020) ***(P-13874)***
Al Industries, Santa Ana *Also called Acrontos Manufacturing Inc* ***(P-13158)***
Al Johnson Company, Camarillo *Also called Gc International Inc* ***(P-17900)***
Al Kramp Specialties.......E.......209 464-7539
1707 El Pinal Dr Stockton (95205) ***(P-17668)***
Al Shellco LLC (HQ).......C.......570 296-6444
9330 Scranton Rd Ste 600 San Diego (92121) ***(P-17756)***
Al's Machine Shop, Ontario *Also called Portable Spndle Repr Spcialist* ***(P-14779)***
Al-Mag Heat Treat.......F.......626 442-8570
9735 Alpaca St South El Monte (91733) ***(P-11792)***
Alabama Metal Industries Corp.......E.......909 350-9280
11093 Beech Ave Fontana (92337) ***(P-12830)***
Alaco Ladder Company, Chino *Also called B E & P Enterprises LLC* ***(P-4607)***
Alaco Ladder Company.......E.......909 591-7561
5167 G St Chino (91710) ***(P-4604)***
Alameda Construction Svcs Inc.......E.......310 635-3277
2528 E 125th St Compton (90222) ***(P-345)***
Alameda Directory Inc.......F.......510 747-1060
1416 Park Ave Alameda (94501) ***(P-6427)***
Alameda Newspapers Inc (HQ).......C.......510 783-6111
22533 Foothill Blvd Hayward (94541) ***(P-5753)***
Alameda Newspapers Inc.......D.......650 348-4321
1080 S Amphlett Blvd San Mateo (94402) ***(P-5754)***
Alameda Newspapers Inc.......B.......209 832-6144
127 Spring St Pleasanton (94566) ***(P-5755)***
Alameda Video Station.......E.......510 523-5200
1929 Broadway Alameda (94501) ***(P-4565)***
Alamillo Radolfo.......F.......323 773-9614
4901 Patata St Ste 404 Cudahy (90201) ***(P-10630)***
Alan Hamilton Industries.......D.......818 885-5121
21020 Lassen St Chatsworth (91311) ***(P-6645)***
Alan Johnson Prfmce Engrg Inc.......E.......805 922-1202
1097 Foxen Canyon Rd Santa Maria (93454) ***(P-20122)***
Alan Lem & Co Inc.......E.......310 538-4282
515 W 130th St Los Angeles (90061) ***(P-10674)***
Alan Pre-Fab Building Corp (PA).......F.......310 538-0333
17817 Evelyn Ave Gardena (90248) ***(P-4566)***
Alan Wofsy Fine Arts LLC.......F.......415 292-6500
1109 Geary Blvd San Francisco (94109) ***(P-6303)***
Alannas Engineer Manufacturing, Chatsworth *Also called Perez Severino* ***(P-13963)***
Alard Machine Products, Gardena *Also called GT Precision Inc* ***(P-13025)***
Alarin Aircraft Hinge Inc.......E.......323 725-1666
6231 Randolph St Commerce (90040) ***(P-11925)***
Alasco Rubber & Plastics Corp.......F.......707 823-5270
1250 Enos Ave Sebastopol (95472) ***(P-9585)***
Alation Inc (PA).......E.......650 779-4440
805 Veterans Blvd Ste 307 Redwood City (94063) ***(P-24346)***
Alatus Aerosystems (PA).......C.......610 251-1000
17055 Gale Ave City of Industry (91745) ***(P-20729)***
Alatus Aerosystems.......D.......714 732-0559
423 Berry Way Brea (92821) ***(P-20730)***
Alatus Aerosystems.......D.......626 498-7376
9301 Mason Ave Chatsworth (91311) ***(P-20731)***
Albanay Aquatic Center, Albany *Also called Albany Swimming Pool* ***(P-23492)***
Albany Swimming Pool.......E.......510 559-6640
1311 Portland Ave Albany (94706) ***(P-23492)***
Albatross USA Inc.......F.......818 543-5850
5439 W San Fernando Rd Los Angeles (90039) ***(P-9187)***
Albers Dairy Equipment. Inc, Chino *Also called Albers Mfg Co Inc* ***(P-14039)***
Albers Mfg Co Inc (PA).......E.......909 597-5537
14323 Albers Way Chino (91710) ***(P-14039)***
Albert Goyenetche Dairy.......F.......661 764-6176
6041 Brandt Rd Buttonwillow (93206) ***(P-708)***
Albion Knitting Mills Inc.......E.......213 624-7740
2152 Sacramento St Los Angeles (90021) ***(P-3370)***
ALC, Fresno *Also called Auernheimer Labs Inc* ***(P-17768)***
Alcast Mfg Inc.......D.......310 542-3581
2910 Fisk Ln Redondo Beach (90278) ***(P-11722)***
Alcatel-Lucent USA, San Jose *Also called Nokia of America Corporation* ***(P-17969)***
Alcatel-Lucent USA Inc.......F.......310 297-2620
2361 Rosecrans Ave # 150 El Segundo (90245) ***(P-15660)***
Alcatel-Lucent USA Inc.......E.......510 475-5000
30971a San Benito St Hayward (94544) ***(P-17918)***
Alcatel-Lucent USA Inc.......B.......408 878-6500
701 E Middlefield Rd Mountain View (94043) ***(P-18677)***
Alcatel-Lucent USA Inc.......E.......818 880-3500
26801 Agoura Rd Calabasas (91301) ***(P-17919)***
Alcine Gazette, El Cajon *Also called East County Gazette* ***(P-5837)***
Alco Designs, Gardena *Also called Vege-Mist Inc* ***(P-15997)***
Alco Engrg & Tooling Corp.......E.......714 556-6060
3001 Oak St Santa Ana (92707) ***(P-12469)***
Alco Manufacturing Inc.......F.......714 549-5007
207 E Alton Ave Santa Ana (92707) ***(P-14474)***
Alco Metal Fab, Santa Ana *Also called Alco Engrg & Tooling Corp* ***(P-12469)***
Alco Plating Corp (PA).......C.......213 749-7561
1400 Long Beach Ave Los Angeles (90021) ***(P-13315)***
Alco Tech Inc.......F.......818 503-9209
12750 Raymer St Unit 2 North Hollywood (91605) ***(P-13161)***
Alcoa, Newbury Park *Also called Arconic Inc* ***(P-11534)***
Alcoa, Fullerton *Also called Arconic Inc* ***(P-11535)***
Alcoa, Fullerton *Also called Arconic Inc* ***(P-11536)***
Alcoa, Torrance *Also called Arconic Inc* ***(P-11537)***
Alcoa, Sylmar *Also called Arconic Inc* ***(P-11538)***
Alcoa Inc.......B.......805 498-4594
1300 Rancho Conejo Blvd Newbury Park (91320) ***(P-11533)***
Alcon Laboratories Inc.......A.......949 753-6488
15800 Alton Pkwy Irvine (92618) ***(P-22320)***
Alcon Lensx Inc (HQ).......D.......949 753-1393
15800 Alton Pkwy Irvine (92618) ***(P-22321)***
Alcon Manufacturing Ltd.......E.......949 753-1393
15800 Alton Pkwy Irvine (92618) ***(P-8008)***
Alcon Research Ltd.......E.......949 387-2142
15800 Alton Pkwy Irvine (92618) ***(P-22322)***
Alcon Surgical, Irvine *Also called Alcon Laboratories Inc* ***(P-22320)***
Alcotrevi Inc.......F.......818 244-0400
1133 S Central Ave 1 Glendale (91204) ***(P-22323)***
Alder & Co LLC.......F.......661 326-0320
412 Wallace St Bakersfield (93307) ***(P-4666)***

ALPHABETIC

Employee Codes: A=Over 500 employees, B=251-500
C=101-250, D=51-100, E=20-50, F=10-19
2019 California
Manfacturers Register
© Mergent Inc. 1-800-342-5647
1051

Alderman Logging, Sonora *Also called Alderman Timber Company Inc* ***(P-3976)***
Alderman Timber Company Inc........F.......209 532-9636
17180 Alderman Rd Sonora (95370) ***(P-3976)***
Aldetec Inc........E.......916 453-3382
3560 Business Dr Ste 100 Sacramento (95820) ***(P-18023)***
Aldila Inc (HQ)........D.......858 513-1801
1945 Kellogg Ave Carlsbad (92008) ***(P-23493)***
Aldila Inc........C.......858 513-1801
13450 Stowe Dr Poway (92064) ***(P-23494)***
Aldila De Poway, Poway *Also called Aldila Inc* ***(P-23494)***
Aldila Golf Corp........C.......858 513-1801
13450 Stowe Dr Poway (92064) ***(P-23495)***
Aldila Golf Corp (HQ)........D.......858 513-1801
1945 Kellogg Ave Carlsbad (92008) ***(P-23496)***
Aldila Materials Technology (HQ)........E.......858 513-1801
13450 Stowe Dr Poway (92064) ***(P-9218)***
Aldo Fragale........F.......310 324-0050
17813 S Main St Ste 111 Gardena (90248) ***(P-16248)***
Aldran Chemical Inc........E.......650 347-8242
1313 N Carolan Ave Burlingame (94010) ***(P-8618)***
Ale USA Inc........A.......818 878-4816
26801 Agoura Rd Calabasas (91301) ***(P-18024)***
Alectro Inc........F.......909 590-9521
6770 Central Ave Ste B Riverside (92504) ***(P-17079)***
Aleeda Wetsuits, Huntington Beach *Also called Sgt Boardriders Inc* ***(P-9677)***
Alegacy Foodservice Products........D.......562 320-3100
12683 Corral Pl Santa Fe Springs (90670) ***(P-5219)***
Alegio Fashions Inc........E.......310 539-0981
25634 Amber Leaf Rd Torrance (90505) ***(P-3371)***
Aleks Corporation........C.......714 245-7191
15640 Laguna Canyon Rd Irvine (92618) ***(P-24347)***
Aleks Educational Systems, Irvine *Also called Aleks Corporation* ***(P-24347)***
Alemad Inc........E.......530 661-1697
2061 Freeway Dr Ste C Woodland (95776) ***(P-5034)***
Alembic Inc........F.......707 523-2611
3005 Wiljan Ct Ste A Santa Rosa (95407) ***(P-23352)***
Aleph Group Inc........E.......951 213-4815
1900 E Alessandro Blvd # 105 Riverside (92508) ***(P-20123)***
Aleph Group Inc........F.......951 213-4815
6920 Sycamore Canyon Blvd Riverside (92507) ***(P-22324)***
Alere Connect LLC........E.......888 876-3327
9975 Summers Ridge Rd San Diego (92121) ***(P-22948)***
Alere Inc........B.......510 732-7200
6465 National Dr Livermore (94550) ***(P-8457)***
Alere San Diego Inc........A.......858 455-4808
9975 Summers Ridge Rd San Diego (92121) ***(P-8458)***
Alert Plating Company........E.......818 771-9304
9939 Glenoaks Blvd Sun Valley (91352) ***(P-13316)***
Alertenterprise Inc........C.......510 440-0840
4350 Starboard Dr Fremont (94538) ***(P-19905)***
Alertlite Neon Co Inc........F.......818 767-2059
11116 Tuxford St Sun Valley (91352) ***(P-17419)***
Alex Design Inc........F.......916 386-8020
8541 Younger Creek Dr # 400 Sacramento (95828) ***(P-4268)***
Alex Tronix, Fresno *Also called GNA Industries Inc* ***(P-17274)***
Alex Velvet Inc........E.......323 255-6900
3334 Eagle Rock Blvd Los Angeles (90065) ***(P-23230)***
Alexander Business Supplies........F.......818 346-1820
21500 Wyandotte St # 110 Canoga Park (91303) ***(P-6646)***
Alexander Color Printing, Canoga Park *Also called Alexander Business Supplies* ***(P-6646)***
Alexander Valley Gourmet LLC........E.......707 473-0116
140 Grove Ct B Healdsburg (95448) ***(P-2448)***
Alexander Valley Vineyards, Healdsburg *Also called AVV Winery Co LLC* ***(P-1648)***
Alexander's Costumes, San Bernardino *Also called Alexanders Textile Pdts Inc* ***(P-3637)***
Alexanders Textile Pdts Inc........F.......951 276-2500
200 N D St San Bernardino (92401) ***(P-3637)***
Alexza Pharmaceuticals Inc (HQ)........E.......650 944-7000
2091 Stierlin Ct Mountain View (94043) ***(P-8009)***
Alfa Scientific Designs Inc........D.......858 513-3888
13200 Gregg St Poway (92064) ***(P-8459)***
Alfonso Jaramillo........F.......951 276-2777
2225 E Cooley Dr Colton (92324) ***(P-13784)***
Alfred Domaine........F.......805 541-9463
7525 Orcutt Rd San Luis Obispo (93401) ***(P-1641)***
Alfred Music Group Inc (PA)........E.......818 891-5999
16320 Roscoe Blvd Ste 100 Van Nuys (91406) ***(P-6304)***
Alfred Music Publishing, Van Nuys *Also called Full Void 2 Inc* ***(P-6489)***
Alfred Picon........F.......562 928-2561
7644 Emil Ave Bell (90201) ***(P-5126)***
Alfred's Machining, Plymouth *Also called Acm Machining Inc* ***(P-16213)***
Alfredo Hernandez........F.......909 971-9320
474 W Arrow Hwy Ste K San Dimas (91773) ***(P-16249)***
Alfresco Concepts, Morgan Hill *Also called Fresco Solar Inc* ***(P-18851)***
Alfresco Software Inc (PA)........D.......888 317-3395
1825 S Grant St Ste 900 San Mateo (94402) ***(P-24348)***
Alger Alternative Energy LLC........F.......317 493-5289
1536 Jones St Brawley (92227) ***(P-11316)***
Alger International, Los Angeles *Also called Alger-Triton Inc* ***(P-17522)***
Alger Precision Machining LLC........C.......909 986-4591
724 S Bon View Ave Ontario (91761) ***(P-13009)***
Alger-Triton Inc........E.......310 229-9500
5600 W Jefferson Blvd Los Angeles (90016) ***(P-17522)***
Algonquin Power Sanger LLC........E.......559 875-0800
1125 Muscat Ave Sanger (93657) ***(P-17080)***
Alhambra Foundry Company Ltd........E.......626 289-4294
1147 S Meridian Ave Alhambra (91803) ***(P-11491)***
Alhambra Reprographics Inc (PA)........F.......909 390-4839
3939 E Guasti Rd Ste B Ontario (91761) ***(P-7226)***
Alhambra Valley Olive Oil Co (PA)........F.......925 370-8500
5371 Stonehurst Dr Martinez (94553) ***(P-1534)***
Alice G Fink-Painter, Santa Fe Springs *Also called Spec Tool Company* ***(P-21436)***
Alien Technology LLC (PA)........E.......408 782-3900
845 Embedded Way San Jose (95138) ***(P-18025)***
Alienvault Inc (HQ)........F.......650 713-3333
1100 Park Pl Ste 300 San Mateo (94403) ***(P-24349)***
Alienvault LLC (HQ)........D.......650 713-3333
1100 Park Pl Ste 300 San Mateo (94403) ***(P-24350)***
Align Aerospace Holding Inc (HQ)........F.......818 727-7800
21123 Nordhoff St Chatsworth (91311) ***(P-11506)***
Align Aerospace LLC (HQ)........C.......818 727-7800
9401 De Soto Ave Chatsworth (91311) ***(P-20732)***
Align Technology Inc (PA)........B.......408 470-1000
2820 Orchard Pkwy San Jose (95134) ***(P-22854)***
Alinabal Inc........E.......661 877-9356
29101 The Old Rd Valencia (91355) ***(P-11839)***
Alion Energy Inc........D.......510 965-0868
870 Harbour Way S Richmond (94804) ***(P-18678)***
Alios Biopharma Inc........E.......650 635-5500
260 E Grand Ave South San Francisco (94080) ***(P-8010)***
Alive & Radiant Foods Inc........E.......510 238-0128
2921 Adeline St Emeryville (94608) ***(P-2373)***
Alivecor Inc........E.......650 396-8650
444 Castro St Ste 600 Mountain View (94041) ***(P-24351)***
Alj, Camarillo *Also called Gc International Inc* ***(P-17899)***
All About Printing, Chatsworth *Also called Barrys Printing Inc* ***(P-6685)***
All Access Apparel Inc (PA)........C.......323 889-4300
1515 Gage Rd Montebello (90640) ***(P-3210)***
All Access Stging Prdctons Inc (PA)........D.......310 784-2464
1320 Storm Pkwy Torrance (90501) ***(P-17669)***
All Ameri Injec Moldi Servi, Temecula *Also called TST Molding LLC* ***(P-10414)***
All American Cabinetry Inc........D.......818 376-0500
13901 Saticoy St Van Nuys (91402) ***(P-5035)***
All American Electric, Covina *Also called Jeff J Polich Inc* ***(P-21781)***
All American Fabrication........F.......831 676-3490
1328 Burton Ave Ste B10 Salinas (93901) ***(P-24029)***
All American Frame & Bedg Corp........E.......323 773-7415
4641 Ardine St Cudahy (90201) ***(P-4822)***
All American Label, Dublin *Also called A A Label Inc* ***(P-5692)***
All American Label........E.......213 622-2222
1700 Wall St Los Angeles (90015) ***(P-2796)***
All American Pipe Bending, Santa Ana *Also called Saf-T-Co Supply* ***(P-17518)***
All American Racers Inc........C.......714 557-2116
2334 S Broadway Santa Ana (92707) ***(P-21087)***
All American Sterile Coat, Van Nuys *Also called All American Cabinetry Inc* ***(P-5035)***
All Bay Pallet Company Inc (PA)........E.......510 636-4131
24993 Tarman Ave Hayward (94544) ***(P-4449)***
All City Printing Inc........F.......415 861-8088
1061 Howard St San Francisco (94103) ***(P-6647)***
All Diameter Grinding Inc........E.......714 744-1200
725 N Main St Orange (92868) ***(P-16250)***
All Energy Inc........F.......619 988-7030
3401 Adams Ave A28 San Diego (92116) ***(P-17670)***
All Forms Express........F.......714 596-8641
17572 Griffin Ln Huntington Beach (92647) ***(P-7227)***
All Good Pallets Inc........E.......209 467-7000
1055 Diamond St Stockton (95205) ***(P-4450)***
All Label Inc........F.......626 964-6744
17989 Arenth Ave City of Industry (91748) ***(P-5694)***
All Manufacturers Inc........E.......951 280-4200
2900 Palisades Dr Corona (92880) ***(P-22325)***
All Metal Fabrication........F.......626 449-6191
617 S Raymond Ave Pasadena (91105) ***(P-12470)***
All Metals Inc (PA)........E.......408 200-7000
705 Reed St Santa Clara (95050) ***(P-11552)***
All Metals Proc San Diego Inc........C.......714 828-8238
8401 Standustrial St Stanton (90680) ***(P-13317)***
All New Stamping Co........C.......626 443-8813
10801 Lower Azusa Rd El Monte (91731) ***(P-13162)***
All One God Faith Inc (PA)........C.......844 937-2551
1335 Park Center Dr Vista (92081) ***(P-8588)***
All Power Manufacturing Co........F.......562 802-2640
13141 Molette St Santa Fe Springs (90670) ***(P-24030)***
All Quality & Services Inc........C.......510 249-5800
401 Kato Ter Fremont (94539) ***(P-18411)***
All Rise Records Inc........F.......951 279-2507
3175 Palisades Dr Corona (92880) ***(P-17385)***
All Sales Manufacturing Inc........E.......916 933-0236
5121 Hillsdale Cir El Dorado Hills (95762) ***(P-20250)***
All Sensors Corporation........E.......408 776-9434
16035 Vineyard Blvd Morgan Hill (95037) ***(P-18679)***
All Source Coatings Inc........E.......858 586-0903
10625 Scripps Ranch Blvd D San Diego (92131) ***(P-13546)***
All Spec Sheet Metal Inc........F.......925 427-4900
547 Bliss Ave Pittsburg (94565) ***(P-12471)***
All Sports Services Inc........F.......909 885-4626
765 S Gifford Ave Ste 1 San Bernardino (92408) ***(P-7228)***
All Star Clothing Inc........F.......323 233-7773
4507 Staunton Ave Vernon (90058) ***(P-3211)***
All Star Precision........E.......909 944-8373
8739 Lion St Rancho Cucamonga (91730) ***(P-14359)***
All Stars Packaging Inc........F.......626 664-3797
13851 Roswell Ave Ste H Chino (91710) ***(P-5339)***
All Stars Packaging & Display, Chino *Also called All Stars Packaging Inc* ***(P-5339)***
All Strong Industry (usa) Inc (PA)........E.......909 598-6494
326 Paseo Tesoro Walnut (91789) ***(P-5178)***
All Technology Machine, Irvine *Also called Lubrication Scientifics Inc* ***(P-13724)***

Mergent e-mail: customerrelations@mergent.com
1052
2019 California
Manufacturers Register
(P-0000) Products & Services Section entry number
(PA)=Parent Co (HQ)=Headquarters (DH)=Div Headquarters

All Time Machine Inc ..... F 909 673-1899
2050 Del Rio Way Ontario (91761) ***(P-16251)***
All Valley Printing Inc ..... F 559 584-5444
110 W 7th St Hanford (93230) ***(P-6648)***
All Weather Inc ..... D 916 928-1000
1065 National Dr Ste 1 Sacramento (95834) ***(P-22158)***
All Weather Insulated Panels, Vacaville *Also called Pre-Insulated Metal Tech Inc* ***(P-12956)***
All Weld Mch & Fabrication Co, San Jose *Also called O-S Inc* ***(P-16801)***
All West Container, San Francisco *Also called Packageone Inc* ***(P-5445)***
All West Fabricators Inc ..... E 510 623-1200
44875 Fremont Blvd Fremont (94538) ***(P-12110)***
All West Plastics Inc ..... E 714 894-9922
5451 Argosy Ave Huntington Beach (92649) ***(P-9736)***
All-American Mfg Co ..... E 323 581-6293
2201 E 51st St Vernon (90058) ***(P-12020)***
All-Battery.com, Fremont *Also called Tenergy Corporation* ***(P-19817)***
All-Star Lettering Inc ..... E 562 404-5995
9419 Ann St Santa Fe Springs (90670) ***(P-7229)***
All-Star Logo, Inglewood *Also called All-Star Mktg & Promotions Inc* ***(P-3826)***
All-Star Mktg & Promotions Inc ..... F 323 582-4880
8715 Aviation Blvd Inglewood (90301) ***(P-3826)***
All-Tech Machine & Engrg Inc ..... E 510 353-2000
2700 Prune Ave Fremont (94539) ***(P-16252)***
All-Truss Inc ..... E 707 938-5595
22700 Broadway Sonoma (95476) ***(P-4389)***
All-Ways Metal Inc ..... E 310 217-1177
401 E Alondra Blvd Gardena (90248) ***(P-12472)***
Allakos Inc ..... E 650 597-5002
75 Shoreway Rd Ste A San Carlos (94070) ***(P-8011)***
Allan Aircraft Supply Co LLC ..... E 818 765-4992
11643 Vanowen St North Hollywood (91605) ***(P-13757)***
Allan Borushek & Assoc Inc ..... F 949 642-8500
16360 Pacific Coast Hwy # 216 Huntington Beach (92649) ***(P-6305)***
Allan Copley Designs, Chula Vista *Also called DStyle Inc* ***(P-13937)***
Allan Kidd ..... E 310 762-1600
3115 E Las Hermanas St Compton (90221) ***(P-17442)***
Allblack Co Inc ..... E 562 946-2955
13090 Park St Santa Fe Springs (90670) ***(P-13318)***
Allbrite Car Care Products ..... F 714 666-8683
1201 N Las Brisas St Anaheim (92806) ***(P-8619)***
Alldata LLC ..... D 916 684-5200
9650 W Taron Dr Ste 100 Elk Grove (95757) ***(P-24352)***
Alldigital Holdings Inc ..... F 949 250-7340
1405 Warner Ave Ste A Tustin (92780) ***(P-24353)***
Allegheny Ludlum LLC ..... F 562 654-3900
8570 Mercury Ln Pico Rivera (90660) ***(P-11376)***
Allegra ..... F 415 824-9610
434 9th St San Francisco (94103) ***(P-6649)***
Allegra Print & Imaging, San Diego *Also called JA Ferrari Print Imaging LLC* ***(P-6905)***
Allegro, South Gate *Also called Conair Corporation* ***(P-17364)***
Allegro Copy & Print, Lafayette *Also called Acp Ventures* ***(P-6640)***
Allegro Creative, El Segundo *Also called Allegro Mfg* ***(P-10556)***
Allegro Mfg ..... F 323 724-0101
500 N Nash St El Segundo (90245) ***(P-10556)***
Allegro Pacific Corporation ..... F 323 724-0101
7250 Oxford Way Commerce (90040) ***(P-10557)***
Allen Industrial Inc ..... F 951 849-4966
960 S Hathaway St Banning (92220) ***(P-13319)***
Allen Mold Inc ..... F 714 538-6517
1100 W Katella Ave Ste N Orange (92867) ***(P-9934)***
Allen Morgan ..... F 714 538-7492
1233 W Collins Ave Orange (92867) ***(P-15249)***
Allen Reed Company Inc ..... F 310 575-8704
23823 Malibu Rd Ste 50275 Malibu (90265) ***(P-5272)***
Allen Sarah & ..... E 415 242-0906
560 Crestlake Dr San Francisco (94132) ***(P-15661)***
Allergan Inc ..... C 512 527-6688
735 Workman Mill Rd Whittier (90601) ***(P-8012)***
Allergan Spclty Thrpeutics Inc ..... A 714 246-4500
2525 Dupont Dr Irvine (92612) ***(P-8013)***
Allergan Usa Inc ..... A 714 427-1900
18581 Teller Ave Irvine (92612) ***(P-8014)***
Allergy Research Group Inc ..... E 510 263-2000
2300 N Loop Rd Alameda (94502) ***(P-8015)***
Allermed Laboratories Inc ..... E 858 292-1060
7203 Convoy Ct San Diego (92111) ***(P-7920)***
Allez Spine LLC (PA) ..... F 949 752-7885
2301 Dupont Dr Ste 510 Irvine (92612) ***(P-22326)***
Allfast Fastening Systems LLC ..... D 626 968-9388
15200 Don Julian Rd City of Industry (91745) ***(P-13057)***
Allhealth Inc ..... C 213 538-0762
515 S Figueroa St # 1300 Los Angeles (90071) ***(P-15388)***
Alliance Air Products Llc ..... C 619 428-9688
2285 Michael Faraday Dr San Diego (92154) ***(P-15935)***
Alliance Analytical Inc ..... E 800 916-5600
355 Fairview Way Milpitas (95035) ***(P-8524)***
Alliance Apparel Inc ..... E 323 888-8900
3422 Garfield Ave Commerce (90040) ***(P-3212)***
Alliance Chemical & Envmtl ..... F 805 385-3330
1721 Ives Ave Oxnard (93033) ***(P-13547)***
Alliance Display & Packaging, Burbank *Also called Westrock Rkt Company* ***(P-5475)***
Alliance Fiber Optic Pdts Inc (HQ) ..... D 408 736-6900
275 Gibraltar Dr Sunnyvale (94089) ***(P-10631)***
Alliance Finishing and Mfg, Oxnard *Also called Alliance Chemical & Envmtl* ***(P-13547)***
Alliance Hose & Extrusions Inc ..... E 714 202-8500
533 W Collins Ave Orange (92867) ***(P-8975)***
Alliance Medical Products Inc ..... C 949 768-4690
9342 9292 Jeronimo Rd Irvine (92618) ***(P-22327)***
Alliance Memory Inc ..... F 650 610-6800
511 Taylor Way San Carlos (94070) ***(P-18680)***
Alliance Metal Products Inc ..... C 818 709-1204
20844 Plummer St Chatsworth (91311) ***(P-12473)***
Alliance Multimedia LLC ..... F 760 522-3455
2033 San Elijo Ave Ste 20 Cardiff (92007) ***(P-7230)***
Alliance Ready Mix Inc ..... F 805 556-3015
310 James Way Ste 210 Pismo Beach (93449) ***(P-11034)***
Alliance Ready Mix Inc ..... F 805 343-0360
915 Sheridan Rd Arroyo Grande (93420) ***(P-11035)***
Alliance Spacesystems LLC ..... C 714 226-1400
4398 Corporate Center Dr Los Alamitos (90720) ***(P-17232)***
Alliance Tags ..... E 858 549-7297
9235 Trade Pl San Diego (92126) ***(P-7231)***
Alliance Technical Svcs Inc ..... F 805 606-3020
1785 Utah Ave Lompoc (93437) ***(P-20983)***
Alliance Trutrus, San Diego *Also called Commercial Truss Co* ***(P-4399)***
Alliance Welding Supplies, San Jose *Also called Tech Air Northern Cal LLC* ***(P-7733)***
Alliance Welding Supplies, Livermore *Also called Tech Air Northern Cal LLC* ***(P-7734)***
Alliance Welding Supplies, Oakland *Also called Tech Air Northern Cal LLC* ***(P-7738)***
Alliant Tchsystems Oprtons LLC ..... F 408 513-3271
151 Martinvale Ln Ste 150 San Jose (95119) ***(P-13686)***
Allied Bio Medical, Ventura *Also called Implantech Associates Inc* ***(P-22750)***
Allied Blnding Ingredients Inc ..... F 562 806-7560
5690 Lindbergh Ln Bell (90201) ***(P-2449)***
Allied Coatings Inc ..... F 800 630-2375
1125 Linda Vista Dr # 104 San Marcos (92078) ***(P-8874)***
Allied Components Intl ..... E 949 356-1780
19671 Descartes Foothill Ranch (92610) ***(P-19317)***
Allied Concrete & Supply Co ..... E 209 524-3177
440 Mitchell Rd Ste B Modesto (95354) ***(P-11036)***
Allied Concrete Rdymx Svcs LLC ..... F 415 282-8117
450 Amador St San Francisco (94124) ***(P-11037)***
Allied Container Systems Inc ..... C 925 944-7600
511 Wilbur Ave Ste B4 Antioch (94509) ***(P-12913)***
Allied Disc Grinding ..... F 209 339-0333
2478 Maggio Cir Ste A Lodi (95240) ***(P-16253)***
Allied Drapery Services Inc ..... F 408 293-1600
365 Lincoln Ave San Jose (95126) ***(P-3688)***
Allied Dvbe Inc ..... F 619 690-4900
260 Bonita Glen Dr Apt V3 Chula Vista (91910) ***(P-3050)***
Allied Dvbe Supply, Chula Vista *Also called Allied Dvbe Inc* ***(P-3050)***
Allied Electric Motor Svc Inc ..... F 559 486-4222
2635 S Sierra Vista Ave Fresno (93725) ***(P-25451)***
Allied Electronic Services ..... F 714 245-2500
1342 E Borchard Ave Santa Ana (92705) ***(P-18412)***
Allied Engineering & Prod Corp (PA) ..... E 510 522-1500
2421 Blanding Ave Alameda (94501) ***(P-16254)***
Allied Engrg & Consulting, Bakersfield *Also called Tringen Corporation* ***(P-285)***
Allied Feather & Down Corp (PA) ..... E 323 581-5677
6905 W Acco St Ste A Montebello (90640) ***(P-24031)***
Allied Fitting LP ..... F 909 390-0101
11040 Inland Ave Mira Loma (91752) ***(P-13093)***
Allied Harbor Aerospace Fas, Corona *Also called All Manufacturers Inc* ***(P-22325)***
Allied International, Sylmar *Also called AWI Acquisition Company* ***(P-13921)***
Allied Litho Products, Los Angeles *Also called Allied Pressroom Products Inc* ***(P-23704)***
Allied Mdular Bldg Systems Inc (PA) ..... E 714 516-1188
642 W Nicolas Ave Orange (92868) ***(P-12914)***
Allied Mechanical Products, Ontario *Also called Tower Mechanical Products Inc* ***(P-21444)***
Allied Mechanical Products, Ontario *Also called Tower Industries Inc* ***(P-17005)***
Allied Pressroom Products Inc ..... F 323 266-6250
3546 Emery St Los Angeles (90023) ***(P-23704)***
Allied Printing Company ..... F 916 442-1373
1912 O St Sacramento (95811) ***(P-6650)***
Allied Signal Aerospace, Torrance *Also called Alliedsignal Arospc Svc Corp* ***(P-11768)***
Allied Telesis Inc ..... D 408 519-6700
468 S Abbott Ave Milpitas (95035) ***(P-15662)***
Allied Telesis Inc ..... E 408 519-8700
3041 Orchard Pkwy San Jose (95134) ***(P-15663)***
Allied Telesis Inc ..... E 408 519-8700
3041 Orchard Pkwy San Jose (95134) ***(P-15664)***
Allied West Paper Corp ..... D 909 349-0710
11101 Etiwanda Ave # 100 Fontana (92337) ***(P-5661)***
Alliedsignal Arospc Svc Corp (HQ) ..... E 310 323-9500
2525 W 190th St Torrance (90504) ***(P-11768)***
Alling Iron Works, West Sacramento *Also called Carter Group* ***(P-12132)***
Allison-Kaufman Co ..... D 818 373-5100
7640 Haskell Ave Van Nuys (91406) ***(P-23231)***
Allman Products Inc ..... E 818 715-0093
21251 Deering Ct Canoga Park (91304) ***(P-9814)***
Alloy De Casting Co, Buena Park *Also called Alloy Die Casting Co* ***(P-11685)***
Alloy Die Casting Co ..... B 714 521-9800
6550 Caballero Blvd Buena Park (90620) ***(P-11685)***
Alloy Machining and Honing Inc ..... F 323 726-8248
2808 Supply Ave Commerce (90040) ***(P-16255)***
Alloy Machining Services Inc ..... F 323 725-2545
2808 Supply Ave Commerce (90040) ***(P-16256)***
Alloy Metal Products, Livermore *Also called Fred Matter Inc* ***(P-16515)***
Alloy Processing, Compton *Also called Kens Spray Equipment Inc* ***(P-13608)***
Alloy Tech Electropolishing ..... F 714 434-6604
2220 S Huron Dr Santa Ana (92704) ***(P-13320)***
Allpakfoam & Packaging ..... F 818 917-5660
20302 Clark St Woodland Hills (91367) ***(P-9815)***
Allstar Microelectronics Inc ..... F 949 546-0888
30191 Avendia De Las Rancho Santa Margari (92688) ***(P-15509)***
Allstarshop.com, Rancho Santa Margari *Also called Allstar Microelectronics Inc* ***(P-15509)***
Allstate Plastics LLC ..... F 510 783-9600
1763 Sabre St Hayward (94545) ***(P-5586)***

A L P H A B E T I C

Employee Codes: A=Over 500 employees, B=251-500
C=101-250, D=51-100, E=20-50, F=10-19
2019 California
Manfacturers Register
© Mergent Inc. 1-800-342-5647
1053

Alltec Integrated Mfg Inc.....E.....805 595-3500
2240 S Thornburg St Santa Maria (93455) ***(P-9935)***
Allteq Industries Inc.....F.....925 833-7666
215 Rustic Pl San Ramon (94582) ***(P-18681)***
Allura Printing Inc.....F.....714 433-0200
185 Paularino Ave Ste B Costa Mesa (92626) ***(P-6651)***
Allure Labs Inc.....E.....510 489-8896
30901 Wiegman Ct Hayward (94544) ***(P-8692)***
Alluxa Inc.....E.....707 284-1040
3660 N Laughlin Rd Santa Rosa (95403) ***(P-22058)***
Allvia Inc.....E.....408 720-3333
657 N Pastoria Ave Sunnyvale (94085) ***(P-18682)***
Allwire Inc.....E.....559 665-4893
16395 Avenue 24 1/2 Chowchilla (93610) ***(P-9774)***
Ally Enterprises.....E.....661 412-9933
5001 E Commercecenter Dr Bakersfield (93309) ***(P-165)***
Allyn James Inc.....F.....925 828-5530
6575 Trinity Ct Ste B Dublin (94568) ***(P-6652)***
Allyo, Sunnyvale *Also called Sass Labs Inc* ***(P-25149)***
Alm Chrome.....E.....714 545-3540
654 Young St Santa Ana (92705) ***(P-13321)***
Alm Media Holdings Inc.....E.....415 490-1054
1035 Market St Ste 500 San Francisco (94103) ***(P-6101)***
Alma Rosa Winery Vineyards LLC (PA).....F.....805 688-9090
181 Industrial Way Ste C Buellton (93427) ***(P-1642)***
Almac Felt Co, Granada Hills *Also called Almac Fixture & Supply Co* ***(P-2985)***
Almac Fixture & Supply Co.....E.....818 360-1706
12932 Jolette Ave Granada Hills (91344) ***(P-2985)***
Almack Liners Inc.....E.....818 718-5878
9541 Cozycroft Ave Chatsworth (91311) ***(P-3291)***
Almaden Press, Santa Clara *Also called Stone Publishing Inc* ***(P-6591)***
Almaden Valley Printing Co.....F.....408 288-6886
16570 Church St Ste 105 Morgan Hill (95037) ***(P-6653)***
Almatron Electronics Inc.....E.....714 557-6000
644 Young St Santa Ana (92705) ***(P-18413)***
Almond Company.....D.....559 665-4405
22782 Road 9 Chowchilla (93610) ***(P-1480)***
Almond Valley Nut Co.....E.....209 480-7300
11255 E Whitmore Ave Denair (95316) ***(P-1481)***
Almore Dye House Inc.....E.....818 506-5444
6850 Tujunga Ave North Hollywood (91605) ***(P-2908)***
Alms Company, Gold River *Also called Markes International Inc* ***(P-21989)***
Alna Envelope Company Inc.....E.....323 235-3161
1567 E 25th St Los Angeles (90011) ***(P-7197)***
Aloha, Fremont *Also called Air Liquide Electronics US LP* ***(P-7750)***
Aloha Bay.....E.....707 994-3267
16275 A Main St Lower Lake (95457) ***(P-24032)***
Alona Apparel Inc.....F.....323 232-1548
1651 Mateo St Los Angeles (90021) ***(P-3132)***
Alor International Ltd.....E.....858 454-0011
4330 La Jolla Village Dr # 100 San Diego (92122) ***(P-23232)***
Alpena Sausage Inc.....F.....818 505-9482
5329 Craner Ave North Hollywood (91601) ***(P-462)***
Alpenhorn Crestline Chronicle.....E.....909 338-8484
23570 Knapps Cutoff Crestline (92325) ***(P-5756)***
Alpha Alarm & Audio Inc.....F.....707 452-8334
1400 Belden Ct Dixon (95620) ***(P-17757)***
Alpha and Omega Semicdtr Inc (HQ).....C.....408 789-0008
475 Oakmead Pkwy Sunnyvale (94085) ***(P-18683)***
Alpha Aviation Components Inc (PA).....E.....818 894-8801
16772 Schoenborn St North Hills (91343) ***(P-16257)***
Alpha Aviation Components Inc.....F.....818 894-8468
16774 Schoenborn St North Hills (91343) ***(P-16258)***
Alpha Corporation of Tennessee.....D.....951 657-5161
19991 Seaton Ave Perris (92570) ***(P-7818)***
Alpha Dental of Utah Inc.....E.....562 467-7759
12898 Towne Center Dr Cerritos (90703) ***(P-22855)***
Alpha Dyno Nobel.....F.....661 824-1356
1682 Sabovich St 30a Mojave (93501) ***(P-9181)***
Alpha Ems Corporation.....C.....510 498-8788
44193 S Grimmer Blvd Fremont (94538) ***(P-18414)***
Alpha Explosives, Mojave *Also called Alpha Dyno Nobel* ***(P-9181)***
Alpha Grinding Inc.....F.....562 803-1509
12402 Benedict Ave Downey (90242) ***(P-16259)***
Alpha I Publishing Inc.....F.....909 862-9572
28400 Coachman Ln Highland (92346) ***(P-6428)***
Alpha Impressions Inc.....F.....323 234-8221
4161 S Main St Los Angeles (90037) ***(P-3874)***
Alpha Laser.....F.....951 582-0285
302 Elizabeth Ln Corona (92880) ***(P-19906)***
Alpha Machine Company Inc.....F.....831 462-7400
933 Chittenden Ln Ste A Capitola (95010) ***(P-16260)***
Alpha Magnetics Inc.....F.....510 732-6698
23453 Bernhardt St Hayward (94545) ***(P-13915)***
Alpha Materials Inc.....E.....951 788-5150
6170 20th St Riverside (92509) ***(P-11038)***
Alpha Omega Swiss Inc.....E.....714 692-8009
23305 La Palma Ave Yorba Linda (92887) ***(P-13010)***
Alpha Omega Winery LLC.....F.....707 963-9999
1155 Mee Ln Rutherford (94573) ***(P-1643)***
Alpha Polishing Corporation (PA).....D.....323 263-7593
1313 Mirasol St Los Angeles (90023) ***(P-13322)***
Alpha Printing & Graphics Inc.....E.....626 851-9800
12758 Schabarum Ave Irwindale (91706) ***(P-6654)***
Alpha Productions Incorporated.....E.....310 559-1364
5830 W Jefferson Blvd Los Angeles (90016) ***(P-12474)***
Alpha Products Inc.....E.....805 981-8666
351 Irving Dr Oxnard (93030) ***(P-19372)***
Alpha Publishing Corporation.....E.....909 464-0500
337 N Vineyard Ave # 240 Ontario (91764) ***(P-6306)***
Alpha Research & Tech Inc.....D.....916 431-9340
5175 Hillsdale Cir # 100 El Dorado Hills (95762) ***(P-15389)***
Alpha Scientific Elec Inc.....F.....510 782-4747
2727 Boeing Way Stockton (95206) ***(P-19439)***
Alpha Sensors Inc.....E.....949 250-6578
125 S Tremont St Ste 100 Oceanside (92054) ***(P-21545)***
Alpha Signs Inc.....F.....916 379-0225
8565 23rd Ave Sacramento (95826) ***(P-23813)***
Alpha Source Inc.....E.....310 515-5560
2415 S Sequoia Dr Compton (90220) ***(P-2820)***
Alpha Technics, Oceanside *Also called Alpha Sensors Inc* ***(P-21545)***
Alpha Technics Inc.....C.....949 250-6578
125 S Tremont St Ste 100 Oceanside (92054) ***(P-22159)***
Alpha Wire Corporation.....A.....310 639-9473
1048 E Burgrove St Carson (90746) ***(P-11642)***
Alpha-Owens Corning, Perris *Also called Alpha Corporation of Tennessee* ***(P-7818)***
Alphabet Lighting.....F.....714 259-0990
15774 Gateway Cir Tustin (92780) ***(P-17581)***
Alphacast Foundry Inc.....F.....213 624-7156
826 S Santa Fe Ave Los Angeles (90021) ***(P-11686)***
Alphacoat Finishing LLC.....E.....949 748-7796
9350 Cabot Dr San Diego (92126) ***(P-13323)***
AlphaGraphics, Sunnyvale *Also called Jsl Partners Inc* ***(P-6916)***
AlphaGraphics, Modesto *Also called Batchlder Bus Cmmnications Inc* ***(P-6686)***
AlphaGraphics, Brea *Also called Herrick Retail Corporation Th* ***(P-6856)***
AlphaGraphics, Roseville *Also called Print & Mail Solutions Inc* ***(P-7038)***
Alphalogix Inc.....D.....714 901-1456
5811 Mcfadden Ave Huntington Beach (92649) ***(P-19855)***
Alphascript Inc.....F.....650 654-2103
1160 Industrial Rd Ste 17 San Carlos (94070) ***(P-8016)***
Alphatec Holdings Inc (PA).....E.....760 431-9286
5818 El Camino Real Carlsbad (92008) ***(P-22328)***
Alphatec Spine Inc (HQ).....C.....760 494-6610
5818 El Camino Real Carlsbad (92008) ***(P-22695)***
Alphatec Spine Inc.....F.....760 431-9286
2150 Palomar Airport Rd Carlsbad (92011) ***(P-22696)***
Alphena Technologies.....F.....626 961-6098
414 Cloverleaf Dr Ste B Baldwin Park (91706) ***(P-9936)***
Alpine Biomed Corp.....C.....650 802-0400
1501 Industrial Rd San Carlos (94070) ***(P-22329)***
Alpine Industries.....F.....530 926-2460
5820 Serrano Dr Mount Shasta (96067) ***(P-13163)***
Alpine Marble.....F.....714 704-9030
917 E Katella Ave Anaheim (92805) ***(P-11228)***
Alpine Meats Inc.....E.....209 477-2691
9850 Lower Sacramento Rd Stockton (95210) ***(P-463)***
Alpine Metals, South Lake Tahoe *Also called Terri Bell* ***(P-25441)***
Alpinestars USA.....F.....310 891-0222
2780 W 237th St Torrance (90505) ***(P-3092)***
Alro Cstm Drapery Installation.....F.....650 847-4343
809 San Antonio Rd Ste 1 Palo Alto (94303) ***(P-5179)***
Alros Label Co Inc.....F.....818 781-2403
14200 Aetna St Van Nuys (91401) ***(P-7232)***
Alros Lebel Co, Van Nuys *Also called Alros Label Co Inc* ***(P-7232)***
Als Garden Art Inc (PA).....B.....909 424-0221
311 W Citrus St Colton (92324) ***(P-11344)***
Alsop Electric Motor Shop, Salinas *Also called Alsop Pump* ***(P-25452)***
Alsop Pump.....F.....831 424-3946
1508 Abbott St Salinas (93901) ***(P-25452)***
Alstom Signaling Operation LLC.....C.....951 343-9699
7337 Central Ave Riverside (92504) ***(P-18307)***
Alston Tascom Inc.....E.....909 517-3660
5171 Edison Ave Ste C Chino (91710) ***(P-17920)***
Alstyle AP & Activewear MGT Co (HQ).....A.....714 765-0400
1501 E Cerritos Ave Anaheim (92805) ***(P-2821)***
Alstyle AP & Activewear MGT Co.....F.....714 765-0400
1501 E Cerritos Ave Anaheim (92805) ***(P-2822)***
Alstyle Apparel, Mira Loma *Also called A and G Inc* ***(P-3129)***
Alstyle Apparel LLC.....A.....714 765-0400
1501 E Cerritos Ave Anaheim (92805) ***(P-2718)***
Alstyle Dyeing & Finishing, Anaheim *Also called A and G Inc* ***(P-2788)***
Alstyle Dyeing & Finishing, Anaheim *Also called Alstyle AP & Activewear MGT Co* ***(P-2822)***
Alta Advanced Technologies Inc.....E.....909 983-2973
760 E Sunkist St Ontario (91761) ***(P-8525)***
Alta Design and Manufacturing.....F.....408 450-5394
885 Auzerais Ave San Jose (95126) ***(P-16261)***
Alta Devices Inc.....C.....408 988-8600
545 Oakmead Pkwy Sunnyvale (94085) ***(P-18684)***
Alta Industries, Santa Rosa *Also called Stx Inc* ***(P-23663)***
Alta Manufacturing Inc.....E.....510 668-1870
47650 Westinghouse Dr Fremont (94539) ***(P-18415)***
Alta Motors, Brisbane *Also called Faster Faster Inc* ***(P-20332)***
Alta Properties Inc.....B.....805 683-1431
879 Ward Dr Santa Barbara (93111) ***(P-19907)***
Alta Properties Inc.....B.....805 683-2575
869 Ward Dr Santa Barbara (93111) ***(P-21717)***
Alta Properties Inc.....B.....805 690-5382
879 Ward Dr Santa Barbara (93111) ***(P-19908)***
Alta Properties Inc.....B.....805 967-0171
839 Ward Dr Santa Barbara (93111) ***(P-10815)***
Alta Properties Inc (PA).....C.....805 967-0171
879 Ward Dr Santa Barbara (93111) ***(P-10816)***
Alta Solutions Inc.....F.....858 668-5200
12580 Stowe Dr Poway (92064) ***(P-21718)***
Alta-Dena Certified Dairy LLC.....C.....805 685-8328
123 Aero Camino Goleta (93117) ***(P-709)***
Alta-Dena Certified Dairy LLC.....C.....800 395-7004
17851 Railroad St City of Industry (91748) ***(P-710)***

Alta-Dena Certified Dairy LLC (HQ)....B....626 964-6401
17637 E Valley Blvd City of Industry (91744) *(P-711)*
Altaflex....D....408 727-6614
336 Martin Ave Santa Clara (95050) *(P-18416)*
Altair Lighting, Comptcn *Also called Jimway Inc (P-17705)*
Altair Technologies Inc....E....650 508-8700
41970 Christy St Fremont (94538) *(P-14905)*
Altamont Manufacturing Inc....F....925 371-5401
241 Rickenbacker Cir Livermore (94551) *(P-14360)*
Altasens Inc (HQ)....E....818 338-9400
2201 E Dominguez St Long Beach (90810) *(P-18685)*
Altaviz LLC (PA)....F....949 656-4003
13766 Alton Pkwy Ste 143 Irvine (92618) *(P-8017)*
Altec Industries Inc....F....707 678-0800
1450 N 1st St Dixon (95620) *(P-20187)*
Altec Industries Inc....D....707 678-0800
325 Industrial Way Dixon (95620) *(P-14140)*
Altera Corporation (HQ)....B....408 544-7000
101 Innovation Dr San Jose (95134) *(P-18686)*
Alterg Inc....D....510 270-5900
48368 Milmont Dr Fremont (94538) *(P-23497)*
Altergy Systems....E....916 458-8590
140 Blue Ravine Rd Folsom (95630) *(P-17329)*
Alternative Hose Inc (PA)....F....714 414-0904
1251 N Sunshine Way Ste B Anaheim (92806) *(P-13736)*
Alternators Starters Etc....F....408 559-3540
1360 White Oaks Rd Ste H Campbell (95008) *(P-19826)*
Altest Corporation....E....408 436-9900
898 Faulstich Ct San Jose (95112) *(P-16262)*
Althea Ajinomoto Inc....C....858 882-0123
11040 Roselle St San Diego (92121) *(P-22330)*
Altia Systems Inc....F....408 996-9710
10020 N De Anza Blvd # 200 Cupertino (95014) *(P-23138)*
Altierre Corporation....E....408 435-7343
1980 Concourse Dr San Jose (95131) *(P-18687)*
Altigen Communications Inc....C....408 597-9000
679 River Oaks Pkwy San Jose (95134) *(P-17921)*
Altinex Inc....E....714 990-0877
592 Apollo St Ste A Brea (92821) *(P-18026)*
Altium LLC....D....800 544-4186
4275 Executive Sq Ste 825 La Jolla (92037) *(P-24354)*
Altmans Products LLC....E....310 559-4093
7136 Kittyhawk Ave Apt 4 Los Angeles (90045) *(P-12013)*
Alto Rey, North Hollywood *Also called Lookout Enterprises Inc (P-2395)*
Altro Usa Inc....F....562 944-8292
12648 Clark St Santa Fe Springs (90670) *(P-24013)*
Alts Tool & Machine Inc (PA)....D....619 562-6653
10926 Woodside Ave N Santee (92071) *(P-16263)*
Altura Pharmaceuticals Inc....E....562 906-9000
12540 Mccann Dr Santa Fe Springs (90670) *(P-8018)*
Alturdyne Power Systems Inc....E....619 343-3204
1405 N Johnson Ave El Cajon (92020) *(P-13987)*
Altus Positioning Systems Inc....F....310 541-8139
20725 S Wstn Ave Ste 100 Torrance (90501) *(P-14597)*
Alu Menziken, Anaheim *Also called Universal Alloy Corporation (P-11608)*
Alum-A-Coat, El Monte *Also called Santoshi Corporation (P-13500)*
Alum-A-Therm, Westminster *Also called Bodycote Imt Inc (P-11795)*
Alum-Alloy Coinc....E....909 986-0410
603 S Hope Ave Ontario (91761) *(P-13119)*
Aluma USA Inc....E....707 545-9344
435 Tesconi Cir Santa Rosa (95401) *(P-23233)*
Alumafab....F....562 630-6440
14335 Iseli Rd Santa Fe Springs (90670) *(P-17582)*
Alumatec Inc....D....818 609-7460
18411 Sherman Way Reseda (91335) *(P-95)*
Alumatherm Incorporated....F....510 832-2819
1717 Kirkham St Oakland (94607) *(P-12291)*
Alumawall Inc....D....408 275-7165
1701 S 7th St Ste 9 San Jose (95112) *(P-12915)*
Alumax Building Products, Sun City *Also called Omnimax International Inc (P-12338)*
Alumen-8, Oceanside *Also called Amerillum LLC (P-17672)*
Alumflam North America....E....562 926-9520
16604 Edwards Rd Cerritos (90703) *(P-13324)*
Alumin-Art Plating Co Inc....E....909 983-1866
803 W State St Ontario (91762) *(P-13325)*
Aluminum Casting Company, Santa Fe Springs *Also called Employee Owned Pacific Cast PR (P-11740)*
Aluminum Coating Tech Inc....E....916 442-1063
8290 Alpine Ave Sacramento (95826) *(P-13326)*
Aluminum Die Casting Co Inc....D....951 681-3900
10775 San Sevaine Way Mira Loma (91752) *(P-11687)*
Aluminum Precision Pdts Inc....C....805 488-4401
1001 Mcwane Blvd Oxnard (93033) *(P-13120)*
Aluminum Precision Pdts Inc....D....714 549-4075
502 E Alton Ave Santa Ana (92707) *(P-13121)*
Aluminum Pros Inc....F....310 366-7696
13917 S Main St Los Angeles (90061) *(P-14831)*
Aluminum Seating Inc....F....909 884-9449
555 Tennis Court Ln San Bernardino (92408) *(P-5007)*
Aluminum Tube Railings, Pomona *Also called Atr Technologies Incorporated (P-12834)*
Alumistar Inc....E....562 633-6673
12711 Imperial Hwy Santa Fe Springs (90670) *(P-11723)*
Aluratek Inc....E....949 468-2046
15241 Barranca Pkwy Irvine (92618) *(P-17758)*
Alva Manufacturing Inc....E....714 237-0925
236 E Orangethorpe Ave Placentia (92870) *(P-13011)*
Alvarado Alta Calidad LLC....F....323 222-0038
2907 Humboldt St Los Angeles (90031) *(P-4904)*
Alvarado Alta Clidad Cstm Furn, Los Angeles *Also called Alvarado Alta Calidad LLC (P-4904)*
Alvarado Dye & Knitting Mill....E....510 324-8892
30542 Union City Blvd Union City (94587) *(P-3093)*
Alvarado Manufacturing Co Inc....D....909 591-8431
12660 Colony Ct Chino (91710) *(P-22160)*
Alvarado Micro Precision Inc....F....760 598-0186
2389 La Mirada Dr Ste 9 Vista (92081) *(P-14361)*
Alvarez Refinishing Inc....E....714 780-0171
23 W Romneya Dr Anaheim (92801) *(P-2900)*
Alvellan Inc....E....925 689-2421
1030 Shary Ct Concord (94518) *(P-16264)*
Alventive Inc (PA)....D....408 969-8000
2790 Walsh Ave Santa Clara (95051) *(P-24355)*
Alvin D Troyer and Associates....F....650 574-0167
310 Shaw Rd Ste F South San Francisco (94080) *(P-11926)*
Alyn Industries Inc....D....818 988-7696
16028 Arminta St Van Nuys (91406) *(P-19440)*
Alza Corporation (HQ)....A....707 453-6400
700 Eubanks Dr Vacaville (95688) *(P-8019)*
Alza Corporation....A....650 564-5000
1010 Joaquin Rd Mountain View (94043) *(P-21899)*
Alza Corporation....A....707 453-6400
700 Eubanks Dr Vacaville (95688) *(P-21900)*
Alza Pharmaceuticals, Vacaville *Also called Alza Corporation (P-8019)*
Alziebler Incorporated (PA)....F....800 430-7536
12734 Branford St Ste 12 Arleta (91331) *(P-16265)*
Alziebler Jos Co, Arleta *Also called Alziebler Incorporated (P-16265)*
AM and S Mfg Inc....F....800 519-5709
1283 Old Mountain View Al Sunnyvale (94089) *(P-16266)*
AM&s Design, Santa Clara *Also called AM&s Mfg Inc (P-13808)*
AM&s Mfg Inc....F....800 519-5709
498 Sapena Ct Santa Clara (95054) *(P-13808)*
AM&s Mnufactruing Design Group, Sunnyvale *Also called AM and S Mfg Inc (P-16266)*
Am-Par Manufacturing Co Inc....F....530 671-1800
959 Von Geldern Way Yuba City (95991) *(P-16267)*
Am-Tek Engineering Inc....F....909 673-1633
1180 E Francis St Ste C Ontario (91761) *(P-16268)*
AMA Plastics (PA)....B....951 734-5600
1100 Citrus St Riverside (92507) *(P-9937)*
Amada Miyachi America Inc (HQ)....C....626 303-5676
1820 S Myrtle Ave Monrovia (91016) *(P-14719)*
Amada Miyachi America Inc....E....626 303-5676
245 E El Norte St Monrovia (91016) *(P-22331)*
Amador Transit Mix Inc....E....209 223-0406
12480 Ridge Rd Sutter Creek (95685) *(P-11039)*
Amag Technology Inc (HQ)....E....310 518-2380
20701 Manhattan Pl Torrance (90501) *(P-15665)*
Amanet, Canoga Park *Also called American Mfg Netwrk Inc (P-16271)*
Amaretto Orchards LLC....E....661 399-9697
32331 Famoso Woody Rd Mc Farland (93250) *(P-24033)*
Amarillo Wind Machine LLC....F....559 592-4256
20513 Avenue 256 Exeter (93221) *(P-14040)*
Amark Industries Inc (PA)....C....951 654-7351
600 W Esplanade Ave San Jacinto (92583) *(P-15250)*
Amato Beverly Hills, Beverly Hills *Also called Rare Elements Hair Care (P-24220)*
Amays Bakery & Noodle Co Inc (PA)....D....213 626-2713
837 E Commercial St Los Angeles (90012) *(P-1347)*
Amazing Facts Inc....D....916 434-3880
1203 W Sunset Blvd Rocklin (95765) *(P-6307)*
Amazing Facts Ministries, Rocklin *Also called Amazing Facts Inc (P-6307)*
Amazing Steel, Montclair *Also called Mitchell Fabrication (P-12212)*
Amazing Steel Company....E....909 590-0393
4564 Mission Blvd Montclair (91763) *(P-12111)*
Amazon Environmental Inc (PA)....E....951 588-0206
779 Palmyrita Ave Riverside (92507) *(P-8875)*
Amazon Paint, Riverside *Also called Amazon Environmental Inc (P-8875)*
Amazon Prsrvation Partners Inc....E....415 775-6355
1501a Vermont St San Francisco (94107) *(P-784)*
Ambarella Inc....A....408 734-8888
3101 Jay St Santa Clara (95054) *(P-18688)*
Ambassador Industries (PA)....F....213 383-1171
2754 W Temple St Los Angeles (90026) *(P-5180)*
Ambay Circuits Inc....F....818 786-8241
16117 Leadwell St Van Nuys (91406) *(P-18417)*
Amber Foods Inc....D....559 591-4782
301 N M St Dinuba (93618) *(P-2450)*
Amber Steel Co., Rialto *Also called H Wayne Lewis Inc (P-12979)*
Amberwood Installation, San Jose *Also called Amberwood Products Inc (P-4269)*
Amberwood Products Inc....C....408 938-1600
1555 S 7th St Bldg 7 San Jose (95112) *(P-4269)*
Ambiance Apparel, Los Angeles *Also called Ambiance USA Inc (P-3372)*
Ambiance USA Inc (PA)....F....323 587-0007
2415 E 15th St Los Angeles (90021) *(P-3372)*
Ambios Technology Inc (PA)....E....831 427-1160
1 Technology Dr Milpitas (95035) *(P-21901)*
Ambit Biosciences Corporation....D....858 334-2100
10201 Wtridge Cir Ste 200 San Diego (92121) *(P-8020)*
Ambrit Engineering Corporation....D....714 557-1074
2640 Halladay St Santa Ana (92705) *(P-14475)*
Ambrit Industries Inc....E....818 243-1224
432 Magnolia Ave Glendale (91204) *(P-14427)*
Ambrx Inc....D....858 875-2400
10975 N Torrey Pines Rd # 100 La Jolla (92037) *(P-8021)*
AMC, Stanton *Also called All Metals Proc San Diego Inc (P-13317)*
AMC, Sylmar *Also called Advanced Mnlythic Ceramics Inc (P-19289)*
AMC Machining Inc....E....805 238-5452
1540 Commerce Way Paso Robles (93446) *(P-12971)*

ALPHABETIC

Employee Codes: A=Over 500 employees, B=251-500
C=101-250, D=51-100, E=20-50, F=10-19
2019 California
Manfacturers Register
© Mergent Inc. 1-800-342-5647
1055

Amcan Beverages Inc ...C ...707 557-0500
1201 Commerce Blvd American Canyon (94503) ***(P-2081)***
Amcan Usa LLC ...F ...858 587-1032
8970 Crestmar Pt San Diego (92121) ***(P-15510)***
Amcc Sales, Santa Clara *Also called Applied Micro Circuits Corp* ***(P-18712)***
Amcells, Vista *Also called Acells Corp* ***(P-21892)***
Amcor Flexibles LLC ...C ...707 257-6481
5425 Broadway St American Canyon (94503) ***(P-5516)***
Amcor Flexibles LLC ...C ...323 721-6777
5416 Union Pacific Ave Commerce (90022) ***(P-5517)***
Amcor Industries Inc ...E ...323 585-2852
2011 E 49th St Vernon (90058) ***(P-20251)***
Amcor Manufacturing Inc ...E ...209 581-9687
500 Winmoore Way Modesto (95358) ***(P-7751)***
Amcor Rigid Plastics Usa LLC ...F ...520 746-0737
14270 Ramona Ave Chino (91710) ***(P-9938)***
Amcor Rigid Plastics Usa LLC ...C ...909 517-2700
14270 Ramona Ave Chino (91710) ***(P-9792)***
AMD International Sls Svc Ltd (HQ) ...E ...408 749-4000
1 Amd Pl Sunnyvale (94085) ***(P-18689)***
AMD International Tech LLC ...E ...909 985-8300
1725 S Campus Ave Ontario (91761) ***(P-12475)***
AMD Ventures LLC ...C ...408 749-4000
1 Amd Pl Sunnyvale (94085) ***(P-18690)***
Ameba Technology Inc ...F ...626 575-8811
4700 Miller Dr Ste B5 Temple City (91780) ***(P-18027)***
Amedica Biotech Inc ...F ...510 785-5980
28301 Industrial Blvd K Hayward (94545) ***(P-22332)***
Ameditech Inc ...C ...858 535-1968
9940 Mesa Rim Rd San Diego (92121) ***(P-22333)***
Amera Machine Inc ...F ...626 577-2819
271 California Ter Pasadena (91105) ***(P-15194)***
Ameramatic Vtech LLC ...F ...760 688-8561
2880 Scott St Ste 106 Vista (92081) ***(P-2703)***
Amerasia Furniture Components ...E ...310 638-0570
2772 Norton Ave Lynwood (90262) ***(P-4759)***
Amergence Technology Inc ...E ...909 859-8400
295 Brea Canyon Rd Walnut (91789) ***(P-14906)***
Ameri-Fax, Orange *Also called Positive Concepts Inc* ***(P-5726)***
America Asia Trade Promotion ...F ...408 970-8868
4633 Old Ironsides Dr # 400 Santa Clara (95054) ***(P-3705)***
America Asian Trade Assn Prom ...D ...408 588-0008
4633 Old Ironside Ste 308 Santa Rosa (95404) ***(P-17583)***
America Manufacturing, Rancho Cucamonga *Also called Mape Engineering Inc* ***(P-20669)***
America Mountain Wldg Inds Inc ...F ...626 698-8066
1613 Chelsea Rd Ste 208 San Marino (91108) ***(P-14720)***
America Printing, Burlingame *Also called Asia America Enterprise Inc* ***(P-6669)***
America Techcode Semicdtr Inc ...E ...408 910-2028
10456 San Fernando Ave Cupertino (95014) ***(P-18691)***
America Wood Finishes Inc ...F ...323 232-8256
728 E 59th St Los Angeles (90001) ***(P-8876)***
American & Efird LLC ...D ...323 724-6884
6098 Rickenbacker Rd Commerce (90040) ***(P-2951)***
American Acrylic Display Inc ...F ...714 738-7990
1061 S Leslie St La Habra (90631) ***(P-23814)***
American Activated Carbon Corp ...F ...310 491-2842
7310 Deering Ave Canoga Park (91303) ***(P-17233)***
American Aerospace Pdts Inc ...F ...714 662-7620
1720 S Santa Fe St Santa Ana (92705) ***(P-12476)***
American Air Liquide Inc (HQ) ...D ...510 624-4000
46409 Landing Pkwy Fremont (94538) ***(P-7689)***
American Aircraft Products Inc ...D ...310 532-7434
15411 S Broadway Gardena (90248) ***(P-12477)***
American Alupack Inds LLC ...E ...805 485-1500
1201 N Rice Ave Oxnard (93030) ***(P-11574)***
American AP Dyg & Finshg Inc ...D ...310 644-4001
747 Warehouse St Los Angeles (90021) ***(P-2789)***
American Apparel, Los Angeles *Also called App Winddown LLC* ***(P-3643)***
American Apparel (usa) LLC ...F ...213 488-0226
747 Warehouse St Los Angeles (90021) ***(P-3638)***
American Apparel ACC Inc (PA) ...E ...626 350-3828
10160 Olney St El Monte (91731) ***(P-9939)***
American Apparel Retail Inc (HQ) ...E ...213 488-0226
747 Warehouse St Los Angeles (90021) ***(P-2719)***
American Audio Component Inc ...E ...909 596-3788
20 Fairbanks Ste 198 Irvine (92618) ***(P-19441)***
American Automated Engrg Inc ...D ...714 898-9951
5382 Argosy Ave Huntington Beach (92649) ***(P-21185)***
American Bath Factory, Corona *Also called Le Elegant Bath Inc* ***(P-9906)***
American Battery Charging Inc ...E ...401 231-5227
15272 Newsboy Cir Huntington Beach (92649) ***(P-17330)***
American Best Car Parts, Anaheim *Also called American Fabrication Corp* ***(P-20254)***
American Bicycle Security Co, Santa Paula *Also called Turtle Storage Ltd* ***(P-5173)***
American Biodiesel Inc ...F ...209 466-4823
809 Snedeker Ave Ste C Stockton (95203) ***(P-8976)***
American Bioscience, Santa Monica *Also called Abraxis Bioscience Inc* ***(P-7990)***
American Blast Systems Inc ...E ...949 244-6859
16182 Gothard St Ste H Huntington Beach (92647) ***(P-11377)***
American Blinds and Drap Inc ...E ...510 487-3500
30776 Huntwood Ave Hayward (94544) ***(P-3689)***
American Board Assembly Inc ...C ...805 523-0274
5456 Endeavour Ct Moorpark (93021) ***(P-18418)***
American Bottling Company ...E ...707 766-9750
2210 S Mcdowell Blvd Ext Petaluma (94954) ***(P-2082)***
American Bottling Company ...F ...707 462-8871
100 Wabash Ave Ukiah (95482) ***(P-2083)***
American Bottling Company ...E ...661 323-7921
230 E 18th St Bakersfield (93305) ***(P-2084)***
American Bottling Company ...D ...559 442-1553
2012 S Pearl St Fresno (93721) ***(P-2085)***
American Bottling Company ...D ...925 938-8777
1981 N Broadway Ste 215 Walnut Creek (94596) ***(P-2086)***
American Bottling Company ...C ...818 898-1471
1166 Arroyo St San Fernando (91340) ***(P-2087)***
American Bottling Company ...E ...805 928-1001
618 Hanson Way Santa Maria (93458) ***(P-2088)***
American Bottling Company ...B ...323 268-7779
3220 E 26th St Vernon (90058) ***(P-2089)***
American Bottling Company ...F ...916 929-3575
2720 Land Ave Sacramento (95815) ***(P-2090)***
American Bottling Company ...D ...916 929-7777
2670 Land Ave Sacramento (95815) ***(P-2091)***
American Bottling Company ...D ...831 632-0777
11205 Commercial Pkwy Castroville (95012) ***(P-2092)***
American Bottling Company ...D ...925 251-3001
6160 Stoneridge Mall Rd # 280 Pleasanton (94588) ***(P-2093)***
American Bow Thruster, Rohnert Park *Also called Arcturus Marine Systems* ***(P-13988)***
American Brass & Alum Fndry Co ...E ...800 545-9988
2060 Garfield Ave Commerce (90040) ***(P-12021)***
American Capacitor Corporation ...E ...626 814-4444
5367 3rd St Irwindale (91706) ***(P-19290)***
American Carousel, Laguna Niguel *Also called S & S Woodcarver Inc* ***(P-4650)***
American Carports Inc (PA) ...F ...866 730-9865
1415 Clay St Colusa (95932) ***(P-12916)***
American Carrier Equipment, Fresno *Also called Ace Trailer Co* ***(P-20492)***
American Carrier Systems ...D ...559 442-1500
2285 E Date Ave Fresno (93706) ***(P-20124)***
American Casting Co, Hollister *Also called Reed Manufacturing Inc* ***(P-11521)***
American Cellar Wine Club, Westlake Village *Also called American Clubs LLC* ***(P-6429)***
American Ceramic Technology (PA) ...F ...619 992-3104
12909 Lomas Verdes Dr Poway (92064) ***(P-22697)***
American Chain & Gear Company ...F ...323 581-9131
3370 Paseo Halcon San Clemente (92672) ***(P-15237)***
American Circuit Tech Inc (PA) ...E ...714 777-2480
5330 E Hunter Ave Anaheim (92807) ***(P-18419)***
American City Bus Journals Inc ...E ...916 447-7661
555 Capitol Mall Ste 200 Sacramento (95814) ***(P-5757)***
American Cleaner and Laundry ...E ...805 925-1571
2230 S Depot St Ste D Santa Maria (93455) ***(P-15927)***
American Clubs LLC ...F ...805 496-1218
4550 E Thousand Oaks Blvd Westlake Village (91362) ***(P-6429)***
American Cnc Inc ...F ...818 890-3400
12430 Montague St Ste 207 Pacoima (91331) ***(P-16269)***
American Coffee Urn Mfg Co Inc ...F ...951 943-1495
5178 Western Way Perris (92571) ***(P-12478)***
American Compaction Eqp Inc ...E ...949 661-2921
29380 Hunco Way Lake Elsinore (92530) ***(P-14141)***
American Concrete Products, Morgan Hill *Also called US Concrete Inc* ***(P-11014)***
American Consumer Products LLC ...E ...310 443-3330
23000 Avalon Blvd Carson (90745) ***(P-9219)***
American Containers Inc ...E ...209 460-1127
813 W Luce St Ste B Stockton (95203) ***(P-5383)***
American Costume Corp ...F ...818 432-4350
12980 Raymer St North Hollywood (91605) ***(P-3639)***
American Craftsmen Corporation ...F ...626 793-3329
273 N Hill Ave Pasadena (91106) ***(P-4667)***
American Crcuit Card Retainers ...F ...714 738-6194
2310 E Orangethorpe Ave Anaheim (92806) ***(P-15390)***
American Custom Coach Inc ...F ...909 796-4747
1255 W Colton Ave Redlands (92374) ***(P-20188)***
American Custom Golf Cars Inc ...F ...909 597-2885
15740 El Prado Rd Chino (91710) ***(P-20125)***
American Custom Meats LLC ...D ...209 839-8800
4276 N Tracy Blvd Tracy (95304) ***(P-464)***
American Cylinder Head Inc ...F ...510 261-1590
499 Lesser St Oakland (94601) ***(P-20252)***
American Cylndr Hd RPR/Excg ...F ...510 536-1764
499 Lesser St Oakland (94601) ***(P-20253)***
American Dart Lines, Santa Maria *Also called Bottelsen Dart Co Inc* ***(P-23411)***
American Dawn Inc (PA) ...D ...310 223-2000
401 W Artesia Blvd Compton (90220) ***(P-2986)***
American Deburring Inc ...E ...949 457-9790
20742 Linear Ln Lake Forest (92630) ***(P-16270)***
American Decal Company, Fountain Valley *Also called Tape Factory Inc* ***(P-5580)***
American Design Inc ...F ...619 429-1995
1672 Industrial Blvd Chula Vista (91911) ***(P-9940)***
American Designs, Los Angeles *Also called Kesmor Associates* ***(P-23281)***
American Die & Rollforming ...F ...916 652-7667
3495 Swetzer Rd Loomis (95650) ***(P-14476)***
American Die Casting Inc ...E ...909 356-7768
14576 Fontlee Ln Fontana (92335) ***(P-11709)***
American Electronics, Carson *Also called Ducommun Labarge Tech Inc* ***(P-20803)***
American Elements, Los Angeles *Also called Merelex Corporation* ***(P-7787)***
American Emperor Inc ...F ...510 536-6868
1900 E 12th St Oakland (94606) ***(P-11927)***
American Etal Technology, Fremont *Also called Axt Inc* ***(P-18738)***
American Etching & Mfg ...E ...323 875-3910
13730 Desmond St Pacoima (91331) ***(P-13548)***
American Fabrication, Bakersfield *Also called Russell Fabrication Corp* ***(P-13903)***
American Fabrication Corp (PA) ...C ...714 632-1709
2891 E Via Martens Anaheim (92806) ***(P-20254)***
American Fashion Group Inc (PA) ...F ...213 748-2100
1430 E Washington Blvd Los Angeles (90021) ***(P-3133)***
American Fine Arts Foundry LLC ...E ...818 848-7593
2520 N Ontario St Ste A Burbank (91504) ***(P-11753)***
American Fleet & Ret Graphics ...E ...909 937-7570
2091 Del Rio Way Ontario (91761) ***(P-23815)***

American Foam Fiber & Sups Inc ......D......626 969-7268
13280 Amar Rd City of Industry (91746) ***(P-2987)***
American Foil & Embosing Inc ......F......949 580-0080
35 Musick Irvine (92618) ***(P-7233)***
American Food Ingredients Inc ......E......760 967-6287
4021 Avenida Plata 501 Oceanside (92056) ***(P-873)***
American Fruits & Flavors LLC (HQ) ......C......818 899-9574
10725 Sutter Ave Pacoima (91331) ***(P-2240)***
American Fruits & Flavors LLC ......E......323 264-7791
1547 Knowles Ave Los Angeles (90063) ***(P-2241)***
American Furniture Aliance Inc ......F......323 804-5242
9141 Arrow Rte Rancho Cucamonga (91730) ***(P-4905)***
American Furniture Systems Inc ......E......626 457-9900
14105 Avalon Blvd Los Angeles (90061) ***(P-4975)***
American Garment Company ......F......562 483-8300
16230 Manning Way Cerritos (90703) ***(P-3640)***
American Garment Finishing ......E......310 962-1929
17941 Lost Canyon Rd # 6 Canyon Country (91387) ***(P-2773)***
American Garment Sewing, Pasadena *Also called AGS Usa LLC* ***(P-3290)***
American Gasket & Die Company ......F......408 441-6200
2275 Paragon Dr San Jose (95131) ***(P-9519)***
American General Tool Group ......E......760 745-7993
929 Poinsettia Ave # 101 Vista (92081) ***(P-9459)***
American Giant Inc ......F......415 529-2429
161 Natoma St Fl 2 San Francisco (94105) ***(P-3094)***
American Graphic Board Inc ......E......323 721-0585
5880 E Slauson Ave Commerce (90040) ***(P-5695)***
American Grip Inc ......E......818 768-8922
8468 Kewen Ave Sun Valley (91352) ***(P-17671)***
American Handgunner and Guns, San Diego *Also called Publishers Development Corp* ***(P-6238)***
American Hi-Tech Petro & Chem, Richmond *Also called Amtecol Inc* ***(P-9422)***
American Highway Technology, Modesto *Also called Dayton Superior Corporation* ***(P-14323)***
American Histology Reagent Co, Lodi *Also called American Mstr Tech Scntfic Inc* ***(P-22334)***
American Historic Inns Inc ......F......949 499-8070
249 Forest Ave Laguna Beach (92651) ***(P-6430)***
American Horse Products ......F......949 248-5300
31896 Plaza Dr Ste C4 San Juan Capistrano (92675) ***(P-3936)***
American Household Company, Commerce *Also called Housewares International Inc* ***(P-10141)***
American HX Auto Trade Inc ......D......909 484-1010
9373 Hyssop Dr Rancho Cucamonga (91730) ***(P-20126)***
American Imex, Irvine *Also called J F Fong Inc* ***(P-22499)***
American Index and Files LLC ......F......714 630-3360
2900 E Miraloma Ave Bc Anaheim (92806) ***(P-5696)***
American Induction Tech Inc ......F......714 456-1122
310 N Palm St Ste B Brea (92821) ***(P-15251)***
American Indus Systems Inc ......E......888 485-6688
1768 Mcgaw Ave Irvine (92614) ***(P-19442)***
American Industrial Corp ......F......714 680-4763
1624 N Orangethorpe Way Anaheim (92801) ***(P-14477)***
American Industrial Pump, Antioch *Also called Tomiko Inc* ***(P-15094)***
American Ingredients Inc ......F......714 630-6000
2929 E White Star Ave Anaheim (92806) ***(P-7921)***
American Innotek Inc (PA) ......D......760 741-6600
2655 Vsta Pcf Drv Ocnside Oceanside Oceanside (92056) ***(P-9941)***
American International Enginee ......E......818 365-8000
860 Arroyo St San Fernando (91340) ***(P-11724)***
American International Inds ......A......323 728-2999
2220 Gaspar Ave Commerce (90040) ***(P-8693)***
American International Mfg Co ......E......530 666-2446
1230 Fortna Ave Woodland (95776) ***(P-14041)***
American International Racing ......F......626 969-7733
1132 W Kirkwall Rd Azusa (91702) ***(P-9942)***
American Israel Public Affairs ......F......323 937-1184
1801 Century Park E # 600 Los Angeles (90067) ***(P-24356)***
American Lab and Systems, Los Angeles *Also called Mjw Inc* ***(P-15085)***
American Label Co, Cerritos *Also called American Non Stop Label Corp* ***(P-7234)***
American Lawyer Media, San Francisco *Also called Alm Media Holdings Inc* ***(P-6101)***
American Licorice Company ......B......510 487-5500
2477 Liston Way Union City (94587) ***(P-1407)***
American Linen Rental, Santa Maria *Also called American Cleaner and Laundry* ***(P-15927)***
American Liquid Packaging Syst (PA) ......E......408 524-7474
440 N Wolfe Rd Sunnyvale (94085) ***(P-7819)***
American Lithium Energy Corp ......F......760 599-7388
2261 Rutherford Rd Carlsbad (92008) ***(P-7752)***
American Lithographers Inc ......D......916 441-5392
2629 5th St Sacramento (95818) ***(P-6655)***
American Made Make Be-Leaves ......F......800 634-1402
5311 Derry Ave Ste C Agoura Hills (91301) ***(P-24034)***
American Maple Inc ......F......310 515-8881
14020 S Western Ave Gardena (90249) ***(P-23498)***
American Marble, Vista *Also called Kammerer Enterprises Inc* ***(P-11258)***
American Marble & Granite Co (PA) ......F......323 268-7979
4084 Whittier Blvd Los Angeles (90023) ***(P-11229)***
American Marble & Onyx Coinc ......E......323 776-0900
10321 S La Cienega Blvd Los Angeles (90045) ***(P-11230)***
American Medical Sales Inc ......E......310 471-8900
218 Bronwood Ave Los Angeles (90049) ***(P-22926)***
American Metal Bearing Company ......E......714 892-5527
7191 Acacia Ave Garden Grove (92841) ***(P-15104)***
American Metal Enterprises Inc ......F......714 894-6810
15855 Chemical Ln Huntington Beach (92649) ***(P-22698)***
American Metal Filter Company ......F......619 628-1917
611 Marsat Ct Chula Vista (91911) ***(P-15143)***
American Metal Processing ......E......619 444-6171
390 Front St El Cajon (92020) ***(P-12479)***
American Mfg Netwrk Inc ......F......818 786-1113
7001 Eton Ave Canoga Park (91303) ***(P-16271)***
American Modular Systems Inc ......D......209 825-1921
787 Spreckels Ave Manteca (95336) ***(P-4567)***
American Mstr Tech Scntfic Inc ......E......209 368-4031
1330 Thurman St Lodi (95240) ***(P-22334)***
American Nail Plate Ltg Inc ......D......909 982-1807
9044 Del Mar Ave Montclair (91763) ***(P-17523)***
American National Mfg Inc ......C......951 273-7888
252 Mariah Cir Corona (92879) ***(P-4850)***
American Non Stop Label Corp ......F......562 921-9437
16221 Arthur St Cerritos (90703) ***(P-7234)***
American Ornamental Studio ......F......650 589-0561
1 Fairview Pl Millbrae (94030) ***(P-10871)***
American Pacific Mortgage Corp ......F......707 746-4920
615 1st St Benicia (94510) ***(P-9220)***
American Pacific Truss Inc ......E......949 363-1691
24265 Rue De Cezanne Laguna Niguel (92677) ***(P-4390)***
American PCF Prtrs College Inc ......E......949 250-3212
17931 Sky Park Cir Irvine (92614) ***(P-6656)***
American Performance Engi ......F......661 256-7309
7347 W Rosamond Blvd Rosamond (93560) ***(P-21088)***
American Plant Services Inc (PA) ......D......562 630-1773
6242 N Paramount Blvd Long Beach (90805) ***(P-11378)***
American Plastic Card Co ......C......818 784-4224
21550 Oxnard St Ste 300 Woodland Hills (91367) ***(P-9943)***
American Plastic Products Inc ......D......818 504-1073
9243 Glenoaks Blvd Sun Valley (91352) ***(P-14478)***
American Pneumatic Tools Inc ......F......562 204-1555
1000 S Grand Ave Santa Ana (92705) ***(P-14428)***
American Poly-Foam Company Inc ......E......510 786-3626
1455 Crocker Ave Hayward (94544) ***(P-9816)***
American Prcision Grinding Mch ......F......626 357-6610
456 Gerona Ave San Gabriel (91775) ***(P-16272)***
American Precision Gear Co ......E......650 627-8060
365 Foster City Blvd Foster City (94404) ***(P-15238)***
American Precision Hydraulics ......E......714 903-8610
5601 Research Dr Huntington Beach (92649) ***(P-14429)***
American Precision Sheet Metal, Chatsworth *Also called Keith E Archambeau Sr Inc* ***(P-12639)***
American Precision Spring ......E......408 986-1020
1513 Arbuckle Ct Santa Clara (95054) ***(P-13785)***
American Premier Corp ......E......909 923-7070
1531 S Carlos Ave Ontario (91761) ***(P-23499)***
American Pride Inc ......E......909 591-7688
12285 Colony Ave Chino (91710) ***(P-10513)***
American Printing & Copy Inc ......F......650 325-2322
1100 Obrien Dr Menlo Park (94025) ***(P-6657)***
American Printing & Design ......E......310 287-0460
14622 Ventura Blvd # 102 Sherman Oaks (91403) ***(P-6658)***
American Printworks, Vernon *Also called P&Y T-Shrts Silk Screening Inc* ***(P-14777)***
American Probe & Tech Inc ......F......408 263-3356
1795 Grogan Ave Merced (95341) ***(P-21719)***
American Production Co Inc ......D......650 368-5334
2734 Spring St Redwood City (94063) ***(P-11854)***
American Publishing Corp ......E......909 390-7548
2143 E Convention Center Ontario (91764) ***(P-6308)***
American Pwdr Coating Pntg Inc ......E......562 861-6348
9445 Washburn Rd Downey (90242) ***(P-13549)***
American Qualex Inc ......F......949 492-8298
920 Calle Negocio Ste A San Clemente (92673) ***(P-10632)***
American Qualex International ......F......949 492-8298
920a Calle Negocio Ste A San Clemente (92673) ***(P-9221)***
American Quality Tools Inc ......E......951 280-4700
12650 Magnolia Ave Ste B Riverside (92503) ***(P-14598)***
American Quilting Company Inc ......E......323 233-2500
1540 Calzona St Los Angeles (90023) ***(P-3827)***
American Range Corporation ......C......818 897-0808
13592 Desmond St Pacoima (91331) ***(P-12480)***
American Ready Mix, Escondido *Also called Superior Ready Mix Concrete LP* ***(P-11193)***
American Ready Mix Inc ......F......760 446-4556
1141 W Graaf Ave Ridgecrest (93555) ***(P-11040)***
American Relays Inc ......E......562 944-0447
15537 Blackburn Ave Norwalk (90650) ***(P-17249)***
American Reliance Inc ......E......626 443-6818
12941 Ramona Blvd Ste F Baldwin Park (91706) ***(P-15391)***
American Rice Inc ......D......530 438-2265
1 Comet Ln Maxwell (95955) ***(P-1073)***
American Rim Supply Inc ......E......760 431-3666
1955 Kellogg Ave Carlsbad (92008) ***(P-20255)***
American River Packaging, Sacramento *Also called Pk1 Inc* ***(P-5451)***
American Rotary Broom Co Inc (PA) ......F......760 591-4025
181 Pawnee St Ste B San Marcos (92078) ***(P-23785)***
American Rotary Broom Co Inc ......E......909 629-9117
688 New York Dr Pomona (91768) ***(P-23786)***
American Rotoform, South San Francisco *Also called Barrango* ***(P-16307)***
American Rv, Santa Clarita *Also called Stiers Rv Centers LLC* ***(P-21242)***
American Safety Technologies ......E......619 575-0590
679 Anita St Ste A Chula Vista (91911) ***(P-13550)***
American Scence Tech As T Corp (PA) ......C......415 251-2800
50 California St Fl 21 San Francisco (94111) ***(P-20538)***
American Scence Tech As T Corp ......D......310 773-1978
2372 Morse Ave Ste 571 Irvine (92614) ***(P-20539)***
American SD Power Inc ......F......909 947-0673
14181 Fern Ave Chino (91710) ***(P-17179)***
American Seals West, Ceres *Also called McMillan - Hendryx Inc* ***(P-9543)***
American Security Educators ......F......562 928-1847
8734 Cleta St Ste E Downey (90241) ***(P-6431)***
American Security Products Co ......C......951 685-9680
11925 Pacific Ave Fontana (92337) ***(P-13916)***

Employee Codes: A=Over 500 employees, B=251-500
C=101-250, D=51-100, E=20-50, F=10-19
2019 California
Manfacturers Register
© Mergent Inc. 1-800-342-5647
1057

American Sheet Metal, El Cajon *Also called Asm Construction Inc* ***(P-12491)***
American Sheet Metal Inc....F....714 780-0155
1430 N Daly St Anaheim (92806) ***(P-12481)***
American Single Sheets, Redlands *Also called Continental Datalabel Inc* ***(P-5706)***
American Skynet Electronics, Milpitas *Also called Silicon Vly World Trade Corp* ***(P-17163)***
American Solar Advantage Inc....E....951 496-1075
7056 Archibald St 102-432 Corona (92880) ***(P-18692)***
American Sport Bags Inc....E....714 547-8013
1485 E Warner Ave Santa Ana (92705) ***(P-3760)***
American Spring Inc....F....310 324-2181
321 W 135th St Los Angeles (90061) ***(P-13747)***
American Steel & Stairways Inc....E....408 848-2992
8525 Forest St Ste A Gilroy (95020) ***(P-12831)***
American Steel Masters Inc....E....626 333-3375
15050 Proctor Ave City of Industry (91746) ***(P-12112)***
American Straw Company LLC....F....213 304-1095
1697 Woods Dr Los Angeles (90069) ***(P-24035)***
American System Publications....E....323 259-1867
3018 Carmel St Los Angeles (90065) ***(P-6432)***
American Tech Supply Inc (PA)....E....925 944-0777
1250 Pine St Ste 105 Walnut Creek (94596) ***(P-18308)***
American Technical Molding Inc....C....909 982-1025
2052 W 11th St Upland (91786) ***(P-9944)***
American Texas Firelog, Sacramento *Also called Conros Corp* ***(P-4614)***
American Thermoform Corp (PA)....F....909 593-6711
1758 Brackett St La Verne (91750) ***(P-14799)***
American Tooth Industries....D....805 487-9868
1200 Stellar Dr Oxnard (93033) ***(P-22856)***
American Trck Trlr Bdy Co Inc (PA)....E....209 836-8985
100 W Valpico Rd Ste D Tracy (95376) ***(P-20189)***
American Truck Dismantling....F....909 429-2166
15303 Arrow Blvd Fontana (92335) ***(P-166)***
American Truss, Laguna Niguel *Also called American Pacific Truss Inc* ***(P-4390)***
American Ultraviolet West Inc....E....310 784-2930
23555 Telo Ave Torrance (90505) ***(P-14264)***
American Underwater Products (HQ)....D....800 435-3483
2002 Davis St San Leandro (94577) ***(P-23500)***
American Vangaurd, Newport Beach *Also called Amvac Chemical Corporation* ***(P-9094)***
American Vanguard Corporation....C....323 526-2372
2110 Davie Ave Commerce (90040) ***(P-9090)***
American Vanguard Corporation (PA)....D....949 260-1200
4695 Macarthur Ct Newport Beach (92660) ***(P-9091)***
American Vanguard Corporation....C....323 264-3910
4100 E Washington Blvd Commerce (90023) ***(P-9092)***
American Vegetable Oils Inc....F....800 728-8089
7244 Condor Ave Commerce (90040) ***(P-1514)***
American Wire Inc....F....909 884-9990
784 S Lugo Ave San Bernardino (92408) ***(P-13809)***
AMERICAN WIRE SALES, Rancho Dominguez *Also called Standard Wire & Cable Co* ***(P-11676)***
American Wood Fibers Inc....F....530 741-3700
4560 Skyway Dr Marysville (95901) ***(P-4028)***
American Yeast Corporation....E....661 834-1050
5455 District Blvd Bakersfield (93313) ***(P-2451)***
American Zabin Intl Inc....E....213 746-3770
3933 S Hill St Los Angeles (90037) ***(P-7235)***
American Zinc Enterprises, Walnut *Also called Sea Shield Marine Products* ***(P-11706)***
Americana Sports Inc....E....626 914-0238
422 S Vermont Ave Glendora (91741) ***(P-23501)***
Americas Finest Products....E....310 450-6555
1639 9th St Santa Monica (90404) ***(P-8589)***
Americas Gold Inc....E....213 688-4904
650 S Hill St Ste 224 Los Angeles (90014) ***(P-23234)***
Americas Gold - Amrcas Damonds, Los Angeles *Also called Americas Gold Inc* ***(P-23234)***
Americawear, Commerce *Also called RDD Enterprises Inc* ***(P-3039)***
Americh Corporation (PA)....C....818 982-1711
13212 Saticoy St North Hollywood (91605) ***(P-22699)***
Americhip Inc (PA)....D....310 323-3697
19032 S Vermont Ave Gardena (90248) ***(P-6659)***
Americon....F....805 987-0412
900 Flynn Rd Camarillo (93012) ***(P-4927)***
Americore Inc....E....209 632-5679
19705 August Ave Hilmar (95324) ***(P-12917)***
Ameriflex Inc....D....951 737-5557
2390 Railroad St Corona (92880) ***(P-13875)***
Amerillum LLC....D....760 727-7675
3728 Maritime Way Oceanside (92056) ***(P-17672)***
Amerimade Technology Inc....E....925 243-9090
449 Mountain Vista Pkwy Livermore (94551) ***(P-9945)***
Amerimax, Anaheim *Also called Euramax Holdings Inc* ***(P-11575)***
Ameripec Inc....C....714 690-9191
6965 Aragon Cir Buena Park (90620) ***(P-2094)***
Amerisink Inc (PA)....F....510 667-9998
835 Fremont Ave San Leandro (94577) ***(P-12022)***
Ameritex International, Los Angeles *Also called Amtex California Inc* ***(P-3690)***
Ameron International Corp....C....425 258-2616
1020 B St Fillmore (93015) ***(P-10872)***
Ameron International Corp....E....909 944-4100
10681 Fthill Blvd Ste 450 Rancho Cucamonga (91730) ***(P-10873)***
Ameron International Corp....C....209 836-5050
10100 W Linne Rd Tracy (95377) ***(P-13758)***
Ameron International Corp....D....805 524-0223
1020 B St Fillmore (93015) ***(P-10874)***
Ameron International Corp....D....909 944-4100
10681 Fthill Blvd Ste 450 Rancho Cucamonga (91730) ***(P-10875)***
Ameron International Corp....C....909 944-4100
10681 Fthill Blvd Ste 450 Rancho Cucamonga (91730) ***(P-11473)***
Ameron International Corp....E....714 256-7755
201 N Berry St Brea (92821) ***(P-23078)***
Ameron International Corp....E....909 944-4100
10681 Fthill Blvd Ste 450 Rancho Cucamonga (91730) ***(P-10876)***
Amertex International Inc....E....626 570-9409
2108 Orange St Alhambra (91803) ***(P-3213)***
Ames Fire Waterworks....D....530 666-2493
1485 Tanforan Ave Woodland (95776) ***(P-17250)***
Ames Industrial, Los Angeles *Also called Ames Rubber Mfg Co Inc* ***(P-9586)***
Ames Rubber Mfg Co Inc....E....818 240-9313
4516 Brazil St Los Angeles (90039) ***(P-9586)***
Amest Corporation....F....949 766-9692
30394 Esperanza Rcho STA Marg (92688) ***(P-18693)***
Ametek Inc....D....949 642-2400
17032 Armstrong Ave Irvine (92614) ***(P-17180)***
Ametek Ameron LLC....E....626 337-4640
4750 Littlejohn St Baldwin Park (91706) ***(P-21255)***
Ametek Ameron LLC (HQ)....D....626 337-4640
4750 Littlejohn St Baldwin Park (91706) ***(P-21546)***
Ametek HCC, Rosemead *Also called Hermetic Seal Corporation* ***(P-19566)***
Ametek Programmable Power Inc (HQ)....C....858 450-0085
9250 Brown Deer Rd San Diego (92121) ***(P-19443)***
Amex Manufacturing Inc....F....619 391-7412
2307 Avenida Costa Este San Diego (92154) ***(P-24036)***
Amex Plating Incorporated....E....408 986-8222
3333 Woodward Ave Santa Clara (95054) ***(P-13327)***
AMF Pharma LLC....E....909 930-9599
1931 S Lynx Ave Ontario (91761) ***(P-8022)***
AMF Support Surfaces Inc (HQ)....C....951 549-6800
1691 N Delilah St Corona (92879) ***(P-4851)***
Amfab, Anaheim *Also called Evert Hancock Incorporated* ***(P-12577)***
Amflex Plastics Incorporated....E....760 643-1756
4039 Calle Platino Ste G Oceanside (92056) ***(P-9946)***
AMG Employee Management Inc....F....323 254-7448
3235 N San Fernando Rd 1d Los Angeles (90065) ***(P-23216)***
AMG Torrance LLC (HQ)....D....310 515-2584
5401 Business Dr Huntington Beach (92649) ***(P-20733)***
Amgen Inc (PA)....A....805 447-1000
1 Amgen Center Dr Thousand Oaks (91320) ***(P-8526)***
Amgen Inc....F....805 499-0512
1909 Oak Terrace Ln Newbury Park (91320) ***(P-8023)***
Amgen Inc....E....650 244-2000
1120 Veterans Blvd South San Francisco (94080) ***(P-8024)***
Amgen Inc....D....805 447-1000
1840 De Havilland Dr Newbury Park (91320) ***(P-8025)***
Amgen Manufacturing Limited....F....787 656-2000
1 Amgen Center Dr Newbury Park (91320) ***(P-24037)***
Amgen USA Inc....D....805 447-1000
1 Amgen Center Dr Thousand Oaks (91320) ***(P-8527)***
Amgraph, Ontario *Also called American Fleet & Ret Graphics* ***(P-23815)***
Amh International Inc....F....805 388-2082
1270 Avenida Acaso Ste J Camarillo (93012) ***(P-16273)***
AMI, El Dorado Hills *Also called All Sales Manufacturing Inc* ***(P-20250)***
AMI, Costa Mesa *Also called Advanced Micro Instruments Inc* ***(P-21893)***
AMI/Coast Magnetics Inc....E....323 936-6188
5333 W Washington Blvd Los Angeles (90016) ***(P-19318)***
Amiad Filtration Systems, Oxnard *Also called Amiad USA Inc* ***(P-16008)***
Amiad USA Inc....E....805 988-3323
1251 Maulhardt Ave Oxnard (93030) ***(P-16008)***
Amico - Diamond Perforated, Visalia *Also called Diamond Perforated Metals Inc* ***(P-13194)***
Amico Fontana, Fontana *Also called Alabama Metal Industries Corp* ***(P-12830)***
Amigo Custom Screen Prints LLC....E....760 452-7964
6351 Yarrow Dr Ste A&B Carlsbad (92011) ***(P-7236)***
Amimon Inc....F....650 641-3191
2350 Mission College Blvd # 190 Santa Clara (95054) ***(P-5340)***
Aminco International USA Inc (PA)....E....949 457-3261
20571 Crescent Bay Dr Lake Forest (92630) ***(P-23235)***
Amino Technologies (us) LLC (HQ)....D....408 861-1400
20823 Stevens Creek Blvd Cupertino (95014) ***(P-18028)***
Amish Country Gazebos Inc....F....800 700-1777
739 E Francis St Ontario (91761) ***(P-4668)***
Amity Rubberized Pen Company....E....626 969-0863
612 N Commercial Ave Covina (91723) ***(P-23697)***
Amity Washer & Stamping Co....E....562 941-1259
10926 Painter Ave Santa Fe Springs (90670) ***(P-13164)***
Amko Restaurant Furniture Inc....E....323 234-0388
5833 Avalon Blvd Los Angeles (90003) ***(P-5220)***
Amkor Technology Inc....D....858 320-6280
5465 Morehouse Dr Ste 210 San Diego (92121) ***(P-18694)***
Amkor Technology Inc....E....949 724-9370
3 Corporate Park Ste 230 Irvine (92606) ***(P-18695)***
Amlogic Inc....E....408 850-9688
2518 Mission College Blvd Santa Clara (95054) ***(P-18696)***
Ammi Publishing Inc....F....415 435-2652
1550 Tiburon Blvd Ste D Belvedere Tiburon (94920) ***(P-5758)***
AMO Corporation....F....916 791-2001
9580 Oak Avenue Pkwy # 9 Folsom (95630) ***(P-14599)***
AMO Usa Inc....C....714 247-8200
1700 E Saint Andrew Pl Santa Ana (92705) ***(P-22335)***
Amobee Inc....F....858 638-1515
10201 Wtridge Cir Ste 200 San Diego (92121) ***(P-21547)***
Amoretti, Oxnard *Also called Noushig Inc* ***(P-1298)***
Amos Art Studio, Northridge *Also called Emanuel Morez Inc* ***(P-4693)***
AMP, Santa Ana *Also called Accelerated Memory Prod Inc* ***(P-18660)***
AMP III LLC....D....408 779-2927
465 Woodview Ave Morgan Hill (95037) ***(P-14600)***
AMP Plus Inc....D....323 231-2600
2042 E Vernon Ave Vernon (90058) ***(P-17659)***
AMP Research, Tustin *Also called Lund Motion Products Inc* ***(P-20390)***
Ampac Analytical, El Dorado Hills *Also called Ampac Fine Chemicals LLC* ***(P-8027)***

Ampac Fine Chemicals LLC (HQ)....B....916 357-6880
Highway 50 And Hazel Ave Rancho Cordova (95741) ***(P-8026)***
Ampac Fine Chemicals LLC....F....916 245-6500
1100 Windfield Way El Dorado Hills (95762) ***(P-8027)***
Ampac USA, Montclair *Also called Nef Tech Inc* ***(P-16078)***
Ampersand Contract Signing Grp, Los Angeles *Also called Ahr Signs Incorporated* ***(P-23811)***
Ampersand Ice Cream LLC....F....559 264-8000
1940 N Echo Ave Fresno (93704) ***(P-655)***
Ampersand Publishing LLC (PA)....E....805 564-5200
715 Anacapa St Santa Barbara (93101) ***(P-5759)***
Amperitech Inc....E....714 523-4068
636 S State College Blvd Fullerton (92831) ***(P-14601)***
Ampex Data Systems Corporation (HQ)....D....650 367-2011
26460 Corporate Ave Hayward (94545) ***(P-15511)***
Amphastar Pharmaceuticals Inc (PA)....C....909 980-9484
11570 6th St Rancho Cucamonga (91730) ***(P-8028)***
Amphenol Corporation....F....805 378-6464
5069 Maureen Ln Ste B Moorpark (93021) ***(P-19373)***
Amphenol DC Electronics Inc....B....408 947-4500
1870 Little Orchard St San Jose (95125) ***(P-17443)***
Amphion, Rancho Cucamonga *Also called Executive Safe and SEC Corp* ***(P-13941)***
Ampine LLC....C....209 223-1690
11610 Ampine Fibreform Rd Sutter Creek (95685) ***(P-4928)***
Amplifier Technologies Inc....E....323 278-0001
1749 Chapin Rd Montebello (90640) ***(P-18029)***
Ampligraphix....F....661 321-3150
1768 Glenwood Dr Bakersfield (93306) ***(P-6660)***
Ampliphi Biosciences Corp (PA)....E....858 829-0829
3579 Valley Centre Dr # 100 San Diego (92130) ***(P-8528)***
Ampro Adlink Technology Inc....D....408 360-0200
5215 Hellyer Ave Ste 110 San Jose (95138) ***(P-15392)***
Ampro Computers, Inc., San Jose *Also called Ampro Adlink Technology Inc* ***(P-15392)***
Ampro Systems Inc....E....510 624-9000
1000 Page Ave Fremont (94538) ***(P-18420)***
Amq Solutions LLC (HQ)....F....877 801-0370
764 Walsh Ave Santa Clara (95050) ***(P-4929)***
AMR Industries Enterprises Inc....E....415 860-5566
2131 19th Ave Ste 203 San Francisco (94116) ***(P-14206)***
Amrapur Overseas Incorporated (PA)....E....714 893-8808
1560 E 6th St Ste 101 Corona (92879) ***(P-2988)***
Amrel, Baldwin Park *Also called American Reliance Inc* ***(P-15391)***
Amrep Inc (PA)....C....909 923-0430
1555 S Cucamonga Ave Ontario (91761) ***(P-20190)***
Amrex Electrotherapy Equipment, Paramount *Also called Amrex-Zetron Inc* ***(P-19909)***
Amrex-Zetron Inc....E....310 527-6868
7034 Jackson St Paramount (90723) ***(P-19909)***
Amrich Energy Inc....F....805 354-0830
1160 Marsh St Ste 105 San Luis Obispo (93401) ***(P-8977)***
Amro Fabricating Corporation....E....951 842-6140
17101 Heacock St Moreno Valley (92551) ***(P-20734)***
Amro Fabricating Corporation (PA)....C....626 579-2200
1430 Adelia Ave South El Monte (91733) ***(P-20735)***
Amron International Inc (PA)....D....760 208-6500
1380 Aspen Way Vista (92081) ***(P-23502)***
Amron Manufacturing Inc....F....714 278-9204
635 Gregory Cir Corona (92881) ***(P-20736)***
Amron Urethane Products, Corona *Also called Amron Manufacturing Inc* ***(P-20736)***
AMS, Manteca *Also called American Modular Systems Inc* ***(P-4567)***
AMS Drilling....F....949 232-1149
120 Tustin Ave Ste C Newport Beach (92663) ***(P-96)***
Amscan Inc....D....714 972-2626
804 W Town And Country Rd Orange (92868) ***(P-5497)***
Amsco US Inc....C....562 630-0333
15341 Texaco Ave Paramount (90723) ***(P-19444)***
Amsec, Fontana *Also called American Security Products Co* ***(P-13916)***
Amtec, Anaheim *Also called Applied Manufacturing Tech Inc* ***(P-14801)***
Amtec Human Capital Inc....E....949 472-0396
21661 Audubon Way El Toro (92630) ***(P-14479)***
Amtech Microelectronics Inc....E....408 612-8888
485 Cochrane Cir Morgan Hill (95037) ***(P-18421)***
Amtecol Inc....E....510 235-7979
810 Wright Ave Richmond (94804) ***(P-9422)***
Amtek, Poway *Also called United Security Products Inc* ***(P-20095)***
Amtek Electronic Inc....E....408 971-8787
1150 N 5th St San Jose (95112) ***(P-15393)***
Amtex California Inc....E....323 859-2200
113 S Utah St Los Angeles (90033) ***(P-3690)***
Amtrend Corporation....D....714 630-2070
1458 Manhattan Ave Fullerton (92831) ***(P-5036)***
Amundson Tom Tmber Flling Cntr....F....530 529-0504
14615 River Oaks Dr Red Bluff (96080) ***(P-3977)***
Amvac Chemical, Commerce *Also called American Vanguard Corporation* ***(P-9092)***
Amvac Chemical Corporation (HQ)....E....323 264-3910
4695 Macarthur Ct # 1200 Newport Beach (92660) ***(P-9093)***
Amvac Chemical Corporation....F....949 260-1212
4695 Macarthur Ct # 1200 Newport Beach (92660) ***(P-9094)***
Amylin Pharmaceuticals LLC....D....858 552-2200
9373 Twn Cntr Dr 150 San Diego (92101) ***(P-8029)***
Amyris Inc (PA)....B....510 450-0761
5885 Hollis St Ste 100 Emeryville (94608) ***(P-8978)***
Amys Kitchen Inc....E....707 568-4500
1650 Corp Cir Ste 200 Petaluma (94954) ***(P-978)***
Amys Kitchen Inc (PA)....A....707 578-7188
2330 Northpoint Pkwy Santa Rosa (95407) ***(P-979)***
Amzart Inc....F....323 404-9372
3260 Casitas Ave Los Angeles (90039) ***(P-2452)***
Amzr Inc....C....800 541-2326
29115 Avenue Valleyview Valencia (91355) ***(P-3937)***
An Environmental Inks....F....909 930-9656
1920 S Quaker Ridge Pl Ontario (91761) ***(P-9188)***
Ana Global LLC....A....619 482-9990
2360 Marconi Ct San Diego (92154) ***(P-4896)***
Anabolic Incorporated....D....949 863-0340
17802 Gillette Ave Irvine (92614) ***(P-8030)***
Anacapa Boatyard, Newport Beach *Also called Anacapa Marine Services* ***(P-21021)***
Anacapa Marine Services (PA)....F....805 985-1818
151 Shipyard Way Ste 5 Newport Beach (92663) ***(P-21021)***
Anaco Inc....C....951 372-2732
1001 El Camino Ave Corona (92879) ***(P-15279)***
Anacom Inc....E....408 519-2062
1961 Concourse Dr San Jose (95131) ***(P-18030)***
Anacom General Corporation....E....714 774-8484
1240 S Claudina St Anaheim (92805) ***(P-17759)***
Anacom Medtek, Anaheim *Also called Anacom General Corporation* ***(P-17759)***
Anacor Pharmaceuticals Inc....E....650 543-7500
1020 E Meadow Cir Palo Alto (94303) ***(P-8031)***
Anacrown Inc....F....310 530-1165
25835 Narbonne Ave # 250 Lomita (90717) ***(P-13917)***
Anadite Cal Restoration Tr....E....562 861-2205
10647 Garfield Ave South Gate (90280) ***(P-13328)***
Anaheim Automation Inc....E....714 992-6990
4985 E Landon Dr Anaheim (92807) ***(P-17251)***
Anaheim Custom Extruders Inc....E....714 693-8508
4640 E La Palma Ave Anaheim (92807) ***(P-9947)***
Anaheim Embroidery Inc....E....714 563-5220
1230 N Jefferson St Ste C Anaheim (92807) ***(P-3828)***
Anaheim Plant, Anaheim *Also called Stepan Company* ***(P-7890)***
ANAHEIM PRECISION MFG, Orange *Also called Anaheim Precision Shtmtl Mfg* ***(P-20540)***
Anaheim Precision Shtmtl Mfg (HQ)....C....714 453-0100
1738 N Neville St Orange (92865) ***(P-20540)***
Anaheim Wire Products Inc (PA)....E....714 563-8300
1009 E Vermont Ave Anaheim (92805) ***(P-13810)***
Anajet LLC....E....714 662-3200
1100 Valencia Ave Tustin (92780) ***(P-14800)***
Analog Bits....E....650 279-9323
945 Stewart Dr Sunnyvale (94085) ***(P-18697)***
Analog Devices Inc....B....408 727-9222
3550 N 1st St San Jose (95134) ***(P-18698)***
Analog Devices Inc....E....714 641-9391
940 S Coast Dr Ste 230 Costa Mesa (92626) ***(P-18699)***
Analogix Semiconductor Inc....E....408 988-8686
3211 Scott Blvd Ste 100 Santa Clara (95054) ***(P-18700)***
Analytcal Scientific Instrs Inc....E....510 669-2250
3023 Research Dr San Pablo (94806) ***(P-21902)***
Analytic and Computational Res....F....310 471-3023
1931 Stradella Rd Los Angeles (90077) ***(P-24357)***
Analytic Endodontics, Orange *Also called Sybron Dental Specialties Inc* ***(P-22914)***
Analytical Industries Inc....E....909 392-6900
2855 Metropolitan Pl Pomona (91767) ***(P-21548)***
Analytik Jena US LLC (HQ)....D....909 946-3197
2066 W 11th St Upland (91786) ***(P-21903)***
Anaplex Corporation....E....714 522-4481
15547 Garfield Ave Paramount (90723) ***(P-13329)***
Anatase Products, Tehachapi *Also called Henway Inc* ***(P-23767)***
Anatesco Inc....F....661 399-6990
128 Bedford Way Bakersfield (93308) ***(P-167)***
Anatometal Inc....E....831 454-9880
411 Ingalls St Santa Cruz (95060) ***(P-23236)***
Anatomic Global Inc....C....800 874-7237
1241 Old Temescal Rd # 103 Corona (92881) ***(P-3706)***
Anayas Cutting Inc....D....323 582-5758
3130 Leonis Blvd Ste 204 Vernon (90058) ***(P-3292)***
Anc Technology....D....805 530-3958
10195 Stockton Rd Moorpark (93021) ***(P-18422)***
Anchen Pharmaceuticals Inc....F....949 639-8100
5 Goodyear Irvine (92618) ***(P-8032)***
Anchor Audio Inc....D....760 827-7100
5931 Darwin Ct Carlsbad (92008) ***(P-17760)***
Anchor Distilling Company....E....415 863-8350
1705 Mariposa St San Francisco (94107) ***(P-1644)***
Anchor Exportation USA LLC....F....310 312-4575
11500 W Olympic Blvd 4 Los Angeles (90064) ***(P-2720)***
Anco International Inc....E....909 887-2521
19851 Cajon Blvd San Bernardino (92407) ***(P-13759)***
Ancra International LLC (HQ)....C....626 765-4800
875 W 8th St Azusa (91702) ***(P-14307)***
Anda Networks Inc....C....408 519-4900
1100 La Avenida St Ste A Mountain View (94043) ***(P-17922)***
Andalou Naturals....F....415 446-9470
7250 Redwood Blvd Ste 208 Novato (94945) ***(P-8694)***
Andari Fashion Inc....C....626 575-2759
9626 Telstar Ave El Monte (91731) ***(P-3134)***
Andeavor....F....310 847-5705
2350 E 223rd St Carson (90810) ***(P-22)***
Anderco Inc....E....714 446-9508
540 Airpark Dr Fullerton (92833) ***(P-4098)***
Andersen Industries Inc....E....760 246-8766
17079 Muskrat Ave Adelanto (92301) ***(P-20493)***
Anderson, Inglewood *Also called Steel Toe Enterprises* ***(P-12999)***
Anderson Bat Company LLC....D....714 524-7500
236 E Orangethorpe Ave Placentia (92870) ***(P-23503)***
Anderson Bros Artistic Iron Co....F....951 898-6880
310 Elizabeth Ln Corona (92880) ***(P-13918)***
Anderson Desk Inc....B....619 671-1040
7510 Airway Rd Ste 7 San Diego (92154) ***(P-4930)***
Anderson Logging Inc....D....707 964-2770
1296 N Main St Fort Bragg (95437) ***(P-3978)***

ALPHABETIC

Employee Codes: A=Over 500 employees, B=251-500
C=101-250, D=51-100, E=20-50, F=10-19
2019 California
Manfacturers Register
© Mergent Inc. 1-800-342-5647
1059

Anderson Moulds Incorporated..........F.......209 943-1145
3131 E Anita St Stockton (95205) ***(P-9948)***
Anderson Signs..........F.......209 367-0120
1240 N Filbert St Stockton (95205) ***(P-23816)***
Anderson Valley Brewing Inc..........E.......707 895-2337
17700 Hwy 253 Boonville (95415) ***(P-1558)***
Anderson Valley Brewing Co, Boonville *Also called Anderson Valley Brewing Inc* ***(P-1558)***
Anderson's Carpet & Linoleum, Oakland *Also called Linoleum Sales Co Inc* ***(P-10600)***
Anderson's Signs & Crane, Stockton *Also called Anderson Signs* ***(P-23816)***
Andre-Boudin Bakeries Inc..........F.......925 935-4375
67 Broadwalk Ln Walnut Creek (94596) ***(P-1173)***
Andre-Boudin Bakeries Inc..........F.......408 249-4101
2855 Stevens Crk 2451 San Jose (95128) ***(P-1174)***
Andrea Bijoux..........F.......213 236-0747
1001 Crocker St Ste 8 Los Angeles (90021) ***(P-3641)***
Andrea Zee Corporation..........F.......209 462-1700
711 S San Joaquin St Stockton (95203) ***(P-11231)***
Andresen, San Francisco *Also called Clic LLC* ***(P-6735)***
Andresen Digital Pre-Press, Santa Monica *Also called Aft Corporation* ***(P-7639)***
Andretti Winery, NAPA *Also called Awg Ltd Inc* ***(P-1649)***
Andrew Alexander Inc..........D.......323 752-0066
1306 S Alameda St Compton (90221) ***(P-10457)***
Andrew LLC..........F.......909 270-9356
1710 S Grove Ave Ste A&B Ontario (91761) ***(P-1024)***
Andrew Morgan Furniture, Vista *Also called California Cstm Furn & Uphl Co* ***(P-3882)***
Andrews Electronics, Valencia *Also called Partsearch Technologies Inc* ***(P-19681)***
Andrews Powder Coating Inc..........E.......818 700-1030
10138 Canoga Ave Chatsworth (91311) ***(P-13551)***
Andromeda Software Inc..........F.......805 379-4109
2965 Potter Ave Thousand Oaks (91360) ***(P-24358)***
Androp Packaging Inc..........E.......909 605-8842
4400 E Francis St Ontario (91761) ***(P-5384)***
Andrus Sheet Metal Inc..........E.......510 232-8687
5021 Seaport Ave Richmond (94804) ***(P-12482)***
Anemostat Products, Carson *Also called Mestek Inc* ***(P-15971)***
Ang Newspaper Group Inc (HQ)..........F.......650 359-6666
1301 Grant Ave B Novato (94945) ***(P-5760)***
Angel Manufacturing, Los Angeles *Also called Angels Garments* ***(P-3135)***
Angeleno Magazine, San Francisco *Also called Modern Luxury Media LLC* ***(P-6221)***
Angell & Giroux Inc..........D.......323 269-8596
2727 Alcazar St Los Angeles (90033) ***(P-4976)***
Angellist LLC..........F.......415 857-0840
90 Gold St San Francisco (94133) ***(P-24359)***
Angels, Los Angeles *Also called Hip & Hip Inc* ***(P-3429)***
Angels Garments..........F.......213 748-0581
525 E 12th St Ste 107 Los Angeles (90015) ***(P-3135)***
Angels Sheet Metal Inc..........F.......209 736-0911
320 N Main St Angels Camp (95222) ***(P-12483)***
Angels Young Inc..........E.......213 614-0742
514 S Broadway Los Angeles (90013) ***(P-3024)***
Angelus Aluminum Foundry Co..........F.......323 268-0145
3479 E Pico Blvd Los Angeles (90023) ***(P-11725)***
Angelus Block Co Inc..........E.......805 485-1137
4575 E Vineyard Ave Oxnard (93036) ***(P-10842)***
Angelus Block Co Inc..........D.......714 637-8594
1705 N Main St Orange (92865) ***(P-10843)***
Angelus Formulations, Santa Fe Springs *Also called Angelus Shoe Polish Co Inc* ***(P-8620)***
Angelus Pacific Company Inc..........F.......714 871-1610
700 E Walnut Ave Fullerton (92831) ***(P-6661)***
Angelus Plating Works..........F.......310 516-1883
1713 W 134th St Gardena (90249) ***(P-20256)***
Angelus Sheet Metal & Plbg Sup, Los Angeles *Also called Angelus Sheet Metal Mfg Co* ***(P-12484)***
Angelus Sheet Metal Mfg Co..........F.......323 221-4191
4800 Valley Blvd Los Angeles (90032) ***(P-12484)***
Angelus Shoe Polish Co Inc..........F.......562 941-4242
12060 Florence Ave Santa Fe Springs (90670) ***(P-8620)***
Angie's Jewelry, Los Angeles *Also called Belair Gold Design Inc* ***(P-23340)***
Angry Horse Brewing, Montebello *Also called Desert Brothers Craft* ***(P-1587)***
Angular Machining Inc..........E.......408 954-8326
2040 Hartog Dr San Jose (95131) ***(P-16274)***
Anheuser-Busch LLC..........C.......818 989-5300
15800 Roscoe Blvd Van Nuys (91406) ***(P-1559)***
Anheuser-Busch LLC..........C.......858 581-7000
5959 Santa Fe St San Diego (92109) ***(P-1560)***
Aniise Skin Care, Los Angeles *Also called Global Sales Inc* ***(P-8755)***
Anillo Industries Inc (PA)..........E.......714 637-7000
2090 N Glassell St Orange (92865) ***(P-13058)***
Anima International Corp..........F.......626 723-4960
234 S 5th Ave City of Industry (91746) ***(P-24038)***
Animal Lovers Pet Center..........F.......360 683-0906
4305 Gravenstein Hwy S Sebastopol (95472) ***(P-24039)***
Animal Nutrition Inds Inc..........F.......949 583-2920
5602 E La Palma Ave Anaheim (92807) ***(P-7922)***
Anin Co (PA)..........F.......415 433-1341
2041 Powell St San Francisco (94133) ***(P-6662)***
Anitas Mexican Foods Corp (PA)..........C.......909 884-8706
3454 N Mike Daley Dr San Bernardino (92407) ***(P-2374)***
Anivive Lifesciences Inc..........F.......714 931-7810
3750 Schaufele Ave # 100 Long Beach (90808) ***(P-8033)***
Anki Inc (PA)..........E.......877 721-2654
55 2nd St Ste 1500 San Francisco (94105) ***(P-23405)***
Anlin Industries..........C.......800 287-7996
1665 Tollhouse Rd Clovis (93611) ***(P-4099)***
Anlin Window Systems, Clovis *Also called Anlin Industries* ***(P-4099)***
Anmar Precision Components..........F.......818 764-0901
7424 Greenbush Ave North Hollywood (91605) ***(P-20737)***
Ann Lilli Corp (PA)..........D.......415 482-9444
1010 B St Ste 209 San Rafael (94901) ***(P-3348)***
Annabelle Candy Inc..........D.......510 783-2900
27211 Industrial Blvd Hayward (94545) ***(P-1408)***
Annianna, Commerce *Also called Siho Corporation* ***(P-3496)***
Annieglass Inc (PA)..........E.......831 761-2041
310 Harvest Dr Watsonville (95076) ***(P-10633)***
Annies Inc (HQ)..........D.......510 558-7500
1610 5th St Berkeley (94710) ***(P-2453)***
Annies Baking LLC (HQ)..........E.......510 558-7500
1610 5th St Berkeley (94710) ***(P-1175)***
Annmar Industries Inc..........F.......714 630-5443
990 S Jay Cir Anaheim (92808) ***(P-9949)***
Annona Company LLC..........F.......858 299-4238
444 S Cedros Ave Ste 175 Solana Beach (92075) ***(P-1054)***
Ano-Tech Metal Finishing, Clovis *Also called Atmf Inc* ***(P-13340)***
Anocote..........F.......858 566-1015
7550 Trade St San Diego (92121) ***(P-13330)***
Anodizing Industries Inc..........E.......323 227-4916
5222 Alhambra Ave Los Angeles (90032) ***(P-13331)***
Anodyne Inc..........E.......714 549-3321
2230 S Susan St Santa Ana (92704) ***(P-13332)***
Anokiwave Inc (PA)..........E.......858 792-9910
11236 El Camino Real # 100 San Diego (92130) ***(P-18701)***
Anoroc Precision Shtmtl Inc..........E.......310 515-6015
19122 S Santa Fe Ave Compton (90221) ***(P-12485)***
Anoto Incorporated..........F.......510 777-0071
7677 Oakport St Ste 1200 Oakland (94621) ***(P-23698)***
Anova Microsystems Inc..........F.......408 941-1888
173 Santa Rita Ct Los Altos (94022) ***(P-15666)***
Anozira Incorporated..........F.......925 771-8400
2415 San Ramon Vly Blvd San Ramon (94583) ***(P-10877)***
Anp Lighting, Montclair *Also called American Nail Plate Ltg Inc* ***(P-17523)***
Anritsu Company, Morgan Hill *Also called Anritsu US Holding Inc* ***(P-21720)***
Anritsu Company (HQ)..........B.......408 201-1551
490 Jarvis Dr Morgan Hill (95037) ***(P-18031)***
Anritsu Instruments Company..........E.......315 797-4449
490 Jarvis Dr Morgan Hill (95037) ***(P-10634)***
Anritsu US Holding Inc (HQ)..........B.......408 778-2000
490 Jarvis Dr Morgan Hill (95037) ***(P-21720)***
Anschutz Film Group LLC (HQ)..........E.......310 887-1000
1888 Century Park E # 1400 Los Angeles (90067) ***(P-23139)***
Ansell Healthcare Products LLC..........E.......205 423-8770
9301 Oakdale Ave Ste 300 Chatsworth (91311) ***(P-22336)***
Ansell Sndel Med Solutions LLC..........E.......818 534-2500
9301 Oakdale Ave Ste 300 Chatsworth (91311) ***(P-22700)***
Ansons Transportation Inc..........E.......559 892-1867
438 E Shaw Ave Ste 434 Fresno (93710) ***(P-14308)***
Ansys Inc..........F.......408 457-2000
2645 Zanker Rd San Jose (95134) ***(P-24360)***
Antaeus Fashions Group Inc..........E.......626 452-0797
2400 Chico Ave South El Monte (91733) ***(P-3136)***
Antaky Quilting Company, Los Angeles *Also called American Quilting Company Inc* ***(P-3827)***
Antcom Corporation..........E.......310 782-1076
367 Van Ness Way Ste 602 Torrance (90501) ***(P-18032)***
Antec Inc..........E.......510 770-1200
47681 Lakeview Blvd Fremont (94538) ***(P-15667)***
Antelope Valley Newspapers Inc..........E.......661 940-1000
44939 10th St W Lancaster (93534) ***(P-5761)***
Antelope Valley Press, Lancaster *Also called Antelope Valley Newspapers Inc* ***(P-5761)***
Antenna Works, Long Beach *Also called Metra Electronics Corporation* ***(P-20400)***
Anterra Group Inc..........F.......949 215-0658
25255 Cabot Rd Ste 215 Laguna Hills (92653) ***(P-8684)***
Antex Electronics Corporation..........F.......310 532-3092
5483 E Oleta St Long Beach (90815) ***(P-15668)***
Antex Knitting Mills, Los Angeles *Also called Tenenblatt Corporation* ***(P-2868)***
Antex Knitting Mills, Los Angeles *Also called Matchmaster Dyg & Finshg Inc* ***(P-2914)***
Antex Knitting Mills, Los Angeles *Also called Guru Knits Inc* ***(P-3241)***
Anthem Music & Media Fund LLC..........F.......310 286-6600
100 N Crescent Dr Ste 323 Beverly Hills (90210) ***(P-6309)***
Anthera Pharmaceuticals Inc..........E.......510 856-5600
25801 Industrial Blvd B Hayward (94545) ***(P-8034)***
Anthony California Inc (PA)..........E.......909 627-0351
14485 Monte Vista Ave Chino (91710) ***(P-17524)***
Anthony Doors Inc..........B.......818 365-9451
12812 Arroyo St Sylmar (91342) ***(P-10675)***
Anthony Doors Inc (HQ)..........A.......818 365-9451
12391 Montero Ave Sylmar (91342) ***(P-15936)***
Anthony International, Sylmar *Also called Anthony Doors Inc* ***(P-10675)***
Anthony International, Sylmar *Also called Anthony Doors Inc* ***(P-15936)***
Anthony Jones..........F.......714 894-3483
14161 Beach Blvd Westminster (92683) ***(P-23504)***
Anthony Welded Products Inc (PA)..........E.......661 721-7211
1447 S Lexington St Delano (93215) ***(P-14309)***
Anthonys Chistmas Tree, Santa Barbara *Also called Anthonys Christmas Trees* ***(P-24040)***
Anthonys Christmas Trees..........E.......805 966-6668
510 Alston Rd Santa Barbara (93108) ***(P-24040)***
Anthonys Rdymx & Bldg Sups Inc (PA)..........F.......310 542-9400
4500 Manhattan Beach Blvd Lawndale (90260) ***(P-11041)***
Antibodies Incorporated..........F.......530 758-4400
25242 County Road 95 Davis (95616) ***(P-8460)***
Antica NAPA Valley, NAPA *Also called Antinori California* ***(P-1645)***
Antigen Discovery Inc., Irvine *Also called Immport Therapeutics Inc* ***(P-22934)***
Antinori California..........E.......707 265-8866
3149 Soda Canyon Rd NAPA (94558) ***(P-1645)***
Antioch Building Materials Co..........E.......925 634-3541
6823 Brentwood Blvd Brentwood (94513) ***(P-11042)***
Antique Apparatus Company, Torrance *Also called Rock-Ola Manufacturing Corp* ***(P-17850)***

Mergent e-mail: customerrelations@mergent.com
1060
2019 California
Manufacturers Register
(P-0000) Products & Services Section entry number
(PA)=Parent Co (HQ)=Headquarters (DH)=Div Headquarters

Antique Designs, Inglewood *Also called Glp Designs Inc* ***(P-5234)***

Antique Designs Ltd Inc ... E ... 310 671-5400
916 W Hyde Park Blvd Inglewood (90302) ***(P-4931)***

Antista Draperies Inc ... F ... 323 935-1912
4048 Tivoli Ave Los Angeles (90066) ***(P-3691)***

Antista's Draperies, Los Angeles *Also called Antista Draperies Inc* ***(P-3691)***

Anto Offset Printing ... F ... 510 843-8454
1101 5th St Berkeley (94710) ***(P-6663)***

Antoninas Artisan Bakery LLC ... E ... 209 665-4176
1316 Dupont Ct Manteca (95336) ***(P-1176)***

Antypas & Associates Inc ... F ... 650 961-4311
749 Thorsen Ct Los Altos (94024) ***(P-18033)***

Anura Plastic Engineergin ... D ... 626 814-9684
5050 Rivergrade Rd Baldwin Park (91706) ***(P-9950)***

Anvil Arts Inc ... F ... 714 630-2870
1137 N Fountain Way Anaheim (92806) ***(P-4823)***

Anvil Cases Inc ... C ... 626 968-4100
15730 Salt Lake Ave City of Industry (91745) ***(P-10514)***

Anvil International LLC ... F ... 909 418-3233
551 N Loop Dr Ontario (91761) ***(P-13876)***

Anvil Iron, Gardena *Also called Anvil Steel Corporation* ***(P-12113)***

Anvil Steel Corporation ... D ... 310 329-5811
134 W 168th St Gardena (90248) ***(P-12113)***

Anwright Corporation ... E ... 818 896-2465
10225 Glenoaks Blvd Pacoima (91331) ***(P-13012)***

Any Budget Printing & Mailing ... F ... 858 278-3151
8170 Ronson Rd Ste L San Diego (92111) ***(P-6664)***

Anydata Corporation (PA) ... E ... 949 900-6040
5405 Alton Pkwy Irvine (92604) ***(P-18034)***

Ao Sky Corporation ... F ... 415 717-9901
4989 Pedro Hill Rd Pilot Hill (95664) ***(P-21256)***

Ao Winery, Rutherford *Also called Alpha Omega Winery LLC* ***(P-1643)***

Aoc LLC ... D ... 951 657-5161
19991 Seaton Ave Perris (92570) ***(P-2956)***

AOC California Plant, Perris *Also called Aoc LLC* ***(P-2956)***

Aonix North America Inc (HQ) ... F ... 858 457-2700
5675 Ruffin Rd Ste 305 San Diego (92123) ***(P-24361)***

Aoptix Technologies Inc ... D ... 408 558-3300
695 Campbell Tech Pkwy # 100 Campbell (95008) ***(P-19910)***

Aot Electronics Inc ... E ... 949 600-6335
23172 Alcalde Dr Ste E Laguna Hills (92653) ***(P-15669)***

Aoxing Pharmaceutical Co Inc ... B ... 646 367-1747
1098 Foster City Blvd Foster City (94404) ***(P-8035)***

AP Parpro Inc ... C ... 760 931-7800
9565 Heinrich Hertz Dr # 1 San Diego (92154) ***(P-15394)***

AP Plastics ... F ... 951 782-0705
4025 Garner Rd Riverside (92501) ***(P-9951)***

AP Precision Metals Inc ... F ... 619 628-0003
1215 30th St San Diego (92154) ***(P-12486)***

AP Tech, NAPA *Also called Advanced Pressure Technology* ***(P-21543)***

Apama Medical Inc ... F ... 408 903-4094
745 Camden Ave Ste A Campbell (95008) ***(P-22337)***

Apartment Directory of L A ... F ... 310 832-0354
2515 S Western Ave Ste 13 San Pedro (90732) ***(P-6433)***

Apartment Drctry L A-South Bay, San Pedro *Also called Apartment Directory of L A* ***(P-6433)***

APC By Scheineder Electric, Costa Mesa *Also called Schneider Electric It Usa* ***(P-19720)***

Apct Inc (PA) ... D ... 408 727-6442
3495 De La Cruz Blvd Santa Clara (95054) ***(P-18423)***

Apem Inc ... D ... 760 598-2518
970 Park Center Dr Vista (92081) ***(P-19445)***

Aperio, Vista *Also called Leica Biosystems Imaging Inc* ***(P-22507)***

Apex Brewing Supply ... F ... 916 250-7950
3237 Rippey Rd Ste 600 Loomis (95650) ***(P-14832)***

Apex Communications Inc (HQ) ... F ... 818 379-8400
21700 Oxnard St Ste 1060 Woodland Hills (91367) ***(P-24362)***

Apex Container Services, Commerce *Also called Apex Drum Company Inc* ***(P-4516)***

Apex Conveyor Corp ... E ... 951 304-7808
41674 Corning Pl Murrieta (92562) ***(P-14265)***

Apex Conveyor Systems Inc ... F ... 951 304-7808
41674 Corning Pl Murrieta (92562) ***(P-14266)***

Apex Design Technology, Anaheim *Also called Apex Technology Holdings Inc* ***(P-21257)***

Apex Die Corporation ... D ... 650 592-6350
840 Cherry Ln San Carlos (94070) ***(P-5650)***

Apex Digital Inc ... F ... 909 923-8686
4401 Eucalyptus Ave # 110 Chino (91710) ***(P-17525)***

Apex Door & Frame, Hesperia *Also called Apex Specialty Cnstr Entps* ***(P-4101)***

Apex Drum Company Inc ... F ... 323 721-8994
6226 Ferguson Dr Commerce (90022) ***(P-4516)***

Apex Interior Source Inc ... E ... 760 343-1919
30555 Roseview Ln Thousand Palms (92276) ***(P-4100)***

Apex Precision Tech Inc ... E ... 317 821-1000
23622 Calabasas Rd # 323 Calabasas (91302) ***(P-20257)***

Apex Specialty Cnstr Entps ... F ... 714 334-1118
17461 Poplar St Hesperia (92345) ***(P-4101)***

Apex Technology Holdings Inc ... C ... 714 688-7188
2850 E Coronado St Anaheim (92806) ***(P-21257)***

Apex Universal Inc (PA) ... F ... 562 944-8878
11033 Forest Pl Santa Fe Springs (90670) ***(P-23817)***

Apexigen Inc ... E ... 650 931-6236
75 Shoreway Rd Ste C San Carlos (94070) ***(P-8036)***

Apffels Coffee Inc ... E ... 562 309-0400
12115 Pacific St Santa Fe Springs (90670) ***(P-2327)***

Aphex LLC ... F ... 818 767-2929
820 S Palm Ave Ste 21 Alhambra (91803) ***(P-18035)***

Aphex Systems Ltd ... E ... 818 767-2929
3500 N San Fernando Blvd Burbank (91505) ***(P-18036)***

API, North Hollywood *Also called Architectural Plywood Inc* ***(P-4376)***

API Marketing ... F ... 916 632-1946
13020 Earhart Ave Auburn (95602) ***(P-6665)***

Apic Corporation ... D ... 310 642-7975
5800 Uplander Way Culver City (90230) ***(P-18702)***

Apical Instruments Inc ... F ... 650 967-1030
2971 Spring St Redwood City (94063) ***(P-22161)***

Apio Inc (HQ) ... D ... 800 454-1355
4575 W Main St Guadalupe (93434) ***(P-2454)***

Aplus Flash Technology Inc ... F ... 408 382-1100
780 Montague Expy Ste 103 San Jose (95131) ***(P-18703)***

Apnea Sciences Corporation ... F ... 949 226-4421
17 Brownsbury Rd Laguna Niguel (92677) ***(P-9587)***

Apoc, Long Beach *Also called Asphalt Products Oil Corp* ***(P-9401)***

Apogee Electronics Corporation ... E ... 310 584-9394
1715 Berkeley St Santa Monica (90404) ***(P-17761)***

Apollo Instruments Inc ... E ... 949 756-3111
55 Peters Canyon Rd Irvine (92606) ***(P-22059)***

Apollo Manufacturing Services ... F ... 858 271-8009
10360 Sorrento Valley Rd A San Diego (92121) ***(P-17331)***

Apollo Metal Spinning Co Inc ... F ... 562 634-5141
15315 Illinois Ave Paramount (90723) ***(P-13136)***

Apollo Printing & Graphics, Anaheim *Also called Tajen Graphics Inc* ***(P-7127)***

Apollo Sprayers Intl Inc ... F ... 760 727-8300
1040 Joshua Way Vista (92081) ***(P-15117)***

App Winddown LLC ... F ... 213 272-1669
16400 Trojan Way La Mirada (90638) ***(P-3642)***

App Winddown LLC (HQ) ... E ... 213 488-0226
747 Warehouse St Los Angeles (90021) ***(P-3643)***

Apparel Enterprises Co Inc ... E ... 619 474-6916
1900 Wilson Ave Ste B National City (91950) ***(P-3373)***

Apparel House USA, Gardena *Also called Stanzino Inc* ***(P-2764)***

Apparel Limited Inc ... D ... 323 859-2430
3011 E Pico Blvd Los Angeles (90023) ***(P-3374)***

Apparel News Group ... E ... 213 327-1002
110 E 9th St Ste A777 Los Angeles (90079) ***(P-6102)***

Apparel Newsgroup, The, Los Angeles *Also called Mnm Corporation* ***(P-6219)***

Apparel Prod Svcs Globl LLC ... E ... 818 700-3700
8954 Lurline Ave Chatsworth (91311) ***(P-3375)***

Apparel Unified LLC ... F ... 562 639-7233
12136 Del Vista Dr La Mirada (90638) ***(P-7237)***

Apparelway Inc ... F ... 323 581-5888
4516 Loma Vista Ave Vernon (90058) ***(P-2965)***

Appbackr Inc ... F ... 650 272-6129
2251 Yale St Palo Alto (94306) ***(P-24363)***

Appdirect Inc (PA) ... D ... 415 852-3924
650 California St Fl 25 San Francisco (94108) ***(P-24364)***

Appdynamics LLC (HQ) ... C ... 415 442-8400
303 2nd St Fl 8 San Francisco (94107) ***(P-24365)***

Appdynamics, Inc., San Francisco *Also called Appdynamics LLC* ***(P-24365)***

Apperson Inc (PA) ... D ... 562 356-3333
17315 Studebaker Rd # 211 Cerritos (90703) ***(P-7548)***

Appery LLC ... D ... 925 602-5504
1340 Treat Blvd Ste 375 Walnut Creek (94597) ***(P-24366)***

Appetize Technologies Inc ... C ... 877 559-4225
6601 Center Dr W Ste 700 Los Angeles (90045) ***(P-24367)***

Appfolio Inc (PA) ... C ... 805 364-6093
50 Castilian Dr Ste 101 Santa Barbara (93117) ***(P-24368)***

Appfolio Inc ... A ... 866 648-1536
9201 Spectrum San Diego (92123) ***(P-24369)***

Appformix Inc ... F ... 408 899-2240
4 N 2nd St Ste 595 San Jose (95113) ***(P-24370)***

Apple Blossom Mould Mill Work, San Ramon *Also called Blossom Apple Moulding & Mllwk* ***(P-4110)***

Apple Inc (PA) ... A ... 408 996-1010
1 Apple Park Way Cupertino (95014) ***(P-18037)***

Apple Inc ... F ... 408 606-5775
1 Infinite Loop Cupertino (95014) ***(P-18038)***

Apple Paper Converting Inc ... E ... 714 632-3195
3800 E Miraloma Ave Anaheim (92806) ***(P-5697)***

Apple Valley News, Hesperia *Also called Hesperia Resorter* ***(P-5878)***

Applecore ... F ... 310 567-6768
1200 Harkness St Manhattan Beach (90266) ***(P-3875)***

Applica Inc ... E ... 818 565-0011
11651 Vanowen St North Hollywood (91605) ***(P-18039)***

Applied Anodize Inc ... D ... 408 435-9191
622 Charcot Ave Ste D San Jose (95131) ***(P-13333)***

Applied Arospc Structures Corp (PA) ... C ... 209 982-0160
3437 S Airport Way Stockton (95206) ***(P-20738)***

Applied Biosystems LLC (HQ) ... C ... 650 638-5000
5791 Van Allen Way Carlsbad (92008) ***(P-24371)***

Applied Business Software Inc ... F ... 562 426-2188
2847 Gundry Ave Signal Hill (90755) ***(P-24372)***

Applied Cardiac Systems Inc ... D ... 949 855-9366
1 Hughes Ste A Irvine (92618) ***(P-22338)***

Applied Ceramics Inc (PA) ... F ... 510 249-9700
48630 Milmont Dr Fremont (94538) ***(P-18704)***

Applied Cmpsite Structures Inc (HQ) ... C ... 714 990-6300
1195 Columbia St Brea (92821) ***(P-20739)***

Applied Coatings & Linings ... E ... 626 280-6354
3224 Rosemead Blvd El Monte (91731) ***(P-13552)***

Applied Control Electronics ... F ... 530 626-5181
5480 Merchant Cir Placerville (95667) ***(P-17252)***

Applied Engineering, San Jose *Also called Electronic Interface Co Inc* ***(P-19958)***

Applied Expert Systems Inc ... E ... 650 617-2400
999 Commercial St Ste 209 Palo Alto (94303) ***(P-24373)***

Applied Films Corporation ... E ... 408 727-5555
3050 Bowers Ave Santa Clara (95054) ***(P-18705)***

Applied Instrument Tech Inc ... E ... 909 204-3700
2121 Aviation Dr Upland (91786) ***(P-21904)***

Applied Liquid Polymer ... F ... 562 402-6300
17213 Roseton Ave Artesia (90701) ***(P-10844)***

ALPHABETIC

Employee Codes: A=Over 500 employees, B=251-500
C=101-250, D=51-100, E=20-50, F=10-19

2019 California
Manfacturers Register

© Mergent Inc. 1-800-342-5647
1061

Applied Manufacturing LLC ....A....949 713-8000
22872 Avenida Empresa Rcho STA Marg (92688) ***(P-22339)***
Applied Manufacturing Tech Inc ....F....714 630-9530
1464 N Hundley St Anaheim Anaheim (92806) ***(P-14801)***
Applied Materials Inc ....E....408 727-5555
3320 Scott Blvd Santa Clara (95054) ***(P-14907)***
Applied Materials Inc ....E....949 244-1600
4675 Macarthur Ct Newport Beach (92660) ***(P-14908)***
Applied Materials Inc ....E....406 752-2107
1285 Walsh Ave Santa Clara (95050) ***(P-18706)***
Applied Materials Inc ....E....408 727-5555
380 Fairview Way Milpitas (95035) ***(P-14909)***
Applied Materials Inc (PA) ....A....408 727-5555
3050 Bowers Ave Santa Clara (95054) ***(P-14910)***
Applied Materials Inc ....D....408 727-5555
3340 Scott Blvd Santa Clara (95054) ***(P-18707)***
Applied Materials Inc ....F....512 272-3692
3101 Scott Blvd Santa Clara (95054) ***(P-14911)***
Applied Materials Inc ....F....916 786-3900
9000 Foothills Blvd Roseville (95747) ***(P-14912)***
Applied Materials Inc ....E....408 727-5555
3535 Garrett Dr Bldg 100 Santa Clara (95054) ***(P-14913)***
Applied Materials Inc ....E....408 727-5555
974 E Arques Ave Sunnyvale (94085) ***(P-14914)***
Applied Materials Inc ....E....510 687-8018
44050 Fremont Blvd Fremont (94538) ***(P-18708)***
Applied Materials Inc ....E....408 727-5555
1285 Walsh Ave Bldg 21 Santa Clara (95050) ***(P-18709)***
Applied Materials Inc ....D....408 727-5555
2821 Scott Blvd Bldg 17 Santa Clara (95050) ***(P-18710)***
Applied Materials Inc ....F....408 727-5555
3330 Scott Blvd Bldg 6 Santa Clara (95054) ***(P-6103)***
Applied Medical Corporation (PA) ....C....949 713-8000
22872 Avenida Empresa Rcho STA Marg (92688) ***(P-22340)***
Applied Medical Distribution, Rcho STA Marg *Also called Applied Medical Resources Corp* ***(P-22341)***
Applied Medical Resources Corp (HQ) ....B....949 713-8000
22872 Avenida Empresa Rcho STA Marg (92688) ***(P-22341)***
Applied Membranes Inc (PA) ....D....760 727-3711
2450 Business Park Dr Vista (92081) ***(P-16009)***
Applied Micro Circuits Corp (HQ) ....C....408 542-8600
4555 Great America Pkwy # 601 Santa Clara (95054) ***(P-18711)***
Applied Micro Circuits Corp ....E....408 523-1000
455 W Maude Ave Sunnyvale (94085) ***(P-15512)***
Applied Micro Circuits Corp ....E....408 542-8600
4555 Great America Pkwy # 601 Santa Clara (95054) ***(P-18712)***
Applied Microstructures Inc ....F....408 907-2885
2381 Bering Dr San Jose (95131) ***(P-21721)***
Applied Photon Technology Inc ....E....510 780-9500
3346 Arden Rd Hayward (94545) ***(P-17420)***
Applied Physics Systems Inc (PA) ....C....650 965-0500
425 Clyde Ave Mountain View (94043) ***(P-22162)***
Applied Polytech Systems Inc ....E....818 504-9261
26000 Springbrook Ave # 102 Santa Clarita (91350) ***(P-4568)***
Applied Powdercoat Inc (PA) ....E....805 981-1991
3101 Camino Del Sol Oxnard (93030) ***(P-13553)***
Applied Process Equipment ....F....650 365-6895
2620 Bay Rd Redwood City (94063) ***(P-16275)***
Applied Science Inc ....F....530 273-8299
983 Golden Gate Ter Grass Valley (95945) ***(P-22342)***
Applied Sewing Resources Inc ....E....707 748-1614
6440 Goodyear Rd Benicia (94510) ***(P-2721)***
Applied Silicone Corporation ....D....805 525-5657
1050 Cindy Ln Carpinteria (93013) ***(P-8979)***
Applied Silver Inc ....F....888 939-4747
26254 Eden Landing Rd Hayward (94545) ***(P-4605)***
Applied Statistics & MGT Inc ....E....951 699-4600
32848 Wolf Store Rd Ste A Temecula (92592) ***(P-24374)***
Applied Systems LLC ....F....909 854-3200
15342 Valencia Ave Fontana (92335) ***(P-12359)***
Applied Technologies Assoc Inc (HQ) ....C....805 239-9100
3025 Buena Vista Dr Paso Robles (93446) ***(P-22163)***
Applied Thin-Film Products (PA) ....C....510 661-4287
3620 Yale Way Fremont (94538) ***(P-19446)***
Applied Thin-Film Products ....F....510 661-4287
3439 Edison Way Fremont (94538) ***(P-19447)***
Appointy Software Inc ....E....408 634-4141
16 Corning Ave Ste 136 Milpitas (95035) ***(P-24375)***
Appress, Berkeley *Also called Apress L P* ***(P-6104)***
Appro International Inc (HQ) ....E....408 941-8100
220 Devcon Dr San Jose (95112) ***(P-15513)***
Approved Aeronautics LLC ....F....951 200-3730
1240 Graphite Dr Corona (92881) ***(P-20740)***
Approved Networks Inc (PA) ....D....800 590-9535
6 Orchard Ste 150 Lake Forest (92630) ***(P-11345)***
Approved Optics, Lake Forest *Also called Approved Networks Inc* ***(P-11345)***
Approved Turbo Components ....F....559 627-3600
1545 E Acequia Ave Visalia (93292) ***(P-20644)***
Appvance Inc ....E....408 871-0122
1250 Oakmead Pkwy Ste 210 Sunnyvale (94085) ***(P-24376)***
Appware Inc ....E....415 732-9298
65 Enterprise Aliso Viejo (92656) ***(P-24377)***
APR Engineering Inc ....E....562 983-3800
1812 W 9th St Long Beach (90813) ***(P-20984)***
Apress L P ....F....510 549-5930
2588 Telegraph Ave Berkeley (94704) ***(P-6104)***
Apricorn ....E....858 513-2000
12191 Kirkham Rd Poway (92064) ***(P-15670)***
Apricot Designs Inc ....E....626 966-3299
677 Arrow Grand Cir Covina (91722) ***(P-22343)***
Apricus Biosciences Inc (PA) ....F....858 222-8041
11975 El Camino Real San Diego (92130) ***(P-8037)***
April Instrument ....F....650 964-8379
1401 Fallen Leaf Ln Los Altos (94024) ***(P-21722)***
APS Marine, National City *Also called Adept Process Services Inc* ***(P-21019)***
APT, Santa Ana *Also called American Pneumatic Tools Inc* ***(P-14428)***
APT Electronics Inc ....C....714 687-6760
241 N Crescent Way Anaheim (92801) ***(P-18424)***
APT Metal Fabricators Inc ....E....818 896-7478
11164 Bradley Ave Pacoima (91331) ***(P-13165)***
Apta Group Inc (PA) ....E....619 710-8170
7580 Britannia Ct San Diego (92154) ***(P-18713)***
Aptan Corp ....F....213 748-5271
2000 S Main St Los Angeles (90007) ***(P-2722)***
Aptco LLC ....D....661 792-2107
31381 Pond Rd Bldg 2 Mc Farland (93250) ***(P-7820)***
Aptean Inc ....F....310 536-6080
2361 Rosecrans Ave # 375 El Segundo (90245) ***(P-24378)***
Apteligent Inc ....D....415 371-1402
1100 La Avenida St Ste A Mountain View (94043) ***(P-24379)***
Aptiv Digital Inc ....D....818 295-6789
2210 W Olive Ave Fl 2 Burbank (91506) ***(P-24380)***
Aptiv Services 3 (us) LLC (HQ) ....F....949 458-3100
30 Corporate Park Ste 303 Irvine (92606) ***(P-20258)***
Apton Biosystems Inc ....F....650 284-6992
24245 Elise Ct Los Altos Hills (94024) ***(P-21905)***
Aqs, Fremont *Also called All Quality & Services Inc* ***(P-18411)***
Aqua Backflow and Chlorination ....F....909 598-7251
1060 Northgate St Ste C Riverside (92507) ***(P-18381)***
Aqua Logic Inc ....E....858 292-4773
9558 Camino Ruiz San Diego (92126) ***(P-15937)***
Aqua Man Inc (PA) ....F....805 499-5707
2568 Turquoise Cir Newbury Park (91320) ***(P-16010)***
Aqua Man Service, Newbury Park *Also called Aqua Man Inc* ***(P-16010)***
Aqua Measure Instrument Co ....F....909 941-7776
9567 Arrow Rte Ste E Rancho Cucamonga (91730) ***(P-22164)***
Aqua Metals Inc (PA) ....D....510 479-7635
1010 Atlantic Ave Alameda (94501) ***(P-11553)***
Aqua Mix Inc ....D....951 256-3040
250 Benjamin Dr Corona (92879) ***(P-8621)***
Aqua Prieta Tees LLC ....F....714 719-2000
102 Via Murcia San Clemente (92672) ***(P-7238)***
Aqua Products Inc ....E....714 670-0691
6860 Oran Cir Ste 6351 Buena Park (90621) ***(P-15918)***
Aqua Sphere, Vista *Also called Aqua-Lung America Inc* ***(P-23505)***
Aqua-Lung America Inc (PA) ....C....760 597-5000
2340 Cousteau Ct Vista (92081) ***(P-23505)***
Aquadyne Computer Corporation ....F....858 495-1040
9434 Chesapeake Dr # 1204 San Diego (92123) ***(P-17253)***
Aquafine Corporation (HQ) ....D....661 257-4770
29010 Avenue Paine Valencia (91355) ***(P-16011)***
Aquahydrate Inc ....D....310 559-5058
5870 W Jefferson Blvd A Los Angeles (90016) ***(P-2095)***
Aquamar Inc ....C....909 481-4700
10888 7th St Rancho Cucamonga (91730) ***(P-2288)***
Aquaneering Inc ....E....858 578-2028
7960 Stromesa Ct San Diego (92126) ***(P-14042)***
Aquantia Corp (PA) ....D....408 228-8300
91 E Tasman Dr Ste 100 San Jose (95134) ***(P-18714)***
Aquarian Accessories Corp ....E....714 632-0230
1140 N Tustin Ave Anaheim (92807) ***(P-23353)***
Aquarian Coatings Corp ....E....714 632-0230
1140 N Tustin Ave Anaheim (92807) ***(P-13334)***
Aquarian Drumheads, Anaheim *Also called Aquarian Accessories Corp* ***(P-23353)***
Aquarius Rags LLC (PA) ....F....213 895-4400
1218 S Santa Fe Ave Los Angeles (90021) ***(P-3293)***
Aquastar Pool Productions, Ventura *Also called Aquastar Pool Products Inc* ***(P-15052)***
Aquastar Pool Products Inc ....F....877 768-2717
2340 Palma Dr Ste 104 Ventura (93003) ***(P-15052)***
Aquasyn LLC ....F....818 350-0423
9525 Owensmouth Ave Ste E Chatsworth (91311) ***(P-13701)***
Aquatec International Inc ....D....949 225-2200
17422 Pullman St Irvine (92614) ***(P-15053)***
Aquatec Water Systems, Irvine *Also called Aquatec International Inc* ***(P-15053)***
Aquatic Av Inc ....F....408 559-1668
282 Kinney Dr San Jose (95112) ***(P-17762)***
Aquatic Co ....C....714 993-1220
8101 E Kaiser Blvd # 200 Anaheim (92808) ***(P-9895)***
Aquatic Co (PA) ....D....714 993-1220
1700 N Delilah St Corona (92879) ***(P-9896)***
Aquatic Industries Inc ....C....800 877-2005
8101 E Kaiser Blvd # 200 Anaheim (92808) ***(P-9897)***
Aqueos Corporation ....E....805 676-4330
2550 Eastman Ave Ventura (93003) ***(P-14207)***
Aqueous Technologies Corp ....E....909 944-7771
1678 N Maple St Corona (92880) ***(P-16012)***
Aqueous Vets ....F....951 764-9384
288 Jasmine Way Danville (94506) ***(P-16013)***
Aquest Inc ....E....831 622-9296
4120 Pine Meadows Way Pebble Beach (93953) ***(P-12023)***
Aquiesse ....F....805 583-4600
2280 Ward Ave Simi Valley (93065) ***(P-24041)***
Aquila Space Inc ....F....650 224-8559
Nasa Ames Research Park Moffett Field (94035) ***(P-18040)***
AR Casting Inc ....F....818 765-1202
7240 Coldwater Canyon Ave B North Hollywood (91605) ***(P-23237)***
AR Square ....F....909 985-5995
8757 Lanyard Ct Ste 150 Rancho Cucamonga (91730) ***(P-10515)***
AR Tech Aerospace, Fontana *Also called A&R Tarpaulins Inc* ***(P-3776)***

Mergent e-mail: customerrelations@mergent.com 2019 California (P-0000) Products & Services Section entry number
1062 Manufacturers Register (PA)=Parent Co (HQ)=Headquarters (DH)=Div Headquarters

AR Wilson Quarry, Aromas *Also called Granite Rock Co* ***(P-360)***

AR-Ce Inc F 310 771-1960
141 E 162nd St Gardena (90248) ***(P-23705)***

ARA Technology E 408 734-8131
1286 Anvilwood Ave Sunnyvale (94089) ***(P-13335)***

Araca Merchandise LP E 818 743-5400
459 Park Ave San Fernando (91340) ***(P-7239)***

Aradigm Corporation (PA) E 510 265-9000
3929 Point Eden Way Hayward (94545) ***(P-8038)***

Aram Precision Tool Die Inc F 818 998-1000
9758 Cozycroft Ave Chatsworth (91311) ***(P-16276)***

Aranda Tooling Inc D 714 379-6565
13950 Yorba Ave Chino (91710) ***(P-16277)***

Arandas Tortilla Company Inc E 209 464-8675
1318 E Scotts Ave Stockton (95205) ***(P-2455)***

Arandas Woodcraft Inc E 310 538-9945
137 W 157th St Gardena (90248) ***(P-4270)***

Aras Power Technologies (PA) F 408 935-8877
371 Fairview Way Milpitas (95035) ***(P-19319)***

ARB, Lake Forest *Also called Juniper Rock Corporation* ***(P-321)***

Arbiter Systems Incorporated (PA) E 805 237-3831
1324 Vendels Cir Ste 121 Paso Robles (93446) ***(P-21723)***

Arbo Box Inc E 562 404-2726
2900 Supply Ave Commerce (90040) ***(P-4433)***

Arbo Inc E 510 658-3700
1205 Stanford Ave Oakland (94608) ***(P-1348)***

Arbon Equipment Corporation F 414 355-2600
22607 Old Canal Rd Yorba Linda (92887) ***(P-14310)***

Arbonne International LLC (HQ) E 949 770-2610
9400 Jeronimo Rd Irvine (92618) ***(P-8695)***

Arbor Fence Inc E 707 938-3133
22725 8th St E Ste C Sonoma (95476) ***(P-12832)***

Arbor Snowboards Inc E 310 577-1120
102 Washington Blvd Marina Del Rey (90292) ***(P-23506)***

ARC Machines Inc (HQ) D 818 896-9556
14320 Arminta St Panorama City (91402) ***(P-14721)***

ARC Plastics Inc E 562 802-3299
14010 Shoemaker Ave Norwalk (90650) ***(P-9952)***

ARC Products, San Diego *Also called Ssco Manufacturing Inc* ***(P-14740)***

Arcadia Inc E 310 665-0490
2323 Firestone Blvd South Gate (90280) ***(P-12292)***

Arcadia Inc E 916 375-1478
2324 Del Monte St West Sacramento (95691) ***(P-11613)***

Arcadia Inc (PA) C 323 269-7300
2301 E Vernon Ave Vernon (90058) ***(P-11614)***

Arcadia Norcal, Vernon *Also called Arcadia Inc* ***(P-11614)***

Arch Foods Inc E 510 868-6000
610 85th Ave Oakland (94621) ***(P-11876)***

Arch Foods Inc (PA) E 510 331-8352
25817 Clawiter Rd Hayward (94545) ***(P-11877)***

Arch-Rite Inc F 714 630-9305
1062 N Armando St Anaheim (92806) ***(P-4102)***

Archangel Investments LLC F 707 944-9261
6236 Silverado Trl NAPA (94558) ***(P-1646)***

Archer-Daniels-Midland Company F 909 783-7574
455 N 6th St Colton (92324) ***(P-1025)***

Archer-Daniels-Midland Company E 323 266-2750
1543 Calada St Los Angeles (90023) ***(P-1026)***

Archer-Daniels-Midland Company C 510 346-3309
2282 Davis Ct Hayward (94545) ***(P-1027)***

Archer-Daniels-Midland Company F 323 269-8175
3691 Noakes St Los Angeles (90023) ***(P-1028)***

Archer-Daniels-Midland Company C 209 339-1252
350 N Guild Ave Lodi (95240) ***(P-1029)***

Archeyy & Friends LLC E 703 579-7649
3630 Andrews Dr Apt 114 Pleasanton (94588) ***(P-1105)***

Archigraphics, Norwalk *Also called Architectural Cathode Lighting* ***(P-17673)***

Archion, La Verne *Also called Postvision Inc* ***(P-15585)***

Archipelago Inc C 213 743-9200
2440 E 38th St Vernon (90058) ***(P-8696)***

Archipelago Botanicals, Vernon *Also called Archipelago Inc* ***(P-8696)***

Architctral Mllwk Slutions Inc F 760 510-6440
2565 Progress St Vista (92081) ***(P-4103)***

Architctral Mllwk Snta Barbara E 805 965-7011
8 N Nopal St Santa Barbara (93103) ***(P-4104)***

Architctural Facades Unlimited D 408 846-5350
600 E Luchessa Ave Gilroy (95020) ***(P-10878)***

Architectural Blomberg LLC E 916 428-8060
1453 Blair Ave Sacramento (95822) ***(P-12293)***

Architectural Cathode Lighting F 323 581-8800
12123 Pantheon St Norwalk (90650) ***(P-17673)***

Architectural Design Signs Inc (PA) D 951 278-0680
1160 Railroad St Corona (92882) ***(P-23818)***

Architectural Enterprises Inc E 323 268-4000
5821 Randolph St Commerce (90040) ***(P-12833)***

Architectural Foam Products F 707 544-2779
3237 Santa Rosa Ave Santa Rosa (95407) ***(P-9817)***

Architectural Foamstone Inc F 818 767-4500
9757 Glenoaks Blvd Sun Valley (91352) ***(P-5651)***

Architectural Plastics Inc E 707 765-9898
1299 N Mcdowell Blvd Petaluma (94954) ***(P-9953)***

Architectural Plywood Inc E 818 255-1900
7104 Case Ave North Hollywood (91605) ***(P-4376)***

Architectural S Weidner E 800 561-7446
5001 24th St Sacramento (95822) ***(P-23819)***

Architectural Wood Design Inc E 559 292-9104
5672 E Dayton Ave Fresno (93727) ***(P-4105)***

Architectural Woodworking Co D 626 570-4125
582 Monterey Pass Rd Monterey Park (91754) ***(P-5037)***

Archrock Inc F 661 321-0271
3333 Gibson St Bakersfield (93308) ***(P-168)***

Archwood Mfg Group Inc F 818 781-7673
15058 Delano St Van Nuys (91411) ***(P-299)***

Arcmate Manufacturing Corp F 760 489-1140
911 S Andreasen Dr Escondido (92029) ***(P-11928)***

Arcmatic Welding Systems Inc (PA) F 707 643-5517
1175 Nimitz Ave Ste 240 Vallejo (94592) ***(P-25386)***

Arco Industries-Western, Tustin *Also called Edwin T Seki Inc* ***(P-5347)***

Arconic Fstening Systems Rings, Carson *Also called Huck International Inc* ***(P-13072)***

Arconic Fstening Systems Rings, Fontana *Also called Forged Metals Inc* ***(P-13100)***

Arconic Fstening Systems Rings, Sylmar *Also called JW Manufacturing Inc* ***(P-13075)***

Arconic Fstening Systems Rings, Sylmar *Also called Valley-Todeco Inc* ***(P-13089)***

Arconic Global Fas & Rings Inc D 714 871-1550
800 S State College Blvd Fullerton (92831) ***(P-11507)***

Arconic Inc B 805 262-4230
1300 Rancho Conejo Blvd Newbury Park (91320) ***(P-11534)***

Arconic Inc B 714 871-1550
800 S State College Blvd Fullerton (92831) ***(P-11535)***

Arconic Inc B 714 278-8981
801 S Placentia Ave Fullerton (92831) ***(P-11536)***

Arconic Inc B 212 836-2674
3016 Lomita Blvd Torrance (90505) ***(P-11537)***

Arconic Inc B 818 367-2261
12975 Bradley Ave Sylmar (91342) ***(P-11538)***

Arctic Fox, San Marcos *Also called Boinca Inc* ***(P-8707)***

Arctic Glacier California Inc D 209 524-3128
1440 Coldwell Ave Modesto (95350) ***(P-2407)***

Arctic Glacier USA Inc C 310 638-0321
17011 Central Ave Carson (90746) ***(P-2408)***

Arctic Silver Incorporated F 559 740-0912
9826 W Legacy Ave Visalia (93291) ***(P-9423)***

Arctic Slope World Svcs Inc A 805 605-7560
225 Bishop Rd Bldg 23 Vandenberg Afb (93437) ***(P-20541)***

Arctic Wolf Networks Inc (PA) F 408 610-3263
111 W Evelyn Ave Ste 115 Sunnyvale (94086) ***(P-24381)***

Arctic Zero Inc E 619 342-1423
4241 Jutland Dr Ste 305 San Diego (92117) ***(P-656)***

Arcturus Marine Systems D 707 586-3155
517a Martin Ave Rohnert Park (94928) ***(P-13988)***

Arcturus Uav Inc F 707 206-9372
539 Martin Ave Rohnert Park (94928) ***(P-21155)***

Ardagh Glass Inc E 559 675-4700
24441 Avenue 12 Madera (93637) ***(P-10615)***

Ardagh Metal Packaging USA Inc C 310 519-2400
936 Barracuda St San Pedro (90731) ***(P-11855)***

Ardax Systems Inc F 650 591-2656
1669 Industrial Rd San Carlos (94070) ***(P-18041)***

Ardella's, Carson *Also called Richandre Inc* ***(P-1011)***

Ardelyx Inc D 510 745-1700
34175 Ardenwood Blvd Fremont (94555) ***(P-8039)***

Arden & Howe Printing Inc F 916 444-7154
430 17th St Sacramento (95811) ***(P-6666)***

Arden Engineering Inc (HQ) E 714 998-6410
3130 E Miraloma Ave Anaheim (92806) ***(P-20741)***

Arden Engineering Inc E 714 998-6410
1878 N Main St Orange (92865) ***(P-20742)***

Arden/Paradise Manufacturing, Victorville *Also called Paradise Manufacturing Co Inc* ***(P-3803)***

Ardent Mills LLC E 951 201-1170
2020 E Steel Rd Colton (92324) ***(P-1030)***

Ardent Mills LLC F 323 725-0771
5471 Ferguson Dr Commerce (90022) ***(P-1031)***

Ardent Mills LLC E 909 887-3407
19684 Cajon Blvd San Bernardino (92407) ***(P-1032)***

Ardent Systems Inc E 408 526-0100
2040 Ringwood Ave San Jose (95131) ***(P-18425)***

Ardian Inc F 650 417-6500
1380 Shorebird Way Mountain View (94043) ***(P-22344)***

Ardica Technologies Inc F 415 568-9270
2325 3rd St Ste 424 San Francisco (94107) ***(P-18715)***

Arecont Vision Costar LLC D 818 937-0700
425 E Colorado St Fl 7700 Glendale (91205) ***(P-17332)***

Areesys Corporation E 510 979-9601
4055 Clipper Ct Fremont (94538) ***(P-19911)***

Aremac Associates Inc E 626 303-8795
2004 S Myrtle Ave Monrovia (91016) ***(P-16278)***

Aremac Heat Treating Inc E 626 333-3898
330 S 9th Ave City of Industry (91746) ***(P-11793)***

Arena Pharmaceuticals Inc (PA) D 858 453-7200
6154 Nancy Ridge Dr San Diego (92121) ***(P-8040)***

Arens Brothers Logging, Pollock Pines *Also called Dan Arens and Son Inc* ***(P-3984)***

Arete Therapeutics Inc F 650 737-4600
52 Buena Vista Ter San Francisco (94117) ***(P-8041)***

Arevalo Tortilleria Inc E 323 888-1711
3033 Supply Ave Commerce (90040) ***(P-2456)***

Arevalo Tortilleria Inc (PA) D 323 888-1711
1537 W Mines Ave Montebello (90640) ***(P-2457)***

Arga Controls Inc F 626 799-3314
10410 Trademark St Rancho Cucamonga (91730) ***(P-21549)***

Arga Controls A Unit, Rancho Cucamonga *Also called Electro Switch Corp* ***(P-19525)***

Arga's Mexican Food Products, City of Industry *Also called Gruma Corporation* ***(P-1269)***

Argee Mfg Co San Diego Inc D 619 449-5050
9550 Pathway St Santee (92071) ***(P-9954)***

Argen Corporation F 858 455-7900
8515 Miralani Dr San Diego (92126) ***(P-22857)***

Argen Corporation (PA) C 858 455-7900
5855 Oberlin Dr San Diego (92121) ***(P-11543)***

Employee Codes: A=Over 500 employees, B=251-500
C=101-250, D=51-100, E=20-50, F=10-19

2019 California
Manfacturers Register

© Mergent Inc. 1-800-342-5647
1063

Argenti Inc ....E....714 666-8084
2870 E Via Martens Anaheim (92806) ***(P-16279)***
Argo Spring Mfg Co Inc ....D....800 252-2740
13930 Shoemaker Ave Norwalk (90650) ***(P-13748)***
Argonaut ....E....310 822-1629
5355 Mcconnell Ave Los Angeles (90066) ***(P-5762)***
Arguello Inc ....E....805 567-1632
17100 Clle Mariposa Reina Goleta (93117) ***(P-125)***
Argus Courier, Petaluma *Also called St Louis Post-Dispatch LLC* ***(P-6057)***
Argyle Precision, Orange *Also called ISI Detention Contg Group Inc* ***(P-16593)***
ARI Industries Inc ....D....714 993-3700
17018 Edwards Rd Cerritos (90703) ***(P-15938)***
Aria Systems Inc (PA) ....D....415 852-7250
100 Pine St Ste 2450 San Francisco (94111) ***(P-24382)***
Aria Technologies Inc ....E....925 292-1616
102 Wright Brothers Ave Livermore (94551) ***(P-11643)***
Arias Industries Inc ....E....310 532-9737
275 Roswell Ave Long Beach (90803) ***(P-20259)***
Arias Pistons, Long Beach *Also called Arias Industries Inc* ***(P-20259)***
Ariat International Inc (PA) ....B....510 477-7000
3242 Whipple Rd Union City (94587) ***(P-10572)***
Ariba Inc (HQ) ....C....650 849-4000
3420 Hillview Ave Bldg 3 Palo Alto (94304) ***(P-24383)***
Aridis Pharmaceuticals Inc ....E....408 385-1742
5941 Optical Ct San Jose (95138) ***(P-8042)***
Aries 33 LLC ....E....310 355-8330
3400 S Main St Los Angeles (90007) ***(P-3137)***
Aries Prepared Beef Company ....E....818 771-0181
11850 Sheldon St Sun Valley (91352) ***(P-1106)***
Aries Research Inc ....F....925 818-1078
46750 Fremont Blvd # 107 Fremont (94538) ***(P-15671)***
Aries Solutions, Fremont *Also called Aries Research Inc* ***(P-15671)***
Arista Foods Corporation ....F....714 666-1001
1240 N Barsten Way Anaheim (92806) ***(P-980)***
Aristamd Inc ....F....858 750-4777
11099 N Torrey Pines Rd # 290 La Jolla (92037) ***(P-24384)***
Ariza Cheese Co Inc ....E....562 630-4144
7602 Jackson St Paramount (90723) ***(P-564)***
Arizona Paper Box Co Inc ....E....619 660-9566
10605 Jamacha Blvd Spring Valley (91978) ***(P-5503)***
Arizona Portland Cement, Glendora *Also called Calportland Company* ***(P-10748)***
Ark Newspaper, The, Belvedere Tiburon *Also called Ammi Publishing Inc* ***(P-5758)***
Arkal Medical Inc ....E....510 933-1950
46575 Fremont Blvd Fremont (94538) ***(P-22345)***
Arkeia Software Inc (HQ) ....F....760 431-1319
1808 Aston Ave Ste 235 Carlsbad (92008) ***(P-24385)***
Arkema Coating Resins, Torrance *Also called Arkema Inc* ***(P-7658)***
Arkema Inc ....C....310 214-5327
19206 Hawthorne Blvd Torrance (90503) ***(P-7658)***
Arktura LLC (PA) ....E....310 532-1050
18225 S Figueroa St Gardena (90248) ***(P-4906)***
Arlon EMD, Rancho Cucamonga *Also called EMD Specialty Materials LLC* ***(P-18474)***
Arlon Graphics LLC ....C....714 985-6300
200 Boysenberry Ln Placentia (92870) ***(P-9696)***
Arlon LLC ....C....714 540-2811
2811 S Harbor Blvd Santa Ana (92704) ***(P-9955)***
Arm Inc ....F....408 576-1500
150 Rose Orchard Way San Jose (95134) ***(P-18716)***
Arm Inc (HQ) ....B....408 576-1500
150 Rose Orchard Way San Jose (95134) ***(P-18717)***
Arm Electronics Inc ....E....916 787-1100
8860 Industrial Ave # 140 Roseville (95678) ***(P-19912)***
Arm Inc ....C....858 453-1900
5375 Mira Sorrento Pl # 540 San Diego (92121) ***(P-18718)***
Armanino Foods Distinction Inc ....E....510 441-9300
30588 San Antonio St Hayward (94544) ***(P-981)***
Armenco Catrg Trck Mfg Co Inc ....F....818 768-0400
11819 Vose St North Hollywood (91605) ***(P-20191)***
Arminak Solutions LLC ....E....626 385-5858
1361 Mountain View Cir Azusa (91702) ***(P-8697)***
Armite Laboratories Inc ....F....949 646-9035
1560 Superior Ave Ste A4 Costa Mesa (92627) ***(P-9424)***
Armo Biosciences Inc ....E....650 779-5075
575 Chesapeake Dr Redwood City (94063) ***(P-8043)***
Armona Frozen Food Lockers ....F....559 584-3948
10870 14th Ave Armona (93202) ***(P-465)***
Armorcast Products Company ....E....909 390-1365
500 S Dupont Ave Ontario (91761) ***(P-9956)***
Armored Group Inc ....E....818 767-3030
11555 Cantara St North Hollywood (91605) ***(P-4434)***
Armored Mobility Inc ....E....831 430-9899
5610 Scotts Valley Dr B332 Scotts Valley (95066) ***(P-9747)***
Armorstruxx LLC ....F....949 366-1300
130 Calle Iglesia San Clemente (92672) ***(P-20743)***
Armorstruxx LLC (PA) ....D....209 365-9400
850 Thurman St Lodi (95240) ***(P-20744)***
Arms Precision Inc ....F....951 273-1800
169 Radio Rd Corona (92879) ***(P-16280)***
Armstrong Petroleum Corp (PA) ....E....949 650-4000
1080 W 17th St Costa Mesa (92627) ***(P-23)***
Armstrong Technology Inc ....E....530 888-6262
12780 Earhart Ave Auburn (95602) ***(P-16281)***
Armtec Countermeasures Co (HQ) ....F....760 398-0143
85901 Avenue 53 Coachella (92236) ***(P-21258)***
Armtec Defense Products Co (HQ) ....B....760 398-0143
85901 Avenue 53 Coachella (92236) ***(P-13694)***
Arna Trading Inc (PA) ....F....760 940-2775
2892 S Santa Fe Ave # 109 San Marcos (92069) ***(P-5265)***
Arnies Supply Service Ltd (PA) ....E....323 263-1696
1541 N Ditman Ave Los Angeles (90063) ***(P-4451)***
Arnold & Egan Manufacturing Co ....E....415 822-2700
1515 Griffith St San Francisco (94124) ***(P-5038)***
Arnold Electronics Inc ....F....714 646-8343
1907 Nancita Cir Placentia (92870) ***(P-18426)***
Arnold-Gonsalves Engrg Inc ....E....909 465-1579
5731 Chino Ave Chino (91710) ***(P-16282)***
Aromyx Corporation ....F....650 430-8100
605 Tasman Dr Apt 1101 Sunnyvale (94089) ***(P-21499)***
Aronson Manufacturing, Van Nuys *Also called Nat Aronson & Associates Inc* ***(P-9501)***
Arrhenius, Santa Clara *Also called Prodigy Surface Tech Inc* ***(P-13483)***
Arrive Technologies Inc ....F....888 864-6959
3693 Westchester Dr Roseville (95747) ***(P-18719)***
Arrive-Ai Inc ....F....949 221-0166
16751 Millikan Ave Irvine (92606) ***(P-24042)***
Arrk Product Dev Group USA Inc ....C....858 552-1587
4747 Executive Dr Ste 550 San Diego (92121) ***(P-12487)***
Arrow Abrasive Company Inc ....F....562 869-2282
12033 1/2 Regentview Ave Downey (90241) ***(P-11288)***
Arrow Diecasting Inc ....F....323 245-8439
4031 Goodwin Ave Los Angeles (90039) ***(P-11688)***
Arrow Electric Motor Service ....F....559 266-0104
645 Broadway St Fresno (93721) ***(P-25453)***
Arrow Engineering ....E....626 960-2806
4946 Azusa Canyon Rd Irwindale (91706) ***(P-16283)***
Arrow Head Regional Med Ctr, Colton *Also called County of San Bernardino* ***(P-21465)***
Arrow Industries, Buellton *Also called Gavial Holdings Inc* ***(P-19550)***
Arrow Screw Products Inc ....E....805 928-2269
941 W Mccoy Ln Santa Maria (93455) ***(P-16284)***
Arrow Sign Co (PA) ....E....209 931-5522
1051 46th Ave Oakland (94601) ***(P-23820)***
Arrow Sign Co ....E....209 931-7852
3133 N Ad Art Rd Stockton (95215) ***(P-23821)***
Arrow Sign Company, Oakland *Also called Arrow Sign Co* ***(P-23820)***
Arrow Steel Products Inc ....F....909 349-1032
13171 Santa Ana Ave Fontana (92337) ***(P-11467)***
Arrow Transit Mix ....E....661 945-7600
507 E Avenue L12 Lancaster (93535) ***(P-11043)***
Arrow Truck Bodies & Equipment ....E....909 947-3991
1639 S Campus Ave Ontario (91761) ***(P-20192)***
Arrow Truck Sales Incorporated ....F....909 829-2365
10175 Cherry Ave Fontana (92335) ***(P-20193)***
Arrowhead Brass & Plumbing LLC ....D....323 221-9137
4900 Valley Blvd Los Angeles (90032) ***(P-12024)***
Arrowhead Ice, Torrance *Also called Southern California Ice Co* ***(P-2421)***
Arrowhead Pharmaceuticals Inc (PA) ....F....626 304-3400
225 S Lake Ave Ste 1050 Pasadena (91101) ***(P-8044)***
Arrowhead Press Inc ....E....626 358-1168
220 W Maple Ave Ste B Monrovia (91016) ***(P-6667)***
Arrowhead Products Corporation ....A....714 828-7770
4411 Katella Ave Los Alamitos (90720) ***(P-20745)***
Arroyo Grande Mushroom Farm, Arroyo Grande *Also called Spawn Mate Inc* ***(P-9074)***
Arroyo Seco Racquet Club ....F....323 258-4178
920 Lohman Ln South Pasadena (91030) ***(P-9588)***
Arroyo Seco Rock, King City *Also called Wm J Clark Trucking Svc Inc* ***(P-393)***
ARS, Burbank *Also called Hutchinson Arospc & Indust Inc* ***(P-20839)***
ARS Enterprises (PA) ....F....562 946-3505
15554 Minnesota Ave Paramount (90723) ***(P-22701)***
Arsenic Inc ....F....310 701-7559
530 S Hewitt St Unit 119 Los Angeles (90013) ***(P-6105)***
Arsh Incorporated ....F....408 971-2722
2300 Stevens Creek Blvd San Jose (95128) ***(P-6668)***
Arsys Inc ....F....714 654-7681
1428 S Grand Ave Santa Ana (92705) ***(P-14915)***
Art, El Dorado Hills *Also called Alpha Research & Tech Inc* ***(P-15389)***
Art & Sign Production Inc ....F....818 245-6945
3651 E Chevy Chase Dr Glendale (91206) ***(P-23822)***
Art Brand Studios LLC (PA) ....E....408 201-5000
18715 Madrone Pkwy Morgan Hill (95037) ***(P-6434)***
Art Bronze Inc ....E....818 897-2222
11275 San Fernando Rd San Fernando (91340) ***(P-11754)***
Art Craft Staturary Inc ....E....510 633-1411
10441 Edes Ave Oakland (94603) ***(P-11232)***
Art Dreams Home Inc ....D....805 642-6444
1834 Palma Dr Ste G Ventura (93003) ***(P-4606)***
Art Glass Etc Inc ....E....805 644-4494
3111 Golf Course Dr Ventura (93003) ***(P-4106)***
Art Impressions Inc ....F....818 591-0105
23586 Calabasas Rd # 210 Calabasas (91302) ***(P-6435)***
Art Manufacturers Inc ....E....714 540-9125
623 Young St Santa Ana (92705) ***(P-17526)***
Art Masterpiece Gallery ....F....323 277-9448
4950 S Santa Fe Ave Vernon (90058) ***(P-3707)***
Art Microelectronics Corp ....F....626 447-7503
5917 Oak Ave Ste 201 Temple City (91780) ***(P-18720)***
Art Mold Die Casting Inc ....F....818 767-6464
11872 Sheldon St Sun Valley (91352) ***(P-14480)***
Art of Muse ....E....510 644-1870
2222 5th St Berkeley (94710) ***(P-4669)***
Art Plates, Rancho Cucamonga *Also called Pitbull Gym Incorporated* ***(P-10275)***
Art Services Melrose ....F....310 247-1452
626 N Almont Dr West Hollywood (90069) ***(P-9957)***
Art Signworks Inc ....F....951 698-8484
41785 Elm St Ste 302 Murrieta (92562) ***(P-23823)***
Artcrafters Cabinets Inc ....E....818 752-8960
5446 Cleon Ave North Hollywood (91601) ***(P-4271)***
Arte De Mexico Inc (PA) ....D....818 753-4559
1000 Chestnut St Burbank (91506) ***(P-4977)***
Arte De Mexico Inc ....E....818 753-4510
5506 Riverton Ave North Hollywood (91601) ***(P-17584)***

Mergent e-mail: customerrelations@mergent.com
1064
2019 California
Manufacturers Register
(P-0000) Products & Services Section entry number
(PA)=Parent Co (HQ)=Headquarters (DH)=Div Headquarters

Artech Industries Inc ....E....951 276-3331
1966 Keats Dr Riverside (92501) ***(P-19448)***
Arteez ....F....916 631-0473
3600 Sunrise Blvd Ste 4 Rancho Cordova (95742) ***(P-7240)***
Arteffex Conceptioneering ....F....818 506-5358
911 Mayo St Los Angeles (90042) ***(P-24043)***
Artehouse, San Rafael *Also called One Bella Casa Inc* ***(P-3736)***
Artemis Pet Food Company Inc ....F....818 771-0700
18010 S Figueroa St Gardena (90248) ***(P-1122)***
Arteris Inc ....E....408 470-7300
595 Millich Dr Ste 200 Campbell (95008) ***(P-18721)***
Arteris Holdings Inc ....E....408 470-7300
591 W Hamilton Ave # 250 Campbell (95008) ***(P-18722)***
Artesa Winery, NAPA *Also called Codorniu Napa Inc* ***(P-1700)***
Artesia Sawdust Products Inc ....E....909 947-5983
13434 S Ontario Ave Ontario (91761) ***(P-4029)***
Arthrex Inc ....D....805 964-8104
460 Ward Dr Ste C Santa Barbara (93111) ***(P-22346)***
Arthur Dogswell LLC (PA) ....E....888 559-8833
11301 W Olympic Blvd Los Angeles (90064) ***(P-1107)***
Arthur P Lamarre & Sons Inc ....F....209 667-6557
1918 Paulson Rd Ste 101 Turlock (95380) ***(P-12488)***
Arthurmade Plastics Inc ....D....323 721-7325
2131 Garfield Ave Commerce (90040) ***(P-9958)***
Artifact Puzzles ....F....650 283-0589
180 Constitution Dr Ste 6 Menlo Park (94025) ***(P-23406)***
Artifacts International, Chula Vista *Also called Califrnia Furn Collections Inc* ***(P-4908)***
Artificial Grass Liquidators ....E....951 677-3377
28071 Diaz Rd Ste A Temecula (92590) ***(P-24044)***
Artisan Brewers LLC ....E....510 567-4926
1933 Davis St Ste 177 San Leandro (94577) ***(P-1561)***
Artisan Crust ....E....323 759-7000
754 E Florence Ave Los Angeles (90001) ***(P-1177)***
Artisan House Inc ....E....818 767-7476
8238 Lankershim Blvd North Hollywood (91605) ***(P-13919)***
Artisan Moss LLC ....F....833 667-7278
3450 Palmer Dr Ste 4 Cameron Park (95682) ***(P-1518)***
Artisan Nameplate Awards Corp ....E....714 556-6222
2730 S Shannon St Santa Ana (92704) ***(P-7241)***
Artisan Screen Printing Inc ....C....626 815-2700
1055 W 5th St Azusa (91702) ***(P-7242)***
Artissimo Designs LLC (HQ) ....E....310 906-3700
2100 E Grand Ave Ste 400 El Segundo (90245) ***(P-5698)***
Artistic Concepts ....F....323 257-8101
3293 N San Fernando Rd Los Angeles (90065) ***(P-4932)***
Artistic Coverings Inc ....E....562 404-9343
14135 Artesia Blvd Cerritos (90703) ***(P-9818)***
Artistic Plastics Inc ....F....951 808-9700
725 E Harrison St Corona (92879) ***(P-9959)***
Artistic Pltg & Met Finshg Inc ....D....619 661-1691
2801 E Miraloma Ave Anaheim (92806) ***(P-13336)***
Artistic Welding Inc ....D....310 515-4922
505 E Gardena Blvd Gardena (90248) ***(P-12489)***
Artistry In Motion Inc ....E....818 994-7388
19411 Londelius St Northridge (91324) ***(P-5699)***
Artiva USA Inc ....E....562 298-8968
12866 Ann St Ste 1 Santa Fe Springs (90670) ***(P-17527)***
Artiva USA Inc (PA) ....E....909 628-1388
13901 Magnolia Ave Chino (91710) ***(P-17528)***
Arto Brick & Tile, Gardena *Also called Arto Brick Veneer Mfgco* ***(P-10772)***
Arto Brick Veneer Mfgco ....E....310 768-8500
15209 S Broadway Gardena (90248) ***(P-10772)***
Arts & Crafts Press, San Diego *Also called Rush Press Inc* ***(P-7091)***
Arts Custom Cabinets Inc ....F....559 562-2766
897 E Tulare Rd Lindsay (93247) ***(P-4670)***
Arts Elegance Inc ....E....626 793-4794
154 W Bellevue Dr Pasadena (91105) ***(P-23238)***
Artsigns, Sunnyvale *Also called Sign Solutions Inc* ***(P-23965)***
Artsons Manufacturing Company ....E....323 773-3469
4915 Cecilia St Cudahy (90201) ***(P-11379)***
Arturo Campos ....F....951 300-2111
796 Palmyrita Ave Ste B Riverside (92507) ***(P-13337)***
Aruba Networks Inc (HQ) ....B....408 227-4500
3333 Scott Blvd Santa Clara (95054) ***(P-15672)***
Aruba Networks Inc ....E....408 227-4500
392 Acoma Way Fremont (94539) ***(P-18042)***
Aruba Networks Inc ....F....408 227-4500
390 W Caribbean Dr Sunnyvale (94089) ***(P-18043)***
Aruba Networks Cafe, Santa Clara *Also called Aruba Networks Inc* ***(P-15672)***
Arvato Services, Valencia *Also called Bertelsmann Inc* ***(P-6312)***
Arvi Manufacturing Inc ....F....408 734-4776
1256 Birchwood Dr Ste B Sunnyvale (94089) ***(P-13920)***
Arvin Tiller Printing, Bakersfield *Also called Reed Print Inc* ***(P-6025)***
Arvinyl Laminates LP ....E....951 371-7800
233 N Sherman Ave Corona (92882) ***(P-9697)***
ARX Pax Labs Inc ....F....408 335-7630
20 S Santa Cruz Ave # 102 Los Gatos (95030) ***(P-21259)***
Arxis Technology Inc ....E....805 306-7890
2468 Tapo Canyon Rd Simi Valley (93063) ***(P-24386)***
Aryzta Holdings IV LLC (HQ) ....C....310 417-4700
6080 Center Dr Ste 900 Los Angeles (90045) ***(P-1349)***
Aryzta LLC ....C....909 472-3500
1220 S Baker Ave Ontario (91761) ***(P-1350)***
Aryzta LLC ....C....949 261-7400
2350 Pullman St Santa Ana (92705) ***(P-1351)***
Aryzta LLC (HQ) ....C....310 417-4700
6080 Center Dr Ste 900 Los Angeles (90045) ***(P-1352)***
Aryzta US Holdings I Corp ....A....800 938-1900
14490 Catalina St San Leandro (94577) ***(P-1353)***

Arzy Company Inc ....F....213 627-7344
650 S Hill St Ste 915 Los Angeles (90014) ***(P-23239)***
Arzy Company Fine Jewelry, Los Angeles *Also called Arzy Company Inc* ***(P-23239)***
AS Match Dyeing Co Inc ....C....323 277-0470
2522 E 37th St Vernon (90058) ***(P-2877)***
Asa, Oxnard *Also called Advanced Structural Tech Inc* ***(P-20244)***
Asa Corporation ....F....530 305-3720
3111 Sunset Blvd Ste V Rocklin (95677) ***(P-21906)***
Asante Technologies Inc (PA) ....E....408 435-8388
2223 Oakland Rd San Jose (95131) ***(P-15673)***
Asante Technologies Inc ....F....408 435-8388
673 S Milpitas Blvd # 100 Milpitas (95035) ***(P-15674)***
Asante Technologies Inc ....E....408 435-8388
47341 Bayside Pkwy Fremont (94538) ***(P-15675)***
Asbury Graphite Inc California ....F....510 799-3636
2855 Franklin Canyon Rd Rodeo (94572) ***(P-9320)***
ASC Group Inc ....C....818 896-1101
12243 Branford St Sun Valley (91352) ***(P-18723)***
ASC Process Systems Inc ....C....818 833-0088
28402 Livingston Ave Valencia (91355) ***(P-15252)***
ASC Profiles Inc ....C....909 823-0401
10905 Beech Ave Fontana (92337) ***(P-12114)***
ASC Profiles LLC ....E....916 376-2899
5001 Bailey Loop McClellan (95652) ***(P-12918)***
Ascendis Pharma Inc ....F....650 352-8389
500 Emerson St Palo Alto (94301) ***(P-8045)***
Ascent Manufacturing LLC ....E....714 540-6414
2545 W Via Palma Anaheim (92801) ***(P-13166)***
Ascent Technology Inc ....E....408 213-1080
838 Jury Ct San Jose (95112) ***(P-12490)***
Ascent Tooling Group LLC ....A....949 455-0665
1395 S Lyon St Santa Ana (92705) ***(P-21260)***
Ascert LLC (PA) ....F....415 339-8500
759 Bridgeway Sausalito (94965) ***(P-24387)***
Asclemed Usa Inc ....F....310 218-4146
379 Van Ness Ave Ste 1403 Torrance (90501) ***(P-8046)***
Asco Automatic Switch ....F....714 937-0811
333 City Blvd W Ste 2140 Orange (92868) ***(P-13702)***
Asco Automatic Switch Co, Orange *Also called Asco Automatic Switch* ***(P-13702)***
Asco Sintering Co ....E....323 725-3550
2750 Garfield Ave Commerce (90040) ***(P-11929)***
Ascor Inc (HQ) ....E....925 328-4650
4650 Norris Canyon Rd San Ramon (94583) ***(P-17254)***
Asd, Canoga Park *Also called Advanced Safety Devices LLC* ***(P-21702)***
Asdak International ....F....714 449-0733
1809 1/2 N Orngethorpe Pa Anaheim (92801) ***(P-10827)***
Asea Power Systems ....E....714 896-9695
15272 Newsboy Cir Huntington Beach (92649) ***(P-19449)***
Aseptic Innovations Inc ....E....714 584-2110
4940 E Landon Dr Anaheim (92807) ***(P-10616)***
Aseptic Sltons USA Vntures LLC ....C....951 736-9230
484 Alcoa Cir Corona (92880) ***(P-2096)***
Aseptic Solutions USA-Corona, Corona *Also called Aseptic Sltons USA Vntures LLC* ***(P-2096)***
Aseptic Technology LLC ....D....714 694-0168
24855 Corbit Pl Yorba Linda (92887) ***(P-10617)***
Ashford Textiles LLC ....E....310 327-4670
1535 W 139th St Gardena (90249) ***(P-2989)***
Ashka Print LLC ....E....323 980-6008
600 E Wash Blvd Ste W4 Los Angeles (90015) ***(P-7243)***
Ashley Furnishing Homestore, Montclair *Also called Ashley Furniture Inds Inc* ***(P-4671)***
Ashley Furniture Inds Inc ....B....909 652-6840
5055 S Montclair Plaza Ln Montclair (91763) ***(P-4671)***
Ashley Furniture Inds Inc ....A....909 825-4900
2250 W Lugonia Ave Redlands (92374) ***(P-4672)***
Ashtel Dental, Ontario *Also called Ashtel Studios Inc* ***(P-22927)***
Ashtel Studios Inc ....E....909 434-0911
1610 E Philadelphia St Ontario (91761) ***(P-22927)***
Asi Semiconductor Inc ....E....818 982-1200
7525 Ethel Ave North Hollywood (91605) ***(P-18724)***
Asi Tooling LLC ....F....760 744-2520
1780 La Costa Meadows Dr # 103 San Marcos (92078) ***(P-14602)***
Asi/Silica Machinery LLC (PA) ....E....818 920-1962
6404 Independence Ave Woodland Hills (91367) ***(P-11755)***
Asia America Enterprise Inc ....E....650 348-2333
1321 N Carolan Ave Burlingame (94010) ***(P-6669)***
Asia Food Inc ....F....626 284-1328
566 Monterey Pass Rd Monterey Park (91754) ***(P-420)***
Asia Pacific California Inc (PA) ....E....650 513-6189
1648 Gilbreth Rd Burlingame (94010) ***(P-5763)***
Asia Pacific California Inc ....E....626 281-8500
2121 W Micaion Rd Ste 207 Alhambra (91803) ***(P-5764)***
Asia Plastics Inc ....E....626 448-8100
9347 Rush St South El Monte (91733) ***(P-5587)***
Asian America Business Journal, San Diego *Also called Vangie L Cortes* ***(P-6078)***
Asian Week (PA) ....F....415 397-0220
809 Sacramento St San Francisco (94108) ***(P-5765)***
Asiana Cuisine Enterprises Inc ....A....310 327-2223
22771 S Wstn Ave Ste 100 Torrance (90501) ***(P-2458)***
Asias Finest ....F....619 297-0800
407 Camino Del Rio S San Diego (92108) ***(P-11878)***
Asic Advantage Inc ....D....408 541-8686
3850 N 1st St San Jose (95134) ***(P-18725)***
Asigma Corporation ....F....760 966-3103
2930 San Luis Rey Rd Oceanside (92058) ***(P-16285)***
Ask Gold Company Inc ....E....213 622-4005
716 S Olive St Fl 3 Los Angeles (90014) ***(P-23240)***
Askgene Pharma Inc ....F....805 807-9868
5217 Verdugo Way Ste A Camarillo (93012) ***(P-8047)***

Employee Codes: A=Over 500 employees, B=251-500
C=101-250, D=51-100, E=20-50, F=10-19
2019 California
Manfacturers Register
© Mergent Inc. 1-800-342-5647
1065

Asm Construction Inc ....E....619 449-1966
1947 John Towers Ave El Cajon (92020) ***(P-12491)***
Asm Precision Inc ....F....707 584-7950
613 Martin Ave Ste 106 Rohnert Park (94928) ***(P-12492)***
Asml Inc ....F....714 754-1912
150 Paularino Ave Costa Mesa (92626) ***(P-6670)***
Asml USA, San Diego *Also called Cymer LLC* ***(P-19940)***
ASPE Inc ....F....951 296-2595
42295 Avenida Alvarado # 5 Temecula (92590) ***(P-14802)***
Aspect Software Inc ....E....408 595-5002
101 Academy Ste 130 Irvine (92617) ***(P-24388)***
Aspen Brands Corporation ....F....702 946-9430
1305 E Wakeham Ave Santa Ana (92705) ***(P-4673)***
Aspen Medical Products ....D....949 681-0200
6481 Oak Cyn Irvine (92618) ***(P-22702)***
Asphalt Fabric and Engrg Inc ....D....562 997-4129
2683 Lime Ave Signal Hill (90755) ***(P-23507)***
Asphalt Products Oil Corp (HQ) ....F....562 423-6471
5903 N Paramount Blvd Long Beach (90805) ***(P-9401)***
Asrc Aerospace Corp ....E....650 604-5946
Nasa Ames Research Ctr Mountain View (94035) ***(P-21261)***
Asrock America Inc ....E....909 590-8308
13848 Magnolia Ave Chino (91710) ***(P-18427)***
Assa Abloy Entrance Sys US Inc ....F....916 686-4116
9733 Kent St 100 Elk Grove (95624) ***(P-19913)***
Assa Abloy Entrance Systems US ....D....714 578-0526
1520 S Sinclair St Anaheim (92806) ***(P-19914)***
Assa Abloy Rsdential Group Inc (HQ) ....C....626 961-0413
15250 Stafford St City of Industry (91744) ***(P-11930)***
Assali Hulling & Shelling ....F....209 883-4263
8618 E Whitmore Ave Hughson (95326) ***(P-1482)***
Assault Industries Inc ....F....714 799-6711
12691 Monarch St Garden Grove (92841) ***(P-21222)***
Assembly Automation Industries ....E....626 303-2777
1849 Business Center Dr Duarte (91010) ***(P-14748)***
Assembly Technologies Co LLC ....F....714 979-4400
2921 W Central Ave Ste B Santa Ana (92704) ***(P-18428)***
Asset Equity Holdings LLC ....F....925 339-5440
34413 Cleveland Ave San Diego (92163) ***(P-21724)***
Asset Science LLC ....E....858 255-7982
17150 Via Del Campo # 200 San Diego (92127) ***(P-24389)***
Assetsmart, Calabasas *Also called PMS Systems Corporation* ***(P-25068)***
Assisvis Inc ....E....909 628-2031
10780 Mulberry Ave Fontana (92337) ***(P-9775)***
Assoc Ready Mixed Concrete ....F....562 923-7281
9645 Washburn Rd Downey (90241) ***(P-11044)***
Assoc Ready Mixed Concrete ....F....949 580-1844
25901 Towne Centre Dr El Toro (92610) ***(P-11045)***
Assoc Students University CA ....E....510 590-7874
112 Hearst Gym Rm 4520 Berkeley (94720) ***(P-6436)***
Associated Arospc Activities ....E....510 483-9020
600 California St Fl 6 San Francisco (94108) ***(P-20645)***
Associated Desert Newspaper (HQ) ....E....760 337-3400
205 N 8th St El Centro (92243) ***(P-5766)***
Associated Desert Shoppers (HQ) ....D....760 346-1729
73400 Highway 111 Palm Desert (92260) ***(P-6437)***
Associated Electrics Inc ....E....949 544-7500
26021 Commercentre Dr Lake Forest (92630) ***(P-23407)***
Associated Gear, Santa Fe Springs *Also called Quality Gears Inc* ***(P-15244)***
Associated Microbreweries Inc ....D....858 587-2739
9675 Scranton Rd San Diego (92121) ***(P-1562)***
Associated Microbreweries Inc ....D....714 546-2739
901 S Coast Dr Ste A Costa Mesa (92626) ***(P-1563)***
Associated Microbreweries Inc (PA) ....E....858 273-2739
5985 Santa Fe St San Diego (92109) ***(P-1564)***
Associated Microbreweries Inc ....C....619 234-2739
1157 Columbia St San Diego (92101) ***(P-1565)***
Associated Plating Company ....E....562 946-5525
9636 Ann St Santa Fe Springs (90670) ***(P-13338)***
Associated Ready Mix Con Inc (PA) ....E....949 253-2800
4621 Teller Ave Ste 130 Newport Beach (92660) ***(P-11046)***
Associated Ready Mix Concrete, Baldwin Park *Also called Standard Concrete Products* ***(P-11186)***
Associated Ready Mix Concrete ....E....818 504-3100
8946 Bradley Ave Sun Valley (91352) ***(P-11047)***
Associated Ready Mixed Con, Gardena *Also called A & A Ready Mixed Concrete Inc* ***(P-11023)***
Associated Screw Machine Pdts ....E....510 783-3831
23978 Connecticut St A Hayward (94545) ***(P-13013)***
Associated Students UCLA ....C....310 825-2787
308 Westwood Plz Ste 118 Los Angeles (90095) ***(P-5767)***
Associated Wire Rope & Rigging ....E....310 448-5444
910 Mahar Ave Wilmington (90744) ***(P-2968)***
Assoluto Inc ....F....213 748-1116
215 S Santa Fe Ave Apt 5 Los Angeles (90012) ***(P-3376)***
AST Power LLC ....E....949 226-2275
54 Coral Reef Newport Coast (92657) ***(P-19827)***
AST Sportswear Inc ....B....714 223-2030
2701 E Imperial Hwy Brea (92821) ***(P-3571)***
Asta Construction Co Inc (PA) ....E....707 374-6472
1090 Saint Francis Way Rio Vista (94571) ***(P-97)***
Astea International Inc ....E....949 784-5000
8 Hughes Irvine (92618) ***(P-24390)***
Astec International Holding, Carlsbad *Also called Aih LLC* ***(P-19438)***
Asteelflash USA Corp (HQ) ....C....510 440-2840
4211 Starboard Dr Fremont (94538) ***(P-18429)***
Astera Software Corporation ....F....805 579-0004
310 N Westlake Blvd # 140 Westlake Village (91362) ***(P-24391)***
Asteres Inc (PA) ....E....858 777-8600
4110 Sorrento Valley Blvd San Diego (92121) ***(P-15893)***
Astex Pharmaceuticals Inc (HQ) ....D....925 560-0100
4420 Rosewood Dr Ste 200 Pleasanton (94588) ***(P-8048)***
Asthmatx Inc ....D....408 419-0100
888 Ross Dr Ste 100 Sunnyvale (94089) ***(P-22347)***
Asti Winery, Cloverdale *Also called Treasury Wine Estates Americas* ***(P-2025)***
Astoria Software ....E....415 956-3917
160 Spear St Ste 1100 San Francisco (94105) ***(P-24392)***
Astourian Jewelry Mfg Inc ....F....213 683-0436
635 S Hill St Ste 407 Los Angeles (90014) ***(P-23241)***
Astra Communications Inc ....F....818 859-7305
1101 Chestnut St Burbank (91506) ***(P-18044)***
Astra Energy Holdings Inc ....C....714 969-6569
301 Main St Ste 201 Huntington Beach (92648) ***(P-9321)***
Astraeus Aerospace LLC ....F....310 907-9205
16255 Ventura Blvd # 625 Encino (91436) ***(P-20542)***
Astrazeneca Pharmaceuticals LP ....E....650 305-2600
200 Cardinal Way Redwood City (94063) ***(P-8049)***
Astro Aerospace ....C....805 684-6641
6384 Via Real Carpinteria (93013) ***(P-21262)***
Astro Aluminum Treating Co Inc ....D....562 923-4344
11040 Palmer Ave South Gate (90280) ***(P-11794)***
Astro Chrome and Polsg Corp ....E....818 781-1463
8136 Lankershim Blvd North Hollywood (91605) ***(P-13339)***
Astro Display Company Inc ....E....909 605-2875
4247 E Airport Dr Ontario (91761) ***(P-23824)***
Astro Haven Enterprises Inc ....F....949 215-3777
555 Anton Blvd Ste 150 Costa Mesa (92626) ***(P-22165)***
Astro Machine Co Inc ....F....310 679-8291
3734 W 139th St Hawthorne (90250) ***(P-16286)***
Astro Packaging, Anaheim *Also called Reliable Packaging Systems Inc* ***(P-9167)***
Astro Seal Inc ....E....951 787-6670
827 Palmyrita Ave Ste B Riverside (92507) ***(P-19450)***
Astro Technology Inc ....E....650 533-5087
3335 Birch St Palo Alto (94306) ***(P-24393)***
Astro-Tek Industries LLC ....D....714 238-0022
1198 N Kraemer Blvd Anaheim (92806) ***(P-20746)***
Astrochef Inc ....D....213 627-9860
1111 Mateo St Los Angeles (90021) ***(P-1389)***
Astrodyne Corporation ....E....714 289-0055
22895 Eastpark Dr Yorba Linda (92887) ***(P-19451)***
Astrodyne Group Inc (PA) ....E....818 709-5440
9555 Owensmouth Ave # 11 Chatsworth (91311) ***(P-16287)***
Astrodynetdi, Yorba Linda *Also called Astrodyne Corporation* ***(P-19451)***
Astrofoam Molding Company Inc ....F....805 482-7276
4117 Calle Tesoro Camarillo (93012) ***(P-9960)***
Astrologie California, Commerce *Also called Ajg Inc* ***(P-3606)***
Astron Corporation ....E....949 458-7277
9 Autry Irvine (92618) ***(P-19320)***
Astronic ....C....949 454-1180
2 Orion Aliso Viejo (92656) ***(P-18430)***
Astronics Company, Pasadena *Also called Sabrin Corporation* ***(P-12748)***
Astronics Test Systems Inc (HQ) ....C....800 722-2528
4 Goodyear Irvine (92618) ***(P-21725)***
Astrophysics Inc (PA) ....C....909 598-5488
21481 Ferrero City of Industry (91789) ***(P-22928)***
Astura Medical ....F....760 814-8047
3186 Lionshead Ave # 100 Carlsbad (92010) ***(P-22348)***
Asturies Manufacturing Co Inc ....E....951 270-1766
310 Cessna Cir Corona (92880) ***(P-20747)***
Asucla Publications, Los Angeles *Also called Associated Students UCLA* ***(P-5767)***
Asv Wines Inc (PA) ....E....661 792-3159
1998 Road 152 Delano (93215) ***(P-1647)***
At Mobile Bottling Line LLC ....F....707 257-3757
413 Saint Andrews Dr NAPA (94558) ***(P-2097)***
At Systems Technologies Inc ....E....317 591-2616
301 N Lake Ave Ste 600 Pasadena (91101) ***(P-15894)***
AT&T Corp ....C....619 521-6100
8954 Rio San Diego Dr # 604 San Diego (92108) ***(P-6438)***
AT&T Corp ....C....209 275-3075
1610 W Yosemite Ave Ste 2 Manteca (95337) ***(P-6439)***
AT&T Corp ....B....415 542-9000
370 3rd St Rm 714 San Francisco (94107) ***(P-6440)***
Ata Boy Inc ....E....323 644-0117
3171 Los Feliz Blvd # 205 Los Angeles (90039) ***(P-24045)***
Atc, Santa Ana *Also called Assembly Technologies Co LLC* ***(P-18428)***
Atdynamics, Hayward *Also called Advanced Transit Dynamics Inc* ***(P-21221)***
Ate Micrographics Inc ....F....510 475-5882
3101 Whipple Rd Ste 22 Union City (94587) ***(P-21907)***
Atech Manufacturing, San Jose *Also called T&S Manufacturing Tech LLC* ***(P-12256)***
Athana International Inc ....F....310 539-7280
602 Faye Ln Redondo Beach (90277) ***(P-15514)***
Athanor Group Inc ....C....909 467-1205
921 E California St Ontario (91761) ***(P-13014)***
Athos Works, Redwood City *Also called Mad Apparel Inc* ***(P-3177)***
ATI Allegheny Ludlum, Pico Rivera *Also called Allegheny Ludlum LLC* ***(P-11376)***
ATI Forged Products, Irvine *Also called Chen-Tech Industries Inc* ***(P-22403)***
ATI Solutions Inc (PA) ....F....818 772-7900
18425 Napa St Northridge (91325) ***(P-18309)***
ATI Windows, Riverside *Also called Nevada Window Supply Inc* ***(P-4199)***
ATI Windows, Riverside *Also called San Joaquin Window Inc* ***(P-12345)***
Atieva Usa Inc ....B....510 648-3553
7500 Gateway Blvd Newark (94560) ***(P-20127)***
Atk, San Diego *Also called Composite Optics Incorporated* ***(P-21189)***
Atk Mission Research, Goleta *Also called Mission Research Corporation* ***(P-20602)***
Atk Space Systems Inc (HQ) ....E....323 722-0222
6033 Bandini Blvd Commerce (90040) ***(P-12360)***
Atk Space Systems Inc ....D....805 685-2262
600 Pine Ave Goleta (93117) ***(P-21186)***

Mergent e-mail: customerrelations@mergent.com
1066
2019 California
Manufacturers Register
(P-0000) Products & Services Section entry number
(PA)=Parent Co (HQ)=Headquarters (DH)=Div Headquarters

Atk Space Systems Inc..........A.......310 343-3799
1960 E Grand Ave Ste 1150 El Segundo (90245) ***(P-21263)***
Atlantic Representations Inc..........E.......562 903-9550
10018 Santa Fe Springs Rd Santa Fe Springs (90670) ***(P-4824)***
Atlantis Computing Inc (PA)..........E.......650 917-9471
900 Glenneyre St Laguna Beach (92651) ***(P-24394)***
Atlas Carpet Mills Inc..........C.......323 724-7930
2200 Saybrook Ave Commerce (90040) ***(P-2924)***
Atlas Computer Centers, Santa Maria *Also called Aegis Industries Inc* ***(P-8873)***
Atlas Copco Compressors LLC..........F.......510 413-5200
6094 Stewart Ave Fremont (94538) ***(P-15118)***
Atlas Copco Compressors LLC..........F.......510 413-5200
48434 Milmont Dr Fremont (94538) ***(P-15119)***
Atlas Copco Mafi-Trench Co LLC (HQ)..........C.......805 352-0112
3037 Industrial Pkwy Santa Maria (93455) ***(P-15144)***
Atlas Foam Products..........F.......818 837-3626
12836 Arroyo St Sylmar (91342) ***(P-9819)***
Atlas Galvanizing LLC..........E.......323 587-6247
2639 Leonis Blvd Vernon (90058) ***(P-13554)***
Atlas Granite & Stone..........F.......916 638-7100
2560 Grennan Ct Rancho Cordova (95742) ***(P-5039)***
Atlas Lithograph Company..........E.......858 560-8273
13561 Elderberry Way San Diego (92130) ***(P-6671)***
Atlas Magnetics Inc..........F.......714 632-9718
1121 N Kraemer Pl Anaheim (92806) ***(P-19452)***
Atlas Match LLC..........D.......714 993-3328
1337 Limerick Dr Placentia (92870) ***(P-24046)***
Atlas Pacific Engineering Co..........D.......559 233-4500
3115 S Willow Ave Fresno (93725) ***(P-14833)***
Atlas Pacific Engineering Co..........E.......209 574-9884
4500 N Star Way Modesto (95356) ***(P-14834)***
Atlas Pallet Corp..........F.......925 432-6261
600 Industry Rd Pittsburg (94565) ***(P-4452)***
Atlas Screw Machine Pdts Co..........F.......415 621-6737
560 Natoma St San Francisco (94103) ***(P-13015)***
Atlas Sheet Metal Inc..........F.......949 600-8787
19 Musick Irvine (92618) ***(P-12493)***
Atlas Shower Door Co, Sacramento *Also called Atlas Specialties Corporation* ***(P-10676)***
Atlas Specialties Corporation (PA)..........E.......503 636-8182
4337 Astoria St Sacramento (95838) ***(P-10676)***
Atlas Sponge Rubber Company..........F.......626 359-5391
114 E Pomona Ave Monrovia (91016) ***(P-9589)***
Atlas Spring Mfgcorp..........C.......310 532-6200
10635 Santa Monica Blvd Los Angeles (90025) ***(P-13786)***
Atlas Survival Shelters LLC..........E.......323 727-7084
7407 Telegraph Rd Montebello (90640) ***(P-4825)***
Atlassian Inc (HQ)..........C.......415 701-1110
1098 Harrison St San Francisco (94103) ***(P-24395)***
Atlona Inc..........D.......408 962-0515
70 Daggett Dr San Jose (95134) ***(P-17763)***
Atm Plus Inc..........F.......619 575-3278
2232 Verus St Ste F San Diego (92154) ***(P-9590)***
Atm Skateboards, Oceanside *Also called Speedskins Inc* ***(P-23658)***
Atmel Corporation (HQ)..........B.......408 735-9110
1600 Technology Dr San Jose (95110) ***(P-18726)***
Atmel Wireless McU Tech Corp..........D.......949 525-4481
1 Spectrum Pointe Dr # 225 Lake Forest (92630) ***(P-18727)***
Atmf Inc..........E.......559 299-6836
807 Lincoln Ave Clovis (93612) ***(P-13340)***
Atmos Engineering Inc..........F.......650 879-1674
443 Dearborn Park Rd Pescadero (94060) ***(P-22166)***
Atomera Incorporated..........F.......408 442-5248
750 University Ave # 280 Los Gatos (95032) ***(P-18728)***
Atomic Aquatics Inc (PA)..........F.......714 375-1433
3585 Cadillac Ave Ste A Costa Mesa (92626) ***(P-23508)***
Atomic Monkey Industries Inc..........F.......949 415-8846
946 Calle Amanecer San Clemente (92673) ***(P-3876)***
Atp, Brisbane *Also called Aircraft Technical Publishers* ***(P-6426)***
Atp, Fremont *Also called Applied Thin-Film Products* ***(P-19446)***
Atp Electronics Inc..........E.......408 732-5000
2590 N 1st St Ste 150 San Jose (95131) ***(P-18729)***
Atr Sales Inc..........E.......714 432-8411
110 E Garry Ave Santa Ana (92707) ***(P-15280)***
Atr Technologies Incorporated..........F.......909 399-9724
805 Towne Center Dr Pomona (91767) ***(P-12834)***
Atra International Traders Inc..........E.......562 864-3885
3301 Leonis Blvd Vernon (90058) ***(P-5518)***
Atra-Flex, Santa Ana *Also called Atr Sales Inc* ***(P-15280)***
Atrevete Inc..........F.......323 277-5551
2055 E 51st St Vernon (90058) ***(P-3214)***
Atrium Door & Win Co Ariz Inc..........B.......714 693-0601
5455 E La Palma Ave Ste A Anaheim (92807) ***(P-12294)***
Ats International, Los Angeles *Also called Parts Out Inc* ***(P-19843)***
Ats Products Inc (PA)..........E.......510 234-3173
2785 Goodrick Ave Richmond (94801) ***(P-9961)***
Ats Systems, Rcho STA Marg *Also called Ats Workholding Inc* ***(P-14603)***
Ats Tool Inc..........E.......949 888-1744
30222 Esperanza Rcho STA Marg (92688) ***(P-14481)***
Ats Workholding, Rcho STA Marg *Also called Ats Tool Inc* ***(P-14481)***
Ats Workholding Inc..........D.......800 321-1833
30222 Esperanza Rcho STA Marg (92688) ***(P-14603)***
Attends Healthcare Pdts Inc..........C.......909 392-1200
1941 N White Ave La Verne (91750) ***(P-5273)***
Attilas Byshore Art Studio LLC..........F.......415 282-2815
2207 Quesada Ave San Francisco (94124) ***(P-11346)***
Atypon Systems LLC (PA)..........D.......408 988-1240
5201 Great America Pkwy # 510 Santa Clara (95054) ***(P-24396)***
Auberry Forest Products Inc..........F.......559 855-6255
32177 Auberry Rd Auberry (93602) ***(P-3979)***
Aubin Industries Inc..........F.......800 324-0051
23833 S Chrisman Rd Tracy (95304) ***(P-9894)***
Auburn Journal Inc (HQ)..........E.......530 885-5656
1030 High St Auburn (95603) ***(P-5768)***
Auburn Journal Inc..........D.......530 346-2232
1030 High St Auburn (95603) ***(P-5769)***
Auburn Printers and Mfg, Auburn *Also called API Marketing* ***(P-6665)***
Auburn Tile Inc..........F.......909 984-2841
545 W Main St Ontario (91762) ***(P-10879)***
Auburn Trader Inc (HQ)..........E.......530 888-7653
1115 Grass Valley Hwy Auburn (95603) ***(P-5770)***
Audaexplore, San Diego *Also called Audatex North America Inc* ***(P-24397)***
Audatex North America Inc (HQ)..........C.......858 946-1900
15030 Ave Of San Diego (92128) ***(P-24397)***
Audentes Therapeutics Inc..........D.......415 818-1001
600 California St Fl 17 San Francisco (94108) ***(P-8529)***
Audeze LLC (PA)..........F.......714 581-8010
3410 S Susan St Santa Ana (92704) ***(P-17764)***
Audience Inc (HQ)..........D.......650 254-2800
331 Fairchild Dr Mountain View (94043) ***(P-18730)***
Audience Inc..........E.......323 413-2370
5670 Wilshire Blvd # 100 Los Angeles (90036) ***(P-6441)***
Audio 2000's, Moorpark *Also called H&F Technologies Inc* ***(P-17807)***
Audio Dynamix Inc..........F.......714 549-5100
2770 S Harbor Blvd Ste D Santa Ana (92704) ***(P-17765)***
Audio Fx LLC..........F.......916 929-2100
1415 Howe Ave Sacramento (95825) ***(P-17766)***
Audio Fx Home Theater, Sacramento *Also called Audio Fx LLC* ***(P-17766)***
Audio Images, Tustin *Also called Henrys Adio Vsual Slutions Inc* ***(P-17811)***
Audio Impressions Inc..........F.......818 532-7360
6592 Oak Springs Dr Oak Park (91377) ***(P-23354)***
Audio Partners Publishing..........F.......530 888-7803
131 E Placer St Auburn (95603) ***(P-17886)***
Audio Video Color Corporation (PA)..........D.......424 213-7500
17707 S Santa Fe Ave Compton (90221) ***(P-5519)***
Audiolink, Thousand Palms *Also called A R Electronics Inc* ***(P-19430)***
Audionics System Inc..........F.......818 345-9599
6860 Canby Ave Ste 104 Reseda (91335) ***(P-17767)***
Audrey 3plus1, Vernon *Also called Three Plus One Inc* ***(P-3278)***
Auernheimer Labs Inc..........F.......559 442-1048
4561 E Florence Ave Fresno (93725) ***(P-17768)***
Auger Industries Inc..........F.......714 577-9350
390 E Crowther Ave Placentia (92870) ***(P-16288)***
August Accessories, Camarillo *Also called August Hat Company Inc* ***(P-3557)***
August Hat Company Inc (PA)..........E.......805 983-4651
850 Calle Plano Ste M Camarillo (93012) ***(P-3557)***
AUL Corp (PA)..........E.......707 257-9700
1250 Main St Ste 300 NAPA (94559) ***(P-25454)***
Auqa Blues, Los Angeles *Also called Shane Hunter LLC* ***(P-3680)***
Aurafin Oroamerica, Burbank *Also called Richline Group Inc* ***(P-23309)***
Auric Blends, Santa Rosa *Also called Teh-Pari International* ***(P-9311)***
Aurident Inc..........E.......714 870-1851
610 S State College Blvd Fullerton (92831) ***(P-22858)***
Auris Health Inc (PA)..........C.......650 610-0750
150 Shoreline Dr Redwood City (94065) ***(P-22349)***
Auritec Pharmaceuticals Inc..........F.......424 272-9501
3200 Santa Monica Blvd # 201 Santa Monica (90404) ***(P-8050)***
Auro Pharmaceuticals Inc..........F.......562 352-9630
511 S Harbor Blvd Ste F La Habra (90631) ***(P-8051)***
Auro Pharmacies Inc..........E.......562 352-9630
511 S Harbor Blvd Ste F La Habra (90631) ***(P-8052)***
Aurora Casting & Engrg Inc..........D.......805 933-2761
1790 E Lemonwood Dr Santa Paula (93060) ***(P-11769)***
Aurum Assembly Plus Inc..........E.......858 578-8710
8829 Production Ave San Diego (92121) ***(P-18431)***
Auspex Pharmaceuticals Inc..........E.......858 558-2400
3333 N Torrey Pines Ct La Jolla (92037) ***(P-8053)***
Austin Horn Collection, Rcho STA Marg *Also called Opulence International* ***(P-2780)***
Austn Creek Materials, Santa Rosa *Also called Bohan & Canelis - Austin Crk* ***(P-325)***
Auto Club Enterprises..........B.......714 885-2376
3333 Fairview Rd Costa Mesa (92626) ***(P-6106)***
Auto Doctor, Temecula *Also called Thompson Magnetics Inc* ***(P-19763)***
Auto Edge Solutions, Pacoima *Also called Moc Products Company Inc* ***(P-9284)***
Auto Lectrics, Campbell *Also called Alternators Starters Etc* ***(P-19826)***
Auto Scrubber, Thousand Oaks *Also called Thousands Oaks Hand Wash* ***(P-16123)***
Auto Tech Engineering Inc..........E.......909 428-9072
3870 Garner Rd Riverside (92501) ***(P-20260)***
Auto Tech Engineering Company, Riverside *Also called Auto Tech Engineering Inc* ***(P-20260)***
Auto Trend Products, Vernon *Also called Punch Press Products Inc* ***(P-14564)***
Auto Wash Concepts Inc..........F.......562 948-2575
11769 Telegraph Rd Santa Fe Springs (90670) ***(P-16014)***
Auto-Chlor System Wash Inc..........F.......818 376-0940
16141 Hart St Van Nuys (91406) ***(P-8622)***
Autoanything Inc..........C.......858 569-8111
6602 Convoy Ct Ste 200 San Diego (92111) ***(P-20128)***
Autobahn Construction Inc..........F.......714 769-7025
933 N Batavia St Ste A Orange (92867) ***(P-14142)***
Autocal Inc..........F.......714 550-7444
1976 E Mcfadden Ave Santa Ana (92705) ***(P-14604)***
Autocam Acquisition Inc..........E.......510 487-7600
1209 San Luis Obispo St Hayward (94544) ***(P-16289)***
Autocam California, Hayward *Also called Autocam Acquisition Inc* ***(P-16289)***
Autocue Inc..........E.......213 627-4570
2701 N Ontario St Burbank (91504) ***(P-23140)***
Autodesk Inc..........D.......415 356-0700
1 Market St San Francisco (94105) ***(P-24398)***

ALPHABETIC

Employee Codes: A=Over 500 employees, B=251-500
C=101-250, D=51-100, E=20-50, F=10-19
2019 California
Manfacturers Register
© Mergent Inc. 1-800-342-5647
1067

Autodesk Inc (PA)	B	415 507-5000
111 Mcinnis Pkwy San Rafael (94903) *(P-24399)*		
Autodesk Inc	C	415 507-5000
3950 Civic Center Dr San Rafael (94903) *(P-24400)*		
Autoflow Products Co	F	310 515-2866
15915 S San Pedro St Gardena (90248) *(P-21550)*		
Autoliv Asp Inc	C	619 661-9347
9355 Airway Rd Ste 3 San Diego (92154) *(P-20261)*		
Autoliv Safety Technology Inc	A	619 662-8000
2475 Paseo D Las Amrcs San Diego (92154) *(P-3938)*		
Autoliv Seatbelt Facility, San Diego *Also called Autoliv Asp Inc (P-20261)*		
Automated Bldg Components Inc	F	559 485-8232
2853 S Orange Ave Fresno (93725) *(P-4391)*		
Automated Packg Systems Inc	F	562 941-1476
10440 Ontiveros Pl Ste 1 Santa Fe Springs (90670) *(P-14200)*		
Automated Tape and Label Inc	E	818 908-4400
7702 Kester Ave Van Nuys (91405) *(P-5547)*		
Automatic Control Engrg Corp	E	510 293-6040
20788 Corsair Blvd Hayward (94545) *(P-22167)*		
Automatic Switch Company	F	714 283-4000
120 S Chaparral Ct # 200 Anaheim (92808) *(P-13703)*		
Automation & Entertainment Inc (PA)	F	408 353-4223
25870 Soquel San Jose Rd Los Gatos (95033) *(P-13704)*		
Automation Electronics, Chatsworth *Also called RJA Industries Inc (P-19708)*		
Automation Gt, Carlsbad *Also called Laurelwood Industries Inc (P-16682)*		
Automation Plating, Glendale *Also called Aero Manufacturing & Pltg Co (P-13311)*		
Automation Plating Corporation	E	323 245-4951
927 Thompson Ave Glendale (91201) *(P-13341)*		
Automation Printing Co (PA)	E	213 488-1230
1230 Long Beach Ave Los Angeles (90021) *(P-7626)*		
Automation West Inc	F	714 556-7381
1605 E Saint Gertrude Pl Santa Ana (92705) *(P-16290)*		
Autometrix Inc	F	530 477-5065
12098 Charles Dr Grass Valley (95945) *(P-14774)*		
Automoco LLC	D	707 544-4761
9142 Independence Ave Chatsworth (91311) *(P-20262)*		
Automotive Electronics Svcs	F	559 292-7851
5465 E Hedges Ave Fresno (93727) *(P-13811)*		
Automotive Engineered Pdts Inc	D	619 229-7797
7149 Mission Gorge Rd San Diego (92120) *(P-14430)*		
Automotive Exch & Sup of Cal (PA)	E	619 282-3207
4354 Twain Ave Ste G San Diego (92120) *(P-20263)*		
Automotive Lease Guide Alg Inc	E	424 258-8026
120 Broadway Ste 200 Santa Monica (90401) *(P-6442)*		
Automotive Racing Products Inc (PA)	D	805 339-2200
1863 Eastman Ave Ventura (93003) *(P-11931)*		
Automotive Racing Products Inc	D	805 525-1497
1760 E Lemonwood Dr Santa Paula (93060) *(P-11932)*		
Auton Motorized Systems, Valencia *Also called Virgil Walker Inc (P-12274)*		
Auton Motorized Systems, Valencia *Also called Virgil Walker Inc (P-19305)*		
Autonomy Interwoven, Sunnyvale *Also called Entco LLC (P-24614)*		
Autosplice Inc (PA)	C	858 535-0077
10431 Wtridge Cir Ste 110 San Diego (92121) *(P-17444)*		
Autotechbizcom Inc	F	949 245-7033
23551 Commerce Center Dr I Laguna Hills (92653) *(P-14916)*		
Autumn Express, Berkeley *Also called Autumn Press Inc (P-6672)*		
Autumn Milling Co Inc	E	310 635-0703
20930 S Alameda St Long Beach (90810) *(P-4030)*		
Autumn Press Inc (PA)	E	510 654-4545
945 Camelia St Berkeley (94710) *(P-6672)*		
Auxin Solar Inc	E	408 225-4380
6835 Via Del Oro San Jose (95119) *(P-18731)*		
AV Now Inc	A	831 425-2500
100 Pioneer St Ste B Santa Cruz (95060) *(P-17769)*		
Ava James, Commerce *Also called C-Quest Inc (P-3223)*		
Avaak Inc	C	858 453-9866
2200 Faraday Ave Ste 150 Carlsbad (92008) *(P-19915)*		
Avab America Inc	E	707 778-8990
11078 Fleetwood St Sun Valley (91352) *(P-17255)*		
Avago Technologies	F	408 433-4068
1730 Fox Dr San Jose (95131) *(P-18732)*		
Avago Technologies US Inc (HQ)	B	800 433-8778
1320 Ridder Park Dr San Jose (95131) *(P-18733)*		
Avalanche Technology Inc	E	510 438-0148
3450 W Warren Ave Fremont (94538) *(P-18734)*		
Avalco Inc	F	310 676-3057
2029 Verdugo Blvd Ste 710 Montrose (91020) *(P-9591)*		
Avalco Valves Inc., Montrose *Also called Avalco Inc (P-9591)*		
Avalent Technologies Inc (PA)	F	408 727-6323
920 Hillview Ct Ste 195 Milpitas (95035) *(P-18432)*		
Avalon Apparel LLC (PA)	C	323 581-3511
2520 W 6th St Los Angeles (90057) *(P-3572)*		
Avalon Chemical Inc	E	714 540-3874
1230 E Saint Gertrude Pl Santa Ana (92707) *(P-9222)*		
Avalon Communications, Hawthorne *Also called Technology Training Corp (P-7130)*		
Avalon Glass & Mirror Company	D	323 321-8806
642 Alondra Blvd Carson (90746) *(P-10677)*		
Avalon Graphics, Roseville *Also called Kkp - Roseville Inc (P-6926)*		
Avalon Machine Products Inc	F	323 979-8656
419 Main St Ste A Huntington Beach (92648) *(P-20748)*		
Avalon Mfg Co Incoirporated	F	951 340-0280
509 Bateman Cir Corona (92880) *(P-14835)*		
Avalon Shutters Inc	C	909 937-4900
3407 N Perris Blvd Perris (92571) *(P-4107)*		
Avanir Pharmaceuticals Inc (HQ)	C	949 389-6700
30 Enterprise Ste 400 Aliso Viejo (92656) *(P-8054)*		
Avantec Manufacturing Inc	E	714 532-6197
1811 N Case St Orange (92865) *(P-18433)*		
Avantec Vascular Corporation	E	408 329-5400
870 Hermosa Ave Sunnyvale (94085) *(P-22350)*		
Avantis Medical Systems Inc	E	408 733-1901
2367 Bering Dr San Jose (95131) *(P-22949)*		
Avanzato Technology Corp	E	312 509-0506
5335 Mcconnell Ave Los Angeles (90066) *(P-14917)*		
Avast Software Inc (PA)	F	844 340-9251
2625 Broadway St Redwood City (94063) *(P-24401)*		
Avatier Corporation (PA)	E	925 217-5170
4733 Chabot Dr Ste 201 Pleasanton (94588) *(P-24402)*		
Avaya Holdings Corp (PA)	E	908 953-6000
4655 Great America Pkwy Santa Clara (95054) *(P-17923)*		
Avc, Compton *Also called Audio Video Color Corporation (P-5519)*		
AVC Specialists Inc	E	513 458-2600
5146 N Commerce Ave Ste G Moorpark (93021) *(P-21500)*		
Avcorp Cmpsite Fabrication Inc	B	310 970-5658
1600 W 135th St Gardena (90249) *(P-20749)*		
Avcorp Cmpstes Fabrication Inc	F	310 527-0700
1551 W 139th St Gardena (90249) *(P-20750)*		
Avd, Newport Beach *Also called American Vanguard Corporation (P-9091)*		
Ave Jewelry Design Mfg, North Hollywood *Also called Ave Jewelry Inc (P-23242)*		
Ave Jewelry Inc	F	213 488-0097
13127 Ebell St North Hollywood (91605) *(P-23242)*		
Aveox Inc	E	805 915-0200
2265 Ward Ave Ste A Simi Valley (93065) *(P-17333)*		
Avermedia Technologies Inc	F	510 403-0006
47358 Fremont Blvd Fremont (94538) *(P-15676)*		
Avery Dennison Corporation (PA)	B	626 304-2000
207 N Goode Ave Ste 500 Glendale (91203) *(P-5548)*		
Avery Dennison Corporation	B	714 674-8500
50 Pointe Dr Brea (92821) *(P-5549)*		
Avery Dennison Corporation	C	626 938-7239
751 N Todd Ave Azusa (91702) *(P-5550)*		
Avery Dennison Corporation	C	909 987-4631
11195 Eucalyptus St Rancho Cucamonga (91730) *(P-5551)*		
Avery Dennison Corporation	C	909 428-4238
10721 Jasmine St Fontana (92337) *(P-5552)*		
Avery Dennison Corporation	C	626 304-2000
2900 Bradley St Pasadena (91107) *(P-5553)*		
Avery Dennison Corporation	C	323 728-8888
5819 Telegraph Rd Commerce (90040) *(P-5554)*		
Avery Dennison Corporation	C	626 304-2000
2743 Thompson Creek Rd Pomona (91767) *(P-5555)*		
Avery Plastics Inc	D	619 696-1230
4070 Goldfinch St Ste A San Diego (92103) *(P-9962)*		
Avery Products Corporation (HQ)	B	714 675-8500
50 Pointe Dr Brea (92821) *(P-5682)*		
Avet Industries Inc	E	818 576-9895
9687 Topanga Canyon Pl Chatsworth (91311) *(P-23509)*		
Avet Reels, Chatsworth *Also called Avet Industries Inc (P-23509)*		
AVI	F	760 451-9379
431 Janemar Rd Fallbrook (92028) *(P-19453)*		
Aviat Networks Inc (PA)	D	408 941-7100
860 N Mccarthy Blvd Milpitas (95035) *(P-18045)*		
Aviat US Inc (HQ)	B	408 941-7100
860 N Mccarthy Blvd # 200 Milpitas (95035) *(P-18046)*		
Aviate Enterprises Inc	E	916 993-4000
5844 Price Ave McClellan (95652) *(P-15939)*		
Aviation and Indus Dev Corp	F	310 373-6057
23870 Hawthorne Blvd Torrance (90505) *(P-9698)*		
Aviation Equipment Processing, Costa Mesa *Also called Flare Group (P-20813)*		
Aviation Publishing Corp	D	626 618-4000
El Monte Airport El Monte (91733) *(P-6107)*		
Aviator Systems Inc	F	949 677-2461
37440 Calle De Lobo Murrieta (92562) *(P-20751)*		
Avibank Mfg Inc (HQ)	C	818 392-2100
11500 Sherman Way North Hollywood (91605) *(P-20752)*		
Avibank Mfg Inc	D	661 257-2329
25323 Rye Canyon Rd Valencia (91355) *(P-11933)*		
Avid Bioservices Inc (PA)	C	714 508-6000
2642 Michelle Dr Ste 200 Tustin (92780) *(P-8055)*		
Avid Bioservices Inc	E	714 508-6000
14191 Myford Rd Tustin (92780) *(P-8056)*		
Avid Idntification Systems Inc (PA)	F	951 371-7505
3185 Hamner Ave Norco (92860) *(P-18735)*		
Avid Ink, Irvine *Also called Advanced Vsual Image Dsign LLC (P-7223)*		
Avid Lyfe Inc	F	888 510-2517
990 Park Center Dr Ste C Vista (92081) *(P-3377)*		
Avid Systems Inc (HQ)	C	650 526-1600
280 Bernardo Ave Mountain View (94043) *(P-18047)*		
Avid Technology Inc	B	510 486-8302
2600 10th St Ste 100 Berkeley (94710) *(P-23141)*		
Avid Technology Inc	E	818 557-2520
101 S 1st St Ste 200 Burbank (91502) *(P-23142)*		
Avid Technology Inc	C	818 779-7860
14007 Runnymede St Van Nuys (91405) *(P-23143)*		
Avilas Garden Art (PA)	D	909 350-4546
14608 Merrill Ave Fontana (92335) *(P-10880)*		
Avinger Inc	D	650 241-7900
400 Chesapeake Dr Redwood City (94063) *(P-22351)*		
Avion Graphics Inc	F	949 472-0438
27192 Burbank Foothill Ranch (92610) *(P-6673)*		
Avion TI Mfg Machining Ctr Inc	F	661 257-2915
29035 The Old Rd Valencia (91355) *(P-16291)*		
Avis Roto Die Co	E	323 255-7070
1560 N San Fernando Rd Los Angeles (90065) *(P-14482)*		
Avista Technologies Inc	D	760 744-0536
140 Bosstick Blvd San Marcos (92069) *(P-9223)*		
Avita Beverage Company Inc (PA)	F	213 477-1979
18401 Burbank Blvd # 121 Tarzana (91356) *(P-2098)*		

Mergent e-mail: customerrelations@mergent.com
1068

2019 California
Manufacturers Register

(P-0000) Products & Services Section entry number
(PA)=Parent Co (HQ)=Headquarters (DH)=Div Headquarters

Aviva Biosciences Corporation .....E.....858 552-0888
6330 Nncy Rdge Dr Ste 103 San Diego (92121) **(P-19916)**
Avm Technologies, Valencia Also called Realwise Inc **(P-25112)**
Avn Media Network Inc .....E.....818 718-5788
9400 Penfield Ave Chatsworth (91311) **(P-6310)**
Avo, Commerce Also called American Vegetable Oils Inc **(P-1514)**
Avogy Inc .....E.....408 684-5200
677 River Oaks Pkwy San Jose (95134) **(P-18736)**
Avolent Inc .....D.....415 553-6400
444 De Haro St Ste 100 San Francisco (94107) **(P-24403)**
Avp Technology LLC .....E.....510 683-0157
4140 Business Center Dr Fremont (94538) **(P-15195)**
AVV Winery Co LLC .....E.....707 433-7209
8644 Highway 128 Healdsburg (95448) **(P-1648)**
AVX Antenna Inc (HQ) .....E.....858 550-3820
5501 Oberlin Dr Ste 100 San Diego (92121) **(P-18048)**
AVX Filters Corporation .....D.....818 767-6770
11144 Penrose St Ste 7 Sun Valley (91352) **(P-15298)**
Aw Industries Inc .....D.....909 629-1500
1810 S Reservoir St Pomona (91766) **(P-4674)**
Awake Inc .....D.....818 365-9361
10711 Walker St Cypress (90630) **(P-3294)**
Award Packaging Spc Corp .....E.....323 727-1200
12855 Midway Pl Cerritos (90703) **(P-5385)**
Aware Products Inc .....E.....818 206-6700
9250 Mason Ave Chatsworth (91311) **(P-8698)**
Aware Products LLC .....C.....818 206-6700
9250 Mason Ave Chatsworth (91311) **(P-8699)**
Awcc Corporation .....F.....949 497-6313
434 N Coast Hwy Laguna Beach (92651) **(P-3607)**
Awesome Products Inc (PA) .....C.....714 562-8873
6370 Altura Blvd Buena Park (90620) **(P-8623)**
Aweta-Autoline (PA) .....E.....559 244-8340
4516 E Citron Fresno (93725) **(P-14043)**
Awg Ltd Inc .....F.....707 259-6777
4162 Big Ranch Rd NAPA (94558) **(P-1649)**
AWI, Sacramento Also called All Weather Inc **(P-22158)**
AWI Acquisition Company (PA) .....D.....818 364-2333
13207 Bradley Ave Sylmar (91342) **(P-13921)**
Awning Matrix .....F.....909 447-5100
4319 Santa Ana St Ste B Ontario (91761) **(P-12494)**
Awnings, Fresno Also called Pacific Tent and Awning **(P-3801)**
Awo, Vista Also called Advanced Web Offset Inc **(P-7224)**
Ax II Inc .....E.....310 292-6523
13921 S Figueroa St Los Angeles (90061) **(P-2797)**
Axceleon Inc .....F.....714 960-5200
1947 Overlook Rd Fullerton (92831) **(P-24404)**
Axcelis Technologies Inc .....B.....949 477-5160
1360 Reynolds Ave Ste 106 Irvine (92614) **(P-22168)**
Axcelis Technologies Inc .....B.....510 979-1970
5673 W Las Positas Blvd # 205 Pleasanton (94588) **(P-22169)**
Axel Johnson Metals, Vallejo Also called NI Industries Inc **(P-11548)**
Axelgaard Manufacturing Co Ltd (PA) .....D.....760 723-7554
520 Industrial Way Fallbrook (92028) **(P-22950)**
Axelgaard Manufacturing Co Ltd .....E.....760 723-7554
329 W Aviation Rd Fallbrook (92028) **(P-22951)**
Axent Corporation Limited (PA) .....F.....949 900-4349
3 Musick Irvine (92618) **(P-5662)**
Axent USA, Irvine Also called Axent Corporation Limited **(P-5662)**
Axeon Water Technologies .....D.....760 723-5417
40980 County Center Dr # 110 Temecula (92591) **(P-16015)**
Axess Products Corp .....F.....818 785-4000
9409 Owensmouth Ave Chatsworth (91311) **(P-17770)**
Axia Technologies LLC .....E.....855 376-2942
4183 State St Santa Barbara (93110) **(P-24405)**
Axial Inc .....F.....949 334-6008
26022 Pala Mission Viejo (92691) **(P-19917)**
Axial Industries Inc .....C.....408 977-7800
1991 Senter Rd San Jose (95112) **(P-12495)**
Axiom Industries Inc .....E.....559 276-1310
4202 W Sierra Madre Ave Fresno (93722) **(P-22703)**
Axiom Label Group, Compton Also called Kmr Label LLC **(P-7205)**
Axiom Materials Inc .....F.....949 623-4400
2320 Pullman St Santa Ana (92705) **(P-9129)**
Axis Group Inc .....F.....510 487-7393
1220 Whipple Rd Union City (94587) **(P-18737)**
Axium Plastics LLC .....D.....909 969-0766
5701 Clark St Ontario (91761) **(P-9963)**
Axl Musical Instruments Ltd .....C.....415 508-1398
31067 San Clemente St Hayward (94544) **(P-23355)**
Axles Now, Anaheim Also called Friedl Corporation **(P-20341)**
Axm Pharma Inc .....C.....909 843-6338
20955 Pathfinder Rd # 100 Diamond Bar (91765) **(P-8057)**
Axp Technology Inc .....F.....510 683-1180
41041 Trimboli Way # 1761 Fremont (94538) **(P-17585)**
Axt Inc .....E.....510 683-5900
4311 Solar Way Fremont (94538) **(P-18738)**
Axt Inc (PA) .....E.....510 438-4700
4281 Technology Dr Fremont (94538) **(P-18739)**
Axxcelera Brdband Wireless Inc (HQ) .....F.....805 968-9621
82 Coromar Dr Santa Barbara (93117) **(P-18049)**
Axxis Corporation .....E.....951 436-9921
1535 Nandina Ave Perris (92571) **(P-16292)**
Axygen Inc (HQ) .....E.....510 494-8900
33210 Central Ave Union City (94587) **(P-9964)**
Axygen Scientific, Union City Also called Axygen Inc **(P-9964)**
Ayala and Son Pallets, Sanger Also called Triple A Pallets Inc **(P-4509)**
Ayantra Inc .....F.....510 623-7526
47873 Fremont Blvd Fremont (94538) **(P-17924)**

Ayca Furniture, Corona Also called Crescent Woodworking Co Ltd **(P-4686)**
Aymar Engineering .....F.....619 562-1121
9434 Abraham Way Santee (92071) **(P-12496)**
AZ Countertops Inc .....E.....909 983-5386
1445 S Hudson Ave Ontario (91761) **(P-11233)**
AZ Displays Inc .....E.....949 831-5000
75 Columbia Aliso Viejo (92656) **(P-19454)**
AZ Manufacturing, Santa Ana Also called A-Z Mfg Inc **(P-13155)**
Az-Iz Case Co, Vernon Also called Procases Inc **(P-4446)**
Aza Industries Inc (PA) .....E.....760 560-0440
1410 Vantage Ct Vista (92081) **(P-23510)**
Azachorok Contract Svcs LLC .....F.....661 951-6566
320 Grand Cypress Ave # 502 Palmdale (93551) **(P-12497)**
Azazie Inc .....F.....650 963-9420
148 E Brokaw Rd San Jose (95112) **(P-3295)**
Azimuth Electronics Inc .....F.....949 492-6481
2605 S El Camino Real San Clemente (92672) **(P-21726)**
Azimuth Industrial Co Inc .....E.....510 441-6000
30593 Un Cy Blvd Ste 110 Union City (94587) **(P-18740)**
Azimuth Semiconductor Assembly, Union City Also called Azimuth Industrial Co
Inc **(P-18740)**
Azitex Knitting Mills, Los Angeles Also called Azitex Trading Corp **(P-2872)**
Azitex Trading Corp .....D.....213 745-7072
1850 E 15th St Los Angeles (90021) **(P-2872)**
Azpire Print & Mediaworks LLC .....F.....310 736-5952
10555 Clarkson Rd Los Angeles (90064) **(P-6674)**
Aztec Containers, Vista Also called Aztec Technology Corporation **(P-12115)**
Aztec Machine Co Inc .....F.....916 638-4894
3156 Fitzgerald Rd Ste A Rancho Cordova (95742) **(P-16293)**
Aztec Perlite Company Inc .....F.....760 741-1733
1518 Simpson Way Escondido (92029) **(P-11317)**
Aztec Technology Corporation (PA) .....E.....760 727-2300
2550 S Santa Fe Ave Vista (92084) **(P-12115)**
Aztec Technology Corporation .....F.....909 350-8830
14022 Slover Ave Fontana (92337) **(P-4453)**
Aztec Tents, Torrance Also called A-Aztec Rents & Sells Inc **(P-3777)**
Azteca Jeans Inc .....E.....323 758-7721
6600 Avalon Blvd Los Angeles (90003) **(P-3378)**
Azteca News .....F.....714 972-9912
1532 E Wellington Ave Santa Ana (92701) **(P-5771)**
Azteca Ornamental Iron Works, Rosemead Also called Azteca Ornamental Metals **(P-12835)**
Azteca Ornamental Metals .....F.....626 280-2822
2738 Stingle Ave Rosemead (91770) **(P-12835)**
Azteca Soccer .....F.....626 768-2704
3022 Durfee Ave Ste E El Monte (91732) **(P-23511)**
Aztech Products International .....E.....858 481-8412
326 10th St Del Mar (92014) **(P-19918)**
Azuma Foods Internatl, Hayward Also called Azuma Foods Intl Inc USA **(P-2308)**
Azuma Foods Intl Inc USA (HQ) .....D.....510 782-1112
20201 Mack St Hayward (94545) **(P-2308)**
Azure Biosystems Inc .....E.....925 307-7127
6747 Sierra Ct Ste A Dublin (94568) **(P-8530)**
Azusa Engineering .....F.....626 966-4071
1542 W Industrial Park St Covina (91722) **(P-20264)**
Azusa Rock LLC (HQ) .....F.....858 530-9444
3901 Fish Canyon Rd Azusa (91702) **(P-309)**
Azusa Rock Inc .....F.....619 440-2363
3605 Dehesa Rd El Cajon (92019) **(P-310)**
Azusa Rock Inc .....E.....209 826-5066
22101 Sunset Dr Los Banos (93635) **(P-11048)**
B & B Battery (usa) Inc (PA) .....E.....323 278-1900
6415 Randolph St Commerce (90040) **(P-19820)**
B & B Doors and Windows Inc .....E.....818 837-8480
11455 Ilex Ave San Fernando (91340) **(P-12295)**
B & B Enameling Inc .....F.....714 848-0044
17591 Sampson Ln Huntington Beach (92647) **(P-13555)**
B & B Jewelry Mfg, Los Angeles Also called Nationwide Jewelry Mfrs Inc **(P-23301)**
B & B Label Inc .....F.....805 922-0332
2357 Thompson Way Santa Maria (93455) **(P-7244)**
B & B Manufacturing Co (PA) .....C.....661 257-2161
27940 Beale Ct Santa Clarita (91355) **(P-16294)**
B & B Pipe and Tool Co (PA) .....F.....562 424-0704
3035 Walnut Ave Long Beach (90807) **(P-16295)**
B & B Pipe and Tool Co .....F.....661 323-8208
2301 Parker Ln Bakersfield (93308) **(P-16296)**
B & B R V Inc .....E.....530 365-7043
3750 Auto Mall Dr Anderson (96007) **(P-20521)**
B & B Red-I-Mix Concrete Inc .....E.....626 359-8371
590 Live Oak Ave Baldwin Park (91706) **(P-11049)**
B & B Refractories Inc .....F.....562 946-4535
12121 Los Nietos Rd Santa Fe Springs (90670) **(P-10798)**
B & B Services, Baldwin Park Also called B & B Red-I-Mix Concrete Inc **(P-11049)**
B & B Specialties Inc (PA) .....C.....714 985-3000
4321 E La Palma Ave Anaheim (92807) **(P-11934)**
B & C Industries, Anaheim Also called B & Cawnings Inc **(P-12498)**
B & C Painting Solutions Inc .....E.....209 982-0422
107 Val Dervin Pkwy Stockton (95206) **(P-13556)**
B & C Plating Co .....E.....323 263-6757
1507 S Sunol Dr Los Angeles (90023) **(P-13342)**
B & Cawnings Inc .....F.....714 632-3303
3082 E Miraloma Ave Anaheim (92806) **(P-12498)**
B & D Litho Group Inc .....F.....909 390-0903
325 N Ponderosa Ave Ontario (91761) **(P-6675)**
B & E Enterprises .....F.....714 630-3731
1380 N Mccan St Anaheim (92806) **(P-21089)**
B & E Manufacturing Co Inc .....E.....714 898-2269
12151 Monarch St Garden Grove (92841) **(P-20753)**
B & G Aerospace Metals .....E.....951 738-8133
1801 Railroad St Corona (92880) **(P-11770)**

Employee Codes: A=Over 500 employees, B=251-500
C=101-250, D=51-100, E=20-50, F=10-19

2019 California
Manfacturers Register

© Mergent Inc. 1-800-342-5647
1069

B & G Electronic Assembly Inc....F....909 608-2077
10350 Regis Ct Rancho Cucamonga (91730) *(P-19455)*
B & G House of Printing, Gardena *Also called Matsuda House Printing Inc (P-6965)*
B & G Metal Inc....F....626 444-8566
9408 Gidley St Temple City (91780) *(P-12499)*
B & G Millworks....F....562 944-4599
12522 Lakeland Rd Santa Fe Springs (90670) *(P-4108)*
B & G Precision Inc....F....510 438-9785
45450 Industrial Pl Ste 9 Fremont (94538) *(P-16297)*
B & H Engineering Company, San Carlos *Also called Begovic Industries Inc (P-16314)*
B & H Labeling Systems, Ceres *Also called B & H Manufacturing Co Inc (P-15196)*
B & H Manufacturing Co Inc (PA)....C....209 537-5785
3461 Roeding Rd Ceres (95307) *(P-15196)*
B & H Signs Inc....D....626 359-6643
926 S Primrose Ave Monrovia (91016) *(P-23825)*
B & H Tool Company, San Marcos *Also called Neville Industries Inc (P-14549)*
B & I Fender Trims Inc....D....718 326-4323
1401 Air Wing Rd San Diego (92154) *(P-20265)*
B & L Casing Service LLC....F....661 589-9080
21054 Kratzmeyer Rd Bakersfield (93314) *(P-169)*
B & M Machine Inc....F....909 355-0998
8439 Cherry Ave Fontana (92335) *(P-16298)*
B & M Racing & Prfmce Pdts, Chatsworth *Also called Automoco LLC (P-20262)*
B & M Upholstery....F....415 621-7447
2525 16th St Ste 201 San Francisco (94103) *(P-2723)*
B & R Accessories Inc....F....213 688-8727
7508 Deering Ave Ste D Canoga Park (91303) *(P-23743)*
B & R Mold Inc....F....805 526-8665
4564 E Los Angeles Ave C Simi Valley (93063) *(P-14483)*
B & R Vinyards Inc....F....408 842-5649
4350 Monterey Rd Gilroy (95020) *(P-1650)*
B & S Plastics Inc....A....805 981-0262
2200 Sturgis Rd Oxnard (93030) *(P-9965)*
B & W Envmtl Solutions LLC....F....415 931-3381
2200 Sacramento St # 1106 San Francisco (94115) *(P-14918)*
B & W Precision Inc....F....714 447-0971
1260 Pioneer St Ste A Brea (92821) *(P-16299)*
B & Y Global Sourcing LLC....F....213 891-1112
801 S Grand Ave Ste 475 Los Angeles (90017) *(P-3296)*
B & Y Machine Co....F....909 795-8588
1060 5th St Calimesa (92320) *(P-16145)*
B and P Plastics Inc....E....619 477-1893
225 W 30th St National City (91950) *(P-9966)*
B and Z Printing Inc....E....714 892-2000
1300 E Wakeham Ave B Santa Ana (92705) *(P-6676)*
B B C, San Jose *Also called Babbitt Bearing Co Inc (P-16304)*
B Braun Medical Inc....A....909 906-7575
1151 Mildred St Ste B Ontario (91761) *(P-22352)*
B Braun Medical Inc....A....610 691-5400
2525 Mcgaw Ave Irvine (92614) *(P-22353)*
B Brays Card Inc....F....760 265-4720
12053 Mariposa Rd Victorville (92394) *(P-6677)*
B C H Manufacturing Co Inc....F....510 569-6586
10012 Denny St Oakland (94603) *(P-14143)*
B C I, San Diego *Also called Brehm Communications Inc (P-6705)*
B C Lighting, Compton *Also called California Metal Group Inc (P-12521)*
B C M, Chula Vista *Also called Bellama Cstm Met Fbrcators Inc (P-12504)*
B C Song International Inc....D....510 785-8383
2509 Technology Dr Hayward (94545) *(P-9322)*
B C T, Laguna Hills *Also called Raintree Business Products (P-7072)*
B C Yellow Pages....F....530 876-8616
1001 Bille Rd Paradise (95969) *(P-6443)*
B Cumming Company A Corp....F....818 504-2571
9990 Glenoaks Blvd Ste B Sun Valley (91352) *(P-9592)*
B D and G Sandblasting Co....F....323 583-1741
2428 E 54th St Vernon (90058) *(P-13343)*
B D L, Brea *Also called Belt Drives Ltd (P-21091)*
B D Pharmingen Inc (HQ)....F....858 812-8800
10975 Torreyana Rd San Diego (92121) *(P-8461)*
B Dazzle Inc....F....310 374-3000
500 Meyer Ln Redondo Beach (90278) *(P-23408)*
B E & P Enterprises LLC (PA)....E....909 591-7561
5167 G St Chino (91710) *(P-4607)*
B E M R, Bakersfield *Also called Bakersfield Elc Mtr Repr Inc (P-25455)*
B F, Riverside *Also called Brenner-Fiedler & Associates (P-22172)*
B F I Labels, Yorba Linda *Also called Beckers Fabrication Inc (P-5556)*
B F Mc Gilla Inc....E....323 581-8288
2020 E Slauson Ave Huntington Park (90255) *(P-13877)*
B Gone Bird Inc....F....949 387-5662
15375 Barranca Pkwy Ste D Irvine (92618) *(P-9737)*
B H Tank Works Inc....F....323 221-1579
1919 N San Fernando Rd Los Angeles (90065) *(P-12361)*
B I A S, Petaluma *Also called Berkley Integrated Audio Softw (P-19856)*
B J Bindery....D....714 835-7342
833 S Grand Ave Santa Ana (92705) *(P-7593)*
B J Embroidery & Screenprint....F....707 463-2767
272 E Smith St Ukiah (95482) *(P-3829)*
B J'S Printing Emporium, Glendale *Also called Glendale Rotary Offset Prtg Co (P-6834)*
B K Harris Inc....F....714 630-8780
3574 E Enterprise Dr Anaheim (92807) *(P-7245)*
B M B, Rancho Cordova *Also called Bmb Metal Products Corporation (P-12506)*
B M I, El Segundo *Also called Bundy Manufacturing Inc (P-16338)*
B M I, San Jose *Also called Berkeley Magnetics Inc (P-17081)*
B Metal Fabrication Inc....E....650 615-7705
318 S Maple Ave South San Francisco (94080) *(P-12500)*
B O A Inc....E....714 256-8960
580 W Lambert Rd Ste L Brea (92821) *(P-3138)*
B P I Corp....F....408 988-7888
1208 Norman Ave Ste B Santa Clara (95054) *(P-16300)*
B P John Hauling, Murrieta *Also called B P John Recycle Inc (P-4031)*
B P John Recycle Inc....E....951 696-1144
38875 Avenida La Cresta Murrieta (92562) *(P-4031)*
B P W, Santa Fe Springs *Also called Brown-Pacific Inc (P-11381)*
B R & F Spray Inc (PA)....F....408 988-7582
3380 De La Cruz Blvd Santa Clara (95054) *(P-13557)*
B R Printers Inc (PA)....D....408 929-5403
665 Lenfest Rd San Jose (95133) *(P-6678)*
B S A, San Jose *Also called Ball Screws & Actuators Coinc (P-15281)*
B S K T Inc....E....818 349-1566
8447 Canoga Ave Canoga Park (91304) *(P-16301)*
B Stephen Cooperage Inc....F....909 591-2929
10746 Vernon Ave Ontario (91762) *(P-11873)*
B T E Deltec Inc (HQ)....C....619 291-4211
2727 Kurtz St San Diego (92110) *(P-19456)*
B T I, City of Industry *Also called Battery Technology Inc (P-19798)*
B T I Areospace & Electronics, Chino *Also called Bti Aerospace & Electronics (P-16335)*
B W I, Anaheim *Also called Bud Wil Inc (P-9822)*
B W Implement Co....E....661 764-5254
288 W Front St Buttonwillow (93206) *(P-14044)*
B W Padilla Inc....E....408 275-9834
197 Ryland St San Jose (95110) *(P-25387)*
B&A Health Products Co, Brea *Also called Lifebloom Corporation (P-8259)*
B&B Hardware Inc....E....805 683-6700
5370 Hollister Ave Ste 2 Santa Barbara (93111) *(P-13059)*
B&B Pallet Company, Compton *Also called Bruce Iversen (P-4456)*
B&B Spring Co, Cerritos *Also called Clio Inc (P-13792)*
B&F Fedelini Inc (PA)....E....213 628-3901
1301 S Main St Ste 226 Los Angeles (90015) *(P-2990)*
B&F Fedelini Inc....E....213 628-3901
305 E 9th St Los Angeles (90015) *(P-2991)*
B&G Machine Shop, Bakersfield *Also called Mc Cain & Mc Cain Inc (P-16724)*
B&K Precision Corporation (PA)....E....714 921-9095
22820 Savi Ranch Pkwy Yorba Linda (92887) *(P-21727)*
B&M Noble Co (PA)....E....619 793-5899
8480 Miralani Dr San Diego (92126) *(P-4073)*
B&W Custom Restaurant Eqp....E....714 578-0332
541 E Jamie Ave La Habra (90631) *(P-16016)*
B&Z Manufacturing Company Inc....E....408 943-1117
1478 Seareel Ln San Jose (95131) *(P-16302)*
B-Air Blowers, Azusa *Also called Intertex Inc (P-15161)*
B-Bridge International Inc....E....408 252-6200
3350 Scott Blvd Bldg 29 Santa Clara (95054) *(P-8531)*
B-Efficient Inc....E....209 663-9199
11545 W Bernardo Ct # 209 San Diego (92127) *(P-17586)*
B-Flat Publishing LLC....F....510 639-7170
9616 Macarthur Blvd Oakland (94605) *(P-6444)*
B-J Machine Inc....F....714 685-0712
1763 N Batavia St Orange (92865) *(P-13167)*
B-K Lighting Inc....D....559 438-5800
40429 Brickyard Dr Madera (93636) *(P-17529)*
B-Lite Optical Inc....F....714 964-8450
18314 Ward St Fountain Valley (92708) *(P-23079)*
B.R. Cohn, Glen Ellen *Also called Vintage Wine Estates Inc (P-2048)*
B.T.i Tool Engineering, Santee *Also called T I B Inc (P-14575)*
B/E Aerospace Inc....C....951 278-4563
350 W Rincon St Corona (92880) *(P-20754)*
B/E Aerospace Inc....D....714 896-9001
7155 Fenwick Ln Westminster (92683) *(P-16303)*
B/E Aerospace Inc....C....714 896-9001
7155 Fenwick Ln Westminster (92683) *(P-20755)*
B/E Aerospace Inc....B....714 688-4200
3355 E La Palma Ave Anaheim (92806) *(P-20756)*
B2 Apparel Inc....F....323 233-0044
219 E 32nd St Los Angeles (90011) *(P-3644)*
B3digigrafx....E....909 259-0153
8759 Lion St Rancho Cucamonga (91730) *(P-6679)*
BA Holdings (HQ)....E....951 684-5110
3016 Kansas Ave Bldg 1 Riverside (92507) *(P-12362)*
Baam Inc....E....818 716-1818
20847 Betron St Woodland Hills (91364) *(P-3558)*
Baatz Enterprises Inc....F....323 660-4866
2910 Allesandro St Los Angeles (90039) *(P-20129)*
Bab Hydraulics, Fontana *Also called Bab Steering Hydraulics (P-20266)*
Bab Steering Hydraulics (PA)....E....208 573-4502
14554 Whittram Ave Fontana (92335) *(P-20266)*
Baba Foods Slo LLC....F....805 439-2250
3889 Long St Ste 100 San Luis Obispo (93401) *(P-982)*
Baba Small Batch, San Luis Obispo *Also called Baba Foods Slo LLC (P-982)*
Babbitt Bearing Co Inc....E....408 298-1101
1170 N 5th St San Jose (95112) *(P-16304)*
Babcock & Wilcox Company....E....707 259-1122
710 Airpark Rd NAPA (94558) *(P-13989)*
Babcock and Wilcox, NAPA *Also called Babcock & Wilcox Company (P-13989)*
Babe Hollywood Inc....F....626 859-7700
113 E Arrow Hwy San Dimas (91773) *(P-3573)*
Babette (PA)....E....510 625-8500
867 Isabella St Oakland (94607) *(P-3379)*
Baby Box Company Inc (PA)....F....844 422-2926
733 Seward St Los Angeles (90038) *(P-5663)*
Baby Einstein Co Llc, The, Burbank *Also called Little Einsteins LLC (P-6359)*
Baby Guess Inc....E....213 765-3100
1444 S Alameda St Los Angeles (90021) *(P-3591)*
Babylon Printing Inc....E....408 519-5000
1800 Dobbin Dr San Jose (95133) *(P-6680)*

Babys World F 714 539-2229
14222 Brookhurst St Garden Grove (92843) ***(P-745)***

Bacchus Press Inc (PA) E 510 420-5800
1287 66th St Emeryville (94608) ***(P-6681)***

Bace Manufacturing Inc (HQ) A 714 630-6002
3125 E Coronado St Anaheim (92806) ***(P-9967)***

Bace Manufacturing Inc D 510 657-5800
45581 Northport Loop W Fremont (94538) ***(P-9968)***

Bachem Americas Inc (HQ) C 310 784-4440
3132 Kashiwa St Torrance (90505) ***(P-8532)***

Bachem Americas Inc F 888 422-2436
1271 Avenida Chelsea Vista (92081) ***(P-8058)***

Bachem Bioscience Inc E 310 784-7322
3132 Kashiwa St Torrance (90505) ***(P-8533)***

Bachem California, Torrance *Also called Bachem Americas Inc* ***(P-8532)***

Bachem Vista BSD, Vista *Also called Bachem Americas Inc* ***(P-8058)***

Bachur & Associates F 408 988-5861
1950 Homestead Rd Santa Clara (95050) ***(P-6682)***

Back Support Systems Inc F 760 329-1472
67688 San Andreas St Desert Hot Springs (92240) ***(P-9820)***

Backflow Apparatus & Valve E 310 639-5231
20435 S Susana Rd Long Beach (90810) ***(P-13760)***

Backstage Equipment Inc F 818 504-6026
8052 Lankershim Blvd North Hollywood (91605) ***(P-12972)***

Backstage Studio Equip, North Hollywood *Also called Backstage Equipment Inc* ***(P-12972)***

Backstage West E 323 525-2356
5055 Wilshire Blvd 5 Los Angeles (90036) ***(P-6108)***

Backyard Unlimited (PA) F 916 630-7433
4765 Pacific St Rocklin (95677) ***(P-4517)***

Bacon Adhesives, Irvine *Also called Royal Adhesives & Sealants LLC* ***(P-9169)***

Bactrack, San Francisco *Also called Khn Solutions Inc* ***(P-22225)***

Badge Co F 714 842-3037
18261 Enterprise Ln Ste D Huntington Beach (92648) ***(P-24047)***

Badger Maps Inc E 415 592-5909
539 Broadway San Francisco (94133) ***(P-24406)***

Badgeville Inc E 650 323-6668
805 Veterans Blvd Ste 307 Redwood City (94063) ***(P-24407)***

Bae Systems Controls Inc C 323 642-5000
5140 W Goldleaf Cir G100 Los Angeles (90056) ***(P-13990)***

Bae Systems Imging Sltions Inc C 408 433-2500
1841 Zanker Rd Ste 50 San Jose (95112) ***(P-18741)***

Bae Systems Info & Elec Sys D 603 885-4321
1930 S Vnyrd Ave M S 1102 Ms Ontario (91761) ***(P-19457)***

Bae Systems Info & Elec Sys C 858 592-5000
10920 Technology Pl San Diego (92127) ***(P-21728)***

Bae Systems Land Armaments LP A 408 289-0111
6331 San Ignacio Ave San Jose (95119) ***(P-21264)***

Bae Systems Land Armaments LP D 408 289-0111
6331 San Ignacio Ave San Jose (95119) ***(P-21214)***

Bae Systcms San Diego (HQ) C 619 238-1000
2205 Belt St San Diego (92113) ***(P-20985)***

Bae Systems San Diego B 619 238-1000
7330 Engineer Rd Ste A San Diego (92111) ***(P-20986)***

Baems, Patterson *Also called Bay Area Ems Solutions LLC* ***(P-18435)***

Baf Industries (PA) E 714 258-8055
1451 Edinger Ave Ste F Tustin (92780) ***(P-8624)***

Baffle Inc F 408 663-6737
2811 Mission College Blvd Santa Clara (95054) ***(P-24408)***

Bagcraftpapercon I LLC D 626 961-6766
515 Turnbull Canyon Rd City of Industry (91745) ***(P-5637)***

Bagelry Inc (PA) E 831 429-8049
320 Cedar St Ste A Santa Cruz (95060) ***(P-1178)***

Baghouse and Indus Shtmtl Svcs, Corona *Also called MS Industrial Shtmtl Inc* ***(P-12689)***

Bagmasters, Corona *Also called CTA Manufacturing Inc* ***(P-3762)***

Baguette World, Los Angeles *Also called Kobi Katz Inc* ***(P-23283)***

Bahne and Company Inc F 760 753-8847
585 Westlake St Ste A Encinitas (92024) ***(P-23512)***

Bahne Single Ski, Encinitas *Also called Bahne and Company Inc* ***(P-23512)***

Bai Inc F 650 872-1700
21 Airport Blvd Ste B South San Francisco (94080) ***(P-20757)***

Baier Marine Company Inc E 800 455-3917
2920 Airway Ave Costa Mesa (92626) ***(P-11935)***

Bailey Essel William Jr F 707 341-3391
1373 Lincoln Ave Calistoga (94515) ***(P-1651)***

Bailey 44 LLC E 213 228-1930
4700 S Boyle Ave Vernon (90058) ***(P-3215)***

Bailey Industries Inc F 949 461-0807
25256 Terreno Dr Mission Viejo (92691) ***(P-20758)***

Bailey Valve Inc E 559 434-2838
264 W Fallbrook Ave # 105 Fresno (93711) ***(P-13705)***

Baise Enterprises Inc F 916 446-0167
3258 Stockton Blvd Sacramento (95820) ***(P-6683)***

Baja Designs, San Marcos *Also called Bestop Baja LLC* ***(P-20268)***

Baja Onyx & Marble Intl, San Ysidro *Also called Betty Stillwell* ***(P-11238)***

Baja Products, Ontario *Also called Chladni & Jariwala Inc* ***(P-13710)***

Bajasys LLC F 619 661-0748
9923 Via De La Amistad # 105 San Diego (92154) ***(P-15677)***

Bakakers Specialty Foods Inc F 209 234-5935
2619 Lycoming St Ste 200 Stockton (95206) ***(P-1033)***

Bake R Us Inc F 310 630-5873
13400 S Western Ave Gardena (90249) ***(P-1179)***

Baked In Sun C 760 591-9045
2560 Progress St Vista (92081) ***(P-1180)***

Bakemark USA LLC (PA) B 562 949-1054
7351 Crider Ave Pico Rivera (90660) ***(P-1095)***

Bakemark USA LLC E 510 487-8188
32621 Central Ave Union City (94587) ***(P-2459)***

Baker Atlas, Bakersfield *Also called Baker Hghes Olfld Oprtions LLC* ***(P-171)***

Baker Commodities Inc (PA) C 323 268-2801
4020 Bandini Blvd Vernon (90058) ***(P-1519)***

Baker Commodities Inc E 559 237-4320
16801 W Jensen Ave Kerman (93630) ***(P-1520)***

Baker Commodities Inc E 559 686-4797
7480 Hanford Armona Rd Hanford (93230) ***(P-1521)***

Baker Commodities Inc E 323 318-8260
3001 Sierra Pine Ave Vernon (90058) ***(P-1522)***

Baker Coupling Company Inc E 323 583-3444
2929 S Santa Fe Ave Vernon (90058) ***(P-13878)***

Baker Filtration, South Gate *Also called Bakercorp* ***(P-17234)***

Baker Filtration E 925 473-9659
2700 California Ave Pittsburg (94565) ***(P-16017)***

Baker Furnace Inc F 714 223-7262
2680 Orbiter St Brea (92821) ***(P-15253)***

Baker Hghes Olfld Oprtions LLC E 661 834-2844
5551 Aldrin Ct Bakersfield (93313) ***(P-170)***

Baker Hghes Olfld Oprtions LLC F 661 831-5200
4730 Armstrong Rd Bakersfield (93313) ***(P-171)***

Baker Hghes Olfld Oprtions LLC D 714 893-8511
5421 Argosy Ave Huntington Beach (92649) ***(P-14208)***

Baker Hghes Olfld Oprtions LLC F 714 891-8544
15421 Assembly Ln Huntington Beach (92649) ***(P-172)***

Baker Hghes Olfld Oprtions LLC E 661 324-9488
4230 Foster Ave Bakersfield (93308) ***(P-173)***

Baker Hghes Olfld Oprtions LLC E 661 834-9654
5700 Doolittle Ave Shafter (93263) ***(P-174)***

Baker Hghes Olfld Oprtions LLC D 310 843-9632
9865 W Olympic Blvd Beverly Hills (90212) ***(P-14209)***

Baker Hughes, Santa Paula *Also called Baker Petrolite LLC* ***(P-183)***

Baker Hughes A GE Company LLC D 714 893-8511
5421 Argosy Ave Huntington Beach (92649) ***(P-14210)***

Baker Hughes A GE Company LLC E 661 834-9654
3901 Fanucchi Way Shafter (93263) ***(P-175)***

Baker Hughes A GE Company LLC D 661 387-1010
1127 Carrier Parkway Ave Bakersfield (93308) ***(P-176)***

Baker Hughes A GE Company LLC D 661 831-7686
3901 Fanucchi Way Shafter (93263) ***(P-177)***

Baker Hughes A GE Company LLC D 661 837-9601
5010 Lisa Marie Ct Bakersfield (93313) ***(P-14211)***

Baker Hughes A GE Company LLC D 800 229-7447
5145 Boylan St Bakersfield (93308) ***(P-178)***

Baker Hughes A GE Company LLC D 661 834-9654
6117 Schirra Ct Bakersfield (93313) ***(P-14212)***

Baker Hughes A GE Company LLC F 661 391-0794
19433 Colombo St Bakersfield (93308) ***(P-179)***

Baker Interiors Furniture Co E 415 626-1414
101 Henry Adams St # 350 San Francisco (94103) ***(P-4907)***

Baker Oil Tools, Bakersfield *Also called Baker Hghes Olfld Oprtions LLC* ***(P-170)***

Baker Oil Tools, Huntington Beach *Also called Baker Hghes Olfld Oprtions LLC* ***(P-172)***

Baker Oil Tools, Bakersfield *Also called Baker Hghes Olfld Oprtions LLC* ***(P-173)***

Baker Petrolite LLC F 925 682-3313
2280 Bates Ave Ste A Concord (94520) ***(P-180)***

Baker Petrolite LLC D 661 325-4138
5125 Boylan St Bakersfield (93308) ***(P-181)***

Baker Petrolite LLC F 562 406-7090
11808 Bloomfield Ave Santa Fe Springs (90670) ***(P-182)***

Baker Petrolite LLC E 805 525-4404
265 Quail Ct Santa Paula (93060) ***(P-183)***

Baker Tanks, Pittsburg *Also called Baker Filtration* ***(P-16017)***

Bakercorp F 562 904-3680
5500 Rawlings Ave South Gate (90280) ***(P-17234)***

Bakersfield Californian (PA) C 661 322-5627
1707 Eye St Bakersfield (93301) ***(P-5772)***

Bakersfield Elc Mtr Repr Inc F 661 327-3583
121 W Sumner St Bakersfield (93301) ***(P-25455)***

Bakersfield Machine Co Inc D 661 393-8441
5605 N Chester Ave Ext Bakersfield (93308) ***(P-16305)***

Bakersfield Refinery, Bakersfield *Also called Paramount Petroleum Corp* ***(P-9346)***

Bakersfield Well Casing LLC F 661 399-2976
17876 Zerker Rd Bakersfield (93308) ***(P-98)***

Bakersfield Woodworks Inc F 661 282-8492
3416 Big Trail Ave Bakersfield (93313) ***(P-4109)***

Bakersfield Yard Asp & Rdymx, Bakersfield *Also called Legacy Vulcan LLC* ***(P-11129)***

Bakerstone International LLC F 855 657-6836
3617 W Macarthur Blvd Santa Ana (92704) ***(P-17363)***

Bakery Depot Inc F 323 261-8388
4489 Bandini Blvd Vernon (90058) ***(P-1181)***

Bal Seal Engineering Inc (PA) B 949 334-8500
19650 Pauling Foothill Ranch (92610) ***(P-13787)***

Balaji Trading Inc D 909 444-7999
4850 Eucalyptus Ave Chino (91710) ***(P-17925)***

Balboa Acquisition LLC E 714 972-4972
1760 E Wilshire Ave Santa Ana (92705) ***(P-1182)***

Balboa Manufacturing Co LLC (PA) E 858 715-0060
9401 Waples St Ste 120 San Diego (92121) ***(P-2823)***

Balboa Water Group LLC (PA) C 714 384-0384
1382 Bell Ave Tustin (92780) ***(P-17256)***

Balda C Brewer Inc (HQ) C 714 630-6810
4501 E Wall St Ontario (91761) ***(P-9969)***

Balda C Brewer Inc F 714 630-6810
4501 E Wall St Ontario (91761) ***(P-9970)***

Balda HK Plastics Inc D 760 757-1100
3229 Roymar Rd Oceanside (92058) ***(P-13016)***

Baldacci Family Vineyard, NAPA *Also called Archangel Investments LLC* ***(P-1646)***

Baldor Electric Company, Commerce *Also called Power Reps Inc* ***(P-25464)***

Baldwin Brass, Foothill Ranch *Also called Baldwin Hardware Corporation* ***(P-11936)***

Baldwin Hardware Corporation (HQ) A 949 672-4000
19701 Da Vinci Foothill Ranch (92610) ***(P-11936)***

Balita Media Inc....E....818 552-4503
2629 Foothill Blvd La Crescenta (91214) *(P-5773)*
Ball Corporation....B....209 848-6500
300 Greger St Oakdale (95361) *(P-11856)*
Ball Metal Beverage Cont Corp....C....707 437-7516
2400 Huntington Dr Fairfield (94533) *(P-11857)*
Ball of Cotton Inc....E....323 888-9448
6400 E Washington Blvd Commerce (90040) *(P-2824)*
Ball Plastic Container, Chino *Also called Amcor Rigid Plastics Usa LLC (P-9792)*
Ball Screws & Actuators Coinc (HQ)....D....408 938-3031
970 Mclaughlin Ave San Jose (95122) *(P-15281)*
Ball TEC, Los Angeles *Also called Micro Surface Engr Inc (P-11843)*
Ballard & Tighe Publishers, Brea *Also called Educational Ideas Incorporated (P-6337)*
Ballast Point Brewing, San Diego *Also called Ballast Point Spirits LLC (P-1566)*
Ballast Point Spirits LLC....C....858 695-2739
9045 Carroll Way San Diego (92121) *(P-1566)*
Ballast Pt Brewing & Spirits, San Diego *Also called Home Brew Mart Inc (P-1600)*
Balletto Vineyards, Santa Rosa *Also called Laguna Oaks Vnyards Winery Inc (P-1850)*
Baltimore Aircoil Company Inc....C....559 673-9231
15341 Road 28 1/2 Madera (93638) *(P-15940)*
Balut Pateros, Westminster *Also called AA Laboratory Eggs Inc (P-2238)*
Bambacigno Steel Company....E....209 524-9681
4930 Mchenry Ave Modesto (95356) *(P-11380)*
Bambeck Systems Inc (PA)....F....949 250-3100
1921 Carnegie Ave Ste 3a Santa Ana (92705) *(P-21551)*
Bamberger Polymers Inc....F....714 672-4740
145 S State College Blvd # 100 Brea (92821) *(P-7821)*
Bamboosa, Culver City *Also called M Group Inc (P-10527)*
Bamford Equipment, Oroville *Also called J W Bamford Inc (P-3995)*
Bananafish Productions Inc....F....714 956-2129
1536 W Embassy St Anaheim (92802) *(P-10678)*
Banbury Precision, Santa Clara *Also called B P I Corp (P-16300)*
Band-It Rubber Company Inc....F....951 735-5072
1711 N Delilah St Corona (92879) *(P-9593)*
Bandag Licensing Corporation....D....562 531-3880
2500 E Thompson St Long Beach (90805) *(P-9594)*
Bandai America Incorporated (HQ)....D....714 816-9751
2120 Park Pl Ste 120 El Segundo (90245) *(P-23409)*
Bandel Mfg Inc....E....818 246-7493
4459 Alger St Los Angeles (90039) *(P-13168)*
Bandmerch LLC....E....818 736-4800
3120 W Empire Ave Burbank (91504) *(P-3877)*
Bandy Manufacturing LLC....D....818 846-9020
3420 N San Fernando Blvd Burbank (91504) *(P-20759)*
Banh An Binh....E....408 935-8950
1965 Stonewood Ln San Jose (95132) *(P-19458)*
Banh MI & Che Cali....E....714 534-6987
13838 Brookhurst St Garden Grove (92843) *(P-1183)*
Bank C Plating Co, Los Angeles *Also called We Five-R Corporation (P-13533)*
Banks Power Products, Azusa *Also called Gale Banks Engineering (P-14028)*
Banner Mattress Inc (PA)....E....909 835-4200
1501 E Cooley Dr Ste B Colton (92324) *(P-4852)*
Bar Manufacturing Inc....D....916 939-0551
3921 Sandstone Dr Ste 1 El Dorado Hills (95762) *(P-18742)*
Bar Media Inc....F....415 861-5019
44 Gough St Ste 204 San Francisco (94103) *(P-5774)*
Bar None Inc....F....714 259-8450
1302 Santa Fe Dr Tustin (92780) *(P-2066)*
Bar-S Foods Co....B....408 941-9958
392 Railroad Ct Milpitas (95035) *(P-466)*
Bar-S Foods Co....B....323 589-3600
4919 Alcoa Ave Vernon (90058) *(P-467)*
Bar-S Foods Co. Los Angeles, Vernon *Also called Bar-S Foods Co (P-467)*
Barbara Lesser, Los Angeles *Also called Wearable Integrity Inc (P-3528)*
Barbee Valve & Supply Inc (HQ)....F....619 585-8484
745 Main St Anaheim (92805) *(P-13706)*
Barber Welding and Mfg Co....E....562 928-2570
7171 Scout Ave Bell Gardens (90201) *(P-16306)*
Barber-Webb Company Inc (PA)....E....541 488-4821
3833 Medford St Los Angeles (90063) *(P-9971)*
Barbosa Cabinets Inc....B....209 836-2501
2020 E Grant Line Rd Tracy (95304) *(P-4272)*
Barbour Vineyards LLC....D....707 257-1829
104 Camino Dorado NAPA (94558) *(P-1652)*
Barco Uniforms Inc....C....310 323-7315
350 W Rosecrans Ave Gardena (90248) *(P-3025)*
Bardex Corporation....D....805 964-7747
6338 Lindmar Dr Goleta (93117) *(P-15299)*
Bare Nothings Inc (PA)....E....714 848-8532
17705 Sampson Ln Huntington Beach (92647) *(P-3380)*
Barebottle Brewing Company Inc....F....415 926-8617
1525 Cortland Ave # 6 San Francisco (94110) *(P-1567)*
Barefoot Cellars, Santa Rosa *Also called Grape Links Inc (P-1794)*
Barfresh Food Group Inc....E....310 598-7113
8383 Wilshire Blvd # 750 Beverly Hills (90211) *(P-2242)*
Bargas Bindery....F....510 357-7901
1658 Scenicview Dr San Leandro (94577) *(P-7594)*
Barger & Associates....E....408 779-5424
140b Mast St Morgan Hill (95037) *(P-9595)*
Bargueiras Rene Inc....F....818 500-8288
621 S Victory Blvd Burbank (91502) *(P-23243)*
Barhena Inc....E....888 383-8800
1085 Bixby Dr Hacienda Heights (91745) *(P-16018)*
Barkens Hardchrome Inc....E....310 632-2000
239 E Greenleaf Blvd Compton (90220) *(P-14919)*
Barker-Canoga Inc....F....760 246-4777
16528 Koala Rd Ste A Adelanto (92301) *(P-14605)*
Barkerblue Inc....E....650 696-2100
363 N Amphlett Blvd San Mateo (94401) *(P-7627)*
Barkevs Inc....F....800 227-7321
707 S Broadway Ste 415 Los Angeles (90014) *(P-23244)*
Barksdale Inc (HQ)....C....323 583-6243
3211 Fruitland Ave Vernon (90058) *(P-22170)*
Barkstrong LLC....E....855 381-5888
4325 Glencoe Ave # 10846 Marina Del Rey (90292) *(P-1108)*
Barletta Dehydrator Inc....F....530 865-9318
4101 County Road S Orland (95963) *(P-874)*
Barlow and Sons Printing Inc....F....707 664-9773
481 Aaron St Cotati (94931) *(P-6684)*
Barlow Printing, Cotati *Also called Barlow and Sons Printing Inc (P-6684)*
Barnana, Santa Monica *Also called Wholesome Valley Foods (P-2700)*
Barnes Plastics Inc....E....310 329-6301
18903 Anelo Ave Gardena (90248) *(P-9699)*
Barnett Performance Products, Ventura *Also called Barnett Tool & Engineering (P-21090)*
Barnett Tool & Engineering....D....805 642-9435
2238 Palma Dr Ventura (93003) *(P-21090)*
Barney & Co California LLC....F....559 442-1752
2925 S Elm Ave Ste 101 Fresno (93706) *(P-2460)*
Barns and Buildings Inc....D....951 678-4571
23100 Baxter Rd Wildomar (92595) *(P-12919)*
Barns By Harrahs....F....530 824-4611
3489 S 99w Corning (96021) *(P-12920)*
Baron & Baron, Huntington Beach *Also called License Frame Inc (P-13611)*
Baron Brand Spices, Fairfield *Also called Abco Laboratories Inc (P-7989)*
Baron Usa LLC....E....931 528-8476
350 Baron Cir Woodland (95776) *(P-15300)*
Barra LLC (HQ)....B....510 548-5442
2100 Milvia St Berkeley (94704) *(P-24409)*
Barra, Inc., Berkeley *Also called Barra LLC (P-24409)*
Barracuda Networks Inc....F....408 342-5400
5225 Hellyer Ave San Jose (95138) *(P-15678)*
Barracuda Networks Inc (HQ)....C....408 342-5400
3175 Winchester Blvd Campbell (95008) *(P-24410)*
Barranca Diamond Products, Torrance *Also called Barranca Holdings Ltd (P-14606)*
Barranca Holdings Ltd....F....310 523-5867
22815 Frampton Ave Torrance (90501) *(P-14606)*
Barrango (PA)....F....650 737-9206
391 Forbes Blvd South San Francisco (94080) *(P-16307)*
Barrel Merchants, Saint Helena *Also called Red River Lumber Co (P-4533)*
Barrel Ten Qarter Cir Land Inc (HQ)....E....707 258-0550
6342 Bystrum Rd Ceres (95307) *(P-1653)*
Barrett Engineering Inc....F....858 256-9194
1725 Burton St San Diego (92111) *(P-19828)*
Barricade Co & Traffic Sup Inc (PA)....F....707 523-2350
3963 Santa Rosa Ave Santa Rosa (95407) *(P-13922)*
Barrick Gold Corporation....D....707 995-6070
26775 Morgan Valley Rd Lower Lake (95457) *(P-1)*
Barrier Systems Sales & Svc, Rio Vista *Also called Lindsay Trnsp Solutions Inc (P-10954)*
Barrot Corporation....E....949 852-1640
1881 Kaiser Ave Irvine (92614) *(P-14484)*
Barrx Medical Inc....D....408 328-7300
540 Oakmead Pkwy Sunnyvale (94085) *(P-22354)*
Barry Avenue Plating Co Inc....D....310 478-0078
2210 Barry Ave Los Angeles (90064) *(P-13344)*
Barry Callebaut USA LLC....F....707 642-8200
1175 Commerce Blvd Ste D American Canyon (94503) *(P-1465)*
Barry Controls Aerospace, Burbank *Also called Hutchinson Arospc & Indust Inc (P-9626)*
Barry Costello....F....530 265-3300
319 Broad St Nevada City (95959) *(P-3608)*
Barrys Cultured Marble Inc....F....707 745-3444
866 Teal Dr Benicia (94510) *(P-11234)*
Barrys Printing Inc....E....818 998-8600
20936 Devonshire St Ste E Chatsworth (91311) *(P-6685)*
Bart Manufacturing Inc....E....408 320-4373
3787 Spinnaker Ct Fremont (94538) *(P-24048)*
Barta-Schoenewald Inc (PA)....C....805 389-1935
3805 Calle Tecate Camarillo (93012) *(P-17181)*
Bartholomew Park Winery, Sonoma *Also called Vineburg Wine Company Inc (P-2044)*
Bartlett Fine Cabinetry Mllwk, Buellton *Also called Cliff Bartlett (P-4287)*
Bartolini Guitars....F....386 517-6823
2133 Research Dr Ste 16 Livermore (94550) *(P-19459)*
Bartolini Pickups, Livermore *Also called Bartolini Guitars (P-19459)*
Barton Perreira LLC (PA)....E....949 305-5360
459 Wald Irvine (92618) *(P-23080)*
Barton Sales, City of Industry *Also called Prime Measurement Products LLC (P-21635)*
Barzillai Manufacturing Co....F....909 947-4200
1410 S Cucamonga Ave Ontario (91761) *(P-12501)*
BAS Recycling Inc....E....951 214-6590
14050 Day St Moreno Valley (92553) *(P-9460)*
Basalite Building Products LLC (HQ)....E....707 678-1901
2150 Douglas Blvd Ste 260 Roseville (95661) *(P-10881)*
Basalite Building Products LLC....C....209 833-3670
11888 W Linne Rd Tracy (95377) *(P-10845)*
Basalite Building Products LLC....E....209 333-6161
104 E Turner Rd Lodi (95240) *(P-10882)*
Basalite-Tracy, Tracy *Also called Basalite Building Products LLC (P-10845)*
Basaw Manufacturing Inc (PA)....E....818 765-6650
7300 Varna Ave North Hollywood (91605) *(P-4435)*
Basaw Services Inc....E....818 765-6650
7300 Varna Ave North Hollywood (91605) *(P-4436)*
Basaw Services Inc....E....818 765-6650
13340 Raymer St North Hollywood (91605) *(P-4437)*
Base Hockey LP (PA)....F....805 405-3650
581 Calle Arroyo Thousand Oaks (91360) *(P-23513)*

Base Lite Corporation ....E....909 444-2776
12260 Eastend Ave Chino (91710) *(P-17530)*
Baselite, Chino *Also called Base Lite Corporation (P-17530)*
BASF Catalysts LLC ....F....510 490-2150
46820 Fremont Blvd Fremont (94538) *(P-8980)*
BASF Construction Chem LLC ....E....909 987-1758
9060 Haven Ave Rancho Cucamonga (91730) *(P-9224)*
BASF Corporation ....E....714 921-1430
138 E Meats Ave Orange (92865) *(P-8981)*
BASF Corporation ....F....510 796-9911
38403 Cherry St Newark (94560) *(P-8982)*
BASF Enzymes LLC ....F....858 431-8520
3550 John Hopkins Ct San Diego (92121) *(P-8983)*
BASF Venture Capital Amer Inc ....F....510 445-6140
46820 Fremont Blvd Fremont (94538) *(P-8984)*
Bashoura Inc ....F....626 963-7600
539 S Glenwood Ave Glendora (91741) *(P-23245)*
Basic American Inc (PA) ....D....925 472-4438
2999 Oak Rd Ste 800 Walnut Creek (94597) *(P-875)*
Basic American Foods, Walnut Creek *Also called Basic American Inc (P-875)*
Basic Business Forms Inc ....E....805 278-4551
561 Kinetic Dr Ste A Oxnard (93030) *(P-7246)*
Basic Electronics Inc ....E....714 530-2400
11371 Monarch St Garden Grove (92841) *(P-19460)*
Basic Energy Services Inc ....E....714 530-0855
12891 Nelson St Garden Grove (92840) *(P-184)*
Basic Energy Services Inc ....E....661 588-3800
6710 Stewart Way Bakersfield (93308) *(P-185)*
Basic Industries Intl Inc ....C....951 226-1500
10850 Wilshire Blvd Los Angeles (90024) *(P-12363)*
Basic Microcom Inc ....F....951 708-1268
38595 Rancho Christina Rd Temecula (92592) *(P-17257)*
Basin Marine Inc ....F....949 673-0360
829 Harbor Island Dr A Newport Beach (92660) *(P-21022)*
Basin Marine Shipyard, Newport Beach *Also called Basin Marine Inc (P-21022)*
Basin Medical, Ontario *Also called Greenwood Products Inc (P-10594)*
Basmat Inc (PA) ....D....310 325-2063
1531 240th St Harbor City (90710) *(P-12502)*
Basque French Bakery, Fresno *Also called Fresno French Bread Bakery Inc (P-1253)*
Bass Angler ....F....925 362-3190
2500 Shadow Mountain Ct San Ramon (94583) *(P-6109)*
Bass Angler Magazine, San Ramon *Also called Bass Angler (P-6109)*
Bassani Exhaust, Anaheim *Also called Bassani Manufacturing (P-13879)*
Bassani Manufacturing ....E....714 630-1821
2900 E La Jolla St Anaheim (92806) *(P-13879)*
Bastan Corporation ....F....619 424-3416
2260 Main St Ste 17 Chula Vista (91911) *(P-746)*
Batchlder Bus Cmmnications Inc ....F....209 577-2222
2900 Standiford Ave Ste 5 Modesto (95350) *(P-6686)*
Bates Industries Inc ....F....562 426-8668
3671 Industry Ave Ste C5 Lakewood (90712) *(P-3609)*
Bates Leathers, Lakewood *Also called Bates Industries Inc (P-3609)*
Bath Petals Inc ....F....310 532-4532
15620 S Figueroa St Gardena (90248) *(P-8700)*
Bath Promotions, Gardena *Also called Bath Petals Inc (P-8700)*
Batida Inc ....F....714 557-4597
3187 Airway Ave Ste B Costa Mesa (92626) *(P-6687)*
Baton Lock & Hardware Co Inc ....E....714 265-3636
14275 Commerce Dr Garden Grove (92843) *(P-11937)*
Baton Security, Garden Grove *Also called Baton Lock & Hardware Co Inc (P-11937)*
Battery Hut, Burbank *Also called Pro Power Products Inc (P-17351)*
Battery Technology Inc (PA) ....D....626 336-6878
16651 E Johnson Dr City of Industry (91745) *(P-19798)*
Battery-Biz Inc ....D....805 437-7777
1380 Flynn Rd Camarillo (93012) *(P-19829)*
Batth Dehydrator LLC ....E....559 864-3501
4624 W Nebraska Ave Caruthers (93609) *(P-876)*
Bau Furniture Manufacturing (PA) ....E....949 643-2729
23811 Aliso Creek Rd # 134 Laguna Niguel (92677) *(P-4675)*
Bauer Industries (PA) ....F....916 648-9200
708 Alhambra Blvd Ste 2 Sacramento (95816) *(P-11938)*
Bauer International Corp ....F....714 259-9800
9251 Irvine Blvd Irvine (92618) *(P-16019)*
Bauers & Collins ....F....818 983-1281
6765 Lankershim Blvd North Hollywood (91606) *(P-22704)*
Baughn Engineering Inc ....F....909 392-0933
2815 Metropolitan Pl Pomona (91767) *(P-21729)*
Baumann Engineering Inc ....D....909 621-4181
212 S Cambridge Ave Claremont (91711) *(P-16308)*
Bausch & Lomb Incorporated ....D....949 788-6000
50 Technology Dr Irvine (92618) *(P-8059)*
Bausch & Lomb Incorporated ....C....949 788-6000
50 Technology Dr Irvine (92618) *(P-23081)*
Bausch & Lomb Surgical Div, Irvine *Also called Eyeonics Inc (P-23099)*
Bausman and Company Inc (PA) ....C....909 947-0139
1500 Crafton Ave Bldg 124 Mentone (92359) *(P-4933)*
Bavco, Long Beach *Also called Backflow Apparatus & Valve (P-13760)*
Baxalta Incorporated ....A....818 240-5600
4501 Colorado Blvd Los Angeles (90039) *(P-8060)*
Baxalta US Inc ....B....805 498-8664
1700 Rancho Conejo Blvd Thousand Oaks (91320) *(P-22355)*
Baxstra Inc ....D....323 770-4171
1224 W 132nd St Gardena (90247) *(P-4074)*
Baxter Bioscience ....A....805 498-8988
1700 Rancho Conejo Blvd Newbury Park (91320) *(P-7923)*
Baxter Healthcare Corporation ....C....303 222-6837
4551 E Philadelphia St Ontario (91761) *(P-8061)*
Baxter Healthcare Corporation ....C....949 474-6301
17511 Armstrong Ave Irvine (92614) *(P-22356)*
Baxter Healthcare Corporation ....F....510 723-2000
2024 W Winton Ave Hayward (94545) *(P-8062)*
Baxter Healthcare Corporation ....D....949 250-2500
1402 Alton Pkwy Irvine (92606) *(P-22357)*
Baxter Healthcare Corporation ....D....503 285-0212
700 Vaughn Rd Dixon (95620) *(P-22358)*
Baxter Medication Delivery, Irvine *Also called Baxter Healthcare Corporation (P-22356)*
Bay AR Yellow Pages ....F....650 558-8888
46292 Warm Springs Blvd Fremont (94539) *(P-6445)*
Bay Area Canvas Inc ....F....408 727-4314
2362 De La Cruz Blvd Santa Clara (95050) *(P-3779)*
Bay Area Circuits Inc ....E....510 933-9000
44358 Old Warm Sprng Blvd Fremont (94538) *(P-18434)*
Bay Area Coffee Inc ....E....707 745-1320
4201 Industrial Way Benicia (94510) *(P-2328)*
Bay Area Drilling Inc ....F....925 427-7574
1860 Loveridge Rd Pittsburg (94565) *(P-346)*
Bay Area Ems Solutions LLC ....F....408 753-3651
147 Walker Ranch Pkwy Patterson (95363) *(P-18435)*
Bay Area Indus Filtration Inc ....E....510 562-6373
6355 Coliseum Way Oakland (94621) *(P-15301)*
Bay Area Pallette Company, Antioch *Also called Chep (usa) Inc (P-4460)*
Bay Area Reporter, San Francisco *Also called Bar Media Inc (P-5774)*
Bay Associates Wire Tech Corp (HQ) ....D....510 988-3800
46840 Lakeview Blvd Fremont (94538) *(P-2969)*
Bay Central Printing Inc ....F....510 429-9111
33401 Western Ave Union City (94587) *(P-6688)*
Bay Cities Container Corp (PA) ....C....562 948-3751
5138 Industry Ave Pico Rivera (90660) *(P-5386)*
Bay Cities Italian Bakery Inc ....F....310 608-1881
1120 W Mahalo Pl Compton (90220) *(P-1184)*
Bay Cities Metal Products, Gardena *Also called Bay Cities Tin Shop Inc (P-12503)*
Bay Cities Tin Shop Inc ....E....310 660-0351
301 E Alondra Blvd Gardena (90248) *(P-12503)*
Bay City Marine Inc (PA) ....E....619 477-3991
1625 Cleveland Ave National City (91950) *(P-12116)*
Bay City Marine Inc ....E....619 477-3991
1625 Cleveland Ave National City (91950) *(P-20987)*
Bay Classifieds Inc ....E....510 636-1867
433 Hegenberger Rd # 205 Oakland (94621) *(P-14803)*
Bay Elctrnic Spport Trnics Inc ....C....408 432-3222
2090 Fortune Dr San Jose (95131) *(P-18436)*
Bay Equipment Co Inc ....F....510 226-8800
44221 S Grimmer Blvd Fremont (94538) *(P-13094)*
Bay Guardian Company ....D....415 255-3100
135 Micaicaippi St San Francisco (94107) *(P-5775)*
Bay Leaf Spice Company ....E....925 330-1918
21c Orinda Way 363 Orinda (94563) *(P-2461)*
Bay Marine Boatworks Inc ....E....510 237-0140
310 W Cutting Blvd Richmond (94804) *(P-21023)*
Bay Ornamental Iron Inc ....E....949 548-1015
757 Newton Way Costa Mesa (92627) *(P-12836)*
Bay Precision Machining Inc ....E....650 365-3010
815 Sweeney Ave Ste D Redwood City (94063) *(P-16309)*
Bay Ship & Yacht Co (PA) ....C....510 337-9122
2900 Main St Ste 2100 Alameda (94501) *(P-20988)*
Bay Tech Manufacturing Inc ....F....510 783-0660
23334 Bernhardt St Hayward (94545) *(P-16310)*
Bay Valve Service & Engrg LLC ....E....707 748-7166
3948 Teal Ct Benicia (94510) *(P-5221)*
Baycorr Packaging Inc (PA) ....C....925 449-1148
6850 Brisa St Livermore (94550) *(P-5387)*
Bayer Corporation ....B....510 705-5000
820 Parker St Berkeley (94710) *(P-22359)*
Bayer Cropscience, West Sacramento *Also called Agraquest Inc (P-9089)*
Bayer Diabetes Care, Sunnyvale *Also called Bayer Healthcare LLC (P-8069)*
Bayer Healthcare LLC ....B....415 437-5800
455 Mission Bay Blvd S # 493 San Francisco (94158) *(P-8063)*
Bayer Healthcare LLC ....C....510 597-6150
5885 Hollis St Emeryville (94608) *(P-8064)*
Bayer Healthcare LLC ....C....510 705-7545
800 Dwight Way Berkeley (94710) *(P-8065)*
Bayer Healthcare LLC ....B....510 705-7539
717 Potter St Street-2 Berkeley (94710) *(P-8066)*
Bayer Healthcare LLC ....C....510 705-4421
747 Grayson St Berkeley (94710) *(P-8067)*
Bayer Healthcare LLC ....C....510 705-4914
2448 6th St Berkeley (94710) *(P-8068)*
Bayer Healthcare LLC ....D....408 499-0606
510 Oakmead Pkwy Sunnyvale (94085) *(P-8069)*
Bayer Hlthcare Phrmcticals Inc ....B....510 262-5000
455 Mission Bay Blvd S San Francisco (94158) *(P-8070)*
Bayfab Metals Inc ....E....510 568-8950
870 Doolittle Dr San Leandro (94577) *(P-12296)*
Bayless Engineering Inc ....C....661 257-3373
26100 Ave Hall Valencia Valencia (91355) *(P-16311)*
Bayless Engineering & Mfg, Valencia *Also called Bayless Engineering Inc (P-16311)*
Bayline, Union City *Also called Compro Packaging LLC (P-5400)*
Bayliss Botanicals LLC ....F....530 868-5466
17 W Rio Bonito Rd Biggs (95917) *(P-8071)*
Bayshore Lights, San Francisco *Also called Ijk & Co Inc (P-19980)*
Bayside Shutters ....F....714 628-9994
1464 N Batavia St Orange (92867) *(P-12297)*
Bayspec Inc ....E....408 512-5928
1101 Mckay Dr San Jose (95131) *(P-10635)*
Bayview Plastic Solutions Inc ....E....510 360-0001
43651 S Grimmer Blvd Fremont (94538) *(P-9972)*
Baywa R.E.renewable Energy, Irvine *Also called Baywa RE Solar Projects LLC (P-18743)*

ALPHABETIC

Employee Codes: A=Over 500 employees, B=251-500
C=101-250, D=51-100, E=20-50, F=10-19
2019 California
Manfacturers Register
© Mergent Inc. 1-800-342-5647
1073

Baywa RE Solar Projects LLC .... E 949 398-3915
17901 Von Karman Ave # 1050 Irvine (92614) ***(P-18743)***
Baywood Cellars Inc .... E 415 606-4640
5573 W Woodbridge Rd Lodi (95242) ***(P-1654)***
Bazz Houston Co, Garden Grove *Also called Houston Bazz Co* ***(P-13220)***
Bb Apparel, Los Angeles *Also called B2 Apparel Inc* ***(P-3644)***
Bb Co Inc .... E 213 747-4701
1753 E 21st St Los Angeles (90058) ***(P-3381)***
BBC Corp .... E 530 677-4009
4286 N Star Dr Shingle Springs (95682) ***(P-6689)***
Bbe Sound Inc (PA) .... E 714 897-6766
2548 Fender Ave Ste D Fullerton (92831) ***(P-23356)***
Bbk Specialties Inc .... F 661 255-2857
24147 Del Monte Dr # 297 Valencia (91355) ***(P-10804)***
Bbs Manufacturing Inc .... F 760 798-8011
1905 Diamond St Ste A San Marcos (92078) ***(P-23514)***
Bbt, Los Angeles *Also called Bhaktivedanta Book Tr Intl Inc* ***(P-6315)***
Bcbg Maxazria Entrmt LLC .... F 323 277-4713
2761 Fruitland Ave Vernon (90058) ***(P-3382)***
BCI Inc .... F 626 579-4234
1822 Belcroft Ave South El Monte (91733) ***(P-16312)***
Bcj Sand and Rock Inc .... F 707 544-0303
3388 Regional Pkwy Ste A Santa Rosa (95403) ***(P-394)***
Bcnu, Los Angeles *Also called Steps Apparel Group Inc* ***(P-3509)***
Bcs International, Hayward *Also called B C Song International Inc* ***(P-9322)***
Bcsi, Sonora *Also called Birchwood Cabinets Sonora Inc* ***(P-4275)***
Bd Biscnces Systems Rgents Inc .... C 408 518-5024
2350 Qume Dr San Jose (95131) ***(P-7753)***
BD Classic Enterprizes Inc .... F 562 944-6177
12903 Sunshine Ave Santa Fe Springs (90670) ***(P-7822)***
Bd Impotex LLC .... F 323 521-1500
2623 S San Pedro St Los Angeles (90011) ***(P-3297)***
Bdfco Inc .... D 714 228-2900
1926 Kauai Dr Costa Mesa (92626) ***(P-18310)***
Bdm Engineering Inc .... E 714 558-6129
1031 S Linwood Ave Santa Ana (92705) ***(P-14144)***
Bdna Corporation (PA) .... D 650 625-9530
339 Bernardo Ave Ste 206 Mountain View (94043) ***(P-24411)***
BDR Industries Inc .... E 818 341-2112
9700 Owensmouth Ave Lbby Chatsworth (91311) ***(P-15679)***
BDS, Brea *Also called Blower Drive Service Co* ***(P-20270)***
BDS Natural Products Inc (PA) .... D 310 518-2227
14824 S Main St Gardena (90248) ***(P-2462)***
Be Beauty, Garden Grove *Also called Cali Chem Inc* ***(P-8712)***
Beach Patrol Inc (HQ) .... F 310 522-2700
3771 Lockland Dr Apt 2 Carson (90745) ***(P-3383)***
Beach Reporter, Rllng HLS Est *Also called National Media Inc* ***(P-5990)***
Beach Reporter, The, Hermosa Beach *Also called National Media Inc* ***(P-5991)***
Beacon Concrete Inc .... E 323 889-7775
1597 S Bluff Rd Montebello (90640) ***(P-11050)***
Beacon Media Inc .... F 626 301-1010
125 E Chestnut Ave Monrovia (91016) ***(P-5776)***
Bead Shoppe .... F 916 782-8642
2030 Douglas Blvd Ste 42 Roseville (95661) ***(P-24049)***
Beals Castings Inc .... E 909 986-3849
520 S Palmetto Ave Ontario (91762) ***(P-11689)***
Beam Dynamics Inc .... F 408 764-4805
5100 Patrick Henry Dr Santa Clara (95054) ***(P-14607)***
Beam On Technology Corporation .... E 408 982-0161
2318 Calle De Luna Santa Clara (95054) ***(P-15302)***
Beam Suntory, Irvine *Also called Jim Beam Brands Co* ***(P-2072)***
Beam Wine Estates, Healdsburg *Also called Constellation Brands US Oprs* ***(P-1706)***
Bear Brothers Enterprises Ltd .... E 914 588-6885
777 E Tahqtz Cyn Way # 200 Palm Springs (92262) ***(P-6110)***
Bear Creek Winery, Lodi *Also called Goldstone Land Company LLC* ***(P-1791)***
Bear Industrial Holdings Inc .... E 562 926-3000
9971 Muirlands Blvd Irvine (92618) ***(P-9776)***
Bear Industrial Supply & Mfg, Irvine *Also called Bear Industrial Holdings Inc* ***(P-9776)***
Bear Label Machines, Gold River *Also called Kirk A Schliger* ***(P-15164)***
Bear Republic Brewing Co Inc (PA) .... F 707 894-2722
110 Sandholm Ln Ste 10 Cloverdale (95425) ***(P-1568)***
Bear Republic Brewing Co Inc .... F 707 433-2337
345 Healdsburg Ave Healdsburg (95448) ***(P-1569)***
Beard Seats, Newport Beach *Also called Redart Corporation* ***(P-5026)***
Beards Custom Cabinets, Redding *Also called David Beard* ***(P-4292)***
Bears For Humanity Inc .... E 866 325-1668
841 Ocean View Ave San Mateo (94401) ***(P-8985)***
Bearsaver, Ontario *Also called Compumeric Engineering Inc* ***(P-12535)***
Beato Inc .... F 310 637-1180
1050 E Dominguez St Carson (90746) ***(P-10516)***
Beato Musical Products, Carson *Also called Beato Inc* ***(P-10516)***
Beats By Dr. Dre, Culver City *Also called Beats Electronics LLC* ***(P-19461)***
Beats By Dre, Culver City *Also called Beats Electronics LLC* ***(P-17771)***
Beats Electronics LLC (PA) .... F 424 268-3055
8600 Hayden Pl Culver City (90232) ***(P-19461)***
Beats Electronics LLC (HQ) .... D 424 326-4679
8600 Hayden Pl Culver City (90232) ***(P-17771)***
Beats Music LLC .... D 415 590-5104
235 2nd St San Francisco (94105) ***(P-24412)***
Beaudry International LLC .... F 213 623-5025
3835 E Thousand Oaks Blvd Westlake Village (91362) ***(P-23339)***
Beaulieu Vineyard, Rutherford *Also called Diageo North America Inc* ***(P-2070)***
Beaumont DC 52, Beaumont *Also called Wolverine World Wide Inc* ***(P-10493)***
Beaumont Juice Inc .... D 951 769-7171
550 B St Beaumont (92223) ***(P-785)***
Beauty & Health International (PA) .... E 714 903-9730
7541 Anthony Ave Garden Grove (92841) ***(P-8072)***
Beauty Craft Furniture Corp .... E 916 428-2238
3316 51st Ave Sacramento (95823) ***(P-4676)***
Bechhold & Son Flasher & Lure .... F 530 367-6650
616 Keller St Petaluma (94952) ***(P-23515)***
Bechler Cams Inc .... F 714 774-5150
1313 S State College Pkwy Anaheim (92806) ***(P-22171)***
Becker Automotive Design USA, Oxnard *Also called Becker Automotive Designs Inc* ***(P-20130)***
Becker Automotive Designs Inc .... E 805 487-5227
1711 Ives Ave Oxnard (93033) ***(P-20130)***
Becker Specialty Corporation .... F 909 356-1095
15310 Arrow Blvd Fontana (92335) ***(P-19321)***
Becker Surfboards Inc .... F 310 372-6554
301 Pier Ave Hermosa Beach (90254) ***(P-23516)***
Becker Woodworking .... F 323 564-2441
847 E 108th St Los Angeles (90059) ***(P-4075)***
Beckers Fabrication Inc .... E 714 692-1600
22465 La Palma Ave Yorba Linda (92887) ***(P-5556)***
Beckman Coulter Inc .... D 909 597-3967
15989 Cypress Ave Chino (91708) ***(P-21908)***
Beckman Coulter Inc .... C 559 784-0800
167 W Poplar Ave Porterville (93257) ***(P-21909)***
Beckman Coulter Inc .... C 760 438-9151
2470 Faraday Ave Carlsbad (92010) ***(P-21910)***
Beckman Coulter Inc .... D 916 374-3511
2040 Enterprise Blvd West Sacramento (95691) ***(P-21911)***
Beckman Coulter Inc .... C 818 970-2161
250 S Kraemer Blvd Brea (92821) ***(P-22360)***
Beckman Industries .... F 805 375-3003
701 Del Nrte Blvd Ste 205 Oxnard (93030) ***(P-23761)***
Beckman Instruments Inc .... E 714 871-4848
2500 N Harbor Blvd Fullerton (92835) ***(P-8462)***
Beckmanns Old World Bakery Ltd .... C 831 423-9242
104 Bronson St Ste 6 Santa Cruz (95062) ***(P-1185)***
Beco Baby Carrier, Costa Mesa *Also called Caperon Designs Inc* ***(P-23415)***
Becs Pacific Ltd .... F 661 397-9400
600 Enterprise Way Bakersfield (93307) ***(P-13137)***
Becton Dickinson and Company .... B 858 812-8800
10975 Torreyana Rd San Diego (92121) ***(P-22361)***
Becton Dickinson and Company .... B 408 432-9475
2350 Qume Dr San Jose (95131) ***(P-22362)***
Bed Time Originals, El Segundo *Also called Lambs & Ivy Inc* ***(P-3730)***
Bedard Machine Inc .... F 714 990-4846
141 Viking Ave Brea (92821) ***(P-16313)***
Bedford Winery .... F 805 344-2107
448 Bell St Los Alamos (93440) ***(P-1655)***
Bee Darlin Inc (PA) .... D 213 749-2116
1875 E 22nd St Los Angeles (90058) ***(P-3298)***
Bee Darlin and Be Smart, Los Angeles *Also called Bee Darlin Inc* ***(P-3298)***
Bee Wire & Cable Inc .... E 909 923-5800
2850 E Spruce St Ontario (91761) ***(P-11644)***
Beef Jerky Factory, Colton *Also called Hawa Corporation* ***(P-490)***
Beejay LLC (PA) .... F 619 220-8697
3450 Kurtz St Ste C San Diego (92110) ***(P-23410)***
Beekee Corp .... F 949 275-5861
3050 Pullman St Costa Mesa (92626) ***(P-24413)***
Beeline Group LLC .... D 510 477-5400
31023 Huntwood Ave Hayward (94544) ***(P-23826)***
Beemak Plastics LLC .... D 310 886-5880
16711 Knott Ave La Mirada (90638) ***(P-9973)***
Beemak-Idl Display Products, La Mirada *Also called Beemak Plastics LLC* ***(P-9973)***
Bega Supply Inc .... F 310 719-1252
1613 W 134th St Ste 3 Gardena (90249) ***(P-17772)***
Bega Video Supplies, Gardena *Also called Bega Supply Inc* ***(P-17772)***
Bega/Us Inc .... D 805 684-0533
1000 Bega Way Carpinteria (93013) ***(P-17674)***
Begovic Industries Inc .... E 650 594-2861
1725 Old County Rd San Carlos (94070) ***(P-16314)***
Behr Paint Corp., Santa Ana *Also called Behr Sales Inc* ***(P-8884)***
Behr Process Corporation .... C 714 545-7101
3001 S Yale St Santa Ana (92704) ***(P-8877)***
Behr Process Corporation .... E 714 545-7101
1603 W Alton Ave Santa Ana (92704) ***(P-8878)***
Behr Process Corporation (HQ) .... A 714 545-7101
1801 E Saint Andrew Pl Santa Ana (92705) ***(P-8879)***
Behr Process Corporation .... D 714 545-7101
3400 W Garry Ave Santa Ana (92704) ***(P-8880)***
Behr Process Corporation .... D 714 545-7101
3130 S Harbor Blvd # 400 Santa Ana (92704) ***(P-8881)***
Behr Process Corporation .... F 714 545-7101
3500 W Segerstrom Ave Santa Ana (92704) ***(P-8882)***
Behr Process Corporation .... D 714 545-7101
1995 S Standard Ave Santa Ana (92707) ***(P-8883)***
Behr Sales Inc (HQ) .... C 714 545-7101
3400 W Segerstrom Ave Santa Ana (92704) ***(P-8884)***
BEI Duncan, Thousand Oaks *Also called Sensata Technologies Inc* ***(P-19723)***
BEI Industrial Encoders, Thousand Oaks *Also called Sensata Technologies Inc* ***(P-15851)***
BEI Industrial Encoders, Thousand Oaks *Also called Carros Sensors Systems Co LLC* ***(P-19480)***
BEI North America LLC (HQ) .... F 805 716-0642
1461 Lawrence Dr Thousand Oaks (91320) ***(P-19462)***
Beko Radiator Cores Inc .... E 925 671-2975
2322 Bates Ave Ste A Concord (94520) ***(P-20267)***
Bel Aire Bridal Inc .... E 310 325-8160
23002 Mariposa Ave Torrance (90502) ***(P-3878)***
Bel Aire Bridal Accessories, Torrance *Also called Bel Aire Bridal Inc* ***(P-3878)***
Bel Power Solutions Inc .... A 866 513-2839
2390 Walsh Ave Santa Clara (95051) ***(P-19322)***

Bel-Air Cases, Ontario *Also called California Quality Plas Inc* ***(P-10006)***
Bel-Air Machining Co..........F.......714 953-6616
1514 E Edinger Ave Ste E Santa Ana (92705) ***(P-16315)***
Belagio Enterprises Inc..........E.......323 731-6934
4801 W Jefferson Blvd Los Angeles (90016) ***(P-2724)***
Belair Gold Design Inc..........E.......213 891-0152
650 S Hill St Ste 914 Los Angeles (90014) ***(P-23340)***
Belching Beaver Brewery..........C.......760 599-5832
1334 Rocky Point Dr Oceanside (92056) ***(P-1570)***
Belco Cabinets Inc..........F.......209 334-5437
1109 Black Diamond Way Lodi (95240) ***(P-12298)***
Belco Packaging Systems Inc..........E.......626 357-9566
910 S Mountain Ave Monrovia (91016) ***(P-15197)***
Belden Inc..........F.......510 438-9071
47823 Westinghouse Dr Fremont (94539) ***(P-11645)***
Belding Golf Bag Company, The, Oxnard *Also called Illah Sports Inc A Corporation* ***(P-23590)***
Belkin Inc..........C.......800 223-5546
12045 Waterfront Dr Playa Vista (90094) ***(P-17773)***
Bell Enterprise, San Bernardino *Also called Kendra Group Inc* ***(P-18338)***
Bell Foundry Co (PA)..........D.......323 564-5701
5310 Southern Ave South Gate (90280) ***(P-23517)***
Bell Powder Coating Inc..........F.......805 658-2233
4747 Mcgrath St Ventura (93003) ***(P-13558)***
Bell Sports Inc (HQ)..........D.......469 417-6600
5550 Scotts Valley Dr Scotts Valley (95066) ***(P-23518)***
Bell-Carter Foods Inc (PA)..........B.......925 284-5933
590 Ygnacio Valley Rd # 300 Walnut Creek (94596) ***(P-786)***
Bell-Carter Foods Inc..........B.......530 528-4820
1012 2nd St Corning (96021) ***(P-910)***
Bell-Carter Foods Inc..........E.......209 549-5939
4207 Finch Rd Modesto (95357) ***(P-787)***
Bell-Carter Olive Company, Walnut Creek *Also called Bell-Carter Foods Inc* ***(P-786)***
Bell-Carter Packaging, Modesto *Also called Bell-Carter Foods Inc* ***(P-787)***
Bell-Carterolive Company, Corning *Also called Bell-Carter Foods Inc* ***(P-910)***
Bella Notte Linens Inc..........E.......415 883-3434
60 Galli Dr Ste 2 Novato (94949) ***(P-2774)***
Bellacanvas, Los Angeles *Also called Color Image Apparel Inc* ***(P-2830)***
Bellama Cstm Met Fbrcators Inc..........F.......619 585-3351
3129 Main St Chula Vista (91911) ***(P-12504)***
Bellas Pillow Inserts Inc..........F.......323 235-3898
150 E Slauson Ave Los Angeles (90011) ***(P-3708)***
Bellasposa Wedding Center..........F.......909 758-0176
11450 4th St Ste 103 Rancho Cucamonga (91730) ***(P-3299)***
Bellaterra Home LLC..........F.......916 896-3188
8372 Tiogawoods Dr # 180 Sacramento (95828) ***(P-4273)***
Bellavuos..........F.......626 653-0121
417 N Azusa Ave West Covina (91791) ***(P-8701)***
Bellou Publishing, San Jose *Also called Times Media Inc* ***(P-6071)***
Bellows Mfg & RES Inc..........F.......818 838-1333
13596 Vaughn St San Fernando (91340) ***(P-16316)***
Belmar Company, San Francisco *Also called B & M Upholstery* ***(P-2723)***
Belmont Publications Inc..........F.......714 825-1234
3621 S Harbor Blvd # 265 Santa Ana (92704) ***(P-6111)***
Belovac LLC..........F.......951 427-4299
435 E Lincoln St Ste A Banning (92220) ***(P-14920)***
Belport Company Inc (PA)..........F.......805 484-1051
4825 Calle Alto Camarillo (93012) ***(P-22859)***
Belt Drives Ltd..........E.......714 693-1313
505 W Lambert Rd Brea (92821) ***(P-21091)***
Belts By Simon Inc..........D.......714 573-0303
14382 Chambers Rd Tustin (92780) ***(P-3626)***
Bema Electronic Mfg Inc..........D.......510 490-7770
4545 Cushing Pkwy Fremont (94538) ***(P-19463)***
Bemco Inc (PA)..........E.......805 583-4970
2255 Union Pl Simi Valley (93065) ***(P-21912)***
Beme International LLC..........E.......858 751-0580
7333 Ronson Rd San Diego (92111) ***(P-3709)***
Ben Davis, San Rafael *Also called Ben F Davis Company* ***(P-3095)***
Ben F Davis Company (PA)..........F.......415 382-1000
3140 Kerner Blvd San Rafael (94901) ***(P-3095)***
Bench 2 Bench Technologies, Fullerton *Also called Winonics Inc* ***(P-18653)***
Bench Depot, Tecate *Also called Benchpro Inc* ***(P-5223)***
Bench-Craft Inc..........F.......714 523-3322
4005 Artesia Ave Fullerton (92833) ***(P-5222)***
Bench-Tek Solutions Llc..........F.......408 653-1100
525 Aldo Ave Santa Clara (95054) ***(P-4978)***
Benchmark Elec Mfg Sltions Inc (HQ)..........D.......408 754-9800
5550 Hellyer Ave San Jose (95138) ***(P-18437)***
Benchmark Elec Mfg Sol Moorpk..........A.......805 532-2800
200 Science Dr Moorpark (93021) ***(P-19464)***
Benchmark Electronics Inc..........D.......510 360-2800
42701 Christy St Fremont (94538) ***(P-18438)***
Benchmark Electronics Inc..........B.......925 363-1151
2301 Arnold Ind Way Ste G Concord (94520) ***(P-18439)***
Benchmark Engineering Div of, Santa Fe Springs *Also called K Metal Products Inc* ***(P-13837)***
Benchmark Thermal, Grass Valley *Also called Manufacturers Coml Fin LLC* ***(P-12075)***
Benchmark Thermal Corporation..........D.......530 477-5011
13185 Nevada City Ave Grass Valley (95945) ***(P-15254)***
Benchpro Inc..........C.......619 478-9400
23949 Tecate Mission Rd Tecate (91980) ***(P-5223)***
Bend-Tek Inc..........E.......714 210-8966
3431 W Maywood Ave Santa Ana (92704) ***(P-12505)***
Benda Tool & Model Works Inc..........E.......510 741-3170
900 Alfred Nobel Dr Hercules (94547) ***(P-14485)***
Bender Ccp Inc..........D.......707 745-9970
2150 E 37th St Vernon Vernon (90058) ***(P-16317)***
Bender US, Vernon *Also called Bender Ccp Inc* ***(P-16317)***
Bendick Precision Inc..........F.......626 445-0217
56 La Porte St Arcadia (91006) ***(P-16318)***
Bendpak Inc..........C.......805 933-9970
1645 E Lemonwood Dr Santa Paula (93060) ***(P-14921)***
Benefit Software Incorporated..........E.......805 679-6200
212 Cottage Grove Ave A Santa Barbara (93101) ***(P-24414)***
Benefits Software, Santa Barbara *Also called Ebix Inc* ***(P-24587)***
Benen Manufacturing LLC..........F.......408 573-7252
1872 Hartog Dr San Jose (95131) ***(P-14608)***
Benicia Fabrication & Mch Inc..........C.......707 745-8111
101 E Channel Rd Benicia (94510) ***(P-12364)***
Benicia Herald, Benicia *Also called Gibson Printing & Publishing* ***(P-5862)***
Benigna..........F.......323 262-2484
4630 Floral Dr Los Angeles (90022) ***(P-3051)***
Benjamin Lewis Inc..........F.......949 859-5119
23042 Alcalde Dr Ste C Laguna Hills (92653) ***(P-6690)***
Benjamin Litho Inc..........F.......408 232-3800
1810 Oakland Rd Ste F San Jose (95131) ***(P-6691)***
Benjamin Moore & Co..........D.......909 444-0390
3441 W Temple Ave Pomona (91768) ***(P-8885)***
Benmar Marine Electronics Inc..........F.......714 540-5120
2225 S Huron Dr Santa Ana (92704) ***(P-21265)***
Bennett & Bennett Inc..........F.......559 896-0200
955 S Commerce Way Lemoore (93245) ***(P-10883)***
Bennett Industries Inc..........F.......415 482-9000
4304 Redwood Hwy 200 San Rafael (94903) ***(P-6692)***
Bennett's Bakery, Sacramento *Also called Bennetts Baking Company* ***(P-1390)***
Bennett's Honey Farm, Fillmore *Also called Honey Bennetts Farm Inc* ***(P-2536)***
Bennetts Baking Company..........F.......916 481-3349
2530 Tesla Way Sacramento (95825) ***(P-1390)***
Bens Alternative Foods..........F.......510 614-6745
2712 Marina Blvd Ste 36 San Leandro (94577) ***(P-983)***
Bent Fir Company..........F.......707 274-6628
3598 Manzanita Ave Nice (95464) ***(P-4677)***
Bent Manufacturing Co Bdaa Inc..........F.......714 842-0600
15442 Chemical Ln Huntington Beach (92649) ***(P-9974)***
Bentec Medical Opco LLC..........E.......530 406-3333
1380 E Beamer St Woodland (95776) ***(P-22363)***
Bentec Scientific LLC..........E.......530 406-3333
1380 E Beamer St Woodland (95776) ***(P-22364)***
Bentek Corporation..........F.......408 954-9600
1911 Lundy Ave San Jose (95131) ***(P-18744)***
Bentek Corporation..........D.......408 954-9600
1991 Senter Rd San Jose (95112) ***(P-19465)***
Bentek Solar, San Jose *Also called Bentek Corporation* ***(P-19465)***
Bentley Management Corporation..........F.......323 653-8060
8060 Melrose Ave Ste 210 Los Angeles (90046) ***(P-6112)***
Bentley Mills Inc..........F.......800 423-4709
315 S 7th Ave City of Industry (91746) ***(P-2925)***
Bentley Mills Inc (PA)..........C.......626 333-4585
14641 Don Julian Rd City of Industry (91746) ***(P-2926)***
Bentley Prtg & Graphics Inc..........F.......714 636-1622
12800 Garden Grove Blvd C Garden Grove (92843) ***(P-6693)***
Bentley-Simonson Inc..........D.......805 650-2794
1746 S Victoria Ave Ste F Ventura (93003) ***(P-24)***
Bento Merge Enterprises, San Francisco *Also called Bento Technologies Inc* ***(P-24415)***
Bento Technologies Inc..........F.......415 887-2028
221 Main St Ste 1325 San Francisco (94105) ***(P-24415)***
Benziger Family Winery, Glen Ellen *Also called Bfw Associates LLC* ***(P-1659)***
Beonca Machine Inc..........F.......909 392-9991
1680 Curtiss Ct La Verne (91750) ***(P-16319)***
Beranek Inc..........E.......310 328-9094
2340 W 205th St Torrance (90501) ***(P-20760)***
Berber Food Manufacturing Inc..........C.......510 553-0444
425 Hester St San Leandro (94577) ***(P-2463)***
Berenice 2 AM Corp..........F.......858 255-8693
8008 Girard Ave Ste 150 La Jolla (92037) ***(P-657)***
Bereshith Inc (PA)..........F.......213 935-8086
1100 S San Pedro St G09 Los Angeles (90015) ***(P-3216)***
Berg Manufacturing Inc..........F.......408 727-2374
408 Aldo Ave Santa Clara (95054) ***(P-24050)***
Berg-Nelson Company Inc..........F.......562 432-3491
1633 W 17th St Long Beach (90813) ***(P-9498)***
Bergandi Machinery Company, Ontario *Also called Bmci Inc* ***(P-14749)***
Bergin Glass Impressions Inc..........E.......707 224-0111
938 Kaiser Rd NAPA (94558) ***(P-10679)***
Bericap LLC..........D.......909 390-5518
1671 Champagne Ave Ste B Ontario (91761) ***(P-9975)***
Bering Technology Inc..........E.......408 364-6500
1608 W Campbell Ave 328 Campbell (95008) ***(P-15680)***
Beringer Vineyards, Saint Helena *Also called Treasury Wine Estates Americas* ***(P-2022)***
Beringer Vinyards, Saint Helena *Also called Treasury Wine Estates Americas* ***(P-2023)***
Berkeley Design Automation Inc..........E.......408 496-6600
46871 Bayside Pkwy Fremont (94538) ***(P-18745)***
Berkeley Farms LLC..........E.......916 689-7613
7444 Reese Rd Sacramento (95828) ***(P-712)***
Berkeley Forge & Tool Inc..........D.......510 525-5117
1331 Eastshore Hwy Berkeley (94710) ***(P-13095)***
Berkeley Magnetics Inc..........E.......408 292-2023
1836 Stone Ave San Jose (95125) ***(P-17081)***
Berkeley Mills, Berkeley *Also called Berkeley Mllwk & Furn Co Inc* ***(P-4678)***
Berkeley Mllwk & Furn Co Inc..........E.......510 549-2854
2830 7th St Berkeley (94710) ***(P-4678)***
Berkeley Nutritional Mfg Corp..........D.......925 243-6300
1852 Rutan Dr Livermore (94551) ***(P-8073)***
Berkeley Scientific..........F.......510 525-1945
21 Westminster Ave Kensington (94708) ***(P-19466)***
Berkley Integrated Audio Softw..........E.......707 782-1866
121 H St Petaluma (94952) ***(P-19856)***

ALPHABETIC

Employee Codes: A=Over 500 employees, B=251-500
C=101-250, D=51-100, E=20-50, F=10-19
2019 California
Manfacturers Register
© Mergent Inc. 1-800-342-5647
1075

Berlex Bioscience, San Francisco *Also called Bayer Hlthcare Phrmcticals Inc* **(P-8070)**

Berlin Food & Lab Equipment Co .....E......650 589-4231
43 S Linden Ave South San Francisco (94080) **(P-21458)**

Bermad Inc (PA) .....E......877 577-4283
3816 S Willow Ave Ste 101 Fresno (93725) **(P-13761)**

Bermad Control Valves, Fresno *Also called Bermad Inc* **(P-13761)**

Bermingham Controls Inc A (PA) .....E......562 860-0463
11144 Business Cir Cerritos (90703) **(P-13707)**

Bernardo Winery Inc .....E......858 487-1866
13330 Pseo Del Vrano Nrte San Diego (92128) **(P-1656)**

Bernardus LLC (PA) .....E......831 659-1900
5 W Carmel Valley Rd Carmel Valley (93924) **(P-1657)**

Bernardus Winery, Carmel Valley *Also called Bernardus LLC* **(P-1657)**

Bernell Hydraulics (PA) .....E......909 899-1751
8810 Etiwanda Ave Rancho Cucamonga (91739) **(P-16162)**

Berney-Karp Inc .....D......323 260-7122
3350 E 26th St Vernon (90058) **(P-10828)**

Bernhardt & Bernhardt Inc .....F......714 544-0708
14771 Myford Rd Ste D Tustin (92780) **(P-14362)**

Bernman Mold and Engineering .....F......909 930-3844
1219 S Bon View Ave Ontario (91761) **(P-14486)**

Berns Bros Inc .....F......562 437-0471
1250 W 17th St Long Beach (90813) **(P-16320)**

Berrett-Koehler Publishers Inc (PA) .....E......510 817-2277
1333 Broadway Ste 1000 Oakland (94612) **(P-6311)**

Berri Pro Inc .....F......909 964-1201
929 Colorado Ave Santa Monica (90401) **(P-2243)**

Berry Global Inc .....F......714 751-2920
3030 S Susan St Santa Ana (92704) **(P-9976)**

Berry Global Inc .....F......714 777-5200
4875 E Hunter Ave Anaheim (92807) **(P-9977)**

Berry Global Inc .....C......909 465-9055
14000 Monte Vista Ave Chino (91710) **(P-9978)**

Berry Global Inc .....E......800 462-3843
13335 Orden Dr Santa Fe Springs (90670) **(P-9979)**

Berry Global Inc .....C......714 777-5200
4875 E Hunter Ave Anaheim (92807) **(P-9980)**

Berry Petroleum Company LLC .....F......661 255-6066
25121 Sierra Hwy Newhall (91321) **(P-25)**

Berry Petroleum Company LLC .....E......661 769-8820
28700 Hovey Hills Rd Taft (93268) **(P-26)**

Berry Petroleum Company LLC (HQ) .....D......661 616-3900
5201 Truxtun Ave Ste 100 Bakersfield (93309) **(P-27)**

Berry Petroleum Company LLC .....F......805 984-0053
5713 W Gonzales Rd Oxnard (93036) **(P-28)**

Berry Petroleum Corporation (PA) .....F......661 616-3900
5201 Truxtun Ave Ste 100 Bakersfield (93309) **(P-29)**

Bert & Rockys Cream Co Inc .....F......909 625-1852
242 Yale Ave Claremont (91711) **(P-658)**

Bert-Co Industries Inc .....E......323 669-5700
2150 S Parco Ave Ontario (91761) **(P-7247)**

Bert-Co Industries Inc (PA) .....C......323 669-5700
2150 S Parco Ave Ontario (91761) **(P-6694)**

Bert-Co. of Ontario CA, Ontario *Also called Edelmann Usa Inc* **(P-23861)**

Bertagna Orchards Inc .....F......530 343-8014
3329 Hegan Ln Chico (95928) **(P-1658)**

Bertelsmann Inc .....B......661 702-2700
29011 Commerce Center Dr Valencia (91355) **(P-6312)**

Bertolin Engineering Corp .....F......408 988-0166
485 Robert Ave Santa Clara (95050) **(P-13169)**

Bertolini Corporation .....C......909 613-1393
2605 E Cedar St Ontario (91761) **(P-4979)**

Beryl Lockhart Enterprises, Sun Valley *Also called Ble Inc* **(P-100)**

Bes Concrete Products, Tracy *Also called Bescal Inc* **(P-10884)**

Besam Entrance Solutions, Elk Grove *Also called Assa Abloy Entrance Sys US Inc* **(P-19913)**

Besam Entrance Solutions, Anaheim *Also called Assa Abloy Entrance Systems US* **(P-19914)**

Bescal Inc .....E......209 836-3492
10304 W Linne Rd Tracy (95377) **(P-10884)**

Bespoke Coachworks Inc .....F......818 571-9900
7641 Burnet Ave Van Nuys (91405) **(P-20131)**

Besser Company, Compton *Also called Concrete Mold Corporation* **(P-14501)**

Best Box Company Inc .....F......323 589-6088
8011 Beach St Los Angeles (90001) **(P-5388)**

Best Carbide Cutting Tools Inc .....D......310 464-8050
1401 W Walnut St Rancho Dominguez (90220) **(P-14363)**

Best Cheer Stone Inc (PA) .....E......714 399-1588
3190 E Miraloma Ave Anaheim (92806) **(P-11235)**

Best Data Products Inc .....F......818 534-1414
21541 Blythe St Canoga Park (91304) **(P-15681)**

Best Engineering, North Hollywood *Also called Karapet Engineering Inc* **(P-16645)**

Best Express Foods Inc .....B......510 782-5338
1742 Sabre St Hayward (94545) **(P-1186)**

Best Formulations Inc .....C......626 912-9998
17758 Rowland St City of Industry (91748) **(P-2464)**

Best Friends By Sheri, Commerce *Also called Sentiments Inc* **(P-24239)**

Best Industrial Supply .....C......626 279-5090
9711 Rush St South El Monte (91733) **(P-14311)**

Best Ink and Thread, Ontario *Also called Medrano Raymundo* **(P-2954)**

Best Label Company Inc (PA) .....C......562 926-1452
13260 Moore St Cerritos (90703) **(P-7248)**

Best Label Company Inc .....E......510 489-5400
2900 Faber St Union City (94587) **(P-15198)**

Best Living International Inc .....F......626 625-2911
12234 Florence Ave Santa Fe Springs (90670) **(P-4826)**

Best Marble Co .....E......510 614-0155
2446 Teagarden St San Leandro (94577) **(P-11236)**

Best Quality Furniture Mfg Inc .....D......909 230-6440
5400 E Francis St Ontario (91761) **(P-4760)**

Best Redwood, San Diego *Also called Rtmex Inc* **(P-4091)**

Best Roll-Up Door Inc .....E......562 802-2233
13202 Arctic Cir Santa Fe Springs (90670) **(P-12299)**

Best Sanitizers Inc .....D......530 265-1800
310 Prvdnce Mine Rd # 120 Nevada City (95959) **(P-8625)**

Best Slip Cover Company, Studio City *Also called Harmony Infinite Inc* **(P-5235)**

Best USA, West Sacramento *Also called Tomra Sorting Inc* **(P-14889)**

Best Value Textbooks LLC .....E......530 222-5980
410 Hemsted Dr Ste 100 Redding (96002) **(P-6313)**

Best Way Marble, Los Angeles *Also called Best-Way Marble & Tile Co Inc* **(P-11237)**

Best- In- West .....E......909 947-6507
2279 Eagle Glen Pkwy Corona (92883) **(P-3830)**

Best-In-West Emblem Co, Corona *Also called Best- In- West* **(P-3830)**

Best-Way Marble & Tile Co Inc .....E......323 266-6794
5037 Telegraph Rd Los Angeles (90022) **(P-11237)**

Bestek Manufacturing Inc .....E......408 321-8834
675 Sycamore Dr Milpitas (95035) **(P-15682)**

Bestest International .....F......714 974-8837
181 W Orangethorpe Ave C Placentia (92870) **(P-21552)**

Bestest Medical, Placentia *Also called Bestest International* **(P-21552)**

Bestop Baja LLC .....E......760 560-2252
185 Bosstick Blvd San Marcos (92069) **(P-20268)**

Bestpro Machining .....F......510 490-6853
45999 Warm Springs Blvd # 3 Fremont (94539) **(P-16321)**

Bestronics, San Jose *Also called Bay Elctrnc Spport Trnics Inc* **(P-18436)**

Bestronics Holdings Inc (PA) .....E......408 385-7777
2090 Fortune Dr San Jose (95131) **(P-19291)**

Bestwall LLC .....C......714 521-4270
15500 Valley View Ave La Mirada (90638) **(P-5389)**

Bestwall LLC .....E......562 435-7094
1401 W Pier D St Long Beach (90802) **(P-11216)**

Bestwall LLC .....C......510 483-7580
1988 Marina Blvd San Leandro (94577) **(P-5274)**

Bestwall LLC .....C......559 485-4900
3630 E Wawona Ave Ste 104 Fresno (93725) **(P-5498)**

Bestway Hydraulics Co Inc .....E......310 639-2507
1518 S Santa Fe Ave Compton (90221) **(P-15054)**

Beta Box Inc .....F......323 383-9820
12021 Wilshire Blvd Los Angeles (90025) **(P-17774)**

Bethebeast Inc .....E......424 206-1081
446 Bayview Dr Hermosa Beach (90254) **(P-24416)**

Better Beverages Inc (PA) .....E......562 924-8321
10624 Midway Ave Cerritos (90703) **(P-2244)**

Better Built Truss Inc .....E......209 869-4545
251 E 4th St Ripon (95366) **(P-4392)**

Better Chinese Llc .....E......650 384-0902
150 W Iowa Ave Ste 104 Sunnyvale (94086) **(P-6314)**

Better Cleaning Systems Inc .....F......559 673-5700
1122 Maple St Madera (93637) **(P-17406)**

Better Instant Copy .....F......323 782-6934
512 S San Vicente Blvd # 1 Los Angeles (90048) **(P-6695)**

Better Mens Clothes, Los Angeles *Also called Hirsh Inc* **(P-223)**

Better Nutritionals LLC .....E......310 502-2277
17120 S Figueroa St B Gardena (90248) **(P-605)**

Better Way Grinding, Santa Fe Springs *Also called Better-Way & Lovell Grinding* **(P-16322)**

Better World Manufacturing Inc (PA) .....F......559 291-4276
3535 N Sabre Dr Fresno (93727) **(P-9981)**

Better-Way & Lovell Grinding .....F......562 693-8722
8333 Chetle Ave Santa Fe Springs (90670) **(P-16322)**

Betterbilt Chemicals .....F......323 266-7111
3137 E 26th St Vernon (90058) **(P-7754)**

Bettercompany Inc .....F......415 501-9692
621 Sansome St San Francisco (94111) **(P-24417)**

Betterline Products Inc .....E......760 535-5030
1101 E Elm Ave Fullerton (92831) **(P-16323)**

Betterworks Systems Inc .....D......650 656-9013
999 Main St Redwood City (94063) **(P-24418)**

Betts Company (PA) .....D......559 498-3304
2843 S Maple Ave Fresno (93725) **(P-13788)**

Betts Company .....E......559 498-3304
2843 S Maple Ave Fresno (93725) **(P-13789)**

Betts Company .....E......559 498-8624
2867 S Maple Ave Fresno (93725) **(P-20194)**

Betts Company .....F......909 427-9988
10771 Almond Ave Ste B Fontana (92337) **(P-13790)**

Betts Spring Manufacturing, Fresno *Also called Betts Company* **(P-13788)**

Betts Truck Parts, Fontana *Also called Betts Company* **(P-13790)**

Betty Clark's Confections, El Monte *Also called California Treats Inc* **(P-790)**

Betty Stillwell .....D......619 428-2001
524 W Calle Primera # 1004 San Ysidro (92173) **(P-11238)**

Beu Industries Inc .....E......310 885-9626
2937 E Maria St E Rncho Dmngz (90221) **(P-5520)**

Beveled Edge Inc .....F......408 467-9900
1740 Junction Ave Ste D San Jose (95112) **(P-10680)**

Beveragefactory.com, San Diego *Also called Cydea Inc* **(P-1584)**

Beverly Hillcrest Oil Corp .....F......949 598-7300
27241 Burbank El Toro (92610) **(P-30)**

Beverly Hills Courier Inc .....E......310 278-1322
499 N Canon Dr Ste 100 Beverly Hills (90210) **(P-5777)**

BEX Engraving Company Inc .....E......714 879-6593
1101 E Ash Ave Ste C Fullerton (92831) **(P-13559)**

Bey-Berk International (PA) .....E......818 773-7534
9145 Deering Ave Chatsworth (91311) **(P-13923)**

Beynon Sports Surfaces Inc .....E......559 237-2590
4668 N Sonora Ave Ste 101 Fresno (93722) **(P-23519)**

Beyond Meat, El Segundo *Also called Savage River Inc* **(P-1014)**

Beyond Meat, El Segundo *Also called Savage River Inc* **(P-1015)**

Beyond Ultimate LLC .....F......626 330-9777
360 S 9th Ave City of Industry (91746) **(P-5266)**

Mergent e-mail: customerrelations@mergent.com
1076

2019 California
Manufacturers Register

(P-0000) Products & Services Section entry number
(PA)=Parent Co (HQ)=Headquarters (DH)=Div Headquarters

Bez Ambar Inc E 213 629-9191
611 Wilshire Blvd Ste 607 Los Angeles (90017) *(P-23246)*
BF Suma Pharmaceuticals Inc F 626 285-8366
5077 Walnut Grove Ave San Gabriel (91776) *(P-606)*
Bfw Associates LLC (HQ) E 707 935-3000
1883 London Ranch Rd Glen Ellen (95442) *(P-1659)*
Bgl Development Inc F 415 256-2525
3070 Kerner Blvd Ste H San Rafael (94901) *(P-24419)*
Bgm Installation Inc F 310 830-3113
528 E D St Wilmington (90744) *(P-9461)*
Bh-Tech Inc A 858 694-0900
7841 Balboa Ave Ste 208 San Diego (92111) *(P-9982)*
Bhaktivedanta Book Tr Intl Inc F 310 837-5284
9701 Venus Blvd Ste A Los Angeles (90034) *(P-6315)*
BHC Industries Inc E 310 632-2000
239 E Greenleaf Blvd Compton (90220) *(P-13345)*
Bhk Inc E 909 983-2973
760 E Sunkist St Ontario (91761) *(P-17421)*
Bhogart LLC E 855 553-3887
1919 Monterey Hwy Ste 80 San Jose (95112) *(P-14836)*
Bi Cmos Foundry, Santa Clara *Also called Onspec Technology Partners Inc (P-19061)*
Bi Nutraceuticals Inc (HQ) E 310 669-2100
2384 E Pacifica Pl Rancho Dominguez (90220) *(P-2245)*
Bi Technologies Corporation F 714 447-2402
413 Rood Rd Ste 7 Calexico (92231) *(P-19467)*
Bi-Search International Inc E 714 258-4500
17550 Gillette Ave Irvine (92614) *(P-19468)*
Biagel One, Ontario *Also called Awning Matrix (P-12494)*
Biale Estate F 707 257-7555
4038 Big Ranch Rd NAPA (94558) *(P-1660)*
Bianchi Orchard Systems Inc C 530 846-5625
1221 Independence Pl Gridley (95948) *(P-14045)*
Bibbero Systems Inc (HQ) E 800 242-2376
1300 N Mcdowell Blvd Petaluma (94954) *(P-6696)*
Bico Inc F 818 842-7179
3116 W Valhalla Dr Burbank (91505) *(P-21459)*
Bico-Braun International, Burbank *Also called Bico Inc (P-21459)*
Bicycle Music Co, The, Beverly Hills *Also called Anthem Music & Media Fund LLC (P-6309)*
Bidchat Inc F 818 631-6212
14570 Benefit St Unit 302 Sherman Oaks (91403) *(P-24420)*
Bidgely, Sunnyvale *Also called Myenersave Inc (P-24941)*
Bidu Inc F 213 748-4433
756 E Wash Blvd Ste B Los Angeles (90021) *(P-3384)*
Bien Air Usa Inc F 949 477-6050
5 Corporate Park Ste 160 Irvine (92606) *(P-22860)*
Bien Padre Foods Inc E 707 442-4585
1459 Railroad St Eureka (95501) *(P-747)*
Big 10 Productions Inc D 310 280-1610
6006 Washington Blvd Culver City (90232) *(P-23827)*
Big 5 Electronics Inc E 562 941-4669
13452 Alondra Blvd Cerritos (90703) *(P-17775)*
Big Accessories, Petaluma *Also called Gmpc LLC (P-23889)*
Big Bang Clothing, Vernon *Also called All Star Clothing Inc (P-3211)*
Big Bang Clothing Inc (PA) F 323 233-7773
4507 Staunton Ave Vernon (90058) *(P-3385)*
Big Bang Clothing Co, Vernon *Also called Big Bang Clothing Inc (P-3385)*
Big D Products, Fairfield *Also called Drake Enterprises Incorporated (P-3942)*
Big Five Electronics, Cerritos *Also called Big 5 Electronics Inc (P-17775)*
Big Front Uniforms, Los Angeles *Also called Bunkerhill Indus Group Inc (P-3096)*
Big Gun Inc F 714 970-0423
190 Business Center Dr B Corona (92880) *(P-20269)*
Big Gun Exhaust, Corona *Also called Big Gun Inc (P-20269)*
Big GZ Pallets F 209 465-0351
1181 S Wilson Way Stockton (95205) *(P-4454)*
Big Heart Pet Brands F 209 547-7200
2 Nestle Way Lathrop (95330) *(P-788)*
Big Heart Pet Brands (HQ) B 415 247-3000
1 Maritime Plz Fl 2 San Francisco (94111) *(P-1109)*
Big Heart Pet Brands C 310 519-3791
24700 Main St Carson (90745) *(P-789)*
Big Hill Logging & Rd Building (PA) E 530 673-4155
680 Sutter St Yuba City (95991) *(P-3980)*
Big Ink Printing F 408 624-1204
1711 Branham Ln Ste A5 San Jose (95118) *(P-6697)*
Big Nickel, Palm Desert *Also called Daniels Inc (P-6468)*
Big Shine Los Angeles Inc F 818 346-0770
27211 Branbury Ct Valencia (91354) *(P-18050)*
Big Sleep Futon Inc E 800 647-2671
760 S Vail Ave Montebello (90640) *(P-4853)*
Big Studio Inc F 562 989-2444
1247 E Hill St Long Beach (90755) *(P-2878)*
Big Switch Networks Inc (PA) D 650 322-6510
3111 Coronado Dr Bldg A Santa Clara (95054) *(P-24421)*
Big Tex Trailer Mfg Inc F 951 845-5344
1425 E Sixth St Beaumont (92223) *(P-14046)*
Big Time Digital F 310 329-1383
6935 Hermosa Cir Buena Park (90620) *(P-6698)*
Big Tree Big Sleep, Montebello *Also called Big Sleep Futon Inc (P-4853)*
Big Tree Furniture & Inds Inc (PA) E 310 894-7500
760 S Vail Ave Montebello (90640) *(P-4679)*
Big Valley Metals F 916 372-2383
620 Houston St Ste 1 West Sacramento (95691) *(P-12117)*
Big Valley Pallet E 209 632-7687
2512 Paulson Rd Turlock (95380) *(P-4455)*
Bigfogg Inc (PA) F 951 587-2460
42095 Zevo Dr Ste A2 Temecula (92590) *(P-15941)*
Bigtribe Corporation F 415 331-3687
89 Crescent Ave Sausalito (94965) *(P-24422)*
Bijan Rad Inc E 818 902-1606
16125 Cantlay St Van Nuys (91406) *(P-14922)*
Bijans Protective Equipment D 707 528-4647
3255 Santa Rosa Ave Santa Rosa (95407) *(P-23520)*
Bikernet.com, Wilmington *Also called 5 Ball Inc (P-6300)*
Bill Williams Welding Co E 562 432-5421
1735 Santa Fe Ave Long Beach (90813) *(P-12118)*
Bill Wood Lathing E 909 628-1733
12188 Central Ave Pmb 621 Chino (91710) *(P-13812)*
Billcom Inc C 650 353-3301
1810 Embarcadero Rd Palo Alto (94303) *(P-24423)*
Billington Welding & Mfg Inc D 209 526-0846
1442 N Emerald Ave Modesto (95351) *(P-14837)*
Bills Pipes Inc F 951 371-1329
226 N Maple St Corona (92880) *(P-21092)*
Billy Beez Usa LLC F 661 383-0050
24201 Valencia Blvd Santa Clarita (91355) *(P-23521)*
Billy Beez Usa LLC F 408 300-9547
925 Blossom Hill Rd # 1397 San Jose (95123) *(P-23522)*
Billy Blues, Commerce *Also called AB&r Inc (P-3367)*
Bimarian Inc E 408 520-2666
3350 Scott Blvd Santa Clara (95054) *(P-24424)*
Bimbo Bakeries U.S.A., Montebello *Also called Bimbo Bakeries Usa Inc (P-1190)*
Bimbo Bakeries Usa Inc F 209 538-6170
1749 Reliance St Modesto (95358) *(P-1187)*
Bimbo Bakeries Usa Inc D 805 544-7687
3580 Sueldo St San Luis Obispo (93401) *(P-1188)*
Bimbo Bakeries Usa Inc F 951 280-9044
385 N Sherman Ave Corona (92882) *(P-1189)*
Bimbo Bakeries Usa Inc F 323 720-6099
480 S Vale Ave Montebello (90640) *(P-1190)*
Bimbo Bakeries Usa Inc F 916 456-3863
3495 Swetzer Rd Loomis (95650) *(P-1191)*
Bimbo Bakeries Usa Inc E 916 681-8069
7601 Wilbur Way Sacramento (95828) *(P-1192)*
Bimbo Bakeries Usa Inc A 916 732-4733
3231 6th Ave Sacramento (95817) *(P-1193)*
Bimbo Bakeries Usa Inc F 760 737-7700
2069 Aldergrove Ave Escondido (92029) *(P-1194)*
Bimbo Bakeries Usa Inc D 858 677-0573
4000 Ruffin Rd Ste B San Diego (92123) *(P-1195)*
Bimbo Bakeries Usa Inc F 559 498-3632
1836 G St Fresno (93706) *(P-1196)*
Bimbo Bakeries Usa Inc F 510 614-4500
14388 Washington Ave San Leandro (94578) *(P-1197)*
Bimbo Bakeries Usa Inc E 650 583-5828
264 S Spruce Ave South San Francisco (94080) *(P-1198)*
Bimbo Bakeries Usa Inc E 714 441-2555
366 S Acacia Ave Fullerton (92831) *(P-1199)*
Bimbo Bakeries Usa Inc D 714 634-8068
1220 Howell St Anaheim (92805) *(P-1200)*
Bimbo Bakeries Usa Inc E 831 633-7100
11400 Commercial Pkwy Castroville (95012) *(P-1201)*
Bimbo Bakeries Usa Inc D 209 532-5185
116 Ponderosa Dr Sonora (95370) *(P-1202)*
Bimbo Bakeries Usa Inc F 661 274-8458
38960 Trade Center Dr A Palmdale (93551) *(P-2465)*
Bimbo Bakeries Usa Inc E 323 913-7214
1771 Blake Ave Los Angeles (90031) *(P-1203)*
Bimbo Bakeries Usa Inc E 650 583-3259
475 S Canal St South San Francisco (94080) *(P-1204)*
Bimbo Bakeries Usa Inc F 805 384-1059
333 Dawson Dr Ste A Camarillo (93012) *(P-1205)*
Bimbo Bakeries Usa Inc F 831 465-1214
2740 Soquel Ave Santa Cruz (95062) *(P-1206)*
Bimbo Bakeries Usa Inc E 916 922-1307
1201 El Camino Ave Sacramento (95815) *(P-1207)*
Bimbo Bakeries Usa Inc C 510 436-5350
3525 Arden Rd Ste 300 Hayward (94545) *(P-1208)*
Bimbo Bakeries Usa Inc E 650 291-3213
2380 N Clovis Ave Fresno (93727) *(P-1209)*
Bimbo Bakeries Usa Inc E 714 533-9436
1215 Alek St Anaheim (92805) *(P-2466)*
Bimbo Bakeries Usa Inc C 559 489-0980
3292 S Willow Ave Ste 101 Fresno (93725) *(P-1210)*
Bimbo Bakeries USA Inc F 818 348-9716
21423 Strathern St Canoga Park (91304) *(P-2467)*
Bimeda Inc F 626 815-1680
5539 Ayon Ave Irwindale (91706) *(P-8074)*
Bindel Bros Grading & F 831 754-1490
1104 Madison Ln Salinas (93907) *(P-14145)*
Binder Metal Products Inc D 323 321-4835
14909 S Broadway Gardena (90248) *(P-13170)*
Binders Express Inc F 310 329-4811
13800 Gramercy Pl Gardena (90249) *(P-7572)*
Bindery , The, San Diego *Also called D A M Bindery Inc (P-7596)*
Biner Ellison Packg Systems, Pasadena *Also called Amera Machine Inc (P-15194)*
Bingo Publishers Incorporated E 949 581-5410
24881 Alicia Pkwy Ste E Laguna Hills (92653) *(P-6446)*
Binh-Nhan D Ngo F 408 641-1721
1751 Fortune Dr Ste F San Jose (95131) *(P-18440)*
Binti Inc E 844 424-6844
1999 Harrison St Ste 1575 Oakland (94612) *(P-24425)*
Bio Check, Inc., South San Francisco *Also called Biocheck Inc (P-22368)*
Bio Creative Enterprises F 714 352-3600
350 Kalmus Dr Costa Mesa (92626) *(P-8702)*
Bio Creative Labs, Costa Mesa *Also called Bio Creative Enterprises (P-8702)*
Bio Cybernetics International F 909 447-7050
2701 Kimball Ave Pomona (91767) *(P-22705)*

ALPHABETIC

Employee Codes: A=Over 500 employees, B=251-500
C=101-250, D=51-100, E=20-50, F=10-19
2019 California
Manfacturers Register
© Mergent Inc. 1-800-342-5647
1077

Bio RAD Laboratories D 510 741-1000
2000 Alfred Nobel Dr Hercules (94547) ***(P-21913)***
Bio-Medical Devices Inc E 949 752-9642
17171 Daimler St Irvine (92614) ***(P-22365)***
Bio-Medical Devices Intl Inc F 800 443-3842
17171 Daimler St Irvine (92614) ***(P-22366)***
Bio-Nutraceuticals Inc D 818 727-0246
21820 Marilla St Chatsworth (91311) ***(P-8075)***
Bio-Nutritional RES Group Inc (PA) D 714 427-6990
6 Morgan Ste 100 Irvine (92618) ***(P-607)***
Bio-RAD Laboratories Inc (PA) B 510 724-7000
1000 Alfred Nobel Dr Hercules (94547) ***(P-21914)***
Bio-RAD Laboratories Inc A 510 741-6916
225 Linus Pauling Dr Hercules (94547) ***(P-21915)***
Bio-RAD Laboratories Inc B 949 789-0685
21 Technology Dr Irvine (92618) ***(P-21916)***
Bio-RAD Laboratories Inc C 949 598-1200
9500 Jeronimo Rd Irvine (92618) ***(P-7924)***
Bio-RAD Laboratories Inc C 510 741-1000
2000 Alfred Nobel Dr Hercules (94547) ***(P-21917)***
Bio-RAD Laboratories Inc C 510 741-6709
4000 Alfred Nobel Dr Hercules (94547) ***(P-21918)***
Bio-RAD Laboratories Inc A 510 232-7000
2000 Alfred Nobel Dr Hercules (94547) ***(P-21919)***
Bio-RAD Laboratories Inc B 510 741-6715
6000 James Watson Dr Hercules (94547) ***(P-21920)***
Bio-RAD Laboratories Inc B 510 741-6999
2000 Alfred Nobel Dr Hercules (94547) ***(P-21921)***
Bio-RAD Laboratories Inc B 510 232-7000
2000 Alfred Nobel Dr Hercules (94547) ***(P-21922)***
Bio-RAD Laboratories Inc E 510 741-5790
5400 E 2nd St Benicia (94510) ***(P-21923)***
Bio-RAD Laboratories Inc B 510 724-7000
2500 Atlas Rd Richmond (94806) ***(P-21924)***
Bio-RAD Labs, Hercules *Also called Bio-RAD Laboratories Inc* ***(P-21922)***
Bio-Zone Laboratories, Pittsburg *Also called Biozone Laboratories Inc* ***(P-8083)***
BIO2, Westminster *Also called Biolargo Inc* ***(P-7755)***
Biocalth International Inc F 909 267-3988
1920 Wright Ave La Verne (91750) ***(P-8076)***
Biocare Medical LLC C 925 603-8000
60 Berry Dr Pacheco (94553) ***(P-22367)***
Biocentury Publications Inc (PA) E 650 595-5333
1235 Radio Rd Ste 100 Redwood City (94065) ***(P-5778)***
Biocheck Inc E 650 573-1968
425 Eccles Ave South San Francisco (94080) ***(P-22368)***
Bioclin Therapeutics Inc F 925 413-6140
1040 Davis St Ste 202 San Leandro (94577) ***(P-8534)***
Biodico Inc F 805 689-9008
121 N Fir St Ste G Ventura (93001) ***(P-8986)***
Biodico Westside LLC F 805 683-8103
426 Donze Ave Santa Barbara (93101) ***(P-8987)***
Biodiesel Industries, Ventura *Also called Biodico Inc* ***(P-8986)***
Biodot Inc (PA) E 949 440-3685
2852 Alton Pkwy Irvine (92606) ***(P-21553)***
Biofilm Inc D 760 727-9030
3225 Executive Rdg Vista (92081) ***(P-22369)***
Biogeneral Inc F 858 453-4451
9925 Mesa Rim Rd San Diego (92121) ***(P-22370)***
Biogenex Laboratories (PA) E 510 824-1400
49026 Milmont Dr Fremont (94538) ***(P-22371)***
Bioinitiatives Inc E 916 780-9100
7641 Galilee Rd Ste 110 Roseville (95678) ***(P-22372)***
Bioject Inc E 503 692-8001
6769 Mesa Ridge Rd Ste 99 San Diego (92121) ***(P-22373)***
Biokey Inc E 510 668-0881
44370 Old Warm Springs Bl Fremont (94538) ***(P-8077)***
Biolargo Inc (PA) F 949 643-9540
14921 Chestnut St Westminster (92683) ***(P-7755)***
Biolase Inc (PA) C 949 361-1200
4 Cromwell Irvine (92618) ***(P-22861)***
Biolegend Inc (PA) C 858 455-9588
9727 Pacific Heights Blvd San Diego (92121) ***(P-8535)***
Biolog Inc E 510 785-2564
21124 Cabot Blvd Hayward (94545) ***(P-21925)***
Biomarin Pharmaceutical Inc (PA) B 415 506-6700
770 Lindaro St San Rafael (94901) ***(P-8078)***
Biomarin Pharmaceutical Inc F 415 218-7386
79 Digital Dr Novato (94949) ***(P-8079)***
Biomatrica Inc E 858 550-0308
5627 Oberlin Dr Ste 120 San Diego (92121) ***(P-5480)***
Biomechanical Analysis & E 714 990-5932
20509 Earlgate St Walnut (91789) ***(P-22706)***
Biomechanical Services, Walnut *Also called Biomechanical Analysis &* ***(P-22706)***
Biomed Instruments Inc F 714 459-5716
1511 Alto Ln Fullerton (92831) ***(P-22952)***
Biomer Technology LLC F 925 426-0787
1233 Quarry Ln 135 Pleasanton (94566) ***(P-8536)***
Biomerica Inc (PA) E 949 645-2111
17571 Von Karman Ave Irvine (92614) ***(P-22374)***
Biomet San Diego LLC F 760 942-2786
1540 Rubenstein Ave Cardiff By The Sea (92007) ***(P-22707)***
Biometric Solutions LLC F 408 625-7763
41829 Albrae St Unit 110 Fremont (94538) ***(P-15683)***
Biomicrolab Inc E 925 689-1200
2500 Dean Lesher Dr Ste A Concord (94520) ***(P-16174)***
Bionano Genomics Inc (PA) D 858 888-7600
9640 Twne Cntre Dr 100 San Diego (92121) ***(P-21926)***
Bioneer Inc E 510 865-0330
1301 Marina Village Pkwy # 110 Alameda (94501) ***(P-8988)***
Bioness Inc C 661 362-4850
25103 Rye Canyon Loop Valencia (91355) ***(P-22953)***
Bionicsound Inc F 714 300-4809
390 Spar Ave Ste 104 San Jose (95117) ***(P-22708)***
Bionikear.com, San Jose *Also called Bionicsound Inc* ***(P-22708)***
Bionorica LLC F 949 361-4900
903 Calle Amanecer # 110 San Clemente (92673) ***(P-8080)***
Biopac Systems Inc E 805 685-0066
42 Aero Camino Goleta (93117) ***(P-21927)***
Biopharmx Corporation (PA) E 650 889-5020
1505 Adams Dr Ste D Menlo Park (94025) ***(P-8081)***
Biorad Inc E 949 598-1200
9500 Jeronimo Rd Irvine (92618) ***(P-21928)***
Bioscience Research Reagents, Temecula *Also called EMD Millipore Corporation* ***(P-21955)***
Bioseal E 714 528-4695
167 W Orangethorpe Ave Placentia (92870) ***(P-22375)***
Biosearch Technologies Inc (HQ) C 415 883-8400
2199 S Mcdowell Blvd Ext Petaluma (94954) ***(P-8537)***
Biosense Webster Inc (HQ) C 909 839-8500
33 Technology Dr Irvine (92618) ***(P-22954)***
Biosense Webster Inc E 909 839-7752
15715 Arrow Hwy Baldwin Park (91706) ***(P-22955)***
Bioserv, San Diego *Also called Nextpharma Tech USA Inc* ***(P-8304)***
Bioserv Corporation E 917 817-1326
5340 Eastgate Mall San Diego (92121) ***(P-8463)***
Bioserve, San Diego *Also called Bioserv Corporation* ***(P-8463)***
Biosource International Inc C 805 659-5759
5791 Van Allen Way Carlsbad (92008) ***(P-8464)***
Biospacific Inc (HQ) F 510 652-6155
5980 Horton St Ste 360 Emeryville (94608) ***(P-8465)***
Biospherical Instruments Inc F 619 686-1888
5340 Riley St San Diego (92110) ***(P-21266)***
Biostar Microtech USA Corp F 909 444-3785
661 Brea Canyon Rd Ste 5 Walnut (91789) ***(P-15684)***
Biosynthetic Technologies LLC (HQ) F 949 390-5910
2 Park Plz Ste 200 Irvine (92614) ***(P-14838)***
Biosys Healthcare, Yorba Linda *Also called Viasys Respiratory Care Inc* ***(P-22675)***
Biota Technology Inc F 650 888-6512
11095 Flintkote Ave Ste B San Diego (92121) ***(P-24426)***
Biotech Energy of America F 714 904-7844
30 Castro Ave San Rafael (94901) ***(P-8989)***
Biotherm Hydronic Inc F 707 794-9660
476 Primero Ct Cotati (94931) ***(P-12058)***
Biotime Inc (PA) D 510 521-3390
1010 Atlantic Ave Ste 102 Alameda (94501) ***(P-8538)***
Biotium Inc F 510 265-1027
46117 Landing Pkwy Fremont (94538) ***(P-8959)***
Biotix Inc (HQ) E 858 875-7696
9880 Mesa Rim Rd San Diego (92121) ***(P-8990)***
Biovail Technologies Ltd C 703 995-2400
1 Enterprise Aliso Viejo (92656) ***(P-8082)***
Biozone Laboratories Inc (HQ) F 925 473-1000
580 Garcia Ave Pittsburg (94565) ***(P-8083)***
Biozone Laboratories Inc E 925 431-1010
701 Willow Pass Rd Ste 8 Pittsburg (94565) ***(P-8084)***
Bipolarics Inc E 408 372-7574
1620 Oakland Rd Ste D103 San Jose (95131) ***(P-18746)***
Birchwood Cabinets of Cal E 209 523-2323
2 Iwanuma Dr NAPA (94558) ***(P-4274)***
Birchwood Cabinets Sonora Inc F 209 532-1417
14375 Cuesta Ct Sonora (95370) ***(P-4275)***
Birchwood Lighting Inc E 714 550-7118
3340 E La Palma Ave Anaheim (92806) ***(P-17675)***
Birdcage Press LLC F 650 462-6300
2320 Bowdoin St Palo Alto (94306) ***(P-6447)***
Birdeye Inc C 800 561-3357
2479 E Bayshore Rd # 100 Palo Alto (94303) ***(P-6448)***
Biscomerica Corp C 909 877-5997
565 W Slover Ave Rialto (92377) ***(P-1354)***
Biscotti and Kate Mack, Oakland *Also called Mack & Reiss Inc* ***(P-3593)***
Bishamon Industries Corp E 909 390-0055
5651 E Francis St Ontario (91761) ***(P-14312)***
Bishop Electronics Corporation E 562 695-0446
3729 Sn Gabril Rvr Pkwy A Pico Rivera (90660) ***(P-19292)***
Bishop-Wisecarver Corporation (PA) D 925 439-8272
2104 Martin Way Pittsburg (94565) ***(P-13924)***
Bison Company F 209 474-8700
9013 Cavendish Ct Stockton (95209) ***(P-99)***
Bison Engineering Company F 562 408-1525
15535 Texaco Ave Paramount (90723) ***(P-16324)***
Bit Group Usa Inc (PA) D 858 613-1200
15870 Bernardo Center Dr San Diego (92127) ***(P-22376)***
Bit Medtech, San Diego *Also called Bit Group Usa Inc* ***(P-22376)***
Bitchin Inc E 760 224-7447
6211 Yarrow Dr Ste C Carlsbad (92011) ***(P-2468)***
Bitchin Sauce, Carlsbad *Also called Bitchin Inc* ***(P-2468)***
Bitmax LLC (PA) E 323 978-7878
6255 W Sunset Blvd # 1515 Los Angeles (90028) ***(P-18311)***
Bitmicro Networks Inc (PA) F 510 743-3124
47929 Fremont Blvd Fremont (94538) ***(P-15515)***
Bitzer Mobile Inc E 866 603-8392
4230 Leonard Stocking Dr Santa Clara (95054) ***(P-24427)***
Bivar Inc E 949 951-8808
4 Thomas Irvine (92618) ***(P-19469)***
Bixby Knolls Prtg & Graphics, Fullerton *Also called Fullerton Printing Inc* ***(P-6830)***
Bixolon America Inc F 858 764-4580
13705 Cimarron Ave Gardena (90249) ***(P-15685)***
Bizinkcom LLC F 818 676-0766
9330 Eton Ave Chatsworth (91311) ***(P-7249)***

Mergent e-mail: customerrelations@mergent.com
1078
2019 California
Manufacturers Register
(P-0000) Products & Services Section entry number
(PA)=Parent Co (HQ)=Headquarters (DH)=Div Headquarters

Bizlink Technology Inc (HQ).....D.....510 252-0786
47211 Bayside Pkwy Fremont (94538) ***(P-17445)***
Bizmatics Inc (PA).....C.....408 873-3030
4010 Moorpark Ave Ste 222 San Jose (95117) ***(P-24428)***
Bjb Enterprises Inc.....E.....714 734-8450
14791 Franklin Ave Tustin (92780) ***(P-7823)***
Bjc.....F.....310 977-6068
1356 Lomita Blvd Apt 1 Harbor City (90710) ***(P-2712)***
BJs Ukiah Embroidery.....F.....707 463-2767
272 E Smith St Ukiah (95482) ***(P-7250)***
BJS&t Enterprises Inc.....F.....619 448-7795
1702 N Magnolia Ave # 101 El Cajon (92020) ***(P-13560)***
Bk Sems Usa Inc.....F.....949 390-7120
4 Executive Park Ste 270 Irvine (92614) ***(P-4608)***
BK Signs Inc.....F.....626 334-5600
1028 W Kirkwall Rd Azusa (91702) ***(P-23828)***
Bkon Interior Soution.....F.....562 408-1655
15330 Allen St Paramount (90723) ***(P-4934)***
Black & Decker (us) Inc.....F.....562 925-7551
9020 Alondra Blvd Bellflower (90706) ***(P-14698)***
Black & Decker Corporation.....F.....909 390-5548
3949 E Guasti Rd Ste A Ontario (91761) ***(P-14699)***
Black Box Distribution LLC.....D.....760 268-1174
371 2nd St Ste 1 Encinitas (92024) ***(P-23523)***
Black Diamond Blade Company (PA).....E.....800 949-9014
234 E O St Colton (92324) ***(P-14146)***
Black Diamond Manufacturing Co.....F.....925 439-9160
755 Bliss Ave Pittsburg (94565) ***(P-16325)***
Black Diamond Video Inc.....D.....510 439-4500
503 Canal Blvd Richmond (94804) ***(P-15686)***
Black Hills Nanosystems Corp.....F.....605 341-3641
1941 Jackson St 9 Oakland (94612) ***(P-18747)***
Black Media News, Winnetka *Also called Life Media Inc* ***(P-6207)***
Black N Gold, Paramount *Also called Kum Kang Trading USAinC* ***(P-8784)***
Black Oxide Industries Inc.....E.....714 870-9610
1745 N Orangethorpe Park Anaheim (92801) ***(P-13346)***
Black Oxide Service Inc.....F.....760 744-8692
1070 Linda Vista Dr Ste A San Marcos (92078) ***(P-13347)***
Black Phoenix Inc.....F.....818 506-9404
12120 Sherman Way North Hollywood (91605) ***(P-8703)***
Black Phoenix Alchemy Lab, North Hollywood *Also called Black Phoenix Inc* ***(P-8703)***
Black Point Products Inc.....E.....510 232-7723
2000 Wright Ave Richmond (94804) ***(P-17926)***
Black Radio Exclusive Magazine, Sherman Oaks *Also called Sidney Millers Black Radio Ex* ***(P-6257)***
Black Ruby Ventures LLC.....F.....619 873-2000
9323 Stevens Rd Ste A Santee (92071) ***(P-23357)***
Black Silver Enterprises Inc (PA).....F.....858 623-9220
6024 Paseo Delicias Rancho Santa Fe (92067) ***(P-3386)***
Black Stallion Winery LLC.....F.....707 253-1400
4089 Silverado Trl NAPA (94558) ***(P-1661)***
Black's Irrigation Systems, Chowchilla *Also called Blacks Irrigations Systems* ***(P-10885)***
Blackbaud Internet Solutions, San Diego *Also called Kintera Inc* ***(P-24833)***
Blackburn Alton Invstments LLC.....E.....714 731-2000
700 E Alton Ave Santa Ana (92705) ***(P-7251)***
Blackcoffee Fabricators Inc.....F.....909 974-4499
4319 Santa Ana St Ste B Ontario (91761) ***(P-23829)***
Blackcoffee Sign Fabricators, Ontario *Also called Blackcoffee Fabricators Inc* ***(P-23829)***
Blackline Systems Inc (HQ).....C.....818 746-4700
21300 Victory Blvd Fl 12 Woodland Hills (91367) ***(P-24429)***
Blacklion Enterprises Inc (PA).....F.....951 328-0400
1731 Bonita Vista Dr San Bernardino (92404) ***(P-12837)***
Blacks Irrigations Systems.....F.....559 665-4891
144 N Chowchilla Blvd Chowchilla (93610) ***(P-10885)***
Blacktalon Industries Inc.....F.....707 256-1812
481 Technology Way NAPA (94558) ***(P-13813)***
Blacoh Fluid Controls Inc (PA).....F.....951 342-3100
601 Columbia Ave Ste D Riverside (92507) ***(P-12365)***
Blaga Precision Inc.....F.....714 891-9509
11650 Seaboard Cir Stanton (90680) ***(P-16326)***
Blaha Oldrih.....F.....760 789-9791
114 10th St Ramona (92065) ***(P-14609)***
Blair Adhesive Products.....F.....562 946-6004
11034 Lockport Pl Santa Fe Springs (90670) ***(P-9130)***
Blairs Metal Polsg Pltg Co Inc.....F.....562 860-7106
17760 Crusader Ave Cerritos (90703) ***(P-13348)***
Blake Manufacturing, City of Industry *Also called Turnham Corporation* ***(P-14690)***
Blake Manufacturing Co, City of Industry *Also called Turnham Corporation* ***(P-14689)***
Blake Sign Company Inc.....F.....714 891-5682
11661 Seaboard Cir Stanton (90680) ***(P-23830)***
Blake Wire & Cable Corp.....F.....818 781-8300
16134 Runnymede St Van Nuys (91406) ***(P-11646)***
Blanchard Signs.....F.....951 354-5050
6750 Central Ave Ste A Riverside (92504) ***(P-23831)***
Blanco Basura Beverage Inc.....C.....888 705-7225
5776 Stoneridge Mall Rd # 338 Pleasanton (94588) ***(P-1571)***
Blank and Cables Inc.....F.....415 648-3842
3100 E 10th St Oakland (94601) ***(P-4680)***
Blanks Plus, Los Angeles *Also called Mj Blanks Inc* ***(P-2851)***
Blast Structures, Huntington Beach *Also called American Blast Systems Inc* ***(P-11377)***
Blasted Wood Products Inc.....F.....714 237-1600
7108 Santa Rita Cir Buena Park (90620) ***(P-4032)***
Blastrac NA.....F.....800 256-3440
5220 Gaines St San Diego (92110) ***(P-14147)***
Blastronix Inc.....F.....209 795-0738
999 W Highway 4 Murphys (95247) ***(P-15687)***
Blazar Communications Corp.....F.....949 336-7115
17951 Sky Park Cir Ste K Irvine (92614) ***(P-7573)***
Blazar Mailing Solutions, Irvine *Also called Blazar Communications Corp* ***(P-7573)***
Blazer Exhibits & Graphics Inc.....F.....408 263-7000
4227 Technology Dr Fremont (94538) ***(P-23832)***
Ble Inc.....F.....818 504-9577
11360 Goss St Sun Valley (91352) ***(P-100)***
Blentech Corporation.....D.....707 523-5949
2899 Dowd Dr Santa Rosa (95407) ***(P-14839)***
Blick Industries LLC.....F.....949 499-5026
2245 Laguna Canyon Rd Laguna Beach (92651) ***(P-15199)***
Blind Man Inc.....F.....951 654-5938
814 S State St San Jacinto (92583) ***(P-5181)***
Blinking Owl Distillery.....F.....949 370-4688
210 N Bush St Santa Ana (92701) ***(P-1572)***
Bliss Holdings LLC.....E.....626 506-8696
745 S Vinewood St Escondido (92029) ***(P-17676)***
Blisslights Inc.....E.....888 868-4603
100 E San Marcos Blvd # 308 San Marcos (92069) ***(P-19919)***
Blisslights LLC.....E.....888 868-4603
100 E San Marcos Blvd # 308 San Marcos (92069) ***(P-17677)***
Blisterpak Inc.....E.....323 728-5555
3020 Supply Ave Commerce (90040) ***(P-9983)***
Blitzers Premium Frozen Yogurt.....F.....951 679-7709
29101 Newport Rd Menifee (92584) ***(P-659)***
Blitz Technology Inc.....E.....949 380-7709
53 Parker Irvine (92618) ***(P-18051)***
Blizzard Entertainment Inc (HQ).....D.....949 955-1380
1 Blizzard Irvine (92618) ***(P-24430)***
Block Alternatives.....F.....661 729-2800
604 W Avenue L Ste 101 Lancaster (93534) ***(P-23524)***
Block Tops Inc (PA).....E.....714 978-5080
1321 S Sunkist St Anaheim (92806) ***(P-5040)***
Blocks Wearables Inc.....F.....650 307-9557
1800 Century Park E Fl 10 Los Angeles (90067) ***(P-23217)***
Blomberg Building Materials (PA).....D.....916 428-8060
1453 Blair Ave Sacramento (95822) ***(P-12300)***
Blomberg Glass, Sacramento *Also called Blomberg Windows Systems* ***(P-10681)***
Blomberg Window Systems, Sacramento *Also called Blomberg Building Materials* ***(P-12300)***
Blomberg Window Systems, Sacramento *Also called Architectural Blomberg LLC* ***(P-12293)***
Blomberg Windows Systems.....C.....916 428-8060
1453 Blair Ave Sacramento (95822) ***(P-10681)***
Blommer Chocolate Co Cal Inc.....C.....510 471-4300
1515 Pacific St Union City (94587) ***(P-1466)***
Bloom Energy Corporation (PA).....B.....408 543-1500
1299 Orleans Dr Sunnyvale (94089) ***(P-18748)***
Bloomboard Inc (PA).....F.....650 567-5656
227 Forest Ave Palo Alto (94301) ***(P-24431)***
Bloomers Metal Stampings Inc.....E.....661 257-2955
28615 Braxton Ave Valencia (91355) ***(P-13171)***
Bloomfield Bakers.....A.....626 610-2253
10711 Bloomfield St Los Alamitos (90720) ***(P-1355)***
Bloss Inc.....E.....626 599-9944
1840 Enterprise Way Monrovia (91016) ***(P-9984)***
Blossom Apple Moulding & Mllwk.....E.....925 820-2345
2411 Old Crow Canyon Rd L San Ramon (94583) ***(P-4110)***
Blossom Valley Foods Inc.....E.....408 848-5520
20 Casey Ln Gilroy (95020) ***(P-2246)***
Blow Molded Products Inc.....E.....951 360-6055
4720 Felspar St Riverside (92509) ***(P-9985)***
Blower Drive Service Co.....E.....562 693-4302
1280 W Lambert Rd Ste B Brea (92821) ***(P-20270)***
Blower-Dempsay Corporation.....D.....714 547-9266
4044 W Garry Ave Santa Ana (92704) ***(P-5390)***
Blowout Tools Inc.....F.....661 746-1700
19484 Broken Ct Shafter (93263) ***(P-186)***
Bltee LLC.....E.....213 802-1736
7101 Telegraph Rd Montebello (90640) ***(P-3217)***
Blu Heaven, Commerce *Also called Alliance Apparel Inc* ***(P-3212)***
Blu Homes Inc (PA).....D.....866 887-7997
1015 Walnut Ave Vallejo (94592) ***(P-4569)***
Blue Book Publishers Inc (PA).....D.....858 454-7939
9820 Willow Creek Rd # 410 San Diego (92131) ***(P-6449)***
Blue California Company, Rcho STA Marg *Also called Phyto Tech Corp* ***(P-8338)***
Blue Can Water (PA).....F.....818 450-3290
8309 Laurel Cny Blvd 219 Sun Valley (91352) ***(P-2099)***
Blue Cedar Networks Inc.....E.....415 329-0401
325 Pacific Ave Fl 1 San Francisco (94111) ***(P-15688)***
Blue Circle Corp.....F.....562 531-2711
7520 Monroe St Paramount (90723) ***(P-13060)***
Blue Coat LLC.....A.....408 220-2200
350 Ellis St Mountain View (94043) ***(P-24432)***
Blue Cross Beauty Products Inc.....E.....818 896-8681
557 Jessie St San Fernando (91340) ***(P-8704)***
Blue Cross Laboratories Inc (PA).....C.....661 255-0955
20950 Centre Pointe Pkwy Santa Clarita (91350) ***(P-8626)***
Blue Danube Systems Inc (PA).....F.....650 316-5010
3131 Jay St Ste 201 Santa Clara (95054) ***(P-18052)***
Blue Desert International Inc.....D.....951 273-7575
510 N Sheridan St Ste A Corona (92880) ***(P-16020)***
Blue Diamond, Turlock *Also called Blue Diamond Growers* ***(P-2470)***
Blue Diamond Growers.....C.....916 446-8464
1701 C St Sacramento (95811) ***(P-2469)***
Blue Diamond Growers.....C.....559 251-4044
10840 E Mckinley Ave Sanger (93657) ***(P-1483)***
Blue Diamond Growers.....D.....209 604-1501
1300 N Washington Rd Turlock (95380) ***(P-2470)***
Blue Eagle Stucco Products.....F.....559 485-4100
1407 N Clark St Fresno (93703) ***(P-11347)***
Blue Engravers, Long Beach *Also called Midonna Inc* ***(P-7407)***
Blue Iron Network Inc.....E.....714 901-1456
5811 Mcfadden Ave Huntington Beach (92649) ***(P-24433)***

ALPHABETIC

Employee Codes: A=Over 500 employees, B=251-500
C=101-250, D=51-100, E=20-50, F=10-19
2019 California
Manfacturers Register
© Mergent Inc. 1-800-342-5647
1079

Blue Lake Roundstock Co LLC.....F.....530 515-7007
19195 Latona Rd Anderson (96007) ***(P-4587)***
Blue Microphones LLC.....F.....818 879-5200
5706 Corsa Ave Ste 102 Westlake Village (91362) ***(P-17776)***
Blue Mtn Ctr of Meditation Inc.....E.....707 878-2369
3600 Tomales Rd Tomales (94971) ***(P-6316)***
Blue PCF Flvors Fragrances Inc.....E.....626 934-0099
1354 Marion Ct City of Industry (91745) ***(P-2247)***
Blue Planet Energy Solutions.....F.....858 947-0100
6540 Lusk Blvd Ste C204 San Diego (92121) ***(P-17587)***
Blue Ribbon Baking Inc.....C.....626 815-8809
823 W 8th St Azusa (91702) ***(P-1211)***
Blue Ribbon Cont & Display Inc.....F.....562 944-1217
11106 Shoemaker Ave Santa Fe Springs (90670) ***(P-5391)***
Blue Ribbon Sheepskin, San Diego *Also called Motorlamb International Acc* ***(P-3955)***
Blue Rock Networks LLC.....F.....415 577-8004
750 Battery St San Francisco (94111) ***(P-21730)***
Blue Sky Energy Inc.....F.....760 597-1642
2598 Fortune Way Ste K Vista (92081) ***(P-17334)***
Blue Sky Home & ACC Inc.....E.....909 930-6200
1360 E Locust St Ontario (91761) ***(P-400)***
Blue Sky Remediation Svcs Inc.....F.....626 961-5736
14000 Valley Blvd La Puente (91746) ***(P-18312)***
Blue Sky Research Incorporated (PA).....E.....408 941-6068
510 Alder Dr Milpitas (95035) ***(P-22060)***
Blue Sphere Inc.....E.....714 953-7555
215 Baker St Ste 100 Costa Mesa (92626) ***(P-3026)***
Blue Squirrel Inc.....D.....858 268-0717
8295 Aero Pl San Diego (92123) ***(P-18313)***
Blue-White Industries Ltd (PA).....D.....714 893-8529
5300 Business Dr Huntington Beach (92649) ***(P-21680)***
Bluebarry Enterprises Inc.....F.....818 956-0912
16525 Sherman Way Ste C11 Van Nuys (91406) ***(P-6699)***
Bluefield Associates Inc.....E.....909 476-6027
1100 N Hellman Ave Ste B Ontario (91764) ***(P-8705)***
Bluefrog Embroidery, San Leandro *Also called Double V Industries* ***(P-3841)***
Bluegate Surface Works Inc.....F.....562 630-9005
15936 Downey Ave Paramount (90723) ***(P-4276)***
Bluelab Corporation USA Ltd.....E.....909 599-1940
437 S Cataract Ave San Dimas (91773) ***(P-15303)***
Bluerun Ventures LP.....F.....650 462-7250
545 Middlefield Rd # 210 Menlo Park (94025) ***(P-24434)***
Bluescope Buildings N Amer Inc.....C.....559 651-5300
7440 W Doe Ave Visalia (93291) ***(P-12921)***
Bluescope Buildings N Amer Inc.....C.....209 667-4951
530 S Tegner Rd Turlock (95380) ***(P-12922)***
Bluesnap Inc.....E.....866 475-4687
5201 Great America Pkwy # 320 Santa Clara (95054) ***(P-24435)***
Bluestack Systems Inc.....E.....408 412-9439
2105 S Bascom Ave Ste 380 Campbell (95008) ***(P-24436)***
Bluetone Muffler Mfg Co.....E.....626 442-1073
9366 Klingerman St South El Monte (91733) ***(P-20271)***
Bluewater Publishing LLC.....F.....925 634-0880
9040 Brentwood Blvd Ste B Brentwood (94513) ***(P-6450)***
Bluewater Wear, Santa Ana *Also called Aftco Mfg Co Inc* ***(P-23489)***
Bluewick Home & Body Co LLC.....F.....626 282-2664
1701 Edgewood Dr Alhambra (91803) ***(P-24051)***
Blum Construction Co Inc.....F.....408 629-3740
404 Umbarger Rd Ste A San Jose (95111) ***(P-12301)***
Bluprint Clothing Corp.....D.....323 780-4347
5600 Bandini Blvd Bell (90201) ***(P-3218)***
Blur Leather, Los Angeles *Also called Luna Mora LLC* ***(P-3904)***
Blurb Inc.....D.....415 364-6300
580 California St Fl 3 San Francisco (94104) ***(P-6317)***
Blythe Energy Inc.....F.....561 304-5126
385 N Buck Blvd Blythe (92225) ***(P-89)***
Bmb Metal Products Corporation.....E.....916 631-9120
11460 Elks Cir Rancho Cordova (95742) ***(P-12506)***
BMC East LLC.....F.....818 842-8139
161 W Cypress Ave Burbank (91502) ***(P-4111)***
BMC Industries, Bakersfield *Also called Bakersfield Machine Co Inc* ***(P-16305)***
BMC Software Inc.....E.....949 752-7281
2020 Main St Ste 700 Irvine (92614) ***(P-24437)***
BMC Technology.....F.....510 429-7000
7968 Country Trail Dr Orangevale (95662) ***(P-16327)***
Bmci Inc.....E.....951 361-8000
1689 S Parco Ave Ontario (91761) ***(P-14749)***
Bmi, Temecula *Also called Bomatic Inc* ***(P-9987)***
Bmi Products Northern Cal Inc.....F.....408 293-4008
990 Ames Ave Milpitas (95035) ***(P-11348)***
Bmp, Riverside *Also called Blow Molded Products Inc* ***(P-9985)***
BMW Precision Machining Inc.....E.....760 439-6813
2379 Industry St Oceanside (92054) ***(P-16328)***
Bni, Chatsworth *Also called Bio-Nutraceuticals Inc* ***(P-8075)***
Bnk Petroleum (us) Inc.....E.....805 484-3613
760 Paseo Camarillo # 350 Camarillo (93010) ***(P-126)***
Bnl Technologies Inc.....E.....310 320-7272
20525 Manhattan Pl Torrance (90501) ***(P-15516)***
BNP Enterprises LLC.....F.....949 770-5438
22902 Roebuck St Lake Forest (92630) ***(P-20272)***
Bnrg, Irvine *Also called Bio-Nutritional RES Group Inc* ***(P-607)***
Bo Dean Co Inc (PA).....E.....707 576-8205
1060 N Dutton Ave Santa Rosa (95401) ***(P-300)***
Bo-Sherrel Corporation.....F.....510 744-3525
3340 Tree Swallow Pl Fremont (94555) ***(P-15689)***
Boardhouse, Gardena *Also called L&F Wood LLC* ***(P-4182)***
Boardriders Inc (HQ).....C.....714 889-2200
5600 Argosy Ave Ste 100 Huntington Beach (92649) ***(P-3139)***
Boards On Nord Inc.....F.....530 513-3922
14822 Meridian Meadows Ln Chico (95973) ***(P-23525)***
Boardwalk Solutions, Gardena *Also called Ocean Direct LLC* ***(P-2320)***
Boatworks.....F.....805 374-9455
2251 Townsgate Rd Westlake Village (91361) ***(P-21024)***
Boatyard-Channel Islands, The, Oxnard *Also called Tbyci LLC* ***(P-21065)***
Bob Lewis Machine Company Inc.....F.....310 538-9406
1324 W 135th St Gardena (90247) ***(P-16329)***
Bob Martin Co, South El Monte *Also called Robert P Martin Company* ***(P-11453)***
BOBBOI, La Jolla *Also called Berenice 2 AM Corp* ***(P-657)***
Bobby Salazar Corporate, Fowler *Also called Bobby Slzars Mxcan Fd Pdts Inc* ***(P-748)***
Bobby Slzars Mxcan Fd Pdts Inc (PA).....E.....559 834-4787
2810 San Antonio Dr Fowler (93625) ***(P-748)***
Bobbys Metal Finishing.....F.....818 837-1928
12423 Gladstone Ave # 25 Sylmar (91342) ***(P-13349)***
Bobs Iron Inc.....E.....510 567-8983
740 Kevin Ct Oakland (94621) ***(P-12119)***
Bobster Eyewear, San Diego *Also called Balboa Manufacturing Co LLC* ***(P-2823)***
Boc Gases, Richmond *Also called Linde LLC* ***(P-7697)***
Bocchi Laboratories, Santa Clarita *Also called Shadow Holdings LLC* ***(P-8838)***
Bocchi Laboratories, Santa Clarita *Also called Shadow Holdings LLC* ***(P-8839)***
Bock Machine Company Inc.....F.....909 947-7250
2141 S Parco Ave Ontario (91761) ***(P-16330)***
Bode Concrete LLC.....D.....415 920-7100
755 Stockton Ave San Jose (95126) ***(P-11051)***
Body Care Resort Inc.....F.....310 328-8888
22125 S Vermont Ave Torrance (90502) ***(P-17386)***
Body Dope, Berkeley *Also called Two Star Dog Inc* ***(P-3281)***
Body Flex Sports, Walnut *Also called Hupa International Inc* ***(P-23587)***
Body Flex Sports Inc (PA).....F.....909 598-9876
21717 Ferrero Walnut (91789) ***(P-23526)***
Body Glove International LLC.....F.....310 374-3441
504 N Broadway Redondo Beach (90277) ***(P-3140)***
Bodycote Imt Inc.....D.....714 893-6561
7474 Garden Grove Blvd Westminster (92683) ***(P-11795)***
Bodycote Thermal Proc Inc.....F.....323 264-0111
2900 S Sunol Dr Vernon (90058) ***(P-11796)***
Bodycote Thermal Proc Inc.....E.....310 604-8000
515 W Apra St Ste A Compton (90220) ***(P-11797)***
Bodycote Thermal Proc Inc.....D.....714 893-6561
7474 Garden Grove Blvd Westminster (92683) ***(P-11798)***
Bodycote Thermal Proc Inc.....D.....323 583-1231
3370 Benedict Way Huntington Park (90255) ***(P-13350)***
Bodycote Thermal Proc Inc.....E.....562 693-3135
11845 Burke St Santa Fe Springs (90670) ***(P-11799)***
Bodycote Thermal Proc Inc.....E.....510 492-4200
4240 Technology Dr Fremont (94538) ***(P-11800)***
Bodycote Thermal Proc Inc.....E.....562 946-1717
9921 Romandel Ave Santa Fe Springs (90670) ***(P-11801)***
Bodycote Usa Inc.....F.....323 264-0111
2900 S Sunol Dr Vernon (90058) ***(P-11802)***
Boeger Winery Inc.....E.....530 622-8094
1709 Carson Rd Placerville (95667) ***(P-1662)***
Boeing Company.....E.....559 998-8260
Lemoore Nval Base Hnger 1 Lemoore (93245) ***(P-20543)***
Boeing Company.....A.....310 662-7286
22308 Harbor Ridge Ln Torrance (90502) ***(P-20544)***
Boeing Company.....B.....714 896-3311
5301 Bolsa Ave Huntington Beach (92647) ***(P-21156)***
Boeing Company.....A.....562 797-5831
2201 Seal Beach Blvd Seal Beach (90740) ***(P-20545)***
Boeing Company.....A.....714 952-1509
5463 Plumeria Ln Cypress (90630) ***(P-20546)***
Boeing Company.....A.....949 452-0259
24172 Via Madrugada Mission Viejo (92692) ***(P-20547)***
Boeing Company.....E.....559 998-8214
210 Reeves Blvd Bldg 210 # 210 Lemoore (93246) ***(P-21267)***
Boeing Company.....A.....661 810-4686
122 E Jones Rd Bldg 151 Edwards (93524) ***(P-20548)***
Boeing Company.....A.....714 317-1070
3521 E Spring St Long Beach (90806) ***(P-20549)***
Boeing Company.....A.....562 593-6668
2400 E Wardlow Rd Long Beach (90807) ***(P-20550)***
Boeing Company.....A.....562 944-6583
12203 Hillwood Dr Whittier (90604) ***(P-20551)***
Boeing Company.....A.....562 425-3613
3460 Cherry Ave Bldg 56 Long Beach (90807) ***(P-20552)***
Boeing Company.....A.....760 246-0273
18310 Readiness St Victorville (92394) ***(P-20553)***
Boeing Company.....E.....310 662-9000
900 N Sepulveda Blvd El Segundo (90245) ***(P-18053)***
Boeing Company.....A.....714 934-9801
15400 Graham St Ste 101 Huntington Beach (92649) ***(P-20554)***
Boeing Company.....D.....310 426-4100
222 N Pacific Coast Hwy # 2050 El Segundo (90245) ***(P-20555)***
Boeing Company.....A.....714 372-5361
2201 Seal Beach Blvd Seal Beach (90740) ***(P-18054)***
Boeing Company.....A.....714 896-3311
5301 Bolsa Ave Huntington Beach (92647) ***(P-20556)***
Boeing Company.....E.....562 593-5511
3855 N Lakewood Blvd D35-0072 Long Beach (90846) ***(P-20557)***
Boeing Company.....A.....562 496-1000
2401 E Wardlow Rd Long Beach (90807) ***(P-20558)***
Boeing Company.....A.....714 896-1301
5301 Bolsa Ave Huntington Beach (92647) ***(P-20559)***
Boeing Company.....B.....661 212-0024
1500 E Avenue M Palmdale (93550) ***(P-21268)***
Boeing Company.....A.....562 593-5511
2401 E Wardlow Rd Long Beach (90807) ***(P-20560)***

Boeing Company ....A.......714 896-1670
14441 Astronautics Ln Huntington Beach (92647) ***(P-20561)***
Boeing Company ....A.......707 437-8574
451 1st St Travis Afb (94535) ***(P-20562)***
Boeing Company ....A.......714 896-1839
5301 Bolsa Ave Huntington Beach (92647) ***(P-20563)***
Boeing Company ....E.......714 896-3311
5222 Rancho Rd Huntington Beach (92647) ***(P-20564)***
Boeing Company ....A.......310 416-9319
1700 E Imperial Ave El Segundo (90245) ***(P-20565)***
Boeing Company ....A.......818 428-1154
8900 De Soto Ave Canoga Park (91304) ***(P-20566)***
Boeing Company ....A.......951 571-0122
5250 Tanker Way March ARB (92518) ***(P-20567)***
Boeing Intellectual ....E.......562 797-2020
3501 Bolsa Ave Huntington Beach (92647) ***(P-20568)***
Boeing Satellite Systems ....D.......310 364-5088
2060 E Imperial Hwy Fl 1 El Segundo (90245) ***(P-21269)***
Boeing Satellite Systems Inc ....F.......310 568-2735
2300 E Imperial Hwy El Segundo (90245) ***(P-20569)***
Boeing Satellite Systems Inc ....E.......310 364-6444
1950 E Imperial Hwy El Segundo (90245) ***(P-20570)***
Boeing Satellite Systems Inc (HQ) ....E.......310 791-7450
900 N Pacific Coast Hwy El Segundo (90245) ***(P-18055)***
Bogner Amplification ....F.......818 765-8929
11411 Vanowen St North Hollywood (91605) ***(P-17777)***
Bohan & Canelis - Austin Crk ....F.......707 632-5296
1528 Copperhill Pkwy F Santa Rosa (95403) ***(P-325)***
Bohns Printing ....F.......661 948-8081
656 W Lancaster Blvd Lancaster (93534) ***(P-6700)***
Boinca Inc ....F.......714 809-6313
15000 S Avalon Blvd Ste F Gardena (90248) ***(P-8706)***
Boinca Inc ....F.......619 398-7252
1611 S Rancho Santa Fe Rd San Marcos (92078) ***(P-8707)***
Boiron Inc ....F.......805 527-9883
4145 Guardian St Simi Valley (93063) ***(P-8085)***
Boise Cascade Company ....E.......209 983-4114
12030 S Harlan Rd Lathrop (95330) ***(P-5275)***
Boise Hexacomb ....F.......562 944-0052
9700 Bell Ranch Dr Santa Fe Springs (90670) ***(P-5276)***
Bojer Inc ....E.......626 334-1711
177 S Peckham Rd Azusa (91702) ***(P-3710)***
Bold Data Technology Inc ....E.......510 490-8296
48363 Fremont Blvd Fremont (94538) ***(P-15395)***
Bolero Inds Inc A Cal Corp ....E.......562 693-3000
11850 Burke St Santa Fe Springs (90670) ***(P-9986)***
Bolero Plastics, Santa Fe Springs *Also called Bolero Inds Inc A Cal Corp* ***(P-9986)***
Bolide International, San Dimas *Also called Bolide Technology Group Inc* ***(P-19920)***
Bolide Technology Group Inc ....D.......909 305-8889
468 S San Dimas Ave San Dimas (91773) ***(P-19920)***
Bolttech Mannings Inc ....D.......310 604-9500
16926 Keegan Ave Carson (90746) ***(P-14700)***
Bolttech Mannings Inc ....D.......707 751-0157
475 Industrial Way Benicia (94510) ***(P-14701)***
Bomark Inc ....E.......626 968-1666
601 S 6th Ave La Puente (91746) ***(P-9189)***
Bomatic Inc (HQ) ....E.......909 947-3900
43225 Business Park Dr Temecula (92590) ***(P-9987)***
Bomatic Inc ....E.......909 947-3900
2181 E Francis St Ontario (91761) ***(P-9988)***
Bombardier Transportation ....D.......323 224-3461
1555 N San Fernando Rd Los Angeles (90065) ***(P-21073)***
Bon Appetit Bakery, Vernon *Also called Bon Appetit Danish Inc* ***(P-1212)***
Bon Appetit Danish Inc ....D.......323 584-9500
4525 District Blvd Vernon (90058) ***(P-1212)***
Bonafide Management Systems ....F.......805 777-7666
241 Lombard St Thousand Oaks (91360) ***(P-24438)***
Bond Furs Inc ....F.......626 471-9912
114 W Lime Ave Monrovia (91016) ***(P-3599)***
Bond Manufacturing Co Inc (PA) ....C.......925 252-1135
1700 W 4th St Antioch (94509) ***(P-10886)***
Bonded Fiberloft Inc ....B.......323 726-7820
2748 Tanager Ave Commerce (90040) ***(P-2725)***
Bonded Window Coverings Inc ....E.......858 974-7700
7831 Ostrow St San Diego (92111) ***(P-5182)***
Bondline Elctrnic Adhsive Corp ....E.......408 830-9200
777 N Pastoria Ave Sunnyvale (94085) ***(P-9131)***
Bonehead Composites, Perris *Also called J F Christopher Inc* ***(P-23598)***
Bonelli Enterprises ....E.......650 873-3222
330 Corey Way South San Francisco (94080) ***(P-12302)***
Bonelli Fine Food Inc ....F.......650 906-9896
3525 Del Mar Heights Rd San Diego (92130) ***(P-558)***
Bonelli Windows and Doors, South San Francisco *Also called Bonelli Enterprises* ***(P-12302)***
Bonjour Fleurette Inc ....F.......415 382-1603
112 Mitchell Blvd Ste A San Rafael (94903) ***(P-10478)***
Bonneau Wines LLC ....F.......707 996-0420
75 Bonneau Rd Sonoma (95476) ***(P-1663)***
Bonner Metal Processing LLC ....E.......925 455-3833
6052 Industrial Way Ste A Livermore (94551) ***(P-12973)***
Bonner Processing Inc ....E.......925 455-3833
6052 Industrial Way Ste A Livermore (94551) ***(P-13351)***
Bonnier Corporation ....D.......760 707-0100
15255 Alton Pkwy Irvine (92618) ***(P-6113)***
Bonny Doon Vineyard (PA) ....F.......831 425-3625
328 Ingalls St Santa Cruz (95060) ***(P-1664)***
Bonny Doon Winery Inc ....D.......831 425-3625
328 Ingalls St Santa Cruz (95060) ***(P-1665)***
Bonsai Ai Inc ....E.......510 900-1112
2150 Shattuck Ave # 1200 Berkeley (94704) ***(P-24439)***
Bonsal American Inc ....E.......714 523-1530
16005 Phoebe Ave La Mirada (90638) ***(P-10887)***
Boochcraft, Chula Vista *Also called Boochery Inc* ***(P-2067)***
Boochery Inc ....F.......619 738-1008
684 Anita St Ste F Chula Vista (91911) ***(P-2067)***
Book Binders, Pico Rivera *Also called Kater-Crafts Incorporated* ***(P-7606)***
Bookette Software Co Inc ....F.......831 484-9250
12795 Corte Cordillera Salinas (93908) ***(P-24440)***
Bookpack Inc ....F.......510 601-8301
3286 Adeline St Ste 1 Berkeley (94703) ***(P-6451)***
Boom Industrial Inc ....D.......909 495-3555
167 University Pkwy Pomona (91768) ***(P-14923)***
Boom Movement LLC ....D.......410 358-3600
1 Viper Way Ste 3 Vista (92081) ***(P-17778)***
Boone Memorials, Sonora *Also called J M Boone & Sons* ***(P-11257)***
Boone Printing & Graphics Inc ....D.......805 683-2349
70 S Kellogg Ave Ste 8 Goleta (93117) ***(P-7252)***
Boosted Inc (PA) ....E.......650 549-4169
915 Linda Vista Ave Mountain View (94043) ***(P-23527)***
Boosted Boards, Mountain View *Also called Boosted Inc* ***(P-23527)***
Boostpower USA Inc ....F.......805 376-6077
2560 Calcite Cir Newbury Park (91320) ***(P-14014)***
Boozak Inc ....E.......951 245-6045
508 Chaney St Ste A Lake Elsinore (92530) ***(P-12507)***
Boral Roofing LLC ....E.......909 796-8324
1990 Riverview Dr San Bernardino (92408) ***(P-10888)***
Boral Roofing LLC ....D.......909 822-4407
3511 N Riverside Ave Rialto (92377) ***(P-10889)***
Bordeaux, Los Angeles *Also called Jamm Industries Corp* ***(P-3434)***
Borden Decal Company Inc ....E.......415 431-1587
870 Harrison St Unit 101 San Francisco (94107) ***(P-7253)***
Borden Lighting ....E.......510 357-0171
460 Roland Way Oakland (94621) ***(P-17588)***
Borden Manufacturing ....E.......530 347-6642
3314 Pacific Trl Cottonwood (96022) ***(P-14431)***
Bordenaves, San Rafael *Also called Bordenaves Marin Baking* ***(P-1213)***
Bordenaves Marin Baking ....D.......415 453-2957
1512 4th St San Rafael (94901) ***(P-1213)***
Border Precast Inc ....F.......760 351-1233
615 Us Highway 111 Brawley (92227) ***(P-10890)***
Bore-Max, El Monte *Also called GAI Manufacturing Co LLC* ***(P-14249)***
Boresha International Inc ....E.......925 676-1400
7041 Koll Center Pkwy # 100 Pleasanton (94566) ***(P-2329)***
Borett Automation Technologies ....F.......818 597-8664
3824 Bowsprit Cir Westlake Village (91361) ***(P-15304)***
Borga Stl Bldngs Cmponents Inc ....E.......559 834-5375
300 W Peach St Fowler (93625) ***(P-12508)***
Borges Rock Product, Sun Valley *Also called Over & Over Ready Mix Inc* ***(P-10971)***
Borin Manufacturing Inc ....E.......310 822-1000
5741 Buckingham Pkwy B Culver City (90230) ***(P-15055)***
Boring Thrading Bars Unlimited, Vista *Also called Alvarado Micro Precision Inc* ***(P-14361)***
Boris Bs Frms Vtrnary Svcs Inc ....D.......916 730-4225
9245 Laguna Springs Dr Elk Grove (95758) ***(P-1123)***
Borland Software Corporation ....D.......650 286-1900
951 Mariners Isl Blvd # 460 San Mateo (94404) ***(P-24441)***
Borsos Engineering Inc ....E.......760 930-0296
5924 Balfour Ct Ste 102 Carlsbad (92008) ***(P-15396)***
Bos, San Marcos *Also called Black Oxide Service Inc* ***(P-13347)***
Bosch Auto Svc Solutions Inc (PA) ....F.......805 966-2000
2030 Alameda Padre Serra Santa Barbara (93103) ***(P-20273)***
Bosch Diagnostics, Santa Barbara *Also called Robert Bosch LLC* ***(P-22607)***
Bosch Enrgy Stor Solutions LLC ....F.......650 320-2933
4005 Miranda Ave Ste 200 Palo Alto (94304) ***(P-17182)***
Boss, Commerce *Also called Norstar Office Products Inc* ***(P-4959)***
Boss Litho Inc ....E.......626 912-7088
2380 Peck Rd City of Industry (90601) ***(P-6701)***
Boss Printing Inc ....F.......714 545-2677
3403 W Macarthur Blvd Santa Ana (92704) ***(P-6702)***
Bostik Inc ....D.......951 296-6425
27460 Bostik Ct Temecula (92590) ***(P-9132)***
Boston Scientific - Valencia, Valencia *Also called Boston Scientific Corporation* ***(P-22379)***
Boston Scientific Corporation ....B.......661 645-6668
28460 Avenue Stanford Valencia (91355) ***(P-22377)***
Boston Scientific Corporation ....C.......408 935-3400
150 Baytech Dr San Jose (95134) ***(P-22378)***
Boston Scientific Corporation ....E.......800 678-2575
25155 Rye Canyon Loop Valencia (91355) ***(P-22379)***
Boston Scientific Corporation ....B.......408 935-3400
150 Baytech Dr San Jose (95134) ***(P-22380)***
Boston Scntfic Nrmdlation Corp ....F.......661 949-4869
25129 Rye Canyon Loop Valencia (91355) ***(P-22709)***
Boston Scntfic Nrmdlation Corp (HQ) ....B.......661 949-4310
25155 Rye Canyon Loop Valencia (91355) ***(P-22710)***
Bot N Bot Inc ....F.......562 906-4873
13005 Los Nietos Rd Santa Fe Springs (90670) ***(P-2375)***
Botanas Mexico Inc ....F.......626 279-1512
11122 Rush St South El Monte (91733) ***(P-2471)***
Botanicalabs Inc ....F.......818 466-5639
21900 Plummer St Chatsworth (91311) ***(P-8708)***
Botanx ....E.......714 854-1601
3357 E Miraloma Ave # 156 Anaheim (92806) ***(P-8709)***
Botner Manufacturing Inc ....F.......510 569-2943
900 Aladdin Ave San Leandro (94577) ***(P-12509)***
Bottelsen Dart Co Inc ....F.......805 922-4519
945 W Mccoy Ln Santa Maria (93455) ***(P-23411)***
Bottle Coatings, Sun Valley *Also called Sundial Powder Coatings Inc* ***(P-13670)***
Bottlemate Inc ....E.......323 887-9009
2095 Leo Ave Commerce (90040) ***(P-9989)***

ALPHABETIC

Bottlers Unlimited Inc......E......707 255-0595
753 Jefferson St NAPA (94559) ***(P-2100)***
Bottling Group LLC......F......559 485-5050
1150 E North Ave Fresno (93725) ***(P-2101)***
Bottling Group LLC......E......951 697-3200
6659 Sycamore Canyon Blvd Riverside (92507) ***(P-2102)***
Bouchaine Vineyards Inc......F......707 252-9065
1075 Buchli Station Rd NAPA (94559) ***(P-1666)***
Bouchaine Winery, NAPA *Also called Bouchaine Vineyards Inc* ***(P-1666)***
Boudin Souerdough BAKery& Cafe, San Jose *Also called Andre-Boudin Bakeries Inc* ***(P-1174)***
Boudoir Spirits Inc......F......909 714-6644
7197 Boulder Ave Ste 12 Highland (92346) ***(P-2068)***
Boudoir Vodka, Highland *Also called Boudoir Spirits Inc* ***(P-2068)***
Boulder Creek Guitars Inc......F......408 842-0222
5810 Obata Way Ste 1 Gilroy (95020) ***(P-23358)***
Boulevard Style Inc......E......213 749-1551
1680 E 40th Pl Los Angeles (90011) ***(P-3219)***
Boulevard Style Inc (PA)......F......213 749-1551
1015 Crocker St Ste 27 Los Angeles (90021) ***(P-3220)***
Boundary Devices LLC......E......602 212-6744
7 Orchard Ste 102 Lake Forest (92630) ***(P-18749)***
Bourns Inc (PA)......C......951 781-5500
1200 Columbia Ave Riverside (92507) ***(P-19323)***
Bourns Inc......C......951 781-5690
1200 Columbia Ave Riverside (92507) ***(P-21731)***
Bourns Inc......F......951 781-5360
8662 Siempre Viva Rd San Diego (92154) ***(P-21732)***
Bowen Enterprises, El Cajon *Also called Bowen Printing Inc* ***(P-5700)***
Bowen Printing Inc......F......619 440-8605
380 Coogan Way El Cajon (92020) ***(P-5700)***
Bowers & Kelly Products Inc......E......714 630-1285
4572 E Eisenhower Cir Anaheim (92807) ***(P-9821)***
Bowers Machining, Anaheim *Also called Aaron Dutt Enterprises Inc* ***(P-13157)***
Bowman Plating Co Inc......C......310 639-4343
2631 E 126th St Compton (90222) ***(P-13352)***
Bowtie Inc (HQ)......E......213 385-2222
500 N Brand Blvd Ste 600 Glendale (91203) ***(P-6114)***
Bowtie Inc......D......949 855-8822
3 Burroughs Irvine (92618) ***(P-6115)***
Box Inc (PA)......C......877 729-4269
900 Jefferson Ave Redwood City (94063) ***(P-24442)***
Box Co Inc......F......619 661-8090
7575 Britannia Park Pl San Diego (92154) ***(P-6703)***
Box Master......E......661 298-2666
17000 Sierra Hwy Canyon Country (91351) ***(P-13172)***
Boxes R Us Inc......D......626 820-5410
15051 Don Julian Rd City of Industry (91746) ***(P-5504)***
Boyd, Modesto *Also called LTI Holdings Inc* ***(P-7907)***
Boyd & Boyd Industries (PA)......F......661 631-8400
3500 Chester Ave Bakersfield (93301) ***(P-15200)***
Boyd Construction, Yorba Linda *Also called Boyd Corporation* ***(P-12120)***
Boyd Corporation, Modesto *Also called A B Boyd Co* ***(P-9579)***
Boyd Corporation (PA)......F......714 533-2375
5832 Ohio St Yorba Linda (92886) ***(P-12120)***
Boyd Corporation (HQ)......F......209 236-1111
5960 Inglewood Dr Ste 115 Pleasanton (94588) ***(P-9133)***
Boyd Corporation......C......888 244-6931
600 S Mcclure Rd Modesto (95357) ***(P-9134)***
Boyd Lighting Fixture Co (PA)......E......415 778-4300
30 Liberty Ship Way # 3150 Sausalito (94965) ***(P-17589)***
Boyd Specialties LLC......D......909 219-5120
1016 E Cooley Dr Ste N Colton (92324) ***(P-468)***
Boyer Inc......E......831 724-0123
105 Thompson Rd Watsonville (95076) ***(P-9058)***
BP Castrol, Richmond *Also called BP Lubricants USA Inc* ***(P-9425)***
BP Lubricants USA Inc......E......510 236-6312
801 Wharf St Richmond (94804) ***(P-9425)***
BP West Coast Products LLC......B......310 816-8787
22600 Wilmington Ave Carson (90745) ***(P-31)***
BP West Coast Products LLC......B......510 231-4724
1306 Canal Blvd Richmond (94804) ***(P-32)***
Bpi Records, Commerce *Also called Bridge Publications Inc* ***(P-6318)***
Bpo Management Services Inc (HQ)......F......714 974-2670
8175 E Kaiser Blvd 100 Anaheim (92808) ***(P-24443)***
Bpo Systems Inc (PA)......E......925 478-4299
1700 Ygnacio Valley Rd # 205 Walnut Creek (94598) ***(P-24444)***
Bps Tactical Inc......F......909 794-2435
2165 E Colton Ave Mentone (92359) ***(P-3052)***
BQE Software Inc......D......310 602-4020
3825 Del Amo Blvd Trrance Torrance Torrance (90503) ***(P-24445)***
Bracton Beer Line Cleaners, Anaheim *Also called Bracton Sosafe Inc* ***(P-8627)***
Bracton Sosafe Inc......F......714 632-8499
1061 N Shepard St Ste E Anaheim (92806) ***(P-8627)***
Brad Barry Company Ltd......E......909 591-9493
14020 Central Ave Ste 580 Chino (91710) ***(P-2330)***
Braden Partners LP A Calif......F......510 562-5501
619 Mccormick St San Leandro (94577) ***(P-22956)***
Bradfield Manufacturing Inc......F......714 543-8348
2633 E Mardi Gras Ave Anaheim (92806) ***(P-12838)***
Bradford Canning Stahl Inc......F......209 257-1535
250 Scottsville Blvd Jackson (95642) ***(P-16331)***
Bradley Corp......F......909 481-7255
5556 Ontario Mills Pkwy Ontario (91764) ***(P-12025)***
Bradley Manufacturing Co Inc......E......562 923-5556
9130 Firestone Blvd Downey (90241) ***(P-9990)***
Bradley Tchnologies-California......E......310 538-0714
447 E Rosecrans Ave Gardena (90248) ***(P-9135)***
Bradley's Plastic Bag Co, Downey *Also called Bradley Manufacturing Co Inc* ***(P-9990)***
Bradshaw Kirchofer Home Furn......F......310 325-0010
22926 Mariposa Ave Torrance (90502) ***(P-4681)***
Brady Sheet Metal Inc......F......818 846-4043
320 N Victory Blvd Burbank (91502) ***(P-12510)***
Bragel International Inc......E......909 598-8808
3383 Pomona Blvd Pomona (91768) ***(P-3547)***
Bragstr LLC......F......818 917-0312
20250 Plummer St Chatsworth (91311) ***(P-24446)***
Braiform Enterprises Inc......D......714 526-0257
576 N Gilbert St Fullerton (92833) ***(P-9991)***
Braille Signs Inc......F......949 797-1570
16782 Von Karman Ave # 30 Irvine (92606) ***(P-23833)***
Brainchip Inc (HQ)......E......949 330-6750
65 Enterprise Aliso Viejo (92656) ***(P-24447)***
Brains Out Media Inc......F......818 296-1036
2629 Foothill Blvd # 111 La Crescenta (91214) ***(P-24448)***
Brainstormproducts LLC......F......760 871-1135
1011 S Andreasen Dr # 100 Escondido (92029) ***(P-23412)***
Brambila's Draperies, Los Angeles *Also called Juan Brambila Sr* ***(P-4709)***
Brampton Mtnesen Fabr Pdts Inc......E......510 483-7771
1688 Abram Ct San Leandro (94577) ***(P-3780)***
Branan Medical Corporation (PA)......E......949 598-7166
9940 Mesa Rim Rd San Diego (92121) ***(P-22381)***
Branch Messenger Inc......F......323 300-4063
130 W Union St Pasadena (91103) ***(P-24449)***
Brand Identity Inc......F......916 553-0000
9520 Flintridge Way Orangevale (95662) ***(P-6704)***
Brand Ink Inc......E......760 721-4465
3801 Oceanic Dr Ste 103 Oceanside (92056) ***(P-7254)***
Brand X Hurarches......E......510 658-9006
4228 Telegraph Ave Oakland (94609) ***(P-10480)***
Branded Spirits USA Ltd......F......415 813-5045
500 Sansome St Ste 600 San Francisco (94111) ***(P-2069)***
Brandelli Arts Inc......E......714 537-0969
12362 9th St Garden Grove (92840) ***(P-11349)***
Branding Irons Unlimited, Canoga Park *Also called Infinity Stamps Inc* ***(P-13224)***
Brandmd Skin Care, Chatsworth *Also called Samuel Raoof* ***(P-8832)***
Brandnew Industries Inc......F......805 964-8251
375 Pine Ave Ste 22 Santa Barbara (93117) ***(P-23714)***
Brandt Consolidated Inc......F......559 499-2100
3654 S Willow Ave Fresno (93725) ***(P-9082)***
Brandt Electronics Inc......E......408 240-0014
1971 Tarob Ct Milpitas (95035) ***(P-19470)***
Brantner and Associates Inc (HQ)......C......619 562-7070
1700 Gillespie Way El Cajon (92020) ***(P-19374)***
Brass Tech, Santa Ana *Also called Newport Metal Finishing Inc* ***(P-13621)***
Brasscraft Corona, Corona *Also called Brasscraft Manufacturing Co* ***(P-13762)***
Brasscraft Manufacturing Co......D......951 735-4375
215 N Smith Ave Corona (92880) ***(P-13762)***
Brasstech Inc......B......949 417-5207
2001 Carnegie Ave Santa Ana (92705) ***(P-12026)***
Brava, Pomona *Also called Bragel International Inc* ***(P-3547)***
Brava Home Inc......E......408 675-2569
312 Chestnut St Redwood City (94063) ***(P-17387)***
Bravo Communications Inc......E......408 297-8700
3463 Meadowlands Ln San Jose (95135) ***(P-15690)***
Bravo Design Inc......F......818 563-1385
150 E Olive Ave Ste 304 Burbank (91502) ***(P-7255)***
Bravo Fono, Palo Alto *Also called Fono Unlimited Inc* ***(P-672)***
Bravo Sports......E......858 408-0083
4370 Jutland Dr San Diego (92117) ***(P-23528)***
Bravo Sports (HQ)......D......562 484-5100
12801 Carmenita Rd Santa Fe Springs (90670) ***(P-23529)***
Bravo Support, Commerce *Also called S Bravo Systems Inc* ***(P-12418)***
Braxton Caribbean Mfg Co Inc......D......714 508-3570
2641 Walnut Ave Tustin (92780) ***(P-23762)***
Brazeau Thoroughbred Farms LP......F......951 925-8957
30500 State St Hemet (92543) ***(P-14047)***
Brea Canon Oil Co Inc......F......310 326-4002
23903 Normandie Ave Harbor City (90710) ***(P-33)***
Bread Basket, Daly City *Also called Westlake Bakery Inc* ***(P-1342)***
Bread Los Angeles......E......323 201-3953
1527 Beach St Montebello (90640) ***(P-1356)***
Breakaway Press Inc......E......818 727-7388
9620 Topanga Canyon Pl A Chatsworth (91311) ***(P-7256)***
Breathe Technologies Inc......E......949 988-7700
175 Technology Dr Ste 100 Irvine (92618) ***(P-22711)***
Bree Engineering Corp......E......760 510-4950
1275 Stone Dr Ste A San Marcos (92078) ***(P-14924)***
Breezaire Products Co......F......858 566-7465
8610 Production Ave Ste A San Diego (92121) ***(P-12366)***
Breg Inc (HQ)......C......760 599-3000
2885 Loker Ave E Carlsbad (92010) ***(P-22382)***
Brehm Communications Inc (PA)......E......858 451-6200
16644 W Bernardo Dr # 300 San Diego (92127) ***(P-6705)***
Brehm Communications Inc......F......916 985-2581
921 Sutter St Folsom (95630) ***(P-5779)***
Breitburn Energy Co, Santa Fe Springs *Also called Strand Energy Company* ***(P-76)***
Breitburn GP LLC......A......213 225-5900
707 Wilshire Blvd # 4600 Los Angeles (90017) ***(P-34)***
Breitburn Operating LP (HQ)......F......213 225-5900
707 Wilshire Blvrd 4600 Los Angeles (90017) ***(P-35)***
Brendan Technologies Inc......E......760 929-7500
1947 Camino Vida Roble # 21 Carlsbad (92008) ***(P-24450)***
Brenner-Fiedler & Associates (PA)......E......562 404-2721
4059 Flat Rock Dr Riverside (92505) ***(P-22172)***
Brent Engineering Inc......F......949 679-5630
81 Shield Irvine (92618) ***(P-14148)***

Mergent e-mail: customerrelations@mergent.com
1082
2019 California
Manufacturers Register
(P-0000) Products & Services Section entry number
(PA)=Parent Co (HQ)=Headquarters (DH)=Div Headquarters

ALPHABETIC SECTION
Brooks Street Companies

Brent-Wood Products Inc ..... E 800 400-7335
777 E Rosecrans Ave Ste D Los Angeles (90059) *(P-4609)*
Brentwood Appliances Inc ..... F 323 266-4600
3088 E 46th St Vernon (90058) *(P-17411)*
Brentwood Home LLC (PA) ..... C 562 949-3759
701 Burning Tree Rd Ste A Fullerton (92833) *(P-4854)*
Brentwood Home LLC ..... F 213 457-7626
2301 E 7th St Ste 417 Los Angeles (90023) *(P-4855)*
Brentwood News, Antioch *Also called Contra Costa Newspapers Inc (P-5816)*
Brentwood Originals Inc (PA) ..... A 310 637-6804
20639 S Fordyce Ave Carson (90810) *(P-3711)*
Brentwood Press & Pubg LLC ..... E 925 516-4757
248 Oak St Brentwood (94513) *(P-5780)*
Brentwood Readymix, Brentwood *Also called Antioch Building Materials Co (P-11042)*
Brentwood Yellow Pages, Brentwood *Also called Brentwood Press & Pubg LLC (P-5780)*
Brett Corp ..... E 858 292-4919
8316 Clairemont Mesa Blvd # 105 San Diego (92111) *(P-7257)*
Brevet Industries, Irvine *Also called Brewer Irvine Inc (P-9992)*
Brevity LLC ..... F 949 250-0701
1405 Warner Ave Ste A Tustin (92780) *(P-24451)*
Brew Building, Fort Bragg *Also called North Coast Brewing Co Inc (P-1613)*
Brew4u LLC ..... F 415 516-8211
935 Washington St San Carlos (94070) *(P-1573)*
Brewer Irvine Inc ..... D 949 474-7000
16661 Jamboree Rd Irvine (92606) *(P-9992)*
Brewmaster Inc ..... E 415 642-3371
1195 Evans Ave San Francisco (94124) *(P-1574)*
Brewster Foods, Reseda *Also called Test Laboratories Inc (P-2680)*
Brg Sports, Scotts Valley *Also called Vista Outdoor Inc (P-23687)*
Brian Klaas Inc ..... F 818 394-9881
11101 Tuxford St Sun Valley (91352) *(P-5127)*
Brian's Welding, San Jose *Also called B W Padilla Inc (P-25387)*
Brice Manufacturing Co Inc ..... E 818 896-2938
10262 Norris Ave Pacoima (91331) *(P-20761)*
Brice Tool & Stamping ..... F 714 630-6400
1170 N Van Horne Way Anaheim (92806) *(P-13173)*
Brickstone Group Inc ..... F 818 242-8569
4722 San Fernando Rd Glendale (91204) *(P-1357)*
Bridge Publications Inc (PA) ..... E 323 888-6200
5600 E Olympic Blvd Commerce (90022) *(P-6318)*
Bridge USA Inc ..... E 310 532-5921
20817 S Western Ave Torrance (90501) *(P-6116)*
Bridgelux Inc (PA) ..... D 925 583-8400
46430 Fremont Blvd Fremont (94538) *(P-18750)*
Bridgeport Products Inc ..... D 949 348-8800
26895 Aliso Creek Rd B Aliso Viejo (92656) *(P-10517)*
Bridgewave Communications Inc ..... E 408 567-6900
17034 Camino San Bernardo San Diego (92127) *(P-11647)*
Bridgford Foods Corporation (HQ) ..... B 714 526-5533
1308 N Patt St Anaheim (92801) *(P-1096)*
Bridlewood Winery ..... E 805 688-9000
3555 Roblar Ave Santa Ynez (93460) *(P-1667)*
Brief Relief, Oceanside *Also called American Innotek Inc (P-9941)*
Briggs & Sons ..... F 707 938-4325
1225 E Macarthur St Sonoma (95476) *(P-5041)*
Bright Business Media LLC ..... F 415 339-9355
475 Gate 5 Rd Ste 235 Sausalito (94965) *(P-6117)*
Bright Glow Candle Company Inc (PA) ..... E 909 469-0119
110 Erie St Pomona (91768) *(P-24052)*
Bright Horizons At Gilead ..... E 650 312-1895
301 Velocity Way Foster City (94404) *(P-8086)*
Bright Lights Candle Company, Lower Lake *Also called Aloha Bay (P-24032)*
Bright Lite Structures LLC ..... F 636 575-7559
90 S Park St San Francisco (94107) *(P-10891)*
Bright People Foods Inc (PA) ..... E 530 669-6870
1640 Tide Ct Woodland (95776) *(P-2472)*
Bright Shark Powder Coating ..... F 909 591-1385
4530 Schaefer Ave Chino (91710) *(P-13561)*
Brightidea Incorporated ..... E 415 814-1387
255 California St # 1100 San Francisco (94111) *(P-24452)*
Brightlight Welding & Mfg Inc ..... E 408 988-0418
3395a Edward Ave Santa Clara (95054) *(P-25388)*
Brighton Collectibles LLC ..... E 925 932-1500
1195 Broadway Plz Walnut Creek (94596) *(P-3645)*
Brighton Collectibles LLC ..... F 650 838-0086
180 El Camino Real Millbrae (94030) *(P-10543)*
Brighton Collectibles LLC ..... E 626 961-9381
10250 Santa Monica Blvd Los Angeles (90067) *(P-3627)*
Brightscope, San Diego *Also called Strategic Insights Inc (P-25227)*
Brightsign LLC ..... D 408 852-9263
983 University Ave Bldg A Los Gatos (95032) *(P-23834)*
Brightwater Medical Inc ..... F 951 290-3410
42580 Rio Nedo Temecula (92590) *(P-22383)*
Briles Aerospace Inc ..... F 310 701-2087
1559 W 135th St Gardena (90249) *(P-13061)*
Brilliant Home Technology Inc ..... F 650 539-5320
241a S San Mateo Dr San Mateo (94401) *(P-17131)*
Brilliant Instruments Inc ..... F 408 866-0426
1622 W Campbell Ave 107 Campbell (95008) *(P-21554)*
Brilliant Solutions, Irvine *Also called Meguiars Inc (P-8655)*
Brilliant Worldwide Inc ..... E 650 468-2966
15 Butte Pl San Francisco (94103) *(P-24453)*
Brion Technologies Inc ..... F 408 653-1500
399 W Trimble Rd San Jose (95131) *(P-18751)*
Bristol - Myers Sqibb Snnyvale ..... F 609 897-2110
700 Bay Rd Redwood City (94063) *(P-8087)*
Bristol Omega Inc ..... E 909 794-6862
9441 Opal Ave Ste 2 Mentone (92359) *(P-5042)*
Bristol Sounds Elec Whse, Santa Ana *Also called Bristol Sounds Electronics (P-17779)*
Bristol Sounds Electronics ..... F 714 549-5923
2604 S Bristol St Santa Ana (92704) *(P-17779)*
Bristolite, Santa Ana *Also called Sundown Liquidating Corp (P-10608)*
Britcan Inc ..... E 760 722-2300
3809 Ocean Ranch Blvd # 110 Oceanside (92056) *(P-5128)*
Brite Lite Enterprises ..... F 310 363-7120
11661 San Vicente Blvd Los Angeles (90049) *(P-17780)*
Brite Plating Co Inc ..... D 323 263-7593
1313 Mirasol St Los Angeles (90023) *(P-13353)*
Brite Vue Div, Visalia *Also called Kawneer Company Inc (P-12870)*
Brite-Lite Neon Corp ..... F 818 763-4798
5514 Satsuma Ave North Hollywood (91601) *(P-23835)*
Britelab ..... D 650 961-0671
6341 San Ignacio Ave San Jose (95119) *(P-21681)*
British American Tl & Die LLC ..... C 714 776-8995
2273 E Via Burton Anaheim (92806) *(P-11886)*
Britz Fertilizers Inc ..... E 559 582-0942
12498 11th Ave Hanford (93230) *(P-14048)*
Brix Beverage, Alameda *Also called Pacific Automated LLC (P-2162)*
Brixen & Sons Inc ..... E 714 566-1444
2100 S Fairview St Santa Ana (92704) *(P-7258)*
Brk Group LLC ..... E 562 949-4394
8357 Loch Lomond Dr Pico Rivera (90660) *(P-2992)*
BRM MANUFACTURING, Los Angeles *Also called Brush Research Mfg Co (P-23787)*
Broach Masters Inc ..... E 530 885-1939
1605 Industrial Dr Auburn (95603) *(P-14610)*
Broadata Communications Inc ..... F 310 530-1416
2545 W 237th St Ste K Torrance (90505) *(P-11648)*
Broadcast Microwave Services (PA) ..... C 858 391-3050
12305 Crosthwaite Cir Poway (92064) *(P-18056)*
Broadcom, San Jose *Also called LSI Corporation (P-18968)*
Broadcom, Santa Clara *Also called Netlogic Microsystems LLC (P-19039)*
Broadcom Corporation ..... E 408 922-7000
250 Innovation Dr San Jose (95134) *(P-18752)*
Broadcom Corporation (HQ) ..... B 408 433-8000
1320 Ridder Park Dr San Jose (95131) *(P-18753)*
Broadcom Corporation ..... E 408 501-8200
250 Innovation Dr San Jose (95134) *(P-18754)*
Broadcom Corporation ..... A 858 385-8800
16340 W Bernardo Dr A San Diego (92127) *(P-18755)*
Broadcom Limited, San Jose *Also called Broadcom Corporation (P-18753)*
Broadley-James-Corporation ..... D 949 829-5555
19 Thomas Irvine (92618) *(P-21555)*
Broadlight Inc (HQ) ..... F 408 982-4210
2901 Tasman Dr Ste 218 Santa Clara (95054) *(P-18756)*
Broadly Inc ..... E 510 400-6039
1500 Broadway Ste 200 Oakland (94612) *(P-24454)*
Broadvision Inc (PA) ..... D 650 331-1000
460 Seaport Ct Ste 102 Redwood City (94063) *(P-24455)*
Broadvision Rcao Broadvisi ..... F 650 261-5100
585 Broadway St Redwood City (94063) *(P-6452)*
Broadway AC Htg & Shtmtl ..... E 310 829-3416
7855 Burnet Ave Santa Monica (90404) *(P-12511)*
Broadway Babe, San Dimas *Also called Babe Hollywood Inc (P-3573)*
Broadway Knitting Mills Corp ..... E 559 456-0955
1766 N Helm Ave Ste 101 Fresno (93727) *(P-2825)*
Broadway Pl, Los Angeles *Also called Promises Promises Inc (P-3335)*
Broadway Sheet Metal, Santa Monica *Also called Broadway AC Htg & Shtmtl (P-12511)*
Broan-Nutone LLC ..... C 262 673-8795
622 Emery Rd Tecate (91980) *(P-12059)*
Brocade Cmmnctions Systems LLC ..... F 408 333-8000
120 Holger Way San Jose (95134) *(P-15691)*
Brocade Cmmnctions Systems LLC (HQ) ..... A 408 333-8000
130 Holger Way San Jose (95134) *(P-15692)*
Brocade It, San Jose *Also called Brocade Cmmnctions Systems LLC (P-15691)*
Brochure Holders 4u, Santa Ana *Also called Clear-Ad Inc (P-10027)*
Brocks Trailers Inc ..... E 661 363-5038
6901 E Brundage Ln Bakersfield (93307) *(P-14049)*
Brodhead Grating Products LLC ..... F 562 598-4314
3651 Sausalito St Los Alamitos (90720) *(P-12839)*
Brodhead Steel Products Co (PA) ..... E 650 871-8251
7550 Alpine Rd La Honda (94020) *(P-12840)*
Broken Earth Winery ..... F 805 239-2562
5625 E Highway 46 Paso Robles (93446) *(P-1668)*
Broken Token ..... F 760 294-1923
541 N Quince St Ste 1 Escondido (92025) *(P-23413)*
Bromack, Los Angeles *Also called LA Cabinet & Millwork Inc (P-5078)*
Bromwell Company (PA) ..... F 800 683-2626
8605 Santa Monica Blvd Los Angeles (90069) *(P-10811)*
Broncs Inc ..... C 310 637-9100
12691 Pala Dr Ste A Garden Grove (92841) *(P-2726)*
Bronze-Way Plating Corporation (PA) ..... E 323 266-6933
3301 E 14th St Los Angeles (90023) *(P-13354)*
Bronze-Way Powder Coating Inc ..... D 323 265-7024
3301 E 14th St Los Angeles (90023) *(P-16332)*
Brookhurst Mill ..... F 951 688-3511
3315 Van Buren Blvd Riverside (92503) *(P-1124)*
Brooks Automation Inc ..... D 510 498-8745
46702 Bayside Pkwy Fremont (94538) *(P-15942)*
Brooks Automation Inc ..... F 858 527-7000
13915 Danielson St # 103 Poway (92064) *(P-14925)*
Brooks Millwork Company ..... F 562 920-3000
17308 1/2 Woodruff Ave Bellflower (90706) *(P-4112)*
Brooks Polycold Systems, Fremont *Also called Brooks Automation Inc (P-15942)*
Brooks Products, Ontario *Also called Heitman Brooks II LLC (P-10936)*
Brooks Street Baking Company, Montclair *Also called Brooks Street Companies (P-1214)*
Brooks Street Companies ..... C 909 983-6090
5560 Brooks St Montclair (91763) *(P-1214)*

ALPHABETIC

Brookshire Innovations LLC ....E.......916 786-7601
502 Giuseppe Ct Ste 7 Roseville (95678) *(P-21093)*
Brookshire Tool & Mfg Co Inc ....F.......562 861-2567
10654 Garfield Ave South Gate (90280) *(P-16333)*
Brothers Enterprises Inc ....F.......619 229-8003
7380 Mission Gorge Rd San Diego (92120) *(P-25389)*
Brothers Intl Desserts ....C.......949 655-0080
2727 S Susan St Santa Ana (92704) *(P-660)*
Brothers Machine & Tool Inc ....E.......951 361-9454
11095 Inland Ave Jurupa Valley (91752) *(P-14432)*
Brothers Machine & Tool Inc (PA) ....F.......951 361-2909
11098 Inland Ave Jurupa Valley (91752) *(P-14433)*
Brothers Optical Laboratory ....D.......714 639-9852
870 N Eckhoff St Orange (92868) *(P-23082)*
Brown & Honeycutt Truss Systms ....E.......760 244-8887
16775 Smoke Tree St Hesperia (92345) *(P-4393)*
Brown Bag Sandwich Company LLC ....C.......714 444-2126
111 E Garry Ave Santa Ana (92707) *(P-2473)*
Brown Estate Vineyard LLC ....F.......707 963-2435
3233 Sage Canyon Rd Saint Helena (94574) *(P-1669)*
Brown Sand Inc ....E.......209 234-1500
800 Mossdale Rd Lathrop (95330) *(P-347)*
Brown Wood Products Inc ....E.......650 593-9875
310 Devonshire Blvd San Carlos (94070) *(P-4518)*
Brown-Pacific Inc ....E.......562 921-3471
13639 Bora Dr Santa Fe Springs (90670) *(P-11381)*
Brownie Baker Inc ....D.......559 277-7070
4870 W Jacquelyn Ave Fresno (93722) *(P-1358)*
Browntrout Publishers Inc ....F.......707 451-8593
4977 Allison Pkwy Ste C Vacaville (95688) *(P-6453)*
Browntrout Publishers Inc (PA) ....E.......424 290-6122
201 Continental Blvd # 200 El Segundo (90245) *(P-6454)*
Bruce Eicher Inc (PA) ....F.......310 657-4630
8755 Melrose Ave Los Angeles (90069) *(P-17531)*
Bruce Iversen ....E.......310 537-4168
439 E Carlin Ave Compton (90222) *(P-4456)*
Bruce Parker ....F.......714 970-2307
5323 Lupine St Yorba Linda (92886) *(P-6706)*
Bruce's Custom Covers, Morgan Hill *Also called Aircraft Covers Inc (P-2717)*
Bruck Braid Company ....E.......213 627-7611
1200 S Santa Fe Ave Los Angeles (90021) *(P-3879)*
Bruder Industry ....D.......916 939-6888
3920 Sandstone Dr El Dorado Hills (95762) *(P-16334)*
Bruker Biosciences Cad, San Jose *Also called Bruker Biospin Corporation (P-21929)*
Bruker Biospin Corporation ....E.......510 683-4300
61 Daggett Dr San Jose (95134) *(P-21929)*
Bruker Corporation ....E.......408 376-4040
1717 Dell Ave Campbell (95008) *(P-15693)*
Brunette Printing, Los Angeles *Also called Brunettes Printing Service (P-6707)*
Brunettes Printing Service ....F.......213 749-7441
742 E Washington Blvd Los Angeles (90021) *(P-6707)*
Brunton Enterprises Inc ....C.......562 945-0013
8815 Sorensen Ave Santa Fe Springs (90670) *(P-12121)*
Brush Dance Inc ....F.......415 491-4950
165 N Redwood Dr Ste 200 San Rafael (94903) *(P-5701)*
Brush Research Mfg Co ....C.......323 261-2193
4642 Floral Dr Los Angeles (90022) *(P-23787)*
Brush Wellman, Fremont *Also called Materion Brush Inc (P-13870)*
Brushy Peak Winery, Livermore *Also called Cedar Mountain Winery Inc (P-1683)*
Brutocao Cellars (PA) ....F.......707 744-1066
1400 Highway 175 Hopland (95449) *(P-1670)*
Bruvado Imports, Pleasanton *Also called Blanco Basura Beverage Inc (P-1571)*
Bryan Edwards Publishing Co ....F.......714 634-0264
2185 N Orange Olive Rd # 3 Orange (92865) *(P-6319)*
Bryan Press Inc ....F.......626 961-9257
1011 S Stimson Ave City of Industry (91745) *(P-6708)*
Bryant Rubber Corp (PA) ....E.......310 530-2530
1112 Lomita Blvd Harbor City (90710) *(P-9520)*
Bryant Rubber Corp ....D.......310 530-2530
1083 W 251st St Bellflower (90706) *(P-9521)*
Bryngelson Prints, Redlands *Also called Duden Enterprises Inc (P-3842)*
Bsh Home Appliances Corp ....E.......949 440-7100
1901 Main St Ste 600 Irvine (92614) *(P-10812)*
Bsh Home Appliances Corp (HQ) ....C.......949 440-7100
1901 Main St Ste 600 Irvine (92614) *(P-17412)*
Bsnap LLC ....F.......657 269-4410
4 Hutton Centre Dr Fl 10 Santa Ana (92707) *(P-24456)*
Bsr, Berkeley *Also called Assoc Students University CA (P-6436)*
Bsst LLC ....F.......626 593-4500
5462 Irwindale Ave Ste A Irwindale (91706) *(P-20274)*
BT Screw Products, Los Angeles *Also called Crellin Machine Company (P-13019)*
BT Sheet Metal Inc ....F.......949 481-5715
1031 Calle Trepadora D San Clemente (92673) *(P-12512)*
Bti Aerospace & Electronics ....E.......909 465-1569
13546 Vintage Pl Chino (91710) *(P-16335)*
Btl Machine, Corona *Also called Acromil LLC (P-16218)*
Btm-Beartech Manufacturing ....F.......714 550-1700
910 S Placentia Ave Ste A Placentia (92870) *(P-13017)*
Btm-Beartech Manufacturing LLC, Placentia *Also called Btm-Beartech Manufacturing (P-13017)*
Btrade LLC ....E.......818 334-4433
655 N Central Ave # 1460 Glendale (91203) *(P-24457)*
Bu LLC ....F.......951 277-7470
9073 Pulsar Ct Ste A Corona (92883) *(P-1575)*
Bubblegum USA, Los Angeles *Also called Komex International Inc (P-3250)*
Bucate Plata Importing Co, Oakland *Also called Brand X Hurarches (P-10480)*
Buchanans Spoke & Rim ....E.......626 969-4655
805 W 8th St Azusa (91702) *(P-21094)*
Buchbinder, Jay Industries, Compton *Also called Jbi LLC (P-4833)*
Bucy Die Casting ....F.......818 843-5044
633 S Glenwood Pl Burbank (91506) *(P-14487)*
Bud Wil Inc ....E.......714 630-1242
1170 N Red Gum St Anaheim (92806) *(P-9822)*
Buddha Teas, Carlsbad *Also called Living Wellness Partners LLC (P-2587)*
Buddy Bar Casting Corporation ....D.......562 861-9664
10801 Sessler St South Gate (90280) *(P-11726)*
Buddy Homes 355, Woodland *Also called Skyline Homes Inc (P-4564)*
Budget Enterprises Inc ....E.......949 697-9544
9301 Research Dr Irvine (92618) *(P-10587)*
Buds Cotton Inc ....E.......714 223-7800
1240 N Fee Ana St Anaheim (92807) *(P-8710)*
Buds Polishing & Metal Finshg ....F.......714 632-0121
1156 N Kraemer Pl Anaheim (92806) *(P-13355)*
Buellton Advanced Materials, Buellton *Also called Lockheed Martin Corporation (P-21324)*
Buena Park Anaheim Independent ....E.......714 952-8505
9551 Valley View St Cypress (90630) *(P-5781)*
Buena Park Tool & Engineering ....F.......714 843-6215
7661 Windfield Dr Huntington Beach (92647) *(P-16336)*
Buff and Shine Mfg Inc ....E.......310 886-5111
2139 E Del Amo Blvd Rancho Dominguez (90220) *(P-11289)*
Buffalo Bills Brewery, Hayward *Also called Steinbeck Brewing Company (P-1626)*
Buffalo Distribution Inc ....E.......510 324-3800
30750 San Clemente St Hayward (94544) *(P-17132)*
Build At Home LLC ....F.......909 949-1601
273 N Benson Ave Upland (91786) *(P-23530)*
Build Your Own Garment, Dublin *Also called Print Ink Inc (P-3185)*
Build-In C & C, Hollister *Also called C & C Built-In Inc (P-4278)*
Builder & Developer Magazines ....F.......949 631-0308
1602 Monrovia Ave Newport Beach (92663) *(P-6118)*
Builders Concrete Inc (HQ) ....E.......559 225-3667
3664 W Ashlan Ave Fresno (93722) *(P-11052)*
Builders Drapery Service Inc ....E.......408 263-3300
1494 Gladding Ct Milpitas (95035) *(P-2727)*
Building Components ....F.......310 274-6516
3148 Abington Dr Beverly Hills (90210) *(P-9993)*
Building Robotics Inc ....F.......510 761-6482
300 Frank H Oakland (94612) *(P-24458)*
Buildit Engineering Co Inc ....F.......818 244-6666
3074 N Lima St Burbank (91504) *(P-11583)*
Buildmat Plus Investments Inc ....F.......909 823-7663
15435 Arrow Blvd Bldg A Fontana (92335) *(P-10892)*
Buisness Leader Media ....E.......510 665-9600
2907 Claremont Ave # 220 Berkeley (94705) *(P-6119)*
Bulb Star, Alhambra *Also called K Live (P-18940)*
Buldoor LLC ....F.......877 388-1366
647 Camino De Los San Clemente (92673) *(P-11939)*
Bull Hn Info Systems Inc ....E.......310 337-3600
6077 Bristol Pkwy Culver City (90230) *(P-15397)*
Bulldog Reporter ....F.......510 596-9300
124 Linden St Oakland (94607) *(P-5782)*
Bullet Guard Corporation ....F.......800 233-5632
3963 Commerce Dr West Sacramento (95691) *(P-13925)*
Bulletproof Brands Co Inc ....F.......916 635-3718
1704 Halifax Way El Dorado Hills (95762) *(P-2103)*
Bullfrog Printing and Graphics ....F.......714 641-0220
1261 S Wright St Santa Ana (92705) *(P-6709)*
Bulls-Eye Marketing Inc ....F.......707 745-5278
6610 Goodyear Rd Benicia (94510) *(P-20275)*
Bullseye, Lancaster *Also called Aerotech News and Review Inc (P-6098)*
Bullseye Leak Detection Inc ....F.......916 760-8944
4015 Seaport Blvd West Sacramento (95691) *(P-16337)*
Bullzeye Mfg ....F.......209 482-5626
13625 Clements Rd Lodi (95240) *(P-11432)*
Bulthaup Corp ....F.......310 288-3875
153 S Robertson Blvd Los Angeles (90048) *(P-4827)*
Bumble Bee, San Diego *Also called Bumble Bee Foods LLC (P-2290)*
Bumble Bee Capital Corp ....C.......858 715-4000
280 10th Ave San Diego (92101) *(P-2289)*
Bumble Bee Foods LLC (HQ) ....B.......858 715-4000
280 10th Ave San Diego (92101) *(P-2290)*
Bumble Bee Holdings Inc (HQ) ....B.......858 715-4000
280 10th Ave San Diego (92101) *(P-469)*
Bumble Bee Plastics Inc ....F.......562 903-0833
10140 Shoemaker Ave Santa Fe Springs (90670) *(P-9994)*
Bumble Bee Seafoods LP ....D.......858 715-4000
280 10th Ave San Diego (92101) *(P-2291)*
Bumble Bee Seafoods Inc ....E.......858 715-4000
280 10th Ave San Diego (92101) *(P-2292)*
Bumble Bee Seafoods Inc ....A.......858 715-4068
280 10th Ave San Diego (92101) *(P-2293)*
Bumble Bee Seafoods LLC ....E.......562 483-7474
13100 Arctic Cir Santa Fe Springs (90670) *(P-2294)*
Bumbleride Inc ....F.......619 615-0475
2245 Kettner Blvd San Diego (92101) *(P-23414)*
Bumjin America Inc (PA) ....F.......619 671-0386
2177 Britannia Blvd # 204 San Diego (92154) *(P-9995)*
Bundy and Sons Inc ....E.......530 246-3868
15196 Mountain Shadows Dr Redding (96001) *(P-3981)*
Bundy Manufacturing Inc ....E.......323 772-3273
507 S Douglas St El Segundo (90245) *(P-16338)*
Bunge Milling Inc ....C.......530 666-1691
845 Kentucky Ave Woodland (95695) *(P-1034)*
Bunge North America, Modesto *Also called Bunge Oils Inc (P-1515)*
Bunge North America Inc ....D.......530 666-1691
845 Kentucky Ave Woodland (95695) *(P-1074)*
Bunge Oils Inc ....D.......209 574-9981
436 S Mcclure Rd Modesto (95357) *(P-1515)*

Bunker Corp (PA) D 949 361-3935
1131 Via Callejon San Clemente (92673) ***(P-20276)***
Bunkerhill Indus Group Inc F 323 227-4222
4535 Huntington Dr S Los Angeles (90032) ***(P-3096)***
Burbank Plating Service Corp F 818 899-1157
13561 Desmond St Pacoima (91331) ***(P-13356)***
Burbank Steel Treating Inc E 818 842-0975
415 S Varney St Burbank (91502) ***(P-11803)***
Burgess Cellars Inc F 707 963-4766
1108 Deer Park Rd Saint Helena (94574) ***(P-1671)***
Burke Display Systems Inc E 949 248-0091
55 S Peak Laguna Niguel (92677) ***(P-5129)***
Burke Industries Inc (HQ) C 408 297-3500
2250 S 10th St San Jose (95112) ***(P-9596)***
Burke Industries Inc C 408 297-3500
2250 S 10th St San Jose (95112) ***(P-9402)***
Burke Je Construction F 661 745-4890
120 E Center St Taft (93268) ***(P-187)***
Burkert Contromatic Corp (PA) F 949 251-1224
2572 White Rd Irvine (92614) ***(P-13708)***
Burkert Contromatic Corp C 949 223-3100
2572 White Rd Irvine (92614) ***(P-13709)***
Burkert Fluid Control Systems, Irvine *Also called Burkert Contromatic Corp* ***(P-13708)***
Burkert Fluid Control Systems, Irvine *Also called Burkert Contromatic Corp* ***(P-13709)***
Burlingame Htg Ventilation Inc F 650 697-9142
821 Malcolm Rd Burlingame (94010) ***(P-12513)***
Burlingame Industries Inc C 909 355-7000
2352 N Locust Ave Rialto (92377) ***(P-11350)***
Burlington Engineering Inc E 714 921-4045
220 W Grove Ave Orange (92865) ***(P-13357)***
Burman Cabinet Corporation E 408 377-6652
864 S Mcglincy Ln B Campbell (95008) ***(P-4277)***
Burner App, Los Angeles *Also called Ad Hoc Labs Inc* ***(P-24317)***
Burnet Machining Inc F 805 964-6321
330 S Kellogg Ave Ste N Goleta (93117) ***(P-16339)***
Burnett & Son Meat Co Inc D 626 357-2165
1420 S Myrtle Ave Monrovia (91016) ***(P-421)***
Burning Torch Inc E 323 733-7700
1738 Cordova St Los Angeles (90007) ***(P-3387)***
Burns Stainless LLC F 949 631-5120
1041 W 18th St Ste B104 Costa Mesa (92627) ***(P-20277)***
Burton Ching Ltd F 415 522-5520
432 N Canal St Ste 5 South San Francisco (94080) ***(P-3712)***
Burton James Inc D 626 961-7221
428 Turnbull Canyon Rd City of Industry (91745) ***(P-4761)***
Burtree Inc E 818 786-4276
13513 Sherman Way Van Nuys (91405) ***(P-16340)***
Bus Services Corporation E 562 231-1770
6801 Suva St Bell Gardens (90201) ***(P-20278)***
Bush Polishing & Chrome F 714 537-7440
2236 W 2nd St Santa Ana (92703) ***(P-13358)***
Bushman Products, Torrance *Also called Momentum Management LLC* ***(P-9642)***
Bushnell Industries Inc F 559 651-9039
7449 Avenue 304 Visalia (93291) ***(P-8628)***
Bushnell Ribbon Corporation D 562 948-1410
300 W Brookdale Pl Fullerton (92832) ***(P-23725)***
Business Extension Bureau E 650 737-5700
500 S Airport Blvd South San Francisco (94080) ***(P-6120)***
Business Journal E 559 490-3400
1315 Van Ness Ave Ste 200 Fresno (93721) ***(P-6121)***
Business Jrnl Publications Inc E 408 295-3800
125 S Market St 11 San Jose (95113) ***(P-5783)***
Business Jrnl Publications Inc E 415 989-2522
275 Battery St Ste 600 San Francisco (94111) ***(P-5784)***
Business Point Impressions, Concord *Also called Hnc Printing Services LLC* ***(P-6860)***
Business Printing and Copies F 916 920-1412
1565 River Park Dr Ste A Sacramento (95815) ***(P-6710)***
Business With Pleasure F 831 430-9711
1 Victor Sq Scotts Valley (95066) ***(P-6711)***
Busseto Foods Inc D 559 237-9591
1090 W Church Ave Fresno (93706) ***(P-470)***
Busseto Foods Inc (PA) C 559 485-9882
1351 N Crystal Ave Fresno (93728) ***(P-471)***
Butane Propane News Inc F 626 357-2168
338 E Foothill Blvd Arcadia (91006) ***(P-6122)***
Butler Home Products LLC F 909 476-3884
9409 Buffalo Ave Rancho Cucamonga (91730) ***(P-23788)***
Butler Inc F 310 323-3114
1600 W 166th St Gardena (90247) ***(P-13062)***
Butler Manufacturing, Visalia *Also called Bluescope Buildings N Amer Inc* ***(P-12921)***
Butte Sand and Gravel E 530 755-0225
10373 S Butte Rd Sutter (95982) ***(P-348)***
Buttonwood Farm Winery Inc F 805 688-3032
1500 Alamo Pintado Rd Solvang (93463) ***(P-1672)***
Buy and Sell Press Inc F 209 223-3333
605 Broadway Jackson (95642) ***(P-6455)***
Buy Insta Slim Inc F 949 263-2301
17662 Armstrong Ave Irvine (92614) ***(P-3097)***
Buzz Converting Inc F 209 948-1341
4343 E Fremont St Stockton (95215) ***(P-5341)***
Buzzworks Inc F 415 863-5964
365 11th St San Francisco (94103) ***(P-1576)***
BV WILMS, Indio *Also called M F G Eurotec Inc* ***(P-4716)***
Bvp Designs Inc F 818 280-2900
21354 Nordhoff St Ste 101 Chatsworth (91311) ***(P-15919)***
BVT Publishing, Redding *Also called Best Value Textbooks LLC* ***(P-6313)***
Bway Corporation E 951 361-4100
11440 Pacific Ave Fontana (92337) ***(P-11858)***
Bwm, Modesto *Also called Billington Welding & Mfg Inc* ***(P-14837)***

Byd Motors LLC (HQ) E 213 748-3980
1800 S Figueroa St Los Angeles (90015) ***(P-20279)***
Byer California (PA) A 415 626-7844
66 Potrero Ave San Francisco (94103) ***(P-3221)***
Byer California D 925 245-0184
3740 Livermore Outlets Dr Livermore (94551) ***(P-3222)***
Byer California B 323 780-7615
1201 Rio Vista Ave Los Angeles (90023) ***(P-2826)***
Byington Steel Treating Inc (PA) E 408 727-6630
1225 Memorex Dr Santa Clara (95050) ***(P-11804)***
Byran Company Inc D 714 841-9808
18092 Redondo Cir Huntington Beach (92648) ***(P-16341)***
Byrnes & Kiefer Co D 714 554-4000
501 Airpark Dr Fullerton (92833) ***(P-2248)***
Byrum Technologies Inc E 760 744-6692
550 S Pacific St Ste 100 San Marcos (92078) ***(P-19921)***
C & A Transducers Inc E 714 554-9188
14329 Commerce Dr Garden Grove (92843) ***(P-19471)***
C & C Built-In Inc E 831 635-5880
2000 Lana Way Hollister (95023) ***(P-4278)***
C & C Die Engraving F 562 944-3399
12510 Mccann Dr Santa Fe Springs (90670) ***(P-16342)***
C & C Signs, Long Beach *Also called Canzone and Company* ***(P-23839)***
C & D Aerospace, Garden Grove *Also called C&D Zodiac Inc* ***(P-20768)***
C & D Precision Components F 626 799-7109
969 S Raymond Ave Pasadena (91105) ***(P-16343)***
C & D Prescision Machining Inc E 408 383-1888
2031 Concourse Dr San Jose (95131) ***(P-16344)***
C & D Semiconductor Svcs Inc (PA) E 408 383-1888
2031 Concourse Dr San Jose (95131) ***(P-18757)***
C & F Foods Inc (PA) D 626 723-1000
15620 E Valley Blvd City of Industry (91744) ***(P-2474)***
C & G Mercury Plastics, Sylmar *Also called C & G Plastics* ***(P-9996)***
C & G Plastics E 818 837-3773
12729 Foothill Blvd Sylmar (91342) ***(P-9996)***
C & Gtool Inc F 916 614-9114
910 Striker Ave Ste B Sacramento (95834) ***(P-14611)***
C & H Enterprises, Fremont *Also called Colleen & Herb Enterprises Inc* ***(P-16394)***
C & H Hydraulics Inc F 949 646-6230
1585 Monrovia Ave Newport Beach (92663) ***(P-20762)***
C & H Letterpress Inc F 714 438-1350
3400 W Castor St Santa Ana (92704) ***(P-7259)***
C & H Machine Inc D 760 746-6459
943 S Andrsen Dr Escndido Escondido Escondido (92029) ***(P-16154)***
C & H Metal Products, Ontario *Also called Daaze Inc* ***(P-12548)***
C & H Molding Incorporated E 951 361-5030
11160 Thurston Ln Mira Loma (91752) ***(P-14488)***
C & H Testing Service Inc (PA) E 661 589-4030
6224 Price Way Bakersfield (93308) ***(P-188)***
C & J Industries, Santa Fe Springs *Also called Custom Steel Fabrication Inc* ***(P-12147)***
C & J Metal Prducts, Paramount *Also called Jeffrey Fabrication LLC* ***(P-12630)***
C & J Metal Products Inc E 562 634-3101
6323 Alondra Blvd Paramount (90723) ***(P-12514)***
C & L Tool and Die Inc F 619 270-8385
8684 Avenida De La Fuente # 12 San Diego (92154) ***(P-14489)***
C & M Manufacturing Company E 619 449-7200
9640 Mission Gorge Rd B Santee (92071) ***(P-9738)***
C & M Spring & Engineering Co E 909 597-2030
5244 Las Flores Dr Chino (91710) ***(P-13791)***
C & M Wood Industries C 760 949-3292
17229 Lemon St Ste D Hesperia (92345) ***(P-5183)***
C & R Extrusions Inc F 626 642-0244
2618 River Ave Rosemead (91770) ***(P-9700)***
C & R Mfg, Colton *Also called C & R Pier Mfg* ***(P-12122)***
C & R Molds Inc E 805 658-7098
2737 Palma Dr Ventura (93003) ***(P-9997)***
C & R Pier Mfg (PA) E 909 872-6444
275 S Rancho Ave Colton (92324) ***(P-12122)***
C & S Assembly Inc F 866 779-8939
1150 N Armando St Anaheim (92806) ***(P-19472)***
C & S Plastics F 818 896-2489
12621 Foothill Blvd Sylmar (91342) ***(P-9998)***
C & S Products CA Inc (PA) F 909 218-8971
1345 S Parkside Pl Ontario (91761) ***(P-8629)***
C & Y Investment Inc F 323 267-9000
946 E 29th St Los Angeles (90011) ***(P-3388)***
C A Botana International Inc (PA) E 858 450-1717
9365 Waples St Ste A San Diego (92121) ***(P-8711)***
C A Buchen Corp E 818 767-5408
9231 Glenoaks Blvd Sun Valley (91352) ***(P-12123)***
C A E, Azusa *Also called Casella Aluminum Extrusions* ***(P-11584)***
C A N Enterprises D 925 939-9736
291 Kinross Dr Walnut Creek (94598) ***(P-2827)***
C A P S, Santa Fe Springs *Also called Central Admxture Phrm Svcs Inc* ***(P-8108)***
C A Schroeder Inc (PA) E 818 365-9561
1318 1st St San Fernando (91340) ***(P-11329)***
C and R Pavers, Escondido *Also called Regina F Barajas* ***(P-14187)***
C and R Sales Inc F 951 686-6864
3750 S Riverside Ave Colton (92324) ***(P-12124)***
C and T Machining, Palmdale *Also called Sharkey Technology Group Inc* ***(P-16941)***
C B Concrete Construction F 408 354-3484
641 University Ave Los Gatos (95032) ***(P-11053)***
C B G, Los Angeles *Also called Gory Electric Motors Inc* ***(P-25462)***
C B Machine Products Inc F 909 517-1828
13735 Iroquois Pl Chino (91710) ***(P-16345)***
C B S, San Marcos *Also called Falmat Inc* ***(P-11660)***
C B S Fasteners Inc E 714 779-6368
1345 N Brasher St Anaheim (92807) ***(P-13063)***

C B Sheets Inc ...... E 562 921-1223
13901 Carmenita Rd Santa Fe Springs (90670) *(P-5342)*

C Brewer Company, Ontario Also called Balda C Brewer Inc *(P-9969)*

C C I, Orange Also called Coastal Component Inds Inc *(P-19495)*

C C I Mling-Shipping Eqp Suppl, Ventura Also called CCI Mail & Shipping Systems *(P-5133)*

C C M D Inc ...... F 310 673-5532
700 Centinela Ave Inglewood (90302) *(P-13359)*

C C Products ...... F 408 295-0205
1990 W San Carlos St San Jose (95128) *(P-21095)*

C C T C North America, Monterey Also called China Circuit Tech Corp N Amer *(P-18447)*

C C T Laser Services Inc ...... F 209 833-1110
25421 S Schulte Rd Tracy (95377) *(P-19922)*

C Case Company Inc ...... E 559 867-3912
7010 W Cerini Ave Riverdale (93656) *(P-189)*

C D International Tech Inc ...... F 408 986-0725
695 Pinnacle Pl Livermore (94550) *(P-19473)*

C D S, Canyon Country Also called Commercial Display Systems LLC *(P-15945)*

C D Video, Santa Ana Also called CD Video Manufacturing Inc *(P-19858)*

C E I, Oakhurst Also called Control Enterprises Inc *(P-13737)*

C Enterprises LP ...... D 760 599-5111
2445 Cades Way Vista (92081) *(P-15694)*

C F Manufacturing ...... F 818 504-9899
11867 Sheldon St Sun Valley (91352) *(P-20280)*

C F W Research & Dev Co ...... F 805 489-8750
338 S 4th St Grover Beach (93433) *(P-11572)*

C Gonshor Fine Jewelry Inc ...... F 213 629-1075
640 S Hill St Ste 546a Los Angeles (90014) *(P-23247)*

C H K Manufacturing Inc ...... E 510 632-5637
960 98th Ave Oakland (94603) *(P-5588)*

C J Precision Industries Inc ...... F 562 426-3708
2817 Cherry Ave Signal Hill (90755) *(P-16346)*

C K Tool Company Inc ...... F 650 968-0261
1033 Wright Ave Mountain View (94043) *(P-16347)*

C L E, Downey Also called Can Lines Engineering Inc *(P-15201)*

C L Hann Industries Inc ...... F 408 293-4800
1020 Timothy Dr San Jose (95133) *(P-16348)*

C L P Inc (PA) ...... E 619 444-3105
1546 E Main St El Cajon (92021) *(P-25390)*

C M Automotive Systems Inc (PA) ...... E 909 869-7912
120 Commerce Way Walnut (91789) *(P-15120)*

C M C, Ontario Also called California Mfg Cabinetry Inc *(P-5044)*

C M C, Fremont Also called Content Management Corporation *(P-7284)*

C M Common Ground Inc ...... F 949 646-9468
888 Production Pl Newport Beach (92663) *(P-17133)*

C M D Products, Lincoln Also called Cmd Products *(P-9827)*

C M H Records Inc ...... E 323 663-8098
2898 Rowena Ave Ste 201 Los Angeles (90039) *(P-17887)*

C M I, Corona Also called Corona Magnetics Inc *(P-19329)*

C M Machine Inc ...... E 951 654-6019
560 S Grand Ave San Jacinto (92582) *(P-16349)*

C M P, San Leandro Also called Peggy S Lane Inc *(P-9910)*

C M Sport, Walnut Creek Also called C A N Enterprises *(P-2827)*

C Magazine, Santa Monica Also called C Publishing LLC *(P-6456)*

C Mondavi & Family (PA) ...... D 707 967-2200
2800 Main St Saint Helena (94574) *(P-1673)*

C N C, San Diego Also called Howco Inc *(P-20365)*

C N C Engineering Inc ...... F 951 674-7486
518 N Riley St Lake Elsinore (92530) *(P-16350)*

C N C Machining Inc ...... F 805 681-8855
510 S Fairview Ave Goleta (93117) *(P-16351)*

C N P Signs & Graphics, San Diego Also called California Neon Products *(P-23837)*

C NC Noodle Co ...... F 510 732-1318
1787 Sabre St Hayward (94545) *(P-2425)*

C P Auto Products Inc ...... E 323 266-3850
3901 Medford St Los Angeles (90063) *(P-13360)*

C P Films Inc ...... E 818 678-1450
21019 Osborne St Canoga Park (91304) *(P-9701)*

C P I, Agoura Hills Also called Chatsworth Products Inc *(P-13929)*

C P P, Pomona Also called Consolidated Foundries Inc *(P-11511)*

C P Products, Long Beach Also called Diamond-U Products Inc *(P-13739)*

C P Shades Inc (PA) ...... F 415 331-4581
403 Coloma St Sausalito (94965) *(P-3389)*

C Pallets From Bkersfield Call ...... F 661 833-2801
2508 E Brundage Ln Bakersfield (93307) *(P-4457)*

C Publishing LLC ...... E 310 393-3800
1543 7th St Ste 202 Santa Monica (90401) *(P-6456)*

C R M, Newport Beach Also called Crm Co LLC *(P-9565)*

C R T, Santa Fe Springs Also called Crt Color Printing Inc *(P-6770)*

C R W Distributors Inc ...... E 310 463-4577
1223 Wilshire Blvd Santa Monica (90403) *(P-472)*

C S America Inc (HQ) ...... E 323 583-7627
13365 Estelle St Corona (92879) *(P-2949)*

C S Bio Co ...... F 650 322-1111
20 Kelly Ct Menlo Park (94025) *(P-8088)*

C S C, Poway Also called Advanced Machining Tooling Inc *(P-14472)*

C S Dash Cover Inc ...... F 562 790-8300
14020 Paramount Blvd Paramount (90723) *(P-3880)*

C S I, Walnut Creek Also called Computers and Structures Inc *(P-24517)*

C S I, Santa Ana Also called Color Science Inc *(P-8961)*

C S L, Santa Clara Also called Csl Operating LLC *(P-13383)*

C S M, Poway Also called Toray Membrane Usa Inc *(P-16126)*

C S T, Thousand Oaks Also called Custom Sensors & Tech Inc *(P-19507)*

C S T I, San Jose Also called Chemical Safety Technology Inc *(P-14927)*

C T F, Perris Also called California Trusframe LLC *(P-4396)*

C T I, San Diego Also called Corrugated Technologies Inc *(P-24528)*

C T L Printing Inds Inc ...... E 714 635-2980
1741 W Lincoln Ave Ste A Anaheim (92801) *(P-7260)*

C T R, Healdsburg Also called Cooling Tower Resources Inc *(P-4616)*

C T V Inc ...... F 408 378-1606
481 Vandell Way Campbell (95008) *(P-6712)*

C Team Inc ...... E 562 866-3887
16706 Lakewood Blvd Bellflower (90706) *(P-16352)*

C W Cole & Company Inc ...... E 626 443-2473
2560 Rosemead Blvd South El Monte (91733) *(P-17590)*

C W Enterprises Inc ...... F 951 786-9999
2111 Iowa Ave Ste D Riverside (92507) *(P-17678)*

C W Moss Auto Parts Inc ...... F 714 639-3083
402 W Chapman Ave Orange (92866) *(P-13138)*

C&C Building Automation Co Inc ...... E 650 292-7450
390 Swift Ave Ste 22 South San Francisco (94080) *(P-22173)*

C&C Metal Form & Tooling Inc ...... E 562 861-9554
10654 Garfield Ave South Gate (90280) *(P-13174)*

C&D Aerodesign, San Diego Also called C&D Zodiac Inc *(P-20769)*

C&D Precision Machining, San Jose Also called C & D Semiconductor Svcs Inc *(P-18757)*

C&D Zodiac Inc ...... C 909 652-9700
8595 Milliken Ave Ste 101 Rancho Cucamonga (91730) *(P-20763)*

C&D Zodiac Inc ...... C 714 901-2672
12472 Industry St Garden Grove (92841) *(P-20764)*

C&D Zodiac Inc (HQ) ...... B 714 934-0000
5701 Bolsa Ave Huntington Beach (92647) *(P-20765)*

C&D Zodiac Inc ...... F 805 922-3013
2850 Skyway Dr Santa Maria (93455) *(P-20766)*

C&D Zodiac Inc ...... C 562 344-4780
11240 Warland Dr Cypress (90630) *(P-20767)*

C&D Zodiac Inc ...... B 714 891-1906
7330 Lincoln Way Garden Grove (92841) *(P-20768)*

C&D Zodiac Inc ...... E 619 671-0430
6754 Calle De Linea # 111 San Diego (92154) *(P-20769)*

C&D Zodiac Inc ...... B 909 947-2725
1945 S Grove Ave Ontario (91761) *(P-20770)*

C&F Wire Products, Stanton Also called Stecher Enterprises Inc *(P-13803)*

C&H Sugar, Crockett Also called C&H Sugar Company Inc *(P-1401)*

C&H Sugar Company, Crockett Also called C&H Sugar Company Inc *(P-1402)*

C&H Sugar Company Inc ...... A 510 787-2121
830 Loring Ave Crockett (94525) *(P-1401)*

C&H Sugar Company Inc ...... B 510 787-6763
830 Loring Ave Crockett (94525) *(P-1402)*

C&J Fab Center Inc ...... F 310 323-0970
1415 W 135th St Gardena (90249) *(P-12515)*

C&M Fine Pack, San Bernardino Also called D&W Fine Pack LLC *(P-10059)*

C&O Manufacturing Company Inc ...... E 562 692-7525
9640 Beverly Rd Pico Rivera (90660) *(P-12516)*

C&S Global Foods Inc ...... F 209 392-2223
20110 State Highway 33 Dos Palos (93620) *(P-2475)*

C&T Publishing Inc ...... E 925 677-0377
1651 Challenge Dr Concord (94520) *(P-6320)*

C-Cube Us Inc ...... A 408 944-6300
1778 Mccarthy Blvd Milpitas (95035) *(P-18758)*

C-Cure, Huntington Beach Also called Custom Building Products Inc *(P-9138)*

C-Cure, Ontario Also called Western States Wholesale Inc *(P-10869)*

C-Fab ...... E 949 646-2616
932 W 17th St Costa Mesa (92627) *(P-11940)*

C-Pak Industries Inc ...... E 909 880-6017
4925 Hallmark Pkwy San Bernardino (92407) *(P-9999)*

C-Quest Inc ...... D 323 980-1400
1439 S Herbert Ave Commerce (90023) *(P-3223)*

C-Scan Corp ...... E 800 953-7888
19630 Allendale Ave Saratoga (95070) *(P-15905)*

C-Thru Sunrooms, Corona Also called Stell Industries Inc *(P-12962)*

C. R. C, Santa Clara Also called Component Re-Engineering Inc *(P-18775)*

C.E.C., Colton Also called Computerized Embroidery Co *(P-3839)*

C.P.s Fine Gems Jwly Collectn, Monrovia Also called CPS Gem Corporation *(P-23253)*

C2 Publishing, Costa Mesa Also called Chet Cooper *(P-6128)*

C3 Biosciences Inc ...... F 949 635-9963
3 Grassy Knoll Ln Rcho STA Marg (92688) *(P-8089)*

C3 Iot Inc ...... C 650 503-2200
1300 Seaport Blvd Ste 500 Redwood City (94063) *(P-24459)*

C3-Ilex LLC (PA) ...... E 510 659-8300
46609 Fremont Blvd Fremont (94538) *(P-21501)*

C4 Litho ...... F 714 259-1073
27020 Daisy Cir Yorba Linda (92887) *(P-6713)*

C8 Medisensors Inc ...... E 408 623-7281
6375 San Ignacio Ave San Jose (95119) *(P-8090)*

Ca Inc ...... C 800 225-5224
3965 Freedom Cir Fl 6 Santa Clara (95054) *(P-24460)*

Ca Inc ...... D 631 342-6000
10180 Telesis Ct Ste 500 San Diego (92121) *(P-24461)*

Ca Inc ...... E 800 405-5540
3013 Douglas Blvd Ste 120 Roseville (95661) *(P-24462)*

CA Signs, Pacoima Also called California Signs Inc *(P-23838)*

CA Skyhook Inc ...... E 619 229-2169
4149 Cartagena Dr Ste B San Diego (92115) *(P-4113)*

CA-Te LP ...... F 559 539-1530
33230 La Colina Dr Springville (93265) *(P-12923)*

Ca-WA Corp ...... E 909 868-0630
1360 W 1st St Pomona (91766) *(P-9597)*

Ca75 Atk, San Diego Also called Northrop Grumman Innovation *(P-21179)*

Ca937 Afjrotc ...... D 818 394-3600
12431 Roscoe Blvd Ste 300 Sun Valley (91352) *(P-24053)*

Cabeau Inc ...... E 877 962-2232
21700 Oxnard St Ste 900 Woodland Hills (91367) *(P-3939)*

Cabinet & Millwork Installers, Santa Clarita Also called Door & Hardware Installers Inc *(P-4145)*

2019 California
Manufacturers Register

(P-0000) Products & Services Section entry number
(PA)=Parent Co (HQ)=Headquarters (DH)=Div Headquarters

Cabinet Company Inc ......F......530 273-7533
416 Crown Point Cir Ste 7 Grass Valley (95945) **(P-5043)**
Cabinet Concepts ......F......909 599-9191
950 W Cienega Ave San Dimas (91773) **(P-4279)**
Cabinet Home, Commerce *Also called Home Paradise LLC* **(P-13219)**
Cabinets & Doors Direct Inc ......F......909 629-3388
858 E 1st St Pomona (91766) **(P-4280)**
Cabinets 2000 Inc ......C......562 868-0909
11100 Firestone Blvd Norwalk (90650) **(P-4281)**
Cabinets By Andy Inc ......F......707 839-0220
2411 Central Ave McKinleyville (95519) **(P-4282)**
Cabinets Galore Oc, San Diego *Also called Cabinets Galore Orange County* **(P-4682)**
Cabinets Galore Orange County ......E......858 586-0555
9279 Cabot Dr Ste D San Diego (92126) **(P-4682)**
Cable Aml Inc (PA) ......F......310 222-5599
2271 W 205th St Ste 101 Torrance (90501) **(P-18057)**
Cable Builders Inc ......F......760 308-0042
2380 Camino Vida Carlsbad (92011) **(P-2970)**
Cable Car Classics Inc ......F......707 433-6810
3239 Rio Lindo Ave Healdsburg (95448) **(P-21074)**
Cable Connection Inc ......D......510 249-9000
1035 Mission Ct Fremont (94539) **(P-17446)**
Cable Devices Incorporated (HQ) ......C......714 554-4370
3008 S Croddy Way Santa Ana (92704) **(P-15695)**
Cable Exchange, Santa Ana *Also called Cable Devices Incorporated* **(P-15695)**
Cable Harness Systems Inc ......E......714 841-9650
7462 Talbert Ave Huntington Beach (92648) **(P-19474)**
Cable Manufacturing Tech ......F......925 687-3700
2455 Bates Ave Ste E Concord (94520) **(P-2971)**
Cable Moore Inc (PA) ......E......510 436-8000
4700 Coliseum Way Oakland (94601) **(P-13814)**
Cable Strand, Long Beach *Also called Cablestrand Corp* **(P-13815)**
Cable-Cisco, San Francisco *Also called Carpenter Group* **(P-14294)**
Cableco, Santa Fe Springs *Also called Carpenter Group* **(P-13818)**
Cableco ......E......562 942-8076
13100 Firestone Blvd Santa Fe Springs (90670) **(P-2972)**
Cablestrand Corp ......F......562 595-4527
2660 Signal Pkwy Long Beach (90755) **(P-13815)**
Cabletek Inc ......F......310 523-5000
525 Finney Ct Gardena (90248) **(P-17447)**
Cabo Gear, Vista *Also called Cabo International* **(P-2728)**
Cabo International ......F......760 597-9199
2345 La Mirada Dr Vista (92081) **(P-2728)**
Caborca Leather LLC ......E......707 463-7607
4275 Peaceful Glen Rd Vacaville (95688) **(P-3628)**
Cabrac Inc ......E......818 834-0177
13250 Paxton St Pacoima (91331) **(P-13175)**
Cac Inc ......F......949 587-3328
20322 Windrow Dr Ste 100 Lake Forest (92630) **(P-19475)**
Cac Fabrication Inc ......F......818 882-2626
9710 Owensmouth Ave Ste C Chatsworth (91311) **(P-12125)**
Cacciatore Fine Wns & Olv Oil (PA) ......F......559 757-9463
1875 S Elm St Pixley (93256) **(P-1674)**
Cachcach, Santa Ana *Also called Funny-Bunny Inc* **(P-3156)**
Cache Creek Foods LLC ......F......530 662-1764
411 N Pioneer Ave Woodland (95776) **(P-2476)**
Cache Phlow Enterprise ......F......925 609-8649
1894 Lynwood Dr Apt D Concord (94519) **(P-7574)**
Cacique Inc (PA) ......C......626 961-3399
800 Royal Oaks Dr Ste 200 Monrovia (91016) **(P-565)**
Cacique Cheese, Monrovia *Also called Cacique Inc* **(P-565)**
Caco-Pacific Corporation (PA) ......C......626 331-3361
813 N Cummings Rd Covina (91724) **(P-14490)**
Cactus Tape, Irwindale *Also called V Himark (usa) Inc* **(P-9178)**
Cad Manufacturing Inc ......F......562 408-1113
7320 Adams St Paramount (90723) **(P-20771)**
Cad Works Inc ......E......626 336-5491
16366 E Valley Blvd La Puente (91744) **(P-12517)**
Cade Corporation ......F......408 292-3435
100 Lewis St San Jose (95112) **(P-9225)**
Caden Concepts LLC ......F......323 651-1190
13412 Ventura Blvd # 300 Sherman Oaks (91423) **(P-3831)**
Cadence Aerospace, Anaheim *Also called Aerospace Parts Holdings Inc* **(P-20723)**
Cadence Aerospace LLC (PA) ......E......949 877-3630
3150 E Miraloma Ave Anaheim (92806) **(P-20772)**
Cadence Design Systems Inc ......E......408 943-1234
2655 Seely Ave San Jose (95134) **(P-24463)**
Cadence Design Systems Inc ......E......949 788-6080
7505 Irvine Center Dr # 250 Irvine (92618) **(P-24464)**
Cadence Design Systems Inc (PA) ......A......408 943-1234
2655 Seely Ave Bldg 5 San Jose (95134) **(P-24465)**
Cadence Design Systems Inc ......F......510 647-2800
2150 Shattuck Ave Fl 10 Berkeley (94704) **(P-24466)**
Cadence Design Systems Inc ......F......925 895-3202
6700 Koll Center Pkwy # 160 Pleasanton (94566) **(P-24467)**
Cadence Gourmet LLC ......E......951 272-5949
155 Klug Cir Corona (92880) **(P-2477)**
Cadence Gourmet Involve Foods, Corona *Also called Cadence Gourmet LLC* **(P-2477)**
Cadence US Inc (PA) ......F......408 943-1234
2655 Seely Ave San Jose (95134) **(P-24468)**
Cadillac Plating Inc ......F......714 639-0342
1147 W Struck Ave Orange (92867) **(P-13361)**
Cae Automation and Test LLC ......F......408 204-0006
44368 Warm Springs Blvd Fremont (94538) **(P-16353)**
Caer Inc ......E......415 879-9864
129 N Laurel Ave Los Angeles (90048) **(P-749)**
Caesar Hardware Intl Ltd (HQ) ......E......800 306-3829
1445 Huntington Dr # 205 South Pasadena (91030) **(P-24054)**
Cafe Champagne, Temecula *Also called Thornton Winery* **(P-2016)**
Cafe Fanny, Berkeley *Also called Le Barbocce Inc* **(P-1067)**
Cafe Niebaum Coppola, San Francisco *Also called Niebam-Cppola Estate Winery LP* **(P-1900)**
Cafe Virtuoso LLC ......F......619 550-1830
1622 National Ave San Diego (92113) **(P-2331)**
Cafecito Organico Oc LLC ......E......213 537-8367
534 N Hoover St Los Angeles (90004) **(P-2332)**
Cafecito Organico Oc LLC ......F......213 537-8367
2916 Heathercliff Rd Malibu (90265) **(P-2333)**
Caffe Cardinale Cof Roasting ......F......831 626-2095
246 The Crossroads Blvd Carmel (93923) **(P-2334)**
Caffe Clabria Cof Roasters LLC ......E......619 683-7787
3933 30th St San Diego (92104) **(P-2335)**
Caffe Classico Foods Inc ......F......925 602-5400
2500 Annalisa Dr Concord (94520) **(P-2336)**
Caffe D'Vita, Chino *Also called Brad Barry Company Ltd* **(P-2330)**
Caffe Del Mar, Solana Beach *Also called Future Wave Technologies Inc* **(P-2349)**
Cageco Inc ......E......800 605-4859
16225 Beaver Rd Adelanto (92301) **(P-14050)**
Cain Cellars Inc ......E......707 963-1616
3800 Langtry Rd Saint Helena (94574) **(P-1675)**
Cain Vineyard & Winery, Saint Helena *Also called Cain Cellars Inc* **(P-1675)**
Caitac Garment Processing Inc ......C......310 217-9888
14725 S Broadway Gardena (90248) **(P-2879)**
Cakebread Cellar Vineyards, Rutherford *Also called Cakebread Cellars* **(P-1676)**
Cakebread Cellars ......D......707 963-5221
8300 Saint Helena Hwy Rutherford (94573) **(P-1676)**
Cal Best Ceilings Inc ......F......909 946-1565
979 Seaboard Ct Upland (91786) **(P-17591)**
Cal Bind ......E......626 338-3699
4700 Littlejohn St Baldwin Park (91706) **(P-7595)**
Cal Coast Acidizing Co ......F......805 934-2411
6226 Dominion Rd Santa Maria (93454) **(P-190)**
Cal Coast Acidizing Service, Santa Maria *Also called Cal Coast Acidizing Co* **(P-190)**
Cal Coast Stucco ......F......818 767-0115
10932 Tuxford St Sun Valley (91352) **(P-11351)**
Cal Coil Magnetics Inc ......E......626 455-0011
2523 Seaman Ave El Monte (91733) **(P-19324)**
Cal Door, Salinas *Also called California Kit Cab Door Corp* **(P-4117)**
Cal Fiber Inc ......F......323 268-0191
1360 S Beverly Glen Blvd # 401 Los Angeles (90024) **(P-2993)**
Cal Flex, San Fernando *Also called California Flex Corporation* **(P-10003)**
Cal Moto ......F......650 966-1183
2490 Old Middlefield Way Mountain View (94043) **(P-21096)**
Cal Nor Design Inc (PA) ......F......925 829-7722
14126 Washington Ave San Leandro (94578) **(P-14491)**
Cal Nor Embroidery & Spc ......F......916 786-3131
4208 Douglas Blvd Ste 100 Granite Bay (95746) **(P-3832)**
Cal Nor Powder Coating Inc ......F......707 462-0217
265 E Clay St Ukiah (95482) **(P-13562)**
Cal Pac Sheet Metal Inc ......E......714 979-2733
2720 S Main St Ste B Santa Ana (92707) **(P-12518)**
Cal Pacific Dyeing & Finishing ......D......310 327-3792
233 E Gardena Blvd Gardena (90248) **(P-2909)**
Cal Partitions Inc ......F......310 539-1911
23814 President Ave Harbor City (90710) **(P-5130)**
Cal Pcific Specialty Foods LLC ......F......831 722-3615
1320 S Main St 302 Salinas (93901) **(P-940)**
Cal Pipe Manufacturing Inc (PA) ......E......562 803-4388
19440 S Dminguez Hills Dr Compton (90220) **(P-13880)**
Cal Plate (PA) ......D......562 403-3000
17110 Jersey Ave Artesia (90701) **(P-14804)**
Cal Portland Cement Co ......E......909 423-0436
695 S Rancho Ave Colton (92324) **(P-11054)**
Cal Precision Inc ......F......951 273-9901
1680 Commerce St Corona (92880) **(P-16354)**
Cal Printing, San Jose *Also called Four Colorcom* **(P-6825)**
Cal Quake Construction Inc ......E......323 931-2969
636 N Formosa Ave Los Angeles (90036) **(P-191)**
Cal Saw Canada, San Francisco *Also called Sawbird Inc* **(P-11921)**
Cal Sheets LLC ......D......209 234-3300
1212 Performance Dr Stockton (95206) **(P-5392)**
Cal Signal Corp ......F......650 343-6100
384 Beach Rd Burlingame (94010) **(P-18314)**
Cal Simba Inc (PA) ......E......805 240-1177
1680 Universe Cir Oxnard (93033) **(P-23335)**
Cal Southern Braiding Inc ......D......562 927-5531
7450 Scout Ave Bell Gardens (90201) **(P-19476)**
Cal Southern Graphics Corp ......D......310 559-3600
8432 Steller Dr Culver City (90232) **(P-6714)**
Cal Spas, Pomona *Also called California Acrylic Inds Inc* **(P-24055)**
Cal Springs LLC ......D......562 943-5599
6250 N Irwindale Ave Irwindale (91702) **(P-7261)**
Cal Star Systems Group Inc ......E......818 922-2000
6613 Valjean Ave Van Nuys (91406) **(P-19923)**
Cal State Rubber, Santa Fe Springs *Also called Duro Roller Company Inc* **(P-9609)**
Cal Stitch Embroidery Inc ......F......909 465-5448
2057 Hunter Rd Chino Hills (91709) **(P-3833)**
Cal Tape & Label, Anaheim *Also called C T L Printing Inds Inc* **(P-7260)**
Cal Tech Precision Inc ......D......714 992-4130
1830 N Lemon St Anaheim (92801) **(P-20773)**
Cal Traders ......F......530 566-1405
1260 Muir Ave Chico (95973) **(P-1484)**
Cal Treehouse Almonds LLC ......C......661 725-6334
2115 Road 144 Delano (93215) **(P-1485)**
Cal Trend Automotive Products, Santa Ana *Also called Cal Trends Accessories LLC* **(P-3940)**

ALPHABETIC

Employee Codes: A=Over 500 employees, B=251-500
C=101-250, D=51-100, E=20-50, F=10-19
2019 California
Manfacturers Register
© Mergent Inc. 1-800-342-5647
1087

Cal Trends Accessories LLC ...E ...714 708-5115
2121 S Anne St Santa Ana (92704) ***(P-3940)***
Cal Vsta Erosion Ctrl Pdts LLC ...E ...530 476-0706
459 Country Rd 99w 99 W Arbuckle (95912) ***(P-14149)***
Cal West Construction Inc ...F ...559 217-3306
4670 N Wilson Ave Fresno (93704) ***(P-14492)***
Cal West Designs, Santa Fe Springs *Also called K S Designs Inc* ***(P-23912)***
Cal West Spcialty Coatings Inc ...F ...408 720-7440
1058 W Evelyn Ave Ste 10 Sunnyvale (94086) ***(P-8886)***
Cal Yuba Investments, Olivehurst *Also called Yuba River Moulding Mllwk Inc* ***(P-4264)***
Cal-Asia Truss Inc ...E ...916 685-5648
10547 E Stockton Blvd Elk Grove (95624) ***(P-4394)***
Cal-Aurum Industries ...E ...714 898-0996
15632 Container Ln Huntington Beach (92649) ***(P-13362)***
Cal-Coast Dairy Systems Inc ...E ...209 634-9026
424 S Tegner Rd Turlock (95380) ***(P-14051)***
Cal-Coast Pkg & Crating Inc ...E ...310 518-7215
2040 E 220th St Carson (90810) ***(P-4438)***
Cal-Comp USA (san Diego) Inc ...C ...858 587-6900
1940 Camino Vida Roble Carlsbad (92008) ***(P-18441)***
Cal-Draulics, Corona *Also called Johnson Caldraul Inc* ***(P-20858)***
Cal-Fab Systems Inc ...E ...760 246-4454
16425 Beaver Rd Adelanto (92301) ***(P-14267)***
Cal-India Foods International ...E ...909 613-1660
13591 Yorba Ave Chino (91710) ***(P-8991)***
Cal-June Inc (PA) ...E ...323 877-4164
5238 Vineland Ave North Hollywood (91601) ***(P-11941)***
Cal-Mil Plastic Products Inc (PA) ...E ...800 321-9069
4079 Calle Platino Oceanside (92056) ***(P-10000)***
Cal-Mold Incorporated ...C ...951 361-6400
3900 Hamner Ave Eastvale (91752) ***(P-10001)***
Cal-Monarch, Corona *Also called California Wire Products Corp* ***(P-13816)***
Cal-Pac Chemical Co Inc ...F ...323 585-2178
6231 Maywood Ave Huntington Park (90255) ***(P-7756)***
Cal-Sensors Inc (PA) ...E ...707 303-3837
1260 Calle Suerte Camarillo (93012) ***(P-21270)***
Cal-Sign Wholesale Inc ...F ...209 523-7446
5260 Jerusalem Ct Modesto (95356) ***(P-23836)***
Cal-Tron Corporation ...E ...760 873-8491
2290 Dixon Ln Bishop (93514) ***(P-10002)***
Cal-Tron Plating Inc ...E ...562 945-1181
11919 Rivera Rd Santa Fe Springs (90670) ***(P-13363)***
Cal-Weld Inc ...C ...510 226-0100
4308 Solar Way Fremont (94538) ***(P-13926)***
Cal-West Machining Inc ...F ...714 637-4161
1734 W Sequoia Ave Orange (92868) ***(P-16155)***
Calamp Corp (PA) ...B ...949 600-5600
15635 Alton Pkwy Ste 250 Irvine (92618) ***(P-18058)***
Calamp Corp ...F ...760 438-9010
2231 Rutherford Rd # 110 Carlsbad (92008) ***(P-18059)***
Calaveras Enterprise, San Andreas *Also called Calaveras First Co Inc* ***(P-5785)***
Calaveras First Co Inc ...E ...209 754-3861
15 Main St San Andreas (95249) ***(P-5785)***
Calaveras Materials Inc (HQ) ...E ...209 883-0448
1100 Lowe Rd Hughson (95326) ***(P-11055)***
Calaveras Materials Inc ...F ...209 883-0448
1100 Lowe Rd Hughson (95326) ***(P-10893)***
Calbiotech Inc ...E ...619 660-6162
1935 Cordell Ct El Cajon (92020) ***(P-22384)***
Calchef Foods LLC ...D ...888 638-7083
4335 N Star Way Ste D Modesto (95356) ***(P-911)***
Calcon Steel Construction ...E ...310 768-8094
1226 W 196th St Torrance (90502) ***(P-12126)***
Calcraft Company, Rialto *Also called Calcraft Corporation* ***(P-12127)***
Calcraft Corporation ...F ...909 879-2900
1426 S Willow Ave Rialto (92376) ***(P-12127)***
Caldera Medical Inc ...D ...818 879-6555
5171 Clareton Dr Agoura Hills (91301) ***(P-22385)***
Caldigit Inc ...F ...714 572-6668
1941 E Miraloma Ave Ste B Placentia (92870) ***(P-15517)***
Caldyn, Los Angeles *Also called California Dynamics Corp* ***(P-22174)***
Caleb Technology Corporation ...E ...310 257-4780
2905 Lomita Blvd Torrance (90505) ***(P-19799)***
Calera Corporation ...E ...831 731-6000
7697 Highway 1 Moss Landing (95039) ***(P-10894)***
Calex Mfg Co Inc ...E ...925 687-4411
2401 Stanwell Dr Frnt Concord (94520) ***(P-19477)***
Calf Canyon Winery LLC ...F ...805 226-8600
679 Calf Canyon Hwy Creston (93432) ***(P-1677)***
Calfabco (PA) ...F ...323 265-1205
1432 Chico Ave South El Monte (91733) ***(P-13176)***
Calgon Carbon Corporation ...F ...707 668-5637
501 Hatchery Rd Blue Lake (95525) ***(P-7757)***
Calgren Renewable Fuels, Pixley *Also called Gfp Ethanol LLC* ***(P-9007)***
Calhoun & Poxon Company Inc ...F ...323 225-2328
5330 Alhambra Ave Los Angeles (90032) ***(P-17134)***
Cali Chem Inc ...E ...714 265-3740
14271 Corp Dr Ste B Garden Grove (92843) ***(P-8712)***
Cali Today Daily Newspaper ...F ...408 297-8271
1310 Tully Rd Ste 105 San Jose (95122) ***(P-5786)***
Cali-Fame Los Angeles Inc ...D ...310 747-5263
20934 S Santa Fe Ave Carson (90810) ***(P-3559)***
Caliame, Sebastopol *Also called Marimar Torres Estate Corp* ***(P-1870)***
Caliber Screenprinting Inc ...F ...760 353-3499
1101 S Hope St El Centro (92243) ***(P-3881)***
Calico Tag & Label Inc ...F ...562 944-6889
13233 Barton Cir Whittier (90605) ***(P-7262)***
Calidad Inc ...E ...909 947-3937
1730 S Balboa Ave Ontario (91761) ***(P-11690)***

Calient Technologies Inc ...D ...805 562-5500
25 Castilian Dr Goleta (93117) ***(P-17927)***
Calient Technologies Inc (PA) ...B ...805 562-5500
27 Castilian Dr Goleta (93117) ***(P-17928)***
Caliente Systems Inc ...D ...510 790-0300
6821 Central Ave Newark (94560) ***(P-12367)***
Calif Frut and Tmto Ktchn LLC ...F ...530 666-6600
1785 Ashby Rd Merced (95348) ***(P-2478)***
Calif Silk Screen, Torrance *Also called California Silkscreen* ***(P-3883)***
Califia Farms LLC (PA) ...E ...213 694-4667
1321 Palmetto St Los Angeles (90013) ***(P-2104)***
Califia Farms LLC ...F ...661 679-1000
33374 Lerdo Hwy Bakersfield (93308) ***(P-2105)***
Califoam Products Inc ...F ...909 364-1600
10775 Silicon Ave Montclair (91763) ***(P-9598)***
California Acrylic Inds Inc (HQ) ...E ...909 623-8781
1462 E 9th St Pomona (91766) ***(P-24055)***
California Acti, Irvine *Also called Acti Corporation Inc* ***(P-17750)***
California Amforge Corporation ...D ...626 334-4931
750 N Vernon Ave Azusa (91702) ***(P-11382)***
California Apparel News, Los Angeles *Also called Apparel News Group* ***(P-6102)***
California Art Products Co, North Hollywood *Also called Capco/Psa* ***(P-10011)***
California Audio Video Distrg, South San Francisco *Also called Cav Distributing Corporation* ***(P-17888)***
California Bag, Woodland *Also called Acme Bag Co Inc* ***(P-5636)***
California Bedrooms Inc ...E ...559 233-7050
95 Santa Fe Ave Fresno (93721) ***(P-4683)***
California Bio-Mass Inc (PA) ...E ...760 246-7946
20055 Shay Rd Victorville (92394) ***(P-4610)***
California Bio-Productex Inc ...E ...559 582-5308
13220 Crown Ave Hanford (93230) ***(P-8992)***
California Blimps ...F ...949 650-1183
738 W 17th St Ste D Costa Mesa (92627) ***(P-20571)***
California Blind Company, North Hollywood *Also called Carl Nersesian* ***(P-4122)***
California Bottling Company ...E ...916 772-1000
8250 Industrial Ave Roseville (95678) ***(P-2106)***
California Box II ...E ...909 944-9202
8949 Toronto Ave Rancho Cucamonga (91730) ***(P-5393)***
California Brazing, Newark *Also called Nevada Heat Treating Inc* ***(P-25424)***
California Broach Company ...F ...323 260-4812
4815 Telegraph Rd Los Angeles (90022) ***(P-16355)***
California Button, Anaheim *Also called United Paper Box Inc* ***(P-5514)***
California Cab & Store Fix ...E ...916 386-1340
8472 Carbide Ct Sacramento (95828) ***(P-4114)***
California Cage Co, San Diego *Also called Specialty Steel Products Inc* ***(P-13853)***
California Calendar, Chino Hills *Also called Ad Industries LLC* ***(P-7571)***
California Candy, El Monte *Also called California Snack Foods Inc* ***(P-1409)***
California Carbon Company Inc ...F ...562 436-1962
2825 E Grant St Wilmington (90744) ***(P-7758)***
California Cart Builder LLC ...F ...951 245-1114
29375 Hunco Way Lake Elsinore (92530) ***(P-20494)***
California Cascade Industries ...C ...916 736-3353
7512 14th Ave Sacramento (95820) ***(P-4588)***
California Cascade-Woodland ...F ...530 666-1261
1492 Churchill Downs Ave Woodland (95776) ***(P-4589)***
California Cedar Products Co (PA) ...E ...209 932-5002
2385 Arch Airport Rd # 500 Stockton (95206) ***(P-4611)***
California Cedar Products Co ...C ...209 944-5800
2385 Arch Airport Rd # 500 Stockton (95206) ***(P-4612)***
California Churros Corporation ...C ...909 370-4777
751 Via Lata Colton (92324) ***(P-1215)***
California Classics, Santa Clarita *Also called California Millworks Corp* ***(P-4118)***
California Clock Co (PA) ...F ...714 545-4321
16060 Abajo Cir Fountain Valley (92708) ***(P-23218)***
California Coast Clothing LLC ...F ...323 923-3870
3690 S Santa Fe Ave Vernon (90058) ***(P-2729)***
California Coating Lab ...E ...510 357-1800
670 Mccormick St San Leandro (94577) ***(P-23083)***
California Cocktails Inc ...F ...714 990-0982
345 Oak Pl Brea (92821) ***(P-2249)***
California Combining Corp ...E ...323 589-5727
5607 S Santa Fe Ave Vernon (90058) ***(P-2957)***
California Commercial Asp Corp (PA) ...F ...858 513-0611
4211 Ponderosa Ave Ste C San Diego (92123) ***(P-9378)***
California Community News LLC (HQ) ...B ...626 472-5297
5091 4th St Irwindale (91706) ***(P-5787)***
California Compactor Svc Inc ...F ...661 298-5556
17000 Sierra Hwy Canyon Country (91351) ***(P-13927)***
California Composite Cont Corp ...E ...951 940-9343
22770 Perry St Perris (92570) ***(P-5481)***
California Composites MGT Inc ...E ...714 258-0405
1935 E Occidental St Santa Ana (92705) ***(P-20774)***
California Concentrate Company ...E ...209 334-9112
18678 N Highway 99 Acampo (95220) ***(P-941)***
California Concrete Pipe Corp ...F ...209 466-4212
2960 S Highway 99 Stockton (95215) ***(P-10895)***
California Costume Int'l, Los Angeles *Also called Califrnia Cstume Cllctions Inc* ***(P-3646)***
California Countertop Inc (PA) ...E ...619 460-0205
7811 Alvarado Rd La Mesa (91942) ***(P-5131)***
California Cstm Frt & Flavors, Irwindale *Also called California Custom Fruits* ***(P-2250)***
California Cstm Furn & Uphl Co ...E ...760 727-1444
2835 La Mirada Dr Ste C Vista (92081) ***(P-3882)***
California Custom Caps ...E ...626 454-1766
2319 Sastre Ave South El Monte (91733) ***(P-3560)***
California Custom Fruits (PA) ...D ...626 736-4130
15800 Tapia St Irwindale (91706) ***(P-2250)***
California Dairies Inc (PA) ...D ...559 625-2200
2000 N Plaza Dr Visalia (93291) ***(P-713)***

California Dairies Inc ....D....209 826-4901
1175 E Pacheco Blvd Los Banos (93635) ***(P-559)***
California Dairies Inc ....D....559 233-5154
755 F St Fresno (93706) ***(P-714)***
California Dairies Inc ....D....562 809-2595
11709 Artesia Blvd Artesia (90701) ***(P-715)***
California Dairies Inc ....D....209 656-1942
475 S Tegner Rd Turlock (95380) ***(P-560)***
California Decor ....E....310 603-9944
541 E Pine St Compton (90222) ***(P-4115)***
California Deluxe Window Indus (PA) ....E....818 349-5566
20735 Superior St Chatsworth (91311) ***(P-4116)***
California Dental Group, North Hollywood *Also called Tech Air of California Inc* ***(P-7739)***
California Die Casting Inc ....E....909 947-9947
1820 S Grove Ave Ontario (91761) ***(P-11710)***
California Digital Inc (PA) ....D....310 217-0500
6 Saddleback Rd Rolling Hills (90274) ***(P-15696)***
California Door, Morgan Hill *Also called California Kit Cab Door Corp* ***(P-4283)***
California Dried Fruit Inc ....E....559 233-0970
9145 W Herndon Ave Fresno (93723) ***(P-877)***
California Dynamics Corp (PA) ....E....323 223-3882
5572 Alhambra Ave Los Angeles (90032) ***(P-22174)***
California Dynasty, Los Angeles *Also called MGT Industries Inc* ***(P-3467)***
California Economizer ....E....714 898-9963
5622 Engineer Dr Huntington Beach (92649) ***(P-17258)***
California Electric Steel ....E....209 736-0465
250 Monte Verda Angels Camp (95222) ***(P-11523)***
California Electric Supply, Anaheim *Also called Ced Anaheim 018* ***(P-19925)***
California Embroidery, Fresno *Also called Holcomb Products Inc* ***(P-3849)***
California Etching Inc ....F....707 224-9966
840 Jackson St NAPA (94559) ***(P-13563)***
California Exotic Novlt LLC ....D....909 606-1950
1455 E Francis St Ontario (91761) ***(P-24056)***
California Expanded Met Pdts (PA) ....D....626 369-3564
13191 Crosrds Pkwy N 32 City of Industry (91746) ***(P-12519)***
California Expanded Met Pdts ....E....925 473-9340
1001a Pttsburg Antoch Hwy Pittsburg (94565) ***(P-12924)***
California Family Foods LLC ....D....530 476-3326
6550 Struckmeyer Rd Arbuckle (95912) ***(P-1075)***
California Farm Equipment Mag ....F....661 589-0435
17045 S Central Vly Hwy Shafter (93263) ***(P-14052)***
California Fashion Club Inc (PA) ....F....626 575-1838
207 S 9th Ave La Puente (91746) ***(P-3349)***
California Faucets Inc ....F....657 400-1639
5231 Argosy Ave Huntington Beach (92649) ***(P-12027)***
California Faucets Inc (PA) ....D....714 890-0450
5271 Argosy Ave Huntington Beach (92649) ***(P-12028)***
California Feather Inds Inc ....F....323 585-5800
2241 E 49th St Vernon (90058) ***(P-3713)***
California Fleet Services Inc (PA) ....F....209 858-0283
1044 Madruga Rd Lathrop (95330) ***(P-20495)***
California Flex Corporation (PA) ....F....818 361-1169
1318 1st St San Fernando (91340) ***(P-10003)***
California Flexrake Corp ....E....626 443-4026
9620 Gidley St Temple City (91780) ***(P-11887)***
California Frames, Los Angeles *Also called Ronald D Teson Inc* ***(P-4090)***
California Fruit Basket, Sanger *Also called Melkonian Enterprises Inc* ***(P-887)***
California Gasket and Rbr Corp (PA) ....E....310 323-4250
533 W Collins Ave Orange (92867) ***(P-9599)***
California Glass & Mirror Div, Santa Ana *Also called Twed-Dells Inc* ***(P-10736)***
California Glass Bending Corp ....E....310 549-5255
2100 W 139th St Gardena (90249) ***(P-10636)***
California Gold Bars Inc (PA) ....F....510 848-9292
1041 Folger Ave Berkeley (94710) ***(P-1467)***
California Heating Equipment, Anaheim *Also called Energy Reconnaissance Inc* ***(P-15259)***
California Heavy Oil Inc ....E....888 848-4754
10889 Wilshire Blvd Los Angeles (90024) ***(P-36)***
California Heritage Mills Inc ....E....530 438-2100
1 Comet Ln Maxwell (95955) ***(P-1076)***
California Hot Springs Water ....F....661 548-6582
42231 Hot Springs Dr Calif Hot Spg (93207) ***(P-2107)***
California House, Sacramento *Also called Beauty Craft Furniture Corp* ***(P-4676)***
California Hydroforming Co Inc ....F....626 912-0036
850 Lawson St City of Industry (91748) ***(P-12520)***
California Industiral Mfg LLC (PA) ....F....530 846-9960
1221 Independence Pl Gridley (95948) ***(P-24057)***
California Industrial Fabrics ....E....619 661-7166
2325 Marconi Ct San Diego (92154) ***(P-2790)***
California Industrial Rbr Co ....E....530 674-2444
1690 Sierra Ave Yuba City (95993) ***(P-7902)***
California Insulated Wire & ....D....818 569-4930
3050 N California St Burbank (91504) ***(P-11649)***
California Integration Coordin ....F....530 626-6168
2929 Grandview St Placerville (95667) ***(P-18442)***
California Interfill Inc ....F....951 351-2619
8178 Mar Vista Ct Riverside (92504) ***(P-8713)***
California Iron Design ....F....818 767-6690
8906 Lankershim Blvd Sun Valley (91352) ***(P-25391)***
California Jig Grinding Co ....F....323 723-4017
861 N Holly Glen Dr Long Beach (90815) ***(P-16356)***
California Kit Cab Door Corp ....C....831 784-5142
1800 Abbott St Salinas (93901) ***(P-4117)***
California Kit Cab Door Corp (PA) ....D....408 782-5700
400 Cochrane Cir Morgan Hill (95037) ***(P-4283)***
California Leisure Products ....F....707 462-2106
265 Thomas St Ukiah (95482) ***(P-4570)***
California Lithographers, Concord *Also called Acme Press Inc* ***(P-6639)***
California Machine Specialties, Chino *Also called Young Machine Inc* ***(P-17075)***
California Master Printers ....F....626 812-8930
796 N Todd Ave Azusa (91702) ***(P-6715)***
California Metal Group Inc ....F....310 609-1400
1205 S Alameda St Compton (90220) ***(P-12521)***
California Metal Processing Co ....E....323 753-2247
1518 W Slauson Ave # 1530 Los Angeles (90047) ***(P-13364)***
California Mfg & Engrg Co LLC ....C....559 842-1500
1401 S Madera Ave Kerman (93630) ***(P-14150)***
California Mfg Cabinetry Inc ....F....909 930-3632
1474 E Francis St Ontario (91761) ***(P-5044)***
California Micro Devices Corp (HQ) ....F....408 542-1051
3001 Stender Way Santa Clara (95054) ***(P-19307)***
California Milling Co, Los Angeles *Also called Grain Craft Inc* ***(P-1043)***
California Millworks Corp ....E....661 294-2345
27772 Avenue Scott Santa Clarita (91355) ***(P-4118)***
California Mini Truck Inc ....F....661 398-9585
12539 Jomani Dr Bakersfield (93312) ***(P-20281)***
California Motor Controls Inco ....F....707 746-6255
3070 Bay Vista Ct Benicia (94510) ***(P-17259)***
California Natural Products ....C....209 858-2525
1250 Lathrop Rd Lathrop (95330) ***(P-2479)***
California Natural Vitamins ....E....818 772-8441
9044 Independence Ave Canoga Park (91304) ***(P-8091)***
California Neon Products ....D....619 283-2191
4530 Mission Gorge Pl San Diego (92120) ***(P-23837)***
California New Foods LLC ....E....831 444-1872
11165 Commercial Pkwy Castroville (95012) ***(P-2480)***
California Newspapers Inc ....A....415 883-8600
150 Alameda Del Prado Novato (94949) ***(P-5788)***
California Newspapers Partnr (PA) ....C....408 920-5333
4 N 2nd St Ste 800 San Jose (95113) ***(P-5789)***
California Nuggets Inc ....E....209 599-7131
23073 S Frederick Rd Ripon (95366) ***(P-2376)***
California Offset Printers Inc ....D....631 274-9530
620 W Elk Ave Glendale (91204) ***(P-6716)***
California Olive and Vine LLC ....F....530 763-7921
1670 Poole Blvd Yuba City (95993) ***(P-1535)***
California Olive Ranch Inc (PA) ....E....530 846-8000
1367 E Lassen Ave Ste A1 Chico (95973) ***(P-1536)***
California Pak Intl Inc ....E....310 223-2500
1700 S Wilmington Ave Compton (90220) ***(P-17082)***
California Panel Systems LLP ....E....619 562-7010
1020 N Marshall Ave El Cajon (92020) ***(P-12522)***
California Paper Bag Inc ....E....818 240-6717
1829 Dana St Ste A Glendale (91201) ***(P-5638)***
California Paperboard, Santa Clara *Also called Caraustar Industries Inc* ***(P-5345)***
California Performance Packg ....B....909 390-4422
33200 Lewis St Union City (94587) ***(P-9823)***
California Pharmaceuticals LLC ....F....805 482-3737
768 Calle Plano Camarillo (93012) ***(P-8092)***
California Pipe Fabricators ....E....707 678-3069
7277 Chevron Way Dixon (95620) ***(P-13881)***
California Plasteck, Ontario *Also called Paramount Panels Inc* ***(P-10266)***
California Plasteck, Ontario *Also called Paramount Panels Inc* ***(P-20903)***
California Plastic Cntrs Inc ....F....562 423-3900
2210 E Artesia Blvd Long Beach (90805) ***(P-10004)***
California Plastics, Riverside *Also called Consolidated Cont Holdings LLC* ***(P-9795)***
California Plastics Inc ....F....805 483-8188
1611 S Rose Ave Oxnard (93033) ***(P-10005)***
California Plastix Inc ....E....909 629-8288
1319 E 3rd St Pomona (91766) ***(P-5589)***
California Portland Cement, Mojave *Also called Calportland Company* ***(P-10744)***
California Pot & Tile Works, Los Angeles *Also called SMD Enterprises Inc* ***(P-10790)***
California Pot & Tile Works, Los Angeles *Also called California Potteries Inc* ***(P-10778)***
California Potteries Inc ....E....323 235-4151
859 E 60th St Los Angeles (90001) ***(P-10778)***
California Poultry, Los Angeles *Also called Western Supreme Inc* ***(P-555)***
California Precast Stone Mfg ....F....951 657-7913
1796 Karen Ct Hemet (92545) ***(P-10896)***
California Precision Pdts Inc ....D....858 638-7300
6790 Flanders Dr San Diego (92121) ***(P-12523)***
California Premium Incentives, Lake Forest *Also called Aminco International USA Inc* ***(P-23235)***
California Pro-Specs Inc ....E....916 455-9890
2240 15th Ave Sacramento (95822) ***(P-4076)***
California Prtg Solutions Inc ....E....909 307-2032
1950 W Park Ave Redlands (92373) ***(P-7263)***
California Quality Plas Inc ....E....909 930-5667
2104 S Cucamonga Ave Ontario (91761) ***(P-10006)***
California Ramp Works Inc ....E....909 949-1601
273 N Benson Ave Upland (91786) ***(P-12925)***
California Reamer Company Inc ....F....562 946-6377
12747 Los Nietos Rd Santa Fe Springs (90670) ***(P-14612)***
California Redwood Products, Colton *Also called Frank Kams & Associates Inc* ***(P-4521)***
California Resources Corp ....E....661 763-6107
1320 4th St Los Osos (93402) ***(P-37)***
California Resources Corp ....E....661 395-8000
5000 Stockdale Hwy Bakersfield (93309) ***(P-38)***
California Resources Corp ....F....661 412-5222
11109 River Run Blvd Bakersfield (93311) ***(P-127)***
California Resources Corp (PA) ....D....888 848-4754
9200 Oakdale Ave Ste 900 Chatsworth (91311) ***(P-128)***
California Resources Corp ....C....562 624-3400
111 W Ocean Blvd Ste 800 Long Beach (90802) ***(P-39)***
California Resources Corp ....E....707 374-4109
2692 Amerada Rd Rio Vista (94571) ***(P-40)***
California Resources Corp ....F....805 641-5566
3055 Pacific Coast Hwy Ventura (93001) ***(P-41)***

ALPHABETIC

Employee Codes: A=Over 500 employees, B=251-500
C=101-250, D=51-100, E=20-50, F=10-19
2019 California
Manfacturers Register
© Mergent Inc. 1-800-342-5647
1089

California Resources Corp....E....310 208-8800
270 Quail Ct Ste 100 Santa Paula (93060) *(P-42)*
California Resources Prod Corp....D....805 483-8017
3450 E 5th St Oxnard (93033) *(P-43)*
California Resources Prod Corp....E....530 671-8201
855 Harter Pkwy Ste 200 Yuba City (95993) *(P-44)*
California Resources Prod Corp (HQ)....C....661 869-8000
11109 River Run Blvd Bakersfield (93311) *(P-45)*
California Respiratory Care....D....818 379-9999
16055 Ventura Blvd # 715 Encino (91436) *(P-9226)*
California Ribbon Carbn Co Inc....D....323 724-9100
10914 Thienes Ave South El Monte (91733) *(P-23726)*
California Sample Services, Ontario *Also called Three Chiefs & No Indians LLC (P-7623)*
California Scene Publishing....F....858 635-9400
8360 Juniper Creek Ln San Diego (92126) *(P-6717)*
California Screw Products Corp....C....562 633-6626
14957 Gwenchris Ct Paramount (90723) *(P-11942)*
California Sensor Corporation....E....760 438-0525
2075 Corte Del Nogal P Carlsbad (92011) *(P-22175)*
California Shellfish Co Inc (PA)....F....415 923-7400
818 E Broadway C San Gabriel (91776) *(P-2309)*
California Signs Inc....E....818 899-1888
10280 Glenoaks Blvd Pacoima (91331) *(P-23838)*
California Silica Products LLC....F....909 947-0028
12808 Rancho Rd Adelanto (92301) *(P-7759)*
California Silkscreen....F....310 320-5111
1507 Plaza Del Amo Torrance (90501) *(P-3883)*
California Smart Foods....E....415 826-0449
2565 3rd St Ste 342 San Francisco (94107) *(P-1216)*
California Snack Foods Inc....E....626 444-4508
2131 Tyler Ave El Monte (91733) *(P-1409)*
California Specialty Farms, Los Angeles *Also called Worldwide Specialties Inc (P-2702)*
California Specialty Painting....F....562 622-7800
9310 Norwalk Blvd Santa Fe Springs (90670) *(P-13564)*
California St UNI Channel Isla....E....805 437-2670
45 Rincon Dr Unit 104a Camarillo (93012) *(P-17083)*
California Stairs, Gilroy *Also called Northern California Stair (P-4204)*
California Stamp Company, San Diego *Also called On-Line Stampco Inc (P-23721)*
California Stay Co Inc....F....310 839-7236
2600 Overland Ave Apt 219 Los Angeles (90064) *(P-10469)*
California Steel and Tube LLC....C....626 968-5511
16049 Stephens St City of Industry (91745) *(P-11474)*
California Steel Inds Inc (HQ)....B....909 350-6300
14000 San Bernardino Ave Fontana (92335) *(P-11383)*
California Steel Inds Inc....E....909 350-6300
1 California Steel Way Fontana (92335) *(P-11384)*
California Steel Products....F....310 603-5645
10851 Drury Ln Lynwood (90262) *(P-12974)*
California Stl Stair Rail Mfr....E....209 824-1785
587 Carnegie St Manteca (95337) *(P-11385)*
California Stone Coating....F....510 284-2554
37911 Von Euw Cmn Fremont (94536) *(P-14151)*
California Sulphur Company....E....562 437-0768
2250 E Pacific Coast Hwy Wilmington (90744) *(P-7760)*
California Supertrucks Inc....E....951 656-2903
14385 Veterans Way Moreno Valley (92553) *(P-20195)*
California Surveying & Draftin....F....707 293-9449
411 Russell Ave Santa Rosa (95403) *(P-15697)*
California Surveying & Draftin (PA)....E....916 344-0232
4733 Auburn Blvd Sacramento (95841) *(P-15698)*
California Swatch Dyers Inc....E....213 748-8425
776 E Washington Blvd Los Angeles (90021) *(P-2901)*
California Technical Pltg Corp....E....818 365-8205
11533 Bradley Ave San Fernando (91340) *(P-13365)*
California Technology, Springville *Also called CA-Te LP (P-12923)*
California Tool & Die, Azusa *Also called Mc William & Son Inc (P-13245)*
California Trade Converters....E....818 899-1455
13299 Louvre St Pacoima (91331) *(P-5343)*
California Treats Inc....D....626 454-4099
2131 Tyler Ave El Monte (91733) *(P-790)*
California Truck Equipment, Downey *Also called Commercial Truck Eqp Co LLC (P-20197)*
California Trusframe LLC....A....951 657-7491
144 Commerce Way Sanger (93657) *(P-4395)*
California Trusframe LLC (PA)....D....951 657-7491
23665 Cajalco Rd Perris (92570) *(P-4396)*
California Truss Company (PA)....D....951 657-7491
23665 Cajalco Rd Perris (92570) *(P-4397)*
California Truss Company....E....209 883-8000
2800 Tully Rd Hughson (95326) *(P-4398)*
California Turbo Inc....F....909 854-2800
10721 Business Dr Fontana (92337) *(P-15145)*
California Webbing Mills Inc....F....323 753-0260
6920 Stanford Ave Los Angeles (90001) *(P-2994)*
California Wire Products Corp....E....951 371-7730
1316 Railroad St Corona (92882) *(P-13816)*
California Woodworking Inc....E....805 982-9090
1726 Ives Ave Oxnard (93033) *(P-4284)*
Californian, The, San Diego *Also called North County Times (P-5999)*
Califrnia Anlytical Instrs Inc....D....714 974-5560
1312 W Grove Ave Orange (92865) *(P-21930)*
Califrnia Cstume Cllctions Inc (PA)....E....323 262-8383
210 S Anderson St Los Angeles (90033) *(P-3646)*
Califrnia Furn Collections Inc....C....619 621-2455
150 Reed Ct Ste A Chula Vista (91911) *(P-4908)*
Califrnia Indus Rfrgn Mchs Inc....F....951 361-0040
3197 Cornerstone Dr Mira Loma (91752) *(P-15943)*
Califrnia Mantel Fireplace Inc (PA)....E....916 925-5775
4141 N Freeway Blvd Sacramento (95834) *(P-4119)*
Califrnia Nwspapers Ltd Partnr (HQ)....B....626 962-8811
605 E Huntington Dr # 100 Monrovia (91016) *(P-5790)*
Califrnia Nwspapers Ltd Partnr....B....909 987-6397
9616 Archibald Ave # 100 Rancho Cucamonga (91730) *(P-5791)*
Califrnia Nwspapers Ltd Partnr....E....909 793-3221
19 E Citrus Ave Ste 102 Redlands (92373) *(P-5792)*
Califrnia Nwspapers Ltd Partnr....C....530 877-4413
5399 Clark Rd Paradise (95969) *(P-5793)*
Califrnia PCF Rice Mil A CA LP....C....530 661-1923
194 W Main St Woodland (95695) *(P-1077)*
Califrnia Rsrces Elk Hills LLC....B....661 412-5000
11109 River Run Blvd Bakersfield (93311) *(P-9323)*
Califrnia Rsurces Long Bch Inc....C....562 624-3204
111 W Ocean Blvd Ste 800 Long Beach (90802) *(P-192)*
Calimesa News Mirror....E....909 795-8145
1007 Calimesa Blvd Ste D Calimesa (92320) *(P-5794)*
Calimmune Inc....F....310 806-6240
129 N Hill Ave Ste 105 Pasadena (91106) *(P-8093)*
Calison Inc....E....626 448-3328
2447 Leef Ave South El Monte (91733) *(P-2810)*
Calistoga Roastery, The, Calistoga *Also called Coffee Guys Inc (P-2337)*
Calithera Biosciences Inc....E....650 870-1000
343 Oyster Point Blvd South San Francisco (94080) *(P-8094)*
Calix Inc (PA)....B....408 514-3000
2777 Orchard Pkwy San Jose (95134) *(P-18060)*
Callaway Golf Company....A....760 804-4502
5858 Dryden Pl Carlsbad (92008) *(P-23531)*
Callaway Golf Company....A....760 345-4653
44500 Indian Wells Ln Indian Wells (92210) *(P-23532)*
Callaway Golf Company (PA)....B....760 931-1771
2180 Rutherford Rd Carlsbad (92008) *(P-23533)*
Callaway Vineyard & Winery....D....951 676-4001
32720 Rancho Cal Rd Temecula (92591) *(P-1678)*
Calleen Cordero Designs Inc....F....818 764-0715
7384 Beverly Blvd Los Angeles (90036) *(P-10494)*
Calleen Cordero Retail, Los Angeles *Also called Calleen Cordero Designs Inc (P-10494)*
Callisto Shoes Rolling Hills, Torrance *Also called J & A Shoe Company Inc (P-10498)*
Calmar Laser, Palo Alto *Also called Calmar Optcom Inc (P-17929)*
Calmar Optcom Inc....E....408 733-7800
951 Commercial St Palo Alto (94303) *(P-17929)*
Calmat Co (HQ)....C....818 553-8821
500 N Brand Blvd Ste 500 # 500 Glendale (91203) *(P-9379)*
Calmat Co....E....661 858-2673
16101 Hwy 156 Maricopa (93252) *(P-311)*
Calmax Technology Inc (PA)....D....408 748-8660
526 Laurelwood Rd Santa Clara (95054) *(P-16357)*
Calmex Fireplace Equip Mfg, Santa Fe Springs *Also called Calmex Fireplace Equipment Mfg (P-11943)*
Calmex Fireplace Equipment Mfg....F....716 645-2901
13629 Talc St Santa Fe Springs (90670) *(P-11943)*
Calmini Products Inc....F....661 398-9500
6951 Mcdivitt Dr Bakersfield (93313) *(P-20282)*
Calmont Engineering & Elec (PA)....E....714 549-0336
420 E Alton Ave Santa Ana (92707) *(P-11650)*
Calmont Wire & Cable, Santa Ana *Also called Calmont Engineering & Elec (P-11650)*
Calmoseptine Inc....F....714 848-2949
16602 Burke Ln Huntington Beach (92647) *(P-8095)*
Calmut Industrial Asphalt, Glendale *Also called Huntmix Inc (P-9387)*
Calnetix Inc (PA)....C....562 293-1660
16323 Shoemaker Ave Cerritos (90703) *(P-17183)*
Calnetix Technologies, Cerritos *Also called Calnetix Inc (P-17183)*
Calnetix Technologies LLC....D....562 293-1660
16323 Shoemaker Ave Cerritos (90703) *(P-17184)*
Calogic LLC (PA)....F....510 656-2900
237 Whitney Pl Fremont (94539) *(P-21733)*
Calor Apparel Group Intl Corp....E....949 548-9095
884 W 16th St Newport Beach (92663) *(P-3534)*
Calpaco Papers Inc (PA)....C....323 767-2800
3155 Universe Dr Mira Loma (91752) *(P-5702)*
Calpak Usa Inc....E....310 937-7335
2110 Artesia Blvd B202 Redondo Beach (90278) *(P-18443)*
Calperf Inc....F....408 829-7779
1810 Richard Ave Santa Clara (95050) *(P-422)*
Calpi Inc....F....661 589-5648
7141 Downing Ave Bakersfield (93308) *(P-193)*
Calpico Inc....E....650 588-2241
1387 San Mateo Ave South San Francisco (94080) *(P-17448)*
Calpipe Security Bollards, Compton *Also called Cal Pipe Manufacturing Inc (P-13880)*
Calportland, Colton *Also called Cal Portland Cement Co (P-11054)*
Calportland....F....760 343-3403
2025 E Financial Way Glendora (91741) *(P-349)*
Calportland....F....760 343-3126
72200 Vista Chino Thousand Palms (92276) *(P-350)*
Calportland Company....D....805 345-3400
219 Tank Farm Rd San Luis Obispo (93401) *(P-10743)*
Calportland Company....C....661 824-2401
9350 Oak Creek Rd Mojave (93501) *(P-10744)*
Calportland Company....E....909 825-4260
695 S Rancho Ave Colton (92324) *(P-10745)*
Calportland Company....F....760 245-5321
19409 National Trails Hwy Oro Grande (92368) *(P-10746)*
Calportland Company....F....209 469-0109
2201 W Washington St # 6 Stockton (95203) *(P-10747)*
Calportland Company (HQ)....D....626 852-6200
2025 E Financial Way Glendora (91741) *(P-10748)*
Calportland Company....E....818 767-0508
8981 Bradley Ave Sun Valley (91352) *(P-10749)*
Calportland Company....F....626 334-3226
1030 W Gladstone St Azusa (91702) *(P-11056)*
Calportland Company....D....626 691-2596
590 Live Oak Ave Irwindale (91706) *(P-10750)*

Calram LLC F 805 987-6205
829 Via Alondra Camarillo (93012) *(P-13928)*
Calspray Inc F 650 325-0096
1905 Bay Rd East Palo Alto (94303) *(P-13565)*
Calstar Products Inc D 262 752-9131
3945 Freedom Cir Ste 560 Santa Clara (95054) *(P-10773)*
Calstone Company F 408 686-9627
13755 Llagas Ave San Martin (95046) *(P-10846)*
Calstone Company E 209 745-2981
421 Crystal Way Galt (95632) *(P-10847)*
Calstrip Industries Inc (PA) E 323 726-1345
3030 Dulles Dr Mira Loma (91752) *(P-11468)*
Calstrip Steel Corporation (HQ) D 323 838-2097
3030 Dulles Dr Mira Loma (91752) *(P-11805)*
Caltex Plastics Inc (PA) E 800 584-7303
2380 E 51st St Vernon (90058) *(P-5590)*
Caltoy, Buena Park *Also called Dream International Usa Inc (P-23396)*
Calva Products Co Inc E 209 339-1516
4351 E Winery Rd Acampo (95220) *(P-716)*
Calwest Galvanizing Corp D 310 549-2200
2226 E Dominguez St Long Beach (90810) *(P-13566)*
Calypto Design Systems Inc F 408 850-2300
2099 Gateway Pl Ste 550 San Jose (95110) *(P-24469)*
Calysta Inc (PA) E 650 492-6880
1140 Obrien Dr Ste B Menlo Park (94025) *(P-8993)*
Calzyme Laboratories Inc (PA) F 805 541-5754
3443 Miguelito Ct San Luis Obispo (93401) *(P-8994)*
CAM, Fullerton *Also called Consolidated Aerospace Mfg LLC (P-21276)*
CAM-Tech, Irvine *Also called Computer Asssted Mfg Tech Corp (P-16396)*
Cambero Metal Works Inc F 626 309-5315
210 Agostino Rd San Gabriel (91776) *(P-25392)*
Cambria Winery, Santa Maria *Also called Jackson Family Wines Inc (P-1825)*
Cambrian, Cambria *Also called McClatchy Newspapers Inc (P-5951)*
Cambridge Laser Laboratories F 510 651-0110
853 Brown Rd Fremont (94539) *(P-10682)*
Cambro Manufacturing Company (PA) B 714 848-1555
5801 Skylab Rd Huntington Beach (92647) *(P-10007)*
Cambro Manufacturing Company F 909 354-8962
21558 Ferrero City of Industry (91789) *(P-24058)*
Cambro Manufacturing Company B 714 848-1555
7601 Clay Ave Huntington Beach (92648) *(P-10008)*
Cambro Manufacturing Company B 714 848-1555
5801 Skylab Rd Huntington Beach (92647) *(P-10009)*
Camco Furnace, San Carlos *Also called Concepts & Methods Co Inc (P-15256)*
Camelbak Acquisition Corp C 707 792-9700
2000 S Mcdowell Blvd Petaluma (94954) *(P-23534)*
Camelbak Products LLC (HQ) D 707 792-9700
2000 S Mcdowell Blvd Petaluma (94954) *(P-23535)*
Camelia City Millwork Inc F 916 451-2454
7831 Clifton Rd Sacramento (95826) *(P-4120)*
Cameo Crafts E 513 381-1480
4995 Hillsdale Cir El Dorado Hills (95762) *(P-7264)*
Camera Ready Cars, Fountain Valley *Also called Gaffoglio Fmly Mtlcrafters Inc (P-10699)*
Cameron & Company, Petaluma *Also called Robert W Cameron & Co Inc (P-6387)*
Cameron International Corp F 661 323-8183
4315 Yeager Way Bakersfield (93313) *(P-14213)*
Cameron International Corp E 707 752-8800
535 Getty Ct Ste A Benicia (94510) *(P-14214)*
Cameron International Corp D 530 242-6965
562 River Park Dr Redding (96003) *(P-14215)*
Cameron International Corp D 510 928-1480
1282 Bayview Farm Rd Pinole (94564) *(P-14216)*
Cameron Metal Cutting, Santa Ana *Also called Automation West Inc (P-16290)*
Cameron Micro Drill Presses, Sonora *Also called Treat Enterprises (P-14419)*
Cameron Technologies Us Inc D 562 222-8440
4040 Capitol Ave Whittier (90601) *(P-21556)*
Cameron Welding Supply (PA) E 714 530-9353
11061 Dale Ave Stanton (90680) *(P-25393)*
Cameron West Coast (PA) F 909 355-8995
9452 Resenda Ave Fontana (92335) *(P-14217)*
Cameron's Measurement Systems, Whittier *Also called Cameron Technologies Us Inc (P-21556)*
Camfil USA Inc D 310 370-3673
3625 Del Amo Blvd Ste 260 Torrance (90503) *(P-15146)*
Camfil USA Inc D 559 992-5118
500 Industrial Ave Corcoran (93212) *(P-15147)*
Camino Neurocare D 858 455-1115
5955 Pacific Center Blvd San Diego (92121) *(P-22386)*
Camino Real Foods Inc B 323 585-6599
2638 E Vernon Ave Vernon (90058) *(P-984)*
Camino Real Foods Inc (PA) B 323 585-6599
2638 E Vernon Ave Vernon (90058) *(P-2481)*
Camino Real Kitchens, Vernon *Also called Camino Real Foods Inc (P-2481)*
Camisasca Automotive Mfg Inc E 949 452-0195
20341 Hermana Cir Lake Forest (92630) *(P-13177)*
Camisasca Automotive Mfg Inc (PA) E 949 452-0195
20352 Hermana Cir Lake Forest (92630) *(P-13178)*
Camland Inc F 805 485-9242
3152 Canopy Dr Camarillo (93012) *(P-25394)*
Camlever Inc F 909 629-9669
954 S East End Ave Pomona (91766) *(P-14152)*
Camp Bow Wow Temecula, Temecula *Also called M & L Haight LLC (P-10575)*
Camp Smidgemore Inc (HQ) E 323 634-0333
3641 10th Ave Los Angeles (90018) *(P-3390)*
Campbell & Loftin Inc F 714 871-1950
1560 N Missile Way Anaheim (92801) *(P-12524)*
Campbell Engineering Inc E 949 859-3306
20412 Barents Sea Cir Lake Forest (92630) *(P-14613)*
Campbell Graphics Inc E 408 371-6411
156 N 2nd St Campbell (95008) *(P-6718)*
Campbell Grinding Inc F 209 339-8838
1003 E Vine St Lodi (95240) *(P-16358)*
Campbell Pump Co, Fresno *Also called Lily Pond Products (P-14984)*
Campbell Soup Company C 707 678-4406
8380 Pedrick Rd Dixon (95620) *(P-750)*
Campbell Soup Company D 916 922-2836
2300 River Plaza Dr # 175 Sacramento (95833) *(P-751)*
Campbell Soup Company E 530 753-2116
28605 County Road 104 Davis (95618) *(P-752)*
Camserv, Pinole *Also called Cameron International Corp (P-14216)*
Camsoft Corporation E 951 674-8100
32295 Mission Trl Ste 8 Lake Elsinore (92530) *(P-19857)*
Camtek LLC F 626 508-1700
2645 Nina St Pasadena (91107) *(P-8096)*
Camtek Usa Inc E 510 624-9905
48389 Fremont Blvd # 112 Fremont (94538) *(P-18759)*
Camtron US, Anaheim *Also called Jeico Security Inc (P-19993)*
Can Lines Engineering Inc (PA) D 562 861-2996
9839 Downey Norwalk Rd Downey (90241) *(P-15201)*
Canaan Company, Fresno *Also called DV Kap Inc (P-3721)*
Canadas Finest Foods Inc D 951 296-1040
26090 Ynez Rd Temecula (92591) *(P-942)*
Canadian Solar (usa) Inc F 925 807-7499
3000 Oak Rd Ste 400 Walnut Creek (94597) *(P-18760)*
Canady Manufacturing Co Inc F 818 365-9181
500 5th St San Fernando (91340) *(P-16359)*
Canam Technology Inc F 562 856-0178
5318 E 2nd St Ste 700 Long Beach (90803) *(P-18061)*
Canandaigua Wine Company Inc A 559 673-7071
12667 Road 24 Madera (93637) *(P-1679)*
Canari, Vista *Also called Leemarc Industries LLC (P-3172)*
Canary Communications Inc F 408 365-0609
6040 Hellyer Ave Ste 150 San Jose (95138) *(P-18062)*
Canay Manufacturing Inc F 661 295-0205
26140 Avenue Hall Valencia (91355) *(P-16360)*
Cancer Genetics Inc C 323 224-3900
1640 Marengo St Ste 7 Los Angeles (90033) *(P-8466)*
Candamar Designs Inc E 714 871-6190
520 E Jamie Ave La Habra (90631) *(P-24059)*
Candella Lighting Co Inc F 323 798-1091
430 S Pecan St Los Angeles (90033) *(P-17592)*
Candella Lighting Company, Los Angeles *Also called 515 W Seventh LLC (P-17575)*
Candies Tolteca E 559 266-9193
2139 N Pleasant Ave Fresno (93705) *(P-1410)*
Candle Crafters, Simi Valley *Also called Globaluxe Inc (P-24111)*
Candlebay Co F 949 307-1807
3440 W Warner Ave Ste Cd Santa Ana (92704) *(P-24060)*
Candlelight Press Inc E 323 299-3798
26752 Oak Ave Ste F Canyon Country (91351) *(P-6719)*
Candlewick-Porterville, Porterville *Also called Tdg Operations LLC (P-2947)*
Candroy Embroidery, San Diego *Also called Epicson Inc (P-7311)*
Candu Graphics F 310 822-1620
5737 Kanan Rd Ste 132 Agoura Hills (91301) *(P-6720)*
Canidae Corporation F 909 599-5190
1975 Tandem Norco (92860) *(P-1110)*
Canidae Pet Foods, Norco *Also called Canidae Corporation (P-1110)*
Canine Caviar Pet Foods Inc E 714 223-1800
4131 Tigris Way Riverside (92503) *(P-1125)*
Cannalink Inc F 310 921-1955
110 W C St Ste 1300 San Diego (92101) *(P-21557)*
Cannalogic F 619 458-0775
5404 Whitsett Ave 219 Valley Village (91607) *(P-24061)*
Cannon Gasket Inc F 909 355-1547
7784 Edison Ave Fontana (92336) *(P-9522)*
Cannon Sleep Products, Fresno *Also called Pleasant Mattress Inc (P-4879)*
Cano Architecture, Ontario *Also called Precast Repair (P-10980)*
Canoga Perkins Corporation (HQ) D 818 718-6300
20600 Prairie St Chatsworth (91311) *(P-18315)*
Cantabio Pharmaceuticals Inc F 408 501-8893
1250 Oakmead Pkwy Ste 210 Sunnyvale (94085) *(P-8097)*
Canterbury Designs Inc E 323 936-7111
5632 W Washington Blvd Los Angeles (90016) *(P-12841)*
Canterbury International, Los Angeles *Also called Canterbury Designs Inc (P-12841)*
Canvas Awning Co Inc F 909 447-5100
325 W Main St Ontario (91762) *(P-3781)*
Canvas Concepts Inc F 619 424-3428
649 Anita St Ste A2 Chula Vista (91911) *(P-3782)*
Canvas Specialty Inc E 323 722-1156
1309 S Eastern Ave Commerce (90040) *(P-3783)*
Canyon Composites Incorporated E 714 991-8181
1548 N Gemini Pl Anaheim (92801) *(P-20775)*
Canyon Engineering Pdts Inc D 661 294-0084
28909 Avenue Williams Valencia (91355) *(P-20776)*
Canyon Graphics Inc D 858 646-0444
6680 Cobra Way San Diego (92121) *(P-4121)*
Canyon Plastics Inc D 661 257-4293
28455 Livingston Ave Valencia (91355) *(P-10010)*
Canyon Road Winery, Healdsburg *Also called Geyser Peak Winery (P-1781)*
Canyon Rock & Asphalt, San Diego *Also called Superior Ready Mix Concrete LP (P-11191)*
Canyon Rock Co Inc E 707 887-2207
7525 Hwy 116 Forestville (95436) *(P-351)*
Canyon Steel Fabricators Inc E 951 683-2352
1751 Spruce St Riverside (92507) *(P-12975)*
Canzone and Company E 714 537-8175
1345 W Cowles St Long Beach (90813) *(P-23839)*

ALPHABETIC

Employee Codes: A=Over 500 employees, B=251-500
C=101-250, D=51-100, E=20-50, F=10-19
2019 California
Manfacturers Register
© Mergent Inc. 1-800-342-5647
1091

Capax Technologies Inc ... E ... 661 257-7666
24842 Avenue Tibbitts Valencia (91355) ***(P-17335)***
Capco/Psa ... E ... 818 762-4276
11125 Vanowen St North Hollywood (91605) ***(P-10011)***
Capella Microsystems Inc ... E ... 408 988-8000
2201 Laurelwood Rd Santa Clara (95054) ***(P-18444)***
Caperon Designs Inc ... F ... 714 552-3201
1733 Monrovia Ave Ste N Costa Mesa (92627) ***(P-23415)***
Capistrano Labs Inc ... E ... 949 492-0390
150 Calle Iglesia Ste B San Clemente (92672) ***(P-22387)***
Capital Cooking Equipment ... E ... 562 903-1168
13211 Florence Ave Santa Fe Springs (90670) ***(P-12060)***
Capital Corrugated and Carton, Sacramento *Also called Capital Corrugated LLC* ***(P-5394)***
Capital Corrugated LLC ... D ... 916 388-7848
8333 24th Ave Sacramento (95826) ***(P-5394)***
Capital Technology Inc ... F ... 909 293-8887
13980 Central Ave Chino (91710) ***(P-17388)***
Capitol Beverage Packers ... D ... 916 929-7777
2670 Land Ave Sacramento (95815) ***(P-2108)***
Capitol Components, Sacramento *Also called Capitol Store Fixtures* ***(P-4935)***
Capitol Iron Works Inc ... E ... 916 381-1554
7009 Power Inn Rd Sacramento (95828) ***(P-12128)***
Capitol Machine Co, Santa Ana *Also called M & W Machine Corporation* ***(P-16701)***
Capitol Neon ... F ... 916 349-1800
5920 Rosebud Ln Ste 1 Sacramento (95841) ***(P-23840)***
Capitol Steel Fabricators Inc ... E ... 323 721-5460
3565 Greenwood Ave Commerce (90040) ***(P-12129)***
Capitol Steel Products ... F ... 916 383-3368
6331 Power Inn Rd Ste B Sacramento (95824) ***(P-11290)***
Capitol Store Fixtures ... E ... 916 646-9096
4220 Pell Dr Ste C Sacramento (95838) ***(P-4935)***
Capitol Tarpaulin Co, Sacramento *Also called Philip A Stitt Agency* ***(P-3804)***
Caplugs, Rancho Dominguez *Also called Protective Industries Inc* ***(P-9665)***
Capo Industries Division, El Cajon *Also called Senior Operations LLC* ***(P-16938)***
Cappac Plastic Products ... E ... 323 721-7542
5835 S Malt Ave Commerce (90040) ***(P-9824)***
Capricor Therapeutics Inc (PA) ... F ... 310 358-3200
8840 Wilshire Blvd Fl 2 Beverly Hills (90211) ***(P-8098)***
Caps, Irvine *Also called Central Admxture Phrm Svcs Inc* ***(P-8107)***
Caps & Tabs Inc ... E ... 619 285-5400
3111 Camino Del Rio N # 400 San Diego (92108) ***(P-608)***
Caps Corporate Office ... E ... 562 941-9515
10370 Slusher Dr Ste 3 Santa Fe Springs (90670) ***(P-8099)***
Capsa Solutions LLC ... E ... 800 437-6633
14000 S Broadway Los Angeles (90061) ***(P-15518)***
Capstan Permaflow ... F ... 310 366-5999
16110 S Figueroa St Gardena (90248) ***(P-16361)***
Capstone Fire Management Inc (PA) ... E ... 760 839-2290
2240 Auto Park Way Escondido (92029) ***(P-15305)***
Capstone Turbine Corporation (PA) ... C ... 818 734-5300
16640 Stagg St Van Nuys (91406) ***(P-13991)***
Captek Softgel Intl Inc (PA) ... C ... 562 921-9511
16218 Arthur St Cerritos (90703) ***(P-1523)***
Captive Ocean Reef Enterprises ... F ... 949 581-8888
34135 Moongate Ct Dana Point (92629) ***(P-15306)***
Captive Plastics Inc ... D ... 209 858-9188
601 Nestle Way Ste A Lathrop (95330) ***(P-10012)***
Captive-Aire Systems Inc ... F ... 951 231-5102
2510 Cloudcrest Way Riverside (92507) ***(P-12525)***
Captive-Aire Systems Inc ... C ... 530 351-7150
6856 Lockheed Dr Redding (96002) ***(P-12526)***
CAr Enterprises Inc ... F ... 760 947-6411
13100 Main St Hesperia (92345) ***(P-15895)***
Car Sound Exhaust System Inc ... D ... 949 858-5900
1901 Corporate Ctr Oceanside (92056) ***(P-20283)***
Car Sound Exhaust System Inc (PA) ... E ... 949 858-5900
1901 Corporate Ctr Oceanside (92056) ***(P-20284)***
Car Sound Exhaust System Inc ... E ... 949 888-1625
1901 Corporate Ctr Oceanside (92056) ***(P-7761)***
Car Sound Exhaust System Inc ... D ... 949 858-5900
30142 Ave De Las Bndra Rcho STA Marg (92688) ***(P-20285)***
Car Sound Exhaust System Inc ... E ... 949 858-5900
23201 Antonio Pkwy Rcho STA Marg (92688) ***(P-20286)***
Caracal Enterprises LLC ... E ... 707 773-3373
1260 Holm Rd Ste A Petaluma (94954) ***(P-15920)***
Caran Precision Engrg Mfg Corp ... D ... 714 447-5400
2830 Orbiter St Brea (92821) ***(P-13179)***
Carando Technologies Inc ... E ... 209 948-6500
345 N Harrison St Stockton (95203) ***(P-14434)***
Caraustar Industries Inc ... C ... 209 464-6590
800b W Church St Stockton (95203) ***(P-5344)***
Caraustar Industries Inc ... E ... 951 685-5544
4502 E Airport Dr Ontario (91761) ***(P-5482)***
Caraustar Industries Inc ... C ... 408 845-7600
525 Mathew St Santa Clara (95050) ***(P-5345)***
Caravan Bakery Inc ... E ... 510 487-2600
33300 Western Ave Union City (94587) ***(P-1217)***
Caravan Manufacturing Co Inc ... F ... 714 220-9722
10814 Los Vaqueros Cir Los Alamitos (90720) ***(P-10013)***
Caravan Trading Company ... D ... 510 487-8090
33300 Western Ave Union City (94587) ***(P-1218)***
Carberry LLC (HQ) ... E ... 800 564-0842
17130 Muskrat Ave Ste B Adelanto (92301) ***(P-1411)***
Carbide Company LLC ... D ... 760 477-1000
2470 Ash St Ste 1 Vista (92081) ***(P-14614)***
Carbide Products Co Inc ... F ... 310 320-7910
22711 S Western Ave Torrance (90501) ***(P-11291)***
Carboline Company ... E ... 909 459-1090
5533 Brooks St Montclair (91763) ***(P-8887)***
Carbomer Inc ... D ... 858 552-0992
6324 Ferris Sq Ste B San Diego (92121) ***(P-7762)***
Carbon Inc ... C ... 650 285-6307
1089 Mills Way Redwood City (94063) ***(P-15699)***
Carbon By Design LLC ... D ... 760 643-1300
4128 Avenida De La Plata A Oceanside (92056) ***(P-20777)***
Carbon California Company LLC ... D ... 805 933-1901
270 Quail Ct Ste B Santa Paula (93060) ***(P-46)***
Carbon Recycling Incorporated ... F ... 619 491-9200
7938 Ivanhoe Ave Ste B La Jolla (92037) ***(P-8995)***
Carbon Recycling Inernational, La Jolla *Also called Carbon Recycling Incorporated* ***(P-8995)***
Carbon Solutions Inc ... F ... 909 234-2738
5094 Victoria Hill Dr Riverside (92506) ***(P-17235)***
Carbonyte Systems Incorporated ... F ... 916 387-0316
3 Wayne Ct Ste A Sacramento (95829) ***(P-8888)***
Carbro Corporation ... E ... 310 643-8400
15724 Condon Ave Lawndale (90260) ***(P-14615)***
Card Nale Tasting Room,, Oakville *Also called Jackson Family Wines Inc* ***(P-1822)***
Card Scanning Solutions, Los Angeles *Also called Acuant Inc* ***(P-15657)***
Cardenas Enterprises Inc ... F ... 323 588-0137
5232 Alcoa Ave Vernon (90058) ***(P-5132)***
Cardiaq Valve Technologies Inc, Irvine *Also called Edwards Lfsciences Cardiaq LLC* ***(P-22433)***
Cardic Machine Products Inc ... F ... 310 884-3400
17000 Keegan Ave Carson (90746) ***(P-16362)***
Cardigan Road Productions ... E ... 310 289-1442
1999 Ave Of The Sts 110 Los Angeles (90067) ***(P-19478)***
Cardinal C G, Moreno Valley *Also called Cardinal Glass Industries Inc* ***(P-10588)***
Cardinal Cg Company, Galt *Also called Cardinal Glass Industries Inc* ***(P-10589)***
Cardinal Cg Company, Los Angeles *Also called Cardinal Glass Industries Inc* ***(P-10683)***
Cardinal Glass Industries Inc ... D ... 951 485-9007
24100 Cardinal Ave Moreno Valley (92551) ***(P-10588)***
Cardinal Glass Industries Inc ... C ... 209 744-8940
680 Industrial Dr Galt (95632) ***(P-10589)***
Cardinal Glass Industries Inc ... E ... 323 319-0070
1125 E Lanzit Ave Los Angeles (90059) ***(P-10683)***
Cardinal Health 414 LLC ... E ... 714 572-9900
640 S Jefferson St Placentia (92870) ***(P-8100)***
Cardinal Industrial Finishes (PA) ... D ... 626 444-9274
1329 Potrero Ave South El Monte (91733) ***(P-8889)***
Cardinal Industrial Finishes ... E ... 408 452-8522
890 Commercial St San Jose (95112) ***(P-8890)***
Cardinal Laboratories Inc ... D ... 626 610-1200
710 S Ayon Ave Azusa (91702) ***(P-8714)***
Cardinal Paint and Powder Inc ... C ... 626 444-9274
1329 Potrero Ave South El Monte (91733) ***(P-8891)***
Cardinal Paint and Powder Inc ... E ... 626 937-6767
15010 Don Julian Rd City of Industry (91746) ***(P-8892)***
Cardinal Pharmaceutical, Santa Fe Springs *Also called Altura Pharmaceuticals Inc* ***(P-8018)***
Cardinal Sheet Metal Inc ... F ... 951 788-8800
3184 Durahart St Riverside (92507) ***(P-12527)***
Cardiomart Inc ... E ... 818 516-6875
11715 Avenida Del Sol Northridge (91326) ***(P-5683)***
Cardiovascular Systems, Tustin *Also called Terumo Americas Holding Inc* ***(P-22028)***
Cardiva Medical Inc ... C ... 408 470-7100
2900 Lakeside Dr Ste 160 Santa Clara (95054) ***(P-22388)***
Cardlogix ... F ... 949 380-1312
16 Hughes Ste 100 Irvine (92618) ***(P-15700)***
Cardona Manufacturing Corp ... E ... 818 841-8358
1869 N Victory Pl Burbank (91504) ***(P-20778)***
Care Fusion ... A ... 858 617-2000
10020 Pacific Mesa Blvd San Diego (92121) ***(P-22389)***
Care Fusion Products, San Diego *Also called Carefusion Corporation* ***(P-22393)***
Care Innovations LLC ... E ... 800 450-0970
950 Iron Point Rd Ste 160 Folsom (95630) ***(P-22957)***
Care Tex Industries Inc (PA) ... D ... 323 567-5074
4583 Firestone Blvd South Gate (90280) ***(P-2828)***
Carecognitics LLC ... F ... 702 355-8201
530 Lytton Ave Fl 2 Palo Alto (94301) ***(P-24470)***
Career Cap Corporation ... E ... 619 575-2277
1680 Industrial Blvd Chula Vista (91911) ***(P-3561)***
Career Tech Circuit Services, Northridge *Also called Circuit Services Llc* ***(P-18451)***
Carefusion 207 Inc ... B ... 760 778-7200
1100 Bird Center Dr Palm Springs (92262) ***(P-22390)***
Carefusion 211 Inc ... A ... 714 283-2228
22745 Savi Ranch Pkwy Yorba Linda (92887) ***(P-22391)***
Carefusion 213 LLC (HQ) ... B ... 800 523-0502
3750 Torrey View Ct San Diego (92130) ***(P-22392)***
Carefusion Corporation ... F ... 888 876-4287
3750 Torrey View Ct San Diego (92130) ***(P-22393)***
Carefusion Corporation (HQ) ... B ... 858 617-2000
3750 Torrey View Ct San Diego (92130) ***(P-22958)***
Carefusion Corporation ... E ... 800 231-2466
22745 Savi Ranch Pkwy Yorba Linda (92887) ***(P-22394)***
Caretex Inc ... D ... 323 567-5074
4581 Firestone Blvd South Gate (90280) ***(P-8960)***
Caretta Inc ... F ... 818 781-9486
13400 Saticoy St Ste 1 North Hollywood (91605) ***(P-23248)***
Carevault Corporation ... F ... 714 333-0556
182 Exbourne Ave Ste 200 San Carlos (94070) ***(P-24471)***
Cargill Incorporated ... D ... 714 449-6708
600 N Gilbert St Fullerton (92833) ***(P-7925)***
Cargill Incorporated ... E ... 323 588-2274
566 N Gilbert St Fullerton (92833) ***(P-1537)***
Cargill Flour Milling Division, San Bernardino *Also called Ardent Mills LLC* ***(P-1032)***
Cargill Meat Solutions Corp ... C ... 559 875-2232
2350 Academy Ave Sanger (93657) ***(P-423)***
Cargill Meat Solutions Corp ... E ... 909 476-3120
10602 N Trademark Pkwy # 500 Rancho Cucamonga (91730) ***(P-424)***

Mergent e-mail: customerrelations@mergent.com
1092
2019 California
Manufacturers Register
(P-0000) Products & Services Section entry number
(PA)=Parent Co (HQ)=Headquarters (DH)=Div Headquarters

Cargill Meat Solutions Corp ... C ... 559 268-5586
3115 S Fig Ave Fresno (93706) ***(P-425)***
Cargill Molasses, Stockton *Also called Westway Feed Products LLC* ***(P-1170)***
Cargo Chief Inc ... F ... 650 560-5001
10 Rollins Rd Ste 202 Millbrae (94030) ***(P-24472)***
Cargo Data Corporation ... F ... 805 650-5922
1502 Eastman Ave Ste A Ventura (93003) ***(P-22176)***
Caribbean Coffee Company Inc ... F ... 805 692-2200
495 Pine Ave Ste A Goleta (93117) ***(P-1055)***
Carl & Irving Printers Inc ... F ... 559 686-8354
161 N N St Tulare (93274) ***(P-6721)***
Carl Herrmann Associates ... E ... 510 683-8554
4201 Business Center Dr Fremont (94538) ***(P-14926)***
Carl Nersesian ... F ... 818 888-0111
13415 Saticoy St North Hollywood (91605) ***(P-4122)***
Carl Zeiss Inc ... E ... 925 557-4100
5160 Hacienda Dr Dublin (94568) ***(P-22061)***
Carl Zeiss Meditec Inc (HQ) ... B ... 925 557-4100
5160 Hacienda Dr Dublin (94568) ***(P-22062)***
Carl Zeiss Meditec Inc ... E ... 858 716-0661
5160 Hacienda Dr Dublin (94568) ***(P-22063)***
Carl Zeiss Meditec Prod LLC ... D ... 877 644-4657
1040 S Vintage Ave Ste A Ontario (91761) ***(P-22395)***
Carl Zeiss Meditec,, Ontario *Also called Aaren Scientific Inc* ***(P-22055)***
Carl Zeiss Ophthalmic Systems ... C ... 925 557-4100
5160 Hacienda Dr Dublin (94568) ***(P-22396)***
Carl Zeiss Vision Inc (HQ) ... D ... 858 790-7700
12121 Scripps Summit Dr San Diego (92131) ***(P-23084)***
Carl Ziss X-Ray Microscopy Inc ... D ... 925 701-3600
4385 Hopyard Rd Ste 100 Pleasanton (94588) ***(P-22929)***
Carley Inc (PA) ... B ... 310 325-8474
1502 W 228th St Torrance (90501) ***(P-10637)***
Carlisle Interconnect, El Segundo *Also called Tri-Star Electronics Intl Inc* ***(P-17502)***
Carlisle Interconnect Tech Inc ... E ... 951 788-0252
4200 Garner Rd Riverside (92501) ***(P-11433)***
Carlos Shower Doors Inc ... F ... 661 327-5594
300 Kentucky St Bakersfield (93305) ***(P-10684)***
Carlsbad Manufacturing, San Diego *Also called Stone Yard Inc* ***(P-4920)***
Carlsbad Technology Inc ... F ... 760 431-8284
5928 Farnsworth Ct Carlsbad (92008) ***(P-8101)***
Carlsbad Technology Inc (HQ) ... D ... 760 431-8284
5922 Farnsworth Ct # 102 Carlsbad (92008) ***(P-8102)***
Carlsbad Technology Inc ... D ... 760 431-8284
5923 Balfour Ct Carlsbad (92008) ***(P-8103)***
Carlson & Beauloye Air Pwr Inc ... F ... 619 232-5719
2143 Newton Ave San Diego (92113) ***(P-16363)***
Carlson & Beauloye Mach Sp Inc ... F ... 619 232-5719
2141 Newton Ave San Diego (92113) ***(P-16364)***
Carlson Wireless Tech Inc ... F ... 707 822-7000
3134 Jacobs Ave Ste C Eureka (95501) ***(P-18063)***
Carlstar Group LLC ... C ... 310 816-1015
1990 S Vintage Ave Ontario (91761) ***(P-9462)***
Carlyle Glasgow Wldg Svcs Inc ... F ... 909 902-1814
4747 E State St Ste A Ontario (91762) ***(P-12130)***
Carmel Communications Inc ... F ... 831 274-8593
734 Lighthouse Ave Pacific Grove (93950) ***(P-5795)***
Carmel Food Group Inc ... E ... 510 471-4889
31128 San Clemente St Hayward (94544) ***(P-2482)***
Carmel Instruments LLC ... F ... 408 866-0426
1622 W Campbell Ave Campbell (95008) ***(P-21558)***
Carmel Pine Cone, The, Pacific Grove *Also called Carmel Communications Inc* ***(P-5795)***
Carmen Abato Enterprises ... F ... 714 895-1887
11258 Monarch St Ste G Garden Grove (92841) ***(P-11651)***
Carmenet Vineyards, Sonoma *Also called Treasury Chateau & Estates* ***(P-2020)***
Carmi Flavors, Commerce *Also called Carmi Flvr & Fragrance Co Inc* ***(P-2251)***
Carmi Flvr & Fragrance Co Inc (PA) ... E ... 323 888-9240
6030 Scott Way Commerce (90040) ***(P-2251)***
Carmine, Newport Beach *Also called Microtelematics Inc* ***(P-24919)***
Carnevale & Lohr Inc ... E ... 562 927-8311
6521 Clara St Bell Gardens (90201) ***(P-11239)***
Caro Nut Company ... E ... 559 439-2365
2904 S Angus Ave Fresno (93725) ***(P-878)***
Carol Anderson Inc (PA) ... E ... 310 638-3333
18700 S Laurel Park Rd Rancho Dominguez (90220) ***(P-3300)***
Carol Anderson By Invitation, Rancho Dominguez *Also called Carol Anderson Inc* ***(P-3300)***
Carol Wior Inc ... D ... 562 927-0052
7533 Garfield Ave Bell (90201) ***(P-3391)***
Carolina Lquid Chmistries Corp ... F ... 336 722-8910
510 W Central Ave Ste C Brea (92821) ***(P-22397)***
Carols Roman Shades Inc (PA) ... E ... 925 674-9622
130 Mason Cir Ste K Concord (94520) ***(P-5184)***
Carols Roman Shades Inc ... F ... 925 674-9622
130 Mason Cir Ste K Concord (94520) ***(P-5185)***
Caron Compactor Co ... E ... 800 448-8236
1204 Ullrey Ave Escalon (95320) ***(P-14153)***
Carousel Carpet Mills Inc ... D ... 415 892-8207
19 Bryan Dr Novato (94945) ***(P-2927)***
Carousel USA, Irwindale *Also called JE Thomson & Company LLC* ***(P-14330)***
Carparts Technologies ... C ... 949 488-8860
32122 Camn Capistrano # 100 San Juan Capistrano (92675) ***(P-24473)***
Carpenter Co ... B ... 951 354-7550
7809 Lincoln Ave Riverside (92504) ***(P-9825)***
Carpenter E R Co, Riverside *Also called Carpenter Co* ***(P-9825)***
Carpenter Group (PA) ... E ... 415 285-1954
222 Napoleon St San Francisco (94124) ***(P-14294)***
Carpenter Group ... F ... 707 562-3543
112 Bgley St Crnr Of Rlro Corner Of Railro Vallejo (94592) ***(P-13817)***
Carpenter Group ... F ... 562 942-8076
13100 Firestone Blvd Santa Fe Springs (90670) ***(P-13818)***
Carpenter Specialty Alloys, Rancho Cucamonga *Also called Carpenter Technology Corp* ***(P-11386)***
Carpenter Technology Corp ... E ... 909 476-4000
8250 Milliken Ave Rancho Cucamonga (91730) ***(P-11386)***
Carpentry Millwork, Fresno *Also called Architectural Wood Design Inc* ***(P-4105)***
Carpod Inc ... F ... 818 395-8676
12132 Gothic Ave Granada Hills (91344) ***(P-10014)***
Carr Corporation (PA) ... E ... 310 587-1113
1547 11th St Santa Monica (90401) ***(P-22930)***
Carr Manufacturing Company Inc ... F ... 949 215-7952
19675 Descartes Foothill Ranch (92610) ***(P-17449)***
Carr Pattern Co Inc ... F ... 951 719-1068
27447 Bostik Ct Temecula (92590) ***(P-13139)***
Carreon Development Inc ... F ... 619 690-4973
4286 Powderhorn Dr San Diego (92154) ***(P-23841)***
Carrera Construction Inc ... F ... 831 728-3299
1961 Main St Ste 261 Watsonville (95076) ***(P-194)***
Carrier Corporation ... B ... 510 347-2000
600 Mccormick St Ste B San Leandro (94577) ***(P-15944)***
Carriercomm Inc ... E ... 805 968-9621
82 Coromar Dr Goleta (93117) ***(P-18064)***
Carris Reels California Inc (HQ) ... E ... 559 674-0804
2100 W Almond Ave Madera (93637) ***(P-4613)***
Carroll Metal Works Inc ... D ... 619 477-9125
740 W 16th St National City (91950) ***(P-12131)***
Carros Sensors Systems Co LLC ... C ... 925 979-4400
355 Lennon Ln Walnut Creek (94598) ***(P-19479)***
Carros Sensors Systems Co LLC (HQ) ... C ... 805 968-0782
1461 Lawrence Dr Thousand Oaks (91320) ***(P-19480)***
Carryoutsupplies.com, Monrovia *Also called S W C Group Inc* ***(P-5500)***
Carson Valley Inc ... F ... 562 906-0062
13215 Barton Cir Whittier (90605) ***(P-12528)***
Carson's Coatings, Galt *Also called Carsons Inc* ***(P-13180)***
Carsons Inc ... E ... 209 745-2387
550 Industrial Dr Ste 200 Galt (95632) ***(P-13180)***
Cartel Industries LLC ... E ... 949 474-3200
17152 Armstrong Ave Irvine (92614) ***(P-12529)***
Carter Group (PA) ... E ... 916 333-5070
511 Houston St West Sacramento (95691) ***(P-12132)***
Carter Holt Harvey Holdings ... D ... 951 272-8180
1230 Railroad St Corona (92882) ***(P-11387)***
Carter Plating Inc ... F ... 818 842-1325
1842 N Keystone St Burbank (91504) ***(P-13366)***
Carter Pump & Machine Inc ... F ... 661 393-8620
635 G St Wasco (93280) ***(P-16365)***
Carton Design, Pico Rivera *Also called CD Container Inc* ***(P-5395)***
Carttronics LLC (HQ) ... E ... 888 696-2278
8 Studebaker Irvine (92618) ***(P-19924)***
Carturner Inc (PA) ... F ... 760 598-7448
929 Poinsettia Ave # 104 Vista (92081) ***(P-22177)***
Caruthers Raisin Pkg Co Inc (PA) ... D ... 559 864-9448
12797 S Elm Ave Caruthers (93609) ***(P-879)***
Carvalho Family Winery LLC ... F ... 916 744-1615
35265 Willow Ave Clarksburg (95612) ***(P-1680)***
Carving Ice, Placentia *Also called R&Js Business Group Inc* ***(P-2419)***
Casa Agria ... F ... 805 485-1454
701 Del Norte Blvd Oxnard (93030) ***(P-1577)***
Casa De Hermandad (PA) ... E ... 310 477-8272
11750 W Pico Blvd Los Angeles (90064) ***(P-23536)***
Casa Grande Woodworks ... E ... 805 226-2040
4230 Cloud Way Paso Robles (93446) ***(P-4123)***
Casa Herrera Inc (PA) ... C ... 909 392-3930
2655 Pine St Pomona (91767) ***(P-14840)***
Casa Mexico Enterprises Inc ... F ... 888 411-9530
3156 Foothill Blvd Ste G La Crescenta (91214) ***(P-7265)***
Casa Sanchez Foods, Hayward *Also called Fante Inc* ***(P-2380)***
Cascade Optical Coating Inc ... F ... 714 543-9777
1225 E Hunter Ave Santa Ana (92705) ***(P-22064)***
Cascade Pump Company ... D ... 562 946-1414
10107 Norwalk Blvd Santa Fe Springs (90670) ***(P-15056)***
Casco Mfg, San Fernando *Also called C A Schroeder Inc* ***(P-11329)***
Case Automation Corporation ... F ... 951 493-6666
208 Jason Ct Corona (92879) ***(P-14268)***
Case Club, Anaheim *Also called Foam Plastics & Rbr Pdts Corp* ***(P-9849)***
Case Hardigg Center ... F ... 413 665-2163
651 Barrington Ave Ste A Ontario (91764) ***(P-4439)***
Case World Co ... F ... 626 330-1000
301 S Doubleday Ave Ontario (91761) ***(P-10558)***
Case's Oil, Riverdale *Also called C Case Company Inc* ***(P-189)***
Casella, Sacramento *Also called Clarus Lighting LLC* ***(P-17680)***
Casella Aluminum Extrusions ... F ... 714 961-8322
824 N Todd Ave Azusa (91702) ***(P-11584)***
Casemaker Inc ... F ... 408 261-8265
1680 Civic Center Dr Frnt Santa Clara (95050) ***(P-24474)***
Caseworx Inc ... E ... 909 799-8550
1130 Research Dr Redlands (92374) ***(P-4936)***
Casey Printing Inc ... E ... 831 385-3221
398 E San Antonio Dr King City (93930) ***(P-6722)***
Cashnet, Oakland *Also called Higher One Payments Inc* ***(P-24733)***
Casmari Inc ... F ... 818 727-1856
9035 Eton Ave Ste C Canoga Park (91304) ***(P-2829)***
Cason Engineering Inc ... E ... 916 939-9311
4952 Windplay Dr Ste D El Dorado Hills (95762) ***(P-16366)***
Caspers, San Leandro *Also called Spar Sausage Co* ***(P-527)***
Caspian Research & Tech LLC ... F ... 310 474-3244
1434 Westwood Blvd Ste 14 Los Angeles (90024) ***(P-24475)***
Caspio Inc (PA) ... E ... 650 691-0900
2953 Bunker Hill Ln # 201 Santa Clara (95054) ***(P-24476)***

Employee Codes: A=Over 500 employees, B=251-500
C=101-250, D=51-100, E=20-50, F=10-19
2019 California
Manfacturers Register
© Mergent Inc. 1-800-342-5647
1093

Cast Parts Inc (HQ)......C......909 595-2252
4200 Valley Blvd Walnut (91789) ***(P-11508)***
Cast Parts Inc......C......626 937-3444
16800 Chestnut St City of Industry (91748) ***(P-11509)***
Cast-Rite Corporation......D......310 532-2080
515 E Airline Way Gardena (90248) ***(P-14493)***
Cast-Rite International Inc (PA)......D......310 532-2080
515 E Airline Way Gardena (90248) ***(P-11771)***
Castaic Brick, Castaic *Also called Clay Castaic Manufacturing Co* ***(P-10775)***
Castaic Clay Products LLC......D......661 259-3066
32201 Castaic Lake Dr Castaic (91384) ***(P-10774)***
Castaic Lake R V Park Inc......F......661 257-3340
31540 Ridge Route Rd Castaic (91384) ***(P-4546)***
Castaic R V Park, Castaic *Also called Castaic Lake R V Park Inc* ***(P-4546)***
Castaic Truck Stop Inc......E......661 295-1374
31611 Castaic Rd Castaic (91384) ***(P-9324)***
Castello Diamorosa, Calistoga *Also called Villa Amorosa* ***(P-2041)***
Castle & Cooke Inc......D......951 245-2460
28251 Lake St Lake Elsinore (92530) ***(P-14154)***
Castle Design & Fabrication, Los Angeles *Also called Multimedia Operations Design* ***(P-5156)***
Castle Hill Holdings Inc......F......925 943-1119
3161 Putnam Blvd Pleasant Hill (94523) ***(P-22712)***
Castle Importing Inc......F......909 428-9200
14550 Miller Ave Fontana (92336) ***(P-566)***
Castlelite Block LLC (PA)......E......707 678-3465
8615 Robben Rd Dixon (95620) ***(P-10848)***
Castor Engineering Inc......F......562 690-4036
450 Commercial Way La Habra (90631) ***(P-11727)***
Castoro Cellars......F......805 467-2002
6465 Von Dollen Rd San Miguel (93451) ***(P-1681)***
Castoro Cellars (PA)......E......805 467-2002
1315 N Bethel Rd Templeton (93465) ***(P-1682)***
Castro Valley Forum, Alameda *Also called Eastbay Publishing Corp* ***(P-5838)***
Casual Fridays Inc......E......858 433-1442
3990 Old Town Ave A203 San Diego (92110) ***(P-6457)***
Casual Lamps California Inc (PA)......E......310 323-0105
15000 S Broadway Gardena (90248) ***(P-17422)***
Casualway Home & Garden, Oxnard *Also called Casualway Usa LLC* ***(P-4828)***
Casualway Usa LLC......D......805 660-7408
1623 Lola Way Oxnard (93030) ***(P-4828)***
Catalina Carpet Mills Inc (PA)......D......562 926-5811
14418 Best Ave Santa Fe Springs (90670) ***(P-2928)***
Catalina Cylinders Inc (PA)......E......714 890-0999
7300 Anaconda Ave Garden Grove (92841) ***(P-12368)***
Catalina Home, Santa Fe Springs *Also called Catalina Carpet Mills Inc* ***(P-2928)***
Catalina Industries Inc......F......818 772-8888
8814 Reseda Blvd Northridge (91324) ***(P-8893)***
Catalina Lifesciences Inc......E......800 898-6888
25 Enterprise Ste 200 Aliso Viejo (92656) ***(P-8104)***
Catalina Pacific Concrete, Sun Valley *Also called Calportland Company* ***(P-10749)***
Catalina Pacific Concrete, Azusa *Also called Calportland Company* ***(P-11056)***
Catalina Pacific Concrete......E......310 532-4600
19030 Normandie Ave Torrance (90502) ***(P-11057)***
Catalina Paint Stores, Northridge *Also called Catalina Industries Inc* ***(P-8893)***
Catalina Spas, Murrieta *Also called Vortex Whirlpool Systems Inc* ***(P-9913)***
Catalina Tempering Inc......E......323 319-0070
1125 E Lanzit Ave Los Angeles (90059) ***(P-10590)***
Catalina Tempering Inc (PA)......E......323 789-7800
1125 E Lanzit Ave Los Angeles (90059) ***(P-11888)***
Catalina Yachts Inc (PA)......C......818 884-7700
21200 Victory Blvd Woodland Hills (91367) ***(P-21025)***
Catalyst Biosciences Inc (PA)......F......650 266-8674
611 Gateway Blvd Ste 710 South San Francisco (94080) ***(P-8105)***
Catalyst Development Corp......E......760 228-9653
56925 Yucca Trl Yucca Valley (92284) ***(P-24477)***
Catalyst Semiconductor Inc......F......408 542-1000
2975 Stender Way Santa Clara (95054) ***(P-18761)***
Catalytic Solutions Inc (HQ)......D......805 486-4649
1700 Fiske Pl Oxnard (93033) ***(P-21502)***
Catame Inc (PA)......E......213 749-2610
1930 Long Beach Ave Los Angeles (90058) ***(P-23763)***
Catapult Communications Corp (HQ)......E......818 871-1800
26601 Agoura Rd Calabasas (91302) ***(P-24478)***
Catawba County Schools, Camarillo *Also called Microsemi Communications Inc* ***(P-19007)***
Cater Line , The, City of Industry *Also called CH Image Inc* ***(P-6726)***
Caterpillar Inc......F......310 921-9811
17364 Hawthorne Blvd Torrance (90504) ***(P-14155)***
Caterpillar Inc......B......909 390-9035
5101 E Airport Dr Ontario (91761) ***(P-14156)***
Caterpillar Pwr Gnrtn Sys......E......858 694-6629
2200 Pacific Hwy San Diego (92101) ***(P-13992)***
Cathera Inc......E......650 388-5088
627 National Ave Mountain View (94043) ***(P-22398)***
Cathy Ireland Home, Chino *Also called Omnia Leather Motion Inc* ***(P-3735)***
Cattaneo Bros Inc......E......805 543-7188
769 Caudill St San Luis Obispo (93401) ***(P-473)***
Caulipower LLC......F......310 606-1648
16200 Ventura Blvd # 400 Encino (91436) ***(P-880)***
Cav Distributing Corporation......F......650 588-2228
253 Utah Ave South San Francisco (94080) ***(P-17888)***
Cavallo & Cavallo Inc......F......909 428-6994
14955 Hilton Dr Fontana (92336) ***(P-16367)***
Cavanaugh Machine Works Inc......E......562 437-1126
1540 Santa Fe Ave Long Beach (90813) ***(P-16368)***
Cavco Industries Inc......D......951 351-0378
7007 Jurupa Ave Riverside (92504) ***(P-4547)***
Cavco Industries Inc......C......951 688-5353
7007 Jurupa Ave Riverside (92504) ***(P-4548)***
Cavern Club LLC......F......323 837-9800
1708 Aeros Way Montebello (90640) ***(P-3224)***
Cavins Oil Well Tools, Signal Hill *Also called Dawson Enterprises* ***(P-14220)***
Cavins Oil Well Tools, Taft *Also called Dawson Enterprises* ***(P-203)***
Cavium Inc (HQ)......C......408 943-7100
5488 Marvell Ln Santa Clara (95054) ***(P-18762)***
Cavium Networks Intl Inc (HQ)......F......650 625-7000
2315 N 1st St San Jose (95131) ***(P-18763)***
Cavotec Dabico US Inc......E......714 947-0005
5665 Corporate Ave Cypress (90630) ***(P-20779)***
Cavotec Inet US Inc......D......714 947-0005
5665 Corporate Ave Cypress (90630) ***(P-14157)***
CB Mill Inc......F......415 386-5309
1232 Connecticut St San Francisco (94107) ***(P-4684)***
CBC Distribution Inc......E......949 553-4240
17352 Daimler St Irvine (92614) ***(P-18764)***
Cbc Steel Buildings LLC......C......209 858-2425
1700 E Louise Ave Lathrop (95330) ***(P-12926)***
Cbj LP......F......818 676-1750
21550 Oxnard St Woodland Hills (91367) ***(P-6123)***
Cbj LP......E......323 549-5225
5700 Wilshire Blvd # 170 Los Angeles (90036) ***(P-6124)***
Cbj LP......E......858 277-6359
4909 Murphy Canyon Rd # 200 San Diego (92123) ***(P-6125)***
Cbj LP......E......949 833-8373
18500 Von Karman Ave # 150 Irvine (92612) ***(P-6126)***
Cbrite Inc......F......805 722-1121
421 Pine Ave Goleta (93117) ***(P-21559)***
CBS Scientific Co Inc (PA)......E......858 755-4959
10805 Vista Sorrento Pkwy # 100 San Diego (92121) ***(P-22178)***
Ccbcc Operations LLC......C......661 723-0714
1123 W Avenue L14 Lancaster (93534) ***(P-2109)***
Ccd, Los Angeles *Also called I T I Electro-Optic Corp* ***(P-21601)***
Ccd, Anaheim *Also called Craftsman Cutting Dies Inc* ***(P-11890)***
Ccda Waters LLC......D......714 991-7031
2121 E Winston Rd Anaheim (92806) ***(P-10618)***
CCI Industries Inc (PA)......E......714 662-3879
350 Fischer Ave Ste A Costa Mesa (92626) ***(P-10015)***
CCI Mail & Shipping Systems......F......805 658-9123
369 Estrella St Ventura (93003) ***(P-5133)***
CCL Label Inc......F......707 938-7800
21481 8th St E Sonoma (95476) ***(P-24062)***
CCL Label Inc......C......909 608-2655
576 College Commerce Way Upland (91786) ***(P-7266)***
CCL Label (delaware) Inc......C......909 608-2260
576 College Commerce Way Upland (91786) ***(P-7267)***
CCL Tube Inc (HQ)......C......310 635-4444
2250 E 220th St Carson (90810) ***(P-10016)***
CCM Assembly & Mfg Inc......E......760 560-1310
2275 Michael Faraday Dr # 6 San Diego (92154) ***(P-19481)***
CCM Enterprises......F......619 562-2605
9366 Abraham Way Santee (92071) ***(P-5045)***
CCM Enterprises (PA)......D......619 562-2605
10848 Wheatlands Ave Santee (92071) ***(P-5046)***
Ccoi Gate & Fence, Hollister *Also called Gregory Patterson* ***(P-12859)***
Ccpu, San Diego *Also called Continuous Computing Corp* ***(P-15403)***
CCS Composites, Fairfield *Also called Yla Inc* ***(P-11375)***
CD Alexander LLC......E......949 250-3306
2802 Willis St Santa Ana (92705) ***(P-15701)***
CD Container Inc......D......562 948-1910
7343 Paramount Blvd Pico Rivera (90660) ***(P-5395)***
CD Video Manufacturing Inc......D......714 265-0770
12650 Westminster Ave Santa Ana (92706) ***(P-19858)***
Cdc Data LLC......F......818 350-5070
9735 Lurline Ave Chatsworth (91311) ***(P-15702)***
Cdeq......E......818 767-5143
9421 Telfair Ave Sun Valley (91352) ***(P-10638)***
Cdg Technology LLC......F......530 243-4451
779 Twin View Blvd Redding (96003) ***(P-17236)***
Cdh Painting Inc......F......707 443-4429
802 Harris St Eureka (95503) ***(P-8894)***
CDI, Irvine *Also called Concept Development Llc* ***(P-18457)***
CDI Torque Products, City of Industry *Also called Consolidated Devices Inc* ***(P-11889)***
CDM Company Inc......E......949 644-2820
12 Corporate Plaza Dr # 200 Newport Beach (92660) ***(P-24063)***
Cds Direct Inc......F......760 747-2734
24583 Avenida Musico Murrieta (92562) ***(P-21560)***
Cdti Advanced Materials Inc (PA)......E......805 639-9458
1700 Fiske Pl Oxnard (93033) ***(P-7763)***
Cebe Co, Paramount *Also called Robert W Wiesmantel* ***(P-16908)***
CEC Print Solutions Inc......F......510 670-0160
30971 San Benito St Hayward (94544) ***(P-6723)***
Cecilias Designs Inc......E......323 584-6151
6862 Vanscoy Ave North Hollywood (91605) ***(P-3834)***
Ceco, Oxnard *Also called Component Equipment Coinc* ***(P-19377)***
Ceco Environmental Corp......E......760 530-1409
4222 E La Palma Ave Anaheim (92807) ***(P-10017)***
Ced Anaheim 018......F......714 956-5156
1304 S Allec St Anaheim (92805) ***(P-19925)***
Cedar Lane North, South San Francisco *Also called Cedarlane Natural Foods North* ***(P-2483)***
Cedar Mountain Winery Inc......F......925 373-6636
10843 Reuss Rd Livermore (94550) ***(P-1683)***
Cedarlane Natural Foods Inc (PA)......D......310 886-7720
1135 E Artesia Blvd Carson (90746) ***(P-985)***
Cedarlane Natural Foods North......E......650 742-0444
150 Airport Blvd South San Francisco (94080) ***(P-2483)***
Cee & Gee Precision, San Jose *Also called Lantin Enterprise Inc* ***(P-16677)***

Cee -Jay Research & Sales LLC ..... E 626 815-1530
920 W 10th St Azusa (91702) *(P-7268)*
Cee Baileys Aircraft Plas Inc ..... E 323 721-4900
6900 W Acco St Montebello (90640) *(P-21097)*
Cee Sportswear ..... E 323 726-8158
6409 Gayhart St Commerce (90040) *(P-3392)*
Ceenee Inc ..... E 408 890-5018
683 River Oaks Pkwy San Jose (95134) *(P-17781)*
Celamark Corp ..... E 415 883-3386
8 Digital Dr Ste 100 Novato (94949) *(P-21561)*
Celebration Cellars LLC ..... E 951 506-5500
33410 Rancho Cal Rd Temecula (92591) *(P-1684)*
Celebrity Publishing LLC ..... F 714 914-4635
17320 Woodentree Ln Riverside (92503) *(P-6458)*
Celerinos Pallets ..... F 626 923-4182
1320 Mateo St Los Angeles (90021) *(P-4458)*
Celeros Corp ..... E 650 325-6900
559 Clyde Ave Ste 220 Mountain View (94043) *(P-15519)*
Celerus Diagnostics Inc ..... E 805 684-0854
100 N Hill Dr Ste 32 Brisbane (94005) *(P-22399)*
Celesco Transducer Products ..... E 818 701-2701
20630 Plummer St Chatsworth (91311) *(P-19482)*
Celestial Lighting, Santa Fe Springs Also called Shimada Enterprises Inc *(P-17731)*
Celestica Aerospace Tech Corp ..... C 512 310-7540
895 S Rockefeller Ave Ontario (91761) *(P-18445)*
Celestica LLC ..... C 510 770-5100
49235 Milmont Dr Fremont (94538) *(P-19483)*
Celestica LLC ..... B 760 357-4880
280 Campillo St Ste G Calexico (92231) *(P-17450)*
Celestica LLC ..... C 408 574-6000
5325 Hellyer Ave San Jose (95138) *(P-18765)*
Celestica Prcsion McHining Ltd ..... E 510 252-2100
40725 Encyclopedia Cir Fremont (94538) *(P-16369)*
Celestica-Aerospace, Ontario Also called Celestica Aerospace Tech Corp *(P-18445)*
Celestron Acquisition LLC ..... D 310 328-9560
2835 Columbia St Torrance (90503) *(P-22065)*
Celestron LLC ..... E 310 328-9560
2835 Columbia St Torrance (90503) *(P-22066)*
Celgene Corporation ..... D 858 558-7500
10300 Campus Point Dr # 100 San Diego (92121) *(P-8106)*
Celigo Inc (PA) ..... E 650 579-0210
1820 Gateway Dr Ste 260 San Mateo (94404) *(P-24479)*
Celite Corporation ..... F 805 736-1221
2500 San Miguelito Rd Lompoc (93436) *(P-408)*
Cell Marque Corporation ..... E 916 746-8900
6600 Sierra College Blvd Rocklin (95677) *(P-8467)*
Cellco Partnership ..... E 714 775-0600
3770 W Mcfadden Ave Ste H Santa Ana (92704) *(P-18065)*
Cellesta Inc ..... F 858 552-0888
10554 Caminito Alvarez San Diego (92126) *(P-8468)*
Cellestis Inc ..... F 661 775-7480
27220 Turnberry Ln # 200 Valencia (91355) *(P-8469)*
Cellfusion Inc ..... F 650 347-4000
1115 Lorne Way Sunnyvale (94087) *(P-24480)*
Cello Jeans, Los Angeles Also called Hidden Jeans Inc *(P-2742)*
Cellotape Inc (HQ) ..... C 510 651-5551
39611 Eureka Dr Newark (94560) *(P-23842)*
Cellphone-Mate Inc ..... D 510 770-0469
48346 Milmont Dr Fremont (94538) *(P-18066)*
Cellscope Inc ..... F 510 282-0674
5537 Claremont Ave Apt 1 Oakland (94618) *(P-17930)*
Celltron Inc ..... F 620 783-1333
19860 Plummer St Chatsworth (91311) *(P-19484)*
Cellu-Con Inc ..... E 559 568-0190
19994 Meredith Dr Strathmore (93267) *(P-9095)*
Cellular Biomedicine Group Inc ..... D 408 973-7884
19925 Stevens Creek Blvd # 100 Cupertino (95014) *(P-8539)*
Cellulo Co Division, Fresno Also called Gusmer Enterprises Inc *(P-15327)*
Cem - Long Bch Terminal, Long Beach Also called Cemex Cnstr Mtls PCF LLC *(P-312)*
Cem - Sacramento Terminal, Sacramento Also called Cemex Cnstr Mtls PCF LLC *(P-11071)*
Cemco, City of Industry Also called California Expanded Met Pdts *(P-12519)*
Cemco, Pittsburg Also called California Expanded Met Pdts *(P-12924)*
Cemcoat Inc ..... E 323 733-0125
4928 W Jefferson Blvd Los Angeles (90016) *(P-13367)*
Cemex (PA) ..... E 916 941-2800
5180 Gldn Fthl Pkwy # 200 El Dorado Hills (95762) *(P-11058)*
Cemex Inc ..... E 909 974-5500
3990 Concours Ste 200 Ontario (91764) *(P-11059)*
Cemex Cement Inc ..... E 805 529-1355
9035 Happy Camp Rd Moorpark (93021) *(P-11060)*
Cemex Cnstr Mtls PCF LLC ..... F 562 435-0195
601 Pier D Ave Long Beach (90802) *(P-312)*
Cemex Cnstr Mtls PCF LLC ..... F 951 377-9657
3221 N Riverside Ave Rialto (92377) *(P-11061)*
Cemex Cnstr Mtls PCF LLC ..... E 925 846-2824
1544 Stanley Blvd Pleasanton (94566) *(P-11062)*
Cemex Cnstr Mtls PCF LLC ..... E 530 626-3590
5481 Davidson Rd El Dorado (95623) *(P-11063)*
Cemex Cnstr Mtls PCF LLC ..... E 209 835-1454
30350 S Tracy Blvd Tracy (95377) *(P-11064)*
Cemex Cnstr Mtls PCF LLC ..... E 707 422-2520
1601 Cement Hill Rd Fairfield (94533) *(P-11065)*
Cemex Cnstr Mtls PCF LLC ..... E 916 645-1949
8705 Camp Far West Rd Sheridan (95681) *(P-11066)*
Cemex Cnstr Mtls PCF LLC ..... F 714 637-9470
1730 N Main St Orange (92865) *(P-11067)*
Cemex Cnstr Mtls PCF LLC ..... E 916 364-2470
9751 Kiefer Blvd Sacramento (95827) *(P-11068)*
Cemex Cnstr Mtls PCF LLC ..... E 925 858-4344
333 23rd Ave Oakland (94606) *(P-11069)*

Cemex Cnstr Mtls PCF LLC ..... E 925 688-1025
3951 Laura Alice Way Concord (94520) *(P-11070)*
Cemex Cnstr Mtls PCF LLC ..... F 916 383-0526
8251 Power Ridge Rd Sacramento (95826) *(P-11071)*
Cemex Cnstr Mtls PCF LLC ..... E 661 725-1819
1100 Garzoli Ave Delano (93215) *(P-11072)*
Cemex Cnstr Mtls PCF LLC ..... E 909 335-3105
8203 Alabama Ave Highland (92346) *(P-11073)*
Cemex Cnstr Mtls PCF LLC ..... E 661 396-0510
11638 Old River Rd Bakersfield (93311) *(P-10897)*
Cemex Cnstr Mtls PCF LLC ..... E 661 746-3423
131 Vultee Ave Shafter (93263) *(P-11074)*
Cemex Cnstr Mtls PCF LLC ..... E 209 862-0182
3407 W Stuhr Rd Newman (95360) *(P-11075)*
Cemex Cnstr Mtls PCF LLC ..... E 530 666-2137
30288 Highway 16 Madison (95653) *(P-9380)*
Cemex Cnstr Mtls PCF LLC ..... E 707 422-2520
1601 Cement Hill Rd Fairfield (94533) *(P-10849)*
Cemex Cnstr Mtls PCF LLC ..... E 707 580-3138
7059 Tremont Rd Dixon (95620) *(P-10850)*
Cemex Cnstr Mtls PCF LLC ..... E 925 862-2201
6527 Calaveras Rd Sunol (94586) *(P-10751)*
Cemex Cnstr Mtls PCF LLC ..... E 909 594-0105
20903 Currier Rd Walnut (91789) *(P-11076)*
Cemex Cnstr Mtls PCF LLC ..... F 909 355-8754
13200 Santa Ana Ave Fontana (92337) *(P-11077)*
Cemex Cnstr Mtls PCF LLC ..... E 209 524-6322
318 Beard Ave Modesto (95354) *(P-11078)*
Cemex Cnstr Mtls PCF LLC ..... F 310 603-9122
2722 N Alameda St Compton (90222) *(P-11079)*
Cemex Cnstr Mtls PCF LLC ..... E 323 221-1828
625 Lamar St Los Angeles (90031) *(P-11080)*
Cemex Cnstr Mtls PCF LLC ..... E 323 466-4928
1000 N La Brea Ave West Hollywood (90038) *(P-11081)*
Cemex Materials LLC ..... E 707 678-4311
7059 Tremont Rd Dixon (95620) *(P-11082)*
Cemex Materials LLC ..... E 510 234-3616
401 Wright Ave Richmond (94804) *(P-11083)*
Cemex Materials LLC ..... E 707 448-7121
1601 Cement Hill Rd Fairfield (94533) *(P-11084)*
Cemex Materials LLC ..... E 707 255-3035
385 Tower Rd NAPA (94558) *(P-11085)*
Cemex Materials LLC ..... E 559 275-2241
4150 N Brawley Ave Fresno (93722) *(P-11086)*
Cemex Materials LLC ..... E 909 825-1500
1205 S Rancho Ave Colton (92324) *(P-11087)*
Cemex USA Inc ..... C 909 798-1144
8731 Orange St Redlands (92374) *(P-11088)*
Cemex USA Inc ..... F 909 974-5500
3990 Concours Ste 200 Ontario (91764) *(P-11089)*
Cemtrol Inc ..... F 714 666-6606
3035 E La Jolla St Anaheim (92806) *(P-15398)*
Cen Cal Rock & Ready Mix, Ripon Also called Ken Anderson *(P-11124)*
Cencal Cnc Inc ..... E 559 897-8706
2491 Simpson St Kingsburg (93631) *(P-16370)*
Cencal Recycling LLC ..... F 209 546-8000
501 Port Road 22 Stockton (95203) *(P-5267)*
Cenergy Solutions Inc ..... F 510 474-7593
40967 Albrae St Fremont (94538) *(P-20287)*
Cengage Learning Inc ..... E 415 839-2300
303 2nd St Ste S500 San Francisco (94107) *(P-6321)*
Cengage Learning Inc ..... E 951 719-1878
40880 County Center Dr G Temecula (92591) *(P-6322)*
Cenic Ntwrk Operations Website ..... F 714 220-3494
5757 Plaza Dr Ste 205 Cypress (90630) *(P-21157)*
Content Company ..... E 714 979-6491
3879 S Main St Santa Ana (92707) *(P-15399)*
Center For Cllbrtive Classroom ..... D 510 533-0213
1001 Marina Village Pkwy # 110 Alameda (94501) *(P-6323)*
Center Health Services ..... F 619 692-2077
2313 El Cajon Blvd San Diego (92104) *(P-21931)*
Center Line Performance Wheels, Huntington Beach Also called Center Line Wheel Corporation *(P-20288)*
Center Line Wheel Corporation ..... D 562 921-9637
19451 Surf Dr Huntington Beach (92648) *(P-20288)*
Center Thatre Group Costume Sp, Los Angeles Also called Center Thtre Group Los Angeles *(P-3647)*
Center Thtre Group Los Angeles ..... E 213 972-3751
2856 E 11th St Los Angeles (90023) *(P-3647)*
Centerline Engineering, Fullerton Also called Centerline Manufacturing Inc *(P-19485)*
Centerline Manufacturing Inc ..... F 714 525-9890
1234 E Ash Ave Ste D Fullerton (92831) *(P-19485)*
Centerline Precision Inc ..... E 408 988-4380
2265 Calle Del Mundo Santa Clara (95054) *(P-8540)*
Centerpoint Mfg Co Inc ..... E 818 842-2147
2625 N San Fernando Blvd Burbank (91504) *(P-16371)*
Centersource Systems LLC ..... F 707 838-1061
60 Commerce Ln Ste D Cloverdale (95425) *(P-6324)*
Centinela Concrete Vault Co ..... E 310 674-2115
720 E Florence Ave Inglewood (90301) *(P-10898)*
Centon Electronics Inc (PA) ..... D 949 855-9111
27412 Aliso Viejo Pkwy Aliso Viejo (92656) *(P-15520)*
Central Admxture Phrm Svcs Inc (HQ) ..... F 949 660-2000
2525 Mcgaw Ave Irvine (92614) *(P-8107)*
Central Admxture Phrm Svcs Inc ..... E 562 941-9595
10370 Slusher Dr Ste 6 Santa Fe Springs (90670) *(P-8108)*
Central Admxture Phrm Svcs Inc ..... E 858 578-1380
7935 Dunbrook Rd Ste C San Diego (92126) *(P-8109)*
Central Blower Co ..... E 626 330-3182
211 S 7th Ave City of Industry (91746) *(P-15148)*

Employee Codes: A=Over 500 employees, B=251-500
C=101-250, D=51-100, E=20-50, F=10-19

2019 California
Manfacturers Register

© Mergent Inc. 1-800-342-5647

1095

Central Business Forms Inc......F......650 548-0918
289 Foster City Blvd B Foster City (94404) *(P-6724)*
Central Cal Metals, Fresno *Also called Robert J Alandt & Sons (P-16907)*
Central California Cnstr Inc......F......661 978-8230
7221 Downing Ave Bakersfield (93308) *(P-195)*
Central California Cont Mfg......E......559 665-7611
800 Commerce Dr Chowchilla (93610) *(P-10018)*
Central Coast Cabinets......F......831 724-2992
111a Lee Rd Watsonville (95076) *(P-4937)*
Central Coast Printing, Grover Beach *Also called David B Anderson (P-6779)*
Central Coast Stainless......E......805 238-0888
825 26th St Paso Robles (93446) *(P-12369)*
Central Coast Water Authority......F......805 463-2122
5250 Annlope Rd Cholame (93461) *(P-16021)*
Central Coast Wine Services, Santa Maria *Also called Central Coast Wine Warehouse (P-1685)*
Central Coast Wine Warehouse (PA)......E......805 928-9210
2717 Aviation Way Ste 101 Santa Maria (93455) *(P-1685)*
Central Coast Yamaha, Santa Maria *Also called Glb Investment Inc (P-23570)*
Central Concrete Supply Coinc (HQ)......D......408 293-6272
755 Stockton Ave San Jose (95126) *(P-11090)*
Central Concrete Supply Coinc......E......408 404-1000
755 Stockton Ave San Jose (95126) *(P-11091)*
Central Drugs, La Habra *Also called Auro Pharmacies Inc (P-8052)*
Central Machine & Sheet Metal, San Jose *Also called Henry Ll (P-12611)*
Central Marble Supply Inc......F......619 595-1800
3754 Main St Ste B San Diego (92113) *(P-11240)*
Central Pallets......F......209 462-3019
1002 Navy Dr Stockton (95206) *(P-4459)*
Central Plastics and Mfg, Tracy *Also called Mother Lode Plas Molding Inc (P-10228)*
Central Precast Concrete Inc......E......925 417-6854
3500 Boulder St Pleasanton (94566) *(P-10899)*
Central Printing & Graphics, Bakersfield *Also called Ampligraphix (P-6660)*
Central Printing Group, Foster City *Also called Central Business Forms Inc (P-6724)*
Central Tech Inc......F......408 955-0919
2271 Ringwood Ave San Jose (95131) *(P-19926)*
Central Tent, Santa Clarita *Also called Frametent Inc (P-3787)*
Central Valley AG Grinding Inc (PA)......E......209 869-1721
5509 Langworth Rd Oakdale (95361) *(P-1035)*
Central Valley Cabinet Mfg......F......559 584-8441
10739 14th Ave Armona (93202) *(P-4285)*
Central Valley Machining Inc......E......559 291-7749
5820 E Harvard Ave Fresno (93727) *(P-12133)*
Central Valley Meat Co Inc......C......559 583-9624
10431 8 3/4 Ave Hanford (93230) *(P-426)*
Central Valley Prof Svcs, Oakdale *Also called Central Valley Professional SE (P-5591)*
Central Valley Professional SE......F......209 847-7832
8207 Mondo Ln Oakdale (95361) *(P-5591)*
Central Valley Tank of Cal......F......559 456-3500
4752 E Carmen Ave Fresno (93703) *(P-12370)*
Central Vly Assembly Packg Inc......E......559 486-4260
5515 E Lamona Ave 103 Fresno (93727) *(P-12029)*
Centric Parts Inc......D......626 961-5775
14528 Bonelli St City of Industry (91746) *(P-20132)*
Centrl Inc......E......650 641-7092
257 Castro St Ste 215 Mountain View (94041) *(P-24481)*
Centron Industries Inc......E......310 324-6443
441 W Victoria St Gardena (90248) *(P-18067)*
Centurion, Merced *Also called Fineline Industries Inc (P-21038)*
Centurum Information Tech Inc......E......619 224-1100
4250 Pacific Hwy Ste 105 San Diego (92110) *(P-11652)*
Century Blinds Inc......D......951 734-3762
451 N Cota St Corona (92880) *(P-5186)*
Century Industries, Orange *Also called Century Precision Machine Inc (P-16374)*
Century Pallets, Lynwood *Also called Roger R Caruso Enterprises Inc (P-4504)*
Century Parts Inc......F......310 328-0281
913 W 223rd St Torrance (90502) *(P-16372)*
Century Pattern Co Inc......F......562 402-1707
15925 Piuma Ave Cerritos (90703) *(P-14464)*
Century Precision Engrg Inc......F......310 538-0015
2141 W 139th St Gardena (90249) *(P-16373)*
Century Precision Machine Inc......F......714 637-3691
1130 W Grove Ave Orange (92865) *(P-16374)*
Century Publishing......F......951 849-4586
218 N Murray St Banning (92220) *(P-7269)*
Century Rubber Company Inc......F......661 366-7009
719 Rooster Dr Bakersfield (93307) *(P-9600)*
Century Sewing Co......E......626 289-0533
421 S Raymond Ave Alhambra (91803) *(P-3301)*
Century Shower Door Co Inc (PA)......E......310 327-8060
20100 Normandie Ave Torrance (90502) *(P-10685)*
Century Snacks LLC......B......323 278-9578
5560 E Slauson Ave Commerce (90040) *(P-1412)*
Century Spring, Commerce *Also called Matthew Warren Inc (P-13752)*
Century Technology Inc......F......650 583-8908
225 Harris Ct South San Francisco (94080) *(P-18446)*
Century Wire & Cable Inc......D......213 236-8879
7400 E Slauson Ave Commerce (90040) *(P-11653)*
Cenveo Worldwide Limited......C......323 262-6000
6250 S Boyle Ave Vernon (90058) *(P-5703)*
Cenveo Worldwide Limited......D......415 821-7171
888 Tennessee St San Francisco (94107) *(P-6725)*
Cenveo Worldwide Limited......D......323 261-7171
150 N Myers St Los Angeles (90033) *(P-5672)*
Cepheid......F......408 541-4191
904 E Caribbean Dr Sunnyvale (94089) *(P-21932)*
Cepheid (HQ)......B......408 541-4191
904 E Caribbean Dr Sunnyvale (94089) *(P-21933)*

Cequal Products Inc......F......310 458-0441
1328 16th St Santa Monica (90404) *(P-6325)*
Cera Inc......E......626 814-2688
14180 Live Oak Ave Ste I Baldwin Park (91706) *(P-21460)*
Ceradyne Inc (HQ)......B......949 862-9600
1922 Barranca Pkwy Irvine (92606) *(P-11352)*
Ceradyne Inc......F......949 756-0642
17466 Daimler St Irvine (92614) *(P-11353)*
Ceramic Tech Inc......E......510 252-8500
46211 Research Ave Fremont (94539) *(P-16375)*
Cercacor Laboratories Inc......F......949 679-6100
40 Parker Irvine (92618) *(P-22179)*
Cerebrotech Medical Systems (PA)......F......925 399-5392
1048 Serpentine Ln # 301 Pleasanton (94566) *(P-22400)*
Cerner Corporation......E......310 247-7700
9100 Wilshire Blvd 655e Beverly Hills (90212) *(P-24482)*
Cerner Life Sciences, Beverly Hills *Also called Cerner Corporation (P-24482)*
Cernex Inc......E......408 541-9226
1710 Zanker Rd Ste 103 San Jose (95112) *(P-19486)*
Certainteed Corona Inc......C......951 272-1300
235 Radio Rd Corona (92879) *(P-10019)*
Certainteed Corporation......D......510 490-0890
6400 Stevenson Blvd Fremont (94538) *(P-9403)*
Certainteed Corporation......B......559 665-4831
17775 Avenue 23 1/2 Chowchilla (93610) *(P-11330)*
Certance LLC (HQ)......B......949 856-7800
141 Innovation Dr Irvine (92617) *(P-15521)*
Certified Distribution Svcs, Santa Fe Springs *Also called Contract Transportation Sys Co (P-8898)*
Certified Enameling Inc......D......323 264-4403
3342 Emery St Los Angeles (90023) *(P-13567)*
Certified Meat Products Inc......E......559 256-1433
4586 E Commerce Ave Fresno (93725) *(P-427)*
Certified Metal Craft Inc......E......619 593-3636
877 Vernon Way El Cajon (92020) *(P-11806)*
Certified Stainless Svc Inc......F......209 356-3300
441 Business Park Way Atwater (95301) *(P-12371)*
Certified Stainless Svc Inc (PA)......C......209 537-4747
2704 Railroad Ave Ceres (95307) *(P-12372)*
Certified Stainless Svc Inc......E......209 537-4747
581 Industry Way Atwater (95301) *(P-12373)*
Certified Steel Treating Corp......E......323 583-8711
2454 E 58th St Vernon (90058) *(P-13368)*
Certified Thermoplastics Inc, Santa Clarita *Also called Certified Thermoplastics LLC (P-10020)*
Certified Thermoplastics LLC......E......661 222-3006
26381 Ferry Ct Santa Clarita (91350) *(P-10020)*
Certifix Inc......F......714 496-3850
700 N Valley St Ste B Anaheim (92801) *(P-24064)*
Certifix Live Scan, Anaheim *Also called Certifix Inc (P-24064)*
Certis USA LLC......E......661 758-8471
720 5th St Wasco (93280) *(P-9096)*
Cerus Corporation (PA)......C......925 288-6000
2550 Stanwell Dr Ste 300 Concord (94520) *(P-22401)*
Ces Electronics Mfg Inc......F......714 505-3441
14731 Franklin Ave Ste E Tustin (92780) *(P-24065)*
Cesca Therapeutics Inc (PA)......D......916 858-5100
2711 Citrus Rd Rancho Cordova (95742) *(P-21461)*
Ceterix Orthopaedics Inc......E......650 316-8660
6500 Kaiser Dr Ste 120 Fremont (94555) *(P-22402)*
Cevians LLC......D......714 619-5135
3128 Red Hill Ave Costa Mesa (92626) *(P-10591)*
CF, Van Nuys *Also called Consolidated Fabricators Corp (P-12378)*
CF&b Manufacturing Inc......E......714 744-8361
1405 N Manzanita St Orange (92867) *(P-5592)*
Cfarms Inc......E......916 375-3000
1244 E Beamer St Woodland (95776) *(P-2484)*
Cff, Valley Springs *Also called Collette Fine Foods LLC (P-2493)*
Cfkba Inc (PA)......D......650 847-3900
150 Jefferson Dr Menlo Park (94025) *(P-11654)*
Cforia Software Inc......E......818 871-9687
4333 Park Terrace Dr # 201 Westlake Village (91361) *(P-24483)*
CFS Income Tax, Simi Valley *Also called CFS Tax Software (P-24484)*
CFS Tax Software......D......805 522-1157
1445 E Los Angeles Ave # 214 Simi Valley (93065) *(P-24484)*
Cfw Precision Metal Components, Grover Beach *Also called C F W Research & Dev Co (P-11572)*
Cg Financial LLC......F......619 656-2919
7020 Alamitos Ave Ste B San Diego (92154) *(P-753)*
Cg Manufacturing Inc......F......818 886-1191
21021 Osborne St Canoga Park (91304) *(P-12530)*
CG Motor Sports Inc......F......909 628-1440
5150 Eucalyptus Ave Ste A Chino (91710) *(P-10021)*
Cg Roxane LLC......D......530 225-1260
1400 Marys Dr Weed (96094) *(P-2110)*
Cg Roxane LLC (PA)......D......760 764-2885
1210 State Hwy 395 Olancha (93549) *(P-2111)*
Cg Roxane Shasta, Weed *Also called Cg Roxane LLC (P-2110)*
CGB, Gardena *Also called California Glass Bending Corp (P-10636)*
Cgm Inc......E......818 609-7088
19611 Ventura Blvd # 211 Tarzana (91356) *(P-23341)*
Cgm Findings, Tarzana *Also called Cgm Inc (P-23341)*
Cgnfm, Valencia *Also called Creations Grdn Natural Fd Mkts (P-7929)*
Cgr/Thompson Industries Inc......D......714 678-4200
7155 Fenwick Ln Westminster (92683) *(P-17084)*
CH Image Inc......F......626 336-6063
15350 Valley Blvd City of Industry (91746) *(P-6726)*

Ch Industrial Technology Inc.....F.....559 485-8011
3160 E California Ave Fresno (93702) *(P-12134)*
CH Laboratories Inc.....E.....310 516-8273
1243 W 130th St Gardena (90247) *(P-8110)*
Ch Products, Vista *Also called Apem Inc (P-19445)*
Cha Bio & Diostech Co Ltd.....D.....213 487-3211
3731 Wilshire Blvd # 850 Los Angeles (90010) *(P-8111)*
Cha Industries, Fremont *Also called Carl Herrmann Associates (P-14926)*
Chad Empey.....F.....707 762-1900
1329 Scott St Ste G Petaluma (94954) *(P-10592)*
Chad Industries Incorporated.....E.....714 938-0080
1565 S Sinclair St Anaheim (92806) *(P-15307)*
Chagall Design Limited.....F.....310 537-9530
20625 Belshaw Ave Carson (90746) *(P-3648)*
Chain & Charm Inc.....D.....213 683-1039
817 San Julian St Ph 1 Los Angeles (90014) *(P-23249)*
Chain & Charm Jewelry Mfg, Los Angeles *Also called Chain & Charm Inc (P-23249)*
Chain Smith Inc.....E.....626 287-3666
5009 Walnut Grove Ave San Gabriel (91776) *(P-23250)*
Chalgren Enterprises.....F.....408 847-3994
380 Tomkins Ct Gilroy (95020) *(P-22959)*
Challenge Graphics Inc.....E.....818 892-0123
16611 Roscoe Pl North Hills (91343) *(P-6727)*
Challenge Publications Inc.....E.....818 700-6868
21835 Nordhoff St Chatsworth (91311) *(P-6127)*
Challenger Ornamental Ir Works.....F.....818 507-7030
437 W Palmer Ave Glendale (91204) *(P-12842)*
Chameleon Beverage Company Inc (PA).....D.....323 724-8223
6444 E 26th St Commerce (90040) *(P-2112)*
Chameleon Books & Journals, Gilroy *Also called Chameleon Like Inc (P-7575)*
Chameleon Like Inc.....E.....408 847-3661
345 Kishimura Dr Gilroy (95020) *(P-7575)*
Chamisal Vineyards LLC.....F.....866 808-9463
7525 Orcutt Rd San Luis Obispo (93401) *(P-1686)*
Champ Co, Campbell *Also called Consoldted Hnge Mnfctured Pdts (P-16401)*
Champion Discs Incorporated.....F.....800 408-8449
950 S Dupont Ave Ontario (91761) *(P-23537)*
Champion Laboratories Inc.....F.....951 275-0715
740 Palmyrita Ave Ste A Riverside (92507) *(P-20289)*
Champion Newspapers, Chino *Also called Champion Pblications Chino Inc (P-5796)*
Champion Pblications Chino Inc.....E.....909 628-5501
13179 9th St Chino (91710) *(P-5796)*
Champion-Arrowhead LLC.....D.....323 221-9137
5147 Alhambra Ave Los Angeles (90032) *(P-12030)*
Champions Choice Inc.....F.....714 635-4491
1910 E Via Burton Anaheim (92806) *(P-9426)*
Champs Sports, Newark *Also called Foot Locker Retail Inc (P-10505)*
Chancellor Oil Tools Inc.....E.....661 324-2213
3521 Gulf St Bakersfield (93308) *(P-14218)*
Chandler Aggregates Inc (PA).....E.....951 277-1341
24867 Maitri Rd Corona (92883) *(P-301)*
Chandler Signs LLC.....D.....760 734-1708
3220 Executive Rdg # 250 Vista (92081) *(P-23843)*
Chandler Wire Products, La Verne *Also called Dhl Wire Products (P-11438)*
Chandlers Palos Verdes Sand A.....F.....310 784-2900
26311 Palos Verdes Dr E Rllng HLS Est (90274) *(P-352)*
Chang Food Company.....E.....714 265-9990
2214 W Knox Ave Santa Ana (92704) *(P-986)*
Changyoucom (us) LLC.....E.....408 889-9866
1654 Hollenbeck Ave # 14 Sunnyvale (94087) *(P-24485)*
Channel Isl Opto Mech.....F.....805 644-2153
1595 Walter St Ste 1 Ventura (93003) *(P-16376)*
Channel Islands Surfboards Inc.....F.....805 745-2823
1115 Mark Ave Carpinteria (93013) *(P-23538)*
Channel Microwave, Thousand Oaks *Also called Trak Microwave Corporation (P-19767)*
Channel Systems Inc.....E.....510 568-7170
74 98th Ave Oakland (94603) *(P-10900)*
Channel Technologies Group, Santa Barbara *Also called International Tranducer Corp (P-21777)*
Channel Vision Technology, Costa Mesa *Also called Djh Enterprises (P-18088)*
Channell Commercial Corp (PA).....D.....951 719-2600
26040 Ynez Rd Temecula (92591) *(P-17931)*
Chantilly.....E.....949 494-7702
202 Park Ave Laguna Beach (92651) *(P-661)*
Chantilly Bakery Inc.....F.....858 693-3300
12714 Chandon Ct San Diego (92130) *(P-1219)*
Chantilly Ice Cream, Laguna Beach *Also called Chantilly (P-661)*
Chapala Iron & Manufacturing.....F.....805 654-9803
1301 Callens Rd Ventura (93003) *(P-11388)*
Chaparral Concrete Company (HQ).....F.....626 359-8371
590 Live Oak Ave Baldwin Park (91706) *(P-11092)*
Chapman Designs Inc.....E.....562 698-4600
8333 Secura Way Santa Fe Springs (90670) *(P-4033)*
Chapman Engineering Corp.....E.....714 542-1942
2321 Cape Cod Way Santa Ana (92703) *(P-16377)*
Chapmn-Wlters Intrcoastal Corp.....E.....949 448-9940
141 Via Lampara Rcho STA Marg (92688) *(P-23539)*
Chappellet Winery Inc (PA).....E.....707 286-4268
1581 Sage Canyon Rd Saint Helena (94574) *(P-1687)*
Charades LLC (PA).....C.....626 435-0077
14438 Don Julian Rd City of Industry (91746) *(P-3649)*
Chargepoint Inc (PA).....C.....408 841-4500
240 E Hacienda Ave Campbell (95008) *(P-17336)*
Chargetek Inc.....E.....805 444-7792
409 Calle San Pablo # 104 Camarillo (93012) *(P-17337)*
Charlaine Graphics, Poway *Also called Imagine That Unlimited (P-23897)*
Charles Gemeiner Cabinets.....E.....323 299-8696
3225 Exposition Pl Los Angeles (90018) *(P-4124)*
Charles Jj Inc.....E.....559 264-6664
4115 S Orange Ave Fresno (93725) *(P-4590)*
Charles Komar & Sons Inc.....B.....951 934-1377
11850 Riverside Dr Mira Loma (91752) *(P-3535)*
Charles Krug Winery, Saint Helena *Also called C Mondavi & Family (P-1673)*
Charles Ligeti Co.....E.....213 612-0831
611 Wilshire Blvd Ste 801 Los Angeles (90017) *(P-23251)*
Charles Meisner Inc.....E.....909 946-8216
201 Sierra Pl Ste A Upland (91786) *(P-14494)*
Charlies Beer Company USA LLC.....F.....909 980-0436
9581 Bus Ctr Dr Ste G Rancho Cucamonga (91730) *(P-1578)*
Charlois Cooperage USA.....F.....707 224-2377
1285 S Foothill Blvd Cloverdale (95425) *(P-4092)*
Charm America, Glendale *Also called Saks Styling Incorporated (P-23314)*
Charman Manufacturing Inc.....E.....213 489-7000
5681 S Downey Rd Vernon (90058) *(P-11475)*
Charming Hawaii, Walnut *Also called New Origins Accessories Inc (P-23754)*
Chart Inc.....E.....408 371-3303
46441 Landing Pkwy Fremont (94538) *(P-12374)*
Charta Global, Anaheim *Also called Paper Max Inc (P-5323)*
Chase Corporation.....F.....626 395-7706
132 E Colorado Blvd Pasadena (91105) *(P-17507)*
Chase Corporation.....F.....714 964-6268
20001 Brookhurst St Huntington Beach (92646) *(P-17508)*
Chase-Durer Ltd (PA).....F.....310 550-7280
8455 Ftn Ave Unit 515 West Hollywood (90069) *(P-23219)*
Chasin Foods Inc.....E.....323 544-0000
1855 E 27th St Vernon (90058) *(P-2310)*
Chassis Unlimited.....F.....925 339-6035
3573 1st St Ste B Livermore (94551) *(P-22713)*
Chateau Diana LLC (PA).....F.....707 433-6992
6195 Dry Creek Rd Healdsburg (95448) *(P-1688)*
Chateau Masson LLC.....E.....408 741-7002
14831 Pierce Rd Saratoga (95070) *(P-1689)*
Chateau Montelena Winery.....E.....707 942-5105
1429 Tubbs Ln Calistoga (94515) *(P-1690)*
Chateau Potelle Inc.....E.....707 255-9440
528 Coombs St NAPA (94559) *(P-1691)*
Chateau Potelle Holdings LLC.....F.....707 255-9440
1200 Dowdell Ln Saint Helena (94574) *(P-1692)*
Chateau St Jean, Kenwood *Also called Treasury Wine Estates Americas (P-2024)*
Chateau Woltner, Angwin *Also called Ladera Winery LLC (P-1848)*
Chatsworth Products Inc (PA).....B.....818 735-6100
29899 Agoura Rd Ste 120 Agoura Hills (91301) *(P-13929)*
Chatsworth Products Inc.....C.....818 882-8595
9353 Winnetka Ave Chatsworth (91311) *(P-13930)*
Chauhan Industries Inc.....F.....805 484-1616
32 Wood Rd Ste A Camarillo (93010) *(P-10022)*
Chavers Gasket Corporation.....E.....949 472-8118
23325 Del Lago Dr Laguna Hills (92653) *(P-9523)*
Chavez Welding & Machining.....E.....408 247-4658
1115 Campbell Ave 1a San Jose (95126) *(P-16378)*
Chawk Technology Intl Inc (PA).....D.....510 330-5299
1256 San Luis Obispo St Hayward (94544) *(P-10023)*
CHE Precision Inc.....F.....805 499-8885
2640 Lavery Ct Ste C Newbury Park (91320) *(P-16379)*
Checchi Enterprises Inc.....F.....530 378-1207
19849 Riverside Ave Anderson (96007) *(P-6728)*
Check It Out, Los Angeles *Also called Nexxen Apparel Inc (P-3469)*
Check Point Software Tech Inc (HQ).....C.....650 628-2000
959 Skyway Rd Ste 300 San Carlos (94070) *(P-24486)*
Check Yourself Inc.....F.....805 967-6190
5785 Thornwood Dr Goleta (93117) *(P-16380)*
Check Yourself Machining, Goleta *Also called Check Yourself Inc (P-16380)*
Checkerspot Inc.....F.....510 239-7921
740 Heinz Ave Berkeley (94710) *(P-8541)*
Checkworks Inc.....D.....626 333-1444
315 Cloverleaf Dr Ste J Baldwin Park (91706) *(P-7576)*
Cheek Engineering & Stamping.....F.....714 832-9480
1732 Mcgaw Ave Irvine (92614) *(P-13181)*
Cheek Machine Corp.....E.....714 279-9486
1312 S Allec St Anaheim (92805) *(P-16381)*
Cheerpak.....F.....818 922-5451
7778 Varna Ave North Hollywood (91605) *(P-1056)*
Cheese Administrative Corp Inc.....E.....209 826-3744
429 H St Los Banos (93635) *(P-567)*
Cheese Cake City Inc.....F.....510 524-9404
1225 4th St Berkeley (94710) *(P-1220)*
Cheesecake Factory Bakery Inc (HQ).....B.....818 880-9323
26950 Agoura Rd Agoura Hills (91301) *(P-1221)*
Chef Brand Foods.....E.....559 651-1696
8637 W Doe Ave Visalia (93291) *(P-1222)*
Chef Brands, Visalia *Also called Chef Brand Foods (P-1222)*
Chef Merito Inc (PA).....D.....818 787-0100
7915 Sepulveda Blvd Van Nuys (91405) *(P-2485)*
Chefmaster.....E.....714 554-4000
501 Airpark Dr Fullerton (92833) *(P-2486)*
Chella, Camarillo *Also called Mosaic Distributors LLC (P-8798)*
Chella Professional Skin Care, Camarillo *Also called Mosaic Marketing Partners LLC (P-8799)*
Chem Arrow Corp.....E.....626 358-2255
13643 Live Oak Ln Irwindale (91706) *(P-9427)*
Chem-Mark of Orange County, Cerritos *Also called Better Beverages Inc (P-2244)*
Chem-O-Lene Co.....F.....805 648-6247
2745 Sherwin Ave Ste 3 Ventura (93003) *(P-196)*
Chem-Tainer Industries Inc.....E.....310 635-5400
135 E Stanley St Compton (90220) *(P-10024)*
Chemat Technology Inc.....E.....818 727-9786
9036 Winnetka Ave Northridge (91324) *(P-21462)*

ALPHABETIC

Chemat Vision, Northridge *Also called Chemat Technology Inc* ***(P-21462)***
Chemco Products Company, Paramount *Also called LMC Enterprises* ***(P-8651)***
Chemcor Chemical Corporation......F......909 590-7234
13770 Benson Ave Chino (91710) ***(P-8630)***
Chemdiv Inc......E......858 794-4860
12760 High Bluff Dr # 370 San Diego (92130) ***(P-9227)***
Chemeor Inc......E......626 966-3808
727 Arrow Grand Cir Covina (91722) ***(P-8685)***
Chemetry, Moss Landing *Also called Calera Corporation* ***(P-10894)***
Chemical & Material Technology......E......408 354-2656
229 Creekside Village Dr Los Gatos (95032) ***(P-22067)***
Chemical Diversity Labs, San Diego *Also called Chemdiv Inc* ***(P-9227)***
Chemical Methods Assoc LLC (HQ)......D......714 898-8781
12700 Knott St Garden Grove (92841) ***(P-16022)***
Chemical Safety Technology Inc......E......408 263-0984
2461 Autumnvale Dr San Jose (95131) ***(P-14927)***
Chemical Systems Div, San Jose *Also called United Technologies Corp* ***(P-20687)***
Chemical Technologies Intl Inc......F......916 638-1315
2747 Merc Dr Ste 200 Rancho Cordova (95742) ***(P-16023)***
Chemicals Incorporated......F......951 681-9697
13560 Colombard Ct Fontana (92337) ***(P-9228)***
Chemocentryx Inc (PA)......D......650 210-2900
850 Maude Ave Mountain View (94043) ***(P-8112)***
Chemring Energetic Devices......C......310 784-2100
24225 Garnier St Torrance (90505) ***(P-21187)***
Chemsil, Pacoima *Also called Flamemaster Corporation* ***(P-9251)***
Chemsil Silicones Inc......E......818 700-0302
21900 Marilla St Chatsworth (91311) ***(P-8996)***
Chemsw Inc......F......707 864-0845
2480 Burskirk Ste 300 Pleasant Hill (94523) ***(P-24487)***
Chemtainer Industries, Compton *Also called Chem-Tainer Industries Inc* ***(P-10024)***
Chemtex International, Sunnyvale *Also called American Liquid Packaging Syst* ***(P-7819)***
Chemtex Print USA Inc......E......310 900-1818
3061 E Maria St Compton (90221) ***(P-7270)***
Chemtool Incorporated......E......661 823-7190
1300 Goodrick Dr Tehachapi (93561) ***(P-9428)***
Chemtrade Chemicals US LLC......E......925 458-7300
501 Nichols Rd Bay Point (94565) ***(P-7764)***
Chemtrade Chemicals US LLC......E......510 232-7193
525 Castro St Richmond (94801) ***(P-7765)***
Chemtreat Inc......E......804 935-2000
8885 Rehco Rd San Diego (92121) ***(P-9229)***
Chemtrol, Santa Barbara *Also called Santa Barbara Control Systems* ***(P-21648)***
Chen-Tech Industries Inc (HQ)......E......949 855-6716
9 Wrigley Irvine (92618) ***(P-22403)***
Chenbro Micom (usa) Inc......E......909 937-0100
2800 Jurupa St Ontario (91761) ***(P-15522)***
Cheol Lee, Los Angeles *Also called Noahs Ark International Inc* ***(P-3262)***
Chep (usa) Inc......D......925 234-4970
2276 Wilbur Ln Antioch (94509) ***(P-4460)***
Cherokee Uniform, Chatsworth *Also called Strategic Partners Inc* ***(P-10491)***
Cherry Pit......F......707 449-8378
812 E Monte Vista Ave Vacaville (95688) ***(P-9429)***
Cherry Valley Sheet Metal......F......951 845-1578
39638 Avenida Sonrisa Cherry Valley (92223) ***(P-14053)***
Chet Cooper......F......949 854-8700
1001 W 17th St Costa Mesa (92627) ***(P-6128)***
Chevron Captain Company LLC (HQ)......C......925 842-1000
6001 Bollinger Canyon Rd San Ramon (94583) ***(P-9325)***
Chevron Corporation (PA)......A......925 842-1000
6001 Bollinger Canyon Rd San Ramon (94583) ***(P-9326)***
Chevron Corporation......A......310 615-5000
324 W El Segundo Blvd El Segundo (90245) ***(P-9327)***
Chevron Corporation......F......805 733-5174
3602 Harris Grade Rd Lompoc (93436) ***(P-47)***
Chevron Corporation......C......310 538-7600
13707 S Broadway Los Angeles (90061) ***(P-9328)***
Chevron Global Energy Inc (HQ)......D......925 842-1000
6001 Bollinger Canyon Rd San Ramon (94583) ***(P-9329)***
Chevron Global Lubricants, San Ramon *Also called Chevron Global Energy Inc* ***(P-9329)***
Chevron Mining Inc......B......760 856-7625
67750 Bailey Rd Mountain Pass (92366) ***(P-16)***
Chevron Oronite Company LLC (HQ)......E......713 432-2500
6001 Bollinger Canyon Rd San Ramon (94583) ***(P-9230)***
Chevron Phillips Chem Co LP......D......909 420-5500
6001 Bollinger Canyon Rd San Ramon (94583) ***(P-9777)***
Chevron Products Company, San Ramon *Also called Chevron Captain Company LLC* ***(P-9325)***
Chevron USA Inc......B......415 733-0063
345 California St Fl 18 San Francisco (94104) ***(P-21503)***
Chevron USA Inc......D......925 842-0855
6001 Bollinger Canyon Rd San Ramon (94583) ***(P-48)***
Chh Lp......E......951 506-5800
28134 Jefferson Ave Temecula (92590) ***(P-2487)***
CHI Fung Plastics Inc......F......510 532-4835
1000 54th Ave Oakland (94601) ***(P-9793)***
CHI-AM Comics Daily Inc......F......626 281-2989
673 Monterey Pass Rd Monterey Park (91754) ***(P-6459)***
Chiapa Welding Inc (PA)......F......559 784-3400
276 E Grand Ave Porterville (93257) ***(P-25395)***
Chicago Brothers, Vernon *Also called Overhill Farms Inc* ***(P-1006)***
Chick Publications Inc......E......909 987-0771
8780 Archibald Ave Rancho Cucamonga (91730) ***(P-6326)***
Chico Community Publishing (PA)......E......530 894-2300
353 E 2nd St Chico (95928) ***(P-5797)***
Chico Community Publishing......D......916 498-1234
1124 Del Paso Blvd Sacramento (95815) ***(P-5798)***
Chico Custom Counter......F......530 894-8123
3080 Thorntree Dr Ste 45 Chico (95973) ***(P-5047)***
Chico Enterprise Record, Chico *Also called Gatehouse Media LLC* ***(P-5859)***
Chico Metal Finishing Inc......F......530 534-7308
3151 Richter Ave Oroville (95966) ***(P-13369)***
Chicobag, Chico *Also called Chicoeco Inc* ***(P-3761)***
Chicoeco Inc......E......530 342-4426
747 Fortress St Chico (95973) ***(P-3761)***
Chicwrap, Malibu *Also called Allen Reed Company Inc* ***(P-5272)***
Chief Neon Sign Co Inc......F......310 327-1317
15027 S Maple Ave Gardena (90248) ***(P-23844)***
Child Evngelism Fellowship Inc......E......661 873-9032
2201 Mount Vernon Ave Bakersfield (93306) ***(P-6729)***
Child To Cherish, Brea *Also called Perine Lowe Inc* ***(P-11865)***
Children's Choice, Danville *Also called Choice Foodservices Inc* ***(P-11728)***
Chili Bar LLC......F......530 622-3325
11380 State Highway 193 Placerville (95667) ***(P-326)***
Chili Bar Slate, Placerville *Also called Chili Bar LLC* ***(P-326)***
Chili's, Santa Maria *Also called Impo International LLC* ***(P-10497)***
Chill Spot Inc......F......818 762-0041
11706 Moorpark St Studio City (91604) ***(P-662)***
Chimes Printing Incorporated......F......510 235-2388
1065 Hensley St Richmond (94801) ***(P-6730)***
China Circuit Tech Corp N Amer......F......831 646-2194
11 Thomas Owens Way Monterey (93940) ***(P-18447)***
China Custom Manufacturing Ltd......A......510 979-1920
44843 Fremont Blvd Fremont (94538) ***(P-10025)***
China Loco Szhou Precise Indus......E......510 429-3700
4125 Business Center Dr Fremont (94538) ***(P-19375)***
China Master USA Entrmt Co......F......626 810-9372
17890 Castleton St # 230 City of Industry (91748) ***(P-11354)***
China Press......F......626 281-8500
2121 W Mission Rd Ste 103 Alhambra (91803) ***(P-5799)***
China Press, The, Burlingame *Also called Asia Pacific California Inc* ***(P-5763)***
China Times Printing Inc......D......626 576-7006
445 Madera St San Gabriel (91776) ***(P-5800)***
Chinese Consumer Yellow Pages, Fremont *Also called Chinese Overseas Mktg Svc Corp* ***(P-6461)***
Chinese Consumer Yellow Pages, Rosemead *Also called Chinese Overseas Mktg Svc Corp* ***(P-6462)***
Chinese Overseas Mktg Svc Corp......E......510 476-0880
33420 Alvarado Niles Rd Union City (94587) ***(P-6460)***
Chinese Overseas Mktg Svc Corp......E......626 280-8588
46292 Warm Springs Blvd Fremont (94539) ***(P-6461)***
Chinese Overseas Mktg Svc Corp (PA)......D......626 280-8588
3940 Rosemead Blvd Rosemead (91770) ***(P-6462)***
Chinese Times, San Francisco *Also called Gum Sun Times Inc* ***(P-5868)***
Chinese-La Daily News, El Monte *Also called LAweb Offset Printing Inc* ***(P-7381)***
Chino Ice Service LLC......E......909 628-2105
3640 Francis Ave Chino (91710) ***(P-2409)***
Chiodo Candy Co......D......510 464-2977
2923 Adeline St Oakland (94608) ***(P-1413)***
Chip-Makers Tooling Supply Inc......F......562 698-5840
7352 Whittier Ave Whittier (90602) ***(P-14495)***
Chipco Manufacturing Co Inc......F......530 751-8150
623 Bridge St Yuba City (95991) ***(P-16382)***
Chipmasters Manufacturing Inc (PA)......F......626 422-2053
798 N Coney Ave Azusa (91702) ***(P-16383)***
Chipstart LLC......F......650 204-7883
5537 Blossom Vista Ave San Jose (95124) ***(P-17451)***
Chipton-Ross Inc......D......310 414-7800
420 Culver Blvd Playa Del Rey (90293) ***(P-20572)***
Chiquita Brands Intl Inc......F......510 732-9500
3586 Arden Rd Hayward (94545) ***(P-943)***
Chladni & Jariwala Inc......E......909 947-5227
1120 E Locust St Ontario (91761) ***(P-13710)***
Chlor Alkali Products & Vinyls, Santa Fe Springs *Also called Olin Chlor Alkali Logistics* ***(P-7666)***
Chlor Alkali Products & Vinyls, Tracy *Also called Olin Chlor Alkali Logistics* ***(P-7667)***
Choice Food Products Inc......F......559 266-1674
1822 W Hedges Ave Fresno (93728) ***(P-474)***
Choice Foodservices Inc......D......925 837-0104
569 San Ramon Valley Blvd Danville (94526) ***(P-11728)***
Choice Lithographics, Buena Park *Also called Cyu Lithographics Inc* ***(P-6774)***
Chol Enterprises Inc......E......310 516-1328
12831 S Figueroa St Los Angeles (90061) ***(P-20780)***
Cholestech, Livermore *Also called Alere Inc* ***(P-8457)***
Chooljian & Sons Inc......D......559 888-2031
Del Rey Ave Del Rey (93616) ***(P-14841)***
Choon Inc (PA)......E......213 225-2500
520 Mateo St Los Angeles (90013) ***(P-3302)***
Choose Manufacturing Co LLC......E......714 327-1698
17925 Sky Park Cir Ste G Irvine (92614) ***(P-18448)***
Chorus.ai, San Francisco *Also called Affectlayer Inc* ***(P-24334)***
Chosen Foods LLC (PA)......F......877 674-2244
1747 Hancock St Ste A San Diego (92101) ***(P-9231)***
Chownow Inc......D......888 707-2469
12181 Bluff Creek Dr # 200 Playa Vista (90094) ***(P-24488)***
Chris French Metal Inc......F......510 238-9339
2500 Union St Oakland (94607) ***(P-12135)***
Chrislie, Azusa *Also called Arminak Solutions LLC* ***(P-8697)***
Christian Herald Inc......F......213 353-0777
520 S La Fayette Park Pl # 520 Los Angeles (90057) ***(P-5801)***
Christian Music Today Inc......F......408 377-9232
80 Gilman Ave Ste 2 Campbell (95008) ***(P-5802)***
Christian Science Church......E......805 966-6661
120 E Valerio St Santa Barbara (93101) ***(P-5803)***
Christian Today Inc......F......323 931-0505
354 S Normandie Ave # 101 Los Angeles (90020) ***(P-5804)***

Christie Digital Systems Inc (HQ) ....F....714 236-8610
10550 Camden Dr Cypress (90630) *(P-23144)*
Christine Alexander Inc ....E....213 488-1114
110 E 9th St Ste B336 Los Angeles (90079) *(P-3835)*
Christine Milne ....F....415 485-5658
1133 Francisco Blvd E H San Rafael (94901) *(P-1391)*
Christy Vault Company (PA) ....E....650 994-1378
1000 Collins Ave Colma (94014) *(P-10901)*
Chroma Systems Solutions Inc (HQ) ....D....949 297-4848
19772 Pauling Foothill Ranch (92610) *(P-21734)*
Chromacode Inc ....E....442 244-4369
2330 Faraday Ave Ste 100 Carlsbad (92008) *(P-21463)*
Chromadex Corporation (PA) ....D....949 419-0288
10005 Muirlands Blvd G Irvine (92618) *(P-7926)*
Chromal Plating & Grinding, Los Angeles *Also called Chromal Plating Company (P-13370)*
Chromal Plating Company ....E....323 222-0119
1748 Workman St Los Angeles (90031) *(P-13370)*
Chromatic Inc Lithographers ....E....818 242-5785
127 Concord St Glendale (91203) *(P-6731)*
Chrome Craft, Sacramento *Also called Mencarini & Jarwin Inc (P-13451)*
Chrome Deposit Corp ....D....925 432-4507
900 Loveridge Rd Pittsburg (94565) *(P-13371)*
Chrome Hearts LLC (PA) ....E....323 957-7544
921 N Mansfield Ave Los Angeles (90038) *(P-3610)*
Chromologic LLC ....E....626 381-9974
1225 S Shamrock Ave Monrovia (91016) *(P-22404)*
Chron Trol, San Diego *Also called Chrontrol Corporation (P-17135)*
Chronicle Books LLC ....C....415 537-4200
680 2nd St San Francisco (94107) *(P-6327)*
Chronomite Laboratories Inc ....E....310 534-2300
17451 Hurley St City of Industry (91744) *(P-21504)*
Chrontel Inc (PA) ....C....408 383-9328
2210 Otoole Ave Ste 100 San Jose (95131) *(P-18766)*
Chrontrol Corporation (PA) ....F....619 282-8686
6611 Jackson Dr San Diego (92119) *(P-17135)*
Chrysler West Coast Bus Ctr, Irvine *Also called FCA US LLC (P-20334)*
Chua & Sons Inc ....E....323 588-8044
3300 E 50th St Vernon (90058) *(P-2798)*
Chuao Chocolatier Inc (HQ) ....F....760 476-1668
2345 Camino Vida Roble Carlsbad (92011) *(P-1414)*
Chubby Gorilla Inc ....E....844 365-5218
10425 Slusher Dr Santa Fe Springs (90670) *(P-10026)*
Chuck L Logging Inc ....E....530 459-3842
6527 Big Springs Rd Montague (96064) *(P-3982)*
Chulada Inc ....E....818 841-6536
640 S Flower St Burbank (91502) *(P-7927)*
Chulada Spices Herbs & Snacks, Burbank *Also called Chulada Inc (P-7927)*
Chunma America, Vernon *Also called Chunma Usa Inc (P-10518)*
Chunma Usa Inc ....F....323 846-0077
2000 E 25th St Vernon (90058) *(P-10518)*
Chup Corporation ....F....949 455-0676
2990 Airway Ave Ste A Costa Mesa (92626) *(P-6732)*
Church & Dwight Co Inc ....E....559 661-2790
31266 Avenue 12 Madera (93638) *(P-7659)*
Church Scientology Intl ....D....323 960-3500
6331 Hollywood Blvd # 801 Los Angeles (90028) *(P-7271)*
Churchill Aerospace LLC ....C....909 266-3116
5091 G St Chino (91710) *(P-14702)*
Churm Publishing Inc (PA) ....E....714 796-7000
1451 Quail St Ste 201 Newport Beach (92660) *(P-6129)*
Ci, Mather *Also called Construction Innovations LLC (P-19931)*
Ci Management LLC ....F....650 654-8900
2039 Seabrook Ct Redwood City (94065) *(P-10470)*
Ci Systems Inc ....F....805 520-2233
759 Cochran St Ste A Simi Valley (93065) *(P-22068)*
Cianna Medical Inc ....D....949 360-0059
6 Journey Ste 125 Aliso Viejo (92656) *(P-9564)*
Ciao Wireless Inc ....D....805 389-3224
4000 Via Pescador Camarillo (93012) *(P-19487)*
Ciasons Industrial Inc ....E....714 259-0838
1615 Boyd St Santa Ana (92705) *(P-9524)*
Cicoil LLC ....D....661 295-1295
24960 Avenue Tibbitts Valencia (91355) *(P-11655)*
Cicon Engineering Inc ....E....818 909-6060
8345 Canoga Ave Canoga Park (91304) *(P-19488)*
Cicon Engineering Inc ....F....818 882-6508
21421 Schoenborn St Canoga Park (91304) *(P-19489)*
Cicon Engineering Inc (PA) ....C....818 909-6060
6633 Odessa Ave Van Nuys (91406) *(P-19490)*
Cidara Therapeutics Inc (PA) ....E....858 752-6170
6310 Nncy Rdge Dr Ste 101 San Diego (92121) *(P-8542)*
Cii, Santee *Also called Compucraft Industries Inc (P-20785)*
Cim, Compton *Also called Circle Industrial Mfg Corp (P-14435)*
Cim Services, Compton *Also called Circle Industrial Mfg Corp (P-15255)*
Cimc Intermodal Equipment LLC (HQ) ....D....562 904-8600
10533 Sessler St South Gate (90280) *(P-20496)*
Cimc Reefer Trailer Inc ....F....951 218-1414
22101 Alessandro Blvd Moreno Valley (92553) *(P-14313)*
Cimmaron Software Inc ....E....858 385-1291
16885 W Bernardo Dr # 345 San Diego (92127) *(P-24489)*
Cimrmaan Ivo ....F....858 693-1536
7550 Trade St San Diego (92121) *(P-13182)*
Cine Mechanics Inc ....F....818 701-7944
20610 Plummer St Chatsworth (91311) *(P-23145)*
Cinemag Inc ....F....818 993-4644
4487 Ish Dr Simi Valley (93063) *(P-19491)*
Cinemills Corporation (PA) ....F....818 843-4560
2021 N Lincoln St Burbank (91504) *(P-17679)*
Cintas Corporation ....F....916 375-8633
1679 Entp Blvd Ste 10 West Sacramento (95691) *(P-3098)*
Cinton ....E....714 961-8808
620 Richfield Rd Placentia (92870) *(P-5557)*
Ciphercloud Inc (PA) ....D....408 519-6930
2581 Junction Ave Ste 200 San Jose (95134) *(P-24490)*
Ciphertex LLC ....F....818 773-8989
9301 Jordan Ave Ste 105a Chatsworth (91311) *(P-15703)*
Ciphertex Data Security, Chatsworth *Also called Ciphertex LLC (P-15703)*
Circa 1605 Inc ....E....217 899-3512
1475 Folsom St Ste 200 San Francisco (94103) *(P-24491)*
Circle Industrial Mfg Corp (PA) ....E....310 638-5101
1613 W El Segundo Blvd Compton (90222) *(P-15255)*
Circle Industrial Mfg Corp ....F....310 638-5101
2727 N Slater Ave Compton (90222) *(P-14435)*
Circle Racing Wheels Inc (PA) ....F....800 959-2100
14955 Don Julian Rd City of Industry (91746) *(P-20290)*
Circle Seal Controls, Corona *Also called Circor Aerospace Inc (P-13711)*
Circlemaster Inc ....F....858 578-3900
7777 Alvarado Rd Ste 320 La Mesa (91942) *(P-12531)*
Circor Aerospace Inc ....B....951 270-6200
2301 Wardlow Cir Corona (92880) *(P-20781)*
Circor Aerospace Inc (HQ) ....C....951 270-6200
2301 Wardlow Cir Corona (92880) *(P-13711)*
Circor Aerospace Inc ....D....951 270-6200
2301 Wardlow Cir Corona (92880) *(P-11944)*
Circor Aerospace Machining Ctr, Corona *Also called Circor Aerospace Inc (P-11944)*
Circor Aerospace Pdts Group ....B....951 270-6200
2301 Wardlow Cir Corona (92880) *(P-11510)*
Circuit Assembly Corp (PA) ....E....949 855-7887
3 Vanderbilt Ste A Irvine (92618) *(P-19376)*
Circuit Automation Inc ....F....714 763-4180
5292 System Dr Huntington Beach (92649) *(P-19492)*
Circuit Bd Test & Insptn Sls, Irvine *Also called Teradyne Inc (P-21868)*
Circuit Check Inc ....D....408 263-7444
1764 Houret Ct Milpitas (95035) *(P-21735)*
Circuit Connections ....E....408 955-9505
2310 Lundy Ave San Jose (95131) *(P-18449)*
Circuit Express Inc ....F....805 581-2172
67 W Easy St Ste 129 Simi Valley (93065) *(P-18450)*
Circuit Services Llc ....E....818 701-5391
18646 Parthenia St Northridge (91324) *(P-18451)*
Circuit Spectrum Inc ....F....408 946-8484
988 Morse St San Jose (95126) *(P-18452)*
Cirexx Corporation ....E....408 988-3980
791 Nuttman St Santa Clara (95054) *(P-18453)*
Cirexx International Inc (PA) ....C....408 988-3980
791 Nuttman St Santa Clara (95054) *(P-18454)*
Cirrent Inc ....F....650 569-1135
2 E 3rd Ave Ste 100 San Mateo (94401) *(P-24492)*
Cirrus Logic Inc ....D....510 226-1204
45630 Northport Loop E Fremont (94538) *(P-18767)*
Cirtec Medical LLC ....D....408 395-0443
101b Cooper Ct Los Gatos (95032) *(P-22405)*
CIS, Santa Ana *Also called Creative Intgrated Systems Inc (P-18790)*
Cisc Semiconductor Corp ....F....847 553-4204
800 W El Camino Real Mountain View (94040) *(P-18768)*
Cisco & Brothers Designs, Los Angeles *Also called Cisco Bros Corp (P-4763)*
Cisco Bros Corp ....F....323 778-8612
938 E 60th St Los Angeles (90001) *(P-4762)*
Cisco Bros Corp (PA) ....C....323 778-8612
5955 S Western Ave Los Angeles (90047) *(P-4763)*
Cisco Ironport Systems LLC (HQ) ....B....650 989-6500
170 W Tasman Dr San Jose (95134) *(P-24493)*
Cisco Mfg Inc ....E....510 584-9626
3185 De La Cruz Blvd Santa Clara (95054) *(P-16384)*
Cisco Systems Inc ....A....408 526-7939
325 E Tasman Dr San Jose (95134) *(P-15704)*
Cisco Systems Inc ....A....408 570-9149
771 Alder Dr Milpitas (95035) *(P-15705)*
Cisco Systems Inc ....F....415 837-6261
500 Terry A Francois Blvd San Francisco (94158) *(P-15706)*
Cisco Systems Inc ....F....714 434-2100
3500 Hyland Ave Costa Mesa (92626) *(P-15707)*
Cisco Systems Inc ....A....408 526-4000
121 Theory Irvine (92617) *(P-15708)*
Cisco Systems Inc ....A....408 225-5248
11 Great Oaks Blvd San Jose (95119) *(P-15709)*
Cisco Systems Inc ....B....949 823-1200
121 Theory Ste 100 Irvine (92617) *(P-17932)*
Cisco Systems Inc ....A....408 526-4000
510 Mccarthy Blvd Milpitas (95035) *(P-15710)*
Cisco Systems Inc ....A....408 525-5669
131 Meadowland Dr Milpitas (95035) *(P-15711)*
Cisco Systems Inc ....A....408 526-6698
3650 Cisco Way Bldg 17 San Jose (95134) *(P-15712)*
Cisco Systems Inc ....A....925 223-1006
4460 Rosewood Dr Ste 100 Pleasanton (94588) *(P-15713)*
Cisco Systems Inc (PA) ....A....408 526-4000
170 W Tasman Dr San Jose (95134) *(P-15714)*
Cisco Systems Inc ....A....408 434-1903
3600 Cisco Way San Jose (95134) *(P-15715)*
Cisco Systems Inc ....A....408 424-4050
110 W Tasman Dr San Jose (95134) *(P-15716)*
Cisco Systems Inc ....A....408 526-5999
3700 Cisco Way San Jose (95134) *(P-15717)*
Ciscos Shop ....F....657 230-9158
2911 E Miraloma Ave # 17 Anaheim (92806) *(P-12031)*
CIT, Santa Fe Springs *Also called Teaze of California Inc (P-3516)*

ALPHABETIC

Employee Codes: A=Over 500 employees, B=251-500
C=101-250, D=51-100, E=20-50, F=10-19
2019 California
Manfacturers Register
© Mergent Inc. 1-800-342-5647
1099

Citizens of Humanity LLC (PA)..........D.......323 923-1240
5715 Bickett St Huntington Park (90255) ***(P-3393)***
Citragen Pharmaceuticals Inc..........F.......510 249-9066
3789 Spinnaker Ct Fremont (94538) ***(P-8113)***
Citrix Online Division..........F.......800 424-8749
7414 Hollister Ave Goleta Los Angeles (90074) ***(P-24494)***
City & County of San Francisco..........E.......415 557-5251
875 Stevenson St Ste 125 San Francisco (94103) ***(P-7272)***
City Baking Company..........D.......650 589-8128
1373 Lowrie Ave South San Francisco (94080) ***(P-1223)***
City Canvas..........F.......408 287-2688
1381 N 10th St San Jose (95112) ***(P-3784)***
City Crane, Bakersfield *Also called Dunbar Electric Sign Company* ***(P-23857)***
City Industrial Tool & Die (PA)..........F.......310 530-1234
25524 Frampton Ave Harbor City (90710) ***(P-11389)***
City of Delano..........E.......661 721-3352
1107 Lytle Ave Delano (93215) ***(P-16024)***
City of Industry, Chino *Also called Balaji Trading Inc* ***(P-17925)***
City of Riverside..........D.......951 351-6140
5950 Acorn St Riverside (92504) ***(P-16025)***
City of San Diego..........E.......619 758-2310
2392 Kincaid Rd San Diego (92101) ***(P-21934)***
City of Santa Fe Springs..........F.......562 868-8761
11641 Florence Ave Santa Fe Springs (90670) ***(P-23540)***
City of Santa Monica Wtr Trtmn, Los Angeles *Also called Santa Monica City of* ***(P-16105)***
City Paper Box Co..........F.......323 231-5990
652 E 61st St Los Angeles (90001) ***(P-5396)***
City Steel Heat Treating Inc..........F.......562 789-7373
1221 W Struck Ave Orange (92867) ***(P-11807)***
City Triangles, Los Angeles *Also called Jodi Kristopher LLC* ***(P-3318)***
City Wide Printing Inc..........F.......818 752-9300
5100 Lankershim Blvd North Hollywood (91601) ***(P-5805)***
Citywide Printing, North Hollywood *Also called City Wide Printing Inc* ***(P-5805)***
Ciuti International Inc..........F.......909 484-1414
8790 Rochester Ave Ste A Rancho Cucamonga (91730) ***(P-1538)***
Civic Center News Inc..........E.......213 481-1448
1264 W 1st St Los Angeles (90026) ***(P-5806)***
CJ Enterprises..........E.......714 898-8558
11530 Western Ave Stanton (90680) ***(P-14496)***
CJ Foods Manufacturing Corp..........E.......714 888-3500
500 S State College Blvd Fullerton (92831) ***(P-2488)***
Cjd Construction Services Inc..........E.......626 335-1116
416 S Vermont Ave Glendora (91741) ***(P-197)***
Cji Process Systems Inc..........D.......562 777-0614
12000 Clark St Santa Fe Springs (90670) ***(P-12375)***
Cjs Toffee & Toppings LLC..........F.......415 929-7852
2269 Chestnut St 298 San Francisco (94123) ***(P-1415)***
CK Manufacturing and Trading..........E.......949 529-3400
6 Piedmont Trabuco Canyon (92679) ***(P-5048)***
CK Technologies Inc (PA)..........E.......805 987-4801
3629 Vista Mercado Camarillo (93012) ***(P-21562)***
Ckcc Inc..........E.......213 629-0939
2125 Bay St Los Angeles (90021) ***(P-3884)***
Ckd Industries Inc..........F.......714 871-5600
501 E Jamie Ave La Habra (90631) ***(P-13183)***
Cks Solution Incorporated..........E.......714 292-6307
556 Vanguard Way Ste C Brea (92821) ***(P-19493)***
Ckt, Camarillo *Also called CK Technologies Inc* ***(P-21562)***
CL Knox Inc..........D.......661 837-0477
34933 Imperial St Bakersfield (93308) ***(P-198)***
CL Olson & Associates Inc..........F.......951 245-6233
508 Central Ave Lake Elsinore (92530) ***(P-14722)***
Cl-One Corporation..........D.......949 364-2895
29582 Spotted Bull Ln San Juan Capistrano (92675) ***(P-2113)***
Clama Products Inc..........F.......714 258-8606
1993 Ritchey St Santa Ana (92705) ***(P-14497)***
Clamp Manufacturing Co Inc..........F.......626 579-5379
1503 Adelia Ave South El Monte (91733) ***(P-11945)***
Clamp Swing Pricing Co Inc..........E.......510 567-1600
8386 Capwell Dr Oakland (94621) ***(P-24066)***
Clamshell Buildings, Oxnard *Also called Clamshell Structures Inc* ***(P-12927)***
Clamshell Structures Inc..........F.......805 988-1340
1101 Maulhardt Ave Oxnard (93030) ***(P-12927)***
Clarcor Air Filtration Pdts..........D.......951 272-1850
1295 E Ontario Ave # 102 Corona (92881) ***(P-15149)***
Clarcor Industrial Air, Sacramento *Also called Pecofacet (us) Inc* ***(P-15351)***
Claremont Courier..........E.......909 621-4761
114 Olive St Claremont (91711) ***(P-5807)***
Claremont Institute Statesmans (PA)..........E.......909 981-2200
1317 W Foothill Blvd # 120 Upland (91786) ***(P-7273)***
Claremont Institute, The, Upland *Also called Claremont Institute Statesmans* ***(P-7273)***
Clariant Corporation..........E.......909 825-1793
926 S 8th St Colton (92324) ***(P-5558)***
Clariant Corporation..........C.......650 494-1749
3350 W Bayshore Rd Palo Alto (94303) ***(P-8997)***
Clariant Corporation..........E.......661 763-5192
801 W 14th St Long Beach (90813) ***(P-8998)***
Clariant Plas Coatings USA Inc..........F.......909 606-1325
14355 Ramona Ave Chino (91710) ***(P-8999)***
Clarify Medical Inc..........E.......877 738-6041
401 W A St Ste 950 San Diego (92101) ***(P-22960)***
Clariphy Communications Inc (HQ)..........D.......949 861-3074
7585 Irvine Center Dr # 100 Irvine (92618) ***(P-18769)***
Clarity H2o LLC..........F.......619 993-4780
752 Pomelo Dr Vista (92081) ***(P-16026)***
Clark - Pacific Corporation (PA)..........B.......916 371-0305
1980 S River Rd West Sacramento (95691) ***(P-10902)***
Clark - Pacific Corporation..........D.......626 962-8751
131 Los Angeles St Irwindale (91706) ***(P-10903)***
Clark - Pacific Corporation..........C.......909 823-1433
13592 Slover Ave Fontana (92337) ***(P-10904)***
Clark - Pacific Corporation..........D.......925 746-7176
3478 Buskirk Ave Ste 1039 Pleasant Hill (94523) ***(P-10905)***
Clark Pacific, West Sacramento *Also called Clark - Pacific Corporation* ***(P-10902)***
Clark Steel Fabricators Inc..........E.......619 390-1502
12610 Vigilante Rd Lakeside (92040) ***(P-12843)***
Clarkdietrich Building Systems, Riverside *Also called Clarkwestern Dietrich Building* ***(P-12532)***
Clarke Engineering Inc..........F.......818 768-0690
8058 Lankershim Blvd North Hollywood (91605) ***(P-15282)***
Clarke Pb & Associates Inc..........E.......714 835-3022
2500 E Francis St Ontario (91761) ***(P-17782)***
Clarkwestern Dietrich Building..........F.......951 360-3500
6510 General Rd Riverside (92509) ***(P-12532)***
Clarmil Manufacturing Corp (PA)..........D.......510 476-0700
30865 San Clemente St Hayward (94544) ***(P-2489)***
Clarus Lighting LLC..........F.......916 363-2888
10183 Croydon Way Ste C Sacramento (95827) ***(P-17680)***
Clary Corporation..........E.......626 359-4486
150 E Huntington Dr Monrovia (91016) ***(P-19494)***
Class A Powdercoat Inc..........E.......916 681-7474
8538 Tiogawoods Dr Sacramento (95828) ***(P-13568)***
Class Twist Inc..........F.......650 646-8235
735 Tehama St San Francisco (94103) ***(P-24495)***
Classdojo, San Francisco *Also called Class Twist Inc* ***(P-24495)***
Classic Components Inc (PA)..........F.......714 619-5690
3420 W Fordham Ave Santa Ana (92704) ***(P-13372)***
Classic Containers Inc..........B.......909 930-3610
1700 S Hellman Ave Ontario (91761) ***(P-9794)***
Classic Cosmetics Inc (PA)..........C.......818 773-9042
9530 De Soto Ave Chatsworth (91311) ***(P-8715)***
Classic Graphix..........F.......562 940-0806
12152 Woodruff Ave Downey (90241) ***(P-3836)***
Classic Innovations, Cloverdale *Also called Classic Mill & Cabinet* ***(P-4286)***
Classic Litho & Design Inc..........E.......310 224-5200
340 Maple Ave Torrance (90503) ***(P-6733)***
Classic Mill & Cabinet..........E.......707 894-9800
590 Santana Dr Cloverdale (95425) ***(P-4286)***
Classic Quilting..........F.......714 558-8312
1471 E Warner Ave Santa Ana (92705) ***(P-3837)***
Classic Salads LLC..........E.......928 726-6196
100 Harrington Rd Royal Oaks (95076) ***(P-2490)***
Classic Slipcover Inc..........E.......323 583-0804
4300 District Blvd Vernon (90058) ***(P-3714)***
Classic Soft Trim Central Cal, Madera *Also called Muscle Road Inc* ***(P-20407)***
Classic Tees Inc..........E.......626 607-0255
4915 Walnut Grove Ave San Gabriel (91776) ***(P-3394)***
Classic Vinegar, Ceres *Also called Classic Wine Vinegar Co Inc* ***(P-2491)***
Classic Wine Vinegar Co Inc..........F.......209 538-7600
4110 Brew Master Dr Ceres (95307) ***(P-2491)***
Classic Wire Cut Company Inc..........C.......661 257-0558
28210 Constellation Rd Valencia (91355) ***(P-16385)***
Classified Flea Market, Oakland *Also called Bay Classifieds Inc* ***(P-14803)***
Classy Inc..........E.......619 961-1892
350 10th Ave Ste 1300 San Diego (92101) ***(P-24496)***
Claudios Specialty Breads..........F.......831 633-5051
11185 Commercial Pkwy Castroville (95012) ***(P-1224)***
Clausen Meat Company Inc..........E.......209 667-8690
19455 W Clausen Rd Turlock (95380) ***(P-428)***
Clay Castaic Manufacturing Co..........D.......661 259-3066
32201 Castaic Lake Dr Castaic (91384) ***(P-10775)***
Clay Designs Inc..........E.......562 432-3991
519 W 15th St Long Beach (90813) ***(P-10829)***
Clay Laguna Co (HQ)..........C.......626 330-0631
14400 Lomitas Ave City of Industry (91746) ***(P-11318)***
Clay Mix LLC..........F.......559 485-0065
1003 N Abby St Fresno (93701) ***(P-11093)***
Clayton Homes Inc..........F.......916 363-2681
9998 Old Placerville Rd Sacramento (95827) ***(P-4549)***
Clayton Homes Inc..........C.......951 657-1611
3100 N Perris Blvd Perris (92571) ***(P-4550)***
Clayton Industries, City of Industry *Also called Clayton Manufacturing Company* ***(P-15308)***
Clayton Manufacturing Company (PA)..........C.......626 443-9381
17477 Hurley St City of Industry (91744) ***(P-15308)***
Clayton Manufacturing Inc (HQ)..........D.......626 443-9381
17477 Hurley St City of Industry (91744) ***(P-15309)***
CLC Work Gear, South Gate *Also called Custom Leathercraft Mfg LLC* ***(P-10573)***
Cleaire Advanced Emission (PA)..........F.......510 347-6103
1001 42nd St Emeryville (94608) ***(P-9330)***
Clean America Inc..........F.......562 694-5990
1400 Pioneer St Brea (92821) ***(P-19927)***
Clean Cut Technologies LLC..........D.......714 864-3500
1145 N Ocean Cir Anaheim (92806) ***(P-9826)***
Clean Sciences Inc..........F.......510 440-8660
301 Whitney Pl Fremont (94539) ***(P-13373)***
Clean Water Technology Inc..........D.......310 380-4648
151 W 135th St Los Angeles (90061) ***(P-16027)***
Clean Wave Management Inc..........F.......949 488-2922
1291 Puerta Del Sol San Clemente (92673) ***(P-20573)***
Clean Wave Management Inc..........E.......949 361-5356
1291 Puerta Del Sol San Clemente (92673) ***(P-15105)***
Cleanflame, Gridley *Also called Wax Box Firelog Corporation* ***(P-12094)***
Cleanlogic LLC..........E.......310 261-3001
4051 S Broadway Los Angeles (90037) ***(P-8631)***
Cleanpartset Inc..........E.......408 886-3300
3530 Bassett St Santa Clara (95054) ***(P-14928)***
Cleanroom Film & Bags, Orange *Also called CF&b Manufacturing Inc* ***(P-5592)***

Cleansmart Solutions Inc............E.......650 871-9123
47422 Kato Rd Fremont (94538) ***(P-5673)***
Cleantech Group, San Francisco *Also called Ctg I LLC* ***(P-6466)***
Cleanworld............F.......916 635-7300
2330 Gold Meadow Way Gold River (95670) ***(P-23541)***
Clear Blue Energy Corp............F.......858 451-1549
17150 Via Del Ca San Diego (92127) ***(P-21563)***
Clear Channel Radio Sales, Los Angeles *Also called Katz Millennium Sls & Mktg Inc* ***(P-18143)***
Clear Image Inc (PA)............E.......916 933-4700
4949 Windplay Dr Ste 100 El Dorado Hills (95762) ***(P-5593)***
Clear Image Printing Inc............E.......818 547-4684
12744 San Fernando Rd # 200 Sylmar (91342) ***(P-6734)***
Clear Path Technologies Inc............F.......951 278-3520
561 W Rincon St Corona (92880) ***(P-19928)***
Clear Skies Solutions Inc............F.......925 570-4471
2345 Mirada Ct Tracy (95377) ***(P-21505)***
Clear View LLC............F.......408 271-2734
1650 Las Plumas Ave Ste A San Jose (95133) ***(P-12303)***
Clear Water Corporation Inc............F.......818 765-8293
14738 Oxnard St Van Nuys (91411) ***(P-16028)***
Clear-Ad Inc............E.......877 899-1002
2410 W 3rd St Santa Ana (92703) ***(P-10027)***
Clear-Com Communications, Alameda *Also called Clear-Com LLC* ***(P-18068)***
Clear-Com LLC............A.......510 337-6600
1301 Marina Vil Pkwy 10 Alameda (94501) ***(P-18068)***
Clearbags, El Dorado Hills *Also called Clear Image Inc* ***(P-5593)***
Clearchem Diagnostics Inc............F.......714 734-8041
1710 E Grevillea Ct Ontario (91761) ***(P-7766)***
Clearlake Capital Group LP (PA)............B.......310 400-8800
233 Wilshire Blvd Ste 800 Santa Monica (90401) ***(P-3885)***
Clearlake Lava Inc............F.......707 995-1515
13329 Point Lakeview Rd Lower Lake (95457) ***(P-11094)***
Clearlight Diagnostics LLC............F.......928 525-4290
428 Oakmead Pkwy Sunnyvale (94085) ***(P-8470)***
Clearslide Inc (HQ)............D.......877 360-3366
45 Fremont St Fl 32 San Francisco (94105) ***(P-24497)***
Clearwater Paper Corporation............A.......925 947-4700
1320 Willow Pass Rd # 550 Concord (94520) ***(P-5277)***
Clearwell Systems Inc............C.......877 253-2793
350 Ellis St Mountain View (94043) ***(P-24498)***
Cleasby Manufacturing Co Inc (PA)............E.......415 822-6565
1414 Bancroft Ave San Francisco (94124) ***(P-14158)***
Cleatech LLC............E.......714 754-6668
2106 N Glassell St Orange Orange (92865) ***(P-21464)***
Clegg Industries Inc............C.......310 225-3800
19032 S Vermont Ave Gardena (90248) ***(P-23845)***
Clegg Promo, Gardena *Also called Clegg Industries Inc* ***(P-23845)***
Clemes & Clemes Inc............F.......510 724-2036
650 San Pablo Ave Pinole (94564) ***(P-11946)***
Clendenen Lindquist Vintners............F.......805 937-9801
4665 Santa Maria Mesa Rd Santa Maria (93454) ***(P-1693)***
Cleophus Quealy Beer Company............F.......510 463-4534
448 Hester St San Leandro (94577) ***(P-1579)***
Cleughs Frozen Foods Inc............E.......714 521-1002
6571 Altura Blvd Ste 200 Buena Park (90620) ***(P-944)***
Cleveland Golf-Srixon, Huntington Beach *Also called Roger Cleveland Golf Co Inc* ***(P-23638)***
Cli Liquidating Corporation............D.......510 354-0300
47266 Benicia St Fremont (94538) ***(P-22961)***
Clic LLC............F.......415 421-2900
601 20th St San Francisco (94107) ***(P-6735)***
Clickscanshare Inc............F.......925 283-1400
3631 Mt Diablo Blvd Ste C Lafayette (94549) ***(P-15718)***
Clickscanshare Inc (PA)............F.......619 461-5880
8055 Clairemont Mesa Blvd # 101 San Diego (92111) ***(P-15719)***
Cliff Bartlett............F.......805 693-1617
250 Industrial Way Ste B Buellton (93427) ***(P-4287)***
Cliff Digital............F.......310 323-5600
14700 S Main St Gardena (90248) ***(P-7274)***
Cliff Vine Winery Inc............F.......707 944-2388
7400 Silverado Trl NAPA (94558) ***(P-1694)***
Cliffdale LLC............F.......818 885-0300
20409 Prairie St Chatsworth (91311) ***(P-21158)***
Cliffdale Manufacturing LLC............C.......818 341-3344
20409 Prairie St Chatsworth (91311) ***(P-21188)***
Clinch-On Cornerbead Company, Orange *Also called Continuous Coating Corp* ***(P-13381)***
Clinical Formula LLC............F.......949 631-0149
888 W 16th St Newport Beach (92663) ***(P-8114)***
Clinicloud Inc............D.......415 801-3283
350 Townsend St Ste 758 San Francisco (94107) ***(P-22962)***
Cliniqa Corporation (HQ)............D.......760 744-1900
495 Enterprise St San Marcos (92078) ***(P-8543)***
Clint Precision Mfg Inc............F.......858 271-4041
7665 Formula Pl Ste A San Diego (92121) ***(P-16386)***
Clio Inc............E.......562 926-3724
12981 166th St Cerritos (90703) ***(P-13792)***
Clipcall Inc............F.......650 285-7597
645 Harrison St Ste 200 San Francisco (94107) ***(P-24499)***
Clipper Windpower PLC............A.......805 690-3275
6305 Carpinteria Ave # 300 Carpinteria (93013) ***(P-13993)***
Clique Brands Inc (PA)............E.......323 648-5619
750 N San Vicnte Blvd Re800 West Hollywood (90069) ***(P-6130)***
Clo Systems LLC............F.......626 939-4226
15312 Valley Blvd City of Industry (91746) ***(P-17185)***
Clockware............F.......650 556-8880
548 Market St San Francisco (94104) ***(P-24500)***
Clonetab Inc............E.......209 292-5663
1660 W Linne Rd Ste 214 Tracy (95377) ***(P-24501)***

Clorox Company (PA)............B.......510 271-7000
1221 Broadway Ste 1300 Oakland (94612) ***(P-8632)***
Clorox Company............F.......209 234-1094
11940 S Harlan Rd Lathrop (95330) ***(P-8633)***
Clorox Company............F.......925 368-6000
4900 Johnson Dr Pleasanton (94588) ***(P-8634)***
Clorox Company Voluntary............F.......510 271-7000
1221 Broadway Ste 1300 Oakland (94612) ***(P-7660)***
Clorox International Company (HQ)............D.......510 271-7000
1221 Broadway Fl 13 Oakland (94612) ***(P-9097)***
Clorox Products Mfg Co............D.......707 437-1051
2600 Huntington Dr Fairfield (94533) ***(P-8635)***
Clorox Products Mfg Co............D.......909 307-2756
2300 W San Bernardino Ave Redlands (92374) ***(P-8636)***
Clorox Products Mfg Co (HQ)............C.......510 271-7000
1221 Broadway Oakland (94612) ***(P-8637)***
Clorox Sales Company............E.......760 432-8362
530 Idaho Ave Escondido (92025) ***(P-7661)***
Clos De La Tech LLC............F.......650 722-3038
575 Eastview Way Woodside (94062) ***(P-1695)***
Clos Du Bois Wines Inc............E.......707 857-1651
19410 Geyserville Ave Geyserville (95441) ***(P-1696)***
Clos Du Val Wine Company Ltd............E.......707 259-2200
5330 Silverado Trl NAPA (94558) ***(P-1697)***
Clos La Chance Wines Inc............E.......408 686-1050
1 Hummingbird Ln San Martin (95046) ***(P-1698)***
Closetmaid Corporation............F.......909 590-4444
5150 Edison Ave Ste C Chino (91710) ***(P-13819)***
Closets By Design Inc............C.......562 699-9945
3860 Capitol Ave City of Industry (90601) ***(P-5049)***
Clothing By Frenzii Inc............F.......213 670-0265
905 Mateo St Los Angeles (90021) ***(P-3225)***
Clothing Illustrated Inc (PA)............E.......213 403-9950
2014 E 15th St Los Angeles (90021) ***(P-3395)***
Cloud Automation Division, Aliso Viejo *Also called Quest Software Inc* ***(P-25099)***
Cloud Company (PA)............E.......805 549-8093
4855 Morabito Pl San Luis Obispo (93401) ***(P-15310)***
Cloud Engines Inc............E.......415 738-8076
77 Geary St Ste 500 San Francisco (94108) ***(P-15523)***
Cloud Nine Comforts, Torrance *Also called Universal Cushion Company Inc* ***(P-3754)***
CLOud&co, San Francisco *Also called Cloudnco Inc* ***(P-24503)***
Cloudburst Inc............E.......805 986-4125
707 E Hueneme Rd Oxnard (93033) ***(P-15150)***
Cloudcar Inc............E.......650 946-1236
2550 Great America Way # 301 Santa Clara (95054) ***(P-24502)***
Cloudminds Technology Inc............F.......650 391-6817
4500 Great America Pkwy # 2 Santa Clara (95054) ***(P-14269)***
Cloudnco Inc............F.......408 605-8755
300 Beale St Apt 613 San Francisco (94105) ***(P-24503)***
Cloudpic Inc............F.......408 786-1098
19925 Stevens Creek Blvd Cupertino (95014) ***(P-24504)***
Cloudscaling Group, San Francisco *Also called EMC Corporation* ***(P-15534)***
Cloudshield Technologies LLC............F.......408 331-6640
212 Gibraltar Dr Sunnyvale (94089) ***(P-24505)***
Cloudvelocity Software, Santa Clara *Also called Cloudvelox Inc* ***(P-24506)***
Cloudvelox Inc............F.......408 841-4800
3945 Freedom Cir Ste 240 Santa Clara (95054) ***(P-24506)***
Clougherty Packing LLC (HQ)............B.......323 583-4621
3049 E Vernon Ave Vernon (90058) ***(P-429)***
Clougherty Packing LLC............F.......559 992-8421
3922 Avenue 120 Corcoran (93212) ***(P-475)***
Clover Garments Inc............D.......415 826-6909
2565 3rd St Ste 232 San Francisco (94107) ***(P-3396)***
Clovis Independent, Sacramento *Also called El Dorado Newspapers Inc* ***(P-5843)***
Clp Apg LLC............D.......510 528-1444
1700 4th St Berkeley (94710) ***(P-6328)***
Clp Apg, Inc., Berkeley *Also called Clp Apg LLC* ***(P-6328)***
Clr Analytics Inc............F.......949 864-6696
25 Mauchly Ste 315 Irvine (92618) ***(P-21223)***
Club Car LLC............E.......951 735-4675
1203 Hall Ave Riverside (92509) ***(P-21224)***
Club Donatello Owners Assn............E.......415 474-7333
501 Post St San Francisco (94102) ***(P-23220)***
Clutches New or Rebuilt, National City *Also called Southland Clutch Inc* ***(P-20451)***
Clw Plastic Bag Mfg Co Inc............F.......562 903-8878
13060 Park St Santa Fe Springs (90670) ***(P-5594)***
CM Brewing Technologies............F.......888 391-9990
13681 Newport Ave 8-261 Tustin (92780) ***(P-16029)***
CM Manufacturing Inc (HQ)............C.......408 284-7200
6321 San Ignacio Ave San Jose (95119) ***(P-18770)***
CMA Dish Machines, Garden Grove *Also called Chemical Methods Assoc LLC* ***(P-16022)***
Cmd Products............F.......916 434-0228
1410 Flightline Dr Ste D Lincoln (95648) ***(P-9827)***
CMF, Long Beach *Also called Commercial Mini Freighters Inc* ***(P-20196)***
CMH Manufacturing West, Sacramento *Also called Clayton Homes Inc* ***(P-4549)***
CMI, Irvine *Also called Cooper Microelectronics Inc* ***(P-18784)***
CMI, Hughson *Also called Calaveras Materials Inc* ***(P-11055)***
CMI, San Clemente *Also called Composite Manufacturing Inc* ***(P-22407)***
CMI Integrated Tech Inc............E.......760 431-7003
11248 Playa Ct Culver City (90230) ***(P-17186)***
CMI Mfg Inc............F.......408 982-9580
35370 Cedar Blvd Newark (94560) ***(P-16387)***
CMI Precision Machining, Placentia *Also called CMi Precision Machining LLC* ***(P-16389)***
CMi Precision Machining LLC............F.......714 528-3000
527 Fee Ana St Placentia (92870) ***(P-16388)***
CMi Precision Machining LLC............F.......714 528-3000
527 Fee Ana St Placentia (92870) ***(P-16389)***
Cmmc, Long Beach *Also called Coastal Marine Maint Co LLC* ***(P-20990)***

ALPHABETIC

Cmos Sensor Inc F 408 366-2898
20045 Stevens Creek Blvd 1a Cupertino (95014) *(P-18771)*
Cmp Display Systems Inc D 805 499-3642
23301 Wilmington Ave Carson (90745) *(P-10028)*
Cmp Healthcare Media, San Francisco *Also called Ubm LLC (P-6278)*
CMr Marketing and RES Inc E 559 499-2100
3594 E Wawona Ave Fresno (93725) *(P-9098)*
CMS, Mission Viejo *Also called Community Merch Solutions LLC (P-15896)*
CMS Products Inc E 714 424-5520
12 Mauchly Ste E Irvine (92618) *(P-15524)*
Cmt, Los Gatos *Also called Chemical & Material Technology (P-22067)*
Cmt, Concord *Also called Cable Manufacturing Tech (P-2971)*
Cmt Sheet Metal F 949 679-9868
22732 Granite Way Ste C Laguna Hills (92653) *(P-12376)*
Cmtg F 310 908-6687
164 W Highland Ave San Bernardino (92405) *(P-24067)*
Cmyk Enterprise Inc F 209 229-7230
25653 Gateway Blvd Tracy (95377) *(P-6736)*
Cmyk Prints and Promotions.com, Tracy *Also called Cmyk Enterprise Inc (P-6736)*
CN Publishing Group, Irvine *Also called Cycle News Inc (P-5819)*
Cnc Clothing, Compton *Also called Kim & Roy Co Inc (P-3108)*
Cnc Industries Inc F 909 445-0300
10635 Monte Vista Ave Montclair (91763) *(P-16390)*
Cnc Machining Service Inc F 559 732-5599
1130 E Acequia Ave Visalia (93292) *(P-13184)*
Cnc Machining Solutions Inc F 951 688-4267
12155 Magnolia Ave 10c Riverside (92503) *(P-22963)*
Cnc Manufacturing, Temecula *Also called Ralc Inc (P-20621)*
Cnc Noodle Corporation F 510 835-2269
325 Fallon St Oakland (94607) *(P-2492)*
Cnex Labs Inc E 408 695-1045
2880 Stevens Creek Blvd San Jose (95128) *(P-18772)*
Cni Mfg Inc E 626 962-6646
15627 Arrow Hwy Irwindale (91706) *(P-16391)*
Cnp Industries Inc F 714 482-2320
351 Thor Pl Brea (92821) *(P-17413)*
Cns Aviation Inc F 714 901-7072
1240 N Simon Cir Anaheim (92806) *(P-20574)*
Co-Color F 909 394-7888
650 W Terrace Dr San Dimas (91773) *(P-6737)*
Co-West Commodities, San Bernardino *Also called Park West Enterprises (P-1531)*
Co/Color Division, San Dimas *Also called Co-Color (P-6737)*
Coach, Commerce *Also called Tapestry Inc (P-10553)*
Coach Inc F 949 365-0771
3333 Bristol St Ste 2883 Costa Mesa (92626) *(P-10544)*
Coach Inc F 805 496-9933
434 W Hillcrest Dr Thousand Oaks (91360) *(P-10545)*
Coachella Valley Rag Company, Lynwood *Also called Linens Exchange Inc (P-3008)*
Coachelle Valley Ice Co E 760 347-3529
83796 Date Ave Indio (92201) *(P-2410)*
Coachworks Holdings Inc B 951 684-9585
1863 Service Ct Riverside (92507) *(P-20133)*
Coadna Photonics Inc (HQ) D 408 736-1100
1012 Stewart Dr Sunnyvale (94085) *(P-17933)*
Coalign Innovations Inc E 888 714-4440
2684 Middlefield Rd Ste A Redwood City (94063) *(P-22406)*
Coalinga Corporation (PA) F 310 578-5900
12575 Beatrice St Los Angeles (90066) *(P-49)*
Coast 2 Coast Cables LLC F 714 666-1062
3162 E La Palma Ave Ste D Anaheim (92806) *(P-11656)*
Coast Aerospace Mfg Inc E 714 893-8066
950 Richfield Rd Placentia (92870) *(P-12136)*
Coast Air Supply Co Inc F 818 898-2288
26501 Summit Cir Santa Clarita (91350) *(P-17452)*
Coast Color Printing Inc F 310 352-3560
16301 S Broadway Gardena (90248) *(P-6738)*
Coast Composites LLC F 949 455-0665
7 Burroughs Irvine (92618) *(P-16392)*
Coast Composites LLC (HQ) C 949 455-0665
5 Burroughs Irvine (92618) *(P-16393)*
Coast Creative Nameplates, San Jose *Also called Coast Engraving Companies (P-7640)*
Coast Custom Cable, Carson *Also called Alpha Wire Corporation (P-11642)*
Coast Cutters Co Inc F 626 444-2965
2500 Royale Pl Fullerton (92833) *(P-11390)*
Coast Dance Shoes, Porter Ranch *Also called Jevin Enterprises Inc (P-9472)*
Coast Engraving Companies E 408 297-2555
1097 N 5th St San Jose (95112) *(P-7640)*
Coast Flagstone Co D 310 829-4010
1810 Colorado Ave Santa Monica (90404) *(P-11241)*
Coast Heat Treating Co E 323 263-6944
1767 Industrial Way Los Angeles (90023) *(P-11808)*
Coast News E 760 436-9737
315 S Coast Highway 101 W Encinitas (92024) *(P-5808)*
Coast Seafoods Company E 707 442-2947
25 Waterfront Dr Eureka (95501) *(P-2295)*
Coast Sheet Metal Inc E 949 645-2224
990 W 17th St Costa Mesa (92627) *(P-12533)*
Coast Sign Display, Anaheim *Also called Coast Sign Incorporated (P-23846)*
Coast Sign Incorporated C 714 520-9144
1500 W Embassy St Anaheim (92802) *(P-23846)*
Coast To Coast Circuits Inc (PA) C 585 254-2980
5331 Mcfadden Ave Huntington Beach (92649) *(P-18455)*
Coast To Coast Circuits Inc D 714 898-4901
5331 Mcfadden Ave Huntington Beach (92649) *(P-18456)*
Coast To Coast Label Inc (PA) F 657 203-2583
18401 Bandilier Cir Fountain Valley (92708) *(P-5704)*
Coast To Coast Met Finshg Corp E 626 282-2122
401 S Raymond Ave Alhambra (91803) *(P-13374)*
Coast To Coast Mfg LLC F 909 798-5024
430 Nevada St Redlands (92373) *(P-10029)*
Coast Wood Preserving Inc (PA) F 209 632-9931
600 W Glenwood Ave Turlock (95380) *(P-4591)*
Coast/A C M, Torrance *Also called Coast/Dvnced Chip Mgnetics Inc (P-19325)*
Coast/Dvnced Chip Mgnetics Inc F 310 370-8188
4225 Spencer St Torrance (90503) *(P-19325)*
Coastal Cocktails Inc (PA) E 949 250-3129
18011 Mitchell S Ste B Irvine (92614) *(P-2114)*
Coastal Component Inds Inc E 714 685-6677
133 E Bristol Ln Orange (92865) *(P-19495)*
Coastal Connections E 805 644-5051
2085 Sperry Ave Ste B Ventura (93003) *(P-17934)*
Coastal Container Inc E 562 801-4595
8455 Loch Lomond Dr Pico Rivera (90660) *(P-5397)*
Coastal Decking Inc E 619 477-0567
2050 Wilson Ave Ste A National City (91950) *(P-20989)*
Coastal Die Cutting Inc F 619 677-3180
4025 Pacific Hwy San Diego (92110) *(P-14436)*
Coastal Enterprises, Fountain Valley *Also called Joy Products California Inc (P-23718)*
Coastal Enterprises E 714 771-4969
1925 W Collins Ave Orange (92867) *(P-7824)*
Coastal Graphics, San Diego *Also called Blue Book Publishers Inc (P-6449)*
Coastal Marine Maint Co LLC (PA) F 562 432-8066
250 W Wardlow Rd Long Beach (90807) *(P-20990)*
Coastal Medical Supply, Anaheim *Also called Orange Cnty Cstl Physcians Inc (P-22574)*
Coastal Products Company Inc F 661 323-0487
2157 Mohawk St Bakersfield (93308) *(P-15057)*
Coastal PVA Opco LLC F 530 406-3303
1380 E Beamer St Woodland (95776) *(P-15400)*
Coastal Tag & Label Inc D 562 946-4318
13233 Barton Cir Whittier (90605) *(P-7275)*
Coastal Vineyard Services LLC F 805 441-4465
120 Callie Ct Arroyo Grande (93420) *(P-1699)*
Coastline High Prfmce Coatings F 714 372-3263
7181 Orangewood Ave Garden Grove (92841) *(P-18069)*
Coastline International C 888 748-7177
1207 Bangor St San Diego (92106) *(P-22964)*
Coastline Metal Finishing Corp D 714 895-9099
7061 Patterson Dr Garden Grove (92841) *(P-13375)*
Coastwide Tag & Label Co E 323 721-1501
7647 Industry Ave Pico Rivera (90660) *(P-7276)*
Coates Incorporated F 530 832-1533
73816 S Delleker Rd Portola (96122) *(P-20291)*
Coating Services Group LLC F 619 596-7444
11649 Rverside Dr Ste 139 Lakeside (92040) *(P-13569)*
Coating Specialties Inc F 310 639-6900
815 E Rosecrans Ave Los Angeles (90059) *(P-20782)*
Coatings By Sandberg Inc F 714 538-0888
856 N Commerce St Orange (92867) *(P-13570)*
Coatings Resource, Huntington Beach *Also called Laird Coatings Corporation (P-8914)*
Cobalt Labs Inc E 415 651-7028
2403 16th St San Francisco (94103) *(P-24507)*
Cobel Technologies Inc E 626 332-2100
822 N Grand Ave Covina (91724) *(P-17136)*
Cobham Adv Elec Sol Inc C 858 560-1301
9404 Chesapeake Dr San Diego (92123) *(P-21271)*
Cobham Adv Elec Sol Inc B 408 624-3000
5300 Hellyer Ave San Jose (95138) *(P-21272)*
Cobra Engineering Inc D 714 692-8180
23801 La Palma Ave Yorba Linda (92887) *(P-20292)*
Cobra Performance Boats Inc F 909 482-0047
5109 Holt Blvd Montclair (91763) *(P-21026)*
Cobra Systems F 714 688-7992
3521 E Enterprise Dr Anaheim (92807) *(P-6463)*
Coc Inc, Los Angeles *Also called Colon Manufacturing Inc (P-3226)*
Coca Cola Btlg of Eureka Cal F 707 443-2796
1335 Albee St Eureka (95501) *(P-2115)*
Coca-Cola, Lancaster *Also called Ccbcc Operations LLC (P-2109)*
Coca-Cola, Eureka *Also called Coca Cola Btlg of Eureka Cal (P-2115)*
Coca-Cola, Santa Maria *Also called Tognazzini Beverage Service (P-2228)*
Coca-Cola Company C 909 975-5200
1650 S Vintage Ave Ontario (91761) *(P-2116)*
Coca-Cola Company E 626 855-4440
13255 Amar Rd City of Industry (91746) *(P-2117)*
Coca-Cola Company C 949 250-5961
3 Park Plz Ste 600 Irvine (92614) *(P-2118)*
Coca-Cola Company E 714 991-7031
2121 E Winston Rd Anaheim (92806) *(P-2119)*
Coca-Cola Company D 909 975-5200
1650 S Vintage Ave Ontario (91761) *(P-2252)*
Coca-Cola Company C 510 476-7048
2025 Pike Ave San Leandro (94577) *(P-2120)*
Coca-Cola Refreshments USA Inc C 805 644-2211
5335 Walker St Ventura (93003) *(P-2121)*
Coca-Cola Refreshments USA Inc D 760 435-7111
3900 Ocean Ranch Blvd Oceanside (92056) *(P-2122)*
Coco Delice F 510 601-1394
1555 Park Ave Ste A Emeryville (94608) *(P-1468)*
Coco Dry, Ontario *Also called C & S Products CA Inc (P-8629)*
Coco Products LLC F 909 218-8971
1345 S Parkside Pl Ontario (91761) *(P-8638)*
Coconut Secret, Mill Valley *Also called Leslies Organics LLC (P-9021)*
Cod USA Inc E 949 381-7367
25954 Commercentre Dr Lake Forest (92630) *(P-5008)*
Coda Automotive Inc E 408 763-4071
4250 Stevens Creek Blvd San Jose (95129) *(P-20293)*
Coda Automotive Inc E 310 820-3611
12101 W Olympic Blvd Los Angeles (90064) *(P-20294)*

Coda Automotive Inc ...E...619 291-2040
1441 Camino Del Rio S San Diego (92108) *(P-20295)*
Coda Automotive Inc ...E...949 830-7000
14 Auto Center Dr Irvine (92618) *(P-20296)*
Coda Energy Holdings LLC ...E...626 775-3900
111 N Artsakh St 300 Glendale (91206) *(P-19929)*
Codan US Corporation ...C...714 430-1300
3511 W Sunflower Ave Santa Ana (92704) *(P-10030)*
Codar Ocean Sensors Ltd (PA) ...F...408 773-8240
1914 Plymouth St Mountain View (94043) *(P-21273)*
Code-In-Motion LLC ...F...949 361-2633
232 Avenida Fabricante # 103 San Clemente (92672) *(P-15311)*
Codefast Inc ...E...408 687-4700
21170 Canyon Oak Way Cupertino (95014) *(P-24508)*
Codexis Inc (PA) ...C...650 421-8100
200 Penobscot Dr Redwood City (94063) *(P-9000)*
Codorniu Napa Inc ...D...707 254-2148
1345 Henry Rd NAPA (94559) *(P-1700)*
Coe Orchard Equipment Inc ...D...530 695-5121
3453 Riviera Rd Live Oak (95953) *(P-14054)*
Coen Company Inc (HQ) ...E...650 522-2100
951 Mariners Island Blvd # 410 San Mateo (94404) *(P-12061)*
Coffee Guys Inc (PA) ...E...707 942-5747
975 Silverado Trl Calistoga (94515) *(P-2337)*
Coffee Klatch, Rancho Cucamonga Also called Klatch Coffee Inc *(P-2358)*
Coffee Works Inc ...F...916 452-1086
3418 Folsom Blvd Sacramento (95816) *(P-2338)*
Cognella Inc ...D...858 552-1120
3970 Sorrento Valley Blvd # 500 San Diego (92121) *(P-6329)*
Coh-Fb LLC ...E...323 923-1240
5715 Bickett St Huntington Park (90255) *(P-3099)*
Coherent Inc ...A...408 764-4000
5100 Patrick Henry Dr Santa Clara (95054) *(P-19930)*
Coherent Inc (PA) ...A...408 764-4000
5100 Patrick Henry Dr Santa Clara (95054) *(P-21935)*
Coherent Asia Inc ...D...408 764-4000
5100 Patrick Henry Dr Santa Clara (95054) *(P-19496)*
Coherent Auburn Group, The, Santa Clara Also called Coherent Inc *(P-19930)*
Coherus Biosciences Inc (PA) ...D...650 649-3530
333 Twin Dolphin Dr # 600 Redwood City (94065) *(P-8115)*
Cohu Inc (PA) ...C...858 848-8100
12367 Crosthwaite Cir Poway (92064) *(P-21736)*
Cohuhd Costar LLC ...D...858 391-1800
7330 Trade St San Diego (92121) *(P-17783)*
Coi Ceramics Inc ...E...858 621-5700
7130 Miramar Rd Ste 100b San Diego (92121) *(P-20783)*
Coi Graphics, City of Industry Also called Smurfit Kappa North Amer LLC *(P-5459)*
Coi Rubber Products Inc ...B...626 965-9966
19255 San Jose Ave City of Industry (91748) *(P-7903)*
Coic, San Diego Also called Coi Ceramics Inc *(P-20783)*
Coil Winding Specialist Inc ...F...714 279-9010
353 W Grove Ave Orange (92865) *(P-19326)*
Coiltech Incorporated ...F...714 708-8715
3545 Cadillac Ave Ste B Costa Mesa (92626) *(P-19327)*
Coin Dealer Newsletter Inc ...F...310 515-7369
2034 262nd St Lomita (90717) *(P-6131)*
Coin Gllery of San Frncsco Inc ...F...510 236-8882
951 Hensley St Richmond (94801) *(P-5134)*
Colbrit Manufacturing Co Inc ...E...818 709-3608
9666 Owensmouth Ave Ste G Chatsworth (91311) *(P-14498)*
Colby Pharmaceutical Company (PA) ...F...650 333-3150
1095 Colby Ave Ste C Menlo Park (94025) *(P-8116)*
Cold Creek Compost Inc ...F...707 485-5966
6000 Potter Valley Rd Ukiah (95482) *(P-9083)*
Cold Jet LLC ...F...513 831-3211
10281 Trademark St Ste A Rancho Cucamonga (91730) *(P-14929)*
Cold Pack System Inc ...F...858 586-0800
9020 Activity Rd Ste A San Diego (92126) *(P-9828)*
Cold Spring Granite Company ...E...559 689-3257
36772 Road 606 Raymond (93653) *(P-11242)*
Cold Spring Granite Company ...E...559 438-2100
802 W Pinedale Ave # 102 Fresno (93711) *(P-11243)*
Coldstone Creamery 256 ...F...951 304-9777
25395 Madison Ave 106d Murrieta (92562) *(P-663)*
Coldstone Mira Mesa 114 ...F...858 695-9771
10716 Westview Pkwy San Diego (92126) *(P-664)*
Cole Instrument Corp ...D...714 556-3100
2650 S Croddy Way Santa Ana (92704) *(P-17187)*
Cole Lighting, South El Monte Also called C W Cole & Company Inc *(P-17590)*
Cole Print & Marketing ...F...925 276-2344
2001 Salvio St Ste 25 Concord (94520) *(P-6739)*
Colfax International ...E...408 730-2275
750 Palomar Ave Sunnyvale (94085) *(P-15401)*
Colfax Record, Auburn Also called Auburn Journal Inc *(P-5769)*
Colimatic Usa Inc ...F...949 600-6440
9272 Jeronimo Rd Ste 115 Irvine (92618) *(P-15202)*
Collabrative DRG Discovery Inc ...F...650 204-3084
1633 Bayshore Hwy Ste 342 Burlingame (94010) *(P-24509)*
Collana Clinics ...F...909 444-1515
20427 Valley Blvd Walnut (91789) *(P-8716)*
Collard Rose Optical Lab, Whittier Also called J G Hernandez Company *(P-23103)*
Collection Development ...F...909 595-8588
710 Nogales St City of Industry (91748) *(P-18773)*
Collection Led, City of Industry Also called Collection Development *(P-18773)*
Colleen & Herb Enterprises Inc ...D...510 226-6083
46939 Bayside Pkwy Fremont (94538) *(P-16394)*
Collette Fine Foods LLC (PA) ...D...209 430-7814
2412 Heinemann Dr Valley Springs (95252) *(P-2493)*
Collicutt Energy Services Inc ...E...562 944-4413
12349 Hawkins St Santa Fe Springs (90670) *(P-12032)*

Collidion Inc (PA) ...F...707 668-7600
1770 Corporate Cir Petaluma (94954) *(P-8117)*
Collier O & P, Pleasant Hill Also called Castle Hill Holdings Inc *(P-22712)*
Collimated Holes Inc ...E...408 374-5080
460 Division St Campbell (95008) *(P-22069)*
Collins Pine Company ...B...530 258-2111
500 Main St Chester (96020) *(P-4034)*
Colloquy LLC ...E...415 863-6171
200 Potrero Ave San Francisco (94103) *(P-3611)*
Collotype Labels USA Inc (HQ) ...D...707 603-2500
21 Executive Way NAPA (94558) *(P-7277)*
Collotype Labels USA Inc ...E...707 931-7400
21684 8th St E Sonoma (95476) *(P-7278)*
Colmol Inc ...E...858 693-7575
8517 Production Ave San Diego (92121) *(P-7279)*
Colombaras Cabinet & Mllwk Inc ...E...530 662-2665
421 4th St Woodland (95695) *(P-4938)*
Colon Manufacturing Inc (PA) ...F...213 749-6149
1100 S San Pedro St Los Angeles (90015) *(P-3226)*
Colonel Lee's Enterprises, Vernon Also called T & T Foods Inc *(P-776)*
Colonial Enterprises Inc ...E...909 822-8700
10620 Mulberry Ave Fontana (92337) *(P-8717)*
Colonial Home Textiles, Corona Also called Amrapur Overseas Incorporated *(P-2988)*
Colonnas Shipyard West LLC ...E...619 557-8373
105 S 31st St San Diego (92113) *(P-20991)*
Color Inc ...E...818 240-1350
1600 Flower St Glendale (91201) *(P-6740)*
Color Depot Inc ...F...818 500-9033
512 State St Glendale (91203) *(P-7280)*
Color Design Laboratory ...E...818 341-5100
19151 Parthenia St Ste H Northridge (91324) *(P-8718)*
Color Digit, Costa Mesa Also called Chup Corporation *(P-6732)*
Color Image Apparel Inc ...E...855 793-3100
860 S Los Angeles St Los Angeles (90014) *(P-2830)*
Color Marble Project Group Inc ...F...909 595-8858
20521 Earlgate St Walnut (91789) *(P-353)*
Color Science Inc ...F...714 434-1033
1230 E Glenwood Pl Santa Ana (92707) *(P-8961)*
Color Service Inc ...E...323 283-4793
40 E Verdugo Ave Burbank (91502) *(P-7641)*
Color Sky Inc ...F...626 338-8565
14439 Joanbridge St Baldwin Park (91706) *(P-11244)*
Color TEC Industrial Finishing ...E...818 897-2669
11231 Ilex Ave Pacoima (91331) *(P-13571)*
Color Tech Commercial Printing, Lake Forest Also called Universal Printing Services *(P-7157)*
Color-Box LLC ...E...559 674-1049
1275 S Granada Dr Madera (93637) *(P-5398)*
Colorado's Bag Manufacture, Rancho Cucamonga Also called AR Square *(P-10515)*
Colorcards 960 ...E...858 535-9311
6224 Via Regla San Diego (92122) *(P-13376)*
Colorcom Inc ...F...323 246-4640
2437 S Eastern Ave Commerce (90040) *(P-6741)*
Colored Solar, Simi Valley Also called Gold Coast Solar LLC *(P-18861)*
Colorfast Dye & Print Hse Inc ...C...323 581-1656
5075 Pacific Blvd Vernon (90058) *(P-6742)*
Colorful Products Corporation ...F...805 498-2195
996 Lawrence Dr Ste 301 Newbury Park (91320) *(P-8719)*
Colorfx Inc ...E...818 767-7671
11050 Randall St Sun Valley (91352) *(P-6743)*
Colorline Inc ...F...714 373-9500
6239 San Ricardo Way Buena Park (90620) *(P-4980)*
Colormarx Corporation (PA) ...F...916 334-0334
4825 Auburn Blvd Sacramento (95841) *(P-6744)*
Colormax Graphics Inc ...F...626 299-1289
1243 Via Del Rey South Pasadena (91030) *(P-7281)*
Colormax Industries Inc (PA) ...E...213 748-6600
1627 Paloma St Los Angeles (90021) *(P-2730)*
Colornet, Van Nuys Also called Niknejad Inc *(P-6994)*
Coloron Jewelry Inc ...F...818 565-1100
7242 Valjean Ave Van Nuys (91406) *(P-23744)*
Coloron Jewelry Manufacturing, Van Nuys Also called Coloron Jewelry Inc *(P-23744)*
Colorplak.com, Temecula Also called Custom Art Services Corp *(P-6772)*
Colorprint ...F...650 697-7611
1570 Gilbreth Rd Burlingame (94010) *(P-6745)*
Colorstitch Inc ...F...714 754-4220
3100 S Croddy Way Santa Ana (92704) *(P-3838)*
Colortech Label Inc ...F...714 999-5545
1230 S Sherman St Anaheim (92805) *(P-5705)*
Colortokens Inc ...E...408 341-6030
2101 Tasman Dr Ste 201 Santa Clara (95054) *(P-24510)*
Colortone, Whittier Also called Windsor House Investments Inc *(P-5660)*
Colorwen International Corp ...E...626 363-8855
951 Lawson St City of Industry (91748) *(P-7740)*
Colour Concepts Inc ...C...951 787-9988
1225 Los Angeles St Glendale (91204) *(P-6746)*
Colour Drop ...F...415 353-5720
1388 Sutter St Ste 508 San Francisco (94109) *(P-7282)*
Colour Impressions, Yorba Linda Also called Bruce Parker *(P-6706)*
Colt Group, Signal Hill Also called Colt Services LP *(P-199)*
Colt Services LP ...F...562 988-2658
1399 E Burnett St Signal Hill (90755) *(P-199)*
Colton Facilities, Colton Also called Hydro Conduit of Texas LP *(P-10939)*
Coltrin Inc ...F...323 266-6872
4466 Worth St Los Angeles (90063) *(P-11476)*
Columbia Aluminum Products LLC ...D...323 728-7361
2565 Sampson Ave Corona (92879) *(P-11585)*

A
L
P
H
A
B
E
T
I
C

Columbia Communications Inc ....F 203 533-0252
22480 Parrotts Ferry Rd Columbia (95310) ***(P-18070)***
Columbia Cosmetics Mfrs Inc (PA) ....D 510 562-5900
1661 Timothy Dr San Leandro (94577) ***(P-8720)***
Columbia Fabricating Co Inc ....E 818 247-4220
5079 Gloria Ave Encino (91436) ***(P-12844)***
Columbia Holding Corp ....B 310 327-4107
14400 S San Pedro St Gardena (90248) ***(P-12304)***
Columbia Products Co, Irvine *Also called Columbia Sanitary Products* ***(P-12033)***
Columbia Sanitary Products ....E 949 474-0777
1622 Browning Irvine (92606) ***(P-12033)***
Columbia Screw Products Inc ....F 714 549-1171
2901 Halladay St Santa Ana (92705) ***(P-13018)***
Columbia Showcase & Cab Co Inc ....C 818 765-9710
11034 Sherman Way Ste A Sun Valley (91352) ***(P-5050)***
Columbia Steel Inc ....D 909 874-8840
2175 N Linden Ave Rialto (92377) ***(P-12137)***
Columbia Stone Products ....F 760 737-3215
663 S Rancho Santa Fe Rd San Marcos (92078) ***(P-11292)***
Columbus Foods LLC ....B 510 921-3400
30977 San Antonio St Hayward (94544) ***(P-430)***
Columbus Manufacturing Inc (HQ) ....D 510 921-3423
30977 San Antonio St Hayward (94544) ***(P-476)***
Colvin-Friedman LLC ....E 707 769-4488
1311 Commerce St Petaluma (94954) ***(P-10031)***
Comac America Corporation ....F 760 616-9614
4350 Von Karman Ave # 400 Newport Beach (92660) ***(P-20575)***
Comant Industries Incorporated (HQ) ....E 714 870-2420
577 Burning Tree Rd Fullerton (92833) ***(P-18071)***
Comar LLC ....C 909 985-2750
9177 Center Ave Rancho Cucamonga (91730) ***(P-10032)***
Combimatrix Corporation (HQ) ....E 949 753-0624
310 Goddard Ste 150 Irvine (92618) ***(P-21936)***
Comchoice, El Segundo *Also called Scenewise Inc* ***(P-19881)***
Comco Inc ....E 818 333-8500
2151 N Lincoln St Burbank (91504) ***(P-16030)***
Comco Sheet Metal Company ....F 510 832-6433
237 Southbrook Pl Clayton (94517) ***(P-12534)***
Comcore Opcital Communication, Fremont *Also called Comcore Technologies Inc* ***(P-22070)***
Comcore Technologies Inc ....E 510 498-8858
48834 Kato Rd Ste 108a Fremont (94538) ***(P-22070)***
Comeback Brewing II Inc ....F 510 526-1160
1404 4th St Berkeley (94710) ***(P-1580)***
Comet Technologies USA Inc ....E 408 325-8770
2370 Bering Dr San Jose (95131) ***(P-22180)***
Comfort Industries Inc ....E 562 692-8288
12266 Rooks Rd Whittier (90601) ***(P-2791)***
Comfort-Pedic Mattress USA ....F 909 810-2600
9080 Charles Smith Ave Rancho Cucamonga (91730) ***(P-4856)***
Comfy, Oakland *Also called Building Robotics Inc* ***(P-24458)***
Cominco Advanced Material, Poway *Also called Teck Advanced Materials Inc* ***(P-19215)***
Command Packaging LLC ....C 323 980-0918
3840 E 26th St Vernon (90058) ***(P-5595)***
Commander Packaging West Inc ....E 714 921-9350
602 S Rockefeller Ave D Ontario (91761) ***(P-5399)***
Commerce, Commerce *Also called Alarin Aircraft Hinge Inc* ***(P-11925)***
Commerce Printers Inc ....E 714 549-5002
3201 Halladay St Santa Ana (92705) ***(P-6747)***
Commerce Velocity LLC ....E 949 756-8950
1 Technology Dr Ste J725 Irvine (92618) ***(P-24511)***
Commercial and Security Labels, Valencia *Also called Quadriga USA Enterprises Inc* ***(P-7455)***
Commercial Casework Inc (PA) ....D 510 657-7933
41780 Christy St Fremont (94538) ***(P-4125)***
Commercial Clear Print Inc ....F 818 709-1220
9025 Fullbright Ave Chatsworth (91311) ***(P-6748)***
Commercial Cooling, City of Industry *Also called Par Engineering Inc* ***(P-17381)***
Commercial Cstm Sting Uphl Inc ....D 714 850-0520
12601 Western Ave Garden Grove (92841) ***(P-5224)***
Commercial Display Systems LLC ....E 818 361-8160
17341 Sierra Hwy Canyon Country (91351) ***(P-15945)***
Commercial Electronics Pho, Newport Beach *Also called Macom Technology Solutions Inc* ***(P-18173)***
Commercial Energy California, Oakland *Also called Commercial Energy Montana Inc* ***(P-50)***
Commercial Energy Montana Inc ....E 510 567-2700
7677 Oakport St Ste 525 Oakland (94621) ***(P-50)***
Commercial Furniture ....E 714 350-7045
1261 N Lakeview Ave Anaheim (92807) ***(P-4939)***
Commercial Intr Resources Inc ....D 562 926-5885
6077 Rickenbacker Rd Commerce (90040) ***(P-4764)***
Commercial Lbr & Pallet Co Inc (PA) ....C 626 968-0631
135 Long Ln City of Industry (91746) ***(P-4461)***
Commercial Manufacturing ....E 559 237-1855
2432 S Railroad Ave Fresno (93706) ***(P-14842)***
Commercial Metal Forming Inc ....D 714 532-6321
341 W Collins Ave Orange (92867) ***(P-13185)***
Commercial Metal Forming Inc (PA) ....E 714 532-6321
341 W Collins Ave Orange (92867) ***(P-13186)***
Commercial Metals Company ....F 909 899-9993
12451 Arrow Rte Etiwanda (91739) ***(P-11391)***
Commercial Mill & Builders Sup, Milpitas *Also called Commercial Mtl & Door Sup Inc* ***(P-4126)***
Commercial Mini Freighters Inc ....E 562 437-2166
1524 W 15th St Long Beach (90813) ***(P-20196)***
Commercial Mtl & Door Sup Inc ....F 408 432-3383
1210 Ames Ave Milpitas (95035) ***(P-4126)***
Commercial Patterns Inc ....F 510 784-1014
3162 Baumberg Ave Ste H Hayward (94545) ***(P-10033)***
Commercial Sand Blast Company ....F 323 581-8672
2678 E 26th St Vernon (90058) ***(P-13377)***
Commercial Sheet Metal Works ....E 213 748-7321
1800 S San Pedro St Los Angeles (90015) ***(P-12138)***
Commercial Truck Eqp Co LLC ....E 562 803-4466
12351 Bellflower Blvd Downey (90242) ***(P-20197)***
Commercial Truss Co ....E 858 693-1771
10731 Treena St Ste 207 San Diego (92131) ***(P-4399)***
Commex Corporation ....F 510 887-4000
20408 Corsair Blvd Hayward (94545) ***(P-9702)***
Commnexus San Diego ....F 888 926-3987
4225 Executive Sq # 1110 La Jolla (92037) ***(P-18774)***
Commodity Resource Envmtl Inc ....E 661 824-2416
11847 United St Mojave (93501) ***(P-11544)***
Commodity Rsource Enviromental, Mojave *Also called Commodity Resource Envmtl Inc* ***(P-11544)***
Commsystems LLC ....F 858 824-0056
12225 World Trade Dr I San Diego (92128) ***(P-18072)***
Communction Systms-Wst/Lnkabit, San Diego *Also called L3 Technologies Inc* ***(P-18159)***
Communicart ....F 408 970-0922
1589 Laurelwood Rd Santa Clara (95054) ***(P-6749)***
Communication Arts, Menlo Park *Also called Coyne & Blanchard Inc* ***(P-6136)***
Communications & Pwr Inds LLC ....C 650 846-3494
607 Hansen Way Palo Alto (94304) ***(P-18382)***
Communications & Pwr Inds LLC ....A 650 846-3729
811 Hansen Way Palo Alto (94304) ***(P-18073)***
Communications & Pwr Inds LLC ....C 650 846-2900
6385 San Ignacio Ave San Jose (95119) ***(P-18074)***
Communications & Pwr Inds LLC ....C 650 846-2900
6385 San Ignacio Ave San Jose (95119) ***(P-19497)***
Communications & Pwr Inds LLC (HQ) ....A 650 846-2900
607 Hansen Way Palo Alto (94304) ***(P-18383)***
Communications & Pwr Inds LLC ....C 650 846-2900
811 Hansen Way Palo Alto (94304) ***(P-18384)***
Communigate Systems, Richmond *Also called Stalker Software Inc* ***(P-25217)***
Community Adviser Newspaper, Banning *Also called Century Publishing* ***(P-7269)***
Community Close-Up Westminster ....D 714 704-5811
1771 S Lewis St Anaheim (92805) ***(P-5809)***
Community Fuels, Stockton *Also called American Biodiesel Inc* ***(P-8976)***
Community Media Corporation ....D 714 220-0292
5119 Ball Rd Cypress (90630) ***(P-5810)***
Community Merch Solutions LLC ....E 877 956-9258
27201 Puerta Real Ste 120 Mission Viejo (92691) ***(P-15896)***
Community Printers Inc ....E 831 426-4682
1827 Soquel Ave Santa Cruz (95062) ***(P-6750)***
Community Vision, North Hollywood *Also called Bauers & Collins* ***(P-22704)***
Compac Engineering Inc ....F 530 872-2042
1111 Noffsinger Ln Paradise (95969) ***(P-21506)***
Compaction American, Lake Elsinore *Also called American Compaction Eqp Inc* ***(P-14141)***
Compass Components Inc (PA) ....C 510 656-4700
48133 Warm Springs Blvd Fremont (94539) ***(P-19498)***
Compass Flooring, Santa Fe Springs *Also called Altro Usa Inc* ***(P-24013)***
Compass Manufacturing Service, Fremont *Also called Compass Components Inc* ***(P-19498)***
Compass Water Solutions Inc (PA) ....D 949 222-5777
15542 Mosher Ave Tustin (92780) ***(P-16031)***
Compatible Software Systems ....F 510 562-1172
10966 Bigge St San Leandro (94577) ***(P-24512)***
Competitor Golf & Tennis AP, Sacramento *Also called AAA Garments & Lettering Inc* ***(P-3822)***
Competitor Group Inc (HQ) ....C 858 450-6510
6420 Sequence Dr San Diego (92121) ***(P-6132)***
Competitor Magazine, San Diego *Also called Competitor Group Inc* ***(P-6132)***
Competitor Magazine ....E 858 768-6800
10179 Hudiken St Ste 100 San Diego (92121) ***(P-6133)***
Complete Clothing Company (PA) ....D 323 277-1470
4950 E 49th St Vernon (90058) ***(P-3303)***
Complete Cutng & Wldg Sups Inc ....F 310 638-1234
401 N Long Beach Blvd Compton (90221) ***(P-25396)***
Complete Garment Inc ....E 323 846-3731
2101 E 38th St Vernon (90058) ***(P-2831)***
Complete Kitchen & Bath, Grass Valley *Also called Cabinet Company Inc* ***(P-5043)***
Complete Metal Design ....F 626 335-3636
154 S Valencia Ave Glendora (91741) ***(P-16395)***
Complete Metal Fabrication Inc ....F 760 353-0260
596 E Main St El Centro (92243) ***(P-12139)***
Complete Welding Supplies, Compton *Also called Complete Cutng & Wldg Sups Inc* ***(P-25396)***
Compliance Poster, Monrovia *Also called Global Compliance Inc* ***(P-6492)***
Compliance Products Usa Inc ....F 619 878-9696
650 Gateway Center Way D San Diego (92102) ***(P-21737)***
Compliance West USA, San Diego *Also called Compliance Products Usa Inc* ***(P-21737)***
Complianceonline, Palo Alto *Also called Metricstream Inc* ***(P-24906)***
Complyright Distribution Svcs ....E 805 981-0992
3451 Jupiter Ct Oxnard (93030) ***(P-7549)***
Component Concepts LLC ....F 760 722-9559
1732 Ord Way Oceanside (92056) ***(P-19800)***
Component Equipment Coinc ....D 805 988-8004
3050 Camino Del Sol Oxnard (93030) ***(P-19377)***
Component Finishing, Rocklin *Also called Diverse McHning Fbrication LLC* ***(P-13934)***
Component Hsing Systems U S A, South Gate *Also called Tony Borges* ***(P-12966)***
Component Re-Engineering Inc ....F 408 562-4000
3508 Bassett St Santa Clara (95054) ***(P-18775)***
Component Surfaces Inc ....F 858 513-3656
11880 Cmnty Rd Ste 380 Poway (92064) ***(P-13378)***

Components For Automation Inc (PA) .... F ...805 582-0065
1737 Lee St Simi Valley (93065) *(P-13712)*
Componetics Inc .... F ...805 498-0939
2492 Turquoise Cir Newbury Park (91320) *(P-19328)*
Composite Engineering, Inc., Sacramento *Also called Kratos Unmanned Aerial Systems (P-10184)*
Composite Manufacturing Inc .... E ...949 361-7580
970 Calle Amanecer Ste D San Clemente (92673) *(P-22407)*
Composite Optics Incorporated .... A ...937 490-4145
7130 Miramar Rd Ste 100b San Diego (92121) *(P-21189)*
Composite Plastic Systems Inc .... F ...805 354-1391
1701a River Rock Rd Santa Maria (93454) *(P-21199)*
Composite Software LLC (HQ) .... D ...800 553-6387
755 Sycamore Dr Milpitas (95035) *(P-24513)*
Composite Support and Sltns In .... F ...310 514-3162
767 W Channel St San Pedro (90731) *(P-5483)*
Composite Technology Intl, Sacramento *Also called Composite Technology Intl Inc (P-4127)*
Composite Technology Intl Inc .... E ...916 551-1850
1730 I St Ste 100 Sacramento (95811) *(P-4127)*
Composites Horizons LLC (HQ) .... C ...626 331-0861
1601 W Industrial Park St Covina (91722) *(P-20784)*
Compressed Air Concepts .... E ...310 537-1350
16207 Carmenita Rd Cerritos (90703) *(P-15121)*
Comprhnsive Crdvsclar Spcalist (PA) .... E ...626 281-8663
220 S 1st St Ste 101 Alhambra (91801) *(P-8118)*
Compro Packaging LLC .... E ...510 475-0118
1600 Atlantic St Union City (94587) *(P-5400)*
Compserv Inc .... F ...415 331-4571
42 Golf Rd Pleasanton (94566) *(P-19499)*
Compu Aire Inc .... C ...562 945-8971
8167 Byron Rd Whittier (90606) *(P-15946)*
Compu Tech Lumber Products .... D ...707 437-6683
1980 Huntington Ct Fairfield (94533) *(P-4400)*
Compu-Fire, Downey *Also called Engine Electronics Inc (P-19832)*
Compucase Corporation .... A ...626 336-6588
16720 Chestnut St Ste C City of Industry (91748) *(P-15525)*
Compucraft Industries Inc .... E ...619 448-0787
8787 Olive Ln Santee (92071) *(P-20785)*
Compugraphics USA Inc (HQ) .... D ...510 249-2600
43455 Osgood Rd Fremont (94539) *(P-18776)*
Compugroup Medical Inc .... E ...949 789-0500
25 B Tech Dr Ste 200 Irvine (92618) *(P-24514)*
Compulink Business Systems Inc .... C ...805 446-2050
1100 Business Center Cir Newbury Park (91320) *(P-24515)*
Compulink Management Ctr Inc .... C ...562 988-1688
3545 Long Beach Blvd Long Beach (90807) *(P-24516)*
Compumeric Engineering Inc .... E ...909 605-1697
1390 S Milliken Ave Ontario (91761) *(P-12535)*
Computational Sensors Corp .... E ...805 962-1175
1042 Via Los Padres Santa Barbara (93111) *(P-21274)*
Computational Systems Inc .... E ...661 832-5306
4301 Resnik Ct Bakersfield (93313) *(P-22181)*
Computed Tool & Engineering .... F ...714 630-3911
2910 E Ricker Way Anaheim (92806) *(P-14499)*
Computer Access Tech Corp .... D ...408 727-6600
3385 Scott Blvd Santa Clara (95054) *(P-15402)*
Computer Asssted Mfg Tech Corp .... D ...949 263-8911
8710 Research Dr Irvine (92618) *(P-16396)*
Computer Exchange, The, Sacramento *Also called Raymar Information Tech Inc (P-17987)*
Computer Intgrted McHining Inc .... E ...619 596-9246
10940 Wheatlands Ave Santee (92071) *(P-16397)*
Computer Metal Products Corp .... D ...805 520-6966
370 E Easy St Simi Valley (93065) *(P-12536)*
Computer Plastics .... E ...510 785-3600
1914 National Ave Hayward (94545) *(P-14500)*
Computer Prompting Service .... F ...818 563-3465
617 S Victory Blvd Burbank (91502) *(P-23146)*
Computer-Nozzles, Irwindale *Also called Cni Mfg Inc (P-16391)*
Computerized Embroidery Co .... F ...909 825-3841
673 E Cooley Dr Ste 101 Colton (92324) *(P-3839)*
Computerized Fashion Svcs Inc .... F ...310 973-0106
3341 Jack Northrop Ave Hawthorne (90250) *(P-3650)*
Computers and Structures Inc .... F ...510 649-2200
1646 N Calif Blvd Ste 600 Walnut Creek (94596) *(P-24517)*
Computrus Inc .... E ...951 245-9103
250 Klug Cir Corona (92880) *(P-12377)*
Computrust Software Corp (PA) .... F ...408 782-7470
18625 Sutter Blvd Ste 500 Morgan Hill (95037) *(P-24518)*
Compuvac Industries Inc .... F ...949 574-5085
18381 Mount Langley St Fountain Valley (92708) *(P-15122)*
Comsat Inc .... F ...805 933-4080
7676 Pine Grove Rd Santa Paula (93060) *(P-18075)*
Comstar Industries Inc .... E ...714 556-1400
4009 W Segerstrom Ave Santa Ana (92704) *(P-17260)*
Comstock Press .... E ...510 522-4115
2117 San Jose Ave Alameda (94501) *(P-6751)*
Comstock Publishing Inc .... F ...916 364-1000
2335 American River Dr # 301 Sacramento (95825) *(P-6134)*
Comstock's Magazine, Sacramento *Also called Comstock Publishing Inc (P-6134)*
Comtech Xicom Technology Inc (HQ) .... C ...408 213-3000
3550 Bassett St Santa Clara (95054) *(P-18076)*
Con Sol Enterprises, Ventura *Also called Trinity Steel Corporation (P-12264)*
Con-Cise Contact Lens Co, Alameda *Also called Lens C-C Inc (P-23105)*
Con-Fab California Corporation (PA) .... E ...209 249-4700
1910 Lathrop Rd Lathrop (95330) *(P-10906)*
Con-Tech Plastics, Brea *Also called Ramtec Associates Inc (P-10324)*
Conagra Brands Inc .... A ...209 847-0321
554 S Yosemite Ave Oakdale (95361) *(P-791)*

Conagra Brands Inc .... D ...559 291-0231
5626 E Shields Ave Fresno (93727) *(P-1486)*
Conagra Brands Inc .... E ...510 536-9555
2201 E 7th St Oakland (94606) *(P-1036)*
Conagra Flour Milling Company .... E ...510 536-9555
2201 E 7th St Oakland (94606) *(P-1037)*
Conair Corporation .... D ...323 724-0101
9350 Rayo Ave South Gate (90280) *(P-17364)*
Conamco SA De CV .... D ...760 586-4356
3008 Palm Hill Dr Vista (92084) *(P-22862)*
Concannon Vineyard, Livermore *Also called Tesla Vineyards Lp (P-2012)*
Concentric Analgesics Inc .... F ...415 771-5129
1824 Jackson St Apt A San Francisco (94109) *(P-8119)*
Concentric Components Inc .... F ...209 529-4840
913 5th St Modesto (95351) *(P-17188)*
Concentric Medical Inc .... E ...650 938-2100
47900 Bayside Pkwy Fremont (94538) *(P-22408)*
Concept Development Llc .... E ...949 623-8000
1881 Langley Ave Irvine (92614) *(P-18457)*
Concept Packaging Group, Ontario *Also called Southland Container Corp (P-5463)*
Concept Part Solutions Inc .... E ...408 748-1244
2047 Zanker Rd San Jose (95131) *(P-14616)*
Concept Studio Inc .... F ...949 759-0606
3195 Red Hill Ave Ste G Costa Mesa (92626) *(P-10779)*
Concept Systems Mfg Inc .... F ...408 855-8595
2047 Zanker Rd San Jose (95131) *(P-18777)*
Concept Transporters, Fresno *Also called Concept Vehicle Technologies (P-20497)*
Concept Vehicle Technologies .... F ...559 233-1313
2695 S Cherry Ave Ste 120 Fresno (93706) *(P-20497)*
Concepts & Methods Co Inc .... E ...650 593-1064
1017 Bransten Rd San Carlos (94070) *(P-15256)*
Concepts & Wood, Huntington Park *Also called Plycraft Industries Inc (P-4382)*
Concepts By J Inc .... E ...323 564-9988
834 E 108th St Los Angeles (90059) *(P-4685)*
Concise Fabricators Inc .... E ...520 746-3226
7550 Panasonic Way San Diego (92154) *(P-12537)*
Concisys Inc .... E ...858 292-5888
5452 Oberlin Dr San Diego (92121) *(P-21738)*
Concord Music Group Inc .... C ...310 385-4455
100 N Crescent Dr Ste 275 Beverly Hills (90210) *(P-6330)*
Concorde Battery Corp (PA) .... E ...626 813-1234
2009 W San Bernardino Rd West Covina (91790) *(P-19821)*
Concrete Inc .... E ...209 830-1962
749 S Stanislaus St Stockton (95206) *(P-11095)*
Concrete Inc .... F ...209 933-6999
10260 Waterman Rd Elk Grove (95624) *(P-11096)*
Concrete Inc (HQ) .... D ...209 933-6999
400 S Lincoln St Stockton (95203) *(P-11097)*
Concrete Mold Corporation .... E ...310 537-5171
2121 E Del Amo Blvd Compton (90220) *(P-14501)*
Concrete Ready Mix Inc .... E ...408 224-2452
33 Hillsdale Ave San Jose (95136) *(P-11098)*
Concreteaccessoriescom .... F ...714 871-9434
130 N Gilbert St Fullerton (92833) *(P-13064)*
Concreteworks Studio Inc .... F ...510 534-7141
1137 57th Ave Oakland (94621) *(P-10907)*
Condeco Software Inc (HQ) .... E ...917 677-7600
2105 S Bascom Ave Ste 150 Campbell (95008) *(P-24519)*
Condor Electronics Inc .... E ...408 745-7141
990 San Antonio Rd Palo Alto (94303) *(P-21564)*
Condor Outdoor Products Inc .... E ...626 358-3270
5268 Rivergrade Rd Baldwin Park (91706) *(P-23542)*
Condor Pacific Inds Cal Inc .... E ...818 889-2150
905 Rancho Conejo Blvd Newbury Park (91320) *(P-20786)*
Condor Reliability Services .... C ...408 486-9600
2175 De La Cruz Blvd # 8 Santa Clara (95050) *(P-18778)*
Conductive Science Inc .... F ...858 699-1837
11643 Rverside Dr Ste 115 Lakeside (92040) *(P-8895)*
Cone Engineering Inc .... F ...714 828-4861
10883 Portal Dr Los Alamitos (90720) *(P-20297)*
Conesco Industries, Riverside *Also called Doka USA Ltd (P-12563)*
Conesys Inc (PA) .... D ...310 618-3737
2280 W 208th St Torrance (90501) *(P-19378)*
Conesys Inc .... F ...310 212-0065
548 Amapola Ave Torrance (90501) *(P-19379)*
Conetech Custom Services LLC .... F ...707 823-2404
2191 Laguna Rd Santa Rosa (95401) *(P-1701)*
Conexant Holdings Inc .... A ...415 983-2706
4000 Macarthur Blvd Newport Beach (92660) *(P-18779)*
Conexant Systems LLC (HQ) .... E ...949 483-4600
1901 Main St Ste 300 Irvine (92614) *(P-18780)*
Conexant Systems Worldwide Inc .... D ...949 483-4600
4000 Macarthur Blvd Newport Beach (92660) *(P-18781)*
Confab, Lathrop *Also called Con-Fab California Corporation (P-10906)*
Confections Michael Recchiuti (PA) .... F ...415 826-2868
2565 3rd St Ste 225 San Francisco (94107) *(P-1416)*
Confident Technologies Inc .... F ...858 345-5640
3830 Vly Cntre Dr Ste 705 San Diego (92130) *(P-24520)*
Confluent Inc (PA) .... E ...650 453-5860
101 University Ave # 111 Palo Alto (94301) *(P-24521)*
Confluent Medical Tech Inc (PA) .... B ...510 683-2000
47533 Westinghouse Dr Fremont (94539) *(P-22409)*
Conglas, Bakersfield *Also called Consolidated Fibrgls Pdts Co (P-11331)*
Conklin & Conklin Incorporated .... E ...510 489-5500
34201 7th St Union City (94587) *(P-13065)*
Conley's Mfg & Sales, Montclair *Also called John L Conley Inc (P-12936)*
Connect Systems Inc .... E ...805 642-7184
1802 Eastman Ave Ste 116 Ventura (93003) *(P-18077)*
Connectec Company Inc (PA) .... D ...949 252-1077
1701 Reynolds Ave Irvine (92614) *(P-17453)*

Employee Codes: A=Over 500 employees, B=251-500
C=101-250, D=51-100, E=20-50, F=10-19

2019 California
Manfacturers Register

© Mergent Inc. 1-800-342-5647

1105

ALPHABETIC

Connectec Company Inc F 949 252-1077
3901 S Main St Santa Ana (92707) *(P-17454)*
Connected Apparel Company LLC (PA) E 323 890-8000
6015 Bandini Blvd Commerce (90040) *(P-3397)*
Connected Holdings LLC F 714 907-6371
4740 Von Karman Ave # 120 Newport Beach (92660) *(P-21275)*
Connectedyard Inc E 415 699-8844
1841 Zanker Rd Ste 10 San Jose (95112) *(P-21937)*
Connection Enterprises Inc F 951 688-8133
4130 Flat Rock Dr Ste 140 Riverside (92505) *(P-17455)*
Connective Solutions LLC F 800 241-2792
14252 Culver Dr Ste A343 Irvine (92604) *(P-10639)*
Connector Kings Corporation F 951 710-1180
2110 Mcallister St Riverside (92503) *(P-19380)*
Connector Plating Corp F 310 323-1622
327 W 132nd St Los Angeles (90061) *(P-13379)*
Connectorkings.com, Riverside *Also called Connector Kings Corporation (P-19380)*
Connell Processing Inc E 818 845-7661
3094 N Avon St Burbank (91504) *(P-13380)*
Connelly Machine Works E 714 558-6855
420 N Terminal St Santa Ana (92701) *(P-16398)*
Conners Oro-Cal Mfg Co F 530 533-5065
1720 Bird St Oroville (95965) *(P-23252)*
Connor J Inc F 626 358-3820
835 Meridian St Irwindale (91010) *(P-21739)*
Connor Manufacturing Svcs Inc (PA) D 650 591-2026
1710 S Amphlett Blvd # 318 San Mateo (94402) *(P-16399)*
Conopco Inc C 209 466-9580
1400 Waterloo Rd Stockton (95205) *(P-8721)*
Conquip Inc D 916 379-8200
11255 Pyrites Way Ste 100 Gold River (95670) *(P-16400)*
Conrad Wood Preserving Co F 530 476-2894
7085 Eddy Rd Unit C Arbuckle (95912) *(P-4592)*
Conros Corp E 916 381-8511
6001 Power Inn Rd Sacramento (95824) *(P-4614)*
Conroy & Knowlton Inc F 323 665-5288
320 S Montebello Blvd Montebello (90640) *(P-10034)*
Consilience Converge, Los Olivos *Also called Escalera-Boulet LLC (P-1752)*
Consilio - A First Advantage E 626 921-1600
605 E Huntington Dr # 211 Monrovia (91016) *(P-24522)*
Consoldted Hnge Mnfctured Pdts F 408 379-6550
1150b Dell Ave Campbell (95008) *(P-16401)*
Consoldted Precision Pdts Corp C 323 773-2363
8333 Wilcox Ave Cudahy (90201) *(P-11729)*
Consoldted Precision Pdts Corp C 805 488-6451
705 Industrial Way Port Hueneme (93041) *(P-11730)*
Consolidated Aerospace Mfg LLC (PA) F 714 989-2797
1425 S Acacia Ave Fullerton (92831) *(P-21276)*
Consolidated Aircraft Coatings, Riverside *Also called Poly-Fiber Inc (P-8924)*
Consolidated Color Corporation E 562 420-7714
12316 Carson St Hawaiian Gardens (90716) *(P-8896)*
Consolidated Cont Holdings LLC E 626 964-9657
17851 Railroad St City of Industry (91748) *(P-10035)*
Consolidated Cont Holdings LLC E 951 340-9390
12165 Madera Way Riverside (92503) *(P-9795)*
Consolidated Container Co LLC E 888 425-7343
1070 Samuelson St City of Industry (91748) *(P-10036)*
Consolidated Container Co LLC D 626 856-2100
4516 Azusa Canyon Rd Irwindale (91706) *(P-10037)*
Consolidated Container Co LLC C 209 820-1700
75 W Valpico Rd Tracy (95376) *(P-10038)*
Consolidated Container Co LLC D 310 952-8736
1500 E 223rd St Carson (90745) *(P-9796)*
Consolidated Container Co LLC F 909 390-6637
5772 Jurupa St Ste B Ontario (91761) *(P-9797)*
Consolidated Container Co LLC D 209 531-9180
1620 Gobel Way Modesto (95358) *(P-9798)*
Consolidated Container Co LP D 714 241-6640
1217 E Saint Gertrude Pl Santa Ana (92707) *(P-9829)*
Consolidated Container Co LP E 909 590-7334
14312 Central Ave Chino (91710) *(P-10039)*
Consolidated Devices Inc (HQ) E 626 965-0668
19220 San Jose Ave City of Industry (91748) *(P-11889)*
Consolidated Fabricators Corp (PA) C 818 901-1005
14620 Arminta St Van Nuys (91402) *(P-12378)*
Consolidated Fabricators Corp D 209 745-4604
901 Simmerhorn Rd Galt (95632) *(P-13187)*
Consolidated Fibrgls Pdts Co D 661 323-6026
3801 Standard St Bakersfield (93308) *(P-11331)*
Consolidated Foundries Inc E 909 595-2252
4200 W Valley Blvd Pomona (91769) *(P-11511)*
Consolidated Geoscience Inc F 909 393-9700
14738 Central Ave Chino (91710) *(P-129)*
Consolidated Graphics Inc D 323 460-4115
3550 Tyburn St Los Angeles (90065) *(P-7283)*
Consolidated Laundry LLC E 323 232-2417
211 Erie St Pomona (91768) *(P-15928)*
Consolidated Laundry Machinery, Pomona *Also called Consolidated Laundry LLC (P-15928)*
Consolidated Printers Inc E 510 843-8524
2630 8th St Berkeley (94710) *(P-6417)*
Consolidated Training LLC E 831 768-8888
144 Holm Rd Spc 47 Watsonville (95076) *(P-24068)*
Consorzio, Berkeley *Also called NAPA Valley Kitchens Inc (P-2614)*
Consteel Industrial Inc E 562 806-4575
15435 Woodcrest Dr Whittier (90604) *(P-12140)*
Constellation Brands Inc E 415 912-3880
1255 Battery St San Francisco (94111) *(P-1702)*
Constellation Brands Inc E 707 467-4840
2399 N State St Ukiah (95482) *(P-1703)*
Constellation Brands US Oprs E 415 912-3700
1255 Battery St Ste 300 San Francisco (94111) *(P-1704)*
Constellation Brands US Oprs A 559 485-0141
12667 Road 24 Madera (93637) *(P-1705)*
Constellation Brands US Oprs A 707 433-8268
349 Healdsburg Ave Healdsburg (95448) *(P-1706)*
Constlltion Brnds US Oprations, Geyserville *Also called Clos Du Bois Wines Inc (P-1696)*
Construction Electrical Pdts, Livermore *Also called R K Larrabee Company Inc (P-17218)*
Construction Innovations LLC C 855 725-9555
10630 Mather Blvd Ste 200 Mather (95655) *(P-19931)*
Construction Masters, Glendale *Also called Mold Masters Inc (P-14543)*
Construction On Time Inc F 408 209-1799
5657 Meridian Ave San Jose (95118) *(P-354)*
Construction Tl & Threading Co F 562 927-1326
8476 Garfield Ave Bell Gardens (90201) *(P-16402)*
Contactual Inc E 650 292-4408
810 W Maude Ave Sunnyvale (94085) *(P-24523)*
Contadina Foods, Woodland *Also called Pacific Coast Producers (P-845)*
Container Decorating Inc F 510 489-9212
12 Homestead Ct Danville (94506) *(P-3886)*
Container Graphics Corp D 209 577-0181
1137 Graphics Dr Modesto (95351) *(P-14805)*
Container Options Inc F 909 478-0045
1493 E San Bernardino Ave San Bernardino (92408) *(P-10040)*
Container Technology Inc (PA) E 805 683-5825
5454 San Patricio Dr Santa Barbara (93111) *(P-10041)*
Containment Consultants Inc F 408 848-6998
110 Old Gilroy St Gilroy (95020) *(P-12379)*
Containment Solutions Inc D 661 399-9556
2600 Pegasus Dr Bakersfield (93308) *(P-12380)*
Contech Engnered Solutions Inc A 714 281-7883
950 S Coast Dr Ste 145 Costa Mesa (92626) *(P-11477)*
Contech Engnered Solutions LLC E 530 243-1207
2245 Canyon Creek Rd Redding (96001) *(P-12381)*
Contech Solutions Incorporated E 510 357-7900
631 Montague St San Leandro (94577) *(P-18782)*
Contempo Window Fashions F 818 768-1773
5721 Newcastle Ave Encino (91316) *(P-2731)*
Contemporary Bath.com, City of Industry *Also called Tonusa LLC (P-4358)*
Contemporary Records, Berkeley *Also called Fantasy Inc (P-17897)*
Content Management Corporation F 510 505-1100
4287 Technology Dr Fremont (94538) *(P-7284)*
Contessa Premium Foods, Vernon *Also called F I O Imports Inc (P-2515)*
Contex Inc F 818 788-5836
4505 Van Nuys Blvd Van Nuys (91403) *(P-23085)*
Contex Inc Contact Lenses, Van Nuys *Also called Contex Inc (P-23085)*
Context Engineering Co E 408 748-9112
1043 Di Giulio Ave Santa Clara (95050) *(P-13188)*
Continental American Corp D 626 964-0164
1333 S Hillward Ave West Covina (91791) *(P-9601)*
Continental Bdr Specialty Corp (PA) C 310 324-8227
407 W Compton Blvd Gardena (90248) *(P-7577)*
Continental Coatings Inc F 909 355-1200
10938 Beech Ave Fontana (92337) *(P-8897)*
Continental Colorcraft, Monterey Park *Also called Graphic Color Systems Inc (P-6837)*
Continental Components LLC F 760 480-4420
243 S Escondido Blvd Escondido (92025) *(P-4615)*
Continental Controls Corp E 858 638-1709
7720 Kenamar Ct C San Diego (92121) *(P-21565)*
Continental Data Graphics, El Segundo *Also called Continental Graphics Corp (P-6755)*
Continental Datalabel Inc E 909 307-3600
211 Business Center Ct Redlands (92373) *(P-5706)*
Continental Engineering Svcs, San Diego *Also called Continental Graphics Corp (P-6752)*
Continental Enterprises, Fowler *Also called Pps Packaging Company (P-5325)*
Continental Feature/ News Svc E 858 492-8696
501 W Broadway Ste C San Diego (92101) *(P-6135)*
Continental Fiberglass Inc (PA) F 760 246-6480
17031 Muskrat Ave Adelanto (92301) *(P-23543)*
Continental Forge Company (PA) D 310 603-1014
412 E El Segundo Blvd Compton (90222) *(P-13122)*
Continental Graphics Corp B 858 552-6520
6910 Carroll Rd San Diego (92121) *(P-6752)*
Continental Graphics Corp A 714 827-1752
4060 N Lakewood Blvd 8015fl Long Beach (90808) *(P-6753)*
Continental Graphics Corp E 909 758-9800
9302 Pttsbrgh Ave Ste 100 Rancho Cucamonga (91730) *(P-6754)*
Continental Graphics Corp E 310 662-2307
222 N Pacific Coast Hwy # 300 El Segundo (90245) *(P-6755)*
Continental Graphix E 415 864-2345
166 Riviera Dr San Rafael (94901) *(P-6756)*
Continental Heat Treating Inc D 562 944-8808
10643 Norwalk Blvd Santa Fe Springs (90670) *(P-11809)*
Continental Industries, Anaheim *Also called International West Inc (P-12625)*
Continental Intelligent Transp E 408 391-9008
3901 N 1st St San Jose (95134) *(P-9463)*
Continental Litho Inc D 760 598-0291
1360 Park Center Dr Vista (92081) *(P-6757)*
Continental Machine Tool Co, Santa Ana *Also called Supreme Abrasives (P-11304)*
Continental Maritime Inds Inc B 619 234-8851
1995 Bay Front St San Diego (92113) *(P-20992)*
Continental Second Shift LLC F 619 985-6038
3008 S Croddy Way Santa Ana (92704) *(P-12382)*
Continental Security Inds F 661 251-8800
19425b Soledad Canyon Rd # 126 Canyon Country (91351) *(P-18316)*
Continental Signs Inc E 714 894-2011
7541 Santa Rita Cir Ste D Stanton (90680) *(P-23847)*
Continental Vitamin Co Inc D 323 581-0176
4510 S Boyle Ave Vernon (90058) *(P-8120)*

Continential Data Graphics, Long Beach *Also called Continental Graphics Corp* ***(P-6753)***
Continuous Cartridge....E....760 929-4808
5973 Avenida Encinas # 140 Carlsbad (92008) ***(P-23147)***
Continuous Coating Corp (PA)....D....714 637-4642
520 W Grove Ave Orange (92865) ***(P-13381)***
Continuous Computing Corp....E....858 882-8800
10431 Wtridge Cir Ste 110 San Diego (92121) ***(P-15403)***
Continuum Electro-Optics Inc....D....408 727-3240
140 Baytech Dr San Jose (95134) ***(P-21938)***
Contour Machining, Chatsworth *Also called Astrodyne Group Inc* ***(P-16287)***
Contra Costa Metal Fabricators, Concord *Also called Monterey Mechanical Co* ***(P-12686)***
Contra Costa Newspapers Inc (HQ)....A....925 935-2525
175 Lennon Ln Ste 100 Walnut Creek (94598) ***(P-5811)***
Contra Costa Newspapers Inc....B....510 748-1683
1516 Oak St Alameda (94501) ***(P-5812)***
Contra Costa Newspapers Inc....D....925 847-2123
127 Spring St Pleasanton (94566) ***(P-5813)***
Contra Costa Newspapers Inc....B....925 943-3925
2800 Camino Diablo Walnut Creek (94597) ***(P-5814)***
Contra Costa Newspapers Inc....C....925 977-8520
2205 Dean Lesher Dr Concord (94520) ***(P-5815)***
Contra Costa Newspapers Inc....F....925 634-2125
1700 Cavallo Rd Antioch (94509) ***(P-5816)***
Contra Costa Newspapers Inc....D....916 786-6500
188 Cirby Way Roseville (95678) ***(P-5817)***
Contra Costa Times, Walnut Creek *Also called Contra Costa Newspapers Inc* ***(P-5811)***
Contraband Control Specialists....F....661 322-3363
26 H St Bakersfield (93304) ***(P-9232)***
Contract Illumination....E....714 771-5223
975 N Enterprise St Orange (92867) ***(P-17593)***
Contract Logging, Weed *Also called M & M Logging Inc* ***(P-3999)***
Contract Metal Products Inc....E....510 979-4811
45535 Northport Loop W Fl Flr 1 Fremont (94538) ***(P-12538)***
Contract Resources, Commerce *Also called Commercial Intr Resources Inc* ***(P-4764)***
Contract Transportation Sys Co....D....562 696-3262
12500 Slauson Ave Ste B2 Santa Fe Springs (90670) ***(P-8898)***
Contrctor Cmpliance Monitoring....E....619 472-9065
2343 Donnington Way San Diego (92139) ***(P-21507)***
Control Components Inc (HQ)....B....949 858-1877
22591 Avenida Empresa Rcho STA Marg (92688) ***(P-13713)***
Control Enterprises Inc....F....559 683-2044
40124 Highway 49 Oakhurst (93644) ***(P-13737)***
Control Switches Inc (PA)....F....562 498-7331
2425 Mira Mar Ave Long Beach (90815) ***(P-17261)***
Control Switches Intl Inc....E....562 498-7331
2425 Mira Mar Ave Long Beach (90815) ***(P-17262)***
Control Systems Intl Inc....E....949 238-4150
1 Sterling Irvine (92618) ***(P-14219)***
Controlled Entrances Inc....F....760 749-1212
27525 Valley Center Rd A Valley Center (92082) ***(P-19932)***
Controlmyspa, Tustin *Also called Balboa Water Group LLC* ***(P-17256)***
Convaid Products Inc....D....310 618-0111
2830 California St Torrance (90503) ***(P-22714)***
Convergent Laser Technologies, Alameda *Also called Xintec Corporation* ***(P-23073)***
Convergent Manufacturing Tech....F....408 987-2770
966 Shulman Ave Santa Clara (95050) ***(P-15720)***
Convergent Mobile Inc....F....707 343-1200
870 Knight St Sonoma (95476) ***(P-18783)***
Converging Systems Inc....F....310 544-2628
32420 Nautilus Dr Ste 100 Pls Vrds Pnsl (90275) ***(P-15721)***
Convergint Technologies LLC....E....714 546-2780
1667 N Batavia St Orange (92867) ***(P-19933)***
Conversion Devices Inc....E....714 898-6551
15481 Electronic Ln Ste D Huntington Beach (92649) ***(P-22965)***
Conversion Technology Co Inc (PA)....E....805 378-0033
5360 N Commerce Ave Moorpark (93021) ***(P-23706)***
Convertly, San Jose *Also called Medianews Group Inc* ***(P-5960)***
Conveyant Systems Inc....F....949 756-7100
1901 Carnegie Ave Ste 1I Santa Ana (92705) ***(P-17935)***
Conveyor Concepts, Los Angeles *Also called Machine Building Specialties* ***(P-14868)***
Conveyor Group, Imperial *Also called Franklin Lee Enterprises LLC* ***(P-7322)***
Conveyor Mfg & Svc Inc....F....909 621-0406
771 Marylind Ave Claremont (91711) ***(P-14270)***
Conxtech Inc....C....510 264-9111
24493 Clawiter Rd Hayward (94545) ***(P-12141)***
Conxtech Inc (PA)....C....510 264-9111
6701 Koll Center Pkwy Pleasanton (94566) ***(P-12142)***
Cook and Cook Incorporated....E....714 680-6669
1000 E Elm Ave Fullerton (92831) ***(P-12383)***
Cook Concrete Products Inc....E....530 243-2562
5461 Eastside Rd Redding (96001) ***(P-10908)***
Cook Induction Heating Co Inc....E....323 560-1327
4925 Slauson Ave Maywood (90270) ***(P-11810)***
Cook King Inc....E....714 739-0502
15120 Desman Rd La Mirada (90638) ***(P-16032)***
Cookie Lovers, Glendale *Also called Interntnal Desserts Delicacies* ***(P-1365)***
Cooks Truck Body Mfg Inc....F....916 784-3220
9600 Del Rd Roseville (95747) ***(P-20198)***
Cool Curtain CCI, Costa Mesa *Also called CCI Industries Inc* ***(P-10015)***
Cool Jams Inc....F....858 566-6165
11206 Spencerport Way San Diego (92131) ***(P-3100)***
Cool Lumens Inc....F....831 471-8084
1334 Brommer St Ste B6 Santa Cruz (95062) ***(P-17594)***
Cool Things, Santa Ana *Also called Ecoolthing Corp* ***(P-13938)***
Cool Touch, Roseville *Also called Cooltouch Corporation* ***(P-22967)***
Cool-Pak LLC....D....805 981-2434
401 N Rice Ave Oxnard (93030) ***(P-10042)***
Coola LLC....E....760 940-2125
3200 Lionshead Ave Carlsbad (92010) ***(P-8722)***
Coola Suncare, Carlsbad *Also called Coola LLC* ***(P-8722)***
Coolhaus, Culver City *Also called Farchitecture Bb LLC* ***(P-669)***
Cooling Source Inc....C....925 292-1293
2021 Las Positas Ct # 101 Livermore (94551) ***(P-11691)***
Cooling Tower Resources Inc (PA)....E....707 433-3900
1470 Grove St Healdsburg (95448) ***(P-4616)***
Cooljet Systems, Brea *Also called Mkt Innovations* ***(P-16760)***
Coolsculpting, Pleasanton *Also called Zeltiq Aesthetics Inc* ***(P-22684)***
Coolssculpting, Dublin *Also called Zeltiq Aesthetics Inc* ***(P-22683)***
Coolsystems Inc (HQ)....C....888 426-3732
1800 Sutter St Ste 500 Concord (94520) ***(P-22966)***
Cooltec Refrigeration Corp....E....909 865-2229
1250 E Franklin Ave B Pomona (91766) ***(P-15947)***
Cooltouch, Roseville *Also called New Star Lasers Inc* ***(P-23026)***
Cooltouch Corporation....F....916 677-1975
9085 Foothills Blvd Roseville (95747) ***(P-22967)***
Cooper & Brain Inc....F....310 834-4411
655 E D St Wilmington (90744) ***(P-51)***
Cooper Bussmann LLC....F....925 924-8500
5735 W Las Positas Blvd # 100 Pleasanton (94588) ***(P-17338)***
Cooper Cameron Valves, Redding *Also called Cameron International Corp* ***(P-14215)***
Cooper Companies Inc (PA)....C....925 460-3600
6140 Stoneridge Mall Rd # 590 Pleasanton (94588) ***(P-23086)***
Cooper Crouse-Hinds LLC....C....805 484-0543
750 W Ventura Blvd Camarillo (93010) ***(P-19381)***
Cooper Crouse-Hinds LLC....C....805 484-0543
705 W Ventura Blvd Camarillo (93010) ***(P-9602)***
Cooper Crouse-Hinds LLC....C....805 484-0543
750 W Ventura Blvd Camarillo (93010) ***(P-9603)***
Cooper Interconnect Inc (HQ)....D....805 484-0543
750 W Ventura Blvd Camarillo (93010) ***(P-17456)***
Cooper Interconnect Inc....D....805 553-9632
750 W Ventura Blvd Camarillo (93010) ***(P-19382)***
Cooper Interconnect Inc....E....805 553-9632
750 W Ventura Blvd Camarillo (93010) ***(P-17509)***
Cooper Lighting LLC....E....909 605-6615
3350 Enterprise Dr Bloomington (92316) ***(P-17681)***
Cooper Microelectronics Inc....E....949 553-8352
1671 Reynolds Ave Irvine (92614) ***(P-18784)***
Cooper Tire & Rubber Company....F....909 481-6437
9363 Lucas Ranch Rd Rancho Cucamonga (91730) ***(P-9464)***
Coopervision Inc....D....925 251-6600
6150 Stoneridge Mall Rd # 370 Pleasanton (94588) ***(P-23087)***
Coordinated Wire Rope No. Ca., San Leandro *Also called Coordnted Wire Rope Rgging Inc* ***(P-2973)***
Coordnted Wire Rope Rgging Inc....F....510 569-6911
790 139th Ave Ste 1 San Leandro (94578) ***(P-2973)***
Coors Brewing Company....E....916 786-2666
3001 Douglas Blvd Ste 200 Roseville (95661) ***(P-1581)***
Coorstek Inc....D....805 644-5583
4544 Mcgrath St Ventura (93003) ***(P-14617)***
Coorstek Inc....C....805 644-5583
4544 Mcgrath St Ventura (93003) ***(P-14618)***
Coorstek Inc....F....310 322-2545
2051 E Maple Ave El Segundo (90245) ***(P-7198)***
Coorstek Inc....D....510 492-6600
42670 Albrae St Fremont (94538) ***(P-16403)***
Coorstek Ventura Geiser Bondin, Ventura *Also called Coorstek Inc* ***(P-14618)***
Coorstek Vista Inc....C....760 542-7065
2065 Thibodo Rd Vista (92081) ***(P-11340)***
Cop Communications, Glendale *Also called California Offset Printers Inc* ***(P-6716)***
Cop Shopper, San Diego *Also called Krasnes Inc* ***(P-3619)***
Copain Wine Cellars LLC....F....707 836-8822
7800 Eastside Rd Healdsburg (95448) ***(P-1707)***
Copain Wine Sellers, Healdsburg *Also called Copain Wine Cellars LLC* ***(P-1707)***
Copenhagen Acquisition LLC (PA)....D....310 899-9200
11400 Olypc Blvd Ste 1400 Los Angeles (90064) ***(P-1392)***
Coplan & Coplan Inc....E....760 268-0583
2270 Camino Vida Roble H Carlsbad (92011) ***(P-14619)***
Copley Press Inc....D....619 718-5200
2375 Northside Dr Ste 300 San Diego (92108) ***(P-24524)***
Copley Press Inc....F....760 752-6700
1152 Armorlite Dr San Marcos (92069) ***(P-5818)***
Copp Industrial Mfg Inc....E....909 593-7448
2837 Metropolitan Pl Pomona (91767) ***(P-12539)***
Coppa Woodworking Inc....F....310 548-4142
1231 Paraiso St San Pedro (90731) ***(P-4128)***
Copper Crm Inc....E....415 231-6360
301 Howard St Ste 600 San Francisco (94105) ***(P-24525)***
Copper Harbor Company Inc....F....510 639-4670
2300 Davis St San Leandro (94577) ***(P-9233)***
Copy 1 Inc....E....415 986-0111
77 Battery St Fl 2 San Francisco (94111) ***(P-6758)***
Copy Mill, San Francisco *Also called Ng John* ***(P-6993)***
Copy Shop & Printing Co, The, San Rafael *Also called Marin County Copy Shops Inc* ***(P-6960)***
Copyland /Zip2print, San Jose *Also called Arsh Incorporated* ***(P-6668)***
Copymat, San Francisco *Also called Digital Mania Inc* ***(P-6786)***
Copymat Salinas LLC....F....831 753-0471
44 W Gabilan St Salinas (93901) ***(P-6759)***
Coraid Inc (PA)....D....650 517-9300
255 Shoreline Dr Ste 650 Redwood City (94065) ***(P-15526)***
Coral Head Inc (PA)....F....310 366-7712
1988 W 169th St Gardena (90247) ***(P-3141)***
Coral Reef Aquarium....E....310 538-4282
515 W 130th St Los Angeles (90061) ***(P-10686)***
Coral Reef Dive Center, Westminster *Also called Anthony Jones* ***(P-23504)***

ALPHABETIC

Employee Codes: A=Over 500 employees, B=251-500 C=101-250, D=51-100, E=20-50, F=10-19
2019 California Manfacturers Register
© Mergent Inc. 1-800-342-5647
1107

Corasia Corp.....F.....408 321-8508
363 Fairview Way Milpitas (95035) ***(P-15203)***
Corazonas Foods Inc.....F.....800 388-8998
3780 Kilroy Airport Way # 430 Long Beach (90806) ***(P-2377)***
Corbell Products, Bloomington *Also called Westco Industries Inc* ***(P-13004)***
Corbell Products Inc.....E.....909 574-9139
14650 Hawthorne Ave Fontana (92335) ***(P-12143)***
Corbin Foods, Santa Ana *Also called Corbin-Hill Inc* ***(P-1225)***
Corbin Pacific Inc.....E.....408 633-2500
11445 Commercial Pkwy Castroville (95012) ***(P-21098)***
Corbin Pacific Inc (PA).....D.....831 634-1100
2360 Technology Pkwy Hollister (95023) ***(P-21099)***
Corbin-Hill Inc.....D.....714 966-6695
2961 W Macarthur Blvd Santa Ana (92704) ***(P-1225)***
Corcen Data International Inc.....F.....714 251-6110
17341 Irvine Blvd Ste 205 Tustin (92780) ***(P-24526)***
Corcept Therapeutics Inc.....C.....650 327-3270
149 Commonwealth Dr Menlo Park (94025) ***(P-8121)***
Corcoran Sawtelle Rosprim Inc.....E.....559 992-2117
542 Otis Ave Corcoran (93212) ***(P-12144)***
Cord Industries Inc.....F.....760 728-4590
541 Industrial Way Ste 2 Fallbrook (92028) ***(P-10043)***
Cord Intrnational/Hana Ola Rec.....F.....805 648-7881
1874 Terrace Dr Ventura (93001) ***(P-17889)***
Cordeiro Vault Co (PA).....E.....707 552-1045
281 5th St Vallejo (94590) ***(P-10909)***
Cordova Industries, Sylmar *Also called International Academy of Fin* ***(P-9013)***
Cordovan & Grey Ltd.....E.....562 699-8300
4826 Gregg Rd Pico Rivera (90660) ***(P-3068)***
Core Industries Inc.....B.....800 228-6635
14410 Myford Rd Irvine (92606) ***(P-23544)***
Core Laboratories LP.....E.....661 325-5657
3437 Landco Dr Bakersfield (93308) ***(P-200)***
Core Supplement Technology.....F.....760 452-7364
4665 North Ave Oceanside (92056) ***(P-8122)***
Core Systems, Poway *Also called Rugged Systems Inc* ***(P-15479)***
Core Tech Products Inc.....F.....661 833-1572
1850 Sunnyside Ct Bakersfield (93308) ***(P-8723)***
Corefact Corporation.....F.....866 777-3986
20936 Cabot Blvd Hayward (94545) ***(P-6418)***
Corelogic Dorado, Oakland *Also called Dorado Network Systems Corp* ***(P-24572)***
Coreslab Structures La Inc.....C.....951 943-9119
150 W Placentia Ave Perris (92571) ***(P-10910)***
Coretest Systems Inc.....F.....408 778-3771
400 Woodview Ave Morgan Hill (95037) ***(P-21939)***
Coretex Products Inc (PA).....F.....661 834-6805
1850 Sunnyside Ct Bakersfield (93308) ***(P-8724)***
Corium International Inc (PA).....C.....650 298-8255
235 Constitution Dr Menlo Park (94025) ***(P-8123)***
Cork Pops.....F.....415 884-6000
7 Commercial Blvd Ste 3 Novato (94949) ***(P-13931)***
Corn Maiden Foods Inc.....D.....310 784-0400
24201 Frampton Ave Harbor City (90710) ***(P-754)***
Corn Products Development Inc (HQ).....F.....209 982-1920
1021 Industrial Dr Stockton (95206) ***(P-1099)***
Corn Products-Stockton Plant, Stockton *Also called Ingredion Incorporated* ***(P-1100)***
Cornerstone Display Group Inc (PA).....E.....661 705-1700
28606 Livingston Ave Valencia (91355) ***(P-23848)***
Cornerstone Ondemand Inc (PA).....C.....310 752-0200
1601 Cloverfield Blvd 620s Santa Monica (90404) ***(P-24527)***
Corningware Corelle & More, Eastvale *Also called Snapware Corporation* ***(P-10380)***
Cornnuts Division of Planters, Fresno *Also called Kraft Heinz Foods Company* ***(P-1494)***
Cornucopia Tool & Plastics Inc.....E.....805 238-7660
448 Sherwood Rd Paso Robles (93446) ***(P-10044)***
Coroc, Bakersfield *Also called Weatherford International LLC* ***(P-297)***
Corona Magnetics Inc.....C.....951 735-7558
201 Corporate Terrace St Corona (92879) ***(P-19329)***
Corona Millworks Company (PA).....D.....909 606-3288
5572 Edison Ave Chino (91710) ***(P-4288)***
Corona Pathology.....F.....818 566-1891
4444 W Riverside Dr # 308 Burbank (91505) ***(P-9001)***
Coronado Eagle, Coronado *Also called Eagle Newspapers LLC* ***(P-5836)***
Coronado Equipment Sales.....F.....877 830-7447
2275 La Crosse Ave # 210 Colton (92324) ***(P-14314)***
Coronado Leather Co Inc.....F.....619 238-0265
1961 Main St San Diego (92113) ***(P-3612)***
Coronado Manufacturing Inc.....E.....818 768-5010
8991 Glenoaks Blvd Sun Valley (91352) ***(P-20787)***
Coronado Stone Products, Fontana *Also called Creative Stone Mfg Inc* ***(P-10911)***
Coronet Concrete Products.....E.....760 398-2441
83801 Avenue 45 Indio (92201) ***(P-11099)***
Coronet Lighting, Gardena *Also called Dasol Inc* ***(P-17424)***
Corp Couch, San Francisco *Also called Corporatecouch* ***(P-18785)***
Corpak of Tulare, Tulare *Also called Westrock Cp LLC* ***(P-5368)***
Corporate Graphics & Printing.....F.....805 529-5333
335 Science Dr Moorpark (93021) ***(P-6760)***
Corporate Graphics Intl Inc.....D.....323 826-3440
4909 Alcoa Ave Vernon (90058) ***(P-6761)***
Corporate Graphics West, Vernon *Also called Corporate Graphics Intl Inc* ***(P-6761)***
Corporate Impressions La Inc.....E.....818 761-9295
10742 Burbank Blvd North Hollywood (91601) ***(P-7285)***
Corporate Sign Systems Inc.....E.....408 292-1600
2464 De La Cruz Blvd Santa Clara (95050) ***(P-23849)***
Corporatecouch.....E.....415 312-6078
260 Vicente St San Francisco (94127) ***(P-18785)***
Corprint Incorporated.....F.....818 839-5316
4235 Mission Oaks Blvd Camarillo (93010) ***(P-7286)***
Corralitos Market & Sausage Co.....F.....831 722-2633
569 Corralitos Rd Watsonville (95076) ***(P-477)***
Correa Pallet Inc (PA).....E.....559 757-1790
13036 Avenue 76 Pixley (93256) ***(P-4462)***
Corrpro Companies Inc.....E.....562 944-1636
10260 Matern Pl Santa Fe Springs (90670) ***(P-11531)***
Corru-Kraft IV.....F.....714 773-0124
1911 E Rosslynn Ave Fullerton (92831) ***(P-5374)***
Corrugados De Baja California.....A.....619 662-8672
2475 Paseo De Las A San Diego (92154) ***(P-5401)***
Corrugated and Packaging LLC.....C.....619 559-1564
9651 Airway Rd Ste F San Diego (92154) ***(P-9830)***
Corrugated Packaging Pdts Inc.....E.....650 615-9180
27403 Industrial Blvd Hayward (94545) ***(P-5402)***
Corrugated Technologies Inc.....E.....858 578-3550
15150 Avenue Of Science San Diego (92128) ***(P-24528)***
Corrwood Containers.....E.....559 651-0335
7182 Rasmussen Ave Visalia (93291) ***(P-4519)***
Corsair Components Inc (PA).....E.....510 657-8747
47100 Bayside Pkwy Fremont (94538) ***(P-15630)***
Corsair Elec Connectors Inc.....C.....949 833-0273
17100 Murphy Ave Irvine (92614) ***(P-19383)***
Corsair Memory Inc.....C.....510 657-8747
47100 Bayside Pkwy Fremont (94538) ***(P-18786)***
Corsican Furniture, Gardena *Also called Victor Martin Inc* ***(P-4847)***
Corte Custom Case, San Jacinto *Also called Wallace Wood Products* ***(P-5118)***
Cortec Precision Shtmtl Inc (PA).....C.....408 278-8540
2231 Will Wool Dr San Jose (95112) ***(P-12540)***
Cortez Furniture Mfg Inc.....F.....323 581-5935
2423 E 58th St Los Angeles (90058) ***(P-4765)***
Cortez Furniture Mfg Inc (PA).....E.....323 581-5935
2444 E 57th St Vernon (90058) ***(P-4766)***
Cortima Co.....E.....760 347-5535
83778 Avenue 45 Indio (92201) ***(P-11245)***
Cortina Systems Inc (HQ).....C.....408 481-2300
2953 Bunker Hill Ln # 300 Santa Clara (95054) ***(P-18787)***
Corvus Pharmaceuticals Inc.....D.....650 900-4520
863 Mitten Rd Ste 102 Burlingame (94010) ***(P-8124)***
Corwin Press Inc.....F.....805 499-9734
2455 Teller Rd Newbury Park (91320) ***(P-6331)***
Cosa Marble Co.....F.....818 364-8800
13040 San Fernando Rd A Sylmar (91342) ***(P-302)***
Cosco Home & Office Products, Ontario *Also called Dorel Juvenile Group Inc* ***(P-10078)***
Cosemi Technologies Inc.....F.....949 623-9816
1370 Reynolds Ave Ste 100 Irvine (92614) ***(P-18788)***
Cosentino Signature Wineries (PA).....E.....707 921-2809
7415 St Helena Hwy Yountville (94599) ***(P-1708)***
Cosentino Winery, Yountville *Also called Cosentino Signature Wineries* ***(P-1708)***
Coskata Inc.....F.....630 657-5800
3945 Freedom Cir Ste 560 Santa Clara (95054) ***(P-9002)***
Coskata Energy, Santa Clara *Also called Coskata Inc* ***(P-9002)***
Cosmedica Skincare.....F.....800 922-5280
2208 Srra Madows Dr Ste A Rocklin (95677) ***(P-8725)***
Cosmetic Design Group LLC.....F.....310 397-9300
5673 Selmaraine Dr Culver City (90230) ***(P-8726)***
Cosmetic Enterprises Ltd.....F.....818 896-5355
12848 Pierce St Pacoima (91331) ***(P-8727)***
Cosmetic Group Usa Inc.....C.....818 767-2889
8430 Tujunga Ave Sun Valley (91352) ***(P-8728)***
Cosmetic Specialties Intl LLC.....C.....805 487-6698
550 E 3rd St Oxnard (93030) ***(P-10045)***
Cosmi Finance LLC.....F.....310 603-5800
1635 Chelsea Rd Ste A San Marino (91108) ***(P-24529)***
Cosmic Fog Vapors.....D.....949 266-1730
3115 Airway Ave Costa Mesa (92626) ***(P-2704)***
Cosmic Plastics Inc (PA).....E.....661 257-3274
28410 Industry Dr Valencia (91355) ***(P-7825)***
Cosmo - Pharm Inc.....E.....818 764-0246
11751 Vose St Ste 53 North Hollywood (91605) ***(P-7928)***
Cosmo Beauty Lab & Mfg, San Dimas *Also called Cosmobeauti Labs & Mfg Inc* ***(P-8729)***
Cosmo Fiber Corporation (PA).....E.....626 256-6098
1802 Santo Domingo Ave Duarte (91010) ***(P-7287)***
Cosmo Import & Export LLC (PA).....E.....916 209-5500
3919 Channel Dr West Sacramento (95691) ***(P-4829)***
Cosmobeauti Labs & Mfg Inc.....F.....909 971-9832
480 E Arrow Hwy San Dimas (91773) ***(P-8729)***
Cosmodyne LLC.....E.....562 795-5990
3010 Old Ranch Pkwy # 300 Seal Beach (90740) ***(P-14930)***
Cosmojet Inc.....F.....818 773-6544
9601 Cozycroft Ave Ste 2 Chatsworth (91311) ***(P-7199)***
Cosmos Food Co Inc.....E.....323 221-9142
16015 Phoenix Dr City of Industry (91745) ***(P-2494)***
Costal Brands, Manteca *Also called Delicato Vineyards* ***(P-1719)***
Cosway Company Inc.....E.....310 527-9135
14805 S Maple Ave Gardena (90248) ***(P-8730)***
Cosway Company Inc (PA).....E.....310 900-4100
20633 S Fordyce Ave Carson (90810) ***(P-8731)***
Cots Journal Magazine, San Clemente *Also called R T C Group* ***(P-6241)***
Cott Manufacturing Company.....E.....818 988-9500
19755 Nordhoff Pl Chatsworth (91311) ***(P-18317)***
Cott Technologies Inc.....F.....626 961-3399
14923 Proctor Ave La Puente (91746) ***(P-13882)***
Cotterman Company, Bakersfield *Also called Material Control Inc* ***(P-13957)***
Cotton Generation Inc.....E.....323 581-8555
6051 Maywood Ave Huntington Park (90255) ***(P-3574)***
Cotton Knits Trading.....E.....310 884-9600
3097 E Ana St Compton (90221) ***(P-2873)***
Cotton Palm Inc.....E.....818 890-3037
12410 Foothill Blvd Ste R Sylmar (91342) ***(P-3142)***

Mergent e-mail: customerrelations@mergent.com
1108
2019 California
Manufacturers Register
(P-0000) Products & Services Section entry number
(PA)=Parent Co (HQ)=Headquarters (DH)=Div Headquarters

Cotton Tale Designs Inc .....E......714 435-9558
16291 Sierra Ridge Way Hacienda Heights (91745) *(P-3715)*
Cotty On, Vernon *Also called Cottyon Inc (P-2732)*
Cottyon Inc .....E......323 589-1563
2202 E Anderson St Vernon (90058) *(P-2732)*
Cougar Biotechnology Inc .....D......310 943-8040
10990 Wilshire Blvd # 1200 Los Angeles (90024) *(P-8125)*
Coughrar: Mechanical Services .....F......707 374-2100
3053 Liberty Island Rd Rio Vista (94571) *(P-16404)*
Coulter Forge Technology Inc .....F......510 420-3500
1494 67th St Emeryville (94608) *(P-13096)*
Coulter Steel and Forge, Emeryville *Also called Coulter Forge Technology Inc (P-13096)*
Counter .....E......310 406-3300
21209 Hawthorne Blvd B Torrance (90503) *(P-10471)*
Counter Fit .....F......916 569-8570
6925 Roseville Rd Sacramento (95842) *(P-11246)*
Counter Fitters, The, Buena Park *Also called Colorline Inc (P-4980)*
Counterpart Automotive Inc .....E......714 771-1732
419 W Brenna Ln Orange (92867) *(P-20298)*
Counterpoint Software Inc .....F......818 222-7777
24528 Palermo Dr Calabasas (91302) *(P-24530)*
Countis Industries Inc .....E......530 272-8334
12295 Charles Dr Grass Valley (95945) *(P-10817)*
Country Almanac, Palo Alto *Also called Embarcadero Publishing Company (P-5846)*
Country Floral Supply Inc .....D......925 960-9823
6909 Las Positas Rd Ste F Livermore (94551) *(P-24069)*
Country House .....F......714 505-8988
2852 Walnut Ave Ste C1 Tustin (92780) *(P-1417)*
Country Plastics Inc .....F......559 597-2556
32501 Road 228 Woodlake (93286) *(P-10046)*
Country Weave, Santa Ana *Also called Newport Plastic Inc (P-10238)*
Countryman Associates Inc .....F......650 364-9988
195 Constitution Dr Menlo Park (94025) *(P-17784)*
County of Alameda .....E......510 272-6964
1225 Fallon St Ste G1 Oakland (94612) *(P-21682)*
County of Los Angeles .....E......626 968-3312
14959 Proctor Ave La Puente (91746) *(P-14159)*
County of Los Angeles .....F......310 456-8014
3637 Winter Canyon Rd Malibu (90265) *(P-14160)*
County of Marin .....D......415 446-4414
1600 Los Gamos Dr Ste 200 San Rafael (94903) *(P-5009)*
County of Monterey .....F......831 755-4790
855 E Laurel Dr Ste C Salinas (93905) *(P-7288)*
County of NAPA .....F......707 259-8620
804 1st St NAPA (94559) *(P-21566)*
County of San Bernardino .....E......909 580-0015
400 N Pepper Ave Colton (92324) *(P-21465)*
County of San Bernardino .....A......909 387-7942
825 E 3rd St San Bernardino (92415) *(P-14161)*
Countywide Metal, El Cajon *Also called Mmix Technologies (P-12681)*
Coupa Software Incorporated (PA) .....C......650 931-3200
1855 S Grant St San Mateo (94402) *(P-24531)*
Courage Production LLC .....D......707 422-6300
2475 Courage Dr Fairfield (94533) *(P-478)*
Courtside Cellars LLC .....E......805 467-2882
2425 Mission St San Miguel (93451) *(P-1709)*
Courtside Cellars LLC (PA) .....E......805 782-0500
4910 Edna Rd San Luis Obispo (93401) *(P-1710)*
Coval Molecular Coatings Inc .....F......707 242-6900
5341 Old Redwood Hwy Petaluma (94954) *(P-9234)*
Covalent Metrology Svcs LLC .....F......408 498-4611
921 Thompson Pl Sunnyvale (94085) *(P-21466)*
Covan Alarm Company, Livermore *Also called Covan Systems Inc (P-17785)*
Covan Systems Inc .....F......510 226-9886
569 Leisure St Livermore (94551) *(P-17785)*
Cove Four-Slide Stamping Corp (PA) .....D......516 379-4232
355 S Hale Ave Fullerton (92831) *(P-13820)*
Cove Four-Slide Stamping Corp. .....E......714 525-2930
335 S Hale Ave Fullerton (92831) *(P-13821)*
Cove West Division, Fullerton *Also called Cove Four-Slide Stamping Corp (P-13820)*
Cove20 LLC .....F......949 297-4930
15 Brookline Aliso Viejo (92656) *(P-18789)*
Cover King, Anaheim *Also called Shrin Corporation (P-20447)*
Coveris, Hanford *Also called Transcontinental US LLC (P-5629)*
Coveris, Ontario *Also called Transcontinental US LLC (P-5630)*
Covert Iron Works .....F......323 560-2792
7821 Otis S Ave Huntington Park (90255) *(P-11503)*
Covia Holdings Corporation .....E......925 634-3575
1300 Camino Diablo Rd Byron (94514) *(P-395)*
Covidien, Costa Mesa *Also called Newport Medical Instrs Inc (P-22557)*
Covidien, Sunnyvale *Also called Barrx Medical Inc (P-22354)*
Covidien Holding Inc .....F......760 603-5020
2101 Faraday Ave Carlsbad (92008) *(P-22410)*
Covidien Holding Inc .....A......619 690-8500
2475 Paseo De Las Amrcs A San Diego (92154) *(P-22411)*
Covidien Kenmex, San Diego *Also called Covidien Holding Inc (P-22411)*
Covidien LP .....B......949 837-3700
9775 Toledo Way Irvine (92618) *(P-22412)*
Covina Welding & Shtmtl Inc .....F......626 332-6293
473 E Front St Covina (91723) *(P-12145)*
Cowboy Direct Response .....E......714 824-3780
130 E Alton Ave Santa Ana (92707) *(P-23850)*
Coy Industries Inc .....D......310 603-2970
2970 E Maria St E Rncho Dmngz (90221) *(P-12541)*
Coyle Reproductions Inc (PA) .....C......866 269-5373
2850 Orbiter St Brea (92821) *(P-6762)*
Coyne & Blanchard Inc .....E......650 326-6040
110 Constitution Dr Menlo Park (94025) *(P-6136)*

Cozad Trailer Sales LLC .....D......209 931-3000
4907 E Waterloo Rd Stockton (95215) *(P-20498)*
Cozza Inc .....F......619 749-5663
9941 Prospect Ave Santee (92071) *(P-16405)*
Cozzia USA LLC .....E......626 667-2272
861 S Oak Park Rd Covina (91724) *(P-19934)*
CP Films Inc .....E......714 634-0900
4110 E La Palma Ave Anaheim (92807) *(P-7826)*
CP Kelco, San Diego *Also called Kelco Bio Polymers (P-9266)*
CP Kelco Us Inc .....E......858 467-6542
2025 Harbor Dr San Diego (92113) *(P-9235)*
CP Kelco US Inc .....F......858 292-4900
8355 Aero Dr San Diego (92123) *(P-9236)*
CP Kelco US Inc .....F......858 292-4900
8225 Aero Dr San Diego (92123) *(P-9237)*
CP Manufacturing Inc (HQ) .....C......619 477-3175
6795 Calle De Linea San Diego (92154) *(P-14931)*
CP Products, Anaheim *Also called Kiva Container Corporation (P-9868)*
Cp-Carrillo Inc .....E......949 567-9000
17401 Armstrong Ave Irvine (92614) *(P-16146)*
Cp-Carrillo Inc (HQ) .....C......949 567-9000
1902 Mcgaw Ave Irvine (92614) *(P-16147)*
Cpacket Networks Inc .....E......650 969-9500
765 Ravendale Dr Mountain View (94043) *(P-15722)*
CPC Fabrication Inc .....F......714 549-2426
2904 Oak St Santa Ana (92707) *(P-12542)*
CPC Group Inc .....F......626 350-8848
11223 Rush St Ste I South El Monte (91733) *(P-10047)*
Cpd Industries .....F......909 465-5596
4665 State St Montclair (91763) *(P-9831)*
Cpfilms Distribution Center, Anaheim *Also called CP Films Inc (P-7826)*
CPI, Palo Alto *Also called Communications & Pwr Inds LLC (P-18382)*
CPI, Palo Alto *Also called Communications & Pwr Inds LLC (P-18073)*
CPI, Palo Alto *Also called Communications & Pwr Inds LLC (P-18383)*
CPI Advanced Inc .....C......909 597-5533
14708 Central Ave Chino (91710) *(P-17085)*
CPI International Inc (HQ) .....F......650 846-2801
811 Hansen Way Palo Alto (94304) *(P-18385)*
CPI International Holding Corp .....F......650 846-2900
811 Hansen Way Palo Alto (94304) *(P-19500)*
CPI Malibu Division .....D......805 383-1829
3760 Calle Tecate Ste A Camarillo (93012) *(P-18078)*
Cpk Manufacturing Inc .....F......408 971-4019
75 Phelan Ave Ste 3 San Jose (95112) *(P-16406)*
Cpp, Sunnyvale *Also called Myers-Briggs Company (P-6534)*
Cpp Cudahy, Cudahy *Also called Consoldted Precision Pdts Corp (P-11729)*
Cpp Ind .....F......909 595-2252
16800 Chestnut St City of Industry (91748) *(P-21277)*
Cpp-Azusa, Azusa *Also called Magparts (P-11746)*
Cpp-City of Industry, City of Industry *Also called Cast Parts Inc (P-11509)*
Cpp-Pomona, Walnut *Also called Cast Parts Inc (P-11508)*
Cpp-Port Hueneme .....C......805 488-6451
705 Industrial Way Port Hueneme (93041) *(P-11772)*
Cpp/Belwin .....E......818 891-5999
16320 Roscoe Blvd Ste 100 Van Nuys (91406) *(P-6332)*
Cppi, San Diego *Also called California Precision Pdts Inc (P-12523)*
Cprint Holdings LLC .....F......213 488-0456
1901 E 7th Pl Los Angeles (90021) *(P-6763)*
CPS Gem Corporation .....F......213 627-4019
1327 S Myrtle Ave Monrovia (91016) *(P-23253)*
CPS Printing .....D......760 494-9000
2304 Faraday Ave Carlsbad (92008) *(P-6764)*
CPS Wood Works Inc .....F......909 326-1102
1257 E 9th St Pomona (91766) *(P-4129)*
Cr & A Custom, Los Angeles *Also called CR & A Custom Apparel Inc (P-7289)*
CR & A Custom Apparel Inc .....E......213 749-4440
312 W Pico Blvd Los Angeles (90015) *(P-7289)*
Cr Laurence, Vernon *Also called CR Laurence Co Inc (P-20299)*
CR Laurence Co Inc (HQ) .....C......323 588-1211
2503 E Vernon Ave Vernon (90058) *(P-20299)*
CR Laurence Co Inc .....F......310 327-9300
14400 S San Pedro St Gardena (90248) *(P-12305)*
Cr Print, Westlake Village *Also called Earth Print Inc (P-6798)*
Cr Spotless, El Cajon *Also called Spotless Water Systems LLC (P-16115)*
Crabtree Glass Company Inc .....E......818 765-1840
13203 Sherman Way North Hollywood (91605) *(P-12845)*
Craft Labor & Support Svcs LLC .....D......619 336-9977
1545 Tidelands Ave Ste C National City (91950) *(P-20993)*
Craftech EDM Corporation .....C......714 630-8117
2941 E La Jolla St Anaheim (92806) *(P-10048)*
Craftech Metal Forming Inc .....E......951 940-6444
24100 Water Ave Ste B Perris (92570) *(P-11731)*
Crafted Metals Inc .....F......619 464-1090
9220 Birch St Spring Valley (91977) *(P-13932)*
Crafters Companion .....E......714 630-2444
2750 E Regal Park Dr Anaheim (92806) *(P-23416)*
Crafton Carton .....E......510 441-5985
31790 Hayman St Hayward (94544) *(P-5505)*
Craftsman Cutting Dies Inc (PA) .....E......714 776-8995
2273 E Via Burton Anaheim (92806) *(P-11890)*
Craftsman Lighting .....F......626 330-8512
14266 Valley Blvd Ste A La Puente (91746) *(P-17532)*
Craftsman Printing, San Jose *Also called United Craftsmen Priniting (P-7156)*
Craftstones, Ramona *Also called Ramona Mining & Manufacturing (P-23346)*
Crafttech, Anaheim *Also called Craftech EDM Corporation (P-10048)*
Craic Technologies Inc .....F......310 573-8180
948 N Amelia Ave San Dimas (91773) *(P-21940)*

Employee Codes: A=Over 500 employees, B=251-500
C=101-250, D=51-100, E=20-50, F=10-19

2019 California
Manfacturers Register

© Mergent Inc. 1-800-342-5647
1109

A
L
P
H
A
B
E
T
I
C

Craig Kackert Design Tech, Simi Valley *Also called Jaxx Manufacturing Inc* ***(P-19595)***
Craig Manufacturing Company (PA) ....D....323 726-7355
8129 Slauson Ave Montebello (90640) ***(P-20300)***
Craig R Williams Cnstr Inc ....F....310 550-9250
100 N Crescent Dr Ste 100 Beverly Hills (90210) ***(P-201)***
Craig Tools Inc ....E....310 322-0614
142 Lomita St El Segundo (90245) ***(P-14620)***
Crain Cutter Company Inc ....D....408 946-6100
1155 Wrigley Way Milpitas (95035) ***(P-11947)***
Cramer Engineering Inc ....E....562 903-5556
302 Elizabeth Ln Corona (92880) ***(P-16407)***
Crane Aerospace Inc ....D....818 526-2600
3000 Winona Ave Burbank (91504) ***(P-21278)***
Crane Co, Signal Hill *Also called Pacific Valves* ***(P-13730)***
Crane Co ....E....310 403-2820
13105 Saticoy St North Hollywood (91605) ***(P-13738)***
Crane Co ....F....707 748-7166
3948 Teal Ct Benicia (94510) ***(P-19501)***
Crane Pro Services, Livermore *Also called Konecranes Inc* ***(P-14300)***
Crane Valves Services Division, Benicia *Also called Crane Co* ***(P-19501)***
Crane, John, Santa Fe Springs *Also called John Crane Inc* ***(P-11322)***
Craneveyor Corp (PA) ....D....626 442-1524
1524 Potrero Ave El Monte (91733) ***(P-14295)***
Craneveyor Corp ....E....909 627-6801
13730 Central Ave Chino (91710) ***(P-12846)***
Craneworks Southwest Inc ....E....760 735-9793
1312 E Barham Dr San Marcos (92078) ***(P-14315)***
Crashcam Industries Corp ....F....310 283-5379
19627 Vision Dr Topanga (90290) ***(P-23148)***
Crave Foods Inc ....E....562 900-7272
2043 Imperial St Los Angeles (90021) ***(P-987)***
Craviotto Drum Co ....F....831 763-0855
81 Hangar Way Ste 8 Watsonville (95076) ***(P-23359)***
Craviotto, John Custom Drums, Watsonville *Also called Craviotto Drum Co* ***(P-23359)***
Crawford Products Company Inc ....F....323 721-6429
409 N Park Ave Montebello (90640) ***(P-8899)***
Cray Cluster Solutions, San Jose *Also called Appro International Inc* ***(P-15513)***
Crazy Industries ....E....619 270-9090
8675 Avenida Costa Norte San Diego (92154) ***(P-23545)***
Crazyondigital Inc ....F....925 294-9432
907 Sunny Brook Way Pleasanton (94566) ***(P-17786)***
CRC Marketing Inc ....F....562 624-3400
111 W Ocean Blvd Ste 800 Long Beach (90802) ***(P-52)***
CRC Services LLC ....F....888 848-4754
9200 Oakdale Ave Fl 9 Chatsworth (91311) ***(P-53)***
Crcm, Long Beach *Also called CRC Marketing Inc* ***(P-52)***
Crd Mfg Inc ....F....714 871-3300
1539 W Orange Grove Ave A Orange (92868) ***(P-11948)***
Creaform USA Inc ....F....855 939-4446
2031 Main St Irvine (92614) ***(P-15723)***
Creamer Printing Co ....F....310 671-9491
1413 N La Brea Ave Inglewood (90302) ***(P-6765)***
Creation Tech Calexico Inc (HQ) ....C....760 336-8543
1778 Zinetta Rd Ste A Calexico (92231) ***(P-18458)***
Creation Tech San Jose Inc ....C....408 954-8055
1873 Barber Ln Milpitas (95035) ***(P-18459)***
Creation Tech Santa Clara Inc ....B....408 235-7500
2801 Northwestern Pkwy Santa Clara (95051) ***(P-18460)***
Creations Grdn Natural Fd Mkts ....C....661 877-4280
24849 Anza Dr Valencia (91355) ***(P-7929)***
Creations Salon, Irvine *Also called Elafree Inc* ***(P-24091)***
Creative Age Publications Inc ....E....818 782-7328
7628 Densmore Ave Van Nuys (91406) ***(P-6137)***
Creative Automation, Sun Valley *Also called Jack J Engel Manufacturing Inc* ***(P-19989)***
Creative Color Printing Inc ....F....951 737-4551
1605 Railroad St Corona (92880) ***(P-6766)***
Creative Computer Products ....F....858 458-1965
6369 Nncy Rdge Dr Ste 200 San Diego (92121) ***(P-10049)***
Creative Concepts and Design ....F....707 812-9320
8460 Freedom Ln Winters (95694) ***(P-4130)***
Creative Concepts Holdings LLC (HQ) ....F....949 705-6584
580 Garcia Ave Pittsburg (94565) ***(P-2253)***
Creative Costuming Designs Inc ....E....714 895-0982
15402 Electronic Ln Huntington Beach (92649) ***(P-3651)***
Creative Design Industries ....C....619 710-2525
2587 Otay Center Dr San Diego (92154) ***(P-3053)***
Creative Electron Inc ....F....760 752-1192
201 Trade St San Marcos (92078) ***(P-21279)***
Creative Extruded Products, West Covina *Also called Yogi Investments Inc* ***(P-10455)***
Creative Foods LLC ....E....858 748-0070
13132 Poway Rd Poway (92064) ***(P-2495)***
Creative Graphic Services, Santa Clarita *Also called Living Way Industries Inc* ***(P-23915)***
Creative Image Systems Inc ....F....909 947-8588
1921 E Acacia St Ontario (91761) ***(P-8732)***
Creative Impressions Inc (PA) ....E....714 521-4441
7697 9th St Buena Park (90621) ***(P-9703)***
Creative Industries, El Cajon *Also called Fuzetron Inc* ***(P-14957)***
Creative Industry Handbooks, Toluca Lake *Also called Gmm Inc* ***(P-6493)***
Creative Inflatables, South El Monte *Also called Promotonal Design Concepts Inc* ***(P-9664)***
Creative Intgrated Systems Inc ....E....949 261-6577
1700 E Garry Ave Ste 112 Santa Ana (92705) ***(P-18790)***
Creative Intl Pastries ....E....415 255-1128
950 Illinois St San Francisco (94107) ***(P-1226)***
Creative Machine Technology, Corona *Also called Cremach Tech Inc* ***(P-14364)***
Creative Machine Technology, Corona *Also called Cremach Tech Inc* ***(P-14365)***
Creative Metal Products Corp ....F....408 281-0797
6284 San Ignacio Ave D San Jose (95119) ***(P-16408)***
Creative Mfg Solutions ....E....408 327-0600
18400 Sutter Blvd Morgan Hill (95037) ***(P-12543)***
Creative Outdoor Distrs USA, Lake Forest *Also called Cod USA Inc* ***(P-5008)***
Creative Pathways Inc ....E....310 530-1965
20815 Higgins Ct Torrance (90501) ***(P-14723)***
Creative Plastic Printing, San Diego *Also called Creative Computer Products* ***(P-10049)***
Creative Press LLC ....D....714 774-5060
1600 E Ball Rd Anaheim (92805) ***(P-6767)***
Creative Shower Door Corp ....F....510 623-9000
43652 S Grimmer Blvd Fremont (94538) ***(P-9898)***
Creative Sign Inc ....F....714 842-4343
17922 Lyons Cir Huntington Beach (92647) ***(P-23851)***
Creative Stone Mfg Inc (PA) ....C....909 357-8295
11191 Calabash Ave Fontana (92337) ***(P-10911)***
Creative Teaching Press Inc (PA) ....D....714 799-2100
6262 Katella Ave Cypress (90630) ***(P-6333)***
Creative Wood Products Inc ....C....510 635-5399
900 77th Ave Oakland (94621) ***(P-4940)***
Credence Id LLC ....E....888 243-5452
5801 Christie Ave Ste 500 Emeryville (94608) ***(P-18079)***
Cree Inc ....E....805 968-9460
340 Storke Rd Ste 100 Goleta (93117) ***(P-18791)***
Creekside Managed Care ....F....707 578-0399
879 2nd St Santa Rosa (95404) ***(P-8126)***
Creftcon Industries Inc ....C....203 377-5944
900 Ajax Ave City of Industry (91748) ***(P-17510)***
Creganna - Tactx Medical, Campbell *Also called Tactx Medical Inc* ***(P-22642)***
Creganna Medical Devices Inc (HQ) ....E....408 364-7100
1353 Dell Ave Campbell (95008) ***(P-22413)***
Creganna-Tactx Medical, Campbell *Also called Creganna Medical Devices Inc* ***(P-22413)***
Crellin Machine Company ....E....323 225-8101
114 W Elmyra St Los Angeles (90012) ***(P-13019)***
Cremach Tech Inc (PA) ....D....951 735-3194
369 Meyer Cir Corona (92879) ***(P-14364)***
Cremach Tech Inc ....E....951 735-3194
400 E Parkridge Ave Corona (92879) ***(P-14365)***
Cremax U S A Corporation ....F....626 956-8800
11740 Clark St Arcadia (91006) ***(P-11949)***
Crenshaw Die and Mfg Corp ....D....949 475-5505
7432 Prince Dr Huntington Beach (92647) ***(P-13189)***
Creo Inc ....F....530 756-1477
50 Fullerton Ct Ste 107 Sacramento (95825) ***(P-7290)***
Crescent Inc ....E....714 992-6030
1196 N Osprey Cir Anaheim (92807) ***(P-6768)***
Crescent Plastics Inc ....F....626 359-9248
1711 S California Ave Monrovia (91016) ***(P-10050)***
Crescent Woodworking Co Ltd ....F....909 673-9955
400 Ramona Ave Ste 212 Corona (92879) ***(P-4686)***
Cresco Manufacturing Inc ....E....714 525-2326
1614 N Orangethorpe Way Anaheim (92801) ***(P-16409)***
Crescomfg.com, Anaheim *Also called Cresco Manufacturing Inc* ***(P-16409)***
Crest Beverage LLC ....B....858 452-2300
8870 Liquid Ct San Diego (92121) ***(P-717)***
Crest Coating Inc ....D....714 635-7090
1361 S Allec St Anaheim (92805) ***(P-13572)***
Crestec Los Angeles, Long Beach *Also called Crestec Usa Inc* ***(P-6769)***
Crestec Usa Inc ....E....310 327-9000
2410 Mira Mar Ave Long Beach (90815) ***(P-6769)***
Crestmark Architractural Mill ....E....707 822-4034
5640 West End Rd Arcata (95521) ***(P-4131)***
Crestone LLC ....E....323 588-8857
1852 E 46th St Vernon (90058) ***(P-3575)***
Crestor Inc ....F....831 475-4435
23 Rockview Dr Santa Cruz (95062) ***(P-11773)***
Crew Knitwear LLC (PA) ....D....323 526-3888
660 S Myers St Los Angeles (90023) ***(P-3398)***
Crew Wine Company LLC ....F....530 662-1032
12300 County Rd 92b Zamora (95698) ***(P-1711)***
CRGsynergy ....E....415 497-0182
21 Commercial Blvd Ste 14 Novato (94949) ***(P-21508)***
Cri 2000 LP (PA) ....E....619 542-1975
2245 San Diego Ave # 125 San Diego (92110) ***(P-4617)***
Cri Sub 1 (HQ) ....E....310 537-1657
1715 S Anderson Ave Compton (90220) ***(P-4941)***
Cricket Company LLC ....E....415 475-4150
68 Leveroni Ct Ste 200 Novato (94949) ***(P-9604)***
Crimson Resource Management, Bakersfield *Also called Delta Trading LP* ***(P-9381)***
Crimson Resource MGT Corp ....E....303 892-8878
5001 California Ave # 206 Bakersfield (93309) ***(P-54)***
Crimson Wine Group Ltd (PA) ....C....800 486-0503
2700 Napa Vly Corp Dr B NAPA (94558) ***(P-1712)***
Crinetics Pharmaceuticals Inc ....E....858 450-6464
10222 Barnes Canyon Rd # 200 San Diego (92121) ***(P-8127)***
Crisi Medical Systems Inc ....F....858 754-8640
9191 Towne Centre Dr # 330 San Diego (92122) ***(P-8128)***
Crisol Metal Finishing ....F....310 516-1165
444 E Gardena Blvd C Gardena (90248) ***(P-13382)***
Crispin Cider Company (HQ) ....E....530 346-9699
1213 S Auburn St Ste A Colfax (95713) ***(P-2496)***
Crispin Cider Works, The, Colfax *Also called Crispinian Inc* ***(P-1582)***
Crispinian Inc ....E....530 346-8411
1213 S Auburn St Ste A Colfax (95713) ***(P-1582)***
Crissair Inc ....C....661 367-3300
28909 Avenue Williams Valencia (91355) ***(P-16163)***
Cristal Materials Inc ....F....323 855-1688
6825 Mckinley Ave Los Angeles (90001) ***(P-4857)***
Cristek Interconnects Inc (PA) ....C....888 265-9162
5395 E Hunter Ave Anaheim (92807) ***(P-19384)***
Criterion Automation Inc ....F....951 683-2400
1722 Production Cir Riverside (92509) ***(P-11478)***

Criterion Catalysts & Tech LP D 925 458-9045
2840 Willow Pass Rd Bay Point (94565) *(P-7767)*
Criterion Composites Inc F 714 554-2717
14349 Commerce Dr Garden Grove (92843) *(P-21100)*
Criterion Machine Works E 949 631-5444
765 W 16th St Costa Mesa (92627) *(P-14621)*
Critical Io LLC F 949 553-2200
36 Executive Park Ste 150 Irvine (92614) *(P-15724)*
Criticalpoint Capital LLC D 909 987-9533
9433 Hyssop Dr Rancho Cucamonga (91730) *(P-7904)*
Crittenden Publishing Inc (HQ) F 415 475-1522
45 Leveroni Ct Ste 204 Novato (94949) *(P-6464)*
Crittenden Research Inc (PA) E 415 475-1576
45 Leveroni Ct Novato (94949) *(P-6465)*
Criveller California Corp F 707 431-2211
185 Grant Ave Healdsburg (95448) *(P-14843)*
Crl Systems Inc D 510 351-3500
14798 Wicks Blvd San Leandro (94577) *(P-18080)*
Crm Co LLC (PA) E 949 263-9100
1301 Dove St Ste 940 Newport Beach (92660) *(P-9565)*
Crockett Graphics Inc (PA) D 805 987-8577
980 Avenida Acaso Camarillo (93012) *(P-5403)*
Crocs Inc F 714 568-0340
2800 N Main St Unit 724 Santa Ana (92705) *(P-9469)*
Crome Gallery, North Hollywood *Also called Alco Tech Inc (P-13161)*
Crookshanks Sales Co Inc E 559 992-5077
2375 Dairy Ave Corcoran (93212) *(P-11100)*
Crosno Construction Inc E 805 343-7437
819 Sheridan Rd Arroyo Grande (93420) *(P-12976)*
Crossbar Inc E 408 884-0281
3200 Patrick Henry Dr # 110 Santa Clara (95054) *(P-18792)*
Crossfield Products Corp (PA) D 310 886-9100
3000 E Harcourt St Compton (90221) *(P-7827)*
Crossing Automation Inc (HQ) E 510 661-5000
46702 Bayside Pkwy Fremont (94538) *(P-14932)*
Crossing Press, The, Emeryville *Also called Elaine Gill Inc (P-6338)*
Crossport Mocean F 949 646-1701
1611 Babcock St Newport Beach (92663) *(P-3027)*
Crossroads Recycled Lumber LLC F 559 877-3645
58500 Hancock Way North Fork (93643) *(P-4035)*
Crossroads Software Inc F 714 990-6433
210 W Birch St Ste 207 Brea (92821) *(P-24532)*
Crosstex International Inc F 562 921-3343
14059 Stage Rd Santa Fe Springs (90670) *(P-22863)*
Crowdoptic, San Francisco *Also called Kba2 Inc (P-24826)*
Crower Cams, San Diego *Also called Crower Engrg & Sls Co Inc (P-20301)*
Crower Engrg & Sls Co Inc C 619 690-7810
6180 Business Center Ct San Diego (92154) *(P-20301)*
Crower's Marketing, Vernon *Also called Pages Produce Company (P-848)*
Crown Carton Company Inc E 323 582-3053
1820 E 48th Pl Vernon (90058) *(P-5404)*
Crown Circuits Inc D 949 922-0144
6070 Avenida Encinas Carlsbad (92011) *(P-18461)*
Crown Citrus Company Inc F 760 344-1930
551 W Main St Brawley (92227) *(P-945)*
Crown Discount Tools, Sylmar *Also called TMW Corporation (P-20952)*
Crown Equipment Corporation E 559 585-8000
1355 E Fntana Ave Ste 102 Fresno (93725) *(P-14316)*
Crown Equipment Corporation D 626 968-0556
1300 Palomares St La Verne (91750) *(P-14317)*
Crown Equipment Corporation C 909 923-8357
4250 Greystone Dr Ontario (91761) *(P-14318)*
Crown Equipment Corporation E 510 471-7272
1400 Crocker Ave Hayward (94544) *(P-14319)*
Crown Equipment Corporation E 916 373-8980
1420 Enterprise Blvd West Sacramento (95691) *(P-14320)*
Crown Equipment Corporation D 310 952-6600
4061 Via Oro Ave Long Beach (90810) *(P-14321)*
Crown Fashion, Los Angeles *Also called Grand West Inc (P-2841)*
Crown Lift Trucks, La Verne *Also called Crown Equipment Corporation (P-14317)*
Crown Lift Trucks, Ontario *Also called Crown Equipment Corporation (P-14318)*
Crown Lift Trucks, Hayward *Also called Crown Equipment Corporation (P-14319)*
Crown Lift Trucks, West Sacramento *Also called Crown Equipment Corporation (P-14320)*
Crown Lift Trucks, Long Beach *Also called Crown Equipment Corporation (P-14321)*
Crown Mfg Co Inc E 510 742-8800
37625 Sycamore St Newark (94560) *(P-10051)*
Crown Micro, Fremont *Also called Bold Data Technology Inc (P-15395)*
Crown Pallet Company Inc E 626 937-6565
15151 Salt Lake Ave La Puente (91746) *(P-4463)*
Crown Paper Converting Inc E 909 923-5226
1380 S Bon View Ave Ontario (91761) *(P-5707)*
Crown Poly Inc C 323 268-1298
5700 Bickett St Huntington Park (90255) *(P-5596)*
Crown Printers, San Bernardino *Also called Shorett Printing Inc (P-7482)*
Crown Printers Anaheim, San Bernardino *Also called Shorett Printing Inc (P-7104)*
Crown Products Inc E 760 471-1188
177 Newport Dr Ste A San Marcos (92069) *(P-12544)*
Crown Steel, San Marcos *Also called Crown Products Inc (P-12544)*
Crown Technical Systems C 909 923-0900
13470 Philadelphia Ave Fontana (92337) *(P-17137)*
CRP Sports LLC F 949 395-7759
3191 Red Hill Ave Ste 250 Costa Mesa (92626) *(P-24070)*
Crt Color Printing Inc F 562 906-1517
13201 Barton Cir Santa Fe Springs (90670) *(P-6770)*
Crucial Power Products F 323 721-5017
14000 S Broadway Los Angeles (90061) *(P-19502)*
Crunch LLC E 650 257-8000
1190 Saratoga Ave San Jose (95129) *(P-24533)*
Crunch Metals Co Inc F 714 897-0552
15645 Commerce Ln Huntington Beach (92649) *(P-12545)*
Crush Master Grinding Corp E 909 595-2249
755 Penarth Ave Walnut (91789) *(P-16410)*
Crydom Inc (HQ) B 619 210-1590
2320 Paseo Delas Amer 2 San Diego (92154) *(P-17263)*
Cryogenic Industries, Murrieta *Also called Hexco International (P-14965)*
Cryogenic Machinery Corp F 818 765-6688
7306 Greenbush Ave North Hollywood (91605) *(P-14933)*
Cryopacific Incorporated F 562 697-7904
641 S Palm St Ste G La Habra (90631) *(P-24071)*
Cryoport Systems Inc (HQ) F 949 540-7204
17305 Daimler St Irvine (92614) *(P-14934)*
Cryoquip LLC (HQ) F 951 677-2060
25720 Jefferson Ave Murrieta (92562) *(P-14935)*
Cryostar USA, Whittier *Also called Linde LLC (P-7695)*
Cryostar USA LLC E 562 903-1290
13117 Meyer Rd Whittier (90605) *(P-15058)*
Cryoworks Inc E 951 360-0920
3309 Grapevine St Mira Loma (91752) *(P-13883)*
Cryptic Studios Inc D 408 399-1969
980 University Ave Los Gatos (95032) *(P-23417)*
Cryst Mark Inc A Swan Techno C E 818 240-7520
613 Justin Ave Glendale (91201) *(P-14936)*
Crystal Basin Cellars F 530 303-3749
3550 Carson Rd Camino (95709) *(P-1713)*
Crystal Bottling Company Inc D 916 568-3300
8631 Younger Creek Dr Sacramento (95828) *(P-2123)*
Crystal Cal Lab Inc E 714 991-1580
3981 E Miraloma Ave Anaheim (92806) *(P-19503)*
Crystal Craft, La Verne *Also called Pf Plastics Inc (P-4916)*
Crystal Cream & Butter Co (HQ) D 916 444-7200
8340 Belvedere Ave Sacramento (95826) *(P-718)*
Crystal Dynamics Inc D 650 421-7600
1400a Saport Blvd Ste 300 Redwood City (94063) *(P-24534)*
Crystal Engineering Corp E 805 595-5477
708 Fiero Ln Ste 9 San Luis Obispo (93401) *(P-21567)*
Crystal Geyser Alpine Spring W, Olancha *Also called Cg Roxane LLC (P-2111)*
Crystal Geyser Water Company E 707 647-4410
5001 Fermi Dr Fairfield (94534) *(P-2124)*
Crystal Geyser Water Company E 661 323-6296
1233 E California Ave Bakersfield (93307) *(P-2125)*
Crystal Geyser Water Company F 661 321-0896
2351 E Brundage Ln Ste A Bakersfield (93307) *(P-2126)*
Crystal Lake Grinders D 559 297-0737
1497 Menlo Ave Ste B Clovis (93611) *(P-16411)*
Crystal Lighting Corp F 562 944-0223
13182 Flores St Santa Fe Springs (90670) *(P-17595)*
Crystal Mark, Glendale *Also called Cryst Mark Inc A Swan Techno C (P-14936)*
Crystal Mining Corporation F 386 479-5823
20380 Stevens Creek Blvd Cupertino (95014) *(P-2)*
Crystal Mountain Springwater, Sacramento *Also called Crystal Bottling Company Inc (P-2123)*
Crystal Solar Inc F 408 490-1340
3050 Coronado Dr Santa Clara (95054) *(P-18793)*
Crystal Technology, Fremont *Also called Gooch & Housego Palo Alto LLC (P-19555)*
Crystal Tex Shoehorn, Downey *Also called Van Grace Quality Injection (P-10428)*
Crystal Vision Packg Systems, Torrance *Also called Aviation and Indus Dev Corp (P-9698)*
Crystaliner Corp E 949 548-0292
1626 Placentia Ave Costa Mesa (92627) *(P-21027)*
Crystolon Inc E 323 725-3482
7223 Sycamore St Commerce (90040) *(P-5135)*
Cs Electronics, Irvine *Also called Cs Systems Inc (P-15725)*
Cs Manfacturing Indus Svcs Inc (PA) F 760 890-7746
619 Paulin Ave Ste 105 Calexico (92231) *(P-19385)*
Cs Systems Inc E 949 475-9100
16781 Noyes Ave Irvine (92606) *(P-15725)*
CSC Ranch, Corcoran *Also called Crookshanks Sales Co Inc (P-11100)*
Csdr International Inc F 844 330-0664
7701 Woodley Ave Van Nuys (91406) *(P-18794)*
CSDS, Sacramento *Also called California Surveying & Draftin (P-15698)*
Csg, Lakeside *Also called Coating Services Group LLC (P-13569)*
Csi Technologies Inc F 760 682-2222
2540 Fortune Way Vista (92081) *(P-19293)*
Csl Operating LLC D 408 727-0893
529 Aldo Ave Santa Clara (95054) *(P-13383)*
CSM Metal Fabricating & Engrg, Los Angeles *Also called Commercial Sheet Metal Works (P-12138)*
Csp Inc F 562 470-7236
6250 N Paramount Blvd Long Beach (90805) *(P-15726)*
Csr Technology Inc (HQ) C 408 523-6500
1060 Rincon Cir San Jose (95131) *(P-19504)*
CSS Global F 530 268-3324
13487 Ranchero Way Grass Valley (95949) *(P-11891)*
CST Power and Construction Inc (HQ) D 310 523-2322
879 W 190th St Ste 1100 Gardena (90248) *(P-11615)*
CT Coachworks LLC F 951 343-8787
9700 Indiana Ave Riverside (92503) *(P-20522)*
CT Oldenkamp LLC F 760 200-9510
78380 Clarke Ct La Quinta (92253) *(P-23789)*
CTA Fixtures Inc D 909 390-6744
5721 Santa Ana St Ste B Ontario (91761) *(P-5051)*
CTA Manufacturing Inc E 951 280-2400
1160 California Ave Corona (92881) *(P-3762)*
Ctc Global Corporation (PA) C 949 428-8500
2026 Mcgaw Ave Irvine (92614) *(P-17457)*
Ctd Machines Inc F 213 689-4455
2382 E 48th St Vernon (90058) *(P-14366)*

A L P H A B E T I C

Employee Codes: A=Over 500 employees, B=251-500
C=101-250, D=51-100, E=20-50, F=10-19
2019 California
Manfacturers Register
© Mergent Inc. 1-800-342-5647
1111

Ctg, Santa Barbara *Also called Alta Properties Inc* ***(P-10816)***
Ctg, Emeryville *Also called I3 Nanotec LLC* ***(P-14967)***
Ctg I LLC....F....415 233-9700
600 California St Fl 11 San Francisco (94108) ***(P-6466)***
CTI, Rancho Cordova *Also called Chemical Technologies Intl Inc* ***(P-16023)***
Cti-Controltech Inc....F....925 208-4250
22 Beta Ct San Ramon (94583) ***(P-17264)***
Ctra Industrial Machine....F....562 698-5188
11817 Slauson Ave Santa Fe Springs (90670) ***(P-14791)***
CTS Cement Manufacturing Corp (PA)....E....714 379-8260
12442 Knott St Garden Grove (92841) ***(P-9136)***
CTS Cement Manufacturing Corp....E....562 802-2660
13846 Firestone Blvd Santa Fe Springs (90670) ***(P-5639)***
CTS Cement Manufacturing Corp....F....310 472-4004
2077 Linda Flora Dr Los Angeles (90077) ***(P-9137)***
CTS Corporation....C....408 955-9001
2271 Ringwood Ave San Jose (95131) ***(P-18462)***
CTS Fabrication USA Inc....F....916 852-6303
11220 Pyrites Way Ste 300 Gold River (95670) ***(P-11573)***
CTS Printing....F....562 941-8420
9920 Jordan Cir Santa Fe Springs (90670) ***(P-6771)***
CTT Inc (PA)....D....408 541-0596
5870 Hellyer Ave Ste 70 San Jose (95138) ***(P-18081)***
Ctu Precast, Olivehurst *Also called Precast Con Tech Unlimited LLC* ***(P-10978)***
Cuadra Associates Inc (PA)....F....310 591-2490
3415 S Sepulveda Blvd # 3 Los Angeles (90034) ***(P-24535)***
Cuahutemoc Tortilleria....E....323 262-0410
3455 E 1st St Los Angeles (90063) ***(P-2497)***
Cubic Corporation (PA)....A....858 277-6780
9333 Balboa Ave San Diego (92123) ***(P-21280)***
Cubic Defense Applications Inc....D....619 661-1010
2055 Dublin Dr Ste 200 San Diego (92154) ***(P-21281)***
Cubic Defense Applications Inc....C....858 505-2870
9333 Balboa Ave San Diego (92123) ***(P-19935)***
Cubic Defense Applications Inc (HQ)....A....858 277-6780
9333 Balboa Ave San Diego (92123) ***(P-19936)***
Cubic Trnsp Systems Inc (HQ)....A....858 268-3100
5650 Kearny Mesa Rd San Diego (92111) ***(P-22182)***
Cubic Trnsp Systems Inc....C....925 348-9163
1800 Sutter St Ste 900 Concord (94520) ***(P-22183)***
Cubic Zee Jewelry Inc....F....213 614-9800
728 S Hill St Ste 900 Los Angeles (90014) ***(P-23254)***
Cucamonga Division, Rancho Cucamonga *Also called Western Metal Dctg Co Coil Div* ***(P-7180)***
Cucina Holdings Inc....F....415 986-8688
4 Embarcadero Ctr Lbby 4 # 4 San Francisco (94111) ***(P-1227)***
Cuddly Toys....F....323 980-0572
1833 N Eastern Ave Los Angeles (90032) ***(P-23394)***
Cue Health Inc....E....256 651-1656
11175 Flintkote Ave San Diego (92121) ***(P-8471)***
Cue Technologies Inc....F....949 362-4002
823 Tumbleweed Ln Fallbrook (92028) ***(P-15527)***
Cuetech, Fallbrook *Also called Cue Technologies Inc* ***(P-15527)***
Cuevas Mattress Inc....F....310 631-8382
3504 E Olympic Blvd Los Angeles (90023) ***(P-4858)***
Cuiti International, Rancho Cucamonga *Also called Ciuti International Inc* ***(P-1538)***
Culinary Brands Inc....C....626 289-3000
3280 E 44th St Vernon (90058) ***(P-988)***
Culinary Farms Inc....E....916 375-3000
1244 E Beamer St Woodland (95776) ***(P-881)***
Culinary International LLC....C....626 289-3000
3280 E 44th St Vernon (90058) ***(P-2498)***
Culinary Specialties Inc....D....760 744-8220
1231 Linda Vista Dr San Marcos (92078) ***(P-2499)***
Cult Cvlt....F....714 435-2858
1555 E Saint Gertrude Pl Santa Ana (92705) ***(P-21101)***
Culture AMP Inc (HQ)....E....415 326-8453
660 Market St Ste 500 San Francisco (94104) ***(P-24536)***
Cultured Stone Corporation (HQ)....A....707 255-1727
Hwy 29 & Tower Rd NAPA (94559) ***(P-10912)***
Cummings Resources LLC....E....951 248-1130
1495 Columbia Ave Riverside (92507) ***(P-23852)***
Cummings Transportation, Shafter *Also called Cummings Vacuum Service Inc* ***(P-202)***
Cummings Vacuum Service Inc....D....661 746-1786
19605 Broken Ct Shafter (93263) ***(P-202)***
Cummins Aerospace, Anaheim *Also called Yeager Manufacturing Corp* ***(P-20976)***
Cummins Electrified Power NA....F....408 624-1231
1181 Cadillac Ct Milpitas (95035) ***(P-20302)***
Cummins Inc....E....510 351-6101
14775 Wicks Blvd San Leandro (94577) ***(P-14015)***
Cummins Pacific LLC....F....707 822-7392
5150 Boyd Rd Arcata (95521) ***(P-14016)***
Cummins Pacific LLC....F....530 244-6898
5125 Caterpillar Rd Redding (96003) ***(P-14017)***
Cummins Pacific LLC....E....916 371-0630
875 Riverside Pkwy West Sacramento (95605) ***(P-14018)***
Cummins Pacific LLC....E....866 934-4373
9520 Stewart And Gray Rd Downey (90241) ***(P-14019)***
Cummins Pacific LLC....E....909 877-0433
3061 S Riverside Ave Bloomington (92316) ***(P-14020)***
Cummins Pacific LLC....D....559 277-6760
5333 N Cornelia Ave Fresno (93722) ***(P-14021)***
Cummins Pacific LLC....E....661 325-9404
4601 E Brundage Ln Bakersfield (93307) ***(P-14022)***
Cummins Pacific LLC (HQ)....D....949 253-6000
1939 Deere Ave Irvine (92606) ***(P-14023)***
Cummins Pacific LLC....E....619 593-3093
310 N Johnson Ave El Cajon (92020) ***(P-14024)***
Cummins Pacific LLC....E....805 644-7281
3958 Transport St Ventura (93003) ***(P-14025)***
Cumulus Networks Inc (PA)....C....650 383-6700
185 E Dana St Mountain View (94041) ***(P-24537)***
Cuora Corporation....E....916 991-3028
2401 Q St Rio Linda (95673) ***(P-4571)***
Cupertronix Inc....F....408 887-5455
2946 Via Torino Santa Clara (95051) ***(P-21941)***
Cura Medical Technologies LLC....F....949 939-4406
1365 S Acacia Ave Fullerton (92831) ***(P-22931)***
Curapharm Inc....F....619 449-7388
10054 Prospect Ave Ste A Santee (92071) ***(P-22414)***
Curbell Plastics Inc....E....619 575-4633
1670 Brandywine Ave Ste B Chula Vista (91911) ***(P-10052)***
Cure Apparel LLC....F....562 927-7460
3338 S Malt Ave Commerce (90040) ***(P-3227)***
Cure Medical LLC (PA)....F....800 570-1778
3471 Via Lido Ste 211 Newport Beach (92663) ***(P-22415)***
Cure Pharmaceutical Corp....E....805 487-7163
1620 Beacon Pl Oxnard (93033) ***(P-8129)***
Curlin Healthcare Products Inc....D....714 893-2200
15751 Graham St Huntington Beach (92649) ***(P-16412)***
Curran Engineering Company Inc....E....800 643-6353
28727 Industry Dr Valencia (91355) ***(P-12847)***
Current Enterprises Modular, Pasadena *Also called Current Modular Inc* ***(P-4572)***
Current Modular Inc....E....909 792-9207
141 S Lake Ave Fl 2 Pasadena (91101) ***(P-4572)***
Current Ways Inc....F....619 596-3984
10221 Buena Vista Ave Santee (92071) ***(P-17339)***
Currie Enterprises....E....714 528-6957
382 N Smith Ave Corona (92880) ***(P-20303)***
Curry Graphics, Hayward *Also called Trade Only Screen Printing Inc* ***(P-7524)***
Curtco Media Group LLC....F....310 589-7700
29160 Heathercliff Rd # 1 Malibu (90265) ***(P-6138)***
Curtco Robb Media LLC (PA)....E....310 589-7700
29160 Heathercliff Rd # 1 Malibu (90265) ***(P-6139)***
Curtis Instruments Inc....D....925 961-1088
235 E Airway Blvd Livermore (94551) ***(P-21683)***
Curtis PMC, Livermore *Also called Curtis Instruments Inc* ***(P-21683)***
Curtis Technology Inc....F....858 453-5797
11391 Sorrento Valley Rd San Diego (92121) ***(P-19505)***
Curtis Winery, Los Olivos *Also called Firestone Vineyard LP* ***(P-1763)***
Curtiss-Wrght Nuclear-Enertech, Brea *Also called Curtiss-Wright Flow Control* ***(P-13715)***
Curtiss-Wright Controls....E....714 982-1860
210 Ranger Ave Brea (92821) ***(P-22715)***
Curtiss-Wright Corporation....E....661 257-4430
28965 Avenue Penn Santa Clarita (91355) ***(P-13714)***
Curtiss-Wright Flow Control....D....714 528-2301
2950 E Birch St Brea (92821) ***(P-13715)***
Cushion Works....F....760 321-7808
68929 Perez Rd Ste B Cathedral City (92234) ***(P-3716)***
Cushion Works Inc....F....415 552-6220
3320 18th St San Francisco (94110) ***(P-3763)***
Custom AG Formulators Inc (PA)....D....559 435-1052
3430 S Willow Ave Fresno (93725) ***(P-9099)***
Custom Aircraft Interiors Inc....F....562 426-5098
3701 Industry Ave Lakewood (90712) ***(P-20788)***
Custom Alloy Light Metals, City of Industry *Also called Custom Alloy Sales Inc* ***(P-11554)***
Custom Alloy Sales Inc (PA)....D....626 369-3641
13191 Crssrds Pkwy N 37 City of Industry (91746) ***(P-11554)***
Custom Art Services Corp....F....951 302-9889
37110 Mesa Rd Temecula (92592) ***(P-6772)***
Custom Aviation Supply, Chatsworth *Also called Custom Control Sensors LLC* ***(P-17138)***
Custom Blenders Corporation....F....510 635-4352
39 California Ave Ste 108 Pleasanton (94566) ***(P-8590)***
Custom Blow Molding, Escondido *Also called Pretium Packaging LLC* ***(P-9806)***
Custom Building Products Inc (HQ)....D....800 272-8786
7711 Center Ave Ste 500 Huntington Beach (92647) ***(P-9138)***
Custom Building Products Inc....D....323 582-0846
6511 Salt Lake Ave Bell (90201) ***(P-9139)***
Custom Building Products Inc....E....209 983-8322
3525 Zephyr Ct Stockton (95206) ***(P-14162)***
Custom Characters Inc....F....818 507-5940
621 Thompson Ave Glendale (91201) ***(P-3652)***
Custom Chemical Formulators, Santa Fe Springs *Also called Morgan Gallacher Inc* ***(P-8656)***
Custom Chemical Formulators, Santa Fe Springs *Also called Jad Chemical Inc* ***(P-9014)***
Custom Chrome Manufacturing....C....408 825-5000
155 E Main Ave Ste 150 Morgan Hill (95037) ***(P-21102)***
Custom Coils Inc....F....707 752-8633
4000 Industrial Way Benicia (94510) ***(P-19330)***
Custom Control Sensors LLC (PA)....C....818 341-4610
21111 Plummer St Chatsworth (91311) ***(P-17138)***
Custom Converting Inc....F....760 724-0664
2625 Temple Heights Dr C Oceanside (92056) ***(P-9832)***
Custom Cooperage Innerstave, Sonoma *Also called Innerstave LLC* ***(P-4524)***
Custom Crushing Industries....F....530 842-5544
2409 E Oberlin Rd Yreka (96097) ***(P-17)***
Custom Deacals & Emblems, El Cajon *Also called Custom Decals & Emblems Inc* ***(P-7291)***
Custom Decals & Emblems Inc....E....619 449-5611
1900 Weld Blvd Ste 120 El Cajon (92020) ***(P-7291)***
Custom Design Iron Works Inc....F....818 700-9182
9182 Kelvin Ave Chatsworth (91311) ***(P-11711)***
Custom Displays Inc....E....323 770-8074
411 W 157th St Gardena (90248) ***(P-5052)***
Custom Enamelers Inc....E....714 540-7884
18340 Mount Baldy Cir Fountain Valley (92708) ***(P-13573)***
Custom Engineering Plastics LP....F....858 452-0961
8558 Miramar Pl San Diego (92121) ***(P-10053)***
Custom Equipment Coinc....F....209 785-9891
90 Rock Creek Rd Ste 9 Copperopolis (95228) ***(P-14055)***

Mergent e-mail: customerrelations@mergent.com 2019 California (P-0000) Products & Services Section entry number
1112 Manufacturers Register (PA)=Parent Co (HQ)=Headquarters (DH)=Div Headquarters

Custom Fabricated Metals LLC ....F....909 822-8828
14580 Manzanita Dr Fontana (92335) ***(P-12546)***
Custom Fibreglass Mfg Co ....C....562 432-5454
1711 Harbor Ave Long Beach (90813) ***(P-21200)***
Custom Foods, Santa Fe Springs *Also called J & J Processing Inc* ***(P-2269)***
Custom Formulations Corp ....F....310 516-8273
1243 W 130th St Gardena (90247) ***(P-7930)***
Custom Framing Service, Van Nuys *Also called Kutzin & Kutzin Inc* ***(P-4630)***
Custom Furniture Design Inc ....E....916 631-6300
3340 Sunrise Blvd Ste F Rancho Cordova (95742) ***(P-4289)***
Custom Goods Warehouse, Rancho Cucamonga *Also called Molex LLC* ***(P-19402)***
Custom Hardtops, Long Beach *Also called Custom Fibreglass Mfg Co* ***(P-21200)***
Custom Hardware Mfg Inc ....E....714 547-7440
2112 E 4th St Ste 228g Santa Ana (92705) ***(P-11950)***
Custom Home Accessories, Rancho Cordova *Also called Penfield Products Inc* ***(P-12712)***
Custom Industries Inc ....E....714 779-9101
1371 N Miller St Anaheim (92806) ***(P-10687)***
Custom Installations ....F....619 445-0692
1452 Hawks Vista Ln Alpine (91901) ***(P-4290)***
Custom Interior Designs, Pico Rivera *Also called Custom Interiors Design Fixs* ***(P-5225)***
Custom Interiors Design Fixs ....E....562 942-7969
7800 Industry Ave Pico Rivera (90660) ***(P-5225)***
Custom Label, Woodland *Also called Sachs Industries Inc* ***(P-5731)***
Custom Label and Decal LLC ....E....510 876-0000
3392 Investment Blvd Hayward (94545) ***(P-7292)***
Custom Labeling & Btlg Corp ....F....408 371-6171
15005 Concord Cir Morgan Hill (95037) ***(P-2127)***
Custom Leathercraft Mfg LLC (PA) ....E....323 752-2221
10240 Alameda St South Gate (90280) ***(P-10573)***
Custom Lithograph ....E....323 778-7751
7006 Stanford Ave Los Angeles (90001) ***(P-6773)***
Custom Marble & Onyx, Modesto *Also called Sharcar Enterprises Inc* ***(P-11278)***
Custom Mechanical Systems LLC ....F....510 347-5500
1830 Embarcadero Ste 103 Oakland (94606) ***(P-15948)***
Custom Metal Finishing Corp ....E....310 532-5075
17804 S Western Ave Gardena (90248) ***(P-14937)***
Custom Metal Works ....F....714 953-5481
2233 W 2nd St Santa Ana (92703) ***(P-12848)***
Custom Mfg LLC ....F....562 944-0245
12946 Los Nietos Rd Santa Fe Springs (90670) ***(P-16413)***
Custom Micro Machining Inc ....E....510 651-9434
707 Brown Rd Fremont (94539) ***(P-16414)***
Custom Microwave Components ....F....510 651-3434
44249 Old Warm Sprng Blvd Fremont (94538) ***(P-19506)***
Custom Molded Devices, Simi Valley *Also called Poly-Tainer Inc* ***(P-9805)***
Custom Muldings Sash Doors Inc ....F....818 787-7367
7732 Densmore Ave Ste A Van Nuys (91406) ***(P-4132)***
Custom Pack Inc ....F....714 534-2201
11621 Cardinal Cir Garden Grove (92843) ***(P-10619)***
Custom Packaging Design, Montclair *Also called Cpd Industries* ***(P-9831)***
Custom Pad and Partition Inc ....D....408 970-9711
1100 Richard Ave Santa Clara (95050) ***(P-5405)***
Custom Paper Products ....D....510 352-6880
2360 Teagarden St San Leandro (94577) ***(P-5375)***
Custom Pipe & Coupling Co Inc, Stanton *Also called Custom Pipe & Fabrication Inc* ***(P-13884)***
Custom Pipe & Fabrication Inc (HQ) ....D....800 553-3058
10560 Fern Ave Stanton (90680) ***(P-13884)***
Custom Plastics LLC (PA) ....F....909 984-0200
1305 Brooks St Ontario (91762) ***(P-10054)***
Custom Printing, Oxnard *Also called Pine Grove Industries Inc* ***(P-7027)***
Custom Quality Door & Trim Inc ....F....951 278-0066
1116 Bradford Cir Corona (92882) ***(P-4133)***
Custom Quilting Inc ....F....949 455-7337
2832 Walnut Ave Ste D Tustin (92780) ***(P-3717)***
Custom Quilting Inc (PA) ....F....714 731-7271
2832 Walnut Ave Ste D Tustin (92780) ***(P-3718)***
Custom Sensors & Tech Inc (PA) ....D....805 716-0322
1461 Lawrence Dr Thousand Oaks (91320) ***(P-19507)***
Custom Silicone Technologies, Pacoima *Also called Kdl Precision Molding Corp* ***(P-21194)***
Custom Source Design Inc ....F....909 597-5221
15642 Dupont Ave Ste A Chino (91710) ***(P-12146)***
Custom Steel Fabrication Inc ....F....562 907-2777
11966 Rivera Rd Santa Fe Springs (90670) ***(P-12147)***
Custom Tooling & Automation, Anaheim *Also called Custom Tooling & Stamping of O* ***(P-14502)***
Custom Tooling & Stamping of O ....F....714 979-6782
1182 N Knollwood Cir Anaheim (92801) ***(P-14502)***
Custom Upholstered Furn Inc ....F....323 731-3033
5000 W Jefferson Blvd Los Angeles (90016) ***(P-4767)***
Custom Wheels and ACC Inc ....F....714 827-5200
41710 Reagan Way Murrieta (92562) ***(P-20304)***
Custom Window Design Inc ....E....760 439-6213
3242 Production Ave Oceanside (92058) ***(P-4134)***
Custom Wire Products ....F....619 469-2328
7580 North Ave Lemon Grove (91945) ***(P-13822)***
Custom Wood Products, Parlier *Also called John Daniel Gonzalez* ***(P-4526)***
Custom X Body Boards, Oceanside *Also called Superior Foam Products Inc* ***(P-23666)***
Customplanetcom Inc ....F....760 508-2648
12180 Ridgecrest Rd # 314 Victorville (92395) ***(P-7293)***
Custopharm Inc (PA) ....F....760 683-0901
2325 Camino Vida Roble A Carlsbad (92011) ***(P-14938)***
Cut & Trim Inc ....F....818 264-0101
20847 Betron St Woodland Hills (91364) ***(P-3228)***
Cut Loose (PA) ....D....415 822-2031
101 Williams Ave San Francisco (94124) ***(P-3399)***
Cutera Inc (PA) ....C....415 657-5500
3240 Bayshore Blvd Brisbane (94005) ***(P-22968)***
Cutie Pie Snack Pies, Lathrop *Also called Horizon Snack Foods Inc* ***(P-1396)***
Cutter Lumber Products ....E....209 982-4477
4004 S El Dorado St Stockton (95206) ***(P-4464)***
Cutting Edge Creative LLC ....D....562 907-7007
8155 Byron Rd Whittier (90606) ***(P-5136)***
Cutting Edge Machining Inc (PA) ....E....408 738-8677
100 San Lucar Ct Sunnyvale (94086) ***(P-13020)***
Cutting Edge Supply, Colton *Also called Black Diamond Blade Company* ***(P-14146)***
Cutting Edge Wood Tech Inc ....E....714 447-3667
130 N Gilbert St Fullerton (92833) ***(P-4135)***
Cutwater Spirits LLC ....E....858 672-3848
9750 Distribution Ave San Diego (92121) ***(P-9238)***
Cv Ice Company Inc ....E....760 347-3529
83796 Date Ave Indio (92201) ***(P-2411)***
Cv of Riverside, Riverside *Also called CV Wndows Dors Riverside Inc* ***(P-10688)***
Cv Sciences Inc ....F....866 290-2157
10070 Barnes Canyon Rd San Diego (92121) ***(P-7931)***
Cv Sciences Inc ....F....619 546-8112
5121 Santa Fe St Ste F La Jolla (92037) ***(P-8130)***
CV Wndows Dors Riverside Inc ....E....951 784-8766
6676 Lance Dr Riverside (92507) ***(P-10688)***
Cvag, Oakdale *Also called Central Valley AG Grinding Inc* ***(P-1035)***
Cvc Audio & Video Supply Inc ....F....714 526-5725
425 Cheyenne Pl Placentia (92870) ***(P-19859)***
Cvc Specialties, Vernon *Also called Continental Vitamin Co Inc* ***(P-8120)***
Cvc Technologies Inc ....E....909 355-0311
10861 Business Dr Fontana (92337) ***(P-15204)***
Cvps Inc ....E....707 998-9364
9514 Glenhaven Dr Glenhaven (95443) ***(P-24538)***
Cvr Nitrogen LP (HQ) ....F....310 571-9800
10877 Wilshire Blvd Fl 10 Los Angeles (90024) ***(P-9059)***
Cw Industries ....F....562 432-5421
1735 Santa Fe Ave Long Beach (90813) ***(P-12148)***
CW Welding Service Inc (PA) ....E....562 432-5421
1735 Santa Fe Ave Long Beach (90813) ***(P-25397)***
Cwi Trading ....F....209 981-7023
714 Elaine Dr Stockton (95207) ***(P-17511)***
Cwic, Rcho STA Marg *Also called Chapmn-Wlters Intrcoastal Corp* ***(P-23539)***
Cwr Labs, Mountain View *Also called Cpacket Networks Inc* ***(P-15722)***
Cws, Orange *Also called Coil Winding Specialist Inc* ***(P-19326)***
Cws Beverage ....F....805 286-2735
2732 Danley Ct Ste 101 Paso Robles (93446) ***(P-1583)***
CWT, Los Angeles *Also called Clean Water Technology Inc* ***(P-16027)***
Cxc Simulations LLC ....F....888 918-2010
3160 W El Segundo Blvd Hawthorne (90250) ***(P-19937)***
Cy Truss ....E....559 888-2160
10715 E American Ave Del Rey (93616) ***(P-4401)***
Cyantek Corporation ....E....510 651-3341
3055 Osgood Ct Fremont (94539) ***(P-9239)***
Cyber Mdia Solutions Ltd Lblty ....E....877 480-8255
23161 Lake Center Dr # 220 Lake Forest (92630) ***(P-24539)***
Cyber Medical Imaging Inc ....E....888 937-9729
11300 W Olympic Blvd # 710 Los Angeles (90064) ***(P-22864)***
Cyber Press, Santa Clara *Also called Nss Enterprises* ***(P-7416)***
Cyber Switching Inc ....E....408 595-3670
2050 Ringwood Ave Frnt San Jose (95131) ***(P-19938)***
Cyberdata Corporation ....E....831 373-2601
3 Justin Ct Monterey (93940) ***(P-15727)***
Cyberlinkcom Corp ....F....408 217-1850
1073 S Winchester Blvd San Jose (95128) ***(P-24540)***
Cybernet Manufacturing Inc ....A....949 600-8000
5 Holland Ste 201 Irvine (92618) ***(P-15404)***
Cybernetic Micro Systems Inc ....F....650 726-3000
3000 La Honda Rd San Gregorio (94074) ***(P-15631)***
Cyberswitchingpatents LLC ....F....408 436-9830
1921 Ringwood Ave San Jose (95131) ***(P-19939)***
Cybertech, Pomona *Also called Bio Cybernetics International* ***(P-22705)***
Cybertouch, Newbury Park *Also called Transparent Devices Inc* ***(P-15874)***
Cyberware Laboratory Inc ....F....831 484-1064
12835 Corte Cordillera Salinas (93908) ***(P-21568)***
Cybortronics Incorporated ....F....949 855-2814
440 Nibus Brea (92821) ***(P-21942)***
Cybrex Consulting Inc ....D....513 999-2109
4470 W Sunset Blvd Los Angeles (90027) ***(P-24541)***
Cycle House LLC ....E....310 358-0888
8511 Melrose Ave West Hollywood (90069) ***(P-23546)***
Cycle News Inc (PA) ....E....949 863-7082
17771 Mitchell N Irvine (92614) ***(P-5819)***
Cycle Shack Inc ....D....650 583-7014
816 Murchison Dr Millbrae (94030) ***(P-21103)***
Cycle World Magazine, Irvine *Also called Hearst Corporation* ***(P-6179)***
Cydea Inc ....E....800 710-9939
8510 Miralani Dr San Diego (92126) ***(P-1584)***
Cydwoq Inc ....E....818 848-8307
2102 Kenmere Ave Burbank (91504) ***(P-10472)***
Cygnet Aerospace Corp ....F....805 528-2376
1971 Fearn Ave Los Osos (93402) ***(P-11732)***
Cygnet Stampng & Fabrictng Inc ....F....818 240-7574
916 Western Ave Glendale (91201) ***(P-13190)***
Cygnet Stampng & Fabrictng Inc (PA) ....E....818 240-7574
613 Justin Ave Glendale (91201) ***(P-13191)***
Cylance Inc (PA) ....C....949 375-3380
400 Spectrum Center Dr Irvine (92618) ***(P-24542)***
Cylinder Division, Corona *Also called Parker-Hannifin Corporation* ***(P-16170)***
Cylinder Head Exchange Inc ....F....818 364-2371
12677 San Fernando Rd Sylmar (91342) ***(P-20305)***
Cymabay Therapeutics Inc (PA) ....E....510 293-8800
7999 Gateway Blvd Ste 100 Newark (94560) ***(P-8131)***

ALPHABETIC

Employee Codes: A=Over 500 employees, B=251-500
C=101-250, D=51-100, E=20-50, F=10-19
2019 California
Manfacturers Register
© Mergent Inc. 1-800-342-5647
1113

Cymer LLC (HQ) .... A 858 385-7300
17075 Thornmint Ct San Diego (92127) *(P-19940)*

Cymmetria Inc .... E 415 568-6870
2557 Park Blvd Apt L106 Palo Alto (94306) *(P-24543)*

Cynergy3 Components Corp (PA) .... F 858 715-7200
2475 Pseo De Las Americas San Diego (92154) *(P-17265)*

Cynthia Garcia .... F 714 897-4654
11782 Western Ave Ste 7 Stanton (90680) *(P-20789)*

Cypress Furniture Inc .... F 510 723-4890
26602 Corporate Ave Hayward (94545) *(P-4687)*

Cypress Grove Chevre Inc .... D 707 825-1100
1330 Q St Arcata (95521) *(P-568)*

Cypress Magnetics Inc .... F 909 987-3570
8753 Industrial Ln Rancho Cucamonga (91730) *(P-19331)*

Cypress Manufacturing LLC .... F 818 772-6592
25620 Rye Canyon Rd Ste B Valencia (91355) *(P-10055)*

Cypress Ridge Winery, King City *Also called Delicato Vineyards (P-1723)*

Cypress Semiconductor Corp .... F 408 943-2600
195 Champion Ct Bldg 2 San Jose (95134) *(P-18795)*

Cypress Semiconductor Corp (PA) .... A 408 943-2600
198 Champion Ct San Jose (95134) *(P-18796)*

Cypress Sponge Rubber Products .... F 714 546-6464
301 Goetz Ave Santa Ana (92707) *(P-9605)*

Cyron Inc .... F 818 772-1900
21029 Itasca St Ste C Chatsworth (91311) *(P-17682)*

Cytec Aerospace Mtls CA Inc .... C 714 899-0400
851 W 18th St Costa Mesa (92627) *(P-2958)*

Cytec Engineered Materials, Costa Mesa *Also called Cytec Aerospace Mtls CA Inc (P-2958)*

Cytec Engineered Materials Inc .... E 714 632-8444
1191 N Hawk Cir Anaheim (92807) *(P-7828)*

Cytec Engineered Materials Inc .... C 714 630-9400
645 N Cypress St Orange (92867) *(P-7829)*

Cytec Engineered Materials Inc .... C 714 632-1174
1440 N Kraemer Blvd Anaheim (92806) *(P-11733)*

Cytec Engineered Materials Inc .... C 714 666-4302
1440 N Cramer Blvd Anaheim (92806) *(P-11734)*

Cytek Biosciences Inc .... F 510 657-0110
46107 Landing Pkwy Fremont (94538) *(P-22969)*

Cytek Development Inc .... F 510 657-0102
4059 Clipper Ct Fremont (94538) *(P-21943)*

Cytobank Inc .... F 650 918-7966
3945 Freedom Cir Ste 540 Santa Clara (95054) *(P-24544)*

Cytokinetics Incorporated (PA) .... C 650 624-3000
280 E Grand Ave South San Francisco (94080) *(P-8132)*

Cytomx Therapeutics Inc .... D 650 515-3185
151 Oyster Point Blvd South San Francisco (94080) *(P-7932)*

Cytori Therapeutics Inc (PA) .... D 858 458-0900
3020 Callan Rd San Diego (92121) *(P-22416)*

Cytosport, Walnut Creek *Also called Gmp Manufacturing Inc (P-2530)*

Cytosport Inc .... C 707 751-3942
1340 Treat Blvd Ste 350 Walnut Creek (94597) *(P-609)*

Cytrx Corporation (PA) .... E 310 826-5648
11726 San Vicente Blvd # 650 Los Angeles (90049) *(P-8544)*

Cytydel Plastics Inc .... E 310 523-2884
17813 S Main St Ste 117 Gardena (90248) *(P-10056)*

Cyu Lithographics Inc .... E 888 878-9898
6951 Oran Cir Buena Park (90621) *(P-6774)*

Cyvex Nutrition Inc .... F 949 622-9030
1851 Kaiser Ave Irvine (92614) *(P-610)*

D & B Precision Shtmtl Inc .... F 209 848-3030
693 Hi Tech Pkwy Oakdale (95361) *(P-12547)*

D & B Supply Corp .... F 714 632-3020
1189 N Grove St Ste A Anaheim (92806) *(P-14271)*

D & D Cbnets - Svage Dsgns Inc .... E 530 634-9713
1478 Sky Harbor Dr Olivehurst (95961) *(P-4291)*

D & D Engineering, Turlock *Also called Donald H Binkley (P-12154)*

D & D Gear Incorporated .... C 714 692-6570
4890 E La Palma Ave Anaheim (92807) *(P-20790)*

D & D Gold Product Corp .... F 714 550-0372
11608 Quartz Ave Fl 2 Fountain Valley (92708) *(P-1038)*

D & D Motorcycle Service Inc .... E 323 567-9480
10401 Alameda St Lynwood (90262) *(P-21104)*

D & D Plastics Incorporated .... F 310 515-1934
1632 W 139th St Gardena (90249) *(P-10057)*

D & D Security Resources Inc (PA) .... E 714 985-9409
716 Richfield Rd Placentia (92870) *(P-19941)*

D & D Technologies USA Inc .... E 949 852-5140
17531 Metzler Ln Huntington Beach (92647) *(P-11434)*

D & F Standler Inc .... F 408 226-8188
195 Lewis Rd Ste 39 San Jose (95111) *(P-16415)*

D & G Manufacturing, Signal Hill *Also called Flex-Mate Inc (P-11894)*

D & H Trucking Equipment, San Diego *Also called Jjs Truck Equipment LLC (P-20211)*

D & J Printing Inc .... D 661 775-4586
600 W Technology Dr Palmdale (93551) *(P-6775)*

D & K Concrete Co, Fontana *Also called Dennie Manning Concrete Inc (P-11101)*

D & L Moulding and Lumber Co .... F 626 444-0134
1044 N Soldano Ave Azusa (91702) *(P-4136)*

D & L Pallet Company, Ontario *Also called Hannibal Lafayette (P-4474)*

D & M Draperies Inc .... F 626 256-1993
323 W Maple Ave Monrovia (91016) *(P-3692)*

D & M Fabrication Inc .... E 209 334-0407
1615 S Stockton St Lodi (95240) *(P-15312)*

D & M Manufacturing .... F 559 834-4668
5400 S Villa Ave Fresno (93725) *(P-14056)*

D & M Precision, Oxnard *Also called Mjolnir Industries LLC (P-14542)*

D & R Brothers Inc .... E 213 747-4309
952 S Broadway 2 Los Angeles (90015) *(P-3229)*

D & S Custom Plating Inc .... F 714 537-5411
11552 Anabel Ave Garden Grove (92843) *(P-20306)*

D & S Industries Inc .... F 714 779-8074
4515 E Eisenhower Cir Anaheim (92807) *(P-20791)*

D & T Fiberglass Inc .... E 916 383-9012
8900 Osage Ave D Sacramento (95828) *(P-5484)*

D & T Machining Inc .... F 408 486-6035
3360 Victor Ct Santa Clara (95054) *(P-16416)*

D A C, Carpinteria *Also called Development Assoc Contrls (P-14370)*

D A C, Carpinteria *Also called Dac International Inc (P-14622)*

D A M Bindery Inc .... F 858 621-7000
7949 Stromesa Ct Ste B San Diego (92126) *(P-7596)*

D and D Tools, San Diego *Also called Shields Enterprises Inc (P-14412)*

D and J Marketing Inc .... E 310 538-1583
580 W 184th St Gardena (90248) *(P-3887)*

D Benham Corporation .... F 619 448-8079
10969 Wheatlands Ave A Santee (92071) *(P-6776)*

D Bindery, Sacramento *Also called Sacramental Color Coil (P-7617)*

D D Office Products Inc .... E 323 582-3400
5025 Hampton St Vernon (90058) *(P-5278)*

D D Wire Co Inc (PA) .... E 626 442-0459
4335 Temple City Blvd Temple City (91780) *(P-12149)*

D D Wire Co Inc .... F 626 285-0298
4942 Encinita Ave Temple City (91780) *(P-12150)*

D Davis Enterprise, Davis *Also called McNaughton Newspapers (P-5954)*

D E I, Santa Fe Springs *Also called Dynamic Enterprises Inc (P-16455)*

D F Stauffer Biscuit Co Inc .... E 714 546-6855
4041 W Garry Ave Santa Ana (92704) *(P-1359)*

D G A Mch Sp Blnchard Grinding, Riverside *Also called DGA Machine Shop Inc (P-16434)*

D G Industries .... F 714 990-3787
226 Viking Ave Brea (92821) *(P-14367)*

D G Motorsports, Oceanside *Also called Advanced Fiberglass Inc (P-10629)*

D G U Trading Corporation .... E 909 469-1288
1999 W Holt Ave Pomona (91768) *(P-10689)*

D Goldenwest Inc .... E 310 564-2641
2700 Pacific Coast Hwy # 2 Torrance (90505) *(P-1228)*

D Hauptman Co Inc .... E 323 734-2507
4856 W Jefferson Blvd Los Angeles (90016) *(P-23547)*

D I Printing, Hidden Valley Lake *Also called Jensen Graphics & Printing (P-6911)*

D J Simpson Company (PA) .... F 650 225-9404
401 S Canal St A South San Francisco (94080) *(P-8900)*

D K Environmental, Vernon *Also called Demenno/Kerdoon Holdings (P-9430)*

D L B Pallets (PA) .... F 951 360-9896
4510 Rutile St Riverside (92509) *(P-4465)*

D L Stoy Logging Co .... F 530 283-3292
17302 Mountain View Rd Greenville (95947) *(P-3983)*

D Laurence Gates Ltd .... E 925 736-8176
2671 Crow Canyon Rd San Ramon (94583) *(P-4036)*

D Mills Grnding Machining Inc .... E 951 697-6847
6131 Quail Valley Ct Riverside (92507) *(P-16417)*

D N G Cummings Inc .... E 650 593-8974
3580 Haven Ave Ste 1 Redwood City (94063) *(P-23853)*

D P I, Porterville *Also called Distributors Processing Inc (P-2255)*

D S McGee Enterprises Inc .... E 951 378-8473
3240 Trade Center Dr Riverside (92507) *(P-4137)*

D W I, Chino *Also called Diamond Wipes Intl Inc (P-8740)*

D W Mack Co Inc .... E 626 969-1817
900 W 8th St Azusa (91702) *(P-10058)*

D X Communications Inc .... E 323 256-3000
3825 Foothill Blvd La Crescenta (91214) *(P-18082)*

D Y U Inc .... C 714 239-2433
223 N Crescent Way Anaheim (92801) *(P-18463)*

D&A Unlimited Inc .... E 562 336-1528
111 W Victoria St Long Beach (90805) *(P-3400)*

D&D Security Enterprises, Placentia *Also called D & D Security Resources Inc (P-19941)*

D&H / R&D, Fremont *Also called D&H Manufacturing Company (P-24072)*

D&H Manufacturing, Fremont *Also called Celestica LLC (P-19483)*

D&H Manufacturing Company .... F 510 770-5100
49235 Milmont Dr Fremont (94538) *(P-24072)*

D&S Brewing Solutions Inc .... E 650 207-4524
6148 E Oakbrook St Long Beach (90815) *(P-1585)*

D&W Fine Pack LLC .... C 206 767-7777
4162 Georgia Blvd San Bernardino (92407) *(P-10059)*

D'Ambrosio Bros, Sunnyvale *Also called Fullfillment Systems Inc (P-486)*

D'Lido Bakery, Los Angeles *Also called Galdaza Food Corporation (P-1259)*

D-1280-X Inc .... F 310 835-6909
126 N Marine Ave Wilmington (90744) *(P-9331)*

D-Mac Inc .... E 714 808-3918
1105 E Discovery Ln Anaheim (92801) *(P-4551)*

D-Tech Optoelectronics Inc (HQ) .... E 626 956-1100
18062 Rowland St City of Industry (91748) *(P-18318)*

D-Tek Manufacturing .... E 408 588-1574
3245 Woodward Ave Santa Clara (95054) *(P-18797)*

D.F. Industries, Chino *Also called Dick Farrell Industries Inc (P-15257)*

D3 Inc (PA) .... D 310 223-2200
3211 Jack Northrop Ave Hawthorne (90250) *(P-4981)*

D3 Go, Encino *Also called D3publisher of America Inc (P-24545)*

D3 Led LLC (PA) .... E 916 669-7408
11370 Sunrise Park Dr Rancho Cordova (95742) *(P-23854)*

D3publisher of America Inc .... D 310 268-0820
15910 Ventura Blvd # 800 Encino (91436) *(P-24545)*

Da Global Energy Inc .... F 408 916-6303
548 Market St Ste 32810 San Francisco (94104) *(P-17423)*

Da Vinci Fine Food, La Mesa *Also called Ritas Fine Food (P-2654)*

Da Vita Tustin Dialysis Ctr .... E 714 835-2450
2090 N Tustin Ave Ste 100 Santa Ana (92705) *(P-22417)*

Da-Ly Glass Corp .... E 323 589-5461
1193 W 2nd St Pomona (91766) *(P-10690)*

Mergent e-mail: customerrelations@mergent.com
1114
2019 California
Manufacturers Register
(P-0000) Products & Services Section entry number
(PA)=Parent Co (HQ)=Headquarters (DH)=Div Headquarters

Da/Pro Rubber Inc ......D......661 775-6290
28635 Braxton Ave Valencia (91355) ***(P-9606)***
Daa Draexlmaier Auto Amer LLC ......D......864 485-1000
801 Challenger St Livermore (94551) ***(P-20307)***
Daaze Inc ......F......626 442-4961
1714 S Grove Ave Ste B Ontario (91761) ***(P-12548)***
Dab Inc ......D......562 623-4773
13415 Marquardt Ave Santa Fe Springs (90670) ***(P-17533)***
Dabmar Lighting Inc (PA) ......E......805 604-9090
2140 Eastman Ave Oxnard (93030) ***(P-17683)***
Dac International Inc (PA) ......E......805 684-8307
6390 Rose Ln Carpinteria (93013) ***(P-14622)***
Dacon Systems Inc ......F......951 735-2100
1891 N Delilah St Corona (92879) ***(P-11657)***
Dacon Systems Inc ......F......310 842-9933
12915 S Spring St Los Angeles (90061) ***(P-11658)***
Dacor ......D......626 799-1000
14425 Clark Ave City of Industry (91745) ***(P-17365)***
Dacor ......F......626 799-1000
14425 Clark Ave City of Industry (91745) ***(P-17366)***
Dacor ......D......626 961-2256
14525 Clark Ave City of Industry (91745) ***(P-17367)***
Dacor Purchasing Industry, City of Industry *Also called Dacor* ***(P-17366)***
Dae Shin Usa Inc ......D......714 578-8900
610 N Gilbert St Fullerton (92833) ***(P-2775)***
Dahlhauser Manufacturing Co ......E......408 988-3717
1855 Russell Ave Santa Clara (95054) ***(P-13823)***
Daicel Safety Systems (HQ) ......F......805 387-1000
2655 1st St Ste 300 Simi Valley (93065) ***(P-20308)***
Daily Breeze, Torrance *Also called Medianews Group Inc* ***(P-5959)***
Daily Californian, Berkeley *Also called Independent Berkeley Student* ***(P-5885)***
Daily Computing Solutions Inc ......F......818 240-5400
3521 Foxglove Rd Glendale (91206) ***(P-5820)***
Daily Democrat, The, Woodland *Also called Medianews Group Inc* ***(P-5962)***
Daily Graphics, Los Angeles *Also called Daily Graphs Inc* ***(P-6140)***
Daily Graphs Inc ......E......310 448-6843
12655 Beatrice St Los Angeles (90066) ***(P-6140)***
Daily Journal ......E......650 344-5200
1720 S Amphlett Blvd # 123 San Mateo (94402) ***(P-5821)***
Daily Journal Corporation (PA) ......C......213 229-5300
915 E 1st St Los Angeles (90012) ***(P-5822)***
Daily Journal Corporation ......D......415 296-2400
44 Montgomery St Ste 500 San Francisco (94104) ***(P-5823)***
Daily Midway Driller, Taft *Also called St Louis Post-Dispatch LLC* ***(P-6058)***
Daily News, Woodland Hills *Also called Medianews Group Inc* ***(P-5958)***
Daily News, Menlo Park *Also called Medianews Group Inc* ***(P-5961)***
Daily News, Valencia *Also called Medianews Group Inc* ***(P-5963)***
Daily Press, Victorville *Also called Lmg National Publishing Inc* ***(P-5915)***
Daily Recorder ......F......916 444-2355
901 H St Ste 312 Sacramento (95814) ***(P-5824)***
Daily Republic, Fairfield *Also called McNaughton Newspapers Inc* ***(P-5955)***
Daily Review ......E......510 783-6111
3317 Arden Rd Hayward (94545) ***(P-5825)***
Daily Sports Seoul Usa Inc ......E......213 487-9331
626 S Kingsley Dr Los Angeles (90005) ***(P-5826)***
Dairy Conveyor Corp ......E......714 891-0883
15212 Connector Ln Huntington Beach (92649) ***(P-14272)***
Dairy Farmers America Inc ......F......951 493-4900
170 N Maple St Ste 106 Corona (92880) ***(P-719)***
Dairy Farmers America Inc ......E......209 883-4461
170 N Maple St Ste 106 Corona (92880) ***(P-720)***
Dairy Farmers America Inc ......D......805 653-0042
4375 N Ventura Ave Ventura (93001) ***(P-721)***
Dairy Farmers America Inc ......D......209 667-9627
600 Trade Way Turlock (95380) ***(P-569)***
Dairymens Feed & Sup Coop Assn ......F......707 763-1585
323 E Washington St Petaluma (94952) ***(P-1126)***
Daisy Publishing Company Inc ......D......661 295-1910
25233 Anza Dr Santa Clarita (91355) ***(P-6141)***
Daisy Scout Publishing ......F......714 630-6611
1200 N Barsten Way Anaheim (92806) ***(P-6467)***
Dakota AG Welding, Ripon *Also called Jackrabbit* ***(P-14074)***
Dakota Press ......F......510 895-1300
14400 Doolittle Dr San Leandro (94577) ***(P-6777)***
Dakota Press Inc ......F......510 895-1300
14400 Doolittle Dr San Leandro (94577) ***(P-5827)***
Dakota Ultrasonics Corporation ......F......831 431-9722
1500 Green Hills Rd # 107 Scotts Valley (95066) ***(P-22184)***
Dakotahouse Industries Inc ......F......310 596-1100
5262 Cartwright Ave Apt 4 North Hollywood (91601) ***(P-409)***
Dal-Tile Corporation ......F......858 565-7767
7865 Ostrow St San Diego (92111) ***(P-7910)***
Dal-Tile Corporation ......E......818 787-3224
16201 Stagg St Van Nuys (91406) ***(P-7911)***
Dal-Tile Corporation ......F......323 257-7553
3550 Tyburn St Los Angeles (90065) ***(P-7912)***
Dale Brisco Inc ......F......559 834-5926
2132 S Temperance Ave Fowler (93625) ***(P-12549)***
Dale C Sannipoli ......F......760 347-2033
27616 Tyler Ave Sun City (92585) ***(P-20309)***
Dale Chavez Company Inc ......F......951 303-0592
35165 La Bonita Donna Temecula (92592) ***(P-10458)***
Dale Grove Corporation ......E......408 251-7220
1501 Stone Creek Dr San Jose (95132) ***(P-14844)***
Dale's Welding & Fabrication, Salinas *Also called Dales Welding Inc* ***(P-14057)***
Dales Welding Inc ......F......831 424-6583
1112 Abbott St A Salinas (93901) ***(P-14057)***
Dallas Electronics Inc ......E......831 457-3610
2151 Delaware Ave Ste A Santa Cruz (95060) ***(P-18464)***

Damac, Costa Mesa *Also called Bdfco Inc* ***(P-18310)***
Dameron Alloy Foundries (PA) ......D......310 631-5165
6330 Gateway Dr Ste B Cypress (90630) ***(P-11524)***
Dan Arens and Son Inc ......F......530 644-6307
5780 Ridgeway Dr Pollock Pines (95726) ***(P-3984)***
Dan Copp Crushing Corp ......E......714 777-6400
22895 Savi Ranch Pkwy C Yorba Linda (92887) ***(P-355)***
Dan Gurneys All Amercn Racers, Santa Ana *Also called All American Racers Inc* ***(P-21087)***
Dan M Swofford ......F......530 343-9994
728 Cherry St Chico (95928) ***(P-6142)***
Dan R Hunt Inc ......F......714 850-9383
2030 S Susan St Santa Ana (92704) ***(P-16418)***
Dan-Loc Bolt & Gasket, Carson *Also called Dan-Loc Group LLC* ***(P-9525)***
Dan-Loc Group LLC ......D......310 538-2822
20444 Tillman Ave Carson (90746) ***(P-9525)***
Dan-Mar Custom Draperies, Monrovia *Also called D & M Draperies Inc* ***(P-3692)***
Dana Creath Designs Ltd ......E......714 662-0111
3030 Kilson Dr Santa Ana (92707) ***(P-17684)***
Dana Innovations ......D......949 492-7777
991 Calle Amanecer San Clemente (92673) ***(P-17787)***
Danaher Corporation ......C......951 652-6811
3255 W Stetson Ave Hemet (92545) ***(P-21684)***
Danair Inc (PA) ......F......559 734-1961
1150 E Acequia Ave Visalia (93292) ***(P-14368)***
Danbee Inc ......F......323 780-0077
3360 E Pico Blvd Los Angeles (90023) ***(P-3304)***
Danchuk Manufacturing Inc ......D......714 540-4363
3201 S Standard Ave Santa Ana (92705) ***(P-20310)***
Danco Anodizing Inc (PA) ......E......626 445-3303
44 La Porte St Arcadia (91006) ***(P-13384)***
Danco Anodizing Inc ......E......909 923-0562
1750 E Monticello Ct Ontario (91761) ***(P-13385)***
Danco Machine, Santa Clara *Also called P M S D Inc* ***(P-16817)***
Danco Metal Surfacing, Arcadia *Also called Danco Anodizing Inc* ***(P-13384)***
Dang Tha ......F......714 898-0989
13050 Hoover St Westminster (92683) ***(P-5010)***
Dangerous Coffee Co LLC ......F......619 405-8291
3644 Midway Dr San Diego (92110) ***(P-24073)***
Daniel Gerard Worldwide Inc ......F......800 635-8296
13055 Jurupa Ave Fontana (92337) ***(P-13824)***
Daniels Inc (PA) ......E......801 621-3355
74745 Leslie Ave Palm Desert (92260) ***(P-6468)***
Danisco US Inc (HQ) ......C......650 846-7500
925 Page Mill Rd Palo Alto (94304) ***(P-8472)***
Dannier Chemical Inc ......E......949 221-8660
2302 Martin Ste 450 Irvine (92612) ***(P-9240)***
Danoc Embroidery, Sacramento *Also called Danoc Manufacturing Corp Inc* ***(P-3350)***
Danoc Manufacturing Corp Inc ......F......916 455-2876
6015 Power Inn Rd Ste A Sacramento (95824) ***(P-3350)***
Danone Us LLC ......B......949 474-9670
3500 Barranca Pkwy # 240 Irvine (92606) ***(P-665)***
Danrich Welding Coinc ......F......562 634-4811
7001 Jackson St Paramount (90723) ***(P-12550)***
Dansig (chapter S Corporation) ......F......661 295-0899
25011 Avenue Stanford G Valencia (91355) ***(P-2128)***
Danso Dental Lab, San Diego *Also called Light Mobile Inc* ***(P-22892)***
Dantel ......E......559 292-1111
2991 N Argyle Ave Fresno (93727) ***(P-17936)***
Danville Materials LLC ......E......714 399-0334
4020 E Leaverton Ct Anaheim (92807) ***(P-22865)***
Danville Materials LLC (HQ) ......E......760 743-7744
2875 Loker Ave E Carlsbad (92010) ***(P-22866)***
Danvo Machining ......F......714 751-1401
2107 S Hathaway St Santa Ana (92705) ***(P-16419)***
Danworth Manufacturing Co ......F......510 487-8290
30991 Huntwood Ave # 401 Hayward (94544) ***(P-16420)***
Danza Del Sol Winery Inc ......F......951 302-6363
39050 De Portola Rd Temecula (92592) ***(P-1714)***
Dar-Ken Inc ......E......760 246-4010
10515 Rancho Rd Adelanto (92301) ***(P-9526)***
Darbo Manufacturing Company ......E......714 529-7693
363 Glenoaks St Brea (92821) ***(P-3401)***
Darcie Kent Vineyards ......F......925 243-9040
4590 Tesla Rd Livermore (94550) ***(P-1715)***
Darcy AK Corporation ......F......949 650-5566
1760 Monrovia Ave Ste A22 Costa Mesa (92627) ***(P-16421)***
Dare Bioscience Inc ......F......858 926-7655
3655 Nobel Dr Ste 260 San Diego (92122) ***(P-8133)***
Dare Lithoworks Inc ......F......213 250-9062
13512 Vintage Pl A Chino (91710) ***(P-6778)***
Dare Technologies Inc (HQ) ......F......714 634-5900
674 Via De La Valle # 100 Solana Beach (92075) ***(P-17937)***
Darioush Khaledi Winery LLC ......E......707 257-2345
4240 Silverado Trl NAPA (94558) ***(P-1716)***
Darko Precision Inc ......D......408 988-6133
470 Gianni St Santa Clara (95054) ***(P-16422)***
Darling Ingredients Inc ......D......415 647-4890
429 Amador St Pier 92 San Francisco (94124) ***(P-1524)***
Darling Ingredients Inc ......E......559 268-5325
795 W Belgravia Ave Fresno (93706) ***(P-1525)***
Darling Ingredients Inc ......D......323 583-6311
2626 E 25th St Los Angeles (90058) ***(P-1526)***
Darling International Inc ......E......209 667-9153
11946 Carpenter Rd Crows Landing (95313) ***(P-1527)***
Darmark Corporation ......D......858 679-3970
13225 Gregg St Poway (92064) ***(P-16423)***
Darnell Corporation ......D......626 912-1688
17915 Railroad St City of Industry (91748) ***(P-11951)***
Darrell Zbrowski ......D......818 324-5961
8465 Vassar Ave Canoga Park (91304) ***(P-14322)***

ALPHABETIC

Employee Codes: A=Over 500 employees, B=251-500
C=101-250, D=51-100, E=20-50, F=10-19
2019 California
Manfacturers Register
© Mergent Inc. 1-800-342-5647
1115

Darrow, Manhattan Beach *Also called Dhy Inc* ***(P-3144)***
Dart Container Corp Calif, Lodi *Also called Dart Container Corp California* ***(P-9834)***
Dart Container Corp California (PA)..........B.......951 735-8115
150 S Maple Ctr Corona (92880) ***(P-9833)***
Dart Container Corp California..........C.......209 333-8088
1400 E Victor Rd Lodi (95240) ***(P-9834)***
Dart Warehouse Corporation (HQ)..........B.......323 981-8205
1430 S Eastman Ave Ste 1 Commerce (90023) ***(P-20499)***
Daryls Pet Shop..........F.......909 793-1788
208 E State St Redlands (92373) ***(P-24074)***
Dasan Zhone Solutions Inc (HQ)..........C.......510 777-7000
7195 Oakport St Oakland (94621) ***(P-17938)***
Dasco Engineering Corp..........C.......310 326-2277
24747 Crenshaw Blvd Torrance (90505) ***(P-20792)***
Dash Sportswear..........E.......323 846-2640
2624 Geraldine St Los Angeles (90011) ***(P-3402)***
Dash Sportwear, Los Angeles *Also called Dash Sportswear* ***(P-3402)***
Dasher Technologies Inc (PA)..........E.......408 409-2607
675 Campbell Technology P Campbell (95008) ***(P-24546)***
Dasol Inc..........C.......310 327-6700
16210 S Avalon Blvd Gardena (90248) ***(P-17424)***
Dassault Systemes Biovia Corp (HQ)..........E.......858 799-5000
5005 Wateridge Vista Dr # 2 San Diego (92121) ***(P-24547)***
DAt Farms Inc..........F.......408 848-8060
24514 Oro Valley Rd Auburn (95602) ***(P-24075)***
Data Advantage Group Inc..........F.......415 947-0400
145 Natoma St Fl 5 San Francisco (94105) ***(P-24548)***
Data Agent LLC..........F.......800 772-8314
1349 Josephine St Berkeley (94703) ***(P-24549)***
Data Aire Inc (HQ)..........C.......800 347-2473
230 W Blueridge Ave Orange (92865) ***(P-15949)***
Data Circle Inc..........F.......949 260-6569
3333 Michelson Dr Ste 735 Irvine (92612) ***(P-18798)***
Data Device Corporation..........E.......631 567-5600
13000 Gregg St Ste C Poway (92064) ***(P-21190)***
Data Device Corporation..........E.......858 503-3300
13000 Gregg St Ste C Poway (92064) ***(P-21191)***
Data Electronic Services, Santa Ana *Also called Humberto Murillo Inc* ***(P-13428)***
Data Label Products Inc..........F.......626 915-6478
840 N Cummings Rd Covina (91724) ***(P-5708)***
Data Line, Santa Clara *Also called Pss Communications Inc* ***(P-17983)***
Data Linkage Software Inc..........F.......310 781-3056
2421 W 205th St Ste D207 Torrance (90501) ***(P-24550)***
Data Physics Corporation..........E.......408 216-8443
9031 Polsa Ct Corona (92883) ***(P-14939)***
Data Scale, Fremont *Also called Terry B Lowe* ***(P-21666)***
Data Solder Inc..........F.......714 429-9866
2915 Kilson Dr Santa Ana (92707) ***(P-17458)***
Data Storm Inc..........F.......818 352-4994
2001 Manistee Dr La Canada Flintridge (91011) ***(P-19942)***
Database Dynamics, Santa Ana *Also called Interactive Entertainment Inc* ***(P-23432)***
Database Works Inc..........F.......714 203-8800
500 S Kraemer Blvd # 110 Brea (92821) ***(P-24551)***
Datadirect Networks Inc (PA)..........C.......818 700-7600
9351 Deering Ave Chatsworth (91311) ***(P-15528)***
Datafox Intelligence Inc..........F.......415 969-2144
835 Howard St 2 San Francisco (94103) ***(P-24552)***
Datagenics Software Inc..........F.......818 487-3900
5527 Satsuma Ave North Hollywood (91601) ***(P-24553)***
Datapage Inc..........F.......323 725-7500
5577 Sheila St Commerce (90040) ***(P-7294)***
Dataray Incorporated..........F.......530 472-1717
1675 Market St Redding (96001) ***(P-21944)***
Datatronic Distribution Inc..........F.......951 928-2058
28151 Us Highway 74 Romoland (92585) ***(P-17086)***
Datatronics Romoland Inc..........D.......951 928-7700
28151 Us Highway 74 Menifee (92585) ***(P-17087)***
Dateline Products LLC..........F.......909 888-9785
1375 E Base Line St Ste B San Bernardino (92410) ***(P-4688)***
Datron Wrld Communications Inc (PA)..........C.......760 597-1500
3055 Enterprise Ct Vista (92081) ***(P-18083)***
Datum Precision Inc..........F.......530 272-8415
345 Crown Point Cir # 800 Grass Valley (95945) ***(P-20793)***
Datum Precision Machining, Anderson *Also called Dpm Inc* ***(P-16449)***
Dauntless Industries Inc..........E.......626 966-4494
806 N Grand Ave Covina (91724) ***(P-14503)***
Dauntless Molds, Covina *Also called Dauntless Industries Inc* ***(P-14503)***
Davco Enterprises Inc..........F.......714 432-0600
3301 W Segerstrom Ave Santa Ana (92704) ***(P-9140)***
Dave Annala..........F.......714 541-8383
1628 E Wilshire Ave Santa Ana (92705) ***(P-12551)***
Dave Humphrey Enterprises Inc..........F.......209 835-2222
145 Gandy Dancer Dr Tracy (95377) ***(P-14163)***
Dave Richardson Trucking..........F.......530 459-5088
8817 Lwer Lttle Shasta Rd Montague (96064) ***(P-3985)***
Dave Schneider's Fine Jewelry, Long Beach *Also called Schneiders Deisgn Studio Inc* ***(P-23316)***
Dave Whipple Sheet Metal Inc..........E.......619 562-6962
1077 N Cuyamaca St El Cajon (92020) ***(P-12552)***
Dave's Donuts & Baking Co, Gardena *Also called Bake R Us Inc* ***(P-1179)***
Davenport International Corp..........E.......818 765-6400
7230 Coldwater Canyon Ave North Hollywood (91605) ***(P-17788)***
Daves Interiors Inc..........E.......714 998-5554
1579 N Main St Orange (92867) ***(P-4768)***
David A Neal Inc..........F.......562 941-5626
9825 Bell Ranch Dr Santa Fe Springs (90670) ***(P-16424)***
David B Anderson..........E.......805 489-0661
921 Huston St Grover Beach (93433) ***(P-6779)***
David Beard..........F.......530 244-1248
821 Twin View Blvd Redding (96003) ***(P-4292)***
David Bruce Winery Inc..........F.......408 354-4214
21439 Bear Creek Rd Los Gatos (95033) ***(P-1717)***
David Corporation..........F.......916 762-8688
925 Highland Pointe Dr # 180 Roseville (95678) ***(P-24554)***
David Duley..........D.......619 449-8556
700 La Cresta Blvd San Marcos (92079) ***(P-5376)***
David Engineering & Mfg, Corona *Also called Specialty Finance Inc* ***(P-13279)***
David Furniture, Gardena *Also called I M Ginsburg Furniture Inc* ***(P-4704)***
David Garment Cutng Fusing Svc..........F.......323 583-9885
5008 S Boyle Ave Vernon (90058) ***(P-3101)***
David H Fell & Co Inc (PA)..........E.......323 722-9992
6009 Bandini Blvd Los Angeles (90040) ***(P-11555)***
David Haid..........E.......323 752-8096
8619 Crocker St Los Angeles (90003) ***(P-5226)***
David Kopf Instruments..........E.......818 352-3274
7324 Elmo St Tujunga (91042) ***(P-22418)***
David L Long..........F.......562 809-5740
16317 Piuma Ave Cerritos (90703) ***(P-4138)***
David Pirrotta Dist Inc..........F.......323 645-7456
7424 1/2 W Sunset Blvd # 5 Los Angeles (90046) ***(P-8733)***
Davids Natural Toothpaste..........F.......949 933-1185
40292 Rosewell Ct Temecula (92591) ***(P-8734)***
Davidson Optronics Inc..........E.......626 962-5181
9087 Arrow Rte Ste 180 Rancho Cucamonga (91730) ***(P-22185)***
Davis Boats..........F.......805 227-1170
2601 Engine Ave Paso Robles (93446) ***(P-21028)***
Davis Gear & Machine Co..........F.......310 337-9881
13625 S Normandie Ave Gardena (90249) ***(P-16425)***
Davis Gregg Enterprises Inc..........F.......619 449-4250
8525 Roland Acres Dr Santee (92071) ***(P-12384)***
Davis Instruments Corporation..........D.......510 732-9229
3465 Diablo Ave Hayward (94545) ***(P-21282)***
Davis Shoe Therapeutics..........F.......415 661-8705
3921 Judah St San Francisco (94122) ***(P-10495)***
Davis Stone Inc..........E.......760 745-7881
519 Venture St Escondido (92029) ***(P-11247)***
Davis Wire Corporation (HQ)..........C.......626 969-7651
5555 Irwindale Ave Irwindale (91706) ***(P-11435)***
Davison Iron Works Inc..........E.......916 381-2121
8845 Elder Creek Rd Ste A Sacramento (95828) ***(P-12151)***
Davita Dialysis Center, San Bruno *Also called Davita Rx LLC* ***(P-8134)***
Davita Rx LLC (HQ)..........E.......650 344-2319
1178 Cherry Ave San Bruno (94066) ***(P-8134)***
Davtron..........F.......650 369-1188
427 Hillcrest Way Emerald Hills (94062) ***(P-21283)***
Dawn Bakery Service Center, Union City *Also called Dawn Food Products Inc* ***(P-1229)***
Dawn Food Products Inc..........F.......517 789-4400
2455 Tenaya Dr Modesto (95354) ***(P-1360)***
Dawn Food Products Inc..........E.......510 487-9007
2845 Faber St Union City (94587) ***(P-1229)***
Dawn Sign Press Inc..........E.......858 625-0600
6130 Nancy Ridge Dr San Diego (92121) ***(P-6334)***
Dawn VME Products..........E.......510 657-4444
47915 Westinghouse Dr Fremont (94539) ***(P-19508)***
Dawson Enterprises (PA)..........E.......562 424-8564
2853 Cherry Ave Signal Hill (90755) ***(P-14220)***
Dawson Enterprises..........F.......661 765-2181
815 Main St Taft (93268) ***(P-203)***
Day Star Industries..........F.......562 926-8800
13727 Excelsior Dr Santa Fe Springs (90670) ***(P-4139)***
Day-Glo Color Corp..........F.......323 560-2000
4615 Ardine St Cudahy (90201) ***(P-7741)***
Daylight Defense LLC..........C.......858 432-7500
15378 Ave Of Science San Diego (92128) ***(P-22970)***
Daylight Solutions Inc (HQ)..........C.......858 432-7500
15378 Ave Of Science # 200 San Diego (92128) ***(P-18799)***
Daymar Corporation..........F.......619 444-1155
460 Cypress Ln Ste B El Cajon (92020) ***(P-2339)***
Daymar Select Fine Coffees, El Cajon *Also called Daymar Corporation* ***(P-2339)***
Daytec Center LLC..........E.......760 995-3515
17469 Lemon St Hesperia (92345) ***(P-21105)***
Dayton Superior Corporation..........E.......909 957-7271
10780 Mulberry Ave Fontana (92337) ***(P-20576)***
Dayton Superior Corporation..........D.......951 782-9517
6001 20th St Riverside (92509) ***(P-11436)***
Dayton Superior Corporation..........E.......209 869-1201
5300 Claus Rd Ste 7 Modesto (95357) ***(P-14323)***
Dayton Superior Corporation..........E.......909 820-0112
562 W Santa Ana Ave Bloomington (92316) ***(P-11437)***
Daz Inc..........F.......949 724-8800
2500 White Rd Ste B Irvine (92614) ***(P-17139)***
Db Building Fasteners, Ontario *Also called DB Building Fasteners Inc* ***(P-12977)***
DB Building Fasteners Inc (PA)..........E.......909 581-6740
5555 E Gibralter Ontario (91764) ***(P-12977)***
Db Studios Inc..........E.......949 833-0100
17032 Murphy Ave Irvine (92614) ***(P-24076)***
DBC Printing Incorporated..........F.......805 988-8855
220 Bernoulli Cir Oxnard (93030) ***(P-6780)***
Dbg Subsidiary Inc..........C.......323 837-3700
1500 N El Centro Ave # 150 Los Angeles (90028) ***(P-3351)***
DC Electronics Inc..........F.......408 947-4531
1870 Little Orchard St San Jose (95125) ***(P-17459)***
DC Partners Inc..........E.......818 285-0692
19329 Bryant St Northridge (91324) ***(P-11735)***
DC Partners Inc (PA)..........D.......714 558-9444
19329 Bryant St Northridge (91324) ***(P-11736)***
DC Partners Inc..........E.......818 718-1221
19408 Londelius St Northridge (91324) ***(P-11737)***

Mergent e-mail: customerrelations@mergent.com
1116
2019 California
Manufacturers Register
(P-0000) Products & Services Section entry number
(PA)=Parent Co (HQ)=Headquarters (DH)=Div Headquarters

DC Shades & Shutters Awnings ......F......818 597-9705
2370 Thunderbird Dr Thousand Oaks (91362) ***(P-12306)***
DC Shoes Inc (HQ) ......D......714 889-4206
5600 Argosy Ave Ste 100 Huntington Beach (92649) ***(P-3143)***
DC Valve Mfg & Precision Mchs, Morgan Hill *Also called Valvex Enterprises Inc* ***(P-17035)***
Dcc General Engrg Contrs Inc ......D......760 480-7400
2180 Meyers Ave Escondido (92029) ***(P-10913)***
Dcg Systems, Fremont *Also called Fei Efa Inc* ***(P-19390)***
DCI, Hayward *Also called Dielectric Coating Industries* ***(P-22073)***
DCI Donor Services Inc ......E......916 567-1600
3940 Industrial Blvd # 100 West Sacramento (95691) ***(P-14058)***
DCI Hollow Metal On Demand, Fontana *Also called Door Components Inc* ***(P-12310)***
Dcl, Fremont *Also called Discopylabs* ***(P-17892)***
Dcl Productions ......F......415 826-2200
1284 Missouri St San Francisco (94107) ***(P-3840)***
Dco Environmental & Recycl LLC ......F......573 204-3844
300 Montgomery St Ste 421 San Francisco (94104) ***(P-10060)***
Dcor LLC (PA) ......D......805 535-2000
290 Maple Ct Ste 290 # 290 Ventura (93003) ***(P-130)***
Dcor LLC ......D......805 576-1200
290 Maple Ct Ste 290 Ventura (93003) ***(P-131)***
Dcx Division, Chatsworth *Also called Dcx-Chol Enterprises Inc* ***(P-18391)***
Dcx-Chol Enterprises Inc (PA) ......D......310 516-1692
12831 S Figueroa St Los Angeles (90061) ***(P-18386)***
Dcx-Chol Enterprises Inc ......D......310 516-1692
12831 S Figueroa St Los Angeles (90061) ***(P-18387)***
Dcx-Chol Enterprises Inc ......D......562 927-5531
7450 Scout Ave Bell (90201) ***(P-19509)***
Dcx-Chol Enterprises Inc ......D......310 516-1692
9330 Desoto Ave Chatsworth (91311) ***(P-18388)***
Dcx-Chol Enterprises Inc ......F......310 516-1692
12831 S Figueroa St Los Angeles (90061) ***(P-18389)***
Dcx-Chol Enterprises Inc ......E......310 525-1205
12831 S Figueroa St Los Angeles (90061) ***(P-18390)***
Dcx-Chol Enterprises Inc ......E......310 715-6946
9330 De Soto Ave Chatsworth (91311) ***(P-18391)***
Dda Holdings Inc ......F......213 624-5200
834 S Broadway Ste 1100 Los Angeles (90014) ***(P-3403)***
Ddh Enterprise Inc (PA) ......C......760 599-0171
2220 Oak Ridge Way Vista (92081) ***(P-17460)***
Ddn, Chatsworth *Also called Datadirect Networks Inc* ***(P-15528)***
DDS, Hayward *Also called Detention Device Systems* ***(P-16433)***
De Anza Manufacturing Svcs Inc ......D......408 734-2020
1271 Reamwood Ave Sunnyvale (94089) ***(P-19510)***
De Anza Muffler Service, Riverside *Also called Vast National Inc* ***(P-11853)***
De Berns Company, Long Beach *Also called Berns Bros Inc* ***(P-16320)***
De La Cruz Products, Paramount *Also called Dlc Laboratories Inc* ***(P-8142)***
De Larshe Cabinetry LLC ......E......909 627-2757
2000 S Reservoir St Pomona (91766) ***(P-4140)***
De Leon Entps Elec Spclist Inc ......E......818 252-6690
11934 Allegheny St Sun Valley (91352) ***(P-18465)***
De Menno-Kerdoon Trading Co (HQ) ......C......310 537-7100
2000 N Alameda St Compton (90222) ***(P-9332)***
De Nora Water Technologies Inc ......D......310 618-9700
1230 Rosecrans Ave # 300 Manhattan Beach (90266) ***(P-16033)***
De Novo Software ......F......213 814-1240
400 N Brand Blvd Ste 850 Glendale (91203) ***(P-24555)***
De Soto Clothing Inc ......F......858 578-6672
7584 Trade St San Diego (92121) ***(P-3404)***
De Soto Sport, San Diego *Also called De Soto Clothing Inc* ***(P-3404)***
De Vries International Inc (PA) ......E......949 252-1212
17671 Armstrong Ave Irvine (92614) ***(P-204)***
Dealzer Com ......F......818 429-1155
9250 Reseda Blvd Northridge (91324) ***(P-8962)***
Deamco Corporation ......D......323 890-1190
6520 E Washington Blvd Commerce (90040) ***(P-14273)***
Dean Distributors Inc ......E......323 587-8147
5015 Hallmark Pkwy San Bernardino (92407) ***(P-2500)***
Dean Distributors Inc ......F......323 923-5400
5015 Hallmark Pkwy San Bernardino (92407) ***(P-2501)***
Dean Foods Company ......F......559 687-1927
605 N J St Tulare (93274) ***(P-722)***
Dean Foods Company Cal Inc ......E......714 684-2160
6408 Regio Ave Buena Park (90620) ***(P-611)***
Deans Certified Welding Inc ......F......951 676-0242
27645 Commerce Center Dr Temecula (92590) ***(P-25398)***
Deanza Tool & Manufacturing, Riverside *Also called M G Deanza Acquisition Inc* ***(P-16702)***
Debbies Delights Inc ......E......805 966-3504
233 E Gutierrez St Santa Barbara (93101) ***(P-1393)***
Debritos Chocolate Factory ......F......831 637-0164
160b Briggs Rd Hollister (95023) ***(P-1418)***
Dec, Santa Ana *Also called Dynasty Electronic Company LLC* ***(P-18469)***
Dec Fabricators Inc ......F......562 403-3626
16916 Gridley Pl Cerritos (90703) ***(P-13933)***
Deca International Corp ......E......714 367-5900
10700 Norwalk Blvd Santa Fe Springs (90670) ***(P-21284)***
Decamilla Brothers LLC ......F......530 865-3379
717 Tehama St Orland (95963) ***(P-1539)***
Decatur Electronics Inc (HQ) ......D......888 428-4315
15890 Bernardo Center Dr San Diego (92127) ***(P-21285)***
Decatur Electronics Inc ......E......619 596-1925
10729 Wheatlands Ave C Santee (92071) ***(P-21286)***
Decco Castings Inc ......E......619 444-9437
1596 Pioneer Way El Cajon (92020) ***(P-11774)***
Decco Graphics Inc ......E......310 534-2861
24411 Frampton Ave Harbor City (90710) ***(P-13192)***
Decco US Post-Harvest Inc (HQ) ......E......800 221-0925
1713 S California Ave Monrovia (91016) ***(P-9100)***
Deccofelt Corporation ......E......626 963-8511
555 S Vermont Ave Glendora (91741) ***(P-2995)***
Decision Medical, Poway *Also called Decision Sciences Med Co LLC* ***(P-22971)***
Decision Sciences Med Co LLC ......E......858 602-1600
12345 First American Way # 100 Poway (92064) ***(P-22971)***
Decisionlogic LLC ......E......858 586-0202
9820 Willow Creek Rd # 310 San Diego (92131) ***(P-24556)***
Deck West Inc ......F......209 939-9700
1900 Sanguinetti Ln Stockton (95205) ***(P-12553)***
Deckers Outdoor Corporation (PA) ......B......805 967-7611
250 Coromar Dr Goleta (93117) ***(P-3653)***
Deckers Outdoor Corporation ......F......805 437-2300
3175 Mission Oaks Blvd Camarillo (93012) ***(P-9470)***
Deco Enterprises Inc ......D......323 726-2575
2917 Vail Ave Commerce (90040) ***(P-17596)***
DECO LIGHTING, Commerce *Also called Deco Enterprises Inc* ***(P-17596)***
Deco Plastics Inc ......F......619 448-6843
160 Denny Way El Cajon (92020) ***(P-10061)***
Decoded USA, Irwindale *Also called Htk Automotive USA Corp* ***(P-19834)***
Decor Auto Inc ......F......323 733-9025
1709 W Washington Blvd Los Angeles (90007) ***(P-3888)***
Decor Fabrics Inc ......E......323 752-2200
6515 Mckinley Ave Los Angeles (90001) ***(P-4769)***
Decor International, Los Angeles *Also called Decor Fabrics Inc* ***(P-4769)***
Decor Shower Door and Glass Co ......F......707 253-0622
1819 Tanen St Ste A NAPA (94559) ***(P-10691)***
Decor Shower Enclosures, NAPA *Also called Decor Shower Door and Glass Co* ***(P-10691)***
Decore Plating Company Inc ......F......310 324-6755
434 W 164th St Gardena (90248) ***(P-13386)***
Decore-Ative Specialties (PA) ......A......626 254-9191
2772 Peck Rd Monrovia (91016) ***(P-4293)***
Decore-Ative Specialties ......C......626 960-7731
4414 Azusa Canyon Rd Irwindale (91706) ***(P-4141)***
Decore-Ative Specialties ......C......916 686-4700
104 Gate Eats Stock Blvd Elk Grove (95624) ***(P-4142)***
Decra Roofing Systems Inc (HQ) ......D......951 272-8180
1230 Railroad St Corona (92882) ***(P-12554)***
Decratek Inc ......E......760 747-1706
2875 Executive Pl Escondido (92029) ***(P-12307)***
Decrevel Incorporated ......F......707 258-8065
1836 Soscol Ave NAPA (94559) ***(P-14504)***
Dee Engineering Inc (PA) ......E......714 979-4990
1600 Sierra Madre Cir Placentia (92870) ***(P-20311)***
Dee Sign Co ......D......818 988-1000
16250 Stagg St Van Nuys (91406) ***(P-23855)***
Deep Foods Inc ......F......510 475-1900
4000 Whipple Rd Union City (94587) ***(P-1361)***
Deep Ocean Engineering Inc ......F......408 436-1102
2403 Qume Dr San Jose (95131) ***(P-21029)***
Deepflight ......F......510 236-3422
1150 Brickyard Cove Rd Point Richmond (94801) ***(P-20994)***
Deerfield Ranch Winery LLC ......F......707 833-5215
1310 Warm Springs Rd Glen Ellen (95442) ***(P-1718)***
Deering Banjo Company Inc ......E......619 464-8252
3733 Kenora Dr Spring Valley (91977) ***(P-23360)***
Deers Merchandise Inc ......F......909 869-8619
347 Enterprise Pl Pomona (91768) ***(P-10830)***
Defense Solutions, Santa Clarita *Also called Curtiss-Wright Corporation* ***(P-13714)***
Define Toys Inc ......F......626 330-8800
1255 Bixby Dr City of Industry (91745) ***(P-23395)***
Definity First, Los Angeles *Also called Sieena Inc* ***(P-25172)***
Defoe Furniture For Kids Inc ......F......909 947-4459
910 S Grove Ave Ontario (91761) ***(P-5011)***
Deft Precision Machining, San Diego *Also called Cimrmaan Ivo* ***(P-13182)***
Dehlinger Winery, Sebastopol *Also called Thomas Dehlinger* ***(P-2014)***
Dei Headquarters Inc ......B......760 598-6200
1 Viper Way Vista (92081) ***(P-18319)***
Dei Holdings Inc (HQ) ......C......760 598-6200
1 Viper Way Ste 3 Vista (92081) ***(P-18320)***
Deiny Automotive Inc ......F......818 362-5865
13040 Bradley Ave Sylmar (91342) ***(P-20134)***
Deist Engineering Inc ......E......818 240-7866
2623 N San Fernando Rd Los Angeles (90065) ***(P-3102)***
Deist Safety, Los Angeles *Also called Flame Out Inc* ***(P-24096)***
Deist Safety Equipment, Los Angeles *Also called Deist Engineering Inc* ***(P-3102)***
Dejagers Inc ......E......760 775-4755
45846 Flower St Indio (92201) ***(P-11248)***
Del Castillo Foods Inc ......E......209 369-2877
2346 Maggio Cir Lodi (95240) ***(P-2502)***
Del Craft Plastics, Laguna Hills *Also called Rls Enterprises* ***(P-10336)***
Del Dotto, NAPA *Also called Hedgeside Vintners* ***(P-1810)***
Del Industries, San Luis Obispo *Also called Del Ozone Holding Company Inc* ***(P-16034)***
Del Logging Inc ......E......530 294-5492
101 Punkin Center Rd Bieber (96009) ***(P-3986)***
Del Mar Database, San Diego *Also called Del Mar Datatrac Inc* ***(P-24557)***
Del Mar Datatrac Inc ......E......858 550-8810
10509 Vista Sorrento Pkwy # 400 San Diego (92121) ***(P-24557)***
Del Mar Die Casting Co, Gardena *Also called Del Mar Industries* ***(P-11712)***
Del Mar Food Products Corp ......B......831 722-3516
1720 Beach Rd Watsonville (95076) ***(P-792)***
Del Mar Industries (PA) ......D......323 321-0600
12901 S Western Ave Gardena (90249) ***(P-11712)***
Del Mar Industries ......E......310 327-2634
12901 S Western Ave Gardena (90249) ***(P-11713)***
Del Mar Seafoods Inc (PA) ......C......831 763-3000
331 Ford St Watsonville (95076) ***(P-2311)***
Del Monte Foods Inc ......D......559 419-9214
1509 Draper St Ste A Kingsburg (93631) ***(P-793)***

ALPHABETIC

Employee Codes: A=Over 500 employees, B=251-500
C=101-250, D=51-100, E=20-50, F=10-19
2019 California
Manfacturers Register
© Mergent Inc. 1-800-342-5647
1117

Del Monte Foods Inc......C......559 639-6160
10652 Jackson Ave Hanford (93230) *(P-794)*
Del Monte Foods Inc......B......209 548-5509
4000 Yosemite Blvd Modesto (95357) *(P-795)*
Del Monte Foods Inc (HQ)......C......925 949-2772
3003 Oak Rd Ste 600 Walnut Creek (94597) *(P-796)*
Del Monte Foods Inc......C......925 944-7300
205 N Wiget Ln Walnut Creek (94598) *(P-797)*
Del Monte Foods 48, Lathrop *Also called Big Heart Pet Brands (P-788)*
Del Ozone Holding Company Inc......E......805 541-1601
3580 Sueldo St San Luis Obispo (93401) *(P-16034)*
Del Ray Packaging, Del Rey *Also called Chooljian & Sons Inc (P-14841)*
Del Real LLC......C......951 681-0395
11041 Inland Ave Mira Loma (91752) *(P-989)*
Del Real Foods, Mira Loma *Also called Del Real LLC (P-989)*
Del Rey Enterprises Inc......F......559 233-4452
8898 E Central Ave Del Rey (93616) *(P-882)*
Del Rey Juice Co......D......559 888-8533
5286 S Del Rey Ave Del Rey (93616) *(P-946)*
Del Rio West Pallets......E......209 983-8215
3845 S El Dorado St Stockton (95206) *(P-4466)*
Del West Engineering Inc (PA)......C......661 295-5700
28128 Livingston Ave Valencia (91355) *(P-20312)*
Del West USA, Valencia *Also called Del West Engineering Inc (P-20312)*
Delafield Corporation (PA)......C......626 303-0740
1520 Flower Ave Duarte (91010) *(P-16426)*
Delafield Fluid Technology, Duarte *Also called Delafield Corporation (P-16426)*
Delafoil Holdings Inc (PA)......B......949 752-4580
18500 Von Karman Ave # 450 Irvine (92612) *(P-12555)*
Delallo Italian Foods, Oroville *Also called George Delallo Company Inc (P-802)*
Delamo Manufacturing Inc......D......323 936-3566
7171 Telegraph Rd Montebello (90640) *(P-10062)*
Delaney Manufacturing Inc......F......661 587-6681
6810 Downing Ave Bakersfield (93308) *(P-12556)*
Delano Growers Grape Products......D......661 725-3255
32351 Bassett Ave Delano (93215) *(P-2254)*
Delano Waste Water Treatment, Delano *Also called City of Delano (P-16024)*
Delaware Systems Technology, San Bernardino *Also called Systems Technology Inc (P-15229)*
Delco Oheb Energy, Los Angeles *Also called Delco Operating Co LP (P-132)*
Delco Operating Co LP......F......310 525-3535
1999 Avenue Of The Stars Los Angeles (90067) *(P-132)*
Delfin Design & Mfg Inc......E......949 888-4644
23301 Antonio Pkwy Rcho STA Marg (92688) *(P-10063)*
Delgado Brothers LLC......E......323 233-9793
647 E 59th St Los Angeles (90001) *(P-4618)*
Delgau Spring, Corona *Also called Spring Delgau Inc (P-13802)*
Delicato Vineyards (PA)......C......209 824-3600
12001 S Highway 99 Manteca (95336) *(P-1719)*
Delicato Vineyards......F......209 824-3501
12001 S Highway 99 Manteca (95336) *(P-1720)*
Delicato Vineyards......E......707 265-1700
455 Devlin Rd Ste 201 NAPA (94558) *(P-1721)*
Delicato Vineyards......E......707 253-1400
4089 Silverado Trl NAPA (94558) *(P-1722)*
Delicato Vineyards......F......831 385-7587
51955 Oasis Rd King City (93930) *(P-1723)*
Delivery Zone LLC......D......323 780-0888
120 S Anderson St Los Angeles (90033) *(P-2503)*
Dell Inc......F......408 206-5466
5450 Great America Pkwy Santa Clara (95054) *(P-15405)*
Della Robbia Inc......E......951 372-9199
796 E Harrison St Corona (92879) *(P-4859)*
Dellarise, Pasadena *Also called Pak Group LLC (P-1374)*
Dellarobbia Inc (PA)......E......949 251-9532
119 Waterworks Way Irvine (92618) *(P-4770)*
Delmar Pharmaceutical Inc......F......650 269-1984
3475 Edison Way Ste R Menlo Park (94025) *(P-8135)*
Delong Manufacturing Co Inc......F......408 727-3348
967 Parker Ct Santa Clara (95050) *(P-16427)*
Delori Foods, City of Industry *Also called Delori Products Inc (P-2504)*
Delori Products Inc......E......626 965-3006
17043 Green Dr City of Industry (91745) *(P-2504)*
Delphi Connection Systems LLC......F......949 458-3155
8662 Siempre Viva Rd San Diego (92154) *(P-20313)*
Delphi Control Systems Inc......F......909 593-8099
2806 Metropolitan Pl Pomona (91767) *(P-21569)*
Delphi Display Systems Inc......D......714 825-3400
3550 Hyland Ave Costa Mesa (92626) *(P-15728)*
Delphix Corp (PA)......E......650 494-1645
1400 Saport Blvd Ste 200a Redwood City (94063) *(P-24558)*
Delphon Industries LLC (PA)......C......510 576-2220
31398 Huntwood Ave Hayward (94544) *(P-10064)*
Delray Lighting Inc......E......818 767-3793
7545 N Lockheed Dr Burbank (91505) *(P-17685)*
Delstar Technologies Inc......E......619 258-1503
9225 Isaac St Santee (92071) *(P-9704)*
Delstar Technologies Inc......E......619 258-1503
1306 Fayette St El Cajon (92020) *(P-9705)*
Delt Industries Inc......F......805 579-0213
90 W Easy St Ste 2 Simi Valley (93065) *(P-11775)*
Delta Coast Beer LLC......F......213 604-2428
2034 E Lincoln Ave Anaheim (92806) *(P-1586)*
Delta Commerce Corporation......F......714 758-0030
1363 S State College Blvd Anaheim (92806) *(P-4077)*
Delta D V H Circuits Inc......E......818 786-8241
16117 Leadwell St Van Nuys (91406) *(P-18466)*
Delta Design Inc (HQ)......B......858 848-8000
12367 Crosthwaite Cir Poway (92064) *(P-15313)*
Delta Design Littleton Inc (HQ)......F......858 848-8100
12367 Crosthwaite Cir Poway (92064) *(P-21740)*
Delta Door Company, Stockton *Also called Masonite International Corp (P-4189)*
Delta Dvh Circuits, Van Nuys *Also called Ambay Circuits Inc (P-18417)*
Delta Engineering and Mfg, Chino *Also called Delta Manufacturing Inc (P-16429)*
Delta Fabrication Inc......D......818 407-4000
9600 De Soto Ave Chatsworth (91311) *(P-12557)*
Delta Floors, Anaheim *Also called Delta Commerce Corporation (P-4077)*
Delta Group Electronics Inc......D......858 569-1681
10180 Scripps Ranch Blvd San Diego (92131) *(P-19511)*
Delta Hi-Tech......C......818 407-4000
9600 De Soto Ave Chatsworth (91311) *(P-16428)*
Delta Ironworks, Salinas *Also called Salomon Dominguez (P-12887)*
Delta Lath & Plaster Inc......E......916 383-6756
5451 Whse Way Ste 105 Sacramento (95826) *(P-14369)*
Delta Machine, San Jose *Also called Delta Matrix Inc (P-16430)*
Delta Manufacturing Inc......E......909 590-4563
6260 Prescott Ct Chino (91710) *(P-16429)*
Delta Matrix Inc......E......408 955-9140
2180 Oakland Rd San Jose (95131) *(P-16430)*
Delta Pacific Activewear Inc......D......714 871-9281
331 S Hale Ave Fullerton (92831) *(P-2832)*
Delta Rebar Services Inc......F......925 798-4220
2410 Bates Ave Concord (94520) *(P-12152)*
Delta Signs, Stockton *Also called Street Graphics Inc (P-23982)*
Delta Sportswear Inc......F......714 568-1102
331 S Hale Ave Fullerton (92831) *(P-3230)*
Delta Stag Manufacturing......D......562 904-6444
1818 E Rosslynn Ave Fullerton (92831) *(P-20199)*
Delta Star Inc......B......650 508-2850
270 Industrial Rd San Carlos (94070) *(P-17088)*
Delta Tau Data Systems Inc Cal (HQ)......C......818 998-2095
21314 Lassen St Chatsworth (91311) *(P-15314)*
Delta Tau International Inc......F......818 998-2095
21314 Lassen St Chatsworth (91311) *(P-15315)*
Delta Tech Industries LLC......F......909 673-1900
1901 S Vineyard Ave Ontario (91761) *(P-17660)*
Delta Trading LP......E......661 834-5560
17731 Millux Rd Bakersfield (93311) *(P-9381)*
Delta Turnstile Controls, Concord *Also called Delta Turnstiles LLC (P-19943)*
Delta Turnstiles LLC......F......925 969-1498
1011 Detroit Ave Concord (94518) *(P-19943)*
Delta Web Printing Inc......E......916 375-0044
1871 Enterprise Blvd West Sacramento (95691) *(P-7295)*
Delta Web Printing & Bindery, West Sacramento *Also called Delta Web Printing Inc (P-7295)*
Delta Yimin Technologies Inc......E......510 487-4411
33170 Central Ave Union City (94587) *(P-10065)*
Delta-Sigma Inc......F......951 343-4005
6690 Doolittle Ave Riverside (92503) *(P-18084)*
Delta-Stag Truck Body, Fullerton *Also called Delta Stag Manufacturing (P-20199)*
Deltatrak Inc......E......209 579-5343
1236 Doker Dr Modesto (95351) *(P-22186)*
Deltatrak Inc (PA)......E......925 249-2250
6140 Stoneridge Mall Rd # 180 Pleasanton (94588) *(P-22187)*
Deltronic Corporation......D......714 545-5800
3900 W Segerstrom Ave Santa Ana (92704) *(P-22071)*
Deluxe Check Printers, Lancaster *Also called Deluxe Corporation (P-7580)*
Deluxe Corporation......D......408 370-8801
1551 Dell Ave Campbell (95008) *(P-7578)*
Deluxe Corporation......B......651 483-7100
2861 Mandela Pkwy Oakland (94608) *(P-7579)*
Deluxe Corporation......B......661 942-1144
42933 Business Ctr Pkwy Lancaster (93535) *(P-7580)*
Deluxe Financial Services, Campbell *Also called Deluxe Corporation (P-7578)*
Deluxe Pckges An Amcor Flexble, Yuba City *Also called Paperboard Packaging Corp (P-5530)*
Demag Cranes & Components Corp......E......909 880-8800
13290 Sabre Blvd Victorville (92394) *(P-14296)*
Demaiz Inc......F......650 518-6268
77 S 28th St San Jose (95116) *(P-755)*
Demandbase Inc (PA)......D......415 683-2660
680 Folsom St Ste 400 San Francisco (94107) *(P-24559)*
Demaria Electric Inc......E......310 549-4980
7048 Marcelle St Paramount (90723) *(P-25456)*
Demaria Electric Motor Svcs, Paramount *Also called Demaria Electric Inc (P-25456)*
Demenno Kerdoon......C......310 537-7100
2000 N Alameda St Compton (90222) *(P-133)*
Demenno-Kerdoon, South Gate *Also called Demenno/Kerdoon Holdings (P-9431)*
Demenno/Kerdoon Holdings......D......323 268-3387
3650 E 26th St Vernon (90058) *(P-9430)*
Demenno/Kerdoon Holdings (HQ)......D......562 231-1550
9302 Garfield Ave South Gate (90280) *(P-9431)*
Demes Gourmet Corporation......E......714 870-6040
327 N State College Blvd Fullerton (92831) *(P-479)*
Demetrius Pohl......F......323 735-1027
2179 W 20th St Los Angeles (90018) *(P-404)*
Demille Marble & Granite Inc......E......760 341-7525
72091 Woburn Ct Ste D Thousand Palms (92276) *(P-11249)*
Demptos NAPA Cooperage (HQ)......E......707 257-2628
1050 Soscol Ferry Rd NAPA (94558) *(P-4520)*
Demtech Services Inc......E......530 621-3200
6414 Capitol Ave Diamond Springs (95619) *(P-10066)*
Den-Mat Corporation (HQ)......B......805 922-8491
236 S Broadway St Orcutt (93455) *(P-8735)*
Den-Mat Corporation......E......800 445-0345
21515 Vanowen St Ste 200 Canoga Park (91303) *(P-8736)*

Den-Mat Holdings LLC (HQ) ...... F 805 346-3700
1017 W Central Ave Lompoc (93436) *(P-22867)*
Denali Software Inc (HQ) ...... E 408 943-1234
2655 Seely Ave San Jose (95134) *(P-24560)*
Denali Therapeutics Inc ...... C 650 866-8548
151 Oyster Point Blvd # 2 South San Francisco (94080) *(P-8545)*
Denbeste Manufacturing Inc ...... F 707 838-1407
810 Den Beste Ct Ste 107 Windsor (95492) *(P-20200)*
Dendreon Pharmaceuticals Inc ...... F 562 253-3931
1700 Saturn Way Seal Beach (90740) *(P-8136)*
Dendreon Pharmaceuticals LLC (HQ) ...... E 562 252-7500
1700 Saturn Way Seal Beach (90740) *(P-8137)*
Denim-Tech LLC ...... D 323 277-8998
2300 E 52nd St Vernon (90058) *(P-15929)*
Denmac Industries Inc ...... E 562 634-2714
7616 Rosecrans Ave Paramount (90723) *(P-13574)*
Dennie Manning Concrete Inc ...... F 909 823-7521
15815 Arrow Blvd Fontana (92335) *(P-11101)*
Dennis Bolton Enterprises Inc ...... E 818 982-1800
7285 Coldwater Canyon Ave North Hollywood (91605) *(P-6781)*
Dennis Reeves Inc ...... F 909 392-9999
1350 Palomares St Ste A La Verne (91750) *(P-5053)*
Dennison Inc ...... E 626 965-8917
17901 Railroad St City of Industry (91748) *(P-12849)*
Denovo Dental Inc ...... E 626 480-0182
5130 Commerce Dr Baldwin Park (91706) *(P-22868)*
Denso International Amer Inc ...... E 760 597-7400
3252 Business Park Dr Vista (92081) *(P-20314)*
Denso Pdts & Svcs Americas Inc ...... C 951 698-3379
41673 Corning Pl Murrieta (92562) *(P-20315)*
Denso Wreless Systems Amer Inc ...... C 760 734-4600
3250 Business Park Dr Vista (92081) *(P-18085)*
Dentium USA (HQ) ...... F 714 226-0229
6731 Katella Ave Cypress (90630) *(P-22869)*
Dentonis Spring and Suspension, Stockton Also called Dentonis Welding Works Inc *(P-25399)*
Dentonis Welding Works Inc (PA) ...... E 209 464-4930
801 S Airport Way Stockton (95205) *(P-25399)*
Dentsply Sirona Inc ...... E 909 795-2080
13553 Calimesa Blvd Yucaipa (92399) *(P-22870)*
Denttio Inc ...... F 323 254-1000
116 N Maryland Ave # 125 Glendale (91206) *(P-22871)*
Dependable Furniture Mfg Co, San Leandro Also called Van Sark Inc *(P-4817)*
Dependable Plas & Pattern Inc ...... F 707 863-4900
4900 Fulton Dr Fairfield (94534) *(P-9835)*
Dependable Precision Mfg Inc ...... F 209 369-1055
1111 S Stockton St Ste A Lodi (95240) *(P-12558)*
Dependble Incontinence Sup Inc ...... F 626 812-0044
590 S Vincent Ave Azusa (91702) *(P-5664)*
Depot 6, The, Apple Valley Also called Valero Energy Corporation *(P-9371)*
Depuy Synthes Products Inc ...... F 408 246-4300
130 Knowles Dr Ste E Los Gatos (95032) *(P-22419)*
Derek and Constance Lee Corp (PA) ...... D 909 595-8831
19355 San Jose Ave City of Industry (91748) *(P-480)*
Derik Plastics Industries Inc ...... A 626 371-7799
2540 Corp Pl Ste B100 Monterey Park (91754) *(P-5346)*
Derma E, Simi Valley Also called Stearns Corporation *(P-8848)*
Dermacare Neuroscience Inst ...... F 323 780-2981
2580 Corporate Pl F109 Monterey Park (91754) *(P-8737)*
Dermal Group, The, Carson Also called Dermalogica LLC *(P-8738)*
Dermalogica LLC (HQ) ...... C 310 900-4000
1535 Beachey Pl Carson (90746) *(P-8738)*
Dermanew LLC (PA) ...... F 626 442-2813
436 Smithwood Dr Beverly Hills (90212) *(P-8739)*
Dermanew LLC ...... F 310 276-0457
9461 Santa Monica Blvd Beverly Hills (90210) *(P-22420)*
Dermanew Institute, Beverly Hills Also called Dermanew LLC *(P-22420)*
Dermira Inc ...... C 650 421-7200
275 Middlefield Rd # 150 Menlo Park (94025) *(P-8138)*
Derosa Enterprises Inc ...... E 760 743-5500
15935 Spring Oaks Rd # 1 El Cajon (92021) *(P-12559)*
Desais Design Craft ...... F 626 285-3189
408 S Gladys Ave San Gabriel (91776) *(P-10640)*
Deschner Corporation ...... E 714 557-1261
3211 W Harvard St Santa Ana (92704) *(P-15316)*
Desco Manufacturing Company (PA) ...... F 949 858-7400
23031 Arroyo Vis Ste A Rcho STA Marg (92688) *(P-16431)*
Desert Block Co Inc ...... F 661 824-2624
11374 Tuxford St Sun Valley (91352) *(P-9382)*
Desert Brand, City of Industry Also called Hill Brothers Chemical Company *(P-7664)*
Desert Brothers Craft ...... F 323 530-0015
603 W Whittier Blvd Montebello (90640) *(P-1587)*
Desert Grafics, Palm Springs Also called Desert Publications Inc *(P-6143)*
Desert Microsystems Inc ...... E 951 682-3867
3387 Chicago Ave Riverside (92507) *(P-21570)*
Desert Publications Inc (PA) ...... E 760 325-2333
303 N Indian Canyon Dr Palm Springs (92262) *(P-6143)*
Desert Redi Mix, Indio Also called Coronet Concrete Products *(P-11099)*
Desert Shades Inc ...... F 323 731-5000
5014 W Jefferson Blvd Los Angeles (90016) *(P-24077)*
Desert Shutters Inc ...... E 949 388-8344
33907 Robles Dr Dana Point (92629) *(P-4078)*
Desert Sky Machining Inc ...... E 925 426-0400
1236 Quarry Ln Ste 104 Pleasanton (94566) *(P-16432)*
Desert Sun Publishing Co (HQ) ...... C 760 322-8889
750 N Gene Autry Trl Palm Springs (92262) *(P-5828)*
Desert Sun, The, Palm Springs Also called Gannett Co Inc *(P-5854)*
Desert Trils Prpratory Academy, Adelanto Also called Adelanto Elementary School Dst *(P-2447)*

Desiccare Inc ...... E 909 444-8272
3400 Pomona Blvd Pomona (91768) *(P-11319)*
Design Concepts Inc ...... F 323 277-4771
4625 E 50th St Vernon (90058) *(P-3405)*
Design Engineering, Canoga Park Also called Infinity Precision Inc *(P-16582)*
Design Form Inc ...... F 714 952-3700
8250 Electric Ave Stanton (90680) *(P-12385)*
Design Imagery ...... F 650 589-6464
3621 Ortega St San Francisco (94122) *(P-5137)*
Design Industries Inc ...... F 559 675-3535
17918 Brook Dr W Madera (93638) *(P-10914)*
Design Journal Inc ...... F 310 394-4394
1720 20th St Ste 201 Santa Monica (90404) *(P-6144)*
Design La, Santa Monica Also called Design Journal Inc *(P-6144)*
Design Octaves ...... E 831 464-8500
2701 Research Park Dr Soquel (95073) *(P-10067)*
Design Polymerics, Santa Ana Also called Davco Enterprises Inc *(P-9140)*
Design Printing, Los Angeles Also called Red Brick Corporation *(P-7080)*
Design Shapes In Steel Inc ...... E 626 579-2032
10315 Rush St South El Monte (91733) *(P-11392)*
Design Todays Inc (PA) ...... D 213 745-3091
725 E Wash Blvd Fl 2nd Los Angeles (90021) *(P-3406)*
Design Veronique, Richmond Also called My True Image Mfg Inc *(P-22776)*
Design West Technologies Inc ...... D 714 731-0201
2701 Dow Ave Tustin (92780) *(P-10068)*
Design Woodworking Inc (PA) ...... E 209 334-6674
709 N Sacramento St Lodi (95240) *(P-4143)*
Design Workshops ...... F 510 434-0727
486 Lesser St Oakland (94601) *(P-5054)*
Designed By Scorpio Inc ...... F 213 612-4440
550 S Hill St Ste 1605 Los Angeles (90013) *(P-23255)*
Designed Metal Connections Inc (HQ) ...... B 310 323-6200
14800 S Figueroa St Gardena (90248) *(P-13021)*
Designer Drinks ...... E 760 444-2355
5050 Avenida Encinas Carlsbad (92008) *(P-2129)*
Designer Fashion Door, Temecula Also called Designer Sash and Door Sys Inc *(P-10069)*
Designer Printing Inc ...... F 415 989-0008
638 Washington St San Francisco (94111) *(P-6782)*
Designer Sash and Door Sys Inc ...... D 951 657-4179
45899 Via Tornado Temecula (92590) *(P-10069)*
Designer Sound SEC Systems ...... E 818 981-9249
13547 Ventura Blvd # 338 Sherman Oaks (91423) *(P-19944)*
Designerx Pharmaceuticals Inc ...... F 707 451-0441
4941 Allison Pkwy Ste B Vacaville (95688) *(P-8139)*
Designline Windows & Doors Inc ...... E 760 931-9422
5674 El Camino Real Ste K Carlsbad (92008) *(P-12308)*
Designs By Batya Inc ...... F 213 746-7844
1200 Santee St Ste 208 Los Angeles (90015) *(P-3028)*
Designs With Fabric, South San Francisco Also called Magnolia Lane Soft HM Furn Inc *(P-3731)*
Deskmakers Inc ...... E 323 264-2260
6525 Flotilla St Commerce (90040) *(P-4942)*
Desserts On US Inc ...... F 707 822-0160
57 Belle Falor Ct Arcata (95521) *(P-1230)*
Destiney Group Inc ...... F 323 581-4477
4800 District Blvd Vernon (90058) *(P-2733)*
Destiny Boutique, Murrieta Also called Tuula Inc *(P-8611)*
Destiny Tool, Santa Clara Also called Step Tools Unlimited Inc *(P-14681)*
Detention Device Systems ...... E 510 783-0771
25545 Seaboard Ln Hayward (94545) *(P-16433)*
Determan Industries Inc ...... F 916 974-1977
4246 Roseville Rd North Highlands (95660) *(P-13193)*
Detoronics Corp ...... E 626 579-7130
13071 Rosecrans Ave Santa Fe Springs (90670) *(P-19386)*
Detroit Diesel Corporation ...... F 562 929-7016
10645 Studebaker Rd Fl 2 Downey (90241) *(P-14026)*
Deutsch Dao, Hemet Also called Te Connectivity Corporation *(P-19421)*
Deutstch Industrial Products, Banning Also called Te Connectivity Corporation *(P-19415)*
Deux Lux Inc (PA) ...... F 213 746-7040
11609 Vanowen St Ste B North Hollywood (91605) *(P-10559)*
Deva, Tustin Also called Distribution Electrnics Vlued *(P-19945)*
Developlus Inc ...... D 951 738-8595
1575 Magnolia Ave Corona (92879) *(P-24078)*
Development Assoc Contrls ...... E 805 684-8307
6390 Rose Ln Carpinteria (93013) *(P-14370)*
Devincenzi Metal Products Inc ...... D 650 692-5800
1809 Castenada Dr Burlingame (94010) *(P-12560)*
Devincnzi Archtctural Pdts Inc ...... E 650 692-5800
1717 Adrian Rd Burlingame (94010) *(P-12850)*
Devita Dialysis, Santa Ana Also called Da Vita Tustin Dialysis Ctr *(P-22417)*
Devoll Rubber Mfg Group, Victorville Also called Devoll Rubber Mfg Group Inc *(P-9607)*
Devoll Rubber Mfg Group Inc ...... F 760 246-0142
18626 Phantom St Victorville (92394) *(P-9607)*
Devon Furniture, San Gabriel Also called R J Vincent Inc *(P-4803)*
Dewalt Service Center 148, Bellflower Also called Black & Decker (us) Inc *(P-14698)*
Deweyl Tool Co Inc ...... E 707 765-5779
959 Transport Way Petaluma (94954) *(P-14623)*
Dex-O-Tex Division, Compton Also called Crossfield Products Corp *(P-7827)*
Dexcom Inc (PA) ...... B 858 200-0200
6340 Sequence Dr San Diego (92121) *(P-22421)*
Dexerials America Corporation ...... E 408 441-0846
2001 Gateway Pl Ste 455e San Jose (95110) *(P-21685)*
Dexin International Inc ...... C 626 859-7475
677 Arrow Grand Cir Covina (91722) *(P-17597)*
Dext Company, Santa Monica Also called Reconserve Inc *(P-1157)*
Dext Company of Maryland (HQ) ...... E 310 458-1574
2811 Wilshire Blvd # 410 Santa Monica (90403) *(P-1127)*

Dexta Corporation...D...707 255-2454
962 Kaiser Rd NAPA (94558) ***(P-22872)***
Dexter Axle Company...C...760 744-1610
135 Sunshine Ln San Marcos (92069) ***(P-20500)***
Dexters Deli...E...760 720-7507
2508 El Cmino Real Ste B2 Carlsbad (92008) ***(P-1111)***
Dezario Shoe Company, North Hollywood *Also called Meco-Nag Corporation* ***(P-10499)***
Df Grafix Inc...F...858 866-0858
13871 Danielson St Poway (92064) ***(P-6783)***
Dfine Inc (HQ)...D...408 321-9999
3047 Orchard Pkwy San Jose (95134) ***(P-22422)***
Dg Displays LLC...E...877 358-5976
355 Parkside Dr San Fernando (91340) ***(P-23856)***
Dg Engineering Corp (PA)...E...818 364-9024
13326 Ralston Ave Sylmar (91342) ***(P-21287)***
Dg Mountz Associates, San Jose *Also called Mountz Inc* ***(P-21621)***
DG Performance Spc Inc...D...714 961-8850
4100 E La Palma Ave Anaheim (92807) ***(P-21225)***
Dga Inc...E...925 299-9000
5325 Industrial Way Benicia (94510) ***(P-8140)***
DGA Machine Shop Inc...F...951 354-2113
5825 Ordway St Riverside (92504) ***(P-16434)***
Dgb LLC...E...858 578-0414
8495 Commerce Ave San Diego (92121) ***(P-23548)***
Dgcc Inc...F...818 787-5007
14745 Keswick St Van Nuys (91405) ***(P-7597)***
Dggr Packaging Crating & Foam, Anaheim *Also called JDC Development Group Inc* ***(P-4525)***
Dharma Mudranalaya (PA)...E...707 847-3380
35788 Hauser Bridge Rd Cazadero (95421) ***(P-6335)***
Dharma Publishing, Cazadero *Also called Dharma Mudranalaya* ***(P-6335)***
Dhl Wire Products...F...909 596-2909
2325 1st St La Verne (91750) ***(P-11438)***
Dhm Enterprises Inc...E...916 688-7767
7609 Wilbur Way Sacramento (95828) ***(P-21226)***
DHm International Corp...D...323 263-3888
901 Monterey Pass Rd Monterey Park (91754) ***(P-3407)***
Dhy Inc...E...310 376-7512
922 Duncan Ave Manhattan Beach (90266) ***(P-3144)***
Di Maxx Technologies LLC...F...530 888-1942
11838 Kemper Rd Auburn (95603) ***(P-22072)***
Diablo Clinical Research Inc...E...925 930-7267
2255 Ygnacio Valley Rd M Walnut Creek (94598) ***(P-8141)***
Diablo Country Magazine Inc...E...925 943-1111
2520 Camino Diablo Walnut Creek (94597) ***(P-6145)***
Diablo Custom Publishing, Walnut Creek *Also called Diablo Country Magazine Inc* ***(P-6145)***
Diablo Molding & Trim Company...E...925 417-0663
5600 Sunol Blvd Ste C Pleasanton (94566) ***(P-12309)***
Diablo Precision Inc...F...831 634-0136
500 Park Center Dr Ste 8 Hollister (95023) ***(P-16435)***
Diageno Chateau & Estate Wines, NAPA *Also called Diageo North America Inc* ***(P-1726)***
Diageo North America Inc...D...707 939-6200
21468 8th St E Ste 1 Sonoma (95476) ***(P-1724)***
Diageo North America Inc...D...707 967-5200
1960 Saint Helena Hwy Rutherford (94573) ***(P-2070)***
Diageo North America Inc...D...415 835-7300
1160 Battery St Ste 30 San Francisco (94111) ***(P-1725)***
Diageo North America Inc...D...707 299-2600
555 Gateway Dr NAPA (94558) ***(P-1726)***
Diagnostic Reagents, Los Angeles *Also called James Stewart* ***(P-8237)***
Diagnostic Solutions Intl LLC...F...909 930-3600
2580 E Philadelphia St C Ontario (91761) ***(P-20794)***
Diagnostics For Real World Ltd (PA)...F...408 773-1511
845 Embedded Way San Jose (95138) ***(P-8473)***
Diagnostixx California Corp...E...909 482-0840
829 Towne Center Dr Pomona (91767) ***(P-22423)***
Dial Act Corporation...F...510 659-8099
45979 Warm Springs Blvd # 3 Fremont (94539) ***(P-9706)***
Dial Precision Inc...D...760 947-3557
17235 Darwin Ave Hesperia (92345) ***(P-16436)***
Dialex, Fremont *Also called Dial Act Corporation* ***(P-9706)***
Dialog Semiconductor, Campbell *Also called Iwatt Inc* ***(P-18933)***
Dialog Semiconductor Inc (HQ)...C...408 845-8500
2560 Mission College Blvd # 110 Santa Clara (95054) ***(P-18800)***
Dialogic Inc...D...800 755-4444
2890 Zanker Rd Ste 107 San Jose (95134) ***(P-17939)***
Diamanti Inc...E...408 645-5111
111 N Market St Ste 800 San Jose (95113) ***(P-15632)***
Diamatic Management Services, San Diego *Also called Global Polishing Solutions LLC* ***(P-14169)***
Diamics Inc...F...415 883-0414
6 Hamilton Landing # 200 Novato (94949) ***(P-22424)***
Diamodent Inc...F...888 281-8850
1577 N Harmony Cir Anaheim (92807) ***(P-22873)***
Diamon Fusion Intl Inc...F...949 388-8000
9361 Irvine Blvd Irvine (92618) ***(P-9241)***
Diamond Baseball Company Inc...E...800 366-2999
1880 E Saint Andrew Pl Santa Ana (92705) ***(P-23549)***
Diamond Creek Vineyard...F...707 942-6926
1500 Diamond Mountain Rd Calistoga (94515) ***(P-1727)***
Diamond Crystal Brands Inc...E...559 651-7782
8700 W Doe Ave Visalia (93291) ***(P-2505)***
Diamond Crystal Brands-Hormel, Visalia *Also called Diamond Crystal Brands Inc* ***(P-2505)***
Diamond Doors, South Lake Tahoe *Also called Diamond Woodcraft* ***(P-4144)***
Diamond Foods LLC (PA)...A...209 467-6000
1050 Diamond St Stockton (95205) ***(P-1487)***
Diamond Foods LLC...F...209 467-6000
600 Montgomery St Fl 17 San Francisco (94111) ***(P-1488)***
Diamond Ground Products Inc...E...805 498-3837
2651 Lavery Ct Newbury Park (91320) ***(P-14724)***
Diamond Injection Molds Inc...F...909 390-2260
4365 E Lowell St Ste E Ontario (91761) ***(P-14505)***
Diamond K2...E...310 539-6116
23911 Garnier St Ste C Torrance (90505) ***(P-11917)***
Diamond Multimedia, Canoga Park *Also called Best Data Products Inc* ***(P-15681)***
Diamond Multimedia Systems...B...408 868-9613
2880 Junction Ave San Jose (95134) ***(P-18467)***
Diamond of California, Stockton *Also called Diamond Foods LLC* ***(P-1487)***
Diamond Perforated Metals Inc...D...559 651-1889
7300 W Sunnyview Ave Visalia (93291) ***(P-13194)***
Diamond Pet Food Processors O...E...209 983-4900
250 Roth Rd Lathrop (95330) ***(P-1112)***
Diamond Precision Products, Placentia *Also called Foremost Precision Pdts Inc* ***(P-16508)***
Diamond Sports, Santa Ana *Also called Diamond Baseball Company Inc* ***(P-23549)***
Diamond Tech Incorporated...F...916 624-1118
4347 Pacific St Rocklin (95677) ***(P-14703)***
Diamond Tool and Die Inc...E...510 534-7050
508 29th Ave Oakland (94601) ***(P-16437)***
Diamond Tree Investments LLC...E...415 627-7730
2841 Octavia St San Francisco (94123) ***(P-3305)***
Diamond Truck Body Mfg Inc...F...209 943-1655
1908 E Fremont St Stockton (95205) ***(P-20201)***
Diamond Truss...F...530 477-1477
12462 Charles Dr Grass Valley (95945) ***(P-4402)***
Diamond Weld Industries Inc...F...559 268-9999
63 W North Ave Fresno (93706) ***(P-14725)***
Diamond Wipes Intl Inc (PA)...D...909 230-9888
4651 Schaefer Ave Chino (91710) ***(P-8740)***
Diamond Woodcraft...F...530 541-0866
2197 Ruth Ave Ste 1 South Lake Tahoe (96150) ***(P-4144)***
Diamond-U Products Inc...F...562 436-8245
515 W Cowles St Long Beach (90813) ***(P-13739)***
Diamonds By Design, Los Angeles *Also called Stardust Diamond Corp* ***(P-23348)***
Diamotec Inc...F...310 539-4994
3545 Lomita Blvd Ste C Torrance (90505) ***(P-14624)***
Dianas Mexican Food Pdts Inc (PA)...B...562 926-5802
16330 Pioneer Blvd Norwalk (90650) ***(P-2506)***
Dianas Mexican Food Pdts Inc...E...626 444-0555
2905 Durfee Ave El Monte (91732) ***(P-2507)***
Diane Markin Inc...F...310 322-0200
112 Penn St El Segundo (90245) ***(P-10692)***
Diaring Inc...F...213 489-3894
550 S Hill St Ste 990 Los Angeles (90013) ***(P-23256)***
Diasol Inc (PA)...F...818 838-7077
1110 Arroyo St San Fernando (91340) ***(P-22425)***
Diasorin Molecular LLC...C...562 240-6500
11331 Valley View St Cypress (90630) ***(P-8474)***
Diassess Inc...F...510 350-8071
1412 62nd St Emeryville (94608) ***(P-22426)***
Diatomaceous Earth.com, Santa Barbara *Also called Esperer Webstores LLC* ***(P-613)***
Dibella Baking Company Inc...D...951 797-4144
3524 Seagate Way Ste 110 Oceanside (92056) ***(P-1362)***
Dicaperl Corporation (HQ)...D...610 667-6640
23705 Crenshaw Blvd Torrance (90505) ***(P-410)***
Dicar Inc...E...408 295-1106
1285 Alma Ct San Jose (95112) ***(P-11659)***
Dicarlo Concrete Inc...F...909 261-4294
8657 Pecan Ave Ste 100 Rancho Cucamonga (91739) ***(P-17890)***
Dick Brown Technical Services...F...707 374-2133
553 Airport Rd Ste B Rio Vista (94571) ***(P-101)***
Dick Farrell Industries Inc...F...909 613-9424
5071 Lindsay Ct Chino (91710) ***(P-15257)***
Dicker & Dicker Beverly Hills, Beverly Hills *Also called Larry B LLC* ***(P-3601)***
Dickinson Corporation...F...415 883-7147
31 Commercial Blvd Ste G Novato (94949) ***(P-21467)***
Dicon Fiberoptics Inc (PA)...C...510 620-5000
1689 Regatta Blvd Bldg W1 Richmond (94804) ***(P-19512)***
Didi of California Inc...E...323 256-4514
5816 Piedmont Ave Los Angeles (90042) ***(P-3231)***
Die & Tool Products Co Inc...F...415 822-2888
1925 Ingalls St San Francisco (94124) ***(P-16438)***
Die Craft Engineering & Mfg Co...F...562 777-8809
11975 Florence Ave Santa Fe Springs (90670) ***(P-14506)***
Die Craft Stamping Inc...E...562 944-2395
10132 Norwalk Blvd Santa Fe Springs (90670) ***(P-13763)***
Die Shop...F...562 630-4400
7302 Adams St Paramount (90723) ***(P-14507)***
Die-Namic Fabrication Inc...F...909 350-2870
378 E Orange Show Rd San Bernardino (92408) ***(P-13195)***
Diecraft, Santa Fe Springs *Also called Die Craft Engineering & Mfg Co* ***(P-14506)***
Diecraft Corporation...E...323 728-2601
5590 Naples Canal Long Beach (90803) ***(P-16439)***
Diego & Son Printing Inc...E...619 233-5373
2104 National Ave San Diego (92113) ***(P-6784)***
Dielectric Coating Industries...F...510 487-5980
30997 Huntwood Ave # 104 Hayward (94544) ***(P-22073)***
Diesel Injection Service, Colton *Also called Ostoich Diesel Service* ***(P-16168)***
Dietrich Industries Inc...D...209 547-9066
2525 S Airport Way Stockton (95206) ***(P-11469)***
Dietzgen Corporation...E...951 278-3259
1522 E Bentley Dr Corona (92879) ***(P-5709)***
Dig Corporation...D...760 727-0914
1210 Activity Dr Vista (92081) ***(P-14059)***
Diggimac Inc DBA Ltg Element...F...858 322-6000
16885 W Bernardo Dr # 380 San Diego (92127) ***(P-17461)***
Digi Group LLC...F...800 521-8467
2421 W 205th St Ste D204 Torrance (90501) ***(P-18086)***

Mergent e-mail: customerrelations@mergent.com
1120
2019 California
Manufacturers Register
(P-0000) Products & Services Section entry number
(PA)=Parent Co (HQ)=Headquarters (DH)=Div Headquarters

Digi Print Plus....F....949 770-5000
9670 Research Dr Irvine (92618) *(P-6785)*
Digicom Electronics Inc....E....510 639-7003
7799 Pardee Ln Oakland (94621) *(P-18468)*
Digilens Inc....E....408 734-0219
1288 Hammerwood Ave Sunnyvale (94089) *(P-22074)*
Digilock, Petaluma *Also called Security People Inc (P-19722)*
Digisight Technologies Inc....F....415 215-4440
535 Mission St Ste 1929 San Francisco (94105) *(P-24561)*
Digital Check Technologies Inc....E....909 204-4638
10231 Trademark St Ste A Rancho Cucamonga (91730) *(P-15729)*
Digital Dynamics Inc....E....831 438-4444
5 Victor Sq Scotts Valley (95066) *(P-21571)*
Digital Factory, Atwater *Also called Certified Stainless Svc Inc (P-12373)*
Digital First Media LLC....A....714 796-7000
625 N Grand Ave Santa Ana (92701) *(P-5829)*
Digital Instruments Div, Goleta *Also called Veeco Process Equipment Inc (P-22047)*
Digital Label Solutions Inc....E....714 982-5000
22745 Old Canal Rd Yorba Linda (92887) *(P-5710)*
Digital Light LLC....E....310 551-9999
1801 Century Park E # 2400 Los Angeles (90067) *(P-18801)*
Digital Loggers Inc....E....408 330-5599
2695 Walsh Ave Santa Clara (95051) *(P-17140)*
Digital Mania Inc....E....415 896-0500
455 Market St Ste 180 San Francisco (94105) *(P-6786)*
Digital Media Vending Intl LLC....F....415 516-3243
105 Duchess Ct Windsor (95492) *(P-15921)*
Digital Music Corporation....F....707 545-0600
3165 Coffey Ln Santa Rosa (95403) *(P-23361)*
Digital One Legal Solutions, San Francisco *Also called Copy 1 Inc (P-6758)*
Digital One Printing Inc....F....858 278-2228
13367 Kirkham Way 110 Poway (92064) *(P-7296)*
Digital Periph Solutions Inc....E....714 998-3440
8015 E Crystal Dr Bldg J Anaheim (92807) *(P-17789)*
Digital Power Corporation (HQ)....E....510 657-2635
48430 Lakeview Blvd Fremont (94538) *(P-19513)*
Digital Pre-Press Intl, South San Francisco *Also called Pre-Press International (P-7032)*
Digital Printing Systems Inc (PA)....D....626 815-1888
777 N Georgia Ave Azusa (91702) *(P-6787)*
Digital Prototype Systems Inc....E....559 454-1600
4955 E Yale Ave Fresno (93727) *(P-18087)*
Digital Room Holdings Inc (PA)....C....310 575-4440
8000 Haskell Ave Van Nuys (91406) *(P-7297)*
Digital Signal Power Mfg, Ontario *Also called Dspm Inc (P-19332)*
Digital Storm, Morgan Hill *Also called Hanaps Enterprises (P-15753)*
Digital Technology Lab Corp....D....530 746-7400
3805 Faraday Ave Davis (95618) *(P-14625)*
Digital Video Systems Inc (PA)....E....650 938-8815
357 Castro St Ste 5 Mountain View (94041) *(P-17790)*
Digital View Inc....F....408 782-7773
18440 Tech Dr Ste 130 Morgan Hill (95037) *(P-19514)*
Digitalpro Inc....D....858 874-7750
13257 Kirkham Way Poway (92064) *(P-7298)*
Digitran, Rancho Cucamonga *Also called Electro Switch Corp (P-17143)*
Digivision Inc....F....858 530-0100
9830 Summers Ridge Rd San Diego (92121) *(P-21572)*
Dilco Industrial Inc....F....714 998-5266
205 E Bristol Ln Orange (92865) *(P-14775)*
Diligent Solutions Inc....E....760 814-8960
3240 Grey Hawk Ct Carlsbad (92010) *(P-16440)*
Dillon Aircraft Deburring....E....818 768-0801
11771 Sheldon St Sun Valley (91352) *(P-13387)*
Dillon Precision Incorporated....E....530 672-6794
3816 Maplewood Ln Placerville (95667) *(P-16441)*
Dima-Tech Inc....E....619 474-7006
301 W 28th St Ste W National City (91950) *(P-17089)*
Dimad Enterprises Inc (PA)....F....626 445-3303
44 La Porte St Arcadia (91006) *(P-13388)*
Dimad Metal Finishing, Arcadia *Also called Dimad Enterprises Inc (P-13388)*
Dime Racing, Huntington Beach *Also called Dime Research and Development (P-20135)*
Dime Research and Development....E....714 969-7879
5542 Research Dr Huntington Beach (92649) *(P-20135)*
Dimension One Spas Inc (HQ)....C....800 345-7727
1819 Aston Ave Ste 105 Carlsbad (92008) *(P-24079)*
Dimensional Plastics Corp....E....305 691-5961
6565 Crescent Park W # 111 Playa Vista (90094) *(P-10070)*
Dimensions In Screen Printing, Irvine *Also called Tomorrows Look Inc (P-2898)*
Dimensions of Dental Hygiene, Santa Ana *Also called Belmont Publications Inc (P-6111)*
Dimensions Unlimited....F....707 552-6800
1080 Nimitz Ave Ste 400 Vallejo (94592) *(P-5055)*
Dimic Steel Tech Inc....E....909 946-6767
145 N 8th Ave Upland (91786) *(P-12561)*
Dimo Gear LLC....E....916 684-1051
1160 Vienna Dr Ste A Lodi (95242) *(P-10560)*
Dimora Enterprises....F....760 832-9070
3475 N Indian Canyon Dr Palm Springs (92262) *(P-20136)*
Dincloud Inc....D....310 929-1101
27520 Hawthorne Blvd # 185 Rllng HLS Est (90274) *(P-24562)*
Dinner On A Dollar Inc....F....858 693-3939
10249 Caminito Pitaya San Diego (92131) *(P-6469)*
Dinsmore & Associates Inc....F....714 641-7111
1681 Kettering Irvine (92614) *(P-9707)*
Dinuba Sentinel, Dinuba *Also called Sentinel Printing & Publishing (P-6042)*
Dion Rostamian....F....877 633-0293
1146 N Central Ave 227 Glendale (91202) *(P-23149)*
Dionex Corporation (HQ)....B....408 737-0700
1228 Titan Way Ste 1002 Sunnyvale (94085) *(P-21945)*
Dionex Corporation....D....408 737-0700
501 Mercury Dr Sunnyvale (94085) *(P-21946)*

Dip Braze Inc....E....818 768-1555
9131 De Garmo Ave Sun Valley (91352) *(P-25400)*
Direct Chemicals, Huntington Beach *Also called Home & Body Company (P-8647)*
Direct Drilling Inc....E....925 472-6850
1255 Treat Blvd Walnut Creek (94597) *(P-102)*
Direct Drive Systems Inc....D....714 872-5500
621 Burning Tree Rd Fullerton (92833) *(P-17189)*
Direct Edge Screenworks Inc....F....714 579-3686
430 W Collins Ave Orange (92867) *(P-7299)*
Direct Label & Tag LLC....E....562 948-4499
11909 Telegraph Rd Santa Fe Springs (90670) *(P-6788)*
Direct Surplus Sales Inc....F....530 533-9999
4801 Feather River Blvd # 3 Oroville (95965) *(P-12562)*
Dis, Azusa *Also called Dependble Incontinence Sup Inc (P-5664)*
Disc Pumps, Santee *Also called Discflo Corporation (P-15059)*
Disc Replicator Inc....F....909 385-0118
21137 Commerce Point Dr Walnut (91789) *(P-17891)*
Discflo Corporation....E....619 596-3181
10850 Hartley Rd Santee (92071) *(P-15059)*
Discopylabs (PA)....E....510 651-5100
48641 Milmont Dr Fremont (94538) *(P-17892)*
Discopylabs....E....909 390-3800
4455 E Philadelphia St Ontario (91761) *(P-17893)*
Discount Blind Center....F....951 678-3980
16074 Grand Ave Lake Elsinore (92530) *(P-5187)*
Discount Instant Printing....F....213 622-4347
175 S Thurston Ave Los Angeles (90049) *(P-6789)*
Discount Medical Supply, San Fernando *Also called Diasol Inc (P-22425)*
Discount Merchant.com, San Diego *Also called MI Technologies Inc (P-18530)*
Discount Outlet, Riverside *Also called Embroidery Outlet (P-3847)*
Discounted Wheel Warehouse, Fullerton *Also called Wheel and Tire Club Inc (P-11429)*
Disguise Inc (HQ)....E....858 391-3600
12120 Kear Pl Poway (92064) *(P-3654)*
Disk Faktory, Tustin *Also called Innovative Diversfd Tech Inc (P-15559)*
Disney Book Group LLC (HQ)....F....818 560-1000
500 S Buena Vista St Burbank (91521) *(P-6336)*
Disney Enterprises Inc....D....407 397-6000
1313 S Harbor Blvd Anaheim (92802) *(P-3655)*
Disney Publishing Worldwide (HQ)....D....212 633-4400
500 S Buena Vista St Burbank (91521) *(P-6146)*
Disorderly Kids, LLC, Los Angeles *Also called Avalon Apparel LLC (P-3572)*
Dispatcher Newspaper....E....415 775-0533
1188 Franklin St Fl 4 San Francisco (94109) *(P-5830)*
Dispensing Dynamics Intl Inc (PA)....D....626 961-3691
1020 Bixby Dr City of Industry (91745) *(P-10071)*
Display Advertising Inc....F....559 266-0231
1837 Van Ness Ave Fresno (93721) *(P-7300)*
Display Fabrication Group Inc....E....714 373-2100
1231 N Miller St Ste 100 Anaheim (92806) *(P-3941)*
Display Integration Tech, Oceanside *Also called 2 S 2 Inc (P-19428)*
Disposable Waste System, Santa Ana *Also called Jwc Environmental LLC (P-16061)*
Distillery Inc....D....415 505-5446
90 Heron Ct San Quentin (94964) *(P-24563)*
Distinct Corporation....E....408 445-3270
175 Bernal Rd Ste 210 San Jose (95119) *(P-24564)*
Distinct Indulgence Inc....E....818 546-1700
5018 Lante St Baldwin Park (91706) *(P-1231)*
Distinctive Inds Texas Inc....E....512 491-3500
10618 Shoemaker Ave Santa Fe Springs (90670) *(P-3613)*
Distinctive Industries....B....800 421-9777
10618 Shoemaker Ave Santa Fe Springs (90670) *(P-3889)*
Distinctive Metals By Angel S, Angels Camp *Also called Angels Sheet Metal Inc (P-12483)*
Distinctive Plastics Inc....D....760 599-9100
1385 Decision St Vista (92081) *(P-10072)*
Distinctive Prpts NAPA Vly....D....707 256-2251
1615 2nd St NAPA (94559) *(P-6147)*
Distribution Center, San Bernardino *Also called Romeros Food Products Inc (P-2659)*
Distribution Electrnics Vlued....E....714 368-1717
2651 Dow Ave Tustin (92780) *(P-19945)*
Distributors Processing Inc....F....559 781-0297
17656 Avenue 168 Porterville (93257) *(P-2255)*
Dita Inc (PA)....E....949 599-2700
1 Columbia Ste 130 Aliso Viejo (92656) *(P-23088)*
Dita Eyewear, Aliso Viejo *Also called Dita Inc (P-23088)*
Ditec Co....F....805 566-7800
1019 Mark Ave Carpinteria (93013) *(P-22427)*
Ditec Mfg., Carpinteria *Also called Ditec Co (P-22427)*
Ditech Networks Inc (HQ)....E....408 883-3636
3099 N 1st St San Jose (95134) *(P-17940)*
Diverse McHning Fbrication LLC....F....916 672-6591
3620 Cincinnati Ave Ste A Rocklin (95765) *(P-13934)*
Diverse Optics Inc....E....909 593-9330
10310 Regis Ct Rancho Cucamonga (91730) *(P-10073)*
Diversfied Mtllrgical Svcs Inc....E....714 895-7777
12101 Industry St Garden Grove (92841) *(P-11811)*
Diversfied Nano Solutions Corp....E....858 924-1017
10531 4s Commons Dr San Diego (92127) *(P-9190)*
Diversfied Tchncal Systems Inc (PA)....E....562 493-0158
1720 Apollo Ct Seal Beach (90740) *(P-19515)*
Diversified Construction, Oxnard *Also called Diversified Panels Systems Inc (P-15950)*
Diversified Hangar Company....F....805 239-8229
5905 Monterey Rd Paso Robles (93446) *(P-12153)*
Diversified Images Inc....F....661 702-0003
27955 Beale Ct Valencia (91355) *(P-7301)*
Diversified Mfg Cal Inc....F....760 599-9280
2555 Progress St Vista (92081) *(P-16442)*
Diversified Mfg Tech Inc....F....714 577-7000
931 S Via Rodeo Placentia (92870) *(P-14508)*

ALPHABETIC

Employee Codes: A=Over 500 employees, B=251-500
C=101-250, D=51-100, E=20-50, F=10-19
2019 California
Manfacturers Register
© Mergent Inc. 1-800-342-5647
1121

Diversified Minerals Inc......E......805 247-1069
1100 Mountain View Ave F Oxnard (93030) ***(P-11102)***
Diversified Nano Corporation (PA)......F......858 673-0387
16885 W Bernardo Dr # 275 San Diego (92127) ***(P-15730)***
Diversified Packaging Inc......E......714 850-9316
2221 S Anne St Santa Ana (92704) ***(P-9836)***
Diversified Panels Systems Inc......F......805 487-9241
2345 Statham Blvd Oxnard (93033) ***(P-15950)***
Diversified Printers Inc......D......714 994-3400
12834 Maxwell Dr Tustin (92782) ***(P-6470)***
Diversified Silicone, Santa Fe Springs *Also called Rogers Corporation* ***(P-9671)***
Diversified Spring Tech......F......562 944-4049
9233 Santa Fe Springs Rd Santa Fe Springs (90670) ***(P-13793)***
Diversified Testing Service......F......714 986-2250
1105 Las Brisas Pl Placentia (92870) ***(P-21741)***
Diversified Tool & Die......E......760 598-9100
2585 Birch St Vista (92081) ***(P-13196)***
Diversitech Corporation......F......760 246-4200
9252 Cassia Rd Adelanto (92301) ***(P-10915)***
Diversity In Steam, Irvine *Also called Diversitycomm Inc* ***(P-6148)***
Diversitycomm Inc......F......949 825-5777
18 Technology Dr Ste 170 Irvine (92618) ***(P-6148)***
Divine Pasta Company (PA)......E......213 542-3300
140 W Providencia Ave Burbank (91502) ***(P-2508)***
Diving Unlimited International......D......619 236-1203
1148 Delevan Dr San Diego (92102) ***(P-23550)***
Divisadero 500 LLC......F......415 572-6062
502 Divisadero St San Francisco (94117) ***(P-5227)***
Dixietruss Inc......F......619 873-0440
12538 Vigilante Rd Lakeside (92040) ***(P-10916)***
Dixon Hard Chrome, Sun Valley *Also called Florence International Company* ***(P-13411)***
Dixon Tribune, Dixon *Also called Gibson Printing & Publishing* ***(P-5865)***
Dixon Tribune......F......707 678-5594
145 E A St Dixon (95620) ***(P-5831)***
Diy Co......F......844 564-6349
3360 20th St San Francisco (94110) ***(P-19946)***
Diy Drones, Berkeley *Also called 3d Robotics Inc* ***(P-19892)***
DJ Bronson Inc (PA)......F......562 945-9609
8427 Secura Way Santa Fe Springs (90670) ***(P-3306)***
DJ Grey Company Inc......F......707 431-2779
455 Allan Ct Healdsburg (95448) ***(P-19516)***
Dj Orthopedics LLC......F......760 727-1280
3151 Scott St Vista (92081) ***(P-22716)***
DJ Safety Inc......E......323 221-0000
2623 N San Fernando Rd Los Angeles (90065) ***(P-3890)***
Dj Tech Tools, Brisbane *Also called Goldensol Music LLC* ***(P-15749)***
Djh Enterprises......E......714 424-6500
234 Fischer Ave Costa Mesa (92626) ***(P-18088)***
Dji Service LLC......F......818 235-0788
17301 Edwards Rd Cerritos (90703) ***(P-20795)***
Dji Technology Inc......E......818 235-0789
201 S Victory Blvd Burbank (91502) ***(P-23150)***
DJM Suspension, Gardena *Also called D and J Marketing Inc* ***(P-3887)***
Djo Global Inc (HQ)......A......760 727-1280
1430 Decision St Vista (92081) ***(P-22717)***
Dkp Designs Inc......F......310 322-6000
110 Maryland St El Segundo (90245) ***(P-24080)***
Dkp Inc......E......559 266-2695
275 N Marks Ave Fresno (93706) ***(P-14060)***
Dkw Precision Machining Inc......E......209 824-7899
17731 Ideal Pkwy Manteca (95336) ***(P-16443)***
Dl Tool and Mfg Co Inc......F......818 837-3451
11828 Glenoaks Blvd San Fernando (91340) ***(P-14509)***
Dla Document Services......E......805 982-4310
4231 San Pedro Rd Port Hueneme (93043) ***(P-6790)***
Dlc Laboratories Inc......F......562 602-2184
7008 Marcelle St Paramount (90723) ***(P-8142)***
Dlive Inc......E......650 397-1777
675 Mariners Island Blvd # 108 San Mateo (94404) ***(P-6471)***
Dlt Co, Los Angeles *Also called E J Y Corporation* ***(P-3843)***
Dm Collective Inc......E......323 923-2400
4536 District Blvd Vernon (90058) ***(P-2833)***
Dm Luxury LLC......B......858 366-9721
875 Prospect St Ste 300 La Jolla (92037) ***(P-7302)***
Dm Software Inc......F......714 953-2653
1842 Park Skyline Rd Santa Ana (92705) ***(P-24565)***
Dmbm LLC......E......714 321-6032
2445 E 12th St Ste C Los Angeles (90021) ***(P-3408)***
DMC Power Inc (PA)......D......310 323-1616
623 E Artesia Blvd Carson (90746) ***(P-17462)***
Dmea MSC......E......916 568-4087
5584 Patrol Rd Bldg 1069 McClellan (95652) ***(P-20796)***
Dmg Mori Manufacturing USA Inc (HQ)......E......530 746-7400
3805 Faraday Ave Davis (95618) ***(P-14371)***
Dmg Mori Usa Inc......F......562 430-3800
5740 Warland Dr Cypress (90630) ***(P-14372)***
Dmh Media Network Corp......F......818 732-4217
1801 Avenue Of The Stars Los Angeles (90067) ***(P-6149)***
Dmi Ready Mix, Oxnard *Also called Diversified Minerals Inc* ***(P-11102)***
Dmoc, Vista *Also called Diversified Mfg Cal Inc* ***(P-16442)***
Dmt, Placentia *Also called Diversified Mfg Tech Inc* ***(P-14508)***
Dn Tanks Inc (PA)......C......619 440-8181
351 Cypress Ln El Cajon (92020) ***(P-21215)***
Dna Health Inst Cyrogenic Div, Ventura *Also called Dna Health Institute Llc* ***(P-9003)***
Dna Health Institute Llc......F......805 654-9363
4562 Westinghouse St B Ventura (93003) ***(P-9003)***
Dna Twopointo Inc......D......650 853-8347
37950 Central Ct Ste C Newark (94560) ***(P-8546)***
Dna2.0, Newark *Also called Dna Twopointo Inc* ***(P-8546)***
Dnfcontrols, Northridge *Also called Universal Ctrl Solutions Corp* ***(P-17317)***
Dnmc......E......707 935-0353
21600 8th St E Sonoma (95476) ***(P-14626)***
Dnp America LLC......F......408 616-1200
2099 Gateway Pl Ste 490 San Jose (95110) ***(P-18802)***
Do Dine Inc......F......510 583-7546
24052 Mission Blvd Hayward (94544) ***(P-24566)***
Do It American Mfg Company LLC......F......951 254-9204
137 Vander St Corona (92880) ***(P-13935)***
Do It Best, Pasadena *Also called George L Throop Co* ***(P-10932)***
Do It Right Products LLC......F......661 722-9664
44321 62nd St W Lancaster (93536) ***(P-10917)***
Do Well Laboratories Inc......F......949 252-0001
14791 Myford Rd Tustin (92780) ***(P-612)***
Do-Nut Wheel Inc......F......408 252-8193
10250 N De Anza Blvd Cupertino (95014) ***(P-1232)***
Doan Inc......F......951 275-2432
2406 John St Riverside (92503) ***(P-14061)***
Dobake Bakeries Inc......D......510 834-3134
810 81st Ave Oakland (94621) ***(P-1233)***
Doble Engineering Company......F......909 923-9390
1520 S Hellman Ave Ontario (91761) ***(P-17141)***
Dockum Research Laboratory......F......626 794-1821
844 E Mariposa St Altadena (91001) ***(P-22874)***
Docrun, Santa Monica *Also called Owl Territory Inc* ***(P-25044)***
Docsend Inc......F......888 258-5951
351 California St # 1200 San Francisco (94104) ***(P-24567)***
Doctor On Demand Inc......D......415 935-4447
275 Battery St Ste 650 San Francisco (94111) ***(P-24568)***
Doctors Signature Sales......E......800 531-4877
495 Raleigh Ave El Cajon (92020) ***(P-7933)***
Document Capture Tech Inc (PA)......E......408 436-9888
41332 Christy St Fremont (94538) ***(P-15731)***
Document Proc Solutions Inc......E......925 839-1182
535 Main St Ste 317 Martinez (94553) ***(P-5279)***
Documotion Research Inc......F......714 662-3800
2020 S Eastwood Ave Santa Ana (92705) ***(P-6791)***
Docupak Inc......E......714 670-7944
17515 Valley View Ave Cerritos (90703) ***(P-7581)***
Docusign Inc (PA)......B......415 489-4940
221 Main St Ste 1000 San Francisco (94105) ***(P-24569)***
Dodge - Wasmund Mfg Inc......F......562 692-8104
4510 Manning Rd Pico Rivera (90660) ***(P-10074)***
Doerksen Precision Products......F......831 476-1843
2725 Chanticleer Ave # 7 Santa Cruz (95065) ***(P-16444)***
Dogeared Inc......D......310 846-4444
6053 Bristol Pkwy Culver City (90230) ***(P-23745)***
Dogg Digital, Cypress *Also called Tr Theater Research Inc* ***(P-17869)***
Dogpatch Wineworks......F......415 525-4440
170 Henry St San Francisco (94114) ***(P-1728)***
Dogsport Inc......F......323 362-6450
244 S Palm Dr Beverly Hills (90212) ***(P-24081)***
Dogsport International, Beverly Hills *Also called Dogsport Inc* ***(P-24081)***
Doi Venture, Rancho Cucamonga *Also called Davidson Optronics Inc* ***(P-22185)***
Doka USA Ltd......F......951 509-0023
6901 Central Ave Riverside (92504) ***(P-12563)***
Dolby Laboratories Inc......F......408 730-5543
432 Lakeside Dr Sunnyvale (94085) ***(P-18089)***
Dolby Laboratories Inc......E......818 562-1101
1020 Chestnut St Burbank (91506) ***(P-17791)***
Dolby Laboratories Inc (PA)......B......415 558-0200
1275 Market St San Francisco (94103) ***(P-17792)***
Dolby Laboratories Inc......D......415 715-2500
175 S Hill Dr Brisbane (94005) ***(P-18090)***
Dolby Labs, Brisbane *Also called Dolby Laboratories Inc* ***(P-18090)***
Dolce Dolci LLC......E......818 343-8400
16745 Saticoy St Ste 112 Van Nuys (91406) ***(P-666)***
Dole Fresh Vegetables Inc (HQ)......C......831 422-8871
2959 Salinas Hwy Monterey (93940) ***(P-2509)***
Dole Packaged Foods LLC (HQ)......A......805 601-5500
3059 Townsgate Rd Ste 400 Westlake Village (91361) ***(P-947)***
Dole Packaged Foods LLC......C......559 875-3354
1117 K St Sanger (93657) ***(P-948)***
Dollar Shave Club Inc (HQ)......E......310 975-8528
13335 Maxella Ave Marina Del Rey (90292) ***(P-14373)***
Dolphin Medical Inc (HQ)......D......800 448-6506
12525 Chadron Ave Hawthorne (90250) ***(P-22972)***
Dolphin Press Inc......F......650 873-9092
264 S Maple Ave South San Francisco (94080) ***(P-7303)***
Dolphin Spas Inc......F......626 334-0099
701 W Foothill Blvd Azusa (91702) ***(P-24082)***
Dolstra Automatic Products......F......714 894-2062
14441 Edwards St Westminster (92683) ***(P-16445)***
Domaine Chandon Inc (HQ)......D......707 944-8844
1 California Dr Yountville (94599) ***(P-1729)***
Domaine De La Terre Rouge......F......209 245-4277
10801 Dickson Rd Plymouth (95669) ***(P-1730)***
Domaine Saint Gregory, Redwood Valley *Also called Gregory Graziano* ***(P-1796)***
Domaine St George Winery, Healdsburg *Also called Pan Magna Group* ***(P-1912)***
Dome Printing and Lithograph, McClellan *Also called Meriliz Incorporated* ***(P-6970)***
Domico Software......F......510 841-4155
1220 Oakland Blvd Ste 300 Walnut Creek (94596) ***(P-24570)***
Domino Data Lab Inc......F......415 570-2425
548 4th St San Francisco (94107) ***(P-24571)***
Domino Plastics Mfg Inc......E......661 396-3744
601 Gateway Ct Bakersfield (93307) ***(P-10075)***
Dominus Estate Corporation......F......707 944-8954
2570 Napa Nook Rd Yountville (94599) ***(P-1731)***
Domries Enterprises Inc......E......559 485-4306
12281 Road 29 Madera (93638) ***(P-14062)***

Don Conibear F 760 728-4590
541 Industrial Way Ste 2 Fallbrook (92028) *(P-10076)*
Don Francisco Cheese, Modesto *Also called Rizo-Lopez Foods Inc (P-595)*
Don Miguel Foods, Orange *Also called Don Miguel Mexican Foods Inc (P-990)*
Don Miguel Mexican Foods Inc (HQ) E 714 385-4500
333 S Anita Dr Ste 1000 Orange (92868) *(P-990)*
Don Pedros Meat F 626 339-3963
725 E Edna Pl Covina (91723) *(P-431)*
Don Sebastiani & Sons Internat E 707 224-0410
520 Airpark Rd NAPA (94558) *(P-1732)*
Don Vito Ozuna Foods Corp E 408 400-0495
180 Cochrane Cir Morgan Hill (95037) *(P-2378)*
Donal Machine Inc E 707 763-6625
591 N Mcdowell Blvd Petaluma (94954) *(P-16446)*
Donald H Binkley F 209 664-9792
2901 Commerce Way Turlock (95380) *(P-12154)*
Donald La Voie, San Jose *Also called La Voies of San Jose (P-5201)*
Donald Tyler Latimes Agency 14, Ontario *Also called Los Angles Tmes Cmmnctions LLC (P-5930)*
Donaldson Company Inc D 661 295-0800
26235 Technology Dr Valencia (91355) *(P-20316)*
Doncasters Gce Integrated, San Diego *Also called Integrated Energy Tech Inc (P-15107)*
Dongbu Electronics Co F 408 330-0330
2953 Bunker Hill Ln # 206 Santa Clara (95054) *(P-18803)*
Dongbu Hi-Tech, Santa Clara *Also called Dongbu Electronics Co (P-18803)*
Donn & Doff Inc F 530 241-4040
2102 Civic Center Dr Redding (96001) *(P-22718)*
Donna Karan Company LLC C 909 484-1201
1 Mills Cir Ontario (91764) *(P-3307)*
Donnashi Enterprises Inc E 760 200-3402
43644 Parkway Esplanade W La Quinta (92253) *(P-21573)*
Donnelley Financial, Irvine *Also called RR Donnelley & Sons Company (P-7474)*
Donnelley Financial, San Francisco *Also called R R Donnelley & Sons Company (P-7211)*
Donoco Industries Inc E 714 893-7889
5642 Research Dr Ste B Huntington Beach (92649) *(P-10641)*
Donovan Aluminum Racing Engine, Torrance *Also called Donovan Engineering Corp (P-20317)*
Donovan Engineering Corp F 310 320-3772
2305 Border Ave Torrance (90501) *(P-20317)*
Donut King, Long Beach *Also called Paris Croissant LLC (P-1306)*
Dony Corp F 323 725-7697
1065 S Vail Ave Montebello (90640) *(P-10519)*
Dony Trading Los Angeles, Montebello *Also called Dony Corp (P-10519)*
Dool Fna Inc C 562 483-4100
16220 Manning Way Cerritos (90703) *(P-2776)*
Door & Glass Unique, Pomona *Also called D G U Trading Corporation (P-10689)*
Door & Hardware Installers Inc E 661 298-9383
14300 Davenport Rd Ste 1a Santa Clarita (91390) *(P-4145)*
Door Components Inc C 909 770-5700
7980 Redwood Ave Fontana (92336) *(P-12310)*
Door Doctor, Anaheim *Also called R & S Overhead Door of So Cal (P-12343)*
Door Service Company F 760 320-0788
680 S Williams Rd Palm Springs (92264) *(P-11439)*
Doorking Inc (PA) C 310 645-0023
120 S Glasgow Ave Inglewood (90301) *(P-19947)*
Doors Plus Inc F 209 463-3667
314 N Main St Lodi (95240) *(P-4146)*
Doors Unlimited F 760 744-5590
1316 Armorlite Dr San Marcos (92069) *(P-4294)*
Dorado Network Systems Corp C 650 227-7300
555 12th St Ste 1100 Oakland (94607) *(P-24572)*
Dorado Pkg, North Hollywood *Also called Corporate Impressions La Inc (P-7285)*
Dorco Electronics Inc F 562 623-1133
13540 Larwin Cir Santa Fe Springs (90670) *(P-5485)*
Dorco Fiberglass Products, Santa Fe Springs *Also called Dorco Electronics Inc (P-5485)*
Dorel Juvenile Group Inc C 909 428-0295
9950 Calabash Ave Fontana (92335) *(P-10077)*
Dorel Juvenile Group Inc C 909 390-5705
5400 Shea Center Dr Ontario (91761) *(P-10078)*
Doremi Cinema LLC E 818 562-1101
1020 Chestnut St Burbank (91506) *(P-23151)*
Doremi Labs, Burbank *Also called Dolby Laboratories Inc (P-17791)*
Doringer Manufacturing Co Inc F 310 366-7766
13400 Estrella Ave Gardena (90248) *(P-14374)*
Dorris Lumber and Moulding Co (PA) C 916 452-7531
2601 Redding Ave Sacramento (95820) *(P-4147)*
Dos Fashions E 626 454-4558
2633 Troy Ave El Monte (91733) *(P-2734)*
Dosa Inc E 213 627-3672
850 S Broadway Ste 700 Los Angeles (90014) *(P-3409)*
Dostal Studio F 415 721-7080
898 Lincoln Ave San Rafael (94901) *(P-23707)*
DOT Blue Safes Corporation E 909 445-8888
2707 N Garey Ave Pomona (91767) *(P-13936)*
DOT Copy Inc E 818 341-6666
9655 De Soto Ave Chatsworth (91311) *(P-6792)*
DOT Graphics, Chatsworth *Also called DOT Copy Inc (P-6792)*
DOT Printer Inc (PA) C 949 474-1100
2424 Mcgaw Ave Irvine (92614) *(P-6793)*
Double K Industries, Chatsworth *Also called Invelop Inc (P-14071)*
Double K Industries Inc E 818 772-2887
9711 Mason Ave Chatsworth (91311) *(P-14063)*
Double Precision Mfg E 408 727-7726
2273 Calle De Luna Santa Clara (95054) *(P-16447)*
Double V Industries E 510 347-3764
717 Whitney St San Leandro (94577) *(P-3841)*
Double-Take Software Inc (HQ) E 949 253-6500
15300 Barranca Pkwy Irvine (92618) *(P-24573)*
Doubleco Incorporated D 909 481-0799
9444 9th St Rancho Cucamonga (91730) *(P-13066)*
Doubledutch Inc (PA) D 800 748-9024
350 Rhode Island St # 375 San Francisco (94103) *(P-24574)*
Doublesight Displays Inc F 949 253-1535
2882 Walnut Ave Ste A Tustin (92780) *(P-15732)*
Douce De France F 650 369-9644
686 Brdwy St Redwood City (94063) *(P-1234)*
Doug Deleo Welding Inc F 559 562-3700
249 N Ashland Ave Lindsay (93247) *(P-25401)*
Doug Mockett & Company Inc E 310 318-2491
1915 Abalone Ave Torrance (90501) *(P-4689)*
Doug Trim Sub Contractor F 661 944-2884
32010 Alaga Ave Pearblossom (93553) *(P-13575)*
Doughpro, Perris *Also called Stearns Product Dev Corp (P-15365)*
Doughtronics Inc (PA) E 510 524-1327
1601 San Pablo Ave Berkeley (94702) *(P-1235)*
Doughtronics Inc E 510 843-2978
2730 9th St Berkeley (94710) *(P-1236)*
Doughtronics Inc E 415 288-2978
1 Ferry Building Ste 15 San Francisco (94111) *(P-1237)*
Douglas & Sturgess Inc F 510 235-8411
1023 Factory St Richmond (94801) *(P-11355)*
Douglas Hunter Inc C 916 288-4464
2080 Enterprise Blvd West Sacramento (95691) *(P-5188)*
Douglas Technologies Group Inc (PA) E 760 758-5560
1340 N Melrose Dr Vista (92083) *(P-20318)*
Douglas Wheel, Vista *Also called Douglas Technologies Group Inc (P-20318)*
Douglass Truck Bodies Inc E 661 327-0258
231 21st St Bakersfield (93301) *(P-20202)*
Doval Industries Inc D 323 226-0335
3961 N Mission Rd Los Angeles (90031) *(P-11952)*
Doval Industries Co, Los Angeles *Also called Doval Industries Inc (P-11952)*
Dove Tree Canyon Software Inc F 619 236-8895
707 Broadway Ste 1240 San Diego (92101) *(P-24575)*
Doves Jewelry Corporation E 818 955-8886
2860 N Naomi St Burbank (91504) *(P-23257)*
Dow Chemical Company D 925 432-3165
901 Loveridge Rd Pittsburg (94565) *(P-7830)*
Dow Chemical Company C 714 228-4700
14445 Alondra Blvd La Mirada (90638) *(P-7768)*
Dow Chemical International E 909 987-6261
11266 Jersey Blvd Rancho Cucamonga (91730) *(P-7831)*
Dow Frosini, San Francisco *Also called Alan Wofsy Fine Arts LLC (P-6303)*
Dow Hydraulic Systems Inc F 909 596-6602
2895 Metropolitan Pl Pomona (91767) *(P-16164)*
Dow Hydraulic Systems Inc (PA) D 909 596-6602
1835 Wright Ave La Verne (91750) *(P-16448)*
Dow Jones & Company Inc E 415 765-6131
201 California St Fl 13 San Francisco (94111) *(P-5832)*
Dow Jones Lmg Stockton Inc C 209 943-6397
530 E Market St Stockton (95202) *(P-5833)*
Dow Phrmaceutical Sciences Inc C 707 793-2600
1330 Redwood Way Ste C Petaluma (94954) *(P-21947)*
Dow Theory Letters Inc F 858 454-0481
7590 Fay Ave Ste 404 La Jolla (92037) *(P-6150)*
Dow-Elco Inc E 323 723-1288
1313 W Olympic Blvd Montebello (90640) *(P-17090)*
Dow-Key Microwave Corporation C 805 650-0260
4822 Mcgrath St Ventura (93003) *(P-17266)*
Dowdys Sales and Services F 559 688-6973
15185 Avenue 224 Tulare (93274) *(P-14064)*
Dowell Aluminum Foundry Inc F 323 877-9645
11342 Hartland St North Hollywood (91605) *(P-11738)*
Dowling Magnets, Sonoma *Also called Sonoma International Inc (P-23466)*
Downey Grinding Co E 562 803-5556
12323 Bellflower Blvd Downey (90242) *(P-14375)*
Downey Manufacturing Inc F 562 862-3311
11421 Downey Ave Downey (90241) *(P-20797)*
Downey Patriot F 562 904-3668
8301 Florence Ave Ste 100 Downey (90240) *(P-5834)*
Downhole Stabilization Inc E 661 631-1044
3515 Thomas Way Bakersfield (93308) *(P-14221)*
Dp Print Services Inc F 310 600-5250
2331 Walling Ave La Habra (90631) *(P-2910)*
Dp Products, San Jose *Also called Papadatos Enterprises Inc (P-16825)*
Dpa Components International, Simi Valley *Also called Dpa Labs Inc (P-18804)*
Dpa Labs Inc E 805 581-9200
2251 Ward Ave Simi Valley (93065) *(P-18804)*
Dpc Woodwork Inc E 323 935-4828
5714 W Pico Blvd Los Angeles (90019) *(P-4148)*
Dpi Direct, Poway *Also called Digitalpro Inc (P-7298)*
DPI Labs Inc E 909 392-5777
1350 Arrow Hwy La Verne (91750) *(P-20798)*
Dpm Inc F 530 378-3420
19641 Hirsch Ct Anderson (96007) *(P-16449)*
Dps Telecom, Fresno *Also called Digital Prototype Systems Inc (P-18087)*
Dpss Lasers Inc E 408 988-4300
2525 Walsh Ave Santa Clara (95051) *(P-19948)*
Dr DBurr Inc F 310 323-6900
12943 S Budlong Ave Gardena (90247) *(P-14376)*
Dr Earth Inc F 707 448-4676
4021 Devon Ct Vacaville (95688) *(P-9060)*
Dr Heater USA, South San Francisco *Also called Tlm International Inc (P-17418)*
Dr J Skinclinic Inc F 714 282-2290
13834 Bettencourt St Cerritos (90703) *(P-8143)*
Dr McDougall's Right Foods, Woodland *Also called Bright People Foods Inc (P-2472)*

Employee Codes: A=Over 500 employees, B=251-500
C=101-250, D=51-100, E=20-50, F=10-19
2019 California
Manfacturers Register
© Mergent Inc. 1-800-342-5647
1123

Dr Pepper/Seven Up Inc.....D.......707 545-7797
1901 Russell Ave Santa Rosa (95403) ***(P-2130)***
DR Radon Boatbuilding Inc (PA).....F.......805 692-2170
67 Depot Rd Goleta (93117) ***(P-21030)***
Dr Smoothie Brands Inc.....E.......714 449-9787
1730 Raymer Ave Fullerton (92833) ***(P-2256)***
Dr Smoothie Enterprises.....E.......714 449-9787
1730 Raymer Ave Fullerton (92833) ***(P-2257)***
Dr Teak Inc.....E.......310 527-2675
13726 Harvard Pl Gardena (90249) ***(P-4690)***
Dr. Bronners Magic Soaps, Vista *Also called All One God Faith Inc* ***(P-8588)***
Dr. J'S Natural, Huntington Beach *Also called Premium Herbal USA LLC* ***(P-646)***
Dr. Jekyll's, Pasadena *Also called Nutraceutical Brews For Lf Inc* ***(P-1614)***
Dr. Shica's Healthy Surprises, Pasadena *Also called Vitafoods America LLC* ***(P-739)***
Draftday Fantasy Sports Inc.....E.......310 306-1828
690 5th St Ste 105 San Francisco (94107) ***(P-24576)***
Draftday Fantasy Sports Inc.....E.......310 306-1828
2058 Broadway Ofc Santa Monica (90404) ***(P-24577)***
Dragon Alliance Inc.....E.......760 931-4900
971 Calle Amanecer San Clemente (92673) ***(P-23089)***
Dragon Herbs, Los Angeles *Also called Ron Teeguarden Enterprises Inc* ***(P-7968)***
Dragon Valves Inc (PA).....E.......562 921-6605
13457 Excelsior Dr Norwalk (90650) ***(P-13764)***
Drake Enterprises Incorporated.....D.......707 864-3077
490 Watt Dr Fairfield (94534) ***(P-3942)***
Drake's Brewing Company, San Leandro *Also called Artisan Brewers LLC* ***(P-1561)***
Drapery Enterprises.....F.......831 458-2578
1334 Brommer St Ste B5 Santa Cruz (95062) ***(P-3693)***
Drapery Productions Inc.....F.......650 340-8555
33 E 4th Ave San Mateo (94401) ***(P-2735)***
Drapes 4 Show Inc.....E.......818 838-0852
12811 Foothill Blvd Sylmar (91342) ***(P-3719)***
Draw Tite, Gardena *Also called Scotch Paint Corporation* ***(P-8939)***
Dream Communications Inc.....F.......619 275-9100
2431 Morena Blvd San Diego (92110) ***(P-6151)***
Dream Homes Magazine, San Diego *Also called Dream Communications Inc* ***(P-6151)***
Dream International Usa Inc.....F.......714 521-6007
7001 Village Dr Ste 280 Buena Park (90621) ***(P-23396)***
Dream Products Incorporated.....E.......818 773-4233
9754 Deering Ave Chatsworth (91311) ***(P-10546)***
Dreamctchers Empwerment Netwrk.....E.......707 558-1775
2201 Tuolumne St Vallejo (94589) ***(P-19517)***
Dreamgear LLC.....E.......310 222-5522
20001 S Western Ave Torrance (90501) ***(P-23418)***
Dreams Closets.....F.......626 641-5070
13030 Ramona Blvd Unit 9 Baldwin Park (91706) ***(P-4295)***
Dreams Duvets & Bed Linens.....F.......415 543-1800
921 Howard St San Francisco (94103) ***(P-3720)***
Dreams Duvets & Linens, San Francisco *Also called Dreams Duvets & Bed Linens* ***(P-3720)***
Dreamteam Business Group LLC.....F.......559 430-7676
5261 E Kings Canyon Rd # 101 Fresno (93727) ***(P-7304)***
Dreamworks Knitting, Santa Ana *Also called Nutrade Inc* ***(P-2755)***
Drees Wood Products Inc.....E.......562 633-7337
14020 Orange Ave Paramount (90723) ***(P-4149)***
Drees Wood Products Inc (PA).....E.......562 633-7337
14003 Orange Ave Paramount (90723) ***(P-4150)***
Dress To Kill Inc.....F.......818 994-3890
15500 Erwin St Ste 1089 Van Nuys (91411) ***(P-3232)***
Dresser-Rand Company.....E.......310 223-0600
18502 Dominguez Hill Dr Rancho Dominguez (90220) ***(P-15123)***
Dresser-Rand LLC.....E.......925 356-5700
5159 Commercial Cir Ste D Concord (94520) ***(P-15124)***
Dresser-Rand Sales, Concord *Also called Dresser-Rand LLC* ***(P-15124)***
Dresses.com, Canoga Park *Also called Odette Christiane LLC* ***(P-3473)***
Dretloh Aircraft Supply Inc (PA).....F.......714 632-6982
2830 E La Cresta Ave Anaheim (92806) ***(P-20799)***
Dreyer's Grand Ice Cream, Bakersfield *Also called Nestle Dreyers Ice Cream Co* ***(P-689)***
Driessen Aircraft Interior.....E.......714 861-7300
14505 Astronautics Ln Huntington Beach (92647) ***(P-20800)***
Driessen Aircraft Interior (HQ).....C.......714 861-7300
17311 Nichols Ln Huntington Beach (92647) ***(P-20801)***
Driessen Galleys USA, Huntington Beach *Also called Driessen Aircraft Interior* ***(P-20801)***
Driftwood Dairy Inc.....C.......626 444-9591
10724 Lower Azusa Rd El Monte (91731) ***(P-723)***
Drilling & Trenching Sup Inc (PA).....F.......510 895-1650
1458 Mariani Ct Tracy (95376) ***(P-14627)***
Drilling World, Tracy *Also called Drilling & Trenching Sup Inc* ***(P-14627)***
Driscoll Inc.....E.......619 226-2500
2500 Shelter Island Dr San Diego (92106) ***(P-21031)***
Driscoll Boat Works, San Diego *Also called Driscoll Inc* ***(P-21031)***
Driscoll Mission Bay LLC.....F.......619 223-5191
1500 Quivira Way Ste 2 San Diego (92109) ***(P-21032)***
Driveai Inc.....C.......650 729-0499
365 Ravendale Dr Mountain View (94043) ***(P-24578)***
Driven Concepts Inc.....F.......714 549-2170
4040 W Carriage Dr Santa Ana (92704) ***(P-3145)***
Driven Raceway and Family Ente.....F.......707 585-3748
4601 Redwood Dr Rohnert Park (94928) ***(P-17512)***
Driver Inc.....D.......415 999-4960
438 Shotwell St San Francisco (94110) ***(P-24579)***
Drivescale Inc.....F.......408 849-4651
1230 Midas Way Ste 210 Sunnyvale (94085) ***(P-24580)***
Drj Organics, Cerritos *Also called Dr J Skinclinic Inc* ***(P-8143)***
Dropbox Inc (PA).....C.......415 857-6800
333 Brannan St San Francisco (94107) ***(P-24581)***
Drs Advanced Isr LLC.....C.......714 220-3800
10600 Valley View St Cypress (90630) ***(P-18805)***
Drs Daylight Solutions, San Diego *Also called Daylight Solutions Inc* ***(P-18799)***
Drs Daylight Solutions Inc., San Diego *Also called Daylight Defense LLC* ***(P-22970)***
Drs Ntwork Imaging Systems LLC.....D.......714 220-3800
10600 Valley View St Cypress (90630) ***(P-18806)***
Drs Snsors Trgting Systems Inc, Cypress *Also called Drs Ntwork Imaging Systems LLC* ***(P-18806)***
Drug Product Services Lab, San Francisco *Also called Ucsf School of Pharmacy* ***(P-8424)***
Drum Magazine, San Jose *Also called Enter Music Publishing Inc* ***(P-6159)***
Drum Workshop Inc (PA).....D.......805 485-6999
3450 Lunar Ct Oxnard (93030) ***(P-23362)***
Druva Inc (HQ).....D.......650 241-3501
150 Mathilda Pl Ste 450 Sunnyvale (94086) ***(P-24582)***
Dry Aged Denim LLC (PA).....F.......323 780-6206
1545 Rio Vista Ave Los Angeles (90023) ***(P-3069)***
Dry Creek Nutrition Inc.....F.......209 341-5696
600 Yosemite Blvd Modesto (95354) ***(P-2258)***
Dry Creek Vineyard Inc.....E.......707 433-1000
3770 Lambert Bridge Rd Healdsburg (95448) ***(P-1733)***
Dry Launch Light Co, Livermore *Also called Sierra Design Mfg Inc* ***(P-17663)***
Dry Vac Environmental Inc (PA).....E.......707 374-7500
864 Saint Francis Way Rio Vista (94571) ***(P-21948)***
Drymax Technologies Inc.....F.......805 239-2555
9900 El Camino Real Atascadero (93422) ***(P-2811)***
Dryvit Systems Inc.....E.......559 564-3591
354 S Acacia St Woodlake (93286) ***(P-9242)***
Drywired Defense LLC.....E.......310 684-3891
9606 Santa Monica Blvd # 4 Beverly Hills (90210) ***(P-13576)***
Ds Cypress Magnetics Inc.....F.......909 987-3570
8753 Industrial Ln Rancho Cucamonga (91730) ***(P-19387)***
Ds Fibertech Corp.....E.......619 562-7001
11015 Mission Park Ct Santee (92071) ***(P-15258)***
Ds Services of America Inc.....D.......323 551-5724
1449 N Avenue 46 Los Angeles (90041) ***(P-2131)***
Dsj Printing Inc.....F.......310 828-8051
1703 Stewart St Santa Monica (90404) ***(P-6794)***
DSM&t Co Inc.....C.......909 357-7960
10609 Business Dr Fontana (92337) ***(P-19830)***
Dspm Inc.....E.......714 970-2304
1921 S Quaker Ridge Pl Ontario (91761) ***(P-19332)***
Dss Networks Inc.....F.......949 981-3473
24462 Redlen St Lake Forest (92630) ***(P-15733)***
Dss-Cctv Inc.....F.......609 850-9498
1280 Activity Dr Ste A Vista (92081) ***(P-18091)***
Dssa AZ, Simi Valley *Also called Daicel Safety Systems* ***(P-20308)***
Dssd Inc.....F.......775 773-8665
4025 Bohannon Dr Menlo Park (94025) ***(P-15529)***
Dst Controls, Benicia *Also called Dusouth Industries* ***(P-21575)***
DStyle Inc.....F.......619 662-0560
3451 Main St Ste 108 Chula Vista (91911) ***(P-13937)***
Dsy Educational Corporation.....F.......805 684-8111
525 Maple St Carpinteria (93013) ***(P-3943)***
DT Mattson Enterprises Inc.....E.......951 849-9781
201 W Lincoln St Banning (92220) ***(P-23419)***
Dtbm Inc.....F.......626 579-7033
1825 Durfee Ave Ste C South El Monte (91733) ***(P-1238)***
DTE Stockton LLC.....E.......209 467-3838
2526 W Washington St Stockton (95203) ***(P-205)***
DTL Mori Seiki, Davis *Also called Digital Technology Lab Corp* ***(P-14625)***
DTL Research & Technical Ctr, Davis *Also called Dmg Mori Manufacturing USA Inc* ***(P-14371)***
Dts LLC.....D.......818 436-1000
5220 Las Virgenes Rd Calabasas (91302) ***(P-17793)***
Du-All Anodizing Corporation.....F.......408 275-6694
730 Chestnut St San Jose (95110) ***(P-13389)***
Du-All Anodizing Inc.....E.......408 275-6694
730 Chestnut St San Jose (95110) ***(P-13390)***
Du-All Safety LLC.....F.......510 651-8289
45950 Hotchkiss St Fremont (94539) ***(P-16450)***
Dualcor Technologies Inc.....E.......831 684-2457
1 Embarcadero Ctr Ste 500 San Francisco (94111) ***(P-15530)***
Dub Custom Auto Show, Santa Fe Springs *Also called Dub Publishing Inc* ***(P-6152)***
Dub Publishing Inc.....F.......626 336-3821
11803 Smith Ave Santa Fe Springs (90670) ***(P-6152)***
Dubon & Sons Inc.....F.......213 923-1182
2852 E 11th St Los Angeles (90023) ***(P-991)***
Duchateau Floors, San Diego *Also called B&M Noble Co* ***(P-4073)***
Duckhorn Wine Company.....E.......707 744-2800
14100 Mountain House Rd Hopland (95449) ***(P-1734)***
Duckhorn Wine Company (HQ).....E.......707 963-7108
1000 Lodi Ln Saint Helena (94574) ***(P-1735)***
Duckhorn Wine Company.....F.......707 895-3202
9200 Highway 128 Philo (95466) ***(P-1736)***
Duclos Lenses.....F.......818 773-0600
20222 Bahama St Chatsworth (91311) ***(P-10079)***
Ducommun Aerostructures Inc (HQ).....B.......310 380-5390
268 E Gardena Blvd Gardena (90248) ***(P-20646)***
Ducommun Aerostructures Inc.....E.......626 358-3211
801 Royal Oaks Dr Monrovia (91016) ***(P-20802)***
Ducommun Aerostructures Inc.....E.......760 246-4191
4001 El Mirage Rd Adelanto (92301) ***(P-14377)***
Ducommun Aerostructures Inc.....F.......714 637-4401
1885 N Batavia St Orange (92865) ***(P-20647)***
Ducommun Aerostructures Inc.....E.......310 513-7200
23301 Wilmington Ave Carson (90745) ***(P-20648)***
Ducommun Arostructures-Gardena, Gardena *Also called Ahf-Ducommun Incorporated* ***(P-20724)***
Ducommun Incorporated (PA).....C.......657 335-3665
200 Sandpointe Ave # 700 Santa Ana (92707) ***(P-19518)***
Ducommun Incorporated.....E.......626 812-9666
1321 Mountain View Cir Azusa (91702) ***(P-19333)***

Mergent e-mail: customerrelations@mergent.com
1124
2019 California
Manufacturers Register
(P-0000) Products & Services Section entry number
(PA)=Parent Co (HQ)=Headquarters (DH)=Div Headquarters

Ducommun Labarge Tech Inc (HQ) ....C.......310 513-7200
23301 Wilmington Ave Carson (90745) ***(P-20803)***
Duda Mobile Inc ....E.......855 790-0003
577 College Ave Palo Alto (94306) ***(P-24583)***
Duden Enterprises Inc ....F.......909 795-0160
2025 W Park Ave Ste 4 Redlands (92373) ***(P-3842)***
Dudes Brewing Company ....E.......424 271-2915
1840 W 208th St Somis (93066) ***(P-1588)***
Duel Systems Inc ....E.......408 453-9500
2025 Galeway Pl Ste 235 San Jose (95110) ***(P-19388)***
Duff Bevill Vineyard Managment ....E.......707 433-6691
4724 Dry Creek Rd Healdsburg (95448) ***(P-1737)***
Duffield Electric Boat Company, Costa Mesa *Also called Duffield Marine Inc* ***(P-21033)***
Duffield Marine Inc (PA) ....E.......760 246-1211
670 W 17th St Ste E7 Costa Mesa (92627) ***(P-21033)***
Duffield Marine Inc ....E.......949 645-6812
2001 W Coast Hwy Newport Beach (92663) ***(P-21034)***
Duffy Electric Boat, Newport Beach *Also called Duffield Marine Inc* ***(P-21034)***
Duke Empirical Inc ....D.......831 420-1104
2829 Mission St Santa Cruz (95060) ***(P-22428)***
Duke Scientific Corporation ....E.......650 424-1177
46360 Fremont Blvd Fremont (94538) ***(P-21468)***
Dukes Research and Mfg Inc ....E.......818 998-9811
9060 Winnetka Ave Northridge (91324) ***(P-20319)***
Dulce Systems Inc ....F.......818 435-6007
26893 Bouquet Canyon Rd L Santa Clarita (91350) ***(P-18321)***
Dumont Printing Inc ....E.......559 485-6311
1333 G St Fresno (93706) ***(P-6795)***
Dumont Printing & Mailing, Fresno *Also called Dumont Printing Inc* ***(P-6795)***
Dunan Sensing LLC ....F.......408 613-1015
1953 Concourse Dr San Jose (95131) ***(P-19949)***
Dunbar Electric Sign Company ....E.......661 323-2600
4020 Rosedale Hwy Bakersfield (93308) ***(P-23857)***
Duncan Carter Corporation (PA) ....D.......805 964-9749
5427 Hollister Ave Santa Barbara (93111) ***(P-23363)***
Duncan Design Inc ....F.......707 636-2300
48 Barham Ave Santa Rosa (95407) ***(P-23858)***
Duncan Enterprises (HQ) ....C.......559 291-4444
5673 E Shields Ave Fresno (93727) ***(P-8901)***
Duncan McIntosh Company Inc (PA) ....E.......949 660-6150
18475 Bandilier Cir Fountain Valley (92708) ***(P-6153)***
Duncan Press Inc ....F.......209 462-5245
25 W Lockeford St Lodi (95240) ***(P-6796)***
Dunham Metal Processing Co ....E.......714 532-5551
936 N Parker St Orange (92867) ***(P-13391)***
Dunlop Manufacturing Inc (PA) ....D.......707 745-2722
150 Industrial Way Benicia (94510) ***(P-23364)***
Dunlop Manufacturing Inc ....E.......707 745-2709
649 Industrial Way Benicia (94510) ***(P-23365)***
Dunn Bros Commercial Prtrs Inc ....E.......323 321-2211
1239 W 130th St Gardena (90247) ***(P-6797)***
Dunnewood Vineyards, Ukiah *Also called Constellation Brands Inc* ***(P-1703)***
Dunstan Enterprises Inc ....F.......562 630-6292
2825 Seaboard Ln Long Beach (90805) ***(P-14378)***
Dunweizer Machine Inc ....F.......562 698-7787
8338 Allport Ave Santa Fe Springs (90670) ***(P-12386)***
Dunweizer Mch & Fabrication, Santa Fe Springs *Also called Dunweizer Machine Inc* ***(P-12386)***
Duo Pane Industries ....F.......707 426-9696
2444 Trevino Way Fairfield (94534) ***(P-10693)***
Duonetics ....F.......951 808-4903
809 E Parkridge Ave # 102 Corona (92879) ***(P-15060)***
Dupaco Inc ....E.......760 758-4550
4144 Avenda De La Plata Oceanside (92056) ***(P-22429)***
Duplan Industries ....E.......760 744-4047
1265 Stone Dr San Marcos (92078) ***(P-16451)***
Dupont Electronic Technologies ....F.......510 784-9105
2520 Barrington Ct Hayward (94545) ***(P-7769)***
Dupree Inc ....E.......909 597-4889
14395 Ramona Ave Chino (91710) ***(P-13067)***
Dur-Red Products ....E.......323 771-9000
4900 Cecilia St Cudahy (90201) ***(P-12564)***
Dura Coat Products Inc (PA) ....D.......951 341-6500
5361 Via Ricardo Riverside (92509) ***(P-13577)***
Dura Imaging Group ....F.......714 254-1400
1596 S Anaheim Blvd Ste A Anaheim (92805) ***(P-23152)***
Dura Micro Inc ....E.......909 947-4590
901 E Cedar St Ontario (91761) ***(P-15531)***
Dura Plastic Products Inc (PA) ....D.......951 845-3161
533 E Third St Beaumont (92223) ***(P-10080)***
Dura Technologies Inc ....C.......909 877-8477
2720 S Willow Ave Ste A Bloomington (92316) ***(P-8902)***
Dura-Chem Inc ....F.......951 245-7778
18327 Pasadena St Lake Elsinore (92530) ***(P-9243)***
Durabag Company Inc ....D.......714 259-8811
1432 Santa Fe Dr Tustin (92780) ***(P-5597)***
Duracite, Fairfield *Also called Halabi Inc* ***(P-11254)***
Duracite ....F.......559 346-1181
2636 N Argyle Ave Fresno (93727) ***(P-5138)***
Duracold Refrigeration Mfg LLC ....E.......626 358-1710
1551 S Primrose Ave Monrovia (91016) ***(P-12928)***
Duraled Ltg Technolgies Corp ....F.......949 753-0162
15285 Alton Pkwy Ste 200 Irvine (92618) ***(P-17425)***
Duralum Products Inc (PA) ....F.......916 452-7021
8269 Alpine Ave Sacramento (95826) ***(P-11616)***
Duralum Products Inc ....F.......951 736-4500
2485 Railroad St Corona (92880) ***(P-11617)***
Duramar Floor Inc ....F.......949 724-8800
2500 White Rd Ste B Irvine (92614) ***(P-10780)***
Duramar Interior Surfaces, Irvine *Also called Duramar Floor Inc* ***(P-10780)***
Duramar Interior Surfaces, Irvine *Also called Daz Inc* ***(P-17139)***
Duramax Building Products, Montebello *Also called US Polymers Inc* ***(P-10423)***
Durand-Wayland Machinery Inc (PA) ....E.......559 591-6904
1041 E Dinuba Ave Reedley (93654) ***(P-14065)***
Durango Foods, Bell *Also called Flores Brothers Inc* ***(P-2522)***
Duray, Downey *Also called J F Duncan Industries Inc* ***(P-16057)***
Durbin Rock Plant, Irwindale *Also called Legacy Vulcan LLC* ***(P-366)***
Durect Corporation (PA) ....D.......408 777-1417
10260 Bubb Rd Cupertino (95014) ***(P-8144)***
Durect Corporation ....F.......408 777-1417
10240 Bubb Rd Cupertino (95014) ***(P-8145)***
Durney Winery Corporation ....F.......831 659-2690
18820 Cachagua Rd Carmel Valley (93924) ***(P-1738)***
Duro Corporation ....F.......626 839-6541
17018 Evergreen Pl City of Industry (91745) ***(P-17368)***
Duro Dyne West Corp ....B.......562 926-1774
10837 Commerce Way Ste C Fontana (92337) ***(P-15951)***
Duro Flex Rubber Products Inc ....F.......562 946-5533
13215 Lakeland Rd Santa Fe Springs (90670) ***(P-9608)***
Duro Roller Company Inc ....F.......562 944-8856
13006 Park St Santa Fe Springs (90670) ***(P-9609)***
Duro-Sense Corp ....F.......310 533-6877
869 Sandhill Ave Carson (90746) ***(P-21574)***
Duron Incorporated ....F.......949 721-0900
4633 Camden Dr Corona Del Mar (92625) ***(P-14940)***
Durston Manufacturing Company ....F.......909 593-1506
1395 Palomares St La Verne (91750) ***(P-11892)***
Dusouth Industries ....E.......707 745-5117
651 Stone Rd Benicia (94510) ***(P-21575)***
Dust Collector Services Inc ....E.......714 237-1690
1280 N Sunshine Way Anaheim (92806) ***(P-15151)***
Dutek Incorporated ....E.......760 599-0171
2228 Oak Ridge Way Vista (92081) ***(P-19950)***
Dutra Materials, Richmond *Also called San Rafael Rock Quarry Inc* ***(P-9397)***
Dutra Materials, San Rafael *Also called San Rafael Rock Quarry Inc* ***(P-333)***
DV Kap Inc ....E.......559 435-5575
426 W Bedford Ave Fresno (93711) ***(P-3721)***
Dvbe Supply, San Diego *Also called Tsf Construction Services Inc* ***(P-2983)***
Dvele Inc ....E.......909 796-2561
25525 Redlands Blvd Loma Linda (92354) ***(P-4552)***
Dvele Omega Corporation ....D.......909 796-2561
25525 Redlands Blvd Loma Linda (92354) ***(P-4553)***
Dvs Sciences Inc ....E.......408 900-7205
7000 Shoreline Ct Ste 100 South San Francisco (94080) ***(P-21949)***
Dvtech Solution Corp ....F.......909 308-0358
13937 Magnolia Ave Chino (91710) ***(P-17142)***
Dvxtreme, Chino *Also called Dvtech Solution Corp* ***(P-17142)***
Dw Drum, Oxnard *Also called Drum Workshop Inc* ***(P-23362)***
Dwa Alminum Composites USA Inc ....E.......818 998-1504
21100 Superior St Chatsworth (91311) ***(P-11739)***
Dwa Nova LLC ....D.......818 695-5000
1000 Flower St Glendale (91201) ***(P-24584)***
Dwam, Vista *Also called Denso International Amer Inc* ***(P-20314)***
Dwaynes Engineering & Cnstr ....D.......661 762-7261
3655 Addie Ave Mc Kittrick (93251) ***(P-206)***
Dwell Home Inc ....F.......877 864-5752
39962 Cedar Blvd Ste 277 Newark (94560) ***(P-4909)***
Dwell Life Inc (PA) ....E.......415 373-5100
595 Pacific Ave 4 San Francisco (94133) ***(P-6154)***
Dwell Records, Los Angeles *Also called C M H Records Inc* ***(P-17887)***
Dwi Enterprises ....E.......714 842-2236
11081 Winners Cir Ste 100 Los Alamitos (90720) ***(P-17794)***
Dxg Technology USA Inc ....E.......626 820-0687
330 Turnbull Canyon Rd City of Industry (91745) ***(P-23153)***
Dxg USA, City of Industry *Also called Dxg Technology USA Inc* ***(P-23153)***
Dyell Machine (PA) ....E.......909 350-4101
160 S Linden Ave Rialto (92376) ***(P-16452)***
Dyell Machine ....F.......760 244-3333
17499 Alder St Hesperia (92345) ***(P-16453)***
Dyell Machine & Hydraulic Shop, Hesperia *Also called Dyell Machine* ***(P-16453)***
Dyk Incorporated (HQ) ....E.......619 440-8181
351 Cypress Ln El Cajon (92020) ***(P-21216)***
Dyk Prestressed Tanks, El Cajon *Also called Dyk Incorporated* ***(P-21216)***
Dylern Incorporated ....E.......530 470-8785
14444 Greenwood Cir Nevada City (95959) ***(P-16454)***
Dyln Inspired, Irvine *Also called Dyln Lifestyle LLC* ***(P-23336)***
Dyln Lifestyle LLC ....F.......949 209-9401
18242 Mcdurmott W Ste A Irvine (92614) ***(P-23336)***
Dyna-King Inc ....F.......707 894-5566
597 Santana Dr Ste A Cloverdale (95425) ***(P-23551)***
Dynabee USA, Anaheim *Also called Dynaflex International* ***(P-23552)***
Dynacast Inc ....C.......949 707-1211
25952 Commercentre Dr Lake Forest (92630) ***(P-11714)***
Dynaflex International ....E.......714 630-0909
1144 N Grove St Anaheim (92806) ***(P-23552)***
Dynaflex Products (PA) ....D.......323 724-1555
6466 Gayhart St Commerce (90040) ***(P-20203)***
Dynalinear Technologies Inc ....F.......408 376-5090
51 E Campbell Ave 108b Campbell (95008) ***(P-14941)***
Dynalloy Inc ....E.......714 436-1206
1562 Reynolds Ave Irvine (92614) ***(P-19519)***
Dynamation Research, Los Angeles *Also called Gali Corporation* ***(P-20821)***
Dynamation Research Inc ....F.......909 864-2310
2301 Pontius Ave Los Angeles (90064) ***(P-20804)***
Dynamet Incorporated ....E.......714 375-3150
16052 Beach Blvd Ste 221 Huntington Beach (92647) ***(P-11627)***
Dynametric Inc ....F.......626 358-2559
1715 Business Center Dr Duarte (91010) ***(P-17941)***

ALPHABETIC

Employee Codes: A=Over 500 employees, B=251-500
C=101-250, D=51-100, E=20-50, F=10-19
2019 California
Manfacturers Register
© Mergent Inc. 1-800-342-5647
1125

Dynamex Corporation....E....310 329-0399
155 E Albertoni St Carson (90746) ***(P-2974)***
Dynamic Bindery Inc....F....909 884-1296
170 S Arrowhead Ave San Bernardino (92408) ***(P-7598)***
Dynamic Cabinet Designs Inc....E....818 700-1658
10215 Canoga Ave Chatsworth (91311) ***(P-4296)***
Dynamic Cooking Systems Inc....A....714 372-7000
695 Town Center Dr # 180 Costa Mesa (92626) ***(P-16035)***
Dynamic Digital Displays, Rancho Cordova *Also called D3 Led LLC* ***(P-23854)***
Dynamic E-Markets LLC....F....619 327-4777
2335 Roll Dr Ste 5 San Diego (92154) ***(P-2705)***
Dynamic Engineering....F....831 457-8891
150 Dubois St Ste C Santa Cruz (95060) ***(P-18807)***
Dynamic Enterprises Inc....E....562 944-0271
10015 Greenleaf Ave Santa Fe Springs (90670) ***(P-16455)***
Dynamic Fabrication Inc....F....714 662-2440
2615 S Hickory St Santa Ana (92707) ***(P-19951)***
Dynamic Finishing, Northridge *Also called Dynamic Shutters Inc* ***(P-4151)***
Dynamic Instruments, San Diego *Also called Technology For Energy Corp* ***(P-21863)***
Dynamic Intgrted Solutions LLC....F....408 737-3400
1710 Fortune Dr San Jose (95131) ***(P-18808)***
Dynamic Intgrted Solutions LLC (PA)....E....408 727-3400
3964 Rivermark Plz # 104 Santa Clara (95054) ***(P-18809)***
Dynamic Machine Inc....F....323 585-0710
3470 Randolph St Huntington Park (90255) ***(P-16456)***
Dynamic Pre-Cast Co Inc....F....707 573-1110
5300 Sebastopol Rd Santa Rosa (95407) ***(P-10918)***
Dynamic Sciences Intl Inc....E....818 226-6262
9400 Lurline Ave Unit B Chatsworth (91311) ***(P-18092)***
Dynamic Services Inc....F....949 458-2553
27091 Burbank El Toro (92610) ***(P-7305)***
Dynamic Shutters Inc....E....818 407-6310
9310 Corbin Ave Northridge (91324) ***(P-4151)***
Dynamic Solutions....F....253 273-7936
631 W Rosecrans Ave # 23 Gardena (90248) ***(P-22188)***
Dynamics O&P, Los Angeles *Also called Dynamics Orthotics & Prostheti* ***(P-22719)***
Dynamics Orthotics & Prostheti....E....213 383-9212
1830 W Olympic Blvd # 123 Los Angeles (90006) ***(P-22719)***
Dynamikos Inc (PA)....F....408 432-1711
720 Charcot Ave San Jose (95131) ***(P-9837)***
Dynamite Sign Group Inc....E....562 595-7725
3080 E 29th St Long Beach (90806) ***(P-23859)***
Dynasty Electronic Company LLC....D....714 550-1197
1790 E Mcfadden Ave Santa Ana (92705) ***(P-18469)***
Dynasty Import Co, San Francisco *Also called FML Inc* ***(P-23747)***
Dynatec Mfg Inc....F....408 265-8471
3326 Famille Ct San Jose (95135) ***(P-16457)***
Dynatect Ro-Lab Inc....E....262 786-1500
8830 W Linne Rd Tracy (95304) ***(P-9566)***
Dynatest Consulting Inc....F....805 648-2230
165 S Chestnut St Ventura (93001) ***(P-21742)***
Dynatex International....E....707 542-4227
5577 Skylane Blvd Santa Rosa (95403) ***(P-14628)***
Dynatrac Products Co Inc....F....714 596-4461
7392 Count Cir Huntington Beach (92647) ***(P-20320)***
Dynavax Technologies Corp (PA)....C....510 848-5100
2929 7th St Ste 100 Berkeley (94710) ***(P-8547)***
Dynglobal California Corp....E....949 584-6198
1139 Baker St Costa Mesa (92626) ***(P-16036)***
Dytran Instruments Inc....C....818 700-7818
21592 Marilla St Chatsworth (91311) ***(P-19520)***
Dz Tranz Group, Canoga Park *Also called Darrell Zbrowski* ***(P-14322)***
E & B Ntral Resources MGT Corp....E....661 766-2501
1848 Perkins Rd New Cuyama (93254) ***(P-134)***
E & B Ntral Resources Mgt Corp (PA)....D....661 679-1714
1600 Norris Rd Bakersfield (93308) ***(P-55)***
E & J Gallo Winery (PA)....A....209 341-3111
600 Yosemite Blvd Modesto (95354) ***(P-1739)***
E & J Gallo Winery....C....559 458-0807
5610 E Olive Ave Fresno (93727) ***(P-1740)***
E & J Gallo Winery....D....559 458-2500
5631 E Olive Ave Fresno (93727) ***(P-1741)***
E & J Gallo Winery....E....707 431-1946
3387 Dry Creek Rd Healdsburg (95448) ***(P-1742)***
E & J Gallo Winery....F....209 341-3111
2101 Yosemite Blvd Modesto (95354) ***(P-1743)***
E & J Gallo Winery....C....209 394-6215
18000 River Rd Livingston (95334) ***(P-1744)***
E & J Gallo Winery....C....805 544-5855
2585 Biddle Ranch Rd San Luis Obispo (93401) ***(P-1745)***
E & J Gallo Winery....B....323 720-6400
2650 Commerce Way Commerce (90040) ***(P-1746)***
E & J Gallo Winery....E....707 963-2736
254 Saint Helena Hwy S Saint Helena (94574) ***(P-1747)***
E & J Gallo Winery....F....209 341-7862
200 E Sandy Blvd Modesto (95354) ***(P-1748)***
E & L Electric Inc....F....562 903-9272
12322 Los Nietos Rd Santa Fe Springs (90670) ***(P-25457)***
E & R Glass Contractors Inc....E....909 624-1763
5369 Brooks St Montclair (91763) ***(P-10694)***
E & R Pallets Inc....F....951 790-1212
4247 Campbell St Riverside (92509) ***(P-4467)***
E & S Precision Machine Inc....F....209 545-6161
4631 Enterprise Way Modesto (95356) ***(P-16458)***
E & S Precision Sheetmetal Mfg....F....760 329-1607
19298 Mclane St North Palm Springs (92258) ***(P-12565)***
E Alko Inc....C....818 587-9700
8201 Woodley Ave Van Nuys (91406) ***(P-23727)***
E and B Natural Resources....D....661 679-1700
1600 Norris Rd Bakersfield (93308) ***(P-135)***
E and J Gallo, Santa Ynez *Also called Bridlewood Winery* ***(P-1667)***
E D D Investment Co....E....714 637-3040
2025 N Tustin St Orange (92865) ***(P-1239)***
E D I, South El Monte *Also called Engineering Design Inds Inc* ***(P-16476)***
E D M Sacramento Inc....E....916 851-9285
11341 Sunrise Park Dr Rancho Cordova (95742) ***(P-16459)***
E E Systems Group Inc....F....626 452-8988
12346 Valley Blvd Unit A El Monte (91732) ***(P-19952)***
E Enterprise Tech, San Jose *Also called Espace Enterprises Tech Inc* ***(P-14950)***
E F T Fast Quality Service....F....714 751-1487
2328 S Susan St Santa Ana (92704) ***(P-13392)***
E G Meat and Provision Inc (PA)....F....323 588-5333
4350 Alcoa Ave Vernon (90058) ***(P-481)***
E H Publishing Inc....E....310 533-2400
3520 Challenger St Torrance (90503) ***(P-6155)***
E J Y Corporation....E....213 748-1700
151 W 33rd St Los Angeles (90007) ***(P-3843)***
E K C Technology/Burmar Chem, Hayward *Also called Ekc Technology Inc* ***(P-9245)***
E L A Custom Architectural Div, City of Industry *Also called Environmental Ltg For Arch Inc* ***(P-17603)***
E L I, San Diego *Also called Energy Labs Inc* ***(P-15953)***
E M C, Moreno Valley *Also called Envirnmntal Mlding Cncepts LLC* ***(P-9610)***
E M E Inc....C....310 639-1621
500 E Pine St Compton (90222) ***(P-13393)***
E M Emergency Power Supplies....E....626 799-3549
1133 Mission St South Pasadena (91030) ***(P-19521)***
E M G Inc....D....707 525-9941
675 Aviation Blvd Ste B Santa Rosa (95403) ***(P-23366)***
E M S, Santa Ana *Also called Sandberg Industries Inc* ***(P-19717)***
E O C, Compton *Also called Cri Sub 1* ***(P-4941)***
E P, Union City *Also called Emerald Packaging Inc* ***(P-5599)***
E P S, Vallejo *Also called Earthquake Protection Systems* ***(P-13123)***
E P S Products, Palm Springs *Also called Xy Corp Inc* ***(P-14463)***
E P Z Inc....F....408 735-1820
2262 Calle Del Mundo Santa Clara (95054) ***(P-14942)***
E Phocus Inc....F....858 646-5462
10455 Pacific Center Ct San Diego (92121) ***(P-23154)***
E R C Company, E Rncho Dmngz *Also called Coy Industries Inc* ***(P-12541)***
E R G International, Oxnard *Also called Ergonom Corporation* ***(P-5231)***
E R Metals Inc....F....760 948-2309
14407 Main St Hesperia (92345) ***(P-11756)***
E S M Plastics Inc....F....909 591-7658
13575 Yorba Ave Chino (91710) ***(P-16460)***
E S Q, Cupertino *Also called Esq Business Services Inc* ***(P-24628)***
E S T, Carlsbad *Also called Electro Surface Tech Inc* ***(P-18470)***
E Sales, Garden Grove *Also called Elasco Inc* ***(P-7833)***
E Seek Inc....F....714 832-7980
9471 Ridgehaven Ct Ste E San Diego (92123) ***(P-15734)***
E Vasquez Distributors Inc....E....805 487-8458
4524 E Pleasant Valley Rd Oxnard (93033) ***(P-4468)***
E Virtual Corporation....F....949 515-3670
192 22nd St Apt D Costa Mesa (92627) ***(P-17795)***
E W Smith Chemical Co....F....909 590-9717
4738 Murietta St Chino (91710) ***(P-9244)***
E Z Buy E Z Sell Recycler Corp (HQ)....C....310 886-7808
4954 Van Nuys Blvd # 201 Sherman Oaks (91403) ***(P-5835)***
E Z Martin Stick Labels Inc....F....562 906-1577
12921 Sunnyside Pl Santa Fe Springs (90670) ***(P-7306)***
E-Band Communications LLC....E....858 408-0660
17034 Camino San Bernardo San Diego (92127) ***(P-18093)***
E-Fab Inc....E....408 727-5218
1075 Richard Ave Santa Clara (95050) ***(P-13578)***
E-Freight Technology Inc....E....626 943-8418
2225 W Cromwell Ave Alhambra (91803) ***(P-24585)***
E-Fuel Corporation....E....408 267-2667
15466 Los Gatos Blvd 37 Los Gatos (95032) ***(P-19953)***
E-Liq Cube Inc (PA)....F....562 537-9454
13515 Alondra Blvd Santa Fe Springs (90670) ***(P-24083)***
E-M Manufacturing Inc....F....209 825-1800
1290 Dupont Ct Manteca (95336) ***(P-12566)***
E-Scepter, City of Industry *Also called Sceptre Inc* ***(P-19719)***
E-Tech, Laguna Hills *Also called Eurotech Showers Inc* ***(P-9900)***
E-Transactions Software Tech....F....408 873-9100
21195 Grenola Dr Cupertino (95014) ***(P-24586)***
E-Z Haul Ready Mix Inc....E....559 233-6603
1538 N Blackstone Ave Fresno (93703) ***(P-11103)***
E-Z Mix Inc....E....909 874-7686
3355 Industrial Dr Bloomington (92316) ***(P-5640)***
E-Z Mix Inc (PA)....E....818 768-0568
11450 Tuxford St Sun Valley (91352) ***(P-5641)***
E-Z Mix Inc....E....510 782-8010
4125 Breakwater Ave Ste E Hayward (94545) ***(P-5642)***
E-Z Plastic Packaging Corp....E....323 887-0123
2051 Garfield Ave Commerce (90040) ***(P-5598)***
E-Z Up Directcom....E....909 426-0060
1900 2nd St Colton (92324) ***(P-3785)***
E-Z-Hook Test Products Div, Arcadia *Also called Tektest Inc* ***(P-19424)***
E. Force Sports, Carlsbad *Also called Efgp Inc* ***(P-23556)***
E/G Electro-Graph Inc....D....760 438-9090
1491 Poinsettia Ave # 138 Vista (92081) ***(P-18810)***
E2 Lighting Inc....E....415 760-7793
1460 Yosemite Ave San Francisco (94124) ***(P-17686)***
E2e Mfg LLC....E....925 862-2057
7139 Koll Center Pkwy Pleasanton (94566) ***(P-13197)***
E8 Denim House LLC....F....310 386-4413
309 E 8th St Fl 5 Los Angeles (90014) ***(P-3146)***
Ea, Redwood City *Also called Electronic Arts Inc* ***(P-24600)***

Ea Sports, Redwood City *Also called Electronic Arts Redwood Inc* ***(P-19861)***
Eagle Access Control Systems ....E.......818 837-7900
12953 Foothill Blvd Sylmar (91342) ***(P-17267)***
Eagle Creek Inc (HQ) ....D.......760 431-6400
5935 Darwin Ct Carlsbad (92008) ***(P-10520)***
Eagle Creek Travel Gear, Carlsbad *Also called Eagle Creek Inc* ***(P-10520)***
Eagle Dominion Energy Corp ....E.......202 380-9649
200 N Hayes Ave Oxnard (93030) ***(P-136)***
Eagle Dominion Trust, Oxnard *Also called Eagle Dominion Energy Corp* ***(P-136)***
Eagle Enterprises Inc ....E.......323 721-4741
604 W Whittier Blvd Montebello (90640) ***(P-20321)***
Eagle Iron Fabrication Inc ....F.......925 686-9510
100 Medburn St Ste A Concord (94520) ***(P-12851)***
Eagle Iron Works, Concord *Also called Eagle Iron Fabrication Inc* ***(P-12851)***
Eagle Laboratories LLC ....D.......909 481-0011
10201a Trademark St Ste A Rancho Cucamonga (91730) ***(P-23090)***
Eagle Labs, Rancho Cucamonga *Also called Eagle Laboratories LLC* ***(P-23090)***
Eagle Mold Technologies Inc ....E.......858 530-0888
12330 Crosthwaite Cir Poway (92064) ***(P-10081)***
Eagle Moulding Company 1 (PA) ....E.......530 673-6517
1625 Tierra Buena Rd Yuba City (95993) ***(P-4152)***
Eagle Newspapers LLC ....E.......619 437-8800
1224 10th St Ste 103 Coronado (92118) ***(P-5836)***
Eagle Products - Plast Indust ....E.......909 465-1548
10811 Fremont Ave Ontario (91762) ***(P-10082)***
Eagle Ridge Paper Ltd (HQ) ....E.......714 780-1799
100 S Anaheim Blvd # 250 Anaheim (92805) ***(P-5280)***
Eagle Rock Incorporated ....F.......530 623-4444
40029 La Grange Rd Junction City (96048) ***(P-14164)***
Eagle Roofing Products Co, Rialto *Also called Burlingame Industries Inc* ***(P-11350)***
Eagle Roofing Products Fla LLC (PA) ....E.......909 822-6000
3546 N Riverside Ave Rialto (92377) ***(P-10801)***
Eagle Signs Inc ....F.......909 923-3034
1028 E Acacia St Ontario (91761) ***(P-23860)***
Eagle Systems Inc ....F.......510 231-2686
1601 Atlas Rd Richmond (94806) ***(P-21075)***
Eagle Tech Manufacturing Inc ....E.......831 768-7467
841 Walker St Watsonville (95076) ***(P-21576)***
Eagle Valley Ginning LLC ....E.......209 826-5002
27480 S Bennett Rd Firebaugh (93622) ***(P-14943)***
Eaglemetric Corp ....F.......949 288-3363
98 Discovery Irvine (92618) ***(P-22189)***
Eagleridge Paper CA, Anaheim *Also called Eagle Ridge Paper Ltd* ***(P-5280)***
Eagleware Manufacturing Co Inc ....E.......562 320-3100
12683 Corral Pl Santa Fe Springs (90670) ***(P-13198)***
Eai-Jr286 Inc ....F.......310 297-6400
20100 S Vermont Ave Torrance (90502) ***(P-23553)***
Eandi Metal Works Inc (PA) ....F.......510 532-8311
976 23rd Ave Oakland (94606) ***(P-12155)***
Ear Charms Inc ....F.......949 494-4147
1855 Laguna Canyon Rd Laguna Beach (92651) ***(P-23258)***
Ear Gear, Laguna Beach *Also called Ear Charms Inc* ***(P-23258)***
Eargo Inc (PA) ....D.......650 996-9508
1600 Technology Dr Fl 6 San Jose (95110) ***(P-22720)***
Earl Hays Press ....F.......818 765-0700
10707 Sherman Way Sun Valley (91352) ***(P-7307)***
Earlens Corporation ....F.......650 366-9000
4045a Campbell Ave Menlo Park (94025) ***(P-22721)***
Early Bird Alert Inc ....F.......415 479-7902
70 Mitchell Blvd Ste 106 San Rafael (94903) ***(P-17942)***
Early Childhood Resources, San Diego *Also called Ecr4kids LP* ***(P-5012)***
Earnest Eats, Solana Beach *Also called Annona Company LLC* ***(P-1054)***
Earth & Vine Provisions Inc ....F.......916 434-8399
160 Flocchini Cir Lincoln (95648) ***(P-798)***
Earth Lab Inc ....F.......310 310-9009
5016 Maplewood Ave Unit B Los Angeles (90004) ***(P-8639)***
Earth Print Inc ....F.......818 879-6050
31115 Via Colinas Ste 301 Westlake Village (91362) ***(P-6798)***
Earthlite LLC (HQ) ....D.......760 599-1112
990 Joshua Way Vista (92081) ***(P-4830)***
Earthologytech LLC ....E.......619 435-5296
928 F Ave Coronado (92118) ***(P-14066)***
Earthpro Inc ....E.......408 294-1920
2010 El Camino Real Santa Clara (95050) ***(P-10851)***
Earthquake Protection Systems ....D.......707 644-5993
451 Azuar Ave Bldg 759 Vallejo (94592) ***(P-13123)***
Earthrise Nutritionals LLC ....F.......760 348-5027
113 E Hoober Rd Calipatria (92233) ***(P-2510)***
Earthsavers Erosion Ctrl LLC ....F.......530 662-7700
12972 County Road 102 Woodland (95776) ***(P-21509)***
Eas Sensorsense Inc ....E.......818 763-9186
13351 Riverside Dr Ste D Sherman Oaks (91423) ***(P-7308)***
Eascare Products USA, Fresno *Also called McGrayel Company Inc* ***(P-9278)***
Easic Corporation ....E.......408 855-9200
3940 Freedom Cir 100 Santa Clara (95054) ***(P-18811)***
East Bay Brass Foundry Inc ....E.......510 233-7171
1200 Chesley Ave Richmond (94801) ***(P-11692)***
East Bay Fixture Company ....E.......510 652-4421
941 Aileen St Oakland (94608) ***(P-4593)***
East Bay Glass Company Inc ....F.......510 834-2535
515 Independent Rd Oakland (94621) ***(P-12311)***
East Bay Machine and Shtmtl, Concord *Also called Alvellan Inc* ***(P-16264)***
East Bay Paint Center Inc ....F.......510 524-6582
990 San Pablo Ave Albany (94706) ***(P-8903)***
East County Gazette ....F.......619 444-5774
270 E Douglas Ave El Cajon (92020) ***(P-5837)***
East Electronics, Fremont *Also called Myntahl Corporation* ***(P-17966)***
East La Lamination Inc ....F.......323 881-9838
616 N Hazard Ave Los Angeles (90063) ***(P-10083)***
East Penn Manufacturing Co ....F.......916 374-9965
2920 Ramco St West Sacramento (95691) ***(P-19801)***
East West Printing ....F.......714 899-7885
7433 Lampson Ave Garden Grove (92841) ***(P-6799)***
East West Tea Company LLC ....F.......310 275-9891
1616 Preuss Rd Los Angeles (90035) ***(P-1057)***
Eastbay Express, Oakland *Also called Village Voice Media* ***(P-6081)***
Eastbay Publishing Corp ....F.......510 537-1792
2117 San Jose Ave Alameda (94501) ***(P-5838)***
Eastern Sports, Thousand Oaks *Also called Easton Hockey Inc* ***(P-23554)***
Easterncctv (usa) LLC ....D.......626 961-8810
110 N California Ave City of Industry (91744) ***(P-19954)***
Eastman Kodak Company ....D.......949 306-9034
3 Santa Elena Rcho STA Marg (92688) ***(P-23155)***
Easton Bell Sports, Scotts Valley *Also called Bell Sports Inc* ***(P-23518)***
Easton Hockey Inc (HQ) ....B.......818 782-6445
3500 Willow Ln Thousand Oaks (91361) ***(P-23554)***
Eastwest Clothing Inc (PA) ....E.......323 980-1177
40 E Verdugo Ave Burbank (91502) ***(P-3233)***
Eastwood Machine LLC ....F.......619 873-3660
9346 Abraham Way Santee (92071) ***(P-16461)***
Easy Ad Incorporated ....E.......951 658-2244
155 S Harvard St Hemet (92543) ***(P-5839)***
Easy Ad Magazine, San Luis Obispo *Also called M G A Investment Co Inc* ***(P-6522)***
Easy Flex, Garden Grove *Also called Easyflex Inc* ***(P-11393)***
Easy Networks Cabling ....F.......951 742-8119
3538 Shelley Way Riverside (92503) ***(P-19522)***
Easy Reader Inc ....E.......310 372-4611
832 Hermosa Ave Hermosa Beach (90254) ***(P-5840)***
Easydial Inc (PA) ....D.......949 916-5851
181 Technology Dr Ste 150 Irvine (92618) ***(P-22430)***
Easyflex Inc ....E.......888 577-8999
7423 Doig Dr Garden Grove (92841) ***(P-11393)***
Eat Like A Woman, Burbank *Also called Staness Jonekos Entps Inc* ***(P-2673)***
Eaton Aerospace LLC ....E.......818 550-4200
2905 Winona Ave Burbank (91504) ***(P-21288)***
Eaton Aerospace LLC ....E.......949 452-9500
9650 Jeronimo Rd Irvine (92618) ***(P-21289)***
Eaton Corporation ....C.......661 396-2557
200 New Stine Rd Bakersfield (93309) ***(P-17268)***
Eaton Industrial Corporation ....B.......949 425-9700
9650 Jeronimo Rd Irvine (92618) ***(P-20805)***
Eaton Leonard Tooling, Vista *Also called Tube Form Solutions LLC* ***(P-14770)***
Eatyourmealscom LLC ....F.......925 984-5452
4418 Deer Ridge Rd Danville (94506) ***(P-24084)***
Eba Design Inc ....F.......714 417-9222
760 W 16th St Ste D Costa Mesa (92627) ***(P-8741)***
Eba Performance Makeup, Costa Mesa *Also called Eba Design Inc* ***(P-8741)***
Ebanista Inc (PA) ....E.......949 650-6397
2015 Newport Blvd Costa Mesa (92627) ***(P-4771)***
Ebara International Corp ....D.......916 920-5451
51 Main Ave Sacramento (95838) ***(P-15061)***
Ebara Technologies Inc (HQ) ....D.......916 920-5451
51 Main Ave Sacramento (95838) ***(P-15125)***
Ebatts.com, Camarillo *Also called Battery-Biz Inc* ***(P-19829)***
Ebix Inc ....E.......805 568-0240
212 Cottage Ave Santa Barbara (93101) ***(P-24587)***
Ebr Systems Inc ....E.......408 720-1906
480 Oakmead Pkwy Sunnyvale (94085) ***(P-22973)***
Ebs Products ....F.......714 896-6700
15134 Goldenwest Cir Westminster (92683) ***(P-14944)***
Ebsco Productions Inc ....E.......323 960-2599
1040 N Las Palmas Ave 1 Los Angeles (90038) ***(P-13199)***
Ebus Inc ....E.......562 904-3474
9250 Washburn Rd Downey (90242) ***(P-20204)***
Eca, Brea *Also called Energy Cnvrsion Applctions Inc* ***(P-17091)***
Eca Medical Instruments (HQ) ....E.......805 376-2509
1107 Tourmaline Dr Newbury Park (91320) ***(P-22431)***
Eca Medical Instruments ....E.......818 998-7284
21615 Parthenia St Canoga Park (91304) ***(P-22432)***
ECB Corp ....E.......916 492-8900
1650 Parkway Blvd West Sacramento (95691) ***(P-12567)***
Eccentric Jewelry, Tarzana *Also called Ggco Inc* ***(P-23266)***
Echelon Corporation (HQ) ....D.......408 938-5200
2901 Patrick Henry Dr Santa Clara (95054) ***(P-21743)***
Echelon Fine Printing, Vernon *Also called The Ligature Inc* ***(P-7517)***
Echelon Fine Printing, Vernon *Also called The Ligature Inc* ***(P-7133)***
Echo Lighting Incorporated ....F.......323 890-9008
5618 E Washington Blvd Commerce (90040) ***(P-17687)***
Echo, A Heatlhstream Company, San Diego *Also called Healthstream Inc* ***(P-24723)***
Eci Fuel Systems, Upland *Also called Exhaust Center Inc* ***(P-12580)***
Eckert Zegler Isotope Pdts Inc ....E.......661 309-1010
1800 N Keystone St Burbank (91504) ***(P-22190)***
Eckert Zegler Isotope Pdts Inc (HQ) ....E.......661 309-1010
24937 Avenue Tibbitts Valencia (91355) ***(P-22191)***
Eckert Zegler Isotope Pdts Inc ....E.......661 309-1010
1800 N Keystone St Burbank (91504) ***(P-22192)***
Ecko Print & Packaging, Ontario *Also called Ecko Products Group LLC* ***(P-5406)***
Ecko Products Group LLC ....E.......909 628-5678
740 S Milliken Ave Ste C Ontario (91761) ***(P-5406)***
Eclipse Chocolate Bar & Bistro ....F.......619 578-2984
2145 Fern St San Diego (92104) ***(P-1469)***
Eclipse Data Technologies Inc ....F.......925 224-8880
5139 Johnson Dr Pleasanton (94588) ***(P-19860)***
Eclipse Design Inc ....F.......707 763-3104
427 Corona Rd Petaluma (94954) ***(P-12852)***
Eclipse Metal Fabrication Inc ....E.......650 298-8731
2901 Spring St Redwood City (94063) ***(P-12568)***

Employee Codes: A=Over 500 employees, B=251-500
C=101-250, D=51-100, E=20-50, F=10-19
2019 California
Manfacturers Register
© Mergent Inc. 1-800-342-5647
1127

Eclipse Microwave Inc...F...408 526-1100
2095 Ringwood Ave Ste 60 San Jose (95131) *(P-19523)*
Eclipse Prtg & Graphics LLC...E...909 390-2452
4462 E Airport Dr Ontario (91761) *(P-6800)*
Eclypse International Corp (PA)...F...951 371-8008
265 N Joy St Ste 150 Corona (92879) *(P-21744)*
Ecmm Services Inc...C...714 988-9388
500 S Kraemer Blvd # 100 Brea (92821) *(P-23728)*
Eco Global Solutions Inc...F...707 254-9844
221 Gateway Rd W Ste 403 NAPA (94558) *(P-21510)*
Eco Sensors, Newark *Also called Kwj Engineering Inc (P-22226)*
Eco Services Operations Corp...E...925 313-8224
100 Mococo Rd Martinez (94553) *(P-7770)*
Eco Services Operations Corp...D...310 885-6719
20720 S Wilmington Ave Long Beach (90810) *(P-7771)*
Eco World USA LLC...F...626 433-1333
9950 Baldwin Pl El Monte (91731) *(P-17598)*
Eco-Gen Distributors Inc...F...760 712-7460
340 Goddard Irvine (92618) *(P-17190)*
Eco-Gen Energy Inc...F...818 756-4700
7247 Hayvenhurst Ave A6 Van Nuys (91406) *(P-17191)*
Eco-Shell Inc...E...530 824-8794
5230 Grange Rd Corning (96021) *(P-24085)*
Ecogear-Products, Sierra Madre *Also called Natus Inc (P-23021)*
Ecolab Inc...F...626 935-1212
18383 Railroad St City of Industry (91748) *(P-8591)*
Ecolab Inc...D...925 215-8008
3160 Crow Canyon Pl # 200 San Ramon (94583) *(P-8592)*
Ecolight Inc...F...310 450-7444
1660 Lincoln Blvd Santa Monica (90404) *(P-24086)*
Ecolink...F...760 431-8804
2055 Corte Del Miguel Carlsbad (92008) *(P-19955)*
Ecolink Intelligent Tech Inc...F...855 432-6546
2055 Corte Del Nogal Carlsbad (92011) *(P-17796)*
Ecologic Engine Tstg Labs LLC...F...714 774-3385
1370 S Acacia Ave Fullerton (92831) *(P-14027)*
Ecoly International Inc...E...818 718-6982
5800 Bristol Pkwy Ste 700 Culver City (90230) *(P-8742)*
Econ-O-Plate Inc...F...310 342-5900
5760 Hannum Ave Culver City (90230) *(P-6801)*
Econocold Refrigerators, Cerritos *Also called Refrigerator Manufacters Inc (P-17382)*
Econoday Inc...F...925 299-5350
3730 Mt Diablo Blvd # 340 Lafayette (94549) *(P-6472)*
Econolite Control Products Inc (PA)...C...714 630-3700
1250 N Tustin Ave Anaheim (92807) *(P-18322)*
Economy Print & Image Inc...F...619 295-4455
7515 Metropolitan Dr San Diego (92108) *(P-6802)*
Economy Printing, San Diego *Also called Economy Print & Image Inc (P-6802)*
Economy Printing...F...858 679-8630
12642 Stoutwood St Poway (92064) *(P-6803)*
Economy Printing Image, Poway *Also called Economy Printing (P-6803)*
Economy Printing Service, Monterey *Also called Montero Printing Inc (P-6983)*
Economy Stock Feed Company...F...559 888-2187
10508 E Central Ave Del Rey (93616) *(P-1128)*
Econotek Inc (PA)...F...714 238-1131
2895 E Blue Star St Anaheim (92806) *(P-22875)*
Econscious, Petaluma *Also called G M P C LLC (P-23885)*
Ecoolthing Corp...E...714 368-4791
1321 E Saint Gertrude Pl A Santa Ana (92705) *(P-13938)*
Ecoplast Corporation Inc...D...909 346-0450
13414 Slover Ave Fontana (92337) *(P-10084)*
Ecosystem Aquarium, Dana Point *Also called Captive Ocean Reef Enterprises (P-15306)*
Ecp Powder Coating...F...619 448-3932
1835 John Towers Ave A El Cajon (92020) *(P-13579)*
Ecr4kids LP...E...619 323-2005
4370 Jutland Dr San Diego (92117) *(P-5012)*
Ecrio Inc...D...408 973-7290
19925 Stevens Creek Blvd # 100 Cupertino (95014) *(P-24588)*
Ecs, Stanton *Also called Electronic Connector Svc Inc (P-17464)*
Ecs Refining, Santa Clara *Also called All Metals Inc (P-11552)*
Ectec Inc...F...661 451-1098
632 E Rancho Vista Blvd A Palmdale (93550) *(P-21290)*
Ectron Corporation...E...858 278-0600
8159 Engineer Rd San Diego (92111) *(P-18094)*
Ecw Technology Inc...F...310 373-0082
609 Deep Valley Dr Rllng HLS Est (90274) *(P-15152)*
Ed Jones Company...F...510 704-0704
2834 8th St Berkeley (94710) *(P-24087)*
Edc-Biosystems Inc...E...510 257-1500
49090 Milmont Dr Fremont (94538) *(P-21577)*
Edcast Inc (PA)...E...650 823-3511
1901 Old Middlefield Way # 21 Mountain View (94043) *(P-24589)*
Edco Die Inc...F...909 985-4417
2199 W Arrow Rte Upland (91786) *(P-16462)*
Edco Plastics Inc...E...714 772-1986
2110 E Winston Rd Anaheim (92806) *(P-10085)*
Eddie Motorsports...F...909 581-7398
11479 6th St Rancho Cucamonga (91730) *(P-11953)*
Eddies Perfume & Cosmtc Co Inc...E...818 341-1717
20929 Ventura Blvd Woodland Hills (91364) *(P-8743)*
Eddy Pump Corporation (PA)...F...619 258-7020
15405 Olde Highway 80 El Cajon (92021) *(P-16165)*
Edelbrock LLC (HQ)...B...310 781-2222
2700 California St Torrance (90503) *(P-21106)*
Edelbrock Foundry Corp...A...951 654-6677
1320 S Buena Vista St San Jacinto (92583) *(P-11693)*
Edelbrock Holdings Inc...C...310 781-2290
2301 Dominguez Way Torrance (90501) *(P-20322)*
Edelbrock Holdings Inc...C...951 654-6677
1380 S Buena Vista St San Jacinto (92583) *(P-20323)*
Edelmann Usa Inc (HQ)...E...323 669-5700
2150 S Parco Ave Ontario (91761) *(P-23861)*
Eden Beauty Concepts Inc...E...760 330-9941
3215 Executive Rdg Vista (92081) *(P-8744)*
Eden Creamery LLC (PA)...F...855 425-6867
4470 W Sunset Blvd # 90182 Los Angeles (90027) *(P-667)*
Eden Equipment Company Inc...F...909 629-2217
5670 Wilshire Blvd # 1400 Los Angeles (90036) *(P-15317)*
Edeniq Inc...D...559 302-1777
2505 N Shirk Rd Visalia (93291) *(P-9004)*
Edessa Inc...E...909 823-1377
11027 Cherry Ave Fontana (92337) *(P-10919)*
Edey Door, Los Angeles *Also called Edey Manufacturing Co Inc (P-12312)*
Edey Manufacturing Co Inc...E...323 566-6151
2159 E 92nd St Los Angeles (90002) *(P-12312)*
Edgate Correlation Svcs LLC...E...858 712-9341
5473 Krny Vlla Rd Ste 300 San Diego (92123) *(P-24088)*
Edge Electronics Corporation...E...510 614-7988
14670 Wicks Blvd San Leandro (94577) *(P-12387)*
Edge Plastics Inc (PA)...E...951 786-4750
3016 Kansas Ave Bldg 3 Riverside (92507) *(P-10086)*
Edge Solutions Consulting Inc (PA)...E...818 591-3500
2801 Townsgate Rd Ste 111 Westlake Village (91361) *(P-15406)*
Edgewave Inc...D...800 782-3762
4225 Executive Sq # 1600 La Jolla (92037) *(P-24590)*
Edgewell Per Care Brands LLC...B...949 466-0131
599 S Barranca Ave Covina (91723) *(P-11879)*
Edgewood Press Inc...F...714 516-2455
1130 N Main St Orange (92867) *(P-6804)*
Edgington Oil Company LLC...D...562 423-1465
2400 E Artesia Blvd Long Beach (90805) *(P-9383)*
Edgy Soul...F...310 800-2861
22337 Pacific Coast Hwy # 143 Malibu (90265) *(P-23746)*
Edi Ideas, Fountain Valley *Also called Freightgate Inc (P-24672)*
Edirect Publishing Inc...F...760 602-8300
3451 Via Montebello # 192 Carlsbad (92009) *(P-6473)*
Edison Opto USA Corporation...F...909 284-9710
1809 Excise Ave Ste 201 Ontario (91761) *(P-18812)*
Edition One Group...F...510 705-1930
2080 2nd St Berkeley (94710) *(P-6805)*
EDM International Logistics...F...626 588-2299
2225 W Commwl Ave Ste 110 Alhambra (91803) *(P-9838)*
EDM Performance Accessories, Brea *Also called Clean America Inc (P-19927)*
Edmodo Inc...E...310 614-6868
1200 Park Pl Ste 400 San Mateo (94403) *(P-24591)*
Edmons Unque Furn Stone Gllery (PA)...F...323 462-5787
5174 Melrose Ave Los Angeles (90038) *(P-4691)*
Edmund A Gray Co (PA)...D...213 625-0376
2277 E 15th St Los Angeles (90021) *(P-13885)*
Edmund Kim International Inc (PA)...E...310 604-1100
18737 S Reyes Ave Compton (90221) *(P-3147)*
Edna Valley Vineyard, San Luis Obispo *Also called E & J Gallo Winery (P-1745)*
Ednas Inc...F...805 541-3563
390 Buckley Rd Ste F San Luis Obispo (93401) *(P-1240)*
Edner Corporation...E...925 831-1248
528 Oakshire Pl Alamo (94507) *(P-1241)*
Edo Rcnnssnce Srvllnce Systems, Van Nuys *Also called Harris Corporation (P-21304)*
Edris Plastics Mfg Inc...E...323 581-7000
4560 Pacific Blvd Vernon (90058) *(P-10087)*
Edro Engineering Inc (HQ)...D...909 594-5751
20500 Carrey Rd Walnut (91789) *(P-14510)*
Edro Specialty Steels Inc...F...800 368-3376
20500 Carrey Rd Walnut (91789) *(P-14511)*
EDS, Tracy *Also called Encompass Dist Svcs LLC (P-18821)*
EDS Wrap and Roll Foods LLC...E...510 266-0888
2545 Barrington Ct Hayward (94545) *(P-756)*
Education Elements Inc...E...650 336-0660
999 Skyway Rd Ste 325 San Carlos (94070) *(P-24592)*
Educational Ideas Incorporated...E...714 990-4332
471 Atlas St Brea (92821) *(P-6337)*
Educational Insights, Gardena *Also called Learning Resources Inc (P-24160)*
Edutone Corporation (PA)...F...888 904-9773
1101 Marina Village Pkwy # 201 Alameda (94501) *(P-24593)*
Edventures Co Inc...F...818 848-1270
1203 W Isabel St Burbank (91506) *(P-25402)*
Edward Koehn Co Inc...F...510 843-0821
820 Folger Ave Berkeley (94710) *(P-13022)*
Edward's Industries, Sun Valley *Also called Normel Inc (P-7414)*
Edwards Assoc Cmmnications Inc (PA)...B...805 658-2626
2277 Knoll Dr Ste A Ventura (93003) *(P-5559)*
Edwards Enterprises...B...805 644-5583
4544 Mcgrath St Ventura (93003) *(P-14629)*
Edwards Industries, Sun Valley *Also called Kimdurla Inc (P-10650)*
Edwards Label, Ventura *Also called Edwards Assoc Cmmnications Inc (P-5559)*
Edwards Lfsciences Cardiaq LLC...F...949 387-2615
2 Jenner Ste 100 Irvine (92618) *(P-22433)*
Edwards Lifescience Fing LLC...F...949 250-3480
1 Edwards Way Irvine (92614) *(P-24089)*
Edwards Lifesciences...F...949 250-3783
17192 Daimler St Irvine (92614) *(P-22434)*
Edwards Lifesciences Corp...F...949 250-3522
1402 Alton Pkwy Irvine (92606) *(P-22722)*
Edwards Lifesciences Corp (PA)...A...949 250-2500
1 Edwards Way Irvine (92614) *(P-22723)*
Edwards Lifesciences Corp...E...949 553-0611
1212 Alton Pkwy Irvine (92606) *(P-22724)*

Mergent e-mail: customerrelations@mergent.com
1128
2019 California
Manufacturers Register
(P-0000) Products & Services Section entry number
(PA)=Parent Co (HQ)=Headquarters (DH)=Div Headquarters

Edwards Lifesciences US Inc ....E....949 250-2500
1 Edwards Way Irvine (92614) *(P-22974)*
Edwards Sheet Metal & Fab, Burbank *Also called Edventures Co Inc (P-25402)*
Edwards Sheet Metal Supply Inc ....E....818 785-8600
7810 Burnet Ave Van Nuys (91405) *(P-12569)*
Edwin T Seki Inc ....F....714 838-1177
14711 Sinclair Cir Tustin (92780) *(P-5347)*
EE Pauley Plastic Extrusion ....F....760 240-3737
17177 Navajo Rd Apple Valley (92307) *(P-10088)*
Eeco, Los Angeles *Also called Elevator Equipment Corporation (P-14246)*
Eema Industries Inc ....E....323 904-0200
5461 W Jefferson Blvd Los Angeles (90016) *(P-17688)*
Eemus Manufacturing Corp ....F....626 443-8841
11111 Rush St South El Monte (91733) *(P-13580)*
Eep Holdings LLC (PA) ....F....909 597-7861
4626 Eucalyptus Ave Chino (91710) *(P-10089)*
Eevelle LLC ....E....760 434-2231
2270 Cosmos Ct Ste 100 Carlsbad (92011) *(P-3944)*
Eeye Digital Security, Aliso Viejo *Also called Eeye Inc (P-24594)*
Eeye Inc (HQ) ....E....949 333-1900
65 Enterprise Ste 100 Aliso Viejo (92656) *(P-24594)*
Eezer Products Inc ....E....559 255-4140
4734 E Home Ave Fresno (93703) *(P-7832)*
Ef Composite Technologies LP ....F....800 433-6723
2151 Las Palmas Dr Ste D Carlsbad (92011) *(P-23555)*
Efaxcom (HQ) ....D....323 817-3207
6922 Hollywood Blvd Fl 5 Los Angeles (90028) *(P-15735)*
Efaxcom ....E....805 692-0064
5385 Hollister Ave # 208 Santa Barbara (93111) *(P-15736)*
Eff Aero, Stockton *Also called Wkf (friedman Enterprises Inc (P-20692)*
Effective Graphics Inc ....D....310 323-2223
40 E Verdugo Ave Burbank (91502) *(P-7642)*
Effector Therapeutics Inc ....E....858 546-3997
11180 Roselle St Ste A San Diego (92121) *(P-22932)*
Efgp Inc ....F....760 692-3900
2080 Las Palmas Dr # 102 Carlsbad (92011) *(P-23556)*
Efi Technology Inc ....E....310 793-2505
4025 Spencer St Ste 102 Torrance (90503) *(P-20324)*
Eg Systems LLC (PA) ....E....510 324-0126
6200 Village Pkwy Dublin (94568) *(P-18813)*
Eg Wear Inc ....F....916 361-1508
4512 Harlin Dr Ste A Sacramento (95826) *(P-24090)*
Egads LLC ....F....951 695-9050
42191 Sarah Way Temecula (92590) *(P-23862)*
Egain Corporation (PA) ....C....408 636-4500
1252 Borregas Ave Sunnyvale (94089) *(P-24595)*
Egain Corporation ....F....408 212-3400
455 W Maude Ave Sunnyvale (94085) *(P-24596)*
Egen, Vernon *Also called 4 You Apparel Inc (P-3288)*
Eggleston Signs ....F....916 920-1750
1558 Juliesse Ave Ste S Sacramento (95815) *(P-23863)*
Eggs West LLC ....E....661 758-9700
14460 Palm Ave Wasco (93280) *(P-537)*
Eggtooth Originals Consulting ....F....530 468-5131
13502 Graveyard Gulch Rd Fort Jones (96032) *(P-23420)*
Egomotion Inc ....E....415 849-4662
729 Minna St San Francisco (94103) *(P-24597)*
Egr Incorporated (HQ) ....C....909 923-7075
4000 Greystone Dr Ontario (91761) *(P-20325)*
Egret, Sonoma *Also called Bonneau Wines LLC (P-1663)*
EH Suda Inc (PA) ....F....650 622-9700
615 Industrial Rd San Carlos (94070) *(P-16463)*
EH Suda Inc ....E....530 778-9830
210 Texas Ave Lewiston (96052) *(P-16464)*
Ehlers Estate, Saint Helena *Also called New Vavin Inc (P-1897)*
Ei-Lo Inc ....F....949 200-6626
2102 Alton Pkwy Ste B Irvine (92606) *(P-3054)*
Eibach Springs Inc ....D....951 256-8300
264 Mariah Cir Corona (92879) *(P-13749)*
Eico Inc (PA) ....D....408 945-9898
1054 Yosemite Dr Milpitas (95035) *(P-21745)*
Eide Industries Inc ....D....562 402-8335
16215 Piuma Ave Cerritos (90703) *(P-3786)*
Eigen, Grass Valley *Also called Zmk Medical Technologies Inc (P-22686)*
Eigen Inc ....E....530 274-1240
13355 Grass Valley Ave A Grass Valley (95945) *(P-17797)*
Eiger Biopharmaceuticals Inc (PA) ....F....650 272-6138
2155 Park Blvd Palo Alto (94306) *(P-8548)*
Eiger Vision Corporation ....F....818 201-0471
7714a Lankershim Blvd North Hollywood (91605) *(P-18095)*
Einflatables, Cerritos *Also called Funtastic Factory Inc (P-16517)*
Einflatables, Buena Park *Also called Spn Investments Inc (P-23659)*
Einstein Noah Rest Group Inc ....F....714 847-4609
16304 Beach Blvd Westminster (92683) *(P-570)*
Einstein Noah Rest Group Inc ....F....408 358-5895
15996 Los Gatos Blvd Los Gatos (95032) *(P-571)*
Eis Group Inc ....C....415 402-2622
731 Sansome St Fl 4 San Francisco (94111) *(P-24598)*
Eisel Enterprises Inc ....E....714 993-1706
714 Fee Ana St Placentia (92870) *(P-10920)*
EJ Diamonds Inc ....F....213 623-2329
631 S Olive St Ste 201 Los Angeles (90014) *(P-23259)*
EJ Lauren LLC ....E....562 803-1113
9400 Hall Rd Downey (90241) *(P-4772)*
Ej Usa Inc ....F....562 528-0258
2020 W 14th St Long Beach (90813) *(P-11492)*
Ejay Filtration Inc ....E....951 683-0805
3036 Durahart St Riverside (92507) *(P-13825)*
Ejays Machine Co Inc ....E....714 879-0558
1108 E Valencia Dr Fullerton (92831) *(P-16465)*
Ejl, Downey *Also called EJ Lauren LLC (P-4772)*
EKA Designs, Westlake Village *Also called EKA Technologies Inc (P-18096)*
EKA Technologies Inc ....E....805 379-8668
2985 E Hillcrest Dr # 203 Westlake Village (91362) *(P-18096)*
Ekc Technology Inc (HQ) ....C....510 784-9105
2520 Barrington Ct Hayward (94545) *(P-9245)*
Ekko Material Hdlg Eqp Mfg Inc ....F....909 212-1962
1761 W Holt Ave Pomona (91768) *(P-21227)*
Eklavya LLC ....F....925 443-3296
2021 Las Positas Ct # 141 Livermore (94551) *(P-15318)*
Eklin Medical Systems Inc ....D....760 918-9626
6359 Paseo Del Lago Carlsbad (92011) *(P-22435)*
Eknowledge Group Inc ....E....951 256-4076
160 W Fthill Pkwy Ste 105 Corona (92882) *(P-24599)*
Eko Devices Inc ....F....844 356-3384
2600 10th St Ste 260 Berkeley (94710) *(P-22975)*
Ekso Bionics Inc (PA) ....D....510 984-1761
1414 Harbour Way S # 1201 Richmond (94804) *(P-14945)*
Ekso Bionics Holdings Inc ....C....510 984-1761
1414 Harbour Way S # 1201 Richmond (94804) *(P-22725)*
El Avisador Magazine ....F....916 903-7490
400 Bremerton Ct Roseville (95661) *(P-5841)*
El Burrito Mxican Fd Pdts Corp ....F....626 369-7828
14944 Don Julian Rd City of Industry (91746) *(P-799)*
El Cajon Plating, El Cajon *Also called Ecp Powder Coating (P-13579)*
El Cajon Sheet Metal Mfg, Santee *Also called ABC Mechanical Inc (P-12455)*
El Camino Machine & Wldg LLC (PA) ....E....831 758-8309
296 El Camino Real S Salinas (93901) *(P-16466)*
El Camino Wood Products ....F....310 768-3447
16816 S Broadway Gardena (90248) *(P-4440)*
El Cerrito Woodworking ....F....510 647-3767
4443 Carson St Oakland (94619) *(P-5056)*
El Chavito Inc ....F....844 424-2848
6020 Progressive Ave # 600 San Diego (92154) *(P-1419)*
El Clasificado ....D....323 278-5310
1125 Goodrich Blvd Commerce (90022) *(P-6474)*
El Dorado Gold Panner Inc ....F....530 626-5057
247 Placerville Dr Placerville (95667) *(P-5842)*
El Dorado Mexican Food Pdts, Los Angeles *Also called Food-O-Mex Corporation (P-2523)*
El Dorado Newspapers Inc (HQ) ....C....916 321-1826
2100 Q St Sacramento (95816) *(P-5843)*
El Dorado Truss Coinc ....E....530 622-1264
300 Industrial Dr Placerville (95667) *(P-4403)*
El Gallito Market Inc ....E....626 442-1190
12242 Valley Blvd El Monte (91732) *(P-2511)*
El Indio Tortillas Fctry, Santa Ana *Also called El Indio Tortilleria (P-2512)*
El Indio Tortilleria ....F....714 542-3114
1502 W 5th St Santa Ana (92703) *(P-2512)*
El Latino Newspaper, Chula Vista *Also called Latina & Associates Inc (P-5909)*
El Metate Foods Inc ....F....714 542-3913
125n Rancho Santiago Blvd Orange (92869) *(P-1242)*
El Metate Foods Inc ....E....949 646-9362
817 W 19th St Costa Mesa (92627) *(P-1243)*
El Metate Market, Costa Mesa *Also called El Metate Foods Inc (P-1243)*
El Metate Mercado, Orange *Also called El Metate Foods Inc (P-1242)*
El Monte Plating Company ....F....626 448-3607
11409 Stewart St El Monte (91731) *(P-13394)*
El Observador Publications Inc ....F....408 938-1700
1042 W Hedding St Ste 250 San Jose (95126) *(P-5844)*
El Paraiso No 2 ....E....323 587-2073
1760 E Florence Ave Los Angeles (90001) *(P-668)*
El Pelado LLC ....E....707 938-2877
1180 Fremont Dr Sonoma (95476) *(P-4469)*
El Popular Spanish Newspaper ....F....661 325-7725
404 Truxtun Ave Bakersfield (93301) *(P-5845)*
El Segundo Bread Bar LLC ....E....310 615-9898
701 E El Segundo Blvd El Segundo (90245) *(P-1244)*
El Sol, Modesto *Also called McClatchy Newspapers Inc (P-5947)*
El Super Leon Pnchin Sncks Inc ....E....619 271-0846
315 Quintard St Chula Vista (91911) *(P-1420)*
El Super Leon Pnchin Sncks Inc ....E....619 426-2968
8650 Avenida Costa Blanca San Diego (92154) *(P-1421)*
Elafree Inc ....F....949 724-9390
17779 Main St Ste F&G Irvine (92614) *(P-24091)*
Elaine Gill Inc ....F....510 559-1600
6001 Shellmound St Fl 4th Emeryville (94608) *(P-6338)*
Elan Blanc, Palm Desert *Also called Equipment De Sport Usa Inc (P-3848)*
Elanco Animal Health, Newbury Park *Also called Eli Lilly and Company (P-8146)*
Elantec Semiconductor Inc (HQ) ....C....408 945-1323
675 Trade Zone Blvd Milpitas (95035) *(P-18814)*
Elasco Inc ....D....714 373-4767
11377 Markon Dr Garden Grove (92841) *(P-7833)*
Elastomer Technologies Inc ....F....951 272-5820
255 Glider Cir Corona (92880) *(P-9527)*
Elation Lighting Inc ....D....323 582-3322
6122 S Eastern Ave Commerce (90040) *(P-17599)*
Elation Lighting Inc ....F....323 213-4552
6122 S Eastern Ave Commerce (90040) *(P-17534)*
Elation Professional, Commerce *Also called Elation Lighting Inc (P-17599)*
Elba Company, San Dimas *Also called Elba Jewelry Inc (P-23260)*
Elba Jewelry Inc ....F....909 394-5803
910 N Amelia Ave San Dimas (91773) *(P-23260)*
Elco Lighting, Vernon *Also called AMP Plus Inc (P-17659)*
Elco Rfrgn Solutions LLC ....A....619 255-5251
2554 Commercial St San Diego (92113) *(P-15952)*

ALPHABETIC

Employee Codes: A=Over 500 employees, B=251-500
C=101-250, D=51-100, E=20-50, F=10-19
2019 California
Manfacturers Register
© Mergent Inc. 1-800-342-5647
1129

Elcon Inc ...E ...408 292-7800
1009 Timothy Dr San Jose (95133) **(P-19524)**
Elcon Power Conectr Pdts Group, Menlo Park *Also called Te Connectivity Corporation* **(P-17497)**
Elcon Precision LLC ...E ...408 292-7800
1009 Timothy Dr San Jose (95133) **(P-14630)**
Eldema Products ...F ...619 661-5113
10145 Via De La Amistad # 5 San Diego (92154) **(P-17661)**
Eldorado National Cal Inc (HQ) ...B ...951 727-9300
9670 Galena St Riverside (92509) **(P-20137)**
Eldorado Stone, North Hollywood *Also called Prime Building Material Inc* **(P-10982)**
Eldridge Products Inc ...E ...831 648-7777
465 Reservation Rd Marina (93933) **(P-21578)**
Eleanor Rigby Leather Co ...E ...619 356-5590
4660 La Jolla Village Dr # 100 San Diego (92122) **(P-10574)**
Elecoco Inc ...E ...213 627-2377
4553 Seville Ave Vernon (90058) **(P-3410)**
Elecraft Incorporated ...E ...831 763-4211
125 Westridge Dr Watsonville (95076) **(P-21746)**
Electrasem Corp ...F ...951 371-6140
372 Elizabeth Ln Corona (92880) **(P-21511)**
Electric Bike Company LLC ...F ...949 264-4080
519 Superior Ave Newport Beach (92663) **(P-21107)**
Electric Designs, Gardena *Also called Gloria Lance Inc* **(P-3238)**
Electric Gate Store Inc (PA) ...C ...818 504-2300
421 Park Ave San Fernando (91340) **(P-19956)**
Electric Gate Store Inc ...C ...818 361-6872
15342 Chatsworth St Mission Hills (91345) **(P-19957)**
Electric Motor Works Inc ...E ...661 327-4271
803 Inyo St Bakersfield (93305) **(P-25458)**
Electric Vehicles Intl LLC (PA) ...E ...209 939-0405
1627 Army Ct Ste 1 Stockton (95206) **(P-20138)**
Electric Visual Evolution LLC (PA) ...E ...949 940-9125
950 Calle Amanecer # 101 San Clemente (92673) **(P-23091)**
Electrical Products Division, Fontana *Also called Southwire Inc* **(P-11580)**
Electrical Products Rep, Irvine *Also called Agents West Inc* **(P-19900)**
Electrical Rebuilders Sls Inc (PA) ...D ...323 249-7545
1559 W 134th St Gardena (90249) **(P-19831)**
Electrical Systems, Corona *Also called Panel Shop Inc* **(P-17153)**
Electriq Power Inc ...F ...408 393-7702
31691 Hayman St Hayward (94544) **(P-21747)**
Electrnic Cmbat Test Evluation, Palmdale *Also called Ectec Inc* **(P-21290)**
Electro Adapter Inc ...D ...818 998-1198
20640 Nordhoff St Chatsworth (91311) **(P-17463)**
Electro Component Assembly, Canoga Park *Also called Eca Medical Instruments* **(P-22432)**
Electro Kinetics Division, Simi Valley *Also called Pacific Scientific Company* **(P-21378)**
Electro Machine & Engrg Co, Compton *Also called E M E Inc* **(P-13393)**
Electro Metal Finishing Corp (PA) ...F ...714 630-8940
1194 N Grove St Anaheim (92806) **(P-13581)**
Electro Optical Industries ...E ...805 964-6701
320 Storke Rd Ste 100 Goleta (93117) **(P-22075)**
Electro Plating Specialties ...E ...510 786-1881
2436 American Ave Hayward (94545) **(P-13395)**
Electro Star Indus Coating Inc ...F ...530 527-5400
1945 Airport Blvd Red Bluff (96080) **(P-13582)**
Electro Star Powder Coatings, Red Bluff *Also called Electro Star Indus Coating Inc* **(P-13582)**
Electro Surface Tech Inc ...D ...760 431-8306
2281 Las Palmas Dr 101 Carlsbad (92011) **(P-18470)**
Electro Switch Corp ...C ...909 581-0855
10410 Trademark St Rancho Cucamonga (91730) **(P-17143)**
Electro Switch Corp ...F ...909 581-0855
10410 Trademark St Rancho Cucamonga (91730) **(P-19525)**
Electro Tech Coatings Inc ...E ...760 746-0292
836 Rancheros Dr Ste A San Marcos (92069) **(P-13583)**
Electro-Comm, Burbank *Also called Y B S Enterprises Inc* **(P-18010)**
Electro-Mech Components Inc (PA) ...F ...626 442-7180
1826 Floradale Ave South El Monte (91733) **(P-17144)**
Electro-Support Systems Corp ...E ...951 676-2751
27449 Colt Ct Temecula (92590) **(P-19526)**
Electro-Tech Machining Div, Long Beach *Also called Kbr Inc* **(P-17238)**
Electro-Tech Products Inc ...E ...909 592-1434
2001 E Gladstone St Ste A Glendora (91740) **(P-19527)**
Electro-Tech's, Corona *Also called R&M Deese Inc* **(P-23948)**
Electrochem Solutions Inc ...F ...510 476-1840
32500 Central Ave Union City (94587) **(P-13396)**
Electrochem Solutions LLC ...D ...510 476-1840
32500 Central Ave Union City (94587) **(P-13397)**
Electrocube Inc (PA) ...D ...909 595-1821
3366 Pomona Blvd Pomona (91768) **(P-19528)**
Electrocut-Pacific, San Carlos *Also called Jerry Carroll Machinery Inc* **(P-16621)**
Electrode Technologies Inc ...E ...714 549-3771
3110 W Harvard St Ste 14 Santa Ana (92704) **(P-13398)**
Electrofab Inc ...E ...408 943-9380
18611 Maude Ave Saratoga (95070) **(P-19529)**
Electrofilm Mfg Co LLC ...D ...661 257-2242
28150 Industry Dr Valencia (91355) **(P-13740)**
Electroglas, Dublin *Also called Eg Systems LLC* **(P-18813)**
Electrograph, Vista *Also called E/G Electro-Graph Inc* **(P-18810)**
Electrolizing Inc ...E ...213 749-7876
1947 Hooper Ave Los Angeles (90011) **(P-13399)**
Electrolurgy Inc (PA) ...E ...949 250-4494
1121 Duryea Ave Irvine (92614) **(P-13400)**
Electrolurgy Inc ...E ...714 641-7488
1217 E Normandy Pl Santa Ana (92705) **(P-13886)**
Electrolurgy Manufacturing, Santa Ana *Also called Electrolurgy Inc* **(P-13886)**
Electromagnetics Division, Los Gatos *Also called Pulver Laboratories Inc* **(P-17295)**
Electromatic Inc ...F ...818 765-3236
7351 Radford Ave North Hollywood (91605) **(P-13401)**
Electromatic Inc (PA) ...F ...805 964-9880
789 S Kellogg Ave Goleta (93117) **(P-13402)**
Electromatic Inc ...F ...562 623-9993
14025 Stage Rd Santa Fe Springs (90670) **(P-13403)**
Electromax Inc ...E ...408 428-9474
1960 Concourse Dr San Jose (95131) **(P-18471)**
Electron Beam Engineering Inc ...F ...714 491-5990
1425 S Allec St Anaheim (92805) **(P-25403)**
Electron Imaging Incorporated ...F ...858 679-1569
14260 Garden Rd Ste A12 Poway (92064) **(P-21950)**
Electron Plating III Inc ...E ...714 554-2210
13932 Enterprise Dr Garden Grove (92843) **(P-13404)**
Electronic Arts Inc (PA) ...B ...650 628-1500
209 Redwood Shores Pkwy Redwood City (94065) **(P-24600)**
Electronic Arts Inc ...F ...310 754-7000
5510 Lincoln Blvd Ste 100 Los Angeles (90094) **(P-24601)**
Electronic Arts Los Angeles, Los Angeles *Also called Electronic Arts Inc* **(P-24601)**
Electronic Arts Redwood Inc (HQ) ...D ...650 628-1500
209 Redwood Shores Pkwy Redwood City (94065) **(P-19861)**
Electronic Auto Systems Inc ...F ...626 280-3855
9855 Joe Vargas Way South El Monte (91733) **(P-17798)**
Electronic Chrome Grinding Co ...E ...562 946-6671
9128 Dice Rd Santa Fe Springs (90670) **(P-13405)**
Electronic Clearing House Inc (HQ) ...D ...805 419-8700
730 Paseo Camarillo Camarillo (93010) **(P-24602)**
Electronic Connector Svc Inc ...E ...714 750-9420
10541 Ashdale St Stanton (90680) **(P-17464)**
Electronic Cooling Solutions ...F ...408 738-8331
2344 Walsh Ave Ste B Santa Clara (95051) **(P-15407)**
Electronic Interface Co Inc ...D ...408 286-2134
6341 San Ignacio Ave # 10 San Jose (95119) **(P-19958)**
Electronic Manufacturing Tech, Irvine *Also called Sparton Irvine LLC* **(P-19733)**
Electronic Mfg Leaders & Qulty, Simi Valley *Also called Emlinq LLC* **(P-19533)**
Electronic Mfg Tech Inc ...E ...858 613-1040
16464 Via Esprillo San Diego (92127) **(P-18472)**
Electronic Precision Spc Inc ...E ...714 256-8950
545 Mercury Ln Brea (92821) **(P-13406)**
Electronic Prtg Solutions LLC ...E ...858 576-3000
4879 Ronson Ct Ste C San Diego (92111) **(P-7309)**
Electronic Resources Network ...F ...530 758-0180
1950 5th St Davis (95616) **(P-15737)**
Electronic Sensor Tech Inc ...F ...805 480-1994
1125 Bsneca Ctr Cir Ste B Newbury Park (91320) **(P-21951)**
Electronic Source Company, Van Nuys *Also called Alyn Industries Inc* **(P-19440)**
Electronic Stamping Corp ...E ...310 639-2120
19920 S Alameda St Compton (90221) **(P-17145)**
Electronic Surfc Mounted Inds ...E ...858 455-1710
6731 Cobra Way San Diego (92121) **(P-18473)**
Electronic Systems Co Esco, Sunnyvale *Also called Northrop Grumman Systems Corp* **(P-20604)**
Electronic Systems Innovation ...F ...310 645-8400
5777 W Century Blvd # 1225 Los Angeles (90045) **(P-15408)**
Electronic Theatre Contrls Inc ...F ...323 461-0216
6640 W Sunset Blvd # 200 Los Angeles (90028) **(P-17689)**
Electronic Waveform Lab Inc ...E ...714 843-0463
5702 Bolsa Ave Huntington Beach (92649) **(P-22436)**
Electrorack, Anaheim *Also called Ortronics Inc* **(P-12697)**
Electrowave Ultrasonics Corp ...E ...858 695-2227
27932 Valley Center Rd Valley Center (92082) **(P-19959)**
Elegance Embroidery Ltd ...E ...510 654-0788
4077 Emery St Emeryville (94608) **(P-3148)**
Elegance Entries and Windows, Anaheim *Also called Elegance Entries Inc* **(P-12313)**
Elegance Entries Inc ...F ...714 632-3667
1130 N Kraemer Blvd Ste G Anaheim (92806) **(P-12313)**
Elegance Upholstery Inc ...F ...562 698-2584
11803 Slauson Ave Unit A Ontario (91762) **(P-5228)**
Elekta Inc ...E ...408 830-8000
100 Mathilda Pl Fl 5 Sunnyvale (94086) **(P-24603)**
Elekta / Impac Medical Systems, Sunnyvale *Also called Impac Medical Systems Inc* **(P-24754)**
Elektron Technology Corp ...F ...760 343-3650
11849 Telegraph Rd Santa Fe Springs (90670) **(P-18815)**
Element Six Tech US Corp ...F ...408 986-8184
3901 Burton Dr Santa Clara (95054) **(P-7772)**
Element Technica LLC ...F ...323 993-5329
4617 W Jefferson Blvd Los Angeles (90016) **(P-23156)**
Elementcxi ...E ...408 935-8090
25 E Trimble Rd San Jose (95131) **(P-18816)**
Elementis Specialties Inc ...E ...760 257-9112
31763 Mountain View Rd Newberry Springs (92365) **(P-401)**
Elements ...E ...310 781-1384
20314a Gramercy Pl Torrance (90501) **(P-23261)**
Elements Architectural Surfaces, Redlands *Also called Fast Access Inc* **(P-10924)**
Elements By Grapevine Inc ...E ...209 727-3711
18251 N Highway 88 Lockeford (95237) **(P-4692)**
Elements Food Group Inc ...D ...909 983-2011
5560 Brooks St Montclair (91763) **(P-1363)**
Elements Manufacturing Inc ...E ...831 421-9440
115 Harvey West Blvd C Santa Cruz (95060) **(P-5057)**
Elephant Filmz & Music Inc ...F ...310 925-8712
3943 Irvine Blvd Ste 430 Irvine (92602) **(P-23157)**
Elevate Inc ...E ...949 276-5428
180 Avenida La Pata San Clemente (92673) **(P-24604)**
Elevator Equipment Corporation (PA) ...D ...323 245-0147
4035 Goodwin Ave Los Angeles (90039) **(P-14246)**
Elevator Industries Inc ...F ...916 921-1495
110 Main Ave Sacramento (95838) **(P-14247)**

ALPHABETIC SECTION
Emisense CA, Ladera Ranch

Elevator Research & Mfg Co......D......213 746-1914
1417 Elwood St Los Angeles (90021) ***(P-14248)***
ELF Beauty Inc (PA)......E......510 778-7787
570 10th St Oakland (94607) ***(P-8745)***
Eli Lilly and Company......C......805 499-5475
63 Via Ricardo Newbury Park (91320) ***(P-8146)***
Elisid Magazine......E......619 990-9999
1450 University Ave F168 Riverside (92507) ***(P-6156)***
Elite 4 Print Inc......E......310 366-1344
851 E Walnut St Carson (90746) ***(P-6806)***
Elite Aviation Products Inc......E......949 536-7199
1641 Reynolds Ave Irvine (92614) ***(P-21291)***
Elite Cabinetry Inc......F......951 698-5050
25755 Jefferson Ave Murrieta (92562) ***(P-5229)***
Elite Color Technologies Inc......F......310 324-3040
851 E Walnut St Carson (90746) ***(P-7310)***
Elite E/M Inc......E......408 988-3505
340 Martin Ave Santa Clara (95050) ***(P-12570)***
Elite Fashion Accessories Inc......F......559 435-0225
7141 N Warren Ave Fresno (93711) ***(P-3629)***
Elite Generators Inc......F......818 718-0200
9007 De Soto Ave Canoga Park (91304) ***(P-17192)***
Elite Global Solutions Inc......F......949 709-4872
19732 Descartes Foothill Ranch (92610) ***(P-7834)***
Elite Leather LLC......D......909 548-8600
3131 E Maria St Compton (90221) ***(P-4773)***
Elite Lighting......C......323 888-1973
5424 E Slauson Ave Commerce (90040) ***(P-17690)***
Elite Lighting Corp., Commerce *Also called Elite Lighting* ***(P-17690)***
Elite Metal Fabrication Inc......E......408 433-9926
2299 Ringwood Ave Ste C1 San Jose (95131) ***(P-16467)***
Elite Metal Finishing, Oceanside *Also called Rose Manufacturing Group Inc* ***(P-13492)***
Elite Metal Finishing LLC......C......805 983-4320
540 Spectrum Cir Oxnard (93030) ***(P-13407)***
Elite Mfg Corp......C......888 354-8356
12143 Altamar Pl Santa Fe Springs (90670) ***(P-4982)***
Elite Optical, Compton *Also called Essilor Laboratories Amer Inc* ***(P-23095)***
Elite Property Maintenance......F......916 275-3956
3759 Pine Hollow Way Antelope (95843) ***(P-14946)***
Elite Ready-Mix LLC......E......916 366-4627
550 Greenville Rd Livermore (94550) ***(P-11104)***
Elite Sports Inc......F......714 634-3835
2120 E Howell Ave Ste 502 Anaheim (92806) ***(P-3149)***
Elixir Industries......F......949 860-5000
24800 Chrisanta Dr # 100 Mission Viejo (92691) ***(P-13200)***
Elixir Medical Corporation (PA)......F......408 636-2000
920 N Mccarthy Blvd Milpitas (95035) ***(P-22437)***
Elizabeth Shutters Inc......E......909 825-1531
525 S Rancho Ave Colton (92324) ***(P-12314)***
Elizabeths Food Co Inc (PA)......E......310 638-2168
19301 S Santa Fe Ave # 104 Compton (90221) ***(P-1245)***
Elk Corporation of Texas......C......661 391-3900
6200 S Zerker Rd Shafter (93263) ***(P-10921)***
Elk Grove Citizen, Elk Grove *Also called Herburger Publications Inc* ***(P-5877)***
Elk Grove Milling Inc......E......916 684-2056
8320 Eschinger Rd Elk Grove (95757) ***(P-1129)***
Elkay Interior Systems Inc......F......800 837-8373
225 Santa Monica Blvd Santa Monica (90401) ***(P-5230)***
Elle Boutique......F......626 307-9882
200 E Garvey Ave Ste 105 Monterey Park (91755) ***(P-3308)***
Ellegra Print & Imaging......F......562 432-2931
1419 Santa Fe Ave Long Beach (90813) ***(P-6807)***
Ellen Lark Farm......F......805 272-8448
410 Bryant Cir Ste A Ojai (93023) ***(P-1058)***
Ellensburg Lamb Company Inc......C......707 678-3091
7390 Rio Dixon Rd Dixon (95620) ***(P-432)***
Ellensburg Lamb Company Inc (HQ)......F......530 758-3091
2530 River Plaza Dr # 200 Sacramento (95833) ***(P-433)***
Ellexar, Santa Ana *Also called Arsys Inc* ***(P-14915)***
Ellie Mae Inc (PA)......C......925 227-7000
4420 Rosewood Dr Ste 500 Pleasanton (94588) ***(P-24605)***
Ellingson Inc......F......714 773-1923
119 W Santa Fe Ave Fullerton (92832) ***(P-16468)***
Elliott Manufacturing Company......F......559 233-6235
2664 S Cherry Ave Fresno (93706) ***(P-16469)***
Ellipsis Health Inc......F......650 906-6117
535 Mission St Fl 25 San Francisco (94105) ***(P-24606)***
Ellis and Ellis Sign, Sacramento *Also called Illuminated Creations Inc* ***(P-23896)***
Ellis Truss Company, Hesperia *Also called Jim Ellis* ***(P-4416)***
Ellison Biner......D......760 598-6500
2685 S Melrose Dr Vista (92081) ***(P-15205)***
Ellison Educational Eqp Inc (PA)......C......949 598-8822
25862 Commercentre Dr Lake Forest (92630) ***(P-14792)***
Elliston Vineyards Inc......D......925 862-2377
463 Kilkare Rd Sunol (94586) ***(P-1749)***
Ellsworth Adhesive Systems, Irvine *Also called Ellsworth Corporation* ***(P-9141)***
Ellsworth Corporation......F......949 341-9329
25 Hubble Irvine (92618) ***(P-9141)***
Elm System Inc......F......408 694-2750
11622 El Carmino Real 1 San Diego (92130) ***(P-19862)***
Elma Electronic Inc (HQ)......C......510 656-3400
44350 S Grimmer Blvd Fremont (94538) ***(P-15409)***
Elmco & Assoc (PA)......F......916 383-0110
11225 Trade Center Dr # 100 Rancho Cordova (95742) ***(P-9899)***
Elmech Inc......F......408 782-2990
195 San Pedro Ave Ste E15 Morgan Hill (95037) ***(P-19530)***
Elro Manufacturing Company (PA)......E......310 380-7444
400 W Walnut St Gardena (90248) ***(P-23864)***
Elro Sign Company, Gardena *Also called Elro Manufacturing Company* ***(P-23864)***

Elsevier Inc......D......619 231-6616
525 B St Ste 1650 San Diego (92101) ***(P-6475)***
Elson Alexander, Anaheim *Also called Universal Directory Publishing* ***(P-6610)***
Elson Electric......F......925 464-7461
3440 Vincent Rd Ste C Pleasant Hill (94523) ***(P-19960)***
Eltron International, Agoura Hills *Also called Zebra Technologies Corporation* ***(P-15891)***
Ely Co Inc......E......310 539-5831
3046 Kashiwa St Torrance (90505) ***(P-16470)***
Elyptol Inc......F......424 500-8099
2500 Broadway Ste F125 Santa Monica (90404) ***(P-7934)***
Elysium Ceramics, Anaheim *Also called Elysium Mosaics Inc* ***(P-10781)***
Elysium Jennings LLC......C......661 679-1700
1600 Norris Rd Bakersfield (93308) ***(P-103)***
Elysium Mosaics Inc......F......714 991-7885
1180 N Anaheim Blvd Anaheim (92801) ***(P-10781)***
Ema, City of Industry *Also called Engineering Model Associates* ***(P-10092)***
Ema Textiles Inc......F......323 589-9800
2947 E 44th St Vernon (90058) ***(P-2834)***
Emac Assembly Corp......F......818 882-2999
21615 Parthenia St Canoga Park (91304) ***(P-19531)***
Emanuel Morez Inc......E......818 780-2787
8754 Yolanda Ave Northridge (91324) ***(P-4693)***
Emazing Lights LLC......F......626 628-6482
240 S Loara St Anaheim (92802) ***(P-17691)***
Embarcadero Publishing Company (PA)......C......650 964-6300
450 Cambridge Ave Palo Alto (94306) ***(P-5846)***
Embedded Designs Inc......E......858 673-6050
16120 W Bernardo Dr Ste A San Diego (92127) ***(P-21579)***
Embedded Systems Inc......E......805 624-6030
2250a Union Pl Simi Valley (93065) ***(P-17269)***
Emberton Machine & Tool Inc......F......619 401-1870
1215 Pioneer Way Ste A El Cajon (92020) ***(P-16471)***
Embolx Inc......F......408 990-2949
530 Lakeside Dr Ste 200 Sunnyvale (94085) ***(P-22438)***
Embroidertex West Ltd (PA)......F......213 749-4319
435 E 16th St Los Angeles (90015) ***(P-3844)***
Embroidery By P & J Inc......F......909 592-2622
301 E Arrow Hwy Ste 104 San Dimas (91773) ***(P-3845)***
Embroidery One Corp......E......213 572-0280
1359 Channing St Los Angeles (90021) ***(P-3846)***
Embroidery Outlet......F......951 687-1750
10460 Magnolia Ave Riverside (92505) ***(P-3847)***
EMC Corporation......D......925 425-1400
6800 Koll Center Pkwy # 200 Pleasanton (94566) ***(P-15532)***
EMC Corporation......D......925 948-9000
6701 Koll Center Pkwy # 150 Pleasanton (94566) ***(P-15533)***
EMC Corporation......E......877 636-8589
455 Market St Fl 4 San Francisco (94105) ***(P-15534)***
EMC Corporation......D......949 794-9999
2201 Dupont Dr Ste 500 Irvine (92612) ***(P-15410)***
EMC Corporation......D......925 600-6800
6801 Koll Center Pkwy Pleasanton (94566) ***(P-15535)***
Emco Fluid Systems Inc......C......661 295-1015
28150 Harrison Pkwy Valencia (91355) ***(P-21580)***
Emcor Group Inc......E......949 475-6020
2 Cromwell Irvine (92618) ***(P-21686)***
Emcore Corporation......F......510 896-2139
8674 Thornton Ave Newark (94560) ***(P-18817)***
Emcore Corporation (PA)......C......626 293-3400
2015 Chestnut St Alhambra (91803) ***(P-18818)***
Emcore Corporation......C......626 293-3400
2015 Chestnut St Alhambra (91803) ***(P-18097)***
EMD Millipore Corporation......C......510 576-1367
25801 Industrial Blvd B Hayward (94545) ***(P-21952)***
EMD Millipore Corporation......F......760 788-9692
26578 Old Julian Hwy Ramona (92065) ***(P-21953)***
EMD Millipore Corporation......C......951 676-8080
28835 Single Oak Dr Temecula (92590) ***(P-21954)***
EMD Millipore Corporation......C......951 676-8080
28820 Single Oak Dr Temecula (92590) ***(P-21955)***
EMD Specialty Materials LLC......F......909 987-9533
9433 Hyssop Dr Rancho Cucamonga (91730) ***(P-18474)***
Emdin International Corp......F......626 813-3740
15841 Business Center Dr Irwindale (91706) ***(P-22876)***
Eme Fan & Motor, Brea *Also called Sunon Inc* ***(P-15178)***
Eme Technologies Inc......E......408 720-8817
3485 Victor St Santa Clara (95054) ***(P-16472)***
Emerald Expositions LLC......D......949 226-5754
31910 Del Obispo St # 200 San Juan Capistrano (92675) ***(P-6157)***
Emerald Expositions LLC......D......323 525-2000
5055 Wilshire Blvd # 600 Los Angeles (90036) ***(P-6158)***
Emerald Kingdom Greenhouse LLC......E......530 215-5670
104 Masonic Ln Weaverville (96093) ***(P-12929)***
Emerald Packaging Inc......C......510 429-5700
33050 Western Ave Union City (94587) ***(P-5599)***
Emergency Preparedness Pdts, Camarillo *Also called Recon 1 Inc* ***(P-9479)***
Emergent Group Inc (HQ)......D......818 394-2800
10939 Pendleton St Sun Valley (91352) ***(P-22726)***
Emerson Process Management......E......858 492-1069
5466 Complex St Ste 203 San Diego (92123) ***(P-21581)***
Emerzian Woodworking Inc......E......559 292-2448
2555 N Argyle Ave Fresno (93727) ***(P-5058)***
EMI Music Publishing Inc......E......310 586-2700
2700 Colorado Ave Ste 100 Santa Monica (90404) ***(P-6476)***
EMI Solutions Inc......F......949 206-9960
13805 Alton Pkwy Ste B Irvine (92618) ***(P-19532)***
Emiliomiti LLC......F......415 621-1171
2129 Harrison St San Francisco (94110) ***(P-14845)***
Emily's Classic Beauty Salon, Long Beach *Also called La Rutan* ***(P-24156)***
Emisense CA, Ladera Ranch *Also called Emisense Technologies LLC* ***(P-18819)***

ALPHABETIC

Employee Codes: A=Over 500 employees, B=251-500
C=101-250, D=51-100, E=20-50, F=10-19
2019 California
Manfacturers Register
© Mergent Inc. 1-800-342-5647
1131

Emisense Technologies LLC (PA) F 949 502-8440
999 Corporate Dr Ste 100 Ladera Ranch (92694) ***(P-18819)***

Emission Methods Inc E 909 605-6800
1307 S Wanamaker Ave Ontario (91761) ***(P-22193)***

Emitcon Inc E 714 632-8595
1175 N Van Horne Way Anaheim (92806) ***(P-21687)***

Emkay Mfg., Redwood City *Also called Bay Precision Machining Inc* ***(P-16309)***

Emlinq LLC D 805 409-4807
2125 N Madera Rd Ste C Simi Valley (93065) ***(P-19533)***

Emmaus Life Sciences Inc (PA) F 310 214-0065
21250 Hawthorne Blvd B Torrance (90503) ***(P-8147)***

Emmaus Medical Inc (HQ) F 310 214-0065
21250 Hawthorne Blvd # 800 Torrance (90503) ***(P-7935)***

Emp Connectors Inc E 310 533-6799
548 Amapola Ave Torrance (90501) ***(P-17465)***

Empire Container Corporation D 310 537-8190
1161 E Walnut St Carson (90746) ***(P-5407)***

Empire Optical of California E 818 997-6474
7633 Varna Ave North Hollywood (91605) ***(P-23092)***

Empire Pre Cast E 951 609-1590
19473 Grand Ave Lake Elsinore (92530) ***(P-10922)***

Empire Sheet Metal Inc F 909 923-2927
1215 S Bon View Ave Ontario (91761) ***(P-12571)***

Empire Shower Doors Inc F 707 773-2898
1217 N Mcdowell Blvd Petaluma (94954) ***(P-10695)***

Empire West Inc E 707 823-1190
9270 Graton Rd Graton (95444) ***(P-10090)***

Empire West Plastics, Graton *Also called Empire West Inc* ***(P-10090)***

Employee Owned Pacific Cast PR E 562 633-6673
12711 Imperial Hwy Santa Fe Springs (90670) ***(P-11740)***

Employerware LLC E 925 283-9735
3687 Mt Diablo Blvd 100a Lafayette (94549) ***(P-6477)***

Employment Screening Resources, Novato *Also called Integrity Support Services Inc* ***(P-9264)***

Emporium Di Sanarrey Corp F 714 780-5474
631 S East St Anaheim (92805) ***(P-11250)***

Empower Rf Systems Inc (PA) D 310 412-8100
316 W Florence Ave Inglewood (90301) ***(P-18098)***

Empower Software Tech LLC F 951 672-6257
41695 Date St Ste A Murrieta (92562) ***(P-24607)***

Emsolutions Inc F 510 668-1118
2152 Zanker Rd San Jose (95131) ***(P-18475)***

Emtec Engineering F 408 779-5800
16840 Joleen Way Ste F1 Morgan Hill (95037) ***(P-12572)***

Emti, San Diego *Also called Electronic Mfg Tech Inc* ***(P-18472)***

Emulex Design & Mfg Corp B 714 662-5600
3333 Susan St Costa Mesa (92626) ***(P-18820)***

Enaba-Kbw USA, Chino *Also called CPI Advanced Inc* ***(P-17085)***

Enablence Systems Inc (HQ) E 510 226-8900
2933 Bayview Dr Fremont (94538) ***(P-24608)***

Enablence USA Components Inc D 510 226-8900
2933 Bayview Dr Fremont (94538) ***(P-17943)***

Enact Systems Inc E 855 503-6228
2600 Cmino Ramon Ste 300b San Ramon (94583) ***(P-24609)***

Enaqua E 760 599-2644
1350 Specialty Dr Ste D Vista (92081) ***(P-16037)***

Enas Media Inc E 626 962-1115
1316 Michillinda Ave Arcadia (91006) ***(P-17894)***

Encinitas Oggis Inc F 760 579-3211
305 Encinitas Blvd Encinitas (92024) ***(P-1589)***

Encompass, Sacramento *Also called Laser Recharge Inc* ***(P-23731)***

Encompass Dist Svcs LLC F 925 249-0988
3502 Mars Way Ste 161 Tracy (95377) ***(P-18821)***

Encore Cases Inc E 818 768-8803
8818 Lankershim Blvd Sun Valley (91352) ***(P-10521)***

Encore Fine Cabinetry Inc F 559 822-4333
14748 Highway 41 Ste B Madera (93636) ***(P-4297)***

Encore Image Inc E 909 986-4632
303 W Main St Ontario (91762) ***(P-23865)***

Encore Image Group Inc (PA) D 310 534-7500
1445 Sepulveda Blvd Torrance (90501) ***(P-23866)***

Encore Industries E 408 416-0501
597 Brennan St San Jose (95131) ***(P-12573)***

Encore Interiors Inc (PA) C 949 559-0930
5511 Skylab Rd Ste 101 Huntington Beach (92647) ***(P-20806)***

Encore International E 949 559-0930
5511 Skylab Rd Huntington Beach (92647) ***(P-20649)***

Encore Plastics, Huntington Beach *Also called Donoco Industries Inc* ***(P-10641)***

Encore Seating Inc E 562 926-1969
13747 Midway St Cerritos (90703) ***(P-4983)***

Encore Seats Inc (PA) F 949 559-0930
5511 Skylab Rd Huntington Beach (92647) ***(P-20807)***

Encore Seats Inc E 949 559-0930
5511 Skylab Rd Huntington Beach (92647) ***(P-20808)***

Endeavor Homes Inc E 530 534-0300
655 Cal Oak Rd Oroville (95965) ***(P-14165)***

Enderle Fuel Injection E 805 526-3838
1830 Voyager Ave Simi Valley (93063) ***(P-20326)***

Enderle Vault Co, Inglewood *Also called Centinela Concrete Vault Co* ***(P-10898)***

Endodent Inc E 626 359-5715
851 Meridian St Duarte (91010) ***(P-22877)***

Endologix Inc (PA) B 949 595-7200
2 Musick Irvine (92618) ***(P-22439)***

Endosee Corporation F 650 383-5156
4546 El Camino Real Los Altos (94022) ***(P-22727)***

Endotec Inc F 714 681-6306
14525 Valley View Ave H Santa Fe Springs (90670) ***(P-22728)***

Endpak Packaging Inc D 562 801-0281
9101 Perkins St Pico Rivera (90660) ***(P-5643)***

Endress & Hauser Conducta Inc E 800 835-5474
4123 E La Palma Ave Anaheim (92807) ***(P-21956)***

Endress+houser Conducta F 714 577-5600
4123 E La Palma Ave # 200 Anaheim (92807) ***(P-21469)***

Endresshauser Conducta, Anaheim *Also called Endress & Hauser Conducta Inc* ***(P-21956)***

Endrun Technologies LLC F 707 573-8633
2270 Northpoint Pkwy Santa Rosa (95407) ***(P-21470)***

Endura Technologies LLC F 858 412-2135
7310 Miramar Rd Fl 5 San Diego (92126) ***(P-18822)***

Endural LLC F 714 434-6533
1685 Scenic Ave Ste A Costa Mesa (92626) ***(P-9748)***

Endurance Ptc F 415 445-9155
8 Madrona St Mill Valley (94941) ***(P-21108)***

Endurequest Corporation E 559 783-9220
1813 Thunderbolt Dr Porterville (93257) ***(P-10091)***

Ener-Core Inc (PA) F 949 616-3300
8965 Research Dr Ste 100 Irvine (92618) ***(P-17193)***

Ener-Core Power Inc (HQ) F 949 428-3300
8965 Research Dr Ste 100 Irvine (92618) ***(P-13994)***

Enerdyne Division, El Cajon *Also called Viasat Inc* ***(P-21454)***

Energent Corporation F 949 885-0365
1831 Carnegie Ave Santa Ana (92705) ***(P-13995)***

Energetic Lighting, Chino *Also called Yankon Industries Inc* ***(P-17658)***

Energetix Solutions Inc F 925 926-6412
2601 Cherry Ln Walnut Creek (94597) ***(P-9182)***

Energous Corporation D 408 963-0200
3590 N 1st St Ste 210 San Jose (95134) ***(P-18099)***

Energy Absorption Systems Inc C 916 645-8181
3617 Cincinnati Ave Rocklin (95765) ***(P-13939)***

Energy Cnvrsion Applctions Inc F 714 256-2166
582 Explorer St Brea (92821) ***(P-17091)***

Energy Exemplar LLC (HQ) F 916 722-1484
3013 Douglas Blvd Ste 120 Roseville (95661) ***(P-24610)***

Energy Labs Inc (HQ) B 619 671-0100
1695 Cactus Rd San Diego (92154) ***(P-15953)***

Energy Lane Inc F 323 962-5020
6767 W Sunset Blvd 8152 Los Angeles (90028) ***(P-7913)***

Energy Link Indus Svcs Inc E 661 765-4444
11439 S Enos Ln Bakersfield (93311) ***(P-16473)***

Energy Management Group Inc (PA) F 949 296-0764
1621 Browning Irvine (92606) ***(P-17692)***

Energy Operations Management F 916 859-4700
2981 Gold Canal Dr Rancho Cordova (95670) ***(P-56)***

Energy Reconnaissance Inc F 714 630-4491
1270 N Red Gum St Anaheim (92806) ***(P-15259)***

Energy Recovery Inc (PA) C 510 483-7370
1717 Doolittle Dr San Leandro (94577) ***(P-14947)***

Energy Recovery Products Inc (HQ) F 805 499-4090
893 Patriot Dr Ste E Moorpark (93021) ***(P-19534)***

Energy Sales LLC (PA) E 503 690-9000
2030 Ringwood Ave San Jose (95131) ***(P-19802)***

Energy Steel Corporation F 925 685-5300
2043 Arnold Indus Way Concord (94520) ***(P-16474)***

Energy Suspension, San Clemente *Also called Bunker Corp* ***(P-20276)***

Energy Systems, Stockton *Also called Es West Coast LLC* ***(P-17194)***

Enersys F 510 887-8080
30069 Ahern Ave Union City (94587) ***(P-19803)***

Enersys D 909 464-8251
5580 Edison Ave Chino (91710) ***(P-19804)***

Enertron Technologies Inc E 800 537-7649
3030 Enterprise Ct Ste D Vista (92081) ***(P-17600)***

Enervault Corporation F 408 636-7519
1100 La Avenida St Ste A Mountain View (94043) ***(P-19805)***

Enevate Corporation E 949 243-0399
101 Theory Ste 200 Irvine (92617) ***(P-19806)***

Enfora Inc D 972 234-1689
9645 Scranton Rd Ste 205 San Diego (92121) ***(P-19535)***

Engage Communication Inc (PA) E 831 688-1021
9565 Soquel Dr Ste 201 Aptos (95003) ***(P-17944)***

Engagio Inc E 650 265-2264
101 S San Mateo Dr Fl 4 San Mateo (94401) ***(P-24611)***

Engel & Gray Inc E 805 925-2771
745 W Betteravia Rd Ste A Santa Maria (93455) ***(P-207)***

Engersall, Riverside *Also called Club Car LLC* ***(P-21224)***

Engine Electronics Inc F 562 803-1700
12155 Pangborn Ave Downey (90241) ***(P-19832)***

Engine World LLC E 510 653-4444
1487 67th St Emeryville (94608) ***(P-20327)***

Engineered Application LLC F 323 585-2894
4727 E 49th St Vernon (90058) ***(P-13584)***

Engineered Coating Tech Inc F 323 588-0260
2838 E 54th St Vernon (90058) ***(P-8904)***

Engineered Food Systems E 714 921-9913
2490 Anselmo Dr Corona (92879) ***(P-16038)***

Engineered Lighting Products, El Monte *Also called R W Swarens Associates Inc* ***(P-17640)***

Engineered Magnetics Inc E 310 649-9000
10524 S La Cienega Blvd Inglewood (90304) ***(P-17340)***

Engineered Outsource Solutions E 408 617-2800
557 E California Ave Sunnyvale (94086) ***(P-18823)***

Engineered Plastic Division, San Jose *Also called Triad Tool & Engineering Inc* ***(P-10410)***

Engineered Products By Lee Ltd F 818 352-3322
10444 Mcvine Ave Sunland (91040) ***(P-16475)***

Engineered Well Svc Intl Inc C 866 913-6283
3120 Standard St Bakersfield (93308) ***(P-208)***

Engineering Design Inds Inc F 626 443-7741
9649 Rush St South El Monte (91733) ***(P-16476)***

Engineering Jk Aerospace & Def F 714 414-6722
23231 La Palma Ave Yorba Linda (92887) ***(P-20809)***

Engineering Materials Co Inc E 562 436-0063
2055 W Cowles St Long Beach (90813) ***(P-23764)***

Mergent e-mail: customerrelations@mergent.com
1132
2019 California
Manufacturers Register
(P-0000) Products & Services Section entry number
(PA)=Parent Co (HQ)=Headquarters (DH)=Div Headquarters

Engineering Model Associates (PA)......E......626 912-7011
1020 Wallace Way City of Industry (91748) ***(P-10092)***
Enginered Pnt Applications LLC......F......626 737-7400
1586 Franklin Ave Redlands (92373) ***(P-8905)***
English Ales Brewers Inc......F......831 883-3000
223 Reindollar Ave Ste A Marina (93933) ***(P-1590)***
Engrade Inc......F......800 305-1367
1337 3rd Street Promenade # 300 Santa Monica (90401) ***(P-24612)***
Enhance America Inc......E......951 361-3000
3463 Grapevine St Mira Loma (91752) ***(P-23867)***
Enhance Electronics, Ontario *Also called Mpeg Industries Inc* ***(P-15463)***
Enhanced Vision Systems Inc (HQ)......E......714 374-1829
5882 Machine Dr Ste A Huntington Beach (92649) ***(P-23093)***
Enjoy Food, Colton *Also called Saab Enterprises Inc* ***(P-521)***
Enjoy Foods International......E......909 823-2228
10601 Beech Ave Fontana (92337) ***(P-482)***
Enjoy Haircare, Oceanside *Also called USP Inc* ***(P-8859)***
Enki Technology Inc......F......408 383-9034
1035 Walsh Ave Santa Clara (95050) ***(P-7773)***
Enlighted Inc (PA)......E......650 964-1094
930 Benecia Ave Sunnyvale (94085) ***(P-17601)***
Enlink Geoenergy Services Inc......E......424 242-1200
2630 Homestead Pl Rancho Dominguez (90220) ***(P-15954)***
Enmo Technologies Inc......F......408 475-6819
3561 Homestead Rd # 233 Santa Clara (95051) ***(P-24613)***
Ennis Inc......C......805 238-1144
298 Sherwood Rd Paso Robles (93446) ***(P-7550)***
Ennis Inc......C......714 765-0400
1600 S Claudina Way Anaheim (92805) ***(P-14512)***
Ennis-Flint Inc......E......661 328-0503
200 2nd St Bakersfield (93304) ***(P-8906)***
Enniss Inc......E......619 561-1101
12535 Vigilante Rd Lakeside (92040) ***(P-356)***
Enormarel Inc......F......818 882-4666
9200 Mason Ave Chatsworth (91311) ***(P-8746)***
Enova Engineering LLC (PA)......F......209 538-3313
1088 Mt Clair Dr Ceres (95307) ***(P-17513)***
Enova Solutions Inc......F......661 327-2405
3553 Landco Dr Ste B Bakersfield (93308) ***(P-9246)***
Enphase Energy Inc (PA)......B......707 774-7000
1420 N Mcdowell Blvd Petaluma (94954) ***(P-18824)***
Enpirion......F......408 904-2800
101 Innovation Dr San Jose (95134) ***(P-18825)***
Enray Inc., Livermore *Also called Truroots Inc* ***(P-2693)***
Ensign US Drlg Cal Inc (HQ)......D......661 589-0111
7001 Charity Ave Bakersfield (93308) ***(P-14379)***
Ensign-Bickford Arospc Def Co......E......805 292-4000
14370 White Sage Rd Moorpark (93021) ***(P-21292)***
Ensphere Solutions Inc......F......408 598-2441
2870 Briarwood Dr San Jose (95125) ***(P-18826)***
Enstrom Mold & Engineering......F......760 744-1880
235 Trade St San Marcos (92078) ***(P-14513)***
Entco LLC (HQ)......B......312 580-9100
1140 Enterprise Way Sunnyvale (94089) ***(P-24614)***
Entech Instruments Inc......D......805 527-5939
2207 Agate Ct Simi Valley (93065) ***(P-21957)***
Entegris Inc......D......858 452-0124
10070 Willow Creek Rd San Diego (92131) ***(P-10093)***
Enter Music Publishing Inc......F......408 971-9794
1346 The Alameda Ste 7 San Jose (95126) ***(P-6159)***
Enterprise Arms, Irwindale *Also called Entreprise Arms Inc* ***(P-13687)***
Enterprise Co, Santa Ana *Also called G G C Inc* ***(P-14794)***
Enterprise Company, Santa Ana *Also called G G C Inc* ***(P-14793)***
Enterprise Informatics Inc......E......858 625-3000
10052 Mesa Ridge Ct Ste 1 San Diego (92121) ***(P-24615)***
Enterprise Printing, Shingle Springs *Also called BBC Corp* ***(P-6689)***
Enterprise Services LLC......F......805 388-8000
333 N Lantana St Ste 287 Camarillo (93010) ***(P-24616)***
Enterprise Signal Inc......D......877 256-8303
440 N Wolfe Rd Sunnyvale (94085) ***(P-24617)***
Enterprise Solutions Group, Santa Clara *Also called Dell Inc* ***(P-15405)***
Entertainment Centers Plus, Rancho Cordova *Also called Custom Furniture Design Inc* ***(P-4289)***
Entertainment Relations, Beverly Hills *Also called Gibson Brands Inc* ***(P-23372)***
Entit Software LLC (HQ)......F......801 861-7000
1140 Entp Way Bldg F Sunnyvale (94089) ***(P-24618)***
Entra Health Systems LLC......E......877 458-2646
1300 N Johnson Ave # 100 El Cajon (92020) ***(P-22440)***
Entrepeneur Magazine, Irvine *Also called Entrepreneur Media Inc* ***(P-6160)***
Entrepreneur Media Inc (PA)......D......949 261-2325
18061 Fitch Irvine (92614) ***(P-6160)***
Entreprise Arms Inc......E......626 962-4692
15509 Arrow Hwy Irwindale (91706) ***(P-13687)***
Entropic Communications LLC (HQ)......D......858 768-3600
5966 La Place Ct Ste 100 Carlsbad (92008) ***(P-18827)***
Entropy Enterprises LLC......F......805 305-1400
170 Seacliff Dr Pismo Beach (93449) ***(P-22441)***
Entrussed LLC......F......916 753-5406
5065 Commercial Pl Sheridan (95681) ***(P-4404)***
Envel Design Corporation......F......805 376-8111
3579 Old Conejo Rd Newbury Park (91320) ***(P-17602)***
Envelope Products Co (PA)......E......925 939-5173
2882 W Cromwell Ave Fresno (93711) ***(P-5281)***
Envia Systems Inc......E......510 509-1367
7979 Gateway Blvd Ste 101 Newark (94560) ***(P-19961)***
Envion LLC......D......818 217-2500
14724 Ventura Blvd Fl 200 Sherman Oaks (91403) ***(P-15153)***
Enviormental Business Intl, San Diego *Also called Informa Media Inc* ***(P-6193)***
Envirnmental Catalyst Tech LLC......E......949 459-3870
3937 Ocean Ranch Blvd Oceanside (92056) ***(P-7774)***
Envirnmental Pdts Applications, La Quinta *Also called Vermillions Environmental* ***(P-21536)***
Envirnmntal Mlding Cncepts LLC......F......951 214-6596
14050 Day St Moreno Valley (92553) ***(P-9610)***
Envirnmntal Pdts Applctons Inc......E......760 779-1814
8-900 Ave 47 Ste 106 La Quinta (92253) ***(P-8640)***
Enviro-Commercial Sweeping......F......408 920-0274
210 San Jose Ave Ste 5 Chico (95927) ***(P-23790)***
Enviro-Intercept Inc......F......818 982-6063
7327 Varna Ave Unit 5 North Hollywood (91605) ***(P-15955)***
Envirocare International Inc......E......707 638-6800
507 Green Island Rd American Canyon (94503) ***(P-15154)***
Envirokinetics Inc (PA)......F......909 621-7599
101 S Milliken Ave Ontario (91761) ***(P-14948)***
Environ Clean Technology, San Jose *Also called Environ-Clean Technology Inc* ***(P-18828)***
Environ-Clean Technology Inc......F......408 487-1770
1710 Ringwood Ave San Jose (95131) ***(P-18828)***
Environment Furniture Inc (HQ)......E......323 782-0296
785 Holmby Ave Los Angeles (90024) ***(P-4694)***
Environmental Inks & Coatings, Ontario *Also called An Environmental Inks* ***(P-9188)***
Environmental Ltg For Arch Inc......E......626 965-0821
17891 Arenth Ave City of Industry (91748) ***(P-17603)***
Environmental Sampling Sup Inc......F......510 465-4988
640 143rd Ave San Leandro (94578) ***(P-10094)***
Environmental Technology Inc......E......707 443-9323
300 S Bay Depot Rd Fields Landing (95537) ***(P-7835)***
Enviroplex Inc......D......209 466-8000
4777 Carpenter Rd Stockton (95215) ***(P-12930)***
Envision Led Lighting Inc......F......213 741-1550
4845 Eastern Ave Bell (90201) ***(P-17426)***
Envision Medical, Goleta *Also called Linvatec Corporation* ***(P-22512)***
Envision Solar Intl Inc......E......858 799-4583
5660 Eastgate Dr San Diego (92121) ***(P-12062)***
Envita Labs LLC......E......800 500-4376
1900 Carnegie Ave Ste A Santa Ana (92705) ***(P-7936)***
Enviz.io, Fremont *Also called Envizio Inc* ***(P-24619)***
Envizio Inc......E......650 814-4302
2400 Country Dr Fremont (94536) ***(P-24619)***
Envy Medical Inc (PA)......F......818 874-2700
9414 Eton Ave Chatsworth (91311) ***(P-8148)***
Envy Wines LLC......F......707 942-4670
1170 Tubbs Ln Calistoga (94515) ***(P-1750)***
Eo Products, San Rafael *Also called Small World Trading Co* ***(P-8842)***
Eoplex Inc......F......408 638-5100
1321 Ridder Park Dr 10 San Jose (95131) ***(P-19962)***
Eoplex Technologies Inc......F......408 638-5100
2940 N 1st St San Jose (95134) ***(P-19963)***
Eoplly Usa Inc......F......650 225-9400
1670 S Amphlett Blvd # 140 San Mateo (94402) ***(P-18829)***
Eos Estate Winery......E......805 239-2562
2300 Airport Rd Paso Robles (93446) ***(P-1751)***
Eos Software Inc......F......855 900-4876
900 E Hamilton Ave # 100 Campbell (95008) ***(P-24620)***
Ep Holdings Inc......E......949 713-4600
30442 Esperanza Rcho STA Marg (92688) ***(P-15536)***
Ep Memory, Rcho STA Marg *Also called Ep Holdings Inc* ***(P-15536)***
Epac Technologies Inc (PA)......C......510 317-7979
2561 Grant Ave San Leandro (94579) ***(P-6808)***
EPC Power Corp......E......858 748-5590
13125 Danielson St # 112 Poway (92064) ***(P-17341)***
Epco, Fresno *Also called Envelope Products Co* ***(P-5281)***
Epe Industries Usa Inc......F......800 315-0336
17654 Newhope St Ste A Fountain Valley (92708) ***(P-9839)***
Epe Industries Usa Inc......F......800 315-0336
1500 Whipple Rd Union City (94587) ***(P-9840)***
Epe Industries Usa Inc (HQ)......F......800 315-0336
17654 Newhope St Ste A Fountain Valley (92708) ***(P-9841)***
Epe Industries USA Dallas, Fountain Valley *Also called Epe Industries Usa Inc* ***(P-9839)***
Epe USA, Union City *Also called Epe Industries Usa Inc* ***(P-9840)***
Epe USA, Fountain Valley *Also called Epe Industries Usa Inc* ***(P-9841)***
Epic Boats LLC (PA)......F......760 542-6060
2755 Dos Aarons Way Ste A Vista (92081) ***(P-21035)***
Epic Plastics, Lodi *Also called Basalite Building Products LLC* ***(P-10882)***
Epic Printing Ink Corp......F......909 598-6771
233 Pioneer Pl Pomona (91768) ***(P-14806)***
Epic Technologies LLC (HQ)......C......818 734-6500
9340 Owensmouth Ave Chatsworth (91311) ***(P-17945)***
Epic Technologies LLC......B......423 461-2020
9340 Owensmouth Ave Chatsworth (91311) ***(P-15738)***
Epica Medical Innovations LLC......F......949 238-6323
2753 Camino Capistrano San Clemente (92672) ***(P-22442)***
Epicor Software Corporation......C......925 361-9900
4120 Dublin Blvd Ste 300 Dublin (94568) ***(P-24621)***
Epicor Software Corporation......D......949 585-4000
17320 Red Hill Ave # 250 Irvine (92614) ***(P-15739)***
Epicson Inc......F......858 558-5757
8250 Cmino Santa Fe Ste A San Diego (92121) ***(P-7311)***
Epicuren Discovery......D......949 588-5807
26081 Merit Cir Ste 116 Laguna Hills (92653) ***(P-8475)***
Epignosis LLC......E......646 797-2799
315 Montgomery St Fl 9 San Francisco (94104) ***(P-24622)***
Epilogue and Arrested, Los Angeles *Also called Rhapsody Clothing Inc* ***(P-3489)***
Epinex Diagnostics Inc......E......949 660-7770
14351 Myford Rd Ste J Tustin (92780) ***(P-22443)***
Eplastics, San Diego *Also called Ridout Plastics Company* ***(P-9724)***
Epmar Corporation......E......562 946-8781
13210 Barton Cir Whittier (90605) ***(P-8907)***

ALPHABETIC

Employee Codes: A=Over 500 employees, B=251-500
C=101-250, D=51-100, E=20-50, F=10-19
2019 California
Manfacturers Register
© Mergent Inc. 1-800-342-5647
1133

Epoca Yocool, South Gate *Also called Win Soon Inc (P-740)*
Epoch International Entps Inc ....D.......714 484-8015
  10542 Calle Lee Ste 114 Los Alamitos (90720) *(P-14949)*
Eps-Cineworks LLC ....F.......818 766-5000
  3330 Chnga Blvd W Ste 200 Los Angeles (90068) *(P-23158)*
Epsilon Plastics Inc ....D.......310 609-1320
  3100 E Harcourt St Compton (90221) *(P-5600)*
Epson America Inc (HQ) ....A.......800 463-7766
  3840 Kilroy Airport Way Long Beach (90806) *(P-15740)*
Epson Electronics America Inc (HQ) ....E.......408 922-0200
  214 Devcon Dr San Jose (95112) *(P-18830)*
Eptronics Inc ....E.......310 536-0700
  19210 S Vermont Ave # 300 Gardena (90248) *(P-17604)*
Epworth Morehouse Cowles, Chino *Also called Morehouse-Cowles LLC (P-14993)*
Eq Technologic Inc ....E.......215 891-9010
  600 Anton Blvd Costa Mesa (92626) *(P-24623)*
Eqh Limited Inc ....E.......310 736-4130
  5440 Mcconnell Ave Los Angeles (90066) *(P-11893)*
Equestrian Designs LLC ....E.......805 686-4455
  91 2nd St Ste A Buellton (93427) *(P-3411)*
Equimine ....F.......877 437-8464
  26457 Rancho Pkwy S Lake Forest (92630) *(P-24624)*
Equipment & Tool Institute, Irvine *Also called Innova Electronics Corporation (P-20372)*
Equipment De Sport Usa Inc ....F.......760 772-5544
  39301 Badger St Ste 500 Palm Desert (92211) *(P-3848)*
Equipment Design & Mfg Inc ....D.......909 594-2229
  119 Explorer St Pomona (91768) *(P-12574)*
Equitex, NAPA *Also called Lixit Corporation (P-24164)*
Equity Ford Research ....F.......858 755-1327
  11722 Sorrento Valley Rd I San Diego (92121) *(P-6478)*
Equus Products Inc ....E.......714 424-6779
  17352 Von Karman Ave Irvine (92614) *(P-21748)*
ERA Furniture, Los Angeles *Also called Environment Furniture Inc (P-4694)*
ERA Products Inc ....F.......310 324-4908
  1130 Benedict Canyon Dr Beverly Hills (90210) *(P-5013)*
Erb Investment Company LLC ....F.......408 727-6908
  3501 Thomas Rd Ste 7 Santa Clara (95054) *(P-16477)*
Erba Organics, Chatsworth *Also called Erbaviva Inc (P-7937)*
Erbaviva Inc ....E.......818 998-7112
  19831 Nordhoff Pl Ste 116 Chatsworth (91311) *(P-7937)*
ERC Concepts Co Inc ....E.......408 734-5345
  1255 Birchwood Dr Sunnyvale (94089) *(P-13201)*
Erg Aerospace Corporation ....D.......510 658-9785
  964 Stanford Ave Oakland (94608) *(P-7775)*
Erg Materials and Aerospace, Oakland *Also called Erg Aerospace Corporation (P-7775)*
Erg Transit Systems (usa) Inc ....C.......925 686-8233
  1800 Sutter St Ste 900 Concord (94520) *(P-16039)*
Erge Designs LLC ....F.......310 614-9197
  4770 E 48th St Vernon (90058) *(P-3234)*
Ergo Baby Carrier Inc (HQ) ....E.......213 283-2090
  617 W 7th St Fl 10 Los Angeles (90017) *(P-23421)*
Ergodirect Inc ....F.......650 654-4300
  1601 Old County Rd San Carlos (94070) *(P-4984)*
Ergonom Corporation ....D.......805 981-9978
  361 Bernoulli Cir Oxnard (93030) *(P-5231)*
Ergononmic Comfort Design Inc ....E.......951 277-1558
  9140 Stellar Ct Ste B Corona (92883) *(P-4985)*
Eri Economic Research Inst Inc ....D.......800 627-3697
  111 Academy Ste 270 Irvine (92617) *(P-24625)*
Ericsson Inc ....F.......805 584-6890
  426 Appleton Rd Simi Valley (93065) *(P-18100)*
Ericsson Inc ....E.......972 583-0000
  1055 La Avenida St Mountain View (94043) *(P-18101)*
Ericsson Inc ....F.......408 776-0600
  18275 Serene Dr Morgan Hill (95037) *(P-18102)*
Ericsson Inc ....D.......949 721-6604
  620 Newport Center Dr # 11 Newport Beach (92660) *(P-15741)*
Ericsson Inc ....E.......408 970-2000
  250 Holger Way San Jose (95134) *(P-18103)*
Eride Inc ....E.......415 848-7800
  1 Letterman Dr Ste 310 San Francisco (94129) *(P-24626)*
Erika Records Inc ....E.......714 228-5420
  6300 Caballero Blvd Buena Park (90620) *(P-17895)*
Eriss ....F.......858 722-2177
  1124 Glen Ellen Pl 201 San Marcos (92078) *(P-19863)*
Ermico Enterprises Inc ....D.......415 822-6776
  1111 17th St Ste B San Francisco (94107) *(P-23557)*
Ermm Corporation ....E.......310 635-0524
  5415 Martin Luther King Lynwood (90262) *(P-20501)*
Ernest Packaging Solutions (PA) ......E.......800 757-4968
  2825 S Elm Ave Ste 103 Fresno (93706) *(P-7776)*
Ernie Ball Inc (PA) ....D.......805 544-7726
  4117 Earthwood Ln San Luis Obispo (93401) *(P-23367)*
Ernie Ball Inc ....D.......800 543-2255
  53973 Polk St Coachella (92236) *(P-23368)*
Ernst Mfg, Bakersfield *Also called Triple E Manufacturing Inc (P-14891)*
Erp Power LLC (PA) ....E.......805 517-1300
  893 Patriot Dr Ste E Moorpark (93021) *(P-21749)*
ES Kluft & Company Inc (PA) ....C.......909 373-4211
  11096 Jersey Blvd Ste 101 Rancho Cucamonga (91730) *(P-4860)*
Es West Coast LLC ....E.......209 870-1900
  7100 Longe St Ste 300 Stockton (95206) *(P-17194)*
Esc, Compton *Also called Electronic Stamping Corp (P-17145)*
Escalera-Boulet LLC ....F.......805 691-1020
  2923 Grand Ave Los Olivos (93441) *(P-1752)*
Escape Communications ....F.......310 997-1300
  2790 Skypark Dr Ste 203 Torrance (90505) *(P-18104)*
Eschaton Foundation (PA) ....D.......831 423-1626
  612 Ocean St Santa Cruz (95060) *(P-6809)*

Escient Pharmaceuticals Inc ....F.......858 617-8236
  3033 Science Park Rd # 230 San Diego (92121) *(P-8149)*
Esco Industries Inc ....F.......951 782-2130
  1755 Iowa Ave Bldg A Riverside (92507) *(P-13097)*
Esco Woodworks ....F.......408 225-2777
  2894 Aiello Dr C San Jose (95111) *(P-4153)*
Escondido Sand & Gravel LLC ....F.......760 432-4690
  500 N Tulip St Escondido (92025) *(P-9384)*
Ese, El Segundo *Also called Mod Electronics Inc (P-23221)*
Eshields LLC ....E.......909 305-8848
  2307 Country Clb Vista St Glendora (91741) *(P-5521)*
Esi, Los Angeles *Also called Electronic Systems Innovation (P-15408)*
Esi Motion, Simi Valley *Also called Embedded Systems Inc (P-17269)*
Esilicon Corporation (PA) ....C.......408 635-6300
  2130 Gold St Ste 100 Alviso (95002) *(P-18831)*
Eska Inc ....E.......323 268-2134
  3631 Union Pacific Ave Los Angeles (90023) *(P-3412)*
Esl Power Systems Inc ....D.......800 922-4188
  2800 Palisades Dr Corona (92880) *(P-17466)*
ESM Aerospace Inc ....E.......818 841-3653
  1203 W Isabel St Burbank (91506) *(P-12575)*
Esmart Source Inc ....F.......408 739-3500
  5159 Commercial Cir Ste H Concord (94520) *(P-24627)*
Esmi, San Diego *Also called Electronic Surfc Mounted Inds (P-18473)*
ESP Corp ....E.......310 639-2535
  1175 W Victoria St Compton (90220) *(P-19536)*
ESP Safety Inc ....F.......408 886-9746
  555 N 1st St San Jose (95112) *(P-22729)*
Espace Enterprises Tech Inc ....F.......408 844-8176
  3010 N 1st St San Jose (95134) *(P-14950)*
Espana Metal Craft Inc ....F.......818 988-4988
  7600 Ventura Canyon Ave Van Nuys (91402) *(P-12576)*
Espe Machine Work / Ver Mfg, San Jose *Also called Neodora LLC (P-14999)*
Especializados Del Aire, San Diego *Also called Alliance Air Products Llc (P-15935)*
Esperanzas Tortilleria Inc ....E.......760 743-5908
  750 Rock Springs Rd Escondido (92025) *(P-2513)*
Esperer Holdings Inc (PA) ....E.......805 880-4220
  3820 State St Santa Barbara (93105) *(P-11556)*
Esperer Webstores LLC ....E.......805 880-1900
  3820 State St Ste B Santa Barbara (93105) *(P-613)*
Esq Business Services Inc (PA) ....D.......925 734-9800
  20660 Stevens Cupertino (95014) *(P-24628)*
Ess Division, Milpitas *Also called Sandisk LLC (P-15598)*
Ess Technology Inc (HQ) ....C.......408 643-8818
  237 S Hillview Dr Milpitas (95035) *(P-18832)*
Essai Inc (PA) ....C.......510 580-1700
  48580 Kato Rd Fremont (94538) *(P-21750)*
Essence Imaging Inc ....E.......909 979-2116
  20651 Golden Springs Dr Walnut (91789) *(P-23159)*
Essence Printing Inc (PA) ....D.......650 952-5072
  270 Oyster Point Blvd South San Francisco (94080) *(P-6810)*
Essence Water Inc ....F.......855 738-7426
  12802 Knott St Garden Grove (92841) *(P-2132)*
Essential Pharmaceutical Corp ....E.......909 623-4565
  1906 W Holt Ave Pomona (91768) *(P-8150)*
Essex Electronics Inc ....E.......805 684-7601
  1130 Mark Ave Carpinteria (93013) *(P-18833)*
Essilor Laboratories Amer Inc ....E.......800 624-6672
  801 N Burke St Visalia (93292) *(P-23094)*
Essilor Laboratories Amer Inc ....E.......310 604-8668
  1450 W Walnut St Compton (90220) *(P-23095)*
Estam, Los Angeles *Also called Orbita Corp (P-3603)*
Estancia Estates ....D.......707 431-1975
  980 Bryant Cyn Soledad (93960) *(P-1753)*
Estar Limited ....E.......310 989-6265
  15216 Daphne Ave Gardena (90249) *(P-17427)*
Estate Cheese Group LLC (PA) ....E.......707 996-1000
  670 W Napa St Ste G Sonoma (95476) *(P-572)*
Estate Granite & Marble ....E.......530 241-7866
  4950 Mtn Lakes Blvd Ste C Redding (96003) *(P-303)*
Estco Enterprises Inc ....F.......760 489-8745
  1549 Simpson Way Escondido (92029) *(P-9611)*
Estephanian Originals Inc ....E.......626 358-7265
  1550 E Mountain St Pasadena (91104) *(P-2880)*
Esterline Power Systems, Buena Park *Also called Leach International Corp (P-19619)*
Esys Energy Control Company ....E.......714 372-3322
  12881 Knott St Ste 227 Garden Grove (92841) *(P-21582)*
ET Balancing Inc ....E.......310 538-9738
  12823 Athens Way Los Angeles (90061) *(P-16478)*
Et Water Systems LLC ....F.......415 945-9383
  384 Bel Marin Keys Blvd # 145 Novato (94949) *(P-22194)*
Eta USA, Morgan Hill *Also called US Eta Inc (P-19778)*
Etc, Los Angeles *Also called Electronic Theatre Contrls Inc (P-17689)*
Etched Media Corporation ....E.......408 374-6895
  101 Gilman Ave Campbell (95008) *(P-13408)*
Etd Precision Ceramics Corp. ....E.......408 577-0405
  580 Charcot Ave San Jose (95131) *(P-18834)*
Eteam Technologies, Aliso Viejo *Also called Appware Inc (P-24377)*
Eternal Star Corporation ....E.......310 768-1945
  17813 S Main St Ste 101 Gardena (90248) *(P-5684)*
Eternity Flooring, Pacoima *Also called LA Hardwood Flooring Inc (P-4083)*
Etha Natural Medicine, El Cajon *Also called Ethos Natural Medicine LLC (P-7939)*
Ethanol Energy Systems LLC ....F.......916 777-5654
  406 Delta Ave Isleton (95641) *(P-9005)*
Ethernal Electric Company, San Diego *Also called Hi-Z Technology Inc (P-17342)*
Ethical Naturals Inc ....F.......650 336-1190
  2731 Fair Oaks Ave Redwood City (94063) *(P-7938)*

Ethicon Inc ....B....949 581-5799
33 Technology Dr Irvine (92618) ***(P-22730)***
Ethos Natural Medicine LLC ....F....858 267-7599
1950 Cordell Ct Ste 105 El Cajon (92020) ***(P-7939)***
Ethosenergy Field Services LLC ....F....707 399-0420
2485 Courage Dr Ste 100 Fairfield (94533) ***(P-209)***
Ethosenergy Field Services LLC (HQ) ....D....310 639-3523
10455 Slusher Dr Bldg 12 Santa Fe Springs (90670) ***(P-210)***
Ethosenergy Pwr Plant Svcs LLC ....E....916 391-2993
3215 47th Ave Sacramento (95824) ***(P-211)***
Eti B Si Professional, Huntington Park *Also called Eti Sound Systems Inc* ***(P-17799)***
Eti Empire Direct, Anaheim *Also called Econotek Inc* ***(P-22875)***
Eti Sound Systems Inc ....E....323 835-6660
3383 E Gage Ave Huntington Park (90255) ***(P-17799)***
Etm—Electromatic Inc (PA) ....D....510 797-1100
35451 Dumbarton Ct Newark (94560) ***(P-18105)***
Etnies, Lake Forest *Also called Sole Technology Inc* ***(P-10510)***
Eton Corporation ....E....650 903-3866
1015 Corporation Way Palo Alto (94303) ***(P-19964)***
Ets Express Inc (PA) ....E....805 278-7771
420 Lombard St Oxnard (93030) ***(P-13585)***
Ettore Products Co ....D....510 748-4130
2100 N Loop Rd Alameda (94502) ***(P-24092)***
Etude Wines Inc ....F....707 257-5300
1250 Cuttings Wharf Rd NAPA (94559) ***(P-1754)***
Eubanks Engineering Co (PA) ....E....909 483-2456
3022 Inland Empire Blvd Ontario (91764) ***(P-14750)***
Eufora, Vista *Also called Eden Beauty Concepts Inc* ***(P-8744)***
Eugenios Sheet Metal Inc ....F....909 923-2002
2151 Maple Privado Ontario (91761) ***(P-13202)***
Eugenus Inc (HQ) ....D....669 235-8244
677 River Oaks Pkwy San Jose (95134) ***(P-21751)***
Eunina Inc ....E....213 747-1672
1100 S San Pedro St J09 Los Angeles (90015) ***(P-3413)***
Euphonix Inc (HQ) ....D....650 526-1600
280 Bernardo Ave Mountain View (94043) ***(P-18106)***
Euramax Holdings Inc ....F....714 563-8260
1411 N Daly St Anaheim (92806) ***(P-11575)***
Euramco Safety Inc ....F....619 670-9590
2746 Via Orange Way Spring Valley (91978) ***(P-15155)***
Eureka Chemical Company (PA) ....F....650 873-5374
234 Lawrence Ave South San Francisco (94080) ***(P-9247)***
Eureka Record Works Inc (PA) ....F....707 442-8121
210 C St Eureka (95501) ***(P-17800)***
Eureka Times-Standard, Eureka *Also called Pasadena Newspapers Inc* ***(P-6011)***
Euri Lighting, Torrance *Also called Irtronix Inc* ***(P-17430)***
Euro Bello USA ....E....213 446-2818
10660 Wilshire Blvd Los Angeles (90024) ***(P-3614)***
Euro Machine Inc ....F....818 998-5198
9627 Owensmouth Ave Ste 1 Chatsworth (91311) ***(P-16479)***
Eurocraft Architectural Met Inc ....E....323 771-1323
5619 Watcher St Bell Gardens (90201) ***(P-12853)***
Eurodesign Ltd (PA) ....F....650 948-5160
62 Chester Cir Los Altos (94022) ***(P-4695)***
Euroline Steel Windows ....E....877 590-2741
22600 Savi Ranch Pkwy E Yorba Linda (92887) ***(P-12315)***
Euroline Steel Windows & Doors, Yorba Linda *Also called Euroline Steel Windows* ***(P-12315)***
European Elegance Woodwork ....F....818 570-9401
8019 Haskell Ave Unit 102 Van Nuys (91406) ***(P-4154)***
European Rolling Shutters, San Jose *Also called Blum Construction Co Inc* ***(P-12301)***
European Services Group ....F....714 898-0595
5062 Caspian Cir Huntington Beach (92649) ***(P-11954)***
European Wholesale Counter ....C....619 562-0565
10051 Prospect Ave Santee (92071) ***(P-5059)***
European Woodwork ....F....714 892-8831
7531 Suzi Ln Westminster (92683) ***(P-4298)***
Europian Investment, Los Angeles *Also called Hunter Digital Ltd* ***(P-15754)***
Eurostampa North America Inc ....F....707 927-4848
2545 Napa Vly NAPA (94558) ***(P-7312)***
Eurotec Seating, La Habra *Also called Orbo Corporation* ***(P-5024)***
Eurotech Showers Inc ....E....949 716-4099
23552 Commerce Center Dr B Laguna Hills (92653) ***(P-9900)***
Eurton Electric Company Inc ....E....562 946-4477
9920 Painter Ave Santa Fe Springs (90670) ***(P-25459)***
Eurus Energy America Corp (HQ) ....F....858 638-7115
9255 Towne Centre Dr # 840 San Diego (92121) ***(P-17195)***
Euv Tech Inc ....F....925 229-4388
2840 Howe Rd Ste A Martinez (94553) ***(P-21958)***
Ev3 Neurovascular, Irvine *Also called Micro Therapeutics Inc* ***(P-22539)***
Evalve Inc ....D....650 330-8100
4045 Campbell Ave Menlo Park (94025) ***(P-22444)***
Evan-Moor Corporation (HQ) ....E....831 649-5901
18 Lower Ragsdale Dr Monterey (93940) ***(P-6339)***
Evan-Moor Educational Publr, Monterey *Also called Evan-Moor Corporation* ***(P-6339)***
Evans Food West Inc (PA) ....F....909 947-3001
1920 S Augusta Ave Ontario (91761) ***(P-2379)***
Evans Industries Inc ....C....626 912-1688
17915 Railroad St City of Industry (91748) ***(P-13940)***
Evans Manufacturing Inc (PA) ....C....714 379-6100
7422 Chapman Ave Garden Grove (92841) ***(P-23868)***
Evans Walker Enterprises ....E....951 784-7223
2304 Fleetwood Dr Riverside (92509) ***(P-20328)***
Evans, Walker Racing, Riverside *Also called Evans Walker Enterprises* ***(P-20328)***
Evantec Corporation ....F....949 632-2811
4007 W Segerstrom Ave Santa Ana (92704) ***(P-9612)***
Evantec Scientific, Santa Ana *Also called Evantec Corporation* ***(P-9612)***
Evapco Inc ....C....559 673-2207
1900 W Almond Ave Madera (93637) ***(P-15956)***
Evapco West, Madera *Also called Evapco Inc* ***(P-15956)***
Evden Enterprises Inc ....F....707 462-0375
2000 Wellmar Dr Ukiah (95482) ***(P-16480)***
Evelozcity Inc ....C....318 849-6327
19951 Mariner Ave Ste 150 Torrance (90503) ***(P-20139)***
Evensphere Incorporation ....E....909 247-3030
1249 S Diamond Bar Blvd Diamond Bar (91765) ***(P-19389)***
Event Farm Inc (PA) ....E....888 444-8162
2448 Main St Santa Monica (90405) ***(P-24629)***
Event Newspapers, Cypress *Also called Community Media Corporation* ***(P-5810)***
Event Spice Wear, Los Angeles *Also called Eska Inc* ***(P-3412)***
Eventure Interactive Inc ....F....855 986-5669
3420 Bristol St Fl 6 Costa Mesa (92626) ***(P-24630)***
Ever-Glory Intl Group Inc ....F....626 859-6638
1009 Becklee Rd Glendora (91741) ***(P-3414)***
Everbrands Inc ....F....855 595-2999
10547 W Pico Blvd Los Angeles (90064) ***(P-22878)***
Everbrite West LLC ....D....909 468-0861
2778 Pomona Blvd Pomona (91768) ***(P-23869)***
Everbrite West LLC ....F....619 444-9000
2733 Via Orange Way Spring Valley (91978) ***(P-23870)***
Eveready Pacific Corp, Riverside *Also called Everpac* ***(P-14776)***
Everest Group Usa Inc ....E....909 923-1818
1885 S Vineyard Ave Ste 3 Ontario (91761) ***(P-2996)***
Everett Charles Tech LLC (HQ) ....D....909 625-5551
14570 Meyer Canyon Dr # 100 Fontana (92336) ***(P-21752)***
Everett Charles Tech LLC ....F....909 625-5551
14570 Meyer Canyon Dr # 100 Fontana (92336) ***(P-21753)***
Everett Graphics Inc ....D....510 577-6777
7300 Edgewater Dr Oakland (94621) ***(P-5506)***
Everfilt, Mira Loma *Also called Puri Tech Inc* ***(P-16094)***
Evergood Fine Foods, San Francisco *Also called Evergood Sausage Co* ***(P-483)***
Evergood Sausage Co ....D....415 822-4660
1932 Van Dyke Ave San Francisco (94124) ***(P-483)***
Evergreen Avionics Inc (PA) ....F....805 445-6492
880 Calle Plano Ste J Camarillo (93012) ***(P-18835)***
Evergreen Environmental Svcs, Gardena *Also called Evergreen Oil Inc* ***(P-9433)***
Evergreen Holdings Inc (PA) ....E....949 757-7770
18952 Macarthur Blvd # 410 Irvine (92612) ***(P-9432)***
Evergreen Industries Inc (HQ) ....E....323 583-1331
2254 E 49th St Vernon (90058) ***(P-21471)***
Evergreen Lighting, Pomona *Also called Yawitz Inc* ***(P-17573)***
Evergreen Oil Inc (HQ) ....E....949 757-7770
18025 S Broadway Gardena (90248) ***(P-9433)***
Evergreen Scientific, Vernon *Also called Evergreen Industries Inc* ***(P-21471)***
Evergreen Systems Intl, Camarillo *Also called Evergreen Avionics Inc* ***(P-18835)***
Everidge Inc ....E....909 605-6419
8886 White Oak Ave Rancho Cucamonga (91730) ***(P-15957)***
Everleigh, Huntington Park *Also called J Heyri Inc* ***(P-3246)***
Everpac ....E....951 686-4560
1499 Palmyrita Ave Riverside (92507) ***(P-14166)***
Everpac ....D....951 774-3274
1499 Palmyrita Ave Riverside (92507) ***(P-14776)***
Everson Spice Company Inc ....E....562 595-4785
2667 Gundry Ave Long Beach (90755) ***(P-2514)***
Everspring Chemical Inc ....D....310 707-1600
11577 W Olympic Blvd Los Angeles (90064) ***(P-9248)***
Evert Hancock Incorporated ....F....714 870-0376
1809 N National St Anaheim (92801) ***(P-12577)***
Everything Mobile, Sunnyvale *Also called Mobile Crossing Inc* ***(P-21349)***
Evissap Inc ....E....408 432-7393
800 Charcot Ave San Jose (95131) ***(P-18107)***
Evk Inc ....E....617 335-3180
5235 Bandera St Montclair (91763) ***(P-9142)***
Evo Manufacturing Inc ....F....714 879-8913
1829 W Commonwealth Ave Fullerton (92833) ***(P-24093)***
Evofem Inc ....F....858 550-1900
12400 High Bluff Dr # 600 San Diego (92130) ***(P-22445)***
Evofem Biosciences Inc (PA) ....F....858 550-1900
12400 High Bluff Dr San Diego (92130) ***(P-8151)***
Evolphin Software Inc (PA) ....F....888 386-4114
2410 Camino Ramon Ste 228 San Ramon (94583) ***(P-24631)***
Evolus Inc (HQ) ....E....949 284-4555
17901 Von Karman Ave Irvine (92614) ***(P-8152)***
Evolution Design Lab Inc ....E....626 960-8388
150 S Los Robles Ave # 100 Pasadena (91101) ***(P-10496)***
Evolution Robotics Inc ....E....626 993-3300
1055 E Colo Blvd Ste 320 Pasadena (91106) ***(P-24632)***
Evolva Inc ....F....415 448-5451
101 Larkspur Landing Cir # 222 Larkspur (94939) ***(P-8549)***
Evolve Dental Technologies Inc ....F....949 713-0909
5 Vanderbilt Irvine (92618) ***(P-22879)***
Evolve Manufacturing Tech Inc ....D....650 968-9292
47300 Bayside Pkwy Fremont (94538) ***(P-22446)***
Evonik Corporation ....E....323 264-0311
3305 E 26th St Vernon (90058) ***(P-9249)***
Evoqua Water Technologies ....F....408 586-9745
960 Ames Ave Milpitas (95035) ***(P-16040)***
Evoqua Water Technologies LLC ....F....916 564-1222
199 Harris Ave Ste 1 Sacramento (95838) ***(P-16041)***
Evy of California Inc (HQ) ....C....213 746-4647
2042 Garfield Ave Commerce (90040) ***(P-3576)***
Evy of California Inc ....F....213 746-4647
1875 E 22nd St Los Angeles (90058) ***(P-3577)***
Ew Corprtion Indus Fabricators (PA) ....D....760 337-0020
1002 E Main St El Centro (92243) ***(P-12156)***
Ewi Worldwide, Foothill Ranch *Also called Exhibit Works Inc* ***(P-23871)***
Exact Cnc Industries Inc ....F....818 527-1908
20640 Bahama St Chatsworth (91311) ***(P-13203)***

ALPHABETIC

Employee Codes: A=Over 500 employees, B=251-500
C=101-250, D=51-100, E=20-50, F=10-19
2019 California
Manufacturers Register
© Mergent Inc. 1-800-342-5647
1135

Exacta-Technology Inc...F.......925 443-6200
378 Wright Brothers Ave Livermore (94551) ***(P-16481)***
Exactacator Inc (PA)...E.......209 464-8979
2237 Stagecoach Rd Stockton (95215) ***(P-23558)***
Exactuals LLC...F.......310 689-7491
1100 Glendon Ave Fl 17 Los Angeles (90024) ***(P-24633)***
Exadel Inc (PA)...D.......925 363-9510
1340 Treat Blvd Walnut Creek (94597) ***(P-24634)***
Exam Room Supply LLC...F.......805 298-3631
2419 Hrbour Blvd Unit 126 Ventura (93001) ***(P-22976)***
Examiner Special Projects Div, Santa Monica *Also called Hearst Corporation* ***(P-6178)***
Exar Corporation (HQ)...C.......669 265-6100
1060 Rincon Cir San Jose (95131) ***(P-18836)***
Exar Corporation...B.......408 927-9975
48760 Kato Rd Fremont (94538) ***(P-18837)***
Exatron Inc...E.......408 629-7600
2842 Aiello Dr San Jose (95111) ***(P-21754)***
Excaliber Systems Inc...E.......805 376-1366
185 Los Vientos Dr Newbury Park (91320) ***(P-7313)***
Excalibur Motorsports, Chino *Also called Hua Rong International Corp* ***(P-21232)***
Excalibur Well Services Corp (PA)...D.......661 589-5338
22034 Rosedale Hwy Bakersfield (93314) ***(P-104)***
Excavo LLC...F.......310 823-7670
13428 Maxella Ave Ste 409 Marina Del Rey (90292) ***(P-4079)***
Excel Bridge Manufacturing Co., Santa Fe Springs *Also called Excel Sheet Metal Inc* ***(P-12578)***
Excel Cabinets Inc...E.......951 279-4545
225 Jason Ct Corona (92879) ***(P-4299)***
Excel Cnc Machining Inc...E.......408 970-9460
3185 De La Cruz Blvd Santa Clara (95054) ***(P-16482)***
Excel Graphix International...E.......949 582-5970
11 Autry Ste B Irvine (92618) ***(P-5560)***
Excel Industries Inc...E.......909 947-4867
1601 Fremont Ct Ontario (91761) ***(P-13204)***
Excel Machining, Santa Clara *Also called Excel Cnc Machining Inc* ***(P-16482)***
Excel Manufacturing Inc...E.......661 257-1900
20409 Prairie St Chatsworth (91311) ***(P-16483)***
Excel Precision Corp USA...E.......408 727-4260
3350 Scott Blvd Bldg 62 Santa Clara (95054) ***(P-21755)***
Excel Sheet Metal Inc (PA)...D.......562 944-0701
12001 Shoemaker Ave Santa Fe Springs (90670) ***(P-12578)***
Excelitas Technologies Corp...D.......510 979-6500
44370 Christy St Fremont (94538) ***(P-17693)***
Excelitas Technologies Corp...C.......626 967-6021
1330 E Cypress St Covina (91724) ***(P-22195)***
Excelity...E.......818 767-1000
11127 Dora St Sun Valley (91352) ***(P-11776)***
Excellence Magazine Inc...F.......415 382-0582
42 Digital Dr Ste 5 Novato (94949) ***(P-6161)***
Excellence Opto Inc...F.......818 674-1921
20047 Tipico St Chatsworth (91311) ***(P-18323)***
Excellent Coatings Inc...F.......760 598-1234
2780 La Mirada Dr Ste E Vista (92081) ***(P-9250)***
Excelligence Learning Corp (PA)...E.......831 333-2000
20 Ryan Ranch Rd Ste 200 Monterey (93940) ***(P-23422)***
Excelline Food Products LLC...C.......818 701-7710
833 N Hollywood Way Burbank (91505) ***(P-992)***
Excelline Foods Inc...F.......818 701-7710
833 N Hollywood Way Burbank (91505) ***(P-993)***
Excello Circuits Inc...E.......714 993-0560
1924 Nancita Cir Placentia (92870) ***(P-18476)***
Excellon Acquisition LLC (HQ)...E.......310 668-7700
20001 S Rancho Way Compton (90220) ***(P-14951)***
Excellon Automation Co, Compton *Also called Excellon Acquisition LLC* ***(P-14951)***
Excelpro Inc (PA)...F.......323 415-8544
1630 Amapola Ave Torrance (90501) ***(P-573)***
Excelsior Metals Inc...E.......559 294-9284
2681 N Business Park Ave Fresno (93727) ***(P-12157)***
Excelsior Nutrition Inc...E.......657 999-5188
1206 N Miller St Unit D Anaheim (92806) ***(P-614)***
Excess Trading Inc...E.......310 212-0020
12350 Montague St Ste L Pacoima (91331) ***(P-22196)***
Exchange, The, Seaside *Also called Monterey County Weekly* ***(P-5977)***
Exclara Inc...E.......408 329-9319
4701 Patrick Henry Dr # 1701 Santa Clara (95054) ***(P-18838)***
Exclusive Powder Coatings Inc...F.......661 294-9812
24922 Anza Dr Ste C Valencia (91355) ***(P-13586)***
Execuprint Inc...F.......818 993-8184
9650 Topanga Canyon Pl E Chatsworth (91311) ***(P-7314)***
Executive Bus Solutions Inc...F.......805 499-3290
21356 Nordhoff St Ste 108 Chatsworth (91311) ***(P-14807)***
Executive Safe and SEC Corp (PA)...E.......909 947-7020
10722 Edison Ct Rancho Cucamonga (91730) ***(P-13941)***
Executive Tool Inc...E.......714 996-1276
1220 N Richfield Rd Anaheim (92807) ***(P-12579)***
Exelis, San Diego *Also called Harris Corporation* ***(P-21598)***
Exelixis Inc...C.......650 837-8254
169 Harbor Way South San Francisco (94080) ***(P-8153)***
Exelixis Inc...B.......650 837-7000
1851 Harbor Bay Pkwy Alameda (94502) ***(P-21688)***
Exelixis Inc...C.......650 837-7000
1851 Harbor Bay Pkwy Alameda (94502) ***(P-8154)***
Exelixis Inc (PA)...D.......650 837-7000
1851 Harbor Bay Pkwy Alameda (94502) ***(P-8155)***
Exemplis LLC...E.......714 995-4800
6280 Artesia Blvd Buena Park (90620) ***(P-4986)***
Exemplis LLC...B.......714 898-5500
6280 Artesia Blvd Buena Park (90620) ***(P-4987)***
Exemplis LLC (PA)...E.......714 995-4800
6415 Katella Ave Cypress (90630) ***(P-4988)***
Exeter Mercantile Company...F.......559 592-2121
258 E Pine St Exeter (93221) ***(P-14067)***
Exhaust Center Inc...F.......951 685-8602
1794 W 11th St Upland (91786) ***(P-12580)***
Exhaust Gas Technologies Inc...F.......909 548-8100
15642 Dupont Ave Ste B Chino (91710) ***(P-20329)***
Exhaust Tech, Commerce *Also called Dynaflex Products* ***(P-20203)***
Exhibit Works Inc...F.......949 470-0850
19531 Pauling Foothill Ranch (92610) ***(P-23871)***
Exide Technologies...E.......951 520-0677
345 Cessna Cir Ste 101 Corona (92880) ***(P-19807)***
Exin LLC...C.......415 359-2600
1213 Evans Ave San Francisco (94124) ***(P-5847)***
Exit Light Co Inc...F.......877 352-3948
3170 Scott St Vista (92081) ***(P-17605)***
Exit Sign Warehouse Inc...F.......888 953-3948
16123 Cohasset St Van Nuys (91406) ***(P-17606)***
Exo Systems Inc...E.......510 655-5033
333 Pali Ct Oakland (94611) ***(P-22977)***
Exodust Collectors LLC...F.......562 808-0842
7045 Jackson St Paramount (90723) ***(P-15156)***
Exotic Silks Inc...F.......650 948-8611
1959 Leghorn St Ste B Mountain View (94043) ***(P-2736)***
Exp Computer...F.......408 530-8080
1296 Kifer Rd Ste 605 Sunnyvale (94086) ***(P-22197)***
Expandable Software Inc (PA)...E.......408 261-7880
900 Lafayette St Ste 400 Santa Clara (95050) ***(P-24635)***
Expedite Precision Works Inc...E.......408 437-1893
931 Berryessa Rd San Jose (95133) ***(P-16484)***
Experimental Aircraft Assn...F.......818 705-2744
7026 Lasaine Ave Van Nuys (91406) ***(P-20577)***
Expert Assembly Services Inc...E.......714 258-8880
1183 Warner Ave Tustin (92780) ***(P-18477)***
Expert Coatings & Graphics LLC...F.......714 476-2086
1570 S Lewis St Anaheim (92805) ***(P-13587)***
Expert Computer Intl Inc (PA)...E.......562 630-3002
6437 Alondra Blvd Paramount (90723) ***(P-15411)***
Expert Reputation LLC...F.......866 407-6020
101 N Acacia Ave Ste 105 Solana Beach (92075) ***(P-24636)***
Expert Semiconductor Tech Inc...E.......831 439-9300
10 Victor Sq Ste 100 Scotts Valley (95066) ***(P-14952)***
Expert Worldwide LLC...F.......818 543-5850
5439 W San Fernando Rd Los Angeles (90039) ***(P-9191)***
Expertech, Scotts Valley *Also called Expert Semiconductor Tech Inc* ***(P-14952)***
Expertpower Direct, Paramount *Also called Expert Computer Intl Inc* ***(P-15411)***
Exploding Kittens LLC...F.......310 788-8699
100 N Crescent Dr Beverly Hills (90210) ***(P-23423)***
Exploramed Nc7 Inc...E.......650 559-5805
201 San Antonio Cir # 172 Mountain View (94040) ***(P-22978)***
Expo Dyeing & Finishing Inc...C.......714 220-9583
1365 N Knollwood Cir Anaheim (92801) ***(P-2911)***
Expo-3 International Inc...E.......714 379-8383
12350 Edison Way 60 Garden Grove (92841) ***(P-23872)***
Expol Inc...F.......408 567-9020
2122 Ronald St Santa Clara (95050) ***(P-16485)***
Exponential Technology Inc...D.......408 378-1850
685 Budd Ct Campbell (95008) ***(P-18839)***
Exportech Worldwide LLC...F.......909 278-9477
14310 Burning Tree Dr Victorville (92395) ***(P-15412)***
Express Business Systems Inc...E.......858 549-9828
9155 Trade Pl San Diego (92126) ***(P-7315)***
Express Chipping...F.......562 789-8058
418 Goetz Ave Santa Ana (92707) ***(P-6479)***
Express Container Inc...E.......909 798-3857
560 Iowa St Redlands (92373) ***(P-5408)***
Express Folding...E.......310 316-6762
21250 Hawthorne Blvd Torrance (90503) ***(P-6480)***
Express ID, Riverside *Also called J&C Tapocik Inc* ***(P-3661)***
Express It Delivers...E.......626 855-1294
168 Mason Way Ste B5 City of Industry (91746) ***(P-6481)***
Express Lens Lab Inc...E.......714 545-1024
17150 Newhope St Ste 305 Fountain Valley (92708) ***(P-23096)***
Express Machining, La Mirada *Also called United States Ball Corporation* ***(P-15115)***
Express Manufacturing Inc (PA)...C.......714 979-2228
3519 W Warner Ave Santa Ana (92704) ***(P-19537)***
Express Pipe & Supply Co LLC (HQ)...E.......310 204-7238
1666 20th St Ste 200a Santa Monica (90404) ***(P-13887)***
Express Sheet Metal Product...F.......562 925-9340
10131 Flora Vista St Bellflower (90706) ***(P-12581)***
Express Sign and Neon...F.......323 291-3333
1720 W Slauson Ave Los Angeles (90047) ***(P-23873)***
Express Systems & Engrg Inc...E.......951 461-1500
41357 Date St Murrieta (92562) ***(P-10095)***
Expression Systems LLC (PA)...E.......877 877-7421
2537 2nd St Davis (95618) ***(P-8550)***
Expressions Home Gallery, Santa Monica *Also called Express Pipe & Supply Co LLC* ***(P-13887)***
Exquisite Corporation...E.......626 856-0200
5000 Rivergrade Rd Baldwin Park (91706) ***(P-8747)***
Exquisite Mfg & Filling Serv, Baldwin Park *Also called Exquisite Corporation* ***(P-8747)***
Extra Lite, Huntington Beach *Also called Pacific Link Corp* ***(P-22119)***
Extreme Group Holdings LLC...E.......310 899-3200
1531 14th St Santa Monica (90404) ***(P-17896)***
Extreme Networks Inc (PA)...B.......408 579-2800
6480 Via Del Oro San Jose (95119) ***(P-17946)***
Extreme Precision Inc...F.......408 275-8365
1717 Little Orchard St B San Jose (95125) ***(P-16486)***
Extreme Precision LLC...F.......949 459-1062
23266 Arroyo Vis Rcho STA Marg (92688) ***(P-16487)***

Mergent e-mail: customerrelations@mergent.com 2019 California (P-0000) Products & Services Section entry number
1136 Manufacturers Register (PA)=Parent Co (HQ)=Headquarters (DH)=Div Headquarters

Extreme Production Music, Santa Monica *Also called Extreme Group Holdings LLC* ***(P-17896)***
Extreme Reach Inc ....F 818 588-3635
1048 N Lake St Burbank (91502) ***(P-6482)***
Extron Contract Mfg Inc ....C 510 353-0177
496 S Abbott Ave Milpitas (95035) ***(P-23424)***
Extron Contract Packaging, Milpitas *Also called Extron Contract Mfg Inc* ***(P-23424)***
Extron Electronics, Anaheim *Also called Rgb Systems Inc* ***(P-15839)***
Extron Electronics, Anaheim *Also called Rgb Systems Inc* ***(P-15840)***
Extrude Hone Abrsve Flw McHng, Paramount *Also called Extrude Hone Deburring Service* ***(P-16488)***
Extrude Hone Deburring Service ....F 562 531-2976
8800 Somerset Blvd Paramount (90723) ***(P-16488)***
Extrumed Inc (HQ) ....E 951 547-7400
547 Trm Cir Corona (92879) ***(P-10096)***
Exxel Media, Cardiff By The Sea *Also called Nutrition Resource Connection* ***(P-17908)***
Exxel Outdoors Inc ....C 626 369-7278
343 Baldwin Park Blvd City of Industry (91746) ***(P-3945)***
Eye Medical Group Santa Cruz ....F 831 426-2550
515 Soquel Ave Santa Cruz (95062) ***(P-22447)***
Eyebrain Medical Inc ....F 949 339-5157
3184 Airway Ave Ste C Costa Mesa (92626) ***(P-23097)***
Eyefluence Inc ....E 408 586-8632
1600 Amphitheatre Pkwy Mountain View (94043) ***(P-23098)***
Eyeonics Inc ....F 949 788-6000
50 Technology Dr Irvine (92618) ***(P-23099)***
Eyeshadow, Los Angeles *Also called Stony Apparel Corp* ***(P-3510)***
Eyvo Inc ....F 888 237-9801
3030 Bridgeway Ste 110 Sausalito (94965) ***(P-24637)***
EZ 2000 Inc ....F 800 273-5033
1800 Century Park E # 600 Los Angeles (90067) ***(P-24638)***
EZ 2000 1 Rated Dental Sftwr, Los Angeles *Also called EZ 2000 Inc* ***(P-24638)***
EZ Inflatables Inc ....E 626 480-9100
1410 Vineland Ave Baldwin Park (91706) ***(P-9613)***
EZ Lube LLC ....A 951 766-1996
532 W Florida Ave Hemet (92543) ***(P-9434)***
EZ Up Factory Store, Colton *Also called E-Z Up Directcom* ***(P-3785)***
Ezaki Glico USA Corp ....F 949 251-0144
17780 Fitch Ste 140 Irvine (92614) ***(P-1422)***
Ezboard Inc ....F 415 773-0400
607 Market St Fl 5 San Francisco (94105) ***(P-24639)***
Ezekiel, Irvine *Also called 3 Point Distribution LLC* ***(P-3128)***
Ezoic Inc ....F 760 444-4995
5870 El Camino Real Carlsbad (92008) ***(P-24640)***
Ezrez Software, San Francisco *Also called Topguest Inc* ***(P-25284)***
F & D Flores Enterprises Inc ....F 909 975-4853
761 E Francis St Ontario (91761) ***(P-22198)***
F & H Plating Co, North Hollywood *Also called F & H Plating LLC* ***(P-13409)***
F & H Plating LLC ....F 818 765-1221
12023 Vose St Ste A North Hollywood (91605) ***(P-13409)***
F & L Tls Precision Machining, Corona *Also called F & L Tools Corporation* ***(P-20810)***
F & L Tools Corporation ....F 951 279-1555
245 Jason Ct Corona (92879) ***(P-20810)***
F C I, San Marcos *Also called Fluid Components Intl LLC* ***(P-21584)***
F Conrad Furlong Inc ....F 213 623-4191
550 S Hill St Ste 1620 Los Angeles (90013) ***(P-23262)***
F D M, Yorba Linda *Also called Fixture Design & Mfg Co* ***(P-5232)***
F E Trailers, Lakeside *Also called McQuaide Brothers Corporation* ***(P-20506)***
F E W Inc ....F 661 323-8319
420 30th St Bakersfield (93301) ***(P-16489)***
F G S Packing Services, Exeter *Also called Fruit Growers Supply Company* ***(P-5411)***
F Gavina & Sons Inc ....B 323 582-0671
2700 Fruitland Ave Vernon (90058) ***(P-2340)***
F I O Imports Inc ....B 323 263-5100
5970 Alcoa Ave Vernon (90058) ***(P-2515)***
F I T, Compton *Also called Fastener Innovation Tech Inc* ***(P-13023)***
F Korbel & Bros (PA) ....B 707 824-7000
13250 River Rd Guerneville (95446) ***(P-1755)***
F Korbel & Bros ....E 661 854-6120
15401 Bear Mtn Winery Rd Di Giorgio (93203) ***(P-1756)***
F M H, Irvine *Also called Fmh Aerospace Corp* ***(P-20816)***
F M I, Santa Ana *Also called Flexible Manufacturing LLC* ***(P-19391)***
F R Industries Inc ....F 818 503-9143
3157 Dona Susana Dr Studio City (91604) ***(P-2997)***
F T B & Son Inc ....E 714 891-8003
11551 Markon Dr Garden Grove (92841) ***(P-12582)***
F T I, Long Beach *Also called Fundamental Tech Intl Inc* ***(P-21589)***
F-J-E Inc ....E 562 437-7466
546 W Esther St Long Beach (90813) ***(P-5060)***
F-P Press, Union City *Also called Fricke-Parks Press Inc* ***(P-6827)***
F.K.a Trmph Strctrs-Los Angles, City of Industry *Also called Alatus Aerosystems* ***(P-20729)***
Faac ....F 800 221-8278
357 S Acacia Ave Unit 357 # 357 Fullerton (92831) ***(P-19965)***
Fab Tron ....F 714 996-4270
1358 N Jefferson St Anaheim (92807) ***(P-12583)***
Fabco Holdings Inc ....A 925 454-9500
151 Lawrence Dr Livermore (94551) ***(P-20330)***
Fabco Steel Fabrication Inc ....E 909 350-1535
14688 San Bernardino Ave Fontana (92335) ***(P-12158)***
Faber Enterprises Inc ....C 310 323-6200
14800 S Figueroa St Gardena (90248) ***(P-13741)***
Fabfad LLC ....F 213 488-0456
1901 E 7th Pl Los Angeles (90021) ***(P-3656)***
Fable Inc ....F 650 598-9616
595 Quarry Rd San Carlos (94070) ***(P-12854)***
Fabnet, Anaheim *Also called Fabrication Network Inc* ***(P-12584)***

Fabri-Corp ....E 650 941-2076
25850 Vinedo Ln Los Altos Hills (94022) ***(P-16490)***
Fabri-Tech Components Inc ....F 510 249-2000
49038 Milmont Dr Fremont (94538) ***(P-19538)***
Fabric Brand, Huntington Park *Also called Coh-Fb LLC* ***(P-3099)***
Fabric Walls Inc ....F 415 863-2711
322 Harriet St San Francisco (94103) ***(P-3722)***
Fabrica Fine Carpet, Santa Ana *Also called Fabrica International Inc* ***(P-2929)***
Fabrica International Inc ....C 949 261-7181
3201 S Susan St Santa Ana (92704) ***(P-2929)***
Fabricast Inc (PA) ....E 626 443-3247
2517 Seaman Ave South El Monte (91733) ***(P-19539)***
Fabricated Components Corp ....C 714 974-8590
130 W Bristol Ln Orange (92865) ***(P-18478)***
Fabricated Extrusion Co LLC (PA) ....E 209 529-9200
2331 Hoover Ave Modesto (95354) ***(P-10097)***
Fabricated Glass Spc Inc ....F 707 429-6160
2350 S Watney Way Ste E Fairfield (94533) ***(P-10696)***
Fabrication Network Inc ....D 714 393-5282
5410 E La Palma Ave Anaheim (92807) ***(P-12584)***
Fabrication Tech Inds Inc ....D 619 477-4141
2200 Haffley Ave National City (91950) ***(P-12159)***
Fabricmate Systems Inc ....F 805 642-7470
2781 Golf Course Dr A Ventura (93003) ***(P-10098)***
Fabricor Products Inc ....F 760 373-8292
22512 Curtis Pl California City (93505) ***(P-12855)***
Fabricor Stamping, California City *Also called Fabricor Products Inc* ***(P-12855)***
Fabrique Delices, Hayward *Also called Sapar Usa Inc* ***(P-523)***
Fabritec Precision Inc (PA) ....F 209 529-8504
1060 Reno Ave Modesto (95351) ***(P-12585)***
Fabritex Inc ....F 213 747-1417
2301 E 7th St Ste D102 Los Angeles (90023) ***(P-2777)***
Fabrix, San Leandro *Also called Osumo Inc* ***(P-3911)***
Fabtex Inc ....C 714 538-0877
1202 W Struck Ave Orange (92867) ***(P-2778)***
Fabtron, San Carlos *Also called EH Suda Inc* ***(P-16463)***
Fabtron, Lewiston *Also called EH Suda Inc* ***(P-16464)***
Fabtron ....F 650 622-9700
615 Industrial Rd San Carlos (94070) ***(P-16491)***
Fabtronic Inc ....E 626 962-3293
5026 Calmview Ave Baldwin Park (91706) ***(P-12586)***
Face First Screen Print Inc ....E 949 443-9895
33049 Calle Aviador Ste C San Juan Capistrano (92675) ***(P-7316)***
Facefirst Inc ....E 805 482-8428
15821 Ventura Blvd # 425 Encino (91436) ***(P-24641)***
Facilitron Inc ....E 800 272-2962
485 Alberto Way Ste 210 Los Gatos (95032) ***(P-24642)***
Factory Direct Dist Corp ....F 619 435-3437
1001 B Ave Ste 100 San Diego (92118) ***(P-8641)***
Factory One Studio Inc ....D 323 752-1670
6700 Avalon Blvd Ste 101 Los Angeles (90003) ***(P-2737)***
Factory Reproductions ....F 909 590-5252
13353 Benson Ave Chino (91710) ***(P-20331)***
Factory Showroom Exchange, Los Angeles *Also called Sofa U Love* ***(P-4811)***
Factron Test Fixtures, Fontana *Also called Everett Charles Tech LLC* ***(P-21752)***
Fafco Inc (PA) ....E 530 332-2100
435 Otterson Dr Chico (95928) ***(P-12063)***
Fair Isaac International Corp (HQ) ....A 415 446-6000
200 Smith Ranch Rd San Rafael (94903) ***(P-24643)***
Fairchild Semicdtr Intl Inc (HQ) ....E 408 822-2000
1272 Borregas Ave Sunnyvale (94089) ***(P-18840)***
Fairmont Designs, Del Mar *Also called Fairmont Global LLC* ***(P-5061)***
Fairmont Global LLC (PA) ....F 415 320-2929
2010 Jimmy Durante Blvd Del Mar (92014) ***(P-5061)***
Fairmont Sign Company ....E 209 365-6490
850 S Guild Ave Lodi (95240) ***(P-23874)***
Fairway Import-Export Inc ....E 310 637-6162
2130 E Gladwick St Rancho Dominguez (90220) ***(P-23559)***
Fairway Injection Molds Inc ....D 909 595-2201
20109 Paseo Del Prado Walnut (91789) ***(P-14514)***
Fairway Trading Inc ....F 323 582-8111
5717 Ferguson Dr Commerce (90022) ***(P-2799)***
Faith Industries Inc ....E 951 351-1486
4117 Pearl St Lake Elsinore (92530) ***(P-4619)***
Faith Knight Inc ....F 213 488-1569
2340 Mountain Ave La Crescenta (91214) ***(P-23263)***
Falcon Abrasive Manufacturing ....F 909 598-3078
5490 Brooks St Montclair (91763) ***(P-11293)***
Falcon Automotive Inc ....E 714 569-1085
1305 E Wakeham Ave Santa Ana (92705) ***(P-3946)***
Falcon Electric, Baldwin Park *Also called Yutaka Electric Intl Inc* ***(P-17361)***
Falcon Electric Inc ....F 626 962-7770
5116 Azusa Canyon Rd Baldwin Park (91706) ***(P-17092)***
Falcon Waterfree Tech LLC (HQ) ....E 310 209-7250
2255 Barry Ave Los Angeles (90064) ***(P-9614)***
Falkner Winery Inc ....D 951 676-6741
40620 Calle Contento Temecula (92591) ***(P-1757)***
Falkor Partners LLC ....D 714 721-8772
333 Mccormick Ave Costa Mesa (92626) ***(P-18841)***
Fallbrook Bonsall Village News, Temecula *Also called Villlage News Inc* ***(P-6082)***
Fallbrook Communications, Fallbrook *Also called Fallbrook Printing Corp* ***(P-6811)***
Fallbrook Industries Inc ....E 760 728-7229
323 Industrial Way Ste 1 Fallbrook (92028) ***(P-13205)***
Fallbrook Printing Corp ....F 760 731-2020
504 E Alvarado St Ste 110 Fallbrook (92028) ***(P-6811)***
Falltech, Compton *Also called Andrew Alexander Inc* ***(P-10457)***
Falmat Inc ....C 800 848-4257
1873 Diamond St San Marcos (92078) ***(P-11660)***

ALPHABETIC

Employee Codes: A=Over 500 employees, B=251-500
C=101-250, D=51-100, E=20-50, F=10-19
2019 California
Manfacturers Register
© Mergent Inc. 1-800-342-5647
1137

Family Loompya Corporation.....E.....619 477-2125
2626 Southport Way Ste F National City (91950) *(P-2516)*
Family Medicine Center Torr.....F.....310 326-8600
2841 Lomita Blvd Ste 220 Torrance (90505) *(P-8156)*
Famoso Nut, Mc Farland *Also called Amaretto Orchards LLC (P-24033)*
Famous Amos Chclat Chip Cookie, Stockton *Also called Murray Biscuit Company LLC (P-1372)*
Famsoft Corp.....F.....408 452-1550
1762 Tech Dr Ste 108 San Jose (95110) *(P-24644)*
Famsoft Corp.....E.....510 683-3940
44946 Osgood Rd Fremont (94539) *(P-24645)*
Fan Fave Inc.....E.....909 975-4999
285 S Dupont Ave Ste 104 Ontario (91761) *(P-23875)*
Fanboys Window Factory Inc (PA).....E.....626 280-8787
10750 Saint Louis Dr El Monte (91731) *(P-12316)*
Fancy Models Corp.....F.....510 683-0819
3500 Yale Way Fremont (94538) *(P-24094)*
Fancy Schmancy Art Frames, Canoga Park *Also called Vitale Home Designs Inc (P-23226)*
Fanfave, Ontario *Also called Fan Fave Inc (P-23875)*
Fanlight Corporation Inc (HQ).....F.....909 930-6868
2000 Sgrove Ave Bldg B Ontario (91761) *(P-17428)*
Fanno Saw Works.....F.....530 895-1762
224 W 8th Ave Chico (95926) *(P-11918)*
Fansteel California Drop Forge, Los Angeles *Also called Fansteel Inc (P-13098)*
Fansteel Inc.....D.....323 221-1134
1033 Alhambra Ave Los Angeles (90012) *(P-13098)*
Fantansty Lingerie, Chatsworth *Also called Pacoima Clothing LLC (P-3542)*
Fantasea Enterprises Inc.....F.....949 673-8545
2901 W Coast Hwy Ste 160 Newport Beach (92663) *(P-21036)*
Fantasia Distribution Inc.....E.....714 817-8300
1566 W Embassy St Anaheim (92802) *(P-2713)*
Fantasia Hookah Tobacco, Anaheim *Also called Fantasia Distribution Inc (P-2713)*
Fantasy Inc.....D.....510 486-2038
2600 10th St Ste 100 Berkeley (94710) *(P-17897)*
Fantasy Activewear Inc (PA).....E.....213 705-4111
5383 Alcoa Ave Vernon (90058) *(P-2835)*
Fantasy Activewear Inc.....E.....323 983-9988
5383 Alcoa Ave Vernon (90058) *(P-2836)*
Fantasy Dyeing & Finishing Inc.....D.....323 983-9988
5383 Alcoa Ave Vernon (90058) *(P-2837)*
Fantasy Manufacturing, Vernon *Also called Fantasy Activewear Inc (P-2835)*
Fantasy Manufacturing Inc.....F.....707 838-7686
7716 Bell Rd Windsor (95492) *(P-16492)*
Fante Inc (PA).....E.....650 697-7525
2898 W Winton Ave Hayward (94545) *(P-2380)*
Fantom Drives, Torrance *Also called Bnl Technologies Inc (P-15516)*
Fanuc America Corporation.....E.....949 595-2700
25951 Commercentre Dr Lake Forest (92630) *(P-14953)*
Fanuc Robotics West, Lake Forest *Also called Fanuc America Corporation (P-14953)*
Far Niente Wine Estates, Oakville *Also called Far Niente Winery Inc (P-1758)*
Far Niente Winery Inc.....D.....707 944-2861
1350 Acacia Dr Oakville (94562) *(P-1758)*
Far West Equipment Rentals.....F.....916 645-2929
649 7th St Lincoln (95648) *(P-11105)*
Far West Meats, Highland *Also called Raemica Inc (P-518)*
Far West Rice Inc.....E.....530 891-1339
3455 Nelson Rd Nelson (95958) *(P-1078)*
Far West Technology Inc.....F.....805 964-3615
330 S Kellogg Ave Goleta (93117) *(P-22199)*
Farad Industries Inc.....F.....310 320-4260
20435 Gramercy Pl Ste 104 Torrance (90501) *(P-7836)*
Farallon Brands Inc (PA).....F.....510 550-4299
33300 Central Ave Union City (94587) *(P-3723)*
Farbotech Color Inc.....F.....909 596-9330
1630 Yeager Ave La Verne (91750) *(P-9192)*
Farchitecture Bb LLC.....E.....917 701-2777
8588 Washington Blvd Culver City (90232) *(P-669)*
Fargo Choice Foods LLC.....E.....510 774-0064
2885 Adeline St Oakland (94608) *(P-1246)*
Farley Interlocking Pav Stones, Palm Desert *Also called Farley Paving Stone Co Inc (P-10923)*
Farley Machine Inc.....F.....661 397-4987
1600 S Union Ave Bakersfield (93307) *(P-14222)*
Farley Paving Stone Co Inc.....D.....760 773-3960
75135 Sheryl Ave Ste A Palm Desert (92211) *(P-10923)*
Farlight LLC.....F.....310 830-0181
460 W 5th St San Pedro (90731) *(P-17607)*
Farlows Scientific Glassblowing, Grass Valley *Also called Farlows Scntfic Glssblwing Inc (P-10642)*
Farlows Scntfic Glssblwing Inc.....E.....530 477-5513
962 Golden Gate Ter Ste B Grass Valley (95945) *(P-10642)*
Farma Pharmaceuticals Inc (PA).....F.....818 638-3113
5240 San Fernando Rd Glendale (91203) *(P-8157)*
Farmdale Creamery Inc.....D.....909 888-4938
1049 W Base Line St San Bernardino (92411) *(P-724)*
Farmer Bros Co.....F.....805 483-8406
1350 Stellar Dr Oxnard (93033) *(P-2341)*
Farmer Bros Co.....E.....858 292-7578
7855 Ostrow St Ste A San Diego (92111) *(P-2342)*
Farmer Bros Co.....F.....510 638-1660
20671 Corsair Blvd Hayward (94545) *(P-2343)*
Farmer Bros Co.....F.....831 633-6521
11460 Commercial Pkwy Castroville (95012) *(P-2344)*
Farmer Bros Co.....F.....661 663-9908
8802 Swigert Ct Bakersfield (93311) *(P-2345)*
Farmer Bros Co.....F.....530 343-3165
480 Ryan Ave Ste 100 Chico (95973) *(P-2346)*
Farmer Bros Co.....F.....818 767-7649
9373 Remick Ave Arleta (91331) *(P-2347)*
Farmer Bros Co.....E.....209 466-0203
4243 Arch Rd Stockton (95215) *(P-2348)*
Farmers Brothers Coffee, Oxnard *Also called Farmer Bros Co (P-2341)*
Farmers Brothers Coffee, Hayward *Also called Farmer Bros Co (P-2343)*
Farmers Brothers Coffee, Castroville *Also called Farmer Bros Co (P-2344)*
Farmers Brothers Coffee, Arleta *Also called Farmer Bros Co (P-2347)*
Farmers Brothers Coffee, Stockton *Also called Farmer Bros Co (P-2348)*
Farmers International, Chico *Also called Cal Traders (P-1484)*
Farmers Rice Cooperative (PA).....E.....916 923-5100
2566 River Plaza Dr Sacramento (95833) *(P-1079)*
Farmers Rice Cooperative.....E.....916 373-5549
1800 Terminal Rd Sacramento (95820) *(P-1080)*
Farmers Rice Cooperative.....C.....916 373-5500
2224 Industrial Blvd West Sacramento (95691) *(P-1081)*
Farmers Rice Cooperative.....C.....916 373-5500
2224 Industrial Blvd West Sacramento (95691) *(P-1082)*
Farmhouse Culture Inc (PA).....E.....831 466-0499
182 Lewis Rd Royal Oaks (95076) *(P-8158)*
Farr West Fashions.....F.....831 661-5039
580 Cathedral Dr Aptos (95003) *(P-3536)*
Farrar Grinding Company.....F.....323 678-4879
347 E Beach Ave Inglewood (90302) *(P-20811)*
Farrell Brothers Holding Corp.....F.....714 630-3417
1137 N Armando St Anaheim (92806) *(P-16493)*
Farrs Custom Carbide Inc.....F.....800 684-0411
1000 Ortega Way Ste B Placentia (92870) *(P-14631)*
Farsi Jewelry Mfg Co Inc.....F.....213 624-0043
631 Suth Olive St Ste 565 Los Angeles (90014) *(P-23264)*
Farstone Technology Inc.....C.....949 336-4321
184 Technology Dr Ste 205 Irvine (92618) *(P-19864)*
Fashion 1001 Nights, Los Angeles *Also called Night Fashion Inc (P-3328)*
Fashion Blacksmith Inc.....F.....707 464-9219
121 Starfish Way Crescent City (95531) *(P-21037)*
Fashion Camp.....E.....714 259-0946
2477 Park Ave Tustin (92782) *(P-2998)*
Fashion Queen Mania Inc.....E.....213 788-7310
800 E 12th St Ste 428 Los Angeles (90021) *(P-3352)*
Fashion Today Inc.....E.....213 744-1636
1100 S San Pedro St Ste A Los Angeles (90015) *(P-3415)*
Fashion Today Inc (PA).....F.....213 744-1636
3100 S Grand Ave Fl 3 Los Angeles (90007) *(P-3416)*
Fast Access Inc.....F.....909 748-1245
1765 Howard Pl Redlands (92373) *(P-10924)*
Fast Ad Inc.....D.....714 835-9353
224 S Center St Santa Ana (92703) *(P-23876)*
Fast Sportswear Inc.....D.....323 720-1078
6400 E Washington Blvd Commerce (90040) *(P-3417)*
Fast Track Energy Drink LLC.....E.....310 281-2045
8447 Wilshire Blvd # 401 Beverly Hills (90211) *(P-2133)*
Fast Turn Machining Inc.....F.....408 720-6888
3087 Lawrence Expy Santa Clara (95051) *(P-16494)*
Fast Undercar, San Diego *Also called Atm Plus Inc (P-9590)*
Fastec Imaging Corporation.....E.....858 592-2342
17150 Via Dl Cmpo 301 San Diego (92127) *(P-23160)*
Fastener Depot Inc.....F.....530 621-3070
6166 Enterprise Dr Ste A Diamond Springs (95619) *(P-13068)*
Fastener Innovation Tech Inc.....D.....310 538-1111
19300 S Susana Rd Compton (90221) *(P-13023)*
Fastener Technology Corp.....D.....818 764-6467
7415 Fulton Ave North Hollywood (91605) *(P-23765)*
Faster Faster Inc.....E.....415 230-0755
185 Valley Dr Brisbane (94005) *(P-20332)*
Fastrak Manufacturing Svcs Inc.....E.....408 298-6414
1275 Alma Ct San Jose (95112) *(P-19540)*
Fastramp, San Diego *Also called Stats Chippac Test Svcs Inc (P-19188)*
Fastramp, Fremont *Also called Stats Chippac Test Svcs Inc (P-19189)*
Fastsigns, Hayward *Also called Justipher Inc (P-23911)*
Fastsigns.....F.....415 537-6900
650 Harrison St San Francisco (94107) *(P-23877)*
Fastsigns.....F.....650 345-0900
2130 S El Camino Real San Mateo (94403) *(P-23878)*
Fat Cuts.....F.....818 367-1540
15140 Bledsoe St Ste B Sylmar (91342) *(P-12160)*
Fat Performance Inc.....F.....714 637-2889
1558 N Case St Orange (92867) *(P-20333)*
Fat Quarters Quilt Shop.....F.....760 758-8308
728 Civic Center Dr Vista (92084) *(P-2738)*
Fat Wreck Chords Inc.....F.....415 284-1790
2196 Palou Ave San Francisco (94124) *(P-17898)*
Fate Therapeutics Inc.....F.....858 875-1800
3535 General Atomics Ct San Diego (92121) *(P-8551)*
Faust Printing Inc.....E.....909 980-1577
8656 Utica Ave Ste 100 Rancho Cucamonga (91730) *(P-6812)*
Faustinos Chair Factory Inc.....E.....323 724-8055
2425 S Malt Ave Commerce (90040) *(P-4943)*
Fax Star, Costa Mesa *Also called S E P E Inc (P-15480)*
Fay & Quartermaine Machining, El Monte *Also called Fay and Qrtrmine McHining Corp (P-14632)*
Fay and Qrtrmine McHining Corp.....F.....323 686-0224
2745 Seaman Ave El Monte (91733) *(P-14632)*
Fay's Foods, North Hollywood *Also called Fayes Foods Inc (P-2517)*
Fayes Foods Inc.....E.....818 508-8392
10650 Burbank Blvd North Hollywood (91601) *(P-2517)*
FBproductions Inc.....D.....818 773-9337
12722 Rverside Dr Ste 204 Valley Village (91607) *(P-6813)*
Fbs Floor Box Systems, Murrieta *Also called Jeluz Electric Ltd LLC (P-19994)*

Fc Global Realty Incorporated .... E 760 602-3300
2375 Camino Vida Roble B Carlsbad (92011) ***(P-22448)***

Fc Management Services .... E 805 499-0050
2580 Azurite Cir Newbury Park (91320) ***(P-14954)***

Fca LLC .... F 805 477-9901
3816 Transport St Ventura (93003) ***(P-4441)***

FCA US LLC .... E 949 450-5111
7700 Irvine Center Dr # 400 Irvine (92618) ***(P-20334)***

FCkingston Co .... D 310 326-8287
23201 Normandie Ave Torrance (90501) ***(P-13716)***

Fcp Inc .... D 951 678-4571
23100 Baxter Rd Wildomar (92595) ***(P-12931)***

Fd, Newbury Park *Also called Follmer Development Inc* ***(P-7691)***

Fdc Aerofilter, El Dorado Hills *Also called Filtration Development Co LLC* ***(P-19335)***

FDS Manufacturing Company (PA) .... D 909 591-1733
2200 S Reservoir St Pomona (91766) ***(P-5711)***

Fear of God LLC .... E 310 466-9751
1200 S Santa Fe Ave Ste A Los Angeles (90021) ***(P-3150)***

Fear of God LLC (PA) .... F 213 235-7985
3940 Laurel Canyon Blvd Studio City (91604) ***(P-3151)***

Feather Farm Inc .... F 707 255-8833
1181 4th Ave NAPA (94559) ***(P-13826)***

Feather Publishing Company Inc (PA) .... E 530 283-0800
287 Lawrence St Quincy (95971) ***(P-5848)***

Feather Publishing Company Inc .... F 530 257-5321
100 Grand Ave Susanville (96130) ***(P-5849)***

Feather River Bulletin, Quincy *Also called Feather Publishing Company Inc* ***(P-5848)***

Feather River Concrete Product .... F 530 532-7915
675 State Box Rd Oroville (95965) ***(P-11106)***

Featherock Inc (PA) .... F 818 882-3888
20219 Bahama St Chatsworth (91311) ***(P-411)***

Featherrock, Chatsworth *Also called United States Pumice Company* ***(P-419)***

Fed Ex Kinkos Ofc & Print Ctr .... F 805 604-6000
255 W Stanley Ave Ventura (93001) ***(P-6814)***

Federal Aviation ADM .... E 310 640-9640
2250 E Imperial Hwy # 140 El Segundo (90245) ***(P-20812)***

Federal Buyers Guide Inc (PA) .... F 805 963-7470
324 Palm Ave Santa Barbara (93101) ***(P-6483)***

Federal Custom Cable LLC .... E 949 851-3114
1891 Alton Pkwy Ste A Irvine (92606) ***(P-19541)***

Federal Heath Sign Company LLC (PA) .... D 760 941-0715
4602 North Ave Oceanside (92056) ***(P-23879)***

Federal Industries Inc .... F 310 297-4040
645 Hawaii St El Segundo (90245) ***(P-13765)***

Federal Manufacturing Corp .... E 818 341-9825
9825 De Soto Ave Chatsworth (91311) ***(P-13069)***

Federal Prison Industries .... E 805 735-2771
3901 Klein Blvd Lompoc (93436) ***(P-23880)***

Federal Prison Industries .... C 805 736-4154
3600 Guard Rd Lompoc (93436) ***(P-4696)***

Federal Signal Corporation .... E 714 871-3336
1108 E Raymond Way Anaheim (92801) ***(P-20140)***

Feedstuffs Processing Co .... F 925 820-5454
112 Lark Ct Alamo (94507) ***(P-1130)***

Feemster Co Inc .... E 909 621-9772
119 Yale Ave Claremont (91711) ***(P-1247)***

Feeney Inc .... E 510 893-9473
2603 Union St Oakland (94607) ***(P-13827)***

Fei Efa Inc .... E 805 560-0404
827 Reddick St Santa Barbara (93103) ***(P-21756)***

Fei Efa Inc (HQ) .... D 510 897-6800
3400 W Warren Ave Fremont (94538) ***(P-19390)***

Fei-Zyfer Inc (HQ) .... E 714 933-4000
7321 Lincoln Way Garden Grove (92841) ***(P-18108)***

Feihe International Inc (PA) .... A 626 757-8885
2275 Huntington Dr # 278 San Marino (91108) ***(P-615)***

Feit Electric Company Inc (PA) .... C 562 463-2852
4901 Gregg Rd Pico Rivera (90660) ***(P-17535)***

Feitian Technologies Us Inc .... F 408 352-5553
4677 Old Ironsides Dr # 312 Santa Clara (95054) ***(P-19966)***

Felbro Inc .... C 323 263-8686
3666 E Olympic Blvd Los Angeles (90023) ***(P-5139)***

Felbro Food Products Inc .... E 323 936-5266
5700 W Adams Blvd Los Angeles (90016) ***(P-2259)***

Felix Tool & Engineering .... E 818 994-9401
14535 Bessemer St Van Nuys (91411) ***(P-14515)***

Fellyr International Inc .... F 626 960-5111
13453 Brooks Dr Ste B Baldwin Park (91706) ***(P-3418)***

Fema Electronics Corporation .... E 714 825-0140
22 Corporate Park Irvine (92606) ***(P-19542)***

Femco, Hollister *Also called Food Equipment Mfg Co* ***(P-14846)***

Femi Data Telecommunication, Harbor City *Also called Adegbesan Adefemi* ***(P-15382)***

Fence Factory .... F 805 462-1362
2650 El Camino Real Atascadero (93422) ***(P-13828)***

Fence Factory .... F 805 644-5482
1482 Callens Rd Ventura (93003) ***(P-12856)***

Fencer Enterprises LLC .... F 916 635-1700
3644 Recycle Rd Rancho Cordova (95742) ***(P-11440)***

Fenchem Inc (HQ) .... F 909 597-8880
15308 El Prado Rd Chino (91710) ***(P-8748)***

Fender Musical Instrs Corp .... D 909 773-1200
1295 E Central Ave San Bernardino (92408) ***(P-23369)***

Fender Musical Instrs Corp .... A 480 596-9690
301 Cessna Cir Corona (92880) ***(P-23370)***

Fenico Precision Castings Inc .... D 562 634-5000
7805 Madison St Paramount (90723) ***(P-11777)***

Fenini, Baldwin Park *Also called Fellyr International Inc* ***(P-3418)***

Fenix International Inc .... B 415 754-9222
30 Cleveland St San Francisco (94103) ***(P-17093)***

Feral Productions LLC .... E 510 791-5392
1935 N Macarthur Dr Tracy (95376) ***(P-16495)***

Ferco Color Inc .... E 909 548-2092
5498 Vine St Chino (91710) ***(P-7837)***

Ferco Plastic Products, Chino *Also called Ferco Color Inc* ***(P-7837)***

Ferminics Opto-Technology Corp .... F 805 582-0155
4555 Runway St Simi Valley (93063) ***(P-17947)***

Fernqvist Labeling Solutions, Mountain View *Also called Fernqvist Retail Systems Inc* ***(P-7200)***

Fernqvist Retail Systems Inc (HQ) .... F 650 428-0330
2544 Leghorn St Mountain View (94043) ***(P-7200)***

Ferrar-Crano Vnyrds Winery LLC (PA) .... C 707 433-6700
8761 Dry Creek Rd Healdsburg (95448) ***(P-1759)***

Ferrari Intrcnnect Sltions Inc .... F 951 684-8034
4385 E Lowell St Ste A Ontario (91761) ***(P-19543)***

Ferro Corporation .... F 442 224-6100
1395 Aspen Way Vista (92081) ***(P-7777)***

Ferrosaur Inc .... F 530 246-7843
4821 Mountain Lakes Blvd Redding (96003) ***(P-12161)***

Ferrotec (usa) Corporation .... E 925 371-4170
4569 Las Positas Rd Ste C Livermore (94551) ***(P-9528)***

Ferrotec Temescal, Livermore *Also called Ferrotec (usa) Corporation* ***(P-9528)***

Fetish Group Inc (PA) .... E 323 587-7873
1013 S Los Angeles St # 700 Los Angeles (90015) ***(P-3152)***

Fetters U.S.A., San Francisco *Also called Mr S Leather* ***(P-3620)***

Fetzer Production Facility, Paso Robles *Also called Fetzer Vineyards* ***(P-1761)***

Fetzer Vineyards (HQ) .... C 707 744-1250
12901 Old River Rd Hopland (95449) ***(P-1760)***

Fetzer Vineyards .... F 805 467-0192
8998 N River Rd Paso Robles (93446) ***(P-1761)***

Fhi Brands, Norwalk *Also called AG Global Products LLC* ***(P-17384)***

Fl, El Segundo *Also called Federal Industries Inc* ***(P-13765)***

Fibco Composites Inc .... F 714 269-1118
1220 Hearthside Ct Fullerton (92831) ***(P-21293)***

Fiber Care Baths Inc .... B 760 246-0019
9832 Yucca Rd Ste A Adelanto (92301) ***(P-9901)***

Fiber Network Engineering Co (PA) .... F 650 726-2639
2085 Touraine Ln Half Moon Bay (94019) ***(P-17948)***

Fiber Optic Cable Shop, Richmond *Also called Support Systems Intl Corp* ***(P-19739)***

Fiber Systems Inc .... E 831 430-0700
380 Encinal St Ste 150 Santa Cruz (95060) ***(P-17949)***

Fiberglass Fabricators, Orange *Also called Lido Industries Inc* ***(P-10191)***

Fiberlite Centrifuge LLC .... D 408 492-1109
422 Aldo Ave Santa Clara (95054) ***(P-22449)***

Fiberoptic Systems Inc .... E 805 579-6600
60 Moreland Rd Ste A Simi Valley (93065) ***(P-11661)***

Fibersense & Signals Inc .... F 408 941-1900
4423 Fortran Ct Ste 111 San Jose (95134) ***(P-17950)***

Fibreform Electronics Inc .... E 714 898-9641
5341 Argosy Ave Huntington Beach (92649) ***(P-16496)***

Fibreform Precision Machining, Huntington Beach *Also called Fibreform Electronics Inc* ***(P-16496)***

Fibrogen Inc (PA) .... C 415 978-1200
409 Illinois St San Francisco (94158) ***(P-8159)***

Ficcare, City of Industry *Also called Visionmax Inc* ***(P-3526)***

Field Applied Cmposite Systems, Monrovia *Also called Air Logistics Corporation* ***(P-9931)***

Field Foundation .... E 562 921-3567
15306 Carmenita Rd Santa Fe Springs (90670) ***(P-212)***

Field Manufacturing Corp (PA) .... D 310 781-9292
1751 Torrance Blvd Ste H Torrance (90501) ***(P-10099)***

Field Stone Winery & Vineyard .... F 707 433-7266
10075 Highway 128 Healdsburg (95448) ***(P-1762)***

Field Time Target Training LLC .... F 714 677-2841
8230 Electric Ave Stanton (90680) ***(P-23560)***

Field To Family Natural Foods .... F 707 765-6756
224 Weller St Ste C Petaluma (94952) ***(P-538)***

Fieldcentrix Inc .... E 949 784-5000
8 Hughes Irvine (92618) ***(P-24646)***

Fieldpiece Instruments Inc .... F 714 634-1844
1636 W Collins Ave Orange (92867) ***(P-21757)***

Fierra Design CL Manufactures, Los Angeles *Also called Fierra Design Inc* ***(P-3153)***

Fierra Design Inc .... E 213 622-2426
1359 Channing St Los Angeles (90021) ***(P-3153)***

Fierrito Metal Stamping .... E 818 362-6136
12358 San Fernando Rd Sylmar (91342) ***(P-16497)***

Fierritos Inc .... E 818 362-6136
12358 San Fernando Rd Sylmar (91342) ***(P-16498)***

Fiesta Concession, Vernon *Also called Mahar Manufacturing Corp* ***(P-23398)***

Fiesta Fashion Co Inc (PA) .... F 213 748-5775
1100 Wall St Ste 106 Los Angeles (90015) ***(P-3235)***

Fiesta Mexican Foods Inc .... E 760 344-3580
979 G St Brawley (92227) ***(P-1248)***

Fife Metal Fabricating Inc .... F 530 243-4696
4191 Eastside Rd Redding (96001) ***(P-12162)***

Figueroa Machining .... F 805 238-7704
1535 Nacimiento Lake Dr Paso Robles (93446) ***(P-16499)***

Figure 8, Torrance *Also called Nothing To Wear Inc* ***(P-3264)***

Filbur Manufacturing LLC .... E 714 228-6000
20 Centerpointe Dr # 110 La Palma (90623) ***(P-15319)***

Filbur Pool & Spa Filtration, La Palma *Also called Filbur Manufacturing LLC* ***(P-15319)***

Filemaker Inc (HQ) .... C 408 987-7000
5201 Patrick Henry Dr Santa Clara (95054) ***(P-24647)***

Filet Menu Inc .... E 310 202-8000
1830 S La Cienega Blvd Los Angeles (90035) ***(P-7201)***

Filetrail Inc .... E 408 289-1300
1990 The Alameda San Jose (95126) ***(P-24648)***

Filipino Channel, Stockton *Also called Aguda Wilson Ramos* ***(P-18018)***

Employee Codes: A=Over 500 employees, B=251-500
C=101-250, D=51-100, E=20-50, F=10-19

2019 California
Manfacturers Register

© Mergent Inc. 1-800-342-5647
1139

Filmagic Inc.......F.......626 339-0120
120 N Fairway Ln West Covina (91791) *(P-8160)*
Filmetrics Inc (PA).......E.......858 573-9300
10655 Roselle St Ste 200 San Diego (92121) *(P-21959)*
Filtec, Torrance *Also called Industrial Dynamics Co Ltd (P-14969)*
Filter Concepts Incorporated.......E.......714 545-7003
22895 Eastpark Dr Yorba Linda (92887) *(P-19334)*
Filter Pump Industries, Sun Valley *Also called Penguin Pumps Incorporated (P-15087)*
Filthy Grill Inc.......F.......818 282-2017
70 N Dewey Ave Newbury Park (91320) *(P-17369)*
Filtration Development Co LLC.......F.......415 884-0555
3920 Sandstone Dr El Dorado Hills (95762) *(P-19335)*
Filtration Group LLC.......D.......707 525-8633
498 Aviation Blvd Santa Rosa (95403) *(P-15157)*
Filtration Technology Group, Cerritos *Also called Ftg Inc (P-20342)*
Filtronics Inc.......F.......714 630-5040
3726 E Miraloma Ave Anaheim (92806) *(P-16042)*
Final Data Inc.......E.......818 835-9560
5950 Canoga Ave Ste 220 Woodland Hills (91367) *(P-6484)*
Final Finish Inc.......E.......562 777-7774
10910 Norwalk Blvd Santa Fe Springs (90670) *(P-2902)*
Finance Department, Hercules *Also called Bio-RAD Laboratories Inc (P-21915)*
Finart Inc (PA).......F.......714 957-1757
201 W Dyer Rd Ste C Santa Ana (92707) *(P-12064)*
Finddoctr Inc.......F.......657 888-2629
9550 Bolsa Ave Ste 213 Westminster (92683) *(P-6485)*
Findly, San Francisco *Also called First Advantage Talent Managem (P-24651)*
Fine Electronic Assembly Inc.......E.......858 573-0887
4887 Mercury St San Diego (92111) *(P-18479)*
Fine Ptch Elctrnic Assmbly LLC.......E.......626 337-2800
5106 Azusa Canyon Rd Irwindale (91706) *(P-18480)*
Fine Quality Metal Finshg Inc.......F.......562 983-7425
1640 Daisy Ave Long Beach (90813) *(P-13410)*
Fineline Carpentry Inc.......E.......650 592-2442
1297 Old County Rd Belmont (94002) *(P-4300)*
Fineline Circuits & Technology.......E.......714 529-2942
594 Apollo St Ste A Brea (92821) *(P-18481)*
Fineline Industries Inc (PA).......C.......209 384-0255
2047 Grogan Ave Merced (95341) *(P-21038)*
Fineline Woodworking Inc.......E.......714 540-5468
1139 Baker St Costa Mesa (92626) *(P-4155)*
Finelite Inc.......C.......510 441-1100
30500 Whipple Rd Union City (94587) *(P-17608)*
Finesse Apparel Inc (PA).......E.......213 747-7077
815 Fairview Ave Unit 101 South Pasadena (91030) *(P-3419)*
Finest Food Inc.......F.......858 699-4746
6491 Weathers Pl Ste A San Diego (92121) *(P-2518)*
Finis Inc (PA).......E.......925 454-0111
7085 Las Positas Rd Ste E Livermore (94551) *(P-23561)*
Finis USA, Livermore *Also called Finis Inc (P-23561)*
Finisar Corporation (PA).......E.......408 548-1000
1389 Moffett Park Dr Sunnyvale (94089) *(P-17951)*
Finisar Corporation.......F.......408 548-1000
41762 Christy St Fremont (94538) *(P-18842)*
Finish Renu Car Care, Corona *Also called Renu Chem Inc (P-8674)*
Finishing Touch Moulding Inc.......D.......760 444-1019
6190 Corte Del Cedro Carlsbad (92011) *(P-4301)*
Finn Industries Inc.......E.......909 930-1500
2000 Chota Rd La Habra Heights (90631) *(P-5348)*
Finntech Inc.......F.......310 323-0790
1930 W 169th St Gardena (90247) *(P-16500)*
Fintech Platform, Los Gatos *Also called Healthywealthyhack Inc (P-24724)*
Fiola Development, Huntington Beach *Also called Fiolas Development LLC (P-10925)*
Fiolas Development LLC.......F.......714 893-7559
5362 Bolsa Ave Ste H Huntington Beach (92649) *(P-10925)*
Fiorano Software Inc.......D.......650 326-1136
230 California Ave # 103 Palo Alto (94306) *(P-24649)*
Fiore Di Pasta Inc.......E.......559 457-0431
4776 E Jensen Ave Fresno (93725) *(P-2519)*
Fiore Stone Inc.......E.......909 424-0221
19930 Jolora Ave Corona (92881) *(P-10926)*
Fiorellos Italian Ice Cream.......F.......415 459-8004
3100 Kerner Blvd Ste Hh San Rafael (94901) *(P-670)*
Firan Tech Group USA Corp (HQ).......F.......818 407-4024
20750 Marilla St Chatsworth (91311) *(P-21294)*
Fire & Earth Ceramics.......F.......303 442-0245
418 Santander Dr San Ramon (94583) *(P-10782)*
Fire & Safety Electronics Inc.......E.......714 850-1320
3160 Pullman St Costa Mesa (92626) *(P-17270)*
Fire and Light Originals LP.......F.......707 825-7500
100 Ericson Ct Ste 100 # 100 Arcata (95521) *(P-10697)*
Fire Mountain Beverage.......E.......661 362-0716
27240 Turnberry Ln # 200 Valencia (91355) *(P-2134)*
Fire Windows and Doors, Redlands *Also called Coast To Coast Mfg LLC (P-10029)*
Fireblast Global Inc.......E.......951 277-8319
545 Monica Cir Corona (92880) *(P-15320)*
Firebrand Media LLC.......E.......949 715-4100
580 Broadway St Ste 301 Laguna Beach (92651) *(P-6815)*
Fireeye Inc (PA).......C.......408 321-6300
601 Mccarthy Blvd Milpitas (95035) *(P-24650)*
Firefighter Gas Safety Pdts, Santa Ana *Also called Little Firefighter Corporation (P-13723)*
Firelight Glass, San Leandro *Also called Vitrico Corp (P-10669)*
Firequick Products Inc.......F.......760 371-4279
1137 Red Rock Inyokern Rd Inyokern (93527) *(P-15321)*
Firestone Vineyard LP.......D.......805 688-3940
5000 Zaca Station Rd Los Olivos (93441) *(P-1763)*
Firestone Walker Inc (PA).......C.......805 225-5911
1400 Ramada Dr Paso Robles (93446) *(P-1591)*
Firestone Walker Brewing Co, Penn Valley *Also called Firestone Walker LLC (P-1592)*
Firestone Walker Brewing Co, Paso Robles *Also called Firestone Walker Inc (P-1591)*
Firestone Walker LLC.......D.......805 225-5911
10130 Commercial Ave Penn Valley (95946) *(P-1592)*
Firetide Inc (HQ).......D.......408 399-7771
2105 S Bascom Ave Ste 220 Campbell (95008) *(P-15742)*
Firmenich.......C.......714 535-2871
424 S Atchison St Anaheim (92805) *(P-9006)*
First Advantage Talent Managem.......E.......415 446-3930
98 Battery St Ste 400 San Francisco (94111) *(P-24651)*
First American Building Svcs.......F.......415 299-7597
6 Commodore Dr Unit 530 Emeryville (94608) *(P-21512)*
First Choice International.......F.......310 537-1500
1201 W Artesia Blvd Compton (90220) *(P-22450)*
First Church Christ, Scientist, Santa Barbara *Also called Christian Science Church (P-5803)*
First Circuit Inc.......F.......760 560-0530
7701 Garboso Pl Carlsbad (92009) *(P-18482)*
First Class Foods, Hawthorne *Also called Firstclass Foods - Trojan Inc (P-434)*
First Class Packaging Inc.......E.......619 579-7166
280 Cypress Ln Ste D El Cajon (92020) *(P-5349)*
First Data Bank, South San Francisco *Also called First Databank Inc (P-6486)*
First Databank Inc (HQ).......D.......800 633-3453
701 Gateway Blvd Ste 600 South San Francisco (94080) *(P-6486)*
First Energy Services Inc.......E.......661 387-1972
1031 Carrier Parkway Ave Bakersfield (93308) *(P-213)*
First Finish Inc.......E.......310 631-6717
11126 Wright Rd Lynwood (90262) *(P-2739)*
First Gold Corp.......F.......530 677-5974
3108 Ponte Morino Dr # 210 Cameron Park (95682) *(P-3)*
First Impressions Printing.......E.......510 784-0811
25030 Viking St Hayward (94545) *(P-6816)*
First Lithium LLC.......F.......310 489-6266
17244 S Main St Carson (90749) *(P-19808)*
First Responder Fire.......F.......562 842-6602
19146 Stare St Northridge (91324) *(P-15322)*
First Solar Inc.......F.......415 935-2500
135 Main St Fl 6 San Francisco (94105) *(P-18843)*
First Solar Electric, San Francisco *Also called First Solar Inc (P-18843)*
First Source Lighting, Auburn *Also called Gara Inc (P-17611)*
First Tactical LLC.......A.......855 665-3410
4335 N Star Way Modesto (95356) *(P-3029)*
Firstar International Group.......F.......918 845-2402
160 W Fthill Pkwy Ste 105 Corona (92882) *(P-14223)*
Firstclass Foods - Trojan Inc.......C.......310 676-2500
12500 Inglewood Ave Hawthorne (90250) *(P-434)*
Firth Rixson Inc.......E.......909 483-2200
11711 Arrow Rte Rancho Cucamonga (91730) *(P-13099)*
Fischer Cstm Cmmunications Inc (PA).......E.......310 303-3300
20603 Earl St Torrance (90503) *(P-21758)*
Fischer Mold Incorporated.......D.......951 279-1140
393 Meyer Cir Corona (92879) *(P-10100)*
Fischler Investments Inc (HQ).......F.......951 479-4682
2026 Cecilia Cir Corona (92881) *(P-2260)*
Fish Bowl, Vernon *Also called Second Generation Inc (P-17855)*
Fish House Foods Inc.......B.......760 597-1270
1263 Linda Vista Dr San Marcos (92078) *(P-2312)*
Fish On Rice LLC.......F.......619 696-6262
3250 Grey Hawk Ct Carlsbad (92010) *(P-1593)*
Fisher & Paykel, Costa Mesa *Also called Dynamic Cooking Systems Inc (P-16035)*
Fisher & Paykel Appliances Inc (HQ).......C.......949 790-8900
695 Town Center Dr # 180 Costa Mesa (92626) *(P-17414)*
Fisher Graphic Inds A Cal Corp.......B.......209 577-0181
1137 Graphics Dr Modesto (95351) *(P-14808)*
Fisher Manufacturing Co Inc (PA).......E.......559 685-5200
1900 S O St Tulare (93274) *(P-12034)*
Fisher Nut Company.......F.......209 527-0108
137 N Hart Rd Modesto (95358) *(P-2520)*
Fisher Printing Inc (PA).......C.......714 998-9200
2257 N Pacific St Orange (92865) *(P-6817)*
Fisher Printing & Stamping Co.......F.......323 933-9193
5038 Venice Blvd Los Angeles (90019) *(P-7317)*
Fisher Sand & Gravel Co.......F.......602 619-0325
24560 Cooperstown Rd Oakdale (95361) *(P-357)*
Fishermans Pride Prcessors Inc.......B.......323 232-1980
4510 S Alameda St Vernon (90058) *(P-2313)*
Fisker Auto & Tech Group LLC.......C.......714 723-3247
3080 Airway Ave Costa Mesa (92626) *(P-20141)*
Fit-Line Inc.......E.......714 549-9091
2901 Tech Ctr Santa Ana (92705) *(P-10101)*
Fitbit Inc (PA).......B.......415 513-1000
199 Fremont St Fl 14 San Francisco (94105) *(P-22200)*
Fitness Warehouse LLC (PA).......E.......858 578-7676
9990 Alesmith Ct Ste 130 San Diego (92126) *(P-23562)*
Fitpro USA LLC.......F.......877 645-5776
1911 2nd St Livermore (94550) *(P-7940)*
Fittings That Fit Inc.......F.......909 248-2808
4628 Mission Blvd Montclair (91763) *(P-13829)*
Fitucci LLC.......F.......818 785-3841
14753 Oxnard St Van Nuys (91411) *(P-4302)*
Fitzgerald Designers & Mfrs, San Francisco *Also called J F Fitzgerald Company Inc (P-4784)*
Fitzgerald Formliners, Santa Ana *Also called Prime Forming & Cnstr Sups (P-10983)*
Five Corner Conservation Inc.......F.......818 792-1805
13654 Victory Blvd # 327 Van Nuys (91401) *(P-16501)*
Five Flavors Herbs.......F.......510 923-0178
344 40th St Oakland (94609) *(P-616)*
Five Keys Inc.......E.......209 358-7971
150 E Broadway Ave Atwater (95301) *(P-3154)*
Five Prime Therapeutics Inc.......E.......415 365-5600
111 Oyster Point Blvd South San Francisco (94080) *(P-8161)*
Five Prime Therapeutics Inc.......C.......415 365-5600
2 Corporate Dr South San Francisco (94080) *(P-8162)*

Five Star Food Containers Inc..........D.......626 437-6219
250 Eastgate Rd Barstow (92311) ***(P-9842)***
Five Star Gourmet Foods Inc..........A.......909 390-0032
3880 Ebony St Ontario (91761) ***(P-994)***
Five Star Juice, Torrance *Also called La Ejuice LLC* ***(P-2714)***
Five Star Lumber Company LLC..........E.......831 422-4493
655 Brunken Ave Salinas (93901) ***(P-4470)***
Five Star Lumber Company LLC (PA)..........E.......510 795-7204
6899 Smith Ave Newark (94560) ***(P-4471)***
Five Star Media Inc..........F.......415 298-2510
155 12th St San Francisco (94103) ***(P-6162)***
Five Star Pallet Co, Newark *Also called Five Star Lumber Company LLC* ***(P-4471)***
Five-Star Graphics Inc..........F.......310 325-6881
2628 Woodbury Dr Torrance (90503) ***(P-6818)***
Five9 Inc (PA)..........C.......925 201-2000
4000 Executive Pkwy # 400 San Ramon (94583) ***(P-24652)***
Fixture Design & Mfg Co..........E.......714 776-3104
4848 Lakeview Ave Ste E Yorba Linda (92886) ***(P-5232)***
Fixtures By Design LLC..........F.......714 572-5406
2951 Saturn St Ste Unitb Brea (92821) ***(P-5062)***
Fixtures Unlimited, Gardena *Also called Tony Glazing Specialties Co* ***(P-5113)***
Fizzy Color LLC..........F.......408 623-6705
3561 Homestead Rd Ste 231 Santa Clara (95051) ***(P-6819)***
Fja Industries Inc..........F.......408 727-0100
1230 Coleman Ave Santa Clara (95050) ***(P-15323)***
Flagcrafters Inc..........E.......619 585-1044
1120 Bay Blvd Ste E Chula Vista (91911) ***(P-3947)***
Flame & Wax Inc..........E.......949 752-4000
2900 Mccabe Way Irvine (92614) ***(P-24095)***
Flame Gard Inc..........D.......323 888-8707
6825 E Washington Blvd Los Angeles (90040) ***(P-15324)***
Flame Out Inc..........E.......323 221-0000
2623 N San Fernando Rd Los Angeles (90065) ***(P-24096)***
Flame-Spray Inc..........E.......619 283-2007
4674 Alvarado Canyon Rd San Diego (92120) ***(P-13588)***
Flamemaster Corporation..........E.......818 890-1401
13576 Desmond St Pacoima (91331) ***(P-9251)***
Flamestower Inc..........D.......415 699-8650
127 Kissling St San Francisco (94103) ***(P-17196)***
Flamous Brands Inc..........F.......626 551-3201
1801 Highland Ave Ste C Duarte (91010) ***(P-2381)***
Flanagan-Gorham Inc (PA)..........F.......818 279-2473
2029 Verdugo Blvd Ste 311 Montrose (91020) ***(P-435)***
Flannery Inc (PA)..........F.......818 837-7585
300 Parkside Dr San Fernando (91340) ***(P-11217)***
Flannigans Merchandising Inc..........E.......818 785-7428
15803 Stagg St Van Nuys (91406) ***(P-7318)***
Flap Happy Inc..........E.......310 453-3527
2857 E 11th St Los Angeles (90023) ***(P-3592)***
Flare Group..........E.......714 850-2080
1571 Macarthur Blvd Costa Mesa (92626) ***(P-20813)***
Flarelink, Santa Ana *Also called Fit-Line Inc* ***(P-10101)***
Flash Anatomy, Orange *Also called Bryan Edwards Publishing Co* ***(P-6319)***
Flash Back USA..........F.......805 434-0321
1535 Templeton Rd Templeton (93465) ***(P-8552)***
Flash Code Solutions LLC..........F.......800 633-7467
4727 Wilshire Blvd # 302 Los Angeles (90010) ***(P-24653)***
Flashco Manufacturing Inc (PA)..........E.......707 824-4448
150 Todd Rd Ste 400 Santa Rosa (95407) ***(P-11628)***
Flathers Precision Inc..........E.......714 966-8505
1311 E Saint Gertrude Pl D Santa Ana (92705) ***(P-16502)***
Flaunt Magazine..........F.......323 836-1044
1422 N Highland Ave Los Angeles (90028) ***(P-6163)***
Flavor House Inc..........E.......760 246-9131
16378 Koala Rd Adelanto (92301) ***(P-2261)***
Flavorchem Corporation..........E.......949 369-7900
271 Calle Pintoresco San Clemente (92672) ***(P-2262)***
Flavors Division, Los Angeles *Also called American Fruits & Flavors LLC* ***(P-2241)***
Fleenor Company Inc (PA)..........E.......800 433-2531
2225 Harbor Bay Pkwy Alameda (94502) ***(P-5712)***
Fleenor Company Inc..........E.......209 932-0329
4201 E Fremont St Stockton (95215) ***(P-5282)***
Fleenor Paper Company, Alameda *Also called Fleenor Company Inc* ***(P-5712)***
Fleet Management Solutions Inc..........E.......800 500-6009
7391 Lincoln Way Garden Grove (92841) ***(P-18109)***
Fleetwood Continental Inc..........D.......310 609-1477
19451 S Susana Rd Compton (90221) ***(P-11757)***
Fleetwood Enterprises Inc (HQ)..........C.......951 354-3000
1351 Pomona Rd Ste 230 Corona (92882) ***(P-21228)***
Fleetwood Enterprises Inc..........B.......951 750-1971
351 Corporate Terrace Cir Corona (92879) ***(P-4554)***
Fleetwood Homes, Riverside *Also called Fleetwood Motor Homes-Califinc* ***(P-20523)***
Fleetwood Homes, Riverside *Also called Cavco Industries Inc* ***(P-4548)***
Fleetwood Homes Arizona Inc..........B.......623 939-2600
7007 Jurupa Ave Riverside (92504) ***(P-4555)***
Fleetwood Homes Arizona Inc (HQ)..........B.......951 351-3000
3125 Myers St Riverside (92503) ***(P-4556)***
Fleetwood Homes California Inc (HQ)..........E.......951 351-2494
7007 Jurupa Ave Riverside (92504) ***(P-4557)***
Fleetwood Homes of Florida (HQ)..........F.......909 261-4274
3125 Myers St Riverside (92503) ***(P-4558)***
Fleetwood Homes of Idaho Inc..........C.......951 354-3000
3125 Myers St Riverside (92503) ***(P-4559)***
Fleetwood Homes of Kentucky (HQ)..........F.......800 688-1745
1351 Pomona Rd Ste 230 Corona (92882) ***(P-4560)***
Fleetwood Homes of Virginia..........C.......951 351-3500
3125 Myers St Riverside (92503) ***(P-4561)***
Fleetwood Motor Homes-Califinc (HQ)..........E.......951 354-3000
3125 Myers St Riverside (92503) ***(P-20523)***
Fleetwood Travel Trlrs Ind Inc (HQ)..........F.......951 354-3000
3125 Myers St Riverside (92503) ***(P-21201)***
Fleis Chmanns Vinegar, Cerritos *Also called AB Mauri Food Inc* ***(P-2446)***
Fleming Metal Fabricators..........E.......323 723-8203
2810 Tanager Ave Commerce (90040) ***(P-20205)***
Fletcher Bldg Holdings USA Inc (HQ)..........D.......951 272-8180
1230 Railroad St Corona (92882) ***(P-12587)***
Fletcher Coating Co..........E.......714 637-4763
426 W Fletcher Ave Orange (92865) ***(P-13589)***
Fleurish Clothing Company, Los Angeles *Also called Evy of California Inc* ***(P-3577)***
Flex Interconnect Tech Inc..........E.......408 956-8204
1603 Watson Ct Milpitas (95035) ***(P-19544)***
Flex Products Inc..........C.......707 525-6866
1402 Mariner Way Santa Rosa (95407) ***(P-22076)***
Flex-Mate Inc..........F.......562 426-7169
1855 E 29th St Ste E Signal Hill (90755) ***(P-11894)***
Flexaust Company Inc (HQ)..........E.......619 232-8429
1200 Prospect St Ste 325 La Jolla (92037) ***(P-16503)***
Flexco Inc..........E.......562 927-2525
6855 Suva St Bell Gardens (90201) ***(P-20814)***
Flexcon Company Inc..........E.......909 465-0408
12840 Reservoir St Chino (91710) ***(P-9708)***
Flexcube Inc..........F.......707 738-4001
1861 Spring Mountain Rd Saint Helena (94574) ***(P-7690)***
Flexfirm Holdings LLC..........F.......323 283-1173
2300 Chico Ave El Monte (91733) ***(P-2959)***
Flexi-Liner, Chino *Also called Liner Technologies Inc* ***(P-10192)***
Flexible Manufacturing LLC..........D.......714 259-7996
1719 S Grand Ave Santa Ana (92705) ***(P-19391)***
Flexible Metal Inc (HQ)..........D.......678 280-0127
1685 Brandywine Ave Chula Vista (91911) ***(P-13888)***
Flexible Video Systems, Marina Del Rey *Also called Sewer Rodding Equipment Co* ***(P-16106)***
Flexline Inc..........E.......562 921-4141
15405 Cornet St Santa Fe Springs (90670) ***(P-7643)***
Flexo-Technologies Inc..........E.......626 444-2595
145 Flowerfield Ln La Habra Heights (90631) ***(P-9193)***
Flexstar Technology, Inc, San Jose *Also called Neosem Technology Inc* ***(P-21815)***
Flexsystems Usa Inc..........E.......619 401-1858
1308 N Magnolia Ave Ste J El Cajon (92020) ***(P-3948)***
Flextronics America LLC (HQ)..........C.......408 576-7000
6201 America Center Dr San Jose (95002) ***(P-18483)***
Flextronics Corporation (HQ)..........B.......803 936-5200
6201 America Center Dr Alviso (95002) ***(P-19545)***
Flextronics International Usa..........A.......408 576-7000
260 S Milpitas Blvd # 15 Milpitas (95035) ***(P-18484)***
Flextronics Intl PA Inc..........F.......408 577-2489
677 Gibraltar Dr Milpitas (95035) ***(P-12588)***
Flextronics Intl USA Inc..........F.......510 814-7000
927 Gibraltar Dr Milpitas (95035) ***(P-15743)***
Flextronics Intl USA Inc..........F.......408 678-3268
1177 Gibraltar Dr Bldg 9 Milpitas (95035) ***(P-18485)***
Flextronics Intl USA Inc..........B.......408 577-2262
925 Lightpost Way Morgan Hill (95037) ***(P-18486)***
Flextronics Intl USA Inc (HQ)..........A.......408 576-7000
6201 America Center Dr San Jose (95002) ***(P-18487)***
Flextronics Semiconductor (HQ)..........E.......408 576-7000
2241 Lundy Ave Bldg 2 San Jose (95131) ***(P-18844)***
Flexy Foam, Chino *Also called Inter Packing Inc* ***(P-9866)***
Flight Environments Inc..........E.......805 226-2912
570 Linne Rd Ste 100 Paso Robles (93446) ***(P-20815)***
Flight Metals LLC..........F.......800 838-9047
879 W 190th St Ste 400 Gardena (90248) ***(P-21295)***
Flight Microwave Corporation..........E.......310 607-9819
410 S Douglas St El Segundo (90245) ***(P-14955)***
Flight Standards District Off, El Segundo *Also called Federal Aviation ADM* ***(P-20812)***
Flint Group US LLC..........E.......626 369-6900
13055 Temple Ave La Puente (91746) ***(P-9194)***
Flint Group US LLC..........F.......562 903-7976
14930 Marquardt Ave Santa Fe Springs (90670) ***(P-9195)***
Flint Ink North America Div, La Puente *Also called Flint Group US LLC* ***(P-9194)***
Flipagram Inc..........F.......415 827-8373
916 Silver Spur Rd # 310 Rllng HLS Est (90274) ***(P-24654)***
Flipcause Inc..........F.......800 523-1950
283 4th St Ste 101 Oakland (94607) ***(P-24655)***
Flir Elctr-Ptcal Comp Bus Unit, Ventura *Also called Flir Eoc LLC* ***(P-21960)***
Flir Eoc LLC..........E.......805 642-4645
2223 Eastman Ave Ste B Ventura (93003) ***(P-21960)***
Flir Motion Ctrl Systems Inc..........E.......650 692-3900
6769 Hollister Ave Goleta (93117) ***(P-14956)***
Flir Systems Inc..........E.......805 964-9797
6769 Hollister Ave # 100 Goleta (93117) ***(P-21296)***
Flo Stor Engineering Inc (PA)..........E.......510 887-7179
21371 Cabot Blvd Hayward (94545) ***(P-14274)***
Flo TV Incorporated..........F.......858 651-1645
5775 Morehouse Dr San Diego (92121) ***(P-18110)***
Flo-Kem, Compton *Also called LMC Enterprises* ***(P-8652)***
Flo-Mac Inc..........E.......323 583-8751
1846 E 60th St Los Angeles (90001) ***(P-13889)***
Flolight, Campbell *Also called Prompter People Inc* ***(P-18225)***
Flood Ctrl Wtr Cnservation Dst, NAPA *Also called County of NAPA* ***(P-21566)***
Flood Ranch Company..........F.......805 937-3616
6600 Foxen Canyon Rd Santa Maria (93454) ***(P-1764)***
Flor De California..........E.......909 673-1968
1930 S Bon View Ave # 18 Ontario (91761) ***(P-671)***
Flora Springs Wine Company..........F.......707 963-5711
1978 Zinfandel Ln Saint Helena (94574) ***(P-1765)***
Floracraft Corporation..........F.......909 620-4410
1315 E 3rd St Pomona (91766) ***(P-9843)***

Employee Codes: A=Over 500 employees, B=251-500
C=101-250, D=51-100, E=20-50, F=10-19
2019 California
Manfacturers Register
© Mergent Inc. 1-800-342-5647
1141

Florence & New Itln Art Co Inc ....E....510 785-9674
27735 Industrial Blvd Hayward (94545) ***(P-10927)***
Florence International Company ....E....818 767-9650
11645 Pendleton St Sun Valley (91352) ***(P-13411)***
Florence Macaroni Company ....F....310 548-5942
1312 W 2nd St San Pedro (90732) ***(P-2426)***
Florentynas Fresh Pasta ....F....213 742-9374
1864 E 22nd St Vernon (90058) ***(P-2521)***
Florentynas Fresh Pasta Fctry, Vernon *Also called Florentynas Fresh Pasta* ***(P-2521)***
Flores Brothers Inc ....E....562 806-9128
7777 Scout Ave Bell (90201) ***(P-2522)***
Flores Design Fine Furn Inc ....E....323 585-3200
4618 Pacific Blvd Vernon (90058) ***(P-4774)***
Florestone Products Co (PA) ....E....559 661-4171
2851 Falcon Dr Madera (93637) ***(P-9902)***
Florian Industries Inc ....F....415 330-9000
151 Industrial Way Brisbane (94005) ***(P-12163)***
Floride Products LLC (PA) ....E....323 201-4363
2867 Vail Ave Commerce (90040) ***(P-7778)***
Flory Industries ....D....209 545-1167
4737 Toomes Rd Salida (95368) ***(P-14068)***
Flostor, Hayward *Also called Flo Stor Engineering Inc* ***(P-14274)***
Flotron Inc ....E....760 727-2700
2630 Progress St Vista (92081) ***(P-14516)***
Flour Fusion ....F....951 245-1166
133 N Main St Lake Elsinore (92530) ***(P-1249)***
Flow Control LLC ....F....949 608-3900
17942 Cowan Irvine (92614) ***(P-15062)***
Flow Dynamics Inc ....F....909 930-5522
1215 E Acacia St Ste 104 Ontario (91761) ***(P-11394)***
Flow N Control Inc ....F....818 330-7425
4452 Ocean View Blvd # 201 Montrose (91020) ***(P-13717)***
Flow Sports Inc (PA) ....E....949 361-5260
1011 Calle Sombra Ste 220 San Clemente (92673) ***(P-23563)***
Floway Pumps, Fresno *Also called Weir Floway Inc* ***(P-15098)***
Flowers Baking Co Modesto LLC ....D....209 857-4600
736 Mariposa Rd Modesto (95354) ***(P-1250)***
Flowers Vineyard & Winery LLC ....F....707 847-3661
28500 Seaview Rd Cazadero (95421) ***(P-1766)***
Flowline Inc ....E....562 598-3015
10500 Humbolt St Los Alamitos (90720) ***(P-22201)***
Flowline Liquid Intelligence, Los Alamitos *Also called Flowline Inc* ***(P-22201)***
Flowmaster Inc ....C....916 371-2345
1500 Overland Ct West Sacramento (95691) ***(P-20335)***
Flowmaster Inc (HQ) ....F....707 544-4761
100 Stony Point Rd # 125 Santa Rosa (95401) ***(P-20336)***
Flowmetrics Inc ....E....818 407-3420
9201 Independence Ave Chatsworth (91311) ***(P-21583)***
Flowserve Corporation ....B....323 584-1890
2300 E Vernon Ave Stop 76 Vernon (90058) ***(P-15063)***
Flowserve Corporation ....E....310 667-4220
1909 E Cashdan St Compton (90220) ***(P-15064)***
Flowserve Corporation ....F....707 745-4710
6077 Egret Ct Benicia (94510) ***(P-15065)***
Flowserve Corporation ....C....951 296-2464
27455 Tierra Alta Way C Temecula (92590) ***(P-15066)***
Floyd Dennee ....F....562 595-6024
2780 Walnut Ave Signal Hill (90755) ***(P-7319)***
Fluid Components Intl LLC (PA) ....C....760 744-6950
1755 La Costa Meadows Dr A San Marcos (92078) ***(P-21584)***
Fluid Industrial Mfg Inc ....E....408 782-9900
374 S Milpitas Blvd Milpitas (95035) ***(P-15958)***
Fluid Line Technology Corp ....E....818 998-8848
9362 Eton Ave Ste A Chatsworth (91311) ***(P-22451)***
Fluid Lubrication & Chem Co ....F....800 826-2415
18400 S Broadway Gardena (90248) ***(P-9435)***
Fluid Power Ctrl Systems Inc ....E....714 525-3727
1400 E Valencia Dr Fullerton (92831) ***(P-21585)***
Fluid Research Corporation ....E....714 258-2350
30281 Esperanza Rcho STA Marg (92688) ***(P-21586)***
Fluid Systems Division, Irvine *Also called Parker-Hannifin Corporation* ***(P-20904)***
Fluidix Inc (PA) ....F....760 935-2016
1422 Mammoth Tav Rd C6 Mammoth Lakes (93546) ***(P-15260)***
Fluidmaster Inc (PA) ....B....949 728-2000
30800 Rancho Viejo Rd San Juan Capistrano (92675) ***(P-12035)***
Fluorescent Supply Co Inc ....E....909 948-8878
9120 Center Ave Rancho Cucamonga (91730) ***(P-17609)***
Fluoresco Lighting & Sign, Pomona *Also called Everbrite West LLC* ***(P-23869)***
Flux Power Inc ....F....760 741-3589
2240 Auto Park Way Escondido (92029) ***(P-21759)***
Flux Power Holdings Inc (PA) ....E....877 505-3589
985 Poinsettia Ave Ste A Vista (92081) ***(P-19809)***
Fluxion Biosciences Inc (PA) ....E....650 241-4777
1600 Harbor Bay Pkwy # 150 Alameda (94502) ***(P-22452)***
Flydive Inc (PA) ....F....844 359-3483
3209 Midway Dr Unit 203 San Diego (92110) ***(P-23564)***
Flyer Defense LLC ....E....310 674-5030
151 W 135th St Los Angeles (90061) ***(P-20142)***
Flying Colors, Walnut *Also called Jakks Pacific Inc* ***(P-23434)***
Flying Machine Factory, Compton *Also called Fmf Racing* ***(P-21109)***
Flyleaf Windows Inc ....E....925 344-1181
11040 Bollinger Canyon Rd San Ramon (94582) ***(P-10698)***
Flynn and Enslow Inc (PA) ....E....415 863-5340
3401 Enterprise Ave Hayward (94545) ***(P-13830)***
Flynn Signs and Graphics Inc ....F....562 498-6655
1345 Coronado Ave Long Beach (90804) ***(P-23881)***
Flynn Signs and Letters, Long Beach *Also called Flynn Signs and Graphics Inc* ***(P-23881)***
Flynt, Larry Publishing, Beverly Hills *Also called L F P Inc* ***(P-6201)***

Flythissim Technologies Inc ....F....844 746-2846
3534 Empleo St Ste B San Luis Obispo (93401) ***(P-19967)***
Flywheel Software Inc ....E....650 260-1700
816 Hamilton St Redwood City (94063) ***(P-24656)***
FM Industries, San Diego *Also called FM Plastics* ***(P-10102)***
FM Industries Inc ....C....510 673-0192
331 E Warren Ave Fremont (94539) ***(P-16504)***
FM Industries Inc (HQ) ....C....510 668-1900
221 E Warren Ave Fremont (94539) ***(P-16505)***
FM Plastics ....E....619 661-5929
9950 Marconi Dr Ste 106 San Diego (92154) ***(P-10102)***
FM Systems Inc ....F....714 979-0537
3877 S Main St Santa Ana (92707) ***(P-18111)***
FMC Corporation ....D....530 753-6718
201 Cousteau Pl Davis (95618) ***(P-7662)***
FMC Technologies Inc ....F....714 872-5574
621 Burning Tree Rd Fullerton (92833) ***(P-14224)***
Fmf Racing ....C....310 631-4363
18033 S Santa Fe Ave Compton (90221) ***(P-21109)***
Fmh Aerospace Corp ....D....714 751-1000
17072 Daimler St Irvine (92614) ***(P-20816)***
FMI, Chula Vista *Also called Flexible Metal Inc* ***(P-13888)***
Fmk Labs Inc ....E....951 736-1212
1690 N Delilah St Corona (92879) ***(P-8749)***
FML Inc ....F....415 864-5084
2765 16th St San Francisco (94103) ***(P-23747)***
Fmw Machine Shop ....F....650 363-1313
980 Obrien Dr Menlo Park (94025) ***(P-16506)***
Fnc Medical Corporation ....E....805 644-7576
6000 Leland St Ventura (93003) ***(P-8750)***
Fntech ....F....714 429-1686
18107 Mount Washington St Fountain Valley (92708) ***(P-17694)***
Foam Concepts Inc ....E....714 693-1037
4729 E Wesley Dr Anaheim (92807) ***(P-9844)***
Foam Depot, La Puente *Also called Jona Global Trading Inc* ***(P-4866)***
Foam Depot, City of Industry *Also called American Foam Fiber & Sups Inc* ***(P-2987)***
Foam Fabricators Inc ....F....310 537-5760
1810 S Santa Fe Ave Compton (90221) ***(P-10103)***
Foam Fabricators Inc ....F....209 523-7002
301 9th St Ste B Modesto (95351) ***(P-9845)***
Foam Factory Inc ....E....310 603-9808
17515 S Santa Fe Ave Compton (90221) ***(P-9846)***
Foam Injection Plastics ....F....510 317-0218
2548 Grant Ave San Lorenzo (94580) ***(P-10104)***
Foam Molders and Specialties (PA) ....D....562 924-7757
11110 Business Cir Cerritos (90703) ***(P-9847)***
Foam Molders and Specialties ....E....562 924-7757
20004 State Rd Cerritos (90703) ***(P-9848)***
Foam Plastics & Rbr Pdts Corp ....F....714 779-0990
4765 E Bryson St Anaheim (92807) ***(P-9849)***
Foam Specialties, Cerritos *Also called Foam Molders and Specialties* ***(P-9847)***
Foam-Craft Inc ....C....714 459-9971
2441 Cypress Way Fullerton (92831) ***(P-9850)***
Foamation Inc ....F....818 837-6613
11852 Glenoaks Blvd San Fernando (91340) ***(P-9851)***
Foamex, San Leandro *Also called Fxi Inc* ***(P-9859)***
Foamex, Orange *Also called Fxi Inc* ***(P-9860)***
Foamex LP ....E....909 824-8981
1400 E Victoria Ave San Bernardino (92408) ***(P-9852)***
Foampro Manufacturing, Irvine *Also called Foampro Mfg Inc* ***(P-23791)***
Foampro Mfg Inc ....D....949 252-0112
1781 Langley Ave Irvine (92614) ***(P-23791)***
Foamtec LLC ....F....916 851-8621
4420 Commodity Way Ste A Shingle Springs (95682) ***(P-10928)***
Focus Enhancements Inc (HQ) ....E....650 230-2400
931 Benecia Ave Sunnyvale (94085) ***(P-18845)***
Focus Enhncments Systems Group, Sunnyvale *Also called Focus Enhancements Inc* ***(P-18845)***
Focus Industries Inc ....D....949 830-1350
25301 Commercentre Dr Lake Forest (92630) ***(P-17610)***
Focus Landscape, Lake Forest *Also called Focus Industries Inc* ***(P-17610)***
Focus Point of Sale ....F....949 336-7500
48 Waterworks Way Irvine (92618) ***(P-24657)***
Focus Pos, Irvine *Also called Focus Point of Sale* ***(P-24657)***
Foh Group Inc (PA) ....E....323 466-5151
6255 W Sunset Blvd # 2212 Los Angeles (90028) ***(P-3548)***
Foil Core Inc ....E....714 891-1695
5452 Mcfadden Ave Huntington Beach (92649) ***(P-24097)***
Foilflex Products Inc ....F....661 702-0775
24963 Avenue Tibbitts Valencia (91355) ***(P-7320)***
Fold-A-Goal, Los Angeles *Also called D Hauptman Co Inc* ***(P-23547)***
Foldimate Inc ....E....805 876-4418
879 White Pine Ct Oak Park (91377) ***(P-17389)***
Folding Cartons, Camarillo *Also called Crockett Graphics Inc* ***(P-5403)***
Folex Co ....F....619 670-5588
2505 Folex Way Spring Valley (91978) ***(P-8593)***
Foley Family Wines Inc (HQ) ....E....805 688-3940
2300 Airport Rd Paso Robles (93446) ***(P-1767)***
Foley Wine Group, Paso Robles *Also called Foley Family Wines Inc* ***(P-1767)***
Folgergraphics Inc ....E....510 293-2294
21093 Forbes Ave Hayward (94545) ***(P-7628)***
Folie A Deux Winery, Saint Helena *Also called Trinchero Family Estates Inc* ***(P-2028)***
Folkmanis Inc ....E....510 658-7677
1219 Park Ave Emeryville (94608) ***(P-24098)***
Follmer Development Inc ....E....805 498-4531
840 Tourmaline Dr Newbury Park (91320) ***(P-7691)***
Folsom Ready Mix Inc ....F....530 365-0191
19291 Latona Rd Anderson (96007) ***(P-11107)***

Folsom Ready Mix Inc (PA) E 916 851-8300
3401 Fitzgerald Rd Rancho Cordova (95742) *(P-10929)*
Folsom Telegraph, Folsom *Also called Brehm Communications Inc (P-5779)*
Fondo De Cultura Economica F 619 429-0455
2293 Verus St San Diego (92154) *(P-6340)*
Fong Brothers Printing Inc (PA) C 415 467-1050
320 Valley Dr Brisbane (94005) *(P-6820)*
Fong Fong Prtrs Lthgrphers Inc E 916 739-1313
3009 65th St Sacramento (95820) *(P-6821)*
Fongs Graphics & Printing Inc E 626 307-1898
7743 Garvey Ave Rosemead (91770) *(P-7202)*
Fono Unlimited Inc (PA) E 650 322-4664
99 Stanford Shopping Ctr Palo Alto (94304) *(P-672)*
Fontal Controls Inc F 818 833-1127
12725 Encinitas Ave Sylmar (91342) *(P-16507)*
Fontana Foundry Corporation E 909 822-6128
8306 Cherry Ave Fontana (92335) *(P-11741)*
Fontana International Inc F 909 854-4532
14978 Ceres Ave Ste B Fontana (92335) *(P-12932)*
Fontana Paper Mills Inc D 909 823-4100
13733 Valley Blvd Fontana (92335) *(P-9404)*
Food Equipment Mfg Co F 831 637-1624
175 Mitchell Rd Hollister (95023) *(P-14846)*
Food For Life Baking Co Inc (PA) D 951 273-3031
2991 Doherty St Corona (92879) *(P-1251)*
Food Machinery Sales Inc D 559 651-2339
7020 W Sunnyview Ave Visalia (93291) *(P-15206)*
Food Makers Bakery Eqp Inc E 626 358-1343
16019 Adelante St Irwindale (91702) *(P-14847)*
Food Pharma, Santa Fe Springs *Also called Food Technology and Design LLC (P-1423)*
Food Processing Equipment Co, Santa Fe Springs *Also called FPec Corporation A Cal Corp (P-14850)*
Food Technology and Design LLC E 562 944-7821
10012 Painter Ave Santa Fe Springs (90670) *(P-1423)*
Food To You Usa Inc F 559 549-0090
1700 Tribute Rd Ste 203 Sacramento (95815) *(P-24658)*
Food-O-Mex Corporation D 323 225-1737
2928 N Main St Los Angeles (90031) *(P-2523)*
Foodlink Online LLC E 408 395-7280
475 Alberto Way Ste 100 Los Gatos (95032) *(P-24659)*
Foodtools Inc (PA) E 805 962-8383
315 Laguna St Santa Barbara (93101) *(P-14848)*
Foot Imprint Inc E 626 991-4430
15373 Proctor Ave City of Industry (91745) *(P-14809)*
Foot In Motion Inc F 312 752-0990
2022 Broadway Ste A Santa Monica (90404) *(P-22731)*
Foot Locker Retail Inc F 510 797-5750
2059 Newpark Mall Fl 2 Newark (94560) *(P-10505)*
Foote Axle & Forge LLC E 323 268-4151
3954 Whiteside St Los Angeles (90063) *(P-20337)*
Foothill Instruments LLC F 818 952-5600
5011 Jarvis Ave La Canada (91011) *(P-22202)*
Foothill Pritnig & Graphics/ C (PA) F 209 736-4332
2245 Highway 49 Angels Camp (95222) *(P-6822)*
Foothill Ready Mix Inc E 530 527-2565
11415 State Highway 99w Red Bluff (96080) *(P-11108)*
FOOTHILL VOCATIONAL OPPORTUNIT, Pasadena *Also called Fvo Solutions Inc (P-13593)*
Foothills Advertiser, Exeter *Also called Foothills Sun-Gazette (P-5850)*
Foothills Sun-Gazette E 559 592-3171
120 N E St Exeter (93221) *(P-5850)*
Foppiano Vineyards, Healdsburg *Also called L Foppiano Wine Co (P-1846)*
For Rent, Roseville *Also called United Advg Publications Inc (P-6281)*
For Rent, Rancho Cucamonga *Also called United Advg Publications Inc (P-6282)*
Forager Project LLC D 855 729-5253
235 Montgomery St Ste 730 San Francisco (94104) *(P-949)*
Forbes Industries Div C 909 923-4559
1933 E Locust St Ontario (91761) *(P-5233)*
Force Fabrication Inc F 805 754-2235
2233 Statham Blvd Oxnard (93033) *(P-12589)*
Force Flow E 925 686-6700
2430 Stanwell Dr Ste 110 Concord (94520) *(P-14633)*
Ford Logging Inc E 707 840-9442
1225 Central Ave Ste 11 McKinleyville (95519) *(P-3987)*
Ford Motor Company C 949 453-9891
1 Glen Bell Way Irvine (92618) *(P-20143)*
Forderer Cornice Works F 415 431-4100
3364 Arden Rd Hayward (94545) *(P-12317)*
Fordon Grind Industries, Torrance *Also called Aeroliant Manufacturing Inc (P-20717)*
Foreal Spectrum Inc E 408 923-1675
2370 Qume Dr Ste A San Jose (95131) *(P-22077)*
Forecross Corporation (PA) F 415 543-1515
505 Montgomery St Fl 11 San Francisco (94111) *(P-24660)*
Forem Manufacturing Inc F 510 577-9500
844 66th Ave Oakland (94621) *(P-11545)*
Forem Metal, Oakland *Also called Forem Manufacturing Inc (P-11545)*
Foremost Enameling Co Inc F 323 321-3941
1608 W 139th St Gardena (90249) *(P-13590)*
Foremost Enmling Powdr Coating, Gardena *Also called Foremost Enameling Co Inc (P-13590)*
Foremost Interiors Inc E 916 635-1423
2318 Gold River Rd Rancho Cordova (95670) *(P-11251)*
Foremost Precision Pdts Inc F 714 961-0165
1940 Petra Ln Ste A Placentia (92870) *(P-16508)*
Foremost Spring & Mfg, Santa Fe Springs *Also called Foremost Spring Company Inc (P-13794)*
Foremost Spring Company Inc F 562 923-0791
11876 Burke St Santa Fe Springs (90670) *(P-13794)*
Foreseeson Custom Displays Inc (PA) E 714 300-0540
2210 E Winston Rd Anaheim (92806) *(P-15744)*
Foresight Sports LLC E 858 880-0179
9825 Businesspark Ave San Diego (92131) *(P-23565)*
Foresite Systems Limited (PA) F 408 855-8600
19925 Stevens Creek Blvd Cupertino (95014) *(P-24661)*
Forespar, Rcho STA Marg *Also called Light Composite Corporation (P-11970)*
Forest Investment Group Inc F 415 459-2330
83 Hamilton Dr Ste 100 Novato (94949) *(P-6823)*
Forest Laboratories LLC D 951 941-0024
12021 Dolly Way Moreno Valley (92555) *(P-8163)*
Forest River Inc E 909 873-3777
255 S Pepper Ave Rialto (92376) *(P-21202)*
Forester Communications Inc E 805 682-1300
2946 De La Vina St Santa Barbara (93105) *(P-6164)*
Forever Young, Oakland *Also called Supernutrition (P-8401)*
Forever Young E 650 355-5481
208 Palmetto Ave Pacifica (94044) *(P-2524)*
Forged Metals Inc C 909 350-9260
10685 Beech Ave Fontana (92337) *(P-13100)*
Forgerock Inc (PA) D 415 599-1100
201 Mission St Ste 2900 San Francisco (94105) *(P-24662)*
Forgerock US Inc (HQ) D 415 599-1100
201 Mission St San Francisco (94105) *(P-24663)*
Forgiato Inc D 818 771-9779
11915 Wicks St Sun Valley (91352) *(P-20338)*
Form & Fusion Mfg Inc F 916 638-8576
11251 Trade Center Dr Rancho Cordova (95742) *(P-13206)*
Form & Fusion Mfg Inc (PA) E 916 638-8576
11261 Trade Center Dr Rancho Cordova (95742) *(P-13207)*
Form Grind Corporation E 949 858-7000
30062 Aventura Rcho STA Marg (92688) *(P-16509)*
Form Products, Rcho STA Marg *Also called Form Grind Corporation (P-16509)*
Formation Inc D 650 257-2277
35 Stillman St San Francisco (94107) *(P-24664)*
Formation Systems, San Francisco *Also called Formation Inc (P-24664)*
Formatop, Campbell *Also called Teammate Builders Inc (P-5170)*
Formax Technologies Inc E 209 668-1001
305 S Soderquist Rd Turlock (95380) *(P-19968)*
Formcraft, Fullerton *Also called Future Foam Inc (P-9858)*
Formex LLC E 858 529-6600
11011 Torreyana Rd # 100 San Diego (92121) *(P-8164)*
Formfactor Inc F 925 290-4000
7545 Longard Rd Livermore (94551) *(P-18846)*
Formfactor Inc (PA) C 925 290-4000
7005 Southfront Rd Livermore (94551) *(P-18847)*
Forming Specialties Inc E 310 639-1122
1309 W Walnut Pkwy Compton (90220) *(P-20817)*
Formosa Meat Company Inc E 909 987-0470
10646 Fulton Ct Rancho Cucamonga (91730) *(P-484)*
Forms Division, Irvine *Also called RR Donnelley & Sons Company (P-7553)*
Formsolver Inc E 323 664-7888
3041 N North Coolidge Ave Los Angeles (90039) *(P-4620)*
Formtran Inc F 949 829-5822
26501 Rancho Pkwy S # 103 Lake Forest (92630) *(P-24665)*
Formula Plastics Inc B 866 307-1362
451 Tecate Rd Ste 2b Tecate (91980) *(P-10105)*
Formulation Technology Inc E 209 847-0331
571 Armstrong Way Oakdale (95361) *(P-8165)*
Formurex Inc F 209 931-2040
2470 Wilcox Rd Stockton (95215) *(P-8166)*
Forrest Machining Inc C 661 257-0231
27756 Avenue Mentry Valencia (91355) *(P-20818)*
Forrester Eastland Corporation E 310 784-2464
1320 Storm Pkwy Torrance (90501) *(P-24099)*
FORRESTMACHINING.COM, Valencia *Also called Forrest Machining Inc (P-20818)*
Forsythe Tech Worldwide F 818 710-8694
23924 Victory Blvd Woodland Hills (91367) *(P-22453)*
Fort Bragg Advocate-News, Fort Bragg *Also called Gatehouse Media LLC (P-5857)*
Fortasa Memory Systems Inc F 888 367-8588
1111 Triton Dr Ste 100 Foster City (94404) *(P-15537)*
Fortemedia Inc (PA) E 408 716-8028
4051 Burton Dr Santa Clara (95054) *(P-18848)*
Fortemedia Inc D 408 716-8011
4051 Burton Dr Santa Clara (95054) *(P-15538)*
Fortemedia Inc D 408 716-8028
4051 Burton Dr Santa Clara (95054) *(P-15539)*
Fortemedia China, Santa Clara *Also called Fortemedia Inc (P-15538)*
Forterra Pipe & Precast LLC F 661 746-3527
30781 San Diego St Shafter (93263) *(P-12590)*
Forterra Pipe & Precast LLC D 916 379-9695
7020 Tokay Ave Sacramento (95828) *(P-10930)*
Forterra Pipe & Precast LLC F 858 715-5600
9229 Harris Plant Rd San Diego (92145) *(P-10931)*
Fortinet Inc (PA) C 408 235-7700
899 Kifer Rd Sunnyvale (94086) *(P-24666)*
Fortner Eng & Mfg Inc D 818 240-7740
918 Thompson Ave Glendale (91201) *(P-20819)*
Fortrend Engineering Corp E 408 734-9311
2220 Otoole Ave San Jose (95131) *(P-21587)*
Fortress Inc E 909 593-8600
1721 Wright Ave La Verne (91750) *(P-4944)*
Fortron/Source Corporation (PA) E 949 766-9240
23181 Antonio Pkwy Rcho STA Marg (92688) *(P-17094)*
Fortuna Tortilla Factory F 209 394-3028
1425 C St Livingston (95334) *(P-2525)*
Fortune Bakery, South El Monte *Also called Dtbm Inc (P-1238)*
Fortune Brands Windows Inc C 707 446-7600
2019 E Monte Vista Ave Vacaville (95688) *(P-10106)*

ALPHABETIC

Employee Codes: A=Over 500 employees, B=251-500 C=101-250, D=51-100, E=20-50, F=10-19
2019 California Manfacturers Register
© Mergent Inc. 1-800-342-5647
1143

Fortune Casuals LLC (PA) ....C....310 733-2100
10119 Jefferson Blvd Culver City (90232) ***(P-3236)***
Fortune Drink Inc ....F....408 805-9526
19925 Stevens Creek Blvd # 100 Cupertino (95014) ***(P-2135)***
Fortune Swimwear LLC (HQ) ....E....310 733-2130
2340 E Olympic Blvd Ste A Los Angeles (90021) ***(P-2838)***
Forty-Niners Publication ....F....562 985-5568
1250 Bellflower Blvd Csul Long Beach (90840) ***(P-6165)***
Forward Integration Technology ....F....408 988-3330
444 Nelo St Santa Clara (95054) ***(P-11662)***
Forward Printing & Design ....F....510 535-2222
9331 Burr St Oakland (94605) ***(P-7321)***
Foss Lampshade Studios Inc (PA) ....F....510 534-4133
1357 International Blvd Oakland (94606) ***(P-24100)***
Foss Maritime Company ....F....562 437-6098
49 W Pier D St Long Beach (90802) ***(P-12164)***
Foster Commodities ....E....559 897-1081
1900 Kern St Kingsburg (93631) ***(P-1131)***
Foster Dairy Farms ....C....707 725-6182
572 State Highway 1 Fortuna (95540) ***(P-617)***
Foster Farms, Livingston *Also called Foster Poultry Farms* ***(P-539)***
Foster Farms, Waterford *Also called Foster Poultry Farms* ***(P-540)***
Foster Farms, Kingsburg *Also called Foster Commodities* ***(P-1131)***
Foster Farms, Livingston *Also called Foster Poultry Farms* ***(P-541)***
Foster Farms LLC ....E....559 897-1081
1900 Kern St Kingsburg (93631) ***(P-1132)***
Foster Planing Mill Co ....F....323 759-9156
1258 W 58th St Los Angeles (90037) ***(P-4621)***
Foster Poultry Farms (PA) ....C....209 394-6914
1000 Davis St Livingston (95334) ***(P-539)***
Foster Poultry Farms ....E....209 394-7901
1307 Ellenwood Rd Waterford (95386) ***(P-540)***
Foster Poultry Farms ....C....209 394-7901
1333 Swan St Livingston (95334) ***(P-541)***
Foster Poultry Farms ....E....209 394-7950
221 Stefani Ave Livingston (95334) ***(P-1133)***
Foster Poultry Farms ....B....559 793-5501
770 N Plano St Porterville (93257) ***(P-542)***
Foster Poultry Farms ....B....310 223-1499
1805 N Santa Fe Ave Compton (90221) ***(P-543)***
Foster Print, Santa Ana *Also called Blackburn Alton Invstments LLC* ***(P-7251)***
Foster Printing Company Inc ....D....714 731-2000
700 E Alton Ave Santa Ana (92705) ***(P-6824)***
Foster Sand & Gravel, Corona *Also called Werner Corporation* ***(P-11212)***
Fotis and Son Imports Inc ....E....714 894-9022
15451 Electronic Ln Huntington Beach (92649) ***(P-14849)***
Found Image Press Inc ....F....619 282-3452
5225 Riley St San Diego (92110) ***(P-7563)***
Foundation 9 Entertainment Inc (PA) ....C....949 698-1500
30211 A De Las Bandera200 Rancho Santa Margari (92688) ***(P-24667)***
Foundation For Nat Progress ....E....415 321-1700
222 Sutter St Ste 600 San Francisco (94108) ***(P-6166)***
Foundry Med Innovations Inc ....F....888 445-2333
1630 Faraday Ave Ste 102 Carlsbad (92008) ***(P-22454)***
Foundry Service & Supplies Inc ....E....909 284-5000
2029 S Parco Ave Ontario (91761) ***(P-11356)***
Foundstone Inc ....D....949 297-5600
27201 Puerta Real Ste 400 Mission Viejo (92691) ***(P-24668)***
Fountainhead Industries ....E....310 248-2444
700 N San Vicente Blvd G910 West Hollywood (90069) ***(P-24101)***
Four Colorcom ....F....408 436-7574
2300 Stevens Creek Blvd San Jose (95128) ***(P-6825)***
Four D Imaging ....F....510 290-3533
808 Gilman St Berkeley (94710) ***(P-22203)***
Four Dimensions Inc ....F....510 782-1843
3140 Diablo Ave Hayward (94545) ***(P-21760)***
Four M Studios ....D....415 249-2362
201 Mission St Fl 12 San Francisco (94105) ***(P-6341)***
Four Seasons Design Inc (PA) ....C....619 761-5151
2451 Britannia Blvd San Diego (92154) ***(P-3891)***
Four Seasons Restaurant Eqp ....E....951 278-9100
412 Jenks Cir Corona (92880) ***(P-12591)***
Four Star Chemical, Vernon *Also called Starco Enterprises Inc* ***(P-15032)***
Four Star Distribution ....D....949 369-4420
206 Calle Conchita San Clemente (92672) ***(P-9471)***
Four Wheel Campers Inc ....E....530 666-1442
109 Pioneer Ave Woodland (95776) ***(P-21203)***
Four-D Metal Finishing Inc ....E....408 730-5722
1065 Memorex Dr Santa Clara (95050) ***(P-13412)***
Fourbro Inc ....F....714 277-3858
13772 A Better Way Garden Grove (92843) ***(P-3155)***
Fourward Machine Inc ....F....858 272-0601
5111 Santa Fe St Ste J&I San Diego (92109) ***(P-16510)***
Fovell Enterprises Inc ....E....951 734-6275
1852 Pomona Rd Corona (92880) ***(P-23882)***
Foveon Inc ....E....408 855-6800
2249 Zanker Rd San Jose (95131) ***(P-18849)***
Fowler Ensinger, Sanger *Also called Midvalley Publishing Inc* ***(P-5972)***
Fowlers Machine Works Inc ....F....209 522-5146
300 S Riverside Dr Modesto (95354) ***(P-16511)***
Fowlie Enterprises Inc ....E....805 583-2800
1143 Fern Oaks Dr Santa Paula (93060) ***(P-1364)***
Fox Barrel Cider Company Inc ....E....530 346-9699
1213 S Auburn St Ste A Colfax (95713) ***(P-1768)***
Fox Factory Inc ....F....619 768-1800
750 Vernon Way El Cajon (92020) ***(P-20339)***
Fox Factory Holding Corp (PA) ....E....831 274-6500
915 Disc Dr Scotts Valley (95066) ***(P-21110)***
Fox Factory Inc (HQ) ....D....831 274-6500
915 Disc Dr Scotts Valley (95066) ***(P-21111)***
Fox Factory Inc (HQ) ....C....831 274-6500
130 Hangar Way Watsonville (95076) ***(P-20340)***
Fox Hills Industries ....E....714 893-1940
5831 Research Dr Huntington Beach (92649) ***(P-11493)***
Fox Hills Machining Inc ....F....714 899-2211
7431 Belva Dr Ste 102 Huntington Beach (92647) ***(P-16512)***
Fox Marble & Granite, San Francisco *Also called Fox Merchandising Intl Inc* ***(P-5140)***
Fox Merchandising Intl Inc ....C....415 671-0635
1315 Armstrong Ave San Francisco (94124) ***(P-5140)***
Fox Racing Shox, Scotts Valley *Also called Fox Factory Inc* ***(P-21111)***
Fox Racing Shox, El Cajon *Also called Fox Factory Inc* ***(P-20339)***
Fox Racing Shox, Watsonville *Also called Fox Factory Inc* ***(P-20340)***
Fox Thermal Instruments Inc ....E....831 384-4300
399 Reservation Rd Marina (93933) ***(P-14634)***
Foxfury Lighting Solution, Oceanside *Also called Foxfury LLC* ***(P-17695)***
Foxfury LLC ....E....760 945-4231
3528 Seagate Way Ste 100 Oceanside (92056) ***(P-17695)***
Foxlink International Inc (HQ) ....E....714 256-1777
925 W Lambert Rd Ste C Brea (92821) ***(P-17467)***
Foxlink World Circuit Tech ....E....714 256-0877
925 W Lambert Rd Ste C Brea (92821) ***(P-18488)***
Foxsemicon Integrated Tech Inc ....F....408 383-9880
96 Bonaventura Dr San Jose (95134) ***(P-18850)***
FP International, Fremont *Also called Free-Flow Packaging Intl Inc* ***(P-5522)***
FP International, Fremont *Also called Free-Flow Packaging Intl Inc* ***(P-9853)***
FP International, Fremont *Also called Free-Flow Packaging Intl Inc* ***(P-9854)***
Fpc Graphics Inc ....E....951 686-0232
2682 Market St Riverside (92501) ***(P-6826)***
FPec Corporation A Cal Corp (PA) ....F....562 802-3727
13623 Pumice St Santa Fe Springs (90670) ***(P-14850)***
Fpg Oc Inc ....D....714 692-2950
24855 Corbit Pl Ste B Yorba Linda (92887) ***(P-2263)***
Fra Mani LLC ....F....510 526-7000
1311 8th St Berkeley (94710) ***(P-485)***
Fra' Mani Handcrafted Salumi, Berkeley *Also called Fra Mani LLC* ***(P-485)***
Fragmob LLC ....F....858 587-6659
9655 Granite Ridge Dr 2f San Diego (92123) ***(P-24669)***
Fralock, Valencia *Also called Lockwood Industries LLC* ***(P-5567)***
Framatic Company, Los Angeles *Also called Formsolver Inc* ***(P-4620)***
Frametent Inc ....E....661 290-3375
26480 Summit Cir Santa Clarita (91350) ***(P-3787)***
Framing Fabrics International, Los Angeles *Also called Frm USA LLC* ***(P-13869)***
Frances Mary Accessories Inc ....A....925 962-2111
3732 Mt Diablo Blvd # 260 Lafayette (94549) ***(P-10547)***
Franchise Update Inc ....F....408 402-5681
6489 Camden Ave Ste 204 San Jose (95120) ***(P-6167)***
Franchise Update Media Group, San Jose *Also called Franchise Update Inc* ***(P-6167)***
Francis Ford Coppola Winery, Geyserville *Also called Francis Ford Cppola Prsnts LLC* ***(P-1769)***
Francis Ford Cppola Prsnts LLC ....E....707 251-3200
300 Via Archimedes Geyserville (95441) ***(P-1769)***
Franciscan Vineyards Inc ....C....707 938-1960
18701 Gehricke Rd Sonoma (95476) ***(P-1770)***
Franciscan Vineyards Inc ....B....209 369-5861
5950 E Woodbridge Rd Acampo (95220) ***(P-1771)***
Franciscan Vineyards Inc (HQ) ....D....707 963-7111
1178 Galleron Rd Saint Helena (94574) ***(P-1772)***
Franciscan Vinyards Inc ....D....707 433-6981
16275 Healdsburg Ave Healdsburg (95448) ***(P-1773)***
Franco American Corporation ....F....323 268-2345
1051 Monterey Pass Rd Monterey Park (91754) ***(P-11310)***
Franco American Textile, Monterey Park *Also called Franco American Corporation* ***(P-11310)***
Frank Kams & Associates Inc ....E....909 382-0047
242 W Hanna St Colton (92324) ***(P-4521)***
Frank Russell Inc ....F....661 324-5575
341 Pacific Ave Shafter (93263) ***(P-16513)***
Frank Stubbs Co Inc ....E....805 278-4300
1830 Eastman Ave Oxnard (93030) ***(P-22732)***
Frank-Lin Distillers Pdts Ltd ....D....408 259-8900
2455 Huntington Dr Fairfield (94533) ***(P-2071)***
Franklin Covey Co ....E....949 788-8102
3333 Michelson Dr Ste 400 Irvine (92612) ***(P-6487)***
Franklin Electric Co Inc ....A....415 467-2693
1129 Brussels St San Francisco (94134) ***(P-17197)***
Franklin Lee Enterprises LLC ....F....760 355-1500
2419 Imprl Bus Park Dr Imperial (92251) ***(P-7322)***
Franklin Logging, Burney *Also called Shasta Green Inc* ***(P-4010)***
Franklin Logging Inc ....E....530 549-4924
11906 Wilson Way Redding (96003) ***(P-3988)***
Franklin Wireless Corp ....D....858 623-0000
9707 Waples St Ste 150 San Diego (92121) ***(P-17952)***
Franklins Inds San Diego Inc ....E....858 486-9399
12135 Dearborn Pl Poway (92064) ***(P-16514)***
Franks Cabinet Shop Inc ....F....661 845-0781
11204 San Diego St Lamont (93241) ***(P-4303)***
Frans Manufacturing Inc ....F....760 741-9135
126 N Vinewood St Escondido (92029) ***(P-22455)***
Franz Inc ....E....510 452-2000
2201 Broadway Ste 715 Oakland (94612) ***(P-24670)***
Franzia Winery, Ripon *Also called Franzia/Sanger Winery* ***(P-1774)***
Franzia/Sanger Winery ....C....209 599-4111
17000 E State Highway 120 Ripon (95366) ***(P-1774)***
Frase Enterprises ....E....510 856-3600
2261 Carion Ct Pittsburg (94565) ***(P-17514)***
Frasinettis Winery & Rest, Sacramento *Also called James Frasinetti & Sons* ***(P-1827)***
Fray Logging Inc ....E....209 984-5968
10619 Jim Brady Rd Jamestown (95327) ***(P-3989)***

Mergent e-mail: customerrelations@mergent.com
1144
2019 California
Manufacturers Register
(P-0000) Products & Services Section entry number
(PA)=Parent Co (HQ)=Headquarters (DH)=Div Headquarters

Frazier Aviation Inc .....E.....818 898-1998
445 N Fox St San Fernando (91340) (P-20820)
Frc, Sacramento Also called Farmers Rice Cooperative (P-1079)
FReal Foods LLC .....D.....800 483-3218
6121 Hollis St Ste 500 Emeryville (94608) (P-618)
Fred Matter Inc .....E.....925 371-1234
7801 Las Positas Rd Livermore (94551) (P-16515)
Frederic Duclos, Huntington Beach Also called A G Artwear Inc (P-23742)
Fredi & Sons Inc .....F.....818 881-1170
58 Calle Cabrillo Foothill Ranch (92610) (P-10479)
Freds Fencing Inc .....F.....619 562-5331
10560 Kenney St Santee (92071) (P-13831)
Free Motion Wakeboards, Encinitas Also called Liquid Force Wakeboards (P-23607)
Free-Flow Packaging Intl Inc .....E.....302 737-2413
34175 Ardenwood Blvd Fremont (94555) (P-5522)
Free-Flow Packaging Intl Inc (HQ) .....E.....650 261-5300
34175 Ardenwood Blvd Fremont (94555) (P-9853)
Free-Flow Packaging Intl Inc .....E.....323 722-5112
34175 Ardenwood Blvd Fremont (94555) (P-9854)
Freeberg Indus Fbrication Corp .....D.....760 737-7614
2874 Progress Pl Escondido (92029) (P-12165)
Freedom Communications Inc .....E.....949 454-7300
22481 Aspan St El Toro (92630) (P-5851)
Freedom Designs Inc .....C.....805 582-0077
2241 N Madera Rd Simi Valley (93065) (P-22733)
Freedom Finishing, Los Angeles Also called Freedom Wood Finishing Inc (P-2912)
Freedom Innovations LLC (HQ) .....E.....949 672-0032
3 Morgan Irvine (92618) (P-22734)
Freedom Meditech Inc .....E.....858 638-1433
5090 Shoreham Pl Ste 109 San Diego (92122) (P-22456)
Freedom of Press Foundation .....F.....415 321-1760
601 Van Ness Ave Ste E731 San Francisco (94102) (P-6168)
Freedom Photonics LLC .....E.....805 967-4900
41 Aero Camino Goleta (93117) (P-19969)
Freedom Wood Finishing Inc .....D.....213 534-6620
600 Wilshire Blvd # 1200 Los Angeles (90017) (P-2912)
Freeform Research & Dev .....F.....949 646-3217
1539 Monrovia Ave Ste 23 Newport Beach (92663) (P-14635)
Freeline Design Surfboards, Santa Cruz Also called Mel & Associates Inc (P-23617)
Freemark Abbey Wnery Ltd Prtnr .....E.....707 963-9694
3022 Saint Helena Hwy N Saint Helena (94574) (P-1775)
Freeport Bakery Inc .....E.....916 442-4256
2966 Freeport Blvd Sacramento (95818) (P-1252)
Freeport-Mcmoran Oil & Gas LLC .....E.....805 567-1601
760 W Hueneme Rd Oxnard (93033) (P-57)
Freeport-Mcmoran Oil & Gas LLC .....E.....661 768-4831
3252 W Crocker Springs Rd Fellows (93224) (P-58)
Freeport-Mcmoran Oil & Gas LLC .....D.....661 322-7600
1200 Discovery Dr Ste 500 Bakersfield (93309) (P-59)
Freeport-Mcmoran Oil & Gas LLC .....E.....323 298-2200
5640 S Fairfax Ave Los Angeles (90056) (P-60)
Freestyle, Costa Mesa Also called Sunburst Products Inc (P-23224)
Freeway Machine & Welding Shop, Orange Also called Lmm Enterprises (P-16689)
Freeze Tag Inc (PA) .....F.....714 210-3850
18062 Irvine Blvd Ste 103 Tustin (92780) (P-24671)
Freightgate Inc .....E.....714 799-2833
10055 Slater Ave Ste 231 Fountain Valley (92708) (P-24672)
Freixenet Sonoma Caves Inc .....E.....707 996-4981
23555 Arnold Dr Sonoma (95476) (P-1776)
Fremarc Designs, City of Industry Also called Fremarc Industries Inc (P-4697)
Fremarc Industries Inc (PA) .....E.....626 965-0802
18810 San Jose Ave City of Industry (91748) (P-4697)
Fremont Amgen Inc .....B.....510 284-6500
6397 Kaiser Dr Fremont (94555) (P-8167)
Fremont Package Express .....F.....916 541-1812
734 Still Breeze Way Sacramento (95831) (P-14324)
French Saml, Los Angeles Also called Samuel French Inc (P-6573)
French Tradition (PA) .....F.....310 719-9977
13700 Crenshaw Blvd Gardena (90249) (P-4698)
Frequency Management Intl (PA) .....F.....714 373-8100
15302 Bolsa Chica St Huntington Beach (92649) (P-19546)
Fresco Plastics Inc .....E.....831 625-9877
5680 Carmel Valley Rd Carmel (93923) (P-10107)
Fresco Solar Inc .....F.....408 497-1579
16875 Joleen Way Unit 170 Morgan Hill (95037) (P-18851)
Fresenius Medical Care, Concord Also called Fresenius Usa Inc (P-8168)
Fresenius Usa Inc (HQ) .....C.....925 288-4218
4040 Nelson Ave Concord (94520) (P-8168)
Fresh & Ready, San Fernando Also called Lehman Foods Inc (P-2582)
Fresh & Ready Foods LLC .....D.....818 837-7600
1145 Arroyo St Ste B San Fernando (91340) (P-2526)
Fresh Creative Foods, Vista Also called Rmjv LP (P-14883)
Fresh Express Incorporated .....E.....831 424-2921
950 E Blanco Rd Salinas (93901) (P-2527)
Fresh Innovations LLC .....E.....805 483-2265
908 E 3rd St Oxnard (93030) (P-2412)
Fresh Jive Manufacturing Inc .....E.....213 748-0129
1317 S Olive St Los Angeles (90015) (P-3055)
Fresh Packing Corporation .....E.....213 612-0136
4333 S Maywood Ave Vernon (90058) (P-757)
Fresh Peaches Incorporated (PA) .....F.....909 980-0172
8423 Rochester Ave # 103 Rancho Cucamonga (91730) (P-2839)
Fresh Peaches Swimwear, Rancho Cucamonga Also called Fresh Peaches
Incorporated (P-2839)
Fresh Start Bakeries, Ontario Also called Aryzta LLC (P-1350)
Freshers, Valencia Also called Dansig (chapter S Corporation) (P-2128)
Fresno Business Journal, Fresno Also called Business Journal (P-6121)
Fresno D", Fresno Also called Fresno Distributing Co (P-17801)

Fresno Distributing Co .....E.....559 442-8800
2055 E Mckinley Ave Fresno (93703) (P-17801)
Fresno Fab-Tech Inc .....E.....559 875-9800
1035 K St Sanger (93657) (P-12166)
Fresno French Bread Bakery Inc .....E.....559 268-7088
2625 Inyo St Fresno (93721) (P-1253)
Fresno Gem & Mineral Society .....F.....559 486-7280
340 W Olive Ave Fresno (93728) (P-23342)
Fresno Glass Plant, Fresno Also called Vitro Flat Glass LLC (P-10611)
Fresno Neon Sign Co Inc .....F.....559 292-2944
5901 E Clinton Ave Fresno (93727) (P-23883)
Fresno Paper Express, Fresno Also called Paper Pulp & Film (P-5724)
Fresno Precision Plastics Inc (PA) .....F.....559 323-9595
998 N Temperance Ave Clovis (93611) (P-10108)
Fresno Precision Plastics Inc .....E.....916 689-5284
8456 Carbide Ct Sacramento (95828) (P-10109)
Fresno Trade Bindery & Mailing, Fresno Also called James Clark (P-7603)
Fresno Valves & Castings Inc (PA) .....C.....559 834-2511
7736 E Springfield Ave Selma (93662) (P-11758)
Freudenberg Medical Inc .....C.....626 814-9684
5050 Rivergrade Rd Baldwin Park (91706) (P-22735)
Freudenberg Medical LLC (HQ) .....B.....805 684-3304
1110 Mark Ave Carpinteria (93013) (P-22736)
Freudenberg-Nok General Partnr .....C.....714 834-0602
2041 E Wilshire Ave Santa Ana (92705) (P-9529)
Freund Baking, Commerce Also called Oakhurst Industries Inc (P-1299)
Fricke-Parks Press Inc .....D.....510 489-6543
33250 Transit Ave Union City (94587) (P-6827)
Friday Flier, Canyon Lake Also called Golding Publications (P-7629)
Friedl Corporation .....F.....714 443-0122
1291 N Patt St Anaheim (92801) (P-20341)
Friendslearn Inc .....F.....734 678-8814
425 Broadway St Redwood City (94063) (P-24673)
Fringe Studio LLC .....F.....949 387-9680
17909 Fitch Irvine (92614) (P-24102)
Frisco Baking Company Inc .....C.....323 225-6111
621 W Avenue 26 Los Angeles (90065) (P-1254)
Frito-Lay North America Inc .....C.....714 562-7260
16701 Trojan Way La Mirada (90638) (P-2382)
Frito-Lay North America Inc .....E.....209 824-3700
1190 Spreckels Rd Manteca (95336) (P-2383)
Frito-Lay North America Inc .....E.....925 689-4260
5045 Forni Dr Concord (94520) (P-2384)
Frito-Lay North America Inc .....E.....805 658-1668
4535 Dupont Ct Ventura (93003) (P-2385)
Frito-Lay North America Inc .....F.....858 576-3300
4953 Paramount Dr San Diego (92123) (P-2386)
Frito-Lay North America Inc .....D.....909 877-0902
635 W Valley Blvd Bloomington (92316) (P-2387)
Frito-Lay North America Inc .....B.....209 544-5400
600 Garner Rd Modesto (95357) (P-2388)
Frito-Lay North America Inc .....A.....661 328-6000
28801 Highway 58 Bakersfield (93314) (P-2389)
Frm USA LLC .....E.....323 469-9006
6001 Santa Monica Blvd Los Angeles (90038) (P-13869)
Froglanders La Jolla .....F.....858 459-3764
915 Pearl St Ste A La Jolla (92037) (P-725)
Frogs Leap Winery .....E.....707 963-4704
8815 Conn Creek Rd Rutherford (94573) (P-1777)
Front Edge Technology Inc .....E.....626 856-8979
13455 Brooks Dr Ste A Baldwin Park (91706) (P-13591)
Frontapp Inc .....D.....415 680-3048
525 Brannan St Ste 300 San Francisco (94107) (P-24674)
Frontera Solutions Inc .....D.....714 368-1631
1913 E 17th St Ste 210 Santa Ana (92705) (P-17237)
Frontier AG Co Inc (PA) .....E.....530 297-1020
46735 County Road 32b Davis (95618) (P-1134)
Frontier Concrete Inc .....F.....760 724-4483
717 Mercantile St Vista (92083) (P-11109)
Frontier Electronics Corp .....F.....805 522-9998
667 Cochran St Simi Valley (93065) (P-19336)
Frontier Engrg & Mfg Tech Inc .....E.....562 606-2655
800 W 16th St Long Beach (90813) (P-16516)
Frontier Semiconductor (PA) .....E.....408 432-8338
165 Topaz St Milpitas (95035) (P-18852)
Frontier Technologies, Long Beach Also called Frontier Engrg & Mfg Tech Inc (P-16516)
Frontiers Magazine, Los Angeles Also called Frontiers Media LLC (P-6488)
Frontiers Media LLC .....E.....323 930-3220
5657 Wilshire Blvd # 470 Los Angeles (90036) (P-6488)
Frontline Environmental TEC .....F.....707 745-1116
3195 Park Rd Ste C Benicia (94510) (P-21588)
Frontline Instrs & Contrls .....F.....707 747-9766
3195 Park Rd Ste C Benicia (94510) (P-22204)
Frontline Military Apparel, San Diego Also called Textile 2000 Screen Printing (P-7516)
Frontline Technologies, Benicia Also called Frontline Environmental TEC (P-21588)
Frontline Technologies, Benicia Also called Frontline Instrs & Contrls (P-22204)
Frontrange Holding Inc .....B.....408 601-2800
490 N Mccarthy Blvd Milpitas (95035) (P-24675)
Frontrange Solutions USA Inc .....F.....925 398-1800
490 N Mccarthy Blvd # 100 Milpitas (95035) (P-24676)
Frost Beacon, Chico Also called Ultramar Inc (P-9369)
Frost Bite Novelties Inc .....E.....714 680-0030
931 S Cypress St La Habra (90631) (P-673)
Frost Magnetics Incorporated .....E.....559 642-2536
49643 Hartwell Rd Oakhurst (93644) (P-19337)
Frozen Bean Inc .....E.....855 837-6936
9238 Bally Ct Rancho Cucamonga (91730) (P-2264)
Frt of America LLC .....E.....408 261-2632
1101 S Winchester Blvd San Jose (95128) (P-14636)

Employee Codes: A=Over 500 employees, B=251-500
C=101-250, D=51-100, E=20-50, F=10-19

2019 California
Manfacturers Register

© Mergent Inc. 1-800-342-5647
1145

A
L
P
H
A
B
E
T
I
C

Fruehe Design, Fresno *Also called Simply Smashing Inc* ***(P-23976)***
Fruit Fillings Inc ....E....559 237-4715
2531 E Edgar Ave Fresno (93706) ***(P-800)***
Fruit Growers Supply Company (PA) ....E....818 986-6480
27770 N Entrmt Dr Fl 3 Flr 3 Valencia (91355) ***(P-5409)***
Fruit Growers Supply Company ....E....530 842-4530
229 S Phillipe Ln Yreka (96097) ***(P-4472)***
Fruit Growers Supply Company ....D....909 390-0190
225 S Wineville Ave Ontario (91761) ***(P-5410)***
Fruit Growers Supply Company ....F....559 592-6550
674 E Myer Ave Exeter (93221) ***(P-5411)***
Fruiti Pops Inc ....F....562 404-2568
15418 Cornet St Santa Fe Springs (90670) ***(P-674)***
Fruitridge Prtg Lithograph Inc (PA) ....E....916 452-9213
3258 Stockton Blvd Sacramento (95820) ***(P-6828)***
Frupaletta, Monterey Park *Also called Sweety Novelty Inc* ***(P-698)***
Frutarom ....F....951 734-6620
790 E Harrison St Corona (92879) ***(P-2265)***
Frutstix Company, Santa Barbara *Also called Von Hoppen Ice Cream* ***(P-703)***
Frutstix Company, San Diego *Also called Von Hoppen Ice Cream* ***(P-704)***
Fry Reglet Corporation (PA) ....C....562 903-9500
12342 Hawkins St Santa Fe Springs (90670) ***(P-11586)***
Fs - Precision Tech Co LLC ....D....310 638-0595
3025 E Victoria St Compton (90221) ***(P-11778)***
FSA, Pleasanton *Also called Full Spectrum Analytics Inc* ***(P-21961)***
Fsc Lighting, Rancho Cucamonga *Also called Fluorescent Supply Co Inc* ***(P-17609)***
FSI Field Specialties Inc ....E....562 685-8300
2020 W 17th St Long Beach (90813) ***(P-15126)***
Fsm, Milpitas *Also called Frontier Semiconductor* ***(P-18852)***
Fsp Group USA Corp ....F....909 606-0960
14284 Albers Way Chino (91710) ***(P-19338)***
Ft Textiles, Orange *Also called Fabtex Inc* ***(P-2778)***
FTC - Forward Threat Control ....F....650 906-7917
234 Jason Way Mountain View (94043) ***(P-18324)***
Ftg Inc (PA) ....E....562 865-9200
12750 Center Court Dr S # 280 Cerritos (90703) ***(P-20342)***
Ftg Aerospace Inc (HQ) ....E....818 407-4024
20740 Marilla St Chatsworth (91311) ***(P-11715)***
Ftg Circuits Inc (HQ) ....D....818 407-4024
20750 Marilla St Chatsworth (91311) ***(P-18489)***
Fti, Turlock *Also called Formax Technologies Inc* ***(P-19968)***
Ftt Holdings Inc ....F....562 430-6262
3020 Old Ranch Pkwy Seal Beach (90740) ***(P-14225)***
Fudge Factory Farm, Placerville *Also called Sierra Foothills Fudge Factory* ***(P-1459)***
Fuel Injection Corporation ....F....925 371-6551
2246 N Macarthur Dr Tracy (95376) ***(P-20343)***
Fuel Injection Engineering, Aliso Viejo *Also called Hilborn Manufacturing Corp* ***(P-20361)***
Fuel Injection Engineering Co ....F....949 360-0909
22892 Glenwood Dr Aliso Viejo (92656) ***(P-20344)***
Fuelbox Inc ....F....919 949-9179
201 W Montecito St Santa Barbara (93101) ***(P-19547)***
Fuji Xerox, Palo Alto *Also called Xerox International Partners* ***(P-14830)***
Fujifilm Dimatix Inc (HQ) ....C....408 565-9150
2250 Martin Ave Santa Clara (95050) ***(P-15745)***
Fujifilm Ultra Pure Sltons Inc (HQ) ....E....831 632-2120
11225 Commercial Pkwy Castroville (95012) ***(P-9252)***
Fujifilm Wako Diagnostics US ....E....650 210-9153
1025 Terra Bella Ave A Mountain View (94043) ***(P-8476)***
Fujikin of America Inc (HQ) ....E....408 980-8269
454 Kato Ter Fremont (94539) ***(P-13742)***
Fujikura Composite America Inc ....E....760 598-6060
1483 Poinsettia Ave # 103 Vista (92081) ***(P-23566)***
Fujikuria Composits, Vista *Also called Fujikura Composite America Inc* ***(P-23566)***
Fujisawa Bristol Corporation ....D....760 324-1488
69848 Highway 111 Rancho Mirage (92270) ***(P-7941)***
Fujisoft America Inc ....F....650 235-9422
1710 S Amphlett Blvd # 215 San Mateo (94402) ***(P-24677)***
Fulcrum International Inc ....E....310 763-6823
993 S Firefly Dr Anaheim (92808) ***(P-2881)***
Fulcrum Microsystems Inc ....D....818 871-8100
26630 Agoura Rd Calabasas (91302) ***(P-18853)***
Fulham Co Inc (HQ) ....E....323 779-2980
12705 S Van Ness Ave Hawthorne (90250) ***(P-17095)***
Full Color Bus Cds & Flyers, Sacramento *Also called Full Color Business* ***(P-6829)***
Full Color Business ....F....916 218-7845
2620 El Camino Ave Sacramento (95821) ***(P-6829)***
Full Potential Motor Sports, Lake Elsinore *Also called Acme Motor Corporation* ***(P-20120)***
Full Spectrum Analytics Inc (PA) ....F....925 485-9000
1252 Quarry Ln Pleasanton (94566) ***(P-21961)***
Full Spectrum Omega Inc ....F....714 866-0039
12832 Nutwood St Garden Grove (92840) ***(P-8751)***
Full Void 2 Inc (PA) ....C....818 891-5999
16320 Roscoe Blvd Ste 100 Van Nuys (91406) ***(P-6489)***
Full-Traction Suspension, Bakersfield *Also called California Mini Truck Inc* ***(P-20281)***
Fullbloom Baking Company Inc ....B....510 456-3638
6500 Overlake Pl Newark (94560) ***(P-1255)***
Fuller Laboratories ....F....714 525-7660
1312 E Valencia Dr Fullerton (92831) ***(P-8477)***
Fuller Manufacturing Inc ....F....209 267-5071
130 Ridge Rd Sutter Creek (95685) ***(P-19970)***
Fullerton Printing Inc ....F....714 870-7500
315 N Lemon St Fullerton (92832) ***(P-6830)***
Fullfillment Systems Inc ....D....408 745-7675
1228 Reamwood Ave Sunnyvale (94089) ***(P-486)***
Fulltone Musical Products Inc ....F....310 204-0155
11018 Washington Blvd Culver City (90232) ***(P-23371)***
Fulton Acres Inc ....F....707 762-2280
1330 Commerce St Ste A Petaluma (94954) ***(P-3892)***
Fun o Cake ....F....323 213-8684
2324 4th Ave Apt 201 Los Angeles (90018) ***(P-1256)***
Fundamental Tech Intl Inc ....E....562 595-0661
2900 E 29th St Long Beach (90806) ***(P-21589)***
Fundex Investment Group, San Francisco *Also called Fundx Investment Group* ***(P-6490)***
Fundx Investment Group ....F....415 986-7979
235 Montgomery St # 1049 San Francisco (94104) ***(P-6490)***
Fungs Village Inc ....E....323 881-1600
5339 E Washington Blvd Commerce (90040) ***(P-2427)***
Funktion Technologies Inc ....F....310 937-7335
2110 Artesia Blvd B202 Redondo Beach (90278) ***(P-21590)***
Funktion USA ....F....760 473-4171
3465 Ann Dr Carlsbad (92008) ***(P-12592)***
Funny-Bunny Inc (PA) ....D....714 957-1114
1513b E Saint Gertrude Pl Santa Ana (92705) ***(P-3156)***
Funtastic Factory Inc ....E....562 777-1140
19703 Meadows Cir Cerritos (90703) ***(P-16517)***
Fur Accents LLC ....F....714 403-5286
1425 E Lincoln Ave Ste O Anaheim (92805) ***(P-3600)***
Furlong, Conrad, Los Angeles *Also called F Conrad Furlong Inc* ***(P-23262)***
Furnace Pros, Orange *Also called Lochaber Cornwall Inc* ***(P-15268)***
Furniture Accessory Ret Group ....E....619 591-1150
180 Knoll Rd San Marcos (92069) ***(P-4699)***
Furniture Technics Inc ....E....562 802-0261
2900 Supply Ave Commerce (90040) ***(P-4700)***
Furniture Techniques, Commerce *Also called Furniture Technics Inc* ***(P-4700)***
Furniture Technologies Inc ....E....760 246-9180
17227 Columbus St Adelanto (92301) ***(P-4080)***
Furst, Los Angeles *Also called Lf Sportswear Inc* ***(P-3252)***
Fusion 360 Inc ....F....209 632-0139
677 E Olive Ave Turlock (95380) ***(P-8553)***
Fusion Coatings Inc ....F....925 443-8083
6589 Las Positas Rd Livermore (94551) ***(P-13592)***
Fusion Diet Systems Inc (PA) ....F....801 783-1194
620 Nwport Ctr Dr Ste 350 Newport Beach (92660) ***(P-619)***
Fusion Food Factory ....E....858 578-8001
9350 Trade Pl Ste A San Diego (92126) ***(P-1257)***
Fusion Mphc Holding Corp ....C....925 201-2500
6800 Koll Center Pkwy Pleasanton (94566) ***(P-24678)***
Fusion Product Mfg Inc ....D....619 819-5521
440 Industrial Rd Tecate (91980) ***(P-14517)***
Fusion Sign & Design Inc (PA) ....D....877 477-8777
680 Columbia Ave Riverside (92507) ***(P-23884)***
Futek Advanced Sensor Tech Inc ....C....949 465-0900
10 Thomas Irvine (92618) ***(P-21591)***
Futon Express ....F....626 443-8684
10309 Vacco St South El Monte (91733) ***(P-4775)***
Futurama, San Mateo *Also called Bears For Humanity Inc* ***(P-8985)***
Future Fibre Tech US Inc (HQ) ....F....650 903-2222
800 W El Cam Mountain View (94040) ***(P-19971)***
Future Fine Foods ....F....805 682-9421
2615 De La Vina St Ste 1 Santa Barbara (93105) ***(P-1258)***
Future Foam Inc ....E....714 871-2344
2451 Cypress Way Fullerton (92831) ***(P-9855)***
Future Foam Inc ....E....209 832-1886
1000 E Grant Line Rd # 100 Tracy (95304) ***(P-9856)***
Future Foam Inc ....C....714 459-9971
2441 Cypress Way Fullerton (92831) ***(P-9857)***
Future Foam Inc ....E....714 459-9971
2441 Cypress Way Fullerton (92831) ***(P-9858)***
Future Home, Los Angeles *Also called Home Portal LLC* ***(P-17098)***
Future Molds Inc ....F....909 989-7398
10349 Regis Ct Rancho Cucamonga (91730) ***(P-14518)***
Future Tech Metals ....E....951 781-4801
2926 Rubidoux Blvd Riverside (92509) ***(P-16518)***
Future Us Inc (HQ) ....D....650 238-2400
1390 Market St Ste 200 San Francisco (94102) ***(P-6169)***
Future Wave Technologies Inc ....E....858 481-1112
1343 Camino Teresa Solana Beach (92075) ***(P-2349)***
Futureflite Inc ....F....818 957-0316
28895 Industry Dr La Crescenta (91214) ***(P-5014)***
Futuris Automotive (ca) LLC ....B....510 771-2300
6601 Overlake Pl Newark (94560) ***(P-3893)***
Fuzebox Software Corporation (HQ) ....F....415 692-4800
150 Spear St Ste 900 San Francisco (94105) ***(P-24679)***
Fuzetron Inc ....F....619 244-5141
2111 Paseo Grande El Cajon (92019) ***(P-14957)***
Fvo Solutions Inc ....D....626 449-0218
789 N Fair Oaks Ave Pasadena (91103) ***(P-13593)***
Fxc Corporation ....D....714 557-8032
3050 Red Hill Ave Costa Mesa (92626) ***(P-3949)***
Fxc Corporation (PA) ....E....714 556-7400
3050 Red Hill Ave Costa Mesa (92626) ***(P-11955)***
Fxi Inc ....D....510 357-2600
2451 Polvorosa Ave San Leandro (94577) ***(P-9859)***
Fxi Inc ....C....714 637-0110
2060 N Batavia St Orange (92865) ***(P-9860)***
Fxp Technologies, Brea *Also called S&B Industry Inc* ***(P-10355)***
Fyfe Co LLC (HQ) ....F....858 444-2970
4995 Murphy Canyon Rd # 110 San Diego (92123) ***(P-12978)***
Fziomed Inc (PA) ....E....805 546-0610
231 Bonetti Dr San Luis Obispo (93401) ***(P-22457)***
G & D Industries Inc ....F....626 331-1250
1202 E Edna Pl Covina (91724) ***(P-10110)***
G & F Horse Trailer Repair ....F....909 820-4600
2175 S Willow Ave Bloomington (92316) ***(P-21229)***
G & F White Wedding Carriages, Bloomington *Also called G & F Horse Trailer Repair* ***(P-21229)***

G & G Quality Case Co Inc ....D.....323 233-2482
2025 E 25th St Vernon (90058) *(P-10522)*
G & H Precision Inc ....F.....818 982-3873
11950 Vose St North Hollywood (91605) *(P-16519)*
G & I Industries, Baldwin Park *Also called G & I Islas Industries Inc* *(P-14851)*
G & I Islas Industries Inc (PA) ....E.....626 960-5020
12860 Schabarum Ave Baldwin Park (91706) *(P-14851)*
G & L Musical Instruments, Fullerton *Also called Bbe Sound Inc* *(P-23356)*
G & L Tooling Inc ....F.....562 802-2857
14526 Carmenita Rd Norwalk (90650) *(P-14380)*
G & N Rubicon Gear Inc 951 278-9860
225 Citation Cir Corona (92880) *(P-13101)*
G & P Dntl Care Former Partnr, Oxnard *Also called Henry J Perez DDS* *(P-22883)*
G & P Group Inc ....F.....323 268-2686
1105 Kearney St Los Angeles (90033) *(P-1489)*
G & S Enterprises, Stockton *Also called G & S Process Equipment Inc* *(P-16520)*
G & S Process Equipment Inc ....F.....209 466-3630
1700 N Broadway Ave Stockton (95205) *(P-16520)*
G A Doors Inc ....D.....714 739-1144
15140 Desman Rd La Mirada (90638) *(P-4156)*
G A Systems, Orange *Also called SA Serving Lines Inc* *(P-12747)*
G A Systems Inc ....F.....714 848-7529
226 W Carleton Ave Orange (92867) *(P-16043)*
G and H Vineyards, Rutherford *Also called Grgich Hills Cellar* *(P-1797)*
G and S Milling Co ....E.....707 459-0294
23205 Live Oak Rd Willits (95490) *(P-4157)*
G B Mold & Tool Design ....F.....408 254-3871
640 Giguere Ct San Jose (95133) *(P-14519)*
G B Remanufacturing Inc 562 272-7333
2040 E Cherry Indus Cir Long Beach (90805) *(P-10111)*
G By Guess, Santa Barbara *Also called Guess Inc* *(P-3072)*
G C S, Torrance *Also called Global Comm Semiconductors LLC* *(P-18859)*
G D M Electronic Assembly Inc 408 945-4100
2070 Ringwood Ave San Jose (95131) *(P-17468)*
G D M S-Gographic Data MGT Sol, Lancaster *Also called Geographic Data Mgt Solutions* *(P-24689)*
G E M Water Systems Intl LLC ....F.....714 736-9990
6351 Orangethorpe Ave Buena Park (90620) *(P-16044)*
G E Shell Core Co 323 773-4242
8346 Salt Lake Ave Cudahy (90201) *(P-14520)*
G F Cole Corporation (PA) ....F.....310 320-0601
21735 S Western Ave Torrance (90501) *(P-9530)*
G G C Inc (PA) 714 835-6530
2624 Rousselle St Santa Ana (92707) *(P-14793)*
G G C Inc ....E.....714 835-0551
2624 Rousselle St Santa Ana (92707) *(P-14794)*
G Girl, Vernon *Also called LAT LLC* *(P-3453)*
G Hartzell & Son Inc 925 798-2206
2372 Stanwell Cir Concord (94520) *(P-22880)*
G L D S, Carlsbad *Also called Great Lakes Data Systems Inc* *(P-24710)*
G L Mezzetta Inc ....D.....707 648-1050
105 Mezzetta Ct American Canyon (94503) *(P-801)*
G L O, Sunnyvale *Also called Glo-Usa Inc* *(P-18858)*
G M I, Anaheim *Also called Gear Manufacturing Inc* *(P-20823)*
G M P C LLC ....F.....707 766-9504
2180 S Mcdowell Blvd Petaluma (94954) *(P-23885)*
G M S, Rancho Cucamonga *Also called General Micro Systems Inc* *(P-15417)*
G O Pallets Inc ....E.....909 823-4663
15642 Slover Ave Fontana (92337) *(P-4473)*
G P Manufacturing Inc ....F.....714 974-0288
541 W Briardale Ave Orange (92865) *(P-16521)*
G Powell Electric ....E.....909 865-2291
1020 Price Ave Pomona (91767) *(P-25460)*
G Printing Inc ....F.....818 246-1156
456 W Broadway Glendale (91204) *(P-7323)*
G Pucci & Sons Inc ....F.....415 468-0452
460 Valley Dr Brisbane (94005) *(P-23567)*
G R C, Chatsworth *Also called General Ribbon Corp* *(P-23729)*
G R Furniture Manufacturing, South El Monte *Also called Ramon Lopez* *(P-4804)*
G R J Fashions 323 537-5814
6750 Foster Bridge Blvd B Bell Gardens (90201) *(P-2952)*
G T C, Whittier *Also called General Transistor Corporation* *(P-18855)*
G T Water Products Inc ....F.....805 529-2900
5239 N Commerce Ave Moorpark (93021) *(P-12036)*
G V Industries Inc ....E.....619 474-3013
1346 Cleveland Ave National City (91950) *(P-16522)*
G W, San Lorenzo *Also called Golden W Ppr Converting Corp* *(P-15207)*
G W Manufacturing Jewelers ....E.....619 234-5850
861 6th Ave Ste 800 San Diego (92101) *(P-23265)*
G&A Apparel Group ....E.....323 234-1746
3610 S Broadway Los Angeles (90007) *(P-3894)*
G&A Bias Les, Los Angeles *Also called G&A Apparel Group* *(P-3894)*
G&L Precision Die Cutting, San Jose *Also called Lohmann Prcision Die Cutng LLC* *(P-5569)*
G-G Distribution & Dev Co Inc ....C.....661 257-5700
28545 Livingston Ave Valencia (91355) *(P-13766)*
G-M Enterprises, Corona *Also called Jhawar Industries Inc* *(P-15265)*
G. Fink & Associates, Laguna Hills *Also called Gregory M Fink* *(P-23891)*
G/G Industries, Valencia *Also called G-G Distribution & Dev Co Inc* *(P-13766)*
G2 Graphic Service Inc ....D.....818 623-3100
5510 Cleon Ave North Hollywood (91601) *(P-7324)*
G2 Metal Fab ....E.....925 443-7903
6954 Preston Ave Livermore (94551) *(P-13942)*
G7 Productivity Systems ....D.....858 675-1095
16885 W Bernardo Dr # 290 San Diego (92127) *(P-24680)*
Gabels Cosmetics Inc ....F.....323 221-2430
126 S Avenue 18 Los Angeles (90031) *(P-8752)*

Gabilan Welding Inc ....F.....831 637-3360
1091 San Felipe Rd Hollister (95023) *(P-16523)*
Gabriel Container Co (PA) ....C.....562 699-1051
8844 Millergrove Dr Santa Fe Springs (90670) *(P-5412)*
Gachupin Enterprises LLC ....E.....714 375-4111
5671 Engineer Dr Huntington Beach (92649) *(P-7325)*
Gadia Polyethylene Supplies Inc ....F.....818 775-0096
21141 Itasca St Chatsworth (91311) *(P-10112)*
GAF Materials, Stockton *Also called Standard Industries Inc* *(P-4602)*
Gaffoglio Fmly Mtlcrafters Inc (PA) ....C.....714 444-2000
11161 Slater Ave Fountain Valley (92708) *(P-10699)*
Gage Wafco Co Inc ....E.....310 532-3106
16625 Gramercy Pl Gardena (90247) *(P-14637)*
Gagne-Mulford Enterprises 925 671-7434
2490 Almond Ave Concord (94520) *(P-9615)*
Gahh LLC (HQ) 800 722-2292
11128 Gault St North Hollywood (91605) *(P-20345)*
Gaia Gelato, Carlsbad *Also called Richard Paola* *(P-691)*
Gail Materials Inc ....E.....951 667-6106
10060 Dawson Canyon Rd Corona (92883) *(P-358)*
Gaines Manufacturing Inc ....E.....858 486-7100
12200 Kirkham Rd Poway (92064) *(P-12593)*
Gaines Well Service Inc (PA) ....E.....916 687-6751
10063 Colony Rd Wilton (95693) *(P-214)*
Gainey Ceramics Inc ....C.....909 596-4464
1200 Arrow Hwy La Verne (91750) *(P-10831)*
GAI Manufacturing Co LLC ....C.....626 443-8616
3380 Gilman Rd El Monte (91732) *(P-14249)*
Galaxy Bearing Company, Valencia *Also called Galaxy Die & Engineering Inc* *(P-11759)*
Galaxy Brazing Co Inc ....E.....562 946-9039
10015 Freeman Ave Santa Fe Springs (90670) *(P-25404)*
Galaxy Desserts ....C.....510 439-3160
1100 Marina Way S Ste D Richmond (94804) *(P-1394)*
Galaxy Die & Engineering Inc ....E.....661 775-9301
24910 Avenue Tibbitts Valencia (91355) *(P-11759)*
Galaxy Energy Systems Inc ....F.....760 778-4254
362 N Palm Canyon Dr Palm Springs (92262) *(P-13996)*
Galaxy Enterprises Inc ....E.....323 728-3980
5411 Sheila St Commerce (90040) *(P-24103)*
GALAXY ENTERPRISES INTERNATION, San Dimas *Also called Gei Inc* *(P-14959)*
Galaxy Manufacturing Inc ....F.....408 654-4583
3200 Bassett St Santa Clara (95054) *(P-13208)*
Galaxy Medical, Commerce *Also called Galaxy Enterprises Inc* *(P-24103)*
Galaxy Pest Control, Malibu *Also called Games Production Company LLC* *(P-23425)*
Galaxy Press, Concord *Also called Print-N-Stuff Inc* *(P-7041)*
Galaxy Press Inc ....E.....323 399-3433
6115-6121 Malburg Way Vernon (90058) *(P-6342)*
Galdaza Food Corporation ....E.....213 747-4025
1147 W Washington Blvd Los Angeles (90015) *(P-1259)*
Gale Banks Engineering ....C.....626 969-9600
546 S Duggan Ave Azusa (91702) *(P-14028)*
Galen Robotics Inc ....E.....408 502-5960
541 Jefferson Ave Ste 100 Redwood City (94063) *(P-22458)*
Gali Corporation ....F.....310 477-1224
2301 Pontius Ave Los Angeles (90064) *(P-20821)*
Galil Motion Control Inc ....E.....800 377-6329
270 Technology Way Rocklin (95765) *(P-21592)*
Gallagher & Burk, Dublin *Also called Oliver De Silva Inc* *(P-330)*
Gallagher Rental Inc ....E.....714 690-1559
15701 Heron Ave La Mirada (90638) *(P-17696)*
Gallery, San Leandro *Also called Lindsay/Barnett Incorporated* *(P-13954)*
Gallery Cabinet Connection ....F.....559 294-7007
5783 E Shields Ave Fresno (93727) *(P-4304)*
Galleys Plus Custom Cabinets ....E.....951 278-4596
1432 E 6th St Corona (92879) *(P-4305)*
Gallien Technology Inc (PA) ....D.....209 234-7300
2234 Industrial Dr Stockton (95206) *(P-17802)*
Galliien Krueger, Stockton *Also called Gallien Technology Inc* *(P-17802)*
Gallo Advertising, Modesto *Also called E & J Gallo Winery* *(P-1748)*
Gallo Glass Company (HQ) ....A.....209 341-3710
605 S Santa Cruz Ave Modesto (95354) *(P-10620)*
Gallo Global Nutrition LLC ....C.....209 394-7984
10561 Highway 140 Atwater (95301) *(P-574)*
Gallo Os Sonoma, Healdsburg *Also called E & J Gallo Winery* *(P-1742)*
Galt Herald, Galt *Also called Herburger Publications Inc* *(P-5876)*
Galt Pipe Company ....F.....209 745-2936
321 Elm Ave Galt (95632) *(P-13767)*
Galt Steel Foundry, Lodi *Also called Lodi Iron Works Inc* *(P-11496)*
Galt Steel Foundry, Galt *Also called Lodi Iron Works Inc* *(P-11497)*
Galtech Computer Corporation ....E.....805 376-1060
501 Flynn Rd Camarillo (93012) *(P-4945)*
Galtech International, Camarillo *Also called Galtech Computer Corporation* *(P-4945)*
Galvin Precision Machining Inc ....F.....707 526-5359
404 Yolanda Ave Santa Rosa (95404) *(P-16524)*
Gamboa Incorporated ....E.....619 448-9995
1355 Presioca St Spring Valley (91977) *(P-12167)*
Gambol Industries Inc ....E.....562 901-2470
1825 W Pier D St Long Beach (90802) *(P-21039)*
Game Ready, Concord *Also called Coolsystems Inc* *(P-22966)*
Gamecloud Studios Inc ....E.....951 677-2345
30111 Tech Dr Ste 110 Murrieta (92563) *(P-24681)*
Gamemine LLC ....E.....310 310-3105
2341 Wilson Ave Venice (90291) *(P-24682)*
Gamepro Magazine, Oakland *Also called Idg Games Media Group Inc* *(P-6189)*
Games Production Company LLC 310 456-0099
21323 Pacific Coast Hwy Malibu (90265) *(P-23425)*
Gaming Fund Group ....F.....510 532-8881
1940 Embarcadero Oakland (94606) *(P-22979)*

Employee Codes: A=Over 500 employees, B=251-500
C=101-250, D=51-100, E=20-50, F=10-19

2019 California
Manfacturers Register

© Mergent Inc. 1-800-342-5647

1147

Gamma, Vernon *Also called Rotax Incorporated* ***(P-3491)***
Gamma Scientific Inc..........E.......858 635-9008
9925 Carroll Canyon Rd San Diego (92131) ***(P-22205)***
Gammalux Lighting Systems..........E.......909 599-9669
248 E Arrow Hwy San Dimas (91773) ***(P-17697)***
Gammell Industries Inc..........F.......562 634-6653
7535 Jackson St Paramount (90723) ***(P-12168)***
Gammon LLC..........F.......707 575-8282
1410 Neotomas Ave Ste 200 Santa Rosa (95405) ***(P-6170)***
Ganar Industries Inc..........F.......310 515-5683
13721 Harvard Pl Gardena (90249) ***(P-2999)***
Gander Publishing Inc..........F.......805 541-5523
450 Front St Avila Beach (93424) ***(P-6343)***
Gandona Inc A California Corp..........F.......707 967-5550
1535 Sage Canyon Rd Saint Helena (94574) ***(P-1778)***
Ganesh Industries LLC..........F.......818 349-9166
20869 Plummer St Chatsworth (91311) ***(P-14751)***
Gang Yan Diamond Products Inc..........F.......909 590-2255
4620 Mission Blvd Montclair (91763) ***(P-14638)***
Gann Products Company Inc..........F.......562 862-2337
9540 Stewart And Gray Rd Downey (90241) ***(P-9499)***
Gannett Co Inc..........E.......800 859-2091
1156 Aster Ave Ste C Sunnyvale (94086) ***(P-6171)***
Gannett Co Inc..........E.......310 444-2120
10960 Wilshire Blvd # 1000 Los Angeles (90024) ***(P-5852)***
Gannett Co Inc..........C.......559 688-0521
330 N West St Tulare (93274) ***(P-5853)***
Gannett Co Inc..........D.......760 322-8889
750 N Gene Autry Trl Palm Springs (92262) ***(P-5854)***
Ganpac Distribution LLC..........E.......858 586-1868
7727 Formula Pl San Diego (92121) ***(P-1260)***
Gans Ink and Supply Co Inc (PA)..........E.......323 264-2200
1441 Boyd St Los Angeles (90033) ***(P-9196)***
Gans Ink and Supply Co Inc..........F.......770 529-7766
1441 Boyd St Los Angeles (90033) ***(P-9197)***
Gantner Instruments Inc..........E.......858 537-2060
9835 Carroll Centre Rd # 100 San Diego (92126) ***(P-21761)***
Gar Enterprises..........E.......909 985-4575
1396 W 9th St Upland (91786) ***(P-19548)***
Gara Inc..........F.......530 887-1110
1730 Industrial Dr Auburn (95603) ***(P-17611)***
Garabedian Bros Inc (PA)..........E.......559 268-5014
2543 S Orange Ave Fresno (93725) ***(P-16525)***
Garage Doors Incorporated..........D.......408 293-7443
147 Martha St San Jose (95112) ***(P-4158)***
Garage Equipment Supply Inc..........F.......805 530-0027
646 Flinn Ave Ste A Moorpark (93021) ***(P-14958)***
Gard Inc..........E.......714 738-5891
524 E Walnut Ave Fullerton (92832) ***(P-12594)***
Garden Highway, Rancho Cordova *Also called Renaissance Food Group LLC* ***(P-2652)***
Garden Pals Inc..........E.......909 605-0200
1300 Valley Vista Dr # 209 Diamond Bar (91765) ***(P-11895)***
Gardena Furniture Mfg..........F.......714 441-8436
11330 Markon Dr Garden Grove (92841) ***(P-4776)***
Gardena Sheet Metal, Gardena *Also called C&J Fab Center Inc* ***(P-12515)***
Gardena Sofa LLC..........F.......714 441-8436
11330 Markon Dr Garden Grove (92841) ***(P-4777)***
Gardena Specialized Processing, Chatsworth *Also called Gsp Acquisition Corporation* ***(P-13420)***
Gardena Textile Inc..........F.......310 327-5060
245 W 135th St Los Angeles (90061) ***(P-2840)***
Gardena Valley News Inc (PA)..........F.......310 329-6351
15005 S Vermont Ave Gardena (90247) ***(P-5855)***
Gardena Valley News Inc..........E.......310 532-4882
15005 S Vermont Ave Gardena (90247) ***(P-5856)***
Gardner Denver Inc..........C.......310 544-5710
28904 Scotsview Dr Rancho Palos Verdes (90275) ***(P-15067)***
Gardner Family Ltd Partnership..........E.......559 675-8149
300 Commerce Dr Madera (93637) ***(P-11956)***
Gardner Systems Inc..........F.......714 668-9018
3321 S Yale St Santa Ana (92704) ***(P-21472)***
Garfield Commercial Entps..........E.......714 690-5959
15977 Heron Ave La Mirada (90638) ***(P-4946)***
Garfield Imaging Center Inc..........F.......626 572-0912
555 N Garfield Ave Monterey Park (91754) ***(P-22980)***
Garhauer Marine Corporation..........E.......909 985-9993
1062 W 9th St Upland (91786) ***(P-11957)***
Garlic Research Labs Inc..........F.......800 424-7990
624 Ruberta Ave Glendale (91201) ***(P-9101)***
Garlic Valley Farm, Glendale *Also called Garlic Research Labs Inc* ***(P-9101)***
Garlic Valley Farms Inc..........F.......818 247-9600
624 Ruberta Ave Glendale (91201) ***(P-912)***
Garlord Manufacturing Company, Ceres *Also called Enova Engineering LLC* ***(P-17513)***
Garmentprinter.com, Santa Fe Springs *Also called Stitch City Industries Inc* ***(P-14780)***
Garmon Corporation..........D.......951 296-6308
27461 Via Industria Temecula (92590) ***(P-24104)***
Garner Heat Treat Inc..........F.......510 568-0587
10001 Denny St Oakland (94603) ***(P-11812)***
Garner Holt Productions Inc..........E.......909 799-3030
825 E Cooley Ave San Bernardino (92408) ***(P-15413)***
Garner Products Inc..........F.......916 784-0200
10620 Industrial Ave # 100 Roseville (95678) ***(P-21297)***
Garnett Sign Studio, South San Francisco *Also called Garnett Signs LLC* ***(P-23886)***
Garnett Signs LLC..........F.......650 871-9518
441 Victory Ave South San Francisco (94080) ***(P-23886)***
Garratt-Callahan Company (PA)..........E.......650 697-5811
50 Ingold Rd Burlingame (94010) ***(P-9253)***
Garrett Precision Inc..........F.......949 855-9710
25082 La Suen Rd Laguna Hills (92653) ***(P-16526)***
Garroutte Inc (PA)..........D.......831 722-2487
151 Kearney St Watsonville (95076) ***(P-14852)***
Garry Electronics, Camarillo *Also called Cooper Crouse-Hinds LLC* ***(P-9602)***
Garvey Nut & Candy, Pico Rivera *Also called Genesis Foods Corporation* ***(P-1424)***
Garvey Nut and Candy, Vernon *Also called S & C Foods Inc* ***(P-1450)***
Gary Bale Redi-Mix Con Inc..........D.......949 786-9441
16131 Construction Cir W Irvine (92606) ***(P-11110)***
Gary Doupnik Manufacturing Inc..........D.......916 652-9291
3237 Rippey Rd Loomis (95650) ***(P-4573)***
Gary Manufacturing Inc..........E.......619 429-4479
2626 Southport Way Ste E National City (91950) ***(P-10113)***
Gary Schroeder Enterprises..........F.......818 565-1133
2080 Floyd St Burbank (91504) ***(P-20346)***
Gary's of California, Granada Hills *Also called Garys Leather Creations Inc* ***(P-10561)***
Gary's Signs & Screen Printing, Lodi *Also called Garys Signs and Screen Prtg* ***(P-23887)***
Garys Leather Creations Inc..........D.......818 831-9977
12644 Bradford Pl Granada Hills (91344) ***(P-10561)***
Garys Signs and Screen Prtg..........F.......209 369-8592
1620 Ackerman Dr Lodi (95240) ***(P-23887)***
Gas Recovery Systems LLC..........F.......949 718-1430
20662 Newport Coast Dr Irvine (92612) ***(P-215)***
Gasket Manufacturing Co..........E.......310 217-5600
18001 S Main St Gardena (90248) ***(P-9531)***
Gasket Specialties Inc..........F.......909 987-4724
8654 Helms Ave Rancho Cucamonga (91730) ***(P-9532)***
Gasketfab Division, Torrance *Also called Industrial Gasket and Sup Co* ***(P-9536)***
Gasser-Olds Inc..........E.......323 583-9031
2618 Fruitland Ave Vernon (90058) ***(P-11760)***
Gate-Or-Door Inc..........E.......209 751-4881
14811 Leroy Ave Ripon (95366) ***(P-24683)***
Gatehouse Media LLC..........F.......707 964-5642
690 S Main St Fort Bragg (95437) ***(P-5857)***
Gatehouse Media LLC..........E.......530 842-5777
309 S Broadway St Yreka (96097) ***(P-5858)***
Gatehouse Media LLC..........D.......530 891-1234
400 E Park Ave Chico (95928) ***(P-5859)***
Gatekeeper Systems Inc (PA)..........E.......949 268-1414
90 Icon Foothill Ranch (92610) ***(P-19972)***
Gateway Inc (HQ)..........C.......949 471-7000
7565 Irvine Center Dr # 150 Irvine (92618) ***(P-15414)***
Gateway Marketing Concepts, Poway *Also called Oussoren Eppel Corporation* ***(P-23938)***
Gateway Precision Inc..........F.......408 855-8849
2300 Calle De Luna Santa Clara (95054) ***(P-16527)***
Gateway US Retail Inc..........C.......949 471-7000
7565 Irvine Center Dr Irvine (92618) ***(P-15415)***
Gateworks Corporation..........F.......805 781-2000
3026 S Higuera St San Luis Obispo (93401) ***(P-21593)***
Gatherapp Inc..........F.......415 409-9476
301 Bryant St Apt 201 San Francisco (94107) ***(P-24684)***
Gator Machinery Company..........F.......909 823-1688
11020 Cherry Ave Fontana (92337) ***(P-14167)***
Gault Millau Inc..........F.......323 617-3982
4311 Wilshire Blvd # 405 Los Angeles (90010) ***(P-6344)***
Gavia, Vernon *Also called F Gavina & Sons Inc* ***(P-2340)***
Gavial Engineering & Mfg, Santa Maria *Also called Gavial Holdings Inc* ***(P-19549)***
Gavial Engineering & Mfg Inc (HQ)..........E.......805 614-0060
1435 W Mccoy Ln Santa Maria (93455) ***(P-18490)***
Gavial Holdings Inc (PA)..........F.......805 614-0060
1435 W Mccoy Ln Santa Maria (93455) ***(P-19549)***
Gavial Holdings Inc..........E.......805 688-6734
139 Industrial Way Buellton (93427) ***(P-19550)***
Gavial Itc LLC..........D.......805 614-0060
869 Ward Dr Santa Barbara (93111) ***(P-19551)***
Gayle Manufacturing Co Inc (PA)..........C.......530 662-0284
1455 E Kentucky Ave Woodland (95776) ***(P-12169)***
Gaylord's Meat Co, Fullerton *Also called Gaylords H R I Meats Inc* ***(P-436)***
Gaylords H R I Meats Inc..........F.......714 526-2278
1100 E Ash Ave Ste C Fullerton (92831) ***(P-436)***
Gaylords Inc (PA)..........F.......562 529-7543
13538 Excelsior Dr Santa Fe Springs (90670) ***(P-20206)***
Gayot Publications..........E.......323 965-3529
1744 Sunset Ave Santa Monica (90405) ***(P-6491)***
Gaze Inc..........F.......415 374-9193
1 Market Spear Twr San Francisco (94105) ***(P-18854)***
Gaze USA Inc..........E.......213 622-0022
1665 Mateo St Los Angeles (90021) ***(P-3420)***
Gaze USA Inc..........F.......213 622-0022
1665 Mateo St Los Angeles (90021) ***(P-3309)***
Gazette Media Co LLC..........F.......916 567-9654
770 L St Ste 950 Sacramento (95814) ***(P-5860)***
Gazette Newspapers..........E.......562 433-2000
5225 E 2nd St Long Beach (90803) ***(P-5861)***
Gb Industrial Spray Inc..........F.......209 825-7176
1140 Bessemer Ave Ste 1 Manteca (95337) ***(P-13594)***
Gb006 Inc..........D.......858 684-1300
3013 Science Park Rd San Diego (92121) ***(P-8169)***
GBF Enterprises Inc..........E.......714 979-7131
2709 Halladay St Santa Ana (92705) ***(P-16528)***
Gbm Manufacturing Inc..........F.......888 862-8397
1188 S Airport Way Stockton (95205) ***(P-10783)***
Gbt, South San Francisco *Also called Global Blood Therapeutics Inc* ***(P-8193)***
Gc Aero Inc (PA)..........F.......310 539-7600
21143 Hawth Blvd Ste 136 Torrance (90503) ***(P-12065)***
Gc International Inc (PA)..........E.......805 389-4631
4671 Calle Carga Camarillo (93012) ***(P-17899)***
Gc International Inc..........E.......805 389-4631
4671 Calle Carga Camarillo (93012) ***(P-17900)***
Gc Labels LLC..........F.......951 270-1664
11927 Burke St Santa Fe Springs (90670) ***(P-7326)***

Mergent e-mail: customerrelations@mergent.com
1148
2019 California
Manufacturers Register
(P-0000) Products & Services Section entry number
(PA)=Parent Co (HQ)=Headquarters (DH)=Div Headquarters

Gc Products Inc ....E....916 645-3870
601 7th St Lincoln (95648) ***(P-14168)***
Gc Valves, Simi Valley *Also called Components For Automation Inc* ***(P-13712)***
Gcg Corporation ....F....818 247-8508
608 Ruberta Ave Glendale (91201) ***(P-13413)***
Gcg Precision Metal Finishing, Glendale *Also called Gcg Corporation* ***(P-13413)***
GCI, San Diego *Also called Goto California Inc* ***(P-17804)***
Gcj, Los Angeles *Also called Gold Craft Jewelry Corp* ***(P-23270)***
Gcm Coating, Vernon *Also called Commercial Sand Blast Company* ***(P-13377)***
Gcm Medical & OEM Division Inc ....D....510 475-0404
1350 Atlantic St Union City (94587) ***(P-12595)***
Gdas-Lincoln Inc ....D....916 645-8961
1501 Aviation Blvd Lincoln (95648) ***(P-20578)***
Gdc, San Jose *Also called Dale Grove Corporation* ***(P-14844)***
Gdca Inc ....E....925 456-9900
1799 Portola Ave Ste 1 Livermore (94551) ***(P-15746)***
Gdm Electronic & Medical, San Jose *Also called G D M Electronic Assembly Inc* ***(P-17468)***
Gdsi, San Jose *Also called Grinding & Dicing Services Inc* ***(P-18863)***
GE, Vista *Also called Suez Wts Services Usa Inc* ***(P-19366)***
GE Aviation Systems LLC ....C....714 692-0200
23695 Via Del Rio Yorba Linda (92887) ***(P-20822)***
GE Digital LLC (HQ) ....B....925 242-6200
2623 Camino Ramon San Ramon (94583) ***(P-24685)***
GE Health Care, San Diego *Also called GE Healthcare Inc* ***(P-7942)***
GE Healthcare Inc ....E....858 279-9382
4877 Mercury St San Diego (92111) ***(P-7942)***
GE Nutrients Inc ....F....949 502-5760
19700 Fairchild Ste 380 Irvine (92612) ***(P-7943)***
GE Vallecitos Nuclear Center, Sunol *Also called Ge-Hitachi Nuclear Energy* ***(P-7779)***
GE Ventures Inc ....E....650 233-3900
2882 Sand Hill Rd Ste 240 Menlo Park (94025) ***(P-22459)***
GE Water & Process Tech, Bakersfield *Also called Suez Wts Usa Inc* ***(P-9309)***
GE Water & Process Tech, Vista *Also called Zenon Environmental Corp* ***(P-9318)***
GE Wind Energy LLC ....C....661 823-6423
13681 Chantico Rd Tehachapi (93561) ***(P-13997)***
Ge-Hitachi Nuclear Energy ....D....925 862-4382
6705 Vallecitos Rd Sunol (94586) ***(P-7779)***
Gea Farm Technologies Inc ....E....559 497-5074
2717 S 4th St Fresno (93725) ***(P-8642)***
Gear Division, Shafter *Also called Lufkin Industries LLC* ***(P-13105)***
Gear Manufacturing Inc ....E....714 792-2895
3701 E Miraloma Ave Anaheim (92806) ***(P-20823)***
Gear Technology, Rancho Cucamonga *Also called Marino Enterprises Inc* ***(P-20873)***
Gear Vendors Inc ....E....619 562-0060
1717 N Magnolia Ave El Cajon (92020) ***(P-20347)***
Gebe Electronic Services Inc ....E....323 731-2439
4112 W Jefferson Blvd Los Angeles (90016) ***(P-13595)***
Geeriraj Inc ....E....760 244-6149
7042 Santa Fe Ave E A1 Hesperia (92345) ***(P-18491)***
Gefen LLC ....E....818 772-9100
1800 S Mcdowell Blvd Ext Petaluma (94954) ***(P-19973)***
Gehr Group Inc (PA) ....E....323 728-5558
7400 E Slauson Ave Commerce (90040) ***(P-11441)***
Gehr Industries Inc (HQ) ....C....323 728-5558
7400 E Slauson Ave Commerce (90040) ***(P-11663)***
Gei Inc ....F....909 592-2234
301 E Arrow Hwy Ste 108 San Dimas (91773) ***(P-14959)***
Geiger Manufacturing Inc ....F....209 464-7746
1110 E Scotts Ave Stockton (95205) ***(P-16529)***
Geiger Plastics Inc ....E....310 327-9926
16150 S Maple Ave A Gardena (90248) ***(P-10114)***
Gekkeikan Sake USAinC ....E....916 985-3111
1136 Sibley St Folsom (95630) ***(P-1779)***
Gelateria Naia, Hercules *Also called Naia Inc* ***(P-688)***
Geltman Industries, Los Angeles *Also called Rezex Corporation* ***(P-2917)***
Gem Box of West ....E....213 748-4875
2430 S Hill St Los Angeles (90007) ***(P-5413)***
Gem Enterprises LLC ....E....760 746-6616
300 N Andreasen Dr Escondido (92029) ***(P-13414)***
Gem Mobile Treatment Svcs Inc (HQ) ....E....562 595-7075
2525 Cherry Ave Ste 105 Signal Hill (90755) ***(P-21513)***
Gemfire Corporation ....D....408 519-6015
2570 N 1st St Ste 440 San Jose (95131) ***(P-19974)***
Gemini - G E L ....E....323 651-0513
8365 Melrose Ave Los Angeles (90069) ***(P-7644)***
Gemini Aluminum Corporation ....E....909 595-7403
3255 Pomona Blvd Pomona (91768) ***(P-11587)***
Gemini Bio Products ....F....916 471-3540
930 Riverside Pkwy Ste 50 Broderick (95605) ***(P-15283)***
Gemini Consultants Inc ....F....925 866-8946
2303 Camino Ramon Ste 106 San Ramon (94583) ***(P-18492)***
Gemini Film & Bag Inc (PA) ....E....323 582-0901
3574 Fruitland Ave Maywood (90270) ***(P-10115)***
Gemini Industries Inc ....D....949 250-4011
2311 Pullman St Santa Ana (92705) ***(P-11557)***
Gemini Industries Inc ....F....949 553-4255
1910 E Warner Ave Ste G Santa Ana (92705) ***(P-24105)***
Gemini Mfg & Engrg Inc ....E....714 999-0010
1020 E Vermont Ave Anaheim (92805) ***(P-14521)***
Gemini Plastics, Maywood *Also called Gemini Film & Bag Inc* ***(P-10115)***
Gems of Fruit Co, Placentia *Also called Packers Food Products Inc* ***(P-961)***
Gemsa Enterprises LLC ....E....714 521-1736
14370 Gannet St La Mirada (90638) ***(P-1540)***
Gemsa Oils, La Mirada *Also called Gemsa Enterprises LLC* ***(P-1540)***
Gemtech Inds Good Earth Mfg ....E....714 848-2517
2737 S Garnsey St Santa Ana (92707) ***(P-13596)***
Gemtech International, Santa Ana *Also called Gemtech Inds Good Earth Mfg* ***(P-13596)***
Gen-Probe Incorporated ....D....858 410-8000
10210 Genetic Center Dr San Diego (92121) ***(P-8478)***
Genalyte Inc ....F....858 956-1200
10520 Wateridge Cir San Diego (92121) ***(P-22460)***
Genbio, San Diego *Also called Innominata* ***(P-8485)***
Gencor, Irvine *Also called GE Nutrients Inc* ***(P-7943)***
Gene Watson Construction A CA ....A....661 763-5254
801 Kern St Taft (93268) ***(P-216)***
Geneforge Inc ....F....650 219-9335
2699 Spring St Redwood City (94063) ***(P-21762)***
Genelabs Technologies Inc (HQ) ....F....415 297-2901
505 Penobscot Dr Redwood City (94063) ***(P-8170)***
Genenco, Bakersfield *Also called James L Craft Inc* ***(P-16613)***
Genencor International, Palo Alto *Also called Danisco US Inc* ***(P-8472)***
Genentech Inc ....E....707 454-1000
1000 New Horizons Way Vacaville (95688) ***(P-8171)***
Genentech Inc ....F....650 225-3639
800 Forbes Blvd South San Francisco (94080) ***(P-8172)***
Genentech Inc (HQ) ....A....650 225-1000
1 Dna Way South San Francisco (94080) ***(P-8173)***
Genentech Inc ....F....408 963-8759
465 E Grand Ave Ms432 South San Francisco (94080) ***(P-8174)***
Genentech Inc ....B....760 231-2440
1 Antibody Way Oceanside (92056) ***(P-8175)***
Genentech Inc ....B....650 216-2900
550 Broadway St Redwood City (94063) ***(P-8176)***
Genentech Inc ....F....650 225-3214
431 Grandview Dr Bldg 27 South San Francisco (94080) ***(P-8177)***
Genentech Inc ....C....650 225-1000
1 Dna Way South San Francisco (94080) ***(P-8178)***
Genentech Inc ....B....760 231-2440
1 Antibody Way Oceanside (92056) ***(P-8554)***
Genentech Usa Inc ....A....650 225-1000
1 Dna Way South San Francisco (94080) ***(P-8179)***
Gener8 LLC ....C....650 940-9898
500 Mercury Dr Sunnyvale (94085) ***(P-19833)***
General Atomic Aeron ....F....858 455-4560
14040 Danielson St Poway (92064) ***(P-20579)***
General Atomic Aeron ....B....858 964-6700
13330 Evening Creek Dr N San Diego (92128) ***(P-20580)***
General Atomic Aeron ....C....760 246-3660
9779 Yucca Rd Adelanto (92301) ***(P-20581)***
General Atomic Aeron ....B....858 455-2810
3550 General Atomics Ct San Diego (92121) ***(P-20582)***
General Atomic Aeron ....B....858 455-4309
16761 Via Del Campo Ct San Diego (92127) ***(P-20583)***
General Atomic Aeron ....C....760 388-8208
73 El Mirage Airport Rd B Adelanto (92301) ***(P-20584)***
General Atomic Aeron (HQ) ....B....858 312-2810
14200 Kirkham Way Poway (92064) ***(P-20585)***
General Atomic Aeron ....B....858 312-2543
14115 Stowe Dr Poway (92064) ***(P-20586)***
General Atomics Intl Svcs Corp ....E....858 455-4141
3483 Dunhill St San Diego (92121) ***(P-20587)***
General Carbon Company ....F....323 588-9291
7542 Maie Ave Los Angeles (90001) ***(P-7742)***
General Coatings, Fresno *Also called Walton Industries Inc* ***(P-8954)***
General Connector, Camarillo *Also called Cooper Crouse-Hinds LLC* ***(P-19381)***
General Container ....D....714 562-8700
5450 Dodds Ave Buena Park (90621) ***(P-5414)***
General Dynamics Adv Info Sys, McClellan *Also called General Dynmics Mssion Systems* ***(P-18327)***
General Dynamics Corporation ....E....619 544-3400
2798 Harbor Dr San Diego (92113) ***(P-20995)***
General Dynamics Glbl IMG Tech ....D....619 671-5400
7603 Saint Andrews Ave H San Diego (92154) ***(P-17271)***
General Dynmics Mssion Systems ....C....916 339-3852
5922 Roseville Rd Sacramento (95842) ***(P-15416)***
General Dynmics Mssion Systems ....B....408 908-7300
2688 Orchard Pkwy San Jose (95134) ***(P-18325)***
General Dynmics Mssion Systems ....C....805 497-5042
112 S Lakeview Canyon Rd Westlake Village (91362) ***(P-18326)***
General Dynmics Mssion Systems ....F....916 565-5316
4235 Forcum Ave Ste 200 McClellan (95652) ***(P-18327)***
General Dynmics Mssion Systems ....D....408 955-1900
2205 Fortune Dr San Jose (95131) ***(P-18328)***
General Dynmics Mtion Ctrl LLC ....F....619 671-5400
7603 Saint Andrews Ave H San Diego (92154) ***(P-17272)***
General Dynmics Ots Ncvlle Inc ....D....707 473-9200
511 Grove St Healdsburg (95448) ***(P-16156)***
General Dynmics Stcom Tech Inc ....D....310 539-6704
3111 Fujita St Torrance (90505) ***(P-18112)***
General Elec Assembly Inc ....E....408 980-8819
1525 Atteberry Ln San Jose (95131) ***(P-18493)***
General Electric Company ....D....925 242-6200
2623 Camino Ramon San Ramon (94583) ***(P-24686)***
General Electric Company ....E....760 530-5200
18000 Phantom St Victorville (92394) ***(P-20588)***
General Electric Company ....B....951 928-2829
26226 Antelope Rd Romoland (92585) ***(P-13998)***
General Electric Company ....E....951 360-2400
11600 Philadelphia Ave Mira Loma (91752) ***(P-17612)***
General Engrg & Mch Works, San Francisco *Also called Robert E Blake Inc* ***(P-21012)***
General Forming Corporation ....E....310 326-0624
2413 Moreton St Torrance (90505) ***(P-12596)***
General Foundry Service Corp ....D....510 297-5040
1390 Business Center Pl San Leandro (94577) ***(P-11742)***
General Graphic Chemicals Co ....F....510 832-4404
2525 Mandela Pkwy Ste 2 Oakland (94607) ***(P-9254)***

Employee Codes: A=Over 500 employees, B=251-500
C=101-250, D=51-100, E=20-50, F=10-19
2019 California
Manfacturers Register
© Mergent Inc. 1-800-342-5647
1149

General Grinding & Mfg Co LLC ....E......562 921-7033
15100 Valley View Ave La Mirada (90638) *(P-16157)*
General Grinding Inc ....E......510 261-5557
801 51st Ave Oakland (94601) *(P-13415)*
General Industrial Repair ....E......323 278-0873
7417 E Slauson Ave Commerce (90040) *(P-16530)*
General Instrument, Santa Clara Also called Ruckus Wireless Inc *(P-17990)*
General Linear Systems ....F......714 994-4822
4332 Artesia Ave Fullerton (92833) *(P-25461)*
General Metal Engraving Inc ....E......626 443-8961
9254 Garvey Ave South El Monte (91733) *(P-23715)*
General Micro Systems Inc (PA) ....D......909 980-4863
8358 Maple Pl Rancho Cucamonga (91730) *(P-15417)*
General Mills Inc ....E......209 334-7061
2000 W Turner Rd Lodi (95242) *(P-1059)*
General Mills Inc ....D......818 553-6777
620 N Kenwood St Glendale (91206) *(P-1060)*
General Mills Inc ....E......323 584-3433
4309 Fruitland Ave Vernon (90058) *(P-1039)*
General Mills Inc ....E......310 605-6108
1055 Sandhill Ave Carson (90746) *(P-726)*
General Mills Inc ....D......951 685-7030
11618 Mulberry Ave Fontana (92337) *(P-1061)*
General Monitors Inc (HQ) ....C......949 581-4464
26776 Simpatica Cir Lake Forest (92630) *(P-18329)*
General Motors LLC ....A......313 556-5000
3050 Lomita Blvd Torrance (90505) *(P-20348)*
General Nucleonics Inc ....F......909 593-4985
2807 Metropolitan Pl Pomona (91767) *(P-22206)*
General Photonics Corp ....E......909 590-5473
14351 Pipeline Ave Chino (91710) *(P-17953)*
General Plating, Los Angeles Also called Alpha Polishing Corporation *(P-13322)*
General Production Services ....F......818 365-4211
670 Arroyo St San Fernando (91340) *(P-16531)*
General Ribbon Corp ....B......818 709-1234
5775 E Ls Angls Ave Ste 2 Chatsworth (91311) *(P-23729)*
General Sealants Inc ....C......626 961-0211
300 Turnbull Canyon Rd City of Industry (91745) *(P-9143)*
General Steel Fabricators Inc ....F......818 897-1300
12179 Branford St Ste B Sun Valley (91352) *(P-12170)*
General Transistor Corporation (PA) .....E......310 578-7344
12449 Putnam St Whittier (90602) *(P-18855)*
General Truck Body Inc ....D......323 276-1933
1130 S Vail Ave Montebello (90640) *(P-20207)*
General Truss Company Inc ....F......916 388-9300
6947 Power Inn Rd Sacramento (95828) *(P-4405)*
General Veneer Mfg Co ....E......323 564-2661
8652 Otis St South Gate (90280) *(P-4377)*
General Wax & Candle Co, North Hollywood Also called General Wax Co Inc *(P-24106)*
General Wax Co Inc (PA) ....D......818 765-5800
6863 Beck Ave North Hollywood (91605) *(P-24106)*
Generation Alpha Inc ....F......888 998-8881
853 Sandhill Ave Carson (90746) *(P-17536)*
Generation Circuits LLC ....E......760 743-7459
621 S Andreasen Dr Ste B Escondido (92029) *(P-18494)*
Generic Manufacturing Corp ....F......951 296-2838
27455 Bostik Ct Temecula (92590) *(P-14853)*
Generitech Corporation ....F......559 346-0233
4967 E Lansing Way Fresno (93727) *(P-8753)*
Generon Igs Inc ....F......925 431-1030
992 Arcy Ln Bldg 992 Pittsburg (94565) *(P-15325)*
Genesis 2000, La Puente Also called Genesis Tc Inc *(P-4778)*
Genesis Computer Systems Inc ....F......714 632-3648
4055 E La Palma Ave Ste C Anaheim (92807) *(P-15418)*
Genesis Engineering Inc ....F......408 249-5034
6053 Wellfleet Way San Jose (95129) *(P-21298)*
Genesis Foods Corporation (HQ) ....D......323 890-5890
8825 Mercury Ln Pico Rivera (90660) *(P-1424)*
Genesis Group Sftwr Developers ....F......714 630-4297
16027 Brookhurst St Ste G Fountain Valley (92708) *(P-24687)*
Genesis Mch & Fabrication Inc ....F......661 324-4366
4321 Turcon Ave Bakersfield (93308) *(P-16532)*
Genesis Natural Products, Chatsworth Also called Nydr Holdings Inc *(P-2626)*
Genesis Printing ....F......323 965-7935
5872 W Pico Blvd Los Angeles (90019) *(P-6831)*
Genesis Supreme Rv Inc ....E......951 337-0254
23129 Cajalco Rd Perris (92570) *(P-21230)*
Genesis Tc Inc ....F......626 968-4455
524 Hofgaarden St La Puente (91744) *(P-4778)*
Genesys Telecom Labs, Daly City Also called Genesys Telecom Labs Inc *(P-24688)*
Genesys Telecom Labs Inc (HQ) ....B......650 466-1100
2001 Junipero Serra Blvd Daly City (94014) *(P-24688)*
Genetix Usa Inc ....F......408 719-6400
120 Baytech Dr San Jose (95134) *(P-21962)*
Genetronics Inc ....E......858 597-6006
11494 Sorrento Valley Rd A San Diego (92121) *(P-21473)*
Genius Tools Americas Corp (PA) ....F......909 230-9588
1440 E Cedar St Ontario (91761) *(P-14639)*
Genoa Corporation ....E......510 979-3000
41762 Christy St Fremont (94538) *(P-18856)*
Genopis Inc ....E......858 875-4700
10390 Pacific Center Ct San Diego (92121) *(P-8180)*
Genovation Incorporated ....F......949 833-3355
17741 Mitchell N Irvine (92614) *(P-15747)*
Gensia Sicor Inc (HQ) ....A......949 455-4700
19 Hughes Irvine (92618) *(P-8181)*
Gentec Manufacturing Inc ....F......408 432-6220
2241 Ringwood Ave San Jose (95131) *(P-16533)*
Gentherm Incorporated ....F......626 593-4500
5462 Irwindale Ave Ste A Irwindale (91706) *(P-20349)*

Gentle Giants Products Inc ....F......951 818-2512
4867 Pedley Ave Norco (92860) *(P-1113)*
Gentry Golf Maintenance ....E......714 630-3541
14893 Ball Rd Anaheim (92806) *(P-23568)*
Gentry Magazine, Menlo Park Also called 18 Media Inc *(P-6094)*
Genuine Parts Distributors, Ontario Also called Tracy Industries Inc *(P-14032)*
Genzyme Corporation ....E......800 255-1616
655 E Huntington Dr Monrovia (91016) *(P-8182)*
Genzyme Genetics, Monrovia Also called Genzyme Corporation *(P-8182)*
Geo A Diack Inc ....E......626 961-2491
1250 S Johnson Dr City of Industry (91745) *(P-5141)*
Geo Drilling Fluids Inc ....E......916 383-2811
7268 Frasinetti Rd Sacramento (95828) *(P-11320)*
Geo Labels Inc ....F......909 923-6832
1180 E Francis St Ste G Ontario (91761) *(P-7327)*
Geo M Martin Company (PA) ....D......510 652-2200
1250 67th St Emeryville (94608) *(P-14795)*
Geo Plastics ....E......323 277-8106
2200 E 52nd St Vernon (90058) *(P-10116)*
Geo Semiconductor Inc (PA) ....E......408 638-0400
101 Metro Dr Ste 620 San Jose (95110) *(P-18857)*
Geodetics Inc ....E......858 729-0872
2649 Ariane Dr San Diego (92117) *(P-21299)*
Geographic Data Mgt Solutions ....F......661 949-1025
42140 10th St W Lancaster (93534) *(P-24689)*
Geolabs Westlake Village, Westlake Village Also called R & R Services Corporation *(P-9666)*
Geometrics Inc ....D......408 428-4244
2190 Fortune Dr San Jose (95131) *(P-22207)*
Georg Fischer Harvel LLC ....D......661 396-0653
7001 Schirra Ct Bakersfield (93313) *(P-9778)*
Georg Fischer Signet LLC ....D......626 571-2770
3401 Aero Jet Ave El Monte (91731) *(P-21594)*
George Coriaty ....E......562 698-7513
7240 Greenleaf Ave Whittier (90602) *(P-6832)*
George Delallo Company Inc ....E......530 533-3303
1800 Idora St Oroville (95966) *(P-802)*
George Fischer Inc (HQ) ....E......626 571-2770
3401 Aero Jet Ave El Monte (91731) *(P-16534)*
George Hood Inc ....E......408 295-6507
890 Faulstich Ct San Jose (95112) *(P-12597)*
George Industries ....B......323 264-6660
4116 Whiteside St Los Angeles (90063) *(P-13416)*
George Jue Mfg Co Inc ....D......562 634-8181
8140 Rosecrans Ave Paramount (90723) *(P-14704)*
George L Kovacs ....E......714 538-8026
1810 W Business Center Dr Orange (92867) *(P-14715)*
George L Throop Co ....E......626 796-0285
444 N Fair Oaks Ave Pasadena (91103) *(P-10932)*
George M Martin Inc ....E......510 652-2200
910 Folger Ave Berkeley (94710) *(P-14796)*
George P Johnson Company ....D......310 965-4300
18500 Crenshaw Blvd Torrance (90504) *(P-23888)*
George Segovia ....F......562 699-8554
9612 Beverly Rd Pico Rivera (90660) *(P-13943)*
George Verhoeven Grain Inc (PA) ....F......909 605-1531
5355 E Airport Dr Ontario (91761) *(P-1135)*
Georgetown Precast Inc ....F......530 333-4404
2420 Georgia Slide Rd Georgetown (95634) *(P-10933)*
Georgia Pacific Holdings Inc ....A......626 926-1474
13208 Hadley St Apt 1 Whittier (90601) *(P-5665)*
Georgia-Pacific, La Mirada Also called Bestwall LLC *(P-5389)*
Georgia-Pacific, Long Beach Also called Bestwall LLC *(P-11216)*
Georgia-Pacific, San Leandro Also called Bestwall LLC *(P-5274)*
Georgia-Pacific, Madera Also called Color-Box LLC *(P-5398)*
Georgia-Pacific, Fresno Also called Bestwall LLC *(P-5498)*
Georgia-Pacific LLC ....C......209 522-5201
2400 Lapham Dr Modesto (95354) *(P-5415)*
Georgia-Pacific LLC ....C......650 873-7800
249 E Grand Ave South San Francisco (94080) *(P-5416)*
Georgia-Pacific LLC ....C......925 757-2870
801 Minaker Dr Antioch (94509) *(P-11218)*
Georgia-Pacific LLC ....C......559 674-4685
24600 Avenue 13 Madera (93637) *(P-5417)*
Georgia-Pacific LLC ....E......510 352-8269
2800 Alvarado St San Leandro (94577) *(P-5283)*
Goris Winery ....F......831 659-1050
4 Pilot Rd Carmel Valley (93924) *(P-1780)*
Gerald Gentellalli ....F......760 789-2094
19360 Camino Vista Rd Ramona (92065) *(P-23569)*
Gerard H Tanzi Inc ....F......209 532-0855
22555 Sawmill Flat Rd Columbia (95310) *(P-14854)*
Gerard Roof Products LLC (HQ) ....E......714 529-0407
721 Monroe Way Placentia (92870) *(P-12598)*
Gerard Roofing Technologies, Placentia Also called Gerard Roof Products LLC *(P-12598)*
Gergay and Associates ....E......415 431-4163
78 Delmar St San Francisco (94117) *(P-13209)*
Gerhardt Gear Co Inc ....E......818 842-6700
133 E Santa Anita Ave Burbank (91502) *(P-20350)*
Gerlinger Fndry Mch Works Inc (PA) ......D......530 243-1053
1527 Sacramento St Redding (96001) *(P-12171)*
Germains Seed Technology Inc ....E......408 848-8120
8333 Swanston Ln Gilroy (95020) *(P-24107)*
German Machine Products, Gardena Also called German Machined Products Inc *(P-16535)*
German Machined Products Inc ....E......310 532-4480
1415 W 178th St Gardena (90248) *(P-16535)*
Germanex Imports Inc ....F......818 700-0441
19015 Parthenia St Northridge (91324) *(P-20351)*
Geron Corporation (PA) ....E......650 473-7700
149 Commonwealth Dr # 2070 Menlo Park (94025) *(P-8183)*

Mergent e-mail: customerrelations@mergent.com
1150

2019 California
Manufacturers Register

(P-0000) Products & Services Section entry number
(PA)=Parent Co (HQ)=Headquarters (DH)=Div Headquarters

Gerson's Machinery Co, Orange *Also called George L Kovacs* ***(P-14715)***
Ges US (new England) Inc ....C....978 459-4434
1051 S East St Anaheim (92805) ***(P-19552)***
Get ....F....562 989-5400
2030 W 17th St Long Beach (90813) ***(P-16045)***
Get Ahead Learning LLC ....F....626 796-8500
70 S Lake Ave Ste 1000 Pasadena (91101) ***(P-24690)***
Get Engineering Corp ....E....619 443-8295
9350 Bond Ave El Cajon (92021) ***(P-21595)***
Getgoing Inc ....F....415 608-7474
610 Bridgeport Ln Foster City (94404) ***(P-24691)***
Geyser Peak Winery ....E....707 857-9463
2306 Magnolia Dr Healdsburg (95448) ***(P-1781)***
Gfbc Inc ....F....858 622-0085
6550 Mira Mesa Blvd San Diego (92121) ***(P-1594)***
Gff Inc ....D....323 232-6255
145 Willow Ave City of Industry (91746) ***(P-913)***
Gfmi Aerospace & Defense Inc ....E....714 361-4444
17375 Mount Herrmann St Fountain Valley (92708) ***(P-20824)***
Gforce Corporation ....F....714 630-0909
1144 N Grove St Anaheim (92806) ***(P-1261)***
Gfp Ethanol LLC ....E....559 757-3850
11704 Road 120 Pixley (93256) ***(P-9007)***
Ggc Administration LLC (PA) ....E....415 983-2700
1 Embarcadero Ctr Fl 39 San Francisco (94111) ***(P-5189)***
Ggco Inc ....E....213 623-3636
18380 Ventura Blvd Tarzana (91356) ***(P-23266)***
Ggf Marble & Supply Inc ....F....925 676-8385
1375 Franquette Ave Ste F Concord (94520) ***(P-11252)***
Ggsdi, Fountain Valley *Also called Genesis Group Sftwr Developers* ***(P-24687)***
Ggtw LLC ....E....619 423-3388
1470 Bay Blvd Chula Vista (91911) ***(P-9255)***
Gh Foods Ca LLC (HQ) ....B....916 844-1140
8425 Carbide Ct Sacramento (95828) ***(P-2528)***
Ghazarian Welding & Repair, Fresno *Also called Ghazarian Wldg Fabrication Inc* ***(P-25405)***
Ghazarian Wldg Fabrication Inc ....F....559 233-1210
2903 E Annadale Ave Fresno (93725) ***(P-25405)***
Ghiringhlli Spcialty Foods Inc ....C....707 561-7670
101 Benicia Rd Vallejo (94590) ***(P-2529)***
Ghs Champion Inc ....E....650 326-8485
550 Waverley St Palo Alto (94301) ***(P-1262)***
Giannelli Cabinet Mfg Co ....F....818 882-9787
8835 Shirley Ave Northridge (91324) ***(P-5142)***
Giannini Garden Ornaments Inc ....E....650 873-4493
225 Shaw Rd South San Francisco (94080) ***(P-10934)***
Gianno Co Ltd ....F....909 628-6928
13546 Vintage Pl Chino (91710) ***(P-3237)***
Giant Horse Printing Inc ....F....650 875-7137
1336 San Mateo Ave South San Francisco (94080) ***(P-6833)***
Giant Mgllan Tlscope Orgnztnal, Pasadena *Also called Gmto Corporation* ***(P-22078)***
Giant Teddy, Anaheim *Also called Raykorvay Inc* ***(P-23401)***
Gibbel Bros Inc ....E....323 875-1367
11145 Tuxford St Sun Valley (91352) ***(P-11111)***
Gibbs Plastic & Rubber Co ....F....707 746-7300
3959 Teal Ct Benicia (94510) ***(P-9616)***
Gibraltar Plastic Pdts Corp ....E....818 365-9318
12885 Foothill Blvd Sylmar (91342) ***(P-10117)***
Gibson and Schaefer Inc (PA) ....E....619 352-3535
1126 Rock Wood Rd Heber (92249) ***(P-11112)***
Gibson Brands Inc ....C....310 300-2369
9350 Civic Center Dr # 130 Beverly Hills (90210) ***(P-23372)***
Gibson Exhaust Systems, Corona *Also called Gibson Performance Corporation* ***(P-20352)***
Gibson Performance Corporation ....D....951 372-1220
1270 Webb Cir Corona (92879) ***(P-20352)***
Gibson Printing & Publishing ....F....707 745-0733
820 1st St Benicia (94510) ***(P-5862)***
Gibson Printing & Publishing (PA) ....E....707 643-2552
544 Curtola Pkwy Vallejo (94590) ***(P-5863)***
Gibson Printing & Publishing ....F....925 228-6400
802 Alhambra Ave Martinez (94553) ***(P-5864)***
Gibson Printing & Publishing ....F....707 678-5594
145 E A St Dixon (95620) ***(P-5865)***
Gibson Radio and Publishing Co, Vallejo *Also called Luther E Gibson Inc* ***(P-6211)***
Gibson Wine Company ....E....559 875-2505
1720 Academy Ave Sanger (93657) ***(P-1782)***
Gifts International Inc ....F....909 854-3977
799 Palmyrita Ave Riverside (92507) ***(P-13944)***
Giga-Tronics Incorporated (PA) ....E....925 328-4650
5990 Gleason Dr Dublin (94568) ***(P-21763)***
Gigamem LLC ....F....949 461-9999
18375 Bandilier Cir Fountain Valley (92708) ***(P-15540)***
Gigamon Inc (HQ) ....C....408 831-4000
3300 Olcott St Santa Clara (95054) ***(P-24692)***
Gigavac LLC ....F....805 684-8401
6382 Rose Ln Carpinteria (93013) ***(P-17273)***
Gilbert Machine & Mfg, San Marcos *Also called Duplan Industries* ***(P-16451)***
Gilbert Martin Wdwkg Co Inc (PA) ....E....800 268-5669
2345 Britannia Blvd San Diego (92154) ***(P-4897)***
Gilbert Spray Coat Inc ....E....408 988-0747
300 Laurelwood Rd Santa Clara (95054) ***(P-13597)***
Gildedtree Inc ....F....925 246-5624
251 Lafayette Cir Ste 310 Lafayette (94549) ***(P-24693)***
Gilderfluke & Company Inc (PA) ....F....818 840-9484
205 S Flower St Burbank (91502) ***(P-17803)***
Gilead Colorado Inc ....C....650 574-3000
333 Lakeside Dr Foster City (94404) ***(P-8184)***
Gilead Palo Alto Inc ....B....909 394-4000
650 Cliffside Dr San Dimas (91773) ***(P-8185)***
Gilead Palo Alto Inc (HQ) ....D....650 384-8500
333 Lakeside Dr Foster City (94404) ***(P-8186)***
Gilead Sciences Inc (PA) ....B....650 574-3000
333 Lakeside Dr Foster City (94404) ***(P-8187)***
Gilead Sciences Inc ....F....909 394-4090
542 W Covina Blvd San Dimas (91773) ***(P-8188)***
Gilead Sciences Inc ....C....909 394-4000
650 Cliffside Dr San Dimas (91773) ***(P-8189)***
Gilead Scientist, San Dimas *Also called Gilead Palo Alto Inc* ***(P-8185)***
Gill Corporation (PA) ....C....626 443-6094
4056 Easy St El Monte (91731) ***(P-10118)***
Gillette Company ....F....949 851-2222
19900 Macarthur Blvd Irvine (92612) ***(P-11880)***
Gilli Inc ....F....213 744-9808
1100 S San Pedro St C07 Los Angeles (90015) ***(P-3657)***
Gillig LLC (HQ) ....B....510 785-1500
451 Discovery Dr Livermore (94551) ***(P-20208)***
Gillig LLC ....B....510 785-1500
451 Discovery Dr Livermore (94551) ***(P-20144)***
Gilwin Company ....E....209 522-9775
2354 Lapham Dr Modesto (95354) ***(P-12318)***
Gim Factory, Santa Fe Springs *Also called Taokaenoi Usa Inc* ***(P-2304)***
Gimelli Vineyards ....F....831 637-5445
403 Grass Valley Rd Hollister (95023) ***(P-1783)***
Gin'l Fabrics, Los Angeles *Also called Ax II Inc* ***(P-2797)***
Gina Designs ....F....707 967-1041
870 Sanitarium Rd Angwin (94576) ***(P-23267)***
Gina T Interior Accents, La Verne *Also called Joann Lammens* ***(P-24138)***
Ginger Golden Products Inc ....E....323 838-1070
5860 Bandini Blvd Commerce (90040) ***(P-914)***
Gingi Pak, Camarillo *Also called Belport Company Inc* ***(P-22859)***
Gino Corporation ....F....323 234-7979
555 E Jefferson Blvd Los Angeles (90011) ***(P-3056)***
Ginza Collection Design Inc ....E....562 531-1116
6015 Obispo Ave Long Beach (90805) ***(P-3310)***
Giovanni Cosmetics Inc ....D....310 952-9960
2064 E University Dr Rancho Dominguez (90220) ***(P-8754)***
Giovanni Hair Care & Cosmetics, Rancho Dominguez *Also called Giovanni Cosmetics Inc* ***(P-8754)***
Girard Food Service, City of Industry *Also called Gff Inc* ***(P-913)***
Girl Talk Clothing, Los Angeles *Also called C & Y Investment Inc* ***(P-3388)***
Gist Inc ....D....530 644-8000
4385 Pleasant Valley Rd Placerville (95667) ***(P-23766)***
Gist Silversmiths, Placerville *Also called Gist Inc* ***(P-23766)***
Git America Inc ....F....714 433-2180
230 Commerce Ste 190 Irvine (92602) ***(P-8479)***
Gitacloud Inc ....F....925 519-5965
5791 Athenour Ct Pleasanton (94588) ***(P-24694)***
Gits Manufacturing Company Inc ....C....641 782-2105
9250 Sepulveda Blvd # 202 North Hills (91343) ***(P-20353)***
Giuliano's Bakery, Carson *Also called Giuliano-Pagano Corporation* ***(P-1263)***
Giuliano-Pagano Corporation ....D....310 537-7700
1264 E Walnut St Carson (90746) ***(P-1263)***
Giustos Specialty Foods LLC (PA) ....E....650 873-6566
344 Littlefield Ave South San Francisco (94080) ***(P-1040)***
Giustos Specialty Foods LLC ....E....650 873-6566
241 E Harris Ave South San Francisco (94080) ***(P-1041)***
Given Imaging Los Angeles LLC ....C....310 641-8492
5860 Uplander Way Culver City (90230) ***(P-22981)***
Givens and Halpern Inc ....E....415 884-9999
1099 Essex Ave Richmond (94801) ***(P-1784)***
Giving Keys Inc ....D....213 935-8791
836 Traction Ave Los Angeles (90013) ***(P-23268)***
Gizmac Accessories LLC ....F....310 320-5563
20410 Earl St Torrance (90503) ***(P-15748)***
GK Foods Inc ....E....760 752-5230
133 Mata Way Ste 101 San Marcos (92069) ***(P-1042)***
GK Welding Inc ....F....510 233-0133
1150 Hensley St Richmond (94801) ***(P-25406)***
GKM International Llc ....D....310 791-7092
1725 Burbury Way San Marcos (92078) ***(P-10119)***
GKN Aerospace Camarillo Inc ....F....805 383-6684
4680 Calle Carga Camarillo (93012) ***(P-12599)***
GKN Aerospace Chem-Tronics Inc ....F....619 258-5012
1148 Bert Acosta St El Cajon (92020) ***(P-20650)***
GKN Aerospace Chem-Tronics Inc (HQ) ....A....619 448-2320
1150 W Bradley Ave El Cajon (92020) ***(P-20651)***
GKN Aerospace Transparency Sys (HQ) ....C....714 893-7531
12122 Western Ave Garden Grove (92841) ***(P-10120)***
GL Woodworking Inc ....D....949 515-2192
14341 Franklin Ave Tustin (92780) ***(P-4622)***
Glacier Design Systems Inc (PA) ....F....714 897-2337
5405 Production Dr Huntington Beach (92649) ***(P-1595)***
Glacier Foods Division, Westlake Village *Also called Dole Packaged Foods LLC* ***(P-947)***
Glacier Foods Division, Sanger *Also called Dole Packaged Foods LLC* ***(P-948)***
Glacier Ice Company, Elk Grove *Also called Glacier Valley Ice Company LP* ***(P-2413)***
Glacier Valley Ice Company LP (PA) ....E....916 394-2939
8580 Laguna Station Rd Elk Grove (95758) ***(P-2413)***
Glad Products Company (HQ) ....C....510 271-7000
1221 Broadway Ste A Oakland (94612) ***(P-9709)***
Gladding McBean, Lincoln *Also called Pabco Clay Products LLC* ***(P-10776)***
Gladding McBean, Lincoln *Also called Pabco Building Products LLC* ***(P-10803)***
Glas Werk Inc ....E....949 766-1296
29710 Ave De Las Bndra Rcho STA Marg (92688) ***(P-10643)***
Glaser Designs Inc ....F....415 552-3188
1469 Pacific Ave San Francisco (94109) ***(P-10548)***
Glasman Shim & Stamping Inc ....F....951 278-8197
226 N Sherman Ave Ste B Corona (92882) ***(P-15326)***
Glaspro, Santa Fe Springs *Also called GP Merger Sub Inc* ***(P-10703)***
Glass Fabrication and Dist, Stanton *Also called Newport Industrial Glass Inc* ***(P-10722)***

A
L
P
H
A
B
E
T
I
C

Employee Codes: A=Over 500 employees, B=251-500
C=101-250, D=51-100, E=20-50, F=10-19
2019 California
Manfacturers Register
© Mergent Inc. 1-800-342-5647
1151

Glass Shop of The North Bay, Petaluma *Also called Chad Empey* **(P-10592)**
Glasslab Inc....E....415 244-5584
209 Redwood Shores Pkwy Redwood City (94065) **(P-24695)**
Glassplax....E....951 677-4800
26605 Madison Ave Murrieta (92562) **(P-10700)**
Glasspoole Masonry Inc....F....805 368-0129
6645 Albatross St Ventura (93003) **(P-10852)**
Glasswerks Group, South Gate *Also called Glasswerks La Inc* **(P-10701)**
Glasswerks La Inc (HQ)....B....323 789-7800
8600 Rheem Ave South Gate (90280) **(P-10701)**
Glasswerks La Inc....E....800 729-1324
42005 Zevo Dr Temecula (92590) **(P-10593)**
Glastar Corporation....E....818 341-0301
8425 Canoga Ave Canoga Park (91304) **(P-14960)**
Glaukos Corporation (PA)....C....949 367-9600
229 Avenida Fabricante San Clemente (92672) **(P-22461)**
Glaxosmithkline Consumer....D....559 650-1550
2020 E Vine Ave Fresno (93706) **(P-8190)**
Glaxosmithkline LLC....E....925 833-1551
11205 Creekside Ct Dublin (94568) **(P-8191)**
Glaxosmithkline LLC....E....619 863-0399
2399 Hummingbird St Chula Vista (91915) **(P-8192)**
Glazier Steel Inc....D....510 471-5300
650 Sandoval Way Hayward (94544) **(P-12172)**
Glb Investment Inc....F....805 925-1971
2004 Preisker Ln Ste B Santa Maria (93454) **(P-23570)**
GLC General Inc....F....714 870-9825
100 W Walnut Ave Fullerton (92832) **(P-4623)**
Gleason Corporation (PA)....F....310 470-6001
10474 Santa Monica Blvd # 400 Los Angeles (90025) **(P-3764)**
Gledhill/Lyons Inc....E....714 502-0274
1521 N Placentia Ave Anaheim (92806) **(P-20825)**
Glen Ellen Carneros Winery, Sonoma *Also called Diageo North America Inc* **(P-1724)**
Glen-Mac Swiss Co....F....310 978-4555
12848 Weber Way Hawthorne (90250) **(P-19392)**
Glenco Manufacturing Company....E....909 984-3348
707 S Hope Ave Ontario (91761) **(P-13024)**
Glencore Ltd....E....562 427-6611
2020 Walnut Ave Long Beach (90806) **(P-9333)**
Glendale Iron....F....818 247-1098
4208 Chevy Chase Dr Los Angeles (90039) **(P-12857)**
Glendale Ready-Mixed Concrete, Los Angeles *Also called Viking Ready Mix Co Inc* **(P-11202)**
Glendale Rotary Offset Prtg Co (PA)....E....818 548-1847
434 Fernando Ct Glendale (91204) **(P-6834)**
Glendale Stl & Orna Ironworks, Los Angeles *Also called Glendale Iron* **(P-12857)**
Glendale Times, Glendale *Also called Los Angles Tmes Cmmnctions LLC* **(P-5922)**
Glengarry Manufacturing Inc....F....951 248-1111
1535 Marlborough Ave Riverside (92507) **(P-16536)**
Glenn Engineering Inc....F....209 667-4555
9850 3rd St Delhi (95315) **(P-20502)**
Glenoaks Food Inc....E....818 768-9091
11030 Randall St Sun Valley (91352) **(P-487)**
Glentek Inc....D....310 322-3026
208 Standard St El Segundo (90245) **(P-17198)**
Glidden Professional Paint Ctr, San Diego *Also called PPG Architectural Finishes Inc* **(P-7874)**
Glide-Write, Milpitas *Also called Marburg Technology Inc* **(P-15799)**
Glima Inc....F....818 980-9686
11133 Vanowen St Ste A North Hollywood (91605) **(P-3421)**
Glimmer Gear....F....619 399-9211
4337 Alabama St San Diego (92104) **(P-23571)**
Glimmerglass Networks Inc....E....510 780-1800
3945 Freedom Cir Ste 560 Santa Clara (95054) **(P-19553)**
Glo-Usa Inc....D....408 598-4400
1225 Bordeaux Dr Sunnyvale (94089) **(P-18858)**
Global Aerospace Tech Corp....E....818 407-5600
25109 Rye Canyon Loop Valencia (91355) **(P-20826)**
Global Aerostructures....F....909 987-4888
10291 Trademark St Ste C Rancho Cucamonga (91730) **(P-20827)**
Global Billiard Mfg Co Inc....E....310 764-5000
1141 Sandhill Ave Carson (90746) **(P-23572)**
Global Blood Therapeutics Inc....C....650 741-7700
171 Oyster Point Blvd South San Francisco (94080) **(P-8193)**
Global Casuals Inc....F....310 817-2828
18505 S Broadway Gardena (90248) **(P-3157)**
Global Circuit Solutions Inc....F....951 353-2780
4130 Flat Rock Dr Unit 1 Riverside (92505) **(P-18495)**
Global Comm Semiconductors LLC (HQ)....E....310 530-7274
23155 Kashiwa Ct Torrance (90505) **(P-18859)**
Global Compliance Inc....E....626 303-6855
438 W Chestnut Ave Ste A Monrovia (91016) **(P-6492)**
Global Contract Manufacturing, Union City *Also called Gcm Medical & OEM Division Inc* **(P-12595)**
Global Custom Security Inc....F....818 889-6900
755 Lakefield Rd Ste B Westlake Village (91361) **(P-19975)**
Global Distribution Services, Glendale *Also called Bowtie Inc* **(P-6114)**
Global Distribution Svcs, Irvine *Also called I-5 Publishing LLC* **(P-6187)**
Global Diversified Inds Inc (PA)....E....559 665-5800
1200 Airport Dr Chowchilla (93610) **(P-4574)**
Global Dolls Corp....F....916 645-3000
1903 Aviation Blvd Lincoln (95648) **(P-24108)**
Global Doors Corp....E....213 622-2003
1340 E 6th St Los Angeles (90021) **(P-4159)**
Global Edge LLC....E....888 315-2692
5230 Las Virgenes Rd # 265 Calabasas (91302) **(P-24696)**
Global Edge LLC (PA)....E....818 207-2694
5230 Las Virgenes Rd # 265 Calabasas (91302) **(P-24697)**
Global Elastomeric Pdts Inc....D....661 831-5380
5551 District Blvd Bakersfield (93313) **(P-14226)**
Global Electronics Intl, Rancho Cucamonga *Also called Mercury United Electronics Inc* **(P-19646)**
Global Enterprise Mfg Inc....E....657 234-1150
1560 S Harris Ct Anaheim (92806) **(P-24109)**
Global Environmental Pdts Inc....D....909 713-1600
5405 Industrial Pkwy San Bernardino (92407) **(P-20145)**
Global Fabricators, Shafter *Also called McM Fabricators Inc* **(P-12205)**
Global Foundries, Santa Clara *Also called Globalfoundries US Inc* **(P-14961)**
Global Future City Holding Inc....F....949 769-3550
2 Park Plz Ste 400 Irvine (92614) **(P-8194)**
Global Grid For Learning, Alameda *Also called Edutone Corporation* **(P-24593)**
Global Infovision Inc....F....714 738-4465
2290 Ardemore Dr Fullerton (92833) **(P-24698)**
Global Link Sourcing Inc....D....951 698-1977
41690 Corporate Center Ct Murrieta (92562) **(P-5523)**
Global Mfg Solutions LLC....E....562 356-3222
2100 E Valencia Dr Ste D Fullerton (92831) **(P-11664)**
Global Micro Solutions Inc....F....310 218-5678
21250 Hawthorne Blvd # 540 Torrance (90503) **(P-24699)**
Global Modular Inc (HQ)....E....559 665-5800
1200 Airport Dr Chowchilla (93610) **(P-4575)**
Global Motorsport Parts Inc....C....408 778-0500
155 E Main Ave Ste 150 Morgan Hill (95037) **(P-21112)**
Global Ocean Trading LLC....F....626 281-0800
430 S Grfield Ave Ste 405 Alhambra (91801) **(P-2296)**
Global Orthopedic Inc....F....480 861-5122
6540 Lusk Blvd Ste C255 San Diego (92121) **(P-22737)**
Global Packaging Solutions Inc....B....619 710-2661
6259 Progressive Dr # 200 San Diego (92154) **(P-5418)**
Global Packing Solutions Inc....F....408 279-4196
2139 S 10th St San Jose (95112) **(P-4522)**
Global Paper Solutions Inc....E....714 687-6102
100 S Anaheim Blvd # 250 Anaheim (92805) **(P-5284)**
Global Pcci (gpc) (PA)....C....757 637-9000
2465 Campus Dr Ste 100 Irvine (92612) **(P-13210)**
Global Plating Inc....E....510 659-8764
44620 S Grimmer Blvd Fremont (94538) **(P-13417)**
Global Polishing Solutions LLC (HQ)....E....619 295-5505
5220 Gaines St San Diego (92110) **(P-14169)**
Global Power Tech Group Inc....F....949 273-4373
20692 Prism Pl Lake Forest (92630) **(P-18860)**
Global Precision Manufacturing....F....831 239-9469
38 Hollins Dr Santa Cruz (95060) **(P-14170)**
Global Printing Sourcing & Dev, San Rafael *Also called Goff Investment Group LLC* **(P-6494)**
Global Pumice LLC....F....760 240-3544
19968 Bear Valley Rd C Apple Valley (92308) **(P-412)**
Global Sales Inc....E....310 474-7700
1732 Westwood Blvd Los Angeles (90024) **(P-8755)**
Global Silicones Inc....F....805 686-4500
49 Industrial Way Buellton (93427) **(P-9008)**
Global Specialties Direct, Oakland *Also called Global Steel Products Corp* **(P-5143)**
Global Steel Products Corp....E....510 652-2060
936 61st St Oakland (94608) **(P-5143)**
Global Sweeping Solutions, San Bernardino *Also called Global Environmental Pdts Inc* **(P-20145)**
Global Syn-Turf Inc....F....562 928-2800
6319 Chalet Dr Commerce (90040) **(P-24110)**
Global Tech Instruments Inc....F....714 375-1811
18380 Enterprise Ln Huntington Beach (92648) **(P-21300)**
Global Truss America LLC....D....323 415-6225
4295 Charter St Vernon (90058) **(P-11588)**
Global Unlimited Export LLC....F....213 365-7051
3407 W 6th St Ste 802 Los Angeles (90020) **(P-10549)**
Global Wave Group LLC....F....949 916-9800
8a Journey Ste 100 Aliso Viejo (92656) **(P-24700)**
Globalex Corporation....D....310 593-4833
2100 Abbot Kinney Blvd A Venice (90291) **(P-24701)**
Globalfoundries US Inc (HQ)....B....408 462-3900
2600 Great America Way Santa Clara (95054) **(P-14961)**
Globalscale Technologies Inc....F....714 632-9239
1200 N Van Buren St Ste D Anaheim (92807) **(P-15541)**
Globalux Lighting LLC....F....909 591-7506
2037 S Vineyard Ave Ontario (91761) **(P-17537)**
Globaluxe Inc....E....805 583-4600
2280 Ward Ave Simi Valley (93065) **(P-24111)**
Globalvision Systems Inc....F....888 227-7967
9401 Oakdale Ave Ste 100 Chatsworth (91311) **(P-15542)**
Globe Iron Foundry Inc (PA)....D....323 723-8983
5649 Randolph St Commerce (90040) **(P-11494)**
Globe Motors Inc....C....408 935-8989
1507 Gladding Ct Milpitas (95035) **(P-17199)**
Globe Plastics Inc....E....909 464-1520
13477 12th St Chino (91710) **(P-10121)**
Globe Rider Distribution, Vista *Also called Wax Research Inc* **(P-9458)**
Glockworx, Oxnard *Also called Zev Technologies Inc* **(P-13693)**
Gloria Ferrer Winery, Sonoma *Also called Freixenet Sonoma Caves Inc* **(P-1776)**
Gloria Lance Inc (PA)....D....310 767-4400
15616 S Broadway Gardena (90248) **(P-3238)**
Gloriann Farms Inc....C....209 221-7121
11104 W Tracy Blvd Tracy (95304) **(P-9861)**
Glovefit International Corp....F....559 243-1110
4705 N Sonora Ave Ste 108 Fresno (93722) **(P-10122)**
Glp Designs Inc....F....310 652-6800
916 W Hyde Park Blvd Inglewood (90302) **(P-5234)**
GLS Apparel Usa Inc....F....213 749-8484
1125 San Julian St C Los Angeles (90015) **(P-3311)**

Gluesmith Industries F 626 282-9390
801 S Raymond Ave Ste 39 Alhambra (91803) ***(P-9144)***
Gluesmith, The, Alhambra *Also called Gluesmith Industries* ***(P-9144)***
GM Associates Inc D 510 430-0806
9824 Kitty Ln Oakland (94603) ***(P-19554)***
GM Marble & Granite Inc F 925 676-8385
1375 Franquette Ave Ste F Concord (94520) ***(P-327)***
GM Nameplate Inc C 408 435-1666
2095 Otoole Ave San Jose (95131) ***(P-5713)***
GME Mfg Inc F 909 989-4478
10641 Pullman Ct Rancho Cucamonga (91730) ***(P-20828)***
GMI, San Diego *Also called Groundmetrics Inc* ***(P-218)***
Gmj Woodworking F 760 294-7428
2365 Mountain View Dr Escondido (92027) ***(P-4160)***
Gmm Inc E 323 874-1600
10152 Riverside Dr Toluca Lake (91602) ***(P-6493)***
Gmp Laboratories America Inc D 714 630-2467
2931 E La Jolla St Anaheim (92806) ***(P-8195)***
Gmp Manufacturing Inc E 707 751-3942
1340 Treat Blvd Ste 350 Walnut Creek (94597) ***(P-2530)***
Gmpc LLC F 707 766-1702
2180 S Mcdowell Blvd Petaluma (94954) ***(P-23889)***
Gms Elevator Services Inc E 909 599-3904
401 Borrego Ct San Dimas (91773) ***(P-14250)***
Gms Landscapes Inc D 805 402-3925
207 Camino Leon Camarillo (93012) ***(P-12037)***
Gms Molds (PA) F 310 684-1168
729 E 223rd St Carson (90745) ***(P-14522)***
Gmto Corporation D 626 204-0500
465 N Halstead St Ste 250 Pasadena (91107) ***(P-22078)***
GNA Industries Inc E 559 276-0953
4761 W Jacquelyn Ave Fresno (93722) ***(P-17274)***
GNB Corporation D 916 233-3543
3200 Dwight Rd Ste 100 Elk Grove (95758) ***(P-14381)***
GNB Vacuum Excellence Defined, Elk Grove *Also called GNB Corporation* ***(P-14381)***
Gnekow Family Winery LLC F 209 463-0697
17347 E Gawne Rd Stockton (95215) ***(P-1785)***
Gnosis International Llc E 858 254-6369
8008 Westbury Ave San Diego (92126) ***(P-8480)***
Go Green Mobile Power LLC F 877 800-4467
171 Pier Ave Ste 105 Santa Monica (90405) ***(P-17200)***
Go Logo, Van Nuys *Also called Dee Sign Co* ***(P-23855)***
Go Rhino, Brea *Also called Iddea California LLC* ***(P-20367)***
Goalsr Inc (PA) E 650 453-5844
3139 Independence Dr Livermore (94551) ***(P-24702)***
Gobeme, San Francisco *Also called Onc Holdings Inc* ***(P-24985)***
Goddard Rotary Tool Co Inc F 760 743-6717
525 Opper St Escondido (92029) ***(P-14382)***
Goddess of Gadgets, South Pasadena *Also called Ximenez Icons* ***(P-3758)***
Godiva Chocolatier Inc E 415 566-5058
3251 20th Ave Ste 154 San Francisco (94132) ***(P-1470)***
Goengineer Inc F 818 716-1650
6400 Canoga Ave Ste 121 Woodland Hills (91367) ***(P-24703)***
Goeppner Industries Inc F 310 784-2800
22924 Lockness Ave Torrance (90501) ***(P-16537)***
Goff Corporation E 415 526-1370
10 Paul Dr San Rafael (94903) ***(P-6345)***
Goff Investment Group LLC F 415 456-2934
980 Lincoln Ave Ste 200b San Rafael (94901) ***(P-6494)***
Goharddrive Inc F 626 593-9927
137 S 8th Ave Ste E La Puente (91746) ***(P-15543)***
Goharddrive.com, La Puente *Also called Goharddrive Inc* ***(P-15543)***
Gold Belt Line Inc F 619 424-5544
1547 Jayken Way Ste C Chula Vista (91911) ***(P-3103)***
Gold Coast Bakeries, Santa Ana *Also called Gold Coast Baking Company Inc* ***(P-1264)***
Gold Coast Baking Company Inc (PA) D 714 545-2253
1590 E Saint Gertrude Pl Santa Ana (92705) ***(P-1264)***
Gold Coast Ironworks F 805 485-6921
531 Montgomery Ave Oxnard (93036) ***(P-12858)***
Gold Coast Label, Santa Fe Springs *Also called Gc Labels LLC* ***(P-7326)***
Gold Coast Solar LLC E 310 351-7229
1975 Hillgate Way Apt G Simi Valley (93065) ***(P-18861)***
Gold Couture 22 K F 760 602-0690
6406 Kinglet Way Carlsbad (92011) ***(P-23269)***
Gold Craft Jewelry Corp (PA) F 213 623-5460
640 S Hill St Ste 650 Los Angeles (90014) ***(P-23270)***
Gold Craft Jewelry Corp E 213 623-8673
640 S Hill St Ste 650 Los Angeles (90014) ***(P-23271)***
Gold Crest Industries Inc E 909 930-9069
1018 E Acacia St Ontario (91761) ***(P-3765)***
Gold Leaf & Metallic Powders E 323 769-4888
6001 Santa Monica Blvd Los Angeles (90038) ***(P-24112)***
Gold Leaf Cigar Co, Azusa *Also called California Master Printers* ***(P-6715)***
Gold Panner, The, Placerville *Also called El Dorado Gold Panner Inc* ***(P-5842)***
Gold Peak Inds N Amer Inc E 858 674-6099
11245 W Bernardo Ct # 104 San Diego (92127) ***(P-19810)***
Gold Prospectors Assn Amer, Temecula *Also called Gold Prospectors Assn of Amer* ***(P-6172)***
Gold Prospectors Assn of Amer E 951 699-4749
43445 Bus Pk Dr Ste 113 Temecula (92590) ***(P-6172)***
Gold River Mills LLC (PA) D 530 661-1923
1620 E Kentucky Ave Woodland (95776) ***(P-1083)***
Gold Rush Kettle Korn Llc E 707 747-6773
4690 E 2nd St Ste 9 Benicia (94510) ***(P-1425)***
Gold Technologies Inc E 408 321-9568
1648 Mabury Rd Ste A San Jose (95133) ***(P-17469)***
Gold Venture Inc C 909 623-1810
1050 S State College Blvd Fullerton (92831) ***(P-9862)***
Goldak Inc E 818 240-2666
15835 Monte St Ste 104 Sylmar (91342) ***(P-21301)***
Golden Altos Corporation E 408 956-1010
402 S Hillview Dr Milpitas (95035) ***(P-21764)***
Golden Applexx Co Inc E 909 594-9788
19805 Harrison Ave Walnut (91789) ***(P-7328)***
Golden Bear Sportswear, San Francisco *Also called Colloquy LLC* ***(P-3611)***
Golden Bolt LLC F 818 626-8261
9361 Canoga Ave Chatsworth (91311) ***(P-13070)***
Golden By-Poducts Inc D 209 668-4855
13000 Newport Rd Ballico (95303) ***(P-14962)***
Golden Coast Sportswear Inc E 714 704-4655
1140 E Howell Ave Anaheim (92805) ***(P-3422)***
Golden Color Printing Inc E 626 455-0850
9353 Rush St South El Monte (91733) ***(P-6835)***
Golden Empire Concrete Co E 661 325-6990
8211 Gosford Rd Bakersfield (93313) ***(P-11113)***
Golden Empire Dental Lab Inc F 661 327-1888
929 21st St Bakersfield (93301) ***(P-22881)***
Golden Farms, Canoga Park *Also called Protemach Inc* ***(P-9032)***
Golden Fleece Designs Inc F 323 849-1901
441 S Victory Blvd Burbank (91502) ***(P-3788)***
Golden Gate Baldor, Hayward *Also called ABB Motors and Mechanical Inc* ***(P-17174)***
Golden Gate Capital, San Francisco *Also called Ggc Administration LLC* ***(P-5189)***
Golden Gate Freightliner Inc C 559 486-4310
2727 E Central Ave Fresno (93725) ***(P-14325)***
Golden Gate Hosiery Inc E 909 464-0805
14095 Laurelwood Pl Chino (91710) ***(P-2812)***
Golden Gate Litho F 510 568-5335
11144 Golf Links Rd Oakland (94605) ***(P-6836)***
Golden Gate Tofu Incorporated F 415 822-5613
1265 Griffith St San Francisco (94124) ***(P-1508)***
Golden Gate Truck Center, Fresno *Also called Golden Gate Freightliner Inc* ***(P-14325)***
Golden Island Jerky Co Inc (HQ) E 844 362-3222
10646 Fulton Ct Rancho Cucamonga (91730) ***(P-488)***
Golden Island Jerky Co Inc F 844 362-3222
9955 6th St Rancho Cucamonga (91730) ***(P-489)***
Golden Kraft Inc D 562 926-8888
15500 Valley View Ave La Mirada (90638) ***(P-5714)***
Golden Mattress Co Inc D 323 887-1888
4231 Firestone Blvd South Gate (90280) ***(P-4861)***
Golden Octagon Inc D 650 369-8573
2537 Middlefield Rd Redwood City (94063) ***(P-1265)***
Golden Office Trailers Inc E 951 678-2177
18257 Grand Ave Lake Elsinore (92530) ***(P-21204)***
Golden Pacific, Pomona *Also called Travelers Choice Travelware* ***(P-10540)***
Golden Pacific Seafoods Inc E 714 589-8888
700 S Raymond Ave Fullerton (92831) ***(P-14855)***
Golden Phoenix Bakery, San Leandro *Also called Triple C Foods Inc* ***(P-1385)***
Golden Plastics Corporation F 510 569-6465
8465 Baldwin St Oakland (94621) ***(P-10123)***
Golden Queen Mining Co LLC C 661 824-4300
2818 Silver Queen Rd Mojave (93501) ***(P-4)***
Golden Rule Bindery Inc E 760 471-2013
242 Bingham Dr Ste 101 San Marcos (92069) ***(P-7599)***
Golden Rule Packaging, San Marcos *Also called Golden Rule Bindery Inc* ***(P-7599)***
Golden Sheaf Bread Co Inc E 831 722-0179
125 Hangar Way Ste 230 Watsonville (95076) ***(P-1266)***
Golden Specialty Foods LLC E 562 802-2537
14605 Best Ave Norwalk (90650) ***(P-2531)***
Golden Spoon Frozen Yogurt E 949 888-8810
31431 Santa Margarita Rcho STA Marg (92688) ***(P-675)***
Golden Spoon of R S M, Rcho STA Marg *Also called Golden Spoon Frozen Yogurt* ***(P-675)***
Golden Star Silk Screen, Commerce *Also called Lucky Star Silkscreen LLC* ***(P-7392)***
Golden State Assembly Inc B 510 226-8155
47823 Westinghouse Dr Fremont (94539) ***(P-11395)***
Golden State Casket Co E 323 268-1783
1705 N Indiana St Los Angeles (90063) ***(P-24011)***
Golden State Donor Services, West Sacramento *Also called DCI Donor Services Inc* ***(P-14058)***
Golden State Drilling Inc D 661 589-0730
3500 Fruitvale Ave Bakersfield (93308) ***(P-105)***
Golden State Engineering Inc C 562 634-3125
15338 Garfield Ave Paramount (90723) ***(P-14752)***
Golden State Foods Corp (PA) E 949 247-8000
18301 Von Karman Ave # 1100 Irvine (92612) ***(P-2266)***
Golden State Foods Corp C 626 968-6431
640 S 6th Ave City of Industry (91746) ***(P-995)***
Golden State Granite Inc F 925 825-5888
1001 Shary Cir Ste 9 Concord (94518) ***(P-5063)***
Golden State Graphics, San Marcos *Also called GSG LLC* ***(P-6842)***
Golden State Medical Sup Inc C 805 477-9866
5187 Camino Ruiz Camarillo (93012) ***(P-8196)***
Golden State Mixing Inc E 209 632-3656
415 D St Turlock (95380) ***(P-727)***
Golden State Shutters, Dixon *Also called Victorian Shutters Inc* ***(P-4252)***
Golden State Steel & Stair Inc (PA) E 707 455-0400
479 Mason St Vacaville (95688) ***(P-12173)***
Golden State Vintners (PA) F 707 254-4900
4596 S Tracy Blvd Tracy (95377) ***(P-1786)***
Golden State Vintners E 707 254-1985
1075 Golden Gate Dr NAPA (94558) ***(P-1787)***
Golden State Vintners E 831 678-3991
1777 Metz Rd Soledad (93960) ***(P-1788)***
Golden State Vintners E 707 553-6480
1175 Commmerce Blvd Vallejo (94503) ***(P-1789)***
Golden Supreme Inc E 562 903-1063
12304 Mccann Dr Santa Fe Springs (90670) ***(P-24113)***
Golden Temple, Los Angeles *Also called East West Tea Company LLC* ***(P-1057)***

A L P H A B E T I C

Employee Codes: A=Over 500 employees, B=251-500
C=101-250, D=51-100, E=20-50, F=10-19
2019 California
Manfacturers Register
© Mergent Inc. 1-800-342-5647
1153

Golden Textile Inc ....F....323 620-2612
2922 S Main St Los Angeles (90007) *(P-2740)*
Golden Tiger, Los Angeles *Also called Ajinomoto Windsor Inc (P-977)*
Golden Valley Dairy Products ....C....559 687-1188
1025 E Bardsley Ave Tulare (93274) *(P-575)*
Golden Valley Industries Inc ....E....209 939-3370
960 Lone Palm Ave Modesto (95351) *(P-437)*
Golden Vantage LLC ....F....626 255-3362
8807 Rochester Ave Rancho Cucamonga (91730) *(P-4624)*
Golden Vly Grape Jice Wine LLC (PA) ....E....559 661-4657
11770 Road 27 1/2 Madera (93637) *(P-1790)*
Golden W Ppr Converting Corp (PA) ....E....510 317-0646
16500 Worthley Dr San Lorenzo (94580) *(P-15207)*
Golden West Envelope Corp ....E....510 452-5419
1009 Morton St Alameda (94501) *(P-5674)*
Golden West Food Group Inc (PA) ....E....888 807-3663
4401 S Downey Rd Vernon (90058) *(P-438)*
Golden West Glass ....F....707 939-9604
18153 Highway 12 Sonoma (95476) *(P-10702)*
Golden West Homes, Perris *Also called Clayton Homes Inc (P-4550)*
Golden West Jewelers, San Diego *Also called G W Manufacturing Jewelers (P-23265)*
Golden West Machine Inc ....E....562 903-1111
9930 Jordan Cir Santa Fe Springs (90670) *(P-16538)*
Golden West Refining Company ....E....562 921-3581
13116 Imperial Hwy Santa Fe Springs (90670) *(P-9334)*
Golden West Shutters, Lake Forest *Also called ABC Custom Wood Shutters Inc (P-4097)*
Golden West Technology ....D....714 738-3775
1180 E Valencia Dr Fullerton (92831) *(P-18496)*
Goldencorr Sheets LLC ....C....626 369-6446
13890 Nelson Ave City of Industry (91746) *(P-5419)*
Goldeneye, Saint Helena *Also called Duckhorn Wine Company (P-1735)*
Goldeneye Winery, Philo *Also called Duckhorn Wine Company (P-1736)*
Goldensol Music LLC ....F....877 246-8958
200 Valley Dr Ste 14 Brisbane (94005) *(P-15749)*
Goldenwood Truss Corporation ....D....805 659-2520
11032 Nardo St Ventura (93004) *(P-4406)*
Goldfarb & Associates, Santa Monica *Also called Adolf Goldfarb (P-23404)*
Goldilocks, Hayward *Also called Clarmil Manufacturing Corp (P-2489)*
Goldilocks Bakeshop and Rest, Santa Fe Springs *Also called Goldilocks Corp California (P-1267)*
Goldilocks Corp California (PA) ....E....562 946-9995
10329 Painter Ave Santa Fe Springs (90670) *(P-1267)*
Golding Publications ....F....951 244-1966
31558 Railroad Canyon Rd Canyon Lake (92587) *(P-7629)*
Goldman Global Greenfield Inc ....F....323 589-3444
2025 E 48th St Vernon (90058) *(P-10124)*
Goldsign, Huntington Park *Also called Citizens of Humanity LLC (P-3393)*
Goldstar Asphalt Products, Perris *Also called Npg Inc (P-9390)*
Goldstone Land Company LLC ....E....209 368-3113
11900 Furry Rd Lodi (95240) *(P-1791)*
Goldtec USA, San Jose *Also called Gold Technologies Inc (P-17469)*
Golet Wine Estates, NAPA *Also called Clos Du Val Wine Company Ltd (P-1697)*
Goleta Coffee Company, Goleta *Also called Grind Food Company Inc (P-16545)*
Golf Apparel Brands Inc ....C....310 327-5188
13621 S Main St Los Angeles (90061) *(P-3423)*
Golf Buddy, Santa Fe Springs *Also called Deca International Corp (P-21284)*
Golf Design Inc ....D....714 899-4040
10523 Humbolt St Los Alamitos (90720) *(P-23573)*
Golf Design USA, Los Alamitos *Also called Golf Design Inc (P-23573)*
Golnex Inc ....E....510 490-6003
4259 Aplicella Ct Manteca (95337) *(P-14753)*
Gomberg Fredrikson & Assoc, Woodside *Also called Wine Company of San Francisco (P-2061)*
Gomen Furniture Mfg Inc ....E....310 635-4894
11612 Wright Rd Lynwood (90262) *(P-4779)*
Gondola Skate Mvg Systems Inc (PA) ....F....619 222-6487
9941 Prospect Ave Santee (92071) *(P-11396)*
Gonz's, Los Angeles *Also called Fresh Jive Manufacturing Inc (P-3055)*
Gonzalez Feliciano ....F....909 236-1372
1583 E Grand Ave Pomona (91766) *(P-4161)*
Gooch & Housego Palo Alto LLC (HQ) ....D....650 856-7911
44247 Nobel Dr Fremont (94538) *(P-19555)*
Gooch and Housego Cal LLC ....D....805 529-3324
5390 Kazuko Ct Moorpark (93021) *(P-22079)*
Good Neighbor Pharmacy, Encino *Also called Zelzah Pharmacy Inc (P-8450)*
Good Worldwide LLC ....E....323 206-6495
6380 Wilshire Blvd # 1500 Los Angeles (90048) *(P-6495)*
Good-West Rubber Corp (PA) ....D....909 987-1774
9615 Feron Blvd Rancho Cucamonga (91730) *(P-9617)*
Goodall Guitars Inc ....F....707 962-1620
541 S Franklin St Fort Bragg (95437) *(P-23373)*
Goodco Inc ....F....415 425-1012
543 Howard St Fl 4 San Francisco (94105) *(P-24704)*
Goodrich Aerostructures, Chula Vista *Also called Goodrich Corporation (P-20830)*
Goodrich Corporation ....F....562 906-7372
11120 Norwalk Blvd Santa Fe Springs (90670) *(P-20829)*
Goodrich Corporation ....D....619 691-4111
850 Lagoon Dr Chula Vista (91910) *(P-20830)*
Goodrich Corporation ....C....714 984-1461
2727 E Imperial Hwy Brea (92821) *(P-20831)*
Goodrich Corporation ....E....707 422-1880
3530 Branscombe Rd Fairfield (94533) *(P-21192)*
Goodrich Corporation ....D....562 944-4441
9920 Freeman Ave Santa Fe Springs (90670) *(P-20832)*
Goodrx Inc (PA) ....F....310 500-6544
233 Wilshire Blvd Ste 990 Santa Monica (90401) *(P-24705)*
Goodway Printing, Poway *Also called Streeter Printing (P-7119)*
Goodwest Linings & Coatings, Rancho Cucamonga *Also called Goodwest Rubber Linings Inc (P-9618)*
Goodwest Rubber Linings Inc ....E....888 499-0085
8814 Industrial Ln Rancho Cucamonga (91730) *(P-9618)*
Goodwin Ammonia Company (PA) ....F....714 894-0531
12102 Industry St Garden Grove (92841) *(P-8643)*
Goodyear Rbr Co Southern Cal, Rancho Cucamonga *Also called Good-West Rubber Corp (P-9617)*
Goomby LLC ....F....323 556-0637
8350 Wilshire Blvd # 200 Beverly Hills (90211) *(P-23574)*
Goomby Skateboarding, Beverly Hills *Also called Goomby LLC (P-23574)*
Goorin Bros Inc (PA) ....E....415 431-9196
1890 Bryant St Ste 208 San Francisco (94110) *(P-3562)*
Goorin Brosinc ....F....
23787 Eichler St Ste E Hayward (94545) *(P-3563)*
Goose Manufacturing Inc ....F....408 747-0940
1853 Little Orchard St San Jose (95125) *(P-16539)*
Goosecross Cellars A Cal Corp ....F....707 944-1986
1119 State Ln Yountville (94599) *(P-1792)*
Goosecross Cellars Coorstek ....F....707 944-1986
1119 State Ln Yountville (94599) *(P-1793)*
Gopro Inc (PA) ....B....650 332-7600
3000 Clearview Way San Mateo (94402) *(P-23161)*
Gordon Biersch Brewing Company ....D....408 792-1546
357 E Taylor St San Jose (95112) *(P-1596)*
Gordon Brush Mfg Co Inc (PA) ....D....323 724-7777
3737 Capitol Ave City of Industry (90601) *(P-23792)*
Gordon Laboratories Inc ....C....310 327-5240
751 E Artesia Blvd Carson (90746) *(P-8756)*
Gores Radio Holdings LLC ....A....310 209-3010
10877 Wilshire Blvd # 1805 Los Angeles (90024) *(P-19976)*
Gorilla Automotive Products, Vernon *Also called Amcor Industries Inc (P-20251)*
Gorilla Circuits (PA) ....C....408 294-9897
1445 Oakland Rd San Jose (95112) *(P-18497)*
Gorlitz Sewer & Drain Inc ....E....562 944-3060
10132 Norwalk Blvd Santa Fe Springs (90670) *(P-16046)*
Gorlitz Sewer and Drain, Santa Fe Springs *Also called Die Craft Stamping Inc (P-13763)*
Gory Electric Motors Inc ....F....323 221-3169
2015 N San Fernando Rd Los Angeles (90065) *(P-25462)*
Gospel Recordings Inc ....E....951 719-1650
41823 Enterprise Cir N Temecula (92590) *(P-17901)*
Gosub 60 ....F....310 394-4760
1334 3rd Street Promenade # 309 Santa Monica (90401) *(P-15750)*
Goto California Inc (HQ) ....C....619 691-8722
6120 Bus Ctr Ct Ste F200 San Diego (92154) *(P-17804)*
Gould & Bass Company Inc ....E....909 623-6793
1431 W 2nd St Pomona (91766) *(P-21765)*
Goulds Pumps ....E....562 949-2113
3951 Capitol Ave City of Industry (90601) *(P-15068)*
Gourmet Coffee Warehouse Inc ....D....818 423-2626
11275 Chandler Blvd North Hollywood (91601) *(P-2350)*
Gourmet Coffee Warehouse Inc (PA) ....E....323 871-8930
920 N Formosa Ave Los Angeles (90046) *(P-2351)*
Government Travel Directory, Santa Barbara *Also called Federal Buyers Guide Inc (P-6483)*
Governmentjobscom Inc ....C....310 426-6304
300 Continental Blvd # 565 El Segundo (90245) *(P-24706)*
GP Batteries, San Diego *Also called Gold Peak Inds N Amer Inc (P-19810)*
GP Color Imaging Group, North Hollywood *Also called Wes Go Inc (P-7537)*
GP Design Inc ....F....310 638-8737
1185 W Mahalo Pl Compton (90220) *(P-3895)*
GP Electric, Pomona *Also called G Powell Electric (P-25460)*
GP Industries Inc ....F....805 227-6565
3230 Rvrsid Ave Ste 110 Paso Robles (93446) *(P-23575)*
GP Machining Inc ....E....805 686-0852
94 Commerce Dr Buellton (93427) *(P-16540)*
GP Merger Sub Inc ....D....562 946-7722
9401 Ann St Santa Fe Springs (90670) *(P-10703)*
Gpr Stabilizer LLC ....F....619 661-0101
8715 Dead Stick Rd San Diego (92154) *(P-21113)*
Gps Logic LLC ....F....949 812-6942
1327 Calle Avanzado San Clemente (92673) *(P-18113)*
Gps Metals Lab Inc ....E....858 433-6125
12396 World Trade Dr San Diego (92128) *(P-11558)*
Grab Green, Camarillo *Also called Maddiebrit Products LLC (P-8916)*
Grace Communications Inc (PA) ....E....213 628-4384
210 S Spring St Los Angeles (90012) *(P-5866)*
Grace Dvson Discovery Sciences, Hesperia *Also called W R Grace & Co - Conn (P-22048)*
Grace Machine Co Inc ....E....323 771-6215
4540 Cecilia St Cudahy (90201) *(P-16541)*
Gracie Collection, Rancho Santa Fe *Also called Black Silver Enterprises Inc (P-3386)*
Grade A Sign LLC ....E....310 652-9700
529 N La Cienega Blvd # 300 West Hollywood (90048) *(P-23890)*
Gradescope Inc ....F....702 985-7442
2054 University Ave # 600 Berkeley (94704) *(P-24707)*
Grading and Excavating Mag, Santa Barbara *Also called Forester Communications Inc (P-6164)*
Graffeo Leather Collection, San Carlos *Also called Meskin Khosrow Kay (P-10568)*
Graffiti Entertainment LLC ....F....650 654-4800
3000 Bridge Pkwy Ste 101 Redwood City (94065) *(P-17805)*
Grafico Inc ....F....562 404-4976
15320 Cornet St Santa Fe Springs (90670) *(P-7645)*
Grafix Screen Printing, Cotati *Also called H & H Enterprises Inc (P-7340)*
Graham Lee Associates Inc ....F....323 581-8203
8674 Atlantic Ave South Gate (90280) *(P-4947)*
Graham Packaging Co Europe LLC ....C....909 989-5367
11555 Arrow Rte Rancho Cucamonga (91730) *(P-9799)*
Graham Packaging Company LP ....D....714 979-1835
3300 W Segerstrom Ave Santa Ana (92704) *(P-10125)*

Mergent e-mail: customerrelations@mergent.com
1154
2019 California
Manufacturers Register
(P-0000) Products & Services Section entry number
(PA)=Parent Co (HQ)=Headquarters (DH)=Div Headquarters

Graham Packaging Company LP ....E 909 484-2900
9041 Pittsburgh Ave Rancho Cucamonga (91730) ***(P-10126)***
Graham Packaging Company LP ....D 209 578-1112
513 S Mcclure Rd Modesto (95357) ***(P-10127)***
Graham Webb International Inc (HQ) ....D 760 918-3600
6109 De Soto Ave Woodland Hills (91367) ***(P-8757)***
Grain Craft Inc ....E 323 585-0131
1861 E 55th St Los Angeles (90058) ***(P-1043)***
Grainless Goodness, Ojai *Also called Ellen Lark Farm* ***(P-1058)***
Gramberg Machine Inc ....F 805 278-4500
500 Spectrum Cir Oxnard (93030) ***(P-16542)***
Gramercy Aerospace Mfg LLC ....F 310 515-0576
17224 Gramercy Pl Gardena (90247) ***(P-21302)***
Gramic Enterprises Inc ....F 714 329-8627
21770 Deveron Cv Yorba Linda (92887) ***(P-1597)***
Gramicci Comfort Engineered, Agoura Hills *Also called Sole Survivor Corporation* ***(P-3501)***
Granatelli Motor Sports Inc ....E 805 486-6644
1000 Yamell Pl Oxnard (93033) ***(P-20354)***
Granath & Granath Inc ....E 310 327-5740
1930 W Rosecrans Ave Gardena (90249) ***(P-13418)***
Granberg International, Pittsburg *Also called Granberg Pump and Meter Ltd* ***(P-14705)***
Granberg Pump and Meter Ltd ....F 707 562-2099
1051 Los Medanos St Pittsburg (94565) ***(P-14705)***
Grand American Millwork, La Mirada *Also called G A Doors Inc* ***(P-4156)***
Grand Casino On Main Inc ....E 310 253-9066
3826 Main St Culver City (90232) ***(P-1268)***
Grand Fusion Housewares Inc (PA) ....F 888 614-7263
12 Partridge Irvine (92604) ***(P-10128)***
Grand General Accessories Mfg ....E 310 631-2589
1965 E Vista Bella Way Rancho Dominguez (90220) ***(P-17096)***
Grand Meadows Inc ....F 714 628-1690
1607 W Orange Grove Ave E Orange (92868) ***(P-8197)***
Grand Metals Inc ....F 310 327-5554
325 N Cota St Corona (92880) ***(P-11397)***
Grand Motif Records ....F 562 698-8538
8304 Enramada Ave Whittier (90605) ***(P-17902)***
Grand Pacific Fire Protection ....F 951 226-8304
13100 Red Corral Dr Corona (92883) ***(P-14127)***
Grand Packaging Pet Tech ....D 209 578-1112
513 S Mcclure Rd Modesto (95357) ***(P-10129)***
Grand Printing, Covina *Also called William J Hammett Inc* ***(P-7187)***
Grand Textile, Cerritos *Also called Dool Fna Inc* ***(P-2776)***
Grand West Inc (PA) ....F 323 235-2700
1441 E Adams Blvd Los Angeles (90011) ***(P-2841)***
Grand-Way Fabri-Graphic Inc ....E 818 206-8560
22550 Lamplight Pl Santa Clarita (91350) ***(P-13598)***
Grandesign Decor Inc ....E 408 436-9969
1727 N 1st St San Jose (95112) ***(P-12319)***
Grandis Inc ....F 408 945-2160
1123 Cadillac Ct Milpitas (95035) ***(P-15544)***
Grandis Metals Intl Corp ....F 949 459-2621
29752 Ave De Las Bndra Rcho STA Marg (92688) ***(P-11629)***
Grandis Titanium, Rcho STA Marg *Also called Grandis Metals Intl Corp* ***(P-11629)***
Granite Construction Inc ....D 805 879-0033
999 Mission Rock Rd Santa Paula (93060) ***(P-9405)***
Granite Gold Inc ....F 858 499-8933
9170 Chesapeake Dr San Diego (92123) ***(P-8644)***
Granite Kitchen Countertops, Concord *Also called GM Marble & Granite Inc* ***(P-327)***
Granite Rock Co (PA) ....D 831 768-2000
350 Technology Dr Watsonville (95076) ***(P-359)***
Granite Rock Co ....E 650 482-3800
365 Blomquist St Redwood City (94063) ***(P-9385)***
Granite Rock Co ....E 831 392-3700
1755 Del Monte Blvd Seaside (93955) ***(P-11114)***
Granite Rock Co ....D 831 768-2300
Quarry Rd Aromas (95004) ***(P-360)***
Granite Software Inc ....F 818 252-1950
7590 N Glenoaks Blvd # 102 Burbank (91504) ***(P-24708)***
Granitize Products Inc ....D 562 923-5438
11022 Vulcan St South Gate (90280) ***(P-8645)***
Grant Piston Rings, Anaheim *Also called Rtr Industries LLC* ***(P-16152)***
Grape Links Inc ....F 707 524-8000
420 Aviation Blvd Ste 106 Santa Rosa (95403) ***(P-1794)***
Grapheex, Simi Valley *Also called Pars Publishing Corp* ***(P-7016)***
Graphic Color Systems Inc ....D 323 283-3000
1166 W Garvey Ave Monterey Park (91754) ***(P-6837)***
Graphic Dies Inc ....F 562 946-1802
12335 Florence Ave Santa Fe Springs (90670) ***(P-7646)***
Graphic Film Group LLC (PA) ....F 310 887-6330
1901 Avenue Of The Stars Los Angeles (90067) ***(P-6173)***
Graphic Fox Inc ....F 530 895-1359
3124 Thorntree Dr Chico (95973) ***(P-6838)***
Graphic Packaging Intl Inc ....C 949 250-0900
1600 Barranca Pkwy Irvine (92606) ***(P-5350)***
Graphic Packaging Intl LLC ....C 559 651-3535
1600 Kelsey Rd Visalia (93291) ***(P-5285)***
Graphic Packaging Intl LLC ....C 530 533-1058
525 Airport Pkwy Oroville (95965) ***(P-7329)***
Graphic Prints Inc ....E 310 768-0474
1200 Kona Dr Compton (90220) ***(P-3896)***
Graphic Research Inc ....E 818 886-7340
9334 Mason Ave Chatsworth (91311) ***(P-18498)***
Graphic Sciences Inc ....F 909 947-3366
4663 E Guasti Rd Ste B Ontario (91761) ***(P-9198)***
Graphic Source, The, San Rafael *Also called Bennett Industries Inc* ***(P-6692)***
Graphic Systems, Lompoc *Also called Henry L Hudson* ***(P-6852)***
Graphic Systems ....F 805 686-0705
1693 Mission Dr Ste C101 Solvang (93463) ***(P-7330)***
Graphic Trends Incorporated ....E 562 531-2339
7301 Adams St Paramount (90723) ***(P-7331)***
Graphic Visions Inc ....E 818 845-8393
7119 Fair Ave North Hollywood (91605) ***(P-6839)***
Graphicom Digital, Santa Fe Springs *Also called Pressline Ink and Sup Co Inc* ***(P-7655)***
Graphicpak Corporation ....F 323 306-3054
760 S Vail Ave Montebello (90640) ***(P-5420)***
Graphics 2000 LLC ....D 714 879-1188
1600 E Valencia Dr Fullerton (92831) ***(P-7332)***
Graphics Bindery ....F 818 886-2463
16611 Roscoe Pl North Hills (91343) ***(P-7600)***
Graphics Factory Inc ....F 818 727-9040
21344 Superior St Chatsworth (91311) ***(P-7333)***
Graphics Ink Lithography LLC ....F 760 438-9052
5531 Foxtail Loop Carlsbad (92010) ***(P-7334)***
Graphics United, Covina *Also called Shift Calendars Inc* ***(P-7103)***
Graphiq LLC ....C 805 335-2433
101a Innovation Pl Santa Barbara (93108) ***(P-6496)***
Graphix Press Inc ....E 818 834-8520
13814 Del Sur St San Fernando (91340) ***(P-6840)***
Graphtec America Inc (HQ) ....E 949 770-6010
17462 Armstrong Ave Irvine (92614) ***(P-21596)***
Grass Manufacturing Co Inc ....F 650 366-2556
2850 Bay Rd Redwood City (94063) ***(P-13211)***
Grass Valley Inc ....A 530 478-3000
125 Crown Point Ct Grass Valley (95945) ***(P-18114)***
Grass Valley Inc (HQ) ....C 530 265-1000
125 Crown Point Ct Grass Valley (95945) ***(P-18115)***
Grass Valley Usa LLC (HQ) ....B 800 547-8949
125 Crown Point Ct Grass Valley (95945) ***(P-18116)***
Grateful Naturals Corp ....F 323 379-4553
213 Walter Ave Newbury Park (91320) ***(P-8758)***
Grating Pacific Inc (PA) ....E 562 598-4314
3651 Sausalito St Los Alamitos (90720) ***(P-12174)***
Grau Design Inc ....F 323 461-4462
1133 N Highland Ave Los Angeles (90038) ***(P-3239)***
Gravity Boarding Company Inc ....F 760 591-4144
2211 S Hcnda Blvd Ste 201 Hacienda Heights (91745) ***(P-23576)***
Graybills Metal Polishing Inc ....F 626 967-5742
1212 E Puente Ave West Covina (91790) ***(P-13419)***
Grayd-A Prcsion Met Fbricators ....E 562 944-8951
13233 Florence Ave Santa Fe Springs (90670) ***(P-12600)***
Graypay LLC ....D 818 387-6735
6345 Balboa Blvd Ste 115 Encino (91316) ***(P-24709)***
Graysix Company ....E 510 845-5936
2427 4th St Berkeley (94710) ***(P-12601)***
Grayson Service Inc ....C 661 589-5444
1845 Greeley Rd Bakersfield (93314) ***(P-217)***
Great American Packaging ....E 323 582-2247
4361 S Soto St Vernon (90058) ***(P-5601)***
Great American Wineries Inc ....E 831 920-4736
2511 Garden Rd Ste B100 Monterey (93940) ***(P-1795)***
Great Lakes Data Systems Inc ....F 760 602-1900
5954 Priestly Dr Carlsbad (92008) ***(P-24710)***
Great Northern Corporation ....E 951 361-4770
12075 Cabernet Dr Fontana (92337) ***(P-5524)***
Great Northern Wheels Deals ....E 530 533-2134
810 Lake Blvd Ste C Redding (96003) ***(P-5867)***
Great River Food, City of Industry *Also called Derek and Constance Lee Corp* ***(P-480)***
Great Spaces USA, Merced *Also called Olde World Corporation* ***(P-5088)***
Great Western Litho, Van Nuys *Also called Investment Enterprises Inc* ***(P-7361)***
Great Western Packaging LLC ....D 818 464-3800
8230-8240 Haskell Ave Van Nuys (91406) ***(P-7335)***
Greatbatch Medical, San Diego *Also called Integer Holdings Corporation* ***(P-19296)***
Greatdad LLC ....F 415 572-8181
2337 Vallejo St San Francisco (94123) ***(P-6174)***
Greathouse Screen Printing ....F 858 279-4939
5644 Kearny Mesa Rd Ste E San Diego (92111) ***(P-7336)***
Grech Motors LLC (PA) ....E 951 688-8347
6915 Arlington Ave Riverside (92504) ***(P-25463)***
Greek Marble Inc ....F 323 221-6624
1600 N San Fernando Rd Los Angeles (90065) ***(P-11253)***
Green Acres Cannabis LLC ....E 415 657-3484
6256 3rd St San Francisco (94124) ***(P-7944)***
Green Circuits Inc ....D 408 526-1700
1130 Ringwood Ct San Jose (95131) ***(P-19556)***
Green Creative LLC ....E 866 774-5433
1200 Bayhill Dr Ste 220 San Bruno (94066) ***(P-17538)***
Green Cures Inc ....E 818 773-3929
20201 Sherman Way Ste 101 Winnetka (91306) ***(P-7945)***
Green Field Paper Company, San Diego *Also called Smithcorp Inc* ***(P-5336)***
Green Flash Brewing, San Diego *Also called Gfbc Inc* ***(P-1594)***
Green Hills Software Inc (PA) ....C 805 965-6044
30 W Sola St Santa Barbara (93101) ***(P-24711)***
Green Lake Investors LLC ....E 707 577-1301
3310 Coffey Ln Santa Rosa (95403) ***(P-23716)***
Green Mattress Inc ....F 323 752-2026
6827 Mckinley Ave Los Angeles (90001) ***(P-2913)***
Green Mochi LLC ....F 213 225-2250
834 S Broadway Ste Mezz Los Angeles (90014) ***(P-3312)***
Green Sheet Inc ....F 707 284-1684
5830 Commerce Blvd Ste B Rohnert Park (94928) ***(P-7337)***
Green Soap Inc (PA) ....F 925 240-5546
450 E Grant Line Rd 1 Tracy (95376) ***(P-8594)***
Green Spot Packaging Inc ....E 909 625-8771
100 S Cambridge Ave Claremont (91711) ***(P-2136)***
Green Valley Foods Product ....F 760 964-1105
25684 Community Blvd Barstow (92311) ***(P-576)***
Green's Metal Cutoff, Long Beach *Also called Dunstan Enterprises Inc* ***(P-14378)***

ALPHABETIC

Employee Codes: A=Over 500 employees, B=251-500
C=101-250, D=51-100, E=20-50, F=10-19
2019 California
Manfacturers Register
© Mergent Inc. 1-800-342-5647
1155

Greenberg Teleprmpt.....F.....714 633-1111
868 N Main St Orange (92868) *(P-17954)*
Greenbox Art and Culture, San Diego *Also called No Boundaries Inc (P-6995)*
Greenbrier Rail Services, San Bernardino *Also called Gunderson Rail Services LLC (P-21076)*
Greenbroz Inc.....F.....844 379-8746
955 Vernon Way El Cajon (92020) *(P-14069)*
Greene Group, Oceanside *Also called Southwest Greene Intl Inc (P-13278)*
Greener Printer, Richmond *Also called Tulip Pubg & Graphics Inc (P-7149)*
Greenfields Outdoor Fitnes Inc.....F.....888 315-9037
2617 W Woodland Dr Anaheim (92801) *(P-23577)*
Greenform LLC.....F.....310 331-1665
12900 Prairie Ave Hawthorne (90250) *(P-14171)*
Greenheck Fan Corporation.....C.....916 626-3400
170 Cyber Ct Rocklin (95765) *(P-15158)*
Greenkraft Inc (PA).....F.....714 545-7777
2530 S Birch St Santa Ana (92707) *(P-20146)*
Greenkraft Inc.....F.....714 545-7777
2530 S Birch St Santa Ana (92707) *(P-20147)*
Greenlee Tempo Operations, Vista *Also called Greenlee Textron Inc (P-21767)*
Greenlee Textron Inc.....D.....858 530-3100
7098 Miratech Dr Ste 130 San Diego (92121) *(P-21766)*
Greenlee Textron Inc.....D.....760 598-8900
1390 Aspen Way Vista (92081) *(P-21767)*
Greenlee Textron Tempo Oper, Vista *Also called Greenlee Tools Inc (P-21768)*
Greenlee Tools Inc.....E.....760 598-8900
1390 Aspen Way Vista (92081) *(P-21768)*
Greenliant Systems Inc.....C.....408 217-7400
3970 Freedom Cir Ste 100 Santa Clara (95054) *(P-18862)*
Greenlots, West Hollywood *Also called Zeco Systems Inc (P-20118)*
Greenscape Solutions Inc.....E.....909 714-8333
7051 27th St Riverside (92509) *(P-10853)*
Greenshine New Energy Co, Lake Forest *Also called Greenshine New Energy LLC (P-17698)*
Greenshine New Energy LLC.....D.....949 609-9636
23661 Birtcher Dr Lake Forest (92630) *(P-17698)*
Greenvity Communications Inc (PA).....E.....408 935-9358
2150 Trade Zone Blvd San Jose (95131) *(P-14963)*
Greenvolts Inc.....D.....415 963-4030
19200 Stevens Creek Blvd # 200 Cupertino (95014) *(P-12066)*
Greenwich Biosciences Inc (HQ).....E.....760 795-2200
5750 Fleet St Ste 200 Carlsbad (92008) *(P-8198)*
Greenwood Products Inc.....F.....909 548-4828
805 Barrington Ave Ontario (91764) *(P-10594)*
Grefco Dicaperl, Torrance *Also called Dicaperl Corporation (P-410)*
Greg Ian Islands Inc.....E.....626 355-0019
123b E Montecito Ave B Sierra Madre (91024) *(P-5064)*
Gregg Hammork Enterprizes Inc.....F.....949 586-7902
23002 Alicia Pkwy Mission Viejo (92692) *(P-61)*
Gregg's Mission Viejo Mobile, Mission Viejo *Also called Gregg Hammork Enterprizes Inc (P-61)*
Gregor Inc.....F.....559 441-7703
3565 N Hazel Ave Fresno (93722) *(P-21040)*
Gregor Boat Co, Fresno *Also called Gregor Inc (P-21040)*
Gregory Associates Inc.....E.....408 446-5725
1233 Belknap Ct Cupertino (95014) *(P-21769)*
Gregory Graziano.....F.....707 485-9463
1170 Bel Arbres Dr Redwood Valley (95470) *(P-1796)*
Gregory M Fink.....F.....949 305-4242
23182 Alcalde Dr Ste H Laguna Hills (92653) *(P-23891)*
Gregory Patterson.....E.....831 636-1015
1741 Shelton Dr Hollister (95023) *(P-12859)*
Greif Inc.....D.....209 383-4396
2400 Cooper Ave Merced (95348) *(P-5486)*
Greif Inc.....D.....408 779-2161
235 San Pedro Ave Morgan Hill (95037) *(P-5487)*
Greif Inc.....D.....714 523-9580
5701 Fresca Dr La Palma (90623) *(P-5488)*
Greif Inc.....E.....909 350-2112
8250 Almeria Ave Fontana (92335) *(P-11874)*
Greige Gods Boking PO AP Group, Vernon *Also called Softmax Inc (P-3554)*
Greka Inc.....C.....805 347-8700
1791 Sinton Rd Santa Maria (93458) *(P-19)*
Greka Integrated Inc (PA).....E.....805 347-8700
1700 Sinton Rd Santa Maria (93458) *(P-137)*
Greneker Furniture.....E.....323 263-9000
3110 E 12th St Los Angeles (90023) *(P-5065)*
Greneker Solutions, Los Angeles *Also called Pacific Manufacturing MGT Inc (P-5160)*
Grenfield Consulting.....E.....310 286-0200
1801 Century Park E Fl 23 Los Angeles (90067) *(P-138)*
Grey Studio Inc.....E.....323 780-8111
629 S Clarence St Los Angeles (90023) *(P-2741)*
Greyheller LLC.....F.....925 415-5053
111 Deerwood Rd Ste 200 San Ramon (94583) *(P-24712)*
Grgich Hills Cellar.....E.....707 963-2784
1829 St Helena Hwy Rutherford (94573) *(P-1797)*
Grico Precision Inc.....F.....626 963-0368
128 S Valencia Ave Ste A Glendora (91741) *(P-16543)*
Grico Precision Inc.....F.....626 963-0368
128 S Valencia Ave Ste A Glendora (91741) *(P-16544)*
Grid Modernization Division, San Jose *Also called Networked Energy Services Corp (P-20026)*
Griff Industries Inc.....F.....661 728-0111
4515 Runway Dr Lancaster (93536) *(P-10130)*
Griffin Laboratories.....F.....951 695-6727
43379 Bus Pk Dr Ste 300 Temecula (92590) *(P-22462)*
Griffiths Printing, Anaheim *Also called Griffiths Services Inc (P-6841)*
Griffiths Services Inc.....E.....714 685-7700
121 S Old Springs Rd Anaheim (92808) *(P-6841)*
Grifols Biologicals LLC (HQ).....B.....323 225-2221
2410 Lillyvale Ave Los Angeles (90032) *(P-8555)*
Grimco Inc.....E.....562 449-4964
13454 Imperial Hwy Santa Fe Springs (90670) *(P-13212)*
Grind Food Company Inc.....F.....805 964-8344
177 S Turnpike Rd Goleta (93111) *(P-16545)*
Grinding & Dicing Services Inc.....E.....408 451-2000
925 Berryessa Rd San Jose (95133) *(P-18863)*
Griswold Controls LLC (PA).....C.....949 559-6000
2803 Barranca Pkwy Irvine (92606) *(P-13768)*
Griswold Pump Company.....E.....909 422-1700
22069 Van Buren St Grand Terrace (92313) *(P-15069)*
Griswold Water Systems, Corona *Also called National Certified Fabricators (P-19348)*
Gritstone Oncology Inc (PA).....D.....510 871-6100
5858 Horton St Ste 210 Emeryville (94608) *(P-8556)*
Gro-Power Inc.....E.....909 393-3744
15065 Telephone Ave Chino (91710) *(P-9061)*
Gro-Tech Systems Inc.....F.....530 432-7012
17282 Cattle Dr Rough and Ready (95975) *(P-12933)*
Groskopf Warehouse & Logistics.....E.....707 939-3100
20580 8th St E Sonoma (95476) *(P-1798)*
Grossi Fabrication Inc.....E.....209 883-2817
3200 Tully Rd Hughson (95326) *(P-13832)*
Ground Control Systems Inc.....F.....805 783-4600
3100 El Camino Real Atascadero (93422) *(P-18117)*
Ground Fueling, Irvine *Also called Eaton Industrial Corporation (P-20805)*
Ground Hog Inc.....E.....909 478-5700
1470 Victoria Ct San Bernardino (92408) *(P-14172)*
Groundmetrics Inc.....F.....619 786-8023
3954 Murphy Canyon Rd D207 San Diego (92123) *(P-218)*
Groundwork Coffee, North Hollywood *Also called Supreme Bean LLC (P-2367)*
Groundwork Coffee Company, North Hollywood *Also called Gourmet Coffee Warehouse Inc (P-2350)*
Groundwork Coffee Company, Los Angeles *Also called Gourmet Coffee Warehouse Inc (P-2351)*
Group Five, Inc., Whittier *Also called Russ Bassett Corp (P-4999)*
Group Manufacturing Services (PA).....D.....408 436-1040
1928 Hartog Dr San Jose (95131) *(P-12602)*
Group Manufacturing Services.....F.....916 858-3270
2751 Merc Dr Ste 900 Rancho Cordova (95742) *(P-12603)*
Group Martin LLC Johnathon.....E.....323 235-1555
3400 S Main St Los Angeles (90007) *(P-3240)*
Grove Aircraft Co, El Cajon *Also called Robert Grove (P-20622)*
Grover City Press, Arroyo Grande *Also called Politezer Newspaers Inc (P-6015)*
Grover Manufacturing, Montebello *Also called Grover Smith Mfg Corp (P-15070)*
Grover Products Co (PA).....E.....323 263-9981
3424 E Olympic Blvd Los Angeles (90023) *(P-20355)*
Grover Products Co.....D.....323 263-9981
3424 E Olympic Blvd Los Angeles (90023) *(P-20356)*
Grover Smith Mfg Corp.....E.....323 724-3444
620 S Vail Ave Montebello (90640) *(P-15070)*
Grow More Inc.....D.....310 515-1700
15600 New Century Dr Gardena (90248) *(P-9102)*
Growdiaries LLC.....F.....626 354-8935
8605 Santa Monica Blvd West Hollywood (90069) *(P-24713)*
Growers Ice Co.....E.....831 424-5781
1124 Abbott St Salinas (93901) *(P-2414)*
Growest Inc (PA).....F.....951 638-1000
10490 Dawson Canyon Rd Corona (92883) *(P-1799)*
Growest Development, Corona *Also called Growest Inc (P-1799)*
Growthstock Inc.....C.....949 660-9473
2921 Daimler St Santa Ana (92705) *(P-19557)*
Gruber Systems Inc.....E.....661 257-0464
29083 The Old Rd Valencia (91355) *(P-14523)*
Gruma Corporation.....F.....858 673-5780
12316 World Trade Dr # 104 San Diego (92128) *(P-2390)*
Gruma Corporation.....C.....562 692-9502
2825 Pellissier Pl City of Industry (90601) *(P-1269)*
Gruma Corporation.....D.....559 498-7820
2849 E Edgar Ave Fresno (93706) *(P-2391)*
Gruma Corporation.....C.....909 980-3566
11559 Jersey Blvd Ste A Rancho Cucamonga (91730) *(P-2392)*
Grundfos CBS Inc.....F.....510 512-1300
25568 Seaboard Ln Hayward (94545) *(P-15071)*
Grunion Gazette, Long Beach *Also called Gazette Newspapers (P-5861)*
Gryphon Mobile Electronics LLC.....F.....626 810-7770
2664 Saturn St Ste B Brea (92821) *(P-18118)*
GS Cosmeceutical Usa Inc.....E.....925 371-5000
131 Pullman St Livermore (94551) *(P-8759)*
Gs Manufacturing.....F.....949 642-1500
985 W 18th St Costa Mesa (92627) *(P-15127)*
Gscm Ventures Inc.....E.....818 303-2600
12924 Pierce St Pacoima (91331) *(P-8760)*
GSG LLC (PA).....E.....760 752-9500
177 Vallecitos De Oro San Marcos (92069) *(P-6842)*
Gsi Capital Partners LLC.....F.....760 745-1768
888 Rancheros Dr Ste A San Marcos (92069) *(P-23578)*
Gsi Technology Inc.....D.....408 980-8388
2360 Owen St Santa Clara (95054) *(P-18864)*
Gsi Technology Inc (PA).....D.....408 331-8800
1213 Elko Dr Sunnyvale (94089) *(P-18865)*
Gsl Fine Lithographers.....E.....916 231-1410
8386 Rovana Cir Sacramento (95828) *(P-6843)*
Gsl Tech Inc.....F.....626 572-9617
3134 Maxson Rd El Monte (91732) *(P-620)*
Gsp, San Diego *Also called Greathouse Screen Printing (P-7336)*
Gsp Acquisition Corporation.....E.....310 532-9430
19745 Lassen St Chatsworth (91311) *(P-13420)*

Mergent e-mail: customerrelations@mergent.com
1156
2019 California
Manufacturers Register
(P-0000) Products & Services Section entry number
(PA)=Parent Co (HQ)=Headquarters (DH)=Div Headquarters

Gsp Precision Inc ......E......818 845-2212
650 Town Center Dr # 950 Costa Mesa (92626) ***(P-16546)***
Gst Inc ......D......949 510-1142
3419 Via Lido Ste 164 Newport Beach (92663) ***(P-15545)***
Gst Industries Inc ......E......818 350-1900
9060 Winnetka Ave Northridge (91324) ***(P-20833)***
GT Precision Inc ......C......310 323-4374
1629 W 132nd St Gardena (90249) ***(P-13025)***
GTC Manufacturing, Benicia *Also called Bulls-Eye Marketing Inc* ***(P-20275)***
Gtr Enterprises Incorporated ......E......760 931-1192
6352 Corte Del Abeto E Carlsbad (92011) ***(P-16547)***
Gtran Inc (PA) ......E......805 445-4500
829 Flynn Rd Camarillo (93012) ***(P-19558)***
Gts Living Foods LLC ......A......323 581-7787
4646 Hampton St Vernon (90058) ***(P-2137)***
Gtx Corp ......F......213 489-3019
117 W 9th St Ste 1214 Los Angeles (90015) ***(P-18119)***
Gu ......E......510 527-4664
1204 10th St Berkeley (94710) ***(P-8199)***
Guadalupe Associates Inc (PA) ......F......415 387-2324
1348 10th Ave San Francisco (94122) ***(P-6497)***
Guano Records LLC ......F......714 263-5398
26298 Jaylene St Murrieta (92563) ***(P-7338)***
Guard-Dogs, Ventura *Also called Abbs Vision Systems Inc* ***(P-23076)***
Guardian Corporate Services ......E......619 295-2646
2814 University Ave Frnt San Diego (92104) ***(P-3789)***
Guardian Industries LLC ......B......559 891-8867
11535 E Mountain View Ave Kingsburg (93631) ***(P-10595)***
Guardian Industries Corp ......D......559 891-8867
11535 E Mountain View Ave Kingsburg (93631) ***(P-10596)***
Guardian Industries Corp ......D......559 638-3588
11535 E Mountain View Ave Kingsburg (93631) ***(P-10597)***
Guardian Survival Gear Inc ......F......760 519-5643
1401 S Hicks Ave Commerce (90023) ***(P-22738)***
Guavus Inc (HQ) ......D......650 243-3400
2860 Junction Ave San Jose (95134) ***(P-24714)***
Guck Ariba ......C......650 390-1445
807 Eleventh Ave Sunnyvale (94089) ***(P-24715)***
Guenoc Winery Inc ......E......707 987-2385
200 Concourse Blvd Santa Rosa (95403) ***(P-1800)***
Guernsey Coating Laboratory ......F......805 642-1508
1788 Goodyear Ave Ventura (93003) ***(P-13599)***
Guess Inc (PA) ......A......213 765-3100
1444 S Alameda St Los Angeles (90021) ***(P-3070)***
Guess Inc ......E......626 856-5555
358 Plaza Dr West Covina (91790) ***(P-3071)***
Guess Inc ......F......805 963-9490
820 State St Santa Barbara (93101) ***(P-3072)***
Guess Inc ......E......408 847-3400
8300 Arroyo Cir Ste 270 Gilroy (95020) ***(P-3158)***
Guess Inc ......E......909 987-7776
1 Mills Cir Ste 313 Ontario (91764) ***(P-3073)***
Guest Chex Inc ......F......714 522-1860
7697 9th St Buena Park (90621) ***(P-6844)***
Guestchex, Buena Park *Also called Guest Chex Inc* ***(P-6844)***
Guidance Software Inc (HQ) ......C......626 229-9191
1055 E Colo Blvd Ste 400 Pasadena (91106) ***(P-24716)***
Guidant Sales LLC ......E......650 965-2634
825 E Middlefield Rd Mountain View (94043) ***(P-22463)***
Guided Wave Inc ......E......916 638-4944
3033 Gold Canal Dr Rancho Cordova (95670) ***(P-22080)***
Guidetech Inc ......E......408 733-6555
1300 Memorex Dr Santa Clara (95050) ***(P-21770)***
Guidewire Software Inc (PA) ......C......650 357-9100
1001 E Hillsdale Blvd # 8 Foster City (94404) ***(P-24717)***
Guiseppe Custom Cue Cases, Buena Park *Also called Guiseppe Inc* ***(P-23579)***
Guiseppe Inc ......F......714 670-7700
6920 Knott Ave Ste H Buena Park (90621) ***(P-23579)***
Guittard Chocolate Co ......C......650 697-4427
10 Guittard Rd Burlingame (94010) ***(P-1471)***
Gulbransen Inc ......F......619 296-5760
2102 Hancock St San Diego (92110) ***(P-23374)***
Gulf Enterprises, Chatsworth *Also called Mercury Magnetics Inc* ***(P-19346)***
Gulf Streams ......F......562 420-1818
4150 E Donald Douglas Dr Long Beach (90808) ***(P-20589)***
Gulfstream Aerospace Corp GA ......A......562 907-9300
9818 Mina Ave Whittier (90605) ***(P-20590)***
Gulfstream California, Lincoln *Also called Gdas-Lincoln Inc* ***(P-20578)***
Gulshan International Corp ......F......408 745-6090
1355 Geneva Dr Sunnyvale (94089) ***(P-18866)***
Gum Sun Times Inc (PA) ......E......415 379-6788
625 Kearny St San Francisco (94108) ***(P-5868)***
Gund Company Inc ......F......909 890-9300
4701 E Airport Dr Ontario (91761) ***(P-17515)***
Gunderson Rail Services LLC ......E......909 478-0541
1475 Cooley Ct San Bernardino (92408) ***(P-21076)***
Gundrill Tech Inc ......E......562 946-9355
10030 Greenleaf Ave Santa Fe Springs (90670) ***(P-16548)***
Gunnebo Entrance Control Inc (HQ) ......F......707 748-0885
535 Getty Ct Ste F Benicia (94510) ***(P-22208)***
Guntert Zmmerman Const Div Inc ......E......209 599-0066
222 E 4th St Ripon (95366) ***(P-14173)***
Gunthers Quality Ice Cream ......F......916 457-3339
2801 Franklin Blvd Sacramento (95818) ***(P-676)***
Guptill Gear Corporation ......F......714 956-2170
874 S Rose Pl Anaheim (92805) ***(P-16549)***
Guru Knits Inc ......D......323 235-9424
225 W 38th St Los Angeles (90037) ***(P-3241)***
GUSB Inc ......F......323 233-0044
219 E 32nd St Los Angeles (90011) ***(P-3242)***
Gusmer Enterprises Inc ......D......908 301-1811
81 M St Fresno (93721) ***(P-15327)***
Gustine Ready Mix, Gustine *Also called Legacy Vulcan LLC* ***(P-10952)***
Gusto, San Francisco *Also called Zenpayroll Inc* ***(P-25370)***
Gutierrez Grading ......F......909 397-8717
1505 E Phillips Blvd Pomona (91766) ***(P-7339)***
Gutterglove Inc ......D......916 624-5000
8860 Industrial Ave # 140 Roseville (95678) ***(P-12604)***
Guy Chaddock & Company (PA) ......C......408 907-9200
1100 La Avenida St Mountain View (94043) ***(P-4780)***
Guy G Veralrud ......F......530 477-7323
10141 Evening Star Dr # 1 Grass Valley (95945) ***(P-17806)***
Guzik Technical Enterprises ......D......650 625-8000
2443 Wyandotte St Mountain View (94043) ***(P-21771)***
Gw Crystal, Rancho Cucamonga *Also called Gw Partners International* ***(P-10644)***
Gw Partners International ......F......909 980-1010
8351 Elm Ave Ste 106 Rancho Cucamonga (91730) ***(P-10644)***
Gw Services LLC (HQ) ......E......760 560-1111
1385 Park Center Dr Vista (92081) ***(P-15922)***
Gwla Acquisition Corp (PA) ......F......323 789-7800
8600 Rheem Ave South Gate (90280) ***(P-10598)***
Gym Parts Depot, Los Angeles *Also called Rtg Investment Group Inc* ***(P-23643)***
Gypsy 05 Inc ......E......323 265-2700
3200 Union Pacific Ave Los Angeles (90023) ***(P-3424)***
Gypsy Heart, Alhambra *Also called Active Knitwear Resources Inc* ***(P-3208)***
H & B Sports Products Div, Ontario *Also called Hillerich & Bradsby Co* ***(P-23585)***
H & H Enterprises Inc ......F......707 794-9988
681 Portal St Cotati (94931) ***(P-7340)***
H & H MANUFACTURING, Pomona *Also called Holland & Herring Mfg Inc* ***(P-16571)***
H & H Specialties Inc ......E......626 575-0776
14850 Don Julian Rd Ste B City of Industry (91746) ***(P-24114)***
H & L Apparel Enterprise Inc ......F......323 589-1563
2202 E Anderson St Vernon (90058) ***(P-3243)***
H & L Tooth Company (PA) ......D......323 721-5146
1540 S Greenwood Ave Montebello (90640) ***(P-14174)***
H & M Cabinet Company ......F......760 744-0559
1565 La Mirada Dr San Marcos (92078) ***(P-5066)***
H & M Four-Slide Inc ......F......951 461-8244
25779 Jefferson Ave Murrieta (92562) ***(P-16550)***
H & M Precision Machining, Santa Clara *Also called H&M Precision Machining* ***(P-13026)***
H & N Tool & Die Co Inc ......F......951 372-9071
201 Jason Ct Ste B Corona (92879) ***(P-14437)***
H & R Aerospace Inc ......F......714 893-1737
1025 N Tustin St Apt 505 Orange (92867) ***(P-20834)***
H 45 Technology, Mountain View *Also called H45 Technology Corporation* ***(P-15751)***
H A I, Placentia *Also called Hai Advnced Mtl Spcialists Inc* ***(P-11840)***
H A Rider & Sons ......E......831 722-3882
2482 Freedom Blvd Watsonville (95076) ***(P-2138)***
H and M Industries LLC ......F......805 499-5100
855 Rancho Conejo Blvd Newbury Park (91320) ***(P-5067)***
H B R Industries Inc ......F......408 988-0800
2261 Fortune Dr Ste B San Jose (95131) ***(P-19339)***
H C I, Rocklin *Also called Hugin Components Inc* ***(P-13222)***
H C Muddox, Sacramento *Also called Pabco Clay Products LLC* ***(P-10777)***
H Co Computer Products ......E......949 833-3222
16812 Hale Ave Irvine (92606) ***(P-15546)***
H F Johnston Mfg Co, Vista *Also called H P Solutions Inc* ***(P-14754)***
H Fam Engineering Inc ......F......909 930-5678
2131 S Hellman Ave Ste F Ontario (91761) ***(P-16551)***
H I S C Inc ......F......949 492-8968
1009 Calle Recodo San Clemente (92673) ***(P-10645)***
H J Harkins Company Inc ......E......805 929-1333
1400 W Grand Ave Ste F Grover Beach (93433) ***(P-8200)***
H J S Graphics ......F......818 782-5490
6825 Valjean Ave Van Nuys (91406) ***(P-6845)***
H K Lighting Group Inc ......F......805 480-4881
3529 Old Conejo Rd # 118 Newbury Park (91320) ***(P-17699)***
H K Prcision Turning Machining, Oceanside *Also called Balda HK Plastics Inc* ***(P-13016)***
H Lima Company Inc ......E......209 239-6787
704 E Yosemite Ave Manteca (95336) ***(P-413)***
H M F, Anaheim *Also called Hitech Metal Fabrication Corp* ***(P-12176)***
H M T, Madera *Also called Horn Machine Tools Inc* ***(P-14438)***
H N Lockwood Inc ......E......650 366-9557
880 Sweeney Ave Redwood City (94063) ***(P-10131)***
H N S, San Diego *Also called Hughes Network Systems LLC* ***(P-18127)***
H P Applications ......F......323 585-2894
4727 E 49th St Vernon (90058) ***(P-11813)***
H P Group ......F......909 364-1069
5070 Lindsay Ct Chino (91710) ***(P-24115)***
H P M, Sunnyvale *Also called Horvath Precision Machining* ***(P-16574)***
H P Solutions Inc ......E......760 727-2880
2475 Ash St Vista (92081) ***(P-14754)***
H Q Machine Tech Inc ......E......714 956-3388
6900 8th St Buena Park (90620) ***(P-16552)***
H R C, Fountain Valley *Also called Headed Reinforcement Corp* ***(P-13215)***
H Roberts Construction ......D......562 590-4825
2165 W Gaylord St Long Beach (90813) ***(P-12934)***
H S N Consultants Inc ......F......805 684-8800
1110 Eugenia Pl Ste 100 Carpinteria (93013) ***(P-6175)***
H Silani & Associates Inc ......F......310 623-4848
210 S Robertson Blvd Beverly Hills (90211) ***(P-22081)***
H Starlet LLC ......F......323 235-8777
3447 S Main St Los Angeles (90007) ***(P-3425)***
H V Food Products Company ......C......510 271-7612
1221 Broadway Oakland (94612) ***(P-915)***
H Wayne Lewis Inc ......E......909 874-2213
312 S Willow Ave Rialto (92376) ***(P-12979)***

Employee Codes: A=Over 500 employees, B=251-500
C=101-250, D=51-100, E=20-50, F=10-19
2019 California
Manfacturers Register
© Mergent Inc. 1-800-342-5647
1157

H&F Technologies Inc........................F......805 523-2759
650 Flinn Ave Unit 4 Moorpark (93021) *(P-17807)*

H&H Imaging Inc........................F......415 431-4731
375 Alabama St Ste 150 San Francisco (94110) *(P-6846)*

H&H Platemakers, San Francisco Also called H&H Imaging Inc *(P-6846)*

H&M Logging........................F......707 964-2340
442 S Franklin St Fort Bragg (95437) *(P-3990)*

H&M Precision Machining........................F......408 982-9184
504 Robert Ave Santa Clara (95050) *(P-13026)*

H-Square Corporation........................E......408 732-1240
3100 Patrick Henry Dr Santa Clara (95054) *(P-18867)*

H.U.M.A.N. Healthy Vending, Culver City Also called Nutrition Without Borders LLC *(P-15923)*

H2 Cards Inc........................F......415 788-7888
638 Washington St San Francisco (94111) *(P-7341)*

H2 Co, Santa Clara Also called H-Square Corporation *(P-18867)*

H2 Environmental........................F......909 628-0369
13122 6th St Chino (91710) *(P-11311)*

H2 Wellness Incorporated........................D......310 362-1888
11999 San Vicente Blvd Los Angeles (90049) *(P-24718)*

H2j Corporation........................F......510 785-2100
3468 Diablo Ave Hayward (94545) *(P-16553)*

H2o Engineering Inc........................F......805 542-9253
189 Granada Dr San Luis Obispo (93401) *(P-16047)*

H2o Plus LLC (PA)........................D......312 377-2132
111 Sutter St Fl 22 San Francisco (94104) *(P-8761)*

H2scan Corporation........................E......661 775-9575
27215 Turnberry Ln Unit A Valencia (91355) *(P-22209)*

H2w Technologies Inc........................F......661 291-1620
26380 Ferry Ct Santa Clarita (91350) *(P-17275)*

H3 High Security Solutions LLC........................E......310 373-2319
434 1/2 Palos Verdes Blvd Redondo Beach (90277) *(P-13683)*

H45 Technology Corporation........................F......650 961-9114
465 Fairchild Dr Ste 103 Mountain View (94043) *(P-15751)*

Hab Enterprises Inc........................F......310 628-9000
15233 Ventura Blvd # 100 Sherman Oaks (91403) *(P-9533)*

Habla Incorporated........................E......703 867-0135
548 Market St San Francisco (94104) *(P-24719)*

Hacker Industries Inc (PA)........................F......949 729-3101
1600 Newport Dr 275 Newport Beach (92660) *(P-11219)*

Hackett Industries Inc.........................E......209 955-8220
4445 E Fremont St Stockton (95215) *(P-14856)*

Hadal Inc........................F......510 864-0600
2107 Livingston St Oakland (94606) *(P-14175)*

Hadco Products Inc........................F......916 966-2409
3345 Sunrise Blvd Ste 5 Rancho Cordova (95742) *(P-5190)*

Haddads Fine Arts Inc........................F......714 996-2100
3855 E Miraloma Ave Anaheim (92806) *(P-9199)*

Hades Performance........................F......925 671-9197
3481 Euclid Ave Concord (94519) *(P-4910)*

Hadley Media Inc........................F......800 270-2084
1665 S Ranch Santa Fe Rd San Marcos (92078) *(P-6498)*

Haeco Americas Cabin Solutions, Pacoima Also called Brice Manufacturing Co Inc *(P-20761)*

Haeger Incorporated (HQ)........................F......209 848-4000
811 Wakefield Dr Oakdale (95361) *(P-14755)*

Haemonetics Corporation........................B......530 774-2081
95 Declaration Dr Ste 3 Chico (95973) *(P-22464)*

Haemonetics Manufacturing Inc (HQ)........................E......626 339-7388
1684 W Industrial Park St Covina (91722) *(P-22465)*

Hagafen Cellars Inc........................F......707 252-0781
4160 Silverado Trl NAPA (94558) *(P-1801)*

Hagen-Renaker Inc (PA)........................C......909 599-2341
914 W Cienega Ave San Dimas (91773) *(P-10832)*

Hager Mfg Inc........................E......714 522-8870
14610 Industry Cir La Mirada (90638) *(P-20835)*

Hagist Welding........................F......707 847-3362
34895 Kruse Ranch Rd Cazadero (95421) *(P-25407)*

Hagle Lumber Company Inc........................E......805 987-3887
3100 Somis Rd Somis (93066) *(P-4037)*

Hahn Estate........................D......831 678-2132
37700 Foothill Rd Soledad (93960) *(P-1802)*

Hahnemann Homeopathic Pharmacy, San Rafael Also called Hahnemann Laboratories Inc *(P-8201)*

Hahnemann Laboratories Inc........................F......415 451-6978
1940 4th St San Rafael (94901) *(P-8201)*

Hai Advnced Mtl Spcialists Inc........................F......714 414-0575
1688 Sierra Madre Cir Placentia (92870) *(P-11840)*

Haig Precision Mfg Corp........................D......408 378-4920
3616 Snell Ave San Jose (95136) *(P-16554)*

Haigs Delicacies LLC........................E......510 782-6285
25673 Nickel Pl Hayward (94545) *(P-2532)*

Haimetal Duct Inc........................F......818 768-2315
625 Arroyo St San Fernando (91340) *(P-12605)*

Hain Celestial Group Inc........................D......707 347-1200
2201 S Mcdowell Boulevard Petaluma (94954) *(P-8762)*

Hair ACC By Mia Minnelli, Pleasant Hill Also called Mosaic Brands Inc *(P-24178)*

Hair By Couture Inc........................F......310 848-7676
1010 W Magnolia Blvd Burbank (91506) *(P-24116)*

Hair Syndicut........................F......909 946-3200
565 N Central Ave Upland (91786) *(P-9256)*

Haisch Construction Co Inc........................F......530 378-6800
1800 S Barney Rd Anderson (96007) *(P-4407)*

Halabi Inc (PA)........................C......707 402-1600
2100 Huntington Dr Fairfield (94533) *(P-11254)*

Halabi Inc........................F......800 660-4167
1009 Martin Ave Santa Clara (95050) *(P-11255)*

Halcore Group Inc........................D......626 575-0880
10941 Weaver Ave South El Monte (91733) *(P-20148)*

Halcyon Microelectronics Inc........................F......626 814-4688
5467 2nd St Irwindale (91706) *(P-18868)*

Haldex Brake Products Corp........................F......909 974-1200
291 Kettering Dr Ontario (91761) *(P-20357)*

Haldor Topsoe Inc........................E......714 621-3800
770 The Cy Dr S Ste 8400 Orange (92868) *(P-7780)*

Halex Corporation (HQ)........................E......909 629-6219
4200 Santa Ana St Ste A Ontario (91761) *(P-11896)*

Haley Bros, Riverside Also called T M Cobb Company *(P-4242)*

Haley Bros Inc (HQ)........................C......714 670-2112
6291 Orangethorpe Ave Buena Park (90620) *(P-4162)*

Haley Brothers, Stockton Also called T M Cobb Company *(P-4243)*

Haley Brothers, San Bernardino Also called T M Cobb Company *(P-5109)*

Haley Indus Ctings Linings Inc........................E......323 588-8086
4185 Charter St Vernon (90058) *(P-13600)*

Half Moon Bay Review, Half Moon Bay Also called Wick Communications Co *(P-6088)*

Hall Associates Racg Pdts Inc........................F......310 326-4111
23104 Normandie Ave Torrance (90502) *(P-21231)*

Hall Health and Longevity Cntr........................F......310 566-6690
916 Main St Venice (90291) *(P-7946)*

Hall Letter Shop Inc........................F......661 327-3228
5200 Rosedale Hwy Bakersfield (93308) *(P-6847)*

Hall Machine, San Diego Also called Rdl Machine Inc *(P-16888)*

Hall Research Technologies LLC (PA)........................F......714 641-6607
1163 Warner Ave Tustin (92780) *(P-15752)*

Halle-Hopper LLC........................E......951 284-7373
630 Parkridge Ave Norco (92860) *(P-4163)*

Hallett Boats........................E......626 969-8844
180 S Irwindale Ave Azusa (91702) *(P-21041)*

Halliburton Company........................D......661 393-8111
34722 7th Standard Rd Bakersfield (93314) *(P-219)*

Hallmark Floors Inc (PA)........................F......909 947-7736
2360 S Archibald Ave Ontario (91761) *(P-4081)*

Hallmark Labs LLC........................C......424 210-3600
3130 Wilshire Blvd # 400 Santa Monica (90403) *(P-7564)*

Hallmark Lighting LLC........................D......818 885-5010
9631 De Soto Ave Chatsworth (91311) *(P-17613)*

Hallmark Metals Inc........................E......626 335-1263
600 W Foothill Blvd Glendora (91741) *(P-12606)*

Hallmark Southwest, Loma Linda Also called Dvele Omega Corporation *(P-4553)*

Halo Neuro Inc........................F......415 851-3338
735 Market St Fl 4 San Francisco (94103) *(P-22982)*

Halo Neuro Inc........................F......650 784-0881
735 Market St Fl 4 San Francisco (94103) *(P-19977)*

Halo Neuroscience, San Francisco Also called Halo Neuro Inc *(P-22982)*

Halo Top, Los Angeles Also called Eden Creamery LLC *(P-667)*

Halo Top Creamery, West Hollywood Also called Halo Top International LLC *(P-677)*

Halo Top International LLC........................E......434 409-2057
1348 N Sierra Bonita Ave # 107 West Hollywood (90046) *(P-677)*

Halozyme Therapeutics Inc (PA)........................D......858 794-8889
11388 Sorrento Valley Rd # 200 San Diego (92121) *(P-8557)*

Halsteel Inc (HQ)........................E......909 937-1001
4190 Santa Ana St Ste A Ontario (91761) *(P-11442)*

Halter Winery LLC........................E......805 226-9455
8910 Adelaida Rd Paso Robles (93446) *(P-1803)*

Hamar Wood Parquet Company........................E......562 944-8885
9303 Greenleaf Ave Santa Fe Springs (90670) *(P-4038)*

Hamax America Inc (PA)........................F......714 641-7528
660 Baker St Ste 405s Costa Mesa (92626) *(P-21963)*

Hambly Studios Inc........................E......408 496-1100
23980 Spalding Ave Los Altos (94024) *(P-3897)*

Hamilton & Associates, Chatsworth Also called Alan Hamilton Industries *(P-6645)*

Hamilton Iron Works, Torrance Also called Calcon Steel Construction *(P-12126)*

Hamilton Metalcraft Inc........................E......626 795-4811
848 N Fair Oaks Ave Pasadena (91103) *(P-12607)*

Hamilton Sundstrand Corp........................C......909 593-3581
2771 N Garey Ave Pomona (91767) *(P-21964)*

Hamilton Sundstrand Spc Systms........................D......909 593-3581
2771 N Garey Ave Pomona (91767) *(P-22210)*

Hamilton Technology Corp........................F......310 217-1191
14900 S Figueroa St Gardena (90248) *(P-17614)*

Hammer Collection Inc........................E......310 515-0276
14427 S Main St Gardena (90248) *(P-4781)*

Hammerhead Industries Inc........................F......805 658-9922
5720 Nicolle St Ventura (93003) *(P-10132)*

Hammitt Inc........................F......310 293-3787
2101 Pacific Coast Hwy A Hermosa Beach (90254) *(P-10523)*

Hammon Plating Corporation........................E......650 494-2691
890 Commercial St Palo Alto (94303) *(P-13421)*

Hammond Enterprises Inc........................E......925 432-3537
549 Garcia Ave Ste C Pittsburg (94565) *(P-13945)*

Hammond Power Solutions Inc........................E......310 537-4690
17715 S Susana Rd Compton (90221) *(P-17097)*

Hampton Fitness Products Ltd........................F......805 339-9733
1913 Portola Rd Ventura (93003) *(P-23580)*

Hampton-Brown Company LLC........................F......831 620-6001
1 Lower Ragsdale Dr # 1200 Monterey (93940) *(P-6419)*

Hamrock Inc........................C......562 944-0255
12521 Los Nietos Rd Santa Fe Springs (90670) *(P-11443)*

Hana Microelectronics Inc........................F......408 452-7474
3100 De La Cruz Blvd # 204 Santa Clara (95054) *(P-19559)*

Hanah Silk Inc........................F......707 442-0886
5155 Myrtle Ave Eureka (95503) *(P-2800)*

Hanaps Enterprises (PA)........................E......669 235-3810
865 Jarvis Dr Morgan Hill (95037) *(P-15753)*

Hancor Inc........................D......661 366-1520
140 Vineland Rd Bakersfield (93307) *(P-9779)*

Hand & Nail Harmony Inc........................D......714 773-9758
1545 Moonstone Brea (92821) *(P-8763)*

Hand and Nail Harmony, Brea *Also called Hand & Nail Harmony Inc* ***(P-8763)***
Hand Biomechanics Lab Inc............F.......916 923-5073
77 Scripps Dr Ste 104 Sacramento (95825) ***(P-22739)***
Hand Crfted Dutchman Doors Inc............E.......209 833-7378
770 Stonebridge Dr Tracy (95376) ***(P-4164)***
Hand Piece Parts and Products............E.......714 997-4331
707 W Angus Ave Orange (92868) ***(P-22882)***
Handa Pharmaceuticals LLC............F.......510 354-2888
1732 N 1st St Ste 200 San Jose (95112) ***(P-8202)***
Handbill Printers LP............E.......951 547-5910
820 E Parkridge Ave Corona (92879) ***(P-6848)***
Handcraft Mattress Company............F.......714 241-8316
1131 Baker St Costa Mesa (92626) ***(P-4862)***
Handcraft Tile Inc............F.......408 262-1140
786 View Dr Pleasanton (94566) ***(P-10799)***
Handelman, Steven Studios, Santa Barbara *Also called Steven Handelman Studios* ***(P-11504)***
Handley Cellars Ltd............F.......707 895-3876
3151 Highway 128 Philo (95466) ***(P-1804)***
Handley Cellars Winery, Philo *Also called Handley Cellars Ltd* ***(P-1804)***
Handshake, San Francisco *Also called Stryder Corp* ***(P-25231)***
Handy Service Corporation............F.......714 632-7832
1043 S Melrose St Ste A Placentia (92870) ***(P-7905)***
Hane & Hane Inc............E.......408 292-2140
650 University Ave San Jose (95110) ***(P-13422)***
Hanergy Holding (america) LLC (HQ)............F.......650 288-3722
1350 Bayshore Hwy Burlingame (94010) ***(P-18869)***
Hanford Ready-Mix Inc............E.......916 405-1918
9800 Kent St Elk Grove (95624) ***(P-11115)***
Hanford Sand & Gravel Inc............F.......916 782-9150
9800 Kent St Elk Grove (95624) ***(P-11116)***
Hanford Sentinel Inc............D.......559 582-0471
300 W 6th St Hanford (93230) ***(P-5869)***
Hang-UPS Unlimited, Santa Monica *Also called Magna-Pole Products Inc* ***(P-5153)***
Hanger............F.......323 238-7738
6099 Malburg Way Vernon (90058) ***(P-22740)***
Hanger Inc............F.......530 528-1795
24 Antelope Blvd Red Bluff (96080) ***(P-22741)***
Hanger Clinic, Los Angeles *Also called Hanger Prosthetics & Ortho* ***(P-22742)***
Hanger Clinic, Irvine *Also called Hanger Prsthetcs & Ortho Inc* ***(P-22744)***
Hanger P&O, Red Bluff *Also called Hanger Inc* ***(P-22741)***
Hanger Prosthetics & Ortho............D.......323 866-2555
6300 Wilshire Blvd # 150 Los Angeles (90048) ***(P-22742)***
Hanger Prsthetcs & Ortho Inc............F.......562 803-3322
7700 Imperial Hwy Ste E2 Downey (90242) ***(P-22743)***
Hanger Prsthetcs & Ortho Inc............D.......949 863-1951
18022 Cowan Ste 285 Irvine (92614) ***(P-22744)***
Hanger Prsthetcs & Ortho Inc............F.......858 487-4516
15725 Pomerado Rd Poway (92064) ***(P-22745)***
Hanger Prsthetcs & Ortho Inc............F.......925 371-5081
4659 Las Positas Rd Ste A Livermore (94551) ***(P-22746)***
Hangers Randy West Coast Ctr............F.......323 728-2253
5350 Zambrano St Commerce (90040) ***(P-11444)***
Hangtags.com, Huntington Beach *Also called Tri Print LLC* ***(P-7145)***
Hank Player Inc............F.......818 856-6079
4303 Lemp Ave Studio City (91604) ***(P-3426)***
Hanley Welding, Hawthorne *Also called Marleon Inc* ***(P-25421)***
Hanmar LLC (PA)............E.......818 240-0170
11441 Bradley Ave Pacoima (91331) ***(P-13213)***
Hanna Fuji Sushi, Santa Fe Springs *Also called Nikko Enterprise Corporation* ***(P-2319)***
Hanna Winery Inc (PA)............F.......707 431-4310
9280 Highway 128 Healdsburg (95448) ***(P-1805)***
Hannah Industries Inc............F.......714 939-7873
401 S Santa Fe St Santa Ana (92705) ***(P-16048)***
Hannahmax Baking Inc............C.......310 380-6778
14601 S Main St Gardena (90248) ***(P-1270)***
Hannan Products Corp (PA)............F.......951 735-1587
220 N Smith Ave Corona (92880) ***(P-15208)***
Hannemann Fiberglass Inc............F.......626 969-7317
1132 W Kirkwall Rd Azusa (91702) ***(P-20358)***
Hannibal Lafayette............F.......909 322-0600
10758 Fremont Ave Ontario (91762) ***(P-4474)***
Hannibal Industries Inc (PA)............C.......323 513-1200
3851 S Santa Fe Ave Vernon (90058) ***(P-11479)***
Hannibal Material Handling............C.......323 587-4060
2230 E 38th St Vernon (90058) ***(P-5144)***
Hannibals Catrg & Events Inc (PA)............E.......916 638-4363
8141 37th Ave Sacramento (95824) ***(P-2533)***
Hansen Bros Enterprises (PA)............D.......530 273-3100
11727 La Barr Meadows Rd Grass Valley (95949) ***(P-361)***
Hansen Haulers Inc............F.......916 443-7755
1628 N C St 1630 Sacramento (95811) ***(P-16555)***
Hansen Information Tech, Rancho Cordova *Also called Infor (us) Inc* ***(P-24766)***
Hansen Machine Works, Sacramento *Also called Hansen Haulers Inc* ***(P-16555)***
Hansen Medical Inc............C.......650 404-5800
800 E Middlefield Rd Mountain View (94043) ***(P-22466)***
Hansens Oak Inc (PA)............F.......209 357-3424
166 E Broadway Ave Atwater (95301) ***(P-4701)***
Hansens Welding Inc............E.......310 329-6888
358 W 168th St Gardena (90248) ***(P-25408)***
Hanson Aggregates LLC............E.......408 996-4000
24001 Stevens Creek Blvd Cupertino (95014) ***(P-362)***
Hanson Aggregates LLC............D.......805 485-3101
3555 E Vineyard Ave Oxnard (93036) ***(P-10752)***
Hanson Aggregates LLC............E.......619 299-8640
5785 Mission Center Rd San Diego (92108) ***(P-10753)***
Hanson Aggregates LLC............E.......626 856-6700
13550 Live Oak Ln Baldwin Park (91706) ***(P-363)***
Hanson Aggregates LLC............F.......858 577-2727
9255 Camino Santa Fe San Diego (92121) ***(P-10754)***
Hanson Aggregates LLC............E.......951 371-7625
19494 River Rock Rd Corona (92881) ***(P-10755)***
Hanson Aggregates LLC............F.......805 934-4931
5325 Foxen Canyon Rd Santa Maria (93454) ***(P-364)***
Hanson Aggregates LLC............E.......805 543-8100
131 Suburban Rd San Luis Obispo (93401) ***(P-365)***
Hanson Aggregates LLC............F.......858 715-5600
12560 Highway 67 Lakeside (92040) ***(P-9386)***
Hanson Aggregates LLC............E.......626 358-1811
13550 Live Oak Ln Irwindale (91706) ***(P-11117)***
Hanson Aggrgtes Md-Pacific Inc............F.......805 928-3764
180 Atascadero Rd Morro Bay (93442) ***(P-11118)***
Hanson Aggrgtes Md-Pacific Inc............F.......925 672-4955
Pine Hollow To Kaiser Rd Clayton (94517) ***(P-11256)***
Hanson Brass Inc............F.......818 767-3501
7530 San Fernando Rd Sun Valley (91352) ***(P-4702)***
Hanson Lab Furniture Inc............E.......805 498-3121
747 Calle Plano Camarillo (93012) ***(P-21474)***
Hanson Lehigh Inc............E.......925 244-6500
12667 Alcosta Blvd # 400 San Ramon (94583) ***(P-10756)***
Hanson Tank, Los Angeles *Also called Roy E Hanson Jr Mfg* ***(P-12416)***
Hanson Truss Inc (PA)............C.......909 591-9256
13950 Yorba Ave Chino (91710) ***(P-4408)***
Hanson Truss Components Inc............D.......530 740-7750
4476 Skyway Dr Olivehurst (95961) ***(P-4409)***
Hantel Technologies Inc............E.......510 400-1164
3496 Breakwater Ct Hayward (94545) ***(P-22467)***
Hantronix Inc............E.......408 252-1100
10080 Bubb Rd Cupertino (95014) ***(P-14964)***
Hanzell Vineyards............F.......707 996-3860
18596 Lomita Ave Sonoma (95476) ***(P-1806)***
Happy Apple, Orosi *Also called Lochirco Fruit and Produce Inc* ***(P-1439)***
Happy Company, The, Hayward *Also called Tender Loving Things Inc* ***(P-8852)***
Happy Daze Rv's, Livermore *Also called Progressive Housing Inc* ***(P-20429)***
Happy Doughnuts, Oakland *Also called Dobake Bakeries Inc* ***(P-1233)***
Happy Girl Kitchen Co............F.......831 373-4475
173 Central Ave Pacific Grove (93950) ***(P-803)***
Happy2ez Inc............F.......714 897-6100
14191 Beach Blvd Ste B Westminster (92683) ***(P-9863)***
Harber All Natural Products............F.......347 921-1004
1440 3rd St Riverside (92507) ***(P-8764)***
Harber Foods LLC (PA)............F.......347 921-1004
1440 3rd St Ste 25 Riverside (92507) ***(P-8765)***
Harbison-Fischer Inc............E.......661 765-7792
116 E Main St Taft (93268) ***(P-220)***
Harbison-Fischer Inc............E.......661 399-0628
200 Carver St Shafter (93263) ***(P-14227)***
Harbison-Fischer Inc............E.......661 387-0166
2801 Pegasus Dr Bakersfield (93308) ***(P-15072)***
Harbor Biosciences Inc (PA)............F.......858 587-9333
9191 Towne Centre Dr # 409 San Diego (92122) ***(P-8203)***
Harbor Custom Canvas............F.......562 436-7708
733 W Anaheim St Long Beach (90813) ***(P-3790)***
Harbor Electronics Inc (PA)............C.......408 988-6544
3021 Kenneth St Santa Clara (95054) ***(P-19560)***
Harbor Furniture Manufacturing (PA)............E.......323 636-1201
12508 Center St South Gate (90280) ***(P-4782)***
Harbor Green Grain LP............E.......310 609-1094
19100 S Susana Rd Compton (90221) ***(P-1136)***
Harbor House, South Gate *Also called Harbor Furniture Manufacturing* ***(P-4782)***
Harbor Medtech Inc............F.......949 679-4800
4 Jenner Ste 190 Irvine (92618) ***(P-22468)***
Harbor Packaging, Poway *Also called Liberty Diversified Intl Inc* ***(P-5435)***
Harbor Products Inc............F.......562 633-8184
15001 Lakewood Blvd Paramount (90723) ***(P-9619)***
Harbor Seal Incorporated............F.......626 305-5754
909 S Myrtle Ave Monrovia (91016) ***(P-9534)***
Harbor Signs Inc............F.......209 463-8686
850 N Union St Stockton (95205) ***(P-23892)***
Harbor Truck Bodies Inc............D.......714 996-0411
255 Voyager Ave Brea (92821) ***(P-20209)***
Harbor Truck Body, Brea *Also called Harbor Truck Bodies Inc* ***(P-20209)***
Harcourt Trade Publishers, San Diego *Also called Houghton Mifflin Harcourt Pubg* ***(P-6351)***
Hardcore Racing Components LLC............F.......661 294-5032
27717 Avenue Scott Valencia (91355) ***(P-23426)***
Hardcraft Industries Inc............D.......408 432-8340
2221 Ringwood Ave San Jose (95131) ***(P-12608)***
Harding Containers Intl Inc............E.......310 549-7272
4000 Santa Fe Ave Long Beach (90810) ***(P-4475)***
Hardware Imports Inc............F.......909 595-6201
161 Commerce Way Walnut (91789) ***(P-20210)***
Hardware Specialties, Ontario *Also called F & D Flores Enterprises Inc* ***(P-22198)***
Hardy Process Solutions............E.......858 278-2900
9440 Carroll Park Dr # 150 San Diego (92121) ***(P-21597)***
Harkham Industries Inc (PA)............E.......323 586-4600
857 S San Pedro St # 300 Los Angeles (90014) ***(P-3244)***
Harley Murray Inc............D.......209 466-0266
1754 E Mariposa Rd Stockton (95205) ***(P-20503)***
Harman Envelopes, North Hollywood *Also called Harman Press* ***(P-6849)***
Harman Press............E.......818 432-0570
6840 Vineland Ave North Hollywood (91605) ***(P-6849)***
Harman Professional Inc............B.......951 242-2927
24950 Grove View Rd Moreno Valley (92551) ***(P-17808)***
Harman Professional Inc (HQ)............B.......818 893-8411
8500 Balboa Blvd Northridge (91329) ***(P-17809)***
Harmless Harvest Inc (PA)............E.......347 688-6286
712 Sansome St San Francisco (94111) ***(P-2534)***

ALPHABETIC

Employee Codes: A=Over 500 employees, B=251-500
C=101-250, D=51-100, E=20-50, F=10-19
2019 California
Manfacturers Register
© Mergent Inc. 1-800-342-5647
1159

Harmonic Design Inc ....E....858 391-9085
13367 Krkrham Way Ste 110 Poway (92064) *(P-17201)*
Harmonic Inc ....F....800 788-1330
4300 N 1st St San Jose (95134) *(P-18120)*
Harmonic Inc (PA) ....B....408 542-2500
4300 N 1st St San Jose (95134) *(P-18121)*
Harmonic Inc ....F....408 542-2500
641 Baltic Way Sunnyvale (94089) *(P-18122)*
Harmony Cellars ....F....805 927-1625
3255 Harmony Valley Rd Harmony (93435) *(P-1807)*
Harmony Foods Corporation (PA) ....C....831 457-3200
2200 Delaware Ave Santa Cruz (95060) *(P-8204)*
Harmony Infinite Inc ....F....818 780-4569
12918 Bloomfield St Studio City (91604) *(P-5235)*
Harmony Kids, San Fernando *Also called Newco International Inc (P-4727)*
Haro Industries Inc ....C....619 407-0500
9635 Heinrich Hertz Dr # 4 San Diego (92154) *(P-12609)*
Haros Anodizing Specialist ....F....408 980-0892
630 Walsh Ave Santa Clara (95050) *(P-13423)*
Harper & Two Inc (PA) ....F....562 424-3030
2937 Cherry Ave Signal Hill (90755) *(P-19561)*
Harpercollins Publishers LLC ....E....415 477-4400
353 Sacramento St Ste 500 San Francisco (94111) *(P-6346)*
Harrington Hoists Inc ....F....717 665-2000
2341 Pomona Rincon Rd # 103 Corona (92880) *(P-14297)*
Harris & Bruno International, Roseville *Also called Harris & Bruno Machine Co Inc (P-14810)*
Harris & Bruno Machine Co Inc (PA) ....D....916 781-7676
8555 Washington Blvd Roseville (95678) *(P-14810)*
Harris Corporation ....B....818 901-2523
7821 Orion Ave Van Nuys (91406) *(P-21303)*
Harris Corporation ....B....408 201-8000
7821 Orion Ave Van Nuys (91406) *(P-21304)*
Harris Corporation ....E....619 684-7511
9201 Spectrum Center Blvd # 105 San Diego (92123) *(P-21305)*
Harris Corporation ....E....408 201-8000
7821 Orion Ave Van Nuys (91406) *(P-17276)*
Harris Corporation ....C....619 296-6900
591 Camno De La Reina 5 San Diego (92108) *(P-21598)*
Harris Industries Inc (PA) ....E....714 898-8048
5181 Argosy Ave Huntington Beach (92649) *(P-5561)*
Harris Organs Inc ....E....562 693-3442
7047 Comstock Ave Whittier (90602) *(P-23375)*
Harris Precision ....F....408 866-4160
161 Lost Lake Ln Campbell (95008) *(P-12610)*
Harris Precision Sheet Metal, Campbell *Also called Harris Precision (P-12610)*
Harris Ranch Beef Company ....A....559 896-3081
16277 S Mccall Ave Selma (93662) *(P-439)*
Harris' Precision Products, Whittier *Also called Harris Organs Inc (P-23375)*
Harrison Beverage Inc ....F....626 961-1959
726 Arabian Ln Walnut (91789) *(P-678)*
Harrison Group, Walnut *Also called Harrison Beverage Inc (P-678)*
Harrys Dye and Wash Inc ....E....714 446-0300
1015 E Orangethorpe Ave Anaheim (92801) *(P-2882)*
Harsco Corporation ....F....909 444-2527
5580 Cherry Ave Long Beach (90805) *(P-12388)*
Harsco Distribution Center, Long Beach *Also called Harsco Corporation (P-12388)*
Hart & Cooley Inc ....E....559 875-1212
1121 Annadale Ave Sanger (93657) *(P-12860)*
Hart Electronic Assembly Inc ....D....818 709-2761
21726 Lassen St Chatsworth (91311) *(P-19562)*
Harten Jewelry Co Inc ....E....562 652-5006
8213 Villaverde Dr Whittier (90605) *(P-23272)*
Hartford Family Winery, Forestville *Also called Hartford Jackson LLC (P-1808)*
Hartford Jackson LLC ....F....707 887-1756
8075 Martinelli Rd Forestville (95436) *(P-1808)*
Harthanks, Ontario *Also called Pennysaver (P-6012)*
Hartle Media Ventures LLC ....E....415 362-7797
680 2nd St San Francisco (94107) *(P-6176)*
Hartley Company ....E....949 646-9643
1987 Placentia Ave Costa Mesa (92627) *(P-23699)*
Hartley-Racon, Costa Mesa *Also called Hartley Company (P-23699)*
Hartman Slicer Div, Compton *Also called United Bakery Equipment Co Inc (P-15232)*
Hartman Slices Division, Compton *Also called United Bakery Equipment Co Inc (P-14893)*
Hartwell Corporation (HQ) ....C....714 993-4200
900 Richfield Rd Placentia (92870) *(P-11958)*
Hartwell Corporation ....D....909 987-4616
9810 6th St Rancho Cucamonga (91730) *(P-13214)*
Hartwick Combustion Tech Inc ....F....562 922-8300
9426 Stewart And Gray Rd Downey (90241) *(P-15328)*
Hartzell Aerospace, Valencia *Also called Electrofilm Mfg Co LLC (P-13740)*
Harvard Card Systems, City of Industry *Also called Harvard Label LLC (P-5286)*
Harvard Label LLC ....C....626 333-8881
111 Baldwin Park Blvd City of Industry (91746) *(P-5286)*
Harvatek International Corp ....F....408 844-9698
3350 Scott Blvd Ste 4101 Santa Clara (95054) *(P-17615)*
Harvest Asia Inc ....F....888 800-3133
7888 Cherry Ave Ste G Fontana (92336) *(P-23427)*
Harvest Container Company ....E....559 562-1394
24476 Road 216 Lindsay (93247) *(P-5421)*
Harvest Farms Inc ....D....661 945-3636
45000 Yucca Ave Lancaster (93534) *(P-996)*
Harvest Printing Company, Anderson *Also called Checchi Enterprises Inc (P-6728)*
Harwil Precision Products ....E....805 988-6800
541 Kinetic Dr Oxnard (93030) *(P-19563)*
Hasa Inc ....E....661 259-5848
1251 Loveridge Rd Pittsburg (94565) *(P-7663)*
Hasala Engineering Inc ....F....310 538-4268
125 W 155th St Gardena (90248) *(P-16556)*
Hasbro Inc ....B....909 393-3248
16047 Mountain Ave Chino (91708) *(P-23428)*
Hasco, Placentia *Also called Hartwell Corporation (P-11958)*
Hasco Fabrication Inc ....F....909 627-0326
13370 Monte Vista Ave Chino (91710) *(P-15209)*
Haskel International LLC (HQ) ....C....818 843-4000
100 E Graham Pl Burbank (91502) *(P-15073)*
Haskon, Div of, Brea *Also called Kirkhill Inc (P-9540)*
Hastings Irrigation Pipe Co ....F....559 675-1200
17619 Road 24 Madera (93638) *(P-11589)*
Hatch Outdoors Inc ....F....760 734-4343
961 Park Center Dr Vista (92081) *(P-23581)*
Hathaway LLC ....E....661 393-2004
4205 Atlas Ct Bakersfield (93308) *(P-62)*
Haug Manufacturing Corporation ....F....408 842-1285
18443 Technology Dr Morgan Hill (95037) *(P-15210)*
Haug Quality Equipment, Morgan Hill *Also called Haug Manufacturing Corporation (P-15210)*
Hauler Racks, Sun City *Also called Dale C Sannipoli (P-20309)*
Haus of Grey LLC ....F....562 270-4739
10641 Calle Lee Ste 161 Los Alamitos (90720) *(P-3104)*
Hausenware Koyo LLC ....F....412 897-3064
2111 Laughlin Rd Windsor (95492) *(P-10646)*
Hauser & Sons Inc ....F....510 234-8850
150 S 2nd St Richmond (94804) *(P-5191)*
Hauser Shade, Richmond *Also called Hauser & Sons Inc (P-5191)*
Hav Holdings & Subsidiaries, Sun Valley *Also called Hollywood Film Company (P-23164)*
Havana Graphic Center Inc ....E....818 841-3774
301 S Flower St Burbank (91502) *(P-6850)*
Hawa Corporation ....E....909 825-8882
125 E Laurel St Colton (92324) *(P-490)*
Hawaii Kai, San Diego *Also called HK Enterprise Group Inc (P-9258)*
Hawaii Pacific Teleport LP ....F....707 938-7057
1145 Beasley Way Sonoma (95476) *(P-18123)*
Hawaiian Host Candies La Inc ....D....310 532-0543
15601 S Avalon Blvd Gardena (90248) *(P-1426)*
Hawaiian Island Creations, Gardena *Also called Coral Head Inc (P-3141)*
Hawk Crest, NAPA *Also called Stags Leap Wine Cellars (P-1988)*
Haworth Inc ....F....310 854-7633
144 N Robertson Blvd # 202 West Hollywood (90048) *(P-4989)*
Hayden Industrial Products, San Bernardino *Also called Hayden Products LLC (P-12389)*
Hayden Products LLC ....D....951 736-2600
1393 E San Bernardino Ave San Bernardino (92408) *(P-12389)*
Haydenshapes Surfboards ....F....310 648-8268
122 Arena St Unit B El Segundo (90245) *(P-23582)*
Hayes Manufacturing Svcs LLC ....E....408 730-5035
1178 Sonora Ct Sunnyvale (94086) *(P-14524)*
Hayes Welding Inc (PA) ....D....760 246-4878
12522 Violet Rd Adelanto (92301) *(P-25409)*
Hayes Welding Inc ....F....760 246-4878
11746 Mariposa Rd Ste 100 Hesperia (92345) *(P-25410)*
Haymarket Worldwide Inc ....E....949 417-6700
17030 Red Hill Ave Irvine (92614) *(P-6177)*
Haynes Publications, Newbury Park *Also called Odcombe Press (nashville) (P-7001)*
Hayward Enterprises Inc ....F....707 261-5100
2700 Napa Valley Corp Dr NAPA (94558) *(P-950)*
Hayward Gordon Us Inc ....E....760 246-3430
9351 Industrial Way Adelanto (92301) *(P-14857)*
Hayward Pallet Company Inc ....F....510 538-3127
4324 Rose Ln Concord (94518) *(P-4476)*
Hayward Quartz Machining Co, Fremont *Also called Hayward Quartz Technology (P-18870)*
Hayward Quartz Technology ....C....510 657-9605
1700 Corporate Way Fremont (94539) *(P-18870)*
Haze Bert and Assossiates ....F....714 557-1567
3188 Airway Ave Ste K1 Costa Mesa (92626) *(P-221)*
Hazel Clothes, Vernon *Also called Crestone LLC (P-3575)*
Hazelcast Inc (PA) ....E....650 521-5453
350 Cambridge Ave Ste 100 Palo Alto (94306) *(P-24720)*
Haztech Systems Inc ....E....209 966-8088
4996 Gold Leaf Dr Mariposa (95338) *(P-8963)*
HB Fuller Company ....D....916 787-6000
10500 Industrial Ave Roseville (95678) *(P-9145)*
HB Products LLC ....E....714 799-6967
5671 Engineer Dr Huntington Beach (92649) *(P-7342)*
Hbc Solutions Holdings LLC ....A....321 727-9100
10877 Wilshire Blvd Fl 18 Los Angeles (90024) *(P-18124)*
Hbe Rental, Grass Valley *Also called Hansen Bros Enterprises (P-361)*
Hbno, Camarillo *Also called IL Helth Buty Natural Oils Inc (P-9260)*
HC Brill ....B....909 825-7343
2111 W Valley Blvd Colton (92324) *(P-1395)*
HCC Industries Inc (HQ) ....F....626 443-8933
4232 Temple City Blvd Rosemead (91770) *(P-19393)*
Hchd ....F....909 923-8889
1175 S Grove Ave Ste 104 Ontario (91761) *(P-20149)*
Hci, San Marcos *Also called Hughes Circuits Inc (P-18500)*
Hco Holding I Corporation ....F....310 684-5320
2270 S Castle Harbour Pl Ontario (91761) *(P-9406)*
Hco Holding II Corporation ....D....310 955-9200
999 N Sepulveda Blvd El Segundo (90245) *(P-9407)*
Hcp Industries Inc ....F....530 899-5591
415 Otterson Dr Ste 10 Chico (95928) *(P-10805)*
HD Carry Inc ....F....949 831-6022
81 Columbia Ste 150 Aliso Viejo (92656) *(P-9864)*
Hd Garment Solutions Inc ....E....323 581-6000
13351 Riverside Dr Sherman Oaks (91423) *(P-3615)*
Hd Window Fashions Inc (HQ) ....B....213 749-6333
1818 Oak St Los Angeles (90015) *(P-5192)*
HDD LLC ....F....707 433-9545
4035 Westside Rd Healdsburg (95448) *(P-1809)*

Hdkaraoke Llc......F......626 296-6200
2400 Lincoln Ave Altadena (91001) *(P-17810)*
Hdp Holdings, San Diego *Also called Wd-40 Company (P-9375)*
Head First Productions Inc......F......714 522-3311
14848 Northam St La Mirada (90638) *(P-14706)*
Headed Reinforcement Corp......F......714 557-1455
11200 Condor Ave Fountain Valley (92708) *(P-13215)*
Headfirst Products, La Mirada *Also called Head First Productions Inc (P-14706)*
Headgear Plus Promo, Petaluma *Also called Fulton Acres Inc (P-3892)*
Headline Graphics Inc......E......760 436-0133
131 Aberdeen Dr Cardiff By The Sea (92007) *(P-7647)*
Headmaster Inc (PA)......E......714 556-5244
3000 S Croddy Way Santa Ana (92704) *(P-3564)*
Headrick Logging, Anderson *Also called James A Headrick Ii/Elizabeth (P-3996)*
Headwaters Construction Inc......E......714 523-1530
16005 Phoebe Ave La Mirada (90638) *(P-10757)*
Headwaters Incorporated......F......909 627-9066
1345 Philadelphia St Pomona (91766) *(P-10935)*
Headway Technologies Inc (HQ)......C......408 934-5300
682 S Hillview Dr Milpitas (95035) *(P-15547)*
Headway Technologies Inc......C......408 934-5300
497 S Hillview Dr Milpitas (95035) *(P-15548)*
Headway Technology......F......408 935-1020
463 S Milpitas Blvd Milpitas (95035) *(P-15549)*
Headwinds......F......626 359-8044
221 W Maple Ave Monrovia (91016) *(P-21114)*
Health Breads Inc......E......760 747-7390
155 Mata Way Ste 112 San Marcos (92069) *(P-1271)*
Health Gorilla Inc......E......844 446-7455
440 N Wolfe Rd Sunnyvale (94085) *(P-24721)*
Health Naturals Inc......F......714 259-1821
13 Navarre Irvine (92612) *(P-8205)*
Health Plus Inc......E......909 627-9393
13837 Magnolia Ave Chino (91710) *(P-8206)*
Healthline Systems LLC (HQ)......E......858 673-1700
9605 Scranton Rd Ste 200 San Diego (92121) *(P-24722)*
Healthsport Inc......F......818 593-4880
1620 Beacon Pl Oxnard (93033) *(P-8207)*
Healthstream Inc......B......800 733-8737
9605 Scranton Rd Ste 200 San Diego (92121) *(P-24723)*
Healthy Times......F......858 513-1550
225 Broadway Ste 450 San Diego (92101) *(P-2535)*
Healthywealthyhack Inc......F......669 225-3745
16979 Frank Ave Los Gatos (95032) *(P-24724)*
Healty Times Natural Products, San Diego *Also called Healthy Times (P-2535)*
Hearsay Social Inc (PA)......D......888 990-3777
185 Berry St Ste 3800 San Francisco (94107) *(P-24725)*
Hearst Communications Inc......B......916 725-8694
7916 Arcade Lake Ln Citrus Heights (95610) *(P-5870)*
Hearst Communications Inc......B......510 645-4250
1350 16th St Oakland (94607) *(P-5871)*
Hearst Communications Inc......C......415 537-4200
680 2nd St San Francisco (94107) *(P-5872)*
Hearst Corporation......F......310 752-1040
3000 Ocean Park Blvd Santa Monica (90405) *(P-6178)*
Hearst Corporation......C......831 582-9605
224 Reindollar Ave Marina (93933) *(P-5873)*
Hearst Corporation......D......760 707-0100
15255 Alton Pkwy Ste 300 Irvine (92618) *(P-6179)*
Hearst Corporation......E......530 964-3131
1 Wyntoon Rd Mccloud (96057) *(P-6180)*
Hearst Corporation......F......415 777-0600
5 3rd St Ste 200 San Francisco (94103) *(P-5874)*
HEARST CORPORATION THE, Marina *Also called Hearst Corporation (P-5873)*
Heart of Haute, La Verne *Also called Heartbreaker Fashion (P-3245)*
Heart Rate Inc......E......714 850-9716
1411 E Wilshire Ave Santa Ana (92705) *(P-23583)*
Heart Wood Manufacturing Inc......D......408 848-9750
5860 Obata Way Gilroy (95020) *(P-4306)*
Heartbreaker Fashion......F......909 599-0715
1925 Mckinley Ave Ste H La Verne (91750) *(P-3245)*
Hearthco Inc......E......530 622-3877
5781 Pleasant Valley Rd El Dorado (95623) *(P-11959)*
Heartland Farms, City of Industry *Also called Sbm Dairies Inc (P-2217)*
Hearts Delight......E......805 648-7123
4035 N Ventura Ave Ventura (93001) *(P-3427)*
Hearts For Long Beach Inc......E......562 433-2000
5225 E 2nd St Long Beach (90803) *(P-5875)*
Heartwood Cabinets, Gilroy *Also called Heart Wood Manufacturing Inc (P-4306)*
Heat Factory Inc......E......760 734-5300
2793 Loker Ave W Carlsbad (92010) *(P-5602)*
Heat Software USA Inc (HQ)......E......408 601-2800
490 N Mccarthy Blvd Milpitas (95035) *(P-24726)*
Heat Transfer Pdts Group LLC......B......714 529-1935
8101 E Kaiser Blvd # 110 Anaheim (92808) *(P-15959)*
Heateflex Corporation......E......626 599-8566
405 E Santa Clara St Arcadia (91006) *(P-12067)*
Heater Designs Inc......E......909 421-0971
2211 S Vista Ave Bloomington (92316) *(P-15261)*
Heatshield Products Inc......E......760 751-0441
938 S Anderson Dr Ste Cd Valley Center (92082) *(P-11341)*
Heaven or Las Vegas, Van Nuys *Also called Kimball Nelson Inc (P-24148)*
Heavy Duty Trucking, Irvine *Also called HIC Corporation (P-6182)*
Heck Cellars, Di Giorgio *Also called F Korbel & Bros (P-1756)*
Heco Inc......F......916 372-5411
2350 Del Monte St West Sacramento (95691) *(P-15239)*
Heco Pacific Manufacturing......E......510 487-1155
1510 Pacific St Union City (94587) *(P-14275)*
Hedgeside Vintners......E......707 963-2134
1055 Atlas Peak Rd NAPA (94558) *(P-1810)*
Hedman Hedders, Whittier *Also called Hedman Manufacturing (P-20359)*
Hedman Manufacturing (PA)......E......562 204-1031
12438 Putnam St Whittier (90602) *(P-20359)*
Hee, Anaheim *Also called Ceco Environmental Corp (P-10017)*
Heeger Inc......F......323 728-5108
6446 Flotilla St Commerce (90040) *(P-17202)*
HEI, San Diego *Also called Oggis Pizza & Brewing Co (P-1616)*
Heidelberg Instruments Inc......F......310 212-5071
2539 W 237th St Ste A Torrance (90505) *(P-14811)*
Heiden's Foods, Anaheim *Also called Heidens Inc (P-804)*
Heidens Inc......F......714 525-3414
2900 E Blue Star St Anaheim (92806) *(P-804)*
Heighten America Inc......E......209 845-0455
1144 Post Rd Oakdale (95361) *(P-16557)*
Heighten Manfacturing, Oakdale *Also called Heighten America Inc (P-16557)*
Heinz Seeds, Stockton *Also called Kraft Heinz Foods Company (P-1493)*
Heinz Weber Incorporated......E......310 477-3561
13025 Park Pl Unit 402 Hawthorne (90250) *(P-7648)*
Heitman Brooks II LLC (PA)......F......909 947-7470
1850 S Parco Ave Ontario (91761) *(P-10936)*
Helados Vallarta Inc......F......559 709-1177
1418 G St Fresno (93706) *(P-679)*
Helen Noble......F......916 457-8990
2120 28th St Sacramento (95818) *(P-6181)*
Helena Agri-Enterprises LLC......E......559 582-0291
12218 11th Ave Hanford (93230) *(P-9103)*
Helens Place Inc......F......909 981-5715
893 W 9th St Upland (91786) *(P-6851)*
Helfer Enterprises......E......714 557-2733
3030 Oak St Santa Ana (92707) *(P-16558)*
Helfer Tool Co, Santa Ana *Also called Helfer Enterprises (P-16558)*
Helica Biosystems Inc......F......714 578-7830
3310 W Macarthur Blvd Santa Ana (92704) *(P-8481)*
Helical Products, Santa Maria *Also called Matthew Warren Inc (P-13751)*
Helicopter Tech Co Ltd Partnr......E......310 523-2750
12902 S Broadway Los Angeles (90061) *(P-20836)*
Heliovolt Corporation......D......512 767-6079
3945 Freedom Cir Ste 560 Santa Clara (95054) *(P-19564)*
Helitek Company Ltd......F......510 933-7688
4033 Clipper Ct Fremont (94538) *(P-18871)*
Helix Medical, Carpinteria *Also called Freudenberg Medical LLC (P-22736)*
Heller Seasoning, Modesto *Also called Newly Weds Foods Inc (P-2621)*
Heller State, Carmel Valley *Also called Durney Winery Corporation (P-1738)*
Hellman Properties LLC......F......562 431-6022
711 First St Seal Beach (90740) *(P-63)*
Hello Network Inc......F......408 891-4727
2 Mint Plz Apt 1004 San Francisco (94103) *(P-24727)*
Hellwig Products Company Inc......E......559 734-7451
16237 Avenue 296 Visalia (93292) *(P-20360)*
Hely & Weber Orthopedic, Santa Paula *Also called Weber Orthopedic Inc (P-22846)*
Hemet Ready Mix, Hemet *Also called Superior Ready Mix Concrete LP (P-11196)*
Hemisphere Design & Mfg LLC......F......661 294-9500
25215 Rye Canyon Rd Valencia (91355) *(P-5068)*
Hemodialysis Inc......E......626 792-0548
806 S Fair Oaks Ave Pasadena (91105) *(P-22469)*
Hemosense Inc......D......408 719-1393
9975 Summers Ridge Rd San Diego (92121) *(P-22983)*
Hemostat Laboratories Inc (PA)......E......707 678-9594
515 Industrial Way Dixon (95620) *(P-8558)*
Hemosure Inc......E......888 436-6787
5358 Irwindale Ave Baldwin Park (91706) *(P-9257)*
Henderson Services Inc......E......559 435-8874
6722 N Stonebridge Dr Fresno (93711) *(P-21042)*
Henkel Corporation......C......310 764-4600
20021 S Susana Rd Compton (90221) *(P-8686)*
Henkel Electronic Mtls LLC......C......888 943-6535
14000 Jamboree Rd Irvine (92606) *(P-9146)*
Henkel US Operations Corp......E......626 968-6511
15051 Don Julian Rd City of Industry (91746) *(P-9147)*
Hennis Enterprises Inc......E......805 477-0257
2646 Palma Dr Ste 430 Ventura (93003) *(P-7838)*
Henry Company, Ontario *Also called Hco Holding I Corporation (P-9406)*
Henry Company LLC (HQ)......D......310 955-9200
999 N Pacific Coast Hwy El Segundo (90245) *(P-9408)*
Henry J Perez DDS......F......805 983-6768
132 S A St Ste B Oxnard (93030) *(P-22883)*
Henry L Hudson (PA)......F......805 736-2737
403 N G St Lompoc (93436) *(P-6852)*
Henry Ll......F......408 944-9100
1020 Rock Ave San Jose (95131) *(P-12611)*
Henry Machine Inc......F......760 734-6792
2316 La Mirada Dr Vista (92081) *(P-16559)*
Henry Plastic Molding Inc......C......510 490-7993
41703 Albrae St Fremont (94538) *(P-10133)*
Henrys Adio Vsual Slutions Inc......E......714 258-7238
1582 Parkway Loop Ste F Tustin (92780) *(P-17811)*
Henrys Metal Polishing Works......F......323 263-9701
3445 Union Pacific Ave Los Angeles (90023) *(P-13424)*
Henway Inc......F......661 822-6873
1314 Goodrick Dr Tehachapi (93561) *(P-23767)*
Hephaestus Innovations......F......831 254-8555
2661 W Bch St Ste 3b Suit Watsonville (95076) *(P-14858)*
Heraeus Prcous Mtls N Amer LLC (HQ)......C......562 921-7464
15524 Carmenita Rd Santa Fe Springs (90670) *(P-11559)*
Herald Printing Ltd (PA)......F......805 647-1870
1242 Los Angeles Ave Ventura (93004) *(P-6853)*

ALPHABETIC

Employee Codes: A=Over 500 employees, B=251-500
C=101-250, D=51-100, E=20-50, F=10-19
2019 California
Manfacturers Register
© Mergent Inc. 1-800-342-5647
1161

Herbal Science International...............F.......626 333-9998
205 Russell St City of Industry (91744) ***(P-7947)***
Herbalife Manufacturing LLC...............D.......949 457-0951
20481 Crescent Bay Dr Lake Forest (92630) ***(P-2267)***
Herbs Yeh Manufacturing Co...............F.......909 946-0794
195 N 2nd Ave Upland (91786) ***(P-621)***
Herburger Publications Inc (PA)...............D.......916 685-5533
604 N Lincoln Way Galt (95632) ***(P-5876)***
Herburger Publications Inc...............F.......916 685-3945
8970 Elk Grove Blvd Elk Grove (95624) ***(P-5877)***
Herdell Printing & Lithography...............E.......707 963-3634
340 Mccormick St Saint Helena (94574) ***(P-6854)***
Herff Jones LLC...............F.......951 541-3938
14321 Goose St Corona (92880) ***(P-23273)***
Heritage Bag Company...............F.......909 899-5554
12320 4th St Rancho Cucamonga (91730) ***(P-5603)***
Heritage Bronze, Hesperia *Also called E R Metals Inc* ***(P-11756)***
Heritage Cabinet Co Inc...............F.......818 786-4900
21740 Marilla St Chatsworth (91311) ***(P-5069)***
Heritage Carbide Inc...............F.......714 974-6377
1591 N Main St Orange (92867) ***(P-16560)***
Heritage Container Inc...............D.......951 360-1900
4777 Felspar St Riverside (92509) ***(P-5422)***
Heritage Design...............F.......949 248-1300
32382 Del Obispo St B1 San Juan Capistrano (92675) ***(P-23893)***
Heritage Distributing Company...............E.......626 333-9526
425 S 9th Ave City of Industry (91746) ***(P-622)***
Heritage Distributing Company (PA)...............E.......323 838-1225
5743 Smithway St Ste 105 Commerce (90040) ***(P-728)***
Heritage Leather Company Inc...............E.......323 983-0420
4011 E 52nd St Maywood (90270) ***(P-10459)***
Heritage Missional Community...............F.......530 605-1990
4302 Shasta Dam Blvd Shasta Lake (96019) ***(P-2352)***
Heritage Paper Co, Livermore *Also called Baycorr Packaging Inc* ***(P-5387)***
Heritage Paper Co...............F.......925 449-1148
17740 Shideler Pkwy Lathrop (95330) ***(P-6855)***
Heritage Paper Co (HQ)...............D.......714 540-9737
2400 S Grand Ave Santa Ana (92705) ***(P-5423)***
Heritage Printing, San Diego *Also called Michael Martella* ***(P-6420)***
Heritage Products LLC...............F.......909 839-1866
20932c Currier Rd Unit C Walnut (91789) ***(P-9749)***
Heritage Roasting Company, Shasta Lake *Also called Heritage Missional Community* ***(P-2352)***
Heritage Truck Painting, San Diego *Also called Brothers Enterprises Inc* ***(P-25389)***
Heritage Woodworking Co Inc...............E.......530 243-7215
4633 Mountain Lakes Blvd Redding (96003) ***(P-4307)***
Herley Industries Inc...............D.......858 812-7300
4820 Estgate Mall Ste 200 San Diego (92121) ***(P-19565)***
Herman Engineering & Mfg Inc...............F.......909 483-1631
4501 E Airport Dr Ste B Ontario (91761) ***(P-10134)***
Herman Miller Inc...............E.......408 432-5730
2740 Zanker Rd Ste 150 San Jose (95134) ***(P-4948)***
Hermes-Microvision Inc...............E.......408 597-8600
1762 Automation Pkwy San Jose (95131) ***(P-18872)***
Hermetic Seal Corporation (HQ)...............C.......626 443-8931
4232 Temple City Blvd Rosemead (91770) ***(P-19566)***
Hernandez Zeferino...............F.......714 953-4010
1924 E Mcfadden Ave Santa Ana (92705) ***(P-9148)***
Hero Arts Rubber Stamps Inc...............D.......510 232-4200
1200 Hrbour Way S Ste 201 Richmond (94804) ***(P-23717)***
Hero Nutritional, Santa Ana *Also called Envita Labs LLC* ***(P-7936)***
Heroku Inc...............E.......650 704-6107
1 Market St Ste 300 San Francisco (94105) ***(P-24728)***
Heron Therapeutics Inc (PA)...............C.......858 251-4400
4242 Campus Point Ct # 200 San Diego (92121) ***(P-8208)***
Herotek Inc...............E.......408 941-8399
155 Baytech Dr San Jose (95134) ***(P-18125)***
Herrick Corporation (PA)...............E.......209 956-4751
3003 E Hammer Ln Stockton (95212) ***(P-12175)***
Herrick Corporation...............C.......209 956-4751
3003 E Hammer Ln Stockton (95212) ***(P-11398)***
Herrick Retail Corporation Th...............F.......714 256-9543
2923 Saturn St Ste D Brea (92821) ***(P-6856)***
Hershey Company...............C.......559 485-8110
2704 S Maple Ave Fresno (93725) ***(P-2428)***
Hertz Entertainment Services, Burbank *Also called 24/7 Studio Equipment Inc* ***(P-18011)***
Herzog Wine Cellars, Oxnard *Also called Royal Wine Corporation* ***(P-1959)***
Hesperia Resorter...............E.......760 244-0021
16925 Main St Ste A Hesperia (92345) ***(P-5878)***
Hesperian Health Guides (PA)...............E.......510 845-1447
1919 Addison St Ste 304 Berkeley (94704) ***(P-6347)***
Hess Collection Import Co, NAPA *Also called Hess Collection Winery* ***(P-1811)***
Hess Collection Winery (HQ)...............E.......707 255-1144
4411 Redwood Rd NAPA (94558) ***(P-1811)***
Hess Precision Laser Inc...............F.......209 575-1634
4747 Stratos Way Ste D Modesto (95356) ***(P-19978)***
Hestan Commercial Corporation...............C.......714 869-2380
3375 E La Palma Ave Anaheim (92806) ***(P-17415)***
Hestan Smart Cooking Inc...............F.......773 710-1538
1 Meyer Plz Vallejo (94590) ***(P-13216)***
Hewitt Industries Los Angeles...............E.......714 891-9300
5492 Bolsa Ave Huntington Beach (92649) ***(P-21599)***
Hewlett Packard Enterprise Co...............D.......916 786-8000
8000 Foothills Blvd Roseville (95747) ***(P-24729)***
Hewlett Packard Enterprise Co...............E.......312 580-9100
1140 Enterprise Way Sunnyvale (94089) ***(P-24730)***
Hewlett Packard Enterprise Co (PA)...............C.......650 687-5817
3000 Hanover St Palo Alto (94304) ***(P-24731)***
Hewlett-Packard Entps LLC (HQ)...............D.......650 687-5817
3000 Hanover St Palo Alto (94304) ***(P-15419)***
Hexacorp Ltd...............E.......760 815-0904
201 Ocean Ave Unit 1108p Santa Monica (90402) ***(P-24732)***
Hexagon Metrology Inc...............E.......949 916-4490
7 Orchard Ste 102 Lake Forest (92630) ***(P-14640)***
Hexagon Metrology Inc...............D.......760 994-1401
3536 Seagate Way Oceanside (92056) ***(P-22211)***
Hexcel Corporation...............D.......925 551-4900
11711 Dublin Blvd Dublin (94568) ***(P-2960)***
Hexco International (PA)...............E.......951 677-2081
25720 Jefferson Ave Murrieta (92562) ***(P-14965)***
Hexion Inc...............F.......714 971-0180
625 The City Dr S Ste 300 Orange (92868) ***(P-9009)***
Hexpol Compounding CA Inc...............D.......626 961-0311
491 Wilson Way City of Industry (91744) ***(P-9620)***
Hexpol Compounding California, Santa Fe Springs *Also called Hexpol Compounding LLC* ***(P-9621)***
Hexpol Compounding LLC...............E.......562 464-4480
8227 Sorensen Ave Santa Fe Springs (90670) ***(P-9621)***
Hexpol Compounding LLC...............E.......562 464-4482
11841 Wakeman St Santa Fe Springs (90670) ***(P-9622)***
Hey Baby of California...............E.......818 504-2060
11238 Peoria St C Sun Valley (91352) ***(P-3428)***
Heyday...............F.......510 549-3564
2120 University Ave Berkeley (94704) ***(P-6348)***
Heyday Books, Berkeley *Also called Heyday* ***(P-6348)***
Hf Group Inc (PA)...............E.......310 605-0755
203 W Artesia Blvd Compton (90220) ***(P-23162)***
Hgc Holdings Inc...............C.......323 567-2226
3303 Mrtn Lthr King Jr Bl Lynwood (90262) ***(P-1427)***
Hgst Inc...............C.......408 418-4148
5601 Great Oaks Pkwy San Jose (95119) ***(P-15550)***
Hgst Inc...............F.......408 801-2394
951 Sandisk Dr Milpitas (95035) ***(P-15551)***
Hgst Inc (HQ)...............F.......408 717-6000
5601 Great Oaks Pkwy San Jose (95119) ***(P-15552)***
Hh Industries, San Diego *Also called Haro Industries Inc* ***(P-12609)***
Hl Desert Forklift Services...............F.......760 241-4575
15603 Tenth St Victorville (92395) ***(P-14326)***
Hl Fashion Productions Inc...............E.......323 722-8200
2850 Tanager Ave Commerce (90040) ***(P-3898)***
Hl Performance Electric Vehicl...............F.......909 923-1973
620 S Magnolia Ave Ste B Ontario (91762) ***(P-17203)***
Hl Rel Connectors Inc...............B.......909 626-1820
760 Wharton Dr Claremont (91711) ***(P-17470)***
Hl Relblity McRelectronics Inc...............E.......408 764-5500
1804 Mccarthy Blvd Milpitas (95035) ***(P-18873)***
Hl Rez Digital Solutions...............F.......760 597-2650
1235 Activity Dr Ste E Vista (92081) ***(P-6857)***
Hl Tech Engineering, Camarillo *Also called Hte Manufacturing Inc* ***(P-14641)***
Hl Tech Heat Treating Inc...............F.......310 532-3705
331 W 168th St Gardena (90248) ***(P-11814)***
Hl Tech Honeycomb Inc...............C.......858 974-1600
9355 Ruffin Ct San Diego (92123) ***(P-13217)***
Hl Tech Solder...............F.......714 572-1200
700 Monroe Way Placentia (92870) ***(P-11630)***
Hi-Craft Metal Products...............E.......310 323-6949
606 W 184th St Gardena (90248) ***(P-12612)***
Hi-Desert Publishing Company...............E.......909 797-9101
35154 Yucaipa Blvd Yucaipa (92399) ***(P-5879)***
Hi-Desert Publishing Company...............E.......909 336-3555
28200 Highway 189 O-1 Lake Arrowhead (92352) ***(P-5880)***
Hi-Desert Publishing Company (HQ)...............D.......760 365-3315
56445 29 Palms Hwy Yucca Valley (92284) ***(P-5881)***
Hi-Flo Corp...............F.......562 468-0800
5161 E El Cedral St Long Beach (90815) ***(P-15074)***
Hi-Grade Materials Co...............E.......661 533-3100
6500 E Avenue T Littlerock (93543) ***(P-11119)***
Hi-Line Industrial Saw and Sup...............F.......714 921-1600
416 W Meats Ave Orange (92865) ***(P-11919)***
Hi-Lite Manufacturing Co Inc...............D.......909 465-1999
13450 Monte Vista Ave Chino (91710) ***(P-17616)***
Hi-Plas, Mira Loma *Also called Highland Plastics Inc* ***(P-10136)***
Hi-Precision Grinding, Santa Ana *Also called Deltronic Corporation* ***(P-22071)***
Hi-Q Environmental Pdts Co Inc...............F.......858 549-2818
7386 Trade St San Diego (92121) ***(P-21965)***
Hi-Rel Plastics & Molding Corp...............E.......951 354-0258
7575 Jurupa Ave Riverside (92504) ***(P-10135)***
Hi-Shear Corporation (HQ)...............A.......310 784-4025
2600 Skypark Dr Torrance (90505) ***(P-13071)***
Hl-Shear Corporation...............E.......310 326-8110
2600 Skypark Dr Torrance (90505) ***(P-11960)***
Hi-Tech Electronic Mfg Corp...............D.......858 657-0908
7420 Carroll Rd San Diego (92121) ***(P-18499)***
Hi-Tech Iron Works, Commerce *Also called Architectural Enterprises Inc* ***(P-12833)***
Hi-Tech Labels Incorporated (PA)...............E.......714 670-2150
8530 Roland St Buena Park (90621) ***(P-7343)***
Hi-Tech Metal Polishing, Santa Fe Springs *Also called Whiting Enterprises* ***(P-13535)***
Hi-Tech Prcision Machining Inc...............F.......408 251-1269
1901 Las Plumas Ave # 50 San Jose (95133) ***(P-16561)***
Hi-Tech Products, Buena Park *Also called Hi-Tech Labels Incorporated* ***(P-7343)***
Hi-Tech Welding & Forming Inc...............E.......619 562-5929
1327 Fayette St El Cajon (92020) ***(P-16562)***
Hi-Temp Forming Co Inc...............D.......714 529-6556
315 Arden Ave Ste 28 Glendale (91203) ***(P-16563)***
Hi-Temp Insulation Inc...............B.......805 484-2774
4700 Calle Alto Camarillo (93012) ***(P-13218)***
Hi-Torque Publications, Santa Clarita *Also called Daisy Publishing Company Inc* ***(P-6141)***

Mergent e-mail: customerrelations@mergent.com
1162
2019 California
Manufacturers Register
(P-0000) Products & Services Section entry number
(PA)=Parent Co (HQ)=Headquarters (DH)=Div Headquarters

Hi-Z Technology Inc....E....858 695-6660
7606 Miramar Rd Ste 7400 San Diego (92126) *(P-17342)*
Hi/Fn Inc (HQ)....F....408 778-2944
48720 Kato Rd Fremont (94538) *(P-18874)*
Hiatus, Los Angeles *Also called Crew Knitwear LLC (P-3398)*
Hibernia Woolen Mills, Manhattan Beach *Also called Stanton Carpet Corp (P-2942)*
HIC Corporation (PA)....F....949 261-1636
38 Executive Park Ste 300 Irvine (92614) *(P-6182)*
Hidden Jeans Inc (PA)....F....213 746-4223
1001 Towne Ave Ste 103 Los Angeles (90021) *(P-2742)*
High Camp Home, Truckee *Also called Recycled Spaces Inc (P-4918)*
High Connection Density Inc....E....408 743-9700
820 Kifer Rd Ste A Sunnyvale (94086) *(P-19394)*
High Country Water, Roseville *Also called California Bottling Company (P-2106)*
High End Seating Solutions LLC....E....714 259-0177
1919 E Occidental St Santa Ana (92705) *(P-21115)*
High Energy Sports Inc....F....714 632-3323
1081 N Shepard St Ste A Anaheim (92806) *(P-3950)*
High Fidelity Textiles, Los Angeles *Also called Padilla Remberto (P-2889)*
High Five Inc....E....714 847-2200
1452 Manhattan Ave Fullerton (92831) *(P-6858)*
High Precision Grinding....E....619 440-0303
1130 Pioneer Way El Cajon (92020) *(P-16564)*
High Sierra Electronics Inc....E....530 273-2080
155 Spring Hill Dr # 106 Grass Valley (95945) *(P-21966)*
High Sierra Plastics, Bishop *Also called RW Wilson Inc (P-10352)*
High Sierra Truss Company Inc....F....559 688-6611
1201 S K St Tulare (93274) *(P-4410)*
High Speed Cnc....F....408 492-0331
3324 Victor Ct Santa Clara (95054) *(P-16565)*
High Tech Etch (PA)....F....760 244-8916
17469 Lemon St Hesperia (92345) *(P-16566)*
High Tech Etch Research & Dev, Hesperia *Also called High Tech Etch (P-16566)*
High Tech Pet Products Inc....E....805 644-1797
2111 Portola Rd A Ventura (93003) *(P-24117)*
High-End Knitwear Inc....E....323 582-6061
1100 S Hope St Ph 202 Los Angeles (90015) *(P-2842)*
High-Tech Coatings Inc....F....714 547-2122
1724 S Santa Fe St Santa Ana (92705) *(P-13601)*
Highball Signal Inc....F....909 341-5367
1871 N Gaffey St Ste C San Pedro (90731) *(P-18330)*
Higher One Payments Inc....E....510 769-9888
80 Swan Way Ste 200 Oakland (94621) *(P-24733)*
Highland Plastics Inc....C....951 360-9587
3650 Dulles Dr Mira Loma (91752) *(P-10136)*
Highland Technology....E....415 551-1700
650 Potrero Ave San Francisco (94110) *(P-22212)*
Highland Wholesale Foods Inc....E....209 933-0580
1604 Tillie Lewis Dr Stockton (95206) *(P-805)*
Highlander Harvesting Aid, Gonzales *Also called Ramsay Highlander Inc (P-14096)*
Highpoint Technologies Inc....F....408 942-5800
41650 Christy St Fremont (94538) *(P-15553)*
Hightower Metal Products....D....714 637-7000
2090 N Glassell St Orange (92865) *(P-16567)*
Hightower Metals, Orange *Also called Hightower Plating & Mfg Co (P-13425)*
Hightower Plating & Mfg Co....E....714 637-9110
2090 N Glassell St Orange (92865) *(P-13425)*
Highway Safety Control, NAPA *Also called Radiator Specialty Company (P-9300)*
Highway Two....F....877 395-8088
1 Columbia Ste 200 Aliso Viejo (92656) *(P-21116)*
Highways Magazine, Oxnard *Also called Tl Enterprises LLC (P-6272)*
Highwire Press Inc (PA)....E....650 721-6388
973 University Ave Los Gatos (95032) *(P-6499)*
Higuchi Inc., USA, Torrance *Also called Kabushiki Kisha Higuchi Shokai (P-17540)*
Hii San Diego Shipyard Inc....B....619 234-8851
1995 Bay Front St San Diego (92113) *(P-20996)*
Hilborn Fuel Injection Company, Aliso Viejo *Also called Fuel Injection Engineering Co (P-20344)*
Hilborn Manufacturing Corp....F....949 360-0909
22892 Glenwood Dr Aliso Viejo (92656) *(P-20361)*
Hile Studio Inc....E....626 359-7210
310 N Sunnyside Ave Sierra Madre (91024) *(P-4783)*
Hilfiker Pipe Co....E....707 443-5091
1902 Hilfiker Ln Eureka (95503) *(P-10937)*
Hilfiker Retaining Walls, Eureka *Also called Hilfiker Pipe Co (P-10937)*
Hilkers Custom Cabinets Inc....F....951 487-7640
504 N Greco Ct San Jacinto (92582) *(P-4308)*
Hill Brothers Chemical Company....F....626 333-2251
15017 Clark Ave City of Industry (91745) *(P-7664)*
Hill Manufacturing Company LLC....E....408 988-4744
3363 Edward Ave Santa Clara (95054) *(P-12613)*
Hill Marine Products LLC....F....714 855-2986
2683 Halladay St Santa Ana (92705) *(P-16568)*
Hill Phoenix Inc....E....909 592-8830
14680 Monte Vista Ave Chino (91710) *(P-15960)*
Hill Products Inc....F....818 877-9256
19160 Arminta St Reseda (91335) *(P-17812)*
Hill Top Winery, Valley Center *Also called Htr LLC (P-1814)*
Hiller Aircraft Corporation....E....559 659-5959
925 M St Firebaugh (93622) *(P-20591)*
Hillerich & Bradsby Co....E....916 652-4267
5960 Jetton Ln Loomis (95650) *(P-23584)*
Hillerich & Bradsby Co....D....800 282-2287
1800 S Archibald Ave Ontario (91761) *(P-23585)*
Hillholder Blocks By Modern....F....619 463-6344
3239 Bancroft Dr Spring Valley (91977) *(P-10938)*
Hillis Printing Co Inc....F....408 450-7910
525 Parrott St San Jose (95112) *(P-6859)*

Hillo America Inc....F....626 570-8899
9094 Las Tunas Dr Temple City (91780) *(P-17813)*
Hills Wldg & Engrg Contr Inc....D....661 746-5400
22038 Stockdale Hwy Bakersfield (93314) *(P-222)*
Hillshire Brands Company....B....909 481-0760
9357 Richmond Pl Ste 101 Rancho Cucamonga (91730) *(P-491)*
Hillshire Brands Company....B....510 276-1300
2411 Baumann Ave San Lorenzo (94580) *(P-492)*
Hillshire Brands Company....E....562 903-9260
10715 Springdale Ave # 5 Santa Fe Springs (90670) *(P-493)*
Hillside Capital Inc....C....650 367-2011
6222 Fallbrook Ave Woodland Hills (91367) *(P-18126)*
Hilltron Corporation....F....408 597-4424
2528 Qume Dr Ste 4 San Jose (95131) *(P-19567)*
Hilmar Cheese Company Inc....D....209 667-6076
3600 W Canal Dr Turlock (95380) *(P-577)*
Hilmar Cheese Company Inc (PA)....B....209 667-6076
8901 Lander Ave Hilmar (95324) *(P-578)*
Hilmar Ingredients, Hilmar *Also called Hilmar Cheese Company Inc (P-578)*
Hilmar Whey Protein Inc (PA)....B....209 667-6076
9001 Lander Ave Hilmar (95324) *(P-623)*
Hilmar Whey Protein Inc....D....209 667-6076
8901 Lander Ave Hilmar (95324) *(P-624)*
Hilz Cable Assemblies Inc....F....951 245-0499
31889 Corydon St Ste 110 Lake Elsinore (92530) *(P-22213)*
Hing WA Lee Inc....E....909 595-3500
19811 Colima Rd Walnut (91789) *(P-23343)*
Hinoichi Tofu, Garden Grove *Also called House Foods America Corp (P-1509)*
Hint Inc....E....415 513-4051
2124 Union St Ste D San Francisco (94123) *(P-2139)*
Hip & Hip Inc (PA)....E....310 494-6742
1100 S San Pedro St D07 Los Angeles (90015) *(P-3429)*
Hiplink Software, Los Gatos *Also called Semotus Inc (P-25161)*
Hire Elegance....F....858 740-7862
8333 Arjons Dr Ste E San Diego (92126) *(P-5236)*
Hirel Connectors, Claremont *Also called Hl Rel Connectors Inc (P-17470)*
Hirok Inc....E....619 713-5066
5644 Kearny Mesa Rd Ste H San Diego (92111) *(P-14176)*
Hirsch Pipe & Supply Co Inc....E....949 487-7009
31920 Del Obispo St # 275 San Juan Capistrano (92675) *(P-12038)*
Hirsh Inc....E....213 622-9441
860 S Los Angeles St # 900 Los Angeles (90014) *(P-223)*
His Company Inc....F....951 493-0200
400 E Parkridge Ave # 101 Corona (92879) *(P-5562)*
His Industries Inc....E....562 407-0512
1202 W Shelley Ct Orange (92868) *(P-15211)*
His Life Woodworks....E....310 756-0170
15107 S Main St Gardena (90248) *(P-4309)*
Hispanic Business Inc....F....805 964-4554
5385 Hollister Ave # 204 Santa Barbara (93111) *(P-6183)*
Hispanic Business Magazine, Santa Barbara *Also called Hispanic Business Inc (P-6183)*
Hitachi Automotive Systems....D....310 212-0200
6200 Gateway Dr Cypress (90630) *(P-17204)*
Hitachi Chem Diagnostics Inc....C....650 961-5501
630 Clyde Ct Mountain View (94043) *(P-21475)*
Hitachi High-Technologies....F....818 280-0745
20770 Nordhoff St Chatsworth (91311) *(P-21967)*
Hitachi Home Elec Amer Inc (HQ)....C....619 591-5200
2420 Fenton St 200 Chula Vista (91914) *(P-17814)*
Hitachi Rail Usa Inc (PA)....F....415 397-7010
101 The Embarcadero # 210 San Francisco (94105) *(P-21077)*
Hitachi Vantara Corporation (HQ)....B....408 970-1000
2845 Lafayette St Santa Clara (95050) *(P-15554)*
Hitachi Via Mechanics USA Inc, San Jose *Also called Via Mechanics (usa) Inc (P-15882)*
Hitco Carbon Composites Inc....D....424 329-5250
1551 W 139th St Gardena (90249) *(P-5489)*
Hitech Global Distribution LLC....E....408 781-8043
2059 Camden Ave Ste 160 San Jose (95124) *(P-18875)*
Hitech Metal Fabrication Corp....D....714 635-3505
1705 S Claudina Way Anaheim (92805) *(P-12176)*
Hitech Plastics and Molds, Valencia *Also called Cypress Manufacturing LLC (P-10055)*
Hitek Lighting Inc....F....805 481-6006
1172 Pradera Ct Arroyo Grande (93420) *(P-17700)*
Hitem, San Diego *Also called Hi-Tech Electronic Mfg Corp (P-18499)*
Hitex Dyeing & Finishing Inc....E....626 363-0160
355 Vineland Ave City of Industry (91746) *(P-3951)*
Hiti Digital America Inc....E....909 594-0099
675 Brea Canyon Rd Ste 7 Walnut (91789) *(P-23163)*
Hits Magazine Inc....D....323 946-7600
6906 Hollywood Blvd Fl 2 Los Angeles (90028) *(P-6184)*
Hitt Companies....E....714 979-1405
3231 W Macarthur Blvd Santa Ana (92704) *(P-9623)*
Hitt Marking Devices I D Tech, Santa Ana *Also called Hitt Companies (P-9623)*
Hive Lighting Inc....F....310 773-4362
525 S Hewitt St Los Angeles (90013) *(P-17539)*
Hixson Metal Finishing....D....800 900-9798
829 Production Pl Newport Beach (92663) *(P-13426)*
Hizco Truck Body, Los Angeles *Also called A A Cater Truck Mfg Co Inc (P-4820)*
HK Canning Inc (PA)....E....805 652-1392
130 N Garden St Ventura (93001) *(P-806)*
HK Enterprise Group Inc....F....858 652-4400
6540 Lusk Blvd Ste C270 San Diego (92121) *(P-9258)*
Hka Elevator Consulting Inc....F....949 348-9711
23211 S Pointe Dr Ste 101 Laguna Hills (92653) *(P-14251)*
HMC Display, Madera *Also called Gardner Family Ltd Partnership (P-11956)*
HMcompany....F....805 650-2651
4464 Mcgrath St Ste 111 Ventura (93003) *(P-16569)*
Hme Hospitality & Specialty Co....E....858 535-6139
14110 Stowe Dr Poway (92064) *(P-18331)*

ALPHABETIC

Employee Codes: A=Over 500 employees, B=251-500
C=101-250, D=51-100, E=20-50, F=10-19
2019 California
Manfacturers Register
© Mergent Inc. 1-800-342-5647
1163

Hmr Building Systems LLC....F....951 749-4700
620 Newport Center Dr # 12 Newport Beach (92660) ***(P-4039)***
Hnc Parent Inc (PA)....D....310 955-9200
999 N Pacific Coast Hwy El Segundo (90245) ***(P-9409)***
Hnc Printing Services LLC....F....925 689-1716
5125 Port Chicago Hwy Concord (94520) ***(P-6860)***
Hni Corporation....B....916 927-0400
3780 Pell Cir Sacramento (95838) ***(P-4990)***
Ho Tai Printing & Book Store, San Francisco *Also called Ho Tai Printing Co Inc* ***(P-6861)***
Ho Tai Printing Co Inc....F....415 421-4218
723 Clay St Ste 725 San Francisco (94108) ***(P-6861)***
Hobie Cat Company....C....760 758-9100
4925 Oceanside Blvd Oceanside (92056) ***(P-21043)***
Hockin Diversfd Holdings Inc....F....760 787-0510
1672 Main St Ste E362 Ramona (92065) ***(P-15159)***
Hocking International Labs Inc (PA)....E....760 432-5277
980 Rancheros Dr San Marcos (92069) ***(P-8646)***
Hodge Products Inc....E....619 444-3147
7365 Mission Gorge Rd F San Diego (92120) ***(P-11961)***
Hoefer Inc....E....415 282-2307
760 National Ct Richmond (94804) ***(P-21968)***
Hoefner Corporation....E....626 443-3258
9722 Rush St South El Monte (91733) ***(P-16570)***
Hoffman Magnetics Inc....E....818 717-5095
19528 Ventura Blvd Tarzana (91356) ***(P-19865)***
Hoffman Plastic Compounds Inc....D....323 636-3346
16616 Garfield Ave Paramount (90723) ***(P-7839)***
Hoffy, Vernon *Also called Square H Brands Inc* ***(P-528)***
Hogan Co Inc....E....909 421-0245
2741 S Lilac Ave Bloomington (92316) ***(P-11445)***
Hogan Mfg Inc (PA)....C....209 838-7323
19527 Mchenry Ave Escalon (95320) ***(P-24118)***
Hogan Mfg Inc....C....209 838-2400
1520 1st St Escalon (95320) ***(P-24119)***
Hoist Fitness Systems, San Diego *Also called Fitness Warehouse LLC* ***(P-23562)***
Hoist Fitness Systems Inc....D....858 578-7676
11900 Community Rd Poway (92064) ***(P-23586)***
Holcomb Products Inc....F....559 822-2067
6751 N Blackstone Ave # 103 Fresno (93710) ***(P-3849)***
Holdrite, Poway *Also called Securus Inc* ***(P-12891)***
Holiday Foliage Inc....E....619 661-9094
2592 Otay Center Dr San Diego (92154) ***(P-24120)***
Holland & Herring Mfg Inc....E....909 469-4700
661 E Monterey Ave Pomona (91767) ***(P-16571)***
Hollands Custom Cabinets Inc....E....619 443-6081
14511 Olde Highway 80 El Cajon (92021) ***(P-4310)***
Holliday Rock Trucking Inc (PA)....D....909 982-1553
1401 N Benson Ave Upland (91786) ***(P-11120)***
Hollinger Metal Edge Inc....E....323 721-7800
6340 Bandini Blvd Commerce (90040) ***(P-5424)***
Hollister Brewing Company LLC....E....805 968-2810
6980 Market Place Dr Goleta (93117) ***(P-1598)***
Hollister Landscape Supply Inc (HQ)....F....831 443-8644
520 Crazy Horse Canyon Rd A Salinas (93907) ***(P-11121)***
Holloway House Publishing Co....E....323 653-8060
8060 Melrose Ave Fl 3 Los Angeles (90046) ***(P-6349)***
Holly Yashi Inc....D....707 822-0389
1300 9th St Arcata (95521) ***(P-23274)***
Hollywood Bed Spring Mfg Inc....D....323 887-9500
5959 Corvette St Commerce (90040) ***(P-11962)***
Hollywood Bike Racks, Los Angeles *Also called Hollywood Engineering Inc* ***(P-11963)***
Hollywood Chairs....F....818 720-9946
1810 Diamond St San Marcos (92078) ***(P-4703)***
Hollywood Engineering Inc....F....310 516-8600
12812 S Spring St Los Angeles (90061) ***(P-11963)***
Hollywood Film Company....D....818 683-1130
9265 Borden Ave Sun Valley (91352) ***(P-23164)***
Hollywood Lamp & Shade Co....F....323 585-3999
2928 Leonis Blvd Vernon (90058) ***(P-17429)***
Hollywood Records Inc....E....818 560-5670
500 S Buena Vista St Burbank (91521) ***(P-17903)***
Hollywood Software Inc....F....818 205-2121
5000 Van Nuys Blvd # 460 Van Nuys (91403) ***(P-24734)***
Hologic Inc....C....408 745-0975
1240 Elko Dr Sunnyvale (94089) ***(P-22933)***
Hologic Inc....E....858 410-8000
10210 Genetic Center Dr San Diego (92121) ***(P-22984)***
Holsum Bakery Inc....E....818 884-6562
21540 Blythe St Canoga Park (91304) ***(P-1272)***
Holt Integrated Circuits, Mission Viejo *Also called W G Holt Inc* ***(P-19267)***
Holt Tool & Machine Inc....E....650 364-2547
2909 Middlefield Rd Redwood City (94063) ***(P-11399)***
Holz Rubber Company Inc....C....209 368-7171
1129 S Sacramento St Lodi (95240) ***(P-9624)***
Holzinger Indus Shtmtl Inc....F....562 944-6337
12440 Mccann Dr Santa Fe Springs (90670) ***(P-12614)***
Home & Body Company (PA)....E....714 842-8000
18352 Enterprise Ln Huntington Beach (92648) ***(P-8647)***
Home Brew Mart Inc....E....858 695-2739
9045 Carroll Way San Diego (92121) ***(P-1599)***
Home Brew Mart Inc (HQ)....C....858 790-6900
9045 Carroll Way San Diego (92121) ***(P-1600)***
Home Land Safe Co, Pico Rivera *Also called Jorge Segovia* ***(P-13952)***
Home of Wine Trees Portfolio, Santa Rosa *Also called A W Direct LLC* ***(P-1638)***
Home Paradise LLC....F....626 284-9999
7000 E Slauson Ave Commerce (90040) ***(P-13219)***
Home Portal LLC....F....310 559-6100
3351 La Cienega Pl Los Angeles (90016) ***(P-17098)***
Home-Flex, Valencia *Also called Valencia Pipe Company* ***(P-9791)***
Homefacts Management LLC....F....949 502-8300
1 Venture Ste 300 Irvine (92618) ***(P-6500)***
Homefacts.com, Irvine *Also called Homefacts Management LLC* ***(P-6500)***
Homegrown Naturals, Berkeley *Also called Annies Inc* ***(P-2453)***
Homestead Fine Foods, South San Francisco *Also called Homestead Ravioli Company Inc* ***(P-758)***
Homestead Publishing Inc....E....307 733-6248
4388 17th St San Francisco (94114) ***(P-6350)***
Homestead Ravioli Company Inc....E....650 615-0750
315 S Maple Ave Ste 106 South San Francisco (94080) ***(P-758)***
Homestead Sheet Metal....E....619 469-4373
9031 Memory Ln Spring Valley (91977) ***(P-12177)***
Hometex Corporation....E....619 661-0400
1743 Continental Ln Escondido (92029) ***(P-3724)***
Homewood Components Inc....D....530 743-8855
5033 Feather River Blvd Marysville (95901) ***(P-4411)***
Homewood Truss, Marysville *Also called Homewood Components Inc* ***(P-4411)***
Homewood Winery....F....707 996-6353
23120 Burndale Rd Sonoma (95476) ***(P-1812)***
Honda Accessory America (HQ)....E....310 781-5300
1900 Harpers Way Torrance (90501) ***(P-20362)***
Honda North America Inc (HQ)....B....310 781-4961
700 Van Ness Ave Torrance (90501) ***(P-20150)***
Hone & Strop Inc....F....424 262-4474
1617 Franklin St Apt 6 Santa Monica (90404) ***(P-8766)***
Honest Company Inc (PA)....C....310 917-9199
12130 Millennium Ste 500 Playa Vista (90094) ***(P-3537)***
Honey Bennetts Farm Inc....E....805 521-1375
3176 Honey Ln Fillmore (93015) ***(P-2536)***
Honey Olivarez Bees Inc....D....530 865-0298
6398 County Road 20 Orland (95963) ***(P-2537)***
Honey Punch, Los Angeles *Also called Klk Forte Industry Inc* ***(P-3448)***
Honey Punch Inc (PA)....F....323 800-3812
1535 Rio Vista Ave Los Angeles (90023) ***(P-3430)***
Honeybee Robotics Ltd....F....510 207-4555
398 W Washington Blvd Pasadena (91103) ***(P-15329)***
Honeywell Authorized Dealer, Rocklin *Also called Jlm Energy Inc* ***(P-14000)***
Honeywell International Inc....E....760 355-3420
510 W Aten Rd Imperial (92251) ***(P-20363)***
Honeywell International Inc....A....310 512-4237
6452 Morion Cir Huntington Beach (92647) ***(P-20652)***
Honeywell International Inc....F....858 513-1223
12800 Brookprinter Pl Poway (92064) ***(P-20653)***
Honeywell International Inc....A....310 323-9500
2525 W 190th St Torrance (90504) ***(P-20654)***
Honeywell International Inc....A....951 500-6086
3105 Prince Valiant Ln Modesto (95350) ***(P-20655)***
Honeywell International Inc....A....949 425-3992
27831 Abadejo Mission Viejo (92692) ***(P-20656)***
Honeywell International Inc....A....209 323-8520
25 S Stockton St Ste C Lodi (95240) ***(P-20657)***
Honeywell International Inc....B....310 410-9605
6201 W Imperial Hwy Los Angeles (90045) ***(P-20658)***
Honeywell International Inc....D....408 962-2000
3500 Garrett Dr Santa Clara (95054) ***(P-7781)***
Honeywell International Inc....B....734 392-5525
2525 W 190th St Torrance (90504) ***(P-21306)***
Honeywell International Inc....C....619 671-5612
2055 Dublin Dr San Diego (92154) ***(P-21514)***
Honeywell International Inc....A....760 312-5300
233 Paulin Ave 8500 Calexico (92231) ***(P-20659)***
Honeywell International Inc....A....858 848-3187
13475 Danielson St # 130 Poway (92064) ***(P-20660)***
Honeywell International Inc....D....858 679-4140
13475 Danielson St # 130 Poway (92064) ***(P-20661)***
Honeywell International Inc....E....858 513-6391
13475 Danielson St # 130 Poway (92064) ***(P-20662)***
Honeywell Safety Pdts USA Inc....C....619 661-8383
7828 Waterville Rd San Diego (92154) ***(P-22747)***
Hong Fat Dye Cutting Co....F....626 452-0382
2103 Sastre Ave South El Monte (91733) ***(P-7601)***
Honomatic Inc....F....562 941-3295
10030 Greenleaf Ave Santa Fe Springs (90670) ***(P-16572)***
Honor Life, Vista *Also called Rayzist Photomask Inc* ***(P-23737)***
Honor Plastics & Molding Inc....F....909 923-9710
730 E Francis St Ontario (91761) ***(P-10137)***
Honulua Surf Co, Irvine *Also called Veezee Inc* ***(P-3286)***
Hood Manufacturing Inc....D....714 979-7681
2621 S Birch St Santa Ana (92707) ***(P-10138)***
Hoojook....F....408 596-9427
1754 Tech Dr Ste 132 San Jose (95148) ***(P-24735)***
Hook It Up....C....714 600-0100
1513 S Grand Ave Santa Ana (92705) ***(P-2706)***
Hook or Crook Cellars, Lodi *Also called Baywood Cellars Inc* ***(P-1654)***
Hoopa Forest Industries....E....530 625-4281
778 Marshall Ln Hoopa (95546) ***(P-3991)***
Hoopla Software Inc....E....408 498-9600
84 W Santa Clara St # 460 San Jose (95113) ***(P-24736)***
Hoosier Plstic Fabrication Inc....C....951 272-3070
1152 California Ave Corona (92881) ***(P-10139)***
Hop Kiln Winery, The, Healdsburg *Also called Overlook Vineyards LLC* ***(P-1910)***
Hope Family Wines (PA)....E....805 238-4112
1585 Live Oak Rd Paso Robles (93446) ***(P-1813)***
Hope Plastic Co Inc....E....818 769-5560
5353 Strohm Ave North Hollywood (91601) ***(P-10140)***
Hopland Brewery, Hopland *Also called Mendocino Brewing Company Inc* ***(P-1610)***
Horiba Automotive Test Systems, Irvine *Also called Horiba Instruments Inc* ***(P-21969)***
Horiba Instruments Inc (HQ)....C....949 250-4811
9755 Research Dr Irvine (92618) ***(P-21969)***

Horiba Instruments Inc....D....408 730-4772
430 Indio Way Sunnyvale (94085) *(P-22214)*
Horiba International Corp (HQ)....D....949 250-4811
9755 Research Dr Irvine (92618) *(P-22215)*
Horizon Bottled Water....F....951 654-0954
1371 S Santa Fe Ave San Jacinto (92583) *(P-2140)*
Horizon Cal Publications....F....760 934-3929
452 Old Mammoth Rd Mammoth Lakes (93546) *(P-5882)*
Horizon Engineering Inc....F....858 679-0785
13200 Kirkham Way Ste 109 Poway (92064) *(P-16573)*
Horizon Hobby LLC....C....909 390-9595
4710 E Guasti Rd Ste A Ontario (91761) *(P-23429)*
Horizon International Ltd....F....559 781-4640
200 E Henderson Ave Porterville (93257) *(P-16049)*
Horizon Publications Inc....F....760 873-3535
407 W Line St Ste 8 Bishop (93514) *(P-5883)*
Horizon Snack Foods Inc....D....925 373-7700
197 Darcy Pkwy Lathrop (95330) *(P-1396)*
Horizon Well Logging Inc....F....805 733-0972
711 Saint Andrews Way Lompoc (93436) *(P-224)*
Hormel Foods Corp Svcs LLC....E....949 753-5350
2 Venture Ste 250 Irvine (92618) *(P-494)*
Horn Machine Tools Inc (PA)....E....559 431-4131
40455 Brickyard Dr # 101 Madera (93636) *(P-14438)*
Hornedo Inc....F....562 490-2120
2424 Brayton Ave Signal Hill (90755) *(P-14966)*
Horstman Manufacturing Co Inc....E....760 598-2100
2371 La Mirada Dr Vista (92081) *(P-20364)*
Hortonworks Inc (PA)....A....408 916-4121
5470 Great America Pkwy Santa Clara (95054) *(P-24737)*
Horvath Precision Machining....F....510 683-0810
930 Thompson Pl Sunnyvale (94085) *(P-16574)*
Hos, Vista *Also called Hruby Orbital Systems Inc (P-16050)*
Hospital Systems Inc....D....925 427-7800
750 Garcia Ave Pittsburg (94565) *(P-22985)*
Hospitality Sleep Systems Inc....F....909 387-9779
107 E Rialto Ave San Bernardino (92408) *(P-4863)*
Hospitality Wood Products Inc....F....562 806-5564
7206 E Gage Ave Commerce (90040) *(P-4165)*
Host Analytics Inc (HQ)....E....650 249-7100
555 Twin Dolphin Dr # 400 Redwood City (94065) *(P-24738)*
Hostrup Industries Inc....F....310 477-6770
2244 Federal Ave Los Angeles (90064) *(P-24121)*
Hot Can Inc....E....707 601-6013
10620 Treena St Ste 230 San Diego (92131) *(P-2353)*
Hot Chillys, San Luis Obispo *Also called Performance Apparel Corp (P-3478)*
Hot Shoppe Designs Inc....F....949 487-2828
1323 Calle Avanzado San Clemente (92673) *(P-3159)*
Hot Spring Spa, Folsom *Also called Xolar Corporation (P-24292)*
Hotech Corporation....E....909 987-8828
9320 Santa Anita Ave # 100 Rancho Cucamonga (91730) *(P-18876)*
Hotlix (PA)....E....805 473-0596
966 Griffin St Grover Beach (93433) *(P-1428)*
Hotlix Candy, Grover Beach *Also called Hotlix (P-1428)*
Hotronic Inc....E....408 378-3883
1875 Winchester Blvd # 100 Campbell (95008) *(P-17955)*
Houghton Mifflin Harcourt Pubg....F....617 351-5000
525 B St Ste 1900 San Diego (92101) *(P-6351)*
House Foods America Corp (HQ)....C....714 901-4350
7351 Orangewood Ave Garden Grove (92841) *(P-1509)*
House of Bagels Inc (PA)....F....650 595-4700
1007 Washington St San Carlos (94070) *(P-1273)*
House of Print & Copy....F....530 273-1000
1501 E Main St Grass Valley (95945) *(P-6862)*
House of Printing Inc....E....626 793-7034
3336 E Colorado Blvd Pasadena (91107) *(P-6863)*
House of Quirky, Los Angeles *Also called Hq Brands LLC (P-3658)*
House of Uniforms, Chatsworth *Also called Warrens Department Store Inc (P-3048)*
Housewares International Inc (PA)....E....323 581-3000
6015 Randolph St Commerce (90040) *(P-10141)*
Houston Bazz Co....D....714 898-2666
12700 Western Ave Garden Grove (92841) *(P-13220)*
Houston Fearless 76, Compton *Also called Hf Group Inc (P-23162)*
Houston Rubber Co Inc....F....818 899-1108
12623 Foothill Blvd Sylmar (91342) *(P-9625)*
Hovey Tile Art....E....909 794-3815
1221 Opal Ave Mentone (92359) *(P-24014)*
How 2 Save Fuel LLC....F....818 882-1189
18017 Chtswrth St Ste 166 Granada Hills (91344) *(P-9010)*
How2savefuel.com, Granada Hills *Also called How 2 Save Fuel LLC (P-9010)*
Howardsoft....F....858 454-0121
7854 Ivanhoe Ave A La Jolla (92037) *(P-24739)*
Howco Inc....F....619 275-1663
1221 W Morena Blvd San Diego (92110) *(P-20365)*
Howell Dick Hole Drilling Svc....F....562 633-9898
2579 E 67th St Long Beach (90805) *(P-106)*
Howell Drilling, Long Beach *Also called Howell Dick Hole Drilling Svc (P-106)*
Howies Moulding Inc....F....562 698-0261
8032 Allport Ave Santa Fe Springs (90670) *(P-4166)*
Howmedica Osteonics Corp....E....714 557-5010
1947 W Collins Ave Orange (92867) *(P-22470)*
Hoya Corporation USA....F....408 654-2200
680 N Mccarthy Blvd # 120 Milpitas (95035) *(P-21307)*
Hoya Corporation USA (HQ)....F....408 492-1069
680 N Mccarthy Blvd # 120 Milpitas (95035) *(P-22082)*
Hoya Holdings Inc....D....626 739-5200
425 E Huntington Dr Monrovia (91016) *(P-22083)*
Hoya Holdings Inc (HQ)....C....408 654-2300
680 N Mccarthy Blvd # 120 Milpitas (95035) *(P-23165)*
Hoya Optical Inc (PA)....D....209 579-7739
1400 Carpenter Ln Modesto (95351) *(P-23100)*
Hoya Surgical Optics Inc....E....909 680-3900
15335 Fairfield Ranch Rd # 250 Chino Hills (91709) *(P-22471)*
HP Core Co Inc....F....323 582-1688
1843 E 58th Pl Los Angeles (90001) *(P-14465)*
HP Hood LLC....B....916 379-9266
8340 Belvedere Ave Sacramento (95826) *(P-729)*
HP Inc (PA)....A....650 857-1501
1501 Page Mill Rd Palo Alto (94304) *(P-15420)*
HP Inc....A....978 687-1501
1140 Enterprise Way Sunnyvale (94089) *(P-15421)*
HP Inc....A....650 857-1501
481 Cottonwood Dr Milpitas (95035) *(P-15422)*
HP Inc....A....650 857-4946
1501 Page Mill Rd Palo Alto (94304) *(P-15423)*
HP Inc....D....650 857-1501
130 Lytton Ave Palo Alto (94301) *(P-15424)*
HP Inc....E....650 857-1501
3495 Deer Creek Rd Palo Alto (94304) *(P-15425)*
HP Inc....D....415 979-3700
303 2nd St Ste S500 San Francisco (94107) *(P-15426)*
HP Precision Inc....E....760 752-9377
548 S Pacific St Ste B100 San Marcos (92078) *(P-12615)*
HP Water Systems Inc....E....559 268-4751
9338 W Whites Bridge Ave Fresno (93706) *(P-15075)*
Hpcwire, San Diego *Also called Tabor Communications Inc (P-6600)*
Hpe Enterprises LLC (HQ)....E....650 857-5817
3000 Hanover St Palo Alto (94304) *(P-24740)*
Hpe Government Llc....D....916 435-9200
46600 Landing Pkwy Fremont (94538) *(P-15633)*
Hpf Corporation (PA)....F....858 566-9710
9920 Prospect Ave Ste 102 Santee (92071) *(P-23376)*
Hpi Cylinders, Santa Fe Springs *Also called Hydraulic Pneumatic Inc (P-16158)*
Hpi Federal LLC (HQ)....F....650 857-1501
1501 Page Mill Rd Palo Alto (94304) *(P-15427)*
Hpl Contract Inc....F....209 892-1717
525 Baldwin Rd Patterson (95363) *(P-4949)*
Hpmi, Fremont *Also called Henry Plastic Molding Inc (P-10133)*
Hpv Technologies Inc....E....949 476-7000
301 E Alton Ave Santa Ana (92707) *(P-17815)*
Hq Brands LLC....F....213 627-7922
860 S Los Angeles St # 706 Los Angeles (90014) *(P-3658)*
Hq Machine Tech LLC....E....714 956-3388
6900 8th St Buena Park (90620) *(P-20837)*
Hr, Lodi *Also called Holz Rubber Company Inc (P-9624)*
Hrh Door Corp....E....916 928-0600
830 Prosessor Ln Sacramento (95834) *(P-12320)*
Hrk Pet Food Products Inc....F....818 897-2521
12924 Pierce St Pacoima (91331) *(P-1137)*
Hruby Orbital Systems Inc....F....760 936-8054
3275 Corporate Vw Vista (92081) *(P-16050)*
Hse Usa Inc (PA)....F....323 278-0888
5832 E 61st St Commerce (90040) *(P-24122)*
HSG Manufacturing Inc....F....909 902-5915
13346 Monte Vista Ave Chino (91710) *(P-13221)*
Hsi Mechanical Inc....E....209 408-0183
1013 N Emerald Ave Modesto (95351) *(P-12616)*
Hsiao & Montano Inc....E....626 588-2528
809 W Santa Anita Ave San Gabriel (91776) *(P-10524)*
Hsin Tung Yang Foods Company....F....650 589-7689
405 S Airport Blvd South San Francisco (94080) *(P-495)*
Hsssi, Pomona *Also called Hamilton Sundstrand Spc Systms (P-22210)*
Ht Multinational Inc....E....626 964-2686
12851 Reservoir St Apt A Chino (91710) *(P-20366)*
Ht Window Fashions Corporation (PA)....D....626 839-8866
770 Epperson Dr City of Industry (91748) *(P-5193)*
Hte Manufacturing Inc....F....805 987-5449
4610 Calle Quetzal Camarillo (93012) *(P-14641)*
Hti Turnkey Manufacturing Svcs....E....408 955-0807
2200 Zanker Rd Ste A San Jose (95131) *(P-19568)*
Htk Automotive USA Corp....F....888 998-9366
5218 Rivergrade Rd Irwindale (91706) *(P-19834)*
Htpg, Anaheim *Also called Heat Transfer Pdts Group LLC (P-15959)*
Htpmi Contract Manufacturing, San Jose *Also called Hi-Tech Prcision Machining Inc (P-16561)*
Htr LLC....F....760 297-4402
30803 Hilltop View Ct Valley Center (92082) *(P-1814)*
Hts Division, Lake Elsinore *Also called Mercury Metal Die & Letter Co (P-13617)*
Hts-Engineering Inc....F....760 631-2070
4079 Oceanside Blvd Ste J Oceanside (92056) *(P-13027)*
Hua Rong International Corp....F....909 591-8800
14020 Cent Ave Ste 530 Chino (91710) *(P-21232)*
Huang Qi....F....626 442-6808
4700 Miller Dr Ste H Temple City (91780) *(P-3313)*
Hub Construction Spc Inc....D....909 379-2100
5310 San Fernando Rd Glendale (91203) *(P-12617)*
Hub Construction Speciality, Glendale *Also called Hub Construction Spc Inc (P-12617)*
Hubbel Wiring Device Kellems, Ontario *Also called Hubbell Incorporated (P-17471)*
Hubbell Incorporated....E....909 390-8002
1392 Sarah Pl Ste A Ontario (91761) *(P-17471)*
Hubbell Incorporated....E....559 783-0470
1829 Thunderbolt Dr Porterville (93257) *(P-17472)*
Hubbell Lighting Inc....B....619 946-1800
2498 Roll Dr San Diego (92154) *(P-17701)*
Hubbell Lighting Inc....D....714 386-5550
17760 Rowland St Rowland Heights (91748) *(P-17617)*
Huck International Inc....C....310 830-8200
900 E Watson Center Rd Carson (90745) *(P-13072)*

ALPHABETIC

Employee Codes: A=Over 500 employees, B=251-500
C=101-250, D=51-100, E=20-50, F=10-19
2019 California
Manfacturers Register
© Mergent Inc. 1-800-342-5647
1165

Hudson & Company LLC...E...916 774-6465
100 Irene Ave Roseville (95678) **(P-3725)**
Hudson Construction, Felton *Also called Hudson Industries Inc* **(P-24123)**
Hudson Industries Inc...F...831 335-4431
11107 Lake Blvd Felton (95018) **(P-24123)**
Hudson Plating Works...F...805 517-1222
11941 Hertz Ave Moorpark (93021) **(P-13427)**
Hudson Printing Inc...E...760 602-1260
2780 Loker Ave W Carlsbad (92010) **(P-7344)**
Hudson Valve Co Inc...E...661 831-6208
5630 District Blvd # 108 Bakersfield (93313) **(P-13718)**
Hues Metal Finishing Inc...F...760 744-5566
977 Linda Vista Dr San Marcos (92078) **(P-13602)**
Hufcor Airwall Since 1900, Long Beach *Also called Hufcor California Inc* **(P-5145)**
Hufcor California Inc (HQ)...D...562 634-3116
2380 E Artesia Blvd Long Beach (90805) **(P-5145)**
Huffman Logging Co Inc...E...707 725-4335
1155 Huffman Dr Fortuna (95540) **(P-3992)**
Huge Usa Inc...F...213 741-1707
1100 S San Pedro St J02 Los Angeles (90015) **(P-2743)**
Hugfun International, City of Industry *Also called Define Toys Inc* **(P-23395)**
Hughes Bros Aircrafters Inc...E...323 773-4541
11010 Garfield Pl South Gate (90280) **(P-14525)**
Hughes Circuits Inc (PA)...E...760 744-0300
546 S Pacific St San Marcos (92078) **(P-18500)**
Hughes Circuits Inc...C...760 744-0300
540 S Pacific St San Marcos (92078) **(P-18501)**
Hughes Network Systems LLC...E...858 455-9550
9605 Scranton Rd Ste 500 San Diego (92121) **(P-18127)**
Hughson Nut Inc (PA)...B...209 883-0403
1825 Verduga Rd Hughson (95326) **(P-1490)**
Hugin Components Inc...F...916 652-1070
4231 Pacific St Ste 23 Rocklin (95677) **(P-13222)**
Hugo Boss Usa Inc...C...310 260-0109
395 Santa Monica Pl # 162 Santa Monica (90401) **(P-3030)**
Hugo Engineering Co Inc...F...310 320-0288
837 Van Ness Ave Torrance (90501) **(P-20838)**
Huhtamaki Inc...F...916 688-4938
8450 Gerber Rd Sacramento (95828) **(P-5490)**
Huhtamaki Inc...B...323 269-0151
4209 Noakes St Commerce (90023) **(P-9865)**
Hulls Norcal Window & Door...F...916 983-5792
104 Stoney Hill Dr Folsom (95630) **(P-10142)**
Humanconcepts LLC...E...650 581-2500
3 Harbor Dr Ste 200 Sausalito (94965) **(P-24741)**
Humangear Inc...F...415 580-7553
636 Shrader St San Francisco (94117) **(P-10143)**
Humberto Murillo Inc...E...714 541-2628
410 Nantucket Pl Santa Ana (92703) **(P-13428)**
Humboldt Newspaper Inc...A...707 442-1711
930 6th St Eureka (95501) **(P-5884)**
Humidtech Inc...F...805 541-9500
1241 Johnson Ave Ste 345 San Luis Obispo (93401) **(P-23275)**
Huneeus Vintners LLC (PA)...E...707 286-2724
1040 Main St Ste 204 NAPA (94559) **(P-1815)**
Hung Tung...F...408 496-1818
3672 Bassett St Santa Clara (95054) **(P-16575)**
Hunkins Enterprises, El Segundo *Also called James Hunkins* **(P-20665)**
Hunnington Dialysis Center, Pasadena *Also called Hemodialysis Inc* **(P-22469)**
Hunt Enterprises, Santa Ana *Also called Dan R Hunt Inc* **(P-16418)**
Huntco Industries LLC...F...818 700-1600
22536 La Quilla Dr Chatsworth (91311) **(P-24124)**
Hunter Digital Ltd...F...310 471-5852
11999 San Vicente Blvd Los Angeles (90049) **(P-15754)**
Hunter Douglas Fabrications...B...408 435-8844
842 Charcot Ave San Jose (95131) **(P-5194)**
Hunter Douglas Inc...C...562 207-0800
17100 Pioneer Blvd # 170 Artesia (90701) **(P-5195)**
Hunter Douglas Inc...C...425 430-6110
2080 Enterprise Blvd West Sacramento (95691) **(P-5196)**
Hunter Industries Incorporated (PA)...B...760 744-5240
1940 Diamond St San Marcos (92078) **(P-9780)**
Hunter Spice Inc...D...805 597-8900
184 Suburban Rd San Luis Obispo (93401) **(P-2538)**
Hunter Technology Corporation (HQ)...C...408 957-1300
1940 Milmont Dr Milpitas (95035) **(P-19569)**
Hunter/Gratzner Industries...F...310 578-9929
4107 Redwood Ave Los Angeles (90066) **(P-24125)**
Huntford Printing...E...408 957-5000
275 Dempsey Rd Milpitas (95035) **(P-6864)**
Huntford Printing & Graphics, Milpitas *Also called Huntford Printing* **(P-6864)**
Hunting Energy Services Inc...D...661 633-4272
4900 California Ave 100a Bakersfield (93309) **(P-225)**
Hunting-Vinson, Bakersfield *Also called Hunting Energy Services Inc* **(P-225)**
Huntington Beach Machining, Huntington Beach *Also called Madsen Products Incorporated* **(P-16708)**
Huntington Company, North Hollywood *Also called John A Thomson PHD* **(P-7953)**
Huntington Mechanical Labs, Grass Valley *Also called Huntington Mechanical Labs Inc* **(P-15128)**
Huntington Mechanical Labs Inc...E...530 273-9533
13355 Nevada City Ave Grass Valley (95945) **(P-15128)**
Huntmix Inc...C...818 548-5200
500 N Brand Blvd Ste 500 Glendale (91203) **(P-9387)**
Huntsman Advanced Materials AM...C...818 265-7221
5121 W San Fernando Rd Los Angeles (90039) **(P-7840)**
Hupa International Inc...E...909 598-9876
21717 Ferrero Walnut (91789) **(P-23587)**
Hupalo Repasky Pipe Organs LLC...F...510 483-6905
2450 Alvarado St San Leandro (94577) **(P-23377)**
Hupp Signs & Lighting Inc...E...530 345-7078
70 Loren Ave Chico (95928) **(P-23894)**
Hurley International LLC...F...323 728-1821
100 Citadel Dr Ste 433 Commerce (90040) **(P-3160)**
Hurley International LLC...C...707 446-6300
321 Nut Tree Rd Vacaville (95687) **(P-3161)**
Hurley International LLC (HQ)...C...949 548-9375
1945g Placentia Ave Costa Mesa (92627) **(P-3162)**
Hurleys LP...D...707 944-2345
1516 King Ave NAPA (94559) **(P-5237)**
Hurleys Restaurant & Bar, NAPA *Also called Hurleys LP* **(P-5237)**
Hurst International, Chatsworth *Also called Labeling Hurst Systems LLC* **(P-5566)**
Husch Vineyards Inc (PA)...E...707 895-3216
4400 Highway 128 Philo (95466) **(P-1816)**
Husk-ITT Distributors Corp...F...951 340-4000
1580 Industrial Ave Norco (92860) **(P-9436)**
Huskey Specialty Lubricants, Norco *Also called Husk-ITT Distributors Corp* **(P-9436)**
Husks Unlimited...D...619 476-8301
1616 Silvas St Chula Vista (91911) **(P-951)**
Husky Injection Molding...F...714 545-8200
3505 Cadillac Ave Ste N4 Costa Mesa (92626) **(P-10144)**
Hussmann Corporation...B...909 590-4910
13770 Ramona Ave Chino (91710) **(P-15961)**
Hutchinson Arospc & Indust Inc...C...818 843-1000
4510 W Vanowen St Burbank (91505) **(P-20839)**
Hutchinson Arospc & Indust Inc...C...818 843-1000
4510 W Vanowen St Burbank (91505) **(P-9626)**
Hutchinson Seal Corporation (HQ)...B...248 375-4190
11634 Patton Rd Downey (90241) **(P-9535)**
Huy Fong Foods Inc...E...626 286-8328
4800 Azusa Canyon Rd Irwindale (91706) **(P-807)**
Hv Industries Inc...F...651 233-5676
13688 Newhope St Garden Grove (92843) **(P-4082)**
Hvi Cat Canyon Inc...C...805 621-5800
2617 E Clark Ave Santa Maria (93455) **(P-226)**
Hw Holdco LLC...E...714 540-8500
555 Anton Blvd Ste 950 Costa Mesa (92626) **(P-6185)**
Hwa In America Inc (PA)...F...619 567-4539
1541 Santiago Ridge Way San Diego (92154) **(P-19570)**
Hwe Mechanical, Bakersfield *Also called Hills Wldg & Engrg Contr Inc* **(P-222)**
HWF Construction Inc...F...661 587-3590
3685 Fruitvale Ave Bakersfield (93308) **(P-6186)**
Hy Jo Mfg Imports Corp...E...619 671-1018
7615 Siempre Viva Rd B San Diego (92154) **(P-13946)**
Hy-Tech Plating Inc...E...650 593-4566
1011 American St San Carlos (94070) **(P-13429)**
Hyatt Die Cast Engrg Corp - S...E...714 622-2131
12250 Industry St Garden Grove (92841) **(P-11694)**
Hyatt Die Cast Engrg Corp - S...E...408 523-7000
1250 Kifer Rd Sunnyvale (94086) **(P-11695)**
Hyatt Die Casting, Sunnyvale *Also called Hyatt Die Cast Engrg Corp - S* **(P-11695)**
Hybrid Kinetic Motors Corp...F...626 683-7330
800 E Colo Blvd Ste 880 Pasadena (91101) **(P-20151)**
Hybrinetics Inc...D...707 585-0333
225 Sutton Pl Santa Rosa (95407) **(P-17099)**
Hycor Biomedical LLC...C...714 933-3000
7272 Chapman Ave Ste A Garden Grove (92841) **(P-22472)**
Hyde, Vernon *Also called Streets Ahead Inc* **(P-3633)**
Hyde Printing and Graphics...F...925 686-4933
2748 Willow Pass Rd Concord (94519) **(P-6865)**
Hydra-Electric Company (PA)...C...818 843-6211
3151 N Kenwood St Burbank (91505) **(P-17146)**
Hydrabrush Inc...F...760 743-5160
701 S Andreasen Dr Ste C Escondido (92029) **(P-8767)**
Hydraforce Incorporated...F...951 689-3987
7383 Orangewood Dr Riverside (92504) **(P-15076)**
Hydraforce Incorporated...F...951 689-3987
7383 Orangewood Dr Riverside (92504) **(P-15077)**
Hydraforce Incorporated...F...951 689-3987
7383 Orangewood Dr Riverside (92504) **(P-15078)**
Hydralift, San Clemente *Also called Innovative Rv Technologies* **(P-227)**
Hydranautics (HQ)...B...760 901-2597
401 Jones Rd Oceanside (92058) **(P-9259)**
Hydraulic Pneumatic Inc...F...562 926-1122
13766 Milroy Pl Santa Fe Springs (90670) **(P-16158)**
Hydraulic Shop Inc...E...909 875-9336
2753 S Vista Ave Bloomington (92316) **(P-14327)**
Hydraulic Technology Inc...F...916 645-3317
3833 Cincinnati Ave Rocklin (95765) **(P-15079)**
Hydraulics International Inc (PA)...B...818 998-1231
9201 Independence Ave Chatsworth (91311) **(P-20840)**
Hydraulics International Inc...D...818 998-1236
9000 Mason Ave Chatsworth (91311) **(P-20841)**
Hydril Company...B...661 588-9332
3237 Patton Way Bakersfield (93308) **(P-14228)**
Hydril USA Distribution LLC...F...661 588-9332
3237 Patton Way Bakersfield (93308) **(P-14229)**
Hydrite Chemical Co...E...559 651-3450
1603 Clancy Ct Visalia (93291) **(P-7782)**
Hydro Components and Tech, Vista *Also called Hydrocomponents & Tech Inc* **(P-16051)**
Hydro Conduit of Texas LP...F...909 825-1500
1205 S Rancho Ave Colton (92324) **(P-10939)**
Hydro Extruder LLC...B...626 964-3411
18111 Railroad St City of Industry (91748) **(P-11590)**
Hydro Fitting Mfg Corp...E...626 967-5151
733 E Edna Pl Covina (91723) **(P-13719)**
Hydro Flow Filtration Sys LLC...F...951 296-0904
42074 Remington Ave Temecula (92590) **(P-23730)**
Hydro Quip, Corona *Also called Blue Desert International Inc* **(P-16020)**

Hydro Systems Inc (PA) ......D......661 775-0686
29132 Avenue Paine Valencia (91355) *(P-12014)*
Hydro-Aire Inc (HQ) ......E......818 526-2600
3000 Winona Ave Burbank (91504) *(P-20842)*
Hydro-Logic Purification ......F......888 426-5644
370 Encinal St Ste 150 Santa Cruz (95060) *(P-15330)*
Hydrochempsc, Bakersfield *Also called PSC Industrial Outsourcing LP (P-263)*
Hydrocomponents & Tech Inc ......F......760 598-0189
1175 Park Center Dr Ste H Vista (92081) *(P-16051)*
Hydrofarm LLC (PA) ......E......800 634-9990
2249 S Mcdowell Blvd Ext Petaluma (94954) *(P-24126)*
Hydroform USA Incorporated ......C......310 632-6353
2848 E 208th St Carson (90810) *(P-20843)*
Hydrohoist Marine Group Inc ......E......925 513-0507
1501 Discovery Bay Blvd Discovery Bay (94505) *(P-14298)*
Hydrokleen Systems, Porterville *Also called Horizon International Ltd (P-16049)*
Hydrolynx Systems Inc ......F......916 374-1800
950 Riverside Pkwy Ste 10 West Sacramento (95605) *(P-21970)*
Hydromach Inc ......E......818 341-0915
20400 Prairie St Chatsworth (91311) *(P-21193)*
Hydronovation Inc ......F......800 778-5092
530 Howard St San Francisco (94105) *(P-16052)*
Hydropoint Data Systems Inc ......E......707 769-9696
1720 Corporate Cir Petaluma (94954) *(P-14070)*
Hygeia II Medical Group Inc ......E......714 515-7571
6241 Yarrow Dr Ste A Carlsbad (92011) *(P-22986)*
Hygeia II Medical Group Inc ......E......714 515-7571
6241 Yarrow Dr Ste A Carlsbad (92011) *(P-22987)*
Hygenia, Camarillo *Also called Medical Packaging Corporation (P-22769)*
Hyghte Holdings, Carlsbad *Also called Astura Medical (P-22348)*
Hygieia Biological Labs (PA) ......E......530 661-1442
1785 E Main St Ste 4 Woodland (95776) *(P-8559)*
Hygiena LLC (PA) ......C......805 388-2383
941 Avenida Acaso Camarillo (93012) *(P-8482)*
Hyland & Associates, San Jose *Also called Nicholas R Hyland (P-4958)*
Hyland Homeopathic, Gardena *Also called Standard Homeopathic Co (P-8394)*
Hyland's Homeopathic, Los Angeles *Also called Standard Homeopathic Co (P-8393)*
Hyperbaric Technologies Inc ......D......619 336-2022
3224 Hoover Ave National City (91950) *(P-22988)*
Hyperion Books For Children, Burbank *Also called Disney Book Group LLC (P-6336)*
Hyponex Corporation ......E......909 597-2811
15978 El Prado Rd Chino (91708) *(P-9062)*
Hyponex Corporation ......D......209 887-3845
23390 E Flood Rd Linden (95236) *(P-9063)*
Hypower Hydraulics, Turlock *Also called Turlock Machine Works (P-16160)*
Hypress Technologies Inc ......F......805 485-4060
340 Hearst Dr Oxnard (93030) *(P-14439)*
Hyspan Precision Products Inc (PA) ......D......619 421-1355
1685 Brandywine Ave Chula Vista (91911) *(P-15284)*
Hyspan Precision Products Inc ......D......619 421-1355
1683 Brandywine Ave Chula Vista (91911) *(P-13947)*
Hysterical Software Inc ......F......415 793-5785
2874 Hillside Dr Burlingame (94010) *(P-24742)*
Hytech Processing, Inglewood *Also called C C M D Inc (P-13359)*
Hytek R&D Inc (PA) ......E......408 761-5271
2044 Corporate Ct Milpitas (95035) *(P-18502)*
Hytron Mfg Co Inc ......E......714 903-6701
15582 Chemical Ln Huntington Beach (92649) *(P-16576)*
Hytrust Inc (PA) ......E......650 681-8100
1975 W El Camino Real # 203 Mountain View (94040) *(P-24743)*
Hyundai Translead (HQ) ......D......619 574-1500
8880 Rio San Diego Dr # 600 San Diego (92108) *(P-12390)*
Hyx Tech Corp ......F......951 907-3386
13620 Benson Ave Ste B Chino (91710) *(P-7345)*
I & A Inc ......E......408 432-8340
2221 Ringwood Ave San Jose (95131) *(P-12618)*
I & E Lath Mill Inc ......E......707 895-3380
8701 School Rd Philo (95466) *(P-4040)*
I & I Deburring Inc ......F......562 802-0058
14504 Carmenita Rd Ste A Norwalk (90650) *(P-14383)*
I & I Sports Supply Company (PA) ......E......310 715-6800
19751 Figueroa St Carson (90745) *(P-23588)*
I Amira Grand Foods Inc (PA) ......F......949 852-4468
1 Park Plz Ste 600 Irvine (92614) *(P-1084)*
I and E Cabinets Inc ......E......818 933-6480
14660 Raymer St Van Nuys (91405) *(P-4311)*
I B E, Sun Valley *Also called Industrial Battery Engrg Inc (P-19811)*
I B P Service Center, Brea *Also called Tyson Fresh Meats Inc (P-453)*
I C C, Fullerton *Also called Interntnal Cnnctors Cable Corp (P-17958)*
I Color Printing & Mailing Inc ......F......310 947-1452
1450 W 228th St Ste 12 Torrance (90501) *(P-6866)*
I Color Printing & Mailing Inc (PA) ......F......310 997-1452
13000 S Broadway Los Angeles (90061) *(P-6867)*
I D T, San Jose *Also called Integrated Device Tech Inc (P-18906)*
I D T, Pasadena *Also called Integrated Design Tools Inc (P-23168)*
I DES Inc ......E......707 374-7500
864 Saint Francis Way Rio Vista (94571) *(P-21600)*
I E P Full Service Printing ......F......415 648-6002
1501 Cortland Ave San Francisco (94110) *(P-7346)*
I E S, Corona *Also called Industrial Eqp Solutions Inc (P-15332)*
I I S Mechanics, San Diego *Also called Port 80 Software Inc (P-25070)*
I J Research Inc ......E......714 546-8522
2919 Tech Ctr Santa Ana (92705) *(P-19571)*
I Joah (PA) ......F......213 742-0500
1721 Wall St Los Angeles (90015) *(P-3431)*
I M B Electronic Products ......D......714 523-2110
1800 E Via Burton Anaheim (92806) *(P-19294)*
I M Ginsburg Furniture Inc ......E......310 243-1260
1441 W 130th St Gardena (90249) *(P-4704)*
I O Interconnect Ltd (PA) ......E......714 564-1111
1202 E Wakeham Ave Santa Ana (92705) *(P-19395)*
I P, Chatsworth *Also called International Precision Inc (P-16590)*
I P C W, Commerce *Also called In Pro Car Wear Inc (P-17703)*
I P E, Norco *Also called Industrial Process Eqp Inc (P-15264)*
I R, El Segundo *Also called Infineon Tech Americas Corp (P-18885)*
I S G, Three Rivers *Also called Innovative Structural GL Inc (P-10705)*
I S G, Inyokern *Also called Intelligence Support Group Ltd (P-19984)*
I S I, Camarillo *Also called Interconnect Systems Inc (P-18920)*
I S T, Santa Clara *Also called Information Scan Tech Inc (P-21772)*
I Source Technical Svcs Inc ......F......949 453-1500
575 Rancho Cir Irvine (92618) *(P-19572)*
I Source Technical Svcs Inc (PA) ......F......949 453-1500
5 Rancho Cir Lake Forest (92630) *(P-19573)*
I T I Electro-Optic Corp (PA) ......E......310 445-8900
11500 W Olympic Blvd Los Angeles (90064) *(P-21601)*
I T I Electro-Optic Corp ......E......310 312-4526
1500 E Olympic Blvd # 400 Los Angeles (90021) *(P-21602)*
I T M Software Corp ......E......650 864-2500
1030 W Maude Ave Sunnyvale (94085) *(P-24744)*
I Transplant Enterprise Tech, Santa Monica *Also called Transplant Connect Inc (P-25291)*
I V C, Irvine *Also called International Vitamin Corp (P-8228)*
I V P, Canoga Park *Also called Interntnal Virtual PDT MGT Inc (P-17959)*
I-5 Publishing LLC (PA) ......C......949 855-8822
5151 California Ave # 100 Irvine (92617) *(P-6187)*
I-Bus Corporation (PA) ......F......408 942-1417
1138 Cadillac Ct Milpitas (95035) *(P-15555)*
I-Coat Company LLC ......E......800 832-2628
12020 Mora Dr Ste 2 Santa Fe Springs (90670) *(P-22084)*
I-Flow LLC ......A......800 448-3569
43 Discovery Ste 100 Irvine (92618) *(P-22473)*
I-Tech Company Ltd Lblty Co ......F......510 226-9226
42978 Osgood Rd Fremont (94539) *(P-15556)*
I. C. O., Gualala *Also called Independent Coast Observer (P-5886)*
I.C.O.N. Salon, Woodland Hills *Also called ICON Line Inc (P-24127)*
I.E. Distribution, Huntington Beach *Also called Seven Wells LLC (P-4652)*
I.V. League Medical, Camarillo *Also called Western Mfg & Distrg LLC (P-21149)*
I/O Controls Corporation (PA) ......D......626 812-5353
1357 W Foothill Blvd Azusa (91702) *(P-17277)*
I/O Interconnect, Santa Ana *Also called I O Interconnect Ltd (P-19395)*
I/O Select Inc ......F......858 537-2060
9835 Carroll Centre Rd # 100 San Diego (92126) *(P-21603)*
I/Omagic Corporation (PA) ......E......949 707-4800
20512 Crescent Bay Dr Lake Forest (92630) *(P-15557)*
I2a Technologies Inc ......E......510 770-0322
3399 W Warren Ave Fremont (94538) *(P-18877)*
I3 Nanotec LLC ......F......510 594-2299
1295 67th St Emeryville (94608) *(P-14967)*
Iac/Interactivecorp ......F......212 314-7300
8800 W Sunset Blvd West Hollywood (90069) *(P-24745)*
IaMplus LLC ......E......323 210-3852
809 N Cahuenga Blvd Los Angeles (90038) *(P-19979)*
Iar Systems Software Inc (HQ) ......F......650 287-4250
1065 E Hillsdale Blvd # 420 Foster City (94404) *(P-24746)*
Ibakeum Inc ......E......562 699-2296
8252 Whittier Blvd Pico Rivera (90660) *(P-1274)*
Ibg Holdings Inc ......E......661 702-8680
24841 Avenue Tibbitts Valencia (91355) *(P-8768)*
Ibisworld Inc ......E......212 626-6794
11755 Wilshire Blvd # 1100 Los Angeles (90025) *(P-6501)*
IBM, Los Angeles *Also called International Bus Mchs Corp (P-15432)*
IC Ink Image Co Inc ......E......209 931-3040
4627 E Fremont St Stockton (95215) *(P-7347)*
Ic Manage Inc (PA) ......F......408 369-9227
2105 S Bascom Ave Ste 120 Campbell (95008) *(P-24747)*
Ic Sensors Inc ......D......510 498-1570
45738 Northport Loop W Fremont (94538) *(P-18878)*
Icad Inc ......D......408 419-2300
345 Potrero Ave Sunnyvale (94085) *(P-9567)*
Ice Link LLC ......F......714 771-6580
954 N Batavia St Orange (92867) *(P-14859)*
Ice Man Inc ......F......562 633-4423
8710 Park St Bellflower (90706) *(P-2415)*
Icebreaker Health Inc ......F......415 926-5818
150 Spear St Ste 350 San Francisco (94105) *(P-24748)*
ICEE Company (HQ) ......D......800 426-4233
1205 S Dupont Ave Ontario (91761) *(P-997)*
ICEE Company ......E......909 974-3518
4250 E Lowell St Ontario (91761) *(P-998)*
ICEE Company ......F......925 828-5807
6800 Sierra Ct Ste M Dublin (94568) *(P-2268)*
Ichia Usa Inc ......C......619 482-2222
509 Telegraph Canyon Rd Chula Vista (91910) *(P-18879)*
Ichor Systems Inc ......C......510 476-8000
34585 7th St Union City (94587) *(P-10145)*
Ichor Systems Inc (HQ) ......E......510 897-5200
3185 Laurelview Ct Fremont (94538) *(P-18880)*
ICI Architectural Millwork Inc ......F......323 759-4993
6820 Brynhurst Ave Los Angeles (90043) *(P-4167)*
ICI Paints Store, Upland *Also called Akzo Nobel Inc (P-8972)*
ICI Paints Store, Costa Mesa *Also called Akzo Nobel Inc (P-8973)*
ICI Paints Store, Escondido *Also called Akzo Nobel Inc (P-8974)*
Iclavis LLC ......F......310 503-6847
8222 Allport Ave Santa Fe Springs (90670) *(P-6868)*

ALPHABETIC

Employee Codes: A=Over 500 employees, B=251-500
C=101-250, D=51-100, E=20-50, F=10-19
2019 California
Manfacturers Register
© Mergent Inc. 1-800-342-5647
1167

ICM Packaging Inc..........E.......714 744-4836
1604 W Collins Ave Orange (92867) **(P-4442)**
Icolorprinting.net, Los Angeles *Also called I Color Printing & Mailing Inc* **(P-6867)**
Icon Aircraft Inc (PA)..........D.......707 564-4000
2141 Icon Way Vacaville (95688) **(P-20844)**
Icon Apparel Group LLC..........E.......916 372-4266
2989 Promenade St Ste 100 West Sacramento (95691) **(P-2792)**
Icon Identity Solutions Inc..........D.......909 942-5100
10156 Sharon Cir Rancho Cucamonga (91730) **(P-23895)**
ICON Line Inc..........F.......818 709-4266
20600 Ventura Blvd Ste C Woodland Hills (91364) **(P-24127)**
Icon Screen Printing, Orange *Also called Icon Screening Inc* **(P-7348)**
Icon Screening Inc..........F.......714 630-4266
1108 W Grove Ave Orange (92865) **(P-7348)**
Iconn Inc..........E.......949 297-8448
8909 Irvine Center Dr Irvine (92618) **(P-19396)**
Iconn Technologies, Irvine *Also called Iconn Inc* **(P-19396)**
Icore International Inc..........C.......707 535-2750
3780 Flightline Dr Santa Rosa (95403) **(P-10146)**
ICP West, Buena Park *Also called Interntional Color Posters Inc* **(P-7360)**
Icpu, Santa Ana *Also called Industrial Cpu Systems Intl* **(P-15428)**
Icrco Inc..........F.......310 921-9559
26 Coromar Dr Goleta (93117) **(P-22989)**
Icrco Inc (PA)..........E.......310 921-9559
26 Coromar Dr Goleta (93117) **(P-22990)**
Icsh Parent Inc..........D.......323 724-8507
1540 S Greenwood Ave Montebello (90640) **(P-5491)**
Icsn Inc..........F.......951 687-2305
521 Princeland Ct Corona (92879) **(P-11696)**
Icu Medical Inc (PA)..........B.......949 366-2183
951 Calle Amanecer San Clemente (92673) **(P-22474)**
Icu Medical Fleet Services LLC..........D.......408 229-0560
5729 Fontanoso Way San Jose (95138) **(P-8209)**
Icu Medical Sales Inc (HQ)..........F.......949 366-2183
951 Calle Amanecer San Clemente (92673) **(P-22475)**
Icy Dock USA, Arcadia *Also called Cremax U S A Corporation* **(P-11949)**
IDB Holdings Inc (HQ)..........F.......909 390-5624
601 S Rockefeller Ave Ontario (91761) **(P-579)**
Iddea California LLC..........F.......714 257-7389
589 Apollo St Brea (92821) **(P-20367)**
Idea, Brea *Also called Instrument Design Eng Assoc I* **(P-19579)**
Idea Printing & Graphics Inc..........F.......559 733-4149
1921 E Main St Visalia (93292) **(P-6869)**
Idea Tooling & Engineering Inc..........D.......310 608-7488
20601 Annalee Ave Carson (90746) **(P-14526)**
Ideal Brands Inc..........E.......213 489-5557
16060 Ventura Blvd Encino (91436) **(P-5666)**
Ideal Envmtl Pdts & Svcs, Gilroy *Also called Containment Consultants Inc* **(P-12379)**
Ideal Fasteners Inc..........E.......714 630-7840
3850 E Miraloma Ave Anaheim (92806) **(P-13073)**
Ideal Graphics Inc..........F.......714 632-3398
1458 N Hundley St Anaheim (92806) **(P-6870)**
Ideal Pallet System Inc..........F.......714 847-9657
7422 Cedar Dr Huntington Beach (92647) **(P-4477)**
Ideal Print Solutions, Oceanside *Also called Solution Box Inc* **(P-7212)**
Ideal Printing Co Inc..........E.......626 964-2019
17855 Maclaren St City of Industry (91744) **(P-6871)**
Ideal Products Inc..........E.......951 727-8600
4501 Etiwanda Ave Mira Loma (91752) **(P-5070)**
Ideas In Motion..........F.......760 635-1181
1435 Eolus Ave Encinitas (92024) **(P-23166)**
Idemia America Corp..........C.......310 884-7900
3150 E Ana St Compton (90221) **(P-10147)**
Identiv Inc (PA)..........B.......949 250-8888
2201 Walnut Ave Ste 100 Fremont (94538) **(P-15755)**
Ideon, Buena Park *Also called Exemplis LLC* **(P-4987)**
Idex Health & Science LLC (HQ)..........D.......707 588-2000
600 Park Ct Rohnert Park (94928) **(P-21476)**
Idex Health & Science LLC..........C.......760 438-2131
2051 Palomar Airpt Rd # 200 Carlsbad (92011) **(P-22085)**
Idg, El Cajon *Also called Inflatable Design Group Inc* **(P-23901)**
Idg Consumer & Smb Inc (HQ)..........C.......415 243-0500
501 2nd St San Francisco (94107) **(P-6188)**
Idg Games Media Group Inc..........E.......510 768-2700
555 12th St Oakland (94607) **(P-6189)**
IDI Tools International LLC..........F.......760 598-8888
2438 Cades Way Vista (92081) **(P-11897)**
IDM, Santa Ana *Also called International Disc Mfr Inc* **(P-17905)**
IDO Cabinet Inc..........F.......415 282-1683
1551 Minnesota St San Francisco (94107) **(P-4312)**
Idrive Inc..........F.......805 308-6094
249 N Turnpike Rd Santa Barbara (93111) **(P-20368)**
Idx Corporation..........C.......408 270-8094
5655 Silver Creek Vly Rd San Jose (95138) **(P-5146)**
Idx Los Angeles LLC..........C.......909 212-8333
5005 E Philadelphia St Ontario (91761) **(P-4168)**
Ied Group, Santa Ana *Also called International Electronic Desig* **(P-19585)**
Iee, Van Nuys *Also called Industrial Electronic Engineer* **(P-15760)**
Ieee Computer Society, Los Alamitos *Also called Institute of Electrical and El* **(P-7203)**
If Copack LLC..........E.......559 875-3354
1912 Industrial Way Sanger (93657) **(P-759)**
Ifco Systems North America Inc..........E.......909 356-0697
14750 Miller Ave Fontana (92336) **(P-4478)**
Ifco Systems Us LLC..........E.......909 484-4332
8950 Rochester Ave # 150 Rancho Cucamonga (91730) **(P-4479)**
Ifiber Optix Inc..........E.......714 665-9796
14450 Chambers Rd Tustin (92780) **(P-10647)**
Ifwe Inc (HQ)..........D.......415 946-1850
848 Battery St San Francisco (94111) **(P-24749)**
Igenica Inc..........E.......650 231-4320
863 Mitten Rd Ste 102 Burlingame (94010) **(P-8210)**
Igi, Sierra Madre *Also called Greg Ian Islands Inc* **(P-5064)**
Ignatius Press, San Francisco *Also called Guadalupe Associates Inc* **(P-6497)**
Ignyta Inc (PA)..........D.......858 255-5959
4545 Towne Centre Ct San Diego (92121) **(P-8211)**
Igo Inc (PA)..........F.......888 205-0093
6001 Oak Cyn Irvine (92618) **(P-18128)**
Igolping Inc..........F.......866 507-4440
43583 Greenhills Way Fremont (94539) **(P-23589)**
Igrad Inc..........E.......858 705-2917
2163 Newcastle Ave # 100 Cardiff By The Sea (92007) **(P-24750)**
Igraphics (PA)..........E.......530 273-2200
165 Spring Hill Dr Grass Valley (95945) **(P-7349)**
Igraphix, San Francisco *Also called H2 Cards Inc* **(P-7341)**
Igraphix, San Francisco *Also called Designer Printing Inc* **(P-6782)**
Igs Inc..........F.......408 733-4621
916 E California Ave Sunnyvale (94085) **(P-10599)**
IHP Operations LLC..........B.......714 549-7782
2701 S Harbor Blvd Santa Ana (92704) **(P-12068)**
Ii-VI Optical Systems Inc..........D.......714 247-7100
14192 Chambers Rd Tustin (92780) **(P-22086)**
Ijk & Co Inc..........E.......415 826-8899
225 Industrial St San Francisco (94124) **(P-19980)**
Ijot Development Inc..........A.......925 258-9909
11360b Pleasant Valley Rd Penn Valley (95946) **(P-5015)**
Ikanos Communications Inc (HQ)..........C.......858 587-1121
5775 Morehouse Dr San Diego (92121) **(P-18881)**
Ikegami Mold Corp America..........F.......619 858-6855
3570 Camino Del Rio N # 106 San Diego (92108) **(P-10148)**
Ikhana Aircraft Services, Murrieta *Also called Ikhana Group Inc* **(P-20845)**
Ikhana Group Inc..........C.......951 600-0009
37260 Sky Canyon Dr # 20 Murrieta (92563) **(P-20845)**
Ikong E-Commerce Inc..........F.......888 556-1522
385 S Lemon Ave Ste E429 Walnut (91789) **(P-14812)**
IL Canto, Santa Fe Springs *Also called Lanshon Inc* **(P-3032)**
IL Fiorello Olive Oil Co..........E.......707 864-1529
2625 Mankas Corner Rd Fairfield (94534) **(P-1541)**
IL Helth Buty Natural Oils Inc..........E.......805 384-0473
322 N Aviador St Camarillo (93010) **(P-9260)**
IL Pastaio Foods Inc..........F.......408 753-9220
1266 E Julian St San Jose (95116) **(P-2539)**
IL Pastaio Fresh Pasta Company, San Jose *Also called IL Pastaio Foods Inc* **(P-2539)**
Ilco Industries Inc..........E.......310 631-8655
1308 W Mahalo Pl Compton (90220) **(P-13890)**
Illah Sports Inc A Corporation..........E.......805 240-7790
1610 Fiske Pl Oxnard (93033) **(P-23590)**
Illinois Tool Works Inc..........E.......805 499-0335
1260 Calle Suerte Camarillo (93012) **(P-18882)**
Illinois Tool Works Inc..........F.......408 468-1230
1980 Lundy Ave San Jose (95131) **(P-7350)**
Illinois Tool Works Inc..........C.......847 724-7500
1050 W 5th St Azusa (91702) **(P-9437)**
Illinois Tool Works Inc..........D.......800 762-7600
3200 Lakeville Hwy Petaluma (94954) **(P-16053)**
Illinois Tool Works Inc..........D.......916 939-4332
5000 Hillsdale Cir El Dorado Hills (95762) **(P-18883)**
Illumina Inc (PA)..........B.......858 202-4500
5200 Illumina Way San Diego (92122) **(P-21971)**
Illumina Inc..........E.......510 670-9300
200 Lincoln Centre Dr Foster City (94404) **(P-21972)**
Illumina Inc..........C.......858 202-4500
9440 Carroll Park Dr # 100 San Diego (92121) **(P-21973)**
Illumina Inc..........B.......800 809-4566
9885 Towne Centre Dr San Diego (92121) **(P-21974)**
Illuminate Education Inc..........E.......951 739-0186
6531 Irvine Center Dr # 100 Irvine (92618) **(P-24751)**
Illuminated Creations Inc..........E.......916 924-1936
1111 Joellis Way Sacramento (95815) **(P-23896)**
Ilona Draperies Inc..........E.......818 840-8811
3130 N Clybourn Ave Burbank (91505) **(P-3694)**
Ilos Corp..........F.......213 255-2060
1300 John Reed Ct Ste B City of Industry (91745) **(P-17702)**
Ilovetocreate A Duncan Entps, Fresno *Also called Duncan Enterprises* **(P-8901)**
Image Apparel For Business Inc..........E.......714 541-5247
1618 E Edinger Ave Santa Ana (92705) **(P-3105)**
Image Capture Review, Goleta *Also called Icrco Inc* **(P-22990)**
Image Casting Inc..........E.......805 986-1106
131 Lombard St Oxnard (93030) **(P-11512)**
Image Distribution Services..........F.......909 599-7680
3191 W Temple Ave Ste 180 Pomona (91768) **(P-6872)**
Image Distribution Services (PA)..........E.......949 754-9000
60 Bunsen Irvine (92618) **(P-6873)**
Image Magazine Inc..........E.......949 608-5188
5001 Birch St Newport Beach (92660) **(P-6190)**
Image Printing Solutions, Irvine *Also called Image Distribution Services* **(P-6873)**
Image Solutions Apparel Inc..........E.......310 464-8991
19571 Magellan Dr Torrance (90502) **(P-3106)**
Image Square Inc..........F.......310 586-2333
1627 Stanford St Santa Monica (90404) **(P-5287)**
Image Square Copy & Print, Santa Monica *Also called Image Square Inc* **(P-5287)**
Image Star LLC..........F.......415 883-5815
42 Digital Dr Ste 10 Novato (94949) **(P-3163)**
Image Technology, Palo Alto *Also called Suss McRtec Prcision Photomask* **(P-23199)**
Imagemover Inc..........F.......818 485-8840
10051 Bradley Ave Pacoima (91331) **(P-6874)**

Mergent e-mail: customerrelations@mergent.com
1168
2019 California
Manufacturers Register
(P-0000) Products & Services Section entry number
(PA)=Parent Co (HQ)=Headquarters (DH)=Div Headquarters

Imagerlabs Inc...F...949 310-9560
1995 S Myrtle Ave Monrovia (91016) ***(P-18884)***
Imageware Systems Inc (PA)...D...858 673-8600
10815 Rncho Brnrdo Rd 3 # 310 San Diego (92127) ***(P-24752)***
Imagex Inc...F...925 474-8100
5990 Stoneridge Dr # 112 Pleasanton (94588) ***(P-6875)***
Imagictech, Victorville *Also called Exportech Worldwide LLC* ***(P-15412)***
Imagine Communications Corp...F...760 936-4000
1493 Poinsettia Ave # 143 Vista (92081) ***(P-18129)***
Imagine That Inc...F...408 365-0305
6830 Via Del Oro Ste 230 San Jose (95119) ***(P-24753)***
Imagine That Unlimited...F...858 566-8868
13100 Kirkham Way Ste 211 Poway (92064) ***(P-23897)***
Imagine This, Irvine *Also called Shye West Inc* ***(P-23960)***
Imaging Technologies...F...858 487-8944
15175 Innovation Dr San Diego (92128) ***(P-15756)***
Imatte Inc...F...818 993-8007
20945 Plummer St Chatsworth (91311) ***(P-17816)***
IMC Networks Corp (PA)...E...949 465-3000
25531 Commercentre Dr Lake Forest (92630) ***(P-15634)***
Imco, Sacramento *Also called Geo Drilling Fluids Inc* ***(P-11320)***
Imcsd, San Diego *Also called Integrated Microwave Corp* ***(P-19580)***
Imdex Technology Usa LLC...E...805 540-2017
3474 Empresa Dr Ste 150 San Luis Obispo (93401) ***(P-22216)***
Imergy Power Systems Inc...E...510 668-1485
3945 Freedom Cir Ste 560 Santa Clara (95054) ***(P-19574)***
Imerys Clays Inc...F...805 737-2445
2500 Miguelito Rd Lompoc (93436) ***(P-399)***
Imerys Filtration Minerals, Lompoc *Also called Imerys Minerals California Inc* ***(P-405)***
Imerys Filtration Minerals...F...408 643-0092
71 Daggett Dr San Jose (95134) ***(P-414)***
Imerys Filtration Minerals Inc (HQ)...E...805 562-0200
1732 N 1st St Ste 450 San Jose (95112) ***(P-415)***
Imerys Minerals California Inc...B...805 736-1221
2500 Miguelito Canyon Rd Lompoc (93436) ***(P-405)***
Imerys Minerals California Inc (HQ)...D...805 736-1221
2500 San Miguelito Rd Lompoc (93436) ***(P-416)***
Imerys Perlite Usa Inc...F...760 745-5900
1450 Simpson Way Escondido (92029) ***(P-15331)***
Imesa, San Diego *Also called Leon Assembly Solutions Inc* ***(P-10819)***
IMG Companies LLC...C...925 273-1100
225 Mountain Vista Pkwy Livermore (94551) ***(P-16577)***
IMI, San Jose *Also called Integrated Materials Inc* ***(P-18908)***
IMI CCI, Rcho STA Marg *Also called Control Components Inc* ***(P-13713)***
Immco, El Monte *Also called Industrial Machine & Mfg Co* ***(P-12178)***
Immersion Corporation (PA)...D...408 467-1900
50 Rio Robles San Jose (95134) ***(P-15757)***
Immport Therapeutics Inc...F...949 679-4068
1 Technology Dr Ste E309 Irvine (92618) ***(P-22934)***
Immunalysis, Pomona *Also called Diagnostixx California Corp* ***(P-22423)***
Immuncellular Therapeutics Ltd...F...818 264-2300
23622 Calabasas Rd # 300 Calabasas (91302) ***(P-8212)***
Immune Design Corp...F...650 225-0214
601 Gateway Blvd Ste 250 South San Francisco (94080) ***(P-8213)***
Immuno Concepts Inc...E...916 363-2649
9825 Goethe Rd Ste 350 Sacramento (95827) ***(P-22476)***
Immunoscience LLC...F...925 400-6055
6780 Sierra Ct Ste M Dublin (94568) ***(P-8483)***
Imp International Inc (PA)...E...909 321-1000
1905 S Lynx Ave Ontario (91761) ***(P-7948)***
Impac International, Ontario *Also called New Greenscreen Incorporated* ***(P-5157)***
Impac Medical Systems Inc (HQ)...E...408 830-8000
100 Mathilda Pl Fl 5 Sunnyvale (94086) ***(P-24754)***
Impac Technologies Inc...D...714 427-2000
3050 Red Hill Ave Costa Mesa (92626) ***(P-18130)***
Impact Bearing, San Clemente *Also called Clean Wave Management Inc* ***(P-20573)***
Impact Bearing, San Clemente *Also called Clean Wave Management Inc* ***(P-15105)***
Impact Displays, Santa Clara *Also called Impact Marketing Displays LLC* ***(P-23898)***
Impact LLC...E...714 546-6000
22521 Avenida Empresa # 107 Rcho STA Marg (92688) ***(P-19575)***
Impact Marketing Displays LLC...F...408 217-6850
1725 De La Cruz Blvd # 4 Santa Clara (95050) ***(P-23898)***
Impact Printing & Graphics...E...909 614-1678
15150 Sierra Bonita Ln Chino (91710) ***(P-7351)***
Impact Project Management Inc...E...760 747-6616
2872 S Santa Fe Ave San Marcos (92069) ***(P-18503)***
Impact Racing Inc (PA)...E...619 449-9455
9335 Stevens Rd Santee (92071) ***(P-25411)***
Impak Corporation...F...323 277-4700
13700 S Broadway Los Angeles (90061) ***(P-9710)***
Impak Worldwide, Los Angeles *Also called Impak Corporation* ***(P-9710)***
Impakt Holdings LLC...F...650 692-5800
490 Gianni St Santa Clara (95054) ***(P-12619)***
Impax Laboratories Inc...D...510 240-6000
31047 Genstar Rd Hayward (94544) ***(P-8214)***
Impax Laboratories LLC (HQ)...A...510 240-6000
30831 Huntwood Ave Hayward (94544) ***(P-8215)***
Impax Laboratories Usa LLC...F...510 240-6000
30831 Huntwood Ave Hayward (94544) ***(P-8216)***
Impco Technologies Inc (HQ)...C...714 656-1200
3030 S Susan St Santa Ana (92704) ***(P-20369)***
Impedimed Inc (HQ)...E...760 585-2100
5900 Pasteur Ct Ste 125 Carlsbad (92008) ***(P-22477)***
Imperative Care Inc...E...650 274-3882
1359 Dell Ave Campbell (95008) ***(P-22748)***
Imperial Cal Products Inc...E...714 990-9100
425 Apollo St Brea (92821) ***(P-13223)***
Imperial Coml Cooking Eqp, Corona *Also called Imperial Manufacturing Co* ***(P-16054)***
Imperial Compost LLC...F...760 351-1900
1698 Jones St Ste 5 Brawley (92227) ***(P-9104)***
Imperial Custom Cabinet Inc...F...619 461-4093
8093 Lemon Grove Way Lemon Grove (91945) ***(P-4705)***
Imperial Designs, Sherman Oaks *Also called Western Imperial Trading Inc* ***(P-23331)***
Imperial Die Cutting Inc...E...916 443-6142
800 Richards Blvd Sacramento (95811) ***(P-5652)***
Imperial Enterprises Inc...E...818 886-5028
9666 Owensmouth Ave Ste A Chatsworth (91311) ***(P-10648)***
Imperial Honing, Santa Fe Springs *Also called Honomatic Inc* ***(P-16572)***
Imperial Manufacturing Co...C...951 281-1830
1128 Sherborn St Corona (92879) ***(P-16054)***
Imperial Marking Systems, Cerritos *Also called Best Label Company Inc* ***(P-7248)***
Imperial Mfg Co, Corona *Also called Spenuzza Inc* ***(P-16112)***
Imperial Mfg Co, Duarte *Also called Spenuzza Inc* ***(P-16113)***
Imperial Pipe Services LLC...E...951 682-3307
12375 Brown Ave Riverside (92509) ***(P-11480)***
Imperial Printers Inc (PA)...F...760 352-4374
430 W Main St El Centro (92243) ***(P-6876)***
Imperial Printers Rocket Copy, El Centro *Also called Imperial Printers Inc* ***(P-6876)***
Imperial Printing, Campbell *Also called C T V Inc* ***(P-6712)***
Imperial Prtg Ppr Box Mfg Inc...E...310 323-7300
1622 W 130th St Gardena (90249) ***(P-5507)***
Imperial Rubber Products Inc...E...909 393-0528
5691 Gates St Chino (91710) ***(P-14813)***
Imperial Shade Venetian Blind, Los Angeles *Also called Imperial Shade Venetian Blind* ***(P-5147)***
Imperial Shade Venetian Blind...F...323 233-4391
909 E 59th St Los Angeles (90001) ***(P-5147)***
Imperial Sugar Company...C...760 344-3110
395 W Keystone Rd Brawley (92227) ***(P-1403)***
Imperial System, Union City *Also called Best Label Company Inc* ***(P-15198)***
Imperial Toy LLC (PA)...C...818 536-6500
16641 Roscoe Pl North Hills (91343) ***(P-23430)***
Imperial Valley Foods Inc...B...760 203-1896
1961 Buchanan Ave Calexico (92231) ***(P-952)***
Imperial Valley Press, El Centro *Also called Associated Desert Newspaper* ***(P-5766)***
Imperials Sand Dunes, Brea *Also called Worldwide Envmtl Pdts Inc* ***(P-21677)***
Impeva Labs Inc (PA)...F...650 559-0103
2570 W El Cam Mountain View (94040) ***(P-19981)***
Implant Direct Sybron Mfg LLC...C...818 444-3300
3050 E Hillcrest Dr Westlake Village (91362) ***(P-22749)***
Implantech Associates Inc...E...805 289-1665
6025 Nicolle St Ste B Ventura (93003) ***(P-22750)***
Implantium, Cypress *Also called Dentium USA* ***(P-22869)***
Imply Data Inc...F...415 685-8187
1633 Old Bayshore Hwy # 232 Burlingame (94010) ***(P-24755)***
Impo International LLC...E...805 922-7753
3510 Black Rd Santa Maria (93455) ***(P-10497)***
Impossible Aerospace Corp...F...707 293-9367
1118 Elko Dr Sunnyvale (94089) ***(P-20592)***
Impresa Aerospace LLC (PA)...F...310 354-1200
344 W 157th St Gardena (90248) ***(P-20846)***
Impresa Aerospace LLC...F...843 553-2021
344 W 157th St Gardena (90248) ***(P-20847)***
Impress Communications Inc...D...818 701-8800
9320 Lurline Ave Chatsworth (91311) ***(P-6877)***
Imprimis Pharmaceuticals Inc (PA)...E...858 704-4040
12264 El Camino Real # 350 San Diego (92130) ***(P-8217)***
Impro Industries Usa Inc (HQ)...F...909 396-6525
21660 Copley Dr Ste 100 Diamond Bar (91765) ***(P-11779)***
Impulse Enterprise...F...858 565-7050
9855 Carroll Canyon Rd San Diego (92131) ***(P-17473)***
Impulse Enterprise...D...858 565-7050
8254 Ronson Rd San Diego (92111) ***(P-17474)***
Impulselogic Inc...F...925 275-1028
2410 Camino Ramon Ste 240 San Ramon (94583) ***(P-24756)***
IMS, South El Monte *Also called Interntnal Mdction Systems Ltd* ***(P-7950)***
IMS, South El Monte *Also called Interntnal Mdction Systems Ltd* ***(P-8230)***
IMS, Chula Vista *Also called Integrated Marine Services Inc* ***(P-20997)***
IMS Products Inc...F...951 653-7720
6240 Box Springs Blvd E Riverside (92507) ***(P-21117)***
IMS-Ess, Temecula *Also called Electro-Support Systems Corp* ***(P-19526)***
IMT, Milpitas *Also called Integrated Mfg Tech Inc* ***(P-16587)***
IMT Analytical, Goleta *Also called Innovative Micro Tech Inc* ***(P-18898)***
IMT International, Milpitas *Also called Integrated Mfg Tech Inc* ***(P-13433)***
IMT Precision Inc...E...510 324-8926
31902 Hayman St Hayward (94544) ***(P-16578)***
IMT-Stason Laboratories, Irvine *Also called Stason Pharmaceuticals Inc* ***(P-8395)***
Imtec Acculine LLC...E...510 770-1800
49036 Milmont Dr Fremont (94538) ***(P-14968)***
In House Custom Decals...F...909 613-1403
2300 S Reservoir St # 308 Pomona (91766) ***(P-7352)***
In House Stickers, Pomona *Also called In House Custom Decals* ***(P-7352)***
In Pro Car Wear Inc...F...323 724-0568
6363 Corsair St Commerce (90040) ***(P-17703)***
In Style, Los Angeles *Also called Boulevard Style Inc* ***(P-3220)***
In Sync Computer Solutions Inc...F...949 837-5000
23282 Mill Creek Dr Laguna Hills (92653) ***(P-24757)***
In To Ink...F...858 271-6363
6959 Colorado Ave La Mesa (91942) ***(P-6878)***
In Win Development USA Inc...E...909 348-0588
188 Brea Canyon Rd Walnut (91789) ***(P-15558)***
In-O-Vate Inc...F...562 806-7515
9301 Garfield Ave South Gate (90280) ***(P-9410)***
Inaba Foods (usa) Inc...F...310 818-2270
19301 Pcf Gtwy Dr Ste 120 Torrance (90502) ***(P-1114)***

ALPHABETIC

Employee Codes: A=Over 500 employees, B=251-500
C=101-250, D=51-100, E=20-50, F=10-19
2019 California
Manfacturers Register
© Mergent Inc. 1-800-342-5647
1169

Inari Medical Inc......E......949 600-8433
9272 Jeronimo Rd Ste 124 Irvine (92618) ***(P-22478)***
Inbenta Technologies Inc......E......408 213-8771
1065 E Hillsdale Blvd # 425 Foster City (94404) ***(P-24758)***
Inc Aerojet Rocketdyne of De......C......818 586-9629
8495 Carla Ln West Hills (91304) ***(P-9011)***
Inc Polycarbon, Valencia *Also called Sgl Technic Inc* ***(P-11326)***
Inca One Corporation......E......310 808-0001
1648 W 134th St Gardena (90249) ***(P-19295)***
Inca Pallets Supply Inc......E......909 622-1414
1349 S East End Ave Pomona (91766) ***(P-4480)***
Inca Plastics Molding Co Inc......D......909 923-3235
948 E Belmont St Ontario (91761) ***(P-10149)***
Incal Technology Inc......E......510 657-8405
46420 Fremont Blvd Fremont (94538) ***(P-15758)***
Incandescent Inc......F......415 464-7975
350 Sansome St San Francisco (94104) ***(P-24759)***
Incarda Therapeutics Inc......E......510 422-5522
39899 Balentine Dr # 185 Newark (94560) ***(P-8218)***
Incelldx Inc......F......650 777-7630
1541 Industrial Rd San Carlos (94070) ***(P-22479)***
Inception Homes Inc......F......714 890-1883
12640 Beach Blvd Stanton (90680) ***(P-4562)***
Incharacter Costumes LLC......E......858 552-3600
4560 Alvarado Canyon Rd 1d San Diego (92120) ***(P-3659)***
Incipio Group, Irvine *Also called Incipio Technologies Inc* ***(P-15759)***
Incipio Technologies Inc (PA)......D......949 250-4929
3347 Michelson Dr Ste 100 Irvine (92612) ***(P-15759)***
Inclinator of California, San Fernando *Also called TL Shield & Associates Inc* ***(P-14260)***
Incline Therapeutics Inc......F......650 241-6800
900 Saginaw Dr Ste 200 Redwood City (94063) ***(P-8219)***
Incredible Cheesecake, San Diego *Also called Princess Brandy Corp* ***(P-1311)***
Indel Engineering Inc......E......562 594-0995
6400 E Marina Dr Long Beach (90803) ***(P-21044)***
Independent Berkeley Student......D......510 548-8300
2483 Hearst Ave Berkeley (94709) ***(P-5885)***
Independent Coast Observer......F......707 884-3501
38500 S Highway 1 Gualala (95445) ***(P-5886)***
Independent Forge Company......E......714 997-7337
692 N Batavia St Orange (92868) ***(P-13124)***
Independent Ink Inc......E......310 523-4657
13700 S Gramac Pl Gardena (90249) ***(P-9261)***
Independent Printing Co Inc (PA)......E......925 229-5050
1530 Franklin Canyon Rd Martinez (94553) ***(P-6879)***
Independent, The, Livermore *Also called Inland Valley Publising Co* ***(P-5890)***
Indepndent Flr Tstg Insptn Inc......F......925 676-7682
2300 Clayton Rd Ste 1240 Concord (94520) ***(P-10940)***
Index Printing Inc......F......209 862-2222
1021 Fresno St Newman (95360) ***(P-7353)***
Indi Molecular Inc......F......310 417-4999
6160 Bristol Pkwy Culver City (90230) ***(P-8484)***
India Journal, Santa Fe Springs *Also called Premier Media Inc* ***(P-6018)***
India Post, Fremont *Also called Rj Media* ***(P-6029)***
India-West Publications Inc (PA)......E......510 383-1140
933 Macarthur Blvd San Leandro (94577) ***(P-5887)***
Indian Head Industries Inc......D......707 894-3333
1184 S Cloverdale Blvd Cloverdale (95425) ***(P-20370)***
Indian Ink Screen Print......E......714 437-0882
1351 Logan Ave Ste A Costa Mesa (92626) ***(P-7354)***
Indian Summer, Rancho Cucamonga *Also called Mizkan Americas Inc* ***(P-2608)***
Indian Wells Brewery, Inyokern *Also called Indian Wells Companies* ***(P-1601)***
Indian Wells Companies......E......760 377-4290
2565 State Highway 14 Inyokern (93527) ***(P-1601)***
Indie Source Inc......E......424 200-2027
1933 S Broadway Ste 1168 Los Angeles (90007) ***(P-3107)***
Indigo Designs......F......909 997-0854
16607 Reed St Fontana (92336) ***(P-4313)***
Indio Products Inc......E......323 720-9117
5331 E Slauson Ave Commerce (90040) ***(P-9262)***
Indium Software Inc......C......408 501-8844
1250 Oakmead Pkwy Ste 210 Sunnyvale (94085) ***(P-24760)***
Individual Software Inc......E......925 734-6767
2301 Armstrong St Ste 101 Livermore (94551) ***(P-24761)***
Indtec Corporation......E......831 582-9388
3348 Paul Davis Dr # 109 Marina (93933) ***(P-18504)***
Indu Fashions......E......619 336-4638
220 W 25th St Ste B National City (91950) ***(P-3074)***
Indu-Electric North Amer Inc......E......310 578-2144
27756 Avenue Hopkins Valencia (91355) ***(P-15285)***
Induction Technology Corp......E......760 246-7333
22060 Bear Valley Rd Apple Valley (92308) ***(P-15262)***
Inductor Supply Inc......F......714 894-9050
11542 Knott St Ste 3 Garden Grove (92841) ***(P-19340)***
Induspac California Inc......F......909 390-4422
1550 Champagne Ave Ontario (91761) ***(P-7841)***
Induspac California Inc (HQ)......E......510 324-3626
21062 Forbes Ave Hayward (94545) ***(P-7842)***
Industrial Battery Engrg Inc......E......818 767-7067
9121 De Garmo Ave Sun Valley (91352) ***(P-19811)***
Industrial Coatings Division, Huntington Beach *Also called PPG Industries Inc* ***(P-8930)***
Industrial Components Div, Simi Valley *Also called Rexnord Industries LLC* ***(P-14881)***
Industrial Cpu Systems Intl......F......714 957-2815
2225 S Grand Ave Santa Ana (92705) ***(P-15428)***
Industrial Design Fabrication......F......209 937-9128
802 S San Joaquin St B Stockton (95206) ***(P-16579)***
Industrial Design Products......F......909 468-0693
2700 Pomona Blvd Pomona (91768) ***(P-14328)***
Industrial Dynamics Co Ltd (PA)......C......310 325-5633
3100 Fujita St Torrance (90505) ***(P-14969)***
Industrial Electric Mfg, Fremont *Also called New Iem LLC* ***(P-17152)***
Industrial Electric Mfg, Fremont *Also called Abd El & Larson Holdings LLC* ***(P-17128)***
Industrial Electronic Engineer......D......818 787-0311
7723 Kester Ave Van Nuys (91405) ***(P-15760)***
Industrial Eqp Solutions Inc......F......951 272-9540
301 N Smith Ave Corona (92880) ***(P-15332)***
Industrial Filtration, Long Beach *Also called La Mar Industries Inc* ***(P-15338)***
Industrial Fire Sprnklr Co Inc......E......619 266-6030
3845 Imperial Ave San Diego (92113) ***(P-15333)***
Industrial Furnace & Insul Inc......F......909 947-2449
2090 S Hellman Ave Ontario (91761) ***(P-15263)***
Industrial Gasket and Sup Co......E......310 530-1771
23018 Normandie Ave Torrance (90502) ***(P-9536)***
Industrial Glass Products Inc......F......323 526-7125
4229 Union Pacific Ave Los Angeles (90023) ***(P-10704)***
Industrial Glass Service, Sunnyvale *Also called Igs Inc* ***(P-10599)***
Industrial Graphic, Santa Ana *Also called Comstar Industries Inc* ***(P-17260)***
Industrial Machine & Mfg Co......F......626 444-0181
2626 Seaman Ave El Monte (91733) ***(P-12178)***
Industrial Machining Co, Columbia *Also called Gerard H Tanzi Inc* ***(P-14854)***
Industrial Manufacturing Inc......F......562 941-5888
10110 Norwalk Blvd Santa Fe Springs (90670) ***(P-12069)***
Industrial Mdfication Repr Inc......F......310 516-7992
1323 W 132nd St Gardena (90247) ***(P-4523)***
Industrial Metal Finishing......F......714 628-8808
1941 Petra Ln Placentia (92870) ***(P-13430)***
Industrial Mineral Company USA......F......562 553-5203
100 Oceangate Ste 600 Long Beach (90802) ***(P-11294)***
Industrial Plating Co, Carlsbad *Also called Industrial Zinc Plating Corp* ***(P-13431)***
Industrial Power Products......E......530 893-0584
355 E Park Ave Chico (95928) ***(P-16580)***
Industrial Process Eqp Inc......F......714 447-0171
1700 Industrial Ave Norco (92860) ***(P-15264)***
Industrial SEC Allianc Ptnrs......F......619 232-7041
3033 5th Ave Ste 400 San Diego (92103) ***(P-23167)***
Industrial Sprockets Gears Inc......E......323 233-7221
13650 Rosecrans Ave Santa Fe Springs (90670) ***(P-15286)***
Industrial Tctnics Brings Corp (HQ)......D......310 537-3750
18301 S Santa Fe Ave E Rncho Dmngz (90221) ***(P-15106)***
Industrial Tool and Die Inc......F......714 549-1686
1330 E Saint Gertrude Pl Santa Ana (92705) ***(P-14527)***
Industrial Tools Inc......E......805 483-1111
1111 S Rose Ave Oxnard (93033) ***(P-14970)***
Industrial Tube Company LLC......D......661 295-4000
28150 Industry Dr Valencia (91355) ***(P-13743)***
Industrial Welding, Redding *Also called Ferrosaur Inc* ***(P-12161)***
Industrial Wiper & Supply Inc......E......408 286-4752
1025 98th Ave A Oakland (94603) ***(P-2801)***
Industrial Zinc Plating Corp......E......760 918-6877
7217 San Luis St Carlsbad (92011) ***(P-13431)***
Industrious Software Solution......F......310 672-8700
8901 S La Cienega Blvd # 202 Inglewood (90301) ***(P-24762)***
Industrious Software Solutions, Inglewood *Also called Industrious Software Solution* ***(P-24762)***
Industry Color Printing Inc......E......626 961-2403
11642 Washington Blvd Whittier (90606) ***(P-6880)***
Industry LLC (HQ)......F......310 463-6157
1811 Micheltorena St Los Angeles (90026) ***(P-24763)***
Industry Terminal Us31, City of Industry *Also called Lhoist North America Ariz Inc* ***(P-11215)***
Inerfab, San Juan Capistrano *Also called American Horse Products* ***(P-3936)***
Inertech Supply Inc......D......626 282-2000
641 Monterey Pass Rd Monterey Park (91754) ***(P-9537)***
Inertia Engrg & Mch Works Inc......E......800 791-9997
6665 Hardaway Rd Stockton (95215) ***(P-17147)***
Inetwork Inc......F......619 401-7334
575 6th Ave Unit 1402 San Diego (92101) ***(P-15429)***
Infab Corporation......D......805 987-5255
1040 Avenida Acaso Camarillo (93012) ***(P-22751)***
Inficold Inc......F......408 464-8007
14654 Placida Ct Saratoga (95070) ***(P-15160)***
Infineon Tech Americas Corp (HQ)......A......310 726-8000
101 N Pacific Coast Hwy El Segundo (90245) ***(P-18885)***
Infineon Tech Americas Corp......A......951 375-2254
233 Kansas St El Segundo (90245) ***(P-18886)***
Infineon Tech Americas Corp......A......310 726-8000
233 Kansas St El Segundo (90245) ***(P-18887)***
Infineon Tech Americas Corp......A......866 951-9519
640 N Mccarthy Blvd Milpitas (95035) ***(P-18888)***
Infineon Tech Americas Corp......A......951 375-6008
41915 Business Park Dr Temecula (92590) ***(P-18889)***
Infineon Tech N Amer Corp (HQ)......B......408 503-2642
640 N Mccarthy Blvd Milpitas (95035) ***(P-18890)***
Infineon Tech US Holdco Inc (HQ)......D......866 951-9519
640 N Mccarthy Blvd Milpitas (95035) ***(P-18891)***
Infineon Technologies AG, Milpitas *Also called Infineon Tech US Holdco Inc* ***(P-18891)***
Infinera Corporation (PA)......B......408 572-5200
140 Caspian Ct Sunnyvale (94089) ***(P-17956)***
Infinera Corporation......E......408 572-5200
1338 Bordeaux Dr Sunnyvale (94089) ***(P-18892)***
Infinisim Inc......F......408 934-9777
2860 Zanker Rd Ste 202 San Jose (95134) ***(P-24764)***
Infinite Electronics Inc (HQ)......E......949 261-1920
17792 Fitch Irvine (92614) ***(P-19576)***
Infinite Electronics Intl Inc (HQ)......C......949 261-1920
17792 Fitch Irvine (92614) ***(P-19397)***
Infinite Engineering Inc......F......714 534-4688
13682 Newhope St Garden Grove (92843) ***(P-16581)***
Infinite Optics Inc......E......714 557-2299
1712 Newport Cir Ste F Santa Ana (92705) ***(P-22087)***

Infiniti, Anaheim *Also called Jenson Custom Furniture Inc* ***(P-4785)***
Infiniti Plastic Technologies.......F.......310 618-8288
11150 Santa Monica Blvd # 1280 Los Angeles (90025) ***(P-10150)***
Infiniti Solutions Usa Inc (PA).......D.......408 923-7300
3910 N 1st St San Jose (95134) ***(P-18505)***
Infiniti Solutions Usa Inc.......D.......408 923-7300
3910 N 1st St San Jose (95134) ***(P-18506)***
Infinity Access Plus Inc.......F.......818 270-8172
12945 Sherman Way Ste 8 North Hollywood (91605) ***(P-12861)***
Infinity Aerospace Inc (PA).......D.......818 998-9811
9060 Winnetka Ave Northridge (91324) ***(P-20663)***
Infinity Kitchen Products Inc.......F.......562 806-5771
7750 Scout Ave Bell Gardens (90201) ***(P-12620)***
Infinity Precision Inc.......F.......818 447-3008
6919 Eton Ave Canoga Park (91303) ***(P-16582)***
Infinity Stainless Products, Bell Gardens *Also called Infinity Kitchen Products Inc* ***(P-12620)***
Infinity Stamps Inc.......F.......818 576-1188
8577 Canoga Ave Canoga Park (91304) ***(P-13224)***
Infinity Systems Inc.......F.......714 692-1722
22715 La Palma Ave Yorba Linda (92887) ***(P-16583)***
Infinity Textile.......F.......562 777-9770
11023 Shoemaker Ave Santa Fe Springs (90670) ***(P-3000)***
Infinity Watch Corporation.......E.......626 289-9878
21078 Commerce Point Dr Walnut (91789) ***(P-23899)***
Inflatable Advertising Co Inc.......F.......213 387-6839
1600 W Olympic Blvd Los Angeles (90015) ***(P-23900)***
Inflatable Design Group Inc.......F.......619 596-6100
1080 W Bradley Ave Ste B El Cajon (92020) ***(P-23901)***
Inflatable Enterprises Inc.......F.......818 482-6509
1418 Vineland Ave Baldwin Park (91706) ***(P-9627)***
Inflight Entrmt & Connectivity, Irvine *Also called Thales Avionics Inc* ***(P-20949)***
Inflight Warning Systems Inc.......F.......714 993-9394
3910 Prospect Ave Unit P Yorba Linda (92886) ***(P-20848)***
Infocus Jupiter, Hayward *Also called Jupiter Systems LLC* ***(P-15636)***
Infofax Inc.......F.......530 895-0431
305 Nord Ave Chico (95926) ***(P-6191)***
Infoimage of California Inc (PA).......D.......650 473-6388
141 Jefferson Dr Menlo Park (94025) ***(P-7355)***
Infokorea Inc.......E.......213 487-1580
626 S Kingsley Dr Los Angeles (90005) ***(P-6192)***
Infor (us) Inc.......C.......678 319-8000
26250 Entp Way Ste 220 Lake Forest (92630) ***(P-24765)***
Infor (us) Inc.......C.......916 921-0883
11000 Olson Dr Ste 201 Rancho Cordova (95670) ***(P-24766)***
Inforce Computing Inc (PA).......F.......510 683-9999
48820 Kato Rd Ste 600b Fremont (94538) ***(P-19577)***
Inform Decisions.......F.......949 709-5838
30162 Tomas 101 Rcho STA Marg (92688) ***(P-24767)***
Inform Solution Incorporated.......F.......805 879-6000
201 Mentor Dr Santa Barbara (93111) ***(P-24768)***
Informa Business Media Inc.......E.......949 252-1146
16815 Von Karman Ave # 150 Irvine (92606) ***(P-6502)***
Informa Media Inc.......E.......619 295-7685
4452 Park Blvd Ste 306 San Diego (92116) ***(P-6193)***
Informa Media Inc.......D.......301 755-0162
11500 W Olympic Blvd Los Angeles (90064) ***(P-6194)***
Informatica LLC (HQ).......C.......650 385-5000
2100 Seaport Blvd Redwood City (94063) ***(P-24769)***
Information Integration Group.......E.......818 956-3744
457 Palm Dr Ste 200 Glendale (91202) ***(P-24770)***
Information Resources Inc.......E.......559 732-0324
400 N Johnson St Visalia (93291) ***(P-24771)***
Information Scan Tech Inc.......F.......408 988-1908
487 Gianni St Santa Clara (95054) ***(P-21772)***
Information Storage Dvcs Inc.......C.......408 943-6666
2727 N 1st St San Jose (95134) ***(P-18893)***
Informer Computer Systems.......F.......714 899-2049
12711 Western Ave Garden Grove (92841) ***(P-15635)***
Infoworld Media Group Inc (HQ).......D.......415 243-4344
501 2nd St Ste 500 San Francisco (94107) ***(P-6195)***
Infrared Dynamics Inc.......E.......714 572-4050
3830 Prospect Ave Yorba Linda (92886) ***(P-12070)***
Infrared Industries Inc.......F.......510 782-8100
25590 Seaboard Ln Hayward (94545) ***(P-21975)***
Infraredvision Technology Corp.......E.......805 686-8848
140 Industrial Way Buellton (93427) ***(P-18894)***
Infrastructureworld LLC.......E.......650 871-3950
1001 Bayhill Dr Ste 200 San Bruno (94066) ***(P-21976)***
Infratab.......E.......805 986-8880
4347 Raytheon Rd Unit 6 Oxnard (93033) ***(P-8560)***
Ingalls Conveyors Inc.......E.......323 837-9900
1005 W Olympic Blvd Montebello (90640) ***(P-14276)***
Ingenu Inc (PA).......E.......858 201-6000
10301 Meanley Dr San Diego (92131) ***(P-18131)***
Ingenue Inc.......D.......323 726-8084
6114 Scott Way Commerce (90040) ***(P-544)***
Ingla Rubber Products, Bellflower *Also called Bryant Rubber Corp* ***(P-9521)***
Inglenook.......F.......707 968-1100
1991 St Helena Hwy Rutherford (94573) ***(P-1817)***
Ingomar Packing Company LLC (PA).......D.......209 826-9494
9950 S Ingomar Grade Los Banos (93635) ***(P-808)***
Ingrasys Technology USA Inc.......E.......863 271-8266
2025 Gateway Pl Ste 190 San Jose (95110) ***(P-21773)***
Ingredients By Nature LLC.......E.......909 230-6200
5555 Brooks St Montclair (91763) ***(P-2540)***
Ingredion Incorporated.......D.......209 982-1920
1021 Industrial Dr Stockton (95206) ***(P-1100)***
Ingrersoll Rand Indus Refrig.......F.......909 477-2037
13770 Ramona Ave Chino (91710) ***(P-10473)***
Ingrooves, San Francisco *Also called Isolation Network Inc* ***(P-17819)***
Ingrooves Fontana.......F.......818 212-2550
15821 Ventura Blvd # 420 Encino (91436) ***(P-6503)***
Inhealth Technologies.......F.......800 477-5969
1110 Mark Ave Carpinteria (93013) ***(P-22752)***
Initiative Foods, Sanger *Also called If Copack LLC* ***(P-759)***
Initiative Foods LLC.......C.......559 875-3354
1912 Industrial Way Sanger (93657) ***(P-760)***
Initio Corporation.......E.......408 943-3189
2050 Ringwood Ave Ste A San Jose (95131) ***(P-18895)***
Initium Eyewear Inc.......F.......714 444-0866
412 Olive Ave Ste 218 Huntington Beach (92648) ***(P-23101)***
Injection Molding, Acampo *Also called AG Ray Inc* ***(P-14036)***
Injekt, Encinitas *Also called Mako Labs LLC* ***(P-24879)***
Ink & Color Inc.......E.......310 280-6060
5920 Bowcroft St Los Angeles (90016) ***(P-6881)***
Ink 2000 Corp.......F.......818 882-0168
19875 Nordhoff St Northridge (91324) ***(P-9200)***
Ink Fx Corporation.......E.......909 673-1950
2031 S Lynx Ave Ontario (91761) ***(P-7356)***
Ink Makers Inc.......F.......323 728-7500
2121 Yates Ave Commerce (90040) ***(P-9201)***
Ink Spot Inc.......E.......626 338-4500
9737 Bell Ranch Dr Santa Fe Springs (90670) ***(P-6882)***
Ink Spots, Montclair *Also called Thomas Burt* ***(P-7134)***
Ink Throwers, Encinitas *Also called R B T Inc* ***(P-3914)***
Inkgrabber.com, Simi Valley *Also called Inkjetmadnesscom Inc* ***(P-9202)***
Inkjetmadnesscom Inc.......F.......805 583-7755
2205 1st St Ste 103 Simi Valley (93065) ***(P-9202)***
Inkovation Inc (PA).......E.......800 465-4174
13659 Excelsior Dr Santa Fe Springs (90670) ***(P-6883)***
Inkovation Inc.......E.......800 465-4174
14906 Spring Ave Santa Fe Springs (90670) ***(P-6884)***
Inktomi Corporation (HQ).......E.......650 653-2800
701 First Ave Sunnyvale (94089) ***(P-24772)***
Inkwright LLC.......E.......714 892-3300
5822 Research Dr Huntington Beach (92649) ***(P-6885)***
Inland Artfl Limb & Brace Inc (PA).......F.......951 734-1835
680 Parkridge Ave Norco (92860) ***(P-22753)***
Inland Color Graphics.......F.......951 493-2999
2054 Tandem Norco (92860) ***(P-7649)***
Inland Empire Cmnty Newspapers.......E.......909 381-9898
1809 Commercenter W San Bernardino (92408) ***(P-5888)***
Inland Empire Drive Line Svc (PA).......F.......909 390-3030
4035 E Guasti Rd Ste 301 Ontario (91761) ***(P-20371)***
Inland Empire Foods Inc (PA).......E.......951 682-8222
5425 Wilson St Riverside (92509) ***(P-883)***
Inland Empire Magazine, Riverside *Also called Inland Empire Media Group Inc* ***(P-6196)***
Inland Empire Media Group Inc.......F.......951 682-3026
3400 Central Ave Ste 160 Riverside (92506) ***(P-6196)***
Inland Empire Truss Inc (PA).......E.......951 300-1758
275 W Rider St Perris (92571) ***(P-4412)***
Inland Envelope Company.......D.......909 622-2016
150 N Park Ave Pomona (91768) ***(P-5675)***
Inland Group, Anaheim *Also called Inland Litho LLC* ***(P-6886)***
Inland Litho LLC.......D.......714 993-6000
4305 E La Palma Ave Anaheim (92807) ***(P-6886)***
Inland Mailing Services Inc.......D.......951 371-6245
160 W Fthill Pkwy Ste 105 Corona (92882) ***(P-6887)***
Inland Marine Industries Inc.......C.......510 785-8555
3245 Depot Rd Hayward (94545) ***(P-13948)***
Inland Metal Technologies, Hayward *Also called Inland Marine Industries Inc* ***(P-13948)***
Inland PCF Resource Recovery.......E.......619 390-1418
12650 Slughter Hse Cyn Rd Lakeside (92040) ***(P-5268)***
Inland Powder Coating Corp.......C.......909 947-1122
1656 S Bon View Ave Ste F Ontario (91761) ***(P-13603)***
Inland Signs Inc.......E.......909 581-0699
10783 Bell Ct Rancho Cucamonga (91730) ***(P-23902)***
Inland Tek Inc.......F.......909 900-8457
7364 Oxford Pl Rancho Cucamonga (91730) ***(P-24773)***
Inland Truss Inc (PA).......D.......951 300-1758
275 W Rider St Perris (92571) ***(P-4413)***
Inland Valley Daily Bulletin, Monrovia *Also called Califrnia Nwspapers Ltd Partnr* ***(P-5790)***
Inland Valley Daily Bulletin, Rancho Cucamonga *Also called Califrnia Nwspapers Ltd Partnr* ***(P-5791)***
Inland Valley News Inc.......F.......909 949-3099
2009 Porter Field Way C Upland (91786) ***(P-5889)***
Inland Valley Publising Co.......F.......925 243-8000
2250 1st St Livermore (94550) ***(P-5890)***
Inland Valley Truss Inc.......F.......209 943-4710
150 N Sinclair Ave Stockton (95215) ***(P-4414)***
Inline Plastics Inc.......E.......909 923-1033
1950 S Baker Ave Ontario (91761) ***(P-10151)***
Inmage Systems Inc (HQ).......E.......408 200-3840
1065 La Avenida St Mountain View (94043) ***(P-24774)***
Inmotion, Sonoma *Also called Monica Bruce Designs Inc* ***(P-3908)***
Inneos LLC.......E.......925 226-0138
5700 Stoneridge Dr # 200 Pleasanton (94588) ***(P-22088)***
Innerspace Cases, North Hollywood *Also called Armored Group Inc* ***(P-4434)***
Innerstave LLC.......E.......707 996-8781
21660 8th St E Ste B Sonoma (95476) ***(P-4524)***
Innerstep BSE (PA).......F.......831 461-5600
4742 Scotts Valley Dr Scotts Valley (95066) ***(P-18507)***
Innespace Productions.......F.......530 241-2800
20172 Charlanne Dr Redding (96002) ***(P-21045)***
Inno Tech Machining Inc.......F.......858 565-4556
8276 Ronson Rd San Diego (92111) ***(P-16584)***
Innocor West LLC.......E.......909 307-3737
300-310 S Tippecanoe Ave San Bernardino (92408) ***(P-9628)***

ALPHABETIC

Employee Codes: A=Over 500 employees, B=251-500 C=101-250, D=51-100, E=20-50, F=10-19
2019 California Manfacturers Register
© Mergent Inc. 1-800-342-5647
1171

Innodisk Usa Corporation......E......510 770-9421
42996 Osgood Rd Fremont (94539) ***(P-18896)***
Innominata......F......858 592-9300
15222 Avenue Of Science A San Diego (92128) ***(P-8485)***
Innopack Usa Inc......F......714 637-4091
238 W Taft Ave Orange (92865) ***(P-7357)***
Innophase Inc......D......619 541-8280
6815 Flanders Dr Ste 150 San Diego (92121) ***(P-18897)***
Innotech Energy Inc......F......510 639-9197
1200 Business Center Dr San Leandro (94577) ***(P-21774)***
Innov8v, Irvine *Also called Innovative Tech & Engrg Inc* ***(P-15761)***
Innova Champion Discs, Ontario *Also called Champion Discs Incorporated* ***(P-23537)***
Innova Electronics Corporation......E......714 241-6800
17352 Von Karman Ave Irvine (92614) ***(P-20372)***
Innovacon Inc......D......858 805-8900
9975 Summers Ridge Rd San Diego (92121) ***(P-8486)***
Innovalight Inc......E......408 419-4400
965 W Maude Ave Sunnyvale (94085) ***(P-17704)***
Innovation Alley LLC......F......559 453-6974
5473 E Hedges Ave Fresno (93727) ***(P-12179)***
Innovative Biosciences Corp......E......760 603-0772
1849 Diamond St San Marcos (92078) ***(P-8769)***
Innovative Body Science, San Marcos *Also called Innovative Biosciences Corp* ***(P-8769)***
Innovative Casework Mfg Inc......E......714 890-9100
12261 Industry St Garden Grove (92841) ***(P-24128)***
Innovative Circuits Engrg, San Jose *Also called Circuit Connections* ***(P-18449)***
Innovative Combustion Tech (PA)......F......510 652-6000
5160 Fulton Dr Fairfield (94534) ***(P-12071)***
Innovative Control Systems Inc......E......610 881-8061
20992 Bake Pkwy Ste 106 Lake Forest (92630) ***(P-16055)***
Innovative Cosmetic Labs Inc......F......818 349-1121
9740 Cozycroft Ave Chatsworth (91311) ***(P-8770)***
Innovative Design and Sheet ME......F......951 222-2270
616 Mrlbrugh Ave Unit S-1 Riverside (92507) ***(P-12621)***
Innovative Designs & Mfg Inc......F......626 812-4422
1067 W 5th St Azusa (91702) ***(P-4831)***
Innovative Diversfd Tech Inc......E......949 455-1701
18062 Irvine Blvd Ste 304 Tustin (92780) ***(P-15559)***
Innovative Earth Products......F......888 588-5955
232 Avenida Fabricante San Clemente (92672) ***(P-23591)***
Innovative Emergency Equipment, Riverside *Also called Innovative Design and Sheet ME* ***(P-12621)***
Innovative Hearth Holdings LLC (PA)......A......714 549-7782
2701 S Harbor Blvd Santa Ana (92704) ***(P-12072)***
Innovative Hearth Products, Santa Ana *Also called IHP Operations LLC* ***(P-12068)***
Innovative Hearth Products IHP, Santa Ana *Also called Innovative Hearth Holdings LLC* ***(P-12072)***
Innovative Hearth Products LLC (PA)......E......615 925-3417
2701 S Harbor Blvd Santa Ana (92704) ***(P-17390)***
Innovative Hearth Products LLC......E......714 549-7782
2701 S Harbor Blvd Santa Ana (92704) ***(P-17391)***
Innovative Integration Inc......E......805 520-3300
741 Flynn Rd Camarillo (93012) ***(P-21604)***
Innovative Machining Inc......E......408 262-2270
845 Yosemite Way Milpitas (95035) ***(P-16585)***
Innovative Manufacturing Inc......F......714 524-5246
1366 N Hundley St Anaheim (92806) ***(P-14726)***
Innovative Metal Inds Inc......D......909 796-6200
1330 Riverview Dr San Bernardino (92408) ***(P-12980)***
Innovative Metal Products Inc......E......760 734-1010
2443 Cades Way Ste 200 Vista (92081) ***(P-13949)***
Innovative Micro Tech Inc......C......805 681-2807
75 Robin Hill Rd Goleta (93117) ***(P-18898)***
Innovative Molding (HQ)......D......707 238-9250
1200 Valley House Dr # 100 Rohnert Park (94928) ***(P-10152)***
Innovative Mounts, Anaheim *Also called Innovative Manufacturing Inc* ***(P-14726)***
Innovative Organics Inc......E......714 701-3900
4905 E Hunter Ave Anaheim (92807) ***(P-9012)***
Innovative Plastics Inc......F......714 891-8800
5502 Buckingham Dr Huntington Beach (92649) ***(P-9750)***
Innovative Products Co, Temecula *Also called IPC Industries Inc* ***(P-21233)***
Innovative R Advanced (PA)......F......949 273-8100
23101 Lake Center Dr # 100 Lake Forest (92630) ***(P-4864)***
Innovative R Advanced......E......949 273-8100
3401 Etiwanda Ave Mira Loma (91752) ***(P-4865)***
Innovative Rv Technologies......E......949 559-5372
205 Via Morada San Clemente (92673) ***(P-227)***
Innovative Skin Care, Burbank *Also called Science of Skincare LLC* ***(P-8837)***
Innovative Stamping Inc......E......310 537-6996
2068 E Gladwick St Compton (90220) ***(P-13225)***
Innovative Steel Structures, Modesto *Also called JR Daniels Commercial Bldrs* ***(P-12982)***
Innovative Structural GL Inc......E......559 561-7000
40220 Pierce Dr Three Rivers (93271) ***(P-10705)***
Innovative Systems, Compton *Also called Innovative Stamping Inc* ***(P-13225)***
Innovative Tech & Engrg Inc......F......949 955-2501
2691 Richter Ave Ste 124 Irvine (92606) ***(P-15761)***
Innovative Technology Inc......F......805 571-8384
1501 Cook Pl Santa Barbara (93117) ***(P-13604)***
Innovativetek Inc......E......909 981-3401
1271 W 9th St Upland (91786) ***(P-19982)***
Innovista Sensors Americas Inc (PA)......E......805 267-7176
2945 Townsgate Rd Ste 200 Westlake Village (91361) ***(P-19578)***
Innoviva Inc (PA)......F......650 238-9600
2000 Sierra Point Pkwy # 500 Brisbane (94005) ***(P-8220)***
Innovive LLC (PA)......E......858 309-6620
10019 Waples Ct San Diego (92121) ***(P-13833)***
Innovtive Rttional Molding Inc......F......559 673-4764
2300 W Pecan Ave Madera (93637) ***(P-10153)***
Innovyze Inc (HQ)......F......626 568-6868
605 E Huntington Dr # 205 Monrovia (91016) ***(P-24775)***
Innowi Inc......E......408 609-9404
3240 Scott Blvd Santa Clara (95054) ***(P-15430)***
Inogen Inc (PA)......C......805 562-0500
326 Bollay Dr Goleta (93117) ***(P-22480)***
Inovate Roofing Products, South Gate *Also called In-O-Vate Inc* ***(P-9410)***
Inovati, Santa Barbara *Also called Innovative Technology Inc* ***(P-13604)***
Inovio Pharmaceuticals Inc......E......267 440-4200
10480 Wateridge Cir San Diego (92121) ***(P-8561)***
Inp, Rancho Cordova *Also called Intercontinental N Mas* ***(P-24130)***
Inphenix Inc......E......925 606-8809
250 N Mines Rd Livermore (94551) ***(P-18899)***
Inphi Corporation (PA)......C......408 217-7300
2953 Bunker Hill Ln # 300 Santa Clara (95054) ***(P-18900)***
Inphi International Pte Ltd......E......805 719-2300
112 S Lakeview Canyon Rd Westlake Village (91362) ***(P-18901)***
Input/Output Technology Inc......E......661 257-1000
28415 Industry Dr Ste 520 Valencia (91355) ***(P-15762)***
Inscopix Inc......F......650 600-3886
2462 Embarcadero Way Palo Alto (94303) ***(P-22089)***
Inseat Solutions LLC......E......562 447-1780
1871 Wright Ave La Verne (91750) ***(P-17392)***
Inserts & Kits Inc......F......714 708-2888
1811 Carnegie Ave Santa Ana (92705) ***(P-16586)***
Inside Park......F......626 964-1800
2353 S Azusa Ave West Covina (91792) ***(P-23592)***
Inside Tennis Associates, Berkeley *Also called Buisness Leader Media* ***(P-6119)***
Insidesalescom Inc......D......385 207-7252
1269 Deep Creek Rd Livermore (94550) ***(P-24776)***
Insieme Networks LLC......F......408 424-1227
210 W Tasman Dr Bldg F San Jose (95134) ***(P-17957)***
Insight Editions LP (PA)......E......415 526-1370
800 A St Ste B San Rafael (94901) ***(P-6352)***
Insight Management Corporation (PA)......E......866 787-3588
1130 E Clark Ave Santa Maria (93455) ***(P-17904)***
Insight Mfg Services, Murphys *Also called Kaiser Enterprises Inc* ***(P-13892)***
Insight Solutions Inc......E......408 725-0213
13095 Paramount Ct Saratoga (95070) ***(P-24777)***
Insight System Exchange, Santa Ana *Also called Limpus Prints Inc* ***(P-7386)***
Insignia, Buena Park *Also called Blasted Wood Products Inc* ***(P-4032)***
Insignia SC Holdings LLC (HQ)......A......925 399-8900
1333 N Calif Blvd Ste 520 Walnut Creek (94596) ***(P-1429)***
Insilixa Inc......F......408 809-3000
1000 Hamlin Ct Sunnyvale (94089) ***(P-18902)***
Insite Vision Incorporated (HQ)......E......510 865-8800
965 Atlantic Ave Alameda (94501) ***(P-8221)***
Insomniac Games Inc (PA)......D......818 729-2400
2255 N Ontario St Ste 550 Burbank (91504) ***(P-23431)***
Inspired Properties LLC......E......818 430-9634
14320 Ventura Blvd 181 Sherman Oaks (91423) ***(P-6353)***
Inspur Systems Inc (HQ)......E......800 697-5893
47451 Fremont Blvd Fremont (94538) ***(P-15431)***
Instacure Healing Products......E......818 222-9600
235 N Moorpark Rd # 2022 Thousand Oaks (91358) ***(P-8222)***
Instagis Inc......F......415 527-6636
218 9th St San Francisco (94103) ***(P-24778)***
Instana Inc......E......415 237-3245
541 Jefferson Ave Ste 100 Redwood City (94063) ***(P-24779)***
Instant Algae, Campbell *Also called Reed Mariculture Inc* ***(P-1158)***
Instant Asphalt Inc......F......408 280-7733
365 Obata Ct Gilroy (95020) ***(P-9149)***
Instant Checkmate, San Diego *Also called Intelicare Direct Inc* ***(P-6892)***
Instant Imprints Franchising......E......858 642-4848
6615 Flanders Dr Ste B San Diego (92121) ***(P-6888)***
Instant Web LLC......C......562 658-2020
7300 Flores St Downey (90242) ***(P-6889)***
Instantfigure, Irvine *Also called Buy Insta Slim Inc* ***(P-3097)***
Instathreads LLC......F......661 470-7841
238 Lakeview Dr Palmdale (93551) ***(P-2953)***
Institute For Intl Studies, Stanford *Also called Leland Stanford Junior Univ* ***(P-6519)***
Institute of Electrical and El......D......714 821-8380
10662 Los Vaqueros Cir Los Alamitos (90720) ***(P-7203)***
Institutional Real Estate (PA)......E......925 933-4040
1475 N Broadway Ste 300 Walnut Creek (94596) ***(P-6504)***
Instrument & Valve Services Co......D......562 633-0179
6851 Walthall Way A Paramount (90723) ***(P-13769)***
Instrument & Valve Services Co......F......707 745-4664
531 Getty Ct Ste D Benicia (94510) ***(P-21605)***
Instrument Bearing Factory USA......E......818 989-5052
19360 Rinaldi St Northridge (91326) ***(P-13074)***
Instrument Design Eng Assoc I......E......714 525-3302
2923 Saturn St Ste F Brea (92821) ***(P-19579)***
Instrumentation Tech Systems......F......818 886-2034
19360 Business Center Dr Northridge (91324) ***(P-15763)***
Instyle Printing Inc......E......626 575-2725
2115 Central Ave South El Monte (91733) ***(P-3549)***
Insua Graphics Incorporated......E......818 767-7007
9121 Glenoaks Blvd Sun Valley (91352) ***(P-6890)***
Insulated Products, Rancho Dominguez *Also called Simple Container Solutions Inc* ***(P-5360)***
Insulated Products Corporation......E......323 838-0900
250 W Artesia Blvd Compton (90220) ***(P-5715)***
Insulfab Inc......D......805 482-2751
4725 Calle Alto Camarillo (93012) ***(P-11332)***
Insultech LLC (PA)......D......714 384-0506
3530 W Garry Ave Santa Ana (92704) ***(P-9263)***
Insurance Journal, San Diego *Also called Wells Publishing Inc* ***(P-6289)***

Mergent e-mail: customerrelations@mergent.com
1172
2019 California
Manufacturers Register
(P-0000) Products & Services Section entry number
(PA)=Parent Co (HQ)=Headquarters (DH)=Div Headquarters

Insync Computer Solutions, Laguna Hills *Also called In Sync Computer Solutions Inc* ***(P-24757)***

Inta Technologies Corporation ....E.......408 748-9955
2281 Calle De Luna Santa Clara (95054) ***(P-13432)***

Intake Screens Inc ....F.......916 665-2727
8417 River Rd Sacramento (95832) ***(P-13834)***

Intapp Inc (PA) ....C.......650 852-0400
200 Portage Ave Palo Alto (94306) ***(P-24780)***

Intec Video Systems Inc (PA) ....E.......949 859-3800
23301 Vista Grande Dr Laguna Hills (92653) ***(P-17817)***

Integenx Inc (HQ) ....D.......925 701-3400
5720 Stoneridge Dr # 300 Pleasanton (94588) ***(P-21477)***

Integer Holdings Corporation ....F.......619 498-9448
8830 Siempre Viva Rd # 100 San Diego (92154) ***(P-19296)***

Integra Lfscnces Holdings Corp ....E.......609 529-9748
5955 Pacific Center Blvd San Diego (92121) ***(P-22481)***

Integra Lifesciences, Carlsbad *Also called Seaspine Inc* ***(P-22808)***

Integra Tech Silicon Vly LLC (HQ) ....C.......408 618-8700
1635 Mccarthy Blvd Milpitas (95035) ***(P-18903)***

Integra Technologies Inc ....E.......310 606-0855
321 Coral Cir El Segundo (90245) ***(P-18904)***

Integra Technologies LLC ....D.......408 923-7300
2006 Martin Ave Santa Clara (95050) ***(P-18905)***

Integral Development Corp (PA) ....C.......650 424-4500
850 Hansen Way Palo Alto (94304) ***(P-24781)***

Integral Engineering, Palo Alto *Also called Integral Development Corp* ***(P-24781)***

Integral Engrg Fabrication Inc ....E.......626 369-0958
520 Hofgaarden St City of Industry (91744) ***(P-12180)***

Integral Products Inc ....E.......310 326-8889
24030 Frampton Ave Harbor City (90710) ***(P-9150)***

Integrated Business Network ....F.......818 879-0670
28310 Roadside Dr Ste 136 Agoura Hills (91301) ***(P-7358)***

Integrated Communications Inc ....E.......310 851-8066
1411 W 190th St Ste 110 Gardena (90248) ***(P-6891)***

Integrated Design Tools Inc (PA) ....F.......850 222-5939
1 W Mountain St Unit 3 Pasadena (91103) ***(P-23168)***

Integrated Device Tech Inc (PA) ....B.......408 284-8200
6024 Silver Creek Vly Rd San Jose (95138) ***(P-18906)***

Integrated Device Tech Inc ....B.......408 284-1433
6024 Silver Creek Vly San Jose (95138) ***(P-18907)***

Integrated Dna Tech Inc ....F.......858 410-6677
6828 Nncy Rdge Dr Ste 400 San Diego (92121) ***(P-8562)***

Integrated Energy Tech Inc ....C.......619 421-1151
9335 Airway Rd Ste 206 San Diego (92154) ***(P-15107)***

Integrated Food Service, Gardena *Also called Lets Do Lunch* ***(P-2584)***

Integrated Magnetics, Culver City *Also called Magnet Sales & Mfg Co Inc* ***(P-10820)***

Integrated Magnetics Inc ....E.......310 391-7213
11250 Playa Ct Culver City (90230) ***(P-17205)***

Integrated Marine Services Inc ....D.......619 429-0300
2320 Main St Chula Vista (91911) ***(P-20997)***

Integrated Marketing Group LLC ....F.......714 771-2401
528 W Briardale Ave Orange (92865) ***(P-2744)***

Integrated Materials Inc ....E.......408 964-7700
135 Nicholson Ln San Jose (95134) ***(P-18908)***

Integrated Mfg Solutions LLC ....E.......760 599-4300
2590 Pioneer Ave Ste C Vista (92081) ***(P-24129)***

Integrated Mfg Tech Inc (HQ) ....F.......408 934-5879
1477 N Milpitas Blvd Milpitas (95035) ***(P-13433)***

Integrated Mfg Tech Inc ....E.......510 366-8793
1477 N Milpitas Blvd Milpitas (95035) ***(P-16587)***

Integrated MGT Concepts Inc ....E.......805 778-1629
3355 Cochran St Ste 201 Simi Valley (93063) ***(P-24782)***

Integrated Microwave Corp ....D.......858 259-2600
11353 Sorrento Valley Rd San Diego (92121) ***(P-19580)***

Integrated Optical Svcs Corp ....E.......408 982-9510
3150 Molinaro St Santa Clara (95054) ***(P-8908)***

Integrated Polymer Inds Inc ....E.......949 788-1050
9741 Irvine Center Dr Irvine (92618) ***(P-9151)***

Integrated Sign Associates ....E.......619 579-2229
1160 Pioneer Way Ste M El Cajon (92020) ***(P-23903)***

Integrity Bio Inc ....E.......805 445-8422
820 Calle Plano Camarillo (93012) ***(P-8223)***

Integrity Municpl Systems LLC ....F.......858 486-1620
13135 Danielson St # 204 Poway (92064) ***(P-16056)***

Integrity Security Svcs Inc ....F.......949 756-0690
7585 Irvine Center Dr Irvine (92618) ***(P-19983)***

Integrity Sheet Metal Inc ....F.......909 608-0449
319 Mcarthur Way Ste 1 Upland (91786) ***(P-12622)***

Integrity Support Services Inc ....F.......415 898-0044
7110 Redwood Blvd Ste C Novato (94945) ***(P-9264)***

Integrity Technology Corp ....E.......270 812-8867
2505 Technology Dr Hayward (94545) ***(P-19581)***

Integrted Silicon Solution Inc ....E.......408 969-6600
1623 Buckeye Dr Milpitas (95035) ***(P-14971)***

Integrted Silicon Solution Inc (PA) ....D.......408 969-6600
1623 Buckeye Dr Milpitas (95035) ***(P-18909)***

Intel Americas Inc (HQ) ....E.......408 765-8080
2200 Mission College Blvd Santa Clara (95054) ***(P-18910)***

Intel Corporation ....D.......916 943-6809
1200 Creekside Dr Folsom (95630) ***(P-18911)***

Intel Corporation (PA) ....B.......408 765-8080
2200 Mission College Blvd Santa Clara (95054) ***(P-15764)***

Intel Corporation ....F.......408 765-8080
111 Theory Ste 100 Irvine (92617) ***(P-18912)***

Intel Corporation ....C.......408 425-8398
2300 Mission College Blvd Santa Clara (95054) ***(P-18913)***

Intel Corporation ....A.......408 544-7000
101 Innovation Dr San Jose (95134) ***(P-15765)***

INTEL Corporation ....E.......510 651-9841
44235 Nobel Dr Fremont (94538) ***(P-18914)***

Intel Corporation ....D.......916 356-8080
1900 Prairie City Rd Folsom (95630) ***(P-18915)***

Intel Federal LLC ....E.......302 644-3756
2200 Mission College Blvd Santa Clara (95054) ***(P-18916)***

INTEL International Limited (HQ) ....F.......408 765-8080
2200 Mission College Blvd Santa Clara (95054) ***(P-18917)***

Intel Network Systems Inc ....E.......408 765-8080
3600 Juliette Ln Santa Clara (95054) ***(P-18918)***

Intel Network Systems Inc ....F.......858 877-4652
12220 Scrps Summit Dr # 300 San Diego (92131) ***(P-15766)***

INTEL Puerto Rico Inc ....E.......408 765-8080
2200 Mission College Blvd Santa Clara (95054) ***(P-18919)***

Intelicare Direct Inc ....F.......702 765-0867
9596 Chesapeake Dr Ste A San Diego (92123) ***(P-6892)***

Intella Interventional Systems ....D.......650 269-1375
605 W California Ave Sunnyvale (94086) ***(P-22482)***

Intelligence Support Group Ltd ....E.......800 504-3341
7100 Monache Mtn Inyokern (93527) ***(P-19984)***

Intelligent Barcode Systems ....F.......626 576-8938
2190 Sherwood Rd San Marino (91108) ***(P-22217)***

Intelligent Blends LP ....E.......858 888-7937
5330 Eastgate Mall San Diego (92121) ***(P-1062)***

Intelligent Cmpt Solutions Inc (PA) ....E.......818 998-5805
8968 Fullbright Ave Chatsworth (91311) ***(P-21775)***

Intelligent Energy Inc ....E.......562 997-3600
1731 Tech Dr Ste 755 San Jose (95110) ***(P-11964)***

Intelligent Fixture ....D.......626 279-1300
3350 Gilman Rd El Monte (91732) ***(P-12181)***

Intelligent Peripherals ....F.......415 564-4366
1123 Judah St San Francisco (94122) ***(P-15767)***

Intelligent Photonics, San Francisco *Also called Invuity Inc* ***(P-22493)***

Intelligent Quartz Solutions, Fremont *Also called Imtec Acculine LLC* ***(P-14968)***

Intelligent Storage Solution ....C.......408 428-0105
2073 Otoole Ave San Jose (95131) ***(P-15560)***

Intelligent Technologies LLC ....C.......858 458-1500
9454 Waples St San Diego (92121) ***(P-17343)***

Intelligrated Systems Inc ....B.......510 263-2300
5903 Christie Ave Emeryville (94608) ***(P-14277)***

Intelligrated Systems Inc ....B.......916 772-6800
3721 Douglas Blvd Ste 345 Roseville (95661) ***(P-14278)***

Intellipower Inc ....D.......714 921-1580
1746 N Saint Thomas Cir Orange (92865) ***(P-19341)***

Intellitime Systems Corp ....F.......714 444-3020
1118 E 17th St Santa Ana (92701) ***(P-24783)***

Intelmail USA Inc ....F.......916 361-9300
9965 Horn Rd Ste D Sacramento (95827) ***(P-15906)***

Intense Cycles Inc ....E.......951 296-9596
42380 Rio Nedo Temecula (92590) ***(P-21118)***

Intense Lighting LLC ....D.......714 630-9877
3340 E La Palma Ave Anaheim (92806) ***(P-17618)***

Intepro America LP (PA) ....E.......714 953-2686
14662 Franklin Ave Ste E Tustin (92780) ***(P-21776)***

Inter City Manufacturing Inc ....E.......831 899-3636
507 Redwood Ave Seaside (93955) ***(P-16588)***

Inter Color Plus Inter ....E.......818 764-5034
13234 Sherman Way Ste 6 North Hollywood (91605) ***(P-7359)***

Inter Mountain Truss & Girder ....F.......209 847-9184
596 Armstrong Way Oakdale (95361) ***(P-4415)***

Inter Packing Inc ....E.......909 465-5555
12315 Colony Ave Chino (91710) ***(P-9866)***

Inter-City Printing Co Inc ....F.......510 451-4775
614 Madison St Oakland (94607) ***(P-6893)***

Interactive Entertainment Inc ....F.......714 460-2343
1800 E Saint Andrew Pl Santa Ana (92705) ***(P-23432)***

Interactive Solutions Inc (HQ) ....D.......510 214-9002
283 4th St Ste 301 Oakland (94607) ***(P-24784)***

Intercept Pharmaceuticals Inc ....F.......646 747-1005
4760 Eastgate Mall San Diego (92121) ***(P-8224)***

Intercity Centerless Grinding ....F.......714 546-5644
11546 Coley River Cir Fountain Valley (92708) ***(P-16589)***

Intercom Energy Inc ....F.......619 863-9644
1330 Orange Ave 300-30 Coronado (92118) ***(P-17100)***

Interconnect Solutions, Santa Ana *Also called Mx Electronics Mfg Inc* ***(P-11666)***

Interconnect Systems Inc (HQ) ....D.......805 482-2870
741 Flynn Rd Camarillo (93012) ***(P-18920)***

Intercontinental Cof Trdg LLC ....F.......619 338-8335
110 W A St Ste 110 # 110 San Diego (92101) ***(P-2354)***

Intercontinental Coffee Trdg, San Diego *Also called Intercontinental Cof Trdg LLC* ***(P-2354)***

Intercontinental N Mas ....E.......916 631-1674
11492 Refinement Rd Rancho Cordova (95742) ***(P-24130)***

Interctive Dsplay Slutions Inc ....F.......949 727-9493
490 Wald Irvine (92618) ***(P-19582)***

Interdigital Inc ....E.......858 210-4800
9276 Scranton Rd Ste 300 San Diego (92121) ***(P-18132)***

Interface Associates Inc (HQ) ....C.......949 448-7056
27721 La Paz Rd Laguna Niguel (92677) ***(P-22483)***

Interface Catheter Solutions, Laguna Niguel *Also called Interface Associates Inc* ***(P-22483)***

Interface Masters Tech Inc ....E.......408 441-9341
150 E Brokaw Rd San Jose (95112) ***(P-19583)***

Intergen Inc ....F.......408 245-2737
1145 Tasman Dr Sunnyvale (94089) ***(P-19985)***

Interglobal Waste Management ....D.......805 388-1588
820 Calle Plano Camarillo (93012) ***(P-21977)***

Interhealth Nutraceuticals Inc ....E.......800 783-4636
5451 Industrial Way Benicia (94510) ***(P-7949)***

Interior Corner Usa Inc ....F.......626 452-8833
2714 Stingle Ave Rosemead (91770) ***(P-5148)***

Interior Wood Design Inc ....F.......530 888-7707
334 Sacramento St Ste 1 Auburn (95603) ***(P-4706)***

Employee Codes: A=Over 500 employees, B=251-500
C=101-250, D=51-100, E=20-50, F=10-19
2019 California
Manfacturers Register
© Mergent Inc. 1-800-342-5647
1173

Company		

Interior Wood of San Diego .....E.....619 295-6469
1215 W Nutmeg St San Diego (92101) *(P-4950)*
Interlink Inc .....D.....714 905-7700
3845 E Coronado St Anaheim (92807) *(P-6894)*
Interlock Industries Inc .....D.....530 668-5690
1326 Paddock Pl Woodland (95776) *(P-12623)*
Interlog Construction, Anaheim *Also called Interlog Corporation (P-19584)*
Interlog Corporation .....E.....714 529-7808
1295 W Knollwood Cir Anaheim (92801) *(P-19584)*
Intermag Inc .....C.....916 568-6744
1650 Santa Ana Ave Sacramento (95838) *(P-19866)*
Intermec Technologies Corp .....F.....925 738-1100
6960 Koll Center Pkwy Pleasanton (94566) *(P-15768)*
Intermed Video Tech Inc .....F.....203 270-9100
38 Waterworks Way Irvine (92618) *(P-17818)*
Intermetro Industries Corp .....E.....909 987-4731
9420 Santa Anita Ave Rancho Cucamonga (91730) *(P-13835)*
Intermolecular Inc (PA) .....C.....408 582-5700
3011 N 1st St San Jose (95134) *(P-18921)*
Intermune Inc (HQ) .....C.....415 466-4383
1 Dna Way South San Francisco (94080) *(P-8225)*
Internacional De Elevadores SA .....E.....619 955-6180
9475 Nicola Tesla Ct San Diego (92154) *(P-14252)*
International Abrasive Mfg Co .....E.....714 779-9970
1221 N Lakeview Ave Anaheim (92807) *(P-8771)*
International Academy of Fin (PA) .....E.....818 361-7724
13177 Foothill Blvd Sylmar (91342) *(P-9013)*
International Apparel, San Diego *Also called Pk Industries Inc (P-10530)*
International Association of S .....F.....916 922-1133
2840 El Centro Rd Ste 110 Sacramento (95833) *(P-12624)*
International Baggyz, Los Angeles *Also called Krissy Op Shins USA Inc (P-3170)*
International Beauty Pdts LLC (PA) .....F.....818 999-1222
8200 Remmet Ave Canoga Park (91304) *(P-8772)*
International Bus Mchs Corp .....A.....310 412-8699
6033 W Century Blvd # 610 Los Angeles (90045) *(P-15432)*
International Co-Packing Co, Fresno *Also called Lidestri Foods Inc (P-820)*
International Coatings Co Inc (PA) .....E.....562 926-1010
13929 166th St Cerritos (90703) *(P-9152)*
International Daily News Inc (PA) .....E.....323 265-1317
870 Monterey Pass Rd Monterey Park (91754) *(P-5891)*
International Decoratives Co .....E.....760 749-2682
27220 N Lake Wohlford Rd Valley Center (92082) *(P-24131)*
International Disc Mfr Inc .....E.....714 210-1780
4906 W 1st St Santa Ana (92703) *(P-17905)*
International E-Z Up Inc (PA) .....D.....800 457-4233
1900 2nd St Norco (92860) *(P-3791)*
International Electronic Desig (PA) .....F.....714 662-1018
2630 S Shannon St Santa Ana (92704) *(P-19585)*
International Forming Tech Inc .....E.....805 278-8060
2331 Sturgis Rd Oxnard (93030) *(P-14440)*
International Group Inc .....F.....510 232-8704
102 Cutting Blvd Richmond (94804) *(P-9335)*
International Group Inc .....D.....510 232-8704
102 Cutting Blvd Richmond (94804) *(P-9336)*
International Immunology Corp .....E.....951 677-5629
25549 Adams Ave Murrieta (92562) *(P-8487)*
International Inboard Mar Inc .....E.....209 384-2566
2556 W 16th St Merced (95348) *(P-21046)*
International Iron Products, San Diego *Also called Price Industries Inc (P-11411)*
International Last Mfg Co .....E.....818 767-2045
5060 Densmore Ave Encino (91436) *(P-10154)*
International Mercantile .....F.....760 438-2205
6102 Avenida Encinas Carlsbad (92011) *(P-20373)*
International Mfg Tech Inc (HQ) .....E.....619 544-7741
2798 Harbor Dr San Diego (92113) *(P-11400)*
International Molders, Van Nuys *Also called Advance Latex Products Inc (P-3532)*
International Paper, Ontario *Also called New-Indy Containerboard LLC (P-5315)*
International Paper, Visalia *Also called Graphic Packaging Intl LLC (P-5285)*
International Paper Company .....E.....510 490-5887
42305 Albrae St Fremont (94538) *(P-5288)*
International Paper Company .....C.....714 776-6060
601 E Ball Rd Anaheim (92805) *(P-5425)*
International Paper Company .....C.....559 651-1416
900 N Plaza Dr Visalia (93291) *(P-5289)*
International Paper Company .....D.....559 592-7279
1111 N Anderson Rd Exeter (93221) *(P-5290)*
International Paper Company .....C.....209 526-4700
660 Mariposa Rd Modesto (95354) *(P-5351)*
International Paper Company .....D.....916 685-9000
10268 Waterman Rd Elk Grove (95624) *(P-5291)*
International Paper Company .....C.....714 736-0296
6211 Descanso Ave Buena Park (90620) *(P-5292)*
International Paper Company .....C.....323 946-6100
11211 Greenstone Ave Santa Fe Springs (90670) *(P-5426)*
International Paper Company .....D.....408 846-2060
6791 Alexander St Gilroy (95020) *(P-5293)*
International Paper Company .....E.....805 933-4347
2000 Pleasant Valley Rd Camarillo (93010) *(P-5294)*
International Paper Company .....F.....310 639-2310
19615 S Susana Rd Compton (90221) *(P-5295)*
International Paper Company .....F.....559 875-3311
1000 Muscat Ave Sanger (93657) *(P-5296)*
International Paper Company .....F.....562 404-1856
14150 Artesia Blvd Cerritos (90703) *(P-5297)*
International Paper Company .....F.....714 889-4900
11205 Knott Ave Ste A Cypress (90630) *(P-5298)*
International Paper Company .....F.....562 483-6680
12851 Alondra Blvd Norwalk (90650) *(P-5299)*
International Paper Company .....F.....831 755-2100
1345 Harkins Rd Salinas (93901) *(P-5300)*

International Paper Company .....D.....408 847-6400
6400 Jamieson Way Gilroy (95020) *(P-5301)*
International Paper Company .....E.....916 371-4634
1714 Cebrian St West Sacramento (95691) *(P-5302)*
International Paper Company .....C.....562 692-9465
9211 Norwalk Blvd Santa Fe Springs (90670) *(P-5303)*
International Paper Company .....D.....909 605-2540
3551 E Francis St Ontario (91761) *(P-5352)*
International Paper Company .....C.....310 549-5525
1350 E 223rd St Carson (90745) *(P-5304)*
International Paper Company .....D.....209 931-9005
3550 Bozzano Rd Stockton (95215) *(P-5427)*
International Paper Company .....D.....562 868-2246
6485 Descanso Ave Buena Park (90620) *(P-5305)*
International Paper Company .....D.....323 724-5010
5110 E Jurupa Ave Ontario (91761) *(P-5428)*
International Paper Company .....A.....510 614-1600
1950 Marina Blvd San Leandro (94577) *(P-5429)*
International Petroleum Produc .....F.....925 556-5530
7600 Dublin Blvd Ste 240 Dublin (94568) *(P-9438)*
International Precision Inc .....E.....818 882-3933
9526 Vassar Ave Chatsworth (91311) *(P-16590)*
International Printing & Typsg .....F.....818 787-6804
14535 Hamlin St Van Nuys (91411) *(P-6895)*
International Processing Corp (HQ) .....E.....310 458-1574
233 Wilshire Blvd Ste 310 Santa Monica (90401) *(P-1138)*
International Rectifier Corp (PA) .....E.....949 453-1008
17885 Von Karman Ave # 100 Irvine (92614) *(P-18922)*
International Rectifier Hirel .....C.....408 944-0239
2520 Junction Ave San Jose (95134) *(P-18923)*
International RES Dev Corp Nev (PA) .....F.....858 488-9900
5212 Chelsea St La Jolla (92037) *(P-19835)*
International Rite-Way Pdts, Ontario *Also called AMD International Tech LLC (P-12475)*
International Rubber Pdts Inc (PA) .....D.....909 947-1244
1035 Calle Amanecer San Clemente (92673) *(P-9629)*
International Sales Inc .....E.....760 722-1455
3210 Production Ave B Oceanside (92058) *(P-23593)*
International Seal Company, Santa Ana *Also called Freudenberg-Nok General Partnr (P-9529)*
International Seals, Santa Ana *Also called Hernandez Zeferino (P-9148)*
International Sensor Tech Inc .....E.....949 452-9000
3 Whatney Ste 100 Irvine (92618) *(P-22218)*
International Stem Cell Corp (PA) .....E.....760 940-6383
5950 Priestly Dr Carlsbad (92008) *(P-8226)*
International Technidyne Corp (HQ) .....C.....858 263-2300
6260 Sequence Dr San Diego (92121) *(P-22484)*
International Technologies .....F.....818 382-2087
15445 Ventura Blvd # 780 Sherman Oaks (91403) *(P-15769)*
International Tents & Supplies .....F.....818 599-6258
1720 1st St San Fernando (91340) *(P-3792)*
International Tranducer Corp .....C.....805 683-2575
869 Ward Dr Santa Barbara (93111) *(P-21777)*
International Trend - 3 Corp .....E.....562 360-5185
7103 Marcelle St Paramount (90723) *(P-3164)*
International Vitamin Corp .....C.....951 361-1120
11010 Hopkins St Ste B Mira Loma (91752) *(P-8227)*
International Vitamin Corp (PA) .....B.....949 664-5500
1 Park Plz Ste 800 Irvine (92614) *(P-8228)*
International West Inc .....D.....714 632-9190
1025 N Armando St Anaheim (92806) *(P-12625)*
International Wind Inc (PA) .....E.....562 240-3963
137 N Joy St Corona (92879) *(P-20664)*
International Wood Products, San Diego *Also called Jeld-Wen Inc (P-4172)*
Internationally Delicious Inc .....E.....925 426-6155
174 Lawrence Dr Ste J Livermore (94551) *(P-1397)*
Internet Industry Publishing .....F.....415 733-5400
315 Pacific Ave San Francisco (94111) *(P-6197)*
Internet Machines Corporation (PA) .....D.....818 575-2100
30501 Agoura Rd Ste 203 Agoura Hills (91301) *(P-15770)*
Internet Science Education Prj .....F.....415 806-3156
805 Chestnut St San Francisco (94133) *(P-21177)*
Internet Strategy Inc .....F.....858 673-6022
10875 Rancho Bernardo Rd # 100 San Diego (92127) *(P-24785)*
Internet Systems Cnsortium Inc (PA) .....F.....650 423-1300
950 Charter St Redwood City (94063) *(P-24786)*
Interniche Technologies Inc (PA) .....F.....408 540-1160
7065 Elmsdale Dr San Jose (95120) *(P-24787)*
Interntional Color Posters Inc .....E.....949 768-1005
8081 Orangethorpe Ave Buena Park (90621) *(P-7360)*
Interntional Photo Plates Corp .....E.....805 496-5031
2641 Townsgate Rd Ste 100 Westlake Village (91361) *(P-13434)*
Interntional Semicdtr Tech Inc .....E.....650 941-7096
3099 Alexis Dr Palo Alto (94304) *(P-18924)*
Interntional Thermal Instr Inc .....F.....858 755-4436
4511 Sun Valley Rd Del Mar (92014) *(P-21978)*
Interntnl Assmbly Specialists, Aliso Viejo *Also called Shugart Corporation (P-15483)*
Interntnl Cnnctors Cable Corp .....C.....888 275-4422
2100 E Valencia Dr Ste D Fullerton (92831) *(P-17958)*
Interntnl Desserts Delicacies .....F.....818 549-0056
743 Milford St Glendale (91203) *(P-1365)*
Interntnl Hmeopathic Mfg Dist .....F.....818 884-8040
7108 De Soto Ave Ste 105 Canoga Park (91303) *(P-8229)*
Interntnl Indian Traty Cuncil .....F.....415 641-4482
2940 16th St Ste 305 San Francisco (94103) *(P-23594)*
Interntnl Mdction Systems Ltd .....F.....626 459-5586
10642 El Poche St South El Monte (91733) *(P-7950)*
Interntnl Mdction Systems Ltd .....A.....626 442-6757
1886 Santa Anita Ave South El Monte (91733) *(P-8230)*
Interntnl Plymr Solutions Inc .....E.....949 458-3731
5 Studebaker Irvine (92618) *(P-13720)*

Mergent e-mail: customerrelations@mergent.com
1174
2019 California
Manufacturers Register
(P-0000) Products & Services Section entry number
(PA)=Parent Co (HQ)=Headquarters (DH)=Div Headquarters

Interntnal Pwr DC Pwr Sups Inc......E......805 981-1188
900 Graves Ave Oxnard (93030) *(P-19586)*
Interntnal Veterinary Sciences, Anaheim *Also called Animal Nutrition Inds Inc (P-7922)*
Interntnal Virtual PDT MGT Inc......F......818 812-9500
8957 De Soto Ave Canoga Park (91304) *(P-17959)*
Interntonal Metallurgical Svcs......F......310 645-7300
6371 Arizona Cir Los Angeles (90045) *(P-11815)*
Interntonal Thermoproducts Div, Santee *Also called Ds Fibertech Corp (P-15258)*
Interocean Industries Inc......E......858 292-0808
3738 Ruffin Rd San Diego (92123) *(P-21308)*
Interocean Systems, San Diego *Also called Interocean Industries Inc (P-21308)*
Interocean Systems LLC......E......858 565-8400
3738 Ruffin Rd San Diego (92123) *(P-21309)*
Interocean Systems, Inc., San Diego *Also called Interocean Systems LLC (P-21309)*
Interorbital Systems......F......661 824-1662
1394 Barnes St Bldg 7 Mojave (93501) *(P-11743)*
Interplastic, Ontario *Also called North American Composites Co (P-7859)*
Interplastic Corporation......E......323 757-1801
12335 S Van Ness Ave Hawthorne (90250) *(P-7843)*
Interplastic Corporation......F......209 932-0396
611 Gilmore Ave Ste C Stockton (95203) *(P-7844)*
Interplex Nascal Inc (HQ)......D......714 505-2900
15777 Gateway Cir Tustin (92780) *(P-13226)*
Interpore Cross Intl Inc (HQ)......D......949 453-3200
181 Technology Dr Irvine (92618) *(P-22754)*
Interpress Technologies Inc (HQ)......E......916 929-9771
1120 Del Paso Rd Sacramento (95834) *(P-5353)*
Interscan Corporation......E......805 823-8301
4590 Ish Dr Ste 110 Simi Valley (93063) *(P-21689)*
Intersect Ent Inc (PA)......B......650 641-2100
1555 Adams Dr Menlo Park (94025) *(P-22485)*
Intershop Communications Inc......E......415 844-1500
461 2nd St Apt 151 San Francisco (94107) *(P-24788)*
Intersil Design Center, San Diego *Also called Renesas Electronics Amer Inc (P-19123)*
Intersil Quellan, Milpitas *Also called Quellan Inc (P-19111)*
Intersil Techwell, Burlingame *Also called Renesas Electronics Amer Inc (P-19122)*
Interson Corp......E......925 462-4948
7150 Koll Center Pkwy Pleasanton (94566) *(P-22991)*
Interspace Battery Inc (PA)......F......626 813-1234
2009 W San Bernardino Rd West Covina (91790) *(P-11631)*
Interstate Cabinet Inc......E......951 736-0777
1631 Pomona Rd Ste B Corona (92880) *(P-24132)*
Interstate Carports Corp......F......951 654-1750
1280 S Buena Vista St A San Jacinto (92583) *(P-12935)*
Interstate Design Industry, Corona *Also called Interstate Cabinet Inc (P-24132)*
Interstate Electronics Corp (HQ)......B......714 758-0500
602 E Vermont Ave Anaheim (92805) *(P-21778)*
Interstate Electronics Corp......E......714 758-3395
604 E Vermont Ave Anaheim (92805) *(P-18133)*
Interstate Meat Co Inc......F......323 838-9400
6114 Scott Way Commerce (90040) *(P-14860)*
Interstate Rebar Inc......F......805 643-6892
2457 N Ventura Ave Ste L Ventura (93001) *(P-11401)*
Interstate Steel Center Co......E......323 583-0855
7001 S Alameda St Los Angeles (90001) *(P-11618)*
Intertex Inc......E......626 385-3300
550 S Ayon Ave Azusa (91702) *(P-15161)*
Intertool Innovative Tooling, San Leandro *Also called Leitch & Co Inc (P-11901)*
Intertrade Aviation Corp......E......714 895-3335
5722 Buckingham Dr Huntington Beach (92649) *(P-20849)*
Interventional Spine Inc......F......949 472-0006
13844 Alton Pkwy Ste 131 Irvine (92618) *(P-22486)*
Interworking Labs Inc......F......831 460-7010
230 Mount Hermon Rd # 208 Scotts Valley (95066) *(P-24789)*
Intest Corporation......E......408 678-9123
47777 Warm Springs Blvd Fremont (94539) *(P-18925)*
Intest Silicon Valley Corp......E......408 678-9123
47777 Warm Springs Blvd Fremont (94539) *(P-18926)*
Intevac Inc (PA)......D......408 986-9888
3560 Bassett St Santa Clara (95054) *(P-14972)*
Intevac Inc......E......408 986-9888
3560 Bassett St Santa Clara (95054) *(P-14973)*
Intevac Photonics Inc (HQ)......F......408 986-9888
3560 Bassett St Santa Clara (95054) *(P-22090)*
Intevac Photonics Inc......E......760 476-0339
5909 Sea Lion Pl Ste A Carlsbad (92010) *(P-22091)*
Intevac Vision Systems, Carlsbad *Also called Intevac Photonics Inc (P-22091)*
Intex Forms Inc......E......650 654-7855
1333 Old County Rd Belmont (94002) *(P-10649)*
Intimate Grooming Escenusals......F......310 230-4544
15332 Antioch St 418 Pacific Palisades (90272) *(P-7951)*
Intimo Industry, Vernon *Also called Pjy Inc (P-2758)*
Intouch Health, Goleta *Also called Intouch Technologies Inc (P-24790)*
Intouch Technologies Inc (PA)......B......805 562-8686
7402 Hollister Ave Goleta (93117) *(P-24790)*
Intraop Medical Services, Sunnyvale *Also called Mc Liquidation Inc (P-23007)*
Intri-Plex Technologies Inc (HQ)......C......805 683-3414
751 S Kellogg Ave Goleta (93117) *(P-13227)*
Intro Designs, Anaheim *Also called Moreno Industries Inc (P-20405)*
Intubrite LLC......F......760 727-1900
2460 Coral St Vista (92081) *(P-22487)*
Intuit Inc......E......858 215-8726
7535 Torrey Santa Fe Rd San Diego (92129) *(P-24791)*
Intuit Inc (PA)......D......650 944-6000
2700 Coast Ave Mountain View (94043) *(P-24792)*
Intuit Inc......C......650 944-6000
2700 Coast Ave Bldg 7 Mountain View (94043) *(P-24793)*
Intuit Inc......F......650 944-6000
2650 Casey Ave Mountain View (94043) *(P-24794)*
Intuit Inc......C......650 944-6000
2535 Garcia Ave Mountain View (94043) *(P-24795)*
Intuit Inc......C......650 944-2840
141 Corona Way Portola Valley (94028) *(P-24796)*
Intuit Inc......C......650 944-6000
180 Jefferson Dr Menlo Park (94025) *(P-24797)*
Intuit Inc......B......858 215-8000
7545 Torrey Santa Fe Rd San Diego (92129) *(P-24798)*
Intuitive Srgcal Oprations Inc......E......408 523-2100
1266 Kifer Rd Sunnyvale (94086) *(P-22488)*
Intuitive Surgical Inc......E......408 523-7314
1250 Kifer Rd Sunnyvale (94086) *(P-22489)*
Intuitive Surgical Inc (PA)......C......408 523-2100
1020 Kifer Rd Sunnyvale (94086) *(P-22490)*
Intuity Medical Inc......D......408 530-1700
3500 W Warren Ave Fremont (94538) *(P-22491)*
Invax Technologies, Sunnyvale *Also called Gulshan International Corp (P-18866)*
Invecas Inc......E......408 758-5636
2901 Tasman Dr Ste 111 Santa Clara (95054) *(P-18927)*
Invelop Inc......E......818 772-2887
9711 Mason Ave Chatsworth (91311) *(P-14071)*
Invenio Imaging Inc......F......408 753-9147
2310 Walsh Ave Santa Clara (95051) *(P-22492)*
Invenios LLC......D......805 962-3333
320 N Nopal St Santa Barbara (93103) *(P-10706)*
Invenlux Corporation......E......626 277-4163
168 Mason Way Ste B5 City of Industry (91746) *(P-18928)*
Invensas Corporation......E......408 324-5100
3025 Orchard Pkwy San Jose (95134) *(P-18929)*
Invensense Inc (HQ)......C......408 501-2200
1745 Tech Dr Ste 200 San Jose (95110) *(P-21310)*
Inventive Resources Inc......F......209 545-1663
5038 Salida Blvd Salida (95368) *(P-12626)*
Inverse Solutions Inc......E......925 931-9500
3922 Valley Ave Ste A Pleasanton (94566) *(P-16591)*
Investment Enterprises Inc (PA)......E......818 464-3800
8230 Haskell Ave Ste 8240 Van Nuys (91406) *(P-7361)*
Investment Land Appraisers......F......310 819-8831
333 E 157th St Gardena (90248) *(P-7602)*
Investors Business Daily Inc (HQ)......C......310 448-6000
12655 Beatrice St Los Angeles (90066) *(P-5892)*
Invia Robotics Inc (PA)......F......818 597-1680
5701 Lindero Canyon Rd 3-100 Westlake Village (91362) *(P-15334)*
Invisalign, San Jose *Also called Align Technology Inc (P-22854)*
Invoice2go Inc (PA)......E......650 300-5180
2317 Broadway St Fl 2 Redwood City (94063) *(P-24799)*
Invotech Systems Inc......F......818 461-9800
20951 Burbank Blvd Ste B Woodland Hills (91367) *(P-24800)*
Invuity Inc......C......415 665-2100
444 De Haro St Ste 100 San Francisco (94107) *(P-22493)*
Inwesco Incorporated (PA)......D......626 334-7115
746 N Coney Ave Azusa (91702) *(P-11446)*
INX Digital Intl, San Leandro *Also called INX International Ink Co (P-9203)*
INX International Ink Co......F......510 895-8001
2125 Williams St San Leandro (94577) *(P-9203)*
INX International Ink Co......F......562 404-5664
13821 Marquardt Ave Santa Fe Springs (90670) *(P-9204)*
INX International Ink Co......F......707 693-2990
1000 Business Park Dr Dixon (95620) *(P-9205)*
INX Prints Inc......D......949 660-9190
1802 Kettering Irvine (92614) *(P-2903)*
Inyo Register, The, Bishop *Also called Horizon Publications Inc (P-5883)*
Iog Products LLC......F......818 350-5070
1025 N Brand Blvd Ste 301 Glendale (91202) *(P-18930)*
Iogyn Inc......F......408 996-2517
150 Baytech Dr San Jose (95134) *(P-22992)*
Iomic Inc......F......714 564-1600
10 Hughes Ste 103 Irvine (92618) *(P-9630)*
Ionetix Corporation (PA)......E......415 944-1440
1 Ferry Building Ste 255 San Francisco (94111) *(P-19986)*
Ionis Pharmaceuticals Inc......E......760 603-3567
2282 Faraday Ave Carlsbad (92008) *(P-8231)*
Ionis Pharmaceuticals Inc (PA)......B......760 931-9200
2855 Gazelle Ct Carlsbad (92010) *(P-8232)*
Ios Optics, Santa Clara *Also called Integrated Optical Svcs Corp (P-8908)*
Iosafe Inc......F......888 984-6723
10600 Industrial Ave # 120 Roseville (95678) *(P-15561)*
IOu International Inc......E......323 846-0056
2624 Geraldine St Los Angeles (90011) *(P-2966)*
Iovance Biotherapeutics Inc (PA)......E......650 260-7120
999 Skyway Rd Ste 150 San Carlos (94070) *(P-8233)*
Iowa Approach Inc......F......650 422-3633
3715 Haven Ave Ste 110 Menlo Park (94025) *(P-22494)*
Ipac, Dublin *Also called International Petroleum Produc (P-9438)*
Ipac Inc......F......925 556-5530
7600 Dublin Blvd Ste 240 Dublin (94568) *(P-9439)*
Iparis LLC......F......866 293-2872
10120 Wexted Way Elk Grove (95757) *(P-15433)*
Ipart Automotive, Fontana *Also called Iparts Inc (P-10155)*
Iparts Inc......F......909 587-6059
14975 Hilton Dr Fontana (92336) *(P-10155)*
IPC Cal Flex Inc......E......714 952-0373
13337 South St 307 Cerritos (90703) *(P-18508)*
IPC Industries Inc (PA)......F......951 695-2720
27230 Madison Ave Ste C2 Temecula (92590) *(P-21233)*
Ipco Printing, Martinez *Also called Independent Printing Co Inc (P-6879)*
Ipex USA LLC......F......209 368-7131
2395 Maggio Cir Lodi (95240) *(P-9781)*

ALPHABETIC

Employee Codes: A=Over 500 employees, B=251-500
C=101-250, D=51-100, E=20-50, F=10-19
2019 California
Manfacturers Register
© Mergent Inc. 1-800-342-5647
1175

Ipitek Group Inc ....C....760 438-8362
2330 Faraday Ave Carlsbad (92008) *(P-18134)*
Ipolipo Inc ....D....408 916-5290
440 N Wolfe Rd Sunnyvale (94085) *(P-24801)*
Ipolymer, Irvine *Also called Interntnl Plymr Solutions Inc (P-13720)*
Ipp Plastics Products Inc ....F....626 357-1178
4610 Littlejohn St Baldwin Park (91706) *(P-7845)*
Ipressroom Inc ....E....310 499-0544
13428 Maxella Ave Ste 222 Marina Del Rey (90292) *(P-24802)*
Ips Corporation (HQ) ....C....310 898-3300
455 W Victoria St Compton (90220) *(P-9153)*
Ips Corporation ....D....310 516-7013
17110 S Main St Gardena (90248) *(P-9154)*
Ips Industries Inc ....D....562 623-2555
12641 166th St Cerritos (90703) *(P-10156)*
Ips Printing Inc ....E....916 442-8961
2020 K St Sacramento (95811) *(P-6896)*
Iq Textile Ind Inc ....F....213 745-2290
3003 S Hill St Los Angeles (90007) *(P-3001)*
Iq-Analog Corporation ....E....858 200-0388
12348 High Bluff Dr # 110 San Diego (92130) *(P-18931)*
Iqair North America Inc ....E....877 715-4247
14351 Firestone Blvd La Mirada (90638) *(P-15162)*
Iqinvision Inc ....D....949 369-8100
27127 Calle Arroyo # 1920 San Juan Capistrano (92675) *(P-23169)*
Ir Hunter, Auburn *Also called IRD Acquisitions LLC (P-23102)*
Ira Gold Group LLC ....F....800 984-6008
9107 Wilshire Blvd # 450 Beverly Hills (90210) *(P-11546)*
Ircamera LLC ....E....805 965-9650
30 S Calle Cesar Chavez Santa Barbara (93103) *(P-22092)*
IRD, La Jolla *Also called International RES Dev Corp Nev (P-19835)*
IRD Acquisitions LLC ....F....530 210-2966
12810 Earhart Ave Auburn (95602) *(P-23102)*
Irene Kasmer Inc ....F....310 553-8986
315 S Bedford Dr Beverly Hills (90212) *(P-3314)*
Irhythm Technologies Inc (PA) ....E....415 632-5700
650 Townsend St Ste 500 San Francisco (94103) *(P-22993)*
Iri, Salida *Also called Inventive Resources Inc (P-12626)*
Iridex, Mountain View *Also called Iris Medical Instruments Inc (P-22994)*
Iridex Corporation (PA) ....C....650 940-4700
1212 Terra Bella Ave Mountain View (94043) *(P-22495)*
Iris Group Inc ....C....760 431-1103
1675 Faraday Ave Carlsbad (92008) *(P-7362)*
Iris Medical Instruments Inc ....C....650 940-4700
1212 Terra Bella Ave Mountain View (94043) *(P-22994)*
Irislogic Inc ....E....408 727-4940
2336 Walsh Ave Ste D Santa Clara (95051) *(P-24803)*
Irisys LLC ....E....858 623-1520
6828 Nncy Rdge Dr Ste 100 San Diego (92121) *(P-8234)*
Irl-Mex Manufacturing Company ....F....818 246-7211
1436 Flower St Glendale (91201) *(P-13028)*
IRM, Madera *Also called Innovtive Rttional Molding Inc (P-10153)*
Iron and Resin, Ventura *Also called Streamline Dsign Slkscreen Inc (P-7500)*
Iron Beds of America, Los Angeles *Also called Wesley Allen Inc (P-4848)*
Iron Dog Fabrication Inc ....F....707 579-7831
3450 Regional Pkwy Ste E Santa Rosa (95403) *(P-12182)*
Iron Grip Barbell Company Inc ....D....714 850-6900
4012 W Garry Ave Santa Ana (92704) *(P-23595)*
Iron Master ....F....818 361-4060
759 Arroyo St Ste D San Fernando (91340) *(P-12862)*
Iron Shield Inc ....F....626 287-4568
5926 Agnes Ave Temple City (91780) *(P-12863)*
Iron Systems Inc ....D....408 943-8000
980 Mission Ct Fremont (94539) *(P-15771)*
Iron Works & Custom Racks ....F....323 581-2222
15337 Illinois Ave Paramount (90723) *(P-25412)*
Iron Works Enterprises Inc ....E....209 572-7450
801 S 7th St Modesto (95351) *(P-20504)*
Ironclad Tool and Machine Inc ....F....661 833-9990
120 Old Yard Dr Bakersfield (93307) *(P-16592)*
Ironhead Studios Inc ....F....818 901-7561
7616 Ventura Canyon Ave Van Nuys (91402) *(P-3660)*
Ironies LLC ....E....510 644-2100
2222 5th St Berkeley (94710) *(P-4951)*
Ironman Magazine ....E....805 385-3500
562 Pacific Cove Dr Port Hueneme (93041) *(P-6198)*
Ironridge Inc (PA) ....D....800 227-9523
28357 Industrial Blvd Hayward (94545) *(P-12073)*
Ironwood Electric Inc ....E....714 630-2350
1239 N Tustin Ave Anaheim (92807) *(P-19987)*
Ironwood Packaging LLC ....E....909 581-0077
8975 Cottage Ave Rancho Cucamonga (91730) *(P-9711)*
Irp, San Clemente *Also called International Rubber Pdts Inc (P-9629)*
Irritec Usa Inc ....F....559 275-8825
1420 N Irritec Way Fresno (93703) *(P-14072)*
Irrometer Company Inc ....F....951 689-1701
1425 Palmyrita Ave Riverside (92507) *(P-22219)*
Irtronix Inc ....F....310 787-1100
20900 Normandie Ave B Torrance (90502) *(P-17430)*
Irvine & Jachens Inc ....F....650 755-4715
6700 Mission St Daly City (94014) *(P-24133)*
Irvine Electronics Inc ....D....949 250-0315
1601 Alton Pkwy Ste A Irvine (92606) *(P-18509)*
Irvine Scientific Sales Co Inc (HQ) ....E....949 261-7800
1830 E Warner Ave Santa Ana (92705) *(P-8563)*
Irvine Sensors Corporation ....E....714 444-8700
3001 Red Hill Ave 3-105 Costa Mesa (92626) *(P-18932)*
Irvine Welding, Lake Elsinore *Also called CL Olson & Associates Inc (P-14722)*
Isabelle Handbags Inc ....E....323 277-9888
3155 Bandini Blvd Unit A Vernon (90058) *(P-10550)*
Isap, San Diego *Also called Industrial SEC Allianc Ptnrs (P-23167)*
ISC Engineering LLC ....D....909 596-3315
4351 Schaefer Ave Chino (91710) *(P-17344)*
Iscience Interventional Corp ....D....650 421-2700
41316 Christy St Fremont (94538) *(P-22496)*
Isec Incorporated ....C....858 279-9085
5735 Krny Vlla Rd Ste 105 San Diego (92123) *(P-21478)*
Isharya Inc ....E....415 462-6294
4340 Stevens Creek Blvd San Jose (95129) *(P-23276)*
ISI, Garden Grove *Also called Inductor Supply Inc (P-19340)*
ISI, Oceanside *Also called International Sales Inc (P-23593)*
ISI Detention Contg Group Inc ....D....714 288-1770
577 N Batavia St Orange (92868) *(P-16593)*
Isign Solutions Inc (PA) ....F....650 802-7888
2025 Gateway Pl Ste 485 San Jose (95110) *(P-15772)*
Isiqalo LLC ....B....714 683-2820
5521 Schaefer Ave Chino (91710) *(P-2843)*
Isis Pharmaceuticals ....F....760 603-2631
1767 Avenida Segovia Oceanside (92056) *(P-8235)*
Island Brewing Co ....F....805 745-8272
5049 6th St Carpinteria (93013) *(P-1602)*
Island Color Inc ....F....714 352-5888
3972 Barranca Pkwy J521 Irvine (92606) *(P-6897)*
Island Mountain Lumber, Willits *Also called G and S Milling Co (P-4157)*
Island Powder Coating ....E....626 279-2460
1830 Tyler Ave South El Monte (91733) *(P-13605)*
Island Products, Buena Park *Also called Island Snacks Inc (P-1430)*
Island Snacks Inc ....E....714 994-1228
7650 Stage Rd Buena Park (90621) *(P-1430)*
Ismart Alarm Inc ....E....408 245-2551
120 San Lucar Ct Sunnyvale (94086) *(P-18332)*
Isolatek International, San Bernardino *Also called United States Mineral Pdts Co (P-11338)*
Isolation Network Inc (PA) ....E....415 489-7000
55 Francisco St Ste 350 San Francisco (94133) *(P-17819)*
Isolink Inc ....E....408 946-1968
880 Yosemite Way Milpitas (95035) *(P-19587)*
Isolutecom Inc (PA) ....E....805 498-6259
9 Northam Ave Newbury Park (91320) *(P-24804)*
Isomedia LLC ....E....510 668-1656
41380 Christy St Fremont (94538) *(P-17906)*
Isotope Products Lab, Valencia *Also called Eckert Zegler Isotope Pdts Inc (P-22191)*
Isp Granule Products Inc ....D....209 274-2930
1900 Hwy 104 Ione (95640) *(P-11321)*
Issac, Tustin *Also called Trelleborg Sealing Solutions (P-22655)*
Issi, Milpitas *Also called Integrted Silicon Solution Inc (P-14971)*
ISU Petasys Corp ....D....818 833-5800
12930 Bradley Ave Sylmar (91342) *(P-18510)*
It Concepts LLC ....F....925 401-0010
1244 Quarry Ln Ste B Pleasanton (94566) *(P-22093)*
It Retail Inc ....F....951 683-4950
191 W Big Springs Rd Riverside (92507) *(P-24805)*
It's Delish, North Hollywood *Also called Mave Enterprises Inc (P-1443)*
Italix Company Inc ....F....408 988-2487
120 Mast St Ste A Morgan Hill (95037) *(P-13606)*
Itc Nexus Holding Company, San Diego *Also called Accriva Dgnostics Holdings Inc (P-22311)*
Itc Sftware Slutions Group LLC (PA) ....F....877 248-2774
201 Sandpointe Ave # 305 Santa Ana (92707) *(P-24806)*
Itcsg, Santa Ana *Also called Itc Sftware Slutions Group LLC (P-24806)*
Itech, San Diego *Also called Intelligent Technologies LLC (P-17343)*
Itech Medical Inc ....F....714 841-2670
17011 Beach Blvd Ste 900 Huntington Beach (92647) *(P-22497)*
Iteris Inc (PA) ....C....949 270-9400
1700 Carnegie Ave Ste 100 Santa Ana (92705) *(P-23170)*
Itouchless Housewares Pdts Inc ....E....650 578-0578
777 Mariners Island Blvd # 125 San Mateo (94404) *(P-10157)*
Its, Brea *Also called ITS Group Inc (P-17278)*
Its, Northridge *Also called Instrumentation Tech Systems (P-15763)*
ITS Group Inc ....F....714 256-4100
266 Viking Ave Brea (92821) *(P-17278)*
Itt LLC ....C....707 523-2300
500 Tesconi Cir Santa Rosa (95401) *(P-17475)*
ITT Aerospace Controls LLC (HQ) ....E....315 568-7258
28150 Industry Dr Valencia (91355) *(P-20850)*
ITT Aerospace Controls LLC ....B....661 295-4000
28150 Industry Dr Valencia (91355) *(P-20851)*
ITT Aerospace Controls LLC ....E....661 295-4000
28150 Industry Dr Valencia (91355) *(P-20852)*
ITT Corporation ....B....714 557-4700
56 Technology Dr Irvine (92618) *(P-17279)*
ITT LLC ....D....562 908-4144
3951 Capitol Ave City of Industry (90601) *(P-17280)*
ITT LLC ....F....626 305-6100
1400 S Shamrock Ave Monrovia (91016) *(P-16166)*
ITT LLC ....F....559 265-4730
3878 S Willow Ave Ste 104 Fresno (93725) *(P-15080)*
Ittavi Inc ....E....866 246-4408
1631 Alhambra Blvd # 120 Sacramento (95816) *(P-24807)*
Ituner Networks Corporation ....F....510 226-6033
47801 Fremont Blvd Fremont (94538) *(P-15773)*
ITW Alpine, Sacramento *Also called ITW Blding Cmponents Group Inc (P-12391)*
ITW Blding Cmponents Group Inc ....E....916 387-0116
8351 Rovana Cir Sacramento (95828) *(P-12391)*
ITW Global Tire Repair Inc ....D....805 489-0490
125 Venture Dr Ste 210 San Luis Obispo (93401) *(P-9465)*
ITW Plymers Salants N Amer Inc ....E....714 898-0025
12271 Monarch St Garden Grove (92841) *(P-7846)*

Mergent e-mail: customerrelations@mergent.com 2019 California (P-0000) Products & Services Section entry number
1176 Manufacturers Register (PA)=Parent Co (HQ)=Headquarters (DH)=Div Headquarters

ALPHABETIC SECTION J Flying Manufacturing

ITW Semisystems Inc E 408 350-0244
625 Wool Creek Dr Ste G San Jose (95112) *(P-11576)*
ITW-Opto Diode, Camarillo *Also called Illinois Tool Works Inc (P-18882)*
IV Welding & Mechanical Inc F 760 482-9353
185 S 3rd St El Centro (92243) *(P-25413)*
Ivalua Inc (HQ) E 650 930-9710
805 Veterans Blvd Ste 203 Redwood City (94063) *(P-24808)*
Ivanti Inc F 408 343-8181
150 Mathilda Pl Ste 302 Sunnyvale (94086) *(P-24809)*
Ivar's Displays, Ontario *Also called Ivars Cabinet Shop Inc (P-5071)*
Ivars Cabinet Shop Inc (PA) C 909 923-2761
2314 E Locust St Ontario (91761) *(P-5071)*
Ivera Medical Corporation, San Diego *Also called Ivera Medical LLC (P-22498)*
Ivera Medical LLC D 888 861-8228
10805 Rancho Bernardo Rd # 100 San Diego (92127) *(P-22498)*
Iverson & Logging Inc F 707 937-0028
41575 Little Lake Rd Mendocino (95460) *(P-3993)*
Ives Inc F 707 498-0311
1918 Highland Cir Eureka (95501) *(P-3994)*
IVEX Ontario, Ontario *Also called IVEX Protective Packaging Inc (P-7847)*
IVEX Protective Packaging Inc E 909 390-4422
1550 Champagne Ave Ontario (91761) *(P-7847)*
Ivoprop Corporation F 562 602-1451
15903 Lakewood Blvd # 103 Bellflower (90706) *(P-20853)*
Ivydoctors Inc F 415 890-3937
555 Bryant St Palo Alto (94301) *(P-24810)*
Iwatt Inc (HQ) E 408 374-4200
675 Campbell Tech Pkwy # 150 Campbell (95008) *(P-18933)*
Iwco Direct - Downey, Downey *Also called Instant Web LLC (P-6889)*
Iwcus, Walnut *Also called Infinity Watch Corporation (P-23899)*
Iwen Naturals F 510 589-8019
4150 Mystic View Ct Hayward (94542) *(P-8773)*
Iwerks Entertainment Inc D 661 678-1800
27509 Avenue Hopkins Santa Clarita (91355) *(P-19988)*
Iwi, Sunnyvale *Also called Intella Interventional Systems (P-22482)*
Iws Predictive Technologies, Yorba Linda *Also called Inflight Warning Systems Inc (P-20848)*
Ix Medical (PA) F 877 902-6446
725 W Anaheim St Long Beach (90813) *(P-22755)*
Ixi Technology, Yorba Linda *Also called Mc2 Sabtech Holdings Inc (P-15449)*
Ixia, Santa Clara *Also called Net Optics Inc (P-24949)*
Ixia (HQ) B 818 871-1800
26601 Agoura Rd Calabasas (91302) *(P-21779)*
Ixia F 818 871-1800
26701 Agoura Rd Calabasas (91302) *(P-21780)*
Ixia Communications, Calabasas *Also called Ixia (P-21780)*
Ixia Inc E 408 988-8703
5301 Stevens Creek Blvd Santa Clara (95051) *(P-17101)*
Ixsystems Inc (PA) D 408 943-4100
2490 Kruse Dr San Jose (95131) *(P-24811)*
Ixys LLC (HQ) D 408 457-9000
1590 Buckeye Dr Milpitas (95035) *(P-18934)*
Ixys Intgrtd Crcts Div AV Inc E 949 831-4622
145 Columbia Aliso Viejo (92656) *(P-18935)*
Ixys Long Beach Inc (HQ) E 562 296-6584
2500 Mira Mar Ave Long Beach (90815) *(P-18936)*
Izorline International Inc F 562 531-6000
6725 Somerset Blvd Paramount (90723) *(P-23596)*
Izurieta Fence Company Inc F 323 661-4759
3000 Gilroy St Los Angeles (90039) *(P-11447)*
J & A Jeffery Inc E 707 678-0369
395 Industrial Way Ste B Dixon (95620) *(P-24134)*
J & A Pallet Accessory Inc F 951 785-1594
6607 Doolittle Ave Ste A Riverside (92503) *(P-4481)*
J & A Shoe Company Inc C 310 324-0139
960 Knox St Bldg A Torrance (90502) *(P-10498)*
J & B Enterprises, Santa Clara *Also called J & B Refining Inc (P-11547)*
J & B Manufacturing Corp C 760 846-6316
2780 La Mirada Dr Ste C Vista (92081) *(P-10707)*
J & B Refining Inc F 408 988-7900
1650 Russell Ave Santa Clara (95054) *(P-11547)*
J & C Apparel E 323 490-8260
757 Towne Ave Unit B Los Angeles (90021) *(P-3075)*
J & C Custom Cabinets Inc E 916 638-3400
11451 Elks Cir Rancho Cordova (95742) *(P-4952)*
J & D Business Forms Inc F 626 914-1777
650 W Terrace Dr San Dimas (91773) *(P-6898)*
J & D Fabricating & Repair Inc F 805 928-9674
2360 Westgate Rd Santa Maria (93455) *(P-13228)*
J & D Laboratories Inc B 844 453-5227
2710 Progress St Vista (92081) *(P-7952)*
J & F Design Inc D 323 526-4444
5578 Bandini Blvd Bell (90201) *(P-3432)*
J & F Machine Inc E 714 527-3499
6401 Global Dr Cypress (90630) *(P-16594)*
J & H Drilling Co Inc F 714 994-0402
7431 Walnut Ave Buena Park (90620) *(P-107)*
J & J Action Inc F 877 327-5268
3210 S Standard Ave Santa Ana (92705) *(P-17393)*
J & J Co, Chatsworth *Also called J & J Products Inc (P-13950)*
J & J Electronics LLC E 949 455-4460
6 Bendix Irvine (92618) *(P-17619)*
J & J Processing Inc E 562 926-2333
14715 Anson Ave Santa Fe Springs (90670) *(P-2269)*
J & J Products Inc F 818 998-4250
9134 Independence Ave Chatsworth (91311) *(P-13950)*
J & J Quality Door Inc E 209 948-5013
741 S Airport Way Stockton (95205) *(P-4169)*
J & J Screen Printing, Rancho Cordova *Also called Arteez (P-7240)*
J & J Snack Foods Corp Cal (HQ) C 323 581-0171
5353 S Downey Rd Vernon (90058) *(P-1366)*
J & J Tape & Label Inc F 951 657-6631
189 Whirlaway St Perris (92571) *(P-7363)*
J & K Orthopedics Inc F 909 621-1180
320 E Bonita Ave Pomona (91767) *(P-22756)*
J & K Resources Inc E 503 252-4009
5205 E Ocean Blvd Apt 10 Long Beach (90803) *(P-6899)*
J & L Cstm Plstic Extrsons Inc E 626 442-0711
1532 Santa Anita Ave South El Monte (91733) *(P-10158)*
J & L Digital Precision Inc F 650 592-0170
551 Taylor Way Ste 15 San Carlos (94070) *(P-19588)*
J & L Imaging Center, Anaheim *Also called Jaguar Litho Incorporated (P-7650)*
J & L Irrigation Company Inc F 559 237-2181
4264 W Jensen Ave Fresno (93706) *(P-14073)*
J & L Metal Products F 951 278-0100
1121 Railroad St Ste 103 Corona (92882) *(P-12627)*
J & L Tank Co, Lynwood *Also called Ermm Corporation (P-20501)*
J & M Printing Inc F 916 652-4600
4321 Anthony Ct Ste 1 Rocklin (95677) *(P-6900)*
J & R Concrete Products Inc E 951 943-5855
440 W Markham St Perris (92571) *(P-10941)*
J & R Engineering Company, Anaheim *Also called Argenti Inc (P-16279)*
J & R Machine Works E 661 945-8826
45420 60th St W Lancaster (93536) *(P-16595)*
J & R Machining Inc F 408 365-7314
164 Martinvale Ln San Jose (95119) *(P-16596)*
J & R Taylor Bros Assoc Inc D 626 334-9301
16321 Arrow Hwy Irwindale (91706) *(P-1115)*
J & S Inc E 310 719-7144
229 E Gardena Blvd Gardena (90248) *(P-16597)*
J & S Machine E 562 945-6419
8112 Freestone Ave Santa Fe Springs (90670) *(P-16598)*
J & S Stakes Inc F 707 668-5647
3157 Greenwood Heights Dr Kneeland (95549) *(P-4625)*
J - Art Co Inc F 310 202-1126
9435 Jefferson Blvd Culver City (90232) *(P-4832)*
J A English II Inc E 760 598-5333
1333 Keystone Way Vista (92081) *(P-10159)*
J A-Co Machine Works LLC E 831 429-8175
4 Carbonero Way Scotts Valley (95066) *(P-16599)*
J and S Machine, Santa Fe Springs *Also called J & S Machine (P-16598)*
J B Enterprises, Sacramento *Also called John Boyd Enterprises Inc (P-20377)*
J B I, La Habra *Also called JB Industries Corp (P-13231)*
J B L Enterprises Inc F 760 754-2727
3219 Roymar Rd Oceanside (92058) *(P-23597)*
J B Manufacturing Co, Adelanto *Also called Barker-Canoga Inc (P-14605)*
J B Precision, Campbell *Also called Jessee Brothers Machine Sp Inc (P-16622)*
J B Tool Inc F 714 993-7173
350 E Orngthrp Ave Ste 6 Placentia (92870) *(P-16600)*
J B'S Private Label, Studio City *Also called Jbs Private Label Inc (P-2844)*
J B3d, Orange *Also called John Bishop Design Inc (P-23908)*
J Brand Inc D 213 749-3500
1318 E 7th St Ste 260 Los Angeles (90021) *(P-2745)*
J Brand Jeans, Los Angeles *Also called J Brand Inc (P-2745)*
J C Ford Company D 714 871-7361
901 S Leslie St La Habra (90631) *(P-14861)*
J C Grinding (PA) F 562 944-3025
10923 Painter Ave Santa Fe Springs (90670) *(P-16601)*
J C Industries Inc F 805 389-4040
3977 Camino Ranchero Camarillo (93012) *(P-24135)*
J C Kitchen, South San Francisco *Also called Jesus Cabezas (P-2544)*
J C Machining, Santa Fe Springs *Also called J C Grinding (P-16601)*
J C Precision, Rancho Cucamonga *Also called JCPM Inc (P-16617)*
J C Rack Systems, Vernon *Also called Cardenas Enterprises Inc (P-5132)*
J C S Volks Machine F 626 338-6003
15626 Cypress Ave Irwindale (91706) *(P-20374)*
J D Heiskell Holdings LLC D 559 757-3135
11518 Road 120 Pixley (93256) *(P-1139)*
J D Industries F 714 542-5517
1636 E Edinger Ave Ste P Santa Ana (92705) *(P-16602)*
J D Tool & Machine Co Inc F 951 371-6652
12321 Sampson St Ste D Riverside (92503) *(P-14528)*
J Deluca Fish Company Inc (PA) E 310 684-5180
2194 Signal Pl San Pedro (90731) *(P-2314)*
J E J Print Inc F 626 281-8989
673 Monterey Pass Rd Monterey Park (91754) *(P-6901)*
J E S Disc Grinding Inc F 909 596-3823
2824 Metropolitan Pl Pomona (91767) *(P-16603)*
J F Christopher Inc F 951 943-1166
3110 Indian Ave Ste D Perris (92571) *(P-23598)*
J F Duncan Industries Inc (PA) D 562 862-4269
9301 Stewart And Gray Rd Downey (90241) *(P-16057)*
J F Fitzgerald Company Inc F 415 648-6161
2750 19th St San Francisco (94110) *(P-4784)*
J F Fong Inc F 949 553-8885
16520 Aston Irvine (92606) *(P-22499)*
J F K & Associates Inc E 925 388-0255
1100 Moraga Way Ste 202 Moraga (94556) *(P-24812)*
J F McCaughin Co E 626 573-3000
2628 River Ave Rosemead (91770) *(P-23708)*
J F Shea Co Inc (PA) E 909 594-9500
655 Brea Canyon Rd Walnut (91789) *(P-11122)*
J F Shea Co Inc E 530 246-2200
17400 Clear Creek Rd Redding (96001) *(P-11123)*
J Flying Manufacturing E 805 839-9229
11000 Brimhall Rd Ste E Bakersfield (93312) *(P-9568)*

ALPHABETIC

Employee Codes: A=Over 500 employees, B=251-500
C=101-250, D=51-100, E=20-50, F=10-19
2019 California
Manfacturers Register
© Mergent Inc. 1-800-342-5647
1177

J G Hernandez Company ....E....562 698-2286
12402 Philadelphia St Whittier (90601) ***(P-23103)***
J Good In Inc ....F....714 257-9391
576 Explorer St Brea (92821) ***(P-23277)***
J H P & Associates Inc ....E....661 799-5888
28005 Smyth Dr Valencia (91355) ***(P-13999)***
J H Textiles Inc ....E....323 585-4124
2301 E 55th St Vernon (90058) ***(P-3002)***
J Hellman Frozen Foods Inc (PA) ....E....213 243-9105
1601 E Olympic Blvd # 200 Los Angeles (90021) ***(P-953)***
J Heyri Inc ....E....323 588-1234
6900 S Alameda St Huntington Park (90255) ***(P-3246)***
J Howard Service Group Inc ....F....562 602-0224
2755 Seaboard Ln Long Beach (90805) ***(P-13795)***
J J and A, Glendale *Also called Jerry V Johnson & Assoc Inc* ***(P-7204)***
J J Engineering, Los Alamitos *Also called James Jackson* ***(P-16612)***
J J Foil Company Inc ....E....714 998-9920
650 W Freedom Ave Orange (92865) ***(P-5653)***
J K Lighting Systems, Stockton *Also called Al Kramp Specialties* ***(P-17668)***
J K Star Corp ....D....310 538-0185
1123 N Stanford Ave Los Angeles (90059) ***(P-3165)***
J L Cooper Electronics Inc ....E....310 322-9990
142 Arena St El Segundo (90245) ***(P-19589)***
J L F/Lone Meadow, Compton *Also called J L Furnishings LLC* ***(P-5016)***
J L Fisher Inc ....D....818 846-8366
1000 W Isabel St Burbank (91506) ***(P-23171)***
J L Furnishings LLC (PA) ....B....310 605-6600
19007 S Reyes Ave Compton (90221) ***(P-5016)***
J L Furnishings LLC ....F....310 856-0412
3145 E Maria St Compton (90221) ***(P-5017)***
J L Haley Enterprises ....C....916 631-6375
3510 Luyung Dr Rancho Cordova (95742) ***(P-16604)***
J L Industries, Commerce *Also called Samson Products Inc* ***(P-5166)***
J L Precision Sheet Metal, San Jose *Also called Laptalo Enterprises Inc* ***(P-12641)***
J L Shepherd and Associates ....E....818 898-2361
1010 Arroyo St San Fernando (91340) ***(P-22220)***
J L Wingert Company (PA) ....D....714 379-5519
11800 Monarch St Garden Grove (92841) ***(P-16058)***
J Lohr Viney, San Jose *Also called J Lohr Winery Corporation* ***(P-1818)***
J Lohr Winery Corporation (PA) ....E....408 288-5057
1000 Lenzen Ave San Jose (95126) ***(P-1818)***
J M A R Precision Systems, Chatsworth *Also called Pacific Precision Labs Inc* ***(P-22248)***
J M Boone & Sons ....F....209 532-2506
22039 Sawmill Flat Rd Sonora (95370) ***(P-11257)***
J M I, Union City *Also called Jenson Mechanical Inc* ***(P-16619)***
J M Mills Communications Inc (HQ) ....E....613 321-2100
4686 Mission Gorge Pl San Diego (92120) ***(P-18135)***
J M R Components, Chatsworth *Also called Jmr Electronics Inc* ***(P-15562)***
J M Smucker Company ....E....805 487-5483
800 Commercial Ave Oxnard (93030) ***(P-809)***
J Manufacturing, Grass Valley *Also called Vossloh Signaling Usa Inc* ***(P-13118)***
J McDowell Wldg Frm Mchy Inc ....F....530 661-6006
29820 County Road 25 Winters (95694) ***(P-25414)***
J Miller Co Inc ....E....818 837-0181
11537 Bradley Ave San Fernando (91340) ***(P-9538)***
J N C O, Los Angeles *Also called J&Company Jeans LLC* ***(P-2746)***
J P B Jewelry Box Co (PA) ....F....323 225-0500
2428 Dallas St Los Angeles (90031) ***(P-5072)***
J P L, Fresno *Also called J P Lamborn Co* ***(P-15962)***
J P Lamborn Co (PA) ....C....559 650-2120
3663 E Wawona Ave Fresno (93725) ***(P-15962)***
J P Specialties Inc ....F....951 763-7077
25811 Jefferson Ave Murrieta (92562) ***(P-10160)***
J P Sportswear, Vernon *Also called Aaron Corporation* ***(P-3366)***
J P Turgeon & Sons Inc ....E....323 773-3105
7758 Scout Ave Bell (90201) ***(P-13435)***
J P Weaver & Company Inc ....F....818 500-1740
941 Air Way Glendale (91201) ***(P-11357)***
J Pedroncelli Winery ....E....707 857-3531
1220 Canyon Rd Geyserville (95441) ***(P-1819)***
J R C Industries Inc ....D....562 698-0171
11804 Wakeman St Santa Fe Springs (90670) ***(P-5306)***
J R Rapid Print Inc ....F....909 947-4868
909 S Cucamonga Ave # 104 Ontario (91761) ***(P-6902)***
J R Schneider Co Inc ....F....707 745-0404
849 Jackson St Benicia (94510) ***(P-15335)***
J R U D E S Holdings LLC ....F....310 281-0800
9200 W Sunset Blvd Ph 2 West Hollywood (90069) ***(P-3031)***
J R V Products Inc ....F....714 259-9772
1314 N Harbor Blvd # 302 Santa Ana (92703) ***(P-19590)***
J Roberts Design, Brea *Also called M3 Products Inc* ***(P-5152)***
J RS Woodworks Inc ....F....707 588-8255
300 W Robles Ave Ste B Santa Rosa (95407) ***(P-4170)***
J S Hackl Archi Signa Inc ....F....510 940-2608
1999 Alpine Way Hayward (94545) ***(P-23904)***
J S M Productions Inc ....F....951 929-5771
537 E Florida Ave Hemet (92543) ***(P-6903)***
J S Paluch Co Inc ....E....562 692-0484
9400 Norwalk Blvd Santa Fe Springs (90670) ***(P-6354)***
J S West Milling Co Inc ....E....209 529-4232
501 9th St Modesto (95354) ***(P-1140)***
J Sheet Metal, Compton *Also called Jaubin Sales & Mfg Corp* ***(P-12628)***
J Summitt Inc ....E....562 236-5744
13834 Bettencourt St Cerritos (90703) ***(P-4171)***
J T I, Pomona *Also called Jacks Technologies & Inds Inc* ***(P-14974)***
J T Walker Industries Inc ....E....909 481-1909
9322 Hyssop Dr Rancho Cucamonga (91730) ***(P-12321)***

J Talley Corporation (PA) ....E....951 654-2123
989 W 7th St San Jacinto (92582) ***(P-12864)***
J W Bamford Inc ....F....530 533-0732
4288 State Highway 70 Oroville (95965) ***(P-3995)***
J W Floor Covering Inc ....D....858 444-1214
3401 Enterprise Ave Hayward (94545) ***(P-2541)***
J&B Mountain Holding, Irvine *Also called Red Mountain Inc* ***(P-21524)***
J&C Tapocik Inc ....F....951 351-4333
2941 Mcallister St Riverside (92503) ***(P-3661)***
J&Company Jeans LLC ....D....323 260-7329
1501 Rio Vista Ave Los Angeles (90023) ***(P-2746)***
J&E Precision Machining Inc ....F....408 281-1195
2814 Aiello Dr Ste A San Jose (95111) ***(P-16605)***
J&J Products ....F....805 544-4288
835 Capitolio Way Ste 4 San Luis Obispo (93401) ***(P-16606)***
J&L Press Inc (PA) ....F....818 549-8344
1218 W 163rd St Gardena (90247) ***(P-6904)***
J&M Analytik AG ....E....626 297-2930
141 California St Apt G Arcadia (91006) ***(P-21979)***
J&M Manufacturing Inc ....E....707 795-8223
430 Aaron St Cotati (94931) ***(P-19591)***
J&S Goodwin Inc (HQ) ....D....714 956-4040
5753 E Sta Ana Cyn G355 Anaheim (92807) ***(P-14329)***
J&S Machine Works, Sylmar *Also called Kay & James Inc* ***(P-16647)***
J&T Designs LLC ....E....310 868-5190
1463 W El Segundo Blvd Compton (90222) ***(P-5238)***
J-Art Ornamental Iron, Culver City *Also called J - Art Co Inc* ***(P-4832)***
J-M Manufacturing Company Inc ....D....951 657-7400
23711 Rider St Perris (92570) ***(P-7848)***
J-M Manufacturing Company Inc (PA) ....C....800 621-4404
5200 W Century Blvd Los Angeles (90045) ***(P-9782)***
J-M Manufacturing Company Inc ....D....909 822-3009
10990 Hemlock Ave Fontana (92337) ***(P-7849)***
J-M Manufacturing Company Inc ....C....209 982-1500
1051 Sperry Rd Stockton (95206) ***(P-7850)***
J-Mark Company, Vista *Also called J-Mark Manufacturing Inc* ***(P-13229)***
J-Mark Manufacturing Inc ....E....760 727-6956
2480 Coral St Vista (92081) ***(P-13229)***
J-T E C H ....C....310 533-6700
548 Amapola Ave Torrance (90501) ***(P-19398)***
J2 Global Communications, Santa Barbara *Also called Efaxcom* ***(P-15736)***
J3 Associates Inc ....F....408 281-4412
2751 Aiello Dr San Jose (95111) ***(P-16607)***
JA Ferrari Print Imaging LLC ....F....619 295-8307
7515 Metro Dr Ste 405 San Diego (92108) ***(P-6905)***
Ja Solar USA Inc ....F....408 586-0000
2570 N 1st St Ste 360 San Jose (95131) ***(P-18937)***
JA Wouters Inc ....F....805 221-5333
2305 Iron Stone Loop Templeton (93465) ***(P-108)***
Jaann Inc ....F....619 336-0584
225 W 15th St National City (91950) ***(P-12183)***
Jabil Chad Automation, Anaheim *Also called Jabil Inc* ***(P-18512)***
Jabil Circuit Inc ....D....408 361-3200
1925 Lundy Ave San Jose (95131) ***(P-18511)***
Jabil Inc ....E....714 938-0080
1565 S Sinclair St Anaheim (92806) ***(P-18512)***
Jabil Inc ....B....408 361-3200
30 Great Oaks Blvd San Jose (95119) ***(P-18513)***
Jabil Silver Creek Inc (HQ) ....C....669 255-2900
5981 Optical Ct San Jose (95138) ***(P-25415)***
Jack B Martin ....F....559 583-1175
109 E 5th St Hanford (93230) ***(P-23905)***
Jack Brain and Associates Inc ....F....510 889-1360
20819 Nunes Ave Castro Valley (94546) ***(P-6505)***
Jack C Drees Grinding Co Inc ....E....818 764-8301
11815 Vose St B North Hollywood (91605) ***(P-16608)***
Jack Frost Ice Service, Modesto *Also called Arctic Glacier California Inc* ***(P-2407)***
Jack J Engel Manufacturing Inc ....E....818 767-6220
11641 Pendleton St Sun Valley (91352) ***(P-19989)***
Jack Martin Signworks, Hanford *Also called Jack B Martin* ***(P-23905)***
Jack McMahon Landscape ....F....707 942-1122
21 Miriam Dr Calistoga (94515) ***(P-4041)***
Jack McMahon Landscaping Svcs, Calistoga *Also called Jack McMahon Landscape* ***(P-4041)***
Jack West Cnc Inc ....F....619 421-1695
3451 Main St Ste 111 Chula Vista (91911) ***(P-16609)***
Jackandjillkidscom, Carson *Also called Jnj Operations LLC* ***(P-24137)***
Jackrabbit (PA) ....D....209 599-6118
471 Industrial Ave Ripon (95366) ***(P-14074)***
Jacks Box & Crate LLC ....E....951 343-1790
6301 Industrial Ave Riverside (92504) ***(P-5430)***
Jacks Technologies & Inds Inc ....F....909 865-2595
225 N Palomares St Pomona (91767) ***(P-14974)***
Jacksam Corp Blackout, Rancho Santa Margari *Also called Jacksam Corporation* ***(P-15212)***
Jacksam Corporation ....E....800 605-3580
30191 Avenida De Las Rancho Santa Margari (92688) ***(P-15212)***
Jackson Engineering Company ....E....818 886-9567
9411 Winnetka Ave A Chatsworth (91311) ***(P-17102)***
Jackson Family Farms LLC (PA) ....E....707 837-1000
425 Aviation Blvd Santa Rosa (95403) ***(P-1820)***
Jackson Family Farms LLC ....E....707 836-2047
5660 Skylane Blvd Santa Rosa (95403) ***(P-1821)***
Jackson Family Wines Inc ....E....707 948-2643
7600 Saint Helena Hwy Oakville (94562) ***(P-1822)***
Jackson Family Wines Inc ....E....707 528-6278
3690 Laughlin Rd Windsor (95492) ***(P-1823)***
Jackson Family Wines Inc (PA) ....D....707 544-4000
421 And 425 Aviation Blvd Santa Rosa (95403) ***(P-1824)***

Mergent e-mail: customerrelations@mergent.com
1178
2019 California
Manufacturers Register
(P-0000) Products & Services Section entry number
(PA)=Parent Co (HQ)=Headquarters (DH)=Div Headquarters

Jackson Family Wines Inc ....E....805 938-7300
5475 Chardonnay Ln Santa Maria (93454) *(P-1825)*
Jackson Family Wines Inc ....E....707 433-9463
7111 Highway 128 Healdsburg (95448) *(P-1826)*
Jackson-Mitchell Inc (PA) ....E....209 667-0786
1240 South Ave Turlock (95380) *(P-730)*
Jaco Engineering ....E....714 991-1680
879 S East St Anaheim (92805) *(P-16610)*
Jaco Machine Works, Scotts Valley *Also called J A-Co Machine Works LLC (P-16599)*
Jacobellis, Burbank *Also called V J Provision Inc (P-454)*
Jacobs Technology Inc ....E....661 275-6100
8 Draco Dr Bldg 8350 Edwards (93524) *(P-21159)*
Jacobsen Trailer Inc ....E....559 834-5971
1128 E South Ave Fowler (93625) *(P-20505)*
Jacobson Plastics Inc ....D....562 433-4911
1401 Freeman Ave Long Beach (90804) *(P-10161)*
Jacquard Products, Healdsburg *Also called Rupert Gibbon & Spider Inc (P-8938)*
Jacuzzi Brands LLC (PA) ....E....909 606-1416
13925 City Center Dr # 200 Chino Hills (91709) *(P-22757)*
Jacuzzi Brands LLC ....E....909 606-1416
13925 City Center Dr Chino Hills (91709) *(P-24136)*
Jacuzzi Group Worldwide, Chino Hills *Also called Jacuzzi Brands LLC (P-22757)*
Jacuzzi Inc (HQ) ....C....909 606-7733
14525 Monte Vista Ave Chino (91710) *(P-16059)*
Jacuzzi Inc ....E....909 606-1416
13925 City Center Dr # 200 Chino Hills (91709) *(P-9903)*
Jacuzzi Outdoor Products, Chino *Also called Jacuzzi Inc (P-16059)*
Jacuzzi Products Co (HQ) ....C....909 606-1416
13925 City Center Dr # 200 Chino Hills (91709) *(P-9904)*
Jacuzzi Whirlpool Bath Inc ....B....909 548-7732
14525 Monte Vista Ave Chino (91710) *(P-9905)*
Jad Chemical Inc ....F....310 833-7457
8707 Millergrove Dr Santa Fe Springs (90670) *(P-9014)*
Jada Group Inc ....D....626 810-8382
938 Hatcher Ave City of Industry (91748) *(P-23433)*
Jada Toys, City of Industry *Also called Jada Group Inc (P-23433)*
Jade Apparel Inc ....E....323 867-9800
1625 S Greenwood Ave Montebello (90640) *(P-3315)*
Jade Products, Brea *Also called Jade Range LLC (P-17370)*
Jade Range LLC ....C....714 961-2400
2650 Orbiter St Brea (92821) *(P-17370)*
Jade Spec LLC ....F....310 933-4338
15932 Downey Ave Ste A Paramount (90723) *(P-2747)*
Jadespec, Paramount *Also called Jade Spec LLC (P-2747)*
Jaf International Inc ....F....510 656-1718
2917 Bayview Dr Fremont (94538) *(P-15434)*
Jaffa Precision Engrg Inc ....F....951 278-8797
12117 Madera Way Riverside (92503) *(P-16611)*
JAGUAR ANIMAL HEALTH, San Francisco *Also called Jaguar Health Inc (P-8236)*
Jaguar Health Inc (PA) ....E....415 371-8300
201 Mission St Ste 2375 San Francisco (94105) *(P-8236)*
Jaguar Litho Incorporated ....F....714 978-1821
1500 S Sunkist St Ste I Anaheim (92806) *(P-7650)*
Jaguar Mfg Cstm Wrought Ir, Bakersfield *Also called Jaguars Wroght Iron (P-12865)*
Jaguars Wroght Iron ....E....661 323-5015
300 Union Ave Bakersfield (93307) *(P-12865)*
Jain Irrigation Inc ....C....559 485-7171
2851 E Florence Ave Fresno (93721) *(P-14075)*
Jake Stehelin Etienne ....D....818 998-4250
8551 Canoga Ave Canoga Park (91304) *(P-10162)*
Jakks Pacific Inc ....E....909 594-7771
21749 Baker Pkwy Walnut (91789) *(P-23434)*
Jakks Pacific Inc (PA) ....B....424 268-9444
2951 28th St Ste 51 Santa Monica (90405) *(P-23435)*
Jal-Vue Window Company, Oakland *Also called East Bay Glass Company Inc (P-12311)*
Jam Design Inc ....F....818 505-1680
5415 Cleon Ave North Hollywood (91601) *(P-23748)*
Jamac Steel Inc ....E....909 983-7592
533 E Belmont St Ontario (91761) *(P-12184)*
Jamaco Enterprises Inc ....F....818 991-2050
5331 Derry Ave Ste L Agoura Hills (91301) *(P-5377)*
James A Headrick Ii/Elizabeth ....D....530 247-8000
7194 Bridge St Anderson (96007) *(P-3996)*
James Betts Enterprises Inc ....E....530 581-1331
100 Sierra Terrace Rd Tahoe City (96145) *(P-21047)*
James Clark ....F....559 456-3893
1766 N Helm Ave Ste 105 Fresno (93727) *(P-7603)*
James Frasinetti & Sons ....E....916 383-2447
7395 Frasinetti Rd Sacramento (95828) *(P-1827)*
James Gang Company ....F....619 225-1283
4851 Newport Ave San Diego (92107) *(P-3899)*
James Gang Custom Printing ....F....619 225-1283
4851 Newport Ave San Diego (92107) *(P-6906)*
James Gang Graphics & Printing, San Diego *Also called James Gang Custom Printing (P-6906)*
James Hardie Trading Co Inc ....C....949 582-2378
26300 La Alameda Ste 400 Mission Viejo (92691) *(P-9411)*
James Hunkins ....F....310 640-8243
601 Lairport St El Segundo (90245) *(P-20665)*
James Jackson ....F....562 493-1402
11021 Via El Mercado Los Alamitos (90720) *(P-16612)*
James Jeans, Los Angeles *Also called Dry Aged Denim LLC (P-3069)*
James Jones Company ....C....909 418-2558
1470 S Vintage Ave Ontario (91761) *(P-13721)*
James Kim Young ....E....310 605-5328
1215 W Walnut St Compton (90220) *(P-3433)*
James L Craft Inc ....E....661 323-8251
1101 33rd St Bakersfield (93301) *(P-16613)*
James L Hall Co Incorporated (PA) ....D....707 547-0775
360 Tesconi Cir Ste B Santa Rosa (95401) *(P-19592)*
James L Hall Co Incorporated ....D....707 544-2436
218 Roberts Ave Santa Rosa (95401) *(P-19342)*
James Litho, Ontario *Also called Eclipse Prtg & Graphics LLC (P-6800)*
James P McNair Cc Inc ....F....415 681-2200
2236 Irving St San Francisco (94122) *(P-11965)*
James Stewart ....E....323 778-1687
8931 S Vermont Ave Los Angeles (90044) *(P-8237)*
James Stout ....E....408 988-8582
481 Gianni St Santa Clara (95054) *(P-16614)*
James Tobin Cellars Inc ....E....805 239-2204
8950 Union Rd Paso Robles (93446) *(P-1828)*
James West Inc (PA) ....F....310 380-1510
13344 S Main St Ste B Los Angeles (90061) *(P-3076)*
Jamis Software Corporation ....F....858 300-5542
4909 Murphy Canyon Rd # 460 San Diego (92123) *(P-24813)*
Jamm Industries Corp ....E....213 622-0555
2425 E 12th St Los Angeles (90021) *(P-3434)*
Jampro Antennas Inc ....D....916 383-1177
6340 Sky Creek Dr Sacramento (95828) *(P-18136)*
Jan-Al Cases, Los Angeles *Also called Jan-Al Innerprizes Inc (P-10525)*
Jan-Al Innerprizes Inc ....E....323 260-7212
3339 Union Pacific Ave Los Angeles (90023) *(P-10525)*
Janco Airless Center, Berkeley *Also called Janco Chemical Corporation (P-8909)*
Janco Chemical Corporation ....F....510 527-9770
1235 5th St Berkeley (94710) *(P-8909)*
Janda Company Inc ....E....951 734-1935
226 N Sherman Ave Ste A Corona (92882) *(P-14727)*
Jandy Industries Inc (HQ) ....E....805 529-2000
6000 Condor Dr Moorpark (93021) *(P-16060)*
Jandy Pool Products, Vista *Also called Zodiac Pool Systems LLC (P-16144)*
Jane Mohr Design, Van Nuys *Also called Dress To Kill Inc (P-3232)*
Janel Glass Company Inc ....E....323 661-8621
2960 Marsh St Los Angeles (90039) *(P-10708)*
Jano Graphics, Ventura *Also called National Graphics LLC (P-6989)*
Jansen Ornamental Supply Co ....E....626 442-0271
10926 Schmidt Rd El Monte (91733) *(P-12866)*
Jansport Inc (HQ) ....F....510 814-7400
2601 Harbor Bay Pkwy Alameda (94502) *(P-3766)*
Janssen Research & Dev LLC ....C....858 450-2000
3210 Merryfield Row San Diego (92121) *(P-8238)*
Jantek Electronics Inc ....F....626 350-4198
4820 Arden Dr Temple City (91780) *(P-19990)*
Janteq Corp (PA) ....E....949 215-2603
9975 Toledo Way Ste 150 Irvine (92618) *(P-18137)*
Janus International Group LLC ....E....714 503-6120
2535 W La Palma Ave Anaheim (92801) *(P-12322)*
Japan Engine Inc ....E....510 532-7878
1951 Williams St San Leandro (94577) *(P-19836)*
Japan Graphics Corp ....E....310 222-8639
1820 W 220th St Ste 210 Torrance (90501) *(P-6907)*
Japanese Truck Dismantling ....F....310 835-3100
940 Alameda St Wilmington (90744) *(P-20152)*
Japanese Weekend Inc (PA) ....E....415 621-0555
496 S Airport Blvd South San Francisco (94080) *(P-3435)*
Japonesque LLC ....F....925 866-6670
2420 Camino Ramon Ste 250 San Ramon (94583) *(P-8774)*
Jar Ventures Inc ....E....530 224-9655
1355 Hartnell Ave Redding (96002) *(P-23906)*
Jarden Corporation ....D....800 755-9520
23610 Banning Blvd Carson (90745) *(P-10163)*
Jardine Performance Products, Corona *Also called Summit Industries Inc (P-12252)*
Jari Electro Supply, Gilroy *Also called Chalgren Enterprises (P-22959)*
Jariet Technologies Inc ....E....310 698-1001
103 W Torrance Blvd Redondo Beach (90277) *(P-21311)*
Jarrow Industries Inc ....C....562 906-1919
12246 Hawkins St Santa Fe Springs (90670) *(P-8239)*
Jarvis ....E....707 255-5280
2970 Monticello Rd NAPA (94558) *(P-1829)*
Jarvis Manufacturing Inc ....F....408 226-2600
195 Lewis Rd Ste 36 San Jose (95111) *(P-16615)*
Jarvis Winery, NAPA *Also called Jarvis (P-1829)*
Jasmine La Belle, Irwindale *Also called Merestone Merchandise Corp (P-8794)*
Jason Incorporated ....E....562 921-9821
13006 Philadelphia St # 305 Whittier (90601) *(P-11295)*
Jason Markk Inc ....E....213 687-7060
329 E 2nd St Los Angeles (90012) *(P-8648)*
Jason Tool & Engineering Inc ....E....714 895-5067
7101 Honold Cir Garden Grove (92841) *(P-10164)*
Jasper Display Corp ....E....408 831-5788
2952 Bunker Hill Ln # 110 Santa Clara (95054) *(P-14975)*
Jasper Electronics ....E....714 917-0749
1580 N Kellogg Dr Anaheim (92807) *(P-19593)*
Jasper Engine Exchange Inc ....F....800 827-7455
1477 E Cedar St Ste D Ontario (91761) *(P-20375)*
Jasper Sinclaire Media MGT Inc ....C....559 380-7853
505 Montgomery St Fl 11 San Francisco (94111) *(P-6355)*
Jaton Corporation ....B....510 933-8888
47677 Lakeview Blvd Fremont (94538) *(P-18514)*
Jaubin Sales & Mfg Corp ....F....310 631-8647
2006 E Gladwick St Compton (90220) *(P-12628)*
Jaunt Inc ....E....650 618-6579
951 Mariners Island Blvd # 500 San Mateo (94404) *(P-24814)*
Jaunt Vr, San Mateo *Also called Jaunt Inc (P-24814)*
Java Printing Inc ....E....323 888-1601
5754 Grace Pl Commerce (90022) *(P-7364)*
Javad Ems Inc ....D....408 770-1700
900 Rock Ave San Jose (95131) *(P-19594)*

ALPHABETIC

Employee Codes: A=Over 500 employees, B=251-500
C=101-250, D=51-100, E=20-50, F=10-19
2019 California
Manfacturers Register
© Mergent Inc. 1-800-342-5647
1179

Javo Beverage Company Inc ... D ... 760 560-5286
1311 Specialty Dr Vista (92081) ***(P-2270)***
Jawen Enterprises, San Diego *Also called Jay Brewer* ***(P-6908)***
Jaxx Manufacturing Inc ... E ... 805 526-4979
1912 Angus Ave Simi Valley (93063) ***(P-19595)***
Jay Bellach Custom Harvesting ... F ... 559 846-9785
4140 N Madera Ave Kerman (93630) ***(P-16616)***
Jay Brewer ... F ... 858 488-4871
926 Turquoise St Ste A San Diego (92109) ***(P-6908)***
Jay Edward Group LLC ... E ... 858 799-1227
12250 El Camino Real # 200 San Diego (92130) ***(P-5239)***
Jay Edward Hospitality Furn, San Diego *Also called Jay Edward Group LLC* ***(P-5239)***
Jay Gee Sales ... F ... 818 365-1311
703 Arroyo St San Fernando (91340) ***(P-10833)***
Jay Manufacturing Corp ... F ... 818 255-0500
7425 Fulton Ave North Hollywood (91605) ***(P-13230)***
Jay Mfg, North Hollywood *Also called Jay Manufacturing Corp* ***(P-13230)***
Jay-Cee Blouse Co Inc ... C ... 213 622-0116
823 Maple Ave Ste 200 Los Angeles (90014) ***(P-3316)***
Jaya Apparel Group LLC (PA) ... D ... 323 584-3500
5175 S Soto St Vernon (90058) ***(P-3436)***
Jayco Hawaii California ... F ... 510 601-9916
1468 66th St Emeryville (94608) ***(P-11619)***
Jayco Interface Technology Inc ... E ... 951 738-2000
1351 Pico St Corona (92881) ***(P-19596)***
Jayco Mmi Inc ... E ... 951 738-2000
1351 Pico St Corona (92881) ***(P-19597)***
Jayone Foods Inc ... E ... 562 633-7400
7212 Alondra Blvd Paramount (90723) ***(P-2542)***
Jaz Distribution Inc ... F ... 714 521-3888
8485 Artesia Blvd Ste B Buena Park (90621) ***(P-13102)***
Jaz Products, Santa Paula *Also called Westlake Engrg Roto Form* ***(P-10443)***
Jazz Imaging LLC ... F ... 567 234-5299
800 Chartot Ave Ste 100 San Jose (95131) ***(P-22884)***
Jazz Pharmaceuticals Inc (HQ) ... C ... 650 496-3777
3170 Porter Dr Palo Alto (94304) ***(P-8240)***
Jazz Semiconductor, Newport Beach *Also called Newport Fab LLC* ***(P-19040)***
Jazz Semiconductor Inc (HQ) ... A ... 949 435-8000
4321 Jamboree Rd Newport Beach (92660) ***(P-18938)***
Jazzyexpo.com, Vista *Also called Starship Worldwide LLC* ***(P-4968)***
JB Britches Inc ... D ... 818 898-4046
2279 Ward Ave Simi Valley (93065) ***(P-3077)***
JB Industries Corp ... F ... 562 691-2105
451 Commercial Way La Habra (90631) ***(P-13231)***
JB Plastics Inc ... E ... 714 541-8500
1921 E Edinger Ave Santa Ana (92705) ***(P-10165)***
JB Radiator Specialties, Sacramento *Also called John Boyd Enterprises Inc* ***(P-20376)***
JB&a Distribution, San Rafael *Also called Jeff Burgess & Associates Inc* ***(P-17820)***
Jbb Inc ... E ... 888 538-9287
880 W Crowther Ave Placentia (92870) ***(P-19991)***
Jbi LLC (PA) ... C ... 310 886-8034
2650 E El Presidio St Long Beach (90810) ***(P-5240)***
Jbi LLC ... E ... 310 537-2910
18521 S Santa Fe Ave Compton (90221) ***(P-4833)***
Jbi Interiors, Long Beach *Also called Jbi LLC* ***(P-5240)***
Jbr Inc (PA) ... C ... 916 258-8000
1731 Aviation Blvd Lincoln (95648) ***(P-2543)***
Jbr Gourmet Foods, Lincoln *Also called Jbr Inc* ***(P-2543)***
Jbs Case Ready, Riverside *Also called Swift Beef Company* ***(P-530)***
Jbs Private Label Inc ... E ... 818 762-3736
4383 Irvine Ave Studio City (91604) ***(P-2844)***
Jbt Food Tech Madera, Madera *Also called John Bean Technologies Corp* ***(P-14862)***
JBW Precision Inc ... E ... 805 499-1973
2650 Lavery Ct Newbury Park (91320) ***(P-12629)***
JC Ford, La Habra *Also called J C Ford Company* ***(P-14861)***
JC Hanscom Inc ... F ... 562 789-9955
11830 Wakeman St Santa Fe Springs (90670) ***(P-4378)***
JC Industries, Los Angeles *Also called JC Trimming Company Inc* ***(P-3317)***
JC Metal ... F ... 650 827-1618
238 Michelle Ct South San Francisco (94080) ***(P-13951)***
JC Metal Specialists Inc (PA) ... E ... 415 822-3878
220 Michelle Ct San Francisco (94124) ***(P-12185)***
JC Pallet Co ... F ... 661 393-2229
5800 State Rd Spc 13 Bakersfield (93308) ***(P-4482)***
JC Supply & Manufacturing, Ontario *Also called Lightcap Industries, Inc.* ***(P-12196)***
JC Trimming Company Inc ... D ... 323 235-4458
3800 S Hill St Los Angeles (90037) ***(P-3317)***
JC Window Fashions Inc ... E ... 909 364-8888
6400 Fleet St Commerce (90040) ***(P-5197)***
Jc's Pie Pops, Chatsworth *Also called We The Pie People LLC* ***(P-705)***
Jci Jones Chemicals Inc ... E ... 310 523-1629
1401 Del Amo Blvd Torrance (90501) ***(P-7665)***
Jci Metal Products (PA) ... D ... 619 229-8206
6540 Federal Blvd Lemon Grove (91945) ***(P-12186)***
Jcm Engineering Corp ... D ... 909 923-3730
2690 E Cedar St Ontario (91761) ***(P-20854)***
JCM Industries Inc (PA) ... E ... 714 902-9000
15302 Pipeline Ln Huntington Beach (92649) ***(P-5149)***
JCPM Inc ... F ... 909 484-9040
8576 Red Oak St Rancho Cucamonga (91730) ***(P-16617)***
Jcr Aircraft Deburring LLC ... E ... 714 870-4427
221 Foundation Ave La Habra (90631) ***(P-14384)***
Jcr Deburring, La Habra *Also called Jcr Aircraft Deburring LLC* ***(P-14384)***
Jcs, Irwindale *Also called J C S Volks Machine* ***(P-20374)***
JD Business Solutions Inc ... E ... 805 962-8193
1351 Holiday Hill Rd Goleta (93117) ***(P-6909)***
JD Engineering & Assoc Inc ... E ... 408 866-0822
905 Dell Ave Campbell (95008) ***(P-16618)***
JD Printing and Mailing, San Dimas *Also called J & D Business Forms Inc* ***(P-6898)***
JD Processing Inc ... E ... 714 972-8161
2220 Cape Cod Way Santa Ana (92703) ***(P-13436)***
JDC Development Group Inc ... E ... 714 575-1108
1321 N Blue Gum St Anaheim (92806) ***(P-4525)***
Jdh Pacific Inc (PA) ... E ... 562 926-8088
14821 Artesia Blvd La Mirada (90638) ***(P-11495)***
Jdi Display America Inc (PA) ... E ... 408 501-3720
1740 Tech Dr Ste 460 San Jose (95110) ***(P-19598)***
JDM Properties ... E ... 209 632-0616
410 S Golden State Blvd Turlock (95380) ***(P-9015)***
Jdr Engineering Cons Inc ... C ... 714 751-7084
3122 Maple St Santa Ana (92707) ***(P-10166)***
Jds Technologies ... F ... 858 486-8787
12200 Thatcher Ct Poway (92064) ***(P-19599)***
Jdsu, San Jose *Also called Viavi Solutions Inc* ***(P-20099)***
Jdsu Photonic Power (HQ) ... F ... 408 546-5000
1768 Automation Pkwy San Jose (95131) ***(P-19992)***
Je Nard's Window Covering, San Jose *Also called Jenards Window Coverings* ***(P-5198)***
JE Thomson & Company LLC ... F ... 626 334-7190
6370 N Irwindale Ave Irwindale (91702) ***(P-14330)***
Jeannine's Bakery, Santa Barbara *Also called Jeannines Bkg Co Santa Barbara* ***(P-1275)***
Jeannines Bkg Co Santa Barbara (PA) ... E ... 805 966-1717
15 E Figueroa St Santa Barbara (93101) ***(P-1275)***
Jeb-PHI Inc ... E ... 562 861-0863
10417 Lakewood Blvd Downey (90241) ***(P-6910)***
Jeditron Technologies Corp ... F ... 510 226-1383
44137 Fremont Blvd Fremont (94538) ***(P-15774)***
Jeff Burgess & Associates Inc (PA) ... E ... 415 256-2800
1050 Northgate Dr Ste 200 San Rafael (94903) ***(P-17820)***
Jeff Frank ... F ... 831 469-8208
120 Encinal St Santa Cruz (95060) ***(P-23907)***
Jeff J Polich Inc ... F ... 626 339-3070
281 E San Bernardino Rd Covina (91723) ***(P-21781)***
Jeffrey Court Inc ... D ... 951 340-3383
620 Parkridge Ave Norco (92860) ***(P-10784)***
Jeffrey Fabrication LLC ... E ... 562 634-3101
6323 Alondra Blvd Paramount (90723) ***(P-12630)***
Jeffrey Rudes LLC ... F ... 310 281-0800
9550 Heather Rd Beverly Hills (90210) ***(P-3166)***
JEI ... E ... 530 677-3210
3087 Alhambra Dr Cameron Park (95682) ***(P-18138)***
Jeico Security Inc ... F
1525 N Endeavor Ln Ste Q Anaheim (92801) ***(P-19993)***
Jejomi Designs Inc ... E ... 323 584-4211
2626 Fruitland Ave Vernon (90058) ***(P-3616)***
Jeld-Wen Inc ... E ... 800 468-3667
3760 Convoy St Ste 111 San Diego (92111) ***(P-4172)***
Jeld-Wen Inc ... C ... 916 782-4900
3901 Cincinnati Ave Rocklin (95765) ***(P-4173)***
Jelenko, San Diego *Also called Argen Corporation* ***(P-11543)***
Jellco Container Inc ... D ... 714 666-2728
1151 N Tustin Ave Anaheim (92807) ***(P-5431)***
Jelly Belly Candy Company (PA) ... B ... 707 428-2800
1 Jelly Belly Ln Fairfield (94533) ***(P-1431)***
Jelly Belly Candy Company ... E ... 707 428-2800
2400 N Watney Way Fairfield (94533) ***(P-1432)***
Jeluz Electric Ltd LLC ... E ... 800 216-8307
25060 Hancock Ave Murrieta (92562) ***(P-19994)***
Jem America Corp ... E ... 510 683-9234
3000 Laurelview Ct Fremont (94538) ***(P-21782)***
Jem Sportswear, Cypress *Also called Awake Inc* ***(P-3294)***
Jem-Hd Co Inc ... D ... 619 710-1443
10030 Via De La Amistad F San Diego (92154) ***(P-10167)***
Jemstep Inc ... E ... 650 966-6500
5150 El Camino Real C20 Los Altos (94022) ***(P-24815)***
Jemstone, Los Angeles *Also called Oak Apparel Inc* ***(P-3472)***
Jenards Window Coverings ... F ... 408 434-5937
2299 Ringwood Ave Ste C2 San Jose (95131) ***(P-5198)***
Jenavalve Technology Inc ... E ... 949 396-7555
7545 Irvine Center Dr Irvine (92618) ***(P-22995)***
Jeneric/Pentron Incorporated (HQ) ... C ... 203 265-7397
1717 W Collins Ave Orange (92867) ***(P-22885)***
Jennings Aeronautics Inc ... E ... 805 544-0932
3183 Duncan Ln Ste C San Luis Obispo (93401) ***(P-21312)***
Jennings Technology Co LLC (HQ) ... D ... 408 292-4025
970 Mclaughlin Ave San Jose (95122) ***(P-19297)***
Jennis Group LLC ... F ... 714 227-7972
1631 Placentia Ave Costa Mesa (92627) ***(P-6506)***
Jenny Sammon ... F ... 951 926-4326
600 Anton Blvd Ste 1100 Costa Mesa (92626) ***(P-20855)***
Jensen Door Systems Inc ... F ... 760 736-4036
160 Vallecitos De Oro San Marcos (92069) ***(P-4174)***
Jensen Enterprises Inc ... F ... 530 865-4277
7210 State Highway 32 Orland (95963) ***(P-10942)***
Jensen Enterprises Inc ... B ... 909 357-7264
14221 San Bernardino Ave Fontana (92335) ***(P-10943)***
Jensen Graphics & Printing ... F ... 707 987-8966
18270 Spyglass Rd Hidden Valley Lake (95467) ***(P-6911)***
Jensen Meat Company Inc ... D ... 619 754-6400
2550 Britannia Blvd # 101 San Diego (92154) ***(P-496)***
Jensen Precast, Fontana *Also called Jensen Enterprises Inc* ***(P-10943)***
Jenson Custom Furniture Inc ... D ... 714 634-8145
2161 S Dupont Dr Anaheim (92806) ***(P-4785)***
Jenson Mechanical Inc ... E ... 510 429-8078
32420 Central Ave Union City (94587) ***(P-16619)***
Jerames Industries Inc ... E ... 619 334-2204
460 Cypress Ln Ste F El Cajon (92020) ***(P-16620)***
Jerames Tool & Mfg, El Cajon *Also called Jerames Industries Inc* ***(P-16620)***

Mergent e-mail: customerrelations@mergent.com
1180
2019 California
Manufacturers Register
(P-0000) Products & Services Section entry number
(PA)=Parent Co (HQ)=Headquarters (DH)=Div Headquarters

Jeremiahs Pick Coffee Company ....F....415 206-9900
1495 Evans Ave San Francisco (94124) *(P-2355)*
Jerome Russell, Canoga Park *Also called International Beauty Pdts LLC (P-8772)*
Jerry Carroll Machinery Inc ....F....650 591-3302
993 E San Carlos Ave San Carlos (94070) *(P-16621)*
Jerry Melton & Sons Cnstr, Taft *Also called Jerry Melton & Sons Cnstr (P-228)*
Jerry Melton & Sons Cnstr ....D....661 765-5546
100 Jamison Ln Taft (93268) *(P-228)*
Jerry Slmon Cstm Picture Frmng, Los Angeles *Also called Jerry Solomon Enterprises Inc (P-4626)*
Jerry Solomon Enterprises Inc ....E....323 556-2265
5221 W Jefferson Blvd Los Angeles (90016) *(P-4626)*
Jerry V Johnson & Assoc Inc ....F....818 543-6710
720 S Glendale Ave Glendale (91205) *(P-7204)*
Jess Howard ....F....530 533-3888
2800 Richter Ave Oroville (95966) *(P-10168)*
Jessee Brothers Machine Sp Inc ....F....408 866-1755
1640 Dell Ave Campbell (95008) *(P-16622)*
Jessica McClintock Inc (PA) ....C....415 553-8200
2307 Broadway St San Francisco (94115) *(P-3578)*
Jessie A Laurent, San Rafael *Also called Laurent Culinary Service (P-2580)*
Jessie Steele Inc ....F....510 204-0991
2112 Adams Ave San Leandro (94577) *(P-3952)*
Jessies Grove Winery ....F....209 368-0880
1973 W Turner Rd Lodi (95242) *(P-1830)*
Jessop Industries ....F....805 581-6976
4645 Industrial St Ste 2c Simi Valley (93063) *(P-16623)*
Jessup Cellars Inc ....E....707 944-8523
6740 Washington St Yountville (94599) *(P-1831)*
Jesta Digital Entrmt Inc (HQ) ....F....323 648-4200
15303 Ventura Blvd # 900 Sherman Oaks (91403) *(P-24816)*
Jesus Cabezas ....F....650 583-0469
145 Utah Ave South San Francisco (94080) *(P-2544)*
Jet & Western Abrasives, Placentia *Also called Jet Abrasives Inc (P-11296)*
Jet Abrasives Inc ....E....323 588-1245
1891 E Miraloma Ave Placentia (92870) *(P-11296)*
Jet Air Fbo LLC ....E....619 448-5991
681 Kenney St El Cajon (92020) *(P-20856)*
Jet Cutting Solutions Inc ....F....909 948-2424
10853 Bell Ct Rancho Cucamonga (91730) *(P-4576)*
Jet I, Fontana *Also called Jeti Inc (P-25416)*
Jet Performance Products Inc ....E....714 848-5500
17491 Apex Cir Huntington Beach (92647) *(P-19837)*
Jet Plastics (PA) ....D....323 268-6706
941 N Eastern Ave Los Angeles (90063) *(P-10169)*
Jet Products, San Diego *Also called Senior Operations LLC (P-16939)*
Jet Set California, San Leandro *Also called Jetset California Inc (P-10758)*
Jet Transmission, Huntington Beach *Also called Jet Performance Products Inc (P-19837)*
Jet/Brella Inc ....E....818 786-5480
6849 Hayvenhurst Ave Van Nuys (91406) *(P-20666)*
Jetair Technologies LLC ....F....805 654-7000
1756 Eastman Ave Ste 100 Ventura (93003) *(P-15163)*
Jetco, Irwindale *Also called Connor J Inc (P-21739)*
Jetco Torque Tools LLC ....F....626 359-2881
835 Meridian St Duarte (91010) *(P-15240)*
Jeteffect Inc (PA) ....F....562 989-8800
3250 Airflite Way Fl 3 Long Beach (90807) *(P-20593)*
Jetfax, Los Angeles *Also called Efaxcom (P-15735)*
Jeti Inc (PA) ....F....909 357-2966
14578 Hawthorne Ave Fontana (92335) *(P-25416)*
Jetlore LLC ....E....650 485-1822
1528 S El Camino Real # 101 San Mateo (94402) *(P-24817)*
Jetnexus LLC ....E....800 568-9921
3201 Great America Pkwy Ste 320 Santa Clara (95054) *(P-15435)*
Jetronics Company, Santa Rosa *Also called James L Hall Co Incorporated (P-19342)*
Jetset California Inc ....F....510 632-7800
2150 Edison Ave San Leandro (94577) *(P-10758)*
Jetstream Trading Co ....F....818 921-7158
1005 E Las Tunas Dr U356 San Gabriel (91776) *(P-20857)*
Jevin Enterprises Inc ....E....818 408-0488
11548 Apulia Ct Porter Ranch (91326) *(P-9472)*
Jewel Date Company Inc ....E....760 399-4474
84675 60th Ave Thermal (92274) *(P-1433)*
Jewelry Club House Inc ....F....213 362-7888
606 S Olive St Ste 2000 Los Angeles (90014) *(P-23278)*
Jewelry Manufacturing, Los Angeles *Also called Gold Craft Jewelry Corp (P-23271)*
Jewels By Angelo Inc ....F....562 862-6293
9221 Rives Ave Downey (90240) *(P-23279)*
JEWISH JOURNAL, THE, Los Angeles *Also called Tribe Media Corp (P-6073)*
Jewish News, Sherman Oaks *Also called Phil Blazer Enterprises Inc (P-6014)*
JF FIXTURES & DESIGN, Long Beach *Also called F-J-E Inc (P-5060)*
Jff Uniforms, Torrance *Also called Just For Fun (P-3058)*
JG Boswell Tomato - Kern LLC ....E....661 764-9000
36889 Hwy 58 Buttonwillow (93206) *(P-810)*
JG Plastics Group LLC ....E....714 751-4266
335 Fischer Ave Costa Mesa (92626) *(P-10170)*
JGA Inc ....F....310 672-4000
1123 E Redondo Blvd Inglewood (90302) *(P-4786)*
JGM Automotive Tooling Inc ....E....714 895-7001
5355 Industrial Dr Huntington Beach (92649) *(P-14976)*
JH Baxter A Cal Ltd Partnr (PA) ....E....650 349-0201
1700 S El Camino Real San Mateo (94402) *(P-4594)*
Jh Biotech Inc (PA) ....E....805 650-8933
4951 Olivas Park Dr Ventura (93003) *(P-9084)*
Jhawar Industries Inc (PA) ....E....951 340-4646
525 Klug Cir Corona (92880) *(P-15265)*
JIC Industrial Co Inc ....F....408 935-9880
978 Hanson Ct Milpitas (95035) *(P-19600)*
Jifco Inc (PA) ....D....925 449-4665
571 Exchange Ct Livermore (94550) *(P-13891)*
Jifco Fabaricated Piping, Livermore *Also called Jifco Inc (P-13891)*
Jifflenow, Sunnyvale *Also called Ipolipo Inc (P-24801)*
Jigmasters Tool & Gauge, Santa Ana *Also called Aluminum Precision Pdts Inc (P-13121)*
Jigsaw Data Corporation ....F....650 235-8400
900 Concar Dr San Mateo (94402) *(P-6507)*
Jim & Lees Optical, Modesto *Also called Jims Optical (P-22094)*
Jim Beam Brands Co ....F....949 200-7200
17901 Von Karman Ave Irvine (92614) *(P-2072)*
Jim Beauregard ....D....831 423-9453
1661 Pine Flat Rd Santa Cruz (95060) *(P-1832)*
Jim Ellis ....F....760 244-8566
16797 Live Oak St Hesperia (92345) *(P-4416)*
Jim Graham Inc ....E....707 374-5114
4 Hill Ct Rio Vista (94571) *(P-229)*
Jim James Enterprises Inc ....F....818 772-8595
9148 Jordan Ave Chatsworth (91311) *(P-12631)*
Jim Little Raymonds Print Shop, Fremont *Also called Raymonds Little Print Shop Inc (P-7077)*
Jim Perry ....E....909 947-0747
13611 Northlands Rd Corona (92880) *(P-7604)*
Jim Wheeler Logging, Miranda *Also called Wheeler Lumber Co Inc (P-4023)*
Jim's Machining, Camarillo *Also called Thiessen Products Inc (P-16998)*
Jim-Buoy, North Hollywood *Also called Cal-June Inc (P-11941)*
Jlmachine Company Inc ....E....858 695-1787
9720 Distribution Ave San Diego (92121) *(P-16624)*
Jimenes Food Inc ....E....562 602-2505
7046 Jackson St Paramount (90723) *(P-2545)*
Jimenez Mexican Foods Inc ....E....951 351-0102
11010 Wells Ave Riverside (92505) *(P-761)*
Jimo Enterprises ....E....323 469-0805
6001 Santa Monica Blvd Los Angeles (90038) *(P-4627)*
Jims Optical ....F....209 549-2517
5253 Jerusalem Ct Ste G Modesto (95356) *(P-22094)*
Jimway Inc ....D....310 886-3718
20101 S Santa Fe Ave Compton (90221) *(P-17705)*
Jinelle, Los Angeles *Also called Rose Genuine Inc (P-3586)*
Jinkosolar (us) Inc ....F....415 402-0502
595 Market St Ste 2200 San Francisco (94105) *(P-18939)*
Jishan Usa Inc ....F....408 609-3286
15257 Don Julian Rd City of Industry (91745) *(P-17620)*
Jisoncase (usa) Limited ....F....888 233-8880
9674 Telstar Ave Ste A El Monte (91731) *(P-10460)*
Jivago Inc (PA) ....F....310 205-5535
9454 Wilshire Blvd # 600 Beverly Hills (90212) *(P-8775)*
Jj Lithographics Inc ....F....562 698-0280
8607 Dice Rd Santa Fe Springs (90670) *(P-6912)*
Jj Printing, Santa Fe Springs *Also called Jj Lithographics Inc (P-6912)*
Jjs Truck Equipment LLC ....E....858 566-1155
9685 Via Excelencia # 200 San Diego (92126) *(P-20211)*
Jkf Construction Inc ....F....805 583-4228
460 E Easy St Ste 102 Simi Valley (93065) *(P-4314)*
JKL Components Corporation ....E....818 896-0019
13343 Paxton St Pacoima (91331) *(P-17662)*
Jl Design Enterprises Inc ....D....714 479-0240
1821 Newport Cir Santa Ana (92705) *(P-3057)*
JL Mallard Inc ....E....909 593-3403
4747 Live Oak Canyon Rd La Verne (91750) *(P-12187)*
Jl Racing.com, Santa Ana *Also called Jl Design Enterprises Inc (P-3057)*
Jlab Audio, Carlsbad *Also called Jlab LLC (P-19601)*
Jlab Audio, Carlsbad *Also called Peag LLC (P-19683)*
Jlab LLC ....E....405 445-7219
2281 Las Palmas Dr # 101 Carlsbad (92011) *(P-19601)*
Jlcooper, El Segundo *Also called J L Cooper Electronics Inc (P-19589)*
Jlg Industries Inc ....C....951 509-1227
7820 Lincoln Ave Riverside (92504) *(P-14177)*
Jlg Serviceplus, Riverside *Also called Jlg Industries Inc (P-14177)*
Jlm Energy Inc ....E....916 304-1603
3735 Placer Corp Dr Ste A Rocklin (95765) *(P-14000)*
JM Eagle, Perris *Also called J-M Manufacturing Company Inc (P-7848)*
JM Eagle, Los Angeles *Also called J-M Manufacturing Company Inc (P-9782)*
JM Eagle, Los Angeles *Also called Pw Eagle Inc (P-9786)*
JM Kitchen Cabinets ....F....323 752-6520
702 E Gage Ave Los Angeles (90001) *(P-4315)*
Jmg Machine Inc ....E....562 926-2848
17037 Industry Pl La Mirada (90638) *(P-16625)*
Jmgj Group Inc ....F....866 293-2872
10120 Wexted Way Elk Grove (95757) *(P-23749)*
Jmi Steel Inc ....E....818 768-3955
8983 San Fernando Rd Sun Valley (91352) *(P-12867)*
Jml Textile Inc ....D....323 584-2323
5801 S 2nd St Vernon (90058) *(P-2748)*
Jmp Electronics Inc ....F....714 730-2086
2685 Dow Ave Ste A1 Tustin (92780) *(P-18515)*
Jmr Electronics Inc ....E....818 993-4801
8968 Fullbright Ave Chatsworth (91311) *(P-15562)*
Jmt Inc ....F....562 404-2014
14926 Bloomfield Ave Norwalk (90650) *(P-16626)*
Jmu Dental Inc ....F....909 676-0000
16273 Gale Ave City of Industry (91745) *(P-22886)*
Jmw Truss and Components, San Diego *Also called Trademark Construction Co Inc (P-19847)*
Jnc Machining ....F....408 920-2520
1834 Stone Ave San Jose (95125) *(P-16627)*
JNJ Apparel Inc ....E....323 584-9700
3838 S Santa Fe Ave Vernon (90058) *(P-3437)*

Employee Codes: A=Over 500 employees, B=251-500
C=101-250, D=51-100, E=20-50, F=10-19
2019 California
Manfacturers Register
© Mergent Inc. 1-800-342-5647
1181

Jnj Operations LLC .....E.......855 525-6545
859 E Sepulveda Blvd Carson (90745) *(P-24137)*
Jns Industries Inc .....F.......909 923-8334
2320 S Vineyard Ave Ontario (91761) *(P-16628)*
Jo Sonjas Folk Art Studio 707 445-9306
2136 3rd St Eureka (95501) *(P-6356)*
Joa Corporation (PA) .....E.......951 785-4411
7254 Magnolia Ave Riverside (92504) *(P-22758)*
Joanka Inc .....F.......310 326-8940
25510 Frampton Ave Harbor City (90710) *(P-12323)*
Joann Lammens .....F.......909 593-8478
2152 Bonita Ave La Verne (91750) *(P-24138)*
Joaos A Tin Fish Bar & Eatery .....E.......619 794-2192
2750 Dewey Rd San Diego (92106) *(P-11632)*
Joar Labs Inc .....E.......818 243-0700
4115 San Fernando Rd Glendale (91204) *(P-8776)*
Job Shop Managers, Valencia Also called Skm Industries Inc *(P-13276)*
Jobbers Meat Packing Co Inc .....F.......323 585-6328
3336 Fruitland Ave Vernon (90058) *(P-440)*
Jobs & Careers Newspapers Inc .....F.......650 367-6885
1480 Oddstad Dr Redwood City (94063) *(P-5893)*
Jodel Enterprises .....F.......650 343-4510
340 Gateway Dr Apt 105 Pacifica (94044) *(P-17821)*
Jodi Kristopher LLC (PA) .....C.......323 890-8000
1950 Naomi Ave Los Angeles (90011) *(P-3318)*
Jody Maronis Italian .....E.......310 822-5639
2011 Ocean Front Walk Venice (90291) *(P-497)*
Jody of California, Los Angeles Also called Private Brand Mdsg Corp *(P-3333)*
Joe Blasco Cosmetics, Palm Springs Also called Joe Blasco Enterprises Inc *(P-24139)*
Joe Blasco Enterprises Inc .....D.......323 467-4949
1285 N Valdivia Way A Palm Springs (92262) *(P-24139)*
Joe Montana Footwear .....D.......310 318-3100
228 Manhattan Beach Blvd Manhattan Beach (90266) *(P-9473)*
Joe's Jeans, Los Angeles Also called Dbg Subsidiary Inc *(P-3351)*
Joe's Trailer Repair, Fontana Also called Wagonmasters Corporation *(P-21246)*
Joes Custom Furn & Frames .....F.......323 721-1881
6402 Whittier Blvd Los Angeles (90022) *(P-4707)*
Johansing Iron Works Inc .....F.......707 361-8190
849 Jackson St Benicia (94510) *(P-12392)*
Johanson Dielectrics Inc (HQ) .....C.......818 364-9800
15191 Bledsoe St Sylmar (91342) *(P-19298)*
Johanson Innovations Inc 805 544-4697
2975 Hawk Hill Ln San Luis Obispo (93405) *(P-22221)*
Johanson Technology Inc .....C.......805 389-1166
4001 Calle Tecate Camarillo (93012) *(P-19299)*
Johasee Rebar Inc .....E.......661 589-0972
18059 Rosedale Hwy Bakersfield (93314) *(P-12188)*
Johasee Rebar LP (PA) .....F.......604 598-9930
18059 Rosedale Hwy Bakersfield (93314) *(P-12981)*
John A Thomson PHD .....E.......323 877-5186
12610 Saticoy St S North Hollywood (91605) *(P-7953)*
John B Campbell MD A Prof Corp .....F.......858 576-9960
9292 Chesapeake Dr # 100 San Diego (92123) *(P-9016)*
John B Sanfilippo & Son Inc .....B.......209 854-2455
29241 Cottonwood Rd Gustine (95322) *(P-1491)*
John Bean Technologies Corp 559 661-3200
2300 W Industrial Ave Madera (93637) *(P-14862)*
John Bean Technologies Corp 951 222-2300
1660 Iowa Ave Ste 100 Riverside (92507) *(P-14863)*
John Bean Technologies Corp .....C.......559 651-8300
9829 W Legacy Ave Visalia (93291) *(P-14864)*
John Bishop Design Inc .....E.......714 744-2300
731 N Main St Orange (92868) *(P-23908)*
John Boyd Enterprises Inc 916 504-3622
8441 Specialty Cir Sacramento (95828) *(P-20376)*
John Boyd Enterprises Inc (PA) .....C.......916 381-4790
8401 Specialty Cir Sacramento (95828) *(P-20377)*
John Crane Inc .....E.......562 802-2555
12760 Florence Ave Santa Fe Springs (90670) *(P-11322)*
John Daniel Gonzalez 559 646-6621
13458 E Industrial Dr Parlier (93648) *(P-4526)*
John Deere Authorized Dealer, City of Industry Also called Valley Power Systems Inc *(P-14035)*
John Fitzpatrick & Sons .....F.......530 241-3216
1480 Beltline Rd Redding (96003) *(P-2141)*
John Henry Packaging West, Petaluma Also called MPS Lansing Inc *(P-5572)*
John L Conley Inc .....D.......909 627-0981
4344 Mission Blvd Montclair (91763) *(P-12936)*
John L Perry Studio Inc .....E.......805 981-9665
3000 Paseo Mercado # 102 Oxnard (93036) *(P-10171)*
John L Staton Inc .....D.......510 527-3114
1214 5th St Berkeley (94710) *(P-4175)*
John List Corporation .....E.......818 882-7848
9732 Cozycroft Ave Chatsworth (91311) *(P-14716)*
John Lompa 510 965-6501
720 Harbour Way S Ste A Richmond (94804) *(P-7365)*
John M Phillips LLC .....F.......661 327-3118
2800 Gibson St Bakersfield (93308) *(P-230)*
John M Phillips Oil Field Eqp, Bakersfield Also called John M Phillips LLC *(P-230)*
John N Hansen Co Inc (PA) 650 652-9833
369 Adrian Rd Millbrae (94030) *(P-23436)*
John Pina Jr & Sons .....E.......707 944-2229
7960 Silverado Trl NAPA (94558) *(P-1833)*
John Russo Industrial Metal, Newark Also called Jri Inc *(P-12633)*
John Wheeler Logging Inc 530 527-2993
13570 State Highway 36 E Red Bluff (96080) *(P-3997)*
John Wiley & Sons Inc .....C.......415 433-1740
1 Montgomery St Ste 1200 San Francisco (94104) *(P-6357)*

Johnny Was Collection Inc (PA) .....E.......323 231-8222
2423 E 23rd St Los Angeles (90058) *(P-3319)*
Johnny Was Showroom, Los Angeles Also called Johnny Was Collection Inc *(P-3319)*
Johns Formica Shop Inc .....F.......707 544-8585
2439 Piner Rd Santa Rosa (95403) *(P-5150)*
Johns Incredible Pizza Co .....D.......760 951-1111
14766 Bear Valley Rd Victorville (92395) *(P-2546)*
Johns Manville Corporation .....B.......530 934-6243
5916 County Road 49 Willows (95988) *(P-11333)*
Johns Manville Corporation .....D.......323 568-2220
4301 Firestone Blvd South Gate (90280) *(P-11334)*
Johnson & Johnson .....E.......408 273-4100
510 Cottonwood Dr Milpitas (95035) *(P-22500)*
Johnson & Johnson .....B.......909 839-8650
15715 Arrow Hwy Irwindale (91706) *(P-22759)*
Johnson & Johnson .....D.......650 237-4878
3509 Langdon Cmn Fremont (94538) *(P-5667)*
Johnson & Johnson (HQ) .....B.......714 247-8200
1700 E Saint Andrew Pl Santa Ana (92705) *(P-22996)*
Johnson & Johnson .....E.......909 839-8690
5110 Commerce Dr Baldwin Park (91706) *(P-22760)*
Johnson & Johnson 714 247-8200
2501 Pullman St Santa Ana (92705) *(P-22095)*
Johnson & Johnson Consumer Inc .....E.......310 642-1150
5670 W 96th St Los Angeles (90045) *(P-8777)*
Johnson & Johnson Vision, Milpitas Also called Johnson & Johnson *(P-22500)*
Johnson Art Studio Inc .....F.......831 763-2744
375 W Beach St Watsonville (95076) *(P-17621)*
Johnson Art Studio, Watsonville Also called Johnson Art Studio Inc *(P-17621)*
Johnson Caldraul Inc .....E.......951 340-1067
220 N Delilah St Ste 101 Corona (92879) *(P-20858)*
Johnson Contrls Authorized Dlr, Hayward Also called Automatic Control Engrg Corp *(P-22167)*
Johnson Controls .....C.......858 633-9100
3568 Ruffin Rd San Diego (92123) *(P-18333)*
Johnson Controls 925 273-0100
6952 Preston Ave Ste A Livermore (94551) *(P-18334)*
Johnson Controls .....F.......530 893-0110
13504 Skypark Industrial Chico (95973) *(P-18335)*
Johnson Controls .....D.......916 283-0300
4650 Beloit Dr Sacramento (95838) *(P-18336)*
Johnson Controls Inc .....C.......562 799-8882
5770 Warland Dr Ste A Cypress (90630) *(P-5018)*
Johnson Controls Inc .....B.......925 447-9200
6383 Las Positas Rd Livermore (94551) *(P-20378)*
Johnson Doc Enterprises .....E.......818 764-1543
11933 Vose St North Hollywood (91605) *(P-10172)*
Johnson Farm Machinery Co Inc .....F.......530 662-1788
38574 Kentucky Ave Woodland (95695) *(P-14076)*
Johnson Industrial Sheet Metal .....F.......916 927-8244
2131 Barstow St Sacramento (95815) *(P-12632)*
Johnson Laminating Coating Inc .....D.......310 635-4929
20701 Annalee Ave Carson (90746) *(P-9751)*
Johnson Leather Corporation (PA) .....F.......415 775-7393
1833 Polk St San Francisco (94109) *(P-3617)*
Johnson Leather Corporation .....F.......415 863-8819
3265 17th St Ste 204 San Francisco (94110) *(P-3618)*
Johnson Manufacturing, Woodland Also called Johnson Farm Machinery Co Inc *(P-14076)*
Johnson Manufacturing Inc .....E.......714 903-0393
15201 Connector Ln Huntington Beach (92649) *(P-16629)*
Johnson Marble Machinery Inc .....F.......818 764-6186
7325 Varna Ave North Hollywood (91605) *(P-14977)*
Johnson Outdoors Inc .....E.......619 402-1023
1166 Fesler St Ste A El Cajon (92020) *(P-23599)*
Johnson Precision Products Inc .....F.......714 824-6971
1308 E Wakeham Ave Santa Ana (92705) *(P-16630)*
Johnson Racing, Santa Maria Also called Alan Johnson Prfmce Engrg Inc *(P-20122)*
Johnson United Inc (PA) .....E.......209 543-1320
5201 Pentecost Dr Modesto (95356) *(P-23909)*
Johnson Wilshire Inc .....E.......562 777-0088
17343 Freedom Way City of Industry (91748) *(P-22761)*
Johnsons Orthopedic, Riverside Also called Joa Corporation *(P-22758)*
Johnston Aircraft Service Inc .....F.......559 686-1795
6679 Dale Fry Rd Tulare (93274) *(P-21313)*
Johnstons Trading Post Inc .....E.......530 661-6152
11 N Pioneer Ave Woodland (95776) *(P-4527)*
Joico Laboratories Inc .....C.......626 321-4100
488 E Santa Clara St # 301 Arcadia (91006) *(P-8778)*
Joint Technologies Limited .....F.......949 361-1158
5120 E La Palma Ave # 205 Anaheim (92807) *(P-15436)*
Jolly Jumps Inc 805 484-0026
600 Via Alondra Camarillo (93012) *(P-16631)*
Jolly Roger Games, Commerce Also called Ultra Pro International LLC *(P-7588)*
Jolo Industries Inc .....E.......714 554-6840
10432 Brightwood Dr Santa Ana (92705) *(P-19602)*
Jolyn Clothing Company LLC .....E.......714 794-2149
150 5th St Ste 100 Huntington Beach (92648) *(P-3438)*
Jomar Machining Inc .....F.......650 324-2143
180 Constitution Dr Ste 8 Menlo Park (94025) *(P-19603)*
Jon Brooks Inc (PA) .....C.......626 330-0631
14400 Lomitas Ave City of Industry (91746) *(P-11323)*
Jon Davler Inc .....E.......626 941-6558
9440 Gidley St Temple City (91780) *(P-8779)*
Jon Steel Erectors Inc .....E.......909 799-0005
1431 S Gage St San Bernardino (92408) *(P-25417)*
Jona Global Trading Inc .....F.......626 855-2588
245 S 8th Ave La Puente (91746) *(P-4866)*
Jonathan Engnred Slutions Corp (PA) .....E.......714 665-4400
250 Commerce Ste 100 Irvine (92602) *(P-11966)*

Mergent e-mail: customerrelations@mergent.com
1182
2019 California
Manufacturers Register
(P-0000) Products & Services Section entry number
(PA)=Parent Co (HQ)=Headquarters (DH)=Div Headquarters

Jonathan Louis Intl Ltd.....B.....213 622-6114
12919 S Figueroa St Los Angeles (90061) *(P-4787)*
Jonathan Louis Intl Ltd (PA).....C.....323 770-3330
544 W 130th St Gardena (90248) *(P-4788)*
Jonathan Martin, Los Angeles *Also called Harkham Industries Inc (P-3244)*
Jondo.....E.....714 394-4344
10556 Industrial Ave # 100 Roseville (95678) *(P-2749)*
Jondo Ltd.....E.....714 279-2300
22700 Savi Ranch Pkwy Yorba Linda (92887) *(P-7366)*
Jonel Engineering.....E.....714 879-2360
500 E Walnut Ave Fullerton (92832) *(P-16175)*
Jonell Oil Corporation.....F.....626 303-4691
13649 Live Oak Ln Irwindale (91706) *(P-9440)*
Jones Glyn Productions Inc.....F.....760 431-8955
1945 Camino Vida Roble M Carlsbad (92008) *(P-6508)*
Jones Iron Works.....F.....323 386-2368
2658 Griffith Park Blvd Los Angeles (90039) *(P-12868)*
Joong-Ang Daily News Cal Inc (HQ).....C.....213 368-2500
690 Wilshire Pl Los Angeles (90005) *(P-5894)*
Joong-Ang Daily News Cal Inc.....F.....714 638-2341
8269 Garden Grove Blvd Garden Grove (92844) *(P-5895)*
Joongang Dily Nwssan Francisco, Union City *Also called Korea Central Daily News (P-5899)*
Jordan Companies.....E.....949 492-0804
2122 S El Camino Real E San Clemente (92672) *(P-14642)*
Jordan Vineyard & Winery, Healdsburg *Also called Jvw Corporation (P-1836)*
Jordan Vineyard & Winery LP.....E.....707 431-5250
1474 Alexander Valley Rd Healdsburg (95448) *(P-1834)*
Jorge Segovia.....E.....562 699-8554
9612 Beverly Rd Pico Rivera (90660) *(P-13952)*
Jorlind Enterprises Inc.....F.....949 364-2309
28570 Marguerite Pkwy # 108 Mission Viejo (92692) *(P-6913)*
Jose Martinez.....F.....323 263-6230
1281 S Hicks Ave Los Angeles (90023) *(P-1434)*
Jose Martinez Candy, Los Angeles *Also called Jose Martinez (P-1434)*
Josef Mendelovitz.....F.....619 231-3555
11240 Explorer Rd La Mesa (91941) *(P-6914)*
Joseph Charles Whitson.....F.....707 694-8806
154 Auburn Way Vacaville (95688) *(P-6509)*
Joseph Company International.....E.....949 474-2200
1711 Langley Ave Irvine (92614) *(P-11859)*
Joseph Farms, Atwater *Also called Gallo Global Nutrition LLC (P-574)*
Joseph Phelps Vineyards, Saint Helena *Also called Stone Bridge Cellars Inc (P-1997)*
Joslyn Sunbank Company LLC.....B.....805 238-2840
1740 Commerce Way Paso Robles (93446) *(P-19399)*
Jossey-Bass Publishers, San Francisco *Also called John Wiley & Sons Inc (P-6357)*
Jostens Inc.....C.....559 622-5200
231 S Kelsey St Visalia (93291) *(P-23280)*
Jostens Printing & Publishing, Visalia *Also called Jostens Inc (P-23280)*
Jot Engineering Inc.....F.....818 727-7572
8385 Canoga Ave Canoga Park (91304) *(P-16632)*
Jouer Cosmetics LLC.....F.....310 312-0500
1929 Pontius Ave Los Angeles (90025) *(P-8780)*
Journal of Bocommunication Inc.....F.....310 475-4708
2772 Woodwardia Dr Los Angeles (90077) *(P-5896)*
Journeyworks Publishing.....F.....831 423-1400
763 Chestnut St Santa Cruz (95060) *(P-6510)*
Joy Active.....D.....310 660-0022
13324 Estrella Ave Gardena (90248) *(P-3439)*
Joy of Cookies, Oakland *Also called Arbo Inc (P-1348)*
Joy Processed Foods Inc.....E.....562 435-1106
1330 Seabright Ave Long Beach (90813) *(P-2547)*
Joy Products California Inc.....F.....714 437-7250
17281 Mount Wynne Cir Fountain Valley (92708) *(P-23718)*
Joy Signal Technology LLC.....E.....530 891-3551
1020 Marauder St Ste A Chico (95973) *(P-17476)*
Joybird, Commerce *Also called Stitch Industries Inc (P-4813)*
JP Graphics Inc.....E.....408 235-8821
3310 Woodward Ave Santa Clara (95054) *(P-7367)*
JP Graphics Inc.....E.....408 235-8821
3310 Woodward Ave Santa Clara (95054) *(P-6915)*
JP Products LLC.....E.....310 237-6237
2054 Davie Ave Commerce (90040) *(P-4708)*
Jpm Finishing Company, Hesperia *Also called Daytec Center LLC (P-21105)*
JR Daniels Commercial Bldrs.....D.....209 545-6040
907 Maze Blvd Modesto (95351) *(P-12982)*
Jr Grease Services.....E.....323 318-2096
5900 S Eastrn Ave Ste 104 Commerce (90040) *(P-1528)*
JR Machine Company Inc.....E.....562 903-9477
13245 Florence Ave Santa Fe Springs (90670) *(P-16633)*
JR Simplot Company.....E.....559 866-5681
12688 S Colorado Ave Helm (93627) *(P-9080)*
JR Simplot Company.....D.....559 439-3900
12688 S Colorado Ave Fresno (93729) *(P-954)*
JR Stephens Company.....E.....707 825-0100
5208 Boyd Rd Arcata (95521) *(P-4316)*
JR Watkins LLC.....E.....415 477-8500
101 Mission St San Francisco (94105) *(P-3726)*
Jr3 Inc.....F.....530 661-3677
22 Harter Ave Ste 1 Woodland (95776) *(P-21606)*
Jrd Precision Machining Inc.....F.....408 246-9327
1158 Campbell Ave San Jose (95126) *(P-16634)*
Jri Inc.....E.....510 494-5300
38021 Cherry St Newark (94560) *(P-12633)*
Js Apparel Inc.....D.....310 631-6333
1751 E Del Amo Blvd Carson (90746) *(P-3167)*
Js Glass Wholesale.....F.....213 746-5577
2035 E 37th St Vernon (90058) *(P-10709)*
Js Manufacturing, Oceanside *Also called Schuman Enterprises Inc (P-13972)*
Js Trade Bindery Services Inc.....D.....650 486-1475
435 Harbor Blvd Belmont (94002) *(P-7605)*
Jsdu, Santa Rosa *Also called Viavi Solutions Inc (P-20098)*
Jsj Electrical Display Corp.....F.....707 747-5595
167 Grobric Ct Fairfield (94534) *(P-23910)*
Jsj Inc Corrugated.....F.....909 987-4746
10700 Jersey Blvd Rancho Cucamonga (91730) *(P-5432)*
Jsl Foods Inc (PA).....C.....323 223-2484
3550 Pasadena Ave Los Angeles (90031) *(P-2548)*
Jsl Foods Inc.....D.....323 727-9999
2222 1/2 Davie Ave Commerce (90040) *(P-2549)*
Jsl Partners Inc.....F.....408 747-9000
1294 Anvilwood Ct Sunnyvale (94089) *(P-6916)*
Jsn Industries Inc.....D.....949 458-0050
9700 Jeronimo Rd Irvine (92618) *(P-10173)*
Jsn Packaging Products Inc.....D.....949 458-0050
9700 Jeronimo Rd Irvine (92618) *(P-9739)*
Jsr Micro Inc (HQ).....C.....408 543-8800
1280 N Mathilda Ave Sunnyvale (94089) *(P-9017)*
JT Design Studio Inc (PA).....E.....213 891-1500
860 S Los Angeles St # 912 Los Angeles (90014) *(P-3440)*
Jt Manufacturing Inc.....F.....408 674-4338
1122 Wrigley Way Milpitas (95035) *(P-24140)*
Jtb Supply Company Inc.....F.....714 639-9558
1030 N Batavia St Ste A Orange (92867) *(P-18337)*
Jtea Inc.....E.....847 878-2226
1421 Valane Dr Glendale (91208) *(P-24818)*
Jts Modular Inc.....E.....661 835-9270
7001 Mcdivitt Dr Ste B Bakersfield (93313) *(P-12937)*
Juan Brambila Sr.....F.....323 939-8312
5018 Venice Blvd Los Angeles (90019) *(P-4709)*
Juanitas Foods.....C.....310 834-5339
645 Eubank Ave Wilmington (90744) *(P-762)*
Juda's Custom Cabinets, North Hollywood *Also called Vaknin Juda (P-4363)*
Judd Wire Inc.....F.....760 744-7720
870 Los Vallecitos Blvd San Marcos (92069) *(P-11665)*
Judith Von Hopf Inc.....E.....909 481-1884
8750 Prestige Ct Rancho Cucamonga (91730) *(P-5073)*
Judson Studios Inc.....F.....323 255-0131
200 S Avenue 66 Los Angeles (90042) *(P-10710)*
Judy Ann, Culver City *Also called Fortune Casuals LLC (P-3236)*
Judy O Productions Inc.....E.....323 938-8513
4858 W Pico Blvd Ste 331 Los Angeles (90019) *(P-6358)*
Judy's Candy Company, Berkeley *Also called Shelton Inc (P-1473)*
Juell Machine Coinc.....F.....909 594-8164
150 Pacific St Pomona (91768) *(P-16635)*
Juengermann Inc.....E.....805 644-7165
1899 Palma Dr Ste A Ventura (93003) *(P-13750)*
Juice Division, Pacoima *Also called American Fruits & Flavors LLC (P-2240)*
Juice Heads Inc.....F.....909 386-7933
735 E Base Line St San Bernardino (92410) *(P-811)*
Juicebot & Co LLC.....F.....651 270-8860
999 Corporate Dr Ste 100 Ladera Ranch (92694) *(P-14865)*
Juicy Couture Inc.....C.....888 824-8826
12723 Wentworth St Arleta (91331) *(P-2779)*
Juicy Whip Inc.....E.....909 392-7500
1668 Curtiss Ct La Verne (91750) *(P-14866)*
July Systems Inc (PA).....F.....650 685-2460
533 Airport Blvd Ste 395 Burlingame (94010) *(P-19867)*
Jumio Software & Dev LLC.....E.....650 388-0264
1971 Landings Dr Mountain View (94043) *(P-24819)*
Jump Start Juice Bar.....F.....949 754-3120
8001 Irvine Center Dr # 40 Irvine (92618) *(P-955)*
Jumping Cracker Beans LLC.....F.....408 265-0658
1588 Camden Village Cir San Jose (95124) *(P-7565)*
Jumpstart Juice, Irvine *Also called Jump Start Juice Bar (P-955)*
June Precision Mfg Inc.....F.....949 855-9121
22276 Chestnut Ln Lake Forest (92630) *(P-13029)*
Jungle Jumps, Pacoima *Also called Twin Peak Industries Inc (P-23679)*
Juniper Networks Inc (PA).....B.....408 745-2000
1133 Innovation Way Sunnyvale (94089) *(P-15775)*
Juniper Networks (us) Inc.....A.....408 745-2000
1133 Innovation Way Sunnyvale (94089) *(P-15776)*
Juniper Rock Corporation.....B.....949 500-1797
26000 Commercentre Dr Lake Forest (92630) *(P-321)*
Juno Graphics.....F.....310 329-0126
16334 S Avalon Blvd Gardena (90248) *(P-6917)*
Junopacific Inc.....C.....831 462-1141
2840 Res Pk Dr Ste 160 Soquel (95073) *(P-10174)*
Jupiter Systems LLC.....D.....510 675-1000
31015 Huntwood Ave Hayward (94544) *(P-15636)*
Just Inc.....C.....844 423-6637
2000 Folsom St San Francisco (94110) *(P-916)*
Just Cellular Inc.....E.....818 701-3039
9327 Deering Ave Chatsworth (91311) *(P-18139)*
Just For Fun.....E.....310 320-1327
557 Van Ness Ave Torrance (90501) *(P-3058)*
Just For Kids, Redondo Beach *Also called Sunset Islandwear (P-2896)*
Just For Wraps Inc (PA).....C.....213 239-0503
5745 Rickenbacker Rd Commerce (90040) *(P-3441)*
Just Johnsons Inc.....D.....661 396-0200
5850 District Blvd Ste 1 Bakersfield (93313) *(P-4628)*
Just Light Technology Inc.....F.....510 585-5652
46560 Fremont Blvd # 105 Fremont (94538) *(P-24820)*
Just Off Melrose Inc.....E.....714 533-4566
1196 Montalvo Way Palm Springs (92262) *(P-1367)*
Just Saying Inc.....F.....888 512-5007
800 S Date Ave Alhambra (91803) *(P-3662)*
Justenough Software Corp Inc (HQ).....E.....949 706-5400
15440 Laguna Canyon Rd # 100 Irvine (92618) *(P-24821)*

ALPHABETIC

Employee Codes: A=Over 500 employees, B=251-500
C=101-250, D=51-100, E=20-50, F=10-19
2019 California
Manfacturers Register
© Mergent Inc. 1-800-342-5647
1183

Justice Bros Dist Co Inc....E....626 359-9174
2734 Huntington Dr Duarte (91010) ***(P-8687)***
Justice Bros-J B Car Care Pdts, Duarte *Also called Justice Bros Dist Co Inc* ***(P-8687)***
Justin Inc....E....626 444-4516
2663 Lee Ave El Monte (91733) ***(P-17103)***
Justin Vineyards & Winery LLC (HQ)....E....805 238-6932
11680 Chimney Rock Rd Paso Robles (93446) ***(P-1835)***
Justipher Inc....F....510 918-6800
1248 W Winton Ave Hayward (94545) ***(P-23911)***
Juul Labs Inc (PA)....C....415 829-2336
560 20th St San Francisco (94107) ***(P-24141)***
Jvic Catalyst Services LLC....E....310 327-0991
18025 S Broadway Carson (90745) ***(P-7783)***
Jvr Sheetmetal Fabrication Inc....E....714 841-2464
7101 Patterson Dr Garden Grove (92841) ***(P-20594)***
Jvw Corporation....D....707 431-5250
1474 Alexander Valley Rd Healdsburg (95448) ***(P-1836)***
JW Manufacturing Inc....D....805 498-4594
12989 Bradley Ave Sylmar (91342) ***(P-13075)***
JW Molding Inc....F....805 499-2682
2523 Calcite Cir Newbury Park (91320) ***(P-14529)***
JW Wireless....F....626 532-2511
846 E Valley Blvd Ste A San Gabriel (91776) ***(P-18140)***
Jwc Carbide Inc....F....714 540-8870
33700 Calle Vis Temecula (92592) ***(P-14385)***
Jwc Environmental LLC....D....714 662-5829
2600 S Garnsey St Santa Ana (92707) ***(P-16061)***
JWP Manufacturing LLC....E....408 970-0641
3500 De La Cruz Blvd Santa Clara (95054) ***(P-16636)***
K & B Foam Inc....C....619 661-1870
9335 Airway Rd Ste 100 San Diego (92154) ***(P-9867)***
K & D Graphics....E....714 639-8900
1432 N Main St Ste C Orange (92867) ***(P-5654)***
K & D Graphics Prtg & Packg, Orange *Also called K & D Graphics* ***(P-5654)***
K & E Inc....F....310 675-3309
3906 W 139th St Hawthorne (90250) ***(P-20859)***
K & E Manufacturing Inc....F....562 494-7570
1966 Freeman Ave Signal Hill (90755) ***(P-12634)***
K & E Printing Ink, La Verne *Also called Farbotech Color Inc* ***(P-9192)***
K & J Wire Products Corp....E....714 816-0360
1220 N Lance Ln Anaheim (92806) ***(P-12869)***
K & K Laboratories Inc....E....760 758-2352
2160 Warmlands Ave Vista (92084) ***(P-8241)***
K & L Anodizing Corporation....D....323 849-6815
272 W Elm Ave Burbank (91502) ***(P-13437)***
K & L Precision Grinding Co....F....323 564-5151
9309 Atlantic Ave South Gate (90280) ***(P-16637)***
K & M Meat Co, Vernon *Also called K & M Packing Co Inc* ***(P-441)***
K & M Packing Co Inc....C....323 585-5318
2443 E 27th St Vernon (90058) ***(P-441)***
K & M Software Design LLC....F....805 583-0403
2828 Cochran St Ste 351 Simi Valley (93065) ***(P-24822)***
K & N Engineering Inc (PA)....A....951 826-4000
1455 Citrus St Riverside (92507) ***(P-21119)***
K & S Enterprises, Adelanto *Also called Dar-Ken Inc* ***(P-9526)***
K & W Manufacturing Co Inc....F....951 277-3300
23107 Temescal Canyon Rd Corona (92883) ***(P-11967)***
K & Z Cabinet Co Inc....D....909 947-3567
1450 S Grove Ave Ontario (91761) ***(P-4317)***
K A Tool & Technology Inc....E....408 957-9600
1700 Sango Ct Milpitas (95035) ***(P-16638)***
K C A Engineered Plastics Inc (PA)....D....415 433-4494
580 California St Ste 22 San Francisco (94104) ***(P-7851)***
K C B, Valencia *Also called Kcb Precision* ***(P-17477)***
K C Photo Engraving Co....E....626 795-4127
2666 Nina St Pasadena (91107) ***(P-14814)***
K C Sheetmetal Inc....F....408 441-6620
943 Berryessa Rd Ste B3 San Jose (95133) ***(P-12635)***
K C Welding Inc....F....760 352-3832
1549 Dogwood Rd El Centro (92243) ***(P-25418)***
K G Bags, San Rafael *Also called ONeil KG Bags* ***(P-10529)***
K I C, San Diego *Also called Embedded Designs Inc* ***(P-21579)***
K I K, Santa Fe Springs *Also called Kik-Socal Inc* ***(P-8649)***
K I O Kables Inc....F....925 778-7500
2525 W 10th St Antioch (94509) ***(P-13836)***
K K Molds Inc....F....818 548-8988
926 Western Ave Ste D Glendale (91201) ***(P-12324)***
K Live....F....626 289-2885
300 W Valley Blvd 33 Alhambra (91803) ***(P-18940)***
K M I, Anaheim *Also called Kanstul Musical Instrs Inc* ***(P-23378)***
K Metal Products Inc....C....562 693-5425
11935 Baker Pl Santa Fe Springs (90670) ***(P-13837)***
K P Graphics, Stockton *Also called Kp LLC* ***(P-7370)***
K P I, Fremont *Also called Knightsbridge Plastics Inc* ***(P-10182)***
K S Designs Inc....E....562 929-3973
9515 Sorensen Ave Santa Fe Springs (90670) ***(P-23912)***
K S Equipment Inc....F....831 722-7173
17 Hangar Way Watsonville (95076) ***(P-19604)***
K S Printing Inc....F....951 268-5180
710 E Parkridge Ave # 105 Corona (92879) ***(P-7368)***
K S Telecom Inc....F....916 652-4735
2350 Humphrey Rd Penryn (95663) ***(P-17960)***
K Short Inc....F....626 358-8511
126 W Walnut Ave Monrovia (91016) ***(P-12189)***
K Squared Metals, Lake Elsinore *Also called Boozak Inc* ***(P-12507)***
K Tech Telecommunications Inc....F....818 773-0333
28231 Avenue Crocker # 90 Santa Clarita (91355) ***(P-18141)***
K Too....E....213 747-7766
800 E 12th St Ste 117 Los Angeles (90021) ***(P-3247)***
K Tube Technologies, Poway *Also called K-Tube Corporation* ***(P-11481)***
K V R Investment Group Inc....D....818 896-1102
12113 Branford St Sun Valley (91352) ***(P-14978)***
K&K World Inc....E....714 234-6237
721 W Wedgewood Ln La Habra (90631) ***(P-5241)***
K&M Jewellery, Burbank *Also called Makse Inc* ***(P-23292)***
K-1 Packaging Group....E....626 964-9384
2001 W Mission Blvd Pomona (91766) ***(P-6918)***
K-1 Packaging Group (PA)....D....626 964-9384
17989 Arenth Ave City of Industry (91748) ***(P-6919)***
K-Bros, Canoga Park *Also called Cg Manufacturing Inc* ***(P-12530)***
K-Max Health Products Internat....F....909 455-0158
1468 E Mission Blvd Pomona (91766) ***(P-625)***
K-P Engineering Corp....F....714 545-7045
2126 S Lyon St Ste A Santa Ana (92705) ***(P-16639)***
K-Swiss Inc (HQ)....C....323 675-2700
523 W 6th St Ste 534 Los Angeles (90014) ***(P-9474)***
K-Swiss Sales Corp....C....818 706-5100
31248 Oak Crest Dr # 150 Westlake Village (91361) ***(P-9475)***
K-Tech Machine Inc....C....800 274-9424
1377 Armorlite Dr San Marcos (92069) ***(P-16640)***
K-Tek, Vista *Also called M Klemme Technology Corp* ***(P-17827)***
K-Too, Los Angeles *Also called K Too* ***(P-3247)***
K-Tops Plastic Mfg Inc....E....626 575-9679
15051 Don Julian Rd City of Industry (91746) ***(P-24142)***
K-Tube Corporation....D....858 513-9229
13400 Kirkham Way Frnt Poway (92064) ***(P-11481)***
K-V Engineering Inc....E....714 229-9977
2411 W 1st St Santa Ana (92703) ***(P-14386)***
K.G.S.electronics Inc., Upland *Also called Gar Enterprises* ***(P-19548)***
K1 Packaging, City of Industry *Also called All Label Inc* ***(P-5694)***
K2 Pure Solutions LP....D....925 203-1196
950 Loveridge Rd Pittsburg (94565) ***(P-16062)***
K2 Pure Solutions Nocal LP....E....647 776-0273
950 Loveridge Rd Pittsburg (94565) ***(P-9265)***
K9 Ballistics Inc....F....805 233-8103
708 Via Alondra Camarillo (93012) ***(P-24143)***
Kaar Drect Mail Flfillment LLC....E....619 382-3670
1225 Expo Way Ste 160 San Diego (92154) ***(P-5897)***
Kabushiki Kisha Higuchi Shokai....F....310 212-7234
2281 W 205th St Ste 107 Torrance (90501) ***(P-17540)***
Kacee Company....F....916 348-3204
3570 Hiawatha North Highlands (95660) ***(P-16641)***
Kacee Discount Abrasives, North Highlands *Also called Kacee Company* ***(P-16641)***
Kadan Consultants Incorporated....F....562 988-1165
5662 Research Dr Huntington Beach (92649) ***(P-16642)***
Kadbanou LLC....F....818 409-0118
1951 Gardena Ave Glendale (91204) ***(P-812)***
Kadi Enterprises Inc....F....818 556-3400
802 N Victory Blvd Burbank (91502) ***(P-498)***
Kafp, Foothill Ranch *Also called Kaiser Aluminum Fab Pdts LLC* ***(P-11577)***
Kaga (usa) Inc....E....714 540-2697
2620 S Susan St Santa Ana (92704) ***(P-13232)***
Kaged Muscle LLC....E....208 850-0174
101 Main St Ste 360 Huntington Beach (92648) ***(P-626)***
Kagome Inc (HQ)....C....209 826-8850
333 Johnson Rd Los Banos (93635) ***(P-813)***
Kahoots Inc....F....619 337-0825
6525 Bisby Lake Ave San Diego (92119) ***(P-24144)***
Kai Os Technologies Sftwr Inc....F....858 547-3940
7310 Miramar Rd Ste 440 San Diego (92126) ***(P-24823)***
Kaic, Foothill Ranch *Also called Kaiser Aluminum Investments Co* ***(P-11578)***
Kainos Dental Technologies LLC (PA)....E....800 331-4834
1844 San Miguel Dr 308b Walnut Creek (94596) ***(P-22887)***
Kaise Perma San Franc Medic Ce....E....415 833-2000
2425 Geary Blvd San Francisco (94115) ***(P-22762)***
Kaiser Aluminum Corporation....E....323 726-8011
6250 Bandini Blvd Commerce (90040) ***(P-11591)***
Kaiser Aluminum Corporation (PA)....D....949 614-1740
27422 Portola Pkwy # 350 Foothill Ranch (92610) ***(P-11539)***
Kaiser Aluminum Fab Pdts LLC....C....323 722-7151
6250 Bandini Blvd Commerce (90040) ***(P-11592)***
Kaiser Aluminum Fab Pdts LLC (HQ)....A....949 614-1740
27422 Portola Pkwy # 200 Foothill Ranch (92610) ***(P-11577)***
Kaiser Aluminum Investments Co (HQ)....C....949 614-1740
27422 Portola Pkwy # 350 Foothill Ranch (92610) ***(P-11578)***
Kaiser Enterprises Inc....D....209 728-2091
798 Murphys Creek Rd Murphys (95247) ***(P-13892)***
Kakuichi America Inc....D....310 539-1590
23540 Telo Ave Torrance (90505) ***(P-9783)***
Kal Machining Inc....F....408 782-8989
18450 Sutter Blvd Morgan Hill (95037) ***(P-16643)***
Kal Plastics, Vernon *Also called Tom York Enterprises Inc* ***(P-10407)***
Kal-Cameron Manufacturing (HQ)....D....626 338-7308
4265 Puente Ave Baldwin Park (91706) ***(P-11898)***
Kalanico Inc....F....714 532-5770
1036 Chantilly Cir Santa Ana (92705) ***(P-5074)***
Kalila Medical Inc....E....408 819-5175
1400 Dell Ave Ste C Campbell (95008) ***(P-22222)***
Kalman Manufacturing Inc....E....408 776-7664
780 Jarvis Dr Ste 150 Morgan Hill (95037) ***(P-16644)***
Kaltec Electronics Inc (PA)....F....813 888-9555
16220 Bloomfield Ave Cerritos (90703) ***(P-23172)***
Kaltec Enterprises, Cerritos *Also called Kaltec Electronics Inc* ***(P-23172)***
Kalypsys Inc....C....858 552-0674
333 S Grand Ave Ste 4070 Los Angeles (90071) ***(P-8242)***
Kama Interconnect Inc....F....818 713-9810
8030 Remmet Ave Ste 3 Canoga Park (91304) ***(P-19605)***
Kama Sutra, Thousand Oaks *Also called Kamsut Incorporated* ***(P-8781)***

Kama-Tech Corporation ....F.......619 421-7858
3451 Main St Ste 109 Chula Vista (91911) ***(P-22096)***
Kamashian Engineering Inc ....F.......562 920-9692
9128 Rose St Bellflower (90706) ***(P-14530)***
Kamet, Milpitas *Also called Khuus Inc* ***(P-16653)***
Kamikaze 7 Sushi Joint, Carlsbad *Also called Fish On Rice LLC* ***(P-1593)***
Kamiran Inc ....F.......213 746-9161
1415 Maple Ave Ste 220 Los Angeles (90015) ***(P-3248)***
Kamm Industries Inc ....E.......800 317-6253
27555 Commerce Center Dr Temecula (92590) ***(P-20379)***
Kammerer Enterprises Inc ....D.......760 560-0550
1280 N Melrose Dr Vista (92083) ***(P-11258)***
Kamper Fabrication Inc ....E.......209 599-7137
20107 N Ripon Rd Ripon (95366) ***(P-14077)***
Kamsut Incorporated ....E.......805 495-7479
2151 Anchor Ct Thousand Oaks (91320) ***(P-8781)***
Kan Group Corp ....F.......213 383-1236
3807 Wilshire Blvd # 518 Los Angeles (90010) ***(P-6511)***
Kana Software Inc (HQ) ....D.......650 614-8300
2550 Walsh Ave Ste 120 Santa Clara (95051) ***(P-24824)***
Kanamax International Inc (PA) ....F.......213 399-3398
10618 Rush St South El Monte (91733) ***(P-8243)***
Kandi Usa Inc ....F.......909 941-4588
738 Epperson Dr City of Industry (91748) ***(P-20153)***
Kane Aerospace, Chino *Also called Kanetic Ltd LLC* ***(P-13438)***
Kanetic Ltd LLC ....F.......505 228-5692
7000 Merrill Ave Chino (91710) ***(P-13438)***
Kanex ....E.......888 975-1368
3 Pointe Dr Ste 300 Brea (92821) ***(P-19995)***
Kangol, Los Angeles *Also called Apparel Limited Inc* ***(P-3374)***
Kanstul Musical Instrs Inc (PA) ....E.......714 563-1000
1332 S Claudina St Anaheim (92805) ***(P-23378)***
Kant-Twist, South El Monte *Also called Clamp Manufacturing Co Inc* ***(P-11945)***
Kap Manufacturing Inc ....E.......909 599-2525
327 W Allen Ave San Dimas (91773) ***(P-21314)***
Kap Medical ....E.......951 340-4360
1395 Pico St Corona (92881) ***(P-22223)***
Kapan - Kent Company Inc ....E.......760 631-1716
2675 Vista Pacific Dr Oceanside (92056) ***(P-3900)***
Kapsch Trafficcom Usa Inc ....F.......925 225-1600
4256 Hacienda Dr Ste 100 Pleasanton (94588) ***(P-17281)***
Kar Ice Service Inc (PA) ....F.......760 256-2648
2521 Solar Way Barstow (92311) ***(P-2416)***
Karapet Engineering Inc ....F.......818 255-0838
11455 Vanowen St North Hollywood (91605) ***(P-16645)***
Karbz Inc ....F.......760 567-9953
77806 Flora Rd Ste E Palm Desert (92211) ***(P-20380)***
Kareem Cart Commissary & Mfg, Los Angeles *Also called Kareem Corporation* ***(P-23600)***
Kareem Corporation ....F.......323 234-0724
4423 S Vermont Ave Los Angeles (90037) ***(P-23600)***
Karel Manufacturing, Calexico *Also called Lorenz Inc* ***(P-20007)***
Karen Kane Inc (PA) ....C.......323 588-0000
2275 E 37th St Vernon (90058) ***(P-3442)***
Kargo Master Inc ....E.......916 638-8703
11261 Trade Center Dr Rancho Cordova (95742) ***(P-12636)***
Karl M Smith Inc ....E.......559 992-4109
1204 Dairy Ave Corcoran (93212) ***(P-12637)***
Karl Storz Endscpy-America Inc ....E.......508 248-9011
2151 E Grand Ave Ste 100 El Segundo (90245) ***(P-22501)***
Karl Storz Endscpy-America Inc (HQ) ....B.......424 218-8100
2151 E Grand Ave El Segundo (90245) ***(P-22502)***
Karl Storz Imaging Inc (HQ) ....B.......805 968-5563
1 S Los Carneros Rd Goleta (93117) ***(P-22224)***
Karl Strauss Brewery & Rest, San Diego *Also called Associated Microbreweries Inc* ***(P-1565)***
Karl Strauss Brewery Garden, San Diego *Also called Associated Microbreweries Inc* ***(P-1564)***
Karl Strauss Brewing Company (PA) ....D.......858 273-2739
5985 Santa Fe St San Diego (92109) ***(P-1603)***
Karl's Sash & Doors, Huntington Beach *Also called Karls Custom Sash and Doors* ***(P-4176)***
Karls Custom Sash and Doors ....E.......714 842-7877
18292 Gothard St Huntington Beach (92648) ***(P-4176)***
Karma Automotive LLC (HQ) ....B.......714 723-3247
9950 Jeronimo Rd Irvine (92618) ***(P-20154)***
Karoun Dairies Inc ....F.......323 666-6222
5117 Santa Monica Blvd Los Angeles (90029) ***(P-580)***
Karoun Dairies Inc (PA) ....D.......818 767-7000
13023 Arroyo St San Fernando (91340) ***(P-581)***
Karrior Electric Vehicles Inc ....F.......310 515-7600
570 W 184th St Gardena (90248) ***(P-14331)***
Karrior Indus Elc Vehicles, Gardena *Also called Karrior Electric Vehicles Inc* ***(P-14331)***
Kasco Fab Inc ....D.......559 442-1018
4529 S Chestnut Ave Lowr Fresno (93725) ***(P-12190)***
Kaser Corporation ....F.......510 657-9002
801 Vista Hill Ter Fremont (94539) ***(P-15437)***
Kashi Company ....E.......858 274-8870
140 Marine View Ave # 101 Solana Beach (92075) ***(P-1044)***
Kashiyama USA Inc ....F.......510 979-0070
41432 Christy St Fremont (94538) ***(P-21607)***
Kasper, Milpitas *Also called Nine West Holdings Inc* ***(P-3356)***
Kastle Stair Inc (PA) ....E.......714 596-2600
7422 Mountjoy Dr Huntington Beach (92648) ***(P-4177)***
Katadyn Desalination LLC ....E.......415 526-2780
2220 S Mcdowell Blvd Ext Petaluma (94954) ***(P-17394)***
Katana Software Inc ....F.......562 495-1366
333 W Broadway Ste 105 Long Beach (90802) ***(P-24825)***
Katch Precision Machining Inc ....F.......310 676-4989
3953 W 139th St Hawthorne (90250) ***(P-16646)***
Katchall Fltration Systems LLC ....F.......866 528-2425
263 W Fourth St Beaumont (92223) ***(P-16063)***
Kate Farms Inc ....C.......805 845-2446
101 Innovation Pl Santa Barbara (93108) ***(P-2550)***
Kate Somerville Skincare LLC (HQ) ....D.......323 655-7546
144 S Beverly Dr Ste 500 Beverly Hills (90212) ***(P-8244)***
Kateeva Inc ....B.......510 953-7600
7015 Gateway Blvd Newark (94560) ***(P-18142)***
Kater-Crafts Incorporated ....E.......562 692-0665
4860 Gregg Rd Pico Rivera (90660) ***(P-7606)***
Katerra Inc (PA) ....D.......650 422-3572
2494 Sand Hill Rd Ste 100 Menlo Park (94025) ***(P-231)***
Katerra Inc ....A.......623 236-5322
2302 Paradise Rd Tracy (95304) ***(P-4417)***
Katherine Baumann Collectibles, West Hollywood *Also called Kathrine Baumann Beverly Hills* ***(P-3320)***
Katherine Shih, Monterey Park *Also called CHI-AM Comics Daily Inc* ***(P-6459)***
Kathrine Baumann Beverly Hills ....E.......310 274-7441
9040 W Sunset Blvd # 208 West Hollywood (90069) ***(P-3320)***
Kathryn M Ireland Inc (PA) ....E.......323 965-9888
5285 W Washington Blvd Los Angeles (90016) ***(P-2750)***
Kathy Ireland Worldwide ....F.......310 557-2700
39 Princeton Dr Rancho Mirage (92270) ***(P-3249)***
Katie K Inc ....F.......323 589-3030
5601 Bickett St Vernon (90058) ***(P-3663)***
Katlan Industries Inc ....F.......562 618-0940
3202 Blume Dr Los Alamitos (90720) ***(P-13233)***
Katolec Development Inc ....E.......619 710-0075
6120 Business Center Ct San Diego (92154) ***(P-19606)***
Katz & Klein ....E.......916 444-2024
9901 Horn Rd Ste D Sacramento (95827) ***(P-23104)***
Katz Millennium Sls & Mktg Inc ....D.......323 966-5066
5700 Wilshire Blvd # 100 Los Angeles (90036) ***(P-18143)***
Katzirs Floor & HM Design Inc ....F.......818 988-9663
14742 Calvert St Van Nuys (91411) ***(P-4178)***
Katzkin Leather Interiors Inc ....F.......323 725-1243
6868 W Acco St Montebello (90640) ***(P-10562)***
Kav America Ag Inc ....E.......855 528-8721
422 Commercial Rd San Bernardino (92408) ***(P-2356)***
Kavi Skin Solutions Inc (PA) ....E.......415 839-5156
700 Larkspur Landing Cir Larkspur (94939) ***(P-8245)***
Kavlico Corporation (HQ) ....A.......805 523-2000
1461 Lawrence Dr Thousand Oaks (91320) ***(P-19607)***
Kavlico Corporation ....E.......805 523-2000
2475 Pseo De Las Americas San Diego (92154) ***(P-19608)***
Kawasaki Micro Elec Amer, San Jose *Also called Megachips Technology Amer Corp* ***(P-18988)***
Kaweah Container Inc (HQ) ....D.......559 651-7850
7101 Avenue 304 Visalia (93291) ***(P-5433)***
Kawneer Company Inc ....C.......559 651-4000
7200 W Doe Ave Visalia (93291) ***(P-12870)***
Kay & James Inc ....D.......818 998-0357
14062 Balboa Blvd Sylmar (91342) ***(P-16647)***
Kay and Associates Inc ....E.......559 410-0917
300 Reeves Blvd Lemoore (93246) ***(P-20595)***
Kay Chesterfield Inc ....F.......510 533-5565
6365 Coliseum Way Oakland (94621) ***(P-4789)***
Kaye Sandy Enterprises Inc ....E.......650 961-5334
1074 Independence Ave Mountain View (94043) ***(P-21048)***
Kayline Enterprises Inc ....E.......562 595-4515
3400 E Airport Way Long Beach (90806) ***(P-24145)***
Kayo Corp (PA) ....F.......760 918-0405
6351 Yarrow Dr Ste D Carlsbad (92011) ***(P-23601)***
Kayo of California (PA) ....E.......323 233-6107
161 W 39th St Los Angeles (90037) ***(P-3353)***
Kayo of California ....F.......310 605-2693
11854 Alameda St Lynwood (90262) ***(P-3443)***
Kayo Store, The, Carlsbad *Also called Kayo Corp* ***(P-23601)***
Kazan Networks Corporation ....E.......916 259-0087
1544 Eureka Rd Ste 250 Roseville (95661) ***(P-15438)***
Kazmere Entertainment ....F.......323 448-9009
400 N La Brea Ave Ste 500 Inglewood (90302) ***(P-17822)***
KB Delta Inc ....E.......310 530-1539
3340 Fujita St Torrance (90505) ***(P-13234)***
KB Delta Comprsr Valve Parts, Torrance *Also called KB Delta Inc* ***(P-13234)***
KB Design Enterprises, Anaheim *Also called Anaheim Embroidery Inc* ***(P-3828)***
KB Sheetmetal Fabrication Inc ....E.......714 979-1780
17371 Mount Wynne Cir B Fountain Valley (92708) ***(P-12638)***
KB Wines LLC ....E.......707 823-7430
220 Morris St Sebastopol (95472) ***(P-1837)***
Kba Engineering LLC ....D.......661 323-0487
2157 Mohawk St Bakersfield (93308) ***(P-14230)***
Kba Ltd of Kern County LLP ....F.......661 323-0487
2152 Mohawk St Bakersfield (93308) ***(P-232)***
Kba2 Inc ....F.......415 528-5500
55 New Montgomery St # 606 San Francisco (94105) ***(P-24826)***
Kbc Networks USA, Aliso Viejo *Also called Cove20 LLC* ***(P-18789)***
Kbr Inc ....E.......562 436-9281
2000 W Gaylord St Long Beach (90813) ***(P-17238)***
Kc Exclusive Inc (PA) ....D.......213 749-0088
1100 S San Pedro St Los Angeles (90015) ***(P-3444)***
KC Metal Products Inc (PA) ....D.......408 436-8754
1960 Hartog Dr San Jose (95131) ***(P-12191)***
Kc Metals, San Jose *Also called KC Metal Products Inc* ***(P-12191)***
Kc Pharmaceuticals Inc ....E.......909 598-9499
3220 Producer Way Pomona (91768) ***(P-8246)***
Kca Electronics Inc ....C.......714 239-2433
223 N Crescent Way Anaheim (92801) ***(P-18516)***
Kcb Precision ....F.......661 295-5695
29009 Avenue Penn Valencia (91355) ***(P-17477)***
Kdc-One, Chatsworth *Also called Thibiant International Inc* ***(P-8853)***

ALPHABETIC

Employee Codes: A=Over 500 employees, B=251-500
C=101-250, D=51-100, E=20-50, F=10-19

2019 California
Manfacturers Register

© Mergent Inc. 1-800-342-5647
1185

KDF Inc.....E.....408 779-3731
15875 Concord Cir Morgan Hill (95037) ***(P-21120)***
Kdl Precision Molding Corp.....D.....818 896-9899
11381 Bradley Ave Pacoima (91331) ***(P-21194)***
Kds Ingredients LLC.....F.....760 310-5245
3460 Mrron Rd Ste 103-229 Oceanside (92056) ***(P-2551)***
Kds Nail Products.....F.....916 381-9358
8580 Younger Creek Dr Sacramento (95828) ***(P-24146)***
Kearney Pattern Works & Fndry.....E.....408 293-7414
40 S Montgomery St San Jose (95110) ***(P-11744)***
Kearneys Aluminum Foundry Inc (PA).....E.....559 233-2591
2660 S Dearing Ave Fresno (93725) ***(P-11697)***
KEBERT REPROGRAPHICS, Santee *Also called D Benham Corporation* ***(P-6776)***
Kechika, Rcho STA Marg *Also called Point Conception Inc* ***(P-3483)***
Keck & Schmidt Tool & Die Inc.....F.....626 579-3890
2610 Troy Ave El Monte (91733) ***(P-14531)***
Keco Inc.....F.....619 546-9533
3475 Kurtz St San Diego (92110) ***(P-16167)***
Keebler Company.....D.....714 228-1555
14000 183rd St La Palma (90623) ***(P-1368)***
Keen-Kut Products Inc.....F.....510 785-5168
3190 Diablo Ave Hayward (94545) ***(P-14643)***
Keene Engineering Inc (PA).....F.....818 485-2681
20201 Bahama St Chatsworth (91311) ***(P-15081)***
Keene Industries, Chatsworth *Also called Keene Engineering Inc* ***(P-15081)***
Keepcup Ltd.....F.....310 957-2070
431 Colyton St Los Angeles (90013) ***(P-10175)***
Keesee Tank Company.....F.....714 528-1814
721 S Melrose St Placentia (92870) ***(P-12393)***
Kehoe Custom Wood Designs.....F.....714 993-0444
1320 N Miller St Ste D Anaheim (92806) ***(P-4710)***
Keiser Corporation (PA).....D.....559 256-8000
2470 S Cherry Ave Fresno (93706) ***(P-23602)***
Keiser Sports Health Equipment, Fresno *Also called Keiser Corporation* ***(P-23602)***
Keith E Archambeau Sr Inc.....E.....818 718-6110
20615 Plummer St Chatsworth (91311) ***(P-12639)***
Keith Nichols.....E.....310 305-0397
8180 Manitoba St Apt 356 Playa Del Rey (90293) ***(P-1838)***
Keithco Manufacturing Inc.....F.....714 258-8933
15031 Parkway Loop Ste C Tustin (92780) ***(P-16648)***
Kelco, Oxnard *Also called Kim Laube & Company Inc* ***(P-8783)***
Kelco Bio Polymers.....E.....619 595-5000
2025 Harbor Dr San Diego (92113) ***(P-9266)***
Kelco Sales & Engineering, Norwalk *Also called Polley Inc* ***(P-15354)***
Kelcourt Plastics Inc (HQ).....D.....949 361-0774
1000 Calle Recodo San Clemente (92673) ***(P-9740)***
Keller Classics Inc (PA).....E.....805 524-1322
19628 Country Oaks St Tehachapi (93561) ***(P-3354)***
Keller Engineering.....F.....310 532-0554
136 W 157th St Gardena (90248) ***(P-16649)***
Keller Engineering Inc.....E.....310 326-6291
3203 Kashiwa St Torrance (90505) ***(P-16650)***
Keller Entertainment Group Inc.....F.....818 981-4950
1093 Broxton Ave Ste 246 Los Angeles (90024) ***(P-15777)***
Kellermyer Bergensons Svcs LLC (PA).....F.....760 631-5111
1959 Avenida Plaza Real Oceanside (92056) ***(P-16064)***
Kelley Blue Book Co Inc (HQ).....D.....949 770-7704
217 Technology Dr Irvine (92618) ***(P-6199)***
Kellogg Company.....B.....925 952-8423
2001 N Main St Ste 450 Walnut Creek (94596) ***(P-1063)***
Kellogg Company.....C.....408 295-8656
475 Eggo Way San Jose (95116) ***(P-1064)***
Kellogg Garden Product, Lockeford *Also called Kellogg Supply Inc* ***(P-9064)***
Kellogg Sales Company.....E.....916 787-0414
300 Harding Blvd Ste 215 Roseville (95678) ***(P-1065)***
Kellogg Supply Inc.....E.....209 727-3130
12686 Locke Rd Lockeford (95237) ***(P-9064)***
Kelly & Thome.....E.....909 623-2559
228 San Lorenzo St Pomona (91766) ***(P-16651)***
Kelly Computer Systems Inc.....E.....650 960-1010
1060 La Avenida St Mountain View (94043) ***(P-15778)***
Kelly Network Solutions Inc.....E.....650 364-7201
473 Sapena Ct Ste 24 Santa Clara (95054) ***(P-21783)***
Kelly Pipe Company, Riverside *Also called Imperial Pipe Services LLC* ***(P-11480)***
Kelly Pneumatics Inc.....F.....949 278-5721
711 W 17th St Ste F8 Costa Mesa (92627) ***(P-19996)***
Kelly Teegarden Organics LLC.....F.....818 518-0707
6524 Platt Ave Ste 224 West Hills (91307) ***(P-8782)***
Kelly Tool & Mfgcoinc.....F.....626 289-7962
433 S Palm Ave Alhambra (91803) ***(P-13235)***
Kelly-Moore Paint Company Inc (PA).....C.....650 592-8337
987 Commercial St San Carlos (94070) ***(P-8910)***
Kelly-Moore Paint Company Inc.....E.....510 505-9834
3954 Decoto Rd Fremont (94555) ***(P-8911)***
Kelly-Moore Paint Company Inc.....E.....650 595-0333
1075 Commercial St San Carlos (94070) ***(P-8912)***
Kelly-Moore Paints, San Carlos *Also called Kelly-Moore Paint Company Inc* ***(P-8910)***
Kelly-Moore Paints, Fremont *Also called Kelly-Moore Paint Company Inc* ***(P-8911)***
Kelly-Moore Paints, San Carlos *Also called Kelly-Moore Paint Company Inc* ***(P-8912)***
Kelmscott Communications LLC.....F.....949 475-1900
2485 Da Vinci Irvine (92614) ***(P-6920)***
Kelpac Medical, San Clemente *Also called Kelcourt Plastics Inc* ***(P-9740)***
Kelpac Medical.....D.....619 710-2550
2189 Britannia Blvd San Diego (92154) ***(P-9741)***
Kelsey See Canyon Vineyards.....F.....805 595-9700
1945 See Canyon Rd San Luis Obispo (93405) ***(P-1839)***
Kelytech Corporation.....E.....408 935-0888
1482 Gladding Ct Milpitas (95035) ***(P-19609)***
Kem-Mil-Co, Hayward *Also called H2j Corporation* ***(P-16553)***
Kemco, Ontario *Also called Kitchen Equipment Mfg Co Inc* ***(P-13238)***
Kemeera Incorporated.....F.....510 281-9000
315 Jefferson St Oakland (94607) ***(P-15779)***
Kemira Water Solutions Inc.....E.....909 350-5678
14000 San Bernardino Ave Fontana (92335) ***(P-7784)***
Kemira Water Solutions Inc.....F.....909 429-4001
14000 San Bernardino Ave Fontana (92335) ***(P-9267)***
Kemira Water Solutions Inc.....E.....909 350-5678
14000 San Bernardino Ave Fontana (92335) ***(P-9268)***
Kemiron Pacific, Fontana *Also called Kemira Water Solutions Inc* ***(P-9268)***
Kemper Enterprises Inc.....E.....909 627-6191
13595 12th St Chino (91710) ***(P-11899)***
Kempton Machine Works Inc.....F.....714 990-0596
4070 E Leaverton Ct Anaheim (92807) ***(P-14644)***
Ken Anderson.....E.....209 604-8579
904 Frontage Rd Ripon (95366) ***(P-11124)***
Ken Hoffmann Inc.....E.....760 325-6012
345 Del Sol Rd Palm Springs (92262) ***(P-13439)***
Ken Mason Tile Inc.....E.....562 432-7574
14600 S Western Ave Gardena (90249) ***(P-10785)***
Ken-Wor Corp.....E.....714 554-6210
13962 Enterprise Dr Garden Grove (92843) ***(P-11402)***
Kenai Drilling Limited (HQ).....E.....805 937-7871
6430 Cat Canyon Rd Santa Maria (93454) ***(P-109)***
Kenco Engineering Inc.....E.....916 782-8494
2155 Pfe Rd Roseville (95747) ***(P-14178)***
Kendall-Jackson Wine Estates (HQ).....B.....707 544-4000
425 Aviation Blvd Santa Rosa (95403) ***(P-1840)***
Kendra Group Inc.....F.....909 473-7206
2394 Saratoga Way San Bernardino (92407) ***(P-18338)***
Keney Manufacturing Co (PA).....F.....209 358-6474
586 Broadway Ave Atwater (95301) ***(P-4318)***
Keney's Cabinets, Atwater *Also called Keney Manufacturing Co* ***(P-4318)***
Kenlor Industries Inc.....F.....714 647-0770
1560 E Edinger Ave Ste A1 Santa Ana (92705) ***(P-22503)***
Kennedy Athletics, Carson *Also called Cali-Fame Los Angeles Inc* ***(P-3559)***
Kennedy Engineered Products.....F.....661 272-1147
38830 17th St E Palmdale (93550) ***(P-20381)***
Kennedy Hills Enterprises LLC.....F.....714 596-7444
19486 Woodlands Dr Huntington Beach (92648) ***(P-18)***
Kennedy Hills Materials, Huntington Beach *Also called Kennedy Hills Enterprises LLC* ***(P-18)***
Kennedy Name Plate Co Inc.....E.....323 585-0121
4501 Pacific Blvd Vernon (90058) ***(P-13607)***
Kennerley-Spratling Inc (PA).....C.....510 351-8230
2116 Farallon Dr San Leandro (94577) ***(P-10176)***
Kennerley-Spratling Inc.....C.....408 944-9407
2308 Zanker Rd San Jose (95131) ***(P-10177)***
Kenneth Cronon Inc.....F.....818 632-4972
10413 Haines Canyon Ave Tujunga (91042) ***(P-3579)***
Kenneth Miller Clothing Inc.....E.....213 746-8866
210 E Olympic Blvd # 208 Los Angeles (90015) ***(P-3445)***
Kenny Giannini Putters LLC.....F.....760 851-9475
74755 N Cove Dr Indian Wells (92210) ***(P-23603)***
Kenny The Printer, Irvine *Also called American PCF Prtrs College Inc* ***(P-6656)***
Kens Spray Equipment Inc (HQ).....D.....310 635-9995
1900 W Walnut St Compton (90220) ***(P-13608)***
Kens Stakes & Supplies.....F.....559 747-1313
193 S Mariposa Ave Visalia (93292) ***(P-4629)***
Kensington Laboratories LLC (PA).....F.....510 324-0126
6200 Village Pkwy Dublin (94568) ***(P-17282)***
Kensington Protective Products.....F.....909 469-1240
151 N Reservoir St Pomona (91767) ***(P-3793)***
Kenwalt Die Casting Corp.....E.....818 768-5800
8719 Bradley Ave Sun Valley (91352) ***(P-11698)***
Kenwood Vineyards, Kenwood *Also called Pernod Ricard Usa LLC* ***(P-1921)***
Keopsys Inc (HQ).....F.....610 758-8428
7001 Briza Loop San Ramon (94582) ***(P-18144)***
Kepner Plas Fabricators Inc.....E.....310 325-3162
3131 Lomita Blvd Torrance (90505) ***(P-10178)***
Kerber Industries Inc.....E.....909 319-0877
166 San Lorenzo St Pomona (91766) ***(P-24147)***
Keri Systems Inc (PA).....D.....408 435-8400
302 Enzo Dr San Jose (95138) ***(P-19997)***
Keriligthing, City of Industry *Also called Jishan Usa Inc* ***(P-17620)***
Kern Valley Sun, Lake Isabella *Also called Wick Communications Co* ***(P-6087)***
Kern Water Bank Authority.....F.....661 398-4900
1620 Mill Rock Way # 500 Bakersfield (93311) ***(P-21608)***
Kerning Data Systems Inc.....F.....818 882-8712
9301 Jordan Ave Ste 102 Chatsworth (91311) ***(P-14815)***
Kerr Corporation (HQ).....C.....714 516-7400
1717 W Collins Ave Orange (92867) ***(P-22888)***
Kerr Group LLC.....C.....805 278-9155
3301 Sturgis Rd Oxnard (93030) ***(P-10179)***
Kerrock Countertops Inc (PA).....E.....510 441-2300
33220 Western Ave Union City (94587) ***(P-4711)***
Kerry Inc.....D.....760 396-2116
64405 Lincoln St Mecca (92254) ***(P-627)***
Kerry Ingredients and Flavours, Commerce *Also called Mastertaste Inc* ***(P-2272)***
Kersting Library Products, Fallbrook *Also called Accurate Wire & Display Inc* ***(P-13807)***
Kesclo Financial Inc.....E.....800 322-8676
150 W 6th St Ste 205 San Pedro (90731) ***(P-12871)***
Kesmor Associates.....E.....213 629-2300
610 S Broadway Ste 717 Los Angeles (90014) ***(P-23281)***
Ketan Automated Equipment Inc.....F.....909 930-0780
1451 S Cucamonga Ave Ontario (91761) ***(P-15213)***
Ketera Technologies Inc (HQ).....E.....408 572-9500
3055 Olin Ave Ste 2200 San Jose (95128) ***(P-24827)***
Kett.....F.....714 974-8837
9581 Featherhill Dr Villa Park (92861) ***(P-21980)***

Mergent e-mail: customerrelations@mergent.com
1186
2019 California
Manufacturers Register
(P-0000) Products & Services Section entry number
(PA)=Parent Co (HQ)=Headquarters (DH)=Div Headquarters

Kett U S, Villa Park *Also called Kett* ***(P-21980)***
Kettle Pop, Benicia *Also called Gold Rush Kettle Korn Llc* ***(P-1425)***
Keurig Dr Pepper Inc ... D ... 951 341-7500
1188 Mt Vernon Ave Riverside (92507) ***(P-2142)***
Keurig Dr Pepper Inc ... E ... 530 893-4501
306 Otterson Dr Chico (95928) ***(P-2143)***
Keurig Dr Pepper Inc ... D ... 925 938-8777
1981 N Broadway Walnut Creek (94596) ***(P-2144)***
Kevin Orthopedic, Santa Monica *Also called Foot In Motion Inc* ***(P-22731)***
Kevin Whaley ... E ... 619 596-4000
9565 Pathway St Santee (92071) ***(P-13838)***
Kevin's San Lorenzo Awnings, Santa Cruz *Also called Kevins Awnings Inc* ***(P-3794)***
Kevins Awnings Inc ... F ... 831 423-7918
907 River St Santa Cruz (95060) ***(P-3794)***
Kevita Inc (HQ) ... D ... 805 200-2250
2220 Celsius Ave Ste A Oxnard (93030) ***(P-2145)***
Key Container, South Gate *Also called Liberty Container Company* ***(P-5434)***
Key Energy Services Inc ... E ... 661 334-8100
5080 California Ave # 150 Bakersfield (93309) ***(P-233)***
Key Energy Services Inc ... E ... 805 653-1300
3587 N Ventura Ave Ventura (93001) ***(P-234)***
Key Item Sales Inc ... F ... 818 885-0928
21037 Superior St Chatsworth (91311) ***(P-23750)***
Key Items Sales Inc ... F ... 818 885-0586
21037 Superior St Chatsworth (91311) ***(P-23173)***
Key Line Litho, Gardena *Also called Keyline Lithography Inc* ***(P-6921)***
Key Material Handling Inc ... F ... 805 520-6007
4790 Alamo St Simi Valley (93063) ***(P-14332)***
Key Solutions Inc ... F ... 510 456-4500
2803 Lakeview Ct Fremont (94538) ***(P-24828)***
Key Source International (PA) ... F ... 510 562-5000
7711 Oakport St Oakland (94621) ***(P-15637)***
Key-Bak, Ontario *Also called West Coast Chain Mfg Co* ***(P-20109)***
Keyfax Newmedia Inc ... F ... 831 477-1205
911 Center St Ste A Santa Cruz (95060) ***(P-17823)***
Keyin Inc ... F ... 562 690-3888
511 S Harbor Blvd Ste C La Habra (90631) ***(P-19868)***
Keyline Lithography Inc ... F ... 310 538-8618
1726 W 180th St Gardena (90248) ***(P-6921)***
Keypr, Los Angeles *Also called Project Cloudkey Inc* ***(P-25083)***
Keys Cabinetry Inc ... F ... 415 382-1466
20 Pimentel Ct Ste B14 Novato (94949) ***(P-5075)***
Keysight Technologies Inc (PA) ... B ... 800 829-4444
1400 Fountaingrove Pkwy Santa Rosa (95403) ***(P-21784)***
Keysight Technologies Inc ... E ... 310 524-4600
700 Lairport St El Segundo (90245) ***(P-21785)***
Keysight Technologies Inc ... E ... 408 553-3290
5301 Stevens Creek Blvd Santa Clara (95051) ***(P-21786)***
Keysource Foods LLC ... E ... 310 879-4888
2263 W 190th St Torrance (90504) ***(P-2297)***
Keyssa Inc (PA) ... E ... 408 637-2300
655 Campbell Technology P Campbell (95008) ***(P-18941)***
Keyssa Systems Inc ... F ... 408 637-2300
655 Campbell Technology P Campbell (95008) ***(P-14979)***
Keystone Cabinetry Inc ... F ... 818 565-3330
3110 N Clybourn Ave Burbank (91505) ***(P-4319)***
Keystone Coffee Company ... F ... 408 998-2221
2230 Will Wool Dr Ste 100 San Jose (95112) ***(P-2357)***
Keystone Engineering Company (HQ) ... E ... 562 497-3200
4401 E Donald Douglas Dr Long Beach (90808) ***(P-16652)***
Kezar Life Sciences Inc ... E ... 650 822-5600
4000 Shoreline Ct Ste 300 South San Francisco (94080) ***(P-8247)***
Kf Fiberglass Inc (PA) ... E ... 562 869-1536
8247 Phlox St Downey (90241) ***(P-20382)***
KG Technologies Inc ... F ... 888 513-1874
6028 State Farm Dr Rohnert Park (94928) ***(P-19610)***
Kh Construction, Fresno *Also called Nevocal Enterprises Inc* ***(P-375)***
Khan Academy Inc ... D ... 650 336-5426
1200 Villa St Ste 200 Mountain View (94041) ***(P-24829)***
Khmca, Oakland *Also called Kyoho Manufacturing California* ***(P-13140)***
Khn Solutions Inc ... F ... 877 334-6876
300 Broadway Ste 26 San Francisco (94133) ***(P-22225)***
Khuus Inc ... D ... 408 522-8000
1778 Mccarthy Blvd Milpitas (95035) ***(P-16653)***
Khyber Foods Incorporated ... E ... 714 879-0900
500 S Acacia Ave Fullerton (92831) ***(P-2552)***
Kia Group, San Diego *Also called Kia Incorporated* ***(P-10506)***
Kia Incorporated (PA) ... E ... 858 824-2999
16516 Via Esprillo # 100 San Diego (92127) ***(P-10506)***
Kiana Analytics Inc ... F ... 650 575-3871
440 N Wolfe Rd W050 Sunnyvale (94085) ***(P-24830)***
Kibblwhite Precision Machining ... E ... 650 359-4704
580 Crespi Dr Ste H Pacifica (94044) ***(P-21121)***
Kicksend, Mountain View *Also called Receivd Inc* ***(P-25115)***
Kiddo By Katie, Vernon *Also called Love Marks Inc* ***(P-3254)***
Kids Line LLC ... C ... 310 660-0110
10541 Humbolt St Los Alamitos (90720) ***(P-3727)***
Kieran Label Corp ... E ... 619 449-4457
2321 Siempre Viva Ct # 101 San Diego (92154) ***(P-5563)***
Kiewit Corporation ... E ... 760 377-3117
Hwy 395 And Cinder Rd Little Lake (93542) ***(P-322)***
Kifuki USA Co Inc (HQ) ... D ... 626 334-8090
15547 1st St Irwindale (91706) ***(P-545)***
Kik Custom Products, Torrance *Also called Prestone Products Corporation* ***(P-9298)***
Kik Pool Additives Inc ... C ... 909 390-9912
5160 E Airport Dr Ontario (91761) ***(P-9269)***
Kik-Socal Inc ... A ... 562 946-6427
9028 Dice Rd Santa Fe Springs (90670) ***(P-8649)***
Kikkoman Foods Inc ... E ... 916 355-8078
1000 Glenn Dr Folsom (95630) ***(P-917)***
Kilgore Machine Company Inc ... E ... 714 540-3659
2312 S Susan St Santa Ana (92704) ***(P-16654)***
Killion Industries Inc (PA) ... D ... 760 727-5102
1380 Poinsettia Ave Vista (92081) ***(P-5076)***
Kilovac, Carpinteria *Also called Te Connectivity Corporation* ***(P-17315)***
Kim & Cami Productions Inc ... E ... 323 584-1300
2950 Leonis Blvd Vernon (90058) ***(P-3446)***
Kim & Roy Co Inc ... F ... 310 762-1896
2924 E Ana St Compton (90221) ***(P-3108)***
Kim and Cami, Vernon *Also called Kim & Cami Productions Inc* ***(P-3446)***
Kim Laube & Company Inc ... E ... 805 240-1300
2221 Statham Blvd Oxnard (93033) ***(P-8783)***
Kim Seng Jewelry Inc ... F ... 213 628-8566
818 N Broadway Ste 202 Los Angeles (90012) ***(P-23344)***
Kim's Fence, Fullerton *Also called Kims Welding and Iron Works* ***(P-13103)***
Kim's Jewelry Manufacturer, Los Angeles *Also called Y Y K Inc* ***(P-23332)***
Kimball Electronics Indiana ... E ... 669 234-1110
5215 Hellyer Ave Ste 130 San Jose (95138) ***(P-21787)***
Kimball Nelson Inc ... F ... 310 636-0081
7740 Lemona Ave Van Nuys (91405) ***(P-24148)***
Kimball Office Inc ... F ... 415 397-1557
330 Pine St San Francisco (94104) ***(P-4991)***
Kimberley Wine Vinegars, Acampo *Also called California Concentrate Company* ***(P-941)***
Kimberly Lighting, Vernon *Also called Hollywood Lamp & Shade Co* ***(P-17429)***
Kimberly Machine Inc ... F ... 714 539-1360
12822 Joy St Garden Grove (92840) ***(P-16655)***
Kimberly-Clark Corporation ... B ... 714 578-0705
2001 E Orangethorpe Ave Fullerton (92831) ***(P-5307)***
Kimberly-Clark Corporation ... F ... 818 986-2430
15260 Ventura Blvd # 1410 Van Nuys (91403) ***(P-5308)***
Kimco Magnetics, Vista *Also called Sensata Technologies Inc* ***(P-17222)***
Kimdurla Inc ... E ... 818 504-4041
9983 Glenoaks Blvd Sun Valley (91352) ***(P-10650)***
Kims Welding and Iron Works ... E ... 714 680-7700
2331 E Orangethorpe Ave Fullerton (92831) ***(P-13103)***
Kimzey Welding Works Inc ... F ... 530 662-9331
164 Kentucky Ave Woodland (95695) ***(P-16656)***
Kinamad, Camarillo *Also called VME Acquisition Corp* ***(P-22844)***
Kinamed Inc ... E ... 805 384-2748
820 Flynn Rd Camarillo (93012) ***(P-22763)***
Kinary Inc ... E ... 626 575-7873
2542 Troy Ave South El Monte (91733) ***(P-3664)***
Kind Led Grow Lights, Santa Rosa *Also called Supercloset* ***(P-11912)***
Kinder Scientific Company LLC ... F ... 858 679-1515
12675 Danielson Ct # 406 Poway (92064) ***(P-17345)***
Kindred Biosciences Inc (PA) ... E ... 650 701-7901
1555 Bayshore Hwy Ste 200 Burlingame (94010) ***(P-8248)***
Kindred Litho Incorporated ... F ... 909 944-4015
10833 Bell Ct Rancho Cucamonga (91730) ***(P-6922)***
Kinematic Automation Inc ... D ... 209 532-3200
21085 Longeway Rd Sonora (95370) ***(P-22504)***
Kinestral Technologies Inc (PA) ... C ... 650 416-5200
3955 Trust Way Hayward (94545) ***(P-10711)***
Kinetic Electric Corporation ... E ... 619 654-1157
944 Industrial Blvd 946 Chula Vista (91911) ***(P-19998)***
Kinetic Farm Inc ... F ... 650 503-3279
210 Industrial Rd Ste 102 San Carlos (94070) ***(P-24831)***
Kinetico Quality Water Systems, Riverside *Also called US Environmental* ***(P-9316)***
King Abrasives Inc ... F ... 510 785-8100
1942 National Ave Hayward (94545) ***(P-5564)***
King Graphics, San Diego *Also called Colmol Inc* ***(P-7279)***
King Henrys Inc ... E ... 661 295-5566
29124 Hancock Pkwy 1 Valencia (91355) ***(P-2393)***
King Instrument Company Inc ... E ... 714 891-0008
12700 Pala Dr Garden Grove (92841) ***(P-21609)***
King Nutronics Corporation ... E ... 818 887-5460
6421 Independence Ave Woodland Hills (91367) ***(P-21610)***
King Plastics Inc ... D ... 714 997-7540
840 N Elm St Orange (92867) ***(P-10180)***
King Precision Inc ... E ... 831 426-2704
111 Harrison Ct Santa Cruz (95062) ***(P-13236)***
King Rustler ... F ... 831 385-4880
522 Broadway St Ste A King City (93930) ***(P-5898)***
King Shock Technology Inc ... E ... 714 530-8701
12472 Edison Way Garden Grove (92841) ***(P-20383)***
King Wire Partitions Inc ... E ... 323 256-4846
6044 N Figueroa St Los Angeles (90042) ***(P-12983)***
King's Printing, San Diego *Also called Kings Printing Corp* ***(P-6923)***
Kingcom(us) LLC (HQ) ... C ... 424 744-5697
3100 Ocean Park Blvd Santa Monica (90405) ***(P-24832)***
Kingdom Matress Company, Gardena *Also called Kingdom Mattress Inc* ***(P-4867)***
Kingdom Mattress Inc ... E ... 562 630-5531
17920 S Figueroa St Gardena (90248) ***(P-4867)***
Kingfa Global Inc ... F ... 909 212-5413
1910 S Archibald Ave D Ontario (91761) ***(P-13076)***
Kingman Industries Inc ... E ... 951 698-1812
26370 Beckman Ct Ste A Murrieta (92562) ***(P-8595)***
Kings Asian Gourmet Inc ... E ... 415 222-6100
683 Brannan St Unit 304 San Francisco (94107) ***(P-763)***
Kings Cabinet Systems ... F ... 559 584-9662
426 Park Ave Hanford (93230) ***(P-4953)***
Kings Crating Inc (PA) ... E ... 619 590-1664
1364 Pioneer Way El Cajon (92020) ***(P-20667)***
Kings Crating Inc ... E ... 619 590-2631
1364 Pioneer Way El Cajon (92020) ***(P-13237)***
Kings Printing Corp ... E ... 619 297-6000
5401 Linda Vista Rd # 401 San Diego (92110) ***(P-6923)***

Employee Codes: A=Over 500 employees, B=251-500
C=101-250, D=51-100, E=20-50, F=10-19
2019 California
Manfacturers Register
© Mergent Inc. 1-800-342-5647
1187

Kings River Casting Inc.......F.......559 875-8250
1350 North Ave Sanger (93657) **(P-5019)**
Kings Silk Embroidery Art.......F.......714 505-0731
14321 Franklin Ave Tustin (92780) **(P-3850)**
Kings Way Sales and Mktg LLC.......F.......530 722-0272
6680 Lockheed Dr Redding (96002) **(P-15336)**
Kingsburg Cabinet Inc.......F.......559 897-7716
1000 14th Ave Ste A Kingsburg (93631) **(P-4320)**
Kingsburg Cultivator Inc.......F.......559 897-3662
40190 Road 36 Kingsburg (93631) **(P-14078)**
Kingsbury Cabinets, Kingsburg *Also called Kingsburg Cabinet Inc* **(P-4320)**
Kingsford Products Company LLC (HQ).......D.......510 271-7000
1221 Broadway Ste 1300 Oakland (94612) **(P-8958)**
Kingsley Mfg Co (PA).......F.......949 645-4401
1984 Placentia Ave Costa Mesa (92627) **(P-22764)**
Kingsolver Inc.......F.......562 945-7590
8417 Secura Way Santa Fe Springs (90670) **(P-23793)**
Kingson Mold & Machine Inc.......E.......714 871-0221
1350 Titan Way Brea (92821) **(P-14532)**
Kingspan Insulated Panels Inc.......D.......209 531-9091
2000 Morgan Rd Modesto (95358) **(P-12938)**
Kingston Digital Inc (HQ).......E.......714 435-2600
17600 Newhope St Fountain Valley (92708) **(P-15780)**
Kingston Technology Corp (PA).......B.......714 445-3495
17600 Newhope St Fountain Valley (92708) **(P-15781)**
Kinkisharyo International LLC (HQ).......F.......424 276-1803
300 N Cntntl Blvd Ste 300 El Segundo (90245) **(P-21078)**
Kintera Inc (HQ).......D.......858 795-3000
9605 Scranton Rd Ste 200 San Diego (92121) **(P-24833)**
Kinwai USA Inc.......E.......510 780-9388
2265 Davis Ct Hayward (94545) **(P-4712)**
Kio Kables, Antioch *Also called K I O Kables Inc* **(P-13836)**
Kion Technology Inc.......F.......408 435-3008
2190 Oakland Rd San Jose (95131) **(P-13609)**
Kip Steel Inc.......E.......714 461-1051
1650 Valley Ln Fullerton (92833) **(P-11470)**
Kipe Molds Inc.......F.......714 572-9576
340 E Crowther Ave Placentia (92870) **(P-14533)**
Kirby Manufacturing Inc (PA).......D.......209 723-0778
484 S St 59 Merced (95341) **(P-14079)**
Kirby Manufacturing Inc.......F.......559 686-1571
1478 N J St Tulare (93274) **(P-14080)**
Kirby-Tulare Manufacturing, Tulare *Also called Kirby Manufacturing Inc* **(P-14080)**
Kirk A Schliger.......F.......916 638-8433
11240 Pyrites Way Gold River (95670) **(P-15164)**
Kirk API Containers.......E.......323 278-5400
2131 Garfield Ave Commerce (90040) **(P-10181)**
Kirk Containers, Commerce *Also called Arthurmade Plastics Inc* **(P-9958)**
Kirkhill Inc.......D.......562 803-1117
12023 Woodruff Ave Downey (90241) **(P-9631)**
Kirkhill Inc (HQ).......E.......714 529-4901
300 E Cypress St Brea (92821) **(P-7906)**
Kirkhill Inc.......A.......714 529-4901
300 E Cypress St Brea (92821) **(P-9539)**
Kirkhill Inc.......A.......714 529-4901
300 E Cypress St Brea (92821) **(P-9540)**
Kirsen Technologies Inc.......F.......510 540-5383
2041 Bancroft Way Ste 201 Berkeley (94704) **(P-18145)**
Kisca, Los Angeles *Also called Komarov Enterprises Inc* **(P-3355)**
Kisco Conformal Coating LLC (PA).......F.......408 224-6533
6292 San Ignacio Ave C San Jose (95119) **(P-18942)**
Kiss Packaging Systems, Vista *Also called Accutek Packaging Equipment Co* **(P-15192)**
Kitanica Manufacturing.......F.......707 272-7286
867 Isabella St Oakland (94607) **(P-24149)**
Kitch Engineering Inc.......E.......818 897-7133
12320 Montague St Pacoima (91331) **(P-16657)**
Kitchen Cuts LLC.......E.......323 560-7415
6045 District Blvd Maywood (90270) **(P-499)**
Kitchen Equipment Mfg Co Inc.......E.......909 923-3153
2102 Maple Privado Ontario (91761) **(P-13238)**
Kitchens Now Inc.......F.......916 229-8222
20 Blue Sky Ct Sacramento (95828) **(P-4321)**
Kitcor Corporation.......E.......323 875-2820
9959 Glenoaks Blvd Sun Valley (91352) **(P-13239)**
Kite Hill, Hayward *Also called Lyrical Foods Inc* **(P-591)**
Kitsch LLC (PA).......F.......424 240-5551
307 N New Hampshire Ave Los Angeles (90004) **(P-23282)**
Kittrich Corporation (PA).......C.......714 736-1000
1585 W Mission Blvd Pomona (91766) **(P-5199)**
Kitty Hawk Corporation (PA).......C.......650 641-0076
2700 Broderick Way Mountain View (94043) **(P-20596)**
Kitty Textile Inc (PA).......F.......213 749-7278
2812 S Grand Ave Los Angeles (90007) **(P-3447)**
Kittyhawk Products, Garden Grove *Also called Kpi Services Inc* **(P-11817)**
Kiva Container Corporation.......E.......714 630-3850
2700 E Regal Park Dr Anaheim (92806) **(P-9868)**
Kiva Designs, Benicia *Also called Applied Sewing Resources Inc* **(P-2721)**
Kizanis Custom Cabinets, San Leandro *Also called Steve and Cynthia Kizanis* **(P-4353)**
Kizure Hair Products & Irons, Compton *Also called Kizure Product Co Inc* **(P-17395)**
Kizure Product Co Inc.......E.......310 604-0058
1950 N Central Ave Compton (90222) **(P-17395)**
Kj Aero Holdings LLC.......F.......714 891-6060
5142 Argosy Ave Huntington Beach (92649) **(P-6924)**
Kjl Fasteners, Chilcoot *Also called Pau Hana Group LLC* **(P-11983)**
Kjm Enterprises Inc.......E.......858 537-2490
8148 Auberge Cir San Diego (92127) **(P-7369)**
Kk Audio Inc.......F.......818 765-2921
12620 Raymer St North Hollywood (91605) **(P-23174)**
Kk-Graphics Printing.......F.......415 468-1057
1336 San Mateo Ave South San Francisco (94080) **(P-6925)**
Kkp - Roseville Inc.......F.......916 786-8573
106 N Sunrise Ave Ste B2 Roseville (95661) **(P-6926)**
Kl Electronics Inc.......E.......714 751-5611
3083 S Harbor Blvd Santa Ana (92704) **(P-18517)**
Kl-Megla America LLC.......E.......818 334-5311
2221 Celsius Ave Ste A Oxnard (93030) **(P-11968)**
KLA Tencor.......E.......510 887-2647
2260 American Ave Ste 1 Hayward (94545) **(P-15287)**
KLA-Tencor Asia-Pac Dist Corp.......E.......408 875-4144
1 Technology Dr Milpitas (95035) **(P-18943)**
KLA-Tencor Corporation (PA).......B.......408 875-3000
1 Technology Dr Milpitas (95035) **(P-21788)**
KLA-Tencor Corporation.......D.......408 496-2055
3530 Bassett St Santa Clara (95054) **(P-21789)**
KLA-Tencor Corporation.......D.......510 456-2490
850 Auburn Ct Fremont (94538) **(P-21790)**
Klatch Coffee Inc.......E.......909 981-4031
8767 Onyx Ave Rancho Cucamonga (91730) **(P-2358)**
Klean Kanteen Inc.......E.......530 592-4552
3960 Morrow Ln Chico (95928) **(P-11860)**
Kleen Maid Inc.......E.......323 581-3000
11450 Sheldon St Sun Valley (91352) **(P-3728)**
Kleenrite, Madera *Also called Better Cleaning Systems Inc* **(P-17406)**
Klein Bros Holdings Ltd.......E.......209 465-5033
1515 S Fresno Ave Stockton (95206) **(P-1492)**
Klein Bros Snacks, Stockton *Also called Klein Bros Holdings Ltd* **(P-1492)**
Klein Electronics Inc.......E.......760 781-3220
349 N Vinewood St Escondido (92029) **(P-18146)**
Klein Industries Inc.......F.......415 695-9117
2380 Jerrold Ave San Francisco (94124) **(P-16658)**
Klinky Manufacturing Co.......F.......818 766-6256
4000 W Magnolia Blvd D Burbank (91505) **(P-11969)**
Klippenstein Corporation.......E.......559 834-4258
5399 S Villa Ave Fresno (93725) **(P-15214)**
Klj Mobile Notary Inc.......F.......562 852-8253
9502 Oak St Apt D Bellflower (90706) **(P-23719)**
Klk Forte Industry Inc (PA).......E.......323 415-9181
1535 Rio Vista Ave Los Angeles (90023) **(P-3448)**
Kln Precision Machining Corp.......D.......510 770-5001
40725 Encyclopedia Cir Fremont (94538) **(P-16659)**
Klooma Holdings Inc.......E.......305 747-3315
113 N San Vicente Blvd Beverly Hills (90211) **(P-24834)**
Kloudgin, Sunnyvale *Also called Enterprise Signal Inc* **(P-24617)**
Kls Doors LLC.......E.......909 605-6468
501 Kettering Dr Ontario (91761) **(P-4179)**
Klune Industries Inc (HQ).......B.......818 503-8100
7323 Coldwater Canyon Ave North Hollywood (91605) **(P-20860)**
Km Printing Production Inc.......F.......626 821-0008
218 Longden Ave Irwindale (91706) **(P-6927)**
Kmb Foods Inc (PA).......E.......626 447-0545
1010 S Sierra Way San Bernardino (92408) **(P-500)**
Kmg Chemicals Inc.......E.......800 956-7467
2340 Bert Dr Hollister (95023) **(P-9270)**
Kmg Electronic Chemicals Inc.......F.......831 636-5151
2340 Bert Dr Hollister (95023) **(P-7692)**
Kmic Technology Inc.......E.......408 240-3600
2095 Ringwood Ave Ste 10 San Jose (95131) **(P-18147)**
Kmp Numatech Pacific, Pomona *Also called Numatech West (kmp) LLC* **(P-5440)**
Kmr Label LLC.......E.......310 603-8910
1360 W Walnut Pkwy Compton (90220) **(P-7205)**
Kmt International Inc.......E.......510 713-1400
344 De Leon Ave Fremont (94539) **(P-14231)**
KMW Communications, Fullerton *Also called KMW USA Inc* **(P-19611)**
KMW USA Inc (HQ).......E.......714 515-1100
1818 E Orangethorpe Ave Fullerton (92831) **(P-19611)**
Knauf Insulation Inc.......C.......530 275-9665
3100 Ashby Rd Shasta Lake (96019) **(P-11335)**
Knife River, Sutter Creek *Also called Amador Transit Mix Inc* **(P-11039)**
Knight LLC (HQ).......D.......949 595-4800
15340 Barranca Pkwy Irvine (92618) **(P-15337)**
Knight Publishing Corp.......E.......323 653-8060
8060 Melrose Ave Ste 210 Los Angeles (90046) **(P-6200)**
Knights Bridge Winery, Calistoga *Also called Bailey Essel William Jr* **(P-1651)**
Knightsbridge Plastics Inc.......D.......510 249-9722
3075 Osgood Ct Fremont (94539) **(P-10182)**
Knightscope Inc.......F.......650 924-1025
1070 Terra Bella Ave Mountain View (94043) **(P-19999)**
Knit Fit Inc.......F.......213 673-4731
112 W 9th St Ste 230 Los Angeles (90015) **(P-3901)**
Knk Apparel Inc.......C.......310 768-3333
223 W Rosecrans Ave Gardena (90248) **(P-3109)**
Kno Inc.......D.......408 844-8120
2200 Mission College Blvd Santa Clara (95054) **(P-24835)**
Knorr Beeswax Products Inc.......F.......760 431-2007
14906 Via De La Valle Del Mar (92014) **(P-24150)**
Knorr Brake Company LLC.......F.......510 475-0770
29471 Kohoutek Way Union City (94587) **(P-21079)**
Knott's Berry Farm, Buena Park *Also called Knotts Berry Farm LLC* **(P-2553)**
Knotts Berry Farm LLC (HQ).......B.......714 827-1776
8039 Beach Blvd Buena Park (90620) **(P-2553)**
Knova Software Inc (HQ).......E.......408 863-5800
10201 Torre Ave Ste 350 Cupertino (95014) **(P-24836)**
Knt Inc.......C.......510 651-7163
39760 Eureka Dr Newark (94560) **(P-16660)**
Knt Manufacturing, Newark *Also called Knt Inc* **(P-16660)**
Knt Manufacturing Inc.......E.......510 896-1699
39760 Eureka Dr Newark (94560) **(P-24151)**

Koala Kountry Folage, Valley Center *Also called International Decoratives Co* ***(P-24131)***
Koam Knitech Inc..........E.......310 515-1121
18118 S Broadway Gardena (90248) ***(P-2845)***
Kobelco Compressors Amer Inc..........D.......951 739-3030
301 N Smith Ave Corona (92880) ***(P-15129)***
Kobelco Compressors Amer Inc (HQ)..........B.......951 739-3030
1450 W Rincon St Corona (92880) ***(P-15130)***
Kobi Katz Inc..........D.......213 689-0076
801 S Flower St Fl 3 Los Angeles (90017) ***(P-23283)***
Kobis Windows & Doors Mfg Inc..........E.......818 764-6400
7326 Laurel Canyon Blvd North Hollywood (91605) ***(P-4322)***
Kobus Business Systems LLC..........F.......559 595-1915
254 N Alta Ave Dinuba (93618) ***(P-15897)***
Kobus Harmse, Dinuba *Also called Kobus Business Systems LLC* ***(P-15897)***
Koch Feeds Inc..........E.......209 725-8253
10916 Amsterdam Rd Winton (95388) ***(P-1141)***
Koch Filter Corporation..........F.......951 361-9017
10290 Birtcher Dr Mira Loma (91752) ***(P-15963)***
Koco Motion Us LLC..........F.......408 612-4970
335 Cochrane Cir Morgan Hill (95037) ***(P-21611)***
Koda Farms Inc..........E.......209 392-2191
22540 Russell Ave South Dos Palos (93665) ***(P-1085)***
Koda Farms Milling Inc..........E.......209 392-2191
22540 Russell Ave South Dos Palos (93665) ***(P-1086)***
Kodiak Cartoners Inc..........E.......559 266-4844
2550 S East Ave Ste 101 Fresno (93706) ***(P-15215)***
Kodiak Precision Inc (PA)..........F.......510 234-4165
444 S 1st St Richmond (94804) ***(P-16661)***
Kodiak Sciences Inc (PA)..........E.......650 281-0850
2631 Hanover St Palo Alto (94304) ***(P-8564)***
Kofax Limited (HQ)..........E.......949 783-1000
15211 Laguna Canyon Rd Irvine (92618) ***(P-24837)***
Kohler & Clark Screw Products..........E.......559 688-1194
4088 S K St Tulare (93274) ***(P-16662)***
Kohler Co..........E.......909 890-4291
675 E Central Ave San Bernardino (92408) ***(P-12015)***
Kois & Ponds Inc..........F.......800 936-3638
4460 Brooks St Ste B Montclair (91763) ***(P-1142)***
Koito Aviation LLC..........F.......661 257-2878
25011 Avenue Stanford D Valencia (91355) ***(P-20861)***
Kokatat Inc..........D.......707 822-7621
5350 Ericson Way Arcata (95521) ***(P-3168)***
Kolkka John..........E.......707 554-3660
1300 Green Island Rd Vallejo (94503) ***(P-4834)***
Kolkka Furniture Design & Mfg, Vallejo *Also called Kolkka John* ***(P-4834)***
Kollmorgen Corporation..........B.......805 696-1236
33 S La Patera Ln Santa Barbara (93117) ***(P-17206)***
Koltov Inc (PA)..........E.......805 764-0280
300 S Lewis Rd Ste A Camarillo (93012) ***(P-10563)***
Komag Incorporated..........F.......408 576-2150
1710 Automation Pkwy San Jose (95131) ***(P-10818)***
Komar Apparel Supply, Los Angeles *Also called Mdc Interior Solutions LLC* ***(P-3671)***
Komar Distribution Services, Mira Loma *Also called Charles Komar & Sons Inc* ***(P-3535)***
Komarov Enterprises Inc..........D.......213 244-7000
1936 Mateo St Los Angeles (90021) ***(P-3355)***
Komax Systems Inc..........E.......310 830-4320
15301 Graham St Huntington Beach (92649) ***(P-14179)***
Komex International Inc..........E.......323 233-9005
736 E 29th St Los Angeles (90011) ***(P-3250)***
Komfy Kings Inc..........D.......818 899-8929
10445 Glenoaks Blvd Pacoima (91331) ***(P-4911)***
Kona Bar LLC..........F.......808 927-1934
2601 Ocean Park Blvd # 310 Santa Monica (90405) ***(P-1435)***
Konami Digital Entrmt Inc (HQ)..........D.......310 220-8100
2381 Rosecrans Ave # 200 El Segundo (90245) ***(P-24838)***
Koncept Technologies Inc..........F.......323 261-8999
429 E Huntington Dr Monrovia (91016) ***(P-17541)***
Konecranes Inc..........E.......661 397-9700
2900 E Belle Ter Bldg A Bakersfield (93307) ***(P-14299)***
Konecranes Inc..........F.......925 273-0140
5637 Blaribera St Livermore (94550) ***(P-14300)***
Kong Veterinary Products..........F.......626 633-0077
16018 Adelante St Ste C Irwindale (91702) ***(P-22505)***
Kontech USA LLC..........F.......626 622-1325
18045 Rowland St City of Industry (91748) ***(P-17622)***
Kontron America Inc..........D.......800 822-7522
9477 Waples St Ste 150 San Diego (92121) ***(P-15439)***
Kontron America Incorporated (HQ)..........C.......858 677-0877
9477 Waples St Ste 150 San Diego (92121) ***(P-15440)***
Kool Star, Long Beach *Also called Three Star Rfrgn Engrg Inc* ***(P-15981)***
Koolfog Inc (PA)..........F.......760 321-9203
31290 Plantation Dr Thousand Palms (92276) ***(P-15964)***
Kopaskie Metallurgical Inc..........E.......626 333-3898
330 S 9th Ave City of Industry (91746) ***(P-11816)***
Kopin Corporation..........E.......831 636-5556
501 Tevis Trl Hollister (95023) ***(P-18944)***
Kopykake Enterprises Inc (PA)..........F.......310 373-8906
3699 W 240th St Torrance (90505) ***(P-13240)***
Koral LLC..........E.......323 391-1060
5124 Pacific Blvd Vernon (90058) ***(P-3169)***
Koral Active Wear, Vernon *Also called Koral LLC* ***(P-3169)***
Koral Industries LLC (PA)..........D.......323 585-5343
5124 Pacific Blvd Vernon (90058) ***(P-3449)***
Koral Los Angeles, Vernon *Also called Koral Industries LLC* ***(P-3449)***
Korbel Champagne Cellers, Guerneville *Also called F Korbel & Bros* ***(P-1755)***
Korda & Geis Engineering LLC..........E.......805 968-5648
132 Easy St Ste D Buellton (93427) ***(P-16663)***
Korden Inc..........F.......909 988-8979
611 S Palmetto Ave Ontario (91762) ***(P-4992)***
Kore Infrastructure LLC..........F.......310 367-1003
200 N Pacific Coast Hwy # 340 El Segundo (90245) ***(P-9018)***
Kore Print Solutions Inc..........F.......510 445-1638
46711 Fremont Blvd Fremont (94538) ***(P-6928)***
Korea Aerospace Industries Ltd..........F.......714 868-8560
16700 Valley View Ave # 205 La Mirada (90638) ***(P-20597)***
Korea Central, Garden Grove *Also called Joong-Ang Daily News Cal Inc* ***(P-5895)***
Korea Central Daily News..........F.......213 368-2500
33288 Central Ave Union City (94587) ***(P-5899)***
Korea Daily, Los Angeles *Also called Joong-Ang Daily News Cal Inc* ***(P-5894)***
Korea Daily News & Korea Times..........E.......510 777-1111
8134 Capwell Dr Oakland (94621) ***(P-5900)***
Korea Times Los Angeles Inc..........E.......510 777-1111
8134 Capwell Dr Oakland (94621) ***(P-5901)***
Korea Times Los Angeles Inc..........F.......714 530-6001
9572 Garden Grove Blvd Garden Grove (92844) ***(P-5902)***
Korea Times San Francisco, The, Oakland *Also called Korea Times Los Angeles Inc* ***(P-5901)***
Koros USA Inc..........E.......805 529-0825
610 Flinn Ave Moorpark (93021) ***(P-22506)***
Kortick Manufacturer Co, Pittsburg *Also called Frase Enterprises* ***(P-17514)***
Kosakura Associates, Trabuco Canyon *Also called CK Manufacturing and Trading* ***(P-5048)***
Kosan Biosciences Incorporated..........D.......650 995-7356
3832 Bay Center Pl Hayward (94545) ***(P-8249)***
Kosta Browne, Sebastopol *Also called KB Wines LLC* ***(P-1837)***
Kosta Browne Winery, Sebastopol *Also called Kosta Browne Wines LLC* ***(P-1841)***
Kosta Browne Wines LLC..........E.......707 823-7430
220 Morris St Sebastopol (95472) ***(P-1841)***
Koto Inc..........F.......310 327-7359
22857 Lockness Ave Torrance (90501) ***(P-23397)***
Koto Bukiya, Torrance *Also called Koto Inc* ***(P-23397)***
Kotonica Inc..........F.......818 898-0978
3226 N Frederic St Burbank (91504) ***(P-10183)***
Kott Inc..........F.......949 770-5055
27161 Burbank El Toro (92610) ***(P-8913)***
Kouzouian Custom Furniture, Granada Hills *Also called Kouzouians Fine Custom Furn* ***(P-5242)***
Kouzouians Fine Custom Furn..........E.......818 772-1212
18586 Caspian Ct Granada Hills (91344) ***(P-5242)***
Kovin Corporation Inc..........E.......858 558-0100
9240 Mira Este Ct San Diego (92126) ***(P-6929)***
Kozlowski Farms A Corporation..........E.......707 887-1587
5566 Hwy 116 Forestville (95436) ***(P-814)***
Kozy Shack Enterprises LLC..........D.......209 634-2131
600 S Tegner Rd Turlock (95380) ***(P-2554)***
Kp LLC (PA)..........B.......510 346-0729
13951 Washington Ave San Leandro (94578) ***(P-6930)***
Kp LLC..........E.......510 346-0729
13951 Washington Ave San Leandro (94578) ***(P-6931)***
Kp LLC..........E.......209 466-6761
1134 Enterprise St Stockton (95204) ***(P-7370)***
Kpi Agency Inc..........F.......949 232-0220
32 Via Jacobea San Clemente (92673) ***(P-6512)***
Kpi Services Inc..........E.......714 895-5024
11651 Monarch St Garden Grove (92841) ***(P-11817)***
Kpisoft Inc..........D.......415 439-5228
50 California St Ste 1500 San Francisco (94111) ***(P-24839)***
Kraemer & Co Mfg Inc..........F.......530 865-7982
3778 County Road 99w Orland (95963) ***(P-12939)***
Kraft Foods, Buena Park *Also called Mondelez Global LLC* ***(P-509)***
Kraft Foods, Oakland *Also called Nestle Pizza Company Inc* ***(P-1001)***
Kraft Foods, Anaheim *Also called Mondelez Global LLC* ***(P-1292)***
Kraft Heinz Foods Company..........C.......209 942-0102
3735 Imperial Way Stockton (95215) ***(P-582)***
Kraft Heinz Foods Company..........E.......209 832-4269
57 Stonebridge Ct Tracy (95376) ***(P-764)***
Kraft Heinz Foods Company..........B.......714 870-8235
1500 E Walnut Ave Fullerton (92831) ***(P-2555)***
Kraft Heinz Foods Company..........E.......209 932-5700
6755 C E Dixon St Stockton (95206) ***(P-1493)***
Kraft Heinz Foods Company..........F.......909 605-7201
3971 E Airport Dr Ontario (91761) ***(P-2556)***
Kraft Heinz Foods Company..........B.......559 441-8515
2494 S Orange Ave Fresno (93725) ***(P-815)***
Kraft Heinz Foods Company..........F.......925 242-4504
2603 Camino Ramon Ste 180 San Ramon (94583) ***(P-816)***
Kraft Heinz Foods Company..........D.......559 237-9206
4343 E Florence Ave Fresno (93725) ***(P-1494)***
Kraft Heinz Foods Company..........B.......209 552-6021
1905 Mchenry Ave Escalon (95320) ***(P-817)***
Kraft Heinz Foods Company..........C.......949 250-4080
2450 White Rd Irvine (92614) ***(P-765)***
Kraft Tech Inc..........F.......818 837-3520
661 Arroyo St San Fernando (91340) ***(P-21122)***
Krallcast Inc..........F.......626 333-0678
16205 Ward Way City of Industry (91745) ***(P-11513)***
Kramarz Enterprises..........F.......408 293-1187
1065 Delmas Ave San Jose (95125) ***(P-16664)***
Kranem Corporation..........C.......650 319-6743
560 S Winchester Blvd San Jose (95128) ***(P-24840)***
Krasnes Inc..........D.......619 232-2066
2222 Commercial St San Diego (92113) ***(P-3619)***
Kratos Def & SEC Solutions Inc (PA)..........B.......858 812-7300
10680 Treena St Ste 600 San Diego (92131) ***(P-18148)***
Kratos Tech Trning Sltions Inc (HQ)..........C.......858 812-7300
10680 Treena St Fl 6 San Diego (92131) ***(P-24841)***
Kratos Unmanned Aerial Systems..........B.......916 431-7977
5381 Raley Blvd Sacramento (95838) ***(P-10184)***

ALPHABETIC

Employee Codes: A=Over 500 employees, B=251-500
C=101-250, D=51-100, E=20-50, F=10-19
2019 California
Manfacturers Register
© Mergent Inc. 1-800-342-5647
1189

Krave Jerky, Sonoma *Also called Krave Pure Foods Inc* ***(P-501)***
Krave Pure Foods Inc..........D.......707 939-9176
117 W Napa St Ste A Sonoma (95476) ***(P-501)***
Krego Corporation..........F.......818 837-1494
12971 Arroyo St San Fernando (91340) ***(P-17148)***
Kretzschmar Steel, Colton *Also called C and R Sales Inc* ***(P-12124)***
Kri Star Enterprises Inc (PA)..........E.......800 579-8819
360 Sutton Pl Santa Rosa (95407) ***(P-10944)***
Krieger Speciality Products, Pico Rivera *Also called Metal Tite Products* ***(P-12332)***
Krinos Foods LLC..........F.......805 922-6700
1105 E Foster Rd Ste E Santa Maria (93455) ***(P-918)***
Krisalis Inc..........F.......209 286-1637
3366 Golden Gate Ct San Andreas (95249) ***(P-16665)***
Krisalis Inc (PA)..........F.......510 786-0858
28216 Industrial Blvd Hayward (94545) ***(P-16666)***
Krisalis Precision Machining, Hayward *Also called Krisalis Inc* ***(P-16666)***
Krissy Op Shins USA Inc..........D.......213 747-2591
2408 S Broadway Los Angeles (90007) ***(P-3170)***
Kristich-Monterey Pipe Co Inc..........F.......831 724-4186
225 Salinas Rd Ste B Royal Oaks (95076) ***(P-10945)***
Kritech Corporation (PA)..........F.......310 538-9940
333 W 131st St Los Angeles (90061) ***(P-19612)***
Kronos Incorporated..........D.......800 580-7374
240 Commerce Irvine (92602) ***(P-24842)***
Kruger Foods Inc..........C.......209 941-8518
18362 E Highway 4 Stockton (95215) ***(P-919)***
Krupp Brothers LLC..........F.......707 226-2215
1345 Hestia Way NAPA (94558) ***(P-1842)***
Kruse and Son Inc..........E.......626 358-4536
235 Kruse Ave Monrovia (91016) ***(P-502)***
Kryler Corp..........E.......714 871-9611
1217 E Ash Ave Fullerton (92831) ***(P-13440)***
Krytar Inc..........E.......408 734-5999
1288 Anvilwood Ave Sunnyvale (94089) ***(P-19613)***
KS Engineering Inc..........F.......562 483-7788
14948 Shoemaker Ave Santa Fe Springs (90670) ***(P-20862)***
KS Industries..........F.......858 344-1146
3160 Camino Del Rio S # 116 San Diego (92108) ***(P-24152)***
Ksc Industries Inc..........E.......619 671-0110
9771 Clairemont Mesa Blvd E San Diego (92124) ***(P-17824)***
KSD Inc..........F.......951 849-7669
161 W Lincoln St Banning (92220) ***(P-16667)***
Ksm Corp..........B.......408 514-2400
1959 Concourse Dr San Jose (95131) ***(P-18945)***
Ksm Vacuum Products Inc..........F.......408 514-2400
1959 Concourse Dr San Jose (95131) ***(P-12394)***
Ksu Corporation..........F.......951 409-7055
3 Emmy Ln Ladera Ranch (92694) ***(P-12192)***
KT Engineering Corporation..........F.......310 537-3818
2016 E Vista Bella Way Rancho Dominguez (90220) ***(P-16668)***
Kt Industries Inc..........F.......323 255-7143
3203 Fletcher Dr Los Angeles (90065) ***(P-17149)***
Kti Incorporated..........D.......909 434-1888
3009 N Laurel Ave Rialto (92377) ***(P-10946)***
Kto, West Hills *Also called Kelly Teegarden Organics LLC* ***(P-8782)***
Kts Kitchens Inc..........C.......310 764-0850
1065 E Walnut St Ste C Carson (90746) ***(P-2557)***
Kuantum Brands LLC..........C.......760 412-2432
1747 Hancock St Ste A San Diego (92101) ***(P-2146)***
Kubota Authorized Dealer, Chico *Also called Industrial Power Products* ***(P-16580)***
Kubota Tractor Corporation..........F.......209 334-9910
1175 S Guild Ave Lodi (95240) ***(P-14081)***
KUDos&co Inc..........E.......650 799-9104
470 Ramona St Palo Alto (94301) ***(P-6513)***
Kui Co Inc..........E.......949 369-7949
266 Calle Pintoresco San Clemente (92672) ***(P-5309)***
Kulayful Silicone Bracelets..........E.......626 610-3816
2267 Joshua Tree Way West Covina (91791) ***(P-23751)***
Kuleto Estate, Santa Rosa *Also called Kuleto Villa LLC* ***(P-1843)***
Kuleto Villa LLC..........E.......707 967-8577
200 Concourse Blvd Santa Rosa (95403) ***(P-1843)***
Kulicke & Soffa Industries, Santa Ana *Also called Kulicke Sffa Wedge Bonding Inc* ***(P-20000)***
Kulicke Sffa Wedge Bonding Inc..........C.......949 660-0440
1821 E Dyer Rd Ste 200 Santa Ana (92705) ***(P-20000)***
Kulthorn North America, San Diego *Also called Elco Rfrgn Solutions LLC* ***(P-15952)***
Kum Kang Trading USAinC..........F.......562 531-6111
6433 Alondra Blvd Paramount (90723) ***(P-8784)***
Kumi Kookoon..........F.......310 515-8811
18018 S Western Ave Gardena (90248) ***(P-3729)***
Kumjian Enterprises, South El Monte *Also called General Metal Engraving Inc* ***(P-23715)***
Kuna Systems Corporation..........F.......650 263-8257
883 Sneath Ln Ste 222 San Bruno (94066) ***(P-15441)***
Kunde Enterprises Inc..........D.......707 833-5501
9825 Sonoma Hwy Kenwood (95452) ***(P-1844)***
Kunde Estate Winery, Kenwood *Also called Kunde Enterprises Inc* ***(P-1844)***
Kunin Wines LLC..........F.......805 963-9633
28 Anacapa St Ste A Santa Barbara (93101) ***(P-1845)***
Kuraray America Inc..........F.......949 476-9600
2 Park Plz Ste 480 Irvine (92614) ***(P-7852)***
Kurdex Corporation..........F.......408 734-8181
343 Gibraltar Dr Sunnyvale (94089) ***(P-15782)***
Kurtz Family Corporation..........F.......707 823-1213
1450 Industrial Ave Sebastopol (95472) ***(P-10185)***
Kurz Transfer Products LP..........E.......951 738-9521
415 N Smith Ave Corona (92880) ***(P-24153)***
Kushwood Chair Inc..........C.......909 930-2100
1290 E Elm St Ontario (91761) ***(P-4713)***
Kuster Co Oil Well Services..........E.......562 595-0661
2900 E 29th St Long Beach (90806) ***(P-110)***
Kuster Company, Long Beach *Also called Kuster Co Oil Well Services* ***(P-110)***
Kustom Lighting Products Inc..........E.......626 443-0166
2107 Chico Ave South El Monte (91733) ***(P-17706)***
Kustomer Kinetics Inc..........F.......626 445-6161
136 E Saint Joseph St A Arcadia (91006) ***(P-8785)***
Kuton Welding Inc..........F.......818 771-0964
11380 Luddington St Sun Valley (91352) ***(P-14728)***
Kutzin & Kutzin Inc..........F.......818 994-0242
14726 Oxnard St Van Nuys (91411) ***(P-4630)***
KVA Inc..........F.......760 489-1500
2802 Luciernaga St Carlsbad (92009) ***(P-11403)***
Kva Stainless, Carlsbad *Also called KVA Inc* ***(P-11403)***
Kval Inc..........C.......707 762-4363
825 Petaluma Blvd S Petaluma (94952) ***(P-14785)***
Kval Machinery Co, Petaluma *Also called Kval Inc* ***(P-14785)***
KVP, Irwindale *Also called Kong Veterinary Products* ***(P-22505)***
KVP International Inc..........E.......888 411-7387
13775 Ramona Ave Chino (91710) ***(P-22765)***
Kw Automotive North Amer Inc..........E.......800 445-3767
300 W Pontiac Way Clovis (93612) ***(P-20384)***
Kw Plastics Recycling Division..........D.......661 392-0500
1861 Sunnyside Ct Bakersfield (93308) ***(P-9712)***
Kwan Software Engineering Inc..........E.......408 496-1200
1879 Lundy Ave Ste 286 San Jose (95131) ***(P-24843)***
Kwdz Manufacturing LLC (PA)..........D.......323 526-3526
337 S Anderson St Los Angeles (90033) ***(P-3580)***
Kwik Kopy Printing, Mission Viejo *Also called Jorlind Enterprises Inc* ***(P-6913)***
Kwikparts.com, Torrance *Also called Probe Racing Components Inc* ***(P-16150)***
Kwj Engineering Inc (PA)..........E.......510 794-4296
8430 Central Ave Ste C Newark (94560) ***(P-22226)***
Kworld (usa) Computer Inc..........F.......626 581-0867
499 Nibus Ste D Brea (92821) ***(P-18149)***
Kyles Rock & Redi-Mix Inc..........E.......916 681-4848
1221 San Simeon Dr Roseville (95661) ***(P-11125)***
Kymera Industries Inc..........F.......909 228-7194
14735 Manzanita Dr Fontana (92335) ***(P-24154)***
Kymsta Corp..........E.......213 380-8118
1506 W 12th St Los Angeles (90015) ***(P-3450)***
Kyocera International Inc (HQ)..........C.......858 492-1456
8611 Balboa Ave San Diego (92123) ***(P-18946)***
Kyocera International Inc..........D.......858 614-2581
8611 Balboa Ave San Diego (92123) ***(P-18947)***
Kyocera Precision Tools Inc..........C.......714 428-3600
3565 Cadillac Ave Costa Mesa (92626) ***(P-14387)***
Kyocharo USA LLC..........F.......213 383-1236
3807 Wilshire Blvd # 518 Los Angeles (90010) ***(P-5903)***
Kyoho Manufacturing California..........C.......209 941-6200
809 Walker Ave Oakland (94610) ***(P-13140)***
Kyowa Hakko Kirin Cal Inc (HQ)..........E.......858 952-7000
9420 Athena Cir La Jolla (92037) ***(P-8250)***
Kyriba Corp (HQ)..........E.......858 210-3560
9620 Towne Cntre Dr 200 San Diego (92121) ***(P-24844)***
Kythera Biopharmaceuticals Inc..........C.......818 587-4500
30930 Russell Ranch Rd # 300 Westlake Village (91362) ***(P-8251)***
Kyung In Printing Inc..........C.......619 662-3920
7920 Airway Rd Ste A8 San Diego (92154) ***(P-6932)***
L & A Plastics, Yorba Linda *Also called Loritz & Associates Inc* ***(P-10194)***
L & B Laboratories Inc..........F.......408 251-7888
1660 Mabury Rd San Jose (95133) ***(P-24155)***
L & H Industries..........F.......714 635-1555
925 E Arlee Pl Anaheim (92805) ***(P-956)***
L & H Iron Inc..........F.......408 287-8797
1049 Felipe Ave San Jose (95122) ***(P-12872)***
L & H Mold & Engineering Inc (PA)..........E.......909 930-1547
2239 1st St La Verne (91750) ***(P-10186)***
L & H Molds, La Verne *Also called L & H Mold & Engineering Inc* ***(P-10186)***
L & L Custom Shutters Inc..........C.......714 996-9539
3133 Yukon Ave Costa Mesa (92626) ***(P-4180)***
L & L Louvers Inc..........E.......951 735-9300
12355 Doherty St Riverside (92503) ***(P-12325)***
L & L Printers Carlsbad LLC..........E.......760 438-3456
6200 Yarrow Dr Carlsbad (92011) ***(P-6933)***
L & L Printers Inc..........F.......858 278-4300
6200 Yarrow Dr Carlsbad (92011) ***(P-6934)***
L & M Electronics..........F.......650 341-1608
541 Taylor Way Ste 10 San Carlos (94070) ***(P-18948)***
L & M Machining Center Inc..........F.......760 437-3810
1497 Poinsettia Ave # 156 Vista (92081) ***(P-16669)***
L & M Machining Corporation..........D.......714 414-0923
550 S Melrose St Placentia (92870) ***(P-19400)***
L & N Fixtures Inc..........E.......323 686-0041
2214 Tyler Ave El Monte (91733) ***(P-5077)***
L & P Button & Trimming Co..........F.......626 796-0903
2477 Ridgeway Rd San Marino (91108) ***(P-23768)***
L & S Machine Inc..........F.......562 924-9007
711 W 17th St Ste H2 Costa Mesa (92627) ***(P-13030)***
L & S Stone and Fireplace Shop, San Marcos *Also called L&S Stone LLC* ***(P-11259)***
L & T Precision Corporation..........C.......858 513-7874
12105 Kirkham Rd Poway (92064) ***(P-12640)***
L & T Precision Engrg Inc..........E.......408 441-1890
2395 Qume Dr San Jose (95131) ***(P-16670)***
L A Air Line Inc..........E.......323 585-1088
3844 S Santa Fe Ave Vernon (90058) ***(P-2883)***
L A Japanese Daily News, Los Angeles *Also called Rafu Shimpo* ***(P-6022)***
L A Lighting, El Monte *Also called Los Angeles Ltg Mfg Co Inc* ***(P-17629)***
L A P C O, La Palma *Also called Lapco West LLC* ***(P-20385)***
L A PRESS, Los Angeles *Also called LA Printing & Graphics Inc* ***(P-6937)***
L A S A M Inc..........F.......323 586-8717
3844 S Santa Fe Ave Vernon (90058) ***(P-3581)***

L A Steel Craft Products (PA).....E.....626 798-7401
1975 Lincoln Ave Pasadena (91103) ***(P-23604)***
L A Supply Co.....E.....949 470-9900
18005 Sky Park Cir Ste A Irvine (92614) ***(P-7371)***
L A Times Olympic Plant, Los Angeles *Also called Los Angles Tmes Cmmnctions LLC* ***(P-5928)***
L A Weekly, Los Angeles *Also called La Weekly* ***(P-5906)***
L C Miller Company.....E.....323 268-3611
717 Monterey Pass Rd Monterey Park (91754) ***(P-15266)***
L C Miller Company (PA).....F.....323 268-3611
717 Monterey Pass Rd Monterey Park (91754) ***(P-15267)***
L C Pringle Sales Inc (PA).....E.....714 892-1524
12020 Western Ave Garden Grove (92841) ***(P-5200)***
L F P Inc (PA).....D.....323 651-3525
8484 Wilshire Blvd # 900 Beverly Hills (90211) ***(P-6201)***
L Foppiano Wine Co.....E.....707 433-2736
12707 Old Redwood Hwy Healdsburg (95448) ***(P-1846)***
L J L Engineering Co, Santa Ana *Also called Laszlo J Lak* ***(P-16681)***
L J R Grinding Corp.....F.....310 532-7232
445 W 164th St Gardena (90248) ***(P-16671)***
L J Smith Inc.....F.....949 609-0544
25956 Commercentre Dr Lake Forest (92630) ***(P-4181)***
L K Lehman Trucking.....E.....209 532-5586
19333 Industrial Dr Sonora (95370) ***(P-10947)***
L M I, Ontario *Also called Larry Mthvin Installations Inc* ***(P-10712)***
L N L Anodizing Inc.....E.....818 768-9224
9900 Glenoaks Blvd Ste 3 Sun Valley (91352) ***(P-13441)***
L P Glassblowing Inc.....E.....408 988-7561
2322 Calle Del Mundo Santa Clara (95054) ***(P-19614)***
L P McNear Brick Co Inc.....D.....415 453-7702
1 Mcnear Brickyard Rd San Rafael (94901) ***(P-10854)***
L R Associates, Simi Valley *Also called Maury Razon* ***(P-3670)***
L Space, Irvine *Also called Lspace America LLC* ***(P-3255)***
L T C, Ukiah *Also called Liqua-Tech Corporation* ***(P-21690)***
L T Litho & Printing Co.....E.....949 863-1340
16811 Noyes Ave Irvine (92606) ***(P-6935)***
L T S, City of Industry *Also called Lt Security Inc* ***(P-20009)***
L T Seroge Inc.....F.....951 354-7141
7400 Jurupa Ave Riverside (92504) ***(P-20001)***
L W Lefort, Placentia *Also called Richfield Engineering Inc* ***(P-12414)***
L Y A Group Inc.....F.....213 683-1123
1317 S Grand Ave Los Angeles (90015) ***(P-3451)***
L&F Wood LLC.....F.....310 400-5569
416 E Alondra Blvd Gardena (90248) ***(P-4182)***
L&H Enterprises.....F.....760 230-2275
2111 Montgomery Ave Cardiff By The Sea (92007) ***(P-15783)***
L&S Machine Enterprises, Costa Mesa *Also called L & S Machine Inc* ***(P-13030)***
L&S Stone LLC (HQ).....E.....760 736-3232
1370 Grand Ave Ste B San Marcos (92078) ***(P-11259)***
L-3 Applied Technologies, Inc., San Diego *Also called L3 Applied Technologies Inc* ***(P-18151)***
L-3 Cmmnications Sonoma Eo Inc.....C.....707 568-3000
428 Aviation Blvd Santa Rosa (95403) ***(P-23175)***
L-3 Communication, San Leandro *Also called L3 Technologies Inc* ***(P-18162)***
L-3 Communications Corporation.....F.....858 694-7500
9020 Balboa Ave San Diego (92123) ***(P-18150)***
L-3 Communications Infrared, Buellton *Also called Infraredvision Technology Corp* ***(P-18894)***
L-3 Communications Wescam.....E.....707 568-3000
428 Aviation Blvd Ste 3I Santa Rosa (95403) ***(P-21315)***
L-3 Interstate Electronics, Anaheim *Also called Interstate Electronics Corp* ***(P-21778)***
L-3 Pacord, National City *Also called Pacord Inc* ***(P-21008)***
L-3 Telemetry & Rf Products, San Diego *Also called L3 Technologies Inc* ***(P-18153)***
L-G Wood Products, Pomona *Also called De Larshe Cabinetry LLC* ***(P-4140)***
L-Nutra Inc.....F.....310 245-1724
8240 Zitola Ter Playa Del Rey (90293) ***(P-8252)***
L3 Applied Technologies Inc (HQ).....C.....858 404-7824
10180 Barnes Canyon Rd San Diego (92121) ***(P-18151)***
L3 Applied Technologies Inc.....C.....858 404-7824
10180 Barnes Canyon Rd San Diego (92121) ***(P-18152)***
L3 Cincinnati Electronics Corp.....E.....626 395-7460
150 N San Gabriel Blvd Pasadena (91107) ***(P-15965)***
L3 Communications Link.....E.....559 998-5295
210 Franklin Blvd Lemoore (93245) ***(P-20002)***
L3 Electron Devices Inc (HQ).....A.....310 517-6000
3100 Lomita Blvd Torrance (90505) ***(P-18392)***
L3 Technologies Inc.....B.....858 279-0411
9020 Balboa Ave San Diego (92123) ***(P-18153)***
L3 Technologies Inc.....C.....818 833-2500
15825 Roxford St Sylmar (91342) ***(P-21316)***
L3 Technologies Inc.....B.....650 591-8411
3100 Lomita Blvd Torrance (90505) ***(P-18154)***
L3 Technologies Inc.....C.....714 758-4222
602 E Vermont Ave Anaheim (92805) ***(P-18155)***
L3 Technologies Inc.....D.....916 363-6581
9795 Bus Park Dr Ste K Sacramento (95827) ***(P-15442)***
L3 Technologies Inc.....C.....916 351-4556
107 Woodmere Rd Folsom (95630) ***(P-18156)***
L3 Technologies Inc.....D.....858 552-9716
10180 Barnes Canyon Rd San Diego (92121) ***(P-18157)***
L3 Technologies Inc.....C.....760 431-6800
5957 Landau Ct Carlsbad (92008) ***(P-18339)***
L3 Technologies Inc.....D.....805 584-1717
200 W Los Angeles Ave Simi Valley (93065) ***(P-18158)***
L3 Technologies Inc.....B.....858 552-9500
9890 Towne Centre Dr # 100 San Diego (92121) ***(P-18159)***
L3 Technologies Inc.....C.....650 326-9500
130 Constitution Dr Menlo Park (94025) ***(P-18160)***
L3 Technologies Inc.....C.....818 367-0111
15825 Roxford St Sylmar (91342) ***(P-18161)***
L3 Technologies Inc.....C.....858 499-0284
2700 Merced St San Leandro (94577) ***(P-18162)***
La Aloe LLC.....E.....888 968-2563
2301 E 7th St Ste A152 Los Angeles (90023) ***(P-957)***
La Barca Tortilleria Inc.....E.....323 268-1744
3047 Whittier Blvd Los Angeles (90023) ***(P-2558)***
La Bath Vanity Inc.....F.....909 303-3323
2222 Davie Ave Commerce (90040) ***(P-4323)***
La Blanca Swimwear, Cypress *Also called Manhattan Beachwear Inc* ***(P-3459)***
La Bonita, Norwalk *Also called Dianas Mexican Food Pdts Inc* ***(P-2506)***
La Bottleworks Inc.....E.....323 724-4076
1605 Beach St Montebello (90640) ***(P-2147)***
La Boulangerie, Stockton *Also called Toufic Inc* ***(P-1334)***
La Brea Bakery Holdings Inc.....B.....818 742-4242
14490 Catalina St San Leandro (94577) ***(P-1276)***
La Brothers Enterprise Inc.....E.....415 626-8818
57 Columbia Sq San Francisco (94103) ***(P-6936)***
LA Cabinet & Millwork Inc.....E.....323 227-5000
3005 Humboldt St Los Angeles (90031) ***(P-5078)***
La Campana Tortilla Factory, Lodi *Also called Del Castillo Foods Inc* ***(P-2502)***
La Canada Valley Sun, La Canada Flintridge *Also called Los Angles Tmes Cmmnctions LLC* ***(P-5925)***
La Candelaria Furniture Mfr, Lynwood *Also called La Candelaria Manufacturing* ***(P-4714)***
La Candelaria Manufacturing.....F.....310 763-0112
2790 M L King Jr Blvd Lynwood (90262) ***(P-4714)***
La Carreta Food Products.....F.....909 825-0737
302 S La Cadena Dr Colton (92324) ***(P-2559)***
La Carreta Mexican Foods, Colton *Also called La Carreta Food Products* ***(P-2559)***
La Chapalita Inc (PA).....E.....626 443-8556
1724 Chico Ave El Monte (91733) ***(P-2560)***
La Chic, Vernon *Also called Rmla Inc* ***(P-3594)***
La Colonial, San Jose *Also called Robles Bros Inc* ***(P-2657)***
La Colonial Mexican Foods, Monterey Park *Also called La Colonial Tortilla Pdts Inc* ***(P-2561)***
La Colonial Tortilla Pdts Inc.....C.....626 289-3647
543 Monterey Pass Rd Monterey Park (91754) ***(P-2561)***
La Crema Winery, Windsor *Also called Jackson Family Wines Inc* ***(P-1823)***
La Ejuice LLC.....E.....310 531-3888
22871 Lockness Ave Torrance (90501) ***(P-2714)***
LA Envelope Incorporated.....E.....323 838-9300
1053 S Vail Ave Montebello (90640) ***(P-5676)***
La Espanola Meats Inc.....E.....310 539-0455
25020 Doble Ave Harbor City (90710) ***(P-503)***
La Estrellita Market & Deli, East Palo Alto *Also called La Estrellita Tizapan Mercado* ***(P-2562)***
La Estrellita Tizapan Mercado.....F.....650 328-0799
2387 University Ave East Palo Alto (94303) ***(P-2562)***
La Famosa Manufacture Inc.....F.....323 241-3100
6600 Mckinley Ave Los Angeles (90001) ***(P-4790)***
La Fe Tortilla Factory Inc (PA).....E.....760 752-8350
446 W Mission Rd Ste 126 San Marcos (92069) ***(P-2563)***
La Fe Tortilleria Factory, San Marcos *Also called La Fe Tortilla Factory Inc* ***(P-2563)***
La Flora Del Sur, Los Angeles *Also called Walker Foods Inc* ***(P-2699)***
La Follette Wines, Healdsburg *Also called Tandem Wines LLC* ***(P-2008)***
La Fortaleza Inc.....D.....323 261-1211
525 N Ford Blvd Los Angeles (90022) ***(P-2564)***
LA Gauge Co Inc.....D.....818 767-7193
7440 San Fernando Rd Sun Valley (91352) ***(P-16672)***
LA Gem and Jwly Design Inc.....D.....213 488-1290
659 S Broadway Fl 7 Los Angeles (90014) ***(P-23284)***
La Gloria Flour Tortillas, Los Angeles *Also called La Gloria Foods Corp* ***(P-2566)***
La Gloria Foods Corp (PA).....D.....323 262-0410
3455 E 1st St Los Angeles (90063) ***(P-2565)***
La Gloria Foods Corp.....D.....323 263-6755
3285 E Cesar E Chavez Ave Los Angeles (90063) ***(P-2566)***
La Gloria Tortilleria, Los Angeles *Also called La Gloria Foods Corp* ***(P-2565)***
La Habra Cabinet Inc.....C.....562 691-0681
540 S Cypress St La Habra (90631) ***(P-4324)***
La Habra Plating Co Inc.....F.....562 694-2704
900 S Cypress St La Habra (90631) ***(P-13442)***
La Habra Welding Inc.....F.....562 923-2229
10819 Koontz Ave Santa Fe Springs (90670) ***(P-25419)***
LA Hardwood Flooring Inc (PA).....F.....818 361-0099
9880 San Fernando Rd Pacoima (91331) ***(P-4083)***
La Indiana Tamales Inc.....E.....323 262-4682
15268 Proctor Ave City of Industry (91745) ***(P-766)***
La Jolla Baking Co, San Diego *Also called Fusion Food Factory* ***(P-1257)***
La Jolla Sport USA Inc (HQ).....D.....855 554-5930
14350 Myford Rd Irvine (92606) ***(P-3171)***
La La Land Production & Design.....E.....323 267-8485
2155 E 7th St Ste 300 Los Angeles (90023) ***(P-10461)***
La Mamba LLC.....E.....323 526-3526
242 S Anderson St Los Angeles (90033) ***(P-3251)***
La Mano Tortilleria.....F.....626 350-4229
9529 Garvey Ave South El Monte (91733) ***(P-2567)***
La Mar Industries Inc.....F.....562 436-4228
1500 Daisy Ave Long Beach (90813) ***(P-15338)***
La Mejor Restaurant, Farmersville *Also called Tortilleria La Mejor* ***(P-2686)***
La Mode, Los Angeles *Also called Golf Apparel Brands Inc* ***(P-3423)***
La Mousse.....D.....310 478-6051
11150 La Grange Ave Los Angeles (90025) ***(P-999)***
La Natura, Los Angeles *Also called New Fragrance Continental* ***(P-8804)***
La Opinion LP (HQ).....D.....213 896-2196
915 Wilshire Blvd Ste 800 Los Angeles (90017) ***(P-5904)***
La Palm Furniture and ACC, Gardena *Also called National Premium Merchandising* ***(P-3855)***
La Parent Magazine (PA).....E.....818 264-2222
5855 Topanga Canyon Blvd # 150 Woodland Hills (91367) ***(P-6202)***

ALPHABETIC

La Paz Products Inc.....F.....714 990-0982
345 Oak Pl Brea (92821) (P-2271)
La Princesita Tortilleria (PA).....E.....323 267-0673
3432 E Cesar E Chavez Ave Los Angeles (90063) (P-2568)
LA Printing & Graphics Inc.....E.....310 527-4526
13951 S Main St Los Angeles (90061) (P-6937)
La Propoint Inc.....E.....818 767-6800
10870 La Tuna Canyon Rd Sun Valley (91352) (P-13953)
La Rancherita Tortilla, Santa Ana Also called M R S Foods Inc (P-2592)
La Reina, Los Angeles Also called Old Pueblo Ranch Inc (P-2628)
La Rocks, Los Angeles Also called LA Gem and Jwly Design Inc (P-23284)
La Rose of California, Los Angeles Also called Jay-Cee Blouse Co Inc (P-3316)
La Rutan.....E.....310 940-7956
6284 Long Beach Blvd Long Beach (90805) (P-24156)
La Selva Beach Spice Company.....E.....831 724-4500
453 Mcquaide Dr Watsonville (95076) (P-2569)
La Sentinel Newspaper, Los Angeles Also called Los Angeles Sentinel Inc (P-5917)
La Siciliana Dressmaking, Culver City Also called La Siciliana Inc (P-3321)
La Siciliana Inc.....E.....323 870-4155
8674 Washington Blvd Culver City (90232) (P-3321)
La Sleeve, Santa Fe Springs Also called Los Angeles Sleeve Co Inc (P-20388)
La Spec Industries Inc.....F.....323 588-8746
2315 E 52nd St Vernon (90058) (P-17623)
LA Supply Company LLC.....F.....562 404-1502
13700 Rosecrans Ave Santa Fe Springs (90670) (P-9019)
La Swim LLC.....F.....213 689-4575
719 S Los Angeles St # 400 Los Angeles (90014) (P-2846)
La Tapatia - Norcal Inc.....C.....510 783-2045
23423 Cabot Blvd Hayward (94545) (P-2570)
La Tapatia Tortilleria Inc.....C.....559 441-1030
104 E Belmont Ave Fresno (93701) (P-2571)
La Terra Fina Usa Inc.....D.....510 404-5888
1300 Atlantic St Union City (94587) (P-2572)
La Times.....F.....213 237-2279
202 W 1st St Ste 500 Los Angeles (90012) (P-5905)
La Tortilla Factory Inc.....E.....707 586-4000
3645 Standish Ave Santa Rosa (95407) (P-2573)
La Touch, Commerce Also called Evy of California Inc (P-3576)
LA Triumph Inc.....E.....562 404-7657
13336 Alondra Blvd Cerritos (90703) (P-3110)
LA Turbine (PA).....D.....661 294-8290
28557 Industry Dr Valencia (91355) (P-14001)
La Viena Ranch.....E.....559 674-6725
9408 Road 23 Madera (93637) (P-884)
La Villeta De Sonoma.....E.....707 939-9392
23000 Arnold Dr Sonoma (95476) (P-12395)
La Voies of San Jose.....F.....408 297-1285
2096 Lincoln Ave San Jose (95125) (P-5201)
La Weekly.....C.....310 574-7100
724 S Spring St Ste 700 Los Angeles (90014) (P-5906)
La Xpress Air & Heating Svcs.....D.....310 856-9678
6400 E Wash Blvd Ste 121 Commerce (90040) (P-6514)
La Zamorana Candy.....F.....323 583-7100
7100 Wilson Ave Los Angeles (90001) (P-1436)
La- Rochelle, Livermore Also called Steven Kent LLC (P-1994)
Lab Clear, Oakland Also called Diamond Tool and Die Inc (P-16437)
Lab Surf Company.....F.....760 757-1975
3205 Production Ave Ste G Oceanside (92058) (P-23605)
Lab Vision Corporation (HQ).....F.....510 979-5000
46500 Kato Rd Fremont (94538) (P-21981)
Lab-Clean LLC.....E.....714 689-0063
3627 Briggeman Dr Los Alamitos (90720) (P-8650)
Labcon North America.....C.....707 766-2100
3700 Lakeville Hwy # 200 Petaluma (94954) (P-10187)
Labeda Inline Wheels & Frames, Lake Elsinore Also called Precision Sports Inc (P-23629)
Label Art of California, Oakland Also called Tags & Labels (P-5739)
Label Art of California, Oakland Also called Label Art-Easy Stik Labels (P-7372)
Label Art-Easy Stik Labels.....E.....510 465-1125
290 27th St Oakland (94612) (P-7372)
Label Gallery, Los Angeles Also called All American Label (P-2796)
Label House, Irvine Also called L A Supply Co (P-7371)
Label ID Technologies Inc.....F.....619 661-5566
2275 Michael Faraday Dr San Diego (92154) (P-7373)
Label Impressions Inc.....E.....714 634-3466
1831 W Sequoia Ave Orange (92868) (P-7374)
Label Masters Inc.....F.....559 445-1208
3188 N Marks Ave Ste 112 Fresno (93722) (P-7375)
Label Productions of Cal.....F.....951 296-1881
42068 Winchester Rd Temecula (92590) (P-7376)
Label Service Inc.....F.....310 329-5605
20008 Normandie Ave Torrance (90502) (P-5565)
Label Specialties Inc.....F.....714 961-8074
704 Dunn Way Placentia (92870) (P-7377)
Label Technology Inc.....C.....209 384-1000
2050 Wardrobe Ave Merced (95341) (P-7378)
Labeling Hurst Systems LLC.....F.....818 701-0710
20747 Dearborn St Chatsworth (91311) (P-5566)
Labeltex Mills Inc (PA).....C.....323 582-0228
6100 Wilmington Ave Los Angeles (90001) (P-23769)
Labeltronix LLC.....D.....800 429-4321
2419 E Winston Rd Anaheim (92806) (P-7379)
Laboratorios Camacho Inc.....F.....818 764-2748
9349 Melvin Ave Ste 1 Northridge (91324) (P-8253)
Labtronix, Hayward Also called Akas Manufacturing Corporation (P-12468)
Labworks Inc.....F.....714 549-1981
2950 Airway Ave Ste A16 Costa Mesa (92626) (P-19615)
Lac Bleu Inc.....F.....213 973-5335
3817 S Santa Fe Ave Vernon (90058) (P-3452)
Lace Music Products, Cypress Also called Actodyne General Inc (P-17752)
Lacey Milling Company Inc.....F.....559 584-6634
217 W 5th St Ste 231 Hanford (93230) (P-1045)
Lackey Woodworking Inc.....F.....831 462-0528
2730 Chanticleer Ave Santa Cruz (95065) (P-4325)
Laclede Inc.....E.....310 605-4280
2103 E University Dr Rancho Dominguez (90220) (P-22889)
Laclede Research Center, Rancho Dominguez Also called Laclede Inc (P-22889)
Ladera Foods Inc.....F.....650 823-7186
1061 Lucky Ave Menlo Park (94025) (P-1066)
Ladera Vineyards LLC.....F.....707 965-2445
150 White Cottage Rd S Angwin (94508) (P-1847)
Ladera Winery LLC.....E.....707 965-2445
150 White Cottage Rd S Angwin (94508) (P-1848)
Lady Jayne LP.....F
10833 Valley View St # 420 Cypress (90630) (P-5685)
Laetitia Vineyard & Winery Inc.....D.....805 481-1772
453 Laetitia Vineyard Dr Arroyo Grande (93420) (P-1849)
Laetitia Winery, Arroyo Grande Also called Laetitia Vineyard & Winery Inc (P-1849)
Lagier Ranches Inc.....F.....209 982-5618
16161 Murphy Rd Escalon (95320) (P-7914)
Lagun Engineering Solutions, Harbor City Also called Republic Machinery Co Inc (P-14403)
Laguna Beach Magazine, Laguna Beach Also called Firebrand Media LLC (P-6815)
Laguna Clay Company, City of Industry Also called Jon Brooks Inc (P-11323)
Laguna Cookie Company Inc.....D.....714 546-6855
4041 W Garry Ave Santa Ana (92704) (P-1369)
Laguna County Sanatation Dist.....F.....805 934-6282
3500 Black Rd Santa Maria (93455) (P-9271)
Laguna Oaks Vnyards Winery Inc.....F.....707 568-2455
5700 Occidental Rd Santa Rosa (95401) (P-1850)
Lahlouh Inc.....C.....650 692-6600
1649 Adrian Rd Burlingame (94010) (P-6938)
Laila Jayde Dda, Cerritos Also called American Garment Company (P-3640)
Laird Coatings Corporation.....E.....714 894-5252
15541 Commerce Ln Huntington Beach (92649) (P-8914)
Laird Family Estate LLC (PA).....E.....707 257-0360
5055 Solano Ave NAPA (94558) (P-1851)
Laird Manufacturing, Merced Also called Laird Mfg LLC (P-14082)
Laird Mfg LLC (PA).....E.....209 722-4145
531 S State Highway 59 Merced (95341) (P-14082)
Laird R & F Products Inc (HQ).....E.....760 916-9410
2091 Rutherford Rd Carlsbad (92008) (P-21317)
Laird Technologies Inc.....E.....408 544-9500
2040 Fortune Dr Ste 102 San Jose (95131) (P-21612)
Lake County Publishing Co (HQ).....D.....707 263-5636
2150 S Main St Lakeport (95453) (P-5907)
Lake County Record-Bee, Lakeport Also called Lake County Publishing Co (P-5907)
Lake County Walnut Inc.....F.....707 279-1200
4545 Loasa Dr Kelseyville (95451) (P-1495)
Lakeview Innovations Inc.....F.....212 502-6702
7777 Greenback Ln Ste 100 Citrus Heights (95610) (P-3665)
Lakim Industries Incorporated (PA).....E.....310 637-8900
389 Rood Rd Calexico (92231) (P-23794)
Lakin Industries Inc (PA).....F.....714 968-6438
18330 Ward St Fountain Valley (92708) (P-13443)
Lam Enterprises Inc.....F.....209 586-2217
824 S Center St Stockton (95206) (P-2574)
Lam Research Corporation.....E.....408 434-6109
3590 N 1st St Ste 200 San Jose (95134) (P-18949)
Lam Research Corporation.....D.....510 572-2186
3724 Dawn Cir Union City (94587) (P-14980)
Lam Research Corporation (PA).....D.....510 572-0200
4650 Cushing Pkwy Fremont (94538) (P-18950)
Lam Research Corporation.....E.....510 572-8400
1 Portola Ave Livermore (94551) (P-18951)
Lam Research Corporation.....D.....510 572-3200
46555 Landing Pkwy Fremont (94538) (P-14981)
Lam Research Corporation.....D.....510 572-0200
4400 Cushing Pkwy Fremont (94538) (P-18952)
Lam Research Intl Holdg Co (HQ).....F.....510 572-0200
4650 Cushing Pkwy Fremont (94538) (P-14982)
Lamar Tool and Die Casting Inc.....E.....209 545-5525
4230 Technology Dr Modesto (95356) (P-11404)
Lamart California Inc.....E.....973 772-6262
33428 Alvarado Niles Rd Union City (94587) (P-11336)
Lamart Corporation.....C.....510 489-8100
2600 Central Ave Ste E Union City (94587) (P-11312)
Lamb Fuels Inc.....E.....619 216-6940
725 Main St Ste B Chula Vista (91911) (P-9020)
Lambda Research Optics Inc.....D.....714 327-0600
1695 Macarthur Blvd Costa Mesa (92626) (P-21982)
Lambert Bridge Winery Inc.....F.....707 431-9600
4085 W Dry Creek Rd Healdsburg (95448) (P-1852)
Lambs & Ivy Inc.....D.....310 322-3800
2042 E Maple Ave El Segundo (90245) (P-3730)
Laminating Company of America, Lake Forest Also called Tri-Star Laminates Inc (P-18629)
Laminating Company of America.....E.....949 587-3300
20322 Windrow Dr Ste 100 Lake Forest (92630) (P-18518)
Laminating Technologies, Anaheim Also called Yti Enterprises Inc (P-4665)
Lamons Gasket Company.....F.....310 886-1133
20009 S Rancho Way Compton (90220) (P-9541)
Lamorenita Tortillera & Mt Mkt.....F.....831 394-3770
1876 Fremont Blvd Seaside (93955) (P-2575)
Lamps Plus Inc.....F.....805 642-9007
4723 Telephone Rd Ventura (93003) (P-17624)
Lamsco West Inc.....C.....661 295-8620
29101 The Old Rd Santa Clarita (91355) (P-20863)
Lamvin Inc.....E.....760 806-6400
4675 North Ave Oceanside (92056) (P-11337)

Lancaster Estate, Santa Rosa *Also called Lancaster Vineyards Inc* ***(P-1853)***
Lancaster Vineyards Inc ....F.......707 433-8178
200 Concourse Blvd Santa Rosa (95403) ***(P-1853)***
Lancer Orthodontics Inc (PA) ....E.......760 744-5585
1493 Poinsettia Ave # 143 Vista (92081) ***(P-22890)***
Land N Top Cleaning Services ....E.......760 624-8845
20953 Sioux Rd Apple Valley (92308) ***(P-2930)***
Land O'Lakes, Turlock *Also called Kozy Shack Enterprises LLC* ***(P-2554)***
Land OLakes Inc ....D.......559 687-8287
400 S M St Tulare (93274) ***(P-583)***
Land OLakes Inc ....E.......530 865-7626
3601 County Road C Orland (95963) ***(P-584)***
Landec Corporation (PA) ....C.......650 306-1650
5201 Great America Pkwy Santa Clara (95054) ***(P-818)***
Landmark Label Manufacturing ....E.......510 651-5551
39611 Eureka Dr Newark (94560) ***(P-7380)***
Landmark Lcds Inc ....F.......408 386-4257
12453 Blue Meadow Ct Saratoga (95070) ***(P-19616)***
Landmark Luggage & Gifts, Sherman Oaks *Also called Safcor Inc* ***(P-10533)***
Landmark Mfg Inc ....E.......760 941-6626
4112 Avenida De La Plata Oceanside (92056) ***(P-16673)***
Landmark Motor Cycle ACC, Oceanside *Also called Landmark Mfg Inc* ***(P-16673)***
Landmark Technology Inc ....E.......408 435-8890
1660 Mckee Rd San Jose (95116) ***(P-19617)***
Landmark Vineyards, Kenwood *Also called Overlook Vineyards LLC* ***(P-1909)***
Landscape Communications Inc ....E.......714 979-5276
14771 Plaza Dr Ste A Tustin (92780) ***(P-6203)***
Landscape Contract National, Tustin *Also called Landscape Communications Inc* ***(P-6203)***
Landscape Contractor, Salinas *Also called Uv Landscaping LLC* ***(P-10866)***
Lane Bennett Winery ....F.......707 942-6684
3340 State Highway 128 Calistoga (94515) ***(P-1854)***
Lane International Trading Inc (PA) ....D.......510 489-7364
33155 Transit Ave Union City (94587) ***(P-10481)***
Lange Precision Inc ....F.......714 870-5420
1106 E Elm Ave Fullerton (92831) ***(P-16674)***
Langer Juice Company Inc ....C.......626 336-3100
16195 Stephens St City of Industry (91745) ***(P-958)***
Langers Juice, City of Industry *Also called Langer Juice Company Inc* ***(P-958)***
Langetwins Wine Company Inc ....E.......209 334-9780
1525 E Jahant Rd Acampo (95220) ***(P-1855)***
Langetwins Winery & Vineyards, Acampo *Also called Langetwins Wine Company Inc* ***(P-1855)***
Langills General Machine Inc ....E.......916 452-0167
7850 14th Ave Sacramento (95826) ***(P-16675)***
Langley Hill Quarry ....F.......650 851-0179
12 Langley Hill Rd Woodside (94062) ***(P-328)***
Langlois Company ....E.......951 360-3900
10810 San Sevaine Way Mira Loma (91752) ***(P-1097)***
Langlois Flour Company, Mira Loma *Also called Langlois Company* ***(P-1097)***
Langston Companies Inc ....E.......559 688-3839
2500 S K St Tulare (93274) ***(P-5644)***
Langtry Estates and Vineyards, Santa Rosa *Also called Guenoc Winery Inc* ***(P-1800)***
Language Los Angeles, Burbank *Also called Eastwest Clothing Inc* ***(P-3233)***
Lanic Aerospace, Rancho Cucamonga *Also called Lanic Engineering Inc* ***(P-20864)***
Lanic Engineering Inc (PA) ....E.......877 763-0411
12144 6th St Rancho Cucamonga (91730) ***(P-20864)***
Lanpar Inc ....B.......541 484-1962
1333 S Bon View Ave Ontario (91761) ***(P-4715)***
Lansair Corporation ....F.......661 294-9503
25228 Anza Dr Santa Clarita (91355) ***(P-16676)***
Lansas Products, Lodi *Also called Vanderlans & Sons Inc* ***(P-16129)***
Lanshon Inc ....E.......562 777-1688
12995 Los Nietos Rd Santa Fe Springs (90670) ***(P-3032)***
Lansing Industries Inc ....F.......858 523-0719
12671 High Bluff Dr # 150 San Diego (92130) ***(P-24157)***
Lanstreetcom ....E.......626 964-2000
17050 Evergreen Pl City of Industry (91745) ***(P-15638)***
Lantic Inc ....F.......949 830-9951
27081 Burbank Foothill Ranch (92610) ***(P-10188)***
Lantic USA, Rancho Dominguez *Also called Fairway Import-Export Inc* ***(P-23559)***
Lantin Enterprise Inc ....F.......408 935-9327
2290 Trade Zone Blvd San Jose (95131) ***(P-16677)***
Lantiq North America Inc ....F.......408 503-8700
2880 Zanker Rd Ste 100 San Jose (95134) ***(P-18953)***
Lantor, Lomita *Also called Anacrown Inc* ***(P-13917)***
Lantronix Inc (PA) ....C.......949 453-3990
7535 Irvine Center Dr # 100 Irvine (92618) ***(P-15784)***
Lanty Inc ....C.......626 582-8001
9660 Flair Dr El Monte (91731) ***(P-2576)***
Lanza Research International ....D.......310 393-5227
429 Santa Monica Blvd # 510 Santa Monica (90401) ***(P-8786)***
Lapco West LLC ....E.......714 773-1380
6901 Marlin Cir La Palma (90623) ***(P-20385)***
Laperla Del Mayab, Santa Ana *Also called Laperla Spice Co Inc* ***(P-2577)***
Laperla Spice Co Inc ....F.......714 543-0159
555 N Fairview St Santa Ana (92703) ***(P-2577)***
Laprensa San Diego ....F.......619 425-7400
220 Glover Ave Apt E Chula Vista (91910) ***(P-5908)***
Laptalo Enterprises Inc ....D.......408 727-6633
2360 Zanker Rd San Jose (95131) ***(P-12641)***
Laptop Lunches, Santa Cruz *Also called Obentec Inc* ***(P-4530)***
Lares Research ....E.......530 345-1767
295 Lockheed Ave Chico (95973) ***(P-22891)***
Larin Corp ....E.......909 464-0605
5651 Schaefer Ave Chino (91710) ***(P-11900)***
Laritech Inc ....D.......805 529-5000
387 Zachary St Unit 102 Moorpark (93021) ***(P-18519)***
Larkin Precision Machining ....E.......831 438-2700
175 El Pueblo Rd Ste 10 Scotts Valley (95066) ***(P-16678)***
Larosa Tortilla Factory ....D.......831 728-5332
26 Menker St Watsonville (95076) ***(P-2578)***
Larry B LLC ....F.......310 652-3877
215 S Robertson Blvd Beverly Hills (90211) ***(P-3601)***
Larry Mthvin Installations Inc (HQ) ....C.......909 563-1700
501 Kettering Dr Ontario (91761) ***(P-10712)***
Larry Mthvin Installations Inc ....E.......209 368-2105
128 N Cluff Ave Lodi (95240) ***(P-10713)***
Larry Schlussler ....F.......707 822-9095
824 L St Ste 7 Arcata (95521) ***(P-17379)***
Larry Spun Products Inc ....E.......323 881-6300
1533 S Downey Rd Los Angeles (90023) ***(P-13241)***
Larryron Enterprises Inc ....F.......310 645-4707
805 W Manchester Blvd Inglewood (90301) ***(P-1277)***
Larsens Inc ....F.......831 476-3009
1041 17th Ave Ste A Santa Cruz (95062) ***(P-3795)***
Larson Al Boat Shop ....D.......310 514-4100
1046 S Seaside Ave San Pedro (90731) ***(P-20998)***
Larson Brothers ....F.......559 292-8161
5665 E Westover Ave # 101 Fresno (93727) ***(P-6515)***
Larson Electronic Glass Inc ....F.......650 369-6734
2840 Bay Rd Redwood City (94063) ***(P-10651)***
Larson Family Winery Inc ....F.......707 938-3031
23355 Millerick Rd Sonoma (95476) ***(P-1856)***
Larson Packaging Company LLC ....E.......408 946-4971
1000 Yosemite Dr Milpitas (95035) ***(P-4483)***
Larson Picture Frames, Santa Fe Springs *Also called Larson-Juhl US LLC* ***(P-4631)***
Larson-Juhl US LLC ....E.......562 946-6873
12206 Bell Ranch Dr Santa Fe Springs (90670) ***(P-4631)***
Larson-Juhl US LLC ....E.......707 747-0555
5365 Industrial Way Benicia (94510) ***(P-4632)***
Lartech, San Jose *Also called L & H Iron Inc* ***(P-12872)***
LArtisan Valley Baking Co ....F.......760 343-2888
31130 Plantation Dr Thousand Palms (92276) ***(P-1278)***
Las Animas Con & Bldg Sup Inc ....E.......831 425-4084
146 Encinal St Santa Cruz (95060) ***(P-14180)***
Las Colinas ....F.......714 528-8100
600 S Jefferson St Ste M Placentia (92870) ***(P-16065)***
Las Cuatros Milpas ....F.......909 885-3344
856 N Mount Vernon Ave San Bernardino (92411) ***(P-1279)***
Lasalle Intl Hldings Group Inc ....E.......818 233-8000
9667 Owensmouth Ave Chatsworth (91311) ***(P-14232)***
Lasani-Felt Co ....E.......323 233-5278
830 E 59th St Los Angeles (90001) ***(P-3003)***
Lasdos Victorias Candy Company, Rosemead *Also called Ldvc Inc* ***(P-1437)***
Laser Division, Santa Clara *Also called Spectra-Physics Inc* ***(P-20078)***
Laser Excel, Santa Rosa *Also called Green Lake Investors LLC* ***(P-23716)***
Laser Imaging International, Van Nuys *Also called E Alko Inc* ***(P-23727)***
Laser Industries Inc ....D.......714 532-3271
1351 Manhattan Ave Fullerton (92831) ***(P-16679)***
Laser Operations LLC ....E.......818 986-0000
15632 Roxford St Sylmar (91342) ***(P-18954)***
Laser Recharge Inc (PA) ....E.......916 737-6360
9935 Horn Rd Ste A Sacramento (95827) ***(P-23731)***
Laser Reference Inc ....E.......408 361-0220
151 Martinvale Ln San Jose (95119) ***(P-21479)***
Laser Tech, Riverside *Also called L T Seroge Inc* ***(P-20001)***
Laser Toner & Computer Supply ....F.......805 529-3300
940 Enchanted Way Ste 106 Simi Valley (93065) ***(P-23732)***
Laserbeam Software LLC ....E.......925 459-2595
1647 Willow Pass Rd Concord (94520) ***(P-24845)***
Lasercare Technologies Inc (PA) ....E.......310 202-4200
3375 Robertson Pl Los Angeles (90034) ***(P-23733)***
Laserfiche Document Imaging, Long Beach *Also called Compulink Management Ctr Inc* ***(P-24516)***
Lasergraphics Inc ....E.......949 753-8282
20 Ada Irvine (92618) ***(P-15785)***
Lasergraphics General Business, Irvine *Also called Lasergraphics Inc* ***(P-15785)***
Laserod Technologies LLC ....E.......310 328-5869
20312 Gramercy Pl Torrance (90501) ***(P-20003)***
Lasertron Inc ....E.......954 846-8600
909 Summit Way Laguna Beach (92651) ***(P-16680)***
Laspec Lighting, Vernon *Also called La Spec Industries Inc* ***(P-17623)***
Lassen County Times, Susanville *Also called Feather Publishing Company Inc* ***(P-5849)***
Lassen Forest Products Inc ....E.......530 527-7677
22829 Casale Rd Red Bluff (96080) ***(P-4418)***
Lasseter Family Winery LLC ....F.......707 933-2800
1 Vintage Ln Glen Ellen (95442) ***(P-1857)***
Lassonde Pappas and Co Inc ....D.......909 923-4041
1755 E Acacia St Ontario (91761) ***(P-2579)***
Lastline Inc ....C.......805 456-7075
6950 Hollister Ave # 101 Goleta (93117) ***(P-24846)***
Lastline Inc (PA) ....E.......805 456-7075
203 Redwood Shores Pkwy Redwood City (94065) ***(P-24847)***
Laszlo J Lak ....F.......714 850-0141
3621 W Moore Ave Santa Ana (92704) ***(P-16681)***
LAT LLC ....E.......323 233-3017
2052 E Vernon Ave Vernon (90058) ***(P-3453)***
Lataz Product, Brea *Also called California Cocktails Inc* ***(P-2249)***
Latcham Granite Inc ....F.......530 620-6642
2860 Omo Ranch Rd Somerset (95684) ***(P-1858)***
Latcham Vineyards, Somerset *Also called Latcham Granite Inc* ***(P-1858)***
Lathrop Engineering, Morgan Hill *Also called Paramit Corporation* ***(P-22580)***
Lathrop Woodworks, Lathrop *Also called Rafael Sandoval* ***(P-4048)***
Laticrete International Inc ....F.......951 277-1776
22740 Temescal Canyon Rd Corona (92883) ***(P-10759)***

ALPHABETIC

Employee Codes: A=Over 500 employees, B=251-500
C=101-250, D=51-100, E=20-50, F=10-19
2019 California
Manfacturers Register
© Mergent Inc. 1-800-342-5647
1193

Latina & Associates Inc (PA)..................E......619 426-1491
1105 Broadway Chula Vista (91911) ***(P-5909)***
Latino Americanos Revista..................F......760 342-2312
82723 Miles Ave Indio (92201) ***(P-6204)***
Latitude 38 Publishing Company..................F......415 383-8200
15 Locust Ave Mill Valley (94941) ***(P-6205)***
Latourette Lift Services..................F......323 262-9111
4368 Bandini Blvd Vernon (90058) ***(P-14333)***
Lats International, Los Angeles *Also called Los Angles Tmes Cmmnctions LLC* ***(P-5927)***
Lattice Data Inc..................E......650 800-7262
801 El Camino Real Menlo Park (94025) ***(P-24848)***
Lattice Semiconductor Corp..................B......408 826-6000
2115 Onel Dr San Jose (95131) ***(P-18955)***
Laufer Media Inc..................F......818 291-8408
330 N Brand Blvd Ste 1150 Glendale (91203) ***(P-6206)***
Launchpoint Technologies Inc..................F......805 683-9659
5735 Hollister Ave Ste B Goleta (93117) ***(P-15288)***
Laundry By Shelli Segal, Commerce *Also called LCI Laundry Inc* ***(P-3324)***
Laura Chenels Chevre Inc..................D......707 996-4477
22085 Carneros Vinyrd Way Sonoma (95476) ***(P-585)***
Laura Scudders Company LLC..................E......714 444-3700
1537 E Mcfadden Ave Ste B Santa Ana (92705) ***(P-2394)***
Lauras French Baking Co Inc..................E......323 585-5144
722 S Oxford Ave Apt 107 Los Angeles (90005) ***(P-1280)***
Laurelwood Industries Inc..................E......760 705-1649
1939 Palomar Oaks Way B Carlsbad (92011) ***(P-16682)***
Laurent Culinary Service..................F......415 485-1122
1945 Francisco Blvd E # 44 San Rafael (94901) ***(P-2580)***
Lava Cap Winery, Placerville *Also called Lava Springs Inc* ***(P-1859)***
Lava Products Inc..................E......949 951-7191
3168 Airway Ave Costa Mesa (92626) ***(P-6939)***
Lava Springs Inc..................E......530 621-0175
2221 Fruitridge Rd Placerville (95667) ***(P-1859)***
Lavang Tech Prcsion Sheet Mtls..................F......714 901-2782
14480 Hoover St Westminster (92683) ***(P-14756)***
Lavante Inc..................E......408 754-1410
5225 Hellyer Ave Ste 200 San Jose (95138) ***(P-24849)***
Lavash Corporation..................E......323 663-5249
2835 Newell St Los Angeles (90039) ***(P-1281)***
Lavender Alley, Los Angeles *Also called S Sedghi Inc* ***(P-3588)***
Lavey Craft Prfmce Boats Inc..................F......951 273-9690
175 Vander St Corona (92880) ***(P-21049)***
Lavi Industries (PA)..................D......877 275-5284
27810 Avenue Hopkins Valencia (91355) ***(P-12873)***
Lavi Systems Inc..................F......818 373-5400
13731 Saticoy St Van Nuys (91402) ***(P-20865)***
Lavinder Inc..................F......310 278-2456
8687 Melrose Ave Ste B310 West Hollywood (90069) ***(P-3004)***
Lavish Clothing Inc..................F......213 745-5400
245 W 28th St Los Angeles (90007) ***(P-3322)***
LAweb Offset Printing Inc..................C......626 454-2469
9639 Telstar Ave El Monte (91731) ***(P-7381)***
Lawinfocom Inc..................D......760 510-3000
5901 Priestly Dr Ste 200 Carlsbad (92008) ***(P-24850)***
Lawleys Inc..................F......209 572-1700
4554 Qantas Ln Stockton (95206) ***(P-1143)***
Lawrence Equipment Inc (PA)..................C......626 442-2894
2034 Peck Rd El Monte (91733) ***(P-14867)***
Lawrence O Lawrence Ltd..................F......323 935-1100
8104 Beverly Blvd Los Angeles (90048) ***(P-3005)***
Lawrence of La Brea, Los Angeles *Also called Lawrence O Lawrence Ltd* ***(P-3005)***
Lawrence Roll Up Doors Inc (PA)..................E......626 962-4163
4525 Littlejohn St Baldwin Park (91706) ***(P-12326)***
Lawrence Roll Up Doors Inc..................F......818 837-1963
11035 Stranwood Ave Mission Hills (91345) ***(P-12327)***
Lawrence Roll Up Doors Inc..................F......626 338-6041
1406 Virginia Ave Ste 10 Baldwin Park (91706) ***(P-12328)***
Layered Luxe Inc..................E......323 513-8200
1443 S Lorena St Los Angeles (90023) ***(P-3323)***
Layne Laboratories Inc..................F......805 242-7918
4303 Huasna Rd Arroyo Grande (93420) ***(P-3006)***
Layton Printing & Mailing..................F......909 592-4419
1538 Arrow Hwy La Verne (91750) ***(P-7382)***
Lazestar..................E......925 443-5293
346 Earhart Way Livermore (94551) ***(P-25420)***
Lazy Daze Inc..................E......909 627-1103
4303 Mission Blvd Montclair (91763) ***(P-20524)***
Lb Manufacturing LLC..................F......413 222-2857
1403 S Coast Hwy Oceanside (92054) ***(P-24158)***
Lbi - USA, Chatsworth *Also called Lehrer Brllnprfktion Werks Inc* ***(P-10189)***
Lca Promotions Inc..................E......818 773-9170
9545 Cozycroft Ave Chatsworth (91311) ***(P-7383)***
LCD&d, Chatsworth *Also called Lighting Control & Design Inc* ***(P-17708)***
LCI Laundry Inc..................C......323 767-1900
5835 S Eastrn Ave Ste 100 Commerce (90040) ***(P-3324)***
Lcl Pacific, Los Angeles *Also called Precision Wire Products Inc* ***(P-11410)***
Lcoa, Lake Forest *Also called Laminating Company of America* ***(P-18518)***
Lcptracker Inc..................E......714 669-0052
117 E Chapman Ave Orange (92866) ***(P-24851)***
Lcr-Dixon Corporation..................F......404 307-1695
2048 Union St Apt 4 San Francisco (94123) ***(P-24852)***
Ld Smart Inc..................F......626 581-8887
1971 W Holt Ave Pomona (91768) ***(P-15443)***
Ldvc Inc..................E......626 448-4611
9606 Valley Blvd Rosemead (91770) ***(P-1437)***
Le Barbocce Inc..................E......510 526-7664
1328 6th St Frnt Frnt Berkeley (94710) ***(P-1067)***
Le Belge Chocolatier Inc..................E......707 258-9200
761 Skyway Ct NAPA (94558) ***(P-1438)***
Le Cache Premium Wine Cabinets, Petaluma *Also called Planet One Products Inc* ***(P-5094)***
Le Chef Costumier Inc..................E......818 242-0868
825 Western Ave Ste 21 Glendale (91201) ***(P-3666)***
Le Elegant Bath Inc..................C......951 734-0238
13405 Estelle St Corona (92879) ***(P-9906)***
Le Hung Tuan..................F......818 700-1008
20952 Itasca St Chatsworth (91311) ***(P-16683)***
Le Vu..................E......916 231-1594
4234 54th St McClellan (95652) ***(P-19618)***
Leach International Corp (HQ)..................B......714 736-7537
6900 Orangethorpe Ave Buena Park (90620) ***(P-19619)***
Leach International Corp..................B......714 739-0770
6900 Orangethorpe Ave Buena Park (90620) ***(P-17283)***
Leadcrunch Inc (PA)..................F......888 708-6649
2159 India St San Diego (92101) ***(P-24853)***
Leading Biosciences Inc..................F......858 395-6099
5800 Armada Dr Ste 210 Carlsbad (92008) ***(P-8254)***
Leadmasters..................F......760 949-6566
17229 Lemon St Ste E11 Hesperia (92345) ***(P-23606)***
Leads360 LLC..................E......888 843-1777
207 Hindry Ave Inglewood (90301) ***(P-24854)***
Leaf Healthcare Inc..................F......925 621-1800
5994 W Las Positas Blvd # 217 Pleasanton (94588) ***(P-22997)***
Lean Manufacturing Group LLC..................F......661 702-9400
29170 Avenue Penn Valencia (91355) ***(P-14388)***
Leaner Creamer LLC..................F......818 621-5274
9107 Wilshire Blvd # 450 Beverly Hills (90210) ***(P-628)***
Leap Motion Inc (PA)..................E......954 234-6321
321 11th St San Francisco (94103) ***(P-15444)***
Leapfrog Enterprises Inc (HQ)..................B......510 420-5000
6401 Hollis St Ste 100 Emeryville (94608) ***(P-23437)***
Lear Baylor Inc..................E......714 799-9396
7215 Garden Grove Blvd C Garden Grove (92841) ***(P-21050)***
Learners Digest Intl LLC..................C......818 240-7500
450 N Brand Blvd Ste 900 Glendale (91203) ***(P-24159)***
Learners Guild Ltd..................F......415 448-7054
492 9th St Oakland (94607) ***(P-24855)***
Learning Resources Inc..................E......800 995-4436
152 W Walnut St Ste 201 Gardena (90248) ***(P-24160)***
Leather Cpr, Los Angeles *Also called Wonder Marketing Inc* ***(P-8957)***
Leather Pro Inc..................E......818 833-8822
12900 Bradley Ave Sylmar (91342) ***(P-10564)***
Leatherock International Inc..................E......619 299-7625
5285 Lovelock St San Diego (92110) ***(P-10462)***
Lebata Inc..................E......949 253-2800
4621 Teller Ave Ste 130 Newport Beach (92660) ***(P-10948)***
Lebec - Ncc CA Cement Company, Lebec *Also called National Cement Co Cal Inc* ***(P-11145)***
Lecroy Prtocol Solutions Group, Milpitas *Also called Teledyne Lecroy Inc* ***(P-21865)***
Led One Distribution Inc (PA)..................E......510 770-1189
45885 Hotchkiss St Fremont (94539) ***(P-18956)***
Leda Corporation..................E......714 841-7821
7080 Kearny Dr Huntington Beach (92648) ***(P-21195)***
Leda Multimedia, Chino *Also called Shop4techcom* ***(P-15607)***
Ledconn Corp..................F......714 256-2111
301 Thor Pl Brea (92821) ***(P-18957)***
Ledengin Inc (PA)..................E......408 922-7200
651 River Oaks Pkwy San Jose (95134) ***(P-18958)***
Ledpac LLC..................D......760 489-8067
9850 Siempre Viva Rd # 5 San Diego (92154) ***(P-23913)***
Ledtronics Inc..................C......310 534-1505
23105 Kashiwa Ct Torrance (90505) ***(P-18959)***
Lee & Fields Publishing Inc..................F......213 380-5858
3731 Wilshire Blvd # 940 Los Angeles (90010) ***(P-6516)***
Lee Aerospace Products Inc..................F......805 527-1811
90 W Easy St Ste 5 Simi Valley (93065) ***(P-20866)***
Lee Augustyn Inc..................F......909 483-0688
9390 7th St Ste A Rancho Cucamonga (91730) ***(P-6940)***
Lee Brothers Inc..................D......650 964-9650
1011 Timothy Dr San Jose (95133) ***(P-920)***
Lee Brothers Truck Body Inc..................F......310 532-7980
18915 Roselle Ave Torrance (90504) ***(P-20212)***
Lee Central Cal Newspapers..................E......559 896-1976
2045 Grant St Selma (93662) ***(P-5910)***
Lee Enterprises Incorporated..................C......805 925-2691
3200 Skyway Dr Santa Maria (93455) ***(P-5911)***
Lee Fasteners Inc..................F......626 287-6848
230 Clary Ave San Gabriel (91776) ***(P-11841)***
Lee Kum Kee (usa) Foods Inc..................D......626 709-1888
14455 Don Julian Rd City of Industry (91746) ***(P-2581)***
Lee Machine Products..................F......626 301-4105
2030 Central Ave Duarte (91010) ***(P-14534)***
Lee Maxton Inc..................F......909 483-0688
10844 Edison Ct Rancho Cucamonga (91730) ***(P-6941)***
Lee Pharmaceuticals..................D......626 442-3141
1434 Santa Anita Ave South El Monte (91733) ***(P-8787)***
Lee Ray Sandblasting, Santa Fe Springs *Also called Cji Process Systems Inc* ***(P-12375)***
Lee Sandusky Corporation..................E......661 854-5551
16125 Widmere Rd Arvin (93203) ***(P-4835)***
Lee Thomas Inc (PA)..................E......310 532-7560
13800 S Figueroa St Los Angeles (90061) ***(P-3454)***
Lee's Enterprise, Chatsworth *Also called Molnar Engineering Inc* ***(P-16763)***
Leejay Industries, Los Alamitos *Also called Katlan Industries Inc* ***(P-13233)***
Leemah Corporation (PA)..................C......415 394-1288
155 S Hill Dr Brisbane (94005) ***(P-18393)***
Leemarc Industries LLC..................D......760 598-0505
2471 Coral St Vista (92081) ***(P-3172)***
Leemax International Inc..................E......619 208-2355
1182 Via Escalante Chula Vista (91910) ***(P-3173)***
Leemco Inc (PA)..................F......909 422-0088
360 S Mount Vernon Ave Colton (92324) ***(P-13722)***

Mergent e-mail: customerrelations@mergent.com
1194
2019 California
Manufacturers Register
(P-0000) Products & Services Section entry number
(PA)=Parent Co (HQ)=Headquarters (DH)=Div Headquarters

Leeper's Stair Products, Corona *Also called Leepers Wood Turning Co Inc* ***(P-4183)***
Leepers Wood Turning Co Inc (PA) ....D....562 422-6525
341 Bonnie Cir Ste 104 Corona (92880) ***(P-4183)***
Lees Concrete Materials Inc ....F....559 486-2440
200 S Pine St Madera (93637) ***(P-11126)***
Lees Fashions Inc ....E....760 753-2408
1157 Monterey Pl Encinitas (92024) ***(P-3325)***
Lees Imperial Welding Inc ....C....510 657-4900
3300 Edison Way Fremont (94538) ***(P-12193)***
Lees Precision Tooling ....F....562 926-1302
16751 Parkside Ave Cerritos (90703) ***(P-16684)***
Leeway Iron Works Inc ....F....510 357-8637
565 Estabrook St San Leandro (94577) ***(P-12194)***
Leewood Press Inc ....E....415 896-0513
1407 Indiana St San Francisco (94107) ***(P-6942)***
Leeyo Software Inc (HQ) ....E....408 988-5800
2841 Junction Ave Ste 201 San Jose (95134) ***(P-24856)***
Left Coast Brewing Company ....F....949 218-3961
1245 Puerta Del Sol San Clemente (92673) ***(P-1604)***
Leftbank Art, La Mirada *Also called Outlook Resources Inc* ***(P-3856)***
Lefton Technologies Inc ....E....818 986-1728
1140 Brooklawn Dr Los Angeles (90077) ***(P-17284)***
Legacy Bands Inc ....F....818 890-2527
13261 Paxton St Pacoima (91331) ***(P-23285)***
Legacy Glass Studios, Menlo Park *Also called Legacy Us LLC* ***(P-10652)***
Legacy Graphics LLC ....F....619 585-1044
1120 Bay Blvd Ste E Chula Vista (91911) ***(P-7384)***
Legacy Systems Incorporated ....F....510 651-2312
4160 Technology Dr Ste E Fremont (94538) ***(P-14983)***
Legacy Us LLC ....F....650 714-9750
1800 El Camino Real Ste D Menlo Park (94027) ***(P-10652)***
Legacy Vulcan LLC ....E....626 856-6150
13000 Los Angeles St Irwindale (91706) ***(P-366)***
Legacy Vulcan LLC ....E....909 875-1150
2400 W Highland Ave San Bernardino (92407) ***(P-367)***
Legacy Vulcan LLC ....F....626 856-6153
6232 Santos Diaz St Irwindale (91702) ***(P-368)***
Legacy Vulcan LLC ....E....714 737-2922
Parkridge & Quarry Sts Corona (92877) ***(P-313)***
Legacy Vulcan LLC ....E....818 983-1323
11447 Tuxford St Sun Valley (91352) ***(P-369)***
Legacy Vulcan LLC ....E....661 822-4158
655 W Tehachapi Blvd Tehachapi (93561) ***(P-11127)***
Legacy Vulcan LLC ....F....925 284-4686
3195 Andreasen Dr Lafayette (94549) ***(P-10949)***
Legacy Vulcan LLC ....E....805 647-1161
6029 E Vineyard Ave Oxnard (93036) ***(P-11128)***
Legacy Vulcan LLC ....E....626 633-4258
16001 1/2 E Foothill Blvd Irwindale (91702) ***(P-9388)***
Legacy Vulcan LLC ....E....661 533-2127
6851 E Avenue T Littlerock (93543) ***(P-370)***
Legacy Vulcan LLC ....D....661 835-4800
8517 E Panama Ln Bakersfield (93307) ***(P-11129)***
Legacy Vulcan LLC ....F....626 856-6148
16013 E Foothill Blvd Irwindale (91702) ***(P-10950)***
Legacy Vulcan LLC ....E....909 875-5180
20350 Highland Ave Rialto (92377) ***(P-371)***
Legacy Vulcan LLC ....E....661 858-2673
Hwy W 166 Of Old Rver Rd Bakersfield (93313) ***(P-10951)***
Legacy Vulcan LLC ....F....209 854-3088
28525 Bambouer Rd Gustine (95322) ***(P-10952)***
Legacy Vulcan LLC ....F....760 439-0624
2925 Industry St Oceanside (92054) ***(P-10953)***
Legacy Vulcan LLC ....D....559 434-1202
11099 Old Friant Rd Fresno (93730) ***(P-11260)***
Legacy Vulcan LLC ....E....661 252-1010
13900 Lang Station Rd Canyon Country (91387) ***(P-372)***
Legacy Vulcan LLC ....E....858 566-2730
7220 Trade St Ste 200 San Diego (92121) ***(P-11130)***
Legacy Vulcan LLC ....F....916 682-0850
11501 Florin Rd Sacramento (95830) ***(P-11131)***
Legacy Vulcan LLC ....E....626 856-6143
16001 E Foothill Blvd Irwindale (91702) ***(P-373)***
Legacy Vulcan LLC ....E....925 373-1802
365 N Canyon Pkwy Livermore (94551) ***(P-314)***
Legacy Vulcan LLC ....E....661 533-2125
7107 E Avenue T Littlerock (93543) ***(P-11132)***
Legacy Vulcan LLC ....E....818 983-0146
11401 Tuxford St Sun Valley (91352) ***(P-11133)***
Legend Pump & Well Service Inc ....E....909 384-1000
1324 W Rialto Ave San Bernardino (92410) ***(P-111)***
Legend Silicon Corp ....E....408 735-9888
22 Stirling Way Hayward (94542) ***(P-18163)***
Legendary Headwear, San Diego *Also called Legendary Holdings Inc* ***(P-3565)***
Legendary Holdings Inc ....E....619 872-6100
2295 Paseo De Las America San Diego (92154) ***(P-3565)***
Legends Apparel & I C Ink, Stockton *Also called IC Ink Image Co Inc* ***(P-7347)***
Leggett & Platt Incorporated ....D....909 937-1010
1050 S Dupont Ave Ontario (91761) ***(P-4868)***
Leggett & Platt 0302, Valencia *Also called Leggett & Platt Incorporated* ***(P-5079)***
Leggett & Platt 0768, Poway *Also called Valley Metals LLC* ***(P-11489)***
Leggett & Platt Incorporated ....D....562 945-2641
12352 Whittier Blvd Whittier (90602) ***(P-4869)***
Leggett & Platt Incorporated ....E....661 775-8500
29120 Commerce Center Dr # 1 Valencia (91355) ***(P-5079)***
Legion Creative Group ....E....323 498-1100
1680 Vine St Ste 700 Los Angeles (90028) ***(P-7385)***
Leham Millet West, Santa Ana *Also called Lehman Millet Incorporated* ***(P-8488)***
Lehigh Hanson, Morro Bay *Also called Hanson Aggrgtes Md-Pacific Inc* ***(P-11118)***
Lehigh Hanson, Lakeside *Also called Hanson Aggregates LLC* ***(P-9386)***
Lehigh Southwest Cement Co ....C....661 822-4445
13573 E Tehachapi Blvd Tehachapi (93561) ***(P-10760)***
Lehigh Southwest Cement Co ....F....408 996-4271
24001 Stevens Creek Blvd Cupertino (95014) ***(P-10761)***
Lehigh Southwest Cement Co (HQ) ....F....972 653-5500
2300 Clayton Rd Ste 300 Concord (94520) ***(P-10762)***
Lehigh Southwest Cement Co ....C....530 275-1581
15390 Wonderland Blvd Redding (96003) ***(P-11134)***
Lehigh Southwest Cement Co ....F....209 465-2624
2201 W Washington St Stockton (95203) ***(P-10763)***
Lehman Foods Inc ....E....818 837-7600
1145 Arroyo St Ste B San Fernando (91340) ***(P-2582)***
Lehman Millet Incorporated ....F....714 850-7900
3 Macarthur Pl Ste 700 Santa Ana (92707) ***(P-8488)***
Lehmans Manufacturing Co Inc ....F....559 486-1700
4960 E Jensen Ave Fresno (93725) ***(P-12195)***
Lehrer Brllnprfktion Werks Inc (PA) ....E....818 407-1890
20801 Nordhoff St Chatsworth (91311) ***(P-10189)***
Leica Biosystems Imaging Inc ....C....760 539-1100
1360 Park Center Dr Vista (92081) ***(P-22507)***
Leica Geosystems Hds LLC ....D....925 790-2300
5000 Executive Pkwy # 500 San Ramon (94583) ***(P-15786)***
Leidos Inc ....E....619 524-2581
4025 Hancock St Ste 210 San Diego (92110) ***(P-15787)***
Leiner Health Products Inc (HQ) ....A....631 200-2000
901 E 233rd St Carson (90745) ***(P-8255)***
Leiner Health Products Inc ....B....714 898-9936
7366 Orangewood Ave Garden Grove (92841) ***(P-8256)***
Leiner Health Products Inc ....D....661 775-1422
27655b Avenue Hopkins Valencia (91355) ***(P-8257)***
Leisure Components, Cerritos *Also called Sedenquist-Fraser Entps Inc* ***(P-20445)***
Leitch & Co Inc ....F....510 483-2323
1607 Abram Ct San Leandro (94577) ***(P-11901)***
Leiter's Compounding, San Jose *Also called Leiters Enterprises Inc* ***(P-8258)***
Leiters Enterprises Inc ....D....800 292-6772
17 Great Oaks Blvd San Jose (95119) ***(P-8258)***
Leitz Tooling Systems LP ....F....909 799-8494
1145 Orange Show Rd San Bernardino (92408) ***(P-14389)***
Lejon of California Inc ....E....951 736-1229
1229 Railroad St Corona (92882) ***(P-3630)***
Lejon Tulliani, Corona *Also called Lejon of California Inc* ***(P-3630)***
Lekos Dye & Finishing Inc ....D....310 763-0900
3131 E Harcourt St Compton (90221) ***(P-2793)***
Leland Stanford Junior Univ ....E....650 723-9434
500 Broadway St Redwood City (94063) ***(P-5912)***
Leland Stanford Junior Univ ....C....650 723-5553
557 Escondido Mall Stanford (94305) ***(P-6517)***
Leland Stanford Junior Univ ....C....650 723-3052
424 Matison Ave Stanford (94305) ***(P-6518)***
Leland Stanford Junior Univ ....D....650 723-4455
559 Nathan Abbott Way Stanford (94305) ***(P-6519)***
Lemonaid Health, San Francisco *Also called Icebreaker Health Inc* ***(P-24748)***
Lemor Trims Inc ....F....213 741-1646
830 Venice Blvd Los Angeles (90015) ***(P-3902)***
Lengthwise Brewing Company ....E....661 836-2537
7700 District Blvd Bakersfield (93313) ***(P-1605)***
Lennox, Santa Ana *Also called Innovative Hearth Products LLC* ***(P-17390)***
Lennox ....F....800 953-6669
4000 Hamner Ave Eastvale (91752) ***(P-15966)***
Lennox Industries Inc ....C....805 288-8200
2221 Eastman Ave Oxnard (93030) ***(P-15967)***
Lenntek Corporation ....E....310 534-2738
1610 Lockness Pl Torrance (90501) ***(P-18164)***
Lens C-C Inc (PA) ....D....800 772-3911
1750 N Loop Rd Ste 150 Alameda (94502) ***(P-23105)***
Lens Technology I LLC ....F....714 690-6470
45 Parker Ste 100 Irvine (92618) ***(P-22097)***
Lensvector Inc ....D....408 542-0300
6203 San Ignacio Ave San Jose (95119) ***(P-23106)***
Lenus Handcrafted ....F....619 200-4266
3323 Thorn St San Diego (92104) ***(P-8788)***
Lenz Precision Technology Inc ....E....650 966-1784
355 Pioneer Way Ste A Mountain View (94041) ***(P-16685)***
Lenz Technology, Mountain View *Also called Lenz Precision Technology Inc* ***(P-16685)***
Leo Lam Inc ....E....925 484-3690
3589 Nevada St Ste A Pleasanton (94566) ***(P-6943)***
Leo Molds ....F....562 714-4807
125 W Victoria St Gardena (90248) ***(P-14535)***
Leoch Battery Corporation (PA) ....E....949 588-5853
19751 Descartes Unit A Foothill Ranch (92610) ***(P-17207)***
Leon Assembly Solutions Inc ....D....858 397-2826
10650 Scripps Ranch Blvd # 123 San Diego (92131) ***(P-10819)***
Leon Krous Drilling Inc ....E....818 833-4654
9300 Borden Ave Sun Valley (91352) ***(P-112)***
Leonard Craft Co LLC ....D....714 549-0678
3501 W Segerstrom Ave Santa Ana (92704) ***(P-23286)***
Leonards Carpet Service Inc (PA) ....D....714 630-1930
1121 N Red Gum St Anaheim (92806) ***(P-5080)***
Leonards Molded Products Inc ....E....661 253-2227
25031 Anza Dr Valencia (91355) ***(P-9632)***
Leonesse Cellars, Temecula *Also called Temecula Valley Winery MGT LLC* ***(P-2009)***
Leonesse Cellars LLC ....E....951 302-7601
38311 De Portola Rd Temecula (92592) ***(P-1860)***
Leons Powder Coating ....F....510 437-9224
834 49th Ave Oakland (94601) ***(P-13610)***
Leos Cabinets ....F....323 759-7649
7007 Avalon Blvd Los Angeles (90003) ***(P-5243)***
Leos Metal Polishing ....F....310 635-5257
10980 Alameda St Lynwood (90262) ***(P-13444)***
Leos Metal Polishing Works, Lynwood *Also called Leos Metal Polishing* ***(P-13444)***

Leotek Electronics USA LLC ....E......408 380-1788
1955 Lundy Ave San Jose (95131) *(P-23914)*
Lepera Enterprises Inc ....E......818 767-5110
8207 Lankershim Blvd North Hollywood (91605) *(P-21123)*
Leprino Foods Company ....B......209 835-8340
2401 N Macarthur Dr Tracy (95376) *(P-586)*
Leprino Foods Company ....B......559 924-7722
490 F St Lemoore (93245) *(P-587)*
Leprino Foods Company ....C......559 924-7939
351 Belle Haven Dr Lemoore (93245) *(P-588)*
Lequios Japan Co Ltd ....F......410 629-8694
14241 Firestone Blvd La Mirada (90638) *(P-2583)*
Lerexa Winery, Livingston *Also called E & J Gallo Winery* *(P-1744)*
Les Schwab, Portola *Also called Coates Incorporated* *(P-20291)*
Lesco, Torrance *Also called American Ultraviolet West Inc* *(P-14264)*
Leslie-Locke, Carson *Also called Jarden Corporation* *(P-10163)*
Leslies Organics LLC ....F......415 383-9800
298 Miller Ave Mill Valley (94941) *(P-9021)*
Lester Box Inc ....F......562 437-5123
1470 Seabright Ave Long Beach (90813) *(P-4528)*
Lester Box & Manufacturing, Long Beach *Also called Lester Box Inc* *(P-4528)*
Lester Lithograph Inc ....E......714 491-3981
1128 N Gilbert St Anaheim (92801) *(P-6944)*
Lets Do Lunch ....D......310 523-3664
310 W Alondra Blvd Gardena (90248) *(P-2584)*
Lets Go Apparel Inc (PA) ....F......213 863-1767
1729 E Washington Blvd Los Angeles (90021) *(P-3667)*
Letterhead Factory Inc ....F......310 538-3321
1007 E Dominguez St Ste H Carson (90746) *(P-6945)*
Leucadia Pharmaceuticals, Carlsbad *Also called Custopharm Inc* *(P-14938)*
Levac Specialties Inc ....F......916 362-3795
2305 Cemo Cir Gold River (95670) *(P-21080)*
Levco Fab Inc ....F......909 465-0840
10757 Fremont Ave Ontario (91762) *(P-13893)*
Levecke LLC ....D......951 681-8600
10810 Inland Ave Mira Loma (91752) *(P-1861)*
Level 5 Networks Inc ....E......408 245-9300
840 W California Ave Sunnyvale (94086) *(P-18960)*
Level Labs LP ....E......408 499-6839
435 Hamilton Ave Palo Alto (94301) *(P-24857)*
Level Trek Corp ....F......626 689-4829
5670 Schaefer Ave Ste N Chino (91710) *(P-10190)*
Levi Strauss & Co (PA) ....A......415 501-6000
1155 Battery St San Francisco (94111) *(P-3078)*
Levi Strauss & Co ....F......415 677-9927
1155 Battery St San Francisco (94111) *(P-3079)*
Levi Strauss & Co ....F......310 246-9044
316 N Beverly Dr Beverly Hills (90210) *(P-3080)*
Levi Strauss & Co ....F......951 674-2694
17600 Collier Ave Lake Elsinore (92530) *(P-3081)*
Levi Strauss International (HQ) ....F......415 501-6000
1155 Battery St San Francisco (94111) *(P-3174)*
Levine Gifts, San Jose *Also called Pottery By Levine Acquisition* *(P-10834)*
Leviton Manufacturing Co Inc ....E......631 812-6041
3760 Kilroy Airport Way # 660 Long Beach (90806) *(P-17478)*
Leviton Manufacturing Co Inc ....B......619 205-8600
860 Harold Pl Chula Vista (91914) *(P-17479)*
Levolor, Irvine *Also called Sampling International LLC* *(P-3963)*
Lewis Barricade Inc ....E......661 363-0912
4000 Westerly Pl Ste 100 Newport Beach (92660) *(P-9389)*
Lewis John Glass Studio ....F......510 635-4607
10229 Pearmain St Oakland (94603) *(P-10653)*
Lewis Lifetime Tools, San Diego *Also called Richmond Engineering Co Inc* *(P-24223)*
Lewis-Goetz and Company Inc ....F......209 944-0791
4848c Frontier Way Stockton (95215) *(P-9500)*
Lex Products LLC ....F......818 768-4474
11847 Sheldon St Sun Valley (91352) *(P-22227)*
Lexington Quarry, Los Gatos *Also called Vulcan Aggregates Company LLC* *(P-387)*
Lexisnexis Matthew Bender, San Francisco *Also called Relx Inc* *(P-6246)*
Lexmark International Inc ....E......714 641-1007
575 Anton Blvd Fl 3 Costa Mesa (92626) *(P-15788)*
Lexmark International Inc ....E......714 368-0015
2211 Michelson Dr Ste 600 Irvine (92612) *(P-15789)*
Lexor Inc ....D......714 444-4144
7400 Hazard Ave Westminster (92683) *(P-24161)*
Lexstar Inc (PA) ....E......845 947-1415
4959 Kalamis Way Oceanside (92056) *(P-17625)*
Ley Grand Foods Corporation ....E......626 336-2244
287 S 6th Ave La Puente (91746) *(P-1282)*
Leyvas Mexican Food ....E......626 350-6328
4032 Tyler Ave El Monte (91731) *(P-1283)*
Lf Illumination LLC ....D......818 885-1335
9200 Deering Ave Chatsworth (91311) *(P-17626)*
LF Industries Inc ....F......951 471-0372
6352 Corte Del Abeto G Carlsbad (92011) *(P-16686)*
Lf Sportswear Inc (PA) ....E......310 437-4100
5333 Mcconnell Ave Los Angeles (90066) *(P-3252)*
Lf Visuals Inc ....E......760 345-5571
39620 Entrepreneur Ln Palm Desert (92211) *(P-3007)*
Lg Innotek Usa Inc (HQ) ....E......408 955-0364
2540 N 1st St Ste 400 San Jose (95131) *(P-19620)*
Lg Nanoh2o Inc ....E......424 218-4000
21250 Hawthorne Blvd # 330 Torrance (90503) *(P-9272)*
Lg-Ericsson USA Inc ....E......877 828-2673
20 Mason Irvine (92618) *(P-17961)*
LGarde Inc ....E......714 259-0771
15181 Woodlawn Ave Tustin (92780) *(P-15563)*
Lgc Wireless Inc ....C......408 952-2400
541 E Trimble Rd San Jose (95131) *(P-18165)*

Lgm Company, El Monte *Also called Smj Inc* *(P-9073)*
Lgphilips Lcd Amer Fin Corp ....E......408 350-7600
150 E Brokaw Rd San Jose (95112) *(P-20004)*
Lhoist North America Ariz Inc ....F......626 336-4578
14931 Salt Lake Ave City of Industry (91746) *(P-11215)*
Lhv Power Corporation (PA) ....E......619 258-7700
10221 Buena Vista Ave A Santee (92071) *(P-19621)*
Lialee Inc ....F......213 765-7788
525 E 87th Pl Los Angeles (90003) *(P-2847)*
Liantronics, Fremont *Also called Manutronics Co* *(P-15447)*
Liantronics LLC ....E......510 438-0588
46722 Fremont Blvd Fremont (94538) *(P-17627)*
Libby Laboratories Inc ....E......510 527-5400
1700 6th St Berkeley (94710) *(P-8789)*
Liberty Cafe ....E......415 695-8777
410 Cortland Ave San Francisco (94110) *(P-1284)*
Liberty Container Company ....C......323 564-4211
4224 Santa Ana St South Gate (90280) *(P-5434)*
Liberty Diversified Intl Inc ....C......858 391-7302
13100 Danielson St Poway (92064) *(P-5435)*
Liberty Foods Trading Co LLC ....E......209 367-8800
631 N Cluff Ave Lodi (95240) *(P-819)*
Liberty Industries ....F......626 575-3206
10754 Lower Azusa Rd El Monte (91731) *(P-16687)*
Liberty Love, Commerce *Also called Cure Apparel LLC* *(P-3227)*
Liberty Packg & Extruding Inc ....E......323 722-5124
3015 Supply Ave Commerce (90040) *(P-5604)*
Liberty Paper, Vernon *Also called D D Office Products Inc* *(P-5278)*
Liberty Printing Inc ....E......209 467-8800
2601 Teepee Dr Stockton (95205) *(P-6946)*
Liberty School, Paso Robles *Also called Treana Winery LLC* *(P-2019)*
Liberty Vegetable Oil Company ....E......562 921-3567
15306 Carmenita Rd Santa Fe Springs (90670) *(P-1542)*
Liboon Group Inc ....F......714 639-3639
1746 W Katella Ave Ste 6 Orange (92867) *(P-14390)*
Libra Cable Technologies Inc ....F......310 618-8182
Monterey Business Park 27 Torrance (90503) *(P-19622)*
Library Mosacis, Los Angeles *Also called Yenor Inc* *(P-7546)*
Library Reproduction Service, Los Angeles *Also called The Microfilm Company of Cal* *(P-6400)*
License Frame Inc ....E......714 903-7550
15462 Electronic Ln Huntington Beach (92649) *(P-13611)*
Licher Direct Mail Inc ....E......626 795-3333
980 Seco St Pasadena (91103) *(P-6947)*
Lida Childrens Wear Inc ....E......626 967-8868
3113 E California Blvd Pasadena (91107) *(P-3582)*
Lidestri Foods Inc ....D......559 251-1000
568 S Temperance Ave Fresno (93727) *(P-820)*
Lido Industries Inc ....F......714 633-3731
456 S Montgomery Way Orange (92868) *(P-10191)*
Lids Corporation ....F......925 609-9516
357 Sun Valley Mall Ste C Concord (94520) *(P-3566)*
Lieder Development Inc ....F......909 947-7722
1839 S Lake Pl Ontario (91761) *(P-19623)*
Life Force International, El Cajon *Also called Doctors Signature Sales* *(P-7933)*
Life Line Packaging Inc ....F......619 444-2737
1250 Pierre Way El Cajon (92021) *(P-5525)*
Life Line Products, El Cajon *Also called Life Line Packaging Inc* *(P-5525)*
Life Media Inc ....E......800 201-9440
7657 Winnetka Ave Ste 504 Winnetka (91306) *(P-6207)*
Life Paint Company (PA) ....E......562 944-6391
12927 Sunshine Ave Santa Fe Springs (90670) *(P-8915)*
Life Science Outsourcing Inc ....D......714 672-1090
830 Challenger St Brea (92821) *(P-22508)*
Life Style West, Orange *Also called Daves Interiors Inc* *(P-4768)*
Life Technologies Corporation ....C......760 603-7200
500 Lincoln Centre Dr Foster City (94404) *(P-21983)*
Life Technologies Corporation (HQ) ....C......760 603-7200
5781 Van Allen Way Carlsbad (92008) *(P-8489)*
Life Technologies Corporation ....D......760 918-4259
5791 Van Allen Way Carlsbad (92008) *(P-8565)*
Lifeaid Beverage Co ....D......800 855-1113
2833 Mission St Santa Cruz (95060) *(P-2148)*
Lifebloom Corporation ....E......562 944-6800
925 W Lambert Rd Ste B Brea (92821) *(P-8259)*
Lifefactory Inc ....E......415 729-9820
3 Harbor Dr Ste 200 Sausalito (94965) *(P-10621)*
Lifegas, Burbank *Also called Linde Gas North America LLC* *(P-7693)*
Lifegas, City of Industry *Also called Linde Gas North America LLC* *(P-7694)*
Lifekind Products Inc ....E......530 477-5395
1415 Whispering Pines Ln # 100 Grass Valley (95945) *(P-8596)*
Lifeline Food Co Inc ....E......831 899-5040
118 Cypress Lakes Ct Marina (93933) *(P-589)*
Lifeline SEC & Automtn Inc ....E......916 285-9078
2081 Arena Blvd Ste 260 Sacramento (95834) *(P-20005)*
Lifeline Systems Company ....C......831 755-0788
450 E Romie Ln Salinas (93901) *(P-18340)*
Lifemed of California ....E......800 543-3633
13948 Mountain Ave Chino (91710) *(P-22509)*
Lifeome Biolabs Inc ....E......619 302-0129
10054 Mesa Ridge Ct San Diego (92121) *(P-8490)*
Lifescan Inc ....F......408 263-9789
901 Wrigley Way Milpitas (95035) *(P-8491)*
Lifescan Inc ....F......408 263-9789
542 Gibraltar Dr Milpitas (95035) *(P-8492)*
Lifescan Inc ....F......408 263-9789
1051 S Milpitas Blvd # 2 Milpitas (95035) *(P-8493)*
Lifescan Products LLC (HQ) ....D......408 719-8443
1000 Gibraltar Dr Milpitas (95035) *(P-22510)*

Mergent e-mail: customerrelations@mergent.com
1196

2019 California
Manufacturers Register

(P-0000) Products & Services Section entry number
(PA)=Parent Co (HQ)=Headquarters (DH)=Div Headquarters

Lifescience, Hercules *Also called Bio-RAD Laboratories Inc* ***(P-21921)***
Lifescience Plus Inc ....F.......650 565-8172
2520 Wyandotte St Ste A Mountain View (94043) ***(P-22998)***
Lifesource Water Systems Inc (PA) ....E.......626 792-9996
523 S Fair Oaks Ave Pasadena (91105) ***(P-16066)***
Lifetime Camper Shells Inc ....E.......909 885-2814
1375 N E St San Bernardino (92405) ***(P-21205)***
Lifetime Memory Products Inc ....E.......949 794-9000
2505 Da Vinci Ste A Irvine (92614) ***(P-18520)***
Lifetouch Nat Schl Studios Inc ....D.......530 345-3993
2860 Fair St Chico (95928) ***(P-7582)***
Lifetrak Incorporated ....F.......510 413-9030
8371 Central Ave Ste A Newark (94560) ***(P-22999)***
Lifi Labs Inc (PA) ....F.......650 739-5563
350 Townsend St Ste 830 San Francisco (94107) ***(P-10654)***
Lifoam Industries LLC ....E.......323 587-1934
2340 E 52nd St Vernon (90058) ***(P-9713)***
Lifoam Mfg, Vernon *Also called Lifoam Industries LLC* ***(P-9713)***
Lift By Encore, Huntington Beach *Also called Encore Interiors Inc* ***(P-20806)***
Lift By Encore, Huntington Beach *Also called Encore Seats Inc* ***(P-20807)***
Lift Off, San Diego *Also called Motsenbocker Advanced Developm* ***(P-8657)***
Lifx, San Francisco *Also called Lifi Labs Inc* ***(P-10654)***
Ligand Pharmaceuticals Inc ....E.......858 550-7500
10275 Science Center Dr San Diego (92121) ***(P-8260)***
Ligand Pharmaceuticals Inc (PA) ....E.......858 550-7500
3911 Sorrento Valley Blvd # 110 San Diego (92121) ***(P-8261)***
Light & Motion Industries ....D.......831 645-1525
711 Neeson Rd Marina (93933) ***(P-17707)***
Light Composite Corporation ....D.......949 858-8820
22322 Gilberto Rcho STA Marg (92688) ***(P-11970)***
Light Fixture Industries, Vista *Also called Exit Light Co Inc* ***(P-17605)***
Light Guard Systems Inc ....F.......707 542-4547
2292 Airport Blvd Santa Rosa (95403) ***(P-17285)***
Light House, Torrance *Also called Takuyo Corporation* ***(P-6066)***
Light Impressions, Santa Fe Springs *Also called Ncd Acquisition Inc* ***(P-9720)***
Light Labs Inc ....D.......650 272-6942
636 Ramona St Palo Alto (94301) ***(P-22098)***
Light Mobile Inc ....F.......858 278-1750
7968 Arjons Dr Ste D San Diego (92126) ***(P-22892)***
Lightcap Industries, Inc. ....E.......909 930-3772
1612 S Cucamonga Ave Ontario (91761) ***(P-12196)***
Lightclub USA, Chatsworth *Also called Lightcraft Outdoor Environmnts* ***(P-17542)***
Lightcraft Outdoor Environmnts ....F.......818 349-2663
9811 Owensmouth Ave Ste 1 Chatsworth (91311) ***(P-17542)***
Lightcross Inc ....E.......626 236-4500
2630 Corporate Pl Monterey Park (91754) ***(P-19624)***
Lightech Fiberoptic Inc ....E.......510 567-8700
1987 Adams Ave San Leandro (94577) ***(P-19625)***
Lightera, Sunnyvale *Also called Luminus Inc* ***(P-17633)***
Lighthouse Trucking, Montebello *Also called Beacon Concrete Inc* ***(P-11050)***
Lighting Company, The, Irvine *Also called Energy Management Group Inc* ***(P-17692)***
Lighting Control & Design Inc (HQ) ....E.......323 226-0000
9144 Deering Ave Chatsworth (91311) ***(P-17708)***
Lightning Dversion Systems LLC ....F.......714 841-1080
16572 Burke Ln Huntington Beach (92647) ***(P-17480)***
Lightprint Labs, San Francisco *Also called Allen Sarah &* ***(P-15661)***
Lights Fantastic ....E.......408 266-2787
2408 Lincoln Village Dr San Jose (95125) ***(P-6948)***
Lights of America Inc (PA) ....B.......909 594-7883
611 Reyes Dr Walnut (91789) ***(P-17543)***
Lightstreams Inc ....F.......408 492-1689
1111 Comstock St Santa Clara (95054) ***(P-10655)***
Lightwave Laser, Santa Rosa *Also called Macon Industries Inc* ***(P-20011)***
Lightwave Pdl Inc ....F.......909 548-3677
1246 E Lexington Ave Pomona (91766) ***(P-17544)***
Lightway Industries Inc ....E.......661 257-0286
28435 Industry Dr Valencia (91355) ***(P-17628)***
Lignum Vitae Cabinet ....F.......510 444-2030
1625 16th St Oakland (94607) ***(P-4954)***
Likom Caseworks USA Inc (HQ) ....E.......210 587-7824
17890 Castleton St # 309 City of Industry (91748) ***(P-15639)***
Lili Butler Studio Inc ....F.......707 793-0222
7950 Redwood Dr Ste 16 Cotati (94931) ***(P-3253)***
Lilly Biotechnology Center ....F.......858 597-4990
10290 Campus Point Dr San Diego (92121) ***(P-8262)***
Lilly Tortilleria ....E.......619 281-2890
4271 University Ave San Diego (92105) ***(P-2585)***
Lily Pond Products ....F.......559 431-5203
351 W Cromwell Ave # 105 Fresno (93711) ***(P-14984)***
Limited Access Unlimited Inc ....F.......619 294-3682
5220 Anna Ave Ste A San Diego (92110) ***(P-406)***
Limos By Tiffany Inc ....E.......951 657-2680
23129 Cajalco Rd Perris (92570) ***(P-20213)***
Limpus Prints Inc ....F.......714 545-5078
1820 S Santa Fe St Santa Ana (92705) ***(P-7386)***
Lin Consulting LLC ....F.......714 650-8595
15086 Beach Blvd Midway City (92655) ***(P-21206)***
Lin Engineering Inc ....C.......408 919-0200
16245 Vineyard Blvd Morgan Hill (95037) ***(P-17208)***
Lin Frank Distillers ....F.......707 437-1092
2455 Huntington Dr Fairfield (94533) ***(P-2073)***
Lin MAI Inc ....E.......818 890-1220
6333 San Fernando Rd Glendale (91201) ***(P-24162)***
Linabond Inc ....F.......805 484-7373
1161 Avenida Acaso Camarillo (93012) ***(P-13612)***
Lincoln Iron Works ....E.......310 684-2543
507 7th St Santa Monica (90402) ***(P-11405)***
Lind Marine Inc (PA) ....E.......707 762-7251
100 E D St Petaluma (94952) ***(P-1144)***
Lindahl Enterprises Ltd Inc ....E.......909 391-7052
936 N Oaks Ave Ontario (91762) ***(P-21613)***
Lindblade Metal Works, La Mirada *Also called Lindblade Metalworks Inc* ***(P-12874)***
Lindblade Metalworks Inc ....E.......714 670-7172
14355 Macaw St La Mirada (90638) ***(P-12874)***
Linde Gas North America LLC ....F.......626 855-8344
614 S Glenwood Pl Burbank (91506) ***(P-7693)***
Linde Gas North America LLC ....F.......626 780-3104
680 Baldwin Park Blvd City of Industry (91746) ***(P-7694)***
Linde LLC ....F.......562 903-1290
13117 Meyer Rd Whittier (90605) ***(P-7695)***
Linde LLC ....E.......310 533-8394
2535 Del Amo Blvd Torrance (90503) ***(P-7696)***
Linde LLC ....F.......510 233-8911
731 W Cutting Blvd Richmond (94804) ***(P-7697)***
Linde LLC ....E.......916 381-1606
5858 88th St Sacramento (95828) ***(P-7698)***
Linde LLC ....E.......925 371-4170
4569 Las Positas Rd Ste C Livermore (94551) ***(P-7699)***
Linde LLC ....D.......626 855-8366
660 Baldwin Park Blvd City of Industry (91746) ***(P-7700)***
Linde LLC ....D.......408 496-1177
2041 Mission College Blvd Santa Clara (95054) ***(P-15082)***
Linden Nut, Linden *Also called Pearl Crop Inc* ***(P-2636)***
Lindgren Lumber Co ....F.......707 822-6519
3851 W End Ct Arcata (95521) ***(P-4042)***
Lindquist Robert N & Assoc (PA) ....F.......805 937-9801
4665 Santa Maria Mesa Rd Santa Maria (93454) ***(P-1862)***
Lindsay Trnsp Solutions Inc (HQ) ....D.......707 374-6800
180 River Rd Rio Vista (94571) ***(P-10954)***
Lindsay/Barnett Incorporated ....F.......510 483-6300
2194 Edison Ave Ste H San Leandro (94577) ***(P-13954)***
Lindsey Doors Inc ....E.......760 775-1959
81101 Indio Blvd Ste D16 Indio (92201) ***(P-9752)***
Lindsey International Co., Azusa *Also called Lindsey Manufacturing Co* ***(P-13125)***
Lindsey Manufacturing Co ....C.......626 969-3471
760 N Georgia Ave Azusa (91702) ***(P-13125)***
Lindsey Mfg, Indio *Also called Lindsey Doors Inc* ***(P-9752)***
Line 6, Inc, Calabasas *Also called Yamaha Guitar Group Inc* ***(P-23393)***
Line Euro-Americas Corp ....F.......323 591-0380
5750 Wilshire Blvd # 640 Los Angeles (90036) ***(P-24858)***
Line One Laboratories Inc USA ....E.......818 886-2288
9600 Lurline Ave Chatsworth (91311) ***(P-9633)***
Line Publications Inc ....F.......310 234-9501
9800 S La Cienega Blvd # 10 Inglewood (90301) ***(P-6208)***
Linea Pelle Inc (PA) ....F.......310 231-9950
7107 Valjean Ave Van Nuys (91406) ***(P-10463)***
Linear Express, Milpitas *Also called Linear Technology Corporation* ***(P-18962)***
Linear Integrated Systems Inc ....F.......510 490-9160
4042 Clipper Ct Fremont (94538) ***(P-18961)***
Linear Technology Corporation ....F.......408 428-2050
720 Sycamore Dr Milpitas (95035) ***(P-18962)***
Linear Technology Corporation ....D.......408 434-6237
1530 Buckeye Dr Milpitas (95035) ***(P-18963)***
Linear Technology LLC (HQ) ....A.......408 432-1900
1630 Mccarthy Blvd Milpitas (95035) ***(P-18964)***
Linear Technology LLC ....D.......805 965-6400
911 Olive St Santa Barbara (93101) ***(P-18965)***
Linear Technology LLC ....D.......408 432-1900
5465 Morehouse Dr Ste 155 San Diego (92121) ***(P-18966)***
Linen Liners, Fullerton *Also called GLC General Inc* ***(P-4623)***
Linens Exchange Inc ....F.......310 638-5507
3148 Martin Luther King Lynwood (90262) ***(P-3008)***
Liner Technologies Inc ....E.......909 594-6610
4821 Chino Ave Chino (91710) ***(P-10192)***
Linfinity Microelectronics, Garden Grove *Also called Microsemi Corp-Analog* ***(P-19011)***
Lingle Bros Coffee Inc ....E.......562 927-3317
6500 Garfield Ave Bell Gardens (90201) ***(P-2359)***
Link Depot, Pomona *Also called Ld Smart Inc* ***(P-15443)***
Link4 Corporation ....F.......714 524-0004
175 E Freedom Ave Anaheim (92801) ***(P-21515)***
Linkbit Inc ....F.......408 969-9940
3180 De La Cruz Blvd # 200 Santa Clara (95054) ***(P-15790)***
Links Medical Products Inc (PA) ....E.......949 753-0001
9247 Research Dr Irvine (92618) ***(P-22511)***
Linktech Quick Couplings Inc ....E.......805 339-0055
3000 Bunsen Ave Ste A Ventura (93003) ***(P-13894)***
Linkus Corp ....F.......530 342-0738
13251 Whitchurch Ln Chico (95973) ***(P-18166)***
Linmarr Associates Inc ....F.......949 215-5466
8 Hammond Ste 108 Irvine (92618) ***(P-15108)***
Linnco LLC ....A.......661 616-3900
5201 Truxtun Ave Bakersfield (93309) ***(P-64)***
Linoleum Sales Co Inc (PA) ....D.......661 327-4053
1000 W Grand Ave Oakland (94607) ***(P-10600)***
Linpeng International Inc ....F.......909 923-9881
1939 S Campus Ave Ontario (91761) ***(P-24163)***
Lintelle Engineering Inc ....E.......831 439-8400
380 El Pueblo Rd Ste 105 Scotts Valley (95066) ***(P-20006)***
Linvatec Corporation ....D.......805 571-8100
26 Castilian Dr Ste B Goleta (93117) ***(P-22512)***
Linx & More, Woodland Hills *Also called Linx Bracelets Inc* ***(P-23287)***
Linx Bracelets Inc ....F.......818 224-4050
23147 Ventura Blvd # 250 Woodland Hills (91364) ***(P-23287)***
Lion Packing Co, Selma *Also called Lion Raisins Inc* ***(P-885)***
Lion Raisins Inc (PA) ....B.......559 834-6677
9500 S De Wolf Ave Selma (93662) ***(P-885)***
Lion Semiconductor Inc ....F.......415 462-4933
332 Townsend St San Francisco (94107) ***(P-18967)***

ALPHABETIC

Employee Codes: A=Over 500 employees, B=251-500
C=101-250, D=51-100, E=20-50, F=10-19
2019 California
Manfacturers Register
© Mergent Inc. 1-800-342-5647
1197

Lion Tank Line Inc ....E....323 726-1966
5801 Randolph St Commerce (90040) ***(P-9337)***
Lip Hing Metal Inc ....F....714 871-9220
738 Phillips Rowland Heights (91748) ***(P-14441)***
Lip Hing Metal Mfg Amer Inc ....F....626 810-8204
738 Phillips Rowland Heights (91748) ***(P-14757)***
Lippert Components Inc ....D....909 873-0061
168 S Spruce Ave Rialto (92376) ***(P-20155)***
Lippert Components Mfg Inc ....E....909 628-5557
1021 Walnut Ave Pomona (91766) ***(P-10714)***
Liqua-Tech Corporation ....F....800 659-3556
3501 N State St Ukiah (95482) ***(P-21690)***
Liqui-Box Corporation ....E....909 390-4646
5772 Jurupa St Ste C Ontario (91761) ***(P-9800)***
Liqui-Box Corporation ....D....916 381-7052
5000 Warehouse Way Sacramento (95826) ***(P-10193)***
Liquid Bioscience Inc ....F....949 432-9559
26895 Aliso Creek Rd B800 Aliso Viejo (92656) ***(P-8263)***
Liquid Force Wakeboards ....E....760 943-8364
364 2nd St Ste 7 Encinitas (92024) ***(P-23607)***
Liquid Graphics Inc ....C....949 486-3588
2701 S Harbor Blvd Unit A Santa Ana (92704) ***(P-3175)***
Liquid Packaging, Paramount *Also called Vast Enterprises* ***(P-9453)***
Liquid Robotics Inc (HQ) ....D....408 636-4200
1329 Moffett Park Dr Sunnyvale (94089) ***(P-20386)***
Liquid Robotics Federal Inc ....F....408 636-4200
1329 Moffett Park Dr Sunnyvale (94089) ***(P-21791)***
Liquid Technologies Inc ....E....909 393-9475
14425 Yorba Ave Chino (91710) ***(P-8790)***
Liquidmetal Technologies Inc (PA) ....E....949 635-2100
20321 Valencia Cir Lake Forest (92630) ***(P-11525)***
Liquidspring Technologies Inc ....F....562 941-4344
10400 Pioneer Blvd Ste 1 Santa Fe Springs (90670) ***(P-21234)***
Liqwiz LLC ....F....925 285-3100
5375 Black Ave Apt 1 Pleasanton (94566) ***(P-22099)***
Lisa & Lesley Fashion ACC, Sherman Oaks *Also called Lisa and Lesley Co* ***(P-3455)***
Lisa & ME, La Puente *Also called California Fashion Club Inc* ***(P-3349)***
Lisa and Lesley Co ....F....323 877-9878
14140 Ventura Blvd # 101 Sherman Oaks (91423) ***(P-3455)***
Lisac Construction, Union City *Also called Kerrock Countertops Inc* ***(P-4711)***
Lisi Aerospace, City of Industry *Also called Monadnock Company* ***(P-11977)***
Lisi Medical Jeropa Inc (HQ) ....D....760 432-9785
950 Borra Pl Escondido (92029) ***(P-14391)***
List Biological Labs Inc ....E....408 866-6363
540 Division St Campbell (95008) ***(P-8566)***
List Labs, Campbell *Also called List Biological Labs Inc* ***(P-8566)***
Lite Extrusions Manufacturing ....E....323 770-4298
15025 S Main St Gardena (90248) ***(P-9753)***
Lite Line Frame Bags ....E....562 905-3150
535 N Puente St Brea (92821) ***(P-10565)***
Lite Machines Corporation ....F....765 463-0959
2222 Faraday Ave Carlsbad (92008) ***(P-21318)***
Lite On Technology Intl Inc (HQ) ....E....408 945-0222
720 S Hillview Dr Milpitas (95035) ***(P-15791)***
Lite Stone Concrete LLC ....F....619 596-9151
12650 Highway 67 Ste B Lakeside (92040) ***(P-10955)***
Litel Instruments Inc ....E....858 546-3788
10650 Scripps Ranch Blvd # 105 San Diego (92131) ***(P-21792)***
Litepanels Inc ....F....818 752-7009
20600 Plummer St Chatsworth (91311) ***(P-17431)***
Lites On West Soho, Oceanside *Also called Lexstar Inc* ***(P-17625)***
Lith-O-Roll Corporation ....E....626 579-0340
9521 Telstar Ave El Monte (91731) ***(P-14816)***
Lithium Technologies LLC (PA) ....D....415 757-3100
1 Pier Ste 1 # 1 San Francisco (94111) ***(P-24859)***
Lithiumstart Inc ....E....800 520-8864
865 Hinckley Rd Burlingame (94010) ***(P-19626)***
Lithocraft Co, Anaheim *Also called Man-Grove Industries Inc* ***(P-6959)***
Lithograph Reproductions ....F....510 658-2367
4120 Martin Luther King J Oakland (94609) ***(P-6949)***
Lithographix Inc (PA) ....B....323 770-1000
12250 Crenshaw Blvd Hawthorne (90250) ***(P-6950)***
Lithographix Inc ....D....760 438-3456
6200 Yarrow Dr Carlsbad (92011) ***(P-7387)***
Lithonia Lighting, Ontario *Also called Acuity Brands Lighting Inc* ***(P-17580)***
Lithotech International LLC ....E....626 443-4210
9950 Baldwin Pl El Monte (91731) ***(P-7388)***
Lithotechs Inc ....F....626 433-1333
9950 Baldwin Pl El Monte (91731) ***(P-7389)***
Lithotype Company Inc (PA) ....D....650 871-1750
333 Point San Bruno Blvd South San Francisco (94080) ***(P-6951)***
Lito ....E....323 260-4692
3730 Union Pacific Ave Los Angeles (90023) ***(P-3538)***
Lito Childrens Wear Inc ....E....323 260-4692
3730 Union Pacific Ave Los Angeles (90023) ***(P-3033)***
Liton Lighting, Los Angeles *Also called Eema Industries Inc* ***(P-17688)***
Little Bliss Cakery, Granite Bay *Also called Sweets 4jc LLC* ***(P-1328)***
Little Brothers Bakery LLC ....D....310 225-3790
320 W Alondra Blvd Gardena (90248) ***(P-1285)***
Little Castle Furniture Co Inc ....E....805 278-4646
301 Todd Ct Oxnard (93030) ***(P-4791)***
Little Digger Mining & Sup LLC ....E....626 856-3366
3524 Maine Ave Baldwin Park (91706) ***(P-5)***
Little Einsteins LLC ....F....818 560-1000
500 S Buena Vista St Burbank (91521) ***(P-6359)***
Little Firefighter Corporation ....F....714 834-0410
204 S Center St Santa Ana (92703) ***(P-13723)***
Little Folk Visuals, Palm Desert *Also called Lf Visuals Inc* ***(P-3007)***
Little Saigon News Inc ....F....714 265-0800
13861 Seaboard Cir Garden Grove (92843) ***(P-5913)***
Litton Navigation Systems Div, Woodland Hills *Also called Northrop Grumman Systems Corp* ***(P-20605)***
Litus Global Solutions, San Diego *Also called Sigma 6 Electronics Inc* ***(P-20069)***
Live and Let Live, La Puente *Also called Oneworld Apparel LLC* ***(P-3330)***
Live Fresh Corporation ....C....909 478-0895
1055 E Cooley Ave San Bernardino (92408) ***(P-959)***
Live Journal Inc ....E....415 230-3600
430 Main St San Francisco (94105) ***(P-5914)***
Liveaction Inc (PA) ....E....415 837-3303
3500 W Bayshore Rd Palo Alto (94303) ***(P-24860)***
Liveoffice LLC ....D....877 253-2793
900 Corporate Pointe Culver City (90230) ***(P-24861)***
Liverpool Jeans, Montebello *Also called Cavern Club LLC* ***(P-3224)***
Livetime Software Inc ....E....415 905-4009
276 Avocado St Apt C102 Costa Mesa (92627) ***(P-24862)***
Livewire Innovation, Camarillo *Also called Livewire Test Labs Inc* ***(P-21793)***
Livewire Test Labs Inc ....F....801 293-8300
808 Calle Plano Camarillo (93012) ***(P-21793)***
Living Tree Community Foods ....E....510 526-7106
1455 5th St Berkeley (94710) ***(P-2586)***
Living Waters Logging Inc ....F....707 822-3955
1159 Stromberg Ave Arcata (95521) ***(P-3998)***
Living Way Industries Inc ....F....661 298-3200
20734 Centre Pointe Pkwy Santa Clarita (91350) ***(P-23915)***
Living Wellness Partners LLC ....E....800 642-3754
5130 Avenida Encinas Carlsbad (92008) ***(P-2587)***
Livingstone Jewelry Co Inc ....F....213 683-1040
631 S Olive St Ste 340 Los Angeles (90014) ***(P-23288)***
Livingstons Concrete Svc Inc (PA) ....D....916 334-4313
5416 Roseville Rd North Highlands (95660) ***(P-11135)***
Livingstons Concrete Svc Inc ....E....916 334-4313
5416 Roseville Rd North Highlands (95660) ***(P-11136)***
Livingstons Concrete Svc Inc ....E....916 334-4313
2915 Lesvos Ct Lincoln (95648) ***(P-11137)***
Lixit Corporation (PA) ....D....800 358-8254
100 Coombs St NAPA (94559) ***(P-24164)***
Liz Palacios Designs Ltd ....E....415 626-4630
1 Stanton Way Mill Valley (94941) ***(P-23752)***
Lizal Inc ....E....408 252-5200
19503 Stevens Creek Blvd Cupertino (95014) ***(P-5605)***
Ljr Blanchard Grinding, Gardena *Also called L J R Grinding Corp* ***(P-16671)***
LL Baker Inc ....F....760 741-9899
431 N Hale Ave Escondido (92029) ***(P-6952)***
Llamas Plastics Inc ....C....818 362-0371
12970 Bradley Ave Sylmar (91342) ***(P-20867)***
LLC Lindero Learning Center, Irvine *Also called Wanada Investments LLC* ***(P-25342)***
LLC Marsh Perkins ....F....760 880-4558
80080 Via Pessaro La Quinta (92253) ***(P-3668)***
Lloyd Design Corporation ....D....818 768-6001
19731 Nordhoff St Northridge (91324) ***(P-2931)***
Lloyd E Hennessey Jr ....E....408 842-8437
7200 Alexander St Gilroy (95020) ***(P-16688)***
Lloyd Mats, Northridge *Also called Lloyd Design Corporation* ***(P-2931)***
LM Scofield Company (HQ) ....E....323 720-3000
12767 Imperial Hwy Santa Fe Springs (90670) ***(P-9273)***
Lmb Heeger, Commerce *Also called Heeger Inc* ***(P-17202)***
LMC Enterprises (PA) ....D....562 602-2116
6401 Alondra Blvd Paramount (90723) ***(P-8651)***
LMC Enterprises ....E....310 632-7124
19402 S Susana Rd Compton (90221) ***(P-8652)***
Lmg National Publishing Inc ....D....760 241-7744
13891 Park Ave Victorville (92392) ***(P-5915)***
LMI, Lodi *Also called Larry Mthvin Installations Inc* ***(P-10713)***
LMI Aerospace Inc ....C....760 597-7066
1351 Specialty Dr Vista (92081) ***(P-20868)***
LMI Aerospace Inc ....C....760 599-4477
1377 Specialty Dr Vista (92081) ***(P-12197)***
Lmm Enterprises ....F....714 543-8044
1348 E Sunview Dr Orange (92865) ***(P-16689)***
Lmw Enterprises LLC ....E....562 944-1969
12309 Telegraph Rd Santa Fe Springs (90670) ***(P-15968)***
Lni Custom Manufacturing Inc ....E....310 978-2000
12536 Chadron Ave Hawthorne (90250) ***(P-12875)***
Loaded Boards Inc ....F....310 839-1800
10575 Virginia Ave Culver City (90232) ***(P-21124)***
Loanhero Inc ....F....888 912-4376
750 B St Ste 1410 San Diego (92101) ***(P-24863)***
Loard's Ice Cream and Candies, San Leandro *Also called Loco Ventures Inc* ***(P-680)***
Lob-Ster Inc (PA) ....F....818 764-6000
7340 Fulton Ave North Hollywood (91605) ***(P-23608)***
Lobob Laboratories Inc ....E....408 324-0381
1440 Atteberry Ln San Jose (95131) ***(P-8264)***
Lobostar Inc ....D....310 516-9812
14601 S Broadway Gardena (90248) ***(P-13955)***
Lobster Sports, North Hollywood *Also called Lob-Ster Inc* ***(P-23608)***
Lobue Laser & Eye Medical Ctrs ....E....951 696-1135
40740 California Oaks Rd Murrieta (92562) ***(P-23000)***
Local 162, Sacramento *Also called International Association of S* ***(P-12624)***
Local Neon Co Inc ....E....310 978-2000
12536 Chadron Ave Hawthorne (90250) ***(P-23916)***
Lochaber Cornwall Inc (PA) ....F....714 935-0302
675 N Eckhoff St Ste D Orange (92868) ***(P-15268)***
Lochirco Fruit and Produce Inc ....E....559 528-4194
41899 Road 120 Orosi (93647) ***(P-1439)***
Locix Inc ....F....650 231-2180
1150 Bayhill Dr Ste 205 San Bruno (94066) ***(P-17286)***

Mergent e-mail: customerrelations@mergent.com
1198
2019 California
Manufacturers Register
(P-0000) Products & Services Section entry number
(PA)=Parent Co (HQ)=Headquarters (DH)=Div Headquarters

Lock America Inc ....F......951 277-5180
9168 Stellar Ct Corona (92883) *(P-11971)*
Lock-N-Stitch Inc ....E......209 632-2345
1015 S Soderquist Rd Turlock (95380) *(P-14645)*
Lock-Ridge Tool Company Inc ....D......909 865-8309
2000 Pomona Blvd Pomona (91768) *(P-13242)*
Lockhart Collection, Santa Fe Springs *Also called Lockhart Furniture Mfg Inc (P-4792)*
Lockhart Furniture Mfg Inc ....D......562 404-0561
13710 Milroy Pl Santa Fe Springs (90670) *(P-4792)*
Lockheed Martin (HQ) ....E......408 834-9741
1111 Lockheed Martin Way Sunnyvale (94089) *(P-20598)*
Lockheed Martin Aeronautics Co, Edwards *Also called Lockheed Martin Corporation (P-21330)*
Lockheed Martin Aeronautics Co, Palmdale *Also called Lockheed Martin Corporation (P-21334)*
Lockheed Martin Corporation ....A......831 425-6000
4203 Smith Grade Santa Cruz (95060) *(P-21319)*
Lockheed Martin Corporation ....B......408 756-1400
1523 Crom St Manteca (95337) *(P-21320)*
Lockheed Martin Corporation ....A......408 734-4980
2770 De La Cruz Blvd Santa Clara (95050) *(P-21321)*
Lockheed Martin Corporation ....B......925 756-4594
4524 Chancery Ln Dublin (94568) *(P-21322)*
Lockheed Martin Corporation ....D......831 425-6000
16020 Empire Grade Santa Cruz (95060) *(P-21160)*
Lockheed Martin Corporation ....B......408 756-1868
1105 Remington Ct Sunnyvale (94087) *(P-21323)*
Lockheed Martin Corporation ....B......805 686-4069
153 Industrial Way Buellton (93427) *(P-21324)*
Lockheed Martin Corporation ....D......408 756-5751
1111 Lockheed Martin Way Sunnyvale (94089) *(P-21161)*
Lockheed Martin Corporation ....A......408 473-3000
3130 Zanker Rd San Jose (95134) *(P-18167)*
Lockheed Martin Corporation ....A......650 424-2000
3251 Hanover St Palo Alto (94304) *(P-21325)*
Lockheed Martin Corporation ....B......805 606-4860
Bldg 8310 Lompoc (93437) *(P-18168)*
Lockheed Martin Corporation ....F......408 781-8570
266 Caspian Dr Sunnyvale (94089) *(P-21326)*
Lockheed Martin Corporation ....F......650 424-2000
3251 Hanover St C Palo Alto (94304) *(P-21327)*
Lockheed Martin Corporation ....A......408 473-7498
3100 Zanker Rd San Jose (95134) *(P-21328)*
Lockheed Martin Corporation ....B......408 747-2626
160 E Tasman Dr San Jose (95134) *(P-21162)*
Lockheed Martin Corporation ....A......805 614-3671
3201 Airpark Dr Ste 204 Santa Maria (93455) *(P-21329)*
Lockheed Martin Corporation ....A......661 277-0691
225 N Flightline Rd Edwards (93524) *(P-21330)*
Lockheed Martin Corporation ....E......408 742-6688
1111 Lockheed Martin Way Sunnyvale (94089) *(P-21331)*
Lockheed Martin Corporation ....A......408 742-4321
1111 Lockheed Martin Way Sunnyvale (94089) *(P-21163)*
Lockheed Martin Corporation ....C......858 740-5100
10325 Meanley Dr San Diego (92131) *(P-21332)*
Lockheed Martin Corporation ....E......805 650-4600
2895 Golf Course Dr Ventura (93003) *(P-21333)*
Lockheed Martin Corporation ....A......661 572-7428
1011 Lockheed Way Palmdale (93599) *(P-21334)*
Lockheed Martin Corporation ....D......831 425-6375
16020 Empire Grade Santa Cruz (95060) *(P-21335)*
Lockheed Martin Corporation ....D......805 571-2346
346 Bollay Dr Goleta (93117) *(P-21336)*
Lockheed Martin Corporation ....A......408 756-5836
1111 Lockheed Martin Way Sunnyvale (94089) *(P-21337)*
Lockheed Martin Corporation ....C......858 740-5100
10325 Meanley Dr San Diego (92131) *(P-21338)*
Lockheed Martin Corporation ....B......661 572-7363
22630 Aguadero Pl Santa Clarita (91350) *(P-21339)*
Lockheed Martin Corporation ....B......408 756-3008
2655 S Macarthur Dr Tracy (95376) *(P-20599)*
Lockheed Martin Corporation ....B......408 756-4386
1643 Kitchener Dr Sunnyvale (94087) *(P-21340)*
Lockheed Martin Corporation ....F......408 742-4321
1111 Lockheed Martin Way Sunnyvale (94089) *(P-21341)*
Lockheed Martin Corporation ....B......408 742-5219
1374 Holland Ct San Jose (95118) *(P-20600)*
Lockheed Martin Corporation ....C......760 446-1700
1121 W Reeves Ave Ridgecrest (93555) *(P-21342)*
Lockheed Martin Corporation ....B......619 298-8453
1330 30th St Ste A San Diego (92154) *(P-20601)*
Lockheed Martin Naval, Ridgecrest *Also called Lockheed Martin Corporation (P-21342)*
Lockheed Martin Skunk Works ....F......661 572-2974
1001 Lockheed Way Palmdale (93599) *(P-21343)*
Lockheed Martin Space Sys, Santa Cruz *Also called Lockheed Martin Corporation (P-21335)*
Lockheed Martin Space Systems, Palo Alto *Also called Lockheed Martin Corporation (P-21327)*
Lockwood Industries LLC ....C......661 702-6999
28525 Industry Dr Valencia (91355) *(P-5567)*
Lockwood Vineyard (PA) ....F......831 642-9566
9777 Blue Larkspur Ln # 101 Monterey (93940) *(P-1863)*
Loco Ventures Inc ....E......510 351-0405
2000 Wayne Ave San Leandro (94577) *(P-680)*
Locrian Networks Inc ....F......408 988-2288
120 San Lucar Ct Sunnyvale (94086) *(P-15083)*
Loctronics Inc ....E......916 638-4900
3212 Luyung Dr Rancho Cordova (95742) *(P-18341)*
Lodestone LLC ....F......714 970-0900
4769 E Wesley Dr Anaheim (92807) *(P-14729)*

Lodestone Pacific, Anaheim *Also called R H Barden Inc (P-19357)*
Lodi Iron Works Inc (PA) ....E......209 368-5395
820 S Sacramento St Lodi (95240) *(P-11496)*
Lodi Iron Works Inc ....F......209 368-5395
609 W Amador St Galt (95632) *(P-11497)*
Lodi Mail Express, Lodi *Also called Lodi News Sentinel (P-5916)*
Lodi News Sentinel ....D......209 369-2761
125 N Church St Lodi (95240) *(P-5916)*
Log(n) LLC ....F......415 500-2558
564 Market St Ste 500 San Francisco (94104) *(P-6520)*
Logan Smith Machine Co ....F......916 632-2692
4190 Citrus Ave Rocklin (95677) *(P-16690)*
Logi Graphics Incorporated ....F......714 841-3686
17592 Metzler Ln Huntington Beach (92647) *(P-18521)*
Logic Beach Inc (PA) ....F......619 698-3300
8363 Center Dr Ste 6f La Mesa (91942) *(P-21614)*
Logic Technology Inc (PA) ....F......408 530-1007
1138 W Evelyn Ave Sunnyvale (94086) *(P-5568)*
Logical Clean Air Solutions, Westlake Village *Also called Logical Trading Co (P-20387)*
Logical Trading Co ....F......805 230-0099
3625 E Thousand Oaks Blvd Westlake Village (91362) *(P-20387)*
Logicool Inc ....E......408 907-1344
1825 De La Cruz Blvd # 201 Santa Clara (95050) *(P-24864)*
Logicube Inc (PA) ....E......818 700-8488
19755 Nordhoff Pl Chatsworth (91311) *(P-15792)*
Logisterra Inc ....E......619 280-9992
6190 Fairmount Ave Ste K San Diego (92120) *(P-10526)*
Logistical Support LLC ....C......818 341-3344
20409 Prairie St Chatsworth (91311) *(P-20668)*
Logitech Inc ....E......510 795-8500
3 Jenner Ste 180 Irvine (92618) *(P-15793)*
Logitech Inc (HQ) ....B......510 795-8500
7700 Gateway Blvd Newark (94560) *(P-15794)*
Logitech Streaming Media Inc ....E......510 795-8500
7600 Gateway Blvd Newark (94560) *(P-19627)*
Logos Plus Inc ....F......562 634-3009
8130 Rosecrans Ave Paramount (90723) *(P-3903)*
Logos Unlimited, Woodland Hills *Also called Baam Inc (P-3558)*
Lohmann Prcision Die Cutng LLC ....F......408 453-9400
1766 Junction Ave San Jose (95112) *(P-5569)*
Lois A Valeskie ....F......415 641-2570
2200 Jerrold Ave Ste K San Francisco (94124) *(P-22228)*
Loleta Cheese Company Inc ....F......707 733-5470
252 Loleta Dr Loleta (95551) *(P-590)*
Lollicup Tea Zone, Chino *Also called Lollicup USA Inc (P-5499)*
Lollicup USA Inc (PA) ....E......626 965-8882
6185 Kimball Ave Chino (91708) *(P-5499)*
Loma Linda University ....E......909 558-4552
24951 Stewart St Loma Linda (92350) *(P-6953)*
Loma Scientific International ....E......310 539-8655
3115 Kashiwa St Torrance (90505) *(P-18169)*
Loma Vista Medical Inc ....F......650 490-4747
863a Mitten Rd Ste 100a Burlingame (94010) *(P-22513)*
Lombard Enterprises Inc ....E......562 692-7070
3619 San Gbriel Rver Pkwy Pico Rivera (90660) *(P-6954)*
Lombard Graphics, Pico Rivera *Also called Lombard Enterprises Inc (P-6954)*
Lombard Medical Tech Inc (HQ) ....E......949 379-3750
6440 Oak Cyn Ste 200 Irvine (92618) *(P-22514)*
Lomeli's Gardens, Lockeford *Also called Lomelis Statuary Inc (P-11358)*
Lomelis Statuary Inc (PA) ....E......209 367-1131
11921 E Brandt Rd Lockeford (95237) *(P-11358)*
Lompoc Record, Lompoc *Also called Pulitzer Inc (P-6021)*
Lompoc Tortilla Shop, Lompoc *Also called Rodriguez Ismael (P-2400)*
Long Bar Grinding Inc ....F......562 921-1983
13121 Arctic Cir Santa Fe Springs (90670) *(P-16691)*
Long Beach Business Journal, Long Beach *Also called South Coast Publishing Inc (P-6051)*
Long Beach City of, Long Beach *Also called Stearns Park (P-5029)*
Long Beach Creamery LLC ....F......562 252-2730
4141 Long Beach Blvd Long Beach (90807) *(P-681)*
Long Beach Enterprise Inc (PA) ....F......562 944-8945
12319 Florence Ave Santa Fe Springs (90670) *(P-2315)*
Long Beach Navy Dispatch, San Diego *Also called Western States Weeklies Inc (P-6086)*
Long Beach Seafoods Co ....E......562 432-7300
4643 Hackett Ave Lakewood (90713) *(P-2316)*
Long Beach Woodworks LLC ....F......562 437-2293
1261 Highland Ave Glendale (91202) *(P-4484)*
Long Machine Inc ....E......951 296-0194
27450 Colt Ct Temecula (92590) *(P-16692)*
Long Pine Leathers, Vernon *Also called Jejomi Designs Inc (P-3616)*
Long Properties LLC (PA) ....F......209 948-4644
4651 Quail Lakes Dr Stockton (95207) *(P-13104)*
Longevity Global Inc ....E......877 566-4462
23591 Foley St Hayward (94545) *(P-14730)*
Lonix Pharmaceutical Inc ....F......626 287-4700
5001 Earle Ave Rosemead (91770) *(P-629)*
Looka Patisserie, Pacifica *Also called The French Patisserie Inc (P-1333)*
Looker Data Sciences Inc (PA) ....D......831 244-0340
101 Church St Fl 4 Santa Cruz (95060) *(P-15564)*
Lookout Enterprises Inc ....F......323 969-0178
11468 Dona Teresa Dr North Hollywood (91604) *(P-2395)*
Lopez Pallets Inc ....F......909 823-0865
11080 Redwood Ave Fontana (92337) *(P-4485)*
Lopez Water Treatment Plant ....F......805 473-7152
2845 Lopez Dr Arroyo Grande (93420) *(P-16067)*
Lor-Van Manufacturing LLC ....E......408 980-1045
3307 Edward Ave Santa Clara (95054) *(P-12642)*
Loran Inc ....E......405 340-0660
1/05 E Colton Ave Redlands (92374) *(P-17104)*

Employee Codes: A=Over 500 employees, B=251-500
C=101-250, D=51-100, E=20-50, F=10-19

2019 California
Manfacturers Register

© Mergent Inc. 1-800-342-5647
1199

A
L
P
H
A
B
E
T
I
C

Lorber Industries California......B......310 275-1568
823 N Roxbury Dr Beverly Hills (90210) ***(P-2884)***
Lorber Industries of Claif, Beverly Hills *Also called Lorber Industries California* ***(P-2884)***
Lord Leviason Enterprises LLC......E......818 453-8245
17337 Ventura Blvd Ste 10 Encino (91316) ***(P-1606)***
Lord's Light Logging, Eureka *Also called Ives Inc* ***(P-3994)***
Loren Electric Sign & Lighting, Whittier *Also called Loren Industries* ***(P-23917)***
Loren Industries......E......562 699-1122
12226 Coast Dr Whittier (90601) ***(P-23917)***
Lorenz Inc......B......760 356-1019
280 Campillo St Ste G Calexico (92231) ***(P-20007)***
Lorimar Communications, El Cajon *Also called Lorimar Group Inc* ***(P-18170)***
Lorimar Group Inc......F......619 954-9300
1488 Pioneer Way Ste 14 El Cajon (92020) ***(P-18170)***
Loritz & Associates Inc......E......714 694-0200
24895 La Palma Ave Yorba Linda (92887) ***(P-10194)***
Lormac Plastics Inc (PA)......F......760 745-9115
2225 Meyers Ave Escondido (92029) ***(P-10195)***
Lorna Jane Usa Inc (HQ)......E......310 828-0022
1674 20th St Santa Monica (90404) ***(P-3456)***
Lorom West, Fremont *Also called Cable Connection Inc* ***(P-17446)***
Lorton's Fresh Squeezed Juices, San Bernardino *Also called Juice Heads Inc* ***(P-811)***
Lortz & Son Mfg Co......C......281 241-9418
4042 Patton Way Bakersfield (93308) ***(P-13445)***
Lortz Manufacturing, Bakersfield *Also called Lortz & Son Mfg Co* ***(P-13445)***
Los Altos Town Crier, Los Altos *Also called Select Communications Inc* ***(P-6255)***
Los Angeles Ale Works LLC......F......213 422-6569
12918 Cerise Ave Hawthorne (90250) ***(P-1607)***
Los Angeles Board Mills Inc......C......323 685-8900
6027 S Eastern Ave Commerce (90040) ***(P-5354)***
Los Angeles Brass Products, Huntington Park *Also called Los Angles Pump Valve Pdts Inc* ***(P-15084)***
Los Angeles Bus Jurnl Assoc......E......323 549-5225
5700 Wilshire Blvd # 170 Los Angeles (90036) ***(P-6209)***
Los Angeles Business Journal, Los Angeles *Also called Cbj LP* ***(P-6124)***
Los Angeles Downtown News, Los Angeles *Also called Civic Center News Inc* ***(P-5806)***
Los Angeles Fiber Co, Vernon *Also called Marspring Corporation* ***(P-4871)***
Los Angeles Galvanizing Co......D......323 583-2263
2518 E 53rd St Huntington Park (90255) ***(P-13613)***
Los Angeles Ltg Mfg Co Inc......D......626 454-8300
10141 Olney St El Monte (91731) ***(P-17629)***
Los Angeles Mills Inc......E......424 307-0075
2331 E 8th St Los Angeles (90021) ***(P-2751)***
Los Angeles Plant, Cypress *Also called Hitachi Automotive Systems* ***(P-17204)***
Los Angeles Poultry Co Inc......D......323 232-3475
4816 Long Beach Ave Los Angeles (90058) ***(P-546)***
Los Angeles Ppr Box & Bd Mills, Commerce *Also called Los Angeles Board Mills Inc* ***(P-5354)***
Los Angeles Refinery, Carson *Also called Phillips 66* ***(P-9351)***
Los Angeles Refining Co......F......310 522-6000
2101 E Pacific Coast Hwy Wilmington (90744) ***(P-9338)***
Los Angeles Sales Office-North, Simi Valley *Also called Weyerhaeuser Company* ***(P-5478)***
Los Angeles Sentinel Inc......D......323 299-3800
3800 Crenshaw Blvd Los Angeles (90008) ***(P-5917)***
Los Angeles Sleeve Co Inc......E......562 945-7578
12051 Rivera Rd Santa Fe Springs (90670) ***(P-20388)***
Los Angeles Wraps, Torrance *Also called Sirena Incorporated* ***(P-7485)***
Los Angles Pump Valve Pdts Inc......E......323 277-7788
2528 E 57th St Huntington Park (90255) ***(P-15084)***
Los Angles Tmes Cmmnctions LLC (PA)......C......213 237-5000
2300 E Imperial Hwy El Segundo (90245) ***(P-5918)***
Los Angles Tmes Cmmnctions LLC......D......310 450-6666
1717 4th St Ste 100 Santa Monica (90401) ***(P-5919)***
Los Angles Tmes Cmmnctions LLC......C......213 237-7203
1245 S Longwood Ave Los Angeles (90019) ***(P-5920)***
Los Angles Tmes Cmmnctions LLC......B......714 966-5600
10540 Talbert Ave 300w Fountain Valley (92708) ***(P-5921)***
Los Angles Tmes Cmmnctions LLC......D......818 637-3203
1011 E Wilson Ave Fl 2 Glendale (91206) ***(P-5922)***
Los Angles Tmes Cmmnctions LLC......E......805 238-2720
705 Pine St Paso Robles (93446) ***(P-5923)***
Los Angles Tmes Cmmnctions LLC......F......415 274-9000
388 Market St Ste 1550 San Francisco (94111) ***(P-5924)***
Los Angles Tmes Cmmnctions LLC......E......818 790-8774
1061 Valley Sun Ln La Canada Flintridge (91011) ***(P-5925)***
Los Angles Tmes Cmmnctions LLC......E......951 683-6066
10427 San Sevaine Way E Mira Loma (91752) ***(P-5926)***
Los Angles Tmes Cmmnctions LLC......E......213 237-7987
145 S Spring St Los Angeles (90012) ***(P-5927)***
Los Angles Tmes Cmmnctions LLC......C......213 237-5691
2000 E 8th St Los Angeles (90021) ***(P-5928)***
Los Angles Tmes Cmmnctions LLC......E......909 980-3707
5091 4th St Baldwin Park (91706) ***(P-5929)***
Los Angles Tmes Cmmnctions LLC......E......909 980-3707
5555 Ontario Mills Pkwy F Ontario (91764) ***(P-5930)***
Los Angles Tmes Cmmnctions LLC......F......310 638-9414
2001 E Cashdan St Compton (90220) ***(P-5931)***
Los Banos Abattoir Co Inc......E......209 826-2212
1312 W Pacheco Blvd Los Banos (93635) ***(P-442)***
Los Banos Enterprise, Los Banos *Also called McClatchy Newspapers Inc* ***(P-5948)***
Los Banos Rock and Ready Mix, Los Banos *Also called Azusa Rock Inc* ***(P-11048)***
Los Cabos Mexican Foods, Santa Fe Springs *Also called M C I Foods Inc* ***(P-2591)***
Los Gatos Tomato Products LLC (PA)......E......559 945-2700
7041 N Van Ness Blvd Fresno (93711) ***(P-821)***
Los Olivos Packaging Inc (PA)......C......323 261-2218
929 Ridgecrest St Monterey Park (91754) ***(P-822)***
Los Pericos Food Products LLC......E......909 623-5625
2301 Valley Blvd Pomona (91768) ***(P-2588)***
Lost Art Liquids, Los Angeles *Also called Lost Art Liquids LLC* ***(P-24165)***
Lost Art Liquids LLC......F......213 816-2988
155 W Washington Blvd Los Angeles (90015) ***(P-24165)***
Lost Coast Brewery & Cafe, Eureka *Also called Table Bluff Brewing Inc* ***(P-1628)***
Lost Dutchmans Minings Assn (HQ)......E......951 699-4749
43445 Bus Pk Dr Ste 113 Temecula (92590) ***(P-6)***
Lost International LLC......F......949 600-6950
170 Technology Dr Irvine (92618) ***(P-3176)***
Lostcost, Eureka *Also called Table Bluff Brewing Inc* ***(P-1629)***
Lotus Beverages......F......213 216-1434
2542 San Gabriel Blvd Rosemead (91770) ***(P-1864)***
Lotus Hygiene Systems Inc......E......714 259-8805
1621 E Saint Andrew Pl Santa Ana (92705) ***(P-10806)***
Lotus Labels, Brea *Also called President Enterprise Inc* ***(P-7442)***
Lotus Orient Corp (PA)......F......626 285-5796
411 S California St San Gabriel (91776) ***(P-3326)***
Lotusflare Inc......F......626 695-5634
530 Lakeside Dr Ste 130 Sunnyvale (94085) ***(P-24865)***
Lotusse LLC......E......909 218-7757
10700 Jersey Blvd Ste 610 Rancho Cucamonga (91730) ***(P-10464)***
Lou Ana Foods, Brea *Also called Ventura Foods LLC* ***(P-1553)***
Loud Mouth Inc......E......619 743-0370
3840 Edna Pl Apt 1 San Diego (92116) ***(P-23609)***
Louden Madelon, Vernon *Also called National Corset Supply House* ***(P-3540)***
Louidar LLC......E......951 676-5047
33820 Rancho Cal Rd Temecula (92591) ***(P-1865)***
Louie Foods International......F......559 264-2745
471 S Teilman Ave Fresno (93706) ***(P-2589)***
Louis Levin & Son Inc......F......562 802-8066
13550 Larwin Cir Santa Fe Springs (90670) ***(P-14442)***
Louis M. Martini Winery, Saint Helena *Also called E & J Gallo Winery* ***(P-1747)***
Louis Roesch Company......F......650 212-2052
289 Foster City Blvd B Foster City (94404) ***(P-6955)***
Louis Sardo Upholstery Inc (PA)......D......310 327-0532
512 W Rosecrans Ave Gardena (90248) ***(P-5020)***
Louis Vuitton US Mfg Inc......F......909 599-2411
321 W Covina Blvd San Dimas (91773) ***(P-10566)***
Louis W Osborn Co., La Mirada *Also called Headwaters Construction Inc* ***(P-10757)***
Louise Green Millinery Co Inc......F......310 479-1881
1616 Cotner Ave Los Angeles (90025) ***(P-3567)***
Lounge Fly, Chatsworth *Also called Loungefly LLC* ***(P-23753)***
Loungefly LLC......E......818 718-5600
20310 Plummer St Chatsworth (91311) ***(P-23753)***
Love In, Los Angeles *Also called Bereshith Inc* ***(P-3216)***
Love Marks Inc (PA)......F......323 859-8770
2050 E 51st St Vernon (90058) ***(P-3254)***
Love Stitch, Los Angeles *Also called Clothing Illustrated Inc* ***(P-3395)***
Low Voltage Architecture Inc......E......310 573-7588
11715 San Vicente Blvd Los Angeles (90049) ***(P-20008)***
Lowers Industrial Supply, Santa Fe Springs *Also called Lowers Wldg & Fabrication Inc* ***(P-16693)***
Lowers Wldg & Fabrication Inc......F......562 946-4521
10847 Painter Ave Santa Fe Springs (90670) ***(P-16693)***
Lowpensky Moulding......F......415 822-7422
900 Palou Ave San Francisco (94124) ***(P-4184)***
Loyyal Corporation......F......415 419-9590
44 Tehama St Fl 5 San Francisco (94105) ***(P-24866)***
Lozano Enterprises, Los Angeles *Also called La Opinion LP* ***(P-5904)***
Lpa Insurance Agency Inc......D......916 286-7850
4030 Truxel Rd Ste B Sacramento (95834) ***(P-24867)***
Lpcc 6008, Ontario *Also called Leggett & Platt Incorporated* ***(P-4868)***
Lpj Aerospace LLC......F......310 834-5700
741 E 223rd St Carson (90745) ***(P-20869)***
Lpn Wireless Inc......F......707 781-9210
4170 Redwood Hwy San Rafael (94903) ***(P-18171)***
Lps Agency Sales and Posting......E......714 247-7500
3210 El Camino Real # 200 Irvine (92602) ***(P-7390)***
LR Baggs Corporation......E......805 929-3545
483 N Frontage Rd Nipomo (93444) ***(P-23379)***
Lrad Corporation (PA)......E......858 676-1112
16262 W Bernardo Dr San Diego (92127) ***(P-17825)***
Lrb Millwork & Casework Inc......F......951 328-0105
2760 S Iowa Ave Colton (92324) ***(P-5081)***
Lrc Coil Company, Santa Fe Springs *Also called Lmw Enterprises LLC* ***(P-15968)***
LSI Corporation (HQ)......A......408 433-8000
1320 Ridder Park Dr San Jose (95131) ***(P-18968)***
LSI Corporation......E......619 312-0903
9745 Prospect Ave Santee (92071) ***(P-18969)***
LSI Corporation......E......800 372-2447
2 Park Plz Ste 440 Irvine (92614) ***(P-18970)***
LSI Corporation......F......408 436-8379
1310 Ridder Park Dr San Jose (95131) ***(P-18971)***
LSI Logic, Irvine *Also called LSI Corporation* ***(P-18970)***
LSI Products Inc......D......951 343-9270
12885 Wildflower Ln Riverside (92503) ***(P-20389)***
Lsl Instruments, Santa Clarita *Also called Manzanita* ***(P-23380)***
Lso, San Diego *Also called Cri 2000 LP* ***(P-4617)***
Lspace America LLC......E......949 596-8726
9821 Irvine Center Dr Irvine (92618) ***(P-3255)***
Lt Security Inc (PA)......E......626 435-2838
18738 San Jose Ave City of Industry (91748) ***(P-20009)***
Ltd Tech Inc......F......805 480-1886
2630 Lavery Ct Ste B Newbury Park (91320) ***(P-14758)***
LTI, Irvine *Also called Lens Technology I LLC* ***(P-22097)***

Mergent e-mail: customerrelations@mergent.com 2019 California (P-0000) Products & Services Section entry number
1200 Manufacturers Register (PA)=Parent Co (HQ)=Headquarters (DH)=Div Headquarters

LTI Boyd A 800 554-0200
600 S Mcclure Rd Modesto (95357) ***(P-14759)***

LTI Holdings Inc (HQ) F 209 236-1111
600 S Mcclure Rd Modesto (95357) ***(P-7907)***

Ltr, South Gate *Also called Lunday-Thagard Company* ***(P-9456)***

Lubeco Inc E 562 602-1791
6859 Downey Ave Long Beach (90805) ***(P-9441)***

Lubricating Specialties Co (PA) C 562 776-4000
8015 Paramount Blvd Pico Rivera (90660) ***(P-9442)***

Lubricating Specialties Co E 562 776-4000
3365 E Slauson Ave Vernon (90058) ***(P-9443)***

Lubrication Scientifics Inc F 714 557-0664
17651 Armstrong Ave Irvine (92614) ***(P-13724)***

Lubrication Scientifics LLC E 714 557-0664
17651 Armstrong Ave Irvine (92614) ***(P-15339)***

Lubrigreen, Irvine *Also called Biosynthetic Technologies LLC* ***(P-14838)***

LUBRIZOL ADVANCED MATERIALS, INC., Paso Robles *Also called Lubrizol Advanced Mtls Inc* ***(P-9274)***

Lubrizol Advanced Mtls Inc D 805 239-1550
3115 Propeller Dr Paso Robles (93446) ***(P-9274)***

Lubrizol Corporation F 949 212-1863
30211 Ave D Las Bandras Rancho Santa Margari (92688) ***(P-9275)***

Luca International Group LLC (PA) F 510 498-8829
39650 Liberty St Ste 490 Fremont (94538) ***(P-139)***

Lucas Labs, Gilroy *Also called Lucas/Signatone Corporation* ***(P-21794)***

Lucas Oil Products Inc (PA) C 951 270-0154
302 N Sheridan St Corona (92880) ***(P-9444)***

Lucas/Signatone Corporation (PA) E 408 848-2851
393 Tomkins Ct Ste J Gilroy (95020) ***(P-21794)***

Luce Communications LLC E 951 361-7404
3810 Wabash Dr Mira Loma (91752) ***(P-6956)***

Lucerne Foods Inc E 925 951-4724
5918 Stoneridge Mall Rd Pleasanton (94588) ***(P-2590)***

Lucero Cables Inc C 408 536-0340
193 Stauffer Blvd San Jose (95125) ***(P-19628)***

Lucero Olive Oil Mnfacture LLC (PA) E 530 824-2190
2120 Loleta Ave Corning (96021) ***(P-1543)***

Lucid Motors, Inc, Newark *Also called Atieva Usa Inc* ***(P-20127)***

Lucidport Technology Inc F 408 720-8800
19287 San Marcos Rd Saratoga (95070) ***(P-17481)***

Lucious Jewels F 760 779-1304
10 Via Dulcinea Palm Desert (92260) ***(P-23289)***

Lucix Corporation (HQ) D 805 987-6645
800 Avenida Acaso Ste E Camarillo (93012) ***(P-19629)***

Lucky Brand Dungarees LLC E 310 587-3515
1427 3rd S Santa Monica (90401) ***(P-3082)***

Lucky Brand Dungarees LLC (HQ) D 213 443-5700
540 S Santa Fe Ave Los Angeles (90013) ***(P-3083)***

Lucky Devil LLC F 714 990-2237
431 Atlas St Brea (92821) ***(P-7391)***

Lucky Foods, San Francisco *Also called Sin MA Imports Company* ***(P-1101)***

Lucky Luke Brewing Company F 661 270-5588
610 W Avenue O Ste 104 Palmdale (93551) ***(P-1608)***

Lucky Picture Frame Co Inc E 323 583-6710
1948 Mairemont Dr Walnut (91789) ***(P-4633)***

Lucky Star Silkscreen LLC E 323 728-4071
5767 E Washington Blvd Commerce (90040) ***(P-7392)***

Lucky Strike Entertainment Inc (PA) E 818 933-3752
15260 Ventura Blvd # 1110 Sherman Oaks (91403) ***(P-23610)***

Lucky-13 Apparel, Costa Mesa *Also called Blue Sphere Inc* ***(P-3026)***

Lucy Ann, Torrance *Also called Obatake Inc* ***(P-23304)***

Lufft Usa Inc F 805 335-8500
1110 Eugenia Pl Ste 200 Carpinteria (93013) ***(P-22229)***

Lufkin Industries LLC F 661 746-0792
31127 Coberly Rd Shafter (93263) ***(P-13105)***

Lugos of California Inc E 323 582-5164
7719 Cecilia St Downey (90241) ***(P-3457)***

Luis Wtkins Cstm Wrught Ir LLC E 310 836-5655
3737 S Durango Ave Los Angeles (90034) ***(P-4836)***

Luma Comfort LLC E 855 963-9247
6600 Katella Ave Cypress (90630) ***(P-17396)***

Lumar Metals, Pomona *Also called Lur Inc* ***(P-12876)***

Lumascape USA Inc F 650 595-5862
1300 Industrial Rd Ste 19 San Carlos (94070) ***(P-17630)***

Lumasense Tech Holdings Inc (HQ) D 408 727-1600
3301 Leonard Ct Santa Clara (95054) ***(P-23001)***

Lumatronix Mfg Inc F 408 435-7820
1141 Ringwood Ct Ste 150 San Jose (95131) ***(P-17346)***

Lumenetix Inc E 877 805-7284
4742 Scotts Valley Dr Scotts Valley (95066) ***(P-18972)***

Lumenis, Livermore *Also called Rh Usa Inc* ***(P-22606)***

Lumenis Inc (HQ) C 408 764-3000
2077 Gateway Pl Ste 300 San Jose (95110) ***(P-22515)***

Lumens Audio Visual Inc F 970 988-6268
127 27th St Apt A Newport Beach (92663) ***(P-18342)***

Lumens Integration Inc F 510 657-8367
4116 Clipper Ct Fremont (94538) ***(P-23176)***

Lumenton Inc E 323 904-0202
5461 W Jefferson Blvd Los Angeles (90016) ***(P-17709)***

Lumenton Lighting, Los Angeles *Also called Lumenton Inc* ***(P-17709)***

Lumentum Holdings Inc (PA) C 408 546-5483
400 N Mccarthy Blvd Milpitas (95035) ***(P-18343)***

Lumentum Operations LLC (HQ) C 408 546-5483
400 N Mccarthy Blvd Milpitas (95035) ***(P-18344)***

Lumentum Operations LLC F 408 546-5483
1750 Automation Pkwy # 400 San Jose (95131) ***(P-22100)***

Lumenyte International Corp F 949 279-8687
535 4th St San Fernando (91340) ***(P-17710)***

Lumigrow Inc E 800 514-0487
1480 64th St Ste 150 Emeryville (94608) ***(P-17631)***

Lumileds LLC (HQ) E 408 964-2900
370 W Trimble Rd San Jose (95131) ***(P-21795)***

Luminar Creations E 818 843-0010
420 N Moss St Burbank (91502) ***(P-23290)***

Lumination Lighting & Tech Inc C 855 283-1100
1515 240th St Harbor City (90710) ***(P-17632)***

Luminit LLC E 310 320-1066
1850 W 205th St Torrance (90501) ***(P-22101)***

Luminus Inc (HQ) C 408 708-7000
1145 Sonora Ct Sunnyvale (94086) ***(P-17633)***

Luminus Devices Inc E 978 528-8000
1145 Sonora Ct Sunnyvale (94086) ***(P-17711)***

Lumio Inc F 586 861-2408
6355 Topanga Canyon Blvd # 335 Woodland Hills (91367) ***(P-18973)***

Lumistar Inc (HQ) F 760 431-2181
2270 Camino Vida Roble L Carlsbad (92011) ***(P-18522)***

Luna Imaging Inc F 323 908-1400
2702 Media Center Dr Los Angeles (90065) ***(P-24868)***

Luna Mora LLC F 310 550-6979
1240 S Corning St Apt 306 Los Angeles (90035) ***(P-3904)***

Luna Sciences Corporation F 949 225-0000
18218 Mcdurmott E Ste A Irvine (92614) ***(P-17545)***

Luna Vineyards Inc E 707 255-2474
2921 Silverado Trl NAPA (94558) ***(P-1866)***

Lunas Sheet Metal Inc F 408 492-1260
3125 Molinaro St Ste 102 Santa Clara (95054) ***(P-12643)***

Lund Motion Products Inc E 949 221-0023
15651 Mosher Ave Tustin (92780) ***(P-20390)***

Lunday-Thagard Company (HQ) C 562 928-7000
9302 Garfield Ave South Gate (90280) ***(P-9456)***

Lunday-Thagard Company E 562 928-6990
9301 Garfield Ave South Gate (90280) ***(P-9412)***

Lundberg Designs, San Francisco *Also called Thomas Lundberg* ***(P-4844)***

Lundberg Family Farms, Richvale *Also called Wehah Farm Inc* ***(P-1094)***

Lundberg Studios Inc E 831 423-2532
131 Old Coast Rd Davenport (95017) ***(P-10715)***

Lundberg Survey Inc E 805 383-2400
911 Via Alondra Camarillo (93012) ***(P-6210)***

Lupitas Bakery Inc (PA) F 323 752-2391
1848 W Florence Ave Los Angeles (90047) ***(P-1286)***

Luppen Holdings Inc (PA) E 323 581-8121
3050 Leonis Blvd Vernon (90058) ***(P-13243)***

Lur Inc F 909 623-4999
599 S East End Ave Pomona (91766) ***(P-12876)***

Luran Inc F 661 257-6303
24927 Avenue Tibbitts K Valencia (91355) ***(P-16694)***

Lusk Quality Machine Products E 661 272-0630
39457 15th St E Palmdale (93550) ***(P-16695)***

Luster Cote Inc F 909 355-9995
10841 Business Dr Fontana (92337) ***(P-13614)***

Lustre-Cal Nameplate Corp D 209 370-1600
715 S Guild Ave Lodi (95240) ***(P-12984)***

Luther E Gibson Inc E 707 643-6104
544 Curtola Pkwy Vallejo (94590) ***(P-6211)***

Luus Family Corp E 209 466-1952
302 S San Joaquin St Stockton (95203) ***(P-547)***

Luxe Laboratory F 714 221-2330
7052 Orangewood Ave Ste 8 Garden Grove (92841) ***(P-23107)***

Luxfer Gas Cylinder, Riverside *Also called Luxfer Inc* ***(P-20870)***

Luxfer Inc (HQ) D 336 578-4515
3016 Kansas Ave Bldg 1 Riverside (92507) ***(P-20870)***

Luxfer Inc C 951 684-5110
1995 3rd St Riverside (92507) ***(P-11593)***

Luxfer Inc E 951 351-4100
6825 Jurupa Ave Riverside (92504) ***(P-13126)***

Luxfer-GTM Technologies LLC (PA) E 415 856-0570
1619 Shattuck Ave Berkeley (94709) ***(P-12396)***

Luxor Industries International E 909 469-4757
1250 E Franklin Ave Pomona (91766) ***(P-4185)***

Luxtera Inc C 760 448-3520
2320 Camino Vida Roble # 100 Carlsbad (92011) ***(P-18974)***

Lvusm, San Dimas *Also called Louis Vuitton US Mfg Inc* ***(P-10566)***

Lw Consulting Services LLC F 650 919-3001
13292 Rhoda Dr Los Altos Hills (94022) ***(P-24869)***

Ly Brothers Corporation (PA) E 510 782-2118
1963 Sabre St Hayward (94545) ***(P-1287)***

Ly Brothers Corporation C 510 782-2118
20389 Corsair Blvd Hayward (94545) ***(P-1288)***

Lynam Industries Inc D 951 360-1919
13050 Santa Ana Ave Fontana (92337) ***(P-12644)***

Lyncean Technologies Inc F 650 320-8300
44755 S Grimmer Blvd B Fremont (94538) ***(P-22935)***

Lynch Ready Mix Concrete Co F 805 647-2817
11011 Azahar St Ste 4 Ventura (93004) ***(P-11138)***

Lynco Grinding Company Inc F 562 927-2631
5950 Clara St Bell (90201) ***(P-16696)***

Lyncole Grunding Solutions LLC E 310 214-4000
3547 Voyager St Ste 204 Torrance (90503) ***(P-17482)***

Lyncole Xit Grounding, Torrance *Also called Lyncole Grunding Solutions LLC* ***(P-17482)***

Lynde-Ordway Company Inc F 714 957-1311
3308 W Warner Ave Santa Ana (92704) ***(P-15907)***

Lynex Company Inc F 408 778-7884
375 Digital Dr Morgan Hill (95037) ***(P-8791)***

Lynn Lugo, Downey *Also called Lugos of California Inc* ***(P-3457)***

Lynn Products Inc A 310 530-5966
2645 W 237th St Torrance (90505) ***(P-15795)***

Lynwood Pattern Service Inc F 310 631-2225
2528 E 127th St Compton (90222) ***(P-11745)***

ALPHABETIC

Employee Codes: A=Over 500 employees, B=251-500
C=101-250, D=51-100, E=20-50, F=10-19
2019 California
Manfacturers Register
© Mergent Inc. 1-800-342-5647
1201

Lynx Enterprises Inc ....D....209 833-3400
724 E Grant Line Rd Ste B Tracy (95304) ***(P-12645)***
Lynx Grills Inc (HQ) ....F....323 722-4324
7300 Flores St Downey (90242) ***(P-17371)***
Lynx Grills Inc ....F....323 838-1770
7300 Flores St Downey (90242) ***(P-17372)***
Lynx Phtnic Ntworks A Del Corp ....F....818 878-7500
6303 Owensmouth Ave Fl 10 Woodland Hills (91367) ***(P-17962)***
Lynx Software Technologies Inc (PA) ....D....408 979-3900
855 Embedded Way San Jose (95138) ***(P-24870)***
Lynx Studio Technology Inc ....F....714 545-4700
190 Mccormick Ave Costa Mesa (92626) ***(P-17826)***
Lyon Technologies Inc ....E....619 216-3400
1690 Brandywine Ave Ste A Chula Vista (91911) ***(P-14083)***
Lyons Magnus Inc (PA) ....B....559 268-5966
3158 E Hamilton Ave Fresno (93702) ***(P-823)***
Lyons Magnus Inc ....E....559 268-5966
1636 S 2nd St Fresno (93702) ***(P-824)***
Lyra Corporation ....F....415 668-2546
1802 Hays St San Francisco (94129) ***(P-6521)***
Lyric Culture LLC ....F....323 581-3511
2520 W 6th St Ste 250 Los Angeles (90057) ***(P-3256)***
Lyrical Foods Inc ....C....510 784-0955
3180 Corporate Pl Hayward (94545) ***(P-591)***
Lyris Inc ....E....800 768-2929
4 N 2nd St Fl 11 San Jose (95113) ***(P-24871)***
Lyru Engineering Inc ....F....510 357-5951
965 San Leandro Blvd San Leandro (94577) ***(P-16697)***
Lyten Inc ....F....650 400-5635
933 Kifer Rd Ste B Sunnyvale (94086) ***(P-14985)***
Lytx Inc (PA) ....B....858 430-4000
9785 Towne Centre Dr San Diego (92121) ***(P-21344)***
M & A Custom Doors, Harbor City *Also called Joanka Inc* ***(P-12323)***
M & A Plastics Inc ....E....818 768-0479
11735 Sheldon St Sun Valley (91352) ***(P-10196)***
M & B Window Fashions, Los Angeles *Also called Hd Window Fashions Inc* ***(P-5192)***
M & G Custom Polishing ....F....714 995-0261
8356 Standustrial St Stanton (90680) ***(P-13446)***
M & H Creative Design Inc ....F....213 627-8881
550 S Hill St Ste 1030 Los Angeles (90013) ***(P-23291)***
M & H Type Composition & Fndry, San Francisco *Also called Lyra Corporation* ***(P-6521)***
M & K Builders Inc ....F....209 478-7531
3212 Bixby Way Stockton (95209) ***(P-12940)***
M & L Haight LLC ....E....951 587-2267
42192 Sarah Way Temecula (92590) ***(P-10575)***
M & L Pharmaceuticals Inc ....F....909 890-0078
629 S Allen St San Bernardino (92408) ***(P-8265)***
M & L Precision Machining Inc (PA) ....E....408 436-3955
18665 Madrone Pkwy Morgan Hill (95037) ***(P-16698)***
M & M Logging Inc ....F....530 938-0745
7800 N Old Stage Rd Weed (96094) ***(P-3999)***
M & M Machine & Tool, Auburn *Also called Mitchell-Duckett Corporation* ***(P-16758)***
M & M Printed Bag Inc ....E....909 393-5537
5651 Kimball Ct Chino (91710) ***(P-5606)***
M & M Sportswear Manufacturing ....F....209 984-5632
18267 4th Ave Jamestown (95327) ***(P-2848)***
M & O Perry Industries Inc ....E....951 734-9838
412 N Smith Ave Corona (92880) ***(P-15216)***
M & R Engineering Co ....F....714 991-8480
227 E Meats Ave Orange (92865) ***(P-16699)***
M & R Plating Corporation ....F....818 896-2700
12375 Montague St Arleta (91331) ***(P-13447)***
M & W Engineering Inc ....E....530 676-7185
3880 Dividend Dr Ste 100 Shingle Springs (95682) ***(P-16700)***
M & W Machine Corporation ....F....714 541-2652
1642 E Edinger Ave Ste A Santa Ana (92705) ***(P-16701)***
M and M Apparel, Chino *Also called M and M Sports* ***(P-3851)***
M and M Cabinets Inc ....F....510 324-4034
33238 Central Ave Union City (94587) ***(P-4326)***
M and M Sports ....F....909 548-3371
14288 Central Ave Ste A Chino (91710) ***(P-3851)***
M and W Glass ....E....909 517-3585
10745 Vernon Ave Ontario (91762) ***(P-10716)***
M Argeso & Co Inc ....F....626 573-3000
2628 River Ave Rosemead (91770) ***(P-9339)***
M B C Reprographics Inc ....E....858 541-1500
5560 Ruffin Rd Ste 5 San Diego (92123) ***(P-7393)***
M B I Ready-Mix L L C ....E....530 346-2432
44 Central St Colfax (95713) ***(P-11139)***
M B S Inc ....F....714 693-9952
18514 Yorba Linda Blvd Yorba Linda (92886) ***(P-19812)***
M C C, Torrance *Also called Medical Chemical Corporation* ***(P-9279)***
M C E, Salinas *Also called Magnetic Circuit Elements Inc* ***(P-19633)***
M C E, Torrance *Also called Magnetic Component Engrg Inc* ***(P-13956)***
M C I Foods Inc ....C....562 977-4000
13013 Molette St Santa Fe Springs (90670) ***(P-2591)***
M C I Manufacturing Inc (PA) ....E....408 456-2700
1020 Rock Ave San Jose (95131) ***(P-12646)***
M C Metal Inc ....F....415 822-2288
1347 Donner Ave San Francisco (94124) ***(P-12877)***
M C O Inc ....F....909 627-3574
13925 Benson Ave Chino (91710) ***(P-20391)***
M C Woodwork ....F....323 233-0954
747 E 60th St Los Angeles (90001) ***(P-4486)***
M D D, Burbank *Also called US Steel Rule Dies Inc* ***(P-14586)***
M D H Burner & Boiler Co Inc ....F....562 630-2875
12106 Center St South Gate (90280) ***(P-15165)***
M D Resource, Livermore *Also called Medical Device Resource Corp* ***(P-22525)***
M D Software Inc ....F....909 881-7599
1226 E 42nd Pl San Bernardino (92404) ***(P-24872)***
M DAmico Inc ....E....619 390-5858
12650 Highway 67 Ste E Lakeside (92040) ***(P-5244)***
M E D Inc ....D....562 921-0464
14001 Marquardt Ave Santa Fe Springs (90670) ***(P-20392)***
M E I, Santa Barbara *Also called Motion Engineering Inc* ***(P-15808)***
M E T, Murrieta *Also called Medical Extrusion Tech Inc* ***(P-9742)***
M F G Eurotec Inc ....E....760 863-0033
84464 Cabazon Center Dr Indio (92201) ***(P-4716)***
M F G West, Adelanto *Also called Molded Fiber GL Companies - W* ***(P-10220)***
M G A Investment Co Inc ....F....805 543-9050
3211 Broad St Ste 201 San Luis Obispo (93401) ***(P-6522)***
M G Deanza Acquisition Inc ....F....951 683-3080
4010 Garner Rd Riverside (92501) ***(P-16702)***
M G Generon, Pittsburg *Also called Generon Igs Inc* ***(P-15325)***
M G Industries Inc ....F....562 436-9095
1427 W 16th St Long Beach (90813) ***(P-9542)***
M G Industries Inc Gaskts, Long Beach *Also called M G Industries Inc* ***(P-9542)***
M G Watanabe Inc ....F....562 402-8989
17031 Roseton Ave Artesia (90701) ***(P-18172)***
M Group Inc ....E....843 221-7830
9808 Venice Blvd Ste 706 Culver City (90232) ***(P-10527)***
M I E, Temecula *Also called Molding Intl & Engrg Inc* ***(P-10222)***
M I P, Covina *Also called Moores Ideal Products LLC* ***(P-23448)***
M I T Inc ....F....714 899-6066
15202 Pipeline Ln Huntington Beach (92649) ***(P-14536)***
M K Products Inc ....D....949 798-1425
16882 Armstrong Ave Irvine (92606) ***(P-14731)***
M Klemme Technology Corp ....F....760 727-0593
1384 Poinsettia Ave Ste F Vista (92081) ***(P-17827)***
M L Interiors Inc ....E....949 723-5001
151 Shipyard Way Ste 4 Newport Beach (92663) ***(P-3695)***
M L Z Inc ....F....562 436-3540
1800 W 9th St Long Beach (90813) ***(P-13244)***
M M Book Bindery ....F....310 532-0780
1826 W 169th St Gardena (90247) ***(P-7607)***
M M P, Long Beach *Also called Maruhide Marine Products Inc* ***(P-2317)***
M M S, Montclair *Also called Micro Matrix Systems* ***(P-13251)***
M N Enterprises, San Diego *Also called Mohammad Khan* ***(P-10218)***
M N M Manufacturing Inc ....D....310 898-1099
3019 E Harcourt St Compton (90221) ***(P-12329)***
M Nexon Inc ....E....213 858-5930
222 N Pacific Coast Hwy # 300 El Segundo (90245) ***(P-24873)***
M O S Plastics, San Jose *Also called Kennerley-Spratling Inc* ***(P-10177)***
M P A, Ione *Also called Mp Associates Inc* ***(P-9183)***
M P C Industrial Products Inc ....E....949 863-0106
2150 Mcgaw Ave Irvine (92614) ***(P-13448)***
M P C Industries, Irvine *Also called M P C Industrial Products Inc* ***(P-13448)***
M P I, San Jose *Also called Micro-Probe Incorporated* ***(P-21805)***
M P M Building Services Inc ....D....818 708-9676
7011 Hayvenhurst Ave F Van Nuys (91406) ***(P-8653)***
M P S, Escondido *Also called Manufacturing & Prod Svcs Corp* ***(P-20395)***
M R F Techniques Inc ....F....408 433-1941
2245b Fortune Dr Ste B San Jose (95131) ***(P-19630)***
M R S Foods Inc (PA) ....D....714 554-2791
4408 W 5th St Santa Ana (92703) ***(P-2592)***
M S E, Burbank *Also called Matthews Studio Equipment Inc* ***(P-23177)***
M S E Media Solutions, Commerce *Also called MSE Media Solutions* ***(P-19873)***
M S F Inc ....F....650 592-0239
1100 Industrial Rd Ste 18 San Carlos (94070) ***(P-5151)***
M Stevens Inc ....F....323 661-2147
1925 Blake Ave Los Angeles (90039) ***(P-3458)***
M T S, Bakersfield *Also called MTS Stimulation Services Inc* ***(P-241)***
M V Outer Limits ....F....858 689-1828
11464 Eastridge Pl San Diego (92131) ***(P-21051)***
M W Reid Welding Inc ....D....619 401-5880
781 Oconner St El Cajon (92020) ***(P-12198)***
M Wave Design Corporation ....F....805 499-8825
94 W Cochran St Ste B Simi Valley (93065) ***(P-19631)***
M&G Duravent Inc (HQ) ....B....707 446-1786
877 Cotting Ct Vacaville (95688) ***(P-12647)***
M&L Metals Inc ....F....510 732-1745
25362 Cypress Ave Hayward (94544) ***(P-12648)***
M-5 Steel Mfg Inc (PA) ....E....323 263-9383
1450 Mirasol St Los Angeles (90023) ***(P-12397)***
M-I LLC ....E....661 321-5400
4400 Fanucchi Way Shafter (93263) ***(P-235)***
M-Pulse Microwave Inc ....E....408 432-1480
576 Charcot Ave San Jose (95131) ***(P-18975)***
M-T Metal Fabrications Inc ....F....510 357-5262
536 Lewelling Blvd Ste A San Leandro (94579) ***(P-12649)***
M2 Antenna Systems Inc ....F....559 221-2271
4402 N Selland Ave Fresno (93722) ***(P-19632)***
M2 Marketplace Inc ....F....310 354-3600
2555 W 190th St 201 Torrance (90504) ***(P-15445)***
M29 Technology and Design ....F....805 489-9402
133 Bridge St Ste B Arroyo Grande (93420) ***(P-24874)***
M3 Products Inc ....F....626 371-1900
335 N Puente St Ste E Brea (92821) ***(P-5152)***
M360, San Francisco *Also called Medicines360* ***(P-8271)***
MA Cher (usa) Inc (HQ) ....F....310 581-5222
1518 Abbot Kinney Blvd Venice (90291) ***(P-24166)***
Maas-Rowe Carillons Inc ....E....760 743-1311
2255 Meyers Ave Escondido (92029) ***(P-20010)***
Mabel Baas Inc ....E....805 520-8075
3960 Royal Ave Simi Valley (93063) ***(P-13615)***

Mergent e-mail: customerrelations@mergent.com
1202
2019 California
Manufacturers Register
(P-0000) Products & Services Section entry number
(PA)=Parent Co (HQ)=Headquarters (DH)=Div Headquarters

Mabrey Products Inc...F...530 895-3799
200 Ryan Ave Chico (95973) ***(P-4186)***
Mabvax Thrpeutics Holdings Inc (PA)...F...858 259-9405
11535 Sorrento Valley Rd San Diego (92121) ***(P-8266)***
Mac Cal Company...D...408 441-1435
1737 Junction Ave San Jose (95112) ***(P-12650)***
Mac Cal Manufacturing, San Jose *Also called Mac Cal Company* ***(P-12650)***
Mac Donald, Richard Galleries, Monterey *Also called Richard Macdonald Studios Inc* ***(P-11369)***
Mac Engineering & Components...F...408 286-3030
5122 Calle Del Sol Santa Clara (95054) ***(P-11972)***
Mac M McCully Co, Moorpark *Also called Mc Cully Mac M Corporation* ***(P-17210)***
Mac Performance Exhaust, Temecula *Also called MAC Products Inc* ***(P-11406)***
MAC Products Inc...D...951 296-3077
43214 Black Deer Loop # 113 Temecula (92590) ***(P-11406)***
Mac Publishing LLC (HQ)...E...415 243-0505
501 2nd St Ste 500 San Francisco (94107) ***(P-6212)***
Mac Thin Films Inc...E...707 791-1650
2721 Giffen Ave Santa Rosa (95407) ***(P-10717)***
Macdermid Prtg Solutions LLC...D...760 510-6277
260 S Pacific St San Marcos (92078) ***(P-14817)***
Macdonald Carbide Co...E...626 960-4034
4510 Littlejohn St Baldwin Park (91706) ***(P-14537)***
Macdonald Screen Print, Modesto *Also called Sign Designs Inc* ***(P-23962)***
Macgregor Yacht Corporation...D...310 621-2206
1631 Placentia Ave Costa Mesa (92627) ***(P-21052)***
Mach Oil Corp...F...818 783-3567
17835 Ventura Blvd # 301 Encino (91316) ***(P-9445)***
Machinables Inc...F...415 216-9467
1101 Cowper St Berkeley (94702) ***(P-15796)***
Machine Arts Incorporated...F...805 965-5344
2105 S Hathaway St Santa Ana (92705) ***(P-16703)***
Machine Building Specialties...E...323 666-8289
1977 Blake Ave Los Angeles (90039) ***(P-14868)***
Machine Control Tech Inc...F...951 808-0973
210 Crouse Dr Corona (92879) ***(P-21796)***
Machine Control Tech Inc...F...951 808-0973
210 Crouse Dr Corona (92879) ***(P-17150)***
Machine Craft of San Diego...E...858 642-0509
9822 Waples St San Diego (92121) ***(P-16704)***
Machine Exprnce & Design Inc...E...559 291-7710
2964 Phillip Ave Clovis (93612) ***(P-16705)***
Machine Precision Components...F...562 404-0500
14014 Dinard Ave Santa Fe Springs (90670) ***(P-16706)***
Machine Vision Products Inc (PA)...D...760 438-1138
3270 Corporate Vw Ste D Vista (92081) ***(P-22102)***
Machinetek LLC...F...760 438-6644
1985 Palomar Oaks Way Carlsbad (92011) ***(P-20871)***
Machining and Frame Division, San Jose *Also called Mass Precision Inc* ***(P-12654)***
Machining Specialist Corp...E...714 847-1214
7125 Fenwick Ln Ste O Westminster (92683) ***(P-16707)***
Machinist Cooperative, Gilroy *Also called Lloyd E Hennessey Jr* ***(P-16688)***
Machnet Inc...F...310 909-2020
11835 W Olympic Blvd 1280e Los Angeles (90064) ***(P-14646)***
Mack & Reiss Inc...D...510 434-9122
5601 San Leandro St Ste 3 Oakland (94621) ***(P-3593)***
Mack Wall Bed Systems, Petaluma *Also called McGunagle William H & Sons Mfg* ***(P-4718)***
Mackenzie Laboratories Inc...E...909 394-9007
1163 Nicole Ct Glendora (91740) ***(P-18976)***
Mackie International Inc (PA)...E...951 346-0530
7344 Magnolia Ave Ste 205 Riverside (92504) ***(P-682)***
Maclac Co, San Francisco *Also called R J McGlennon Company Inc* ***(P-8937)***
Macom, Newport Beach *Also called Mindspeed Technologies Inc* ***(P-19019)***
Macom Technology Solutions Inc...F...310 320-6160
4000 Macarthur Blvd # 101 Newport Beach (92660) ***(P-18173)***
Macon Industries Inc...F...707 566-2116
3186 Coffey Ln Santa Rosa (95403) ***(P-20011)***
Macquarie Electronics Inc...F...408 965-3860
2153 Otoole Ave Ste 20 San Jose (95131) ***(P-18977)***
Macro Air Technologies, San Bernardino *Also called Macroair Technologies Inc* ***(P-15166)***
Macro Plastics Inc (HQ)...E...707 437-1200
2250 Huntington Dr Fairfield (94533) ***(P-10197)***
Macroair Technologies Inc (PA)...E...909 890-2270
794 S Allen St San Bernardino (92408) ***(P-15166)***
Macrogenics West Inc...F...650 624-2600
3280 Byshore Blvd Ste 200 Brisbane (94005) ***(P-8267)***
Macs Lift Gate Inc (PA)...E...562 634-5962
2801 E South St Long Beach (90805) ***(P-24167)***
Macs Lift Gate Inc...F...562 634-5962
2715 Seaboard Ln Long Beach (90805) ***(P-14334)***
Mactech Magazine, Westlake Village *Also called Xplain Corporation* ***(P-6298)***
Macworld Magazine, San Francisco *Also called Mac Publishing LLC* ***(P-6212)***
Mad Apparel Inc...E...800 714-9697
201 Arch St Redwood City (94062) ***(P-3177)***
Mad Engine LLC (PA)...E...858 558-5270
6740 Cobra Way Ste 100 San Diego (92121) ***(P-2885)***
Mad Hueys, The, Carlsbad *Also called Outdoor Lfstyle Collective LLC* ***(P-3267)***
Mad Wills Food Company, Auburn *Also called Nor Cal Food Solutions LLC* ***(P-923)***
Mad Zone, San Francisco *Also called Divisadero 500 LLC* ***(P-5227)***
Madcap Software Inc (PA)...F...858 320-0387
7777 Fay Ave Ste 210 La Jolla (92037) ***(P-24875)***
Maddiebrit Products LLC...F...818 483-0096
537 Constitution Ave B Camarillo (93012) ***(P-8916)***
Maddox Defense Inc...F...818 378-8246
6549 Mission Gorge Rd # 112 San Diego (92120) ***(P-3953)***
Made In L.A. Fitness, Los Angeles *Also called 5150 Fitness LLC* ***(P-23481)***
Madera Carports Inc...F...559 662-1815
17462 Baldwin St Madera (93638) ***(P-12941)***
Madera Concepts...F...805 692-0053
55b Depot Rd Goleta (93117) ***(P-4634)***
Madera Fina, Fremont *Also called Commercial Casework Inc* ***(P-4125)***
Madera Glass...F...559 673-3583
1825 Howard Rd Madera (93637) ***(P-10601)***
Madera Printing & Pubg Co Inc...E...559 674-2424
2890 Falcon Dr Madera (93637) ***(P-5932)***
Madesolid Inc...F...510 858-5567
2340 Powell St 298 Emeryville (94608) ***(P-7853)***
Madison Industries (HQ)...E...323 583-4061
18000 Studebaker Rd # 305 Cerritos (90703) ***(P-12942)***
Madison Industries Inc Arizona...E...602 252-3083
18000 Studebaker Rd # 305 Cerritos (90703) ***(P-12199)***
Madison Street Press, Oakland *Also called Inter-City Printing Co Inc* ***(P-6893)***
Madrid Inc...F...562 404-9941
7800 Industry Ave Pico Rivera (90660) ***(P-4379)***
Madrigal Vineyards, Calistoga *Also called Madrigal Vineyard Management* ***(P-1867)***
Madrigal Vineyard Management...E...707 942-8691
3718 Saint Helena Hwy Calistoga (94515) ***(P-1867)***
Madrone Hospice Inc...E...530 842-2547
217 W Miner St Yreka (96097) ***(P-10718)***
Madruga Iron Works Inc...E...209 832-7003
305 Gandy Dancer Dr Tracy (95377) ***(P-12200)***
Madsen Products Incorporated...F...714 894-1816
15321 Connector Ln Huntington Beach (92649) ***(P-16708)***
Maestro Cellers, Anaheim *Also called Two Blind Mice LLC* ***(P-2036)***
Maf Industries Inc (HQ)...D...559 897-2905
36470 Highway 99 Traver (93673) ***(P-15217)***
Mag Aerospace Industries Inc...B...310 631-3800
1500 Glenn Curtiss St Carson (90746) ***(P-12016)***
Mag High Tech...F...818 786-8366
14718 Arminta St Panorama City (91402) ***(P-12651)***
Mag Instrument Inc (PA)...B...909 947-1006
2001 S Hellman Ave Ontario (91761) ***(P-17712)***
Magazine Publishers Svc Inc...D...707 571-7610
350 E St Santa Rosa (95404) ***(P-6213)***
Magcomp Inc...F...714 532-3584
1020 N Batavia St Ste T Orange (92867) ***(P-17105)***
Magellan Gold Corporation...E...707 884-3766
2010a Harbison Dr 312 Vacaville (95687) ***(P-11)***
Magellan International Corp...F...510 656-6661
4453 Enterprise St Fremont (94538) ***(P-11594)***
Magellan West LLC...E...408 324-0620
1580 Oakland Rd Ste C107 San Jose (95131) ***(P-24876)***
Magerack, Fremont *Also called Magellan International Corp* ***(P-11594)***
Magic Gumball International...E...818 716-1888
9310 Mason Ave Chatsworth (91311) ***(P-1440)***
Magic Plastics Inc...D...800 369-0303
25215 Avenue Stanford Santa Clarita (91355) ***(P-10198)***
Magic Touch Software Intl...F...800 714-6490
330 Rancheros Dr Ste 258 San Marcos (92069) ***(P-24877)***
Magic-Flight General Mfg Inc...C...619 288-4638
3417 Hancock St San Diego (92110) ***(P-4635)***
Magicall Inc...E...805 484-4300
4550 Calle Alto Camarillo (93012) ***(P-17209)***
Magico LLC...E...510 649-9700
3170 Corporate Pl Hayward (94545) ***(P-17828)***
Magito & Company LLC...F...707 567-1521
1446 Industrial Ave Sebastopol (95472) ***(P-1868)***
Magma, Escondido *Also called One Stop Systems Inc* ***(P-15818)***
Magma Products Inc...D...562 627-0500
3940 Pixie Ave Lakewood (90712) ***(P-17373)***
Magna Charger Inc...D...805 642-8833
1990 Knoll Dr Ste A Ventura (93003) ***(P-3905)***
Magna Tool Inc...E...714 826-2500
5594 Market Pl Cypress (90630) ***(P-16709)***
Magna-Pole Products Inc (PA)...F...310 453-3806
1904 14th St Ste 107 Santa Monica (90404) ***(P-5153)***
Magnabiosciences LLC...D...858 481-4400
6325 Lusk Blvd San Diego (92121) ***(P-22516)***
Magnaflow, Oceanside *Also called Car Sound Exhaust System Inc* ***(P-20284)***
Magnamosis Inc...F...707 484-8774
953 Indiana St Rm 212 San Francisco (94107) ***(P-22517)***
Magnaslow, Rcho STA Marg *Also called Car Sound Exhaust System Inc* ***(P-20285)***
Magnebit Holding Corporation (PA)...E...858 573-0727
9590 Chesapeake Dr Ste 5 San Diego (92123) ***(P-21797)***
Magnell Associate Inc...F...626 271-1320
17708 Rowland St City of Industry (91748) ***(P-15446)***
Magnesium Alloy Pdts Co Inc...E...310 605-1440
2420 N Alameda St Compton (90222) ***(P-11699)***
Magnesium Alloy Products Co LP...E...323 636-2276
2420 N Alameda St Compton (90222) ***(P-11700)***
Magnet Sales & Mfg Co Inc (HQ)...D...310 391-7213
11248 Playa Ct Culver City (90230) ***(P-10820)***
Magnet Source Tm, The, Anaheim *Also called A-L-L Magnetics* ***(P-13913)***
Magnet Systems Inc...E...650 329-5904
2300 Geng Rd Ste 100 Palo Alto (94303) ***(P-24878)***
Magnetic Circuit Elements Inc...E...831 757-8752
1540 Moffett St Salinas (93905) ***(P-19633)***
Magnetic Coils Inc...E...707 459-5994
150 San Hedrin Cir Willits (95490) ***(P-19343)***
Magnetic Component Engrg Inc (PA)...D...310 784-3100
2830 Lomita Blvd Torrance (90505) ***(P-13956)***
Magnetic Design Labs Inc...F...714 558-3355
1636 E Edinger Ave Ste H Santa Ana (92705) ***(P-19634)***
Magnetic Insight Inc...F...510 291-1200
980 Atlantic Ave Ste 102 Alameda (94501) ***(P-21984)***
Magnetic Metals Corporation...E...714 828-4625
2475 W La Palma Ave Anaheim (92801) ***(P-14443)***

ALPHABETIC

Magnetic Moments, Goleta *Also called Launchpoint Technologies Inc* ***(P-15288)***
Magnetic Rcrding Solutions Inc.......E.......408 970-8266
3080 Oakmead Village Dr Santa Clara (95051) ***(P-21798)***
Magnetic Sensors Corp.......E.......714 630-8380
1365 N Mccan St Anaheim (92806) ***(P-19635)***
Magnetron Power Inventions Inc.......E.......310 462-6970
2226 W 232nd St Torrance (90501) ***(P-140)***
Magnitude Electronics LLC.......F.......650 551-1850
926 Bransten Rd San Carlos (94070) ***(P-19636)***
Magnolia Lane Soft HM Furn Inc.......E.......650 624-0700
187 Utah Ave South San Francisco (94080) ***(P-3731)***
Magnolia Pub & Brewery, San Francisco *Also called McLean Brewery Inc* ***(P-1609)***
Magnotek Manufacturing Inc.......D.......951 653-8461
6510 Box Springs Blvd Riverside (92507) ***(P-19344)***
Magnum Abrasives Inc.......E.......909 890-1100
758 S Allen St San Bernardino (92408) ***(P-11297)***
Magnum Data Inc.......F.......800 869-2589
28130 Avenue Crocker # 303 Valencia (91355) ***(P-23734)***
Magnum Fence and Security Inc.......F.......805 641-3656
1070 N Ventura Ave Ventura (93001) ***(P-12878)***
Magnum Semiconductor Inc.......C.......408 934-3700
6024 Silver Creek Vly Rd San Jose (95138) ***(P-18978)***
Magnuson Products LLC.......E.......805 642-8833
1990 Knoll Dr Ste A Ventura (93003) ***(P-20393)***
Magnuson Superchargers, Ventura *Also called Magnuson Products LLC* ***(P-20393)***
Magnussen Home Furnishings Inc.......F.......336 841-4424
2155 Excise Ave Ste B Ontario (91761) ***(P-4717)***
Magor Mold LLC.......D.......909 592-5729
420 S Lone Hill Ave San Dimas (91773) ***(P-14538)***
Magorian Mine Services (PA).......F.......530 269-1960
10310 Sierra Hills Ln Auburn (95602) ***(P-374)***
Magparts (HQ).......D.......626 334-7897
1545 W Roosevelt St Azusa (91702) ***(P-11746)***
Magtech & Power Conversion Inc.......E.......714 451-0106
1146 E Ash Ave Fullerton (92831) ***(P-19345)***
Magtek Inc.......F.......562 631-8602
20725 Annalee Ave Carson (90746) ***(P-18979)***
Magtek Inc (PA).......C.......562 546-6400
1710 Apollo Ct Seal Beach (90740) ***(P-15797)***
Mahar Manufacturing Corp (PA).......E.......323 581-9988
2834 E 46th St Vernon (90058) ***(P-23398)***
Mahindra Genze, Fremont *Also called Mahindra Tractor Assembly Inc* ***(P-21125)***
Mahindra Tractor Assembly Inc (HQ).......E.......650 779-5180
2901 Bayview Dr Fremont (94538) ***(P-21125)***
Mahivr.......F.......949 559-5470
5405 Alton Pkwy Irvine (92604) ***(P-5645)***
Mahmood Izadi Inc.......F.......310 325-0463
3115 Lomita Blvd Torrance (90505) ***(P-15340)***
MAI Systems, Lake Forest *Also called Infor (us) Inc* ***(P-24765)***
Maidenform LLC.......C.......323 724-9558
100 Citadel Dr Ste 323 Commerce (90040) ***(P-3539)***
Maier Manufacturing Inc.......E.......530 272-9036
416 Crown Point Cir Ste 1 Grass Valley (95945) ***(P-21126)***
Maier Racing Enterprises Inc.......F.......510 581-7600
22215 Meekland Ave Hayward (94541) ***(P-20394)***
Mailrite Print & Mail Inc.......E.......916 927-6245
834 Striker Ave Ste C Sacramento (95834) ***(P-6957)***
Mailworks Inc.......E.......619 670-2365
2513 Folex Way Spring Valley (91978) ***(P-5310)***
Main Steel LLC.......D.......951 789-3010
3100 Jefferson St Riverside (92504) ***(P-13449)***
Main Street Banner, Carpinteria *Also called Dsy Educational Corporation* ***(P-3943)***
Main Street Kitchens.......F.......925 944-0153
37 Quail Ct Ste 200 Walnut Creek (94596) ***(P-5716)***
Mainetti USA Inc.......F.......562 741-2920
5350 Zambrano St Commerce (90040) ***(P-7394)***
Mainland Machine.......E.......805 543-7149
2930 Mcmillan Ave Ste E San Luis Obispo (93401) ***(P-16710)***
Mainline Equipment Inc.......D.......800 444-2288
20917 Higgins Ct Torrance (90501) ***(P-18174)***
Mainstreet Media Group LLC.......C.......408 842-6400
6400 Monterey Rd Gilroy (95020) ***(P-5933)***
Maitlen & Benson Inc.......E.......562 597-2200
1395 Obispo Ave Long Beach (90804) ***(P-14732)***
Majestic Garlic Inc.......F.......951 677-0555
2222 Foothill Blvd Ste E La Canada (91011) ***(P-921)***
Major Brass Foundry Inc (PA).......F.......310 324-0177
16206 S Main St Gardena (90248) ***(P-11761)***
Major Fulfillment Inc.......F.......310 323-2326
13707 S Figueroa St Los Angeles (90061) ***(P-6958)***
Make Beverage Holdings LLC.......E.......949 923-8238
2569 Tea Leaf Ln Tustin (92782) ***(P-5245)***
Makeit Inc.......F.......626 470-7938
612 S Marengo Ave Alhambra (91803) ***(P-15798)***
Makerplace Inc.......F.......619 435-1279
684 Margarita Ave Coronado (92118) ***(P-23438)***
Makers Usa Inc.......F.......323 582-1800
5000 District Blvd Vernon (90058) ***(P-3065)***
Makerskit LLC.......E.......213 973-7019
7600 Melrose Ave Ste E Los Angeles (90046) ***(P-23439)***
Makerskit.com, Los Angeles *Also called Makerskit LLC* ***(P-23439)***
Making It Big Inc.......E.......707 795-1995
525 Portal St Cotati (94931) ***(P-3257)***
Making Scents, Canoga Park *Also called Spa La La Inc* ***(P-24249)***
Makino Inc.......E.......714 444-4334
17800 Newhope St Ste K Fountain Valley (92708) ***(P-14647)***
Mako Inc.......E.......323 262-2168
736 Monterey Pass Rd Monterey Park (91754) ***(P-2802)***
Mako Industries SC Inc.......E.......714 632-1400
1280 N Red Gum St Anaheim (92806) ***(P-21985)***
Mako Labs LLC.......E.......619 786-3618
169 Saxony Rd Ste 107 Encinitas (92024) ***(P-24879)***
Mako Overhead Door Inc.......F.......714 998-0122
5618 E La Palma Ave Anaheim (92807) ***(P-12330)***
Makplate LLC.......F.......408 842-7572
5780 Obata Way Gilroy (95020) ***(P-13450)***
Makse Inc.......F.......213 622-5030
52 E Santa Anita Ave Burbank (91502) ***(P-23292)***
Malakan Inc.......E.......818 915-0014
307 W Broadway Apt 6 Glendale (91204) ***(P-4380)***
Malco Manufacturing, Los Angeles *Also called Aluminum Pros Inc* ***(P-14831)***
Malcolm Demille Inc.......F.......805 929-4353
650 S Frontage Rd Nipomo (93444) ***(P-23293)***
Malibu Ceramic Works.......E.......310 455-2485
903 Fairbanks Ave Long Beach (90813) ***(P-10786)***
Malibu Enterprises Inc.......E.......310 457-2112
28990 Pacific Coast Hwy # 108 Malibu (90265) ***(P-5934)***
Malibu Kitchen, Malibu *Also called Marys Country Kitchen* ***(P-1398)***
Malibu Times Inc.......F.......310 456-5507
3864 Las Flores Canyon Rd Malibu (90265) ***(P-5935)***
Malikco LLC.......E.......925 974-3555
2121 N Calif Blvd Ste 290 Walnut Creek (94596) ***(P-24880)***
Mallin Casual Furniture, Montebello *Also called Minson Corporation* ***(P-4798)***
Mallinckrodt Inc.......F.......805 553-9303
3298 Morning Ridge Ave Thousand Oaks (91362) ***(P-22518)***
Mama Sues Gourmet Pasta Inc.......E.......626 241-2394
2621 Lee Ave South El Monte (91733) ***(P-2593)***
Mamma Lina Ravioli Co, San Diego *Also called Mamma Linas Incorporated* ***(P-2594)***
Mamma Linas Incorporated.......F.......858 535-0620
10741 Roselle St San Diego (92121) ***(P-2594)***
Mammoth Media Inc.......D.......310 393-3024
1447 2nd St Santa Monica (90401) ***(P-5936)***
Mammoth Times, Mammoth Lakes *Also called Horizon Cal Publications* ***(P-5882)***
Mammoth Water, Montebello *Also called Unix Packaging Inc* ***(P-2230)***
Man-Grove Industries Inc.......D.......714 630-3020
1201 N Miller St Anaheim (92806) ***(P-6959)***
Manchester Feeds Inc (PA).......F.......714 637-7062
1520 E Barham Dr San Marcos (92078) ***(P-1145)***
Manchester Feeds San Marcos, San Marcos *Also called Manchester Feeds Inc* ***(P-1145)***
Mancias Steel Company Inc.......F.......408 295-5096
519 Horning St San Jose (95112) ***(P-12201)***
Mandala, Carlsbad *Also called Oceanside Glasstile Company* ***(P-10787)***
Mandego Apparel, Hollister *Also called Mandego Inc* ***(P-2886)***
Mandego Inc.......F.......831 637-5241
2300 Tech Pkwy Ste 2 Hollister (95023) ***(P-2886)***
Maneri Sign Co Inc.......E.......310 327-6261
1928 W 135th St Gardena (90249) ***(P-23918)***
Manetti Group, Commerce *Also called Hangers Randy West Coast Ctr* ***(P-11444)***
Maney Aircraft Inc.......E.......909 390-2500
1305 S Wanamaker Ave Ontario (91761) ***(P-20872)***
Mangia Inc.......F.......949 581-1274
1 Marconi Ste F Irvine (92618) ***(P-825)***
Manhattan Beachwear Inc (PA).......C.......714 892-7354
10700 Valley View St Cypress (90630) ***(P-3459)***
Manhattan Beachwear Inc.......D.......714 892-7354
10700 Valley View St Cypress (90630) ***(P-3460)***
Manhattan Components Inc.......F.......714 761-7249
5920 Lakeshore Dr Cypress (90630) ***(P-10199)***
Manley Laboratories Inc.......E.......909 627-4256
13880 Magnolia Ave Chino (91710) ***(P-17829)***
Manna Pro Feeds, Fresno *Also called Manna Pro Products LLC* ***(P-1146)***
Manna Pro Products LLC.......E.......559 486-1810
2962 S Cedar Ave Fresno (93725) ***(P-1146)***
Manning Holoff Co Inc.......E.......818 407-2500
15610 Moorpark St Apt 3 Encino (91436) ***(P-21615)***
Mannings Beef LLC.......D.......562 908-1089
9531 Beverly Rd Pico Rivera (90660) ***(P-443)***
Mannis Communications Inc.......E.......858 270-3103
1621 Grand Ave Ste C San Diego (92109) ***(P-5937)***
Mannis Communications Inc.......E.......858 270-3103
4645 Caca St Fl 2 Flr 2 San Diego (92109) ***(P-5938)***
Mansoor Amarna Corp.......F.......818 894-8937
16923 Kinzie St Northridge (91343) ***(P-23709)***
Manta Instruments.......F.......858 449-5801
6370 Lusk Blvd Ste F208 San Diego (92121) ***(P-21986)***
Manta Solar Corporation.......F.......928 853-6216
5420 Fulton St San Francisco (94121) ***(P-12074)***
Manteca Bulletin, Manteca *Also called Morris Newspaper Corp Cal* ***(P-5980)***
Manti-Machine Co Inc.......F.......714 902-1465
11782 Western Ave Ste 15 Stanton (90680) ***(P-16711)***
Manufacture Resource Pdts Inc.......E.......909 839-2988
19907 E Walnut Dr S Ste C Walnut (91789) ***(P-2975)***
Manufacturers Coml Fin LLC.......E.......530 477-5011
13185 Nevada City Ave Grass Valley (95945) ***(P-12075)***
Manufacturers Import & Export, San Jose *Also called Amtek Electronic Inc* ***(P-15393)***
Manufacturers of Wood Products, Santa Barbara *Also called Architctral Mllwk Snta Barbara* ***(P-4104)***
Manufacturers/Hyland Ltd.......F.......408 748-1806
650 Reed St Santa Clara (95050) ***(P-10719)***
Manufacturing & Prod Svcs Corp.......F.......760 796-4300
2222 Enterprise St Escondido (92029) ***(P-20395)***
Manufacturing USA Enterprises.......E.......818 409-3070
632 Irving Ave Glendale (91201) ***(P-23294)***
Manutech Mfg & Dist.......F.......831 655-8794
2080 Sunset Dr Pacific Grove (93950) ***(P-14128)***
Manutronics Inc.......F.......408 262-6579
736 S Hillview Dr Milpitas (95035) ***(P-19637)***

Mergent e-mail: customerrelations@mergent.com
1204
2019 California
Manufacturers Register
(P-0000) Products & Services Section entry number
(PA)=Parent Co (HQ)=Headquarters (DH)=Div Headquarters

Manutronics Co ....E......510 438-0588
46722 Fremont Blvd Fremont (94538) *(P-15447)*
Manzana Products Co Inc ....E......707 823-5313
9141 Green Valley Rd Sebastopol (95472) *(P-826)*
Manzanita ....F......818 785-1111
26559 Ruether Ave Santa Clarita (91350) *(P-23380)*
Manzer Corporation ....E......619 295-6031
3801 30th St San Diego (92104) *(P-3696)*
Map Masters, Poway Also called Traylor Management Inc *(P-6606)*
Mape Engineering Inc ....F......626 338-7964
9840 6th St Rancho Cucamonga (91730) *(P-20669)*
Mapei Corporation ....E......909 475-4100
5415 Industrial Pkwy San Bernardino (92407) *(P-7854)*
Maple Consumer Foods, Fair Oaks Also called Wholesome Harvest Baking Inc *(P-458)*
Maple Leaf Bakery, Richmond Also called Wholesome Harvest Baking LLC *(P-1343)*
Maplegrove Gluten Free Foods ....E......909 334-7828
5010 Eucalyptus Ave Chino (91710) *(P-2595)*
Maquet Medical Systems USA LLC ....A......408 635-3900
120 Baytech Dr San Jose (95134) *(P-23002)*
Mar & Company Inc (PA) ....E......818 241-8882
1763 Flower St Glendale (91201) *(P-3461)*
Mar Cor Purification Inc ....E......800 633-3080
6351 Orangethorpe Ave Buena Park (90620) *(P-16068)*
Mar Engineering Company ....E......818 765-4805
7350 Greenbush Ave North Hollywood (91605) *(P-16712)*
Mar Vista Resources LLC ....F......559 992-4535
745 North Ave Corcoran (93212) *(P-9065)*
Mar Vista Wood Products Inc ....F......562 698-2024
7343 Pierce Ave Whittier (90602) *(P-4187)*
Maranti Networks Inc ....D......408 834-4000
1452 N Vasco Rd Livermore (94551) *(P-15565)*
Marathon Machine Inc ....E......858 578-8670
7588 Trade St San Diego (92121) *(P-16713)*
Marathon Products Incorporated ....F......510 562-6450
627 Mccormick St San Leandro (94577) *(P-22230)*
Marbil Industries Inc ....E......714 974-4032
2201 N Glassell St Orange (92865) *(P-21987)*
Marble City Company Inc ....F......650 802-8189
611 Taylor Way Ste 6 San Carlos (94070) *(P-11261)*
Marble Palace, Stockton Also called Andrea Zee Corporation *(P-11231)*
Marble Security Inc ....E......408 737-4300
68 Willow Rd Menlo Park (94025) *(P-24881)*
Marble Shop Inc (PA) ....E......925 439-6910
180 Bliss Ave Pittsburg (94565) *(P-11262)*
Marble Works of San Diego, San Diego Also called Central Marble Supply Inc *(P-11240)*
Marburg Technology Inc ....C......408 262-8400
304 Turquoise St Milpitas (95035) *(P-15799)*
Marcaflex Inc ....F......415 472-4423
2 Seville Dr San Rafael (94903) *(P-5570)*
Marcea Inc ....F......213 746-5191
1742 Crenshaw Blvd Torrance (90501) *(P-3462)*
Marcel Electronics Inc ....F......714 974-8590
240 W Bristol Ln Orange (92865) *(P-18523)*
Marcel Electronics Inc ....F......714 974-8590
130 W Bristol Ln Orange (92865) *(P-18524)*
March Vision Care Inc ....E......310 665-0975
6701 Center Dr W Ste 790 Los Angeles (90045) *(P-23108)*
Marchem Solvay Group, Long Beach Also called Solvay USA Inc *(P-7806)*
Marco Fine Arts ....D......310 615-1818
4860 W 147th St Hawthorne (90250) *(P-7395)*
Marco Fine Furniture Inc ....E......415 285-3235
650 Potrero Ave San Francisco (94110) *(P-4793)*
Marcoa Media LLC (PA) ....E......858 635-9627
9955 Black Mountain Rd San Diego (92126) *(P-6523)*
Marcoa Quality Publishing LLC ....D......858 695-9600
9955 Black Mountain Rd San Diego (92126) *(P-6524)*
Mardian Equipment Co Inc ....E......619 938-8071
10168 Channel Rd Lakeside (92040) *(P-14335)*
Mare Island Dry Dock LLC ....D......707 652-7356
1180 Nimitz Ave Vallejo (94592) *(P-20999)*
Mareblu Naturals, Anaheim Also called 180 Snacks *(P-1479)*
Marflex, Vernon Also called Marspring Corporation *(P-2932)*
Margaret OLeary Inc (PA) ....D......415 354-6663
50 Dorman Ave San Francisco (94124) *(P-3463)*
Marge Carson Inc (PA) ....D......626 571-1111
1260 E Grand Ave Pomona (91766) *(P-4794)*
MARGEAUX AND LINDA'S VEGAN KIT, Los Angeles Also called Amzart Inc *(P-2452)*
Margus Automotive Elc Exch ....D......323 232-5281
165 E Jefferson Blvd Los Angeles (90011) *(P-20396)*
Maria Corporation ....F......714 751-2460
2760 S Harbor Blvd Ste C Santa Ana (92704) *(P-7396)*
Mariani Bros, Marysville Also called Mariani Packing Co Inc *(P-886)*
Mariani Packing Co Inc ....E......530 749-6565
9281 Highway 70 Marysville (95901) *(P-886)*
Mariani Winery, Saratoga Also called Savannah Chanelle Vineyards *(P-1967)*
Mariannes Ice Cream LLC ....E......831 713-4746
218 State Park Dr Aptos (95003) *(P-683)*
Mariannes Ice Cream LLC (PA) ....E......831 457-1447
2100 Delaware Ave Ste B Santa Cruz (95060) *(P-684)*
Mariba Corporation ....F......626 963-6775
158 N Glendora Ave Ste W Glendora (91741) *(P-4529)*
Marich Confectionery Co Inc ....C......831 634-4700
2101 Bert Dr Hollister (95023) *(P-1441)*
Marie Joann Designs Inc ....F......714 996-0550
630 S Jefferson St Ste H Placentia (92870) *(P-3954)*
Marietta Cellars Incorporated ....F......707 433-2747
22295 Chianti Rd Geyserville (95441) *(P-1869)*
Marietta Marketing, Geyserville Also called Marietta Cellars Incorporated *(P-1869)*

Marika LLC ....D......323 888-7755
5553-B Bandini Blvd Bell (90201) *(P-3464)*
Marimar Torres Estate Corp ....F......707 823-4365
11400 Graton Rd Sebastopol (95472) *(P-1870)*
Marimix Company Inc ....F......714 633-7300
987 N Enterprise St Orange (92867) *(P-1442)*
Marin County Copy Shops Inc ....F......415 457-5600
901 C St San Rafael (94901) *(P-6960)*
Marin Food Specialties Inc ....E......925 634-6126
14800 Byron Hwy Byron (94514) *(P-767)*
Marin French Cheese Company ....F......707 762-6001
7500 Red Hill Rd Petaluma (94952) *(P-592)*
Marin Independent Journal, Novato Also called California Newspapers Inc *(P-5788)*
Marin Magazine Inc ....F......415 332-4800
1 Harbor Dr Ste 208 Sausalito (94965) *(P-6214)*
Marin Manufacturing Inc ....F......415 453-1825
195 Mill St San Rafael (94901) *(P-12202)*
Marin Scope Incorporated ....E......415 892-1516
1301b Grant Ave Novato (94945) *(P-5939)*
Marin Scope Incorporated ....E......415 892-1516
700 Larkspur Landing Cir Larkspur (94939) *(P-5940)*
Marin Scope Newspapers, Novato Also called Marin Scope Incorporated *(P-5939)*
Marin USA ....E......415 382-6000
265 Bel Marin Keys Blvd Novato (94949) *(P-11973)*
Marina Industries, Los Angeles Also called Marina Sportswear Inc *(P-3465)*
Marina Shipyard, Long Beach Also called Indel Engineering Inc *(P-21044)*
Marina Sportswear Inc ....D......323 232-2012
3766 S Main St Los Angeles (90007) *(P-3465)*
Marine & Industrial Services ....F......925 757-8791
2391 W 10th St Antioch (94509) *(P-13895)*
Marine & Rest Fabricators Inc ....E......619 232-7267
3768 Dalbergia St San Diego (92113) *(P-12652)*
Marine Fenders Intl Inc ....E......310 834-7037
909 Mahar Ave Wilmington (90744) *(P-13141)*
Marine Group Boat Works LLC ....C......619 427-6767
997 G St Chula Vista (91910) *(P-21000)*
Marine Spill Response Corp ....E......707 442-6087
990 W Waterfront Dr Eureka (95501) *(P-21988)*
Marine Tech ....E......619 225-0448
1500 Quivira Way Ste 1 San Diego (92109) *(P-21053)*
Marinesync Corporation ....F......619 578-2953
3235 Hancock St San Diego (92110) *(P-21616)*
Marino Enterprises Inc ....E......909 476-0343
10671 Civic Center Dr Rancho Cucamonga (91730) *(P-20873)*
Marinpak ....F......707 996-3931
21684 8th St E Ste 100 Sonoma (95476) *(P-2596)*
Mariposa Gazette & Miner ....F......209 966-2500
5180 Hwy 140 Ste B Mariposa (95338) *(P-5941)*
Marisa Foods LLC ....F......562 437-7775
1401 Santa Fe Ave Long Beach (90813) *(P-504)*
Maritime Solutions LLC ....E......619 234-2676
1616 Newton Ave San Diego (92113) *(P-21054)*
Marjorie Baer Accessories ....E......650 872-2272
1389 Lowrie Ave South San Francisco (94080) *(P-23295)*
Mark Crawford Logging Inc ....F......530 496-3272
26 Walker Creek Rd Seiad Valley (96086) *(P-4000)*
Mark Ease Products Inc ....E......209 462-8632
132 S Aurora St Stockton (95202) *(P-23919)*
Mark IV Metal Products Inc ....F......310 217-9700
544 W 132nd St Gardena (90248) *(P-13896)*
Mark Levine Window Coverings, Newport Beach Also called M L Interiors Inc *(P-3695)*
Mark One Counter Top Designs, Fresno Also called Duracite *(P-5138)*
Mark Optics Inc ....E......714 545-6684
1424 E Saint Gertrude Pl Santa Ana (92705) *(P-22103)*
Mark Resources LLC (PA) ....F......415 515-5540
1962 22nd Ave San Francisco (94116) *(P-4993)*
Mark Sheffield Construction ....E......661 589-8520
9105 Langley Rd Bakersfield (93312) *(P-236)*
Mark V Products, Corona Also called 2nd Gen Productions Inc *(P-8614)*
Mark V Products, Corona Also called 2nd Gen Productions Inc *(P-8615)*
Markap Inc ....E......949 240-1418
20382 Hermana Cir Lake Forest (92630) *(P-3631)*
Markes International Inc ....D......513 745-0241
2355 Gold Meadow Way # 120 Gold River (95670) *(P-21989)*
Marketing Bulletin Board ....F......805 455-2255
639 Olive Rd Santa Barbara (93108) *(P-5942)*
Marketing Bus Advantage Inc ....F......925 933-3637
1940 Olivera Rd Ste E Concord (94520) *(P-14986)*
Marketing Pro Consulting Inc ....F......619 233-8591
1230 Columbia St Ste 500 San Diego (92101) *(P-24882)*
Marketron Mobile LLC ....F......415 981-0812
388 Market St Ste 854 San Francisco (94111) *(P-24883)*
Marki Microwave Inc ....E......408 778-4200
215 Vineyard Ct Morgan Hill (95037) *(P-19638)*
Markland Industries Inc (PA) ....D......714 245-2850
1111 E Mcfadden Ave Santa Ana (92705) *(P-21127)*
Marko Foam Products, Irvine Also called Marko Products Inc *(P-9869)*
Marko Products Inc (PA) ....D......800 862-7561
2500 White Rd Ste A Irvine (92614) *(P-9869)*
Marksman Products, Santa Fe Springs Also called S/R Industries Inc *(P-23646)*
Markwins International Corp (PA) ....C......909 595-8898
22067 Ferrero Walnut (91789) *(P-8792)*
Markzware ....F......949 756-5100
1805 E Dyer Rd Ste 101 Santa Ana (92705) *(P-24884)*
Markzware Software, Santa Ana Also called Markzware *(P-24884)*
Marlee Manufacturing Inc ....E......909 390-3222
4711 E Guasti Rd Ontario (91761) *(P-22519)*
Marleon Inc ....E......310 679-1242
3202 W Rosecrans Ave Hawthorne (90250) *(P-25421)*

Employee Codes: A=Over 500 employees, B=251-500
C=101-250, D=51-100, E=20-50, F=10-19

2019 California
Manfacturers Register

© Mergent Inc. 1-800-342-5647

1205

Marler Precision, San Andreas *Also called Krisalis Inc* ***(P-16665)***

Marlin Designs LLC ....C....949 637-7257
1900 E Warner Ave Ste J Santa Ana (92705) ***(P-4795)***

Marlin Machine Products ....F....951 275-0050
4071 Brewster Way Riverside (92501) ***(P-16714)***

Marna Ro LLC ....F....310 801-5788
818 S Broadway Ste 800 Los Angeles (90014) ***(P-3583)***

Maroney Company ....F....818 882-2722
9016 Winnetka Ave Northridge (91324) ***(P-16715)***

Marples Gears Inc ....E....626 570-1744
808 W Santa Anita Ave San Gabriel (91776) ***(P-15241)***

Marpo Kinetics Inc ....F....925 606-6919
1306 Stealth St Livermore (94551) ***(P-23611)***

Marquez & Marquez Food PR, South Gate *Also called Marquez Marquez Inc* ***(P-2396)***

Marquez Brothers Intl Inc ....E....559 276-7800
4393 N Golden State Blvd Fresno (93722) ***(P-593)***

Marquez Marquez Inc ....E....562 408-0960
11821 Industrial Ave South Gate (90280) ***(P-2396)***

Marrone Bio Innovations Inc ....C....530 750-2800
1540 Drew Ave Davis (95618) ***(P-9105)***

Marrs Printing Inc ....D....909 594-9459
860 Tucker Ln City of Industry (91789) ***(P-6961)***

Mars Air Systems LLC ....D....310 532-1555
14716 S Broadway Gardena (90248) ***(P-15167)***

MArs Engineering Company Inc ....E....510 483-0541
699 Montague St San Leandro (94577) ***(P-13031)***

Mars Food Us LLC (HQ) ....B....310 933-0670
2001 E Cashdan St Ste 201 Rancho Dominguez (90220) ***(P-1087)***

Mars Food Us LLC ....B....562 616-7347
6875 Pacific View Dr Los Angeles (90068) ***(P-1088)***

Mars Medical Ride Corp ....F....310 518-1024
23702 Main St Carson (90745) ***(P-20156)***

Mars Petcare Us Inc ....E....909 887-8131
2765 Lexington Way San Bernardino (92407) ***(P-1116)***

Mars Petcare Us Inc ....E....760 261-7900
13243 Nutro Way Victorville (92395) ***(P-1117)***

Mars Printing and Packaging, City of Industry *Also called Marrs Printing Inc* ***(P-6961)***

Marsal Packaging & Rfrgn ....F....714 812-6775
931 S Cypress St La Habra (90631) ***(P-15969)***

Marsha Vicki Originals Inc ....E....714 895-6371
5292 Production Dr Huntington Beach (92649) ***(P-3034)***

Marshall & Swift/Boeckh LLC ....F....213 683-9000
777 S Figueroa St Fl 12 Los Angeles (90017) ***(P-6360)***

Marshall Genuine Products LLC ....F....619 754-4099
616 Marsat Ct Chula Vista (91911) ***(P-14648)***

Marspring Corporation (PA) ....E....323 589-5637
4920 S Boyle Ave Vernon (90058) ***(P-2932)***

Marspring Corporation ....E....800 522-5252
4920 S Boyle Ave Vernon (90058) ***(P-4870)***

Marspring Corporation ....E....310 484-6849
4920 S Boyle Ave Vernon (90058) ***(P-4871)***

Martek Power, Torrance *Also called Sure Power Inc* ***(P-19740)***

Martellotto Inc ....F....619 567-9244
12934 Francine Ter Poway (92064) ***(P-1871)***

Marteq Process Solutions Inc ....F....714 495-4275
1721 S Grand Ave Santa Ana (92705) ***(P-18980)***

Martha Olsons Great Foods Inc ....F....209 234-5935
4407 Giannecchini Ln Stockton (95206) ***(P-1370)***

Martha's All Natural, Stockton *Also called Martha Olsons Great Foods Inc* ***(P-1370)***

Martha's All Natural, Stockton *Also called Bakakers Specialty Foods Inc* ***(P-1033)***

Martin Aerospace Corporation ....F....310 231-0055
11150 Tennessee Ave 1b Los Angeles (90064) ***(P-13744)***

Martin Archery, Los Angeles *Also called Martin Sports Inc* ***(P-23612)***

Martin Brass Foundry ....D....951 698-7041
22427 Bear Creek Dr N Murrieta (92562) ***(P-11762)***

Martin Company, The, Los Angeles *Also called Martin Aerospace Corporation* ***(P-13744)***

Martin Engineering Co Inc ....F....626 960-5153
5454 2nd St Irwindale (91706) ***(P-14869)***

Martin Erattrud Co, Gardena *Also called Baxstra Inc* ***(P-4074)***

Martin Fischer Logging Inc ....F....209 293-4847
1165 Skull Flat Rd West Point (95255) ***(P-4001)***

Martin Furniture, San Diego *Also called Gilbert Martin Wdwkg Co Inc* ***(P-4897)***

Martin Marietta Materials Inc ....E....951 682-0918
1500 Rubidoux Blvd Riverside (92509) ***(P-323)***

Martin Marietta Materials Inc ....F....530 534-4517
2216 Table Mountain Blvd Oroville (95965) ***(P-315)***

Martin Purefoods Corporation ....F....909 865-4440
1713 W 2nd St Pomona (91766) ***(P-505)***

Martin Sports Inc (PA) ....E....509 529-2554
1100 Glendon Ave Ste 920 Los Angeles (90024) ***(P-23612)***

Martin Sprocket & Gear Inc ....E....916 441-7172
1199 Vine St Sacramento (95811) ***(P-15242)***

Martin Sprocket & Gear Inc ....F....323 728-8117
5920 Triangle Dr Commerce (90040) ***(P-15243)***

Martin Sweeping, La Quinta *Also called CT Oldenkamp LLC* ***(P-23789)***

Martin Weyrich Winery LLC ....F....805 226-9296
4230 Buena Vista Dr Paso Robles (93446) ***(P-1872)***

Martin-Chandler Inc ....F....323 321-5119
122 E Alondra Blvd Gardena (90248) ***(P-16716)***

Martin/Brattrud Inc ....D....323 770-4171
1224 W 132nd St Gardena (90247) ***(P-4796)***

Martinek Manufacturing ....E....510 438-0357
42650 Osgood Rd Fremont (94539) ***(P-16717)***

Martinelli Envmtl Graphics, San Francisco *Also called Martinelli Envmtl Graphics* ***(P-23920)***

Martinelli Envmtl Graphics ....F....415 468-4000
1829 Egbert Ave San Francisco (94124) ***(P-23920)***

Martinez & Turek, Rialto *Also called Martinez and Turek Inc* ***(P-16718)***

Martinez and Turek Inc ....C....909 820-6800
300 S Cedar Ave Rialto (92376) ***(P-16718)***

Martinez News Gazette, Vallejo *Also called Gibson Printing & Publishing* ***(P-5863)***

Martinez News Gazette, Martinez *Also called Gibson Printing & Publishing* ***(P-5864)***

Martinez Pallet Services LLC ....F....209 968-1393
671 Mariposa Rd Modesto (95354) ***(P-4487)***

Martini Prati Winery, Santa Rosa *Also called Conetech Custom Services LLC* ***(P-1701)***

Martinic Engineering Inc (HQ) ....E....714 527-8988
10932 Chestnut Ave Stanton (90680) ***(P-16719)***

Marton Precision Mfg LLC ....E....714 808-6523
1365 S Acacia Ave Fullerton (92831) ***(P-20670)***

Martronic Engineering Inc (PA) ....F....805 583-0808
874 Patriot Dr Unit D Moorpark (93021) ***(P-20012)***

Maruchan Inc (HQ) ....B....949 789-2300
15800 Laguna Canyon Rd Irvine (92618) ***(P-2597)***

Maruchan Inc ....C....949 789-2300
1902 Deere Ave Irvine (92606) ***(P-2429)***

Maruhachi Ceramics America Inc ....E....800 736-6221
1985 Sampson Ave Corona (92879) ***(P-10802)***

Maruhide Marine Products Inc ....D....562 435-6509
2145 W 17th St Long Beach (90813) ***(P-2317)***

Maruichi American Corporation ....D....562 903-8600
11529 Greenstone Ave Santa Fe Springs (90670) ***(P-11482)***

Marukan Vinegar U S A Inc (HQ) ....C....562 630-6060
16203 Vermont Ave Paramount (90723) ***(P-2598)***

Marukome USA Inc ....F....949 863-0110
17132 Pullman St Irvine (92614) ***(P-2599)***

Marvac Scientific Mfg Co ....F....925 825-4636
3231 Monument Way Ste I Concord (94518) ***(P-21480)***

Marvell Semiconductor Inc ....E....408 855-8839
5450 Bayfront Plz Santa Clara (95054) ***(P-21799)***

Marvell Semiconductor Inc (HQ) ....A....408 222-2500
5488 Marvell Ln Santa Clara (95054) ***(P-18981)***

Marvell Technology Group Ltd (HQ) ....E....408 222-2500
5488 Marvell Ln Santa Clara (95054) ***(P-18982)***

Marvin Engineering Co Inc (PA) ....A....310 674-5030
261 W Beach Ave Inglewood (90302) ***(P-20874)***

Marvin Group The, Inglewood *Also called Marvin Land Systems Inc* ***(P-20157)***

Marvin Group, The, Inglewood *Also called Marvin Engineering Co Inc* ***(P-20874)***

Marvin Land Systems Inc ....E....310 674-5030
261 W Beach Ave Inglewood (90302) ***(P-20157)***

Marvin Test Solutions Inc ....D....949 263-2222
1770 Kettering Irvine (92614) ***(P-21800)***

Marway Power Solutions, Santa Ana *Also called Marway Power Systems Inc* ***(P-15800)***

Marway Power Systems Inc (PA) ....E....714 917-6200
1721 S Grand Ave Santa Ana (92705) ***(P-15800)***

Marwell Corporation ....F....909 794-4192
1094 Wabash Ave Mentone (92359) ***(P-17151)***

Marx Digital Cnc Machine Shop, Santa Clara *Also called Marx Digital Mfg Inc* ***(P-16720)***

Marx Digital Mfg Inc (PA) ....E....408 748-1783
3551 Victor St Santa Clara (95054) ***(P-16720)***

Mary Anns Baking Co Inc ....C....916 681-7444
8371 Carbide Ct Sacramento (95828) ***(P-1289)***

Mary Matava ....F....760 439-9920
3210 Oceanside Blvd Oceanside (92056) ***(P-9106)***

Marybelle Farms Inc ....E....916 645-8568
3761 Nicolaus Rd Lincoln (95648) ***(P-1147)***

Marys Country Kitchen ....F....310 456-7845
3900 Cross Creek Rd Ste 3 Malibu (90265) ***(P-1398)***

Marzetti West, Milpitas *Also called Tmarzetti Company* ***(P-936)***

Mas Metals Inc ....F....510 259-1426
600 Montague St San Leandro (94577) ***(P-12879)***

Masco Corporation ....D....313 274-7400
19914 Via Baron Way Rancho Dominguez (90220) ***(P-12039)***

Mascorro Leather Inc ....D....323 724-6759
1303 S Gerhart Ave Commerce (90022) ***(P-10567)***

Mashindustries Inc ....E....714 736-9600
1700 E Via Burton Anaheim (92806) ***(P-5246)***

Masimo Corporation ....E....949 297-7000
40 Parker Irvine (92618) ***(P-23003)***

Masimo Corporation ....E....949 297-7000
9600 Jeronimo Rd Irvine (92618) ***(P-23004)***

Masimo Corporation (PA) ....B....949 297-7000
52 Discovery Irvine (92618) ***(P-23005)***

Masimo Semiconductor Inc ....E....603 595-8900
40 Parker Irvine (92618) ***(P-18983)***

Mask Technology Inc ....E....714 557-3383
2601 Oak St Santa Ana (92707) ***(P-19639)***

Mask U S Inc ....F....619 476-9041
3121 Main St Ste F Chula Vista (91911) ***(P-3669)***

Mask-Off Company Inc ....F....626 303-8015
345 W Maple Ave Monrovia (91016) ***(P-9155)***

Maskell Fusion Tech Services, Corona *Also called Maskell Pipe & Supply Inc* ***(P-11483)***

Maskell Pipe & Supply Inc (PA) ....F....909 574-8662
560 W Rincon St Corona (92880) ***(P-11483)***

Maskless Lithography Inc ....F....408 433-1864
2550 Zanker Rd San Jose (95131) ***(P-6962)***

Mason Electric Co ....B....818 361-3366
13955 Balboa Blvd Sylmar (91342) ***(P-20875)***

Masonite Entry Door Corp ....F....951 243-2261
25100 Globe St Moreno Valley (92551) ***(P-4188)***

Masonite International Corp ....E....209 948-0637
433 W Scotts Ave Stockton (95203) ***(P-4189)***

Mass Group ....E....310 214-2000
1959 Kingsdale Ave Redondo Beach (90278) ***(P-6963)***

Mass Precision Inc ....C....408 954-0200
46555 Landing Pkwy Fremont (94538) ***(P-12653)***

Mass Precision Inc (PA) ....C....408 954-0200
2110 Oakland Rd San Jose (95131) ***(P-12654)***

Mass Press, Redondo Beach *Also called Mass Group* ***(P-6963)***

Mass Systems, Baldwin Park *Also called Ametek Ameron LLC* ***(P-21546)***

Mergent e-mail: customerrelations@mergent.com
1206
2019 California
Manufacturers Register
(P-0000) Products & Services Section entry number
(PA)=Parent Co (HQ)=Headquarters (DH)=Div Headquarters

Mast Biosurgery USA Inc ....E....858 550-8050
6749 Top Gun St Ste 108 San Diego (92121) *(P-22766)*
Masten Space Systems Inc ....F....661 824-3423
1570 Sabovich St 25 Mojave (93501) *(P-21164)*
Master Arts Engraving, Anaheim *Also called Master Arts Inc (P-7651)*
Master Arts Inc ....F....714 240-4550
3737 E Miraloma Ave Anaheim (92806) *(P-7651)*
Master Body Works Inc ....E....323 564-6901
9824 Atlantic Ave South Gate (90280) *(P-20214)*
Master Designs Sofa Inc ....F....626 444-1477
9800 Rush St South El Monte (91733) *(P-4797)*
Master Enterprises Inc ....E....626 442-1821
2025 Lee Ave South El Monte (91733) *(P-12655)*
Master Fab Inc ....F....951 277-4772
9210 Stellar Ct Corona (92883) *(P-12656)*
Master Inds Worldwide LLC ....F....949 660-0644
1001 S Linwood Ave Santa Ana (92705) *(P-24168)*
Master Industries Inc ....E....949 660-0644
1001 S Linwood Ave Santa Ana (92705) *(P-23613)*
Master Link Sausage, Fullerton *Also called Demes Gourmet Corporation (P-479)*
Master Machine Products, Riverside *Also called Metric Machining (P-14394)*
Master Metal Products Company ....F....408 275-1210
495 Emory St San Jose (95110) *(P-12657)*
Master Metal Works Inc ....E....626 444-8818
1805 Potrero Ave South El Monte (91733) *(P-12880)*
Master Plastics Incorporated ....E....707 451-3168
820 Eubanks Dr Ste I Vacaville (95688) *(P-10200)*
Master Powder Coating Inc ....E....562 863-4135
13721 Bora Dr Santa Fe Springs (90670) *(P-8917)*
Master Precision Machining ....E....408 727-0185
2199 Ronald St Santa Clara (95050) *(P-16721)*
Master Productions Inc ....F....858 677-0037
8310 Miramar Mall Ste A San Diego (92121) *(P-6964)*
Master Research & Mfg Inc ....D....562 483-8789
13528 Pumice St Norwalk (90650) *(P-20876)*
Master Washer Stamping Svc Co ....F....323 722-0969
80899 Camino San Lucas Indio (92203) *(P-14539)*
Master-Halco Inc ....E....909 350-4740
8008 Church Ave Highland (92346) *(P-11448)*
Masterbrand Cabinets Inc ....E....951 686-3614
3700 S Riverside Ave Colton (92324) *(P-4327)*
Mastercraft Safety, Santee *Also called Impact Racing Inc (P-25411)*
Mastering Lab Inc ....F....805 640-2900
911 Bryant Pl Ojai (93023) *(P-17907)*
Masterite Division, Los Angeles *Also called Dcx-Chol Enterprises Inc (P-18389)*
Masterpiece Cookies, Livermore *Also called Internationally Delicious Inc (P-1397)*
Masterpiece Leaded Windows ....E....858 391-3344
11651 Rverside Dr Ste 143 Lakeside (92040) *(P-10720)*
Masters In Metal Inc ....E....805 988-1992
131 Lombard St Oxnard (93030) *(P-10813)*
Mastertaste Inc ....D....323 727-2100
1916 S Tubeway Ave Commerce (90040) *(P-2272)*
Mastey De Paris Inc ....E....661 257-4814
25413 Rye Canyon Rd Valencia (91355) *(P-8793)*
Mastini Designs ....F....800 979-4848
9454 Wilshire Blvd # 600 Beverly Hills (90212) *(P-23296)*
Mat Cactus Mfg Co ....E....626 969-0444
930 W 10th St Azusa (91702) *(P-2933)*
Mat Mat ....F....818 678-9392
21029 Itasca St Chatsworth (91311) *(P-11861)*
Matanzas Creek Winery ....E....707 528-6464
6097 Bennett Valley Rd Santa Rosa (95404) *(P-1873)*
Matchless LLC ....E....310 473-5100
8423 Wilshire Blvd Beverly Hills (90211) *(P-18175)*
Matchmaster Dyg & Finshg Inc (PA) ....C....323 232-2061
3750 S Broadway Los Angeles (90007) *(P-2914)*
Matchmaster Dyg & Finshg Inc ....D....323 232-2061
3750 Broadway Pl Los Angeles (90007) *(P-2866)*
Matchpoint Solutions (PA) ....F....925 829-4455
6690 Amador Plaza Rd # 225 Dublin (94568) *(P-24885)*
Materia Inc (PA) ....C....626 584-8400
60 N San Gabriel Blvd Pasadena (91107) *(P-7785)*
Material Control Inc ....E....661 617-6033
6901a District Blvd Bakersfield (93313) *(P-13957)*
Material Handling Division, Victorville *Also called Demag Cranes & Components Corp (P-14296)*
Material Handling Solutions ....F....909 908-9663
12359 Meritage Ct Rancho Cucamonga (91739) *(P-14336)*
Material In Motion Inc (PA) ....C....650 967-3300
385 Moffett Park Dr # 115 Sunnyvale (94089) *(P-15448)*
Material Supply Inc (PA) ....C....951 801-5004
11700 Industry Ave Fontana (92337) *(P-12658)*
Materials Development Corp (PA) ....F....818 700-8290
21541 Nordhoff St Ste B Chatsworth (91311) *(P-21801)*
Materials Innovation, Sunnyvale *Also called Jsr Micro Inc (P-9017)*
Materion Brush Inc ....E....510 623-1500
44036 S Grimmer Blvd Fremont (94538) *(P-13870)*
Matheson Tri-Gas Inc ....E....626 334-2905
16125 Ornelas St Irwindale (91706) *(P-7701)*
Matheson Tri-Gas Inc ....F....510 714-3026
6925 Central Ave Newark (94560) *(P-7702)*
Matheson Tri-Gas Inc ....E....909 758-5464
8800 Utica Ave Rancho Cucamonga (91730) *(P-7703)*
Matheson Tri-Gas Inc ....D....510 793-2559
6775 Central Ave Newark (94560) *(P-7704)*
Matheson Tri-Gas Inc ....F....323 773-2777
5555 District Blvd Vernon (90058) *(P-7705)*
Mathews Ready Mix LLC ....E....530 671-2400
249 Lamon St Yuba City (95991) *(P-11140)*
Mathews Readymix, Yuba City *Also called Mathews Ready Mix LLC (P-11140)*
Mathews Readymix Inc ....F....530 893-8856
1619 Skyway Chico (95928) *(P-11141)*
Mathy Machine Inc ....E....619 448-0404
9315 Wheatlands Rd Santee (92071) *(P-14444)*
Matko, San Bernardino *Also called Mkkr Inc (P-14654)*
Matrix Cab Parts Inc ....F....818 782-7022
7950 Woodley Ave Ste B Van Nuys (91406) *(P-4190)*
Matrix Concepts LLC ....F....661 253-1592
28010 Industry Dr Valencia (91355) *(P-21128)*
Matrix Document Imaging Inc ....D....626 966-9959
527 E Rowland St Ste 214 Covina (91723) *(P-7397)*
Matrix Logic Corporation ....F....415 893-9897
1380 East Ave Ste 124240 Chico (95926) *(P-24886)*
Matrix Millwork, Van Nuys *Also called Matrix Cab Parts Inc (P-4190)*
Matrix Shafts ....E....714 970-9977
4992 E Hunter Ave Anaheim (92807) *(P-23614)*
Matrix USA Inc ....E....714 825-0404
2730 S Main St Santa Ana (92707) *(P-18525)*
Matsmatsmats.com, Woodland Hills *Also called Tinyinklingcom LLC (P-9686)*
Matsuda House Printing Inc ....E....310 532-1533
1825 W 169th St Ste A Gardena (90247) *(P-6965)*
Matsui International Co Inc ....C....310 767-7812
1501 W 178th St Gardena (90248) *(P-9276)*
Matsun America Corp ....F....909 930-0779
4070 Greystone Dr Ste B Ontario (91761) *(P-3111)*
Matsusada Precision Inc ....F....650 877-0151
299 Harbor Way South San Francisco (94080) *(P-22936)*
Mattco Forge Inc (PA) ....D....562 634-8635
16443 Minnesota Ave Paramount (90723) *(P-13106)*
Matte Grey, Los Alamitos *Also called Haus of Grey LLC (P-3104)*
Mattel Inc (PA) ....A....310 252-2000
333 Continental Blvd El Segundo (90245) *(P-23440)*
Mattel Inc ....F....310 252-6434
2043 E Mariposa Ave El Segundo (90245) *(P-23441)*
Mattel Inc ....E....310 252-3384
333 Continental Blvd El Segundo (90245) *(P-23442)*
Mattel Inc ....F....909 382-3780
1456 E Harry Shepard Blvd San Bernardino (92408) *(P-23443)*
Mattel Direct Import Inc (HQ) ....F....310 252-2000
333 Continental Blvd El Segundo (90245) *(P-23444)*
Matteo LLC ....E....213 617-2813
1000 E Cesar E Chavez Ave Los Angeles (90033) *(P-3732)*
Matterhorn Filter Corporation ....F....310 329-8073
125 W Victoria St Gardena (90248) *(P-7786)*
Matterhorn Ice Cream Inc ....D....208 287-8916
1221 66th St Sacramento (95819) *(P-685)*
Matternet Inc ....E....650 260-2727
3511 Edison Way Menlo Park (94025) *(P-20877)*
Matthew Warren Inc ....E....805 928-3851
901 W Mccoy Ln Santa Maria (93455) *(P-13751)*
Matthew Warren Inc ....D....800 237-5225
5959 Triumph St Commerce (90040) *(P-13752)*
Matthews International Corp ....E....951 537-6615
442 W Esplanade Ave 105 San Jacinto (92583) *(P-11763)*
Matthews International Corp ....E....562 921-0994
5555 Fresca Dr La Palma (90623) *(P-14818)*
Matthews Manufacturing Inc ....E....323 980-4373
3301 E 14th St Los Angeles (90023) *(P-12659)*
Matthews Skyline Logging Inc ....E....707 743-2890
10100 East Rd Potter Valley (95469) *(P-4002)*
Matthews Studio Equipment Inc ....E....818 843-6715
4520 W Valerio St Burbank (91505) *(P-23177)*
Matthey Johnson Inc ....C....858 716-2400
12205 World Trade Dr San Diego (92128) *(P-11560)*
Matthey Johnson Inc ....C....858 716-2400
12205 World Trade Dr San Diego (92128) *(P-11561)*
Matthey Johnson Inc ....E....408 727-2221
1070 Coml St Ste 110 San Jose (95112) *(P-22520)*
Matthias Rath Inc (HQ) ....F....408 567-5000
1260 Memorex Dr Santa Clara (95050) *(P-630)*
Mattson Technology Inc (HQ) ....C....510 657-5900
47131 Bayside Pkwy Fremont (94538) *(P-14987)*
Matz Rubber Co Inc ....E....323 849-5170
1209 Chestnut St Burbank (91506) *(P-9634)*
Maui Imaging Inc ....F....408 744-1127
256 Gibraltar Dr Ste 110 Sunnyvale (94089) *(P-23006)*
Maui Toys ....E....330 747-4333
2951 28th St Ste 1000 Santa Monica (90405) *(P-23615)*
Maul Mfg Inc (PA) ....E....714 641-0727
3041 S Shannon St Santa Ana (92704) *(P-16722)*
Maurer Marine Inc ....F....949 645-7673
873 W 17th St Costa Mesa (92627) *(P-21055)*
Maurice & Maurice Engrg Inc ....E....760 949-5151
17579 Mesa St Ste B4 Hesperia (92345) *(P-11540)*
Maurice Carrie Winery ....E....951 676-1711
34225 Rancho Cal Rd Temecula (92591) *(P-1874)*
Maurice Landstrass ....E....650 355-5532
1667 Rosita Rd Pacifica (94044) *(P-21802)*
Maury Microwave Inc ....C....909 987-4715
2900 Inland Empire Blvd Ontario (91764) *(P-19640)*
Maury Razon ....F....818 989-6246
74 W Cochran St Ste A Simi Valley (93065) *(P-3670)*
Mave Enterprises Inc ....E....818 767-4533
11555 Cantara St Ste B-E North Hollywood (91605) *(P-1443)*
Mavens Creamery LLC ....E....408 216-9270
1701 S 7th St Ste 7 San Jose (95112) *(P-686)*
Maverick Abrasives Corporation ....E....714 854-9531
4340 E Miraloma Ave Anaheim (92807) *(P-11298)*

ALPHABETIC

Employee Codes: A=Over 500 employees, B=251-500
C=101-250, D=51-100, E=20-50, F=10-19
2019 California
Manfacturers Register
© Mergent Inc. 1-800-342-5647
1207

Maverick Aerospace Inc ....F.......714 578-1700
3718 Capitol Ave City of Industry (90601) ***(P-20878)***
Maverick Aerospace LLC ....F.......714 578-1700
3718 Capitol Ave City of Industry (90601) ***(P-20879)***
Maverick Aerospace LLC ....E.......714 578-1700
3718 Capitol Ave City of Industry (90601) ***(P-20880)***
Maverick Enterprises Inc ....C.......707 463-5591
751 E Gobbi St Ukiah (95482) ***(P-11579)***
Max Fischer & Sons Inc ....E.......213 624-8756
1327 Palmetto St Los Angeles (90013) ***(P-3733)***
Max Leon Inc (PA) ....D.......626 797-6886
3100 New York Dr Pasadena (91107) ***(P-3466)***
Max Muscle, Anaheim *Also called Peak Franchising Inc* ***(P-643)***
Max Precision Machine Inc ....F.......408 956-8986
2467 Autumnvale Dr San Jose (95131) ***(P-16723)***
Max Q, Ontario *Also called Maximum Quality Metal Pdts Inc* ***(P-12660)***
Max Smt Corp ....F.......877 589-9422
5675 Kimball Ct Chino (91710) ***(P-15131)***
Max Studio.com, Pasadena *Also called Max Leon Inc* ***(P-3466)***
Max-Q Systems Inc ....F.......714 259-0181
3449 Summerset Cir Costa Mesa (92626) ***(P-8654)***
Maxair Systems, Irvine *Also called Bio-Medical Devices Inc* ***(P-22365)***
Maxco Supply Inc ....D.......559 638-8449
2059 E Olsen Ave Reedley (93654) ***(P-5355)***
Maxford Technology LLC ....F.......408 855-8288
2225 Calle De Luna Santa Clara (95054) ***(P-11359)***
Maxim Integrated Products Inc (PA) ....A.......408 601-1000
160 Rio Robles San Jose (95134) ***(P-18984)***
Maxim Lighting ....C.......626 956-4200
253 Vineland Ave City of Industry (91746) ***(P-17546)***
Maxim Lighting Intl Inc (PA) ....C.......626 956-4200
253 Vineland Ave City of Industry (91746) ***(P-17547)***
Maxim Lighting Intl Inc ....D.......626 956-4200
247 Vineland Ave City of Industry (91746) ***(P-17548)***
Maxim-Dallas Direct Inc ....F.......800 659-5909
120 San Gabriel Dr Sunnyvale (94086) ***(P-18985)***
Maxima Racing Oils, Santee *Also called South West Lubricants Inc* ***(P-9450)***
Maxims Mattress Inc ....F.......323 721-5616
2553 Garfield Ave Commerce (90040) ***(P-4872)***
Maximum Quality Metal Pdts Inc ....E.......909 902-5018
1017 E Acacia St Ontario (91761) ***(P-12660)***
Maximus Holdings Inc ....A.......650 935-9500
2475 Hanover St Palo Alto (94304) ***(P-24887)***
Maxit Designs Inc ....F.......916 489-1023
4044 Wayside Ln Ste A Carmichael (95608) ***(P-2849)***
Maxlinear Inc (PA) ....E.......760 692-0711
5966 La Place Ct Ste 100 Carlsbad (92008) ***(P-18986)***
Maxlite Inc ....F.......714 678-5000
1148 N Ocean Cir Anaheim (92806) ***(P-17713)***
Maxon Crs LLC ....E.......424 236-4660
5400 W Rosecrans Ave # 105 Hawthorne (90250) ***(P-21001)***
Maxon Industries Inc ....D.......562 464-0099
11921 Slauson Ave Santa Fe Springs (90670) ***(P-20397)***
Maxstraps Inc ....D.......707 829-3000
925 Gravenstein Ave Sebastopol (95472) ***(P-2803)***
Maxtor Corporation (HQ) ....D.......831 438-6550
4575 Scotts Valley Dr Scotts Valley (95066) ***(P-15566)***
Maxtrol Corporation ....E.......714 245-0506
1701 E Edinger Ave Ste B6 Santa Ana (92705) ***(P-19641)***
Maxus Group, Walnut *Also called Prophecy Technology LLC* ***(P-15830)***
Maxwell Alarm Screen Mfg Inc ....E.......818 773-5533
20327 Nordhoff St Chatsworth (91311) ***(P-23921)***
Maxwell Sign and Decal Div, Chatsworth *Also called Maxwell Alarm Screen Mfg Inc* ***(P-23921)***
Maxwell Technologies Inc (PA) ....B.......858 503-3300
3888 Calle Fortunada San Diego (92123) ***(P-19838)***
Maxxess Systems Inc (PA) ....E.......714 772-1000
22661 Old Canal Rd Yorba Linda (92887) ***(P-24888)***
Maxxon Company, City of Industry *Also called Dennison Inc* ***(P-12849)***
Maya Steels Fabrication Inc ....D.......310 532-8830
301 E Compton Blvd Gardena (90248) ***(P-12203)***
Mayer Baking Co, Torrance *Also called Kopykake Enterprises Inc* ***(P-13240)***
Mayoni Enterprises ....D.......818 896-0026
10320 Glenoaks Blvd Pacoima (91331) ***(P-12661)***
Maysoft Inc ....F.......978 635-1700
1727 Santa Barbara St Santa Barbara (93101) ***(P-24889)***
Mazzei Injector Company LLC ....E.......661 363-6500
500 Rooster Dr Bakersfield (93307) ***(P-16069)***
MB Calram LLC, Camarillo *Also called Calram LLC* ***(P-13928)***
MB Sports Inc ....E.......209 357-4153
280 Airpark Rd Atwater (95301) ***(P-21056)***
MBA Electronics, Fremont *Also called William Ho* ***(P-15886)***
MBC Mattress Co Inc ....E.......951 371-8044
19270 Envoy Ave Corona (92881) ***(P-4873)***
Mbf Interiors Inc ....E.......858 565-2944
7831 Ostrow St San Diego (92111) ***(P-3697)***
Mbf Transportation LLC ....F.......562 282-0540
13610 Imperial Hwy Ste 6 Santa Fe Springs (90670) ***(P-21081)***
MBK Enterprises Inc ....E.......818 998-1477
9959 Canoga Ave Chatsworth (91311) ***(P-22767)***
MBK Tape Solutions, Chatsworth *Also called MBK Enterprises Inc* ***(P-22767)***
Mbtechnology ....E.......559 233-2181
188 S Teilman Ave Fresno (93706) ***(P-9413)***
Mc Allister Industries Inc (PA) ....E.......858 755-0683
731 S Highway 101 Ste 2 Solana Beach (92075) ***(P-7206)***
Mc Cain & Mc Cain Inc ....F.......661 322-7764
3801 Gilmore Ave Bakersfield (93308) ***(P-16724)***
Mc Clellan Bottling Group ....F.......530 241-2600
4712 Mountain Lakes Blvd Redding (96003) ***(P-2149)***
Mc Cormick G R Engrg & Mfg Co ....F.......818 848-8511
416 N Varney St Burbank (91502) ***(P-16725)***
Mc Cully Mac M Corporation ....E.......805 529-0661
12012 Hertz Ave Moorpark (93021) ***(P-17210)***
Mc Electronics LLC ....B.......831 637-1651
1891 Airway Dr Hollister (95023) ***(P-19642)***
Mc Intyre Coil, San Leandro *Also called Edge Electronics Corporation* ***(P-12387)***
Mc Lane Manufacturing Inc ....D.......562 633-8158
7110 Rosecrans Ave Paramount (90723) ***(P-14129)***
Mc Laughlin Mine, Lower Lake *Also called Barrick Gold Corporation* ***(P-1)***
Mc Liquidation Inc ....E.......408 636-1020
570 Del Rey Ave Sunnyvale (94085) ***(P-23007)***
Mc Products Inc ....F.......949 888-7100
23331 Antonio Pkwy Rcho STA Marg (92688) ***(P-9277)***
Mc William & Son Inc ....F.......626 969-1821
421 S Irwindale Ave Azusa (91702) ***(P-13245)***
Mc-Dowell-Craig Mfgco (PA) ....F.......714 521-7170
13146 Firestone Blvd Santa Fe Springs (90670) ***(P-4994)***
Mc2 Sabtech Holdings Inc (PA) ....E.......714 692-3800
22705 Savi Ranch Pkwy Yorba Linda (92887) ***(P-15449)***
McAero LLC ....F.......310 787-9911
12711 Imperial Hwy Santa Fe Springs (90670) ***(P-16726)***
McAfee Inc ....D.......858 967-2342
6707 Barnhurst Dr San Diego (92117) ***(P-24890)***
McAfee LLC (HQ) ....C.......888 847-8766
2821 Mission College Blvd Santa Clara (95054) ***(P-24891)***
McAfee Finance 2 LLC ....A.......888 847-8766
2821 Mission College Blvd Santa Clara (95054) ***(P-24892)***
McAfee Security LLC ....A.......866 622-3911
2821 Mission College Blvd Santa Clara (95054) ***(P-24893)***
McBain Instruments Inc ....F.......805 581-6800
1650 Voyager Ave Ste B Simi Valley (93063) ***(P-22104)***
McC Controls LLC ....E.......218 847-1317
859 Cotting Ct Ste G Vacaville (95688) ***(P-16070)***
McCain Manufacturing Inc ....D.......760 295-9290
2633 Progress St Vista (92081) ***(P-12204)***
McCalls Country Canning Inc ....F.......951 461-2277
41735 Cherry St Murrieta (92562) ***(P-24169)***
McCarthy Ranch ....F.......408 356-2300
15425 Los Gatos Blvd # 102 Los Gatos (95032) ***(P-4577)***
McCarthys Draperies Inc ....E.......916 422-0155
6955 Luther Dr Sacramento (95823) ***(P-3698)***
McCash Manufacturing Inc ....E.......408 748-8991
1256 Washoe Dr San Jose (95120) ***(P-22521)***
McClatchy Company (PA) ....C.......916 321-1844
2100 Q St Sacramento (95816) ***(P-5943)***
McClatchy Newspapers Inc (HQ) ....A.......916 321-1855
2100 Q St Sacramento (95816) ***(P-5944)***
McClatchy Newspapers Inc ....B.......559 441-6111
1626 E St Fresno (93706) ***(P-5945)***
McClatchy Newspapers Inc ....F.......209 578-2007
948 11th St Ste 30 Modesto (95354) ***(P-5946)***
McClatchy Newspapers Inc ....B.......209 238-4636
1325 H St Modesto (95354) ***(P-5947)***
McClatchy Newspapers Inc ....D.......209 826-3831
907 6th St Los Banos (93635) ***(P-5948)***
McClatchy Newspapers Inc ....C.......209 722-1511
3033 G St Merced (95340) ***(P-5949)***
McClatchy Newspapers Inc ....B.......209 587-2250
948 11th St Ste 30 Modesto (95354) ***(P-5950)***
McClatchy Newspapers Inc ....D.......805 927-8652
2068 Main St Cambria (93428) ***(P-5951)***
McClatchy Newspapers Inc ....D.......408 200-1000
4 N 2nd St Ste 800 San Jose (95113) ***(P-5952)***
McClatchy Newspapers Inc ....C.......805 781-7800
3825 S Higuera St San Luis Obispo (93401) ***(P-5953)***
McCoppin Enterprises ....E.......818 240-4840
6641 San Fernando Rd Glendale (91201) ***(P-16727)***
McCormacks Guides Inc ....F.......925 229-1869
3211 Elmquist Ct Martinez (94553) ***(P-6525)***
McCormick & Company Inc ....D.......714 685-0934
180 N Riverview Dr Anaheim (92808) ***(P-2600)***
McCormick & Company Inc ....D.......831 775-3350
340 El Cam Ste 20 Salinas (93901) ***(P-2601)***
McCormick & Company Inc ....C.......831 758-2411
340 El Camino Real S # 20 Salinas (93901) ***(P-2602)***
McCormick Fresh Herbs LLC ....D.......323 278-9750
1575 W Walnut Pkwy Compton (90220) ***(P-2603)***
McCrometer Inc ....C.......951 652-6811
3255 W Stetson Ave Hemet (92545) ***(P-21691)***
McCullough Aero Company, Santa Fe Springs *Also called McAero LLC* ***(P-16726)***
McDaniel Inc ....F.......909 591-8353
10807 Monte Vista Ave Montclair (91763) ***(P-11514)***
McDaniel Manufacturing Inc ....F.......530 626-6336
6180 Enterprise Dr Ste D Diamond Springs (95619) ***(P-11974)***
McDowell & Craig Off Systems ....D.......562 921-4441
13146 Firestone Blvd Norwalk (90650) ***(P-4995)***
McDowell Craig, Santa Fe Springs *Also called Mc-Dowell-Craig Mfgco* ***(P-4994)***
McDowell Publishers, Ontario *Also called Alpha Publishing Corporation* ***(P-6306)***
McDowell-Craig Office Furn, Norwalk *Also called McDowell & Craig Off Systems* ***(P-4995)***
McE, Rancho Cordova *Also called Nidec Motor Corporation* ***(P-14254)***
McElroy Metal Mill Inc ....E.......760 246-5545
17031 Koala Rd Adelanto (92301) ***(P-12943)***
McEvoy of Marin LLC ....D.......707 778-2307
5935 Red Hill Rd Petaluma (94952) ***(P-1544)***
McEvoy Properties LLC ....C.......415 537-4200
680 2nd St San Francisco (94107) ***(P-6361)***
McEvoy Ranch, Petaluma *Also called McEvoy of Marin LLC* ***(P-1544)***
McGrath Rentcorp ....C.......951 360-6600
11450 Mission Blvd Mira Loma (91752) ***(P-12944)***

McGrayel Company Inc .... E 559 299-7660
5361 S Villa Ave Fresno (93725) **(P-9278)**
McGuff Pharmaceuticals Inc .... E 714 918-7277
2921 W Macarthur Blvd # 142 Santa Ana (92704) **(P-8268)**
McGuire Furniture, San Francisco *Also called Baker Interiors Furniture Co* **(P-4907)**
McGunagle William H & Sons Mfg (PA) .... F 707 762-7900
971 Transport Way Ste B Petaluma (94954) **(P-4718)**
McHale Sign Company Inc .... F 530 223-2030
3707 Electro Way Redding (96002) **(P-23922)**
McIntire Tool Die & Machine (PA) .... F 909 888-0440
308 S Mountain View Ave San Bernardino (92408) **(P-13246)**
McIntyre Industries, San Leandro *Also called Optimization Corporation* **(P-15169)**
McKeague Patpatrick .... F 805 541-4593
1339 Marsh St San Luis Obispo (93401) **(P-6362)**
McKeever Danlee Confectionary .... E 626 334-8964
760 N Mckeever Ave Azusa (91702) **(P-1444)**
McKenna Boiler Works Inc .... F 323 221-1171
1510 N Spring St Los Angeles (90012) **(P-12398)**
McKenna Labs Inc (PA) .... E 714 687-6888
1601 E Orangethorpe Ave Fullerton (92831) **(P-8269)**
McKenzie Machining Inc .... F 408 748-8885
481 Perry Ct Santa Clara (95054) **(P-16728)**
McKinnon Enterprises .... E 858 571-1818
4577 Viewridge Ave San Diego (92123) **(P-6215)**
McLaren Industries Inc (PA) .... E 310 212-1333
12440 Carson St Hawaiian Gardens (90716) **(P-9466)**
McLean Brewery Inc .... E 415 864-7468
1398 Haight St San Francisco (94117) **(P-1609)**
McLellan Equipment Inc (PA) .... D 650 873-8100
251 Shaw Rd South San Francisco (94080) **(P-20215)**
McLellan Equipment Inc .... D 559 582-8100
13221 Crown Ave Hanford (93230) **(P-20216)**
McLellan Industries Inc .... D 650 873-8100
13221 Crown Ave Hanford (93230) **(P-20217)**
McLeod Racing LLC .... F 714 630-2764
1570 Lakeview Loop Anaheim (92807) **(P-20398)**
McM Fabricators Inc .... C 661 589-2774
720 Commerce Way Shafter (93263) **(P-12205)**
McMahon Steel Company Inc .... C 619 671-9700
1880 Nirvana Ave Chula Vista (91911) **(P-11975)**
McMillan - Hendryx Inc .... F 209 538-2300
3924 Starlite Dr Ste B Ceres (95307) **(P-9543)**
McMillin Mfg Corp .... D 323 981-8585
40 E Verdugo Ave Burbank (91502) **(P-12662)**
McMillin Wire Products, Burbank *Also called McMillin Mfg Corp* **(P-12662)**
McMurtrie & Mcmurtrie Inc .... D 626 815-0177
915 W 5th St Azusa (91702) **(P-4084)**
McNab Ridge Winery, Ukiah *Also called Plc LLC* **(P-1927)**
McNab Ridge Winery LLC .... F 707 462-2423
2350 Mcnab Ranch Rd Ukiah (95482) **(P-1875)**
McNaughton Newspapers .... D 530 756-0800
315 G St Davis (95616) **(P-5954)**
McNaughton Newspapers Inc (PA) .... D 707 425-4646
1250 Texas St Fairfield (94533) **(P-5955)**
McNeal Enterprises Inc .... D 408 922-7290
2031 Ringwood Ave San Jose (95131) **(P-10201)**
McNear Brick & Block, San Rafael *Also called L P McNear Brick Co Inc* **(P-10854)**
McNeilus Truck and Mfg Inc .... E 909 370-2100
401 N Pepper Ave Colton (92324) **(P-20218)**
MCP Industries Inc (PA) .... F 951 736-1881
708 S Temescal St Ste 101 Corona (92879) **(P-9635)**
MCP Industries Inc .... E 951 736-1313
1660 Leeson Ln Corona (92879) **(P-12040)**
McQuaide Brothers Corporation .... F 619 444-9932
11919 Woodside Ave Lakeside (92040) **(P-20506)**
McRoskey Mattress, San Francisco *Also called Pleasant Mattress Inc* **(P-4878)**
McRoskey Mattress, San Francisco *Also called Pleasant Mattress Inc* **(P-4880)**
McStarlite, Harbor City *Also called Basmat Inc* **(P-12502)**
McUbe Inc (PA) .... E 408 637-5503
2570 N 1st St Ste 300 San Jose (95131) **(P-15450)**
McV Microwave, San Diego *Also called McV Technologies Inc* **(P-18176)**
McV Technologies Inc .... F 858 450-0468
6349 Nancy Ridge Dr San Diego (92121) **(P-18176)**
McWane Inc (PA) .... C 510 632-3467
7825 San Leandro St Oakland (94621) **(P-11498)**
McWhirter Steel Inc .... F 661 951-8998
42211 7th St E Lancaster (93535) **(P-12206)**
MD Engineering Inc .... E 951 736-5390
1550 Consumer Cir Corona (92880) **(P-16729)**
MD Manufacturing Inc .... F 661 283-7550
34970 Mcmurtrey Ave Bakersfield (93308) **(P-16071)**
MD Software Enterprise, San Bernardino *Also called M D Software Inc* **(P-24872)**
MD Stainless Services .... E 562 904-7022
8241 Phlox St Downey (90241) **(P-13897)**
Md-Staff, Temecula *Also called Applied Statistics & MGT Inc* **(P-24374)**
Mda Cmmunications Holdings LLC .... A 650 852-4000
3825 Fabian Way Palo Alto (94303) **(P-18177)**
Mdc Interior Solutions LLC .... D 800 621-4006
6900 E Washington Blvd Los Angeles (90040) **(P-3671)**
Mdc Vacuum Products LLC (PA) .... D 510 265-3500
30962 Santana St Hayward (94544) **(P-18987)**
Mdc Vacuum Products LLC .... D 510 265-3500
23874b Cabot Blvd Hayward (94545) **(P-13725)**
MDE Semiconductor Inc .... D 760 564-8656
78150 Calle Tampico # 210 La Quinta (92253) **(P-17347)**
Mdi, Riverside *Also called Molded Devices Inc* **(P-10219)**
Mdi East Inc (HQ) .... E 951 509-6918
6918 Ed Perkic St Riverside (92504) **(P-10202)**
Mds, Tarzana *Also called Universal Merchandise Inc* **(P-3047)**
ME & ME Costumes Inc .... F 323 876-4432
1117 N Formosa Ave West Hollywood (90046) **(P-23178)**
Meade Instruments Corp .... D 949 451-1450
27 Hubble Irvine (92618) **(P-22105)**
Meadow Decor Inc .... F 909 923-2558
1477 E Cedar St Ste A Ontario (91761) **(P-4912)**
Meadow Farms Sausage Co Inc .... F 323 752-2300
6215 S Western Ave Los Angeles (90047) **(P-506)**
Meadows Mechanical, Gardena *Also called Meadows Sheet Metal and AC Inc* **(P-12663)**
Meadows Sheet Metal and AC Inc .... E 310 615-1125
333 Crown Vista Dr Gardena (90248) **(P-12663)**
Mealenders, San Francisco *Also called Willpower Labs Inc* **(P-8444)**
Mean Well Usa Inc .... F 510 683-8886
44030 Fremont Blvd Fremont (94538) **(P-19643)**
Means Engineering Inc .... D 760 931-9452
5927 Geiger Ct Carlsbad (92008) **(P-21990)**
Measurement Specialties Inc .... D 818 701-2750
20630 Plummer St Chatsworth (91311) **(P-22231)**
Measurement Specialties Inc .... D 530 273-4608
424 Crown Point Cir Grass Valley (95945) **(P-21803)**
Meat Packers Butchers Sup Inc .... F 323 268-8514
2820 E Washington Blvd Los Angeles (90023) **(P-14870)**
Meca Aerospace, Santa Ana *Also called Mecadaq Aerospace LLC* **(P-14649)**
Mecadaq Aerospace LLC .... F 714 442-9703
2806 S Susan St Santa Ana (92704) **(P-14649)**
Mechancal Systm-Rial Refueling, Yorba Linda *Also called GE Aviation Systems LLC* **(P-20822)**
Mechanical and Mch Repr Svcs .... F 909 625-8705
10584 Silicon Ave Montclair (91763) **(P-16730)**
Mechanical Bookbinding, Baldwin Park *Also called Cal Bind* **(P-7595)**
Mechanix Wear Inc (PA) .... D 800 222-4296
28525 Witherspoon Pkwy Valencia (91355) **(P-3602)**
Mechanized Engineering Systems .... F 310 830-9763
737 E 223rd St Carson (90745) **(P-14337)**
Mechanized Enterprises Inc .... F 714 630-5512
1140 N Kraemer Blvd Ste M Anaheim (92806) **(P-16731)**
Mechanized Science Seals Inc .... E 714 898-5602
5322 Mcfadden Ave Huntington Beach (92649) **(P-22232)**
Meco-Nag Corporation .... D 818 764-2020
7306 Laurel Canyon Blvd North Hollywood (91605) **(P-10499)**
Mecoptron Inc .... E 510 226-9966
3115 Osgood Ct Fremont (94539) **(P-16732)**
Mecpro Inc .... E 408 727-9757
980 George St Santa Clara (95054) **(P-16733)**
Mectec Molds Inc .... F 909 981-3636
1525 Howard Access Rd D Upland (91786) **(P-14540)**
Med, Clovis *Also called Machine Exprnce & Design Inc* **(P-16705)**
Med Mart, San Leandro *Also called Braden Partners LP A Calif* **(P-22956)**
Med-Fit Systems Inc .... C 760 723-3618
3553 Rosa Way Fallbrook (92028) **(P-23616)**
Med-Pharmex Inc .... F 909 593-7875
2727 Thompson Creek Rd Pomona (91767) **(P-8270)**
Med-Safe Systems Inc .... C 855 236-2772
10975 Torreyana Rd San Diego (92121) **(P-22522)**
Medallia Inc (PA) .... C 650 321-3000
450 Concar Dr San Mateo (94402) **(P-24894)**
Medata Inc (PA) .... D 714 918-1310
5 Peters Canyon Rd # 250 Irvine (92606) **(P-24895)**
Medconx Inc .... E 408 330-0003
2901 Tasman Dr Ste 211 Santa Clara (95054) **(P-9636)**
Mededge Inc .... F 310 745-2290
11965 Venice Blvd Ste 407 Los Angeles (90066) **(P-22523)**
Medegen LLC (HQ) .... E 909 390-9080
4501 E Wall St Ontario (91761) **(P-10203)**
Medelita LLC .... F 949 542-4100
23456 S Pointe Dr Ste A Laguna Hills (92653) **(P-3035)**
Medennium Inc (PA) .... E 949 789-9000
9 Parker Ste 150 Irvine (92618) **(P-23109)**
Medgear, Cerritos *Also called LA Triumph Inc* **(P-3110)**
Medi Kid Company .... F 951 925-8800
448 S Palm Ave Ste A Hemet (92543) **(P-22768)**
Media Blast & Abrasive Inc .... F 714 257-0484
591 Apollo St Brea (92821) **(P-16072)**
Media Gobbler Inc .... F 323 203-3222
6427 W Sunset Blvd Los Angeles (90028) **(P-24896)**
Media King Inc .... E 626 288-4558
140 W Valley Blvd 201a San Gabriel (91776) **(P-20013)**
Media Nation Enterprises LLC (PA) .... E 888 502-8222
15271 Barranca Pkwy Irvine (92618) **(P-23923)**
Media Nation USA, Irvine *Also called Media Nation Enterprises LLC* **(P-23923)**
Media News, Paradise *Also called Califrnia Nwspapers Ltd Partnr* **(P-5793)**
Media News Group .... F 707 459-4643
77 W Commercial St Willits (95490) **(P-5956)**
Media News Groups, Vacaville *Also called Reporter* **(P-6026)**
Media Products, San Jose *Also called Dynamikos Inc* **(P-9837)**
Medianews Group Inc .... D 562 435-1161
300 Oceangate Ste 150 Long Beach (90802) **(P-5957)**
Medianews Group Inc .... A 818 713-3000
21860 Burbank Blvd # 200 Woodland Hills (91367) **(P-5958)**
Medianews Group Inc .... C 310 540-5511
5215 Torrance Blvd Torrance (90503) **(P-5959)**
Medianews Group Inc .... B 408 920-5713
4 N 2nd St Ste 800 San Jose (95113) **(P-5960)**
Medianews Group Inc .... C 650 391-1000
255 Constitution Dr Menlo Park (94025) **(P-5961)**
Medianews Group Inc .... E 530 662-5421
711 Main St Woodland (95695) **(P-5962)**
Medianews Group Inc .... C 661 257-5200
24800 Ave Rockefeller Valencia (91355) **(P-5963)**

ALPHABETIC

Employee Codes: A=Over 500 employees, B=251-500
C=101-250, D=51-100, E=20-50, F=10-19
2019 California
Manfacturers Register
© Mergent Inc. 1-800-342-5647
1209

Medianews Group Inc......C......707 994-6656
14913 Lakeshore Dr Clearlake (95422) *(P-5964)*
Medianews Group Inc......E......530 527-2151
728 Main St Red Bluff (96080) *(P-5965)*
Mediapointe Inc......F......805 480-3700
3952 Camino Ranchero Camarillo (93012) *(P-17830)*
Mediatek USA Inc (PA)......C......408 526-1899
2840 Junction Ave San Jose (95134) *(P-15451)*
Mediatek USA Inc......F......408 526-1899
96 Corporate Park Ste 300 Irvine (92606) *(P-15452)*
Medic I D'S Internatl, Woodland Hills *Also called Medic Ids (P-24170)*
Medic Ids......F......818 705-0595
20350 Ventura Blvd # 140 Woodland Hills (91364) *(P-24170)*
Medical Aesthetics Menlo Park......F......650 336-3358
885 Oak Grove Ave Ste 101 Menlo Park (94025) *(P-22524)*
Medical Analysis Systems Inc (HQ)......C......510 979-5000
46360 Fremont Blvd Fremont (94538) *(P-8494)*
Medical Breakthrough Massage......E......408 677-7702
28016 Industry Dr Valencia (91355) *(P-24171)*
Medical Chemical Corporation......E......310 787-6800
19430 Van Ness Ave Torrance (90501) *(P-9279)*
Medical Data Recovery Inc......F......949 251-0073
17310 Red Hill Ave # 270 Irvine (92614) *(P-24897)*
Medical Device Manufacturing, Brea *Also called Life Science Outsourcing Inc (P-22508)*
Medical Device Resource Corp......F......510 732-9950
5981 Graham Ct Livermore (94550) *(P-22525)*
Medical Devices Manufacturer, Morgan Hill *Also called Oncogenesis Inc (P-22569)*
Medical Extrusion Tech Inc (PA)......E......951 698-4346
26608 Pierce Cir Ste A Murrieta (92562) *(P-9742)*
Medical Instr Dev Labs Inc......E......510 357-3952
557 Mccormick St San Leandro (94577) *(P-22526)*
Medical Packaging Corporation......D......805 388-2383
941 Avenida Acaso Camarillo (93012) *(P-22769)*
Medical Tactile Inc......F......310 641-8228
5757 W Century Blvd # 600 Los Angeles (90045) *(P-22527)*
Medical Transcription Billing......A......800 869-3700
405 Kenyon St Ste 300 San Diego (92110) *(P-24898)*
Medicines360......F......415 951-8700
353 Sacramento St Ste 300 San Francisco (94111) *(P-8271)*
Medicinova Inc (PA)......F......858 373-1500
4275 Executive Sq Ste 300 La Jolla (92037) *(P-8272)*
Medicool Inc......F......310 782-2200
20460 Gramercy Pl Torrance (90501) *(P-22528)*
Medifarm So Cal Inc......E......855 447-6967
2040 Main St Ste 225 Irvine (92614) *(P-14084)*
Medigreens, Huntington Beach *Also called Mgfso LLC (P-8282)*
Medika Health Care, Fremont *Also called Medika Therapeutics Inc (P-22529)*
Medika Therapeutics Inc......F......510 377-0898
4046 Clipper Ct Fremont (94538) *(P-22529)*
Mediland Corporation......D......562 630-9696
7027 Motz St Paramount (90723) *(P-10602)*
Medimmune LLC......B......650 603-2000
297 Bernardo Ave Mountain View (94043) *(P-8273)*
Medimmune LLC......D......650 603-2000
319 Bernardo Ave Mountain View (94043) *(P-8274)*
Medimmune Vaccines, Mountain View *Also called Medimmune LLC (P-8273)*
Medina Medical Inc......F......650 396-7756
39684 Eureka Dr Newark (94560) *(P-22530)*
Medina Wood Products Inc......F......209 832-4523
26342 S Banta Rd Tracy (95304) *(P-4488)*
Mediostream Inc......E......650 625-8900
4962 El Camino Real # 120 Los Altos (94022) *(P-19869)*
Medisense, Alameda *Also called Abbott Diabetes Care Inc (P-8454)*
Meditab Software Inc......C......510 632-2021
333 Hegenberger Rd # 800 Oakland (94621) *(P-24899)*
Medium Entertainment Inc......E......469 951-2688
501 Folsom St Fl 1 San Francisco (94105) *(P-23445)*
Medius, San Jose *Also called Babylon Printing Inc (P-6680)*
Medivation Inc (HQ)......C......415 543-3470
525 Market St Ste 3600 San Francisco (94105) *(P-8275)*
Medivision Inc......F......714 563-2772
4883 E La Palma Ave # 503 Anaheim (92807) *(P-23008)*
Medivision Optics, Anaheim *Also called Medivision Inc (P-23008)*
Medleycom Incorporated......F......408 745-5418
910 E Hamilton Ave Fl 6 Campbell (95008) *(P-5966)*
Medlin & Son Engrg Servinc......D......562 464-5889
12484 Whittier Blvd Whittier (90602) *(P-16734)*
Medlin & Sons, Whittier *Also called Medlin & Son Engrg Servinc (P-16734)*
Medlin Equipment, Santa Fe Springs *Also called Medlin Material Handling Eqp (P-14445)*
Medlin Material Handling Eqp......F......562 229-1991
14903 Marquardt Ave Santa Fe Springs (90670) *(P-14445)*
Medline Industires, Temecula *Also called Medline Industries Inc (P-22770)*
Medline Industries Inc......F......951 296-2600
42500 Winchester Rd Temecula (92590) *(P-22770)*
Medplast Group Inc......D......951 273-1700
3125 E Coronado St Anaheim (92806) *(P-10204)*
Medplast Group Inc......C......510 657-5800
45581 Northport Loop W Fremont (94538) *(P-10205)*
Medrano Raymundo......E......909 947-5507
1752 S Bon View Ave Ontario (91761) *(P-2954)*
Medrio Inc (PA)......E......415 963-3700
345 California St Ste 325 San Francisco (94104) *(P-24900)*
Medtronic Inc......B......949 798-3934
1659 Gailes Blvd San Diego (92154) *(P-23009)*
Medtronic Inc......C......510 985-9670
2200 Powell St Emeryville (94608) *(P-23010)*
Medtronic Inc......F......805 571-3769
125 Cremona Dr Goleta (93117) *(P-23011)*
Medtronic Inc......C......300 646-4633
18000 Devonshire St Northridge (91325) *(P-23012)*
Medtronic Inc......F......949 486-9973
9 Parker Irvine (92618) *(P-23013)*
Medtronic Inc......D......707 541-3281
3576 Unocal Pl Bldg B Santa Rosa (95403) *(P-22771)*
Medtronic Inc......E......949 837-3700
9775 Toledo Way Irvine (92618) *(P-23014)*
Medtronic Inc......E......707 541-3144
5345 Skyllane Blvd Santa Rosa (95403) *(P-22531)*
Medtronic Inc......D......949 474-3943
1851 E Deere Ave Santa Ana (92705) *(P-23015)*
Medtronic Inc......E......408 548-6618
1860 Barber Ln Milpitas (95035) *(P-23016)*
Medtronic Inc......E......951 332-3600
11811 Landon Dr Mira Loma (91752) *(P-23017)*
Medtronic Ats Medical Inc......E......949 380-9333
1851 E Deere Ave Santa Ana (92705) *(P-22532)*
Medtronic Minimed Inc (HQ)......A......800 646-4633
18000 Devonshire St Northridge (91325) *(P-23018)*
Medtronic PS Medical Inc (HQ)......C......805 571-3769
125 Cremona Dr Goleta (93117) *(P-22533)*
Medtronic Spine LLC (HQ)......C......408 548-6500
1221 Crossman Ave Sunnyvale (94089) *(P-22534)*
Medwaves Inc (PA)......F......858 946-0015
16760 W Bernardo Dr San Diego (92127) *(P-22535)*
Medway Plastics Corporation......C......562 630-1175
2250 E Cherry Indus Cir Long Beach (90805) *(P-10206)*
Medweb, San Francisco *Also called Nexsys Electronics Inc (P-15813)*
Mee Audio, City of Industry *Also called S2e Inc (P-17852)*
Mee Industries Inc (PA)......F......626 359-4550
16021 Adelante St Irwindale (91702) *(P-15970)*
Meeder Equipment Company (PA)......E......559 485-0979
3495 S Maple Ave Fresno (93725) *(P-14988)*
Meerkat Inc......F......909 877-0093
434 S Yucca Ave Rialto (92376) *(P-16735)*
Meese Inc......E......714 739-4005
16404 Knott Ave La Mirada (90638) *(P-10207)*
Meese Obitron Dunn Co, La Mirada *Also called Meese Inc (P-10207)*
Meetville Inc......C......415 755-0822
1465 Civic Ct Concord (94520) *(P-6526)*
Mega Brands America Inc (HQ)......D......949 727-9009
3 Ada Ste 200 Irvine (92618) *(P-23446)*
Mega Force Corporation......E......408 956-9989
2035 Otoole Ave San Jose (95131) *(P-15801)*
Mega Led Technology, Commerce *Also called Mega Sign Inc (P-23924)*
Mega Machinery Inc......F......951 300-9300
6688 Doolittle Ave Riverside (92503) *(P-14989)*
Mega Plus Pcb Incorporated......F......714 550-0265
4091 E La Palma Ave Ste M Anaheim (92807) *(P-18526)*
Mega Precision O Rings Inc......F......310 530-1166
23206 Normandie Ave Ste 5 Torrance (90502) *(P-16736)*
Mega Sign Inc......E......888 315-7446
6500 Flotilla St Commerce (90040) *(P-23924)*
Megachips Technology Amer Corp (HQ)......E......408 570-0555
2755 Orchard Pkwy San Jose (95134) *(P-18988)*
Megacycle Cams, San Rafael *Also called Megacycle Engineering Inc (P-21129)*
Megacycle Engineering Inc......F......415 472-3195
90 Mitchell Blvd San Rafael (94903) *(P-21129)*
Megaforce, San Jose *Also called Mega Force Corporation (P-15801)*
Megaprint Digital Prtg Corp......F......650 517-0200
1404 Old County Rd Belmont (94002) *(P-6966)*
Megavision Inc......F......805 964-1400
5765 Thornwood Dr Goleta (93117) *(P-20014)*
Meggitt......C......877 666-0712
1785 Voyager Ave Ste 100 Simi Valley (93063) *(P-20881)*
Meggitt (orange County) Inc (HQ)......B......949 493-8181
14600 Myford Rd Irvine (92606) *(P-22233)*
Meggitt (orange County) Inc......F......408 739-3533
355 N Pastoria Ave Sunnyvale (94085) *(P-21345)*
Meggitt (san Diego) Inc (HQ)......C......858 824-8976
6650 Top Gun St San Diego (92121) *(P-20882)*
Meggitt Aerospace, Sunnyvale *Also called Meggitt (orange County) Inc (P-21345)*
Meggitt Airdynamics Inc (HQ)......E......951 734-0070
2616 Research Dr Corona (92882) *(P-15168)*
Meggitt Arcft Braking Systems, Gardena *Also called Nasco Aircraft Brake Inc (P-20895)*
Meggitt Control Systems, Simi Valley *Also called Meggitt Safety Systems Inc (P-20015)*
Meggitt Control Systems, North Hollywood *Also called Meggitt North Hollywood Inc (P-13726)*
Meggitt Defense Systems Inc......C......949 465-7700
9801 Muirlands Blvd Irvine (92618) *(P-20883)*
Meggitt North Hollywood Inc (HQ)......C......818 765-8160
12838 Saticoy St North Hollywood (91605) *(P-13726)*
Meggitt Polymers & Composites, Simi Valley *Also called Meggitt-Usa Inc (P-20884)*
Meggitt Polymers & Composites, San Diego *Also called Meggitt (san Diego) Inc (P-20882)*
Meggitt Safety Systems Inc (HQ)......C......805 584-4100
1785 Voyager Ave Simi Valley (93063) *(P-20015)*
Meggitt Safety Systems Inc......C......805 584-4100
1785 Voyager Ave Ste 100 Simi Valley (93063) *(P-21346)*
Meggitt Sensing Systems, Irvine *Also called Meggitt (orange County) Inc (P-22233)*
Meggitt-Usa Inc (HQ)......B......805 526-5700
1955 Surveyor Ave Simi Valley (93063) *(P-20884)*
Megiddo Global LLC......F......818 267-6686
153 W Rosecrans Ave Gardena (90248) *(P-24172)*
Meguiars Inc (HQ)......E......949 752-8000
17991 Mitchell S Irvine (92614) *(P-8655)*
MEI Pharma Inc......E......858 369-7100
3611 Vly Cntre Dr Ste 500 San Diego (92130) *(P-8276)*

Mergent e-mail: customerrelations@mergent.com 2019 California (P-0000) Products & Services Section entry number
1210 Manufacturers Register (PA)=Parent Co (HQ)=Headquarters (DH)=Div Headquarters

Meisei Corporation ....F 805 497-2626
3350 Willow Ln Thousand Oaks (91361) *(P-14707)*

Meister Eye & Laser, Citrus Heights Also called Nvision Laser Eye Centers Inc *(P-23111)*

Meivac Incorporated ....E 408 362-1000
5830 Hellyer Ave San Jose (95138) *(P-18989)*

Mekong Printing Inc ....E 714 558-9595
2421 W 1st St Santa Ana (92703) *(P-6967)*

Mel & Associates Inc (PA) ....F 831 476-2950
821 41st Ave Santa Cruz (95062) *(P-23617)*

Melamed International Inc (PA) ....F 310 271-8585
113 N Palm Dr Beverly Hills (90210) *(P-3178)*

Melcast, Cerritos Also called Molino Company *(P-6979)*

Melco Engineering Corporation ....F 818 591-1000
3605 Avenida Cumbre Calabasas (91302) *(P-22536)*

Melco Steel Inc ....E 626 334-7875
1100 W Foothill Blvd Azusa (91702) *(P-12399)*

Melfred Borzall Inc ....F 562 946-7524
12115 Shoemaker Ave Santa Fe Springs (90670) *(P-16737)*

Melfred Borzall Inc ....E 805 614-4344
2712 Airpark Dr Santa Maria (93455) *(P-14392)*

Melian Labs Inc ....F 888 423-1944
988 Market St Ste 600 San Francisco (94102) *(P-24901)*

Melkes Machine Inc ....E 626 448-5062
9928 Hayward Way South El Monte (91733) *(P-16738)*

Melkonian Enterprises Inc ....E 559 485-6191
2730 S De Wolf Ave Sanger (93657) *(P-887)*

Mellace Family Brands Inc ....C 760 448-1940
6195 El Camino Real Carlsbad (92009) *(P-1496)*

Mellace Family Brands Cal Inc ....E 760 448-1940
6195 El Camino Real Carlsbad (92009) *(P-1497)*

Mellanox Technologies Inc ....E 408 970-3400
350 Oakmead Pkwy Ste 100 Sunnyvale (94085) *(P-18990)*

Mellanox Technologies Inc (HQ) ......C 408 970-3400
350 Oakmead Pkwy Sunnyvale (94085) *(P-18991)*

Melles Griot Inc ....F 760 438-2131
2072 Corte Del Nogal Carlsbad (92011) *(P-22106)*

Melling Sintered Metals, Gardena Also called Melling Tool Rush Metals LLC *(P-11842)*

Melling Tool Rush Metals LLC ....D 580 725-3295
16100 S Figueroa St Gardena (90248) *(P-11842)*

Melmarc Products Inc ....F 714 460-6691
752 S Campus Ave Ontario (91761) *(P-3179)*

Melmarc Products Inc (PA) ....B 714 549-2170
752 S Campus Ave Ontario (91761) *(P-3852)*

Melrose Bakery, Los Angeles Also called Napoleon Bakery Inc *(P-1294)*

Melrose Mac Inc ....F 818 840-8466
2400 W Olive Ave Burbank (91506) *(P-15453)*

Melrose Metal Products Inc ....E 510 657-8771
44533 S Grimmer Blvd Fremont (94538) *(P-12664)*

Melrose Nameplate and Label Co (PA) ...E 510 732-3100
26575 Corporate Ave Hayward (94545) *(P-13616)*

Melville Winery LLC ....F 805 735-7030
5185 E Highway 246 Lompoc (93436) *(P-1876)*

Membrane Switch and Panel Inc ......F 714 957-6905
3198 Arprt Loop Dr Ste K Costa Mesa (92626) *(P-19644)*

Memjet Labels Inc (HQ) ....F 858 798-3300
10920 Via Frontera # 120 San Diego (92127) *(P-15802)*

Memjet Labels Inc ....E 858 798-3061
10918 Technology Pl San Diego (92127) *(P-15803)*

Memory Experts Intl USA Inc (HQ) .....E 714 258-3000
1651 E Saint Andrew Pl Santa Ana (92705) *(P-15567)*

Memory Glass LLC ....F 805 682-6469
325 Rutherford St Ste E Goleta (93117) *(P-10656)*

Memory Makers Photo ACC, Chatsworth Also called Key Items Sales Inc *(P-23173)*

Memoryten Inc (PA) ....D 408 516-4141
2800 Bowers Ave Santa Clara (95051) *(P-15568)*

Memoryx, Santa Clara Also called Memoryten Inc *(P-15568)*

Memry Corporation ....C 650 463-3400
4065 Campbell Ave Menlo Park (94025) *(P-19645)*

Menasha Packaging Company LLC ....E 951 374-5281
305 Resource Dr Ste 100 Bloomington (92316) *(P-5436)*

Menasha Packaging Company LLC ....D 562 698-3705
8110 Sorensen Ave Santa Fe Springs (90670) *(P-5437)*

Mencarini & Jarwin Inc ....F 916 383-1660
5950 88th St Sacramento (95828) *(P-13451)*

Menches Tool & Die Inc ....E 650 592-2328
30995 San Benito St Hayward (94544) *(P-20885)*

Mendias Imports, Rosemead Also called Lotus Beverages *(P-1864)*

Mendicino Wine Company, Ukiah Also called Parducci Wine Estates LLC *(P-1915)*

Mendo Litho, Fort Bragg Also called Mendocino Lithographers *(P-6968)*

Mendocino Brewing Company Inc .....E 707 744-1015
13351 S Highway 101 Hopland (95449) *(P-1610)*

Mendocino Brewing Company Inc (HQ) ...D 707 463-2627
1601 Airport Rd Ukiah (95482) *(P-1611)*

Mendocino Lithographers ....F 707 964-0062
100 N Franklin St Fort Bragg (95437) *(P-6968)*

Menezes Hay Co ....F 209 394-3111
5030 Dwight Way Livingston (95334) *(P-1148)*

Menlo Energy LLC ....E 415 762-8200
555 California St # 4600 San Francisco (94104) *(P-9022)*

Menlo Microsystems Inc ....E 949 903-2369
49 Discovery Ste 150 Irvine (92618) *(P-18992)*

Menlo Therapeutics Inc ....E 650 486-1416
200 Cardinal Way Fl 2 Redwood City (94063) *(P-8277)*

Mens Wearhouse ....E 510 657-9821
6100 Stevenson Blvd Fremont (94538) *(P-3112)*

Mensi, Carson Also called Mechanized Engineering Systems *(P-14337)*

Mentor Graphics Corporation ....F 949 790-3200
18301 Von Karman Ave # 760 Irvine (92612) *(P-24902)*

Mentor Worldwide LLC (HQ) ....C 800 636-8678
33 Technology Dr Irvine (92618) *(P-22772)*

Mentzer Electronics ....E 650 697-2642
858 Stanton Rd Burlingame (94010) *(P-23019)*

Menu Services, Buena Park Also called Advertising Services *(P-6643)*

Mepco Label Systems ....D 209 946-0201
1313 S Stockton St Lodi (95240) *(P-7398)*

Meps Real-Time Inc ....E 760 448-9500
6451 El Camino Real Ste C Carlsbad (92009) *(P-22234)*

Mer-Mar Electronics, Hesperia Also called Geeriraj Inc *(P-18491)*

Mercado Latino Inc ....F 310 537-1062
1420 W Walnut St Compton (90220) *(P-24173)*

Merced County Times, Merced Also called Mid Valley Publication *(P-5970)*

Merced Screw Products Inc ....E 209 723-7706
1861 Grogan Ave Merced (95341) *(P-13032)*

Merced Sun Star, Merced Also called McClatchy Newspapers Inc *(P-5949)*

Mercer Foods LLC ....F 209 529-0150
1836 Lapham Dr Modesto (95354) *(P-888)*

Merchandising Systems Inc ....E 510 477-9100
31801 Hayman St Hayward (94544) *(P-5154)*

Merchants Metals LLC ....F 916 381-8243
6829 Mccomber St Sacramento (95828) *(P-13839)*

Merchants Metals LLC ....F 818 896-6111
10401 Glenoaks Blvd Pacoima (91331) *(P-13840)*

Merchants Metals LLC ....F 951 686-1888
6466 Mission Blvd Riverside (92509) *(P-11449)*

Merck & Co Inc ....D 650 496-6400
901 California Ave Palo Alto (94304) *(P-8278)*

Merck Sharp & Dohme Corp ....D 619 292-4900
8355 Aero Dr San Diego (92123) *(P-8279)*

Merco Manufacturing Co, Placentia Also called Aero Pacific Corporation *(P-20710)*

Mercotac Inc ....F 760 431-7723
6195 Corte Del Cedro # 100 Carlsbad (92011) *(P-17483)*

Mercury Broach Company Inc ....F 626 443-5904
2546 Seaman Ave El Monte (91733) *(P-14650)*

Mercury Engineering Corp ....F 562 861-7816
5630 Imperial Hwy South Gate (90280) *(P-16739)*

Mercury Interactive LLC ....E 949 476-3780
5000 Birch Ste 3000 Newport Beach (92660) *(P-24903)*

Mercury Interactive LLC (HQ) ....B 650 857-1501
3000 Hanover St Palo Alto (94304) *(P-24904)*

Mercury Interactive LLC ....E 818 957-2087
4452 Ocean View Blvd # 200 Montrose (91020) *(P-24905)*

Mercury Magnetics Inc ....E 818 998-7791
10050 Remmet Ave Chatsworth (91311) *(P-19346)*

Mercury Metal Die & Letter Co (PA) ....F 951 674-8717
600 3rd St Ste A Lake Elsinore (92530) *(P-13617)*

Mercury Networks LLC ....F 408 859-1345
1800 Wyatt Dr Ste 2 Santa Clara (95054) *(P-18178)*

Mercury Plastics Inc ....D 323 264-2400
2939 E Washington Blvd Los Angeles (90023) *(P-9714)*

Mercury Plastics Inc ....B 626 961-0165
14825 Salt Lake Ave City of Industry (91746) *(P-5607)*

Mercury Security Products LLC ....F 562 986-9105
2355 Mira Mar Ave Long Beach (90815) *(P-20016)*

Mercury Systems Inc ....C 805 388-1345
1000 Avenida Acaso Camarillo (93012) *(P-18527)*

Mercury Systems Inc ....F 669 226-5800
85 Nicholson Ln San Jose (95134) *(P-18528)*

Mercury Systms-Trstd Mssn Sltn (HQ) ...D 510 252-0870
47200 Bayside Pkwy Fremont (94538) *(P-15454)*

Mercury United Electronics Inc ......E 909 466-0427
9804 Cres Ctr Dr Ste 603 Rancho Cucamonga (91730) *(P-19646)*

Meredith Publishing, San Francisco Also called Four M Studios *(P-6341)*

Merelex Corporation ....E 310 208-0551
10884 Weyburn Ave Los Angeles (90024) *(P-7787)*

Merestone Merchandise Corp ....F 626 337-6262
12823 Schabarum Ave Irwindale (91706) *(P-8794)*

Merex Inc ....F 805 446-2700
1283 Flynn Rd Camarillo (93012) *(P-21804)*

Meri Gol Products Limited, Palmdale Also called Park-Rand Enterprises Inc *(P-8663)*

Merial Limited ....F 916 780-9292
1640 Lead Hill Blvd Roseville (95661) *(P-8280)*

Meridian Gold Inc ....C 209 785-3222
4461 Rock Creek Rd Copperopolis (95228) *(P-7)*

Meridian Graphics Inc ....D 949 833-3500
2652 Dow Ave Tustin (92780) *(P-6969)*

Meridian Jewelry & Design Inc ....F 510 428-2095
3814 La Cresta Ave Oakland (94602) *(P-23297)*

Meridian Technical Sales Inc ....E 408 526-2000
520 Alder Dr Milpitas (95035) *(P-6363)*

Meriliz Incorporated (PA) ....C 916 923-3663
2031 Dome Ln McClellan (95652) *(P-6970)*

Merit Aluminum Inc (PA) ....D 951 735-1770
2480 Railroad St Corona (92880) *(P-11595)*

Merit Cables Incorporated ....E 714 547-3054
830 N Poinsettia St Santa Ana (92701) *(P-22537)*

Merit Ends Inc ....E 925 427-2500
620 Clark Ave Pittsburg (94565) *(P-12665)*

Merit Printing Ink Company ....F 323 268-1807
1451 S Lorena St Los Angeles (90023) *(P-9206)*

Merit USA, Pittsburg Also called Merit Ends Inc *(P-12665)*

Merito.com, Van Nuys Also called Chef Merito Inc *(P-2485)*

Meritor Specialty Products LLC ....F 248 435-1000
151 Lawrence Dr Livermore (94551) *(P-20399)*

Meritronics Inc (PA) ....E 408 969-0888
500 Yosemite Dr Ste 108 Milpitas (95035) *(P-18529)*

Merkle Loyalty Solutions, San Francisco Also called 500friends Inc *(P-24300)*

Merle Norman Cosmetics Inc (PA) ....B....310 641-3000
9130 Bellanca Ave Los Angeles (90045) ***(P-8795)***
Merlex Stucco Inc ....E....877 547-8822
2911 N Orange Olive Rd Orange (92865) ***(P-11360)***
Merlex Stucco Mfg, Orange *Also called Merlex Stucco Inc* ***(P-11360)***
Merlin Solar Technologies Inc ....E....678 650-8892
5891 Rue Ferrari San Jose (95138) ***(P-18993)***
Merlin-Alltec Mold Making Inc ....F....562 529-5050
15543 Minnesota Ave Paramount (90723) ***(P-10208)***
Merlos Precast Products ....F....310 323-0234
13115 S Broadway Los Angeles (90061) ***(P-10956)***
Merrick Engineering Inc (PA) ....C....951 737-6040
1275 Quarry St Corona (92879) ***(P-10209)***
Merrill Corporation ....D....213 253-5900
350 S Grand Ave Ste 3000 Los Angeles (90071) ***(P-7399)***
Merrill Corporation ....D....714 690-2200
10716 Reagan St Los Alamitos (90720) ***(P-7400)***
Merrill Corporation ....E....650 493-1400
1731 Embarcadero Rd # 100 Palo Alto (94303) ***(P-7401)***
Merrill Corporation ....D....858 623-0300
8899 University Center Ln # 200 San Diego (92122) ***(P-7402)***
Merrill Corporation ....F....831 759-9300
14500 Reservation Rd Salinas (93908) ***(P-7403)***
Merrill Corporation ....F....949 252-9449
1900 Avenue Of The Stars # 1200 Los Angeles (90067) ***(P-7404)***
Merrill Corporation Inc ....E....310 552-5288
10635 Santa Monica Blvd # 350 Los Angeles (90025) ***(P-7405)***
Merrill's Packaging Supply, Burlingame *Also called Merrills Packaging Inc* ***(P-9715)***
Merrill/Orange County, Los Angeles *Also called Merrill Corporation* ***(P-7404)***
Merrills Packaging Inc ....D....650 259-5959
1529 Rollins Rd Burlingame (94010) ***(P-9715)***
Merryvale Vineyards LLC ....E....707 963-2225
1000 Main St Saint Helena (94574) ***(P-1877)***
Meru Networks Inc (HQ) ....D....408 215-5300
894 Ross Dr Sunnyvale (94089) ***(P-18345)***
Mes Enterprises ....F....909 484-6863
10096 6th St Ste L Rancho Cucamonga (91730) ***(P-5202)***
Mesa Castings Inc (PA) ....C....714 962-1064
22401 Harwich Ln Huntington Beach (92646) ***(P-11499)***
Mesa Industries Inc ....E....626 359-9361
1726 S Magnolia Ave Monrovia (91016) ***(P-14181)***
Mesa Label Express Inc ....F....858 668-2820
13257 Kirkham Way Poway (92064) ***(P-7406)***
Mesa Machining, Huntington Beach *Also called Mesa Castings Inc* ***(P-11499)***
Mesa Reprographics, San Diego *Also called M B C Reprographics Inc* ***(P-7393)***
Mesa Safe Company Inc ....E....714 202-8000
337 W Freedom Ave Orange (92865) ***(P-13958)***
Mesa/Boogie Limited (PA) ....D....707 765-1805
1317 Ross St Petaluma (94954) ***(P-17831)***
Mesgona Corporation ....F....310 926-3238
12534 Moorpark St Apt H Studio City (91604) ***(P-6527)***
Meskin Khosrow Kay ....E....650 595-3090
661 Laurel St San Carlos (94070) ***(P-10568)***
Mesmerize, Los Angeles *Also called Kamiran Inc* ***(P-3248)***
Mesotech International Inc ....F....916 368-2020
4531 Harlin Dr Sacramento (95826) ***(P-21991)***
Messana Inc ....F....855 729-6244
4105 Soquel Dr Ste B Soquel (95073) ***(P-15269)***
Messana Radiant Cooling, Soquel *Also called Messana Inc* ***(P-15269)***
Messer Logging Inc ....E....559 855-3160
32111 Rock Hill Ln Auberry (93602) ***(P-4003)***
Mestek Inc ....C....310 835-7500
1220 E Watson Center Rd Carson (90745) ***(P-15971)***
Metabasis Therapeutics Inc ....F....858 550-7500
11085 N Torrey Pines Rd # 300 La Jolla (92037) ***(P-8281)***
Metacrylics, Gilroy *Also called Instant Asphalt Inc* ***(P-9149)***
Metal Art of California Inc ....D....714 532-7100
640 N Cypress St Orange (92867) ***(P-23925)***
Metal Art of California Inc (PA) ....D....714 532-7100
640 N Cypress St Orange (92867) ***(P-23926)***
Metal Building Components Mbci, Atwater *Also called Nci Group Inc* ***(P-12954)***
Metal Cast Inc ....E....714 285-9792
2002 W Chestnut Ave Santa Ana (92703) ***(P-11526)***
Metal Chem Inc ....E....818 727-9951
21514 Nordhoff St Chatsworth (91311) ***(P-13452)***
Metal Coaters, Rancho Cucamonga *Also called Nci Group Inc* ***(P-12953)***
Metal Coaters California Inc ....D....909 987-4681
9123 Center Ave Rancho Cucamonga (91730) ***(P-13618)***
Metal Coaters System, Rancho Cucamonga *Also called Metal Coaters California Inc* ***(P-13618)***
Metal Container Corporation ....C....951 354-0444
7155 Central Ave Riverside (92504) ***(P-11862)***
Metal Container Corporation ....C....951 360-4500
10980 Inland Ave Mira Loma (91752) ***(P-11863)***
Metal Cutting Service Inc ....F....626 968-4764
16233 Gale Ave City of Industry (91745) ***(P-16740)***
Metal Engineering & Mfg ....F....626 334-5271
1031b W Kirkwall Rd Azusa (91702) ***(P-12666)***
Metal Etch Services Inc ....E....760 510-9476
1165 Linda Vista Dr # 106 San Marcos (92078) ***(P-21992)***
Metal Fabrication and Art LLC ....F....323 980-9595
3499 E 15th St Los Angeles (90023) ***(P-12207)***
Metal Fd Hhld Pdts Pckging Div, Oakdale *Also called Ball Corporation* ***(P-11856)***
Metal Finishing Division, South Gate *Also called Anadite Cal Restoration Tr* ***(P-13328)***
Metal Finishing Solutions Inc ....F....408 988-8642
870 Comstock St Santa Clara (95054) ***(P-12667)***
Metal Improvement Company LLC ....E....323 585-2168
2588 Industry Way A Lynwood (90262) ***(P-11818)***
Metal Improvement Company LLC ....D....818 983-1952
6940 Farmdale Ave North Hollywood (91605) ***(P-11819)***
Metal Improvement Company LLC ....E....949 855-8010
35 Argonaut Ste A1 Laguna Hills (92656) ***(P-11820)***
Metal Improvement Company LLC ....D....818 407-6280
20751 Superior St Chatsworth (91311) ***(P-11821)***
Metal Improvement Company LLC ....E....925 960-1090
7655 Longard Rd Bldg A Livermore (94551) ***(P-11822)***
Metal Improvement Company LLC ....F....714 546-4160
2151 S Hathaway St Santa Ana (92705) ***(P-11823)***
Metal Improvement Company LLC ....F....323 563-1533
2588a Industry Way Lynwood (90262) ***(P-11824)***
Metal Manufacturing Co Inc ....E....916 922-3484
2240 Evergreen St Sacramento (95815) ***(P-12331)***
Metal Master Inc ....E....858 292-8880
4611 Overland Ave San Diego (92123) ***(P-12668)***
Metal Preparations ....E....213 628-5176
1000 E Ocean Blvd # 416 Long Beach (90802) ***(P-13453)***
Metal Products Engineering, Vernon *Also called Luppen Holdings Inc* ***(P-13243)***
Metal Products Engineering ....E....323 581-8121
3050 Leonis Blvd Vernon (90058) ***(P-11825)***
Metal Sales Manufacturing Corp ....F....909 829-8618
14213 Whittram Ave Fontana (92335) ***(P-12669)***
Metal Supply LLC ....D....562 634-9940
11810 Center St South Gate (90280) ***(P-12208)***
Metal Surfaces Inc ....C....562 927-1331
6060 Shull St Bell Gardens (90201) ***(P-13454)***
Metal Tek Engineering Inc ....E....909 821-4158
7426 Cherry Ave Ste 210 Fontana (92336) ***(P-4191)***
Metal Tite Products (PA) ....D....562 695-0645
4880 Gregg Rd Pico Rivera (90660) ***(P-12332)***
Metal Works Supply, Oroville *Also called Smb Industries Inc* ***(P-12243)***
Metal X Direct Inc ....F....949 336-0055
1304 Logan Ave Ste A Costa Mesa (92626) ***(P-12881)***
Metal-Fab Services Industries ....E....714 630-7771
2500 E Miraloma Way Anaheim (92806) ***(P-12670)***
Metalcast, Santa Ana *Also called Metal Cast Inc* ***(P-11526)***
Metalco ....F....510 652-7470
1475 67th St Emeryville (94608) ***(P-13455)***
Metalfab, Santa Clara *Also called Sutter P Dahlglen Entps Inc* ***(P-16977)***
Metalfx, Willits *Also called Advanced Mfg & Dev Inc* ***(P-12461)***
Metalite Manufacturing, Pacoima *Also called Hanmar LLC* ***(P-13213)***
Metalite Manufacturing Company ....E....818 890-2802
11441 Bradley Ave Pacoima (91331) ***(P-13247)***
Metalite Mfg Companys, Pacoima *Also called Metalite Manufacturing Company* ***(P-13247)***
Metalore Inc ....E....310 643-0360
750 S Douglas St El Segundo (90245) ***(P-16741)***
Metalpro Industries Inc ....E....661 294-0764
28064 Avenue Stanford H Santa Clarita (91355) ***(P-12671)***
Metals Direct Inc ....E....530 605-1931
6771 Eastside Rd Redding (96001) ***(P-12672)***
Metals USA Building Pdts LP ....D....714 522-7852
6450a Caballero Blvd Buena Park (90620) ***(P-12209)***
Metals USA Building Pdts LP (HQ) ....A....713 946-9000
955 Columbia St Brea (92821) ***(P-11620)***
Metals USA Building Pdts LP ....E....800 325-1305
1951 S Parco Ave Ste C Ontario (91761) ***(P-11621)***
Metals USA Building Pdts LP ....E....916 635-2245
11340 White Rock Rd Ste B Rancho Cordova (95742) ***(P-11622)***
Metals USA Building Pdts LP ....E....714 529-0407
955 Columbia St Brea (92821) ***(P-11623)***
Metalset Inc ....E....510 233-9998
1200 Hensley St Richmond (94801) ***(P-12210)***
Metamaterial Tech USA Inc ....F....650 993-9223
5880 W Las Positas Blvd Pleasanton (94588) ***(P-22107)***
Metco Fourslide Manufacturing, Gardena *Also called Metco Manufacturing Inc* ***(P-13248)***
Metco Manufacturing Inc ....E....310 516-6547
17540 S Denver Ave Gardena (90248) ***(P-13248)***
Metech Recycling Inc ....E....408 848-3050
6200 Engle Way Gilroy (95020) ***(P-11562)***
Meteor Lighting, City of Industry *Also called Ilos Corp* ***(P-17702)***
Method Home Products ....F....415 568-4600
637 Commercial St Fl 3 San Francisco (94111) ***(P-5311)***
Metlsaw Systems Inc ....E....707 746-6200
2950 Bay Vista Ct Benicia (94510) ***(P-14393)***
Metra Biosystems Inc (HQ) ....E....408 616-4300
2981 Copper Rd Santa Clara (95051) ***(P-8495)***
Metra Electronics Corporation ....F....562 470-6601
3201 E 59th St Long Beach (90805) ***(P-20400)***
Metrex Valve Corp ....E....626 335-4027
505 S Vermont Ave Glendora (91741) ***(P-13727)***
Metric Design & Manufacturing ....F....408 378-4544
217 E Hacienda Ave Campbell (95008) ***(P-14541)***
Metric Machining (PA) ....E....909 947-9222
3263 Trade Center Dr Riverside (92507) ***(P-14394)***
Metric Precision, Huntington Beach *Also called AMG Torrance LLC* ***(P-20733)***
Metric Products Inc (PA) ....E....310 815-9000
4630 Leahy St Culver City (90232) ***(P-3550)***
Metric Systems Corporation ....F....760 560-0348
3055 Enterprise Ct Vista (92081) ***(P-18179)***
Metricstream Inc (PA) ....C....650 620-2900
2479 E Byshore Rd Ste 260 Palo Alto (94303) ***(P-24906)***
Metro Digital Printing Inc ....E....714 545-8400
3311 W Macarthur Blvd Santa Ana (92704) ***(P-6971)***
Metro Novelty & Pleating Co ....D....213 748-1201
906 Thayer Ave Los Angeles (90024) ***(P-3906)***
Metro Poly Corporation ....E....510 357-9898
1651 Aurora Dr San Leandro (94577) ***(P-5608)***
Metro Print, Long Beach *Also called J & K Resources Inc* ***(P-6899)***

Metro Publishing Inc ... F ... 831 457-9000
1205 Pacific Ave Ste 301 Santa Cruz (95060) ***(P-5967)***

Metro Publishing Inc ... F ... 707 527-1200
847 5th St Santa Rosa (95404) ***(P-5968)***

Metro Ready Mix ... F ... 661 829-7851
1635 James Rd Bakersfield (93308) ***(P-11142)***

Metro Roof Products, Oceanside *Also called Metrotile Manufacturing LLC* ***(P-9414)***

Metro Santa Cruz Newspaper, Santa Cruz *Also called Metro Publishing Inc* ***(P-5967)***

Metro Steel, Spring Valley *Also called Gamboa Incorporated* ***(P-12167)***

Metro Truck Body Incorporated ... E ... 310 532-5570
1201 W Jon St Torrance (90502) ***(P-20219)***

Metro World Plastics Inc ... F ... 415 255-8515
344348 Shell St San Francisco (94102) ***(P-9716)***

Metrolaser Inc ... F ... 949 553-0688
22941 Mill Creek Dr Laguna Hills (92653) ***(P-21993)***

Metroll, Fontana *Also called Buildmat Plus Investments Inc* ***(P-10892)***

Metromedia Technologies Inc ... E ... 818 552-6500
370 Amapola Ave Ste 200 Torrance (90501) ***(P-15804)***

Metrophones Unlimited Inc ... E ... 650 630-5400
15675 La Jolla Ct Morgan Hill (95037) ***(P-17963)***

Metropolitan News Company, Los Angeles *Also called Grace Communications Inc* ***(P-5866)***

Metropolitan News Company ... E ... 951 369-5890
3540 12th St Riverside (92501) ***(P-5969)***

Metrosa, Santa Rosa *Also called Metro Publishing Inc* ***(P-5968)***

Metrotech Corporation (PA) ... D ... 408 734-3880
3251 Olcott St Santa Clara (95054) ***(P-21347)***

Metrotile Manufacturing LLC ... E ... 760 435-9842
3093 Industry St Ste A Oceanside (92054) ***(P-9414)***

Mettler Electronics Corp ... E ... 714 533-2221
1333 S Claudina St Anaheim (92805) ***(P-22538)***

Mettler-Toledo Rainin LLC (HQ) ... C ... 510 564-1600
7500 Edgewater Dr Oakland (94621) ***(P-22235)***

Mevsa, Cypress *Also called Mitsubishi Electric Visual* ***(P-19655)***

Mexapparel Inc (PA) ... F ... 323 364-8600
2344 E 38th St Vernon (90058) ***(P-3113)***

Meyco Machine and Tool Inc ... E ... 714 435-1546
11579 Martens River Cir Fountain Valley (92708) ***(P-14651)***

Meyenburg Goat Milk Products, Turlock *Also called Jackson-Mitchell Inc* ***(P-730)***

Meyer & Reeder Inc ... F ... 714 388-0148
1255 N Patt St Anaheim (92801) ***(P-5082)***

Meyer Cookware Industries Inc ... E ... 707 551-2800
1 Meyer Plz Vallejo (94590) ***(P-13249)***

Meyer Corporation US (HQ) ... D ... 707 551-2800
1 Meyer Plz Vallejo (94590) ***(P-13250)***

Meyer Sound Laboratories Inc (PA) ... C ... 510 486-1166
2832 San Pablo Ave Berkeley (94702) ***(P-17832)***

Meyer Sound Labs, Berkeley *Also called Meyer Sound Laboratories Inc* ***(P-17832)***

Meyer Wines, Vallejo *Also called Meyer Corporation US* ***(P-13250)***

Meyers Publishing Inc ... F ... 805 445-8881
799 Camarillo Springs Rd Camarillo (93012) ***(P-6216)***

Meyers Sheet Metal Box Inc ... F ... 650 873-8889
138 W Harris Ave South San Francisco (94080) ***(P-12673)***

Meza Pallet Inc ... F ... 909 829-0223
14619 Merrill Ave Fontana (92335) ***(P-4443)***

Meziere Enterprises Inc ... E ... 800 208-1755
220 S Hale Ave Ste A Escondido (92029) ***(P-16742)***

Mf Inc ... C ... 213 627-2498
2010 E 15th St Los Angeles (90021) ***(P-3258)***

Mfb Worldwide Inc (PA) ... F ... 323 562-2339
4901 Patata St 201-204 Cudahy (90201) ***(P-3009)***

Mfg Packaging Products ... F ... 714 984-2300
3200 Enterprise St Brea (92821) ***(P-15218)***

Mfi Inc ... F ... 949 313-6450
363 San Miguel Dr Ste 200 Newport Beach (92660) ***(P-24174)***

Mgb Industries Inc ... F ... 619 247-9284
679 Anita St Ste B Chula Vista (91911) ***(P-20886)***

MGF Graphics, Northridge *Also called N M H Inc* ***(P-6987)***

Mgfso LLC ... F ... 949 500-7645
7372 Siena Dr Huntington Beach (92648) ***(P-8282)***

MGM Brakes, Cloverdale *Also called Indian Head Industries Inc* ***(P-20370)***

MGM Brakes ... D ... 707 894-3333
1184 S Cloverdale Blvd Cloverdale (95425) ***(P-20401)***

MGM Transformer Co ... D ... 323 726-0888
5701 Smithway St Commerce (90040) ***(P-17106)***

Mgp Caliper Covers, Chula Vista *Also called Marshall Genuine Products LLC* ***(P-14648)***

Mgr Design International Inc ... C ... 805 981-6400
1950 Williams Dr Oxnard (93036) ***(P-24175)***

MGT Industries Inc (PA) ... C ... 310 516-5900
13889 S Figueroa St Los Angeles (90061) ***(P-3467)***

Mgx Copy (PA) ... F ... 877 649-5463
8840 Kenamar Dr Ste 405 San Diego (92121) ***(P-6972)***

MI Rancho Tortilla Inc ... D ... 559 299-3183
801 Purvis Ave Clovis (93612) ***(P-2604)***

MI Rancho Tortilla Factory, San Leandro *Also called Berber Food Manufacturing Inc* ***(P-2463)***

MI Technologies Inc ... C ... 619 710-2637
2215 Pseo De Las Americas San Diego (92154) ***(P-18530)***

Mi9, Pleasanton *Also called Software Development Inc* ***(P-25192)***

Miasole ... B ... 408 919-5700
2590 Walsh Ave Santa Clara (95051) ***(P-18994)***

Miasole Hi-Tech Corp (HQ) ... C ... 408 919-5700
2590 Walsh Ave Santa Clara (95051) ***(P-18995)***

Mic Labs ... F ... 925 822-2847
7643 Corrinne Pl San Ramon (94583) ***(P-237)***

Mica Lighting Company Inc ... F ... 714 738-8448
717 S State College Blvd K Fullerton (92831) ***(P-17714)***

Micawrap Moulding Company, Riverbank *Also called Overholtzer Elvan* ***(P-4640)***

Michael and Company, Lockeford *Also called Woodside Investment Inc* ***(P-13985)***

Michael BS LLC ... E ... 310 320-0141
22625 S Western Ave Torrance (90501) ***(P-768)***

Michael D Wilson Inc ... F ... 559 568-1115
19774 Orange Belt Dr Strathmore (93267) ***(P-13959)***

Michael Hagan ... E ... 909 213-5916
17858 Laurel Dr Fontana (92336) ***(P-23618)***

Michael Martella ... C ... 858 695-9600
9955 Black Mountain Rd San Diego (92126) ***(P-6420)***

Michael Somers Attorney At Law, Long Beach *Also called Aci Postal System* ***(P-6638)***

Michael T Mingione ... F ... 408 365-1544
2885 Aiello Dr Ste D San Jose (95111) ***(P-5155)***

Michaels Furniture Company Inc ... B ... 916 381-9086
15 Koch Rd Ste J Corte Madera (94925) ***(P-4719)***

Michel-Schlmberger Partners LP ... E ... 707 433-7427
4155 Wine Creek Rd Healdsburg (95448) ***(P-1878)***

Michel-Schlumberger Fine Wine, Healdsburg *Also called Michel-Schlmberger Partners LP* ***(P-1878)***

Michelsen Packaging California, Fresno *Also called Michelsen Packaging Co Cal* ***(P-5526)***

Michelsen Packaging Co Cal ... E ... 559 237-3819
4165 S Cherry Ave Fresno (93706) ***(P-5526)***

Michigan Metal Partitions, Anaheim *Also called Weis/Robart Partitions Inc* ***(P-12905)***

Micile Inc ... F ... 626 381-9974
1225 S Shamrock Ave Monrovia (91016) ***(P-15455)***

Micrel LLC ... A ... 408 944-0800
2180 Fortune Dr San Jose (95131) ***(P-18996)***

Micrel LLC ... C ... 408 944-0800
1849 Fortune Dr San Jose (95131) ***(P-18997)***

Micrel LLC ... C ... 408 944-0800
1931 Fortune Dr San Jose (95131) ***(P-18998)***

Micrel Semiconductor, San Jose *Also called Micrel LLC* ***(P-18997)***

Micro Analog Inc ... C ... 909 392-8277
1861 Puddingstone Dr La Verne (91750) ***(P-18531)***

Micro Chips of America Inc ... E ... 818 577-9543
5302 Comercio Ln Apt 1 Woodland Hills (91364) ***(P-19647)***

Micro Connectors Inc ... E ... 510 266-0299
2700 Mccone Ave Hayward (94545) ***(P-15805)***

Micro Express, Irvine *Also called A S A Engineering Inc* ***(P-15379)***

Micro Filtration Systems, Dublin *Also called Advantec Mfs Inc* ***(P-15138)***

Micro Gage Inc ... E ... 626 443-1741
9537 Telstar Ave Ste 131 El Monte (91731) ***(P-18999)***

Micro Grow Greenhouse Systems ... F ... 951 296-3340
42065 Zevo Dr Ste B1 Temecula (92590) ***(P-21516)***

Micro Lambda Wireless Inc ... E ... 510 770-9221
46515 Landing Pkwy Fremont (94538) ***(P-19648)***

Micro Lithography Inc ... C ... 408 747-1769
1247 Elko Dr Sunnyvale (94089) ***(P-21617)***

Micro Matic Usa Inc ... E ... 818 701-9765
19761 Bahama St 19791 Northridge (91324) ***(P-15972)***

Micro Matic Usa Inc ... E ... 818 882-8012
19791 Bahama St Northridge (91324) ***(P-13728)***

Micro Matrix Systems (PA) ... E ... 909 626-8544
4651 Brooks St Montclair (91763) ***(P-13251)***

Micro Plastics Inc ... E ... 818 882-0244
20821 Dearborn St Chatsworth (91311) ***(P-17484)***

Micro Semicdtr Researches LLC ... E ... 408 492-1369
805 Aldo Ave Ste 101 Santa Clara (95054) ***(P-19000)***

Micro Space Products, Hawthorne *Also called K & E Inc* ***(P-20859)***

Micro Steel Inc ... E ... 818 348-8701
7850 Alabama Ave Canoga Park (91304) ***(P-21196)***

Micro Surface Engr Inc (PA) ... E ... 323 582-7348
1550 E Slauson Ave Los Angeles (90011) ***(P-11843)***

Micro Tech Systems, Fremont *Also called Mt Systems Inc* ***(P-14995)***

Micro Therapeutics Inc (HQ) ... F ... 949 837-3700
9775 Toledo Way Irvine (92618) ***(P-22539)***

Micro Tool & Manufacturing Inc ... E ... 619 582-2884
6494 Federal Blvd Lemon Grove (91945) ***(P-14652)***

Micro Trim Inc ... F ... 714 241-7046
3613 W Macarthur Blvd # 605 Santa Ana (92704) ***(P-11596)***

Micro-DOT, Los Angeles *Also called Zada Graphics Inc* ***(P-7193)***

Micro-Metric Inc ... F ... 408 452-8505
1050 Commercial St San Jose (95112) ***(P-22236)***

Micro-Mode Products Inc ... C ... 619 449-3844
1870 John Towers Ave El Cajon (92020) ***(P-18180)***

Micro-OHM Corporation ... E ... 626 357-5377
1088 Hamilton Rd Duarte (91010) ***(P-19308)***

Micro-Probe Incorporated (HQ) ... D ... 408 457-3900
617 River Oaks Pkwy San Jose (95134) ***(P-21805)***

Micro-TEC, Chatsworth *Also called Wallace E Miller Inc* ***(P-17049)***

Micro-Tech Scientific Inc ... F ... 760 597-9088
3059 Palm Hill Dr Vista (92084) ***(P-21994)***

Micro-Tracers Inc ... F ... 415 822-1100
1370 Van Dyke Ave San Francisco (94124) ***(P-9280)***

Micro-Tronics, Sonora *Also called O M Jones Inc* ***(P-19666)***

Micro-Vu Corp California (PA) ... D ... 707 838-6272
7909 Conde Ln Windsor (95492) ***(P-22108)***

Micro/Sys Inc ... E ... 818 244-4600
3730 Park Pl Montrose (91020) ***(P-15456)***

Microbar Inc ... B ... 510 659-9770
45473 Warm Springs Blvd Fremont (94539) ***(P-14990)***

Microbiotic Health Foods Inc ... F ... 858 273-5775
4901 Morena Blvd Ste 403 San Diego (92117) ***(P-1371)***

Microchip Technology Inc ... C ... 408 735-9110
450 Holger Way San Jose (95134) ***(P-19001)***

Microcool ... F ... 760 322-1111
72216 Northshore St # 103 Thousand Palms (92276) ***(P-21618)***

Microcosm Inc ... E ... 310 219-2700
3111 Lomita Blvd Torrance (90505) ***(P-21178)***

Microdyn-Nadir Us Inc (HQ) ... D ... 805 964-8003
93 S La Patera Ln Goleta (93117) ***(P-16073)***

Employee Codes: A=Over 500 employees, B=251-500
C=101-250, D=51-100, E=20-50, F=10-19

2019 California
Manfacturers Register

© Mergent Inc. 1-800-342-5647
1213

Microdyne Plastics Inc D 909 503-4010
1901 E Cooley Dr Colton (92324) ***(P-10210)***
Microfab Manufacturing Inc F 760 744-7240
220 Distribution St San Marcos (92078) ***(P-12674)***
Microfab Mfg Shtmtl Pdts, San Marcos *Also called Microfab Manufacturing Inc* ***(P-12674)***
Microfabrica Inc E 888 964-2763
7911 Haskell Ave Van Nuys (91406) ***(P-19649)***
Microflex Technologies LLC F 714 937-1507
430 W Collins Ave Orange (92867) ***(P-19002)***
Microform Precision LLC D 916 419-0580
4244 S Market Ct Ste A Sacramento (95834) ***(P-12675)***
Microgenics Corporation (HQ) C 510 979-9147
46500 Kato Rd Fremont (94538) ***(P-8283)***
Microlux Inc F 408 435-1700
1065 Asbury St San Jose (95126) ***(P-20017)***
Micromega Systems Inc F 415 924-4700
2 Fifer Ave Ste 120 Corte Madera (94925) ***(P-24907)***
Micrometals Inc (PA) D 714 970-9400
5615 E La Palma Ave Anaheim (92807) ***(P-19650)***
Micrometals/Texas Inc C 325 677-8753
5615 E La Palma Ave Anaheim (92807) ***(P-19651)***
Micromold Inc F 951 684-7130
2100 Iowa Ave Riverside (92507) ***(P-10211)***
Micron Consumer Pdts Group Inc (HQ) F 669 226-3000
540 Alder Dr Fremont (94538) ***(P-15569)***
Micron Instruments, Simi Valley *Also called Piezo-Metrics Inc* ***(P-19075)***
Micron Machine Company E 858 486-5900
12530 Stowe Dr Poway (92064) ***(P-16743)***
Micron Technology Inc E 408 855-4000
570 Alder Dr Bldg 2 Milpitas (95035) ***(P-19003)***
Micron Technology Inc A 916 458-3003
2235 Iron Point Rd Folsom (95630) ***(P-19004)***
Micronas USA Inc C 408 625-1200
560 S Winchester Blvd San Jose (95128) ***(P-17833)***
Micronova Manufacturing Inc E 310 784-6990
3431 Lomita Blvd Torrance (90505) ***(P-3734)***
Microplate, Inglewood *Also called Multichrome Company Inc* ***(P-13460)***
Microplex Inc F 714 630-8220
1070 Ortega Way Placentia (92870) ***(P-19005)***
Micropoint Bioscience Inc E 408 588-1682
3521 Leonard Ct Santa Clara (95054) ***(P-8496)***
Microprint Inc E 626 369-1950
133 Puente Ave City of Industry (91746) ***(P-6973)***
Microscale Industries Inc F 714 593-1422
18435 Bandilier Cir Fountain Valley (92708) ***(P-6974)***
Microsemi Communications Inc E 805 388-3700
4721 Calle Carga Camarillo (93012) ***(P-19006)***
Microsemi Communications Inc (HQ) C 805 388-3700
4721 Calle Carga Camarillo (93012) ***(P-19007)***
Microsemi Corp - Pwr Prdts Grp F 408 986-8031
3000 Oakmead Village Dr Santa Clara (95051) ***(P-19008)***
Microsemi Corp - Rf Power Pdts D 408 986-8031
3000 Oakmead Village Dr Santa Clara (95051) ***(P-19009)***
Microsemi Corp - Santa Ana, Garden Grove *Also called Microsemi Corporation* ***(P-19012)***
Microsemi Corp- Rf Integrated (HQ) C 916 850-8640
105 Lake Forest Way Folsom (95630) ***(P-19010)***
Microsemi Corp-Analog (HQ) D 714 898-8121
11861 Western Ave Garden Grove (92841) ***(P-19011)***
Microsemi Corp-Power MGT Group C 714 994-6500
11861 Western Ave Garden Grove (92841) ***(P-17287)***
Microsemi Corporation B 714 898-7112
11861 Western Ave Garden Grove (92841) ***(P-19012)***
Microsemi Corporation (HQ) E 949 380-6100
1 Enterprise Aliso Viejo (92656) ***(P-19013)***
Microsemi Corporation C 707 568-5900
3843 Brickway Blvd # 100 Santa Rosa (95403) ***(P-19014)***
Microsemi Corporation F 408 643-6000
3850 N 1st St San Jose (95134) ***(P-19015)***
Microsemi Frequency Time Corp D 707 528-1230
3750 Westwind Blvd Santa Rosa (95403) ***(P-17964)***
Microsemi Frequency Time Corp F 408 433-0910
2300 Orchard Pkwy San Jose (95131) ***(P-24908)***
Microsemi Rfis, Folsom *Also called Microsemi Corp- Rf Integrated* ***(P-19010)***
Microsemi Semiconductor US Inc D 707 568-5900
3843 Brickway Blvd # 100 Santa Rosa (95403) ***(P-19652)***
Microsemi Soc Corp (HQ) C 408 643-6000
3870 N 1st St San Jose (95134) ***(P-19016)***
Microsemi Soc Corp E 650 318-4200
2051 Stierlin Ct Mountain View (94043) ***(P-19017)***
Microsemi Stor Solutions Inc (HQ) D 408 239-8000
1380 Bordeaux Dr Sunnyvale (94089) ***(P-19018)***
Microsoft Corporation E 949 680-3000
75 Enterprise Ste 100 Aliso Viejo (92656) ***(P-24909)***
Microsoft Corporation E 858 909-3800
9255 Towne Centre Dr # 400 San Diego (92121) ***(P-24910)***
Microsoft Corporation D 650 964-7200
680 Vaqueros Ave Sunnyvale (94085) ***(P-24911)***
Microsoft Corporation D 619 849-5872
7007 Friars Rd San Diego (92108) ***(P-24912)***
Microsoft Corporation E 916 369-3600
1415 L St Ste 200 Sacramento (95814) ***(P-24913)***
Microsoft Corporation C 650 693-1009
1020 Entp Way Bldg B Sunnyvale (94089) ***(P-24914)***
Microsoft Corporation C 650 693-4000
680 Vaqueros Ave Sunnyvale (94085) ***(P-15806)***
Microsoft Corporation C 949 263-3000
3 Park Plz Ste 1800 Irvine (92614) ***(P-24915)***
Microsoft Corporation D 213 806-7300
13031 W Jefferson Blvd # 200 Playa Vista (90094) ***(P-24916)***
Microsoft Corporation C 415 972-6400
555 California St Ste 200 San Francisco (94104) ***(P-24917)***
Microsoft Corporation D 408 987-9608
2045 Lafayette St Santa Clara (95050) ***(P-24918)***
Microsource Inc D 925 328-4650
5990 Gleason Dr Dublin (94568) ***(P-21806)***
Microtech LLC E 714 966-1645
17260 Newhope St Fountain Valley (92708) ***(P-22893)***
Microtech Scientific, Vista *Also called Micro-Tech Scientific Inc* ***(P-21994)***
Microtech Systems Inc F 650 596-1900
5617 Scotts Valley Dr # 100 Scotts Valley (95066) ***(P-19870)***
Microtek Electronics Inc F 949 297-4930
25691 Atlantic Ocean Dr Lake Forest (92630) ***(P-18181)***
Microtelematics Inc F 888 651-7133
1500 Quail St Ste 280 Newport Beach (92660) ***(P-24919)***
Microunity Systems Engineering E 408 734-8100
2010 El Camino Real Santa Clara (95050) ***(P-18346)***
Microvention Inc (HQ) B 714 258-8000
35 Enterprise Aliso Viejo (92656) ***(P-22540)***
Microvention Terumo, Aliso Viejo *Also called Microvention Inc* ***(P-22540)***
Microvision Development Inc E 760 438-7781
3142 Tiger Run Ct Ste 103 Carlsbad (92010) ***(P-24920)***
Microvoice Corporation E 805 389-2922
345 Willis Ave Camarillo (93010) ***(P-18182)***
Microvoice Systems, Camarillo *Also called Microvoice Corporation* ***(P-18182)***
Microwave Dynamics F 949 679-7788
16541 Scientific Irvine (92618) ***(P-18183)***
Microwave Power Products Div, Palo Alto *Also called Communications & Pwr Inds LLC* ***(P-18384)***
Microwave Technology Inc (HQ) E 510 651-6700
4268 Solar Way Fremont (94538) ***(P-19653)***
Micrus Endovascular LLC (HQ) C 408 433-1400
821 Fox Ln San Jose (95131) ***(P-22541)***
Mid Century Imports Inc F 818 509-3050
5333 Cahuenga Blvd North Hollywood (91601) ***(P-4720)***
Mid Labs, San Leandro *Also called Medical Instr Dev Labs Inc* ***(P-22526)***
Mid Michigan Trading Post Ltd D 517 323-9020
5200 Lankershim Blvd # 350 North Hollywood (91601) ***(P-6528)***
Mid Ohio Field Services LLC F 614 755-5067
4686 Ontario Mills Pkwy Ontario (91764) ***(P-238)***
Mid Valley Dairy, Turlock *Also called Super Store Industries* ***(P-696)***
Mid Valley Grinding Co Inc F 818 764-1086
7352 Radford Ave North Hollywood (91605) ***(P-24176)***
Mid Valley Mfg Inc F 559 864-9441
2039 W Superior Ave Caruthers (93609) ***(P-16744)***
Mid Valley Milk Co F 661 721-8419
10786 Avenue 144 Tipton (93272) ***(P-731)***
Mid Valley Publication E 209 383-0433
2221 K St Merced (95340) ***(P-5970)***
Mid Valley Publications, Winton *Also called Winton Times* ***(P-6089)***
Mid-State Concrete Products E 805 928-2855
1625 E Donovan Rd Ste C Santa Maria (93454) ***(P-10957)***
Mid-Valley Tarp Service, Modesto *Also called Modesto Tent and Awning Inc* ***(P-3796)***
Mid-West Fabricating Co E 562 698-9615
8623 Dice Rd Santa Fe Springs (90670) ***(P-20402)***
Midas Technology Inc E 818 937-4774
16 Goodyear Ste 120 Irvine (92618) ***(P-17834)***
Middle Atlantic Products Inc E 800 266-7225
11150 Inland Ave Ste A Mira Loma (91752) ***(P-12676)***
Middle East Baking Co E 650 348-7200
1380 Marsten Rd Burlingame (94010) ***(P-1290)***
Middle Sales, Woodland *Also called Interlock Industries Inc* ***(P-12623)***
Midern Computer Inc E 626 964-8682
18005 Cortney Ct City of Industry (91748) ***(P-15457)***
Midmark Corporation F 310 516-5100
690 Knox St Torrance (90502) ***(P-17715)***
Midonna Inc F 562 983-5140
1375 Caspian Ave Long Beach (90813) ***(P-7407)***
Midrange Software Inc E 818 762-8539
12716 Riverside Dr Studio City (91607) ***(P-24921)***
Midthrust Imports Inc E 213 749-6651
830 E 14th Pl Los Angeles (90021) ***(P-2874)***
Midvalley Publishing Inc E 559 638-2244
1130 G St Reedley (93654) ***(P-5971)***
Midvalley Publishing Inc E 559 875-2511
740 N St Sanger (93657) ***(P-5972)***
Midway Farms, Fresno *Also called California Dried Fruit Inc* ***(P-877)***
Midwest Rubber, Ontario *Also called Ace Calendering Enterprises* ***(P-9582)***
Midwestern Pipeline Svcs Inc (PA) F 707 557-6633
160 Klamath Ct American Canyon (94503) ***(P-9415)***
Mighty Mover Trailers Inc E 951 736-0225
224 N Sherman Ave Corona (92882) ***(P-21235)***
Mighty Soy Inc F 323 266-6969
1227 S Eastern Ave Los Angeles (90022) ***(P-14871)***
Miholin Inc F 213 820-8225
1500 S Bradshawe Ave Monterey Park (91754) ***(P-3180)***
Mika Color F 323 254-1450
6000 Monterey Rd Los Angeles (90042) ***(P-7652)***
Mikailian Meat Product Inc F 661 257-1055
25310 Avenue Stanford Santa Clarita (91355) ***(P-507)***
Mikawaya (PA) E 323 587-5504
5563 Alcoa Ave Vernon (90058) ***(P-1291)***
Mike Fellows E 707 938-0278
28913 Arnold Dr Sonoma (95476) ***(P-3907)***
Mike Kenney Tool Inc E 714 577-9262
2900 Saturn St Ste A Brea (92821) ***(P-16745)***
Mike Murach & Associates F 559 440-9071
4340 N Knoll Ave Fresno (93722) ***(P-6364)***

Mike Printer Inc ......F......818 902-9922
6933 Woodley Ave Van Nuys (91406) ***(P-6975)***
Mikelson Machine Shop Inc ......E......626 448-3920
2546 Merced Ave South El Monte (91733) ***(P-20887)***
Mikes Metal Works Inc ......F......619 440-8804
3552 Fowler Canyon Rd Jamul (91935) ***(P-11407)***
Mikes Micro Parts Inc ......E......626 443-0675
1901 Potrero Ave South El Monte (91733) ***(P-16746)***
Mikes Precision Welding Inc ......F......951 676-4744
28073 Diaz Rd Ste D Temecula (92590) ***(P-25422)***
Mikes Sheet Metal Products ......E......916 348-3800
3315 Elkhorn Blvd North Highlands (95660) ***(P-12677)***
Mikhail Darafeev Inc (PA) ......E......909 613-1818
5075 Edison Ave Chino (91710) ***(P-4721)***
Mikron Products Inc ......D......323 245-1251
2600 Homestead Pl Compton (90220) ***(P-9569)***
Mikroscan Technologies Inc ......F......760 893-8095
2764 Gateway Rd 100 Carlsbad (92009) ***(P-22542)***
Mil-Spec Magnetics Inc ......E......909 598-8116
169 Pacific St Pomona (91768) ***(P-19347)***
Mila Usa Inc ......E......415 734-8540
11 Laurel Ave Belvedere Tiburon (94920) ***(P-17397)***
Milco Waterjet, Huntington Beach *Also called Milco Wire Edm Inc* ***(P-16747)***
Milco Wire Edm Inc ......F......714 373-0098
15221 Connector Ln Huntington Beach (92649) ***(P-16747)***
Milcomm Inc ......F......626 523-8305
10291 Trademark St Ste C Rancho Cucamonga (91730) ***(P-20888)***
Mildara Blass Inc ......C......707 836-5000
205 Concourse Blvd Santa Rosa (95403) ***(P-1879)***
Mildef Inc (PA) ......F......703 224-8835
630 W Lambert Rd Brea (92821) ***(P-15458)***
Milestones Products Inc ......F......323 728-3434
1965 S Tubeway Ave Commerce (90040) ***(P-8796)***
Milgard Manufacturing Inc ......C......831 636-0114
2451 Bert Dr Hollister (95023) ***(P-12333)***
Milgard Manufacturing Inc ......C......805 581-6325
355 E Easy St Simi Valley (93065) ***(P-10721)***
Milgard Manufacturing Inc ......F......480 763-6000
26879 Diaz Rd Temecula (92590) ***(P-10212)***
Milgard Manufacturing Inc ......C......916 387-0700
6050 88th St Sacramento (95828) ***(P-12334)***
Milgard Windows, Temecula *Also called Milgard Manufacturing Inc* ***(P-10212)***
Milgard Windows, Sacramento *Also called Milgard Manufacturing Inc* ***(P-12334)***
Milgard-Simi Valley, Simi Valley *Also called Milgard Manufacturing Inc* ***(P-10721)***
Military Aircraft Parts ......E......916 635-8010
11265 Sunrise Gold Cir G Rancho Cordova (95742) ***(P-16748)***
Military Aircraft Parts (PA) ......E......916 635-8010
116 Oxburough Dr Folsom (95630) ***(P-16749)***
Military Magazine, Sacramento *Also called Helen Noble* ***(P-6181)***
Military Press Newspaper, San Diego *Also called Richard Matz* ***(P-6027)***
Mill 42 Inc ......F......714 979-4200
5331 Production Dr Huntington Beach (92649) ***(P-2850)***
Mill Creek Vneyards Winery Inc ......F......707 433-4788
1401 Westside Rd Healdsburg (95448) ***(P-1880)***
Millbrook Kitchens Inc ......F......310 684-3366
15960 Downey Ave Paramount (90723) ***(P-4328)***
Millcraft Inc ......D......714 632-9621
2850 E White Star Ave Anaheim (92806) ***(P-4192)***
Millennial Brands LLC ......F......925 230-0617
126 W 9th St Los Angeles (90015) ***(P-10500)***
Millennium Automation ......F......510 683-5942
1300 Fulton Pl Fremont (94539) ***(P-15341)***
Millennium Graphics Inc ......F......925 602-0635
3443 Park Pl Pleasanton (94588) ***(P-7207)***
Millennium Metalcraft Inc ......E......510 657-4700
3201 Osgood Cmn Fremont (94539) ***(P-12678)***
Millennium Space Systems Inc (HQ) ......E......310 683-5840
2265 E El Segundo Blvd El Segundo (90245) ***(P-21348)***
Millenworks ......D......714 426-5500
1361 Valencia Ave Tustin (92780) ***(P-20158)***
Miller & Pidskalny Cstm Wdwrk ......F......949 250-8508
1940 Blair Ave Santa Ana (92705) ***(P-4722)***
Miller Castings Inc (PA) ......D......562 695-0461
2503 Pacific Park Dr Whittier (90601) ***(P-11515)***
Miller Castings Inc ......F......562 695-0461
12251 Coast Dr Whittier (90601) ***(P-11516)***
Miller Cnc, San Diego *Also called Miller Machine Works LLC* ***(P-16751)***
Miller Electric Mfg Co ......C......805 520-7494
2523 Ellington Ct Simi Valley (93063) ***(P-14733)***
Miller Gasket Co, San Fernando *Also called J Miller Co Inc* ***(P-9538)***
Miller Hot Dogs, Lodi *Also called Miller Packing Company* ***(P-508)***
Miller Machine Inc ......E......814 723-5700
4055 Calle Platino # 200 Oceanside (92056) ***(P-16750)***
Miller Machine Works LLC ......F......619 501-9866
1905 Broadway San Diego (92102) ***(P-16751)***
Miller Manufacturing Inc ......F......707 584-9528
165 Cascade Ct Rohnert Park (94928) ***(P-5203)***
Miller Marine ......E......619 791-1500
2275 Manya St San Diego (92154) ***(P-21002)***
Miller Milling Company LLC ......E......559 441-8133
2908 S Maple Ave Fresno (93725) ***(P-1046)***
Miller Packing Company ......E......209 339-2310
1122 Industrial Way Lodi (95240) ***(P-508)***
Miller Products Inc ......D......209 467-2470
2315 Station Dr Stockton (95215) ***(P-5571)***
Millercoors LLC ......D......626 969-6811
15801 1st St Irwindale (91706) ***(P-1612)***
Millers American Honey Inc ......E......909 825-1722
1455 Riverview Dr San Bernardino (92408) ***(P-2605)***
Millers Fab & Weld Corp ......E......951 359-3100
6100 Industrial Ave Riverside (92504) ***(P-12211)***
Millers Woodworking, Tustin *Also called GL Woodworking Inc* ***(P-4622)***
Millerton Builders Inc ......E......559 252-0490
4714 E Home Ave Fresno (93703) ***(P-5204)***
Millipart Inc (PA) ......F......626 963-4101
412 W Carter Dr Glendora (91740) ***(P-16752)***
Millpledge North America Inc ......F......310 215-0400
5310 Derry Ave Ste S&T Agoura Hills (91301) ***(P-8497)***
Mills Acquisition Corporation ......E......650 365-2801
1035 22nd Ave Oakland (94606) ***(P-12679)***
Mills ASAP Reprographics (PA) ......F......805 772-2019
495 Morro Bay Blvd Morro Bay (93442) ***(P-5686)***
Mills Iron Works ......D......323 321-6520
14834 S Maple Ave Gardena (90248) ***(P-13770)***
Millwood Cabinet Co Inc ......E......661 327-0371
2321 Virginia Ave Bakersfield (93307) ***(P-4329)***
Millwork Co ......F......760 788-1533
607 Brazos St Ste C Ramona (92065) ***(P-4193)***
Millwork Div, Oroville *Also called Setzer Forest Products Inc* ***(P-4055)***
Millworks Etc Inc (PA) ......E......805 499-3400
2586 Calcite Cir Newbury Park (91320) ***(P-12335)***
Millworks By Design Inc ......E......818 597-1326
2248 Townsgate Rd Ste 1 Westlake Village (91361) ***(P-4194)***
Millworx Prcsion Machining Inc ......E......951 371-2683
506 Malloy Ct Corona (92880) ***(P-16753)***
Milners Anodizing ......F......707 584-1188
3330 Mcmaude Pl Santa Rosa (95407) ***(P-13456)***
Milo Engineering, Torrance *Also called Milo Machining Inc* ***(P-16754)***
Milo Machining Inc ......F......310 530-0925
2675 Skypark Dr Ste 304 Torrance (90505) ***(P-16754)***
Milodon Incorporated ......E......805 577-5950
2250 Agate Ct Simi Valley (93065) ***(P-20403)***
Milpitas Post Newspapers Inc ......F......408 262-2454
59 Marylinn Dr Milpitas (95035) ***(P-5973)***
Milwright, Sebastopol *Also called Kurtz Family Corporation* ***(P-10185)***
Mimo, Los Angeles *Also called 2bb Unlimited Inc* ***(P-3023)***
Min-E-Con LLC ......D......949 250-0087
17312 Eastman Irvine (92614) ***(P-19401)***
Mina Product Development Inc ......F......714 966-2150
3020 Red Hill Ave Costa Mesa (92626) ***(P-10213)***
Mina-Tree Signs Incorporated (PA) ......E......209 941-2921
1233 E Ronald St Stockton (95205) ***(P-23927)***
Minachee Inc ......F......213 745-8100
1248 S Flower St Los Angeles (90015) ***(P-3114)***
Minatronic Inc ......F......805 239-8864
1139 13th St Paso Robles (93446) ***(P-19654)***
Mindjolt ......F......415 543-7800
144 2nd St Fl 4 San Francisco (94105) ***(P-23447)***
Mindrum Precision Inc ......E......909 989-1728
10000 4th St Rancho Cucamonga (91730) ***(P-21692)***
Mindrum Precision Products, Rancho Cucamonga *Also called Mindrum Precision Inc* ***(P-21692)***
Mindsai Inc ......F......831 239-4644
101 Cooper St Ste 218 Santa Cruz (95060) ***(P-24922)***
Mindsnacks Inc ......E......415 875-9817
1479 Folsom St San Francisco (94103) ***(P-24923)***
Mindspeed Technologies Inc (HQ) ......D......949 579-3000
4000 Macarthur Blvd Newport Beach (92660) ***(P-19019)***
Mineral Essence, North Hollywood *Also called Advanced Inst of Skin Care* ***(P-8690)***
Mineral King Minerals Inc (PA) ......F......559 582-9228
7600 N Ingram Ave Ste 105 Fresno (93711) ***(P-9066)***
Minerva Surgical Inc ......F......650 399-1770
101 Saginaw Dr Redwood City (94063) ***(P-22543)***
Minestone ......F......818 775-5999
17739 Valley Vista Blvd Encino (91316) ***(P-304)***
Mingo Enterprises Inc ......F......510 528-3044
1209b Solano Ave Albany (94706) ***(P-6217)***
Mini Vac Inc ......F......818 244-6777
634 E Colorado St Glendale (91205) ***(P-17407)***
Mini-Flex Corporation ......F......805 644-1474
2472 Eastman Ave Ste 29 Ventura (93003) ***(P-16755)***
Miniature Precision Inc ......F......530 244-4131
4488 Mountain Lakes Blvd Redding (96003) ***(P-16756)***
Minitouch Inc ......F......510 651-5000
47853 Warm Springs Blvd Fremont (94539) ***(P-22544)***
Minorities & Success, Torrance *Also called Minority Success Pubg Group* ***(P-6218)***
Minority Success Pubg Group ......E......310 373-2868
3711 Lomita Blvd Ste 196 Torrance (90505) ***(P-6218)***
Minsley Inc ......E......909 458-1100
989 S Monterey Ave Ontario (91761) ***(P-2606)***
Minson Corporation ......B......323 513-1041
1 Minson Way Montebello (90640) ***(P-4798)***
Mint Grips, Benicia *Also called Gibbs Plastic & Rubber Co* ***(P-9616)***
Mint Software Inc ......F......650 944-6000
280 Hope St Mountain View (94041) ***(P-24924)***
Mintie Corporation ......F......510 351-5868
1114 N San Fernando Rd Los Angeles (90065) ***(P-12680)***
Minton-Spidell Inc (PA) ......F......310 836-0403
8467 Steller Dr Culver City (90232) ***(P-4723)***
Mintronix Inc ......F......805 482-1298
6090 Cielo Vista Ct Camarillo (93012) ***(P-15459)***
Minus K Technology Inc ......C......310 348-9656
460 Hindry Ave Ste C Inglewood (90301) ***(P-19020)***
Minute Man Envmtl Systems Inc ......E......949 637-5446
830 W 16th St Costa Mesa (92627) ***(P-6976)***
Minuteman Press, Van Nuys *Also called Printcom Inc* ***(P-7042)***
Minuteman Press, Rancho Cucamonga *Also called Lee Maxton Inc* ***(P-6941)***
Mio Technology, Fremont *Also called Mitac Usa Inc* ***(P-15460)***

Employee Codes: A=Over 500 employees, B=251-500
C=101-250, D=51-100, E=20-50, F=10-19
2019 California
Manfacturers Register
© Mergent Inc. 1-800-342-5647
1215

Mips Tech Inc (HQ)..........D.......408 530-5000
3201 Scott Blvd Santa Clara (95054) *(P-19021)*
Mir Printing & Graphics..........F.......818 313-9333
21333 Deering Ct Canoga Park (91304) *(P-6977)*
Miracle Bedding Corporation..........E.......562 908-2370
3700 Capitol Ave City of Industry (90601) *(P-4874)*
Miracle Cover (PA)..........F.......714 842-8863
20721 Goshawk Ln Huntington Beach (92646) *(P-8918)*
Miracle Greens Inc..........C.......800 521-5867
8477 Steller Dr Culver City (90232) *(P-631)*
Miracle Sealants Company LLC..........E.......626 443-6433
12318 Lower Azusa Rd Arcadia (91006) *(P-9281)*
Mirage Sprtfshng & Commrcl..........F.......805 983-0975
1810 Kapalua Dr Oxnard (93036) *(P-23619)*
Miramar Labs Inc..........E.......408 940-8700
2790 Walsh Ave Santa Clara (95051) *(P-22773)*
Miramonte Winery, Temecula *Also called Celebration Cellars LLC (P-1684)*
Miranda, Grass Valley *Also called Grass Valley Inc (P-18115)*
Mirapoint Software, Inc...........D.......650 286-7200
1600 Seaport Blvd Ste 400 Redwood City (94063) *(P-18184)*
Mirati Therapeutics Inc..........D.......858 332-3410
9393 Towne Centre Dr # 200 San Diego (92121) *(P-8284)*
Mirion Technologies Inc (PA)..........C.......925 543-0800
3000 Executive Pkwy # 518 San Ramon (94583) *(P-22237)*
Mirth Corporation..........E.......714 389-1200
611 Anton Blvd Ste 500 Costa Mesa (92626) *(P-24925)*
Miss Cristina, Los Angeles *Also called Miss Kim Inc (P-3327)*
Miss Kim Inc..........F.......213 747-4011
1015 San Julian St Los Angeles (90015) *(P-3327)*
Mission AG Resources LLC..........E.......559 591-3333
6801 Avenue 430 Unit A Reedley (93654) *(P-632)*
Mission Bell Mfg Co Inc..........E.......209 229-7280
25656 Schulte Ct Tracy (95377) *(P-4330)*
Mission Bell Winery, Madera *Also called Constellation Brands US Oprs (P-1705)*
Mission Bindery Inc..........E.......510 623-8260
7140 Via Solana San Jose (95135) *(P-7608)*
Mission Concrete Products, Gilroy *Also called Quinn Development Co (P-10858)*
Mission Crtical Composites LLC..........E.......714 831-2100
15400 Graham St Ste 102 Huntington Beach (92649) *(P-20889)*
Mission Custom Extrusion Inc..........E.......909 822-1581
10904 Beech Ave Fontana (92337) *(P-10214)*
Mission Flavors Fragrances Inc..........F.......949 461-3344
25882 Wright El Toro (92610) *(P-2273)*
Mission Foods, Fresno *Also called Gruma Corporation (P-2391)*
Mission Foods, Rancho Cucamonga *Also called Gruma Corporation (P-2392)*
Mission Foods Dc60, San Diego *Also called Gruma Corporation (P-2390)*
Mission Hockey Company (PA)..........F.......949 585-9390
12 Goodyear Ste 100 Irvine (92618) *(P-23620)*
Mission Kleensweep Prod Inc..........D.......323 223-1405
13644 Live Oak Ln Baldwin Park (91706) *(P-8597)*
Mission Laboratories, Baldwin Park *Also called Mission Kleensweep Prod Inc (P-8597)*
Mission Microwave Tech LLC..........E.......951 893-4925
9924 Norwalk Blvd Santa Fe Springs (90670) *(P-18185)*
Mission Plastics Inc..........C.......909 947-7287
1930 S Parco Ave Ontario (91761) *(P-10215)*
Mission Ready Mix, Ventura *Also called Lynch Ready Mix Concrete Co (P-11138)*
Mission Research Corporation (HQ)..........F.......805 690-2447
6750 Navigator Way # 200 Goleta (93117) *(P-20602)*
Mission Rubber, Corona *Also called MCP Industries Inc (P-12040)*
Mission Rubber Co, Corona *Also called MCP Industries Inc (P-9635)*
Mission Rubber Company LLC (HQ)..........D.......951 736-1313
1660 Leeson Ln Corona (92879) *(P-13771)*
Mission Tool and Mfg Co Inc..........E.......510 782-8383
3440 Arden Rd Hayward (94545) *(P-16757)*
Mission Truss, Lakeside *Also called Dixietruss Inc (P-10916)*
Mission Valley Regional Occu..........E.......510 657-1865
5019 Stevenson Blvd Fremont (94538) *(P-9282)*
Mist & Cool LLC..........F.......805 986-4125
707 E Hueneme Rd Oxnard (93033) *(P-17398)*
Mist Incorporated..........E.......818 678-5619
9006 Fullbright Ave Chatsworth (91311) *(P-14653)*
Mistras Group Inc..........E.......310 793-7173
3551 Voyager St Ste 104 Torrance (90503) *(P-22238)*
Misyd Corp (PA)..........D.......213 742-1800
30 Fremont Pl Los Angeles (90005) *(P-3584)*
Mitac Information Systems..........E.......510 668-3679
39889 Eureka Dr Newark (94560) *(P-15807)*
Mitac Information Systems Corp (HQ)..........C.......510 284-3000
39889 Eureka Dr Newark (94560) *(P-15570)*
Mitac Usa Inc (HQ)..........E.......510 661-2800
47988 Fremont Blvd Fremont (94538) *(P-15460)*
Mitann Inc (HQ)..........E.......408 782-2500
400 Jarvis Dr Ste A Morgan Hill (95037) *(P-9283)*
Mitchell Dean Collins..........F.......714 894-6767
12771 Monarch St Garden Grove (92841) *(P-4331)*
Mitchell Fabrication..........E.......909 590-0393
4564 Mission Blvd Montclair (91763) *(P-12212)*
Mitchell Instruments, San Marcos *Also called Mitchell Test & Safety Inc (P-22239)*
Mitchell Instruments Co Inc..........F.......760 744-2690
1570 Cherokee St San Marcos (92078) *(P-21807)*
Mitchell Processing LLC..........E.......909 519-5759
2778 Pomona Blvd Pomona (91768) *(P-9637)*
Mitchell Repair Info Co LLC (HQ)..........E.......858 391-5000
14145 Danielson St Ste A Poway (92064) *(P-6529)*
Mitchell Rubber Products LLC (PA)..........C.......951 681-5655
10220 San Sevaine Way Mira Loma (91752) *(P-9638)*
Mitchell Rubber Products LLC..........D.......951 681-5655
10220 San Sevaine Way Mira Loma (91752) *(P-9639)*
Mitchell Test & Safety Inc..........F.......760 744-2690
1570 Cherokee St San Marcos (92078) *(P-22239)*
Mitchell-Duckett Corporation..........F.......530 268-2112
10074 Streeter Rd Ste B Auburn (95602) *(P-16758)*
Mitchell1, Poway *Also called Mitchell Repair Info Co LLC (P-6529)*
Mitchellamazing, Montclair *Also called Amazing Steel Company (P-12111)*
Mitco Industries Inc (PA)..........E.......909 877-0800
2235 S Vista Ave Bloomington (92316) *(P-16759)*
Mitel Networks Inc (HQ)..........C.......613 592-2122
960 Stewart Dr Sunnyvale (94085) *(P-17965)*
Mitrani USA Corp..........F.......818 888-9994
7451 Westcliff Dr West Hills (91307) *(P-9907)*
Mitratech Holdings Inc..........F.......323 964-0000
5900 Wilshire Blvd # 1500 Los Angeles (90036) *(P-24926)*
Mitsubishi Cement Corporation..........C.......760 248-7373
5808 State Highway 18 Lucerne Valley (92356) *(P-10764)*
Mitsubishi Chemical Crbn Fbr..........C.......800 929-5471
1822 Reynolds Ave Irvine (92614) *(P-9156)*
Mitsubishi Chemical Crbn Fbr (HQ)..........C.......916 386-1733
5900 88th St Sacramento (95828) *(P-17239)*
Mitsubishi Elc Auto Amer Inc..........E.......714 902-1900
5800 Skylab Rd Huntington Beach (92647) *(P-19839)*
Mitsubishi Electric Visual..........C.......800 553-7278
10833 Valley View St # 300 Cypress (90630) *(P-19655)*
Mitxpc Inc..........F.......510 226-6883
45437 Warm Springs Blvd Fremont (94539) *(P-15461)*
Mitxpc Embedded Sys Solutions, Fremont *Also called Mitxpc Inc (P-15461)*
Miwa Inc..........E.......510 261-5999
5733 San Leandro St Ofc Oakland (94621) *(P-13841)*
Mix Garden Inc..........F.......707 433-4327
1083 Vine St Healdsburg (95448) *(P-11143)*
Mixamo Inc..........E.......415 255-7455
2415 3rd St Ste 239 San Francisco (94107) *(P-24927)*
Mixed Bag Designs Inc..........D.......650 239-5358
1744 Rollins Rd Burlingame (94010) *(P-5609)*
Mixed Chicks LLC..........F.......818 888-4008
21208 Vanowen St Canoga Park (91303) *(P-8797)*
Mixed Nuts Inc..........E.......323 587-6887
3366 Fruitland Ave Vernon (90058) *(P-1498)*
Mixmor Inc..........F.......323 664-1941
3131 Casitas Ave Los Angeles (90039) *(P-14182)*
Mixonic..........F.......866 838-5067
1145 Polk St Ste A San Francisco (94109) *(P-7408)*
Miyako Oriental Foods Inc..........F.......626 962-9633
4287 Puente Ave Baldwin Park (91706) *(P-1510)*
Miyokos Kitchen..........E.......415 448-5807
2086 Marina Ave Petaluma (94954) *(P-561)*
Mizkan Americas Inc..........F.......831 728-2061
46 Walker St Watsonville (95076) *(P-2607)*
Mizkan Americas Inc..........E.......909 484-8743
10037 8th St Rancho Cucamonga (91730) *(P-2608)*
Mizu Inc (PA)..........F.......307 690-3219
2225 Faraday Ave Ste E Carlsbad (92008) *(P-9640)*
Mizuho Orthopedic Systems Inc (HQ)..........B.......510 429-1500
30031 Ahern Ave Union City (94587) *(P-22545)*
Mizuho OSI, Union City *Also called Mizuho Orthopedic Systems Inc (P-22545)*
Mj Blanks Inc..........E.......213 629-0006
1155 S Grand Ave Apt 614 Los Angeles (90015) *(P-2851)*
Mja Vineyards LLC..........F.......408 353-6000
24900 Highland Way Los Gatos (95033) *(P-1881)*
Mjc Engineering and Tech Inc..........F.......714 890-0618
15401 Assembly Ln Huntington Beach (92649) *(P-14446)*
Mjck Corporation..........E.......888 992-8437
3222 E Washington Blvd Vernon (90058) *(P-2852)*
Mjd Cabinets, Lakeside *Also called M DAmico Inc (P-5244)*
MJM Expert Pipe Fbrcation Wldg..........E.......661 330-8698
3404 Wrenwood St Bakersfield (93309) *(P-12213)*
Mjolnir Industries LLC..........F.......805 488-3550
5701 Perkins Rd Oxnard (93033) *(P-14542)*
Mjus LLC (fka Mindjet Llc)..........D.......415 229-4344
275 Battery St Ste 1000 San Francisco (94111) *(P-24928)*
Mjw Inc..........D.......323 778-8900
1328 W Slauson Ave Los Angeles (90044) *(P-15085)*
Mk Diamond Products Inc (PA)..........C.......310 539-5221
1315 Storm Pkwy Torrance (90501) *(P-14708)*
Mk Digital Direct Inc..........F.......619 661-0628
861 Harold Pl Ste 209 Chula Vista (91914) *(P-21995)*
Mk Magnetics Inc..........D.......760 246-6373
17030 Muskrat Ave Adelanto (92301) *(P-11450)*
Mk Manufacturing, Irvine *Also called M K Products Inc (P-14731)*
Mk Printing, Santa Ana *Also called Mekong Printing Inc (P-6967)*
Mk Tool and Abrasive Inc..........F.......562 776-8818
4710 S Eastern Ave Los Angeles (90040) *(P-11299)*
Mkkr Inc..........F.......909 890-5994
430 E Parkcenter Cir N San Bernardino (92408) *(P-14654)*
Mkm Customs, Roseville *Also called Sinister Mfg Company Inc (P-20449)*
Mks Color Composite, Compton *Also called Permalite Plastics Corp (P-8965)*
Mkt Innovations, Brea *Also called Mike Kenney Tool Inc (P-16745)*
Mkt Innovations..........D.......714 524-7668
2900 Saturn St Ste A Brea (92821) *(P-16760)*
ML Kishigo Mfg Co LLC..........D.......949 852-1963
2901 Daimler St Santa Ana (92705) *(P-3672)*
Mlabs, Lakeport *Also called Mountain Lake Labs (P-21353)*
Mlim LLC..........A.......619 299-3131
350 Camino De La Reina San Diego (92108) *(P-5974)*
Mline Transportation Company..........E.......916 729-1053
6621 Clear Creek Ct Citrus Heights (95610) *(P-1511)*
Mmi Services Inc..........C.......661 589-9366
4042 Patton Way Bakersfield (93308) *(P-239)*

Mmix Technologies ... F ... 619 631-6644
1348 Pioneer Way El Cajon (92020) ***(P-12681)***
Mmp Sheet Metal Inc ... E ... 562 691-1055
501 Commercial Way La Habra (90631) ***(P-12682)***
MMR Technologies Inc (PA) ... F ... 650 962-9620
41 Daggett Dr San Jose (95134) ***(P-14991)***
Mmw Operation, South El Monte *Also called Master Metal Works Inc* ***(P-12880)***
MNC Bliss Enterprises Inc ... F ... 916 483-1167
1715 Fulton Ave Sacramento (95825) ***(P-17716)***
Mnd Engineering, Sylmar *Also called Vallin Alida* ***(P-17034)***
Mng Newspapers, San Jose *Also called California Newspapers Partnr* ***(P-5789)***
Mnm Corporation (PA) ... D ... 213 627-3737
110 E 9th St Ste A777 Los Angeles (90079) ***(P-6219)***
Mobil Pallets Exchange ... F ... 831 758-5203
140 Villa Pacheco Ct Hollister (95023) ***(P-4489)***
Mobile Crossing Inc ... F ... 916 485-2773
1230 Oakmead Pkwy Ste 304 Sunnyvale (94085) ***(P-21349)***
Mobile Designs Inc ... F ... 530 244-1050
4650 Caterpillar Rd Redding (96003) ***(P-11597)***
Mobile Equipment Appraisers, Bakersfield *Also called Mobile Equipment Company* ***(P-14301)***
Mobile Equipment Company ... E ... 661 327-8476
3610 Gilmore Ave Bakersfield (93308) ***(P-14301)***
Mobile Home Board ... E ... 408 744-1011
1240 Mountain Vw Alviso C Sunnyvale (94089) ***(P-6220)***
Mobile Home Park Magazines, Sunnyvale *Also called Mobile Home Board* ***(P-6220)***
Mobile Management, Mira Loma *Also called McGrath Rentcorp* ***(P-12944)***
Mobile Mini Inc ... F ... 510 252-9326
44580 Old Warm Sprng Blvd Fremont (94538) ***(P-12945)***
Mobile Mini Inc ... E ... 530 345-7645
3902 Esplanade Chico (95973) ***(P-12946)***
Mobile Mini Inc ... E ... 916 381-1351
8160 Junipero St Sacramento (95828) ***(P-12947)***
Mobile Mini Inc ... E ... 209 858-9300
16351 Mckinley Ave Lathrop (95330) ***(P-12948)***
Mobile Mini Inc ... C ... 909 356-1690
42207 3rd St E Lancaster (93535) ***(P-12949)***
Mobile Mini Inc ... E ... 858 578-9222
12345 Crosthwaite Cir Poway (92064) ***(P-12950)***
Mobile Mini Storage, Poway *Also called Mobile Mini Inc* ***(P-12950)***
Mobile Tone Inc ... F ... 323 939-6928
5430 Westhaven St Los Angeles (90016) ***(P-18186)***
Mobile Wireless Tech Llc ... F ... 714 239-1535
125 W Cerritos Ave Anaheim (92805) ***(P-18347)***
Mobileiron Inc (PA) ... C ... 650 919-8100
401 E Middlefield Rd Mountain View (94043) ***(P-24929)***
Mobileops Corporation ... F ... 408 203-0243
1422 Wright Ave Sunnyvale (94087) ***(P-24930)***
Mobility Specialist Inc ... E ... 714 674-0480
490 Capricorn St Brea (92821) ***(P-24177)***
Mobilityware, Irvine *Also called Upstanding LLC* ***(P-25317)***
Mobis Parts America LLC ... B ... 949 450-0014
10550 Talbert Ave 4 Fountain Valley (92708) ***(P-20404)***
Mobius Photonics Inc ... F ... 408 496-1084
110 Pioneer Way Ste A Mountain View (94041) ***(P-20018)***
Mobiveil Inc ... F ... 408 791-2977
890 Hillview Ct Ste 250 Milpitas (95035) ***(P-19022)***
Moc Products Company Inc (PA) ... D ... 818 794-3500
12306 Montague St Pacoima (91331) ***(P-9284)***
Mockingbird Networks ... D ... 408 342-5300
10040 Bubb Rd Cupertino (95014) ***(P-15462)***
Mod 2, Los Angeles *Also called Mod2 Inc* ***(P-24931)***
Mod Electronics Inc ... E ... 310 322-2136
142 Sierra St El Segundo (90245) ***(P-23221)***
Mod Shop ... E ... 310 523-1008
15610 S Main St Gardena (90248) ***(P-4724)***
Mod2 Inc ... F ... 213 747-8424
3317 S Broadway Los Angeles (90007) ***(P-24931)***
Moda Enterprises Inc ... F ... 714 484-0076
1334 N Knollwood Cir Anaheim (92801) ***(P-20159)***
Mode Analytics Inc ... F ... 415 271-7599
208 Utah St Ste 400 San Francisco (94103) ***(P-24932)***
Mode Tek, Pasadena *Also called Modetek Inc* ***(P-10658)***
Modern Aire Ventilating, North Hollywood *Also called Modern-Aire Ventilating Inc* ***(P-12683)***
Modern Bamboo Incorporated ... F ... 925 820-2804
5853 Virmar Ave Oakland (94618) ***(P-4725)***
Modern Blind Factory, San Diego *Also called Mbf Interiors Inc* ***(P-3697)***
Modern Ceramics Mfg Inc ... E ... 408 383-0554
2240 Lundy Ave San Jose (95131) ***(P-10657)***
Modern Combat Solutions, Gilroy *Also called Real Action Paintball Inc* ***(P-23634)***
Modern Concepts Inc ... D ... 310 637-0013
3121 E Ana St E Rncho Dmngz (90221) ***(P-10216)***
Modern Custom Fabrication ... E ... 559 264-4741
2421 E California Ave Fresno (93721) ***(P-12400)***
Modern Dev Co A Ltd Partnr ... F ... 805 239-1167
3380 Branch Rd Paso Robles (93446) ***(P-1882)***
Modern Engine Inc ... E ... 818 409-9494
701 Sonora Ave Glendale (91201) ***(P-16761)***
Modern Gold Design Inc ... E ... 213 614-1818
650 S Hill St Ste 509 Los Angeles (90014) ***(P-23298)***
Modern Gourmet Foods, Irvine *Also called Coastal Cocktails Inc* ***(P-2114)***
Modern Luxury Media LLC (HQ) ... E ... 404 443-0004
243 Vallejo St San Francisco (94111) ***(P-6221)***
Modern Manufacturing Inc ... E ... 714 254-0156
4110 E La Palma Ave Anaheim (92807) ***(P-16762)***
Modern Metal Installations ... F ... 916 316-0997
4400 Shady Oak Way Fair Oaks (95628) ***(P-12882)***
Modern Metals Industries Inc ... E ... 800 437-6633
14000 S Broadway Los Angeles (90061) ***(P-22546)***
Modern Pattern & Fndry Co Inc ... E ... 323 583-4921
5610 Alcoa Ave Vernon (90058) ***(P-11517)***
Modern Plating, Los Angeles *Also called Alco Plating Corp* ***(P-13315)***
Modern Postcard, Carlsbad *Also called Iris Group Inc* ***(P-7362)***
Modern Stairways Inc ... F ... 619 466-1484
3239 Bancroft Dr Spring Valley (91977) ***(P-10958)***
Modern Studio Equipment Inc ... F ... 818 764-8574
7414 Bellaire Ave North Hollywood (91605) ***(P-23179)***
Modern Times Beer ... E ... 619 269-5222
3000 Upas St Ste 102 San Diego (92104) ***(P-5975)***
Modern Wall Graphics LLC ... E ... 760 787-0346
2191 W Esplanade Ave San Jacinto (92582) ***(P-9717)***
Modern Woodworks, Canoga Park *Also called Mww Inc* ***(P-4638)***
Modern-Aire Ventilating Inc ... E ... 818 765-9870
7319 Lankershim Blvd North Hollywood (91605) ***(P-12683)***
Modernpro LLC ... F ... 949 232-2148
15 Woodcrest Ln Aliso Viejo (92656) ***(P-6530)***
Modesto Bee Circulation, Modesto *Also called McClatchy Newspapers Inc* ***(P-5950)***
Modesto Bee, The, Modesto *Also called McClatchy Newspapers Inc* ***(P-5946)***
Modesto Pltg & Powdr Coating ... F ... 209 526-2696
436 Mitchell Rd Ste D Modesto (95354) ***(P-13457)***
Modesto Tent and Awning Inc ... F ... 209 545-1607
4448 Sisk Rd Modesto (95356) ***(P-3796)***
Modetek Inc ... E ... 760 431-4190
1720 San Pasqual St Pasadena (91106) ***(P-10658)***
Modified Plastics Inc (PA) ... E ... 714 546-4667
1240 E Glenwood Pl Santa Ana (92707) ***(P-10217)***
Moducom, Los Angeles *Also called Modular Communications Systems* ***(P-18187)***
Modular Communications Systems ... E ... 818 764-1333
373 N Western Ave Ste 15 Los Angeles (90004) ***(P-18187)***
Modular Metal Fabricators Inc ... C ... 951 242-3154
24600 Nandina Ave Moreno Valley (92551) ***(P-12684)***
Modular Office Solutions Inc ... D ... 909 476-4200
11701 6th St Rancho Cucamonga (91730) ***(P-4996)***
Modular Process Tech Corp ... F ... 408 325-8640
1675 Walsh Ave Ste E Santa Clara (95050) ***(P-15270)***
Modular Wind Energy Inc ... D ... 562 304-6782
1709 Apollo Ct Seal Beach (90740) ***(P-14002)***
Modulex Inc ... E ... 626 256-9508
2392 Bateman Ave Duarte (91010) ***(P-12336)***
Modulus Inc ... F ... 408 457-3712
518 Sycamore Dr Milpitas (95035) ***(P-18532)***
Modus Advanced Inc ... E ... 925 960-8700
1575 Greenville Rd Livermore (94550) ***(P-9641)***
Modutek Corp ... E ... 408 362-2000
6387 San Ignacio Ave San Jose (95119) ***(P-21619)***
Moebius Color, San Diego *Also called Moebius Design* ***(P-7653)***
Moebius Design ... E ... 858 450-4486
9770 Carroll Centre Rd San Diego (92126) ***(P-7653)***
Moeller Mfg & Sup Inc, Anaheim *Also called Moeller Mfg & Sup LLC* ***(P-11976)***
Moeller Mfg & Sup LLC ... E ... 714 999-5551
805 E Cerritos Ave Anaheim (92805) ***(P-11976)***
Moen Industries ... E ... 562 946-6381
10330 Pioneer Blvd # 235 Santa Fe Springs (90670) ***(P-14797)***
Mogan David Wine, Ripon *Also called Wine Group Inc* ***(P-2062)***
Mohammad Khan ... F ... 619 231-1664
2606 Imperial Ave San Diego (92102) ***(P-10218)***
Mohawk Industries Inc ... D ... 909 357-1064
9687 Transportation Way Fontana (92335) ***(P-2934)***
Mohawk Industries Inc ... C ... 510 440-8790
41490 Boyce Rd Fremont (94538) ***(P-2935)***
Mohawk Land & Cattle Co Inc ... D ... 408 436-1800
1660 Old Bayshore Hwy San Jose (95112) ***(P-444)***
Mohawk Western Plastics Inc ... E ... 909 593-7547
1496 Arrow Hwy La Verne (91750) ***(P-5610)***
Moisture Register Products, Rancho Cucamonga *Also called Aqua Measure Instrument Co* ***(P-22164)***
Mojado Bros, Placentia *Also called Soft Touch Inc* ***(P-7488)***
Mojave Copy & Printing Inc ... F ... 760 241-7898
12402 Industrial Blvd E10 Victorville (92395) ***(P-6978)***
Mojave Foods Corporation ... C ... 323 890-8900
6200 E Slauson Ave Commerce (90040) ***(P-2609)***
Moki International (usa) Inc ... E ... 205 208-0179
21700 Oxnard St Ste 850 Woodland Hills (91367) ***(P-17835)***
Mokume Software Inc ... F ... 408 839-7000
4131 Mackin Woods Ln San Jose (95135) ***(P-24933)***
Mold Masters Inc ... F ... 323 999-2599
715 Ruberta Ave Glendale (91201) ***(P-14543)***
Mold USA ... F ... 310 823-6653
322 Culver Blve Apt 6 Playa Del Rey (90293) ***(P-14544)***
Mold Vision Inc ... F ... 951 245-8020
18351 Pasadena St Lake Elsinore (92530) ***(P-14545)***
Molded Devices, Riverside *Also called Mdi East Inc* ***(P-10202)***
Molded Devices Inc (PA) ... E ... 480 785-9100
6918 Ed Perkic St Riverside (92504) ***(P-10219)***
Molded Fiber GL Companies - W ... D ... 760 246-4042
9400 Holly Rd Adelanto (92301) ***(P-10220)***
Molded Interconnect Industries, Foothill Ranch *Also called Lantic Inc* ***(P-10188)***
Moldex-Metric Inc ... B ... 310 837-6500
10111 Jefferson Blvd Culver City (90232) ***(P-22774)***
Molding Acquisition Corp ... F ... 209 723-5000
2651 Cooper Ave Merced (95348) ***(P-7855)***
Molding Company ... E ... 408 748-6968
1987 Russell Ave Santa Clara (95054) ***(P-4636)***
Molding Corporation America ... E ... 818 890-7877
10349 Norris Ave Pacoima (91331) ***(P-10221)***

ALPHABETIC

Employee Codes: A=Over 500 employees, B=251-500
C=101-250, D=51-100, E=20-50, F=10-19
2019 California
Manfacturers Register
© Mergent Inc. 1-800-342-5647
1217

Molding Intl & Engrg Inc ....D....951 296-5010
42136 Avenida Alvarado Temecula (92590) *(P-10222)*
Molding Solutions Inc (PA) ....D....707 575-1218
3225 Regional Pkwy Santa Rosa (95403) *(P-10223)*
Moldings Plus Inc ....E....909 947-3310
1856 S Grove Ave Ontario (91761) *(P-4195)*
Molecular Databank, Burlingame *Also called Collabrative DRG Discovery Inc (P-24509)*
Molecular Devices LLC (HQ) ....C....408 747-1700
3860 N 1st St San Jose (95134) *(P-21996)*
Moleculum ....F....714 619-5139
3128 Red Hill Ave Costa Mesa (92626) *(P-9340)*
Molekule Inc (PA) ....F....352 871-3803
1184 Harrison St San Francisco (94103) *(P-21517)*
Moles Farm ....D....559 444-0324
9503 S Hughes Ave Fresno (93706) *(P-889)*
Molex LLC ....E....909 803-1362
12200 Arrow Rte Rancho Cucamonga (91739) *(P-19402)*
Molinari Salami Co, San Francisco *Also called P G Molinari & Sons Inc (P-511)*
Molino Company ....D....323 726-1000
13712 Alondra Blvd Cerritos (90703) *(P-6979)*
Moller International Inc ....F....530 756-5086
1855 N 1st St Unit C Dixon (95620) *(P-20603)*
Molly Max, Los Angeles *Also called Assoluto Inc (P-3376)*
Molly's Custom Silver, Riverside *Also called Paradise Ranch (P-3674)*
Molnar Engineering Inc ....E....818 734-5685
20731 Marilla St Chatsworth (91311) *(P-16763)*
Mom Enterprises Inc ....F....415 526-2710
1003 W Cutting Blvd # 110 Richmond (94804) *(P-8285)*
Momeni Engineering LLC ....E....714 897-9301
15662 Commerce Ln Huntington Beach (92649) *(P-16764)*
Momentum Management LLC ....F....310 329-2599
1206 W Jon St Torrance (90502) *(P-9642)*
Mon Amie, Los Angeles *Also called Fashion Today Inc (P-3415)*
Mon Amie, Los Angeles *Also called Fashion Today Inc (P-3416)*
Monaco Baking Company, Fullerton *Also called Phenix Gourmet LLC (P-1375)*
Monaco Sheet Metal ....F....858 272-0297
5131 Santa Fe St Ste A San Diego (92109) *(P-12685)*
Monadnock Company ....C....626 964-6581
16728 Gale Ave City of Industry (91745) *(P-11977)*
Monaero Engineering Inc ....F....714 994-5463
17011 Industry Pl La Mirada (90638) *(P-20890)*
Monarch Art & Frame Inc ....E....818 373-6180
7700 Gloria Ave Van Nuys (91406) *(P-4637)*
Monarch Litho Inc (PA) ....E....323 727-0300
1501 Date St Montebello (90640) *(P-6980)*
Monarch Precision Deburring ....F....714 258-0342
1514 E Edinger Ave Ste C Santa Ana (92705) *(P-14395)*
Monarchy Diamond Inc ....B....213 924-1161
550 S Hill St Ste 1088 Los Angeles (90013) *(P-417)*
Monco Products Inc ....E....714 891-2788
7562 Acacia Ave Garden Grove (92841) *(P-10224)*
Mondelez Global LLC ....A....714 690-7428
6201 Knott Ave Buena Park (90620) *(P-509)*
Mondelez Global LLC ....E....714 634-2773
1220 Howell St Anaheim (92805) *(P-1292)*
Mongabay Org Corporation ....E....209 315-5573
15 Clinton St Redwood City (94062) *(P-6531)*
Monica Bruce Designs Inc ....F....707 938-0277
28913 Arnold Dr Sonoma (95476) *(P-3908)*
Monier Lifetile, Rialto *Also called Boral Roofing LLC (P-10889)*
Monitise Inc ....F....650 286-1059
1 Embarcadero Ctr Ste 900 San Francisco (94111) *(P-24934)*
Mono Engineering Corp ....E....818 772-4998
20977 Knapp St Chatsworth (91311) *(P-16765)*
Monobind Inc (PA) ....E....949 951-2665
100 N Pointe Dr Lake Forest (92630) *(P-22547)*
Monogram Aerospace Fas Inc (HQ) ....C....323 722-4760
3423 Garfield Ave Commerce (90040) *(P-11978)*
Monogram Biosciences Inc ....B....650 635-1100
345 Oyster Point Blvd South San Francisco (94080) *(P-8498)*
Monogram Systems, Carson *Also called Zodiac WATer&waste Aero System (P-20981)*
Monogram Systems, Carson *Also called Mag Aerospace Industries Inc (P-12016)*
Monogram Systems ....F....801 400-7944
1500 Glenn Curtiss St Carson (90746) *(P-20891)*
Monographx Inc ....F....310 325-6780
1052 251st St Harbor City (90710) *(P-23928)*
Monolith Materials Inc ....E....650 933-4957
1700 Seaport Blvd Ste 110 Redwood City (94063) *(P-7788)*
Monolithic Power Systems Inc (PA) ....C....408 826-0600
79 Great Oaks Blvd San Jose (95119) *(P-19023)*
Monopole Inc ....F....818 500-8585
4661 Alger St Los Angeles (90039) *(P-8919)*
Monopoly Music, Whittier *Also called Grand Motif Records (P-17902)*
Monrow Inc ....E....213 741-6007
1404 S Main St Ste C Los Angeles (90015) *(P-3259)*
Monsanto Company ....C....831 623-7016
500 Lucy Brown Rd San Juan Bautista (95045) *(P-9107)*
Monson Machine Inc ....F....951 736-6615
1802 Pomona Rd Corona (92880) *(P-16766)*
Monster Beverage 1990 Corp (HQ) ....D....951 739-6200
1 Monster Way Corona (92879) *(P-2150)*
Monster Beverage Company ....A....866 322-4466
1990 Pomona Rd Corona (92880) *(P-2151)*
Monster Beverage Corporation (PA) ....D....951 739-6200
1 Monster Way Corona (92879) *(P-2152)*
Monster Route Inc ....F....650 368-1628
3559 Haven Ave Ste A Menlo Park (94025) *(P-12214)*
Monster Tool Company, Vista *Also called Carbide Company LLC (P-14614)*

Mont St John Cellars Inc ....F....707 255-8864
5400 Old Sonoma Rd NAPA (94559) *(P-1883)*
Montage Technology Inc ....F....408 982-2788
101 Metro Dr Ste 500 San Jose (95110) *(P-19024)*
Montague Company ....C....510 785-8822
1830 Stearman Ave Hayward (94545) *(P-16074)*
Montavista Software LLC (HQ) ....C....408 572-8000
2315 N 1st St Fl 4 San Jose (95131) *(P-24935)*
Montblanc North America LLC ....F....408 241-5188
2855 Stevens Creek Blvd Santa Clara (95050) *(P-23299)*
Montblanc Santa Clara, Santa Clara *Also called Montblanc North America LLC (P-23299)*
Montbleau & Associates Inc (PA) ....D....619 263-5550
555 Raven St San Diego (92102) *(P-4955)*
Montclair Bronze Inc (PA) ....E....909 986-2664
5621 State St Montclair (91763) *(P-11764)*
Montclair Machine Shop Inc ....F....909 986-2664
5621 State St Montclair (91763) *(P-16767)*
Montclair Wood Corporation ....C....909 985-0302
545 N Mountain Ave # 104 Upland (91786) *(P-4085)*
Monte Allen Interiors Inc ....E....310 380-4640
1505 W 139th St Gardena (90249) *(P-4799)*
Monte De Oro Winery ....F....951 491-6551
35820 Rancho Cal Rd Temecula (92591) *(P-1884)*
Montebello Container Co LLC ....D....714 994-2351
14333 Macaw St La Mirada (90638) *(P-5438)*
Montebello Container Co LLC ....E....562 948-3483
13220 Molette St Santa Fe Springs (90670) *(P-5439)*
Montebello Plastics LLC ....E....323 728-6814
601 W Olympic Blvd Montebello (90640) *(P-9718)*
Monterey Bay Beverage Co Inc ....E....818 784-4885
14535 Benefit St Unit 4 Sherman Oaks (91403) *(P-827)*
Monterey Bay Office Pdts Inc ....F....408 727-4627
1700 Wyatt Dr Santa Clara (95054) *(P-7208)*
Monterey Bay Rebar Inc (PA) ....F....831 724-3013
547 Airport Blvd Watsonville (95076) *(P-12215)*
Monterey Canyon LLC (PA) ....D....213 741-0209
1515 E 15th St Los Angeles (90021) *(P-3468)*
Monterey Coast Brewing LLC ....F....831 758-2337
165 Main St Salinas (93901) *(P-14872)*
Monterey Coun Graphic Comm, Salinas *Also called County of Monterey (P-7288)*
Monterey County Herald Company (HQ) ....E....831 372-3311
2200 Garden Rd Monterey (93940) *(P-5976)*
Monterey County Weekly ....E....831 393-3348
668 Williams Ave Seaside (93955) *(P-5977)*
Monterey Design Systems Inc ....C....408 747-7370
2171 Landings Dr Mountain View (94043) *(P-19871)*
Monterey Foam Company Inc ....F....408 279-6756
1716 Stone Ave Ste A San Jose (95125) *(P-11361)*
Monterey Graphics Inc ....F....310 787-3370
23505 Crenshaw Blvd # 137 Torrance (90505) *(P-6981)*
Monterey Herald, Monterey *Also called Monterey County Herald Company (P-5976)*
Monterey Machine Products ....F....626 967-2242
1504 W Industrial Park St Covina (91722) *(P-16768)*
Monterey Mechanical Co ....F....925 689-6670
1126 Landini Ln Concord (94520) *(P-12686)*
Monterey Signs Inc ....F....831 632-0490
555 Broadway Ave Seaside (93955) *(P-6982)*
Montero Printing Inc ....E....831 655-5511
2 Harris Ct Ste A6 Monterey (93940) *(P-6983)*
Montery Wine Company LLC ....F....831 386-1100
1010 Industrial Way King City (93930) *(P-1885)*
Montesquieu Winery, San Diego *Also called WG Best Weinkellerei Inc (P-2052)*
Montevina Winery, Plymouth *Also called Sierra Sunrise Vineyard Inc (P-1975)*
Montgomery Marble Co ....F....916 383-1563
8711 Younger Creek Dr Sacramento (95828) *(P-11263)*
Monthly Grapevine, The, Vacaville *Also called S & J Advertising Inc (P-6251)*
Monticello Cellars Inc ....F....707 253-2802
4242 Big Ranch Rd NAPA (94558) *(P-1886)*
Montoya & Jaramillo Inc ....F....408 727-5776
1161 Richard Ave Santa Clara (95050) *(P-13458)*
Monty Ventsam Inc ....F....818 768-6424
9495 San Fernando Rd Sun Valley (91352) *(P-4196)*
Moo Time, San Diego *Also called Nadolife Inc (P-687)*
Moog Aircraft Group, Torrance *Also called Moog Inc (P-21352)*
Moog Inc ....C....818 341-5156
21339 Nordhoff St Chatsworth (91311) *(P-21350)*
Moog Inc ....B....805 618-3900
7406 Hollister Ave Goleta (93117) *(P-21351)*
Moog Inc ....B....310 533-1178
1218 W Jon St Torrance (90502) *(P-17288)*
Moog Inc ....B....310 533-1178
20263 S Western Ave Torrance (90501) *(P-21352)*
Moog Jon Street Warehouse, Torrance *Also called Moog Inc (P-17288)*
Mooney Industries ....F....818 998-0199
8744 Remmet Ave Canoga Park (91304) *(P-16769)*
Mooney International, Chino *Also called Soaring America Corporation (P-20627)*
Moonshine Ink ....E....530 587-3607
10137 Riverside Dr Truckee (96161) *(P-5978)*
Moore Business Forms, Vacaville *Also called R R Donnelley & Sons Company (P-7070)*
Moore Epitaxial Inc ....E....209 833-0100
1422 Harding Ave Tracy (95376) *(P-14992)*
Moore Farms Inc ....F....661 854-5588
916 S Derby St Arvin (93203) *(P-2610)*
Moore Quality Galvanizing Inc ....E....559 673-2822
3001 Falcon Dr Madera (93637) *(P-13619)*
Moore Quality Galvanizing LP ....E....559 673-2822
3001 Falcon Dr Madera (93637) *(P-13620)*
Moore Technologies, Tracy *Also called Moore Epitaxial Inc (P-14992)*

Moore Tool Co ...E...760 949-4142
16701 Chestnut St Ste 8 Hesperia (92345) *(P-11979)*
Moores Ideal Products LLC ...F...626 339-9007
830 W Golden Grove Way Covina (91722) *(P-23448)*
Moose Boats Inc ...F...707 778-9828
1175 Nimitz Ave Ste 115 Vallejo (94592) *(P-21057)*
Mophie Inc (HQ) ...E...888 866-7443
15101 Red Hill Ave Tustin (92780) *(P-18188)*
Moquin Press Inc ...D...650 592-0575
555 Harbor Blvd Belmont (94002) *(P-6984)*
Moran Tools ...E...760 801-3570
2515 Bella Vista Dr Vista (92084) *(P-14447)*
Moravek Biochemicals Inc (PA) ...E...714 990-2018
577 Mercury Ln Brea (92821) *(P-7789)*
Moreau Wetzel Engineering Co ...F...310 830-5479
24424 Main St Ste 604 Carson (90745) *(P-14546)*
Morehouse Foods Inc ...E...626 854-1655
760 Epperson Dr City of Industry (91748) *(P-922)*
Morehouse-Cowles LLC ...E...909 627-7222
13930 Magnolia Ave Chino (91710) *(P-14993)*
Moreno Industries Inc ...F...714 229-9696
1225 N Knollwood Cir Anaheim (92801) *(P-20405)*
Morgan Advanced Ceramics Inc ...C...530 823-3401
13079 Earhart Ave Auburn (95602) *(P-7790)*
Morgan Gallacher Inc ...E...562 695-1232
8707 Millergrove Dr Santa Fe Springs (90670) *(P-8656)*
Morgan Hill Plastics Inc ...E...408 779-2118
8118 Arroyo Cir Gilroy (95020) *(P-10225)*
Morgan Hill Precision Inc ...F...408 778-7895
15500 Concord Cir Ste 100 Morgan Hill (95037) *(P-16770)*
Morgan Manufacturing Inc ...F...707 763-6848
521 2nd St Petaluma (94952) *(P-11902)*
Morgan Marine, Woodland Hills *Also called Catalina Yachts Inc* *(P-21025)*
Morgan Medesign Inc ...F...707 568-2929
7700 Bell Rd Ste B Windsor (95492) *(P-22548)*
Morgan Polymer Seals LLC (PA) ...E...858 679-4946
2475 A Paseo De Las San Diego (92154) *(P-9544)*
Morgan Products Inc ...F...661 257-3022
28103 Avenue Stanford Santa Clarita (91355) *(P-16771)*
Morgan Technical Ceramics Inc ...F...510 491-1100
2425 Whipple Rd Hayward (94544) *(P-11362)*
Morgan Truck Body LLC ...D...951 689-0800
7888 Lincoln Ave Riverside (92504) *(P-20220)*
Morgan Winery Inc (PA) ...F...831 751-7777
590 Brunken Ave Ste C Salinas (93901) *(P-1887)*
Morin Corp ...E...909 428-3747
10707 Commerce Way Fontana (92337) *(P-12951)*
Morin Industrial Technology, Huntington Beach *Also called M I T Inc* *(P-14536)*
Morin West, Fontana *Also called Morin Corp* *(P-12951)*
Morinaga Nutritional Foods Inc ...F...310 787-0200
3838 Del Amo Blvd Ste 201 Torrance (90503) *(P-2611)*
Morning Star Company ...D...209 827-2724
13448 Volta Rd Los Banos (93635) *(P-828)*
Morning Star Packing, Los Banos *Also called Morning Star Company* *(P-828)*
Morning Star Packing Co LP ...E...530 473-3642
2211 Old Highway 99 Williams (95987) *(P-829)*
Morningstar Foods, Gustine *Also called Saputo Dairy Foods Usa LLC* *(P-735)*
Morrell's Metal Finishing, Compton *Also called Morrells Electro Plating Inc* *(P-13459)*
Morrells Electro Plating Inc ...E...310 639-1024
432 E Euclid Ave Compton (90222) *(P-13459)*
Morrill Industries Inc ...D...209 838-2550
24754 E River Rd Escalon (95320) *(P-13772)*
Morris Enterprises Inc ...E...818 894-9103
16799 Schoenborn St North Hills (91343) *(P-10226)*
Morris Group International, City of Industry *Also called Acorn Engineering Company* *(P-12909)*
Morris Group International (PA) ...F...626 336-4561
15125 Proctor Ave City of Industry (91746) *(P-12952)*
Morris Multimedia Inc ...D...661 259-1234
24000 Creekside Rd Santa Clarita (91355) *(P-5979)*
Morris Newspaper Corp Cal (HQ) ...D...209 249-3500
531 E Yosemite Ave Manteca (95336) *(P-5980)*
Morris Publications (PA) ...E...209 847-3021
122 S 3rd Ave Oakdale (95361) *(P-5981)*
Morris Roberts LLC ...E...800 672-3974
20251 Sw Acacia St # 120 Newport Beach (92660) *(P-23929)*
Morris Welding Co Inc ...F...707 987-1114
11210 Socrates Mine Rd Middletown (95461) *(P-25423)*
Morrison Engineering ...F...909 796-5319
9879 Juniper Ct Yucaipa (92399) *(P-16772)*
Morrison Mar & Intermodal Inc ...E...925 362-4599
753 Tunbridge Rd Ste A150 Danville (94526) *(P-21003)*
Morrissey Bros Printers Inc ...E...323 233-7197
929 E Slauson Ave Los Angeles (90011) *(P-7409)*
Mortan Industries Inc ...E...951 682-2215
880 Columbia Ave Ste 2 Riverside (92507) *(P-9643)*
Mortech Manufacturing Co Inc ...E...626 334-1471
411 N Aerojet Dr Azusa (91702) *(P-5021)*
Mortensen Precision Shtmtl, San Jose *Also called Mortenson Precision* *(P-12687)*
Mortenson Precision ...E...408 441-7380
1943 Hartog Dr San Jose (95131) *(P-12687)*
Mortgageplannercrm, San Diego *Also called Marketing Pro Consulting Inc* *(P-24882)*
Morton Grinding Inc ...C...661 298-0895
201 E Avenue K15 Lancaster (93535) *(P-23770)*
Morton Manufacturing, Lancaster *Also called Morton Grinding Inc* *(P-23770)*
Morton Salt Inc ...F...562 437-0071
1050 Pier F Ave Long Beach (90802) *(P-402)*
Morts Custom Sheetmetal ...F...530 241-7013
18121 Clear Creek Rd Redding (96001) *(P-12688)*

Mosaic Brands Inc ...E...925 322-8700
3266 Buskirk Ave Pleasant Hill (94523) *(P-24178)*
Mosaic Distributors LLC ...F...805 383-7711
507 Calle San Pablo Camarillo (93012) *(P-8798)*
Mosaic Marketing Partners LLC ...F...805 383-7711
507 Calle San Pablo Camarillo (93012) *(P-8799)*
Mosaic Vineyards & Winery Inc ...F...707 857-2000
2001 Highway 128 Geyserville (95441) *(P-1888)*
Moseley Associates Inc (HQ) ...C...805 968-9621
82 Coromar Dr Goleta (93117) *(P-18189)*
Mosier Bros ...F...559 564-3304
19580 Avenue 344 Woodlake (93286) *(P-12401)*
MOSplastics Inc ...C...408 944-9407
2308 Zanker Rd San Jose (95131) *(P-10227)*
Moss Landing Cement Co LLC ...F...831 731-6000
7697 Highway 1 Moss Landing (95039) *(P-10765)*
Mosys Inc (PA) ...D...408 418-7500
2309 Bering Dr San Jose (95131) *(P-19025)*
Mota Group Inc (PA) ...E...408 370-1248
60 S Market St Ste 1100 San Jose (95113) *(P-19872)*
Motec USA, Huntington Beach *Also called JGM Automotive Tooling Inc* *(P-14976)*
Motek Industries ...F...626 960-6005
14434 Joanbridge St Baldwin Park (91706) *(P-16773)*
MOTHER JONES MAGAZINE, San Francisco *Also called Foundation For Nat Progress* *(P-6166)*
Mother Lode Plas Molding Inc ...E...209 532-5146
1905 N Macarthur Dr # 100 Tracy (95376) *(P-10228)*
Mother Lode Printing & Pubg Co ...D...530 344-5030
2889 Ray Lawyer Dr Placerville (95667) *(P-5982)*
Mother Plucker Feather Co Inc ...F...213 637-0411
2511 W 3rd St Ste 102 Los Angeles (90057) *(P-24179)*
Motherly Inc ...E...917 860-9926
1725 Oakdell Dr Menlo Park (94025) *(P-6532)*
Moticont ...E...818 785-1800
6901 Woodley Ave Van Nuys (91406) *(P-20019)*
Motion Engineering Inc (HQ) ...D...805 696-1200
33 S La Patera Ln Santa Barbara (93117) *(P-15808)*
Motion Industries Inc ...E...818 768-1200
7915 Ajay Dr Sun Valley (91352) *(P-21620)*
Motionloft Inc ...E...415 580-7671
550 15th St Ste 29 San Francisco (94103) *(P-21997)*
Motiv Design Group Inc ...E...408 441-0611
430 Perrymont Ave San Jose (95125) *(P-17240)*
Motivational Systems Inc ...E...800 748-6584
2200 Cleveland Ave National City (91950) *(P-23930)*
Motivational Systems Inc ...E...916 635-0234
11437 Sunrise Gold Cir A Rancho Cordova (95742) *(P-23931)*
Motoart LLC ...F...310 375-4531
21809 S Western Ave Torrance (90501) *(P-11363)*
Motor Technology Inc ...E...951 270-6200
2301 Wardlow Cir Corona (92880) *(P-17211)*
Motorcar Parts of America Inc (PA) ...A...310 212-7910
2929 California St Torrance (90503) *(P-20406)*
Motorlamb International Acc ...F...858 569-8111
8055 Clairemont Mesa Blvd # 108 San Diego (92111) *(P-3955)*
Motorola Mobility LLC ...D...206 383-7785
1633 Bayshore Hwy Burlingame (94010) *(P-18190)*
Motorola Mobility LLC ...D...847 576-5000
809 Eleventh Ave Bldg 4 Sunnyvale (94089) *(P-18191)*
Motorola Solutions Inc ...C...510 217-7400
1101 Marina Village Pkwy # 200 Alameda (94501) *(P-18192)*
Motorola Solutions Inc ...E...213 362-6706
725 S Figueroa St # 1855 Los Angeles (90017) *(P-18193)*
Motorola Solutions Inc ...F...858 541-2163
9665 Chesapeake Dr # 220 San Diego (92123) *(P-19026)*
Motorola Solutions Inc ...C...954 723-4730
6101 W Century Blvd Los Angeles (90045) *(P-18194)*
Motorola Solutions Inc ...E...510 420-7400
6001 Shellmound St Fl 4th Emeryville (94608) *(P-15640)*
Motors & Controls Intl Inc (PA) ...E...714 956-0480
1440 N Burton Pl Anaheim (92806) *(P-14655)*
Motorshield LLC ...F...323 396-9200
3364 Garfield Ave Commerce (90040) *(P-8920)*
Motorsport Aftrmrket Group Inc (HQ) ...F...949 440-5500
17771 Mitchell N Ste A Irvine (92614) *(P-21130)*
Motoshieldpro, Commerce *Also called Motorshield LLC* *(P-8920)*
Motran Industries Inc ...F...661 257-4995
3037 Golf Course Dr Ste 4 Ventura (93003) *(P-17212)*
Motsenbocker Advanced Developm (PA) ...F...858 581-0222
4901 Morena Blvd Ste 806 San Diego (92117) *(P-8657)*
Motu Global LLC ...F...801 471-7800
924 W 9th St Upland (91786) *(P-830)*
Mount Palomar Winery, Temecula *Also called Louidar LLC* *(P-1865)*
Mount Rose Publishing Co Inc ...F...530 587-6061
10775 Pioneer Trl Truckee (96161) *(P-5983)*
Mount Rose Publishing Co Inc (PA) ...F...530 583-3487
395 N Lake Blvd Ste A Tahoe City (96145) *(P-5984)*
Mount Seven, Atwater *Also called Five Keys Inc* *(P-3154)*
Mountain Democrat, Placerville *Also called Mother Lode Printing & Pubg Co* *(P-5982)*
Mountain Lake Labs ...F...707 331-3297
2675 Lands End Dr Lakeport (95453) *(P-21353)*
Mountain Life, Mariposa *Also called Mariposa Gazette & Miner* *(P-5941)*
Mountain News & Shopper, Lake Arrowhead *Also called Hi-Desert Publishing Company* *(P-5880)*
Mountain View Voice ...E...650 326-8210
450 Cambridge Ave Palo Alto (94306) *(P-5985)*
Mountain Winery, Saratoga *Also called Chateau Masson LLC* *(P-1689)*
Mountz Inc (PA) ...E...408 292-2214
1080 N 11th St San Jose (95112) *(P-21621)*

Mouse Graphics, Costa Mesa *Also called Orange Coast Reprographics Inc* ***(P-7006)***
Mousepad Designs, Cerritos *Also called Mpd Holdings Inc* ***(P-15810)***
Mova Stone Inc....E....916 922-2080
4361 Pell Dr Ste 100 Sacramento (95838) ***(P-11264)***
Moveel Fuel LLC....F....213 748-1444
15000 S Avalon Blvd Ste K Gardena (90248) ***(P-9023)***
Movement Products Inc....F....949 206-0000
22365 El Toro Rd Ste 295 Lake Forest (92630) ***(P-21131)***
Movie Star, Los Angeles *Also called Foh Group Inc* ***(P-3548)***
Movieline Magazine, Inglewood *Also called Line Publications Inc* ***(P-6208)***
Moving Image Technologies LLC....E....714 751-7998
17760 Newhope St Ste B Fountain Valley (92708) ***(P-23180)***
Movits, Carson *Also called O W I Inc* ***(P-17840)***
Moxa Americas Inc....E....714 528-6777
601 Valencia Ave Ste 100 Brea (92823) ***(P-15809)***
Moz Designs Inc....E....510 632-0853
711 Kevin Ct Oakland (94621) ***(P-12883)***
Mozaik LLC....F....562 207-1900
2330 Artesia Ave Ste B Fullerton (92833) ***(P-5378)***
Mp Associates Inc....C....209 274-4715
6555 Jackson Valley Rd Ione (95640) ***(P-9183)***
Mp Biomedical, Burlingame *Also called Rapid Diagnostics Inc* ***(P-22597)***
Mp Mine Operations LLC....C....702 277-0848
67750 Bailey Rd Mountain Pass (92366) ***(P-407)***
MP Tool Inc....F....661 294-7711
28110 Avenue Stanford E Valencia (91355) ***(P-16774)***
MPA, Torrance *Also called Motorcar Parts of America Inc* ***(P-20406)***
Mpb Furniture Corporation....F....760 375-4800
414 W Ridgecrest Blvd Ridgecrest (93555) ***(P-4800)***
Mpbs Industries, Los Angeles *Also called Meat Packers Butchers Sup Inc* ***(P-14870)***
Mpc Networkcom Inc....F....949 873-1002
440 Fair Dr Ste 233 Costa Mesa (92626) ***(P-6533)***
Mpd Holdings Inc....E....562 777-1051
16200 Commerce Way Cerritos (90703) ***(P-15810)***
Mpeg Industries Inc....F....562 677-1268
1951 S Parco Ave Ste A Ontario (91761) ***(P-15463)***
Mpi, Newbury Park *Also called Multilayer Prototypes Inc* ***(P-18534)***
Mpi Label Systems, Stockton *Also called Miller Products Inc* ***(P-5571)***
Mpj Recycling LLC....F....916 761-5740
2100 21st St Ste B Sacramento (95818) ***(P-14994)***
MPK Sonoma, Sonoma *Also called Marinpak* ***(P-2596)***
Mpm & Associates, Van Nuys *Also called M P M Building Services Inc* ***(P-8653)***
Mpo Videotronics Inc (PA)....D....805 499-8513
5069 Maureen Ln Moorpark (93021) ***(P-23181)***
MPS Industries Incorporated (PA)....E....310 325-1043
19210 S Vermont Ave # 405 Gardena (90248) ***(P-17107)***
MPS International Ltd....A....408 826-0600
79 Great Oaks Blvd San Jose (95119) ***(P-19027)***
MPS Lansing Inc....E....707 778-1250
101 H St Ste M Petaluma (94952) ***(P-5572)***
MPS Medical Inc....E....714 672-1090
830 Challenger St Ste 200 Brea (92821) ***(P-22549)***
Mr Gears Inc....F....650 364-7793
428 Stanford Ave Redwood City (94063) ***(P-16775)***
Mr Lock, Corona *Also called Lock America Inc* ***(P-11971)***
MR Mold & Engineering Corp....E....714 996-5511
2700 E Imperial Hwy Ste C Brea (92821) ***(P-14547)***
Mr S Leather....E....415 863-7764
385 8th St San Francisco (94103) ***(P-3620)***
Mr T Transport....F....562 602-5536
15535 Garfield Ave Paramount (90723) ***(P-240)***
Mr Washerman, South El Monte *Also called Calfabco* ***(P-13176)***
Mr. Nature, Los Angeles *Also called G & P Group Inc* ***(P-1489)***
Mri, San Fernando *Also called Simon Harrison* ***(P-22270)***
Mri Interventions Inc....E....949 900-6833
5 Musick Irvine (92618) ***(P-22550)***
Mrp Holdings Corp., City of Industry *Also called Hexpol Compounding CA Inc* ***(P-9620)***
MRr Moulding Industries Inc....F....510 794-8116
125 N Mary Ave Spc 42 Sunnyvale (94086) ***(P-4197)***
Mrs Appletree's Bakery, Baldwin Park *Also called Distinct Indulgence Inc* ***(P-1231)***
Mrs Baird's Bakeries, Los Angeles *Also called Bimbo Bakeries Usa Inc* ***(P-1203)***
Mrs Grossmans Paper Company....D....707 763-1700
3810 Cypress Dr Petaluma (94954) ***(P-5687)***
Mrs Redds Pie Co Inc....E....909 825-4800
150 S La Cadena Dr Colton (92324) ***(P-1293)***
Mrv Communications Inc (PA)....C....818 773-0900
20520 Nordhoff St Chatsworth (91311) ***(P-19028)***
Mrv Systems LLC....E....800 645-7114
6370 Lusk Blvd Ste F100 San Diego (92121) ***(P-21808)***
MS Aerospace Inc....B....818 833-9095
13928 Balboa Blvd Sylmar (91342) ***(P-13077)***
Ms Aerospace Materials LLC....F....323 813-4105
180 Erma Ct Ste 160 Chico (95928) ***(P-20892)***
Ms Bellows, Huntington Beach *Also called Mechanized Science Seals Inc* ***(P-22232)***
Ms Cast Stone Inc....E....760 754-9697
235 Via Del Monte Oceanside (92058) ***(P-11144)***
MS Industrial Shtmtl Inc....C....951 272-6610
1731 Pomona Rd Corona (92880) ***(P-12689)***
MS Intertrade Inc (PA)....E....707 837-8057
2221 Bluebell Dr Ste A Santa Rosa (95403) ***(P-2318)***
Ms2 Technologies LLC....F....310 277-4110
2448 E 25th St Vernon (90058) ***(P-11633)***
MSA West LLC....E....213 536-9880
16161 Ventura Blvd C326 Encino (91436) ***(P-3551)***
Mscsoftware Corporation (HQ)....C....714 540-8900
4675 Macarthur Ct Ste 900 Newport Beach (92660) ***(P-24936)***
MSE Media Solutions....E....323 721-1656
6013 Scott Way Commerce (90040) ***(P-19873)***
MSI Hvac, Fontana *Also called Material Supply Inc* ***(P-12658)***
Msnap, Inc., San Francisco *Also called Marketron Mobile LLC* ***(P-24883)***
MSP Group Inc....E....310 660-0022
206 W 140th St Los Angeles (90061) ***(P-2752)***
Msquared, Fresno *Also called M2 Antenna Systems Inc* ***(P-19632)***
Mt, Oxnard *Also called Travis Mike Inc* ***(P-13288)***
Mt Systems Inc....F....510 651-5277
49040 Milmont Dr Fremont (94538) ***(P-14995)***
MTI De Baja Inc....E....951 654-2333
42941 Madio St Ste 2 Indio (92201) ***(P-21354)***
MTI Laboratory Inc....D....310 955-3700
201 Continental Blvd # 300 El Segundo (90245) ***(P-18195)***
MTI Technology Corporation (PA)....C....949 251-1101
15461 Red Hill Ave # 200 Tustin (92780) ***(P-15571)***
Mtil, El Segundo *Also called MTI Laboratory Inc* ***(P-18195)***
Mtm Industrial Inc....F....760 967-1346
3230 Production Ave Ste B Oceanside (92058) ***(P-16776)***
MTS Stimulation Services Inc (PA)....E....661 589-5804
7131 Charity Ave Bakersfield (93308) ***(P-241)***
Mu Gallery Makers, Vernon *Also called Makers Usa Inc* ***(P-3065)***
Mueller Gages Company....F....626 287-2911
318 Agostino Rd San Gabriel (91776) ***(P-14656)***
Mufich Engineering Inc....E....714 283-0599
341 W Blueridge Ave Orange (92865) ***(P-16777)***
Muhlhauser Enterprises Inc (PA)....E....909 877-2792
2437 S Willow Ave Bloomington (92316) ***(P-12216)***
Muhlhauser Steel, Bloomington *Also called Muhlhauser Enterprises Inc* ***(P-12216)***
Muhlhauser Steel Inc....E....909 877-2792
2437 S Willow Ave Bloomington (92316) ***(P-12217)***
Muirsis Inc....F....714 579-1555
2841 Saturn St Ste J Brea (92821) ***(P-12041)***
Mulesoft Inc....A....415 229-2009
50 Fremont St Ste 300 San Francisco (94105) ***(P-24937)***
Mulfat LLC....E....818 367-0149
15835 Monte St Ste 103 Sylmar (91342) ***(P-15464)***
Mulgrew Arcft Components Inc....D....626 256-1375
1810 S Shamrock Ave Monrovia (91016) ***(P-20893)***
Mulherin Monumental Inc....F....760 353-7717
1000 S 2nd St El Centro (92243) ***(P-11265)***
Mulholland Brothers (PA)....E....415 824-5995
1710 4th St Berkeley (94710) ***(P-4801)***
Mullen Technologies Inc (PA)....F....714 613-1900
1405 Pioneer St Brea (92821) ***(P-20160)***
Muller Company....F....858 587-9955
3366 N Torrey Pines Ct # 140 La Jolla (92037) ***(P-22775)***
Multani Logistics, Hayward *Also called Do Dine Inc* ***(P-24566)***
Multi Packaging Solutions Inc....E....818 638-0216
1212 S Flower St Ste 100 Los Angeles (90015) ***(P-6985)***
Multi Power Products Inc....F....415 883-6300
47931 Westinghouse Dr Fremont (94539) ***(P-20020)***
Multi-Fineline Electronix Inc (HQ)....A....949 453-6800
101 Academy Ste 250 Irvine (92617) ***(P-18533)***
Multi-Link International Corp....E....562 941-5380
12235 Los Nietos Rd Santa Fe Springs (90670) ***(P-9870)***
Multibeam Corporation....E....408 980-1800
3951 Burton Dr Santa Clara (95054) ***(P-14996)***
Multichrome Company Inc (PA)....E....310 216-1086
1013 W Hillcrest Blvd Inglewood (90301) ***(P-13460)***
Multicoat Products Inc....F....949 888-7100
23331 Antonio Pkwy Rcho STA Marg (92688) ***(P-8921)***
Multicolor, Sonoma *Also called Collotype Labels USA Inc* ***(P-7278)***
Multilayer Prototypes Inc....F....805 498-9390
2513 Teller Rd Newbury Park (91320) ***(P-18534)***
Multimedia Led Inc (PA)....F....951 280-7500
4225 Prado Rd Ste 108 Corona (92880) ***(P-19656)***
Multimedia Operations Design (PA)....E....818 848-1303
3816 Medford St Los Angeles (90063) ***(P-5156)***
Multimek Inc....E....408 653-1300
357 Reed St Santa Clara (95050) ***(P-18535)***
Multimetrixs LLC....F....510 527-6769
1025 Solano Ave Albany (94706) ***(P-17348)***
Multiquip Industries Corp....F....888 996-7267
22605 La Palma Ave # 507 Yorba Linda (92887) ***(P-12337)***
Multis Inc....E....510 441-2653
766 S 12th St San Jose (95112) ***(P-24180)***
Multitest Elctrnic Systems Inc (HQ)....B....408 988-6544
3021 Kenneth St Santa Clara (95054) ***(P-21809)***
Multivitamin Direct Inc....E....408 573-7276
2178 Paragon Dr San Jose (95131) ***(P-7954)***
Mumm NAPA Valley, Rutherford *Also called Pernod Ricard Usa LLC* ***(P-1922)***
Munchkin Inc (PA)....C....818 893-5000
7835 Gloria Ave Van Nuys (91406) ***(P-9801)***
Municon Consultants, San Francisco *Also called Lois A Valeskie* ***(P-22228)***
Munkyfun Inc....E....415 281-3837
415 Jackson St Fl 1 San Francisco (94111) ***(P-24938)***
Munselle Vineyards LLC....F....707 857-9988
3660 Highway 128 Geyserville (95441) ***(P-1889)***
Murad LLC (HQ)....C....310 726-0600
2121 Park Pl Fl 1 El Segundo (90245) ***(P-8286)***
Murray Biscuit Company LLC....E....209 472-3718
5250 Claremont Ave Stockton (95207) ***(P-1372)***
Murray Trailers, Stockton *Also called Harley Murray Inc* ***(P-20503)***
Murrey International Inc....E....310 532-6091
25701 Weston Dr Laguna Niguel (92677) ***(P-23621)***
Muscardini Cellars LLC....F....707 933-9305
9380 Sonoma Hwy Kenwood (95452) ***(P-1890)***
Muscle & Fitness Flex M&F Hers, Los Angeles *Also called Weider Publications LLC* ***(P-6288)***
Muscle Dynamics Corporation....F....562 926-3232
14133 Freeway Dr Santa Fe Springs (90670) ***(P-23622)***

Muscle Road Inc..........F.......559 499-6888
28838 Ave 15 One Half Madera (93638) ***(P-20407)***
Musclepharm Corporation (PA)..........D.......303 396-6100
4400 W Vanowen St Burbank (91505) ***(P-633)***
Musco Family Olive Co, Tracy *Also called Olive Musco Products Inc* ***(P-841)***
Music Connection Inc..........F.......818 995-0101
16130 Ventura Blvd # 540 Encino (91436) ***(P-6222)***
Music Connection Magazine, Encino *Also called Music Connection Inc* ***(P-6222)***
Music Market Update, Los Angeles *Also called Hits Magazine Inc* ***(P-6184)***
Musicmatch Inc..........C.......858 485-4300
16935 W Bernardo Dr # 270 San Diego (92127) ***(P-24939)***
Mustang Hills LLC..........E.......661 888-5810
16409 K St Mojave (93501) ***(P-2950)***
Mustard Seed Technologies Inc..........C.......714 556-7007
3000 W Warner Ave Santa Ana (92704) ***(P-19657)***
Muth Machine Works (HQ)..........E.......714 527-2239
8042 Katella Ave Stanton (90680) ***(P-16778)***
Mv Excel..........F.......619 223-7493
2838 Garrison St San Diego (92106) ***(P-23623)***
Mvm Products LLC..........D.......949 366-1470
946 Calle Amanecer Ste E San Clemente (92673) ***(P-23182)***
Mvp Rv Inc..........E.......951 848-4288
40 E Verdugo Ave Burbank (91502) ***(P-21207)***
Mvp Technology Intl Inc..........F.......510 651-2425
44911 Industrial Dr Fremont (94538) ***(P-24181)***
Mw McWong International Inc..........D.......916 371-8080
1921 Arena Blvd Sacramento (95834) ***(P-17717)***
MWsausse & Co Inc (PA)..........D.......661 257-3311
28744 Witherspoon Pkwy Valencia (91355) ***(P-17289)***
Mww Inc..........E.......800 575-3475
7945 Deering Ave Canoga Park (91304) ***(P-4638)***
Mx Electronics Mfg Inc..........D.......714 258-0200
1651 E Saint Andrew Pl Santa Ana (92705) ***(P-11666)***
MXF Designs Inc..........D.......323 266-1451
1601 Perrino Pl Ste A Los Angeles (90023) ***(P-3260)***
My Burbankcom Inc..........F.......818 842-2140
10061 Rverside Dr Ste 520 Toluca Lake (91602) ***(P-5986)***
My Dirty Jobs LLC..........F.......310 393-5522
1207 4th St Ph 1 Santa Monica (90401) ***(P-8598)***
My Eye Media LLC (HQ)..........E.......818 559-7200
2211 N Hollywood Way Burbank (91505) ***(P-24940)***
My Fruity Faces LLC..........F.......877 358-9210
2400 Lincoln Ave Altadena (91001) ***(P-1545)***
My Machine Inc..........F.......626 214-9223
5140 Commerce Dr Baldwin Park (91706) ***(P-16779)***
My Michelle, La Puente *Also called Mymichelle Company LLC* ***(P-3261)***
My Sign Design LLC..........F.......818 384-0800
4821 Lankershim Blvd F145 North Hollywood (91601) ***(P-6986)***
My True Image Mfg Inc..........D.......510 970-7990
999 Marina Way S Richmond (94804) ***(P-22776)***
My World Styles LLC..........F.......800 355-4008
16 Dutton Ave San Leandro (94577) ***(P-8800)***
Mya International Inc..........F.......619 429-6012
10030 Marconi Dr Ste 1 San Diego (92154) ***(P-8287)***
Myc Direct Inc..........F.......909 287-9919
19977 Harrison Ave Walnut (91789) ***(P-21481)***
Mycase, San Diego *Also called Appfolio Inc* ***(P-24369)***
Mydax Inc..........F.......530 888-6662
12260 Shale Ridge Ln # 4 Auburn (95602) ***(P-15973)***
Mydyer.com, Long Beach *Also called Providence Industries LLC* ***(P-3117)***
Mye Technologies Inc..........E.......661 964-0217
28460 Westinghouse Pl Valencia (91355) ***(P-20021)***
Myenersave Inc..........F.......408 464-6385
440 N Wolfe Rd Sunnyvale (94085) ***(P-24941)***
Myers & Sons Hi-Way Safety Inc..........E.......909 591-1781
520 W Grand Ave Escondido (92025) ***(P-18348)***
Myers & Sons Hi-Way Safety Inc (PA)..........C.......909 591-1781
13310 5th St Chino (91710) ***(P-18349)***
Myers Container LLC..........E.......800 406-9377
21508 Ferrero B Walnut (91789) ***(P-11875)***
Myers Mixers LLC..........E.......323 560-4723
8376 Salt Lake Ave Cudahy (90201) ***(P-15342)***
Myers Wine Cntry Kitchens LLC..........E.......707 252-9463
511 Alexis Ct NAPA (94558) ***(P-10622)***
Myers-Briggs Company (PA)..........D.......650 969-8901
185 N Wolfe Rd Sunnyvale (94086) ***(P-6534)***
Mygrant Glass Company Inc..........E.......858 455-8022
10220 Camino Santa Fe San Diego (92121) ***(P-20408)***
Mymichelle Company LLC (HQ)..........B.......626 934-4166
13077 Temple Ave La Puente (91746) ***(P-3261)***
Myntahl Corporation..........E.......510 413-0002
48273 Lakeview Blvd Fremont (94538) ***(P-17966)***
Myogenix Incorporated..........F.......800 950-0348
2309 A St Santa Maria (93455) ***(P-8288)***
Myojo USA Inc..........F.......909 464-1411
6220 Prescott Ct Chino (91710) ***(P-2430)***
Myokardia Inc..........D.......650 741-0900
333 Allerton Ave South San Francisco (94080) ***(P-8289)***
Myosci Technologies Inc..........F.......760 433-5376
1211 Liberty Way Ste B Vista (92081) ***(P-634)***
Myricom Inc..........E.......626 821-5555
3871 E Colo Blvd Ste 101 Pasadena (91107) ***(P-15465)***
Myron L Company..........D.......760 438-2021
2450 Impala Dr Carlsbad (92010) ***(P-21622)***
Mytee Products Inc..........E.......858 679-1191
13655 Stowe Dr Poway (92064) ***(P-16075)***
Mytek America, La Canada Flintridge *Also called Data Storm Inc* ***(P-19942)***
Mytime, San Francisco *Also called Melian Labs Inc* ***(P-24901)***
Mytrex Inc..........F.......949 800-9725
4070 N Palm St Ste 707 Fullerton (92835) ***(P-14085)***
Myvoicegig LLC..........F.......714 702-6006
12517 Wedgwood Cir Tustin (92780) ***(P-6535)***
Myway Learning Company Inc..........F.......415 937-1722
47 Laurel Ave Larkspur (94939) ***(P-24942)***
Mywi Fabricators Inc..........F.......626 279-6994
2115-2119 Edwards Ave South El Monte (91733) ***(P-12218)***
N A Suez..........E.......310 414-0183
1935 S Hughes Way El Segundo (90245) ***(P-21623)***
N A T C O, Glendale *Also called North American Textile Co LLC* ***(P-3910)***
N C Industries..........F.......951 296-9603
42147 Roick Dr Temecula (92590) ***(P-16780)***
N C W G Inc..........F.......530 265-9463
321 Spring St Nevada City (95959) ***(P-1891)***
N D E Inc..........E.......408 727-3955
3301 Keller St Santa Clara (95054) ***(P-18536)***
N D Industries, Santa Fe Springs *Also called ND Industries Inc* ***(P-13078)***
N G S, Sacramento *Also called New Generation Software Inc* ***(P-24960)***
N H Research Incorporated..........D.......949 474-3900
16601 Hale Ave Irvine (92606) ***(P-21810)***
N J P Sports Inc..........F.......818 247-3914
548 Arden Ave Glendale (91203) ***(P-3797)***
N M Floor Coverings Inc..........F.......760 931-8274
5651 Palmer Way Ste D Carlsbad (92010) ***(P-4086)***
N M H Inc..........F.......818 843-8522
19426 Londelius St Northridge (91324) ***(P-6987)***
N S Ceramic Molding Co..........E.......909 947-3231
1336 E Francis St Unit 1 Ontario (91761) ***(P-14548)***
N Stitches Prints Inc..........F.......310 323-7777
16009 S Broadway Gardena (90248) ***(P-3853)***
N T S, Woodland Hills *Also called Network Telephone Services Inc* ***(P-5083)***
N V Cast Stone LLC..........D.......707 261-6615
1111 Green Island Rd Vallejo (94503) ***(P-10959)***
N W D T, Hayward *Also called Keen-Kut Products Inc* ***(P-14643)***
N Z Pump Co Inc..........F.......626 458-8023
801 S Palm Ave Alhambra (91803) ***(P-15086)***
N-Synch Technologies..........F.......949 218-7761
30100 Town Center Dr 0-204 Laguna Niguel (92677) ***(P-15641)***
N-Tek Inc..........E.......408 735-8442
823 Kifer Rd Sunnyvale (94086) ***(P-14997)***
N/S Corporation (PA)..........D.......310 412-7074
235 W Florence Ave Inglewood (90301) ***(P-16076)***
N2 Aero, Glendale *Also called N2 Development Inc* ***(P-20894)***
N2 Development Inc..........F.......323 210-3251
1819 Dana St Ste A Glendale (91201) ***(P-20894)***
Nabors Well Services Co..........C.......661 588-6140
1025 Earthmover Ct Bakersfield (93314) ***(P-113)***
Nabors Well Services Co..........B.......661 589-3970
7515 Rosedale Hwy Bakersfield (93308) ***(P-242)***
Nabors Well Services Co..........C.......310 639-7074
19431 S Santa Fe Ave Compton (90221) ***(P-243)***
Nabors Well Services Co..........D.......661 392-7668
1954 James Rd Bakersfield (93308) ***(P-244)***
Nac Mfg Inc..........E.......909 472-3033
601 Kettering Dr Ontario (91761) ***(P-9067)***
Nadalie USA, Calistoga *Also called Tonnellerie Francaise French C* ***(P-4538)***
Nadin Company..........E.......818 500-8908
1815 Flower St Glendale (91201) ***(P-8290)***
Nadolife Inc..........D.......619 522-6890
2709 Newton Ave San Diego (92113) ***(P-687)***
Nady Systems Inc..........E.......510 652-2411
870 Harbour Way S Richmond (94804) ***(P-17836)***
Nafhc, Santa Maria *Also called North American Fire Hose Corp* ***(P-9502)***
Nafm LLC (PA)..........F.......951 738-1114
1521 Pomona Rd Ste A Corona (92880) ***(P-15219)***
Nafm Engineering Service, Corona *Also called Nafm LLC* ***(P-15219)***
Naftex Westside Partners Limit..........E.......310 277-9004
1900 Avenue Of The Stars Los Angeles (90067) ***(P-65)***
Nagles Veal Inc..........E.......909 383-7075
1411 E Base Line St San Bernardino (92410) ***(P-445)***
Nagra, San Francisco *Also called Opentv Inc* ***(P-24989)***
Naia Inc..........E.......510 724-2479
736 Alfred Nobel Dr Hercules (94547) ***(P-688)***
Nailpro, Van Nuys *Also called Creative Age Publications Inc* ***(P-6137)***
Nails 2000 International Inc..........F.......714 265-1983
10892 Forbes Ave Ste A2 Garden Grove (92843) ***(P-24182)***
Nakagawa Manufacturing USA Inc..........E.......510 782-0197
8652 Thornton Ave Newark (94560) ***(P-5312)***
Nakamura-Beeman Inc..........E.......562 696-1400
8520 Wellsford Pl Santa Fe Springs (90670) ***(P-4956)***
Naked Princess Worldwide LLC (PA)..........F.......310 271-1199
11766 Wilshire Blvd Fl 9 Los Angeles (90025) ***(P-8801)***
Nalco Company LLC..........F.......661 864-7955
4900 California Ave 420b Bakersfield (93309) ***(P-9285)***
Nalco Company LLC..........F.......800 798-2247
1000 Burnett Ave Ste 430 Concord (94520) ***(P-9286)***
Nalco Company LLC..........F.......805 584-9950
980 Enchanted Way Ste 203 Simi Valley (93065) ***(P-9287)***
Nalco Wtr Prtrtment Sltons LLC..........E.......714 792-0708
704 Richfield Rd Placentia (92870) ***(P-16077)***
Nally & Millie, Los Angeles *Also called MXF Designs Inc* ***(P-3260)***
Nana's Cookie Company, San Diego *Also called Microbiotic Health Foods Inc* ***(P-1371)***
Nancys Specialty Foods..........B.......510 494-1100
2400 Olympic Blvd Ste 8 Walnut Creek (94595) ***(P-2612)***
Nancys Tortilleria & Mini Mkt..........E.......909 629-5889
348 S Towne Ave Pomona (91766) ***(P-2613)***
Nanka Seimen Co..........F.......323 585-9967
3030 Leonis Blvd Vernon (90058) ***(P-2431)***
Nankai Enviro-Tech Corporation..........C.......619 754-2250
2320 Paseo De Las America San Diego (92154) ***(P-10229)***

Nannette Keller, Tehachapi *Also called Keller Classics Inc* ***(P-3354)***
Nanofilm, Westlake Village *Also called Interntional Photo Plates Corp* ***(P-13434)***
Nanoimaging Services Inc......F......888 675-8261
4940 Carroll Canyon Rd # 115 San Diego (92121) ***(P-21998)***
Nanometer Technologies Inc......F......805 226-7332
2985 Theatre Dr Ste 3 Paso Robles (93446) ***(P-17967)***
Nanometrics Incorporated (PA)......B......408 545-6000
1550 Buckeye Dr Milpitas (95035) ***(P-14998)***
Nanoprecision Products Inc......E......310 597-4991
802 Calle Plano Camarillo (93012) ***(P-13252)***
Nanoscale Combinatorial......E......408 987-2000
3100 Central Expy Santa Clara (95051) ***(P-9288)***
Nanosilicon Inc......E......408 263-7341
2461 Autumnvale Dr San Jose (95131) ***(P-19029)***
Nanostellar Inc......E......650 368-1010
3696 Haven Ave Ste B Redwood City (94063) ***(P-21165)***
Nanostim Inc......F......408 530-0700
776 Palomar Ave Sunnyvale (94085) ***(P-23020)***
Nanostone Water Inc......F......442 232-2595
2463 Impala Dr Carlsbad (92010) ***(P-2961)***
Nanosyn, Santa Clara *Also called Nanoscale Combinatorial* ***(P-9288)***
Nanosys Inc......C......408 240-6700
233 S Hillview Dr Milpitas (95035) ***(P-19030)***
Nanotech Entertainment Inc (PA)......F......408 414-7355
311 Santa Rosa Dr Los Gatos (95032) ***(P-24943)***
Nanotronics Automation, Hollister *Also called Nanotronics Imaging Inc* ***(P-20022)***
Nanotronics Imaging Inc......F......831 630-0700
777 Flynn Rd Hollister (95023) ***(P-20022)***
Nanovea Inc (PA)......F......949 461-9292
6 Morgan Ste 156 Irvine (92618) ***(P-21999)***
Nantkwest Inc (HQ)......E......805 633-0300
3530 John Hopkins Ct San Diego (92121) ***(P-8567)***
NAPA Beaucanon Estate......F......707 254-1460
1006 Monticello Rd NAPA (94558) ***(P-1892)***
NAPA Desktop Publishing, NAPA *Also called NAPA Printing & Graphics Ctr* ***(P-6988)***
NAPA Industries Inc......F......310 293-1209
1379 Beckwith Ave Los Angeles (90049) ***(P-24183)***
NAPA Printing & Graphics Ctr (PA)......F......707 257-6555
630 Airpark Rd Ste D NAPA (94558) ***(P-6988)***
NAPA Register, NAPA *Also called NAPA Valley Publishing Co* ***(P-5988)***
NAPA Valley Cast Stone, Vallejo *Also called N V Cast Stone LLC* ***(P-10959)***
NAPA Valley Coffee Roasting Co (PA)......F......707 224-2233
948 Main St NAPA (94559) ***(P-2360)***
NAPA Valley Kitchens Inc......D......510 558-7500
1610 5th St Berkeley (94710) ***(P-2614)***
NAPA Valley Publishing Co......D......707 226-3711
1615 Soscol Ave NAPA (94559) ***(P-5987)***
NAPA Valley Publishing Co (PA)......E......707 226-3711
1615 Soscol Ave NAPA (94559) ***(P-5988)***
NAPA Valley Register, NAPA *Also called NAPA Valley Publishing Co* ***(P-5987)***
NAPA Wine Company LLC......E......707 944-8669
7830 St Helena Hwy 40 Oakville (94562) ***(P-1893)***
Napoleon Bakery Inc......D......323 651-3822
7356 Melrose Ave Los Angeles (90046) ***(P-1294)***
Napro, Los Alamitos *Also called North American Petroleum* ***(P-9291)***
Naprotek Inc......D......408 830-5000
90 Rose Orchard Way San Jose (95134) ***(P-18537)***
Naptech Test Equipment Inc......F......707 995-7145
11270 Clayton Creek Rd Lower Lake (95457) ***(P-21811)***
Narayan Corporation......E......310 719-7330
13432 Estrella Ave Gardena (90248) ***(P-9802)***
Narcotics Anonymous World Serv......E......818 773-9999
19737 Nordhoff Pl Chatsworth (91311) ***(P-6365)***
Nareg Jewelry Inc......E......213 683-1660
640 S Hill St Ste 542a Los Angeles (90014) ***(P-23300)***
Nasco Aircraft Brake Inc......D......310 532-4430
13300 Estrella Ave Gardena (90248) ***(P-20895)***
Nasco Gourmet Foods Inc......D......714 279-2100
22720 Savi Ranch Pkwy Yorba Linda (92887) ***(P-831)***
Nasco Petroleum LLC......F......949 461-5212
20532 El Toro Rd Ste 102 Mission Viejo (92692) ***(P-245)***
Nashua Corporation......D......323 583-8828
13341 Cambridge St Santa Fe Springs (90670) ***(P-5313)***
Nasmyth Tmf Inc......D......818 954-9504
29102 Hancock Pkwy Valencia (91355) ***(P-13461)***
Naso Industries Corporation......E......805 650-1231
3007 Bunsen Ave Ste Q Ventura (93003) ***(P-18538)***
Naso Technologies, Ventura *Also called Naso Industries Corporation* ***(P-18538)***
Nassco, San Diego *Also called National Stl & Shipbuilding Co* ***(P-21004)***
Nassco, Santa Cruz *Also called National Stock Sign Company* ***(P-23933)***
Nassco, San Diego *Also called International Mfg Tech Inc* ***(P-11400)***
Nat Aronson & Associates Inc......F......818 787-5160
7640 Gloria Ave Ste J Van Nuys (91406) ***(P-9501)***
Natel, Chatsworth *Also called Epic Technologies LLC* ***(P-17945)***
Natel Energy Inc......F......510 342-5269
2401 Monarch St Alameda (94501) ***(P-14003)***
Natel Engineering Company Inc (PA)......C......818 734-6523
9340 Owensmouth Ave Chatsworth (91311) ***(P-19031)***
Natel Engineering Company Inc......E......818 734-6552
9340 Owensmouth Ave Chatsworth (91311) ***(P-18539)***
Natel Engineering Company Inc......C......408 228-5462
2243 Lundy Ave San Jose (95131) ***(P-18540)***
Natel Engineering Company Inc......C......760 737-6777
2066 Aldergrove Ave Escondido (92029) ***(P-18541)***
Nates Fine Foods LLC......E......310 897-2690
8880 Industrial Ave # 100 Roseville (95678) ***(P-1000)***
Nathan Anthony Furniture, Vernon *Also called Yen-Nhai Inc* ***(P-4819)***
Nathan Kimmel Company LLC......F......213 627-8556
1213 S Santa Fe Ave Los Angeles (90021) ***(P-3798)***

National Advertising Centre, Canoga Park *Also called Video Reporter Inc* ***(P-6617)***
National Band Saw Company......F......661 294-9552
1055 W Avenue L12 Lancaster (93534) ***(P-14873)***
National Bedding Company LLC......C......925 373-1350
6818 Patterson Pass Rd Livermore (94550) ***(P-4875)***
National Bevpak, Hayward *Also called Shasta Beverages Inc* ***(P-2223)***
National Bright Lighting Inc......E......909 818-9188
1480 Adelia Ave South El Monte (91733) ***(P-17718)***
National Casein of California......F......714 979-8400
3435 W Macarthur Blvd Santa Ana (92704) ***(P-9157)***
National Cement Co Cal Inc......F......661 248-6733
5 Miles East Of I 5 Ofc H Lebec (93243) ***(P-11145)***
National Cement Co Cal Inc (HQ)......E......818 728-5200
15821 Ventura Blvd # 475 Encino (91436) ***(P-11146)***
National Cement Company Inc (HQ)......E......818 728-5200
15821 Ventura Blvd # 475 Encino (91436) ***(P-10766)***
National Certified Fabricators......F......951 278-8992
1525 E 6th St Corona (92879) ***(P-19348)***
National Cnstr Rentals Inc......F......323 838-1800
1045 S Greenwood Ave Montebello (90640) ***(P-246)***
National Cnstr Rentals Inc......E......909 574-1400
11029 Beech Ave Fontana (92337) ***(P-19349)***
National Copy Cartridge, El Cajon *Also called US Print & Toner Inc* ***(P-23740)***
National Corset Supply House (PA)......D......323 261-0265
3240 E 26th St Vernon (90058) ***(P-3540)***
National Diamond Lab Cal......F......818 240-5770
4650 Alger St Los Angeles (90039) ***(P-14657)***
National Directory Services......E......530 268-8636
19698 View Forever Ln Grass Valley (95945) ***(P-6366)***
National Diversified Sales Inc (HQ)......C......559 562-9888
21300 Victory Blvd # 215 Woodland Hills (91367) ***(P-10230)***
National Dragster Magazine, Glendora *Also called National Hot Rod Association* ***(P-5989)***
National Dyeing, Vernon *Also called AS Match Dyeing Co Inc* ***(P-2877)***
National Emblem Inc (PA)......C......310 515-5055
3925 E Vernon St Long Beach (90815) ***(P-3854)***
National Ewp Inc......F......510 236-6282
1961 Meeker Ave Richmond (94804) ***(P-12)***
National Ewp Inc......E......909 931-4014
5566 Arrow Hwy Montclair (91763) ***(P-13)***
National Explrtion Wells Pumps, Montclair *Also called National Ewp Inc* ***(P-13)***
National Filter Media Corp......D......760 246-4551
17130 Muskrat Ave Ste B Adelanto (92301) ***(P-15343)***
National Graphics LLC......E......805 644-9212
4893 Mcgrath St Ventura (93003) ***(P-6989)***
National Hardwood Flooring & M, Van Nuys *Also called Katzirs Floor & HM Design Inc* ***(P-4178)***
National Hot Rod Association......E......626 250-2300
2035 E Financial Way Glendora (91741) ***(P-5989)***
National Instruments Corp......B......408 610-6800
4600 Patrick Henry Dr Santa Clara (95054) ***(P-21812)***
National Law Digest Inc......E......310 791-9975
23844 Hawthorne Blvd # 200 Torrance (90505) ***(P-6367)***
National Media Inc (HQ)......E......310 377-6877
609 Deep Valley Dr # 200 Rllng HLS Est (90274) ***(P-5990)***
National Media Inc......E......310 372-0388
2615 Pcf Cast Hwy Ste 329 Hermosa Beach (90254) ***(P-5991)***
National Medical Products Inc......F......949 768-1147
57 Parker Unit A Irvine (92618) ***(P-10231)***
National Metal Fabricators......E......510 887-6231
28435 Century St Hayward (94545) ***(P-12219)***
National Metal Stampings Inc......D......661 945-1157
42110 8th St E Lancaster (93535) ***(P-13253)***
National Mustang Racers Assn, Santa Ana *Also called Promedia Companies* ***(P-6237)***
National O Rings, Downey *Also called Hutchinson Seal Corporation* ***(P-9535)***
National Oilwell Varco Inc......E......714 978-1900
1701 W Sequoia Ave Orange (92868) ***(P-14233)***
National Oilwell Varco Inc......F......530 682-0571
1438b Ohm Rd Arbuckle (95912) ***(P-247)***
National Oilwell Varco Inc......E......714 978-1900
759 N Eckhoff St Orange (92868) ***(P-14234)***
National Oilwell Varco Inc......E......714 978-1900
743 N Eckhoff St Orange (92868) ***(P-14235)***
National Oilwell Varco Inc......E......714 978-1900
752 N Poplar St Orange (92868) ***(P-14236)***
National Oilwell Varco LP......F......661 387-9316
19417 Colombo St Bakersfield (93308) ***(P-248)***
National Oilwell Varco LP......F......714 456-1244
743 N Eckhoff St Orange (92868) ***(P-114)***
National Packaging Products, Commerce *Also called Yavar Manufacturing Co Inc* ***(P-5515)***
National Pecan Shelling (HQ)......F......800 952-7771
1050 Diamond St Stockton (95205) ***(P-1499)***
National Pecan-Youn, Stockton *Also called National Pecan Shelling* ***(P-1499)***
National Pen Co LLC (HQ)......C......866 388-9850
12121 Scripps Summit Dr # 200 San Diego (92131) ***(P-23700)***
National Premium Merchandising (PA)......D......310 217-2700
1650 W Artesia Blvd Gardena (90248) ***(P-3855)***
National Raisin Company, Fowler *Also called Sunshine Raisin Corporation* ***(P-1460)***
National Ready Mix, Duarte *Also called Viking Ready Mix Co Inc* ***(P-11209)***
National Ready Mixed Con Co......F......323 245-5539
4549 Brazil St Los Angeles (90039) ***(P-11147)***
National Ready Mixed Con Co......F......818 884-0893
6969 Deering Ave Canoga Park (91303) ***(P-11148)***
National Ready Mixed Con Co (HQ)......E......818 728-5200
15821 Ventura Blvd # 475 Encino (91436) ***(P-11149)***
National Ready Mixed Con Co......F......562 865-6211
11725 Artesia Blvd Artesia (90701) ***(P-11150)***
National Recycling Corporation......F......510 268-1022
1312 Kirkham St Oakland (94607) ***(P-5717)***

Mergent e-mail: customerrelations@mergent.com 2019 California (P-0000) Products & Services Section entry number
1222 Manufacturers Register (PA)=Parent Co (HQ)=Headquarters (DH)=Div Headquarters

National Sales Inc F 916 912-2894
825 F St Ste 600 West Sacramento (95605) ***(P-5314)***

National Scientific Sup Co Inc F 909 621-4585
260 York Pl Claremont (91711) ***(P-10232)***

National Semiconductor Corp (HQ) A 408 721-5000
2900 Semiconductor Dr Santa Clara (95051) ***(P-19032)***

National Sign & Marketing Corp D 909 591-4742
13580 5th St Chino (91710) ***(P-23932)***

National Signal Inc E 714 441-7707
2440 Artesia Ave Fullerton (92833) ***(P-21236)***

National Stabilizers Inc F 626 969-5700
611 S Duggan Ave Azusa (91702) ***(P-2615)***

National Stl & Shipbuilding Co (HQ) B 619 544-3400
2798 Harbor Dr San Diego (92113) ***(P-21004)***

National Stock Sign Company F 831 476-2020
1040 El Dorado Ave Santa Cruz (95062) ***(P-23933)***

National Sweetwater Inc F 951 303-0999
43394 Calle De Velardo Temecula (92592) ***(P-9289)***

Nationals Elite Athletics Inc (PA) F 866 253-6614
5000 Birch St Newport Beach (92660) ***(P-7410)***

Nations Petroleum Cal LLC D 661 387-6402
9600 Ming Ave Ste 300 Bakersfield (93311) ***(P-141)***

Nationwide Boiler Incorporated (PA) D 510 490-7100
42400 Christy St Fremont (94538) ***(P-12402)***

Nationwide Jewelry Mfrs Inc F 213 489-1215
631 S Olive St Ste 790 Los Angeles (90014) ***(P-23301)***

Nationwide Plastic Products E 310 366-7585
16809 Gramercy Pl Gardena (90247) ***(P-9719)***

Nationwide Printing Svcs Inc F 714 258-7899
400 Camino Vista Verde San Clemente (92673) ***(P-7411)***

Native American Media F 310 475-6845
10806 1/2 Wilshire Blvd Los Angeles (90024) ***(P-6223)***

Native Canadian Media, Los Angeles *Also called Native American Media* ***(P-6223)***

Native Kjalii Foods Inc E 415 592-8670
1474 29th Ave San Francisco (94122) ***(P-2616)***

Nato LLC E 760 934-8677
38 Laurel Mountain Rd Mammoth Lakes (93546) ***(P-24184)***

Natren Inc D 805 371-4737
3105 Willow Ln Thousand Oaks (91361) ***(P-2617)***

Natrol LLC (HQ) C 818 739-6000
21411 Prairie St Chatsworth (91311) ***(P-8291)***

Natura-Genics Inc F 909 597-6676
6952 Buckeye St Chino (91710) ***(P-8292)***

Natural Balance Pet Foods Inc (HQ) E 800 829-4493
100 N First St Ste 200 Burbank (91502) ***(P-1149)***

Natural Decadence LLC F 707 444-2629
3750 Harris St Eureka (95503) ***(P-1399)***

Natural Elements, Vernon *Also called L A S A M Inc* ***(P-3581)***

Natural Envmtl Protection Co E 909 620-8028
750 S Reservoir St Pomona (91766) ***(P-7856)***

Natural Food Mill, Corona *Also called Food For Life Baking Co Inc* ***(P-1251)***

Natural Medicine Intl, Upland *Also called Herbs Yeh Manufacturing Co* ***(P-621)***

Natural Pest Controls & Firewd (PA) F 916 726-0855
8864 Little Creek Dr Orangevale (95662) ***(P-9108)***

Natural Sourcing International, Encino *Also called Nsi Group LLC* ***(P-890)***

Natural Std RES Collaboration E 617 591-3300
3120 W March Ln Fl 1 Stockton (95219) ***(P-6368)***

Natural Wonders Ca Inc F 818 593-2001
7240 Eton Ave Canoga Park (91303) ***(P-7955)***

Naturalife Eco Vite Labs D 310 370-1563
20433 Earl St Torrance (90503) ***(P-635)***

Naturas Foods California Inc F 909 594-7838
334 Paseo Sonrisa Walnut (91789) ***(P-769)***

Nature Creation, Canoga Park *Also called Natural Wonders Ca Inc* ***(P-7955)***

Nature Zone Pet Products E 530 343-5199
265 Boeing Ave Chico (95973) ***(P-24185)***

Nature's Baby Organics, Rancho Mirage *Also called Natures Baby Products Inc* ***(P-8802)***

Nature's Bounty, Anaheim *Also called Nbty Manufacturing LLC* ***(P-8294)***

Nature's Flavors, Orange *Also called Newport Flavors & Fragrances* ***(P-2274)***

Nature's Glory, North Hollywood *Also called Cosmo - Pharm Inc* ***(P-7928)***

Nature-Cide, Canoga Park *Also called Pacific Shore Holdings Inc* ***(P-8325)***

Naturemaker Inc E 760 438-4244
6225 El Camino Real Carlsbad (92009) ***(P-24186)***

Naturener Usa LLC (HQ) E 415 217-5500
435 Pacific Ave Fl 4 San Francisco (94133) ***(P-17213)***

Natures Baby Products Inc F 818 521-5054
58 Dartmouth Dr Rancho Mirage (92270) ***(P-8802)***

Natures Bounty Co F 310 952-7107
901 E 233rd St Carson (90745) ***(P-7956)***

Natures Bounty Co F 714 898-9936
7366 Orangewood Ave Garden Grove (92841) ***(P-7957)***

Natures Dream, West Covina *Also called Filmagic Inc* ***(P-8160)***

Natures Pwr Ntraceuticals Corp E 310 694-3031
15161 15171 S Figueroa St Gardena (90248) ***(P-636)***

Naturestar Bio Tech Inc F 909 930-1878
1175 S Grove Ave Ste 101 Ontario (91761) ***(P-8293)***

Naturvet, Temecula *Also called Garmon Corporation* ***(P-24104)***

Natus Inc F 626 355-3746
19 Suffolk Ave Ste C Sierra Madre (91024) ***(P-23021)***

Natus Medical Incorporated E 303 962-1800
1501 Industrial Rd San Carlos (94070) ***(P-23022)***

Natus Medical Incorporated D 858 260-2590
5955 Pacific Center Blvd San Diego (92121) ***(P-23023)***

Natus Medical Incorporated (PA) B 925 223-6700
6701 Koll Center Pkwy # 120 Pleasanton (94566) ***(P-23024)***

Natutac, Cerritos *Also called Winning Laboratories Inc* ***(P-7983)***

Natvar, City of Industry *Also called Tekni-Plex Inc* ***(P-5742)***

Nautilus Seafood, San Pedro *Also called J Deluca Fish Company Inc* ***(P-2314)***

Navajo Concrete Inc F 805 238-0955
2484 Ramada Dr Paso Robles (93446) ***(P-11151)***

Navajo Rock & Block, Paso Robles *Also called Navajo Concrete Inc* ***(P-11151)***

Naval Maint Training Group, Port Hueneme *Also called United States Dept of Navy* ***(P-20965)***

Navarro Vineyard, Philo *Also called Navarro Winery* ***(P-1894)***

Navarro Winery D 707 895-3686
5601 Highway 128 Philo (95466) ***(P-1894)***

Navcom Defense Electronics Inc (PA) D 951 268-9205
9129 Stellar Ct Corona (92883) ***(P-21355)***

Navcom Technology Inc (HQ) E 310 381-2000
20780 Madrona Ave Torrance (90503) ***(P-18196)***

Navigational Services Inc F 619 409-6992
34 E 17th St Ste C National City (91950) ***(P-21005)***

Navigator Yachts and Pdts Inc C 951 657-2117
364 Malbert St Perris (92570) ***(P-21058)***

Navistar Inc D 818 907-0129
14651 Ventura Blvd Sherman Oaks (91403) ***(P-20161)***

Naylor Corp E 415 421-1789
Spc 112 Pier 39 San Francisco (94133) ***(P-1472)***

Nazca Solutions Inc E 612 279-6100
4 First American Way Santa Ana (92707) ***(P-24944)***

Nbp, Claremont *Also called New Bedford Panoramex Corp* ***(P-17719)***

Nbty Manufacturing LLC C 714 765-8323
5115 E La Palma Ave Anaheim (92807) ***(P-8294)***

NC Dynamics Incorporated C 562 634-7392
6925 Downey Ave Long Beach (90805) ***(P-20896)***

NC Dynamics LLC C 562 634-7392
3401 E 69th St Long Beach (90805) ***(P-16781)***

NC Engineering Inc F 310 532-4810
13439 S Budlong Ave Gardena (90247) ***(P-16782)***

NC Interactive LLC D 650 393-2200
1900 S Norfolk St Ste 125 San Mateo (94403) ***(P-24945)***

Nca Laboratories Inc F 916 852-7029
11305 Sunrise Gold Cir D Rancho Cordova (95742) ***(P-17837)***

Ncd Acquisition Inc (PA) E 203 565-8707
10425 Slusher Dr Santa Fe Springs (90670) ***(P-9720)***

Ncdi, Long Beach *Also called NC Dynamics Incorporated* ***(P-20896)***

Nci Group Inc D 909 987-4681
9123 Center Ave Rancho Cucamonga (91730) ***(P-12953)***

Nci Group Inc C 209 357-1000
550 Industry Way Atwater (95301) ***(P-12954)***

Ncla Inc F 562 926-6252
16031 Carmenita Rd Cerritos (90703) ***(P-5718)***

ND Industries Inc E 562 926-3321
13929 Dinard Ave Santa Fe Springs (90670) ***(P-13078)***

Nds, Woodland Hills *Also called National Diversified Sales Inc* ***(P-10230)***

Nds, Fresno *Also called Agrifim Irrigation Pdts Inc* ***(P-14037)***

Ndsp Crp, San Jose *Also called Ndsp Delaware Inc* ***(P-19033)***

Ndsp Delaware Inc D 408 626-1640
224 Airport Pkwy Ste 400 San Jose (95110) ***(P-19033)***

NDT Systems Inc E 714 893-2438
5542 Buckingham Dr Ste A Huntington Beach (92649) ***(P-22240)***

Nea Electronics Inc E 805 292-4010
14370 White Sage Rd Moorpark (93021) ***(P-19403)***

Neal Family Vineyards LLC F 707 965-2800
716 Liparita Ave Angwin (94508) ***(P-1895)***

Neal Feay Company D 805 967-4521
133 S La Patera Ln Goleta (93117) ***(P-11598)***

Nearfield Systems Inc D 310 525-7000
19730 Magellan Dr Torrance (90502) ***(P-21813)***

Neato Robotics Inc (HQ) D 510 795-1351
8100 Jarvis Ave Ste 100 Newark (94560) ***(P-14760)***

Neatpocket LLC F 323 632-7440
8033 W Sunset Blvd West Hollywood (90046) ***(P-24946)***

Neb Cal Printing, San Diego *Also called Kovin Corporation Inc* ***(P-6929)***

Nebia Inc F 203 570-6222
375 Alabama St Ste 200 San Francisco (94110) ***(P-9644)***

Neclec E 559 797-0103
5945 E Harvard Ave Fresno (93727) ***(P-13462)***

Nectave Inc F 714 393-0144
6700 Caballero Blvd Buena Park (90620) ***(P-2618)***

Nef Tech Inc F 909 548-4900
5255 State St Montclair (91763) ***(P-16078)***

Nefab Packaging Inc D 408 678-2500
8477 Central Ave Newark (94560) ***(P-4444)***

Nefful USA Inc F 626 839-6657
18563 Gale Ave City of Industry (91748) ***(P-3541)***

Neighboring LLC F 818 271-0640
2427 Sentinel Ln San Marcos (92078) ***(P-22894)***

Neil A Kjos Music Company (PA) E 858 270-9800
4382 Jutland Dr San Diego (92117) ***(P-6536)***

Neil A Kjos Music Company F 619 225-6710
4382 Jutland Dr San Diego (92117) ***(P-6537)***

Neil Jones Food Company D 831 637-0573
711 Sally St Hollister (95023) ***(P-832)***

Neil Jones Food Company E 559 659-5100
2502 N St Firebaugh (93622) ***(P-833)***

Neil Patel Digital LLC E 619 356-8119
750 B St Ste 2600 San Diego (92101) ***(P-6538)***

Neill Aircraft Co B 562 432-7981
1260 W 15th St Long Beach (90813) ***(P-20897)***

Neilmed Pharmaceuticals Inc B 707 525-3784
601 Aviation Blvd Santa Rosa (95403) ***(P-8295)***

Neiman & Company, Van Nuys *Also called Neiman/Hoeller Inc* ***(P-23934)***

Neiman/Hoeller Inc D 818 781-8600
6842 Valjean Ave Van Nuys (91406) ***(P-23934)***

Neko World Inc E 301 649-1188
21041 S Wstn Ave Ste 200 Torrance (90501) ***(P-23449)***

Employee Codes: A=Over 500 employees, B=251-500
C=101-250, D=51-100, E=20-50, F=10-19
2019 California
Manfacturers Register
© Mergent Inc. 1-800-342-5647
1223

Nektar Therapeutics ....E.......650 622-1790
150 Industrial Rd San Carlos (94070) ***(P-8296)***
Nektar Therapeutics (PA) ....B.......415 482-5300
455 Mission Bay Blvd S San Francisco (94158) ***(P-8297)***
Nelco Products Inc (HQ) ....C.......714 879-4293
1100 E Kimberly Ave Anaheim (92801) ***(P-9754)***
Nelco Products Inc ....E.......714 879-4293
1100 E Kimberly Ave Anaheim (92801) ***(P-18542)***
Nelgo Industries Inc ....E.......760 433-6434
3265 Production Ave Ste A Oceanside (92058) ***(P-16783)***
Nelgo Manufacturing, Oceanside *Also called Nelgo Industries Inc* ***(P-16783)***
Nellson Nutraceutical Inc (PA) ....B.......626 812-6522
5801 Ayala Ave Irwindale (91706) ***(P-1445)***
Nellson Nutraceutical LLC (PA) ....B.......714 765-7000
5115 E La Palma Ave Anaheim (92807) ***(P-1446)***
Nelson & Sons Electric Inc ....E.......209 667-4343
401 N Walnut Rd Turlock (95380) ***(P-20023)***
Nelson & Sons Inc ....E.......707 462-3755
550 Nelson Ranch Rd Ukiah (95482) ***(P-1896)***
Nelson Adams Inc ....E.......909 256-8938
160 N Cactus Ave Rialto (92376) ***(P-5022)***
Nelson Adams Naco Corporation ....E.......909 256-8938
160 N Cactus Ave Rialto (92376) ***(P-4726)***
Nelson Banner Inc ....E.......707 585-9942
5720 Labath Ave Rohnert Park (94928) ***(P-5611)***
Nelson Case Corporation ....F.......714 528-2215
650 S Jefferson St Ste A Placentia (92870) ***(P-4445)***
Nelson Engineering Llc ....E.......714 893-7999
11600 Monarch St Garden Grove (92841) ***(P-16784)***
Nelson Family Vineyard, Ukiah *Also called Nelson & Sons Inc* ***(P-1896)***
Nelson Jewellery (usa) Inc ....F.......213 489-3323
631 S Olive St Ste 300 Los Angeles (90014) ***(P-23345)***
Nelson Name Plate Company (PA) ....C.......323 663-3971
2800 Casitas Ave Los Angeles (90039) ***(P-7412)***
Nelson Sports Inc ....E.......562 944-8081
10528 Pioneer Blvd Santa Fe Springs (90670) ***(P-10507)***
Nelson Thread Grinding Inc ....F.......818 768-2578
8205 Lankershim Blvd North Hollywood (91605) ***(P-16785)***
Nelson-Miller, Los Angeles *Also called Nelson Name Plate Company* ***(P-7412)***
Nemco, Irvine *Also called Nexsun Electronics Inc* ***(P-19660)***
Nemco Electronics Corp ....C.......650 571-1234
40 Roan Pl Woodside (94062) ***(P-19300)***
Neo Pacific Holdings Inc ....E.......818 786-2900
14940 Calvert St Van Nuys (91411) ***(P-10233)***
Neo Superwater Corp ....F.......800 604-7051
535 Mission St Ste 1820 San Francisco (94105) ***(P-2153)***
Neo Tech Aqua Solutions Inc ....F.......858 571-6590
3853 Calle Fortunada San Diego (92123) ***(P-9290)***
Neo Tech Natel Epic Oncore, Chatsworth *Also called Oncore Manufacturing Svcs Inc* ***(P-18550)***
Neocatena Networks Inc ....F.......650 200-7340
6300 Old School Rd Pleasanton (94588) ***(P-20024)***
Neoconix Inc ....E.......408 530-9393
4020 Moorpark Ave Ste 108 San Jose (95117) ***(P-19034)***
Neodora LLC ....E.......650 283-3319
1545 Berger Dr San Jose (95112) ***(P-14999)***
Neogen Corporation ....E.......800 995-1607
1355 Paulson Rd Turlock (95380) ***(P-8658)***
Neogov, El Segundo *Also called Governmentjobscom Inc* ***(P-24706)***
Neology Inc (HQ) ....E.......858 391-0260
13520 Evening Creek Dr N # 460 San Diego (92128) ***(P-21814)***
Neomen, Palm Springs *Also called Pleros LLC* ***(P-8820)***
Neomend Inc ....D.......949 783-3300
60 Technology Dr Irvine (92618) ***(P-22551)***
Neon Ideas ....F.......805 648-7681
1635 Buena Vista St Ventura (93001) ***(P-23935)***
Neonode Inc (PA) ....D.......408 496-6722
2880 Zanker Rd San Jose (95134) ***(P-22000)***
Neonroots LLC ....C.......310 907-9210
8560 W Sunset Blvd # 500 West Hollywood (90069) ***(P-24947)***
Neophotonics Corporation ....F.......510 933-4100
40931 Encyclopedia Cir Fremont (94538) ***(P-19035)***
Neophotonics Corporation (PA) ....B.......408 232-9200
2911 Zanker Rd San Jose (95134) ***(P-19036)***
Neoplast Inc ....F.......951 300-9300
1350 Citrus St Riverside (92507) ***(P-10234)***
Neosem Technology Inc (HQ) ....E.......408 643-7000
1965 Concourse Dr San Jose (95131) ***(P-21815)***
Neotech, Chatsworth *Also called Natel Engineering Company Inc* ***(P-19031)***
Neotract Inc (HQ) ....F.......925 401-0700
4473 Willow Rd Ste 100 Pleasanton (94588) ***(P-22552)***
Nepco, Pomona *Also called Natural Envmtl Protection Co* ***(P-7856)***
Neptec Optical Solutions, Fremont *Also called Neptec Os Inc* ***(P-11667)***
Neptec Optical Solutions Inc ....E.......510 687-1101
48603 Warm Springs Blvd Fremont (94539) ***(P-10659)***
Neptec Os Inc ....E.......510 687-1101
48603 Warm Springs Blvd Fremont (94539) ***(P-11667)***
Neptune Foods, Vernon *Also called Fishermans Pride Prcessors Inc* ***(P-2313)***
Neptune Trading Inc ....F.......909 923-0236
4021 Greystone Dr Ontario (91761) ***(P-11881)***
Nerdist Channel LLC ....E.......818 333-2705
2525 N Naomi St Burbank (91504) ***(P-18197)***
Nerdist Industries, Burbank *Also called Nerdist Channel LLC* ***(P-18197)***
Nerveda Inc ....D.......858 705-2365
3888 Quarter Mile Dr San Diego (92130) ***(P-8298)***
Nest Environments Inc ....F.......714 979-5500
530 E Dyer Rd Santa Ana (92707) ***(P-4198)***
Nestle Confections Factory, Modesto *Also called Nestle Usa Inc* ***(P-639)***
Nestle Dist Ctr & Logistics, Mira Loma *Also called Nestle Usa Inc* ***(P-1002)***
Nestle Dreyers Ice Cream Co ....F.......661 398-5448
7301 District Blvd Bakersfield (93313) ***(P-689)***
Nestle Dsd, Fresno *Also called Nestle Usa Inc* ***(P-638)***
Nestle Holdings Inc (HQ) ....F.......818 549-6000
800 N Brand Blvd Glendale (91203) ***(P-637)***
Nestle Pizza Company Inc ....F.......510 261-8001
2530 E 11th St Oakland (94601) ***(P-1001)***
Nestle Purina Factory, Maricopa *Also called Nestle Purina Petcare Company* ***(P-24187)***
Nestle Purina Petcare Company ....D.......661 769-8261
1710 Golden Cat Rd Maricopa (93252) ***(P-24187)***
Nestle Purina Petcare Company ....C.......314 982-1000
800 N Brand Blvd Fl 5 Glendale (91203) ***(P-1118)***
Nestle Refrigerated Food Co ....B.......818 549-6000
800 N Brand Blvd Fl 5 Glendale (91203) ***(P-2432)***
Nestle Usa Inc ....F.......559 834-2554
4065 E Therese Ave Fresno (93725) ***(P-638)***
Nestle Usa Inc ....D.......209 574-2000
736 Garner Rd Modesto (95357) ***(P-639)***
Nestle Usa Inc ....F.......951 360-7200
3450 Dulles Dr Mira Loma (91752) ***(P-1002)***
Net Clearly ....F.......510 465-0101
300 Frank H Ogawa Plz # 234 Oakland (94612) ***(P-24948)***
Net Optics Inc ....D.......408 737-7777
5301 Stevens Creek Blvd Santa Clara (95051) ***(P-24949)***
Net Shapes Inc ....C.......909 947-3231
1336 E Francis St Ste B Ontario (91761) ***(P-11518)***
Netaphor Software Inc ....F.......949 470-7955
15510 Rockfield Blvd C100 Irvine (92618) ***(P-24950)***
Netapp Inc (PA) ....A.......408 822-6000
1395 Crossman Ave Sunnyvale (94089) ***(P-15572)***
Netcube Systems Inc ....D.......650 862-7858
1275 Arbor Ave Los Altos (94024) ***(P-24951)***
Netgear Inc (PA) ....C.......408 907-8000
350 E Plumeria Dr San Jose (95134) ***(P-17968)***
Nethra Imaging Inc (PA) ....F.......408 257-5880
2855 Bowers Ave Santa Clara (95051) ***(P-19037)***
Netlist Inc (PA) ....D.......949 435-0025
175 Technology Dr Ste 150 Irvine (92618) ***(P-19038)***
Netlogic Microsystems LLC ....A.......408 454-3000
3975 Freedom Cir Ste 900 Santa Clara (95054) ***(P-19039)***
Netmarble Us Inc ....F.......714 276-1196
6131 Orangethorpe Ave # 160 Buena Park (90620) ***(P-6539)***
Netsarang Inc ....F.......669 204-3301
4701 P Henry Dr 137 Santa Clara (95054) ***(P-24952)***
Netsol Technologies Inc (PA) ....E.......818 222-9197
24025 Park Sorrento # 410 Calabasas (91302) ***(P-24953)***
Netsuite Inc (HQ) ....C.......650 627-1000
2955 Campus Dr Ste 100 San Mateo (94403) ***(P-24954)***
Network Automation Inc ....E.......213 738-1700
3530 Wilshire Blvd # 1800 Los Angeles (90010) ***(P-24955)***
Network Chemistry Inc ....F.......650 858-3120
1804 Embarcadero Rd # 201 Palo Alto (94303) ***(P-20025)***
Network Pcb Inc ....E.......408 943-8760
1914 Otoole Way San Jose (95131) ***(P-18543)***
Network Printing & Copy Center ....F.......858 695-8221
12155 Flint Pl Poway (92064) ***(P-6990)***
Network Telephone Services Inc (PA) ....B.......800 742-5687
21135 Erwin St Woodland Hills (91367) ***(P-5083)***
Network Vigilance LLC ....F.......858 695-8676
12121 Scripps Summit Dr # 320 San Diego (92131) ***(P-24956)***
Networked Energy Services Corp (HQ) ....E.......408 622-9900
5215 Hellyer Ave Ste 150 San Jose (95138) ***(P-20026)***
Networks Electronic Co LLC ....E.......818 341-0440
9750 De Soto Ave Chatsworth (91311) ***(P-13695)***
Netwrix Corporation (PA) ....E.......888 638-9749
300 Spectrum Center Dr # 200 Irvine (92618) ***(P-24957)***
Neural Analytics Inc ....F.......818 317-4999
2440 S Sepulveda Blvd # 115 Los Angeles (90064) ***(P-22553)***
Neural Id LLC ....F.......650 394-8800
203 Redwood Shr Pkwy # 250 Redwood City (94065) ***(P-19874)***
Neurocrine Biosciences Inc (PA) ....C.......858 617-7600
12780 El Camino Real # 100 San Diego (92130) ***(P-8299)***
Neurohacker Collective LLC ....F.......855 281-2328
179 Calle Magdalena # 100 Encinitas (92024) ***(P-640)***
Neurolenses, Costa Mesa *Also called Eyebrain Medical Inc* ***(P-23097)***
Neuroptics Inc ....F.......949 250-9792
23041 Ave D L Carlota 1 Laguna Hills (92653) ***(P-22554)***
Neurosmith LLC ....E.......562 296-1100
1000 N Studebaker Rd # 3 Long Beach (90815) ***(P-23450)***
Neurostructures Inc ....F.......800 352-6103
199 Technology Dr Ste 110 Irvine (92618) ***(P-22777)***
Neutraderm Inc ....E.......818 534-3190
20660 Nordhoff St Chatsworth (91311) ***(P-8803)***
Neutrogena, Los Angeles *Also called Johnson & Johnson Consumer Inc* ***(P-8777)***
Neutron Plating Inc ....D.......714 632-9241
2993 E Blue Star St Anaheim (92806) ***(P-13463)***
Neutronic Stamping & Plating ....E.......714 964-8900
10550 Lawson River Ave Fountain Valley (92708) ***(P-13464)***
Nevada City Winery, Nevada City *Also called N C W G Inc* ***(P-1891)***
Nevada County Publishing Co ....A.......530 273-9561
464 Sutton Way Grass Valley (95945) ***(P-5992)***
Nevada Heat Treating Inc (PA) ....E.......510 790-2300
37955 Central Ct Ste D Newark (94560) ***(P-25424)***
Nevada Window Supply Inc ....F.......951 300-0100
1455 Columbia Ave Riverside (92507) ***(P-4199)***
Never Scrub ....F.......951 272-9922
4225 Prado Rd Ste 103 Corona (92880) ***(P-8599)***
Neville Industries Inc ....F.......760 471-8949
285 Pawnee St Ste D San Marcos (92078) ***(P-14549)***

Mergent e-mail: customerrelations@mergent.com
1224
2019 California
Manufacturers Register
(P-0000) Products & Services Section entry number
(PA)=Parent Co (HQ)=Headquarters (DH)=Div Headquarters

Nevion Usa Inc....D....805 247-8575
400 W Ventura Blvd # 155 Camarillo (93010) *(P-18198)*
Nevocal Enterprises Inc....D....559 277-0700
5320 N Barcus Ave Fresno (93722) *(P-375)*
Nevro Corp....B....650 251-0005
1800 Bridge Pkwy Redwood City (94065) *(P-22555)*
Nevwest Inc....E....619 420-8100
1225 S Expo Way Ste 140 San Diego (92154) *(P-21356)*
New Age Enclosures, Santa Maria *Also called Alltec Integrated Mfg Inc (P-9935)*
New Age Metal Finishing LLC....E....559 498-8585
2169 N Pleasant Ave Fresno (93705) *(P-13465)*
New American Industries Inc....E....559 251-1581
5475 E Hedges Ave # 102 Fresno (93727) *(P-3767)*
New Bedford Panoramex Corp....E....909 982-9806
1480 N Claremont Blvd Claremont (91711) *(P-17719)*
New Bi US Gaming LLC....D....858 592-2472
10920 Via Frontera # 420 San Diego (92127) *(P-24958)*
New Brunswick Industries Inc....E....619 448-4900
1850 Gillespie Way El Cajon (92020) *(P-18544)*
New Cal Metals Inc....F....916 652-7424
3495 Swetzer Rd Granite Bay (95746) *(P-12690)*
New CAM Commerce Solutions LLC....D....714 338-0200
5555 Garden Grove Blvd # 100 Westminster (92683) *(P-24959)*
New Century Gold LLC....F....818 936-2676
6303 Owensmouth Ave Fl 10 Woodland Hills (91367) *(P-23302)*
New Century Industries Inc....E....562 634-9551
7231 Rosecrans Ave Paramount (90723) *(P-20409)*
New Century Machine Tools Inc....F....562 906-8455
9641 Santa Fe Springs Rd Santa Fe Springs (90670) *(P-14396)*
New Century Snacks, Commerce *Also called Snak Club LLC (P-1503)*
New Chef Fashion Inc....D....323 581-0300
3223 E 46th St Vernon (90058) *(P-3026)*
New Cntury Mtals Southeast Inc....F....562 356-6804
15723 Shoemaker Ave Norwalk (90650) *(P-11634)*
New Dimension Electronics, Santa Clara *Also called N D E Inc (P-18536)*
New Direction Silk Screen....F....916 971-3939
2328 Auburn Blvd Ste 2 Sacramento (95821) *(P-7413)*
New Fragrance Continental....F....323 766-0060
5033 Exposition Blvd Los Angeles (90016) *(P-8804)*
New Generation Software Inc....E....916 920-2200
3835 N Freeway Blvd # 200 Sacramento (95834) *(P-24960)*
New Generation Sourcing, Carlsbad *Also called Designer Drinks (P-2129)*
New Global Food....F....562 404-9953
13577 Larwin Cir Santa Fe Springs (90670) *(P-2619)*
New Gold Manufacturing Inc....D....818 847-1020
2150 N Lincoln St Burbank (91504) *(P-23303)*
New Gordon Industries LLC....E....562 483-7378
13750 Rosecrans Ave Santa Fe Springs (90670) *(P-13254)*
New Green Day LLC....E....323 566-7603
1710 E 111th St Los Angeles (90059) *(P-5269)*
New Greenscreen Incorporated....E....951 685-9660
11445 Pacific Ave Fontana (92337) *(P-12691)*
New Greenscreen Incorporated....E....800 767-9378
5500 Jurupa St Ontario (91761) *(P-5157)*
New Harbinger Publications Inc (PA)....E....510 652-0215
5674 Shattuck Ave Oakland (94609) *(P-6369)*
New Haven Companies Inc....D....213 749-8181
13571 Vaughn St Unit E San Fernando (91340) *(P-3010)*
New Hong Kong Noodle Co Inc....E....650 588-6425
360 Swift Ave Ste 22 South San Francisco (94080) *(P-2433)*
New Horizon, South San Francisco *Also called Hsin Tung Yang Foods Company (P-495)*
New Horizon Foods Inc....E....510 489-8600
33440 Western Ave Union City (94587) *(P-2620)*
New Iem LLC....D....510 656-1600
48205 Warm Springs Blvd Fremont (94539) *(P-17152)*
New Image Foam Products LLC....E....916 388-0741
6835 Power Inn Rd Sacramento (95828) *(P-9871)*
New Incorporation Now....F....562 484-3020
12323 Imperial Hwy Norwalk (90650) *(P-5993)*
New Logic Research Inc....D....510 655-7305
5040 Commercial Cir Ste A Concord (94520) *(P-15000)*
New Maverick Desk Inc....C....310 217-1554
15100 S Figueroa St Gardena (90248) *(P-4957)*
New Method Fur Dressing Co....E....650 583-9881
131 Beacon St South San Francisco (94080) *(P-24188)*
New Ngc Inc....C....562 435-4465
1850 Pier B St Long Beach (90813) *(P-11220)*
New Origins Accessories Inc (PA)....F....909 869-7559
3980 Valley Blvd Ste D Walnut (91789) *(P-23754)*
New Paradise, South El Monte *Also called CPC Group Inc (P-10047)*
New Printing, Van Nuys *Also called Digital Room Holdings Inc (P-7297)*
New Product Integration Solutn....D....408 944-9178
685 Jarvis Dr Ste A Morgan Hill (95037) *(P-11451)*
New Quantum Living, Arcadia *Also called Quantum Corporation (P-15589)*
New Relic Inc (PA)....C....650 777-7600
188 Spear St Ste 1200 San Francisco (94105) *(P-24961)*
New Rise Brand Holdings LLC....E....323 233-9005
801 S Figueroa St # 1000 Los Angeles (90017) *(P-3084)*
New Source Technology LLC....F....925 462-6888
6678 Owens Dr Ste 105 Pleasanton (94588) *(P-23025)*
New Star Lasers Inc....E....916 677-1900
8331 Sierra College Blvd # 204 Roseville (95661) *(P-23026)*
New Technology Plastics Inc....E....562 941-6034
12989 Los Nietos Rd Santa Fe Springs (90670) *(P-7857)*
New Times Media Group, San Luis Obispo *Also called Slo New Times Inc (P-6048)*
New Vavin Inc....E....707 963-5972
3222 Ehlers Ln Saint Helena (94574) *(P-1897)*
New Vision Display Inc (HQ)....E....916 786-8111
1430 Blue Oaks Blvd # 100 Roseville (95747) *(P-19658)*
New Wave Industries Ltd (PA)....F....800 882-8854
3315 Orange Grove Ave North Highlands (95660) *(P-16079)*
New Wave Research Incorporated (HQ)....C....510 249-1550
48660 Kato Rd Fremont (94538) *(P-20027)*
New World Library, Novato *Also called Whatever Publishing Inc (P-6408)*
New World Machining Inc....E....408 227-3810
2799 Aiello Dr San Jose (95111) *(P-16786)*
New World Manufacturing Inc....F....707 894-5257
27627 Dutcher Creek Rd Cloverdale (95425) *(P-9645)*
New World Medical Incorporated....F....909 466-4304
10763 Edison Ct Rancho Cucamonga (91730) *(P-22556)*
New York Frozen Foods Inc....E....626 338-3000
5100 Rivergrade Rd Baldwin Park (91706) *(P-1295)*
New York Toy Exchange Inc....F....626 327-4547
11955 Jack Benny Dr Ste 1 Rancho Cucamonga (91739) *(P-23451)*
New Zealand Pump Company, Alhambra *Also called N Z Pump Co Inc (P-15086)*
New-Indy Containerboard, Ontario *Also called New-Indy Ontario LLC (P-5316)*
New-Indy Containerboard, Oxnard *Also called New-Indy Oxnard LLC (P-5317)*
New-Indy Containerboard LLC (HQ)....D....909 296-3400
3500 Porsche Way Ste 150 Ontario (91764) *(P-5315)*
New-Indy Ontario LLC....C....909 390-1055
5100 Jurupa St Ontario (91761) *(P-5316)*
New-Indy Oxnard LLC....C....805 986-3881
5936 Perkins Rd Oxnard (93033) *(P-5317)*
Newage Pavilions LLC....F....818 701-9600
9360 Penfield Ave Chatsworth (91311) *(P-20028)*
Neways Inc....E....949 264-1542
28202 Cabot Rd Ste 100 Laguna Niguel (92677) *(P-19659)*
Newbasis West LLC....C....951 787-0600
2626 Kansas Ave Riverside (92507) *(P-10960)*
Newbold Cleaners....F....916 481-1130
4211 Arden Way Ste A Sacramento (95864) *(P-15930)*
Newby Rubber Inc....E....661 327-5137
320 Industrial St Bakersfield (93307) *(P-9646)*
Newco International Inc....B....818 834-7100
13600 Vaughn St San Fernando (91340) *(P-4727)*
Newcomb Spring Corp....E....714 995-5341
8380 Cerritos Ave Stanton (90680) *(P-13796)*
Newcomb Spring of California, Stanton *Also called Newcomb Spring Corp (P-13796)*
Newegg.com, City of Industry *Also called Magnell Associate Inc (P-15446)*
Newell Brands Inc....F....760 246-2700
17182 Nevada St Victorville (92394) *(P-10235)*
Newera Software Inc....F....408 520-7100
18625 Sutter Blvd Ste 950 Morgan Hill (95037) *(P-24962)*
Newfield Technology Corp (PA)....E....909 931-4405
4230 E Airport Dr Ste 105 Ontario (91761) *(P-20162)*
Newhall Signal, Santa Clarita *Also called Signal (P-6045)*
Newhouse Upholstery....E....626 444-1370
2309 Edwards Ave El Monte (91733) *(P-5023)*
Newhouse Upholstery Mfg, El Monte *Also called Newhouse Upholstery (P-5023)*
Newlight Technologies Inc....E....714 556-4500
14382 Astronautics Ln Huntington Beach (92647) *(P-10236)*
Newline Rubber Company....F....408 214-0359
13165 Monterey Hwy # 100 San Martin (95046) *(P-9647)*
Newlon Rouge LLC....F....310 458-7737
1640 5th St Ste 218 Santa Monica (90401) *(P-5994)*
Newly Weds Foods Inc....E....209 491-7777
437 S Mcclure Rd Modesto (95357) *(P-2621)*
Newman and Sons Inc (PA)....E....805 522-1646
2655 1st St 210 Simi Valley (93065) *(P-10961)*
Newman Bros California Inc (PA)....E....951 782-0102
1901 Massachusetts Ave Riverside (92507) *(P-4200)*
Newman Flange & Fitting Co....D....209 862-2977
1649 L St Newman (95360) *(P-13107)*
Newmatic Engineering Inc (PA)....F....415 824-2664
355 Goddard Ste 250 Irvine (92618) *(P-21518)*
Newnex Technology Corp....F....408 986-9988
3041 Olcott St Santa Clara (95054) *(P-15811)*
Newpacket Wireless Corporation....F....408 747-1003
1600 Wyatt Dr Ste 10 Santa Clara (95054) *(P-15812)*
Newport Brass, Santa Ana *Also called Brasstech Inc (P-12026)*
Newport Corporation (HQ)....B....949 863-3144
1791 Deere Ave Irvine (92606) *(P-21482)*
Newport Corporation....A....408 980-4300
3635 Peterson Way Santa Clara (95054) *(P-20029)*
Newport Custom Woodworking....F....949 631-6397
1835 Whittier Ave Ste C10 Costa Mesa (92627) *(P-4201)*
Newport Electronics, Santa Ana *Also called Omega Engineering Inc (P-15002)*
Newport Energy LLC....E....408 230-7545
19200 Von Karman Ave # 400 Irvine (92612) *(P-142)*
Newport Fab LLC....D....949 435-8000
4321 Jamboree Rd Newport Beach (92660) *(P-19040)*
Newport Fish, South San Francisco *Also called Tardio Enterprises Inc (P-2326)*
Newport Flavors & Fragrances....E....714 771-2200
833 N Elm St Orange (92867) *(P-2274)*
Newport Glass Works Ltd....F....714 484-8100
10564 Fern Ave Stanton (90680) *(P-22109)*
Newport Glassworks, Stanton *Also called Newport Optical Industries (P-22110)*
Newport Industrial Glass Inc....E....714 484-7500
8610 Central Ave Stanton (90680) *(P-10722)*
Newport Laminates Inc....E....714 545-8335
3121 W Central Ave Santa Ana (92704) *(P-10237)*
Newport Medical Instrs Inc....D....949 642-3910
1620 Sunflower Ave Costa Mesa (92626) *(P-22557)*
Newport Mesa Usd Campus C....F....714 424-8939
2985 Bear St Costa Mesa (92626) *(P-6991)*
Newport Metal Finishing Inc....D....714 556-8411
3230 S Standard Ave Santa Ana (92705) *(P-13621)*

ALPHABETIC

Employee Codes: A=Over 500 employees, B=251-500
C=101-250, D=51-100, E=20-50, F=10-19
2019 California
Manfacturers Register
© Mergent Inc. 1-800-342-5647
1225

Newport Optical Industries (PA).....E.....714 484-8100
10564 Fern Ave Stanton (90680) ***(P-22110)***
Newport Plastic Inc.....E.....714 549-1955
1525 E Edinger Ave Santa Ana (92705) ***(P-10238)***
Newport Plastics LLC (PA).....E.....800 854-8402
1525 E Edinger Ave Santa Ana (92705) ***(P-10239)***
Newport Thin Film Lab Inc.....F.....909 591-0276
13824 Magnolia Ave Chino (91710) ***(P-10240)***
Newport Vessels, Monrovia *Also called Torero Specialty Products LLC* ***(P-23674)***
News Media Corporation.....D.....831 761-7300
100 Westridge Dr Watsonville (95076) ***(P-5995)***
News Media Inc.....E.....805 237-6060
502 First St Paso Robles (93446) ***(P-5996)***
News Publishers' Press, Glendale *Also called P E N Inc* ***(P-7426)***
News Review, The, Ridgecrest *Also called Sierra View Inc* ***(P-6044)***
Newtex Industries Inc.....D.....323 277-0900
9654 Hermosa Ave Rancho Cucamonga (91730) ***(P-24189)***
Newton Heat Treating Company.....D.....626 964-6528
19235 E Walnut Dr N City of Industry (91748) ***(P-11826)***
Newton Vineyard LLC (HQ).....E.....707 963-9000
2555 Madrona Ave Saint Helena (94574) ***(P-1898)***
Nexenta Systems Inc.....C.....408 791-3341
2025 Gateway Pl Ste 160 San Jose (95110) ***(P-24963)***
Nexfon Corporation.....F.....925 200-2233
7172 Regional St Dublin (94568) ***(P-10660)***
Nexgen Pharma Inc (PA).....C.....949 863-0340
46 Corporate Park Ste 100 Irvine (92606) ***(P-8300)***
Nexgen Pharma Inc.....E.....949 260-3702
17802 Gillette Ave Irvine (92614) ***(P-8301)***
Nexgen Pharma Inc.....F.....949 863-0340
17802 Gillette Ave Irvine (92614) ***(P-8302)***
Nexgen Power Systems Inc.....E.....408 230-7698
2010 El Camino Real Santa Clara (95050) ***(P-19041)***
Nexlogic Technologies Inc.....D.....408 436-8150
2085 Zanker Rd San Jose (95131) ***(P-18545)***
Nexon America, El Segundo *Also called M Nexon Inc* ***(P-24873)***
Nexrange Industries, City of Industry *Also called Duro Corporation* ***(P-17368)***
Nexsan Technologies Inc (HQ).....E.....408 724-9809
325 E Hillcrest Dr # 150 Thousand Oaks (91360) ***(P-15573)***
Nexsan Technologies Inc.....E.....760 745-3550
302 Enterprise St Escondido (92029) ***(P-15574)***
Nexstar Pharmaceutical, San Dimas *Also called Gilead Sciences Inc* ***(P-8189)***
Nexsteppe Inc.....E.....650 887-5700
400 E Jamie Ct Ste 202 South San Francisco (94080) ***(P-1150)***
Nexsteppe Seeds Inc.....E.....650 887-5700
400 E Jamie Ct Ste 202 South San Francisco (94080) ***(P-9024)***
Nexsun Corp.....E.....213 382-2220
3250 Wilshire Blvd # 1410 Los Angeles (90010) ***(P-9025)***
Nexsun Electronics Inc.....E.....949 680-4725
142 Technology Dr Ste 150 Irvine (92618) ***(P-19660)***
Nexsys Electronics Inc (PA).....F.....415 541-9980
70 Zoe St Ste 100 San Francisco (94107) ***(P-15813)***
Next Day Flyers, Van Nuys *Also called Postcard Press Inc* ***(P-7441)***
Next Day Frame Inc.....D.....310 886-0851
11560 Wright Rd Lynwood (90262) ***(P-4913)***
Next Day Printed Tees.....F.....619 420-8618
3523 Main St Ste 601 Chula Vista (91911) ***(P-3909)***
Next ERA, Vernon *Also called Peter K Inc* ***(P-3479)***
Next Generation, Bell *Also called J & F Design Inc* ***(P-3432)***
Next Intent Inc.....E.....805 781-6755
865 Via Esteban San Luis Obispo (93401) ***(P-16787)***
Next Level Elevator Inc.....F.....888 959-6010
2199 N Batavia St Ste S Orange (92865) ***(P-14253)***
Next Level Warehouse Solutions.....F.....916 922-7225
555 Display Way Sacramento (95838) ***(P-14279)***
Next Pharmaceuticals Inc.....E.....831 621-8712
360 Espinosa Rd Salinas (93907) ***(P-8303)***
Next Phase Solar, Berkeley *Also called Sunsystem Technology LLC* ***(P-19205)***
Next System Inc.....E.....661 257-1600
20605 Soledad Canyon Rd # 222 Canyon Country (91351) ***(P-2936)***
Next Up, Commerce *Also called Connected Apparel Company LLC* ***(P-3397)***
Nextag Inc (PA).....D.....650 645-4700
555 Twin Dolphin Dr # 370 Redwood City (94065) ***(P-6540)***
Nextclientcom Inc.....F.....818 550-8989
25012 Avenue Kearny Valencia (91355) ***(P-6541)***
Nextec Microwave & Rf Inc.....F.....408 727-1189
3010 Scott Blvd Santa Clara (95054) ***(P-18199)***
Nextest Systems Corporation.....C.....408 960-2400
875 Embedded Way San Jose (95138) ***(P-21816)***
Nextest Systems Teradyne Co, San Jose *Also called Nextest Systems Corporation* ***(P-21816)***
NEXTEX INTERNATIONAL, South Gate *Also called Nextrade Inc* ***(P-3011)***
Nextgen Healthcare Inc (PA).....C.....949 255-2600
18111 Von Karman Ave Irvine (92612) ***(P-24964)***
Nextinput Inc (PA).....F.....408 770-9293
980 Linda Vista Ave Mountain View (94043) ***(P-17290)***
Nextivity Inc (PA).....D.....858 485-9442
16550 W Bernardo Dr # 550 San Diego (92127) ***(P-18200)***
Nextpharma Tech USA Inc.....E.....858 450-3123
5340 Eastgate Mall San Diego (92121) ***(P-8304)***
Nextrade Inc (PA).....E.....562 944-9950
12411 Industrial Ave South Gate (90280) ***(P-3011)***
Nexus Automation, Livermore *Also called Eklavya LLC* ***(P-15318)***
Nexus California Inc.....F.....909 937-1000
4551 Brickell Privado St Ontario (91761) ***(P-9721)***
Nexus Dx Inc.....B.....858 410-4600
6759 Mesa Ridge Rd San Diego (92121) ***(P-22558)***
Nexxen Apparel Inc (PA).....F.....323 267-9900
1555 Los Palos St Los Angeles (90023) ***(P-3469)***

Nexyn Corporation.....F.....408 962-0895
1287 Forgewood Ave Sunnyvale (94089) ***(P-19661)***
Neyenesch Printers Inc.....D.....619 297-2281
2750 Kettner Blvd San Diego (92101) ***(P-6992)***
NFC Innovation Center, San Jose *Also called Thin Film Electronics Inc* ***(P-19762)***
Nfi Industries.....F.....951 681-6455
11888 Mission Blvd Mira Loma (91752) ***(P-24190)***
Ng John.....F.....415 929-7188
780 Van Ness Ave San Francisco (94102) ***(P-6993)***
Ngcodec Inc.....E.....408 766-4382
440 N Wolfe Rd Ste 2187 Sunnyvale (94085) ***(P-19042)***
Ngd Systems Inc.....E.....949 510-6327
355 Goddard Ste 200 Irvine (92618) ***(P-15575)***
NGK Spark Plugs (usa) Inc.....E.....949 580-2639
68 Fairbanks Irvine (92618) ***(P-19840)***
Nguoi Viet Newspaper, Westminster *Also called Nguoi Vietnamese People Inc* ***(P-5997)***
Nguoi Vietnamese People Inc (PA).....E.....714 892-9414
14771 Moran St Westminster (92683) ***(P-5997)***
Nguyen Hiep Corp.....E.....408 451-9042
1641 Rogers Ave San Jose (95112) ***(P-16788)***
Nhk Laboratories (PA).....D.....562 903-5835
12230 Florence Ave Santa Fe Springs (90670) ***(P-8305)***
Nhs Inc.....D.....831 459-7800
104 Bronson St Ste 9 Santa Cruz (95062) ***(P-23624)***
Ni Industries Inc.....E.....309 283-3355
7300 E Slauson Ave Commerce (90040) ***(P-12985)***
Ni Microwave Components, Santa Clara *Also called National Instruments Corp* ***(P-21812)***
Ni Microwave Components, Santa Clara *Also called Phase Matrix Inc* ***(P-21825)***
Nia Energy LLC.....F.....818 422-8000
23679 Calabasas Rd Calabasas (91302) ***(P-17432)***
Niagara Bottling LLC.....F.....909 230-5000
1401 Alder Ave Rialto (92376) ***(P-2154)***
Nibco Inc.....C.....951 737-5599
1375 Sampson Ave Corona (92879) ***(P-13960)***
Nic Protection Inc.....F.....818 249-2539
7135 Foothill Blvd Tujunga (91042) ***(P-17549)***
Nicewell Inc.....F.....626 455-0099
2411 Loma Ave South El Monte (91733) ***(P-3115)***
Nicholas Michael Designs Inc.....C.....714 562-8101
2330 Raymer Ave Fullerton (92833) ***(P-4914)***
Nicholas R Hyland.....F.....408 392-0600
227 San Jose Ave San Jose (95125) ***(P-4958)***
Nichols Farms, Hanford *Also called Nichols Pistachio* ***(P-1500)***
Nichols Lumber, Baldwin Park *Also called Survey Stake and Marker Inc* ***(P-4658)***
Nichols Manufacturing Inc.....F.....408 945-0911
913 Hanson Ct Milpitas (95035) ***(P-16789)***
Nichols Pistachio.....C.....559 584-6811
13762 1st Ave Hanford (93230) ***(P-1500)***
Nichols Winery & Cellars, Playa Del Rey *Also called Keith Nichols* ***(P-1838)***
Nicholson Ranch LLC.....E.....707 938-8822
4200 Napa Rd Sonoma (95476) ***(P-1899)***
Nick Sciabica & Sons A Corp.....E.....209 577-5067
2150 Yosemite Blvd Modesto (95354) ***(P-1546)***
Nick's Cabinet Doors, Azusa *Also called Nicks Doors Inc* ***(P-4202)***
Nicks Doors Inc.....F.....626 812-6491
1052 W Kirkwall Rd Azusa (91702) ***(P-4202)***
Nicksons Machine Shop Inc.....E.....805 925-2525
914 W Betteravia Rd Santa Maria (93455) ***(P-16790)***
Nico Nat Mfg Corp.....E.....323 721-1900
2624 Yates Ave Commerce (90040) ***(P-5084)***
Nicola, Commerce *Also called Protrend Ltd* ***(P-3336)***
Nicole Fullerton.....F.....661 257-0406
27821 Pine Crest Pl Castaic (91384) ***(P-3673)***
Niconat Manufacturing, Commerce *Also called Nico Nat Mfg Corp* ***(P-5084)***
Nidec Motor Corporation.....B.....916 638-4011
11380 White Rock Rd Rancho Cordova (95742) ***(P-14254)***
Nidi Tec Inc.....F.....714 777-9323
3936 E Coronado St Anaheim (92807) ***(P-11266)***
Niebam-Cppola Estate Winery LP.....E.....415 291-1700
916 Kearny St San Francisco (94133) ***(P-1900)***
Niebam-Cppola Estate Winery LP (PA).....C.....707 968-1100
1991 St Helena Hwy Rutherford (94573) ***(P-1901)***
Nieco Corporation.....D.....707 838-3226
7950 Cameron Dr Windsor (95492) ***(P-16080)***
Niedwick Corporation.....E.....714 771-9999
967 N Eckhoff St Orange (92867) ***(P-16791)***
Niedwick Machine Co, Orange *Also called Niedwick Corporation* ***(P-16791)***
Night Fashion Inc.....E.....213 747-8740
628 W 30th St Ofc C Los Angeles (90007) ***(P-3328)***
Night Optics Usa Inc.....F.....714 899-4475
605 Oro Dam Blvd E Oroville (95965) ***(P-18350)***
Nightingale Vantagemed Corp (HQ).....D.....916 638-4744
10670 White Rock Rd Rancho Cordova (95670) ***(P-24965)***
Nightscaping Outdoor Lighting, Redlands *Also called Loran Inc* ***(P-17104)***
Nihon Kohden Orangemed Inc.....F.....949 502-6448
15375 Barranca Pkwy C109 Irvine (92618) ***(P-23027)***
Nike Inc.....F.....949 768-4000
20001 Ellipse Foothill Ranch (92610) ***(P-3568)***
Nike Inc.....E.....310 670-6770
222 E Redondo Beach Blvd C Gardena (90248) ***(P-9476)***
Niki-Viki Apparel Inc.....F.....323 587-5055
2141 E 52nd St Vernon (90058) ***(P-2753)***
Nikkel Iron Works Corporation.....F.....661 746-4904
17045 S Central Vly Hwy Shafter (93263) ***(P-14086)***
Nikko Enterprise Corporation.....E.....562 941-6080
13168 Sandoval St Santa Fe Springs (90670) ***(P-2319)***
Niknejad Inc.....E.....310 478-8363
6855 Hayvenhurst Ave Van Nuys (91406) ***(P-6994)***

Nikon Research Corp America ....E.......800 446-4566
1399 Shoreway Rd Belmont (94002) ***(P-21817)***
Nilgiri Press, Tomales *Also called Blue Mtn Ctr of Meditation Inc* ***(P-6316)***
Nils Inc (PA) ....F.......714 755-1600
3151 Airway Ave Ste V Costa Mesa (92626) ***(P-3470)***
Nils Skiwear, Costa Mesa *Also called Nils Inc* ***(P-3470)***
Nilson Report, The, Carpinteria *Also called H S N Consultants Inc* ***(P-6175)***
Nima LLC ....E.......949 404-1990
3857 Birch St Ste 406 Newport Beach (92660) ***(P-17838)***
Nima Sports, Newport Beach *Also called Nima LLC* ***(P-17838)***
Nimble Storage Inc (HQ) ....C.......408 432-9600
211 River Oaks Pkwy San Jose (95134) ***(P-15576)***
Nimbus Data Inc ....E.......650 276-4500
5151 California Ave # 100 Irvine (92617) ***(P-15577)***
Nimbus Water Systems ....F.......951 984-2800
42445 Avenida Alvarado Temecula (92590) ***(P-16081)***
Nina Mia Inc ....D.......714 773-5588
826 Enterprise Way Fullerton (92831) ***(P-2622)***
Nina Religion, Huntington Park *Also called Saydel Inc* ***(P-8836)***
Ninas Mexican Foods Inc ....E.......909 468-5888
20631 Valley Blvd Ste A Walnut (91789) ***(P-2623)***
Nine West Holdings Inc ....F.......408 946-2570
232 Great Mall Dr Milpitas (95035) ***(P-3356)***
Niner Wine Estates LLC ....F.......805 239-2233
2400 W Highway 46 Paso Robles (93446) ***(P-1902)***
Ninja Jump Inc ....D.......323 255-5418
3221 N San Fernando Rd Los Angeles (90065) ***(P-23452)***
Ninth Avenue Foods, City of Industry *Also called Heritage Distributing Company* ***(P-622)***
Nippon Industries Inc ....E.......707 427-3127
2430 S Watney Way Fairfield (94533) ***(P-1003)***
Nippon Trends Food Service Inc ....D.......408 214-0511
631 Giguere Ct Ste A1 San Jose (95133) ***(P-2624)***
Niron Inc ....E.......909 598-1526
20541 Earlgate St Walnut (91789) ***(P-14550)***
Nis America Inc ....E.......714 540-1199
4 Hutton Cntre Dr Ste 650 Santa Ana (92707) ***(P-24966)***
Nishiba Industries Corporation ....A.......619 661-8866
2360 Marconi Ct San Diego (92154) ***(P-10241)***
Nissi Trim, Los Angeles *Also called Ckcc Inc* ***(P-3884)***
Nissin Foods USA Company Inc (HQ) ....C.......310 327-8478
2001 W Rosecrans Ave Gardena (90249) ***(P-2434)***
Niterider Technical Lighting & ....E.......858 268-9316
8295 Aero Pl Ste 200 San Diego (92123) ***(P-17720)***
Nitinol Development Corp ....A.......510 683-2000
47533 Westinghouse Dr Fremont (94539) ***(P-23110)***
Nitinol Devices & Components, Fremont *Also called Nitinol Development Corp* ***(P-23110)***
Nitro 2 Go Inc ....E.......909 864-4886
1420 Richardson St San Bernardino (92408) ***(P-7958)***
Nitto Americas Inc (HQ) ....C.......510 445-5400
48500 Fremont Blvd Fremont (94538) ***(P-5573)***
Nitto Avecia Pharma Svcs Inc ....E.......949 462-0814
4 Chrysler Irvine (92618) ***(P-8306)***
Nittobo America Inc ....D.......951 677-5629
25549 Adams Ave Murrieta (92562) ***(P-8568)***
Nixsys Inc ....F.......714 435-9610
34 Mauchly Ste B Irvine (92618) ***(P-15466)***
Nkok Inc ....F.......626 330-1988
5354 Irwindale Ave Ste A Irwindale (91706) ***(P-23453)***
Nl Industries Inc ....E.......707 552-4850
403 Ryder St Vallejo (94590) ***(P-11548)***
NL&a Collections Inc ....E.......323 277-6266
6323 Maywood Ave Huntington Park (90255) ***(P-17550)***
Nlp Furniture Industries Inc ....C.......619 661-5170
1425 Corporate Center Dr # 200 San Diego (92154) ***(P-5247)***
Nls, San Diego *Also called Non-Linear Systems* ***(P-21624)***
Nlyte Software Americas Ltd (HQ) ....C.......650 561-8200
2800 Campus Dr Ste 135 San Mateo (94403) ***(P-24967)***
NM Laser Products Inc ....F.......408 227-8299
337 Piercy Rd San Jose (95138) ***(P-20030)***
NM Machining Inc ....E.......408 972-8978
175 Lewis Rd Ste 25 San Jose (95111) ***(P-16792)***
Nmc Corporation ....E.......209 986-0899
2427 Bonniebrook Dr Stockton (95207) ***(P-19404)***
No Boundaries Inc ....E.......619 266-2349
789 Gateway Center Way San Diego (92102) ***(P-6995)***
No Lift Nails Inc ....F.......714 897-0070
3211 S Shannon St Santa Ana (92704) ***(P-7858)***
No Second Thoughts Inc ....D.......619 428-5992
1333 30th St Ste D San Diego (92154) ***(P-3037)***
No Starch Press Inc ....F.......415 863-9900
245 8th St San Francisco (94103) ***(P-6370)***
No Static Pro Audio Inc ....F.......818 729-8554
3223 Burton Ave Burbank (91504) ***(P-17839)***
Noah's, Los Gatos *Also called Einstein Noah Rest Group Inc* ***(P-571)***
Noah's New York Bagels, Westminster *Also called Einstein Noah Rest Group Inc* ***(P-570)***
Noahs Ark International Inc ....F.......714 521-1235
2319 E 8th St Los Angeles (90021) ***(P-3262)***
Noahs Bottled Water ....E.......209 526-2945
416 Hosmer Ave Modesto (95351) ***(P-2155)***
Noark Electric (usa) Inc ....F.......626 330-7007
2188 Pomona Blvd Pomona (91768) ***(P-20031)***
Noatex Corporation ....F.......310 783-0133
2711 Plaza Del Amo # 511 Torrance (90503) ***(P-14551)***
Nobbe Orthopedics Inc ....F.......805 687-7508
3010 State St Santa Barbara (93105) ***(P-22778)***
Nobel Biocare Usa LLC ....B.......714 282-4800
22715 Savi Ranch Pkwy Yorba Linda (92887) ***(P-22895)***
Nobix Inc ....E.......925 659-3500
2682 Bishop Dr Ste 211 San Ramon (94583) ***(P-24968)***
Noble Concrete Plants, Tracy *Also called Dave Humphrey Enterprises Inc* ***(P-14163)***
Noble Energy, Seal Beach *Also called Samedan Oil Corporation* ***(P-73)***
Noble Metals, San Diego *Also called Matthey Johnson Inc* ***(P-11560)***
Noble Methane Inc ....F.......530 668-7961
104 Matmor Rd Woodland (95776) ***(P-249)***
Nod, Calabasas *Also called Nova-One Diagnostics LLC* ***(P-8499)***
Noel Burt ....E.......925 439-7030
880 Howe Rd Ste F Martinez (94553) ***(P-16148)***
Noel Technologies, Campbell *Also called Semi Automation & Tech Inc* ***(P-19139)***
Noels Lighting Inc ....E.......562 908-6181
9335 Stephens St Unit I Pico Rivera (90660) ***(P-17634)***
Nok Nok Labs Inc ....F.......650 433-1300
2100 Geng Rd Ste 105 Palo Alto (94303) ***(P-24969)***
Nokia of America Corporation ....F.......408 363-5906
5390 Hellyer Ave San Jose (95138) ***(P-17969)***
Noll Inc ....F.......805 543-3602
390 Buckley Rd Frnt San Luis Obispo (93401) ***(P-14448)***
Nol!/Norwesco LLC ....C.......209 234-1600
1320 Performance Dr Stockton (95206) ***(P-12692)***
Nolo ....C.......510 549-1976
950 Parker St Berkeley (94710) ***(P-6371)***
Nology Engineering Inc ....F.......760 591-0888
1333 Keystone Way Vista (92081) ***(P-20410)***
Noma Bearing Corporation ....F.......310 329-1800
1555 W Rosecrans Ave Gardena (90249) ***(P-15109)***
Non-Linear Systems ....F.......619 521-2161
4561 Mission Gorge Pl F San Diego (92120) ***(P-21624)***
Nonprofiteasy Inc (PA) ....F.......707 929-3563
1300 Valley House Dr # 100 Rohnert Park (94928) ***(P-24970)***
Nonstop Printing Inc ....F.......323 464-1640
6226 Santa Monica Blvd Los Angeles (90038) ***(P-6996)***
Noodle Theory ....F.......510 595-6988
6099 Claremont Ave Oakland (94618) ***(P-2435)***
Nooshin Inc ....F.......310 559-5766
555 Chalette Dr Beverly Hills (90210) ***(P-3471)***
Nooshin Blanque, Beverly Hills *Also called Nooshin Inc* ***(P-3471)***
Nor Cal Food Solutions LLC ....F.......530 823-8527
2043 Airpark Ct Auburn (95602) ***(P-923)***
Nor Cal Truck Sales & Mfg ....F.......925 787-9735
200 Industrial Way Benicia (94510) ***(P-14338)***
Nor Car Truck Sales, Benicia *Also called Nor Cal Truck Sales & Mfg* ***(P-14338)***
Nor-Cal Beverage Co Inc ....E.......916 372-1700
1375 Terminal St West Sacramento (95691) ***(P-2156)***
Nor-Cal Metal Fabricators ....D.......510 350-0121
1121 3rd St Oakland (94607) ***(P-12693)***
Nor-Cal Products Inc (HQ) ....C.......530 842-4457
1967 S Oregon St Yreka (96097) ***(P-13773)***
Norac Inc (PA) ....B.......626 334-2907
405 S Motor Ave Azusa (91702) ***(P-9026)***
Norac Pharma, Azusa *Also called S&B Pharma Inc* ***(P-7969)***
Norberg Crushing Inc ....F.......619 390-4200
592 Tyrone St El Cajon (92020) ***(P-329)***
Norberts Athletic Products ....F.......310 830-6672
354 W Gardena Blvd Gardena (90248) ***(P-23625)***
Norcal Printing Inc (PA) ....F.......415 282-8856
1555 Yosemite Ave Ste 28 San Francisco (94124) ***(P-6997)***
Norcal Recycled Rock Aggregate (PA) ....F.......707 459-9636
291a Shell Ln Willits (95490) ***(P-11152)***
Norcal Respiratory Inc ....E.......530 246-1200
3075 Crossroads Dr Ste A Redding (96003) ***(P-23028)***
Norcal Waste Equipment Co ....E.......510 568-8336
299 Park St San Leandro (94577) ***(P-20221)***
Norchem Corporation (PA) ....D.......323 221-0221
5649 Alhambra Ave Los Angeles (90032) ***(P-15001)***
Norco Injection Molding Inc ....D.......909 393-4000
14325 Monte Vista Ave Chino (91710) ***(P-10242)***
Norco Plastics, Chino *Also called Norco Injection Molding Inc* ***(P-10242)***
Norco Plastics Inc ....D.......909 393-4000
14325 Monte Vista Ave Chino (91710) ***(P-10243)***
Norco Printing Inc ....F.......510 569-2200
440 Hester St San Leandro (94577) ***(P-7630)***
Norden Millimeter Inc ....E.......530 642-9123
5441 Merchant Cir Ste C Placerville (95667) ***(P-18201)***
Nordic Naturals Inc (PA) ....C.......800 662-2544
111 Jennings Way Watsonville (95076) ***(P-1529)***
Nordic Saw & Tool Mfrs ....E.......209 634-9015
2114 Divanian Dr Turlock (95382) ***(P-11920)***
Nordson Asymtek, Carlsbad *Also called Nordson California Inc* ***(P-19875)***
Nordson Asymtek Inc ....F.......760 727-2880
2475 Ash St Vista (92081) ***(P-21625)***
Nordson Asymtek Inc (HQ) ....C.......760 431-1919
2747 Loker Ave W Carlsbad (92010) ***(P-21626)***
Nordson California Inc ....D.......760 918-8490
2747 Loker Ave W Carlsbad (92010) ***(P-19875)***
Nordson Dage Inc ....E.......440 985-4496
2747 Loker Ave W Carlsbad (92010) ***(P-22937)***
Nordson Medical (ca) LLC ....D.......657 215-4200
7612 Woodwind Dr Huntington Beach (92647) ***(P-22559)***
Nordson Yestech Inc ....E.......949 361-2714
2747 Loker Ave W Carlsbad (92010) ***(P-22111)***
Norell Prsthtics Orthotics Inc (PA) ....F.......510 770-9010
48521 Warm Sprnigs 305 Fremont (94539) ***(P-22779)***
Norm Harboldt ....E.......714 596-4242
17592 Gothard St Huntington Beach (92647) ***(P-13622)***
Norm Tessier Cabinets Inc ....E.......909 987-8955
11989 6th St Rancho Cucamonga (91730) ***(P-4332)***
Normal Centrix Inc ....F.......310 715-9977
14101 Valleyheart Dr # 104 Sherman Oaks (91423) ***(P-24191)***
Norman Fox & Co ....F.......626 581-5600
14970 Don Julian Rd City of Industry (91746) ***(P-8600)***

ALPHABETIC

Employee Codes: A=Over 500 employees, B=251-500
C=101-250, D=51-100, E=20-50, F=10-19
2019 California
Manfacturers Register
© Mergent Inc. 1-800-342-5647
1227

Norman & Globus Inc ....F......510 222-2638
5215 Central Ave Ste A Richmond (94804) *(P-6372)*
Norman International, Vernon *Also called Norman Paper and Foam Co Inc* *(P-5527)*
Norman Paper and Foam Co Inc ....E......323 582-7132
4501 S Santa Fe Ave Vernon (90058) *(P-5527)*
Norman Wireline Service Inc ....F......661 399-5697
1301 James Rd Bakersfield (93308) *(P-250)*
Normandie Country Bakery Inc (PA) ....E......323 939-5528
3022 S Cochran Ave Los Angeles (90016) *(P-1296)*
Normandy Refinishers Inc ....E......626 792-9202
355 S Rosemead Blvd Pasadena (91107) *(P-13466)*
Normel Inc ....F......818 504-4041
9983 Glenoaks Blvd Sun Valley (91352) *(P-7414)*
Norotos Inc ....C......714 662-3113
201 E Alton Ave Santa Ana (92707) *(P-16793)*
Norpak, Hayward *Also called Norton Packaging Inc* *(P-10244)*
Norquist Salvage Corp Inc ....E......916 454-0435
5005 Stockton Blvd Ste B Sacramento (95820) *(P-3181)*
Norquist Salvage Corp Inc ....E......916 922-9942
410 El Camino Ave Sacramento (95815) *(P-3182)*
Norsal Printing Inc ....F......818 886-4164
20255 Prairie St Chatsworth (91311) *(P-6998)*
Norsco Inc ....F......209 845-2327
1816 Ackley Cir Oakdale (95361) *(P-13033)*
Norstar Office Products Inc (PA) ....E......323 262-1919
5353 Jillson St Commerce (90040) *(P-4959)*
Nortek Security & Control LLC ....F......760 438-7000
12471 Riverside Dr Eastvale (91752) *(P-20032)*
North America Pwr & Infra ....E......562 403-4337
19112 Gridley Rd 2001 Cerritos (90703) *(P-10767)*
North American Composites, Stockton *Also called Interplastic Corporation* *(P-7844)*
North American Composites Co ....E......909 605-8977
4990 Vanderbilt St Ontario (91761) *(P-7859)*
North American Fire Hose Corp ....D......805 922-7076
910 Noble Way Santa Maria (93454) *(P-9502)*
North American Foam & Packg, Fullerton *Also called Gold Venture Inc* *(P-9862)*
North American Pet Products, Corona *Also called Pet Partners Inc* *(P-24208)*
North American Petroleum ....E......562 598-6671
11072 Via El Mercado Los Alamitos (90720) *(P-9291)*
North American Textile Co LLC (PA) ....E......818 409-0019
346 W Cerritos Ave Glendale (91204) *(P-3910)*
North Amrcn Specialty Pdts LLC ....F......209 365-7500
300 S Beckman Rd Lodi (95240) *(P-7860)*
NORTH ATLANTIC BOOKS, Berkeley *Also called Society For The Study O* *(P-6393)*
North Bay Industries, Rohnert Park *Also called North Bay Rhblitation Svcs Inc* *(P-3956)*
North Bay Industries, Monterey *Also called North Bay Rhblitation Svcs Inc* *(P-3263)*
North Bay Plywood Inc ....E......707 224-7849
510 Northbay Dr NAPA (94559) *(P-4203)*
North Bay Rhblitation Svcs Inc (PA) ....C......707 585-1991
649 Martin Ave Rohnert Park (94928) *(P-3956)*
North Bay Rhblitation Svcs Inc ....E......831 372-4094
875 Airport Rd Monterey (93940) *(P-3263)*
North Cal Wood Products Inc ....E......707 462-0686
700 Kunzler Ranch Rd Ukiah (95482) *(P-4043)*
North Coast Brewing Co Inc (PA) ....E......707 964-2739
455 N Main St Fort Bragg (95437) *(P-1613)*
North Coast Industries, Sausalito *Also called Tony Marterie & Associates* *(P-3342)*
North Coast Journal Inc ....F......707 442-1400
310 F St Eureka (95501) *(P-5998)*
North County Polishing ....E......760 480-0847
220 S Hale Ave Ste A Escondido (92029) *(P-13467)*
North County Sand and Grav Inc ....F......951 928-2881
26227 Sherman Rd Sun City (92585) *(P-376)*
North County Times (HQ) ....C......800 533-8830
350 Camino De La Reina San Diego (92108) *(P-5999)*
North County Times ....E......951 676-4315
28441 Rancho California R Temecula (92590) *(P-6000)*
North Face, The, Alameda *Also called Vf Outdoor LLC* *(P-3203)*
North Face, The, San Francisco *Also called Vf Outdoor LLC* *(P-23684)*
North Hollywood Uniform Group, North Hollywood *Also called North Hollywood Uniform Inc* *(P-3357)*
North Hollywood Uniform Inc ....F......818 503-5931
7328 Laurel Canyon Blvd North Hollywood (91605) *(P-3357)*
North Pacific International ....F......909 628-2224
5944 Sycamore Ct Chino (91710) *(P-13871)*
North Sails Group LLC ....D......619 226-1415
4630 Santa Fe St San Diego (92109) *(P-3799)*
North Sails One Design, San Diego *Also called North Sails Group LLC* *(P-3799)*
North State Rendering Co Inc ....E......530 343-6076
15 Shippee Rd Oroville (95965) *(P-1530)*
North Valley Candle Molds ....E......530 247-0447
6928 Danyeur Rd Redding (96001) *(P-24192)*
North Valley Newspapers Inc ....F......530 365-2797
2676 Gateway Dr Anderson (96007) *(P-6001)*
North Valley Rain Gutters ....F......530 894-3347
27 Freight Ln Ste C Chico (95973) *(P-12694)*
North West Pharmanaturals, Inc ....E......714 529-0980
1000 Beacon St Brea (92821) *(P-7959)*
Northbay Stone Wrks Cntertops ....F......415 898-0200
849 Sweetser Ave Novato (94945) *(P-5085)*
Northern Aggregates Inc ....E......707 459-3929
500 Cropley Ln Willits (95490) *(P-377)*
Northern Cal Pet Imaging Ctr ....F......916 737-3211
3195 Folsom Blvd Sacramento (95816) *(P-22938)*
Northern California Labels Inc ....F......562 802-8528
12809 Marquardt Ave Santa Fe Springs (90670) *(P-7415)*
Northern California Power Agcy ....F......209 728-1387
477 Bret Harte Ln Murphys (95247) *(P-17214)*

Northern California Stair ....F......408 847-0106
7150 Alexander St Gilroy (95020) *(P-4204)*
Northern Quinoa Prod Corp ....E......806 535-8118
200 Kansas St Ste 215 San Francisco (94103) *(P-1068)*
Northland Process Piping Inc ....D......559 925-9724
400 E St Lemoore (93245) *(P-11408)*
Northrdge Tr-Mdlity Imging Inc ....F......818 709-2468
9457 De Soto Ave Chatsworth (91311) *(P-21483)*
Northrop Grumman Corporation ....A......626 812-2842
14099 Champlain Ct Fontana (92336) *(P-21357)*
Northrop Grumman Corporation ....A......818 715-3264
9736 Trigger Pl Chatsworth (91311) *(P-21358)*
Northrop Grumman Corporation ....C......310 332-1000
1 Hornet Way El Segundo (90245) *(P-21359)*
Northrop Grumman Corporation ....A......858 967-1221
18701 Caminito Pasadero San Diego (92128) *(P-21360)*
Northrop Grumman Corporation ....A......310 332-0412
28063 Liana Ln Valencia (91354) *(P-21361)*
Northrop Grumman Corporation ....A......310 332-6653
17311 Santa Barbara St Fountain Valley (92708) *(P-21362)*
Northrop Grumman Corporation ....A......310 764-3000
18701 Wilmington Ave Carson (90746) *(P-21363)*
Northrop Grumman Corporation ....A......858 618-7617
10806 Willow Ct San Diego (92127) *(P-21364)*
Northrop Grumman Corporation ....A......858 514-9259
4010 Sorrento Valley Blvd San Diego (92121) *(P-21365)*
Northrop Grumman Corporation ....F......310 812-4321
4020 Redondo Beach Ave Redondo Beach (90278) *(P-21366)*
Northrop Grumman Info Systems, McClellan *Also called Northrop Grumman Systems Corp* *(P-20616)*
Northrop Grumman Innovation ....B......858 621-5700
9617 Distribution Ave San Diego (92121) *(P-21179)*
Northrop Grumman Innovation ....B......818 887-8100
9401 Corvin Ave Woodland Hills (91367) *(P-21367)*
Northrop Grumman Innovation ....D......951 520-7300
250 Klug Cir Corona (92880) *(P-21180)*
Northrop Grumman Innovation ....D......805 961-8600
6750 Navigator Way # 200 Goleta (93117) *(P-21181)*
Northrop Grumman Intl Trdg Inc ....A......818 715-3607
21240 Burbank Blvd Woodland Hills (91367) *(P-21368)*
Northrop Grumman Mar Systems, Sunnyvale *Also called Northrop Grumman Systems Corp* *(P-20613)*
Northrop Grumman Space, San Diego *Also called Northrop Grumman Systems Corp* *(P-21374)*
Northrop Grumman Systems Corp ....B......408 735-2241
401 E Hendy Ave Sunnyvale (94086) *(P-20604)*
Northrop Grumman Systems Corp ....C......310 812-5149
1 Space Park Blvd Redondo Beach (90278) *(P-18202)*
Northrop Grumman Systems Corp ....A......818 715-4040
21240 Burbank Blvd Ms29 Woodland Hills (91367) *(P-20605)*
Northrop Grumman Systems Corp ....B......310 632-1846
1 Hornet Way Dept Mt00w5 El Segundo (90245) *(P-20606)*
Northrop Grumman Systems Corp ....B......661 272-7000
3520 E Avenue M Palmdale (93550) *(P-20607)*
Northrop Grumman Systems Corp ....A......805 278-2074
2700 Camino Del Sol Oxnard (93030) *(P-21369)*
Northrop Grumman Systems Corp ....F......858 514-9020
9112 Spectrum Center Blvd San Diego (92123) *(P-20608)*
Northrop Grumman Systems Corp ....E......818 715-2597
21200 Burbank Blvd Woodland Hills (91367) *(P-21370)*
Northrop Grumman Systems Corp ....A......858 618-4349
17066 Goldentop Rd San Diego (92127) *(P-21371)*
Northrop Grumman Systems Corp ....C......626 812-1000
1100 W Hollyvale St Azusa (91702) *(P-21372)*
Northrop Grumman Systems Corp ....B......661 540-0446
3520 E Avenue M Palmdale (93550) *(P-20609)*
Northrop Grumman Systems Corp ....E......916 570-4454
5441 Luce Ave McClellan (95652) *(P-21373)*
Northrop Grumman Systems Corp ....B......310 812-4321
2477 Manhattan Beach Blvd Redondo Beach (90278) *(P-20610)*
Northrop Grumman Systems Corp ....B......626 812-1464
1111 W 3rd St Azusa (91702) *(P-20611)*
Northrop Grumman Systems Corp ....C......858 514-9000
9326 Spectrum Center Blvd San Diego (92123) *(P-21374)*
Northrop Grumman Systems Corp ....C......310 332-1000
1 Hornet Way El Segundo (90245) *(P-20612)*
Northrop Grumman Systems Corp ....A......408 735-3011
401 E Hendy Ave Ms33-3 Sunnyvale (94086) *(P-20613)*
Northrop Grumman Systems Corp ....B......310 812-1089
1 Space Park Blvd Redondo Beach (90278) *(P-20614)*
Northrop Grumman Systems Corp ....B......310 812-4321
1 Space Park Blvd D Redondo Beach (90278) *(P-20615)*
Northrop Grumman Systems Corp ....A......408 531-2524
5441 Luce Ave McClellan (95652) *(P-20616)*
Norths Bakery California Inc ....E......818 761-2892
5430 Satsuma Ave North Hollywood (91601) *(P-1297)*
Northwest Circuits Corp ....D......619 661-1701
8660 Avenida Costa Blanca San Diego (92154) *(P-18546)*
Northwest Pallets, Woodland *Also called Ricardo Ochoa* *(P-5455)*
Northwest Pipe Company ....B......760 246-3191
12351 Rancho Rd Adelanto (92301) *(P-11484)*
Northwest Signs, Santa Cruz *Also called Jeff Frank* *(P-23907)*
Northwest Skyline Logging Inc ....F......530 493-5150
725 Lower Airport Rd Happy Camp (96039) *(P-4004)*
Northwestern Converting Co ....D......800 959-3402
2395 Railroad St Corona (92880) *(P-23795)*
Northwood Design Partners Inc ....E......510 731-6505
1550 Atlantic St Union City (94587) *(P-4960)*
Norton Company, Fullerton *Also called Penhall Diamond Products Inc* *(P-14661)*

Mergent e-mail: customerrelations@mergent.com
1228

2019 California
Manufacturers Register

(P-0000) Products & Services Section entry number
(PA)=Parent Co (HQ)=Headquarters (DH)=Div Headquarters

Norton Packaging Inc (PA).....C.....510 786-1922
20670 Corsair Blvd Hayward (94545) ***(P-10244)***
Norton Packaging Inc.....D.....323 588-6167
5800 S Boyle Ave Vernon (90058) ***(P-10245)***
Nortra Cables Inc.....D.....408 942-1106
570 Gibraltar Dr Milpitas (95035) ***(P-19662)***
Norwesco Inc.....F.....559 585-1668
13241 11th Ave Hanford (93230) ***(P-10246)***
Norwich Aero Products Inc (HQ).....D.....607 336-7636
6900 Orangethorpe Ave B Buena Park (90620) ***(P-21375)***
Not Only Jeans Inc.....E.....213 765-9725
3004 S Main St Los Angeles (90007) ***(P-2754)***
Nothing To Wear Inc (PA).....E.....310 328-0408
630 Maple Ave Torrance (90503) ***(P-3264)***
Noticiero Semanal Advertising.....D.....559 784-5000
115 E Oak Ave Porterville (93257) ***(P-6002)***
Notron Manufacturing Inc.....F.....818 247-7739
801 Milford St Glendale (91203) ***(P-16794)***
Noushig Inc.....E.....805 983-2903
451 Lombard St Oxnard (93030) ***(P-1298)***
Nov, Orange *Also called National Oilwell Varco Inc* ***(P-14233)***
Nov Orange Warehouse, Orange *Also called National Oilwell Varco Inc* ***(P-14236)***
Nova, Huntington Park *Also called NL&a Collections Inc* ***(P-17550)***
Nova Care Orthtics Prosthetics, Poway *Also called Hanger Prsthetcs & Ortho Inc* ***(P-22745)***
Nova Drilling Services Inc.....E.....408 732-6682
1500 Buckeye Dr Milpitas (95035) ***(P-18547)***
Nova Lifestyle Inc (PA).....E.....323 888-9999
6565 E Washington Blvd Commerce (90040) ***(P-4728)***
Nova Measuring Instruments Inc (HQ).....E.....408 200-4344
3090 Oakmead Village Dr Santa Clara (95051) ***(P-21818)***
Nova Measuring Instruments Inc.....F.....408 746-9921
1270 Oakmead Pkwy Ste 215 Sunnyvale (94085) ***(P-21819)***
Nova Mobile Systems Inc.....F.....800 734-9885
2888 Loker Ave E Ste 311 Carlsbad (92010) ***(P-19405)***
Nova Print Inc.....F.....951 525-4040
2100 S Fairview St Santa Ana (92704) ***(P-3329)***
Nova Tool Co.....F.....925 828-7172
27736 Industrial Blvd Hayward (94545) ***(P-23720)***
Nova-One Diagnostics LLC.....D.....818 348-1543
22287 Mulholland Hwy Calabasas (91302) ***(P-8499)***
Novabay Pharmaceuticals Inc.....E.....510 899-8800
2000 Powell St Ste 1150 Emeryville (94608) ***(P-8307)***
Novacap LLC.....B.....661 295-5920
25111 Anza Dr Valencia (91355) ***(P-19301)***
Novacart.....F.....510 215-8999
510 W Ohio Ave Richmond (94804) ***(P-5318)***
Novacart USA, Richmond *Also called Novacart* ***(P-5318)***
Novanta Corporation.....E.....510 770-1417
4575 Cushing Pkwy Fremont (94538) ***(P-19663)***
Novanta Corporation.....E.....408 754-4176
5750 Hellyer Ave San Jose (95138) ***(P-19664)***
Novaray Medical Inc.....F.....510 619-9200
39655 Eureka Dr Newark (94560) ***(P-22939)***
Novartis Biophrmctcl Ops-Vcvll, Vacaville *Also called Novartis Pharmaceuticals Corp* ***(P-8500)***
Novartis Corporation.....D.....858 812-1741
3115 Merryfield Row San Diego (92121) ***(P-8308)***
Novartis Corporation.....D.....510 879-9500
5300 Chiron Way Emeryville (94608) ***(P-9109)***
Novartis Corporation.....D.....650 631-3100
150 Industrial Rd San Carlos (94070) ***(P-8309)***
Novartis Pharmaceuticals Corp.....E.....707 452-8081
2010 Cessna Dr Vacaville (95688) ***(P-8500)***
Novasentis Inc.....E.....814 238-7400
25 Edwards Ct Ste 17 Burlingame (94010) ***(P-20033)***
Novastor Corporation (PA).....E.....805 579-6700
29209 Canwood St Ste 200 Agoura Hills (91301) ***(P-24971)***
Novastruxx Composite Materials, San Clemente *Also called Armorstruxx LLC* ***(P-20743)***
Novato Advance Newspaper, Novato *Also called St Louis Post-Dispatch LLC* ***(P-6056)***
Novatorque Inc.....E.....510 933-2700
281 Greenoaks Dr Atherton (94027) ***(P-17215)***
Novela Designs Inc.....F.....213 505-4092
643 S Olive St Ste 421 Los Angeles (90014) ***(P-23755)***
Novipax Inc (HQ).....D.....909 392-1750
1941 N White Ave La Verne (91750) ***(P-5719)***
Novtek Inc.....F.....408 441-9934
7018 Mariposa St Santee (92071) ***(P-21820)***
Novtek Test Systems, Santee *Also called Novtek Inc* ***(P-21820)***
Novus Therapeutics Inc.....F.....617 225-4305
19900 Macarthur Blvd # 550 Irvine (92612) ***(P-8310)***
Novvi LLC.....E.....281 488-0833
5885 Hollis St Ste 100 Emeryville (94608) ***(P-9341)***
Novx Corporation.....E.....408 998-5555
1750 N Loop Rd Ste 100 Alameda (94502) ***(P-21821)***
NP Nutra, Gardena *Also called Natures Pwr Ntraceuticals Corp* ***(P-636)***
Npc Firewood, Orangevale *Also called Natural Pest Controls & Firewd* ***(P-9108)***
Npg Inc (PA).....D.....951 940-0200
1354 Jet Way Perris (92571) ***(P-9390)***
Nphase Inc.....E.....805 750-8580
323 Neptune Ave Encinitas (92024) ***(P-24972)***
Npi Services Inc.....F.....714 850-0550
1580 Corporate Dr Ste 124 Costa Mesa (92626) ***(P-18548)***
Npi Solutions, Morgan Hill *Also called New Product Integration Solutn* ***(P-11451)***
Npms Natural Products Mil Svcs, Gardena *Also called BDS Natural Products Inc* ***(P-2462)***
Nq Engineering Inc.....F.....209 836-3255
1852 W 11th St Pmb 532 Tracy (95376) ***(P-16795)***
NRC Manufacturing Inc.....F.....510 438-9400
47690 Westinghouse Dr Fremont (94539) ***(P-19665)***
NRC USA Inc.....F.....213 325-2780
3700 Wilshire Blvd # 300 Los Angeles (90010) ***(P-17416)***
NRG Energy Services LLC.....D.....702 815-2023
100302 Yates Well Rd Nipton (92364) ***(P-17108)***
NRG Evgo.....F.....310 268-8017
11390 W Olympic Blvd Fl 2 Los Angeles (90064) ***(P-19841)***
NS Wash Systems, Inglewood *Also called N/S Corporation* ***(P-16076)***
Nsd Industries Inc.....F.....626 813-2001
5027 Gayhurst Ave Baldwin Park (91706) ***(P-16796)***
Nsi Architectural, Anaheim *Also called Onesolution Light and Control* ***(P-17721)***
Nsi Group LLC (PA).....E.....818 639-8335
17031 Ventura Blvd Encino (91316) ***(P-890)***
Nss Enterprises.....E.....408 970-9200
3380 Viso Ct Santa Clara (95054) ***(P-7416)***
Nst, San Diego *Also called No Second Thoughts Inc* ***(P-3037)***
Ntek, Sunnyvale *Also called N-Tek Inc* ***(P-14997)***
NTL Precision Machining Inc.....F.....408 298-6650
1355 Vander Way San Jose (95112) ***(P-16797)***
Ntrust Infotech Inc.....D.....562 207-1600
230 Commerce Ste 180 Irvine (92602) ***(P-24973)***
Nu Engineering.....E.....714 894-1206
12121 Bartlett St Garden Grove (92845) ***(P-16798)***
Nu Health Products, Walnut *Also called Nu-Health Products Co* ***(P-7960)***
Nu TEC Powdercoating.....F.....714 632-5045
2990 E Blue Star St Anaheim (92806) ***(P-13623)***
Nu Venture Diving Co.....E.....805 815-4044
1600 Beacon Pl Oxnard (93033) ***(P-15132)***
Nu Visions De Mexico SA De Cv.....C.....619 987-0518
9355 Airway Rd San Diego (92154) ***(P-24193)***
Nu-Health California LLC.....F.....800 806-0519
16910 Cherie Pl Carson (90746) ***(P-834)***
Nu-Health Products Co.....E.....909 869-0666
20875 Currier Rd Walnut (91789) ***(P-7960)***
Nu-Hope Laboratories Inc.....E.....818 899-7711
12640 Branford St Pacoima (91331) ***(P-22780)***
Nuance Communications Inc.....C.....781 565-5000
1198 E Arques Ave Sunnyvale (94085) ***(P-24974)***
Nubile, Los Angeles *Also called Semore Inc* ***(P-3087)***
Nubs Plastics Inc.....E.....760 598-2525
991 Park Center Dr Vista (92081) ***(P-10247)***
Nucast Industries Inc.....F.....951 277-8888
23220 Park Canyon Dr Corona (92883) ***(P-10962)***
Nuconic Packaging LLC.....E.....323 588-9033
4889 Loma Vista Ave Vernon (90058) ***(P-10248)***
Nugen Technologies Inc.....E.....650 590-3600
900 Chesapeake Dr Redwood City (94063) ***(P-7791)***
Nugeneration Technologies LLC (PA).....F.....707 820-4080
1155 Park Ave Emeryville (94608) ***(P-9292)***
Nugentec, Emeryville *Also called Nugeneration Technologies LLC* ***(P-9292)***
Nugentec Oilfield Chem LLC.....E.....707 891-3012
1155 Park Ave Emeryville (94608) ***(P-8601)***
Nugier Hydraulics, Gardena *Also called Nugier Press Company Inc* ***(P-14449)***
Nugier Press Company Inc.....F.....310 515-6025
18031 La Salle Ave Gardena (90248) ***(P-14449)***
Numano Sake Company, Berkeley *Also called Takara Sake USA Inc* ***(P-2079)***
Numatech West (kmp) LLC.....D.....909 706-3627
1201 E Lexington Ave Pomona (91766) ***(P-5440)***
Numatic Engineering, Sun Valley *Also called Motion Industries Inc* ***(P-21620)***
Numecent Inc.....E.....949 833-2800
15635 Alton Pkwy Ste 100 Irvine (92618) ***(P-24975)***
Numeri Tech Inc.....F.....209 463-1910
124 N E St Stockton (95205) ***(P-16799)***
Numotech Inc.....D.....818 772-1579
9420 Reseda Blvd Ste 504 Northridge (91324) ***(P-22560)***
Nuorder Inc.....E.....310 954-1313
900 Hilgard Ave Los Angeles (90024) ***(P-24976)***
Nuphoton Technologies Inc.....F.....951 696-8366
41610 Corning Pl Murrieta (92562) ***(P-20034)***
Nupla Corporation.....C.....818 768-6800
11912 Sheldon St Sun Valley (91352) ***(P-11903)***
Nuprodx Inc.....F.....925 292-0866
161 S Vasco Rd Ste G Livermore (94551) ***(P-22781)***
Nursery Supplies Inc.....E.....714 538-0251
534 W Struck Ave Orange (92867) ***(P-10249)***
Nursesbond Inc.....F.....951 286-8537
26386 Primrose Way Moreno Valley (92555) ***(P-24977)***
Nurseweek Publishing, Sunnyvale *Also called Gannett Co Inc* ***(P-6171)***
Nuset Inc.....E.....626 246-1668
1364 Marion Ct City of Industry (91745) ***(P-11980)***
Nusil Silicone Technology, Carpinteria *Also called Nusil Technology LLC* ***(P-7861)***
Nusil Technology LLC.....D.....805 684-8780
1000 Cindy Ln Carpinteria (93013) ***(P-7861)***
Nusil Technology LLC.....D.....661 391-4750
2343 Pegasus Dr Bakersfield (93308) ***(P-9648)***
Nusil Technology LLC.....D.....805 684-8780
1150 Mark Ave Carpinteria (93013) ***(P-9649)***
Nustar Logistics LP.....F.....925 427-6880
1100 Willow Pass Rd Pittsburg (94565) ***(P-66)***
Nutec Rehab, Sacramento *Also called Tri Quality Inc* ***(P-22835)***
Nutiva (PA).....D.....510 255-2700
213 W Cutting Blvd Richmond (94804) ***(P-2625)***
Nutra Blend LLC.....D.....559 661-6161
2140 W Industrial Ave Madera (93637) ***(P-1151)***
Nutraceutical Brews For Lf Inc.....F.....310 273-8339
825 Cambridge Ct Pasadena (91107) ***(P-1614)***
Nutrade Inc.....E.....949 477-2300
2808 Willis St Santa Ana (92705) ***(P-2755)***
Nutrawise Corporation, Irvine *Also called Nutrawise Health & Beauty Corp* ***(P-8311)***

ALPHABETIC

Employee Codes: A=Over 500 employees, B=251-500
C=101-250, D=51-100, E=20-50, F=10-19
2019 California
Manfacturers Register
© Mergent Inc. 1-800-342-5647
1229

Nutrawise Health & Beauty Corp (PA) ....D....949 900-2400
9600 Toledo Way Irvine (92618) ***(P-8311)***
Nutri Granulations Inc ....D....714 994-7855
16024 Phoebe Ave La Mirada (90638) ***(P-641)***
Nutribiotic, Lakeport *Also called Nutrition Resource Inc* ***(P-8312)***
Nutricology, Alameda *Also called Allergy Research Group Inc* ***(P-8015)***
Nutrien AG Solutions Inc ....F....805 488-3646
2150 Eastman Ave Oxnard (93030) ***(P-9068)***
Nutrien AG Solutions Inc ....E....209 551-1424
3348 Claus Rd Modesto (95355) ***(P-9085)***
Nutrient Technologies Inc (PA) ....F....559 595-8090
1092 E Kamm Ave Dinuba (93618) ***(P-9069)***
Nutrition Resource Inc (PA) ....F....707 263-0411
865 Parallel Dr Lakeport (95453) ***(P-8312)***
Nutrition Resource Connection ....F....760 803-8234
254 May Ct Cardiff By The Sea (92007) ***(P-17908)***
Nutrition Without Borders LLC ....F....310 845-7745
4641 Leahy St Culver City (90232) ***(P-15923)***
Nutritional Engineering Inc ....F....760 599-5200
1208 Avenida Chelsea Vista (92081) ***(P-8313)***
Nutrius LLC ....E....559 897-5862
39494 Clarkson Dr Kingsburg (93631) ***(P-1152)***
Nuvair, Oxnard *Also called Nu Venture Diving Co* ***(P-15132)***
Nuvasive Inc (PA) ....D....858 909-1800
7475 Lusk Blvd San Diego (92121) ***(P-22561)***
Nuvasive Spclzed Orthpdics Inc ....D....949 837-3600
101 Enterprise Ste 100 Aliso Viejo (92656) ***(P-22562)***
Nuvet Labs, Westlake Village *Also called Vitavet Labs Inc* ***(P-24283)***
Nuvora Inc ....E....408 856-2200
3350 Scott Blvd Ste 502 Santa Clara (95054) ***(P-8805)***
Nuwest Milling LLC ....F....209 883-1163
4636 Geer Rd Hughson (95326) ***(P-1153)***
Nuzee Inc ....F....858 549-6893
2865 Scott St Ste 101 Vista (92081) ***(P-2361)***
Nvent Thermal LLC (HQ) ....B....650 474-7414
899 Broadway St Redwood City (94063) ***(P-21519)***
Nvidia Corporation (PA) ....B....408 486-2000
2788 San Tomas Expy Santa Clara (95051) ***(P-19043)***
Nvidia Corporation ....F....408 566-5364
2001 Walsh Ave Santa Clara (95050) ***(P-19044)***
Nvidia Development Inc ....E....408 486-2000
2701 San Tomas Expy Santa Clara (95050) ***(P-19045)***
Nvidia US Investment Company ....A....408 615-2500
2701 San Tomas Expy Santa Clara (95050) ***(P-18203)***
Nvision Laser Eye Centers Inc ....F....916 723-7400
5959 Greenback Ln Ste 310 Citrus Heights (95621) ***(P-23111)***
Nwe Technology Inc ....C....408 919-6100
1688 Richard Ave Santa Clara (95050) ***(P-15578)***
Nwp Services Corporation (HQ) ....C....949 253-2500
535 Anton Blvd Ste 1100 Costa Mesa (92626) ***(P-24978)***
NWT Infotech Services ....F....831 335-6500
5779 Winfield Blvd Ste A2 San Jose (95123) ***(P-15642)***
Nxp Usa Inc ....D....408 518-5500
2680 Zanker Rd Ste 200 San Jose (95134) ***(P-19046)***
Nxp Usa Inc ....B....408 518-5500
411 E Plumeria Dr San Jose (95134) ***(P-19047)***
Nxp Usa Inc ....E....408 991-2700
690 E Arques Ave Sunnyvale (94085) ***(P-19048)***
Nxp Usa Inc ....E....408 991-2000
440 N Wolfe Rd Sunnyvale (94085) ***(P-19049)***
Nxp Usa Inc ....F....949 399-4000
9 Cushing Ste 100 Irvine (92618) ***(P-19050)***
Nyabenga Llc ....F....925 418-4221
9020 Brentwood Blvd Ste A Brentwood (94513) ***(P-6542)***
Nyansa Inc ....E....650 446-7818
430 Cowper St Ste 250 Palo Alto (94301) ***(P-24979)***
Nycetek Inc ....F....714 671-3860
555 W Lambert Rd Ste F Brea (92821) ***(P-5086)***
Nydr Holdings Inc ....F....818 626-8174
9525 Cozycroft Ave Ste M Chatsworth (91311) ***(P-2626)***
Nylok LLC ....E....714 635-3993
313 N Euclid Way Anaheim (92801) ***(P-13079)***
Nylok Western Fastener, Anaheim *Also called Nylok LLC* ***(P-13079)***
Nypro Healthcare Baja, Chula Vista *Also called Nypro Inc* ***(P-10250)***
Nypro Healthcare Baja Inc ....A....619 498-9250
2195 Britannia Blvd # 107 San Diego (92154) ***(P-22563)***
Nypro Inc ....D....619 498-9250
505 Main St Rm 107 Chula Vista (91911) ***(P-10250)***
Nypro Precision Assemblies, San Diego *Also called Nypro Healthcare Baja Inc* ***(P-22563)***
Nypro San Diego Inc ....D....619 482-7033
505 Main St Chula Vista (91911) ***(P-10251)***
Nyx Industries Inc ....F....909 937-3923
1930 S Rochester Ste 111 Ontario (91761) ***(P-14087)***
O & S California Inc ....B....619 661-1800
9731 Siempre Viva Rd E San Diego (92154) ***(P-20035)***
O & S Precision Inc ....E....818 718-8876
20630 Nordhoff St Chatsworth (91311) ***(P-16800)***
O and Y Precision Inc ....F....408 362-1333
312 Piercy Rd San Jose (95138) ***(P-14658)***
O C M, Los Angeles *Also called Old Country Millwork Inc* ***(P-14717)***
O C P, Calabasas *Also called Optical Communication Pdts Inc* ***(P-17974)***
O D I, Riverside *Also called Edge Plastics Inc* ***(P-10086)***
O H I Company ....E....209 466-8921
820 S Pershing Ave Stockton (95206) ***(P-14874)***
O Industries Corporation ....F....310 719-2289
1930 W 139th St Gardena (90249) ***(P-4087)***
O K Color America Corporation ....F....310 320-9343
578 Amapola Ave Torrance (90501) ***(P-10252)***
O M Jones Inc ....E....209 532-1008
18897 Microtronics Way Sonora (95370) ***(P-19666)***
O M Y A, Lucerne Valley *Also called Omya California Inc* ***(P-7793)***
O O Campbell, San Leandro *Also called Oriental Odysseys Inc* ***(P-24195)***
O P F, Oxnard *Also called Oxnard Prcsion Fabrication Inc* ***(P-12698)***
O W I Inc ....F....310 515-1900
17141 Kingsview Ave Carson (90746) ***(P-17840)***
O'Brien Iron Works, Concord *Also called Energy Steel Corporation* ***(P-16474)***
O'Connor Engineering Labs, Burbank *Also called Autocue Inc* ***(P-23140)***
O'Neil Data Systems, Inc., Los Angeles *Also called ONeil Capital Management* ***(P-7209)***
O'Neill Sportswear, Irvine *Also called La Jolla Sport USA Inc* ***(P-3171)***
O-S Inc ....F....408 946-5890
541 W Capitol Expy Ste 10 San Jose (95136) ***(P-16801)***
O.C. Metro Magazine, Newport Beach *Also called Churm Publishing Inc* ***(P-6129)***
Oak Apparel Inc ....F....213 489-9766
1363 Elwood St Los Angeles (90021) ***(P-3472)***
Oak Design Corporation ....E....909 628-9597
13272 6th St Chino (91710) ***(P-4961)***
Oak Land Company, Chula Vista *Also called Oak Land Furniture* ***(P-4837)***
Oak Land Furniture ....F....619 424-8758
2462 Main St Ste D Chula Vista (91911) ***(P-4837)***
Oak Manufacturing Company Inc ....F....323 581-8087
2850 E Vernon Ave Vernon (90058) ***(P-15924)***
Oak Ridge Winery LLC ....E....209 369-4768
6100 E Hwy 12 Victor Rd Lodi (95240) ***(P-1903)***
Oak Tree Furniture Inc ....D....562 944-0754
13615 Excelsior Dr Santa Fe Springs (90670) ***(P-4729)***
Oak-It Inc ....E....951 735-5973
143 Business Center Dr Corona (92880) ***(P-4205)***
Oak-It Inc ....E....310 719-3999
845 Sandhill Ave Carson (90746) ***(P-5087)***
Oakdale Cheese & Specialties ....F....209 848-3139
10040 State Highway 120 Oakdale (95361) ***(P-594)***
Oakhurst Industries Inc (PA) ....C....323 724-3000
2050 S Tubeway Ave Commerce (90040) ***(P-1299)***
Oakland Magazine, Alameda *Also called Alameda Directory Inc* ***(P-6427)***
Oakland Production Center, Oakland *Also called Kemeera Incorporated* ***(P-15779)***
Oakland Tribune Inc ....A....510 208-6300
600 Grand Ave 308 Oakland (94610) ***(P-6003)***
Oakley Inc ....D....949 672-6849
20081 Ellipse Foothill Ranch (92610) ***(P-23112)***
Oakley Inc (HQ) ....A....949 951-0991
1 Icon Foothill Ranch (92610) ***(P-3265)***
Oakley Sales Corp ....F....949 951-0991
1 Icon El Toro (92610) ***(P-23113)***
Oakmead Prtg & Reproduction ....E....408 734-5505
233 E Weddell Dr Ste G Sunnyvale (94089) ***(P-6999)***
Oakridge, Oxnard *Also called Scully Sportswear Inc* ***(P-3622)***
Oakwood Interiors, Ontario *Also called Lanpar Inc* ***(P-4715)***
Oasis Alloy Wheels Inc ....F....714 533-3286
400 S Lemon St Anaheim (92805) ***(P-11747)***
Oasis Breads, San Marcos *Also called Health Breads Inc* ***(P-1271)***
Oasis Date Garden Inc ....E....760 399-5665
59111 Grapefruit Blvd Thermal (92274) ***(P-2627)***
Oasis Foods Inc ....E....209 382-0263
10881 Toews Ave Le Grand (95333) ***(P-835)***
Oasis Materials Company LP ....E....858 486-8846
12131 Community Rd Ste D Poway (92064) ***(P-19667)***
Oasis Medical Inc (PA) ....D....909 305-5400
510-528 S Vermont Ave Glendora (91741) ***(P-23114)***
Oasis Metal Works, Anaheim *Also called Oasis Alloy Wheels Inc* ***(P-11747)***
Oasis Structures & Water Works ....F....707 839-1683
273 Anker Ln McKinleyville (95519) ***(P-16082)***
Oatey Co ....E....800 321-9532
6600 Smith Ave Newark (94560) ***(P-9158)***
Obagi Cosmeceuticals LLC (PA) ....D....800 636-7546
3760 Kilroy Airport Way Long Beach (90806) ***(P-8314)***
Obagi Medical, Long Beach *Also called Obagi Cosmeceuticals LLC* ***(P-8314)***
Obalon Therapeutics Inc ....C....760 795-6558
5421 Avd Encinas Ste F Carlsbad (92008) ***(P-22564)***
Obatake Inc ....E....310 782-2730
20309 Gramercy Pl Ste A Torrance (90501) ***(P-23304)***
Obentec Inc (PA) ....F....831 457-0301
500 Chestnut St Ste 225 Santa Cruz (95060) ***(P-4530)***
Oberon Co ....D....408 227-3730
7216 Via Colina San Jose (95139) ***(P-19668)***
Oberon Fuels Inc (PA) ....F....619 255-9361
2159 India St Ste 200 San Diego (92101) ***(P-9342)***
Observables Inc ....F....805 272-9255
117 N Milpas St Santa Barbara (93103) ***(P-20036)***
Observer Newspaper ....E....310 452-9900
1844 Lincoln Blvd Santa Monica (90404) ***(P-6004)***
Oc Baking Company ....D....714 998-2253
1960 N Glassell St Orange (92865) ***(P-1300)***
Oc Fleet Service Inc ....F....714 460-8069
8270 Monroe Ave Stanton (90680) ***(P-21006)***
Oc Glass, Irvine *Also called USA Fire Glass* ***(P-10739)***
Oc Metals Inc ....E....714 668-0783
2720 S Main St Ste B Santa Ana (92707) ***(P-12695)***
Oc Waterjet ....F....714 685-0851
2280 N Batavia St Orange (92865) ***(P-12220)***
Occam Networks Inc (HQ) ....E....805 692-2900
6868 Cortona Dr Santa Barbara (93117) ***(P-17970)***
Occidental Manufacturing Inc ....E....707 824-2560
4200 Ross Rd Sebastopol (95472) ***(P-10576)***
Oce Dsplay Grphics Systems Inc ....D....773 714-8500
2811 Orchard Pkwy San Jose (95134) ***(P-14819)***

Mergent e-mail: customerrelations@mergent.com
1230
2019 California
Manufacturers Register
(P-0000) Products & Services Section entry number
(PA)=Parent Co (HQ)=Headquarters (DH)=Div Headquarters

Ocean Aero Inc ....E....858 945-3768
10350 Sorrento Valley Rd San Diego (92121) *(P-21376)*
Ocean Avenue Brewing Co ....E....949 497-3381
237 Ocean Ave Laguna Beach (92651) *(P-1615)*
Ocean Beauty Seafoods LLC ....C....213 624-2101
629 S Central Ave Los Angeles (90021) *(P-2298)*
Ocean Blue Inc ....E....909 478-9910
494 Commercial Rd San Bernardino (92408) *(P-9872)*
Ocean Brewing Company, Laguna Beach *Also called Ocean Avenue Brewing Co (P-1615)*
Ocean Direct LLC (PA) ....E....424 266-9300
13771 Gramercy Pl Gardena (90249) *(P-2320)*
Ocean Divers USA LLC ....F....760 599-6898
975 Park Center Dr Vista (92081) *(P-10253)*
Ocean Fresh LLC (PA) ....E....707 964-1389
350 N Main St Fort Bragg (95437) *(P-2299)*
Ocean Fresh Seafood Products, Fort Bragg *Also called Ocean Fresh LLC (P-2299)*
Ocean Heat Inc ....F....951 208-1923
13610 Imperial Hwy Ste 4 Santa Fe Springs (90670) *(P-22782)*
Ocean Protecta Incorporated ....E....714 891-2628
10743 Progress Way Cypress (90630) *(P-21059)*
Ocean Technology Systems, Santa Ana *Also called Undersea Systems Intl Inc (P-20094)*
Ocean Wayne Media Inc ....F....626 966-8808
100 N Citrus St Ste 530 West Covina (91791) *(P-6543)*
Oceania Inc ....E....562 926-8886
14209 Gannet St La Mirada (90638) *(P-9722)*
Oceania International LLC ....E....949 407-8904
23661 Birtcher Dr Lake Forest (92630) *(P-11635)*
Oceanic, San Leandro *Also called American Underwater Products (P-23500)*
Oceans Flavor Foods LLC ....F....619 793-5269
4492 Camino De La Plz San Ysidro (92173) *(P-9293)*
Oceanscience, Poway *Also called Tern Design Ltd (P-21665)*
Oceanside Glasstile Company (PA) ....B....760 929-4000
5858 Edison Pl Carlsbad (92008) *(P-10787)*
Oceanside Marine Center Inc (PA) ....F....760 722-1833
1550 Harbor Dr N Oceanside (92054) *(P-21060)*
Oceanside Plastic Enterprises ....F....760 433-0779
3038 Industry St Ste 108 Oceanside (92054) *(P-14552)*
Oceanside Ready Mix, Oceanside *Also called Legacy Vulcan LLC (P-10953)*
Oceanwide Repairs, Long Beach *Also called APR Engineering Inc (P-20984)*
Ocg Inc ....D....714 375-4024
17952 Lyons Cir Huntington Beach (92647) *(P-19669)*
Oci, Santa Fe Springs *Also called Office Chairs Inc (P-4962)*
Oclaro Inc (PA) ....D....408 383-1400
225 Charcot Ave San Jose (95131) *(P-19051)*
Oclaro (north America) Inc (HQ) ....B....408 383-1400
252 Charcot Ave San Jose (95131) *(P-17971)*
Oclaro Fiber Optics Inc (HQ) ....E....408 383-1400
225 Charcot Ave San Jose (95131) *(P-19052)*
Oclaro Photonics Inc (HQ) ....D....408 383-1400
225 Charcot Ave San Jose (95131) *(P-22112)*
Oclaro Subsystems Inc ....C....408 383-1400
225 Charcot Ave San Jose (95131) *(P-17972)*
Oclaro Technology Inc (HQ) ....D....408 383-1400
225 Charcot Ave San Jose (95131) *(P-17973)*
Ocli, Santa Rosa *Also called Optical Coating Laboratory LLC (P-13625)*
OCP Group Inc ....E....858 279-7400
7130 Engineer Rd San Diego (92111) *(P-15643)*
Ocpc Inc ....D....949 475-1900
2485 Da Vinci Irvine (92614) *(P-7000)*
Oct Medical Imaging Inc ....F....949 701-6656
1002 Health Sciences Rd Irvine (92617) *(P-22565)*
Octillion Power Systems Inc ....F....510 397-5952
721 Sandoval Way Hayward (94544) *(P-20411)*
Oculeve Inc ....F....415 745-3784
4410 Rosewood Dr Pleasanton (94588) *(P-22566)*
Ocunexus Therapeutics Inc ....F....858 480-2403
12481 High Bluff Dr D San Diego (92130) *(P-8315)*
Od Signs, Hayward *Also called Oki Doki Signs (P-23936)*
Odcombe Press (nashville) ....E....615 793-5414
859 Lawrence Dr Newbury Park (91320) *(P-7001)*
Oddbox Holdings Inc ....F....714 602-8864
17332 Von Irvine (92614) *(P-7417)*
Oddworld Inhabitants Inc ....D....805 503-3000
869 Monterey St San Luis Obispo (93401) *(P-24980)*
Odette Christiane LLC ....F....818 883-0410
21521 Blythe St Canoga Park (91304) *(P-3473)*
Odonate Therapeutics Inc ....E....858 731-8180
4747 Executive Dr Ste 510 San Diego (92121) *(P-8316)*
ODonnell Manufacturing Inc ....F....562 944-9671
14811 Via Defrancesco Ave Riverside (92508) *(P-16802)*
Odusa, Vista *Also called Ocean Divers USA LLC (P-10253)*
Odwalla Inc ....E....310 342-3920
700 Isis Ave Inglewood (90301) *(P-836)*
Odwalla Inc ....E....408 254-5800
1805 Las Plumas Ave San Jose (95133) *(P-837)*
Odyssey Innovative Designs, San Gabriel *Also called Hsiao & Montano Inc (P-10524)*
OEM LLC ....E....714 449-7500
311 S Highland Ave Fullerton (92832) *(P-16803)*
OEM Materials & Supplies Inc ....E....714 564-9600
1500 Ritchey St Santa Ana (92705) *(P-5319)*
Oepic Semiconductors Inc ....E....408 747-0388
1231 Bordeaux Dr Sunnyvale (94089) *(P-19053)*
Off Broadway, La Verne *Also called Fortress Inc (P-4944)*
Off Dock USA Inc ....F....310 522-4400
22700 S Alameda St Carson (90810) *(P-14339)*
Off Grid Labs Inc ....E....415 344-0953
555 De Haro St Ste 220 San Francisco (94107) *(P-19054)*
Off Lead Inc ....F....209 931-6909
9751 N Highway 99 Stockton (95212) *(P-10577)*
Off Price Network LLC ....E....213 477-8205
10544 Dunleer Dr Los Angeles (90064) *(P-3358)*
Offenhauser Sales Corp ....F....323 225-1307
5300 Alhambra Ave Los Angeles (90032) *(P-20412)*
Offerman Industries ....F....951 676-5016
43154 Via Dos Picos Ste F Temecula (92590) *(P-16804)*
Office Chairs Inc ....D....562 802-0464
14815 Radburn Ave Santa Fe Springs (90670) *(P-4962)*
Office Furniture Solutions, Temecula *Also called Tradeincom Inc (P-4971)*
Office Master Inc ....D....909 392-5678
1110 Mildred St Ontario (91761) *(P-4997)*
Offline Inc (PA) ....E....213 742-9001
2250 Maple Ave Los Angeles (90011) *(P-3552)*
Offshore Promotion Inc (PA) ....F....619 690-2622
3065 Beyer Blvd Ste 103 San Diego (92154) *(P-10254)*
Oggi, Anaheim *Also called Asdak International (P-10827)*
Oggis Pizza & Brewing Co ....E....858 481-7883
12840 Carmel Country Rd San Diego (92130) *(P-1616)*
Ogio International Inc ....D....801 619-4100
2180 Rutherford Rd Carlsbad (92008) *(P-10528)*
Ogletree's, Saint Helena *Also called Ronald F Ogletree Inc (P-12741)*
OH Juice Inc ....F....619 318-0207
5631 Palmer Way Ste A Carlsbad (92010) *(P-838)*
Ohadi Management Corporation ....F....909 625-2000
11088 Elm Ave Rancho Cucamonga (91730) *(P-22567)*
Ohanyan's Deli, Fresno *Also called Ohanyans Inc (P-510)*
Ohanyans Inc (PA) ....F....559 225-4290
3296 W Sussex Way Fresno (93722) *(P-510)*
OHara Metal Products ....E....707 863-9090
4949 Fulton Dr Ste E Fairfield (94534) *(P-13753)*
Oheck LLC ....C....323 923-2700
5830 Bickett St Huntington Park (90255) *(P-3621)*
Ohio Inc ....F....415 647-6446
630 Treat Ave San Francisco (94110) *(P-4963)*
Ohno America Inc ....E....770 773-3820
18781 Winnwood Ln Santa Ana (92705) *(P-2937)*
Ohp Inc (HQ) ....E....800 659-6745
4695 Macarthur Ct # 1200 Newport Beach (92660) *(P-7792)*
Oil Country Manufacturing ....C....805 643-1200
300 W Stanley Ave Ventura (93001) *(P-14237)*
Oil Well Service Company (PA) ....C....562 612-0600
10840 Norwalk Blvd Santa Fe Springs (90670) *(P-251)*
Oil Well Service Company ....E....661 589-2333
10255 Enos Ln Shafter (93263) *(P-252)*
Oil Well Service Company ....E....805 525-2103
1015 Mission Rock Rd Santa Paula (93060) *(P-253)*
Oil-Dri Corporation America ....F....661 765-7194
950 Petroleum Club Rd Taft (93268) *(P-8659)*
Ojo De Agua Produce, Dos Palos *Also called C&S Global Foods Inc (P-2475)*
OK Mine Company Incorporated ....F....323 440-4333
520 Chestnut Ave Long Beach (90802) *(P-14)*
Okamoto Corporation ....F....408 654-8400
7175 Via Corona San Jose (95139) *(P-19055)*
Oki Doki Signs ....F....510 940-7446
1680 W Winton Ave Ste 7 Hayward (94545) *(P-23936)*
Oki Graphics Inc ....F....408 451-9294
2148 Zanker Rd San Jose (95131) *(P-7002)*
Okonite Company ....C....805 922-6682
2900 Skyway Dr Santa Maria (93455) *(P-11668)*
Okta Inc ....F....650 348-2620
172 Lakeshore Dr San Mateo (94402) *(P-24981)*
Ola Corporate Services Inc ....F....323 655-1005
6404 Wilshire Blvd # 525 Los Angeles (90048) *(P-15908)*
Olaes Design & Marketing, Poway *Also called Olaes Enterprises Inc (P-3183)*
Olaes Enterprises Inc ....E....858 679-4450
13860 Stowe Dr Poway (92064) *(P-3183)*
Olam Spices and Vegetables, Woodland *Also called Olam West Coast Inc (P-840)*
Olam Tomato Processors Inc ....D....559 447-1390
205 E River Park Cir # 310 Fresno (93720) *(P-839)*
Olam West Coast Inc ....A....530 473-4290
1400 Churchill Downs Ave Woodland (95776) *(P-840)*
Olaplex LLC (PA) ....F....805 258-7680
1482 E Valley Rd Ste 701 Santa Barbara (93108) *(P-8806)*
Olark, San Francisco *Also called Habla Incorporated (P-24719)*
Old An Inc ....E....949 263-1400
17651 Armstrong Ave Irvine (92614) *(P-24194)*
Old Bones Co ....F....714 641-2800
641 Paularino Ave Costa Mesa (92626) *(P-4802)*
Old Bones Company, Costa Mesa *Also called Old Bones Co (P-4802)*
Old California Lantern Company, Orange *Also called Contract Illumination (P-17593)*
Old Castle Inclosure Solution, Madera *Also called Oldcastle Precast Inc (P-10967)*
Old Country Bakery, South San Francisco *Also called Bimbo Bakeries Usa Inc (P-1204)*
Old Country Millwork Inc ....E....323 234-2940
5855 Hooper Ave Los Angeles (90001) *(P-14717)*
Old Creek Ranch Winery Inc ....F....805 649-4132
10024 Creek Rd Oak View (93022) *(P-1904)*
Old English Mil & Woodworks, Santa Clarita *Also called Old English Mil & Woodworks (P-4206)*
Old English Mil & Woodworks (PA) ....E....661 294-9171
27772 Avenue Scott Santa Clarita (91355) *(P-4206)*
Old Fashion Lavash, Los Angeles *Also called Lavash Corporation (P-1281)*
Old Guys Rule, Ventura *Also called Streamline Dsign Slkscreen Inc (P-3192)*
Old New York Bagel & Deli Co (PA) ....F....805 484-3354
4972 Verdugo Way Camarillo (93012) *(P-1301)*
Old New York Deli & Bagel Co, Camarillo *Also called Old New York Bagel & Deli Co (P-1301)*
Old Pueblo Ranch Inc (PA) ....C....323 268-2791
316 N Ford Blvd Los Angeles (90022) *(P-2628)*

A L P H A B E T I C

Employee Codes: A=Over 500 employees, B=251-500
C=101-250, D=51-100, E=20-50, F=10-19
2019 California
Manfacturers Register
© Mergent Inc. 1-800-342-5647
1231

Oldcast Precast (HQ) .... E 951 788-9720
2434 Rubidoux Blvd Riverside (92509) ***(P-10963)***
Oldcastle Apg West Inc .... E 909 355-6422
10714 Poplar Ave Fontana (92337) ***(P-10768)***
Oldcastle Apg West Inc .... F 209 983-1609
4202 Gibralter Ct Stockton (95206) ***(P-9391)***
Oldcastle Buildingenvelope Inc .... D 510 651-2292
6850 Stevenson Blvd Fremont (94538) ***(P-10723)***
Oldcastle Buildingenvelope Inc .... D 323 722-2007
5631 Ferguson Dr Commerce (90022) ***(P-10724)***
Oldcastle Precast Inc .... C 909 428-3700
10650 Hemlock Ave Fontana (92337) ***(P-10964)***
Oldcastle Precast Inc .... E 619 390-2251
10441 Vine St Lakeside (92040) ***(P-10965)***
Oldcastle Precast Inc .... E 209 235-1173
2960 S Highway 99 Stockton (95215) ***(P-10966)***
Oldcastle Precast Inc .... E 559 674-8093
801 S Pine St Madera (93637) ***(P-13961)***
Oldcastle Precast Inc .... F 559 675-1813
801 S Pine St Madera (93637) ***(P-10967)***
Oldcastle Precast Inc .... E 530 742-8368
5236 Arboga Rd Marysville (95901) ***(P-10968)***
Oldcastle Precast Inc .... E 951 683-8200
2434 Rubidoux Blvd Riverside (92509) ***(P-10969)***
Olde World Corporation .... E 209 384-1337
360 Grogan Ave Merced (95341) ***(P-5088)***
Olea Kiosks Inc .... E 562 924-2644
13845 Artesia Blvd Cerritos (90703) ***(P-15814)***
Oleumtech Corporation .... E 949 305-9009
19762 Pauling Foothill Ranch (92610) ***(P-21627)***
Olin Chlor Alkali Logistics .... C 562 692-0510
11600 Pike St Santa Fe Springs (90670) ***(P-7666)***
Olin Chlor Alkali Logistics .... E 209 835-5424
26700 S Banta Rd Tracy (95304) ***(P-7667)***
Olio Devices Inc .... E 650 918-6546
1100 La Avenida St Ste A Mountain View (94043) ***(P-23222)***
Oliphant Tool Company .... E 714 903-6336
15652 Chemical Ln Huntington Beach (92649) ***(P-14553)***
Oliso, Richmond *Also called Unovo LLC* ***(P-17410)***
Oliso Inc .... F 415 864-7600
1200 Harbour Way S 215 Richmond (94804) ***(P-17399)***
Olive Bari Oil Company .... F 559 595-9260
40063 Road 56 Dinuba (93618) ***(P-1547)***
Olive Bariani Oil LLC .... F 415 864-1917
1330 Waller St San Francisco (94117) ***(P-1548)***
Olive Corto L P .... F 209 888-8100
10201 Live Oak Rd Stockton (95212) ***(P-1549)***
Olive Musco Products Inc (PA) .... B 209 836-4600
17950 Via Nicolo Tracy (95377) ***(P-841)***
Olive Musco Products Inc .... E 530 865-4111
Swift & 5th St # 5 Orland (95963) ***(P-924)***
Olive Press LLC (PA) .... F 707 939-8900
24724 Arnold Dr Sonoma (95476) ***(P-1550)***
Oliver De Silva Inc (PA) .... E 925 829-9220
11555 Dublin Blvd Dublin (94568) ***(P-330)***
Olivera Egg Ranch LLC .... D 408 258-8074
3315 Sierra Rd San Jose (95132) ***(P-548)***
Olivera Foods, San Jose *Also called Olivera Egg Ranch LLC* ***(P-548)***
Olli Salumeria Americana LLC .... F 804 427-7866
1301 Rocky Point Dr Oceanside (92056) ***(P-446)***
Ols Controls .... F 408 353-6564
15215 Old Ranch Rd Los Gatos (95033) ***(P-21520)***
Olson and Co Steel .... D 559 224-7811
3488 W Ashlan Ave Fresno (93722) ***(P-12221)***
Olson and Co Steel (PA) .... C 510 489-4680
1941 Davis St San Leandro (94577) ***(P-12884)***
Olson Industrial Systems, Santee *Also called Olson Irrigation Systems* ***(P-14088)***
Olson Irrigation Systems .... E 619 562-3100
10910 Wheatlands Ave A Santee (92071) ***(P-14088)***
Olson Technology Inc .... E 209 586-1022
24926 State Highway 108 Ml Wuk Village (95346) ***(P-18204)***
Olt Solar, San Jose *Also called Orbotech Lt Solar LLC* ***(P-19065)***
Oly, Berkeley *Also called Art of Muse* ***(P-4669)***
Olympia Trading, Los Angeles *Also called Silver Textile Incorporated* ***(P-2807)***
Olympic Cascade Publishing (HQ) .... E 916 321-1000
2100 Q St Sacramento (95816) ***(P-6005)***
Olympic Coatings .... E 760 745-3322
2200 Micro Pl Escondido (92029) ***(P-13624)***
Olympic Press Inc .... F 408 496-6222
461 Nelo St Santa Clara (95054) ***(P-7418)***
Olympus America Inc .... B 408 935-5000
2400 Ringwood Ave San Jose (95131) ***(P-22568)***
OLYMPUS AMERICA INC., San Jose *Also called Olympus America Inc* ***(P-22568)***
Omana Group LLC .... F 714 891-9488
11562 Knott St Ste 5 Garden Grove (92841) ***(P-642)***
Omega 2000 Group Corp .... D 951 775-5815
160 S Carmalita St Hemet (92543) ***(P-17400)***
Omega Case Company Inc .... E 818 238-9263
2231 N Hollywood Way Burbank (91505) ***(P-4531)***
Omega Diamond Inc .... F 916 652-8122
10125 Ophir Rd Newcastle (95658) ***(P-14659)***
Omega Engineering Inc .... D 714 540-4914
2229 S Yale St Santa Ana (92704) ***(P-15002)***
Omega Extruding, Rancho Cucamonga *Also called Omega Plastics Corp* ***(P-5612)***
Omega Fire Inc .... F 818 404-6212
441 W Allen Ave Ste 109 San Dimas (91773) ***(P-9503)***
Omega Graphics, Corona *Also called Rivas Industries Inc* ***(P-7085)***
Omega Graphics Printing Hollyw .... F 213 784-5200
6000 Fountain Ave Los Angeles (90028) ***(P-7003)***
Omega Graphics Printing Inc .... F 818 374-9189
7710 Kester Ave Van Nuys (91405) ***(P-7419)***
Omega Industrial Supply Inc .... E 707 864-8164
101 Grobric Ct Fairfield (94534) ***(P-8660)***
Omega Interconnect Inc .... F 909 986-1933
1207 Brooks St Ontario (91762) ***(P-16805)***
Omega Leads Inc .... E 310 394-6786
1509 Colorado Ave Santa Monica (90404) ***(P-19670)***
Omega Plastics Corp .... C 909 987-8716
9614 Lucas Ranch Rd Ste D Rancho Cucamonga (91730) ***(P-5612)***
Omega Precision .... E 562 946-2491
13040 Telegraph Rd Santa Fe Springs (90670) ***(P-16806)***
Omega Precision Machine .... F 209 833-6502
320 W Larch Rd Ste 15 Tracy (95304) ***(P-16807)***
Omega Products Corp (HQ) .... D 916 635-3335
8111 Fruitridge Rd Sacramento (95826) ***(P-11364)***
Omega Products Corp .... E 714 935-0900
282 S Anita Dr Fl 3 Orange (92868) ***(P-11365)***
Omega Products International, Sacramento *Also called Omega Products Corp* ***(P-11364)***
Omega Technologies Inc .... F 818 264-7970
31125 Via Colinas Ste 905 Westlake Village (91362) ***(P-11904)***
Omega Tool Die & Machine, San Bernardino *Also called McIntire Tool Die & Machine* ***(P-13246)***
Omega Turnstiles, Benicia *Also called Gunnebo Entrance Control Inc* ***(P-22208)***
Omf Performance Products .... F 951 354-8272
8199 Mar Vista Ct Riverside (92504) ***(P-21237)***
OMI, Yuba City *Also called Organic Mattresses Inc* ***(P-4876)***
Omicron Engineering Inc .... F 310 328-4017
1513 Plaza Del Amo Torrance (90501) ***(P-16808)***
Omics Group Inc .... B 650 268-9744
731 Gull Ave Foster City (94404) ***(P-6224)***
Oml Inc .... F 408 779-2698
300 Digital Dr Morgan Hill (95037) ***(P-21822)***
Omneon Inc (HQ) .... C 408 585-5000
4300 N 1st St San Jose (95134) ***(P-18205)***
Omni Connection Intl Inc .... B 951 898-6232
126 Via Trevizio Corona (92879) ***(P-19671)***
Omni Duct Systems, West Sacramento *Also called ECB Corp* ***(P-12567)***
Omni Enclosures Inc .... E 619 579-6664
505 Raleigh Ave El Cajon (92020) ***(P-5089)***
Omni Metal Finishing Inc (PA) .... D 714 979-9414
11665 Coley River Cir Fountain Valley (92708) ***(P-13468)***
Omni Optical Products Inc (PA) .... E 714 634-5700
17282 Eastman Irvine (92614) ***(P-22241)***
Omni Pacific, El Cajon *Also called Omni Enclosures Inc* ***(P-5089)***
Omni Seals, Inc., Rancho Cucamonga *Also called Smith International Inc* ***(P-275)***
Omnia Leather Motion Inc .... C 909 393-4400
4950 Edison Ave Chino (91710) ***(P-3735)***
Omnical Inc .... F 818 837-7531
557 Jessie St San Fernando (91340) ***(P-22783)***
Omnicell Inc .... F 408 907-8868
725 Sycamore Dr Milpitas (95035) ***(P-15467)***
Omnicell Inc (PA) .... B 650 251-6100
590 E Middlefield Rd Mountain View (94043) ***(P-15468)***
Omnimax International Inc .... C 951 928-1000
28921 Us Highway 74 Sun City (92585) ***(P-12338)***
Omniprint Inc .... E 949 833-0080
1923 E Deere Ave Santa Ana (92705) ***(P-15815)***
Omnirax, Sausalito *Also called Sausalito Craftworks Inc* ***(P-23315)***
Omnisil .... E 805 644-2514
5401 Everglades St Ventura (93003) ***(P-19056)***
Omnitec Precision Mfg Inc .... F 408 437-9056
435 Queens Ln San Jose (95112) ***(P-16809)***
Omnitek Engineering Corp (PA) .... F 760 591-0089
1333 Keystone Way Ste 101 Vista (92081) ***(P-20413)***
Omnitracs Midco LLC (PA) .... E 858 651-5812
9276 Scranton Rd Ste 200 San Diego (92121) ***(P-24982)***
Omnitron Systems Tech Inc .... D 949 250-6510
38 Tesla Irvine (92618) ***(P-15816)***
Omnivision Technologies Inc (HQ) .... C 408 567-3000
4275 Burton Dr Santa Clara (95054) ***(P-19057)***
Omnivore Technologies Inc .... E 800 293-4058
1191 B St Hayward (94541) ***(P-24983)***
Omniyig Inc .... E 408 988-0843
3350 Scott Blvd Bldg 66 Santa Clara (95054) ***(P-19672)***
Omron Adept Technologies Inc (HQ) .... C 925 245-3400
4550 Norris Canyon Rd # 150 San Ramon (94583) ***(P-14280)***
Omron Scientific Tech Inc (HQ) .... C 510 608-3400
6550 Dumbarton Cir Fremont (94555) ***(P-21628)***
Omstar Environmental Products, Wilmington *Also called D-1280-X Inc* ***(P-9331)***
Omtek Inc .... E 805 687-9629
3722 Calle Cita Santa Barbara (93105) ***(P-19058)***
Omxie, Chino *Also called Max Smt Corp* ***(P-15131)***
Omya California Inc .... D 760 248-7306
7299 Crystal Creek Rd Lucerne Valley (92356) ***(P-7793)***
On Press Printing Service Inc .... F 909 799-9599
1440 Richardson St San Bernardino (92408) ***(P-7004)***
On-Gard Metals Inc .... F 562 622-9057
8638 Cleta St Downey (90241) ***(P-11563)***
On-Line Power Incorporated (PA) .... E 323 721-5017
14000 S Broadway Los Angeles (90061) ***(P-17109)***
On-Line Power Incorporated .... D 323 720-4125
14000 S Broadway Los Angeles (90061) ***(P-17110)***
On-Line Stampco Inc .... F 800 373-5614
3341 Hancock St San Diego (92110) ***(P-23721)***
On24 Inc (PA) .... B 877 202-9599
50 Beale St Ste 800 San Francisco (94105) ***(P-24984)***
Onanon Inc .... E 408 262-8990
720 S Milpitas Blvd Milpitas (95035) ***(P-19406)***

Onc Holdings Inc.....F.....415 243-3343
832 Folsom St Ste 1001 San Francisco (94107) ***(P-24985)***
Oncogenesis Inc.....F.....408 636-7725
385 Woodview Ave Ste 150 Morgan Hill (95037) ***(P-22569)***
Oncology Care Systems Group, Concord *Also called Siemens Med Solutions USA Inc* ***(P-23047)***
Oncomed Pharmaceuticals Inc.....D.....650 995-8200
800 Chesapeake Dr Redwood City (94063) ***(P-8317)***
Oncore Manufacturing LLC.....C.....760 737-6777
237 Via Vera Cruz San Marcos (92078) ***(P-18549)***
Oncore Manufacturing Svcs Inc.....C.....510 360-2222
9340 Owensmouth Ave Chatsworth (91311) ***(P-18550)***
Oncore Velocity, San Marcos *Also called Oncore Manufacturing LLC* ***(P-18549)***
Ondax Inc.....F.....626 357-9600
850 E Duarte Rd Monrovia (91016) ***(P-22113)***
One At A Time.....F.....805 461-1784
3518 El Camino Real 195 Atascadero (93422) ***(P-23399)***
One Bella Casa Inc.....E.....707 746-8300
101 Lucas Valley Rd # 130 San Rafael (94903) ***(P-3736)***
One Color Communications, Alameda *Also called ONe Color Communications LLC* ***(P-7654)***
ONe Color Communications LLC.....D.....510 263-1840
1851 Harbor Bay Pkwy Alameda (94502) ***(P-7654)***
One Hat One Hand LLC.....E.....415 822-2020
1335 Yosemite Ave San Francisco (94124) ***(P-3569)***
One Lambda Inc (HQ).....C.....818 702-0042
21001 Kittridge St Canoga Park (91303) ***(P-7961)***
One Natural Experience, Monrovia *Also called One World Enterprises LLC* ***(P-2157)***
One Park Place, San Diego *Also called Internet Strategy Inc* ***(P-24785)***
One Resonance Sensors LLC.....F.....407 637-0771
8291 Aero Pl Ste 120 San Diego (92123) ***(P-19059)***
One Source Automation Inc.....F.....619 422-4010
310 Trousdale Dr Ste B Chula Vista (91910) ***(P-14761)***
One Stop Label Corporation.....F.....909 230-9380
1641 S Baker Ave Ontario (91761) ***(P-5720)***
One Stop Systems Inc (PA).....D.....760 745-9883
2235 Entp St Ste 110 Escondido (92029) ***(P-15817)***
One Stop Systems Inc.....E.....858 530-2511
2235 Entp St Ste 110 Escondido (92029) ***(P-15818)***
One Time Utilities Sales, Santa Ana *Also called One Time Utility Sales Inc* ***(P-17516)***
One Time Utility Sales Inc.....E.....714 953-5700
501 N Garfield St Santa Ana (92701) ***(P-17516)***
ONE TOUCH OFFICE TECHNOLOGY, Torrance *Also called One Touch Solutions Inc* ***(P-14820)***
One Touch Solutions Inc.....F.....310 320-6868
370 Amapola Ave Ste 106 Torrance (90501) ***(P-14820)***
One Up Manufacturing LLC.....E.....310 749-8347
2555 E Del Amo Blvd Compton (90221) ***(P-5356)***
One Vine Wines, Poway *Also called Martellotto Inc* ***(P-1871)***
One World Apparel Inc.....E.....213 222-1010
13071 Temple Ave La Puente (91746) ***(P-3266)***
One World Enterprises LLC.....E.....310 802-4220
1333 S Mayflower Ave # 100 Monrovia (91016) ***(P-2157)***
One-Way Manufacturing Inc.....E.....714 630-8833
1195 N Osprey Cir Anaheim (92807) ***(P-13898)***
ONeil Capital Management.....D.....310 448-6400
12655 Beatrice St Los Angeles (90066) ***(P-7209)***
ONeil Digital Solutions LLC.....C.....310 448-6407
12655 Beatrice St Los Angeles (90066) ***(P-7005)***
ONeil KG Bags.....F.....415 460-0111
124 Belvedere St Ste 12 San Rafael (94901) ***(P-10529)***
ONeill Wetsuits LLC (PA).....D.....831 475-7500
1071 41st Ave Santa Cruz (95062) ***(P-9650)***
Onesolution Light and Control.....E.....714 490-5540
225 S Loara St Anaheim (92802) ***(P-17721)***
Onesun LLC.....F.....415 230-4277
27 Gate 5 Rd Sausalito (94965) ***(P-19060)***
Oneto Manufacturing Company.....F.....650 875-1710
146 S Maple Ave South San Francisco (94080) ***(P-12696)***
Oneworld Apparel LLC (HQ).....E.....213 222-1010
13071 Temple Ave La Puente (91746) ***(P-3330)***
Onex Automation, Duarte *Also called Onex Enterprises Corporation* ***(P-15344)***
Onex Enterprises Corporation.....F.....626 358-6639
1824 Flower Ave Duarte (91010) ***(P-15344)***
Onex Rf Automation Inc.....F.....626 358-6639
1824 Flower Ave Duarte (91010) ***(P-14734)***
Onki Corp.....F.....510 567-8875
294 Hegenberger Rd Oakland (94621) ***(P-20414)***
Only You Rx Skin Care, Valencia *Also called Professional Skin Care Inc* ***(P-8826)***
Onnet Usa Inc.....E.....408 457-3992
2870 Zanker Rd Ste 205 San Jose (95134) ***(P-6544)***
Onnik Shoe Company Inc.....E.....818 506-5353
11443 Chandler Blvd North Hollywood (91601) ***(P-10501)***
Onq Solutions Inc (PA).....E.....650 262-4150
24540 Clawiter Rd Hayward (94545) ***(P-5158)***
Onset Medical Corporation.....E.....949 716-1100
13900 Alton Pkwy Ste 120 Irvine (92618) ***(P-22570)***
Onshore Technologies Inc.....E.....310 533-4888
2771 Plaza Dl Amo 802-8 Torrance (90503) ***(P-19673)***
Onspec Technology Partners Inc.....E.....408 654-7627
975 Comstock St Santa Clara (95054) ***(P-19061)***
Ontario Binding Company Inc.....D.....909 947-7866
15951 Promontory Rd Chino Hills (91709) ***(P-7609)***
Ontario Foam Products, Ontario *Also called Androp Packaging Inc* ***(P-5384)***
Onyx Industries Inc (PA).....D.....310 539-8830
1227 254th St Harbor City (90710) ***(P-13034)***
Onyx Industries Inc.....E.....310 851-6161
521 W Rosecrans Ave Gardena (90248) ***(P-13035)***
Onyx Optics Inc.....F.....925 833-1969
6551 Sierra Ln Dublin (94568) ***(P-22114)***
Onyx Pharmaceuticals Inc.....A.....650 266-0000
1 Amgen Center Dr Newbury Park (91320) ***(P-8318)***
Onyx Shutters, City of Industry *Also called Tje Company* ***(P-12351)***
Oogolow Enterprises.....F.....530 899-9927
1608 W 5th St A Chico (95928) ***(P-2629)***
Oopston Inc.....F.....800 881-5901
748 S Glasgow Ave Inglewood (90301) ***(P-24986)***
Ooshirts Inc (PA).....B.....866 660-8667
41454 Christy St Fremont (94538) ***(P-7420)***
Op-Test, Redding *Also called Sof-Tek Integrators Inc* ***(P-21850)***
Opal Moon Winery LLC.....F.....707 996-0420
21660 8th St E Ste A Sonoma (95476) ***(P-1905)***
Opal Service Inc (PA).....E.....714 935-0900
282 S Anita Dr Orange (92868) ***(P-11366)***
Openclovis Solutions Inc.....E.....707 981-7120
765 Baywood Dr Ste 336 Petaluma (94954) ***(P-24987)***
Openpro Erp Software, Fountain Valley *Also called Openpro Inc* ***(P-24988)***
Openpro Inc.....F.....714 378-4600
10061 Talbert Ave Ste 228 Fountain Valley (92708) ***(P-24988)***
Opentv Inc (HQ).....C.....415 962-5000
275 Sacramento St Ste Sl1 San Francisco (94111) ***(P-24989)***
Openwave Mobility Inc (PA).....E.....650 480-7200
400 Seaport Ct Ste 104 Redwood City (94063) ***(P-24990)***
Openx Technologies Inc.....E.....626 466-1141
888 E Walnut St Fl 2 Pasadena (91101) ***(P-24991)***
Opera Commerce LLC.....F.....650 625-1262
1875 S Grant St Ste 800 San Mateo (94402) ***(P-24992)***
Opera Patisserie Fines Inc (PA).....E.....858 536-5800
8480 Redwood Creek Ln San Diego (92126) ***(P-1400)***
Opera Software Americas LLC.....F.....650 625-1262
1875 S Grant St Ste 750 San Mateo (94402) ***(P-24993)***
Ophir Rf Inc.....E.....310 306-5556
5300 Beethoven St Fl 3 Los Angeles (90066) ***(P-18206)***
Ophthonix, San Diego *Also called Trex Enterprises Corporation* ***(P-15500)***
Ophthonix Inc.....D.....760 842-5600
900 Glenneyre St Laguna Beach (92651) ***(P-23115)***
Opi, San Diego *Also called Offshore Promotion Inc* ***(P-10254)***
Opiant Pharmaceuticals Inc.....F.....301 598-5410
201 Santa Monica Blvd B Santa Monica (90401) ***(P-8319)***
Opmp, Tracy *Also called Omega Precision Machine* ***(P-16807)***
Opnext, Inc., San Jose *Also called Oclaro Fiber Optics Inc* ***(P-19052)***
Opolo Vineyards Inc (PA).....E.....805 238-9593
7110 Vineyard Dr Paso Robles (93446) ***(P-1906)***
Opotek Inc.....F.....760 929-0770
2233 Faraday Ave Ste E Carlsbad (92008) ***(P-23029)***
Oppo Original Corp.....F.....909 444-3000
108 Brea Canyon Rd 118 Walnut (91789) ***(P-10502)***
Ops Technology, San Francisco *Also called Realpage Inc* ***(P-25109)***
Opsveda Inc.....F.....408 628-0461
4030 Moorpark Ave Ste 107 San Jose (95117) ***(P-24994)***
Optasense Inc.....F.....408 970-3500
3350 Scott Blvd Bldg 1 Santa Clara (95054) ***(P-19062)***
Optasense Inc.....F.....714 482-1922
3060 Saturn St Ste 101 Brea (92821) ***(P-143)***
Optec Laser Systems LLC.....E.....858 220-1070
11622 El Camino Real San Diego (92130) ***(P-7421)***
Optek Group Inc.....E.....949 629-2558
23 Corporate Plaza Dr # 150 Newport Beach (92660) ***(P-23030)***
Optel-Matic Inc.....F.....626 444-2671
11221 Thienes Ave El Monte (91733) ***(P-16810)***
Optex Incorporated.....F.....800 966-7839
18730 S Wilmington Ave # 100 Compton (90220) ***(P-18351)***
Opti Lite Optical.....E.....323 932-6828
5552 W Adams Blvd Los Angeles (90016) ***(P-23116)***
Opti-Forms Inc.....D.....951 296-1300
42310 Winchester Rd Temecula (92590) ***(P-13469)***
Optibase Inc (HQ).....E.....800 451-5101
931 Benecia Ave Sunnyvale (94085) ***(P-15819)***
Optic Arts Inc.....E.....213 250-6069
1130 Monterey Pass Rd Monterey Park (91754) ***(P-17433)***
Optical Coating Laboratory LLC (HQ).....B.....707 545-6440
2789 Northpoint Pkwy Santa Rosa (95407) ***(P-13625)***
Optical Communication Pdts Inc.....A.....818 876-8700
26850 Agoura Rd Fl 1 Calabasas (91301) ***(P-17974)***
Optical Physics Company.....F.....818 880-2907
4133 Guardian St G Simi Valley (93063) ***(P-22115)***
Optical Sensor Division, Fremont *Also called Omron Scientific Tech Inc* ***(P-21628)***
Optical Zonu Corporation.....F.....818 780-9701
7510 Hazeltine Ave Van Nuys (91405) ***(P-17975)***
Opticolor Inc.....F.....714 893-8839
15281 Graham St Huntington Beach (92649) ***(P-10255)***
Opticomm Corp.....E.....626 293-3400
2015 Chestnut St Alhambra (91803) ***(P-11669)***
Optim Microwave Inc.....E.....805 482-7093
4020 Adolfo Rd Camarillo (93012) ***(P-18207)***
Optima Industries Inc.....F.....310 533-8448
22771 S Wstn Ave Ste 201b Torrance (90501) ***(P-14397)***
Optima Technology Corporation.....B.....949 253-5768
17062 Murphy Ave Irvine (92614) ***(P-15820)***
Optimedica Corporation.....C.....408 850-8600
510 Cottonwood Dr Milpitas (95035) ***(P-22571)***
Optimis Services Inc.....E.....310 230-2780
225 Mantua Rd Pacific Palisades (90272) ***(P-24995)***
Optimization Corporation.....F.....510 614-5890
14680 Wicks Blvd San Leandro (94577) ***(P-15169)***
Optimum Bioenergy Intl Corp.....F.....714 903-8872
2463 Pomona Rd Corona (92880) ***(P-7962)***
Optimum Design Associates Inc (PA).....D.....925 401-2004
1075 Serpentine Ln Ste A Pleasanton (94566) ***(P-19674)***

A
L
P
H
A
B
E
T
I
C

Employee Codes: A=Over 500 employees, B=251-500
C=101-250, D=51-100, E=20-50, F=10-19
2019 California
Manfacturers Register
© Mergent Inc. 1-800-342-5647
1233

Optimum Solutions Group LLC..........C......415 954-7100
419 Ponderosa Ct Lafayette (94549) ***(P-24996)***
Optiscan Biomedical Corp..........E......510 342-5800
24590 Clawiter Rd Hayward (94545) ***(P-22572)***
Optiscan Ltd..........F......760 777-9595
48290 Vista Calico Ste A La Quinta (92253) ***(P-22116)***
Optivus Proton Therapy Inc..........D......909 799-8300
1475 Victoria Ct San Bernardino (92408) ***(P-22242)***
Optiworks Inc (PA)..........D......510 438-4560
47211 Bayside Pkwy Fremont (94538) ***(P-10661)***
Opto 22..........C......951 695-3000
43044 Business Park Dr Temecula (92590) ***(P-19675)***
Opto Diode Corporation..........E......805 465-8700
1260 Calle Suerte Camarillo (93012) ***(P-19063)***
Optodyne Incorporation..........E......310 635-7481
1180 W Mahalo Pl Rancho Dominguez (90220) ***(P-18208)***
Optoelectronix Inc (PA)..........F......408 437-9488
111 W Saint John St # 588 San Jose (95113) ***(P-19064)***
Optoma Technology Inc..........C......510 897-8600
47697 Westinghouse Dr # 100 Fremont (94539) ***(P-23183)***
Optoplex Corporation (PA)..........D......510 490-9930
48500 Kato Rd Fremont (94538) ***(P-17976)***
Optosigma Corporation..........E......949 851-5881
3210 S Croddy Way Santa Ana (92704) ***(P-22117)***
Optovue Inc (PA)..........D......510 623-8868
2800 Bayview Dr Fremont (94538) ***(P-22573)***
Optron Scientific Company Inc..........F......818 883-6103
7051 Eton Ave Canoga Park (91303) ***(P-22243)***
Optronics, Goleta *Also called Karl Storz Imaging Inc* ***(P-22224)***
Opulence International..........E......949 360-7611
30085 Comercio Rcho STA Marg (92688) ***(P-2780)***
Opus One Winery LLC (PA)..........D......707 944-9442
7900 St Helena Hwy Oakville (94562) ***(P-1907)***
or Technology, Chula Vista *Also called Mk Digital Direct Inc* ***(P-21995)***
Oracle, San Mateo *Also called Netsuite Inc* ***(P-24954)***
Oracle America Inc..........C......408 276-4300
4220 Network Cir Santa Clara (95054) ***(P-24997)***
Oracle America Inc (HQ)..........A......650 506-7000
500 Oracle Pkwy Redwood City (94065) ***(P-15469)***
Oracle America Inc..........F......303 272-6473
1001 Sunset Blvd Rocklin (95765) ***(P-24998)***
Oracle America Inc..........D......415 908-3609
475 Sansome St Fl 15 San Francisco (94111) ***(P-24999)***
Oracle America Inc..........F......408 702-5945
600 Oracle Pkwy Redwood City (94065) ***(P-25000)***
Oracle America Inc..........D......925 694-3314
5815 Owens Dr Pleasanton (94588) ***(P-25001)***
Oracle America Inc..........E......818 905-0200
15821 Ventura Blvd # 270 Encino (91436) ***(P-25002)***
Oracle America Inc..........B......408 635-3072
80 Railroad Ave Milpitas (95035) ***(P-25003)***
Oracle America Inc..........D......858 625-5044
9540 Towne Centre Dr San Diego (92121) ***(P-25004)***
Oracle America Inc..........F......909 605-0222
3401 Centre Lake Dr # 410 Ontario (91761) ***(P-25005)***
Oracle America Inc..........C......408 276-7534
4230 Leonard Stocking Dr Santa Clara (95054) ***(P-25006)***
Oracle Corporation..........C......713 654-0919
279 Barnes Rd Tustin (92782) ***(P-25007)***
Oracle Corporation..........E......415 834-9731
475 Sansome St Fl 15 San Francisco (94111) ***(P-25008)***
Oracle Corporation..........B......650 607-5402
214 Clarence Ave Sunnyvale (94086) ***(P-25009)***
Oracle Corporation..........B......650 678-3612
1408 Antigua Ln Foster City (94404) ***(P-25010)***
Oracle Corporation..........B......408 421-2890
1490 Newhall St Santa Clara (95050) ***(P-25011)***
Oracle Corporation..........B......408 276-5552
231 Kerry Dr Santa Clara (95050) ***(P-25012)***
Oracle Corporation..........B......408 276-3822
3084 Thurman Dr San Jose (95148) ***(P-25013)***
Oracle Corporation..........C......858 202-0648
9515 Towne Centre Dr San Diego (92121) ***(P-25014)***
Oracle Corporation..........B......650 506-9864
3532 Eastin Pl Santa Clara (95051) ***(P-25015)***
Oracle Corporation..........B......408 390-8623
372 Calero Ave San Jose (95123) ***(P-25016)***
Oracle Corporation..........C......415 402-7200
475 Sansome St Fl 15 San Francisco (94111) ***(P-25017)***
Oracle Corporation..........B......916 435-8342
6224 Hummingbird Ln Rocklin (95765) ***(P-25018)***
Oracle Corporation..........B......877 767-2253
5805 Owens Dr Pleasanton (94588) ***(P-25019)***
Oracle Corporation..........B......925 694-6258
3925 Emerald Isle Ln San Jose (95135) ***(P-25020)***
Oracle Corporation..........B......510 471-6971
5863 Carmel Way Union City (94587) ***(P-25021)***
Oracle Corporation..........B......310 258-7500
5750 Hannum Ave Ste 200 Culver City (90230) ***(P-25022)***
Oracle Corporation..........B......310 343-7405
200 N Pacific Coast Hwy # 400 El Segundo (90245) ***(P-25023)***
Oracle Corporation..........B......916 315-3500
1001 Sunset Blvd Rocklin (95765) ***(P-25024)***
Oracle Corporation..........E......650 506-7000
475 Sansome St Fl 15 San Francisco (94111) ***(P-25025)***
Oracle Systems Corporation..........D......818 817-2900
200 N Pacific Coast Hwy # 400 El Segundo (90245) ***(P-25026)***
Oracle Systems Corporation..........D......650 506-8648
102 Santa Barbara Ave Daly City (94014) ***(P-25027)***
Oracle Systems Corporation..........B......650 654-7606
301 Island Pkwy Belmont (94002) ***(P-25028)***
Oracle Systems Corporation..........C......650 506-6780
500 Oracle Pwky San Mateo (94403) ***(P-25029)***
Oracle Systems Corporation..........F......650 506-5062
501 Island Pkwy Belmont (94002) ***(P-25030)***
Oracle Systems Corporation..........B......650 506-0300
10 Twin Dolphin Dr Redwood City (94065) ***(P-25031)***
Oracle Systems Corporation..........F......650 378-1351
1840 Gateway Dr Ste 250 San Mateo (94404) ***(P-25032)***
Oracle Systems Corporation..........E......650 506-5887
300 Oracle Pkwy Redwood City (94065) ***(P-25033)***
Oracle Systems Corporation..........B......925 694-3000
5840 Owens Dr Pleasanton (94588) ***(P-25034)***
Oracle Systems Corporation..........D......949 224-1000
2010 Main St Ste 450 Irvine (92614) ***(P-25035)***
Oracle Systems Corporation..........B......949 623-9460
17901 Von Karman Ave # 800 Irvine (92614) ***(P-25036)***
Oracle Taleo LLC..........A......925 452-3000
4140 Dublin Blvd Ste 400 Dublin (94568) ***(P-25037)***
Oral Essentials Inc..........F......888 773-5273
436 N Roxbury Dr Beverly Hills (90210) ***(P-8807)***
Orange Bang Inc..........E......818 833-1000
13115 Telfair Ave Sylmar (91342) ***(P-2158)***
Orange Circle Studio Corp..........E......949 727-0800
8687 Research Dr Ste 150 Irvine (92618) ***(P-7422)***
Orange Cnty Cstl Physcians Inc..........F......808 545-2500
4879 E La Palma Ave Anaheim (92807) ***(P-22574)***
Orange Cnty Mlt-Hsing Svc Corp..........F......714 245-9500
525 Cabrillo Park Dr # 125 Santa Ana (92701) ***(P-6225)***
Orange Cnty Name Plate Co Inc..........D......714 522-7693
13201 Arctic Cir Santa Fe Springs (90670) ***(P-23937)***
Orange Coast Kommunications..........E......949 862-1133
1124 Main St Ste A Irvine (92614) ***(P-6226)***
Orange Coast Magazine, Irvine *Also called Orange Coast Kommunications* ***(P-6226)***
Orange Coast Reprographics Inc..........E......949 548-5571
659 W 19th St Costa Mesa (92627) ***(P-7006)***
Orange Container Inc..........D......714 547-9617
1984 E Mcfadden Ave Santa Ana (92705) ***(P-5441)***
Orange Corporation..........F......323 266-0700
1430 S Grande Vista Ave Los Angeles (90023) ***(P-3553)***
Orange County Business Journal, Irvine *Also called Cbj LP* ***(P-6126)***
Orange County Erectors Inc..........E......714 502-8455
517 E La Palma Ave Anaheim (92801) ***(P-12955)***
Orange County Label Co Inc..........F......714 437-1010
301 W Dyer Rd Ste D Santa Ana (92707) ***(P-7423)***
Orange County Plating Coinc..........E......714 532-4610
940 N Parker St 960 Orange (92867) ***(P-13470)***
Orange County Printing, Irvine *Also called Kelmscott Communications LLC* ***(P-6920)***
Orange County Register, El Toro *Also called Freedom Communications Inc* ***(P-5851)***
Orange County Register, The, Santa Ana *Also called Digital First Media LLC* ***(P-5829)***
Orange County Screw Products..........E......714 630-7433
2993 E La Palma Ave Anaheim (92806) ***(P-16811)***
Orange Cove Mountain Times, Reedley *Also called Midvalley Publishing Inc* ***(P-5971)***
Orange Metal Spinning and Stam..........F......714 754-0770
2601 Orange Ave Santa Ana (92707) ***(P-13255)***
Orange Pack Solution, San Diego *Also called Hwa In America Inc* ***(P-19570)***
Orangegrid LLC..........E......657 220-1519
145 S State College Blvd # 350 Brea (92821) ***(P-25038)***
Oratec Interventions Inc (HQ)..........F......901 396-2121
3696 Haven Ave Redwood City (94063) ***(P-23031)***
Oraya Therapeutics Inc..........E......510 456-3700
3 Twin Dolphin Dr Ste 175 Redwood City (94065) ***(P-22575)***
Orb Media Broadcasting Inc..........F......323 246-4524
3125 W Beverly Blvd Montebello (90640) ***(P-6545)***
Orban, San Leandro *Also called Crl Systems Inc* ***(P-18080)***
Orbit Industries, Grass Valley *Also called Countis Industries Inc* ***(P-10817)***
Orbit Systems, Laguna Hills *Also called Aot Electronics Inc* ***(P-15669)***
Orbita Corp (PA)..........F......213 746-4783
1136 Crocker St Los Angeles (90021) ***(P-3603)***
Orbital Sciences Corporation..........D......703 406-5000
20 Ryan Ranch Rd Ste 214 Monterey (93940) ***(P-19676)***
Orbital Sciences Corporation..........D......805 734-5400
Talo Rd Bldg 1555 Lompoc (93437) ***(P-21166)***
Orbits Lightwave Inc..........F......626 795-0667
41 S Chester Ave Pasadena (91106) ***(P-10662)***
Orbo Corporation..........E......562 806-6171
1000 S Euclid St La Habra (90631) ***(P-5024)***
Orbotech Lt Solar LLC..........E......408 414-3777
5970 Optical Ct San Jose (95138) ***(P-19065)***
Orca Arms LLC..........D......858 586-0503
9825 Carroll Centre Rd # 100 San Diego (92126) ***(P-23626)***
Orca Systems Inc..........E......858 679-9295
3990 Old Town Ave San Diego (92110) ***(P-18551)***
Orchard Equipment Mfg, Gridley *Also called Bianchi Orchard Systems Inc* ***(P-14045)***
Orchard Harvest, Yuba City *Also called Orchard Machinery Corporation* ***(P-14089)***
Orchard Machinery Corporation (PA)..........D......530 673-2822
2700 Colusa Hwy Yuba City (95993) ***(P-14089)***
Orchard Printing..........F......510 490-1736
325 Aleut Ct Fremont (94539) ***(P-7007)***
Orchard's Metal Fabrication, Riverside *Also called Omf Performance Products* ***(P-21237)***
Orco Block & Hardscape (PA)..........D......714 527-2239
11100 Beach Blvd Stanton (90680) ***(P-10855)***
Orco Block & Hardscape..........E......760 757-1780
3501 Oceanside Blvd Oceanside (92056) ***(P-10856)***
Orco Block & Hardscape..........E......951 928-3619
26380 Palomar Rd Romoland (92585) ***(P-10857)***
Orcon Aerospace, Union City *Also called Lamart Corporation* ***(P-11312)***
Orcon Aerospace..........C......510 489-8100
2600 Central Ave Ste E Union City (94587) ***(P-20898)***

Ordway Metal Polishing E 323 225-3373
1901 N San Fernando Rd Los Angeles (90065) *(P-13471)*
OReilly Media Inc (PA) C 707 827-7000
1005 Gravenstein Hwy N Sebastopol (95472) *(P-6373)*
Orexigen Therapeutics Inc (HQ) D 858 875-8600
3344 N Torrey Pines Ct # 200 La Jolla (92037) *(P-8320)*
Orfila Vineyards & Winery, Escondido *Also called Orfila Vineyards Inc (P-1908)*
Orfila Vineyards Inc (PA) E 760 738-6500
13455 San Pasqual Rd Escondido (92025) *(P-1908)*
Orfium, Santa Monica *Also called Hexacorp Ltd (P-24732)*
Orgain Inc F 949 930-0039
16631 Millikan Ave Irvine (92606) *(P-2159)*
Organ-O-Sil Fiber Co Inc E 714 847-8310
17616 Gothard St Ste B Huntington Beach (92647) *(P-20415)*
Organic Bottle Dctg Co LLC E 951 335-4600
575 Alcoa Cir Ste B Corona (92880) *(P-5357)*
Organic Horseradish Co E 530 664-3862
7890 County Road 120 Tulelake (96134) *(P-925)*
Organic Infusions Inc (PA) F 805 419-4118
2390 Las Posas Rd Camarillo (93010) *(P-9343)*
Organic Mattresses Inc E 530 790-6723
1335 Harter Pkwy Yuba City (95993) *(P-4876)*
Organic Milling Inc D 800 638-8686
505 W Allen Ave San Dimas (91773) *(P-1069)*
Organic Milling Corporation (PA) C 909 599-0961
505 W Allen Ave San Dimas (91773) *(P-1070)*
Organic Milling Corporation F 909 305-0185
305 S Acacia St Unit A San Dimas (91773) *(P-1071)*
Organic Spices (PA) E 510 440-1044
4180 Business Center Dr Fremont (94538) *(P-2630)*
Organicgirl LLC A 831 758-7800
900 Work St Salinas (93901) *(P-2631)*
Organicsorb LLC F 310 795-4011
630 S Los Angeles St Los Angeles (90014) *(P-418)*
Organosil Fiber Co, Huntington Beach *Also called Organ-O-Sil Fiber Co Inc (P-20415)*
Organovo Inc C 858 224-1000
6275 Nncy Rdge Dr Ste 110 San Diego (92121) *(P-8569)*
Orgatech Omegalux, Orange *Also called Western Lighting Inds Inc (P-17571)*
Oric Pharmaceuticals Inc E 650 918-8818
240 E Grand Ave South San Francisco (94080) *(P-8321)*
Orient & Flume Art Glass Co E 530 893-0373
2161 Park Ave Chico (95928) *(P-10663)*
Oriental Odysseys Inc E 510 357-6100
14557 Griffith St San Leandro (94577) *(P-24195)*
Orientex, Pittsburg *Also called Ramar International Corp (P-449)*
Orientex Foods, Pittsburg *Also called Ramar International Corp (P-690)*
Origin LLC (HQ) E 818 848-1648
119 E Graham Pl Burbank (91502) *(P-24196)*
Original Distributor Exchange F 323 583-8707
2538 E 52nd St Huntington Park (90255) *(P-19842)*
Original Glass Design, San Jose *Also called Beveled Edge Inc (P-10680)*
Original Jack's Baking Co, Pico Rivera *Also called Ibakeum Inc (P-1274)*
Original Letterman Jacket Co, Paramount *Also called Logos Plus Inc (P-3903)*
Original Watermen Inc F 760 599-0990
1198 Joshua Way Vista (92081) *(P-3038)*
Originals 22 Inc F 909 993-5050
3675 Placentia Ct Chino (91710) *(P-17551)*
Originclear Inc (PA) E 323 939-6645
525 S Hewitt St Los Angeles (90013) *(P-16083)*
Orion Chandelier Inc F 714 668-9668
2202 S Wright St Santa Ana (92705) *(P-17552)*
Orion Group, The, Kensington *Also called Sempervirens Group (P-9111)*
Orion Manufacturing Inc C 408 955-9001
5550 Hellyer Ave San Jose (95138) *(P-18552)*
Orion Ornamental Iron Inc E 818 752-0688
6918 Tujunga Ave North Hollywood (91605) *(P-11981)*
Orion Plastics Corporation D 310 223-0370
700 W Carob St Compton (90220) *(P-7862)*
Orion Tech, City of Industry *Also called Compucase Corporation (P-15525)*
Orion Woodcraft, San Diego *Also called T L Clark Co Inc (P-4355)*
Orlando Spring Corp E 562 594-8411
5341 Argosy Ave Huntington Beach (92649) *(P-13797)*
Orly International Inc D 818 994-1001
7710 Haskell Ave Van Nuys (91406) *(P-8808)*
Ormco Corporation (HQ) D 714 516-7400
1717 W Collins Ave Orange (92867) *(P-22896)*
Ormet Circuits Inc E 858 831-0010
6555 Nncy Rdge Dr Ste 200 San Diego (92121) *(P-19677)*
Orora Visual LLC D 714 879-2400
1600 E Valencia Dr Fullerton (92831) *(P-7424)*
Orora Visual TX LLC D 323 258-4111
3116 W Avenue 32 Los Angeles (90065) *(P-7425)*
Oroweat, Sacramento *Also called Bimbo Bakeries Usa Inc (P-1207)*
Oroweat Foods, San Diego *Also called Bimbo Bakeries Usa Inc (P-1195)*
Oroweat Foods, Anaheim *Also called Bimbo Bakeries Usa Inc (P-1200)*
Ortech Inc E 916 549-9696
6720 Folsom Blvd Ste 219 Sacramento (95819) *(P-10788)*
Ortech Advanced Ceramics, Sacramento *Also called Ortech Inc (P-10788)*
Ortega Manufacturing Inc F 951 766-9363
3960 Industrial Ave Hemet (92545) *(P-24197)*
Ortel A Division Emcore Co (HQ) F 626 293-3400
2015 Chestnut St Alhambra (91803) *(P-19066)*
Orthaheel, San Rafael *Also called Vionic Group LLC (P-10492)*
Ortho Engineering Inc (PA) E 310 559-5996
5759 Uplander Way Culver City (90230) *(P-22784)*
Ortho Organizers Inc C 760 448-8600
1822 Aston Ave Carlsbad (92008) *(P-22897)*
Ortho-Clinical Diagnostics Inc E 908 704-5910
1401 Red Hawk Cir E307 Fremont (94538) *(P-8501)*
Ortho-Clinical Diagnostics Inc E 714 639-2323
612 W Katella Ave Ste B Orange (92867) *(P-8502)*
Orthodental International Inc D 760 357-8070
280 Campillo St Ste J Calexico (92231) *(P-22898)*
Orthor Engineering Inc D 310 604-0000
3737 Martin Luther King J Lynwood (90262) *(P-22785)*
Ortronics Inc C 714 776-5420
1443 S Sunkist St Anaheim (92806) *(P-12697)*
Oryx Advanced Materials Inc (PA) E 510 249-1158
46458 Fremont Blvd Fremont (94538) *(P-15579)*
Osca-Arcosa, San Diego *Also called O & S California Inc (P-20035)*
Oscar Printing, San Francisco *Also called La Brothers Enterprise Inc (P-6936)*
Ose Usa Inc (HQ) F 408 452-9080
1737 N 1st St Ste 350 San Jose (95112) *(P-19067)*
OSI Electronics Inc (HQ) C 310 978-0516
12533 Chadron Ave Hawthorne (90250) *(P-18553)*
OSI Industries LLC E 951 684-4500
1155 Mt Vernon Ave Riverside (92507) *(P-24198)*
OSI Optoelectronics Inc E 805 987-0146
1240 Avenida Acaso Camarillo (93012) *(P-19068)*
OSI Subsidiary Inc B 310 978-0516
12525 Chadron Ave Hawthorne (90250) *(P-20037)*
OSI Systems Inc (PA) B 310 978-0516
12525 Chadron Ave Hawthorne (90250) *(P-19069)*
Osio International Inc F 714 935-9700
2550 E Cerritos Ave Anaheim (92806) *(P-5528)*
Osmosis Technology Inc E 714 670-9303
6900 Hermosa Cir Buena Park (90620) *(P-16084)*
Osmotik, Buena Park *Also called Osmosis Technology Inc (P-16084)*
Osr Enterprises Inc E 805 925-1831
1910 E Stowell Rd Santa Maria (93454) *(P-25039)*
Osram Sylvania Inc B 858 748-5077
13350 Gregg St Ste 101 Poway (92064) *(P-17434)*
OSS, Escondido *Also called One Stop Systems Inc (P-15817)*
Osseon LLC F 707 636-5940
2301 Circadian Way # 300 Santa Rosa (95407) *(P-22576)*
Ossic Corporation F 206 227-8585
1612 Calle Plumerias Encinitas (92024) *(P-25040)*
Ossur Americas Inc (HQ) B 949 362-3883
27051 Towne Centre Dr Foothill Ranch (92610) *(P-22786)*
Ossur Americas Inc F 949 382-3883
27051 Towne Centre Dr Foothill Ranch (92610) *(P-22787)*
Ossur Americas Inc E 805 484-2600
742 Pancho Rd Camarillo (93012) *(P-22788)*
Ossur North America, Camarillo *Also called Ossur Americas Inc (P-22788)*
Ostoich Diesel Service F 909 885-0590
1690 Ashley Way Colton (92324) *(P-16168)*
Osumo Inc F 510 346-6888
1933 Republic Ave San Leandro (94577) *(P-3911)*
OT Precision Inc E 408 435-8818
1450 Seareel Ln San Jose (95131) *(P-16812)*
Otanez New Creations F 951 808-9663
7179 E Columbus Dr Anaheim (92807) *(P-5090)*
Otonomy Inc D 619 323-2200
4796 Executive Dr San Diego (92121) *(P-8322)*
Otsuka America Inc (HQ) F 415 986-5300
1 Embarcadero Ctr # 2020 San Francisco (94111) *(P-22244)*
Otsuka America Foods Inc (HQ) F 424 219-9425
1 Embarcadero Ctr # 2020 San Francisco (94111) *(P-2632)*
Ottano Inc F 805 547-2088
11555 Los Osos Valley Rd # 201 San Luis Obispo (93405) *(P-1617)*
Otto ARC Systems Inc F 916 939-3400
3921 Sandstone Dr Ste 1 El Dorado Hills (95762) *(P-14735)*
Otto Instrument Service Inc (PA) C 909 930-5800
1441 Valencia Pl Ontario (91761) *(P-20899)*
Ottos Pizza Stix Inc F 562 519-5304
9040 Sunland Blvd Sun Valley (91352) *(P-1004)*
Oudimentary LLC F 510 501-5057
43170 Osgood Rd Fremont (94539) *(P-9294)*
Oupiin America Inc F 661 294-0228
27795 Avenue Hopkins Valencia (91355) *(P-17216)*
Our Powder Coating Inc F 562 946-0525
10103 Freeman Ave Santa Fe Springs (90670) *(P-13626)*
Oussoren Eppel Corporation F 858 483-6770
12232 Thatcher Ct Poway (92064) *(P-23938)*
Ouster Inc D 415 949-0108
350 Treat Ave San Francisco (94110) *(P-22245)*
Outback Inc F 559 369-7261
4201 W Shaw Ave Ste 106 Fresno (93722) *(P-11153)*
Outdoor Creations Inc F 530 365-6106
2270 Barney Rd Anderson (96007) *(P-10970)*
Outdoor Dimensions LLC C 714 578-9555
5325 E Hunter Ave Anaheim (92807) *(P-4639)*
Outdoor Galore Inc F 661 831-8662
5010 Young St Bakersfield (93311) *(P-15909)*
Outdoor Lfstyle Collective LLC F 858 336-5580
829 Windcrest Dr Carlsbad (92011) *(P-3267)*
Outdoor Products, View Park *Also called Outdoor Recreation Group (P-3768)*
Outdoor Recreation Group (PA) E 323 226-0830
3450 Mount Vernon Dr View Park (90008) *(P-3768)*
Outdoor Sign System Inc (PA) F 714 692-2052
22603 La Palma Ave # 309 Yorba Linda (92887) *(P-23939)*
Outer Limits Sports Fishing, San Diego *Also called M V Outer Limits (P-21051)*
Outlaw Beverage Inc F 310 424-5077
405 14th St Ste 1000 Oakland (94612) *(P-1618)*
Outlook Resources Inc D 714 522-2452
14930 Alondra Blvd La Mirada (90638) *(P-3856)*

ALPHABETIC

Employee Codes: A=Over 500 employees, B=251-500
C=101-250, D=51-100, E=20-50, F=10-19
2019 California
Manfacturers Register
© Mergent Inc. 1-800-342-5647
1235

Output Inc	F	310 795-6099
1418 N Spring St Ste 102 Los Angeles (90012) *(P-25041)*		
Outreach Corporation	E	888 938-7356
55 Union St 2 San Francisco (94111) *(P-25042)*		
Outreach Slutions As A Svc LLC	F	800 824-8573
980 9th St Fl 16 Sacramento (95814) *(P-6546)*		
Outsol Inc	F	760 415-8060
5910 Sea Lion Pl Ste 120 Carlsbad (92010) *(P-9908)*		
Outsystems Inc	F	925 804-6189
2603 Camino Ramon Ste 210 San Ramon (94583) *(P-25043)*		
Outword News Magazine	E	916 329-9280
1 Ebbtide Ct Sacramento (95831) *(P-6006)*		
Outword Newsmagazine, Sacramento *Also called Outword News Magazine* *(P-6006)*		
Ovation R&G LLC (PA)	E	310 430-7575
2850 Ocean Park Blvd # 225 Santa Monica (90405) *(P-18209)*		
Oven Fresh Bakery Incorporated	F	650 366-9201
23188 Foley St Hayward (94545) *(P-1302)*		
Over & Over Ready Mix Inc	D	818 983-1588
8216 Tujunga Ave Sun Valley (91352) *(P-10971)*		
Overbeck Machine	E	831 425-5912
2620 Mission St Santa Cruz (95060) *(P-16813)*		
Overhill Farms Inc	C	323 587-5985
431 Isis Ave Inglewood (90301) *(P-1005)*		
Overhill Farms Inc (HQ)	E	323 582-9977
2727 E Vernon Ave Vernon (90058) *(P-1006)*		
Overhill Farms Inc	C	323 584-4375
3055 E 44th St Vernon (90058) *(P-1007)*		
Overholtzer Elvan	E	209 869-2536
3142 Talbot Ave Riverbank (95367) *(P-4640)*		
Overland Storage Inc (HQ)	C	858 571-5555
4542 Ruffner St Ste 250 San Diego (92111) *(P-15580)*		
Overlook Vineyards LLC (HQ)	E	707 833-0053
101 Adobe Canyon Rd Kenwood (95452) *(P-1909)*		
Overlook Vineyards LLC	E	707 433-6491
58 W North St Ste 101 Healdsburg (95448) *(P-1910)*		
Owen Magic Supreme Inc	F	626 969-4519
734 N Mckeever Ave Azusa (91702) *(P-24199)*		
Owen Oil Tools Inc	E	661 637-1380
5001 Standard St Bakersfield (93308) *(P-9184)*		
Owen Trailers Inc	E	951 361-4557
9020 Jurupa Rd Riverside (92509) *(P-20507)*		
Owen Weldon Inc (HQ)	E	415 291-0100
1045 Sansome St Ste 100 San Francisco (94111) *(P-6374)*		
Owen Weldon Publishing Inc (HQ)	F	415 291-0100
1045 Sansome St Ste 100 San Francisco (94111) *(P-6375)*		
Owens Corning Sales LLC	C	310 631-1062
1501 N Tamarind Ave Compton (90222) *(P-9416)*		
Owens Design Incorporated	E	510 659-1800
47427 Fremont Blvd Fremont (94538) *(P-16814)*		
Owens Printing Co	F	818 773-8900
9170 Independence Ave Chatsworth (91311) *(P-7008)*		
Owens-Brockway Glass Cont Inc	D	510 436-2000
3600 Alameda Ave Oakland (94601) *(P-10623)*		
Owl Territory Inc	F	800 607-0677
227 Broadway Ste 303 Santa Monica (90401) *(P-25044)*		
Oxbo International Corporation	F	559 897-7012
10825 W Goshen Ave Visalia (93291) *(P-14090)*		
Oxbow Activated Carbon LLC	E	760 630-5724
2535 Jason Ct Oceanside (92056) *(P-7794)*		
Oxford Instrs Asylum RES Inc (HQ)	D	805 696-6466
6310 Hollister Ave Santa Barbara (93117) *(P-22001)*		
Oxford Instruments X-Ray Tech	D	831 439-9729
360 El Pueblo Rd Scotts Valley (95066) *(P-19678)*		
Oxnard Lemon Company	F	805 483-1173
2001 Sunkist Cir Oxnard (93033) *(P-960)*		
Oxnard Pallet Company, Oxnard *Also called E Vasquez Distributors Inc* *(P-4468)*		
Oxnard Prcsion Fabrication Inc	E	805 985-0447
2200 Teal Club Rd Oxnard (93030) *(P-12698)*		
OXY USA Inc	C	661 869-8000
9600 Ming Ave Ste 300 Bakersfield (93311) *(P-67)*		
Ozeki Sake U S A Inc (HQ)	E	831 637-9217
249 Hillcrest Rd Hollister (95023) *(P-1911)*		
Ozmo Inc	E	650 515-3524
1600 Technology Dr San Jose (95110) *(P-15581)*		
Ozmo Devices, San Jose *Also called Ozmo Inc* *(P-15581)*		
Ozotech Inc (PA)	E	530 842-4189
2401 E Oberlin Rd Yreka (96097) *(P-16085)*		
P & E Rubber Processing Inc	E	760 241-2643
15380 Lyons Valley Rd Jamul (91935) *(P-9651)*		
P & F Machine Inc	F	209 667-2515
301 S Broadway Turlock (95380) *(P-16815)*		
P & F Metals, Turlock *Also called Turlock Sheet Metal & Wldg Inc* *(P-1049)*		
P & L Concrete Products Inc	E	209 838-1448
1900 Roosevelt Ave Escalon (95320) *(P-11154)*		
P & L Development LLC	C	323 567-2482
11865 Alameda St Lynwood (90262) *(P-8602)*		
P & L Development LLC	E	310 763-1377
11840 Alameda St Lynwood (90262) *(P-8323)*		
P & L Specialties	F	707 573-3141
1650 Almar Pkwy Santa Rosa (95403) *(P-15003)*		
P & R Pallets Inc	E	213 327-1104
2301 Porter St Los Angeles (90021) *(P-4490)*		
P & R Paper Supply Co Inc	F	619 671-2400
1350 Piper Ranch Rd San Diego (92154) *(P-5721)*		
P & S Sales Inc	F	510 732-2628
20943 Cabot Blvd Hayward (94545) *(P-20416)*		
P A C, San Rafael *Also called Packaging Aids Corporation* *(P-15221)*		
P A P, Anaheim *Also called Precision Anodizing & Pltg Inc* *(P-13478)*		
P A S U Inc	C	619 421-1151
1891 Nirvana Ave Chula Vista (91911) *(P-12699)*		
P A X Industries, Costa Mesa *Also called Tk Pax Inc* *(P-9510)*		
P C I Manufacturing Division	F	714 543-3496
2103 N Ross St Santa Ana (92706) *(P-18210)*		
P C S, Hollister *Also called Pride Conveyance Systems Inc* *(P-14281)*		
P C S C, Torrance *Also called Proprietary Controls Systems* *(P-22252)*		
P C Teas, Burlingame *Also called Prestige Chinese Teas Co* *(P-2641)*		
P E N Inc	E	818 954-0775
215 Allen Ave Glendale (91201) *(P-7426)*		
P G Molinari & Sons Inc	F	415 822-5555
1401 Yosemite Ave San Francisco (94124) *(P-511)*		
P H Machining Inc	E	408 980-9895
1099 N 5th St San Jose (95112) *(P-18211)*		
P J Machining Co Inc	F	760 948-2722
17056 Hercules St Ste 101 Hesperia (92345) *(P-16816)*		
P J Milligan & Associates, Santa Barbara *Also called P J Milligan Company LLC* *(P-4730)*		
P J Milligan Company LLC (PA)	F	805 963-4038
436 E Gutierrez St Santa Barbara (93101) *(P-4730)*		
P K C, Santa Ana *Also called Mustard Seed Technologies Inc* *(P-19657)*		
P K Engineering & Mfg Co Inc	E	805 628-9556
200 E Shell Rd 2b Ventura (93001) *(P-22577)*		
P K Metal, Los Angeles *Also called P Kay Metal Inc* *(P-11636)*		
P K Selective Metal Pltg Inc	F	408 988-1910
415 Mathew St Santa Clara (95050) *(P-13472)*		
P Kay Metal Inc (PA)	E	323 585-5058
2448 E 25th St Los Angeles (90058) *(P-11636)*		
P L D S, Milpitas *Also called Philips & Lite-On Digital* *(P-15583)*		
P L M, Los Angeles *Also called Prudential Lighting Corp* *(P-17639)*		
P M D, Gardena *Also called Pedavena Mould and Die Co Inc* *(P-16836)*		
P M I, San Diego *Also called Pacific Maritime Inds Corp* *(P-12224)*		
P M S D Inc	D	408 988-5235
950 George St Santa Clara (95054) *(P-16817)*		
P P I, Corona *Also called Preproduction Plastics Inc* *(P-10308)*		
P P Mfg Co Inc	F	562 921-3640
13130 Arctic Cir Santa Fe Springs (90670) *(P-13256)*		
P P T, Rancho Cucamonga *Also called Pacific Plastic Technology Inc* *(P-9755)*		
P R P Multisource Inc	E	951 681-6100
3836 Wacker Dr Mira Loma (91752) *(P-15220)*		
P S C Manufacturing Inc	E	408 988-5115
3424 De La Cruz Blvd Santa Clara (95054) *(P-10256)*		
P S E Boilers, Santa Fe Springs *Also called Pacific Steam Equipment Inc* *(P-12404)*		
P S I, Beaumont *Also called Precision Stampings Inc* *(P-17487)*		
P T I, Torrance *Also called Plasma Technology Incorporated* *(P-13636)*		
P T I, Bloomington *Also called Products/Techniques Inc* *(P-8934)*		
P T I, Santa Ana *Also called Parpro Technologies Inc* *(P-18557)*		
P T Industries Inc	F	562 961-3431
3220 Industry Dr Signal Hill (90755) *(P-12700)*		
P T M Inc	E	559 673-1552
10842 Road 28 1/2 Madera (93637) *(P-4491)*		
P T P, Carson *Also called Pacific Toll Processing Inc* *(P-11409)*		
P V I, Oxnard *Also called Poole Ventura Inc* *(P-15134)*		
P V T Supply, Paramount *Also called Wagner Plate Works West Inc* *(P-12439)*		
P W Pipe, Perris *Also called Pw Eagle Inc* *(P-9787)*		
P W Pipe, Shingle Springs *Also called Pw Eagle Inc* *(P-9788)*		
P W Wiring Systems LLC	E	562 463-9055
9415 Kruse Rd Pico Rivera (90660) *(P-19407)*		
P&P Enterprises	F	213 802-0890
1246 W 7th St Los Angeles (90017) *(P-23940)*		
P&Y T-Shrts Silk Screening Inc	D	323 585-4604
2126 E 52nd St Vernon (90058) *(P-14777)*		
P-Americas LLC	E	510 732-9500
3586 Arden Rd Hayward (94545) *(P-2160)*		
P-Americas LLC	C	805 641-4200
4375 N Ventura Ave Ventura (93001) *(P-2161)*		
P-W Western Inc	D	562 463-9055
9415 Kruse Rd Pico Rivera (90660) *(P-12403)*		
P.E.P., Pomona *Also called Performnce Engineered Pdts Inc* *(P-10272)*		
Pabco Building Products LLC	D	510 792-9555
37851 Cherry St Newark (94560) *(P-11221)*		
Pabco Building Products LLC	E	510 792-1577
37849 Cherry St Newark (94560) *(P-11222)*		
Pabco Building Products LLC (HQ)	E	510 792-1577
10600 White Rock Rd # 100 Rancho Cordova (95670) *(P-11223)*		
Pabco Building Products LLC	D	323 581-6113
4460 Pacific Blvd Vernon (90058) *(P-11224)*		
Pabco Building Products LLC	D	916 645-3341
601 7th St Lincoln (95648) *(P-10803)*		
Pabco Clay Products LLC	C	916 645-3341
601 7th St Lincoln (95648) *(P-10776)*		
Pabco Clay Products LLC	D	916 859-6320
4875 Bradshaw Rd Sacramento (95827) *(P-10777)*		
Pabco Gypsum, Newark *Also called Pabco Building Products LLC* *(P-11221)*		
Pabco Paper, Vernon *Also called Pabco Building Products LLC* *(P-11224)*		
Pabst Brewing Company LLC (PA)	B	310 470-0962
10635 Santa Monica Blvd Los Angeles (90025) *(P-1619)*		
Pac 21	F	714 891-7000
11888 Western Ave Stanton (90680) *(P-21629)*		
Pac Fill Inc	E	818 409-0117
5471 W San Fernando Rd Los Angeles (90039) *(P-732)*		
Pac Foundries Inc	E	805 986-1308
705 Industrial Way Port Hueneme (93041) *(P-11748)*		
Pac Litho, Huntington Beach *Also called Kj Aero Holdings LLC* *(P-6924)*		
Pac Powder Inc	F	707 826-1630
148 S G St Ste 9 Arcata (95521) *(P-13627)*		
Pac Tech USA Packg Tech Inc	F	408 588-1925
328 Martin Ave Santa Clara (95050) *(P-19070)*		
Pac Trim, Rocklin *Also called Pacific Mdf Products Inc* *(P-4209)*		

Mergent e-mail: customerrelations@mergent.com
1236
2019 California
Manufacturers Register
(P-0000) Products & Services Section entry number
(PA)=Parent Co (HQ)=Headquarters (DH)=Div Headquarters

ALPHABETIC SECTION
Pacific Foam, Ontario

Pac-Com International F 562 903-3900
11217 Shoemaker Ave Santa Fe Springs (90670) ***(P-11300)***

Pac-Rancho Inc (HQ) C 909 987-4721
11000 Jersey Blvd Rancho Cucamonga (91730) ***(P-11519)***

Pac-West Rubber Products LLC F 760 891-0911
120 Venture St San Marcos (92078) ***(P-9570)***

Pace Americas Inc E 310 606-8300
887 N Douglas St 200 El Segundo (90245) ***(P-18212)***

Pace International LLC E 559 651-4877
1104 N Nevada St Visalia (93291) ***(P-8661)***

Pace Punches Inc D 949 428-2750
297 Goddard Irvine (92618) ***(P-14554)***

Pace Sportswear Inc F 714 891-8716
12781 Monarch St Garden Grove (92841) ***(P-3474)***

Pacer Technology, Ontario *Also called Super Glue Corporation* ***(P-9173)***

Pacer Technology D 909 987-0550
11201 Jersey Blvd Rancho Cucamonga (91730) ***(P-9159)***

Pacesetter Inc (HQ) A 818 362-6822
15900 Valley View Ct Sylmar (91342) ***(P-23032)***

Pacesetter Fabrics LLC (HQ) F 213 741-9999
11450 Sheldon St Sun Valley (91352) ***(P-3012)***

Pacful Inc (PA) D 916 233-1488
11311 White Rock Rd # 100 Rancho Cordova (95742) ***(P-7009)***

Pacful Inc D 650 200-4252
131 Glenn Way Ste 4 San Carlos (94070) ***(P-7010)***

Pachunga Gas Station F 951 506-4575
45000 Pechanga Pkwy Temecula (92592) ***(P-254)***

Pacific Accent Incorporated F 909 563-1600
623 S Doubleday Ave Ontario (91761) ***(P-17401)***

Pacific Accesory, Ontario *Also called Clarke Pb & Associates Inc* ***(P-17782)***

Pacific Aero Components Inc (PA) F 818 841-9258
28887 Industry Dr Valencia (91355) ***(P-20900)***

Pacific Aerodynamic Inc F 714 450-9140
889 N Main St Orange (92868) ***(P-20671)***

Pacific Aerospace Machine Inc E 714 534-1444
3002 S Rosewood Ave Santa Ana (92707) ***(P-16818)***

Pacific Aggregates Inc D 951 245-2460
28251 Lake St Lake Elsinore (92530) ***(P-11155)***

Pacific Air Industries Inc E 310 829-4345
9650 De Soto Ave Chatsworth (91311) ***(P-20901)***

Pacific Alliance Capital Inc F 949 360-1796
27141 Aliso Creek Rd # 215 Aliso Viejo (92656) ***(P-15582)***

Pacific Analogix Semiconductor, Santa Clara *Also called Analogix Semiconductor Inc* ***(P-18700)***

Pacific Archtectural Mllwk Inc (PA) D 562 905-3200
1435 Pioneer St Brea (92821) ***(P-4207)***

Pacific Artglass Corporation E 310 516-7828
125 W 157th St Gardena (90248) ***(P-10725)***

Pacific Athletic Wear Inc D 714 751-8006
1545 Macarthur Blvd Costa Mesa (92626) ***(P-3475)***

Pacific Automated LLC F 800 372-5098
1951 Monarch St 200 Alameda (94501) ***(P-2162)***

Pacific Avalon Yacht Charters, Newport Beach *Also called Fantasea Enterprises Inc* ***(P-21036)***

Pacific Award Metals Inc (HQ) D 626 814-4410
1450 Virginia Ave Baldwin Park (91706) ***(P-12701)***

Pacific Award Metals Inc E 626 814-4410
13169 Slover Ave Fontana (92337) ***(P-12702)***

Pacific Award Metals Inc D 626 814-4410
1450 Virginia Ave Baldwin Park (91706) ***(P-12703)***

Pacific Barcode Inc F 951 587-8717
27531 Enterprise Cir W 201c Temecula (92590) ***(P-14821)***

Pacific Biosciences Cal Inc (PA) B 650 521-8000
1305 Obrien Dr Menlo Park (94025) ***(P-22002)***

Pacific Biotech Inc C 858 552-1100
10165 Mckellar Ct San Diego (92121) ***(P-8503)***

Pacific Boat Trailers Inc (PA) E 909 902-0094
13643 5th St Chino (91710) ***(P-21238)***

Pacific Boulevard Inc F 323 581-1656
5075 Pacific Blvd Vernon (90058) ***(P-3331)***

Pacific Bridge Packaging Inc F 909 598-1988
103 Exchange Pl Pomona (91768) ***(P-11864)***

Pacific Broach & Engrg Assoc F 714 632-5678
1513 N Kraemer Blvd Anaheim (92806) ***(P-16819)***

Pacific Bulletproof Co F 714 630-5447
4985 E Landon Dr Anaheim (92807) ***(P-21167)***

Pacific Capacitor Co F 408 778-6670
288 Digital Dr Morgan Hill (95037) ***(P-19302)***

Pacific Cast Products, Santa Fe Springs *Also called Alumistar Inc* ***(P-11723)***

Pacific Casual LLC E 805 445-8310
1060 Avenida Acaso Camarillo (93012) ***(P-4838)***

Pacific Catch Inc F 415 504-6905
770 Tamalpais Dr Ste 400 Corte Madera (94925) ***(P-1154)***

Pacific Ceramics Inc E 408 747-4600
824 San Aleso Ave Sunnyvale (94085) ***(P-10821)***

Pacific Choice Brands Inc (PA) B 559 892-5365
4667 E Date Ave Fresno (93725) ***(P-926)***

Pacific Clears, Eureka *Also called Schmidbauer Lumber Inc* ***(P-4052)***

Pacific Cnc Machine Co F 760 431-7558
2702 Gateway Rd Carlsbad (92009) ***(P-16820)***

Pacific Coachworks Inc C 951 686-7294
3411 N Perris Blvd Bldg 1 Perris (92571) ***(P-21208)***

Pacific Coast Bach Label Co E 213 612-0314
3015 S Grand Ave Los Angeles (90007) ***(P-2915)***

Pacific Coast Bindery Inc E 562 908-5900
12250 Coast Dr Whittier (90601) ***(P-7610)***

Pacific Coast Bus Times Inc F 805 560-6950
14 E Carrillo St Ste A Santa Barbara (93101) ***(P-6007)***

Pacific Coast Coml Interiors, Carlsbad *Also called N M Floor Coverings Inc* ***(P-4086)***

Pacific Coast Fabricators Inc F 909 627-3833
14375 Telephone Ave Chino (91710) ***(P-12222)***

Pacific Coast Feather LLC C 562 222-5560
8500 Rex Rd Pico Rivera (90660) ***(P-3737)***

Pacific Coast Feather Cushion (HQ) C 562 801-9995
7600 Industry Ave Pico Rivera (90660) ***(P-3738)***

Pacific Coast Home Furn Inc (PA) F 323 838-7808
2424 Saybrook Ave Commerce (90040) ***(P-3739)***

Pacific Coast Ironworks Inc F 323 585-1320
8831 Miner St Los Angeles (90002) ***(P-12223)***

Pacific Coast Laboratories F 510 351-2770
1031 San Leandro Blvd San Leandro (94577) ***(P-22789)***

Pacific Coast Lighting, Ventura *Also called Lamps Plus Inc* ***(P-17624)***

Pacific Coast Lighting Inc (PA) C 818 886-9751
20238 Plummer St Chatsworth (91311) ***(P-17722)***

Pacific Coast Mfg Inc D 909 627-7040
5270 Edison Ave Chino (91710) ***(P-17374)***

Pacific Coast Optics Inc E 916 789-0111
10604 Industrial Ave # 100 Roseville (95678) ***(P-22118)***

Pacific Coast Pallets Inc E 626 937-6565
15151 Salt Lake Ave La Puente (91746) ***(P-4492)***

Pacific Coast Producers, Lodi *Also called Liberty Foods Trading Co LLC* ***(P-819)***

Pacific Coast Producers D 209 334-3352
741 S Stockton St Lodi (95240) ***(P-842)***

Pacific Coast Producers (PA) B 209 367-8800
631 N Cluff Ave Lodi (95240) ***(P-843)***

Pacific Coast Producers C 530 533-4311
1601 Mitchell Ave Oroville (95965) ***(P-844)***

Pacific Coast Producers B 530 662-8661
1376 Lemen Ave Woodland (95776) ***(P-845)***

Pacific Coast Producers C 530 534-1344
1376 Lemen Ave Woodland (95776) ***(P-846)***

Pacific Coast Products LLC (PA) F 831 316-7137
170 Technology Cir Scotts Valley (95066) ***(P-2275)***

Pacific Coast Products LLC E 831 316-7137
200 Technology Cir Scotts Valley (95066) ***(P-2276)***

Pacific Coast Sportswear, Fountain Valley *Also called Watt Enterprise Inc* ***(P-3205)***

Pacific Coast Supply LLC E 559 651-2185
30158 Road 68 Visalia (93291) ***(P-11225)***

Pacific Coast Supply LLC F 916 339-8100
5550 Roseville Rd North Highlands (95660) ***(P-4419)***

Pacific Collision Equipment, Signal Hill *Also called Hornedo Inc* ***(P-14966)***

Pacific Color Graphics Inc F 925 600-3006
6336 Patterson Pass Rd A Livermore (94550) ***(P-7427)***

Pacific Communications, Irvine *Also called Allergan Usa Inc* ***(P-8014)***

Pacific Composites Inc F 949 498-8600
221 Calle Pintoresco San Clemente (92672) ***(P-11520)***

Pacific Computer Products Inc E 714 549-7535
2210 S Huron Dr Santa Ana (92704) ***(P-23735)***

Pacific Consolidated Inds LLC D 951 479-0860
12201 Magnolia Ave Riverside (92503) ***(P-15345)***

Pacific Containerprint Inc E 909 465-0365
5951 Riverside Dr Apt 4 Chino (91710) ***(P-7428)***

Pacific Contntl Textiles Inc (HQ) E 310 604-1100
18737 S Reyes Ave Compton (90221) ***(P-2916)***

Pacific Contntl Textiles Inc F 310 639-1500
2880 E Ana St E Rncho Dmngz (90221) ***(P-2887)***

Pacific Controls E D M, Encino *Also called Pacific Controls Inc* ***(P-20038)***

Pacific Controls Inc F 818 345-1970
4949 Newcastle Ave Encino (91316) ***(P-20038)***

Pacific Corrugated Pipe, Fontana *Also called W E Hall Co* ***(P-12814)***

Pacific Corrugated Pipe Co, Newport Beach *Also called WE Hall Company Inc* ***(P-11472)***

Pacific Corrugated Pipe Co, Sacramento *Also called WE Hall Company Inc* ***(P-11020)***

Pacific Design Tech Inc E 805 961-9110
6300 Lindmar Dr Goleta (93117) ***(P-21377)***

Pacific Die Cast Inc F 562 407-1390
15980 Bloomfield Ave Cerritos (90703) ***(P-14555)***

Pacific Die Casting Corp C 323 725-1308
6155 S Eastern Ave Commerce (90040) ***(P-11701)***

Pacific Die Cut Industries D 510 732-8103
3399 Arden Rd Hayward (94545) ***(P-9545)***

Pacific Die Services Inc F 562 907-4463
7626 Baldwin Pl Whittier (90602) ***(P-14556)***

Pacific Diversified Capital Co A 619 696-2000
101 Ash St San Diego (92101) ***(P-22246)***

Pacific Door & Cabinet Company E 559 439-3822
7050 N Harrison Ave Pinedale (93650) ***(P-4208)***

Pacific Drapery, San Diego *Also called Manzer Corporation* ***(P-3696)***

Pacific Drilling, San Diego *Also called Limited Access Unlimited Inc* ***(P-406)***

Pacific Dry Goods Inc F 925 288-2929
1085 Essex Ave Richmond (94801) ***(P-2794)***

Pacific Duct Inc E 909 635-1335
5499 Brooks St Montclair (91763) ***(P-12704)***

Pacific Eagle USA Inc E 626 455-0033
9707 El Poche St Ste H South El Monte (91733) ***(P-9652)***

Pacific Earthscape, McKinleyville *Also called Ford Logging Inc* ***(P-3987)***

Pacific Energy Resources Ltd (PA) F 562 628-1526
111 W Ocean Blvd Ste 1240 Long Beach (90802) ***(P-68)***

Pacific Ethanol Central LLC (HQ) D 916 403-2123
400 Capitol Mall Ste 2060 Sacramento (95814) ***(P-9027)***

Pacific Ethanol West LLC C 916 403-2123
400 Capitol Mall Ste 2060 Sacramento (95814) ***(P-9028)***

Pacific Fibre & Rope Co Inc F 310 834-4567
903 Flint Ave 927 Wilmington (90744) ***(P-2976)***

Pacific Fixture Company Inc F 818 362-2130
12860 San Fernando Rd B1 Sylmar (91342) ***(P-5159)***

Pacific Flyway Decoy Assn F 925 754-4978
300 Marble Dr Antioch (94509) ***(P-23627)***

Pacific Foam, Ontario *Also called Induspac California Inc* ***(P-7841)***

ALPHABETIC

Employee Codes: A=Over 500 employees, B=251-500
C=101-250, D=51-100, E=20-50, F=10-19
2019 California
Manfacturers Register
© Mergent Inc. 1-800-342-5647
1237

Pacific Forge Inc.......D.......909 390-0701
10641 Etiwanda Ave Fontana (92337) ***(P-13108)***
Pacific Galvanizing Inc.......E.......510 261-7331
715 46th Ave Oakland (94601) ***(P-13628)***
Pacific Gaming.......E.......510 562-8900
1975 Adams Ave San Leandro (94577) ***(P-23454)***
Pacific Ginning Company LLC.......E.......559 829-9446
33370 W Nebraska Ave Cantua Creek (93608) ***(P-15004)***
Pacific Glass, Gardena *Also called Pacific Artglass Corporation* ***(P-10725)***
Pacific Green Trucking Inc.......F.......310 830-4528
512 E C St Wilmington (90744) ***(P-21082)***
Pacific Handy Cutter Inc.......E.......714 662-1033
17819 Gillette Ave Irvine (92614) ***(P-11905)***
Pacific Hardware Sales, Anaheim *Also called A J Fasteners Inc* ***(P-13056)***
Pacific Hardwood Cabinetry.......E.......707 528-8627
2811 Dowd Dr Santa Rosa (95407) ***(P-4333)***
Pacific Imaging.......F.......858 536-2600
9687 Distribution Ave San Diego (92121) ***(P-7011)***
Pacific Impressions Inc.......F.......408 727-4200
3494 Edward Ave Santa Clara (95054) ***(P-2888)***
Pacific Inspection, Arbuckle *Also called National Oilwell Varco Inc* ***(P-247)***
Pacific Instruments Inc.......E.......925 827-9010
4080 Pike Ln Concord (94520) ***(P-22247)***
Pacific Integrated Mfg Inc.......C.......619 921-3464
4364 Bonita Rd Ste 454 Bonita (91902) ***(P-22578)***
Pacific International Stl Corp.......E.......209 931-0900
2889 Navone Rd Stockton (95215) ***(P-12986)***
Pacific Intl Rice Mills, Woodland *Also called Bunge North America Inc* ***(P-1074)***
Pacific Intrlock Pvngstone Inc (PA).......F.......831 637-9163
1895 San Felipe Rd Hollister (95023) ***(P-10972)***
Pacific Kiln Insulations Inc.......F.......951 697-4422
14370 Veterans Way Moreno Valley (92553) ***(P-15271)***
Pacific Label Inc.......D.......714 237-1276
1511 E Edinger Ave Santa Ana (92705) ***(P-5574)***
Pacific Lasertec Inc.......E.......760 450-4095
3821 Sienna St Oceanside (92056) ***(P-24200)***
Pacific Light Blown Glass, Cudahy *Also called Alamillo Radolfo* ***(P-10630)***
Pacific Lighting & Electrical, Sacramento *Also called Mw McWong International Inc* ***(P-17717)***
Pacific Link Corp.......F.......714 897-3525
15865 Chemical Ln Huntington Beach (92649) ***(P-22119)***
Pacific Lock Company (PA).......E.......661 294-3707
25605 Hercules St Valencia (91355) ***(P-11982)***
Pacific Ltg & Standards Co.......E.......310 603-9344
2815 Los Flores Blvd Lynwood (90262) ***(P-17635)***
Pacific Magnetics, Chula Vista *Also called Pacmag Inc* ***(P-19679)***
Pacific Manufacturing MGT Inc.......D.......323 263-9000
3110 E 12th St Los Angeles (90023) ***(P-5160)***
Pacific Marine Shtmtl Corp.......C.......858 869-8900
2650 Jamacha Rd El Cajon (92019) ***(P-12705)***
Pacific Maritime Inds Corp.......C.......619 575-8141
1790 Dornoch Ct San Diego (92154) ***(P-12224)***
Pacific Mdf Products Inc (PA).......D.......916 660-1882
4312 Anthony Ct Ste A Rocklin (95677) ***(P-4209)***
Pacific Metal Fab & Design, Madera *Also called Pacific Sheet Metal Inc* ***(P-12708)***
Pacific Metal Finishing Inc.......F.......805 237-8886
440 Sherwood Rd Paso Robles (93446) ***(P-13629)***
Pacific Metal Products, Los Angeles *Also called Basic Industries Intl Inc* ***(P-12363)***
Pacific Metal Stampings Inc.......E.......661 257-7656
28415 Witherspoon Pkwy Valencia (91355) ***(P-13257)***
Pacific Metals Group LLC.......E.......909 218-8889
787 S Wanamaker Ave Ontario (91761) ***(P-12706)***
Pacific Mfg Inc San Diego.......E.......619 423-0316
1520 Corporate Center Dr San Diego (92154) ***(P-16821)***
Pacific Millennium US Corp.......F.......858 450-1505
12526 High Bluff Dr # 300 San Diego (92130) ***(P-5320)***
Pacific Miniatures, Fullerton *Also called Pacmin Incorporated* ***(P-24203)***
Pacific Modern Homes Inc.......E.......916 685-9514
9723 Railroad St Elk Grove (95624) ***(P-12707)***
pacific Molding Inc.......F.......951 683-2100
1390 Dodson Way Riverside (92507) ***(P-10257)***
Pacific Natural Spices, Commerce *Also called Pacific Spice Company Inc* ***(P-2633)***
Pacific Naturals, Pacoima *Also called Gscm Ventures Inc* ***(P-8760)***
Pacific Neon.......E.......916 927-0527
2939 Academy Way Sacramento (95815) ***(P-23941)***
Pacific Northwest Pubg Co Inc.......B.......916 321-1828
2100 Q St Sacramento (95816) ***(P-6008)***
Pacific Operators Inc.......E.......805 899-3144
205 E Carrillo St Ste 200 Santa Barbara (93101) ***(P-115)***
Pacific Packaging McHy LLC (HQ).......E.......949 369-2425
200 River Rd Corona (92880) ***(P-14875)***
Pacific Pallet Co, Glendale *Also called Long Beach Woodworks LLC* ***(P-4484)***
Pacific Pallet Exchange Inc.......E.......916 448-5589
3350 51st Ave Sacramento (95823) ***(P-4493)***
Pacific Panel Products Corp.......E.......626 851-0444
15601 Arrow Hwy Irwindale (91706) ***(P-4381)***
Pacific Paper Box Company (PA).......E.......323 771-7733
3928 Encino Hills Pl Encino (91436) ***(P-5379)***
Pacific Paper Tube Inc (PA).......E.......510 562-8823
4343 E Fremont St Stockton (95215) ***(P-5492)***
Pacific Perforating Inc.......E.......661 768-9224
25090 Highway 33 Fellows (93224) ***(P-255)***
Pacific Pharmascience Inc.......F.......949 916-6955
23052 Alcalde Dr Ste A Laguna Hills (92653) ***(P-8324)***
Pacific Pickle Works Inc.......F.......805 765-1779
718 Union Ave Snta Brbara Santa Barbara Santa Barbara (93103) ***(P-927)***
Pacific Piston Ring Co Inc.......D.......310 836-3322
3620 Eastham Dr Culver City (90232) ***(P-16149)***
Pacific Plastic Technology Inc.......E.......909 987-4200
9555 Hyssop Dr Rancho Cucamonga (91730) ***(P-9755)***
Pacific Plastics Inc.......D.......714 990-9050
111 S Berry St Brea (92821) ***(P-9784)***
Pacific Plastics Design Inc.......E.......818 364-6677
15570 Roxford St Sylmar (91342) ***(P-10258)***
Pacific Plating, Sun Valley *Also called K V R Investment Group Inc* ***(P-14978)***
Pacific Play Tents Inc.......F.......323 269-0431
2801 E 12th St Los Angeles (90023) ***(P-3800)***
Pacific Plaza Imports Inc (PA).......E.......925 349-4000
3018 Willow Pass Rd # 102 Concord (94519) ***(P-2300)***
Pacific Plstcs-Njction Molding, Vista *Also called J A English II Inc* ***(P-10159)***
Pacific Powder Coating, Arcata *Also called Pac Powder Inc* ***(P-13627)***
Pacific Powder Coating Inc.......E.......916 381-1154
8637 23rd Ave Sacramento (95826) ***(P-13630)***
Pacific Pprbd Converting LLC (PA).......E.......909 476-6466
8865 Utica Ave Ste A Rancho Cucamonga (91730) ***(P-5722)***
Pacific Precision Labs Inc.......E.......818 700-8977
9430 Lurline Ave Chatsworth (91311) ***(P-22248)***
Pacific Precision Metals Inc.......C.......951 226-1500
1100 E Orangethorpe Ave Anaheim (92801) ***(P-13258)***
Pacific Press, Anaheim *Also called Wasser Filtration Inc* ***(P-15373)***
Pacific Press Corporation.......E.......408 292-3422
2350 S 10th St San Jose (95112) ***(P-6009)***
Pacific Printing, San Diego *Also called Pacific Imaging* ***(P-7011)***
Pacific Process Systems Inc (PA).......D.......661 321-9681
7401 Rosedale Hwy Bakersfield (93308) ***(P-256)***
Pacific Pulp Molding Inc.......E.......619 977-5617
11285 Forestview Ln San Diego (92131) ***(P-5321)***
Pacific Quality Packaging Corp.......D.......714 257-1234
660 Neptune Ave Brea (92821) ***(P-5442)***
Pacific Quartz Inc.......E.......714 546-8133
1404 E Saint Gertrude Pl Santa Ana (92705) ***(P-22120)***
Pacific Rim Printers & Mailers, Culver City *Also called Econ-O-Plate Inc* ***(P-6801)***
Pacific Rim Publishing, Fremont *Also called T C Media Inc* ***(P-6266)***
Pacific Scientific Company (HQ).......E.......805 526-5700
1785 Voyager Ave Simi Valley (93063) ***(P-21378)***
Pacific Scientific Energetic (HQ).......B.......831 637-3731
3601 Union Rd Hollister (95023) ***(P-9295)***
Pacific Screw Products Inc.......D.......650 583-9682
1331c Old County Rd Belmont (94002) ***(P-13036)***
Pacific Seismic Products Inc.......E.......661 942-4499
233 E Avenue H8 Lancaster (93535) ***(P-13729)***
Pacific Sheet Metal Inc.......F.......559 661-4044
497 S Pine St Madera (93637) ***(P-12708)***
Pacific Ship Repr Fbrction Inc (PA).......B.......619 232-3200
1625 Rigel St San Diego (92113) ***(P-21007)***
Pacific Shore Holdings Inc.......F.......818 998-0996
8236 Remmet Ave Canoga Park (91304) ***(P-8325)***
Pacific Sky Supply Inc.......D.......818 768-3700
8230 San Fernando Rd Sun Valley (91352) ***(P-20902)***
Pacific Southwest Cont LLC (PA).......B.......209 526-0444
4530 Leckron Rd Modesto (95357) ***(P-5529)***
Pacific Southwest Cont LLC.......D.......559 651-5500
9525 W Nicholas Ct Visalia (93291) ***(P-5443)***
Pacific Southwest Cont LLC.......E.......209 373-2900
4530 Leckron Rd Modesto (95357) ***(P-5444)***
Pacific Southwest Molds.......F.......562 803-9811
12307 Woodruff Ave Downey (90241) ***(P-14557)***
Pacific Spice Company Inc.......D.......323 726-9190
6430 E Slauson Ave Commerce (90040) ***(P-2633)***
Pacific Stainless, Colton *Also called S & S Installations Inc* ***(P-16104)***
Pacific Standard Print, Sacramento *Also called American Lithographers Inc* ***(P-6655)***
Pacific States Felt Mfg Co Inc.......F.......510 783-2357
23850 Clawiter Rd Ste 20 Hayward (94545) ***(P-9546)***
Pacific States Treating Inc.......F.......530 938-4408
422 Mill St Weed (96094) ***(P-4595)***
Pacific Steam Equipment Inc.......E.......562 906-9292
11748 Slauson Ave Santa Fe Springs (90670) ***(P-12404)***
Pacific Steel Fabricators Inc.......E.......209 464-9474
8275 San Leandro St Oakland (94621) ***(P-12225)***
Pacific Steel Group (PA).......D.......858 251-1100
4805 Murphy Canyon Rd San Diego (92123) ***(P-12987)***
Pacific Steel Group.......E.......707 669-3136
2301 Napa Vallejo Hwy NAPA (94558) ***(P-12988)***
Pacific Stone Design Inc.......E.......714 836-5757
1201 E Wakeham Ave Santa Ana (92705) ***(P-10973)***
Pacific Sun.......F.......415 488-8100
847 5th St Santa Rosa (95404) ***(P-6227)***
Pacific Sunshine Enterprises.......F.......530 673-1888
857 Gray Ave Ste B Yuba City (95991) ***(P-24201)***
Pacific Supply, Visalia *Also called Pacific Coast Supply LLC* ***(P-11225)***
Pacific Supply, North Highlands *Also called Pacific Coast Supply LLC* ***(P-4419)***
Pacific Tank Ltd.......F.......760 246-6136
17177 Muskrat Ave Adelanto (92301) ***(P-12405)***
Pacific Tchnical Eqp Engrg Inc.......F.......714 835-3088
1298 N Blue Gum St Anaheim (92806) ***(P-15133)***
Pacific Tech Products Ontario, Union City *Also called California Performance Packg* ***(P-9823)***
Pacific Tek, Anaheim *Also called Pacific Tchnical Eqp Engrg Inc* ***(P-15133)***
Pacific Tent and Awning.......F.......559 436-8147
7295 N Palm Bluffs Ave Fresno (93711) ***(P-3801)***
Pacific Testtronics Inc.......F.......323 721-1077
5983 Smithway St Commerce (90040) ***(P-24202)***
Pacific Thermography.......E.......323 938-3349
9550 Jellico Ave Northridge (91325) ***(P-7429)***
Pacific Timber Contracting.......F.......707 498-1374
690 Jacobsen Way Ferndale (95536) ***(P-4005)***

Pacific Toll Processing Inc......E......310 952-4992
24724 Wilmington Ave Carson (90745) *(P-11409)*
Pacific Transformer Corp......C......714 779-0450
5399 E Hunter Ave Anaheim (92807) *(P-17111)*
Pacific Trendz, Ontario *Also called Sunny Products Inc (P-7586)*
Pacific Truck Equipment Inc......D......562 464-9674
11655 Washington Blvd Whittier (90606) *(P-20222)*
Pacific Truck Tank Inc......E......916 379-9280
7029 Florin Perkins Rd A Sacramento (95828) *(P-20223)*
Pacific Urethanes LLC......C......909 390-8400
1671 Champagne Ave Ste A Ontario (91761) *(P-3740)*
Pacific Utility Products Inc......F......909 923-1800
2950 E Philadelphia St Ontario (91761) *(P-21693)*
Pacific Valves......D......562 426-2531
3201 Walnut Ave Signal Hill (90755) *(P-13730)*
Pacific Vial Mfg Inc......E......323 721-7004
2738 Supply Ave Commerce (90040) *(P-10624)*
Pacific Vista Foods Llc......E......760 908-9840
2380 Back Nine St Oceanside (92056) *(P-8964)*
Pacific Wave Systems Inc......D......714 893-0152
7151 Patterson Dr Garden Grove (92841) *(P-18213)*
Pacific WD Prserving-New Stine......F......661 617-6385
5601 District Blvd Bakersfield (93313) *(P-4596)*
Pacific Weaving Corporation......E......650 592-9434
1068 American St San Carlos (94070) *(P-2756)*
Pacific West Forest Products......F......530 899-7313
13434 Browns Valley Dr Chico (95973) *(P-12989)*
Pacific West Litho Inc......D......714 579-0868
3291 E Miraloma Ave Anaheim (92806) *(P-7012)*
Pacific Western Container, Santa Ana *Also called Blower-Dempsay Corporation (P-5390)*
Pacific Western Systems Inc (PA)......E......650 961-8855
505 E Evelyn Ave Mountain View (94041) *(P-21823)*
Pacific Westline Inc......D......714 956-2442
1536 W Embassy St Anaheim (92802) *(P-5091)*
Pacific Wire Products Inc......E......818 755-6400
10725 Vanowen St North Hollywood (91605) *(P-13842)*
Pacific Wood Milling Reload, Cottonwood *Also called Plum Valley Inc (P-4046)*
Pacific World Corporation (PA)......C......949 598-2400
75 Enterprise Ste 300 Aliso Viejo (92656) *(P-8809)*
Pacific Wstn Arostructures Inc......F......661 607-0100
27771 Avenue Hopkins Valencia (91355) *(P-16822)*
Pacific Wtrprfing Rstrtion Inc......E......909 444-3052
2845 Pomona Blvd Pomona (91768) *(P-9296)*
Pacific Yacht Towers......F......760 744-4831
165 Balboa St Ste C10 San Marcos (92069) *(P-21061)*
Pacifica Foods LLC......E......951 371-3123
13415 Estelle St Corona (92879) *(P-847)*
Pacifica Foods LLC (PA)......E......951 371-3123
13415 Estelle St Corona (92879) *(P-928)*
Pacifica Tribune, Novato *Also called Ang Newspaper Group Inc (P-5760)*
Pacificgmp......F......858 550-4094
8810 Rehco Rd Ste E San Diego (92121) *(P-8570)*
Pacifico Bindery Inc......E......714 744-1510
544 W Angus Ave Orange (92868) *(P-7611)*
Pacifictech Molded Pdts Inc......F......714 279-9928
22805 Savi Ranch Pkwy F Yorba Linda (92887) *(P-9653)*
Pacifitek Systems Inc......F......619 401-1968
344 Coogan Way El Cajon (92020) *(P-18214)*
Paciolan LLC (HQ)......D......949 476-2050
5171 California Ave # 200 Irvine (92617) *(P-25045)*
Pacira Pharmaceuticals Inc......D......858 678-3950
10450 Science Center Dr San Diego (92121) *(P-8326)*
Pack West Machinery, Corona *Also called Pacific Packaging McHy LLC (P-14875)*
Pack West Machinery Co, Corona *Also called W J Ellison Co Inc (P-15235)*
Packageone Inc (PA)......E......650 761-3339
1100 Union St San Francisco (94109) *(P-5445)*
Packaging Aids Corporation (PA)......E......415 454-4868
25 Tiburon St San Rafael (94901) *(P-15221)*
Packaging America - Sacramento, McClellan *Also called PCA Central Cal Corrugated LLC (P-5450)*
Packaging Corporation America......D......323 263-7581
4240 Bandini Blvd Vernon (90058) *(P-5446)*
Packaging Corporation America......C......562 927-7741
9700 E Frontage Rd Ste 20 South Gate (90280) *(P-5447)*
Packaging Dist Assembly Group......F......661 607-0600
24730 Avenue Rockefeller Valencia (91355) *(P-5358)*
Packaging Plus......E......209 858-9200
3816 S Willow Ave Ste 102 Fresno (93725) *(P-5448)*
Packaging Resource Group, Sherman Oaks *Also called Hab Enterprises Inc (P-9533)*
Packaging Specialists Inc......F......530 742-8441
3663 Feather River Blvd Plumas Lake (95961) *(P-4494)*
Packaging Spectrum, Los Angeles *Also called Advance Paper Box Company (P-5382)*
Packaging Systems Inc......E......661 253-5700
26435 Summit Cir Santa Clarita (91350) *(P-9160)*
Packers Bar M, Los Angeles *Also called Serv-Rite Meat Company Inc (P-525)*
Packers Food Products Inc......E......913 262-6200
701 W Kimberly Ave # 210 Placentia (92870) *(P-961)*
Packers Manufacturing Inc......E......559 732-4886
4212 W Hemlock Ave Visalia (93277) *(P-14876)*
Packit LLC......F......805 496-2999
875 S Westlake Blvd Westlake Village (91361) *(P-5613)*
Packline Technologies Inc......E......559 591-3150
5929 Avenue 408 Dinuba (93618) *(P-15222)*
Paclights LLC (PA)......E......888 983-2165
15830 El Prado Rd Ste F Chino (91708) *(P-17636)*
Pacmag Inc......F......619 872-0343
87 Georgina St Chula Vista (91910) *(P-19679)*
Pacmet Aerospace, Ontario *Also called Pacific Metals Group LLC (P-12706)*
Pacmin Incorporated (PA)......D......714 447-4478
2021 Raymer Ave Fullerton (92833) *(P-24203)*
Paco Plastics & Engrg Inc......F......562 698-0916
8540 Dice Rd Santa Fe Springs (90670) *(P-10259)*
Paco Pumps By Grundfos, Hayward *Also called Grundfos CBS Inc (P-15071)*
Pacobond Inc......E......818 768-5002
9800 Glenoaks Blvd Sun Valley (91352) *(P-5646)*
Pacoima Clothing LLC......E......818 897-8009
21345 Lassen St Chatsworth (91311) *(P-3542)*
Pacon Inc......C......626 814-4654
4249 Puente Ave Baldwin Park (91706) *(P-10260)*
Pacon Mfg Inc......E......925 961-0445
4777 Bennett Dr Ste H Livermore (94551) *(P-16823)*
Pacord Inc......E......619 336-2200
240 W 30th St National City (91950) *(P-21008)*
Pactiv Corp, Visalia *Also called Pactiv LLC (P-10263)*
Pactiv Corporation......E......562 944-0052
9700 Bell Ranch Dr Santa Fe Springs (90670) *(P-5723)*
Pactiv LLC......B......661 392-4000
2024 Norris Rd Bakersfield (93308) *(P-10261)*
Pactiv LLC......A......209 983-1930
4545 Qantas Ln Stockton (95206) *(P-5449)*
Pactiv LLC......D......562 693-1451
12500 Slauson Ave Ste H1 Santa Fe Springs (90670) *(P-10262)*
Pactiv LLC......C......909 622-1151
8201 W Elowin Ct Visalia (93291) *(P-10263)*
Pactiv Packaging Inc (HQ)......D......323 513-9000
3751 Seville Ave Vernon (90058) *(P-7863)*
Paddack Almond Hlling Shelling, Escalon *Also called Paddack Enterprises (P-1501)*
Paddack Enterprises......E......209 838-1536
27052 State Highway 120 Escalon (95320) *(P-1501)*
Paderia LLC......F......949 478-5273
18279 Brookhurst St Ste 1 Fountain Valley (92708) *(P-1373)*
Padilla Jewelers Inc......F......323 931-1678
6118 Venice Blvd Fl 2 Los Angeles (90034) *(P-23305)*
Padilla Remberto......F......323 268-1111
3524 Union Pacific Ave Los Angeles (90023) *(P-2889)*
Padywell Corp......E......626 359-9149
835 Meridian St Duarte (91010) *(P-7430)*
Pagecorp Industries, Santa Ana *Also called P C I Manufacturing Division (P-18210)*
Pages Produce Company......D......323 277-3660
4601 Pacific Blvd Vernon (90058) *(P-848)*
Pai Enterprises, Los Angeles *Also called Pai Gp Inc (P-10726)*
Pai Gp Inc......D......323 549-5355
5914 Crenshaw Blvd Los Angeles (90043) *(P-10726)*
Paige LLC (PA)......D......310 733-2100
10119 Jefferson Blvd Culver City (90232) *(P-3116)*
PAIGE FLOOR COVERING SPECIALIS, National City *Also called Paige Sitta & Associates Inc (P-21009)*
Paige Premium Denim, Culver City *Also called Paige LLC (P-3116)*
Paige Sitta & Associates Inc (PA)......E......619 233-5912
2050 Wilson Ave Ste B National City (91950) *(P-21009)*
Paiho North America Corp......E......661 257-6611
16051 El Prado Rd Chino (91708) *(P-23771)*
Paint Chem, Burbank *Also called Slickote (P-13659)*
Paint Specialists Inc......E......818 771-0552
8629 Bradley Ave Sun Valley (91352) *(P-13631)*
Paint-Chem Inc......F......213 747-7725
1680 Miller Ave Los Angeles (90063) *(P-8922)*
Painted Rhino Inc......E......951 656-5524
14310 Veterans Way Moreno Valley (92553) *(P-9909)*
Pair of Thieves, Culver City *Also called Stateside Merchants LLC (P-3066)*
Paisano Publications LLC (PA)......C......818 889-8740
28210 Dorothy Dr Agoura Hills (91301) *(P-6228)*
Paisano Publications Inc......D......818 889-8740
28210 Dorothy Dr Agoura Hills (91301) *(P-6229)*
Pak Group LLC......E......626 316-6555
236 N Chester Ave Ste 200 Pasadena (91106) *(P-1374)*
Pakedge Device & Software Inc......E......714 880-4511
17011 Beach Blvd Ste 600 Huntington Beach (92647) *(P-25046)*
Palace Press International, San Rafael *Also called Goff Corporation (P-6345)*
Palace Printing & Design LP......E......415 526-1370
800 A St San Rafael (94901) *(P-6376)*
Palace Textile Inc......D......323 587-7756
8453 Terradell St Pico Rivera (90660) *(P-14778)*
Palace Textiles, Pico Rivera *Also called Palace Textile Inc (P-14778)*
Paladar Mfg Inc......D......760 775-4222
53973 Polk St Coachella (92236) *(P-23381)*
Palermo Products LLC......F......949 201-9066
16935 Saticoy St Van Nuys (91406) *(P-3741)*
Palette Unlimited......E......916 408-1914
2390 Athens Ave Lincoln (95648) *(P-4495)*
Palex Metals Inc......E......408 496-6111
3601 Thomas Rd Santa Clara (95054) *(P-12709)*
Palihuse Hllway Rsidences Assn......F......323 656-4100
8465 Holloway Dr West Hollywood (90069) *(P-3332)*
Palisades Beach Club, Los Angeles *Also called Fortune Swimwear LLC (P-2838)*
Pall Corporation......D......858 455-7264
4116 Sorrento Valley Blvd San Diego (92121) *(P-15346)*
Pall Corporation......B......626 339-7388
1630 W Industrial Park St Covina (91722) *(P-15347)*
Pallet Depot Inc (PA)......E......916 645-0490
19049 Avenue 242 Lindsay (93247) *(P-4496)*
Pallet Masters Inc......D......323 758-1713
655 E Florence Ave Los Angeles (90001) *(P-4497)*
Pallet Recovery Service Inc......F......209 496-5074
3401 Gaffery Rd Tracy (95304) *(P-4498)*
Pallets 4 Less Inc......F......213 377-7813
750 Ceres Ave Los Angeles (90021) *(P-4499)*

ALPHABETIC

Employee Codes: A=Over 500 employees, B=251-500
C=101-250, D=51-100, E=20-50, F=10-19
2019 California
Manfacturers Register
© Mergent Inc. 1-800-342-5647
1239

Palm Inc (HQ) ....B 408 617-7000
950 W Maude Ave Sunnyvale (94085) ***(P-18215)***
Palm Springs Plating, Palm Springs *Also called Ken Hoffmann Inc* ***(P-13439)***
Palmdale Heat Treating Inc ....F 661 274-8604
38834 17th St E Palmdale (93550) ***(P-12406)***
Palmdale Rock and Asphalt, Littlerock *Also called Legacy Vulcan LLC* ***(P-370)***
Palmer Tank & Construction Inc ....E 661 834-1110
2464 S Union Ave Bakersfield (93307) ***(P-257)***
Palo Alto Awning Inc ....F 650 968-4270
1381 N 10th St San Jose (95112) ***(P-3802)***
Palo Alto Cafe ....F 650 322-8644
2675 Middlefield Rd Palo Alto (94306) ***(P-2362)***
Palo Alto Networks Inc (PA) ....B 408 753-4000
3000 Tannery Way Santa Clara (95054) ***(P-15821)***
Palomar Casework Inc ....F 760 941-9860
4275 Clearview Dr Carlsbad (92008) ***(P-5161)***
Palomar Display Products Inc ....E 760 931-3200
5803 Newton Dr Ste C Carlsbad (92008) ***(P-19680)***
Palomar Products Inc ....D 949 858-8836
23042 Arroyo Vis Rcho STA Marg (92688) ***(P-18352)***
Palomar Technologies Inc (PA) ....D 760 931-3600
2728 Loker Ave W Carlsbad (92010) ***(P-15005)***
Palpilot International Corp ....E 714 460-0718
15991 Red Hill Ave # 102 Tustin (92780) ***(P-18554)***
Palpilot International Corp (PA) ....E 408 855-8866
500 Yosemite Dr Milpitas (95035) ***(P-18555)***
Palyon Medical Corporation ....E 661 705-5601
28432 Constellation Rd Valencia (91355) ***(P-23033)***
Pam Dee Publishing ....F 707 542-1528
303 Talbot Ave Santa Rosa (95405) ***(P-6377)***
Pamarco Global Graphics Inc ....E 714 739-0700
6907 Marlin Cir La Palma (90623) ***(P-14822)***
Pamarco Western, La Palma *Also called Pamarco Global Graphics Inc* ***(P-14822)***
Pamco, Sun Valley *Also called Precision Arcft Machining Inc* ***(P-16853)***
Pamco Machine Works Inc ....E 909 941-7260
9359 Feron Blvd Rancho Cucamonga (91730) ***(P-16824)***
Pamelas Products Incorporated ....D 707 462-6605
1 Carousel Ln Ste D Ukiah (95482) ***(P-1303)***
Pampanga Foods Company Inc ....F 714 773-0537
1835 N Orngthrp Park A Anaheim (92801) ***(P-512)***
Pampanga Foods Incorporated ....E 714 331-7206
1835 N Orngthrp Park A Anaheim (92801) ***(P-1008)***
Pan Magna Group ....E 707 433-5508
1141 Grant Ave Healdsburg (95448) ***(P-1912)***
Pan Pacific Plastics Mfg Inc ....E 510 785-6888
26551 Danti Ct Hayward (94545) ***(P-10264)***
Pan Probe Biotech Inc ....F 858 689-9936
7396 Trade St San Diego (92121) ***(P-22579)***
Pan-A-Lite Products Inc ....F 714 258-7111
1601 Ritchey St Santa Ana (92705) ***(P-17723)***
Pan-O-Rama Baking Inc ....E 415 522-5500
500 Florida St San Francisco (94110) ***(P-1304)***
Pana-Pacific Corporation ....C 559 457-4700
838 N Laverne Ave Fresno (93727) ***(P-20417)***
Panadent Corporation ....E 909 783-1841
580 S Rancho Ave Colton (92324) ***(P-22899)***
Panasonic Appliances Ref ....D 619 661-1134
2001 Sanyo Ave San Diego (92154) ***(P-17380)***
Panavision Hollywood, Los Angeles *Also called Panavision Inc* ***(P-23184)***
Panavision Inc ....D 323 464-3800
6735 Selma Ave Los Angeles (90028) ***(P-23184)***
Panavision International LP (HQ) ....B 818 316-1080
6101 Variel Ave Woodland Hills (91367) ***(P-23185)***
Panchos Bakery ....E 323 582-9109
1759 E Florence Ave Los Angeles (90001) ***(P-1305)***
Panco Mens Products Inc ....F 760 342-4368
45605 Citrus Ave Indio (92201) ***(P-8810)***
Panda Bowl ....F 714 418-0299
11940 Edinger Ave Fountain Valley (92708) ***(P-5248)***
Panel Products Inc ....E 310 830-3331
21818 S Wilmington Ave # 411 Long Beach (90810) ***(P-21379)***
Panel Shop Inc ....E 951 739-7000
2800 Palisades Dr Corona (92880) ***(P-17153)***
Panel Shop, The, San Fernando *Also called Krego Corporation* ***(P-17148)***
Panel Works, Santa Fe Springs *Also called JC Hanscom Inc* ***(P-4378)***
Pangea Silkscreen ....E 707 778-0110
110 Howard St Ste A Petaluma (94952) ***(P-3912)***
Panic Plastics ....F 909 946-5529
1652 W 11th St Upland (91786) ***(P-5614)***
Pankl Aerospace Systems ....D 562 207-6300
16615 Edwards Rd Cerritos (90703) ***(P-11780)***
Pannaway, Fremont *Also called Enablence Systems Inc* ***(P-24608)***
Pano Logic Inc ....D 650 743-1773
1100 La Avenida St Ste A Mountain View (94043) ***(P-15822)***
Panob Corp ....E 909 947-8008
1531 E Cedar St Ontario (91761) ***(P-10265)***
Panolam Industries Intl Inc ....E 909 581-1970
8535 Oakwood Pl Ste A Rancho Cucamonga (91730) ***(P-4600)***
Panorama Intl CL Co Inc ....F 415 891-8478
200 Toland St San Francisco (94124) ***(P-770)***
Panoramic Software Corporation ....F 877 558-8526
9650 Research Dr Irvine (92618) ***(P-25047)***
Panosoft, Irvine *Also called Panoramic Software Corporation* ***(P-25047)***
Panrosa Enterprises Inc ....D 951 339-5888
550 Monica Cir Ste 101 Corona (92880) ***(P-8603)***
Pantronix Corporation ....C 510 656-5898
2710 Lakeview Ct Fremont (94538) ***(P-19071)***
Pantry Retail Inc ....F 415 234-3574
3095 Kerner Blvd Ste N San Rafael (94901) ***(P-15925)***
Papa Cantella's Sausage Plant, Vernon *Also called Papa Cantellas Incorporated* ***(P-513)***
Papa Cantellas Incorporated ....D 323 584-7272
3341 E 50th St Vernon (90058) ***(P-513)***
Papadatos Enterprises Inc ....F 408 299-0190
2015 Stone Ave San Jose (95125) ***(P-16825)***
Papago Inc ....F 909 595-6896
376 Lemon Creek Dr Ste E Walnut (91789) ***(P-21380)***
Papco Parts, Chatsworth *Also called Papco Screw Products Inc* ***(P-14398)***
Papco Screw Products Inc ....F 818 341-2266
9410 De Soto Ave Ste A Chatsworth (91311) ***(P-14398)***
Pape Material Handling Inc ....D 562 692-9311
2600 Peck Rd City of Industry (90601) ***(P-14340)***
Paper Pulp & Film ....E 559 233-1151
2822 S Maple Ave Fresno (93725) ***(P-5724)***
Paper Group Company LLC ....E 714 566-0025
15201 Woodlawn Ave # 200 Tustin (92780) ***(P-5322)***
Paper Max Inc (PA) ....F 714 780-0595
100 S Anaheim Blvd # 250 Anaheim (92805) ***(P-5323)***
Paper Surce Converting Mfg Inc ....E 323 583-3800
4800 S Santa Fe Ave Vernon (90058) ***(P-5324)***
Paper Works Corporation ....F 310 781-9400
19168 Van Ness Ave Torrance (90501) ***(P-7431)***
Paper-Pak Industries, La Verne *Also called Novipax Inc* ***(P-5719)***
Paperboard Packaging Corp (HQ) ....D 530 671-9000
800 N Walton Ave Yuba City (95993) ***(P-5530)***
Papercon Packaging Division, City of Industry *Also called Bagcraftpapercon I LLC* ***(P-5637)***
Papercutters Inc ....E 323 888-1330
6023 Bandini Blvd Los Angeles (90040) ***(P-5531)***
Pappalecco ....F 619 906-5566
3650 5th Ave Ste 104 San Diego (92103) ***(P-13962)***
Pappy's Fine Foods, Fresno *Also called Pappys Meat Company Inc* ***(P-2634)***
Pappys Meat Company Inc ....E 559 291-0218
5663 E Fountain Way Fresno (93727) ***(P-2634)***
Paprsa, San Diego *Also called Panasonic Appliances Ref* ***(P-17380)***
Par Engineering Inc ....E 626 964-8700
17855 Arenth Ave City of Industry (91748) ***(P-17381)***
Par Global Resources Inc ....F 408 982-5515
2005 De La Cruz Blvd # 111 Santa Clara (95050) ***(P-7013)***
Par Orthodontic Laboratory ....E 949 472-4788
23141 La Cadena Dr Ste K Laguna Hills (92653) ***(P-22900)***
Para Plate & Plastics Co Inc ....E 562 404-3434
15910 Shoemaker Ave Cerritos (90703) ***(P-14823)***
Para Tech Coating, Laguna Hills *Also called Metal Improvement Company LLC* ***(P-11820)***
Parabilis Space Tech Inc ....F 855 727-2245
1195 Linda Vista Dr Ste F San Marcos (92078) ***(P-21168)***
Paracor Medical Inc ....E 408 207-1050
19200 Stevns Crk Blvd # 200 Cupertino (95014) ***(P-23034)***
Paradigm Contract Mfg LLC ....F 714 889-7074
11562 Knott St Ste 13 Garden Grove (92841) ***(P-24204)***
Paradigm Label Inc ....F 951 372-9212
10258 Birtcher Dr Mira Loma (91752) ***(P-5725)***
Paradigm Packaging West, Rancho Cucamonga *Also called Comar LLC* ***(P-10032)***
Paradigm Winery ....F 707 944-1683
683 Dwyer Rd Oakville (94562) ***(P-1913)***
Paradise Kitchen Doors, Pomona *Also called Gonzalez Feliciano* ***(P-4161)***
Paradise Manufacturing Co Inc ....C 909 477-3460
13364 Aerospace Dr 100 Victorville (92394) ***(P-3803)***
Paradise Printing Inc ....E 714 228-9628
13474 Pumice St Norwalk (90650) ***(P-7014)***
Paradise Ranch ....F 951 776-7736
2900 Adams St Ste C8 Riverside (92504) ***(P-3674)***
Paradise Ridge Winery ....F 707 528-9463
4545 Thomas Lk Harris Dr Santa Rosa (95403) ***(P-1914)***
Paradise Road LLC ....E 714 894-1779
5872 Engineer Dr Huntington Beach (92649) ***(P-8662)***
Paragon Building Products Inc (PA) ....E 951 549-1155
2191 5th St Ste 111 Norco (92860) ***(P-10974)***
Paragon Controls Incorporated ....F 707 579-1424
2371 Circadian Way Santa Rosa (95407) ***(P-21521)***
Paragon Label, Petaluma *Also called Mrs Grossmans Paper Company* ***(P-5687)***
Paragon Laboratories, Torrance *Also called Naturalife Eco Vite Labs* ***(P-635)***
Paragon Machine Works Inc ....D 510 232-3223
253 S 25th St Richmond (94804) ***(P-16826)***
Paragon Precision Inc ....E 661 257-1380
25620 Rye Canyon Rd Ste A Valencia (91355) ***(P-20672)***
Paragon Products LLC (PA) ....E 916 941-9717
4475 Golden Foothill Pkwy El Dorado Hills (95762) ***(P-21083)***
Paragon Swiss Inc ....E 408 748-1617
545 Aldo Ave Ste 1 Santa Clara (95054) ***(P-16827)***
Paragon Tactical Inc ....F 951 736-9440
1580 Commerce St Corona (92880) ***(P-23628)***
Parallax Incorporated ....E 916 624-8333
599 Menlo Dr Ste 100 Rocklin (95765) ***(P-15470)***
Parallax Research, Rocklin *Also called Parallax Incorporated* ***(P-15470)***
Parallocity Inc ....E 408 524-1530
440 N Wolfe Rd Sunnyvale (94085) ***(P-19876)***
Parametric Manufacturing Inc ....F 408 654-9845
3465 Edward Ave Santa Clara (95054) ***(P-16828)***
Paramit Corporation (PA) ....B 408 782-5600
18735 Madrone Pkwy Morgan Hill (95037) ***(P-22580)***
Paramont Metal & Supply Co, Paramount *Also called George Jue Mfg Co Inc* ***(P-14704)***
Paramount Asphalt, Paramount *Also called Paramount Petroleum Corp* ***(P-9345)***
Paramount Dairy Inc (PA) ....E 949 265-8077
17801 Cartwright Rd Irvine (92614) ***(P-733)***
Paramount Dairy Inc ....E 949 265-8000
15255 Texaco Ave Paramount (90723) ***(P-734)***
Paramount Extrusions Company (PA) ....E 562 634-3291
6833 Rosecrans Ave Paramount (90723) ***(P-11599)***

Mergent e-mail: customerrelations@mergent.com
1240
2019 California
Manufacturers Register
(P-0000) Products & Services Section entry number
(PA)=Parent Co (HQ)=Headquarters (DH)=Div Headquarters

Paramount Extrusions Company ....E....562 634-3291
6833 Rosecrans Ave Ste A Paramount (90723) ***(P-11600)***
Paramount Fabricators, Rancho Cucamonga *Also called Paramunt Plstic Fbricators Inc* ***(P-10267)***
Paramount Farms, Los Angeles *Also called Wonderful Pstchios Almonds LLC* ***(P-1507)***
Paramount Food Processing, Del Rey *Also called Del Rey Juice Co* ***(P-946)***
Paramount Grinding Service ....F....562 630-6940
7311 Madison St Ste C Paramount (90723) ***(P-16829)***
Paramount Laminates Inc ....F....562 531-7580
15527 Vermont Ave Paramount (90723) ***(P-9756)***
Paramount Laminates & Cabinets, Paramount *Also called Paramount Laminates Inc* ***(P-9756)***
Paramount Machine Co Inc ....E....909 484-3600
10824 Edison Ct Rancho Cucamonga (91730) ***(P-16830)***
Paramount Mattress Inc ....F....323 264-3451
2900 E Olympic Blvd Los Angeles (90023) ***(P-4877)***
Paramount Panels Inc (PA) ....E....909 947-8008
1531 E Cedar St Ontario (91761) ***(P-10266)***
Paramount Panels Inc ....E....909 947-5168
1531 E Cedar St Ontario (91761) ***(P-20903)***
Paramount Petroleum Corp ....F....562 633-4332
8835 Somerset Blvd Paramount (90723) ***(P-9344)***
Paramount Petroleum Corp ....F....916 685-9253
10090 Waterman Rd Elk Grove (95624) ***(P-9392)***
Paramount Petroleum Corp (HQ) ....C....562 531-2060
14700 Downey Ave Paramount (90723) ***(P-9345)***
Paramount Petroleum Corp ....E....661 326-4200
6451 Rosedale Hwy Bakersfield (93308) ***(P-9346)***
Paramount Petroleum Corp ....F....661 392-3630
1201 China Grade Loop Bakersfield (93308) ***(P-9347)***
Paramount Ready Mix Con Inc ....E....562 404-4125
13949 Stage Rd Santa Fe Springs (90670) ***(P-11156)***
Paramount Roll Forming Co Inc ....E....562 944-6151
12120 Florence Ave Santa Fe Springs (90670) ***(P-12226)***
Paramount Tool & Machine Co, Redwood City *Also called Talos Corporation* ***(P-16986)***
Paramunt Plstic Fbricators Inc ....F....909 987-4757
11251 Jersey Blvd Rancho Cucamonga (91730) ***(P-10267)***
Parasound Products Inc ....F....415 397-7100
2250 Mckinnon Ave San Francisco (94124) ***(P-17841)***
Paratech Inc ....E....562 633-2045
15940 Minnesota Ave Paramount (90723) ***(P-11324)***
Parco Inc (PA) ....C....909 947-2200
1801 S Archibald Ave Ontario (91761) ***(P-9547)***
Parcor, Garden Grove *Also called Ken-Wor Corp* ***(P-11402)***
Parducci Wine Estates LLC ....E....707 463-5350
501 Parducci Rd Ukiah (95482) ***(P-1915)***
Parent Is Sas Ltries H Trbllat, Sonoma *Also called Laura Chenels Chevre Inc* ***(P-585)***
Parex Usa Inc (HQ) ....E....714 778-2266
4125 E La Palma Ave # 250 Anaheim (92807) ***(P-11367)***
Parex Usa Inc ....E....209 983-8002
11290 Vallejo Ct French Camp (95231) ***(P-11368)***
Paris Croissant LLC (PA) ....E....562 630-8711
6890 Cherry Ave Long Beach (90805) ***(P-1306)***
Parisa Lingerie & Swim Wear, Northridge *Also called Afr Apparel International Inc* ***(P-3533)***
Park Electrochemical Corp ....E....714 459-4400
1100 E Kimberly Ave Anaheim (92801) ***(P-18556)***
Park Engineering and Mfg Co ....E....714 521-4660
6430 Roland St Buena Park (90621) ***(P-16831)***
Park O Mate, Van Nuys *Also called Bijan Rad Inc* ***(P-14922)***
Park Pets and Boulders, Paso Robles *Also called Sport Rock International Inc* ***(P-23660)***
Park Steel Co Inc ....F....310 638-6101
515 E Pine St Compton (90222) ***(P-12227)***
Park West Enterprises ....E....909 383-8341
2586 Shenandoah Way San Bernardino (92407) ***(P-1531)***
Park's Prtg & Lithographic Co, Modesto *Also called Village Instant Printing Inc* ***(P-7169)***
Park-Rand Enterprises Inc ....F....818 362-2565
39630 Fairway Dr Apt 218 Palmdale (93551) ***(P-8663)***
Parker Aerospace, Irvine *Also called Parker-Hannifin Corporation* ***(P-20905)***
Parker Boiler Co, Commerce *Also called Sid E Parker Boiler Mfg Co Inc* ***(P-12420)***
Parker House International, Eastvale *Also called Parker House Mfg Co Inc* ***(P-4898)***
Parker House Mfg Co Inc ....E....800 628-1319
6300 Providence Way Eastvale (92880) ***(P-4898)***
Parker Plastics Inc ....E....707 994-6363
12762 Highway 29 Lower Lake (95457) ***(P-10268)***
Parker Powis Inc ....D....510 848-2463
2929 5th St Berkeley (94710) ***(P-15910)***
Parker Printing Inc ....F....714 444-4550
11240 Young River Ave Fountain Valley (92708) ***(P-7015)***
Parker Pumper Helmet Co, Mira Loma *Also called Racing Plus Inc* ***(P-22801)***
Parker Service Center, Buena Park *Also called Parker-Hannifin Corporation* ***(P-9504)***
Parker-Hannifin Corporation ....E....714 522-8840
8460 Kass Dr Buena Park (90621) ***(P-9504)***
Parker-Hannifin Corporation ....D....310 308-0389
13850 Van Ness Ave Gardena (90249) ***(P-16832)***
Parker-Hannifin Corporation ....C....619 661-7000
7664 Panasonic Way San Diego (92154) ***(P-16169)***
Parker-Hannifin Corporation ....B....949 833-3000
16666 Von Karman Ave Irvine (92606) ***(P-20673)***
Parker-Hannifin Corporation ....D....510 235-9590
250 Canal Blvd Richmond (94804) ***(P-21630)***
Parker-Hannifin Corporation ....D....216 896-2663
16666 Von Karman Ave Irvine (92606) ***(P-20904)***
Parker-Hannifin Corporation ....C....949 833-3000
14300 Alton Pkwy Irvine (92618) ***(P-20905)***
Parker-Hannifin Corporation ....E....951 280-3800
221 Helicopter Cir Corona (92880) ***(P-16170)***
Parker-Hannifin Corporation ....C....949 833-3000
16666 Von Karman Ave Irvine (92606) ***(P-16171)***
Parker-Hannifin Corporation ....F....805 658-2984
3007 Bunsen Ave Ste K Ventura (93003) ***(P-16172)***
Parker-Hannifin Corporation ....C....707 584-7558
5500 Business Park Dr Rohnert Park (94928) ***(P-17291)***
Parker-Hannifin Corporation ....A....949 833-3000
14300 Alton Pkwy Irvine (92618) ***(P-20906)***
Parker-Hannifin Corporation ....E....562 404-1938
14087 Borate St Santa Fe Springs (90670) ***(P-12407)***
Parker-Hannifin Corporation ....A....209 521-7860
3400 Finch Rd Modesto (95354) ***(P-15348)***
Parker-Hannifin Corporation ....C....805 604-3400
2340 Eastman Ave Oxnard (93030) ***(P-15349)***
Parker-Hannifin Corporation ....C....805 419-7000
3800 Calle Tecate Camarillo (93012) ***(P-20907)***
Parks and Open Space, San Rafael *Also called County of Marin* ***(P-5009)***
Parks Optical Inc ....E....805 522-6722
80 W Easy St Ste 3 Simi Valley (93065) ***(P-22121)***
Parmatech Corporation ....D....707 778-2266
2221 Pine View Way Petaluma (94954) ***(P-11844)***
Parpro Technologies Inc ....C....714 545-8886
2700 S Fairview St Santa Ana (92704) ***(P-18557)***
Parquet By Dian Inc ....D....310 527-3779
16601 S Main St Gardena (90248) ***(P-4088)***
Parrot Communications Intl Inc ....E....818 567-4700
26321 Ferry Ct Santa Clarita (91350) ***(P-6547)***
Parrot Media Network, Santa Clarita *Also called Parrot Communications Intl Inc* ***(P-6547)***
Pars Publishing Corp ....D....818 280-0540
4485 Runway St Simi Valley (93063) ***(P-7016)***
Part Handling Engrg & Dev Corp ....F....951 308-4450
42175 Zevo Dr Temecula (92590) ***(P-23035)***
Parter Medical Products Inc ....C....310 327-4417
17015 Kingsview Ave Carson (90746) ***(P-21484)***
Partner Printing, Glendale *Also called Colour Concepts Inc* ***(P-6746)***
Partnership Of Paramount Petro, Long Beach *Also called Tidelands Oil Production Inc* ***(P-78)***
Parts Expediting and Dist Co ....E....562 944-3199
10805 Artesia Blvd # 112 Cerritos (90703) ***(P-20418)***
Parts Out Inc (PA) ....F....626 560-1540
1875 Century Park E # 2200 Los Angeles (90067) ***(P-19843)***
Partsearch Technologies Inc (HQ) ....E....800 289-0300
27460 Avenue Scott D Valencia (91355) ***(P-19681)***
Party Time Ice Inc ....F....310 833-0187
983 N Pacific Ave San Pedro (90731) ***(P-2417)***
PARTYAID, Santa Cruz *Also called Lifeaid Beverage Co* ***(P-2148)***
Parylene USA Inc ....F....949 452-0770
23 Spectrum Pointe Dr # 201 Lake Forest (92630) ***(P-24205)***
Pasadena Bio Cllbrtive Incbtor ....F....626 507-8487
2265 E Foothill Blvd Pasadena (91107) ***(P-21485)***
Pasadena Bscence Colloborative, Pasadena *Also called Pasadena Bio Cllbrtive Incbtor* ***(P-21485)***
Pasadena Newspapers Inc (PA) ....C....626 578-6300
2 N Lake Ave Ste 150 Pasadena (91101) ***(P-6010)***
Pasadena Newspapers Inc ....C....707 442-1711
930 6th St Eureka (95501) ***(P-6011)***
Pasadena Star-News, Pasadena *Also called Pasadena Newspapers Inc* ***(P-6010)***
Pasadena Weekly, Pasadena *Also called Southland Publishing* ***(P-6585)***
Pascal Systems, West Sacramento *Also called Heco Inc* ***(P-15239)***
Pasco, Buena Park *Also called Yeager Enterprises Corp* ***(P-11309)***
Pasco Corporation of America ....E....503 289-6500
19191 S Vt Ave Ste 420 Torrance (90502) ***(P-1009)***
Pasco Industries Inc ....F....714 992-2051
2040 Redondo Pl Fullerton (92835) ***(P-23796)***
Paso Robles Press, Paso Robles *Also called News Media Inc* ***(P-5996)***
Pasport Communications, Sausalito *Also called Pasport Software Programs Inc* ***(P-25048)***
Pasport Software Programs Inc ....F....415 331-2606
307 Bridgeway Sausalito (94965) ***(P-25048)***
Pass, Orange *Also called Prototype & Short-Run Svcs Inc* ***(P-13267)***
Pass & Seymour Inc ....A....562 505-4072
9415 Kruse Rd Pico Rivera (90660) ***(P-17485)***
Pass Laboratories Inc ....F....530 878-5350
13395 New Airport Rd Auburn (95602) ***(P-17842)***
Passport Food Group LLC (PA) ....C....909 627-7312
2539 E Philadelphia St Ontario (91761) ***(P-2635)***
Passy-Muir Inc ....F....949 833-8255
1212 Mcgaw Ave Irvine (92614) ***(P-22790)***
Passy-Muir Inc (PA) ....E....949 833-8255
17992 Mitchell S Ste 200 Irvine (92614) ***(P-22791)***
Pasta Mia, Fullerton *Also called Nina Mia Inc* ***(P-2622)***
Pasta Prima, Benicia *Also called Valley Fine Foods Company Inc* ***(P-1050)***
Pasta Sonoma LLC ....F....707 584-0800
640 Martin Ave Ste 1 Rohnert Park (94928) ***(P-2436)***
Pastries By Edie Inc ....E....818 340-0203
7226 Topanga Canyon Blvd Canoga Park (91303) ***(P-1307)***
Patch Place ....E....909 947-3023
1724 S Grove Ave Ste A Ontario (91761) ***(P-3957)***
Patientpop Inc ....D....844 487-8399
214 Wilshire Blvd Santa Monica (90401) ***(P-25049)***
Patina Products, Arroyo Grande *Also called Layne Laboratories Inc* ***(P-3006)***
Patio & Door Outlet Inc (PA) ....E....714 974-9900
410 W Fletcher Ave Orange (92865) ***(P-4915)***
Patio Outlet, Orange *Also called Patio & Door Outlet Inc* ***(P-4915)***
Patio Paradise Inc ....F....626 715-4869
444 Athol St San Bernardino (92401) ***(P-17553)***
Patricia Edwards, Commerce *Also called Superb Chair Corporation* ***(P-4815)***
Patricks Cabinets ....F....909 823-2524
10160 Redwood Ave Fontana (92335) ***(P-4334)***

ALPHABETIC

Employee Codes: A=Over 500 employees, B=251-500
C=101-250, D=51-100, E=20-50, F=10-19
2019 California
Manfacturers Register
© Mergent Inc. 1-800-342-5647
1241

Patriot Lighting Inc ....F....213 741-9757
2305 S Main St Los Angeles (90007) ***(P-17637)***
Patriot Memory LLC (PA) ....C....510 979-1021
47027 Benicia St Fremont (94538) ***(P-19072)***
Patriot Mritime Compliance LLC ....F....925 296-2000
1320 Willow Pass Rd # 485 Concord (94520) ***(P-21010)***
Patriot Polishing Company ....F....310 903-7409
47260 Wrangler Rd Aguanga (92536) ***(P-8664)***
Patriot Products, Irwindale *Also called Pertronix Inc* ***(P-19844)***
Patron Solutions LLC ....C....949 823-1700
5171 California Ave # 200 Irvine (92617) ***(P-25050)***
Pats Decorating Service Inc ....F....323 585-5073
2532 Strozier Ave South El Monte (91733) ***(P-3699)***
Patsons Media Group, Santa Clara *Also called Patsons Press* ***(P-7017)***
Patsons Press ....E....408 567-0911
831 Martin Ave Santa Clara (95050) ***(P-7017)***
Patten Systems Inc ....F....714 799-5656
15598 Producer Ln Huntington Beach (92649) ***(P-21631)***
Patterson Frozen Foods Inc ....F....209 892-5060
10 S 3rd St Patterson (95363) ***(P-962)***
Patterson Kincaid LLC ....F....323 584-3559
5175 S Soto St Vernon (90058) ***(P-3476)***
Patton Door and Gate, Palm Springs *Also called Door Service Company* ***(P-11439)***
Patz and Hall Wine Company (HQ) ....F....707 265-7700
21200 8th St E Sonoma (95476) ***(P-1916)***
Pau Hana Group LLC ....F....530 993-6800
94601 State Rte 70 Chilcoot (96105) ***(P-11983)***
Paul A Evans Inc ....F....530 859-2505
1215 Audubon Rd Mount Shasta (96067) ***(P-14183)***
Paul Baker Printing Inc ....E....916 969-8317
220 Riverside Ave Roseville (95678) ***(P-7018)***
Paul Brown Hawaii, Sun Valley *Also called Pbh Marketing Inc* ***(P-8811)***
Paul Crist Studios Inc ....F....562 696-9992
8317 Secura Way Santa Fe Springs (90670) ***(P-10727)***
Paul Dosier Associates Inc ....F....714 556-7075
913 Chicago Ave Placentia (92870) ***(P-14399)***
Paul Graham Drilling & Svc Co ....C....707 374-5123
2500 Airport Rd Rio Vista (94571) ***(P-116)***
Paul Hobbs Winery LP ....F....707 824-9879
3355 Gravenstein Hwy N Sebastopol (95472) ***(P-1917)***
Paul Hubbs Construction Inc (PA) ....F....951 360-3990
542 W C St Colton (92324) ***(P-331)***
Paul Merrill Company Inc ....F....562 691-1871
912 Bonnie Way Brea (92821) ***(P-11267)***
Paul Silver Enterprises Inc ....F....818 998-9900
9155 Alabama Ave Ste F Chatsworth (91311) ***(P-7019)***
Paula Keller ....F....310 833-1894
1044 S Gaffey St San Pedro (90731) ***(P-4210)***
Paulco Precision Inc ....F....310 679-4900
13916 Cordary Ave Hawthorne (90250) ***(P-16833)***
Pauli Systems Inc ....E....707 429-2434
1820 Walters Ct Fairfield (94533) ***(P-16834)***
Paulsen White Oak LP ....F....530 656-2201
3976 Garden Hwy Nicolaus (95659) ***(P-9110)***
Paulson Manufacturing Corp (PA) ....D....951 676-2451
46752 Rainbow Canyon Rd Temecula (92592) ***(P-22792)***
Paulsson Inc ....F....310 780-2219
16543 Arminta St Van Nuys (91406) ***(P-144)***
Pavement Recycling Systems Inc ....F....661 948-5599
46205 Division St Lancaster (93535) ***(P-9393)***
Pavestone LLC ....E....530 795-4400
27600 County Road 90 Winters (95694) ***(P-11268)***
Pavex Construction Co, Seaside *Also called Granite Rock Co* ***(P-11114)***
Pavilion Integration Corp ....F....408 453-8801
2528 Qume Dr Ste 1 San Jose (95131) ***(P-22249)***
Pavilion Products Inc ....F....818 345-4841
4520 Azalia Dr Tarzana (91356) ***(P-3742)***
Paw Prints Inc ....F....650 365-4077
3166 Bay Rd Redwood City (94063) ***(P-7432)***
Paxata Inc ....D....650 542-7897
1800 Seaport Blvd Fl 3 Redwood City (94063) ***(P-25051)***
Paxvax Inc ....F....858 450-9595
4122 Sorrento Valley Blvd San Diego (92121) ***(P-8571)***
Paydivvy Inc ....F....949 313-3451
3121 Michelson Dr Ste 150 Irvine (92612) ***(P-25052)***
Paylocity Holding Corporation ....B....847 956-4850
2107 Livingston St Oakland (94606) ***(P-25053)***
Paymentmax Processing Inc ....D....805 557-1692
600 Hampshire Rd Ste 120 Westlake Village (91361) ***(P-15898)***
Payne Magnetics Inc ....D....626 332-6207
854 W Front St Covina (91722) ***(P-19350)***
Paysonic, Union City *Also called Spacesonics Incorporated* ***(P-12766)***
Payton Technology Corporation ....C....714 885-8000
17665 Newhope St Ste B Fountain Valley (92708) ***(P-19073)***
Pazzulla Plastics Inc ....E....714 847-2541
165 Emilia Ln Fallbrook (92028) ***(P-5092)***
Pb Fasteners, Gardena *Also called SPS Technologies LLC* ***(P-13083)***
Pbf Energy Inc ....F....310 212-2800
3700 W 190th St Torrance (90504) ***(P-9348)***
Pbf Energy Western Region LLC (HQ) ....B....973 455-7500
111 W Ocean Blvd Ste 1500 Long Beach (90802) ***(P-9349)***
Pbh Marketing Inc ....F....818 374-9000
9960 Glenoaks Blvd Ste C Sun Valley (91352) ***(P-8811)***
Pby Plastics Inc ....F....909 930-6700
2571 Lindsey Privado Dr Ontario (91761) ***(P-10269)***
PC Mechanical Inc ....E....805 925-2888
2803 Industrial Pkwy Santa Maria (93455) ***(P-258)***
PC Recycle, Newbury Park *Also called Fc Management Services* ***(P-14954)***
PC Vaughan Mfg Corp (PA) ....F....805 278-2555
1278 Mercantile St Oxnard (93030) ***(P-20419)***
PC World Online, San Francisco *Also called Idg Consumer & Smb Inc* ***(P-6188)***
PCA, Santa Clara *Also called Polishing Corporation America* ***(P-19080)***
PCA Aerospace Inc (PA) ....D....714 841-1750
17800 Gothard St Huntington Beach (92647) ***(P-20908)***
PCA Central Cal Corrugated LLC ....C....916 614-0580
4841 Urbani Ave McClellan (95652) ***(P-5450)***
PCA Electronics Inc ....E....818 892-0761
16799 Schoenborn St North Hills (91343) ***(P-19351)***
PCA Summit Service, Escondido *Also called Summit Services Inc* ***(P-10865)***
PCA/Los Angeles 349, Vernon *Also called Packaging Corporation America* ***(P-5446)***
PCA/South Gate 378, South Gate *Also called Packaging Corporation America* ***(P-5447)***
Pcb Fabrication Facility, San Marcos *Also called Hughes Circuits Inc* ***(P-18501)***
PCC Rollmet Inc ....D....949 221-5333
1822 Deere Ave Irvine (92606) ***(P-11549)***
PCC Structurals Inc ....C....510 568-6400
414 Hester St San Leandro (94577) ***(P-11781)***
PCC Structurals-San Leandro, San Leandro *Also called PCC Structurals Inc* ***(P-11781)***
Pch International USA Inc (PA) ....E....415 643-5463
135 Mississippi St Fl 1 San Francisco (94107) ***(P-19682)***
Pch Lime Lab, San Francisco *Also called Pch International USA Inc* ***(P-19682)***
PCI, Riverside *Also called Pacific Consolidated Inds LLC* ***(P-15345)***
PCI, Santa Rosa *Also called Paragon Controls Incorporated* ***(P-21521)***
PCI Holding Company Inc (PA) ....C....951 479-0860
12201 Magnolia Ave Riverside (92503) ***(P-15350)***
PCI Industries Inc ....D....323 728-0004
6501 Potello St Commerce (90040) ***(P-12710)***
PCL Communications, San Leandro *Also called Pacific Coast Laboratories* ***(P-22789)***
Pcs Company, Sunnyvale *Also called Pcs Machining Service Inc* ***(P-16835)***
Pcs Machining Service Inc ....F....408 735-9974
784 Edale Dr Sunnyvale (94087) ***(P-16835)***
Pct, Compton *Also called Pacific Contntl Textiles Inc* ***(P-2916)***
Pct, Fremont *Also called Printed Circuit Technology* ***(P-18567)***
Pct-Gw Carbide Tools Usa Inc ....E....562 921-7898
13701 Excelsior Dr Santa Fe Springs (90670) ***(P-7795)***
Pd Group ....E....760 674-3028
41945 Boardwalk Ste L Palm Desert (92211) ***(P-23942)***
Pda Group, Valencia *Also called Packaging Dist Assembly Group* ***(P-5358)***
PDC, Valencia *Also called Precision Dynamics Corporation* ***(P-5575)***
Pdc LLC ....E....626 334-5000
4675 Vinita Ct Chino (91710) ***(P-14558)***
Pdf Print Communications Inc (PA) ....D....562 426-6978
2630 E 28th St Long Beach (90755) ***(P-7020)***
Pdi, Silverado *Also called Program Data Incorporated* ***(P-21830)***
Pdi, San Carlos *Also called Precision Design Inc* ***(P-18565)***
Pdl Biopharma Inc ....E....650 454-1000
1500 Seaport Blvd Redwood City (94063) ***(P-8572)***
PDM Solutions Inc ....E....858 348-1000
8451 Miralani Dr Ste J San Diego (92126) ***(P-18558)***
Pdma Ventures Inc ....E....714 777-8770
22951 La Palma Ave Yorba Linda (92887) ***(P-24206)***
PDQ Engineering Inc ....E....805 482-1334
1199 Avenida Acaso Ste F Camarillo (93012) ***(P-20617)***
Pdr-America, Shingle Springs *Also called White Industrial Corporation* ***(P-14744)***
PDT, Goleta *Also called Pacific Design Tech Inc* ***(P-21377)***
Peabody Engineering & Sup Inc ....E....951 734-7711
13435 Estelle St Corona (92879) ***(P-15006)***
Peachpit Press ....E....415 336-6831
1301 Sansome St San Francisco (94111) ***(P-6548)***
Peag LLC ....F....520 349-9371
2281 Las Palmas Dr Rm 101 Carlsbad (92011) ***(P-19683)***
Peak Franchising Inc ....E....714 456-0700
1500 S Sunkist St Ste D Anaheim (92806) ***(P-643)***
Peak Seasons, Riverside *Also called Tom Leonard Investment Co Inc* ***(P-24272)***
Peak Servo Corp / Eltrol, Carlsbad *Also called Peak Servo Corporation* ***(P-17292)***
Peak Servo Corporation ....F....760 438-4986
5931 Sea Lion Pl Ste 108 Carlsbad (92010) ***(P-17292)***
Peanut Shell, Union City *Also called Farallon Brands Inc* ***(P-3723)***
Pear Valley Vineyard Inc ....F....805 237-2861
4900 Union Rd Paso Robles (93446) ***(P-1918)***
Pearl Crop Inc ....E....209 887-3731
8452 Demartini Ln Linden (95236) ***(P-2636)***
Pearl Crop Inc ....E....209 982-9933
17641 French Camp Rd Ripon (95366) ***(P-1516)***
Pearl Rove Inc ....F....858 869-1827
9570 Ridgehaven Ct Ste B San Diego (92123) ***(P-23756)***
Pearlman Enterprises Inc (HQ) ....C....800 969-5561
6210 Garfield Ave Commerce (90040) ***(P-11301)***
Pearpoint Inc ....E....760 343-7350
39740 Garand Ln Ste B Palm Desert (92211) ***(P-18216)***
Pearson Education Inc ....F....800 653-1918
3700 Inland Empire Blvd Ontario (91764) ***(P-6378)***
Pearson Education Inc ....E....415 402-2500
1301 Sansome St San Francisco (94111) ***(P-6379)***
Pearson Electronics Inc ....F....650 494-6444
4009 Transport St Palo Alto (94303) ***(P-19352)***
Pearson Engineering Corp ....F....626 442-7436
2505 Loma Ave South El Monte (91733) ***(P-13632)***
Peay Vineyards LLC ....F....707 894-8720
207a N Cloverdale Blvd Cloverdale (95425) ***(P-1919)***
Pebble Technology Corp ....E....888 224-5820
900 Middlefield Rd Ste 5 Redwood City (94063) ***(P-23223)***
PEC Manufacturing Inc ....F....408 577-1839
2110 Ringwood Ave San Jose (95131) ***(P-20039)***
PEC of America Corporation (HQ) ....F....619 710-8131
2320 Pso De Las Amer # 107 San Diego (92154) ***(P-17154)***
PEC Tool, Torrance *Also called Products Engineering Corp* ***(P-11907)***

ALPHABETIC SECTION Perez Severino

Peca Corporation ....E....626 452-8873
9707 El Poche St Ste H El Monte (91733) *(P-9654)*

Pecific Grinding, Fullerton *Also called Kryler Corp (P-13440)*

Peck Road Gravel Pit ....E....626 574-7570
128 Live Oak Ave Monrovia (91016) *(P-378)*

Peco Controls Corporation ....F....209 576-3345
1616 Culpepper Ave Ste A Modesto (95351) *(P-17293)*

Peco Inspx, Modesto *Also called Peco Controls Corporation (P-17293)*

Pecofacet (us) Inc ....F....916 689-2328
8314 Tiogawoods Dr Sacramento (95828) *(P-15351)*

Pecowood Inc ....F....562 633-2538
7707 Alondra Blvd Paramount (90723) *(P-11984)*

Pedavena Mould and Die Co Inc ....E....310 327-2814
12464 Mccann Dr Gardena (90249) *(P-16836)*

Pedco, Cerritos *Also called Parts Expediting and Dist Co (P-20418)*

Pedi, Carlsbad *Also called Providien Injction Molding Inc (P-10316)*

Pednar Products Inc ....F....626 960-9883
1823 Enterprise Way Monrovia (91016) *(P-9873)*

Pedro Pallan ....F....310 638-1763
344 W Rosecrans Ave Compton (90222) *(P-1308)*

Peei, Los Angeles *Also called Playboy Enterprises Intl Inc (P-6552)*

Peek Arent You Curious Inc (PA) ....D....415 512-7335
425 2nd St Ste 405 San Francisco (94107) *(P-3585)*

Peen-Rite Inc ....F....818 767-3676
11662 Sheldon St Sun Valley (91352) *(P-11827)*

Peep Inc ....E....213 748-5500
720 Towne Ave Los Angeles (90021) *(P-3477)*

Peep Studio, Los Angeles *Also called Peep Inc (P-3477)*

Peerles Coffee and Tea, Oakland *Also called Peerless Coffee Company Inc (P-2363)*

Peerless Coffee Company Inc ....D....510 763-1763
260 Oak St Oakland (94607) *(P-2363)*

Peerless Injection Molding LLC ....E....714 689-1920
14321 Corp Dr Garden Grove (92843) *(P-10270)*

Peerless Materials Company (PA) ....E....323 266-0313
4442 E 26th St Vernon (90058) *(P-8665)*

Peets Coffee & Tea LLC (HQ) ....B....510 594-2100
1400 Park Ave Emeryville (94608) *(P-2364)*

Pega Precision Inc ....E....408 776-3700
18800 Adams Ct Morgan Hill (95037) *(P-12711)*

Pegasus Foods, Los Angeles *Also called Astrochef Inc (P-1389)*

Pegasus Interprint ....E....800 926-9873
7111 Hayvenhurst Ave Van Nuys (91406) *(P-7021)*

Pegasus Med Services/Renalab ....F....805 226-8350
3570 Sibley Ln Templeton (93465) *(P-8327)*

Pegasus Press 2010 LLC ....D....818 989-3600
7111 Hayvenhurst Ave Van Nuys (91406) *(P-7022)*

Peggy S Lane Inc ....D....510 483-1202
2701 Merced St San Leandro (94577) *(P-9910)*

Peking Noodle Co Inc ....E....323 223-0897
1514 N San Fernando Rd Los Angeles (90065) *(P-2437)*

Pel Manufacturing Leasng Corp ....F....310 530-7145
3200 Kashiwa St Torrance (90505) *(P-7612)*

Pel Mfg & Leasing, Torrance *Also called Pel Manufacturing Leasng Corp (P-7612)*

Pelagic Pressure Systems Corp ....D....510 569-3100
2002 Davis St San Leandro (94577) *(P-14660)*

Pelican Products Inc (PA) ....B....310 326-4700
23215 Early Ave Torrance (90505) *(P-17724)*

Pelican Rope Works ....F....714 545-0116
1600 E Mcfadden Ave Santa Ana (92705) *(P-2977)*

Pelican Sign Service Inc ....F....408 246-3833
1565 Lafayette St Santa Clara (95050) *(P-23943)*

Pelican Woodworks ....E....951 674-7821
560 Birch St Ste 2 Lake Elsinore (92530) *(P-4335)*

Pellegrine Wine Company, Santa Rosa *Also called Pellegrini Ranches (P-1920)*

Pellegrini Ranches ....F....707 545-8680
4055 W Olivet Rd Santa Rosa (95401) *(P-1920)*

Pellenc America Inc (HQ) ....E....707 568-7286
3171 Guerneville Rd Santa Rosa (95401) *(P-14091)*

Pelton-Shepherd Industries Inc (PA) ....E....209 460-0893
812 W Luce St Ste B Stockton (95203) *(P-2418)*

Pem, Buena Park *Also called Park Engineering and Mfg Co (P-16831)*

Pencil Grip Inc (PA) ....F....310 315-3545
21200 Superior St Ste A Chatsworth (91311) *(P-5688)*

Pencom Accuracy Inc ....D....510 785-5022
1300 Industrial Rd Ste 21 San Carlos (94070) *(P-13037)*

Pendarvis Manufacturing Inc ....E....714 992-0950
1808 N American St Anaheim (92801) *(P-16837)*

Pendragon Costumes, Castaic *Also called Nicole Fullerton (P-3673)*

Penfield Products Inc ....E....916 635-0231
11300 Trade Center Dr A Rancho Cordova (95742) *(P-12712)*

Penguin Pumps Incorporated ....E....818 504-2391
7932 Ajay Dr Sun Valley (91352) *(P-15087)*

Penguin Random House LLC ....E....916 787-7000
3000 Lava Ridge Ct # 100 Roseville (95661) *(P-6380)*

Penhall Diamond Products Inc ....D....714 776-0937
1345 S Acacia Ave Fullerton (92831) *(P-14661)*

Penhouse Media Group Inc ....E....310 575-4835
11601 Wilshire Blvd Fl 5 Los Angeles (90025) *(P-6230)*

Peninsula Engrg Solutions Inc ....F....925 837-2243
288 Love Ln Danville (94526) *(P-18217)*

Peninsula Light Metals LLC (HQ) ....F....626 765-4856
875 W 8th St Azusa (91702) *(P-11702)*

Peninsula Metal Fabrication, San Jose *Also called I & A Inc (P-12618)*

Peninsula Metal Fabrication, San Jose *Also called Hardcraft Industries Inc (P-12608)*

Peninsula Packaging LLC (HQ) ....D....559 594-6813
1030 N Anderson Rd Exeter (93221) *(P-24207)*

Peninsula Packaging LLC ....C....831 634-0940
2401 Bert Dr Ste A Hollister (95023) *(P-10271)*

Peninsula Packaging Company, Exeter *Also called Peninsula Packaging LLC (P-24207)*

Peninsula Pharmaceuticals ....E....510 337-1060
1751 Harbor Bay Pkwy Alameda (94502) *(P-8328)*

Peninsula Publishing, Newport Beach *Also called Builder & Developer Magazines (P-6118)*

Peninsula Publishing Inc ....E....949 631-1307
1602 Monrovia Ave Newport Beach (92663) *(P-6231)*

Peninsula Spring Corporation ....F....408 848-3361
6750 Silacci Way Gilroy (95020) *(P-13798)*

Pennoyer-Dodge Co ....E....818 547-2100
6650 San Fernando Rd Glendale (91201) *(P-14662)*

Penny & Giles Drive Technology, Brea *Also called Curtiss-Wright Controls (P-22715)*

Pennysaver ....E....909 467-8500
1520 N Mountain Ave # 121 Ontario (91762) *(P-6012)*

Pennzoil-Quaker State Company ....F....510 748-1331
2015 Grand St Alameda (94501) *(P-9446)*

Penrose Coping Company, Sun Valley *Also called Precision Tile Co (P-10981)*

Penrose Studios Inc ....F....703 354-1801
223 Mississippi St Ste 3 San Francisco (94107) *(P-6549)*

Penta Biotech Inc ....F....650 598-9328
1100 Industrial Rd Ste 4 San Carlos (94070) *(P-9029)*

Penta Financial Inc ....E....818 882-3872
7868 Deering Ave Canoga Park (91304) *(P-18394)*

Penta Laboratories, Canoga Park *Also called Penta Financial Inc (P-18394)*

Penta Laboratories LLC ....F....818 882-3872
7868 Deering Ave Canoga Park (91304) *(P-18395)*

Pentair, Huntington Beach *Also called STA-Rite Industries LLC (P-15092)*

Pentair Aquatic Systems, Chino *Also called Pentair Water Pool and Spa Inc (P-16087)*

Pentair Flow Technologies LLC ....C....559 266-0516
2445 S Gearhart Ave Fresno (93725) *(P-16086)*

Pentair Pool Products, Moorpark *Also called Pentair Water Pool and Spa Inc (P-16088)*

Pentair Water Group, Fresno *Also called Pentair Flow Technologies LLC (P-16086)*

Pentair Water Pool and Spa Inc ....E....909 287-7800
13950 Mountain Ave Chino (91710) *(P-16087)*

Pentair Water Pool and Spa Inc ....E....805 553-5003
10951 W Los Angeles Ave Moorpark (93021) *(P-16088)*

Pentrate Metal Processing ....E....323 269-2121
3517 E Olympic Blvd Los Angeles (90023) *(P-13473)*

Penumbra Inc (PA) ....B....510 748-3200
1 Penumbra Alameda (94502) *(P-22581)*

Penumbra Brands Inc ....F....385 336-6120
1010 S Coast Highway 101 Encinitas (92024) *(P-19684)*

People Center Inc ....E....781 864-1232
2443 Fillmore St San Francisco (94115) *(P-25054)*

People For Peace, Los Angeles *Also called 2016 Montgomery Inc (P-2715)*

People Trend Inc ....F....213 995-5555
4801 Staunton Ave Vernon (90058) *(P-3184)*

Peoples Sausage Company ....F....213 627-8633
1132 E Pico Blvd Los Angeles (90021) *(P-514)*

PeopleSoft, San Mateo *Also called Oracle Systems Corporation (P-25032)*

Pepper Plant, The, Gilroy *Also called Blossom Valley Foods Inc (P-2246)*

Pepsi Co, Oakland *Also called Svc Mfg Inc A Corp (P-2227)*

Pepsi Cola Btlg of Bkersfield ....C....661 327-9992
215 E 21st St Bakersfield (93305) *(P-2163)*

Pepsi-Cola, Fresno *Also called Roger Enrico (P-2214)*

Pepsi-Cola Bottling Group ....C....661 635-1100
215 E 21st St Bakersfield (93305) *(P-2164)*

Pepsi-Cola Metro Btlg Co Inc ....D....805 739-2160
2345 Thompson Way Santa Maria (93455) *(P-2165)*

Pepsi-Cola Metro Btlg Co Inc ....B....714 522-9635
6261 Caballero Blvd Buena Park (90620) *(P-2166)*

Pepsi-Cola Metro Btlg Co Inc ....C....408 617-2200
4699 Old Ironsides Dr # 150 Santa Clara (95054) *(P-2167)*

Pepsi-Cola Metro Btlg Co Inc ....A....310 327-4222
19700 Figueroa St Carson (90745) *(P-2168)*

Pepsi-Cola Metro Btlg Co Inc ....B....916 423-1000
7550 Reese Rd Sacramento (95828) *(P-2169)*

Pepsi-Cola Metro Btlg Co Inc ....E....209 367-7140
4225 Pepsi Pl Stockton (95215) *(P-2170)*

Pepsi-Cola Metro Btlg Co Inc ....B....909 885-0741
6659 Sycamore Canyon Blvd Riverside (92507) *(P-2171)*

Pepsi-Cola Metro Btlg Co Inc ....B....858 560-6735
7995 Armour St San Diego (92111) *(P-2172)*

Pepsi-Cola Metro Btlg Co Inc ....C....831 796-2000
135 Martella St Salinas (93901) *(P-2173)*

Pepsi-Cola Metro Btlg Co Inc ....D....661 824-2051
2471 Nadeau St Mojave (93501) *(P-2174)*

Pepsi-Cola Metro Btlg Co Inc ....F....760 775-2660
83801 Citrus Ave Indio (92201) *(P-2175)*

Pepsi-Cola Metro Btlg Co Inc ....B....510 781-3600
29000 Hesperian Blvd Hayward (94545) *(P-2176)*

Pepsi-Cola Metro Btlg Co Inc ....C....949 643-5700
27717 Aliso Creek Rd Aliso Viejo (92656) *(P-2177)*

Pepsico, Santa Maria *Also called Pepsi-Cola Metro Btlg Co Inc (P-2165)*

Pepsico, Hayward *Also called P-Americas LLC (P-2160)*

Pepsico, Redding *Also called John Fitzpatrick & Sons (P-2141)*

Pepsico, Stockton *Also called Pepsi-Cola Metro Btlg Co Inc (P-2170)*

Pepsico, San Diego *Also called Pepsi-Cola Metro Btlg Co Inc (P-2172)*

Pepsico, Bakersfield *Also called Pepsi-Cola Bottling Group (P-2164)*

Pepsico, Ventura *Also called P-Americas LLC (P-2161)*

Pepsico, Aliso Viejo *Also called Pepsi-Cola Metro Btlg Co Inc (P-2177)*

Pepsico, Riverside *Also called Bottling Group LLC (P-2102)*

Perceptimed Inc ....E....650 941-7000
365 San Antonio Rd Mountain View (94040) *(P-15007)*

Peregrine Mobile Bottling LLC ....F....707 637-7584
20590 Pueblo Ave Sonoma (95476) *(P-2178)*

Perez Severino ....F....818 701-1522
9710 Owensmouth Ave Lbby Chatsworth (91311) *(P-13963)*

ALPHABETIC

Employee Codes: A=Over 500 employees, B=251-500
C=101-250, D=51-100, E=20-50, F=10-19
2019 California
Manfacturers Register
© Mergent Inc. 1-800-342-5647
1243

Perez Bros Ornamental Iron, Northridge *Also called Perez Brothers* **(P-4839)**
Perez Brothers........F.......818 780-8482
19607 Prairie St Northridge (91324) **(P-4839)**
Perez Distributing Fresno Inc (PA)........E.......800 638-3512
103 S Academy Ave Sanger (93657) **(P-8329)**
Perez Machine Inc........F.......310 217-9090
1501 W 134th St Gardena (90249) **(P-16838)**
Perfect Image Printing Inc........F.......916 631-8350
3223 Monier Cir Rancho Cordova (95742) **(P-7433)**
Perfect Plank Co........F.......530 533-7606
2850 S 5th Ave Oroville (95965) **(P-4211)**
Perfect Puree of NAPA Vly LLC........F.......707 261-5100
2700 Napa Valley Corp Dr NAPA (94558) **(P-963)**
Perfection Machine & Tl Works, Los Angeles *Also called Perfection Machine and Tl Work* **(P-16839)**
Perfection Machine and Tl Work........E.......213 749-5095
1568 E 22nd St Los Angeles (90011) **(P-16839)**
Perfectvips Inc........F.......408 912-2316
2099 Gateway Pl Ste 240 San Jose (95110) **(P-19074)**
Perfekt Beauty, Culver City *Also called Cosmetic Design Group LLC* **(P-8726)**
Performance Agriculture, Kerman *Also called Pinnacle Agriculture Dist Inc* **(P-14093)**
Performance Aluminum Products........E.......909 391-4131
520 S Palmetto Ave Ontario (91762) **(P-11703)**
Performance Apparel Corp........F.......805 541-0989
4145 Santa Fe Rd Ste 1 San Luis Obispo (93401) **(P-3478)**
Performance Cnc Inc........F.......760 722-1129
3210 Production Ave Ste A Oceanside (92058) **(P-16840)**
Performance Coatings Inc........E.......707 462-3023
360 Lake Mendocino Dr Ukiah (95482) **(P-8923)**
Performance Composites Inc........D.......310 328-6661
1418 S Alameda St Compton (90221) **(P-10664)**
Performance Forged Products........E.......323 722-3460
7401 Telegraph Rd Montebello (90640) **(P-13109)**
Performance Label Intl Inc........F.......619 429-6870
6825 Gateway Park Dr # 1 San Diego (92154) **(P-7434)**
Performance Machine Tech Inc........E.......661 294-8617
25141 Avenue Stanford Valencia (91355) **(P-16841)**
Performance Materials Corp (PA)........D.......805 482-1722
1150 Calle Suerte Camarillo (93012) **(P-7864)**
Performance Pipe Div, San Ramon *Also called Chevron Phillips Chem Co LP* **(P-9777)**
Performance Plastics Inc........C.......619 482-5031
7919 Saint Andrews Ave San Diego (92154) **(P-20909)**
Performance Plus Laboratories........C.......805 383-7871
3609 Vista Mercado Camarillo (93012) **(P-21486)**
Performance Polymer Tech LLC........E.......916 677-1414
8801 Washington Blvd # 109 Roseville (95678) **(P-9571)**
Performance Powder Inc........E.......714 632-0600
2940 E La Jolla St Ste A Anaheim (92806) **(P-13633)**
Performance Printing Center........E.......415 485-5878
4380 Redwood Hwy Ste B8 San Rafael (94903) **(P-7023)**
Performance Sealing Inc........F.......714 662-5918
1821 Langley Ave Irvine (92614) **(P-9548)**
Performance Trailers Inc........E.......559 673-6300
2901 Falcon Dr Madera (93637) **(P-20508)**
Performance Truck and Trlr LLC........F.......909 605-0323
500 Etiwanda Ave Ontario (91761) **(P-20509)**
Performance Tube Bending Inc........F.......626 939-9000
5462 Diaz St Baldwin Park (91706) **(P-13899)**
Performance Welding........F.......559 233-0042
2540 S Sarah St Fresno (93706) **(P-25425)**
Performex Machining Inc........E.......650 595-2228
963 Terminal Way San Carlos (94070) **(P-16842)**
Performnce Engineered Pdts Inc........D.......909 594-7487
3270 Pomona Blvd Pomona (91768) **(P-10272)**
Perfumer's Apprentice, Scotts Valley *Also called Pacific Coast Products LLC* **(P-2275)**
Perfumer's Apprentice, Scotts Valley *Also called Pacific Coast Products LLC* **(P-2276)**
Peri Formwork Systems Inc........E.......909 356-5797
15369 Valencia Ave Fontana (92335) **(P-12713)**
Peric Oil Tool, Bakersfield *Also called Weatherford Completion Systems* **(P-294)**
Pericom Semiconductor Corp (HQ)........E.......408 232-9100
1545 Barber Ln Milpitas (95035) **(P-21824)**
Peridot Corporation........D.......925 461-8830
1072 Serpentine Ln Pleasanton (94566) **(P-13799)**
Perimeter Solutions LP........E.......909 983-0772
10667 Jersey Blvd Rancho Cucamonga (91730) **(P-7796)**
Perine Lowe Inc........F.......714 990-1590
400 N Berry St Brea (92821) **(P-11865)**
Periodico El Vida........E.......805 483-1008
130 Palm Dr Oxnard (93030) **(P-6013)**
Perkins........E.......818 764-9293
7312 Varna Ave Ste A North Hollywood (91605) **(P-14736)**
Perkins Family Restaurant, North Hollywood *Also called Perkins* **(P-14736)**
Perkins Market, Descanso *Also called Yaldo Enterprises Inc* **(P-2424)**
Permacel-Automotive, Fremont *Also called Nitto Americas Inc* **(P-5573)**
Permalite Plastics Corp........E.......310 669-9492
3121 E Ana St Compton (90221) **(P-8965)**
Permaswage USA, Gardena *Also called Designed Metal Connections Inc* **(P-13021)**
Permeco........F.......909 599-9600
1970 Walker St La Verne (91750) **(P-11269)**
Pernod Ricard Usa LLC........D.......707 833-5891
9592 Sonoma Hwy Kenwood (95452) **(P-1921)**
Pernod Ricard Usa LLC........D.......707 967-7770
8445 Silverado Trl Rutherford (94573) **(P-1922)**
Pernstner Sons Fabrication Inc........F.......209 345-2430
712 W Harding Rd Turlock (95380) **(P-13900)**
Perpetual Motion Group Inc........D.......818 982-4300
11939 Sherman Rd North Hollywood (91605) **(P-12228)**
Perrault Corporation........F.......760 466-1024
30640 N River Rd Bonsall (92003) **(P-379)**
Perricone Juices, Beaumont *Also called Beaumont Juice Inc* **(P-785)**
Perrin Craft, City of Industry *Also called Dispensing Dynamics Intl Inc* **(P-10071)**
Perrins Registration Office........F.......818 832-1332
17727 Chatsworth St Granada Hills (91344) **(P-13259)**
Perris Skyventure........F.......951 940-4290
2093 Goetz Rd Perris (92570) **(P-12408)**
Perris Wind Tunnel, Perris *Also called Perris Skyventure* **(P-12408)**
Perry Creek Winery........F.......530 620-5175
7400 Perry Creek Rd Somerset (95684) **(P-1923)**
Perry Tool & Research Inc........E.......510 782-9226
3415 Enterprise Ave Hayward (94545) **(P-11845)**
Perrys Custom Chopping........F.......209 667-8777
21365 Williams Ave Hilmar (95324) **(P-14092)**
Perseption, Vernon *Also called W & W Concept Inc* **(P-3527)**
Pershing Foods........F.......323 589-1658
3680 S Santa Fe Ave Vernon (90058) **(P-2397)**
Person & Covey Inc........E.......818 937-5000
616 Allen Ave Glendale (91201) **(P-8812)**
Persona International, Sausalito *Also called Personal Awareness Systems* **(P-6550)**
Personal Awareness Systems........F.......415 331-3900
767 Bridgeway Ste 3b Sausalito (94965) **(P-6550)**
Persys Engineering Inc........E.......831 471-9300
815 Swift St Santa Cruz (95060) **(P-15008)**
Pertronix Inc (PA)........E.......909 599-5955
440 E Arrow Hwy San Dimas (91773) **(P-21522)**
Pertronix Inc........E.......909 599-5955
15601 Cypress Ave Unit B Irwindale (91706) **(P-19844)**
Pesenti Winery, Saint Helena *Also called Turley Wine Cellars Inc* **(P-2032)**
Pet Carousel Inc........E.......316 291-2500
2350 Academy Ave Sanger (93657) **(P-1119)**
Pet Partners Inc (PA)........C.......951 279-9888
450 N Sheridan St Corona (92880) **(P-24208)**
Pet Product News, Irvine *Also called Bowtie Inc* **(P-6115)**
Petalumaidence Opco LLC........D.......707 763-4109
101 Monroe St Petaluma (94954) **(P-1924)**
Peter Cohen Companies, Los Angeles *Also called Piet Retief Inc* **(P-3482)**
Peter K Inc (PA)........E.......323 585-5343
5175 S Soto St Vernon (90058) **(P-3479)**
Peter Michael Winery, Calistoga *Also called Sugarloaf Farming Corporation* **(P-2001)**
Peter Pugger Manufacturing........F.......707 463-1333
3661 Christy Ln Ukiah (95482) **(P-14184)**
Petersen Precision Engrg LLC........C.......650 365-4373
611 Broadway St Redwood City (94063) **(P-16843)**
Peterson Sheet Metal Inc........F.......925 830-1766
12925 Alcosta Blvd Ste 2 San Ramon (94583) **(P-12714)**
Peterson Sheetmetal, San Ramon *Also called Peterson Sheet Metal Inc* **(P-12714)**
Petit Pot Inc........F.......650 488-7432
158 S Spruce Ave South San Francisco (94080) **(P-2637)**
Petite Porcelain By Barbara, Modesto *Also called Phoenix Custom Promotions* **(P-23400)**
Petits Pains & Co LP........F.......650 692-6000
1730 Gilbreth Rd Burlingame (94010) **(P-1309)**
Petra-1 LP........F.......866 334-3702
12386 Osborne Pl Pacoima (91331) **(P-8813)**
Petro-Lud Inc........F.......661 747-4779
12625 Jomani Dr Ste 104 Bakersfield (93312) **(P-117)**
Petrochem Marketing........F.......323 526-4084
3033 E Washington Blvd Los Angeles (90023) **(P-9394)**
Petroil Americas Limited........F.......323 931-3720
5651 W Pico Blvd Ste 102 Los Angeles (90019) **(P-9350)**
Petroleum Sales Inc........D.......415 256-1600
2066 Redwood Hwy Greenbrae (94904) **(P-69)**
Petsport Usa Inc........F.......925 439-9243
1160 Railroad Ave Pittsburg (94565) **(P-24209)**
Pettigrew & Sons Casket Co........E.......916 383-0777
6151 Power Inn Rd Sacramento (95824) **(P-24012)**
Petunia Pickle Bottom Corp........F.......805 643-6697
3567 Old Conejo Rd Newbury Park (91320) **(P-2757)**
Pew Forest Products Inc........E.......530 284-7882
390 Arlington Rd Crescent Mills (95934) **(P-4044)**
Pew Forestry, Crescent Mills *Also called Pew Forest Products Inc* **(P-4044)**
Pezeme, Los Angeles *Also called Choon Inc* **(P-3302)**
Pf Candle Co, Commerce *Also called Pommes Frites Candle Co* **(P-24212)**
Pf Plastics Inc........F.......909 392-4488
2044 Wright Ave La Verne (91750) **(P-4916)**
Pfanner Communications Inc........F.......714 227-3579
3334 E Coast Hwy Ste 162 Corona Del Mar (92625) **(P-6232)**
Pfanstiel Printing, Long Beach *Also called Pfanstiel Publishers & Prtrs* **(P-7024)**
Pfanstiel Publishers & Prtrs........F.......562 438-5641
3010 E Anaheim St Long Beach (90804) **(P-7024)**
Pfenex Inc........D.......858 352-4400
10790 Roselle St San Diego (92121) **(P-8330)**
Pfister Faucets, Foothill Ranch *Also called Price Pfister Inc* **(P-12045)**
Pfizer Health Solutions Inc........F.......310 586-2550
2400 Broadway Ste 500 Santa Monica (90404) **(P-8331)**
Pfizer Inc........C.......858 622-7325
11095 Torreyana Rd San Diego (92121) **(P-8332)**
Pfizer Inc........A.......858 622-3001
10646 Science Center Dr San Diego (92121) **(P-8333)**
Pfp, Milpitas *Also called Precision Fiber Products Inc* **(P-11670)**
Pfs, Sylmar *Also called Professional Finishing Systems* **(P-13264)**
PG Emminger Inc........E.......925 313-5830
4036 Pacheco Blvd A Martinez (94553) **(P-5093)**
Pg Imtech of California LLC........F.......562 945-8943
8424 Secura Way Santa Fe Springs (90670) **(P-13474)**
Pgac Corp (PA)........D.......858 560-8213
9630 Ridgehaven Ct Ste B San Diego (92123) **(P-5532)**
Pgi Pacific Graphics Intl........E.......626 336-7707
14938 Nelson Ave City of Industry (91744) **(P-7025)**

Mergent e-mail: customerrelations@mergent.com
1244
2019 California
Manufacturers Register
(P-0000) Products & Services Section entry number
(PA)=Parent Co (HQ)=Headquarters (DH)=Div Headquarters

Pgm Metal Finishing......F......714 282-9193
409 W Blueridge Ave Orange (92865) ***(P-13634)***
Pgp International Inc (HQ)......C......530 662-5056
351 Hanson Way Woodland (95776) ***(P-2638)***
PH Labs Advanced Nutrition......F......619 240-3263
9760 Via De La Amistad San Diego (92154) ***(P-8334)***
Phantom, Beverly Hills *Also called Melamed International Inc* ***(P-3178)***
Phantom Carriage Brewery......E......310 538-5834
18525 S Main St Gardena (90248) ***(P-14877)***
Phantom Cyber Corporation......E......650 208-5151
2479 E Byshore Rd Ste 185 Palo Alto (94303) ***(P-25055)***
Phantom Tool & Die Co......F......760 240-4249
23535 Us Highway 18 Apple Valley (92307) ***(P-14450)***
Phaostron Instr Electronic Co, Azusa *Also called Phaostron Instr Electronic Co* ***(P-17155)***
Phaostron Instr Electronic Co......D......626 969-6801
717 N Coney Ave Azusa (91702) ***(P-17155)***
Pharma Pac, Grover Beach *Also called H J Harkins Company Inc* ***(P-8200)***
Pharmaceutic Litho Label Inc......D......805 285-5162
3990 Royal Ave Simi Valley (93063) ***(P-8335)***
Pharmachem Laboratories LLC......F......714 630-6000
2929 E White Star Ave Anaheim (92806) ***(P-644)***
Pharmaco-Kinesis Corporation......E......310 641-2700
6053 W Century Blvd # 600 Los Angeles (90045) ***(P-22582)***
Pharmacyclics LLC (HQ)......C......408 215-3000
995 E Arques Ave Sunnyvale (94085) ***(P-8336)***
Pharmapack North America Corp......F......909 390-1888
5095 E Airport Dr Ontario (91761) ***(P-7865)***
Pharmavite LLC......B......818 221-6200
1150 Aviation Pl San Fernando (91340) ***(P-7963)***
Pharmavite LLC (HQ)......C......818 221-6200
8510 Balboa Blvd Ste 300 Northridge (91325) ***(P-7964)***
Pharr-Palomar Inc......A......714 522-4811
6781 8th St Buena Park (90620) ***(P-2946)***
Phase 5 Tactical, Roseville *Also called Phase 5 Weapon Systems Inc* ***(P-13688)***
Phase 5 Weapon Systems Inc......F......916 787-4273
501 Giuseppe Ct Ste C Roseville (95678) ***(P-13688)***
Phase II Products Inc (PA)......E......619 236-9699
501 W Broadway Ste 2090 San Diego (92101) ***(P-5205)***
Phase Matrix Inc......E......408 610-6810
4600 Patrick Henry Dr Santa Clara (95054) ***(P-21825)***
Phase Research, Costa Mesa *Also called Fire & Safety Electronics Inc* ***(P-17270)***
Phase-A-Matic Inc......F......661 947-8485
39360 3rd St E Ste C301 Palmdale (93550) ***(P-20040)***
Phasespace Inc (PA)......F......925 945-6533
1937 Oak Park Blvd Ste A Pleasant Hill (94523) ***(P-23186)***
Phat N Jicy Burgers Brands LLC......E......310 420-7983
25876 The Old Rd 305 Stevenson Ranch (91381) ***(P-2639)***
Phat N Juicy Brands, Stevenson Ranch *Also called Phat N Jicy Burgers Brands LLC* ***(P-2639)***
PHC, Irvine *Also called Pacific Handy Cutter Inc* ***(P-11905)***
Phenix Enterprises Inc (PA)......E......909 469-0411
1785 Mount Vernon Ave Pomona (91768) ***(P-20224)***
Phenix Gourmet LLC......C......562 404-5028
4225 N Palm St Fullerton (92835) ***(P-1375)***
Phenix Truck Bodies and Eqp, Pomona *Also called Phenix Enterprises Inc* ***(P-20224)***
Phenomenex Inc (HQ)......C......310 212-0555
411 Madrid Ave Torrance (90501) ***(P-22003)***
Pheonicia Inc......F......951 268-5180
710 E Parkridge Ave # 105 Corona (92879) ***(P-7435)***
PHI......E......626 968-9680
14955 Salt Lake Ave E City of Industry (91746) ***(P-14451)***
PHI Hydraulics, City of Industry *Also called PHI* ***(P-14451)***
Phiaro Incorporated......E......949 727-1261
9016 Research Dr Irvine (92618) ***(P-24210)***
Phibro Animal Health Corp......E......562 698-8036
8851 Dice Rd Santa Fe Springs (90670) ***(P-9297)***
Phibro-Tech Inc......E......562 698-8036
8851 Dice Rd Santa Fe Springs (90670) ***(P-7797)***
Phil Blazer Enterprises Inc......F......818 786-4000
15315 Magnolia Blvd # 101 Sherman Oaks (91403) ***(P-6014)***
Phil Wood & Company......F......408 292-4137
1125 N 7th St A San Jose (95112) ***(P-13964)***
Philadelphia Gear, Santa Fe Springs *Also called Timken Gears & Services Inc* ***(P-13114)***
Philatron International (PA)......C......562 802-0452
15315 Cornet St Santa Fe Springs (90670) ***(P-20041)***
Philbrick Inc......E......707 964-2277
32180 Airport Rd Fort Bragg (95437) ***(P-4006)***
Philbrick Logging & Trucking, Fort Bragg *Also called Philbrick Inc* ***(P-4006)***
Philip A Stitt Agency......F......916 451-2801
3900 Stockton Blvd Sacramento (95820) ***(P-3804)***
Philip Morris USA Inc......D......949 453-3500
185 Technology Dr Irvine (92618) ***(P-2707)***
Philippe Charriol USA, San Diego *Also called Alor International Ltd* ***(P-23232)***
Philips & Lite-On Digital (HQ)......E......510 687-1800
726 S Hillview Dr Milpitas (95035) ***(P-15583)***
Philips Elec N Amer Corp......C......626 480-0755
13700 Live Oak Ave Baldwin Park (91706) ***(P-22122)***
Philips Medical Systems Clevel......F......805 681-0463
5290 Overpass Rd Ste 209 Santa Barbara (93111) ***(P-22583)***
Philips North America LLC......E......909 574-1800
11201 Iberia St Ste A Jurupa Valley (91752) ***(P-17554)***
Philips Semiconductors, Sunnyvale *Also called Nxp Usa Inc* ***(P-19048)***
Phillips 66......D......310 522-9300
1520 E Sepulveda Blvd Carson (90745) ***(P-9351)***
Phillips 66 Co Carbon Group......F......805 489-4050
2555 Willow Rd Arroyo Grande (93420) ***(P-15009)***
Phillips 66 Spectrum Corp......F......707 745-6100
6100 Egret Ct Benicia (94510) ***(P-9447)***
Phillips Bros Plastics Inc......E......310 532-8020
17831 S Western Ave Gardena (90248) ***(P-9757)***
Phillips Lobue & Wilson Mllwk......F......951 331-5714
300 E Santa Ana St Anaheim (92805) ***(P-4212)***
Phillips Machine & Wldg Co Inc......E......626 855-4600
16125 Gale Ave City of Industry (91745) ***(P-25426)***
Phillips-Medisize......C......949 477-9495
3545 Harbor Blvd Costa Mesa (92626) ***(P-22584)***
Phin, San Jose *Also called Connectedyard Inc* ***(P-21937)***
Phl Associates Inc......F......530 753-5881
24711 County Road 100a Davis (95616) ***(P-8573)***
Phoenix Aerial Systems Inc......F......323 577-3366
10131 National Blvd Los Angeles (90034) ***(P-22250)***
Phoenix Arms......E......909 937-6900
4231 E Brickell St Ontario (91761) ***(P-13689)***
Phoenix Audio Technologies, Irvine *Also called Midas Technology Inc* ***(P-17834)***
Phoenix Cars LLC......F......909 987-0815
401 S Doubleday Ave Ontario (91761) ***(P-20163)***
Phoenix Custom Promotions......F......209 579-1557
2005 Casa Grande Ct Modesto (95355) ***(P-23400)***
Phoenix Day Co Inc......F......415 822-4414
3431 Regatta Blvd Richmond (94804) ***(P-17555)***
Phoenix Deventures Inc......E......408 782-6240
18655 Madrone Pkwy # 180 Morgan Hill (95037) ***(P-9655)***
Phoenix Engineering, Orange *Also called His Industries Inc* ***(P-15211)***
Phoenix Footwear Group Inc (PA)......E......760 602-9688
5937 Darwin Ct Ste 109 Carlsbad (92008) ***(P-10482)***
Phoenix Improving Life LLC......F......650 248-0655
148 Farley St Mountain View (94043) ***(P-22793)***
Phoenix Marine Corporation (PA)......D......415 464-8116
700 Larkspur Landing Cir # 175 Larkspur (94939) ***(P-21826)***
Phoenix Motorcars, Ontario *Also called Phoenix Cars LLC* ***(P-20163)***
Phoenix Pharmaceuticals Inc......E......650 558-8898
330 Beach Rd Burlingame (94010) ***(P-8337)***
Phoenix Research Labs, Pleasanton *Also called Phoenix Technology Group Inc* ***(P-22123)***
Phoenix Software Intl Inc (PA)......E......310 338-0400
831 N Park View Dr El Segundo (90245) ***(P-25056)***
Phoenix Technologies Ltd (HQ)......E......408 570-1000
910 E Hamilton Ave # 110 Campbell (95008) ***(P-25057)***
Phoenix Technology Group Inc......F......925 485-1100
6630 Owens Dr Pleasanton (94588) ***(P-22123)***
Phonak LLC......F......510 743-3939
47257 Fremont Blvd Fremont (94538) ***(P-22794)***
Phonesuit Inc......E......310 774-0282
1431 7th St Ste 201 Santa Monica (90401) ***(P-18218)***
Phorus LLC......F......310 995-2521
16255 Ventura Blvd # 310 Encino (91436) ***(P-17843)***
Photo Fabricators Inc......D......818 781-1010
7648 Burnet Ave Van Nuys (91405) ***(P-18559)***
Photo Sciences Incorporated (PA)......E......310 634-1500
2542 W 237th St Torrance (90505) ***(P-15823)***
Photobacks LLC......F......760 582-2550
40 Paseo Montecillo Palm Desert (92260) ***(P-25058)***
Photoflex Inc......F......831 786-1370
1800 Green Hills Rd # 104 Scotts Valley (95066) ***(P-23187)***
Photographer's Forum, Santa Barbara *Also called Serbin Communications Inc* ***(P-6256)***
Photon Inc......F......408 226-1000
1671 Dell Ave Ste 208 Campbell (95008) ***(P-21632)***
Photon Dynamics Inc (HQ)......C......408 226-9900
5970 Optical Ct San Jose (95138) ***(P-21827)***
Photonic Corp......F......310 642-7975
5800 Uplander Way Ste 100 Culver City (90230) ***(P-7026)***
Photonics Division, Carlsbad *Also called L3 Technologies Inc* ***(P-18339)***
Photostone LLC......F......858 274-3400
8495 Redwood Creek Ln San Diego (92126) ***(P-14824)***
Photronics California, Burbank *Also called Photronics Inc* ***(P-23188)***
Photronics Inc (HQ)......B......203 740-5653
2428 N Ontario St Burbank (91504) ***(P-23188)***
Phu Huong Foods Co Inc......F......626 280-8607
9008 Garvey Ave Ste I Rosemead (91770) ***(P-549)***
Phygen, Irvine *Also called Allez Spine LLC* ***(P-22326)***
Phyn LLC......F......310 400-4001
1855 Del Amo Blvd Torrance (90501) ***(P-21633)***
Phynexus Inc......F......408 267-7214
3670 Charter Park Dr B San Jose (95136) ***(P-22004)***
Physicans Formula Holdings Inc (HQ)......E......626 334-3395
22067 Ferrero Walnut (91789) ***(P-8814)***
Physicians Formula Inc (HQ)......D......626 334-3395
22067 Ferrero City of Industry (91789) ***(P-8815)***
Physicians Formula Inc......D......626 334-3395
250 S 9th Ave City of Industry (91746) ***(P-8816)***
Physicians Formula Inc......D......626 334-3395
753 Arrow Grand Cir Covina (91722) ***(P-8817)***
Physicians Formula Cosmt Inc......C......626 334-3395
22067 Ferrero City of Industry (91789) ***(P-8818)***
Physicians Trust, San Clemente *Also called Srsb Inc* ***(P-25214)***
Phyto Animal Health LLC......E......888 871-4505
550 W C St Ste 2040 San Diego (92101) ***(P-645)***
Phyto Tech Corp......E......949 635-1990
30111 Tomas Rcho STA Marg (92688) ***(P-8338)***
Pi-Coral Inc......D......408 516-5150
600 California St Fl 6 San Francisco (94108) ***(P-15584)***
Piano Exchange, San Diego *Also called Gulbransen Inc* ***(P-23374)***
Pic Flick, Glendale *Also called Dion Rostamian* ***(P-23149)***
Pic Manufacturing Inc......F......805 238-5451
410 Sherwood Rd Paso Robles (93446) ***(P-14825)***
Picarro Inc (PA)......E......408 962-3900
3105 Patrick Henry Dr Santa Clara (95054) ***(P-22005)***

ALPHABETIC

Employee Codes: A=Over 500 employees, B=251-500
C=101-250, D=51-100, E=20-50, F=10-19
2019 California
Manfacturers Register
© Mergent Inc. 1-800-342-5647
1245

Piccone Apparel Corp ....E....310 559-6702
3740 Motor Ave Los Angeles (90034) ***(P-3480)***
Pickering Laboratories Inc ....E....650 694-6700
1280 Space Park Way Mountain View (94043) ***(P-7798)***
Picnic At Ascot Inc ....E....310 674-3098
3237 W 131st St Hawthorne (90250) ***(P-4532)***
Pico Corporation, Camarillo *Also called Pico Crimping Tools Co* ***(P-14663)***
Pico Crimping Tools Co ....F....805 388-5510
444 Constitution Ave Camarillo (93012) ***(P-14663)***
Pico Digital Inc (HQ) ....D....858 546-5050
8880 Rehco Rd San Diego (92121) ***(P-18219)***
Pico Pica Foods, Wilmington *Also called Juanitas Foods* ***(P-762)***
Picotrack ....F....408 988-7000
309 Laurelwood Rd Ste 21 Santa Clara (95054) ***(P-15010)***
Pictron Inc ....F....408 725-8888
1250 Oakmead Pkwy Ste 210 Sunnyvale (94085) ***(P-25059)***
Pictsweet Company ....B....805 928-4414
732 Hanson Way Santa Maria (93458) ***(P-1010)***
Picture Source of California, El Monte *Also called Sybman Inc* ***(P-4659)***
Picture This Framing Inc ....F....714 447-8749
631 S State College Blvd Fullerton (92831) ***(P-4641)***
Piedras Machine Corporation ....F....562 602-1500
15154 Downey Ave Ste B Paramount (90723) ***(P-20910)***
Piercan Usa Inc ....F....760 599-4543
160 Bosstick Blvd San Marcos (92069) ***(P-9656)***
Pierce Textile Inc ....E....562 220-1177
13984 Orange Ave Paramount (90723) ***(P-2869)***
Pierco, Eastvale *Also called Cal-Mold Incorporated* ***(P-10001)***
Pierco Incorporated ....F....909 251-7100
680 Main St Riverside (92501) ***(P-24211)***
Pierre Mitri (PA) ....F....213 747-1838
1138 Wall St Los Angeles (90015) ***(P-3481)***
Pierry Inc (PA) ....E....800 860-7953
557 Grand St Redwood City (94062) ***(P-25060)***
Piet Retief Inc ....E....323 732-8312
1914 6th Ave Los Angeles (90018) ***(P-3482)***
Pietri Bersage Store Design, Anaheim *Also called Emporium Di Sanarrey Corp* ***(P-11250)***
Piezo-Metrics Inc (PA) ....E....805 522-4676
4509 Runway St Simi Valley (93063) ***(P-19075)***
Pigs Tail USA LLC ....F....714 566-0011
925 W Lambert Rd Brea (92821) ***(P-10273)***
Pilkington Glass Co, Lathrop *Also called Pilkington North America Inc* ***(P-10603)***
Pilkington North America Inc ....B....209 858-6249
500 E Louise Ave Lathrop (95330) ***(P-10603)***
Pillar Data Systems Inc ....B....408 503-4000
2840 Junction Ave San Jose (95134) ***(P-25061)***
Pillsbury Company LLC ....D....818 522-3952
220 S Kenwood St Ste 202 Glendale (91205) ***(P-1047)***
Pilot Automotive, City of Industry *Also called Pilot Inc* ***(P-20420)***
Pilot Inc (PA) ....D....626 937-6988
13000 Temple Ave City of Industry (91746) ***(P-20420)***
Pilot Software Inc ....F....650 230-2830
3410 Hillview Ave Palo Alto (94304) ***(P-25062)***
Pimco, Corona *Also called Precision Injection Molding Co* ***(P-10303)***
Pin Concepts, Sun Valley *Also called Pin Craft Inc* ***(P-23757)***
Pin Craft Inc ....E....818 248-0077
7933 Ajay Dr Sun Valley (91352) ***(P-23757)***
Pina Cellars, NAPA *Also called John Pina Jr & Sons* ***(P-1833)***
Pine Grove Group Inc ....E....209 295-7733
25500 State Highway 88 Pioneer (95666) ***(P-20042)***
Pine Grove Industries Inc ....E....805 485-3700
2001 Cabot Pl Oxnard (93030) ***(P-7027)***
Pine Ridge Vineyards, NAPA *Also called Pine Ridge Winery LLC* ***(P-1925)***
Pine Ridge Winery LLC ....D....707 253-7500
5901 Silverado Trl NAPA (94558) ***(P-1925)***
Pinecone Press, Costa Mesa *Also called Jennis Group LLC* ***(P-6506)***
Pinecraft Custom Shutters Inc ....E....949 642-9317
946 W 17th St Costa Mesa (92627) ***(P-4213)***
Pinky Los Angeles, Burbank *Also called Vesture Group Incorporated* ***(P-3598)***
Pinnacle, La Puente *Also called Tristar Global Inc* ***(P-20469)***
Pinnacle Agriculture Dist Inc ....F....559 842-4601
1100 S Madera Ave Kerman (93630) ***(P-14093)***
Pinnacle Diversified Inc ....F....408 562-0111
1248 San Luis Obispo St Hayward (94544) ***(P-7436)***
Pinnacle Manufacturing Corp ....E....408 778-6100
17680 Butterfield Blvd # 100 Morgan Hill (95037) ***(P-12715)***
Pinnacle Precision Shtmtl Corp (PA) ....C....714 777-3129
5410 E La Palma Ave Anaheim (92807) ***(P-12716)***
Pinnacle Precision Shtmtl Corp ....D....714 777-3129
5410 E La Palma Ave Anaheim (92807) ***(P-12717)***
Pinnacle Press, Hayward *Also called Pinnacle Diversified Inc* ***(P-7436)***
Pinnacle Systems Inc ....F....650 237-1900
280 Bernardo Ave Mountain View (94043) ***(P-18220)***
Pinnacle Worldwide Inc ....F....909 628-2200
435 S Detroit St Apt 209 Los Angeles (90036) ***(P-17349)***
Pinpoint Media Group Inc ....F....714 545-5640
3188 Airway Ave Ste L Costa Mesa (92626) ***(P-6233)***
Pioneer Automotive Tech Inc ....F....937 746-6600
8701 Siempre Viva Rd San Diego (92154) ***(P-18221)***
Pioneer Balloon Co, West Covina *Also called Continental American Corp* ***(P-9601)***
Pioneer Broach Company (PA) ....E....323 728-1263
6434 Telegraph Rd Commerce (90040) ***(P-14664)***
Pioneer Circuits Inc ....B....714 641-3132
3000 S Shannon St Santa Ana (92704) ***(P-18560)***
Pioneer Custom Elec Pdts Corp ....D....562 944-0626
10640 Springdale Ave Santa Fe Springs (90670) ***(P-17112)***
Pioneer Diecasters Inc ....F....323 245-6561
4209 Chevy Chase Dr Los Angeles (90039) ***(P-11704)***
Pioneer Electronics (usa) Inc (HQ) ....B....310 952-2000
2050 W 190th St Ste 100 Torrance (90504) ***(P-17844)***
Pioneer French Bakery, Oxnard *Also called Wholesome Harvest Baking LLC* ***(P-1344)***
Pioneer Materials Inc ....E....650 357-7130
548 Trinidad Ln Foster City (94404) ***(P-22124)***
Pioneer Natural Foods, Marina Del Rey *Also called Barkstrong LLC* ***(P-1108)***
Pioneer Photo Albums Inc (PA) ....C....818 882-2161
9801 Deering Ave Chatsworth (91311) ***(P-7583)***
Pioneer Sands LLC ....E....661 746-5789
9952 Enos Ln Bakersfield (93314) ***(P-396)***
Pioneer Sands LLC ....D....949 728-0171
31302 Ortega Hwy San Juan Capistrano (92675) ***(P-397)***
Pioneer Speakers Inc (HQ) ....E....310 952-2000
2050 W 190th St Ste 100 Torrance (90504) ***(P-17845)***
Pionetics Corporation ....F....650 551-0250
151 Old County Rd Ste H San Carlos (94070) ***(P-10274)***
Pionite, Rancho Cucamonga *Also called Panolam Industries Intl Inc* ***(P-4600)***
PIP Printing, Downey *Also called Jeb-PHI Inc* ***(P-6910)***
PIP Printing, Van Nuys *Also called Bluebarry Enterprises Inc* ***(P-6699)***
PIP Printing, Hemet *Also called J S M Productions Inc* ***(P-6903)***
PIP Printing, Sun Valley *Also called Pipnsv Inc* ***(P-7028)***
PIP Printing, Sacramento *Also called Colormarx Corporation* ***(P-6744)***
PIP Printing, San Francisco *Also called Anin Co* ***(P-6662)***
Pipe Fabricating & Supply Co (PA) ....D....714 630-5200
1235 N Kraemer Blvd Anaheim (92806) ***(P-13901)***
Pipe Fabricators International, El Cajon *Also called Al & Krla Pipe Fabricators Inc* ***(P-13874)***
Pipe Guard Inc ....E....818 765-2424
10723 Sherman Way Sun Valley (91352) ***(P-12042)***
Pipeline, Compton *Also called Graphic Prints Inc* ***(P-3896)***
Pipeline Products Inc ....F....760 744-8907
1650 Linda Vista Dr # 110 San Marcos (92078) ***(P-15352)***
Pipeliner Crm ....E....424 280-6445
15243 La Cruz Dr Unit 492 Pacific Palisades (90272) ***(P-25063)***
Pipelinersales Inc (PA) ....F....323 317-7426
15243 La Cruz Dr Ste 492 Marina Del Rey (90292) ***(P-25064)***
Pipnsv Inc ....F....818 768-0550
8422 Sunland Blvd Sun Valley (91352) ***(P-7028)***
Piranha Ems Inc ....E....408 520-3963
2681 Zanker Rd Ste B San Jose (95134) ***(P-17350)***
Piranha Pipe & Precast Inc ....E....559 665-7473
16000 Avenue 25 Chowchilla (93610) ***(P-10975)***
Piranha Propeller, Jackson *Also called Bradford Canning Stahl Inc* ***(P-16331)***
Pirates Press Inc ....F....415 738-2268
1260 Powell St Emeryville (94608) ***(P-17909)***
Pisani Printing II, Santa Clara *Also called Theater Publications Inc* ***(P-6269)***
Pisor Industries Inc ....E....916 944-2851
7201 32nd St North Highlands (95660) ***(P-16844)***
Piston Hydraulic System Inc ....F....626 350-0100
11614 Mcbean Dr El Monte (91732) ***(P-15353)***
Pitbull Energy Bar, Los Angeles *Also called Energy Lane Inc* ***(P-7913)***
Pitbull Gym Incorporated ....F....909 980-7960
10782 Edison Ct Rancho Cucamonga (91730) ***(P-10275)***
Pitman Family Farms ....D....559 585-3330
10365 Iona Ave Hanford (93230) ***(P-1155)***
Pitney Bowes Inc ....D....949 855-7844
25531 Commercentre Dr # 110 Lake Forest (92630) ***(P-15911)***
Pitney Bowes Inc ....E....415 330-9423
71 Park Ln Brisbane (94005) ***(P-15912)***
Pitney Bowes Inc ....E....310 312-4288
11355 W Olympic Blvd Fl 2 Los Angeles (90064) ***(P-15913)***
Pittman Outdoors, La Mirada *Also called Pittman Products International* ***(P-10276)***
Pittman Products International ....F....562 926-6660
15330 Valley View Ave # 2 La Mirada (90638) ***(P-10276)***
Pittsburgh Glass Works LLC ....C....916 419-1853
815 Professor Ln Sacramento (95834) ***(P-10604)***
Pivotal Systems Corporation ....E....510 770-9125
48389 Fremont Blvd # 100 Fremont (94538) ***(P-17294)***
Pixelworks Inc (PA) ....D....408 200-9200
224 Airport Pkwy Ste 400 San Jose (95110) ***(P-19076)***
Pixi Inc ....F....310 670-7767
10351 Santa Monica Blvd # 410 Los Angeles (90025) ***(P-8819)***
Pixi Beauty, Los Angeles *Also called Pixi Inc* ***(P-8819)***
Pixley Construction Inc ....F....510 783-3020
27607 Industrial Blvd Hayward (94545) ***(P-259)***
Pixon Imaging Inc ....E....858 352-0100
4930 Longford St San Diego (92117) ***(P-22006)***
Pixonimaging, San Diego *Also called Pixon Imaging Inc* ***(P-22006)***
Pixscan ....F....510 595-2222
1259 Park Ave Emeryville (94608) ***(P-7437)***
Pjk Winery LLC ....E....707 431-8333
4900 W Dry Creek Rd Healdsburg (95448) ***(P-1926)***
Pjy Inc ....E....323 583-7737
3251 Leonis Blvd Vernon (90058) ***(P-2758)***
Pk Industries Inc ....F....619 428-6382
1533 Olivella Way San Diego (92154) ***(P-10530)***
Pk1 Inc (HQ) ....D....916 858-1300
4225 Pell Dr Sacramento (95838) ***(P-5451)***
Pl Development, Lynwood *Also called P & L Development LLC* ***(P-8602)***
Pl Development, Lynwood *Also called P & L Development LLC* ***(P-8323)***
Pla-Cor Incorporated ....F....619 478-2139
10207 Buena Vista Ave D Santee (92071) ***(P-10277)***
Placer Waterworks Inc ....E....530 742-9675
1325 Furneaux Rd Plumas Lake (95961) ***(P-12229)***
Planar Monolithics Inds Inc ....E....916 542-1401
4921 Robert J Mathews El Dorado Hills (95762) ***(P-19685)***
Planet Green Cartridges Inc ....D....818 725-2596
20724 Lassen St Chatsworth (91311) ***(P-23736)***

Mergent e-mail: customerrelations@mergent.com
1246
2019 California
Manufacturers Register
(P-0000) Products & Services Section entry number
(PA)=Parent Co (HQ)=Headquarters (DH)=Div Headquarters

Planet Inc .... F 250 478-8171
15791 Coleman Valley Rd Occidental (95465) ***(P-8666)***
Planet One Products Inc (PA) .... E 707 794-8000
1445 N Mcdowell Blvd Petaluma (94954) ***(P-5094)***
Planet Plexi Corp .... F 949 206-1183
23282 Verdugo Dr Laguna Hills (92653) ***(P-10278)***
Planet Products, Occidental *Also called Planet Inc* ***(P-8666)***
Planet Star, Northridge *Also called 5 Star Redemption Inc* ***(P-24018)***
Planetary Machine and Engrg .... F 760 489-5571
976 S Andreasen Dr Ste A Escondido (92029) ***(P-14665)***
Plangrid Inc (PA) .... E 415 349-7440
2111 Mission St Ste 400 San Francisco (94110) ***(P-25065)***
Planit Solutions .... F 530 666-6647
1240 Commerce Ave Woodland (95776) ***(P-25066)***
Planned Parenthood Los Angeles .... E 323 256-1717
1578 Colorado Blvd Ste 13 Los Angeles (90041) ***(P-6551)***
Plant 1, North Highlands *Also called Livingstons Concrete Svc Inc* ***(P-11136)***
Plant 3, Lincoln *Also called Livingstons Concrete Svc Inc* ***(P-11137)***
Plantation Coffee Roasters .... E 916 714-2633
9583 Elk Grove Florin Rd Elk Grove (95624) ***(P-2365)***
Plantronics Inc (PA) .... B 831 426-5858
345 Encinal St Santa Cruz (95060) ***(P-17977)***
Plantronics Inc .... F 831 458-7089
1470 Expo Way Ste 130 San Diego (92154) ***(P-17978)***
Plantronics Inc .... E 831 426-5858
345 Encinal St Santa Cruz (95060) ***(P-17979)***
Plantronics BV, San Diego *Also called Plantronics Inc* ***(P-17978)***
Plantronics BV, Santa Cruz *Also called Plantronics Inc* ***(P-17979)***
Plas-Tal Manufacturing Co, Santa Fe Springs *Also called Brunton Enterprises Inc* ***(P-12121)***
Plas-Tech Sealing Tech LLC .... E 951 737-2228
252 Mariah Cir Fl 2 Corona (92879) ***(P-9161)***
Plascene Inc .... F 562 695-0240
1600 Pacific Ave Oxnard (93033) ***(P-10279)***
Plascor Inc .... C 951 328-1010
972 Columbia Ave Riverside (92507) ***(P-9803)***
Plasidyne Engineering & Mfg .... E 562 531-0510
3230 E 59th St Long Beach (90805) ***(P-10280)***
Plaskolite West LLC .... E 310 637-2103
2225 E Del Amo Blvd Compton (90220) ***(P-7866)***
Plaskolite West, Inc., Compton *Also called Plaskolite West LLC* ***(P-7866)***
Plasma Biolife Services L P .... D 818 947-5600
15903 Strathern St Van Nuys (91406) ***(P-8504)***
Plasma Coating Corporation .... E 310 532-1951
13309 S Western Ave Gardena (90249) ***(P-16845)***
Plasma Control Technologies, San Jose *Also called Comet Technologies USA Inc* ***(P-22180)***
Plasma Division, Corona *Also called PVA Tepla America Inc* ***(P-16866)***
Plasma Rggedized Solutions Inc .... E 714 893-6063
5452 Business Dr Huntington Beach (92649) ***(P-13475)***
Plasma Rggedized Solutions Inc (PA) .... D 408 954-8405
2284 Ringwood Ave Ste A San Jose (95131) ***(P-13635)***
Plasma Technology Incorporated (PA) .... D 310 320-3373
1754 Crenshaw Blvd Torrance (90501) ***(P-13636)***
Plasmetex Industries .... F 760 744-8300
1425 Linda Vista Dr San Marcos (92078) ***(P-10281)***
Plastech Molding & Fabricating, Hesperia *Also called Plastech Moulding & Fabg* ***(P-10282)***
Plastech Moulding & Fabg .... E 760 244-8078
16717 Spruce St Hesperia (92345) ***(P-10282)***
Plastech Specialties Company (PA) .... F 626 357-6839
4645 Portofino Cir Cypress (90630) ***(P-3913)***
Plasthec Molding Inc .... D 909 947-4267
1945 S Grove Ave Ontario (91761) ***(P-10283)***
Plasti-Print Inc .... F 650 652-4950
1620 Gilbreth Rd Burlingame (94010) ***(P-7438)***
Plastic and Metal Center Inc .... E 949 770-0610
23162 La Cadena Dr Laguna Hills (92653) ***(P-10284)***
Plastic Color Technology .... F 909 597-9230
3010 Spyglass Ct Chino Hills (91709) ***(P-7743)***
Plastic Dress-Up Company .... D 626 442-7711
11077 Rush St South El Monte (91733) ***(P-10285)***
Plastic Fabrication Tech LLC .... D 773 509-1700
2320 E Cherry Indus Cir Long Beach (90805) ***(P-10286)***
Plastic Innovations Inc .... F 951 361-0251
10513 San Sevaine Way Mira Loma (91752) ***(P-9758)***
Plastic Mart Inc .... E 310 268-1404
43535 Gadsden Ave Ste F Lancaster (93534) ***(P-7867)***
Plastic Molding Shop, The, Oroville *Also called Jess Howard* ***(P-10168)***
Plastic Package LLC (PA) .... D 916 921-3399
4600 Beloit Dr Sacramento (95838) ***(P-10287)***
Plastic Processing Co, Gardena *Also called Narayan Corporation* ***(P-9802)***
Plastic Processing Corp .... E 310 719-7330
13432 Estrella Ave Gardena (90248) ***(P-10288)***
Plastic Service Center, Santa Clara *Also called P S C Manufacturing Inc* ***(P-10256)***
Plastic Tops Inc (PA) .... F 714 738-8128
521 E Jamie Ave La Habra (90631) ***(P-5162)***
Plastic View Atc Inc .... F 805 520-9390
4585 Runway St Ste B Simi Valley (93063) ***(P-5206)***
Plastics Development Corp .... E 949 492-0217
960 Calle Negocio San Clemente (92673) ***(P-10289)***
Plastics Plus Technology Inc .... E 909 747-0555
1495 Research Dr Redlands (92374) ***(P-10290)***
Plastics Research Corporation .... D 909 391-9050
1400 S Campus Ave Ontario (91761) ***(P-9759)***
Plastifab Inc .... E 909 596-1927
1425 Palomares St La Verne (91750) ***(P-9760)***
Plastifab San Diego .... F 858 679-6600
12145 Paine St Poway (92064) ***(P-9761)***
Plastifab/Leed Plastics, La Verne *Also called Plastifab Inc* ***(P-9760)***
Plastiject LLC .... F 562 926-6705
14811 Spring Ave Santa Fe Springs (90670) ***(P-10291)***
Plastikon Industries Inc (PA) .... B 510 400-1010
688 Sandoval Way Hayward (94544) ***(P-14559)***
Plastique Unique Inc .... E 310 839-3968
3383 Livonia Ave Los Angeles (90034) ***(P-10292)***
Plasto Tech International Inc .... E 949 458-1880
4 Autry Irvine (92618) ***(P-10293)***
Plastpro 2000 Inc (PA) .... C 310 693-8600
5200 W Century Blvd Fl 9 Los Angeles (90045) ***(P-10294)***
Plastpro Doors, Los Angeles *Also called Plastpro 2000 Inc* ***(P-10294)***
Plastruct Inc .... D 626 912-7017
1020 Wallace Way City of Industry (91748) ***(P-10295)***
Plasvacc USA Inc .... F 805 434-0321
1535 Templeton Rd Templeton (93465) ***(P-8574)***
Plateronics Processing Inc .... E 818 341-2191
9164 Independence Ave Chatsworth (91311) ***(P-13476)***
Platescan Inc .... E 949 851-1600
20101 Sw Birch St Ste 250 Newport Beach (92660) ***(P-13260)***
Plating, Chatsworth *Also called Electro Adapter Inc* ***(P-17463)***
Platinum Distribution, Yorba Linda *Also called Nasco Gourmet Foods Inc* ***(P-831)***
Platron Company West .... F 510 781-5588
26260 Eden Landing Rd Hayward (94545) ***(P-16846)***
Platt Medical Center, Rancho Mirage *Also called Tfx International* ***(P-8413)***
Plaxicon Co, Rancho Cucamonga *Also called Plaxicon Holding Corporation* ***(P-9804)***
Plaxicon Holding Corporation .... C 909 944-6868
10660 Acacia St Rancho Cucamonga (91730) ***(P-9804)***
Playa Tool & Marine Inc .... F 714 972-2722
1746 E Borchard Ave Santa Ana (92705) ***(P-16847)***
Playboy Enterprises Intl Inc .... D 310 424-1800
10960 Wilshire Blvd # 2200 Los Angeles (90024) ***(P-6552)***
Playboy Japan Inc .... F 310 424-1800
9346 Civic Center Dr # 200 Beverly Hills (90210) ***(P-6234)***
Players Circle Barbershop, San Leandro *Also called My World Styles LLC* ***(P-8800)***
Players International Publ, Los Angeles *Also called Bentley Management Corporation* ***(P-6112)***
Players Music Accessories, San Jose *Also called Thunder Products Inc* ***(P-23391)***
Players Press Inc .... E 818 789-4980
Fulton Ave Studio City (91604) ***(P-6381)***
Playhut Inc .... E 909 869-8083
18560 San Jose Ave City of Industry (91748) ***(P-23455)***
Plaze De Caviar, Concord *Also called Pacific Plaza Imports Inc* ***(P-2300)***
Plc LLC .... F 707 462-2423
2350 Mcnab Ranch Rd Ukiah (95482) ***(P-1927)***
Pleasant Mattress Inc .... F 415 874-7540
1400 Minnesota St San Francisco (94107) ***(P-4878)***
Pleasant Mattress Inc (PA) .... D 559 268-6446
375 S West Ave Fresno (93706) ***(P-4879)***
Pleasant Mattress Inc .... E 415 861-4532
1400 Minnesota St San Francisco (94107) ***(P-4880)***
Pleasanton Main St Brewry Inc .... F 925 462-8218
830 Main St Ste Frnt Pleasanton (94566) ***(P-1620)***
Pleasanton Ready Mix Concrete .... F 925 846-3226
3400 Boulder St Pleasanton (94566) ***(P-11157)***
Pleasanton Readymix Concrete, Pleasanton *Also called Pleasanton Ready Mix Concrete* ***(P-11157)***
Pleasanton Steel Supply, Livermore *Also called Stretch-Run Inc* ***(P-12250)***
Pleasanton Tool & Mfg Inc .... E 925 426-0500
1181 Quarry Ln Ste 450 Pleasanton (94566) ***(P-16848)***
Pleros LLC .... F 442 275-6764
2825 E Tahquitz Cyn W Palm Springs (92262) ***(P-8820)***
Plexi Fab Inc .... F 714 447-8494
1142 E Elm Ave Fullerton (92831) ***(P-7868)***
Plexus Corp .... C 510 668-9000
431 Kato Ter Fremont (94539) ***(P-18561)***
Plexxikon Inc .... E 510 647-4000
91 Bolivar Dr Berkeley (94710) ***(P-8339)***
Plh Products Inc .... E 714 739-6622
6655 Knott Ave Buena Park (90620) ***(P-4578)***
Pls Diabetic Shoe Company Inc .... E 818 734-7080
21500 Osborne St Canoga Park (91304) ***(P-9477)***
Plt Enterprises Inc .... D 805 389-5335
809 Calle Plano Camarillo (93012) ***(P-17486)***
Plum Inc .... F 510 225-4018
1485 Park Ave Ste 101 Emeryville (94608) ***(P-1072)***
Plum Creek Timberlands LP .... C 909 949-2255
615 N Benson Ave Upland (91786) ***(P-4045)***
Plum Organics, Emeryville *Also called Plum Inc* ***(P-1072)***
Plum Valley Inc .... E 530 262-6262
3308 Cyclone Ct Cttonwood Cottonwood Cottonwood (96022) ***(P-4046)***
Plumberex Specialty Pdts Inc .... E 760 343-7363
72170 Dunham Way Ste A Thousand Palms (92276) ***(P-12043)***
Plumbing Products Inc .... F 760 343-3306
77551 El Duna Ct Ste I Palm Desert (92211) ***(P-12044)***
Plumjack Winery, NAPA *Also called Villa Encinal Partners LP* ***(P-2042)***
Pluot Communications Inc .... F 202 258-9223
1925 48th Ave San Francisco (94116) ***(P-17846)***
Plural Publishing Inc .... F 858 492-1555
5521 Ruffin Rd San Diego (92123) ***(P-6382)***
Plush Home Inc .... E 323 852-1912
8323 Melrose Ave Los Angeles (90069) ***(P-4731)***
Plush Printing, Fullerton *Also called Sticker Hub Inc* ***(P-7498)***
Plusrite and Ledirect, Ontario *Also called Fanlight Corporation Inc* ***(P-17428)***
Plustek Technology Inc .... F 562 777-1888
9830 Norwalk Blvd Ste 155 Santa Fe Springs (90670) ***(P-15824)***
Plutoz, Oakland *Also called Net Clearly* ***(P-24948)***
Plx Technology Inc .... C 408 435-7400
1320 Ridder Park Dr San Jose (95131) ***(P-25067)***

ALPHABETIC

Employee Codes: A=Over 500 employees, B=251-500
C=101-250, D=51-100, E=20-50, F=10-19
2019 California
Manfacturers Register
© Mergent Inc. 1-800-342-5647
1247

Plycraft Industries Inc ....C....323 587-8101
2100 E Slauson Ave Huntington Park (90255) ***(P-4382)***
PM Corporate Group Inc ....C....619 498-9199
6425 Randolph St Commerce (90040) ***(P-7029)***
PM Lithographers Inc ....F....818 704-2626
7600 Linley Ln Canoga Park (91304) ***(P-7030)***
PM Packaging, Commerce *Also called PM Corporate Group Inc* ***(P-7029)***
Pmc Inc (HQ) ....E....818 896-1101
12243 Branford St Sun Valley (91352) ***(P-20911)***
PMC Global Inc (PA) ....A....818 896-1101
12243 Branford St Sun Valley (91352) ***(P-9874)***
PMC Leaders In Chemicals Inc (HQ) ....C....818 896-1101
12243 Branford St Sun Valley (91352) ***(P-9875)***
PMC-Sierra Us Inc ....F....408 239-8000
1380 Bordeaux Dr Sunnyvale (94089) ***(P-19077)***
Pmic, Los Angeles *Also called Practice Management Info Corp* ***(P-6383)***
Pmp Products Inc ....F....310 549-5122
1210 W Jon St Torrance (90502) ***(P-10531)***
Pmr Precision Mfg & Rbr Co Inc ....E....909 605-7525
1330 Etiwanda Ave Ontario (91761) ***(P-9657)***
Pmrca Inc (PA) ....F....661 822-6760
20437 Brian Way Ste B Tehachapi (93561) ***(P-7031)***
PMS Systems Corporation ....F....310 450-2566
26707 Agoura Rd Ste 201 Calabasas (91302) ***(P-25068)***
PNa Construction Tech Inc ....E....661 326-1700
301 Espee St Ste E Bakersfield (93301) ***(P-12718)***
PNC Proactive Nthrn Cont LLC ....E....909 390-5624
602 S Rockefeller Ave A Ontario (91761) ***(P-5452)***
Pneudraulics Inc ....B....909 980-5366
8575 Helms Ave Rancho Cucamonga (91730) ***(P-21381)***
Pneumatic Scale Angelus, Rancho Cucamonga *Also called Pneumatic Scale Corporation* ***(P-15223)***
Pneumatic Scale Corporation ....F....909 527-7600
10860 6th St Rancho Cucamonga (91730) ***(P-15223)***
Pneumatic Tube Carrier, Duarte *Also called Lee Machine Products* ***(P-14534)***
Pneumrx Inc ....E....650 625-4440
4255 Burton Dr Santa Clara (95054) ***(P-22585)***
Pnm Company ....E....559 291-1986
2547 N Business Park Ave Fresno (93727) ***(P-16849)***
Pny Technologies Inc ....E....408 392-4100
2099 Gateway Pl Ste 220 San Jose (95110) ***(P-19078)***
Pocino Foods Company ....D....626 968-8000
14250 Lomitas Ave City of Industry (91746) ***(P-515)***
Pocket Gems Inc ....C....415 371-1333
220 Montgomery St Ste 750 San Francisco (94104) ***(P-23456)***
Poco Dolce Confections Inc ....F....415 817-1551
1020 Illinois St San Francisco (94107) ***(P-1447)***
Poetry Corporation (PA) ....E....213 765-8957
2111 Long Beach Ave Los Angeles (90058) ***(P-3359)***
Point Blanks Inc ....F....805 643-8616
43 S Olive St Ventura (93001) ***(P-2074)***
Point Conception Inc ....E....949 589-6890
23121 Arroyo Vis Ste A Rcho STA Marg (92688) ***(P-3483)***
Point Lakeview Rock & Redi-Mix, Lower Lake *Also called Clearlake Lava Inc* ***(P-11094)***
Point Nine Technologies Inc (PA) ....F....805 375-6600
2697 Lavery Ct Ste 8 Newbury Park (91320) ***(P-19079)***
Pointech ....E....415 822-8704
Hunters Point Shpyd San Francisco (94124) ***(P-11765)***
Pokka Beverages, American Canyon *Also called Amcan Beverages Inc* ***(P-2081)***
Pol Tech Precision Co, Fremont *Also called Pol-Tech Precision Inc* ***(P-13261)***
Pol-Tech Precision Inc ....F....510 656-6832
4447 Enterprise St Fremont (94538) ***(P-13261)***
Polara Engineering Inc ....D....951 547-5500
9153 Stellar Ct Corona (92883) ***(P-19686)***
Polargy Inc ....E....408 752-0186
1148 Sonora Ct Sunnyvale (94086) ***(P-12409)***
Polarion Software Inc ....D....877 572-4005
1001 Marina Village Pkwy # 403 Alameda (94501) ***(P-25069)***
Polaris E-Commerce Inc ....E....714 907-0582
1941 E Occidental St Santa Ana (92705) ***(P-15088)***
Polaris Pharmaceuticals Inc ....E....858 452-6688
9373 Towne Centre Dr # 150 San Diego (92121) ***(P-8340)***
Pole Danzer ....E....760 419-9514
3777 Paseo De Olivos Fallbrook (92028) ***(P-10976)***
Polerax USA ....F....323 477-1866
909 S Greenwood Ave Ste K Montebello (90640) ***(P-3675)***
Polishing Corporation America ....E....888 892-3377
442 Martin Ave Santa Clara (95050) ***(P-19080)***
Polit Farms Inc ....F....530 438-2759
4334 Old Hwy 99w 99 W Maxwell (95955) ***(P-1089)***
Politezer Newspaers Inc ....F....805 929-3864
260 Station Way Ste F Arroyo Grande (93420) ***(P-6015)***
Polk Audio LLC ....E....888 267-5495
1 Viper Way Ste 3 Vista (92081) ***(P-17847)***
Polley Inc (PA) ....E....562 868-9861
11936 Front St Norwalk (90650) ***(P-15354)***
Pollstar LLC (PA) ....D....559 271-7900
4697 W Jacquelyn Ave Fresno (93722) ***(P-6235)***
Pollstar.com, Fresno *Also called Pollstar LLC* ***(P-6235)***
Pollution Control Specialists ....E....949 474-0137
1354 Ritchey St Santa Ana (92705) ***(P-15170)***
Polly's Tasty Foods & Pies, Orange *Also called E D D Investment Co* ***(P-1239)***
Pollybyrd Publications Limited, Beverly Hills *Also called Ppl Entertainment Group Inc* ***(P-6555)***
Poly Masters Industries Inc ....E....323 564-7824
2821 Century Blvd South Gate (90280) ***(P-10296)***
Poly Processing Company LLC ....B....209 982-4904
8055 Ash St French Camp (95231) ***(P-7869)***
Poly-Fiber Inc (PA) ....E....951 684-4280
4343 Fort Dr Riverside (92509) ***(P-8924)***
Poly-Seal Industries ....F....510 843-9722
725 Channing Way Berkeley (94710) ***(P-9658)***
Poly-Tainer Inc (PA) ....B....805 526-3424
450 W Los Angeles Ave Simi Valley (93065) ***(P-9805)***
Polyair Inter Pack Inc ....D....951 737-7125
1692 Jenks Dr Ste 102 Corona (92880) ***(P-3805)***
Polyalloys ....D....310 715-9800
14000 Avalon Blvd Los Angeles (90061) ***(P-14201)***
Polycom Inc ....E....209 830-5083
25212 S Schulte Rd Tracy (95377) ***(P-17980)***
Polycom Inc (HQ) ....B....408 586-6000
6001 America Center Dr San Jose (95002) ***(P-17981)***
Polycom Inc ....C....925 924-6151
4750 Willow Rd Pleasanton (94588) ***(P-17982)***
Polycore Optical - USA, Santa Fe Springs *Also called Polyvision Inc* ***(P-7873)***
Polycraft Inc ....E....951 296-0860
42075 Avenida Alvarado Temecula (92590) ***(P-7439)***
Polyfet Rf Devices Inc ....E....805 484-9582
1110 Avenida Acaso Camarillo (93012) ***(P-19081)***
Polymer Concepts Technologies ....F....760 240-4999
13522 Manhasset Rd Apple Valley (92308) ***(P-9549)***
Polymer Logistics Inc ....F....951 567-2900
1725 Sierra Ridge Dr Riverside (92507) ***(P-10297)***
Polymerex Medical Corp ....F....858 695-0765
7358 Trade St San Diego (92121) ***(P-9743)***
Polymeric Technology Inc ....E....510 895-6001
1900 Marina Blvd San Leandro (94577) ***(P-9659)***
Polymond Dk Inc ....E....213 327-0771
777 E 10th St Ste 110 Los Angeles (90021) ***(P-3484)***
Polynetics, Corona *Also called Duonetics* ***(P-15060)***
Polynt Composites USA Inc ....F....310 886-1070
2801 Lynwood Rd Lynwood (90262) ***(P-7870)***
Polyone Corporation ....D....310 513-7100
2104 E 223rd St Carson (90810) ***(P-7871)***
Polyone Corporation ....E....909 987-0253
11400 Newport Dr Ste A Rancho Cucamonga (91730) ***(P-7872)***
Polyplex Plastics of N Amer ....E....818 768-8866
8511 Lankershim Blvd Sun Valley (91352) ***(P-9660)***
Polypure, Los Angeles *Also called Snf Holding Company* ***(P-9307)***
Polystak Inc ....F....408 441-1400
1159 Sonora Ct 109 Sunnyvale (94086) ***(P-19082)***
Polytec Products Corporation ....E....650 322-7555
1190 Obrien Dr Menlo Park (94025) ***(P-16850)***
Polytech Color & Compounding ....F....909 923-7008
847 S Wanamaker Ave Ontario (91761) ***(P-10298)***
Polytex Manufacturing Inc (PA) ....F....323 726-0140
1140 S Hope St Los Angeles (90015) ***(P-2955)***
Polyvision Inc (PA) ....E....562 944-3924
9830 Norwalk Blvd Ste 174 Santa Fe Springs (90670) ***(P-7873)***
Polywell Company Inc ....E....650 583-7222
1461 San Mateo Ave Ste 1 South San Francisco (94080) ***(P-15471)***
Polywell Computers, South San Francisco *Also called Polywell Company Inc* ***(P-15471)***
Poma GL Specialty Windows Inc ....D....951 321-0116
813 Palmyrita Ave Riverside (92507) ***(P-10605)***
Pomar Junction Cellars LLC ....E....805 238-9940
5036 S El Pomar Rd Templeton (93465) ***(P-1928)***
Pometta's, Sonoma *Also called Sonoma Gourmet Inc* ***(P-933)***
Pommes Frites Candle Co ....E....213 488-2016
7300 E Slauson Ave Commerce (90040) ***(P-24212)***
Pomona Quality Foam LLC ....D....909 628-7844
1279 Philadelphia St Pomona (91766) ***(P-9876)***
Pong Research Corporation ....F....858 914-5299
1010 S Coast Highway 101 # 105 Encinitas (92024) ***(P-22795)***
Pool Doctor, Glendale *Also called World Industries International* ***(P-10451)***
Poole Ventura Inc ....F....805 981-1784
321 Bernoulli Cir Oxnard (93030) ***(P-15134)***
Poolmaster Inc ....D....916 567-9800
770 Del Paso Rd Sacramento (95834) ***(P-23457)***
Poor Richard's Press, San Luis Obispo *Also called Prpco* ***(P-7453)***
Poor Richards Press, San Luis Obispo *Also called Ws Packaging-Blake Printery* ***(P-7191)***
Pop 82 Inc ....F....714 523-8500
8211 Orangethorpe Ave Buena Park (90621) ***(P-2781)***
Pop Chips, E Rncho Dmngz *Also called Sonora Mills Foods Inc* ***(P-1380)***
Pop Plastics Acrylic Disp Inc ....E....714 523-8500
8211 Orangethorpe Ave Buena Park (90621) ***(P-10299)***
Popcorn Tree, Glendora *Also called Tom Clark Confections* ***(P-1463)***
Popcornopolis LLC (PA) ....C....310 414-6700
3200 E Slauson Ave Vernon (90058) ***(P-1448)***
Pope, Canoga Park *Also called Jake Stehelin Etienne* ***(P-10162)***
Pope Plastics Inc ....E....818 701-1850
9134 Independence Ave Chatsworth (91311) ***(P-14560)***
Popkoff's, City of Industry *Also called Whittier Enterprise LLC* ***(P-1021)***
Popla International Inc ....E....909 923-6899
1740 S Sacramento Ave Ontario (91761) ***(P-1098)***
Popsalot Gourmet Popcorn, Paramount *Also called Popsalot LLC* ***(P-2398)***
Popsalot LLC ....E....213 761-0156
7723 Somerset Blvd Paramount (90723) ***(P-2398)***
Popsugar Inc (PA) ....C....415 391-7576
111 Sutter St Fl 16 San Francisco (94104) ***(P-6553)***
Popular Printers Inc ....F....626 307-4281
3210 San Gabriel Blvd Rosemead (91770) ***(P-7440)***
Popular TV Networks LLC ....F....323 822-3324
8307 Rugby Pl Los Angeles (90046) ***(P-6016)***
Porifera Inc ....F....510 695-2775
1575 Alvarado St San Leandro (94577) ***(P-16089)***
Port 80 Software Inc ....E....858 274-4497
2105 Garnet Ave Ste E San Diego (92109) ***(P-25070)***

Mergent e-mail: customerrelations@mergent.com
1248
2019 California
Manufacturers Register
(P-0000) Products & Services Section entry number
(PA)=Parent Co (HQ)=Headquarters (DH)=Div Headquarters

Port Brewing LLC.....E.....800 918-6816
155 Mata Way Ste 104 San Marcos (92069) *(P-1621)*
Porta-Bote International, Mountain View *Also called Kaye Sandy Enterprises Inc (P-21048)*
Portable Spndle Repr Spcialist.....F.....909 591-7220
10803 Fremont Ave Ste A Ontario (91762) *(P-14779)*
Portapaint, Ventura *Also called Wombat Products Inc (P-10449)*
Portellus Inc.....D.....949 250-9600
2522 Chambers Rd Ste 100 Tustin (92780) *(P-25071)*
Porter Powder Coating Inc.....F.....714 956-2010
510 S Rose St Anaheim (92805) *(P-13637)*
Porterville Concrete Pipe Inc.....F.....559 784-6187
474 S Main St Porterville (93257) *(P-10977)*
Porterville Recorder, Porterville *Also called Noticiero Semanal Advertising (P-6002)*
Portocork America Inc.....F.....707 258-3930
560 Technology Way NAPA (94558) *(P-4642)*
Portola Pharmaceuticals Inc (PA).....C.....650 246-7000
270 E Grand Ave South San Francisco (94080) *(P-8341)*
Portos Food Product Inc.....D.....323 480-8400
2085 Garfield Ave Commerce (90040) *(P-1310)*
Portworx Inc.....E.....650 241-3222
4940 El Camino Real # 200 Los Altos (94022) *(P-25072)*
Pos Portal Inc (HQ).....E.....530 695-3005
180 Promenade Cir Ste 215 Sacramento (95834) *(P-15899)*
Posey Co, Arcadia *Also called Posey Products LLC (P-22796)*
Posey Products LLC (HQ).....C.....626 443-3143
5635 Peck Rd Arcadia (91006) *(P-22796)*
Positano, Los Angeles *Also called Alona Apparel Inc (P-3132)*
Positex Inc.....F.....307 201-0601
2569 Mccabe Way Ste 210 Irvine (92614) *(P-20618)*
Positive Concepts Inc (PA).....E.....714 685-5800
2021 N Glassell St Orange (92865) *(P-5726)*
Positive Energy Beverages LLC.....F.....949 735-6080
101 Academy Ste 100 Irvine (92617) *(P-2179)*
Positive Publishing Inc.....F.....858 551-0889
449 Nautilus St La Jolla (92037) *(P-6554)*
Positron Access Solutions Inc.....F.....951 272-9100
1640 2nd St Ste 207 Norco (92860) *(P-18222)*
Positronics Incorporated.....F.....925 931-0211
173 Spring St Ste 120 Pleasanton (94566) *(P-14762)*
Post Montgomery Center, San Francisco *Also called Sas Institute Inc (P-25146)*
Post-Srgcal Rhab Spcalists LLC.....F.....562 236-5600
12774 Florence Ave Santa Fe Springs (90670) *(P-22586)*
Postcard Press Inc (PA).....E.....310 747-3800
8000 Haskell Ave Van Nuys (91406) *(P-7441)*
Poster Compliance Center, Lafayette *Also called Employerware LLC (P-6477)*
Postvision Inc.....F.....818 840-0777
2120 Foothill Blvd # 111 La Verne (91750) *(P-15585)*
Potentia Labs Inc.....F.....951 603-3531
2870 4th Ave Apt 212 San Diego (92103) *(P-25073)*
Potential Design Inc.....F.....559 834-5361
4185 E Jefferson Ave Fresno (93725) *(P-14878)*
Pottery By Levine Acquisition.....E.....408 773-0418
1185 Campbell Ave San Jose (95126) *(P-10834)*
Pouches Incorporated.....F.....909 923-1135
1901 S Bon View Ave Ontario (91761) *(P-5533)*
Powder Coating Plus, Valencia *Also called Canay Manufacturing Inc (P-16360)*
Powder Coating Usa Inc.....F.....805 237-8886
440 Sherwood Rd Paso Robles (93446) *(P-13638)*
Powder Painting By Sundial, Sun Valley *Also called Sundial Industries Inc (P-13669)*
Powdercoat Services LLC.....E.....714 533-2251
1747 W Lincoln Ave Ste K Anaheim (92801) *(P-13639)*
Powdercoat Services, Inc., Anaheim *Also called Powdercoat Services LLC (P-13639)*
Power - Trim Co.....F.....714 523-8560
11150 Dana Cir Cypress (90630) *(P-14130)*
Power Aire Inc.....E.....800 526-7661
8055 E Crystal Dr Anaheim (92807) *(P-17156)*
Power Automation Systems, Lathrop *Also called California Natural Products (P-2479)*
Power Brake Exchange Inc.....F.....562 806-6661
6853 Suva St Bell (90201) *(P-20421)*
Power Circuits Inc.....B.....714 327-3000
2630 S Harbor Blvd Santa Ana (92704) *(P-18562)*
Power Design Manufacturing LLC.....E.....408 437-1931
121 E Brokaw Rd San Jose (95112) *(P-18563)*
Power Design Services, San Jose *Also called Power Design Manufacturing LLC (P-18563)*
Power Distribution Inc.....F.....714 513-1500
4011 W Carriage Dr Santa Ana (92704) *(P-19353)*
Power Efficiency Corporation.....F.....858 750-3875
5744 Pcf Ctr Blvd Ste 311 San Diego (92121) *(P-17217)*
Power Fasteners Inc.....E.....323 232-4362
650 E 60th St Los Angeles (90001) *(P-13080)*
Power Integrations Inc (PA).....B.....408 414-9200
5245 Hellyer Ave San Jose (95138) *(P-19083)*
Power Knot LLC.....F.....408 480-2758
2290 Ringwood Ave Ste A San Jose (95131) *(P-16090)*
Power Magnetics, Gardena *Also called Power Paragon Inc (P-17114)*
Power One, Santa Clara *Also called Bel Power Solutions Inc (P-19322)*
Power Paragon Inc (HQ).....A.....714 956-9200
901 E Ball Rd Anaheim (92805) *(P-17113)*
Power Paragon Inc.....B.....714 956-9200
901 E Ball Rd Anaheim (92805) *(P-20043)*
Power Paragon Inc.....F.....310 523-4443
711 W Knox St Gardena (90248) *(P-17114)*
Power Printing, La Mesa *Also called Josef Mendelovitz (P-6914)*
Power Pros Exhaust Systems, Placentia *Also called Power Pros Racg Exhust Systems (P-20422)*
Power Pros Racg Exhust Systems.....F.....714 777-3278
817 S Lakeview Ave Ste J Placentia (92870) *(P-20422)*
Power Pt Inc.....E.....951 490-4149
23120 Oleander Ave Perris (92570) *(P-14341)*
Power Reps Inc (PA).....E.....323 724-6771
6480 Flotilla St Commerce (90040) *(P-25464)*
Power Services, Los Angeles *Also called On-Line Power Incorporated (P-17109)*
Power Standards Lab Inc.....E.....510 522-4400
980 Atlantic Ave Ste 100 Alameda (94501) *(P-21828)*
Power Systems Group, Anaheim *Also called Power Paragon Inc (P-17113)*
Power Systems Group, Anaheim *Also called Power Paragon Inc (P-20043)*
Powercords, Santa Clara *Also called Volex Inc (P-10432)*
Powercube, Chatsworth *Also called Natel Engineering Company Inc (P-18539)*
Powerflare Corporation.....F.....650 208-2580
37 Ringwood Ave Atherton (94027) *(P-20044)*
Powerlift Dumbwaiters Inc.....E.....800 409-5438
2444 Georgia Slide Rd Georgetown (95634) *(P-14255)*
Powerlux Corporation.....F.....760 727-2360
1260 Liberty Way Ste E Vista (92081) *(P-17725)*
Powerplus Cleaning Solutions.....E.....714 635-9264
1525 N Endeavor Ln Ste O Anaheim (92801) *(P-8667)*
Powers Bros Machine Inc.....F.....323 728-2010
8100 Slauson Ave Montebello (90640) *(P-16851)*
Powerschool Group LLC (HQ).....C.....916 288-1636
150 Parkshore Dr Folsom (95630) *(P-25074)*
Powerstorm Ess, Rancho Palos Verdes *Also called Powerstorm Holdings Inc (P-19813)*
Powerstorm Holdings Inc.....F.....424 327-2991
31244 Palos Verdes Dr W # 245 Rancho Palos Verdes (90275) *(P-19813)*
Powertronix Corporation.....E.....650 345-6800
1120 Chess Dr Foster City (94404) *(P-17115)*
Powertye Manufacturing.....F.....714 993-7400
1640 E Miraloma Ave Placentia (92870) *(P-17157)*
Powerware, San Diego *Also called B T E Deltec Inc (P-19456)*
Powwow Inc.....E.....415 515-4947
594 Howard St Ste 301 San Francisco (94105) *(P-25075)*
PPG 9721, Lancaster *Also called PPG Industries Inc (P-8928)*
PPG 9722, Palm Desert *Also called PPG Industries Inc (P-8929)*
PPG 9726, Los Angeles *Also called PPG Industries Inc (P-8927)*
PPG Aerospace, Valencia *Also called PRC - Desoto International Inc (P-9162)*
PPG Aerospace, Mojave *Also called PRC - Desoto International Inc (P-9163)*
PPG Aerospace, Sylmar *Also called Sierracin/Sylmar Corporation (P-10375)*
PPG Aerospace, Mojave *Also called PRC - Desoto International Inc (P-9164)*
PPG Architectural Finishes Inc.....F.....619 284-2772
4388 Vandever Ave San Diego (92120) *(P-7874)*
PPG Industries Inc.....F.....925 798-0539
5750 Imhoff Dr Ste A Concord (94520) *(P-8925)*
PPG Industries Inc.....F.....562 692-4010
10060 Mission Mill Rd City of Industry (90601) *(P-8926)*
PPG Industries Inc.....E.....310 559-2335
1128 N Highland Ave Los Angeles (90038) *(P-8927)*
PPG Industries Inc.....E.....661 945-7871
43639 10th St W Lancaster (93534) *(P-8928)*
PPG Industries Inc.....E.....760 340-1762
74240 Highway 111 Palm Desert (92260) *(P-8929)*
PPG Industries Inc.....E.....714 894-5252
15541 Commerce Ln Huntington Beach (92649) *(P-8930)*
PPG Industries Inc.....E.....661 824-4532
11601 United St Mojave (93501) *(P-8931)*
Ppl Entertainment Group Inc (PA).....E.....310 860-7499
468 N Camden Dr Beverly Hills (90210) *(P-6555)*
Ppm Products Inc.....F.....408 946-4710
1538 Gladding Ct Milpitas (95035) *(P-16852)*
Pport Com Inc.....F.....516 393-6759
1200 Crossman Ave Ste 240 Sunnyvale (94089) *(P-25076)*
Ppp LLC.....F.....323 581-6058
5991 Alcoa Ave Vernon (90058) *(P-7875)*
Ppp LLC.....E.....323 832-9627
601 W Olympic Blvd Montebello (90640) *(P-10300)*
Pps Packaging Company.....D.....559 834-1641
3189 E Manning Ave Fowler (93625) *(P-5325)*
Ppst Inc (PA).....E.....800 421-1921
17692 Fitch Irvine (92614) *(P-19687)*
PQ Corporation.....F.....323 326-1100
8401 Quartz Ave South Gate (90280) *(P-7799)*
Practice Management Info Corp (PA).....E.....323 954-0224
4727 Wilshire Blvd # 302 Los Angeles (90010) *(P-6383)*
Pranalytica Inc.....F.....310 458-3345
1101 Colorado Ave Santa Monica (90401) *(P-22587)*
Prather Ranch, Macdoel *Also called Ralphs Ranches (P-448)*
Pratt.....E.....818 586-1000
6633 Canoga Ave Canoga Park (91303) *(P-20674)*
Pratt Industries Inc.....E.....805 348-1097
2643 Industrial Pkwy Ofc Santa Maria (93455) *(P-5326)*
Pratt Industries Inc.....E.....760 966-9170
3931 Oceanic Dr Oceanside (92056) *(P-5327)*
Pratt Industries Inc.....C.....770 922-0117
2131 E Louise Ave Lathrop (95330) *(P-5328)*
Pratt Industries Inc.....F.....760 966-9170
3931 Oceanic Dr Oceanside (92056) *(P-5329)*
Pratt Industries Inc.....E.....831 763-0630
223 W Riverside Dr Watsonville (95076) *(P-5330)*
Pratt Industries Inc.....E.....805 483-5331
1051 S Rose Ave Oxnard (93030) *(P-5331)*
Praxair Inc.....F.....925 866-6800
2430 Camino Ramon Ste 310 San Ramon (94583) *(P-7706)*
Praxair Inc.....D.....925 427-1051
2000 Loveridge Rd Pittsburg (94565) *(P-7707)*
Praxair Inc.....E.....310 816-1066
2006 E 223rd St Long Beach (90810) *(P-7708)*

ALPHABETIC

Employee Codes: A=Over 500 employees, B=251-500
C=101-250, D=51-100, E=20-50, F=10-19
2019 California
Manfacturers Register
© Mergent Inc. 1-800-342-5647
1249

Praxair Inc....E....619 596-4558
10728 Prospect Ave Ste A Santee (92071) ***(P-7709)***
Praxair Inc....E....559 674-7306
3481 Yeager Rd Madera (93637) ***(P-7710)***
Praxair Inc....E....510 223-9593
2995 Atlas Rd San Pablo (94806) ***(P-7711)***
Praxair Inc....F....805 966-0829
305 E Haley St Ste A Santa Barbara (93101) ***(P-7712)***
Praxair Inc....E....925 427-1950
1950 Loveridge Rd Pittsburg (94565) ***(P-14737)***
Praxair Inc....F....323 562-5200
8300 Atlantic Ave Cudahy (90201) ***(P-7713)***
Praxair Inc....E....661 861-6421
3331 Buck Owens Blvd Bakersfield (93308) ***(P-7714)***
Praxair Inc....E....661 327-5336
3505 Buck Owens Blvd Bakersfield (93308) ***(P-7715)***
Praxair Inc....E....515 963-3872
1011 W Collins Ave Orange (92867) ***(P-7716)***
Praxair Inc....E....415 657-9880
3994 Bayshore Blvd Brisbane (94005) ***(P-7717)***
Praxair Inc....E....323 588-8181
5700 S Alameda St Vernon (90058) ***(P-7718)***
Praxair Inc....D....909 390-0283
5705 E Airport Dr Ontario (91761) ***(P-7719)***
Praxair Inc....F....916 786-3900
7501 Foothills Blvd Roseville (95747) ***(P-7720)***
Praxair Inc....E....707 745-5328
331 E Channel Rd Benicia (94510) ***(P-7721)***
Praxair Distribution Inc....E....559 237-5521
2771 S Maple Ave Fresno (93725) ***(P-7722)***
Praxair Distribution Inc....E....951 736-8113
500 Harrington St Ste G Corona (92880) ***(P-7723)***
Praxair Distribution Inc....E....805 966-0829
305 E Haley St Santa Barbara (93101) ***(P-7724)***
Praxair Distribution Inc....F....818 760-2011
5508 Vineland Ave North Hollywood (91601) ***(P-7725)***
Praxair Distribution Inc....F....805 487-2742
455 E Wooley Rd Oxnard (93030) ***(P-7726)***
Praxair Distribution Inc....F....619 232-7341
2205 Newton Ave San Diego (92113) ***(P-7727)***
Praxair Distribution Inc....F....408 995-6089
215 San Jose Ave San Jose (95125) ***(P-7728)***
Praxair Distribution Inc....E....714 547-6684
1545 E Edinger Ave Santa Ana (92705) ***(P-7729)***
Praxair Distribution Inc....E....408 748-1722
2020 De La Cruz Blvd Santa Clara (95050) ***(P-7730)***
Praxair Distribution Inc....D....310 371-1254
19200 Hawthorne Blvd Torrance (90503) ***(P-7731)***
Prb Logics Corp....F....951 255-8963
1901 Newport Blvd Ste 350 Costa Mesa (92627) ***(P-19688)***
PRC, Ontario *Also called Plastics Research Corporation* ***(P-9759)***
PRC - Desoto International Inc (HQ)....B....661 678-4209
24811 Ave Rockefeller Valencia (91355) ***(P-9162)***
PRC - Desoto International Inc....F....949 474-0400
11601 United St Mojave (93501) ***(P-9163)***
PRC - Desoto International Inc....C....661 824-4532
11601 United St Mojave (93501) ***(P-9164)***
PRC Composites LLC....D....909 391-2006
1400 S Campus Ave Ontario (91761) ***(P-4917)***
Pre-Insulated Metal Tech Inc (HQ)....E....707 359-2280
929 Aldridge Rd Vacaville (95688) ***(P-12956)***
Pre-Peeled Potato Co Inc....F....209 469-6911
1585 S Union St Stockton (95206) ***(P-2640)***
Pre-Press International....E....415 216-0031
20 S Linden Ave Ste 4a South San Francisco (94080) ***(P-7032)***
Pre/Plastics Inc....E....530 823-1820
12600 Locksley Ln Ste 100 Auburn (95602) ***(P-10301)***
Precast Con Tech Unlimited LLC....E....530 749-6501
1260 Furneaux Rd Olivehurst (95961) ***(P-10978)***
Precast Innovations Inc....E....714 921-4060
1670 N Main St Orange (92867) ***(P-10979)***
Precast Repair....E....909 627-5477
5494 Morgan St Ontario (91762) ***(P-10980)***
Precinct Reporter....F....909 889-0597
357 W 2nd St Ste 1a San Bernardino (92401) ***(P-6017)***
Precinct Reporter Newsprs, San Bernardino *Also called Precinct Reporter* ***(P-6017)***
Precious Metals Plating Co Inc....F....714 546-6271
2635 Orange Ave Santa Ana (92707) ***(P-13477)***
Precise Aero Products Inc....F....951 340-4554
4120 Indus Way Riverside (92503) ***(P-20912)***
Precise Aerospace Mfg Inc....E....951 898-0500
224 Glider Cir Corona (92880) ***(P-10302)***
Precise Industries Inc....C....714 482-2333
610 Neptune Ave Brea (92821) ***(P-12719)***
Precise Media Services Inc....E....909 481-3305
888 Vintage Ave Ontario (91764) ***(P-17910)***
Precise Plastic Products, Corona *Also called Precise Aerospace Mfg Inc* ***(P-10302)***
Precise Technology Inc....F....949 453-1997
33 Hammond Ste 210 Irvine (92618) ***(P-19084)***
Precise-Full Service Media, Ontario *Also called Precise Media Services Inc* ***(P-17910)***
Precision Aerospace & Tech Inc....E....714 543-2966
2320 E Orangethorpe Ave A Anaheim (92806) ***(P-14666)***
Precision Aerospace Corp....D....909 945-9604
11155 Jersey Blvd Ste A Rancho Cucamonga (91730) ***(P-20913)***
Precision Anodizing & Pltg Inc....D....714 996-1601
1601 N Miller St Anaheim (92806) ***(P-13478)***
Precision Arcft Machining Inc....E....818 768-5900
10640 Elkwood St Sun Valley (91352) ***(P-16853)***
Precision Babbitt Co Inc....F....562 531-9173
1007 S Whitemarsh Ave Compton (90220) ***(P-15289)***

Precision Circuits San Diego, Carlsbad *Also called First Circuit Inc* ***(P-18482)***
Precision Circuits West Inc....F....714 435-9670
3310 W Harvard St Santa Ana (92704) ***(P-18564)***
Precision Cnc Mil & Turning, Scotts Valley *Also called Larkin Precision Machining* ***(P-16678)***
Precision Coatings Inc....F....510 525-3600
1220 4th St Berkeley (94710) ***(P-8932)***
Precision Coil Spring Company....D....626 448-9731
10107 Rose Ave El Monte (91731) ***(P-13800)***
Precision Companies Inc....F....909 548-2700
15088 La Palma Dr Chino (91710) ***(P-4214)***
Precision Contacts Inc....E....916 939-4147
990 Suncast Ln El Dorado Hills (95762) ***(P-18223)***
Precision Corepins, Santa Ana *Also called West Coast Form Grinding* ***(P-17058)***
Precision Cutting Tools Inc....E....562 921-7898
13701 Excelsior Dr Santa Fe Springs (90670) ***(P-14667)***
Precision Deburring Services....D....562 944-4497
4440 Manning Rd Pico Rivera (90660) ***(P-14400)***
Precision Design Inc....E....650 508-8041
1160 Industrial Rd Ste 16 San Carlos (94070) ***(P-18565)***
Precision Designed Products, Pacoima *Also called Excess Trading Inc* ***(P-22196)***
Precision Die Cutting Inc....E....510 636-9654
150 Doolittle Dr San Leandro (94577) ***(P-20423)***
Precision Diecut, Chino *Also called Pdc LLC* ***(P-14558)***
Precision Doors & Millwork, Chino *Also called Precision Companies Inc* ***(P-4214)***
Precision Dynamics Corporation (HQ)....C....818 897-1111
27770 N Entmt Dr Ste 200 Valencia (91355) ***(P-5575)***
Precision Energy Efficient Ltg, Yorba Linda *Also called Precision Fluorescent West Inc* ***(P-17638)***
Precision Engineered Products, Sunland *Also called Engineered Products By Lee Ltd* ***(P-16475)***
Precision Engineering Inds....F....818 767-8590
11627 Cantara St North Hollywood (91605) ***(P-19689)***
Precision Engineering Industry, North Hollywood *Also called Precision Engineering Inds* ***(P-19689)***
Precision Enterprises, Stanton *Also called CJ Enterprises* ***(P-14496)***
Precision European Inc....F....714 241-9657
11594 Coley River Cir Fountain Valley (92708) ***(P-15011)***
Precision Fastener Tooling....F....714 898-8558
11530 Western Ave Stanton (90680) ***(P-14452)***
Precision Fiber Products Inc....F....408 946-4040
142 N Milpitas Blvd # 298 Milpitas (95035) ***(P-11670)***
Precision Fiberglass Products....E....310 539-7470
3105 Kashiwa St Torrance (90505) ***(P-17517)***
Precision Film & Tape, San Leandro *Also called Precision Die Cutting Inc* ***(P-20423)***
Precision Flight Controls....F....916 414-1310
2747 Merc Dr Ste 100 Rancho Cordova (95742) ***(P-20045)***
Precision Fluorescent West Inc (HQ)....D....352 692-5900
23281 La Palma Ave Yorba Linda (92887) ***(P-17638)***
Precision Forging Dies Inc....E....562 861-1878
10710 Sessler St South Gate (90280) ***(P-14561)***
Precision Forklift....F....559 805-5487
15389 Avenue 288 Visalia (93292) ***(P-14342)***
Precision Forming Group LLC....F....562 501-1985
511 Commercial Way La Habra (90631) ***(P-14453)***
Precision Frrites Ceramics Inc....D....714 901-7622
5432 Production Dr Huntington Beach (92649) ***(P-10822)***
Precision Glass Bevelling Inc....E....818 989-2727
15201 Keswick St Ste A Van Nuys (91405) ***(P-10665)***
Precision Granite Company, Azusa *Also called Precision Granite USA Inc* ***(P-11270)***
Precision Granite USA Inc....E....562 696-8328
174 N Aspan Ave Azusa (91702) ***(P-11270)***
Precision Graphics, Redwood City *Also called Tilley Manufacturing Co Inc* ***(P-9561)***
Precision Hermetic Tech Inc....D....909 381-6011
1940 W Park Ave Redlands (92373) ***(P-19690)***
Precision Identity Corporation....E....408 374-2346
804 Camden Ave Campbell (95008) ***(P-16854)***
Precision Injection Molding Co....F....951 272-8028
206 Lewis Ct Corona (92882) ***(P-10303)***
Precision Jewelry Tools & Sups....E....408 251-7990
1555 Alum Rock Ave San Jose (95116) ***(P-11906)***
Precision Label Inc....E....760 757-7533
659 Benet Rd Oceanside (92058) ***(P-5534)***
Precision Litho Inc....E....760 727-9400
1185 Joshua Way Vista (92081) ***(P-7033)***
Precision Machining, Glendale *Also called Premac Inc* ***(P-16857)***
Precision Metal Crafts....F....562 468-7080
16920 Gridley Pl Cerritos (90703) ***(P-12230)***
Precision Metal Products Inc (HQ)....C....619 448-2711
850 W Bradley Ave El Cajon (92020) ***(P-13110)***
Precision Milling, Burbank *Also called BMC East LLC* ***(P-4111)***
Precision Millwork LLC....F....661 402-5021
14300 Davenport Rd Ste 4a Agua Dulce (91390) ***(P-4215)***
Precision Molded Plastics Inc....F....909 981-9662
880 W 9th St Upland (91786) ***(P-10304)***
Precision Mtal Fabrication Inc....F....562 941-2169
1942 Sunny Side Pl Santa Fe Springs (90670) ***(P-12720)***
Precision Offset Inc....D....949 752-1714
15201 Woodlawn Ave Tustin (92780) ***(P-7034)***
Precision One Medical Inc....D....760 945-7966
3923 Oceanic Dr Ste 200 Oceanside (92056) ***(P-22901)***
Precision Optical, Costa Mesa *Also called Sellers Optical Inc* ***(P-22134)***
Precision Plastic LLC....C....510 324-8676
555 Twin Dolphin Dr Redwood City (94065) ***(P-10305)***
Precision Plastics Printing, Anaheim *Also called Interlink Inc* ***(P-6894)***
Precision Plus, Huntington Beach *Also called Urabe Incorporated* ***(P-17026)***
Precision Printers, Grass Valley *Also called Igraphics* ***(P-7349)***

Precision Pwdred Met Parts Inc .... E 909 595-5656
145 Atlantic St Pomona (91768) ***(P-11846)***
Precision Resource Inc .... B 714 891-4439
5803 Engineer Dr Huntington Beach (92649) ***(P-13262)***
Precision Resource Cal Div, Huntington Beach *Also called Precision Resource Inc* ***(P-13262)***
Precision Resources, Hawthorne *Also called Paulco Precision Inc* ***(P-16833)***
Precision Services Group, Tustin *Also called Precision Offset Inc* ***(P-7034)***
Precision Sheet Metal, Gardena *Also called Artistic Welding Inc* ***(P-12489)***
Precision Silicones, Chino *Also called Wacker Chemical Corporation* ***(P-9052)***
Precision Sports Inc .... D 951 674-1665
29910 Ohana Cir Lake Elsinore (92532) ***(P-23629)***
Precision Stampings Inc (PA) .... E 951 845-1174
500 Egan Ave Beaumont (92223) ***(P-17487)***
Precision Steel Products Inc .... E 310 523-2002
13124 Avalon Blvd Los Angeles (90061) ***(P-12721)***
Precision Surfaces Inc .... E 951 680-9279
8081 Orangethorpe Ave Buena Park (90621) ***(P-5095)***
Precision Technology and Mfg .... E 951 788-0252
3147 Durahart St Riverside (92507) ***(P-13038)***
Precision Tile Co .... F 818 767-7673
11140 Penrose St Sun Valley (91352) ***(P-10981)***
Precision Tube Bending .... D 562 921-6723
13626 Talc St Santa Fe Springs (90670) ***(P-20914)***
Precision Waterjet, Placentia *Also called Jbb Inc* ***(P-19991)***
Precision Waterjet Inc .... E 888 538-9287
880 W Crowther Ave Placentia (92870) ***(P-16855)***
Precision Welding Inc .... E 661 729-3436
241 Enterprise Pkwy Lancaster (93534) ***(P-12231)***
Precision Wire Products Inc (PA) .... C 323 890-9100
6150 Sheila St Commerce (90040) ***(P-13843)***
Precision Wire Products Inc .... E 323 569-8165
11215 Wilmington Ave Los Angeles (90059) ***(P-11410)***
Preco Aircraft Motors Inc .... E 626 799-3549
1133 Mission St South Pasadena (91030) ***(P-19845)***
Precon Gage, Anaheim *Also called Precon Inc* ***(P-14401)***
Precon Inc .... E 714 630-7632
3131 E La Palma Ave Anaheim (92806) ***(P-14401)***
Pred Technologies USA Inc .... D 858 999-2114
7855 Fay Ave Ste 310 La Jolla (92037) ***(P-19691)***
Predator Motorsports Inc .... F 760 734-1749
1250 Distribution Way Vista (92081) ***(P-10306)***
Predii Inc .... E 650 666-2524
2211 Park Blvd Palo Alto (94306) ***(P-25077)***
Predpol Inc .... F 831 331-4550
920 41st Ave Ste D Santa Cruz (95062) ***(P-25078)***
Preferred Mfg Svcs Inc (PA) .... D 530 677-2675
4261 Business Dr Cameron Park (95682) ***(P-16856)***
Preferred Milling Inc .... E 714 754-4230
3151 Airway Ave Ste A1 Costa Mesa (92626) ***(P-4047)***
Preferred Pallets Inc .... F 909 875-7540
288 E Santa Ana Ave Bloomington (92316) ***(P-4500)***
Preferred Pharmaceuticals Inc .... F 714 777-3729
1250 N Lakeview Ave Ste O Anaheim (92807) ***(P-8342)***
Preferred Wire Products Inc .... F 559 324-0140
401 N Minnewawa Ave Clovis (93611) ***(P-13844)***
Pregis .... E 909 469-8100
159 N San Antonio Ave Pomona (91767) ***(P-9877)***
Pregnancy Magazine, San Francisco *Also called Greatdad LLC* ***(P-6174)***
Premac Inc .... F 818 241-8370
625 Thompson Ave Glendale (91201) ***(P-16857)***
Premco Forge Inc .... F 323 564-6666
5200 Tweedy Blvd South Gate (90280) ***(P-13111)***
Premier Bag Company LLC .... E 805 237-1910
1603 Commerce Way Paso Robles (93446) ***(P-5535)***
Premier Barricades .... F 877 345-9700
28441 Felix Valdez Ave Temecula (92590) ***(P-13965)***
Premier Coatings Inc .... D 209 982-5585
7910 Longe St Stockton (95206) ***(P-13640)***
Premier Color Graphics Inc .... E 559 625-8606
1899 N Helm Ave Fresno (93727) ***(P-7035)***
Premier Finishing, Stockton *Also called Premier Coatings Inc* ***(P-13640)***
Premier Gear & Machining Inc .... E 951 278-5505
2360 Pomona Rd Corona (92880) ***(P-13112)***
Premier Magnetics Inc .... E 949 452-0511
20381 Barents Sea Cir Lake Forest (92630) ***(P-19354)***
Premier Media Inc .... F 562 802-9720
13353 Alondra Blvd # 115 Santa Fe Springs (90670) ***(P-6018)***
Premier Metal Processing Inc .... F 760 415-9027
971 Vernon Way El Cajon (92020) ***(P-13479)***
Premier Mop & Broom, Corona *Also called Northwestern Converting Co* ***(P-23795)***
Premier Packaging Group, LLC, Paso Robles *Also called Premier Bag Company LLC* ***(P-5535)***
Premier Steel Structures Inc .... E 951 356-6655
13345 Estelle St Corona (92879) ***(P-12232)***
Premier Tank Service Inc .... E 661 833-2960
34933 Imperial St Bakersfield (93308) ***(P-21217)***
Premier Trailer Manufacturing .... E 559 651-2212
30517 Ivy Rd Visalia (93291) ***(P-21239)***
Premiere Recycle Co .... E 408 297-7910
348 Phelan Ave San Jose (95112) ***(P-12410)***
Premio Inc (PA) .... C 626 839-3100
918 Radecki Ct City of Industry (91748) ***(P-15472)***
Premium Herbal USA LLC .... F 800 567-7878
15121 Graham St Ste 108 Huntington Beach (92649) ***(P-646)***
Premium Pallet Inc .... F 909 868-9621
2000 Pomona Blvd Pomona (91768) ***(P-4501)***
Premium Pet Foods, Irwindale *Also called J & R Taylor Bros Assoc Inc* ***(P-1115)***
Premium Plastics Machine Inc .... F 323 979-3889
15956 Downey Ave Paramount (90723) ***(P-10307)***
Premium Windows, Paramount *Also called Mediland Corporation* ***(P-10602)***
Prenav Inc .... F 650 264-7279
121 Beech St Redwood City (94063) ***(P-21382)***
Preplastics, Auburn *Also called Pre/Plastics Inc* ***(P-10301)***
Preproduction Plastics Inc .... E 951 340-9680
210 Teller St Corona (92879) ***(P-10308)***
Presbia, Irvine *Also called Presbibio LLC* ***(P-23117)***
Presbibio LLC .... E 949 502-7010
8845 Irvine Center Dr Irvine (92618) ***(P-23117)***
Presentation Folder Inc .... E 714 289-7000
1130 N Main St Orange (92867) ***(P-5655)***
Presentation Systems, Richmond *Also called Coin Gllery of San Frncsco Inc* ***(P-5134)***
Preserved Treescapes Intl, San Marcos *Also called Preserved Treescapes Intl Inc* ***(P-24213)***
Preserved Treescapes Intl Inc (PA) .... E 760 631-6789
180 Vallecitos De Oro San Marcos (92069) ***(P-24213)***
President Enterprise Inc .... E 714 671-9577
700 Columbia St Brea (92821) ***(P-7442)***
President Global Corporation (HQ) .... F 714 994-2990
6965 Aragon Cir Buena Park (90620) ***(P-1376)***
Presidio Pharmaceuticals Inc .... F 415 655-7560
1700 Owens St Ste 585 San Francisco (94158) ***(P-8343)***
Presquile Winery .... F 805 937-8110
5391 Presquile Dr Santa Maria (93455) ***(P-1929)***
Press Brothers Juicery LLC .... E 213 389-3645
2551 Beverly Blvd Ste A Los Angeles (90057) ***(P-849)***
Press Colorcom, Santa Fe Springs *Also called Ace Commercial Inc* ***(P-6636)***
Press Democrat, The, Santa Rosa *Also called Santa Rosa Press Democrat Inc* ***(P-6040)***
Press Forge Company .... D 562 531-4962
7700 Jackson St Paramount (90723) ***(P-13127)***
Press-Enterprise Company (PA) .... A 951 684-1200
3450 14th St Riverside (92501) ***(P-6019)***
Press-Enterprise Company .... F 951 684-1200
3450 14th St Riverside (92501) ***(P-6020)***
Pressed Right LLC .... F 866 257-5774
23615 El Toro Rd Lake Forest (92630) ***(P-11882)***
Pressline Ink and Sup Co Inc .... E 562 907-1891
12117 Slauson Ave Santa Fe Springs (90670) ***(P-7655)***
Pressnet Express Inc .... F 858 694-0070
7283 Engineer Rd Ste Ab San Diego (92111) ***(P-7036)***
Presstime, Anaheim *Also called B K Harris Inc* ***(P-7245)***
Pressure Cast Products Corp .... E 510 532-7310
4210 E 12th St Oakland (94601) ***(P-11716)***
Pressure Profile Systems Inc .... F 310 641-8100
5757 W Century Blvd # 600 Los Angeles (90045) ***(P-21634)***
Prestige Chinese Teas Co .... F 650 697-8989
882 Mahler Rd Burlingame (94010) ***(P-2641)***
Prestige Cosmetics Inc .... F 714 375-0395
17780 Gothard St Huntington Beach (92647) ***(P-8821)***
Prestige Flag & Banner Co .... D 619 497-2220
591 Camino Dela Reina 917 San Diego (92108) ***(P-3958)***
Prestige Foil Inc .... F 714 556-1431
13531 Fairmont Way Tustin (92780) ***(P-7443)***
Prestige Limousine, Stockton *Also called Ramon Lopez* ***(P-20166)***
Prestige Mold Incorporated .... D 909 980-6600
11040 Tacoma Dr Rancho Cucamonga (91730) ***(P-14562)***
Prestige Printing, San Ramon *Also called Sorenson Publishing Inc* ***(P-7106)***
Prestige Printing & Graphics, San Ramon *Also called Trinity Marketing LLC* ***(P-7148)***
Preston Cinema Systems Inc .... F 310 453-1852
1659 11th St Ste 100 Santa Monica (90404) ***(P-23189)***
Preston Vineyards & Winery, Healdsburg *Also called Preston Vineyards Inc* ***(P-1930)***
Preston Vineyards Inc .... F 707 433-3372
9282 W Dry Creek Rd Healdsburg (95448) ***(P-1930)***
Prestone Products Corporation .... E 424 271-4836
19500 Mariner Ave Torrance (90503) ***(P-9298)***
Pretika Corporation .... E 949 481-8818
16 Salermo Laguna Niguel (92677) ***(P-8822)***
Pretium Packaging LLC .... C 760 737-7995
946 S Andreasen Dr Escondido (92029) ***(P-9806)***
Pretzelmaker, Santa Paula *Also called Fowlie Enterprises Inc* ***(P-1364)***
Prevail Wines, Healdsburg *Also called Ferrar-Crano Vnyrds Winery LLC* ***(P-1759)***
Prezant Company .... F 650 342-7413
940 S Amphlett Blvd San Mateo (94402) ***(P-14798)***
Prezi Inc (PA) .... E 415 398-8012
450 Bryant St San Francisco (94107) ***(P-25079)***
Price Industries Inc .... D 858 673-4451
10883 Thornmint Rd San Diego (92127) ***(P-11411)***
Price Manufacturing Co Inc .... E 951 371-5660
372 N Smith Ave Corona (92880) ***(P-13039)***
Price Pfister Inc .... C 949 672-4003
19701 Da Vinci Foothill Ranch (92610) ***(P-12045)***
Price Pfister Inc (HQ) .... A 949 672-4000
19701 Da Vinci Foothill Ranch (92610) ***(P-12046)***
Price Pfister Brass Mfg, Foothill Ranch *Also called Price Pfister Inc* ***(P-12046)***
Price Products Incorporated .... E 760 233-8704
106 State Pl Escondido (92029) ***(P-16858)***
Price Rubber Company Inc .... F 209 239-7478
17760 Ideal Pkwy Manteca (95336) ***(P-9505)***
Price-Leho Co Inc .... F 805 482-8967
3841 Mission Oaks Blvd Camarillo (93012) ***(P-13263)***
Pride Conveyance Systems Inc .... D 831 637-1787
1781 Shelton Dr Hollister (95023) ***(P-14281)***
Pride Industries One Inc .... A 916 788-2100
10030 Foothills Blvd Roseville (95747) ***(P-24214)***
Pride Line Products, Stockton *Also called Value Products Inc* ***(P-8613)***
Pride Metal Polishing Inc .... F 626 350-1326
10822 Saint Louis Dr El Monte (91731) ***(P-13480)***

ALPHABETIC

Pride Sash, Hawthorne *Also called Computerized Fashion Svcs Inc* ***(P-3650)***

Prieto Sports, Temple City *Also called Zeeni Inc* ***(P-3206)***

Prima Fleur Botanicals Inc ... F ... 415 455-0957
84 Galli Dr Novato (94949) ***(P-8823)***

Prima Games, Roseville *Also called Penguin Random House LLC* ***(P-6380)***

Prima Games Inc ... C ... 916 787-7000
2990 Lava Ridge Ct # 120 Roseville (95661) ***(P-6384)***

Prima Lighting Corp ... F ... 562 407-3079
13615 Marquardt Ave Santa Fe Springs (90670) ***(P-17556)***

Prima Publishing, Roseville *Also called Prima Games Inc* ***(P-6384)***

Prima-Tex Industries Cal Inc ... D ... 714 521-6104
6237 Descanso Cir Buena Park (90620) ***(P-2890)***

Primal Essence Inc ... F ... 805 981-2409
1351 Maulhardt Ave Oxnard (93030) ***(P-2277)***

Primal Pet Foods Inc ... F ... 415 642-7400
535 Watt Dr Ste B Fairfield (94534) ***(P-1120)***

Primapharma Inc ... E ... 858 259-0969
3443 Tripp Ct San Diego (92121) ***(P-8344)***

Primarch Manufacturing Inc ... F ... 760 730-8572
1211 Liberty Way Vista (92081) ***(P-24215)***

Primary Color Systems Corp (PA) ... B ... 949 660-7080
11130 Holder St Cypress (90630) ***(P-7037)***

Primary Color Systems Corp ... D ... 310 841-0250
401 Coral Cir El Segundo (90245) ***(P-7444)***

Primary Concepts Inc ... F ... 510 559-5545
1338 7th St Berkeley (94710) ***(P-23458)***

Prime Alliance LLC ... E ... 310 764-1000
360 W Victoria St Compton (90220) ***(P-2870)***

Prime Alloy Steel Casting, Port Hueneme *Also called Pac Foundries Inc* ***(P-11748)***

Prime Alloy Steel Castings Inc ... C ... 805 488-6451
717 Industrial Way Port Hueneme (93041) ***(P-11782)***

Prime Building Material Inc ... F ... 818 503-4242
7811 Lankershim Blvd North Hollywood (91605) ***(P-10982)***

Prime Conduit Inc ... E ... 530 669-0160
1776 E Beamer St Woodland (95776) ***(P-7876)***

Prime Converting Corporation ... E ... 909 476-9500
9121 Pttsbrgh Ave Ste 100 Rancho Cucamonga (91730) ***(P-5727)***

Prime Engineering, Fresno *Also called Axiom Industries Inc* ***(P-22703)***

Prime Forming & Cnstr Sups ... E ... 714 547-6710
1500a E Chestnut Ave Santa Ana (92701) ***(P-10983)***

Prime Heat Incorporated ... F ... 619 449-6623
1844 Friendship Dr Ste A El Cajon (92020) ***(P-15272)***

Prime Measurement Products LLC (PA) ... B ... 626 961-2547
900 Turnbull Canyon Rd City of Industry (91745) ***(P-21635)***

Prime Plating, Sun Valley *Also called Schmidt Industries Inc* ***(P-13501)***

Prime Plating Aerospace Inc ... F ... 818 768-9100
11321 Goss St Sun Valley (91352) ***(P-13481)***

Prime Solutions Inc ... F ... 510 490-2255
4261 Business Center Dr Fremont (94538) ***(P-19085)***

Prime Surfaces Inc ... F ... 310 448-2292
25111 Normandie Ave Harbor City (90710) ***(P-11271)***

Prime Wheel Corporation ... B ... 310 326-5080
23920 Vermont Ave Harbor City (90710) ***(P-20424)***

Prime Wheel Corporation ... E ... 310 516-9126
250 W Apra St Compton (90220) ***(P-20425)***

Prime Wheel Corporation (PA) ... A ... 310 516-9126
17705 S Main St Gardena (90248) ***(P-20426)***

Prime Wire & Cable Inc (HQ) ... E ... 888 445-9955
280 Machlin Ct Walnut (91789) ***(P-11671)***

Primebore Directional Boring ... F ... 909 821-4643
10822 Vernon Ave Ontario (91762) ***(P-118)***

Primed Productions Inc ... F ... 626 216-5822
1443 E Washington Blvd Pasadena (91104) ***(P-5025)***

Primedia Enthsast Pblctons Inc (HQ) ... C ... 717 657-9555
831 S Douglas St Ste 100 El Segundo (90245) ***(P-6236)***

Primetech Silicones Inc ... F ... 951 509-6655
6655 Doolittle Ave Riverside (92503) ***(P-9030)***

Primex, Vacaville *Also called SJ Electro Systems Inc* ***(P-16108)***

Primex, Vacaville *Also called McC Controls LLC* ***(P-16070)***

Primex Farms LLC (PA) ... E ... 661 758-7790
16070 Wildwood Rd Wasco (93280) ***(P-1502)***

Primo Powder Coating & Sndblst ... F ... 714 596-4242
17592 Gothard St Huntington Beach (92647) ***(P-13641)***

Primo Sandblasting, Huntington Beach *Also called Norm Harboldt* ***(P-13622)***

Primus Inc (PA) ... D ... 714 527-2261
17901 Jamestown Ln Huntington Beach (92647) ***(P-23944)***

Primus Inc ... F ... 714 527-2261
17901 Jamestown Ln Huntington Beach (92647) ***(P-23945)***

Primus Lighting Inc ... F ... 626 442-4600
3570 Lexington Ave El Monte (91731) ***(P-17726)***

Primus Power Corporation ... E ... 510 342-7600
3967 Trust Way Hayward (94545) ***(P-19822)***

Prince Development LLC ... F ... 866 774-6234
23302 Oxnard St Woodland Hills (91367) ***(P-8824)***

Prince Lionheart Inc (PA) ... E ... 805 922-2250
2421 Westgate Rd Santa Maria (93455) ***(P-10309)***

Prince Reigns, Woodland Hills *Also called Prince Development LLC* ***(P-8824)***

Princess Brandy Corp (PA) ... F ... 619 563-9722
3161 Adams Ave San Diego (92116) ***(P-1311)***

Princess Paper Inc ... E ... 323 588-4777
4455 Fruitland Ave Vernon (90058) ***(P-5668)***

Princeton Case West Inc ... E ... 805 928-8840
1444 W Mccoy Ln Santa Maria (93455) ***(P-10310)***

Princeton Technology Inc ... E ... 949 851-7776
1691 Browning Irvine (92606) ***(P-15825)***

Principia Biopharma Inc ... D ... 650 416-7700
400 E Jamie Ct Ste 302 South San Francisco (94080) ***(P-8345)***

Principle Plastics ... E ... 310 532-3411
1136 W 135th St Gardena (90247) ***(P-9478)***

Pringle's Draperies, Garden Grove *Also called L C Pringle Sales Inc* ***(P-5200)***

Prinko Image Co (usa) Inc (HQ) ... F ... 626 389-8988
5021 Tyler Ave Ste D Temple City (91780) ***(P-15826)***

Prinsco Inc ... E ... 559 485-5542
2839 S Cherry Ave Fresno (93706) ***(P-9785)***

Print & Mail Solutions Inc ... F ... 916 782-5489
1322 Blue Oaks Blvd # 100 Roseville (95678) ***(P-7038)***

Print Ink Inc ... E ... 925 829-3950
6918 Sierra Ct Dublin (94568) ***(P-3185)***

Print N Save Inc ... F ... 714 634-1133
2120 E Howell Ave Ste 414 Anaheim (92806) ***(P-7039)***

Print Shop, San Bernardino *Also called San Brnrdino Cmnty College Dst* ***(P-7477)***

Print Shop, The, La Mirada *Also called Wintflash Inc* ***(P-7543)***

Print Smith Inc ... F ... 831 688-1538
8047 Soquel Dr Aptos (95003) ***(P-7040)***

Print-N-Stuff Inc ... F ... 925 798-3212
1300 Galaxy Way Ste 3 Concord (94520) ***(P-7041)***

Printcom Inc ... F ... 818 891-8282
14675 Titus St Van Nuys (91402) ***(P-7042)***

Printec Ht Electronics LLC ... E ... 714 484-7597
501 Sally Pl Fullerton (92831) ***(P-19086)***

Printech, Fullerton *Also called High Five Inc* ***(P-6858)***

Printed Circuit Solutions Inc ... F ... 714 825-1090
2040 S Yale St Santa Ana (92704) ***(P-18566)***

Printed Circuit Technology ... D ... 510 659-1866
44081 Old Warm Sprng Blvd Fremont (94538) ***(P-18567)***

Printed Image, The, Chico *Also called Srl Apparel Inc* ***(P-2895)***

Printefex Inc ... F ... 818 240-2400
401 W Los Feliz Rd Ste C Glendale (91204) ***(P-7043)***

Printegra Corp ... E ... 925 373-6368
379 Earhart Way Livermore (94551) ***(P-7551)***

Printer Cartridge USA ... F ... 858 538-7630
14276 Barrymore St San Diego (92129) ***(P-23190)***

Printery Inc ... F ... 949 757-1930
1762 Kaiser Ave Irvine (92614) ***(P-7044)***

Printfirm Inc ... F ... 818 992-1005
21333 Deering Ct Canoga Park (91304) ***(P-7445)***

PRINTING 4HIM, Ontario *Also called Ultimate Print Source Inc* ***(P-7153)***

Printing and Marketing Inc ... F ... 510 931-7000
33200 Transit Ave Union City (94587) ***(P-7446)***

Printing Connection , The, Van Nuys *Also called H J S Graphics* ***(P-6845)***

Printing Division Inc ... F ... 714 685-0111
1933 N Main St Orange (92865) ***(P-7045)***

Printing Impressions, Goleta *Also called JD Business Solutions Inc* ***(P-6909)***

Printing Island Corporation ... F ... 714 668-1000
11535 Martens River Cir Fountain Valley (92708) ***(P-7046)***

Printing Management Associates (PA) ... F ... 562 407-9977
17128 Edwards Rd Cerritos (90703) ***(P-7047)***

Printing Manufacturer, San Diego *Also called Kyung In Printing Inc* ***(P-6932)***

Printing Palace Inc ... E ... 310 451-5151
2300 Lincoln Blvd Santa Monica (90405) ***(P-7048)***

Printing Place, The, Palm Desert *Also called Wanda Matranga* ***(P-7172)***

Printing Rsources Southern Cal, Upland *Also called Helens Place Inc* ***(P-6851)***

Printing Safari Co ... F ... 818 709-3752
9855 Topanga Canyon Blvd Chatsworth (91311) ***(P-7049)***

Printing Shoppe, The, San Diego *Also called Wissings Inc* ***(P-7189)***

Printing Solutions, Escondido *Also called LL Baker Inc* ***(P-6952)***

Printograph Inc ... F ... 818 252-3000
7625 N San Fernando Rd Burbank (91505) ***(P-7050)***

Printpack Inc ... C ... 925 469-0601
5870 Stoneridge Mall Rd # 200 Pleasanton (94588) ***(P-5615)***

Printronix LLC (PA) ... C ... 714 368-2300
6440 Oak Cyn Ste 200 Irvine (92618) ***(P-15827)***

Printronix Holding Corp ... C ... 714 368-2300
6440 Oak Cyn Ste 200 Irvine (92618) ***(P-15828)***

Printrunner LLC ... E ... 888 296-5760
8000 Haskell Ave Van Nuys (91406) ***(P-7447)***

Prints Charmn Inc (PA) ... F ... 310 312-0904
11560 Tennessee Ave Los Angeles (90064) ***(P-7051)***

Printworx Inc ... F ... 831 722-7147
195 Aviation Way Ste 201 Watsonville (95076) ***(P-15829)***

Printyourcompany ... F ... 714 380-3900
2661 Dow Ave Tustin (92780) ***(P-7448)***

Priority Pallet Inc ... C ... 951 769-9399
1060 E Third St Beaumont (92223) ***(P-4502)***

Priority Posting and Pubg Inc ... E ... 714 338-2568
17501 Irvine Blvd Ste 1 Tustin (92780) ***(P-6556)***

Priority Tech Systems Inc ... F ... 818 756-5413
14040 Runnymede St Van Nuys (91405) ***(P-20046)***

Prisha Cosmetics Inc ... F ... 818 773-8784
9260 Owensmouth Ave Chatsworth (91311) ***(P-8825)***

Prism Aerospace ... E ... 951 582-2850
3087 12th St Riverside (92507) ***(P-12722)***

Prism Mfg ... E ... 310 538-3857
3057 12th St Riverside (92507) ***(P-20915)***

Prism Skylabs Inc ... F ... 415 243-0834
799 Market St Fl 8 San Francisco (94103) ***(P-18224)***

Prism Software Corporation ... E ... 949 855-3100
15500 Rockfield Blvd C Irvine (92618) ***(P-25080)***

Prison Ride Share Network ... E ... 314 703-5245
1541 S California Ave Compton (90221) ***(P-6557)***

Prison Rideshare Network, Compton *Also called Prison Ride Share Network* ***(P-6557)***

Private Brand Mdsg Corp ... E ... 213 749-0191
214 W Olympic Blvd Los Angeles (90015) ***(P-3333)***

Private Label By G Inc (PA) ... E ... 562 531-1116
6015 Obispo Ave Long Beach (90805) ***(P-3334)***

Prl Aluminum Inc ... D ... 626 968-7507
14760 Don Julian Rd City of Industry (91746) ***(P-11541)***

Pro American Premium Tools, Baldwin Park *Also called Kal-Cameron Manufacturing* ***(P-11898)***
Pro Cal, South Gate *Also called Productivity California Inc* ***(P-10313)***
Pro Circuit Products Inc....F....951 734-3320
2388 Railroad St Corona (92880) ***(P-21132)***
Pro Coat Powder Coating, Lake Elsinore *Also called Rick Palenshus* ***(P-15020)***
Pro Colorflex Ink Corp....F....510 293-3033
3588 Arden Rd Hayward (94545) ***(P-9207)***
Pro Comp, Chula Vista *Also called Tap Manufacturing LLC* ***(P-20459)***
Pro Design Group Inc....E....310 767-1032
438 E Alondra Blvd Gardena (90248) ***(P-10311)***
Pro Detention Inc....D....714 881-3680
2238 N Glassell St Ste K Orange (92865) ***(P-11452)***
Pro Document Solutions Inc (PA)....D....805 238-6680
1760 Commerce Way Paso Robles (93446) ***(P-7052)***
Pro Fab Manufacturing, Fremont *Also called United Pro Fab Mfg Inc* ***(P-19248)***
Pro Fab Tech LLC....F....626 804-7200
970 W Foothill Blvd Azusa (91702) ***(P-13642)***
Pro Food Inc....F....818 341-4040
19431 Bus Center Dr # 35 Northridge (91324) ***(P-2642)***
Pro Form Labs, Benicia *Also called Dga Inc* ***(P-8140)***
Pro Group, Irvine *Also called Professnal Rprgraphic Svcs Inc* ***(P-7450)***
Pro Imaging, Chula Vista *Also called Professional Imaging Svcs Inc* ***(P-22007)***
Pro Line Paint Company....E....619 232-8968
2646 Main St San Diego (92113) ***(P-8933)***
Pro Metal Products....F....760 480-0212
25559 Jesmond Dene Rd Escondido (92026) ***(P-12723)***
Pro Mold Inc....F....951 776-0555
415 Grumman Dr Riverside (92508) ***(P-14563)***
Pro Pack Systems Inc....F....831 771-1300
1354 Dayton St Ste A Salinas (93901) ***(P-15224)***
Pro Power Products Inc....F....818 558-6222
913 S Victory Blvd Burbank (91502) ***(P-17351)***
Pro Products Inc....E....909 605-0545
2967 Avenida De Autlan Ontario (91764) ***(P-20427)***
Pro Systems Fabricators Inc (PA)....F....909 350-9147
14643 Hawthorne Ave Fontana (92335) ***(P-20047)***
Pro Tag Corp....E....213 272-9606
8122 Maie Ave Unit C Los Angeles (90001) ***(P-2853)***
Pro Tool Services Inc....E....661 393-9222
1704 Sunnyside Ct Bakersfield (93308) ***(P-14668)***
Pro Tour Memorabilia LLC....E....424 303-7200
700 N San Vicente Blvd G696 West Hollywood (90069) ***(P-4643)***
Pro Vac....F....661 765-7298
26857 Henry Rd Fellows (93224) ***(P-260)***
Pro Wax, Tustin *Also called Baf Industries* ***(P-8624)***
Pro-Action Products, Van Nuys *Also called Neo Pacific Holdings Inc* ***(P-10233)***
PRO-CISION MACHINING, Morgan Hill *Also called KDF Inc* ***(P-21120)***
Pro-Dex Inc (PA)....D....949 769-3200
2361 Mcgaw Ave Irvine (92614) ***(P-22588)***
Pro-Lite Inc....F....714 668-9988
3505 Cadillac Ave Ste D Costa Mesa (92626) ***(P-23946)***
Pro-Mart Industries Inc (PA)....E....949 428-7700
17421 Von Karman Ave Irvine (92614) ***(P-3743)***
Pro-Spot International Inc....F....760 407-1414
5932 Sea Otter Pl Carlsbad (92010) ***(P-20048)***
Pro-Tech Mats Industries Inc....F....760 343-3667
72370 Quarry Trl Ste A Thousand Palms (92276) ***(P-9661)***
Pro-Tek Manufacturing Inc....E....925 454-8100
4849 Southfront Rd Livermore (94551) ***(P-12724)***
Proactive Packg & Display Inc (PA)....D....909 390-5624
602 S Rockefeller Ave Ontario (91761) ***(P-5453)***
Probactive Biotech Inc....E....714 903-1000
11555 Monarch St Ste B Garden Grove (92841) ***(P-7915)***
Probe Racing Components Inc....E....310 784-2977
5022 Onyx St Torrance (90503) ***(P-16150)***
Probe-Logic Inc....D....408 416-0777
1885 Lundy Ave Ste 101 San Jose (95131) ***(P-15473)***
Probe-Rite Corp....E....408 727-0100
600 Mission St Santa Clara (95050) ***(P-21829)***
Procases Inc....F....323 585-4447
4626 E 48th St Vernon (90058) ***(P-4446)***
Procede Software LP....E....858 450-4800
6815 Flanders Dr Ste 200 San Diego (92121) ***(P-25081)***
Proceilingtiles, Bakersfield *Also called Udecor Inc* ***(P-10416)***
Process Advanced Filtration, Oxnard *Also called Parker-Hannifin Corporation* ***(P-15349)***
Process Materials Inc....F....925 245-9626
5625 Brisa St Ste B Livermore (94550) ***(P-11564)***
Process Solutions Inc....E....408 370-6540
1077 Dell Ave Ste A Campbell (95008) ***(P-21636)***
Process Specialties Inc....E....209 832-1344
1660 W Linne Rd Ste A Tracy (95377) ***(P-13845)***
Process Stainless Lab Inc (PA)....E....408 980-0535
1280 Memorex Dr Santa Clara (95050) ***(P-13482)***
Processexchange Inc....E....661 799-2548
25876 The Old Rd 159 Santa Clarita (91381) ***(P-19877)***
Processors Mailing Inc....E....626 358-5075
761 N Dodsworth Ave Covina (91724) ***(P-7053)***
Processors The, Covina *Also called Processors Mailing Inc* ***(P-7053)***
Proco Products Inc (PA)....E....209 943-6088
2431 Wigwam Dr Stockton (95205) ***(P-9662)***
Procoat, San Marcos *Also called Prowest Technologies Inc* ***(P-8935)***
Procter & Gamble Mfg Co....C....916 383-3800
8201 Fruitridge Rd Sacramento (95826) ***(P-8604)***
Procter & Gamble Mfg Co....B....513 627-4678
18125 Rowland St City of Industry (91748) ***(P-8605)***
Procter & Gamble Paper Pdts Co....B....805 485-8871
800 N Rice Ave Oxnard (93030) ***(P-5669)***
Prodigy Press Inc....F....408 962-0396
1136 W Evelyn Ave Sunnyvale (94086) ***(P-7449)***
Prodigy Surface Tech Inc....E....408 492-9390
807 Aldo Ave Ste 103 Santa Clara (95054) ***(P-13483)***
Produce Apparel Inc....F....949 472-9434
23383 Saint Andrews Mission Viejo (92692) ***(P-3485)***
Produce Available Inc (PA)....D....805 483-5292
910 Commercial Ave Oxnard (93030) ***(P-14094)***
Produce World Inc....D....510 441-1449
30611 San Antonio St Hayward (94544) ***(P-2643)***
Product Design Developments....E....714 898-6895
15611 Container Ln Huntington Beach (92649) ***(P-10312)***
Product Solutions Inc....E....714 545-9757
1182 N Knollwood Cir Anaheim (92801) ***(P-16091)***
Product Virtual Gt, Costa Mesa *Also called E Virtual Corporation* ***(P-17795)***
Productboard Inc....F....844 472-6273
392 Staten Ave Oakland (94610) ***(P-14343)***
Production Assmbly Systems Inc....E....858 748-6700
12568 Kirkham Ct Poway (92064) ***(P-14763)***
Production Car Care Products, Stockton *Also called Production Chemical Mfg Inc* ***(P-8668)***
Production Chemical Mfg Inc (PA)....F....209 943-7337
1000 E Channel St Stockton (95205) ***(P-8668)***
Production Data Inc....F....661 327-4776
1210 33rd St Bakersfield (93301) ***(P-261)***
Production Embroidery Inc....F....760 727-7407
1235 Activity Dr Ste D Vista (92081) ***(P-3857)***
Production Engineering & Mch, Fontana *Also called Cavallo & Cavallo Inc* ***(P-16367)***
Production Industries, Brea *Also called Production Systems Group Inc* ***(P-5249)***
Production Lapping Company....E....626 359-0611
124 E Chestnut Ave Monrovia (91016) ***(P-16859)***
Production Saw....F....818 765-6100
9790 Glenoaks Blvd Ste 8 Sun Valley (91352) ***(P-14402)***
Production Specialties, San Francisco *Also called Klein Industries Inc* ***(P-16658)***
Production Specialties, Sacramento *Also called California Pro-Specs Inc* ***(P-4076)***
Production Systems Group Inc....E....714 990-8997
895 Beacon St Brea (92821) ***(P-5249)***
Productivity California Inc....D....562 923-3100
10533 Sessler St South Gate (90280) ***(P-10313)***
Productplan LLC....E....805 618-2975
10 E Yanonali St Ste 2a Santa Barbara (93101) ***(P-25082)***
Products Engineering Corp (PA)....D....310 787-4500
2645 Maricopa St Torrance (90503) ***(P-11907)***
Products Usa LLC....F....770 960-1120
2933 Bunker Hill Ln # 200 Santa Clara (95054) ***(P-9299)***
Products/Techniques Inc....F....909 877-3951
3271 S Riverside Ave Bloomington (92316) ***(P-8934)***
Professional Bearing Svc Inc....E....562 596-5023
3831 Catalina St Ste K Los Alamitos (90720) ***(P-16860)***
Professional Finishing Inc....D....510 233-7629
770 Market Ave Richmond (94801) ***(P-13484)***
Professional Finishing Systems....F....818 365-8888
12341 Gladstone Ave Sylmar (91342) ***(P-13264)***
Professional Imaging Svcs Inc....F....858 565-4217
1548 Jayken Way Ste C Chula Vista (91911) ***(P-22007)***
Professional McHy Group Inc....F....209 832-0100
1885 N Macarthur Dr Tracy (95376) ***(P-14786)***
Professional Print & Mail Inc....E....559 237-7468
2818 E Hamilton Ave Fresno (93721) ***(P-7054)***
Professional Skin Care Inc (PA)....E....661 257-7771
25028 Avenue Kearny Valencia (91355) ***(P-8826)***
Professnal Rprgraphic Svcs Inc....E....949 748-5400
17731 Cowan Irvine (92614) ***(P-7450)***
Profile Planing Mill, Santa Ana *Also called Strata Forest Products Inc* ***(P-4067)***
Proformance Manufacturing Inc....E....951 279-1230
1922 Elise Cir Corona (92879) ***(P-13265)***
Proformative Inc....F....408 400-3993
99 Almaden Blvd Ste 975 San Jose (95113) ***(P-6558)***
Program Data Incorporated....F....714 649-2122
16291 Jackson Ranch Rd Silverado (92676) ***(P-21830)***
Program Precision Co, San Diego *Also called Fourward Machine Inc* ***(P-16510)***
Programmed Composites Inc....C....951 520-7300
250 Klug Cir Corona (92880) ***(P-20916)***
Prographics Inc....E....626 287-0417
9200 Lower Azusa Rd Rosemead (91770) ***(P-7055)***
Prographics Screenprinting Inc....E....760 744-4555
1975 Diamond St San Marcos (92078) ***(P-7451)***
Progress Group....F....714 630-9017
1600 E Miraloma Ave Placentia (92870) ***(P-20428)***
Progressive Concepts Machining, Pleasanton *Also called Desert Sky Machining Inc* ***(P-16432)***
Progressive Housing Inc....F....916 920-8255
5605 Southfront Rd Livermore (94551) ***(P-20429)***
Progressive Label Inc....E....323 415-9770
2545 Yates Ave Commerce (90040) ***(P-5728)***
Progressive Manufacturing, Anaheim *Also called Progrssive Intgrated Solutions* ***(P-7452)***
Progressive Marketing Pdts Inc....D....714 888-1700
2620 Palisades Dr Corona (92882) ***(P-12957)***
Progressive Packg Group Inc (PA)....E....831 424-2942
18931 Portola Dr Ste C Salinas (93908) ***(P-5454)***
Progressive Products Inc....F....951 784-9930
1650 7th St Riverside (92507) ***(P-3013)***
Progressive Technology Inc....E....916 632-6715
4130 Citrus Ave Ste 17 Rocklin (95677) ***(P-10789)***
Progressive Tool & Die Inc....F....310 327-0569
17016 S Broadway Gardena (90248) ***(P-14669)***
Progressive Woodwork....F....530 343-2211
2255 Ceanothus Ave Chico (95926) ***(P-4336)***
Progrip Cargo Control, Lodi *Also called USA Products Group Inc* ***(P-3970)***

ALPHABETIC

Employee Codes: A=Over 500 employees, B=251-500
C=101-250, D=51-100, E=20-50, F=10-19
2019 California
Manfacturers Register
© Mergent Inc. 1-800-342-5647
1253

Progrssive Intgrated Solutions ....D......714 237-0980
3700 E Miraloma Ave Anaheim (92806) *(P-7452)*

Project 1920 Inc ....E......415 990-9788
251 Post St Ste 412 San Francisco (94108) *(P-10551)*

Project Cloudkey Inc ....F......310 596-8160
600 Wilshire Blvd Ste 700 Los Angeles (90017) *(P-25083)*

Project Mustang Dev LLC ....C......323 275-4098
10115 Jefferson Blvd Culver City (90232) *(P-8346)*

Project Social T LLC ....E......323 266-4500
615 S Clarence St Los Angeles (90023) *(P-3268)*

Project Steel Company Inc ....F......760 947-0531
6826 Cupeno Ave Hesperia (92345) *(P-12233)*

Projectoris Inc ....F......917 972-5553
582 Market St Ste 1901 San Francisco (94104) *(P-25084)*

Projex International Inc ....F......661 268-0999
9555 Hierba Rd Santa Clarita (91390) *(P-24216)*

Prolab Orthotics Inc ....E......707 257-4400
575 Airpark Rd NAPA (94558) *(P-9663)*

Prolacta Bioscience Inc ....E......626 599-9260
1800 Highland Ave Duarte (91010) *(P-647)*

Prolacta Bioscience Inc (PA) ....C......626 599-9260
757 Baldwin Park Blvd City of Industry (91746) *(P-8575)*

Proline Concrete Tools Inc ....E......760 758-7240
2664 Vista Pacific Dr Oceanside (92056) *(P-15012)*

Proline Manufacturing, Banning Also called DT Mattson Enterprises Inc *(P-23419)*

Proma Inc ....E......310 327-0035
730 Kingshill Pl Carson (90746) *(P-22902)*

Promag, South Gate Also called C&C Metal Form & Tooling Inc *(P-13174)*

Promarksvac Corporation ....F......909 923-3888
1915 E Acacia St Ontario (91761) *(P-15225)*

Promart Dazz, Irvine Also called Pro-Mart Industries Inc *(P-3743)*

Promedia Companies ....F......714 444-2426
3518 W Lake Center Dr D Santa Ana (92704) *(P-6237)*

Promedia Printers, Canoga Park Also called PM Lithographers Inc *(P-7030)*

Promega Biosciences LLC ....D......805 544-8524
277 Granada Dr San Luis Obispo (93401) *(P-7965)*

Promega Bsystems Sunnyvale Inc ....E......408 636-2400
3945 Freedom Cir Ste 200 Santa Clara (95054) *(P-22251)*

Prometheus Laboratories Inc ....B......858 824-0895
9410 Carroll Park Dr San Diego (92121) *(P-8347)*

Promex Industries Incorporated ....E......858 674-4676
10987 Via Frontera San Diego (92127) *(P-19087)*

Promex Industries Incorporated (PA) ....D......408 496-0222
3075 Oakmead Village Dr Santa Clara (95051) *(P-19088)*

Promex International Plas Inc ....E......818 367-5352
12860 San Fernando Rd D Sylmar (91342) *(P-10314)*

Promises Promises Inc ....E......213 749-7725
3121 S Grand Ave Los Angeles (90007) *(P-3335)*

Promotion West, Glendale Also called Lin MAI Inc *(P-24162)*

Promotion Xpress Prtg Graphics, San Leandro Also called Akido Printing Inc *(P-6644)*

Promotonal Design Concepts Inc ....D......626 579-4454
9872 Rush St South El Monte (91733) *(P-9664)*

Prompt Precision Metals Inc ....D......209 531-1210
1649 E Whitmore Ave Ceres (95307) *(P-12725)*

Prompter People Inc ....F......408 353-6000
126 Dillon Ave Campbell (95008) *(P-18225)*

Pronk Technologies Inc (PA) ....E......818 768-5600
8933 Lankershim Blvd Sun Valley (91352) *(P-21831)*

Pronto Drilling Inc (PA) ....E......562 777-0900
9501 Santa Fe Springs Rd Santa Fe Springs (90670) *(P-16861)*

Pronto Products Co (PA) ....D......619 661-6995
9850 Siempre Viva Rd San Diego (92154) *(P-16092)*

Propel Biofuels Inc (PA) ....F......800 871-0773
1815 19th St Sacramento (95811) *(P-9031)*

Propel Fuels, Sacramento Also called Propel Biofuels Inc *(P-9031)*

Propertyradar.com, Truckee Also called Acureo Inc *(P-24316)*

Prophecy Technology LLC ....E......909 598-7998
339 Cheryl Ln Walnut (91789) *(P-15830)*

Proplas Technologies, Garden Grove Also called Peerless Injection Molding LLC *(P-10270)*

Proprietary Controls Systems ....E......310 303-3600
3541 Challenger St Torrance (90503) *(P-22252)*

Pros Incorporated ....D......661 589-5400
3400 Patton Way Bakersfield (93308) *(P-262)*

Proseries LLC ....F......213 533-6400
3400 Airport Ave Bldg E Santa Monica (90405) *(P-23630)*

Proshot Golf, Irvine Also called Proshot Investors LLC *(P-18226)*

Proshot Investors LLC ....F......949 586-9500
13865 Alton Pkwy Ste 100 Irvine (92618) *(P-18226)*

Prosound Communications Inc ....F......818 367-9593
233 N Maclay Ave Ste 403 San Fernando (91340) *(P-10474)*

Prostat First Aid LLC ....F......661 705-1256
24922 Anza Dr Ste A Valencia (91355) *(P-22797)*

Prosthetic and Orthotic Group (PA) ....F......562 595-6445
2669 Myrtle Ave Ste 101 Signal Hill (90755) *(P-22798)*

Prosurg Inc ....E......408 945-4040
2195 Trade Zone Blvd San Jose (95131) *(P-22589)*

Protab Laboratories ....D......949 635-1930
25902 Towne Centre Dr Foothill Ranch (92610) *(P-8348)*

Protagonist Therapeutics Inc ....E......510 474-0170
7707 Gateway Blvd Ste 140 Newark (94560) *(P-8349)*

Protec Arisawa America Inc ....E......760 599-4800
2455 Ash St Vista (92081) *(P-12411)*

Protech Design & Manufacturing, San Diego Also called PDM Solutions Inc *(P-18558)*

Protech Materials Inc ....F......510 887-5870
20919 Cabot Blvd Hayward (94545) *(P-11717)*

Protech Minerals Inc ....F......760 245-3441
17092 S D St Victorville (92395) *(P-10800)*

Protech Systems, Riverside Also called Alectro Inc *(P-17079)*

Protective Industries Inc ....D......310 537-2300
18704 S Ferris Pl Rancho Dominguez (90220) *(P-9665)*

Protein Research, Livermore Also called Berkeley Nutritional Mfg Corp *(P-8073)*

Protemach Inc ....F......310 622-2693
7133 Remmet Ave Canoga Park (91303) *(P-9032)*

Proterra Inc (PA) ....C......864 438-0000
1815 Rollins Rd Burlingame (94010) *(P-20164)*

Proteus Digital Health Inc ....C......650 632-4031
3956 Point Eden Way Hayward (94545) *(P-8576)*

Proteus Digital Health Inc (PA) ....C......650 632-4031
2600 Bridge Pkwy Redwood City (94065) *(P-8577)*

Proteus Industries Inc ....E......650 964-4163
340 Pioneer Way Mountain View (94041) *(P-21637)*

Prothena Corp Pub Ltd Co ....E......650 837-8550
331 Oyster Point Blvd South San Francisco (94080) *(P-7966)*

Proto Homes LLC ....E......310 271-7544
917 W 17th St Los Angeles (90015) *(P-21209)*

Proto Laminations Inc ....E......562 926-4777
13666 Bora Dr Santa Fe Springs (90670) *(P-13266)*

Proto Services Inc ....E......408 321-8688
1991 Concourse Dr San Jose (95131) *(P-18353)*

Proto Space Engineering Inc ....E......626 442-8273
2214 Loma Ave South El Monte (91733) *(P-16862)*

Protocast, Chatsworth Also called John List Corporation *(P-14716)*

Protonex LLC ....F......707 566-2260
2331 Circadian Way Santa Rosa (95407) *(P-19089)*

Protool Co, Tustin Also called Bernhardt & Bernhardt Inc *(P-14362)*

Protoquick Inc ....F......510 264-0101
3412 Investment Blvd Hayward (94545) *(P-16863)*

Prototype & Short-Run Svcs Inc ....E......714 449-9661
1310 W Collins Ave Orange (92867) *(P-13267)*

Prototype Express LLC ....F......714 751-3533
3506 W Lake Center Dr D Santa Ana (92704) *(P-20049)*

Prototype Industries Inc (PA) ....F......310 255-0021
1545 26th St Ste 200 Santa Monica (90404) *(P-6559)*

Prototype Solutions, San Jose Also called Binh-Nhan D Ngo *(P-18440)*

Protrend Ltd (HQ) ....F......323 832-9323
6001 E Washington Blvd Commerce (90040) *(P-3336)*

Protype, Orange Also called G P Manufacturing Inc *(P-16521)*

Proulx Manufacturing Inc ....E......909 980-0662
11433 6th St Rancho Cucamonga (91730) *(P-10315)*

Provac Sales Inc ....E......831 462-8900
2535 7th Ave Ste 4 Santa Cruz (95062) *(P-15089)*

Provasis Therapeutics Inc ....E......858 712-2101
9177 Sky Park Ct B San Diego (92123) *(P-22590)*

Provena Foods Inc (HQ) ....D......909 627-1082
5010 Eucalyptus Ave Chino (91710) *(P-516)*

Provena Foods Inc ....E......209 858-5555
251 Darcy Pkwy Lathrop (95330) *(P-517)*

Provenance Vineyards ....F......707 968-3633
1695 Saint Helena Hwy S Saint Helena (94574) *(P-1931)*

Provence Stone ....F......650 631-5600
1040 Varian St San Carlos (94070) *(P-11272)*

Providence Industries LLC ....D......562 420-9091
3833 Mcgowen St Long Beach (90808) *(P-3117)*

Providence Publications LLC ....E......916 774-4000
1620 Santa Clara Dr Roseville (95661) *(P-6560)*

Providenet Communications Corp ....E......408 398-6335
20 Great Oaks Blvd San Jose (95119) *(P-25085)*

Providien Injction Molding Inc ....D......760 931-1844
2731 Loker Ave W Carlsbad (92010) *(P-10316)*

Providien Thermoforming Inc (HQ) ....E......858 850-1591
6740 Nancy Ridge Dr San Diego (92121) *(P-9723)*

Provivi Inc ....E......310 828-2307
1701 Colorado Ave Santa Monica (90404) *(P-9033)*

Prowave Manufacturing, San Marcos Also called Action Electronic Assembly Inc *(P-18406)*

Prowest Technologies Inc ....E......760 510-9003
2872 S Santa Fe Ave San Marcos (92069) *(P-8935)*

Proxim Wireless Corporation (PA) ....D......408 383-7600
2114 Ringwood Ave San Jose (95131) *(P-18354)*

Proximex Corporation (HQ) ....F......408 215-9000
300 Santana Row Ste 200 San Jose (95128) *(P-25086)*

Prozyme Inc ....E......510 638-6900
3832 Bay Center Pl Hayward (94545) *(P-8505)*

Prp Seats, Temecula Also called Kamm Industries Inc *(P-20379)*

Prpco ....E......805 543-6844
2226 Beebee St San Luis Obispo (93401) *(P-7453)*

Prs Industries, Ontario Also called Inland Powder Coating Corp *(P-13603)*

Prudential Lighting Corp (PA) ....C......213 477-1694
1774 E 21st St Los Angeles (90058) *(P-17639)*

Pryor Products ....E......760 724-8244
1819 Peacock Blvd Oceanside (92056) *(P-22591)*

Prysm Inc (PA) ....D......408 586-1100
180 Baytech Dr Ste 200 San Jose (95134) *(P-24217)*

PS Intl Inc ....F......626 333-8168
655 Vineland Ave City of Industry (91746) *(P-13846)*

PS Print, LLC, Oakland Also called TYT LLC *(P-7151)*

PS Support Inc ....F......301 351-9366
800 W El Camin Real Mountain View (94040) *(P-25087)*

PSC, Visalia Also called Pacific Southwest Cont LLC *(P-5443)*

PSC Circuits Inc ....E......626 373-1728
5160 Rivergrade Rd Baldwin Park (91706) *(P-19692)*

PSC Industrial Outsourcing LP ....F......661 833-9991
200 Old Yard Dr Bakersfield (93307) *(P-263)*

Pscmb Repairs Inc ....E......626 448-7778
12145 Slauson Ave Santa Fe Springs (90670) *(P-12990)*

Psemi Corporation (HQ) ....D......858 731-9400
9369 Carroll Park Dr San Diego (92121) *(P-19090)*

Psg, San Diego Also called Pacific Steel Group *(P-12987)*

PSI, San Jose *Also called Proto Services Inc (P-18353)*

PSI, Irvine *Also called Performance Sealing Inc (P-9548)*

PSI, El Cajon *Also called Derosa Enterprises Inc (P-12559)*

PSI, Campbell *Also called Process Solutions Inc (P-21636)*

PSI, Plumas Lake *Also called Packaging Specialists Inc (P-4494)*

Psiber Data Systems Inc ....F....619 287-9970
7075 Mission Gorge Rd K San Diego (92120) ***(P-19091)***

Psitech Inc ....F....714 964-7818
18368 Bandilier Cir Fountain Valley (92708) ***(P-15474)***

PSM Industries Inc (PA) ....D....888 663-8256
14000 Avalon Blvd Los Angeles (90061) ***(P-13966)***

Pss Communications Inc ....F....408 496-3330
3066 Scott Blvd Santa Clara (95054) ***(P-17983)***

Pssc Labs ....F....949 380-7288
20432 N Sea Cir Lake Forest (92630) ***(P-15586)***

PSW Inc ....F....951 371-7100
149 Via Trevizio Corona (92879) ***(P-2644)***

Pt Welding Inc ....F....530 406-0267
1960 E Main St Woodland (95776) ***(P-25427)***

Ptb Sales Inc (PA) ....E....626 334-0500
1361 Mountain View Cir Azusa (91702) ***(P-15135)***

Ptec Solutions Inc ....D....510 358-3578
48633 Warm Springs Blvd Fremont (94539) ***(P-16864)***

Pti Technologies Inc (HQ) ....C....805 604-3700
501 Del Norte Blvd Oxnard (93030) ***(P-20917)***

Ptm & W Industries Inc ....E....562 946-4511
10640 Painter Ave Santa Fe Springs (90670) ***(P-9762)***

Ptm Images, West Hollywood *Also called Pro Tour Memorabilia LLC (P-4643)*

Ptr Manufacturing Inc ....E....510 477-9654
33390 Transit Ave Union City (94587) ***(P-16865)***

Ptr Sheet Metal & Fabrication, Union City *Also called Ptr Manufacturing Inc (P-16865)*

Pts Security, Van Nuys *Also called Priority Tech Systems Inc (P-20046)*

Pubinno Inc ....F....669 251-6538
1040 Mariposa St San Francisco (94107) ***(P-25088)***

Public Utilites Emts, San Diego *Also called City of San Diego (P-21934)*

Public Works Dept, San Bernardino *Also called County of San Bernardino (P-14161)*

Public Works, Dept of, La Puente *Also called County of Los Angeles (P-14159)*

Public Works, Dept of, Malibu *Also called County of Los Angeles (P-14160)*

Publishers Development Corp ....E....858 605-0200
12345 World Trade Dr San Diego (92128) ***(P-6238)***

Puente Ready Mix Inc (PA) ....E....626 968-0711
209 N California Ave City of Industry (91744) ***(P-11158)***

Pulitzer Community Newspapers, Hanford *Also called Hanford Sentinel Inc (P-5869)*

Pulitzer Inc ....E....805 735-1132
115 N H St Lompoc (93436) ***(P-6021)***

Pull String Inc ....E....415 758-3339
133 Kearny St 400 San Francisco (94108) ***(P-25089)***

Pull-N-Pac, Huntington Park *Also called Crown Poly Inc (P-5596)*

Pulltarps Manufacturing, El Cajon *Also called Transportation Equipment Inc (P-3816)*

Pulmonx Corporation (PA) ....E....650 364-0400
700 Chesapeake Dr Redwood City (94063) ***(P-22592)***

Pulp Story, Orange *Also called Quality Produced LLC (P-965)*

Pulsar Vascular Inc ....F....408 246-4300
130 Knowles Dr Ste E Los Gatos (95032) ***(P-22593)***

Pulse Electronics Inc (HQ) ....B....858 674-8100
15255 Innovation Dr # 100 San Diego (92128) ***(P-17116)***

Pulse Electronics Corporation (HQ) ....D....858 674-8100
15255 Innovation Dr # 100 San Diego (92128) ***(P-19693)***

Pulse Instruments ....E....310 515-5330
1234 Francisco St Torrance (90502) ***(P-21832)***

Pulse Metric Inc ....F....760 842-8224
2100 Hawley Dr Vista (92084) ***(P-22594)***

Pulse Systems LLC ....E....925 798-4080
4090 Nelson Ave Concord (94520) ***(P-22799)***

Pulver Laboratories Inc ....F....408 399-7000
320 N Santa Cruz Ave Los Gatos (95030) ***(P-17295)***

Puma Biotechnology Inc (PA) ....D....424 248-6500
10880 Wilshire Blvd # 2150 Los Angeles (90024) ***(P-8350)***

Pump-A-Head, San Diego *Also called Keco Inc (P-16167)*

Pumptop TV, Garden Grove *Also called Adtek Media Inc (P-23809)*

Punch Press Products Inc ....D....323 581-7151
2035 E 51st St Vernon (90058) ***(P-14564)***

Punkpost Inc ....E....415 818-7677
41 Federal St Unit 4 San Francisco (94107) ***(P-7566)***

Pur-Clean Pressure Car Wash, North Highlands *Also called New Wave Industries Ltd (P-16079)*

Pura Naturals Inc (HQ) ....F....949 273-8100
23101 Lake Center Dr # 100 Lake Forest (92630) ***(P-8827)***

Pura Naturals Inc ....E....949 273-8100
3401 Etiwanda Ave Mira Loma (91752) ***(P-4881)***

Puratos Corporation ....E....310 632-1361
18831 S Laurel Park Rd Compton (90220) ***(P-14879)***

Puratos West Coast, Compton *Also called Puratos Corporation (P-14879)*

Pure Allure Accessories, Oceanside *Also called Pure Allure Inc (P-3486)*

Pure Allure Inc ....D....760 966-3650
4005 Avenida De La Plata Oceanside (92056) ***(P-3486)***

Pure Bioscience Inc (PA) ....F....619 596-8600
1725 Gillespie Way El Cajon (92020) ***(P-8669)***

Pure Cotton Incorporated ....D....213 507-3270
2221 S Main St Fl 2 Los Angeles (90007) ***(P-3118)***

Pure Flo Water, Santee *Also called Pure-Flo Water Co (P-2180)*

Pure Forge ....F....760 201-0951
13011 Kirkham Way Poway (92064) ***(P-20430)***

Pure Nature Foods LLC ....E....530 723-5269
700 Santa Anita Dr Woodland (95776) ***(P-2399)***

Pure One Business Svc Group, Santa Ana *Also called Pure One Environmental Inc (P-9034)*

Pure One Environmental Inc ....F....714 641-1430
3400 W Warner Ave Ste A Santa Ana (92704) ***(P-9034)***

Pure Storage Inc (PA) ....B....800 379-7873
650 Castro St Ste 400 Mountain View (94041) ***(P-15587)***

Pure Water Centers Inc ....F....818 316-1250
8860 Corbin Ave Ste 382 Northridge (91324) ***(P-16093)***

Pure-Chem Products Company Inc ....F....714 995-4141
8371 Monroe Ave Stanton (90680) ***(P-8606)***

Pure-Flo Water Co (PA) ....D....619 596-4130
7737 Mission Gorge Rd Santee (92071) ***(P-2180)***

Puredepth Inc (PA) ....F....408 394-9146
303 Twin Dolphin Dr Fl 6 Redwood City (94065) ***(P-15831)***

Pureformance Cables, Torrance *Also called Lynn Products Inc (P-15795)*

Purelife Dental ....F....310 587-0783
201 Santa Monica Blvd # 400 Santa Monica (90401) ***(P-22903)***

Pureline Oralcare Inc ....F....831 662-9500
804 Estates Dr Ste 104 Aptos (95003) ***(P-22904)***

Puretek Corporation ....C....818 361-3949
7900 Nelson Rd Unit A Panorama City (91402) ***(P-8351)***

Puretek Corporation (PA) ....E....818 361-3316
7900 Nelson Rd Panorama City (91402) ***(P-8352)***

Purewave Networks Inc ....E....650 528-5200
3951 Burton Dr Santa Clara (95054) ***(P-18227)***

Purfect Packaging ....F....909 460-7363
5420 Brooks St Montclair (91763) ***(P-5616)***

Puri Tech Inc ....E....951 360-8380
3167 Progress Cir Mira Loma (91752) ***(P-16094)***

Puricle Inc ....E....909 466-7125
11799 Jersey Blvd Rancho Cucamonga (91730) ***(P-8670)***

Purina Animal Nutrition LLC ....E....209 634-9101
1125 Paulson Rd Turlock (95380) ***(P-1156)***

Puritan Bakery Inc ....C....310 830-5451
1624 E Carson St Carson (90745) ***(P-1312)***

Purity Organic LLC ....E....415 440-7777
405 14th St Ste 1000 Oakland (94612) ***(P-964)***

Purity Organics Inc ....E....559 842-5600
14900 W Belmont Ave Kerman (93630) ***(P-850)***

Purity Pool Inc ....F....530 472-3298
30411 Whitmore Rd Whitmore (96096) ***(P-16095)***

Puroflux Corporation ....F....805 579-0216
2121 Union Pl Simi Valley (93065) ***(P-19355)***

Purolator Pdts A Filtration Co ....F....510 785-4800
20671 Corsair Blvd Hayward (94545) ***(P-15171)***

Puronics Incorporated ....E....925 456-7000
5775 Las Positas Rd Livermore (94551) ***(P-16096)***

Purosil LLC ....F....951 271-3900
1660 Leeson Ln Corona (92879) ***(P-9035)***

Purosil LLC (HQ) ....D....951 271-3900
708 S Temescal St Ste 102 Corona (92879) ***(P-9036)***

Purotecs Inc ....F....925 215-0380
6678 Owens Dr Ste 104 Pleasanton (94588) ***(P-15013)***

Purple Platypus, Irvine *Also called Oddbox Holdings Inc (P-7417)*

Purple Wine Company LLC ....E....707 829-6100
9119 Graton Rd Graton (95444) ***(P-1932)***

Purveyors Kitchen ....E....530 823-8527
2043 Airpark Ct Ste 30 Auburn (95602) ***(P-851)***

Pushtotest Inc ....F....408 436-8203
1735 Tech Dr Ste 820 San Jose (95110) ***(P-25090)***

Puyallup Herald, Sacramento *Also called Olympic Cascade Publishing (P-6005)*

PVA Tepla America Inc (HQ) ....E....951 371-2500
251 Corporate Terrace St Corona (92879) ***(P-16866)***

Pvc Pipe Fttngs Irrgation Pdts, Galt *Also called Galt Pipe Company (P-13767)*

Pvd Coatings II LLC ....F....714 899-4892
5271 Argosy Ave Huntington Beach (92649) ***(P-13643)***

Pvh Neckwear Inc (HQ) ....A....213 688-7970
1735 S Santa Fe Ave Los Angeles (90021) ***(P-3067)***

Pvp Advanced Eo Systems Inc ....E....714 508-2740
14312 Franklin Ave # 100 Tustin (92780) ***(P-22125)***

Pw Brands LLC ....F....949 916-0600
32565 Golden Lantern St B Dana Point (92629) ***(P-11302)***

Pw Eagle Inc ....B....800 621-4404
5200 W Century Blvd Fl 10 Los Angeles (90045) ***(P-9786)***

Pw Eagle Inc ....B....951 657-7400
23711 Rider St Perris (92570) ***(P-9787)***

Pw Eagle Inc ....D....530 677-2286
3500 Robin Ln Shingle Springs (95682) ***(P-9788)***

PW Gillibrand Co Inc ....D....805 526-2195
4537 Ish Dr Simi Valley (93063) ***(P-398)***

Pw Wiring Systems, Pico Rivera *Also called P W Wiring Systems LLC (P-19407)*

Pwp, Vernon *Also called Pactiv Packaging Inc (P-7863)*

Pwp Manufacturing LLC ....E....408 748-0120
1325 Norman Ave Santa Clara (95054) ***(P-12726)***

Pyr Preservation Services ....E....619 338-8395
2393 Newton Ave Ste B San Diego (92113) ***(P-21011)***

Pyramid Alhuse At Wllnut Creek, Walnut Creek *Also called Pyramid Breweries Inc (P-1622)*

Pyramid Breweries Inc ....D....925 946-1520
1410 Locust St Walnut Creek (94596) ***(P-1622)***

Pyramid Granite & Metals Inc ....E....760 745-6309
660 Superior St Escondido (92029) ***(P-11273)***

Pyramid Graphics ....F....650 871-0290
325 Harbor Way South San Francisco (94080) ***(P-7056)***

Pyramid Mold & Tool ....E....909 476-2555
10155 Sharon Cir Rancho Cucamonga (91730) ***(P-14565)***

Pyramid Powder Coating Inc ....E....818 768-5898
12251 Montague St Pacoima (91331) ***(P-13644)***

Pyramid Precision Machine Inc ....D....858 642-0713
6721 Cobra Way San Diego (92121) ***(P-16867)***

Pyramid Printing and Graphics, South San Francisco *Also called Pyramid Graphics (P-7056)*

ALPHABETIC

Pyramid Semiconductor Corp....F....408 542-9430
1249 Reamwood Ave Sunnyvale (94089) ***(P-19092)***
Pyramid Systems Inc....E....559 582-9345
10105 8 3/4 Ave Hanford (93230) ***(P-5096)***
Pyramids Winery Inc....E....707 765-2768
5875 Lakeville Hwy Petaluma (94954) ***(P-1933)***
Pyrenees French Bakery Inc....E....661 322-7159
717 E 21st St Bakersfield (93305) ***(P-1313)***
Pyron Solar III LLC....F....760 599-5100
1216 Liberty Way Ste A Vista (92081) ***(P-12076)***
Q & B Foods Inc (HQ)....D....626 334-8090
15547 1st St Irwindale (91706) ***(P-929)***
Q C A, San Jose *Also called Quality Circuit Assembly Inc* ***(P-18573)***
Q C M Inc....E....714 414-1173
285 Gemini Ave Brea (92821) ***(P-17352)***
Q C Poultry, Commerce *Also called Ingenue Inc* ***(P-544)***
Q Corporation....E....805 383-8998
4880 Adohr Ln Camarillo (93012) ***(P-22008)***
Q I S Inc....F....951 244-0500
28005 Oregon Pl Quail Valley (92587) ***(P-18355)***
Q M C, Fountain Valley *Also called Quik Mfg Co* ***(P-14185)***
Q Microwave Inc....D....619 258-7322
1591 Pioneer Way El Cajon (92020) ***(P-19694)***
Q Perfumes, Commerce *Also called Milestones Products Inc* ***(P-8796)***
Q Team....F....714 228-4465
6400 Dale St Buena Park (90621) ***(P-7057)***
Q Tech Corporation....C....310 836-7900
10150 Jefferson Blvd Culver City (90232) ***(P-19695)***
Q Trade International Corp (PA)....E....949 766-0070
16205 Distribution Way Cerritos (90703) ***(P-2645)***
Q&A7 LLC....F....323 364-4250
2155 E 7th St Ste 150 Los Angeles (90023) ***(P-3487)***
Q-Flex Inc....E....714 664-0101
1301 E Hunter Ave Santa Ana (92705) ***(P-18568)***
Q-Lite Usa LLC....C....310 736-2977
3691 Lenawee Ave Los Angeles (90016) ***(P-17488)***
Q-Mark Manufacturing Inc....F....949 457-1913
30051 Comercio Rcho STA Marg (92688) ***(P-21638)***
Q-See, Anaheim *Also called Digital Periph Solutions Inc* ***(P-17789)***
Q-Vio LLC....F....858 777-8299
10211 Pacific Mesa Blvd San Diego (92121) ***(P-19696)***
Q1 Test Inc....F....909 390-9718
1100 S Grove Ave Ste B2 Ontario (91761) ***(P-20918)***
Q3-Cnc Inc....F....858 790-0002
9091 Kenamar Dr San Diego (92121) ***(P-16868)***
Qad Inc (PA)....C....805 566-6000
100 Innovation Pl Santa Barbara (93108) ***(P-25091)***
Qantel Technologies Inc....E....510 731-2080
3506 Breakwater Ct Hayward (94545) ***(P-15475)***
Qc Manufacturing Inc....D....951 325-6340
43352 Business Park Dr Temecula (92590) ***(P-15172)***
Qcept Technologies California, Fremont *Also called Qcept Technologies Inc* ***(P-19408)***
Qcept Technologies Inc....E....510 490-1120
47354 Fremont Blvd Fremont (94538) ***(P-19408)***
QED Inc....E....714 546-6010
2920 Halladay St Santa Ana (92705) ***(P-21639)***
QED Software LLC....E....310 214-3118
304 Tejon Pl Palos Verdes Estates (90274) ***(P-25092)***
QED Systems Inc....E....619 424-3225
1330 30th St Ste C San Diego (92154) ***(P-20050)***
Qep, Ontario *Also called QEP Co Inc* ***(P-4089)***
QEP Co Inc....F....909 622-3537
4200 Santa Ana St Ontario (91761) ***(P-4089)***
Qf Liquidation Inc....E....949 399-4500
25242 Arctic Ocean Dr Lake Forest (92630) ***(P-20431)***
Qf Liquidation Inc (PA)....C....949 930-3400
25242 Arctic Ocean Dr Lake Forest (92630) ***(P-20432)***
Qfi Prv Aerospace, Torrance *Also called Quality Forming LLC* ***(P-20919)***
Qg LLC....A....209 384-0444
2201 Cooper Ave Merced (95348) ***(P-7058)***
Qg Printing Corp....C....951 571-2500
6688 Box Springs Blvd Riverside (92507) ***(P-6239)***
Qg Printing II Corp....A....925 432-9740
1221 California Ave Pittsburg (94565) ***(P-7059)***
Qg Printing II Corp....A....951 571-2500
6688 Box Springs Blvd Riverside (92507) ***(P-7060)***
Qingmu International Inc....E....626 965-7277
1055 Park View Dr Ste 119 Covina (91724) ***(P-7454)***
Qjm Corp....F....213 622-0264
606 S Olive St Ste 2170 Los Angeles (90014) ***(P-23306)***
Qlogic LLC (HQ)....C....949 389-6000
15485 Sand Canyon Ave Irvine (92618) ***(P-19093)***
Qmat Inc....E....498 228-5858
2424 Walsh Ave Santa Clara (95051) ***(P-19094)***
Qmp Inc....E....661 294-6860
25070 Avenue Tibbitts Valencia (91355) ***(P-16097)***
Qontrol Devices Inc....F....626 968-4268
167 Mason Way Ste A7 City of Industry (91746) ***(P-15014)***
Qor LLC....F....707 658-2539
775 Baywood Dr Ste 312 Petaluma (94954) ***(P-3186)***
Qortstone Inc....F....877 899-7678
7733 Lemona Ave Van Nuys (91405) ***(P-11274)***
Qorvo California Inc....E....805 480-5050
950 Lawrence Dr Newbury Park (91320) ***(P-19697)***
Qorvo US, Newbury Park *Also called Qorvo California Inc* ***(P-19697)***
Qorvo Us Inc....E....805 480-5099
950 Lawrence Dr Newbury Park (91320) ***(P-19698)***
Qorvo Us Inc....E....408 493-4304
3099 Orchard Dr San Jose (95134) ***(P-19095)***
Qorvo Us Inc....B....408 577-6200
3099 Orchard Dr San Jose (95134) ***(P-19096)***
Qostronics Inc....E....408 719-1286
2044 Corporate Ct San Jose (95131) ***(P-18569)***
Qpc Fiber Optic LLC....E....949 361-8855
27612 El Lazo Laguna Niguel (92677) ***(P-11672)***
Qpc Laser, Sylmar *Also called Laser Operations LLC* ***(P-18954)***
Qpc Lasers Inc....F....818 986-0000
15632 Roxford St Sylmar (91342) ***(P-23036)***
Qpe Inc....F....949 263-0381
1372 Mcgaw Ave Irvine (92614) ***(P-7210)***
Qre Operating LLC....C....213 225-5900
707 Wilshire Blvd # 4600 Los Angeles (90017) ***(P-145)***
Qrtstone, Van Nuys *Also called Qortstone Inc* ***(P-11274)***
Qsc LLC (PA)....B....714 754-6175
1675 Macarthur Blvd Costa Mesa (92626) ***(P-17848)***
Qsi 2011 Inc (PA)....F....949 855-6885
2302 Martin Ste 475 Irvine (92612) ***(P-25093)***
Qspac Industries Inc (PA)....D....562 407-3868
15020 Marquardt Ave Santa Fe Springs (90670) ***(P-9165)***
Qst Ingredients and Packg Inc....F....909 989-4343
9734-40 6th St Rancho Cucamonga (91730) ***(P-2646)***
QTRADE TEAS & HERBS, Cerritos *Also called Q Trade International Corp* ***(P-2645)***
Quad Express Printing Inc....F....415 861-3433
3324 Investment Blvd Hayward (94545) ***(P-7061)***
Quad Graphics, Riverside *Also called Qg Printing II Corp* ***(P-7060)***
Quad R Tech, Harbor City *Also called Onyx Industries Inc* ***(P-13034)***
Quad R Tech....C....310 851-6161
521 W Rosecrans Ave Gardena (90248) ***(P-23307)***
Quad/Graphics Inc....F....310 751-3900
17871 Park Plaza Dr # 150 Cerritos (90703) ***(P-7062)***
Quad/Graphics Inc....C....951 689-1122
7190 Jurupa Ave Riverside (92504) ***(P-7063)***
Quad/Graphics Inc....A....415 267-3700
350 Rhode Island St # 110 San Francisco (94103) ***(P-7064)***
Quad/Graphics Inc....A....415 398-0624
100 North Pt Ste 105 San Francisco (94133) ***(P-7065)***
Quad/Graphics Inc....B....209 384-0444
2201 Cooper Ave Merced (95348) ***(P-7066)***
Quadbase Systems Inc....F....408 982-0835
990 Linden Dr Ste 230 Santa Clara (95050) ***(P-25094)***
Quadco Printing Inc....F....530 894-4061
2535 Zanella Way Chico (95928) ***(P-7067)***
Quadrant Solutions Inc....F....408 463-9451
561 Monterey Rd Morgan Hill (95037) ***(P-13967)***
Quadrant Technology, Morgan Hill *Also called Quadrant Solutions Inc* ***(P-13967)***
Quadriga Americas LLC....E....424 634-4900
17800 S Main St Ste 113 Gardena (90248) ***(P-6561)***
Quadriga USA Enterprises Inc....F....888 669-9994
28410 Witherspoon Pkwy Valencia (91355) ***(P-7455)***
Quadrtech Corporation....C....310 523-1697
521 W Rosecrans Ave Gardena (90248) ***(P-11908)***
Quady LLC (PA)....E....559 673-8068
13181 Road 24 Madera (93637) ***(P-1934)***
Quady Winery Inc....F....559 673-8068
13181 Road 24 Madera (93637) ***(P-1935)***
Quake Global Inc (PA)....D....858 277-7290
4711 Vewridge Ave Ste 150 San Diego (92123) ***(P-17984)***
Quaker, Whittier *Also called AC Products Inc* ***(P-9126)***
Quaker City Plating....C....562 945-3721
11729 Washington Blvd Whittier (90606) ***(P-13485)***
Quaker City Plating & Silvrsm, Whittier *Also called Quaker City Plating* ***(P-13485)***
Quaker Oats Company....C....510 261-5800
5625 International Blvd Oakland (94621) ***(P-2278)***
Qual-Pro Corporation (HQ)....C....310 329-7535
18510 S Figueroa St Gardena (90248) ***(P-18570)***
Qual-Tronix, Saratoga *Also called Electrofab Inc* ***(P-19529)***
Qualcomm Atheros Inc (HQ)....A....408 773-5200
1700 Technology Dr San Jose (95110) ***(P-19097)***
Qualcomm Datacenter Tech Inc (HQ)....D....858 567-1121
5775 Morehouse Dr San Diego (92121) ***(P-19098)***
Qualcomm Incorporated....C....408 216-2500
3165 Kifer Rd Santa Clara (95051) ***(P-18228)***
Qualcomm Incorporated....B....858 651-8481
2016 Palomar Airport Rd # 100 Carlsbad (92011) ***(P-19099)***
Qualcomm Incorporated....B....408 216-6797
3135 Kifer Rd Santa Clara (95051) ***(P-19100)***
Qualcomm Incorporated (PA)....B....858 587-1121
5775 Morehouse Dr San Diego (92121) ***(P-18229)***
Qualcomm Incorporated....F....858 587-1121
3165 Kifer Rd Santa Clara (95051) ***(P-19101)***
Qualcomm Incorporated....B....858 909-0316
5751 Pacific Center Blvd San Diego (92121) ***(P-19102)***
Qualcomm Incorporated....B....858 587-1121
9393 Waples St Ste 150 San Diego (92121) ***(P-19103)***
Qualcomm Incorporated....D....858 587-1121
5525 Morehouse Dr San Diego (92121) ***(P-18230)***
Qualcomm Incorporated....B....858 587-1121
10160 Pacific Mesa Blvd # 100 San Diego (92121) ***(P-19104)***
Qualcomm Innovation Center Inc (HQ)....E....858 587-1121
4365 Executive Dr # 1100 San Diego (92121) ***(P-25095)***
Qualcomm Limited Partner Inc....E....858 587-1121
5775 Morehouse Dr San Diego (92121) ***(P-19105)***
Qualcomm Mems Technologies Inc....E....858 587-1121
5775 Morehouse Dr San Diego (92121) ***(P-18356)***
Qualcomm Technologies Inc (HQ)....C....858 587-1121
5525 Morehouse Dr San Diego (92121) ***(P-19106)***
Qualectron Systems Corporation....F....408 986-1686
321 E Brokaw Rd San Jose (95112) ***(P-21833)***

Quali-Tech Manufacturing, Calexico *Also called Lakim Industries Incorporated* ***(P-23794)***
Quali-Tech Mold ......F......909 464-8124
5939 Sycamore Ct Chino (91710) ***(P-10317)***
Qualigen Inc (PA) ......E......760 918-9165
2042 Corte Del Nogal A Carlsbad (92011) ***(P-21487)***
Qualitask Incorporated ......F......714 237-0900
2840 E Gretta Ln Anaheim (92806) ***(P-16869)***
Qualitau Incorporated (PA) ......D......650 282-6226
830 Maude Ave Mountain View (94043) ***(P-21834)***
Qualitek Inc (HQ) ......D......408 734-8686
1116 Elko Dr Sunnyvale (94089) ***(P-18571)***
Qualitek Inc ......D......408 752-8422
1272 Forgewood Ave Sunnyvale (94089) ***(P-18572)***
Quality Aerostructures Company ......F......909 987-4888
10291 Trademark St Ste A Rancho Cucamonga (91730) ***(P-20675)***
Quality Aluminum Forge LLC (HQ) ......D......714 639-8191
794 N Cypress St Orange (92867) ***(P-13128)***
Quality Aluminum Forge LLC ......F......714 633-1195
793 N Cypress St Orange (92867) ***(P-11601)***
Quality Cabinet and Fixture Co (HQ) ......E......619 266-1011
7955 Saint Andrews Ave San Diego (92154) ***(P-4337)***
Quality Car Care Products Inc ......E......626 359-9174
2734 Huntington Dr Duarte (91010) ***(P-7800)***
Quality Circle Institute Inc ......F......530 893-4095
555 East Ave Chico (95926) ***(P-6240)***
Quality Circuit Assembly Inc ......D......408 441-1001
1709 Junction Ct Ste 380 San Jose (95112) ***(P-18573)***
Quality Coating, North Hollywood *Also called Quality Powder Coating LLC* ***(P-13646)***
Quality Components Co, Rcho STA Marg *Also called Q-Mark Manufacturing Inc* ***(P-21638)***
Quality Container Corp ......F......909 482-1850
866 Towne Center Dr Pomona (91767) ***(P-5536)***
Quality Control Plating Inc ......E......909 605-0206
4425 E Airport Dr Ste 113 Ontario (91761) ***(P-13486)***
Quality Control Solutions Inc ......E......951 676-1616
43339 Bus Pk Dr Ste 101 Temecula (92590) ***(P-22253)***
Quality Controlled Mfg Inc ......D......619 443-3997
9429 Abraham Way Santee (92071) ***(P-16870)***
Quality Countertops Inc ......F......909 597-6888
17853 Santiago Blvd # 107 Villa Park (92861) ***(P-5097)***
Quality Craft Cabinets Inc ......F......626 358-2021
504 E Duarte Rd Monrovia (91016) ***(P-4338)***
Quality Craft Mold Inc ......F......530 873-7790
6424 Woodward Dr Magalia (95954) ***(P-11412)***
Quality Digest, Chico *Also called Quality Circle Institute Inc* ***(P-6240)***
Quality Door & Trim, Stockton *Also called J & J Quality Door Inc* ***(P-4169)***
Quality Doors & Trim, Lakeport *Also called Young & Family Inc* ***(P-4263)***
Quality Edm Inc ......F......714 283-9220
8025 E Crystal Dr Anaheim (92807) ***(P-16871)***
Quality Fabrication ......D......818 407-5015
9631 Irondale Ave Chatsworth (91311) ***(P-12727)***
Quality First Woodworks Inc ......C......714 632-0480
1264 N Lakeview Ave Anaheim (92807) ***(P-4644)***
QUALITY FOAM PACKAGING, Lake Elsinore *Also called Aerofoam Industries Inc* ***(P-5005)***
Quality Foam Packaging Inc ......E......951 245-4429
31855 Corydon St Lake Elsinore (92530) ***(P-9878)***
Quality Forming LLC ......D......310 539-2855
22906 Frampton Ave Torrance (90501) ***(P-20919)***
Quality Gears Inc ......F......562 921-9938
12139 Slauson Ave Santa Fe Springs (90670) ***(P-15244)***
Quality Grinding Company Inc ......F......714 228-2100
6800 Caballero Blvd Buena Park (90620) ***(P-14670)***
Quality Heat Treating Inc ......E......818 840-8212
3305 Burton Ave Burbank (91504) ***(P-11828)***
Quality Image Inc ......E......562 259-9872
15130 Illinois Ave Paramount (90723) ***(P-7877)***
Quality Industry Repair, Santa Fe Springs *Also called Pscmb Repairs Inc* ***(P-12990)***
Quality Lift and Equipment Inc ......F......562 903-2131
10845 Norwalk Blvd Santa Fe Springs (90670) ***(P-14344)***
Quality Machine Engrg Inc ......E......707 528-1900
2559 Grosse Ave Santa Rosa (95404) ***(P-16872)***
Quality Machine Shop Inc ......F......805 653-7944
1676 N Ventura Ave Ventura (93001) ***(P-16873)***
Quality Machining, Ramona *Also called Blaha Oldrih* ***(P-14609)***
Quality Machining & Design Inc ......E......408 224-7976
2857 Aiello Dr San Jose (95111) ***(P-15015)***
Quality Magnetics Corporation ......F......310 632-1941
18025 Adria Maru Ln Carson (90746) ***(P-13968)***
Quality Marble & Granite, Ontario *Also called Regards Enterprises Inc* ***(P-4601)***
Quality Metal Fabrication LLC ......E......530 887-7388
2350 Wilbur Way Auburn (95602) ***(P-12728)***
Quality Metal Spinning and ......E......650 858-2491
4047 Transport St Palo Alto (94303) ***(P-13268)***
Quality Packaging and Engrg, Irvine *Also called Qpe Inc* ***(P-7210)***
Quality Painting Co ......E......626 964-2529
19136 San Jose Ave Rowland Heights (91748) ***(P-13645)***
Quality Plating, San Jose *Also called Sal Rodriguez* ***(P-13496)***
Quality Powder Coating LLC ......F......818 982-8322
7373 Atoll Ave Ste B North Hollywood (91605) ***(P-13646)***
Quality Produced LLC ......F......310 592-8834
987 N Enterprise St Orange (92867) ***(P-965)***
Quality Quartz Engineering Inc (PA) ......E......510 791-1013
8484 Central Ave Newark (94560) ***(P-19699)***
Quality Service Pac Industry, Santa Fe Springs *Also called Qspac Industries Inc* ***(P-9165)***
Quality Sheds Inc ......F......951 672-6750
33210 Bailey Park Blvd Menifee (92584) ***(P-4732)***
Quality Steel Fabricators Inc ......E......858 748-8400
13275 Gregg St Poway (92064) ***(P-12991)***
Quality Systems Intgrated Corp (PA) ......B......858 587-9797
6720 Cobra Way San Diego (92121) ***(P-18574)***
Quality Tech Machining, Santa Clara *Also called Hung Tung* ***(P-16575)***
Quality Tech Mfg Inc ......E......909 465-9565
170 W Mindanao St Bloomington (92316) ***(P-20619)***
Quality Transformer & Elec ......E......408 935-0231
963 Ames Ave Milpitas (95035) ***(P-17117)***
Quality Transformer & Elec Co, Milpitas *Also called Quality Transformer & Elec* ***(P-17117)***
Quality Vessel Engineering Inc ......F......562 696-2100
8515 Chetle Ave Santa Fe Springs (90670) ***(P-12412)***
Quality Woodworks Inc ......E......760 744-4748
261a Redel Rd San Marcos (92078) ***(P-4339)***
Quallion LLC ......C......818 833-2000
12744 San Fernando Rd # 100 Sylmar (91342) ***(P-19823)***
Qualontime Corporation ......F......714 523-4751
19 Senisa Irvine (92612) ***(P-16874)***
Qualstar Corporation (PA) ......E......805 583-7744
130 W Cochran St Ste C Simi Valley (93065) ***(P-15588)***
Qualtech Circuits Inc ......F......408 727-4125
1101 Comstock St Santa Clara (95054) ***(P-18575)***
Quaneco, Woodland Hills *Also called Quantum Energy LLC* ***(P-146)***
Quanergy Systems Inc (PA) ......D......408 245-9500
482 Mercury Dr Sunnyvale (94085) ***(P-21383)***
Quantal International Inc ......E......415 644-0754
455 Market St Ste 1200 San Francisco (94105) ***(P-25096)***
Quantam Signs & Graphics, Lake Forest *Also called To Industries Inc* ***(P-23991)***
Quantech Machining Inc ......E......661 775-3990
25647 Rye Canyon Rd Valencia (91355) ***(P-16875)***
Quantenna Communications Inc (PA) ......E......669 209-5500
1704 Automation Pkwy San Jose (95131) ***(P-19107)***
Quantimetrix Corporation ......D......310 536-0006
2005 Manhattan Beach Blvd Redondo Beach (90278) ***(P-8506)***
Quantum 3d Headquarters ......F......408 361-9999
6330 San Ignacio Ave San Jose (95119) ***(P-19108)***
Quantum Chromodynamics Inc ......F......310 329-5000
3703 W 190th St Torrance (90504) ***(P-7456)***
Quantum Clean, San Jose *Also called Quantum Global Tech LLC* ***(P-8671)***
Quantum Corporation, Irvine *Also called Certance LLC* ***(P-15521)***
Quantum Corporation ......C......213 248-2481
1441 Melanie Ln Arcadia (91007) ***(P-15589)***
Quantum Corporation ......D......949 856-7800
141 Innovation Dr Ste 100 Irvine (92617) ***(P-15590)***
Quantum Design Inc (PA) ......C......858 481-4400
10307 Pacific Center Ct San Diego (92121) ***(P-22009)***
Quantum Design International, San Diego *Also called Quantum Design Inc* ***(P-22009)***
Quantum Digital Technology Inc ......F......310 325-4949
1525 W Alton Ave Santa Ana (92704) ***(P-19700)***
Quantum Dynasty ......F......347 469-1047
5934 Rancho Mission Rd # 118 San Diego (92108) ***(P-15591)***
Quantum Energy LLC ......E......800 950-3519
22801 Ventura Blvd # 200 Woodland Hills (91364) ***(P-146)***
Quantum Focus Instruments Corp ......F......760 599-1122
2385 La Mirada Dr Vista (92081) ***(P-21835)***
Quantum Global Tech LLC ......E......408 487-1770
1710 Ringwood Ave San Jose (95131) ***(P-8671)***
Quantum Global Tech LLC ......E......510 687-8000
44010 Fremont Blvd Fremont (94538) ***(P-8672)***
Quantum Group Inc ......D......858 566-9959
6827 Nancy Ridge Dr San Diego (92121) ***(P-22254)***
Quantum Performance Developmen ......F......510 870-6381
32537 Jean Dr Union City (94587) ***(P-15592)***
Quantum Solar Inc ......F......415 924-8140
6 Endeavor Dr Corte Madera (94925) ***(P-19109)***
Quantum Technologies, Lake Forest *Also called Qf Liquidation Inc* ***(P-20432)***
Quantum Technologies Inc ......C......949 399-4500
25242 Arctic Ocean Dr Lake Forest (92630) ***(P-70)***
Quantum-Dynamics Co Inc ......F......818 719-0142
6414 Independence Ave Woodland Hills (91367) ***(P-21640)***
Quantum3d Inc (PA) ......F......408 600-2500
1759 Mccarthy Blvd Milpitas (95035) ***(P-21384)***
Quantumclean, Fremont *Also called Quantum Global Tech LLC* ***(P-8672)***
Quantumscape Corporation ......C......408 452-2000
1730 Technology Dr San Jose (95110) ***(P-19110)***
Quark Pharmaceuticals Inc (HQ) ......E......510 402-4020
7999 Gateway Blvd Ste 310 Newark (94560) ***(P-8353)***
Quartet Mechanics Inc ......F......510 490-1886
4055 Clipper Ct Fremont (94538) ***(P-14764)***
Quartic West Technologies ......F......909 202-7038
425 W 235th St Carson (90745) ***(P-19878)***
Quarton USA Inc ......F......888 532-2221
3230 Fallow Field Dr Diamond Bar (91765) ***(P-20051)***
Quashnick Tool Corporation ......E......209 334-5283
225 N Guild Ave Lodi (95240) ***(P-10318)***
Quatro Composites LLC ......E......712 707-9200
13250 Gregg St Ste A1 Poway (92064) ***(P-17241)***
Queen Beach Printers Inc ......E......562 436-8201
937 Pine Ave Long Beach (90813) ***(P-7068)***
Queens Bakery Inc (PA) ......F......323 222-6447
2311 Pasadena Ave Los Angeles (90031) ***(P-1314)***
Queenship Publishing Company ......F......805 692-0043
5951 Encina Rd Ste 100 Goleta (93117) ***(P-6385)***
Quellan Inc ......E......408 546-3487
1001 Murphy Ranch Rd Milpitas (95035) ***(P-19111)***
Quemetco Inc ......C......626 937-3239
720 S 7th Ave City of Industry (91746) ***(P-11565)***
Quemetco West LLC ......E......626 330-2294
720 S 7th Ave City of Industry (91746) ***(P-11566)***
Quenta Material, Santa Clara *Also called Qmat Inc* ***(P-19094)***
Quest Diagnostics Nichols Inst (HQ) ......A......949 728-4000
33608 Ortega Hwy San Juan Capistrano (92675) ***(P-22010)***
Quest Inds - Stockton Plant, Stockton *Also called Quest Industries LLC* ***(P-7457)***

ALPHABETIC

Employee Codes: A=Over 500 employees, B=251-500
C=101-250, D=51-100, E=20-50, F=10-19
2019 California
Manfacturers Register
© Mergent Inc. 1-800-342-5647
1257

Quest Industries LLC.....F.....209 234-0202
2518 Boeing Way Stockton (95206) ***(P-7457)***
Quest Nutrition LLC (PA).....E.....888 212-0601
777 S Aviation Blvd El Segundo (90245) ***(P-2647)***
Quest Nutrition LLC.....E.....562 446-3321
2221 Park Pl El Segundo (90245) ***(P-2648)***
Quest Software Inc.....D.....415 373-2222
118 2nd St Fl 6 San Francisco (94105) ***(P-25097)***
Quest Software Inc.....F.....408 899-3823
5450 Great America Pkwy Santa Clara (95054) ***(P-25098)***
Quest Software Inc.....D.....949 754-8000
4 Polaris Way Aliso Viejo (92656) ***(P-25099)***
Questivity Inc.....F.....408 615-1781
1680 Civic Center Dr # 209 Santa Clara (95050) ***(P-25100)***
Questys Solutions, Irvine *Also called Qsi 2011 Inc* ***(P-25093)***
Quick Deck Inc.....F.....925 516-0603
15390 Byron Hwy Byron (94514) ***(P-12958)***
Quick Mount Pv, Walnut Creek *Also called Wencon Development Inc* ***(P-12815)***
Quick Silver Prtg & Graphics, Chatsworth *Also called Paul Silver Enterprises Inc* ***(P-7019)***
Quickie Designs, Fresno *Also called Vcp Mobility Holdings Inc* ***(P-22840)***
Quicklogic Corporation.....D.....408 990-4000
1277 Orleans Dr Sunnyvale (94089) ***(P-21641)***
Quickrete, Corona *Also called Quikrete California LLC* ***(P-10984)***
Quicksilver Aeronautics LLC.....F.....951 506-0061
40084 Villa Venecia Temecula (92591) ***(P-20620)***
Quidel Corporation (PA).....B.....858 552-1100
12544 High Bluff Dr # 200 San Diego (92130) ***(P-8507)***
Quidel Corporation.....F.....858 552-1100
10165 Mckellar Ct San Diego (92121) ***(P-8508)***
Quiel Bros Elc Sign Svc Co Inc.....E.....909 885-4476
272 S I St San Bernardino (92410) ***(P-23947)***
Quiet Ride Solutions LLC.....F.....209 942-4777
1122 S Wilson Way Ste 1 Stockton (95205) ***(P-10319)***
Quik Mfg Co.....E.....714 754-0337
18071 Mount Washington St Fountain Valley (92708) ***(P-14185)***
Quik-Pak, San Diego *Also called Promex Industries Incorporated* ***(P-19087)***
Quikrete California LLC.....C.....951 277-3155
3940 Temescal Canyon Rd Corona (92883) ***(P-10984)***
Quikrete Companies Inc.....F.....559 781-1949
14200 Road 284 Porterville (93257) ***(P-10985)***
Quikrete Companies LLC.....E.....510 490-4670
7705 Wilbur Way Sacramento (95828) ***(P-10986)***
Quikrete Companies LLC.....E.....858 549-2371
9265 Camino Santa Fe San Diego (92121) ***(P-10987)***
Quikrete Companies LLC.....D.....510 490-4670
6950 Stevenson Blvd Fremont (94538) ***(P-10988)***
Quikrete Companies LLC.....D.....323 875-1367
11145 Tuxford St Sun Valley (91352) ***(P-10989)***
Quikrete Companies LLC.....E.....916 689-8840
7705 Wilbur Way Sacramento (95828) ***(P-10990)***
Quikrete Northern California, Porterville *Also called Quikrete Companies Inc* ***(P-10985)***
Quikrete of Atlanta, Fremont *Also called Quikrete Companies LLC* ***(P-10988)***
Quikstor, Van Nuys *Also called Cal Star Systems Group Inc* ***(P-19923)***
Quikturn Prof Scrnprinting Inc.....F.....800 784-5419
567 S Melrose St Placentia (92870) ***(P-7458)***
Quilter Laboratories LLC.....F.....714 519-6114
1700 Sunflower Ave Costa Mesa (92626) ***(P-23382)***
Quilting House.....E.....949 476-7090
16872 Millikan Ave Irvine (92606) ***(P-3744)***
Quinn Development Co.....F.....408 842-9320
5787 Obata Way Gilroy (95020) ***(P-10858)***
Quinn Medical Inc.....F.....949 784-0310
1000 Calle Cordillera San Clemente (92673) ***(P-22800)***
Quint Graphics, Walnut Creek *Also called Quint Measuring Systems Inc* ***(P-22255)***
Quint Measuring Systems Inc.....F.....510 351-9405
2922 Saklan Indian Dr Walnut Creek (94595) ***(P-22255)***
Quintel Corporation.....E.....408 776-5190
685 Jarvis Dr Ste A Morgan Hill (95037) ***(P-14826)***
Quintessa Vinyards, NAPA *Also called Huneeus Vintners LLC* ***(P-1815)***
Quintron Systems Inc (PA).....D.....805 928-4343
2105 S Blosser Rd Santa Maria (93458) ***(P-17985)***
Quivera Hospitality, Palm Springs *Also called Quivera Marketing Inc* ***(P-3014)***
Quivera Marketing Inc.....F.....213 746-8200
611 S Palm Canyon Dr Palm Springs (92264) ***(P-3014)***
Quivira Vineyards, Healdsburg *Also called Pjk Winery LLC* ***(P-1926)***
Qulsar Inc (PA).....F.....408 715-1098
1798 Tech Dr Ste 139 San Jose (95110) ***(P-17296)***
Qulsar Usa Inc.....F.....408 715-1098
1798 Tech Dr Ste 292 San Jose (95110) ***(P-18231)***
Qumu Inc.....D.....650 396-8530
1100 Grundy Ln Ste 110 San Bruno (94066) ***(P-25101)***
Quorex Pharm Inc (PA).....E.....760 602-1910
2232 Rutherford Rd Carlsbad (92008) ***(P-8354)***
Quorum Systems Inc.....F.....858 546-0895
5960 Cornerstone Ct W # 200 San Diego (92121) ***(P-19112)***
Qve Inc.....E.....626 961-0114
7829 Industry Ave Pico Rivera (90660) ***(P-13731)***
Qwilt Inc (PA).....F.....866 824-8009
275 Shoreline Dr Ste 510 Redwood City (94065) ***(P-25102)***
Qxq Inc.....E.....510 252-1522
44113 S Grimmer Blvd Fremont (94538) ***(P-21836)***
Qycell Corporation.....E.....909 390-6644
600 Etiwanda Ave Ontario (91761) ***(P-9879)***
Qyk Brands LLC.....E.....949 312-7119
9 Macarthur Pl Santa Ana (92707) ***(P-17402)***
Qyksonic, Santa Ana *Also called Qyk Brands LLC* ***(P-17402)***
R & B Logging, Montague *Also called Dave Richardson Trucking* ***(P-3985)***
R & B Plastics Inc.....F.....714 229-8419
227 E Meats Ave Orange (92865) ***(P-16876)***
R & B Research & Development, Loomis *Also called Hillerich & Bradsby Co* ***(P-23584)***
R & B Wire Products Inc.....E.....714 549-3355
2902 W Garry Ave Santa Ana (92704) ***(P-13847)***
R & D Fasteners, Rancho Cucamonga *Also called Doubleco Incorporated* ***(P-13066)***
R & D Mfg Services, San Jose *Also called R Stephenson & D Cram Mfg Inc* ***(P-16881)***
R & D Nova Inc.....F.....951 781-7332
833 Marlborough Ave 200 Riverside (92507) ***(P-23037)***
R & D Racing Products USA Inc.....F.....562 906-1190
12983 Los Nietos Rd Santa Fe Springs (90670) ***(P-21062)***
R & D Tech, Milpitas *Also called Hytek R&D Inc* ***(P-18502)***
R & I Industries Inc.....E.....909 923-7747
2910 S Archibald Ave A Ontario (91761) ***(P-12234)***
R & J Fabricators Inc.....E.....951 817-0300
1121 Railroad St Ste 102 Corona (92882) ***(P-5250)***
R & J Leathercraft.....F.....951 688-1685
12155 Magnolia Ave Ste 8d Riverside (92503) ***(P-10578)***
R & J Paper Box, La Habra *Also called R & J Rule & Die Inc* ***(P-5656)***
R & J Rule & Die Inc.....F.....562 945-7535
701 Sturbridge Dr La Habra (90631) ***(P-5656)***
R & J Wldg Met Fabrication Inc.....F.....909 930-2900
2182 Maple Privado Ontario (91761) ***(P-17158)***
R & K Industrial Products Co.....E.....510 234-7212
1945 7th St Richmond (94801) ***(P-13969)***
R & L Enterprises Inc.....E.....559 233-1608
1955 S Mary St Fresno (93721) ***(P-16877)***
R & M Coils.....F.....951 672-9855
27547 Terrytown Rd Sun City (92586) ***(P-19356)***
R & M Energy System, Bakersfield *Also called National Oilwell Varco LP* ***(P-248)***
R & R Ductwork LLC.....F.....562 944-9660
12820 Lakeland Rd Santa Fe Springs (90670) ***(P-12729)***
R & R Industries, San Clemente *Also called Rosen & Rosen Industries Inc* ***(P-23640)***
R & R Industries Inc.....E.....323 581-6000
1923 S Santa Fe Ave Los Angeles (90021) ***(P-3858)***
R & R Industries Inc.....E.....949 361-9238
204 Avenida Fabricante San Clemente (92672) ***(P-3676)***
R & R Machine Products Inc.....F.....909 885-7500
760 W Mill St San Bernardino (92410) ***(P-13040)***
R & R Maintenance Group.....F.....707 863-0328
1255 Treat Blvd Ste 300 Walnut Creek (94597) ***(P-14131)***
R & R Metal Fabricators.....F.....626 960-6400
14846 Ramona Blvd Baldwin Park (91706) ***(P-13970)***
R & R Pumping Unit Repr & Svc, Ventura *Also called Richard Yarbrough* ***(P-265)***
R & R Rubber Molding Inc.....E.....626 575-8105
2444 Loma Ave South El Monte (91733) ***(P-9572)***
R & R Services Corporation.....E.....818 889-2562
31119 Via Colinas Ste 502 Westlake Village (91362) ***(P-9666)***
R & R Stamping Four Slide Corp.....D.....909 595-6444
2440 Railroad St Corona (92880) ***(P-13269)***
R & S Automation Inc.....F.....800 962-3111
283 W Bonita Ave Pomona (91767) ***(P-12339)***
R & S Erection Incorporated (PA).....F.....510 483-3710
2057 W Avenue 140th San Leandro (94577) ***(P-12340)***
R & S Manufacturing Inc (HQ).....E.....510 429-1788
33955 7th St Union City (94587) ***(P-12341)***
R & S Manufacturing & Sup Inc.....F.....909 622-5881
16616 Garfield Ave Paramount (90723) ***(P-8936)***
R & S Mfg, Pomona *Also called R & S Mfg Southern Cal Inc* ***(P-12342)***
R & S Mfg Southern Cal Inc.....F.....909 596-2090
283 W Bonita Ave Pomona (91767) ***(P-12342)***
R & S Overhead Door of So Cal.....E.....714 680-0600
1617 N Orangethorpe Way Anaheim (92801) ***(P-12343)***
R & S Processing Co Inc.....D.....562 531-0738
15712 Illinois Ave Paramount (90723) ***(P-9667)***
R & S Rolling Door Products, Union City *Also called R & S Manufacturing Inc* ***(P-12341)***
R & V Sheet Metal Inc.....F.....951 361-9455
3197 Grapevine St Mira Loma (91752) ***(P-12730)***
R A Industries Llc.....E.....714 557-2322
3207 W Pendleton Ave Santa Ana (92704) ***(P-16878)***
R A Jenson Manufacturing Co.....F.....415 822-2732
1337 Van Dyke Ave San Francisco (94124) ***(P-4340)***
R A Phillips Industries Inc.....B.....562 781-2100
12070 Burke St Santa Fe Springs (90670) ***(P-20510)***
R A Reed Electric Company (PA).....E.....323 587-2284
5503 S Boyle Ave Vernon (90058) ***(P-25465)***
R B I, Burbank *Also called Bargueiras Rene Inc* ***(P-23243)***
R B III Associates Inc.....C.....760 471-5370
166 Newport Dr San Marcos (92069) ***(P-3360)***
R B R Meat Company Inc.....D.....323 973-4868
5151 Alcoa Ave Vernon (90058) ***(P-447)***
R B S Inc.....F.....949 766-2924
31941 La Subida Dr Trabuco Canyon (92679) ***(P-15832)***
R B T Inc.....F.....619 781-8802
2240 Encinitas Blvd Encinitas (92024) ***(P-3914)***
R B Welding Inc.....F.....310 324-8680
155 E Redondo Beach Blvd Gardena (90248) ***(P-25428)***
R C I, Auburn *Also called Ron & Diana Vanatta* ***(P-5098)***
R C I P Inc.....F.....714 630-1239
1476 N Hundley St Anaheim (92806) ***(P-16879)***
R C Industries, Anaheim *Also called R C I P Inc* ***(P-16879)***
R C Products Corp.....D.....949 858-8820
22322 Gilberto Rcho STA Marg (92688) ***(P-11985)***
R C S, Rancho Cordova *Also called Residential Ctrl Systems Inc* ***(P-21525)***
R C Westburg Engineering Inc.....F.....949 859-4648
23302 Vista Grande Dr Laguna Hills (92653) ***(P-10320)***
R D Mathis Company.....E.....562 426-7049
2840 Gundry Ave Signal Hill (90755) ***(P-11430)***

Mergent e-mail: customerrelations@mergent.com
1258
2019 California
Manufacturers Register
(P-0000) Products & Services Section entry number
(PA)=Parent Co (HQ)=Headquarters (DH)=Div Headquarters

R D Rubber Technology Corp E 562 941-4800
12870 Florence Ave Santa Fe Springs (90670) ***(P-9573)***

R E Atckison Co Inc F 626 334-0266
1801 W Gladstone St Azusa (91702) ***(P-14186)***

R E Dillard 1 LLC D 415 675-1500
300 California St Fl 7 San Francisco (94104) ***(P-12077)***

R E Michel, Long Beach *Also called R E Michel Company LLC* ***(P-15974)***

R E Michel Company LLC E 310 885-9820
155 W Victoria St Long Beach (90805) ***(P-15974)***

R F Circuits and Assembly Inc F 805 499-7788
3533 Old Conejo Rd # 107 Newbury Park (91320) ***(P-18576)***

R F P & Welding F 805 526-3425
310 E Easy St Ste E Simi Valley (93065) ***(P-20433)***

R G B Display Corporation F 530 268-2222
22525 Kingston Ln Grass Valley (95949) ***(P-15644)***

R G Hansen Associates (PA) F 805 564-3388
5951 Encina Rd Ste 106 Goleta (93117) ***(P-21642)***

R Goodloe & Associates Inc F 714 380-3900
25602 Alicia Pkwy Laguna Hills (92653) ***(P-7069)***

R H Barden Inc F 714 970-0900
4769 E Wesley Dr Anaheim (92807) ***(P-19357)***

R H Pattern E 909 484-9141
10700 Jersey Blvd Ste 590 Rancho Cucamonga (91730) ***(P-14466)***

R I M, Santa Clara *Also called Rimnetics Inc* ***(P-10335)***

R J McGlennon Company Inc (PA) E 415 552-0311
198 Utah St San Francisco (94103) ***(P-8937)***

R J R Technologies Inc (PA) C 510 638-5901
7875 Edgewater Dr Oakland (94621) ***(P-20052)***

R J Reynolds Tobacco Company C 858 625-8453
8380 Miramar Mall Ste 117 San Diego (92121) ***(P-2708)***

R J Vincent Inc E 626 448-1509
1030 Abbot Ave San Gabriel (91776) ***(P-4803)***

R K Fabrication Inc F 714 630-9654
1283 N Grove St Anaheim (92806) ***(P-7878)***

R K Larrabee Company Inc D 925 828-9420
7800 Las Positas Rd Livermore (94551) ***(P-17218)***

R Kern Engineering & Mfg Corp D 909 664-2440
13912 Mountain Ave Chino (91710) ***(P-19409)***

R L Anodizing F 818 252-3804
11331 Penrose St Sun Valley (91352) ***(P-13487)***

R L Anodizing & Plating, Sun Valley *Also called R L Anodizing* ***(P-13487)***

R Lang Company D 559 651-0701
8240 W Doe Ave Visalia (93291) ***(P-12344)***

R M A Geoscience, Chino *Also called Consolidated Geoscience Inc* ***(P-129)***

R M Baker Machine & Tool Inc F 562 697-4007
815 W Front St Covina (91722) ***(P-16880)***

R M I, Van Nuys *Also called Rothlisberger Mfg A Cal Corp* ***(P-16917)***

R M I, Gardena *Also called Rotational Molding Inc* ***(P-10343)***

R M P, San Jose *Also called Rose Metal Products Inc* ***(P-12239)***

R O S, San Diego *Also called Remote Ocean Systems Inc* ***(P-17728)***

R P M, Concord *Also called Renaissance Precision Mfg Inc* ***(P-16896)***

R P M Centerless Grinding, Norco *Also called RPM Grinding Co Inc* ***(P-16920)***

R P M Electric Motors F 714 638-4174
11352 Westminster Ave Garden Grove (92843) ***(P-25466)***

R R Donnelley, San Diego *Also called R R Donnelley & Sons Company* ***(P-7462)***

R R Donnelley & Sons Company E 909 930-1605
1600 Proforma Ave Ontario (91761) ***(P-7459)***

R R Donnelley & Sons Company F 310 789-4100
1888 Century Park E # 1650 Los Angeles (90067) ***(P-7460)***

R R Donnelley & Sons Company E 415 362-2300
1 Embarcadero Ctr Ste 200 San Francisco (94111) ***(P-7211)***

R R Donnelley & Sons Company E 213 928-0967
333 S Grand Ave Ste 4350 Los Angeles (90071) ***(P-7461)***

R R Donnelley & Sons Company F 707 446-6195
1050 Aviator Dr Vacaville (95688) ***(P-7070)***

R R Donnelley & Sons Company C 619 527-4600
955 Gateway Center Way San Diego (92102) ***(P-7462)***

R R Donnelley & Sons Company C 619 527-4600
960 Gateway Center Way San Diego (92102) ***(P-7463)***

R R Donnelley Coml Press Plant, San Diego *Also called R R Donnelley & Sons Company* ***(P-7463)***

R R Donnelley Financial, Los Angeles *Also called R R Donnelley & Sons Company* ***(P-7460)***

R R Donnelley Financial, Los Angeles *Also called R R Donnelley & Sons Company* ***(P-7461)***

R S R Steel Fabrication Inc E 760 244-2210
11040 I Ave Hesperia (92345) ***(P-11413)***

R Stephenson & D Cram Mfg Inc E 408 452-0882
800 Faulstich Ct San Jose (95112) ***(P-16881)***

R T C Group E 949 226-2000
905 Calle Amanecer # 250 San Clemente (92673) ***(P-6241)***

R T I, Morgan Hill *Also called Robson Technologies Inc* ***(P-16910)***

R Torre & Company Inc (PA) C 800 775-1925
233 E Harris Ave South San Francisco (94080) ***(P-2279)***

R Torre & Company Inc E 650 624-2830
400 Littlefield Ave South San Francisco (94080) ***(P-2280)***

R V Gambler F 928 927-5966
6966 Saxon Rd Spc 14 Adelanto (92301) ***(P-20511)***

R W Lyall & Company Inc (HQ) C 951 270-1500
2665 Research Dr Corona (92882) ***(P-147)***

R W Swarens Associates Inc E 626 579-0943
10768 Lower Azusa Rd El Monte (91731) ***(P-17640)***

R Zamora Inc E 760 597-1130
2826 La Mirada Dr Ste D Vista (92081) ***(P-13270)***

R&D Altanova Inc E 408 225-7011
6389 San Ignacio Ave San Jose (95119) ***(P-18577)***

R&Js Business Group Inc F 714 224-1455
900 S Placentia Ave Ste B Placentia (92870) ***(P-2419)***

R&K Industrial Wheels, Richmond *Also called R & K Industrial Products Co* ***(P-13969)***

R&M Deese Inc E 951 734-7342
1875 Sampson Ave Corona (92879) ***(P-23948)***

R-Cold Inc D 951 436-5476
1221 S G St Perris (92570) ***(P-15975)***

R-Quest Technologies LLC F 530 621-9916
4710 Oak Hill Rd Placerville (95667) ***(P-15833)***

R2 Semiconductor Inc E 408 745-7400
1196 Borregas Ave Ste 201 Sunnyvale (94089) ***(P-19113)***

Ra Medical Systems Inc D 760 804-1648
2070 Las Palmas Dr Carlsbad (92011) ***(P-22595)***

Ra-White Inc F 661 725-1840
2736 W Industry Rd Delano (93215) ***(P-16882)***

Rabbit Lithographics, Chino *Also called Dare Lithoworks Inc* ***(P-6778)***

Racaar Circuit Industries Inc E 818 998-7566
9225 Alabama Ave Ste F Chatsworth (91311) ***(P-18578)***

Race Pak, Rcho STA Marg *Also called Racepak LLC* ***(P-20165)***

Race Technologies LLC F 714 438-1118
17422 Murphy Ave Irvine (92614) ***(P-20434)***

Racehorse Supply, Fontana *Also called Michael Hagan* ***(P-23618)***

Racemate Alternators, San Diego *Also called Barrett Engineering Inc* ***(P-19828)***

Racepak LLC E 949 709-5555
30402 Esperanza Rcho STA Marg (92688) ***(P-20435)***

Racepak LLC E 888 429-4709
30402 Esperanza Rcho STA Marg (92688) ***(P-20165)***

Racer Media & Marketing Inc F 949 417-6700
17030 Red Hill Ave Irvine (92614) ***(P-6242)***

Rache Corporation F 805 389-6868
1160 Avenida Acaso Camarillo (93012) ***(P-20053)***

Racing Beat Inc E 714 779-8677
4789 E Wesley Dr Anaheim (92807) ***(P-14029)***

Racing Plus Inc F 951 360-5906
3834 Wacker Dr Mira Loma (91752) ***(P-22801)***

Rack & Riddle, Healdsburg *Also called RB Wine Associates LLC* ***(P-1941)***

Rack Master, Brea *Also called Nycetek Inc* ***(P-5086)***

Raco Manufacturing & Engrg Co F 510 658-6713
1400 62nd St Emeryville (94608) ***(P-20054)***

Rada Industry F 323 265-3727
1060 S Ditman Ave Los Angeles (90023) ***(P-24218)***

Radarsonics Inc F 714 630-7288
1190 N Grove St Anaheim (92806) ***(P-19701)***

Radcal Partners IA California E 626 359-4575
426 W Duarte Rd Monrovia (91016) ***(P-22256)***

Radex Stereo Co Inc F 310 516-9015
13228 Crenshaw Blvd Gardena (90249) ***(P-23191)***

Radflo Suspension Technology F 714 965-7828
11233 Condor Ave Fountain Valley (92708) ***(P-20436)***

Radford Cabinets Inc D 661 729-8931
216 E Avenue K8 Lancaster (93535) ***(P-4733)***

Radian Audio Engineering Inc E 714 288-8900
600 N Batavia St Orange (92868) ***(P-18232)***

Radian Heat Sinks, Santa Clara *Also called Radian Thermal Products Inc* ***(P-11783)***

Radian Thermal Products Inc D 408 988-6200
2160 Walsh Ave Santa Clara (95050) ***(P-11783)***

Radiant Detector Tech LLC F 818 709-2468
19355 Bus Center Dr Ste 8 Northridge (91324) ***(P-22257)***

Radiant Genomics Inc F 646 450-7332
5980 Horton St Ste 105 Emeryville (94608) ***(P-7967)***

Radiation Protection & Spc Inc F 714 771-7702
1531 W Orangewood Ave Orange (92868) ***(P-12731)***

Radiator Specialty Company E 707 252-0122
935 Enterprise Way NAPA (94558) ***(P-9300)***

Radicom Research Inc (PA) F 408 383-9006
671 E Brokaw Rd San Jose (95112) ***(P-17986)***

Radio Frequency Simulation E 714 974-7377
25371 Diana Cir Mission Viejo (92691) ***(P-21837)***

Radio Frequency Systems Inc F 408 281-6100
6276 San Ignacio Ave E San Jose (95119) ***(P-18233)***

Radio Frqency Systems Ferrocom, San Jose *Also called Radio Frequency Systems Inc* ***(P-18233)***

Radio Korea USA, Los Angeles *Also called Infokorea Inc* ***(P-6192)***

Radiology Support Devices E 310 518-0527
1904 E Dominguez St Long Beach (90810) ***(P-22596)***

Raditek Inc (PA) D 408 266-7404
1702 Meridian Ave Ste L San Jose (95125) ***(P-18234)***

Raditek Inc F 408 266-7404
44253 Old Warm Sprng Blvd Fremont (94538) ***(P-18235)***

Radius Product Development Inc A 408 361-6000
6375 San Ignacio Ave San Jose (95119) ***(P-10321)***

Radlink Inc E 310 643-6900
815 N Nash St El Segundo (90245) ***(P-23038)***

Radtec Engineering Inc F 760 510-2715
1780 La Costa Meadows Dr # 102 San Marcos (92078) ***(P-21385)***

Radx Technologies Inc F 619 677-1849
10650 Scripps Ranch Blvd # 100 San Diego (92131) ***(P-21838)***

Rae Systems Inc (HQ) C 408 952-8200
1349 Moffett Park Dr Sunnyvale (94089) ***(P-22258)***

Rael Inc E 800 573-1516
6940 Beach Blvd Unit D608 Buena Park (90621) ***(P-5670)***

Raemica Inc E 909 864-1990
7759 Victoria Ave Highland (92346) ***(P-518)***

Rafael Sandoval E 209 858-4173
16175 Mckinley Ave Lathrop (95330) ***(P-4048)***

Rafco Products Brickform, Rancho Cucamonga *Also called Rafco-Brickform LLC* ***(P-14671)***

Rafco-Brickform LLC (PA) D 909 484-3399
11061 Jersey Blvd Rancho Cucamonga (91730) ***(P-14671)***

Raffaello Research Labs F 310 618-8754
120 The Village Unit 109 Redondo Beach (90277) ***(P-8355)***

Rafi Systems Inc D 909 861-6574
23453 Golden Springs Dr Diamond Bar (91765) ***(P-23118)***

ALPHABETIC

Employee Codes: A=Over 500 employees, B=251-500
C=101-250, D=51-100, E=20-50, F=10-19

2019 California
Manfacturers Register

© Mergent Inc. 1-800-342-5647
1259

Rafu Shimpo...E...213 629-2231
701 E 3rd St Ste 130 Los Angeles (90013) ***(P-6022)***
Rago & Son Inc...D...510 536-5700
1029 51st Ave Oakland (94601) ***(P-13271)***
Rago Neon Inc...F...510 537-1903
235 Laurel Ave Hayward (94541) ***(P-23949)***
Rahn Industries Incorporated (PA)...D...562 908-0680
2630 Pacific Park Dr Whittier (90601) ***(P-15976)***
Raika Inc...E...818 503-5911
13150 Saticoy St North Hollywood (91605) ***(P-10569)***
Railmakers Inc...F...949 642-6506
864 W 18th St Costa Mesa (92627) ***(P-11986)***
Rain Bird Corporation (PA)...C...626 812-3400
970 W Sierra Madre Ave Azusa (91702) ***(P-13774)***
Rain Bird Corporation...E...626 812-3400
970 W Sierra Madre Ave Azusa (91702) ***(P-12047)***
Rain Bird Golf Division, Azusa *Also called Rain Bird Corporation* ***(P-12047)***
Rain Mstr Irrgtion Systems Inc...E...805 527-4498
5825 Jasmine St Riverside (92504) ***(P-21643)***
Rainbo Record Mfg Corp (PA)...C...818 280-1100
8960 Eton Ave Canoga Park (91304) ***(P-17911)***
Rainbo Records & Cassettes, Canoga Park *Also called Rainbo Record Mfg Corp* ***(P-17911)***
Rainbow Fin Company Inc...E...831 728-2998
677 Beach Dr Watsonville (95076) ***(P-23631)***
Rainbow Magnetics Incorporated...E...714 540-4777
1 Whatney Irvine (92618) ***(P-7071)***
Rainbow Manufacturing Co Inc...F...323 778-2093
1504 W 58th St Los Angeles (90062) ***(P-4964)***
Rainbow Novelty Creations Co...E...323 855-9464
3431 E Olympic Blvd Los Angeles (90023) ***(P-2891)***
Rainbow Orchards...F...530 644-1594
2569 Larsen Dr Camino (95709) ***(P-2181)***
Rainbow Sublymation Inc...E...213 489-5001
2438 E 11th St Los Angeles (90021) ***(P-7464)***
Rainbow Symphony Inc...F...818 708-8400
6860 Canby Ave Ste 120 Reseda (91335) ***(P-5657)***
Raindrip Inc...E...818 710-4023
2250 Agate Ct Simi Valley (93065) ***(P-14095)***
Rainguard International, Huntington Beach *Also called Weatherman Products Inc* ***(P-8955)***
Raintree Business Products...E...949 859-0801
23101 Terra Dr Laguna Hills (92653) ***(P-7072)***
Raj Manufacturing LLC...F...714 838-3110
2692 Dow Ave Tustin (92780) ***(P-3488)***
Rakar Incorporated...E...805 487-2721
1700 Emerson Ave Oxnard (93033) ***(P-10322)***
Rakshak...E...404 513-5867
2518 Alvin St Mountain View (94043) ***(P-25103)***
Ralc Inc...F...951 693-0098
42158 Sarah Way Temecula (92590) ***(P-20621)***
Rallio, Irvine *Also called Socialwise Inc* ***(P-6581)***
Ralph E Ames Machine Works...E...310 328-8523
2301 Dominguez Way Torrance (90501) ***(P-16883)***
Ralph L Florimonte...F...714 960-4470
517 Alondra Dr Huntington Beach (92648) ***(P-9506)***
Ralphs Ranches...F...530 398-4182
1833 W Ball Mountain Rd Macdoel (96058) ***(P-448)***
Ralphs-Pugh Co Inc...D...707 745-6222
3931 Oregon St Benicia (94510) ***(P-14282)***
Ram Aerospace Inc...F...714 853-1703
4010 N Palm St Ste 101 Fullerton (92835) ***(P-20920)***
Ram Centrifical Products, Spring Valley *Also called Euramco Safety Inc* ***(P-15155)***
Ram Centrifugal Products Inc...F...619 670-9590
2746 Via Orange Way Spring Valley (91978) ***(P-15173)***
Ram Off Road Accessories Inc...E...323 266-3850
3901 Medford St Los Angeles (90063) ***(P-20437)***
Rama Corporation...E...951 654-7351
600 W Esplanade Ave San Jacinto (92583) ***(P-15273)***
Rama Food Manufacture Corp...E...909 923-5305
1486 E Cedar St Ontario (91761) ***(P-2649)***
Ramador Inc (PA)...F...209 245-6979
12225 Steiner Rd Plymouth (95669) ***(P-1936)***
Ramar International Corp (PA)...E...925 439-9009
1101 Railroad Ave Pittsburg (94565) ***(P-690)***
Ramar International Corp...E...925 432-4267
539 Garcia Ave Ste E Pittsburg (94565) ***(P-449)***
Rambus Inc...E...440 397-2549
1050 Entp Way Ste 700 Sunnyvale (94089) ***(P-19114)***
Rambus Inc (PA)...B...408 462-8000
1050 Entp Way Ste 700 Sunnyvale (94089) ***(P-19115)***
Rambus Inc...F...408 462-8000
1050 Enterprise Way # 700 Sunnyvale (94089) ***(P-19116)***
Ramco, Simi Valley *Also called Recycled Aggregate Mtls Co Inc* ***(P-9395)***
Ramda Metal Specialties Inc...E...310 538-2136
13012 Crenshaw Blvd Gardena (90249) ***(P-12732)***
Rami Designs Inc...F...949 588-8288
24 Hammond Ste E Irvine (92618) ***(P-12885)***
Ramko Injection Inc...D...951 652-3510
3500 Tanya Ave Hemet (92545) ***(P-10323)***
Ramon Lopez...F...626 575-3891
9729 Alpaca St South El Monte (91733) ***(P-4804)***
Ramon Lopez...F...209 478-9500
4752 Ijams Rd Stockton (95210) ***(P-20166)***
Ramona Home Journal...F...760 788-8148
726 D St Ramona (92065) ***(P-6023)***
Ramona Mining & Manufacturing...F...760 789-1620
505 Elm St Ramona (92065) ***(P-23346)***
Ramonas Food Group LLC...C...310 323-1950
13633 S Western Ave Gardena (90249) ***(P-771)***
Ramp Engineering Inc...F...562 531-8030
6850 Walthall Way Paramount (90723) ***(P-12235)***
Rampone Industries LLC...E...949 581-8701
14235 Commerce Dr Garden Grove (92843) ***(P-13848)***
Rams Gate Winery LLC...E...707 721-8700
28700 Arnold Dr Sonoma (95476) ***(P-1937)***
Ramsay Highlander Inc...E...831 675-3453
45 Gonzales River Rd Gonzales (93926) ***(P-14096)***
Ramspur Winery LLC...F...707 251-3948
3100 Old Sonoma Rd NAPA (94558) ***(P-1938)***
Ramtec Associates Inc...E...714 996-7477
3200 E Birch St Ste B Brea (92821) ***(P-10324)***
Ranboy Sportswear, Chula Vista *Also called Leemax International Inc* ***(P-3173)***
Ranch Systems LLC...F...415 884-2770
37 Commercial Blvd # 101 Novato (94949) ***(P-14097)***
Rancho Bernardo Printing Inc...F...858 486-4540
1519 Industrial Ave Ste D Escondido (92029) ***(P-7073)***
Rancho Cucamonga Division, Rancho Cucamonga *Also called Gasket Specialties Inc* ***(P-9532)***
Rancho Cucamonga Maverick...F...909 466-6445
7349 Milliken Ave Ste 110 Rancho Cucamonga (91730) ***(P-6024)***
Rancho Cucamonga Today, Rancho Cucamonga *Also called Rancho Cucamonga Maverick* ***(P-6024)***
Rancho De Solis Winery Inc...F...408 847-6306
3920 Hecker Pass Rd Gilroy (95020) ***(P-1939)***
Rancho Ready Mix (PA)...E...951 674-0488
28251 Lake St Lake Elsinore (92530) ***(P-11159)***
Rancho Safari, Ramona *Also called Gerald Gentellalli* ***(P-23569)***
Rancho Sisquoc Winery, Santa Maria *Also called Flood Ranch Company* ***(P-1764)***
Rancho Technology Inc...F...909 987-3966
10783 Bell Ct Rancho Cucamonga (91730) ***(P-15834)***
Rand Machine Works, Fresno *Also called R & L Enterprises Inc* ***(P-16877)***
Randal Optimal Nutrients LLC...E...707 528-1800
1595 Hampton Way Santa Rosa (95407) ***(P-8356)***
Randell Equipment & Mfg, Delano *Also called Randell Equiptment & Mfg* ***(P-14098)***
Randell Equiptment & Mfg...E...661 725-6380
15260 County Line Rd Delano (93215) ***(P-14098)***
Randolph & Hein...F...323 233-6010
720 E 59th St Los Angeles (90001) ***(P-4734)***
Random Technologies LLC...F...415 255-1267
2325 3rd St Ste 404 San Francisco (94107) ***(P-10666)***
Randtron Antenna Systems, Menlo Park *Also called L3 Technologies Inc* ***(P-18160)***
Randy Nix Cstm Wldg & Mfg Inc...F...559 562-1958
22700 Road 196 Lindsay (93247) ***(P-25429)***
Randy's Donuts, Inglewood *Also called Larryron Enterprises Inc* ***(P-1277)***
Rang Dong Joint Stock Company...F...707 259-9446
3 Executive Way NAPA (94558) ***(P-1940)***
Rang Dong Winery, NAPA *Also called Rang Dong Joint Stock Company* ***(P-1940)***
Rangefinder Publishing Co Inc...F...310 846-4770
11835 W Olympic Blvd 550e Los Angeles (90064) ***(P-6243)***
Rangeme Inc...F...415 351-9268
665 3rd St Ste 415 San Francisco (94107) ***(P-6562)***
Rank Technology Corp...E...408 737-1488
1190 Miraloma Way Ste Q Sunnyvale (94085) ***(P-15593)***
Rankin-Delux Inc (PA)...F...951 685-0081
3245 Corridor Dr Eastvale (91752) ***(P-16098)***
Ranks Big Data...C...510 830-6926
2453 Naglee Rd Tracy (95304) ***(P-3959)***
Ranroy Company...E...858 571-8800
8320 Camino Santa Fe # 200 San Diego (92121) ***(P-7074)***
Ransome Manufacturing, Fresno *Also called Meeder Equipment Company* ***(P-14988)***
Rantec Microwave Systems Inc...E...760 744-1544
2066 Wineridge Pl Escondido (92029) ***(P-19702)***
Rantec Microwave Systems Inc (PA)...D...818 223-5000
31186 La Baya Dr Westlake Village (91362) ***(P-21386)***
Rantec Power Systems Inc...D...805 596-6000
1173 Los Olivos Ave Los Osos (93402) ***(P-19703)***
Raoul Textiles Inc...F...805 965-1694
110 Los Aguajes Ave Santa Barbara (93101) ***(P-7465)***
Raoul's Hand-Screened Yardage, Santa Barbara *Also called Raoul Textiles Inc* ***(P-7465)***
Raouls Printworks...F...805 965-1694
110 Los Aguajes Ave Santa Barbara (93101) ***(P-2892)***
RAP Security Inc...D...323 560-3493
4630 Cecilia St Cudahy (90201) ***(P-5163)***
Rap4...E...408 434-0434
7700 Arroyo Cir Gilroy (95020) ***(P-23632)***
Rapco-West Asbestos, Malibu *Also called West Rapco Environmental Svcs* ***(P-14591)***
Raphaels Inc...F...619 670-7999
2780 Sweetwater Spgs Blvd Spring Valley (91977) ***(P-4645)***
Rapid Accu-Form Inc...F...707 745-1879
3825 Sprig Dr Benicia (94510) ***(P-10325)***
Rapid Anodizing Inc...F...323 753-5255
1216 W Slauson Ave Los Angeles (90044) ***(P-15016)***
Rapid Diagnostics Inc...E...650 558-0395
1429 Rollins Rd Burlingame (94010) ***(P-22597)***
Rapid Displays Inc...B...510 471-6955
33195 Lewis St Union City (94587) ***(P-23950)***
Rapid Industries...F...323 753-5255
1216 W Slauson Ave Los Angeles (90044) ***(P-13488)***
Rapid Lasergraphics, San Francisco *Also called Rapid Typographers Company* ***(P-7632)***
Rapid Lasergraphics (HQ)...F...415 957-5840
836 Harrison St San Francisco (94107) ***(P-7631)***
Rapid Manufacturing (PA)...F...818 899-4377
9724 Eton Ave Chatsworth (91311) ***(P-24219)***
Rapid Manufacturing A (PA)...C...714 974-2432
8080 E Crystal Dr Anaheim (92807) ***(P-13849)***
Rapid Plating, Los Angeles *Also called Rapid Industries* ***(P-13488)***
Rapid Precision Mfg Inc...E...408 617-0771
1516 Montague Expy San Jose (95131) ***(P-16884)***

Mergent e-mail: customerrelations@mergent.com 2019 California Manufacturers Register (P-0000) Products & Services Section entry number
1260 (PA)=Parent Co (HQ)=Headquarters (DH)=Div Headquarters

Rapid Printers of Monterey....E....831 373-1822
201 Foam St Monterey (93940) *(P-7075)*
Rapid Product Solutions Inc....E....805 485-7234
2240 Celsius Ave Ste D Oxnard (93030) *(P-16885)*
Rapid Ramen Inc....F....916 479-7003
9381 E Stockton Blvd # 230 Elk Grove (95624) *(P-16099)*
Rapid Typographers Company (PA)....E....415 957-5840
836 Harrison St San Francisco (94107) *(P-7632)*
Rapidwerks Incorporated....E....925 417-0124
1257 Quarry Ln Ste 140 Pleasanton (94566) *(P-10326)*
Rapiscan Laboratories Inc (HQ)....D....408 961-9700
3793 Spinnaker Ct Fremont (94538) *(P-22940)*
Rapiscan Systems Inc (HQ)....C....310 978-1457
2805 Columbia St Torrance (90503) *(P-22941)*
Rapt Touch Inc....F....415 994-1537
1875 S Grant St Ste 925 San Mateo (94402) *(P-15476)*
Raptor Pharmaceuticals Inc....E....415 408-6200
7 Hamilton Landing # 100 Novato (94949) *(P-8357)*
Rare Breed Distilling LLC (HQ)....E....415 315-8060
55 Francisco St Ste 100 San Francisco (94133) *(P-2075)*
Rare Elements Hair Care....F....310 277-6524
8950 W Olympic Blvd 641 Beverly Hills (90211) *(P-24220)*
Rasmussen Iron Works Inc....E....562 696-8718
12028 Philadelphia St Whittier (90601) *(P-12078)*
Raspadoxpress....F....818 892-6969
8610 Van Nuys Blvd Panorama City (91402) *(P-6563)*
Rastergraf Inc (PA)....F....510 849-4801
7145 Marlborough Ter Berkeley (94705) *(P-18579)*
Ratebeer LLC....D....302 476-2337
1381 Velma Ave Santa Rosa (95403) *(P-6564)*
Ratebeer.com, Santa Rosa *Also called Ratebeer LLC (P-6564)*
Ratermann Manufacturing Inc (PA)....E....800 264-7793
601 Pinnacle Pl Livermore (94550) *(P-10327)*
Rau Restoration....F....310 445-1128
2027 Pontius Ave Los Angeles (90025) *(P-4216)*
Rau William Automotive Wdwrk, Los Angeles *Also called Rau Restoration (P-4216)*
Raven's Deli, Armona *Also called Armona Frozen Food Lockers (P-465)*
Ravenswood Winery, Sonoma *Also called Franciscan Vineyards Inc (P-1770)*
Raveon Technologies Corp....E....760 444-5995
2320 Cousteau Ct Vista (92081) *(P-18236)*
Rawson Custom Cabinets Inc (PA)....E....408 779-9838
16890 Church St Bldg 1a Morgan Hill (95037) *(P-4341)*
Raxium Inc....E....408 712-1648
1250 Reliance Way Fremont (94539) *(P-17727)*
Ray Chinn Construction Inc....E....661 327-2731
424 24th St Bakersfield (93301) *(P-14454)*
Ray Foster Dental Equipment....F....714 897-7795
5421 Commercial Dr Huntington Beach (92649) *(P-22905)*
Ray-Bar Engineering Corp....F....626 969-1818
697 W Foothill Blvd Azusa (91702) *(P-22802)*
Raychem, Menlo Park *Also called Te Connectivity Corporation (P-9508)*
Raychem Product Division, Redwood City *Also called Te Connectivity Corporation (P-17496)*
Raychem Wire Division, Redwood City *Also called Te Connectivity Corporation (P-17498)*
Rayco B Products, Monrovia *Also called Rayco Burial Products Inc (P-12733)*
Rayco Burial Products Inc....E....626 357-1996
1601 Raymond Ave Monrovia (91016) *(P-12733)*
Rayco Electronic Mfg Inc....E....310 329-2660
1220 W 130th St Gardena (90247) *(P-19358)*
Raycon Technology Inc (PA)....F....714 799-4100
5252 Mcfadden Ave Huntington Beach (92649) *(P-19410)*
Raykorvay Inc....F....714 632-8680
1070 N Kraemer Pl Anaheim (92806) *(P-23401)*
Raymar Information Tech Inc (PA)....F....916 783-1951
7325 Roseville Rd Sacramento (95842) *(P-17987)*
Raymert Press Incorporated....E....858 576-0880
1604 Sunburst Dr El Cajon (92021) *(P-7076)*
Raymonds Little Print Shop Inc....B....510 353-3608
41454 Christy St Fremont (94538) *(P-7077)*
Raynguard Protective Mtls Inc....F....916 454-2560
8280 14th Ave Sacramento (95826) *(P-9166)*
Rayotek Scientific Inc....D....858 558-3671
11499 Sorrento Valley Rd San Diego (92121) *(P-10728)*
Rayotek Sight Windows, San Diego *Also called Rayotek Scientific Inc (P-10728)*
Raypak Inc (HQ)....B....805 278-5300
2151 Eastman Ave Oxnard (93030) *(P-12079)*
Rayspan Corporation....F....858 259-9596
1493 Poinsettia Ave # 139 Vista (92081) *(P-17988)*
Raytheon Applied Signal (HQ)....C....408 749-1888
460 W California Ave Sunnyvale (94086) *(P-18357)*
Raytheon Applied Signal....F....714 917-0255
160 N Rverview Dr Ste 300 Anaheim (92808) *(P-18358)*
Raytheon Company....C....805 967-5511
6380 Hollister Ave Goleta (93117) *(P-20055)*
Raytheon Company....F....310 334-0430
14471 Danes Cir Huntington Beach (92647) *(P-21387)*
Raytheon Company....D....310 647-1000
1921 Mariposa St El Segundo (90245) *(P-21388)*
Raytheon Company....C....626 675-2584
16035 E Bridger St Covina (91722) *(P-21389)*
Raytheon Company....F....714 446-2584
1801 Hughes Dr Fullerton (92833) *(P-21390)*
Raytheon Company....D....714 446-3513
1801 Hughes Dr Fullerton (92833) *(P-21391)*
Raytheon Company....E....760 384-3295
350 E Ridgecrest Blvd # 202 Ridgecrest (93555) *(P-21392)*
Raytheon Company....C....619 628-3345
8650 Balboa Ave San Diego (92123) *(P-21393)*
Raytheon Company....D....714 446-2287
1801 Hughes Dr Dd311 Fullerton (92833) *(P-22259)*
Raytheon Company....C....714 732-0119
1801 Hughes Dr Fullerton (92833) *(P-21394)*
Raytheon Company....B....310 647-1000
2000 E El Segundo Blvd El Segundo (90245) *(P-21395)*
Raytheon Company....F....805 562-2730
26 Castilian Dr Goleta (93117) *(P-15477)*
Raytheon Company....B....310 647-8334
2000 Elsegundo Blvd El Segundo (90245) *(P-21396)*
Raytheon Company....F....805 985-6851
Bldg 471 North End Port Hueneme (93043) *(P-21397)*
Raytheon Company....F....310 334-2050
2200 E Imperial Hwy El Segundo (90245) *(P-21398)*
Raytheon Company....D....310 338-1324
6150 W Century Blvd Los Angeles (90045) *(P-21399)*
Raytheon Company....A....310 647-9438
2000 E El Segundo Blvd El Segundo (90245) *(P-21400)*
Raytheon Company....B....310 647-1000
2000 E El Segundo Blvd El Segundo (90245) *(P-21401)*
Raytheon Company....E....310 647-1000
2000 E El Segundo Blvd El Segundo (90245) *(P-21402)*
Raytheon Company....C....310 884-1825
9400 Santa Fe Springs Rd Santa Fe Springs (90670) *(P-20167)*
Raytheon Company....D....805 562-4611
75 Coromar Dr Goleta (93117) *(P-21403)*
Raytheon Company....B....714 446-3232
1901 W Malvern Ave 618 Fullerton (92833) *(P-21404)*
Raytheon Company....D....909 483-4040
10606 7th St Rancho Cucamonga (91730) *(P-21405)*
Raytheon Company....E....310 334-7675
2175 Park Pl El Segundo (90245) *(P-21406)*
Raytheon Company....D....805 562-4611
75 Coromar Dr Goleta (93117) *(P-21407)*
Raytheon Company....A....310 647-9438
2000 E El Segundo Blvd El Segundo (90245) *(P-21408)*
Raytheon Company....D....858 571-6598
8650 Balboa Ave San Diego (92123) *(P-21409)*
Raytheon Company....C....805 967-5511
63 Hollister St Goleta (93117) *(P-21410)*
Raytheon Dgital Force Tech LLC....E....858 546-1244
6779 Mesa Ridge Rd # 150 San Diego (92121) *(P-21411)*
Rayzist Photomask Inc (PA)....D....760 727-8561
955 Park Center Dr Vista (92081) *(P-23737)*
RB Design, Escondido *Also called Generation Circuits LLC (P-18494)*
RB Machining Inc....F....661 274-4611
39360 3rd St E Ste B203 Palmdale (93550) *(P-16886)*
RB Racing....F....310 515-5720
1234 W 134th St Gardena (90247) *(P-20438)*
RB Wine Associates LLC....D....707 433-8400
499 Moore Ln Healdsburg (95448) *(P-1941)*
Rbc Transport Dynamics Corp....C....203 267-7001
3131 W Segerstrom Ave Santa Ana (92704) *(P-15290)*
Rbf Group International....F....626 333-5700
1441 W 2nd St Pomona (91766) *(P-4965)*
Rbf Lifestyle Holdings, Pomona *Also called Rbf Group International (P-4965)*
Rbg Holdings Corp (PA)....F....818 782-6445
7855 Haskell Ave Ste 350 Van Nuys (91406) *(P-23633)*
Rbm Conveyor Systems Inc....E....909 620-1333
1570 W Mission Blvd Pomona (91766) *(P-14880)*
Rbs Glass Designs, Van Nuys *Also called Precision Glass Bevelling Inc (P-10665)*
Rbz Vineyards LLC....E....805 542-0133
2324 W Highway 46 Paso Robles (93446) *(P-1942)*
RC Apparel Inc....F....818 541-1994
3104 Markridge Rd La Crescenta (91214) *(P-3915)*
RC Furniture Inc....D....626 964-4100
1111 Jellick Ave City of Industry (91748) *(P-4805)*
RC Readymix Co Inc....E....925 449-7785
1227 Greenville Rd Livermore (94550) *(P-11160)*
Rcd Engineering Inc....E....530 292-3133
17100 Salmon Mine Rd Nevada City (95959) *(P-17297)*
Rch Associates Inc....F....510 657-7846
4115 Business Center Dr Fremont (94538) *(P-15017)*
Rci Rack Cnvyor Instltion Inc....E....909 381-4818
346 S I St Ste 9 San Bernardino (92410) *(P-14283)*
RCP Block & Brick Inc (PA)....D....619 460-9101
8240 Broadway Lemon Grove (91945) *(P-10859)*
RCP Block & Brick Inc....E....619 448-2240
8755 N Magnolia Ave Santee (92071) *(P-10860)*
RCP Block & Brick Inc....E....619 474-1516
75 N 4th Ave Chula Vista (91910) *(P-10861)*
RCP Block & Brick Inc....E....760 753-1164
577 N Vulcan Ave Encinitas (92024) *(P-10862)*
Rcrv Inc....F....323 235-7332
4619 S Alameda St Vernon (90058) *(P-5617)*
Rcs, Los Angeles *Also called Rider Circulation Services (P-6028)*
Rcs Custom Stoneworks....F....714 309-0620
3280 Vine St Ste 201 Riverside (92507) *(P-11275)*
Rd Jean, Vernon *Also called California Coast Clothing LLC (P-2729)*
Rd Metal Polishing Inc....E....909 594-8393
244 Pioneer Pl Pomona (91768) *(P-13489)*
Rdc Machine Inc....E....408 970-0721
384 Laurelwood Rd Santa Clara (95054) *(P-16887)*
RDD Enterprises Inc....F....213 746-0020
4638 E Washinton Blvd Commerce (90040) *(P-3039)*
RDfabricators Inc....F....714 634-2078
11880 Western Ave Stanton (90680) *(P-12734)*
Rdl Machine Inc....E....858 693-3975
7775 Arjons Dr San Diego (92126) *(P-16888)*
RDm Industrial Products Inc....F....408 945-8400
1652 Watson Ct Milpitas (95035) *(P-4998)*

ALPHABETIC

Employee Codes: A=Over 500 employees, B=251-500
C=101-250, D=51-100, E=20-50, F=10-19
2019 California
Manfacturers Register
© Mergent Inc. 1-800-342-5647
1261

RDM Multi-Enterprises Inc ...F...562 924-1820
20428 Belshire Ave Lakewood (90715) ***(P-11325)***
RDS Group Inc ...F...909 923-8831
1714 E Grevillea Ct Ontario (91761) ***(P-7078)***
RDS Printing and Graphics Ctr, Ontario *Also called RDS Group Inc* ***(P-7078)***
RE Bilt Metalizing Co ...F...323 277-8200
2229 E 38th St Vernon (90058) ***(P-16889)***
RE Tranquillity 8 LLC ...D...415 675-1500
300 California St Fl 7 San Francisco (94104) ***(P-12080)***
Reach International, Buena Park *Also called Leach International Corp* ***(P-17283)***
Reach Technology, San Jose *Also called Novanta Corporation* ***(P-19664)***
Reaction Technology Inc (PA) ...E...408 970-9601
3400 Bassett St Santa Clara (95054) ***(P-19117)***
Read Corp ...E...408 705-2123
16012a Flintlock Rd Cupertino (95014) ***(P-25104)***
Read It Later Inc ...E...415 692-6111
233 Sansome St Ste 1200 San Francisco (94104) ***(P-25105)***
Reader Magazine ...F...909 335-8100
108 Orange St Ste 11 Redlands (92373) ***(P-6244)***
Ready Industries Inc ...F...213 749-2041
1520 E 15th St Los Angeles (90021) ***(P-7079)***
Ready Pac Foods Inc (HQ) ...B...626 856-8686
4401 Foxdale St Irwindale (91706) ***(P-2650)***
Ready Reproductions, Los Angeles *Also called Ready Industries Inc* ***(P-7079)***
Ready Stamps, San Diego *Also called United Cerebral Palsy Assn San* ***(P-23723)***
Readymix - Delano Rm, Delano *Also called Cemex Cnstr Mtls PCF LLC* ***(P-11072)***
Readymix - Fairfield R/M, Fairfield *Also called Cemex Cnstr Mtls PCF LLC* ***(P-10849)***
Readymix - Old River Rm, Bakersfield *Also called Cemex Cnstr Mtls PCF LLC* ***(P-10897)***
Readymix - Tremont R/M, Dixon *Also called Cemex Cnstr Mtls PCF LLC* ***(P-10850)***
Readymix -Compton Rm, Compton *Also called Cemex Cnstr Mtls PCF LLC* ***(P-11079)***
Readymix -Concord Rm Dual, Concord *Also called Cemex Cnstr Mtls PCF LLC* ***(P-11070)***
Readymix -Fontana Rm, Fontana *Also called Cemex Cnstr Mtls PCF LLC* ***(P-11077)***
Readymix -Hollywood Rm Dual, West Hollywood *Also called Cemex Cnstr Mtls PCF LLC* ***(P-11081)***
Readymix -Los Angeles Rm Dual, Los Angeles *Also called Cemex Cnstr Mtls PCF LLC* ***(P-11080)***
Readymix -Modesto Rm, Modesto *Also called Cemex Cnstr Mtls PCF LLC* ***(P-11078)***
Readymix -Newman Rm, Newman *Also called Cemex Cnstr Mtls PCF LLC* ***(P-11075)***
Readymix -Oakland Rm, Oakland *Also called Cemex Cnstr Mtls PCF LLC* ***(P-11069)***
Readymix -Orange Rm Dual, Orange *Also called Cemex Cnstr Mtls PCF LLC* ***(P-11067)***
Readymix -Redlands Rm Dual, Highland *Also called Cemex Cnstr Mtls PCF LLC* ***(P-11073)***
Readymix -Tracy Rm Dual, Tracy *Also called Cemex Cnstr Mtls PCF LLC* ***(P-11064)***
Readymix -Walnut Rm, Walnut *Also called Cemex Cnstr Mtls PCF LLC* ***(P-11076)***
Readysmart, Mountain View *Also called Phoenix Improving Life LLC* ***(P-22793)***
Readytech Corporation ...F...510 834-3344
2201 Broadway Ste 725 Oakland (94612) ***(P-25106)***
Reagent Chemical & RES Inc ...E...909 796-4059
1454 S Sunnyside Ave San Bernardino (92408) ***(P-7801)***
Real Action Paintball Inc ...F...408 848-2846
7700 Arroyo Cir Gilroy (95020) ***(P-23634)***
Real Goods Solar Inc ...C...951 304-3301
41567 Cherry St Murrieta (92562) ***(P-12081)***
Real Marketing ...E...858 847-0335
9955 Black Mountain Rd San Diego (92126) ***(P-6565)***
Real Meat Company, The, Montrose *Also called Flanagan-Gorham Inc* ***(P-435)***
Real Plating Inc ...E...909 623-2304
1245 W 2nd St Pomona (91766) ***(P-13490)***
Real Seal, Escondido *Also called REAL Seal Co Inc* ***(P-9550)***
REAL Seal Co Inc ...E...760 743-7263
1971 Don Lee Pl Escondido (92029) ***(P-9550)***
Real Software Systems LLC (PA) ...D...818 313-8000
21255 Burbank Blvd # 220 Woodland Hills (91367) ***(P-25107)***
Real-Time Radiography Inc ...E...925 416-1903
3825 Hopyard Rd Ste 220 Pleasanton (94588) ***(P-23039)***
Realization Technologies Inc ...E...408 271-1720
440 N Wolfe Rd 52 Sunnyvale (94085) ***(P-25108)***
Realpage Inc ...E...415 222-6996
333 3rd St San Francisco (94107) ***(P-25109)***
Realscout Inc ...F...650 397-6500
480 Ellis St Ste 203 Mountain View (94043) ***(P-25110)***
Realtalkla, Los Angeles *Also called Transformationnet Media LLC* ***(P-6274)***
Realware Inc ...F...510 382-9045
444 Haas Ave San Leandro (94577) ***(P-25111)***
Realwise Inc ...F...661 295-9399
28042 Avenue Stanford E Valencia (91355) ***(P-25112)***
Reason8 Inc ...F...505 220-3683
490 Post St Ste 526 San Francisco (94102) ***(P-25113)***
Rebas Inc ...C...562 941-4155
12907 Imperial Hwy Santa Fe Springs (90670) ***(P-14345)***
Rebecca Beeson Collection Tees, San Francisco *Also called Rebecca Beeson Inc* ***(P-3269)***
Rebecca Beeson Inc ...F...415 865-0471
1345 Howard St San Francisco (94103) ***(P-3269)***
Rebecca International Inc ...E...323 973-2602
4587 E 48th St Vernon (90058) ***(P-3859)***
Rebelkingsnugus LLc ...F...323 667-8565
112 W 9th St Los Angeles (90015) ***(P-2759)***
Rebol Technologies Inc ...F...707 485-0599
301 S State St Ukiah (95482) ***(P-25114)***
Rebuilt Metalizing Chrome Pltg, Vernon *Also called RE Bilt Metalizing Co* ***(P-16889)***
Rec Inc ...F...760 727-8006
2442 Cades Way Vista (92081) ***(P-15355)***
Rec Solar Commercial Corp ...C...844 732-7652
3450 Broad St Ste 105 San Luis Obispo (93401) ***(P-21523)***
Recarbco, Martinez *Also called Noel Burt* ***(P-16148)***
Recchiuti Confections, San Francisco *Also called Confections Michael Recchiuti* ***(P-1416)***
Receivd Inc ...F...650 336-5817
655 Castro St Ste 2 Mountain View (94041) ***(P-25115)***
Recoating-West Inc (PA) ...E...916 652-8290
4170 Douglas Blvd Ste 120 Granite Bay (95746) ***(P-12735)***
Recognition Products Mfg, San Jose *Also called Stryker Enterprises Inc* ***(P-13976)***
Recomax Software Inc ...F...408 592-0851
706 La Para Ave Palo Alto (94306) ***(P-18237)***
Recommind Inc (HQ) ...D...415 394-7899
550 Kearny St Ste 700 San Francisco (94108) ***(P-19879)***
Recon 1 Inc ...F...805 388-3911
4045 Via Pescador Camarillo (93012) ***(P-9479)***
Recon Services Inc ...F...951 682-1400
2255 Via Cerro Jurupa Valley (92509) ***(P-12413)***
Reconserve Inc (HQ) ...E...310 458-1574
2811 Wilshire Blvd # 410 Santa Monica (90403) ***(P-1157)***
Reconserve of Maryland, Santa Monica *Also called Dext Company of Maryland* ***(P-1127)***
Recor Medical Inc (PA) ...F...631 676-2730
1049 Elwell Ct Palo Alto (94303) ***(P-22598)***
Record Technology Inc ...E...805 484-2747
486 Dawson Dr Ste 4s Camarillo (93012) ***(P-17912)***
Record The, Stockton *Also called Dow Jones Lmg Stockton Inc* ***(P-5833)***
Recortec Inc ...F...408 928-1488
2231 Fortune Dr Ste A San Jose (95131) ***(P-15835)***
Recruitment Services Inc ...F...213 364-1960
3600 Wilshire Blvd Ste 15 Los Angeles (90010) ***(P-6245)***
Rectangular Tubing Inc ...F...626 333-7884
333 Newquist Pl City of Industry (91745) ***(P-5493)***
Recycled Aggregate Mtls Co Inc (PA) ...E...805 522-1646
2655 1st St 210 Simi Valley (93065) ***(P-9395)***
Recycled Paper Products, Santa Fe Springs *Also called Gabriel Container Co* ***(P-5412)***
Recycled Spaces Inc ...F...530 587-3394
10191 Donner Pass Rd # 1 Truckee (96161) ***(P-4918)***
Recycler Classified, Sherman Oaks *Also called E Z Buy E Z Sell Recycler Corp* ***(P-5835)***
Red Bluff Daily News, Red Bluff *Also called Medianews Group Inc* ***(P-5965)***
Red Brick Corporation ...F...323 549-9444
5364 Venice Blvd Los Angeles (90019) ***(P-7080)***
Red Bull North America Inc ...D...310 393-4647
1630 Stewart St Ste A Santa Monica (90404) ***(P-2182)***
Red Caboose of Colorado, Crescent City *Also called William McClung* ***(P-23479)***
Red Digital Cinema Camera Co, Irvine *Also called Redcom LLC* ***(P-23192)***
Red Engine Inc ...F...213 742-8858
1850 E 15th St Los Angeles (90021) ***(P-3085)***
Red Engine Jeans, Los Angeles *Also called Red Engine Inc* ***(P-3085)***
Red Gate Software Inc ...E...626 993-3949
144 W Colo Blvd Ste 200 Pasadena (91105) ***(P-25116)***
Red Hat Inc ...F...650 567-9039
444 Castro St Ste 1200 Mountain View (94041) ***(P-25117)***
Red Line Engineering Inc ...F...530 333-2134
4616 Weed Patch Ct Greenwood (95635) ***(P-16890)***
Red Line Synthetic Oil, Benicia *Also called Phillips 66 Spectrum Corp* ***(P-9447)***
Red Mountain Inc ...F...949 595-4475
17767 Mitchell N Irvine (92614) ***(P-21524)***
Red River Lumber Co ...E...707 963-1251
2959 Saint Helena Hwy N Saint Helena (94574) ***(P-4533)***
Red Robot Labs Inc ...F...650 762-8058
1935 Landings Dr Mountain View (94043) ***(P-23459)***
Red Shell Foods Inc ...F...626 937-6501
825 Baldwin Park Blvd City of Industry (91746) ***(P-930)***
Red Star Coffee, Goleta *Also called Santa Barbara Coffee LLC* ***(P-2366)***
Red Star Fertilizer Co ...D...909 597-4801
17132 Hellman Ave Corona (92880) ***(P-9070)***
Redacted-Studios LLC ...F...510 333-0030
4100 Redwood Rd Oakland (94619) ***(P-25118)***
Redart Corporation ...F...714 774-9444
2549 Eastbluff Dr Newport Beach (92660) ***(P-5026)***
Redcom LLC (HQ) ...D...949 206-7900
34 Parker Irvine (92618) ***(P-23192)***
Redcort Software Inc ...F...559 434-8544
619 Woodworth Ave Ste 200 Clovis (93612) ***(P-25119)***
Redding Metal Crafters Inc ...F...530 222-4400
3871 Rancho Rd Redding (96002) ***(P-12736)***
Redding Printing Co Inc (PA) ...E...530 243-0525
1130 Continental St Redding (96001) ***(P-7081)***
Reddit Inc ...E...415 666-2330
420 Taylor St San Francisco (94102) ***(P-6566)***
Reddy Ice Corporation ...E...760 344-0535
462 N 8th St Brawley (92227) ***(P-2420)***
Redfern Integrated Optics Inc ...E...408 970-3500
3350 Scott Blvd Bldg 1 Santa Clara (95054) ***(P-22126)***
Redi Shades, Cotati *Also called Shades Unlimited Inc* ***(P-5209)***
Redlands CCI Inc ...E...909 307-6500
721 Nevada St Ste 308 Redlands (92373) ***(P-21133)***
Redlands Daily Facts, Redlands *Also called Califrnia Nwspapers Ltd Partnr* ***(P-5792)***
Redline Detection LLC ...F...714 451-1411
828 W Taft Ave Orange (92865) ***(P-15018)***
Redline Prcision Machining Inc ...F...909 483-1273
907 E Francis St Ontario (91761) ***(P-11414)***
Redline Solutions Inc ...F...408 562-1700
3350 Scott Blvd Bldg 5 Santa Clara (95054) ***(P-15836)***
Redpine Signals Inc (PA) ...E...408 748-3385
2107 N 1st St Ste 540 San Jose (95131) ***(P-19118)***
Redseal Inc ...D...408 641-2200
940 Stewart Dr Ste 101 Sunnyvale (94085) ***(P-25120)***
Redshark Group Inc ...F...925 837-3490
166 Saint Helena Ct Danville (94526) ***(P-7082)***
Redtrac, Bakersfield *Also called Water Associates LLC* ***(P-18298)***
Redwood Apps Inc ...F...408 348-3808
805 Veterans Blvd Ste 322 Redwood City (94063) ***(P-25121)***

Mergent e-mail: customerrelations@mergent.com
1262
2019 California
Manufacturers Register
(P-0000) Products & Services Section entry number
(PA)=Parent Co (HQ)=Headquarters (DH)=Div Headquarters

Redwood Empire Awng & Furn Co....F....707 633-8156
3547 Santa Rosa Ave Santa Rosa (95407) *(P-3806)*
Redwood Milling Company LLC....E....707 433-1343
12055 Old Redwood Hwy Healdsburg (95448) *(P-4217)*
Redwood Scientific Tech Inc....E....310 693-5401
820 N Mountain Ave # 100 Upland (91786) *(P-8358)*
Redwood Valley Gravel Products....F....707 485-8585
11200 East Rd Redwood Valley (95470) *(P-10991)*
Redworks Industries LLC....E....949 334-7081
23986 Aliso Creek Rd Laguna Niguel (92677) *(P-4646)*
Reed LLC....E....909 287-2100
13822 Oaks Ave Chino (91710) *(P-15090)*
Reed & Graham Inc (PA)....E....408 287-1400
690 Sunol St San Jose (95126) *(P-9352)*
Reed & Graham Inc....E....888 381-0800
26 Light Sky Ct Sacramento (95828) *(P-9396)*
Reed & Graham Inc....F....916 381-9900
26 Light Sky Ct Sacramento (95828) *(P-9353)*
Reed Electric & Field Service, Vernon *Also called R A Reed Electric Company (P-25465)*
Reed Group....F....209 334-0790
686 E Lockeford St Lodi (95240) *(P-332)*
Reed International (HQ)....E....209 874-2357
13024 Lake Rd Hickman (95323) *(P-14202)*
Reed Manufacturing, Chino *Also called Reed LLC (P-15090)*
Reed Manufacturing Inc....E....831 637-5641
51 Fallon Rd Hollister (95023) *(P-11521)*
Reed Mariculture Inc....F....408 377-1065
900 E Hamilton Ave # 100 Campbell (95008) *(P-1158)*
Reed Print Inc (PA)....E....661 845-3704
5409 Aldrin Ct Bakersfield (93313) *(P-6025)*
Reedex Inc....E....714 894-0311
15526 Commerce Ln Huntington Beach (92649) *(P-19704)*
Reeds Inc....E....310 217-9400
13000 S Spring St Los Angeles (90061) *(P-2183)*
Reel Efx Inc....E....818 762-1710
5539 Riverton Ave North Hollywood (91601) *(P-24221)*
Reel Picture Productions LLC....D....858 587-0301
5330 Eastgate Mall San Diego (92121) *(P-19880)*
Reeve Store Equipment Company (PA)....D....562 949-2535
9131 Bermudez St Pico Rivera (90660) *(P-5164)*
Reeves Enterprises, La Verne *Also called Dennis Reeves Inc (P-5053)*
Reeves Extruded Products Inc....D....661 854-5970
1032 Stockton Ave Arvin (93203) *(P-9744)*
Refining Technology Division, Orange *Also called Haldor Topsoe Inc (P-7780)*
Reflectech Inc....F....916 388-7821
5861 88th St Ste 100 Sacramento (95828) *(P-8673)*
Reflection Shoes, Sun Valley *Also called Polyplex Plastics of N Amer (P-9660)*
Reflection Technology, Sacramento *Also called Reflectech Inc (P-8673)*
Reflective Images, Novato *Also called Image Star LLC (P-3163)*
Reflex Corporation....E....760 931-9009
1825 Aston Ave Ste A Carlsbad (92008) *(P-3960)*
Reflex Photonics Inc....E....408 501-8886
1250 Oakmead Pkwy Sunnyvale (94085) *(P-19119)*
Reflexion Medical Inc....E....650 239-9070
25821 Industrial Blvd # 200 Hayward (94545) *(P-23040)*
Refresco Beverages US Inc....D....909 915-1400
631 S Waterman Ave San Bernardino (92408) *(P-2184)*
Refresco Beverages US Inc....D....951 461-3328
26205 Cottonwood St Murrieta (92563) *(P-2185)*
Refrigerator Manufacters Inc (PA)....E....562 926-2006
17018 Edwards Rd Cerritos (90703) *(P-17382)*
Refrigerator Manufacturers LLC....E....562 926-2006
17018 Edwards Rd Cerritos (90703) *(P-15977)*
Refunds Today LLC....E....323 261-0240
10430 Pioneer Blvd Ste 2 Santa Fe Springs (90670) *(P-25122)*
Regal Cultured Marble Inc....E....909 802-2388
1239 E Franklin Ave Pomona (91766) *(P-11276)*
Regal Custom Millwork Inc....F....714 632-2488
301 E Santa Ana St Anaheim (92805) *(P-4049)*
Regal Electronics Inc (PA)....E....408 988-2288
2029 Otoole Ave San Jose (95131) *(P-19705)*
Regal Furniture Manufacturing....F....323 971-9185
6007 S St Andrews Pl # 2 Los Angeles (90047) *(P-4806)*
Regal III LLC....D....707 836-2100
1190 Kittyhawk Blvd Windsor (95492) *(P-1943)*
Regal Kitchens LLC....C....786 953-6578
3480 Sunset Ln Oxnard (93035) *(P-4342)*
Regal Machine & Engrg Inc....E....323 773-7462
5200 E 60th St Maywood (90270) *(P-16891)*
Regal Mfg Co, City of Industry *Also called Creftcon Industries Inc (P-17510)*
Regal Wine Co, Windsor *Also called Regal III LLC (P-1943)*
Regards Enterprises Inc....F....909 983-0655
731 S Taylor Ave Ontario (91761) *(P-4601)*
Regency Fine Furniture, Los Angeles *Also called Roman Empire Furn Parts Mfg (P-4808)*
Regent Publishing Services....E....760 510-1936
5355 Mira Sorrento Pl # 100 San Diego (92121) *(P-6567)*
Regina F Barajas....F....760 500-0809
629 Fern St Escondido (92027) *(P-14187)*
Regional Mtls Recovery Inc....E....760 727-0878
2142 Industrial Ct Ste D Vista (92081) *(P-305)*
Registrar of Voters Office, Oakland *Also called County of Alameda (P-21682)*
Regusci Vineyard MGT Inc....E....707 254-0403
5584 Silverado Trl NAPA (94558) *(P-1944)*
Regusci Winery, NAPA *Also called Regusci Vineyard MGT Inc (P-1944)*
Rehau Constructions, Corona *Also called Rehau Incorporated (P-9789)*
Rehau Incorporated....F....951 549-9017
1250 Corona Pointe Ct # 301 Corona (92879) *(P-9789)*
Rehrig Pacific Company (HQ)....C....800 421-6244
4010 E 26th St Vernon (90058) *(P-10328)*
Rehrig Pacific Holdings Inc (PA)....F....323 262-5145
4010 E 26th St Vernon (90058) *(P-10329)*
Reichert Enterprises Inc....E....714 513-9199
2720 S Harbor Blvd Santa Ana (92704) *(P-23951)*
Reichert's Signs, Santa Ana *Also called Reichert Enterprises Inc (P-23951)*
Reichhold Chemicals, Azusa *Also called Reichhold Industries Inc (P-7879)*
Reichhold Industries Inc....F....626 334-4974
237 S Motor Ave Azusa (91702) *(P-7879)*
Reid & Clark Screen Arts Co....F....619 233-7541
722 33rd St San Diego (92102) *(P-2904)*
Reid Metal Finishing, Santa Ana *Also called Electrode Technologies Inc (P-13398)*
Reid Plastics, Ontario *Also called Consolidated Container Co LLC (P-9797)*
Reid Plastics Customer Svcs, City of Industry *Also called Consolidated Container Co LLC (P-10036)*
Reid Products Inc....E....760 240-1355
21430 Waalew Rd Apple Valley (92307) *(P-16892)*
Reinhart Oil & Gas Inc....F....760 753-3330
1953 San Elijo Ave # 200 Cardiff By The Sea (92007) *(P-71)*
Reinhold Industries Inc (HQ)....C....562 944-3281
12827 Imperial Hwy Santa Fe Springs (90670) *(P-10330)*
Reisner Enterprises Inc....F....951 786-9478
1403 W Linden St Riverside (92507) *(P-16893)*
Relateiq Inc....E....650 409-2336
502 Emerson St Palo Alto (94301) *(P-25123)*
Relational Center....E....323 935-1807
2717 S Robertson Blvd # 1 Los Angeles (90034) *(P-25124)*
Relativity Space Inc....F....972 978-8946
8701 Aviation Blvd Inglewood (90301) *(P-11749)*
Relaxis, San Clemente *Also called Sensory Neurostimulation Inc (P-8377)*
Relcomm Inc....F....209 736-0421
4868 Highway 4 Ste G Angels Camp (95222) *(P-19706)*
Reldom Corporation....E....562 498-3346
3241 Industry Dr Signal Hill (90755) *(P-20056)*
Relectric Inc....E....408 467-2222
2390 Zanker Rd San Jose (95131) *(P-17159)*
Reliable Mill Supply Co....F....707 462-1458
1550 Millview Rd Ukiah (95482) *(P-11415)*
Reliable Packaging Systems Inc....F....714 572-1094
3845 E Miraloma Ave Ste A Anaheim (92806) *(P-9167)*
Reliable Powder Coatings LLC....F....510 895-5551
1577 Factor Ave San Leandro (94577) *(P-13647)*
Reliable Rubber Products Inc....F....209 525-9750
2600 Yosemite Blvd Ste B Modesto (95354) *(P-9668)*
Reliable Sheet Metal Works, Fullerton *Also called Gard Inc (P-12594)*
Reliable Tape Products, Vernon *Also called Chua & Sons Inc (P-2798)*
Reliance Carpet Cushion, Huntington Park *Also called Reliance Upholstery Sup Co Inc (P-3745)*
Reliance Carpet Cushion, Vernon *Also called Reliance Upholstery Supply Inc (P-3015)*
Reliance Computer Corp....C....408 492-1915
2451 Mission College Blvd Santa Clara (95054) *(P-19120)*
Reliance Machine Products Inc....E....510 438-6760
4265 Solar Way Fremont (94538) *(P-16894)*
Reliance Rock, Irwindale *Also called Legacy Vulcan LLC (P-373)*
Reliance Upholstery Sup Co Inc....D....323 321-2300
5942 Santa Fe Ave Huntington Park (90255) *(P-3745)*
Reliance Upholstery Supply Inc....F....800 522-5252
4920 S Boyle Ave Vernon (90058) *(P-3015)*
Reliant Foodservice, Temecula *Also called Canadas Finest Foods Inc (P-942)*
Reloaded Technologies Inc....F....949 870-3123
17011 Beach Blvd Ste 320 Huntington Beach (92647) *(P-25125)*
Rels Foods Inc (PA)....F....510 652-2747
1814 Franklin St Ste 310 Oakland (94612) *(P-2651)*
Relton Corporation....D....800 423-1505
317 Rolyn Pl Arcadia (91007) *(P-9301)*
Relx Inc....E....415 908-3200
201 Mission St Fl 26 San Francisco (94105) *(P-6246)*
Relypsa Inc....B....650 421-9500
100 Cardinal Way Redwood City (94063) *(P-8359)*
Remanfctured Converter MBL LLC....F....714 744-8988
582 N Batavia St Orange (92868) *(P-15291)*
Remanufactured Converter MBL, Orange *Also called Remanfctured Converter MBL LLC (P-15291)*
Remba Partners LLC....F....310 858-8495
1419 E Adams Blvd Los Angeles (90011) *(P-6568)*
Remco, Livermore *Also called Rock Engineered McHy Co Inc (P-9355)*
Remco Mch & Fabrication Inc....F....909 877-3530
1966 S Date Ave Bloomington (92316) *(P-16895)*
Remcor Technical Industries....E....619 424-8878
7025 Alamitos Ave San Diego (92154) *(P-21412)*
Remec Broadband Wire....C....858 312-6900
17034 Camino San Bernardo San Diego (92127) *(P-18238)*
Remec Broadband Wireless LLC (PA)....C....858 312-6900
17034 Camino San Bernardo San Diego (92127) *(P-18239)*
Remedy Blinds Inc....D....714 245-0186
220 W Central Ave Santa Ana (92707) *(P-5207)*
Remington Inc....E....661 257-9400
28165 Avenue Crocker Valencia (91355) *(P-16100)*
Remington Roll Forming Inc....F....626 350-5196
2445 Chico Ave El Monte (91733) *(P-11471)*
Remo Inc (PA)....B....661 294-5600
28101 Industry Dr Valencia (91355) *(P-23383)*
Remote Ocean Systems Inc (PA)....E....858 565-8500
5618 Copley Dr San Diego (92111) *(P-17728)*
Rempex Pharmaceuticals Inc....E....858 875-2840
3013 Science Park Rd Fl 1 San Diego (92121) *(P-8360)*
Ren Acquisition Inc....F....209 245-6979
12225 Steiner Rd Plymouth (95669) *(P-1945)*

A L P H A B E T I C

Employee Codes: A=Over 500 employees, B=251-500
C=101-250, D=51-100, E=20-50, F=10-19
2019 California
Manfacturers Register
© Mergent Inc. 1-800-342-5647
1263

Ren Corporation.....F.....916 739-2000
2201 Francisco Dr El Dorado Hills (95762) ***(P-14099)***
Renaissance Doors & Windows, Rcho STA Marg *Also called Renaissnce Frnch Dors Sash Inc* ***(P-4219)***
Renaissance Food Group LLC (HQ).....E.....916 638-8825
11020 White Rock Rd # 100 Rancho Cordova (95670) ***(P-2652)***
Renaissance Food Inc.....F.....818 778-6230
14540 Friar St Van Nuys (91411) ***(P-1377)***
Renaissance Pastry, Van Nuys *Also called Renaissance Food Inc* ***(P-1377)***
Renaissance Precision Mfg Inc.....F.....925 691-5997
2551 Stanwell Dr Concord Concord (94520) ***(P-16896)***
Renaissance Wdwrk & Design Inc.....F.....818 787-7238
7605 Hazeltine Ave Unit B Van Nuys (91405) ***(P-4218)***
Renaissnce Frnch Dors Sash Inc (PA).....C.....714 578-0090
38 Segada Rcho STA Marg (92688) ***(P-4219)***
Renau Corporation.....E.....818 341-1994
9309 Deering Ave Chatsworth (91311) ***(P-21644)***
Renau Electronic Laboratories, Chatsworth *Also called Renau Corporation* ***(P-21644)***
Renee C.....F.....213 741-0095
127 E 9th St Ste 506 Los Angeles (90015) ***(P-3361)***
Renee Claire Inc, Los Angeles *Also called Camp Smidgemore Inc* ***(P-3390)***
Renee Rivera Hair Accessories.....F.....415 776-6613
2295 Chestnut St Ste 2 San Francisco (94123) ***(P-9669)***
Renesas Electronics Amer Inc.....A.....408 546-3434
205 Llagas Rd Morgan Hill (95037) ***(P-19121)***
Renesas Electronics Amer Inc (HQ).....B.....408 432-8888
1001 Murphy Ranch Rd Milpitas (95035) ***(P-19707)***
Renesas Electronics Amer Inc.....A.....408 588-6750
1541 Rollins Rd Burlingame (94010) ***(P-19122)***
Renesas Electronics Amer Inc.....A.....858 451-7240
10865 Rancho Bernardo Rd San Diego (92127) ***(P-19123)***
Renkus-Heinz Inc.....D.....949 588-9997
19201 Cook St Foothill Ranch (92610) ***(P-17849)***
Rennovia Inc.....F.....650 804-7400
3040 Oakmead Village Dr Santa Clara (95051) ***(P-9037)***
Reno News & Review, Chico *Also called Chico Community Publishing* ***(P-5797)***
Reno Tenco, Boron *Also called Rio Tinto Minerals Inc* ***(P-20)***
Renos Floor Covering Inc.....F.....415 459-1403
61 Paul Dr San Rafael (94903) ***(P-24015)***
Renovare International Inc (PA).....F.....510 748-9993
849 Balra Dr El Cerrito (94530) ***(P-16101)***
Rent All Party Works Inc.....F.....707 964-6661
18550 N Highway 1 Fort Bragg (95437) ***(P-25430)***
Rent What, Compton *Also called Sew What Inc* ***(P-3703)***
Rentech Inc (PA).....D.....310 571-9800
10880 Wilshire Blvd # 1101 Los Angeles (90024) ***(P-9457)***
Rentech Ntrgn Pasadena Spa LLC.....F.....310 571-9805
10877 Wilshire Blvd # 710 Los Angeles (90024) ***(P-9071)***
Renu Chem Inc.....F.....951 736-8072
572 Malloy Ct Corona (92880) ***(P-8674)***
Renwood Winery, Plymouth *Also called Ramador Inc* ***(P-1936)***
Reny & Co Inc.....F.....626 962-3078
4505 Littlejohn St Baldwin Park (91706) ***(P-10331)***
Renymed, Baldwin Park *Also called Reny & Co Inc* ***(P-10331)***
Rep-Kote Products Inc.....E.....909 355-1288
10938 Beech Ave Fontana (92337) ***(P-9417)***
Repet Inc.....C.....909 594-5333
14207 Monte Vista Ave Chino (91710) ***(P-9763)***
Replacement Parts Inds Inc.....E.....818 882-8611
625 Cochran St Simi Valley (93065) ***(P-22906)***
Replenish Inc.....F.....626 219-7867
73 N Vinedo Ave Pasadena (91107) ***(P-22599)***
Reporter.....D.....707 448-6401
916 Cotting Ln Vacaville (95688) ***(P-6026)***
Repose Corp.....F.....562 921-9299
16826 Edwards Rd Cerritos (90703) ***(P-17403)***
Repro Magic.....F.....858 277-2488
8585 Miramar Pl San Diego (92121) ***(P-7083)***
Reprodox, Santa Ana *Also called Maria Corporation* ***(P-7396)***
Repsco Inc.....E.....303 294-0364
5300 Claus Rd Ste 3 Modesto (95357) ***(P-10332)***
Republic Bag Inc (PA).....C.....951 734-9740
580 E Harrison St Corona (92879) ***(P-5618)***
Republic Furniture Mfg Inc.....E.....323 235-2144
2241 E 49th St Vernon (90058) ***(P-4807)***
Republic Machinery Co Inc (PA).....E.....310 518-1100
800 Sprucelake Dr Harbor City (90710) ***(P-14403)***
Res Med Inc.....E.....858 746-2400
9001 Spectrum Center Blvd San Diego (92123) ***(P-22600)***
Rescue 42 Inc.....F.....530 891-3473
370 Ryan Ave Ste 120 Chico (95973) ***(P-15356)***
Research & Dev GL Pdts &, Berkeley *Also called Research & Dev GL Pdts & Eqp* ***(P-10729)***
Research & Dev GL Pdts & Eqp.....F.....510 547-6464
1808 Harmon St Berkeley (94703) ***(P-10729)***
Research Metal Industries Inc.....E.....310 352-3200
1970 W 139th St Gardena (90249) ***(P-16897)***
Research Way Ll LLC.....F.....608 830-6300
1900 Main St Ste 375 Irvine (92614) ***(P-8361)***
Research Way Partners, Irvine *Also called Research Way Ll LLC* ***(P-8361)***
Residential Ctrl Systems Inc.....E.....916 635-6784
11481 Sunrise Gold Cir # 1 Rancho Cordova (95742) ***(P-21525)***
Resina.....F.....951 296-6585
27455 Bostik Ct Temecula (92590) ***(P-15914)***
Resinart Corporation.....E.....949 642-3665
1621 Placentia Ave Costa Mesa (92627) ***(P-10333)***
Resinart Plastics, Costa Mesa *Also called Resinart Corporation* ***(P-10333)***
Resmed Inc (PA).....B.....858 836-5000
9001 Spectrum Center Blvd San Diego (92123) ***(P-22601)***
Resmed Motor Technologies Inc.....C.....818 428-6400
9540 De Soto Ave Chatsworth (91311) ***(P-17219)***
Resonance Technology Inc.....F.....818 882-1997
18121 Parthenia St Ste A Northridge (91325) ***(P-23041)***
Resonant Inc (PA).....E.....805 308-9803
110 Castilian Dr Ste 100 Goleta (93117) ***(P-19124)***
Resource Cementing LLC.....F.....707 374-3350
2500 Airport Rd Rio Vista (94571) ***(P-264)***
Resource Ctr For Nonviolence, Santa Cruz *Also called Eschaton Foundation* ***(P-6809)***
Resource Label Group LLC.....E.....510 477-0707
30803 San Clemente St Hayward (94544) ***(P-7466)***
Respiratory Support Products.....E.....619 710-1000
9255 Customhouse Plz N San Diego (92154) ***(P-22602)***
Respironics Inc.....F.....562 483-6805
14101 Rosecrans Ave Ste F La Mirada (90638) ***(P-22803)***
Response Envelope Inc (PA).....C.....909 923-5855
1340 S Baker Ave Ontario (91761) ***(P-7467)***
Response Graphics In Print.....F.....949 376-8701
1065 La Mirada St Laguna Beach (92651) ***(P-7468)***
Resq Manufacturing.....E.....916 638-6786
11365 Sunrise Park Dr # 200 Rancho Cordova (95742) ***(P-24222)***
Resta Mattress, Rancho Cucamonga *Also called Comfort-Pedic Mattress USA* ***(P-4856)***
Restonic/San Francisco, Burlingame *Also called Sleeprite Industries Inc* ***(P-4887)***
Restoration Robotics Inc (PA).....D.....408 883-6888
128 Baytech Dr San Jose (95134) ***(P-22603)***
Resumemailman, Carlsbad *Also called Edirect Publishing Inc* ***(P-6473)***
Retail Print Media Inc.....E.....424 488-6950
2355 Crenshaw Blvd # 135 Torrance (90501) ***(P-7469)***
Retail Solutions Incorporated (PA).....E.....650 390-6100
201 Ravendale Dr Mountain View (94043) ***(P-25126)***
Retech Systems LLC.....C.....707 462-6522
100 Henry Station Rd Ukiah (95482) ***(P-12082)***
Rethink Label Systems, Anaheim *Also called Labeltronix LLC* ***(P-7379)***
Retrophin Inc (PA).....D.....760 260-8600
3721 Vly Cntre Dr Ste 200 San Diego (92130) ***(P-8362)***
Retrospect Inc.....E.....888 376-1078
44 Westwind Rd Lafayette (94549) ***(P-25127)***
Rettig Machine Inc.....E.....909 793-7811
301 Kansas St Redlands (92373) ***(P-25431)***
Reuland Electric Co (PA).....C.....626 964-6411
17969 Railroad St City of Industry (91748) ***(P-17220)***
Reuser Inc.....F.....707 894-4224
370 Santana Dr Cloverdale (95425) ***(P-4050)***
Reuters Television La, Los Angeles *Also called Thomson Reuters Corporation* ***(P-18286)***
Rev Co Spring Mfanufacturing.....F.....562 949-1958
9915 Alburtis Ave Santa Fe Springs (90670) ***(P-13801)***
Reva Medical Inc.....E.....858 966-3000
5751 Copley Dr Ste B San Diego (92111) ***(P-22804)***
Revance Therapeutics Inc.....C.....510 742-3400
7555 Gateway Blvd Newark (94560) ***(P-8363)***
Reveal Imaging Tech Inc.....D.....858 826-9909
10260 Campus Point Dr # 6133 San Diego (92121) ***(P-21413)***
Reveal Windows & Doors, Brea *Also called Pacific Archtectural Mllwk Inc* ***(P-4207)***
Revera Incorporated.....E.....408 510-7400
3090 Oakmead Village Dr Santa Clara (95051) ***(P-15837)***
Revere Packaging, Sacramento *Also called Plastic Package LLC* ***(P-10287)***
Reverie On Diamond Mtn LLC.....F.....707 942-6800
4410 Lake County Hwy Calistoga (94515) ***(P-1946)***
Reverie Winery, Calistoga *Also called Reverie On Diamond Mtn LLC* ***(P-1946)***
Reverse Medical Corporation.....F.....949 215-0660
13700 Alton Pkwy Ste 167 Irvine (92618) ***(P-22604)***
Reversica Design Inc.....F.....831 459-9033
1900 Commercial Way Ste A Santa Cruz (95065) ***(P-11987)***
Review Concierge, Solana Beach *Also called Expert Reputation LLC* ***(P-24636)***
Revivogen, Los Angeles *Also called Advanced Skin & Hair Inc* ***(P-8691)***
Revjet.....C.....650 508-2215
981 Industrial Rd Ste F San Carlos (94070) ***(P-25128)***
Revlon Inc.....E.....760 599-2900
1125 Joshua Way Ste 12 Vista (92081) ***(P-8828)***
Revo Payments, Venice *Also called Globalex Corporation* ***(P-24701)***
Revolution Enterprises Inc.....F.....858 679-5785
12170 Dearborn Pl Poway (92064) ***(P-23635)***
Revolution Lighting, Simi Valley *Also called Seesmart Inc* ***(P-17560)***
Revolution Lighting Tech Inc.....F.....248 969-3800
2280 Ward Ave Simi Valley (93065) ***(P-19125)***
Revolutionario, Los Angeles *Also called Susan Zadi* ***(P-2325)***
Rex Creamery, Commerce *Also called Heritage Distributing Company* ***(P-728)***
Rexhall Industries Inc.....E.....661 726-5470
26857 Tannahill Ave Canyon Country (91387) ***(P-20525)***
Rexnord Industries LLC.....F.....602 682-1764
1150 Etiwanda Ave Ontario (91761) ***(P-15292)***
Rexnord Industries LLC.....C.....805 583-5514
2175 Union Pl Simi Valley (93065) ***(P-14881)***
Rexnord LLC.....C.....909 467-8102
3690 Jurupa St Ontario (91761) ***(P-15245)***
Rey Nelson Printing Inc.....F.....909 947-3505
1955 S Starfire Ave Corona (92879) ***(P-7084)***
Reyes Coca-Cola Bottling LLC (PA).....B.....213 744-8616
3 Park Plz Ste 600 Irvine (92614) ***(P-2186)***
Reyes Coca-Cola Bottling LLC.....D.....661 324-6531
4320 Ride St Bakersfield (93313) ***(P-2187)***
Reyes Coca-Cola Bottling LLC.....D.....408 436-3700
1555 Old Bayshore Hwy San Jose (95112) ***(P-2188)***
Reyes Coca-Cola Bottling LLC.....D.....562 803-8100
8729 Cleta St Downey (90241) ***(P-2189)***
Reyes Coca-Cola Bottling LLC.....D.....510 476-7000
1551 Atlantic St Union City (94587) ***(P-2190)***

Mergent e-mail: customerrelations@mergent.com
1264
2019 California
Manufacturers Register
(P-0000) Products & Services Section entry number
(PA)=Parent Co (HQ)=Headquarters (DH)=Div Headquarters

Reyes Coca-Cola Bottling LLC .... C 510 667-6300
14655 Wicks Blvd San Leandro (94577) ***(P-2191)***
Reyes Coca-Cola Bottling LLC .... D 559 264-4631
3220 E Malaga Ave Fresno (93725) ***(P-2192)***
Reyes Coca-Cola Bottling LLC .... D 805 644-2211
5335 Walker St Ventura (93003) ***(P-2193)***
Reyes Coca-Cola Bottling LLC .... E 209 466-9501
1467 El Pinal Dr Stockton (95205) ***(P-2194)***
Reyes Coca-Cola Bottling LLC .... D 760 396-4500
86375 Industrial Way Coachella (92236) ***(P-2195)***
Reyes Coca-Cola Bottling LLC .... D 831 755-8300
715 Vandenberg St Salinas (93905) ***(P-2196)***
Reyes Coca-Cola Bottling LLC .... C 909 980-3121
10670 6th St Rancho Cucamonga (91730) ***(P-2197)***
Reyes Coca-Cola Bottling LLC .... D 805 614-3702
1000 Fairway Dr Santa Maria (93455) ***(P-2198)***
Reyes Coca-Cola Bottling LLC .... E 530 241-4315
1580 Beltline Rd Redding (96003) ***(P-2199)***
Reyes Coca-Cola Bottling LLC .... C 562 803-8165
8729 Cleta St Downey (90241) ***(P-2200)***
Reyes Coca-Cola Bottling LLC .... E 619 266-6300
1348 47th St San Diego (92102) ***(P-2201)***
Reyes Coca-Cola Bottling LLC .... D 323 278-2600
666 Union St Montebello (90640) ***(P-2202)***
Reyes Coca-Cola Bottling LLC .... E 530 743-6533
1430 Melody Rd Marysville (95901) ***(P-2203)***
Reyes Coca-Cola Bottling LLC .... C 714 974-1901
700 W Grove Ave Orange (92865) ***(P-2204)***
Reyes Coca-Cola Bottling LLC .... C 707 747-2000
530 Getty Ct Benicia (94510) ***(P-2205)***
Reyes Coca-Cola Bottling LLC .... E 213 744-8659
1338 E 14th St Los Angeles (90021) ***(P-2206)***
Reyes Coca-Cola Bottling LLC .... D 925 830-6500
2603 Camino Ramon Ste 550 San Ramon (94583) ***(P-2207)***
Reyes Coca-Cola Bottling LLC .... C 310 965-2653
19875 Pacific Gateway Dr Torrance (90502) ***(P-2208)***
Reyes Coca-Cola Bottling LLC .... E 760 241-2653
15346 Anacapa Rd Victorville (92392) ***(P-2209)***
Reyes Coca-Cola Bottling LLC .... E 760 352-1561
126 S 3rd St El Centro (92243) ***(P-2210)***
Reyes Machining, El Cajon *Also called Kings Crating Inc* ***(P-13237)***
Reyes Machining, El Cajon *Also called Kings Crating Inc* ***(P-20667)***
Reynaldos Mexican Food Co LLC (PA) .... C 562 803-3188
3301 E Vernon Ave Vernon (90058) ***(P-772)***
Reynard Corporation .... E 949 366-8866
1020 Calle Sombra San Clemente (92673) ***(P-22127)***
Reynolds Systems Inc .... F 707 928-5244
18649 State Highway 175 Middletown (95461) ***(P-13684)***
Reyrich Plastics Inc .... F 909 484-8444
1734 S Vineyard Ave Ontario (91761) ***(P-10334)***
Rezex Corporation .... E 213 622-2015
1901 Sacramento St Los Angeles (90021) ***(P-2917)***
Rf Communiactions, San Diego *Also called Harris Corporation* ***(P-21305)***
Rf Digital Corporation .... C 949 610-0008
1601 Pcf Cast Hwy Ste 290 Hermosa Beach (90254) ***(P-19126)***
Rf Industries Ltd (PA) .... D 858 549-6340
7610 Miramar Rd Ste 6000 San Diego (92126) ***(P-19411)***
Rf Precision Cables Inc .... F 714 772-7567
1600 S Anaheim Blvd Ste A Anaheim (92805) ***(P-11673)***
Rf Surgical Systems LLC .... D 855 522-7027
5927 Landau Ct Carlsbad (92008) ***(P-22605)***
Rf Techniques, San Jose *Also called M R F Techniques Inc* ***(P-19630)***
Rf-Lambda Usa LLC .... F 972 767-5998
10509 Vista Sorrento Pkwy # 120 San Diego (92121) ***(P-17298)***
Rfa Medical Solutions .... F 510 583-9500
40874 Calido Pl Fremont (94539) ***(P-23042)***
Rfc Wire Forms Inc .... D 909 467-0559
525 Brooks St Ontario (91762) ***(P-13850)***
Rfid4u, Concord *Also called Esmart Source Inc* ***(P-24627)***
Rfl Global Inc .... F 323 235-2580
732 E Jefferson Blvd Los Angeles (90011) ***(P-25129)***
RG Costumes & Accessories Inc .... E 626 858-9559
726 Arrow Grand Cir Covina (91722) ***(P-3677)***
Rga, Laguna Hills *Also called R Goodloe & Associates Inc* ***(P-7069)***
Rgb Spectrum .... D 510 814-7000
950 Marina Village Pkwy Alameda (94501) ***(P-15838)***
Rgb Systems Inc (PA) .... C 714 491-1500
1025 E Ball Rd Ste 100 Anaheim (92805) ***(P-15839)***
Rgb Systems Inc .... D 714 491-1500
1025 E Ball Rd Ste 100 Anaheim (92805) ***(P-15840)***
Rgblase LLC .... F 510 585-8449
3984 Washington Blvd # 306 Fremont (94538) ***(P-20057)***
RGF Enterprises Inc .... E 951 734-6922
220 Citation Cir Corona (92880) ***(P-13648)***
Rgm Products Inc .... B 559 499-2222
3301 Navone Rd Stockton (95215) ***(P-9418)***
Rgr Diversified Services Inc .... F 562 522-0028
5635 Panorama Dr Whittier (90601) ***(P-4882)***
Rh Products Inc .... E 510 794-6676
6756 Central Ave Ste E Newark (94560) ***(P-4503)***
RH Strasbaugh (PA) .... D 805 541-6424
825 Buckley Rd San Luis Obispo (93401) ***(P-14404)***
Rh Usa Inc .... E 925 245-7900
455 N Canyons Pkwy Ste B Livermore (94551) ***(P-22606)***
Rh Wood Products, Newark *Also called Rh Products Inc* ***(P-4503)***
Rhapsody Clothing Inc .... D 213 614-8887
3140 E Pico Blvd Unit A Los Angeles (90023) ***(P-3489)***
Rheetech Sales & Services Inc .... F 213 749-9111
2401 S Main St Los Angeles (90007) ***(P-7470)***
Rheosense Inc .... F 925 866-3801
2420 Camino Ramon Ste 240 San Ramon (94583) ***(P-22260)***
Rhino Linings Corporation (PA) .... D 858 450-0441
9747 Businesspark Ave San Diego (92131) ***(P-15136)***
Rhino Manufacturing Group Inc .... F 858 869-4010
14440 Meadowrun St San Diego (92129) ***(P-11416)***
Rhino Valve Usa Inc .... F 661 587-0220
5833 Pembroke Ave Bakersfield (93308) ***(P-13732)***
Rhodes Publications Inc .... F 213 385-4781
3600 Wilshire Blvd # 1526 Los Angeles (90010) ***(P-6247)***
RHS Gas Inc .... F 310 710-2331
520 W Pacific Coast Hwy Long Beach (90806) ***(P-9354)***
Rhubcommunications Inc .... F 408 899-2830
4340 Stevens Creek Blvd San Jose (95129) ***(P-20058)***
Rhys Vineyards LLC .... F 650 419-2050
11715 Skyline Blvd Los Gatos (95033) ***(P-1947)***
Rl, Santa Clara *Also called Roos Instruments Inc* ***(P-21841)***
Riah Fashion Inc .... F 323 325-7308
1820 E 46th St Vernon (90058) ***(P-3490)***
Rialto Concrete Products, Rialto *Also called Kti Incorporated* ***(P-10946)***
Rialto Record, San Bernardino *Also called Inland Empire Cmnty Newspapers* ***(P-5888)***
Ricardo Ochoa .... F 530 668-1152
281 N Pioneer Ave Woodland (95776) ***(P-5455)***
Ricaurte Precision Inc .... E 714 667-0632
1550 E Mcfadden Ave Santa Ana (92705) ***(P-16898)***
Rice Field Corporation .... C 626 968-6917
14500 Valley Blvd City of Industry (91746) ***(P-519)***
Rich Chicks LLC .... E 209 879-4104
13771 Gramercy Pl Gardena (90249) ***(P-550)***
Rich Chicks LLC (PA) .... E 209 879-4104
4276 N Tracy Blvd Tracy (95304) ***(P-551)***
Rich Chicks, Rich In Nutrition, Tracy *Also called Rich Chicks LLC* ***(P-551)***
Rich Limited, Oceanside *Also called Britcan Inc* ***(P-5128)***
Rich Products .... F 510 234-7547
1041 Broadway Ave San Pablo (94806) ***(P-20439)***
Rich Products Corporation .... C 559 486-7380
320 O St Fresno (93721) ***(P-2321)***
Rich Xiberta Usa Inc .... F 707 795-1800
450 Aaron St Cotati (94931) ***(P-4647)***
Richandre Inc .... F 310 762-1560
1170 Sandhill Ave Carson (90746) ***(P-1011)***
Richard Paola .... F 442 500-8231
300 Carlsbad Village Dr # 104 Carlsbad (92008) ***(P-691)***
Richard E Cox Interprizes, Rocklin *Also called Vanishing Vistas* ***(P-6615)***
Richard J Trevino MD .... F 408 926-5300
175 N Jackson Ave Ste 200 San Jose (95116) ***(P-22805)***
Richard K Gould Inc .... E 916 371-5943
788 Northport Dr West Sacramento (95691) ***(P-9302)***
Richard Macdonald Studios Inc (PA) .... F 831 655-0424
16 Lower Ragsdale Dr Monterey (93940) ***(P-11369)***
Richard Matz .... E 858 537-2280
6780 Miramar Rd Ste 202 San Diego (92121) ***(P-6027)***
Richard Ray Custom Designs .... F 323 937-5685
11350 Alethea Dr Sunland (91040) ***(P-17557)***
Richard Tyler, Alhambra *Also called Tyler Trafficante Inc* ***(P-3046)***
Richard Veeck .... F 209 667-0872
9966 Golf Link Rd Hilmar (95324) ***(P-15019)***
Richard Yarbrough .... E 805 643-1021
2493 N Ventura Ave Ventura (93001) ***(P-265)***
Richards Label Co Inc .... F 714 529-1791
17291 Mount Herrmann St Fountain Valley (92708) ***(P-5576)***
Richards Machining Co Inc .... F 408 526-9219
2161 Del Franco St San Jose (95131) ***(P-16899)***
Richards Neon Shop Inc .... E 951 279-6767
4375 Prado Rd Ste 102 Corona (92880) ***(P-23952)***
Richardson Steel Inc .... E 619 697-5892
9102 Harness St Ste A Spring Valley (91977) ***(P-12236)***
Richee Lighting Inc .... F 213 814-1638
1600 W Washington Blvd Los Angeles (90007) ***(P-17729)***
Richer Poorer Inc .... F 949 388-9994
27132 Paseo Espada B1225 San Juan Capistrano (92675) ***(P-2813)***
Riches International Inc .... F 760 598-3366
2530 Fortune Way Vista (92081) ***(P-21134)***
Richfield Engineering Inc .... E 714 524-3741
1135 Fee Ana St Placentia (92870) ***(P-12414)***
Richline Group Inc .... C 818 848-5555
455 N Moss St Burbank (91502) ***(P-23308)***
Richline Group Inc .... C 818 848-5555
443 N Varney St Burbank (91502) ***(P-23309)***
Richline Textile Inc .... E 323 792-1030
1706 Maple Ave Los Angeles (90015) ***(P-2760)***
Richmond Engineering Co Inc .... D 800 589-7058
15472 Markar Rd San Diego (92154) ***(P-24223)***
Richmond Metal Painting .... F 510 232-7541
1143 Marina Way S Richmond (94804) ***(P-13649)***
Richmond Optical Co .... F 510 783-1420
923 Berryessa Rd San Jose (95133) ***(P-23119)***
Richter Furniture Mfg 2002 .... C 323 588-7900
28720 Canwood St Ste 108 Agoura Hills (91301) ***(P-5251)***
Richter Furniture Mfr Rfm, Agoura Hills *Also called Richter Furniture Mfg 2002* ***(P-5251)***
Richview By Tehdex, City of Industry *Also called Ht Window Fashions Corporation* ***(P-5193)***
Richwood Meat Company Inc .... D 209 722-8171
2751 N Santa Fe Ave Merced (95348) ***(P-450)***
Rick Palenshus .... F 951 245-2100
560 3rd St Lake Elsinore (92530) ***(P-15020)***
Rick's Hitches & Welding, El Cajon *Also called C L P Inc* ***(P-25390)***
Ricks America Inc .... F 323 232-6800
2828 Stanford Ave Los Angeles (90011) ***(P-2864)***

ALPHABETIC

Employee Codes: A=Over 500 employees, B=251-500
C=101-250, D=51-100, E=20-50, F=10-19
2019 California
Manfacturers Register
© Mergent Inc. 1-800-342-5647
1265

Rickshaw Bagworks Inc...E...415 904-8368
904 22nd St San Francisco (94107) **(P-3769)**
Ricky Reader LLC...F...323 231-4322
6715 Mckinley Ave Unit B Los Angeles (90001) **(P-6386)**
Ricman Mfg Inc...E...510 670-1785
2273 American Ave Ste 1 Hayward (94545) **(P-16900)**
Rico Corporation (HQ)...E...818 394-2700
8484 San Fernando Rd Sun Valley (91352) **(P-23384)**
Rico Holdings Inc...C...818 394-2700
8484 San Fernando Rd Sun Valley (91352) **(P-23385)**
Rico Products, Sun Valley *Also called Rico Corporation* **(P-23384)**
Ricoh Development California, Tustin *Also called Ricoh Electronics Inc* **(P-23193)**
Ricoh Electronics Inc (HQ)...B...714 566-2500
1100 Valencia Ave Tustin (92780) **(P-23193)**
Ricoh Electronics Inc...B...714 259-1220
1100 Valencia Ave Tustin (92780) **(P-15915)**
Ricoh Prtg Systems Amer Inc (HQ)...B...805 578-4000
2390 Ward Ave Ste A Simi Valley (93065) **(P-15841)**
Ricon Corp (HQ)...C...818 267-3000
1135 Aviation Pl San Fernando (91340) **(P-24224)**
Rideau Vineyard LLC...F...805 688-0717
1562 Alamo Pintado Rd Solvang (93463) **(P-1948)**
Rider Circulation Services...F...323 344-1200
1324 Cypress Ave Los Angeles (90065) **(P-6028)**
Ridge Cast Metals, San Leandro *Also called Ridge Foundry Inc* **(P-11500)**
Ridge Cementing LLC...F...530 476-3333
7085 Eddy Rd G Arbuckle (95912) **(P-266)**
Ridge Foundry Inc...E...510 352-0551
1554 Doolittle Dr San Leandro (94577) **(P-11500)**
Ridgeline, Stockton *Also called Rgm Products Inc* **(P-9418)**
Ridgeline Engineering Company, Vista *Also called Rec Inc* **(P-15355)**
Ridgeline Power LLC...E...800 504-5844
12100 Wilshire Blvd 805 Los Angeles (90025) **(P-19127)**
Ridout Plastics Company...E...858 560-1551
5535 Ruffin Rd San Diego (92123) **(P-9724)**
Riedel Communications Inc...F...818 559-6900
2508 N Ontario St Burbank (91504) **(P-18359)**
Riedon Inc...F...562 926-2304
13065 Tom White Way Ste F Norwalk (90650) **(P-21839)**
Riedon Inc (PA)...C...626 284-9901
300 Cypress Ave Alhambra (91801) **(P-19309)**
Rieke Corporation...C...707 238-9250
1200 Valley House Dr # 100 Rohnert Park (94928) **(P-13148)**
Riffyn Inc (PA)...F...510 542-9868
360 17th St Ste 100 Oakland (94612) **(P-25130)**
Rigel Pharmaceuticals Inc (PA)...C...650 624-1100
1180 Veterans Blvd South San Francisco (94080) **(P-8364)**
Riggins Engineering Inc...E...818 782-7010
13932 Saticoy St Van Nuys (91402) **(P-16901)**
Right Away Concrete Pmpg Inc...E...510 536-1900
401 Kennedy St Oakland (94606) **(P-11161)**
Right Hand Manufacturing Inc...C...619 819-5056
180 Otay Lakes Rd Ste 205 Bonita (91902) **(P-17299)**
Right Height, Yorba Linda *Also called Arbon Equipment Corporation* **(P-14310)**
Right Manufacturing LLC...E...858 566-7002
7949 Stromesa Ct Ste G San Diego (92126) **(P-13902)**
Rightway, Vernon *Also called R B R Meat Company Inc* **(P-447)**
Rigiflex Technology Inc...E...714 688-1500
1166 N Grove St Anaheim (92806) **(P-18580)**
Rignoli Pacific, Monterey Park *Also called Rigoli Enterprises Inc* **(P-20059)**
Rigoli Enterprises Inc...F...626 573-0242
1983 Potrero Grande Dr Monterey Park (91755) **(P-20059)**
Rigos Equipment Mfg LLC...E...626 813-6621
14501 Joanbridge St Baldwin Park (91706) **(P-12737)**
Rigos Sheet Metal, Baldwin Park *Also called Rigos Equipment Mfg LLC* **(P-12737)**
Rileys TANks/D&j Service...F...559 237-1403
3261 S Elm Ave Fresno (93706) **(P-12415)**
Rima Enterprises Inc...D...714 893-4534
5340 Argosy Ave Huntington Beach (92649) **(P-14827)**
Rima-System, Huntington Beach *Also called Rima Enterprises Inc* **(P-14827)**
Rimnetics Inc...E...650 969-6590
3445 De La Cruz Blvd Santa Clara (95054) **(P-10335)**
Rinat Neuroscience Corp...F...650 615-7300
230 E Grand Ave South San Francisco (94080) **(P-8365)**
Rinco International Inc...F...510 785-1633
31056 Genstar Rd Hayward (94544) **(P-9880)**
Rincon Engineering Corporation...E...805 684-0935
6325 Carpinteria Ave Carpinteria (93013) **(P-16902)**
Ring Container Tech LLC...E...209 238-3426
3643 Finch Rd Modesto (95357) **(P-9807)**
Ring Container Tech LLC...E...909 350-8416
8275 Almeria Ave Fontana (92335) **(P-9808)**
Ring LLC (HQ)...B...800 656-1918
1523 26th St Santa Monica (90404) **(P-17118)**
Ring of Fire, Van Nuys *Also called Rof LLC* **(P-3119)**
Rinsekit, Carlsbad *Also called Outsol Inc* **(P-9908)**
Rio Pluma Company LLC (HQ)...E...530 846-5200
1900 Highway 99 Gridley (95948) **(P-852)**
Rio Tinto Minerals Inc...C...760 762-7121
14486 Borax Rd Boron (93516) **(P-20)**
Rios-Lovell Estate Winery...E...925 443-0434
6500 Tesla Rd Livermore (94550) **(P-1949)**
Rios-Lovell Winery, Livermore *Also called Rios-Lovell Estate Winery* **(P-1949)**
Rip Curl Inc (HQ)...D...714 422-3600
3030 Airway Ave Costa Mesa (92626) **(P-23636)**
Rip Curl USA, Costa Mesa *Also called Rip Curl Inc* **(P-23636)**
Rip-Tie Inc...F...510 577-0200
883 San Leandro Blvd San Leandro (94577) **(P-2978)**

Ripon Mfg Co...E...209 599-2148
652 S Stockton Ave Ripon (95366) **(P-14882)**
Ripon Milling LLC (PA)...E...209 599-4269
30636 E Carter Rd Farmington (95230) **(P-1159)**
Ripon Volunteer Firemans Assn...F...209 599-4209
142 S Stockton Ave Ripon (95366) **(P-20168)**
Rippling, San Francisco *Also called People Center Inc* **(P-25054)**
Risco Inc...E...951 769-2899
390 Risco Cir Beaumont (92223) **(P-13081)**
Rising Beverage Company LLC...D...310 556-4500
10351 Santa Monica Blvd # 210 Los Angeles (90025) **(P-2211)**
Risvolds Inc...D...323 770-2674
1234 W El Segundo Blvd Gardena (90247) **(P-2653)**
Rita Medical Systems Inc (HQ)...D...510 771-0400
46421 Landing Pkwy Fremont (94538) **(P-23043)**
Ritas Felicita...F...760 975-3302
1875 S Centre City Pkwy Escondido (92025) **(P-692)**
Ritas Fine Food...F...619 698-3925
8900 Grossmont Blvd Ste 5 La Mesa (91941) **(P-2654)**
Ritchey Design Inc (PA)...F...650 368-4018
236 N Santa Cruz Ave # 238 Los Gatos (95030) **(P-21135)**
Rite Screen, Rancho Cucamonga *Also called J T Walker Industries Inc* **(P-12321)**
Rite Track Equipment Svcs Inc...F...408 432-0131
2151 Otoole Ave Ste 40 San Jose (95131) **(P-15021)**
Ritec, Simi Valley *Also called Rugged Info Tech Eqp Corp* **(P-15844)**
Ritemp Refrigeration Inc...F...909 941-0444
9155 Archibald Ave # 503 Rancho Cucamonga (91730) **(P-17383)**
Ritescreen Inc...F...800 949-4174
33444 Western Ave Union City (94587) **(P-4220)**
Rivas Industries Inc...F...951 880-8638
6687 Havenhurst St Corona (92880) **(P-7085)**
River City...E...707 253-1111
505 Lincoln Ave NAPA (94558) **(P-5252)**
River City Lithography, Rocklin *Also called J & M Printing Inc* **(P-6900)**
River City Millwork Inc...E...916 364-8981
3045 Fite Cir Sacramento (95827) **(P-4221)**
River City Print and Mail Inc...F...916 638-8400
2431 Mercantile Dr Ste G Rancho Cordova (95742) **(P-7086)**
River City Printers LLC...E...916 638-8400
2431 Mercantile Dr Ste G Rancho Cordova (95742) **(P-7087)**
River City Restaurant, NAPA *Also called River City* **(P-5252)**
River Ready Mix, Forestville *Also called Canyon Rock Co Inc* **(P-351)**
River Valley Precast Inc...E...928 764-3839
14796 Washington Dr Fontana (92335) **(P-10992)**
Rivera Yarn Products Inc...E...619 661-6306
1690 Cactus Rd San Diego (92154) **(P-2804)**
Riverbed Technology Inc (HQ)...D...415 247-8800
680 Folsom St Ste 500 San Francisco (94107) **(P-15842)**
Riverbend Rice Mill Inc...F...530 458-8561
234 Main St Colusa (95932) **(P-1090)**
Rivermeadow Software Inc...F...408 217-6498
2107 N 1st St Ste 660 San Jose (95131) **(P-25131)**
Riverside Bulletin & Jurupa Th, Riverside *Also called Metropolitan News Company* **(P-5969)**
Riverside Foundary, Riverside *Also called Oldcast Precast* **(P-10963)**
Riverside Lamination Corp...F...951 682-0100
3016 Kansas Ave Bldg 6 Riverside (92507) **(P-9168)**
Riverside Machine Works Inc...F...951 685-7416
6301 Baldwin Ave Riverside (92509) **(P-16903)**
Riverside Tent & Awning Co...F...951 683-1925
231 E Alcandro Blvd Ste A Riverside (92508) **(P-3770)**
Riviana Foods Inc...D...559 485-8110
2704 S Maple Ave Fresno (93725) **(P-2655)**
Riviera Beverages LLC...E...714 895-5169
12782 Monarch St Garden Grove (92841) **(P-2212)**
Rizo-Lopez Foods Inc...C...800 626-5587
201 S Mcclure Rd Modesto (95357) **(P-595)**
RJ Acquisition Corp (PA)...C...323 318-1107
3260 E 26th St Vernon (90058) **(P-7471)**
Rj Boudreau Inc...F...209 480-3172
1641 Princeton Ave Ste 6 Modesto (95350) **(P-14100)**
RJ Jewelry Inc...F...213 627-9936
650 S Hill St Ste 414 Los Angeles (90014) **(P-23310)**
Rj Machine Inc...F...858 547-9482
7985 Dunbrook Rd Ste E San Diego (92126) **(P-16904)**
Rj Media...F...510 938-8667
1860 Mowry Ave Ste 200 Fremont (94538) **(P-6029)**
RJ Mfg...F...209 632-9708
1201 S Blaker Rd Turlock (95380) **(P-2979)**
RJ Singer International Inc...D...323 735-1717
4801 W Jefferson Blvd Los Angeles (90016) **(P-10532)**
RJA Industries Inc...E...818 998-5124
9640 Topanga Canyon Pl J Chatsworth (91311) **(P-19708)**
Rjb, Modesto *Also called Rj Boudreau Inc* **(P-14100)**
Rjw & Assoc...F...818 706-0289
31700 Dunraven Ct Ste 100 Thousand Oaks (91361) **(P-6569)**
Rk Sport Inc...E...951 894-7883
26900 Jefferson Ave Murrieta (92562) **(P-20440)**
Rkd Engineering Corp Inc...F...831 430-9464
316 S Navarra Dr Scotts Valley (95066) **(P-19128)**
Rks Inc (HQ)...F...858 571-4444
1955 Cordell Ct Ste 104 El Cajon (92020) **(P-20060)**
Rlf Print Shop, Fresno *Also called Dreamteam Business Group LLC* **(P-7304)**
Rlh Industries Inc (PA)...E...714 532-1672
936 N Main St Orange (92867) **(P-17989)**
Rls Enterprises...E...714 493-1735
25072 Wilkes Pl Laguna Hills (92653) **(P-10336)**
Rlt Seafood Supermarket Inc...F...909 888-6520
333 S E St San Bernardino (92401) **(P-2301)**

Mergent e-mail: customerrelations@mergent.com
1266
2019 California
Manufacturers Register
(P-0000) Products & Services Section entry number
(PA)=Parent Co (HQ)=Headquarters (DH)=Div Headquarters

Rlv Tuned Exhaust Products ....E....805 925-5461
2351 Thompson Way Bldg A Santa Maria (93455) *(P-20441)*
Rm 518 Management LLC ....E....213 624-6788
719 S Los Angeles St Los Angeles (90014) *(P-3678)*
RMC, Ripon *Also called Ripon Mfg Co (P-14882)*
RMC Engineering Co Inc (PA) ....E....408 842-2525
255 Mayock Rd Gilroy (95020) *(P-16905)*
RMC Pacific Materials Inc ....E....209 835-1454
30350 S Tracy Blvd Tracy (95377) *(P-10769)*
RMC Pacific Materials Inc ....C....831 429-7200
700 Highway 1 Davenport (95017) *(P-10770)*
RMC Pacific Materials Inc (HQ) ....C....925 426-8787
6601 Koll Center Pkwy Pleasanton (94566) *(P-10771)*
RMC Pacific Materials Inc ....E....925 846-2824
1544 Stanley Blvd Pleasanton (94566) *(P-11162)*
Rmf Salt Holdings LLC ....F....510 477-9600
30984 Santana St Hayward Hayward (94544) *(P-8829)*
Rmi, Livermore *Also called Ratermann Manufacturing Inc (P-10327)*
Rmjv LP ....B....503 526-5752
3285 Corporate Vw Vista (92081) *(P-14883)*
Rmla Inc ....D....213 749-4333
1972 E 20th St Vernon (90058) *(P-3594)*
RMR Products Inc (PA) ....E....818 890-0896
11011 Glenoaks Blvd Ste 1 Pacoima (91331) *(P-10993)*
RMS Monty Crystal, Cardiff By The Sea *Also called Reinhart Oil & Gas Inc (P-71)*
RMS Printing LLC ....F....818 707-2625
5331 Derry Ave Ste N Agoura Hills (91301) *(P-7088)*
Rnb Vending Inc ....F....714 548-6993
9353 Bolsa Ave Ste A49 Westminster (92683) *(P-15926)*
Rnc, Los Angeles *Also called Rnovate Inc (P-15293)*
Rnd Contractors Inc ....E....909 429-8500
14796 Jurupa Ave Ste A Fontana (92337) *(P-12237)*
Rnd Enterprises, Chatsworth *Also called BDR Industries Inc (P-15679)*
Rnj Printing Corporation ....F....310 638-7768
16005 S Broadway Gardena (90248) *(P-7089)*
Rnk Industries Co ....F....323 446-0777
2816 E 11th St Los Angeles (90023) *(P-2761)*
Rnovate Inc ....E....213 489-1617
834 S Broadway Los Angeles (90014) *(P-15293)*
RNS Channel Letters, Corona *Also called Richards Neon Shop Inc (P-23952)*
Ro Gar Mfg, El Centro *Also called Rogar Manufacturing Inc (P-19710)*
Ro Generation Inc ....F....323 771-5416
1528 Highland Ave Duarte (91010) *(P-5729)*
Roa Pacific Inc ....F....619 565-2800
1225 Exposition Way San Diego (92154) *(P-7880)*
Roach Bros Inc (PA) ....E....707 964-9240
23550 Shady Ln Fort Bragg (95437) *(P-4007)*
Road Champs Inc (HQ) ....E....310 456-7799
22619 Pacific Coast Hwy Malibu (90265) *(P-23460)*
Road Vista, San Diego *Also called Gamma Scientific Inc (P-22205)*
Roadracing World Publishing ....F....951 245-6411
581 Birch St Ste C Lake Elsinore (92530) *(P-6248)*
Roadrunner Circuit Technology ....F....714 671-9517
23201 Mill Creek Dr Laguna Hills (92653) *(P-18581)*
Roadster Wheels Inc ....F....626 333-3007
14955 Don Julian Rd City of Industry (91746) *(P-20442)*
Roadwire Distinctive Inds, Santa Fe Springs *Also called Distinctive Inds Texas Inc (P-3613)*
Roan Mills LLC ....F....818 249-4686
11069 Penrose St Sun Valley (91352) *(P-1048)*
Rob Inc (PA) ....D....562 806-5589
6760 Foster Bridge Blvd Bell Gardens (90201) *(P-3086)*
Robanda International Inc ....E....619 276-7660
8260 Cmino Santa Fe Ste A San Diego (92121) *(P-8830)*
Robar Enterprises Inc (PA) ....C....760 244-5456
17671 Bear Valley Rd Hesperia (92345) *(P-11163)*
Robb Curtco Media LLC ....E....310 589-7700
29160 Heathercliff Rd # 200 Malibu (90265) *(P-6249)*
Robb-Jack Corporation (PA) ....D....916 645-6045
3300 Nicolaus Rd Ste 1 Lincoln (95648) *(P-14405)*
Robbins Auto Top LLC ....D....805 278-8249
321 Todd Ct Oxnard (93030) *(P-10337)*
Robbins Precast, Corona *Also called Nucast Industries Inc (P-10962)*
Robecks Wldg & Fabrication Inc ....E....408 287-0202
1150 Mabury Rd Ste 1 San Jose (95133) *(P-12238)*
Robeks Corporation ....F....310 642-7800
8905 S Sepulveda Blvd Los Angeles (90045) *(P-2656)*
Robeks Corporation ....F....310 838-2332
3891 Overland Ave Culver City (90232) *(P-853)*
Robeks Juice, Los Angeles *Also called Robeks Corporation (P-2656)*
Robeks Juice, Culver City *Also called Robeks Corporation (P-853)*
Robert A Kerl ....E....818 341-9281
8930 Quartz Ave Northridge (91324) *(P-7613)*
Robert Biale Vineyards, NAPA *Also called Biale Estate (P-1660)*
Robert Bosch LLC ....E....805 966-2000
2030 Alameda Padre Serra Santa Barbara (93103) *(P-22607)*
Robert Bosch Stiftung GMBH, Palo Alto *Also called Bosch Enrgy Stor Solutions LLC (P-17182)*
Robert Bosch Tool Corporation ....C....760 357-5603
302 E 3rd St 31-1812 Calexico (92231) *(P-14709)*
Robert Crowder & Co Inc ....F....323 248-7737
901 S Greenwood Ave Ste L Montebello (90640) *(P-9670)*
Robert E Blake Inc ....F....415 391-2255
135 Clara St San Francisco (94107) *(P-21012)*
Robert F Chapman Inc ....D....661 940-9482
43100 Exchange Pl Lancaster (93535) *(P-12738)*
Robert Grove ....F....619 562-1268
1860 Joe Crosson Dr El Cajon (92020) *(P-20622)*
Robert H Oliva Inc ....E....818 700-1035
19863 Nordhoff St Northridge (91324) *(P-16906)*
Robert J Alandt & Sons ....E....559 275-1391
4692 N Brawley Ave Fresno (93722) *(P-16907)*
Robert M Hadley Company Inc ....D....805 658-7286
4054 Transport St Ste B Ventura (93003) *(P-19359)*
Robert Mann Packaging, Oceanside *Also called Pratt Industries Inc (P-5327)*
Robert Mondavi Corporation (HQ) ....D....707 967-2100
166 Gateway Rd E NAPA (94558) *(P-1950)*
Robert Mondavi Corporation ....E....209 365-2995
770 N Guild Ave Lodi (95240) *(P-1951)*
Robert P Martin Company ....F....323 686-2220
2209 Seaman Ave South El Monte (91733) *(P-11453)*
Robert P Von Zabern ....F....951 734-7215
4121 Tigris Way Riverside (92503) *(P-22608)*
Robert R Wix Inc (PA) ....E....209 537-4561
2140 Pine St Ceres (95307) *(P-7472)*
Robert Snell Cast Specialist ....F....530 273-8958
110 Spring Hill Dr Ste 20 Grass Valley (95945) *(P-23347)*
Robert Talbott Inc (PA) ....E....831 649-6000
24560 Silver Cloud Ct Monterey (93940) *(P-3040)*
Robert W Cameron & Co Inc ....F....707 769-1617
149 Kentucky St Ste 7 Petaluma (94952) *(P-6387)*
Robert W Wiesmantel ....F....562 634-0442
15345 Allen St Paramount (90723) *(P-16908)*
Robert Yick Company Inc ....E....415 282-9707
261 Bay Shore Blvd San Francisco (94124) *(P-16102)*
Robert's Engineering, Anaheim *Also called Roberts Precision Engrg Inc (P-16909)*
Roberto Martinez Inc ....F....800 257-6462
1050 Calle Cordillera # 103 San Clemente (92673) *(P-23311)*
Roberts Ferry Nut Company Inc ....F....209 874-3247
20493 Yosemite Blvd Waterford (95386) *(P-1449)*
Roberts Precision Engrg Inc ....E....714 635-4485
1345 S Allec St Anaheim (92805) *(P-16909)*
Roberts Research Laboratory ....F....310 320-7310
23150 Kashiwa Ct Torrance (90505) *(P-13696)*
Roberts Tool Company Inc (PA) ....C....818 341-3344
20409 Prairie St Chatsworth (91311) *(P-16159)*
Robertson Precision Inc ....F....650 363-2212
2971 Spring St Redwood City (94063) *(P-19129)*
Robertson-Ceco II Corporation ....C....209 727-5504
12101 E Brandt Rd Lockeford (95237) *(P-12959)*
Robertsons Distributors Inc ....F....951 849-4766
1990 N Hargrave St Banning (92220) *(P-11164)*
Robertsons Rdy Mix Ltd A Cal ....F....909 337-7577
2975 Hwy 18 Lake Arrowhead (92352) *(P-11165)*
Robertsons Rdy Mix Ltd A Cal ....F....760 246-4000
12203 Violet Rd Adelanto (92301) *(P-11166)*
Robertsons Ready Mix Ltd (HQ) ....D....951 493-6500
200 S Main St Ste 200 # 200 Corona (92882) *(P-11167)*
Robertsons Ready Mix Ltd ....E....909 623-9185
2470 Pomona Blvd Pomona (91768) *(P-11168)*
Robertsons Ready Mix Ltd ....E....800 834-7557
200 S Main St Ste 200 # 200 Corona (92882) *(P-11169)*
Robertsons Ready Mix Ltd ....E....909 425-2930
27401 3rd St Highland (92346) *(P-11170)*
Robeworks, Alhambra *Also called Victoire LLC (P-3605)*
Robin's Jeans, Bell Gardens *Also called Rob Inc (P-3086)*
Robinson Engineering Corp ....F....951 361-8000
3575 Grapevine St Mira Loma (91752) *(P-14718)*
Robinson Family Winery ....F....707 287-8428
5880 Silverado Trl NAPA (94558) *(P-1952)*
Robinson Farms Feed Company ....F....209 466-7915
7000 S Inland Dr Stockton (95206) *(P-1160)*
Robinson Helicopter Co Inc ....A....310 539-0508
2901 Airport Dr Torrance (90505) *(P-20623)*
Robinson Pharma Inc (PA) ....B....714 241-0235
3330 S Harbor Blvd Santa Ana (92704) *(P-8366)*
Robinson Pharma Inc ....C....714 241-0235
2811 S Harbor Blvd Santa Ana (92704) *(P-8367)*
Robinson Printing Inc ....E....951 296-0300
42685 Rio Nedo Temecula (92590) *(P-7473)*
Robinson Textiles Inc ....E....310 527-8110
24532 Woodward Ave Lomita (90717) *(P-3041)*
Robledo Family Winery Inc (PA) ....F....707 939-6903
21901 21903 Bonness Rd Sonoma (95476) *(P-1953)*
Robles Bros Inc (PA) ....E....408 436-5551
1700 Rogers Ave San Jose (95112) *(P-2657)*
Roboworm Inc ....F....805 389-1636
764 Calle Plano Camarillo (93012) *(P-23637)*
Robson Technologies Inc ....E....408 779-8008
135 E Main Ave Ste 130 Morgan Hill (95037) *(P-16910)*
ROC-Aire Corp ....E....909 784-3385
2198 Pomona Blvd Pomona (91768) *(P-16911)*
Rocateq North America ....F....925 648-7794
4155 Blackhwk Lasas Cir Danville (94506) *(P-13851)*
Rochas Cabinets ....F....209 239-2367
108 Industrial Park Dr # 17 Manteca (95337) *(P-4343)*
Roche Pharmaceuticals ....E....908 635-5692
4300 Hacienda Dr Pleasanton (94588) *(P-8368)*
Rochester Midland Corporation ....E....800 388-4762
7275 Sycamore Canyon Blvd # 101 Riverside (92508) *(P-5671)*
Rock & Roll Custom Paint Works ....E....714 744-0631
1630 S Sunkist St Ste N Anaheim (92806) *(P-15022)*
Rock & Sand Plant, San Diego *Also called Legacy Vulcan LLC (P-11130)*
Rock Engineered McHy Co Inc ....F....925 447-0805
263 S Vasco Rd Livermore (94551) *(P-9355)*
Rock Rag Inc ....F....818 919-9364
913 N Highland Ave Los Angeles (90038) *(P-6570)*
Rock Revival, Vernon *Also called Rcrv Inc (P-5617)*

ALPHABETIC

Employee Codes: A=Over 500 employees, B=251-500
C=101-250, D=51-100, E=20-50, F=10-19
2019 California
Manfacturers Register
© Mergent Inc. 1-800-342-5647
1267

Rock Solid Stone LLC...F.......760 731-6191
308 Industrial Way Ste B Fallbrook (92028) ***(P-10994)***
Rock Wall Wine Company Inc...E.......510 522-5700
2301 Monarch St Alameda (94501) ***(P-1954)***
Rock West Composites Inc (PA)...E.......801 566-3402
1602 Precision Park Ln San Diego (92173) ***(P-9764)***
Rock-Ola Manufacturing Corp...D.......310 328-1306
2335 W 208th St Torrance (90501) ***(P-17850)***
Rocker Industries, Harbor City *Also called Rocker Solenoid Company* ***(P-19709)***
Rocker Solenoid Company...D.......310 534-5660
1500 240th St Harbor City (90710) ***(P-19709)***
Rocket Ems Inc...C.......408 727-3700
2950 Patrick Henry Dr Santa Clara (95054) ***(P-18582)***
Rocket Shop, Folsom *Also called Aerojet Rocketdyne Inc* ***(P-20716)***
Rocketstar Robotics Inc...F.......805 529-7769
177 Estaban Dr Camarillo (93010) ***(P-17221)***
Rockstar Inc...C.......323 785-2820
8530 Wilshire Blvd Fl 3 Beverly Hills (90211) ***(P-2213)***
Rockstar Energy Drink, Beverly Hills *Also called Rockstar Inc* ***(P-2213)***
Rockwell Automation Inc...D.......714 938-9000
2125 E Katella Ave # 250 Anaheim (92806) ***(P-17300)***
Rockwell Automation Inc...E.......714 828-1800
5836 Corporate Ave Cypress (90630) ***(P-17301)***
Rockwell Automation Inc...D.......408 443-5425
111 N Market St Ste 200 San Jose (95113) ***(P-17302)***
Rockwell Automation Inc...E.......925 242-5700
3000 Executive Pkwy # 210 San Ramon (94583) ***(P-17303)***
Rockwell Collins Inc...C.......310 751-3298
4553 Glencoe Ave Ste 100 Marina Del Rey (90292) ***(P-21414)***
Rockwell Collins Inc...D.......714 929-3000
1733 Alton Pkwy Irvine (92606) ***(P-21415)***
Rockwell Collins Inc...E.......760 540-2232
1757 Carr Rd Calexico (92231) ***(P-21416)***
Rockwell Collins Optronics Inc...F.......319 295-1000
2752 Loker Ave W Carlsbad (92010) ***(P-21417)***
Rocky Label Mills Inc...E.......323 278-0080
1930 Doreen Ave South El Monte (91733) ***(P-2805)***
Rod L Electronics Inc (PA)...F.......650 322-0711
935 Sierra Vista Ave F Mountain View (94043) ***(P-21840)***
Rodak Plastics Co Inc...F.......510 471-0898
31721 Knapp St Hayward (94544) ***(P-10338)***
Rode Microphones LLC...C.......310 328-7456
2745 Raymond Ave Signal Hill (90755) ***(P-17851)***
Rodon Products Inc...E.......714 898-3528
15481 Electronic Ln Ste A Huntington Beach (92649) ***(P-19360)***
Rodriguez Ismael...F.......805 736-7362
138 N D St Lompoc (93436) ***(P-2400)***
Rods Unfinished Furniture...E.......626 281-9855
1121 S Meridian Ave Alhambra (91803) ***(P-4735)***
Roettele Industries...F.......909 606-8252
15485 Dupont Ave Chino (91710) ***(P-9551)***
Rof LLC...E.......818 933-4000
7800 Arprt Bus Pkwy Ste B Van Nuys (91406) ***(P-3119)***
Rogar Manufacturing Inc...C.......760 335-3700
866 E Ross Ave El Centro (92243) ***(P-19710)***
Roger Cleveland Golf Co Inc (PA)...C.......714 889-1300
5601 Skylab Rd Huntington Beach (92647) ***(P-23638)***
Roger Enrico...B.......559 485-5050
1150 E North Ave Fresno (93725) ***(P-2214)***
Roger Industry...F.......714 896-0765
11552 Knott St Ste 5 Garden Grove (92841) ***(P-18583)***
Roger R Caruso Enterprises Inc...E.......714 778-6006
2911 Norton Ave Lynwood (90262) ***(P-4504)***
Rogers Corporation...D.......562 404-8942
13937 Rosecrans Ave Santa Fe Springs (90670) ***(P-9671)***
Rogers Holding Company Inc...E.......714 257-4850
1130 Columbia St Brea (92821) ***(P-20921)***
Rogerson Aircraft Corporation (PA)...C.......949 660-0666
2201 Alton Pkwy Irvine (92606) ***(P-21418)***
Rogerson Kratos...C.......626 449-3090
403 S Raymond Ave Pasadena (91105) ***(P-21419)***
Rogue River Rifleworks Inc...F.......805 227-4611
570 Linne Rd Ste 110 Paso Robles (93446) ***(P-23639)***
Rogue River Super Scopes, Paso Robles *Also called Rogue River Rifleworks Inc* ***(P-23639)***
Rohr Inc (HQ)...A.......619 691-4111
850 Lagoon Dr Chula Vista (91910) ***(P-20922)***
Rohrback Cosasco Systems Inc (HQ)...D.......562 949-0123
11841 Smith Ave Santa Fe Springs (90670) ***(P-21645)***
Rolenn Manufacturing Inc...E.......951 682-1185
1549 Marlborough Ave Riverside (92507) ***(P-24225)***
Rolenn Manufacturing Inc (PA)...E.......951 682-1185
2065 Roberta St Riverside (92507) ***(P-10339)***
Roll Technology West, Pittsburg *Also called Chrome Deposit Corp* ***(P-13371)***
Roll-A-Shade Inc (PA)...E.......951 245-5077
12101 Madera Way Riverside (92503) ***(P-5208)***
Roller Bones, Santa Barbara *Also called Skate One Corp* ***(P-23651)***
Rollin Industries, San Diego *Also called Yellow Inc* ***(P-23694)***
Rollin J. Lobaugh, Belmont *Also called Pacific Screw Products Inc* ***(P-13036)***
Rolls-Royce Corporation...B.......510 635-1500
7200 Earhart Rd Oakland (94621) ***(P-20676)***
Roltec Gasket Manufacturing, Corona *Also called Elastomer Technologies Inc* ***(P-9527)***
Roma Bakery Inc...D.......408 294-0123
655 S Almaden Ave San Jose (95110) ***(P-1315)***
Roma Fabricating Corporation...E.......760 727-8040
2638 S Santa Fe Ave San Marcos (92069) ***(P-10995)***
Roma Marble & Tile, San Marcos *Also called Roma Fabricating Corporation* ***(P-10995)***
Roma Moulding Inc...E.......626 334-2539
6230 N Irwindale Ave Irwindale (91702) ***(P-4648)***
Romac Supply Co Inc...D.......323 721-5810
7400 Bandini Blvd Commerce (90040) ***(P-17160)***
Romakk Engineering, Northridge *Also called Robert H Oliva Inc* ***(P-16906)***
Roman Empire Furn Parts Mfg...E.......323 264-8857
4466 Worth St Los Angeles (90063) ***(P-4808)***
Roman Global Resources Inc...F.......949 276-4100
1027 Calle Trepadora # 2 San Clemente (92673) ***(P-9552)***
Roman Kruchowhy...F.......805 386-7939
6486 Palomino Cir Somis (93066) ***(P-19711)***
Roman Upholstery Manufacturing...F.......310 479-3252
2008 Cotner Ave Los Angeles (90025) ***(P-4809)***
Romance Ring, Moorpark *Also called Star Ring Inc* ***(P-23319)***
Rombauer Vineyards Inc...D.......707 963-5170
3522 Silverado Trl N Saint Helena (94574) ***(P-1955)***
Romeo Packing Company...E.......650 728-3393
106 Princeton Ave Half Moon Bay (94019) ***(P-5647)***
Romeo Power, Vernon *Also called Romeo Systems Inc* ***(P-20061)***
Romeo Systems Inc...C.......323 675-2180
4380 Ayers Ave Vernon (90058) ***(P-20061)***
Romeros Food Products Inc (PA)...D.......562 802-1858
15155 Valley View Ave Santa Fe Springs (90670) ***(P-2658)***
Romeros Food Products Inc...F.......909 884-5531
993 S Waterman Ave San Bernardino (92408) ***(P-2659)***
Romeros Welding & Mar Svcs Inc...F.......925 550-0518
519 Waterfront Ave Vallejo (94592) ***(P-25432)***
Romi Industries Inc...F.......661 294-1142
25443 Rye Canyon Rd Valencia (91355) ***(P-16912)***
Romi Machine Shop, Valencia *Also called Romi Industries Inc* ***(P-16912)***
Romla Co...E.......619 946-1224
9668 Heinrich Hertz Dr D San Diego (92154) ***(P-12739)***
Romla Ventilator Co, San Diego *Also called Romla Co* ***(P-12739)***
Ron & Diana Vanatta...F.......530 888-0200
332 Sacramento St Auburn (95603) ***(P-5098)***
Ron Grose Racing Inc...F.......209 368-2571
488 E Kettleman Ln Lodi (95240) ***(P-16913)***
Ron Kehl Engineering...F.......408 629-6632
384 Umbarger Rd Ste B San Jose (95111) ***(P-13491)***
Ron Nunes Enterprises LLC...F.......925 371-0220
7703 Las Positas Rd Livermore (94551) ***(P-12740)***
Ron Teeguarden Enterprises Inc (PA)...E.......323 556-8188
5670 Wilshire Blvd # 1500 Los Angeles (90036) ***(P-7968)***
Ron Ungar...F.......805 642-3555
4700 Aurora Dr Spc 114 Ventura (93003) ***(P-15226)***
Ron Witherspoon Inc...D.......831 633-3568
13525 Blackie Rd Castroville (95012) ***(P-16914)***
Ronald D Teson Inc...E.......310 532-5987
13945 Mckinley Ave Los Angeles (90059) ***(P-4090)***
Ronald F Ogletree Inc...E.......707 963-3537
935 Vintage Ave Saint Helena (94574) ***(P-12741)***
Ronan Engineering Company (PA)...D.......661 702-1344
28209 Avenue Stanford Valencia (91355) ***(P-21646)***
Ronan Engnrng/Rnan Msrment Div, Valencia *Also called Ronan Engineering Company* ***(P-21646)***
Ronatec C2c Inc...F.......760 476-1890
5651 Palmer Way Ste H Carlsbad (92010) ***(P-9303)***
Roncelli Plastics Inc...D.......626 359-2551
330 W Duarte Rd Monrovia (91016) ***(P-7881)***
Ronco Plastics Incorporated...E.......714 259-1385
15022 Parkway Loop Ste B Tustin (92780) ***(P-10340)***
Rondor Music International (PA)...F.......310 235-4800
2440 S Sepulveda Blvd # 119 Los Angeles (90064) ***(P-6571)***
Ronford Products Inc...E.......909 622-7446
1116 E 2nd St Pomona (91766) ***(P-10341)***
Ronlo Engineering Ltd...E.......805 388-3227
955 Flynn Rd Camarillo (93012) ***(P-16915)***
Ronpak Inc...E.......951 685-3800
10900 San Sevaine Way Mira Loma (91752) ***(P-5332)***
Rooke Manufacturing Co...F.......714 540-6943
3360 W Harvard St Santa Ana (92704) ***(P-16916)***
Roos Instruments Inc...E.......408 748-8589
2285 Martin Ave Santa Clara (95050) ***(P-21841)***
Rootlieb Inc...F.......209 632-2203
815 S Soderquist Rd Turlock (95380) ***(P-13142)***
Ropak Corporation (HQ)...E.......714 845-2845
10540 Talbert Ave 200w Fountain Valley (92708) ***(P-10342)***
Ropak Packaging, Fountain Valley *Also called Ropak Corporation* ***(P-10342)***
Roplast Industries Inc...C.......530 532-9500
3155 S 5th Ave Oroville (95965) ***(P-5619)***
Rosa Brothers Milk Co Inc (PA)...E.......559 582-8825
10090 2nd Ave Hanford (93230) ***(P-693)***
Rosa's Cafe & Tortilla Factory, Temecula *Also called Chh Lp* ***(P-2487)***
Rosco Laboratories Inc...F.......800 767-2652
9420 Chivers Ave Sun Valley (91352) ***(P-23194)***
Roscoe Moss Company, Los Angeles *Also called Roscoe Moss Manufacturing Co* ***(P-11485)***
Roscoe Moss Manufacturing Co (PA)...D.......323 261-4185
4360 Worth St Los Angeles (90063) ***(P-11485)***
Roscoe Moss Manufacturing Co...D.......323 263-4111
4360 Worth St Los Angeles (90063) ***(P-11486)***
Rose Art Industries, Irvine *Also called Mega Brands America Inc* ***(P-23446)***
Rose Business Solutions Inc...E.......858 794-9401
875 Chelsea Ln Encinitas (92024) ***(P-25132)***
Rose Chem Intl - USA Corp...E.......678 510-8864
25 Rainbow Fls Irvine (92603) ***(P-8369)***
Rose Genuine Inc...F.......213 747-4120
834 S Broadway Ste 1100 Los Angeles (90014) ***(P-3586)***
Rose Manufacturing Group Inc...F.......760 407-0232
2525 Jason Ct Ste 102 Oceanside (92056) ***(P-13492)***
Rose Metal Products Inc...D.......417 865-1676
1754 Tech Dr Ste 100 San Jose (95110) ***(P-12239)***

Rosedale Medical, Fremont *Also called Intuity Medical Inc* ***(P-22491)***
Roselm Industries Inc.....E.....626 442-6840
2510 Seaman Ave South El Monte (91733) ***(P-18240)***
Rosemead Oil Products Inc.....F.....562 941-3261
12402 Los Nietos Rd Santa Fe Springs (90670) ***(P-9448)***
Rosen & Rosen Industries Inc.....D.....949 361-9238
204 Avenida Fabricante San Clemente (92672) ***(P-23640)***
Rosenkranz Enterprises Inc.....F.....323 583-9021
2447 E 54th St Los Angeles (90058) ***(P-13493)***
Rosetti Gennaro Furniture.....E.....323 750-7794
6833 Brynhurst Ave Los Angeles (90043) ***(P-4736)***
Roseville Press-Tribune, Roseville *Also called Contra Costa Newspapers Inc* ***(P-5817)***
Rosewill Inc.....E.....626 271-1420
17708 Rowland St City of Industry (91748) ***(P-15478)***
Ross Bindery Inc.....C.....562 623-4565
15310 Spring Ave Santa Fe Springs (90670) ***(P-7614)***
Ross Fabrication & Welding Inc.....F.....661 393-1242
1154 Basta Ave Bakersfield (93308) ***(P-4649)***
Ross Hay, Lincoln *Also called Marybelle Farms Inc* ***(P-1147)***
Ross Name Plate Company.....E.....323 725-6812
2 Red Plum Cir Monterey Park (91755) ***(P-23953)***
Ross Periodicals, Novato *Also called Excellence Magazine Inc* ***(P-6161)***
Ross Publications Inc.....E.....562 691-5013
113 W Amerige Ave Fullerton (92832) ***(P-6572)***
Ross Racing Pistons.....D.....310 536-0100
625 S Douglas St El Segundo (90245) ***(P-16151)***
Rossmoor Pastries MGT Inc.....D.....562 498-2253
2325 Redondo Ave Signal Hill (90755) ***(P-1316)***
Rostar Auto Filter Mfg Corp.....C.....805 278-2555
1278 Mercantile St Oxnard (93030) ***(P-15357)***
Rostar Filters, Oxnard *Also called Rostar Auto Filter Mfg Corp* ***(P-15357)***
Rotary Club of Ajai West.....E.....805 646-3794
1129 Maricopa Hwy Ojai (93023) ***(P-1956)***
Rotary Corp.....F.....559 445-1108
3359 E North Ave Ste 102 Fresno (93725) ***(P-14132)***
Rotating Prcsion McHanisms Inc.....E.....818 349-9774
8750 Shirley Ave Northridge (91324) ***(P-18241)***
Rotational Molding Inc.....D.....310 327-5401
17038 S Figueroa St Gardena (90248) ***(P-10343)***
Rotax Incorporated.....E.....323 589-5999
2940 Leonis Blvd Vernon (90058) ***(P-3491)***
Rotech Engineering Inc.....E.....714 632-0532
1020 S Melrose St Ste A Placentia (92870) ***(P-19712)***
Rotex Punch Company Inc (PA).....F.....510 357-3600
2350 Alvarado St San Leandro (94577) ***(P-14566)***
Roth Wood Products Ltd.....E.....408 723-8888
2260 Canoas Garden Ave San Jose (95125) ***(P-5253)***
Rothlisberger Mfg A Cal Corp.....F.....818 786-9462
14718 Arminta St Van Nuys (91402) ***(P-16917)***
Roto Lite Inc.....E.....909 923-4353
2161 Maple Privado Ontario (91761) ***(P-10344)***
Roto Power Inc.....F.....951 751-9850
191 Granite St Ste A Corona (92879) ***(P-10345)***
Roto West Enterprises Inc.....F.....714 899-2030
15651 Container Ln Huntington Beach (92649) ***(P-10346)***
Roto-Die Company Inc.....F.....714 991-8701
712 N Valley St Ste B Anaheim (92801) ***(P-14567)***
Rotometrics, Anaheim *Also called Roto-Die Company Inc* ***(P-14567)***
Rotoplas, Merced *Also called Molding Acquisition Corp* ***(P-7855)***
Rotork Controls Inc.....F.....707 769-4880
419 1st St Petaluma (94952) ***(P-17304)***
Rotron Incorporated.....F.....619 593-7400
474 Raleigh Ave El Cajon (92020) ***(P-15174)***
Rotta Winery Inc.....F.....805 237-0510
250 Winery Rd Templeton (93465) ***(P-1957)***
Rouchon Industries Inc.....F.....310 763-0336
3729 San Gabriel River Pk Pico Rivera (90660) ***(P-15843)***
Roudybush Inc (PA).....F.....530 668-6196
340 Hanson Way Woodland (95776) ***(P-1161)***
Rouge & Noir, Petaluma *Also called Marin French Cheese Company* ***(P-592)***
Round Hill Cellars.....D.....707 968-3200
1680 Silverado Trl S Saint Helena (94574) ***(P-1958)***
Rounds Logging Company.....E.....530 247-0517
4350 Lynbrook Loop Apt 1 Redding (96003) ***(P-4008)***
Rox Medical Inc (PA).....E.....949 276-8968
150 Calle Iglesia Ste A San Clemente (92672) ***(P-23044)***
Roxwood Medical Inc.....F.....650 779-4555
400 Seaport Ct Ste 103 Redwood City (94063) ***(P-22609)***
Roy & Val Tool Grinding Inc.....F.....818 341-2434
10131 Canoga Ave Chatsworth (91311) ***(P-16918)***
Roy E Hanson Jr Mfg (PA).....D.....213 747-7514
1600 E Washington Blvd Los Angeles (90021) ***(P-12416)***
Royal Adhesives & Sealants LLC.....F.....949 863-1499
16731 Hale Ave Irvine (92606) ***(P-9169)***
Royal Angelus Macaroni Company.....C.....909 627-7312
2539 E Philadelphia St Ontario (91761) ***(P-2660)***
Royal Apparel Inc.....D.....626 579-5168
4331 Baldwin Ave El Monte (91731) ***(P-3492)***
Royal Blue Inc.....E.....310 888-0156
9025 Wilshire Blvd # 301 Beverly Hills (90211) ***(P-3746)***
Royal Cabinets, Pomona *Also called Royal Industries Inc* ***(P-4345)***
Royal Cabinets Inc.....A.....909 629-8565
1299 E Phillips Blvd Pomona (91766) ***(P-4344)***
Royal Chemical Company Ltd.....F.....510 782-8727
2498 American Ave Hayward (94545) ***(P-8607)***
Royal Circuit Solutions Inc (PA).....E.....831 636-7789
21 Hamilton Ct Hollister (95023) ***(P-18584)***
Royal Coatings, Simi Valley *Also called Mabel Baas Inc* ***(P-13615)***
Royal Custom Designs Inc.....C.....909 591-8990
13951 Monte Vista Ave Chino (91710) ***(P-4810)***
Royal Custom Parquet, Santa Fe Springs *Also called Hamar Wood Parquet Company* ***(P-4038)***
Royal Drapery and Interiors, NAPA *Also called Royal Drapery Manufacturing* ***(P-3700)***
Royal Drapery Manufacturing.....F.....707 226-2022
3149 California Blvd K NAPA (94558) ***(P-3700)***
Royal Flex Circuits Inc.....E.....562 404-0626
15320 Cornet St Santa Fe Springs (90670) ***(P-18585)***
Royal Industries, Eastvale *Also called Royal Range California Inc* ***(P-17375)***
Royal Industries Inc.....C.....909 629-8565
1299 E Phillips Blvd Pomona (91766) ***(P-4345)***
Royal Interpack Midwest Inc.....F.....626 675-0637
475 Palmyrita Ave Riverside (92507) ***(P-10347)***
Royal Interpack North Amer Inc.....E.....951 787-6925
475 Palmyrita Ave Riverside (92507) ***(P-10348)***
Royal Manufacturing Inds Inc.....F.....714 668-9199
600 W Warner Ave Santa Ana (92707) ***(P-12742)***
Royal Metal, Santa Ana *Also called Ted Rieck Enterprises Inc* ***(P-12785)***
Royal Mountain King, Copperopolis *Also called Meridian Gold Inc* ***(P-7)***
Royal Paper Box Co California (PA).....C.....323 728-7041
1105 S Maple Ave Montebello (90640) ***(P-5508)***
Royal Range California Inc.....D.....951 360-1600
3245 Corridor Dr Eastvale (91752) ***(P-17375)***
Royal Riders.....F.....408 779-1997
120 Mast St Ste B Morgan Hill (95037) ***(P-3961)***
Royal Robbins LLC.....E.....209 529-6913
1524 Princeton Ave Modesto (95350) ***(P-23641)***
Royal Stall.....F.....559 875-8100
1865 Industrial Way Sanger (93657) ***(P-12886)***
Royal Systems Group.....F.....818 717-5010
18301 Napa St Northridge (91325) ***(P-14765)***
Royal Trim.....E.....323 583-2121
2529 Chambers St Vernon (90058) ***(P-3916)***
Royal Welding & Fabricating, Fullerton *Also called Cook and Cook Incorporated* ***(P-12383)***
Royal Wine Corporation.....E.....805 983-1560
3201 Camino Del Sol Oxnard (93030) ***(P-1959)***
Royal-Pedic Mattress Mfg LLC.....E.....310 518-5420
331 N Fries Ave Wilmington (90744) ***(P-4883)***
Royale Energy Funds Inc.....F.....619 383-6600
1870 Cordell Ct Ste 210 El Cajon (92020) ***(P-72)***
Royalite Mfg Inc.....F.....650 637-1440
1055 Terminal Way San Carlos (94070) ***(P-12743)***
Royalpedic Mattress Mfg, Wilmington *Also called Royal-Pedic Mattress Mfg LLC* ***(P-4883)***
Royce Records, Oakland *Also called B-Flat Publishing LLC* ***(P-6444)***
Rozak Engineering Inc.....F.....714 446-8855
556 S State College Blvd Fullerton (92831) ***(P-16919)***
Rozendal Associates Inc.....F.....619 562-5596
9530 Pathway St Ste 101 Santee (92071) ***(P-21420)***
Rpc Inc.....F.....619 647-9911
9457 Adlai Ter Lakeside (92040) ***(P-267)***
RPC Legacy Inc.....D.....818 787-9000
14600 Arminta St Van Nuys (91402) ***(P-11988)***
RPI, Simi Valley *Also called Replacement Parts Inds Inc* ***(P-22906)***
RPM, Northridge *Also called Rotating Prcsion McHanisms Inc* ***(P-18241)***
RPM Embroidery Inc.....F.....949 650-0085
1614 Babcock St Costa Mesa (92627) ***(P-3860)***
RPM Grinding Co Inc.....F.....951 273-0602
1755 Commerce St Norco (92860) ***(P-16920)***
RPM Plastic Molding Inc.....E.....714 630-9300
2821 E Miraloma Ave Anaheim (92806) ***(P-10349)***
RPM Products Inc (PA).....E.....949 888-8543
23272 Arroyo Vis Rcho STA Marg (92688) ***(P-9553)***
RPS Inc.....E.....818 350-8088
20331 Corisco St Chatsworth (91311) ***(P-13852)***
Rpsz Construction LLC.....E.....314 677-5831
1201 W 5th St Ste T340 Los Angeles (90017) ***(P-23642)***
RR Donnelley, Ontario *Also called R R Donnelley & Sons Company* ***(P-7459)***
RR Donnelley & Sons Company.....B.....209 983-6700
3837 Producers Dr Stockton (95206) ***(P-7090)***
RR Donnelley & Sons Company.....E.....949 852-1933
19200 Von Karman Ave # 700 Irvine (92612) ***(P-7474)***
RR Donnelley & Sons Company.....A.....310 516-3100
19681 Pacific Gateway Dr Torrance (90502) ***(P-7475)***
RR Donnelley & Sons Company.....F.....916 929-8632
1765 Challenge Way # 220 Sacramento (95815) ***(P-7552)***
RR Donnelley & Sons Company.....E.....949 476-0505
19200 Von Karman Ave # 700 Irvine (92612) ***(P-7553)***
RR Donnelley & Sons Company.....E.....650 845-6600
855 N California Ave A Palo Alto (94303) ***(P-7584)***
RR Donnelley Financial, Palo Alto *Also called RR Donnelley & Sons Company* ***(P-7584)***
Rrds Inc (PA).....F.....949 284-6239
12 Goodyear Ste 100 Irvine (92618) ***(P-22128)***
Rs Machining Co Inc.....F.....818 718-0097
9726 Cozycroft Ave Chatsworth (91311) ***(P-16921)***
RS Technical Services Inc (PA).....D.....707 778-1974
1327 Clegg St Petaluma (94954) ***(P-22011)***
Rsa Engineered Products LLC.....D.....805 584-4150
110 W Cochran St Ste A Simi Valley (93065) ***(P-20923)***
Rsdg International Inc.....E.....626 256-4190
2127 Aralia St Newport Beach (92660) ***(P-3587)***
Rsg/Aames Security Inc.....E.....562 529-5100
3300 E 59th St Long Beach (90805) ***(P-18360)***
RSI Home Products Inc (HQ).....A.....714 449-2200
400 E Orangethorpe Ave Anaheim (92801) ***(P-4840)***
RSI Home Products Inc.....A.....949 720-1116
620 Newport Center Dr # 1200 Newport Beach (92660) ***(P-4841)***
RSI Home Products Mfg Inc.....D.....714 449-2200
400 E Orangethorpe Ave Anaheim (92801) ***(P-4842)***
Rsk Tool Incorporated.....E.....310 537-3302
410 W Carob St Compton (90220) ***(P-10350)***

ALPHABETIC

Employee Codes: A=Over 500 employees, B=251-500
C=101-250, D=51-100, E=20-50, F=10-19
2019 California
Manfacturers Register
© Mergent Inc. 1-800-342-5647
1269

RSR Metal Spinning Inc......F......626 814-2339
850 E Edna Pl Covina (91723) *(P-12744)*
Rss Manufacturing......F......714 361-4800
1261 Logan Ave Costa Mesa (92626) *(P-12048)*
Rta Sales Inc......F......661 942-3553
210 E Avenue L Ste A Lancaster (93535) *(P-4222)*
RTC Aerospace, Chatsworth *Also called Cliffdale Manufacturing LLC (P-21188)*
RTC Aerospace, Chatsworth *Also called Logistical Support LLC (P-20668)*
Rte Welding, Fontana *Also called Tikos Tanks Inc (P-25444)*
Rtec-Instruments Inc......E......408 456-0801
1810 Oakland Rd Ste B San Jose (95131) *(P-22012)*
Rtg Inc......F......310 534-3016
4030 Spencer St Ste 108 Torrance (90503) *(P-19130)*
Rtg Investment Group Inc......F......310 444-5554
149 S Barrington Ave Los Angeles (90049) *(P-23643)*
Rti, City of Industry *Also called Rectangular Tubing Inc (P-5493)*
Rti, Gardena *Also called D & D Plastics Incorporated (P-10057)*
Rti Los Angeles, Norwalk *Also called New Cntury Mtals Southeast Inc (P-11634)*
Rtie Holdings LLC......D......714 765-8200
1800 E Via Burton Anaheim (92806) *(P-19713)*
Rtl Electronics......F......310 320-0451
1972 Del Amo Blvd Ste D Torrance (90501) *(P-23701)*
Rtm Products Inc......E......562 926-2400
13120 Arctic Cir Santa Fe Springs (90670) *(P-11417)*
Rtmex Inc......C......619 391-9913
1202 Piper Ranch Rd San Diego (92154) *(P-4091)*
Rtr Industries LLC......E......714 996-0050
1360 N Jefferson St Anaheim (92807) *(P-16152)*
RTS Oil Holdings Inc......E......714 665-8777
1306 E Edinger Ave Ste C Santa Ana (92705) *(P-148)*
RTS Packaging LLC......D......209 722-2787
1900 Wardrobe Ave Merced (95341) *(P-5730)*
RTS Powder Coating Inc (PA)......E......909 393-5404
15121 Sierra Bonita Ln Chino (91710) *(P-13650)*
Rubber Plastic & Metal Pdts, Rcho STA Marg *Also called RPM Products Inc (P-9553)*
Rubber Teck Division, Long Beach *Also called Rubbercraft Corp Cal Ltd (P-9574)*
Rubbercraft Corp Cal Ltd (HQ)......C......562 354-2800
3701 E Conant St Long Beach (90808) *(P-9574)*
Rubberite Corp (PA)......F......714 546-6464
301 Goetz Ave Santa Ana (92707) *(P-9672)*
Rubberite Cypress Sponge Rubbe, Santa Ana *Also called Rubberite Corp (P-9672)*
Rubberite Cypress Sponge Rubbe, Santa Ana *Also called Cypress Sponge Rubber Products (P-9605)*
Rubel Marguerite Mfg Co......F......415 362-2626
27 Pier San Francisco (94111) *(P-3362)*
Ruben and Sharam, Los Angeles *Also called RJ Singer International Inc (P-10532)*
Ruben Ortiz, Sacramento *Also called Capitol Steel Products (P-11290)*
Rubens Jewelry Mfg, Los Angeles *Also called RJ Jewelry Inc (P-23310)*
Rubicon Express (PA)......F......916 858-8575
3290 Monier Cir Ste 100 Rancho Cordova (95742) *(P-15023)*
Rubicon Manufacturing, Rancho Cordova *Also called Rubicon Express (P-15023)*
Rubio Fabrics, Sacramento *Also called McCarthys Draperies Inc (P-3698)*
Ruby Rox, Los Angeles *Also called Misyd Corp (P-3584)*
Rucci Inc......F......323 778-9000
6700 11th Ave Los Angeles (90043) *(P-24226)*
Rucker & Knolls, Milpitas *Also called Rucker & Kolls Inc (P-15024)*
Rucker & Kolls Inc (HQ)......E......408 934-9875
1064 Yosemite Dr Milpitas (95035) *(P-15024)*
Rucker Mill & Cabinet Works......F......530 621-0236
5828 Mother Lode Dr Placerville (95667) *(P-4346)*
Ruckus Wireless Inc......E......408 235-5500
2450 Walsh Ave Santa Clara (95051) *(P-17990)*
Rudd Winery, Oakville *Also called Rudd Wines Inc (P-1960)*
Rudd Wines Inc (PA)......E......707 944-8577
500 Oakville Xrd Oakville (94562) *(P-1960)*
Rudex Broadcasting Ltd Corp......F......213 494-3377
12272 Sarazen Pl Granada Hills (91344) *(P-18242)*
Rudolph Foods Company Inc......D......909 388-2202
920 W Fourth St Beaumont (92223) *(P-2401)*
Rudolph International Inc......E......714 529-5696
1150 Beacon St Brea (92821) *(P-8831)*
Rugged Info Tech Eqp Corp (PA)......E......805 577-9710
25 E Easy St Simi Valley (93065) *(P-15844)*
Rugged Portable Systems, Santa Ana *Also called Secure Comm Systems Inc (P-18247)*
Rugged Systems Inc......C......858 391-1006
13000 Danielson St Ste Q Poway (92064) *(P-15479)*
Ruggeri Marble and Granite Inc......D......310 513-2155
16001 S San Pedro St C Gardena (90248) *(P-11277)*
Ruhe Corporation (PA)......C......714 777-8321
901 S Leslie St La Habra (90631) *(P-2402)*
Ruiz Flour Tortillas, Riverside *Also called Ruiz Mexican Foods Inc (P-2661)*
Ruiz Food Products Inc (PA)......A......559 591-5510
501 S Alta Ave Dinuba (93618) *(P-1012)*
Ruiz Industries Inc......F......818 582-6882
13027 Telfair Ave Sylmar (91342) *(P-10570)*
Ruiz Mexican Foods Inc (PA)......C......909 947-7811
1200 Marlborough Ave A Riverside (92507) *(P-2661)*
Rumble Entertainment Inc......E......650 316-8819
2121 S El Cmino Real C1 San Mateo (94403) *(P-23461)*
Rumble Games, San Mateo *Also called Rumble Entertainment Inc (P-23461)*
Rumiano Cheese Co (PA)......C......530 934-5438
1629 County Road E Willows (95988) *(P-596)*
Rumiano Cheese Co......E......707 465-1535
511 9th St Crescent City (95531) *(P-597)*
Runa Inc......F......508 253-5000
2 W 5th Ave Ste 300 San Mateo (94402) *(P-25133)*
Runners World Magazine......F......310 615-4567
2101 Rosecrans Ave # 6200 El Segundo (90245) *(P-6250)*
Rupert Gibbon & Spider Inc......E......800 442-0455
1147 Healdsburg Ave Healdsburg (95448) *(P-8938)*
Rurisond Inc......F......650 395-7136
2725 Ohio Ave Redwood City (94061) *(P-18243)*
Rush Pcb Inc......F......408 469-6013
2149 Otoole Ave Ste 20 San Jose (95131) *(P-18586)*
Rush Press Inc......E......619 296-7874
955 Gateway Center Way San Diego (92102) *(P-7091)*
Russ Bassett Corp......C......562 945-2445
8189 Byron Rd Whittier (90606) *(P-4999)*
Russ International Inc......E......310 329-7121
1658 W 132nd St Gardena (90249) *(P-12745)*
Russell Fabrication Corp......E......661 861-8495
4940 Gilmore Ave Bakersfield (93308) *(P-13903)*
Russell Kc & Son......E......559 686-3236
375 E Paige Ave Tulare (93274) *(P-14101)*
Russell-Stanley......D......909 980-7114
9449 Santa Anita Ave Rancho Cucamonga (91730) *(P-10351)*
Russell-Stanley West, Rancho Cucamonga *Also called Russell-Stanley (P-10351)*
Russian River Brewing Co, Santa Rosa *Also called 23 Bottles of Beer LLC (P-1556)*
Russian River Utility Inc......F......707 887-7735
7131 Mirabel Rd Forestville (95436) *(P-20225)*
Russian River Winery Inc......E......707 824-2005
2191 Laguna Rd Santa Rosa (95401) *(P-1961)*
Rusty Surfboards, San Diego *Also called Dgb LLC (P-23548)*
Rusty Surfboards Inc (PA)......E......858 578-0414
8495 Commerce Ave San Diego (92121) *(P-23644)*
Rusty Surfboards Inc......F......858 551-0262
2170 Avenida De La Playa La Jolla (92037) *(P-23645)*
Ruth Training Center Sew Mchs......F......213 748-8033
328 E 24th St Los Angeles (90011) *(P-3962)*
Rutherford Wine Company, Saint Helena *Also called Round Hill Cellars (P-1958)*
Ruxco Engineering Inc......F......530 622-4122
6051 Entp Dr Ste 105 Diamond Springs (95619) *(P-22610)*
Rvision Inc (HQ)......F......619 233-1403
2365 Paragon Dr Ste D San Jose (95131) *(P-22129)*
RW Wilson Inc......E......760 873-5600
375 Joe Smith Rd Bishop (93514) *(P-10352)*
Rwi, Granite Bay *Also called Recoating-West Inc (P-12735)*
Rwnm Inc......D......760 489-1245
1240 Simpson Way Escondido (92029) *(P-17119)*
Rxsafe LLC......F......760 593-7161
2453 Cades Way Bldg A Vista (92081) *(P-15025)*
Ryadon Inc......E......949 768-8333
25932 Wright Foothill Ranch (92610) *(P-11989)*
Ryan Press, Buena Park *Also called Q Team (P-7057)*
Ryangmw Inc......F......530 305-2499
13861 Dry Creek Rd Auburn (95602) *(P-20226)*
Ryko Plastic Products Inc......F......909 773-0050
701 E Francis St Ontario (91761) *(P-10353)*
Ryko Solutions Inc......E......916 372-8815
3939 W Capitol Ave Ste D West Sacramento (95691) *(P-16103)*
Rypple......F......888 479-7753
577 Howard St Fl 3 San Francisco (94105) *(P-25134)*
Ryss Lab Inc......F......510 477-9570
29540 Kohoutek Way Union City (94587) *(P-21488)*
Rytan Inc......F......310 328-6553
455 Maple Ave Torrance (90503) *(P-14406)*
Ryvec Inc......E......714 520-5592
251 E Palais Rd Anaheim (92805) *(P-7744)*
S & C Electric Company......E......510 864-9300
1135 Atlantic Ave Ste 100 Alameda (94501) *(P-17305)*
S & C Foods Inc......E......323 205-6887
6094 Malburg Way Vernon (90058) *(P-1450)*
S & C Precision Inc......F......626 338-7149
5045 Calmview Ave Baldwin Park (91706) *(P-19714)*
S & H Cabinets and Mfg Inc......E......909 357-0551
10860 Mulberry Ave Fontana (92337) *(P-4966)*
S & H Enterprises Inc......F......530 626-8043
6200 Enterprise Dr Diamond Springs (95619) *(P-14256)*
S & H Machine Inc (PA)......F......818 846-9847
900 N Lake St Burbank (91502) *(P-16922)*
S & H Welding Inc......F......916 386-8921
8604 Elder Creek Rd Sacramento (95828) *(P-12417)*
S & J Advertising Inc (PA)......F......707 448-6446
555 Mason St Ste 250 Vacaville (95688) *(P-6251)*
S & J Carpet Cleaning......F......916 630-9330
1911 Douglas Blvd 85394 Roseville (95661) *(P-17408)*
S & J Pro Clean Services, North Hills *Also called S & J Prof Property Svcs (P-90)*
S & J Prof Property Svcs......F......818 892-0181
9615 Aqueduct Ave North Hills (91343) *(P-90)*
S & K Plating Inc......E......310 632-7141
2727 N Compton Ave Compton (90222) *(P-13494)*
S & K Theatrical Drap Inc......F......818 503-0596
7313 Varna Ave North Hollywood (91605) *(P-3701)*
S & L Contracting......E......661 371-6379
900 W Kern Ave Ste 900 # 900 Mc Farland (93250) *(P-12746)*
S & R Cnc Machining......F......818 767-5200
13183 Kelowna St Pacoima (91331) *(P-20677)*
S & S Bakery, Vista *Also called Baked In Sun (P-1180)*
S & S Bindery Inc......E......909 596-2213
2366 1st St La Verne (91750) *(P-7615)*
S & S Foods LLC......C......626 633-1609
1120 W Foothill Blvd Azusa (91702) *(P-520)*
S & S Installations Inc......E......909 370-1730
294 W Olive St Colton (92324) *(P-16104)*
S & S Numerical Control Inc......E......818 341-4141
19841 Nordhoff St Northridge (91324) *(P-16923)*

S & S Precision Mfg Inc ....E....714 754-6664
2509 S Broadway Santa Ana (92707) **(P-16924)**
S & S Precision Sheetmetal, Canoga Park *Also called B S K T Inc* **(P-16301)**
S & S Printers ....E....714 535-5592
2100 W Lincoln Ave Ste A Anaheim (92801) **(P-7092)**
S & S Woodcarver Inc ....E....714 258-2222
13 San Rafael Pl Laguna Niguel (92677) **(P-4650)**
S 2 K, Chatsworth *Also called S2k Graphics Inc* **(P-23954)**
S A C O Your Manufacturing Co, Newbury Park *Also called Saco* **(P-20062)**
S A Fields Inc ....F....559 292-1221
3328 N Duke Ave Fresno (93727) **(P-3807)**
S A Hartman Productions, Sherman Oaks *Also called SA Hartman & Associates Inc* **(P-23195)**
S and H Rubber Company Inc ....E....714 526-2583
1141 E Elm Ave Fullerton (92831) **(P-9673)**
S and S Carbide Tool Inc ....E....619 670-5214
2830 Via Orange Way Ste D Spring Valley (91978) **(P-14568)**
S B I F Inc ....F....805 683-1711
873 S Kellogg Ave Goleta (93117) **(P-13651)**
S Bravo Systems Inc ....E....323 888-4133
2929 Vail Ave Commerce (90040) **(P-12418)**
S C Coatings Corporation ....E....951 461-9777
41745 Elm St Ste 101 Murrieta (92562) **(P-13652)**
S C P, Berkeley *Also called Spiritual Counterfeits Prj Inc* **(P-6261)**
S C R Molding Inc ....F....951 736-5490
2340 Pomona Rd Corona (92880) **(P-10354)**
S C S, North Highlands *Also called Security Contractor Svcs Inc* **(P-12890)**
S D Drilling ....F....760 789-5658
24660 E Old Julian Hwy Ramona (92065) **(P-268)**
S D I, Visalia *Also called Spraying Devices Inc* **(P-14134)**
S D I, Camarillo *Also called Structural Diagnostics Inc* **(P-21855)**
S D M, Chino *Also called Syntech Development & Mfg Inc* **(P-10397)**
S D M Furniture Co Inc ....F....323 936-0295
4620 W Jefferson Blvd Los Angeles (90016) **(P-4737)**
S D S, Ontario *Also called Specialized Dairy Service Inc* **(P-14106)**
S E M, Fremont *Also called Streamline Electronics Mfg Inc* **(P-18617)**
S E P E Inc ....E....714 241-7373
245 Fischer Ave Ste C4 Costa Mesa (92626) **(P-15480)**
S F Enterprises Incorporated ....F....650 455-3223
707 Warrington Ave Redwood City (94063) **(P-16925)**
S F Technology, Cerritos *Also called UFO Designs* **(P-20473)**
S G S, Baldwin Park *Also called Superior Grounding Systems* **(P-17493)**
S Howard Hirsh, Los Angeles *Also called La Swim LLC* **(P-2846)**
S J Helicopter Service, Delano *Also called San-Joaquin Helicopters Inc* **(P-20624)**
S J Sterilized Wiping Rags ....F....408 287-2512
201 San Jose Ave San Jose (95125) **(P-3016)**
S K Digital Imaging Inc ....F....858 408-0732
7686 Miramar Rd Ste A San Diego (92126) **(P-7616)**
S K Laboratories Inc ....E....714 695-9800
5420 E La Palma Ave Anaheim (92807) **(P-8370)**
S K Labs, Anaheim *Also called S K Laboratories Inc* **(P-8370)**
S L Cellars ....F....707 833-5070
9380 Sonoma Hwy Kenwood (95452) **(P-1962)**
S L Fusco Inc (PA) ....E....310 868-1010
1966 E Via Arado Rancho Dominguez (90220) **(P-14407)**
S M G Custom Cabinets Inc ....E....916 381-5999
5750 Alder Ave Sacramento (95828) **(P-4347)**
S M L Industries Inc ....F....619 258-7941
10965 Hartley Rd Ste P Santee (92071) **(P-23462)**
S M S Briners Inc ....F....209 941-8515
17750 E Highway 4 Stockton (95215) **(P-931)**
S M U, Los Angeles *Also called Rm 518 Management LLC* **(P-3678)**
S Martinelli & Company (PA) ....C....831 724-1126
735 W Beach St Watsonville (95076) **(P-2662)**
S P I, Livermore *Also called Sierra Photonics Inc* **(P-18364)**
S R 3, North Hollywood *Also called Sr3 Solutions LLC* **(P-6055)**
S R C Devices Inccustomer (PA) ....F....866 772-8668
6295 Ferris Sq Ste D San Diego (92121) **(P-17306)**
S R Machining-Properties LLC ....C....951 520-9486
640 Parkridge Ave Norco (92860) **(P-16926)**
S R S M Inc ....C....310 952-9000
945 E Church St Riverside (92507) **(P-7882)**
S S I, Irvine *Also called Seal Science Inc* **(P-9556)**
S S Schaffer Co Inc ....F....323 560-1430
5637 District Blvd Vernon (90058) **(P-14408)**
S S Sign Electric, Los Angeles *Also called Soteleo Salvadar* **(P-23978)**
S Sedghi Inc (PA) ....E....213 745-2019
2416 W 7th St Los Angeles (90057) **(P-3588)**
S Studio Inc ....D....213 388-7400
3030 W 6th St Los Angeles (90020) **(P-3363)**
S T Cycle Wear, El Cajon *Also called St Cyclewear/Gallop LLC* **(P-3189)**
S T E U Inc ....E....805 527-0987
1625 Surveyor Ave Simi Valley (93063) **(P-17730)**
S T I, Corona *Also called Paragon Tactical Inc* **(P-23628)**
S V M, Santa Clara *Also called Silicon Vly McRelectronics Inc* **(P-19159)**
S W C Group Inc ....E....888 982-1628
750 Royal Oaks Dr Ste 108 Monrovia (91016) **(P-5500)**
S W G, Union City *Also called Smart Wires Inc* **(P-19363)**
S&B Filters Inc ....D....909 947-0015
15461 Slover Ave Ste A Fontana (92337) **(P-20443)**
S&B Industry Inc ....D....909 569-4155
105 S Puente St Brea (92821) **(P-10355)**
S&B Pharma Inc ....D....626 334-2908
405 S Motor Ave Azusa (91702) **(P-7969)**
S&H International Inc ....F....213 626-7112
1240 Palmetto St Los Angeles (90013) **(P-17558)**
S&H Melkes Inc ....E....626 448-5062
9928 Hayward Way South El Monte (91733) **(P-13745)**
S&J Carrera Constructions, Watsonville *Also called Carrera Construction Inc* **(P-194)**
S&S Flavours, Brea *Also called Scisorek & Son Flavors Inc* **(P-2281)**
S&S Investment Club (PA) ....F....707 747-5508
5340 Gateway Plaza Dr Benicia (94510) **(P-21240)**
S&S Signature Mill Works Inc ....F....916 652-1046
5951 Jetton Ln Ste C6 Loomis (95650) **(P-4651)**
S-Energy America Inc (HQ) ....F....949 281-7897
18022 Cowan Ste 260 Irvine (92614) **(P-19131)**
S-Matrix Corporation ....F....707 441-0404
1594 Myrtle Ave Eureka (95501) **(P-25135)**
S.T. Johnson Company, Fairfield *Also called Innovative Combustion Tech* **(P-12071)**
S/R Industries Inc (HQ) ....F....562 968-5800
10652 Bloomfield Ave Santa Fe Springs (90670) **(P-23646)**
S2e Inc ....F....626 965-1008
817 Lawson St City of Industry (91748) **(P-17852)**
S2k Graphics Inc ....E....818 885-3900
9255 Deering Ave Chatsworth (91311) **(P-23954)**
S3 Graphics Inc ....C....510 687-4900
940 Mission Ct Fremont (94539) **(P-19132)**
S3d Acquisition II Company, San Diego *Also called Overland Storage Inc* **(P-15580)**
SA Hartman & Associates Inc ....E....818 907-9681
14570 Benefit St Sherman Oaks (91403) **(P-23195)**
SA Serving Lines Inc ....F....714 848-7529
226 W Carleton Ave Orange (92867) **(P-12747)**
Saab Enterprises, Fontana *Also called Enjoy Foods International* **(P-482)**
Saab Enterprises Inc ....D....909 823-2228
1433 Miller Dr Colton (92324) **(P-521)**
Saags Products LLC ....D....510 678-3412
1799 Factor Ave San Leandro (94577) **(P-522)**
Saavy Inc ....F....323 728-2137
516 W Lincoln Ave Montebello (90640) **(P-14409)**
Saaz Micro Inc ....F....805 405-0700
94 W Cochran St Ste A Simi Valley (93065) **(P-19133)**
Saba Motors Inc ....F....408 219-8675
521 Charcot Ave Ste 165 San Jose (95131) **(P-20169)**
Saba Software Inc (PA) ....D....877 722-2101
4120 Dublin Blvd Ste 200 Dublin (94568) **(P-25136)**
Sabel, Vista *Also called Surgistar Inc* **(P-22639)**
Sabert Corporation ....F....951 342-0240
860 Palmyrita Ave Riverside (92507) **(P-10356)**
Sabia Incorporated (PA) ....E....858 217-2200
10915 Technology Pl San Diego (92127) **(P-21647)**
Sabre Sciences Inc ....F....760 448-2750
2233 Faraday Ave Ste K Carlsbad (92008) **(P-7970)**
Sabred International Packg Inc ....E....714 996-2800
3740 Prospect Ave Yorba Linda (92886) **(P-9881)**
Sabrin Corporation ....F....626 792-3813
2836 E Walnut St Pasadena (91107) **(P-12748)**
Sac EDM & Waterjet, Rancho Cordova *Also called E D M Sacramento Inc* **(P-16459)**
Sac Valley Ornamental Ir Outl ....F....916 383-6340
8540 Thys Ct Sacramento (95828) **(P-11454)**
Sac-TEC Labs Inc (PA) ....E....310 375-5295
24301 Wilmington Ave Carson (90745) **(P-19134)**
Sachs & Associates Inc ....F....310 356-7911
1230 Rosecrans Ave # 408 Manhattan Beach (90266) **(P-15594)**
Sachs Industries Inc ....F....631 242-9000
801 Kate Ln Woodland (95776) **(P-5731)**
Saco ....E....805 499-7788
3525 Old Conejo Rd # 107 Newbury Park (91320) **(P-20062)**
Sacramental Color Coil ....E....916 383-9588
8541 Thys Ct Sacramento (95828) **(P-7617)**
Sacramento Baking Co Inc ....E....916 361-2000
9221 Beatty Dr Sacramento (95826) **(P-1317)**
Sacramento Bee, Sacramento *Also called McClatchy Newspapers Inc* **(P-5944)**
Sacramento Business Journal, Sacramento *Also called American City Bus Journals Inc* **(P-5757)**
Sacramento Coca-Cola Btlg Inc (HQ) ....B....916 928-2300
4101 Gateway Park Blvd Sacramento (95834) **(P-2215)**
Sacramento Coca-Cola Btlg Inc ....E....209 541-3200
1733 Morgan Rd Ste 200 Modesto (95358) **(P-2216)**
Sacramento Envelope Co Inc ....F....916 371-4747
773 Northport Dr Ste C-A West Sacramento (95691) **(P-7093)**
Sacramento Gazette, The, Sacramento *Also called Gazette Media Co LLC* **(P-5860)**
Sacramento News & Review, Sacramento *Also called Chico Community Publishing* **(P-5798)**
Sacramento Rendering Co, Sacramento *Also called SRC Milling Co LLC* **(P-1533)**
Saddleback Educational Inc ....E....949 860-2500
151 Kalmus Dr Ste J-1 Costa Mesa (92626) **(P-6388)**
Saddleback Stair & Millwork ....F....949 460-0384
23291 Peralta Dr Ste B4 Laguna Hills (92653) **(P-4223)**
Sadra Medical Inc ....E....408 370-1550
160 Knowles Dr Los Gatos (95032) **(P-22611)**
SAE Engineering Inc ....E....408 492-1784
365 Reed St Santa Clara (95050) **(P-12749)**
Saehan Electronics America Inc (PA) ....F....858 496-1500
7880 Airway Rd Ste B5g San Diego (92154) **(P-18587)**
Saeilo Manufacturing Inds, Santa Fe Springs *Also called SMI Ca Inc* **(P-16948)**
Saemie Corporation ....F....714 632-0530
3199 E La Palma Ave Ste A Anaheim (92806) **(P-11418)**
Saes Pure Gas Inc ....C....805 541-9299
4175 Santa Fe Rd San Luis Obispo (93401) **(P-15358)**
Saeshin America Inc ....E....949 825-6925
216 Technology Dr Ste F Irvine (92618) **(P-22907)**
Saf West, Redding *Also called Southern Alum Finshg Co Inc* **(P-11625)**
Saf-T-Cab Inc (PA) ....D....559 268-5541
3241 S Parkway Dr Fresno (93725) **(P-20227)**

ALPHABETIC

Employee Codes: A=Over 500 employees, B=251-500
C=101-250, D=51-100, E=20-50, F=10-19
2019 California
Manfacturers Register
© Mergent Inc. 1-800-342-5647
1271

Saf-T-Co Supply ....E....714 547-9975
1300 E Normandy Pl Santa Ana (92705) ***(P-17518)***
Saf-T-Kut LLC ....E....657 210-4426
2652 Dow Ave Tustin (92780) ***(P-14410)***
Safari Books Online, Sebastopol *Also called OReilly Media Inc* ***(P-6373)***
Safari Signs, Chatsworth *Also called Printing Safari Co* ***(P-7049)***
Safariland LLC ....B....909 923-7300
3120 E Mission Blvd Ontario (91761) ***(P-10579)***
Safariland LLC (HQ) ....E....925 219-1097
3120 E Mission Blvd Ontario (91761) ***(P-18361)***
Safc Pharma, Carlsbad *Also called Sigma-Aldrich Corporation* ***(P-9304)***
Safcor Inc ....F....818 392-8437
13455 Ventura Blvd 237a Sherman Oaks (91423) ***(P-10533)***
Safe Catch Inc ....F....415 944-4442
85 Liberty Ship Way Sausalito (94965) ***(P-2302)***
Safe Environment Engrg LP ....F....661 295-5500
28474 Westinghouse Pl Valencia (91355) ***(P-19715)***
Safe Plating Inc ....D....626 810-1872
18001 Railroad St City of Industry (91748) ***(P-13495)***
Safe Publishing Company ....D....805 973-1300
5775 Lindero Canyon Rd Westlake Village (91362) ***(P-7476)***
Safeguard Covers, Dana Point *Also called Pw Brands LLC* ***(P-11302)***
Safeland Industrial Supply Inc (PA) ....F....909 786-1967
10278 Birtcher Dr Jurupa Valley (91752) ***(P-11455)***
Safety America Inc ....F....619 660-6968
2766 Via Orange Way Ste D Spring Valley (91978) ***(P-23120)***
Safety-Kleen Systems Inc ....F....559 486-1960
3561 S Maple Ave Fresno (93725) ***(P-15026)***
Safetychain Software Inc (PA) ....E....415 233-9474
7599 Redwood Blvd Ste 205 Novato (94945) ***(P-25137)***
Safeway Sign Company ....E....760 246-7070
9875 Yucca Rd Adelanto (92301) ***(P-23955)***
Saffola Quality Foods, Ontario *Also called Ventura Foods LLC* ***(P-563)***
Safna A Division of Heateflex, Arcadia *Also called Heateflex Corporation* ***(P-12067)***
Safran Elec Def Avnics USA LLC ....C....949 642-2427
3184 Pullman St Costa Mesa (92626) ***(P-21421)***
Safran Pwr Units San Diego LLC ....D....858 223-2228
4255 Ruffin Rd Ste 100 San Diego (92123) ***(P-20678)***
Sage (PA) ....E....925 288-4827
1410 Monument Blvd Concord (94520) ***(P-8578)***
Sage Goddess Inc ....E....650 733-6639
3830 Del Amo Blvd Ste 102 Torrance (90503) ***(P-23312)***
Sage Instruments Inc ....D....831 761-1000
240 Airport Blvd Freedom (95019) ***(P-21842)***
Sage Interior Inc ....F....949 654-0184
9 Aspen Tree Ln Irvine (92612) ***(P-4348)***
Sage Machado Inc ....F....323 931-0595
133 N Gramercy Pl Los Angeles (90004) ***(P-23313)***
Sage Metering Inc ....F....831 242-2030
8 Harris Ct Ste D1 Monterey (93940) ***(P-22013)***
Sage Software Inc ....C....650 579-3628
1380 Tatan Trail Rd Burlingame (94010) ***(P-25138)***
Sage Software Holdings Inc (HQ) ....B....866 530-7243
6561 Irvine Center Dr Irvine (92618) ***(P-25139)***
Sager Co, City of Industry *Also called Midern Computer Inc* ***(P-15457)***
Sager Electrical Supply Co Inc ....F....408 588-1750
2390 Owen St Santa Clara (95054) ***(P-19716)***
Sago Systems Inc ....F....858 646-5300
10455 Pacific Center Ct San Diego (92121) ***(P-21422)***
SAI Industries ....E....818 842-6144
631 Allen Ave Glendale (91201) ***(P-13690)***
Saigon Nho, Garden Grove *Also called Little Saigon News Inc* ***(P-5913)***
Saigon Times Inc ....F....626 288-2696
9234 Valley Blvd Rosemead (91770) ***(P-6030)***
Saint Gobain Containers Inc ....F....707 437-8700
2600 Stanford Ct Fairfield (94533) ***(P-10625)***
Saint-Gobain Ceramics Plas Inc ....E....714 701-3900
4905 E Hunter Ave Anaheim (92807) ***(P-9038)***
Saint-Gobain Prfmce Plas Corp ....C....714 893-0470
7301 Orangewood Ave Garden Grove (92841) ***(P-7883)***
Saint-Gobain Prfmce Plas Corp ....B....714 688-2612
7301 Orangewood Ave Garden Grove (92841) ***(P-10626)***
Saint-Gobain Solar Gard LLC (HQ) ....D....866 300-2674
4540 Viewridge Ave San Diego (92123) ***(P-9725)***
Saintsbury LLC ....F....707 252-0592
1500 Los Carneros Ave NAPA (94559) ***(P-1963)***
Sake Robotics ....F....650 207-4021
570 El Camino Real 150-3 Redwood City (94063) ***(P-14766)***
Saks Styling Incorporated ....E....818 244-0540
641 W Harvard St Glendale (91204) ***(P-23314)***
Sakura Noodle Inc ....F....213 623-2396
620 E 7th St Los Angeles (90021) ***(P-2438)***
Sakura Paper Inc ....F....714 886-3791
1683 Sunflower Ave # 103 Costa Mesa (92626) ***(P-5732)***
Sal J Acsta Sheetmetal Mfg Inc ....D....408 275-6370
930 Remillard Ct San Jose (95122) ***(P-12750)***
Sal Rodriguez ....F....408 993-8091
1680 Almaden Expy Ste I San Jose (95125) ***(P-13496)***
Saladino Sausage Company, Fresno *Also called Choice Food Products Inc* ***(P-474)***
Salco Dynamic Solutions Inc (PA) ....E....714 374-7500
6248 Surfpoint Cir Huntington Beach (92648) ***(P-9449)***
Salco Oil, Huntington Beach *Also called Salco Dynamic Solutions Inc* ***(P-9449)***
Salco Products, Ontario *Also called Nyx Industries Inc* ***(P-14087)***
Sale 121 Corp (PA) ....D....888 233-7667
1467 68th Ave Sacramento (95822) ***(P-15595)***
Saleen Automotive Inc (PA) ....E....800 888-8945
2735 Wardlow Rd Corona (92882) ***(P-13143)***
Saleen Incorporated (PA) ....B....714 400-2121
2735 Wardlow Rd Corona (92882) ***(P-20170)***

Sales & Marketing, San Francisco *Also called Outreach Corporation* ***(P-25042)***
Sales Office, Irwindale *Also called Legacy Vulcan LLC* ***(P-10950)***
Sales Office Accessories Inc ....F....714 896-9600
7211 Patterson Dr Garden Grove (92841) ***(P-23956)***
Salesforcecom Inc ....E....415 323-8685
50 Fremont St San Francisco (94105) ***(P-25140)***
Salesforcecom Inc ....F....703 463-3300
1 Market Ste 300 San Francisco (94105) ***(P-25141)***
Salesforcecom Inc (PA) ....A....415 901-7000
1 Market Ste 300 San Francisco (94105) ***(P-25142)***
Salesforcecom Inc ....E....310 752-7000
1442 2nd St Santa Monica (90401) ***(P-25143)***
Salinas Newspapers Inc, Salinas *Also called Salinas Newspapers LLC* ***(P-6031)***
Salinas Newspapers LLC ....C....831 424-2221
1093 S Main St Ste 101 Salinas (93901) ***(P-6031)***
Salinas Tallow Co Inc ....E....831 422-6436
1 Work Cir Salinas (93901) ***(P-1532)***
Salinas Valley Wax Paper Co ....E....831 424-2747
1111 Abbott St Salinas (93901) ***(P-5733)***
Salis International Inc ....E....303 384-3588
3921 Oceanic Dr Ste 802 Oceanside (92056) ***(P-23710)***
Salomon Dominguez ....F....831 663-1190
15420 Meridian Rd Salinas (93907) ***(P-12887)***
Salon Brandy, Compton *Also called California Decor* ***(P-4115)***
Salpy, Encino *Also called International Last Mfg Co* ***(P-10154)***
Salsam Manufacturing Co, Santa Ana *Also called Kalanico Inc* ***(P-5074)***
Salsbury Industries Inc (PA) ....C....323 846-6700
1010 E 62nd St Los Angeles (90001) ***(P-5165)***
Salus Enterprises of N Amer, Redwood City *Also called Salus North America Inc* ***(P-21526)***
Salus North America Inc ....F....888 387-2587
850 Main St Redwood City (94063) ***(P-21526)***
Salutron Incorporated (PA) ....E....510 795-2876
8371 Central Ave Ste A Newark (94560) ***(P-23045)***
Salwasser Inc ....D....559 843-2882
4087 N Howard Ave Kerman (93630) ***(P-891)***
Sam & Lavi, Los Angeles *Also called Valmas Inc* ***(P-3346)***
Sam Vaziri Vance Inc (PA) ....E....323 822-3955
15120 Keswick St Van Nuys (91405) ***(P-23121)***
Sama Eyewear, Van Nuys *Also called Sam Vaziri Vance Inc* ***(P-23121)***
Samax Precision Inc ....E....408 245-9555
926 W Evelyn Ave Sunnyvale (94086) ***(P-16927)***
Sambrailo Packaging, Watsonville *Also called Samco Plastics Inc* ***(P-5537)***
Samco Plastics Inc ....F....831 761-1392
1260 W Beach St Watsonville (95076) ***(P-5537)***
Samedan Oil Corporation ....B....661 319-5038
1360 Landing Ave Seal Beach (90740) ***(P-73)***
Samil Power US Ltd ....A....925 930-3924
3478 Buskirk Ave Ste 1000 Pleasant Hill (94523) ***(P-19135)***
Samis Sports ....F....323 965-8093
5215 1/2 W Adams Blvd Los Angeles (90016) ***(P-23647)***
Sammons Equipment Mfg Corp ....F....951 340-3419
390 Meyer Cir Ste A Corona (92879) ***(P-5254)***
Sampav Inc ....F....909 984-8646
1394 W 7th St Upland (91786) ***(P-3042)***
Sampe, Diamond Bar *Also called Society For The Advancement of* ***(P-6260)***
Sampling International LLC ....F....949 305-5333
28 Hammond Ste C Irvine (92618) ***(P-3963)***
Sams Crftsman Style Pfab Gzbos, Gardena *Also called Samsgazeboscom Inc* ***(P-4051)***
Sams Tailoring ....F....714 963-6776
18120 Brookhurst St Fountain Valley (92708) ***(P-3043)***
Sams Trade Development Corp ....E....213 225-0188
818 S Main St Los Angeles (90014) ***(P-23758)***
Samsgazeboscom Inc ....F....310 523-3778
132 E 163rd St Gardena (90248) ***(P-4051)***
Samson Pharmaceuticals Inc ....E....323 722-3066
2027 Leo Ave Commerce (90040) ***(P-8371)***
Samson Products Inc ....B....323 726-9070
6285 Randolph St Commerce (90040) ***(P-5166)***
Samsung Sdi America Inc (HQ) ....F....408 544-4470
665 Clyde Ave Mountain View (94043) ***(P-15845)***
Samuel French Inc ....E....323 876-0570
7623 W Sunset Blvd Los Angeles (90046) ***(P-6573)***
Samuel Raoof ....E....818 534-3180
20660 Nordhoff St Chatsworth (91311) ***(P-8832)***
Samyang USA Inc ....F....562 946-9977
3810 Wilshire Blvd # 1212 Los Angeles (90010) ***(P-2439)***
San Antonio Bakery, Compton *Also called Pedro Pallan* ***(P-1308)***
San Antonio Gift Shop, Los Angeles *Also called San Antonio Winery Inc* ***(P-1964)***
San Antonio Winery Inc (PA) ....C....323 223-1401
737 Lamar St Los Angeles (90031) ***(P-1964)***
San Benito Shutter, Hollister *Also called SBS America LLC* ***(P-4225)***
San Benito Supply (PA) ....C....831 637-5526
2984 Monterey Hwy San Jose (95111) ***(P-10996)***
San Bernandina Steel, Stockton *Also called Herrick Corporation* ***(P-12175)***
San Bernardino County Sun, The, San Bernardino *Also called Sun Company San Bernardino Cal* ***(P-6062)***
San Brnrdino Cmnty College Dst ....C....909 888-6511
701 S Mount Vernon Ave San Bernardino (92410) ***(P-7477)***
San Clemente Times LLC ....F....949 388-7700
34932 Calle Del Sol Ste B Capistrano Beach (92624) ***(P-6032)***
San Dego Gographic Info Source ....F....858 874-7000
5510 Overland Ave Ste 230 San Diego (92123) ***(P-6574)***
San Dego HM Grdn Lfestyles Mag, San Diego *Also called McKinnon Enterprises* ***(P-6215)***
San Dego Prcsion Machining Inc ....E....858 499-0379
9375 Ruffin Ct San Diego (92123) ***(P-12751)***
San Dego Prtective Coating Inc ....F....619 448-7795
9344 Wheatlands Rd Ste A Santee (92071) ***(P-13653)***
San Diegan, San Diego *Also called San Diego Guide Inc* ***(P-6575)***

San Diego Ace Inc ....C....619 252-3148
8490 Mathis Pl San Diego (92127) *(P-10357)*
San Diego Afr Amrcn Gnlogy RSC ....E....619 231-5810
5148 Market St San Diego (92114) *(P-24227)*
San Diego Arcft Interiors Inc ....E....619 474-1997
2940 Hoover Ave National City (91950) *(P-4738)*
San Diego Business Journal, San Diego *Also called Cbj LP (P-6125)*
San Diego Cabinets Inc ....E....760 747-3100
2001 Lendee Dr Escondido (92025) *(P-4349)*
San Diego Cmnty Newsppr Group, San Diego *Also called Mannis Communications Inc (P-5938)*
San Diego County Truss Inc ....F....619 286-8787
7462 Mission Gorge Rd San Diego (92120) *(P-4420)*
San Diego Crating & Pkg Inc ....F....858 748-0100
12678 Brookprinter Pl Poway (92064) *(P-5456)*
San Diego Daily Transcript ....D....619 232-4381
34 Emerald Gln Laguna Niguel (92677) *(P-5333)*
San Diego Electric Sign Inc ....F....619 258-1775
1890 Cordell Ct Ste 105 El Cajon (92020) *(P-23957)*
San Diego Family Magazine LLC ....F....619 685-6970
1475 6th Ave Ste 500 San Diego (92101) *(P-6252)*
San Diego Guide Inc ....E....858 877-3217
6370 Lusk Blvd Ste F202 San Diego (92121) *(P-6575)*
San Diego Instruments Inc ....F....858 530-2600
9155 Brown Deer Rd Ste 8 San Diego (92121) *(P-21489)*
San Diego Lgbt Community Ctr, San Diego *Also called Center Health Services (P-21931)*
San Diego Magazine Pubg Co ....E....619 230-9292
707 Broadway Ste 1100 San Diego (92101) *(P-6253)*
San Diego Mirror and Window, Vista *Also called J & B Manufacturing Corp (P-10707)*
San Diego Paper Box Co Inc ....E....619 660-9566
10605 Jamacha Blvd Spring Valley (91978) *(P-5509)*
San Diego Pcb Design LLC ....F....858 271-5722
9909 Mira Mesa Blvd # 250 San Diego (92131) *(P-18588)*
San Diego Powder Coating, El Cajon *Also called BJS&t Enterprises Inc (P-13560)*
San Diego Precast Concrete Inc (HQ) ....E....619 240-8000
2735 Cactus Rd San Diego (92154) *(P-10997)*
San Diego Printers, San Diego *Also called Three Man Corporation (P-7520)*
San Diego Union Tribune, The, San Diego *Also called San Diego Union-Tribune LLC (P-6034)*
San Diego Union-Tribune LLC ....D....619 299-3131
600 B St Ste 1201 San Diego (92101) *(P-6033)*
San Diego Union-Tribune LLC (PA) ....A....619 299-3131
600 B St Ste 1201 San Diego (92101) *(P-6034)*
San Dieguito Printers, San Marcos *Also called San Dieguito Publishers Inc (P-7094)*
San Dieguito Publishers Inc ....D....760 593-5139
1880 Diamond St San Marcos (92078) *(P-7094)*
San Emidio Quarry, Bakersfield *Also called Legacy Vulcan LLC (P-10951)*
San Fernando Valley Bus Jurnl, Woodland Hills *Also called Cbj LP (P-6123)*
San Francisco Bath Salt Co, Hayward *Also called Rmf Salt Holdings LLC (P-8829)*
San Francisco Bay Brand Inc (PA) ....E....510 792-7200
8239 Enterprise Dr Newark (94560) *(P-1162)*
San Francisco Bay Guardian, San Francisco *Also called Bay Guardian Company (P-5775)*
San Francisco Business Time, San Francisco *Also called Business Jrnl Publications Inc (P-5784)*
San Francisco Circuits Inc ....F....650 655-7202
1660 S Amphlett Blvd # 200 San Mateo (94402) *(P-18589)*
San Francisco Daily Journal, San Francisco *Also called Daily Journal Corporation (P-5823)*
San Francisco Elev Svcs Inc ....E....925 829-5400
6517 Sierra Ln Dublin (94568) *(P-14257)*
San Francisco Envelope, Fremont *Also called Cleansmart Solutions Inc (P-5673)*
San Francisco Fine Bakery, Redwood City *Also called Golden Octagon Inc (P-1265)*
San Francisco Foods Inc ....D....510 357-7343
14054 Catalina St San Leandro (94577) *(P-1013)*
San Francisco Network ....E....415 468-1110
2171 Francisco Blvd E G San Rafael (94901) *(P-3543)*
San Francisco Offset Printing, San Jose *Also called Southwest Offset Prtg Co Inc (P-7491)*
San Francisco Pipe & ....E....510 785-9148
23099 Connecticut St Hayward (94545) *(P-13904)*
San Francisco Print Media Co (PA) ....E....415 487-2594
835 Market St Ste 550 San Francisco (94103) *(P-7095)*
San Francisco Victoriana Inc ....F....415 648-0313
2070 Newcomb Ave San Francisco (94124) *(P-4224)*
San Franstitchco Inc ....F....707 795-6891
6819 Redwood Dr Ste E Cotati (94931) *(P-3861)*
San Joaquin Equipment LLC ....E....209 538-3831
2413 Crows Landing Rd Modesto (95358) *(P-14102)*
San Joaquin Facilities MGT Inc (PA) ....F....661 631-8713
4520 California Ave # 300 Bakersfield (93309) *(P-74)*
San Joaquin Orthtics & Prsthtc ....F....209 932-0170
2211 N California St Stockton (95204) *(P-22806)*
San Joaquin Refining Co Inc ....C....661 327-4257
3500 Shell St Bakersfield (93308) *(P-9356)*
San Joaquin Tomato Growers Inc ....F....209 837-4721
22001 E St Crows Landing (95313) *(P-854)*
San Joaquin Valley Dairymen, Turlock *Also called California Dairies Inc (P-560)*
San Joaquin Vly Concentrates, Modesto *Also called E & J Gallo Winery (P-1739)*
San Joaquin Vly Concentrates, Fresno *Also called E & J Gallo Winery (P-1741)*
San Joaquin Window Inc (PA) ....D....909 946-3697
1455 Columbia Ave Riverside (92507) *(P-12345)*
San Joaquin Wine Company Inc ....F....559 673-0066
21081 Avenue 16 Madera (93637) *(P-1965)*
San Jose Awning Company Inc ....F....408 350-7000
755 Chestnut St Ste E San Jose (95110) *(P-3808)*
San Jose BMW, San Jose *Also called C C Products (P-21095)*
San Jose Business Journal ....E....408 295-3800
125 S Market St Ste 1100 San Jose (95113) *(P-6035)*
San Jose Delta Associates Inc ....E....408 727-1448
482 Sapena Ct Santa Clara (95054) *(P-10823)*
San Jose Die Casting Corp ....E....408 262-6500
2475 Autumnvale Dr San Jose (95131) *(P-11705)*
San Jose Mercury-News LLC (HQ) ....A....408 920-5000
4 N 2nd St Ste 8008800 San Jose (95113) *(P-6036)*
San Juan Specialty Pdts Inc ....F....888 342-8262
4149 Avenida De La Plata Oceanside (92056) *(P-4534)*
San Luis Obispo Rdymx Plant, San Luis Obispo *Also called Calportland Company (P-10743)*
San Luis Tribune, San Luis Obispo *Also called McClatchy Newspapers Inc (P-5953)*
San Marco's Tortilla & Market, Los Angeles *Also called Tortilleria San Marcos (P-2687)*
San Marcos Trading Company, San Marcos *Also called GK Foods Inc (P-1042)*
San Mateo Daily News ....E....650 327-9090
255 Constitution Dr Menlo Park (94025) *(P-6037)*
San Mateo Times, San Mateo *Also called Alameda Newspapers Inc (P-5754)*
San Pedro Garage Door and Repr, San Pedro *Also called Paula Keller (P-4210)*
San Pedro Sign Company ....E....310 549-4661
701 Lakme Ave Wilmington (90744) *(P-23958)*
San Rafael Rock Quarry Inc ....E....510 970-7700
961 Western Dr Richmond (94801) *(P-9397)*
San Rafael Rock Quarry Inc (HQ) ....D....415 459-7740
1000 Point San Pedro Rd San Rafael (94901) *(P-333)*
San Rfl-Trra Linda Newspointer, Larkspur *Also called Marin Scope Incorporated (P-5940)*
San-I-Pak Pacific Inc ....E....209 836-2310
23535 S Bird Rd Tracy (95304) *(P-12419)*
San-Joaquin Helicopters Inc ....F....661 725-6603
1408 S Lexington St Delano (93215) *(P-20624)*
Sanarus Medical Incorporated ....F....925 460-6080
7068 Koll Center Pkwy # 425 Pleasanton (94566) *(P-22612)*
Sanctuary Clothing Inc ....E....818 505-0018
3611 N San Fernando Blvd Burbank (91505) *(P-3270)*
Sandberg Furniture Mfg Co Inc (PA) ....C....323 582-0711
5705 Alcoa Ave Vernon (90058) *(P-4739)*
Sandberg Industries Inc (PA) ....D....949 660-9473
2921 Daimler St Santa Ana (92705) *(P-19717)*
Sandee Plastic Extrusions ....E....323 979-4020
14932 Gwenchris Ct Paramount (90723) *(P-9575)*
Sandel Avionics Inc ....C....760 727-4900
2405 Dogwood Way Vista (92081) *(P-21423)*
Sandel Avionics Inc (PA) ....E....760 727-4900
2401 Dogwood Way Vista (92081) *(P-21424)*
Sanders Aircraft Inc ....F....209 274-2955
17149 Lambert Rd Ione (95640) *(P-21425)*
Sanders Aircraft Technologies, Ione *Also called Sanders Aircraft Inc (P-21425)*
Sanders Candy Factory Inc ....E....626 814-2038
5051 Calmview Ave Baldwin Park (91706) *(P-1451)*
Sanders Composites Inc (HQ) ....E....858 571-5220
4075 Ruffin Rd San Diego (92123) *(P-20924)*
Sanders Composites Industries, San Diego *Also called Sanders Composites Inc (P-20924)*
Sanders Industries (HQ) ....F....562 354-2920
3701 E Conant St Long Beach (90808) *(P-7916)*
Sanders Orthodontic Lab Inc ....F....925 251-0019
5653 Stoneridge Dr # 107 Pleasanton (94588) *(P-22908)*
Sanders Prcsion Timber Falling ....E....530 938-4120
9509 N Old Stage Rd Weed (96094) *(P-4009)*
Sandi Duty Free, San Diego *Also called Dynamic E-Markets LLC (P-2705)*
Sandia Plastics Inc ....E....714 901-8400
15571 Container Ln Huntington Beach (92649) *(P-10358)*
Sandisk LLC ....F....408 801-2928
1101 Sandisk Dr Bldg 5 Milpitas (95035) *(P-15596)*
Sandisk LLC (HQ) ....C....408 801-1000
951 Sandisk Dr Milpitas (95035) *(P-15597)*
Sandisk LLC ....D....408 321-0320
630 Alder Dr Ste 202 Milpitas (95035) *(P-15598)*
Sandman Inc (PA) ....E....408 947-0669
1404 S 7th St San Jose (95112) *(P-10998)*
Sandman Inc ....E....408 947-0159
1510 S 7th St San Jose (95112) *(P-10999)*
Sandra Sparks & Associates ....F....805 985-2057
2510 Peninsula Rd Oxnard (93035) *(P-8833)*
Sandstone Designs Inc ....E....818 787-5005
14828 Calvert St Van Nuys (91411) *(P-11000)*
Sandvik Thermal Process Inc ....D....209 533-1990
19500 Nugget Blvd Sonora (95370) *(P-15027)*
Sandys Drapery Inc ....E....510 445-0112
48374 Milmont Dr Bldg A Fremont (94538) *(P-3702)*
Sanford Metal Processing Co ....F....650 327-5172
990 Obrien Dr Menlo Park (94025) *(P-13497)*
Sangfor Technologies Inc ....A....408 520-7898
46721 Fremont Blvd Fremont (94538) *(P-21843)*
Sangis, San Diego *Also called San Dego Gographic Info Source (P-6574)*
Sangstat Medical Corp (HQ) ....F....510 789-4300
6300 Dumbarton Cir Fremont (94555) *(P-22613)*
Sanguine Biosciences Inc ....D....818 926-5196
5000 Van Nuys Blvd # 205 Sherman Oaks (91403) *(P-8579)*
Sani-Tech West Inc (PA) ....D....805 389-0400
1020 Flynn Rd Camarillo (93012) *(P-9507)*
Sanie Manufacturing Company ....F....714 751-7700
2600 S Yale St Santa Ana (92704) *(P-12888)*
Sanitek Products Inc ....F....323 245-6781
3959 Goodwin Ave Los Angeles (90039) *(P-8675)*
Sanitor Corporation ....F....714 799-2722
8400 Cerritos Ave Stanton (90680) *(P-8834)*
Sanko Electronics America Inc (HQ) ....F....310 618-1677
20700 Denker Ave Ste A Torrance (90501) *(P-20444)*
Sanluisina, Ontario *Also called Andrew LLC (P-1024)*
Sanmina Corporation ....A....408 244-0266
425 El Camino Real Bldg A Santa Clara (95050) *(P-18590)*

ALPHABETIC

Employee Codes: A=Over 500 employees, B=251-500
C=101-250, D=51-100, E=20-50, F=10-19
2019 California
Manfacturers Register
© Mergent Inc. 1-800-342-5647
1273

Sanmina Corporation.....E.....408 964-3500
2700 N 1st St San Jose (95134) ***(P-18591)***
Sanmina Corporation.....E.....408 964-3500
2701 Zanker Rd San Jose (95134) ***(P-18592)***
Sanmina Corporation.....B.....408 964-6400
2050 Bering Dr San Jose (95131) ***(P-18593)***
Sanmina Corporation.....B.....408 964-3500
2036 Bering Dr San Jose (95131) ***(P-18594)***
Sanmina Corporation.....B.....408 557-7210
60 E Plumeria Dr B2db San Jose (95134) ***(P-18595)***
Sanmina Corporation.....B.....510 897-2000
42735 Christy St Fremont (94538) ***(P-18596)***
Sanmina Corporation.....D.....408 964-3000
60 E Plumeria Dr San Jose (95134) ***(P-18597)***
Sanmina Corporation.....D.....714 371-2800
2945 Airway Ave Costa Mesa (92626) ***(P-18598)***
Sanmina Corporation (PA).....B.....408 964-3500
2700 N 1st St San Jose (95134) ***(P-18599)***
Sanmina Corporation.....C.....714 913-2200
2950 Red Hill Ave Costa Mesa (92626) ***(P-18600)***
Sanmina-Sci, San Jose *Also called Sanmina Corporation* ***(P-18594)***
Sanofi US Services Inc.....C.....415 856-5000
185 Berry St San Francisco (94107) ***(P-8372)***
Sanovas Inc.....E.....415 729-9391
2597 Kerner Blvd San Rafael (94901) ***(P-22614)***
Santa Ana Packaging Inc.....F.....714 670-6397
14655 Firestone Blvd La Mirada (90638) ***(P-5359)***
Santa Ana Plating Corp (PA).....D.....310 923-8305
1726 E Rosslynn Ave Fullerton (92831) ***(P-13498)***
Santa Barbara Coffee LLC.....F.....805 683-2555
6489 Calle Real Ste G Goleta (93117) ***(P-2366)***
Santa Barbara Control Systems.....F.....805 683-8833
5375 Overpass Rd Santa Barbara (93111) ***(P-21648)***
Santa Barbara Design Studio (PA).....D.....805 966-3883
1600 Pacific Ave Oxnard (93033) ***(P-10835)***
Santa Barbara Independent Inc.....E.....805 965-5205
12 E Figueroa St Santa Barbara (93101) ***(P-6038)***
Santa Barbara Indus Finshg, Goleta *Also called S B I F Inc* ***(P-13651)***
Santa Barbara Magazine, Santa Barbara *Also called Smith Publishing Inc* ***(P-6258)***
Santa Barbara Music Publishing.....E.....805 962-5800
260 Loma Media Rd Santa Barbara (93103) ***(P-6576)***
Santa Barbara News-Press Info, Santa Barbara *Also called Ampersand Publishing LLC* ***(P-5759)***
Santa Barbara Olives Co, Santa Maria *Also called Krinos Foods LLC* ***(P-918)***
Santa Barbara Winery.....E.....805 963-3646
202 Anacapa St Santa Barbara (93101) ***(P-1966)***
Santa Brbara Essntial Fods LLC.....E.....805 965-1948
233 E Gutierrez St Santa Barbara (93101) ***(P-1378)***
Santa Clara Imaging.....E.....408 296-5555
1825 Civic Center Dr # 1 Santa Clara (95050) ***(P-22261)***
Santa Clara Plating Co Inc.....D.....408 727-9315
1773 Grant St Santa Clara (95050) ***(P-13499)***
Santa Clarita Plastic Molding.....F.....661 294-2257
24735 Avenue Rockefeller Valencia (91355) ***(P-10359)***
Santa Cruz Bicycles LLC.....D.....831 459-7560
2841 Mission St Santa Cruz (95060) ***(P-21136)***
Santa Cruz Bikes, Santa Cruz *Also called Santa Cruz Bicycles LLC* ***(P-21136)***
Santa Cruz Biotechnology Inc.....E.....831 457-3800
2145 Delaware Ave Santa Cruz (95060) ***(P-8580)***
Santa Cruz Guitar Corporation.....E.....831 425-0999
151 Harvey West Blvd C Santa Cruz (95060) ***(P-23386)***
Santa Cruz Industries Inc.....F.....831 423-9211
129 Bulkhead Santa Cruz (95060) ***(P-5167)***
Santa Cruz Mtn Pasta Fctry.....F.....831 461-9900
5340 Scotts Valley Dr Scotts Valley (95066) ***(P-2663)***
Santa Cruz Nutritionals, Santa Cruz *Also called Harmony Foods Corporation* ***(P-8204)***
Santa Cruz Pasta Factory, Scotts Valley *Also called Santa Cruz Mtn Pasta Fctry* ***(P-2663)***
Santa Cruz Skateboards, Santa Cruz *Also called Nhs Inc* ***(P-23624)***
Santa Fe Aggregates Inc (HQ).....F.....209 358-3303
11650 Shaffer Rd Winton (95388) ***(P-380)***
Santa Fe Enterprises Inc.....E.....562 692-7596
11654 Pike St Santa Fe Springs (90670) ***(P-14569)***
Santa Fe Extruders Inc.....D.....562 921-8991
15315 Marquardt Ave Santa Fe Springs (90670) ***(P-10360)***
Santa Fe Footwear Corporation.....F.....562 941-9689
9988 Santa Fe Springs Rd Santa Fe Springs (90670) ***(P-10508)***
Santa Fe Machine Works Inc.....E.....909 350-6877
14578 Rancho Vista Dr Fontana (92335) ***(P-16928)***
Santa Fe Packaging Corp.....E.....562 921-8991
9614 Lucas Ranch Rd Ste D Rancho Cucamonga (91730) ***(P-5620)***
Santa Fe Rubber Products Inc.....E.....562 693-2776
12306 Washington Blvd Whittier (90606) ***(P-9674)***
Santa Fe Supply Company, Santa Fe Springs *Also called Philatron International* ***(P-20041)***
Santa Fe Textiles Inc.....F.....949 251-1960
17370 Mount Herrmann St Fountain Valley (92708) ***(P-2806)***
Santa Maria Enrgy Holdings LLC.....E.....805 938-3320
2811 Airpark Dr Santa Maria (93455) ***(P-149)***
Santa Maria Times, Santa Maria *Also called Lee Enterprises Incorporated* ***(P-5911)***
Santa Maria Times Inc.....C.....805 925-2691
3200 Skyway Dr Santa Maria (93455) ***(P-6039)***
Santa Monica City of.....F.....310 826-6712
1228 S Bundy Dr Los Angeles (90025) ***(P-16105)***
Santa Monica Daily Press, Santa Monica *Also called Newlon Rouge LLC* ***(P-5994)***
Santa Monica Plastics Llc.....F.....310 403-2849
1631 Stanford St Santa Monica (90404) ***(P-10361)***
Santa Monica Propeller Svc Inc.....F.....310 390-6233
3135 Dnald Douglas Loop S Santa Monica (90405) ***(P-20925)***
Santa Rosa Lead Products LLC (PA).....F.....800 916-5323
33 S University St Healdsburg (95448) ***(P-14188)***
Santa Rosa Lead Products Inc.....E.....707 431-1477
33 S University St Healdsburg (95448) ***(P-11784)***
Santa Rosa Press Democrat Inc (HQ).....B.....707 546-2020
427 Mendocino Ave Santa Rosa (95401) ***(P-6040)***
Santa Rosa Stain.....E.....707 544-7777
1400 Airport Blvd Santa Rosa (95403) ***(P-21218)***
Santafe Spg PKS&rec Lake Cntr, Santa Fe Springs *Also called City of Santa Fe Springs* ***(P-23540)***
Santan Software Systems Inc.....E.....310 836-2802
19504 Ronald Ave Torrance (90503) ***(P-25144)***
Santana Formal Accessories Inc.....C.....818 898-3677
707 Arroyo St B San Fernando (91340) ***(P-3044)***
Santarus Inc.....E.....858 314-5700
3611 Vly Cntre Dr Ste 400 San Diego (92130) ***(P-8373)***
Santec Inc.....E.....310 542-0063
3501 Challenger St Fl 2 Torrance (90503) ***(P-12049)***
Santee Cosmetics USA.....F.....310 329-2305
13202 Estrella Ave Gardena (90248) ***(P-8835)***
Santier Inc.....D.....858 271-1993
10103 Carroll Canyon Rd San Diego (92131) ***(P-19136)***
Santini Fine Wines, San Lorenzo *Also called Santini Foods Inc* ***(P-648)***
Santini Foods Inc.....C.....510 317-8888
16505 Worthley Dr San Lorenzo (94580) ***(P-648)***
Santos Precision Inc.....E.....714 957-0299
2220 S Anne St Santa Ana (92704) ***(P-20926)***
Santoshi Corporation.....E.....626 444-7118
2439 Seaman Ave El Monte (91733) ***(P-13500)***
Santronics, Sunnyvale *Also called Ahn Enterprises LLC* ***(P-19316)***
Santur Corporation (HQ).....E.....510 933-4100
40931 Encyclopedia Cir Fremont (94538) ***(P-15028)***
Sanyo Foods Corp America (HQ).....E.....714 891-3671
11955 Monarch St Garden Grove (92841) ***(P-2440)***
Sap AG.....C.....650 849-4000
3410 Hillview Ave Palo Alto (94304) ***(P-15599)***
Sapa Extrusions Inc.....C.....909 947-7682
2821 E Philadelphia St A Ontario (91761) ***(P-11602)***
Sapar Usa Inc (PA).....E.....510 441-9500
1610 Delta Ct Ste 1 Hayward (94544) ***(P-523)***
Sapphire Chandelier LLC.....F.....714 630-3660
505 Porter Way Placentia (92870) ***(P-17641)***
Sapphire Energy Inc.....D.....858 768-4700
10996 Torreyana Rd # 280 San Diego (92121) ***(P-7971)***
Sapphire Manufacturing Inc.....E.....714 401-3117
505 Porter Way Placentia (92870) ***(P-12889)***
Sappi North America Inc.....D.....714 456-0600
333 S Anita Dr Ste 840 Orange (92868) ***(P-5734)***
Saputo Cheese USA Inc.....B.....559 687-8411
800 E Paige Ave Tulare (93274) ***(P-598)***
Saputo Cheese USA Inc.....C.....559 687-9999
901 E Levin Ave Tulare (93274) ***(P-599)***
Saputo Cheese USA Inc.....C.....562 862-7686
5611 Imperial Hwy South Gate (90280) ***(P-600)***
Saputo Dairy Foods Usa LLC.....C.....209 854-6461
299 5th Ave Gustine (95322) ***(P-735)***
Saputo Dairy Foods Usa LLC.....C.....714 772-8861
1901 Via Burton Fullerton (92831) ***(P-736)***
Sara Lee, San Lorenzo *Also called Hillshire Brands Company* ***(P-492)***
Sara Lee Bakery Group, Loomis *Also called Bimbo Bakeries Usa Inc* ***(P-1191)***
Sara Lee Fresh Inc.....A.....215 347-5500
5200 S Alameda St Vernon (90058) ***(P-1318)***
Sarahs Leather Mfg.....E.....323 262-2594
3926 Hammel St Los Angeles (90063) ***(P-10580)***
Saramark Inc.....E.....408 971-3881
15660 Mckinley Ave Lathrop (95330) ***(P-12960)***
Saraya Healthcare, Nevada City *Also called Witt Hillard* ***(P-8683)***
Sardee Corporation California.....E.....209 466-1526
2731 E Myrtle St Stockton (95205) ***(P-14284)***
Sardee Industries Inc.....E.....209 466-1526
2731 E Myrtle St Stockton (95205) ***(P-15227)***
Sardo Bus & Coach Upholstery, Gardena *Also called Louis Sardo Upholstery Inc* ***(P-5020)***
Sardo Bus & Coach Upholstery.....D.....800 654-3824
512 W Rosecrans Ave Gardena (90248) ***(P-4967)***
Sargam International Inc.....F.....310 855-9694
719 Huntley Dr West Hollywood (90069) ***(P-17853)***
Sari Art & Printing Inc.....F.....626 305-0888
720 N Todd Ave Azusa (91702) ***(P-7096)***
SARR Industries Inc.....F.....818 998-7735
8975 Fullbright Ave Chatsworth (91311) ***(P-16929)***
Sarris Interiors, Paramount *Also called Sibyl Shepard Inc* ***(P-3747)***
Sars Software Products Inc.....F.....415 226-0040
2175 Francisco Blvd E San Rafael (94901) ***(P-25145)***
Sas Institute Inc.....E.....415 421-2227
50 Post St Ste 50 # 50 San Francisco (94104) ***(P-25146)***
Sas Institute Inc.....F.....919 677-8000
2121 N 1st St Ste 100 San Jose (95131) ***(P-25147)***
Sas Institute Inc.....D.....949 250-9999
1148 N Lemon St Orange (92867) ***(P-25148)***
Sas Manufacturing Inc.....E.....951 734-1808
405 N Smith Ave Corona (92880) ***(P-19718)***
Sas Safety Corporation.....D.....562 427-2775
3031 Gardenia Ave Long Beach (90807) ***(P-22807)***
Sas Stressteel, Fremont *Also called Stressteel Inc* ***(P-11425)***
Sas Textiles Inc.....D.....323 277-5555
3100 E 44th St Vernon (90058) ***(P-2875)***
Sass Labs Inc.....E.....404 731-7284
121 W Washington Ave # 212 Sunnyvale (94086) ***(P-25149)***
Sat, Sacramento *Also called Lpa Insurance Agency Inc* ***(P-24867)***
Satco Inc (PA).....C.....310 322-4719
1601 E El Segundo Blvd El Segundo (90245) ***(P-4505)***

Mergent e-mail: customerrelations@mergent.com
1274
2019 California
Manufacturers Register
(P-0000) Products & Services Section entry number
(PA)=Parent Co (HQ)=Headquarters (DH)=Div Headquarters

Satcom Solutions Corporation ....F 818 991-9794
31119 Via Colinas Ste 501 Westlake Village (91362) *(P-21426)*
Satellite 2000 Systems ....F 818 991-9794
741 Lakefield Rd Ste I Westlake Village (91361) *(P-18244)*
Satellite Telework Centers Inc (PA) ....F 831 222-2100
6265 Highway 9 Felton (95018) *(P-21844)*
Saticoy Rock Asphalt and Rdymx, Oxnard *Also called Legacy Vulcan LLC (P-11128)*
Satori Seal Corporation ....F 909 987-8234
8455 Utica Ave Rancho Cucamonga (91730) *(P-9675)*
Saturn Fasteners Inc ....C 818 973-1807
425 S Varney St Burbank (91502) *(P-11990)*
Saunco Air Technologies, Hickman *Also called Reed International (P-14202)*
Saunders Manufacturing Svcs ....F 714 961-8492
15330 Fairfield Ranch Rd G Chino Hills (91709) *(P-24228)*
Sausalito Craftworks Inc ....F 415 331-4031
2342 Marinship Way Sausalito (94965) *(P-23315)*
Sauvage Inc (PA) ....F 858 408-0100
7717 Formula Pl San Diego (92121) *(P-3187)*
Savage River Inc (PA) ....F 805 669-8673
111 Main St El Segundo (90245) *(P-1014)*
Savage River Inc ....E 310 567-3323
1325 E El Segundo Blvd El Segundo (90245) *(P-1015)*
Savannah Chanelle Vineyards ....E 408 741-2934
23600 Big Basin Way Saratoga (95070) *(P-1967)*
Save-Sorb, Los Angeles *Also called Organicsorb LLC (P-418)*
Savensealcom Ltd ....F 530 478-0238
15478 Applewood Ln Nevada City (95959) *(P-5621)*
Savi Technology Holdings Inc (PA) ....E 650 316-4950
615 Tasman Dr Sunnyvale (94089) *(P-18245)*
Savnik & Company Inc ....F 510 568-4628
601 Mcclary Ave Oakland (94621) *(P-2938)*
Savory Creations International ....E 510 477-0395
32611 Central Ave Union City (94587) *(P-524)*
Savory Creations International ....E 650 638-1024
1900 Ofarrell St Ste 180 San Mateo (94403) *(P-1163)*
Sawbird Inc (PA) ....F 415 861-0644
721 Brannan St San Francisco (94103) *(P-11921)*
Sawhney Garcia Hernandez ....F 619 564-8400
401 B St Ste 2210 San Diego (92101) *(P-3632)*
Sawtelle & Rosprim Machine Sp, Corcoran *Also called Corcoran Sawtelle Rosprim Inc (P-12144)*
Saxco International LLC (PA) ....F 844 766-7819
1855 Gateway Blvd Ste 400 Concord (94520) *(P-10627)*
Saxton Industrial Inc ....F 818 265-0702
1736 Standard Ave Glendale (91201) *(P-12752)*
Saybolt LP ....F 310 518-4400
21730 S Wilmington Ave # 203 Carson (90810) *(P-269)*
Saydel Inc (PA) ....E 323 585-2800
2475 E Slauson Ave Huntington Park (90255) *(P-8836)*
Sazerac Company Inc ....E 310 604-8717
2202 E Del Amo Blvd Carson (90749) *(P-2076)*
SBC, San Francisco *Also called AT&T Corp (P-6440)*
Sbm Dairies Inc (HQ) ....D 626 923-3000
17851 Railroad St City of Industry (91748) *(P-2217)*
Sbmc Solutions LLC ....D 408 732-3200
2960 Copper Rd Santa Clara (95051) *(P-14672)*
Sbragia Family Vineyards LLC ....E 707 473-2992
9990 Dry Creek Rd Geyserville (95441) *(P-1968)*
SBS, Fremont *Also called South Bay Solutions Inc (P-16953)*
SBS America LLC (PA) ....E 831 637-8700
1600 Lana Way Hollister (95023) *(P-4225)*
SC Bluwood Inc ....E 909 519-5470
2604 El Camino Real Ste B Carlsbad (92008) *(P-4597)*
Scafco Corporation ....E 415 852-7974
2177 Jerrold Ave San Francisco (94124) *(P-24229)*
Scafco Corporation ....E 559 256-9911
2443 Foundry Park Ave Fresno (93706) *(P-11847)*
Scafco Corporation ....E 209 670-8053
2525 S Airport Way Stockton (95206) *(P-24230)*
Scafco Corporation ....E 916 624-7700
4301 Jetway Ct North Highlands (95660) *(P-14103)*
Scafco Steel Stud Mfg, San Francisco *Also called Scafco Corporation (P-24229)*
Scafco Steel Stud Mfg, North Highlands *Also called Scafco Corporation (P-14103)*
Scalable Systems RES Labs Inc ....E 650 322-6507
544 Monterey Rd Pacifica (94044) *(P-19137)*
Scale Services Inc ....F 909 266-0896
3553a N Perris Blvd Ste 8 Perris (92571) *(P-16176)*
Scaled Composites LLC ....B 661 824-4541
1624 Flight Line Mojave (93501) *(P-20625)*
Scality Inc ....E 650 356-8500
555 California St # 3050 San Francisco (94104) *(P-15600)*
Scamsafe Inc ....F 800 960-5512
402 E Gutierrez St Santa Barbara (93101) *(P-25150)*
Scanart, Emeryville *Also called Pixscan (P-7437)*
Scantibodies Laboratory Inc (PA) ....C 619 258-9300
9336 Abraham Way Santee (92071) *(P-8509)*
Scapa Tapes North America LLC ....E 310 419-0567
540 N Oak St Inglewood (90302) *(P-5577)*
Scape Goat Ind ....F 760 931-1802
6901 Quail Pl Unit E Carlsbad (92009) *(P-23648)*
Scarlet Saints Softball ....F 530 613-1443
304 Grande Ave Davis (95616) *(P-23649)*
Scarrott Metallurgical Co, Los Angeles *Also called Interntonal Metallurgical Svcs (P-11815)*
Scb Division, Bell Gardens *Also called Cal Southern Braiding Inc (P-19476)*
Scb Division of Dcx-Chol, Bell *Also called Dcx-Chol Enterprises Inc (P-19509)*
SCE Gaskets Inc ....F 661 728-9200
24927 Avenue Tibbitts F Valencia (91355) *(P-9554)*
Scene 53 Inc ....E 415 404-2461
800 E Charleston Rd Apt 7 Palo Alto (94303) *(P-25151)*

Scenewise Inc ....D 310 466-7692
2201 Park Pl Ste 100 El Segundo (90245) *(P-19881)*
Sceptre Inc ....E 626 369-3698
16800 Gale Ave City of Industry (91745) *(P-19719)*
Schaefer Systems Intl Inc ....E 209 365-6030
1250 Thurman St Lodi (95240) *(P-10362)*
Schaeffler Group USA Inc ....B 949 234-9799
34700 Pacific Coast Hwy # 203 Capistrano Beach (92624) *(P-15110)*
Schaffer Laboratories Inc ....F 714 202-1594
8441 Monroe Ave Stanton (90680) *(P-9765)*
Schamas Mfg Coinc ....E 626 334-6870
6356 N Irwindale Ave Irwindale (91702) *(P-14189)*
Schea Holdings Inc ....E 818 888-3818
9812 Independence Ave Chatsworth (91311) *(P-23959)*
Schell & Kampeter Inc ....E 209 983-4900
250 Roth Rd Lathrop (95330) *(P-1121)*
Schellinger Spring Inc ....F 909 373-0799
8477 Utica Ave Rancho Cucamonga (91730) *(P-13754)*
Scheu Manufacturing Co (PA) ....F 909 982-8933
297 Stowell St Upland (91786) *(P-12083)*
Schindler Elevator Corporation ....E 510 382-2075
555 Mccormick St San Leandro (94577) *(P-14258)*
Schlage Lock Company LLC ....E 619 671-0276
2297 Niels Bohr Ct # 209 San Diego (92154) *(P-11991)*
Schley Products Inc ....F 714 693-7666
5350 E Hunter Ave Anaheim (92807) *(P-11909)*
Schlumberger Oilfield Services, Ventura *Also called Schlumberger Technology Corp (P-270)*
Schlumberger Technology Corp ....E 805 642-8230
1710 Callens Rd Ventura (93003) *(P-270)*
Schlumberger Technology Corp ....D 661 864-4750
2841 Pegasus Dr Bakersfield (93308) *(P-271)*
Schlumberger Technology Corp ....D 714 379-7332
12131 Industry St Garden Grove (92841) *(P-272)*
Schlumberger Technology Corp ....F 805 644-8325
3530 Arundell Cir Ventura (93003) *(P-273)*
Schlumberger Well Services, Bakersfield *Also called Schlumberger Technology Corp (P-271)*
Schlumberger Well Services, Ventura *Also called Schlumberger Technology Corp (P-273)*
Schmartboard Inc ....F 510 744-9900
37423 Fremont Blvd Fremont (94536) *(P-17307)*
Schmeiser Farm Equipment, Fresno *Also called T G Schmeiser Co Inc (P-11999)*
Schmid Thermal Systems Inc ....C 831 763-0113
200 Westridge Dr Watsonville (95076) *(P-15274)*
Schmidbauer Lumber Inc (PA) ....C 707 443-7024
1099 W Waterfront Dr Eureka (95501) *(P-4052)*
Schmidbauer Lumber Inc ....E 707 822-7607
1017 Samoa Blvd Arcata (95521) *(P-4053)*
Schmidt Industries Inc ....D 818 768-9100
11321 Goss St Sun Valley (91352) *(P-13501)*
Schmitt Superior Classics, Redding *Also called William R Schmitt (P-4024)*
Schneider Elc Systems USA Inc ....F 949 885-0700
26561 Rancho Pkwy S Lake Forest (92630) *(P-21649)*
Schneider Electric It Usa ....B 714 513-7313
1660 Scenic Ave Costa Mesa (92626) *(P-19720)*
Schneider Electric Usa Inc ....E 714 662-4432
1660 Scenic Ave Costa Mesa (92626) *(P-20063)*
Schneider Electric Usa Inc ....C 858 385-5040
10805 Thornmint Rd # 140 San Diego (92127) *(P-17161)*
Schneiders Deisgn Studio Inc ....F 562 437-0448
245 The Promenade N Fl 2 Long Beach (90802) *(P-23316)*
Schneiders Manufacturing Inc ....E 818 771-0082
11122 Penrose St Sun Valley (91352) *(P-16930)*
Schoenstein & Co ....E 707 747-5858
4001 Industrial Way Benicia (94510) *(P-23387)*
Scholastic Inc ....E 626 337-9996
4821 Charter St Baldwin Park (91706) *(P-6389)*
Scholastic Sports Inc ....D 858 496-9221
4878 Ronson Ct Ste Kl San Diego (92111) *(P-7097)*
Scholle Ipn Corporation ....B 209 384-3100
2500 Cooper Ave Merced (95348) *(P-10363)*
Scholle Ipn Packaging Inc ....B 209 384-3100
2500 Cooper Ave Merced (95348) *(P-10364)*
Scholten Surgical Instrs Inc ....F 209 365-1393
170 Commerce St Ste 101 Lodi (95240) *(P-22615)*
School Apparel Inc (PA) ....C 650 777-4500
838 Mitten Rd Burlingame (94010) *(P-3364)*
School Innovations Achievement (PA) ....D 916 933-2290
5200 Golden Foothill Pkwy El Dorado Hills (95762) *(P-25152)*
Schott Magnetics ....F 619 661-7510
1401 Air Wing Rd San Diego (92154) *(P-13971)*
Schreiber Foods Inc ....C 714 490-7360
1901 Via Burton Fullerton (92831) *(P-601)*
Schrey & Sons Mold Co Inc ....F 661 294-2260
24735 Avenue Rockefeller Valencia (91355) *(P-14570)*
Schrillo Company LLC ....E 818 894-8241
16750 Schoenborn St North Hills (91343) *(P-13082)*
Schroeder Iron Corporation ....E 909 428-6471
8417 Beech Ave Fontana (92335) *(P-12240)*
Schroeder Tool & Die Corp ....E 818 786-9360
25448 Cumberland Ln Calabasas (91302) *(P-16931)*
Schuberth North America LLC ....F 949 215-0893
33 Journey Ste 200 Aliso Viejo (92656) *(P-13272)*
Schulz Engineering, Sylmar *Also called Dg Engineering Corp (P-21287)*
Schulz Industries, Paramount *Also called Schulz Leather Co Inc (P-3809)*
Schulz Leather Co Inc ....E 562 633-1081
16247 Minnesota Ave Paramount (90723) *(P-3809)*
Schuman Enterprises Inc ....F 760 940-1322
1621 Ord Way Oceanside (92056) *(P-13972)*

Schurman Fine Papers......C......951 653-1934
22500 Town Cir Moreno Valley (92553) ***(P-7567)***
Schwarzkopf Inc (HQ)......E......310 641-0990
600 Corporate Pointe # 400 Culver City (90230) ***(P-24231)***
Schwin and Tran Mill & Bakery, Berkeley *Also called Vital Vittles Bakery Inc* ***(P-1338)***
SCI, Santa Clara *Also called Santa Clara Imaging* ***(P-22261)***
SCI, Santa Ana *Also called Semiconductor Components Inc* ***(P-19142)***
SCI, Pomona *Also called Structural Composites Inds LLC* ***(P-12429)***
SCI, National City *Also called Southern California Insulation* ***(P-21014)***
SCI Instruments Inc (PA)......F......760 634-3822
6355 Corte Del Abeto C105 Carlsbad (92011) ***(P-22014)***
SCI Publishing Inc......F......415 382-0580
42 Digital Dr Ste 5 Novato (94949) ***(P-6254)***
SCI-Tech Glassblowing Inc......F......805 523-9790
5555 Tech Cir Moorpark (93021) ***(P-10730)***
Sciabica's, Modesto *Also called Nick Sciabica & Sons A Corp* ***(P-1546)***
Sciambr-Passini French Bky Inc......E......707 252-3072
685 S Freeway Dr NAPA (94558) ***(P-1319)***
Sciambra French Bakery, NAPA *Also called Sciambr-Passini French Bky Inc* ***(P-1319)***
Sciclone Pharmaceuticals Inc (HQ)......E......650 358-3456
950 Tower Ln Ste 900 Foster City (94404) ***(P-8374)***
Science of Skincare LLC......D......818 254-7961
3333 N San Fernando Blvd Burbank (91504) ***(P-8837)***
Science Wiz Summer Camp, Richmond *Also called Norman & Globus Inc* ***(P-6372)***
Scientific Components Systems......F......714 554-3960
1514 N Susan St Ste C Santa Ana (92703) ***(P-17642)***
Scientific Cutting Tools Inc......E......805 584-9495
110 W Easy St Simi Valley (93065) ***(P-14673)***
Scientific Drilling Intl Inc......E......661 831-0636
31101 Coberly Rd Shafter (93263) ***(P-119)***
Scientific Imaging Corporation (PA)......E......408 374-7300
262 E Hamilton Ave Ste H Campbell (95008) ***(P-22130)***
Scientific Imaging Inc......F......408 374-7300
262 E Hamilton Ave Ste H Campbell (95008) ***(P-22131)***
Scientific Instrument Company, Campbell *Also called Scientific Imaging Corporation* ***(P-22130)***
Scientific Instrument Company, Campbell *Also called Scientific Imaging Inc* ***(P-22131)***
Scientific Learning Corp......E......510 444-3500
300 Frank H Ogawa Plz # 600 Oakland (94612) ***(P-25153)***
Scientific Metal Finishing......E......408 970-9011
3180 Molinaro St Santa Clara (95054) ***(P-13654)***
Scientific Molding Corp Ltd......D......707 303-3041
3250 Brickway Blvd Santa Rosa (95403) ***(P-10365)***
Scientific Repair Inc......F......310 214-5092
20720 Earl St Ste 2 Torrance (90503) ***(P-21650)***
Scientific Specialties Inc......D......209 333-2120
1310 Thurman St Lodi (95240) ***(P-9726)***
Scientific Spray Finishes Inc......E......714 871-5541
315 S Richman Ave Fullerton (92832) ***(P-13655)***
Scientific Surface Inds Inc......F......805 499-5100
855 Rancho Conejo Blvd Newbury Park (91320) ***(P-5099)***
Scientific-Atlanta LLC......B......619 679-6000
13112 Evening Creek Dr S San Diego (92128) ***(P-21427)***
Scigen Inc......F......310 324-6576
333 E Gardena Blvd Gardena (90248) ***(P-9039)***
Scigene Corporation......F......408 733-7337
1287 Reamwood Ave Sunnyvale (94089) ***(P-22616)***
Scintera Networks Inc......E......408 636-2600
160 Rio Robles San Jose (95134) ***(P-19138)***
Scion Instruments, Fremont *Also called Techcomp (usa) Inc* ***(P-22026)***
Scisorek & Son Flavors Inc......E......714 524-0550
2951 Enterprise St Brea (92821) ***(P-2281)***
Sciton Inc......D......650 493-9155
925 Commercial St Palo Alto (94303) ***(P-22617)***
SCM Accelerators LLC......F......415 595-8091
2731 California St San Francisco (94115) ***(P-25154)***
Scodan Systems Inc......F......626 444-1020
12373 Barringer St South El Monte (91733) ***(P-13113)***
Scone Henge Inc......F......510 845-5168
2787 Shattuck Ave Berkeley (94705) ***(P-1320)***
Sconza Candy Company......D......209 845-3700
1 Sconza Candy Ln Oakdale (95361) ***(P-1452)***
Scope City (PA)......E......805 522-6646
2978 Topaz Ave Simi Valley (93063) ***(P-22132)***
Scope Packaging Inc......E......714 998-4411
13400 Nelson Ave City of Industry (91746) ***(P-5457)***
Scopely Inc (PA)......C......323 400-6618
3530 Hayden Ave Ste A Culver City (90232) ***(P-25155)***
Scor Industries......F......909 820-5046
2321 S Willow Ave Bloomington (92316) ***(P-24232)***
Scosche Industries Inc......C......805 486-4450
1550 Pacific Ave Oxnard (93033) ***(P-17854)***
Scot Gasket Company Inc......F......323 560-6600
8220 Atlantic Ave Cudahy (90201) ***(P-9555)***
Scotch Paint Corporation......F......310 329-1259
555 W 189th St Gardena (90248) ***(P-8939)***
Scotland Entry Systems Inc......F......818 376-0777
16116 Leadwell St Van Nuys (91406) ***(P-10366)***
Scott Architectural, Fairfield *Also called Scott Lamp Company Inc* ***(P-17643)***
Scott Craft Co (PA)......F......323 560-3949
4601 Cecilia St Cudahy (90201) ***(P-16932)***
Scott Craft Co......F......323 560-3949
5 Stallion Rd Rancho Palos Verdes (90275) ***(P-16933)***
Scott Craft Co & STC, Rancho Palos Verdes *Also called Scott Craft Co* ***(P-16933)***
Scott Engineering Inc......E......909 594-9637
5051 Edison Ave Chino (91710) ***(P-17353)***
Scott Foresman Pearson Educatn, Ontario *Also called Pearson Education Inc* ***(P-6378)***
Scott Industries......D......916 812-7217
736 Central Ave Santa Maria (93454) ***(P-24233)***
Scott Lamp Company Inc......D......707 864-2066
355 Watt Dr Fairfield (94534) ***(P-17643)***
Scott Welsher......F......949 574-4000
2031 S Lynx Ave Ontario (91761) ***(P-10534)***
Scottex Inc......F......310 516-1411
12828 S Broadway Los Angeles (90061) ***(P-3964)***
Scotts Company LLC......F......661 387-9555
742 Industrial Way Shafter (93263) ***(P-9072)***
Scotts Food Products Inc......F......562 630-8448
7331 Alondra Blvd Paramount (90723) ***(P-932)***
Scotts Temecula Operations LLC (HQ)......E......951 719-1700
42375 Remington Ave Temecula (92590) ***(P-14133)***
Scotts Valley Magnetics Inc......E......831 438-3600
300 El Pueblo Rd Ste 107 Scotts Valley (95066) ***(P-19361)***
Scotts- Hyponex, Chino *Also called Hyponex Corporation* ***(P-9062)***
Scotts- Hyponex, Linden *Also called Hyponex Corporation* ***(P-9063)***
Scrap Tire Company, Ballico *Also called Golden By-Products Inc* ***(P-14962)***
Scrape Certified Welding Inc......D......760 728-1308
2525 Old Highway 395 Fallbrook (92028) ***(P-12241)***
Screamin Mimis Inc......F......707 823-5902
6902 Sebastopol Ave Sebastopol (95472) ***(P-694)***
Screaming Squeegee, Sacramento *Also called Creo Inc* ***(P-7290)***
Screen Art Inc......F......714 891-4185
15162 Triton Ln Huntington Beach (92649) ***(P-7478)***
Screen Machine, San Jose *Also called Lights Fantastic* ***(P-6948)***
Screen Printers Resource Inc (PA)......F......714 441-1155
1251 Burton St Fullerton (92831) ***(P-7479)***
Screen Shop Inc......F......408 295-7384
601 Hamline St San Jose (95110) ***(P-12346)***
Screen Tech Inc......D......408 885-9750
4754 Bennett Dr Livermore (94551) ***(P-12753)***
Screen Works......E......714 432-7900
320 E Alton Ave Santa Ana (92707) ***(P-2893)***
Screening Systems Inc (PA)......E......949 855-1751
36 Blackbird Ln Aliso Viejo (92656) ***(P-22015)***
Screenmeet.com, San Francisco *Also called Projectoris Inc* ***(P-25084)***
Screenprintit.com, Sacramento *Also called New Direction Silk Screen* ***(P-7413)***
Screenworks Co Tim......E......310 532-7239
1705 W 134th St Gardena (90249) ***(P-7480)***
Screw Conveyor Pacific Corp......E......559 651-2131
7807 W Doe Ave Visalia (93291) ***(P-14285)***
Screwmatic Inc......D......626 334-7831
925 W 1st St Azusa (91702) ***(P-16934)***
Scribble Press Inc......E......212 288-2928
1109 Montana Ave Santa Monica (90403) ***(P-6577)***
Scribner Engineering Inc......E......916 638-1515
11455 Hydraulics Dr Rancho Cordova (95742) ***(P-10367)***
Scribner Plastics......F......916 638-1515
11455 Hydraulics Dr Rancho Cordova (95742) ***(P-10368)***
Scrimco Inc......F......559 237-7442
2377 S Orange Ave Fresno (93725) ***(P-2782)***
Scripps Laboratories Inc......E......858 546-5800
6838 Flanders Dr San Diego (92121) ***(P-8581)***
Scripps Media Inc......C......805 437-0000
550 Camarillo Center Dr Camarillo (93010) ***(P-6041)***
Scripto-Tokai Corporation (HQ)......D......909 930-5000
2055 S Haven Ave Ontario (91761) ***(P-24234)***
Scully Sportswear Inc......D......805 483-6339
1701 Pacific Ave Oxnard (93033) ***(P-3622)***
Sculptor Body Molding (PA)......F......818 761-3767
10817 W Stallion Ranch Rd Sunland (91040) ***(P-10369)***
SD Desserts LLC......F......702 480-9083
1608 India St Ste 104 San Diego (92101) ***(P-2664)***
SD Fresh Products, San Diego *Also called Cg Financial LLC* ***(P-753)***
SDC Technologies Inc (HQ)......E......714 939-8300
45 Parker Ste 100 Irvine (92618) ***(P-13656)***
Sdi, Simi Valley *Also called Special Devices Incorporated* ***(P-20452)***
Sdi LLC......E......949 351-1866
21 Morgan Ste 150 Irvine (92618) ***(P-16935)***
Sdi Industries Inc (PA)......C......818 890-6002
13000 Pierce St Pacoima (91331) ***(P-14286)***
Sdm, Los Angeles *Also called S D M Furniture Co Inc* ***(P-4737)***
Sdo Communications Corp......D......408 979-0289
47365 Galindo Dr Fremont (94539) ***(P-22133)***
SE Industries Inc......F......714 744-3200
300 W Collins Ave Orange (92867) ***(P-4350)***
SE Software Inc......F......888 504-9876
3340 Ocean Park Blvd # 1005 Santa Monica (90405) ***(P-25156)***
Se-Gl Products Inc......E......951 737-8320
20521 Teresita Way Lake Forest (92630) ***(P-12754)***
Se-Ir Corporation......F......805 571-6800
87 Santa Felicia Dr Goleta (93117) ***(P-22016)***
Sea & Sun Graphics Inc......F......714 897-4020
11721 Seaboard Cir Stanton (90680) ***(P-3917)***
Sea Breeze Technology Inc......F......760 727-6366
1160 Joshua Way Vista (92081) ***(P-20064)***
Sea Con, El Cajon *Also called Brantner and Associates Inc* ***(P-19374)***
Sea Critters, Culver City *Also called Ecoly International Inc* ***(P-8742)***
Sea Magazine, Fountain Valley *Also called Duncan McIntosh Company Inc* ***(P-6153)***
Sea One Seafood, Santa Fe Springs *Also called Long Beach Enterprise Inc* ***(P-2315)***
Sea Shield Marine Products......E......909 594-2507
20832 Currier Rd Walnut (91789) ***(P-11706)***
Sea Snack Foods Inc (PA)......E......213 622-2204
914 E 11th St Los Angeles (90021) ***(P-2322)***
Sea Tek Spars & Rigging Inc......F......310 549-1800
508 E E St Ste B Wilmington (90744) ***(P-21013)***

Mergent e-mail: customerrelations@mergent.com
1276
2019 California
Manufacturers Register
(P-0000) Products & Services Section entry number
(PA)=Parent Co (HQ)=Headquarters (DH)=Div Headquarters

Seaboard Envelope Co Inc...E...626 960-4559
15601 Cypress Ave Irwindale (91706) *(P-5677)*
Seaboard International Inc...D...661 325-5026
3912 Gilmore Ave Bakersfield (93308) *(P-14238)*
Seaborn Canvas...E...310 519-1208
435 N Harbor Blvd Ste B1 San Pedro (90731) *(P-3965)*
Seachrome Corporation...C...310 427-8010
1906 E Dominguez St Long Beach (90810) *(P-12017)*
Seagate Systems (us) Inc (HQ)...D...510 687-5200
46831 Lakeview Blvd Fremont (94538) *(P-15601)*
Seagate Tech Hdd Holdings, Cupertino *Also called Seagate Technology LLC (P-15603)*
Seagate Technology LLC...C...530 410-6594
10042 Wolf Rd Grass Valley (95949) *(P-15602)*
Seagate Technology LLC (HQ)...A...408 658-1000
10200 S De Anza Blvd Cupertino (95014) *(P-15603)*
Seagate Technology LLC...F...405 324-4799
10200 S De Anza Blvd Cupertino (95014) *(P-15604)*
Seagate US LLC...F...408 658-1000
10200 S De Anza Blvd Cupertino (95014) *(P-15605)*
Seagra Technology Inc...E...408 230-8706
816 W Ahwanee Ave Sunnyvale (94085) *(P-15846)*
Seagra Technology Inc (PA)...F...949 419-6796
14252 Culver Dr Irvine (92604) *(P-15847)*
Seagull Solutions Inc...F...408 778-1127
15105 Concord Cir Ste 100 Morgan Hill (95037) *(P-21845)*
Seal For Life Industries LLC...F...619 671-0932
2290 Enrico Fermi Dr San Diego (92154) *(P-24235)*
Seal Innovations Inc...F...626 282-7325
820 S Palm Ave Ste 15 Alhambra (91803) *(P-9676)*
Seal Methods Inc (PA)...D...562 944-0291
11915 Shoemaker Ave Santa Fe Springs (90670) *(P-5578)*
Seal Science Inc (PA)...D...949 253-3130
17131 Daimler St Irvine (92614) *(P-9556)*
Seal Software Inc (PA)...F...650 938-7325
1990 N Calif Blvd Ste 500 Walnut Creek (94596) *(P-25157)*
Sealed Air Corporation...D...909 594-1791
19440 Arenth Ave City of Industry (91748) *(P-9882)*
Sealed Air Corporation...E...201 791-7600
16201 Commerce Way Cerritos (90703) *(P-5622)*
Sealed Air Corporation...C...559 675-0152
1835 W Almond Ave Madera (93637) *(P-9883)*
Sealed Air Corporation...E...619 421-9003
2311 Boswell Rd Ste 8 Chula Vista (91914) *(P-5623)*
Sealing Corporation...F...818 765-7327
7353 Greenbush Ave B North Hollywood (91605) *(P-9557)*
Sealtight Technology, Santa Barbara *Also called B&B Hardware Inc (P-13059)*
Sealy Mattress Mfg Co Inc...C...323 567-7781
4361 Firestone Blvd South Gate (90280) *(P-4884)*
Sealy Mattress Mfg Co Inc...C...510 235-7171
1130 7th St Richmond (94801) *(P-4885)*
Seamaid Manufacturing Corp...E...415 777-9978
960 Mission St San Francisco (94103) *(P-3059)*
Seaman Products of California...F...818 361-2012
12329 Gladstone Ave Sylmar (91342) *(P-20927)*
Seaport Stainless, Richmond *Also called Andrus Sheet Metal Inc (P-12482)*
Searing Industries Inc...C...909 948-3030
8901 Arrow Rte Rancho Cucamonga (91730) *(P-11419)*
Searles Valley Minerals Inc...A...760 372-2259
80201 Trona Rd Trona (93562) *(P-403)*
Searles Valley Minerals Inc...E...760 372-2135
13200 Main St Trona (93562) *(P-9040)*
Seascape Lamps Inc...F...831 728-5699
125a Lee Rd Watsonville (95076) *(P-17559)*
Seaside Printing Co...E...562 437-6437
1220 E 4th St Long Beach (90802) *(P-7098)*
Seasonic Electronics Inc...F...626 969-9966
301 Aerojet Ave Azusa (91702) *(P-19721)*
Seaspace Corporation...E...858 746-1100
13000 Gregg St Ste A Poway (92064) *(P-18246)*
Seaspine Inc...D...760 727-8399
5770 Armada Dr Carlsbad (92008) *(P-22808)*
Seaspine Orthopedics Corp (HQ)...E...866 942-8698
5770 Armada Dr Carlsbad (92008) *(P-22809)*
Seating Component Mfg Inc...F...714 693-3376
3951 E Miraloma Ave Anaheim (92806) *(P-4919)*
Seating Concepts LLC...E...619 491-3159
4229 Ponderosa Ave Ste B San Diego (92123) *(P-5027)*
Seavey Vineyard Ltd Partnr...F...707 963-8339
1310 Conn Valley Rd Saint Helena (94574) *(P-1969)*
Seb, Chino *Also called Specilty Enzymes Btechnologies (P-9043)*
Sebastiani Vineyards Inc...D...707 938-5532
389 4th St E Sonoma (95476) *(P-1970)*
Sebastiani Vineyards & Winery, Sonoma *Also called Sebastiani Vineyards Inc (P-1970)*
SEC, Moorpark *Also called Semiconductor Equipment Corp (P-15029)*
Sechrist Industries Inc...D...714 579-8400
4225 E La Palma Ave Anaheim (92807) *(P-22618)*
Seco Industries, Commerce *Also called Specialty Enterprises Co (P-9884)*
Seco Manufacturing Company Inc...C...530 225-8155
4155 Oasis Rd Redding (96003) *(P-22262)*
Second Generation Inc...D...213 743-8700
4433 Pacific Blvd Vernon (90058) *(P-17855)*
Second Sight Medical Pdts Inc (PA)...818 833-5000
12744 San Fernando Rd Sylmar (91342) *(P-22619)*
Secondwind Products Inc...E...805 239-2555
4301 Second Wind Way Paso Robles (93446) *(P-8676)*
Secret Garden (tsg 1895) LLC...F...562 716-5544
6925 Aragon Cir Ste 1 Buena Park (90620) *(P-24236)*
Secret Road Music Pubg Inc...F...323 464-1234
5850 Foothill Dr Los Angeles (90068) *(P-6390)*
Sector9, San Diego *Also called Bravo Sports (P-23528)*
Secugen Corporation...E...408 834-7712
2065 Martin Ave Ste 108 Santa Clara (95050) *(P-15848)*
Secura Inc...D...760 804-7313
6965 El Camino Re Ste 105 Oceanside (92054) *(P-3120)*
Secura Key, Chatsworth *Also called Soundcraft Inc (P-20077)*
Secure Comm Systems Inc (HQ)...C...714 547-1174
1740 E Wilshire Ave Santa Ana (92705) *(P-18247)*
Secure Comm Systems Inc...F...714 547-1174
1740 E Wilshire Ave Santa Ana (92705) *(P-18248)*
Secure Computing Corporation (HQ)...E...408 979-2020
3965 Freedom Cir 4 Santa Clara (95054) *(P-25158)*
Secured Gold Buyers, Newport Beach *Also called SGB Holdings LLC (P-23317)*
Securedata Inc...F...424 363-8529
3255 Chnga Blvd W Ste 301 Los Angeles (90068) *(P-25159)*
Security Contractor Svcs Inc...E...916 338-4800
5311 Jackson St North Highlands (95660) *(P-12890)*
Security Door Controls (PA)...E...805 494-0622
801 Avenida Acaso Camarillo (93012) *(P-11992)*
Security Front Desk, Mc Kittrick *Also called Aera Energy LLC (P-93)*
Security Metal Products Corp (HQ)...E...310 641-6690
5678 Concours Ontario (91764) *(P-12347)*
Security People Inc...E...707 766-6000
9 Willowbrook Ct Petaluma (94954) *(P-19722)*
Security Pro USA...F...310 841-5845
10530 Venice Blvd Ste 200 Culver City (90232) *(P-22810)*
Security Sales & Integration, Torrance *Also called E H Publishing Inc (P-6155)*
Security Textile Corporation...D...213 747-2673
1457 E Washington Blvd Los Angeles (90021) *(P-3918)*
Securityman, Ontario *Also called Teklink Security Inc (P-20087)*
Securus Inc...E...858 391-0414
14284 Danielson St Poway (92064) *(P-12891)*
Sedas Printing Inc...F...323 469-1034
5335 Santa Monica Blvd Los Angeles (90029) *(P-7099)*
Sedenquist-Fraser Entps Inc...E...562 924-5763
16730 Gridley Rd Cerritos (90703) *(P-20445)*
See's Candies, South San Francisco *Also called Sees Candy Shops Incorporated (P-1454)*
See's Candies, Los Angeles *Also called Sees Candy Shops Incorporated (P-1456)*
Seed Factory Northwest Inc (PA)...E...209 634-8522
4319 Jessup Rd Ceres (95307) *(P-1164)*
Seedorff Acme, Anaheim *Also called A P Seedorff & Company Inc (P-17245)*
Seeger's Printing, Turlock *Also called Seegers Industries Inc (P-7100)*
Seegers Industries Inc...F...209 667-2750
210 N Center St Turlock (95380) *(P-7100)*
Seek Software Inc...F...408 316-4169
1645 Mission Avenida Morgan Hill (95037) *(P-25160)*
Seektech, San Diego *Also called Seescan Inc (P-14710)*
Seelect Inc...F...714 744-3700
833 N Elm St Orange (92867) *(P-2665)*
Seeo Inc...F...510 782-7336
3906 Trust Way Hayward (94545) *(P-19814)*
Sees Candies Inc (HQ)...B...650 761-2490
210 El Camino Real South San Francisco (94080) *(P-1453)*
Sees Candy Shops Incorporated (HQ)...E...650 761-2490
210 El Camino Real South San Francisco (94080) *(P-1454)*
Sees Candy Shops Incorporated...F...562 928-2912
9839 Paramount Blvd Downey (90240) *(P-1455)*
Sees Candy Shops Incorporated...C...310 559-4919
3423 S La Cienega Blvd Los Angeles (90016) *(P-1456)*
Seescan Inc (PA)...C...858 244-3300
3855 Ruffin Rd San Diego (92123) *(P-14710)*
Seesmart Inc...E...203 504-1111
2280 Ward Ave Simi Valley (93065) *(P-17560)*
Sega Holdings USA Inc (HQ)...C...415 701-6000
9737 Lurline Ave Chatsworth (91311) *(P-24237)*
Sega of America Inc (HQ)...E...415 806-0169
6400 Oak Cyn Ste 100 Irvine (92618) *(P-24238)*
Seghesio Wineries Inc...E...707 433-3579
700 Grove St Healdsburg (95448) *(P-1971)*
Seghesio Winery, Healdsburg *Also called Seghesio Wineries Inc (P-1971)*
Segmentio Inc...F...844 611-0621
100 California St Ste 700 San Francisco (94111) *(P-15849)*
Seguin Moreau Holdings Inc (PA)...D...707 252-3408
151 Camino Dorado NAPA (94558) *(P-4535)*
Segundo Metal Products Inc...D...925 667-2009
7855 Southfront Rd Livermore (94551) *(P-12755)*
Sehanson Inc...E...714 778-1900
2121 E Via Burton Anaheim (92806) *(P-20928)*
Seiko Epson, Long Beach *Also called Epson America Inc (P-15740)*
Seirus Innovative ACC Inc...E...858 513-1212
13975 Danielson St Poway (92064) *(P-23650)*
Seismic Reservoir 2020 Inc...E...562 697-9711
3 Pointe Dr Ste 212 Brea (92821) *(P-150)*
Sekai Electronics Inc (PA)...E...949 783-5740
38 Waterworks Way Irvine (92618) *(P-18249)*
Sekisui America Corporation...E...858 452-3198
6659 Top Gun St San Diego (92121) *(P-8510)*
Sel-Tech, Chico *Also called Selken Enterprises Inc (P-25433)*
Selane Products Inc (PA)...D...818 998-7460
9129 Lurline Ave Chatsworth (91311) *(P-22909)*
Selby Inc...F...707 431-1703
498 Moore Ln Ste A Healdsburg (95448) *(P-1972)*
Selby Winery, Healdsburg *Also called Selby Inc (P-1972)*
Select Circuits...F...714 825-1090
3700 W Segerstrom Ave Santa Ana (92704) *(P-18601)*
Select Communications Inc...E...650 948-9000
138 Main St Los Altos (94022) *(P-6255)*
Select Fabrications, Corona *Also called Grand Metals Inc (P-11397)*

ALPHABETIC

Employee Codes: A=Over 500 employees, B=251-500
C=101-250, D=51-100, E=20-50, F=10-19
2019 California
Manfacturers Register
© Mergent Inc. 1-800-342-5647
1277

Select Graphics.....F.....714 537-5250
11931 Euclid St Garden Grove (92840) ***(P-7101)***
Select Office Systems Inc.....F.....818 861-8320
1811 W Magnolia Blvd Burbank (91506) ***(P-9208)***
Select Supplements Inc.....E.....760 431-7509
2390 Oak Ridge Way Vista (92081) ***(P-7972)***
Select Supplements Inc.....F.....760 431-7509
2390 Oak Ridge Way Vista (92081) ***(P-649)***
Selectra Industries Corp.....D.....323 581-8500
5166 Alcoa Ave Vernon (90058) ***(P-3544)***
Self Esteem, Montebello *Also called All Access Apparel Inc* ***(P-3210)***
Selfoptima Inc.....F.....408 217-8667
1601 S De Anza Blvd # 255 Cupertino (95014) ***(P-6578)***
Selken Enterprises Inc.....F.....530 891-4200
108 Boeing Ave Chico (95973) ***(P-25433)***
Sell Lumber Corporation.....F.....530 241-2085
7887 Eastside Rd Redding (96001) ***(P-4054)***
Sellers Optical Inc.....D.....949 631-6800
320 Kalmus Dr Costa Mesa (92626) ***(P-22134)***
Selma Enterprise, Selma *Also called Lee Central Cal Newspapers* ***(P-5910)***
Selma Pallet Inc.....E.....559 896-7171
1651 Pacific St Selma (93662) ***(P-4506)***
Seloah Gourmet Food, Tustin *Also called Country House* ***(P-1417)***
Selvage Concrete Products.....F.....707 542-2762
3309 Sebastopol Rd Santa Rosa (95407) ***(P-11001)***
Semano Inc.....E.....510 489-2360
31757 Knapp St Hayward (94544) ***(P-13502)***
Semco.....E.....909 799-9666
1495 S Gage St San Bernardino (92408) ***(P-22263)***
Semco Aerospace.....F.....818 678-9381
9637 Owensmouth Ave Chatsworth (91311) ***(P-3810)***
Semco Instruments Inc (HQ).....C.....661 257-2000
25700 Rye Canyon Rd Valencia (91355) ***(P-22264)***
Semi Automation & Tech Inc.....E.....408 374-9549
1510 Dell Ave Ste C Campbell (95008) ***(P-19139)***
Semi-Kinetics Inc.....D.....949 830-7364
20191 Windrow Dr Ste A Lake Forest (92630) ***(P-18602)***
Semicndctor Cmponents Inds LLC.....C.....408 542-1000
2975 Stender Way Santa Clara (95054) ***(P-19140)***
Semicoa, Costa Mesa *Also called Falkor Partners LLC* ***(P-18841)***
Semicoa Corporation.....D.....714 979-1900
333 Mccormick Ave Costa Mesa (92626) ***(P-19141)***
Semiconductor Components Inc.....E.....714 547-6059
1353 E Edinger Ave Santa Ana (92705) ***(P-19142)***
Semiconductor Equipment Corp.....F.....805 529-2293
5154 Goldman Ave Moorpark (93021) ***(P-15029)***
Semiconductor Equipment Div, San Jose *Also called Okamoto Corporation* ***(P-19055)***
Semiconductor Logistics Corp.....F.....562 921-0399
14409 Iseli Rd Santa Fe Springs (90670) ***(P-19143)***
Semiconductor Process Eqp Corp.....E.....661 257-0934
27963 Franklin Pkwy Valencia (91355) ***(P-15030)***
Semiconductorstore.com, Hawthorne *Also called Symmetry Electronics LLC* ***(P-19209)***
Semiconix Corp (PA).....F.....408 986-8026
2968 Scott Blvd Santa Clara (95054) ***(P-19144)***
Semifab Inc.....D.....408 414-5928
150 Great Oaks Blvd San Jose (95119) ***(P-21651)***
Seminet Inc.....F.....408 754-8537
150 Great Oaks Blvd San Jose (95119) ***(P-19145)***
Semler Scientific Inc.....E.....877 774-4211
911 Bern Ct Ste 110 San Jose (95112) ***(P-22620)***
Semnur Pharmaceuticals.....F.....650 516-4310
301 N Whisman Rd Mountain View (94043) ***(P-8375)***
Semore Inc.....F.....213 746-4122
1437 Santee St Ste 201 Los Angeles (90015) ***(P-3087)***
Semotus Inc.....E.....408 667-2046
718 University Ave # 110 Los Gatos (95032) ***(P-25161)***
Sempervirens Group.....F.....510 847-0801
820 Coventry Rd Kensington (94707) ***(P-9111)***
Sempra Global (HQ).....D.....619 696-2000
488 8th Ave San Diego (92101) ***(P-17120)***
Semprex Corporation.....F.....408 379-3230
782 Camden Ave Campbell (95008) ***(P-21846)***
Semtech Corporation (PA).....C.....805 498-2111
200 Flynn Rd Camarillo (93012) ***(P-19146)***
Semtech San Diego Corporation.....E.....858 695-1808
10021 Willow Creek Rd San Diego (92131) ***(P-19147)***
Semtek Innvtive Solutions Corp.....E.....858 436-2270
12777 High Bludd Dr 225 San Diego (92130) ***(P-15850)***
Sencha Naturals Inc.....F.....213 353-9908
104 N Union Ave Los Angeles (90026) ***(P-1457)***
Sendx Medical Inc (HQ).....C.....760 930-6300
1945 Palomar Oaks Way # 100 Carlsbad (92011) ***(P-21652)***
Seneca Foods Corporation.....C.....209 572-5201
2801 Finch Rd Modesto (95354) ***(P-855)***
Seneca Foods Corporation.....B.....209 572-5694
2801 Finch Rd Modesto (95354) ***(P-856)***
Senetrics International, Berkeley *Also called Sensys Networks Inc* ***(P-18362)***
Senetur LLC.....F.....650 269-1023
399 Lakeside Dr Ste 400 Oakland (94612) ***(P-25162)***
Seng Cheang Mong Co.....F.....626 442-2899
2661 Merced Ave El Monte (91733) ***(P-2441)***
Seng Cheang Mong Food, El Monte *Also called Seng Cheang Mong Co* ***(P-2441)***
Senga Engineering Inc.....E.....714 549-8011
1525 E Warner Ave Santa Ana (92705) ***(P-16936)***
Senior Aerospace Jet Pdts Corp (HQ).....C.....858 278-8400
9106 Balboa Ave San Diego (92123) ***(P-20679)***
Senior Flexonics, San Diego *Also called Senior Operations LLC* ***(P-16937)***
Senior Operations LLC.....B.....858 278-8400
9106 Balboa Ave San Diego (92123) ***(P-16937)***
Senior Operations LLC.....B.....818 260-2900
2980 N San Fernando Blvd Burbank (91504) ***(P-20929)***
Senior Operations LLC.....D.....909 627-2723
790 Greenfield Dr El Cajon (92021) ***(P-16938)***
Senior Operations LLC.....C.....858 278-8400
9106 Balboa Ave San Diego (92123) ***(P-16939)***
Senju Comtek Corp.....F.....408 792-3830
1171 N 4th St Ste 80 San Jose (95112) ***(P-11848)***
Senju Comtek Corp (HQ).....F.....408 963-5300
2989 San Ysidro Way Santa Clara (95051) ***(P-11849)***
Senju Usa Inc.....F.....818 719-7190
21700 Oxnard St Ste 1070 Woodland Hills (91367) ***(P-8376)***
Senor Snacks Holdings, Fullerton *Also called Senor Snacks Inc* ***(P-2403)***
Senor Snacks Inc.....F.....714 739-1073
2325 Raymer Ave Fullerton (92833) ***(P-2403)***
Senor Snacks Manufacturing Ltd.....D.....714 739-1073
2325 Raymer Ave Fullerton (92833) ***(P-1458)***
Sensata Technologies Inc.....D.....805 968-0782
1461 Lawrence Dr Thousand Oaks (91320) ***(P-15851)***
Sensata Technologies Inc.....C.....805 968-0782
1461 Lawrence Dr Thousand Oaks (91320) ***(P-19723)***
Sensata Technologies Inc.....D.....760 597-7042
1499 Poinsettia Ave # 160 Vista (92081) ***(P-17222)***
Sensbey Inc (PA).....F.....650 697-2032
833 Mahler Rd Ste 3 Burlingame (94010) ***(P-14738)***
Sense Fashion Corporation.....E.....626 454-3381
2415 Merced Ave South El Monte (91733) ***(P-3271)***
Sense Fashions, South El Monte *Also called Sense Fashion Corporation* ***(P-3271)***
Sensient Dehydrated Flavors, Turlock *Also called Sensient Ntral Ingredients LLC* ***(P-893)***
Sensient Ntral Ingredients LLC.....F.....209 394-7979
7474 Cressey Way Livingston (95334) ***(P-892)***
Sensient Ntral Ingredients LLC (HQ).....D.....209 667-2777
151 S Walnut Rd Turlock (95380) ***(P-893)***
Sensient Technologies Corp.....F.....209 394-7971
9984 W Walnut Ave Livingston (95334) ***(P-2666)***
Sensit Inc.....F.....909 793-5816
1652 Plum Ln Ste 106 Redlands (92374) ***(P-21527)***
Senso-Metrics Inc.....F.....805 527-3640
4584 Runway St Simi Valley (93063) ***(P-22265)***
Sensonetics Inc.....F.....714 799-1616
11164 Young River Ave Fountain Valley (92708) ***(P-22266)***
Sensor Concepts Incorporated.....D.....925 443-9001
7950 National Dr Livermore (94550) ***(P-21428)***
Sensor Dynamics Inc.....F.....510 623-1459
4568 Enterprise St Fremont (94538) ***(P-23046)***
Sensor Engineering, Oxnard *Also called Sensortech Systems Inc* ***(P-21653)***
Sensor Systems Inc.....B.....818 341-5366
8929 Fullbright Ave Chatsworth (91311) ***(P-21429)***
Sensoronix Inc.....F.....949 528-0906
16181 Scientific Irvine (92618) ***(P-19148)***
Sensortech Systems Inc.....F.....805 981-3735
341 Bernoulli Cir Oxnard (93030) ***(P-21653)***
Sensory Neurostimulation Inc.....F.....949 492-0550
1235 Puerta Del Sol # 600 San Clemente (92673) ***(P-8377)***
Sensoscientific Inc.....E.....800 279-3101
685 Cochran St Ste 200 Simi Valley (93065) ***(P-21654)***
Sensys Networks Inc (PA).....D.....510 548-4620
1608 4th St Ste 200 Berkeley (94710) ***(P-18362)***
Sentient Energy Inc (PA).....F.....650 523-6680
880 Mitten Rd Ste 105 Burlingame (94010) ***(P-21847)***
Sentiments Inc (PA).....F.....323 843-2080
5635 Smithway St Commerce (90040) ***(P-24239)***
Sentinel Hydrosolutions LLC.....F.....866 410-1134
1223 Pacific Oaks Pl # 104 Escondido (92029) ***(P-22267)***
Sentinel Plastics LLC.....E.....619 734-0213
4492 Camino Dela Plz 23 San Ysidro (92173) ***(P-10370)***
Sentinel Printing & Publishing.....F.....559 591-4632
145 S L St Dinuba (93618) ***(P-6042)***
Sentran L L C (PA).....F.....888 545-8988
4355 E Lowell St Ste F Ontario (91761) ***(P-22268)***
Sentry Industries Inc.....F.....909 986-3642
1245 Brooks St Ontario (91762) ***(P-7884)***
Sentynl Therapeutics Inc.....E.....888 227-8725
420 Stevens Ave Ste 200 Solana Beach (92075) ***(P-8378)***
Separation Engineering Inc.....E.....760 489-0101
931 S Andreasen Dr Ste A Escondido (92029) ***(P-15359)***
Sepasoft Inc.....F.....916 939-1684
1264 Hawks Flight Ct El Dorado Hills (95762) ***(P-25163)***
Sepco, Fremont *Also called Silicon Valley Electro Plating* ***(P-13504)***
Sepor Inc.....F.....310 830-6601
718 N Fries Ave Wilmington (90744) ***(P-21490)***
Sepragen Corporation.....E.....510 475-0650
1205 San Luis Obispo St Hayward (94544) ***(P-22017)***
Sequent Medical Inc.....D.....949 830-9600
11 Columbia Ste A Aliso Viejo (92656) ***(P-22621)***
Sequent Software Inc.....F.....650 419-2713
4699 Old Ironsides Dr # 470 Santa Clara (95054) ***(P-25164)***
Sequenta LLC.....D.....650 243-3900
329 Oyster Point Blvd South San Francisco (94080) ***(P-8511)***
Sequoia Pure Water Inc.....E.....310 637-8500
1640 W 134th St Compton (90222) ***(P-2218)***
Sequoia Works, Rio Linda *Also called Cuora Corporation* ***(P-4571)***
Seradyn Inc.....D.....317 610-3800
46360 Fremont Blvd Fremont (94538) ***(P-8512)***
Serbin Communications Inc.....F.....805 564-7636
813 Reddick St Santa Barbara (93103) ***(P-6256)***
Serco Mold Inc (PA).....E.....626 331-0517
2009 Wright Ave La Verne (91750) ***(P-10371)***
Sercomp LLC (PA).....D.....805 299-0020
5401 Tech Cir Ste 200 Moorpark (93021) ***(P-23738)***

Sereechai Newspaper Inc ....F....323 465-7550
4904 Fountain Ave Los Angeles (90029) ***(P-6043)***

Sergio Shoes, North Hollywood *Also called Onnik Shoe Company Inc* ***(P-10501)***

Serious Energy Inc (PA) ....D....408 541-8000
1250 Elko Dr Sunnyvale (94089) ***(P-5028)***

Serious Windows, Sunnyvale *Also called Serious Energy Inc* ***(P-5028)***

Serpa Packaging Solutions, Visalia *Also called Food Machinery Sales Inc* ***(P-15206)***

Serpac Electronic Enclosures, La Verne *Also called Serco Mold Inc* ***(P-10371)***

Serra Laser and Waterjet Inc ....E....714 680-6211
1740 N Orangethorpe Park Anaheim (92801) ***(P-20065)***

Serra Manufacturing Corp (PA) ....E....310 537-4560
3039 E Las Hermanas St Compton (90221) ***(P-13273)***

Serra Systems Inc (HQ) ....F....707 433-5104
126 Mill St Healdsburg (95448) ***(P-25165)***

Serrano Industries Inc ....E....562 777-8180
9922 Tabor Pl Santa Fe Springs (90670) ***(P-16940)***

Serta International, Livermore *Also called National Bedding Company LLC* ***(P-4875)***

Serv-Rite Meat Company Inc ....D....323 227-1911
2515 N San Fernando Rd Los Angeles (90065) ***(P-525)***

Servers Direct LLC ....C....800 576-7931
20480 Business Pkwy Walnut (91789) ***(P-15481)***

Service Press Inc ....F....650 592-3484
935 Tanklage Rd San Carlos (94070) ***(P-7102)***

Service Rock Products Corp ....E....760 252-1615
2820 E Main St Barstow (92311) ***(P-11171)***

Service Rock Products Corp ....E....760 373-9140
7900 Moss Ave California City (93505) ***(P-11172)***

Service Rock Products Corp ....F....760 245-7997
200 S Main St Ste 200 # 200 Corona (92882) ***(P-11173)***

Service Rock Products Corp ....D....760 446-2606
2157 W Inyokern Rd Ridgecrest (93555) ***(P-11174)***

Service Rock Products Corp ....E....661 533-3443
37790 75th St E Palmdale (93552) ***(P-11175)***

Servo Dynamics Corporation ....E....818 700-8600
28231 Avenue Crocker # 10 Valencia (91355) ***(P-17856)***

Servtech Plastics, Monrovia *Also called Crescent Plastics Inc* ***(P-10050)***

Sesame Software Inc ....E....866 474-7575
5201 Great America Pkwy # 320 Santa Clara (95054) ***(P-25166)***

Sessa Manufacturing & Welding ....E....805 644-2284
2932 Golf Course Dr Ventura (93003) ***(P-13274)***

Sessions ....E....831 461-5080
60 Old El Pueblo Rd Scotts Valley (95066) ***(P-3493)***

Setco LLC ....F....812 424-2904
4875 E Hunter Ave Anaheim (92807) ***(P-10372)***

Seton Scientific Co ....F....707 782-0900
15789 Adams Rdg Los Gatos (95033) ***(P-10373)***

Settlers Jerky Incorporated ....E....909 444-3999
307 Paseo Sonrisa Walnut (91789) ***(P-526)***

Setzer Forest Products Inc (PA) ....C....916 442-2555
2555 3rd St Ste 200 Sacramento (95818) ***(P-4226)***

Setzer Forest Products Inc ....C....530 534-8100
1980 Kusel Rd Oroville (95966) ***(P-4055)***

Sev-Cal Tool Inc ....E....714 549-3347
3231 Halladay St Santa Ana (92705) ***(P-14674)***

Seven For All Mankind LLC- (HQ) ....B....323 406-5300
777 S Alameda St Los Angeles (90021) ***(P-3088)***

Seven Up Bottling, Sacramento *Also called Capitol Beverage Packers* ***(P-2108)***

Seven Up Btlg Co San Francisco (HQ) ....C....925 938-8777
2875 Prune Ave Fremont (94539) ***(P-2219)***

Seven Up Btlg Co San Francisco ....E....831 632-0777
11205 Commercial Pkwy Castroville (95012) ***(P-2220)***

Seven Up Btlg Co San Francisco ....D....916 929-7777
2670 Land Ave Sacramento (95815) ***(P-2221)***

Seven Wel's LLC ....F....213 305-4775
14801 Able Ln Ste 102 Huntington Beach (92647) ***(P-4652)***

Seven-Up Bottling, Fremont *Also called Seven Up Btlg Co San Francisco* ***(P-2219)***

Seven-Up Bottling, Castroville *Also called Seven Up Btlg Co San Francisco* ***(P-2220)***

Seven-Up Bottling, Petaluma *Also called American Bottling Company* ***(P-2082)***

Seven-Up Bottling, Ukiah *Also called American Bottling Company* ***(P-2083)***

Seven-Up Bottling, Sacramento *Also called Seven Up Btlg Co San Francisco* ***(P-2221)***

Seven-Up Btlg Co Marysville, Sacramento *Also called American Bottling Company* ***(P-2090)***

Seven-Up RC of Chico ....E....530 893-4501
306 Otterson Dr Ste 10 Chico (95928) ***(P-2222)***

Seventh Heaven Inc ....E....408 287-8945
1025 S 5th St San Jose (95112) ***(P-3966)***

Sew Forth Inc ....E....323 725-3500
2350 Central Ave Duarte (91010) ***(P-3121)***

Sew Sporty ....E....760 599-0585
2215 La Mirada Dr Vista (92081) ***(P-3494)***

Sew What Inc ....E....310 639-6000
1978 E Gladwick St Compton (90220) ***(P-3703)***

Sew-Eurodrive Inc ....E....510 487-3560
30599 San Antonio St Hayward (94544) ***(P-15246)***

Sewer Rodding Equipment Co (PA) ....E....310 301-9009
3217 Carter Ave Marina Del Rey (90292) ***(P-16106)***

Sewing Collection Inc ....D....323 264-2223
3113 E 26th St Vernon (90058) ***(P-9558)***

Sewing Experts Inc ....E....760 357-8525
227 Lincoln St Calexico (92231) ***(P-3272)***

Sextant Wines, Paso Robles *Also called Rbz Vineyards LLC* ***(P-1942)***

Seychelle Water Filtration ....E....949 234-1999
32963 Calle Perfecto San Juan Capistrano (92675) ***(P-8379)***

Seyi - America Inc ....F....909 839-1151
17534 Von Karman Ave Irvine (92614) ***(P-14455)***

Seymour Duncan, Santa Barbara *Also called Duncan Carter Corporation* ***(P-23363)***

Seymour Levinger & Co ....E....909 673-9800
1455 Citrus St Riverside (92507) ***(P-13144)***

SF Global LLC ....F....888 536-5593
250 Frank H Ogawa Plz Oakland (94612) ***(P-10374)***

SF Tube, Hayward *Also called San Francisco Pipe &* ***(P-13904)***

Sfc, Perris *Also called Stretch Forming Corporation* ***(P-12775)***

Sfc Communications Inc ....F....949 553-8566
65 Post Ste 1000 Irvine (92618) ***(P-21528)***

SFE, Santa Fe Springs *Also called Santa Fe Enterprises Inc* ***(P-14569)***

Sffi Company Inc (PA) ....C....323 586-0000
4383 Exchange Ave Vernon (90058) ***(P-857)***

Sfo Apparel ....C....415 468-8816
41 Park Pl 43 Brisbane (94005) ***(P-3495)***

Sfs, Brea *Also called Kirkhill Inc* ***(P-7906)***

SGB Enterprises Inc ....E....661 294-8306
24844 Anza Dr Ste A Valencia (91355) ***(P-15645)***

SGB Holdings LLC ....E....949 722-1149
16 Cape Woodbury Newport Beach (92660) ***(P-23317)***

Sgk LLC ....D....415 438-6700
650 Townsend St Ste 160 San Francisco (94103) ***(P-7656)***

Sgk LLC ....C....323 258-4111
3116 W Avenue 32 Los Angeles (90065) ***(P-7657)***

Sgl Technic Inc (HQ) ....D....661 257-0500
28176 Avenue Stanford Valencia (91355) ***(P-11326)***

Sgm, Sutter Creek *Also called Sutter Gold Mining Inc* ***(P-9)***

Sgps Inc ....D....310 538-4175
15823 S Main St Gardena (90248) ***(P-24240)***

Sgt Boardriders Inc ....F....714 274-8000
7403 Slater Ave Huntington Beach (92647) ***(P-9677)***

Shades Unlimited Inc ....F....707 285-2233
361 Blodgett St Cotati (94931) ***(P-5209)***

Shadow Holdings LLC (PA) ....E....661 252-3807
26455 Ruether Ave Santa Clarita (91350) ***(P-8838)***

Shadow Holdings LLC ....B....661 252-3807
26421 Ruether Ave Santa Clarita (91350) ***(P-8839)***

Shadow Industries Inc ....F....714 995-4353
8941 Electric St Cypress (90630) ***(P-21210)***

Shadow Trailers, Cypress *Also called Shadow Industries Inc* ***(P-21210)***

Shafer Metal Stake (PA) ....F....559 674-9487
25176 Avenue 5 1/2 Madera (93637) ***(P-12756)***

Shafer Vineyards ....F....707 944-2877
6154 Silverado Trl NAPA (94558) ***(P-1973)***

Shafton Inc ....F....818 985-5025
6932 Tujunga Ave North Hollywood (91605) ***(P-3679)***

Shaka Wear, Los Angeles *Also called Gino Corporation* ***(P-3056)***

Shalon Ventures ....F....650 324-9090
155 Island Dr Palo Alto (94301) ***(P-21491)***

Shamir Insight Inc ....D....858 514-8330
9938 Via Pasar San Diego (92126) ***(P-10667)***

Shammi Industries, Corona *Also called Sammons Equipment Mfg Corp* ***(P-5254)***

Shamrock Die Cutting Company ....E....323 266-4556
3020 Meyerloa Ln Pasadena (91107) ***(P-5658)***

Shamrock Fireplace, San Rafael *Also called Shamrock Materials Inc* ***(P-11178)***

Shamrock Manufacturing, Chino *Also called Shamrock Marketing Co Inc* ***(P-22811)***

Shamrock Marketing Co Inc (HQ) ....F....909 591-8855
5445 Daniels St Chino (91710) ***(P-22811)***

Shamrock Materials Inc (PA) ....E....707 781-9000
181 Lynch Creek Way # 201 Petaluma (94954) ***(P-11176)***

Shamrock Materials Inc ....F....707 792-4695
8150 Gravenstein Hwy Cotati (94931) ***(P-11177)***

Shamrock Materials Inc ....E....415 455-1575
548 Du Bois St San Rafael (94901) ***(P-11178)***

Shamrock Materials of Cotati, Cotati *Also called Shamrock Materials Inc* ***(P-11177)***

Shamrock Materials of Novato ....F....415 892-1571
7552 Redwood Blvd Novato (94945) ***(P-11179)***

Shane Hunter LLC ....E....213 749-9390
1013 S Los Angeles St # 1000 Los Angeles (90015) ***(P-3680)***

Shanghai Anc Electronic Tech, Moorpark *Also called Anc Technology* ***(P-18422)***

Shannon Ridge Inc ....E....707 994-9656
13888 Point Lakeview Rd Lower Lake (95457) ***(P-1974)***

Shannon Side Welding Inc ....F....415 408-3219
214 Shaw Rd Ste I South San Francisco (94080) ***(P-25434)***

Shape Memory Applications, San Jose *Also called Matthey Johnson Inc* ***(P-22520)***

Shape Memory Medical Inc ....F....979 599-5201
807 Aldo Ave Ste 109 Santa Clara (95054) ***(P-22812)***

Shape Products, Oakland *Also called Vulpine Inc* ***(P-9317)***

Shara-Tex Inc ....E....323 587-7200
3338 E Slauson Ave Vernon (90058) ***(P-2867)***

Sharcar Enterprises Inc ....D....209 531-2200
201 Winmoore Way Modesto (95358) ***(P-11278)***

Sharedata Inc ....D....408 490-2500
2465 Augustine Dr Santa Clara (95054) ***(P-25167)***

Sharedta/E Trade Bus Solutions, Santa Clara *Also called Sharedata Inc* ***(P-25167)***

Sharkey Technology Group Inc ....F....661 267-2118
39450 3rd St E Ste 154 Palmdale (93550) ***(P-16941)***

Sharkrack Inc ....F....510 477-7900
23842 Cabot Blvd Hayward (94545) ***(P-15852)***

Sharp Dimension Inc ....E....510 656-8938
4240 Business Center Dr Fremont (94538) ***(P-16942)***

Sharp Dots.com, Azusa *Also called Sharpdots LLC* ***(P-15853)***

Sharp Industries Inc (PA) ....E....310 370-5990
3501 Challenger St Fl 2 Torrance (90503) ***(P-14456)***

Sharp Profiles LLC ....F....760 246-9446
828 W Cienega Ave San Dimas (91773) ***(P-11910)***

Sharp-Rite Tool Inc ....F....909 948-1234
8443 Whirlaway St Alta Loma (91701) ***(P-14675)***

Sharpcast, Los Angeles *Also called Sugarsync Inc* ***(P-25233)***

Sharpdots LLC ....F....626 599-9696
720 N Todd Ave Azusa (91702) ***(P-15853)***

A L P H A B E T I C

Sharpe Energy Services Inc .... F 408 489-3581
  5094 Northlawn Dr San Jose (95130) *(P-151)*
Sharpe Software Inc .... F 530 671-6499
  925 Market St Yuba City (95991) *(P-25168)*
Shasta Beverages Inc (HQ) .... D 954 581-0922
  26901 Indl Blvd Hayward (94545) *(P-2223)*
Shasta Beverages Inc .... D 714 523-2280
  14405 Artesia Blvd La Mirada (90638) *(P-2224)*
Shasta Electronic Mfg Svcs Inc .... E 408 436-1267
  525 E Brokaw Rd San Jose (95112) *(P-15482)*
Shasta Ems, San Jose *Also called Shasta Electronic Mfg Svcs Inc (P-15482)*
Shasta Forest Products Inc (PA) .... E 530 842-0527
  1412 Montague Rd Yreka (96097) *(P-4653)*
Shasta Forest Products Inc .... E 530 842-2787
  1423 Montague Rd Yreka (96097) *(P-4654)*
Shasta Green Inc .... E 530 335-4924
  35586a State Hwy 299 E Burney (96013) *(P-4010)*
Shasta Ready Mix, Redding *Also called J F Shea Co Inc (P-11123)*
Shasta Wood Products .... E 530 378-6880
  19751 Hirsch Ct Anderson (96007) *(P-5100)*
Shaver Specialty Coinc .... E 310 370-6941
  20608 Earl St Torrance (90503) *(P-14884)*
Shaw Industries Group Inc .... B 562 921-7209
  15305 Valley View Ave Santa Fe Springs (90670) *(P-2939)*
Shaw Industries Group Inc .... C 562 430-4445
  11411 Valley View St Cypress (90630) *(P-2940)*
Shawcor Pipe Protection LLC .... F 909 357-9002
  14000 San Bernardino Ave Fontana (92335) *(P-13657)*
Shawver Metal Tech Inc .... F 209 239-9896
  881 Moffat Blvd Manteca (95336) *(P-13275)*
Shaxon Industries Inc .... D 714 779-1140
  4852 E La Palma Ave Anaheim (92807) *(P-15606)*
Shb Instruments Inc .... F 818 773-2000
  19215 Parthenia St Ste A Northridge (91324) *(P-21848)*
Shear Tech, Chatsworth *Also called Y Nissim Inc (P-15917)*
Sheathing Technologies Inc .... E 408 782-2720
  675 Jarvis Dr Ste A Morgan Hill (95037) *(P-22622)*
Sheedy Drayage Co .... F 510 441-7300
  34301 7th St Union City (94587) *(P-14302)*
Sheedy Hoist, Union City *Also called Sheedy Drayage Co (P-14302)*
Sheepskin Specialties, San Diego *Also called Superlamb Inc (P-3623)*
Sheer Design inc .... D 310 306-2121
  6309 Esplanade Playa Del Rey (90293) *(P-8840)*
Sheervision Inc (PA) .... F 310 265-8918
  4030 Palos Verdes Dr N # 104 Rllng HLS Est (90274) *(P-22135)*
Sheet Metal Prototype Inc .... E 818 772-2715
  19420 Londelius St Northridge (91324) *(P-12757)*
Sheet Metal Service .... F 714 446-0196
  2310 E Orangethorpe Ave Anaheim (92806) *(P-12758)*
Sheet Metal Specialist LLC .... E 951 351-6828
  11698 Warm Springs Rd Riverside (92505) *(P-12759)*
Sheet Mtal Fabrication Sup Inc .... D 916 641-6884
  2020 Railroad Dr Sacramento (95815) *(P-12760)*
Sheetmetal Engineering .... E 805 306-0390
  1780 Voyager Ave Simi Valley (93063) *(P-12761)*
Sheffield Manufacturing Inc .... E 818 767-4948
  13849 Magnolia Ave Chino (91710) *(P-16943)*
Sheffield Platers Inc .... E 858 546-8484
  9850 Waples St San Diego (92121) *(P-13503)*
Shelby Carroll Intl Inc (PA) .... E 310 538-2914
  19021 S Figueroa St Gardena (90248) *(P-20171)*
Shelcore Inc (PA) .... F 818 883-2400
  7811 Lemona Ave Van Nuys (91405) *(P-23463)*
Shelcore Toys, Van Nuys *Also called Shelcore Inc (P-23463)*
Sheldons Hobby Shop .... F 408 943-0220
  2135 Oakland Rd San Jose (95131) *(P-18250)*
Shell Chemical LP .... D 925 313-8601
  10 Mococo Rd Martinez (94553) *(P-7802)*
Shell Martinez Refinery, Martinez *Also called Shell Martinez Refining Co (P-9357)*
Shell Martinez Refining Co .... A 925 313-3000
  3485 Pacheco Blvd Martinez (94553) *(P-9357)*
Shellpro Inc .... E 209 334-2081
  18378 Atkins Rd Lodi (95240) *(P-24241)*
Shelter International Inc .... E 323 888-8856
  6310 Corsair St Commerce (90040) *(P-4655)*
Shelter Island Boatyard, San Diego *Also called Shelter Island Yachtways Ltd (P-21063)*
Shelter Island Yachtways Ltd .... E 619 222-0481
  2330 Shelter Island Dr # 1 San Diego (92106) *(P-21063)*
Shelter Systems .... F 650 323-6202
  224 Walnut St Menlo Park (94025) *(P-3811)*
Shelton Inc .... E 510 524-2430
  1225 8th St Berkeley (94710) *(P-1473)*
Sheng-Kee Bakery .... D 415 468-3800
  201 S Hill Dr Brisbane (94005) *(P-1321)*
Sheng-Kee of California Inc .... E 408 865-6000
  10961 N Wolfe Rd Cupertino (95014) *(P-1379)*
Shepard Bros Inc (PA) .... C 562 697-1366
  503 S Cypress St La Habra (90631) *(P-16107)*
Shephard Casters .... F 909 393-0597
  4451 Eucalyptus Ave Chino (91710) *(P-15111)*
Sherbit Health Inc .... F 925 683-8116
  2200 Powell St Ste 460 Emeryville (94608) *(P-25169)*
Shercon Inc .... E 800 228-3218
  18704 S Ferris Pl Rancho Dominguez (90220) *(P-9678)*
Sherline Products Incorporated .... E 760 727-5181
  3235 Executive Rdg Vista (92081) *(P-14411)*
Sherman Corporation .... E 310 671-2117
  10803 Los Jardines E Fountain Valley (92708) *(P-16944)*
Sherry Kline, Commerce *Also called Pacific Coast Home Furn Inc (P-3739)*

Sherwin-Williams Company .... E 323 726-7272
  5501 E Slauson Ave Commerce (90040) *(P-2962)*
Shg Holdings Corp (PA) .... D 310 410-4907
  201 Hindry Ave Inglewood (90301) *(P-14711)*
Shield CA, Chino *Also called Shield Realty California Inc (P-7732)*
Shield Realty California Inc (PA) .... E 909 628-4707
  5165 G St Chino (91710) *(P-7732)*
Shieldnseal, Nevada City *Also called Savensealcom Inc (P-5621)*
Shields Enterprises Inc .... E 619 276-9100
  8740 Avenida Costa Blanca San Diego (92154) *(P-14412)*
Shift Calendars Inc .... E 626 967-5862
  809 N Glendora Ave Covina (91724) *(P-7103)*
Shift Management Inc .... F 916 381-4700
  1060 National Dr Ste 3 Sacramento (95834) *(P-20446)*
Shihs Printing .... E 626 281-2989
  673 Monterey Pass Rd Monterey Park (91754) *(P-7481)*
Shikai Products, Santa Rosa *Also called Trans-India Products Inc (P-8855)*
Shim-It Corporation .... F 562 467-8600
  1691 California Ave Corona (92881) *(P-20930)*
Shimada Enterprises Inc .... E 562 802-8811
  14009 Dinard Ave Santa Fe Springs (90670) *(P-17731)*
Shimmer Fashion .... F 619 426-7781
  555 Broadway Ste 134 Chula Vista (91910) *(P-3273)*
Shimtech Industries US Inc .... D 661 295-8620
  29101 The Old Rd Valencia (91355) *(P-20931)*
Shimtech US, Santa Clarita *Also called Lamsco West Inc (P-20863)*
Shine & Pretty (usa) Corp .... E 805 388-8581
  456 Constitution Ave Camarillo (93012) *(P-8841)*
Shine Company Inc .... F 909 590-5005
  3535 Philadelphia St Chino (91710) *(P-4656)*
Shine Food Inc (PA) .... E 310 329-3829
  19216 Normandie Ave Torrance (90502) *(P-773)*
Shine Food Inc .... E 310 533-6010
  21100 S Western Ave Torrance (90501) *(P-1016)*
Shinestar, Vernon *Also called Elecoco Inc (P-3410)*
Ship Supply International Inc .... F 310 325-3188
  1215 255th St Harbor City (90710) *(P-10824)*
Shiploop, San Francisco *Also called Squamtech Inc (P-25211)*
Shire Rgenerative Medicine Inc .... E 858 202-0673
  10933 N Torrey Pines Rd # 200 La Jolla (92037) *(P-8380)*
Shire Rgenerative Medicine Inc .... D 858 754-3700
  10933 N Torrey Pines Rd # 200 La Jolla (92037) *(P-8582)*
Shire Rgenerative Medicine Inc .... D 858 754-5396
  10933 N Torrey Pines Rd # 200 La Jolla (92037) *(P-8381)*
Shirlee Industries Inc .... F 909 590-4120
  13985 Sycamore Way Chino (91710) *(P-12992)*
Shmaze Custom Coatings, Lake Forest *Also called Shmaze Industries Inc (P-13658)*
Shmaze Industries Inc .... E 949 583-1448
  20792 Canada Rd Lake Forest (92630) *(P-13658)*
Shocking Technologies Inc .... E 831 331-4558
  5870 Hellyer Ave San Jose (95138) *(P-7885)*
Shockwave Medical Inc .... F 510 279-4262
  48501 Warm Springs Blvd Fremont (94539) *(P-22623)*
Shoes For Crews Intl Inc .... E 561 683-5090
  760 Baldwin Park Blvd City of Industry (91746) *(P-10483)*
Shop -Bradshaw Maintenance Sho, Sacramento *Also called Cemex Cnstr Mtls PCF LLC (P-11068)*
Shop -Ncal Rmx Fixed Maint Sho, Fairfield *Also called Cemex Cnstr Mtls PCF LLC (P-11065)*
Shop4techcom .... F 909 248-2725
  13745 Seminole Dr Chino (91710) *(P-15607)*
Shorai Inc .... F 408 720-8821
  16020 Caputo Dr 100 Morgan Hill (95037) *(P-19824)*
Shore Western Manufacturing .... E 626 357-3251
  225 W Duarte Rd Monrovia (91016) *(P-22018)*
Shorecare, Sunnyvale *Also called Mitel Networks Inc (P-17965)*
Shoreline Products Inc .... E 949 388-1919
  120 Calle Iglesia Ste A San Clemente (92672) *(P-23772)*
Shores Press .... F 650 593-2802
  1100 Industrial Rd Ste 2 San Carlos (94070) *(P-6579)*
Shorett Printing Inc (PA) .... E 714 545-4689
  250 W Rialto Ave San Bernardino (92408) *(P-7482)*
Shorett Printing Inc .... E 714 956-9001
  250 W Rialto Ave San Bernardino (92408) *(P-7104)*
Short Run Swiss Inc .... E 626 974-9373
  714 E Edna Pl Covina (91723) *(P-16945)*
Shortcuts Software Inc .... E 714 622-6600
  7711 Center Ave Ste 550 Huntington Beach (92647) *(P-25170)*
Shotspotter Inc .... D 510 794-3100
  7979 Gateway Blvd Ste 210 Newark (94560) *(P-25171)*
Show Group Production Services, Gardena *Also called Sgps Inc (P-24240)*
Show Off Time, Ventura *Also called Fnc Medical Corporation (P-8750)*
Show Offs .... E 909 885-5223
  1696 W Mill St Unit 10 Colton (92324) *(P-5101)*
Showcase Components, Santa Fe Springs *Also called Alumafab (P-17582)*
Showdogs Inc .... E 760 603-3269
  168 S Pacific St San Marcos (92078) *(P-5210)*
Showerdoordirect LLC .... D 310 327-8060
  20100 Normandie Ave Torrance (90502) *(P-12762)*
Showertek Inc .... F 707 224-1480
  2775 Napa Valley Corp Dr NAPA (94558) *(P-10731)*
Shred-Tech Usa LLC .... E 909 923-2783
  1100 S Grove Ave Ontario (91761) *(P-14346)*
Shredding Paper .... F 415 454-2242
  75 Plum Tree Ln Apt 3 San Rafael (94901) *(P-6391)*
Shrin Corporation .... C 714 850-0303
  900 E Arlee Pl Anaheim (92805) *(P-20447)*
Shrink Wrap Pros LLC .... F 805 207-9050
  275 E Hillcrest Dr Ste 16 Thousand Oaks (91360) *(P-15228)*

ALPHABETIC SECTION Sigma 6 Electronics Inc

Shubb Capos............E.......707 876-3001
14471 Hwy 1 Valley Ford (94972) *(P-23388)*
Shugar Soapworks Inc............F.......323 234-2874
5955 Rickenbacker Rd Commerce (90040) *(P-8608)*
Shugart Corporation (PA)............C.......949 488-8779
25 Brookline Aliso Viejo (92656) *(P-15483)*
Shusters Logging Inc............D.......707 459-4131
750 E Valley St Willits (95490) *(P-4011)*
Shuttercraft of California, Santa Fe Springs *Also called Steiner & Mateer Inc (P-4235)*
Shutters By Angel Co, Lancaster *Also called Rta Sales Inc (P-4222)*
Shuttle Computer Group Inc............E.......626 820-9000
17068 Evergreen Pl City of Industry (91745) *(P-15484)*
Shye West Inc (PA)............E.......949 486-4598
43 Corporate Park Ste 102 Irvine (92606) *(P-23960)*
Si, Fontana *Also called California Steel Inds Inc (P-11383)*
Si Manufacturing Inc............E.......714 956-7110
1440 S Allec St Anaheim (92805) *(P-19362)*
Sibyl Shepard Inc............E.......562 531-8612
8225 Alondra Blvd Paramount (90723) *(P-3747)*
Sid E Parker Boiler Mfg Co Inc............D.......323 727-9800
5930 Bandini Blvd Commerce (90040) *(P-12420)*
Sidco Labelling Systems, Santa Clara *Also called Context Engineering Co (P-13188)*
Side Effects of California, Glendale *Also called Mar & Company Inc (P-3461)*
Sidney Millers Black Radio Ex............E.......818 907-9959
15030 Ventura Blvd # 864 Sherman Oaks (91403) *(P-6257)*
Sidus Solutions LLC (PA)............F.......619 275-5533
7352 Trade St San Diego (92121) *(P-20066)*
Sieena Inc............E.......310 455-6188
1901 Avenue Of The Stars Los Angeles (90067) *(P-25172)*
Siegfried Irvine, Irvine *Also called Alliance Medical Products Inc (P-22327)*
Siegwerk USA Inc............E.......707 469-7648
871 Cotting Ct Ste H Vacaville (95688) *(P-9209)*
Siemens Hlthcare Dgnostics Inc............D.......310 645-8200
5210 Pacific Concourse Dr Los Angeles (90045) *(P-8513)*
Siemens Hlthcare Dgnostics Inc............F.......510 982-4000
725 Potter St Berkeley (94710) *(P-17991)*
Siemens Hlthcare Dgnostics Inc............E.......916 372-1900
2040 Enterprise Blvd West Sacramento (95691) *(P-8514)*
Siemens Industry Inc............E.......323 277-1500
5375 S Boyle Ave Vernon (90058) *(P-15360)*
Siemens Industry Inc............D.......949 448-0600
6 Journey Ste 200 Aliso Viejo (92656) *(P-21529)*
Siemens Industry Inc............E.......724 772-1237
1441 E Washington Blvd Los Angeles (90021) *(P-15361)*
Siemens Industry Inc............D.......510 237-2325
2775 Goodrick Ave Richmond (94801) *(P-21530)*
Siemens Industry Inc............F.......916 553-4444
3650 Industrial Blvd # 100 West Sacramento (95691) *(P-21531)*
Siemens Industry Inc............C.......916 681-3000
7464 French Rd Sacramento (95828) *(P-21532)*
Siemens Industry Inc............D.......714 252-3100
10855 Business Center Dr Cypress (90630) *(P-17162)*
Siemens Med Solutions USA Inc............B.......925 246-8200
4040 Nelson Ave Concord (94520) *(P-23047)*
Siemens Medical Solutions, Los Angeles *Also called Siemens Hlthcare Dgnostics Inc (P-8513)*
Siemens Medical Systems, Berkeley *Also called Siemens Hlthcare Dgnostics Inc (P-17991)*
Siemens PLM Software, San Jose *Also called Siemens Product Life Mgmt Sftw (P-25173)*
Siemens Product Life Mgmt Sftw............E.......408 941-4600
2077 Gateway Pl Ste 400 San Jose (95110) *(P-25173)*
Siemens Rail Automation Corp............C.......909 532-5405
9568 Archibald Ave Rancho Cucamonga (91730) *(P-18363)*
Siena Decor Inc............F.......909 895-8585
1250 Philadelphia St Pomona (91766) *(P-23711)*
Sienna Corporation Inc............E.......510 440-0200
41350 Christy St Fremont (94538) *(P-20067)*
Sientra Inc (PA)............C.......805 562-3500
420 S Fairview Ave # 200 Santa Barbara (93117) *(P-22813)*
Sierra Aerospace LLC............F.......805 526-8669
2263 Ward Ave Simi Valley (93065) *(P-20680)*
Sierra Alloys Company............D.......626 969-6711
5467 Ayon Ave Irwindale (91706) *(P-13129)*
Sierra Aluminum Company (HQ)............E.......951 781-7800
2345 Fleetwood Dr Riverside (92509) *(P-11603)*
Sierra Asset Servicing LLC............F.......530 582-7300
10232 Donner Pass Rd # 4 Truckee (96161) *(P-274)*
Sierra Automated Sys/Eng Corp............E.......818 840-6749
2821 Burton Ave Burbank (91504) *(P-18251)*
Sierra Aviation............E.......760 778-2845
3400 E Tahquitz Canyon Wa Palm Springs (92262) *(P-10535)*
Sierra Cascade Aggregate & Asp............F.......530 258-4555
6600 Old Ski Rd Chester (96020) *(P-381)*
Sierra Chemical Company, West Sacramento *Also called Richard K Gould Inc (P-9302)*
Sierra Circuits Inc............C.......408 735-7137
1108 W Evelyn Ave Sunnyvale (94086) *(P-18603)*
Sierra Design Mfg Inc (PA)............E.......925 443-3140
1113 Greenville Rd Livermore (94550) *(P-17663)*
Sierra Energy, Garden Valley *Also called Toms Sierra Company Inc (P-283)*
Sierra Feeds, Reedley *Also called Mission AG Resources LLC (P-632)*
Sierra Foods Inc............F.......562 802-3500
13352 Imperial Hwy Santa Fe Springs (90670) *(P-11883)*
Sierra Foothills Fudge Factory............F.......530 644-3492
2860 High Hill Rd Placerville (95667) *(P-1459)*
Sierra Hygiene Products LLC............F.......925 371-7173
4749 Bennett Dr Ste B Livermore (94551) *(P-5334)*
Sierra Lumber Manufacturers............C.......209 943-7777
375 W Hazelton Ave Stockton (95203) *(P-4227)*
Sierra Metal Fabricators Inc............E.......530 265-4591
529 Searls Ave Nevada City (95959) *(P-12242)*
Sierra Metalk Fabricators, Nevada City *Also called Sierra Metal Fabricators Inc (P-12242)*
Sierra Monitor Corporation (PA)............D.......408 262-6611
1991 Tarob Ct Milpitas (95035) *(P-22269)*
Sierra Monolithics Inc............F.......949 269-4400
5141 California Ave # 150 Irvine (92617) *(P-21430)*
Sierra National Corporation............E.......619 258-8200
5140 Alzeda Dr La Mesa (91941) *(P-15900)*
Sierra Natural Science Inc............F.......831 757-1702
538 Brunken Ave Ste 2 Salinas (93901) *(P-9041)*
Sierra Nevada Brewing Co (PA)............B.......530 893-3520
1075 E 20th St Chico (95928) *(P-1623)*
Sierra Nevada Cheese Co Inc............D.......530 934-8660
6505 County Road 39 Willows (95988) *(P-602)*
Sierra Nevada Corporation............E.......510 446-8400
39465 Paseo Padre Pkwy # 2900 Fremont (94538) *(P-18252)*
Sierra Nevada Corporation............E.......916 985-8799
145 Parkshore Dr Folsom (95630) *(P-20068)*
Sierra Office Supplies & Prtg, Sacramento *Also called Sierra Office Systems Pdts Inc (P-7105)*
Sierra Office Systems Pdts Inc (PA)............D.......916 369-0491
9950 Horn Rd Ste 5 Sacramento (95827) *(P-7105)*
Sierra Pacific Engrg & Pdts, Long Beach *Also called SPEP Acquisition Corp (P-11994)*
Sierra Pacific Industries............F.......530 226-5181
2771 Bechelli Ln Redding (96002) *(P-4056)*
Sierra Pacific Industries (PA)............D.......530 378-8000
19794 Riverside Ave Anderson (96007) *(P-4057)*
Sierra Pacific Industries............F.......530 378-8301
36336 Highway 299 E Burney (96013) *(P-4058)*
Sierra Pacific Industries............C.......530 532-6630
3025 S 5th Ave Oroville (95965) *(P-4059)*
Sierra Pacific Industries............C.......530 335-3681
Hwy 299 E Burney (96013) *(P-4060)*
Sierra Pacific Industries............B.......530 824-2474
Alameda Rd Corning (96021) *(P-4228)*
Sierra Pacific Industries............C.......530 275-8851
3735 El Cajon Ave Shasta Lake (96019) *(P-4061)*
Sierra Pacific Industries............B.......530 365-3721
19758 Riverside Ave Anderson (96007) *(P-4062)*
Sierra Pacific Industries............B.......530 644-2311
3950 Carson Rd Camino (95709) *(P-4063)*
Sierra Pacific Industries............B.......916 645-1631
1440 Lincoln Blvd Lincoln (95648) *(P-4064)*
Sierra Pacific Industries............B.......530 527-9620
11605 Reading Rd Red Bluff (96080) *(P-4065)*
Sierra Pacific Machining Inc............F.......408 924-0281
530 Parrott St San Jose (95112) *(P-16946)*
Sierra Pacific Packaging, Oroville *Also called Graphic Packaging Intl LLC (P-7329)*
Sierra Pharmacy, Rancho Cucamonga *Also called Akaranta Inc (P-8007)*
Sierra Photonics Inc............E.......925 290-2930
7563 Southfront Rd Livermore (94551) *(P-18364)*
Sierra Plastic, Pomona *Also called California Plastix Inc (P-5589)*
Sierra Precast Inc............D.......408 779-1000
1 Live Oak Ave Morgan Hill (95037) *(P-11002)*
Sierra Precision, Anaheim *Also called 3d Instruments LP (P-21539)*
Sierra Precision Optics Inc............E.......530 885-6979
12830 Earhart Ave Auburn (95602) *(P-22136)*
Sierra Proto Express, Sunnyvale *Also called Sierra Circuits Inc (P-18603)*
Sierra Resource Management Inc............E.......209 984-1146
12015 La Grange Rd Jamestown (95327) *(P-4012)*
Sierra Rm / Bm, El Dorado *Also called Cemex Cnstr Mtls PCF LLC (P-11063)*
Sierra Safety Company............F.......916 663-2026
215 Taylor Rd Newcastle (95658) *(P-13973)*
Sierra Scientific Instrs LLC, Culver City *Also called Given Imaging Los Angeles LLC (P-22981)*
Sierra Sculpture Inc............F.......530 887-1581
13333 New Airport Rd Auburn (95602) *(P-11766)*
Sierra Sun Newspaper, Truckee *Also called Mount Rose Publishing Co Inc (P-5983)*
Sierra Sunrise Vineyard Inc............E.......209 245-6942
20680 Shenandoah Schl Rd Plymouth (95669) *(P-1975)*
Sierra Sunscreens, Rancho Cordova *Also called Hadco Products Inc (P-5190)*
Sierra Swiss & Machine Inc............F.......530 346-1110
12854 Earhart Ave Ste 103 Auburn (95602) *(P-13041)*
Sierra Tech, Chatsworth *Also called A F B Systems Inc (P-20638)*
Sierra Technical Services Inc............F.......661 823-1092
101 Commercial Way Apt D Tehachapi (93561) *(P-11522)*
Sierra Traffic Service Inc............F.......805 388-2474
225 W Loop Dr Camarillo (93010) *(P-18365)*
Sierra View Inc............E.......760 371-4301
109 N Sanders St Ridgecrest (93555) *(P-6044)*
Sierra Woodworking Inc............E.......714 538-8440
960 6th St Ste 101a Norco (92860) *(P-4229)*
Sierra-Tahoe Ready Mix Inc............E.......530 541-1877
1526 Emerald Bay Rd South Lake Tahoe (96150) *(P-11180)*
Sierracin Corporation (HQ)............A.......818 741-1656
12780 San Fernando Rd Sylmar (91342) *(P-8940)*
Sierracin/Sylmar Corporation............A.......818 362-6711
12780 San Fernando Rd Sylmar (91342) *(P-10375)*
Sieva Networks Inc (PA)............F.......408 475-1953
281 Countrybrook Loop San Ramon (94583) *(P-21431)*
Sig, San Diego *Also called Strafford Intl Group Inc (P-5169)*
Sigen, San Jose *Also called Silicon Genesis Corporation (P-19150)*
Sight Machine Inc............D.......888 461-5739
243 Vallejo St San Francisco (94111) *(P-25174)*
Sighten Inc............E.......415 965-3000
426 17th St Ste 600 Oakland (94612) *(P-25175)*
Sigma 6 Electronics Inc............F.......858 279-4300
7030 Alamitos Ave Ste E San Diego (92154) *(P-20069)*

ALPHABETIC

Employee Codes: A=Over 500 employees, B=251-500
C=101-250, D=51-100, E=20-50, F=10-19
2019 California
Manfacturers Register
© Mergent Inc. 1-800-342-5647
1281

Sigma Circuit Technology LLC......D......858 523-0146
4624 Calle Mar De Armonia San Diego (92130) ***(P-18604)***
Sigma Mfg & Logistics LLC......E......916 781-3052
10050 Fthlls Blvd Ste 100 Roseville (95747) ***(P-15485)***
Sigma-Aldrich Corporation......E......760 710-6213
6211 El Camino Real Carlsbad (92009) ***(P-9304)***
Sigmatex High Tech Fabrics Inc (HQ)......D......707 751-0573
6001 Egret Ct Benicia (94510) ***(P-17242)***
Sigmatron International Inc......C......510 477-5000
30000 Eigenbrodt Way Union City (94587) ***(P-18605)***
Sigmatronix Inc......F......714 436-1618
2109 S Susan St Santa Ana (92704) ***(P-17857)***
Sign Art Co......F......626 287-2512
423 S California St San Gabriel (91776) ***(P-23961)***
Sign Designs Inc......E......209 524-4484
204 Campus Way Modesto (95350) ***(P-23962)***
Sign Excellence LLC......F......818 308-1044
8515 Telfair Ave Sun Valley (91352) ***(P-23963)***
Sign Industries Inc......E......909 930-0303
2101 Carrillo Privado Ontario (91761) ***(P-23964)***
Sign Mart, Orange *Also called Metal Art of California Inc* ***(P-23926)***
Sign Mart Retail Store, Orange *Also called Metal Art of California Inc* ***(P-23925)***
Sign of Times Inc......E......323 826-9766
4950 S Santa Fe Ave Vernon (90058) ***(P-5735)***
Sign Post, The, Sacramento *Also called Eggleston Signs* ***(P-23863)***
Sign Solutions Inc......F......408 245-7133
532 Mercury Dr Sunnyvale (94085) ***(P-23965)***
Sign Source Inc......F......714 979-9979
204 W Carleton Ave Ste A Orange (92867) ***(P-23966)***
Sign Specialists Corporation......E......714 641-0064
111 W Dyer Rd Ste F Santa Ana (92707) ***(P-23967)***
Sign Technology Inc......E......916 372-1200
1700 Entp Blvd Ste F West Sacramento (95691) ***(P-23968)***
Sign-A-Rama, Redding *Also called Jar Ventures Inc* ***(P-23906)***
Sign-A-Rama, Palm Desert *Also called Pd Group* ***(P-23942)***
Signa Chemistry Inc......E......212 933-4101
720 Olive Dr Ste Cd Davis (95616) ***(P-7803)***
Signage Solutions Corporation......E......714 491-0299
2231 S Dupont Dr Anaheim (92806) ***(P-23969)***
Signal......D......661 259-1234
26330 Diamond Pl Ste 100 Santa Clarita (91350) ***(P-6045)***
Signal Hill Petroleum Inc......E......562 595-6440
2633 Cherry Ave Signal Hill (90755) ***(P-152)***
Signal Newspaper, The, Santa Clarita *Also called Morris Multimedia Inc* ***(P-5979)***
Signature Control Systems Inc......D......949 580-3640
16485 Laguna Canyon Rd # 130 Irvine (92618) ***(P-14104)***
Signature Eyewear Inc (PA)......C......310 330-2700
317 Isis Ave Ste 207 Inglewood (90301) ***(P-23122)***
Signature Flexible Packg Inc......D......323 887-1997
5519 Jillson St Commerce (90040) ***(P-9170)***
Signature Press, Sacramento *Also called Arden & Howe Printing Inc* ***(P-6666)***
Signature Propellers, Santa Ana *Also called Hill Marine Products LLC* ***(P-16568)***
Signature Tech Group Inc......E......818 890-7611
11960 Borden Ave San Fernando (91340) ***(P-19724)***
Signature Woodworks......F......805 685-4080
7334 Hollister Ave Ste B Goleta (93117) ***(P-4230)***
Signgroup/Karman, Chatsworth *Also called Schea Holdings Inc* ***(P-23959)***
Signon San Diego, San Diego *Also called Copley Press Inc* ***(P-24524)***
Signquest......E......310 355-0528
13040 Cerise Ave Hawthorne (90250) ***(P-23970)***
Signs and Services Company......E......714 761-8200
10980 Boatman Ave Stanton (90680) ***(P-23971)***
Signs of Success Inc......F......805 925-7545
2350 Skyway Dr Ste 10 Santa Maria (93455) ***(P-23972)***
Signsource, Orange *Also called Sign Source Inc* ***(P-23966)***
Signtech, West Sacramento *Also called Sign Technology Inc* ***(P-23968)***
Signtech Electrical Advg Inc......C......619 527-6100
4444 Federal Blvd San Diego (92102) ***(P-23973)***
Signtronix Inc (PA)......D......310 534-7500
1445 Sepulveda Blvd Torrance (90501) ***(P-23974)***
Signum Systems Corporation......F......805 383-3682
1211 Flynn Rd Unit 104 Camarillo (93012) ***(P-21849)***
Signworld America Inc (PA)......F......844 900-7446
12023 Arrow Rte Rancho Cucamonga (91739) ***(P-23975)***
Sigtronics Corporation......E......909 305-9399
178 E Arrow Hwy San Dimas (91773) ***(P-18366)***
Siho Corporation......F......323 721-4000
5750 Grace Pl Commerce (90022) ***(P-3496)***
Sii Semiconductor USA Corp......F......310 517-7771
21221 S Wstn Ave Ste 250 Torrance (90501) ***(P-19149)***
Sika Corporation......F......562 941-0231
12767 Imperial Hwy Santa Fe Springs (90670) ***(P-9305)***
Sikama International Inc......F......805 962-1000
118 E Gutierrez St Santa Barbara (93101) ***(P-14739)***
Sil, Santa Maria *Also called Space Information Labs LLC* ***(P-21435)***
Sila Nanotechnologies Inc......E......408 475-7452
2450 Mariner Square Loop Alameda (94501) ***(P-7804)***
Silao Tortilleria Inc......E......626 961-0761
250 N California Ave City of Industry (91744) ***(P-2667)***
Silent Servant, Rohnert Park *Also called Miller Manufacturing Inc* ***(P-5203)***
Silenus Vintners......F......707 299-3930
5225 Solano Ave NAPA (94558) ***(P-1976)***
Silenx Corporation......F......562 941-4200
10606 Shoemaker Ave Ste A Santa Fe Springs (90670) ***(P-21655)***
Silfine America Inc......D......408 823-8663
1750 Cleveland Ave San Jose (95126) ***(P-7886)***
Silgan Can Company......F......916 422-8030
6200 Franklin Blvd # 100 Sacramento (95824) ***(P-774)***
Silgan Containers Corporation (HQ)......D......818 348-3700
21600 Oxnard St Ste 1600 Woodland Hills (91367) ***(P-11866)***
Silgan Containers LLC (HQ)......D......818 710-3700
21600 Oxnard St Ste 1600 Woodland Hills (91367) ***(P-11867)***
Silgan Containers Mfg Corp......D......209 521-6469
4000 Yosemite Blvd Modesto (95357) ***(P-11868)***
Silgan Containers Mfg Corp......E......925 778-8000
2200 Wilbur Ave Antioch (94509) ***(P-11869)***
Silgan Containers Mfg Corp......E......209 869-3601
3250 Patterson Rd Riverbank (95367) ***(P-11870)***
Silgan Containers Mfg Corp (HQ)......B......818 710-3700
21600 Oxnard St Ste 1600 Woodland Hills (91367) ***(P-11871)***
Silica Engineering Group, Santa Clara *Also called Superior Quartz Inc* ***(P-11550)***
Silicon 360 LLC......F......408 432-1790
801 Buckeye Ct Milpitas (95035) ***(P-5648)***
Silicon Energy LLC (PA)......F......360 618-6500
9 Cushing Ste 200 Irvine (92618) ***(P-12084)***
Silicon Genesis Corporation......D......408 228-5858
145 Baytech Dr San Jose (95134) ***(P-19150)***
Silicon Graphics Intl Corp (HQ)......B......669 900-8000
940 N Mccarthy Blvd Milpitas (95035) ***(P-15854)***
Silicon Image Inc (HQ)......D......408 616-4000
2115 Onel Dr San Jose (95131) ***(P-19151)***
Silicon Laboratories, Sunnyvale *Also called Silicon Labs Integration Inc* ***(P-19152)***
Silicon Labs Integration Inc (HQ)......F......408 702-1400
940 Stewart Dr Sunnyvale (94085) ***(P-19152)***
Silicon Light Machines Corp (HQ)......F......408 240-4700
820 Kifer Rd Sunnyvale (94086) ***(P-19153)***
Silicon Microstructures Inc......D......408 473-9700
1701 Mccarthy Blvd Milpitas (95035) ***(P-17308)***
Silicon Motion Inc......D......408 501-5300
690 N Mccarthy Blvd # 200 Milpitas (95035) ***(P-19154)***
Silicon Specialists Inc......F......510 732-9796
2487 Industrial Pkwy W Hayward (94545) ***(P-19155)***
Silicon Spread Corp......D......855 446-7634
19925 S Creek Blvd 100 Cupertino (95014) ***(P-19156)***
Silicon Standard Corp......E......408 234-6964
4701 Patrick Henry Dr # 16 Santa Clara (95054) ***(P-19157)***
Silicon Tech Inc......C......949 476-1130
3009 Daimler St Santa Ana (92705) ***(P-15608)***
Silicon Turnkey Solutions Inc (HQ)......F......408 904-0200
1804 Mccarthy Blvd Milpitas (95035) ***(P-19158)***
Silicon Valley Electro Plating......E......408 945-1444
44727 Aguila Ter Fremont (94539) ***(P-13504)***
Silicon Valley Express......F......408 292-0677
1250 Aviation Ave Ste 105 San Jose (95110) ***(P-20626)***
Silicon Valley Launch, Redwood City *Also called Sposato John* ***(P-18262)***
Silicon Valley Mfg Inc......E......510 791-9450
6520 Central Ave Newark (94560) ***(P-11456)***
Silicon Valley Precision Mch, San Jose *Also called Nguyen Hiep Corp* ***(P-16788)***
Silicon Vly Cmnty Newspapers, San Jose *Also called McClatchy Newspapers Inc* ***(P-5952)***
Silicon Vly McRelectronics Inc......E......408 844-7100
2985 Kifer Rd Santa Clara (95051) ***(P-19159)***
Silicon Vly World Trade Corp......F......408 945-6355
1474 Gladding Ct Milpitas (95035) ***(P-17163)***
Siliconcore Technology Inc......E......408 946-8185
890 Hillview Ct Ste 120 Milpitas (95035) ***(P-19160)***
Siliconix Incorporated (HQ)......A......408 988-8000
2585 Junction Ave San Jose (95134) ***(P-19161)***
Silicontech, Santa Ana *Also called Silicon Tech Inc* ***(P-15608)***
Silk Screen Shirts Inc......E......760 233-3900
6185 El Camino Real Carlsbad (92009) ***(P-2894)***
Siller Aviation, Yuba City *Also called Siller Brothers Inc* ***(P-4013)***
Siller Brothers Inc (PA)......D......530 673-0734
1250 Smith Rd Yuba City (95991) ***(P-4013)***
Silmar Division, Hawthorne *Also called Interplastic Corporation* ***(P-7843)***
Silo City Inc......E......661 387-0179
1401 S Union Ave Bakersfield (93307) ***(P-14190)***
Silpak Inc (PA)......F......909 625-0056
470 E Bonita Ave Pomona (91767) ***(P-7908)***
Siluria Technologies Inc......E......415 978-2170
409 Illinois St San Francisco (94158) ***(P-75)***
Silve Rest Innov Sleep Produ, Pico Rivera *Also called Brk Group LLC* ***(P-2992)***
Silver Eagle Corporation......E......916 925-6843
2655 Land Ave Sacramento (95815) ***(P-3748)***
Silver Horse Vineyards Inc......F......805 467-9463
1205 Beaver Creek Ln Paso Robles (93446) ***(P-1977)***
Silver Moon Lighting Inc......F......858 613-3600
12225 World Trade Dr F San Diego (92128) ***(P-17561)***
Silver Oak Wine Cellars LP (PA)......F......707 942-7022
915 Oakville Cross Rd Oakville (94562) ***(P-1978)***
Silver Peak Systems Inc (PA)......C......408 935-1800
2860 De La Cruz Blvd # 100 Santa Clara (95050) ***(P-19162)***
Silver Press Inc......F......408 435-0449
940 Rincon Cir San Jose (95131) ***(P-7618)***
Silver Ranch and Winery, Paso Robles *Also called Silver Horse Vineyards Inc* ***(P-1977)***
Silver Star Exchange......E......626 300-6668
240 S Raymond Ave Alhambra (91801) ***(P-3497)***
Silver Textile Incorporated......F......213 747-2221
2101 S Flower St Los Angeles (90007) ***(P-2807)***
Silverado Brewing Co L L C......E......707 341-3089
4104 Saint Helena Hwy Calistoga (94515) ***(P-1624)***
Silveron Industries Inc......F......909 598-4533
182 S Brent Cir City of Industry (91789) ***(P-17309)***
Silverrest, Fullerton *Also called Brentwood Home LLC* ***(P-4854)***
Silvester California, Los Angeles *Also called Silvestri Studio Inc* ***(P-24242)***
Silvestri Studio Inc (PA)......D......323 277-4420
8125 Beach St Los Angeles (90001) ***(P-24242)***

Mergent e-mail: customerrelations@mergent.com
1282
2019 California
Manufacturers Register
(P-0000) Products & Services Section entry number
(PA)=Parent Co (HQ)=Headquarters (DH)=Div Headquarters

Silvestri Studio Inc......F......323 735-1481
1733 Cordova St Los Angeles (90007) **(P-24243)**
Silvias Costumes......E......323 661-2142
4964 Hollywood Blvd Los Angeles (90027) **(P-3681)**
Silvus Technologies Inc (PA)......E......310 479-3333
10990 Wilshire Blvd # 1500 Los Angeles (90024) **(P-18253)**
Simba Recycling, San Marcos *Also called Arna Trading Inc* **(P-5265)**
Simcardz4u Inc......F......213 359-0602
818 W 7th St Fl 6 Los Angeles (90017) **(P-20932)**
Simco-Ion Technology Group (PA)......C......510 217-0600
1601 Harbor Bay Pkwy # 150 Alameda (94502) **(P-17354)**
Simex-Iwerks, Santa Clarita *Also called Iwerks Entertainment Inc* **(P-19988)**
Simi Winery, Healdsburg *Also called Franciscan Vinyards Inc* **(P-1773)**
Simmitri Inc......E......408 779-3333
1999 S Bascom Ave Ste 700 Campbell (95008) **(P-19163)**
Simmitri Energy Efficiency, Campbell *Also called Simmitri Inc* **(P-19163)**
Simmons Stairways Inc......E......408 920-0105
830 Jury Ct Ste 4 San Jose (95112) **(P-4231)**
Simon Harrison......E......818 898-1036
551 5th St Ste A San Fernando (91340) **(P-22270)**
Simon of California (PA)......F......310 559-4871
9545 Sawyer St Los Angeles (90035) **(P-10536)**
Simons Brick Corporation......E......951 279-1000
4301 Firestone Blvd South Gate (90280) **(P-11342)**
Simonton Windows, Vacaville *Also called Fortune Brands Windows Inc* **(P-10106)**
Simpa Networks Inc......F......415 216-3204
2595 Mission St Ste 300 San Francisco (94110) **(P-22271)**
Simplay Labs LLC......E......408 616-4000
1140 E Arques Ave Sunnyvale (94085) **(P-22624)**
Simple Container Solutions Inc......E......310 638-0900
250 W Artesia Blvd Rancho Dominguez (90220) **(P-5360)**
Simple Green, Huntington Beach *Also called Sunshine Makers Inc* **(P-8678)**
Simple Orthotic Solutions LLC......F......951 353-8127
9960 Indiana Ave Ste 15 Riverside (92503) **(P-10475)**
Simplefeed Inc......F......650 947-7445
289 S San Antonio Rd # 2 Los Altos (94022) **(P-25176)**
Simplelegal Inc......F......415 763-5366
488 Ellis St Mountain View (94043) **(P-25177)**
Simplex Filler Co, NAPA *Also called Wild Horse Industrial Corp* **(P-15236)**
Simplex Isolation Systems, Fontana *Also called Simplex Strip Doors LLC* **(P-9727)**
Simplex Strip Doors LLC (HQ)......E......800 854-7951
14500 Miller Ave Fontana (92336) **(P-9727)**
Simpliphi Power Inc......F......805 640-6700
420 Bryant Cir Ste A-B Ojai (93023) **(P-19815)**
Simply Automated Inc......F......760 431-2100
6108 Avd Encinas Ste B Carlsbad (92011) **(P-17489)**
Simply Country Inc......F......530 615-0565
10110 Harvest Ln Rough and Ready (95975) **(P-14105)**
Simply Fresh Foods Inc......F......714 562-5000
11215 Knott Ave Ste A Cypress (90630) **(P-2323)**
Simply Fresh Fruit, Vernon *Also called Sffi Company Inc* **(P-857)**
Simply Fresh Fruit Inc......D......323 586-0000
4383 Exchange Ave Vernon (90058) **(P-858)**
Simply Smashing Inc......E......559 658-2367
4790 W Jacquelyn Ave Fresno (93722) **(P-23976)**
Simpson Coatings Group Inc......E......650 873-5990
401 S Canal St A South San Francisco (94080) **(P-8941)**
Simpson Coatings Group, The, South San Francisco *Also called D J Simpson Company* **(P-8900)**
Simpson Industries Inc......E......310 605-1224
1093 E Bedmar St Carson (90746) **(P-8382)**
Simpson Manufacturing Co Inc (PA)......C......925 560-9000
5956 W Las Positas Blvd Pleasanton (94588) **(P-11850)**
Simpson Manufacturing Co Inc......B......209 234-7775
5151 S Airport Way Stockton (95206) **(P-11303)**
Simpson Performance Pdts Inc......D......310 325-6035
1407 240th St Harbor City (90710) **(P-22814)**
Simpson Strong-Tie Company Inc (HQ)......C......925 560-9000
5956 W Las Positas Blvd Pleasanton (94588) **(P-12993)**
Simpson Strong-Tie Company Inc......C......714 871-8373
12246 Holly St Riverside (92509) **(P-4421)**
Simpson Strong-Tie Company Inc......D......209 234-7775
5151 S Airport Way Stockton (95206) **(P-12994)**
Simpson Strong-Tie Company Inc......D......714 871-8373
12246 Holly St Riverside (92509) **(P-12995)**
Simpson Strong-Tie Intl Inc (HQ)......D......925 560-9000
5956 W Las Positas Blvd Pleasanton (94588) **(P-12996)**
Simpson Timber Company......F......707 668-4566
1165 Maple Creek Rd Korbel (95550) **(P-4066)**
Simpsonsimpson Industries, Carson *Also called Simpson Industries Inc* **(P-8382)**
Sims Recycling Solutions Inc......E......916 772-5600
8855 Washington Blvd Roseville (95678) **(P-11567)**
Simso Tex Sublimation (PA)......D......310 885-9717
3028 E Las Hermanas St E Rncho Dmngz (90221) **(P-3919)**
Simsolve......F......951 898-6880
310 Elizabeth Ln Corona (92880) **(P-11420)**
Simwon America Corp......F......925 276-3412
400 Darcy Pkwy Lathrop (95330) **(P-20448)**
Sin MA Imports Company......F......415 285-9369
1425 Minnesota St San Francisco (94107) **(P-1101)**
Sinbad Foods LLC......D......559 674-4445
2401 W Almond Ave Madera (93637) **(P-2668)**
Sincere Food Co, El Monte *Also called Agra-Farm Foods Inc* **(P-1053)**
Sincere Orient Commercial Corp......D......626 333-8882
15222 Valley Blvd City of Industry (91746) **(P-2669)**
Sincere Orient Food Company, City of Industry *Also called Sincere Orient Commercial Corp* **(P-2669)**
Sinclair & Valentine, Watsonville *Also called Smith & Vandiver Corporation* **(P-8844)**
Sinclair Companies......C......714 826-5886
7760 Crescent Ave Buena Park (90620) **(P-9358)**
Sinclair Companies......D......559 997-3617
5792 N Palm Ave Fresno (93704) **(P-9359)**
Sinclair Companies......D......559 351-1916
1703 W Olive Ave Fresno (93728) **(P-9360)**
Sinclair Printing Company, Palmdale *Also called D & J Printing Inc* **(P-6775)**
Sinclair Systems, Fresno *Also called Atlas Pacific Engineering Co* **(P-14833)**
Sinclair Systems Intl LLC......F......559 233-4500
3115 S Willow Ave Fresno (93725) **(P-7483)**
Sine-Tific Solutions Inc......F......408 432-3434
1701 Fortune Dr Ste C San Jose (95131) **(P-7484)**
Sing Tao Daily, Burlingame *Also called Sing Tao Newspapers* **(P-6046)**
Sing Tao Newspapers (HQ)......D......650 808-8800
1818 Gilbreth Rd Ste 108 Burlingame (94010) **(P-6046)**
Sing Tao Newspapers Ltd......D......626 839-8200
17059 Green Dr City of Industry (91745) **(P-6047)**
Sing Tao Nwspapers Los Angeles, City of Industry *Also called Sing Tao Newspapers Ltd* **(P-6047)**
Singha North America Inc......F......714 206-5097
303 Twin Dolphin Dr # 600 Redwood City (94065) **(P-1625)**
Singular Bio Inc......F......415 553-8773
455 Mission Bay Blvd S # 145 San Francisco (94158) **(P-8515)**
Sinister Mfg Company Inc......E......916 772-9253
2025 Opportunity Dr Ste 7 Roseville (95678) **(P-20449)**
Sinkpad LLC......F......714 660-2944
511 Princeland Ct Corona (92879) **(P-19725)**
Sinosource Intl Co Inc......F......650 697-6668
230 Adrian Rd Millbrae (94030) **(P-11279)**
Sinusys Corporation......F......650 213-9988
4030 Fabian Way Palo Alto (94303) **(P-8583)**
Sios Technology Corp (HQ)......F......650 645-7000
155 Bovet Rd Ste 476 San Mateo (94402) **(P-25178)**
Sipex Corporation (HQ)......C......510 668-7000
48720 Kato Rd Fremont (94538) **(P-19164)**
Sipi Company Inc......F......650 201-1169
34734 Williams Way Union City (94587) **(P-23464)**
Sipix Imaging Inc (HQ)......E......510 743-2928
47428 Fremont Blvd Fremont (94538) **(P-15486)**
Sir Speedy, Whittier *Also called George Coriaty* **(P-6832)**
Sirena Incorporated......F......866 548-5353
22717 S Western Ave Torrance (90501) **(P-7485)**
Sirf Technology Holdings Inc (HQ)......D......408 523-6500
1060 Rincon Cir San Jose (95131) **(P-19165)**
Sirna Therapeutics Inc......D......415 512-7200
1700 Owens St San Francisco (94158) **(P-8383)**
Siskiyou County Family Plng R, Mount Shasta *Also called Sousa Ready Mix LLC* **(P-11181)**
Siskiyou Daily News, Yreka *Also called Gatehouse Media LLC* **(P-5858)**
Siskiyou Forest Products (PA)......E......530 378-6980
6275 State Highway 273 Anderson (96007) **(P-4232)**
Sisneros Inc......E......562 777-9797
12717 Los Nietos Rd Santa Fe Springs (90670) **(P-5000)**
Sisneros Office Furntiure, Santa Fe Springs *Also called Sisneros Inc* **(P-5000)**
Sissell Bros......F......323 261-0106
4322 E 3rd St Los Angeles (90022) **(P-11003)**
Sistema US Inc (PA)......E......707 773-2200
775 Southpoint Blvd Petaluma (94954) **(P-10376)**
Sistone Inc......E......818 988-9918
15530 Lanark St Van Nuys (91406) **(P-5102)**
Sit On It, Buena Park *Also called Exemplis LLC* **(P-4986)**
Sitek Process Solutions......F......916 797-9000
233 Technology Way Ste 3 Rocklin (95765) **(P-19166)**
Sitime Corporation (HQ)......D......408 328-4400
5451 Patrick Henry Dr Santa Clara (95054) **(P-19167)**
Sitonit, Cypress *Also called Exemplis LLC* **(P-4988)**
Siui America Inc......F......408 432-8881
780 Montague Expy Ste 608 San Jose (95131) **(P-23048)**
Sius Products-Distributor Inc (PA)......F......510 382-1700
700 Kevin Ct Oakland (94621) **(P-5624)**
Six Pac Campers Inc......F......800 242-1442
109 Pioneer Ave Woodland (95776) **(P-21211)**
Six Sigma, Milpitas *Also called Winslow Automation Inc* **(P-19273)**
Six Sigma Precision Inc......F......707 836-0869
7706 Bell Rd Ste C Windsor (95492) **(P-16947)**
Sixteen Rivers Press Inc......F......415 273-1303
1195 Green St San Francisco (94109) **(P-6580)**
Size Control Plating Co......F......626 369-3014
13349 Temple Ave La Puente (91746) **(P-13505)**
Sizto Tech Corporation......F......650 856-8833
892 Commercial St Palo Alto (94303) **(P-13733)**
Sizzix, Lake Forest *Also called Ellison Educational Eqp Inc* **(P-14792)**
SJ Electro Systems Inc......E......707 449-0341
859 Cotting Ct Ste G Vacaville (95688) **(P-16108)**
Sj Valley Plating Inc......F......408 988-5502
491 Perry Ct Santa Clara (95054) **(P-13506)**
SJ&I Bias Binding & Tex Co Inc......E......213 747-5271
1950 E 20th St Vernon (90058) **(P-3920)**
SJcontrols Inc......F......562 494-1400
2248 Obispo Ave Ste 203 Long Beach (90755) **(P-21656)**
Sjm Facility, Irvine *Also called St Jude Medical LLC* **(P-8391)**
Sjt Tech Industries Inc......F......408 980-9547
1400 Coleman Ave Ste E28 Santa Clara (95050) **(P-19168)**
Sjwc, Madera *Also called San Joaquin Wine Company Inc* **(P-1965)**
Sk Drapes, North Hollywood *Also called S & K Theatrical Drap Inc* **(P-3701)**
Sk Hynix Memory Solutions Inc (HQ)......E......408 514-3500
3103 N 1st St San Jose (95134) **(P-19169)**
Skagfield Corporation......B......858 635-7777
2225 Avenida Costa Este San Diego (92154) **(P-5211)**

ALPHABETIC

Employee Codes: A=Over 500 employees, B=251-500
C=101-250, D=51-100, E=20-50, F=10-19
2019 California
Manfacturers Register
© Mergent Inc. 1-800-342-5647
1283

Skalli Vineyards, Rutherford *Also called St Supery Inc (P-1987)*
Skandia Industries, San Diego *Also called Skagfield Corporation (P-5211)*
Skasol Incorporated......F......510 839-1000
1696 W Grand Ave Oakland (94607) *(P-9306)*
Skat-Trak Inc......C......909 795-2505
654 Avenue K Calimesa (92320) *(P-9467)*
Skate Group Inc......F......213 749-6651
830 E 14th Pl Los Angeles (90021) *(P-3682)*
Skate One Corp......D......805 964-1330
30 S La Patera Ln Ste 9 Santa Barbara (93117) *(P-23651)*
Skateboard, Hacienda Heights *Also called Gravity Boarding Company Inc (P-23576)*
Skaug Truck Body Works......F......818 365-9123
1404 1st St San Fernando (91340) *(P-20228)*
SKB Corporation (PA)......B......714 637-1252
434 W Levers Pl Orange (92867) *(P-10377)*
SKB Corporation......B......714 637-1572
1633 N Leslie Way Orange (92867) *(P-10537)*
Skechers Collection LLC (HQ)......E......310 318-3100
228 Manhattan Beach Blvd Manhattan Beach (90266) *(P-9480)*
Skechers Direct......D......310 318-3100
228 Manhattan Beach Blvd Manhattan Beach (90266) *(P-9481)*
Skechers Factory Outlet 198, Barstow *Also called Skechers USA Inc (P-9482)*
Skechers Factory Outlet 346, Livermore *Also called Skechers USA Inc (P-9483)*
Skechers USA, Manhattan Beach *Also called Skechers Direct (P-9481)*
Skechers USA Inc......F......760 253-3707
2796 Tanger Way Barstow (92311) *(P-9482)*
Skechers USA Inc......F......925 447-2622
3320 Livermore Outlets Dr Livermore (94551) *(P-9483)*
Skechers USA Inc......E......310 318-3100
330 S Sepulveda Blvd Manhattan Beach (90266) *(P-9484)*
Skechers USA Inc (PA)......D......310 318-3100
228 Manhattan Beach Blvd # 200 Manhattan Beach (90266) *(P-10509)*
Skechers USA Inc II (HQ)......D......310 318-3100
225 S Sepulveda Blvd Manhattan Beach (90266) *(P-9485)*
Sketchers, Manhattan Beach *Also called Skechers Collection LLC (P-9480)*
SKF Aptitude Exchange, San Diego *Also called SKF Condition Monitoring Inc (P-22272)*
SKF Condition Monitoring Inc (HQ)......C......858 496-3400
9444 Balboa Ave Ste 150 San Diego (92123) *(P-22272)*
Skirt Inc......F......213 553-1134
2600 E 8th St Los Angeles (90023) *(P-3122)*
Skiva Graphics Screen Prtg Inc......E......760 602-9124
2258 Rutherford Rd Ste A Carlsbad (92008) *(P-7486)*
Skjonberg Controls Inc......F......805 650-0877
1363 Donlon St Ste 6 Ventura (93003) *(P-17310)*
Skm Industries Inc......F......661 294-8373
28966 Hancock Pkwy Valencia (91355) *(P-13276)*
Skog Furniture, Pomona *Also called Aw Industries Inc (P-4674)*
Sks Die Cast & Machining Inc (PA)......E......510 523-2541
1849 Oak St Alameda (94501) *(P-11707)*
Skullduggery Inc......F......714 777-6425
5433 E La Palma Ave Anaheim (92807) *(P-23465)*
Skurka Aerospace Inc (HQ)......C......216 706-2939
4600 Calle Bolero Camarillo (93012) *(P-17223)*
Sky Global Services Inc......F......949 291-5511
23 Corporate Plaza Dr # 100 Newport Beach (92660) *(P-24244)*
Sky Jeans Inc......E......323 778-2065
6600 Avalon Blvd Ste 102 Los Angeles (90003) *(P-2762)*
Sky Luxury Corp......E......323 940-0111
3001 Humboldt St Los Angeles (90031) *(P-3498)*
Sky One Inc......F......909 622-3333
1793 W 2nd St Pomona (91766) *(P-10810)*
Sky Rider Equipment Co Inc......E......714 632-6890
1180 N Blue Gum St Anaheim (92806) *(P-4886)*
Sky Signs & Graphics......F......818 898-3802
15340 San Fernnd Missn Bl Mission Hills (91345) *(P-3862)*
Skyco Shading Systems Inc......E......714 708-3038
3411 W Fordham Ave Santa Ana (92704) *(P-4233)*
Skyco Skylights Inc......E......949 629-4090
2995 Airway Ave Unit B Costa Mesa (92626) *(P-10606)*
Skydio Inc......F......408 203-8497
114 Hazel Ave Redwood City (94061) *(P-21432)*
Skyepharma Inc......F......858 678-3950
10450 Science Center Dr San Diego (92121) *(P-8384)*
Skyera, San Jose *Also called Hgst Inc (P-15550)*
Skyguard LLC......E......703 262-0500
2945 Townsgate Rd Ste 200 Westlake Village (91361) *(P-20070)*
Skylight Software Inc......E......408 858-3933
3792 Bertini Ct Apt 1 San Jose (95117) *(P-25179)*
Skyline Cabinet & Millworks, Bakersfield *Also called Spalinger Enterprises Inc (P-5103)*
Skyline Concrete, Sun Valley *Also called Viking Ready Mix Co Inc (P-11208)*
Skyline Concrete, Canoga Park *Also called Viking Ready Mix Co Inc (P-11210)*
Skyline Digital Images Inc......E......562 944-1677
10420 Pioneer Blvd Santa Fe Springs (90670) *(P-23977)*
Skyline Homes Inc......C......951 654-9321
499 W Esplanade Ave San Jacinto (92583) *(P-4563)*
Skyline Homes Inc......C......530 666-0974
1720 E Beamer St Woodland (95776) *(P-4564)*
Skyline Seating, Westminster *Also called Dang Tha (P-5010)*
Skylock Industries......D......626 334-2391
1290 W Optical Dr Azusa (91702) *(P-20933)*
Skymicro Inc......E......805 491-8935
2060 E Ave Arboles 344 Thousand Oaks (91362) *(P-15855)*
Skyreach L S Extrsons USA Corp......F......909 204-3550
9281 Pittsburgh Ave Ste A Rancho Cucamonga (91730) *(P-11624)*
Skyworks Solutions......F......301 874-6408
1767 Carr Rd Ste 105 Calexico (92231) *(P-17355)*
Skyworks Solutions Inc......D......949 231-3000
5221 California Ave Irvine (92617) *(P-19726)*
Skyworks Solutions Inc......D......805 480-4400
2427 W Hillcrest Dr Newbury Park (91320) *(P-19170)*
Skyworks Solutions Inc......D......805 480-4227
730 Lawrence Dr Newbury Park (91320) *(P-19171)*
SL Power Electronics Corp (PA)......D......800 235-5929
6050 King Dr Ste A Ventura (93003) *(P-19727)*
Slack Technologies Inc (PA)......C......415 579-9153
500 Howard St San Francisco (94105) *(P-25180)*
Slam Specialties LLC (PA)......F......559 348-9038
5845 E Terrace Ave Fresno (93727) *(P-20450)*
Slashpoint Share Drive, Simi Valley *Also called Xmultiple Technologies Inc (P-17506)*
Slawomira Sobczyk, Milpitas *Also called Yuhas Tooling & Machining (P-17076)*
SLC, Livermore *Also called Software Licensing Consultants (P-25193)*
Sld Laser, Goleta *Also called Soraa Laser Diode Inc (P-20075)*
Sledge Usa Inc......E......213 747-4400
940 W Washington Blvd Los Angeles (90015) *(P-3499)*
Sleep Therapy, Escondido *Also called Wickline Bedding Entp Corp (P-4893)*
Sleep-N-Aire Mattress Co Inc......F......661 835-0200
5101 White Ln Ste F Bakersfield (93309) *(P-3749)*
Sleepow Ltd......E......646 688-0808
11706 Darlington Ave Los Angeles (90049) *(P-2763)*
Sleeprite Industries Inc......E......650 344-1980
1492 Rollins Rd Burlingame (94010) *(P-4887)*
Slickote......F......818 749-3066
730 University Ave Burbank (91504) *(P-13659)*
Slide Systems Inc......F......310 539-3416
1448 240th St Harbor City (90710) *(P-13277)*
Sligh Cabinets Inc......F......805 239-2550
105 Calle Propano Paso Robles (93446) *(P-4351)*
Slimsuit, Bell *Also called Carol Wior Inc (P-3391)*
Sling-Light, Newport Beach *Also called Freeform Research & Dev (P-14635)*
Slivnik Machining Inc......E......760 744-8692
1070 Linda Vista Dr Ste A San Marcos (92078) *(P-23652)*
Slj Wholesale LLC......E......323 662-8900
13850 Del Sur St San Fernando (91340) *(P-1322)*
Slo New Times Inc......E......805 546-8208
1010 Marsh St San Luis Obispo (93401) *(P-6048)*
Sloanled, Ventura *Also called The Sloan Company Inc (P-17737)*
Slp Limited LLC......F......714 517-1955
2031 E Cerritos Ave Ste H Anaheim (92806) *(P-18606)*
SM Asian Market, San Bernardino *Also called Rlt Seafood Supermarket Inc (P-2301)*
SMA America Production LLC......C......720 347-6000
6020 West Oaks Blvd # 300 Rocklin (95765) *(P-12085)*
Smac, Carlsbad *Also called Systems Machines Automatio (P-17314)*
Small Paper Co Inc......F......323 277-0525
2559 E 56th St Huntington Park (90255) *(P-5335)*
Small Precision Tools Inc......D......707 765-4545
1330 Clegg St Petaluma (94954) *(P-11370)*
Small Wnders Hndcrfted Mntures......F......818 703-7450
7033 Canoga Ave Ste 5 Canoga Park (91303) *(P-24245)*
Small World Trading Co......C......415 945-1900
90 Windward Way San Rafael (94901) *(P-8842)*
Smart Action Company LLC......E......310 776-9200
300 Continental Blvd # 350 El Segundo (90245) *(P-25181)*
Smart Caregiver Corporation......E......707 781-7450
1229 N Mcdowell Blvd Petaluma (94954) *(P-23049)*
Smart Elec & Assembly Inc......C......714 772-2651
2000 W Corporate Way Anaheim (92801) *(P-18607)*
Smart Foam Pads, Lake Forest *Also called Innovative R Advanced (P-4864)*
Smart Global Holdings Inc (PA)......F......510 623-1231
39870 Eureka Dr Newark (94560) *(P-19172)*
Smart Inc......E......310 674-8135
14108 S Western Ave Gardena (90249) *(P-10378)*
Smart Machines Inc......E......510 661-5000
46702 Bayside Pkwy Fremont (94538) *(P-14287)*
Smart Meetings, Sausalito *Also called Bright Business Media LLC (P-6117)*
Smart Modular Tech De Inc (HQ)......C......510 623-1231
45800 Northport Loop W Fremont (94538) *(P-19173)*
Smart Modular Technologies Inc......E......949 753-0117
15635 Alton Pkwy Ste 155 Irvine (92618) *(P-19174)*
Smart Storage Systems Inc (HQ)......F......510 623-1231
39672 Eureka Dr Newark (94560) *(P-15609)*
Smart TV & Sound, Chico *Also called Videomaker Inc (P-6284)*
Smart Wax, Gardena *Also called Smart Inc (P-10378)*
Smart Wires Inc (PA)......F......415 800-5555
3292 Whipple Rd Union City (94587) *(P-19363)*
Smart-Tek Automated Svcs Inc (HQ)......F......858 798-1644
11838 Bernardo Plaza Ct # 250 San Diego (92128) *(P-25182)*
Smartdraw Software LLC......E......858 225-3300
9909 Mira Mesa Blvd San Diego (92131) *(P-25183)*
Smartlogic Semaphore Inc......F......408 213-9500
111 N Market St Ste 300 San Jose (95113) *(P-25184)*
Smartqed Inc......F......925 922-4618
421 37th Ave San Mateo (94403) *(P-25185)*
Smartrunk Systems Inc......E......619 426-3781
867 Bowsprit Rd Chula Vista (91914) *(P-18254)*
Smartwash Solutions LLC......F......831 676-9750
1129 Harkins Rd Salinas (93901) *(P-7805)*
Smashbox Beauty Cosmetics Inc......C......310 558-1490
8538 Warner Dr Culver City (90232) *(P-8843)*
Smashbox Cosmetics, Culver City *Also called Smashbox Beauty Cosmetics Inc (P-8843)*
Smb Clothing Inc......F......213 489-4949
1016 Towne Ave Unit 104 Los Angeles (90021) *(P-3500)*
Smb Industries Inc (PA)......D......530 534-6266
550 Georgia Pacific Way Oroville (95965) *(P-12243)*
SMD Enterprises Inc......E......323 235-4151
859 E 60th St Los Angeles (90001) *(P-10790)*
SMI, Sacramento *Also called Shift Management Inc (P-20446)*

Mergent e-mail: customerrelations@mergent.com
1284
2019 California
Manufacturers Register
(P-0000) Products & Services Section entry number
(PA)=Parent Co (HQ)=Headquarters (DH)=Div Headquarters

SMI Ca Inc ....E....562 926-9407
14340 Iseli Rd Santa Fe Springs (90670) *(P-16948)*
Smi, Scb, Los Angeles *Also called Dcx-Chol Enterprises Inc (P-18386)*
Smiley Group Inc ....F....323 290-4690
4434 Crenshaw Blvd Los Angeles (90043) *(P-6392)*
Smith & Company, Los Angeles *Also called A S G Corporation (P-24020)*
Smith & Hook Winery Inc, Soledad *Also called Hahn Estate (P-1802)*
Smith & Nephew Inc ....E....925 681-3300
4085 Nelson Ave Ste E Concord (94520) *(P-22815)*
Smith & Vandiver Corporation ....D....831 722-9526
480 Airport Blvd Watsonville (95076) *(P-8844)*
Smith Bros Cstm Met Fbrication, South El Monte *Also called Smith Bros Strl Stl Pdts Inc (P-11421)*
Smith Bros Strl Stl Pdts Inc ....F....626 350-1872
1535 Potrero Ave South El Monte (91733) *(P-11421)*
Smith Brothers Manufacturing ....F....619 296-3171
5304 Banks St San Diego (92110) *(P-16949)*
Smith International Inc ....C....909 906-7900
11031 Jersey Blvd Ste A Rancho Cucamonga (91730) *(P-275)*
Smith International Inc ....F....661 589-8304
3101 Steam Ct Bakersfield (93308) *(P-276)*
Smith Micro Software Inc (PA) ....C....949 362-5800
51 Columbia Aliso Viejo (92656) *(P-25186)*
Smith Precision Products Co ....E....805 498-6616
1299 Lawrence Dr Newbury Park (91320) *(P-15091)*
Smith Publishing Inc ....F....805 965-5999
2064 Alameda Padre Serra # 120 Santa Barbara (93103) *(P-6258)*
Smith Pumps, Newbury Park *Also called Smith Precision Products Co (P-15091)*
Smithco Plastics Inc (PA) ....F....714 545-9107
3330 W Harvard St Santa Ana (92704) *(P-10379)*
Smithcorp Inc ....F....888 402-9979
7196 Clairemont Mesa Blvd San Diego (92111) *(P-5336)*
Smithfield Foods, Vernon *Also called Clougherty Packing LLC (P-429)*
Smithfield Packaged Meats Corp ....C....408 392-0442
1660 Old Bayshore Hwy San Jose (95112) *(P-451)*
Smiths Action Plastic Inc (PA) ....F....714 836-4141
645 S Santa Fe St Santa Ana (92705) *(P-9911)*
Smiths Detection LLC ....A....714 258-4400
1251 E Dyer Rd Ste 140 Santa Ana (92705) *(P-22019)*
Smiths Intrcnnect Americas Inc ....B....714 371-1100
1550 Scenic Ave Costa Mesa (92626) *(P-19728)*
Smiths Medical Asd Inc ....E....619 710-1000
9255 Customhouse Plz N San Diego (92154) *(P-22816)*
Smiths Medical Asd Inc ....C....760 602-4400
2231 Rutherford Rd Carlsbad (92008) *(P-22625)*
Smj Inc ....F....626 448-8042
2213 Chico Ave El Monte (91733) *(P-9073)*
SMK Manufacturing Inc ....E....619 216-6400
1055 Tierra Del Rey Ste H Chula Vista (91910) *(P-15646)*
Sml Space Maintainers Labs, Chatsworth *Also called Selane Products Inc (P-22909)*
Smooth Operator LLC ....E....619 233-8177
3388 Main St San Diego (92113) *(P-23653)*
Smooth Run Equine Inc ....F....760 751-8988
11590 W Bernardo Ct # 110 San Diego (92127) *(P-1165)*
Smoothie Operator Inc ....F....916 773-9541
8690 Sierra College Blvd Roseville (95661) *(P-966)*
Smoothreads Inc ....E....800 536-5959
13750 Stowe Dr Ste A Poway (92064) *(P-3921)*
Smp Robotics Systems Corp ....D....415 572-2316
851 Burlway Rd Ste 216 Burlingame (94010) *(P-14288)*
SMS Fabrications Inc ....E....951 351-6828
11698 Warm Springs Rd Riverside (92505) *(P-12763)*
SMS Industrial Inc ....F....831 337-4271
1628 N Main St Salinas (93906) *(P-12421)*
Smt Centre, Fremont *Also called Surface Mount Tech Centre (P-15860)*
Smt Electronics Mfg Inc ....E....714 751-8894
2630 S Shannon St Santa Ana (92704) *(P-19175)*
SMt Mfg Incorporataed ....E....714 738-9999
970 S Loyola Dr Anaheim (92807) *(P-19729)*
Smtc Corporation ....D....510 737-0700
431 Kato Ter Fremont (94539) *(P-20071)*
Smtc Manufacturing Corp Cal ....A....408 934-7100
2302 Trade Zone Blvd San Jose (95131) *(P-18608)*
Smtcl Usa Inc ....F....626 667-1192
17038 Gale Ave City of Industry (91745) *(P-14676)*
Smucker Natural Foods Inc (HQ) ....C....530 899-5000
37 Speedway Ave Chico (95928) *(P-2225)*
Smurfit Kappa North Amer LLC ....B....626 333-6363
13400 Nelson Ave City of Industry (91746) *(P-5458)*
Smurfit Kappa North Amer LLC (HQ) ....B....626 333-6363
13400 Nelson Ave City of Industry (91746) *(P-5459)*
Smurfit Kappa North Amer LLC ....B....626 322-2123
440 Baldwin Park Blvd City of Industry (91746) *(P-5460)*
Smurfit-Stone Container, Milpitas *Also called Westrock Cp LLC (P-5467)*
Smurfit-Stone Container, Santa Fe Springs *Also called Westrock Cp LLC (P-5468)*
Sna Electronics Inc ....E....510 656-3903
3249 Laurelview Ct Fremont (94538) *(P-18609)*
Snak Club LLC ....E....323 278-9578
5560 E Slauson Ave Commerce (90040) *(P-1503)*
Snap, Sunnyvale *Also called Spiracur Inc (P-22634)*
Snap Creative Manufacturing ....F....818 735-3830
3760 Calle Tecate Ste B Camarillo (93012) *(P-23402)*
Snaplogic Inc (PA) ....C....888 494-1570
1825 S Grant St Ste 550 San Mateo (94402) *(P-25187)*
Snapmd Inc ....F....310 953-4800
121 W Lexington Dr # 412 Glendale (91203) *(P-25188)*
Snaptracs Inc ....F....858 587-1121
5775 Morehouse Dr San Diego (92121) *(P-21433)*
Snapware Corporation ....C....951 361-3100
3900 Hamner Ave Eastvale (91752) *(P-10380)*
Snei, San Diego *Also called Sony Interactive Entrmt LLC (P-25202)*
Snf Holding Company ....F....323 266-4435
4690 Worth St Los Angeles (90063) *(P-9307)*
Snl Group Inc ....F....530 222-5048
9818 Holton Way Redding (96003) *(P-14191)*
Snowflake Designs ....E....559 291-6234
2893 Larkin Ave Clovis (93612) *(P-2854)*
Snowline Engineering, Cameron Park *Also called Preferred Mfg Svcs Inc (P-16856)*
Snowpure LLC ....E....949 240-2188
130 Calle Iglesia Ste A San Clemente (92672) *(P-16109)*
Snowpure Water Technologies, San Clemente *Also called Snowpure LLC (P-16109)*
Snowsound USA, Santa Fe Springs *Also called Atlantic Representations Inc (P-4824)*
Snyder Industries Inc ....D....559 665-7612
800 Commerce Dr Chowchilla (93610) *(P-10381)*
So Cal Graphics, San Diego *Also called Brett Corp (P-7257)*
So Cal Soft-Pak Incorporated ....E....619 283-2338
8525 Gibbs Dr Ste 300 San Diego (92123) *(P-25189)*
So Cal Tractor Sales Co Inc ....E....818 252-1900
30517 The Old Rd Castaic (91384) *(P-25435)*
So Calif Oil Tool Co, Cudahy *Also called Scot Gasket Company Inc (P-9555)*
So California Biodiesel, Bloomington *Also called Southern California Biodiesel (P-9361)*
So-Cal Value Added, Camarillo *Also called Plt Enterprises Inc (P-17486)*
So-Cal Value Added LLC ....E....805 389-5335
809 Calle Plano Camarillo (93012) *(P-19730)*
Soap & Water LLC ....E....310 639-3990
11450 Sheldon St Sun Valley (91352) *(P-8845)*
Soaptronic LLC ....E....949 465-8955
20562 Crescent Bay Dr Lake Forest (92630) *(P-8677)*
Soaring America Corporation ....E....909 270-2628
8354 Kimball Ave F360 Chino (91708) *(P-20627)*
Soberlink Healthcare LLC ....F....714 975-7200
16787 Beach Blvd 211 Huntington Beach (92647) *(P-22273)*
Socal Skateshop ....F....949 305-5321
24002 Via Fabricante # 205 Mission Viejo (92691) *(P-23654)*
Soccer 90 ....F....650 599-9900
1235 Veterans Blvd Redwood City (94063) *(P-23655)*
Soccer Learning Systems Inc ....F....209 858-4300
17610 Murphy Pkwy Lathrop (95330) *(P-6259)*
Socco Plastic Coating Company ....E....909 987-4753
11251 Jersey Blvd Rancho Cucamonga (91730) *(P-13660)*
Social Brands LLC ....E....415 728-1761
6575 Simson St Oakland (94605) *(P-24246)*
Social Imprints LLC ....E....415 956-0269
969 Folsom St San Francisco (94107) *(P-7487)*
Social Media Day San Diego, San Diego *Also called Casual Fridays Inc (P-6457)*
Socialight, The, Campbell *Also called Afn Services LLC (P-5218)*
Socialize Inc ....E....415 529-4019
450 Townsend St 102 San Francisco (94107) *(P-25190)*
Socialwise Inc ....F....949 861-3900
300 Spectrum Center Dr # 950 Irvine (92618) *(P-6581)*
Societe Brewing Company LLC ....F....858 598-5415
8262 Clairemont Mesa Blvd Del Mar (92014) *(P-1979)*
Society For The Advancement of ....F....626 521-9460
21680 Gateway Center Dr # 300 Diamond Bar (91765) *(P-6260)*
Society For The Study O ....E....510 549-4270
2526 M Luthr King Jr Way Berkeley (94704) *(P-6393)*
Socket Mobile Inc ....E....510 933-3000
39700 Eureka Dr Newark (94560) *(P-18255)*
Socksmith Design Inc (PA) ....E....831 426-6416
1515 Pacific Ave Santa Cruz (95060) *(P-2814)*
Sodamail LLC ....F....707 794-1289
1300 Valley House Dr # 100 Rohnert Park (94928) *(P-6582)*
Soderberg Manufacturing Co Inc ....D....909 595-1291
20821 Currier Rd Walnut (91789) *(P-17664)*
Soex West Tex Recycl USA LLC ....D....559 233-1765
2360 S Orange Ave Fresno (93725) *(P-2941)*
Sof-Tek Integrators Inc ....F....530 242-0527
4712 Mtn Lakes Blvd # 200 Redding (96003) *(P-21850)*
Sofa U Love (PA) ....E....323 464-3397
1207 N Western Ave Los Angeles (90029) *(P-4811)*
Sofi Clothing, Los Angeles *Also called Skirt Inc (P-3122)*
Sofi Enterprises, Los Angeles *Also called Sonmez Emre (P-3967)*
Sofie Biosciences Inc (PA) ....E....310 215-3159
6162 Bristol Pkwy Culver City (90230) *(P-8516)*
Soft Flex Co ....E....707 938-3539
22678 Broadway Sonoma (95476) *(P-11457)*
Soft Gel Technologies Inc (HQ) ....D....323 726-0700
6982 Bandini Blvd Commerce (90040) *(P-8385)*
Soft Pak, San Diego *Also called So Cal Soft-Pak Incorporated (P-25189)*
Soft Touch Inc ....F....714 524-3382
1830 E Miraloma Ave Ste C Placentia (92870) *(P-7488)*
Soft-Touch Tissue, Vernon *Also called Paper Surce Converting Mfg Inc (P-5324)*
Softmax Inc ....F....213 718-2100
2341 E 49th St Fl 2 Vernon (90058) *(P-3554)*
Softsell Business Systems, Sausalito *Also called Ascert LLC (P-24387)*
Softub Inc (PA) ....D....858 602-1920
13495 Gregg St Poway (92064) *(P-24247)*
Software Ag Inc ....C....408 490-5300
2901 Tasman Dr Ste 219 Santa Clara (95054) *(P-25191)*
Software AG of Virginia, Santa Clara *Also called Software Ag Inc (P-25191)*
Software Development Inc ....E....925 847-8823
5000 Hopyard Rd Ste 160 Pleasanton (94588) *(P-25192)*
Software Licensing Consultants ....E....925 371-1277
1001 Shannon Ct Ste B Livermore (94550) *(P-25193)*
Software Motor Company ....F....408 601-7781
1295 Forgewood Ave Sunnyvale (94089) *(P-17224)*

ALPHABETIC

Employee Codes: A=Over 500 employees, B=251-500
C=101-250, D=51-100, E=20-50, F=10-19
2019 California
Manfacturers Register
© Mergent Inc. 1-800-342-5647
1285

Software Partners LLC..........E.......760 944-8436
906 2nd St Encinitas (92024) **(P-25194)**
Soho Carpet & Rugs, Santa Ana *Also called Ohno America Inc* **(P-2937)**
Soil Retention Products Inc (PA)..........F.......951 928-8477
2501 State St Carlsbad (92008) **(P-10863)**
Soil Retention Products Inc..........F.......951 928-8477
1765 Watson Rd Romoland (92585) **(P-10864)**
Soilmoisture Equipment Corp..........E.......805 964-3525
801 S Kellogg Ave Goleta (93117) **(P-22274)**
Sola Products, San Clemente *Also called Shoreline Products Inc* **(P-23772)**
Soladigm, Milpitas *Also called View Inc* **(P-10740)**
Solaicx..........D.......408 988-5000
600 Clipper Dr Belmont (94002) **(P-19176)**
Solano Clinical Research, Petaluma *Also called Dow Phrmaceutical Sciences Inc* **(P-21947)**
Solano County Water Agency..........F.......707 455-1105
810 Vaca Valley Pkwy # 203 Vacaville (95688) **(P-2226)**
Solano Diagnostics Imaging..........F.......707 646-4646
1101 B Gale Wilson Blvd # 100 Fairfield (94533) **(P-22275)**
Solar Art, Irvine *Also called Budget Enterprises Inc* **(P-10587)**
Solar Art, Irvine *Also called Window Solutions* **(P-23212)**
Solar Atmospheres Inc..........E.......909 217-7400
8606 Live Oak Ave Fontana (92335) **(P-11829)**
Solar Electronics Company, North Hollywood *Also called A T Parker Inc* **(P-19893)**
Solar Enrgy World Ltd Lblty Co..........E.......973 887-1082
1300 Park Newport Apt 209 Newport Beach (92660) **(P-12086)**
Solar Industries Inc..........E.......916 567-9650
731 N Market Blvd Ste J Sacramento (95834) **(P-12087)**
Solar Region Inc..........F.......909 595-8500
19575 E Walnut Dr S C16 City of Industry (91748) **(P-15487)**
Solar Turbines Incorporated (HQ)..........A.......619 544-5000
2200 Pacific Hwy San Diego (92101) **(P-14004)**
Solar Turbines Incorporated..........E.......619 544-5352
2200 Pacific Hwy San Diego (92101) **(P-15247)**
Solar Turbines Incorporated..........C.......858 715-2060
9250a Sky Park Ct San Diego (92123) **(P-14005)**
Solar Turbines Incorporated..........F.......949 450-0870
18 Morgan Ste 100 Irvine (92618) **(P-14006)**
Solar Turbines Intl Co (HQ)..........E.......619 544-5000
2200 Pacific Hwy San Diego (92101) **(P-14007)**
Solar Turbines Intl Co..........E.......858 694-1616
9330 Sky Park Ct San Diego (92123) **(P-14008)**
Solara Engineering, Sun Valley *Also called Excelity* **(P-11776)**
Solarbos..........D.......925 456-7744
310 Stealth Ct Livermore (94551) **(P-17164)**
Solaredge Technologies Inc (PA)..........D.......510 498-3200
47505 Seabridge Dr Fremont (94538) **(P-17356)**
Solarflare Communications Inc..........C.......949 581-6830
7505 Irvine Center Dr Irvine (92618) **(P-15488)**
Solarius Development Inc..........F.......408 541-0151
2390 Bering Dr San Jose (95131) **(P-21851)**
Solaron Pool Heating Inc (PA)..........F.......916 858-8146
3480 Sunrise Blvd Ste 100 Rancho Cordova (95742) **(P-15362)**
Solarreserve LLC (PA)..........E.......310 315-2200
520 Broadway Fl 6 Santa Monica (90401) **(P-12088)**
Solarroofscom Inc..........F.......916 481-7200
5840 Gibbons Dr Ste H Carmichael (95608) **(P-12089)**
Solartech Power Inc..........F.......909 673-0178
901 E Cedar St Ontario (91761) **(P-19177)**
Solatron Enterprises, Torrance *Also called Mahmood Izadi Inc* **(P-15340)**
Solatube International Inc (PA)..........D.......888 765-2882
2210 Oak Ridge Way Vista (92081) **(P-12348)**
Soldermask Inc..........F.......714 842-1987
17905 Metzler Ln Huntington Beach (92647) **(P-18610)**
SOLE Designs Inc..........F.......626 452-8642
11685 Mcbean Dr El Monte (91732) **(P-4812)**
Sole Society Group Inc..........C.......310 220-0808
8511 Steller Dr Culver City (90232) **(P-10476)**
Sole Survivor Corporation..........C.......818 338-3760
28632 Roadside Dr Ste 200 Agoura Hills (91301) **(P-3501)**
Sole Technology Inc (PA)..........C.......949 460-2020
26921 Fuerte Lake Forest (92630) **(P-10510)**
Sole Technology Inc..........F.......949 460-2020
17300 Slover Ave Fontana (92337) **(P-10511)**
Solecta Inc (PA)..........E.......760 630-9643
4113 Avenida De La Plata Oceanside (92056) **(P-2963)**
Solectek Corporation..........E.......858 450-1220
8375 Cmino Santa Fe Ste A San Diego (92121) **(P-18256)**
Soledad Bee, King City *Also called South County Newspapers LLC* **(P-6052)**
Soleno Therapeutics Inc (PA)..........F.......650 213-8444
1235 Radio Rd Ste 110 Redwood City (94065) **(P-8386)**
Solera Laboratories Inc..........F.......408 200-3131
3940 Freedom Cir Santa Clara (95054) **(P-19178)**
Solflower Computer Inc..........F.......408 733-8100
3337 Kifer Rd Santa Clara (95051) **(P-15856)**
Solher Iron..........F.......415 822-9900
1555 Galvez Ave Ste 400 San Francisco (94124) **(P-12997)**
Soli-Bond Inc..........E.......661 631-1633
4230 Foster Ave Bakersfield (93308) **(P-277)**
Soliant Energy Inc..........E.......626 396-9500
1100 La Avenida St Ste A Mountain View (94043) **(P-20072)**
Solid 21 Incorporated..........F.......213 688-0900
22287 Mulholland Hwy # 82 Calabasas (91302) **(P-23318)**
Solid Data Systems Inc..........F.......408 845-5700
3542 Bassett St Santa Clara (95054) **(P-15610)**
Solid State Devices Inc..........C.......562 404-4474
14701 Firestone Blvd La Mirada (90638) **(P-19179)**
Solid-Scope Machining Co Inc..........F.......310 523-2366
17925 Adria Maru Ln Carson (90746) **(P-11993)**
Soligen 2006, Northridge *Also called DC Partners Inc* **(P-11735)**
Soligen 2006, Northridge *Also called DC Partners Inc* **(P-11736)**
Soligen 2006, Northridge *Also called DC Partners Inc* **(P-11737)**
Solimar Energy LLC..........F.......805 643-4100
121 N Fir St Ste H Ventura (93001) **(P-153)**
Solmetric Corporation..........E.......707 823-4600
117 Morris St Ste 100 Sebastopol (95472) **(P-22276)**
Solo Enterprise Corp..........E.......626 961-3591
220 N California Ave City of Industry (91744) **(P-16950)**
Solo Golf, City of Industry *Also called Solo Enterprise Corp* **(P-16950)**
Solo Steel Erectors Inc..........F.......530 893-2293
762 Portal Dr Chico (95973) **(P-12961)**
Solomon Colors Inc..........E.......909 484-9156
1371 Laurel Ave Rialto (92376) **(P-7745)**
Solonics Inc (PA)..........F.......650 589-9798
31082 San Antonio St Hayward (94544) **(P-17992)**
Solow..........E.......323 664-7772
2907 Glenview Ave Los Angeles (90039) **(P-3502)**
Solta Medical Inc (HQ)..........F.......510 786-6946
7031 Koll Center Pkwy # 260 Pleasanton (94566) **(P-23050)**
Solta Medical Inc..........C.......510 782-2286
25901 Industrial Blvd Hayward (94545) **(P-23051)**
Soltech Solar Inc..........F.......909 890-2282
1836 Commercenter Cir San Bernardino (92408) **(P-14009)**
Solution Box Inc..........F.......949 387-3223
1923 Avenida Plaza Real Oceanside (92056) **(P-7212)**
Solutions Safety Services Inc..........D.......714 843-5653
16182 Gothard St Ste J Huntington Beach (92647) **(P-3017)**
Solutions Unlimited, Fullerton *Also called Wilsons Art Studio Inc* **(P-7542)**
Solutionsoft Systems Inc..........E.......408 346-1491
2350 Mission College Blvd Santa Clara (95054) **(P-25195)**
Solv Inc..........F.......858 622-4040
16798 W Bernardo Dr San Diego (92127) **(P-25196)**
Solvaira, Bell *Also called Allied Blnding Ingredients Inc* **(P-2449)**
Solvay USA Inc..........F.......310 669-5300
20851 S Santa Fe Ave Long Beach (90810) **(P-7806)**
Soma Magnetics Corporation..........E.......714 447-0782
585 S State College Blvd Fullerton (92831) **(P-17121)**
Somacis Inc..........C.......858 513-2200
13500 Danielson St Poway (92064) **(P-18611)**
Somar Corporation..........F.......310 329-1446
13006 Halldale Ave Gardena (90249) **(P-12764)**
Some Crust Bakery, Claremont *Also called Feemster Co Inc* **(P-1247)**
Somerset Printing, Belmont *Also called Somerset Traveller Inc* **(P-7619)**
Somerset Traveller Inc..........F.......650 593-7350
2765 Comstock Cir Belmont (94002) **(P-7619)**
Sonance, San Clemente *Also called Dana Innovations* **(P-17787)**
Sonant Corporation..........F.......858 623-8180
6215 Ferris Sq Ste 220 San Diego (92121) **(P-17993)**
Sonasoft Corp (PA)..........E.......408 708-4000
6920 Santa Teresa Blvd # 108 San Jose (95119) **(P-25197)**
Sonatech Division, Santa Barbara *Also called Alta Properties Inc* **(P-19907)**
Soncell North America Inc (HQ)..........E.......619 795-4600
10729 Whelt Lands Ave C San Diego (92107) **(P-21434)**
Sonendo Inc (PA)..........E.......949 766-3636
26061 Merit Cir Ste 102 Laguna Hills (92653) **(P-22910)**
Sonfarrel Inc..........D.......714 630-7286
3000 E La Jolla St 3010 Anaheim (92806) **(P-16951)**
Song Beoung..........F.......510 670-8788
501 Murphy Ranch Rd # 148 Milpitas (95035) **(P-7585)**
Songbird Ocarinas LLC..........F.......323 269-2524
2751 E 11th St Los Angeles (90023) **(P-23389)**
Songs Music Publishing LLC..........F.......323 939-3511
7656 W Sunset Blvd Los Angeles (90046) **(P-6583)**
Sonic Air Systems Inc..........E.......714 255-0124
1050 Beacon St Brea (92821) **(P-15175)**
Sonic Dry Clean, Ramona *Also called Hockin Diversfd Holdings Inc* **(P-15159)**
Sonic Manufacturing Tech Inc..........B.......510 580-8500
47951 Westinghouse Dr Fremont (94539) **(P-18612)**
Sonic Plating Company, Gardena *Also called Granath & Granath Inc* **(P-13418)**
Sonic Solutions Holdings Inc..........B.......408 562-8400
2830 De La Cruz Blvd Santa Clara (95050) **(P-25198)**
Sonic Studio LLC..........F.......415 944-7642
93 Madrone Rd Fairfax (94930) **(P-25199)**
Sonic Technology Products Inc..........E.......530 272-4607
108 Boulder St Nevada City (95959) **(P-19180)**
Sonic Vr LLC..........F.......206 227-8585
225 Broadway Ste 650 San Diego (92101) **(P-25200)**
Sonicsensory Inc (PA)..........F.......818 256-7900
1161 Logan St Los Angeles (90026) **(P-9486)**
Sonix, Torrance *Also called Lenntek Corporation* **(P-18164)**
Sonmez Emre..........F.......323 589-6000
1370 E Washington Blvd Los Angeles (90021) **(P-3967)**
Sonnet Technologies Inc..........E.......949 587-3500
8 Autry Irvine (92618) **(P-20073)**
Sonnet Tool..........E.......310 219-7790
3348 W El Segundo Blvd Hawthorne (90250) **(P-14677)**
Sonoco Corrflex LLC..........F.......818 507-7477
1225 Grand Central Ave Glendale (91201) **(P-5461)**
Sonoco Industrial Products Div, City of Industry *Also called Sonoco Products Company* **(P-5361)**
Sonoco Products Company..........D.......626 369-6611
166 Baldwin Park Blvd City of Industry (91746) **(P-5361)**
Sonoco Products Company..........D.......562 921-0881
12851 Leyva St Norwalk (90650) **(P-5362)**
Sonoco Prtective Solutions Inc..........D.......510 785-0220
3466 Enterprise Ave Hayward (94545) **(P-5462)**
Sonoma Access Ctrl Systems Inc..........E.......707 935-3458
21600 8th St E Sonoma (95476) **(P-12892)**

Mergent e-mail: customerrelations@mergent.com
1286
2019 California
Manufacturers Register
(P-0000) Products & Services Section entry number
(PA)=Parent Co (HQ)=Headquarters (DH)=Div Headquarters

Sonoma Beverage Company LLC (PA) ....E....707 431-1099
2710 Giffen Ave Santa Rosa (95407) ***(P-967)***
Sonoma Business Magazine, Santa Rosa *Also called Gammon LLC* ***(P-6170)***
Sonoma Cast Stone Corporation ....E....877 283-2400
133 Copeland St Ste A Petaluma (94952) ***(P-11004)***
Sonoma Cider Mill ....F....707 433-8212
1083 Vine St Healdsburg (95448) ***(P-2670)***
Sonoma Creek Winery, Sonoma *Also called Larson Family Winery Inc* ***(P-1856)***
Sonoma Foods, Santa Rosa *Also called MS Intertrade Inc* ***(P-2318)***
Sonoma Gourmet Inc ....E....707 939-3700
21684 8th St E Ste 100 Sonoma (95476) ***(P-933)***
Sonoma Index-Tribune ....D....707 938-2111
117 W Napa St Ste A Sonoma (95476) ***(P-6049)***
Sonoma International Inc ....E....707 935-0710
462 W Napa St Fl 2 Sonoma (95476) ***(P-23466)***
Sonoma Orthopedic Products Inc ....F....847 807-4378
2735 Sand Hill Rd Ste 205 Menlo Park (94025) ***(P-22626)***
Sonoma Pacific Company, Sonoma *Also called El Pelado LLC* ***(P-4469)***
Sonoma Pacific Company LLC ....D....707 938-2877
1180 Fremont Dr Sonoma (95476) ***(P-4507)***
Sonoma Pharmaceuticals Inc (PA) ....D....707 283-0550
1129 N Mcdowell Blvd Petaluma (94954) ***(P-8387)***
Sonoma Photonics Inc ....E....707 568-1202
1750 Northpoint Pkwy C Santa Rosa (95407) ***(P-19364)***
Sonoma Pins Etc Corporation ....D....707 996-9956
841 W Napa St Sonoma (95476) ***(P-7489)***
Sonoma Promotional Solutions, Sonoma *Also called Sonoma Pins Etc Corporation* ***(P-7489)***
Sonoma Sparkler, Healdsburg *Also called Sonoma Cider Mill* ***(P-2670)***
Sonoma Tilemakers Inc (HQ) ....D....707 837-8177
7750 Bell Rd Windsor (95492) ***(P-10791)***
Sonoma Valley Foods Inc ....E....707 585-2200
3645 Standish Ave Santa Rosa (95407) ***(P-775)***
Sonoma Valley Publishing, Sonoma *Also called Sonoma Index-Tribune* ***(P-6049)***
Sonoma West Publishers Inc (PA) ....F....707 823-7845
135 S Main St Sebastopol (95472) ***(P-6050)***
Sonoma West Times & News, Sebastopol *Also called Sonoma West Publishers Inc* ***(P-6050)***
Sonoma Wine Company LLC ....C....707 829-6100
9119 Graton Rd Graton (95444) ***(P-1980)***
Sonoma Wine Hardware Inc ....E....650 866-3020
360 Swift Ave Ste 34 South San Francisco (94080) ***(P-1981)***
Sonora Face Co ....E....323 560-8188
5233 Randolph St Maywood (90270) ***(P-4383)***
Sonora Mills Foods Inc (PA) ....C....310 639-5333
3064 E Maria St E Rncho Dmngz (90221) ***(P-1380)***
Sonos Inc (PA) ....D....805 965-3001
614 Chapala St Santa Barbara (93101) ***(P-17858)***
Sonosim Inc ....F....323 473-3800
1738 Berkeley St Ste A Santa Monica (90404) ***(P-25201)***
Sonus-USA, San Jose *Also called Richard J Trevino MD* ***(P-22805)***
Sony Biotechnology Inc ....D....800 275-5963
1730 N 1st St Fl 2 San Jose (95112) ***(P-20074)***
Sony Broadcast Products, San Jose *Also called Sony Electronics Inc* ***(P-15857)***
Sony Corporation of America (PA) ....E....212 833-8000
16530 Via Esprillo Mz7190 San Diego (92127) ***(P-15489)***
Sony Dadc US Inc ....E....310 760-8500
4499 Glencoe Ave Marina Del Rey (90292) ***(P-19882)***
Sony Electronics Inc (HQ) ....A....858 942-2400
16535 Via Esprillo Bldg 1 San Diego (92127) ***(P-17859)***
Sony Electronics Inc ....E....408 352-4000
1730 N 1st St San Jose (95112) ***(P-15857)***
Sony Electronics Inc ....C....858 942-2400
16530 Via Esprillo San Diego (92127) ***(P-17860)***
Sony Electronics Inc ....C....858 942-2400
16530 Via Esprillo San Diego (92127) ***(P-18396)***
Sony Electronics Inc ....E....858 824-6960
5510 Morehouse Dr Ste 100 San Diego (92121) ***(P-17913)***
Sony Interactive Entrmt LLC ....E....858 207-1500
16535 Via Esprillo San Diego (92127) ***(P-25202)***
Sony Mobile Communications USA ....C....866 766-9374
2207 Bridgepoint Pkwy San Mateo (94404) ***(P-18257)***
Sony Network Studios Division, San Diego *Also called Sony Electronics Inc* ***(P-17913)***
Sony Optical Archive Inc ....F....844 725-0398
1730 N 1st St San Jose (95112) ***(P-15611)***
Sony Style, San Diego *Also called Sony Electronics Inc* ***(P-17860)***
Sony/Atv Music Publishing LLC ....E....310 441-1300
10635 Santa Monica Blvd # 300 Los Angeles (90025) ***(P-6584)***
Soojians Inc ....E....559 875-5511
89 Academy Ave Sanger (93657) ***(P-1381)***
Sooraksan Soojebi ....F....213 389-2818
4003 Wilshire Blvd Ste I Los Angeles (90010) ***(P-11884)***
Soper-Wheeler Company LLC (PA) ....E....530 675-2343
19855 Barton Hill Rd Strawberry Valley (95981) ***(P-4014)***
Sora Power Inc (PA) ....F....951 479-9880
1141 Olympic Dr Corona (92881) ***(P-19731)***
Soraa Inc (PA) ....D....510 456-2200
6500 Kaiser Dr Ste 110 Fremont (94555) ***(P-19181)***
Soraa Laser Diode Inc (PA) ....E....805 696-6999
485 Pine Ave Goleta (93117) ***(P-20075)***
Soraa Laser Diode Inc ....E....805 696-6999
6500 Kaiser Dr Fremont (94555) ***(P-20076)***
Sorenson Engineering Inc (PA) ....C....909 795-2434
32032 Dunlap Blvd Yucaipa (92399) ***(P-13042)***
Sorenson Publishing Inc ....F....925 866-1514
12925 Alcosta Blvd Ste 6 San Ramon (94583) ***(P-7106)***
Sorma USA LLC ....B....559 651-1269
9810 W Ferguson Ave Visalia (93291) ***(P-5625)***
Sorrento Networks Corporation (HQ) ....F....510 577-1400
7195 Oakport St Oakland (94621) ***(P-17994)***
Sotcher Measurement Inc ....F....408 574-0112
115 Phelan Ave Ste 10 San Jose (95112) ***(P-21852)***
Soteleo Salvadar ....E....213 621-2040
620 Imperial St Los Angeles (90021) ***(P-23978)***
Sotera Wireless Inc ....C....858 427-4620
10020 Huennekens St San Diego (92121) ***(P-23052)***
Sound Imaging Inc ....F....858 622-0082
7580 Trade St Ste A San Diego (92121) ***(P-23053)***
Sound Storm Laboratory LLC ....E....805 983-8008
3451 Lunar Ct Oxnard (93030) ***(P-17861)***
Sound United, Vista *Also called Dei Headquarters Inc* ***(P-18319)***
Sound Waves Insullation Inc ....E....714 556-2110
1406 Ritchey St Ste D Santa Ana (92705) ***(P-21657)***
Soundcoat Company Inc ....E....631 242-2200
16901 Armstrong Ave Irvine (92606) ***(P-17311)***
Soundcraft Inc ....E....818 882-0020
20301 Nordhoff St Chatsworth (91311) ***(P-20077)***
Soundview Applications Inc ....F....530 888-7593
2390 Lindbergh St Ste 101 Auburn (95602) ***(P-17862)***
Soup Bases Loaded Inc ....E....909 230-6890
2355 E Francis St Ontario (91761) ***(P-894)***
Source Bio Inc ....F....951 676-1000
43379 Bus Pk Dr Ste 100 Temecula (92590) ***(P-8517)***
Source of Health Inc ....E....619 409-9500
1055 Bay Blvd Ste A Chula Vista (91911) ***(P-650)***
Source Photonics Usa Inc (HQ) ....C....818 773-9044
8521 Fllbrook Ave Ste 200 Canoga Park (91304) ***(P-19182)***
Source Print Media Solutions ....F....661 263-1880
29108 Summer Oak Ct Santa Clarita (91390) ***(P-7107)***
Source Scientific LLC ....E....949 231-5096
2144 Michelson Dr Irvine (92612) ***(P-22627)***
Source Surgical Inc ....F....415 861-7040
3130 20th St Ste 200 San Francisco (94110) ***(P-22628)***
Sourcing Group LLC ....E....510 471-4749
1672 Delta Ct Hayward (94544) ***(P-7108)***
Sourcing Group LLC ....F....530 346-1280
148 Whitcomb Ave Colfax (95713) ***(P-7109)***
Souriau Usa Inc (HQ) ....E....805 238-2840
1750 Commerce Way Paso Robles (93446) ***(P-17490)***
Sousa Ready Mix LLC ....F....530 926-4485
100 Upton Rd Mount Shasta (96067) ***(P-11181)***
South Alliance Industrial Mch ....F....626 442-3744
2423 Troy Ave South El Monte (91733) ***(P-16952)***
South Amrcn Imging Sltions Inc ....F....805 824-4036
2360 Eastman Ave Ste 110 Oxnard (93030) ***(P-17225)***
South Bay Cable Corp (PA) ....D....951 659-2183
54125 Maranatha Dr Idyllwild (92549) ***(P-11674)***
South Bay Cable Corp ....F....951 296-9900
42033 Rio Nedo Temecula (92590) ***(P-11675)***
South Bay Chrome, Santa Ana *Also called Classic Components Inc* ***(P-13372)***
South Bay Circuits Inc ....C....408 978-8992
210 Hillsdale Ave San Jose (95136) ***(P-19732)***
South Bay Corporation ....F....310 532-5353
1335 W 134th St Gardena (90247) ***(P-9679)***
South Bay Cstm Plstic Extrders ....E....619 544-0808
2554 Commercial St San Diego (92113) ***(P-10382)***
South Bay Diversfd Systems Inc ....F....510 784-3094
1841 National Ave Hayward (94545) ***(P-12765)***
South Bay International Inc ....E....909 718-5000
13169 Slover Ave Ste B Fontana (92337) ***(P-4888)***
South Bay Marble Inc (PA) ....F....650 594-4251
15745 E Alta Vista Way San Jose (95127) ***(P-11280)***
South Bay Neon, San Diego *Also called Carreon Development Inc* ***(P-23841)***
South Bay Salt Works, Chula Vista *Also called Ggtw LLC* ***(P-9255)***
South Bay Solutions Inc (PA) ....E....650 843-1800
37399 Centralmont Pl Fremont (94536) ***(P-16953)***
South Bay Solutions Texas LLC ....E....936 494-0180
37399 Centralmont Pl Fremont (94536) ***(P-17357)***
SOUTH BAY WELDING, El Cajon *Also called M W Reid Welding Inc* ***(P-12198)***
South Coast Baking LLC (HQ) ....D....949 851-9654
1722 Kettering Irvine (92614) ***(P-1382)***
South Coast Baking Co., Irvine *Also called South Coast Baking LLC* ***(P-1382)***
South Coast Circuits Inc ....D....714 966-2108
3506 W Lake Center Dr A Santa Ana (92704) ***(P-18613)***
South Coast Materials Co, San Diego *Also called Forterra Pipe & Precast LLC* ***(P-10931)***
South Coast Mold Inc ....F....949 253-2000
1852 Mcgaw Ave Irvine (92614) ***(P-14571)***
South Coast Publishing Inc ....F....562 988-1222
2599 E 28th St Ste 212 Long Beach (90755) ***(P-6051)***
South Coast Screen and Casing ....F....310 632-3200
19112 S Santa Fe Ave Compton (90221) ***(P-278)***
South Coast Sewing Company Inc ....E....310 350-0535
2009 S Grand Ave Santa Ana (92705) ***(P-3595)***
South Coast Stairs Inc ....E....949 858-1685
30251 Tomas Rcho STA Marg (92688) ***(P-4234)***
South Coast Water, Santa Ana *Also called Hannah Industries Inc* ***(P-16048)***
South Coast Winery Inc ....E....951 587-9463
34843 Rancho Cal Rd Temecula (92591) ***(P-1982)***
South Coast Winery Resort Spa, Temecula *Also called South Coast Winery Inc* ***(P-1982)***
South County Newspapers LLC ....F....831 385-4880
522 Broadway St Ste B King City (93930) ***(P-6052)***
South Gate Engineering LLC ....C....909 628-2779
13477 Yorba Ave Chino (91710) ***(P-12422)***
South Orange County Ww Auth ....F....949 234-5400
34156 Del Obispo St Dana Point (92629) ***(P-9308)***
South Pacific Tuna Corporation ....F....619 233-2060
501 W Broadway San Diego (92101) ***(P-2303)***
South Plastic Molds, Anaheim *Also called Medplast Group Inc* ***(P-10204)***

ALPHABETIC

Employee Codes: A=Over 500 employees, B=251-500
C=101-250, D=51-100, E=20-50, F=10-19

2019 California
Manfacturers Register

1287

South Street Inc................................F.....562 984-6240
2231 E Curry St Long Beach (90805) *(P-23656)*
South Swell Screen Arts................................F.....858 566-3095
8440 Production Ave San Diego (92121) *(P-7490)*
South Valley Materials Inc (HQ)................D.....559 277-7060
7673 N Ingram Ave Ste 101 Fresno (93711) *(P-11182)*
South Valley Materials Inc................................E.....559 582-0532
7761 Hanford Armona Rd Hanford (93230) *(P-11183)*
South Valley Oil Field Electri................................F.....661 665-9809
309 Windsor Park Dr Bakersfield (93311) *(P-279)*
South West Lubricants Inc................................619 449-5000
9266 Abraham Way Santee (92071) *(P-9450)*
South Western Paving Company................F.....714 577-5750
2250 E Orangethorpe Ave Fullerton (92831) *(P-9398)*
Southcoast Cabinet Inc (PA)................F.....909 594-3089
755 Pinefalls Ave Walnut (91789) *(P-4352)*
Southcoast Welding & Mfg LLC................B.....619 429-1337
2591 Faivre St Ste 1 Chula Vista (91911) *(P-25436)*
Southeast Kern Weekender, Tehachapi Also called Tehachapi News Inc *(P-6068)*
Souther Archtctural Cast Stone, Oceanside Also called Ms Cast Stone Inc *(P-11144)*
Souther Cast Stone Inc................................E.....760 754-9697
235 Via Del Monte Oceanside (92058) *(P-11005)*
Southern Alum Finshg Co Inc................D.....530 244-7518
4356 Caterpillar Rd Redding (96003) *(P-11625)*
Southern Cal Bndery Miling Inc................D.....909 829-1949
10661 Business Dr Fontana (92337) *(P-7620)*
Southern Cal Gold Pdts Inc................F.....805 988-0777
2350 Santiago Ct Oxnard (93030) *(P-11422)*
Southern Cal Tchnical Arts Inc................E.....714 524-2626
370 E Crowther Ave Placentia (92870) *(P-16954)*
Southern California Biodiesel................F.....951 377-4007
18760 6th St Ste C Bloomington (92316) *(P-9361)*
Southern California Carbide................E.....858 513-7777
12216 Thatcher Ct Poway (92064) *(P-14413)*
Southern California Components................D.....760 949-5144
9927 C Ave Hesperia (92345) *(P-4422)*
Southern California Ice Co................F.....310 325-1040
22921 Lockness Ave Torrance (90501) *(P-2421)*
Southern California Insulation................E.....619 477-1303
2050 Wilson Ave Ste C National City (91950) *(P-21014)*
Southern California Mtl Hdlg................E.....714 773-9630
168 E Freedom Ave Anaheim (92801) *(P-14347)*
Southern California Mulch Inc................F.....951 352-5355
30141 Antelope Rd 116 Menifee (92584) *(P-4657)*
Southern California Plas Inc................D.....714 751-7084
3122 Maple St Santa Ana (92707) *(P-7887)*
Southern California Soap Co................F.....323 888-1332
2700 Tanager Ave Commerce (90040) *(P-8609)*
Southern California Tow Eqp, Anaheim Also called Moda Enterprises Inc *(P-20159)*
Southern California Trane, Brea Also called Trane US Inc *(P-15985)*
Southern Counties Oil Co................E.....408 251-0811
2075 Alum Rock Ave San Jose (95116) *(P-9451)*
Southern Electronics, Pomona Also called Electrocube Inc *(P-19528)*
Southern International Packg, Rancho Palos Verdes Also called Western Summit Mfg Corp *(P-9735)*
Southern Valley Chemical Co................F.....661 366-3308
S Derby & Sycamore Rd Arvin (93203) *(P-9112)*
Southland Clutch Inc................F.....619 477-2105
101 E 18th St National City (91950) *(P-20451)*
Southland Container Corp................F.....909 937-9781
1600 Champagne Ave Ontario (91761) *(P-5463)*
Southland Enterprises, Escondido Also called Southland Manufacturing Inc *(P-14678)*
Southland Envelope Company Inc................C.....619 449-3553
10111 Riverford Rd Lakeside (92040) *(P-5678)*
Southland Industries................A.....714 901-5800
12131 Western Ave Garden Grove (92841) *(P-24248)*
Southland Manufacturing Inc................F.....760 745-7913
210 Market Pl Escondido (92029) *(P-14678)*
Southland Mixer Service................F.....760 246-6080
12231 Hibiscus Rd Adelanto (92301) *(P-20229)*
Southland Polymers Inc................E.....562 921-0444
14030 Gannet St Santa Fe Springs (90670) *(P-7888)*
Southland Publishing................E.....626 584-1500
50 S De Lacey Ave Ste 200 Pasadena (91105) *(P-6585)*
Southland Publishing Inc................E.....626 584-1500
50 S Delacey Ave Ste 200 Pasadena (91105) *(P-6053)*
Southland Ready Mix Concrete, Escondido Also called Superior Ready Mix Concrete LP *(P-11195)*
Southland Tool Mfg Inc................F.....714 632-8198
1430 N Hundley St Anaheim (92806) *(P-14679)*
Southwall Technologies Inc (HQ)................E.....650 798-1285
3788 Fabian Way Palo Alto (94303) *(P-9728)*
Southwest Data Products, San Bernardino Also called Innovative Metal Inds Inc *(P-12980)*
Southwest Greene Intl Inc................C.....760 639-4960
4055 Calle Platino # 200 Oceanside (92056) *(P-13278)*
Southwest Machine & Plastic Co................E.....626 963-6919
620 W Foothill Blvd Glendora (91741) *(P-20934)*
Southwest Manufacturing Svcs, El Cajon Also called Pacific Marine Shtmtl Corp *(P-12705)*
Southwest Offset Prtg Co Inc (PA)................B.....310 965-9154
13650 Gramercy Pl Gardena (90249) *(P-7110)*
Southwest Offset Prtg Co Inc................D.....408 232-5160
587 Charcot Ave San Jose (95131) *(P-7491)*
Southwest Plastics, Glendora Also called Southwest Machine & Plastic Co *(P-20934)*
Southwest Plating Co Inc................F.....323 753-3781
1344 W Slauson Ave Los Angeles (90044) *(P-13507)*
Southwest Processors Inc................F.....323 269-9876
4120 Bandini Blvd Vernon (90058) *(P-1166)*
Southwest Products Corporation................F.....360 887-7400
2875 Cherry Ave Signal Hill (90755) *(P-14030)*

Southwest Products Corporation................E.....209 745-6000
85 Enterprise Ct Ste B Galt (95632) *(P-14031)*
Southwest Products LLC................C.....619 263-8000
8411 Siempre Viva Rd San Diego (92154) *(P-2671)*
Southwest Shutter Shaque, Orange Also called Bayside Shutters *(P-12297)*
Southwest Sign Company, Corona Also called Fovell Enterprises Inc *(P-23882)*
Southwest Sign Systems, El Centro Also called Western Electrical Advg Co *(P-24003)*
Southwest Trade Bindery, Northridge Also called Robert A Kerl *(P-7613)*
Southwest Treatment Systems, Vernon Also called Southwest Processors Inc *(P-1166)*
Southwest Wine & Spirits LLC (PA)................F.....213 765-3213
144 S Beverly Dr Fl 600 Beverly Hills (90212) *(P-1983)*
Southwestern Industries Inc (PA)................D.....310 608-4422
2615 Homestead Pl Rancho Dominguez (90220) *(P-14414)*
Southwire Inc (HQ)................F.....310 884-8500
11695 Pacific Ave Fontana (92337) *(P-11580)*
Sova Pharmaceuticals Inc................E.....858 750-4700
11099 N Torrey Pines Rd La Jolla (92037) *(P-8388)*
Sovereign Packaging Inc................E.....714 670-6811
8420 Kass Dr Buena Park (90621) *(P-5464)*
Soxnet Inc................F.....626 855-3200
235 S 6th Ave La Puente (91746) *(P-2815)*
Soyfoods of America................E.....626 358-3836
1091 Hamilton Rd Duarte (91010) *(P-1512)*
Sp, City of Industry Also called Scope Packaging Inc *(P-5457)*
Sp Controls Inc................E.....650 392-7880
930 Linden Ave South San Francisco (94080) *(P-15858)*
SP&s, Valencia Also called Specialty Polymers & Svcs Inc *(P-9171)*
Sp3 Diamond Technologies Inc................F.....877 773-9940
1605 Wyatt Dr Santa Clara (95054) *(P-15363)*
Spa Girl Corporation................E.....714 444-1040
3100 W Warner Ave Ste 11 Santa Ana (92704) *(P-8846)*
Spa La La Inc................F.....605 321-1276
21430 Strathern St Unit I Canoga Park (91304) *(P-24249)*
Space Components, Commerce Also called Atk Space Systems Inc *(P-12360)*
Space Exploration Tech Corp (PA)................A.....310 363-6000
1 Rocket Rd Hawthorne (90250) *(P-21169)*
Space Information Labs LLC................F.....805 925-9010
2260 Meredith Ln Ste A Santa Maria (93455) *(P-21435)*
Space Jam Juice LLC................D.....714 660-7467
1041 Calle Trepadora San Clemente (92673) *(P-2709)*
Space Micro Inc................D.....858 332-0700
10237 Flanders Ct San Diego (92121) *(P-18258)*
Space Propulsions Div, San Jose Also called United Technologies Corp *(P-20688)*
Space Spring and Stamping Co................F.....714 255-9800
5341 Argosy Ave Huntington Beach (92649) *(P-13755)*
Space Systems Group, Monterey Also called Orbital Sciences Corporation *(P-19676)*
Space Systems/Loral LLC................E.....916 605-5448
5130 Rbert J Mathews Pkwy El Dorado Hills (95762) *(P-18259)*
Space Time Insight Inc................F.....650 513-8550
1850 Gateway Dr Ste 125 San Mateo (94404) *(P-25203)*
Space-Lok Inc................C.....310 527-6150
13306 Halldale Ave Gardena (90249) *(P-20935)*
Spaceage Control Inc................F.....661 206-6666
4001 Inglewood Ave # 101 Redondo Beach (90278) *(P-20936)*
Spaceship Company, The, Mojave Also called Tsc LLC *(P-21173)*
Spacesonics Incorporated................D.....650 610-0999
30300 Union City Blvd Union City (94587) *(P-12766)*
Spacesystems Holdings LLC................C.....714 226-1400
4398 Corporate Center Dr Los Alamitos (90720) *(P-17243)*
Spacetron Metal Billows Corp................F.....818 633-1075
15303 Ventura Blvd # 900 Sherman Oaks (91403) *(P-16955)*
Spacewall Inc................F.....714 961-1300
350 E Crowther Ave Placentia (92870) *(P-4384)*
Spacewall West Slotwall Mfg, Placentia Also called Spacewall Inc *(P-4384)*
Spacex, Hawthorne Also called Space Exploration Tech Corp *(P-21169)*
Spadia Inc................F.....562 206-2505
10440 Pioneer Blvd Ste 1 Santa Fe Springs (90670) *(P-17562)*
Spalinger Enterprises Inc................F.....661 834-4550
800 S Mount Vernon Ave Bakersfield (93307) *(P-5103)*
Span-O-Matic Inc................E.....714 256-4700
825 Columbia St Brea (92821) *(P-12767)*
Spanish Castle Inc................F.....818 222-4496
22201 Camay Ct Calabasas (91302) *(P-1984)*
Spansion Inc (HQ)................E.....408 962-2500
198 Champion Ct San Jose (95134) *(P-19183)*
Spansion LLC (HQ)................D.....512 691-8500
198 Champion Ct San Jose (95134) *(P-19184)*
Spar Sausage Co................F.....510 614-8100
688 Williams St San Leandro (94577) *(P-527)*
Sparitual, Van Nuys Also called Orly International Inc *(P-8808)*
Spark Stone LLC................F.....714 772-7575
2300 E Winston Rd Anaheim (92806) *(P-306)*
Sparkcentral Inc (PA)................E.....866 559-6229
650 California St # 1850 San Francisco (94108) *(P-6586)*
Sparkletts Water, Los Angeles Also called Ds Services of America Inc *(P-2131)*
Sparling Instruments LLC................E.....626 444-0571
4097 Temple City Blvd El Monte (91731) *(P-21658)*
Sparqtron Corporation................D.....510 657-7198
5079 Brandin Ct Fremont (94538) *(P-17358)*
Spartak Enterprises Inc................E.....951 360-0610
11186 Venture Dr Mira Loma (91752) *(P-4899)*
Spartan................E.....800 743-6950
444 E Taylor St San Jose (95112) *(P-7492)*
Spartan Inc................D.....661 327-1205
3030 M St Bakersfield (93301) *(P-12244)*
Spartan Manufacturing Co................E.....714 894-1955
7081 Patterson Dr Garden Grove (92841) *(P-16956)*

Spartan Truck Company Inc ....E....818 899-1111
12266 Branford St Sun Valley (91352) ***(P-20230)***
Spartech LLC ....F....714 523-2260
14263 Gannet St La Mirada (90638) ***(P-9766)***
Sparton Irvine LLC ....D....949 855-6625
2802 Kelvin Ave Ste 100 Irvine (92614) ***(P-19733)***
Spates Fabricators Inc ....D....760 397-4122
85435 Middleton Thermal (92274) ***(P-4423)***
Spatial Photonics Inc ....E....408 940-8800
930 Hamlin Ct Sunnyvale (94089) ***(P-19185)***
Spatial Wave Inc ....F....949 540-6400
23461 S Pointe Dr Ste 300 Laguna Hills (92653) ***(P-25204)***
Spatz Corporation ....C....805 487-2122
1600 Westar Dr Oxnard (93033) ***(P-8847)***
Spatz Laboratories, Oxnard *Also called Spatz Corporation* ***(P-8847)***
Spaulding Crusher Parts, Perris *Also called Spaulding Equipment Company* ***(P-14203)***
Spaulding Equipment Company (PA) ....E....951 943-4531
75 Paseo Adelanto Perris (92570) ***(P-14203)***
Spawn Mate Inc ....E....805 473-7250
4000 Huasna Rd Arroyo Grande (93420) ***(P-9074)***
Speakeasy Ales & Lagers, San Francisco *Also called Brewmaster Inc* ***(P-1574)***
Spec, Valencia *Also called Semiconductor Process Eqp Corp* ***(P-15030)***
Spec Engineering Co Inc ....E....818 780-3045
13754 Saticoy St Van Nuys (91402) ***(P-16957)***
Spec Formliners Inc ....E....714 429-9500
1038 E 4th St Santa Ana (92701) ***(P-10383)***
Spec Iron Inc ....F....818 765-4070
7244 Varna Ave North Hollywood (91605) ***(P-12245)***
Spec Tool Company ....E....323 723-9533
11805 Wakeman St Santa Fe Springs (90670) ***(P-21436)***
Spec-Built Systems Inc ....D....619 661-8100
2150 Michael Faraday Dr San Diego (92154) ***(P-12768)***
Specfoam LLC ....F....951 685-3626
13215 Marlay Ave Fontana (92337) ***(P-4889)***
Special Devices Incorporated (HQ) ....B....805 387-1000
2655 1st St Ste 300 Simi Valley (93065) ***(P-20452)***
Special Forces Custom Gear Inc ....E....619 241-5453
2949 Hoover Ave National City (91950) ***(P-3771)***
Special Iron Security Systems ....F....626 443-7877
2030 Rosemead Blvd El Monte (91733) ***(P-12893)***
Special Products Group, Chula Vista *Also called Sealed Air Corporation* ***(P-5623)***
Special-T, North Hollywood *Also called Specialty Coatings & Chem Inc* ***(P-8943)***
Specialist Media Group, Carlsbad *Also called L & L Printers Carlsbad LLC* ***(P-6933)***
Specialists In Cstm Sftwr Inc ....E....310 315-9660
2574 Wellesley Ave Los Angeles (90064) ***(P-25205)***
Speciality Labs, Fullerton *Also called Magtech & Power Conversion Inc* ***(P-19345)***
Specialized Coating, Huntington Beach *Also called Specilized Crmic Powdr Coating* ***(P-13662)***
Specialized Coating Services ....D....510 226-8700
42680 Christy St Fremont (94538) ***(P-18614)***
Specialized Dairy Service Inc ....E....909 923-3420
1710 E Philadelphia St Ontario (91761) ***(P-14106)***
Specialized Elevator Corp ....D....562 407-1200
14320 Iseli Rd Santa Fe Springs (90670) ***(P-14259)***
Specialized Graphics Inc ....E....925 680-0265
3951 Industrial Way Ste A Concord (94520) ***(P-23979)***
Specialized Milling Corp ....F....909 357-7890
10330 Elm Ave Fontana (92337) ***(P-8942)***
Specialized Products & Design ....F....714 289-1428
1428 N Manzanita St Orange (92867) ***(P-9042)***
Specialized Screen Printing ....E....714 964-1230
18435 Bandilier Cir Fountain Valley (92708) ***(P-7493)***
Specialteam Medical Svc Inc ....F....714 694-0348
22445 La Palma Ave Ste F Yorba Linda (92887) ***(P-22629)***
Specialty Car Wash System ....F....909 869-6300
146 Mercury Cir Pomona (91768) ***(P-16110)***
Specialty Cellular Products Co ....F....925 454-3010
2763 Boeing Way Stockton (95206) ***(P-11371)***
Specialty Coating Systems Inc ....E....909 390-8818
4435 E Airport Dr Ste 100 Ontario (91761) ***(P-13661)***
Specialty Coatings & Chem Inc ....E....818 983-0055
7360 Varna Ave North Hollywood (91605) ***(P-8943)***
Specialty Concepts Inc ....F....818 998-5238
2393 Teller Rd Ste 106 Newbury Park (91320) ***(P-17165)***
Specialty Division, Santa Fe Springs *Also called Distinctive Industries* ***(P-3889)***
Specialty Enterprises Co ....D....323 726-9721
6858 E Acco St Commerce (90040) ***(P-9884)***
Specialty Equipment Co ....E....714 258-1622
1921 E Pomona St Santa Ana (92705) ***(P-20231)***
Specialty Fabrications Inc ....E....805 579-9730
2674 Westhills Ct Simi Valley (93065) ***(P-12769)***
Specialty Finance Inc ....E....951 735-5200
1230 Quarry St Corona (92879) ***(P-13279)***
Specialty Finishes, Fontana *Also called Specialized Milling Corp* ***(P-8942)***
Specialty Granules LLC ....E....209 274-5323
1900 State Hwy 104 Ione (95640) ***(P-11327)***
Specialty Graphics Inc ....F....510 351-7705
1998 Republic Ave San Leandro (94577) ***(P-7621)***
Specialty International Inc ....D....818 768-8810
11144 Penrose St Ste 11 Sun Valley (91352) ***(P-13280)***
Specialty Manufacturing, Inc., San Diego *Also called Providien Thermoforming Inc* ***(P-9723)***
Specialty Metal Fabrication, Goleta *Also called Tan Set Corporation* ***(P-12257)***
Specialty Minerals Inc ....C....760 248-5300
6565 Meridian Rd Lucerne Valley (92356) ***(P-316)***
Specialty Motions Inc ....E....951 735-8722
5480 Smokey Mountain Way Yorba Linda (92887) ***(P-15112)***
Specialty Polymers & Svcs Inc ....F....661 294-1790
27822 Fremont Ct Valencia (91355) ***(P-9171)***
Specialty Products Design Inc ....F....916 635-8108
11252 Sunco Dr Rancho Cordova (95742) ***(P-20453)***
Specialty Rock Inc ....F....909 334-2265
5405 Alton Pkwy Irvine Irvine (92604) ***(P-382)***
Specialty Science Counter Tops, Newbury Park *Also called H and M Industries LLC* ***(P-5067)***
Specialty Steel Products Inc ....F....664 637-6704
1202 Piper Ranch Rd San Diego (92154) ***(P-13853)***
Specialty Surface Grinding ....F....310 538-4352
345 W 131st St Los Angeles (90061) ***(P-16958)***
Specilized Crmic Powdr Coating ....F....714 901-2628
5862 Research Dr Huntington Beach (92649) ***(P-13662)***
Specilized Packg Solutions Inc ....E....510 494-5670
38505 Cherry St Ste H Newark (94560) ***(P-4536)***
Specilty Enzymes Btechnologies, Chino *Also called Cal-India Foods International* ***(P-8991)***
Specilty Enzymes Btechnologies ....F....909 613-1660
13591 Yorba Ave Chino (91710) ***(P-9043)***
Specilty Mtals Fabrication Inc ....F....619 937-6100
11222 Woodside Ave N Santee (92071) ***(P-2964)***
Specilzed Packg Solutions-Wood, Newark *Also called Specilized Packg Solutions Inc* ***(P-4536)***
Speck Products, San Mateo *Also called Speculative Product Design LLC* ***(P-10539)***
Specks Industries LLC ....E....800 511-0497
10957 Grass Valley Cir Moreno Valley (92557) ***(P-24250)***
Spectra Color Inc ....E....951 277-0200
9116 Stellar Ct Corona (92883) ***(P-7746)***
Spectra USA, Chino *Also called Isiqalo LLC* ***(P-2843)***
Spectra Watermakers, Petaluma *Also called Katadyn Desalination LLC* ***(P-17394)***
Spectra Watermakers Inc (HQ) ....F....415 526-2780
2220 S Mcdowell Blvd Ext Petaluma (94954) ***(P-16111)***
Spectra-Physics Inc ....A....650 961-2550
3635 Peterson Way Santa Clara (95054) ***(P-20078)***
Spectra-Physics Laser Div, Santa Clara *Also called Newport Corporation* ***(P-20029)***
Spectral Dynamics Inc (PA) ....E....760 761-0440
2199 Zanker Rd San Jose (95131) ***(P-22277)***
Spectral Labs Incorporated ....E....858 451-0540
15920 Bernardo Center Dr San Diego (92127) ***(P-22278)***
Spectranetics ....F....408 592-2111
6531 Dumbarton Cir Fremont (94555) ***(P-23054)***
Spectranetics Corporation ....D....510 933-7964
5055 Brandin Ct Fremont (94538) ***(P-22630)***
Spectraprint Inc ....F....415 460-1228
24 Moody Ct San Rafael (94901) ***(P-7494)***
Spectrasensors Inc ....E....909 980-4238
11027 Arrow Rte Rancho Cucamonga (91730) ***(P-22020)***
Spectraswitch Inc ....E....707 568-7000
445 Tesconi Cir Santa Rosa (95401) ***(P-17995)***
Spectratek Technologies Inc (PA) ....D....310 822-2400
9834 Jordan Cir Santa Fe Springs (90670) ***(P-7111)***
Spectre Performance, Riverside *Also called Seymour Levinger & Co* ***(P-13144)***
Spectrolab Inc ....B....818 365-4611
12500 Gladstone Ave Sylmar (91342) ***(P-19186)***
Spectrum Accessory Distrs ....C....858 653-6470
9770 Carroll Centre Rd San Diego (92126) ***(P-20454)***
Spectrum Assembly Inc ....D....760 930-4000
6300 Yarrow Dr Ste 100 Carlsbad (92011) ***(P-18615)***
Spectrum Bags, Cerritos *Also called Ips Industries Inc* ***(P-10156)***
Spectrum Brands Inc ....C....805 222-3611
5144 N Commerce Ave Ste A Moorpark (93021) ***(P-24251)***
Spectrum Electronics, Carlsbad *Also called Spectrum Assembly Inc* ***(P-18615)***
Spectrum Grafix Inc ....F....415 648-2400
141 10th St San Francisco (94103) ***(P-7112)***
Spectrum Instruments Inc ....F....909 971-9710
570 E Arrow Hwy Ste D San Dimas (91773) ***(P-21853)***
Spectrum Lighting, Santa Fe Springs *Also called Dab Inc* ***(P-17533)***
Spectrum Lithograph Inc ....E....510 438-9192
4300 Business Center Dr Fremont (94538) ***(P-7113)***
Spectrum Naturals, Petaluma *Also called Spectrum Organic Products LLC* ***(P-1551)***
Spectrum Organic Products LLC ....D....888 343-6637
2201 S Mcdowell Blvd Ext Petaluma (94954) ***(P-1551)***
Spectrum Plating Company Inc ....E....310 533-0748
202 W 140th St Los Angeles (90061) ***(P-13508)***
Spectrum Prosthetics/Orthotics ....F....530 243-4500
1844 South St Redding (96001) ***(P-22817)***
Spectrum Scientific Inc ....F....949 260-9900
16692 Hale Ave Ste A Irvine (92606) ***(P-22137)***
Speculative Product Design LLC ....F....650 462-9086
303 Bryant St Mountain View (94041) ***(P-10538)***
Speculative Product Design LLC (HQ) ....D....650 462-2040
177 Bovet Rd Ste 200 San Mateo (94402) ***(P-10539)***
Speed-O-Pin International ....F....562 433-4911
1401 Freeman Ave Long Beach (90804) ***(P-5212)***
Speedplay Inc ....E....858 453-4707
10151 Pacific Mesa Blvd # 107 San Diego (92121) ***(P-23657)***
Speedpress Sign Supply, Carlsbad *Also called Coplan & Coplan Inc* ***(P-14619)***
Speedskins Inc ....F....760 439-3119
2919 San Luis Rey Rd Oceanside (92058) ***(P-23658)***
Speedwear.com, Huntington Beach *Also called Gachupin Enterprises LLC* ***(P-7325)***
Speedy Bindery Inc ....E....619 275-0261
4386 Jutland Dr San Diego (92117) ***(P-7622)***
Speedy Circuits, Huntington Beach *Also called Coast To Coast Circuits Inc* ***(P-18455)***
Spellbound Development Group ....F....949 474-8577
17192 Gillette Ave Irvine (92614) ***(P-23123)***
Spellbound Entertainment, Irvine *Also called Spellbound Development Group* ***(P-23123)***
Spencer Home Decor, City of Industry *Also called Spencer N Enterprises LLC* ***(P-3750)***
Spencer N Enterprises LLC (HQ) ....D....909 895-8495
425 S Lemon Ave City of Industry (91789) ***(P-3750)***

ALPHABETIC

Employee Codes: A=Over 500 employees, B=251-500
C=101-250, D=51-100, E=20-50, F=10-19
2019 California
Manfacturers Register
© Mergent Inc. 1-800-342-5647
1289

Spenco Machine & Manufacturing ....F....951 699-5566
27556 Commerce Center Dr Temecula (92590) ***(P-16959)***
Spenuzza Inc (PA) ....C....951 281-1830
1128 Sherborn St Corona (92879) ***(P-16112)***
Spenuzza Inc ....E....626 358-8063
913 Oak Ave Duarte (91010) ***(P-16113)***
SPEP Acquisition Corp (PA) ....D....310 608-0693
4041 Via Oro Ave Long Beach (90810) ***(P-11994)***
Sphere Alliance Inc ....E....951 352-2400
3051 Myers St Riverside (92503) ***(P-7889)***
Spices Unlimited Inc ....F....831 636-3596
2339 Tech Pkwy Ste J Hollister (95023) ***(P-2672)***
Spidell Publishing Inc ....E....714 776-7850
1134 N Gilbert St Anaheim (92801) ***(P-6587)***
Spiegel's Jewelry Factory, North Hollywood *Also called Caretta Inc* ***(P-23248)***
Spigit Inc ....D....855 774-4480
275 Battery St Ste 1000 San Francisco (94111) ***(P-25206)***
Spike Chunsoft Inc ....F....562 786-5080
5000 Airport Plaza Dr # 230 Long Beach (90815) ***(P-25207)***
Spikey Wear, Monterey Park *Also called Miholin Inc* ***(P-3180)***
Spill Magic Inc ....E....714 557-2001
630 Young St Santa Ana (92705) ***(P-5337)***
Spin Products Inc ....E....909 590-7000
13878 Yorba Ave Chino (91710) ***(P-10384)***
Spin Shades Corporation ....E....805 650-4849
3115 Breaker Dr Ventura (93003) ***(P-17732)***
Spin Tek Machining Inc ....F....408 298-8223
540 Parrott St Ste A San Jose (95112) ***(P-16960)***
Spinal and Orthopedic Devices ....F....818 908-9000
5920 Noble Ave Van Nuys (91411) ***(P-22818)***
Spinalmotion Inc ....F....650 947-3472
201 San Antonio Cir # 115 Mountain View (94040) ***(P-22631)***
Spine View Inc ....D....510 490-1753
3167 Skyway Ct Fremont (94539) ***(P-22632)***
Spineex Inc ....F....510 573-1093
4046 Clipper Ct Fremont (94538) ***(P-22633)***
Spinelli Graphic Inc ....F....562 431-3232
10631 Bloomfield St Ste 2 Los Alamitos (90720) ***(P-7495)***
Spinergy Inc ....D....760 496-2121
1914 Palomar Oaks Way # 100 Carlsbad (92008) ***(P-21137)***
Spinmedia Group Inc ....C....323 203-1333
6464 W Sunset Blvd # 650 Los Angeles (90028) ***(P-6588)***
Spinner Toys & Gifts, San Diego *Also called Beejay LLC* ***(P-23410)***
Spintek Filtration Inc ....F....714 236-9190
10863 Portal Dr Los Alamitos (90720) ***(P-15364)***
Spira Manufacturing Corp ....E....818 764-8222
650 Jessie St San Fernando (91340) ***(P-9559)***
Spiracle Technology LLC ....F....714 418-1091
10601 Calle Lee Ste 190 Los Alamitos (90720) ***(P-22279)***
Spiracur Inc (PA) ....D....650 364-1544
1180 Bordeaux Dr Sunnyvale (94089) ***(P-22634)***
Spiral Ppr Tube & Core Co Inc ....E....562 801-9705
5200 Industry Ave Pico Rivera (90660) ***(P-5494)***
Spiral Water Technologies Inc ....F....415 259-4929
999 Andersen Dr Ste 140 San Rafael (94901) ***(P-16114)***
Spire Manufacturing Inc ....E....510 226-1070
49016 Milmont Dr Fremont (94538) ***(P-17491)***
Spirent Communications Inc (HQ) ....B....818 676-2300
27349 Agoura Rd Calabasas (91301) ***(P-18260)***
Spirent Communications Inc ....E....408 894-7015
2708 Orchard Pkwy Ste 20 San Jose (95134) ***(P-18261)***
Spirit Activewear, Vernon *Also called Spirit Clothing Company* ***(P-3503)***
Spirit Clothing Company ....E....213 784-0251
2211 E 37th St Vernon (90058) ***(P-3503)***
Spirit Foodservice Inc ....D....323 724-0503
5951 Rickenbacker Rd Commerce (90040) ***(P-10385)***
Spirit Sciences Usa Inc (PA) ....F....310 568-1030
6733 S Sepulveda Blvd # 108 Los Angeles (90045) ***(P-8389)***
Spirit Throws, Roseville *Also called Hudson & Company LLC* ***(P-3725)***
Spirit West Coast, Campbell *Also called Christian Music Today Inc* ***(P-5802)***
Spiritbrands, Commerce *Also called Spirit Foodservice Inc* ***(P-10385)***
Spiritual Counterfeits Prj Inc ....F....510 540-0300
2606 Dwight Way Berkeley (94704) ***(P-6261)***
Spitzlift, San Diego *Also called Hirok Inc* ***(P-14176)***
Splunk Inc (PA) ....C....415 848-8400
270 Brannan St San Francisco (94107) ***(P-25208)***
Spm, Anaheim *Also called Bace Manufacturing Inc* ***(P-9967)***
Spn Investments Inc ....E....562 777-1140
6481 Orangethorpe Ave # 12 Buena Park (90620) ***(P-23659)***
Spoety Cuts Corporation ....F....310 908-1512
6510 Wooster Ave Los Angeles (90056) ***(P-9044)***
Spooners Woodworks Inc ....D....858 679-9086
12460 Kirkham Ct Poway (92064) ***(P-5104)***
Sport Boat Trailers Inc ....F....209 892-5388
430 C St Patterson (95363) ***(P-21241)***
Sport Kites Inc ....F....714 998-6359
500 W Blueridge Ave Orange (92865) ***(P-20628)***
Sport Pins International Inc ....F....909 985-4549
888 Berry Ct Ste A Upland (91786) ***(P-23759)***
Sport Rock International Inc ....F....805 434-5474
450 Marquita Ave Paso Robles (93446) ***(P-23660)***
Sportrx Inc ....E....858 571-0240
5076 Santa Fe St Ste A San Diego (92109) ***(P-23124)***
Sports Hoop Inc ....F....626 387-6027
12669 Beryl Way Jurupa Valley (92509) ***(P-23661)***
Sports Medicine Info Network ....F....310 659-6889
8737 Beverly Blvd Ste 303 West Hollywood (90048) ***(P-6054)***
Sports Rack Vehicle Outfitters, Sacramento *Also called Bauer Industries* ***(P-11938)***
Sportscar, Corona Del Mar *Also called Pfanner Communications Inc* ***(P-6232)***
Sportscar International, Novato *Also called SCI Publishing Inc* ***(P-6254)***
Sportsco, San Bernardino *Also called All Sports Services Inc* ***(P-7228)***
Sportsman Steel Gun Safe, Long Beach *Also called Sportsmen Steel Safe Fabg Co* ***(P-13974)***
Sportsmen Steel Safe Fabg Co (PA) ....E....562 984-0244
6311 N Paramount Blvd Long Beach (90805) ***(P-13974)***
Sportsrobe Inc (PA) ....E....310 559-3999
8654 Hayden Pl Culver City (90232) ***(P-3188)***
Sposato John ....F....408 215-8727
257 Vera Ave Redwood City (94061) ***(P-18262)***
Spot On Treats, Santa Ana *Also called Balboa Acquisition LLC* ***(P-1182)***
Spotless Water Systems LLC ....F....858 530-9993
372 Coogan Way El Cajon (92020) ***(P-16115)***
Spotlite America Corporation (PA) ....E....310 829-0200
9937 Jefferson Blvd # 110 Culver City (90232) ***(P-10668)***
Spotlite Media Inc ....E....650 447-9135
7083 Hollywood Blvd Los Angeles (90028) ***(P-25209)***
Spotlite Power Corporation ....E....310 838-2367
9937 Jefferson Blvd # 110 Culver City (90232) ***(P-17644)***
Spoton Computing Inc ....E....650 293-7464
209 9th St Fl 3 San Francisco (94103) ***(P-25210)***
Spragg Industries Inc ....F....661 424-9673
20049 Crestview Dr Canyon Country (91351) ***(P-24252)***
Spragues Ready Mix, Irwindale *Also called Spragues Rock and Sand Company* ***(P-11184)***
Spragues Ready Mix Concrete, Simi Valley *Also called Spragues Rock and Sand Company* ***(P-11185)***
Spragues Rock and Sand Company (PA) ....E....626 445-2125
230 Longden Ave Irwindale (91706) ***(P-11184)***
Spragues Rock and Sand Company ....F....805 522-7010
5400 Bennett Rd Simi Valley (93063) ***(P-11185)***
Spray Enclosure Technologies ....E....909 419-7011
1427 N Linden Ave Rialto (92376) ***(P-12770)***
Spray Tech, Rialto *Also called Spray Enclosure Technologies* ***(P-12770)***
Spraying Devices Inc ....F....559 734-5555
447 E Caldwell Ave Visalia (93277) ***(P-14134)***
Sprayline Enterprises Inc ....E....909 627-8411
10774 Grand Ave Ontario (91762) ***(P-13663)***
Sprayline Manufacturing ....F....562 941-5313
10110 Greenleaf Ave Santa Fe Springs (90670) ***(P-15137)***
Spraytronics Inc ....E....408 988-3636
6001 Butler Ln Ste 204 Scotts Valley (95066) ***(P-13664)***
Spreadco Inc ....E....760 351-0747
803 Us Highway 78 Brawley (92227) ***(P-2905)***
Spreckels Sugar, Brawley *Also called Imperial Sugar Company* ***(P-1403)***
Spreckels Sugar Company Inc ....B....760 344-3110
395 W Keystone Rd Brawley (92227) ***(P-1404)***
Spring Delgau Inc ....F....951 371-1000
322 N Garfield Ave Corona (92882) ***(P-13802)***
Spring Industries, Ventura *Also called Juengermann Inc* ***(P-13750)***
Spring Mountain Vineyards Inc ....E....707 967-4188
2805 Spring Mountain Rd Saint Helena (94574) ***(P-1985)***
Springpudic, Los Angeles *Also called Cuevas Mattress Inc* ***(P-4858)***
Springs Industries Inc ....C....323 887-3920
5770 Peachtree St Commerce (90040) ***(P-3018)***
Sprint Copy Center Inc ....F....707 823-3900
175 N Main St Sebastopol (95472) ***(P-7114)***
Sprite Industries Incorporated ....E....951 735-1015
1791 Railroad St Corona (92880) ***(P-22021)***
Sprite Showers, Corona *Also called Sprite Industries Incorporated* ***(P-22021)***
Sprizzi Drink Co ....F....909 528-7779
897 Via Lata Ste C Colton (92324) ***(P-15978)***
Sprout Inc ....F....415 894-9629
475 Brannan St Ste 410 San Francisco (94107) ***(P-6589)***
Sproutling Inc ....F....415 323-3270
8 California St Ste 300 San Francisco (94111) ***(P-17996)***
SPS Inc ....F....714 632-7131
3000 E Miraloma Ave Anaheim (92806) ***(P-4424)***
SPS Studios Inc ....E....858 456-2336
7917 Ivanhoe Ave La Jolla (92037) ***(P-7568)***
SPS Technologies LLC ....B....714 545-9311
1224 E Warner Ave Santa Ana (92705) ***(P-23773)***
SPS Technologies LLC ....B....310 323-6222
1700 W 132nd St Gardena (90249) ***(P-13083)***
SPS Technologies LLC ....E....714 892-5571
12570 Knott St Garden Grove (92841) ***(P-13084)***
SPS Technologies LLC ....B....714 371-1925
1224 E Warner Ave Santa Ana (92705) ***(P-23774)***
SPS Technologies LLC ....D....562 426-9411
14800 S Figueroa St Gardena (90248) ***(P-13775)***
Spt Microtechnologies USA Inc ....E....408 571-1400
1150 Ringwood Ct San Jose (95131) ***(P-15031)***
Spun Products, Long Beach *Also called M L Z Inc* ***(P-13244)***
SPX Cooling Technologies Inc ....E....714 529-6080
550 Mercury Ln Brea (92821) ***(P-12423)***
SPX Corporation ....D....714 434-2576
17815 Newhope St Ste M Fountain Valley (92708) ***(P-12424)***
SPX Corporation ....F....714 634-3855
1515 S Harris Ct Anaheim (92806) ***(P-12425)***
SPX Corporation ....D....951 781-4484
1531 7th St Riverside (92507) ***(P-12426)***
SPX Flow Us LLC ....D....949 455-8150
26561 Rancho Pkwy S Lake Forest (92630) ***(P-14885)***
Spy Inc (PA) ....D....760 804-8420
1896 Rutherford Rd Carlsbad (92008) ***(P-23125)***
Spyder Manufacturing Inc ....F....714 528-8010
545 Porter Way Placentia (92870) ***(P-14135)***
Spyglass Entrmt Group LLC ....F....310 443-5800
245 N Beverly Dr Beverly Hills (90210) ***(P-23196)***

Spyke Inc..........E.......562 803-1700
12155 Pangborn Ave Downey (90241) ***(P-21138)***
Spyrus Inc (PA)..........E.......408 392-9131
103 Bonaventura Dr San Jose (95134) ***(P-15859)***
Squaglia Manufacturing (PA)..........E.......650 965-9644
275 Polaris Ave Mountain View (94043) ***(P-16961)***
Squamtech Inc..........F.......415 867-8300
2023 22nd St San Francisco (94107) ***(P-25211)***
Square Inc (PA)..........E.......415 375-3176
1455 Market St Ste 600 San Francisco (94103) ***(P-25212)***
Square Deal Mat Fctry & Uphl, Chico *Also called Square Deal Mattress Factory* ***(P-4890)***
Square Deal Mattress Factory..........E.......530 342-2510
1354 Humboldt Ave Chico (95928) ***(P-4890)***
Square H Brands Inc..........C.......323 267-4600
2731 S Soto St Vernon (90058) ***(P-528)***
Squarebar Inc..........F.......530 412-0209
1035 22nd Ave Unit 8 Oakland (94606) ***(P-8390)***
Sr Machining Inc..........F.......951 520-9486
692 Parkridge Ave Norco (92860) ***(P-16962)***
Sr Plastics Company LLC (PA)..........F.......951 520-9486
640 Parkridge Ave Norco (92860) ***(P-10386)***
Sr Plastics Company LLC..........E.......951 479-5394
692 Parkridge Ave Norco (92860) ***(P-10387)***
Sr2020 Inc..........E.......714 482-1922
3 Pointe Dr Ste 212 Brea (92821) ***(P-154)***
Sr3 Solutions LLC..........F.......818 255-3131
13136 Saticoy St North Hollywood (91605) ***(P-6055)***
Sra Oss Inc..........C.......408 855-8200
5201 Great America Pkwy # 419 Santa Clara (95054) ***(P-25213)***
SRC, Linden *Also called Stockton Rubber Mfgcoinc* ***(P-9680)***
SRC Milling Co LLC..........E.......916 363-4821
11350 Kiefer Blvd Sacramento (95830) ***(P-1533)***
Srco Inc..........F.......626 350-8321
2305 Merced Ave El Monte (91733) ***(P-16963)***
Sream Inc..........E.......951 245-6999
12869 Temescal Canyon Rd A Corona (92883) ***(P-10732)***
SRI Instruments, Torrance *Also called Scientific Repair Inc* ***(P-21650)***
Srl Apparel Inc..........E.......530 898-9525
2209 Park Ave Chico (95928) ***(P-2895)***
Srm Contracting & Paving, San Diego *Also called Superior Ready Mix Concrete LP* ***(P-11190)***
SRS, Sunnyvale *Also called Stanford Research Systems Inc* ***(P-22022)***
Srsb Inc..........F.......949 234-1881
5004 Cmino Escllo Ste 200 San Clemente (92673) ***(P-25214)***
Srss LLC..........F.......707 544-7777
1400 Airport Blvd Santa Rosa (95403) ***(P-12998)***
Ss Brewtech, Tustin *Also called CM Brewing Technologies* ***(P-16029)***
Ss Metal Fabricators..........F.......949 631-4272
1626 Ohms Way Costa Mesa (92627) ***(P-12246)***
Ssb Manufacturing Company..........C.......770 512-7700
20100 S Alameda St Compton (90221) ***(P-4891)***
SSC, Santa Clara *Also called Silicon Standard Corp* ***(P-19157)***
SSC Racing, Palm Desert *Also called Karbz Inc* ***(P-20380)***
Ssco Manufacturing Inc..........E.......619 628-1022
1245 30th St San Diego (92154) ***(P-14740)***
Sscor Inc..........F.......818 504-4054
11064 Randall St Sun Valley (91352) ***(P-22635)***
Ssdi, La Mirada *Also called Solid State Devices Inc* ***(P-19179)***
Ssg Alliance LLC (PA)..........F.......925 526-6050
2550 Smrsville Rd Unit 55 Brentwood (94513) ***(P-20079)***
Ssi, Lodi *Also called Scientific Specialties Inc* ***(P-9726)***
Ssi G Debbas Chocolatier LLC..........E.......559 294-2071
2794 N Larkin Ave Fresno (93727) ***(P-1474)***
Ssi Surfaces, Newbury Park *Also called Scientific Surface Inds Inc* ***(P-5099)***
SSS, Carlsbad *Also called Silk Screen Shirts Inc* ***(P-2894)***
SST, Newark *Also called Shotspotter Inc* ***(P-25171)***
Sst International, Downey *Also called Sst Technologies* ***(P-21659)***
Sst Technologies..........E.......562 803-3361
9801 Everest St Downey (90242) ***(P-21659)***
St Cyclewear/Gallop LLC..........F.......619 449-9191
1200 Billy Mitchell Dr D El Cajon (92020) ***(P-3189)***
St George Spirits Inc..........E.......510 769-1601
2601 Monarch St Alameda (94501) ***(P-1986)***
St John Knits Inc (HQ)..........C.......949 863-1171
17522 Armstrong Ave Irvine (92614) ***(P-3504)***
St John Knits Intl Inc (HQ)..........C.......949 863-1171
17622 Armstrong Ave Irvine (92614) ***(P-3505)***
St John Knits Intl Inc..........B.......949 399-8200
17622 Armstrong Ave Irvine (92614) ***(P-2855)***
ST Johnson Company LLC..........E.......510 652-6000
5160 Fulton Dr Fairfield (94534) ***(P-12090)***
St Jude Medical LLC..........E.......949 769-5000
2375 Morse Ave Irvine (92614) ***(P-8391)***
St Jude Medical LLC..........B.......408 738-4883
645 Almanor Ave Sunnyvale (94085) ***(P-22636)***
St Louis Post-Dispatch LLC..........E.......415 892-1516
1068 Machin Ave Novato (94945) ***(P-6056)***
St Louis Post-Dispatch LLC..........E.......707 762-4541
830 Petaluma Blvd N Petaluma (94952) ***(P-6057)***
St Louis Post-Dispatch LLC..........F.......661 763-3171
800 Center St Taft (93268) ***(P-6058)***
St Paul Brands, Garden Grove *Also called Probactive Biotech Inc* ***(P-7915)***
St Pierre Gonzalez Enterprises..........E.......714 491-2191
419 E La Palma Ave Anaheim (92801) ***(P-13665)***
St Supertec, Paramount *Also called Supertec Machinery Inc* ***(P-14415)***
St Supery Inc (HQ)..........E.......707 963-4507
8440 St Helena Hwy Rutherford (94573) ***(P-1987)***
STA Pharmaceutical US LLC..........E.......609 606-6499
6114 Nancy Ridge Dr San Diego (92121) ***(P-8392)***

STA-Brite Anodizing, Westminster *Also called STA-Brite-Ano* ***(P-13666)***
STA-Brite-Ano..........F.......323 581-1432
8602 Orwell Ave Westminster (92683) ***(P-13666)***
STA-Rite Industries LLC..........B.......714 371-1550
16261 Tisbury Cir Huntington Beach (92649) ***(P-15092)***
STA-Slim Products Inc..........F.......310 514-1155
600 N Pacific Ave San Pedro (90731) ***(P-23662)***
Staar Surgical Company (PA)..........C.......626 303-7902
1911 Walker Ave Monrovia (91016) ***(P-23126)***
Staar Surgical Company..........F.......626 303-7902
15102 Redhill Ave Tustin (92780) ***(P-23127)***
Stabile Plating Company Inc..........E.......626 339-9091
1150 E Edna Pl Covina (91724) ***(P-13509)***
Stablcor Technology Inc..........F.......714 375-6644
17011 Beach Blvd Ste 900 Huntington Beach (92647) ***(P-5495)***
Staccato, Vernon *Also called Atrevete Inc* ***(P-3214)***
Stack Labs Inc..........E.......503 453-5172
10052 Pasadena Ave Ste A Cupertino (95014) ***(P-17645)***
Stack Lighting, Cupertino *Also called Stack Labs Inc* ***(P-17645)***
Stack Plastics Inc..........E.......650 361-8600
3525 Haven Ave Menlo Park (94025) ***(P-10388)***
Stackla Inc..........D.......415 528-4910
33 New Montgomery St San Francisco (94105) ***(P-25215)***
Stackrox Inc..........E.......650 489-6769
700 E El Camino Real # 200 Mountain View (94040) ***(P-25216)***
Staco Switch, Irvine *Also called Staco Systems Inc* ***(P-17166)***
Staco Systems Inc (HQ)..........D.......949 297-8700
7 Morgan Irvine (92618) ***(P-17166)***
Stadco (PA)..........C.......323 227-8888
107 S Avenue 20 Los Angeles (90031) ***(P-14680)***
Stadium Printing Inc..........F.......951 371-3890
3700 Temescal Ave Norco (92860) ***(P-7115)***
Staffing Industry Analysts Inc..........E.......650 390-6200
1975 W El Cmno Rl 304 Mountain View (94040) ***(P-6590)***
Staffing Industry Report, Mountain View *Also called Staffing Industry Analysts Inc* ***(P-6590)***
Stafford Soap Candle Co..........F.......951 302-3476
S Pmb 130-31805 Temecula (92592) ***(P-10807)***
Stags Leap Wine Cellars..........C.......707 944-2020
5766 Silverado Trl NAPA (94558) ***(P-1988)***
Stailess Polishing Co., Oakland *Also called General Grinding Inc* ***(P-13415)***
Stainless Fixtures Inc..........E.......909 622-1615
1250 E Franklin Ave Pomona (91766) ***(P-5255)***
Stainless Industrial Companies..........D.......310 575-9400
11111 Santa Monica Blvd # 1120 Los Angeles (90025) ***(P-14572)***
Stainless Micro-Polish Inc..........F.......714 632-8903
1286 N Grove St Anaheim (92806) ***(P-13510)***
Stainless Process Systems Inc..........F.......805 483-7100
1650 Beacon Pl Oxnard (93033) ***(P-12247)***
Stainless Technologies LLC..........F.......559 651-0460
19425 W Grove Ave Visalia (93291) ***(P-25437)***
Stainless Works Inc..........F.......559 688-4310
201 E Owens Ave Tulare (93274) ***(P-25438)***
Stainless Works Mfg Inc..........E.......831 728-5097
225 Salinas Rd Bldg 5a Royal Oaks (95076) ***(P-14886)***
Stair Service, San Jose *Also called Simmons Stairways Inc* ***(P-4231)***
Stake Fastener, Chino *Also called Dupree Inc* ***(P-13067)***
Stalfab..........F.......831 786-1600
131 Algen Ln Watsonville (95076) ***(P-14887)***
Stalker Software Inc..........E.......415 569-2280
125 Park Pl Ste 210 Richmond (94801) ***(P-25217)***
Stama Winery LLC..........F.......209 727-3314
17521 N Davis Rd Lodi (95242) ***(P-1989)***
Stamats Communications Inc..........E.......800 358-0388
550 Montgomery St Ste 750 San Francisco (94111) ***(P-6394)***
Stamats Travel Group, San Francisco *Also called Stamats Communications Inc* ***(P-6394)***
Stan's San Frncsco Cheesecakes, San Francisco *Also called Stans Michegaas* ***(P-1323)***
Standard Armament, Glendale *Also called SAI Industries* ***(P-13690)***
Standard Bias Binding Co Inc..........E.......323 277-9763
4621 Pacific Blvd Vernon (90058) ***(P-3922)***
Standard Cognition Corp..........E.......201 707-7782
164 Townsend St Unit 9 San Francisco (94107) ***(P-25218)***
Standard Concrete Products (HQ)..........E.......310 829-4537
13550 Live Oak Ln Baldwin Park (91706) ***(P-11186)***
Standard Crystal Corp..........F.......626 443-2121
17626 Barber Ave Artesia (90701) ***(P-19734)***
Standard Filter Corporation (PA)..........E.......323 663-2184
5928 Balfour Ct Carlsbad (92008) ***(P-15176)***
Standard Homeopathic Co (PA)..........D.......310 768-0700
204 W 131st St Los Angeles (90061) ***(P-8393)***
Standard Homeopathic Co..........E.......424 224-4127
108 W Walnut St Fl 1 Gardena (90248) ***(P-8394)***
Standard Industries Inc..........D.......209 931-1277
3301 Navone Rd Stockton (95215) ***(P-4602)***
Standard Lumber Company Inc (HQ)..........E.......559 651-2037
8009 W Doe Ave Visalia (93291) ***(P-4508)***
Standard Metal Products Inc..........E.......310 532-9861
1541 W 132nd St Gardena (90249) ***(P-13511)***
Standard Tool & Die Co, Los Angeles *Also called Stadco* ***(P-14680)***
Standard Wire & Cable Co (PA)..........E.......310 609-1811
2050 E Vista Bella Way Rancho Dominguez (90220) ***(P-11676)***
Standardvision LLC..........E.......323 222-3630
3370 N San Fernando Rd # 206 Los Angeles (90065) ***(P-23980)***
Standish Precision Products, Fallbrook *Also called Fallbrook Industries Inc* ***(P-13205)***
Standridge Granite Corporation..........E.......562 946-6334
9437 Santa Fe Springs Rd Santa Fe Springs (90670) ***(P-11281)***
Staness Jonekos Entps Inc..........E.......818 606-2710
4000 W Magnolia Blvd D Burbank (91505) ***(P-2673)***
Stanford Advanced Materials, Lake Forest *Also called Oceania International LLC* ***(P-11635)***

ALPHABETIC

Employee Codes: A=Over 500 employees, B=251-500
C=101-250, D=51-100, E=20-50, F=10-19
2019 California
Manfacturers Register
© Mergent Inc. 1-800-342-5647
1291

Stanford Daily Publishing Corp...E...650 723-2555
456 Panama Mall Stanford (94305) ***(P-6059)***
Stanford Daily, The, Stanford *Also called Stanford Daily Publishing Corp* ***(P-6059)***
Stanford Furniture Mfg Inc...E...916 387-5300
5851 Alder Ave Ste A Sacramento (95828) ***(P-5256)***
Stanford Humanities Review, Stanford *Also called Leland Stanford Junior Univ* ***(P-6518)***
Stanford Materials Corporation...F...949 380-7362
23661 Birtcher Dr Lake Forest (92630) ***(P-7747)***
Stanford Mu Corporation...E...310 605-2888
20725 Annalee Ave Carson (90746) ***(P-21197)***
Stanford Research Systems Inc...C...408 744-9040
1290 Reamwood Ave Ste D Sunnyvale (94089) ***(P-22022)***
Stanford Sign & Awning Inc (PA)...E...619 423-6200
2556 Faivre St Chula Vista (91911) ***(P-23981)***
Stanford University Libraries, Stanford *Also called Leland Stanford Junior Univ* ***(P-6517)***
Stanford University Press, Redwood City *Also called Leland Stanford Junior Univ* ***(P-5912)***
Stang Industrial Products, Corona *Also called Stang Industries Inc* ***(P-24253)***
Stang Industries Inc...F...714 556-0222
2616 Research Dr Ste B Corona (92882) ***(P-24253)***
Stangenes Industries Inc (PA)...C...650 855-9926
1052 E Meadow Cir Palo Alto (94303) ***(P-19365)***
Stanislaus Distributing Co, Modesto *Also called Varni Brothers Corporation* ***(P-2231)***
Stanislaus Food Products Co (PA)...C...209 548-3537
1202 D St Modesto (95354) ***(P-859)***
Stanley Access Tech LLC...C...909 628-9272
4230 E Airport Dr Ste 107 Ontario (91761) ***(P-11911)***
Stanley Electric Motor Co Inc...E...209 464-7321
1520 E Miner Ave Stockton (95205) ***(P-25467)***
Stans Michegaas (PA)...E...415 839-8442
1022 Revere Ave San Francisco (94124) ***(P-1323)***
Stantec Consulting Svcs Inc...F...916 434-5062
1245 Fiddyment Rd Lincoln (95648) ***(P-16116)***
Stanton Carpet Corp...F...562 945-8711
2209 Pine Ave Manhattan Beach (90266) ***(P-2942)***
Stanza, San Francisco *Also called Spoton Computing Inc* ***(P-25210)***
Stanzino Inc...C...213 746-8822
16325 S Avalon Blvd Gardena (90248) ***(P-2764)***
Staples Inc...F...213 623-4395
731 S Spring St Ste 300 Los Angeles (90014) ***(P-3506)***
Star Ave...E...213 623-5799
514 E 8th St Ste 500 Los Angeles (90014) ***(P-3507)***
Star Building Products, Fresno *Also called E-Z Haul Ready Mix Inc* ***(P-11103)***
Star Building Systems, Lockeford *Also called Robertson-Ceco II Corporation* ***(P-12959)***
Star Concrete, San Jose *Also called Sandman Inc* ***(P-10998)***
Star Die Casting Inc...D...562 698-0627
12209 Slauson Ave Santa Fe Springs (90670) ***(P-11995)***
Star Finishes Inc...F...559 261-1076
40429 Brickyard Dr Madera (93636) ***(P-13512)***
Star Fish Inc...F...415 468-6688
410 Talbert St Daly City (94014) ***(P-3923)***
Star Lion, Los Angeles *Also called Starlion Inc* ***(P-3060)***
Star Milling Co...C...951 657-3143
24067 Water Ave Perris (92570) ***(P-1167)***
Star News Publishing Co Inc...F...619 427-3000
296 Third Ave Chula Vista (91910) ***(P-6060)***
Star One Investments LLC...F...916 858-1178
1304 Buttercup Ct Roseville (95661) ***(P-11996)***
Star Pacific Inc...E...510 471-6555
27462 Sunrise Farm Rd Los Altos Hills (94022) ***(P-8610)***
Star Plastic Design...D...310 530-7119
25914 President Ave Harbor City (90710) ***(P-10389)***
Star Products...E...408 727-8421
312 Brokaw Rd Santa Clara (95050) ***(P-16964)***
Star Racecars, Pacoima *Also called Valley Motor Center Inc* ***(P-20181)***
Star Ring Inc...D...818 773-4900
4429 Summerglen Ct Moorpark (93021) ***(P-23319)***
Star Route LLC...F...805 405-8510
4522 Henley Ct Westlake Village (91361) ***(P-7569)***
Star Sanitation Services...F...831 754-6794
4 Harris Rd Salinas (93908) ***(P-10390)***
Star Shield Solutions LLC...D...866 662-4477
4315 Santa Ana St Ontario (91761) ***(P-10391)***
Star Stainless Screw Co...F...510 489-6569
30150 Ahern Ave Union City (94587) ***(P-11423)***
Star Tool & Engineering Co Inc...E...510 742-0500
49235 Milmont Dr Fremont (94538) ***(P-16965)***
Star Trac, Irvine *Also called Core Industries Inc* ***(P-23544)***
Star-Kist, Carson *Also called Big Heart Pet Brands* ***(P-789)***
Star-Luck Enterprise Inc...F...661 665-9999
11807 Harrington St Bakersfield (93311) ***(P-21660)***
Starco Enterprises Inc (PA)...D...323 266-7111
3137 E 26th St Vernon (90058) ***(P-15032)***
Stardust Diamond Corp...F...213 239-9999
550 S Hill St Ste 1420 Los Angeles (90013) ***(P-23348)***
Starix Technology Inc...E...949 387-8120
9120 Irvine Center Dr # 200 Irvine (92618) ***(P-18263)***
Stark Awning & Canvas, Chula Vista *Also called Stark Mfg Co* ***(P-3812)***
Stark Mfg Co...E...619 425-5880
76 Broadway Chula Vista (91910) ***(P-3812)***
Starled Inc...F...310 603-0403
2059 E Del Amo Blvd Rancho Dominguez (90220) ***(P-19735)***
Starlineoem Inc...F...949 342-8889
3183 Airway Ave Ste 112f Costa Mesa (92626) ***(P-17122)***
Starlion Inc...E...323 233-8823
706 E 32nd St Los Angeles (90011) ***(P-3060)***
Starmont Winery, Saint Helena *Also called Merryvale Vineyards LLC* ***(P-1877)***
Starr Design Fabrics Inc...F...530 467-5121
440 Pig Aly Etna (96027) ***(P-2918)***
Starscroll, Los Angeles *Also called Twelve Signs Inc* ***(P-6275)***
Starship Worldwide LLC...F...760 727-1190
3030 Enterprise Ct Ste C Vista (92081) ***(P-4968)***
Starview Inc...E...406 890-5910
2841 Junction Ave Ste 110 San Jose (95134) ***(P-25219)***
Stason Pharmaceuticals Inc (PA)...E...949 380-0752
11 Morgan Irvine (92618) ***(P-8395)***
Stat Clinical Systems Inc...F...510 705-8700
2560 9th St Ste 317 Berkeley (94710) ***(P-25220)***
Stat Systems, Berkeley *Also called Stat Clinical Systems Inc* ***(P-25220)***
State Hornet...D...916 278-6583
6000 J St Sacramento (95819) ***(P-6061)***
State Ready Mix Inc...E...805 647-2817
3127 Los Angeles Ave Oxnard (93036) ***(P-11187)***
State Ready Mix Inc (PA)...E...805 647-2817
1011 Azahar St Ste 1 Ventura (93004) ***(P-11188)***
Statek Corporation (HQ)...D...714 639-7810
512 N Main St Orange (92868) ***(P-19736)***
Stateside Merchants LLC...E...424 251-5190
5813 Washington Blvd Culver City (90232) ***(P-3066)***
Statewide Distributors, Ontario *Also called USA Sales Inc* ***(P-2710)***
Statewide Safety and Signs I...B...714 468-1919
522 Lindon Ln Nipomo (93444) ***(P-18367)***
Stats Chippac Inc (HQ)...E...510 979-8000
46429 Landing Pkwy Fremont (94538) ***(P-19187)***
Stats Chippac Test Svcs Inc...E...858 228-4084
9710 Scranton Rd Ste 360 San Diego (92121) ***(P-19188)***
Stats Chippac Test Svcs Inc (HQ)...F...510 979-8000
46429 Landing Pkwy Fremont (94538) ***(P-19189)***
Statue Factory LLC...E...415 468-4870
10 Industrial Way Brisbane (94005) ***(P-11372)***
Status Collection & Co Inc...F...310 432-7788
8383 Wilshire Blvd # 112 Beverly Hills (90211) ***(P-23320)***
Stauber Prfmce Ingredients (HQ)...C...714 441-3900
4120 N Palm St Fullerton (92835) ***(P-7973)***
Stavatti Industries Ltd...D...651 238-5369
1443 S Gage St San Bernardino (92408) ***(P-8)***
Stci, Rancho Cucamonga *Also called Superior Tank Co Inc* ***(P-12431)***
Steady Clothing Inc...F...714 444-2058
1711 Newport Cir Santa Ana (92705) ***(P-3190)***
Steadymed Therapeutics Inc...F...925 361-7111
2603 Camino Ramon Ste 350 San Ramon (94583) ***(P-8396)***
Stealth Security Inc...F...844 978-3258
100 S Murphy Ave Ste 300 Sunnyvale (94086) ***(P-25221)***
Stearns Corporation...E...805 582-2710
2130 Ward Ave Simi Valley (93065) ***(P-8848)***
Stearns Park...E...562 570-1685
4520 E 23rd St Long Beach (90815) ***(P-5029)***
Stearns Product Dev Corp (PA)...D...951 657-0379
20281 Harvill Ave Perris (92570) ***(P-15365)***
Stec Inc (HQ)...B...415 222-9996
3355 Michelson Dr Ste 100 Irvine (92612) ***(P-15612)***
Stec International Holding Inc...D...949 476-1180
3001 Daimler St Santa Ana (92705) ***(P-15613)***
Stecher Enterprises Inc...F...714 484-6900
8536 Central Ave Stanton (90680) ***(P-13803)***
Steecon Inc...F...714 895-5313
5362 Indl Dr Huntington Beach (92649) ***(P-20937)***
Steel Products International, Los Angeles *Also called Precision Steel Products Inc* ***(P-12721)***
Steel Services Co, Vernon *Also called S S Schaffer Co Inc* ***(P-14408)***
Steel Structures Inc...E...559 673-8021
28777 Avenue 15 1/2 Madera (93638) ***(P-12427)***
Steel Toe Enterprises...F...310 828-9677
967 W Hyde Park Blvd Inglewood (90302) ***(P-12999)***
Steel Unlimited Inc (PA)...D...909 873-1222
3200 Myers St Riverside (92503) ***(P-12428)***
Steel Works Etc, Newbury Park *Also called Millworks Etc Inc* ***(P-12335)***
Steelcase Inc...B...415 865-0261
111 Rhode Island St San Francisco (94103) ***(P-5001)***
Steelcase Inc...B...619 671-1040
7510 Airway Rd Ste 7 San Diego (92154) ***(P-4969)***
Steelclad Inc...E...714 529-0277
2664 Saturn St Ste A Brea (92821) ***(P-280)***
Steelco USA, Chino *Also called West Coast Steel & Proc LLC* ***(P-11530)***
Steelcraft West...F...909 548-2696
14575 Yorba Ave Chino (91710) ***(P-23337)***
Steeldeck Inc...E...323 290-2100
3339 Exposition Pl Los Angeles (90018) ***(P-24254)***
Steeldyne Industries...E...714 630-6200
2871 E La Cresta Ave Anaheim (92806) ***(P-12771)***
Steele Wines Inc...E...707 279-9475
4350 Thomas Dr Kelseyville (95451) ***(P-1990)***
Steeler Inc...F...916 483-3600
2901 Orange Grove Ave North Highlands (95660) ***(P-12772)***
Steelscape Inc...F...909 987-4711
11200 Arrow Rte Rancho Cucamonga (91730) ***(P-13667)***
Steico Industries Inc...C...760 438-8015
1814 Ord Way Oceanside (92056) ***(P-13281)***
Stein Industries Inc (PA)...E...714 522-4560
4005 Artesia Ave Fullerton (92833) ***(P-12773)***
Steinbeck Brewing Company...D...510 888-0695
1082 B St Hayward (94541) ***(P-1626)***
Steiner & Mateer Inc...E...562 464-9082
8333 Secura Way Santa Fe Springs (90670) ***(P-4235)***
Steinhausen Inc...F...661 702-1400
28478 Westinghouse Pl Valencia (91355) ***(P-23349)***
Stell Industries Inc...E...951 369-8777
1477 Davril Cir Corona (92880) ***(P-12962)***
Stella Carakasi, Berkeley *Also called Two Star Dog Inc* ***(P-3343)***

Mergent e-mail: customerrelations@mergent.com
1292
2019 California
Manufacturers Register
(P-0000) Products & Services Section entry number
(PA)=Parent Co (HQ)=Headquarters (DH)=Div Headquarters

Stella Cheese, Tulare *Also called Saputo Cheese USA Inc* ***(P-599)***
Stella Fashions Inc ....E....213 746-6889
1015 Crocker St Ste Q04 Los Angeles (90021) ***(P-3508)***
Stellar Biotechnologies Inc ....F....805 488-2147
332 E Scott St Port Hueneme (93041) ***(P-8397)***
Stellar Exploration Inc ....F....805 459-1425
835 Airport Dr San Luis Obispo (93401) ***(P-21170)***
Stellarvue ....F....530 823-7796
11820 Kemper Rd Auburn (95603) ***(P-22138)***
Stem Inc ....C....415 937-7836
100 Rollins Rd Millbrae (94030) ***(P-21854)***
Stem Consultants Inc ....F....612 987-8008
645 Chestnut Ave Apt 202 Long Beach (90802) ***(P-21694)***
Stemrad Inc ....F....650 933-3377
228 Hamilton Ave Fl 3 Palo Alto (94301) ***(P-22819)***
Stencil Master Inc ....F....408 428-9695
780 Charcot Ave San Jose (95131) ***(P-23722)***
Step Mobile Inc ....F....203 913-9229
2765 Sand Hill Rd Ste 201 Menlo Park (94025) ***(P-25222)***
Step Tools Unlimited Inc ....F....408 988-8898
3233 De La Cruz Blvd C Santa Clara (95054) ***(P-14681)***
Stepan Company ....E....714 776-9870
1208 N Patt St Anaheim (92801) ***(P-7890)***
Steps Apparel Group Inc (PA) ....E....323 261-2233
1105 S Boyle Ave Los Angeles (90023) ***(P-3509)***
Steps Mobile Inc ....F....408 806-5178
2035 5th St Davis (95618) ***(P-25223)***
Stepstone Inc (PA) ....E....310 327-7474
17025 S Main St Gardena (90248) ***(P-11006)***
Stepstone Inc ....E....310 327-7474
13238 S Figueroa St Los Angeles (90061) ***(P-11007)***
Steril-Aire Inc ....E....818 565-1128
2840 N Lima St Burbank (91504) ***(P-15177)***
Steripax Inc ....E....714 892-8811
5412 Research Dr Huntington Beach (92649) ***(P-5538)***
Steris Corporation ....F....800 614-6789
324 Martin Ave Santa Clara (95050) ***(P-22820)***
Steris Corporation ....D....858 586-1166
9020 Activity Rd Ste D San Diego (92126) ***(P-20080)***
Sterisyn Inc ....E....805 991-9694
11969 Challenger Ct Moorpark (93021) ***(P-8398)***
Sterling Foods, Union City *Also called Caravan Trading Company* ***(P-1218)***
Sterling Pacific Meat Co., Commerce *Also called Interstate Meat Co Inc* ***(P-14860)***
Sterling Shutters, Costa Mesa *Also called Pinecraft Custom Shutters Inc* ***(P-4213)***
Sterling Vineyards Inc (PA) ....E....707 942-3300
1111 Dunaweal Ln Calistoga (94515) ***(P-1991)***
Sterling Vineyards Inc ....E....707 252-7410
1105 Oak Knoll Ave NAPA (94558) ***(P-1992)***
Sterling Vineyards Inc ....F....707 942-9602
3690 Santa Lina Hwy Calistoga (94515) ***(P-1993)***
Sterno Group LLC (HQ) ....E....800 669-6699
1880 Compton Ave Ste 101 Corona (92881) ***(P-16117)***
Sterno Products LLC (HQ) ....E....951 682-9600
1880 Compton Ave Ste 101 Corona (92881) ***(P-16118)***
Sternocandlelamp, Corona *Also called Sterno Products LLC* ***(P-16118)***
Steve and Cynthia Kizanis ....F....510 352-2832
2483 Washington Ave San Leandro (94577) ***(P-4353)***
Steve Bruner ....E....707 744-1103
81 Hwy 175 Hopland (95449) ***(P-4236)***
Steve Leshner Clear Systems ....F....818 764-9223
13438 Wyandotte St North Hollywood (91605) ***(P-10392)***
Steve Morris ....F....707 822-8537
1500 Glendale Dr McKinleyville (95519) ***(P-4015)***
Steve Morris Logging & Contg, McKinleyville *Also called Steve Morris* ***(P-4015)***
Steve Rock & Ready Mix ....F....916 966-1600
5044 Osgood Way Fair Oaks (95628) ***(P-11189)***
Steve Zappetini & Son Inc ....E....415 454-2511
885 Penny Royal Ln San Rafael (94903) ***(P-12894)***
Steven Handelman Studios (PA) ....E....805 884-9070
716 N Milpas St Santa Barbara (93103) ***(P-11504)***
Steven Kent LLC ....E....925 243-6442
5443 Tesla Rd Livermore (94550) ***(P-1994)***
Steven Label Corporation ....F....562 906-2612
9046 Sorensen Ave Santa Fe Springs (90670) ***(P-7496)***
Steven Label Corporation ....F....562 698-9971
11926 Burke St Santa Fe Springs (90670) ***(P-7497)***
Steven Madden Ltd ....D....323 656-0012
938 N Fairfax Ave West Hollywood (90046) ***(P-10484)***
Steven Madden Ltd ....D....818 713-9681
6600 Topanga Canyon Blvd # 98 Canoga Park (91303) ***(P-10485)***
Steven Madden Ltd ....D....661 753-9510
24201 Valencia Blvd # 3506 Santa Clarita (91355) ***(P-10486)***
Steven Madden Ltd ....D....619 690-9761
4345 Camino De La Plz San Diego (92173) ***(P-10487)***
Steven Madden Ltd ....D....818 205-9563
14006 Riverside Dr Sherman Oaks (91423) ***(P-10488)***
Steven Madden Ltd ....D....323 346-0205
100 Citadel Dr Commerce (90040) ***(P-10489)***
Steven Madden Ltd ....D....909 393-7575
6725 Kimball Ave Chino (91708) ***(P-10490)***
Steven Rhoades Ceramic Designs ....F....949 250-1076
17595 Harvard Ave Ste C Irvine (92614) ***(P-10836)***
Steven Varrati ....F....209 545-0107
5237 American Ave Modesto (95356) ***(P-16966)***
Stevens, M Dancewear & Design, Los Angeles *Also called M Stevens Inc* ***(P-3458)***
Steves Plating Corporation ....C....818 842-2184
3111 N San Fernando Blvd Burbank (91504) ***(P-5168)***
Steward Terra Inc ....E....619 713-0028
4323 Palm Ave La Mesa (91941) ***(P-17123)***
Stewart & Jasper Marketing Inc (PA) ....C....209 862-9600
3500 Shiells Rd Newman (95360) ***(P-1504)***
Stewart & Jasper Orchards, Newman *Also called Stewart & Jasper Marketing Inc* ***(P-1504)***
Stewart Audio (HQ) ....F....209 588-8111
100 W El Camino Real # 72 Mountain View (94040) ***(P-19737)***
Stewart Filmscreen Corp (PA) ....C....310 326-1422
1161 Sepulveda Blvd Torrance (90502) ***(P-23197)***
Stewart Tool Company ....D....916 635-8321
3647 Omec Cir Rancho Cordova (95742) ***(P-14682)***
Stewart/Walker Company, Tracy *Also called Consolidated Container Co LLC* ***(P-10038)***
Stg Machine, Santa Clara *Also called James Stout* ***(P-16614)***
Stic-Adhesive Products Co Inc ....C....323 268-2956
3950 Medford St Los Angeles (90063) ***(P-9172)***
Sticker City, Sherman Oaks *Also called Vpro Inc* ***(P-24002)***
Sticker Hub Inc ....F....714 912-8457
1452 Manhattan Ave Fullerton (92831) ***(P-7498)***
Stico, San Diego *Also called Solar Turbines Intl Co* ***(P-14007)***
Stiers Rv Centers LLC ....F....661 254-6000
25410 The Old Rd Santa Clarita (91381) ***(P-21242)***
Stigtec Manufacturing LLC ....F....760 744-7239
1125 Linda Vista Dr # 110 San Marcos (92078) ***(P-16967)***
Stiles Custom Metal Inc ....D....209 538-3667
1885 Kinser Rd Ceres (95307) ***(P-12349)***
Stiles Paint Manufacturing Inc ....F....510 887-8868
21595 Curtis St Hayward (94545) ***(P-8944)***
Stillhouse LLC ....E....323 498-1111
8201 Beverly Blvd Ste 300 Los Angeles (90048) ***(P-2077)***
Stines Machine Inc ....E....760 599-9955
2481 Coral St Vista (92081) ***(P-16968)***
Stinger Solar Kits, San Diego *Also called Maddox Defense Inc* ***(P-3953)***
Stingray Shields Corp ....F....619 325-9003
Stingray Shields 16870 W San Diego (92127) ***(P-22821)***
Stion Corporation (PA) ....D....408 284-7200
333 S Grand Ave Ste 4070 Los Angeles (90071) ***(P-19190)***
Stir ....F....626 657-0918
2210 Lincoln Ave Pasadena (91103) ***(P-20081)***
Stir Foods LLC ....E....714 871-9231
1820 E Walnut Ave Fullerton (92831) ***(P-1017)***
Stir Foods LLC (PA) ....C....714 637-6050
1581 N Main St Orange (92867) ***(P-1018)***
Stirworks Inc ....E....800 657-2427
2010 Lincoln Ave Pasadena (91103) ***(P-10581)***
Stitch and Hide LLC ....F....310 377-6912
4 Bowie Rd Rolling Hills (90274) ***(P-10465)***
Stitch City Industries Inc (PA) ....F....562 408-6144
11823 Slauson Ave Ste 31 Santa Fe Springs (90670) ***(P-14780)***
Stitch Factory ....F....310 523-3337
120 W 131st St Los Angeles (90061) ***(P-3863)***
Stitch Industries Inc ....E....310 977-5556
6055 E Wash Blvd Ste 900 Commerce (90040) ***(P-4813)***
Stitch Service, Los Angeles *Also called Stitch Factory* ***(P-3863)***
Stj Orthotic Services Inc ....E....951 279-5650
225 Benjamin Dr Ste 103 Corona (92879) ***(P-22822)***
Stl Fabrication Inc ....F....909 823-5033
10207 Elm Ave Fontana (92335) ***(P-12248)***
Stm Networks Inc ....E....949 273-6800
2 Faraday Irvine (92618) ***(P-18264)***
Stm Wireless, Irvine *Also called Stm Networks Inc* ***(P-18264)***
Stmicroelectronics Inc ....E....949 347-0717
85 Enterprise Ste 300 Aliso Viejo (92656) ***(P-19191)***
Stmicroelectronics Inc ....E....408 919-8400
2755 Great America Way Santa Clara (95054) ***(P-19192)***
Sto-Kar Enterprises ....E....818 886-5600
1112 Arroyo St Ste 2 San Fernando (91340) ***(P-12249)***
Stockon Mailing & Printing ....F....209 466-6741
4133 Postal Ave Stockton (95204) ***(P-7116)***
Stockton Propeller Inc ....F....209 982-4000
2478 Wilcox Rd Stockton (95215) ***(P-20938)***
Stockton Rubber Mfgcoinc ....E....209 887-1172
5023 N Flood Rd Linden (95236) ***(P-9680)***
Stockton Tri-Industries Inc ....D....209 948-9701
2141 E Anderson St Stockton (95205) ***(P-14289)***
Stokes Ladders Inc ....F....707 279-4306
4545 Renfro Dr Kelseyville (95451) ***(P-13975)***
Stoll Metalcraft Inc ....C....661 295-0401
24808 Anza Dr Valencia (91355) ***(P-12774)***
Stolo Cabinets Inc (PA) ....E....714 529-7303
860 Challenger St Brea (92821) ***(P-4970)***
Stolo Custom Cabinets, Brea *Also called Stolo Cabinets Inc* ***(P-4970)***
Stolpman Vineyards LLC (PA) ....F....805 736-5000
2434 Alamo Pintado Rd Los Olivos (93441) ***(P-1995)***
Stolpman Vineyards LLC ....E....805 736-5000
1700 Industrial Way B Lompoc (93436) ***(P-1996)***
Stone Boat Yard Inc ....F....510 523-3030
2517 Blanding Ave Alameda (94501) ***(P-21064)***
Stone Bridge Cellars Inc (PA) ....D....707 963-2745
200 Taplin Rd Saint Helena (94574) ***(P-1997)***
Stone Candles, Santa Monica *Also called Ecolight Inc* ***(P-24086)***
Stone Edge Farm, Sonoma *Also called Stone Edge Winery LLC* ***(P-1998)***
Stone Edge Winery LLC ....F....707 935-6520
19330 Carriger Rd Sonoma (95476) ***(P-1998)***
Stone Harbor Inc ....F....323 277-2777
5015 District Blvd Vernon (90058) ***(P-3019)***
Stone Impressions, San Diego *Also called Photostone LLC* ***(P-14824)***
Stone Manufacturing Company, Gardena *Also called Tomorrows Heirlooms Inc* ***(P-12001)***
Stone Merchants LLC ....D....310 471-1815
889 Linda Flora Dr Los Angeles (90049) ***(P-11282)***
Stone Publishing Inc (PA) ....D....408 450-7910
2549 Scott Blvd Santa Clara (95050) ***(P-6591)***

ALPHABETIC

Employee Codes: A=Over 500 employees, B=251-500
C=101-250, D=51-100, E=20-50, F=10-19
2019 California
Manfacturers Register
© Mergent Inc. 1-800-342-5647
1293

Stone Truss LLC (PA) ....F....951 255-6958
507 Jones Rd Oceanside (92058) ***(P-4425)***
Stone Valley Materials LLC ....F....951 681-7830
3500b Pyrite St Riverside (92509) ***(P-383)***
Stone Yard Inc ....E....858 586-1580
8980 Crestmar Pt San Diego (92121) ***(P-4920)***
Stonecrop Technologies LLC ....E....781 659-0007
103 H St Ste B Petaluma (94952) ***(P-18265)***
Stonecushion Inc (PA) ....E....707 433-1911
1400 Lytton Springs Rd Healdsburg (95448) ***(P-1999)***
Stoneside LLC ....E....650 422-2154
228 Hamilton Ave Ste 300 Palo Alto (94301) ***(P-5213)***
Stoneware Design Co ....F....562 432-8145
5332 Polis Dr La Palma (90623) ***(P-10837)***
Stoneybrook Publishing Inc ....E....858 674-4600
16772 W Bernardo Dr San Diego (92127) ***(P-6395)***
Stony Apparel Corp (PA) ....C....323 981-9080
1500 S Evergreen Ave Los Angeles (90023) ***(P-3510)***
Stony Point Rock Quarry Inc (PA) ....F....707 795-1775
7171 Stony Point Rd Cotati (94931) ***(P-384)***
Stop Look Plastics Inc, La Habra *Also called Stop-Look Sign Co Intl Inc* ***(P-9729)***
Stop Staring Designs ....E....213 627-1480
1151 Goodrick Dr Tehachapi (93561) ***(P-3337)***
Stop-Look Sign Co Intl Inc ....F....562 690-7576
401 Commercial Way La Habra (90631) ***(P-9729)***
Storage and Sanitation, Fontana *Also called National Cnstr Rentals Inc* ***(P-19349)***
Storm Industries Inc (PA) ....D....310 534-5232
23223 Normandie Ave Torrance (90501) ***(P-14107)***
Storm Manufacturing, Torrance *Also called FCkingston Co* ***(P-13716)***
Storm Manufacturing Group Inc ....D....310 326-8287
23201 Normandie Ave Torrance (90501) ***(P-13734)***
Storm8 Inc ....F....650 596-8600
2400 Bridge Pkwy 2 Redwood City (94065) ***(P-25224)***
Storm8 Entertainment, Redwood City *Also called Storm8 Inc* ***(P-25224)***
Stormpath, San Mateo *Also called Okta Inc* ***(P-24981)***
Storopack Inc ....E....408 435-1095
2210 Junction Ave San Jose (95131) ***(P-9730)***
Storopack Inc ....E....562 803-1584
12007 Woodruff Ave Downey (90241) ***(P-7891)***
Storus Corporation ....F....925 322-8700
3266 Buskirk Ave Pleasant Hill (94523) ***(P-11997)***
Stoughton Printing Co ....E....626 961-3678
130 N Sunset Ave City of Industry (91744) ***(P-7117)***
Stracon Inc ....F....949 851-2288
1672 Kaiser Ave Ste 1 Irvine (92614) ***(P-20082)***
Strada Wheels Inc ....F....626 336-1634
560 S Magnolia Ave Ontario (91762) ***(P-11424)***
Strafford Intl Group Inc ....F....619 446-6960
877 Island Ave Unit 704 San Diego (92101) ***(P-5169)***
Strahmcolor ....F....415 459-5409
3000 Kerner Blvd San Rafael (94901) ***(P-7118)***
Straight Down Clothing Co, San Luis Obispo *Also called Straight Down Sportswear* ***(P-3191)***
Straight Down Sportswear (PA) ....E....805 543-3086
625 Clarion Ct San Luis Obispo (93401) ***(P-3191)***
Straightline Mechanical Inc ....F....714 204-0940
1051 E 6th St Santa Ana (92701) ***(P-13776)***
Strand Art Company Inc ....E....714 777-0444
4700 E Hunter Ave Anaheim (92807) ***(P-10393)***
Strand Energy Company ....C....562 944-9580
10350 Heritage Park Dr Santa Fe Springs (90670) ***(P-76)***
Strand Products Inc ....E....805 568-0304
721 E Yanonali St Santa Barbara (93103) ***(P-2980)***
Strand Products Inc (PA) ....E....805 568-0304
725 E Yanonali St Santa Barbara (93103) ***(P-23055)***
Strat Edge, Santee *Also called Stratedge Corporation* ***(P-19194)***
Strata Forest Products Inc (PA) ....E....714 751-0800
2600 S Susan St Santa Ana (92704) ***(P-4067)***
Strata Technologies ....E....714 368-9785
1800 Irvine Blvd Ste 205 Tustin (92780) ***(P-17359)***
Stratamet Inc ....E....510 651-7176
46009 Hotchkiss St Fremont (94539) ***(P-19193)***
Stratamet Advanced Mtls Corp ....F....510 440-1697
2718 Prune Ave Fremont (94539) ***(P-10792)***
Stratasys Direct Inc (HQ) ....C....661 295-4400
28309 Avenue Crocker Valencia (91355) ***(P-10394)***
Stratasys Direct Manufacturing, Valencia *Also called Stratasys Direct Inc* ***(P-10394)***
Stratcitycom LLC ....D....408 858-0006
1317 Monterosso St Danville (94506) ***(P-25225)***
Stratedge Corporation ....E....866 424-4962
9424 Abraham Way Ste A Santee (92071) ***(P-19194)***
Strategic Distribution L P ....C....818 671-2100
9800 De Soto Ave Chatsworth (91311) ***(P-3123)***
Strategic Info Group Inc ....E....760 697-1050
1953 San Elijo Ave # 201 Cardiff By The Sea (92007) ***(P-25226)***
Strategic Insights Inc ....D....858 452-7500
9191 Towne Centre Dr # 401 San Diego (92122) ***(P-25227)***
Strategic Materials Corp ....E....323 567-2195
8616 Otis St South Gate (90280) ***(P-11527)***
Strategic Medical Ventures LLC (PA) ....E....949 355-5212
280 Newport Center Dr Newport Beach (92660) ***(P-22942)***
Strategic Partners Inc (PA) ....C....818 671-2100
9800 De Soto Ave Chatsworth (91311) ***(P-10491)***
Strategic Prtg Solution Inc ....F....562 242-5880
12110 Slauson Ave Ste 9 Santa Fe Springs (90670) ***(P-7499)***
Strategy Companion Corp ....D....714 460-8398
3240 El Camino Real # 120 Irvine (92602) ***(P-25228)***
Strathmore Ladder, Strathmore *Also called Michael D Wilson Inc* ***(P-13959)***
Stratoflex Product Division, Camarillo *Also called Parker-Hannifin Corporation* ***(P-20907)***
Stratoflight (HQ) ....D....949 622-0700
25540 Rye Canyon Rd Valencia (91355) ***(P-20939)***
Stratus Coml Cooking Eqp Inc ....F....626 969-7041
1760 W 1st St Irwindale (91702) ***(P-13282)***
Straus Family Creamery Inc ....D....707 776-2887
1105 Industrial Ave # 200 Petaluma (94952) ***(P-562)***
Strauss Karl Brewery and Rest ....E....858 551-2739
1044 Wall St Ste C La Jolla (92037) ***(P-1627)***
Streak Technology Inc ....F....408 206-2373
43575 Mission Blvd 614 Fremont (94539) ***(P-23467)***
Streamline Avionics Inc ....E....949 861-8151
17672 Armstrong Ave Irvine (92614) ***(P-17124)***
Streamline Circuits Corp ....C....408 727-1418
1410 Martin Ave Santa Clara (95050) ***(P-18616)***
Streamline Development LLC (HQ) ....E....415 499-3355
100 Smith Ranch Rd # 124 San Rafael (94903) ***(P-25229)***
Streamline Dsign Slkscreen Inc ....F....805 884-1025
1328 N Ventura Ave Ventura (93001) ***(P-7500)***
Streamline Dsign Slkscreen Inc (PA) ....D....805 884-1025
1299 S Wells Rd Ventura (93004) ***(P-3192)***
Streamline Electronics Mfg Inc ....E....408 263-3600
4285 Technology Dr Fremont (94538) ***(P-18617)***
Streamline Solutions, San Rafael *Also called Streamline Development LLC* ***(P-25229)***
Street Glow Inc ....D....310 631-1881
2710 E El Presidio St Carson (90810) ***(P-17665)***
Street Graphics Inc ....E....209 948-1713
1834 W Euclid Ave Stockton (95204) ***(P-23982)***
Streeter Printing ....E....858 278-6611
13865 Sagewood Dr Ste C Poway (92064) ***(P-7119)***
Streeter Printing Inc ....F....858 566-0866
9880 Via Pasar Ste C San Diego (92126) ***(P-7120)***
Streets Ahead Inc ....E....323 277-0860
5510 S Soto St Unit B Vernon (90058) ***(P-3633)***
Streetwise Reports LLC ....E....707 981-8999
755 Baywood Dr Fl 2 Petaluma (94954) ***(P-6592)***
Streivor Inc ....F....925 960-9090
2150 Kitty Hawk Rd Livermore (94551) ***(P-23338)***
Streivor Air Systems, Livermore *Also called Streivor Inc* ***(P-23338)***
Stremicks Heritage Foods LLC (PA) ....B....714 775-5000
4002 Westminster Ave Santa Ana (92703) ***(P-737)***
Stremicks Heritage Foods LLC ....D....951 352-1344
11503 Pierce St Riverside (92505) ***(P-695)***
Strenumed Inc ....F....805 477-1000
4864 Market St Ste D Ventura (93003) ***(P-22823)***
Stressteel Inc ....F....888 284-8752
47375 Fremont Blvd Fremont (94538) ***(P-11425)***
Stretch Inc ....D....408 543-2700
48720 Kato Rd Fremont (94538) ***(P-19195)***
Stretch Art, Gardena *Also called AR-Ce Inc* ***(P-23705)***
Stretch Film Center, Santa Fe Springs *Also called Our Powder Coating Inc* ***(P-13626)***
Stretch Forming Corporation ....C....951 443-0911
804 S Redlands Ave Perris (92570) ***(P-12775)***
Stretch-Run Inc ....F....925 606-1599
6621 Brisa St Livermore (94550) ***(P-12250)***
Streuter Technologies ....E....949 369-7630
208 Avenida Fabricante # 200 San Clemente (92672) ***(P-11008)***
Strevus Inc ....D....415 704-8182
455 Market St Ste 1670 San Francisco (94105) ***(P-25230)***
Strike Technology Inc ....E....562 437-3428
24311 Wilmington Ave Carson (90745) ***(P-19738)***
String Letter Publishing Inc ....E....510 215-0010
501 Canal Blvd Ste J Richmond (94804) ***(P-6593)***
Stroppini Enterprises ....F....916 635-8181
2546 Mercantile Dr Ste A Rancho Cordova (95742) ***(P-14348)***
Structural Composites Inds LLC (HQ) ....E....909 594-7777
336 Enterprise Pl Pomona (91768) ***(P-12429)***
Structural Diagnostics Inc ....E....805 987-7755
650 Via Alondra Camarillo (93012) ***(P-21855)***
Structural Wood Systems ....F....760 375-2772
505 San Bernardino Blvd Ridgecrest (93555) ***(P-4426)***
Structurecast ....D....661 833-4490
8261 Mccutchen Rd Bakersfield (93311) ***(P-11009)***
Structures Unlimited ....F....951 688-6300
7671 Arlington Ave Riverside (92503) ***(P-12050)***
Stryder Corp ....D....415 981-8400
225 Bush St Fl 12 San Francisco (94104) ***(P-25231)***
Stryker Corporation ....E....510 413-2500
47900 Bayside Pkwy Fremont (94538) ***(P-22637)***
Stryker Corporation ....E....714 764-1700
3407 E La Palma Ave Anaheim (92806) ***(P-22638)***
Stryker Enterprises Inc ....E....408 295-6300
1358 E San Fernando St San Jose (95116) ***(P-13976)***
Stryker Neurovascular, Fremont *Also called Stryker Corporation* ***(P-22637)***
STS, Tehachapi *Also called Sierra Technical Services Inc* ***(P-11522)***
STS, Hawthorne *Also called System Technical Support Corp* ***(P-17313)***
STS Instruments Inc ....F....580 223-4773
17711 Mitchell N Irvine (92614) ***(P-21856)***
Stuart Cellars LLC ....F....951 676-6414
41006 Simi Ct Temecula (92591) ***(P-2000)***
Stuart David Inc (PA) ....E....209 537-7449
3419 Railroad Ave Ceres (95307) ***(P-4740)***
Stuart's Fine Furniture, Ceres *Also called Stuart David Inc* ***(P-4740)***
Stuart-Dean Co Inc ....F....714 544-4460
14731 Franklin Ave Ste L Tustin (92780) ***(P-13513)***
Stud Welding Systems Inc ....E....626 330-7434
15306 Proctor Ave City of Industry (91745) ***(P-13085)***
Student Sports ....F....310 791-1142
23954 Madison St Torrance (90505) ***(P-2943)***
Studer Creative Packaging Inc ....F....818 344-1665
5652 Mountain View Ave Yorba Linda (92886) ***(P-10395)***

Mergent e-mail: customerrelations@mergent.com
1294
2019 California
Manufacturers Register
(P-0000) Products & Services Section entry number
(PA)=Parent Co (HQ)=Headquarters (DH)=Div Headquarters

Studex, Gardena *Also called Quadrtech Corporation* ***(P-11908)***
Studio 311 Inc .... F 707 795-6599
466 Primero Ct Ste E Cotati (94931) ***(P-23321)***
Studio Krp LLC .... F 310 589-5777
6133 Bonsall Dr Malibu (90265) ***(P-3338)***
Studio Systems Inc (PA) .... E 323 634-3400
5700 Wilshire Blvd # 600 Los Angeles (90036) ***(P-6594)***
Studio Two Black Diamond Prtg, Laguna Hills *Also called Benjamin Lewis Inc* ***(P-6690)***
Studio Two Graphics and Prtg, Laguna Hills *Also called Studio Two Printing Inc* ***(P-7121)***
Studio Two Printing Inc .... E 949 859-5119
23042 Alcalde Dr Ste C Laguna Hills (92653) ***(P-7121)***
Studio9d8 Inc .... E 626 350-0832
9743 Alesia St South El Monte (91733) ***(P-2856)***
Stumbleupon Inc (HQ) .... E 415 979-0640
535 Mission St Fl 11 San Francisco (94105) ***(P-25232)***
Sturdy Gun Safe Manufactruing .... F 559 485-8361
2030 S Sarah St Fresno (93721) ***(P-13977)***
Sturdy Safe, Fresno *Also called Sturdy Gun Safe Manufactruing* ***(P-13977)***
Stutz Packing Company .... F 760 342-1666
82689 Avenue 45 Indio (92201) ***(P-895)***
Stutzman Plating, Los Angeles *Also called Virgil M Stutzman Inc* ***(P-13532)***
Stx Inc .... E 707 284-3549
418 Aviation Blvd Santa Rosa (95403) ***(P-23663)***
Style Knits Inc .... D 323 890-9080
1745 Chapin Rd Montebello (90640) ***(P-2857)***
Style Media Group Inc .... E 916 988-9888
120 Blue Ravine Rd Ste 5 Folsom (95630) ***(P-6262)***
Style Plus Inc (PA) .... F 213 205-8408
2807 S Olive St Los Angeles (90007) ***(P-3274)***
Style Up America Inc .... F 213 553-1134
2600 E 8th St Los Angeles (90023) ***(P-23664)***
Styrotek Inc .... C 661 725-4957
345 Road 176 Delano (93215) ***(P-9885)***
Su Mano Inc .... F 562 529-8835
536 Milton Dr San Gabriel (91775) ***(P-10466)***
Sub-One Technology Inc .... F 925 924-1020
161 S Vasco Rd Ste L Livermore (94551) ***(P-13668)***
Suba Mfg Inc .... E 707 745-0358
921 Bayshore Rd Benicia (94510) ***(P-5105)***
Suba Technology Inc .... E 408 434-6500
551 Lundy Pl Milpitas (95035) ***(P-18618)***
Subco, Fresno *Also called Subdirect LLC* ***(P-6263)***
Subdirect LLC .... E 559 321-0449
653 W Fallbrook Ave # 101 Fresno (93711) ***(P-6263)***
Sublitex Inc .... E 323 582-9596
1515 E 15th St Los Angeles (90021) ***(P-3339)***
Sublitex Sublimation Tech, Los Angeles *Also called Sublitex Inc* ***(P-3339)***
Submersible Systems Inc .... F 714 842-6566
7413 Slater Ave Huntington Beach (92647) ***(P-23665)***
Subsidy of Be Aerospace, Fullerton *Also called ADB Industries* ***(P-11790)***
Suburban Steel Inc (PA) .... E 559 268-6281
706 W California Ave Fresno (93706) ***(P-12251)***
Sue Wong, Los Angeles *Also called S Studio Inc* ***(P-3363)***
Suez Wts Services Usa Inc .... F 760 598-1800
1800 Thibodo Rd Ste 210 Vista (92081) ***(P-19366)***
Suez Wts Services Usa Inc .... C 408 360-5900
5900 Silver Creek Vly Rd San Jose (95138) ***(P-16119)***
Suez Wts Services Usa Inc .... D 562 942-2200
7777 Industry Ave Pico Rivera (90660) ***(P-16120)***
Suez Wts Services Usa Inc .... F 951 681-5555
11689 Pacific Ave Fontana (92337) ***(P-16121)***
Suez Wts Usa Inc .... E 661 393-3035
3050 Pegasus Dr Bakersfield (93308) ***(P-9309)***
Sugar Bowl Bakery, Hayward *Also called Ly Brothers Corporation* ***(P-1287)***
Sugar Bowl Bakery, Hayward *Also called Ly Brothers Corporation* ***(P-1288)***
Sugar Foods Corporation .... D 323 727-8290
6190 E Slauson Ave Commerce (90040) ***(P-1324)***
Sugar Free, Santa Fe Springs *Also called DJ Bronson Inc* ***(P-3306)***
Sugared + Bronzed LLC .... C 747 264-0477
13033 Ventura Blvd Studio City (91604) ***(P-3555)***
Sugarloaf Farming Corporation .... E 707 942-4459
12400 Ida Clayton Rd Calistoga (94515) ***(P-2001)***
Sugarsync Inc .... E 650 571-5105
6922 Hollywood Blvd # 500 Los Angeles (90028) ***(P-25233)***
Sui Companies, Riverside *Also called Steel Unlimited Inc* ***(P-12428)***
Suitable Technologies Inc (PA) .... F 650 294-3170
921 E Charleston Rd Palo Alto (94303) ***(P-14767)***
Sukarne, City of Industry *Also called Viz Cattle Corporation* ***(P-456)***
Sullins Connector Solutions, San Marcos *Also called Sullins Electronics Corp* ***(P-17492)***
Sullins Electronics Corp (PA) .... E 760 744-0125
801 E Mission Rd B San Marcos (92069) ***(P-17492)***
Sullivan & Brampton, San Leandro *Also called Brampton Mthesen Fabr Pdts Inc* ***(P-3780)***
Sullivan Counter Tops Inc .... E 510 652-2337
1189 65th St Oakland (94608) ***(P-5106)***
Sully Miller Contracting, Brea *Also called United Rock Products Corp* ***(P-318)***
Sulzer Bingham Pumps, Santa Fe Springs *Also called Sulzer Pump Services (us) Inc* ***(P-25439)***
Sulzer Pump Services (us) Inc .... E 562 903-1000
9856 Jordan Cir Santa Fe Springs (90670) ***(P-25439)***
Sulzer Pump Solutions US Inc .... E 916 925-8508
1650 Bell Ave Ste 140 Sacramento (95838) ***(P-15093)***
Sumas Media, City of Industry *Also called Solar Region Inc* ***(P-15487)***
Sumbody Union Street LLC .... E 707 823-4043
118 N Main St Sebastopol (95472) ***(P-8849)***
Sumco Phoenix Corporation .... D 408 352-3880
2099 Gateway Pl Ste 400 San Jose (95110) ***(P-19196)***
Sumi Office Services, Carson *Also called Sumi Printing & Binding Inc* ***(P-7122)***
Sumi Printing & Binding Inc .... F 310 769-1600
1139 E Janis St Carson (90746) ***(P-7122)***
Sumicom-Usa .... F 408 385-2046
1729 Little Orchard St San Jose (95125) ***(P-15490)***
Sumiden Wire Products Corp (HQ) .... E 209 466-8924
1412 El Pinal Dr Stockton (95205) ***(P-11458)***
Sumitomo Electric Interconn (HQ) .... D 760 761-0600
915 Armorlite Dr San Marcos (92069) ***(P-9681)***
Sumitronics USA Inc .... E 619 661-0450
9335 Airway Rd Ste 203c San Diego (92154) ***(P-18619)***
Summer Rio Corp (PA) .... E 626 854-1498
17501 Rowland St City of Industry (91748) ***(P-9487)***
Summertree Interiors Inc .... F 951 549-0590
4111 Buchanan St Riverside (92503) ***(P-4741)***
Summit Electric & Data Inc .... E 661 775-9901
28338 Constellation Rd # 920 Valencia (91355) ***(P-20083)***
Summit Forest Products, Cerritos *Also called J Summitt Inc* ***(P-4171)***
Summit Furniture Inc (PA) .... F 831 375-7811
5 Harris Ct Bldg W Monterey (93940) ***(P-4742)***
Summit Industries Inc .... E 951 739-5900
1280 Graphite Dr Corona (92881) ***(P-12252)***
Summit Interconnect - Anaheim, Anaheim *Also called Kca Electronics Inc* ***(P-18516)***
Summit Interconnect Orange, Orange *Also called Fabricated Components Corp* ***(P-18478)***
Summit International Packg Inc .... D 626 333-3333
30200 Cartier Dr Rancho Palos Verdes (90275) ***(P-5539)***
Summit Machine LLC .... C 909 923-2744
2880 E Philadelphia St Ontario (91761) ***(P-16969)***
Summit Microelectronics Inc (HQ) .... E 408 523-1000
757 N Mary Ave Sunnyvale (94085) ***(P-19197)***
Summit Services Inc .... F 760 737-7630
1430 Valle Grande Escondido (92025) ***(P-10865)***
Summit Window Products Inc .... D 408 526-1600
6336 Patterson Pass Rd F Livermore (94550) ***(P-4237)***
Summit Wireless Tech Inc .... E 408 627-4716
6840 Via Del Oro Ste 280 San Jose (95119) ***(P-19198)***
Sumopti .... F 650 331-1126
742 Moreno Ave Palo Alto (94303) ***(P-25234)***
Sun & Sun Industries Inc .... D 714 210-5141
2101 S Yale St Santa Ana (92704) ***(P-17646)***
Sun Badge Co .... E 909 930-1444
2248 S Baker Ave Ontario (91761) ***(P-24255)***
Sun Basket Inc .... D 408 669-4418
1 Clarence Pl Unit 14 San Francisco (94107) ***(P-2674)***
Sun Chemical Corporation .... F 925 695-2601
120 Mason Cir Concord (94520) ***(P-9210)***
Sun Chemical Corporation .... E 562 946-2327
12963 Park St Santa Fe Springs (90670) ***(P-9211)***
Sun Chemical Corporation .... E 510 618-1302
1599 Factor Ave San Leandro (94577) ***(P-9212)***
Sun Coast Calamari Inc .... C 805 385-0056
928 E 3rd St Oxnard (93030) ***(P-2324)***
Sun Company San Bernardino Cal (PA) .... B 909 889-9666
4030 Georgia Blvd San Bernardino (92407) ***(P-6062)***
Sun Company San Bernardino Cal .... C 909 889-9666
290 N D St Ste 100 San Bernardino (92401) ***(P-9362)***
Sun Dairy, Los Angeles *Also called Pac Fill Inc* ***(P-732)***
Sun Deep Cosmetics, Hayward *Also called Sun Deep Inc* ***(P-8850)***
Sun Deep Inc .... E 510 441-2525
31285 San Clemente St B Hayward (94544) ***(P-8850)***
Sun Dog International, Fullerton *Also called Sun Trade Group Inc* ***(P-2859)***
Sun Dyeing and Finishing Co .... F 310 329-0844
15621 Broadway Center St Gardena (90248) ***(P-2858)***
Sun Frost, Arcata *Also called Larry Schlussler* ***(P-17379)***
Sun Glo Foods, Fullerton *Also called Khyber Foods Incorporated* ***(P-2552)***
Sun Ice USA, Riverside *Also called Mackie International Inc* ***(P-682)***
Sun Marble Inc .... E 510 783-9900
1300 Norman Ave Santa Clara (95054) ***(P-11283)***
Sun Marble/Home Express, Santa Clara *Also called Sun Marble Inc* ***(P-11283)***
Sun Microsystems, Santa Clara *Also called Oracle America Inc* ***(P-24997)***
Sun Microsystems, Redwood City *Also called Oracle America Inc* ***(P-15469)***
Sun Microsystems, Rocklin *Also called Oracle America Inc* ***(P-24998)***
Sun Microsystems, Pleasanton *Also called Oracle America Inc* ***(P-25001)***
Sun Microsystems, Encino *Also called Oracle America Inc* ***(P-25002)***
Sun Microsystems, Milpitas *Also called Oracle America Inc* ***(P-25003)***
Sun Microsystems, San Diego *Also called Oracle America Inc* ***(P-25004)***
Sun Microsystems, Ontario *Also called Oracle America Inc* ***(P-25005)***
Sun Microsystems, Santa Clara *Also called Oracle America Inc* ***(P-25006)***
Sun Mountain Inc .... E 415 852-2320
2 Henry Adams St Ste 150 San Francisco (94103) ***(P-4238)***
Sun Plastics Inc .... E 323 888-6999
7140 E Slauson Ave Commerce (90040) ***(P-5626)***
Sun Power Security Gates Inc .... F 209 722-3990
438 Tyler Rd Merced (95341) ***(P-11459)***
Sun Power Source (PA) .... F 805 644-2520
1650 Palma Dr Ventura (93003) ***(P-17733)***
Sun Precision Machining Inc .... F 951 817-0056
1651 Market St Ste A Corona (92880) ***(P-16970)***
Sun Reporter Newspaper, San Francisco *Also called Sun Reporter Publishing Inc* ***(P-6063)***
Sun Reporter Publishing Inc .... F 415 671-1000
1286 Fillmore St San Francisco (94115) ***(P-6063)***
Sun Rich Foods Intl Corp .... F 714 632-7577
1240 N Barsten Way Anaheim (92806) ***(P-2675)***
Sun Sheet Metal, San Diego *Also called Monaco Sheet Metal* ***(P-12685)***
Sun Sheetmetal Solutions Inc .... E 408 445-8047
3565 Charter Park Dr San Jose (95136) ***(P-12776)***
Sun Stone Sales, Temecula *Also called Sunstone Components Group Inc* ***(P-13283)***

ALPHABETIC

Employee Codes: A=Over 500 employees, B=251-500
C=101-250, D=51-100, E=20-50, F=10-19
2019 California
Manfacturers Register
© Mergent Inc. 1-800-342-5647
1295

Sun Tees F 805 434-0074
310 S Main St Templeton (93465) ***(P-7501)***

Sun Trade Group Inc (PA) F 714 525-4888
1251 Burton St Fullerton (92831) ***(P-2859)***

Sun Tropics Inc F 925 202-2221
2430 Camino Ramon Ste 111 San Ramon (94583) ***(P-968)***

Sun Valley Extrusion, Los Angeles *Also called Sun Valley Products Inc* ***(P-11604)***

Sun Valley Floral Group LLC A 707 826-8700
3160 Upper Bay Rd Arcata (95521) ***(P-24256)***

Sun Valley Ltg Standards Inc B 661 233-2000
660 W Avenue O Palmdale (93551) ***(P-17647)***

Sun Valley Products Inc E 818 247-8350
4640 Sperry St Los Angeles (90039) ***(P-11604)***

Sun Valley Products Inc (HQ) D 818 247-8350
4626 Sperry St Los Angeles (90039) ***(P-11605)***

Sun Valley Rice Company LLC D 530 476-3000
7050 Eddy Rd Arbuckle (95912) ***(P-1091)***

Sun Valley Rock and Asphalt, Sun Valley *Also called Legacy Vulcan LLC* ***(P-11133)***

Sun Valley Skylights Inc F 818 686-0032
12884 Pierce St Pacoima (91331) ***(P-10607)***

Sun Vlley Rsins Inc A Cal Corp F 559 233-8070
9595 S Hughes Ave Fresno (93706) ***(P-896)***

Sun Vlly Skylghts Plus Windws, Pacoima *Also called Sun Valley Skylights Inc* ***(P-10607)***

Sun, The, San Bernardino *Also called Sun Company San Bernardino Cal* ***(P-9362)***

Sun-Gro Commodities Inc (PA) E 661 393-2612
34575 Famoso Rd Bakersfield (93308) ***(P-1168)***

Sun-Mate Corp F 818 700-0572
19730 Ventura Blvd Ste 18 Woodland Hills (91364) ***(P-23468)***

Sunar Rf Motion Inc F 925 833-9936
6780 Sierra Ct Ste R Dublin (94568) ***(P-18266)***

Sunbeam Trailer Products Inc E 714 373-5000
5312 Production Dr Huntington Beach (92649) ***(P-17666)***

Sunbritetv LLC E 805 214-7250
2001 Anchor Ct Thousand Oaks (91320) ***(P-18267)***

Sunburst Products Inc E 949 722-0158
1570 Corporate Dr Ste F Costa Mesa (92626) ***(P-23224)***

Suncore Inc E 949 450-0054
3200 El Camino Real # 100 Irvine (92602) ***(P-19199)***

Sundance Spas, Chino Hills *Also called Jacuzzi Brands LLC* ***(P-24136)***

Sundance Spas Inc (HQ) D 909 606-7733
14525 Monte Vista Ave Chino (91710) ***(P-24257)***

Sundance Uniform & Embroidery F 530 676-6900
4050 Durock Rd Ste 13 Shingle Springs (95682) ***(P-3864)***

Sundance Uniforms & Embroidery, Shingle Springs *Also called Sundance Uniform & Embroidery* ***(P-3864)***

Sunday Brunch, San Rafael *Also called San Francisco Network* ***(P-3543)***

Sundial Industries Inc E 818 767-4477
8421 Telfair Ave Sun Valley (91352) ***(P-13669)***

Sundial Orchrds Hulling Drying E 530 846-6155
1500 Kirk Rd Gridley (95948) ***(P-1505)***

Sundial Powder Coatings Inc E 818 767-4477
8421 Telfair Ave Sun Valley (91352) ***(P-13670)***

Sundown Foods USA Inc E 909 606-6797
10891 Business Dr Fontana (92337) ***(P-860)***

Sundown Liquidating Corp (PA) C 714 540-8950
401 Goetz Ave Santa Ana (92707) ***(P-10608)***

Sundry Clothing, Los Angeles *Also called Sunnyside Llc* ***(P-3545)***

Sunearth Inc E 909 434-3100
8425 Almeria Ave Fontana (92335) ***(P-12091)***

Sunesis Pharmaceuticals Inc (PA) E 650 266-3500
395 Oyster Point Blvd # 400 South San Francisco (94080) ***(P-8399)***

Suneva Medical Inc (PA) E 858 550-9999
5870 Pacific Center Blvd San Diego (92121) ***(P-8851)***

Sunex Inc (PA) F 760 597-2966
3160 Lionshead Ave Ste 2 Carlsbad (92010) ***(P-22139)***

Suneye, Sebastopol *Also called Solmetric Corporation* ***(P-22276)***

Sunflower Imports Inc F 213 748-3444
412 W Pico Blvd Los Angeles (90015) ***(P-3193)***

Sunfoods LLC F 530 661-1923
194 W Main St Ste 200 Woodland (95695) ***(P-1092)***

Sungear Inc E 858 549-3166
8535 Arjons Dr Ste G San Diego (92126) ***(P-20940)***

Sunland Aerospace Fasteners F 818 485-8929
12920 Pierce St Pacoima (91331) ***(P-13086)***

Sunland Tool Inc F 714 974-6500
1819 N Case St Orange (92865) ***(P-16971)***

Sunline Energy Inc E 858 997-2408
7546 Trade St San Diego (92121) ***(P-19200)***

Sunlink Corporation (PA) F 415 925-9650
2 Belvedere Pl Ste 210 Mill Valley (94941) ***(P-19201)***

Sunny America & Global Autotec D 714 544-0400
2681 Dow Ave Ste A Tustin (92780) ***(P-20455)***

Sunny Delight Beverages Co C 714 630-6251
1230 N Tustin Ave Anaheim (92807) ***(P-861)***

Sunny Products Inc F 909 947-5028
1989 S Campus Ave Ontario (91761) ***(P-7586)***

Sunnygem LLC B 661 758-0491
500 N F St Wasco (93280) ***(P-862)***

Sunnyside Llc F 213 745-3070
3763 S Hill St Los Angeles (90007) ***(P-3545)***

Sunnytech F 408 943-8100
2243 Ringwood Ave San Jose (95131) ***(P-18620)***

Sunnyvalley Smoked Meats Inc C 209 825-0288
2475 W Yosemite Ave Manteca (95337) ***(P-529)***

Sunon Inc (PA) E 714 255-0208
1075 W Lambert Rd Ste A Brea (92821) ***(P-15178)***

Sunopta Food Solutions, Scotts Valley *Also called Sunopta Glbal Orgnic Ing Inc* ***(P-934)***

Sunopta Fruit Group Inc (HQ) E 323 774-6000
12128 Center St South Gate (90280) ***(P-2282)***

Sunopta Glbal Orgnic Ing Inc (HQ) E 831 685-6506
100 Enterprise Way Ste B1 Scotts Valley (95066) ***(P-934)***

Sunoptics Prismatic Skylights, Sacramento *Also called Washoe Equipment Inc* ***(P-17570)***

Sunpower Corporation (HQ) A 408 240-5500
77 Rio Robles San Jose (95134) ***(P-19202)***

Sunpower USA, Union City *Also called Aei Electech Corp* ***(P-19436)***

Sunpreme Inc E 408 245-1112
615 Palomar Ave Sunnyvale (94085) ***(P-19203)***

Sunrise Bakery F 209 632-9400
1561 Geer Rd Turlock (95380) ***(P-1325)***

Sunrise Bakery and Cafe, Turlock *Also called Sunrise Bakery* ***(P-1325)***

Sunrise Fresh LP E 209 932-0192
2716 E Miner Ave Stockton (95205) ***(P-897)***

Sunrise Imaging Inc F 949 252-3003
1813 E Dyer Rd Ste 410 Santa Ana (92705) ***(P-23198)***

Sunrise Jewelry Mfg Corp B 619 270-5624
4425 Convoy St Ste 226 San Diego (92111) ***(P-23322)***

Sunrise Luxury Living Room Inc E 562 803-1301
12160 Woodruff Ave Downey (90241) ***(P-4814)***

Sunrise Med HM Hlth Care Group, Chula Vista *Also called Vcp Mobility Holdings Inc* ***(P-22839)***

Sunrise Medical (us) LLC D 559 292-2171
2842 N Business Park Ave Fresno (93727) ***(P-22824)***

Sunrise Medical Inc E 619 930-1500
2382 Faraday Ave Ste 200 Carlsbad (92008) ***(P-22825)***

Sunrise Mfg Inc (PA) E 916 635-6262
2665 Mercantile Dr Rancho Cordova (95742) ***(P-5736)***

Sunrise Pillow Co Inc F 626 401-9283
2215 Merced Ave El Monte (91733) ***(P-3751)***

Sunrise Shutters, Los Angeles *Also called Sunrise Wood Products Inc* ***(P-4239)***

Sunrise Specialty Company F 510 729-7277
61 Skyway Ln Oakland (94619) ***(P-12051)***

Sunrise Wood Products Inc E 323 971-6540
6701 11th Ave Los Angeles (90043) ***(P-4239)***

Suns Out Inc F 714 556-2314
2915 Red Hill Ave A210c Costa Mesa (92626) ***(P-23469)***

Sunsation Inc E 909 542-0280
100 S Cambridge Ave Claremont (91711) ***(P-969)***

Sunset Islandwear F 310 372-7960
601 Mary Ann Dr Redondo Beach (90278) ***(P-2896)***

Sunset Leather Group E 310 388-4898
8527 Melrose Ave West Hollywood (90069) ***(P-10582)***

Sunset Magazine, Oakland *Also called Sunset Publishing Corporation* ***(P-6264)***

Sunset Moulding Co (PA) E 530 790-2700
2231 Paseo Rd Live Oak (95953) ***(P-4068)***

Sunset Printing, Gardena *Also called Coast Color Printing Inc* ***(P-6738)***

Sunset Publishing Corporation (HQ) C 650 324-5558
55 Harrison St Ste 150 Oakland (94607) ***(P-6264)***

Sunset Signs and Printing F 714 255-9104
2981 E White Star Ave Anaheim (92806) ***(P-7502)***

Sunshine Enterprises, Monterey Park *Also called DHm International Corp* ***(P-3407)***

Sunshine Makers Inc (PA) D 562 795-6000
15922 Pacific Coast Hwy Huntington Beach (92649) ***(P-8678)***

Sunshine Raisin Corporation (PA) C 559 834-5981
626 S 5th St Fowler (93625) ***(P-1460)***

Sunsil Inc (PA) F 925 648-7779
3174 Danville Blvd Ste 1 Alamo (94507) ***(P-19204)***

Sunsports LP C 949 273-6202
7 Holland Irvine (92618) ***(P-10477)***

Sunstar Spa Covers Inc (HQ) E 858 602-1950
13495 Gregg St Poway (92064) ***(P-24258)***

Sunstone Components Group Inc (HQ) D 951 296-5010
42136 Avenida Alvarado Temecula (92590) ***(P-13283)***

Sunsweet Dryers F 530 824-5854
23760 Loleta Ave Corning (96021) ***(P-898)***

Sunsweet Dryers D 530 846-5578
26 E Evans Reimer Rd Gridley (95948) ***(P-899)***

Sunsweet Dryers Inc F 559 673-4140
28390 Avenue 12 Madera (93637) ***(P-900)***

Sunsweet Growers Inc (PA) A 800 417-2253
901 N Walton Ave Yuba City (95993) ***(P-901)***

Sunsystem Technology LLC B 510 984-2027
2802 10th St Berkeley (94710) ***(P-19205)***

Suntech America Inc (PA) F 415 882-9922
2721 Shattuck Ave Berkeley (94705) ***(P-12092)***

Suntech Power, Berkeley *Also called Suntech America Inc* ***(P-12092)***

Sunvair Inc (HQ) D 661 294-3777
29145 The Old Rd Valencia (91355) ***(P-16972)***

Sunvair Overhaul Inc E 661 257-6123
29145 The Old Rd Valencia (91355) ***(P-20941)***

Sunwater Solar Inc F 650 739-5297
865 Marina Bay Pkwy # 39 Richmond (94804) ***(P-12093)***

Sunway Mechanical & Elec Tech F 909 673-7959
1650 S Grove Ave Ste A Ontario (91761) ***(P-20512)***

Sunwest Printing Inc F 909 890-3898
118 E Airport Dr Ste 209 San Bernardino (92408) ***(P-7503)***

Sunwood Doors Inc E 562 951-9401
1143 N Stanford Ave Los Angeles (90059) ***(P-4240)***

Sunworks Inc (PA) D 916 409-6900
1030 Winding Creek Rd # 100 Roseville (95678) ***(P-19206)***

Super Binge Media Inc F 714 688-6231
530 Bush St Ste 600 San Francisco (94108) ***(P-25235)***

Super Chef, Redwood City *Also called American Production Co Inc* ***(P-11854)***

Super Color Digital LLC (PA) C 949 622-0010
16761 Hale Ave Irvine (92606) ***(P-7504)***

Super Glue Corporation (HQ) C 909 987-0550
3281 E Guasti Rd Ste 260 Ontario (91761) ***(P-9173)***

Super Glue Corporation F 909 987-0550
4970 Vanderbilt St Ontario (91761) ***(P-9174)***

Mergent e-mail: customerrelations@mergent.com
1296
2019 California
Manufacturers Register
(P-0000) Products & Services Section entry number
(PA)=Parent Co (HQ)=Headquarters (DH)=Div Headquarters

Super Machining Inc .... F 714 662-2021
2008 S Susan St Santa Ana (92704) ***(P-16973)***
Super Micro Computer Inc (PA) .... A 408 503-8000
980 Rock Ave San Jose (95131) ***(P-15491)***
Super Store Industries .... D 209 668-2100
2600 Spengler Way Turlock (95380) ***(P-696)***
Super Vias & Trim .... F 323 233-2556
3651 S Main St E Los Angeles (90007) ***(P-3924)***
Super Welding Southern Cal Inc .... E 619 239-8003
609 Anita St Chula Vista (91911) ***(P-14741)***
Superb Chair Corporation .... E 562 776-1771
6861 Watcher St Commerce (90040) ***(P-4815)***
Supercloset .... E 831 588-7829
3555 Airway Dr Santa Rosa (95403) ***(P-11912)***
Superfish Inc .... F 650 752-6564
2595 E Byshore Rd Ste 150 Palo Alto (94303) ***(P-21661)***
Superform USA Incorporated .... E 951 351-4100
6825 Jurupa Ave Riverside (92504) ***(P-13130)***
Superheat Fgh Services Inc .... F 925 808-6711
1333 Willow Pass Rd Concord (94520) ***(P-11830)***
Superior Automation Inc .... F 408 227-4898
47770 Westinghouse Dr Fremont (94539) ***(P-15033)***
Superior Awning Inc .... E 818 780-7200
14555 Titus St Panorama City (91402) ***(P-3813)***
Superior Bias Trims, Vernon *Also called SJ&I Bias Binding & Tex Co Inc* ***(P-3920)***
Superior Building Products .... E 909 930-1802
27040 San Bernardino Ave Redlands (92374) ***(P-12350)***
Superior Coffee & Foods, Santa Fe Springs *Also called Hillshire Brands Company* ***(P-493)***
Superior Connector Plating Inc .... E 714 774-1174
1901 E Cerritos Ave Anaheim (92805) ***(P-13514)***
Superior Dairy Products Co .... E 559 582-0481
325 N Douty St Hanford (93230) ***(P-697)***
Superior Duct Fabrication Inc .... C 909 620-8565
1683 Mount Vernon Ave Pomona (91768) ***(P-12777)***
Superior Electric Mtr Svc Inc .... F 323 583-1040
4622 Alcoa Ave Vernon (90058) ***(P-25468)***
Superior Electrical Advg (PA) .... D 562 495-3808
1700 W Anaheim St Long Beach (90813) ***(P-23983)***
Superior Electrical Advg .... F 209 334-3337
125 Houston Ln Lodi (95240) ***(P-23984)***
Superior Emblem & Embroidery .... E 213 747-4103
2601 S Hill St Los Angeles (90007) ***(P-3865)***
Superior Equipment Solutions .... D 323 722-7900
1085 Bixby Dr Hacienda Heights (91745) ***(P-17376)***
Superior Essex Inc .... F 909 481-4804
5250 Ontario Mills Pkwy # 300 Ontario (91764) ***(P-11677)***
Superior Farms, Vernon *Also called Transhumance Holding Co Inc* ***(P-532)***
Superior Farms, Dixon *Also called Transhumance Holding Co Inc* ***(P-452)***
Superior Farms, Sacramento *Also called Ellensburg Lamb Company Inc* ***(P-433)***
Superior Filtration Pdts LLC .... F 951 681-1700
3401 Etiwanda Ave 811b Mira Loma (91752) ***(P-15179)***
Superior Foam Products Inc .... F 760 722-1585
394 Via El Centro Oceanside (92058) ***(P-23666)***
Superior Food Machinery Inc .... E 562 949-0396
8311 Sorensen Ave Santa Fe Springs (90670) ***(P-14888)***
Superior Graphic Packaging Inc .... D 323 263-8400
3055 Bandini Blvd Vernon (90058) ***(P-7123)***
Superior Grounding Systems .... E 626 814-1981
16021 Arrow Hwy Ste A Baldwin Park (91706) ***(P-17493)***
Superior Honey Company, San Bernardino *Also called Millers American Honey Inc* ***(P-2605)***
Superior Inds Intl Hldings LLC (HQ) .... E 818 781-4973
7800 Woodley Ave Van Nuys (91406) ***(P-20456)***
Superior Jig Inc .... E 714 525-4777
1540 N Orangethorpe Way Anaheim (92801) ***(P-14573)***
Superior Labs Inc .... F 888 708-5227
9921 Carmel Mountain Rd # 297 San Diego (92129) ***(P-8400)***
Superior Lithographics, Vernon *Also called Superior Graphic Packaging Inc* ***(P-7123)***
Superior Manufacturing, Bell *Also called Alfred Picon* ***(P-5126)***
Superior Metal Fabricators .... F 951 360-2474
4768 Felspar St Riverside (92509) ***(P-12778)***
Superior Metal Finishing Inc .... F 310 464-8010
1733 W 134th St Gardena (90249) ***(P-13515)***
Superior Metal Shapes Inc .... E 909 947-3455
4730 Eucalyptus Ave Chino (91710) ***(P-11606)***
Superior Metals Inc .... F 408 938-3488
838 Jury Ct Ste B San Jose (95112) ***(P-12779)***
Superior Millwork of Sb Inc .... E 805 685-1744
7330 Hollister Ave Ste B Goleta (93117) ***(P-4354)***
Superior Mold Co Inc .... E 909 947-7028
1927 E Francis St Ontario (91761) ***(P-10396)***
Superior On Site Service Inc .... F 760 744-4420
237 S Bent Ave San Marcos (92078) ***(P-21243)***
Superior Packing Co, Dixon *Also called Ellensburg Lamb Company Inc* ***(P-432)***
Superior Panoramic Hand Prnts .... D 805 445-7770
840 Via Alondra Camarillo (93012) ***(P-2897)***
Superior Pipe Fabricators Inc .... F 323 569-6500
10211 S Alameda St Los Angeles (90002) ***(P-13905)***
Superior Plating, Anaheim *Also called Superior Connector Plating Inc* ***(P-13514)***
Superior Plating Inc .... E 818 252-1088
9001 Glenoaks Blvd Sun Valley (91352) ***(P-13516)***
Superior Press, Santa Fe Springs *Also called Superior Printing Inc* ***(P-7505)***
Superior Printing Inc .... D 562 368-1700
9440 Norwalk Blvd Santa Fe Springs (90670) ***(P-7505)***
Superior Processing .... F 714 524-8525
1115 Las Brisas Pl Placentia (92870) ***(P-13517)***
Superior Quartz Inc .... F 408 844-9663
3370 Edward Ave Santa Clara (95054) ***(P-11550)***
Superior Radiant Insul Inc .... F 909 305-1450
451 W Covina Blvd San Dimas (91773) ***(P-5737)***
Superior Ready Mix Concrete LP .... E 619 265-0955
7192 Mission Gorge Rd San Diego (92120) ***(P-11190)***
Superior Ready Mix Concrete LP .... E 619 265-0296
7500 Mission Gorge Rd San Diego (92120) ***(P-11191)***
Superior Ready Mix Concrete LP .... E 760 352-4341
802 E Main St El Centro (92243) ***(P-11192)***
Superior Ready Mix Concrete LP .... F 760 728-1128
1508 W Mission St Escondido (92029) ***(P-11193)***
Superior Ready Mix Concrete LP .... E 951 277-3553
24635 Temescal Canyon Rd Corona (92883) ***(P-11194)***
Superior Ready Mix Concrete LP (PA) .... E 760 745-0556
1508 Mission Rd Escondido (92029) ***(P-11195)***
Superior Ready Mix Concrete LP .... E 951 658-9225
1130 N State St Hemet (92543) ***(P-11196)***
Superior Ready Mix Concrete LP .... E 619 443-7510
12494 Highway 67 Lakeside (92040) ***(P-11197)***
Superior Ready Mix Concrete LP .... E 760 343-3418
72270 Varner Rd Thousand Palms (92276) ***(P-11198)***
Superior Sheet Metal, Anaheim *Also called Campbell & Loftin Inc* ***(P-12524)***
Superior Sndblst & Coating .... F 909 428-9994
8315 Beech Ave Fontana (92335) ***(P-8945)***
Superior Software Inc .... F 818 990-1135
16055 Ventura Blvd # 650 Encino (91436) ***(P-25236)***
Superior Sound Technology LLC .... F 707 863-7431
707 Vintage Ave Suisun City (94534) ***(P-22826)***
Superior Spring Company .... E 714 490-0881
1260 S Talt Ave Anaheim (92806) ***(P-13804)***
Superior Stone Products Inc .... F 714 635-7775
923 E Arlee Pl Anaheim (92805) ***(P-11284)***
Superior Storage Tank Inc .... F 714 226-1914
14700 Industry Cir La Mirada (90638) ***(P-12430)***
Superior Tank Co Inc (PA) .... E 909 912-0580
9500 Lucas Ranch Rd Rancho Cucamonga (91730) ***(P-12431)***
Superior Tbeppe Bnding Fbrctn, Hayward *Also called Superior Tube Pipe Bnding Fbco* ***(P-13906)***
Superior Tech Inc .... F 909 364-2300
13850 Benson Ave Chino (91710) ***(P-11487)***
Superior Technologies, Chino *Also called Superior Tech Inc* ***(P-11487)***
Superior Trailer Works .... E 909 350-0185
13700 Slover Ave Fontana (92337) ***(P-14349)***
Superior Tube Pipe Bnding Fbco .... E 510 782-9311
2407 Industrial Pkwy W Hayward (94545) ***(P-13906)***
Superior Window Coverings Inc .... E 818 762-6685
7683 N San Fernando Rd Burbank (91505) ***(P-3704)***
Superior-Studio Spc Inc .... E 323 278-0100
2239 Yates Ave Commerce (90040) ***(P-24259)***
Superlamb Inc .... F 858 566-2031
8026 Miramar Rd San Diego (92126) ***(P-3623)***
Supermedia LLC .... B 209 472-6011
1215 W Center St Ste 102 Manteca (95337) ***(P-6595)***
Supermedia LLC .... B 909 390-5000
3401 Centre Lake Dr # 500 Ontario (91761) ***(P-6596)***
Supermedia LLC .... B 626 331-9440
1270 E Garvey St Covina (91724) ***(P-6597)***
Supermedia LLC .... B 562 594-5101
3131 Katella Ave Los Alamitos (90720) ***(P-6598)***
Supermedia LLC .... B 916 782-6866
1200 Melody Ln Ste 100 Roseville (95678) ***(P-6599)***
Supermicro, San Jose *Also called Super Micro Computer Inc* ***(P-15491)***
Supernova Spirits Inc .... E 415 819-3154
10288 Richwood Dr Cupertino (95014) ***(P-2078)***
Supernutrition, Pacifica *Also called Forever Young* ***(P-2524)***
Supernutrition .... E 510 446-7980
1925 Brush St Oakland (94612) ***(P-8401)***
Superprint Lithographics Inc .... F 562 698-8001
8332 Secura Way Santa Fe Springs (90670) ***(P-7124)***
Supersonic ADS Inc .... E 650 825-6010
17 Bluxome St San Francisco (94107) ***(P-23985)***
Supersprings International .... F 805 745-5553
505 Maple St Carpinteria (93013) ***(P-13756)***
Supertec Machinery Inc .... F 562 220-1675
6435 Alondra Blvd Paramount (90723) ***(P-14415)***
Supertex Inc (HQ) .... D 408 222-8888
1235 Bordeaux Dr Sunnyvale (94089) ***(P-19207)***
Supervision Eyewear Suppliers, Beverly Hills *Also called H Silani & Associates Inc* ***(P-22081)***
Supplier Diversity Program, Carlsbad *Also called Life Technologies Corporation* ***(P-8565)***
Support Equipment, Escondido *Also called C & H Machine Inc* ***(P-16154)***
Support Systems Intl Corp .... D 510 234-9090
136 S 2nd St Dept B Richmond (94804) ***(P-19739)***
Support Technologies Inc (PA) .... F 949 442-2957
1939 Deere Ave Irvine (92606) ***(P-25237)***
Supportpay, Sacramento *Also called Ittavi Inc* ***(P-24807)***
Suppress Fire Atmtc Sprinklers .... F 714 671-5939
363 Cliffwood Park St G Brea (92821) ***(P-15366)***
Supreme Abrasives .... F 949 250-8644
1021 Fuller St Santa Ana (92701) ***(P-11304)***
Supreme Bean LLC .... C 818 506-6020
5457 Cleon Ave North Hollywood (91601) ***(P-2367)***
Supreme Bindery, Gardena *Also called Investment Land Appraisers* ***(P-7602)***
Supreme Corporation .... C 951 656-6101
22135 Alessandro Blvd Moreno Valley (92553) ***(P-20232)***
Supreme Enterprise, Santa Fe Springs *Also called Kingsolver Inc* ***(P-23793)***
Supreme Graphics Inc .... F 310 531-8300
3403 Jack Northrop Ave Hawthorne (90250) ***(P-7125)***
Supreme Legends USA, Anaheim *Also called Supreme Pta Investments Corp* ***(P-21139)***
Supreme Machine Products Inc .... F 909 974-0349
302 Sequoia Ave Ontario (91761) ***(P-16974)***

Employee Codes: A=Over 500 employees, B=251-500
C=101-250, D=51-100, E=20-50, F=10-19
2019 California
Manfacturers Register
© Mergent Inc. 1-800-342-5647
1297

Supreme Pta Investments Corp........F.......949 707-0288
221 N Loara St Anaheim (92801) ***(P-21139)***
Supreme Steel Treating Inc........E.......626 350-5865
2466 Seaman Ave El Monte (91733) ***(P-11831)***
Supreme Truck Body, Moreno Valley *Also called Supreme Corporation* ***(P-20232)***
Surco Products Inc........F.......310 323-2520
14001 S Main St Los Angeles (90061) ***(P-12895)***
Sure Guard Socal........F.......714 556-5497
11702 Anabel Ave Garden Grove (92843) ***(P-4241)***
Sure Guard Windows, Garden Grove *Also called Sure Guard Socal* ***(P-4241)***
Sure Power Inc........E.......310 542-8561
1111 Knox St Torrance (90502) ***(P-19740)***
Surecall, Fremont *Also called Cellphone-Mate Inc* ***(P-18066)***
Surefire LLC........E.......714 545-9444
18300 Mount Baldy Cir Fountain Valley (92708) ***(P-17734)***
Surefire LLC (PA)........B.......714 545-9444
18300 Mount Baldy Cir Fountain Valley (92708) ***(P-22827)***
Suregrip International Co........D.......562 923-0724
5519 Rawlings Ave South Gate (90280) ***(P-23667)***
Surf City Garage........E.......714 894-1707
5872 Engineer Dr Huntington Beach (92649) ***(P-8679)***
Surf More Products Inc........E.......949 492-0753
250 Calle Pintoresco San Clemente (92672) ***(P-23668)***
Surf Ride........F.......760 433-4020
1609 Ord Way Oceanside (92056) ***(P-3194)***
Surf To Summit Inc........F.......805 964-1896
7234 Hollister Ave Goleta (93117) ***(P-23669)***
Surface Art Engineering Inc........E.......408 433-4700
81 Bonaventura Dr San Jose (95134) ***(P-19208)***
Surface Engineering Spc........E.......408 734-8810
919 Hamlin Ct Sunnyvale (94089) ***(P-14781)***
Surface Manufacturing Inc........F.......530 885-0700
2025 Airpark Ct Ste 10 Auburn (95602) ***(P-16975)***
Surface Mdfication Systems Inc........F.......562 946-7472
12917 Park St Santa Fe Springs (90670) ***(P-13671)***
Surface Mount Tech Centre........B.......408 935-9548
431 Kato Ter Fremont (94539) ***(P-15860)***
Surface Optics Corp........E.......858 675-7404
11555 Rancho Bernardo Rd San Diego (92127) ***(P-21857)***
Surface Techniques Corporation (PA)........E.......510 887-6000
25673 Nickel Pl Hayward (94545) ***(P-5107)***
Surface Technologies Corp........E.......619 564-8320
3170 Commercial St San Diego (92113) ***(P-17312)***
Surface Technology, Hayward *Also called Surface Techniques Corporation* ***(P-5107)***
Surfaces Tile Craft Inc........F.......818 609-0719
7900 Andasol Ave Northridge (91325) ***(P-10793)***
Surfacing Solutions Inc........F.......951 699-0035
27637 Commerce Center Dr Temecula (92590) ***(P-13518)***
Surfside News, Malibu *Also called Malibu Enterprises Inc* ***(P-5934)***
Surfy Surfy........F.......760 452-7687
974 N Coast Highway 101 Encinitas (92024) ***(P-23670)***
Surgeon Worldwide Inc........E.......707 501-7962
4000 Broadway Pl Los Angeles (90037) ***(P-10503)***
Surgistar Inc (PA)........E.......760 598-2480
2310 La Mirada Dr Vista (92081) ***(P-22639)***
Suri Steel Inc........F.......323 224-3166
5851 Towne Ave Los Angeles (90003) ***(P-12253)***
Surplus Ctys Fbrction Mfg Wldg, Oroville *Also called Direct Surplus Sales Inc* ***(P-12562)***
Surprisesilkcom........F.......626 568-9889
628 Madre St Pasadena (91107) ***(P-2783)***
Surrounding Elements LLC........E.......949 582-9000
33051 Calle Aviador Ste A San Juan Capistrano (92675) ***(P-4843)***
Surtec Inc........E.......209 820-3700
1880 N Macarthur Dr Tracy (95376) ***(P-8680)***
Surtec System , The, Tracy *Also called Surtec Inc* ***(P-8680)***
Surveillance Solutions, Van Nuys *Also called Harris Corporation* ***(P-21303)***
Survey Stake and Marker Inc........F.......626 960-4802
13470 Dalewood St Baldwin Park (91706) ***(P-4658)***
Survivor Industries Inc........E.......805 385-5560
1621 Emerson Ave Oxnard (93033) ***(P-2676)***
Susan Biegel MD........F.......909 985-1908
1113 Alta Ave Ste 220 Upland (91786) ***(P-8402)***
Susan Zadi........F.......424 223-3526
4220 Beverly Blvd Los Angeles (90004) ***(P-2325)***
Suspender Factory Inc........E.......510 547-5400
1425 63rd St Emeryville (94608) ***(P-3683)***
Suspender Factory of S F, Emeryville *Also called Suspender Factory Inc* ***(P-3683)***
Suspension Technologies Inc........F.......559 875-8883
1075 North Ave Sanger (93657) ***(P-20457)***
Suss McRtec Phtnic Systems Inc........D.......951 817-3700
220 Klug Cir Corona (92880) ***(P-20084)***
Suss McRtec Prcision Photomask........E.......415 494-3113
821 San Antonio Rd Palo Alto (94303) ***(P-23199)***
Suss Microtec Inc (HQ)........C.......408 940-0300
220 Klug Cir Corona (92880) ***(P-15034)***
Sust Manufacturing Company........F.......209 931-9571
2380 Wilcox Rd Stockton (95215) ***(P-16976)***
Sustain Technologies Inc (PA)........F.......213 229-5300
915 E 1st St Los Angeles (90012) ***(P-19883)***
Sustainable Fibr Solutions LLC (PA)........F.......949 265-8287
30950 Rancho Viejo Rd San Juan Capistrano (92675) ***(P-5540)***
Susy Clothing Co........E.......818 500-7879
2256 Hollister Ter Glendale (91206) ***(P-3511)***
Sutherland Presses........F.......310 453-6981
22561 Carbon Mesa Rd Malibu (90265) ***(P-14457)***
Sutro Biopharma Inc (PA)........C.......650 392-8412
310 Utah Ave Ste 150 South San Francisco (94080) ***(P-8403)***
Sutter Buttes Olive Oil, Yuba City *Also called California Olive and Vine LLC* ***(P-1535)***
Sutter Gold Mining Company, Sutter Creek *Also called Usecb Joint Venture Inc* ***(P-10)***
Sutter Gold Mining Inc........F.......209 736-2708
11500 Stringbean Aly Sutter Creek (95685) ***(P-9)***
Sutter Home Winery Inc (PA)........C.......707 963-3104
100 Saint Helena Hwy S Saint Helena (94574) ***(P-2002)***
Sutter Home Winery Inc........E.......707 963-3104
560 Gateway Dr NAPA (94558) ***(P-2003)***
Sutter P Dahlglen Entps Inc........F.......408 727-4640
1650 Grant St Santa Clara (95050) ***(P-16977)***
Sutter Printing, Sacramento *Also called Baise Enterprises Inc* ***(P-6683)***
Suttini, Oceanside *Also called Secura Inc* ***(P-3120)***
Suttons Forest Products........F.......530 741-2747
8222 Hallwood Blvd Marysville (95901) ***(P-24260)***
Sutura Inc........E.......714 427-0398
17080 Newhope St Fountain Valley (92708) ***(P-22828)***
Suvolta Inc........E.......408 866-4125
130 Knowles Dr Ste D Los Gatos (95032) ***(P-15035)***
Suzhou South........B.......626 322-0101
18351 Colima Rd Ste 82 Rowland Heights (91748) ***(P-15901)***
Suzuki Motor of America Inc (HQ)........C.......714 996-7040
3251 E Imperial Hwy Brea (92821) ***(P-21140)***
Suzuki Music USA, Santee *Also called Black Ruby Ventures LLC* ***(P-23357)***
Suzuki Musical Instruments, Santee *Also called Hpf Corporation* ***(P-23376)***
Suzuki USA, Brea *Also called Suzuki Motor of America Inc* ***(P-21140)***
Sv Probe Inc........D.......480 635-4700
6680 Via Del Oro San Jose (95119) ***(P-21858)***
Sv Probe Inc........F.......408 653-2387
535 E Brokaw Rd San Jose (95112) ***(P-21859)***
Sv Probe Inc........C.......408 727-6341
535 E Brokaw Rd San Jose (95112) ***(P-21860)***
Svc Mfg Inc A Corp........F.......510 261-5800
5625 International Blvd Oakland (94621) ***(P-2227)***
Sven Design Handbag Outlet, Berkeley *Also called Sven Design Inc* ***(P-10552)***
Sven Design Inc........F.......510 848-7836
2301 4th St Berkeley (94710) ***(P-10552)***
Svetwheel LLC........F.......650 245-6080
121 Arundel Rd San Carlos (94070) ***(P-22140)***
Svm Machining Inc........E.......510 791-9450
6520 Central Ave Newark (94560) ***(P-12254)***
Svp Winery LLC........F.......805 237-8693
111 Clark Rd Shandon (93461) ***(P-2004)***
SW Fixtures Inc........F.......909 595-2506
3940 Valley Blvd Ste C Walnut (91789) ***(P-5108)***
SW Safety Solutions Inc........E.......510 429-8692
33278 Central Ave Ste 102 Union City (94587) ***(P-2876)***
Swa Mountain Gate........F.......530 221-3406
20285 Radcliffe Redding (96003) ***(P-385)***
Swabplus Inc........E.......909 987-7898
9669 Hermosa Ave Rancho Cucamonga (91730) ***(P-9560)***
Swaner Hardwood Co Inc (PA)........D.......818 953-5350
5 W Magnolia Blvd Burbank (91502) ***(P-4385)***
Swedcom Corporation........F.......650 348-1190
851 Burlway Rd Ste 300 Burlingame (94010) ***(P-17997)***
Sweeneys Ale House, Encino *Also called Lord Leviason Enterprises LLC* ***(P-1606)***
Sweet Air, Placerville *Also called Sweet Septic Systems Inc* ***(P-11010)***
Sweet Donaldson Met Spinning........F.......323 268-8730
3535 Union Pacific Ave Los Angeles (90023) ***(P-12780)***
Sweet Earth Inc........D.......831 375-8673
3080 Hilltop Rd Moss Landing (95039) ***(P-2677)***
Sweet Earth Natural Foods, Moss Landing *Also called Sweet Earth Inc* ***(P-2677)***
Sweet Girl, Los Angeles *Also called Bd Impotex LLC* ***(P-3297)***
Sweet Inspirations Inc........E.......310 886-9010
17770 Ridgeway Rd Granada Hills (91344) ***(P-3340)***
Sweet Lady Jane, San Fernando *Also called Slj Wholesale LLC* ***(P-1322)***
Sweet Ovations LLC........D.......310 719-2600
16911 S Normandie Ave Gardena (90247) ***(P-9045)***
Sweet Production Inc........D.......650 631-7777
915 Terminal Way Ste B San Carlos (94070) ***(P-1326)***
Sweet Septic Systems Inc (PA)........F.......530 622-8768
7121 Green Valley Rd Placerville (95667) ***(P-11010)***
Sweet Xo LP........F.......818 889-9696
5825 Kanan Rd Agoura Hills (91301) ***(P-738)***
Sweetie Pies LLC........F.......707 257-7280
520 Main St NAPA (94559) ***(P-1327)***
Sweets 4jc LLC........F.......916 791-6453
5741 Oak Creek Pl Granite Bay (95746) ***(P-1328)***
Sweetspot Labs, Pacific Palisades *Also called Intimate Grooming Escenusals* ***(P-7951)***
Sweetwater Technologies, Temecula *Also called National Sweetwater Inc* ***(P-9289)***
Sweety Novelty Inc........F.......626 282-4482
633 Monterey Pass Rd Monterey Park (91754) ***(P-698)***
Swenson Group Inc........F.......650 655-4990
1620 S Amphlett Blvd San Mateo (94402) ***(P-23200)***
Swenson Group Inc Xerox, San Mateo *Also called Swenson Group Inc* ***(P-23200)***
Swift Beef Company........C.......951 571-2237
15555 Meridian Pkwy Riverside (92518) ***(P-530)***
Swift Fab........F.......310 366-7295
515 E Alondra Blvd Gardena (90248) ***(P-12781)***
Swift Health Systems Inc........E.......877 258-8677
111 Academy Ste 150 Irvine (92617) ***(P-22911)***
Swift Metal Finishing, Santa Clara *Also called Montoya & Jaramillo Inc* ***(P-13458)***
Swift Navigation Inc........D.......415 484-9026
650 Townsend St Ste 410 San Francisco (94103) ***(P-18268)***
Swift-Cor Precision Inc........D.......310 354-1207
344 W 157th St Gardena (90248) ***(P-12782)***
Swiftech, Pico Rivera *Also called Rouchon Industries Inc* ***(P-15843)***
Swiftstack Inc (PA)........E.......415 625-0293
333 Bush St Ste 1650 San Francisco (94104) ***(P-25238)***
Swiftstack Inc........E.......408 642-1865
1054 S De Anza Blvd San Jose (95129) ***(P-25239)***

Swim Cap Company , The, Chula Vista *Also called Next Day Printed Tees* ***(P-3909)***
Swimwear ....E 323 584-7536
1961 Hawkins Cir Los Angeles (90001) ***(P-3512)***
Swimwear Expert Inc ....F 310 941-4880
4025 Spencer St Ste 401 Torrance (90503) ***(P-2860)***
Swinerton Builders, San Diego *Also called Solv Inc* ***(P-25196)***
Swiss House, Glendora *Also called Grico Precision Inc* ***(P-16544)***
Swiss Machine Products, Anaheim *Also called Farrell Brothers Holding Corp* ***(P-16493)***
Swiss Pattern Corp ....F 714 545-8040
2611 S Yale St Santa Ana (92704) ***(P-14467)***
Swiss Productions Inc ....E 805 654-8379
2801 Golf Course Dr Ventura (93003) ***(P-9767)***
Swiss Screw Products Inc ....E 408 748-8400
339 Mathew St Santa Clara (95050) ***(P-16978)***
Swiss Wire EDM ....F 714 540-2903
3505 Cadillac Ave Ste J1 Costa Mesa (92626) ***(P-16979)***
Swiss-Micron Inc ....D 949 589-0430
22361 Gilberto Ste A Rcho STA Marg (92688) ***(P-13043)***
Swiss-Tech Machining LLC ....E 916 797-6010
10564 Industrial Ave # 130 Roseville (95678) ***(P-13044)***
Swissdigital USA Co Ltd ....F 626 351-1999
49 S Baldwin Ave Ste D Sierra Madre (91024) ***(P-24261)***
Swisstrax LLC ....F 760 347-3330
82579 Fleming Way Ste A Indio (92201) ***(P-10794)***
Swm, El Cajon *Also called Delstar Technologies Inc* ***(P-9705)***
Sworn Virgins, Vernon *Also called Ema Textiles Inc* ***(P-2834)***
Syagen Technology LLC ....E 714 258-4400
1251 E Dyer Rd Ste 140 Santa Ana (92705) ***(P-22023)***
Syapse Inc ....D 650 924-1461
303 2nd St Ste S650 San Francisco (94107) ***(P-25240)***
Syar Industries Inc ....D 707 643-3261
885 Lake Herman Rd Vallejo (94591) ***(P-317)***
Sybman Inc ....F 626 579-9911
9911 Gidley St El Monte (91731) ***(P-4659)***
Sybron Dental Specialties Inc ....A 650 340-0393
824 Cowan Rd Burlingame (94010) ***(P-22912)***
Sybron Dental Specialties Inc ....A 909 596-0276
1332 S Lone Hill Ave Glendora (91740) ***(P-22913)***
Sybron Dental Specialties Inc (HQ) ....C 949 255-8700
1717 W Collins Ave Orange (92867) ***(P-22914)***
Sybron Endo, Orange *Also called Ormco Corporation* ***(P-22896)***
Sygma Inc ....F 562 906-8880
13168 Flores St Santa Fe Springs (90670) ***(P-14683)***
Sylvester Winery Inc ....E 805 227-4000
5115 Buena Vista Dr Paso Robles (93446) ***(P-2005)***
Symbol Technologies LLC ....C 510 684-2974
208 Channing Way Alameda (94502) ***(P-15861)***
Symbolic Displays Inc ....D 714 258-2811
1917 E Saint Andrew Pl Santa Ana (92705) ***(P-20942)***
Symcoat Metal Processing Inc ....E 858 451-3313
7887 Dunbrook Rd Ste C San Diego (92126) ***(P-13519)***
Symmetricom Inc ....E 408 433-0910
3870 N 1st St San Jose (95134) ***(P-17998)***
Symmetry Electronics LLC (HQ) ....E 310 536-6190
5400 W Rosecrans Ave Hawthorne (90250) ***(P-19209)***
Symphonix Devices Inc ....F 408 323-8218
1735 N 1st St San Jose (95112) ***(P-22829)***
Symphony Talent LLC ....E 415 968-3389
98 Battery St Ste 400 San Francisco (94111) ***(P-25241)***
Symphonyrm Inc ....F 650 336-8430
530 University Ave Palo Alto (94301) ***(P-25242)***
Symprotek Co ....E 408 956-0700
950 Yosemite Dr Milpitas (95035) ***(P-18621)***
Symrise Inc ....F 949 276-4600
332 Forest Ave Laguna Beach (92651) ***(P-2283)***
Synapsense Corporation ....F 916 294-0110
340 Palladio Pkwy Ste 530 Folsom (95630) ***(P-15614)***
Synaptics Incorporated ....F 408 904-1100
1109 Mckay Dr San Jose (95131) ***(P-15862)***
Synaptics Incorporated (PA) ....B 408 904-1100
1251 Mckay Dr San Jose (95131) ***(P-15863)***
Synbiotics LLC ....E 858 451-3771
16420 Via Esprillo San Diego (92127) ***(P-8518)***
Synchronized Technologies Inc ....F 213 368-3760
3333 Wilshire Blvd # 806 Los Angeles (90010) ***(P-15864)***
Synchrotech, Los Angeles *Also called Synchronized Technologies Inc* ***(P-15864)***
Synder Inc (PA) ....E 707 451-6060
4941 Allison Pkwy Vacaville (95688) ***(P-19367)***
Synder California Container, Chowchilla *Also called Central California Cont Mfg* ***(P-10018)***
Synder Filtration, Vacaville *Also called Synder Inc* ***(P-19367)***
Synectic Packaging Inc ....F 650 474-0132
1201 San Luis Obispo St Hayward (94544) ***(P-7506)***
Synergetic Tech Group Inc ....F 909 305-4711
1712 Earhart La Verne (91750) ***(P-11998)***
Synergex International Corp ....D 916 635-7300
2330 Gold Meadow Way Gold River (95670) ***(P-25243)***
Synergeyes Inc (PA) ....D 760 476-9410
2232 Rutherford Rd Carlsbad (92008) ***(P-23128)***
Synergistic Research Inc ....F 949 642-2800
1736 E Borchard Ave Santa Ana (92705) ***(P-13854)***
Synergy Beverages, Vernon *Also called Gts Living Foods LLC* ***(P-2137)***
Synergy Direct Response, Santa Ana *Also called Cowboy Direct Response* ***(P-23850)***
Synergy Global Inc ....F 415 766-3540
4 Embarcadero Ctr # 1400 San Francisco (94111) ***(P-25244)***
Synergy Microsystems Inc (HQ) ....D 858 452-0020
28965 Avenue Penn Valencia (91355) ***(P-15492)***
Synergy Oil LLC ....E 888 333-1933
1201 Dove St Ste 475 Newport Beach (92660) ***(P-15367)***
Synergy Prosthetics, Fremont *Also called Norell Prsthtics Orthotics Inc* ***(P-22779)***
Syneron Inc (HQ) ....D 866 259-6661
3 Goodyear Ste A Irvine (92618) ***(P-23056)***
Syneron Candela, Irvine *Also called Syneron Inc* ***(P-23056)***
Synertech PM Inc ....F 714 898-9151
11711 Monarch St Garden Grove (92841) ***(P-11785)***
Synnex Corporation ....F 510 656-3333
6551 W Schulte Rd Ste 100 Tracy (95377) ***(P-15493)***
Synopsys Inc (PA) ....B 650 584-5000
690 E Middlefield Rd Mountain View (94043) ***(P-25245)***
Synopsys Inc ....D 626 795-9101
199 S Los Robles Ave # 400 Pasadena (91101) ***(P-25246)***
Synplicity Inc (HQ) ....C 650 584-5000
690 E Middlefield Rd Mountain View (94043) ***(P-25247)***
Syntech Development & Mfg Inc ....E 909 465-5554
13948 Mountain Ave Chino (91710) ***(P-10397)***
Syntest Technologies Inc ....F 408 720-9956
4320 Stevens Creek Blvd # 100 San Jose (95129) ***(P-25248)***
Synthesis ....E 530 899-7708
210 W 6th St Chico (95928) ***(P-6265)***
Synthesys Research Inc (HQ) ....D 408 753-1630
4250 Burton Dr Santa Clara (95054) ***(P-21861)***
Syntonic Microwave Inc ....F 408 866-5900
275 E Hacienda Ave Campbell (95008) ***(P-18269)***
Syntron Bioresearch Inc ....B 760 930-2200
2774 Loker Ave W Carlsbad (92010) ***(P-8519)***
Synvasive Technology Inc ....E 916 939-3913
4925 R J Mathews Park 1 El Dorado Hills (95762) ***(P-22640)***
Sypris Data Systems Inc (HQ) ....E 909 962-9400
160 Via Verde San Dimas (91773) ***(P-15615)***
Sysmaster Corporation ....E 925 891-7813
2700 Ygnacio Valley Rd # 210 Walnut Creek (94598) ***(P-15647)***
Sysop Tools Inc ....F 310 598-3885
815 Moraga Dr Los Angeles (90049) ***(P-25249)***
Systech Corporation ....E 858 674-6500
10908 Technology Pl San Diego (92127) ***(P-18368)***
System Studies Incorporated (PA) ....E 831 475-5777
21340 E Cliff Dr Santa Cruz (95062) ***(P-17999)***
System Technical Support Corp ....E 310 845-9400
13826 Prairie Ave Hawthorne (90250) ***(P-17313)***
Systems Machines Automatio (PA) ....C 760 929-7575
5807 Van Allen Way Carlsbad (92008) ***(P-17314)***
Systems Integrated LLC ....E 714 998-0900
2200 N Glassell St Ste A Orange (92865) ***(P-22280)***
Systems L C Womack ....F 909 593-7304
1615 Yeager Ave La Verne (91750) ***(P-22281)***
Systems Plus Lumber, Anderson *Also called Haisch Construction Co Inc* ***(P-4407)***
Systems Printing Inc ....F 714 832-4677
14311 Chambers Rd Tustin (92780) ***(P-7633)***
Systems Technology Inc ....D 909 799-9950
1350 Riverview Dr San Bernardino (92408) ***(P-15229)***
Systems Upgrade Inc ....F 949 429-8900
806 Avenida Pico Ste I San Clemente (92673) ***(P-15616)***
Systems Wire & Cable Limited ....F 310 532-7870
1165 N Stanford Ave Los Angeles (90059) ***(P-13855)***
Systron Donner Inertial, Walnut Creek *Also called Carros Sensors Systems Co LLC* ***(P-19479)***
Systron Donner Inertial Inc ....C 925 979-4400
2700 Systron Dr Concord (94518) ***(P-19741)***
T & D Services Inc ....F 951 304-1190
42363 Guava St Murrieta (92562) ***(P-120)***
T & F Sheet Metals Fab ....E 310 516-8548
15607 New Century Dr Gardena (90248) ***(P-20943)***
T & H Store Fixtures, Commerce *Also called Teichman Enterprises Inc* ***(P-5171)***
T & J Sausage Kitchen, Anaheim *Also called T&J Sausage Kitchen Inc* ***(P-531)***
T & M Machining Inc ....E 805 983-6716
331 Irving Dr Oxnard (93030) ***(P-16980)***
T & R Lumber Company (PA) ....D 909 899-2383
8685 Etiwanda Ave Rancho Cucamonga (91739) ***(P-4537)***
T & S Die Cutting ....F 562 802-1731
13301 Alondra Blvd Ste A Santa Fe Springs (90670) ***(P-14574)***
T & T Box Company Inc ....E 909 465-0848
1353 Philadelphia St Pomona (91766) ***(P-5510)***
T & T Foods Inc ....E 323 588-2158
3080 E 50th St Vernon (90058) ***(P-776)***
T & V Printing Inc ....F 951 353-8470
7101 Jurupa Ave Ste 3 Riverside (92504) ***(P-7126)***
T and T Industries Inc (PA) ....F 714 284-6555
1835 Dawns Way Ste A Fullerton (92831) ***(P-13856)***
T B C, Santa Rosa *Also called Barricade Co & Traffic Sup Inc* ***(P-13922)***
T Bags LLC ....F 323 225-9525
1530 E 25th St Los Angeles (90011) ***(P-3513)***
T C I, San Diego *Also called Turbine Components Inc* ***(P-20686)***
T C Media Inc ....F 510 656-5100
40748 Encyclopedia Cir Fremont (94538) ***(P-6266)***
T C Quality Machining Inc ....F 951 509-4633
12155 Magnolia Ave 10d Riverside (92503) ***(P-16981)***
T D I Signs ....E 562 436-5188
1419 Seabright Ave Long Beach (90813) ***(P-23986)***
T E B Inc ....F 909 941-8100
8754 Lion St Rancho Cucamonga (91730) ***(P-16982)***
T E M P, Gardena *Also called Thermally Engineered Manufactu* ***(P-12435)***
T E R, Santa Clara *Also called Ter Inc* ***(P-16995)***
T F S, Camarillo *Also called Technical Film Systems Inc* ***(P-23201)***
T F X, Oxnard *Also called Trans Fx Inc* ***(P-24275)***
T G Schmeiser Co Inc ....E 559 486-4569
3160 E California Ave Fresno (93702) ***(P-11999)***
T Hasegawa USA Inc (HQ) ....E 714 522-1900
14017 183rd St Cerritos (90703) ***(P-2284)***

Employee Codes: A=Over 500 employees, B=251-500
C=101-250, D=51-100, E=20-50, F=10-19
2019 California
Manfacturers Register
© Mergent Inc. 1-800-342-5647
1299

T I B Inc.......F.......619 562-3071
9525 Pathway St Santee (92071) **(P-14575)**
T L Care Inc.......F.......650 589-3659
1459 San Mateo Ave South San Francisco (94080) **(P-3546)**
T L Clark Co Inc.......F.......619 230-1400
3430 Kurtz St San Diego (92110) **(P-4355)**
T L Machine Inc.......D.......714 554-4154
14272 Commerce Dr Garden Grove (92843) **(P-13045)**
T L Timmerman Construction.......E.......760 244-2532
9845 Santa Fe Ave E Hesperia (92345) **(P-4427)**
T M C, Berkeley *Also called Terminal Manufacturing Co LLC* **(P-12259)**
T M Cobb Company (PA).......E.......951 248-2400
500 Palmyrita Ave Riverside (92507) **(P-4242)**
T M Cobb Company.......D.......209 948-5358
2651 E Roosevelt St Stockton (95205) **(P-4243)**
T M Cobb Company.......C.......909 796-6969
1592 E San Bernardino Ave San Bernardino (92408) **(P-5109)**
T M Cobb Company.......E.......714 670-2112
6291 Orangethorpe Ave Buena Park (90620) **(P-4244)**
T M I, Santa Clara *Also called Tool Makers International Inc* **(P-14418)**
T M I, Gardena *Also called Timbucktoo Manufacturing Inc* **(P-16124)**
T M Industries Incorporated.......F.......408 736-5202
1085 Di Giulio Ave Santa Clara (95050) **(P-12255)**
T M O, Rancho Cucamonga *Also called Thermostatic Industries Inc* **(P-11313)**
T M P Services Inc (PA).......E.......951 213-3900
2929 Kansas Ave Riverside (92507) **(P-12963)**
T M W Engineering Inc.......F.......310 768-8211
14810 S San Pedro St Gardena (90248) **(P-20944)**
T McGee Electric Inc.......F.......909 591-6461
12375 Mills Ave Ste 2 Chino (91710) **(P-17494)**
T N T Auto Inc.......D.......310 715-1117
535 Patrice Pl Gardena (90248) **(P-10467)**
T P S, Stockton *Also called Transworld Printing Svcs Inc* **(P-7214)**
T Q M Apparel Group, Los Angeles *Also called High-End Knitwear Inc* **(P-2842)**
T R I, Yucaipa *Also called Technical Resource Industries* **(P-17499)**
T S M, Los Angeles *Also called Tubular Specialties Mfg Inc* **(P-10808)**
T S Manufacturing Inc.......D.......209 586-1025
24926 State Highway 108 MI Wuk Village (95346) **(P-19742)**
T S Microtech Inc.......F.......626 839-8998
17109 Gale Ave City of Industry (91745) **(P-15865)**
T T E Products Inc.......F.......408 955-0100
1701 Fortune Dr Ste N San Jose (95131) **(P-16983)**
T Ultra Equipment Company Inc.......F.......510 440-3900
41980 Christy St Fremont (94538) **(P-15036)**
T W I, Sunnyvale *Also called Thomas West Inc* **(P-3752)**
T&D Trenchless, Murrieta *Also called T & D Services Inc* **(P-120)**
T&J Sausage Kitchen Inc.......E.......714 632-8350
2831 E Miraloma Ave Anaheim (92806) **(P-531)**
T&L Air Conditioning Inc.......F.......626 294-9888
164 W Live Oak Ave Arcadia (91007) **(P-21533)**
T&S Manufacturing Tech LLC.......E.......408 441-0285
1530 Oakland Rd Ste 120 San Jose (95112) **(P-12256)**
T&T Precision Machining.......F.......323 583-0064
9812 Atlantic Ave South Gate (90280) **(P-16984)**
T-1 Lighting Inc.......F.......626 234-2328
9929 Pioneer Blvd Santa Fe Springs (90670) **(P-17648)**
T-Ram Semiconductor Inc.......E.......408 597-3670
2109 Landings Dr Mountain View (94043) **(P-19210)**
T-Rex Grilles, Corona *Also called T-Rex Truck Products Inc* **(P-13145)**
T-Rex Products Incorporated.......F.......619 482-4424
7920 Airway Rd Ste A6 San Diego (92154) **(P-24262)**
T-Rex Truck Products Inc.......D.......800 287-5900
2365 Railroad St Corona (92880) **(P-13145)**
T. H. E. Swimwear, Los Angeles *Also called Swimwear* **(P-3512)**
T/Q Systems Inc.......E.......949 455-0478
25131 Arctic Ocean Dr Lake Forest (92630) **(P-16985)**
T3 Micro Inc (PA).......E.......310 452-2888
228 Main St Ste 12 Venice (90291) **(P-24263)**
T3m Inc.......E.......909 464-1535
3403 10th St Ste 709 Riverside (92501) **(P-21141)**
Ta Aerospace Co (HQ).......C.......661 775-1100
28065 Franklin Pkwy Valencia (91355) **(P-9682)**
Ta Aerospace Co.......C.......661 702-0448
28065 Franklin Pkwy Valencia (91355) **(P-7892)**
Ta Division, Valencia *Also called Ta Aerospace Co* **(P-7892)**
Tab Label Inc.......F.......510 638-4411
21 Hegenberger Ct Oakland (94621) **(P-5738)**
Tabc Inc (HQ).......C.......562 984-3305
6375 N Paramount Blvd Long Beach (90805) **(P-20458)**
Tabco Precision, Fallbrook *Also called Workman Holdings Inc* **(P-22682)**
Tablas Creek Vineyard LLC.......F.......805 237-1231
9339 Adelaida Rd Paso Robles (93446) **(P-2006)**
Table Bluff Brewing Inc (PA).......E.......707 445-4480
617 4th St Eureka (95501) **(P-1628)**
Table Bluff Brewing Inc.......F.......707 445-4484
1600 Sunset Dr Eureka (95503) **(P-1629)**
Table De France Inc.......F.......909 923-5205
2020 S Haven Ave Ontario (91761) **(P-1329)**
Table Mountain Quarry, Oroville *Also called Martin Marietta Materials Inc* **(P-315)**
Tabor Communications Inc.......E.......858 625-0070
8445 Camino Santa Fe # 101 San Diego (92121) **(P-6600)**
Tachyon Networks Incorporated.......D.......858 882-8100
9339 Carroll Park Dr # 150 San Diego (92121) **(P-18270)**
Tackett Volume Press Inc.......E.......916 374-8991
1348 Terminal St West Sacramento (95691) **(P-7507)**
Taco Works Inc.......E.......805 541-1556
3424 Sacramento Dr San Luis Obispo (93401) **(P-2404)**
Tacoma News Inc (HQ).......B.......916 321-1846
2100 Q St Sacramento (95816) **(P-6064)**
Tacsense Inc.......F.......530 797-0008
10 N East St Ste 108 Woodland (95776) **(P-22641)**
Tactical Communications Corp.......E.......805 987-4100
473 Post St Camarillo (93010) **(P-18369)**
Tacticombat Inc.......F.......626 315-4433
11640 Mcbean Dr El Monte (91732) **(P-13691)**
Tactx Medical Inc (HQ).......C.......408 364-7100
1353 Dell Ave Campbell (95008) **(P-22642)**
Tacupeto Chips & Salsa Inc.......F.......760 597-9400
1330 Distribution Way A Vista (92081) **(P-2405)**
Tadashi Shoji & Associates Inc (PA).......D.......213 627-7145
3016 E 44th St Vernon (90058) **(P-3341)**
Tae Gwang Inc.......F.......323 233-2882
4922 S Figueroa St Los Angeles (90037) **(P-23987)**
Tae Life Sciences LLC.......F.......949 830-2117
19641 Da Vinci Foothill Ranch (92610) **(P-23057)**
Taft Production Company.......D.......661 765-7194
950 Petroleum Club Rd Taft (93268) **(P-21)**
Taft Street Inc.......E.......707 823-2049
2030 Barlow Ln Sebastopol (95472) **(P-2007)**
Taft Street Winery, Sebastopol *Also called Taft Street Inc* **(P-2007)**
Tag Pax & Label Inc.......E.......626 579-2000
9528 Rush St Ste C El Monte (91733) **(P-7508)**
Tag Rag, Los Angeles *Also called Fetish Group Inc* **(P-3152)**
Tag Toys Inc.......D.......310 639-4566
1810 S Acacia Ave Compton (90220) **(P-24264)**
Tag-Connect LLC.......F.......877 244-4156
433 Airport Blvd Ste 425 Burlingame (94010) **(P-11678)**
Tag-It Pacific Inc.......E.......818 444-4100
21900 Burbank Blvd # 270 Woodland Hills (91367) **(P-2919)**
Tags & Labels.......E.......510 465-1125
290 27th St Oakland (94612) **(P-5739)**
Tagtime U S A Inc.......B.......323 587-1555
4601 District Blvd Vernon (90058) **(P-5740)**
Tagtrends Inc.......F.......714 903-7792
1340 Reynolds Ave Ste 101 Irvine (92614) **(P-2920)**
Tagtrends USA, Irvine *Also called Tagtrends Inc* **(P-2920)**
Tahiti Cabinets Inc.......D.......714 693-0618
5419 E La Palma Ave Anaheim (92807) **(P-5257)**
Tahiti Trading Company, Riverside *Also called Tropical Functional Labs LLC* **(P-651)**
Tahoe House Inc.......F.......530 583-1377
625 W Lake Blvd Tahoe City (96145) **(P-1330)**
Tahoe Rf Semiconductor Inc.......F.......530 823-9786
12834 Earhart Ave Auburn (95602) **(P-19211)**
Tahoe World, Tahoe City *Also called Mount Rose Publishing Co Inc* **(P-5984)**
Taiga Embroidery Inc.......F.......626 448-4812
12368 Valley Blvd Ste 114 El Monte (91732) **(P-3866)**
Tailgate Printing Inc.......C.......714 966-3035
2930 S Fairview St Santa Ana (92704) **(P-7509)**
Tailgater Inc.......F.......831 424-7710
881 Vertin Ave Salinas (93901) **(P-21212)**
Tait & Associates Inc.......D.......714 560-8222
2131 S Dupont Dr Anaheim (92806) **(P-12432)**
Tait Cabinetry Woodworks.......F.......951 776-1192
6572 Whitman Ct Riverside (92506) **(P-4245)**
Tajen Graphics Inc.......E.......714 527-3122
2100 W Lincoln Ave Ste B Anaheim (92801) **(P-7127)**
Tajima /Crl, Vernon *Also called Tajima USA Dissolving Corp* **(P-12896)**
Tajima USA Dissolving Corp.......F.......323 588-1281
2503 E Vernon Ave Vernon (90058) **(P-12896)**
Tajima USA Inc.......E.......310 604-8200
19925 S Susana Rd Compton (90221) **(P-14782)**
Takane USA Inc (HQ).......E.......310 212-1411
369 Van Ness Way Ste 715 Torrance (90501) **(P-23225)**
Takara Sake USA Inc (HQ).......E.......510 540-8250
708 Addison St Berkeley (94710) **(P-2079)**
Take A Break Paper.......E.......323 333-7773
263 W Olive Ave 307 Burbank (91502) **(P-6065)**
Take It For Granite Inc.......E.......408 790-2812
345 Phelan Ave San Jose (95112) **(P-307)**
Takex America Inc.......E.......877 371-2727
151 San Zeno Way Sunnyvale (94086) **(P-19212)**
Takipi Inc.......F.......408 203-9585
797 Bryant St San Francisco (94107) **(P-25250)**
Takt Manufacturing Inc.......F.......408 250-4975
1300 E Victor Rd Lodi (95240) **(P-24265)**
Takuyo Corporation.......F.......310 782-6927
2958 Columbia St Torrance (90503) **(P-6066)**
Talamo Food Service Inc.......E.......408 612-8751
18675 Madrone Pkwy 100 Morgan Hill (95037) **(P-603)**
Talamo Foods, Morgan Hill *Also called Talamo Food Service Inc* **(P-603)**
Talbott Ties, Monterey *Also called Robert Talbott Inc* **(P-3040)**
Talco Foam Inc (PA).......F.......916 492-8840
1631 Entp Blvd Ste 30 West Sacramento (95691) **(P-9683)**
Talco Foam Products, West Sacramento *Also called Talco Foam Inc* **(P-9683)**
Talco Plastics Inc.......E.......562 630-1224
3270 E 70th St Long Beach (90805) **(P-10398)**
Tali Pak Lumber Milling, Hopland *Also called Steve Bruner* **(P-4236)**
Talimar Systems Inc.......E.......714 557-4884
3105 W Alpine St Santa Ana (92704) **(P-5030)**
Talins Company.......F.......310 378-3715
17800 S Main St Ste 121 Gardena (90248) **(P-12783)**
Talis Biomedical Corporation.......E.......650 433-3000
230 Constitution Dr Menlo Park (94025) **(P-22024)**
Talisman Systems Group Inc.......F.......415 357-1751
1111 Oak St San Francisco (94117) **(P-25251)**

Mergent e-mail: customerrelations@mergent.com
1300
2019 California
Manufacturers Register
(P-0000) Products & Services Section entry number
(PA)=Parent Co (HQ)=Headquarters (DH)=Div Headquarters

Talix Inc D 628 220-3885
660 3rd St Ste 302 San Francisco (94107) *(P-25252)*
Talkdesk Inc (PA) E 888 743-3044
535 Mission St Fl 12 San Francisco (94105) *(P-25253)*
Talladium Inc (PA) E 661 295-0900
27360 Muirfield Ln Valencia (91355) *(P-22915)*
Talley Metal Fabrication, San Jacinto *Also called J Talley Corporation (P-12864)*
Tallygo Inc (PA) F 510 858-1969
4133 Redwood Ave # 1015 Los Angeles (90066) *(P-25254)*
Talon Therapeutics Inc C 949 788-6700
157 Technology Dr Irvine (92618) *(P-8404)*
Talos Corporation E 650 364-7364
512 2nd Ave Redwood City (94063) *(P-16986)*
TALSCO, Garden Grove *Also called Jvr Sheetmetal Fabrication Inc (P-20594)*
Talyarps Corporation E 310 559-2335
3465 S La Cienega Blvd Los Angeles (90016) *(P-8946)*
Tam Printing Inc F 714 224-4488
2961 E White Star Ave Anaheim (92806) *(P-7128)*
Tamaki Rice Corporation E 530 473-2862
1701 Abel Rd Williams (95987) *(P-1093)*
Tamalpais Coml Cabinetry Inc E 510 231-6800
200 9th St Richmond (94801) *(P-5110)*
Tamarco Contractor Specialties, San Diego *Also called Tomarco Contractor Spc Inc (P-23776)*
Tamco Inc (HQ) D 909 899-0660
12459 Arrow Rte Rancho Cucamonga (91739) *(P-13000)*
Tamco Steel, Rancho Cucamonga *Also called Tamco Inc (P-13000)*
Tammy Taylor Nails Inc E 949 250-9287
2001 E Deere Ave Santa Ana (92705) *(P-7893)*
Tampico Spice Co Incorporated E 323 235-3154
5901 S Central Ave 5941 Los Angeles (90001) *(P-2678)*
Tampico Spice Company, Los Angeles *Also called Tampico Spice Co Incorporated (P-2678)*
Tamshell Corp D 951 272-9395
237 Glider Cir Corona (92880) *(P-10399)*
Tan Set Corporation F 805 967-4567
1 S Fairview Ave Goleta (93117) *(P-12257)*
Tanbil Bakery Inc F 626 280-2638
8150 Garvey Ave Ste 104 Rosemead (91770) *(P-1331)*
Tanbit Bakery, Rosemead *Also called Tanbil Bakery Inc (P-1331)*
Tandem Design Inc E 714 978-7272
1846 W Sequoia Ave Orange (92868) *(P-24266)*
Tandem Diabetes Care Inc (PA) C 858 366-6900
11075 Roselle St San Diego (92121) *(P-22643)*
Tandem Exhibit, Orange *Also called Tandem Design Inc (P-24266)*
Tandem Wines LLC F 707 395-3902
4900 W Dry Creek Rd Healdsburg (95448) *(P-2008)*
Tanfield Engrg Systems US Inc F 559 443-6602
2686 S Maple Ave Fresno (93725) *(P-14192)*
Tangent Computer Inc D 650 342-9388
45800 Northport Loop W Fremont (94538) *(P-15494)*
Tangent Computer Inc (PA) D 888 683-2881
191 Airport Blvd Burlingame (94010) *(P-15495)*
Tanget Fastnet, Burlingame *Also called Tangent Computer Inc (P-15495)*
Tangle Inc E 650 616-7900
385 Oyster Point Blvd 8b South San Francisco (94080) *(P-23470)*
Tango Systems Inc D 408 526-2330
1980 Concourse Dr San Jose (95131) *(P-19743)*
Tangoe Inc D 858 452-6800
9920 Pcf Hts Blvd Ste 200 San Diego (92121) *(P-25255)*
Tangome Inc E 650 375-2620
440 N Wolfe Rd Sunnyvale (94085) *(P-18271)*
Tanko Streetlighting Inc E 415 254-7579
220 Bay Shore Blvd San Francisco (94124) *(P-17649)*
Tanko Streetlighting Services, San Francisco *Also called Tanko Streetlighting Inc (P-17649)*
Tanox Inc (HQ) C 650 851-1607
1 Dna Way South San Francisco (94080) *(P-8405)*
Tanvex Biologics Inc E 858 210-4100
10421 Pacific Center Ct San Diego (92121) *(P-8406)*
Taokaenoi Usa Inc F 562 404-9888
13767 Milroy Pl Santa Fe Springs (90670) *(P-2304)*
Tap Manufacturing LLC F 619 216-1444
2360 Boswell Rd Chula Vista (91914) *(P-20459)*
Tap Plastics Inc A Cal Corp (PA) F 510 357-3755
3011 Alvarado St Ste A San Leandro (94577) *(P-7894)*
Tapatio Foods LLC F 323 587-8933
4685 District Blvd Vernon (90058) *(P-935)*
Tapatio Hot Sauce, Vernon *Also called Tapatio Foods LLC (P-935)*
Tapclicks, San Jose *Also called Taponix Inc (P-25257)*
Tape & Label Converters Inc E 562 945-3486
8231 Allport Ave Santa Fe Springs (90670) *(P-5579)*
Tape Factory Inc E 714 979-7742
11899 Lotus Ave Fountain Valley (92708) *(P-5580)*
Tape Service Ltd F 909 627-8811
4510 Carter Ct Chino (91710) *(P-9684)*
Tapemation Machining Inc (PA) F 831 438-3069
13 Janis Way Scotts Valley (95066) *(P-16987)*
Tapestry Inc F 323 725-6792
100 Citadel Dr Ste 709 Commerce (90040) *(P-10553)*
Tapestry Inc F 909 337-5207
28200 Highway 189 Lake Arrowhead (92352) *(P-10554)*
Tapinfluence Inc E 720 726-4071
67 E Evelyn Ave Ste 5 Mountain View (94041) *(P-25256)*
Tapioca Express F 408 999-0128
81 Curtner Ave San Jose (95125) *(P-1102)*
Tapioca Express F 619 286-0484
6145 El Cajon Blvd Ste G San Diego (92115) *(P-1103)*
Taponix Inc F 408 725-2942
5300 Stevens Creek Blvd San Jose (95129) *(P-25257)*

Tapp Label Inc F 707 253-8250
580 Gateway Dr NAPA (94558) *(P-7129)*
Tapp Label Inc (HQ) F 707 252-8300
161 S Vasco Rd L Livermore (94551) *(P-5741)*
Tara Enterprises Inc F 661 510-2206
27023 Mack Bean Pkwy Valencia (91355) *(P-4356)*
Tara Materials Inc E 619 671-1018
7615 Siempre Viva Rd San Diego (92154) *(P-23712)*
Tarana Wireless Inc E 510 868-3359
2105 M L King Jr Way J Berkeley (94704) *(P-18272)*
Tarazi Specialty Foods LLC F 909 628-3601
13727 Seminole Dr Chino (91710) *(P-2679)*
Tardif Sheet Metal & AC F 714 547-7135
412 N Santa Fe St Santa Ana (92701) *(P-12258)*
Tardio Enterprises Inc E 650 877-7200
457 S Canal St South San Francisco (94080) *(P-2326)*
Target Media Partners Oper LLC E 323 930-3123
5900 Wilshire Blvd # 550 Los Angeles (90036) *(P-6067)*
Target Technology Company LLC (PA) F 949 788-0909
564 Wald Irvine (92618) *(P-19884)*
Targeted Medical Pharma Inc (PA) E 310 474-9809
2980 N Beverly Glen Cir # 1 Los Angeles (90077) *(P-8407)*
Tarina Tarantino Designs LLC F 213 533-8070
910 S Broadway Fl 6 Los Angeles (90015) *(P-23323)*
Tarpin Corporation E 714 891-6944
5361 Business Dr Huntington Beach (92649) *(P-14576)*
Tarps & Tie-Downs Inc (PA) F 510 782-8772
24967 Huntwood Ave Hayward (94544) *(P-3814)*
Tarrica Wine Cellars, Shandon *Also called Svp Winery LLC (P-2004)*
Tarsal Pharmaceuticals Inc E 818 919-9723
3909 Oceanic Dr Ste 401 Oceanside (92056) *(P-8408)*
Tartan Fashion Inc E 626 575-2828
4357 Rowland Ave El Monte (91731) *(P-3195)*
Tartine LP E 415 487-2600
600 Guerrero St San Francisco (94110) *(P-1332)*
Tartine Bakery & Cafe, San Francisco *Also called Tartine LP (P-1332)*
TAS Group Inc F 925 551-3700
2333 San Ramon Vly Blvd San Ramon (94583) *(P-7634)*
Tascent Inc F 650 799-4611
475 Alberto Way Ste 200 Los Gatos (95032) *(P-20085)*
Taschen America LLC (PA) F 323 463-4441
6671 W Sunset Blvd Los Angeles (90028) *(P-6396)*
Tasco Molds Inc F 909 613-1926
6260 Prescott Ct Chino (91710) *(P-14577)*
Taseon Inc D 408 240-7800
515 S Flower St Fl 25 Los Angeles (90071) *(P-21862)*
Tasker Metal Products Inc F 213 765-5400
1823 S Hope St Los Angeles (90015) *(P-20460)*
Taste Adventure, Ontario *Also called Will Pak Foods Inc (P-908)*
Taste Nirvana International, Corona *Also called PSW Inc (P-2644)*
Tate Shoes, Sun Valley *Also called Tatiossian Bros Inc (P-10504)*
Tatiossian Bros Inc D 818 768-3200
11144 Penrose St Ste 11 Sun Valley (91352) *(P-10504)*
Tatung Company America Inc (HQ) D 310 637-2105
2850 E El Presidio St Long Beach (90810) *(P-18273)*
Tatung Telecom Corporation D 650 961-2288
2660 Marine Way Mountain View (94043) *(P-18000)*
Tay Ho, Santa Ana *Also called West Lake Food Corporation (P-457)*
Tay Ho Food Corporation E 714 973-2286
2430 Cape Cod Way Santa Ana (92703) *(P-777)*
Tayco Engineering Inc C 714 952-2240
10874 Hope St Cypress (90630) *(P-21171)*
Taylor Cabinet Door Company, Stockton *Also called Taylor Company (P-4357)*
Taylor Coml Foodservice Inc E 714 255-7200
221 S Berry St Brea (92821) *(P-15979)*
Taylor Communications Inc E 951 203-9011
8972 Cuyamaca St Corona (92883) *(P-7554)*
Taylor Communications Inc F 916 927-1891
1300 Ethan Way Ste 675 Sacramento (95825) *(P-7555)*
Taylor Communications Inc F 866 541-0937
5151 Murphy Canyon Rd # 100 San Diego (92123) *(P-7556)*
Taylor Communications Inc D 916 340-0200
3885 Seaport Blvd Ste 40 West Sacramento (95691) *(P-7557)*
Taylor Communications Inc E 714 708-2005
535 Anton Blvd Ste 530 Costa Mesa (92626) *(P-7558)*
Taylor Communications Inc E 714 664-8865
400 N Tustin Ave Ste 275 Santa Ana (92705) *(P-7559)*
Taylor Communications Inc F 916 368-1200
10390 Coloma Rd Ste 7 Rancho Cordova (95670) *(P-7560)*
Taylor Communications Inc F 866 541-0937
330 E Lambert Rd Ste 100 Brea (92821) *(P-7213)*
Taylor Company F 209 933-9747
4646 Qantas Ln Ste B14 Stockton (95206) *(P-4357)*
Taylor Graphics Inc E 949 752-5200
1582 Browning Irvine (92606) *(P-7510)*
Taylor Guitars, El Cajon *Also called Taylor-Listug Inc (P-23390)*
Taylor Made Golf Company Inc C 760 918-6000
5545 Fermi Ct Carlsbad (92008) *(P-23671)*
Taylor Maid Farms LLC E 707 824-9110
6790 Mckinley Ave Sebastopol (95472) *(P-2368)*
Taylor Scott Collection, The, Inglewood *Also called JGA Inc (P-4786)*
Taylor Wings Inc E 916 851-9464
3720 Omec Cir Rancho Cordova (95742) *(P-12784)*
Taylor-Dunn Manufacturing Co (HQ) D 714 956-4040
2114 W Ball Rd Anaheim (92804) *(P-14350)*
Taylor-Listug Inc (PA) B 619 258-6957
1980 Gillespie Way El Cajon (92020) *(P-23390)*
Taylormade Golf Company Inc (HQ) B 877 860-8624
5545 Fermi Ct Carlsbad (92008) *(P-23672)*

Tazi Designs F 415 503-0013
2660 Bridgeway Sausalito (94965) ***(P-4921)***
Tb Kawashima Usa Inc F 714 389-5310
19200 Von Karman Ave # 870 Irvine (92612) ***(P-3968)***
TBs Irrigation Products Inc E 619 579-0520
1532 N Johnson Ave El Cajon (92020) ***(P-12052)***
Tbyci LLC F 805 985-6800
3615 Victoria Ave Oxnard (93035) ***(P-21065)***
Tc Communications Inc E 949 852-1972
17881 Cartwright Rd Irvine (92614) ***(P-18370)***
Tc Cosmotronic Inc D 949 660-0740
4663 E Guasti Rd Ste A Ontario (91761) ***(P-18622)***
TC Steel E 707 773-2150
464 Sonoma Mountain Rd Petaluma (94954) ***(P-25440)***
Tca Precision Products LLC F 714 257-4850
1130 Columbia St Brea (92821) ***(P-20945)***
Tcho Ventures Inc F 415 981-0189
1900 Powell St Ste 600 Emeryville (94608) ***(P-1475)***
Tcho Ventures Inc (PA) E 844 877-8246
3100 San Pablo Ave Berkeley (94702) ***(P-1476)***
TCI Engineering Inc D 909 984-1773
1416 Brooks St Ontario (91762) ***(P-20172)***
TCI International Inc (HQ) C 510 687-6100
3541 Gateway Blvd Fremont (94538) ***(P-18274)***
TCI Texarkana Inc F 562 808-8000
5855 Obispo Ave Long Beach (90805) ***(P-11581)***
Tcj Manufacturing LLC E 213 488-8400
2744 E 11th St Los Angeles (90023) ***(P-3514)***
Tck Membrane America Inc F 714 678-8832
3390 E Miraloma Ave Anaheim (92806) ***(P-9310)***
Tck USA Corporation F 323 269-2969
2580 Corp Pl Ste F101 Monterey Park (91754) ***(P-9175)***
Tcomt Inc D 408 351-3340
111 N Market St Ste 670 San Jose (95113) ***(P-18275)***
TCS, Chatsworth *Also called Telemtry Cmmnctons Systems Inc* ***(P-18279)***
Tct Advanced Machining Inc F 714 871-9371
2454 Fender Ave Ste C Fullerton (92831) ***(P-16988)***
Tcth Screenworks, Gardena *Also called Screenworks Co Tim* ***(P-7480)***
Tcw Trends Inc F 310 533-5177
2886 Columbia St Torrance (90503) ***(P-3515)***
Tda Magnetics LLC F 424 213-1585
1175 W Victoria St Rancho Dominguez (90220) ***(P-13978)***
Tdc Medical California, Sunnyvale *Also called Vention Med Design & Dev Inc* ***(P-22670)***
Tdg Aerospace Inc F 760 466-1040
545 Corporate Dr Escondido (92029) ***(P-20946)***
Tdg Operations LLC D 559 781-4116
600 S E St Porterville (93257) ***(P-2947)***
Tdg Operations LLC D 323 724-9000
340 S Avenue 17 Los Angeles (90031) ***(P-2944)***
Tdg Operations LLC F 323 724-9000
6433 Gayhart St Commerce (90040) ***(P-2945)***
Tdi2 Custom Packaging Inc F 714 751-6782
3400 W Fordham Ave Santa Ana (92704) ***(P-5627)***
Tdk Electronics Inc F 858 485-4640
11770 Bernardo Plaza Ct San Diego (92128) ***(P-19744)***
Tdk Machining F 714 554-4166
10772 Capital Ave Ste 7n Garden Grove (92843) ***(P-20947)***
Tdk-Lambda Americas Inc C 619 575-4400
401 Mile Of Cars Way # 325 National City (91950) ***(P-19745)***
Tdl Aero Enterprises F 209 722-7300
44 Macready Dr Merced (95341) ***(P-20629)***
Tdo Software Inc E 858 558-3696
6235 Lusk Blvd San Diego (92121) ***(P-25258)***
Te Circuit Protection, Menlo Park *Also called Te Connectivity Ltd* ***(P-19746)***
Te Connectivity, Grass Valley *Also called Measurement Specialties Inc* ***(P-21803)***
Te Connectivity F 951 765-2200
5733 W Whittier Ave Hemet (92545) ***(P-19412)***
Te Connectivity Corporation E 650 361-3333
305 Constitution Dr Menlo Park (94025) ***(P-19413)***
Te Connectivity Corporation B 650 361-3333
305 Constitution Dr Menlo Park (94025) ***(P-19414)***
Te Connectivity Corporation A 650 361-3333
305 Constitution Dr Menlo Park (94025) ***(P-17495)***
Te Connectivity Corporation F 650 361-2495
501 Oakside Ave Side Redwood City (94063) ***(P-17496)***
Te Connectivity Corporation B 650 361-3333
308 Constitution Dr Menlo Park (94025) ***(P-17167)***
Te Connectivity Corporation C 805 684-4560
550 Linden Ave Carpinteria (93013) ***(P-17315)***
Te Connectivity Corporation E 650 361-3306
307 Constitution Dr Menlo Park (94025) ***(P-17497)***
Te Connectivity Corporation B 951 929-3323
700 S Hathaway St Banning (92220) ***(P-19415)***
Te Connectivity Corporation D 951 765-2250
5733 W Whittier Ave Hemet (92545) ***(P-19416)***
Te Connectivity Corporation A 760 757-7500
250 Eddie Jones Way Oceanside (92058) ***(P-19417)***
Te Connectivity Corporation C 650 361-3302
1455 Adams Dr Menlo Park (94025) ***(P-19418)***
Te Connectivity Corporation B 650 361-3333
305 Constitution Dr Menlo Park (94025) ***(P-9508)***
Te Connectivity Corporation B 408 624-3000
5300 Hellyer Ave San Jose (95138) ***(P-19419)***
Te Connectivity Corporation F 650 361-3333
501 Oakside Ave Side Redwood City (94063) ***(P-11679)***
Te Connectivity Corporation B 650 361-2495
501 Oakside Ave Side Redwood City (94063) ***(P-17498)***
Te Connectivity Corporation E 619 454-5176
9543 Henrich Dr Ste 7 San Diego (92154) ***(P-19420)***
Te Connectivity Corporation B 760 757-7500
5733 W Whittier Ave Hemet (92545) ***(P-19421)***
Te Connectivity Corporation A 650 361-3615
6900 Paseo Padre Pkwy Fremont (94555) ***(P-19422)***
Te Connectivity Corporation B 951 765-2200
5733 W Whittier Ave Hemet (92545) ***(P-19423)***
Te Connectivity Ltd E 650 361-4923
305 Constitution Dr Menlo Park (94025) ***(P-19746)***
Teacher Created Materials Inc C 714 891-2273
5301 Oceanus Dr Huntington Beach (92649) ***(P-6397)***
Teacher Created Resources Inc D 714 230-7060
12621 Western Ave Garden Grove (92841) ***(P-6398)***
Teachers Curriculum Inst LLC (PA) E 800 497-6138
2440 W El Cam Mountain View (94040) ***(P-6399)***
Teaching Channel Inc E 415 800-4288
2 Embarcadero Ctr Fl 8 San Francisco (94111) ***(P-25259)***
Teal Electronics Corporation (PA) D 858 558-9000
10350 Sorrento Valley Rd San Diego (92121) ***(P-17316)***
Team Inc D 310 514-2312
2580 W 237th St Torrance (90505) ***(P-11832)***
Team Air Inc (PA) E 909 823-1957
12771 Brown Ave Riverside (92509) ***(P-15980)***
Team Air Conditioning Eqp, Riverside *Also called Team Air Inc* ***(P-15980)***
Team C High Performance Center, Bellflower *Also called C Team Inc* ***(P-16352)***
Team Casing F 530 743-5424
5073 Arboga Rd Marysville (95901) ***(P-281)***
Team China California LLC F 714 424-9999
3138 Madeira Ave Costa Mesa (92626) ***(P-22025)***
Team Color Inc E 949 646-6486
837 W 18th St Costa Mesa (92627) ***(P-3925)***
Team Color Screen Printing, Costa Mesa *Also called Team Color Inc* ***(P-3925)***
Team Econolite F 408 577-1733
1810 Oakland Rd Ste E San Jose (95131) ***(P-18371)***
Team Fashion F 323 589-3388
2303 E 55th St Vernon (90058) ***(P-3275)***
Team Industrial Services, Torrance *Also called Team Inc* ***(P-11832)***
Team Manufacturing Inc E 310 639-0251
2625 Homestead Pl Rancho Dominguez (90220) ***(P-13284)***
Team Simpson Racing, Harbor City *Also called Simpson Performance Pdts Inc* ***(P-22814)***
Teamifier Inc F 408 591-9872
514 Live Oak Ln Emerald Hills (94062) ***(P-25260)***
Teammate Builders Inc F 408 377-9000
281 E Mcglincy Ln Frnt Campbell (95008) ***(P-5170)***
Teamwork Athletic Apparel, San Marcos *Also called R B III Associates Inc* ***(P-3360)***
Teamwork Packaging, San Bernardino *Also called Ocean Blue Inc* ***(P-9872)***
Tearlab Corporation (PA) F 858 455-6006
150 La Terraza Blvd # 101 Escondido (92025) ***(P-22644)***
Teasdale Foods Inc (PA) B 209 358-5616
901 Packers St Atwater (95301) ***(P-778)***
Teasdale Latin Foods, Atwater *Also called Teasdale Foods Inc* ***(P-778)***
Teaze of California Inc C 562 944-8995
9900 Bell Ranch Dr # 105 Santa Fe Springs (90670) ***(P-3516)***
TEC, Compton *Also called Thermal Equipment Corporation* ***(P-12434)***
TEC Color Craft (PA) E 909 392-9000
1860 Wright Ave La Verne (91750) ***(P-7511)***
TEC Color Craft Products, La Verne *Also called TEC Color Craft* ***(P-7511)***
TEC Lighting Inc F 714 529-5068
115 Arovista Cir Brea (92821) ***(P-17735)***
Tecan Systems Inc D 408 953-3100
2450 Zanker Rd San Jose (95131) ***(P-21492)***
Tecfar Manufacturing Inc F 818 767-0677
8525 Telfair Ave Sun Valley (91352) ***(P-16989)***
Tech 22, Vista *Also called Sea Breeze Technology Inc* ***(P-20064)***
Tech Air Northern Cal LLC F 408 293-9353
140 S Montgomery St San Jose (95110) ***(P-7733)***
Tech Air Northern Cal LLC F 925 449-9353
800 Greenville Rd Livermore (94550) ***(P-7734)***
Tech Air Northern Cal LLC F 510 524-9353
1224 6th St Berkeley (94710) ***(P-7735)***
Tech Air Northern Cal LLC F 925 568-9353
1135 Erickson Rd Concord (94520) ***(P-7736)***
Tech Air Northern Cal LLC F 650 593-9353
820 Industrial Rd San Carlos (94070) ***(P-7737)***
Tech Air Northern Cal LLC F 510 533-9353
4445 Jensen St Oakland (94601) ***(P-7738)***
Tech Air of California Inc F 818 787-6010
7254 Coldwater Canyon Ave North Hollywood (91605) ***(P-7739)***
Tech Electronic Systems Inc F 909 986-4395
592 E State St Ontario (91761) ***(P-19747)***
Tech Powers, Santa Fe Springs *Also called Turbine Eng Cmpnents Tech Corp* ***(P-13131)***
Tech West Vacuum Inc E 559 291-1650
2625 N Argyle Ave Fresno (93727) ***(P-22916)***
Tech-Semi Inc F 408 451-9588
2355 Paragon Dr Ste A San Jose (95131) ***(P-19213)***
Tech-Star Industries Inc F 650 369-7214
1171 Sonora Ct Sunnyvale (94086) ***(P-16990)***
Tech4learning Inc (PA) F 619 283-6028
10981 San Diego 120 San Diego (92108) ***(P-25261)***
Techcomp (usa) Inc E 510 683-4300
3500 W Warren Ave Fremont (94538) ***(P-22026)***
Techflex Packaging LLC D 424 266-9400
13771 Gramercy Pl Gardena (90249) ***(P-5541)***
Techko Inc A 949 486-0678
27301 Calle De La Rosa San Juan Capistrano (92675) ***(P-20086)***
Techko Kobot Inc F 949 380-7300
11 Marconi Ste A Irvine (92618) ***(P-17409)***
Techko Maid, Irvine *Also called Techko Kobot Inc* ***(P-17409)***
Techmer Pm Inc B 310 632-9211
18420 S Laurel Park Rd Compton (90220) ***(P-7895)***

Techmo Entertainment Inc ....F....408 309-3039
3191 17 Mile Dr Pebble Beach (93953) *(P-25262)*
Techni-Cast Corp ....D....562 923-4585
11220 Garfield Ave South Gate (90280) *(P-11786)*
Technibuilders Iron Inc ....E....408 287-8797
1049 Felipe Ave San Jose (95122) *(P-12897)*
Technic Inc ....E....714 632-0200
1170 N Hawk Cir Anaheim (92807) *(P-13520)*
Technical America Inc ....D....951 272-9540
301 N Smith Ave Corona (92880) *(P-24267)*
Technical Anodize ....F....909 865-9034
1142 Price Ave Pomona (91767) *(P-11582)*
Technical Associates, Canoga Park *Also called Optron Scientific Company Inc (P-22243)*
Technical Devices, Torrance *Also called Winther Technologies Inc (P-14745)*
Technical Devices Company ....E....310 618-8437
560 Alaska Ave Torrance (90503) *(P-14742)*
Technical Film Systems Inc ....F....805 384-9470
4650 Calle Quetzal Camarillo (93012) *(P-23201)*
Technical Heaters Inc ....F....818 361-7185
10959 Tuxford St Sun Valley (91352) *(P-9509)*
Technical Manufacturing W LLC ....E....661 295-7226
24820 Avenue Tibbitts Valencia (91355) *(P-24268)*
Technical Resource Industries (PA) ....E....909 446-1109
12854 Daisy Ct Yucaipa (92399) *(P-17499)*
Technical Sales Intl LLC (HQ) ....F....866 493-6337
910 Pleasant Grove Blvd # 120 Roseville (95678) *(P-25263)*
Technical Screen Printing Inc ....E....714 541-8590
677 N Hariton St Orange (92868) *(P-7512)*
Technical Trouble Shooting Inc ....E....661 257-1202
27822 Fremont Ct B Valencia (91355) *(P-16991)*
Techniche International, Vista *Also called Techniche Solutions (P-3124)*
Techniche Solutions ....E....619 818-0071
2575 Pioneer Ave Ste 101 Vista (92081) *(P-3124)*
Technicolor Connected USA, Lebec *Also called Technicolor Usa Inc (P-17864)*
Technicolor Content Services, Glendale *Also called Technicolor Usa Inc (P-17866)*
Technicolor Disc Services Corp (PA) ....C....805 445-1122
3233 Mission Oaks Blvd Camarillo (93012) *(P-19885)*
Technicolor Thomson Group ....A....805 445-7652
3233 Mission Oaks Blvd Camarillo (93012) *(P-17863)*
Technicolor Usa Inc ....C....661 496-1309
4049 Industrial Pkwy Dr Lebec (93243) *(P-17864)*
Technicolor Usa Inc ....C....818 500-9090
1507 Railroad St Glendale (91204) *(P-17865)*
Technicolor Usa Inc ....C....818 260-3651
440 W Los Feliz Rd Glendale (91204) *(P-17866)*
Technicolor Usa Inc ....A....530 478-3000
400 Providence Mine Rd Nevada City (95959) *(P-18276)*
Technicote Inc ....E....951 372-0627
1141 California Ave Corona (92881) *(P-9176)*
Technifex Products LLC ....E....661 294-3800
25261 Rye Canyon Rd Valencia (91355) *(P-11305)*
Techniform International Corp ....C....909 877-6886
375 S Cactus Ave Rialto (92376) *(P-16992)*
Techniglove International Inc ....F....951 582-0890
3750 Pierce St Riverside (92503) *(P-22830)*
Technipfmc US Holdings Inc ....F....661 283-1069
5200 Northspur Ct Bakersfield (93308) *(P-14239)*
Technipfmc US Holdings Inc ....F....310 328-1236
810 Manley Dr San Gabriel (91776) *(P-14240)*
Technipfmc US Holdings Inc ....E....530 753-6718
260 Cousteau Pl Davis (95618) *(P-14241)*
Technique Designs Inc ....F....760 904-6223
63665 19th Ave North Palm Springs (92258) *(P-5111)*
Technisoil Global Inc ....F....530 605-4881
5660 Westside Rd Redding (96001) *(P-9113)*
Technlogy Knwldgable Machining ....F....310 608-7756
1920 Kona Dr Compton (90220) *(P-13285)*
Technology For Energy Corp ....F....858 278-4900
9440 Carroll Park Dr # 150 San Diego (92121) *(P-21863)*
Technology Training Corp ....D....310 644-7777
3238 W 131st St Hawthorne (90250) *(P-7130)*
Technolube Products, Pico Rivera *Also called Lubricating Specialties Co (P-9442)*
Technolube Products, Vernon *Also called Lubricating Specialties Co (P-9443)*
Technoprobe America Inc ....E....408 573-9911
2526 Qume Dr Ste 27 San Jose (95131) *(P-19214)*
Technotronix Inc ....E....714 630-9200
1381 N Hundley St Anaheim (92806) *(P-18623)*
Techpro Sales & Service Inc ....F....562 594-7878
3429 Cerritos Ave Los Alamitos (90720) *(P-9177)*
Techserve Industries Inc ....E....714 505-2755
6032 E West View Dr Orange (92869) *(P-18624)*
Techshop San Jose LLC ....F....408 916-4144
300 S 2nd St San Jose (95113) *(P-14468)*
Techtron Products Inc ....E....510 293-3500
2694 W Winton Ave Hayward (94545) *(P-17563)*
Teck Advanced Materials Inc (HQ) ....F....858 391-2935
13670 Danielson St Ste H Poway (92064) *(P-19215)*
Tecnadyne, San Diego *Also called Tecnova Advanced Systems Inc (P-21437)*
Tecnico Corporation ....E....619 426-7385
1670 Brandywine Ave Ste D Chula Vista (91911) *(P-21015)*
Tecno Industrial Engineering ....E....562 623-4517
13528 Pumice St Norwalk (90650) *(P-16993)*
Tecnova Advanced Systems Inc ....E....858 586-9660
9770 Carroll Centre Rd San Diego (92126) *(P-21437)*
Teco Diagnostics ....D....714 693-7788
1268 N Lakeview Ave Anaheim (92807) *(P-8520)*
Tecomet Inc ....A....626 334-1519
503 S Vincent Ave Azusa (91702) *(P-22645)*
Tecxel, Vista *Also called R Zamora Inc (P-13270)*
Ted Rieck Enterprises Inc ....F....714 542-4763
1228 S Wright St Santa Ana (92705) *(P-12785)*
Tedco, Livermore *Also called Thomas E Davis Inc (P-12790)*
Tee -N -Jay Manufacturing Inc ....E....818 504-2961
9145 Glenoaks Blvd Sun Valley (91352) *(P-12786)*
Teeco Products Inc ....E....916 688-3535
7471 Reese Rd Sacramento (95828) *(P-20461)*
Teefor 2 Inc ....F....909 613-0055
5460 Vine St Ontario (91710) *(P-7131)*
Teen Bell, Los Angeles *Also called Touch ME Fashion Inc (P-3520)*
Tegerstrand Orthtics Prsthtics, Redding *Also called Donn & Doff Inc (P-22718)*
Teh-Pari International ....E....707 829-9116
334 Ohair Ct Ste B Santa Rosa (95407) *(P-9311)*
Tehachapi News Inc (PA) ....F....661 822-6828
411 N Mill St Tehachapi (93561) *(P-6068)*
Tei Struthers Wells, Santa Fe Springs *Also called Wells Struthers Corporation (P-12441)*
Teichert Inc (PA) ....C....916 484-3011
3500 American River Dr Sacramento (95864) *(P-11199)*
Teichert Aggregates, Truckee *Also called A Teichert & Son Inc (P-335)*
Teichert Aggregates, Tracy *Also called A Teichert & Son Inc (P-336)*
Teichert Aggregates, Woodland *Also called A Teichert & Son Inc (P-337)*
Teichert Aggregates, Tracy *Also called A Teichert & Son Inc (P-338)*
Teichert Aggregates, Cool *Also called A Teichert & Son Inc (P-339)*
Teichert Aggregates, Marysville *Also called A Teichert & Son Inc (P-340)*
Teichert Aggregates, Marysville *Also called A Teichert & Son Inc (P-341)*
Teichert Aggregates, Rancho Cordova *Also called A Teichert & Son Inc (P-342)*
Teichert Aggregates, Sacramento *Also called A Teichert & Son Inc (P-343)*
Teichert Readymix, Pleasant Grove *Also called A Teichert & Son Inc (P-11030)*
Teichert Readymix, Sacramento *Also called A Teichert & Son Inc (P-11031)*
Teichert Readymix, Folsom *Also called A Teichert & Son Inc (P-11032)*
Teichert Readymix, Roseville *Also called A Teichert & Son Inc (P-11033)*
Teichman Enterprises Inc ....E....323 278-9000
6100 Bandini Blvd Commerce (90040) *(P-5171)*
Teikoku Pharma Usa Inc (HQ) ....D....408 501-1800
1718 Ringwood Ave San Jose (95131) *(P-8409)*
Tek Enterprises Inc ....E....818 785-5971
7730 Airport Bus Pkwy Van Nuys (91406) *(P-19748)*
Tek Labels and Printing Inc ....E....408 586-8107
472 Vista Way Milpitas (95035) *(P-7132)*
Tek84 Engineering Group LLC ....F....858 676-5382
13230 Evening Creek Dr S # 202 San Diego (92128) *(P-22282)*
Teka Illumination Inc ....F....559 438-5800
40429 Brickyard Dr Madera (93636) *(P-17736)*
Tekever Corporation ....D....408 730-2617
5201 Great America Pkwy Santa Clara (95054) *(P-25264)*
Tekia Inc ....E....949 699-1300
17 Hammond Ste 414 Irvine (92618) *(P-23129)*
Teklam, Corona *Also called B/E Aerospace Inc (P-20754)*
Teklink Security Inc ....E....909 230-6668
4601 E Airport Dr Ontario (91761) *(P-20087)*
Tekma, Compton *Also called Technlogy Knwldgable Machining (P-13285)*
Tekni-Plex Inc ....C....909 589-4366
19555 Arenth Ave City of Industry (91748) *(P-5742)*
Teknor Apex Company ....C....626 968-4656
420 S 6th Ave City of Industry (91746) *(P-7896)*
Tekram Usa Inc ....F....714 961-0800
14228 Albers Way Chino (91710) *(P-15617)*
Teksun Inc ....F....310 479-0794
1549 N Poinsettia Pl # 1 Los Angeles (90046) *(P-10400)*
Tektest Inc ....E....626 446-6175
225 N 2nd Ave Arcadia (91006) *(P-19424)*
Tektronix Inc ....E....408 496-0800
2368 Walsh Ave Santa Clara (95051) *(P-21864)*
Tekvisions Inc (PA) ....F....951 506-9709
40970 Anza Rd Temecula (92592) *(P-22283)*
Tela Innovations Inc ....E....408 558-6300
475 Alberto Way Ste 120 Los Gatos (95032) *(P-19216)*
Telatemp Corporation ....F....714 414-0343
2910 E La Palma Ave Ste C Anaheim (92806) *(P-22284)*
Telco Food, Colton *Also called HC Brill (P-1395)*
Telecard LLC ....F....760 752-1700
220 Bingham Dr Ste 101 San Marcos (92069) *(P-7513)*
Telechem International Inc (HQ) ....E....408 744-1331
927 Thompson Pl Sunnyvale (94085) *(P-23471)*
Telecommunications Engrg Assoc ....F....650 590-1801
1160 Industrial Rd Ste 15 San Carlos (94070) *(P-18277)*
Teledesign Systems ....F....408 941-1808
1729 S Main St Milpitas (95035) *(P-18278)*
Teledyne Advanced Pollution ....E....858 657-9800
9970 Carroll Canyon Rd San Diego (92131) *(P-21662)*
Teledyne Analytical Instrs, City of Industry *Also called Teledyne Instruments Inc (P-21663)*
Teledyne API, San Diego *Also called Teledyne Instruments Inc (P-22286)*
Teledyne Battery Products, Redlands *Also called Teledyne Technologies Inc (P-19816)*
Teledyne Blueview, Poway *Also called Teledyne Instruments Inc (P-20088)*
Teledyne Controls, El Segundo *Also called Teledyne Technologies Inc (P-19753)*
Teledyne Controls LLC ....A....310 765-3600
501 Continental Blvd El Segundo (90245) *(P-21438)*
Teledyne Cougar, Sunnyvale *Also called Teledyne Technologies Inc (P-19220)*
Teledyne Defense Elec LLC ....C....323 777-0077
12525 Daphne Ave Hawthorne (90250) *(P-19749)*
Teledyne Defense Elec LLC ....F....310 823-5491
1001 Knox St Torrance (90502) *(P-19750)*
Teledyne Defense Elec LLC ....C....916 638-3344
11361 Sunrise Park Dr Rancho Cordova (95742) *(P-19751)*
Teledyne Defense Elec LLC ....C....408 737-0992
765 Sycamore Dr Milpitas (95035) *(P-19217)*

ALPHABETIC

Employee Codes: A=Over 500 employees, B=251-500
C=101-250, D=51-100, E=20-50, F=10-19
2019 California
Manfacturers Register
© Mergent Inc. 1-800-342-5647
1303

Teledyne Defense Elec LLC (HQ) ... E ... 650 691-9800
1274 Terra Bella Ave Mountain View (94043) ***(P-19752)***
Teledyne Dgital Imaging US Inc ... F ... 408 736-6000
765 Sycamore Dr Milpitas (95035) ***(P-22285)***
Teledyne E2v, Inc. ... E ... 408 737-0992
765 Sycamore Dr Milpitas (95035) ***(P-19218)***
Teledyne Elctronic Safety Pdts, Chatsworth *Also called Teledyne Risi Inc* ***(P-20681)***
Teledyne Hirel Electronics, Milpitas *Also called Teledyne Defense Elec LLC* ***(P-19217)***
Teledyne Hirel Electronics, Milpitas *Also called Teledyne E2v, Inc.* ***(P-19218)***
Teledyne Impulse, San Diego *Also called Impulse Enterprise* ***(P-17473)***
Teledyne Impulse, San Diego *Also called Impulse Enterprise* ***(P-17474)***
Teledyne Impulse, San Diego *Also called Teledyne Instruments Inc* ***(P-17500)***
Teledyne Instruments Inc ... D ... 619 239-5959
9970 Carroll Canyon Rd A San Diego (92131) ***(P-22286)***
Teledyne Instruments Inc ... E ... 858 842-3127
9855 Carroll Canyon Rd San Diego (92131) ***(P-19219)***
Teledyne Instruments Inc ... C ... 626 934-1500
16830 Chestnut St City of Industry (91748) ***(P-21663)***
Teledyne Instruments Inc ... E ... 760 754-2400
14020 Stowe Dr Poway (92064) ***(P-21664)***
Teledyne Instruments Inc ... C ... 858 842-2600
14020 Stowe Dr Poway (92064) ***(P-21439)***
Teledyne Instruments Inc ... E ... 425 492-7400
14020 Stowe Dr Poway (92064) ***(P-20088)***
Teledyne Instruments Inc ... D ... 619 239-5959
9970 Carroll Canyon Rd B San Diego (92131) ***(P-14768)***
Teledyne Instruments Inc ... E ... 818 882-7266
9810 Variel Ave Chatsworth (91311) ***(P-22027)***
Teledyne Instruments Inc ... D ... 858 565-7050
9855 Carroll Canyon Rd San Diego (92131) ***(P-17500)***
Teledyne Lecroy Inc ... E ... 408 727-6600
765 Sycamore Dr Milpitas (95035) ***(P-21865)***
Teledyne Microwave, Santa Clara *Also called Teledyne Wireless Inc* ***(P-17377)***
Teledyne Microwave Solutions, Mountain View *Also called Teledyne Wireless LLC* ***(P-19757)***
Teledyne Microwave Solutions, Rancho Cordova *Also called Teledyne Defense Elec LLC* ***(P-19751)***
Teledyne Microwave Solutions, Mountain View *Also called Teledyne Defense Elec LLC* ***(P-19752)***
Teledyne Oceanscience, Poway *Also called Teledyne Instruments Inc* ***(P-21664)***
Teledyne RAD-Icon Imaging, Milpitas *Also called Teledyne Dgital Imaging US Inc* ***(P-22285)***
Teledyne Rd Instruments, Poway *Also called Teledyne Instruments Inc* ***(P-21439)***
Teledyne Reynolds, Torrance *Also called Teledyne Defense Elec LLC* ***(P-19750)***
Teledyne Risi Inc (HQ) ... E ... 925 456-9700
32727 W Corral Hollow Rd Tracy (95376) ***(P-9185)***
Teledyne Risi Inc ... F ... 818 718-6640
19735 Dearborn St Chatsworth (91311) ***(P-20681)***
Teledyne Seabotix, San Diego *Also called Teledyne Instruments Inc* ***(P-14768)***
Teledyne Technologies Inc ... F ... 310 893-1600
12870 Panama St Los Angeles (90066) ***(P-21440)***
Teledyne Technologies Inc ... B ... 310 765-3600
501 Continental Blvd El Segundo (90245) ***(P-19753)***
Teledyne Technologies Inc ... B ... 310 820-4616
3350 Moore St Los Angeles (90066) ***(P-19754)***
Teledyne Technologies Inc (PA) ... C ... 805 373-4545
1049 Camino Dos Rios Thousand Oaks (91360) ***(P-19755)***
Teledyne Technologies Inc ... B ... 310 822-8229
12964 Panama St Los Angeles (90066) ***(P-19756)***
Teledyne Technologies Inc ... D ... 909 793-3131
840 W Brockton Ave Redlands (92374) ***(P-19816)***
Teledyne Technologies Inc ... B ... 408 773-8814
290 Santa Ana Ct Sunnyvale (94085) ***(P-19220)***
Teledyne Wireless LLC ... C ... 650 691-9800
1274 Terra Bella Ave Mountain View (94043) ***(P-19757)***
Teledyne Wireless LLC ... C ... 916 638-3344
11361 Sunrise Park Dr Rancho Cordova (95742) ***(P-19758)***
Teledyne Wireless Inc ... C ... 408 986-5060
3236 Scott Blvd Santa Clara (95054) ***(P-17377)***
Telegent Systems Usa Inc ... E ... 408 523-2800
10180 Telesis Ct Ste 500 San Diego (92121) ***(P-19221)***
Telegraph Brewing Co Inc ... F ... 805 963-5018
418 N Salsipuedes St Santa Barbara (93103) ***(P-1630)***
Telemetria Telephony Tech Inc ... F ... 408 428-0101
2635 N 1st St Ste 205 San Jose (95134) ***(P-19846)***
Telemtry Cmmnctons Systems Inc ... E ... 818 718-6248
10020 Remmet Ave Chatsworth (91311) ***(P-18279)***
Telenav Inc (PA) ... C ... 408 245-3800
4655 Great America Pkwy # 300 Santa Clara (95054) ***(P-21441)***
Telepathy Inc ... E ... 408 306-8421
1202 Kifer Rd Sunnyvale (94086) ***(P-15866)***
Telesign Holdings Inc (HQ) ... E ... 310 740-9700
13274 Fiji Way Ste 600 Marina Del Rey (90292) ***(P-25265)***
Telesynergy Research USA Inc ... F ... 408 200-9879
40101 Spady St Fremont (94538) ***(P-15867)***
Telewave Inc ... E ... 408 929-4400
660 Giguere Ct San Jose (95133) ***(P-18280)***
Telexca Inc ... F ... 760 247-4277
13463 Nomwaket Rd Apple Valley (92308) ***(P-20630)***
Telic Company, Valencia *Also called Westwood Group* ***(P-22147)***
Telirite Technical Svcs Inc ... E ... 510 440-3888
2857 Lakeview Ct Fremont (94538) ***(P-18625)***
Tellme Networks Inc ... B ... 650 693-1009
1065 La Avenida St Mountain View (94043) ***(P-6601)***
Tellus Solutions Inc ... E ... 408 850-2942
3350 Scott Blvd Bldg 34a Santa Clara (95054) ***(P-25266)***
Telsor Corporation ... F ... 951 296-3066
42181 Avenida Alvarado B Temecula (92590) ***(P-21866)***
Tembo Systems Inc ... E ... 408 300-9236
2933 Bunker Hill Ln # 100 Santa Clara (95054) ***(P-15868)***
Temecula Precision Mfg, Temecula *Also called Temecula Precison Fabrication* ***(P-14769)***
Temecula Precison Fabrication ... F ... 951 699-4066
42201 Sarah Way Temecula (92590) ***(P-14769)***
Temecula Quality Plating Inc ... F ... 951 296-9875
43095 Black Deer Loop Temecula (92590) ***(P-15037)***
Temecula T-Shirt Printers Inc ... F ... 951 296-0184
41607 Enterprise Cir N A Temecula (92590) ***(P-7514)***
Temecula Valley Winery MGT LLC ... D ... 951 699-8896
27495 Diaz Rd Temecula (92590) ***(P-2009)***
Temeka Advertising Inc ... D ... 951 277-2525
9073 Pulsar Ct Corona (92883) ***(P-5112)***
Temeka Group, Corona *Also called Temeka Advertising Inc* ***(P-5112)***
Tempco Engineering Inc ... C ... 818 767-2326
8866 Laurel Canyon Blvd A Sun Valley (91352) ***(P-16994)***
Tempest Technology Corporation ... E ... 559 277-7577
4708 N Blythe Ave Fresno (93722) ***(P-15180)***
Templock Enterprises LLC ... F ... 805 962-3100
1 N Calle Cesar Chavez # 170 Santa Barbara (93103) ***(P-9886)***
Tempo Automation Inc ... E ... 415 320-1261
2460 Alameda St San Francisco (94103) ***(P-19759)***
Tempo Industries, Irvine *Also called Tempo Lighting Inc* ***(P-17650)***
Tempo Lighting Inc ... E ... 949 442-1601
1961 Mcgaw Ave Irvine (92614) ***(P-17650)***
Tempo Plastic Co ... F ... 559 651-7711
1227 N Miller Park Ct Visalia (93291) ***(P-9887)***
Tempted Apparel Corp ... E ... 323 859-2480
4516 Loma Vista Ave Vernon (90058) ***(P-3517)***
Temptrol Industries Inc ... D ... 916 344-4457
3909 Onawa Ct Antelope (95843) ***(P-3815)***
Temptron Engineering Inc ... E ... 818 346-4900
7823 Deering Ave Canoga Park (91304) ***(P-22287)***
Ten Enthusiast Network LLC ... C ... 760 722-7777
2052 Corte Del Nogal # 100 Carlsbad (92011) ***(P-6267)***
Ten Fu Company Limited, El Monte *Also called Uncle Lees Tea Inc* ***(P-2695)***
Tenacore Holdings Inc ... D ... 714 444-4643
1525 E Edinger Ave Santa Ana (92705) ***(P-22646)***
Tencate Performance Composite, Camarillo *Also called Performance Materials Corp* ***(P-7864)***
Tender Corporation ... E ... 510 261-7414
1141 Harbor Bay Pkwy # 103 Alameda (94502) ***(P-22831)***
Tender Loving Things Inc ... E ... 510 300-1260
26203 Prod Ave Ste 4 Hayward (94545) ***(P-8852)***
Tenenblatt Corporation ... C ... 323 232-2061
3750 Broadway Pl Los Angeles (90007) ***(P-2868)***
Tenergy Corporation ... D ... 510 687-0388
436 Kato Ter Fremont (94539) ***(P-19817)***
Tenex Health Inc ... D ... 949 454-7500
26902 Vista Ter Lake Forest (92630) ***(P-22647)***
Tenneco Automotive Oper Co Inc ... D ... 562 630-0700
6925 Atlantic Ave Long Beach (90805) ***(P-20462)***
Tennis Media Co LLC ... F ... 310 966-8182
814 S Westgate Ave # 100 Los Angeles (90049) ***(P-6268)***
Tension Envelope Corporation ... C ... 951 296-0500
40750 County Center Dr Temecula (92591) ***(P-5679)***
Tensorcom Inc ... E ... 760 496-3264
3530 John Hopkins Ct San Diego (92121) ***(P-19222)***
Tensys Medical Inc ... E ... 858 552-1941
12625 High Bluff Dr # 213 San Diego (92130) ***(P-23058)***
Tent City Canvas House, Fresno *Also called S A Fields Inc* ***(P-3807)***
Teohc California Inc ... B ... 209 234-1600
1320 Performance Dr Stockton (95206) ***(P-12787)***
Ter Inc ... E ... 408 986-9920
306 Mathew St Santa Clara (95050) ***(P-16995)***
Ter Precision Machining Inc ... E ... 408 986-9920
306 Mathew St Santa Clara (95050) ***(P-16996)***
Terabit Radios Inc ... F ... 408 431-6032
1551 Mccarthy Blvd # 210 Milpitas (95035) ***(P-18281)***
Teradyne Inc ... C ... 818 991-9700
30801 Agoura Rd Agoura Hills (91301) ***(P-21867)***
Teradyne Inc ... B ... 818 991-2900
30701 Agoura Rd Agoura Hills (91301) ***(P-19760)***
Teradyne Inc ... D ... 949 453-0900
5251 California Ave # 100 Irvine (92617) ***(P-21868)***
Teradyne Inc ... C ... 408 960-2400
875 Embedded Way San Jose (95138) ***(P-21869)***
Terarecon Inc (PA) ... D ... 650 372-1100
4000 E 3rd Ave Ste 200 Foster City (94404) ***(P-15869)***
Teridian Semiconductor Corp (HQ) ... D ... 714 508-8800
6440 Oak Cyn Ste 100 Irvine (92618) ***(P-19223)***
Terminal Freezers, Oxnard *Also called Fresh Innovations LLC* ***(P-2412)***
Terminal Manufacturing Co LLC ... E ... 510 526-3071
707 Gilman St Berkeley (94710) ***(P-12259)***
Terminix Intl Co Ltd Partnr ... F ... 916 376-8770
950 Riverside Pkwy Ste 40 West Sacramento (95605) ***(P-9114)***
Termo Company ... E ... 562 595-7401
3275 Cherry Ave Long Beach (90807) ***(P-77)***
Tern, Davis *Also called Electronic Resources Network* ***(P-15737)***
Tern Design Ltd ... E ... 760 754-2400
14020 Stowe Dr Poway (92064) ***(P-21665)***
Terra Furniture Inc ... E ... 626 912-8523
549 E Edna Pl Covina (91723) ***(P-4816)***
Terra Nova Technologies Inc ... D ... 619 596-7400
10770 Rockville St Ste A Santee (92071) ***(P-14290)***
Terra Tech Corp (PA) ... E ... 855 447-6967
2040 Main St Ste 225 Irvine (92614) ***(P-14108)***
Terra Universal Inc ... C ... 714 526-0100
800 S Raymond Ave Fullerton (92831) ***(P-15181)***

Mergent e-mail: customerrelations@mergent.com
1304
2019 California
Manufacturers Register
(P-0000) Products & Services Section entry number
(PA)=Parent Co (HQ)=Headquarters (DH)=Div Headquarters

Terrajoule Corporation..........F.......650 269-0494
1051 Fife Ave Palo Alto (94301) ***(P-14010)***
Terralink Communications Inc..........F.......916 439-4367
5145 Golden Foothill Pkwy # 140 El Dorado Hills (95762) ***(P-18282)***
Terramar Graphics Inc..........F.......805 529-8845
5345 Townsgate Rd Ste 330 Westlake Village (91361) ***(P-7515)***
Terran Orbital Corporation (PA)..........E.......212 496-2300
15330 Barranca Pkwy Irvine (92618) ***(P-21172)***
Terrasat Communications Inc..........E.......408 782-5911
315 Digital Dr Morgan Hill (95037) ***(P-18283)***
Terravant Wine Company LLC..........E.......805 686-9400
35 Industrial Way Buellton (93427) ***(P-2010)***
Terravant Wine Company LLC..........C.......805 688-4245
70 Industrial Way Buellton (93427) ***(P-2011)***
Terre Rouge Winery, Plymouth *Also called Domaine De La Terre Rouge* ***(P-1730)***
Terri Bell..........F.......530 541-4180
2152 Ruth Ave Ste 4 South Lake Tahoe (96150) ***(P-25441)***
Terry B Lowe..........F.......510 651-7350
42430 Blacow Rd Fremont (94539) ***(P-21666)***
Terry Hinge & Hardware, Van Nuys *Also called RPC Legacy Inc* ***(P-11988)***
Terry Town Corporation..........F.......619 421-5354
1440 Innov Dr 200& San Diego (92154) ***(P-3604)***
Terryberry Company LLC..........D.......661 257-9971
25600 Rye Canyon Rd # 109 Santa Clarita (91355) ***(P-23324)***
Terumo Americas Holding Inc..........C.......714 258-8001
1311 Valencia Ave Tustin (92780) ***(P-22028)***
Tervita (us Operations) LLC..........F.......909 899-7504
12459 Arrow Rte Rancho Cucamonga (91739) ***(P-121)***
Tesco Products..........F.......661 257-0153
25601 Avenue Stanford Santa Clarita (91355) ***(P-14416)***
Teseda Corporation..........F.......650 320-8188
160 Rio Robles Bldg D San Jose (95134) ***(P-21870)***
Teselagen Biotechnology Inc..........F.......650 387-5932
1501 Mariposa St Ste 312 San Francisco (94107) ***(P-25267)***
Tesla Inc..........F.......310 219-4652
3203 Jack Northrop Ave Hawthorne (90250) ***(P-20463)***
Tesla Inc..........F.......209 647-7037
18260 S Harlan Rd Lathrop (95330) ***(P-20173)***
Tesla Inc..........A.......510 896-6400
38503 Cherry St Ste I Newark (94560) ***(P-20174)***
Tesla Inc..........E.......707 373-4035
1055 Page Ave Fremont (94538) ***(P-20175)***
Tesla Inc (PA)..........C.......650 681-5000
3500 Deer Creek Rd Palo Alto (94304) ***(P-20176)***
Tesla Motors Store Santana Row..........F.......408 249-2815
333 Santana Row San Jose (95128) ***(P-20177)***
Tesla Vineyards Lp..........F.......925 456-2500
4590 Tesla Rd Livermore (94550) ***(P-2012)***
Teslaire..........F.......310 590-5357
263 W Olive Ave 307 Burbank (91502) ***(P-16122)***
Tesoro, Carson *Also called Andeavor* ***(P-22)***
Tesoro Refining & Mktg Co LLC..........A.......925 372-3100
150 Solano Way Pacheco (94553) ***(P-9363)***
Tesoro Refining & Mktg Co LLC..........B.......562 728-2215
5905 N Paramount Blvd Long Beach (90805) ***(P-9364)***
Tesorx Pharma LLC (PA)..........F.......909 595-0500
3670 W Temple Ave Pomona (91768) ***(P-8410)***
Tessenderio Kerly Inc..........E.......559 582-9200
10724 Energy St Hanford (93230) ***(P-9086)***
Tessenderlo Kerley Inc..........E.......559 485-0114
5247 E Central Ave Fresno (93725) ***(P-7807)***
Tessera Inc (HQ)..........F.......408 321-6000
3025 Orchard Pkwy San Jose (95134) ***(P-19224)***
Tessera Intellectual Prpts Inc..........D.......408 321-6000
3025 Orchard Pkwy San Jose (95134) ***(P-19225)***
Tessera Intllctual Prprty Corp..........E.......408 321-6000
3025 Orchard Pkwy San Jose (95134) ***(P-19226)***
Tessera Technologies Inc (HQ)..........E.......408 321-6000
3025 Orchard Pkwy San Jose (95134) ***(P-19227)***
Test Connections Inc..........F.......909 981-1810
1146 W 9th St Upland (91786) ***(P-21871)***
Test Electronics..........E.......831 763-2000
821 Smith Rd Watsonville (95076) ***(P-21872)***
Test Enterprises Inc (PA)..........E.......408 542-5900
1288 Reamwood Ave Sunnyvale (94089) ***(P-21667)***
Test Enterprises Inc..........E.......408 778-0234
1288 Reamwood Ave Sunnyvale (94089) ***(P-21873)***
Test Laboratories Inc (PA)..........F.......818 881-4251
7121 Canby Ave Reseda (91335) ***(P-2680)***
Test-Um Inc..........F.......818 464-5021
430 N Mccarthy Blvd Milpitas (95035) ***(P-21874)***
Testarossa Vineyards LLC..........E.......408 354-6150
300 College Ave Apt A Los Gatos (95030) ***(P-2013)***
Testmetrix Inc..........E.......408 730-5511
426 S Hillview Dr Milpitas (95035) ***(P-21875)***
Testronic Laboratories Inc..........E.......818 845-3223
111 N First St Ste 304 Burbank (91502) ***(P-21876)***
Tetra Pak Processing Equip..........D.......209 599-4634
1408 W Main St Ste E Ripon (95366) ***(P-5542)***
Tetra Tech Ec Inc..........E.......949 809-5000
17885 Von Karman Ave # 500 Irvine (92614) ***(P-22029)***
Tetracam Inc..........F.......818 718-2119
21601 Devonshire St # 310 Chatsworth (91311) ***(P-23202)***
Tetrad Services Inc..........F.......530 527-5889
960 Diamond Ave Red Bluff (96080) ***(P-16997)***
Tetrafluor, El Segundo *Also called Coorstek Inc* ***(P-7198)***
Teva Foods Inc..........E.......323 267-8110
4401 S Downey Rd Vernon (90058) ***(P-2681)***
Teva Parenteral Medicines Inc..........A.......949 455-4700
19 Hughes Irvine (92618) ***(P-8411)***
Teva Pharmaceuticals Usa Inc..........E.......949 457-2828
19 Hughes Irvine (92618) ***(P-8412)***
Tex Shoemaker & Son Inc..........F.......909 592-2071
19034 E Donington St Glendora (91741) ***(P-3624)***
Tex-Cote, Los Angeles *Also called Textured Coatings America Inc* ***(P-8947)***
Texas Boom Company Inc..........F.......281 441-2002
2433 Sagebrush Ct La Jolla (92037) ***(P-14242)***
Texas Instruments Incorporated..........E.......408 541-9900
165 Gibraltar Ct Sunnyvale (94089) ***(P-19228)***
Texas Instruments Incorporated..........E.......669 721-5000
2900 Semiconductor Dr Santa Clara (95051) ***(P-19229)***
Texas Instruments Incorporated..........C.......714 731-7110
14351 Myford Rd Tustin (92780) ***(P-19230)***
Texas Tst Inc..........E.......951 685-2155
13428 Benson Ave Chino (91710) ***(P-11568)***
Texchem Chemical, Sacramento *Also called Kds Nail Products* ***(P-24146)***
Texollini Inc..........C.......310 537-3400
2575 E El Presidio St Long Beach (90810) ***(P-2967)***
Textile 2000 Screen Printing..........E.......858 735-8521
8675 Miralani Dr San Diego (92126) ***(P-7516)***
Textile Products Inc..........E.......714 761-0401
2512-2520 W Woodland Dr Anaheim (92801) ***(P-2784)***
Textile Unlimited Corporation (PA)..........E.......310 263-7400
20917 Higgins Ct Torrance (90501) ***(P-3061)***
Textron Inc..........D.......707 763-8855
1309 Dynamic St Petaluma (94954) ***(P-19231)***
Texture Design, Anaheim *Also called Textured Design Furniture* ***(P-4743)***
Textured Coatings America Inc..........E.......323 233-3111
5950 Avalon Blvd Los Angeles (90003) ***(P-8947)***
Textured Design Furniture..........E.......714 502-9121
1303 S Claudina St Anaheim (92805) ***(P-4743)***
TFC Manufacturing Inc..........D.......562 426-9559
4001 Watson Plaza Dr Lakewood (90712) ***(P-12788)***
Tfd Incorporated..........E.......714 630-7127
1180 N Tustin Ave Anaheim (92807) ***(P-22141)***
Tfn Architectural Signage Inc (PA)..........E.......714 556-0990
3411 W Lake Center Dr Santa Ana (92704) ***(P-23988)***
Tfx International..........F.......760 836-3232
72785 Frank Sinatra Dr Rancho Mirage (92270) ***(P-8413)***
Tgs Molding LLC..........F.......909 890-1707
425 E Parkcenter Cir S San Bernardino (92408) ***(P-10401)***
Tgs Plastic, San Bernardino *Also called Tgs Molding LLC* ***(P-10401)***
Thai Silks, Mountain View *Also called Exotic Silks Inc* ***(P-2736)***
Thai Thai Noodle..........F.......415 441-5551
1400 California St San Francisco (94109) ***(P-2442)***
Thai Union International Inc (HQ)..........F.......858 558-9662
9330 Scranton Rd Ste 500 San Diego (92121) ***(P-2305)***
Thales Alenia Space North Amer..........F.......408 973-9845
20400 Stevens Creek Blvd # 245 Cupertino (95014) ***(P-21182)***
Thales Avionics..........F.......949 381-3033
48 Discovery Irvine (92618) ***(P-20948)***
Thales Avionics Inc..........C.......949 790-2500
51 Discovery Irvine (92618) ***(P-20949)***
That Casting Place Inc..........F.......323 258-5691
6229 Outlook Ave Los Angeles (90042) ***(P-23350)***
Thats It Nutrition LLC..........F.......818 782-1701
834 S Broadway Ste 800 Los Angeles (90014) ***(P-1461)***
Thawte Inc..........E.......650 426-7400
487 E Middlefield Rd Mountain View (94043) ***(P-18284)***
Thawte Consulting USA, Mountain View *Also called Thawte Inc* ***(P-18284)***
The Badge Company, Huntington Beach *Also called Badge Co* ***(P-24047)***
The Beacon, San Diego *Also called Mannis Communications Inc* ***(P-5937)***
The Black & Decker Inc..........B.......949 672-4000
19701 Da Vinci El Toro (92610) ***(P-14712)***
The Bristol Group, San Rafael *Also called Bgl Development Inc* ***(P-24419)***
The China Press, Alhambra *Also called Asia Pacific California Inc* ***(P-5764)***
The Clearwater Company, Rancho Cordova *Also called Nca Laboratories Inc* ***(P-17837)***
The French Patisserie Inc..........D.......650 738-4990
1080 Palmetto Ave Pacifica (94044) ***(P-1333)***
The Hispanic News, La Puente *Also called Total Media Enterprises Inc* ***(P-6604)***
The Ligature Inc..........F.......800 421-8703
4909 Alcoa Ave Vernon (90058) ***(P-7517)***
The Ligature Inc (HQ)..........E.......323 585-6000
4909 Alcoa Ave Vernon (90058) ***(P-7133)***
The Ligature Inc..........E.......510 526-5181
750 Gilmore St Berkeley (94710) ***(P-7518)***
The Mayflower Group, Santa Barbara *Also called Maysoft Inc* ***(P-24889)***
The Microfilm Company of Cal..........F.......310 354-2610
14214 S Figueroa St Los Angeles (90061) ***(P-6400)***
The Orange County Printing Co, Irvine *Also called Ocpc Inc* ***(P-7000)***
The Orgnal Los Angeles APT Mag, Costa Mesa *Also called Pinpoint Media Group Inc* ***(P-6233)***
The Rupp Butler Studio, Cotati *Also called Lili Butler Studio Inc* ***(P-3253)***
The Rutter Group, Los Angeles *Also called West Publishing Corporation* ***(P-6407)***
The Sloan Company Inc (PA)..........C.......805 676-3200
5725 Olivas Park Dr Ventura (93003) ***(P-17737)***
The Valley Business Jurnl Inc..........F.......951 461-0400
40335 Winchester Rd # 128 Temecula (92591) ***(P-6069)***
The Vitamin Barn, Canoga Park *Also called California Natural Vitamins* ***(P-8091)***
The Wave, Los Angeles *Also called Wave Community Newspapers Inc* ***(P-6083)***
The White Sheet, Palm Desert *Also called Associated Desert Shoppers* ***(P-6437)***
Theater Publications Inc..........F.......408 748-1600
3485 Victor St Santa Clara (95054) ***(P-6269)***
Theboom Headsets, Petaluma *Also called Ume Voice Inc* ***(P-17872)***
Thebrain Technologies LP..........F.......310 390-0100
11522 W Washington Blvd Los Angeles (90066) ***(P-25268)***

ALPHABETIC

Employee Codes: A=Over 500 employees, B=251-500
C=101-250, D=51-100, E=20-50, F=10-19
2019 California
Manfacturers Register
© Mergent Inc. 1-800-342-5647
1305

Theft Patrol LLC.....F.....858 880-5841
4740 Von Karman Ave Newport Beach (92660) ***(P-18285)***
Thehomemag Bay Area, Brentwood *Also called Nyabenga Llc* ***(P-6542)***
Themis, Fremont *Also called Mercury Systms-Trstd Mssn Sltn* ***(P-15454)***
Theranos Inc (PA).....D.....650 838-9292
7373 Gateway Blvd Newark (94560) ***(P-22648)***
Therapak LLC.....C.....626 357-5900
651 Wharton Dr Claremont (91711) ***(P-21493)***
Therapeutic Industries Inc.....F.....760 343-2502
72096 Dunham Way Ste E Thousand Palms (92276) ***(P-22649)***
Therapy Tubs.....F.....951 553-7001
27973 Diaz Rd Temecula (92590) ***(P-9912)***
Therasense Inc.....F.....510 749-5400
1360 S Loop Rd Alameda (94502) ***(P-22650)***
Theravance Biopharma Us Inc.....C.....650 808-6000
901 Gateway Blvd South San Francisco (94080) ***(P-8414)***
Theravnce Bphrma Antbotics Inc.....C.....877 275-6930
901 Gateway Blvd South San Francisco (94080) ***(P-8415)***
Therm-O-Namel Inc.....F.....310 631-7866
2780 M L King Jr Blvd Lynwood (90262) ***(P-13672)***
Therm-X of California Inc (PA).....C.....510 441-7566
3200 Investment Blvd Hayward (94545) ***(P-22288)***
Therma LLC.....A.....408 347-3400
1601 Las Plumas Ave San Jose (95133) ***(P-12789)***
Therma-Tek Range Corp.....E.....570 455-9491
9121 Atlanta Ave Ste 331 Huntington Beach (92646) ***(P-17417)***
Thermal Bags By Ingrid Inc.....F.....847 836-4400
5801 Skylab Rd Huntington Beach (92647) ***(P-5511)***
Thermal Dynamics, Ontario *Also called Yinlun Tdi LLC* ***(P-20490)***
Thermal Electronics Inc.....F.....951 674-3555
403 W Minthorn St Lake Elsinore (92530) ***(P-19761)***
Thermal Engrg Intl USA Inc (HQ).....C.....323 726-0641
18000 Studebaker Rd # 400 Cerritos (90703) ***(P-12433)***
Thermal Equipment Corporation.....E.....310 328-6600
2030 E University Dr Compton (90220) ***(P-12434)***
THERMAL SOLUTIONS MANUFACTURING INC., San Bernardino *Also called Thermal Solutions Mfg Inc* ***(P-20464)***
Thermal Solutions Mfg Inc.....E.....909 796-0754
1390 S Tippecanoe Ave B San Bernardino (92408) ***(P-20464)***
Thermal Structures Inc (HQ).....B.....951 736-9911
2362 Railroad St Corona (92880) ***(P-20682)***
Thermal-Vac Technology Inc.....E.....714 997-2601
1221 W Struck Ave Orange (92867) ***(P-11833)***
Thermally Engineered Manufactu.....E.....310 523-9934
543 W 135th St Gardena (90248) ***(P-12435)***
Thermalrite, Rancho Cucamonga *Also called Everidge Inc* ***(P-15957)***
Thermalsun Glass Products Inc.....E.....707 579-9534
3950 Brickway Blvd Santa Rosa (95403) ***(P-10733)***
Thermapak Technologies Inc.....F.....909 612-9380
1210 E Green St Ste 102 Pasadena (91106) ***(P-12000)***
Thermaprint Corp.....E.....949 583-0800
11 Autry Ste B Irvine (92618) ***(P-23203)***
Thermcore, Grass Valley *Also called Thermo Products Inc* ***(P-11834)***
Thermcraft Inc.....F.....916 363-9411
3762 Bradview Dr Sacramento (95827) ***(P-7519)***
Thermech Corporation.....E.....714 533-3183
1773 W Lincoln Ave Ste I Anaheim (92801) ***(P-5543)***
Thermech Engineering, Anaheim *Also called Thermech Corporation* ***(P-5543)***
Thermeon Corporation (PA).....F.....714 731-9191
1175 Warner Ave Tustin (92780) ***(P-25269)***
Thermionics Metal Processing, Hayward *Also called Tli Enterprises Inc* ***(P-13521)***
Thermo Finnigan LLC (HQ).....B.....408 965-6000
355 River Oaks Pkwy San Jose (95134) ***(P-22030)***
Thermo Fischer Scientific Inc.....F.....747 494-1413
22801 Roscoe Blvd West Hills (91304) ***(P-22031)***
Thermo Fisher, Sunnyvale *Also called Dionex Corporation* ***(P-21946)***
Thermo Fisher Scientific, Fremont *Also called Lab Vision Corporation* ***(P-21981)***
Thermo Fisher Scientific, Santa Clara *Also called Fiberlite Centrifuge LLC* ***(P-22449)***
Thermo Fisher Scientific.....E.....408 731-5056
3380 Central Expy Santa Clara (95051) ***(P-22032)***
Thermo Fisher Scientific.....B.....408 894-9835
355 River Oaks Pkwy San Jose (95134) ***(P-22033)***
Thermo Fisher Scientific Inc.....B.....909 393-3205
15982 San Antonio Ave Chino (91710) ***(P-22034)***
Thermo Fisher Scientific Inc.....F.....408 988-1103
422 Aldo Ave Santa Clara (95054) ***(P-22035)***
Thermo Fisher Scientific Inc.....B.....858 481-6386
675 S Sierra Ave Solana Beach (92075) ***(P-22036)***
Thermo Fisher Scientific Inc.....D.....650 876-1949
200 Oyster Point Blvd South San Francisco (94080) ***(P-22037)***
Thermo Fisher Scientific Inc.....E.....510 979-5000
46500 Kato Rd Fremont (94538) ***(P-22038)***
Thermo Fisher Scientific Inc.....F.....650 246-5265
180 Oyster Point Blvd South San Francisco (94080) ***(P-22039)***
Thermo Fisher Scientific Inc.....F.....858 453-7551
9389 Waples St San Diego (92121) ***(P-22040)***
Thermo Fisher Scientific Inc.....C.....650 638-6409
7000 Shoreline Ct South San Francisco (94080) ***(P-22041)***
Thermo Fisher Scientific Inc.....F.....317 490-5809
46500 Kato Rd Fremont (94538) ***(P-22042)***
Thermo Fisher Scientific Inc.....F.....858 882-1286
10010 Mesa Rim Rd San Diego (92121) ***(P-22043)***
Thermo Gamma-Metrics LLC (HQ).....E.....858 450-9811
10010 Mesa Rim Rd San Diego (92121) ***(P-21695)***
Thermo Kevex X-Ray Inc.....E.....831 438-5940
320 El Pueblo Rd Scotts Valley (95066) ***(P-18397)***
Thermo Products Inc.....D.....909 888-2882
13185 Nevada City Ave Grass Valley (95945) ***(P-11834)***
Thermo Trilogy, Wasco *Also called Certis USA LLC* ***(P-9096)***
Thermobile, Santa Ana *Also called Hood Manufacturing Inc* ***(P-10138)***
Thermodyne International Ltd.....C.....909 923-9945
1841 S Business Pkwy Ontario (91761) ***(P-10402)***
Thermofinnegan, San Jose *Also called Thermo Fisher Scientific* ***(P-22033)***
Thermolab, Sun Valley *Also called Technical Heaters Inc* ***(P-9509)***
Thermometrics Corporation (PA).....E.....818 886-3755
18714 Parthenia St Northridge (91324) ***(P-21668)***
Thermonics, Sunnyvale *Also called Test Enterprises Inc* ***(P-21667)***
Thermoplaque Company Inc.....F.....818 988-1080
14928 Calvert St Van Nuys (91411) ***(P-24269)***
Thermoquest Corporation.....A.....408 965-6000
355 River Oaks Pkwy San Jose (95134) ***(P-22044)***
Thermostatic Industries, Rancho Cucamonga *Also called Newtex Industries Inc* ***(P-24189)***
Thermostatic Industries Inc.....E.....323 277-0900
9654 Hermosa Ave Rancho Cucamonga (91730) ***(P-11313)***
Thermtronix Corporation (PA).....E.....760 246-4500
17129 Muskrat Ave Adelanto (92301) ***(P-15275)***
Thermx Southwest, San Diego *Also called Thermx Temperature Tech* ***(P-21669)***
Thermx Temperature Tech.....F.....858 573-0983
7370 Opportunity Rd Ste S San Diego (92111) ***(P-21669)***
Theta Digital Corporation.....E.....818 572-4300
1749 Chapin Rd Montebello (90640) ***(P-17867)***
Thibiant International Inc.....B.....818 709-1345
20320 Prairie St Chatsworth (91311) ***(P-8853)***
Thiele Technologies Inc.....B.....559 638-8484
1949 E Manning Ave Reedley (93654) ***(P-15230)***
Thienes Apparel Inc.....C.....626 575-2818
1811 Floradale Ave South El Monte (91733) ***(P-2861)***
Thiessen Products Inc.....C.....805 482-6913
555 Dawson Dr Ste A Camarillo (93012) ***(P-16998)***
Thin Film Devices, Anaheim *Also called Tfd Incorporated* ***(P-22141)***
Thin Film Electronics Inc.....D.....408 503-7300
2581 Junction Ave San Jose (95134) ***(P-19762)***
Thin-Lite Corporation.....E.....805 987-5021
530 Constitution Ave Camarillo (93012) ***(P-17738)***
Thingap LLC.....E.....805 477-9741
4035 Via Pescador Camarillo (93012) ***(P-17226)***
Thingap Holdings LLC.....F.....805 477-9741
4035 Via Pescador Camarillo (93012) ***(P-17227)***
Thingap.com, Camarillo *Also called Thingap Holdings LLC* ***(P-17227)***
Think Surgical Inc.....C.....510 249-2300
47201 Lakeview Blvd Fremont (94538) ***(P-22832)***
Thinkcp Technologies, Irvine *Also called H Co Computer Products* ***(P-15546)***
Thinksmart LLC.....F.....888 489-4284
530 Jackson St Fl 3 San Francisco (94133) ***(P-25270)***
Thinkwave Inc.....F.....707 824-6200
7959 Covert Ln Sebastopol (95472) ***(P-19886)***
Third Degree Sportswear Inc.....F.....714 890-9828
5402 Commercial Dr Huntington Beach (92649) ***(P-3518)***
Third Floor North Company, Santa Ana *Also called Tfn Architectural Signage Inc* ***(P-23988)***
Third Mllennium Test Solutions.....F.....650 949-1120
3101 Alexis Dr Palo Alto (94304) ***(P-21877)***
Thirdmotion Inc.....F.....415 848-2724
795 Folsom St Fl 1 San Francisco (94107) ***(P-25271)***
Thirdrock Software.....F.....408 777-2910
7098 Chiala Ln San Jose (95129) ***(P-25272)***
Thirsty Bear Brewing Co LLC.....D.....415 974-0905
661 Howard St San Francisco (94105) ***(P-1631)***
Thirty Three Threads Inc.....E.....877 486-3769
1330 Park Center Dr Vista (92081) ***(P-2816)***
Thistle Roller Co Inc.....E.....323 685-5322
209 Van Norman Rd Montebello (90640) ***(P-14828)***
Thomas Burt.....F.....626 301-9065
5095 Brooks St Montclair (91763) ***(P-7134)***
Thomas Cnc Machining.....F.....714 692-9373
23650 Via Del Rio Yorba Linda (92887) ***(P-16999)***
Thomas Container & Packaging, Pomona *Also called T & T Box Company Inc* ***(P-5510)***
Thomas Craven Wood Finishers.....F.....805 341-7713
15746 W Arminta St Simi Valley (93065) ***(P-5258)***
Thomas Dehlinger.....F.....707 823-2378
4101 Ginehill Rd Sebastopol (95472) ***(P-2014)***
Thomas E Davis Inc.....F.....925 373-1373
6736 Preston Ave Ste A Livermore (94551) ***(P-12790)***
Thomas Lavin, West Hollywood *Also called Lavinder Inc* ***(P-3004)***
Thomas Leonardini.....F.....707 963-9454
1563 Saint Helena Hwy S Saint Helena (94574) ***(P-2015)***
Thomas Lundberg.....F.....415 695-0110
2620 3rd St San Francisco (94107) ***(P-4844)***
Thomas Manufacturing Co LLC.....E.....530 893-8940
1308 W 8th Ave Chico (95926) ***(P-25442)***
Thomas Products, Madera *Also called Nutra Blend LLC* ***(P-1151)***
Thomas T Bernstein.....E.....626 351-0570
1160 Daveric Dr Pasadena (91107) ***(P-13046)***
Thomas Tellez.....E.....707 668-1825
100 Taylor Way Blue Lake (95525) ***(P-4246)***
Thomas Welding & Mch Sp Inc.....E.....530 893-8940
1308 W 8th Ave Chico (95926) ***(P-25443)***
Thomas West Inc (PA).....E.....408 481-3850
470 Mercury Dr Sunnyvale (94085) ***(P-3752)***
Thomas-Swan Sign Company Inc.....E.....415 621-1511
2717 Goodrick Ave Richmond (94801) ***(P-23989)***
Thomes Creek Rock Co Inc.....F.....530 824-0191
6069 99w Corning (96021) ***(P-386)***
Thompson ADB Industries, Westminster *Also called Thompson Industries Ltd* ***(P-20950)***
Thompson Aerospace Inc (PA).....F.....949 264-1600
8687 Research Dr Ste 250 Irvine (92618) ***(P-20683)***
Thompson Building Materials, Fontana *Also called Edessa Inc* ***(P-10919)***
Thompson Gundrilling Inc.....E.....323 873-4045
13840 Saticoy St Van Nuys (91402) ***(P-11501)***

Thompson Industries Ltd....E....310 679-9193
7155 Fenwick Ln Westminster (92683) *(P-20950)*
Thompson Magnetics Inc....F....951 676-0243
42255 Baldaray Cir Ste C Temecula (92590) *(P-19763)*
Thompson Multimedia, Camarillo *Also called Technicolor Thomson Group (P-17863)*
Thompson Tank Inc....F....562 869-7711
8029 Phlox St Downey (90241) *(P-12436)*
Thompson Type Inc....E....619 224-3137
3687 Voltaire St San Diego (92106) *(P-7635)*
Thomson Higher Education, San Francisco *Also called Cengage Learning Inc (P-6321)*
THOMSON REUTERS (MARKETS) LLC, San Francisco *Also called Thomson Reuters (markets) LLC (P-6270)*
Thomson Reuters (markets) LLC....B....415 344-6000
1 Sansome St Lbby 3 San Francisco (94104) *(P-6270)*
Thomson Reuters Corporation....B....949 400-7782
163 Albert Pl Costa Mesa (92627) *(P-6602)*
Thomson Reuters Corporation....F....877 518-2761
633 W 5th St Ste 2300 Los Angeles (90071) *(P-18286)*
Thor Electronics of California, Salinas *Also called Abrams Electronics Inc (P-17438)*
Thor Fiber, Torrance *Also called Digi Group LLC (P-18086)*
Thoratec Corporation (HQ)....C....925 847-8600
6035 Stoneridge Dr Pleasanton (94588) *(P-23059)*
Thoreen Designs Inc....E....949 645-0981
930 W 16th St Ste C1 Costa Mesa (92627) *(P-3753)*
Thornton Steel & Ir Works Inc....E....714 491-8800
1323 S State College Pkwy Anaheim (92806) *(P-12898)*
Thornton Winery....D....951 699-0099
32575 Rancho Cal Rd Temecula (92591) *(P-2016)*
Thoro—Packaging (HQ)....C....951 278-2100
1467 Davril Cir Corona (92880) *(P-5512)*
Thorock Metals Inc....E....310 537-1597
1213 S Pacific Coast Hwy Redondo Beach (90277) *(P-11569)*
Thorx Laboratories Inc....F....510 240-6000
30831 Huntwood Ave Hayward (94544) *(P-8416)*
Thought Inc....F....415 836-9199
5 3rd St Ste 1030 San Francisco (94103) *(P-25273)*
Thoughtspot Inc....F....800 508-7008
3000 El Camino Real Palo Alto (94306) *(P-25274)*
Thousandeyes Inc (PA)....D....415 513-4526
201 Mission St Ste 1700 San Francisco (94105) *(P-25275)*
Thousands Oaks Hand Wash....F....805 379-2732
2725 E Thousand Oaks Blvd Thousand Oaks (91362) *(P-16123)*
Thousandshores Inc....F....510 477-0249
33442 Western Ave Union City (94587) *(P-15496)*
Three Brothers Cutting....F....323 564-4774
8416 Otis St South Gate (90280) *(P-3276)*
Three Chiefs & No Indians LLC....C....909 465-6314
4200 E Mission Blvd Ontario (91761) *(P-7623)*
Three Dots LLC....D....714 799-6333
7340 Lampson Ave Garden Grove (92841) *(P-3277)*
Three Guys Holding Co LLC....F....855 711-7686
430 Pacific Ave San Francisco (94133) *(P-3089)*
Three Man Corporation....E....858 684-5200
10025 Huennekens St San Diego (92121) *(P-7520)*
Three Plus One Inc....F....213 623-3070
3007 Fruitland Ave Vernon (90058) *(P-3278)*
Three Sisters Design Inc....F....760 230-2813
967 S Coast Highway 101 # 109 Encinitas (92024) *(P-23325)*
Three Sisters Jewelry Design, Encinitas *Also called Three Sisters Design Inc (P-23325)*
Three Star Rfrgn Engrg Inc....E....310 327-9090
21720 S Wilmington Ave # 309 Long Beach (90810) *(P-15981)*
Three Sticks Wines LLC....E....707 996-3328
21692 8th St E Ste 280 Sonoma (95476) *(P-2017)*
Three Stone Hearth....F....510 981-1334
1581 University Ave Berkeley (94703) *(P-11872)*
Three Twins Organic Ice Cream, Petaluma *Also called Three Twins Organic Inc (P-699)*
Three Twins Organic Inc (PA)....E....707 763-8946
419 1st St Petaluma (94952) *(P-699)*
Three-D Plastics Inc....F....323 849-1316
424 N Varney St Burbank (91502) *(P-10403)*
Three-D Plastics Inc (PA)....E....323 849-1316
430 N Varney St Burbank (91502) *(P-10404)*
Three-D Traffic Works, Burbank *Also called Three-D Plastics Inc (P-10403)*
Three-D Traffics Works, Burbank *Also called Three-D Plastics Inc (P-10404)*
Threshold Enterprises Ltd....F....831 425-3955
165 Technology Dr Watsonville (95076) *(P-7974)*
Threshold Enterprises Ltd (PA)....B....831 438-6851
23 Janis Way Scotts Valley (95066) *(P-7975)*
Threshold Enterprises Ltd....D....831 461-6413
11 Janis Way Scotts Valley (95066) *(P-7976)*
Threshold Enterprises Ltd....E....831 461-6343
19 Janis Way Scotts Vly Scotts Valle Scotts Valley (95066) *(P-7977)*
Threshold Enterprises Ltd....E....831 466-4014
2280 Delaware Ave Santa Cruz (95060) *(P-7978)*
Thrift Town, Sacramento *Also called Norquist Salvage Corp Inc (P-3181)*
Thrift Town, Sacramento *Also called Norquist Salvage Corp Inc (P-3182)*
Thrun Mfg Inc....E....949 677-2461
31947 Corydon St Ste 170 Lake Elsinore (92530) *(P-20684)*
Thunder Products Inc....F....408 270-7800
2469 Klein Rd San Jose (95148) *(P-23391)*
Thunderbird Industries Inc....E....909 394-1633
695 W Terrace Dr San Dimas (91773) *(P-14578)*
Thunderbolt Manufacturing Inc....E....714 632-0397
641 S State College Blvd Fullerton (92831) *(P-17000)*
Thunderbolt Sales Inc....E....209 869-4561
3400 Patterson Rd Riverbank (95367) *(P-4598)*
Thunderbolt WD Treating Co Inc (PA)....E....209 869-4561
3400 Patterson Rd Riverbank (95367) *(P-4599)*
Thunderworks Division, Santee *Also called Decatur Electronics Inc (P-21286)*

Thyssenkrupp Bilstein Amer Inc....E....858 386-5900
14102 Stowe Dr Poway (92064) *(P-20465)*
TI Inc....F....559 972-1475
13802 Avenue 352 Visalia (93292) *(P-9075)*
TI Limited LLC (PA)....D....323 877-5991
20335 Ventura Blvd Woodland Hills (91364) *(P-25276)*
TI Wire, Walnut *Also called Tree Island Wire (usa) Inc (P-11460)*
Tianello Inc....C....323 231-0599
138 W 38th St Los Angeles (90037) *(P-3279)*
Tianello By Steve Barraza, Los Angeles *Also called Tianello Inc (P-3279)*
Tibban Manufacturing Inc....F....760 961-1160
12593 Highline Dr Apple Valley (92308) *(P-24270)*
Tibbetts Newport Corporation....F....714 546-6662
2337 S Birch St Santa Ana (92707) *(P-8948)*
Tibco Software Inc....F....415 344-0339
575 Market St Fl 15 San Francisco (94105) *(P-25277)*
Ticketswest, Irvine *Also called Paciolan LLC (P-25045)*
Tidelands Oil Production Inc (HQ)....E....562 436-9918
301 E Ocean Blvd Ste 300 Long Beach (90802) *(P-78)*
Tidelands Oil Production Inc....E....562 436-2836
705 Pico Ave Long Beach (90813) *(P-79)*
Tidings....E....213 637-7360
3424 Wilshire Blvd Los Angeles (90010) *(P-6070)*
Tien-Hu Knitting Co (us) Inc....D....510 268-8833
3996 San Pablo Ave Ste A Emeryville (94608) *(P-2862)*
Tiffany Coach Builders, Perris *Also called Warlock Industries (P-20182)*
Tiffany Coachworks, Perris *Also called Limos By Tiffany Inc (P-20213)*
Tiffany Coachworks Inc....C....951 657-2680
1771 N Delilah St Corona (92879) *(P-20178)*
Tiffany Structures....E....619 905-9684
13162 Hwy 8 Bus Spc 205 El Cajon (92021) *(P-12964)*
Tig/M LLC....E....818 709-8500
9160 Jordan Ave Chatsworth (91311) *(P-14291)*
Tiger Beat Magazine, Glendale *Also called Laufer Media Inc (P-6206)*
Tiger Cased Hole Services Inc....F....562 426-4044
2828 Junipero Ave Signal Hill (90755) *(P-14109)*
Tiger Construction Inc....F....408 244-8124
6930 Rainbow Dr San Jose (95129) *(P-8949)*
Tiger Jet Network Inc....F....408 437-7727
50 Airport Pkwy Ofc San Jose (95110) *(P-21878)*
Tiger Tanks Inc....E....661 363-8335
3397 Edison Hwy Bakersfield (93307) *(P-21219)*
Tiger-Sul Products LLC....F....209 451-2725
61 Stork Rd Stockton (95203) *(P-7808)*
Tigers Plastics Inc....F....818 901-9393
14721 Lull St Van Nuys (91405) *(P-10405)*
Tikos Tanks Inc....E....951 757-8014
14561 Hawthorne Ave Fontana (92335) *(P-25444)*
Tile Artisans Inc....F....800 601-4199
4288 State Highway 70 Oroville (95965) *(P-10795)*
Tile Guild Inc....F....323 581-3770
2424 E 55th St Vernon (90058) *(P-10796)*
Tilley Manufacturing Co Inc (PA)....E....650 365-3598
2734 Spring St Redwood City (94063) *(P-9561)*
Tilton Engineering Inc....E....805 688-2353
25 Easy St Buellton (93427) *(P-20466)*
Tim Guzzy Services Inc....F....626 813-0626
5136 Calmview Ave Baldwin Park (91706) *(P-17001)*
Tim Hoover Enterprises....D....951 237-9210
8532 Yarrow Ln Riverside (92508) *(P-18287)*
Timber Products Co Ltd Partnr....C....530 842-2310
130 N Phillipe Ln Yreka (96097) *(P-4386)*
Timberline Molding, San Marcos *Also called Doors Unlimited (P-4294)*
Timbucktoo Manufacturing Inc....E....310 323-1134
1633 W 134th St Gardena (90249) *(P-16124)*
Timbuk2 Designs Inc (PA)....D....415 252-4300
583 Shotwell St San Francisco (94110) *(P-3772)*
Timco, Hesperia *Also called T L Timmerman Construction (P-4427)*
Timco Aluminum Alloys, Chino *Also called Tst Inc (P-11571)*
Timco/Cal Rf Inc....E....805 582-1777
3910 Royal Ave Ste A Simi Valley (93063) *(P-19425)*
Time Inc....E....415 434-5244
2 Embarcadero Ctr # 1900 San Francisco (94111) *(P-6271)*
Time Masters, Los Angeles *Also called AMG Employee Management Inc (P-23216)*
Time Prtg Solutions Provider....F....916 446-6152
1614 D St Sacramento (95814) *(P-7135)*
Timely Data Resources Inc....F....831 462-2510
107 Washburn Ave Capitola (95010) *(P-25278)*
Timemed Labeling Systems Inc (HQ)....D....818 897-1111
27770 N Entrmt Dr Ste 200 Valencia (91355) *(P-9685)*
Times Herald, Hayward *Also called Alameda Newspapers Inc (P-5753)*
Times Litho Inc....E....503 359-0300
300 S Grand Ave Ste 1200 Los Angeles (90071) *(P-7136)*
Times Media Inc....F....408 494-7000
1900 Camden Ave San Jose (95124) *(P-6071)*
Times Publishing, Torrance *Also called National Law Digest Inc (P-6367)*
Times-Standard, Eureka *Also called Humboldt Newspaper Inc (P-5884)*
Timet, Vallejo *Also called Titanium Metals Corporation (P-11637)*
Timevalue Software....E....949 727-1800
22 Mauchly Irvine (92618) *(P-25279)*
Timken Company....B....714 484-2400
4422 Corporate Center Dr Los Alamitos (90720) *(P-15113)*
Timken Gears & Services Inc....E....310 605-2600
12935 Imperial Hwy Santa Fe Springs (90670) *(P-13114)*
Timkev International Inc....F....562 232-1691
9050 Rosecrans Ave Bellflower (90706) *(P-1383)*
Timlin Industries Inc....E....541 947-6771
6777 Nancy Ridge Dr San Diego (92121) *(P-23990)*

Employee Codes: A=Over 500 employees, B=251-500
C=101-250, D=51-100, E=20-50, F=10-19
2019 California
Manfacturers Register
© Mergent Inc. 1-800-342-5647
1307

Timmons Wood Products Inc F 951 940-4700
4675 Wade Ave Perris (92571) ***(P-4660)***
Tini Aerospace Inc E 415 524-2124
2505 Kerner Blvd San Rafael (94901) ***(P-18288)***
Tink Inc E 530 895-0897
2361 Durham Dayton Hwy Durham (95938) ***(P-14193)***
Tinker & Rasor Inc E 909 890-0700
791 S Waterman Ave San Bernardino (92408) ***(P-21442)***
Tiny Hero, San Francisco *Also called Northern Quinoa Prod Corp* ***(P-1068)***
Tinyinklingcom LLC F 877 777-6287
6303 Owensmouth Ave Fl 10 Woodland Hills (91367) ***(P-9686)***
Tiodize Co Inc (PA) D 714 898-4377
5858 Engineer Dr Huntington Beach (92649) ***(P-13673)***
Tiodize Co Inc F 248 348-6050
5858 Engineer Dr Huntington Beach (92649) ***(P-13674)***
Tipestry Inc F 650 421-1344
940 Stewart Dr 203 Sunnyvale (94085) ***(P-25280)***
Titan Frozen Fruit LLC (PA) E 831 540-4110
585 Auto Center Dr Ste A Watsonville (95076) ***(P-970)***
Titan Gaming F 310 869-3326
1351 4th St Fl 4 Santa Monica (90401) ***(P-23472)***
Titan Medical Dme Inc F 818 889-9998
803 Camarillo Springs Rd A Camarillo (93012) ***(P-22651)***
Titan Medical Enterprises Inc F 562 903-7236
11100 Greenstone Ave Santa Fe Springs (90670) ***(P-8417)***
Titan Metal Fabricators Inc (PA) D 805 487-5050
352 Balboa Cir Camarillo (93012) ***(P-12260)***
Titan Metal Products, Sacramento *Also called Tmp LLC* ***(P-12352)***
Titan Oilfield Services Inc F 661 861-1630
21535 Kratzmeyer Rd Bakersfield (93314) ***(P-282)***
Titan Pharmaceuticals Inc (PA) F 650 244-4990
400 Oyster Point Blvd # 505 South San Francisco (94080) ***(P-8418)***
Titan Photonics Inc E 510 687-0488
1241 Quarry Ln Ste 140 Pleasanton (94566) ***(P-18001)***
Titan Steel Fabricators Inc F 619 449-1271
1069 E Bradley Ave El Cajon (92021) ***(P-25445)***
Titanium Metals Corporation D 707 552-4850
403 Ryder St Vallejo (94590) ***(P-11637)***
Titleist, Carlsbad *Also called Acushnet Company* ***(P-23486)***
Tivix Inc (PA) F 415 680-1299
2845 California St San Francisco (94115) ***(P-25281)***
Tivoli LLC E 714 957-6101
15602 Mosher Ave Tustin (92780) ***(P-17435)***
Tivoli Industries Inc E 714 957-6101
1550 E Saint Gertrude Pl Santa Ana (92705) ***(P-17739)***
Tj Aerospace Inc E 714 891-3564
12601 Monarch St Garden Grove (92841) ***(P-14417)***
Tj Giant Llc A 562 906-1060
12623 Cisneros Ln Santa Fe Springs (90670) ***(P-7521)***
Tje Company F 909 869-7777
18343 Gale Ave City of Industry (91748) ***(P-12351)***
Tjeker LLC E 424 240-7696
730 Arizona Ave Santa Monica (90401) ***(P-18289)***
Tjs Metal Manufacturing Inc E 310 604-1545
10847 Drury Ln Lynwood (90262) ***(P-12899)***
Tk and Company Watches F 213 545-1971
5827 W Pico Blvd Los Angeles (90019) ***(P-23326)***
Tk Classics LLC E 916 209-5500
3771 Channel Dr 100 West Sacramento (95691) ***(P-4845)***
Tk Pax Inc E 714 850-1330
1561 Macarthur Blvd Costa Mesa (92626) ***(P-9510)***
Tl Enterprises LLC (HQ) E 805 981-8393
2750 Park View Ct Ste 240 Oxnard (93036) ***(P-6272)***
TL Shield & Associates Inc (PA) E 818 509-8228
1030 Arroyo St San Fernando (91340) ***(P-14260)***
TLC Logistics Inc F 323 665-0474
3109 Casitas Ave Los Angeles (90039) ***(P-5743)***
TLC Machining Incorporated E 408 321-9002
2571 Chant Ct San Jose (95122) ***(P-14684)***
Tli Enterprises Inc (PA) E 510 538-3304
23950 Clawiter Rd Hayward (94545) ***(P-21494)***
Tli Enterprises Inc D 510 786-0680
3118 Depot Rd Hayward (94545) ***(P-13521)***
Tlk Industries Inc F 714 692-9373
23650 Via Del Rio Yorba Linda (92887) ***(P-24271)***
Tlm International Inc F 650 952-2257
239 Harbor Way South San Francisco (94080) ***(P-17418)***
Tm Microscopes Vco Metrlgy Grp D 805 967-2700
112 Robin Hill Rd Goleta (93117) ***(P-22142)***
Tm Noodle F 916 486-2579
4110 Manzanita Ave Carmichael (95608) ***(P-2443)***
Tmarzetti Company C 408 263-7540
876 Yosemite Dr Milpitas (95035) ***(P-936)***
TMC Aero, Murrieta *Also called TMC Ice Protection Systems LLC* ***(P-21443)***
TMC Aerospace Inc E 949 250-4999
2865 Pullman St Santa Ana (92705) ***(P-20951)***
TMC Ice Protection Systems LLC E 951 677-6934
25775 Jefferson Ave Murrieta (92562) ***(P-21443)***
TMI, San Marcos *Also called Trade Marker International* ***(P-2982)***
TMJ Concepts, Ventura *Also called TMJ Solutions Inc* ***(P-22833)***
TMJ Products Inc F 626 576-4063
515 S Palm Ave Ste 6 Alhambra (91803) ***(P-20685)***
TMJ Solutions Inc F 805 650-3391
2233 Knoll Dr Ventura (93003) ***(P-22833)***
Tmk Manufacturing D 408 732-3200
2110 Oakland Rd San Jose (95131) ***(P-14579)***
Tmk Manufacturing Inc E 408 844-8289
2233 Calle Del Mundo Santa Clara (95054) ***(P-14685)***
Tmp, Los Angeles *Also called Targeted Medical Pharma Inc* ***(P-8407)***
Tmp LLC E 916 920-2555
3011 Academy Way Sacramento (95815) ***(P-12352)***
Tmr Executive Interiors Inc F 559 346-0631
2677 N Argyle Ave Fresno (93727) ***(P-4247)***
TMW Corporation (PA) C 818 362-5665
15148 Bledsoe St Sylmar (91342) ***(P-20952)***
TMW Corporation E 818 374-1074
14647 Arminta St Panorama City (91402) ***(P-13522)***
Tmx Engineering and Mfg Corp D 714 641-5884
2141 S Standard Ave Santa Ana (92707) ***(P-17002)***
TN Sheet Metal Inc F 714 593-0100
18385 Bandilier Cir Fountain Valley (92708) ***(P-12791)***
Tncoopers, Sonoma *Also called Toneleria Nacional Usa Inc* ***(P-4093)***
Tnp Instruments Inc F 310 532-2222
119 Star Of India Ln Carson (90746) ***(P-19764)***
TNT Assembly LLC E 760 410-1750
1331 Specialty Dr Vista (92081) ***(P-2981)***
TNT Cable Industries, Vista *Also called TNT Assembly LLC* ***(P-2981)***
TNT Electric Signs Co, Long Beach *Also called Dynamite Sign Group Inc* ***(P-23859)***
TNT Industrial Contractors Inc (PA) E 916 395-8400
3800 Happy Ln Sacramento (95827) ***(P-14194)***
TNT Plastic Molding Inc (PA) C 951 808-9700
725 E Harrison St Corona (92879) ***(P-10406)***
To Die For, Ontario *Also called Scott Welsher* ***(P-10534)***
To Industries Inc F 949 454-6078
23180 Del Lago Dr Lake Forest (92630) ***(P-23991)***
Toad & Co International Inc (PA) E 805 957-1474
2020 Alameda Padre Serra Santa Barbara (93103) ***(P-3196)***
Toad Hollow Vineyards Inc F 707 431-1441
4024 Westside Rd Healdsburg (95448) ***(P-2018)***
TOAd&co, Santa Barbara *Also called Toad & Co International Inc* ***(P-3196)***
Tobar Industries D 408 494-3530
912 Olinder Ct San Jose (95122) ***(P-17501)***
Tobin Steel Company Inc D 714 541-2268
817 E Santa Ana Blvd Santa Ana (92701) ***(P-12261)***
Tocabi America Corporation E 619 661-6136
333 H St Ste 5007 Chula Vista (91910) ***(P-4900)***
Tocagen Inc D 858 412-8400
4242 Campus Point Ct # 500 San Diego (92121) ***(P-8419)***
Today Pvc Bending Inc F 714 953-5707
501 N Garfield St Santa Ana (92701) ***(P-17519)***
Toffee Boutique Inc F 916 638-8462
11353 Pyrites Way Rancho Cordova (95670) ***(P-1462)***
Toffee Tops, San Francisco *Also called Cjs Toffee & Toppings LLC* ***(P-1415)***
Tofu Shop Specialty Foods Inc E 707 822-7401
65 Frank Martin Ct Arcata (95521) ***(P-2682)***
Tognazzini Beverage Service F 805 928-1144
241 Roemer Way Santa Maria (93454) ***(P-2228)***
Tok America, Milpitas *Also called Tokyo Ohka Kogyo America Inc* ***(P-7809)***
Tokbox Inc F 415 284-4688
501 2nd St Ste 310 San Francisco (94107) ***(P-25282)***
Toky Inc F 844 332-6433
530 Lytton Ave Fl 2 Palo Alto (94301) ***(P-25283)***
Tokyo Ohka Kogyo America Inc F 408 956-9901
190 Topaz St Milpitas (95035) ***(P-7809)***
Tokyopop Inc D 323 920-5967
5200 W Century Blvd Fl 7 Los Angeles (90045) ***(P-6401)***
Tolar Manufacturing Co Inc E 951 808-0081
258 Mariah Cir Corona (92879) ***(P-12262)***
Tolco Incorporated E 951 656-3111
6480 Box Springs Blvd Riverside (92507) ***(P-12965)***
Toleeto Fastener International E 619 662-1355
1580 Jayken Way Chula Vista (91911) ***(P-23775)***
Tolemar Inc E 714 362-8166
5221 Oceanus Dr Huntington Beach (92649) ***(P-21142)***
Tolemar Manufacturing, Huntington Beach *Also called Tolemar Inc* ***(P-21142)***
Tolerance Technology Inc F 408 586-8811
1756 Junction Ave Ste C San Jose (95112) ***(P-23702)***
Tolosa Winery, San Luis Obispo *Also called Courtside Cellars LLC* ***(P-1710)***
Tom Bengard Ranch Inc F 831 758-5770
375 W Market St Salinas (93901) ***(P-15982)***
Tom Clark Confections E 909 599-4700
1193 Nicole Ct Glendora (91740) ***(P-1463)***
Tom Garcia Inc F 619 232-4881
2777 Newton Ave San Diego (92113) ***(P-25469)***
Tom Harris Inc D 951 352-5700
5821 Wilderness Ave Riverside (92504) ***(P-2683)***
Tom Leonard Investment Co Inc E 951 351-7778
7240 Sycamore Canyon Blvd Riverside (92508) ***(P-24272)***
Tom York Enterprises Inc E 323 581-6194
2050 E 48th St Vernon (90058) ***(P-10407)***
Toma Tek, Firebaugh *Also called Neil Jones Food Company* ***(P-833)***
Tomahawk Power LLC F 619 255-7478
402 W Broadway Ste 810 San Diego (92101) ***(P-17360)***
Tomarco Contractor Spc Inc F 858 547-0700
9372 Cabot Dr San Diego (92126) ***(P-23776)***
Tomasini Inc E 323 231-2349
1001 E 60th St Los Angeles (90001) ***(P-2785)***
Tomi Engineering Inc D 714 556-1474
414 E Alton Ave Santa Ana (92707) ***(P-17003)***
Tomiko Inc F 925 754-5694
1615 W 10th St Antioch (94509) ***(P-15094)***
Tomorrows Heirlooms Inc E 310 323-6720
1636 W 135th St Gardena (90249) ***(P-12001)***
Tomorrows Look Inc D 949 596-8400
17462 Von Karman Ave Irvine (92614) ***(P-2898)***
Tomra Sorting Inc (HQ) D 720 870-2240
875 Embarcadero Dr West Sacramento (95605) ***(P-14889)***

Mergent e-mail: customerrelations@mergent.com
1308
2019 California
Manufacturers Register
(P-0000) Products & Services Section entry number
(PA)=Parent Co (HQ)=Headquarters (DH)=Div Headquarters

Toms Metal Specialists Inc ....E....415 822-7971
1416 Wallace Ave San Francisco (94124) *(P-25446)*
Toms Printing Inc ....F....916 444-7788
1819 E St Sacramento (95811) *(P-7137)*
Toms Sierra Company Inc ....F....530 333-4620
4710 Marshall Rd Garden Valley (95633) *(P-283)*
Toms Welding & Fabrication, San Francisco *Also called Toms Metal Specialists Inc* *(P-25446)*
Toneleria Nacional Usa Inc ....F....707 501-8728
21481 8th St E Ste 20c Sonoma (95476) *(P-4093)*
Toner2print Inc ....F....909 972-9656
9450 7th St Ste J Rancho Cucamonga (91730) *(P-15870)*
Tonnellerie Francaise French C ....F....707 942-9301
1401 Tubbs Ln Calistoga (94515) *(P-4538)*
Tonnellerie Radoux Usa Inc ....F....707 284-2888
480 Aviation Blvd Santa Rosa (95403) *(P-4539)*
Tonusa LLC ....F....626 961-8700
16770 E Johnson Dr City of Industry (91745) *(P-4358)*
Tony Borges ....E....310 962-8700
8685 Bowers Ave South Gate (90280) *(P-12966)*
Tony Glazing Specialties Co ....F....323 770-8400
13011 S Normandie Ave Gardena (90249) *(P-5113)*
Tony Hawk Inc ....F....760 477-2477
1161-A S Melrose Dr 362 Vista (92081) *(P-23673)*
Tony Marterie & Associates (PA) ....E....415 331-7150
28 Liberty Ship Way Fl 2 Sausalito (94965) *(P-3342)*
Tool & Jig Plating Co, Whittier *Also called Aguilar Williams Inc* *(P-13313)*
Tool Makers International Inc ....F....408 980-8888
3390 Woodward Ave Santa Clara (95054) *(P-14418)*
Toolander Engineering Inc ....F....949 498-8339
1110 Via Callejon San Clemente (92673) *(P-13286)*
Toolbox Medical Innovations, Carlsbad *Also called Foundry Med Innovations Inc* *(P-22454)*
Tools & Production Inc ....E....626 286-0213
466 W Arrow Hwy Ste C San Dimas (91773) *(P-14580)*
Toolster Belts Inc ....F....858 583-0681
3525a Del Mar Heights Rd San Diego (92130) *(P-14686)*
Toomey Racing USA ....F....805 239-8870
5050 Wing Way Paso Robles (93446) *(P-21143)*
Top Art LLC ....F....858 554-0102
8830 Rehco Rd Ste G San Diego (92121) *(P-6603)*
Top Brands Distribution Inc ....F....858 578-0319
9675 Distribution Ave San Diego (92121) *(P-604)*
Top Greener Inc ....F....626 254-3367
1701 E Edinger Ave Ste A1 Santa Ana (92705) *(P-10825)*
Top Heavy Clothing Company Inc (PA) ....D....951 442-8839
28381 Vincent Moraga Dr Temecula (92590) *(P-3062)*
Top Line Mfg Inc ....E....562 633-0605
7032 Alondra Blvd Paramount (90723) *(P-12002)*
Top Notch Manufacturing Inc ....F....619 588-2033
1488 Pioneer Way Ste 17 El Cajon (92020) *(P-13287)*
Top Printing & Graphic Inc ....F....714 484-9200
1210 N Knollwood Cir Anaheim (92801) *(P-7522)*
Top Quality Sports Wear, Los Angeles *Also called Top Quality Sportswear* *(P-3197)*
Top Quality Sportswear ....F....323 262-0399
4740 E Olympic Blvd Los Angeles (90022) *(P-3197)*
Top Quest Inc ....F....626 839-8618
13872 Magnolia Ave Chino (91710) *(P-22652)*
Top Shelf Manufacturing LLC ....F....209 834-8185
1851 Paradise Rd Ste B Tracy (95304) *(P-22653)*
Top Ten, Los Angeles *Also called Smb Clothing Inc* *(P-3500)*
Top-Shelf Fixtures LLC (PA) ....D....909 627-7423
5263 Schaefer Ave Chino (91710) *(P-13857)*
Topaz Systems Inc (PA) ....E....805 520-8282
875 Patriot Dr Ste A Moorpark (93021) *(P-15871)*
Topcon Med Laser Systems Inc ....E....888 760-8657
606 Enterprise Ct Livermore (94550) *(P-23060)*
Topcon Positioning Systems Inc (HQ) ....C....925 245-8300
7400 National Dr Livermore (94550) *(P-22289)*
Topguest Inc ....E....646 415-9402
601 Montgomery St Fl 17 San Francisco (94111) *(P-25284)*
Topi Systems Inc ....F....408 807-5124
20650 4th St Apt 2 Saratoga (95070) *(P-25285)*
Topline Game Labs LLC ....F....310 461-0350
10351 Santa Monica Blvd # 410 Los Angeles (90025) *(P-25286)*
Topnotch Foods Inc ....F....323 586-2007
1988 E 57th St Vernon (90058) *(P-2684)*
Topnotch Quality Works Inc ....F....818 897-7679
12455 Branford St Ste 8 Pacoima (91331) *(P-20953)*
Toppage Inc ....F....510 471-6366
3101 Whipple Rd Ste 28 Union City (94587) *(P-25287)*
Topper Manufacturing Corp ....F....310 375-5000
23880 Madison St Torrance (90505) *(P-16125)*
Topper Plastics Inc ....F....626 331-0561
461 E Front St Covina (91723) *(P-9888)*
Tops Slt Inc ....C....562 968-2000
8550 Chetle Ave Ste B Whittier (90606) *(P-5659)*
Topslide International, Huntington Beach *Also called European Services Group* *(P-11954)*
Topson Downs California Inc ....E....310 558-0300
3545 Motor Ave Los Angeles (90034) *(P-3365)*
Topstar International Inc ....F....909 595-8807
13668 Valley Blvd Unit D2 City of Industry (91746) *(P-17436)*
Tor C A M Industries Inc ....E....562 531-8463
2160 E Cherry Indus Cir Long Beach (90805) *(P-16153)*
Torah-Aura Productions Inc ....F....323 585-1847
2710 Supply Ave Commerce (90040) *(P-6402)*
Torani Syrups & Flavors, South San Francisco *Also called R Torre & Company Inc* *(P-2279)*
Toray Membrane Usa Inc ....F....714 678-8832
13435 Danielson St Poway (92064) *(P-16126)*
Toray Membrane Usa Inc (HQ) ....D....858 218-2360
13435 Danielson St Poway (92064) *(P-9312)*
Torcano Industries Inc ....E....855 359-3339
20381 Lk Frest Dr Ste B10 Lake Forest (92630) *(P-21144)*
Torco International Corp ....F....909 980-1495
1720 S Carlos Ave Ontario (91761) *(P-9365)*
Torero Specialty Products LLC ....F....415 520-3481
222 E Huntington Dr # 225 Monrovia (91016) *(P-23674)*
Torian Group Inc ....F....559 733-1940
519 W Center Ave Visalia (93291) *(P-25288)*
Torn Ranch Inc (PA) ....D....415 506-3000
2198 S Mcdowell Blvd Ext Petaluma (94954) *(P-1464)*
Toro Company ....D....619 562-2950
1588 N Marshall Ave El Cajon (92020) *(P-14110)*
Toro Company ....D....951 688-9221
5825 Jasmine St Riverside (92504) *(P-14111)*
Toro Company ....D....760 321-8396
70221 Dinah Shore Dr Rancho Mirage (92270) *(P-14112)*
Torrance Manufacturing, Chatsworth *Also called Torrance Precision Machining* *(P-17004)*
Torrance Precision Machining ....F....818 709-7838
9530 Owensmouth Ave Ste 8 Chatsworth (91311) *(P-17004)*
Torrance Refinery, Torrance *Also called Pbf Energy Inc* *(P-9348)*
Torrance Refining Company LLC ....A....310 483-6900
3700 W 190th St Torrance (90504) *(P-9366)*
Torrance Steel Window Co Inc ....E....310 328-9181
1819 Abalone Ave Torrance (90501) *(P-12353)*
Torrence Aluminum Window, Redlands *Also called Window Enterprises Inc* *(P-12355)*
Torrence Trading Inc ....E....310 649-1188
21041 S Wstn Ave Ste 200 Torrance (90501) *(P-23473)*
Torrey Pines Scientific Inc ....F....760 930-9400
2713 Loker Ave W Carlsbad (92010) *(P-21495)*
Tortilla Land, San Diego *Also called Southwest Products LLC* *(P-2671)*
Tortilleria La California Inc ....E....323 221-8940
2241 Cypress Ave Los Angeles (90065) *(P-2685)*
Tortilleria La Mejor ....D....559 747-0739
684 S Farmersville Blvd Farmersville (93223) *(P-2686)*
Tortilleria San Marcos ....E....323 263-0208
1927 E 1st St Los Angeles (90033) *(P-2687)*
Tortilleria Santa Fe ....E....619 585-0350
387 Zenith St Chula Vista (91911) *(P-2688)*
Tortilleria Temecula ....F....951 676-5272
28780 Old Town Front St A7 Temecula (92590) *(P-2689)*
Tortolani Inc ....F....323 268-1488
1313 Mirasol St Los Angeles (90023) *(P-23992)*
Toscanella Inc ....E....818 506-7283
9935 Toluca Lake Ave Toluca Lake (91602) *(P-4744)*
Tosco - Tool Specialty Company ....E....323 232-3561
1011 E Slauson Ave Los Angeles (90011) *(P-14687)*
Toshiba Amer Info Systems Inc ....D....949 587-6378
2 Musick Irvine (92618) *(P-15497)*
Toshiba America Electronic (HQ) ....B....949 462-7700
5231 California Ave Irvine (92617) *(P-17868)*
Toshiba America Electronic ....E....408 526-2400
2610 Orchard Pkwy San Jose (95134) *(P-19765)*
Toska Inc ....F....213 746-0088
1100 S San Pedro St I06 Los Angeles (90015) *(P-3519)*
Total Brand Delivery, Camarillo *Also called Corprint Incorporated* *(P-7286)*
Total Concept Enterprises Inc ....F....559 485-8413
3745 E Jensen Ave Fresno (93725) *(P-23777)*
Total Cost Involved, Ontario *Also called TCI Engineering Inc* *(P-20172)*
Total Media Enterprises Inc ....F....626 961-7887
16235 Montbrook St La Puente (91744) *(P-6604)*
Total Paper and Packaging Inc ....F....818 885-1072
2175 Agate Ct Unit A Simi Valley (93065) *(P-5744)*
Total Phase Inc ....F....408 850-6500
2350 Mission College Blvd # 1100 Santa Clara (95054) *(P-15618)*
Total Process Solutions LLC ....E....661 829-7910
1400 Norris Rd Bakersfield (93308) *(P-15095)*
Total Resources Intl Inc (PA) ....D....909 594-1220
420 S Lemon Ave Walnut (91789) *(P-22834)*
Total Source Manufacturing ....A....760 598-2146
1445 Engineer St Vista (92081) *(P-21496)*
Total Source Manufacturing Co, Vista *Also called Total Source Manufacturing* *(P-21496)*
Total Structures Inc ....E....805 676-3322
1696 Walter St Ventura (93003) *(P-17740)*
Total Technologies, Irvine *Also called Turn-Luckily International Inc* *(P-15876)*
Total-Western Inc (HQ) ....E....562 220-1450
8049 Somerset Blvd Paramount (90723) *(P-284)*
Totally Bamboo, San Marcos *Also called Hollywood Chairs* *(P-4703)*
Totally Radical Associates Inc ....F....714 630-2740
1025 Ortega Way Ste A Placentia (92870) *(P-14581)*
Totalthermalimagingcom ....F....619 303-5884
8341 La Mesa Blvd La Mesa (91942) *(P-15872)*
Totex Manufacturing Inc ....D....310 326-2028
3050 Lomita Blvd Torrance (90505) *(P-10408)*
Totty Printing ....F....714 633-7081
1208 W Collins Ave Orange (92867) *(P-7523)*
Toucaned Inc ....F....831 464-0508
1716 Brommer St Santa Cruz (95062) *(P-6605)*
Touch Coffee & Beverages LLC ....F....626 968-0300
15312 Valley Blvd City of Industry (91746) *(P-17404)*
Touch Litho Company ....F....562 927-8899
7215 E Gage Ave Commerce (90040) *(P-7138)*
Touch ME Fashion Inc ....E....323 234-9200
906 E 60th St Los Angeles (90001) *(P-3520)*
Touchdown Technologies Inc ....C....626 472-6732
5188 Commerce Dr Baldwin Park (91706) *(P-19232)*
Touchmark, Hayward *Also called Delphon Industries LLC* *(P-10064)*
Touchpint Elctrnic Sltions LLC ....F....951 734-8083
38372 Innovation Ct # 306 Murrieta (92563) *(P-15498)*

ALPHABETIC

Employee Codes: A=Over 500 employees, B=251-500
C=101-250, D=51-100, E=20-50, F=10-19
2019 California
Manfacturers Register
© Mergent Inc. 1-800-342-5647
1309

Touchpoint Solutions ....F....714 740-7242
18426 Brookhurst St # 207 Fountain Valley (92708) *(P-25289)*
Touchsport Footwear LLC....F....310 763-0208
2969 E Pcf Commerce Dr E Rncho Dmngz (90221) *(P-9488)*
Toufic Inc ....F....209 478-4780
2324 Grand Canal Blvd # 1 Stockton (95207) *(P-1334)*
Tourism Development Corp (PA) ....F....310 280-2880
3679 Motor Ave Ste 300 Los Angeles (90034) *(P-6273)*
Toutapp Inc....F....866 548-1927
535 Mission St Fl 14 San Francisco (94105) *(P-25290)*
Tow Industries, Los Angeles *Also called Baatz Enterprises Inc (P-20129)*
Tower Industries Inc....C....909 947-2723
1720 S Bon View Ave Ontario (91761) *(P-17005)*
Tower Mechanical Products Inc ....C....714 947-2723
1720 S Bon View Ave Ontario (91761) *(P-21444)*
Tower Semiconductor Usa Inc....F....408 770-1320
2570 N 1st St Ste 480 San Jose (95131) *(P-19233)*
Towerjazz, Newport Beach *Also called Jazz Semiconductor Inc (P-18938)*
Towerjazz Texas Inc (PA)....D....949 435-8000
4321 Jamboree Rd Newport Beach (92660) *(P-19766)*
Towne Park Brew Inc....E....714 844-2492
1566 W Lincoln Ave Anaheim (92801) *(P-1632)*
Toye Corporation ....E....818 882-4000
9230 Deering Ave Chatsworth (91311) *(P-15873)*
Toykidz Inc....F....213 688-2999
100 S Doheny Dr Ph 10 Los Angeles (90048) *(P-24273)*
Toyo Ink International Corp ....E....714 899-2377
11190 Valley View St Cypress (90630) *(P-9213)*
Toyo Ink North America, Cypress *Also called Toyo Ink International Corp (P-9213)*
Toyo Tire Hldings Americas Inc (HQ)....E....562 431-6502
5900 Katella Ave Ste 200a Cypress (90630) *(P-9468)*
Toyota Motor Engineering & Man....D....562 428-3604
6375 N Paramount Blvd Lakewood (90805) *(P-20179)*
Toyota-Lift of Los Angeles, Santa Fe Springs *Also called Rebas Inc (P-14345)*
TP Products, San Fernando *Also called Triumph Precision Products (P-13047)*
TP Solar Inc....E....562 808-2171
16310 Downey Ave Paramount (90723) *(P-15276)*
TPC Advance Technology Inc ....F....626 810-4337
18519 Gale Ave City of Industry (91748) *(P-22917)*
TPC Industries LLC....E....310 849-9574
5920 W Birch Ave Fresno (93722) *(P-24274)*
Tpg Growth, San Francisco *Also called Tpg Partners III LP (P-80)*
Tpg Partners III LP (HQ) ....E....415 743-1500
345 California St # 3300 San Francisco (94104) *(P-80)*
Tpi, Covina *Also called Topper Plastics Inc (P-9888)*
Tpi Marketing LLC....F....302 703-0283
14985 Hilton Dr Fontana (92336) *(P-14890)*
Tpl Communications, La Crescenta *Also called D X Communications Inc (P-18082)*
Tpsi, Paramount *Also called TP Solar Inc (P-15276)*
Tr Engineering Inc....F....831 430-9920
1350 Green Hills Rd 10 Scotts Valley (95066) *(P-15096)*
Tr Manufacturing LLC (HQ)....C....510 657-3850
33210 Central Ave Union City (94587) *(P-20089)*
Tr Theater Research Inc (PA) ....F....714 894-5888
11150 Hope St Cypress (90630) *(P-17869)*
Tra Medical, Placentia *Also called Totally Radical Associates Inc (P-14581)*
Tracet Manufacturing Inc....F....408 779-8846
40 Kirby Ave Morgan Hill (95037) *(P-17006)*
Trackstar Printing Inc ....F....310 216-1275
1140 W Mahalo Pl Compton (90220) *(P-7139)*
Tracy Industries Inc....C....562 692-9034
3200 E Guasti Rd Ste 100 Ontario (91761) *(P-14032)*
Tracy Press Inc....E....209 835-3030
145 W 10th St Tracy (95376) *(P-6072)*
Trade Lithography, Richmond *Also called John Lompa (P-7365)*
Trade Marker International....F....760 602-4864
445 Ryan Dr Ste 101 San Marcos (92078) *(P-2982)*
Trade Only Screen Printing Inc....E....510 887-2020
23482 Foley St Hayward (94545) *(P-7524)*
Trade Printing Services LLC....E....760 496-0230
2080 Las Palmas Dr Carlsbad (92011) *(P-7140)*
Tradeincom Inc....F....951 296-5566
28441 Rancho Cal Rd Ste Z Temecula (92590) *(P-4971)*
Trademark Construction Co Inc (PA) ....D....760 489-5647
15916 Bernardo Center Dr San Diego (92127) *(P-19847)*
Trademark Cosmetic Inc....E....951 683-2631
545 Columbia Ave Riverside (92507) *(P-8854)*
Trademark Hoist Inc....E....909 455-0801
1369 Ridgeway St Pomona (91768) *(P-14303)*
Trademark Hoist & Crane, Pomona *Also called Trademark Hoist Inc (P-14303)*
Trademark Plastics Inc....C....909 941-8810
807 Palmyrita Ave Riverside (92507) *(P-15038)*
Tradenet Enterprise Inc....D....888 595-3956
1930 S Vineyard Ave Ontario (91761) *(P-23993)*
Tradesman Trucktops, Winters *Also called Access Mfg Inc (P-20186)*
Tradewinds, Monrovia *Also called Headwinds (P-21114)*
Traditional Baking Inc ....D....909 877-8471
2575 S Willow Ave Bloomington (92316) *(P-1384)*
Traditional Medicinals Inc (PA)....C....707 823-8911
4515 Ross Rd Sebastopol (95472) *(P-2690)*
Traffic Control & Safety Corp....F....858 679-7292
13755 Blaisdell Pl Poway (92064) *(P-23994)*
Traffic Sensor Corporation....F....909 468-4625
3205 Pomona Blvd Pomona (91768) *(P-19848)*
Traffic Works Inc....E....323 582-0616
5720 Soto St Huntington Park (90255) *(P-9731)*
Traffix Devices Inc ....E....760 246-7171
12128 Yucca Rd Adelanto (92301) *(P-9687)*
Traffix Devices Inc (PA) ....F....949 361-5663
160 Avenida La Pata San Clemente (92673) *(P-18372)*
Tragara Pharmaceuticals Inc ....F....760 208-6900
12481 High Bluff Dr # 150 San Diego (92130) *(P-8420)*
Train Reaction, Huntington Beach *Also called West Coast Trends Inc (P-23689)*
Trak Microwave Corporation....F....805 267-0100
375 Conejo Ridge Ave Thousand Oaks (91361) *(P-19767)*
Trams International, Bell Gardens *Also called Bus Services Corporation (P-20278)*
Trane US Inc....F....408 257-5212
1601 S De Anza Blvd 235 Cupertino (95014) *(P-15983)*
Trane US Inc....C....408 481-3600
310 Soquel Way Sunnyvale (94085) *(P-15984)*
Trane US Inc....D....626 913-7123
3253 E Imperial Hwy Brea (92821) *(P-15985)*
Trane US Inc....E....626 913-7913
20450 E Walnut Dr N Walnut (91789) *(P-15986)*
Trane US Inc....D....951 801-6020
2222 Kansas Ave Ste C Riverside (92507) *(P-15987)*
Trane US Inc....D....408 437-0390
890 Service St Ste A San Jose (95112) *(P-15988)*
Trane US Inc....D....310 971-4555
1930 E Carson St Ste 101 Carson (90810) *(P-15989)*
Trane US Inc....E....858 292-0833
3565 Corporate Ct Fl 1 San Diego (92123) *(P-15990)*
Trane US Inc....E....559 271-4625
3026 N Bus Park Ave # 104 Fresno (93727) *(P-15991)*
Tranpak Inc....E....800 827-2474
2860 S East Ave Fresno (93725) *(P-10409)*
Trans Bay Steel Corporation (PA) ....E....510 277-3756
536 Cleveland Ave Berkeley (94710) *(P-12263)*
Trans Fx Inc....F....805 485-6110
2361 Eastman Ave Oxnard (93030) *(P-24275)*
Trans Western Polymers Inc....B....925 449-7800
7539 Las Positas Rd Livermore (94551) *(P-5628)*
Trans-India Products Inc....E....707 544-0298
3330 Coffey Ln Ste A&B Santa Rosa (95403) *(P-8855)*
Transcend Medical Inc....F....650 325-2050
127 Independence Dr Menlo Park (94025) *(P-22654)*
Transcendia Inc....F....909 944-9981
9000 9th St Ste 140 Rancho Cucamonga (91730) *(P-9732)*
Transchem Coatings, Los Angeles *Also called Paint-Chem Inc (P-8922)*
Transco, El Monte *Also called Transgo (P-20467)*
Transcontinental Nrthern CA 20....C....510 580-7700
47540 Kato Rd Fremont (94538) *(P-7525)*
Transcontinental US LLC....C....559 585-2040
10801 Iona Ave Hanford (93230) *(P-5629)*
Transcontinental US LLC ....E....909 390-8866
5601 Santa Ana St Ontario (91761) *(P-5630)*
Transdigm Inc....E....323 269-9181
5000 Triggs St Commerce (90022) *(P-20954)*
Transdigm Inc....C....323 269-9181
5000 Triggs St Commerce (90022) *(P-20955)*
Transdigm Inc....C....323 269-9181
5000 Triggs St Commerce (90022) *(P-20956)*
Transducer Techniques LLC....E....951 719-3965
42480 Rio Nedo Temecula (92590) *(P-19768)*
Transfer Engineering & Mfg Inc....E....510 651-3000
1100 La Avenida St Ste A Mountain View (94043) *(P-15231)*
Transfirst Corporation....E....831 424-2911
900 E Blanco Rd Salinas (93901) *(P-21534)*
Transformationnet Media LLC ....E....310 476-5259
1640 N Spring St Los Angeles (90012) *(P-6274)*
Transglobal Apparel Group Inc....F....714 890-9200
12362 Knott St Garden Grove (92841) *(P-3521)*
Transgo....E....626 443-7456
2621 Merced Ave El Monte (91733) *(P-20467)*
Transhumance Holding Co Inc ....F....323 583-5503
2851 E 44th St Vernon (90058) *(P-532)*
Transhumance Holding Co Inc....C....707 693-2303
7390 Rio Dixon Rd Dixon (95620) *(P-452)*
Transit Care Inc (PA)....F....818 267-3002
7900 Nelson Rd Panorama City (91402) *(P-10609)*
Transko Electronics Inc....F....714 528-8000
3981 E Miraloma Ave Anaheim (92806) *(P-19769)*
Translarity Inc....F....510 371-7900
46575 Fremont Blvd Fremont (94538) *(P-21879)*
Translattice Inc (PA)....E....408 749-8478
3398 Londonderry Dr Santa Clara (95050) *(P-15499)*
Transline Technology Inc....E....714 533-8300
1106 S Technology Cir Anaheim (92805) *(P-18626)*
Translogic Incorporated....E....714 890-0058
5641 Engineer Dr Huntington Beach (92649) *(P-21670)*
Transmeta Corp....E....408 327-9831
3940 Freedom Cir Santa Clara (95054) *(P-19234)*
Transonic Combustion Inc....E....805 465-5145
461 Calle San Pablo Camarillo (93012) *(P-14033)*
Transparent Devices Inc....E....805 499-5000
853 Lawrence Dr Newbury Park (91320) *(P-15874)*
Transparent Products Inc....E....661 294-9787
28064 Avenue Stanford E Valencia (91355) *(P-15648)*
Transplant Connect Inc....E....310 392-1400
2701 Ocean Park Blvd # 222 Santa Monica (90405) *(P-25291)*
Transportation Equipment Inc (PA)....E....619 449-8860
1404 N Marshall Ave El Cajon (92020) *(P-3816)*
Transportation Power Inc....E....858 248-4255
2415 Auto Park Way Escondido (92029) *(P-20468)*
Transpower, Escondido *Also called Transportation Power Inc (P-20468)*
Transworld Printing Svcs Inc....F....209 982-1511
2857 Transworld Dr Stockton (95206) *(P-7214)*

Mergent e-mail: customerrelations@mergent.com
1310
2019 California
Manufacturers Register
(P-0000) Products & Services Section entry number
(PA)=Parent Co (HQ)=Headquarters (DH)=Div Headquarters

Trantronics Inc .....E.....949 553-1234
1822 Langley Ave Irvine (92614) *(P-18627)*
Trashy Lingerie, West Hollywood *Also called 402 Shoes Inc* *(P-3531)*
Trattoria Amici/Americana LLC .....F.....818 502-1220
783 Americana Way Glendale (91210) *(P-5259)*
Travcom, Los Angeles *Also called Travel Computer Systems Inc* *(P-25292)*
Travel Computer Systems Inc .....F.....310 558-3130
1990 Westwood Blvd # 310 Los Angeles (90025) *(P-25292)*
Travelers Choice Travelware .....D.....909 529-7688
2805 S Reservoir St Pomona (91766) *(P-10540)*
Travidia Inc (PA) .....C.....530 343-6400
265 Airpark Blvd Ste 500 Chico (95973) *(P-25293)*
Travis American Group LLC .....C.....714 258-1200
11450 Sheldon St Sun Valley (91352) *(P-4248)*
Travis Industries, Sun Valley *Also called Travis American Group LLC* *(P-4248)*
Travis Mike Inc .....F.....805 201-3363
2420 Celsius Ave Ste D Oxnard (93030) *(P-13288)*
Travismathew LLC .....F.....562 799-6900
15202 Graham St Huntington Beach (92649) *(P-3198)*
Traxx Corporation .....D.....909 623-8032
1201 E Lexington Ave Pomona (91766) *(P-24276)*
Trayer Engineering Corporation .....F.....415 285-7770
1569 Alvarado St San Leandro (94577) *(P-17168)*
Traylor Management Inc (PA) .....F.....858 486-7700
12120 Tech Center Dr B Poway (92064) *(P-6606)*
TRC Cocoa LLC .....F.....916 847-2390
3721 Douglas Blvd Ste 375 Roseville (95661) *(P-1477)*
TRC Operating Company Inc .....F.....661 763-0081
805 Blackgold Ct Taft (93268) *(P-81)*
Treana Winery LLC .....E.....805 237-2932
4280 Second Wind Way Paso Robles (93446) *(P-2019)*
Treasury Chateau & Estates .....F.....707 996-5870
1700 Moon Mountain Rd Sonoma (95476) *(P-2020)*
Treasury Wine Estates Americas (HQ) .....B.....707 259-4500
555 Gateway Dr NAPA (94558) *(P-2021)*
Treasury Wine Estates Americas .....D.....707 963-7115
2000 Main St Saint Helena (94574) *(P-2022)*
Treasury Wine Estates Americas .....B.....707 963-4812
1000 Pratt Ave Saint Helena (94574) *(P-2023)*
Treasury Wine Estates Americas .....E.....707 833-4134
8555 Sonoma Hwy Kenwood (95452) *(P-2024)*
Treasury Wine Estates Americas .....E.....707 894-2541
26150 Asti Rd Cloverdale (95425) *(P-2025)*
Treasury Wine Estates Americas .....D.....707 963-7115
2000 Saint Helena Hwy N Saint Helena (94574) *(P-2026)*
Treat Enterprises .....F.....209 532-2220
19401 Rawhide Rd Sonora (95370) *(P-14419)*
Tree House Pad & Paper Inc 800 213-4184
2341 Pomona Rd Ste 108 Corona (92880) *(P-5689)*
Tree Island Wire (usa) Inc (HQ) .....C.....909 594-7511
3880 Valley Blvd Walnut (91789) *(P-11460)*
Tree Island Wire (usa) Inc .....D.....909 594-7511
13470 Philadelphia Ave Fontana (92337) *(P-11461)*
Tree Island Wire (usa) Inc .....B.....909 595-6617
3880 W Valley Blvd Pomona (91769) *(P-11462)*
Tree Island Wire (usa) Inc .....D.....800 255-6974
12459 Arrow Rte Rancho Cucamonga (91739) *(P-11463)*
Tree Top Inc .....C.....509 697-7251
1250 E 3rd St Oxnard (93030) *(P-863)*
Trefethen Family Vineyards, NAPA *Also called Trefethen Vineyards Winery Inc* *(P-2027)*
Trefethen Vineyards Winery Inc .....E.....707 255-7700
1160 Oak Knoll Ave NAPA (94558) *(P-2027)*
Trek Armor Incorporated .....F.....951 319-4008
41795 Elm St Ste 401 Murrieta (92562) *(P-24277)*
Trekell & Co Inc .....F.....800 378-3867
17459 Lilac St Ste B Hesperia (92345) *(P-23713)*
Trelleborg Sealing Solutions (HQ) .....C.....714 415-0280
2761 Walnut Ave Tustin (92780) *(P-22655)*
Trelleborg Sealing Solutions E .....D.....310 322-8030
2051 E Maple Ave El Segundo (90245) *(P-9562)*
Tremco Incorporated .....F.....323 587-3014
3060 E 44th St Vernon (90058) *(P-9419)*
Trend Chasers LLC .....E.....213 749-2661
2311 S Santa Fe Ave Vernon (90058) *(P-10583)*
Trend Frames, San Diego *Also called Trend Marketing Corporation* *(P-4661)*
Trend Manor Furn Mfg Co Inc .....E.....626 964-6493
17047 Gale Ave City of Industry (91745) *(P-4745)*
Trend Marketing Corporation .....D.....800 468-7363
3025 Beyer Blvd Ste 102 San Diego (92154) *(P-4661)*
Trend Offset Printing Svcs Inc .....C.....859 449-2900
3701 Catalina St Los Alamitos (90720) *(P-7141)*
Trend Offset Printing Svcs Inc (PA) .....A.....562 598-2446
3701 Catalina St Los Alamitos (90720) *(P-7142)*
Trend Offset Printing Svcs Inc .....B.....562 598-2446
3791 Catalina St Los Alamitos (90720) *(P-7143)*
Trend Offset Printing Svcs Inc .....D.....714 826-2360
3722 Catalina St Los Alamitos (90720) *(P-7144)*
Trend Technologies LLC (HQ) .....C.....909 597-7861
4626 Eucalyptus Ave Chino (91710) *(P-12792)*
Trendpoint Systems Inc .....F.....925 855-0600
283 Winfield Cir Corona (92880) *(P-21880)*
Trent Beverage Company LLC .....F.....310 384-6776
47230 Golden Bush Ct Palm Desert (92260) *(P-2229)*
Trent Beverages, Palm Desert *Also called Trent Beverage Company LLC* *(P-2229)*
Trepanning Spcialty A Cal Corp .....E.....562 408-0044
16201 Illinois Ave Paramount (90723) *(P-17007)*
Trepanning Specialties, Paramount *Also called Trepanning Spcialty A Cal Corp* *(P-17007)*
Tres Bien Inc (PA) .....F.....213 747-3366
1016 Towne Ave Unit 113 Los Angeles (90021) *(P-3522)*

Tresco Paint Co .....F.....510 887-7254
21595 Curtis St Hayward (94545) *(P-8950)*
Trex Enterprises Corporation (PA) .....C.....858 646-5300
10455 Pacific Center Ct San Diego (92121) *(P-15500)*
Trexta Inc .....F.....858 536-9100
8969 Kenamar Dr Ste 105 San Diego (92121) *(P-18290)*
Tri A Machine Inc .....F.....714 408-8907
7221 Garden Grove Blvd Ab Garden Grove (92841) *(P-14458)*
Tri All, San Clemente *Also called Try All 3 Sports* *(P-21146)*
Tri C Machine Shop, West Sacramento *Also called Tri-C Machine Corporation* *(P-17009)*
Tri City Voice, Fremont *Also called Whats Happening Tri City* *(P-7541)*
Tri County Spring & Stamping, Ventura *Also called Tricoss Inc* *(P-13805)*
Tri Dental Innovators Corp .....F.....714 554-1170
13902 West St Garden Grove (92843) *(P-22918)*
Tri Electronics Inc .....F.....858 571-4881
4667 Mission Gorge Pl B San Diego (92120) *(P-22290)*
Tri Fab Associates Inc .....D.....510 651-7628
48351 Lakeview Blvd Fremont (94538) *(P-12793)*
Tri Map International Inc .....E.....209 234-0100
111 Val Dervin Pkwy Stockton (95206) *(P-15501)*
Tri Models Inc .....D.....714 896-0823
5191 Oceanus Dr Huntington Beach (92649) *(P-20631)*
Tri Power Electric Inc .....F.....714 630-6445
1211 N La Loma Cir Anaheim (92806) *(P-20090)*
Tri Precision Sheetmetal Inc .....F.....714 632-8838
845 N Elm St Orange (92867) *(P-12794)*
Tri Print LLC .....F.....714 847-1400
7573 Slater Ave Ste C Huntington Beach (92647) *(P-7145)*
Tri Quality Inc .....F.....916 388-5939
5840 S Watt Ave Ste A Sacramento (95829) *(P-22835)*
Tri Service Co Inc .....F.....626 442-3270
2465 Loma Ave South El Monte (91733) *(P-9313)*
Tri Star Metals Inc .....F.....707 678-1140
8749 Pedrick Rd Dixon (95620) *(P-13001)*
Tri State Manufacturing Inc .....F.....949 855-9121
27212 Burbank El Toro (92610) *(P-17008)*
Tri State Truss Corporation .....F.....760 326-3868
600 River Rd Needles (92363) *(P-4428)*
Tri Tek Electronics Inc .....F.....661 295-0020
25358 Avenue Stanford Valencia (91355) *(P-19770)*
Tri-C Machine Corporation (PA) .....F.....916 371-8090
520 Harbor Blvd West Sacramento (95691) *(P-17009)*
Tri-C Manufacturing Inc .....F.....916 371-1700
517 Houston St West Sacramento (95691) *(P-15039)*
Tri-City Print & Mail, West Sacramento *Also called Tri-City Technologies Inc* *(P-7526)*
Tri-City Technologies Inc .....F.....916 503-5300
2615 Del Monte St West Sacramento (95691) *(P-7526)*
Tri-Co Building Supply Inc .....D.....805 343-2555
695 Obispo St Guadalupe (93434) *(P-4429)*
Tri-Continent Scientific Inc .....D.....530 273-8888
12740 Earhart Ave Auburn (95602) *(P-21696)*
Tri-Dim Filter Corporation .....E.....626 826-5893
15271 Fairfield Ranch Rd # 150 Chino Hills (91709) *(P-15182)*
Tri-Fitting Mfg Company .....E.....626 442-2000
10414 Rush St South El Monte (91733) *(P-20957)*
Tri-J Metal Heat Treating Co (PA) .....F.....909 622-9999
327 E Commercial St Pomona (91767) *(P-11835)*
Tri-J Metal Heat Treating Co .....F.....909 622-9999
327 E Commercial St Pomona (91767) *(P-11836)*
Tri-K Truss Company .....F.....559 784-8511
453 S Main St Porterville (93257) *(P-4430)*
Tri-M Co .....E.....760 744-5115
528 E Mission Rd San Marcos (92069) *(P-12795)*
Tri-Mag Inc .....F.....559 651-2222
1601 Clancy Ct Visalia (93291) *(P-19771)*
Tri-Net Inc .....F.....909 483-3555
14721 Hilton Dr Fontana (92336) *(P-21881)*
Tri-Net Technology Inc .....D.....909 598-8818
21709 Ferrero Walnut (91789) *(P-15875)*
Tri-Phase Inc .....C.....408 284-7700
6190 San Ignacio Ave San Jose (95119) *(P-18628)*
Tri-Star Dyeing & Finshg Inc .....D.....562 483-0123
15125 Marquardt Ave Santa Fe Springs (90670) *(P-2795)*
Tri-Star Electronics Intl Inc (HQ) .....B.....310 536-0444
2201 Rosecrans Ave El Segundo (90245) *(P-17502)*
Tri-Star Laminates Inc .....E.....949 587-3200
20322 Windrow Dr Ste 100 Lake Forest (92630) *(P-18629)*
Tri-Star Technologies Inc .....E.....310 536-0444
2201 Rosecrans Ave El Segundo (90245) *(P-23061)*
Tri-State Manufacturing, Lake Forest *Also called June Precision Mfg Inc* *(P-13029)*
Tri-State Stairway Corp .....F.....559 268-0875
706 W California Ave Fresno (93706) *(P-12900)*
Tri-Tech Precision Inc .....F.....714 970-1363
1863 N Case St Orange (92865) *(P-20958)*
Tri-Union Seafoods LLC .....F.....858 558-9662
4510 Executive Dr Ste 300 San Diego (92121) *(P-2306)*
Tri-Valley Herald, Pleasanton *Also called Alameda Newspapers Inc* *(P-5755)*
Tria Beauty Inc .....D.....925 701-2500
7999 Gateway Blvd Ste 100 Newark (94560) *(P-23062)*
Triactive America Inc .....E.....805 595-1005
1244 Trail View Pl Nipomo (93444) *(P-23675)*
Triad Bellows Design & Mfg Inc .....E.....714 204-4444
2897 E La Cresta Ave Anaheim (92806) *(P-17010)*
Triad Energy Resources Inc .....D.....209 527-0607
204 Kerr Ave Modesto (95354) *(P-9087)*
Triad Tool & Engineering Inc .....E.....408 436-8411
1750 Rogers Ave San Jose (95112) *(P-10410)*
Triad Waste Management, Modesto *Also called Triad Energy Resources Inc* *(P-9087)*
Trialgraphix Inc .....F.....213 621-4400
600 Wilshire Blvd Ste 700 Los Angeles (90017) *(P-7146)*

Employee Codes: A=Over 500 employees, B=251-500
C=101-250, D=51-100, E=20-50, F=10-19
2019 California
Manfacturers Register
© Mergent Inc. 1-800-342-5647
1311

Triangle Brass Mfg Co Inc (PA) ....D....323 262-4191
1351 Rocky Point Dr Oceanside (92056) *(P-12003)*
Triangle Rock Products, Sacramento *Also called Legacy Vulcan LLC (P-11131)*
Triangle Rock Products LLC ....E....818 553-8820
500 N Brand Blvd Ste 500 # 500 Glendale (91203) *(P-334)*
Triangle Tool & Die Corp ....F....562 944-2117
13189 Flores St Santa Fe Springs (90670) *(P-17011)*
Tribal Print Source ....F....760 597-2650
36146 Pala Temecula Rd Pala (92059) *(P-7147)*
Tribe Media Corp ....E....213 368-1661
3250 Wilshire Blvd Los Angeles (90010) *(P-6073)*
Tribeworx LLC ....D....800 949-3432
4 San Joaquin Plz Ste 150 Newport Beach (92660) *(P-25294)*
Tribune Los Angeles Inc ....F....213 237-5000
202 W 1st St Ste 500 Los Angeles (90012) *(P-6074)*
Tribune Studios, Los Angeles *Also called 5800 Sunset Productions Inc (P-5750)*
Tribune, The, Oakland *Also called Oakland Tribune Inc (P-6003)*
Trical Inc ....F....559 651-0736
28679 Rd 68 Visalia (93277) *(P-9115)*
Trical Inc (PA) ....E....831 637-0195
8100 Arroyo Cir Gilroy (95020) *(P-9116)*
Trical Inc ....D....831 637-0195
8770 Hwy 25 Hollister (95023) *(P-9117)*
Trical Inc ....F....951 737-6960
1029 Railroad St Corona (92882) *(P-9118)*
Trical Inc ....E....661 824-2494
1667 Purdy Rd Mojave (93501) *(P-9119)*
Tricida Inc ....D....415 429-7800
7000 Shoreline Ct Ste 201 South San Francisco (94080) *(P-8421)*
Tricir Technologies, City of Industry *Also called Lanstreetcom (P-15638)*
Trico Sports Inc ....D....818 899-7705
13541 Desmond St Pacoima (91331) *(P-21145)*
Tricom Research Inc ....D....949 250-6024
17791 Sky Park Cir Ste J Irvine (92614) *(P-18291)*
Triconex, Lake Forest *Also called Schneider Elc Systems USA Inc (P-21649)*
Tricor Refining LLC ....E....661 393-7110
1134 Manor St Bakersfield (93308) *(P-9367)*
Tricoss Inc ....F....805 644-4107
4450 Dupont Ct Ste A Ventura (93003) *(P-13805)*
Tridecs Corporation ....E....510 785-2620
3513 Arden Rd Hayward (94545) *(P-17012)*
Trident Diving Equipment ....E....818 998-7518
9616 Owensmouth Ave Chatsworth (91311) *(P-23676)*
Trident Plating Inc ....E....562 906-2556
10046 Romandel Ave Santa Fe Springs (90670) *(P-13523)*
Trident Products Inc ....D....760 510-1160
1370 W San Marcos Blvd # 120 San Marcos (92078) *(P-10411)*
Trident Technologies, San Diego *Also called Chemtreat Inc (P-9229)*
Tridus International Inc ....F....310 884-3200
1145 W Victoria St Compton (90220) *(P-13979)*
Tridus Magnetics and Assenblie, Compton *Also called Tridus International Inc (P-13979)*
Trifoil Imaging, Chatsworth *Also called Northrdge Tr-Mdlity Imging Inc (P-21483)*
Trigon Components Inc ....E....714 990-1367
939 Mariner St Brea (92821) *(P-19303)*
Trigon Electronics Inc ....F....714 633-7442
22765 Savi Ranch Pkwy C Yorba Linda (92887) *(P-20091)*
Trilibis Inc (PA) ....F....650 646-2400
66 Bovet Rd Ste 285 San Mateo (94402) *(P-25295)*
Trilibis Mobile, San Mateo *Also called Trilibis Inc (P-25295)*
Trilogy Glass and Packg Inc ....E....707 521-1300
975 Corporate Cntr Pkwy # 120 Santa Rosa (95407) *(P-10734)*
Trilore Technologies Inc ....E....925 295-0734
3000 Danville Blvd 525f Alamo (94507) *(P-11750)*
Trim Quick, Corona *Also called Vinylvisions Company LLC (P-8953)*
Trim Quick Co, Norco *Also called Halle-Hopper LLC (P-4163)*
Trim To Trade, Palm Desert *Also called Plumbing Products Inc (P-12044)*
Trim-Lok Inc ....C....714 562-0500
6855 Hermosa Cir Buena Park (90620) *(P-10412)*
Trimatic, Pasadena *Also called C & D Precision Components (P-16343)*
Trimble Inc ....F....408 481-8490
945 Stewart Dr Ste 100 Sunnyvale (94085) *(P-21445)*
Trimble Inc (PA) ....A....408 481-8000
935 Stewart Dr Sunnyvale (94085) *(P-21446)*
Trimble Inc ....E....916 294-2000
1720 Prairie City Rd Folsom (95630) *(P-21447)*
Trimble Inc ....F....408 481-8000
510 Deguigne Dr Sunnyvale (94085) *(P-21448)*
Trimble Military & Advnced Sys ....D....408 481-8000
510 De Guigne Dr Sunnyvale (94085) *(P-21449)*
Trimco, Oceanside *Also called Triangle Brass Mfg Co Inc (P-12003)*
Trimedyne Inc (PA) ....E....949 951-3800
5 Holland Ste 223 Irvine (92618) *(P-23063)*
Trimek Inc (HQ) ....F....858 571-7475
900 Lane Ave Ste 170 Chula Vista (91914) *(P-4922)*
Trimknit Inc ....E....818 768-7878
7542 San Fernando Rd Sun Valley (91352) *(P-2808)*
Trina Solar (us) Inc ....E....800 696-7114
100 Century Center Ct # 501 San Jose (95112) *(P-19235)*
Trinchero Family Estates, Saint Helena *Also called Sutter Home Winery Inc (P-2002)*
Trinchero Family Estates Inc ....F....707 963-1160
3070 Saint Helena Hwy N Saint Helena (94574) *(P-2028)*
Trinet Construction Inc ....F....415 695-7814
2560 Marin St San Francisco (94124) *(P-15368)*
Tringen Corporation ....F....661 393-3039
238 E Norris Rd Bakersfield (93308) *(P-285)*
Trinidad Benham Holding Co ....E....909 627-7535
5177 Chino Ave Chino (91710) *(P-2691)*
Trinity - 4, Paramount *Also called International Trend - 3 Corp (P-3164)*
Trinity Engineering ....E....707 585-2959
583 Martin Ave Rohnert Park (94928) *(P-5172)*
Trinity Lighweight, Frazier Park *Also called Trnlwb LLC (P-24278)*
Trinity Marketing LLC ....F....925 866-1514
12925 Alcosta Blvd Ste 6 San Ramon (94583) *(P-7148)*
Trinity Office Furniture Inc ....D....909 888-5551
1050 W Rialto Ave San Bernardino (92410) *(P-4972)*
Trinity Process Solutions Inc ....E....714 701-1112
4740 E Bryson St Anaheim (92807) *(P-13907)*
Trinity River Lumber Company (PA) ....C....530 623-5561
1375 Main St Weaverville (96093) *(P-4069)*
Trinity Steel Corporation ....F....805 648-3486
184 Rocklite Rd Ventura (93001) *(P-12264)*
Trinity Woodworks Inc ....E....760 639-5351
2620 Temple Heights Dr Oceanside (92056) *(P-4249)*
Trinium Technologies, Palos Verdes Estates *Also called QED Software LLC (P-25092)*
Trio Engineered Products Inc (HQ) ....E....626 851-3966
12823 Schabarum Ave Irwindale (91706) *(P-14195)*
Trio Manufacturing Inc ....D....310 640-6123
601 Lairport St El Segundo (90245) *(P-20959)*
Trio Metal Stamping Inc ....D....626 336-1228
15318 Proctor Ave City of Industry (91745) *(P-12796)*
Trio Tool & Die Co (PA) ....F....310 644-4431
3340 W El Segundo Blvd Hawthorne (90250) *(P-14582)*
Trio-Tech International (PA) ....F....818 787-7000
16139 Wyandotte St Van Nuys (91406) *(P-15040)*
Trion World Network Inc ....F....650 394-1000
1200 Bridge Pkwy Ste 201 Redwood City (94065) *(P-25296)*
Trion Worlds, Inc ....B....650 631-9800
2400 Bridge Pkwy 100 Redwood City (94065) *(P-25297)*
Triple A Pallets Inc ....F....559 313-7636
3555 S Academy Ave Sanger (93657) *(P-4509)*
Triple C Foods Inc ....D....510 357-8880
1465 Factor Ave San Leandro (94577) *(P-1385)*
Triple DOT Corp ....E....714 241-0888
3302 S Susan St Santa Ana (92704) *(P-9809)*
Triple E Manufacturing Inc ....E....661 831-7553
2121 S Union Ave Bakersfield (93307) *(P-14891)*
Triple H Food Processors LLC ....D....951 352-5700
5821 Wilderness Ave Riverside (92504) *(P-2692)*
Triplett Harps ....F....805 544-2777
220 Suburban Rd Ste C San Luis Obispo (93401) *(P-23392)*
Tripos Industries Inc ....E....323 669-0488
2448 Glendower Ave Los Angeles (90027) *(P-12053)*
Triprism Inc ....F....858 675-7552
15950 Bernardo Center Dr B San Diego (92127) *(P-23204)*
Tripus Industries, Los Angeles *Also called Tripos Industries Inc (P-12053)*
Triquint Wj Inc ....E....408 577-6200
3099 Orchard Dr San Jose (95134) *(P-18292)*
Trireme Medical LLC ....D....925 931-1300
7060 Koll Center Pkwy Pleasanton (94566) *(P-22656)*
Trisar Inc ....E....714 972-2626
950 W Town And Country Rd Orange (92868) *(P-7527)*
Trisep Corporation, Goleta *Also called Microdyn-Nadir Us Inc (P-16073)*
Tristar Global Inc ....F....626 363-6978
526 Coralridge Pl La Puente (91746) *(P-20469)*
Triton Chandelier Inc ....E....714 957-9600
1301 Dove St Ste 900 Newport Beach (92660) *(P-17651)*
Triumph Actuation Systms-Valen ....C....661 295-1015
28150 Harrison Pkwy Valencia (91355) *(P-20960)*
Triumph Aerostructures LLC ....A....310 322-1000
3901 Jack Northrop Ave Hawthorne (90250) *(P-20632)*
Triumph Equipment Inc ....E....909 947-5983
13434 S Ontario Ave Ontario (91761) *(P-20961)*
Triumph Fabrications ....C....619 440-2504
203 N Johnson Ave El Cajon (92020) *(P-20962)*
Triumph Fbrication - San Diego, El Cajon *Also called Triumph Fabrications (P-20962)*
Triumph Group Inc ....B....714 546-9842
2136 S Hathaway St Santa Ana (92705) *(P-11837)*
Triumph Insulation Systems ....F....760 768-1700
2401 Portico Blvd Calexico (92231) *(P-20963)*
Triumph Precision Products ....F....818 897-4700
13636 Vaughn St Ste A San Fernando (91340) *(P-13047)*
Triumph Processing Inc ....C....323 563-1338
2605 Industry Way Lynwood (90262) *(P-13524)*
Triumph Structures - Brea, Brea *Also called Alatus Aerosystems (P-20730)*
Triune Enterprises Inc ....E....310 719-1600
13711 S Normandie Ave Gardena (90249) *(P-5544)*
Triune Enterprises Mfg, Gardena *Also called Triune Enterprises Inc (P-5544)*
Trius Therapeutics LLC ....D....858 452-0370
4747 Executive Dr # 1100 San Diego (92121) *(P-8422)*
Trivascular Inc (HQ) ....E....707 543-8800
3910 Brickway Blvd Santa Rosa (95403) *(P-22657)*
Trivascular Technologies Inc (HQ) ....F....707 543-8800
3910 Brickway Blvd Santa Rosa (95403) *(P-22658)*
Trivec-Avant Corporation ....E....714 841-4976
17831 Jamestown Ln Huntington Beach (92647) *(P-18293)*
Triview Glass Industries LLC ....D....626 363-7980
711 S Stimson Ave City of Industry (91745) *(P-10735)*
Trixxi Clothing Company Inc (PA) ....E....323 585-4200
6817 E Acco St Commerce (90040) *(P-3280)*
Triyar Capital California LLC (PA) ....F....310 441-5654
10850 Wilshire Blvd Los Angeles (90024) *(P-20964)*
Trlg Intermediate Holdings LLC (PA) ....F....323 266-3072
1888 Rosecrans Ave Manhattan Beach (90266) *(P-3596)*
TRM Manufacturing Inc ....C....951 256-8550
375 Trm Cir Corona (92879) *(P-9733)*
Trmc Sale Corporation ....D....800 290-7073
4215 E Airport Dr Ontario (91761) *(P-15992)*

Trnlwb LLC ....A....661 245-3736
17410 Lockwood Valley Rd Frazier Park (93225) ***(P-24278)***
Troesh Readymix Inc ....D....805 928-3764
2280 Hutton Rd Nipomo (93444) ***(P-11200)***
Trojan Battery Company LLC (PA) ....B....800 423-6569
10375 Slusher Dr Santa Fe Springs (90670) ***(P-19825)***
Tronex Technology Incorporated ....E....707 426-2550
2860 Cordelia Rd Ste 230 Fairfield (94534) ***(P-11913)***
Tronson Manufacturing Inc ....E....408 533-0369
3421 Yale Way Fremont (94538) ***(P-17013)***
Tropian Inc ....D....408 865-1300
20813 Stevens Creek Blvd Cupertino (95014) ***(P-19236)***
Tropical Asphalt LLC (PA) ....F....714 739-1408
14435 Macaw St La Mirada (90638) ***(P-9420)***
Tropical Functional Labs LLC ....F....951 688-2619
7111 Arlington Ave Ste F Riverside (92503) ***(P-651)***
Tropical Preserving Co Inc ....E....213 748-5108
1711 E 15th St Los Angeles (90021) ***(P-864)***
Tropical Roofing Products CA, La Mirada *Also called Tropical Asphalt LLC* ***(P-9420)***
Tropicale Foods Inc ....E....909 635-0390
1237 W State St Ontario (91762) ***(P-700)***
Tropicana Products Inc ....C....626 968-1299
240 N Orange Ave City of Industry (91744) ***(P-865)***
Tropitone Furniture Co Inc (HQ) ....E....949 595-2000
5 Marconi Irvine (92618) ***(P-4846)***
Trosak Cabinets Inc ....F....760 744-9042
1478 Alpine Pl San Marcos (92078) ***(P-5114)***
Trouble At The Mill, Huntington Park *Also called Cotton Generation Inc* ***(P-3574)***
Trov Inc (PA) ....E....925 478-5500
347 Hartz Ave Danville (94526) ***(P-25298)***
Trovagene Inc ....D....858 952-7570
11055 Flintkote Ave Ste A San Diego (92121) ***(P-8521)***
Troy Metal Products, Goleta *Also called Neal Feay Company* ***(P-11598)***
Troy Products, Montebello *Also called Troy Sheet Metal Works Inc* ***(P-13146)***
Troy Sheet Metal Works Inc ....E....323 720-4100
1024 S Vail Ave Montebello (90640) ***(P-13146)***
Troy-Csl Lighting Inc ....D....626 336-4511
14508 Nelson Ave City of Industry (91744) ***(P-17564)***
Trs International Mfg Inc ....F....949 855-0673
27152 Burbank Foothill Ranch (92610) ***(P-17503)***
TRT Bsness Ntwrk Solutions Inc ....F....714 380-3888
15551 Red Hill Ave Ste A Tustin (92780) ***(P-21882)***
Tru Form Industries, Santa Fe Springs *Also called Tru-Form Industries Inc* ***(P-13289)***
Tru Machining ....F....510 573-3408
45979 Warm Springs Blvd Fremont (94539) ***(P-17014)***
Tru-Cut Inc ....E....310 630-0422
141 E 157th St Gardena (90248) ***(P-14136)***
Tru-Duct Inc ....E....619 660-3858
2500 Swetwater Sprng Blvd Spring Valley (91978) ***(P-12797)***
Tru-Fit Manufacturing, Lathrop *Also called Accurate Heating & Cooling Inc* ***(P-12457)***
Tru-Form Industries Inc (PA) ....D....562 802-2041
14511 Anson Ave Santa Fe Springs (90670) ***(P-13289)***
Tru-Form Plastics Inc ....E....310 327-9444
14600 Hoover St Westminster (92683) ***(P-10413)***
Tru-Trailers Inc ....F....559 251-7591
4444 E Lincoln Ave Fresno (93725) ***(P-20513)***
Tru-Trailers Manufacturing, Fresno *Also called Tru-Trailers Inc* ***(P-20513)***
Tru-Wood Products, Azusa *Also called McMurtrie & Mcmurtrie Inc* ***(P-4084)***
Truabutment Inc ....D....714 956-1488
17742 Cowan Irvine (92614) ***(P-22919)***
Truck Accessories Group LLC ....C....530 666-0176
1686 E Beamer St Woodland (95776) ***(P-21213)***
Truck Club Publishing Inc ....E....323 726-8620
7807 Telegraph Rd Ste H Montebello (90640) ***(P-6403)***
True Cast Concrete Products, Sun Valley *Also called Gibbel Bros Inc* ***(P-11111)***
True Cast Concrete Products, Sun Valley *Also called Quikrete Companies LLC* ***(P-10989)***
True Circuits Inc ....F....650 949-3400
4300 El Camino Real # 200 Los Altos (94022) ***(P-19772)***
True Design Inc ....F....562 699-2001
9427 Norwalk Blvd Santa Fe Springs (90670) ***(P-4359)***
True Fresh Hpp LLC ....F....949 531-6519
6535 Caballero Blvd B Buena Park (90620) ***(P-21535)***
True Grit, Newport Beach *Also called Calor Apparel Group Intl Corp* ***(P-3534)***
True Leaf Farms LLC ....B....831 623-4667
1275 San Justo Rd San Juan Bautista (95045) ***(P-902)***
True Leaf Technologies, Cotati *Also called Biotherm Hydronic Inc* ***(P-12058)***
True Organic Products Inc ....F....559 866-3001
20225 W Kamm Ave Helm (93627) ***(P-9088)***
True Position Technologies LLC ....D....661 294-0030
24900 Avenue Stanford Valencia (91355) ***(P-17015)***
True Precision Machining Inc ....E....805 964-4545
175 Indstrial Way Bellton Buellton Buellton (93427) ***(P-17016)***
True Protein, Vista *Also called Myosci Technologies Inc* ***(P-634)***
True Religion Apparel Inc (HQ) ....B....323 266-3072
1888 Rosecrans Ave # 1000 Manhattan Beach (90266) ***(P-3597)***
True Religion Brand Jeans, Manhattan Beach *Also called True Religion Apparel Inc* ***(P-3597)***
True Temper Sports Inc ....E....858 404-0405
9401 Waples St Ste 140 San Diego (92121) ***(P-23677)***
True Vision Displays Inc ....F....562 407-0630
16402 Berwyn Rd Cerritos (90703) ***(P-19773)***
True Warrior LLC ....E....661 237-6588
21226 Lone Star Way Santa Clarita (91390) ***(P-3684)***
Truer Medical Inc ....F....714 628-9785
1050 N Batavia St Ste C Orange (92867) ***(P-22659)***
Truett-Hurst Inc (PA) ....E....707 431-4423
125 Foss Creek Cir Healdsburg (95448) ***(P-2029)***
Truevision 3d Surgical, Goleta *Also called Truevision Systems Inc* ***(P-22660)***
Truevision Systems Inc ....E....805 963-9700
315 Bollay Dr Ste 101 Goleta (93117) ***(P-22660)***
Trufocus Corporation ....F....831 761-9981
468 Westridge Dr Watsonville (95076) ***(P-22943)***
Truframe, Visalia *Also called R Lang Company* ***(P-12344)***
Truitt Oilfield Maint Corp ....B....661 871-4099
1051 James Rd Bakersfield (93308) ***(P-286)***
Trulite GL Alum Solutions LLC ....F....800 877-8439
19430 San Jose Ave City of Industry (91748) ***(P-11607)***
Truly Green Solutions LLC ....E....818 206-4404
9601 Variel Ave Chatsworth (91311) ***(P-17741)***
Trumaker Inc ....E....415 662-3836
228 Grant Ave Fl 2 San Francisco (94108) ***(P-3045)***
Trumaker & Co., San Francisco *Also called Trumaker Inc* ***(P-3045)***
Trumed Systems Incorporated ....E....844 878-6331
4350 Executive Dr Ste 120 San Diego (92121) ***(P-15993)***
Trumer Brauerei, Berkeley *Also called Comeback Brewing II Inc* ***(P-1580)***
Trupart Manufacturing Inc ....F....805 644-4107
4450 Dupont Ct Ste A Ventura (93003) ***(P-14420)***
Trupart Mfg, Ventura *Also called Trupart Manufacturing Inc* ***(P-14420)***
Truroots Inc (HQ) ....E....925 218-2205
6999 Southfront Rd Livermore (94551) ***(P-2693)***
Truroots Inc ....F....925 218-2205
37 Speedway Ave Chico (95928) ***(P-2694)***
Truspro, Guadalupe *Also called Tri-Co Building Supply Inc* ***(P-4429)***
Truss Engineering Inc ....E....209 527-6387
477 Zeff Rd Modesto (95351) ***(P-4431)***
Trussworks International Inc ....D....714 630-2772
2850 E Coronado St Anaheim (92806) ***(P-12265)***
Trusted Energy LLC ....F....818 646-3137
5478 Wilshire Blvd # 303 Los Angeles (90036) ***(P-82)***
Truston, Santa Barbara *Also called Scamsafe Inc* ***(P-25150)***
Trutouch Technologies Inc ....F....909 703-5963
2020 Iowa Ave Ste 102 Riverside (92507) ***(P-22291)***
Truwest Inc ....E....714 895-2444
5592 Engineer Dr Huntington Beach (92649) ***(P-3199)***
Try All 3 Sports ....F....949 492-2255
931 Calle Negocio Ste O San Clemente (92673) ***(P-21146)***
Tryad Service Corporation ....D....661 391-1524
5900 E Lerdo Hwy Shafter (93263) ***(P-287)***
Trymax ....F....661 391-1572
5900 E Lerdo Hwy Shafter (93263) ***(P-13908)***
TS Logging ....F....707 895-3751
18121 Rays Rd Philo (95466) ***(P-4016)***
Tsc LLC ....A....661 824-6600
16555 Spcship Landing Way Mojave (93501) ***(P-21173)***
Tschida Engineering ....F....707 224-4482
1812 Yajome St NAPA (94559) ***(P-17017)***
TSE Worldwide Press Inc ....E....909 989-8282
9830 6th St Ste 101 Rancho Cucamonga (91730) ***(P-6607)***
Tset, Inc., Santa Clara *Also called Cleanpartset Inc* ***(P-14928)***
Tsf Construction Services Inc ....F....619 202-7615
4805 Mercury St Ste E San Diego (92111) ***(P-2983)***
Tsg 1895 USA, Buena Park *Also called Secret Garden (tsg 1895) LLC* ***(P-24236)***
Tsi Tech Devmnt & Commercializ ....F....916 786-3900
7501 Foothills Blvd Roseville (95747) ***(P-19237)***
Tsi/Protherm, Orange *Also called Allen Morgan* ***(P-15249)***
Tsmc Technology Inc ....D....408 382-8052
2585 Junction Ave San Jose (95134) ***(P-19238)***
TSS El Segundo, El Segundo *Also called Trelleborg Sealing Solutions E* ***(P-9562)***
TSS Embroidery Inc ....F....909 590-1383
3432 Royal Ridge Rd Chino Hills (91709) ***(P-3867)***
TSS Software Corporation ....E....443 321-5600
200 Commerce Irvine (92602) ***(P-25299)***
Tst Inc ....E....951 727-3169
13428 Benson Ave Chino (91710) ***(P-11570)***
Tst Inc (PA) ....B....951 685-2155
13428 Benson Ave Chino (91710) ***(P-11571)***
TST Molding LLC ....E....951 296-6200
42322 Avenida Alvarado Temecula (92590) ***(P-10414)***
TST Water LLC ....F....951 541-9517
42188 Rio Nedo Ste B Temecula (92590) ***(P-16127)***
Tst/Impreso California Inc ....F....909 357-7190
10589 Business Dr Fontana (92337) ***(P-7561)***
TT Machine Corp ....E....714 534-5288
11651 Anabel Ave Garden Grove (92843) ***(P-14688)***
Ttb Products Inc (PA) ....F....949 369-1475
220 Calle Pintoresco San Clemente (92672) ***(P-18373)***
TTI Floor Care North Amer Inc ....B....440 996-2802
13055 Valley Blvd Fontana (92335) ***(P-9511)***
TTI Performance Exhaust, Corona *Also called Tube Technologies Inc* ***(P-20470)***
Ttl Holdings LLC (HQ) ....F....909 597-7861
4626 Eucalyptus Ave Chino (91710) ***(P-10415)***
Ttm Printed Circuit Group Inc ....C....408 486-3100
407 Mathew St Santa Clara (95050) ***(P-18630)***
Ttm Printed Circuit Group Inc (HQ) ....D....714 327-3000
2630 S Harbor Blvd Santa Ana (92704) ***(P-18631)***
Ttm Technologies Inc ....B....408 486-3100
407 Mathew St Santa Clara (95050) ***(P-18632)***
Ttm Technologies Inc (PA) ....B....714 327-3000
1665 Scenic Ave Ste 250 Costa Mesa (92626) ***(P-18633)***
Ttm Technologies Inc ....B....714 688-7200
3140 E Coronado St Anaheim (92806) ***(P-18634)***
Ttm Technologies Inc ....D....858 874-2701
5037 Ruffner St San Diego (92111) ***(P-18635)***
Ttm Technologies Inc ....B....714 327-3000
2630 S Harbor Blvd Santa Ana (92704) ***(P-18636)***
Ttm Technologies Inc ....C....408 280-0422
355 Turtle Creek Ct San Jose (95125) ***(P-18637)***

ALPHABETIC

Ttm Technologies N Amer LLC....C....408 719-4000
355 Turtle Creek Ct San Jose (95125) ***(P-18638)***
Ttn Machining Inc....F....619 303-4573
9105 Olive Dr Spring Valley (91977) ***(P-17018)***
Tts Products, Los Angeles *Also called Tvs Distributors Inc* ***(P-23778)***
TTT Concrete, Lakeside *Also called Superior Ready Mix Concrete LP* ***(P-11197)***
Tu-K Industries Inc....E....562 927-3365
5702 Firestone Pl South Gate (90280) ***(P-8856)***
Tua Fashion Inc (PA)....F....213 422-2384
8936 Appian Way Los Angeles (90046) ***(P-2765)***
Tua USA, Los Angeles *Also called Tua Fashion Inc* ***(P-2765)***
Tube Bending Llc....F....562 692-5829
4747 Citrus Dr Pico Rivera (90660) ***(P-13909)***
Tube Form Solutions LLC....F....760 599-5001
1398 Poinsettia Ave # 101 Vista (92081) ***(P-14770)***
Tube Lighting Products, El Cajon *Also called Tujayar Enterprises Inc* ***(P-17652)***
Tube One Industries Inc....F....951 300-2998
4055 Garner Rd Riverside (92501) ***(P-11488)***
Tube Rags....F....323 264-7770
4382 Bandini Blvd Vernon (90058) ***(P-2871)***
Tube Technologies Inc....E....951 371-4878
1555 Consumer Cir Corona (92880) ***(P-20470)***
Tube-Tainer Inc....E....562 945-3711
8174 Byron Rd Whittier (90606) ***(P-5496)***
Tubemogul Inc....D....510 653-0126
1250 53rd St Ste 1 Emeryville (94608) ***(P-25300)***
Tubing Seal Cap Co, Anaheim *Also called Pacific Precision Metals Inc* ***(P-13258)***
Tubit Enterprises Inc....E....530 335-5085
21640 S Vallejo St Burney (96013) ***(P-4017)***
Tuboscope Nat Oilwell Varco, Bakersfield *Also called Tuboscope Pipeline Svcs Inc* ***(P-288)***
Tuboscope Pipeline Svcs Inc....E....661 321-3400
4621 Burr St Bakersfield (93308) ***(P-288)***
Tubular Specialties Mfg Inc....D....310 515-4801
13011 S Spring St Los Angeles (90061) ***(P-10808)***
Tuesday Review, The, Newman *Also called Index Printing Inc* ***(P-7353)***
Tuff Boy Holding Inc....E....209 239-1361
5151 Almondwood Rd Manteca (95337) ***(P-20514)***
Tuff Boy Trailers, Manteca *Also called Tuff Boy Holding Inc* ***(P-20514)***
Tuff Kote Systems Inc....F....714 522-7341
7033 Orangethorpe Ave B Buena Park (90621) ***(P-8951)***
Tuff Shed Inc....E....559 268-8833
2431 Sarah Dr Fresno (93706) ***(P-4579)***
Tuff Shed Inc....F....626 334-0748
850 W Foothill Blvd Azusa (91702) ***(P-4580)***
Tuff Shed Inc....F....408 935-8833
931 Cadillac Ct Milpitas (95035) ***(P-4581)***
Tuff Shed Inc....F....925 681-3492
1401 Franquette Ave Concord (94520) ***(P-4582)***
Tuff Stuff Products....B....559 535-5778
9600 Road 256 Terra Bella (93270) ***(P-7897)***
Tuffer Manufacturing Co Inc....E....714 526-3077
163 E Liberty Ave Anaheim (92801) ***(P-21450)***
Tuffstuff Fitness Intl Inc....C....909 629-1600
13971 Norton Ave Chino (91710) ***(P-23678)***
Tuftex Carpet Mills, Santa Fe Springs *Also called Shaw Industries Group Inc* ***(P-2939)***
Tujayar Enterprises Inc....E....619 442-0577
1346 Pioneer Way El Cajon (92020) ***(P-17652)***
Tukko Group LLC....E....408 598-1251
530 Alameda Del Prado Novato (94949) ***(P-25301)***
Tukko Labs, Novato *Also called Tukko Group LLC* ***(P-25301)***
Tul Inc....D....909 444-0577
663 Brea Canyon Rd Ste 6 Walnut (91789) ***(P-12004)***
Tulare Advance Register, Tulare *Also called Gannett Co Inc* ***(P-5853)***
Tulare County Septic Tank Inc....F....559 686-8531
19412 Road 96 Tulare (93274) ***(P-11011)***
Tulip Pubg & Graphics Inc....E....510 898-0000
1003 Canal Blvd Richmond (94804) ***(P-7149)***
Tulkoff Food Products West Inc....E....925 427-5157
705 Bliss Ave Pittsburg (94565) ***(P-937)***
Tullys Coffee Co Inc (HQ)....E....415 929-8808
2455 Fillmore St San Francisco (94115) ***(P-2369)***
Tullys Coffee Co Inc....F....415 213-8791
1509 Sloat Blvd San Francisco (94132) ***(P-2370)***
Tulocay Winery....F....707 255-4064
1426 Coombsville Rd NAPA (94558) ***(P-2030)***
Tung Fei Plastic Inc....F....510 783-9688
1859 Sabre St Hayward (94545) ***(P-5631)***
Tung Tai Group....F....408 573-8681
1726 Rogers Ave San Jose (95112) ***(P-13290)***
Tungsten Heavy Powder Inc (PA)....D....858 693-6100
6170 Cornerstone Ct E # 310 San Diego (92121) ***(P-11431)***
Tungsten Heavy Powder & Parts, San Diego *Also called Tungsten Heavy Powder Inc* ***(P-11431)***
Tur-Bo Jet Products Co Inc....D....626 285-1294
5025 Earle Ave Rosemead (91770) ***(P-19368)***
Turbine Components Inc....E....858 678-8568
8985 Crestmar Pt San Diego (92121) ***(P-20686)***
Turbine Eng Cmpnents Tech Corp....C....562 908-0200
8839 Pioneer Blvd Santa Fe Springs (90670) ***(P-13131)***
Turbo Coil Inc....F....626 644-6254
1532 Sinaloa Ave Pasadena (91104) ***(P-15994)***
Turbo Coil Manufacturing Inc....E....626 599-7777
1740 Evergreen St Duarte (91010) ***(P-19369)***
Turbo International....F....760 476-1444
2151 Las Palmas Dr Ste E Carlsbad (92011) ***(P-13115)***
Turbo Refrigeration Systems....E....626 599-9777
1740 Evergreen St Duarte (91010) ***(P-15995)***
Turbonetics Holdings Inc....E....805 581-0333
14399 Princeton Ave Moorpark (93021) ***(P-20471)***
Turbosand, Anderson *Also called Voorwood Company* ***(P-14787)***
Turbotax, San Diego *Also called Intuit Inc* ***(P-24798)***
Turbotools Corporation....F....415 759-5599
2190 31st Ave San Francisco (94116) ***(P-25302)***
Turf Star Inc (PA)....F....800 585-8001
2438 Radley Ct Hayward (94545) ***(P-14113)***
Turkhan Nuts, Ripon *Also called Pearl Crop Inc* ***(P-1516)***
Turley Wine Cellars....F....805 434-1030
2900 Vineyard Dr Templeton (93465) ***(P-2031)***
Turley Wine Cellars Inc....F....707 968-2700
3358 Saint Helena Hwy N Saint Helena (94574) ***(P-2032)***
Turlock Cabinet Shop Inc....F....209 632-1311
1475 West Ave S Turlock (95380) ***(P-4360)***
Turlock Journal....F....209 634-9141
138 S Center St Turlock (95380) ***(P-6075)***
Turlock Machine Works....E....209 632-2275
1240 S 1st St Turlock (95380) ***(P-16160)***
Turlock Sheet Metal & Wldg Inc....E....209 667-4716
301 S Broadway Turlock (95380) ***(P-1049)***
Turn-Luckily International Inc....F....949 465-0200
9710 Research Dr Irvine (92618) ***(P-15876)***
Turnbull Wine Cellars....F....707 963-5839
8210 St Helena Hwy Oakville (94562) ***(P-2033)***
Turner Designs Inc....E....408 749-0994
1995 N 1st St San Jose (95112) ***(P-22045)***
Turner Designs Hydrocarbon Ins....E....559 253-1414
2027 N Gateway Blvd # 109 Fresno (93727) ***(P-20092)***
Turner Fiberfill Inc....E....323 724-7957
1600 Date St Montebello (90640) ***(P-7917)***
Turner Group Publications Inc....F....408 297-3299
27788 Klaus Ct Hayward (94542) ***(P-7528)***
Turner Precision, Gardena *Also called Aldo Fragale* ***(P-16248)***
Turnham Corporation (PA)....F....626 330-0415
15312 Proctor Ave City of Industry (91745) ***(P-14689)***
Turnham Corporation....F....626 968-6481
15310 Proctor Ave City of Industry (91745) ***(P-14690)***
Turnkey Technologies Inc....E....707 745-9520
4650 E 2nd St Ste C Benicia (94510) ***(P-17019)***
Turret Lathe Specialists Inc....F....714 520-0058
875 S Rose Pl Anaheim (92805) ***(P-17020)***
Turret Punch Co Inc....F....909 587-1820
7780 Edison Ave Fontana (92336) ***(P-9768)***
Turtle Beach Corporation (PA)....C....914 345-2255
11011 Via Frontera Ste A San Diego (92127) ***(P-19774)***
Turtle Storage Ltd....E....805 933-3688
401 S Beckwith Rd Santa Paula (93060) ***(P-5173)***
Turtleback Case, Sylmar *Also called Leather Pro Inc* ***(P-10564)***
Tuscany Pavers Inc....F....866 596-4092
241 S Twin Oaks Valley Rd San Marcos (92078) ***(P-14196)***
Tusco Casting Corporation....E....209 368-5137
934 E Victor Rd Lodi (95240) ***(P-11528)***
Tutti, Los Angeles *Also called Adwear Inc* ***(P-3091)***
Tuula Inc....F....858 761-6045
26019 Jefferson Ave Ste D Murrieta (92562) ***(P-8611)***
Tvs Distributors Inc (PA)....F....323 268-1347
2822 E Olympic Blvd Los Angeles (90023) ***(P-23778)***
Twed-Dells Inc....E....714 754-6900
1900 S Susan St Santa Ana (92704) ***(P-10736)***
Twelve Signs Inc....D....310 553-8000
3369 S Robertson Blvd Los Angeles (90034) ***(P-6275)***
Twelve Strike, Long Beach *Also called South Street Inc* ***(P-23656)***
Twentieth Century Spring Mfg, Campbell *Also called 20th Century Spring Mfg* ***(P-13149)***
Twenty Niners Club, Vernon *Also called Twenty-Niners Provisions Inc* ***(P-552)***
Twenty-Niners Provisions Inc....E....323 233-7864
1784 E Vernon Ave Vernon (90058) ***(P-552)***
Twilight Technology Inc (PA)....E....714 257-2257
325 N Shepard St Anaheim (92806) ***(P-19239)***
Twin Coast Metrology Inc (PA)....F....310 709-2308
333 Wshngton Blvd Ste 362 Marina Del Rey (90292) ***(P-22143)***
Twin Creeks Technologies Inc (PA)....F....408 368-3733
3930 N 1st St Ste 10 San Jose (95134) ***(P-19240)***
Twin Design Co LLC....F....510 329-4991
18458 Carlwyn Dr Castro Valley (94546) ***(P-15369)***
Twin Eagles Inc....D....562 802-3488
13259 166th St Cerritos (90703) ***(P-17378)***
Twin Glass Industries Inc....F....408 779-8801
16880 Joleen Way Ste 2 Morgan Hill (95037) ***(P-10737)***
Twin Industries, San Ramon *Also called Gemini Consultants Inc* ***(P-18492)***
Twin Industries Inc....D....925 866-8946
2303 Camino Ramon Ste 106 San Ramon (94583) ***(P-18639)***
Twin Peak Industries Inc....E....800 259-5906
12420 Montague St Ste E Pacoima (91331) ***(P-23679)***
Twin Peaks Ingrdients, Fontana *Also called Tpi Marketing LLC* ***(P-14890)***
Twin Peaks Winery Inc....F....707 945-0855
1473 Yountville Cross Rd Yountville (94599) ***(P-2034)***
Twindom, Berkeley *Also called Machinables Inc* ***(P-15796)***
Twist Bioscience Corporation....C....800 719-0671
455 Mission Bay Blvd S San Francisco (94158) ***(P-8584)***
Twist Frozen Yogurt, Los Angeles *Also called Venture Capital Entps LLC* ***(P-702)***
Twist Tite Mfg Inc....E....562 229-0990
13344 Cambridge St Santa Fe Springs (90670) ***(P-13087)***
Twisted Oak Winery LLC (PA)....E....209 728-3000
4280 Red Hill Rd Vallecito (95251) ***(P-2035)***
Two Bears Metal Products....E....310 326-2533
723 N Meyler St San Pedro (90731) ***(P-17021)***
Two Blind Mice LLC....F....714 279-0600
5016 E Crescent Dr Anaheim (92807) ***(P-2036)***
Two Brothers Racing Inc....F....714 550-6070
401 S Grand Ave Santa Ana (92705) ***(P-21147)***

Mergent e-mail: customerrelations@mergent.com
1314
2019 California
Manufacturers Register
(P-0000) Products & Services Section entry number
(PA)=Parent Co (HQ)=Headquarters (DH)=Div Headquarters

Two Hands, Los Angeles *Also called Lialee Inc* ***(P-2847)***
Two Lads Inc (PA) ....E.......323 584-0064
5001 Hampton St Vernon (90058) ***(P-23779)***
Two Pore Guys Inc ....F.......831 515-8515
2161 Delaware Ave Ste B Santa Cruz (95060) ***(P-19241)***
Two Star Dog Inc ....F.......510 525-1100
1329 9th St Berkeley (94710) ***(P-3343)***
Two Star Dog Inc (PA) ....E.......510 525-1100
1329 9th St Berkeley (94710) ***(P-3281)***
Two Thirty Two Productins Inc ....E.......714 317-5317
7108 Katella Ave Ste 440 Stanton (90680) ***(P-23205)***
Twpm Inc ....F.......714 522-8881
15320 Valley View Ave La Mirada (90638) ***(P-5513)***
Txc Technology Inc (HQ) ....F.......714 990-5510
451 W Lambert Rd Ste 201 Brea (92821) ***(P-19775)***
Txd International Usa Inc ....F.......909 947-6568
2336 S Vineyard Ave A Ontario (91761) ***(P-6076)***
Tyco Electronics, San Diego *Also called Te Connectivity Corporation* ***(P-19420)***
Tyco Fire Products LP ....C.......925 687-6957
6952 Preston Ave Livermore (94551) ***(P-15370)***
Tyco Fire Protection Products, Livermore *Also called Tyco Fire Products LP* ***(P-15370)***
Tyco International MGT Co LLC ....B.......650 361-3333
300 Constitution Dr Menlo Park (94025) ***(P-11680)***
Tyco Simplexgrinnell ....E.......707 578-3212
3077 Wiljan Ct Ste B Santa Rosa (95407) ***(P-15371)***
Tyflong International Inc ....F.......530 746-3001
606 Pena Dr Davis (95618) ***(P-11306)***
Tyler Camera Systems, Van Nuys *Also called Tyler Technologies Inc* ***(P-25303)***
Tyler Technologies Inc ....F.......818 989-4420
14218 Aetna St Van Nuys (91401) ***(P-25303)***
Tyler Trafficante Inc (PA) ....D.......323 869-9299
700 S Palm Ave Alhambra (91803) ***(P-3046)***
Tylerco Inc ....E.......949 769-3991
17831 Sky Park Cir Ste A Irvine (92614) ***(P-17565)***
Tyloon Media Corporation ....F.......626 330-5838
15713 E Valley Blvd City of Industry (91744) ***(P-6608)***
Typecraft Inc ....E.......626 795-8093
2040 E Walnut St Pasadena (91107) ***(P-7150)***
Typecraft Wood & Jones, Pasadena *Also called Typecraft Inc* ***(P-7150)***
Typehaus Inc ....F.......760 334-3555
2262 Rutherford Rd # 103 Carlsbad (92008) ***(P-15619)***
Tyson Fresh Meats Inc ....F.......714 528-5543
500 S Kraemer Blvd # 380 Brea (92821) ***(P-453)***
TYT LLC (HQ) ....C.......510 444-3933
2861 Mandela Pkwy Oakland (94608) ***(P-7151)***
Tyvak Nn-Satellite Systems Inc ....D.......949 753-1020
15330 Barranca Pkwy Irvine (92618) ***(P-21174)***
Tz, Los Angeles *Also called Toska Inc* ***(P-3519)***
Tz Holdings LP ....A.......949 719-2200
567 San Nicolas Dr # 120 Newport Beach (92660) ***(P-25304)***
U M S Inc ....E.......661 324-5454
317 Mount Vernon Ave Bakersfield (93307) ***(P-13525)***
U P C, Huntington Beach *Also called Urethane Products Corporation* ***(P-10421)***
U P I, Fontana *Also called Urethane Polymer International* ***(P-9315)***
U R M, Vista *Also called United Research & Mfg* ***(P-20476)***
U R U, Escondido *Also called URu By Kristine St Rrik Inc* ***(P-3345)***
U S Air Filtration Inc (PA) ....F.......951 491-7282
23811 Washington Ave C110176 Murrieta (92562) ***(P-21671)***
U S Architectural Lighting, Palmdale *Also called US Pole Company Inc* ***(P-17742)***
U S Bearings ....E.......626 358-0181
5001b Commerce Dr Baldwin Park (91706) ***(P-15114)***
U S Bowling Corporation ....F.......909 548-0644
5480 Schaefer Ave Chino (91710) ***(P-23680)***
U S Chrome Corp California ....F.......562 437-2825
1480 Canal Ave Long Beach (90813) ***(P-13526)***
U S Circuit Inc ....D.......760 489-1413
2071 Wineridge Pl Escondido (92029) ***(P-19776)***
U S Cold Storage, Bakersfield *Also called United States Cold Storage Inc* ***(P-2423)***
U S Divers Co Inc ....C.......760 597-5000
2340 Cousteau Ct Vista (92081) ***(P-23681)***
U S Enterprise Corporation ....E.......510 487-8877
30560 San Antonio St Hayward (94544) ***(P-938)***
U S Fabrications, Hayward *Also called South Bay Diversfd Systems Inc* ***(P-12765)***
U S I, Saratoga *Also called United Supertek Inc* ***(P-18640)***
U S L, San Luis Obispo *Also called Ultra-Stereo Labs Inc* ***(P-20093)***
U S Label Corporation ....F.......818 558-3703
3100 W Vanowen St Burbank (91505) ***(P-5745)***
U S Medical Instruments Inc (PA) ....E.......619 661-5500
888 Prospect St Ste 100 La Jolla (92037) ***(P-22661)***
U S Precision Manufacturing, Riverside *Also called US Precision Sheet Metal Inc* ***(P-12802)***
U S Saw & Blades, Santa Ana *Also called US Saws Inc* ***(P-14197)***
U S Technical Institute, Placentia *Also called US Computers Inc* ***(P-15879)***
U S Weatherford L P ....D.......661 589-9483
2815 Fruitvale Ave Bakersfield (93308) ***(P-289)***
U S Weatherford L P ....E.......661 746-3415
19608 Broken Ct Shafter (93263) ***(P-155)***
U S Weatherford L P ....F.......661 746-1391
19468 Creek Rd Bakersfield (93314) ***(P-13910)***
U S Wheel Corporation ....E.......714 892-0021
15702 Producer Ln Huntington Beach (92649) ***(P-20472)***
U-Blox San Diego Inc ....F.......858 847-9611
12626 High Bluff Dr San Diego (92130) ***(P-18002)***
U-C Components Inc (PA) ....E.......408 782-1929
18700 Adams Ct Morgan Hill (95037) ***(P-13088)***
U-Nited Printing and Copy Ctr, Van Nuys *Also called Printrunner LLC* ***(P-7447)***
U.S. Concrete Precast Group, Morgan Hill *Also called Sierra Precast Inc* ***(P-11002)***
U.S. Horizon Mfg, Valencia *Also called US Horizon Manufacturing Inc* ***(P-10610)***
U.S. Patriot Lite, Los Angeles *Also called Patriot Lighting Inc* ***(P-17637)***
U.S. Specialty Vehicles, Rancho Cucamonga *Also called American HX Auto Trade Inc* ***(P-20126)***
Uber Technologies Inc ....E.......415 986-2715
555 Market St San Francisco (94105) ***(P-25305)***
Ubi Energy Corporation ....C.......310 283-6978
9465 Wilshire Blvd # 300 Beverly Hills (90212) ***(P-9368)***
Ubicom Inc ....D.......408 433-3330
195 Baypointe Pkwy San Jose (95134) ***(P-19242)***
Ubiome Inc ....F.......415 275-2461
360 Langton St Ste 301 San Francisco (94103) ***(P-8423)***
Ubm Canon LLC (HQ) ....C.......310 445-4200
2901 28th St Ste 100 Santa Monica (90405) ***(P-6276)***
Ubm LLC ....D.......415 947-6770
18301 Von Karman Ave # 920 Irvine (92612) ***(P-6277)***
Ubm LLC ....C.......415 947-6488
303 2nd St Ste 900s San Francisco (94107) ***(P-6278)***
Ubm Techweb (HQ) ....F.......415 947-6000
303 Secon St Tower Fl 9 9 Stower San Francisco (94107) ***(P-6279)***
UBS Printing Group Inc ....D.......951 273-7900
2577 Research Dr Corona (92882) ***(P-7152)***
Ubst Inc ....F.......424 222-9908
373 Van Ness Ave Torrance (90501) ***(P-3282)***
Ubtech Robotics Corp ....E.......213 261-7153
767 S Alameda St Los Angeles (90021) ***(P-14771)***
UC Plastic Manufacture Inc ....E.......510 785-6777
3202 Diablo Ave Hayward (94545) ***(P-5632)***
Uc2, San Diego *Also called Biota Technology Inc* ***(P-24426)***
Ucan Zippers, Los Angeles *Also called Catame Inc* ***(P-23763)***
Ucsf School of Pharmacy ....F.......415 476-1444
3333 California St San Francisco (94118) ***(P-8424)***
Uct, Hayward *Also called Ultra Clean Technology Systems* ***(P-21672)***
Ucview, Northridge *Also called ATI Solutions Inc* ***(P-18309)***
Udecor Inc (PA) ....F.......877 550-0600
8302 Espresso Dr Ste 130 Bakersfield (93312) ***(P-10416)***
UFO Designs (PA) ....F.......714 892-4420
5812 Machine Dr Huntington Beach (92649) ***(P-10417)***
UFO Designs ....E.......562 924-5763
16730 Gridley Rd Cerritos (90703) ***(P-20473)***
UFO Inc ....E.......323 588-5450
2110 Belgrave Ave Huntington Park (90255) ***(P-10418)***
Ufp Technologies Inc ....E.......714 662-0277
20211 S Susana Rd Compton (90221) ***(P-9889)***
Uhv Sputtering Inc ....F.......408 779-2826
275 Digital Dr Morgan Hill (95037) ***(P-19243)***
Ukiah Brewing Co LLC ....E.......707 468-5898
551 Cypress Ave Ukiah (95482) ***(P-1633)***
Ullman Sails Inc (PA) ....F.......714 432-1860
2710 S Croddy Way Santa Ana (92704) ***(P-3817)***
Ulmer Industries Inc ....E.......909 823-7111
15243 Valley Blvd Fontana (92335) ***(P-12266)***
Ultera Systems Inc ....F.......949 367-8800
28241 Crown Valley Pkwy F115 Laguna Niguel (92677) ***(P-15877)***
Ulti-Mate Connector Inc ....E.......714 637-7099
1872 N Case St Orange (92865) ***(P-19426)***
Ultimate Ears Consumer LLC ....E.......949 502-8340
3 Jenner Ste 180 Irvine (92618) ***(P-22836)***
Ultimate Game Chair Inc ....E.......925 756-6944
5089 Lone Tree Way Antioch (94531) ***(P-17870)***
Ultimate Jumpers Inc ....F.......626 337-3086
14924 Arrow Hwy Ste A Baldwin Park (91706) ***(P-5260)***
Ultimate Metal Finishing Corp ....F.......323 890-9100
6150 Sheila St Commerce (90040) ***(P-13675)***
Ultimate Paper Box Company, City of Industry *Also called Boxes R Us Inc* ***(P-5504)***
Ultimate Print Source Inc ....E.......909 947-5292
2070 S Hellman Ave Ontario (91761) ***(P-7153)***
Ultimate Rail Equipment Inc ....F.......510 324-5000
30914 San Antonio St Hayward (94544) ***(P-20474)***
Ultimate Software Group Inc ....E.......949 214-2710
5 Hutton Centre Dr # 130 Santa Ana (92707) ***(P-25306)***
Ultimate Solutions, Huntington Beach *Also called Sandia Plastics Inc* ***(P-10358)***
Ultimate Sound Inc ....B.......909 861-6200
1200 S Diamond Bar Blvd # 200 Diamond Bar (91765) ***(P-17871)***
Ultimatte Corporation ....E.......818 993-8007
20945 Plummer St Chatsworth (91311) ***(P-18294)***
Ultimo Software Solutions Inc ....C.......408 943-1490
33268 Central Ave 2 Union City (94587) ***(P-25307)***
Ultra Built Kitchens Inc ....E.......323 232-3362
1814 E 43rd St Los Angeles (90058) ***(P-4361)***
Ultra Chem Labs Corp ....F.......909 605-1640
4581 Brickell Privado St Ontario (91761) ***(P-8681)***
Ultra Clean Technology Systems (HQ) ....C.......510 576-4400
26462 Corporate Ave Hayward (94545) ***(P-21672)***
Ultra Glass ....F.......916 338-3911
4001 Vista Park Ct Ste 1 Sacramento (95834) ***(P-10738)***
Ultra Gro LLC ....E.......559 661-0977
1043 S Granada Dr Madera (93637) ***(P-9076)***
Ultra Pro Acquisition LLC ....C.......323 725-1975
6049 E Slauson Ave Commerce (90040) ***(P-7587)***
Ultra Pro International LLC (PA) ....D.......323 890-2100
6049 E Slauson Ave Commerce (90040) ***(P-7588)***
Ultra TEC Manufacturing Inc ....F.......714 542-0608
1025 E Chestnut Ave Santa Ana (92701) ***(P-15041)***
Ultra-Pure Metal Finishing ....F.......714 637-3150
1764 N Case St Orange (92865) ***(P-13527)***
Ultra-Stereo Labs Inc ....E.......805 549-0161
181 Bonetti Dr San Luis Obispo (93401) ***(P-20093)***
Ultracast LLC ....E.......860 253-5015
3701 E Conant St Long Beach (90808) ***(P-11502)***
Ultracor, Stockton *Also called Specialty Cellular Products Co* ***(P-11371)***

ALPHABETIC

Employee Codes: A=Over 500 employees, B=251-500
C=101-250, D=51-100, E=20-50, F=10-19
2019 California
Manfacturers Register
© Mergent Inc. 1-800-342-5647
1315

Ultragenyx Pharmaceutical Inc (PA) ....C....415 483-8800
60 Leveroni Ct Novato (94949) *(P-8425)*
Ultramar Inc ....F....530 345-7901
2233 Esplanade Chico (95926) *(P-9369)*
Ultramar Inc ....F....661 944-2496
9508 E Palmdale Blvd Palmdale (93591) *(P-9370)*
Ultramar Inc ....E....310 834-7254
961 S La Paloma Ave Wilmington (90744) *(P-290)*
Ultramet ....D....818 899-0236
12173 Montague St Pacoima (91331) *(P-13528)*
Ultraneon Sign Company, San Diego *Also called Ultraneon Sign Corp (P-23995)*
Ultraneon Sign Corp ....E....858 569-6716
5458 Complex St Ste 401 San Diego (92123) *(P-23995)*
Ultrasil Corp ....E....510 266-3700
3527 Breakwater Ave Hayward (94545) *(P-19244)*
Ultratech Inc (HQ) ....C....408 321-8835
3050 Zanker Rd San Jose (95134) *(P-15042)*
Ultratype & Graphics ....F....858 541-1894
1929 Hancock St Ste D San Diego (92110) *(P-7636)*
Ultron Systems Inc ....F....805 529-1485
5105 Maureen Ln Moorpark (93021) *(P-15043)*
Ulysses Press, Berkeley *Also called Bookpack Inc (P-6451)*
Umc Acquisition Corp (PA) ....E....562 940-0300
9151 Imperial Hwy Downey (90242) *(P-11638)*
Umc Group(usa) ....D....408 523-7800
488 De Guigne Dr Sunnyvale (94085) *(P-19245)*
Ume Voice Inc ....F....707 939-8607
1435 Technology Ln Ste B4 Petaluma (94954) *(P-17872)*
Umec, Hayward *Also called United Mech Met Fbricators Inc (P-12800)*
Umex, Downey *Also called Universal Mlding Extrusion Inc (P-11609)*
Umeya Inc ....E....213 626-8341
414 Crocker St Los Angeles (90013) *(P-1386)*
Umeya Rice Cake Co, Los Angeles *Also called Umeya Inc (P-1386)*
Umgee USA Inc ....F....323 526-9138
500 S Anderson St Los Angeles (90033) *(P-3283)*
Umo Steel, Union City *Also called United Misc & Orna Stl Inc (P-13002)*
Ump, Corona *Also called United Metal Products Inc (P-11851)*
Umpco Inc ....D....714 897-3531
7100 Lampson Ave Garden Grove (92841) *(P-12005)*
Umx, Walnut *Also called Universal Mercantile Exchange (P-23997)*
Uncks Unique Plastics Inc ....F....909 983-5181
1215 Brooks St Ontario (91762) *(P-10419)*
Uncle Ben's, Los Angeles *Also called Mars Food Us LLC (P-1088)*
Uncle Bum's Gourmet Sauces, Riverside *Also called Tom Harris Inc (P-2683)*
Uncle Lees Tea Inc ....E....626 350-3309
11020 Rush St El Monte (91733) *(P-2695)*
Under Armour Inc ....E....707 451-4736
321 Nut Tree Rd Vacaville (95687) *(P-3200)*
Undercar Express Inc ....F....626 683-2787
57 N Altadena Dr Pasadena (91107) *(P-20180)*
Underground Autowerks Inc (PA) ....F....619 336-9000
106 E 17th St National City (91950) *(P-11914)*
Underground Energy Inc ....E....805 455-6042
7 W Figueroa St Fl 3 Santa Barbara (93101) *(P-156)*
Underground Games Inc ....F....310 379-0100
2356 253rd St Lomita (90717) *(P-23474)*
Underground Labs Inc ....F....925 297-5333
1114 Oakwood Cir Clayton (94517) *(P-25308)*
Undersea Systems Intl Inc ....D....714 754-7848
3133 W Harvard St Santa Ana (92704) *(P-20094)*
Underwraps Costume Corporation ....F....818 349-5300
9600 Irondale Ave Chatsworth (91311) *(P-3685)*
Underwraps Costumes Inc., Chatsworth *Also called Underwraps Costume Corporation (P-3685)*
Ungar, Ron Engineering, Ventura *Also called Ron Ungar (P-15226)*
Unger Fabrik LLC (PA) ....C....213 222-1010
13071 Temple Ave La Puente (91746) *(P-3284)*
UNI Filter Inc ....D....714 535-6933
1468 Manhattan Ave Fullerton (92831) *(P-20475)*
UNI Sport Inc ....E....310 217-4587
16933 Gramercy Pl Gardena (90247) *(P-7154)*
UNI-Caps LLC ....E....714 529-8400
540 Lambert Rd Brea (92821) *(P-7979)*
UNI-Pixel Displays Inc ....F....281 825-4500
4699 Old Ironsides Dr Santa Clara (95054) *(P-15649)*
UNI-Poly Inc ....F....510 357-9898
2040 Williams St San Leandro (94577) *(P-5633)*
Unichem, Bakersfield *Also called Baker Hughes A GE Company LLC (P-179)*
Unichem Enterprises, Ontario *Also called Imp International Inc (P-7948)*
Unico Incorporated ....F....619 209-6124
8880 Rio San Diego Dr # 8 San Diego (92108) *(P-15)*
Unicom Electric Inc ....E....626 964-7873
565 Brea Canyon Rd Ste A Walnut (91789) *(P-18374)*
Unicor, Lompoc *Also called Federal Prison Industries (P-23880)*
Unicor, Lompoc *Also called Federal Prison Industries (P-4696)*
Unicorn Group, Novato *Also called Forest Investment Group Inc (P-6823)*
Unifi Software Inc ....E....732 614-9522
1810 Gateway Dr Ste 380 San Mateo (94404) *(P-25309)*
Unifyid Inc ....F....650 887-3760
425 2nd St Ste 201 San Francisco (94107) *(P-25310)*
Unilabel, Santa Fe Springs *Also called Universal Label Printers Inc (P-7530)*
Unilete Inc ....F....714 557-1271
18774 Ashford Ln Huntington Beach (92648) *(P-3201)*
Unimark, Gardena *Also called Matsui International Co Inc (P-9276)*
Unimark International Inc ....F....949 497-1235
22601 Allview Ter Laguna Beach (92651) *(P-14892)*

Union Carbide Corporation ....D....310 214-5300
19206 Hawthorne Blvd Torrance (90503) *(P-5363)*
Union Electric Motor Service, San Diego *Also called Tom Garcia Inc (P-25469)*
Union Flavors Inc ....F....626 333-1612
14145 Proctor Ave Ste 15 City of Industry (91746) *(P-2285)*
Union Ice Company ....F....323 277-1000
2970 E 50th St Vernon (90058) *(P-2422)*
Union Pacific Lines, Long Beach *Also called Union Pacific Railroad Company (P-12901)*
Union Pacific Railroad Company ....B....562 490-7000
2401 E Sepulveda Blvd Long Beach (90810) *(P-12901)*
Union Planing Mill (PA) ....E....209 466-9617
965 Oakhurst Way Stockton (95209) *(P-4250)*
Union Publications Inc ....F....510 525-6300
653 Wellesley Ave Kensington (94708) *(P-6280)*
Union Solutions Inc ....F....510 483-1222
15355 Bittern Ct San Leandro (94579) *(P-25311)*
Union Swiss Manufacturing Co, Glendale *Also called Irl-Mex Manufacturing Company (P-13028)*
Union Tank Car Company ....C....312 431-3111
175 W Jackson Blvd Bakersfield (93311) *(P-21084)*
Union Technology Corp ....E....323 266-6603
718 Monterey Pass Rd Monterey Park (91754) *(P-19304)*
Union Tribune, San Marcos *Also called Copley Press Inc (P-5818)*
Union Wine Company, Calabasas *Also called Spanish Castle Inc (P-1984)*
Union, The, Grass Valley *Also called Nevada County Publishing Co (P-5992)*
Uniproducts, North Highlands *Also called Mikes Sheet Metal Products (P-12677)*
Uniq Vision Inc ....C....408 330-0818
2924 Scott Blvd Santa Clara (95054) *(P-23206)*
Unique Apparel Inc ....D....213 321-8192
3777 S Main St Los Angeles (90007) *(P-3523)*
Unique Bindery, Van Nuys *Also called Dgcc Inc (P-7597)*
Unique Drawer Boxes Inc ....F....619 873-4240
9435 Bond Ave El Cajon (92021) *(P-4447)*
Unique Functional Products, San Marcos *Also called Dexter Axle Company (P-20500)*
Unique Garage Door Inc (PA) ....E....714 223-1493
6259 Descanso Ave Buena Park (90620) *(P-12354)*
Unique Image Inc ....F....818 727-7785
19365 Bus Center Dr Ste 4 Northridge (91324) *(P-7155)*
Unique Media Inc ....F....408 733-9999
2991 Corvin Dr Santa Clara (95051) *(P-17914)*
Unique Plex Inc ....F....951 653-2500
2900 Adams St Ste C130 Riverside (92504) *(P-7918)*
Unique Sales, Vernon *Also called Zk Enterprises Inc (P-3207)*
Unique Screen Printing Inc ....E....626 575-2725
2115 Central Ave South El Monte (91733) *(P-3926)*
Uniquify Inc ....E....408 235-8810
2030 Fortune Dr Ste 200 San Jose (95131) *(P-19777)*
Unirex Corp ....F....323 589-4000
2288 E 27th St Vernon (90058) *(P-19246)*
Unirex Technology, Vernon *Also called Unirex Corp (P-19246)*
Unisem (sunnvale) Inc (PA) ....F....408 734-3222
2241 Calle De Luna Santa Clara (95054) *(P-19247)*
Unisoft Corporation ....F....650 259-1290
10 Rollins Rd Ste 118 Millbrae (94030) *(P-25312)*
Unisorb Inc ....F....626 793-1000
101 N Indian Hill Blvd C2-201 Claremont (91711) *(P-13980)*
Unistrut International Corp ....F....510 476-1200
1679 Atlantic St Union City (94587) *(P-12267)*
Unisun Multinational, Chino *Also called Ht Multinational Inc (P-20366)*
Unit Industries Inc (PA) ....E....714 871-4161
3122 Maple St Santa Ana (92707) *(P-19427)*
Unitech Deco Inc ....E....818 700-1373
19731 Bahama St Northridge (91324) *(P-7529)*
Unitech Industries, Northridge *Also called Unitech Deco Inc (P-7529)*
Unitech Tool & Machine Inc ....E....408 566-0333
3025 Stender Way Santa Clara (95054) *(P-17022)*
United Advg Publications Inc ....E....916 746-2300
3017 Douglas Blvd Roseville (95661) *(P-6281)*
United Advg Publications Inc ....F....909 466-1480
8250 White Oak Ave # 101 Rancho Cucamonga (91730) *(P-6282)*
United Audio Video Group Inc ....E....818 980-6700
6855 Vineland Ave North Hollywood (91605) *(P-19887)*
United Bakery Equipment Co Inc (PA) ....D....310 635-8121
19216 S Laurel Park Rd Compton (90220) *(P-15232)*
United Bakery Equipment Co Inc ....E....310 635-8121
19216 S Laurel Park Rd Compton (90220) *(P-14893)*
United Bakery Inc ....E....818 843-1892
727 S Flower St Burbank (91502) *(P-1335)*
United Brands Company Inc ....E....619 461-5220
5930 Cornerstone Ct W # 170 San Diego (92121) *(P-2286)*
United Cabinet Company Inc ....F....909 796-3015
1510 S Mountain View Ave San Bernardino (92408) *(P-5002)*
United California, Downey *Also called United Drill Bushing Corp (P-14691)*
United California Corporation ....C....562 803-1521
12200 Woodruff Ave Downey (90241) *(P-14583)*
United Carports LLC ....F....800 757-6742
7280 Sycamore Canyon Blvd # 1 Riverside (92508) *(P-12967)*
United Castings Inc ....F....909 627-7645
5154 F St Chino (91710) *(P-11787)*
United Cerebral Palsy Assn San ....F....619 282-8790
10405 Sn Dgo Mssn Rd 10 San Diego (92108) *(P-23723)*
United Craftsmen Priniting ....E....408 224-6464
6660 Via Del Oro San Jose (95119) *(P-7156)*
United Distlrs Vintners N Amer, San Francisco *Also called Diageo North America Inc (P-1725)*
United Drill Bushing Corp ....C....562 803-1521
12200 Woodruff Ave Downey (90241) *(P-14691)*

United Drilling Co ....E....562 945-8833
11807 Slauson Ave Santa Fe Springs (90670) ***(P-17023)***
United Duralume Products Inc ....F....714 773-4011
350 S Raymond Ave Fullerton (92831) ***(P-12798)***
United Fabrication Inc ....F....805 482-2354
1250 Avenida Acaso Ste C Camarillo (93012) ***(P-12799)***
United Foods Intl USA Inc (HQ) ....E....510 264-5850
23447 Cabot Blvd Hayward (94545) ***(P-2696)***
United Granite & Cabinets LLC ....F....510 558-8999
5225 Central Ave Richmond (94804) ***(P-4362)***
United Launch Alliance LLC ....D....303 269-5876
1579 Utah Ave Bldg 7525 Vandenberg Afb (93437) ***(P-21175)***
United Mech Met Fbricators Inc ....E....510 537-4744
548 Claire St Hayward (94541) ***(P-12800)***
United Memorial Products Inc ....D....562 699-3578
4845 Pioneer Blvd Whittier (90601) ***(P-11012)***
United Memorial/Matthews Intl, Whittier *Also called United Memorial Products Inc* ***(P-11012)***
United Metal Products Inc ....F....951 739-9535
234 N Sherman Ave Corona (92882) ***(P-11851)***
United Misc & Orna Stl Inc ....E....510 429-8755
4700 Horner St Union City (94587) ***(P-13002)***
United Optronics Inc ....F....408 503-8900
1323 Great Mall Dr Milpitas (95035) ***(P-18003)***
United Orthopedic Group LLC ....F....760 729-8585
2885 Loker Ave E Carlsbad (92010) ***(P-22662)***
United Pacific Designs, Vernon *Also called UPD INC* ***(P-23403)***
United Pallet Services Inc ....C....209 538-5844
4043 Crows Landing Rd Modesto (95358) ***(P-4510)***
United Paper Box Inc ....E....714 777-8383
1530 Lakeview Loop Anaheim (92807) ***(P-5514)***
United Partition Systems Inc ....F....909 947-1077
2180 S Hellman Ave Ontario (91761) ***(P-4583)***
United Pet Group, Moorpark *Also called Spectrum Brands Inc* ***(P-24251)***
United Pharma LLC ....C....714 738-8999
2317 Moore Ave Fullerton (92833) ***(P-9314)***
United Precision Corp ....F....818 576-9540
20810 Plummer St Chatsworth (91311) ***(P-13806)***
United Pro Fab Mfg Inc ....F....510 651-5570
45300 Industrial Pl Ste 5 Fremont (94538) ***(P-19248)***
United Reporting Pubg Corp ....E....916 542-7501
1835 Iron Point Rd # 100 Folsom (95630) ***(P-6609)***
United Research & Mfg ....F....760 727-4320
2630 Progress St Vista (92081) ***(P-20476)***
United Rock Products Corp ....E....626 358-4558
135 S State College Blvd # 400 Brea (92821) ***(P-318)***
United Rotary Brush Corp ....E....909 629-9117
688 New York Dr Pomona (91768) ***(P-23797)***
United Rotary Brush Corp ....E....913 888-8450
160 Enterprise Ct Ste B Galt (95632) ***(P-23798)***
United Security Products Inc ....E....800 227-1592
13250 Gregg St Ste B Poway (92064) ***(P-20095)***
United Sheetmetal Inc ....F....510 257-1858
44153 S Grimmer Blvd Fremont (94538) ***(P-12801)***
United Sign Systems, Modesto *Also called Johnson United Inc* ***(P-23909)***
United Snshine Amrcn Inds Corp ....E....801 972-5124
2808 E Marywood Ln Orange (92867) ***(P-13858)***
United States Ball Corporation ....F....714 521-6500
15919 Phoebe Ave La Mirada (90638) ***(P-15115)***
United States Cold Storage Inc ....E....661 834-2371
4701 Stine Rd Bakersfield (93313) ***(P-2423)***
United States Dept of Navy ....E....805 989-5402
672 13th St Ste 1 Port Hueneme (93042) ***(P-20965)***
United States Dept of Navy ....A....559 998-2488
Vfa 122 Hanger 5 Lemoore (93246) ***(P-14034)***
United States Gypsum Company ....B....760 358-3200
3810 Evan Hewes Hwy Imperial (92251) ***(P-11226)***
United States Logistics Group ....E....562 989-9555
2700 Rose Ave Ste A Signal Hill (90755) ***(P-20515)***
United States Mineral Pdts Co ....D....909 473-6993
4062 Georgia Blvd San Bernardino (92407) ***(P-11338)***
United States Pumice Company (PA) ....F....818 882-0300
20219 Bahama St Chatsworth (91311) ***(P-419)***
United States Thermoelectric ....E....530 345-8000
13267 Contractors Dr Chico (95973) ***(P-22046)***
United Supertek Inc ....E....408 922-0730
14930 Vintner Ct Saratoga (95070) ***(P-18640)***
United Technologies Corp ....A....408 779-9121
600 Metcalf Rd San Jose (95138) ***(P-20687)***
United Technologies Corp ....A....408 779-9121
600 Metcalf Rd San Jose (95138) ***(P-20688)***
United Technologies Corp ....B....510 438-1300
4384 Enterprise Pl Fremont (94538) ***(P-20689)***
United Technologies Corp ....E....562 944-6244
11120 Norwalk Blvd Santa Fe Springs (90670) ***(P-20966)***
United Technologies Corp ....E....951 351-5400
8200 Arlington Ave Riverside (92503) ***(P-20967)***
United Testing Systems Inc ....D....714 638-2322
1375 S Acacia Ave Ste A Fullerton (92831) ***(P-22292)***
United Tote Company ....E....858 279-4250
4205 Ponderosa Ave San Diego (92123) ***(P-15878)***
United Traffic Services & Sup, La Puente *Also called Blue Sky Remediation Svcs Inc* ***(P-18312)***
United Uniform Mfrs Inc ....F....909 381-2682
1096 W Rialto Ave San Bernardino (92410) ***(P-3063)***
United Wealth Control, Bakersfield *Also called B & L Casing Service LLC* ***(P-169)***
United Western Enterprises Inc ....E....805 389-1077
850 Flynn Rd Ste 200 Camarillo (93012) ***(P-13676)***
United Western Industries Inc ....E....559 226-7236
3515 N Hazel Ave Fresno (93722) ***(P-17024)***
United Wholesale Lumber Co, Visalia *Also called Standard Lumber Company Inc* ***(P-4508)***
United Yearbook Printing Svcs, Rancho Cucamonga *Also called TSE Worldwide Press Inc* ***(P-6607)***
Unitek Technology Inc ....F....909 930-5700
10211 Bellegrave Ave Mira Loma (91752) ***(P-15502)***
Unitex International, Vernon *Also called Destiney Group Inc* ***(P-2733)***
Unity Clothing Company, El Monte *Also called Unity Clothing Inc* ***(P-23682)***
Unity Clothing Inc ....F....626 579-5588
3788 Rockwell Ave El Monte (91731) ***(P-23682)***
Unity Digital, Costa Mesa *Also called Unity Sales International Inc* ***(P-23207)***
Unity Forest Products Inc ....E....530 671-7152
1162 Putman Ave Yuba City (95991) ***(P-4251)***
Unity Sales International Inc ....F....714 800-1700
2950 Airway Ave Ste A12 Costa Mesa (92626) ***(P-23207)***
Universal Alloy Corporation ....B....714 630-7200
2871 E John Ball Way Anaheim (92806) ***(P-11608)***
Universal Cell Site Svcs Inc ....E....925 447-4500
2428 Research Dr Livermore (94550) ***(P-12268)***
Universal Ctrl Solutions Corp ....F....818 898-3380
19770 Bahama St Northridge (91324) ***(P-17317)***
Universal Cushion Company Inc (PA) ....E....323 887-8000
3121 Fujita St Torrance (90505) ***(P-3754)***
Universal Custom Design, Elk Grove *Also called Universal Custom Display* ***(P-23996)***
Universal Custom Display ....C....916 714-2505
9104 Elkmont Dr Ste 100 Elk Grove (95624) ***(P-23996)***
Universal Defense ....E....909 626-4178
412 Cucamonga Ave Claremont (91711) ***(P-12437)***
Universal Directory Publishing ....E....714 994-6025
2995 E White Star Ave Anaheim (92806) ***(P-6610)***
Universal Dyeing & Printing ....D....213 746-0818
2303 E 11th St Los Angeles (90021) ***(P-2906)***
Universal Dynamics Inc ....F....626 480-0035
5313 3rd St Irwindale (91706) ***(P-157)***
Universal Electronics Inc (PA) ....C....714 918-9500
201 Sandpointe Ave Fl 8 Santa Ana (92707) ***(P-17873)***
Universal Filtration Inc ....F....626 308-1832
914 Westminster Ave Alhambra (91803) ***(P-16128)***
Universal Forest Products, Ontario *Also called Idx Los Angeles LLC* ***(P-4168)***
Universal Hosiery Inc ....D....661 702-8444
28337 Constellation Rd Valencia (91355) ***(P-2817)***
Universal Imaging Tech Inc ....F....310 961-2098
4733 Torrance Blvd 997 Torrance (90503) ***(P-23739)***
Universal Interior Industries ....F....951 743-5446
4111 Buchanan St Riverside (92503) ***(P-4746)***
Universal Label Printers Inc ....E....562 944-0234
13003 Los Nietos Rd Santa Fe Springs (90670) ***(P-7530)***
Universal Maritime, Harbor City *Also called Ship Supply International Inc* ***(P-10824)***
Universal McLoud USA Corp ....F....613 222-5904
580 California St San Francisco (94104) ***(P-25313)***
Universal Meat Company, Rancho Cucamonga *Also called Formosa Meat Company Inc* ***(P-484)***
Universal Medical Press Inc ....F....415 436-9790
2443 Fillmore St San Francisco (94115) ***(P-6283)***
Universal Mercantile Exchange (PA) ....F....909 839-0556
21128 Commerce Point Dr Walnut (91789) ***(P-23997)***
Universal Merchandise Inc ....F....818 344-2044
5422 Aura Ave Tarzana (91356) ***(P-3047)***
Universal Metal Plating ....F....626 969-7932
704 S Taylor Ave Montebello (90640) ***(P-13529)***
Universal Metal Spinning Inc ....F....510 782-0980
2543 W Winton Ave Ste 5j Hayward (94545) ***(P-17653)***
Universal Mlding Extrusion Inc (HQ) ....E....562 401-1015
9151 Imperial Hwy Downey (90242) ***(P-11609)***
Universal Molding Company, Downey *Also called Umc Acquisition Corp* ***(P-11638)***
Universal Molding Company (HQ) ....C....310 886-1750
9151 Imperial Hwy Downey (90242) ***(P-11639)***
Universal Music Pubg Group ....F....310 235-4700
2100 Colorado Ave Santa Monica (90404) ***(P-6611)***
Universal Plant Svcs Cal Inc (HQ) ....F....310 618-1600
20545a Belshaw Ave Carson (90746) ***(P-17025)***
Universal Plastic Mold, Baldwin Park *Also called Upm Inc* ***(P-14584)***
Universal Precast Concrete Inc ....F....530 243-6477
16538 Clear Creek Rd Redding (96001) ***(P-11013)***
Universal Printing Services ....F....951 788-1500
26012 Atlantic Ocean Dr Lake Forest (92630) ***(P-7157)***
Universal Products, Rancho Cucamonga *Also called Proulx Manufacturing Inc* ***(P-10315)***
Universal Punch Corp ....D....714 556-4488
4001 W Macarthur Blvd Santa Ana (92704) ***(P-14459)***
Universal Screw Products Inc ....E....310 371-1170
20421 Earl St Torrance (90503) ***(P-13048)***
Universal Specialty Vehicles ....F....951 943-7747
7879 Pine Crest Dr Riverside (92506) ***(P-20526)***
Universal Steel Services Inc ....F....626 960-1455
5034 Heintz St Baldwin Park (91706) ***(P-12269)***
Universal Surface Techlgy Inc ....E....310 352-6969
13023 S Main St Los Angeles (90061) ***(P-8612)***
Universal Systems, Placentia *Also called Diversified Testing Service* ***(P-21741)***
Universal Trailers Inc ....F....951 784-0543
2750 Mulberry St Riverside (92501) ***(P-21244)***
Universal Turbo Technology ....D....714 600-9585
1120 E Elm Ave Fullerton (92831) ***(P-14011)***
Universal Wire Inc ....F....626 285-2288
1705 S Campus Ave Ontario (91761) ***(P-13859)***
Universe Industries, Anaheim *Also called American Industrial Corp* ***(P-14477)***
University Blanket & Flag Corp (PA) ....F....619 435-4100
1111 Orange Ave Ste C Coronado (92118) ***(P-3969)***
University Cal Press Fundation (PA) ....D....510 642-4247
155 Grand Ave Ste 400 Oakland (94612) ***(P-6404)***
University Cal Press Fundation ....E....510 642-4247
2000 Center St Ste 303 Berkeley (94704) ***(P-6405)***

ALPHABETIC

University California Berkeley .... E 510 642-4247
155 Grand Ave Ste 400 Oakland (94612) *(P-6406)*
University Frames Inc .... E 714 575-5100
3060 E Miraloma Ave Anaheim (92806) *(P-4662)*
University of California Press, Oakland *Also called University California Berkeley* *(P-6406)*
University Plating Co, San Jose *Also called Hane & Hane Inc* *(P-13422)*
University Printing, Loma Linda *Also called Loma Linda University* *(P-6953)*
University Readers, San Diego *Also called Cognella Inc* *(P-6329)*
University Southern California .... F 323 442-3858
2250 Alcazar St Ste B7 Los Angeles (90089) *(P-8426)*
Univocity Media Inc .... F 760 904-5200
2901 E Alejo Rd Bldg 4 Palm Springs (92262) *(P-6612)*
Uniweb Inc (PA) .... D 951 279-7999
222 S Promenade Ave Corona (92879) *(P-5174)*
Unix Packaging Inc .... C 213 627-5050
9 Minson Way Montebello (90640) *(P-2230)*
Unlimited Trck Trlr Maint Inc .... E 323 727-2500
825 S Maple Ave Ste D Montebello (90640) *(P-20516)*
Unmanned Innovation Inc (PA) .... D 877 714-4828
460 Bryant St Ste 200 San Francisco (94107) *(P-20633)*
Unocal, Lompoc *Also called Chevron Corporation* *(P-47)*
Unocal Corporation (HQ) .... B 310 726-7600
6001 Bollinger Canyon Rd San Ramon (94583) *(P-83)*
Unorth, San Jose *Also called Mota Group Inc* *(P-19872)*
Unovo LLC .... F 415 864-7600
1200 Hrbour Way S Ste 215 Richmond (94804) *(P-17410)*
Unshackled, Palo Alto *Also called Level Labs LP* *(P-24857)*
Untangle Holdings Inc .... E 408 598-4299
100 W San Fernando St # 565 San Jose (95113) *(P-25314)*
UOP LLC .... E 714 870-7590
2100 E Orangethorpe Ave Anaheim (92806) *(P-5545)*
UPD INC .... D 323 588-8811
4507 S Maywood Ave Vernon (90058) *(P-23403)*
UPF Corporation .... E 661 323-8227
3747 Standard St Bakersfield (93308) *(P-11339)*
Upguard Inc (PA) .... E 888 882-3223
909 San Rafael Ave Mountain View (94043) *(P-25315)*
Uphold Inc .... E 415 730-3988
301 Battery St Fl 7 San Francisco (94111) *(P-25316)*
Upholstery By Wayne Stoec .... F 559 233-1960
3316 E Annadale Ave Fresno (93725) *(P-2766)*
Upholstery Workroom, Los Angeles *Also called Custom Upholstered Furn Inc* *(P-4767)*
Upland Fab Inc .... E 909 933-9185
1445 Brooks St Ste L Ontario (91762) *(P-10420)*
Upm Inc .... B 626 962-4001
13245 Los Angeles St Baldwin Park (91706) *(P-14584)*
Upm Raflatac Inc .... E 909 390-4657
1105 Auto Center Dr Ontario (91761) *(P-5581)*
Upper Crust, San Rafael *Also called Christine Milne* *(P-1391)*
Upper Crust Enterprises Inc .... E 213 625-0038
411 Center St Los Angeles (90012) *(P-2697)*
Upper Deck Company .... C 800 873-7332
5830 El Camino Real Carlsbad (92008) *(P-6613)*
Upper Deck Company LLC .... B 800 873-7332
5830 El Camino Real Carlsbad (92008) *(P-7158)*
Upright, Fresno *Also called Tanfield Engrg Systems US Inc* *(P-14192)*
Upstanding LLC .... C 949 788-9900
440 Exchange Ste 100 Irvine (92602) *(P-25317)*
Upton Engineering & Mfg Co, South El Monte *Also called BCI Inc* *(P-16312)*
Uptown, Los Angeles *Also called Lets Go Apparel Inc* *(P-3667)*
Urabe Incorporated .... F 714 377-9701
16742 Westfield Ln Huntington Beach (92649) *(P-17026)*
Urban Decal LLC (HQ) .... E 949 574-9712
833 W 16th St Newport Beach (92663) *(P-8857)*
Urban Decay Cosmetics, Newport Beach *Also called Urban Decal LLC* *(P-8857)*
Urban Empire, San Diego *Also called Quantum Dynasty* *(P-15591)*
Urban Expressions Inc .... E 310 593-4574
5500 Union Pacific Ave Commerce (90022) *(P-10555)*
Urban Outfitters Inc .... E 626 449-1818
139 W Colorado Blvd Pasadena (91105) *(P-3344)*
Urban Outfitters Store 18, Pasadena *Also called Urban Outfitters Inc* *(P-3344)*
Urban Trading Software Inc .... E 877 633-6171
21227 Foothill Blvd Hayward (94541) *(P-25318)*
Urbanista, South Gate *Also called YH Texpert Corporation* *(P-3529)*
Uremet Corporation .... E 714 641-8813
3026 Orange Ave Santa Ana (92707) *(P-7898)*
Urethane Polymer International .... E 909 357-7200
10880 Poplar Ave Fontana (92337) *(P-9315)*
Urethane Products Corporation .... F 800 913-0062
17842 Sampson Ln Huntington Beach (92647) *(P-10421)*
Urethane Science Inc .... F 714 828-3210
8357 Standustrial St Stanton (90680) *(P-10422)*
Urgent Upfits, Rancho Cordova *Also called Form & Fusion Mfg Inc* *(P-13207)*
Uri Tech Inc .... F 408 456-0115
1340 Norman Ave Santa Clara (95054) *(P-18641)*
Uriman Inc (HQ) .... C 714 257-2080
650 N Puente St Brea (92821) *(P-19849)*
Urocare Products Inc .... F 909 621-6013
2735 Melbourne Ave Pomona (91767) *(P-9688)*
Urolift, Pleasanton *Also called Neotract Inc* *(P-22552)*
Urovant Sciences Inc (PA) .... E 949 226-6029
5151 California Ave # 250 Irvine (92617) *(P-8427)*
URu By Kristine St Rrik Inc .... F 760 745-1800
622 Aero Way Escondido (92029) *(P-3345)*
Uruhu Highlands Ltd .... F 424 213-9725
14360 Valerio St Apt 311 Van Nuys (91405) *(P-13685)*
US Apothecary Crown Labs, Santa Fe Springs *Also called Titan Medical Enterprises Inc* *(P-8417)*
US Architectural Lighting, Palmdale *Also called Sun Valley Ltg Standards Inc* *(P-17647)*
US Armor Corporation .... E 562 207-4240
10715 Bloomfield Ave Santa Fe Springs (90670) *(P-22837)*
US Bioservices (PA) .... D 800 801-1140
5100 E Hunter Ave Anaheim (92807) *(P-8952)*
US Blanks LLC (PA) .... E 310 225-6774
14700 S San Pedro St Gardena (90248) *(P-7899)*
US Borax Inc .... A 760 762-7000
14486 Borax Rd Boron (93516) *(P-7810)*
US Borax Inc .... C 310 522-5300
300 Falcon St Wilmington (90744) *(P-7811)*
US Composite Pipe South, Rialto *Also called Uscps* *(P-24280)*
US Computers Inc .... F 714 528-0514
181 W Orangethorpe Ave C Placentia (92870) *(P-15879)*
US Concrete Inc .... E 408 779-1000
1 Live Oak Ave Morgan Hill (95037) *(P-11014)*
US Concrete Inc .... F 408 947-8606
755 Stockton Ave San Jose (95126) *(P-11201)*
US Concrete Precast, San Diego *Also called San Diego Precast Concrete Inc* *(P-10997)*
US Container and Housing Co .... E 844 762-8242
22320 Fthill Blvd Ste 450 Hayward (94541) *(P-4584)*
US Continental Marketing Inc (PA) .... D 951 808-8888
310 Reed Cir Corona (92879) *(P-8682)*
US Cotton LLC .... B 559 651-3015
7100 W Sunnyview Ave Visalia (93291) *(P-8858)*
US Cover LLC .... F 323 838-2700
1309 S Eastern Ave Commerce (90040) *(P-12968)*
US Critical, Lake Forest *Also called US Critical LLC* *(P-15620)*
US Critical LLC (PA) .... E 949 916-9326
6 Orchard Ste 150 Lake Forest (92630) *(P-15620)*
US Critical LLC .... E 800 884-8945
25422 Trabuco Rd 320 Lake Forest (92630) *(P-15621)*
US Dental Inc .... E 562 404-3500
13043 166th St Cerritos (90703) *(P-22920)*
US Dies Inc (PA) .... E 209 664-1402
1992 Rockefeller Dr # 300 Ceres (95307) *(P-14585)*
US Direct LLC .... E 949 491-3342
1700 Barranca Pkwy Irvine (92606) *(P-7531)*
US Door and Fence LLC .... F 951 300-0010
3880 Garner Rd Riverside (92501) *(P-4018)*
US Environmental .... F 951 359-9002
7085 Jurupa Ave Ste 1 Riverside (92504) *(P-9316)*
US Eta Inc .... F 408 778-5875
16170 Vineyard Blvd # 180 Morgan Hill (95037) *(P-19778)*
US Fiberglass Inc .... F 760 246-3822
17031 Muskrat Ave Adelanto (92301) *(P-23683)*
US Garment LLC .... E 323 415-6464
4440 E 26th St Vernon (90058) *(P-3125)*
US Gear & Pumps .... E 909 525-3026
1249 S Diamond Bar Blvd # 325 Diamond Bar (91765) *(P-15248)*
US Gold Trading Inc .... F 818 558-7766
117 E Providencia Ave Burbank (91502) *(P-23327)*
US Gov GA Aeronautical Uav, Poway *Also called General Atomic Aeron* *(P-20585)*
US Hanger Company LLC .... E 310 323-8030
17501 S Denver Ave Gardena (90248) *(P-11464)*
US Horizon Manufacturing Inc .... E 661 775-1675
28539 Industry Dr Valencia (91355) *(P-10610)*
US Hosiery Inc .... F 213 742-0101
1415 S Main St Los Angeles (90015) *(P-2818)*
US Hybrid Corporation (PA) .... E 310 212-1200
445 Maple Ave Torrance (90503) *(P-20477)*
US Industrial Tool & Sup Co .... E 310 464-8400
14083 S Normandie Ave Gardena (90249) *(P-14460)*
US Logistics, Signal Hill *Also called United States Logistics Group* *(P-20515)*
US Lubricants Inc .... E 909 469-1860
10735 Kadota Ave Montclair (91763) *(P-9452)*
US Machining, San Jose *Also called TLC Machining Incorporated* *(P-14684)*
US Motor Works LLC (PA) .... C 562 404-0488
14722 Anson Ave Santa Fe Springs (90670) *(P-20478)*
US Niutang Chemical Inc .... E 909 631-2895
14266 Euclid Ave Chino (91710) *(P-8966)*
US Nuclear Corp (PA) .... F 818 296-0746
7051 Eton Ave Canoga Park (91303) *(P-22293)*
US Packagers Inc .... E 310 327-7721
13620 Crenshaw Blvd Gardena (90249) *(P-7589)*
US Pipe Fabrication LLC .... E 530 742-5171
3387 Plumas Arboga Rd Marysville (95901) *(P-9790)*
US Plastic Inc .... E 951 300-9360
1561 Estridge Ave Ste 102 Riverside (92507) *(P-9810)*
US Pole Company Inc (PA) .... C 800 877-6537
660 W Avenue O Palmdale (93551) *(P-17742)*
US Polymers Inc .... E 323 727-6888
5910 Bandini Blvd Commerce (90040) *(P-11610)*
US Polymers Inc (PA) .... D 323 728-3023
1057 S Vail Ave Montebello (90640) *(P-10423)*
US Precision Sheet Metal Inc .... D 951 276-2611
4020 Garner Rd Riverside (92501) *(P-12802)*
US Premier Inc .... F 323 267-4463
624 S Clarence St Los Angeles (90023) *(P-3285)*
US Print & Toner Inc .... E 619 562-6995
1990 Friendship Dr El Cajon (92020) *(P-23740)*
US Rack Inc .... F 559 661-3050
2850 Falcon Dr Madera (93637) *(P-12006)*
US Radiator Corporation (PA) .... E 323 826-0965
4423 District Blvd Vernon (90058) *(P-20479)*
US Rigging Supply Corp .... E 714 545-7444
1600 E Mcfadden Ave Santa Ana (92705) *(P-13860)*

Mergent e-mail: customerrelations@mergent.com
1318
2019 California
Manufacturers Register
(P-0000) Products & Services Section entry number
(PA)=Parent Co (HQ)=Headquarters (DH)=Div Headquarters

US Rockets .... F 707 267-3393
Munsey Rd Mile 11 Cantil (93519) *(P-21176)*
US Rubber Roller Company Inc .... F 951 682-2221
1516 7th St Riverside (92507) *(P-14829)*
US Saws Inc (PA) .... F 860 668-2402
3702 W Central Ave Santa Ana (92704) *(P-14197)*
US Sensor Corp .... D 714 639-1000
1832 W Collins Ave Orange (92867) *(P-19249)*
US Steel Rule Dies Inc .... E 562 921-0690
40 E Verdugo Ave Burbank (91502) *(P-14586)*
US Tower Corp .... D 559 564-6000
1099 W Ropes Ave Woodlake (93286) *(P-12270)*
US Toyo Fan Corporation (HQ) .... F 626 338-1111
16025 Arrow Hwy Ste F Irwindale (91706) *(P-15183)*
US Union Tool Inc (HQ) .... E 714 521-6242
1260 N Fee Ana St Anaheim (92807) *(P-14421)*
US Wheel, Huntington Beach *Also called U S Wheel Corporation (P-20472)*
US Wholesale Drug Corp .... F 323 227-4258
2611 N San Fernando Rd Los Angeles (90065) *(P-8428)*
Us1com Inc .... F 707 781-2560
715 Southpoint Blvd Ste D Petaluma (94954) *(P-7532)*
USA Extruded Plastics Inc .... F 714 991-6061
965 E Discovery Ln Anaheim (92801) *(P-10424)*
USA Fire Glass .... F 949 302-7728
6789 Quail Hill Pkwy # 613 Irvine (92603) *(P-10739)*
USA Industries, Orange *Also called United Snshine Amrcn Inds Corp (P-13858)*
USA Printer Company .... F 800 279-7768
41571 Corning Pl Ste 115 Murrieta (92562) *(P-7159)*
USA Printer Guy, Murrieta *Also called USA Printer Company (P-7159)*
USA Printing, West Hollywood *Also called A & J Enterprises Inc (P-6632)*
USA Products Group Inc (PA) .... E 209 334-1460
1300 E Vine St Lodi (95240) *(P-3970)*
USA Sales Inc .... E 909 390-9606
1560 S Archibald Ave Ontario (91761) *(P-2710)*
USA Solar Technology Inc .... F 714 356-8360
28381 Vincent Moraga Dr Temecula (92590) *(P-24279)*
USA Topdon LLC .... F 833 233-5535
18351 Colima Rd Unit 255 Rowland Heights (91748) *(P-20096)*
USA Vision Systems Inc (HQ) .... E 949 583-1519
9301 Irvine Blvd Irvine (92618) *(P-20097)*
USAopoly Inc .... E 760 431-5910
5607 Palmer Way Carlsbad (92010) *(P-23475)*
Usc Molecular Imaging Center, Los Angeles *Also called University Southern California (P-8426)*
Uscps .... D 909 434-1888
3009 N Laurel Ave Rialto (92377) *(P-24280)*
Usecb Joint Venture Inc .... F 209 267-5594
11500 String Bean Aly Sutter Creek (95685) *(P-10)*
Used Pellet Co, Fresno *Also called Charles Jj Inc (P-4590)*
Usglobalsat Inc .... F 909 597-8525
14740 Yorba Ct Chino (91710) *(P-18295)*
Ushio America Inc .... E 714 236-8600
14 Mason Irvine (92618) *(P-17654)*
USI Manufacturing Services Inc .... D 408 636-9600
1255 E Arques Ave Sunnyvale (94085) *(P-15880)*
Usit Co, Gardena *Also called US Industrial Tool & Sup Co (P-14460)*
Usk Manufacturing Inc .... E 510 471-7555
720 Zwissig Way Union City (94587) *(P-12803)*
Usl Parallel Products Cal .... E 909 980-1200
12281 Arrow Rte Rancho Cucamonga (91739) *(P-9046)*
USP Inc .... D 760 842-7700
1818 Ord Way Oceanside (92056) *(P-8859)*
Uspar Enterprises Inc .... E 909 591-7506
2037 S Vineyard Ave Ontario (91761) *(P-17566)*
USS-Psco Inds A Cal Jint Ventr (PA) .... A 800 877-7672
900 Loveridge Rd Pittsburg (94565) *(P-11426)*
UST, Los Angeles *Also called Universal Surface Techlgy Inc (P-8612)*
Ustc, Chico *Also called United States Thermoelectric (P-22046)*
Utak Laboratories Inc .... E 661 294-3935
25020 Avenue Tibbitts Valencia (91355) *(P-9047)*
Utap Printing Co Inc .... F 650 588-2818
1423 San Mateo Ave South San Francisco (94080) *(P-7160)*
Utbbb Inc .... C 562 594-4411
10711 Bloomfield St Los Alamitos (90720) *(P-1387)*
UTC Aerospace Systems, Santa Fe Springs *Also called United Technologies Corp (P-20966)*
UTC Aerospace Systems, Fairfield *Also called Goodrich Corporation (P-21192)*
UTC Aerospace Systems, Riverside *Also called United Technologies Corp (P-20967)*
UTC Aerospace Systems Company, Chula Vista *Also called Rohr Inc (P-20922)*
Utility Composite Solutions In (PA) .... F 858 442-3187
4600 Pavlov Ave Unit 221 San Diego (92122) *(P-11015)*
Utility Refrigerator .... F 818 764-6200
12160 Sherman Way North Hollywood (91605) *(P-15996)*
Utility Trailer Mfg Co (PA) .... B 626 964-7319
17295 Railroad St Ste A City of Industry (91748) *(P-20517)*
Utility Trailer Mfg Co .... B 909 594-6026
301 Paseo Tesoro Walnut (91789) *(P-20518)*
Utility Trailer Mfg Co .... E 909 428-8300
15567 Valley Blvd Fontana (92335) *(P-20519)*
Utility Trlr Sls Southern Cal, Fontana *Also called Utility Trailer Mfg Co (P-20519)*
Utility Vault, Fontana *Also called Oldcastle Precast Inc (P-10964)*
Utility Vault, Madera *Also called Oldcastle Precast Inc (P-13961)*
Utility Vault, Riverside *Also called Oldcastle Precast Inc (P-10969)*
Utopia Lighting .... F 310 327-7711
2329 E Pacifica Pl Compton (90220) *(P-17125)*
Uv Landscaping LLC .... F 831 275-5296
477 Old Natividad Rd Salinas (93906) *(P-10866)*
Uv Skinz Inc .... F 209 536-9200
13775 Mono Way Ste A Sonora (95370) *(P-3202)*
Uvexs Incorporated .... F 408 734-4402
1287 Hammerwood Ave Sunnyvale (94089) *(P-9214)*
Uvify Inc .... F 628 200-4469
1 Market Spear Twr Fl 36 San Francisco (94105) *(P-21451)*
Uvp, LLC, Upland *Also called Analytik Jena US LLC (P-21903)*
Uwe, Camarillo *Also called United Western Enterprises Inc (P-13676)*
V & F Fabrication Company Inc .... E 714 265-0630
13902 Seaboard Cir Garden Grove (92843) *(P-12271)*
V & M Plating Co .... F 310 532-5633
14024 Avalon Blvd Los Angeles (90061) *(P-13530)*
V & M Precision Grinding Co., Brea *Also called Rogers Holding Company Inc (P-20921)*
V & P Scientific Inc .... F 858 455-0643
9823 Pacific Heights Blvd San Diego (92121) *(P-10425)*
V & S Engineering Company Ltd .... F 714 898-7869
5766 Research Dr Huntington Beach (92649) *(P-17027)*
V & V Manufacturing Inc .... F 626 330-0641
15320 Proctor Ave City of Industry (91745) *(P-23760)*
V 3, Oxnard *Also called V3 Printing Corporation (P-7161)*
V Fly, El Monte *Also called Vfly Corporation (P-3868)*
V H Paris Co, La Habra Heights *Also called Viet Hung Paris Inc (P-534)*
V Himark (usa) Inc .... F 626 305-5766
16019 E Foothill Blvd Irwindale (91702) *(P-9178)*
V I P Ironworks Inc .... F 310 216-2890
8319 Hindry Ave Los Angeles (90045) *(P-12902)*
V J Provision Inc .... F 818 843-3945
410 S Varney St Burbank (91502) *(P-454)*
V M P Inc .... F 661 294-9934
24830 Avenue Tibbitts Valencia (91355) *(P-13049)*
V M I, Visalia *Also called Voltage Multipliers Inc (P-19265)*
V Manufacturing Logistics Inc .... E 909 869-6200
20501 Earlgate St Walnut (91789) *(P-8860)*
V Q Orthocare, Irvine *Also called Vision Quest Industries Inc (P-22842)*
V Tech, Sunnyvale *Also called V-Tech Manufacturing Inc (P-17028)*
V Twest Inc .... F 714 521-2167
16222 Phoebe Ave La Mirada (90638) *(P-5115)*
V Twin Magazine, Agoura Hills *Also called Paisano Publications LLC (P-6228)*
V&H Performance LLC .... D 562 921-7461
13861 Rosecrans Ave Santa Fe Springs (90670) *(P-21148)*
V&M Prcsion Machining Grinding, Brea *Also called Tca Precision Products LLC (P-20945)*
V-A Optical Company Inc .... F 415 459-1919
60 Red Hill Ave San Anselmo (94960) *(P-22144)*
V-Silicon Inc .... F 510 897-0168
47467 Fremont Blvd Fremont (94538) *(P-19250)*
V-T Industries Inc .... F 714 521-2008
16222 Phoebe Ave La Mirada (90638) *(P-10426)*
V-Tech Manufacturing Inc .... F 408 730-9200
1140 W Evelyn Ave Sunnyvale (94086) *(P-17028)*
V/ Twins, Agoura Hills *Also called Paisano Publications Inc (P-6229)*
V2 Lighting Group Inc .... F 707 383-4600
276 E Gish Rd San Jose (95112) *(P-17743)*
V3, Oxnard *Also called Ventura Printing Inc (P-7533)*
V3 Printing Corporation .... D 805 981-2600
200 N Elevar St Oxnard (93030) *(P-7161)*
Va-Tran Systems Inc .... F 619 423-4555
677 Anita St Ste A Chula Vista (91911) *(P-15044)*
Vaca Energy LLC .... F 310 385-3684
4407 Sturgis Rd Oxnard (93030) *(P-158)*
Vacaville Fruit Co Inc .... E 707 448-5292
2055 Cessna Dr Vacaville (95688) *(P-903)*
Vacco Industries (HQ) .... C 626 443-7121
10350 Vacco St South El Monte (91733) *(P-13777)*
Vacmet Inc .... E 909 948-9344
8740 Hellman Ave Rancho Cucamonga (91730) *(P-13677)*
Vacumed, Ventura *Also called Vacumetrics Inc (P-22663)*
Vacumetrics Inc .... F 805 644-7461
4538 Wstnghouse St Unit A Ventura (93003) *(P-22663)*
Vacuum Engrg & Mtls Co Inc .... E 408 871-9900
390 Reed St Santa Clara (95050) *(P-7812)*
Vacuum Tube Logic of America .... F 909 627-5944
4774 Murietta St Ste 10 Chino (91710) *(P-18398)*
Vaga Industries, South El Monte *Also called Pearson Engineering Corp (P-13632)*
Vagrant Records Inc .... E 323 302-0100
6351 Wilshire Blvd # 101 Los Angeles (90048) *(P-7590)*
Vahe Enterprises Inc .... D 323 235-6657
750 E Slauson Ave Los Angeles (90011) *(P-20233)*
Vaider Inc .... F 707 584-3655
553 Martin Ave Ste 1 Rohnert Park (94928) *(P-13678)*
Vaider Manufacturing, Rohnert Park *Also called Vaider Inc (P-13678)*
Vaknin Juda .... F 818 503-8872
7359 Fulton Ave North Hollywood (91605) *(P-4363)*
Val Pak Products .... F 661 252-0115
20731 Centre Pointe Pkwy Santa Clarita (91350) *(P-9689)*
Val Plastic USA L L C .... F 909 390-9600
4570 Eucalyptus Ave Ste C Chino (91710) *(P-14114)*
Val-Aero Industries Inc .... F 661 252-1047
25319 Rye Canyon Rd Valencia (91355) *(P-17029)*
Valadons Plumbing Service Inc .... F 661 201-1460
315 Coleshill St Bakersfield (93312) *(P-12054)*
Valco Boats, Fresno *Also called Henderson Services Inc (P-21042)*
Valco Planer Works Inc .... E 323 582-6355
6131 Maywood Ave Huntington Park (90255) *(P-14587)*
Valco Precision Works, Huntington Park *Also called Valco Planer Works Inc (P-14587)*
Valdor Fiber Optics Inc (PA) .... E 510 293-1212
1838 D St Hayward (94541) *(P-21883)*
Valeant Pharmaceuticals Intl .... F 800 548-5100
50 Technology Dr Irvine (92618) *(P-8429)*
Valence Surface Tech LLC .... E 323 770-0240
1000 Commercial St San Carlos (94070) *(P-21452)*

ALPHABETIC

Employee Codes: A=Over 500 employees, B=251-500
C=101-250, D=51-100, E=20-50, F=10-19
2019 California
Manfacturers Register
© Mergent Inc. 1-800-342-5647
1319

Valencia Pipe Company...E...661 257-3923
28839 Industry Dr Valencia (91355) ***(P-9791)***
Valent Dublin Laboratories, Dublin *Also called Valent USA LLC* ***(P-9120)***
Valent USA LLC...E...925 256-2700
6560 Trinity Ct Dublin (94568) ***(P-9120)***
Valerie Trading Inc...E...323 231-4255
870 E 59th St Los Angeles (90001) ***(P-2921)***
Valero, Wilmington *Also called Ultramar Inc* ***(P-290)***
Valero Energy Corporation...B...707 745-7011
3400 E 2nd St Benicia (94510) ***(P-9048)***
Valero Energy Corporation...E...760 946-3322
17928 Us Highway 18 Apple Valley (92307) ***(P-9371)***
Valero Ref Company-California...B...707 745-7011
3400 E 2nd St Benicia (94510) ***(P-9372)***
Valero Ref Company-California...B...562 491-6754
2401 E Anaheim St Wilmington (90744) ***(P-9373)***
Valew Welding & Fabrication, Adelanto *Also called Hayes Welding Inc* ***(P-25409)***
Valew Welding & Fabrication, Hesperia *Also called Hayes Welding Inc* ***(P-25410)***
Valiantica Inc (PA)...F...408 694-3803
1340 S De Anza Blvd San Jose (95129) ***(P-25319)***
Valid Woodworks, Cerritos *Also called David L Long* ***(P-4138)***
Valimet Inc (PA)...D...209 444-1600
431 Sperry Rd Stockton (95206) ***(P-11852)***
Vallejo Electric Motor Inc...F...707 552-7488
925 Maine St Vallejo (94590) ***(P-25470)***
Valley Business Printers Inc...D...818 362-7771
16230 Filbert St Sylmar (91342) ***(P-7162)***
Valley Cabinet, El Cajon *Also called Vcsd Inc* ***(P-4365)***
Valley Casework Inc...D...619 579-6886
1112 Cleghorn Way Alpine (91901) ***(P-4364)***
Valley Chrome Plating Inc...D...559 298-8094
1028 Hoblitt Ave Clovis (93612) ***(P-13531)***
Valley Circuits...F...661 294-0077
24940 Avenue Tibbitts Valencia (91355) ***(P-18642)***
Valley Community Newspaper...F...916 429-9901
1109 Markham Way Sacramento (95818) ***(P-6077)***
Valley Controls Inc...F...559 638-5115
583 E Dinuba Ave Reedley (93654) ***(P-21673)***
Valley Cutting System Inc...E...559 684-1229
1455 N Belmont Rd Exeter (93221) ***(P-14422)***
Valley Decorating Company...E...559 495-1100
2829 E Hamilton Ave Fresno (93721) ***(P-10427)***
Valley Department Store, Upland *Also called Sampav Inc* ***(P-3042)***
Valley Drapery Inc...D...818 892-7744
16616 Schoenborn St North Hills (91343) ***(P-2786)***
Valley Drapery and Upholstery, North Hills *Also called Valley Drapery Inc* ***(P-2786)***
Valley Engravers, Santa Clarita *Also called Valley Precision Metal Product* ***(P-12804)***
Valley Fabrication Inc...D...831 757-5151
1056 Pellet Ave Salinas (93901) ***(P-14115)***
Valley Fine Foods Company Inc...F...530 671-7200
300 Epley Dr Yuba City (95991) ***(P-1019)***
Valley Fine Foods Company Inc (PA)...B...707 746-6888
3909 Park Rd Ste H Benicia (94510) ***(P-1050)***
Valley Forge Acquisition Corp...F...626 969-8701
444 S Motor Ave Azusa (91702) ***(P-13116)***
Valley Fresh Inc (HQ)...E...209 943-5411
1404 S Fresno Ave Stockton (95206) ***(P-553)***
Valley Garlic Inc...E...559 934-1763
500 Enterprise Pkwy Coalinga (93210) ***(P-939)***
Valley Images...F...408 279-6777
1925 Kyle Park Ct San Jose (95125) ***(P-3927)***
Valley Lahvosh Baking Co Inc...E...559 485-2700
502 M St Fresno (93721) ***(P-1336)***
Valley Metal Treating Inc...E...909 623-6316
355 S East End Ave Pomona (91766) ***(P-11838)***
Valley Metals LLC...E...858 513-1300
13125 Gregg St Poway (92064) ***(P-11489)***
Valley Mfg & Engrg Inc...F...818 504-6085
9105 De Garmo Ave Sun Valley (91352) ***(P-14588)***
Valley Motor Center Inc...F...818 686-3350
10639 Glenoaks Blvd Pacoima (91331) ***(P-20181)***
Valley News Gardens, Gardena *Also called Gardena Valley News Inc* ***(P-5855)***
Valley Oak Cabinets, Santa Ynez *Also called Valley Oaks Industries* ***(P-4973)***
Valley Oaks Industries...F...805 688-2754
3550 E Highway 246 Ste Ae Santa Ynez (93460) ***(P-4973)***
Valley of Moon Winery...E...707 939-4500
777 Madrone Rd Glen Ellen (95442) ***(P-2037)***
Valley Packline Solutions...E...559 638-7821
5259 Avenue 408 Reedley (93654) ***(P-14894)***
Valley Perforating LLC...D...661 324-4964
3201 Gulf St Bakersfield (93308) ***(P-17030)***
Valley Pipe & Supply Inc...E...559 233-0321
1801 Santa Clara St Fresno (93721) ***(P-13778)***
Valley Post, Anderson *Also called North Valley Newspapers Inc* ***(P-6001)***
Valley Power Services Inc...E...909 969-9345
425 S Hacienda Blvd City of Industry (91745) ***(P-17228)***
Valley Power Systems Inc (PA)...D...626 333-1243
425 S Hacienda Blvd City of Industry (91745) ***(P-14035)***
Valley Precision Inc...F...209 847-1758
536 Hi Tech Pkwy Oakdale (95361) ***(P-17031)***
Valley Precision Metal Product...E...661 607-0100
27771 Avenue Hopkins Santa Clarita (91355) ***(P-12804)***
Valley Printers, Sylmar *Also called Valley Business Printers Inc* ***(P-7162)***
Valley Printing, Ceres *Also called Robert R Wix Inc* ***(P-7472)***
Valley Protein LLC...D...559 498-7115
1828 E Hedges Ave Fresno (93703) ***(P-533)***
Valley Publications...F...661 298-5330
27259 One Half Camp Plnty Canyon Country (91351) ***(P-6614)***
Valley Rock Lndscpe Material (PA)...F...916 652-7209
4018 Taylor Rd Loomis (95650) ***(P-10867)***
Valley Rubber & Gasket, Stockton *Also called Lewis-Goetz and Company Inc* ***(P-9500)***
Valley Sailboards, Oxnard *Also called Advantage Engineering Corp* ***(P-23488)***
Valley Services Electronics, San Jose *Also called Tri-Phase Inc* ***(P-18628)***
Valley Sleurry Seal Co, Redding *Also called Vss Emultech Inc* ***(P-9399)***
Valley Spuds of Oxnard, Oxnard *Also called Produce Available Inc* ***(P-14094)***
Valley Stairway Inc...F...559 299-0151
5684 E Shields Ave Fresno (93727) ***(P-12903)***
Valley Stamping Inc...F...661 259-4562
24304 Creekside Dr Newhall (91321) ***(P-13291)***
Valley Syncom Circuits, Valencia *Also called Valley Circuits* ***(P-18642)***
Valley Tool & Mfg Co Inc...E...209 883-4093
2507 Tully Rd Hughson (95326) ***(P-17032)***
Valley Tool and Machine Co Inc...E...909 595-2205
111 Explorer St Pomona (91768) ***(P-17033)***
Valley View Foods Inc...D...530 673-7356
7547 Sawtelle Ave Yuba City (95991) ***(P-866)***
Valley View Packing Co Inc...E...408 289-8300
1764 The Alameda San Jose (95126) ***(P-904)***
Valley Water Management Co...F...661 410-7500
7500 Meany Ave Bakersfield (93308) ***(P-291)***
Valley Welding & Machine Works, Fresno *Also called Garabedian Bros Inc* ***(P-16525)***
Valley Yellow Pages, Fresno *Also called Agi Publishing Inc* ***(P-6423)***
Valley Yellow Pages, Fresno *Also called Agi Publishing Inc* ***(P-6424)***
Valley-Todeco Inc (HQ)...E...800 992-4444
12975 Bradley Ave Sylmar (91342) ***(P-13089)***
Vallin Alida...F...818 361-9020
12473 Gladstone Ave Sylmar (91342) ***(P-17034)***
Valma Properties, San Francisco *Also called James P McNair Co Inc* ***(P-11965)***
Valmas Inc...E...323 677-2211
1233 S Boyle Ave Los Angeles (90023) ***(P-3346)***
Valmont Industries Inc...D...323 264-6660
4116 Whiteside St Los Angeles (90063) ***(P-12272)***
Valmont Industries Inc...F...760 253-3070
3970 Lenwood Rd Barstow (92311) ***(P-12273)***
Valmont Newmark, Barstow *Also called Valmont Industries Inc* ***(P-12273)***
Valprint, Fresno *Also called Zip Print Inc* ***(P-7195)***
Valterra Products LLC (PA)...E...818 898-1671
15230 San Fernando Mission Hills (91345) ***(P-13779)***
Valuable Market, Huntington Beach *Also called Third Degree Sportswear Inc* ***(P-3518)***
Value Products Inc...E...209 345-3817
2128 Industrial Dr Stockton (95206) ***(P-8613)***
Valves & Cylinders, San Leandro *Also called Rotex Punch Company Inc* ***(P-14566)***
Valvex Enterprises Inc...E...408 928-2510
885 Jarvis Dr Morgan Hill (95037) ***(P-17035)***
Vampire Penguin LLC (PA)...F...916 553-4197
907 K St Sacramento (95814) ***(P-701)***
Van Brunt Foundry Inc...F...323 569-2832
5136 Chakemco St South Gate (90280) ***(P-11751)***
Van Craeynest Inc...F...415 362-1025
27 E State St Redlands (92373) ***(P-23328)***
Van Grace Quality Injection...F...323 931-5255
9164 Appleby St Downey (90240) ***(P-10428)***
Van Heusen Factory Outlet...F...951 674-1190
17600 Collier Ave D134 Lake Elsinore (92530) ***(P-3064)***
Van Howd Studios, Auburn *Also called Sierra Sculpture Inc* ***(P-11766)***
Van R Dental Products Inc...F...805 488-1122
600 E Hueneme Rd Oxnard (93033) ***(P-22921)***
Van Sark Inc (PA)...E...510 635-1111
888 Doolittle Dr San Leandro (94577) ***(P-4817)***
Van Tisse Inc...F...415 543-2404
2565 3rd St Ste 319 San Francisco (94107) ***(P-2865)***
Vanard Lithographers Inc...E...619 291-5571
3220 Kurtz St San Diego (92110) ***(P-7163)***
Vance & Hines, Santa Fe Springs *Also called V&H Performance LLC* ***(P-21148)***
Vander-Bend Manufacturing Inc...A...408 245-5150
2701 Orchard Pkwy San Jose (95134) ***(P-19779)***
Vanderhulst Associates Inc...E...408 727-1313
3300 Victor Ct Santa Clara (95054) ***(P-17036)***
Vanderlans & Sons Inc (PA)...E...209 334-4115
1320 S Sacramento St Lodi (95240) ***(P-16129)***
Vandersteen Audio Inc...E...559 582-0324
116 W 4th St Hanford (93230) ***(P-17874)***
Vanderveer Industrial Plas LLC (PA)...E...714 579-7700
515 S Melrose St Placentia (92870) ***(P-9769)***
Vandorn Plastering...F...530 671-2748
657 Lincoln Rd Ste D Yuba City (95991) ***(P-11373)***
Vangie L Cortes...E...858 578-6807
9466 Black Mountain Rd San Diego (92126) ***(P-6078)***
Vanguard Elect, Huntington Beach *Also called Vanguard Networing Products* ***(P-18375)***
Vanguard Fabrication Corp...F...909 355-0832
14578 Hawthorne Ave Fontana (92335) ***(P-12805)***
Vanguard Industries East Inc...D...800 433-1334
2440 Impala Dr Carlsbad (92010) ***(P-3971)***
Vanguard Industries West Inc (PA)...C...760 438-4437
2440 Impala Dr Carlsbad (92010) ***(P-3972)***
Vanguard Instruments, Ontario *Also called Doble Engineering Company* ***(P-17141)***
Vanguard Marketing, Scotts Valley *Also called Threshold Enterprises Ltd* ***(P-7975)***
Vanguard Networing Products...B...714 842-3330
7412 Prince Dr Huntington Beach (92647) ***(P-18375)***
Vanguard Printing, Oxnard *Also called DBC Printing Incorporated* ***(P-6780)***
Vanguard Tool & Manufacturing, Rancho Cucamonga *Also called Vanguard Tool & Mfg Co Inc* ***(P-13292)***
Vanguard Tool & Mfg Co Inc...E...909 980-9392
8388 Utica Ave Rancho Cucamonga (91730) ***(P-13292)***
Vaniman Manufacturing, Fallbrook *Also called Vmc International LLC* ***(P-22923)***

Mergent e-mail: customerrelations@mergent.com
1320
2019 California
Manufacturers Register
(P-0000) Products & Services Section entry number
(PA)=Parent Co (HQ)=Headquarters (DH)=Div Headquarters

Vanishing Vistas ....E.......916 624-1237
5043 Midas Ave Rocklin (95677) *(P-6615)*
Vannelli Brands LLC ....F.......916 824-1717
4031 Alvis Ct Rocklin (95677) *(P-867)*
Vans Inc ....F.......310 390-7548
6000 Sepulveda Blvd # 2155 Culver City (90230) *(P-9489)*
Vans Inc ....F.......818 990-1098
14006 Riverside Dr Sherman Oaks (91423) *(P-9490)*
Vans Inc ....F.......650 401-3542
1354 Burlingame Ave Burlingame (94010) *(P-9491)*
Vans Inc ....F.......562 856-1695
5232 E 2nd St Long Beach (90803) *(P-9492)*
Vans Inc ....F.......415 566-3762
3251 20th Ave Ste 237 San Francisco (94132) *(P-9493)*
Vans Inc ....F.......909 517-3141
13920 Cy Ctr Dr Ste 4035 Chino Hills (91709) *(P-9494)*
Vans Inc (HQ) ....B.......855 909-8267
1588 S Coast Dr Costa Mesa (92626) *(P-9495)*
Vans Inc ....F.......415 479-1284
5800 Northgate Dr Ste 44 San Rafael (94903) *(P-9496)*
Vans Instant Printers Inc ....F.......626 966-1708
221 E San Bernardino Rd Covina (91723) *(P-7164)*
Vans Manufacturing Inc ....F.......805 522-6267
330 E Easy St Ste C Simi Valley (93065) *(P-17037)*
Vans Shoes, Costa Mesa *Also called Vans Inc (P-9495)*
Vantage Associates Inc ....E.......619 477-6940
900 Civic Center Dr National City (91950) *(P-20968)*
Vantage Associates Inc (PA) ....E.......619 477-6940
900 Civic Center Dr National City (91950) *(P-21198)*
Vantage Associates Inc ....D.......562 968-1400
12333 Los Nietos Rd Santa Fe Springs (90670) *(P-10429)*
Vantage Led, Ontario *Also called Tradenet Enterprise Inc (P-23993)*
Vantage Master Machine Company, National City *Also called Vantage Associates Inc (P-20968)*
Vantage Point Products Corp (PA) ....D.......562 946-1718
9115 Dice Rd Ste 18 Santa Fe Springs (90670) *(P-17875)*
Vantage Vehicle Group, Corona *Also called Vantage Vehicle Intl Inc (P-19850)*
Vantage Vehicle Intl Inc ....E.......951 735-1200
1740 N Delilah St Corona (92879) *(P-19850)*
Vantari Medical LLC ....F.......949 783-5300
15440 Laguna Canyon Rd Irvine (92618) *(P-22294)*
Vantiq Inc ....F.......303 377-2882
1990 N Calif Blvd Ste 400 Walnut Creek (94596) *(P-25320)*
Vapex-Genex-Precision, Gardena *Also called Electrical Rebuilders Sls Inc (P-19831)*
Vapor Cleaners (PA) ....F.......831 423-4646
285 Water St Santa Cruz (95060) *(P-23329)*
Vapor Cleaners & Shirt Laundry, Santa Cruz *Also called Vapor Cleaners (P-23329)*
Vaporbrothers Inc ....F.......310 618-1188
2908 Oregon Ct Ste I9 Torrance (90503) *(P-17405)*
Vaquero Energy Inc ....E.......661 616-0600
5060 California Ave Bakersfield (93309) *(P-292)*
Vaquero Energy Incorporated ....E.......661 363-7240
15545 Hermosa Rd Bakersfield (93307) *(P-84)*
Varco Heat Treating, Garden Grove *Also called Diversfied Mtllrgical Svcs Inc (P-11811)*
Varedan Technologies LLC ....F.......310 542-2320
3860 Del Amo Blvd Ste 401 Torrance (90503) *(P-17318)*
Variable Image Printing ....F.......949 296-1444
16540 Aston Ste A Irvine (92606) *(P-7165)*
Variable Image Printing ....E.......858 530-2443
9020 Kenamar Dr Ste 204 San Diego (92121) *(P-7166)*
Varian Associates Limited ....E.......650 493-4000
3100 Hansen Way Palo Alto (94304) *(P-22664)*
Varian Medical Systems Inc (PA) ....A.......650 493-4000
3100 Hansen Way Palo Alto (94304) *(P-22944)*
Varian Medical Systems Inc ....E.......408 321-4468
3120 Hansen Way Palo Alto (94304) *(P-22665)*
Varian Medical Systems Inc ....F.......650 493-4000
3175 Hanover St Palo Alto (94304) *(P-18399)*
Varian Medical Systems Inc ....C.......408 321-9400
660 N Mccarthy Blvd Milpitas (95035) *(P-22666)*
Varian Medical Systems Inc ....C.......650 493-4000
3045 Hanover St Palo Alto (94304) *(P-22667)*
Varian Thin Film Systems, Palo Alto *Also called Varian Medical Systems Inc (P-18399)*
Variant Technology Inc ....F.......626 278-4343
635 Hampton Rd Arcadia (91006) *(P-17744)*
Various Technologies Inc ....E.......408 972-4460
2720 Aiello Dr Ste C San Jose (95111) *(P-17319)*
Varni Brothers Corporation (PA) ....D.......209 521-1777
400 Hosmer Ave Modesto (95351) *(P-2231)*
Varni Brothers Corporation ....E.......209 464-7778
1109 W Anderson St Stockton (95206) *(P-2232)*
Varni Lite, Hayward *Also called Varni-Lite Coatings Associates (P-9179)*
Varni-Lite Coatings Associates ....F.......510 887-8997
21595 Curtis St Hayward (94545) *(P-9179)*
Vas Engineering Inc ....E.......858 569-1601
4750 Viewridge Ave San Diego (92123) *(P-19780)*
Vasari Plaster and Stucco LLC ....F.......805 845-2497
1725 N Ventura Ave Ventura (93001) *(P-11374)*
Vascular Imaging Professionals (PA) ....F.......949 278-5622
1340 N Dynamics St Ste A Anaheim (92806) *(P-22668)*
Vascular Therapies, Irvine *Also called Covidien LP (P-22412)*
Vast Enterprises ....F.......562 633-3224
7739 Monroe St Paramount (90723) *(P-9453)*
Vast National Inc ....F.......951 788-7030
4398 Market St Riverside (92501) *(P-11853)*
Vastcircuits & Mfg LLC ....F.......805 421-4299
2226 Goodyear Ave Unit B Ventura (93003) *(P-19781)*
Vat Incorporated ....E.......408 813-2700
655 River Oaks Pkwy San Jose (95134) *(P-13735)*
Vave Health Inc ....F.......650 387-7059
2955 Campus Dr Ste 110 San Mateo (94403) *(P-23064)*
Vaxart Inc (PA) ....F.......650 550-3500
290 Utah Ave Ste 200 South San Francisco (94080) *(P-8430)*
Vclad Laminates Inc ....E.......626 442-2100
2103 Seaman Ave South El Monte (91733) *(P-9770)*
Vcp Mobility Inc ....B.......559 292-2171
2842 N Business Park Ave Fresno (93727) *(P-22838)*
Vcp Mobility Holdings Inc ....B.......619 213-6500
745 Design Ct Ste 602 Chula Vista (91911) *(P-22839)*
Vcp Mobility Holdings Inc ....B.......303 218-4500
2842 N Business Park Ave Fresno (93727) *(P-22840)*
Vcsd Inc ....E.......619 579-6886
585 Vernon Way El Cajon (92020) *(P-4365)*
Vdi Motor Sports, Lake Elsinore *Also called Vertical Doors Inc (P-5214)*
Vdp Direct LLC (PA) ....E.......858 300-4510
5520 Ruffin Rd Ste 111 San Diego (92123) *(P-7167)*
Vector Electronics & Tech Inc ....E.......818 985-8208
11115 Vanowen St North Hollywood (91605) *(P-18643)*
Vector Fabrication Inc (PA) ....E.......408 942-9800
1629 Watson Ct Milpitas (95035) *(P-18644)*
Vector Laboratories Inc (PA) ....D.......650 697-3600
30 Ingold Rd Burlingame (94010) *(P-8585)*
Veeco C V C, Santa Clara *Also called Veeco Instruments Inc (P-19251)*
Veeco Electro Fab Inc (PA) ....F.......714 630-8020
1176 N Osprey Cir Anaheim (92807) *(P-18645)*
Veeco Instruments Inc ....E.......510 657-8523
3100 Laurelview Ct Santa Clara (95054) *(P-19251)*
Veeco Process Equipment Inc ....C.......805 967-1400
112 Robin Hill Rd Goleta (93117) *(P-22047)*
Veeco Process Equipment Inc ....D.......805 967-2700
112 Robin Hill Rd Goleta (93117) *(P-17038)*
Veeva Systems Inc (PA) ....C.......925 452-6500
4280 Hacienda Dr Pleasanton (94588) *(P-25321)*
Veex Inc ....F.......510 651-0500
2827 Lakeview Ct Fremont (94538) *(P-21674)*
Veezee Inc ....E.......949 265-0800
121 Waterworks Way Irvine (92618) *(P-3286)*
Vefo Inc ....E.......909 598-3856
3202 Factory Dr Pomona (91768) *(P-9890)*
Vega Textile Inc ....F.......323 923-0600
2751 S Alameda St Los Angeles (90058) *(P-2809)*
Vege - Kurl Inc ....D.......818 956-5582
412 W Cypress St Glendale (91204) *(P-8861)*
Vege-Mist Inc ....E.......310 353-2300
407 E Redondo Beach Blvd Gardena (90248) *(P-15997)*
Vege-Tech Company, Glendale *Also called Vege - Kurl Inc (P-8861)*
Velco Tool & Die Inc ....F.......949 855-6638
20431 Barents Sea Cir Lake Forest (92630) *(P-14589)*
Vellios Automotive Machine Sp, Lawndale *Also called Vellios Machine Shop Inc (P-17039)*
Vellios Machine Shop Inc ....F.......310 643-8540
4625 29th Mnhattan Bch Bl Lawndale (90260) *(P-17039)*
Vello Systems Inc ....D.......650 324-7688
1530 Obrien Dr Menlo Park (94025) *(P-18004)*
Velo3d Inc ....C.......408 666-5309
511 Division St Campbell (95008) *(P-7168)*
Velocity Imaging Products Inc ....F.......619 433-8000
8139 Center St La Mesa (91942) *(P-23208)*
Velodyne Acoustics Inc ....D.......408 465-2800
345 Digital Dr Morgan Hill (95037) *(P-17876)*
Velodyne Lidar Inc ....B.......408 465-2800
345 Digital Dr Morgan Hill (95037) *(P-21453)*
Velos Inc ....E.......510 739-4010
42840 Christy St Ste 201 Fremont (94538) *(P-25322)*
Velox Cnc, Orange *Also called Liboon Group Inc (P-14390)*
Velti Inc (HQ) ....E.......415 362-2077
150 California St Fl 10 San Francisco (94111) *(P-25323)*
Velti USA, San Francisco *Also called Velti Inc (P-25323)*
Velvet Heart, Los Angeles *Also called Tcj Manufacturing LLC (P-3514)*
Vena Engineering Corp ....F.......831 724-5738
7 Hangar Way Watsonville (95076) *(P-22295)*
Venator Americas LLC ....D.......323 269-7311
3700 E Olympic Blvd Los Angeles (90023) *(P-7748)*
Vending Security Products ....F.......949 646-1474
770 Newton Way Costa Mesa (92627) *(P-12438)*
Venice Baking Co ....E.......310 322-7357
134 Main St El Segundo (90245) *(P-1337)*
Venoco Inc ....E.......805 644-1400
4483 Mcgrath St Ste 101 Ventura (93003) *(P-85)*
Venoco Inc ....E.......805 961-2305
7979 Hollister Ave Goleta (93117) *(P-9374)*
Venolia Pistons, Long Beach *Also called Tor C A M Industries Inc (P-16153)*
Venstar Inc ....F.......818 341-8760
9250 Owensmouth Ave Chatsworth (91311) *(P-15998)*
Venta Medical Inc ....E.......510 429-9300
1971 Milmont Dr Milpitas (95035) *(P-22669)*
Ventek International, Petaluma *Also called Caracal Enterprises LLC (P-15920)*
Vention Med Design & Dev Inc ....F.......603 707-8753
610 Palomar Ave Sunnyvale (94085) *(P-22670)*
Ventritex, Sylmar *Also called Pacesetter Inc (P-23032)*
Ventsam Sash & Door Mfg Co, Sun Valley *Also called Monty Ventsam Inc (P-4196)*
Ventura Aerospace Inc ....F.......818 540-3130
31355 Agoura Rd Westlake Village (91361) *(P-20969)*
Ventura Coastal LLC (PA) ....D.......805 653-7000
2325 Vista Del Mar Dr Ventura (93001) *(P-971)*
Ventura Coastal LLC ....F.......559 737-9836
12310 Avenue 368 Visalia (93291) *(P-972)*
Ventura County Reporter, Pasadena *Also called Southland Publishing Inc (P-6053)*
Ventura County Star, Camarillo *Also called Scripps Media Inc (P-6041)*

Ventura County Star.......F.......805 437-0138
151 Factory Stores Dr Camarillo (93010) ***(P-6079)***
Ventura Foods LLC.......C.......714 257-3700
2900 Jurupa St Ontario (91761) ***(P-1552)***
Ventura Foods LLC.......C.......323 262-9157
2900 Jurupa St Ontario (91761) ***(P-563)***
Ventura Foods LLC (PA).......C.......714 257-3700
40 Pointe Dr Brea (92821) ***(P-1553)***
Ventura GL Inc.......F.......818 890-1886
12595 Foothill Blvd Sylmar (91342) ***(P-11285)***
Ventura Harbor Boatyard Inc.......E.......805 654-1433
1415 Spinnaker Dr Ventura (93001) ***(P-21066)***
Ventura Hydrulic Mch Works Inc.......E.......805 656-1760
1555 Callens Rd Ventura (93003) ***(P-16161)***
Ventura Printing Inc (PA).......D.......805 981-2600
200 N Elevar St Oxnard (93030) ***(P-7533)***
Ventura Technology Group.......E.......805 581-0800
855 E Easy St Ste 104 Simi Valley (93065) ***(P-19252)***
Venture Capital Entps LLC.......F.......914 275-7305
10669 Wellworth Ave Los Angeles (90024) ***(P-702)***
Venture Electronics Intl Inc.......F.......510 744-3720
6701 Mowry Ave Newark (94560) ***(P-18646)***
Venturedyne Ltd.......D.......909 793-2788
1320 W Colton Ave Redlands (92374) ***(P-15184)***
Ventus Medical Inc.......E.......408 200-5299
1100 La Avenida St Ste A Mountain View (94043) ***(P-22671)***
Venus Alloys Inc (PA).......E.......714 635-8800
1415 S Allec St Anaheim (92805) ***(P-11708)***
Venus Bridal Gowns, San Gabriel *Also called Lotus Orient Corp* ***(P-3326)***
Venus Foods Inc.......E.......626 369-5188
770 S Stimson Ave City of Industry (91745) ***(P-455)***
Venus Laboratories Inc.......D.......714 891-3100
11150 Hope St Cypress (90630) ***(P-7813)***
Veoneer Santa Barbara, Goleta *Also called Veoneer Us Inc* ***(P-19851)***
Veoneer Us Inc.......E.......805 571-1777
420 S Fairview Ave Goleta (93117) ***(P-19851)***
Vera Security Inc.......E.......844 438-8372
318 Cambridge Ave Palo Alto (94306) ***(P-25324)***
Veratex Inc (PA).......C.......818 994-6487
20362 Plummer St Chatsworth (91311) ***(P-2767)***
Verbio Inc.......E.......650 862-8935
2225 E Byshore Rd Ste 200 Palo Alto (94303) ***(P-25325)***
Verco Decking Inc.......F.......909 822-8079
8333 Lime Ave Fontana (92335) ***(P-12806)***
Verco Decking Inc.......F.......925 778-2102
607 Wilbur Ave Antioch (94509) ***(P-12807)***
Verde, Vernon *Also called Pacific Boulevard Inc* ***(P-3331)***
Verde Cosmetic Labs LLC.......F.......818 284-4080
19845 Nordhokk St Northridge (91324) ***(P-8862)***
Verdugo Tool & Engrg Co Inc.......F.......818 998-1101
20600 Superior St Chatsworth (91311) ***(P-13293)***
Veredatech LLC.......F.......858 342-6468
4645 Vereda Mar Del Sol San Diego (92130) ***(P-6616)***
Veridiam Inc (HQ).......C.......619 448-1000
1717 N Cuyamaca St El Cajon (92020) ***(P-14743)***
Verifone Inc (HQ).......C.......408 232-7800
88 W Plumeria Dr San Jose (95134) ***(P-15902)***
Verifone Inc.......C.......408 232-7800
2455 Augustine Dr Santa Clara (95054) ***(P-15903)***
Verifone Inc.......E.......858 436-2270
10590 W Ocean Air Dr # 250 San Diego (92130) ***(P-15881)***
Verifone Systems Inc (HQ).......D.......408 232-7800
88 W Plumeria Dr San Jose (95134) ***(P-15904)***
Verilogix Inc.......F.......310 527-5100
960 Knox St Bldg A Torrance (90502) ***(P-25326)***
Verint, Santa Clara *Also called Kana Software Inc* ***(P-24824)***
Veripic, San Jose *Also called Kwan Software Engineering Inc* ***(P-24843)***
Veris Manufacturing, Brea *Also called Q C M Inc* ***(P-17352)***
Verisilicon Inc (HQ).......F.......408 844-8560
2150 Gold St Ste 200 San Jose (95002) ***(P-19253)***
Veritas Software Global LLC.......F.......650 335-8000
1600 Plymouth St Mountain View (94043) ***(P-25327)***
Verizon, Los Alamitos *Also called Supermedia LLC* ***(P-6598)***
Verizon, Santa Ana *Also called Cellco Partnership* ***(P-18065)***
Verizon, Roseville *Also called Supermedia LLC* ***(P-6599)***
Verlo Industries Inc.......E.......714 236-2191
10762 Chestnut Ave Stanton (90680) ***(P-5175)***
Vermillion's Environmental, La Quinta *Also called Envirnmntal Pdts Applctons Inc* ***(P-8640)***
Vermillions Environmental.......E.......760 777-8035
78900 Avenue 47 Ste 106 La Quinta (92253) ***(P-21536)***
Vern Lackey, Armona *Also called Central Valley Cabinet Mfg* ***(P-4285)***
Vernon Machine and Foundry.......F.......323 277-0550
5420 S Santa Fe Ave Vernon (90058) ***(P-24281)***
Veronica Foods Company.......E.......510 535-6833
1991 Dennison St Oakland (94606) ***(P-1554)***
Veros Software Inc.......E.......714 415-6300
2333 N Broadway Ste 350 Santa Ana (92706) ***(P-25328)***
Versa Stage, Torrance *Also called Forrester Eastland Corporation* ***(P-24099)***
Versacall Technologies Inc.......F.......858 677-6766
7047 Carroll Rd San Diego (92121) ***(P-18376)***
Versacheck, San Diego *Also called G7 Productivity Systems* ***(P-24680)***
Versaclimber, Santa Ana *Also called Heart Rate Inc* ***(P-23583)***
Versaco Manufacturing Inc.......F.......408 848-2880
550 E Luchessa Ave Gilroy (95020) ***(P-14895)***
Versafab Corp (PA).......E.......800 421-1822
15919 S Broadway Gardena (90248) ***(P-12808)***
Versaform Corporation.......D.......760 599-0961
1377 Specialty Dr Vista (92081) ***(P-12809)***

Versant Corporation (HQ).......F.......650 232-2400
500 Arguello St Ste 200 Redwood City (94063) ***(P-25329)***
Versarack, Salinas *Also called Tailgater Inc* ***(P-21212)***
Versatile Power Inc.......F.......408 341-4600
743 Camden Ave B Campbell (95008) ***(P-22672)***
Verseon Corporation (PA).......E.......510 668-1622
48820 Kato Rd Ste 100b Fremont (94538) ***(P-8431)***
Versicolor Inc.......F.......949 361-9698
934 Calle Negocio Ste E San Clemente (92673) ***(P-14783)***
Versicolor Screenprinting, San Clemente *Also called Versicolor Inc* ***(P-14783)***
Vertechs Enterprises Inc (PA).......D.......858 578-3900
1071 Industrial Pl El Cajon (92020) ***(P-11718)***
Vertek, Grass Valley *Also called Guy G Veralrud* ***(P-17806)***
Vertex China, Pomona *Also called Sky One Inc* ***(P-10810)***
Vertex Diamond Tool Company.......D.......909 599-1129
940 W Cienega Ave San Dimas (91773) ***(P-14692)***
Vertex Industrial Inc.......F.......909 626-2100
5138 Brooks St Montclair (91763) ***(P-15372)***
Vertex Lcd Inc.......E.......714 223-7111
600 S Jefferson St Ste K Placentia (92870) ***(P-19782)***
Vertex Water Products, Montclair *Also called Vertex Industrial Inc* ***(P-15372)***
Vertical Communication (HQ).......D.......408 969-9600
3979 Freedom Cir Ste 400 Santa Clara (95054) ***(P-18005)***
Vertical Doors Inc.......F.......951 273-1069
542 3rd St Lake Elsinore (92530) ***(P-5214)***
Vertical Fiber Technologies, Montebello *Also called Vft Inc* ***(P-3755)***
Vertical Hydro Garden Inc.......F.......916 458-4987
1676 W Lincoln Ave Anaheim (92801) ***(P-14137)***
Vertiflex Inc.......E.......442 325-5900
2714 Loker Ave W Ste 100 Carlsbad (92010) ***(P-23065)***
Vertimass LLC.......F.......949 417-1396
2 Park Plz Ste 700 Irvine (92614) ***(P-9049)***
Vertiv Corporation.......B.......925 734-8660
6960 Koll Center Pkwy # 300 Pleasanton (94566) ***(P-17169)***
Vertiv Corporation.......F.......760 768-7522
2340 Rockwood Ave Calexico (92231) ***(P-17170)***
Vertiv Corporation.......E.......949 457-3600
35 Parker Irvine (92618) ***(P-21675)***
Vertos Medical Inc.......D.......949 349-0008
95 Enterprise Ste 325 Aliso Viejo (92656) ***(P-22673)***
Vertox Company.......F.......714 530-4541
11752 Garden Grove Blvd # 113 Garden Grove (92843) ***(P-21884)***
Verus Pharmaceuticals Inc.......F.......858 436-1600
11455 El Camino Real # 460 San Diego (92130) ***(P-8432)***
Very Special Chocolats Inc.......C.......626 334-7838
760 N Mckeever Ave Azusa (91702) ***(P-1478)***
Vescio Manufacturing Intl, Santa Fe Springs *Also called Vescio Threading Co* ***(P-17040)***
Vescio Threading Co.......D.......562 802-1868
14002 Anson Ave Santa Fe Springs (90670) ***(P-17040)***
Vest Inc.......D.......800 421-6370
6023 Alcoa Ave Vernon (90058) ***(P-11490)***
Vesta, Corona *Also called Extrumed Inc* ***(P-10096)***
Vesta Medical LLC.......F.......949 660-8648
3750 Torrey View Ct San Diego (92130) ***(P-22674)***
Vesta Solutions Inc (HQ).......B.......951 719-2100
42555 Rio Nedo Temecula (92590) ***(P-18006)***
Vesta Technology Inc.......F.......408 519-5800
3973 Soutirage Ln San Jose (95135) ***(P-19254)***
Vestara, San Diego *Also called Vesta Medical LLC* ***(P-22674)***
Vesture Group Incorporated.......E.......818 842-0200
3405 W Pacific Ave Burbank (91505) ***(P-3598)***
Veterans Employment Agency Inc.......F.......650 245-0599
3906 Ginko Way Sacramento (95834) ***(P-11286)***
Vetpowered LLC.......F.......619 269-7116
2970 Main St San Diego (92113) ***(P-25447)***
Vf Contemporary Brands Inc.......F.......213 747-7002
777 S Alameda St Bldg 1 Los Angeles (90021) ***(P-3090)***
Vf Engineering USA, Anaheim *Also called Zurich Engineering Inc* ***(P-20693)***
Vf Outdoor LLC (HQ).......C.......510 618-3500
2701 Harbor Bay Pkwy Alameda (94502) ***(P-3203)***
Vf Outdoor LLC.......E.......415 433-3223
180 Post St San Francisco (94108) ***(P-23684)***
Vfa 122 Power Plants, Lemoore *Also called United States Dept of Navy* ***(P-14034)***
Vfly Corporation.......F.......626 575-3115
4137 Peck Rd El Monte (91732) ***(P-3868)***
Vft Inc.......E.......323 728-2280
1040 S Vail Ave Montebello (90640) ***(P-3755)***
Vgw Us Inc.......F.......415 240-0498
442 Post St Fl 9 San Francisco (94102) ***(P-25330)***
Vi-Star Gear Co Inc.......E.......323 774-3750
7312 Jefferson St Paramount (90723) ***(P-13117)***
Vi-TEC Manufacturing Inc.......F.......925 447-8200
288 Boeing Ct Livermore (94551) ***(P-17041)***
Via Mechanics (usa) Inc (HQ).......F.......408 392-9650
150 Charcot Ave Ste C San Jose (95131) ***(P-15882)***
Via Telecom Inc.......C.......858 350-5560
3390 Carmel Mountain Rd # 100 San Diego (92121) ***(P-19255)***
Viade Products Inc.......E.......805 484-2114
354 Dawson Dr Camarillo (93012) ***(P-22922)***
Viader Vineyard & Winery, Deer Park *Also called Viader Vineyards* ***(P-2038)***
Viader Vineyards.......F.......707 963-3816
1120 Deer Park Rd Deer Park (94576) ***(P-2038)***
Vianh Company Inc.......E.......714 590-9808
13841 A Better Way 10c Garden Grove (92843) ***(P-17042)***
Viant Medical LLC.......F.......510 657-5800
45581 Northport Loop W Fremont (94538) ***(P-10430)***
Viasat Inc.......D.......619 438-6000
1935 Cordell Ct El Cajon (92020) ***(P-21454)***

Mergent e-mail: customerrelations@mergent.com
1322
2019 California
Manufacturers Register
(P-0000) Products & Services Section entry number
(PA)=Parent Co (HQ)=Headquarters (DH)=Div Headquarters

Viasat Inc (PA)...B...760 476-2200
6155 El Camino Real Carlsbad (92009) ***(P-18296)***
Viasys Respiratory Care Inc...C...714 283-2228
22745 Savi Ranch Pkwy Yorba Linda (92887) ***(P-22675)***
Viatech Pubg Solutions Inc...D...323 721-3629
5668 E 61st St Commerce (90040) ***(P-7591)***
Viavi Solutions Inc...C...408 577-1478
80 Rose Orchard Way San Jose (95134) ***(P-19256)***
Viavi Solutions Inc (PA)...B...408 404-3600
6001 America Center Dr # 6 San Jose (95002) ***(P-19257)***
Viavi Solutions Inc...C...707 545-6440
2789 Northpoint Pkwy Santa Rosa (95407) ***(P-20098)***
Viavi Solutions Inc...D...805 465-1875
3601 Calle Tecate Camarillo (93012) ***(P-18007)***
Viavi Solutions Inc...C...408 546-5000
430 N Mccarthy Blvd Milpitas (95035) ***(P-19258)***
Viavi Solutions Inc...C...408 546-5000
1750 Automation Pkwy San Jose (95131) ***(P-20099)***
Vibes Audio LLC...F...949 769-6806
15635 Alton Pkwy Ste 475 Irvine (92618) ***(P-17877)***
Vibra Finish Co (PA)...E...805 578-0033
2220 Shasta Way Simi Valley (93065) ***(P-11307)***
Vibrahone, Simi Valley *Also called Vibra Finish Co* ***(P-11307)***
Vibrant Care Pharmacy Inc...F...510 638-9851
7400 Macarthur Blvd Ste B Oakland (94605) ***(P-8433)***
Vibration Impact & Pres...F...949 429-3558
32242 Paseo Adelanto C San Juan Capistrano (92675) ***(P-15045)***
Vibrex, Valencia *Also called MWsausse & Co Inc* ***(P-17289)***
Vibrynt Inc...E...650 362-6100
2570 W El Camino Real # 310 Mountain View (94040) ***(P-23066)***
Vic Company, Santa Fe Springs *Also called Victor Wieteski* ***(P-19783)***
Vical Incorporated (PA)...D...858 646-1100
10390 Pacific Center Ct San Diego (92121) ***(P-8586)***
Vicki Marsha Uniforms, Huntington Beach *Also called Marsha Vicki Originals Inc* ***(P-3034)***
Vicolo Pizza, Hayward *Also called Vicolo Wholesale* ***(P-1051)***
Vicolo Wholesale (PA)...E...510 475-6019
31112 San Clemente St Hayward (94544) ***(P-1051)***
Vicom Systems Inc...E...408 588-1286
2336 Walsh Ave Ste H Santa Clara (95051) ***(P-15622)***
Victoire LLC...F...323 225-0101
955 S Meridian Ave Alhambra (91803) ***(P-3605)***
Victor Martin Inc...C...323 587-3101
1640 W 132nd St Gardena (90249) ***(P-4847)***
Victor Packing Inc...E...559 673-5908
11687 Road 27 1/2 Madera (93637) ***(P-905)***
Victor Wieteski...F...562 946-9715
9427 Santa Fe Springs Rd Santa Fe Springs (90670) ***(P-19783)***
Victor Wire & Cable, Los Angeles *Also called Dacon Systems Inc* ***(P-11658)***
Victor Wire and Cable LLC...F...310 842-9933
12915 S Spring St Los Angeles (90061) ***(P-11681)***
Victoria Skimboards...E...949 494-0059
2955 Laguna Canyon Rd # 1 Laguna Beach (92651) ***(P-23685)***
Victorian Shutters Inc (PA)...F...707 678-1776
305 Industrial Way Frnt Dixon (95620) ***(P-4252)***
Victory Custom Athletics...D...818 349-8476
2001 Anchor Ct Ste A Newbury Park (91320) ***(P-3524)***
Victory Koredrry, Huntington Beach *Also called Victory Professional Products* ***(P-3525)***
Victory Oil Company...E...310 519-9500
461 W 6th St Ste 300 San Pedro (90731) ***(P-86)***
Victory Professional Products...E...714 887-0621
5601 Engineer Dr Huntington Beach (92649) ***(P-3525)***
Victory Studio...F...818 972-0737
1840 Victory Blvd Glendale (91201) ***(P-23209)***
Vida Corporation...E...626 839-4912
17807 Maclaren St Ste A City of Industry (91744) ***(P-19888)***
Vida Newspaper, Oxnard *Also called Periodico El Vida* ***(P-6013)***
VIDA NUEVA, Los Angeles *Also called Tidings* ***(P-6070)***
Video Reporter Inc...E...800 266-9104
21107 Vanowen St Canoga Park (91303) ***(P-6617)***
Video Simplex Inc...F...858 467-9762
5160 Mercury Pt Ste C San Diego (92111) ***(P-20100)***
Videoamp Inc (PA)...F...949 294-0351
560 Mission St Ste 1379 San Francisco (94105) ***(P-25331)***
Videomaker Inc...E...530 891-8410
645 Mangrove Ave Chico (95926) ***(P-6284)***
Videssence LLC (PA)...E...626 579-0943
10768 Lower Azusa Rd El Monte (91731) ***(P-17567)***
Videssence LLC...E...626 579-0943
10768 Lower Azusa Rd El Monte (91731) ***(P-17745)***
Vie Products Inc...E...310 684-3566
9663 Santa Monica Blvd Beverly Hills (90210) ***(P-8863)***
Vie-Del Company (PA)...D...559 834-2525
11903 S Chestnut Ave Fresno (93725) ***(P-868)***
Vie-Del Company...E...559 896-3065
13363 S Indianola Ave Kingsburg (93631) ***(P-2039)***
Vien Dong Daily News, Westminster *Also called Vietnmese Amrcn Mdia Corp Vamc* ***(P-6080)***
Vierra Bros Dairy, Oakdale *Also called Vierra Bros Farms LLC* ***(P-14116)***
Vierra Bros Farms LLC...F...209 247-3468
6960 Crane Rd Oakdale (95361) ***(P-14116)***
Viet Hung Paris Inc...F...562 944-4919
1975 Chota Rd La Habra Heights (90631) ***(P-534)***
Viet Nam Daily Newspaper, San Jose *Also called Pacific Press Corporation* ***(P-6009)***
Vietnmese Amrcn Mdia Corp Vamc...F...714 379-2851
14891 Moran St Westminster (92683) ***(P-6080)***
View Inc (PA)...D...408 263-9200
195 S Milpitas Blvd Milpitas (95035) ***(P-10740)***
View Rite Manufacturing...E...415 468-3856
455 Allan St Daly City (94014) ***(P-5116)***
Vigilant Ballistics Inc...F...213 212-3232
1055 W 7th St Ph 33 Los Angeles (90017) ***(P-10868)***
Vigilant Marine Systems LLC...F...909 597-9508
2045 S Baker Ave Ontario (91761) ***(P-20480)***
Vigilent Corporation (PA)...E...888 305-4451
1111 Broadway Fl 3 Oakland (94607) ***(P-21537)***
Vigitron Inc...F...858 484-5209
7810 Trade St 100 San Diego (92121) ***(P-20101)***
Vignette Winery LLC...F...707 637-8821
45 Enterprise Ct Ste 3 NAPA (94558) ***(P-2040)***
Vigor Systems Inc...E...866 748-4467
4660 La Jolla Village Dr # 500 San Diego (92122) ***(P-18297)***
Viking Access Systems LLC...E...949 753-1280
631 Wald Irvine (92618) ***(P-20102)***
Viking Fabrication, Riverside *Also called Tolco Incorporated* ***(P-12965)***
Viking Products, Orange *Also called Pro Detention Inc* ***(P-11452)***
Viking Products Inc...E...949 379-5100
20 Doppler Irvine (92618) ***(P-14693)***
Viking Ready Mix Co Inc...E...818 243-4243
4549 Brazil St Los Angeles (90039) ***(P-11202)***
Viking Ready Mix Co Inc...E...323 564-1866
4988 Firestone Blvd South Gate (90280) ***(P-11203)***
Viking Ready Mix Co Inc...E...559 225-3667
1641 Tollhouse Clovis (93611) ***(P-11204)***
Viking Ready Mix Co Inc...F...559 344-7931
12100 11th Ave Hanford (93230) ***(P-11205)***
Viking Ready Mix Co Inc...E...562 865-6211
11725 Artesia Blvd Artesia (90701) ***(P-11206)***
Viking Ready Mix Co Inc...E...818 786-2210
15203 Oxnard St Van Nuys (91411) ***(P-11207)***
Viking Ready Mix Co Inc...E...818 768-0050
9010 Norris Ave Sun Valley (91352) ***(P-11208)***
Viking Ready Mix Co Inc...E...626 303-7755
2620 Buena Vista St Duarte (91010) ***(P-11209)***
Viking Ready Mix Co Inc...E...818 884-0893
6969 Deering Ave Canoga Park (91303) ***(P-11210)***
Viking Rubber Products Inc...D...310 868-5200
2600 Homestead Pl Compton (90220) ***(P-9690)***
Viking Therapeutics Inc...F...858 704-4660
12340 El Camino Real # 250 San Diego (92130) ***(P-8434)***
Viko Test Labs, Santa Clara *Also called Integra Technologies LLC* ***(P-18905)***
Villa Amorosa...D...707 942-8200
4045 Saint Helena Hwy Calistoga (94515) ***(P-2041)***
Villa Dolce Gelato, Van Nuys *Also called Dolce Dolci LLC* ***(P-666)***
Villa Encinal Partners LP...F...707 945-1220
620 Oakville Cross Rd NAPA (94558) ***(P-2042)***
Villa Firenze, Studio City *Also called F R Industries Inc* ***(P-2997)***
Villa Furniture Mfg Co...C...714 535-7272
13760 Midway St Cerritos (90703) ***(P-5031)***
Villa International, Cerritos *Also called Villa Furniture Mfg Co* ***(P-5031)***
Villa Pallet LLC...F...510 794-6676
6756 Central Ave Hayward (94544) ***(P-4511)***
Villa Toscano Winery...E...209 245-3800
10600 Shenandoah Rd Plymouth (95669) ***(P-2043)***
Village Center Ultramar, Palmdale *Also called Ultramar Inc* ***(P-9370)***
Village Collection Inc...F...650 594-1635
1303 Elmer St A Belmont (94002) ***(P-4366)***
Village Instant Printing Inc...E...209 576-2568
1515 10th St Modesto (95354) ***(P-7169)***
Village Voice Media...D...510 879-3700
318 Harrison St Ste 302 Oakland (94607) ***(P-6081)***
Villanueva Plastic Company Inc...F...909 581-3870
372 W Tullock St Rialto (92376) ***(P-9771)***
Villlage News Inc...E...760 451-3488
41740 Enterprise Cir S Temecula (92590) ***(P-6082)***
Vim Tools, La Verne *Also called Durston Manufacturing Company* ***(P-11892)***
Vimco, Santa Rosa *Also called Randal Optimal Nutrients LLC* ***(P-8356)***
Vin-Max, San Leandro *Also called MArs Engineering Company Inc* ***(P-13031)***
Vinaco Engineering Company, Chatsworth *Also called Le Hung Tuan* ***(P-16683)***
Vinatronic Inc...E...714 845-3480
15571 Industry Ln Huntington Beach (92649) ***(P-18647)***
Vincent Electic Motor Company, Oakland *Also called Vincent Electric Company* ***(P-25471)***
Vincent Electric Company (PA)...E...510 639-4500
8383 Baldwin St Oakland (94621) ***(P-25471)***
Vindicia Inc...C...650 264-4700
2988 Campus Dr Ste 300 San Mateo (94403) ***(P-25332)***
Vineburg Wine Company Inc (PA)...E...707 938-5277
2000 Denmark St Sonoma (95476) ***(P-2044)***
Vineyard 29 LLC...F...707 963-9292
2929 Saint Helena Hwy N Saint Helena (94574) ***(P-2045)***
Vineyard 7 & 8, Saint Helena *Also called 7 & 8 LLC* ***(P-1637)***
Vineyard Post Acute, Petaluma *Also called Petalumaidence Opco LLC* ***(P-1924)***
Vineyards of Monterey, Santa Rosa *Also called Jackson Family Wines Inc* ***(P-1824)***
Vinotemp International Corp (PA)...D...310 886-3332
16782 Von Karman Ave # 15 Irvine (92606) ***(P-4923)***
Vinotheque Wine Cellars...F...209 466-9463
1738 E Alpine Ave Stockton (95205) ***(P-15999)***
Vintage 99 Label Mfg Inc...E...925 294-5270
611 Enterprise Ct Livermore (94550) ***(P-5582)***
Vintage Aero Engines...F...661 822-4107
1582 Goodrick Dr Ste 8a Tehachapi (93561) ***(P-21067)***
Vintage Image, South San Francisco *Also called Wine Appreciation Guild Ltd* ***(P-6410)***
Vintage Point LLC...E...707 939-6766
564 Broadway Sonoma (95476) ***(P-2046)***
Vintage Production California, Bakersfield *Also called California Resources Prod Corp* ***(P-45)***
Vintage Transport Inc...F...530 622-3046
161 Fair Ln Placerville (95667) ***(P-20520)***

ALPHABETIC

Employee Codes: A=Over 500 employees, B=251-500
C=101-250, D=51-100, E=20-50, F=10-19
2019 California
Manfacturers Register
© Mergent Inc. 1-800-342-5647
1323

Vintage Wine Estates Inc....F....707 942-4981
1060 Dunaweal Ln Calistoga (94515) *(P-2047)*
Vintage Wine Estates Inc....E....707 933-9675
15000 Hwy 12 Glen Ellen (95442) *(P-2048)*
Vintique Inc....E....714 634-1932
1828 W Sequoia Ave Orange (92868) *(P-20481)*
Vinyl Fabrications Inc....F....530 532-1236
2690 5th Ave Oroville (95965) *(P-3818)*
Vinyl Specialties, Fresno *Also called Millerton Builders Inc (P-5204)*
Vinyl Technology Inc....C....626 443-5257
200 Railroad Ave Monrovia (91016) *(P-5546)*
Vinylvisions Company LLC....E....800 321-8746
1233 Enterprise Ct Corona (92882) *(P-8953)*
Violin Mmory Fdral Systems Inc....F....650 396-1500
4555 Great America Pkwy Santa Clara (95054) *(P-19259)*
Violin Systems LLC....C....650 396-1501
2560 N 1st St Ste 300 San Jose (95131) *(P-15623)*
Vionic Group LLC....D....415 526-6932
4040 Civic Center Dr # 430 San Rafael (94903) *(P-10492)*
Vioski Inc....F....626 359-4571
1625 S Magnolia Ave Monrovia (91016) *(P-4818)*
VIP Manufacturing & Engrg Corp....F....408 727-6545
1084 Martin Ave Santa Clara (95050) *(P-20690)*
VIP Mfg & Engr, Santa Clara *Also called VIP Manufacturing & Engrg Corp (P-20690)*
VIP Rubber Company Inc (PA)....C....714 774-7635
540 S Cypress St La Habra (90631) *(P-9691)*
VIP Sensors, San Juan Capistrano *Also called Vibration Impact & Pres (P-15045)*
Vipology Inc....F....626 502-8661
1278 Center Court Dr Covina (91724) *(P-6618)*
Virage Logic Corporation (HQ)....B....650 584-5000
700 E Middlefield Rd Mountain View (94043) *(P-19260)*
Virco Mfg Corporation (PA)....B....310 533-0474
2027 Harpers Way Torrance (90501) *(P-5032)*
Virgil M Stutzman Inc....E....323 732-9146
5045 Exposition Blvd Los Angeles (90016) *(P-13532)*
Virgil Walker Inc....F....661 797-4101
24856 Avenue Rockefeller Valencia (91355) *(P-12274)*
Virgil Walker Inc....E....661 294-9142
29102 Hancock Pkwy Valencia (91355) *(P-19305)*
Virgin Orbit LLC....B....562 384-4400
4022 E Conant St Long Beach (90808) *(P-13697)*
Virginia Park LLC....F....816 592-0776
2225 Via Cerro Ste A Riverside (92509) *(P-2698)*
Virginia Park Foods, Riverside *Also called Virginia Park LLC (P-2698)*
Virsec Systems Inc....F....978 274-7260
226 Airport Pkwy Ste 350 San Jose (95110) *(P-25333)*
Virtual Composites Co Inc....F....714 256-8850
584 Explorer St Brea (92821) *(P-7900)*
Virtus Nutrition LLC....F....559 992-5033
520 Industrial Ave Corcoran (93212) *(P-1169)*
Vis Tech, Modesto *Also called Vistech Mfg Solutions LLC (P-15233)*
Visage Ladies Fashions, Los Angeles *Also called D & R Brothers Inc (P-3229)*
Visage Software Inc....F....949 614-0759
5151 California Ave # 230 Irvine (92617) *(P-25334)*
Visalia Cams, Visalia *Also called Visalia Ctr 4 Ambltry Med & Sv (P-22841)*
Visalia Ctr 4 Ambltry Med & Sv....E....559 740-4094
842 S Akers St Visalia (93277) *(P-22841)*
Visalia Electric Motor Service, Visalia *Also called Visalia Electric Motor Sp Inc (P-25472)*
Visalia Electric Motor Sp Inc....F....559 651-0606
7515 W Sunnyview Ave Visalia (93291) *(P-25472)*
Viscon California LLC....F....661 327-7061
3121 Standard St Bakersfield (93308) *(P-9050)*
Visger Precision Inc....F....408 988-0184
1815 Russell Ave Santa Clara (95054) *(P-17043)*
Vishay Intertechnology Inc....F....626 331-0502
677 Arrow Grand Cir Covina (91722) *(P-19310)*
Vishay Siliconix LLC....A....408 988-8000
2585 Junction Ave San Jose (95134) *(P-9051)*
Vishay Spectoral Electronics, Ontario *Also called Vishay Thin Film LLC (P-19261)*
Vishay Spectrol, Ontario *Also called Vishay Thin Film LLC (P-19311)*
Vishay Techno Components LLC....D....909 923-3313
4051 Greystone Dr Ontario (91761) *(P-17320)*
Vishay Techno Components Corp, Ontario *Also called Vishay Techno Components LLC (P-17320)*
Vishay Thin Film LLC....D....909 923-3313
4051 Greystone Dr Ontario (91761) *(P-19261)*
Vishay Thin Film LLC....E....909 923-3313
4051 Greystone Dr Ontario (91761) *(P-19311)*
Vishay Transducers Ltd....E....626 363-7500
2930 Inland Empire Blvd # 100 Ontario (91764) *(P-19262)*
Visibility Solutions Inc....F....714 434-7040
320 E Dyer Rd Santa Ana (92707) *(P-5261)*
Visible Graphics Inc....F....818 787-0477
9736 Eton Ave Chatsworth (91311) *(P-23998)*
Visier Inc (PA)....F....888 277-9331
550 S Winchester Blvd San Jose (95128) *(P-25335)*
Vision Aquatics Inc....F....818 749-2178
4542 Skidmore Ct Moorpark (93021) *(P-23686)*
Vision Design Studio, Long Beach *Also called Vision Publications Inc (P-6619)*
Vision Engrg Met Stamping Inc....D....661 575-0933
114 Grand Cypress Ave Palmdale (93551) *(P-17655)*
Vision Envelope & Prtg Co Inc (PA)....E....310 324-7062
13707 S Figueroa St Los Angeles (90061) *(P-5680)*
Vision Imaging Supplies Inc....E....818 710-7200
7920 Deering Ave Canoga Park (91304) *(P-23741)*
Vision Plastics Mfg Inc....F....855 476-2767
9888 Waples St Ste B San Diego (92121) *(P-23476)*
Vision Press, San Ramon *Also called TAS Group Inc (P-7634)*
Vision Publications Inc....E....562 597-4000
1342 Coronado Ave Long Beach (90804) *(P-6619)*
Vision Quest Industries Inc (PA)....D....949 261-6382
18011 Mitchell S Ste A Irvine (92614) *(P-22842)*
Vision Quest Industries Inc....D....760 734-1550
1390 Decision St Ste A Vista (92081) *(P-22843)*
Vision Smart Center Inc....F....213 625-1740
123 Astronaut E S Onizuka Los Angeles (90012) *(P-7980)*
Vision Systems Inc....D....619 258-7300
11322 Woodside Ave N Santee (92071) *(P-11611)*
Visionaire Lighting LLC....A....310 512-6480
19645 S Rancho Way Compton (90220) *(P-17656)*
Visionary Electronics Inc....D....415 751-8811
141 Parker Ave San Francisco (94118) *(P-19263)*
Visionary Inc....E....714 237-1900
2940 E Miraloma Ave Anaheim (92806) *(P-23130)*
Visionary Sleep LLC....D....909 605-2010
2060 S Wineville Ave A Ontario (91761) *(P-4892)*
Visionary Solutions Inc....F....805 845-8900
2060 Alameda Padre Serra Santa Barbara (93103) *(P-20103)*
Visioneer Inc (HQ)....E....925 251-6300
5673 Gibraltar Dr Ste 150 Pleasanton (94588) *(P-15883)*
Visioneered Image Systems Inc....F....818 613-7600
444 W Ocean Blvd Ste 1400 Long Beach (90802) *(P-23999)*
Visionmax Inc....F....626 839-1602
17232 Railroad St City of Industry (91748) *(P-3526)*
Visoy Food Products & Mfg Inc....F....323 221-4079
111 W Elmyra St Los Angeles (90012) *(P-1513)*
Vista Coatings Inc....E....310 635-7697
1440 6th St Manhattan Beach (90266) *(P-13679)*
Vista Landscape Lighting, Simi Valley *Also called S T E U Inc (P-17730)*
Vista Metals Corp (PA)....C....909 823-4278
13425 Whittram Ave Fontana (92335) *(P-11612)*
Vista Outdoor Inc....E....831 461-7500
5550 Scotts Valley Dr Scotts Valley (95066) *(P-23687)*
Vista Powder Coatings, Manhattan Beach *Also called Vista Coatings Inc (P-13679)*
Vista Steel Co Inc (PA)....E....805 964-4732
6100 Francis Botello Rd C Goleta (93117) *(P-13003)*
Vistagen Therapeutics Inc....F....650 577-3600
343 Allerton Ave South San Francisco (94080) *(P-8435)*
Vistan Corporation....F....510 351-0560
855 Montague St San Leandro (94577) *(P-14896)*
Vistanomics Inc....F....818 249-1236
3450 Ocean View Blvd Frnt Glendale (91208) *(P-6285)*
Vistech Mfg Solutions LLC (PA)....E....209 544-9333
1156 Scenic Dr Ste 120 Modesto (95350) *(P-15233)*
Visualon Inc....C....408 645-6618
2590 N 1st St Ste 100 San Jose (95131) *(P-25336)*
Vit Best, Tustin *Also called Vitabest Nutrition Inc (P-8436)*
VIT Products Inc....E....760 480-6702
2063 Wineridge Pl Escondido (92029) *(P-12007)*
Vita Science Health Products, Long Beach *Also called Get (P-16045)*
Vita-Pakt Citrus Products Co (PA)....E....626 332-1101
203 E Badillo St Covina (91723) *(P-869)*
Vitabest Nutrition Inc....B....714 832-9700
2802 Dow Ave Tustin (92780) *(P-8436)*
Vitachrome Graphics Inc (PA)....E....818 957-0900
3710 Park Pl Montrose (91020) *(P-7534)*
Vitacig Inc....D....310 402-6937
433 N Camden Dr Fl 6 Beverly Hills (90210) *(P-2711)*
Vitafoods America LLC....F....800 695-4750
680 E Colo Blvd Ste 180 Pasadena (91101) *(P-739)*
Vitajoy USA Inc....F....626 965-8830
14165 Ramona Ave Chino (91710) *(P-7981)*
Vital Connect Inc....E....408 963-4600
224 Airport Pkwy Ste 300 San Jose (95110) *(P-23067)*
Vital Therapies Inc....F....858 673-6840
15222 Avenue Of Science B San Diego (92128) *(P-8437)*
Vital Therapies Inc....D....858 673-6840
15010 Avenue Of Science San Diego (92128) *(P-8438)*
Vital Vittles Bakery Inc....F....510 644-2022
2810 San Pablo Ave Berkeley (94702) *(P-1338)*
Vitale Home Designs Inc....F....818 888-2481
24425 Woolsey Canyon Rd # 46 Canoga Park (91304) *(P-23226)*
Vitalhue....F....323 646-8775
2036 Nevada City Hwy # 188 Grass Valley (95945) *(P-24282)*
Vitality Furniture Group Inc....F....323 937-4900
5042 Wilshire Blvd # 265 Los Angeles (90036) *(P-5262)*
Vitamer Laboratories, Irvine *Also called Anabolic Incorporated (P-8030)*
Vitamin Friends Llc....E....310 502-2277
5300 Beethoven St Los Angeles (90066) *(P-652)*
Vitamins Unlimited, Brea *Also called North West Pharmanaturals, Inc (P-7959)*
Vitavet Labs Inc....E....818 865-2600
5717 Corsa Ave Westlake Village (91362) *(P-24283)*
Vitek Indus Video Pdts Inc....E....661 294-8043
28492 Constellation Rd Valencia (91355) *(P-23210)*
Vitesse Manufacturing & Dev....C....805 388-3700
4721 Calle Carga Camarillo (93012) *(P-19264)*
Vitesse Semiconductor, Camarillo *Also called Vitesse Manufacturing & Dev (P-19264)*
Vitrek LLC....F....858 689-2755
12169 Kirkham Rd Ste C Poway (92064) *(P-21885)*
Vitrico Corp....F....510 652-6731
2181 Williams St San Leandro (94577) *(P-10669)*
Vitro Flat Glass LLC....C....559 485-4660
3333 S Peach Ave Fresno (93725) *(P-10611)*
Vitro Flat Glass LLC....C....559 485-4660
3333 S Peach Ave Fresno (93725) *(P-10612)*
Vitron Electronic Services Inc....D....408 251-1600
5400 Hellyer Ave San Jose (95138) *(P-18648)*
Vitron Electronics Mfg & Svcs, San Jose *Also called Vitron Electronic Services Inc (P-18648)*

Mergent e-mail: customerrelations@mergent.com
1324
2019 California
Manufacturers Register
(P-0000) Products & Services Section entry number
(PA)=Parent Co (HQ)=Headquarters (DH)=Div Headquarters

Viv Labs Inc....F....650 268-9837
60 S Market St Ste 900 San Jose (95113) *(P-25337)*
Viva Concepts, Glendale *Also called Viva Holdings LLC (P-5690)*
Viva Holdings LLC (PA)....F....818 243-1363
1025 N Brand Blvd Ste 300 Glendale (91202) *(P-5690)*
Viva Photo Albums Company, Milpitas *Also called Song Beoung (P-7585)*
Viva Print LLC (HQ)....F....818 243-1363
1025 N Brand Blvd Ste 300 Glendale (91202) *(P-5691)*
Vivax-Metrotech, Santa Clara *Also called Metrotech Corporation (P-21347)*
Viver Co Inc....F....310 327-4578
1934 W 144th St Gardena (90249) *(P-12810)*
Viver Sheet Metal, Gardena *Also called Viver Co Inc (P-12810)*
Vivid Inc....D....408 982-9101
1250 Memorex Dr Santa Clara (95050) *(P-12811)*
Viviglo Technologies Inc....E....949 933-9738
620 Lunar Ave Ste B Brea (92821) *(P-24284)*
Vivometrics Inc....E....805 667-2225
16030 Ventura Blvd # 470 Encino (91436) *(P-23068)*
Vivus Inc (PA)....E....650 934-5200
900 E Hamilton Ave # 550 Campbell (95008) *(P-8439)*
Viz Cattle Corporation....E....310 884-5260
17890 Castleton St # 350 City of Industry (91748) *(P-456)*
Viz Media LLC....C....415 546-7073
1355 Market St Ste 200 San Francisco (94103) *(P-6286)*
Viz Media Music, San Francisco *Also called Viz Media LLC (P-6286)*
Vizio Inc (PA)....C....949 428-2525
39 Tesla Irvine (92618) *(P-17878)*
Vline Industries, Simi Valley *Also called Computer Metal Products Corp (P-12536)*
Vlsi Standards Inc....E....408 428-1800
5 Technology Dr Milpitas (95035) *(P-21886)*
Vm Custom Boat Trailers....E....559 486-0410
5200 S Peach Ave Fresno (93725) *(P-21245)*
Vm Discovery Inc....F....510 818-1018
45535 Northport Loop E Fremont (94538) *(P-8440)*
Vm International, Riverside *Also called S R S M Inc (P-7882)*
Vm Provider Inc (PA)....F....800 674-3233
1135 1/2 N Berendo St Los Angeles (90029) *(P-2819)*
Vmanoo Inc....F....626 662-1342
480 Rosemarie Dr Arcadia (91007) *(P-20104)*
Vmc Holdings Group Corp....E....818 993-1466
9667 Owensmouth Ave # 202 Chatsworth (91311) *(P-15503)*
Vmc International LLC....F....760 723-1498
140 N Brandon Rd Ste C Fallbrook (92028) *(P-22923)*
VME Acquisition Corp (PA)....E....805 384-2748
820 Flynn Rd Camarillo (93012) *(P-22844)*
Vmg Engineering Inc....F....818 837-6320
1046 Griswold Ave San Fernando (91340) *(P-17044)*
Vml Winery, Healdsburg *Also called HDD LLC (P-1809)*
Vnomic Inc....F....408 890-2220
1250 Oakmead Pkwy Sunnyvale (94085) *(P-25338)*
Vnu Business, San Juan Capistrano *Also called Emerald Expositions LLC (P-6157)*
Vnus Medical Technologies Inc....C....408 360-7200
5799 Fontanoso Way San Jose (95138) *(P-22676)*
Vocera Communications Inc (PA)....C....408 882-5100
525 Race St Ste 150 San Jose (95126) *(P-18377)*
Vode Lighting LLC....F....707 996-9898
21684 8th St E Ste 700 Sonoma (95476) *(P-17568)*
Voelker Sensors Inc....F....650 361-0570
3790 El Camino Real Palo Alto (94306) *(P-3928)*
Vogt Western Silver Ltd....F....530 669-6840
1210 Commerce Ave Ste 1 Woodland (95776) *(P-23330)*
Vogue Sign Inc....F....805 487-7222
715 Commercial Ave Oxnard (93030) *(P-24000)*
Voice Assist Inc....F....949 655-1611
15 Enterprise Ste 350 Aliso Viejo (92656) *(P-19784)*
Voiceboard Corporation....F....805 389-3100
473 Post St Camarillo (93010) *(P-15504)*
Volant Cool Air Intakes Inc....F....909 476-7225
10285 Indiana Ct Rancho Cucamonga (91730) *(P-10431)*
Volcano Corporation (HQ)....B....800 228-4728
3721 Vly Cntre Dr Ste 500 San Diego (92130) *(P-23069)*
Volcano Corporation....B....916 281-2932
2451 Merc Dr Ste 200 Rancho Cordova (95742) *(P-23070)*
Volcano Corporation....B....650 938-5300
1931 Old Middlefield Way Mountain View (94043) *(P-23071)*
Volcano Corporation....B....916 638-8008
2870 Kilgore Rd Rancho Cordova (95670) *(P-23072)*
Volcano Therapeutics, Rancho Cordova *Also called Volcano Corporation (P-23070)*
Volex Inc (HQ)....E....669 444-1740
3110 Coronado Dr Santa Clara (95054) *(P-10432)*
Volex Inc....E....619 205-4900
511 E San Ysidro Blvd San Ysidro (92173) *(P-10433)*
Volk Enterprises Inc....D....209 632-3826
618 S Kilroy Rd Turlock (95380) *(P-13861)*
Voltage Multipliers Inc (PA)....C....559 651-1402
8711 W Roosevelt Ave Visalia (93291) *(P-19265)*
Voltage Valet Division, Santa Rosa *Also called Hybrinetics Inc (P-17099)*
Volterra Semiconductor Corp, San Jose *Also called Volterra Semiconductor LLC (P-19266)*
Volterra Semiconductor LLC (HQ)....E....408 601-1000
160 Rio Robles San Jose (95134) *(P-19266)*
Voluspa, Irvine *Also called Flame & Wax Inc (P-24095)*
Volvo Construction Eqp & Svcs....E....951 277-7620
22099 Knabe Rd Corona (92883) *(P-14198)*
Vomar Products Inc....E....818 610-5115
7800 Deering Ave Canoga Park (91304) *(P-7535)*
Vomela Specialty Company....E....562 944-3853
9810 Bell Ranch Dr Santa Fe Springs (90670) *(P-7170)*
Vomela Specialty Company....E....650 877-8000
1342 San Mateo Ave South San Francisco (94080) *(P-24001)*
Von Hoppen Ice Cream (HQ)....F....805 965-2009
1525 State St Ste 203 Santa Barbara (93101) *(P-703)*
Von Hoppen Ice Cream....F....858 695-9111
8221 Arjons Dr Ste A San Diego (92126) *(P-704)*
Vonnic Inc....E....626 964-2345
16610 Gale Ave City of Industry (91745) *(P-23211)*
Voorwood Company....E....530 365-3311
2350 Barney Rd Anderson (96007) *(P-14787)*
Vortech Engineering Inc....E....805 247-0226
1650 Pacific Ave Oxnard (93033) *(P-15185)*
Vortex Engineering LLC....F....619 258-9660
9425 Wheatlands Ct Santee (92071) *(P-12275)*
Vortex Enterprise, Santa Fe Springs *Also called Spadia Inc (P-17562)*
Vortex Whirlpool Systems Inc....D....951 940-4556
26035 Jefferson Ave Murrieta (92562) *(P-9913)*
Vortran Laser Technology Inc....F....916 283-8208
21 Golden Land Ct Ste 200 Sacramento (95834) *(P-20105)*
Vortran Medical Technology 1 (PA)....E....916 648-8460
21 Golden Land Ct Ste 100 Sacramento (95834) *(P-22677)*
Vossloh Signaling Usa Inc....E....530 272-8194
12799 Loma Rica Dr Grass Valley (95945) *(P-13118)*
Votaw Precision Tech Inc....F....562 944-0661
13153 Lakeland Rd Santa Fe Springs (90670) *(P-21455)*
Voteblast Inc....E....650 387-9147
8478 Hollywood Blvd Los Angeles (90069) *(P-6620)*
Voxara LLC....F....844 869-2721
5737 Kanan Rd Ste 700 Agoura Hills (91301) *(P-6621)*
Voyage Medical Inc....E....650 503-7500
610 Galveston Dr Redwood City (94063) *(P-22678)*
Voyager Learning Company....F....909 923-3120
2060 Lynx Pl Unit G Ontario (91761) *(P-6622)*
Voyant Aviation Broadband, Mountain View *Also called Voyant International Corp (P-25339)*
Voyant International Corp....F....800 710-6637
444 Castro St Ste 318 Mountain View (94041) *(P-25339)*
Vp Footwear Inc....F....626 443-2186
2536 Loma Ave South El Monte (91733) *(P-9497)*
Vpro Inc....F....818 905-5678
4638 Van Nuys Blvd Sherman Oaks (91403) *(P-24002)*
Vpt Direct, Santa Fe Springs *Also called Vantage Point Products Corp (P-17875)*
Vq Orthocare, Vista *Also called Vision Quest Industries Inc (P-22843)*
Vra Manufacturing, Cameron Park *Also called Vultures Row Aviation LLC (P-17045)*
Vs Vincenzo Ltd Inc....F....949 388-8791
34700 Pacific Coast Hwy Capistrano Beach (92624) *(P-8864)*
Vsc Incorporated (PA)....F....909 877-0975
2038 S Sycamore Ave Bloomington (92316) *(P-12276)*
Vsmpo Tirus US....E....909 230-9020
2850 E Cedar St Ontario (91761) *(P-11640)*
Vsmpo-Tirus US Inc....E....909 230-9020
2850 E Cedar St Ontario (91761) *(P-11641)*
Vsp Labs Inc (PA)....E....866 569-8800
3333 Quality Dr Rancho Cordova (95670) *(P-22145)*
Vsp Products Inc....D....209 862-1200
3324 Orestimba Rd Newman (95360) *(P-906)*
Vspone, Rancho Cordova *Also called Vsp Labs Inc (P-22145)*
VSR Network Technologies LLC....E....530 889-1500
11760 Atwood Rd Auburn (95603) *(P-18008)*
Vss Countertops Inc....E....916 681-8677
7640 Wilbur Way Sacramento (95828) *(P-5117)*
Vss Emultech Inc (HQ)....F....530 243-0111
7200 Pit Rd Redding (96001) *(P-9399)*
Vss Emultech Inc....F....916 371-8480
3785 Channel Dr West Sacramento (95691) *(P-9400)*
Vti Instruments Corporation (HQ)....E....949 955-1894
2031 Main St Irvine (92614) *(P-20106)*
Vti-Valtronics Inc....F....209 754-0707
3463 Double Springs Rd Valley Springs (95252) *(P-22296)*
Vtl Amplifiers Inc....E....909 627-5944
4774 Murietta St Ste 10 Chino (91710) *(P-17879)*
Vts Medical Systems, Santa Clara *Also called Steris Corporation (P-22820)*
Vts Sheetmetal Specialist Co....E....714 237-1420
1041 N Grove St Anaheim (92806) *(P-12812)*
Vue-Temp Inc (PA)....D....209 634-2914
618 S Kilroy Rd Turlock (95380) *(P-554)*
Vulcan Aggregates Company LLC....F....408 354-7904
18500 Limekiln Canyon Rd Los Gatos (95033) *(P-387)*
Vulcan Construction Mtls LLC....F....408 213-4270
346 Mathew St Santa Clara (95050) *(P-388)*
Vulcan Materials, Glendale *Also called Calmat Co (P-9379)*
Vulcan Materials Co....E....760 737-3486
849 W Washington Ave Escondido (92025) *(P-11211)*
Vulcan Materials Company....F....619 440-2363
3605 Dehesa Rd El Cajon (92019) *(P-319)*
Vulcan Materials Company....F....626 334-4913
16005 E Foothill Blvd Irwindale (91702) *(P-389)*
Vulcan Materials Company....F....818 241-7356
500 N Brand Blvd Ste 500 Glendale (91203) *(P-320)*
VULCAN STEEL COMPANY, Bloomington *Also called Vsc Incorporated (P-12276)*
Vulpine Inc....F....510 534-1186
1127 57th Ave Oakland (94621) *(P-9317)*
Vultures Row Aviation LLC....F....530 676-9245
3152 Cameron Park Dr Cameron Park (95682) *(P-17045)*
Vuze Inc....E....650 963-4750
489 S El Camino Real San Mateo (94402) *(P-15884)*
Vybion Inc....F....607 227-2502
584 Oak St Monterey (93940) *(P-7919)*
Vycom America Inc....E....800 235-9195
39252 Winchester Rd 107-3 Murrieta (92563) *(P-18649)*
Vycon Inc....D....562 282-5500
16323 Shoemaker Ave # 600 Cerritos (90703) *(P-19818)*

ALPHABETIC

W & J Dairy, Oakdale *Also called Willie Bylsma* ***(P-14898)***
W & M Textile, Vernon *Also called Jml Textile Inc* ***(P-2748)***
W & W Concept Inc.....D.....323 233-9202
4890 S Alameda St Vernon (90058) ***(P-3527)***
W A Call Manufacturing Co Inc.....F.....408 436-1450
1710 Rogers Ave San Jose (95112) ***(P-12813)***
W A Murphy Inc.....F.....760 245-8711
26550 National Trails Hwy Helendale (92342) ***(P-9186)***
W B Powell Inc.....E.....951 270-0095
630 Parkridge Ave Norco (92860) ***(P-4253)***
W C Q, Fremont *Also called West Coast Quartz Corporation* ***(P-10670)***
W D Schock Corp.....E.....951 277-3377
364 Malbert St Perris (92570) ***(P-21068)***
W E Hall Co.....F.....909 829-4235
13680 Slover Ave Fontana (92337) ***(P-12814)***
W E Plemons McHy Svcs Inc.....E.....559 646-6630
13479 E Industrial Dr Parlier (93648) ***(P-15234)***
W G Holt Inc.....D.....949 859-8800
23351 Madero Mission Viejo (92691) ***(P-19267)***
W J Ellison Co Inc.....E.....626 814-4766
200 River Rd Corona (92880) ***(P-15235)***
W J Keenan.....E.....916 783-5201
408 Sunrise Ave Roseville (95661) ***(P-21887)***
W L Gore & Associates Inc.....C.....928 864-2705
2890 De La Cruz Blvd Santa Clara (95050) ***(P-22679)***
W L Rubottom Co.....D.....805 648-6943
320 W Lewis St Ventura (93001) ***(P-4367)***
W Machine Works Inc.....E.....818 890-8049
13814 Del Sur St San Fernando (91340) ***(P-17046)***
W P Keith Co Inc.....E.....562 948-3636
8323 Loch Lomond Dr Pico Rivera (90660) ***(P-15277)***
W Plastics Inc.....E.....800 442-9727
2543 41573 Dendy Pkwy Temecula (92590) ***(P-9734)***
W R E Colortech, Berkeley *Also called Western Roto Engravers Inc* ***(P-7539)***
W R Grace & Co.....F.....562 927-8513
7237 E Gage Ave Commerce (90040) ***(P-7814)***
W R Grace & Co.....C.....209 839-2800
252 W Larch Rd Ste H Tracy (95304) ***(P-7815)***
W R Grace & Co - Conn.....E.....714 979-4682
2502 S Garnsey St Santa Ana (92707) ***(P-9891)***
W R Grace & Co - Conn.....F.....909 466-4610
9541 Bus Ctr Dr Ste B Rancho Cucamonga (91730) ***(P-9180)***
W R Grace & Co - Conn.....D.....760 244-6107
17434 Mojave St Hesperia (92345) ***(P-22048)***
W R Grace Construction Pdts, Commerce *Also called W R Grace & Co* ***(P-7814)***
W R Grace Construction Pdts, Santa Ana *Also called W R Grace & Co - Conn* ***(P-9891)***
W R Meadows Inc.....E.....909 469-2606
2300 Valley Blvd Pomona (91768) ***(P-11016)***
W S Dodge Oil Co Inc.....F.....323 583-3478
3710 Fruitland Ave Maywood (90270) ***(P-9454)***
W S West, Fresno *Also called Gea Farm Technologies Inc* ***(P-8642)***
W T E, Ontario *Also called Wallner Expac Inc* ***(P-14772)***
W Three Co.....E.....760 344-5841
1679 River Dr D Brawley (92227) ***(P-14117)***
W. R. Meadows Southern Cal, Pomona *Also called W R Meadows Inc* ***(P-11016)***
W/S Packaging Group Inc.....D.....714 992-2574
531 Airpark Dr Fullerton (92833) ***(P-5746)***
W2 Optronics Inc.....F.....510 220-2796
39523 Pardee Ct Fremont (94538) ***(P-19268)***
W5 Concepts Inc.....E.....323 231-2415
2049 E 38th St Vernon (90058) ***(P-3287)***
Waag, Van Nuys *Also called Wsw Corp* ***(P-20489)***
Wabash Technologies Inc.....F.....760 768-9343
1778 Carr Rd Calexico (92231) ***(P-17321)***
WAbenjamin Electric Co.....E.....213 749-7731
1615 Staunton Ave Los Angeles (90021) ***(P-17171)***
Wac Lighting, Ontario *Also called Wangs Alliance Corporation* ***(P-17569)***
Wacker Chemical Corporation.....E.....909 590-8822
13910 Oaks Ave Chino (91710) ***(P-9052)***
Wacker Development Inc.....F.....408 356-0208
36 Hollywood Ave Los Gatos (95030) ***(P-17047)***
Waco Products, Santa Ana *Also called Ackley Metal Products Inc* ***(P-16212)***
Wadco Industries Inc.....E.....909 874-7800
2625 S Willow Ave Bloomington (92316) ***(P-12277)***
Wadco Steel Sales, Bloomington *Also called Wadco Industries Inc* ***(P-12277)***
Waddington North America Inc.....C.....626 913-4022
1135 Samuelson St City of Industry (91748) ***(P-10434)***
Wade Metal Products.....F.....559 237-9233
1818 Los Angeles St Fresno (93721) ***(P-12278)***
Wafer Process Systems Inc.....F.....408 445-3010
3641 Charter Park Dr San Jose (95136) ***(P-15046)***
Wafer Reclaim Services LLC (PA).....C.....408 945-8112
2240 Ringwood Ave San Jose (95131) ***(P-19269)***
Wafernet Inc.....F.....408 437-9747
2142 Paragon Dr San Jose (95131) ***(P-19270)***
Waggl Inc (PA).....F.....415 399-9949
3 Harbor Dr Ste 200 Sausalito (94965) ***(P-25340)***
Wagner Die Supply (PA).....E.....909 947-3044
2041 Elm Ct Ontario (91761) ***(P-14590)***
Wagner Plate Works West Inc (PA).....E.....562 531-6050
14015 Garfield Ave Paramount (90723) ***(P-12439)***
Wagonmasters Corporation.....F.....909 823-6188
11060 Cherry Ave Fontana (92337) ***(P-21246)***
Wah Fung Noodles Inc.....F.....626 442-0588
4443 Rowland Ave El Monte (91731) ***(P-2444)***
Wah Hung Group Inc (PA).....E.....626 571-8700
1000 E Garvey Ave Monterey Park (91755) ***(P-20482)***
Wah Hung Group Inc.....E.....626 571-8700
283 E Garvey Ave Monterey Park (91755) ***(P-20483)***
Wahlco Inc.....C.....714 979-7300
15 Marconi Ste B Irvine (92618) ***(P-17048)***
Waiakea Inc.....F.....855 924-2532
5800 Hannum Ave Ste A135 Culver City (90230) ***(P-2233)***
Waiakea Investments LLC (PA).....F.....805 450-0981
736 Cima Linda Ln Santa Barbara (93108) ***(P-2234)***
Wain Industries.....F.....805 581-5900
1567 Shadowglen Ct Westlake Village (91361) ***(P-19785)***
Wako Life Sciences, Inc., Mountain View *Also called Fujifilm Wako Diagnostics US* ***(P-8476)***
Walashek Industrial & Mar Inc.....F.....206 624-2880
2826 Eighth St Berkeley (94710) ***(P-21016)***
Walashek Industrial & Mar Inc.....E.....619 498-1711
1428 Mckinley Ave National City (91950) ***(P-21017)***
Walco Machines Co.....E.....909 483-3333
9017 Arrow Rte Rancho Cucamonga (91730) ***(P-15047)***
Walden Structures Inc (PA).....D.....909 389-9100
1000 Bristol St N 126 Newport Beach (92660) ***(P-4585)***
Waleeds Food Inc.....F.....951 694-8800
42170 Sarah Way Temecula (92590) ***(P-779)***
Walker Bags, San Francisco *Also called Walker/Dunham Corp* ***(P-10541)***
Walker Corporation.....E.....909 390-4300
1555 S Vintage Ave Ontario (91761) ***(P-13862)***
Walker Creations.....F.....805 349-0755
907 Vista Del Rio Santa Maria (93458) ***(P-22845)***
Walker Design Inc.....E.....818 252-7788
9255 San Fernando Rd Sun Valley (91352) ***(P-21018)***
Walker Engineering Enterprises, Sun Valley *Also called Walker Design Inc* ***(P-21018)***
Walker Foods Inc.....D.....323 268-5191
237 N Mission Rd Los Angeles (90033) ***(P-2699)***
Walker Lithograph.....F.....530 527-2142
20869 Walnut St Red Bluff (96080) ***(P-7171)***
Walker Printing, Red Bluff *Also called Walker Lithograph* ***(P-7171)***
Walker Products (PA).....E.....714 554-5151
14291 Commerce Dr Garden Grove (92843) ***(P-20484)***
Walker Spring & Stamping Corp.....C.....909 390-4300
1555 S Vintage Ave Ontario (91761) ***(P-13294)***
Walker Street Pallets LLC.....F.....831 724-6088
801 Ohlone Pkwy Watsonville (95076) ***(P-4512)***
Walker/Dunham Corp.....F.....415 821-3070
445 Barneveld Ave San Francisco (94124) ***(P-10541)***
Wallaby Financial LLC.....E.....626 600-2604
680 E Colo Blvd Ste 350 Pasadena (91101) ***(P-25341)***
Wallaby Financial, Inc., Pasadena *Also called Wallaby Financial LLC* ***(P-25341)***
Wallace, Blue Lake *Also called Thomas Tellez* ***(P-4246)***
Wallace E Miller Inc.....F.....818 998-0444
9155 Alabama Ave Ste B Chatsworth (91311) ***(P-17049)***
Wallace Wood Products.....F.....951 654-9311
1247 S Buena Vista St C San Jacinto (92583) ***(P-5118)***
Wallboard Tool Co Inc.....C.....562 437-0701
1697 Seabright Ave Long Beach (90813) ***(P-11915)***
Wallner Expac Inc (PA).....D.....909 481-8800
1274 S Slater Cir Ontario (91761) ***(P-14772)***
Wally International Inc (PA).....C.....805 444-7764
20520 E Walnut Dr N Walnut (91789) ***(P-5364)***
Walmsley Design.....F.....310 836-0772
3825 Willat Ave Bldg A Culver City (90232) ***(P-4747)***
Walt Disney Imagineering.....C.....714 781-3152
1200 N Miller St Unit D Anaheim (92806) ***(P-3686)***
Waltco Lift Corp.....D.....323 321-4131
227 E Compton Blvd Gardena (90248) ***(P-14351)***
Walter N Coffman Inc.....D.....619 266-2642
5180 Naranja St San Diego (92114) ***(P-9892)***
Walters & Wolf Glass Company.....D.....510 226-9800
41450 Cowbell Rd Fremont (94538) ***(P-11017)***
Walters & Wolf Precast.....C.....510 226-9800
41450 Boscell Rd Fremont (94538) ***(P-11018)***
Walters Manufacturing Company.....F.....831 724-1377
135 Aviation Way Ste 1 Watsonville (95076) ***(P-16130)***
Walters Steamworks, Watsonville *Also called Walters Manufacturing Company* ***(P-16130)***
Walton Company Inc.....F.....714 847-8800
17900 Sampson Ln Huntington Beach (92647) ***(P-4663)***
Walton Industries Inc.....F.....559 233-6300
1220 E North Ave Fresno (93725) ***(P-8954)***
Walz Caps Inc.....E.....760 683-9259
2215 La Mirada Dr Vista (92081) ***(P-3625)***
Wan Ll Industrial Dev Inc.....F.....909 594-1818
141 Mercury Cir Pomona (91768) ***(P-19852)***
Wanada Investments LLC.....E.....818 292-8627
5 Corporate Park Ste 110 Irvine (92606) ***(P-25342)***
Wanda Matranga.....F.....760 773-4701
41651 Corporate Way Ste 5 Palm Desert (92260) ***(P-7172)***
Waneshear Technologies LLC.....E.....707 462-4761
3471 N State St Ukiah (95482) ***(P-14788)***
Wang Nmr Inc.....E.....925 443-0212
550 N Canyons Pkwy Livermore (94551) ***(P-22680)***
Wangs Alliance Corporation.....E.....909 230-9401
1750 S Archibald Ave Ontario (91761) ***(P-17569)***
Wanna B, Los Angeles *Also called Style Plus Inc* ***(P-3274)***
Warco, Orange *Also called West American Rubber Co LLC* ***(P-9692)***
Warco, Orange *Also called West American Rubber Co LLC* ***(P-9693)***
Ward Automatic Machine Pdts.....F.....661 822-7543
1265 Goodrick Dr Ste E Tehachapi (93561) ***(P-13050)***
Ward E Waldo & Son Inc.....F.....626 355-1218
273 E Highland Ave Sierra Madre (91024) ***(P-870)***
Ward E Waldo & Son Marmalades, Sierra Madre *Also called Ward E Waldo & Son Inc* ***(P-870)***
Ward Enterprises.....F.....661 251-4890
10332 Trumbull St California City (93505) ***(P-17050)***

Mergent e-mail: customerrelations@mergent.com 2019 California (P-0000) Products & Services Section entry number
1326 Manufacturers Register (PA)=Parent Co (HQ)=Headquarters (DH)=Div Headquarters

Wardley Industrial Inc....E....209 932-1088
907 Stokes Ave Stockton (95215) ***(P-9893)***
Wardrobe Specialties Ltd....F....209 523-2094
607 Glass Ln Modesto (95356) ***(P-10741)***
Warlock Industries....E....951 657-2680
23129 Cajalco Rd Ste A Perris (92570) ***(P-20182)***
Warmboard Inc....E....831 685-9276
8035 Soquel Dr Ste 41a Aptos (95003) ***(P-15278)***
Warmelin Precision Pdts LLC....D....323 777-5003
12705 Daphne Ave Hawthorne (90250) ***(P-17051)***
Warnaco Swimwear Inc (HQ)....E....213 481-4300
1201 W 5th St Ste 1200 Los Angeles (90017) ***(P-3204)***
Warnaco Swimwear Products, Los Angeles *Also called Warnaco Swimwear Inc* ***(P-3204)***
Warner Enterprises Inc....E....530 241-4000
1577 Beltline Rd Redding (96003) ***(P-4019)***
Warner Music Group Corp....F....818 846-9090
3300 Warner Blvd Burbank (91505) ***(P-17915)***
Warner Music Inc....D....818 953-2600
3400 W Riverside Dr # 900 Burbank (91505) ***(P-17916)***
Warner/Chappell Music Inc (HQ)....C....310 441-8600
10585 Santa Monica Blvd # 300 Los Angeles (90025) ***(P-6623)***
Warnock Food Products Inc....D....559 661-4845
20237 Masa St Madera (93638) ***(P-2406)***
Warren & Baerg Mfg Inc....E....559 591-6790
39950 Road 108 Dinuba (93618) ***(P-14118)***
Warren Printing & Mailing Inc....F....323 258-2621
5000 Eagle Rock Blvd Los Angeles (90041) ***(P-7173)***
Warrens Department Store Inc....E....888 577-2735
9800 De Soto Ave Chatsworth (91311) ***(P-3048)***
Wartsila Dynmc Positioning Inc (HQ)....E....858 679-5500
12131 Community Rd Ste A Poway (92064) ***(P-17322)***
Wasatch Co....F....310 637-6160
11000 Wright Rd Lynwood (90262) ***(P-3756)***
Wasatch Import, Lynwood *Also called Wasatch Co* ***(P-3756)***
Wasco Hardfacing Co....E....559 485-5860
4585 E Citron Fresno (93725) ***(P-14119)***
Wasco Hardfacing Co....D....559 485-5860
2660 S East Ave Fresno (93706) ***(P-14120)***
Wasco Manufacturing Co....E....559 485-5860
2660 S East Ave Fresno (93706) ***(P-14121)***
Wasco Sales & Marketing Inc....E....805 739-2747
2245 A St Santa Maria (93455) ***(P-17504)***
Wash System and Dry Wall Works, Sacramento *Also called Delta Lath & Plaster Inc* ***(P-14369)***
Washburn Grove Management Inc....E....909 322-4690
27781 Fairview Ave Hemet (92544) ***(P-4020)***
Washington Garment Dyeing (PA)....D....213 747-1111
1341 E Washington Blvd Los Angeles (90021) ***(P-2907)***
Washington Garment Dyeing....E....213 747-1111
1332 E 18th St Los Angeles (90021) ***(P-2899)***
Washington Orna Ir Works Inc....E....310 327-8660
17913 S Main St Gardena (90248) ***(P-12904)***
Washoe Equipment Inc....E....916 395-4700
6201 27th St Sacramento (95822) ***(P-17570)***
Wask Engineering Inc....F....530 672-2795
3905 Dividend Dr Cameron Park (95682) ***(P-21183)***
Wasser Filtration Inc (PA)....D....714 982-5600
1215 N Fee Ana St Anaheim (92807) ***(P-15373)***
Watch L.A., Los Angeles *Also called Pierre Mitri* ***(P-3481)***
Water Associates LLC....E....661 281-6077
34929 Flyover Ct Bakersfield (93308) ***(P-18298)***
Water Filter Exchange Inc....F....818 808-2541
980 Kirkton Pl Glendale (91207) ***(P-15374)***
Water One Industries Inc....F....707 747-4300
2913 Pattern St Unit D Brea (92821) ***(P-16131)***
Water One Industries Inc (PA)....E....707 747-4300
5410 Gateway Plaza Dr Benicia (94510) ***(P-16132)***
Water Planet Engineering LLC....F....424 331-7700
8915 S La Cienega Blvd C Inglewood (90301) ***(P-16133)***
Water Resources Cal Dept....D....916 651-9203
901 P St Lbby Sacramento (95814) ***(P-21676)***
Water Studio Inc....F....310 313-5553
5681 Selmaraine Dr Culver City (90230) ***(P-13981)***
Water Treatment Plant, Riverside *Also called City of Riverside* ***(P-16025)***
Water Works Manufacturing, Marysville *Also called US Pipe Fabrication LLC* ***(P-9790)***
Wateranywhere, Vista *Also called Applied Membranes Inc* ***(P-16009)***
Watercrest Inc....D....909 390-3944
4850 E Airport Dr Ontario (91761) ***(P-12440)***
Waterdog Products Inc....F....619 441-9688
1148 Pioneer Way El Cajon (92020) ***(P-10435)***
Waterfountainscom Inc....F....760 946-0525
13870 Riverside Dr Apple Valley (92307) ***(P-13982)***
Waterguru Inc....F....415 692-3310
150 Post St Ste 650 San Francisco (94108) ***(P-16134)***
Watergush Inc....E....408 524-3074
440 N Wolfe Rd Ste E252 Sunnyvale (94085) ***(P-11019)***
Waterhealth International Inc....C....949 716-5790
9601 Irvine Center Dr Irvine (92618) ***(P-16135)***
Waterless Co Inc....F....760 727-7723
1050 Joshua Way Vista (92081) ***(P-12055)***
Waterman Valve LLC (HQ)....C....559 562-4000
25500 Road 204 Exeter (93221) ***(P-16136)***
Watermans Guild....F....714 751-0603
260 E Dyer Rd Ste L Santa Ana (92707) ***(P-23688)***
Watermark, Riverside *Also called Irrometer Company Inc* ***(P-22219)***
Waters Technologies Corp....F....949 474-4320
18271 Mcdurmott St Irvine (92614) ***(P-22049)***
Watersentinel, Temecula *Also called TST Water LLC* ***(P-16127)***
Waterstone Faucets, Murrieta *Also called Waterstone LLC* ***(P-12056)***
Waterstone LLC....C....951 304-0520
41180 Raintree Ct Murrieta (92562) ***(P-12056)***
Waterway Plastics, Oxnard *Also called B & S Plastics Inc* ***(P-9965)***
Watkins Manufacturing Corp (HQ)....B....760 598-6464
1280 Park Center Dr Vista (92081) ***(P-24285)***
Watkins Manufacturing Corp....F....760 598-6464
1325 Hot Springs Way Vista (92081) ***(P-9914)***
Watkins Wellness, Vista *Also called Watkins Manufacturing Corp* ***(P-24285)***
Watkins, Luis, Los Angeles *Also called Luis Wtkins Cstm Wrught Ir LLC* ***(P-4836)***
Watson ME Inc (PA)....F....661 763-5254
801 Kern St Taft (93268) ***(P-293)***
Watsons Profiling Corp....F....909 923-5500
1460 S Balboa Ave Ontario (91761) ***(P-17052)***
Watsonvlle Register-Pajaronian, Watsonville *Also called News Media Corporation* ***(P-5995)***
Watt Enterprise Inc....F....714 963-0781
10575 Bechler River Ave Fountain Valley (92708) ***(P-3205)***
Watt Stopper Inc (HQ)....E....408 988-5331
2700 Zanker Rd Ste 168 San Jose (95134) ***(P-17505)***
Watt Stopper Le Grand, San Jose *Also called Watt Stopper Inc* ***(P-17505)***
Watts Liquidation Corporation....F....310 328-5999
555 Van Ness Ave Torrance (90501) ***(P-2922)***
Watts Machining Inc....E....408 654-9300
2339 Calle Del Mundo Santa Clara (95054) ***(P-17053)***
Wave 80 Biosciences Inc....F....415 487-7976
1100 26th St San Francisco (94107) ***(P-22681)***
Wave Circuits....E....805 987-3008
1260 Avenida Acaso Ste H Camarillo (93012) ***(P-19786)***
Wave Community Newspapers Inc (PA)....E....323 290-3000
3731 Wilshire Blvd # 840 Los Angeles (90010) ***(P-6083)***
Wave Precision Inc....D....805 529-3324
5390 Kazuko Ct Moorpark (93021) ***(P-22146)***
Wavenet Inc....E....310 885-4200
707 E Sepulveda Blvd Carson (90745) ***(P-11465)***
Wavestream Corporation (HQ)....C....909 599-9080
545 W Terrace Dr San Dimas (91773) ***(P-19787)***
Wavexing Inc....F....408 896-1982
3200 Scott Blvd Santa Clara (95054) ***(P-19271)***
Wawa, Cupertino *Also called Sheng-Kee of California Inc* ***(P-1379)***
Wawona Frozen Foods (PA)....A....559 299-2901
100 W Alluvial Ave Clovis (93611) ***(P-973)***
Wax Box Firelog Corporation....E....530 846-2200
1791 State Highway 99 Gridley (95948) ***(P-12094)***
Wax Research Inc....F....760 607-0850
1212 Distribution Way Vista (92081) ***(P-9458)***
Way of The World Inc....F....408 616-7700
170 Commercial St Sunnyvale (94086) ***(P-7536)***
Way Out West Inc....E....310 769-6937
1440 W 135th St Gardena (90249) ***(P-3126)***
Wayfarers, Alamo *Also called Edner Corporation* ***(P-1241)***
Wayne - Dalton Sacramento, Sacramento *Also called Hrh Door Corp* ***(P-12320)***
Wayne J Sand & Gravel Inc....F....805 529-1323
9455 Buena Vista St Moorpark (93021) ***(P-390)***
Wayne Tool & Die Co....E....818 364-1611
15853 Olden St Sylmar (91342) ***(P-11427)***
Wb Machining & Mech Design....E....408 453-5005
1670 Zanker Rd San Jose (95112) ***(P-17054)***
Wbp Associates Inc....F....626 575-0747
2017 Seaman Ave South El Monte (91733) ***(P-5176)***
Wbt Group LLC....E....323 735-1201
1401 S Shamrock Ave Monrovia (91016) ***(P-24286)***
Wbt Industries, Monrovia *Also called Wbt Group LLC* ***(P-24286)***
WBwalton Enterprises Inc....E....951 683-0930
4185 Hallmark Pkwy San Bernardino (92407) ***(P-18299)***
Wc, Fairfield *Also called West-Com Nrse Call Systems Inc* ***(P-18300)***
Wcbm Company (PA)....E....323 262-3274
1812 W 135th St Gardena (90249) ***(P-23780)***
Wce Products Inc....F....714 895-4381
7542 Santa Rita Cir Stanton (90680) ***(P-7909)***
WCI, Santa Ana *Also called Wright Capacitors Inc* ***(P-19306)***
Wcitiescom Inc....F....415 495-8090
1212 Broadway Ste 910 Oakland (94612) ***(P-6624)***
WCP Inc....D....562 860-9040
17730 Crusader Ave Cerritos (90703) ***(P-10436)***
Wct, Garden Grove *Also called Broncs Inc* ***(P-2726)***
Wct/Pac Data, Aliso Viejo *Also called Pacific Alliance Capital Inc* ***(P-15582)***
WD, San Jose *Also called Western Digital Tech Inc* ***(P-15625)***
WD Media LLC....B....408 576-2000
1710 Automation Pkwy San Jose (95131) ***(P-19889)***
WD-40 Company (PA)....B....619 275-1400
9715 Businesspark Ave San Diego (92131) ***(P-9455)***
Wd-40 Company....C....619 275-1400
9715 Businesspark Ave San Diego (92131) ***(P-9375)***
We Can Foundation, Los Angeles *Also called West E Cmnty Access Netwrk Inc* ***(P-20634)***
We Do Graphics Inc....E....714 997-7390
1150 N Main St Orange (92867) ***(P-7174)***
We Five-R Corporation....F....323 263-6757
1507 S Sunol Dr Los Angeles (90023) ***(P-13533)***
WE Hall Company Inc (PA)....D....949 650-4555
471 Old Newport Blvd # 205 Newport Beach (92663) ***(P-11472)***
WE Hall Company Inc....F....916 383-4891
5999 Power Inn Rd Sacramento (95824) ***(P-11020)***
We Imagine Inc....D....818 709-0064
9371 Canoga Ave Chatsworth (91311) ***(P-18650)***
We The Pie People LLC....E....818 349-1880
9909 Topanga Canyon Blvd # 159 Chatsworth (91311) ***(P-705)***
We-Cel Creations, San Fernando *Also called Jay Gee Sales* ***(P-10833)***
Wearable Integrity Inc....E....213 748-6044
1360 E 17th St Los Angeles (90021) ***(P-3528)***

Employee Codes: A=Over 500 employees, B=251-500
C=101-250, D=51-100, E=20-50, F=10-19
2019 California
Manfacturers Register
© Mergent Inc. 1-800-342-5647
1327

Weartech International Inc (HQ) ....E....714 683-2430
1177 N Grove St Anaheim (92806) ***(P-15116)***
Weather TEC Corp ....F....559 291-5555
5645 E Clinton Ave Fresno (93727) ***(P-14122)***
Weatherby Inc ....E....307 675-7800
1605 Commerce Way Paso Robles (93446) ***(P-13692)***
Weatherford Artificia ....E....661 654-8120
21728 Rosedale Hwy Bakersfield (93314) ***(P-15097)***
Weatherford Completion Systems ....E....661 746-1391
19468 Creek Rd Bakersfield (93314) ***(P-294)***
Weatherford International LLC ....E....805 933-0242
201 Hallock Dr Santa Paula (93060) ***(P-295)***
Weatherford International LLC ....D....805 781-3580
1880 Santa Barbara Ave # 220 San Luis Obispo (93401) ***(P-296)***
Weatherford International LLC ....D....661 587-9753
21728 Rosedale Hwy Bakersfield (93314) ***(P-297)***
Weatherford International LLC ....E....661 589-2146
3701 Enterprise St Shafter (93263) ***(P-14243)***
Weatherford International LLC ....D....805 933-0200
201 Hallock Dr Santa Paula (93060) ***(P-13911)***
Weatherford International LLC ....F....805 643-1279
400 Rocklite Rd Ventura (93001) ***(P-298)***
Weatherford International Inc ....F....562 595-0931
3356 Lime Ave Long Beach (90755) ***(P-14244)***
Weatherman Products Inc (PA) ....F....949 515-8800
21622 Surveyor Cir Huntington Beach (92646) ***(P-8955)***
Web CAM, Riverside *Also called Web CAM Inc* ***(P-20485)***
Web CAM Inc ....F....951 341-0112
1815 Massachusetts Ave Riverside (92507) ***(P-20485)***
Web Traffic School, Oakland *Also called Interactive Solutions Inc* ***(P-24784)***
Webalo Inc ....F....310 828-7335
1990 S Bundy Dr Ste 350 Los Angeles (90025) ***(P-19890)***
Webb Designs Inc ....F....559 641-5400
40300 Greenwood Way Oakhurst (93644) ***(P-5215)***
Webb Massey Co Inc ....E....714 639-6012
201 W Carleton Ave Orange (92867) ***(P-4901)***
Webb-Stotler Engineering ....F....951 735-2040
1701 Commerce St Corona (92880) ***(P-17055)***
Webber EMI, Ontario *Also called Emission Methods Inc* ***(P-22193)***
Webbshade, Oakhurst *Also called Webb Designs Inc* ***(P-5215)***
Webcloak LLC ....F....949 417-9940
2 Park Plz Ste 700 Irvine (92614) ***(P-25343)***
Webedoctor Inc ....E....714 990-3999
471 W Lambert Rd Ste 105 Brea (92821) ***(P-25344)***
Weber Drilling Co Inc ....E....310 670-7708
401 Hindry Ave Inglewood (90301) ***(P-14204)***
Weber Metals Inc ....B....562 602-0260
16706 Garfield Ave Paramount (90723) ***(P-13132)***
Weber Orthopedic Inc (PA) ....E....805 525-8474
1185 E Main St Santa Paula (93060) ***(P-22846)***
Weber Precision Graphics, Santa Ana *Also called Artisan Nameplate Awards Corp* ***(P-7241)***
Weber Printing Company Inc ....E....310 639-5064
1124 E Del Amo Blvd Carson (90746) ***(P-7175)***
Webers Auto Parts, Montebello *Also called Eagle Enterprises Inc* ***(P-20321)***
Weckworth Electric Group Inc ....F....916 933-3066
1261 Hawks Flight Ct A El Dorado Hills (95762) ***(P-20107)***
Weddingchannelcom Inc ....C....213 599-4100
5757 Wilshire Blvd # 504 Los Angeles (90036) ***(P-6625)***
Wedemeyer Bakery, South San Francisco *Also called Windmill Corporation* ***(P-1345)***
Weekend Balita, La Crescenta *Also called Balita Media Inc* ***(P-5773)***
Wefea Inc ....E....925 218-1839
4695 Chabot Dr Ste 200 Pleasanton (94588) ***(P-19891)***
Wehah Farm Inc ....B....530 538-3500
5311 Midway Richvale (95974) ***(P-1094)***
WEI Laboratories Inc ....E....408 970-8700
2880 Zanker Rd Ste 205 San Jose (95134) ***(P-780)***
Weibel Champagne Vineyards, Lodi *Also called Weibel Incorporated* ***(P-2049)***
Weibel Incorporated ....E....209 365-9463
1 Winemaster Way Ste D Lodi (95240) ***(P-2049)***
Weider Health and Fitness ....B....818 884-6800
21100 Erwin St Woodland Hills (91367) ***(P-2287)***
Weider Leasing Inc ....D....818 884-6800
21100 Erwin St Woodland Hills (91367) ***(P-6287)***
Weider Publications LLC (HQ) ....D....818 884-6800
3699 Wilshire Blvd # 1220 Los Angeles (90010) ***(P-6288)***
WEIDNERCA, Sacramento *Also called Architectural S Weidner* ***(P-23819)***
Wein Products Inc ....E....213 749-6250
880 W 1st St Apt 315 Los Angeles (90012) ***(P-20108)***
Weir Floway Inc (HQ) ....C....559 442-4000
2494 S Railroad Ave Fresno (93706) ***(P-15098)***
Weir Seaboard, Bakersfield *Also called Seaboard International Inc* ***(P-14238)***
Weis/Robart Partitions Inc ....F....714 666-0822
3501 E La Palma Ave Anaheim (92806) ***(P-12905)***
Weiser Iron Inc ....E....909 429-4600
10700 Jersey Blvd Ste 680 Rancho Cucamonga (91730) ***(P-11428)***
Weiser Litho Inc ....F....818 707-2708
9025 Owensmouth Ave Canoga Park (91304) ***(P-7176)***
Weiser Lock Corporation ....F....949 672-4000
19701 Da Vinci Foothill Ranch (92610) ***(P-12008)***
Weiss-Mcnair LLC (HQ) ....D....530 891-6214
100 Loren Ave Chico (95928) ***(P-14123)***
Welaco, Bakersfield *Also called Well Analysis Corporation Inc* ***(P-4021)***
Weld Design, Santa Ana *Also called Dave Annala* ***(P-12551)***
Weld-On Adhesives, Compton *Also called Ips Corporation* ***(P-9153)***
Weldcraft Industries ....F....559 784-4322
18794 Avenue 96 Terra Bella (93270) ***(P-14124)***
Weldex Corporation (PA) ....E....714 761-2100
6751 Katella Ave Cypress (90630) ***(P-19272)***
Weldlogic Inc ....D....805 375-1670
2651 Lavery Ct Newbury Park (91320) ***(P-25448)***
Weldmac Manufacturing Company ....C....619 440-2300
1451 N Johnson Ave El Cajon (92020) ***(P-17056)***
Weldon Company, Gardena *Also called Ips Corporation* ***(P-9154)***
Weldonowen, San Francisco *Also called Owen Weldon Inc* ***(P-6374)***
Weldstone Portable Welders, Anaheim *Also called Lodestone LLC* ***(P-14729)***
Weldtek Inc ....D....714 210-8966
3431 W Maywood Ave Santa Ana (92704) ***(P-14461)***
Weldway Inc ....E....209 847-8083
521 Hi Tech Pkwy Oakdale (95361) ***(P-12279)***
Well Analysis Corporation Inc (PA) ....E....661 283-9510
5500 Woodmere Dr Bakersfield (93313) ***(P-4021)***
Welland Industries LLC ....F....714 528-9900
3860 Prospect Ave Yorba Linda (92886) ***(P-24287)***
Wellbore Navigation Inc (PA) ....F....714 259-7760
1240 N Jefferson St Ste M Anaheim (92807) ***(P-22297)***
Wellex Corporation (PA) ....C....510 743-1818
551 Brown Rd Fremont (94539) ***(P-19788)***
Wellington Foods Inc ....E....562 989-0111
1930 California Ave Corona (92881) ***(P-781)***
Wellprint Inc ....F....714 838-3962
380 E 1st St Ste B Tustin (92780) ***(P-7177)***
Wells Dental Inc ....F....707 937-0521
5860 Flynn Creek Rd Comptche (95427) ***(P-22924)***
Wells Mfg USA Inc ....F....626 575-2886
9698 Telstar Ave Ste 312 El Monte (91731) ***(P-19853)***
Wells Precision Machining, Comptche *Also called Wells Dental Inc* ***(P-22924)***
Wells Publishing Inc (PA) ....E....619 584-1100
3570 Camino Delrio N 20 San Diego (92108) ***(P-6289)***
Wells Struthers Corporation ....E....814 726-1000
10375 Slusher Dr Santa Fe Springs (90670) ***(P-12441)***
Welmark Textile Inc ....F....310 516-7289
14824 S Main St Gardena (90248) ***(P-3020)***
Welnav, Anaheim *Also called Wellbore Navigation Inc* ***(P-22297)***
Welovefine, Los Angeles *Also called Mf Inc* ***(P-3258)***
Wemo Media Inc ....F....310 399-8058
550 Rose Ave Venice (90291) ***(P-25345)***
Wems Electronics, Hawthorne *Also called Wems Inc* ***(P-15186)***
Wems Inc (PA) ....D....310 644-0251
4650 W Rosecrans Ave Hawthorne (90250) ***(P-15186)***
Wems Inc ....E....310 644-0255
4652 W Rosecrans Ave Hawthorne (90250) ***(P-17323)***
Wencon Development Inc ....D....925 687-6686
2700 Mitchell Dr 2 Walnut Creek (94598) ***(P-12815)***
Wenner Media LLC ....E....323 930-3300
5700 Wilshire Blvd # 345 Los Angeles (90036) ***(P-6290)***
Wente Bros (PA) ....D....925 456-2300
5565 Tesla Rd Livermore (94550) ***(P-2050)***
Wente Bros ....E....831 674-5642
37995 Elm Ave Greenfield (93927) ***(P-2051)***
Wente Brothers Winery, Greenfield *Also called Wente Bros* ***(P-2051)***
Wente Vineyards, Livermore *Also called Wente Bros* ***(P-2050)***
Wep Transport Holdings LLC ....F....858 756-1010
16909 Via De Santa Fe Rancho Santa Fe (92067) ***(P-159)***
Wepower LLC ....F....866 385-9463
32 Journey Ste 250 Aliso Viejo (92656) ***(P-14012)***
Werner Co ....F....209 383-3989
1810 Grogan Ave Merced (95341) ***(P-13983)***
Werner Corporation ....F....951 277-4586
25050 Maitri Rd Corona (92883) ***(P-11212)***
Werner Systems Inc ....E....714 838-4444
14321 Myford Rd Tustin (92780) ***(P-11626)***
Wes Go Inc ....E....818 504-1200
8211 Lankershim Blvd North Hollywood (91605) ***(P-7537)***
Wes Manufacturing Inc ....E....408 727-0750
3241 Keller St Santa Clara (95054) ***(P-17057)***
Wesanco Inc ....E....714 739-4989
14870 Desman Rd La Mirada (90638) ***(P-20970)***
Wescam Sonoma Operations, Santa Rosa *Also called L-3 Cmmnications Sonoma Eo Inc* ***(P-23175)***
Wescam Usa Inc (HQ) ....F....707 236-1077
424 Aviation Blvd Santa Rosa (95403) ***(P-21456)***
Wesco Enterprises Inc ....F....562 944-3100
12681 Corral Pl Santa Fe Springs (90670) ***(P-10437)***
Wesco Mounting & Finishing Inc ....E....714 562-0122
5450 Dodds Ave Buena Park (90621) ***(P-7624)***
Wesfac Inc ....D....562 861-2160
9300 Hall Rd Downey (90241) ***(P-16137)***
Weslan Systems Inc ....F....530 668-3304
1244 Commerce Ave Woodland (95776) ***(P-15048)***
Wesley Allen Inc (PA) ....C....323 231-4275
1001 E 60th St Los Angeles (90001) ***(P-4848)***
Wespac, Downey *Also called Wesfac Inc* ***(P-16137)***
Wessco International Ltd A C (PA) ....E....310 477-4272
11400 W Olympic Blvd # 450 Los Angeles (90064) ***(P-3773)***
Wessex Industries Inc ....E....562 944-5760
8619 Red Oak St Rancho Cucamonga (91730) ***(P-13912)***
West American Energy Corp ....F....661 747-7732
4949 Buckley Way Ste 207 Bakersfield (93309) ***(P-122)***
West American Rubber Co LLC (PA) ....B....714 532-3355
1337 W Braden Ct Orange (92868) ***(P-9692)***
West American Rubber Co LLC ....C....714 406-5860
750 N Main St Orange (92868) ***(P-9693)***
WEST AREA OPPORTUNITY CENTER, Los Angeles *Also called Casa De Hermandad* ***(P-23536)***
West Bent Bolt Division, Santa Fe Springs *Also called Mid-West Fabricating Co* ***(P-20402)***

West Bond Inc (PA)....E....714 978-1551
1551 S Harris Ct Anaheim (92806) ***(P-15375)***
West Bsin Wtr Rclamation Plant, El Segundo *Also called N A Suez* ***(P-21623)***
West Cast Architectural Shtmtl....F....408 776-2700
2215 Oakland Rd San Jose (95131) ***(P-12906)***
West Coast Aerospace Inc (PA)....D....310 518-3167
220 W E St Wilmington (90744) ***(P-23781)***
West Coast Aerospace Inc....F....310 632-2064
3017 E Las Hermanas St Compton (90221) ***(P-23782)***
West Coast Aggregate Supply....E....760 342-7598
92500 Airport Blvd Thermal (92274) ***(P-391)***
West Coast Airlines, Riverside *Also called West Coast Unlimited* ***(P-20183)***
West Coast Asm, San Jose *Also called West Cast Architectural Shtmtl* ***(P-12906)***
West Coast Binders, Gardena *Also called US Packagers Inc* ***(P-7589)***
West Coast Business Prtrs Inc....F....818 709-4980
9822 Independence Ave Chatsworth (91311) ***(P-7178)***
West Coast Button Mfg Co, Gardena *Also called Wcbm Company* ***(P-23780)***
West Coast Canvas (PA)....F....209 333-0243
14900 W Highway 12 Ste C Lodi (95242) ***(P-3819)***
West Coast Catrg Trcks Mfg Inc....F....323 278-1279
1217 Goodrich Blvd Commerce (90022) ***(P-4748)***
West Coast Chain Mfg Co....E....909 923-7800
4245 Pacific Privado Ontario (91761) ***(P-20109)***
West Coast Clinical RES LLC....F....818 776-0820
5525 Etiwanda Ave Ste 202 Tarzana (91356) ***(P-8441)***
West Coast Consulting LLC (PA)....C....949 250-4102
9233 Research Dr Ste 200 Irvine (92618) ***(P-25346)***
West Coast Consulting LLC....E....949 336-7700
9233 Research Dr Ste 200 Irvine (92618) ***(P-25347)***
West Coast Cryogenics Inc....F....209 914-6989
503 W Larch Rd Ste K Tracy (95304) ***(P-15049)***
West Coast Custom Sheet Metal....F....818 252-7500
9045 Glenoaks Blvd Sun Valley (91352) ***(P-12816)***
West Coast Digital, Chatsworth *Also called West Coast Business Prtrs Inc* ***(P-7178)***
West Coast Enterprizes, Stanton *Also called Wce Products Inc* ***(P-7909)***
West Coast Fab Inc....F....510 529-0177
700 S 32nd St Richmond (94804) ***(P-12817)***
West Coast Fixtures Inc (PA)....E....707 752-6373
511 Stone Rd Benicia (94510) ***(P-5119)***
West Coast Form Grinding....F....714 540-5621
2548 S Fairview St Santa Ana (92704) ***(P-17058)***
West Coast Foundry LLC (HQ)....E....323 583-1421
2450 E 53rd St Huntington Park (90255) ***(P-11529)***
West Coast Garment Mfg....E....415 896-1772
70 Elmira St San Francisco (94124) ***(P-3127)***
West Coast Gasket Co....D....714 869-0123
300 Ranger Ave Brea (92821) ***(P-9563)***
West Coast Growers Inc....E....559 843-2294
1849 N Helm Ave Ste 110 Fresno (93727) ***(P-907)***
West Coast Labels, Placentia *Also called Cinton* ***(P-5557)***
West Coast Laboratories Inc....E....310 527-6163
156 E 162nd St Gardena (90248) ***(P-8442)***
West Coast Laboratories Inc (PA)....F....323 321-4774
116 E Alondra Blvd Gardena (90248) ***(P-8443)***
West Coast Laminating LLC....F....562 906-2489
13833 Borate St Santa Fe Springs (90670) ***(P-4586)***
West Coast Lanyards Inc....F....877 447-6030
10661 Fulton Ct Rancho Cucamonga (91730) ***(P-24288)***
West Coast Machining Inc....F....562 229-1087
14560 Marquardt Ave Santa Fe Springs (90670) ***(P-17059)***
West Coast Magnetics, Stockton *Also called Wjlp Company Inc* ***(P-19370)***
West Coast Manufacturing Inc....E....714 897-4221
1822 Western Ave Stanton (90680) ***(P-13295)***
West Coast Metal Stamping Inc....E....714 792-0322
550 W Crowther Ave Placentia (92870) ***(P-13296)***
West Coast Microwave, Artesia *Also called M G Watanabe Inc* ***(P-18172)***
West Coast Milling, Lancaster *Also called Pavement Recycling Systems Inc* ***(P-9393)***
West Coast Orthotic/Prosthetic....F....209 942-4166
3215 N California St # 2 Stockton (95204) ***(P-22847)***
West Coast Plastics Inc....F....562 777-8024
10025 Shoemaker Ave Santa Fe Springs (90670) ***(P-10438)***
West Coast Porcelain Inc....E....951 278-8680
133 N Sherman Ave Corona (92882) ***(P-10838)***
West Coast Products, Orland *Also called Decamilla Brothers LLC* ***(P-1539)***
West Coast Quartz Corporation (HQ)....D....510 249-2160
1000 Corporate Way Fremont (94539) ***(P-10670)***
West Coast Sand Gravel....E....559 625-9426
7715 Avenue 296 Visalia (93291) ***(P-392)***
West Coast Service Center, Ontario *Also called Vsmpo-Tirus US Inc* ***(P-11641)***
West Coast Sheepskin Import....F....562 945-5151
14056 Whittier Blvd Whittier (90605) ***(P-3973)***
West Coast Steel & Proc LLC (PA)....D....909 393-8405
3534 Philadelphia St Chino (91710) ***(P-11530)***
West Coast Switchgear (HQ)....D....562 802-3441
13837 Bettencourt St Cerritos (90703) ***(P-17172)***
West Coast Timber Corp....F....714 893-4374
6221 Apache Rd Westminster (92683) ***(P-4022)***
West Coast Trends Inc....E....714 843-9288
17811 Jamestown Ln Huntington Beach (92647) ***(P-23689)***
West Coast Unlimited....F....951 352-1234
11161 Pierce St Riverside (92505) ***(P-20183)***
West Coast Venture Capital LLC (PA)....A....408 725-0700
10050 Bandley Dr Cupertino (95014) ***(P-18009)***
West Coast Vinyl Windows, Cerritos *Also called WCP Inc* ***(P-10436)***
West Coast Welding & Cnstr....F....805 604-1222
390 S Del Norte Blvd Oxnard (93030) ***(P-25449)***
West Coast Windows & Doors....F....925 681-1776
2170 Commerce Ave Ste C Concord (94520) ***(P-10439)***
West Coast-Accudyne Inc....E....562 927-2546
7180 Scout Ave Bell (90201) ***(P-14462)***
West E Cmnty Access Netwrk Inc....D....323 967-0520
646 W 60th St Los Angeles (90044) ***(P-20634)***
West Lake Food Corporation....D....714 973-2286
2430 Cape Cod Way Santa Ana (92703) ***(P-457)***
West Newport Oil Company....F....949 631-1100
1080 W 17th St Costa Mesa (92627) ***(P-87)***
West Pacific Cabinet Mfg....F....916 652-6840
3121 Swetzer Rd Ste A Loomis (95650) ***(P-4368)***
West Publishing Corporation....E....800 747-3161
633 W 5th St Ste 2300 Los Angeles (90071) ***(P-6407)***
West Rapco Environmental Svcs....E....310 450-3335
23852 Pacific Coast Hwy # 941 Malibu (90265) ***(P-14591)***
West Rock, Milpitas *Also called Westrock Cp LLC* ***(P-5471)***
West Star Industries, Stockton *Also called Hackett Industries Inc* ***(P-14856)***
West Valley Plating Inc....F....818 709-1684
21061 Superior St Ste A Chatsworth (91311) ***(P-13534)***
West World Manufacturing Inc....F....619 287-4403
6420 Federal Blvd Ste F Lemon Grove (91945) ***(P-4749)***
West World Productions Inc....E....310 273-9874
420 N Camden Dr Beverly Hills (90210) ***(P-6291)***
West-Bag Inc....E....323 264-0750
1161 Monterey Pass Rd Monterey Park (91754) ***(P-10440)***
West-Com Nrse Call Systems Inc (PA)....E....707 428-5900
2200 Cordelia Rd Fairfield (94534) ***(P-18300)***
West-Mark, Ceres *Also called Certified Stainless Svc Inc* ***(P-12372)***
West-World Co, Lemon Grove *Also called West World Manufacturing Inc* ***(P-4749)***
Westaire Engineering Inc....F....323 587-3347
5820 S Alameda St Vernon (90058) ***(P-16000)***
Westak, Sunnyvale *Also called Qualitek Inc* ***(P-18572)***
Westak Inc (PA)....D....408 734-8686
1116 Elko Dr Sunnyvale (94089) ***(P-18651)***
Westamerica....F....707 863-6000
4550 Mangels Blvd Fairfield (94534) ***(P-23477)***
Westar Metal Fabrication Inc....F....626 350-0718
1926 Potrero Ave South El Monte (91733) ***(P-12280)***
Westar Nutrition Corp....C....949 645-6100
350 Paularino Ave Costa Mesa (92626) ***(P-7982)***
Westbase Inc (PA)....F....626 969-6801
717 N Coney Ave Azusa (91702) ***(P-17173)***
Westbridge Agricultural Pdts....F....760 599-8855
1260 Avenida Chelsea Vista (92081) ***(P-9121)***
Westbridge Research Group (PA)....F....760 599-8855
1260 Avenida Chelsea Vista (92081) ***(P-9122)***
Westco Industries Inc....E....909 874-8700
2625 S Willow Ave Bloomington (92316) ***(P-13004)***
Westco Iron Works Inc (PA)....D....925 961-9152
5828 S Naylor Rd Livermore (94551) ***(P-11916)***
Westcoast Brush Mfg Inc....E....909 627-7170
1330 Philadelphia St Pomona (91766) ***(P-23799)***
Westcoast Business Solutions, Agoura Hills *Also called Jamaco Enterprises Inc* ***(P-5377)***
Westcoast Companies Inc....F....626 794-9330
725-729 E Washington Blvd Pasadena (91104) ***(P-3820)***
Westcoast Elevator Pads, Pasadena *Also called Westcoast Companies Inc* ***(P-3820)***
Westcoast Grinding Corporation....F....818 890-1841
10517 San Fernando Rd Pacoima (91331) ***(P-17060)***
Westcoast Inksolutions LLC....F....323 726-8100
5928 Garfield Ave Commerce (90040) ***(P-9215)***
Westcoast Precision Inc....E....408 943-9998
2091 Fortune Dr San Jose (95131) ***(P-17061)***
Westcoast Rotor Inc....E....310 327-5050
119 W 154th St Gardena (90248) ***(P-15099)***
Westcoast Tool Products, Sun Valley *Also called Accu-Grinding Inc* ***(P-14595)***
Westcorp Engineering, Riverside *Also called Reisner Enterprises Inc* ***(P-16893)***
Westcott Press Inc....F....626 794-7716
1121 W Isabel St Burbank (91506) ***(P-7179)***
Westech Inv Advisors LLC (PA)....E....650 234-4300
104 La Mesa Dr 102 Portola Valley (94028) ***(P-1020)***
Westech Metal Fabrication Inc....F....619 702-9353
3420 E St San Diego (92102) ***(P-12281)***
Westek Electronics Inc....E....831 740-6300
185 Westridge Dr Watsonville (95076) ***(P-18378)***
Westend Software Inc (PA)....F....310 370-0367
1905 Speyer Ln Redondo Beach (90278) ***(P-25348)***
Westerly Marine Inc....E....714 966-8550
3535 W Garry Ave Santa Ana (92704) ***(P-21069)***
Western Abrasives Inc....F....323 588-1245
4383 Fruitland Ave Vernon (90058) ***(P-11308)***
Western Bagel Baking Corp (PA)....C....818 786-5847
7814 Sepulveda Blvd Van Nuys (91405) ***(P-1339)***
Western Bagel Baking Corp....E....818 887-5451
21749 Ventura Blvd Woodland Hills (91364) ***(P-1340)***
Western Bagel Baking Corp....E....310 479-4823
11628 Santa Monica Blvd # 12 Los Angeles (90025) ***(P-1341)***
Western Bagel Too, Los Angeles *Also called Western Bagel Baking Corp* ***(P-1341)***
Western Bay Sheet Metal Inc....E....619 233-1753
1410 Hill St El Cajon (92020) ***(P-12282)***
Western Cactus Growers Inc....E....760 726-1710
1860 Monte Vista Dr Vista (92084) ***(P-14138)***
Western Case Incorporated....F....714 838-8460
6400 Sycamore Canyon Blvd B Riverside (92507) ***(P-10441)***
Western Case Incorporated (PA)....E....951 214-6380
6400 Sycam Canyo Blvd Ste Riverside (92507) ***(P-10442)***
Western Cnc Inc....D....760 597-7000
1001 Park Center Dr Vista (92081) ***(P-17062)***
Western Combustion Engrg Inc....F....310 834-9389
640 E Realty St Carson (90745) ***(P-12442)***
Western Concrete Products, Pleasanton *Also called Central Precast Concrete Inc* ***(P-10899)***

Western Corrugated Design Inc.....E.....562 695-5718
8741 Pioneer Blvd Santa Fe Springs (90670) *(P-5465)*
Western Die & Printing Corp.....F.....323 665-0474
3109 Casitas Ave Los Angeles (90039) *(P-7538)*
Western Die Cutting and Prtg, Los Angeles *Also called TLC Logistics Inc (P-5743)*
Western Digital, Milpitas *Also called Sandisk LLC (P-15597)*
Western Digital Corporation (PA).....A.....408 717-6000
5601 Great Oaks Pkwy San Jose (95119) *(P-15624)*
Western Digital Tech Inc (HQ).....A.....949 672-7000
5601 Great Oaks Pkwy San Jose (95119) *(P-15625)*
Western Division, Morgan Hill *Also called Greif Inc (P-5487)*
Western Division, Tehachapi *Also called Legacy Vulcan LLC (P-11127)*
Western Division, Rialto *Also called Legacy Vulcan LLC (P-371)*
Western Dning - Schneider Cafe.....E.....559 292-1981
3500 Pelco Way Clovis (93612) *(P-20110)*
Western Dovetail Incorporated.....E.....707 556-3683
1101 Nimitz Ave Ste 209 Vallejo (94592) *(P-4750)*
Western Edge Inc.....F.....661 947-3900
37957 Sierra Hwy Palmdale (93550) *(P-13680)*
Western Electrical Advg Co.....E.....760 352-0471
853 Dogwood Ave El Centro (92243) *(P-24003)*
Western Energy Production LLC.....F.....858 756-1010
16909 Via De Santa Fe Rancho Santa Fe (92067) *(P-160)*
Western Equipment Mfg, Corona *Also called Western Equipment Mfg Inc (P-14199)*
Western Equipment Mfg Inc.....F.....951 284-2000
1160 Olympic Dr Corona (92881) *(P-14199)*
Western Fab Inc.....F.....760 949-1441
9823 E Ave Hesperia (92345) *(P-13984)*
Western Fabrication & Eqp, Bakersfield *Also called F E W Inc (P-16489)*
Western Fabricators, Hesperia *Also called Western Fab Inc (P-13984)*
Western Fiber Co Inc.....E.....661 854-5556
4234a Sandrini Rd Arvin (93203) *(P-14423)*
Western Foam, Hayward *Also called Induspac California Inc (P-7842)*
Western Foods LLC (PA).....E.....530 601-5991
420 N Pioneer Ave Woodland (95776) *(P-1052)*
Western Forge Die, Huntington Beach *Also called Tarpin Corporation (P-14576)*
Western Gage Corporation.....E.....805 445-1410
3316 Maya Linda Ste A Camarillo (93012) *(P-14694)*
Western Glass Co, Pomona *Also called Da-Ly Glass Corp (P-10690)*
Western Glove Manufacturing.....D.....562 634-3720
10747 Norwalk Blvd Santa Fe Springs (90670) *(P-22848)*
Western Golf Inc.....F.....800 448-4409
1340 N Jefferson St Anaheim (92807) *(P-23690)*
Western Golf Car Mfg Inc.....D.....760 671-6691
69391 Dillon Rd Desert Hot Springs (92241) *(P-23691)*
Western Golf Car Sales Co, Desert Hot Springs *Also called Western Golf Car Mfg Inc (P-23691)*
Western Grinding Service Inc.....E.....650 591-2635
2375 De La Cruz Blvd Santa Clara (95050) *(P-13051)*
Western Hardware Company, Walnut *Also called Hardware Imports Inc (P-20210)*
Western Hardware Company.....F.....909 595-6201
161 Commerce Way Walnut (91789) *(P-12009)*
Western Hellenic Journal Inc.....E.....925 939-3900
1839 Ygnacio Valley Rd Walnut Creek (94598) *(P-6084)*
Western Highway Products, Huntington Beach *Also called Primus Inc (P-23944)*
Western Hose & Gasket, National City *Also called Westflex Inc (P-9512)*
Western Hydrostatics Inc (PA).....E.....951 784-2133
1956 Keats Dr Riverside (92501) *(P-16173)*
Western Illuminated Plas Inc.....F.....714 895-3067
14451 Edwards St Westminster (92683) *(P-17657)*
Western Imperial Trading Inc.....F.....818 907-0768
13946 Ventura Blvd Sherman Oaks (91423) *(P-23331)*
Western Integrated Mtls Inc (PA).....E.....562 634-2823
3310 E 59th St Long Beach (90805) *(P-4254)*
Western Lighting Inds Inc.....E.....626 969-6820
205 W Blueridge Ave Orange (92865) *(P-17571)*
Western Lithographics, Costa Mesa *Also called Batida Inc (P-6687)*
Western Mesquite Mines Inc.....E.....928 341-4653
6502 E Us Highway 78 Brawley (92227) *(P-11551)*
Western Metal Dctg Co Coil Div.....F.....909 987-2506
8875 Industrial Ln Rancho Cucamonga (91730) *(P-7180)*
Western Metal Spinning & Mfg.....F.....951 657-0711
5055 Western Way Perris (92571) *(P-13297)*
Western Metal Spinning Farming, Perris *Also called Western Metal Spinning & Mfg (P-13297)*
Western Metal Supply Co Inc.....F.....760 233-7800
2115 E Valley Pkwy Ste B Escondido (92027) *(P-12969)*
Western Methods, Valencia *Also called Stratoflight (P-20939)*
Western Methods Machinery Corp.....C.....949 252-6600
2344 Pullman St Santa Ana (92705) *(P-20971)*
Western Mfg & Distrg LLC.....E.....805 988-1010
835 Flynn Rd Camarillo (93012) *(P-21149)*
Western Mill Fabricators Inc.....E.....714 993-3667
615 Fee Ana St Placentia (92870) *(P-5263)*
Western Motor Works Inc.....F.....310 382-6896
8332 Osage Ave Los Angeles (90045) *(P-14789)*
Western Mountaineering, San Jose *Also called Seventh Heaven Inc (P-3966)*
Western Nutrients Corporation.....E.....661 327-9604
245 Industrial St Bakersfield (93307) *(P-9077)*
Western Organics Inc.....E.....209 982-4936
4343 Mckinley Ave Stockton (95206) *(P-9078)*
Western Outdoor News, San Clemente *Also called Western Outdoors Publications (P-6085)*
Western Outdoors Publications (PA).....E.....949 366-0030
901 Calle Amanecer # 300 San Clemente (92673) *(P-6085)*
Western Pacific Pulp and Paper (HQ).....D.....562 803-4401
9400 Hall Rd Downey (90241) *(P-5270)*
Western Pacific Signal LLC.....F.....510 276-6400
15890 Foothill Blvd San Leandro (94578) *(P-18379)*
Western Pad.....E.....714 671-1900
391 Thor Pl Brea (92821) *(P-7181)*
Western PCF Stor Solutions Inc (PA).....D.....909 451-0303
300 E Arrow Hwy San Dimas (91773) *(P-5177)*
Western Plastic Products, Stanton *Also called Schaffer Laboratories Inc (P-9765)*
Western Plastics Temecula, Temecula *Also called W Plastics Inc (P-9734)*
Western Precision Aero LLC.....E.....714 893-7999
11600 Monarch St Garden Grove (92841) *(P-20691)*
Western Printing and Label, Irvine *Also called Western Prtg & Graphics LLC (P-7182)*
Western Prtg & Graphics LLC (PA).....E.....714 532-3946
17931 Sky Park Cir Irvine (92614) *(P-7182)*
Western Ready Mix Concrete Co (PA).....F.....530 934-2185
Gyle Rd Willows (95988) *(P-11213)*
Western Real Estate News, South San Francisco *Also called Business Extension Bureau (P-6120)*
Western Roto Engravers Inc.....F.....510 525-2950
1225 6th St Berkeley (94710) *(P-7539)*
Western Saw Manufacturers Inc.....E.....805 981-0999
3200 Camino Del Sol Oxnard (93030) *(P-11922)*
Western Screw Products Inc.....E.....562 698-5793
11770 Slauson Ave Santa Fe Springs (90670) *(P-13052)*
Western Sheld Acquisitions LLC.....E.....310 527-6212
2146 E Gladwick St Rancho Dominguez (90220) *(P-7215)*
Western Shield Label, Rancho Dominguez *Also called Western Sheld Acquisitions LLC (P-7215)*
Western Sign Company Inc.....E.....916 933-3765
6221a Enterprise Dr Ste A Diamond Springs (95619) *(P-24004)*
Western Square Industries Inc.....E.....209 944-0921
1621 N Brdwy Stockton (95205) *(P-12907)*
Western Stabilization, Dixon *Also called J & A Jeffery Inc (P-24134)*
Western States Envelope Corp.....D.....714 449-0909
2301 Raymer Ave Fullerton (92833) *(P-5681)*
Western States Glass, Sacramento *Also called Wsglass Holdings Inc (P-22150)*
Western States Glass, Fremont *Also called Wsglass Holdings Inc (P-10613)*
Western States Packaging Inc.....E.....818 686-6045
13276 Paxton St Pacoima (91331) *(P-5634)*
Western States Weeklies Inc.....F.....619 280-2988
6312 Riverdale St San Diego (92120) *(P-6086)*
Western States Wholesale Inc (PA).....C.....909 947-0028
1420 S Bon View Ave Ontario (91761) *(P-10869)*
Western Strata Exploration Inc.....F.....916 744-1440
52360 Willow Point Rd Clarksburg (95612) *(P-123)*
Western Summit Manufacturing, Rancho Palos Verdes *Also called Summit International Packg Inc (P-5539)*
Western Summit Mfg Corp.....D.....626 333-3333
30200 Cartier Dr Rancho Palos Verdes (90275) *(P-9735)*
Western Supreme Inc.....C.....213 627-3861
865 Produce Ct Los Angeles (90021) *(P-555)*
Western Telematic Inc.....E.....949 586-9950
5 Sterling Irvine (92618) *(P-15885)*
Western Trade Printing Inc.....F.....559 251-8595
5695 E Shields Ave Fresno (93727) *(P-7183)*
Western Tube & Conduit Corp (HQ).....C.....310 537-6300
2001 E Dominguez St Long Beach (90810) *(P-17520)*
Western Web Inc.....E.....707 444-6236
1900 Bendixsen St Ste 2 Samoa (95564) *(P-7184)*
Western Widgets Cnc Inc.....F.....408 436-1230
915 Commercial St San Jose (95112) *(P-17063)*
Western Wire Works Inc.....F.....909 483-1186
7923 Cartilla Ave Rancho Cucamonga (91730) *(P-13863)*
Western Wood, Lake Elsinore *Also called Faith Industries Inc (P-4619)*
Western Wood Treating, Woodland *Also called California Cascade-Woodland (P-4589)*
Western Yankee Inc.....E.....562 944-6889
13233 Barton Cir Whittier (90605) *(P-7540)*
Western Yarn Dyeing Inc.....E.....714 578-9500
2011 Raymer Ave Fullerton (92833) *(P-2923)*
Westfab Manufacturing Inc.....E.....408 727-0550
3370 Keller St Santa Clara (95054) *(P-12818)*
Westfield Hydraulics Inc.....F.....818 896-6414
13834 Del Sur St San Fernando (91340) *(P-13746)*
Westflex Inc (PA).....E.....619 474-7400
325 W 30th St National City (91950) *(P-9512)*
Westgate Hardwoods Inc (PA).....E.....530 892-0300
9296 Midway Durham (95938) *(P-4255)*
Westgate Mfg Inc.....F.....877 805-2252
2462 E 28th St Vernon (90058) *(P-20111)*
Westinghouse A Brake Tech Corp.....E.....707 459-5563
452 E Hill Rd Willits (95490) *(P-10809)*
Westlake Bakery Inc.....F.....650 994-7741
7099 Mission St Daly City (94014) *(P-1342)*
Westlake Engrg Roto Form.....E.....805 525-8800
1041 E Santa Barbara St Santa Paula (93060) *(P-10443)*
Westlam Foods, Chino *Also called Trinidad Benham Holding Co (P-2691)*
Westland Technologies Inc.....D.....800 877-7734
107 S Riverside Dr Modesto (95354) *(P-9576)*
Westmark, Atwater *Also called Certified Stainless Svc Inc (P-12371)*
Westminster Press Inc.....E.....714 210-2881
4906 W 1st St Santa Ana (92703) *(P-7185)*
Westmont Industries (PA).....D.....562 944-6137
10805 Painter Ave Uppr Santa Fe Springs (90670) *(P-14304)*
Westpak Usa Inc.....F.....714 530-6995
1235 N Red Gum St Anaheim (92806) *(P-20112)*
Westport Scandinavia, Watsonville *Also called Nordic Naturals Inc (P-1529)*
Westridge Laboratories Inc.....E.....714 259-9400
1671 E Saint Andrew Pl Santa Ana (92705) *(P-8865)*

Westrock Converting Company........F.......951 601-4164
16110 Cosmos St Moreno Valley (92551) ***(P-5466)***
Westrock Cp LLC........C.......408 946-3600
201 S Hillview Dr Milpitas (95035) ***(P-5467)***
Westrock Cp LLC........C.......714 523-3550
13833 Freeway Dr Santa Fe Springs (90670) ***(P-5468)***
Westrock Cp LLC........C.......831 424-1831
1078 Merrill St Salinas (93901) ***(P-5469)***
Westrock Cp LLC........C.......951 734-1870
185 N Smith Ave Corona (92880) ***(P-5470)***
Westrock Cp LLC........F.......661 327-3841
2710 O St Bakersfield (93301) ***(P-5365)***
Westrock Cp LLC........E.......770 448-2193
205 E Alma Ave San Jose (95112) ***(P-5366)***
Westrock Cp LLC........C.......408 946-3600
201 S Hillview Dr Milpitas (95035) ***(P-5471)***
Westrock Cp LLC........F.......559 441-1166
24 S Thorne Ave Fresno (93706) ***(P-5367)***
Westrock Cp LLC........D.......559 685-1102
701 E Continental Ave Tulare (93274) ***(P-5368)***
Westrock Cp LLC........E.......916 379-2200
4800 Florin Perkins Rd Sacramento (95826) ***(P-5369)***
Westrock Cp LLC........E.......714 641-8891
2540 S Main St Santa Ana (92707) ***(P-5370)***
Westrock Cp LLC........C.......559 519-7240
3366 E Muscat Ave Fresno (93725) ***(P-5472)***
Westrock Cp LLC........D.......714 523-3550
15300 Marquardt Ave Santa Fe Springs (90670) ***(P-5371)***
Westrock CP LLC........E.......818 557-1500
3003 N San Fernando Blvd Burbank (91504) ***(P-5372)***
Westrock CP LLC........D.......925 946-0842
2363 Boulevard Cir Ste 4 Walnut Creek (94595) ***(P-5583)***
Westrock Mwv LLC........B.......909 597-2197
15750 Mountain Ave Chino (91708) ***(P-5373)***
Westrock Rkt LLC........F.......559 441-1181
1854 E Home Ave Fresno (93703) ***(P-5380)***
Westrock Rkt Company........C.......714 978-2895
749 N Poplar St Orange (92868) ***(P-5473)***
Westrock Rkt Company........C.......559 497-1662
3366 E Muscat Ave Fresno (93725) ***(P-5474)***
Westrock Rkt Company........E.......818 729-0610
100 E Tujunga Ave Ste 102 Burbank (91502) ***(P-5475)***
Westrock Rkt Company........C.......626 859-7633
536 S 2nd Ave Covina (91723) ***(P-5476)***
Westrock Usc Inc........F.......562 282-4200
13833 Freeway Dr Santa Fe Springs (90670) ***(P-5477)***
Westside Accessories Inc (PA)........E.......626 858-5452
8920 Vernon Ave Ste 128 Montclair (91763) ***(P-3634)***
Westside Building Materials, San Jose *Also called Central Concrete Supply Coinc* ***(P-11090)***
Westside Concrete Materials, San Jose *Also called US Concrete Inc* ***(P-11201)***
Westside Pallet Inc........D.......209 862-3941
2138 L St Newman (95360) ***(P-4513)***
Westside Research Inc........F.......530 330-0085
4293 County Road 99w Orland (95963) ***(P-3929)***
Westside Resources Inc........E.......800 944-3939
2967 Michelson Dr Ste G Irvine (92612) ***(P-22925)***
Westway Feed Products LLC........F.......209 466-4391
2130 W Washington St Stockton (95203) ***(P-1170)***
Westway Magazine, Costa Mesa *Also called Auto Club Enterprises* ***(P-6106)***
Westwood Group........F.......661 702-8603
28478 Westinghouse Pl Valencia (91355) ***(P-22147)***
Westwood Laboratories, Azusa *Also called Cardinal Laboratories Inc* ***(P-8714)***
Westwood Laboratories Inc (PA)........E.......626 969-3305
710 S Ayon Ave Azusa (91702) ***(P-8866)***
Wesval Inc........F.......714 870-0990
1621 N Orangethorpe Way Anaheim (92801) ***(P-17064)***
Wetmore Cutting Tools, Chino *Also called Wetmore Tool and Engrg Co* ***(P-14695)***
Wetmore Tool and Engrg Co........D.......909 364-1000
5091 G St Chino (91710) ***(P-14695)***
Wetzels Pretzels LLC (HQ)........F.......626 432-6900
35 Hugus Aly Ste 300 Pasadena (91103) ***(P-1388)***
Weyerhaeuser Company........C.......800 238-3676
543 Country Club Dr Simi Valley (93065) ***(P-5478)***
Weyerhaeuser Company........F.......209 942-1825
2700 S California St Stockton (95206) ***(P-4070)***
Wg, Santa Fe Springs *Also called Ethosenergy Field Services LLC* ***(P-210)***
WG Best Weinkellerei Inc........F.......858 627-1747
8221 Arjons Dr Ste F San Diego (92126) ***(P-2052)***
Wg Security Products Inc........E.......408 241-8000
2105 S Bascom Ave Ste 316 Campbell (95008) ***(P-20113)***
Whalen Furniture Manufacturing, San Diego *Also called Whalen LLC* ***(P-4752)***
Whalen Furniture Mfg Inc........E.......619 423-9948
1578 Air Wing Rd San Diego (92154) ***(P-4751)***
Whalen LLC (HQ)........C.......619 423-9948
1578 Air Wing Rd San Diego (92154) ***(P-4752)***
Whaley, Kevin Enterprises, Santee *Also called Kevin Whaley* ***(P-13838)***
Whamcloud Inc........E.......925 452-7599
696 San Ramon Valley Blvd Danville (94526) ***(P-25349)***
What Kids Want Inc........F.......818 775-0375
19428 Londelius St Northridge (91324) ***(P-23478)***
Whatever Publishing Inc........F.......415 884-2100
14 Pamaron Way Ste 1 Novato (94949) ***(P-6408)***
Whats Happening Tri City........E.......510 494-1999
39120 Argonaut Way # 335 Fremont (94538) ***(P-7541)***
Wheaton International, Hayward *Also called Tung Fei Plastic Inc* ***(P-5631)***
Wheel and Tire Club Inc........E.......714 422-3505
1301 Burton St Fullerton (92831) ***(P-11429)***
Wheeler & Reeder Inc........F.......323 268-4163
3334 Montrose Ave La Crescenta (91214) ***(P-14292)***
Wheeler Deeler, North Hollywood *Also called Mid Michigan Trading Post Ltd* ***(P-6528)***
Wheeler Lumber Co Inc........F.......707 943-3424
2407 Cathy Rd Miranda (95553) ***(P-4023)***
Wheeler Optical Lab........F.......714 891-2016
8200 Katella Ave Ste A Stanton (90680) ***(P-23131)***
Wheeler Winery Inc........E.......415 979-0630
849 Zinfandel Ln Saint Helena (94574) ***(P-2053)***
Wheels and Deals, Redding *Also called Great Northern Wheels Deals* ***(P-5867)***
Wheels Magazine Inc........E.......310 402-9013
1409 Centinela Ave Inglewood (90302) ***(P-21070)***
Wheelskins Inc........F.......510 841-2128
2821 10th St Berkeley (94710) ***(P-10584)***
Where Orange County Magazine, Los Angeles *Also called Tourism Development Corp* ***(P-6273)***
Whill Inc (PA)........F.......844 699-4455
285 Old County Rd Ste 6 San Carlos (94070) ***(P-21247)***
Whipple Industries Inc........F.......559 442-1261
3292 N Weber Ave Fresno (93722) ***(P-15187)***
Whisperkoll, Stockton *Also called Whisperkool Corporation* ***(P-2054)***
Whisperkool Corporation........F.......800 343-9463
1738 E Alpine Ave Stockton (95205) ***(P-2054)***
Whistle Labs Inc........E.......415 692-0200
1355 Market St Fl 2 San Francisco (94103) ***(P-20114)***
White Fire Tagets, San Bernardino *Also called Reagent Chemical & RES Inc* ***(P-7801)***
White Industrial Corporation........F.......530 676-6262
3869 Dividend Dr Ste 1 Shingle Springs (95682) ***(P-14744)***
White Wave Foods, City of Industry *Also called Wwf Operating Company* ***(P-741)***
Whitefish Enterprises Inc........F.......510 357-6100
14557 Griffith St San Leandro (94577) ***(P-24289)***
Whitehall Lane Winery, Saint Helena *Also called Thomas Leonardini* ***(P-2015)***
Whitehall Manufacturing Inc........A.......626 336-4561
15125 Proctor Ave City of Industry (91746) ***(P-22849)***
Whites Hvac Services Inc........F.......805 801-0167
131 E Knotts St Nipomo (93444) ***(P-16001)***
Whitestone Industries Inc........F.......888 567-2234
2076 White Ln Spc 283 Bakersfield (93304) ***(P-24290)***
Whiting Enterprises........E.......562 946-5100
10140 Romandel Ave Santa Fe Springs (90670) ***(P-13535)***
Whitmor Plstic Wire Cable Corp (PA)........D.......661 257-2400
27737 Avenue Hopkins Santa Clarita (91355) ***(P-13864)***
Whitmor Plstic Wire Cable Corp........E.......661 257-2400
28420 Stanford Ave Valencia (91355) ***(P-13865)***
Whitmor Wire and Cable, Santa Clarita *Also called Whitmor Plstic Wire Cable Corp* ***(P-13864)***
Whitmor Wirenetics, Valencia *Also called Whitmor Plstic Wire Cable Corp* ***(P-13865)***
Whittaker Corporation........E.......805 526-5700
1955 Surveyor Ave Fl 2 Simi Valley (93063) ***(P-20972)***
Whitten Machine Shop........F.......559 686-3428
4770 S K St Tulare (93274) ***(P-17065)***
Whittier Enterprise LLC........E.......844 767-5633
18901 Railroad St City of Industry (91748) ***(P-1021)***
Whittier Fertilizer Company........D.......562 699-3461
9441 Kruse Rd Pico Rivera (90660) ***(P-9079)***
Whittier Filtration Inc (HQ)........E.......714 986-5300
120 S State College Blvd Brea (92821) ***(P-16138)***
Whittier Mailing Products Inc (PA)........E.......562 464-3000
13019 Park St Santa Fe Springs (90670) ***(P-15916)***
Whizz Systems Inc........E.......408 207-0400
3240 Scott Blvd Santa Clara (95054) ***(P-18652)***
Who What Wear, West Hollywood *Also called Clique Brands Inc* ***(P-6130)***
Wholesale Shade, San Marcos *Also called Showdogs Inc* ***(P-5210)***
Wholesale Shutter Company Inc........F.......951 845-8786
411 Olive Ave Beaumont (92223) ***(P-4256)***
Wholesome Harvest Baking Inc........F.......916 967-1633
7840 Madison Ave Ste 135 Fair Oaks (95628) ***(P-458)***
Wholesome Harvest Baking LLC........C.......510 231-7200
3200 Regatta Blvd Ste G Richmond (94804) ***(P-1343)***
Wholesome Harvest Baking LLC........C.......805 487-5191
2701 Statham Blvd Oxnard (93033) ***(P-1344)***
Wholesome Valley Foods (PA)........F.......858 480-1543
1746 Berkeley St Unit B Santa Monica (90404) ***(P-2700)***
Wholesome Yo Curd........F.......909 859-8758
19755 Colima Rd Rowland Heights (91748) ***(P-706)***
Wi2wi Inc (PA)........E.......408 416-4200
2107 N 1st St Ste 680 San Jose (95131) ***(P-18301)***
Wiakea Springs, Culver City *Also called Waiakea Inc* ***(P-2233)***
Wick Communications Co........E.......760 379-3667
6404 Lake Isabella Blvd Lake Isabella (93240) ***(P-6087)***
Wick Communications Co........E.......650 726-4424
714 Kelly St Half Moon Bay (94019) ***(P-6088)***
Wickline Bedding Entp Corp........E.......760 747-7761
455 N Quince St Escondido (92025) ***(P-4893)***
Wide Open Industries LLC........E.......949 635-2292
21088 Bake Pkwy Ste 100 Lake Forest (92630) ***(P-20184)***
Wide USA Corporation........E.......714 300-0540
2210 E Winston Rd Anaheim (92806) ***(P-15650)***
Widescreen Review, Temecula *Also called Wsr Publishing Inc* ***(P-6297)***
Wiegmann & Rose, Oakland *Also called Xchanger Manufacturing Corp* ***(P-12444)***
Wiens Cellars LLC........E.......951 694-9892
35055 Via Del Ponte Temecula (92592) ***(P-2055)***
Wiggins Lift Co Inc........E.......805 485-7821
2571 Cortez St Oxnard (93036) ***(P-14352)***
Wikoff Color Corporation........F.......916 928-6965
1329 N Market Blvd # 160 Sacramento (95834) ***(P-9216)***
Wilbur Curtis Co Inc........B.......323 837-2300
6913 W Acco St Montebello (90640) ***(P-16139)***
Wilbur Curtis Co Inc........B.......323 837-2300
6913 W Acco St Montebello (90640) ***(P-16140)***
Wilbur Manufacturing, Hayward *Also called Nova Tool Co* ***(P-23720)***

A
L
P
H
A
B
E
T
I
C

Employee Codes: A=Over 500 employees, B=251-500
C=101-250, D=51-100, E=20-50, F=10-19
2019 California
Manfacturers Register
© Mergent Inc. 1-800-342-5647
1331

Wilbur-Ellis Company LLC........D.......559 442-1220
2903 S Cedar Ave Fresno (93725) ***(P-14125)***
Wilcox AG Products, Walnut Grove *Also called Wilcox Brothers Inc* ***(P-14126)***
Wilcox Brothers Inc........D.......916 776-1784
14180 State Highway 160 Walnut Grove (95690) ***(P-14126)***
Wilcox Machine Co........D.......562 927-5353
7180 Scout Ave Bell Gardens (90201) ***(P-17066)***
Wild Horse Industrial Corp........F.......707 265-6801
640 Airpark Rd Ste A NAPA (94558) ***(P-15236)***
Wild Lizard, Los Angeles *Also called Bb Co Inc* ***(P-3381)***
Wild Turkey Distillery, San Francisco *Also called Rare Breed Distilling LLC* ***(P-2075)***
Wild Wood Designs Inc........F.......714 543-6549
1607 E Edinger Ave Ste P Santa Ana (92705) ***(P-4753)***
Wildbrine LLC........E.......707 657-7607
322 Bellevue Ave Santa Rosa (95407) ***(P-871)***
Wilden Pump and Engrg LLC (HQ)........B.......909 422-1700
22069 Van Buren St Grand Terrace (92313) ***(P-15100)***
Wilderness Trail Bikes Inc (PA)........F.......415 389-5040
475 Miller Ave Mill Valley (94941) ***(P-21150)***
Wildflower Linen Inc (PA)........E.......714 522-2777
6901 8th St Buena Park (90620) ***(P-3021)***
Wildlife Fur Dressing Inc........F.......209 538-2901
3415 Harold St Ceres (95307) ***(P-10468)***
Wildlife In Wood Inc........F.......714 773-5816
165 E Liberty Ave Anaheim (92801) ***(P-4664)***
Wildthings Snap-Ons Inc........F.......415 457-0112
4 De Luca Pl San Rafael (94901) ***(P-3589)***
Wildwood Designs, Santa Ana *Also called Wild Wood Designs Inc* ***(P-4753)***
Wiley X Eyewear, Livermore *Also called X Wiley Inc* ***(P-23132)***
Wilkins Design and Mfg Inc........E.......714 564-3351
2619 Oak St Santa Ana (92707) ***(P-12283)***
Wilkinson Mfg Inc........F.......408 809-7341
332 Piercy Rd San Jose (95138) ***(P-17067)***
Will Pak Foods Inc........F.......800 874-0883
4471 Santa Ana St Ste C Ontario (91761) ***(P-908)***
Will's Fresh Foods, San Leandro *Also called Woolery Enterprises Inc* ***(P-2701)***
Will-Mann Inc........E.......714 870-0350
225 E Santa Fe Ave Fullerton (92832) ***(P-12819)***
Willard Marine Inc........D.......714 630-4018
1250 N Grove St Anaheim (92806) ***(P-21071)***
Willey Printing Company Inc........E.......209 524-4811
1405 10th St Modesto (95354) ***(P-7186)***
William A Shubeck........E.......909 795-6970
10961 Desert Lawn Dr # 102 Calimesa (92320) ***(P-24016)***
William Bounds Ltd........E.......310 375-0505
23625 Madison St Torrance (90505) ***(P-14897)***
William Getz Corp........E.......714 516-2050
539 W Walnut Ave Orange (92868) ***(P-23692)***
William Hill Winery........E.......707 224-5424
1761 Atlas Peak Rd NAPA (94558) ***(P-2056)***
William Ho........F.......510 226-9089
40760 Encyclopedia Cir Fremont (94538) ***(P-15886)***
William J Hammett Inc........F.......626 966-1708
221 E San Bernardino Rd Covina (91723) ***(P-7187)***
William Kreysler & Assoc Inc........E.......707 552-3500
501 Green Island Rd American Canyon (94503) ***(P-10444)***
William McClung........F.......970 535-4601
987 Keller Ave Crescent City (95531) ***(P-23479)***
William R Schmitt........E.......530 243-3069
18135 Clear Creek Rd Redding (96001) ***(P-4024)***
Williams & Selyem Winery........F.......707 433-6425
7227 Westside Rd Healdsburg (95448) ***(P-2057)***
Williams Aerospace & Mfg Inc........E.......619 660-6220
2820 Via Orange Way Ste G Spring Valley (91978) ***(P-20973)***
Williams Cabinets Inc........F.......530 365-8421
2011 Frontier Trl Anderson (96007) ***(P-4369)***
Williams Comfort Products, Colton *Also called Williams Furnace Co* ***(P-16002)***
Williams Foam Inc........F.......818 833-4343
12961 San Fernando Rd Sylmar (91342) ***(P-4894)***
Williams Furnace Co (HQ)........C.......562 450-3602
250 W Laurel St Colton (92324) ***(P-16002)***
Williams Manufacturing Company........F.......818 898-2272
12727 Foothill Blvd Sylmar (91342) ***(P-13780)***
Williams Metal Blanking Dies........F.......562 634-4592
16222 Minnesota Ave Paramount (90723) ***(P-13298)***
Williams Selyem, Healdsburg *Also called Williams & Selyem Winery* ***(P-2057)***
Williams Sign Co........F.......909 622-5304
111 S Huntington St Pomona (91766) ***(P-24005)***
Willick Engineering Co Inc........F.......562 946-4242
12516 Lakeland Rd Santa Fe Springs (90670) ***(P-22945)***
Willie Bylsma........F.......209 847-3362
10217 Atlas Ct Oakdale (95361) ***(P-14898)***
Willis Construction Co Inc........C.......831 623-2900
2261 San Juan Hwy San Juan Bautista (95045) ***(P-11021)***
Willis Machine Inc........E.......805 604-4500
200 Kinetic Dr Oxnard (93030) ***(P-17068)***
Willits News, Willits *Also called Media News Group* ***(P-5956)***
Willits Redwood Company Inc........E.......707 459-4549
220 Franklin Ave Willits (95490) ***(P-4071)***
Willow & Clay, Vernon *Also called Complete Clothing Company* ***(P-3303)***
Willpower Labs Inc........F.......415 805-1518
3318 California St Apt 4 San Francisco (94118) ***(P-8444)***
Wills Wing, Orange *Also called Sport Kites Inc* ***(P-20628)***
Wilmanco........F.......805 523-2390
5350 Kazuko Ct Moorpark (93021) ***(P-18302)***
Wilmar Oils Fats Stockton LLC........E.......925 627-1600
2008 Port Road B Stockton (95203) ***(P-1517)***
Wilmington Ironworks, Wilmington *Also called Wilmington Machine Inc* ***(P-17069)***
Wilmington Machine Inc........F.......310 518-3213
432 W C St Wilmington (90744) ***(P-17069)***
Wilmington Woodworks Inc........E.......310 834-1015
318 E C St Wilmington (90744) ***(P-4514)***
Wilorco, Carson *Also called Strike Technology Inc* ***(P-19738)***
Wilschur Design and Mfg, Santa Ana *Also called Wilkins Design and Mfg Inc* ***(P-12283)***
Wilsenergy LLC........F.......951 676-7700
42440 Winchester Rd Temecula (92590) ***(P-13681)***
Wilsey Foods Inc........A.......714 257-3700
40 Pointe Dr Brea (92821) ***(P-1555)***
Wilshire Book Company Inc........E.......818 700-1522
22647 Ventura Blvd Woodland Hills (91364) ***(P-6409)***
Wilshire Precision Pdts Inc........E.......818 765-4571
7353 Hinds Ave North Hollywood (91605) ***(P-17070)***
Wilson Artisan Wineries, Healdsburg *Also called Stonecushion Inc* ***(P-1999)***
Wilson Creek Wnery Vnyards Inc........C.......951 699-9463
35960 Rancho Cal Rd Temecula (92591) ***(P-2058)***
Wilson Garment, Alhambra *Also called Silver Star Exchange* ***(P-3497)***
Wilson Imaging and Publishing........F.......909 931-1818
305 N 2nd Ave Pmb 324 Upland (91786) ***(P-6626)***
Wilsons Art Studio Inc........D.......714 870-7030
501 S Acacia Ave Fullerton (92831) ***(P-7542)***
Wilsted & Taylor Pubg Svcs........F.......510 428-9087
430 40th St Oakland (94609) ***(P-7637)***
Wilwood Engineering........C.......805 388-1188
4700 Calle Bolero Camarillo (93012) ***(P-20486)***
Win Fat Food LLC........E.......323 261-1869
700 Monterey Pass Rd A Monterey Park (91754) ***(P-556)***
Win Soon Inc........E.......323 564-5070
4569 Firestone Blvd South Gate (90280) ***(P-740)***
Win-Glo Window Coverings, San Jose *Also called Hunter Douglas Fabrications* ***(P-5194)***
Win-Holt Equipment Corp........F.......909 625-2624
2717 N Towne Ave Pomona (91767) ***(P-14353)***
Winbo Usa Inc........E.......951 738-9978
2120 California Ave Ste 2 Corona (92881) ***(P-12820)***
Winchester Electronics Div, Sacramento *Also called L3 Technologies Inc* ***(P-15442)***
Wind & Shade Screens Inc........F.......760 761-4994
1223 Linda Vista Dr San Marcos (92078) ***(P-2787)***
Wind River Systems Inc (HQ)........C.......510 748-4100
500 Wind River Way Alameda (94501) ***(P-25350)***
Wind River Systems Inc........D.......858 824-3100
10505 Sorrento Valley Rd San Diego (92121) ***(P-25351)***
Windline Marine........C.......310 516-9812
14601 S Broadway Gardena (90248) ***(P-12010)***
Windmill Corporation........E.......650 873-1000
314 Harbor Way South San Francisco (94080) ***(P-1345)***
Window & Door Shop Inc (PA)........F.......415 282-6192
185 Industrial St San Francisco (94124) ***(P-4257)***
Window Enterprises Inc........E.......951 943-4894
430 Nevada St Redlands (92373) ***(P-12355)***
Window Hardware Supply........F.......510 463-0301
1717 Kirkham St Oakland (94607) ***(P-10445)***
Window Products Management Inc........F.......805 677-6800
5917 Olivas Park Dr Ste F Ventura (93003) ***(P-4258)***
Window Solutions........F.......650 349-2499
9301 Research Dr Irvine (92618) ***(P-23212)***
Windshield Pros Incorporated........E.......951 272-2867
4501 E Airport Dr Ontario (91761) ***(P-20487)***
Windsor Foods, Hayward *Also called Ajinomoto Foods North Amer Inc* ***(P-974)***
Windsor Foods, Ontario *Also called Ajinomoto Foods North Amer Inc* ***(P-975)***
Windsor House Investments Inc........E.......323 261-0231
12250 Coast Dr Whittier (90601) ***(P-5660)***
Windsor Mill, Cotati *Also called Windsor Willits Company* ***(P-4259)***
Windsor Mill, Willits *Also called Windsor Willits Company* ***(P-4260)***
Windsor Oaks Vineyards LLP........E.......707 433-4050
10810 Hillview Rd Windsor (95492) ***(P-2059)***
Windsor Textile Corporation........F.......310 323-3997
13122 S Normandie Ave Gardena (90249) ***(P-2948)***
Windsor Vineyards, Santa Rosa *Also called Mildara Blass Inc* ***(P-1879)***
Windsor Willits Company (PA)........E.......707 665-9663
7950 Redwood Dr Ste 4 Cotati (94931) ***(P-4259)***
Windsor Willits Company........E.......707 459-8568
661 Railroad Ave Willits (95490) ***(P-4260)***
Windtamer Tarps........F.......559 584-2080
13704 Hanford Armona Rd B2 Hanford (93230) ***(P-3821)***
Windward Yacht & Repair Inc........F.......310 823-4581
13645 Fiji Way Venice (90292) ***(P-21072)***
Windward Yacht Center, Venice *Also called Windward Yacht & Repair Inc* ***(P-21072)***
Windy Balloon Company, Gardena *Also called South Bay Corporation* ***(P-9679)***
Wine Appreciation Guild Ltd........F.......650 866-3020
360 Swift Ave Ste 34 South San Francisco (94080) ***(P-6410)***
Wine Business Monthly, Sonoma *Also called Wine Communications Group* ***(P-6292)***
Wine Cellar Impressions Inc........F.......408 277-0100
2013 Stone Ave San Jose (95125) ***(P-2060)***
Wine Communications Group........F.......707 939-0822
35 Maple St Sonoma (95476) ***(P-6292)***
Wine Company of San Francisco........F.......650 851-0965
231 Ware Rd Ste 823 Woodside (94062) ***(P-2061)***
Wine Country Cases Inc........D.......707 967-4805
621 Airpark Rd NAPA (94558) ***(P-4540)***
Wine Foundry, NAPA *Also called Vignette Winery LLC* ***(P-2040)***
Wine Group Inc (HQ)........C.......209 599-4111
17000 E State Highway 120 Ripon (95366) ***(P-2062)***
Wine Makers Inc........F.......909 481-5050
8916 Foothill Blvd Ste K3 Rancho Cucamonga (91730) ***(P-2063)***
Wine Tailor, The, Rancho Cucamonga *Also called Wine Makers Inc* ***(P-2063)***
Winery Services Group, Salinas *Also called SMS Industrial Inc* ***(P-12421)***
Wing Hing Noodle Company, Ontario *Also called Passport Food Group LLC* ***(P-2635)***

Wing Inflatables Inc (HQ) ....C....707 826-2887
1220 5th St Arcata (95521) *(P-10446)*
Wing Master, Clovis *Also called Valley Chrome Plating Inc (P-13531)*
Wing Nien Company, Hayward *Also called U S Enterprise Corporation (P-938)*
Winner Industrial Chemicals ....E....909 887-6228
154 W Foothill Blvd Ste A Upland (91786) *(P-9053)*
Winning Laboratories Inc ....F....562 921-6880
16218 Arthur St Cerritos (90703) *(P-7983)*
Winning Team Inc ....F....661 295-1428
24922 Anza Dr Ste E Valencia (91355) *(P-3869)*
Winnov Inc ....F....888 315-9460
3910 Freedom Cir Ste 102 Santa Clara (95054) *(P-17880)*
Winonics Inc ....C....714 626-3755
1257 S State College Blvd Fullerton (92831) *(P-18653)*
Winslow Automation Inc ....D....408 262-9004
905 Montague Expy Milpitas (95035) *(P-19273)*
Winstar Textile Inc ....E....626 357-1133
16815 E Johnson Dr City of Industry (91745) *(P-3590)*
Winstronics, Fremont *Also called Wintronics International Inc (P-11682)*
Wint Corporation ....C....408 532-8356
5686 Country Club Pkwy San Jose (95138) *(P-22148)*
Wintec Industries Inc ....E....510 953-7400
8674 Thornton Ave Newark (94560) *(P-15887)*
Wintec Industries Inc (PA) ....C....510 953-7440
8674 Thornton Ave Newark (94560) *(P-15888)*
Winter & Bain Manufacturing (PA) ....F....213 749-3568
1417 Elwood St Los Angeles (90021) *(P-14261)*
Winter & Bain Manufacturing ....F....213 749-3561
1410 Elwood St Los Angeles (90021) *(P-14262)*
Wintflash Inc ....F....562 944-6548
13720 De Alcala Dr La Mirada (90638) *(P-7543)*
Winther Technologies Inc (PA) ....E....310 618-8437
560 Alaska Ave Torrance (90503) *(P-14745)*
Winton Times ....E....209 358-5311
6950 Gerard Ave Winton (95388) *(P-6089)*
Wintriss Engineering Corp ....E....858 550-7300
9010 Kenamar Dr Ste 101 San Diego (92121) *(P-22149)*
Wintronics International Inc ....E....510 226-7588
3817 Spinnaker Ct Fremont (94538) *(P-11682)*
Winway Usa Inc ....E....203 775-9311
1800 Wyatt Dr Ste 2 Santa Clara (95054) *(P-19274)*
Wire Bonding Tools, Petaluma *Also called Small Precision Tools Inc (P-11370)*
Wire Cut Company Inc ....E....714 994-1170
6750 Caballero Blvd Buena Park (90620) *(P-17071)*
Wire Guard Systems Inc ....F....323 588-2166
2050 E Slauson Ave Huntington Park (90255) *(P-17521)*
Wire Harness & Cable Assembly, Santa Monica *Also called Omega Leads Inc (P-19670)*
Wire Technology Corporation ....E....310 635-6935
9527 Laurel St Los Angeles (90002) *(P-11683)*
Wired Ventures Inc ....C....415 276-8400
520 3rd St Ste 305 San Francisco (94107) *(P-6293)*
Wireless Glue Networks Inc ....F....925 310-4561
4185 Blackhawk Plaza Cir # 220 Danville (94506) *(P-25352)*
Wireless Products, San Diego *Also called Trexta Inc (P-18290)*
Wireless Systems Segment, San Jose *Also called Te Connectivity Corporation (P-19419)*
Wireless Technology Inc ....E....805 339-9696
2064 Eastman Ave Ste 113 Ventura (93003) *(P-17881)*
Wireman Fence Products, Rancho Cordova *Also called Fencer Enterprises LLC (P-11440)*
Wiretech Inc (PA) ....D....323 722-4933
6440 Canning St Commerce (90040) *(P-11466)*
Wirewright Inc ....F....805 499-9194
3563 Old Conejo Rd Newbury Park (91320) *(P-10447)*
Wirta Logging Inc ....E....928 440-3446
970 Kandy Ln Portola (96122) *(P-4025)*
Wirz & Co ....F....909 825-6970
444 Colton Ave Colton (92324) *(P-7188)*
Wise Living Inc ....E....323 541-0410
2001 W 60th St Los Angeles (90047) *(P-4924)*
Wise Villa Winery LLC ....F....916 543-0323
4226 Wise Rd Lincoln (95648) *(P-2064)*
Wissings Inc ....F....858 625-4111
9906 Mesa Rim Rd San Diego (92121) *(P-7189)*
Wit Group ....E....530 243-4447
1822 Buenaventura Blvd # 101 Redding (96001) *(P-2235)*
Witt Hillard ....E....530 510-0756
310 Providence Mine Rd Nevada City (95959) *(P-8683)*
Witten Logging ....F....760 378-3640
4600 Kelso Creek Rd Weldon (93283) *(P-4026)*
Witts Everything For Office, Tehachapi *Also called Pmrca Inc (P-7031)*
Wixen Music Publishing Inc ....F....818 591-7355
24025 Park Sorrento # 130 Calabasas (91302) *(P-6411)*
Wizard Enterprise ....F....323 756-8430
12605 Daphne Ave Hawthorne (90250) *(P-10797)*
Wizard Graphics Inc ....F....530 893-3636
411 Otterson Dr Ste 20 Chico (95928) *(P-7544)*
Wizard Manufacturing Inc ....F....530 342-1861
2244 Ivy St Chico (95928) *(P-1506)*
Wizeline Inc ....F....650 389-7272
456 Montgomery St # 2200 San Francisco (94104) *(P-15505)*
Wjb Bearings Inc ....E....909 598-6238
535 Brea Canyon Rd City of Industry (91789) *(P-13133)*
Wjlp Company Inc ....D....800 628-1123
4848 Frontier Way Ste 100 Stockton (95215) *(P-19370)*
Wkf (friedman Enterprises Inc (PA) ....F....925 673-9100
2334 Stagecoach Rd Ste B Stockton (95215) *(P-20692)*
Wls Coatings Inc ....F....310 538-2155
1680 Miller Ave Los Angeles (90063) *(P-8956)*
Wm J Clark Trucking Svc Inc ....F....831 385-4000
319 Division St King City (93930) *(P-393)*
Wm J Matson Company ....F....805 684-9410
213 N Olive St Ventura (93001) *(P-13682)*
WMC Precision Machining ....F....714 773-0059
1234 E Ash Ave Ste A Fullerton (92831) *(P-17072)*
Wme Bi LLC ....D....877 592-2472
17075 Camino San Diego (92127) *(P-25353)*
Wna City of Industry, City of Industry *Also called Wna Comet West Inc (P-10448)*
Wna City of Industry, City of Industry *Also called Waddington North America Inc (P-10434)*
Wna Comet West Inc ....C....626 913-0724
1135 Samuelson St City of Industry (91748) *(P-10448)*
Wohler Technologies Inc ....E....510 870-0810
1280 San Luis Obispo St Hayward (94544) *(P-18303)*
Wolf Canyon Asia Pacific, Marina *Also called Wolf Canyon of America Inc (P-1104)*
Wolf Canyon of America Inc ....F....831 626-1320
3013 Lighthouse Ln Marina (93933) *(P-1104)*
Wolfe Engineering, Inc., San Jose *Also called Jabil Silver Creek Inc (P-25415)*
Wolfpack Inc ....E....760 736-4500
2440 Grand Ave Ste B Vista (92081) *(P-24006)*
Wolfpack Gear Inc ....F....805 439-1911
3765 S Higuera St Ste 150 San Luis Obispo (93401) *(P-5649)*
Wolfpack Sign Group, Vista *Also called Wolfpack Inc (P-24006)*
Wolfram Inc ....F....209 238-9610
1309 Doker Dr Ste B Modesto (95351) *(P-10671)*
Wolfs Precision Works Inc ....F....650 364-1341
3549 Haven Ave Ste F Menlo Park (94025) *(P-17073)*
Wolfson Knitting Mills Inc ....F....213 627-8746
2124 Sacramento St Los Angeles (90021) *(P-2768)*
Wolverine World Wide Inc ....F....800 253-2184
1020 Prosperity Way Beaumont (92223) *(P-10493)*
Womack International Inc ....E....707 763-1800
3855 Cypress Dr Ste H Petaluma (94954) *(P-15376)*
Wombat Products Inc ....E....805 794-1767
1384 Callens Rd Ste B Ventura (93003) *(P-10449)*
Wonder Grip USA Inc ....F....404 290-2015
3070 Bristol St Ste 440 Costa Mesa (92626) *(P-10450)*
Wonder Marketing Inc ....E....310 235-1469
11601 Wilshire Blvd # 2150 Los Angeles (90025) *(P-8957)*
Wonder Metals Corporation ....F....530 241-3251
4351 Caterpillar Rd Redding (96003) *(P-12356)*
Wonderful Pstchios Almonds LLC (HQ) ....E....310 966-4650
11444 W Olympic Blvd Los Angeles (90064) *(P-1507)*
Wondergrove LLC ....F....800 889-7249
17563 Ventura Blvd Fl 1 Encino (91316) *(P-25354)*
Wonolo Inc ....E....415 766-7692
535 Mission St Fl 14 San Francisco (94105) *(P-25355)*
Wood Box Specialties Inc ....F....510 786-1600
23308 Kidder St Hayward (94545) *(P-4541)*
Wood Connection Inc ....E....209 577-1044
4701 N Star Way Modesto (95356) *(P-4261)*
Wood Tech Inc ....D....510 534-4930
4611 Malat St Oakland (94601) *(P-4754)*
Wood-N-Wood Products Cal, Fresno *Also called Wood-N-Wood Products Inc (P-4544)*
Wood-N-Wood Products Cal Inc (PA) ....E....559 896-3636
2247 W Birch Ave Fresno (93711) *(P-4542)*
Wood-N-Wood Products Cal Inc ....E....559 896-3636
13598 S Golden State Blvd Selma (93662) *(P-4543)*
Wood-N-Wood Products Inc ....F....559 896-3636
2247 W Birch Ave Fresno (93711) *(P-4544)*
Woodbridge Glass, Tustin *Also called Werner Systems Inc (P-11626)*
Woodbridge Winery, Acampo *Also called Franciscan Vineyards Inc (P-1771)*
Wooden Bridge Inc ....F....408 436-9663
483 Reynolds Cir San Jose (95112) *(P-4370)*
Woodford Wicks LLC ....F....614 554-8474
302 Williams Way Hayward (94541) *(P-24291)*
Woodford Wicks Candle Company, Hayward *Also called Woodford Wicks LLC (P-24291)*
Woodland Bedrooms Inc ....D....562 408-1558
3423 Merced St Los Angeles (90065) *(P-4755)*
Woodland Products Co Inc ....F....909 622-3456
10825 7th St Ste C Rancho Cucamonga (91730) *(P-5120)*
Woodland Welding Works ....F....530 666-5531
1955 E Main St Woodland (95776) *(P-12284)*
Woodline Cabinets, Fairfield *Also called Woodline Partners Inc (P-4371)*
Woodline Partners Inc ....E....707 864-5445
5165 Fulton Dr Fairfield (94534) *(P-4371)*
Woodmark Manufacturing, Sacramento *Also called Silver Eagle Corporation (P-3748)*
Woodpecker Cabinet Inc ....E....310 404-4805
21512 Nordhoff St Chatsworth (91311) *(P-4372)*
Woodruff Corporation ....E....310 378-1611
109 Calle Mayor Redondo Beach (90277) *(P-17074)*
Woodside Investment Inc ....D....209 787-8040
12405 E Brandt Rd Lockeford (95237) *(P-13985)*
Woodsmiths Architectural Casew ....F....916 456-8871
2709 Del Monte St West Sacramento (95691) *(P-5121)*
Woodsource International ....F....310 328-9663
2201 Dominguez St Torrance (90501) *(P-4387)*
Woodtech Industries, Santa Clara *Also called Wti Jkb Inc (P-4262)*
Woodward Drilling Company ....E....707 374-4300
550 River Rd Rio Vista (94571) *(P-124)*
Woodward Duarte, Duarte *Also called Woodward Hrt Inc (P-20975)*
Woodward Hrt Inc ....B....626 359-9211
1700 Business Center Dr Duarte (91010) *(P-20974)*
Woodward Hrt Inc (HQ) ....A....661 294-6000
25200 Rye Canyon Rd Santa Clarita (91355) *(P-17324)*
Woodward Hrt Inc ....D....661 702-5552
25200 Rye Canyon Rd Santa Clarita (91355) *(P-17325)*
Woodward Hrt Inc ....C....626 359-9211
1700 Business Center Dr Duarte (91010) *(P-20975)*
Woodworks ....F....831 688-8420
107 Nunes Rd Watsonville (95076) *(P-4756)*

ALPHABETIC

Employee Codes: A=Over 500 employees, B=251-500
C=101-250, D=51-100, E=20-50, F=10-19
2019 California
Manfacturers Register
© Mergent Inc. 1-800-342-5647
1333

Woof & Poof Inc ....E....530 895-0693
388 Orange St Chico (95928) ***(P-3757)***
Woojin Is America Inc ....F....626 386-0101
5108 Azusa Canyon Rd Irwindale (91706) ***(P-21085)***
Woolery Enterprises Inc ....E....510 357-5700
1991 Republic Ave San Leandro (94577) ***(P-2701)***
Wordsmart Corporation ....D....858 565-8068
10025 Mesa Rim Rd San Diego (92121) ***(P-25356)***
Workbook Inc ....E....323 856-0008
110 N Doheny Dr Beverly Hills (90211) ***(P-6412)***
Working Nurse, Los Angeles *Also called Recruitment Services Inc* ***(P-6245)***
Working World, Los Angeles *Also called Rhodes Publications Inc* ***(P-6247)***
Workman Holdings Inc ....F....760 723-5283
525 Industrial Way Fallbrook (92028) ***(P-22682)***
Works Connection ....F....530 642-9488
4130 Product Dr Cameron Park (95682) ***(P-21151)***
Works Performance Products Inc ....E....818 701-1010
21045 Osborne St Canoga Park (91304) ***(P-20488)***
Works, The, Eureka *Also called Eureka Record Works Inc* ***(P-17800)***
Workspot Inc (PA) ....F....408 533-8669
1601 S De Anza Blvd # 230 Cupertino (95014) ***(P-25357)***
Workstation Industries Inc ....E....714 258-7535
1938 E Pomona St Santa Ana (92705) ***(P-5264)***
World Amenities, San Diego *Also called Robanda International Inc* ***(P-8830)***
World Centric ....F....707 241-9190
617 2nd St Ste C Petaluma (94952) ***(P-5747)***
World Harmony Organization ....F....415 246-6886
514 Arballo Dr San Francisco (94132) ***(P-6413)***
World Industries International ....F....818 649-7858
655 N Central Ave Fl 1700 Glendale (91203) ***(P-10451)***
World Journal Inc (PA) ....D....650 692-9936
231 Adrian Rd Millbrae (94030) ***(P-6090)***
World Journal Inc ....E....323 261-6972
1588 Corporate Center Dr Monterey Park (91754) ***(P-6091)***
World Journal La LLC (HQ) ....C....323 268-4982
1588 Corporate Center Dr Monterey Park (91754) ***(P-6092)***
World Manufacturing Inc (PA) ....F....714 662-3539
350 Fischer Ave Ste B Costa Mesa (92626) ***(P-9772)***
World Oil Corp ....E....562 928-0100
9302 Garfield Ave South Gate (90280) ***(P-88)***
World Oil Marketing Company (PA) ....E....562 928-0100
9302 Garfield Ave South Gate (90280) ***(P-9376)***
World Service Office, Chatsworth *Also called Narcotics Anonymous World Serv* ***(P-6365)***
World Tariff Limited ....E....415 391-7501
220 Montgomery St Ste 448 San Francisco (94104) ***(P-6294)***
World Textile and Bag Inc ....E....916 922-9222
1627 Main Ave Ste 4 Sacramento (95838) ***(P-3774)***
World Traditions Inc ....E....951 990-6346
332 Camino De La Luna Perris (92571) ***(P-10839)***
World Trend Inc (PA) ....F....909 620-9945
1920 W Holt Ave Pomona (91768) ***(P-23800)***
World Upholstery & Trim Inc ....F....805 921-0100
1320 E Main St Santa Paula (93060) ***(P-3930)***
World Wine Bottles LLC ....E....707 339-2102
1370 Trancas St Ste 411 NAPA (94558) ***(P-10628)***
World Wine Bottles & Packaging, NAPA *Also called World Wine Bottles LLC* ***(P-10628)***
Worldflash Software Inc ....E....310 745-0632
3853 Marcasel Ave Ste 101 Los Angeles (90066) ***(P-25358)***
Worldlink Media ....F....415 561-2141
38 Keyes Ave Ste 17 San Francisco (94129) ***(P-25359)***
Worldradio Inc ....F....916 457-3655
2120 28th St Sacramento (95818) ***(P-6295)***
Worldradio News, Sacramento *Also called Worldradio Inc* ***(P-6295)***
Worldtariff, San Francisco *Also called World Tariff Limited* ***(P-6294)***
Worldview Project ....F....858 964-0709
2445 Morena Blvd Ste 210 San Diego (92110) ***(P-6414)***
Worldwide Aeros Corp ....D....818 344-3999
1734 Aeros Way Montebello (90640) ***(P-20635)***
Worldwide Energy & Mfg USA Inc (PA) ....E....650 692-7788
1675 Rollins Rd Ste F Burlingame (94010) ***(P-19275)***
Worldwide Envmtl Pdts Inc (PA) ....D....714 990-2700
1100 Beacon St Brea (92821) ***(P-21677)***
Worldwide Gaming Systems Corp ....E....818 678-9150
9205 Alabama Ave Ste E Chatsworth (91311) ***(P-23480)***
Worldwide Specialties Inc ....C....323 587-2200
2420 Modoc St Los Angeles (90021) ***(P-2702)***
Worthington Cylinder Corp ....C....909 594-7777
336 Enterprise Pl Pomona (91768) ***(P-12443)***
Wpi Salem Division, Camarillo *Also called Cooper Crouse-Hinds LLC* ***(P-9603)***
Wpm, Ventura *Also called Window Products Management Inc* ***(P-4258)***
Wpx Energy Inc ....F....510 727-9708
1122 B St Ste 220 Hayward (94541) ***(P-161)***
Wrenchware Inc ....F....951 784-2717
2751 Reche Canyon Rd # 104 Colton (92324) ***(P-10814)***
Wrex Products Inc Chico ....D....530 895-3838
25 Wrex Ct Chico (95928) ***(P-10452)***
Wright Business Forms Inc ....E....909 614-6700
13602 12th St Ste A Chino (91710) ***(P-7562)***
Wright Business Graphics Calif, Chino *Also called Wright Business Forms Inc* ***(P-7562)***
Wright Capacitors Inc ....F....714 546-2490
2610 Oak St Santa Ana (92707) ***(P-19306)***
Wright Engineered Plastics Inc ....D....707 575-1218
3681 N Laughlin Rd Santa Rosa (95403) ***(P-14592)***
Wright Pharma Inc ....E....209 549-9771
700 Kiernan Ave Ste A Modesto (95356) ***(P-8445)***
Wright Technologies Inc ....F....916 773-4424
1352 Blue Oaks Blvd # 140 Roseville (95678) ***(P-19789)***
Wrightspeed Inc ....D....866 960-9482
650 W Tower Ave Alameda (94501) ***(P-13147)***
Write Thought Inc ....F....559 876-2170
1254 Commerce Way Sanger (93657) ***(P-6296)***
Wrought Iron Fencing & Supply ....E....760 591-3110
1370 La Mirada Dr San Marcos (92078) ***(P-12908)***
Wrs Materials, San Jose *Also called Wafer Reclaim Services LLC* ***(P-19269)***
Ws Packaging-Blake Printery (HQ) ....F....805 543-6843
2222 Beebee St San Luis Obispo (93401) ***(P-7190)***
Ws Packaging-Blake Printery ....E....805 543-6844
2224 Beebee St San Luis Obispo (93401) ***(P-7191)***
Wsglass Holdings Inc ....F....916 388-5885
180 Main Ave Sacramento (95838) ***(P-22150)***
Wsglass Holdings Inc (HQ) ....E....510 623-5000
3241 Darby Cmn Fremont (94539) ***(P-10613)***
Wsr Publishing Inc (PA) ....F....951 676-4914
27645 Commerce Center Dr Temecula (92590) ***(P-6297)***
Wsw Corp (PA) ....E....818 989-5008
16000 Strathern St Van Nuys (91406) ***(P-20489)***
Wti, Ventura *Also called Wireless Technology Inc* ***(P-17881)***
Wti Jkb Inc (PA) ....F....408 297-8579
405 Aldo Ave Santa Clara (95054) ***(P-4262)***
Wunder-Mold Inc ....E....707 448-2349
790 Eubanks Dr Vacaville (95688) ***(P-10453)***
WV Communications Inc ....E....805 376-1820
1125 Bus Ctr Cir Ste A Newbury Park (91320) ***(P-18304)***
Wwf Operating Company ....C....626 810-1775
18275 Arenth Ave Bldg 1 City of Industry (91748) ***(P-741)***
Wwt International Inc ....F....714 632-0810
1150 N Tustin Ave Anaheim (92807) ***(P-14245)***
Www.asbworkshop.com, San Francisco *Also called A S Batle Company* ***(P-11343)***
Www.b-Dazzle.com, Redondo Beach *Also called B Dazzle Inc* ***(P-23408)***
Www.masterlocks.com, San Diego *Also called Hodge Products Inc* ***(P-11961)***
Www.slp-Formx.com, Anaheim *Also called Slp Limited LLC* ***(P-18606)***
Www.zerran.com, Pacoima *Also called Zerran International Corp* ***(P-8869)***
Wyatt Precision Machine Inc ....E....562 634-0524
3301 E 59th St Long Beach (90805) ***(P-13053)***
Wyatt Technology Corporation (PA) ....C....805 681-9009
6330 Hollister Ave Goleta (93117) ***(P-22050)***
Wycen Foods Inc (PA) ....F....510 351-1987
560 Estabrook St San Leandro (94577) ***(P-535)***
Wylatti Resource MGT Inc ....E....707 983-8135
23601 Cemetery Ln Covelo (95428) ***(P-4027)***
Wymore Inc ....E....760 352-2045
697 S Dogwood Rd El Centro (92243) ***(P-25450)***
Wyndham Collection LLC ....E....888 522-8476
1175 Aviation Pl San Fernando (91340) ***(P-4373)***
Wypo, Long Beach *Also called Maitlen & Benson Inc* ***(P-14732)***
Wyred 4 Sound LLC ....F....805 466-9973
4235 Traffic Way Atascadero (93422) ***(P-17882)***
Wyrefab Inc ....E....310 523-2147
15711 S Broadway Gardena (90248) ***(P-13866)***
Wyroc Inc (PA) ....F....760 727-0878
2142 Industrial Ct Ste D Vista (92081) ***(P-308)***
Wyroc Materials, Vista *Also called Regional Mtls Recovery Inc* ***(P-305)***
Wyvern Technologies Inc ....E....714 966-0710
1205 E Warner Ave Santa Ana (92705) ***(P-19790)***
X Cell Tool & Manufacturing Co, Gardena *Also called Parker-Hannifin Corporation* ***(P-16832)***
X Controls Inc ....F....858 717-0004
6640 Lusk Blvd Ste A101 San Diego (92121) ***(P-21538)***
X Sublimation Inc ....F....213 700-1024
2837 S Olive St Los Angeles (90007) ***(P-3687)***
X Tri Inc ....F....805 286-4544
8787 Plata Ln Ste 7 Atascadero (93422) ***(P-9217)***
X Wiley Inc (PA) ....D....925 243-9810
7800 Patterson Pass Rd Livermore (94550) ***(P-23132)***
X-Igent Printing Inc ....F....323 837-9779
1001 Goodrich Blvd Commerce (90022) ***(P-7192)***
X-Ray Technology Group, Scotts Valley *Also called Oxford Instruments X-Ray Tech* ***(P-19678)***
Xanadu Bakery, Santa Barbara *Also called Xanadu French Bakery* ***(P-1346)***
Xanadu French Bakery ....E....805 845-7232
1028 Coast Village Rd A Santa Barbara (93108) ***(P-1346)***
Xandex Inc ....D....707 763-7799
1360 Redwood Way Ste A Petaluma (94954) ***(P-21888)***
Xavient Digital, Simi Valley *Also called Xavient Info Systems Inc* ***(P-25360)***
Xavient Info Systems Inc ....A....805 955-4111
2125 N Madera Rd Ste B Simi Valley (93065) ***(P-25360)***
Xceive Corporation ....E....408 486-5610
3900 Freedom Cir Ste 200 Santa Clara (95054) ***(P-19791)***
Xcelaero Corporation ....F....805 547-2660
4540 Broad St Ste 120 San Luis Obispo (93401) ***(P-15188)***
Xceliron Corp ....F....818 700-8404
9540 Vassar Ave Chatsworth (91311) ***(P-14696)***
Xcelmobility Inc ....D....650 320-1728
2225 E Byshore Rd Ste 200 Palo Alto (94303) ***(P-25361)***
Xchanger Manufacturing Corp ....E....510 632-8828
9131 San Leandro St # 220 Oakland (94603) ***(P-12444)***
Xcom Wireless Inc ....F....562 981-0077
2700 Rose Ave Ste E Signal Hill (90755) ***(P-18305)***
Xcvi LLC (PA) ....C....213 749-2661
2311 S Santa Fe Ave Los Angeles (90058) ***(P-2769)***
Xdr Radiology, Los Angeles *Also called Cyber Medical Imaging Inc* ***(P-22864)***
XEL Group, Aliso Viejo *Also called XEL USA Inc* ***(P-19276)***
XEL USA Inc ....E....949 425-8686
66 Argonaut Ste 170 Aliso Viejo (92656) ***(P-19276)***
Xeltek, Sunnyvale *Also called Exp Computer* ***(P-22197)***
Xencor Inc ....C....626 305-5900
111 W Lemon Ave Monrovia (91016) ***(P-8446)***

ALPHABETIC SECTION Yocup Company

Xenonics Inc ....F....760 477-8900
3186 Lionshead Ave # 100 Carlsbad (92010) *(P-20115)*
Xenonics Holdings Inc ....F....760 477-8900
3186 Lionshead Ave # 100 Carlsbad (92010) *(P-17746)*
Xentric Drapery Hardware Inc ....F....818 897-0444
11001 Sutter Ave Pacoima (91331) *(P-5216)*
Xerox Corporation ....F....909 605-7900
2980 Inland Empire Blvd # 105 Ontario (91764) *(P-23213)*
Xerox Corporation ....C....714 565-1200
1851 E 1st St Ste 200 Santa Ana (92705) *(P-23214)*
Xerox International Partners (HQ) ....E....408 953-2700
3174 Porter Dr Palo Alto (94304) *(P-14830)*
Xerxes Corporation ....D....714 630-0012
1210 N Tustin Ave Anaheim (92807) *(P-7901)*
Xgrass Turf Direct, Anaheim *Also called Leonards Carpet Service Inc (P-5080)*
Xhale Distributors ....F....888 942-5355
464 E 4th St Los Angeles (90013) *(P-653)*
Xia LLC ....F....510 494-9020
31057 Genstar Rd Hayward (94544) *(P-22051)*
Xicato Inc (PA) ....E....408 829-4758
101 Daggett Dr San Jose (95134) *(P-17572)*
Xilinx Inc ....D....510 770-9449
42063 Benbow Dr Fremont (94539) *(P-19277)*
Xilinx Inc (PA) ....A....408 559-7778
2100 All Programable San Jose (95124) *(P-18654)*
Xilinx Inc ....F....408 879-6563
2050 All Programable # 4 San Jose (95124) *(P-19278)*
Xilinx Development Corporation (HQ) ....F....408 559-7778
2100 All Programable San Jose (95124) *(P-19279)*
Ximed Medical Systems, San Jose *Also called Prosurg Inc (P-22589)*
Ximenez Icons ....F....310 344-6670
1107 Fair Oaks Ave Ste 11 South Pasadena (91030) *(P-3758)*
Xinet LLC (HQ) ....F....510 845-0555
2560 9th St Ste 312 Berkeley (94710) *(P-25362)*
Xingtera Inc ....F....408 916-4781
2953 Bunker Hill Ln # 202 Santa Clara (95054) *(P-15889)*
Xintec Corporation (PA) ....E....510 832-2130
1660 S Loop Rd Alameda (94502) *(P-23073)*
Xirgo Technologies LLC ....E....805 319-4079
188 Camino Ruiz Fl 2 Camarillo (93012) *(P-20116)*
Xirrus Inc ....C....805 262-1600
2101 Corporate Center Dr A Thousand Oaks (91320) *(P-21678)*
Xitron Technologies, Carlsbad *Also called Impedimed Inc (P-22477)*
Xl Dynamics Inc ....E....562 916-1402
18303 Gridley Rd Cerritos (90703) *(P-25363)*
Xlsoft Corporation (PA) ....F....949 453-2781
12 Mauchly Ste K Irvine (92618) *(P-25364)*
Xmultiple Technologies (PA) ....F....805 579-1100
543 Country Club Dr B-128 Simi Valley (93065) *(P-15506)*
Xmultiple Technologies Inc ....A....805 579-1100
1060 E Los Angeles Ave Simi Valley (93065) *(P-17506)*
Xmultiple/Xrjax, Simi Valley *Also called Xmultiple Technologies (P-15506)*
Xolar Corporation ....E....916 983-6301
1012 E Bidwell St Ste 600 Folsom (95630) *(P-24292)*
Xoma Corporation (PA) ....F....510 204-7200
2200 Powell St Ste 310 Emeryville (94608) *(P-8447)*
Xomv Media Corporation ....E....424 284-4024
9465 Wilshire Blvd Beverly Hills (90212) *(P-6627)*
Xotic Guitars & Effects, San Fernando *Also called Prosound Communications Inc (P-10474)*
Xp Power LLC (HQ) ....D....408 732-7777
990 Benecia Ave Sunnyvale (94085) *(P-19792)*
Xplain Corporation ....F....805 494-9797
705 Lakefield Rd Ste I Westlake Village (91361) *(P-6298)*
Xr LLC ....E....714 847-9292
15251 Pipeline Ln Huntington Beach (92649) *(P-22850)*
Xs Scuba Inc (PA) ....E....714 424-0434
4040 W Chandler Ave Santa Ana (92704) *(P-23693)*
Xsential, Gardena *Also called Techflex Packaging LLC (P-5541)*
Xtandi, San Francisco *Also called Medivation Inc (P-8275)*
Xtime Inc ....E....650 508-4300
1400 Bridge Pkwy Ste 200 Redwood City (94065) *(P-10454)*
Xtreme Manufacturing LLC ....E....559 891-2978
1775 Park St Ste 82 Selma (93662) *(P-12445)*
Xy Corp Inc ....F....760 323-0333
1258 Montalvo Way Ste A Palm Springs (92262) *(P-14463)*
Xylem Inc ....F....559 265-4731
3878 S Willow Ave Fresno (93725) *(P-15101)*
Xylem Water Systems Cal Inc ....E....619 575-7466
830 Bay Blvd Ste 101 Chula Vista (91911) *(P-15102)*
Xyratex, Fremont *Also called Seagate Systems (us) Inc (P-15601)*
XYZ Graphics Inc (PA) ....E....415 227-9972
190 Lombard St San Francisco (94111) *(P-7545)*
XYZ Text Book, San Luis Obispo *Also called McKeague Patpatrick (P-6362)*
Xzavier, Vernon *Also called Mjck Corporation (P-2852)*
Y & D Rubber Corporation ....F....909 517-1683
1451 S Carlos Ave Ontario (91761) *(P-9694)*
Y B S Enterprises Inc ....F....818 848-7790
3116 W Vanowen St Burbank (91505) *(P-18010)*
Y I C, Carson *Also called Yun Industrial Co Ltd (P-18656)*
Y K K U S A, Anaheim *Also called YKK (usa) Inc (P-23783)*
Y Nissim Inc ....F....818 718-9024
9424 Eton Ave Ste H Chatsworth (91311) *(P-15917)*
Y Y K Inc ....F....213 622-0741
411 W 7th St Ste 710 Los Angeles (90014) *(P-23332)*
Y-Change Inc ....F....510 573-2205
43575 Mission Blvd 416 Fremont (94539) *(P-25365)*
Y2k Precision Sheetmetal Inc ....F....714 632-3901
3831 E La Palma Ave Anaheim (92807) *(P-24007)*
Yadav Technology Inc ....F....510 438-0148
48371 Fremont Blvd # 101 Fremont (94538) *(P-19280)*
Yageo America Corporation ....E....408 240-6200
2550 N 1st St Ste 480 San Jose (95131) *(P-19312)*
Yaldo Enterprises Inc ....F....619 445-2578
24680 Viejas Grade Rd B Descanso (91916) *(P-2424)*
Yamachan Ramen, San Jose *Also called Nippon Trends Food Service Inc (P-2624)*
Yamagata America Inc ....F....858 751-1010
3760 Convoy St Ste 219 San Diego (92111) *(P-6628)*
Yamaha Guitar Group Inc (HQ) ....C....818 575-3600
26580 Agoura Rd Calabasas (91302) *(P-23393)*
Yamamoto Manufacturing USA Inc (HQ) ....F....408 387-5250
2025 Gateway Pl Ste 220 San Jose (95110) *(P-18655)*
Yamamoto of Orient Inc ....F....909 591-7654
12475 Mills Ave Chino (91710) *(P-3775)*
Yamamotoyama of America, Chino *Also called Yamamoto of Orient Inc (P-3775)*
Yamasa Enterprises ....E....213 626-2211
515 Stanford Ave Los Angeles (90013) *(P-2307)*
Yamasa Fish Cake, Los Angeles *Also called Yamasa Enterprises (P-2307)*
Yanfeng US Automotive ....E....616 886-3622
30559 San Antonio St Hayward (94544) *(P-5033)*
Yang's Screen Printing, South El Monte *Also called Unique Screen Printing Inc (P-3926)*
Yankon Industries Inc ....E....909 591-2345
13445 12th St Chino (91710) *(P-17658)*
Yara North America Inc ....E....916 375-1109
3961 Channel Dr West Sacramento (95691) *(P-9123)*
Yardney Water MGT Systems, Riverside *Also called Yardney Water MGT Systems Inc (P-16141)*
Yardney Water MGT Systems Inc (PA) ....E....951 656-6716
6666 Box Springs Blvd Riverside (92507) *(P-16141)*
Yaskawa America Inc ....F....949 263-2640
1701 Kaiser Ave Irvine (92614) *(P-15377)*
Yaskawa America Inc ....E....510 651-5204
47215 Lakeview Blvd Fremont (94538) *(P-20117)*
Yaskawa America Inc ....C....408 748-4400
4101 Burton Dr Santa Clara (95054) *(P-17229)*
Yates Gear Inc ....D....530 222-4606
2608 Hartnell Ave Ste 6 Redding (96002) *(P-10585)*
Yavar Manufacturing Co Inc ....E....323 722-2040
1900 S Tubeway Ave Commerce (90040) *(P-5515)*
Yawa Inc ....F....909 391-8888
1706 E Francis St Ontario (91761) *(P-17883)*
Yawitz Inc ....E....909 865-5599
1379 Ridgeway St Pomona (91768) *(P-17573)*
Yayyo Inc ....F....310 926-2643
433 N Camden Dr Ste 600 Beverly Hills (90210) *(P-25366)*
Yb Media LLC ....E....310 467-5804
1534 Plaza Ln 146 Burlingame (94010) *(P-6629)*
Ybcc Inc ....E....626 213-3945
17800 Castleton St # 386 City of Industry (91748) *(P-654)*
YC Textile Inc ....F....323 233-9833
1821 E 48th Pl Vernon (90058) *(P-2770)*
Yeager Enterprises Corp ....D....714 994-2040
7100 Village Dr Buena Park (90621) *(P-11309)*
Yeager Manufacturing Corp (PA) ....E....714 879-2800
2200 E Orangethorpe Ave Anaheim (92806) *(P-20976)*
Yellow Inc ....E....858 689-4851
9350 Trade Pl Ste C San Diego (92126) *(P-23694)*
Yellow Magic Incorporated ....F....951 506-4005
41571 Date St Murrieta (92562) *(P-25367)*
Yellow Pages Inc ....E....714 776-0534
24931 Nellie Gail Rd Laguna Hills (92653) *(P-6630)*
Yellow Springs Instruments, San Diego *Also called Ysi Incorporated (P-22052)*
Yen-Nhai Inc ....E....323 584-1315
4940 District Blvd Vernon (90058) *(P-4819)*
Yenor Inc ....F....310 410-1573
5640 W 63rd St Los Angeles (90056) *(P-7546)*
Yerma Jewelry Mfg Inc ....E....818 551-0690
671 W Broadway Glendale (91204) *(P-23333)*
Yes To Carrots, Pasadena *Also called Yes To Inc (P-8867)*
Yes To Inc ....E....626 365-1976
177 E Colo Blvd Ste 110 Pasadena (91105) *(P-8867)*
Yes-Tek, San Jose *Also called Yield Enhancement Services Inc (P-19282)*
Yesco, Sacramento *Also called Young Electric Sign Company (P-24008)*
Yesco, Mira Loma *Also called Young Electric Sign Company (P-24009)*
Yf Manufacture Inc ....F....626 768-0029
2455 Maple Ave Pomona (91767) *(P-10840)*
YH Texpert Corporation ....F....323 562-8800
5052 Cecelia St South Gate (90280) *(P-3529)*
Yield Engineering Systems Inc ....E....925 373-8353
203 Lawrence Dr Ste A Livermore (94551) *(P-19281)*
Yield Enhancement Services Inc ....F....408 410-5825
364 Sunpark Ct San Jose (95136) *(P-19282)*
Yillik Precision Industries ....D....909 947-2785
1621 S Cucamonga Ave Ontario (91761) *(P-14697)*
Yinlun Tdi LLC ....B....909 390-3944
4850 E Airport Dr Ontario (91761) *(P-20490)*
YKK (usa) Inc ....C....714 701-1200
5001 E La Palma Ave Anaheim (92807) *(P-23783)*
Yla Inc ....D....707 359-3400
2450 Cordelia Rd Fairfield (94534) *(P-11375)*
YMI Jeanswear Inc (PA) ....F....323 581-7700
1155 S Boyle Ave Los Angeles (90023) *(P-3347)*
YMi Jeanswear Inc ....D....213 746-6681
1015 Wall St Ste 115 Los Angeles (90015) *(P-3530)*
Ynez Corporation ....F....805 688-5522
432 2nd St Solvang (93463) *(P-6093)*
Yocup Company ....F....310 884-9888
13711 S Main St Los Angeles (90061) *(P-5501)*

ALPHABETIC

Employee Codes: A=Over 500 employees, B=251-500
C=101-250, D=51-100, E=20-50, F=10-19
2019 California
Manfacturers Register
© Mergent Inc. 1-800-342-5647
1335

Yogi Investments Inc ....F....909 984-5703
419 Capron Ave West Covina (91792) ***(P-10455)***
Yonekyu USA Inc ....D....323 581-4194
3615 E Vernon Ave Vernon (90058) ***(P-536)***
Yong Kee Rice Noodle Co ....F....415 986-3759
946 Stockton St Apt 10c San Francisco (94108) ***(P-2445)***
Yoplait U S A Inc ....E....310 632-9502
1055 Sandhill Ave Carson (90746) ***(P-742)***
Yorba Linda Country Club, Garden Grove *Also called Sanyo Foods Corp America* ***(P-2440)***
York Engineering ....F....323 256-0439
4405 Lincoln Ave Los Angeles (90041) ***(P-14593)***
York Label, El Dorado Hills *Also called Cameo Crafts* ***(P-7264)***
Yosemite Association, El Portal *Also called Yosemite Natural History Assn* ***(P-6415)***
Yosemite Natural History Assn ....D....209 379-2646
5020 El Portal Rd El Portal (95318) ***(P-6415)***
Yosemite Vly Beef Pkg Co Inc ....E....626 435-0170
970 E Sandy Mush Rd Merced (95341) ***(P-459)***
Yoshimasa Display Case Inc ....E....213 637-9999
108 Pico St Pomona (91766) ***(P-5122)***
Youcare Pharma (usa) Inc ....D....951 258-3114
132 Business Center Dr Corona (92880) ***(P-8448)***
Young & Family Inc ....E....707 263-8877
64 Soda Bay Rd Lakeport (95453) ***(P-4263)***
Young American Bindery ....E....310 898-1212
2157 E Del Amo Blvd Compton (90220) ***(P-7625)***
Young Angels Children's Wear, Los Angeles *Also called Angels Young Inc* ***(P-3024)***
Young Dental, Cerritos *Also called US Dental Inc* ***(P-22920)***
Young Electric Sign Company ....E....916 419-8101
875 National Dr Ste 107 Sacramento (95834) ***(P-24008)***
Young Electric Sign Company ....D....909 923-7668
10235 Bellegrave Ave Mira Loma (91752) ***(P-24009)***
Young Engineering & Mfg Inc (PA) ....E....909 394-3225
560 W Terrace Dr San Dimas (91773) ***(P-21679)***
Young Engineers Inc ....D....949 581-9411
25841 Commercentre Dr Lake Forest (92630) ***(P-12011)***
Young Kee, San Francisco *Also called Yong Kee Rice Noodle Co* ***(P-2445)***
Young Knitting Mills ....E....323 980-8677
3499 E 15th St Los Angeles (90023) ***(P-2863)***
Young Machine Inc ....F....909 464-0405
12282 Colony Ave Chino (91710) ***(P-17075)***
Young Nails Inc ....F....714 525-2264
1149 N Patt St Anaheim (92801) ***(P-8868)***
Young Sung USA Inc ....F....213 427-2580
1122 S Alvarado St Los Angeles (90006) ***(P-3974)***
Youngdale Manufacturing Corp ....E....760 727-0644
1216 Liberty Way Ste B Vista (92081) ***(P-12012)***
Younger Mfg Co (PA) ....B....310 783-1533
2925 California St Torrance (90503) ***(P-23133)***
Younger Optics, Torrance *Also called Younger Mfg Co* ***(P-23133)***
Youngs Custom Cabinet Inc ....F....415 822-8313
1760 Yosemite Ave San Francisco (94124) ***(P-4374)***
Youngs Evergreen Nursery Co, Fountain Valley *Also called California Clock Co* ***(P-23218)***
Yreka Division, Yreka *Also called Timber Products Co Ltd Partnr* ***(P-4386)***
Yreka Transit Mix Concrete ....F....530 842-4351
126 Schantz Rd Yreka (96097) ***(P-11214)***
Ys Controls LLC ....E....714 641-0727
3041 S Shannon St Santa Ana (92704) ***(P-22298)***
Ysi Incorporated ....E....858 546-8327
9940 Summers Ridge Rd San Diego (92121) ***(P-22052)***
Yti Enterprises Inc ....F....714 632-8696
1260 S State College Pkwy Anaheim (92806) ***(P-4665)***
Yuba City Steel Products Co ....E....530 673-4554
532 Crestmont Ave Yuba City (95991) ***(P-12285)***
Yuba Cy Wste Wtr Trtmnt Fcilty ....E....530 822-7698
302 Burns Dr Yuba City (95991) ***(P-16142)***
Yuba River Moulding Mllwk Inc (PA) ....E....530 742-2168
3757 Feather River Blvd Olivehurst (95961) ***(P-4264)***
Yucatan Foods LP ....F....310 342-5363
5901 W Century Blvd # 1578 Los Angeles (90045) ***(P-782)***
Yuciapa & Calimesa News Mirror, Yucaipa *Also called Hi-Desert Publishing Company* ***(P-5879)***
Yuhas Tooling & Machining ....F....408 934-9196
1031 Pecten Ct Milpitas (95035) ***(P-17076)***
Yuja Inc ....C....888 257-2278
2168 Ringwood Ave San Jose (95131) ***(P-25368)***
Yukon Trail Inc ....F....909 218-5286
1175 Woodlawn St Ontario (91761) ***(P-21152)***
Yuku.com, San Francisco *Also called Ezboard Inc* ***(P-24639)***
Yumi, Los Angeles *Also called Caer Inc* ***(P-749)***
Yun Industrial Co Ltd ....E....310 715-1898
161 Selandia Ln Carson (90746) ***(P-18656)***
Yutaka Electric Intl Inc ....F....626 962-7770
5116 Azusa Canyon Rd Baldwin Park (91706) ***(P-17361)***
Z B P Inc ....F....323 266-3363
2871 E Pico Blvd Los Angeles (90023) ***(P-5748)***
Z B Wire Works Inc ....F....909 391-0995
1139 Brooks St Ontario (91762) ***(P-13867)***
Z C & R Coating For Optics Inc ....E....310 381-3060
1401 Abalone Ave Torrance (90501) ***(P-22151)***
Z Industries, Los Angeles *Also called Active Window Products* ***(P-12288)***
Z K Celltest Inc ....F....408 541-2620
2310 Walsh Ave Santa Clara (95051) ***(P-21889)***
Z Manufacturing Inc ....E....909 593-2191
2679 Sierra Way La Verne (91750) ***(P-13986)***
Z-Barten Productions, Los Angeles *Also called Z B P Inc* ***(P-5748)***
Z-Communications Inc ....F....858 621-2700
6779 Mesa Ridge Rd # 150 San Diego (92121) ***(P-19793)***
Z-Line Designs Inc (PA) ....D....925 743-4000
2410 San Ramon Valley Blv San Ramon (94583) ***(P-5003)***
Z-Tronix Inc ....E....562 808-0800
6327 Alondra Blvd Paramount (90723) ***(P-19794)***
Zacharon Pharmaceuticals Inc ....F....415 506-6700
105 Digital Dr Novato (94949) ***(P-8449)***
Zacky & Sons Poultry LLC ....C....559 443-2700
13200 Crossroads P City of Industry (91746) ***(P-557)***
Zacky Farms, City of Industry *Also called Zacky & Sons Poultry LLC* ***(P-557)***
Zada Graphics Inc ....F....323 321-8940
13009 S Broadway Los Angeles (90061) ***(P-7193)***
Zada International Printing, Burbank *Also called Havana Graphic Center Inc* ***(P-6850)***
Zadara Storage Inc ....E....949 251-0360
6 Venture Ste 140 Irvine (92618) ***(P-15626)***
Zadro Products Inc ....E....714 892-9200
14462 Astronautics Ln # 101 Huntington Beach (92647) ***(P-10742)***
Zalemark Holding Company Inc ....F....888 682-6885
15260 Vntr Blvd St 1200 Sherman Oaks (91403) ***(P-23334)***
Zaolla ....E....714 736-9270
6650 Caballero Blvd Buena Park (90620) ***(P-17884)***
Zap Printing and Graphics, Corona *Also called Zap Printing Incorporated* ***(P-7194)***
Zap Printing Incorporated ....F....951 734-8181
127 Radio Rd Corona (92879) ***(P-7194)***
Zapworldcom (PA) ....F....707 525-8658
300 Stony Point Rd # 249 Petaluma (94952) ***(P-17230)***
Zarif Companies ....F....805 318-1800
4187 Carpinteria Ave Carpinteria (93013) ***(P-2065)***
Zbe Inc ....E....805 576-1600
1035 Cindy Ln Carpinteria (93013) ***(P-17326)***
Zebra Technologies Corporation ....B....619 661-5465
1440 Innovative Dr # 100 San Diego (92154) ***(P-15890)***
Zebra Technologies Corporation ....B....805 579-1800
30601 Agoura Rd Agoura Hills (91301) ***(P-15891)***
Zebra Technologies Intl LLC ....F....408 473-8500
2940 N 1st St San Jose (95134) ***(P-15892)***
Zeco Systems Inc (HQ) ....E....888 751-8560
925 N La Brea Ave West Hollywood (90038) ***(P-20118)***
Zed Audio Corporation ....F....805 499-5559
2624 Lavery Ct Ste 203 Newbury Park (91320) ***(P-17885)***
Zee Consulting, Bakersfield *Also called Contraband Control Specialists* ***(P-9232)***
Zeeni Inc ....F....626 350-1024
9536 Gidley St Temple City (91780) ***(P-3206)***
Zelco Cabinet Mfg Inc ....F....707 584-1121
298 W Robles Ave Santa Rosa (95407) ***(P-4902)***
Zeltiq Aesthetics Inc ....F....925 474-2519
6723 Sierra Ct Dublin (94568) ***(P-22683)***
Zeltiq Aesthetics Inc (HQ) ....B....925 474-2500
4410 Rosewood Dr Pleasanton (94588) ***(P-22684)***
Zelzah Pharmacy Inc ....F....818 609-0692
17911 Ventura Blvd Encino (91316) ***(P-8450)***
Zen Monkey LLC ....F....310 504-2899
655 N Central Ave Fl 1700 Glendale (91203) ***(P-1022)***
Zenana, Los Angeles *Also called Kc Exclusive Inc* ***(P-3444)***
Zendesk Inc (PA) ....C....415 418-7506
1019 Market St San Francisco (94103) ***(P-25369)***
Zenith Manufacturing Inc ....E....818 767-2106
11129 Dora St Sun Valley (91352) ***(P-20977)***
Zenith Screw Products Inc ....E....562 941-0281
10910 Painter Ave Santa Fe Springs (90670) ***(P-13054)***
Zenith Specialty Bag Co Inc (PA) ....C....626 912-2481
17625 Railroad St City of Industry (91748) ***(P-5635)***
Zenner Performance Meters Inc ....E....951 849-8822
1910 E Westward Ave Banning (92220) ***(P-21697)***
Zenon Environmental Corp ....E....760 598-1800
760 Shadowridge Dr Vista (92083) ***(P-9318)***
Zenpayroll Inc (PA) ....B....800 936-0383
525 20th St San Francisco (94107) ***(P-25370)***
Zentec Group ....F....949 586-3609
26190 Entp Way Ste 200 Lake Forest (92630) ***(P-19795)***
Zentera Systems Inc ....F....408 436-4811
2099 Gateway Pl Ste 420 San Jose (95110) ***(P-25371)***
Zenverge Inc ....D....408 350-5052
2680 Zanker Rd Ste 200 San Jose (95134) ***(P-19283)***
Zenyx Inc ....F....415 741-0170
2870 Zanker Rd Ste 210 San Jose (95134) ***(P-25372)***
Zeons Inc ....B....323 302-8299
291 S Cienega Blvd 102 Beverly Hills (90211) ***(P-10672)***
Zep Solar Llc (HQ) ....E....415 479-6900
161 Mitchell Blvd Ste 104 San Rafael (94903) ***(P-19284)***
Zepco ....F....818 848-0880
440 N Moss St Ste B Burbank (91502) ***(P-10456)***
Zephyr Manufacturing Co Inc ....D....310 410-4907
201 Hindry Ave Inglewood (90301) ***(P-14713)***
Zephyr Tool Group, Inglewood *Also called Zephyr Manufacturing Co Inc* ***(P-14713)***
Zephyr Tool Group, Inglewood *Also called Shg Holdings Corp* ***(P-14711)***
Zepp Labs Inc ....E....314 662-2145
75 E Santa Clara St # 93 San Jose (95113) ***(P-23695)***
Zeptor Corporation ....F....408 432-6001
3087 N 1st St San Jose (95134) ***(P-17244)***
Zero Base, Fremont *Also called Zerobase Energy LLC* ***(P-19819)***
Zero Gravity Corporation ....E....805 388-8803
912 Pancho Rd Ste A Camarillo (93012) ***(P-21153)***
Zero Gravity Group, Camarillo *Also called Zero Gravity Corporation* ***(P-21153)***
Zerobase Energy LLC ....E....888 530-9376
46609 Fremont Blvd Fremont (94538) ***(P-19819)***
Zerouv ....F....714 584-0015
16792 Burke Ln Huntington Beach (92647) ***(P-23134)***
Zerran International Corp ....F....818 897-5494
12880 Pierce St Pacoima (91331) ***(P-8869)***

Mergent e-mail: customerrelations@mergent.com
1336
2019 California
Manufacturers Register
(P-0000) Products & Services Section entry number
(PA)=Parent Co (HQ)=Headquarters (DH)=Div Headquarters

Zest Labs Inc (HQ) ..... E 408 200-6500
2349 Bering Dr San Jose (95131) *(P-19285)*
Zet-Tek Machining, Yorba Linda *Also called Zet-Tek Precision Machining (P-17077)*
Zet-Tek Precision Machining (PA) ..... F 714 777-8770
22951 La Palma Ave Yorba Linda (92887) *(P-17077)*
Zettler Magnetics Inc ..... E 949 831-5000
75 Columbia Aliso Viejo (92656) *(P-17126)*
Zev Technologies Inc (PA) ..... F 805 486-5800
1051 Yarnell Pl Oxnard (93033) *(P-13693)*
Zevia LLC ..... E 310 202-7000
15821 Ventura Blvd # 145 Encino (91436) *(P-2236)*
ZI Chemicals ..... F 818 827-1301
8605 Santa Monica Blvd Los Angeles (90069) *(P-7816)*
Zi Machine Manufacturing, El Dorado Hills *Also called 478826 Limited (P-16180)*
Zico Beverages LLC (HQ) ..... E 866 729-9426
2101 E El Segundo Blvd # 403 El Segundo (90245) *(P-2237)*
Ziegenfelder Company ..... E 909 590-0493
12290 Colony Ave Chino (91710) *(P-707)*
Ziehm Instrumentarium ..... E 407 615-8560
4181 Latham St Riverside (92501) *(P-22946)*
Ziething Cabinets Inc ..... F 949 642-6344
200 Briggs Ave Costa Mesa (92626) *(P-4375)*
Zigzagzoom, Glendale *Also called Jtea Inc (P-24818)*
Zilift Inc ..... F 661 369-8579
3600 Pegasus Dr Unit 7 Bakersfield (93308) *(P-15103)*
Zilog (HQ) ..... E 408 513-1500
1590 Buckeye Dr Milpitas (95035) *(P-19286)*
Zimmer Intermed Inc ..... E 909 392-0882
1647 Yeager Ave La Verne (91750) *(P-22851)*
Zing Racing Products ..... F 760 219-4700
27430 Bostik Ct Ste 101 Temecula (92590) *(P-21154)*
Zinik Wheels, Anaheim *Also called Saemie Corporation (P-11418)*
Zinio Systems Inc ..... D 415 494-2700
114 Sansome St Fl 4 San Francisco (94104) *(P-25373)*
Zinsser Na Inc ..... F 818 341-2906
19145 Parthenia St Ste C Northridge (91324) *(P-22053)*
Zinus Inc (HQ) ..... D 925 417-2100
1951 Fairway Dr Ste A San Leandro (94577) *(P-4895)*
Zion Health Inc ..... F 650 520-4313
430 E Grand Ave South San Francisco (94080) *(P-8870)*
Zion Packaging, Corona *Also called Organic Bottle Dctg Co LLC (P-5357)*
Zip Notes LLC ..... F 415 931-8020
2822 Van Ness Ave San Francisco (94109) *(P-5338)*
Zip Print Inc (PA) ..... E 559 486-3112
1257 G St Fresno (93706) *(P-7195)*
Zip-Chem Products, Morgan Hill *Also called Mitann Inc (P-9283)*
Zipco, Sun Valley *Also called Zenith Manufacturing Inc (P-20977)*
Zipline Medical Inc ..... F 408 412-7228
747 Camden Ave Ste A Campbell (95008) *(P-22685)*
Zircon Corporation (PA) ..... E 408 866-8600
1580 Dell Ave Campbell (95008) *(P-14714)*
Zk Enterprises Inc ..... E 213 622-7012
4368 District Blvd Vernon (90058) *(P-3207)*
Zmb Industries LLC ..... F 858 842-1000
12925 Brookprinter Pl # 400 Poway (92064) *(P-24293)*
Zmk Medical Technologies Inc ..... E 530 274-1240
13366 Grass Valley Ave A Grass Valley (95945) *(P-22686)*
Zmp Aquisition Corporation ..... C 714 278-6500
4141 N Palm St Fullerton (92835) *(P-17327)*
Zo Skin Health Inc (PA) ..... D 949 988-7524
5 Technology Dr Irvine (92618) *(P-8871)*
Zoasis Corporation ..... E 800 745-4725
1960 E Grand Ave Ste 555 El Segundo (90245) *(P-6299)*
Zodiac Aerospace, Huntington Beach *Also called C&D Zodiac Inc (P-20765)*
Zodiac Aerospace, Carson *Also called Monogram Systems (P-20891)*
Zodiac Aerospace ..... F 714 891-0683
7330 Lincoln Way Garden Grove (92841) *(P-20978)*
Zodiac Aerospace ..... F 909 652-9700
11340 Jersey Blvd Rancho Cucamonga (91730) *(P-20636)*
Zodiac Cabin & Structures ..... F 909 947-4115
1945 S Grove Ave Ontario (91761) *(P-20979)*
Zodiac Electrical Inserts USA, Huntington Beach *Also called Driessen Aircraft Interior (P-20800)*
Zodiac Pool Solutions LLC (HQ) ..... B 760 599-9600
2620 Commerce Way Vista (92081) *(P-16143)*
Zodiac Pool Systems LLC (HQ) ..... C 760 599-9600
2620 Commerce Way Vista (92081) *(P-16144)*
Zodiac Seat Shells US LLC ..... A 805 922-5995
2641 Airpark Dr Santa Maria (93455) *(P-20980)*
Zodiac WATer&waste Aero System ..... E 310 884-7000
1500 Glenn Curtiss St Carson (90746) *(P-20981)*
Zodiak Services America ..... E 310 884-7200
6734 Valjean Ave Van Nuys (91406) *(P-20982)*
Zogenix Inc (PA) ..... D 510 550-8300
5858 Horton St Ste 455 Emeryville (94608) *(P-8451)*

Zoho Corporation (HQ) ..... F 925 924-9500
4141 Hacienda Dr Pleasanton (94588) *(P-25374)*
Zola Acai, San Francisco *Also called Amazon Prsrvation Partners Inc (P-784)*
Zoll Circulation Inc ..... C 408 541-2140
2000 Ringwood Ave San Jose (95131) *(P-23074)*
Zoll Medical Corporation ..... F 408 419-2929
2000 Ringwood Ave San Jose (95131) *(P-23075)*
Zollner Electronics Inc ..... E 408 434-5400
575 Cottonwood Dr Milpitas (95035) *(P-18657)*
Zolt Information Sciences Inc ..... F 714 921-7489
2401 N Glassell St Orange (92865) *(P-9054)*
Zombie Industries, Poway *Also called Zmb Industries LLC (P-24293)*
Zonex Systems, Huntington Beach *Also called California Economizer (P-17258)*
Zonson Company Inc ..... E 760 597-0338
3197 Lionshead Ave Carlsbad (92010) *(P-23696)*
Zoo Piks International ..... E 323 724-0503
5951 Rickenbacker Rd Commerce (90040) *(P-5502)*
Zoo Printing Inc (PA) ..... D 310 253-7751
4730 Eastern Ave Bell (90201) *(P-7196)*
Zoo Printing Trade Printer, Bell *Also called Zoo Printing Inc (P-7196)*
Zoo Zoo Wham Whams Blip Blops ..... F 213 248-9591
645 W Rosecrans Ave Compton (90222) *(P-3022)*
Zoom Bookz LLC ..... F 800 662-9982
10000 Fairway Dr Ste 140 Roseville (95678) *(P-6416)*
Zoops Products Inc ..... F 951 922-2396
931 E Lincoln St Ste A Banning (92220) *(P-20491)*
Zoox Inc (PA) ..... C 650 733-9669
1149 Chess Dr Foster City (94404) *(P-20185)*
Zoox Labs, Foster City *Also called Zoox Inc (P-20185)*
Zoran Corporation (HQ) ..... E 972 673-1600
1060 Rincon Cir San Jose (95131) *(P-19287)*
Zosano Pharma Corporation (PA) ..... E 510 745-1200
34790 Ardentech Ct Fremont (94555) *(P-8452)*
Zotos International Inc ..... E 626 321-4100
488 E Santa Clara St # 301 Arcadia (91006) *(P-8872)*
Zpower LLC ..... C 805 445-7789
4765 Calle Quetzal Camarillo (93012) *(P-17362)*
Zs Bag, City of Industry *Also called Zenith Specialty Bag Co Inc (P-5635)*
Zs Pharma Inc ..... F 650 753-1823
1100 Park Pl Fl 3 San Mateo (94403) *(P-8453)*
Zscaler Inc (PA) ..... C 408 533-0288
110 Rose Orchard Way San Jose (95134) *(P-25375)*
Zt Plus ..... F 626 208-3440
1321 Mountain View Cir Azusa (91702) *(P-19288)*
Ztech ..... F 916 635-6784
11481 Sunrise Gold Cir # 1 Rancho Cordova (95742) *(P-16003)*
Zuca Inc ..... E 408 377-9822
320 S Milpitas Blvd Milpitas (95035) *(P-10542)*
Zulip Inc ..... F 617 945-7653
185 Berry St Ste 400 San Francisco (94107) *(P-25376)*
Zumar Industries Inc ..... D 562 941-4633
9719 Santa Fe Springs Rd Santa Fe Springs (90670) *(P-24010)*
Zuo Modern Contemporary Inc (PA) ..... E 510 777-1030
80 Swan Way Ste 300 Oakland (94621) *(P-4974)*
Zuora Inc (PA) ..... B 800 425-1281
3050 S Del St Ste 301 San Mateo (94403) *(P-25377)*
Zurich Engineering Inc ..... F 714 528-0066
1365 N Dynamics St Ste E Anaheim (92806) *(P-20693)*
Zuza, Carlsbad *Also called CPS Printing (P-6764)*
Zuza ..... E 760 438-9411
2304 Faraday Ave Carlsbad (92008) *(P-7547)*
Zx Vecor ..... F 323 587-7100
2833 Leonis Blvd Ste 111 Vernon (90058) *(P-10673)*
Zye Labs LLC ..... F 904 800-9935
310 S Twin Oaks Valley Rd San Marcos (92078) *(P-25378)*
Zygo Corporation ..... E 714 918-7433
2031 Main St Irvine (92614) *(P-22152)*
Zygo Corporation ..... E 408 434-1000
1971 Milmont Dr Milpitas (95035) *(P-22054)*
Zygo Epo ..... F 510 243-7592
3900 Lakeside Dr Richmond (94806) *(P-22153)*
Zygo Optical Systems, Irvine *Also called Zygo Corporation (P-22152)*
Zymed Laboratories ..... E 650 952-0110
458 Carlton Ct South San Francisco (94080) *(P-24294)*
Zynga Inc ..... F 415 621-2391
650 Townsend St San Francisco (94103) *(P-25379)*
Zypcom Inc ..... E 510 324-2501
29400 Kohoutek Way # 170 Union City (94587) *(P-18306)*
Zyrel Inc ..... F 707 995-2551
15322 Lkeshore Dr Ste 301 Clearlake (95422) *(P-18658)*
Zyrion Inc ..... D 408 524-7424
440 N Wolfe Rd Sunnyvale (94085) *(P-25380)*
Zytek Corp ..... E 408 520-4287
1755 Mccarthy Blvd Milpitas (95035) *(P-18659)*
Zytek Ems, Milpitas *Also called Zytek Corp (P-18659)*

Employee Codes: A=Over 500 employees, B=251-500
C=101-250, D=51-100, E=20-50, F=10-19

2019 California
Manfacturers Register

© Mergent Inc. 1-800-342-5647
1337

COUNTY/CITY CROSS-REFERENCE INDEX

Alameda
Alameda
Albany
Berkeley
Castro Valley
Dublin
Emeryville
Fremont
Hayward
Kensington
Livermore
Newark
Oakland
Pleasanton
San Leandro
San Lorenzo
Sunol
Union City

Amador
Ione
Jackson
Pioneer
Plymouth
Sutter Creek

Butte
Biggs
Chico
Durham
Gridley
Magalia
Nelson
Oroville
Paradise
Richvale

Calaveras
Angels Camp
Copperopolis
Murphys
San Andreas
Vallecito
Valley Springs
West Point

Colusa
Arbuckle
Colusa
Maxwell
Princeton
Williams

Contra Costa
Alamo
Antioch
Bay Point
Brentwood
Byron
Clayton
Concord
Crockett
Danville
Discovery Bay
El Cerrito
Hercules
Lafayette
Martinez
Moraga
Orinda

Pacheco
Pinole
Pittsburg
Pleasant Hill
Point Richmond
Richmond
Rodeo
San Pablo
San Ramon
Walnut Creek

Del Norte
Crescent City

El Dorado
Cameron Park
Camino
Cool
Diamond Springs
El Dorado
El Dorado Hills
Garden Valley
Georgetown
Greenwood
Pilot Hill
Placerville
Pollock Pines
Shingle Springs
Somerset
South Lake Tahoe

Fresno
Auberry
Cantua Creek
Caruthers
Clovis
Coalinga
Del Rey
Firebaugh
Fowler
Fresno
Helm
Kerman
Kingsburg
Parlier
Pinedale
Reedley
Riverdale
Sanger
Selma
Tranquillity

Glenn
Orland
Willows

Humboldt
Arcata
Blue Lake
Eureka
Ferndale
Fields Landing
Fortuna
Hoopa
Kneeland
Korbel
Loleta
McKinleyville
Miranda
Samoa

Imperial
Brawley
Calexico
Calipatria
El Centro
Heber
Imperial

Inyo
Bishop
Little Lake
Olancha

Kern
Arvin
Bakersfield
Boron
Buttonwillow
California City
Cantil
Delano
Di Giorgio
Edwards
Fellows
Frazier Park
Inyokern
Lake Isabella
Lamont
Lebec
Maricopa
Mc Farland
Mc Kittrick
Mojave
Ridgecrest
Rosamond
Shafter
Taft
Tehachapi
Wasco
Weldon

Kings
Armona
Corcoran
Hanford
Lemoore

Lake
Clearlake
Glenhaven
Hidden Valley Lake
Kelseyville
Lakeport
Lower Lake
Middletown
Nice

Lassen
Bieber
Susanville

Los Angeles
Agoura Hills
Agua Dulce
Alhambra
Altadena
Arcadia
Arleta
Artesia
Azusa

Baldwin Park
Bell
Bell Gardens
Bellflower
Beverly Hills
Burbank
Calabasas
Canoga Park
Canyon Country
Carson
Castaic
Cerritos
Chatsworth
City of Industry
Claremont
Commerce
Compton
Covina
Cudahy
Culver City
Diamond Bar
Downey
Duarte
E Rncho Dmngz
El Monte
El Segundo
Encino
Gardena
Glendale
Glendora
Granada Hills
Hacienda Heights
Harbor City
Hawaiian Gardens
Hawthorne
Hermosa Beach
Hollywood
Huntington Park
Inglewood
Irwindale
La Canada
La Canada Flintridge
La Crescenta
La Mirada
La Puente
La Verne
Lakewood
Lancaster
Lawndale
Littlerock
Lomita
Long Beach
Los Angeles
Lynwood
Malibu
Manhattan Beach
Marina Del Rey
Maywood
Mission Hills
Monrovia
Montebello
Monterey Park
Montrose
Newhall
North Hills
North Hollywood
Northridge

Norwalk
Pacific Palisades
Pacoima
Palmdale
Palos Verdes Estates
Panorama City
Paramount
Pasadena
Pearblossom
Pico Rivera
Playa Del Rey
Playa Vista
Pls Vrds Pnsl
Pomona
Porter Ranch
Rancho Dominguez
Rancho Palos Verdes
Redondo Beach
Reseda
Rllng HLS Est
Rolling Hills
Rosemead
Rowland Heights
San Dimas
San Fernando
San Gabriel
San Marino
San Pedro
Santa Clarita
Santa Fe Springs
Santa Monica
Sherman Oaks
Sierra Madre
Signal Hill
South El Monte
South Gate
South Pasadena
Stevenson Ranch
Studio City
Sun Valley
Sunland
Sylmar
Tarzana
Temple City
Toluca Lake
Topanga
Torrance
Tujunga
Valencia
Valley Village
Van Nuys
Venice
Vernon
View Park
Walnut
West Covina
West Hills
West Hollywood
Whittier
Wilmington
Winnetka
Woodland Hills

Madera
Chowchilla
Madera
North Fork
Oakhurst

Raymond

Marin
Belvedere Tiburon
Corte Madera
Fairfax
Greenbrae
Larkspur
Mill Valley
Novato
San Anselmo
San Quentin
San Rafael
Sausalito
Tomales

Mariposa
El Portal
Mariposa

Mendocino
Boonville
Comptche
Covelo
Fort Bragg
Gualala
Hopland
Mendocino
Philo
Potter Valley
Redwood Valley
Ukiah
Willits

Merced
Atwater
Ballico
Delhi
Dos Palos
Gustine
Hilmar
Le Grand
Livingston
Los Banos
Merced
South Dos Palos
Winton

Mono
Mammoth Lakes

Monterey
Aromas
Carmel
Carmel Valley
Castroville
Gonzales
Greenfield
King City
Marina
Monterey
Moss Landing
Pacific Grove
Pebble Beach
Salinas
Seaside
Soledad

Napa
American Canyon
Angwin
Calistoga
Deer Park
NAPA

Oakville
Rutherford
Saint Helena
Vallejo
Yountville

Nevada
Grass Valley
Nevada City
Penn Valley
Rough and Ready
Truckee

Orange
Aliso Viejo
Anaheim
Brea
Buena Park
Capistrano Beach
Corona Del Mar
Costa Mesa
Cypress
Dana Point
El Toro
Foothill Ranch
Fountain Valley
Fullerton
Garden Grove
Huntington Beach
Irvine
La Habra
La Habra Heights
La Palma
Ladera Ranch
Laguna Beach
Laguna Hills
Laguna Niguel
Lake Forest
Los Alamitos
Midway City
Mission Viejo
Newport Beach
Newport Coast
Orange
Placentia
Rancho Santa Margari
Rcho STA Marg
San Clemente
San Juan Capistrano
Santa Ana
Seal Beach
Silverado
Stanton
Trabuco Canyon
Tustin
Villa Park
Westminster
Yorba Linda

Placer
Auburn
Colfax
Granite Bay
Lincoln
Loomis
Newcastle
Penryn
Rocklin
Roseville
Sheridan
Tahoe City

Plumas
Chester
Chilcoot
Crescent Mills
Greenville
Portola
Quincy

Riverside
Aguanga
Banning
Beaumont
Blythe
Calimesa
Canyon Lake
Cathedral City
Cherry Valley
Coachella
Corona
Desert Hot Springs
Eastvale
Hemet
Idyllwild
Indian Wells
Indio
Jurupa Valley
La Quinta
Lake Elsinore
March ARB
Mecca
Menifee
Mira Loma
Moreno Valley
Murrieta
Norco
North Palm Springs
Palm Desert
Palm Springs
Perris
Quail Valley
Rancho Mirage
Riverside
Romoland
San Jacinto
Sun City
Temecula
Thermal
Thousand Palms
Wildomar

Sacramento
Antelope
Carmichael
Citrus Heights
Elk Grove
Fair Oaks
Folsom
Galt
Gold River
Isleton
Mather
McClellan
North Highlands
Orangevale
Rancho Cordova
Rio Linda
Sacramento
Walnut Grove
Wilton

San Benito
Hollister
San Juan Bautista

San Bernardino
Adelanto
Alta Loma
Apple Valley
Barstow
Bloomington
Chino
Chino Hills
Colton
Crestline
Etiwanda
Fontana
Grand Terrace
Helendale
Hesperia
Highland
Lake Arrowhead
Loma Linda
Lucerne Valley
Mentone
Montclair
Mountain Pass
Needles
Newberry Springs
Nipton
Oak Hills
Ontario
Oro Grande
Rancho Cucamonga
Redlands
Rialto
San Bernardino
Trona
Upland
Victorville
Yucaipa
Yucca Valley

San Diego
Alpine
Bonita
Bonsall
Cardiff
Cardiff By The Sea
Carlsbad
Chula Vista
Coronado
Del Mar
Descanso
El Cajon
Encinitas
Escondido
Fallbrook
Jamul
La Jolla
La Mesa
Lakeside
Lemon Grove
National City
Oceanside
Pala
Poway
Ramona
Rancho Santa Fe
San Diego
San Marcos
San Ysidro

Santee
Solana Beach
Spring Valley
Tecate
Valley Center
Vista

San Francisco
San Francisco

San Joaquin
Acampo
Escalon
Farmington
French Camp
Lathrop
Linden
Lockeford
Lodi
Manteca
Ripon
Stockton
Tracy

San Luis Obispo
Arroyo Grande
Atascadero
Avila Beach
Cambria
Cholame
Creston
Grover Beach
Harmony
Los Osos
Morro Bay
Nipomo
Paso Robles
Pismo Beach
San Luis Obispo
San Miguel
Shandon
Templeton

San Mateo
Atherton
Belmont
Brisbane
Burlingame
Colma
Daly City
El Granada
Emerald Hills
Foster City
Half Moon Bay
La Honda
Menlo Park
Millbrae
Pacifica
Pescadero
Portola Valley
Redwood City
San Bruno
San Carlos
San Gregorio
San Mateo
South San Francisco
Woodside

Santa Barbara
Buellton
Carpinteria
Goleta
Guadalupe

Lompoc
Los Alamos
Los Olivos
New Cuyama
Orcutt
Santa Barbara
Santa Maria
Santa Ynez
Solvang
Vandenberg Afb

Santa Clara

Alviso
Campbell
Cupertino
East Palo Alto
Gilroy
Los Altos
Los Altos Hills
Los Gatos
Milpitas
Moffett Field
Morgan Hill
Mountain View
Palo Alto
San Jose
San Martin
Santa Clara
Saratoga
Stanford
Sunnyvale

Santa Cruz

Aptos
Capitola
Davenport
Felton

Freedom
Los Gatos
Royal Oaks
Santa Cruz
Scotts Valley
Soquel
Watsonville

Shasta

Anderson
Burney
Cottonwood
Redding
Shasta Lake
Whitmore

Siskiyou

Etna
Fort Jones
Happy Camp
Macdoel
Mccloud
Montague
Mount Shasta
Seiad Valley
Tulelake
Weed
Yreka

Solano

Benicia
Dixon
Fairfield
Rio Vista
Suisun City
Travis Afb
Vacaville

Vallejo

Sonoma

Cazadero
Cloverdale
Cotati
Forestville
Geyserville
Glen Ellen
Graton
Guerneville
Healdsburg
Kenwood
Occidental
Petaluma
Rohnert Park
Santa Rosa
Sebastopol
Sonoma
Valley Ford
Windsor

Stanislaus

Ceres
Crows Landing
Denair
Hickman
Hughson
Modesto
Newman
Oakdale
Patterson
Riverbank
Salida
Turlock
Waterford

Sutter

Live Oak
Nicolaus
Pleasant Grove
Sutter
Yuba City

Tehama

Corning
Red Bluff

Trinity

Junction City
Lewiston
Weaverville

Tulare

Calif Hot Spg
Dinuba
Exeter
Farmersville
Lindsay
Orosi
Pixley
Porterville
Springville
Strathmore
Terra Bella
Three Rivers
Tipton
Traver
Tulare
Visalia
Woodlake

Tuolumne

Columbia

Jamestown
MI Wuk Village
Sonora

Ventura

Camarillo
Fillmore
Moorpark
Newbury Park
Oak Park
Oak View
Ojai
Oxnard
Port Hueneme
Santa Paula
Simi Valley
Somis
Thousand Oaks
Ventura
Westlake Village

Yolo

Broderick
Clarksburg
Davis
Madison
West Sacramento
Winters
Woodland
Zamora

Yuba

Marysville
Olivehurst
Plumas Lake
Strawberry Valley

GEOGRAPHIC SECTION

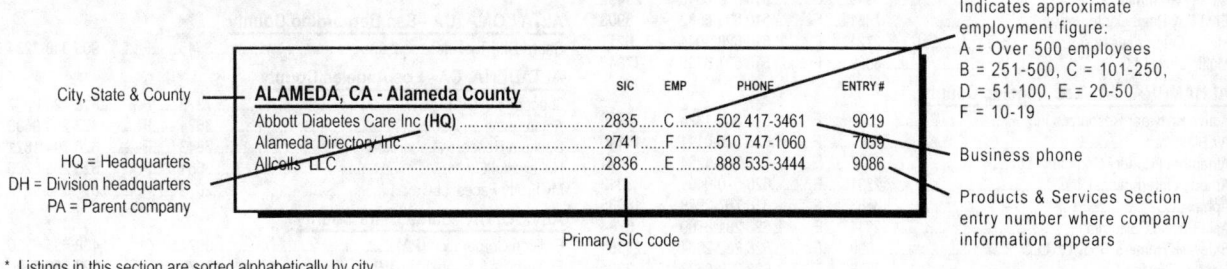

City, State & County → **ALAMEDA, CA - Alameda County**

	SIC	EMP	PHONE	ENTRY #
Abbott Diabetes Care Inc **(HQ)**	2835	C	502 417-3461	9019
Alameda Directory Inc	2741	F	510 747-1060	7059
Allcells LLC	2836	E	888 535-3444	9086

HQ = Headquarters
DH = Division headquarters
PA = Parent company

Primary SIC code

Indicates approximate employment figure:
A = Over 500 employees
B = 251-500, C = 101-250,
D = 51-100, E = 20-50,
F = 10-19

Business phone

Products & Services Section entry number where company information appears

* Listings in this section are sorted alphabetically by city.
* Listings within each city are sorted alphabetically by company name.

ACAMPO, CA - San Joaquin County	SIC	EMP	PHONE	ENTRY #
AG Ray Inc	3523	F	209 334-1999	14036
California Concentrate Company	2037	E	209 334-9112	941
Calva Products Co Inc	2026	E	209 339-1516	716
Franciscan Vineyards Inc	2084	B	209 369-5861	1771
Langetwins Wine Company Inc	2084	E	209 334-9780	1855

ADELANTO, CA - San Bernardino County				
Adelanto Elementary School Dst	2099	E	760 530-7680	2447
Andersen Industries Inc	3715	E	760 246-8766	20493
Barker-Canoga Inc	3545	F	760 246-4777	14605
Cageco Inc	3523	E	800 605-4859	14050
Cal-Fab Systems Inc	3535	F	760 246-4454	14267
California Silica Products LLC	2819	F	909 947-0028	7759
Carberry LLC **(HQ)**	2064	E	800 564-0842	1411
Continental Fiberglass Inc **(PA)**	3949	F	760 246-6480	23543
Dar-Ken Inc	3053	F	760 246-4010	9526
Diversitech Corporation	3272	F	760 246-4200	10915
Ducommun Aerostructures Inc	3541	E	760 246-4191	14377
Fiber Care Baths Inc	3088	B	760 246-0019	9901
Flavor House Inc	2087	E	760 246-9131	2261
Furniture Technologies Inc	2426	E	760 246-9180	4080
General Atomic Aeron	3721	C	760 246-3660	20581
General Atomic Aeron	3721	C	760 388-4280	20584
Hayes Welding Inc **(PA)**	7692	D	760 246-4878	25409
Hayward Gordon Us Inc	3556	F	760 246-3430	14857
McElroy Metal Mill Inc	3448	E	760 246-5545	12943
Mk Magnetics Inc	3315	D	760 246-6373	11450
Molded Fiber GL Companies - W	3089	D	760 246-4042	10220
National Filter Media Corp	3569	D	760 246-4551	15343
Northwest Pipe Company	3317	B	760 246-3191	11484
Pacific Tank Ltd	3443	F	760 246-6136	12405
R V Gambler	3715	F	928 927-5966	20511
Robertsons Rdy Mix Ltd A Cal	3273	F	760 246-4000	11166
Safeway Sign Company	3993	F	760 246-7070	23955
Southland Mixer Service	3713	F	760 246-6080	20229
Thermtronix Corporation **(PA)**	3567	E	760 246-4500	15275
Traffix Devices Inc	3069	E	760 246-7171	9687
US Fiberglass Inc	3949	F	760 246-3822	23683

AGOURA HILLS, CA - Los Angeles County				
Acorn Newspaper Inc	2711	E	818 706-0266	5751
American Made Make Be-Leaves	3999	F	800 634-1402	24034
Caldera Medical Inc	3841	D	818 879-6555	22385
Candu Graphics	2752	F	310 822-1620	6720
Chatsworth Products Inc **(FA)**	3499	B	818 735-6100	13929
Cheesecake Factory Bakery Inc **(HQ)**	2051	B	818 880-9323	1221
Integrated Business Network	2759	F	818 879-0670	7358
Internet Machines Corporation **(PA)**	3577	D	818 575-2100	15770
Jamaco Enterprises Inc	2652	F	818 991-2050	5377
Millpledge North America Inc	2835	F	310 215-0400	8497
Novastor Corporation **(PA)**	7372	F	805 579-6700	24971
Paisano Publications LLC **(PA)**	2721	C	818 889-8740	6228
Paisano Publications Inc	2721	D	818 889-8740	6229
Richter Furniture Mfg 2002	2599	C	323 588-7900	5251
RMS Printing LLC	2752	F	818 707-2625	7088
Sole Survivor Corporation	2339	F	818 338-3760	3501
Sweet Xo LP	2026	F	818 889-9696	738
Teradyne Inc	3825	C	818 991-9700	21867
Teradyne Inc	3679	B	818 991-2900	19760
Voxara LLC	2741	F	844 869-2721	6621
Zebra Technologies Corporation	3577	B	805 579-1800	15891

AGUA DULCE, CA - Los Angeles County	SIC	EMP	PHONE	ENTRY #
Agua Dulce Vineyards LLC	2084	E	661 268-7402	1640
Precision Millwork LLC	2431	F	661 402-5021	4215

AGUANGA, CA - Riverside County				
Patriot Polishing Company	2842	F	310 903-7409	8664

ALAMEDA, CA - Alameda County				
Abbott Diabetes Care Inc **(HQ)**	2835	C	510 749-5400	8454
Alameda Directory Inc	2741	F	510 747-1060	6427
Alameda Video Station	2452	E	510 523-5200	4565
Allergy Research Group Inc	2834	E	510 263-2000	8015
Allied Engineering & Prod Corp **(PA)**	3599	E	510 522-1500	16254
Aqua Metals Inc **(PA)**	3341	D	510 479-7635	11553
Bay Ship & Yacht Co **(PA)**	3731	C	510 337-9122	20988
Bioneer Inc	2869	E	510 865-0330	8988
Biotime Inc **(PA)**	2836	D	510 521-3390	8538
Center For Cllbrtive Classroom	2731	D	510 533-0213	6323
Clear-Com LLC	3663	A	510 337-6600	18068
Comstock Press	2752	E	510 522-4115	6751
Contra Costa Newspapers Inc	2711	B	510 748-1683	5812
Eastbay Publishing Corp	2711	F	510 537-1792	5838
Edutone Corporation **(PA)**	7372	F	888 904-9773	24593
Ettore Products Co	3999	D	510 748-4130	24092
Exelixis Inc	3824	E	650 837-7000	21688
Exelixis Inc	2834	C	650 837-7000	8154
Exelixis Inc **(PA)**	2834	D	650 837-7000	8155
Fleenor Company Inc **(PA)**	2679	E	800 433-2531	5712
Fluxion Biosciences Inc **(PA)**	3841	E	650 241-4777	22452
Golden West Envelope Corp	2677	E	510 452-5419	5674
Insite Vision Incorporated **(DH)**	2834	E	510 865-8800	8221
Jansport Inc **(HQ)**	2393	F	510 814-7400	3766
Lens C-C Inc **(PA)**	3851	D	800 772-3911	23105
Magnetic Insight Inc	3826	E	510 291-1200	21984
Motorola Solutions Inc	3663	C	510 217-7400	18192
Natel Energy Inc	3511	F	510 342-5269	14003
Novx Corporation	3825	E	408 998-5555	21821
ONe Color Communications LLC	2796	D	510 263-1840	7654
Pacific Automated LLC	2086	E	800 372-5098	2162
Peninsula Pharmaceuticals	2834	E	510 337-1060	8328
Pennzoil-Quaker State Company	2992	E	510 748-1331	9446
Penumbra Inc **(PA)**	3841	B	510 748-3200	22581
Polarion Software Inc	7372	D	877 572-4005	25069
Power Standards Lab Inc	3825	E	510 522-4400	21828
Rgb Spectrum	3577	D	510 814-7000	15838
Rock Wall Wine Company Inc	2084	E	510 522-5700	1954
S & C Electric Company	3625	E	510 864-9300	17305
Sila Nanotechnologies Inc	2819	E	408 475-7452	7804
Simco-Ion Technology Group **(PA)**	3629	C	510 217-0600	17354
Sks Die Cast & Machining Inc **(PA)**	3363	E	510 523-2541	11707
St George Spirits Inc	2084	E	510 769-1601	1986
Stone Boat Yard Inc	3732	F	510 523-3030	21064
Symbol Technologies LLC	3577	C	510 684-2974	15861
Tender Corporation	3842	E	510 261-7414	22831
Therasense Inc	3841	F	510 749-5400	22650
Vf Outdoor LLC **(HQ)**	2329	C	510 618-3500	3203
Wind River Systems Inc **(HQ)**	7372	C	510 748-4100	25350
Wrightspeed Inc	3465	D	866 960-9482	13147
Xintec Corporation **(PA)**	3845	E	510 832-2130	23073

ALAMO, CA - Contra Costa County				
Edner Corporation	2051	E	925 831-1248	1241
Feedstuffs Processing Co	2048	F	925 820-5454	1130
Sunsil Inc **(PA)**	3674	F	925 648-7779	19204

GEOGRAPHIC

Employment Codes: A=Over 500 employees, B=251-500,
C=101-250, D=51-100, E=20-50, F=10-19

2019 California
Manufacturers Register

© Mergent Inc. 1-800-342-5647
1343

	SIC	EMP	PHONE	ENTRY #
Trilore Technologies Inc	3365	E	925 295-0734	11750

ALBANY, CA - Alameda County

	SIC	EMP	PHONE	ENTRY #
Albany Swimming Pool	3949	E	510 559-6640	23492
East Bay Paint Center Inc	2851	F	510 524-6582	8903
Mingo Enterprises Inc	2721	F	510 528-3044	6217
Multimetrixs LLC	3629	F	510 527-6769	17348

ALHAMBRA, CA - Los Angeles County

	SIC	EMP	PHONE	ENTRY #
Active Knitwear Resources Inc	2331	F	626 308-1328	3208
Air Blast Inc	3564	F	626 576-0144	15140
Alhambra Foundry Company Ltd	3321	E	626 289-4294	11491
Amertex International Inc	2331	E	626 570-9409	3213
Aphex LLC	3663	F	818 767-2929	18035
Asia Pacific California Inc	2711	E	626 281-8500	5764
Bluewick Home & Body Co LLC	3999	F	626 282-2664	24051
Century Sewing Co	2335	E	626 289-0533	3301
China Press	2711	F	626 281-8500	5799
Coast To Coast Met Finshg Corp	3471	E	626 282-2122	13374
Comprhnsive Crdvsclar Spcalist (PA)	2834	E	626 281-8663	8118
E-Freight Technology Inc	7372	E	626 943-8418	24585
EDM International Logistics	3086	F	626 588-2299	9838
Emcore Corporation (PA)	3674	C	626 293-3400	18818
Emcore Corporation	3663	C	626 293-3400	18097
Global Ocean Trading LLC	2091	F	626 281-0800	2296
Gluesmith Industries	2891	F	626 282-9390	9144
Just Saying Inc	2389	F	888 512-5007	3662
K Live	3674	F	626 289-2885	18940
Kelly Tool & Mfgcoinc	3469	F	626 289-7962	13235
Makeit Inc	3577	F	626 470-7938	15798
N Z Pump Co Inc	3561	F	626 458-8023	15086
Opticomm Corp	3357	F	626 293-3400	11669
Ortel A Division Emcore Co (HQ)	3674	F	626 293-3400	19066
Riedon Inc (PA)	3676	C	626 284-9901	19309
Rods Unfinished Furniture	2511	E	626 281-9855	4735
Seal Innovations Inc	3069	F	626 282-7325	9676
Silver Star Exchange	2339	F	626 300-6668	3497
TMJ Products Inc	3724	F	626 576-4063	20685
Tyler Trafficante Inc (PA)	2311	D	323 869-9299	3046
Universal Filtration Inc	3589	F	626 308-1832	16128
Victoire LLC	2384	E	323 225-0101	3605

ALISO VIEJO, CA - Orange County

	SIC	EMP	PHONE	ENTRY #
Adaptive Inc (PA)	7372	F	888 399-4621	24318
Agile Technologies Inc	3674	F	949 454-8030	18673
Appware Inc	7372	E	415 732-9298	24377
Astronic	3672	C	949 454-1180	18430
Avanir Pharmaceuticals Inc (DH)	2834	C	949 389-6700	8054
AZ Displays Inc	3679	F	949 831-5000	19454
Biovail Technologies Ltd	2834	C	703 995-2400	8082
Brainchip Inc (HQ)	7372	E	949 330-6750	24447
Bridgeport Products Inc	3161	D	949 348-8800	10517
Catalina Lifesciences Inc	2834	E	800 898-6888	8104
Centon Electronics Inc (PA)	3572	D	949 855-9111	15520
Cianna Medical Inc	3061	D	949 360-0059	9564
Cove20 LLC	3674	F	949 297-4930	18789
Dita Inc (PA)	3851	E	949 599-2700	23088
Eeye Inc (HQ)	7372	F	949 333-1900	24594
Fuel Injection Engineering Co	3714	F	949 360-0909	20344
Global Wave Group LLC	7372	F	949 916-9800	24700
HD Carry Inc	3086	F	949 831-6022	9864
Highway Two	3751	F	877 395-8088	21116
Hilborn Manufacturing Corp	3714	F	949 360-0909	20361
Ixys Intgrtd Crcts Div AV Inc	3674	F	949 831-4622	18935
Liquid Bioscience Inc	2834	F	949 432-9559	8263
Microsemi Corporation (HQ)	3674	F	949 380-6100	19013
Microsoft Corporation	7372	F	949 680-3000	24909
Microvention Inc (DH)	3841	B	714 258-8000	22540
Modernpro LLC	2741	F	949 232-2148	6530
Nuvasive Spclzed Orthpdics Inc	3841	D	949 837-3600	22562
Pacific Alliance Capital Inc	3572	F	949 360-1796	15582
Pacific World Corporation (PA)	2844	C	949 598-2400	8809
Pepsi-Cola Metro Btlg Co Inc	2086	C	949 643-5700	2177
Quest Software Inc	7372	D	949 754-8000	25099
Schuberth North America LLC	3469	F	949 215-0893	13272
Screening Systems Inc (PA)	3826	E	949 855-1751	22015
Sequent Medical Inc	3841	D	949 830-9600	22621
Shugart Corporation (PA)	3571	C	949 488-8779	15483
Siemens Industry Inc	3822	E	949 448-0600	21529
Smith Micro Software Inc (PA)	7372	C	949 362-5800	25186
Stmicroelectronics Inc	3674	E	949 347-0717	19191
Vertos Medical Inc	3841	F	949 349-0008	22673
Voice Assist Inc	3679	F	949 655-1611	19784
Wepower LLC	3511	F	866 385-9463	14012
XEL USA Inc	3674	E	949 425-8686	19276
Zettler Magnetics Inc	3612	E	949 831-5000	17126

ALPINE, CA - San Diego County

	SIC	EMP	PHONE	ENTRY #
Custom Installations	2434	F	619 445-0692	4290
Valley Casework Inc	2434	D	619 579-6886	4364

ALTA LOMA, CA - San Bernardino County

	SIC	EMP	PHONE	ENTRY #
Sharp-Rite Tool Inc	3545	F	909 948-1234	14675

ALTADENA, CA - Los Angeles County

	SIC	EMP	PHONE	ENTRY #
3becom Inc (PA)	7372	F	818 726-0007	24299
Acton Inc	3621	F	323 250-0685	17176
Dockum Research Laboratory	3843	F	626 794-1821	22874
Hdkaraoke Llc	3651	F	626 296-6200	17810
My Fruity Faces LLC	2079	F	877 358-9210	1545

ALVISO, CA - Santa Clara County

	SIC	EMP	PHONE	ENTRY #
Esilicon Corporation (PA)	3674	C	408 635-6300	18831
Flextronics Corporation (DH)	3679	B	803 936-5200	19545

AMERICAN CANYON, CA - Napa County

	SIC	EMP	PHONE	ENTRY #
Amcan Beverages Inc	2086	C	707 557-0500	2081
Amcor Flexibles LLC	2671	C	707 257-6481	5516
Barry Callebaut USA LLC	2066	F	707 642-8200	1465
Envirocare International Inc	3564	E	707 638-6800	15154
G L Mezzetta Inc	2033	D	707 648-1050	801
Midwestern Pipeline Svcs Inc (PA)	2952	F	707 557-6633	9415
William Kreysler & Assoc Inc	3089	E	707 552-3500	10444

ANAHEIM, CA - Orange County

	SIC	EMP	PHONE	ENTRY #
180 Snacks (PA)	2068	E	714 238-1192	1479
3d Instruments LP (DH)	3823	E	714 399-9200	21539
3d Machine Co Inc	3599	E	714 777-8985	16179
A & D Precision Mfg Inc	3599	E	714 779-2714	16183
A & G Instr Svc & Calibration	3491	F	714 630-7400	13698
A & R Powder Coating Inc	3479	F	714 630-0709	13536
A and G Inc	2231	C	714 756-0400	2788
A D S Gold Inc	3339	F	714 632-1888	11542
A J Fasteners Inc	3452	F	714 630-1556	13056
A P Seedorff & Company Inc	3625	F	714 252-5330	17245
A&D Fire Sprinklers Inc	3569	F	714 634-3923	15294
A-L-L Magnetics	3499	F	714 632-1754	13913
Aaron Dutt Enterprises Inc	3469	F	714 632-7035	13157
Acra Aerospace LLC	3721	E	714 778-1900	20527
Acrylic Designs Inc	3089	F	714 630-1370	9923
Action Enterprises Inc	3089	E	714 978-0333	9924
Action Innovations Inc	3089	E	714 978-0333	9925
Adcraft Products Co Inc	2759	E	714 776-1230	7221
Advanced Global Tech Group	3678	E	714 281-8020	19371
Advanced Manufacturing Tech	3699	C	714 238-1488	19899
Advanced Tech Plating	3471	F	714 630-7093	13310
Advanced Thermal Sciences	3674	E	714 688-4200	18670
Adwest Technologies Inc (HQ)	3564	E	714 632-8595	15139
Aerofab Corporation	3441	F	714 635-0902	12106
Aerospace Parts Holdings Inc	3728	A	949 877-3630	20723
Affluent Target Marketing Inc	2721	F	714 446-6280	6099
Allbrite Car Care Products	2842	F	714 666-8683	8619
Alpine Marble	3281	F	714 704-9030	11228
Alstyle AP & Activewear MGT Co (HQ)	2253	A	714 765-0400	2821
Alstyle AP & Activewear MGT Co	2253	A	714 765-0400	2822
Alstyle Apparel LLC	2211	A	714 765-0400	2718
Alternative Hose Inc (PA)	3492	F	714 414-0904	13736
Alvarez Refinishing Inc	2262	E	714 780-0171	2900
American Circuit Tech Inc (PA)	3672	F	714 777-2480	18419
American Crcuit Card Retainers	3571	F	714 738-6194	15390
American Fabrication Corp (PA)	3714	C	714 632-1709	20254
American Index and Files LLC	2679	F	714 630-3360	5696
American Industrial Corp	3544	F	714 680-4763	14477
American Ingredients Inc	2833	F	714 630-6000	7921
American Sheet Metal Inc	3444	F	714 780-0155	12481
Anacom General Corporation	3651	E	714 774-8484	17759
Anaheim Automation Inc	3625	E	714 992-6990	17251
Anaheim Custom Extruders Inc	3089	E	714 693-8508	9947
Anaheim Embroidery Inc	2395	E	714 563-5220	3828
Anaheim Wire Products Inc (PA)	3496	E	714 563-8300	13810
Animal Nutrition Inds Inc	2833	F	949 583-2920	7922
Annmar Industries Inc	3089	F	714 630-5443	9949
Anvil Arts Inc	2514	F	714 630-2870	4823
Apex Technology Holdings Inc	3812	C	714 688-7188	21257
Apple Paper Converting Inc	2679	F	714 632-1916	5697
Applied Manufacturing Tech Inc	3555	F	714 630-9530	14801
APT Electronics Inc	3672	C	714 687-6760	18424
Aquarian Accessories Corp	3931	E	714 632-0230	23353
Aquarian Coatings Corp	3471	E	714 632-0230	13334
Aquatic Co	3088	C	714 993-1220	9895
Aquatic Industries Inc	3088	C	800 877-2005	9897
Arch-Rite Inc	2431	F	714 630-9305	4102
Arden Engineering Inc (DH)	3728	E	714 998-6410	20741
Argenti Inc	3599	E	714 666-8084	16279

2019 California
Manufacturers Register

(P-0000) Products & Services Section entry number
(PA)=Parent Co (HQ)=Headquarters (DH)=Div Headquarters

	SIC	EMP	PHONE	ENTRY #
Arista Foods Corporation	2038	F	714 666-1001	980
Artistic Pltg & Met Finshg Inc	3471	D	619 661-1691	13336
Ascent Manufacturing LLC	3469	F	714 540-6414	13166
Asdak International	3269	F	714 449-0733	10827
Aseptic Innovations Inc	3221	E	714 584-2110	10616
Assa Abloy Entrance Systems US	3699	D	714 578-0526	19914
Astro-Tek Industries LLC	3728	D	714 238-0022	20746
Atlas Magnetics Inc	3679	F	714 632-9718	19452
Atrium Door & Win Co Ariz Inc	3442	B	714 693-0601	12294
Automatic Switch Company	3491	F	714 283-4000	13703
B & B Specialties Inc (PA)	3429	C	714 985-3000	11934
B & Cawnings Inc	3444	E	714 632-3303	12498
B & E Enterprises	3751	F	714 630-3731	21089
B K Harris Inc	2759	F	714 630-8780	7245
B/E Aerospace Inc	3728	B	714 688-4200	20756
Bace Manufacturing Inc (HQ)	3089	A	714 630-6002	9967
Bananafish Productions Inc	3231	F	714 956-2129	10678
Barbee Valve & Supply Inc (HQ)	3491	F	619 585-8484	13706
Bassani Manufacturing	3498	E	714 630-1821	13879
Bechler Cams Inc	3829	F	714 774-5150	22171
Berry Global Inc	3089	F	714 777-5200	9977
Berry Global Inc	3089	C	714 777-5200	9980
Best Cheer Stone Inc (PA)	3281	E	714 399-1588	11235
Bimbo Bakeries Usa Inc	2051	D	714 634-8068	1200
Bimbo Bakeries Usa Inc	2099	E	714 533-9436	2466
Birchwood Lighting Inc	3648	E	714 550-7118	17675
Black Oxide Industries Inc	3471	E	714 870-9610	13346
Block Tops Inc (PA)	2541	F	714 978-5080	5040
Botanx	2844	E	714 854-1601	8709
Bowers & Kelly Products Inc	3086	F	714 630-1285	9821
Bpo Management Services Inc (HQ)	7372	F	714 974-2670	24443
Bracton Sosafe Inc	2842	F	714 632-8499	8627
Bradfield Manufacturing Inc	3446	F	714 543-8348	12838
Brice Tool & Stamping	3469	F	714 630-6400	13173
Bridgford Foods Corporation (HQ)	2045	B	714 526-5533	1096
British American TI & Die LLC	3423	C	714 776-8995	11886
Bud Wil Inc	3086	F	714 630-1242	9822
Buds Cotton Inc	2844	E	714 223-7800	8710
Buds Polishing & Metal Finshg	3471	E	714 632-0121	13355
C & S Assembly Inc	3679	F	866 779-8939	19472
C B S Fasteners Inc	3452	F	714 779-6368	13063
C T L Printing Inds Inc	2759	E	714 635-2980	7260
Cadence Aerospace LLC (PA)	3728	E	949 877-3630	20772
Cal Tech Precision Inc	3728	D	714 992-4130	20773
Campbell & Loftin Inc	3444	F	714 871-1950	12524
Canyon Composites Incorporated	3728	E	714 991-8181	20775
Ccda Waters LLC	3221	D	714 991-7031	10618
Ceco Environmental Corp	3089	E	760 530-1409	10017
Ced Anaheim 018	3699	F	714 956-5156	19925
Cemtrol Inc	3571	E	714 666-6606	15398
Certifix Inc	3999	F	714 496-3850	24064
Chad Industries Incorporated	3569	E	714 938-0080	15307
Champions Choice Inc	2992	F	714 635-4491	9426
Cheek Machine Corp	3599	F	714 279-9486	16381
Ciscos Shop	3432	F	657 230-9158	12031
Clean Cut Technologies LLC	3086	D	714 864-3500	9826
Cns Aviation Inc	3721	F	714 901-7072	20574
Coast 2 Coast Cables LLC	3357	F	714 666-1062	11656
Coast Sign Incorporated	3993	C	714 520-9144	23846
Cobra Systems	2741	F	714 688-7992	6463
Coca-Cola Company	2086	E	714 991-7031	2119
Colortech Label Inc	2679	F	714 999-5545	5705
Commercial Furniture	2521	E	714 350-7045	4939
Community Close-Up Westminster	2711	D	714 704-5811	5809
Computed Tool & Engineering	3544	F	714 630-3911	14499
CP Films Inc	2821	E	714 634-0900	7826
Craftech EDM Corporation	3089	C	714 630-8117	10048
Crafters Companion	3944	E	714 630-2444	23416
Craftsman Cutting Dies Inc (PA)	3423	E	714 776-8995	11890
Creative Press LLC	2752	D	714 774-5060	6767
Crescent Inc	2752	F	714 992-6030	6768
Cresco Manufacturing Inc	3599	E	714 525-2326	16409
Crest Coating Inc	3479	D	714 635-7090	13572
Cristek Interconnects Inc (PA)	3678	C	888 265-9162	19384
Crystal Cal Lab Inc	3679	F	714 991-1580	19503
Custom Industries Inc	3231	E	714 779-9101	10687
Custom Tooling & Stamping of O	3544	F	714 979-6782	14502
Cytec Engineered Materials Inc	2821	E	714 632-8444	7828
Cytec Engineered Materials Inc	3365	C	714 632-1174	11733
Cytec Engineered Materials Inc	3365	C	714 666-4302	11734
D & B Supply Corp	3535	C	714 632-3020	14271
D & D Gear Incorporated	3728	C	714 692-6570	20790
D & S Industries Inc	3728	F	714 779-8074	20791
D Y U Inc	3672	C	714 239-2433	18463
D-Mac Inc	2451	E	714 808-3918	4551

	SIC	EMP	PHONE	ENTRY #
Daisy Scout Publishing	2741	F	714 630-6611	6467
Danville Materials LLC	3843	E	714 399-0334	22865
Delta Coast Beer LLC	2082	F	213 604-2428	1586
Delta Commerce Corporation	2426	F	714 758-0030	4077
DG Performance Spc Inc	3799	D	714 961-8850	21225
Diamodent Inc	3843	F	888 281-8850	22873
Digital Periph Solutions Inc	3651	E	714 998-3440	17789
Disney Enterprises Inc	2389	D	407 397-6000	3655
Display Fabrication Group Inc	2399	F	714 373-2100	3941
Dretloh Aircraft Supply Inc (PA)	3728	F	714 632-6982	20799
Dura Imaging Group	3861	F	714 254-1400	23152
Dust Collector Services Inc	3564	F	714 237-1690	15151
Dynaflex International	3949	E	714 630-0909	23552
Eagle Ridge Paper Ltd (HQ)	2621	E	714 780-1799	5280
Econolite Control Products Inc (PA)	3669	C	714 630-3700	18322
Econotek Inc (PA)	3843	F	714 238-1131	22875
Edco Plastics Inc	3089	F	714 772-1986	10085
Electro Metal Finishing Corp (PA)	3479	F	714 630-8940	13581
Electron Beam Engineering Inc	7692	E	714 491-5990	25403
Elegance Entries Inc	3442	F	714 632-3667	12313
Elite Sports Inc	2329	F	714 634-3835	3149
Elysium Mosaics Inc	3253	F	714 991-7885	10781
Emazing Lights LLC	3648	F	626 628-6482	17691
Emticon Inc	3824	E	714 632-8595	21687
Emporium Di Sanarrey Corp	3281	F	714 780-5474	11250
Endress & Hauser Conducta Inc	3826	E	800 835-5474	21956
Endress+houser Conducta	3821	F	714 577-5600	21469
Energy Reconnaissance Inc	3567	F	714 630-4491	15259
Ennis Inc	3544	C	714 765-0400	14512
Euramax Holdings Inc	3353	F	714 563-8260	11575
Evert Hancock Incorporated	3444	F	714 870-0376	12577
Excelsior Nutrition Inc	2023	E	657 999-5188	614
Executive Tool Inc	3444	E	714 996-1276	12579
Expert Coatings & Graphics LLC	3479	F	714 476-2086	13587
Expo Dyeing & Finishing Inc	2269	C	714 220-9583	2911
Fab Tron	3444	F	714 996-4270	12583
Fabrication Network Inc	3444	D	714 393-5282	12584
Fantasia Distribution Inc	2131	E	714 817-8300	2713
Farrell Brothers Holding Corp	3599	F	714 630-3417	16493
Federal Signal Corporation	3711	E	714 871-3336	20140
Filtronics Inc	3589	E	714 630-5040	16042
Firmenich	2869	C	714 535-2871	9006
Foam Concepts Inc	3086	E	714 693-1037	9844
Foam Plastics & Rbr Pdts Corp	3086	F	714 779-0990	9849
Foreseeson Custom Displays Inc (PA)	3577	E	714 300-0540	15744
Friedl Corporation	3714	F	714 443-0122	20341
Fulcrum International Inc	2261	E	310 763-6823	2881
Fur Accents LLC	2371	F	714 403-5286	3600
Gear Manufacturing Inc	3728	E	714 792-2895	20823
Gemini Mfg & Engrg Inc	3544	E	714 999-0010	14521
Genesis Computer Systems Inc	3571	E	714 632-3648	15418
Gentry Golf Maintenance	3949	E	714 630-3541	23568
Ges US (new England) Inc	3679	C	978 459-4434	19552
Gforce Corporation	2051	F	714 630-0909	1261
Gledhill/Lyons Inc	3728	E	714 502-0274	20825
Global Enterprise Mfg Inc	3999	E	657 234-1150	24109
Global Paper Solutions Inc	2621	E	714 687-6102	5284
Globalscale Technologies Inc	3572	E	714 632-9239	15541
Gmp Laboratories America Inc	2834	D	714 630-2467	8195
Golden Coast Sportswear Inc	2339	E	714 704-4655	3422
Greenfields Outdoor Fitnes Inc	3949	F	888 315-9037	23577
Griffiths Services Inc	2752	E	714 685-7700	6841
Guptill Gear Corporation	3599	E	714 996-2170	16549
Haddads Fine Arts Inc	2893	F	714 996-2100	9199
Harrys Dye and Wash Inc	2261	E	714 446-0300	2882
Heat Transfer Pdts Group LLC	3585	B	714 529-1935	15959
Heidens Inc	2033	F	714 525-3414	804
Hestan Commercial Corporation	3639	C	714 869-2380	17415
High Energy Sports Inc	2399	F	714 632-3323	3950
Hitech Metal Fabrication Corp	3441	D	714 635-3505	12176
I M B Electronic Products	3675	D	714 523-2110	19294
Ideal Fasteners Inc	3452	F	714 630-7840	13073
Ideal Graphics Inc	2752	F	714 632-3398	6870
Inland Litho LLC	2752	D	714 993-6000	6886
Innovative Manufacturing Inc	3548	F	714 524-5246	14726
Innovative Organics Inc	2869	E	714 701-3900	9012
Intense Lighting LLC	3646	F	714 630-9877	17618
Interlink Inc	2752	D	714 905-7700	6894
Interlog Corporation	3679	E	714 529-7808	19584
International Abrasive Mfg Co	2844	E	714 779-9910	8771
International Paper Company	2653	C	714 776-6060	5425
International West Inc	3444	D	714 632-9190	12625
Interstate Electronics Corp (HQ)	3825	B	714 758-0500	21778
Interstate Electronics Corp	3663	E	714 758-3395	18133
Ironwood Electric Inc	3699	E	714 630-2350	19987

Employment Codes: A=Over 500 employees, B=251-500,
C=101-250, D=51-100, E=20-50, F=10-19

2019 California
Manufacturers Register

© Mergent Inc. 1-800-342-5647

1345

GEOGRAPHIC

Company	SIC	EMP	PHONE	ENTRY #
J&S Goodwin Inc (HQ)	3537	D	714 956-4040	14329
Jabil Inc	3672	E	714 938-0080	18512
Jaco Engineering	3599	E	714 991-1680	16610
Jaguar Litho Incorporated	2796	F	714 978-1821	7650
Janus International Group LLC	3442	E	714 503-6120	12322
Jasper Electronics	3679	E	714 917-0749	19593
JDC Development Group Inc	2449	E	714 575-1108	4525
Jeico Security Inc	3699	F	-	19993
Jellco Container Inc	2653	D	714 666-2728	5431
Jenson Custom Furniture Inc	2512	D	714 634-8145	4785
Joint Technologies Limited	3571	F	949 361-1158	15436
K & J Wire Products Corp	3446	E	714 816-0360	12869
Kanstul Musical Instrs Inc (PA)	3931	E	714 563-1000	23378
Kca Electronics Inc	3672	C	714 239-2433	18516
Kehoe Custom Wood Designs	2511	F	714 993-0444	4710
Kempton Machine Works Inc	3545	F	714 990-0596	14644
Kiva Container Corporation	3086	D	714 630-3850	9868
L & H Industries	2037	F	714 635-1555	956
L3 Technologies Inc	3663	C	714 758-4222	18155
Labeltronix LLC	2759	D	800 429-4321	7379
Leonards Carpet Service Inc (PA)	2541	D	714 630-1930	5080
Lester Lithograph Inc	2752	F	714 491-3981	6944
Link4 Corporation	3822	F	714 524-0004	21515
Lodestone LLC	3548	F	714 970-0900	14729
Magnetic Metals Corporation	3542	E	714 828-4625	14443
Magnetic Sensors Corp	3679	E	714 630-8380	19635
Mako Industries SC Inc	3826	E	714 632-1400	21985
Mako Overhead Door Inc	3442	F	714 998-0122	12330
Man-Grove Industries Inc	2752	D	714 630-3020	6959
Mashindustries Inc	2599	F	714 736-9600	5246
Master Arts Inc	2796	F	714 240-4550	7651
Matrix Shafts	3949	E	714 970-9977	23614
Maverick Abrasives Corporation	3291	E	714 854-9531	11298
Maxlite Inc	3648	E	714 678-5000	17713
McCormick & Company Inc	2099	D	714 685-0934	2600
McLeod Racing LLC	3714	F	714 630-2764	20398
Mechanized Enterprises Inc	3599	F	714 630-5512	16731
Medivision Inc	3845	E	714 563-2772	23008
Medplast Group Inc	3089	D	951 273-1700	10204
Mega Plus Pcb Incorporated	3672	F	714 550-0265	18526
Metal-Fab Services Industries	3444	E	714 630-7771	12670
Mettler Electronics Corp	3841	E	714 533-2221	22538
Meyer & Reeder Inc	2541	E	714 388-0148	5082
Micrometals Inc (PA)	3679	D	714 970-9400	19650
Micrometals/Texas Inc	3679	C	325 677-8753	19651
Millcraft Inc	2431	D	714 632-9621	4192
Mobile Wireless Tech Llc	3669	F	714 239-1535	18347
Moda Enterprises Inc	3711	F	714 484-0076	20159
Modern Manufacturing Inc	3599	E	714 254-0156	16762
Moeller Mfg & Sup LLC	3429	E	714 999-5551	11976
Mondelez Global LLC	2051	J	714 634-2773	1292
Moreno Industries Inc	3714	F	714 229-9696	20405
Motors & Controls Intl Inc (PA)	3545	E	714 956-0480	14655
Nbty Manufacturing LLC	2834	C	714 765-8323	8294
Nelco Products Inc (HQ)	3083	E	714 879-4293	9754
Nelco Products Inc	3672	E	714 879-4293	18542
Nellson Nutraceutical LLC (PA)	2064	B	714 765-7000	1446
Neutron Plating Inc	3471	D	714 632-9241	13463
Nidi Tec Inc	3281	F	714 777-9323	11266
Nu TEC Powdercoating	3479	E	714 632-5045	13623
Nylok LLC	3452	E	714 635-3993	13079
Oasis Alloy Wheels Inc	3365	F	714 533-3286	11747
One-Way Manufacturing Inc	3498	E	714 630-8833	13898
Onesolution Light and Control	3648	E	714 490-5540	17721
Orange Cnty Cstl Physcians Inc	3841	F	808 545-2500	22574
Orange County Erectors Inc	3448	E	714 502-8455	12955
Orange County Screw Products	3599	E	714 630-7433	16811
Ortronics Inc	3444	C	714 776-5420	12697
Osio International Inc	2671	E	714 935-9700	5528
Otanez New Creations	2541	F	951 808-9663	5090
Outdoor Dimensions LLC	2499	C	714 578-9555	4639
Pacific Broach & Engrg Assoc	3599	F	714 632-5678	16819
Pacific Bulletproof Co	3761	F	714 630-5447	21167
Pacific Precision Metals Inc	3469	C	951 226-1500	13258
Pacific Tchnical Eqp Engrg Inc	3563	F	714 835-3088	15133
Pacific Transformer Corp	3612	C	714 779-0450	17111
Pacific West Litho Inc	2752	F	714 579-0868	7012
Pacific Westline Inc	2541	D	714 956-2442	5091
Pampanga Foods Company Inc	2013	F	714 773-0537	512
Pampanga Foods Incorporated	2038	E	714 331-7206	1008
Paper Max Inc (PA)	2621	F	714 780-0595	5323
Parex Usa Inc (DH)	3299	E	714 778-2266	11367
Park Electrochemical Corp	3672	F	714 459-4400	18556
Peak Franchising Inc	2023	E	714 456-0700	643
Pendarvis Manufacturing Inc	3599	E	714 992-0950	16837
Performance Powder Inc	3479	E	714 632-0600	13633
Pharmachem Laboratories LLC	2023	F	714 630-6000	644
Phillips Lobue & Wilson Mllwk	2431	F	951 331-5714	4212
Pinnacle Precision Shtmtl Corp (PA)	3444	C	714 777-3129	12716
Pinnacle Precision Shtmtl Corp	3444	C	714 777-3129	12717
Pipe Fabricating & Supply Co (PA)	3498	D	714 630-5200	13901
Porter Powder Coating Inc	3479	F	714 956-2010	13637
Powdercoat Services LLC	3479	E	714 533-2251	13639
Power Aire Inc	3613	E	800 526-7661	17156
Power Paragon Inc (HQ)	3612	A	714 956-9200	17113
Power Paragon Inc	3699	B	714 956-9200	20043
Powerplus Cleaning Solutions	2842	E	714 635-9264	8667
Precision Aerospace & Tech Inc	3545	E	714 543-2966	14666
Precision Anodizing & Pltg Inc	3471	D	714 996-1601	13478
Precon Inc	3541	F	714 630-7632	14401
Preferred Pharmaceuticals Inc	2834	F	714 777-3729	8342
Print N Save Inc	2752	F	714 634-1133	7039
Product Solutions Inc	3589	F	714 545-9757	16091
Progrssive Intgrated Solutions	2759	D	714 237-0980	7452
Qualitask Incorporated	3599	F	714 237-0900	16869
Quality Edm Inc	3599	E	714 283-9220	16871
Quality First Woodworks Inc	2499	C	714 632-0480	4644
R & S Overhead Door of So Cal	3442	E	714 680-0600	12343
R C I P Inc	3599	F	714 630-1239	16879
R H Barden Inc	3677	F	714 970-0900	19357
R K Fabrication Inc	2821	E	714 630-9654	7878
Racing Beat Inc	3519	E	714 779-8677	14029
Radarsonics Inc	3679	E	714 630-7288	19701
Rapid Manufacturing A (PA)	3496	C	714 974-2432	13849
Raykorvay Inc	3942	E	714 632-8680	23401
Raytheon Applied Signal	3669	F	714 917-0255	18358
Regal Custom Millwork Inc	2421	F	714 632-2488	4049
Reliable Packaging Systems Inc	2891	F	714 572-1094	9167
Rf Precision Cables Inc	3357	F	714 772-7567	11673
Rgb Systems Inc (PA)	3577	C	714 491-1500	15839
Rgb Systems Inc	3577	D	714 491-1500	15840
Rigiflex Technology Inc	3672	E	714 688-1500	18580
Roberts Precision Engrg Inc	3599	E	714 635-4485	16909
Rock & Roll Custom Paint Works	3559	E	714 744-0631	15022
Rockwell Automation Inc	3625	D	714 938-9000	17300
Roto-Die Company Inc	3544	F	714 991-8701	14567
RPM Plastic Molding Inc	3089	F	714 630-9300	10349
RSI Home Products Inc (HQ)	2514	A	714 449-2200	4840
RSI Home Products Mfg Inc	2514	D	714 449-2200	4842
Rtie Holdings LLC	3679	D	714 765-8200	19713
Rtr Industries LLC	3592	E	714 996-0050	16152
Ryvec Inc	2816	E	714 520-5592	7744
S & S Printers	2752	E	714 535-5592	7092
S K Laboratories Inc	2834	E	714 695-9800	8370
Saemie Corporation	3312	E	714 632-0530	11418
Saint-Gobain Ceramics Plas Inc	2869	E	714 701-3900	9038
Schley Products Inc	3423	F	714 693-7666	11909
Seating Component Mfg Inc	2519	F	714 693-3376	4919
Sechrist Industries Inc	3841	D	714 579-8400	22618
Sehanson Inc	3728	E	714 778-1900	20928
Serra Laser and Waterjet Inc	3699	E	714 680-6211	20065
Setco LLC	3089	F	812 424-2904	10372
Shaxon Industries Inc	3572	D	714 779-1140	15606
Sheet Metal Service	3444	F	714 446-0196	12758
Shrin Corporation	3714	C	714 850-0303	20447
Si Manufacturing Inc	3677	E	714 956-7110	19362
Signage Solutions Corporation	3993	E	714 491-0299	23969
Skullduggery Inc	3944	F	714 777-6425	23465
Sky Rider Equipment Co Inc	2515	E	714 632-6890	4886
Slp Limited LLC	3672	F	714 517-1955	18606
Smart Elec & Assembly Inc	3672	C	714 772-2651	18607
SMt Mfg Incorporataed	3679	E	714 738-9999	19729
Sonfarrel Inc	3599	D	714 630-7286	16951
Southern California Mtl Hdlg	3537	D	714 773-9630	14347
Southland Tool Mfg Inc	3545	F	714 632-8198	14679
Spark Stone LLC	1411	F	714 772-7575	306
Spidell Publishing Inc	2741	F	714 776-7850	6587
SPS Inc	2439	F	714 632-7131	4424
SPX Corporation	3443	F	714 634-3855	12425
St Pierre Gonzalez Enterprises	3479	E	714 491-2191	13665
Stainless Micro-Polish Inc	3471	F	714 632-8903	13510
Steeldyne Industries	3444	E	714 630-6200	12771
Stepan Company	2821	E	714 776-9870	7890
Strand Art Company Inc	3089	E	714 777-0444	10393
Stryker Corporation	3841	E	714 764-1700	22638
Sun Rich Foods Intl Corp	2099	F	714 632-7577	2675
Sunny Delight Beverages Co	2033	C	714 630-6251	861
Sunset Signs and Printing	2759	F	714 255-9104	7502
Superior Connector Plating Inc	3471	E	714 774-1174	13514
Superior Jig Inc	3544	F	714 525-4777	14573

	SIC	EMP	PHONE	ENTRY #
Superior Spring Company	3495	E	714 490-0881	13804
Superior Stone Products Inc	3281	F	714 635-7775	11284
Supreme Pta Investments Corp	3751	E	949 707-0288	21139
T&J Sausage Kitchen Inc	2013	E	714 632-8350	531
Tahiti Cabinets Inc	2599	D	714 693-0618	5257
Tait & Associates Inc	3443	D	714 560-8222	12432
Tajen Graphics Inc	2752	E	714 527-3122	7127
Tam Printing Inc	2752	F	714 224-4488	7128
Taylor-Dunn Manufacturing Co (DH)	3537	D	714 956-4040	14350
Tck Membrane America Inc	2899	F	714 678-8832	9310
Technic Inc	3471	E	714 632-0200	13520
Technotronix Inc	3672	E	714 630-9200	18623
Teco Diagnostics	2835	E	714 693-7788	8520
Telatemp Corporation	3829	F	714 414-0343	22284
Textile Products Inc	2221	E	714 761-0401	2784
Textured Design Furniture	2511	E	714 502-9121	4743
Tfd Incorporated	3827	F	714 630-7127	22141
Thermech Corporation	2671	E	714 533-3183	5543
Thornton Steel & Ir Works Inc	3446	E	714 491-8800	12898
Top Printing & Graphic Inc	2759	F	714 484-9200	7522
Towne Park Brew Inc	2082	E	714 844-2492	1632
Transko Electronics Inc	3679	F	714 528-8000	19769
Transline Technology Inc	3672	E	714 533-8300	18626
Tri Power Electric Inc	3699	F	714 630-6445	20090
Triad Bellows Design & Mfg Inc	3599	F	714 204-4444	17010
Trinity Process Solutions Inc	3498	E	714 701-1112	13907
Trussworks International Inc	3441	E	714 630-2772	12265
Ttm Technologies Inc	3672	B	714 688-7200	18634
Tuffer Manufacturing Co Inc	3812	E	714 526-3077	21450
Turret Lathe Specialists Inc	3599	F	714 520-0058	17020
Twilight Technology Inc (PA)	3674	E	714 257-2257	19239
Two Blind Mice LLC	2084	F	714 279-0600	2036
United Paper Box Inc	2657	E	714 777-8383	5514
Universal Alloy Corporation	3354	B	714 630-7200	11608
Universal Directory Publishing	2741	E	714 994-6025	6610
University Frames Inc	2499	E	714 575-5100	4662
UOP LLC	2671	E	714 870-7590	5545
US Bioservices (PA)	2851	D	800 801-1140	8952
US Union Tool Inc (HQ)	3541	E	714 521-6242	14421
USA Extruded Plastics Inc	3089	F	714 991-6061	10424
Vascular Imaging Professionals (PA)	3841	F	949 278-5622	22668
Veeco Electro Fab Inc (PA)	3672	E	714 630-8020	18645
Venus Alloys Inc (PA)	3363	E	714 635-8800	11708
Vertical Hydro Garden Inc	3524	F	916 458-4987	14137
Visionary Inc	3851	E	714 237-1900	23130
Vts Sheetmetal Specialist Co	3444	E	714 237-1420	12812
Walt Disney Imagineering	2389	C	714 781-3152	3686
Wasser Filtration Inc (PA)	3569	D	714 982-5600	15373
Weartech International Inc (HQ)	3562	E	714 683-2430	15116
Weis/Robart Partitions Inc	3446	F	714 666-0822	12905
Wellbore Navigation Inc (PA)	3829	F	714 259-7760	22297
West Bond Inc (PA)	3569	F	714 978-1551	15375
Western Golf Inc	3949	F	800 448-4409	23690
Westpak Usa Inc	3699	F	714 530-6995	20112
Wesval Inc	3599	F	714 870-0990	17064
Wide USA Corporation	3575	F	714 300-0540	15650
Wildlife In Wood Inc	2499	F	714 773-5816	4664
Willard Marine Inc	3732	D	714 630-4018	21071
Wwt International Inc	3533	F	714 632-0810	14245
Xerxes Corporation	2821	D	714 630-0012	7901
Y2k Precision Sheetmetal Inc	3993	F	714 632-3901	24007
Yeager Manufacturing Corp (PA)	3728	E	714 879-2800	20976
YKK (usa) Inc	3965	C	714 701-1200	23783
Young Nails Inc	2844	E	714 525-2264	8868
Yti Enterprises Inc	2499	F	714 632-8696	4665
Zurich Engineering Inc	3724	F	714 528-0066	20693

ANDERSON, CA - Shasta County

	SIC	EMP	PHONE	ENTRY #
B & B R V Inc	3716	E	530 365-7043	20521
Blue Lake Roundstock Co LLC	2491	F	530 515-7007	4587
Checchi Enterprises Inc	2752	F	530 378-1207	6728
Dpm Inc	3599	F	530 378-3420	16449
Folsom Ready Mix Inc	3273	E	530 365-0191	11107
Haisch Construction Co Inc	2439	F	530 378-6800	4407
James A Headrick Ii/Elizabeth	2411	D	530 247-8000	3996
North Valley Newspapers Inc	2711	F	530 365-2797	6001
Outdoor Creations Inc	3272	F	530 365-6106	10970
Shasta Wood Products	2541	E	530 378-6880	5100
Sierra Pacific Industries (PA)	2421	D	530 378-8000	4057
Sierra Pacific Industries	2421	B	530 365-3721	4062
Siskiyou Forest Products (PA)	2431	E	530 378-6980	4232
Voorwood Company	3553	E	530 365-3311	14787
Williams Cabinets Inc	2434	F	530 365-8421	4369

ANGELS CAMP, CA - Calaveras County

	SIC	EMP	PHONE	ENTRY #
Angels Sheet Metal Inc	3444	F	209 736-0911	12483

	SIC	EMP	PHONE	ENTRY #
California Electric Steel	3325	E	209 736-0465	11523
Foothill Pritnig & Graphics/ C (PA)	2752	F	209 736-4332	6822
Relcomm Inc	3679	F	209 736-0421	19706

ANGWIN, CA - Napa County

	SIC	EMP	PHONE	ENTRY #
Gina Designs	3911	F	707 967-1041	23267
Ladera Vineyards LLC	2084	F	707 965-2445	1847
Ladera Winery LLC	2084	F	707 965-2445	1848
Neal Family Vineyards LLC	2084	F	707 965-2800	1895

ANTELOPE, CA - Sacramento County

	SIC	EMP	PHONE	ENTRY #
Elite Property Maintenance	3559	F	916 275-3956	14946
Temptrol Industries Inc	2394	F	916 344-4457	3815

ANTIOCH, CA - Contra Costa County

	SIC	EMP	PHONE	ENTRY #
Allied Container Systems Inc	3448	C	925 944-7600	12913
Bond Manufacturing Co Inc (PA)	3272	C	925 252-1135	10886
Chep (usa) Inc	2448	D	925 234-4970	4460
Contra Costa Newspapers Inc	2711	F	925 634-2125	5816
Georgia-Pacific LLC	3275	C	925 757-2870	11218
K I O Kables Inc	3496	F	925 778-7500	13836
Marine & Industrial Services	3498	F	925 757-8791	13895
Pacific Flyway Decoy Assn	3949	F	925 754-4978	23627
Silgan Containers Mfg Corp	3411	E	925 778-8000	11869
Tomiko Inc	3561	F	925 754-5694	15094
Ultimate Game Chair Inc	3651	F	925 756-6944	17870
Verco Decking Inc	3444	F	925 778-2102	12807

APPLE VALLEY, CA - San Bernardino County

	SIC	EMP	PHONE	ENTRY #
EE Pauley Plastic Extrusion	3089	F	760 240-3737	10088
Global Pumice LLC	1499	F	760 240-3544	412
Induction Technology Corp	3567	F	760 246-7333	15262
Land N Top Cleaning Services	2273	F	760 624-8845	2930
Phantom Tool & Die Co	3542	F	760 240-4249	14450
Polymer Concepts Technologies	3053	F	760 240-4999	9549
Reid Products Inc	3599	F	760 240-1355	16892
Telexca Inc	3721	F	760 247-4277	20630
Tibban Manufacturing Inc	3999	F	760 961-1160	24270
Valero Energy Corporation	2911	E	760 946-3322	9371
Waterfountainscom Inc	3499	F	760 946-0525	13982

APTOS, CA - Santa Cruz County

	SIC	EMP	PHONE	ENTRY #
Engage Communication Inc (PA)	3661	E	831 688-1021	17944
Farr West Fashions	2341	F	831 661-5039	3536
Mariannes Ice Cream LLC	2024	E	831 713-4746	683
Print Smith Inc	2752	F	831 688-1538	7040
Pureline Oralcare Inc	3843	E	831 662-9500	22904
Warmboard Inc	3567	E	831 685-9276	15278

ARBUCKLE, CA - Colusa County

	SIC	EMP	PHONE	ENTRY #
ADM Milling Co	2041	D	530 476-2662	1023
Cal Vsta Erosion Ctrl Pdts LLC	3531	E	530 476-0706	14149
California Family Foods LLC	2044	E	530 476-3326	1075
Conrad Wood Preserving Co	2491	E	530 476-2894	4592
National Oilwell Varco Inc	1389	F	530 682-0571	247
Ridge Cementing LLC	1389	F	530 476-3333	266
Sun Valley Rice Company LLC	2044	D	530 476-3000	1091

ARCADIA, CA - Los Angeles County

	SIC	EMP	PHONE	ENTRY #
Airsoft Zone Corporation (PA)	3949	F	818 495-6502	23490
Airsoft Zone Corporation	3949	F	818 495-6502	23491
Bendick Precision Inc	3599	F	626 445-0217	16318
Butane Propane News Inc	2721	F	626 357-2168	6122
Cremax U S A Corporation	3429	F	626 956-8800	11949
Danco Anodizing Inc (PA)	3471	E	626 445-3303	13384
Dimad Enterprises Inc (PA)	3471	E	626 445-3303	13388
Enas Media Inc	3652	E	626 962-1115	17894
Heateflex Corporation	3433	E	626 599-8566	12067
J&M Analytik AG	3826	E	626 297-2930	21979
Joico Laboratories Inc	2844	C	626 321-4100	8778
Kustomer Kinetics Inc	2844	E	626 445-6161	8785
Miracle Sealants Company LLC	2899	E	626 443-6433	9281
Posey Products LLC (HQ)	3842	E	626 443-3143	22796
Quantum Corporation	3572	C	213 248-2481	15589
Relton Corporation	2899	D	800 423-1505	9301
T&L Air Conditioning Inc	3822	F	626 294-9888	21533
Tektest Inc	3678	F	626 446-6175	19424
Variant Technology Inc	3648	F	626 278-4343	17744
Vmanoo Inc	3699	F	626 662-1342	20104
Zotos International Inc	2844	E	626 321-4100	8872

ARCATA, CA - Humboldt County

	SIC	EMP	PHONE	ENTRY #
Crestmark Architractural Mill	2431	E	707 822-4034	4131
Cummins Pacific LLC	3519	F	707 822-7392	14016
Cypress Grove Chevre Inc	2022	D	707 825-1100	568
Desserts On US Inc	2051	F	707 822-0160	1230
Fire and Light Originals LP	3231	F	707 825-7500	10697
Holly Yashi Inc	3911	D	707 822-0389	23274

Employment Codes: A=Over 500 employees, B=251-500,
C=101-250, D=51-100, E=20-50, F=10-19

2019 California
Manufacturers Register

© Mergent Inc. 1-800-342-5647

1347

Company	SIC	EMP	PHONE	ENTRY #
JR Stephens Company	2434	E	707 825-0100	4316
Kokatat Inc	2329	D	707 822-7621	3168
Larry Schlussler	3632	F	707 822-9095	17379
Lindgren Lumber Co	2421	F	707 822-6519	4042
Living Waters Logging Inc	2411	F	707 822-3955	3998
Pac Powder Inc	3479	F	707 826-1630	13627
Schmidbauer Lumber Inc	2421	E	707 822-7607	4053
Sun Valley Floral Group LLC	3999	A	707 826-8700	24256
Tofu Shop Specialty Foods Inc	2099	E	707 822-7401	2682
Wing Inflatables Inc (HQ)	3089	C	707 826-2887	10446

ARLETA, CA - Los Angeles County

Company	SIC	EMP	PHONE	ENTRY #
Alziebler Incorporated (PA)	3599	F	800 430-7536	16265
Farmer Bros Co	2095	F	818 767-7649	2347
Juicy Couture Inc	2221	C	888 824-8826	2779
M & R Plating Corporation	3471	F	818 896-2700	13447

ARMONA, CA - Kings County

Company	SIC	EMP	PHONE	ENTRY #
Armona Frozen Food Lockers	2013	F	559 584-3948	465
Central Valley Cabinet Mfg	2434	F	559 584-8441	4285

AROMAS, CA - Monterey County

Company	SIC	EMP	PHONE	ENTRY #
Granite Rock Co	1442	D	831 768-2300	360

ARROYO GRANDE, CA - San Luis Obispo County

Company	SIC	EMP	PHONE	ENTRY #
Alliance Ready Mix Inc	3273	F	805 343-0360	11035
Coastal Vineyard Services LLC	2084	F	805 441-4465	1699
Crosno Construction Inc	3449	E	805 343-7437	12976
Hitek Lighting Inc	3648	F	805 481-6006	17700
Laetitia Vineyard & Winery Inc	2084	D	805 481-1772	1849
Layne Laboratories Inc	2299	F	805 242-7918	3006
Lopez Water Treatment Plant	3589	F	805 473-7152	16067
M29 Technology and Design	7372	F	805 489-9402	24874
Phillips 66 Co Carbon Group	3559	F	805 489-4050	15009
Politezer Newspaers Inc	2711	F	805 929-3864	6015
Spawn Mate Inc	2873	E	805 473-7250	9074

ARTESIA, CA - Los Angeles County

Company	SIC	EMP	PHONE	ENTRY #
Applied Liquid Polymer	3271	F	562 402-6300	10844
Cal Plate (PA)	3555	D	562 403-3000	14804
California Dairies Inc	2026	D	562 809-2595	715
Hunter Douglas Inc	2591	C	562 207-0800	5195
M G Watanabe Inc	3663	F	562 402-8989	18172
National Ready Mixed Con Co	3273	F	562 865-6211	11150
Standard Crystal Corp	3679	F	626 443-2121	19734
Viking Ready Mix Co Inc	3273	F	562 865-6211	11206

ARVIN, CA - Kern County

Company	SIC	EMP	PHONE	ENTRY #
Lee Sandusky Corporation	2514	E	661 854-5551	4835
Moore Farms Inc	2099	F	661 854-5588	2610
Reeves Extruded Products Inc.	3082	D	661 854-5970	9744
Southern Valley Chemical Co	2879	F	661 366-3308	9112
Western Fiber Co Inc	3541	E	661 854-5556	14423

ATASCADERO, CA - San Luis Obispo County

Company	SIC	EMP	PHONE	ENTRY #
Drymax Technologies Inc	2252	F	805 239-2555	2811
Fence Factory	3496	F	805 462-1362	13828
Ground Control Systems Inc	3663	F	805 783-4600	18117
One At A Time	3942	F	805 461-1784	23399
Wyred 4 Sound LLC	3651	F	805 466-9973	17882
X Tri Inc	2893	F	805 286-4544	9217

ATHERTON, CA - San Mateo County

Company	SIC	EMP	PHONE	ENTRY #
Novatorque Inc	3621	E	510 933-2700	17215
Powerflare Corporation	3699	F	650 208-2580	20044

ATWATER, CA - Merced County

Company	SIC	EMP	PHONE	ENTRY #
Certified Stainless Svc Inc	3443	F	209 356-3300	12371
Certified Stainless Svc Inc	3443	E	209 537-4747	12373
Five Keys Inc	2329	F	209 358-7971	3154
Gallo Global Nutrition LLC	2022	C	209 394-7984	574
Hansens Oak Inc (PA)	2511	F	209 357-3424	4701
Keney Manufacturing Co (PA)	2434	F	209 358-6474	4318
MB Sports Inc	3732	E	209 357-4153	21056
Nci Group Inc	3448	C	209 357-1000	12954
Teasdale Foods Inc (PA)	2032	B	209 358-5616	778

AUBERRY, CA - Fresno County

Company	SIC	EMP	PHONE	ENTRY #
Auberry Forest Products Inc	2411	F	559 855-6255	3979
Messer Logging Inc	2411	E	559 855-3160	4003

AUBURN, CA - Placer County

Company	SIC	EMP	PHONE	ENTRY #
Absinthe Group Inc	2033	E	530 823-8527	783
API Marketing	2752	F	916 632-1946	6665
Armstrong Technology Inc	3599	E	530 888-6262	16281
Auburn Journal Inc (HQ)	2711	E	530 885-5656	5768
Auburn Journal Inc	2711	D	530 346-2232	5769
Auburn Trader Inc (DH)	2711	F	530 888-7653	5770
Audio Partners Publishing	3652	F	530 888-7803	17886

Company	SIC	EMP	PHONE	ENTRY #
Broach Masters Inc	3545	E	530 885-1939	14610
DAt Farms Inc	3999	F	408 848-8060	24075
Di Maxx Technologies LLC	3827	F	530 888-1942	22072
Gara Inc	3646	F	530 887-1110	17611
Interior Wood Design Inc	2511	F	530 888-7707	4706
IRD Acquisitions LLC	3851	F	530 210-2966	23102
Magorian Mine Services (PA)	1442	F	530 269-1960	374
Mitchell-Duckett Corporation	3599	F	530 268-2112	16758
Morgan Advanced Ceramics Inc	2819	C	530 823-3401	7790
Mydax Inc	3585	F	530 888-6662	15973
Nor Cal Food Solutions LLC	2035	F	530 823-8527	923
Pass Laboratories Inc	3651	F	530 878-5350	17842
Pre/Plastics Inc	3089	F	530 823-1820	10301
Purveyors Kitchen	2033	E	530 823-8527	851
Quality Metal Fabrication LLC	3444	E	530 887-7388	12728
Ron & Diana Vanatta	2541	F	530 888-0200	5098
Ryangmw Inc	3713	F	530 305-2499	20226
Sierra Precision Optics Inc	3827	F	530 885-6979	22136
Sierra Sculpture Inc	3366	F	530 887-1581	11766
Sierra Swiss & Machine Inc	3451	F	530 346-1110	13041
Soundview Applications Inc	3651	F	530 888-7593	17862
Stellarvue	3827	F	530 823-7796	22138
Surface Manufacturing Inc	3599	F	530 885-0700	16975
Tahoe Rf Semiconductor Inc	3674	F	530 823-9765	19211
Tri-Continent Scientific Inc	3824	D	530 273-8888	21696
VSR Network Technologies LLC	3661	F	530 889-1500	18008

AVILA BEACH, CA - San Luis Obispo County

Company	SIC	EMP	PHONE	ENTRY #
Gander Publishing Inc	2731	F	805 541-5523	6343

AZUSA, CA - Los Angeles County

Company	SIC	EMP	PHONE	ENTRY #
A & B Aerospace Inc	3599	E	626 334-2976	16181
Accu-Blend Corporation	2911	F	626 334-7744	9319
Acme Portable Machines Inc	3571	E	626 610-1888	15381
American International Racing	3089	F	626 969-7733	9942
Ancra International LLC (HQ)	3537	C	626 765-4800	14307
Arminak Solutions LLC	2844	C	626 385-5858	8697
Artisan Screen Printing Inc	2759	C	626 815-2700	7242
Avery Dennison Corporation	2672	C	626 938-7239	5550
Azusa Rock LLC (DH)	1422	C	858 530-9444	309
BK Signs Inc	3993	F	626 334-5600	23828
Blue Ribbon Baking Inc	2051	C	626 815-8809	1211
Bojer Inc	2392	E	626 334-1711	3710
Buchanans Spoke & Rim	3751	E	626 969-4655	21094
California Amforge Corporation	3312	D	626 334-4931	11382
California Master Printers	2752	F	626 812-8930	6715
Calportland Company	3273	C	626 334-3226	11056
Cardinal Laboratories Inc	2844	D	626 610-1200	8714
Casella Aluminum Extrusions	3354	F	714 961-8322	11584
Cee -Jay Research & Sales LLC	2759	E	626 815-1530	7268
Chipmasters Manufacturing Inc (PA)	3599	F	626 422-2053	16383
D & L Moulding and Lumber Co	2431	E	626 444-0134	4136
D W Mack Co Inc	3089	F	626 969-1817	10058
Dependble Incontinence Sup Inc	2676	F	626 812-0044	5664
Digital Printing Systems Inc (PA)	2752	D	626 815-1888	6787
Dolphin Spas Inc	3999	F	626 334-0099	24082
Ducommun Incorporated	3677	C	626 812-9666	19333
Gale Banks Engineering	3519	C	626 969-9600	14028
Hallett Boats	3732	E	626 969-8844	21041
Hannemann Fiberglass Inc	3714	F	626 969-7317	20358
I/O Controls Corporation (PA)	3625	D	626 812-5353	17277
Illinois Tool Works Inc	2992	C	847 724-7500	9437
Innovative Designs & Mfg Inc	2514	F	626 812-4422	4831
Intertex Inc	3564	E	626 385-3300	15161
Inwesco Incorporated (PA)	3315	C	626 334-7115	11446
Lindsey Manufacturing Co	3463	C	626 969-3471	13125
Magparts (DH)	3365	D	626 334-7897	11746
Mat Cactus Mfg Co	2273	F	626 969-0444	2933
Mc William & Son Inc	3469	F	626 969-1821	13245
McKeever Danlee Confectionary	2064	E	626 334-8964	1444
McMurtrie & Mcmurtrie Inc	2426	D	626 815-0177	4084
Melco Steel Inc	3443	E	626 334-7875	12399
Metal Engineering & Mfg	3444	E	626 334-5271	12666
Mortech Manufacturing Co Inc	2531	E	626 334-1471	5021
National Stabilizers Inc	2099	F	626 969-5700	2615
Nicks Doors Inc	2431	F	626 812-6491	4202
Norac Inc (PA)	2869	B	626 334-2907	9026
Northrop Grumman Systems Corp	3812	C	626 812-1000	21372
Northrop Grumman Systems Corp	3721	B	626 812-1464	20611
Owen Magic Supreme Inc	3999	F	626 969-4519	24199
Peninsula Light Metals LLC (HQ)	3363	F	626 765-4856	11702
Phaostron Instr Electronic Co	3613	D	626 969-6801	17155
Precision Granite USA Inc	3281	F	562 696-8328	11270
Pro Fab Tech LLC	3479	F	626 804-7200	13642
Ptb Sales Inc (PA)	3563	E	626 334-0500	15135
R E Atckison Co Inc	3531	F	626 334-0266	14186

Mergent email: customerrelations@mergent.com
1348

2019 California
Manufacturers Register

(P-0000) Products & Services Section entry number
(PA)=Parent Co (HQ)=Headquarters (DH)=Div Headquarters

Company	SIC	EMP	PHONE	ENTRY #
Rain Bird Corporation (PA)	3494	C	626 812-3400	13774
Rain Bird Corporation	3432	E	626 812-3400	12047
Ray-Bar Engineering Corp	3842	F	626 969-1818	22802
Reichhold Industries Inc	2821	F	626 334-4974	7879
S & S Foods LLC	2013	C	626 633-1609	520
S&B Pharma Inc	2833	D	626 334-2908	7969
Sari Art & Printing Inc	2752	F	626 305-0888	7096
Screwmatic Inc	3599	D	626 334-7831	16934
Seasonic Electronics Inc	3679	F	626 969-9966	19721
Sharpdots LLC	3577	F	626 599-9696	15853
Skylock Industries	3728	D	626 334-2391	20933
Tecomet Inc	3841	A	626 334-1519	22645
Tuff Shed Inc	2452	F	626 334-0748	4580
Valley Forge Acquisition Corp	3462	F	626 969-8701	13116
Very Special Chocolats Inc	2066	C	626 334-7838	1478
Westbase Inc (PA)	3613	F	626 969-6801	17173
Westwood Laboratories Inc (PA)	2844	E	626 969-3305	8866
Zt Plus	3674	F	626 208-3440	19288

BAKERSFIELD, CA - Kern County

Company	SIC	EMP	PHONE	ENTRY #
Acco Engineered Systems Inc	3585	F	661 631-1975	15931
Advanced Technologies	7372	E	661 872-4807	24329
Aera Energy LLC (HQ)	1381	A	661 665-5000	92
Airgas Usa LLC	2813	E	661 201-8107	7686
Alder & Co LLC	2511	F	661 326-0320	4666
Ally Enterprises	1389	E	661 412-9933	165
American Bottling Company	2086	E	661 323-7921	2084
American Yeast Corporation	2099	F	661 834-1050	2451
Ampligraphix	2752	F	661 321-3150	6660
Anatesco Inc	1389	F	661 399-6990	167
Archrock Inc	1389	F	661 321-0271	168
B & B Pipe and Tool Co	3599	F	661 323-8208	16296
B & L Casing Service LLC	1389	F	661 589-9080	169
Baker Hghes Olfld Oprtions LLC	1389	F	661 834-2844	170
Baker Hghes Olfld Oprtions LLC	1389	F	661 831-5200	171
Baker Hghes Olfld Oprtions LLC	1389	F	661 324-9488	173
Baker Hughes A GE Company LLC	1389	D	661 387-1010	176
Baker Hughes A GE Company LLC	3533	D	661 837-9601	14211
Baker Hughes A GE Company LLC	1389	D	800 229-7447	178
Baker Hughes A GE Company LLC	3533	D	661 834-9654	14212
Baker Hughes A GE Company LLC	1389	F	661 391-0794	179
Baker Petrolite LLC	1389	D	661 325-4138	181
Bakersfield Californian (PA)	2711	C	661 322-5627	5772
Bakersfield Elc Mtr Repr Inc	7694	F	661 327-3583	25455
Bakersfield Machine Co Inc	3599	D	661 393-8441	16305
Bakersfield Well Casing LLC	1381	F	661 399-2976	98
Bakersfield Woodworks Inc	2431	F	661 282-8492	4109
Basic Energy Services Inc	1389	E	661 588-3800	185
Becs Pacific Ltd	3465	F	661 397-9400	13137
Berry Petroleum Company LLC (HQ)	1311	D	661 616-3900	27
Berry Petroleum Corporation (PA)	1311	E	661 616-3900	29
Boyd & Boyd Industries (PA)	3565	F	661 631-8400	15200
Brocks Trailers Inc	3523	E	661 363-5038	14049
C & H Testing Service Inc (PA)	1389	E	661 589-4030	188
C Pallets From Bkersfield Call	2448	F	661 833-2801	4457
Califia Farms LLC	2086	F	661 679-1000	2105
California Mini Truck Inc	3714	F	661 398-9585	20281
California Resources Corp	1311	E	661 395-8000	38
California Resources Corp	1382	E	661 412-5222	127
California Resources Prod Corp (HQ)	1311	C	661 869-8000	45
Califrnia Rsrces Elk Hills LLC	2911	B	661 412-5000	9323
Calmini Products Inc	3714	F	661 398-9500	20282
Calpi Inc	1389	F	661 589-5648	193
Cameron International Corp	3533	E	661 323-8183	14213
Carlos Shower Doors Inc	3231	E	661 327-5594	10684
Cemex Cnstr Mtls PCF LLC	3272	E	661 396-0510	10897
Central California Cnstr Inc	1389	F	661 978-8230	195
Century Rubber Company Inc	3069	F	661 366-7009	9600
Chancellor Oil Tools Inc	3533	E	661 324-2213	14218
Child Evngelism Fellowship Inc	2752	E	661 873-9032	6729
CL Knox Inc	1389	D	661 837-0477	198
Coastal Products Company Inc	3561	F	661 323-0487	15057
Computational Systems Inc	3829	E	661 832-5306	22181
Consolidated Fibrgls Pdts Co	3296	D	661 323-6026	11331
Containment Solutions Inc	3443	D	661 399-9556	12380
Contraband Control Specialists	2899	F	661 322-3363	9232
Core Laboratories LP	1389	E	661 325-5657	200
Core Tech Products Inc	2844	F	661 833-1572	8723
Coretex Products Inc (PA)	2844	F	661 834-6805	8724
Crimson Resource MGT Corp	1311	E	303 892-8878	54
Crystal Geyser Water Company	2086	E	661 323-6296	2125
Crystal Geyser Water Company	2086	E	661 321-0896	2126
Cummins Pacific LLC	3519	E	661 325-9404	14022
Delaney Manufacturing Inc	3444	F	661 587-6681	12556
Delta Trading LP	2951	E	661 834-5560	9381
Domino Plastics Mfg Inc	3089	E	661 396-3744	10075
Douglass Truck Bodies Inc	3713	E	661 327-0258	20202
Downhole Stabilization Inc	3533	E	661 631-1044	14221
Dunbar Electric Sign Company	3993	E	661 323-2600	23857
E & B Ntral Resources Mgt Corp (PA)	1311	D	661 679-1714	55
E and B Natural Resources	1382	D	661 679-1700	135
Eaton Corporation	3625	C	661 396-2557	17268
El Popular Spanish Newspaper	2711	F	661 325-7725	5845
Electric Motor Works Inc	7694	E	661 327-4271	25458
Elysium Jennings LLC	1381	C	661 679-1700	103
Energy Link Indus Svcs Inc	3599	E	661 765-4444	16473
Engineered Well Svc Intl Inc	1389	C	866 913-6283	208
Ennis-Flint Inc	2851	E	661 328-0503	8906
Enova Solutions Inc	2899	F	661 327-2405	9246
Ensign US Drlg Cal Inc (HQ)	3541	D	661 589-0111	14379
Excalibur Well Services Corp (PA)	1381	E	661 589-5338	104
F E W Inc	3599	F	661 323-8319	16489
Farley Machine Inc	3533	E	661 397-4987	14222
Farmer Bros Co	2095	F	661 663-9908	2345
First Energy Services Inc	1389	E	661 387-1972	213
Freeport-Mcmoran Oil & Gas LLC	1311	D	661 322-7600	59
Frito-Lay North America Inc	2096	A	661 328-6000	2389
Genesis Mch & Fabrication Inc	3599	F	661 324-4366	16532
Georg Fischer Harvel LLC	3084	D	661 396-0653	9778
Global Elastomeric Pdts Inc	3533	E	661 831-5380	14226
Golden Empire Concrete Co	3273	E	661 325-6990	11113
Golden Empire Dental Lab Inc	3843	F	661 327-1888	22881
Golden State Drilling Inc	1381	D	661 589-0730	105
Grayson Service Inc	1389	C	661 589-5444	217
Hall Letter Shop Inc	2752	F	661 327-3228	6847
Halliburton Company	1389	D	661 393-8111	219
Hancor Inc	3084	D	661 366-1520	9779
Harbison-Fischer Inc	3561	E	661 387-0166	15072
Hathaway LLC	1311	E	661 393-2004	62
Hills Wldg & Engrg Contr Inc	1389	D	661 746-5400	222
Hudson Valve Co Inc	3491	E	661 831-6208	13718
Hunting Energy Services Inc	1389	E	661 633-4272	225
HWF Construction Inc	2721	E	661 587-3590	6186
Hydril Company	3533	B	661 588-9332	14228
Hydril USA Distribution LLC	3533	E	661 588-9332	14229
Ironclad Tool and Machine Inc	3599	F	661 833-9990	16592
J Flying Manufacturing	3061	E	805 839-9229	9568
Jaguars Wroght Iron	3446	E	661 323-5015	12865
James L Craft Inc	3599	E	661 323-8251	16613
JC Pallet Co	2448	F	661 393-2229	4482
Johasee Rebar Inc	3441	E	661 589-0972	12188
Johasee Rebar LP (PA)	3449	E	604 598-9930	12981
John M Phillips LLC	1389	F	661 327-3118	230
Jts Modular Inc	3448	E	661 835-9270	12937
Just Johnsons Inc	2499	D	661 396-0200	4628
Kba Engineering LLC	3533	E	661 323-0487	14230
Kba Ltd of Kern County LLP	1389	E	661 323-0487	232
Kern Water Bank Authority	3823	F	661 398-4900	21608
Key Energy Services Inc	1389	E	661 334-8100	233
Konecranes Inc	3536	E	661 397-9700	14299
Kw Plastics Recycling Division	3081	D	661 392-0500	9712
Legacy Vulcan LLC	3273	D	661 835-4800	11129
Legacy Vulcan LLC	3272	E	661 858-2673	10951
Lengthwise Brewing Company	2082	E	661 836-2537	1605
Linnco LLC	1311	A	661 616-3900	64
Lortz & Son Mfg Co	3471	C	281 241-9418	13445
Mark Sheffield Construction	1389	E	661 589-8520	236
Material Control Inc	3499	E	661 617-6033	13957
Mazzei Injector Company LLC	3589	E	661 363-6500	16069
Mc Cain & Mc Cain Inc	3599	F	661 322-7764	16724
MD Manufacturing Inc	3589	F	661 283-7550	16071
Metro Ready Mix	3273	F	661 829-7851	11142
Millwood Cabinet Co Inc	2434	E	661 327-0371	4329
MJM Expert Pipe Fbrcation Wldg	3441	E	661 330-8698	12213
Mmi Services Inc	1389	C	661 589-9366	239
Mobile Equipment Company	3536	E	661 327-8476	14301
MTS Stimulation Services Inc (PA)	1389	E	661 589-5804	241
Nabors Well Services Co	1381	C	661 588-6140	113
Nabors Well Services Co	1389	B	661 589-3970	242
Nabors Well Services Co	1389	D	661 392-7668	244
Nalco Company LLC	2899	F	661 864-7955	9285
National Oilwell Varco LP	1389	E	661 387-9316	248
Nations Petroleum Cal LLC	1382	D	661 387-6402	141
Nestle Dreyers Ice Cream Co	2024	F	661 398-5448	689
Newby Rubber Inc	3069	E	661 327-5137	9646
Norman Wireline Service Inc	1389	F	661 399-5697	250
Nusil Technology LLC	3069	D	661 391-4750	9648
Outdoor Galore Inc	3579	F	661 831-8662	15909
Owen Oil Tools Inc	2892	E	661 637-1380	9184
OXY USA Inc	1311	C	661 869-8000	67
Pacific Process Systems Inc (PA)	1389	F	661 321-9681	256

Employment Codes: A=Over 500 employees, B=251-500, C=101-250, D=51-100, E=20-50, F=10-19

2019 California
Manufacturers Register

© Mergent Inc. 1-800-342-5647

1349

GEOGRAPHIC

AZUSA, CA (continued)

Company	SIC	EMP	PHONE	ENTRY #
Pacific WD Prserving-New Stine	2491	F	661 617-6385	4596
Pactiv LLC	3089	B	661 392-4000	10261
Palmer Tank & Construction Inc	1389	E	661 834-1110	257
Paramount Petroleum Corp	2911	E	661 326-4200	9346
Paramount Petroleum Corp	2911	E	661 392-3630	9347
Pepsi Cola Btlg of Bkersfield	2086	C	661 327-9992	2163
Pepsi-Cola Bottling Group	2086	C	661 635-1100	2164
Petro-Lud Inc	1381	F	661 747-4779	117
Pioneer Sands LLC	1446	E	661 746-5789	396
PNa Construction Tech Inc	3444	E	661 326-1700	12718
Praxair Inc	2813	E	661 861-6421	7714
Praxair Inc	2813	E	661 327-5336	7715
Premier Tank Service Inc	3795	E	661 833-2960	21217
Pro Tool Services Inc	3545	E	661 393-9222	14668
Production Data Inc	1389	F	661 327-4776	261
Pros Incorporated	1389	D	661 589-5400	262
PSC Industrial Outsourcing LP	1389	E	661 833-9991	263
Pyrenees French Bakery Inc	2051	E	661 322-7159	1313
Ray Chinn Construction Inc	3542	E	661 327-2731	14454
Reed Print Inc (PA)	2711	E	661 845-3704	6025
Reyes Coca-Cola Bottling LLC	2086	D	661 324-6531	2187
Rhino Valve Usa Inc	3491	F	661 587-0220	13732
Ross Fabrication & Welding Inc	2499	F	661 393-1242	4649
Russell Fabrication Corp	3498	E	661 861-8495	13903
San Joaquin Facilities MGT Inc (PA)	1311	E	661 631-8713	74
San Joaquin Refining Co Inc	2911	C	661 327-4257	9356
Schlumberger Technology Corp	1389	D	661 864-4750	271
Seaboard International Inc	3533	D	661 325-5026	14238
Silo City Inc	3531	E	661 387-0179	14190
Sleep-N-Aire Mattress Co Inc	2392	F	661 835-0200	3749
Smith International Inc	1389	F	661 589-8304	276
Soli-Bond Inc	1389	E	661 631-1633	277
South Valley Oil Field Electri	1389	F	661 665-9809	279
Spalinger Enterprises Inc	2541	F	661 834-4550	5103
Spartan Inc	3441	D	661 327-1205	12244
Star-Luck Enterprise Inc	3823	F	661 665-9999	21660
Structurecast	3272	D	661 833-4490	11009
Suez Wts Usa Inc	2899	E	661 393-3035	9309
Sun-Gro Commodities Inc (PA)	2048	E	661 393-2612	1168
Technipfmc US Holdings Inc	3533	F	661 283-1069	14239
Tiger Tanks Inc	3795	E	661 363-8335	21219
Titan Oilfield Services Inc	1389	F	661 861-1630	282
Total Process Solutions LLC	3561	E	661 829-7910	15095
Tricor Refining LLC	2911	E	661 393-7110	9367
Tringen Corporation	1389	F	661 393-3039	285
Triple E Manufacturing Inc	3556	F	661 831-7553	14891
Truitt Oilfield Maint Corp	1389	B	661 871-4099	286
Tuboscope Pipeline Svcs Inc	1389	E	661 321-3400	288
U M S Inc	3471	E	661 324-5454	13525
U S Weatherford L P	1389	D	661 589-9483	289
U S Weatherford L P	3498	E	661 746-1391	13910
Udecor Inc (PA)	3089	F	877 550-0600	10416
Union Tank Car Company	3743	C	312 431-3111	21084
United States Cold Storage Inc	2097	E	661 834-2371	2423
UPF Corporation	3296	E	661 323-8227	11339
Valadons Plumbing Service Inc	3432	F	661 201-1460	12054
Valley Perforating LLC	3599	D	661 324-4964	17030
Valley Water Management Co	1389	F	661 410-7500	291
Vaquero Energy Inc	1389	E	661 616-0600	292
Vaquero Energy Incorporated	1311	E	661 363-7240	84
Viscon California LLC	2869	E	661 327-7061	9050
Water Associates LLC	3663	E	661 281-6077	18298
Weatherford Artificia	3561	E	661 654-8120	15097
Weatherford Completion Systems	1389	E	661 746-1391	294
Weatherford International LLC	1389	D	661 587-9753	297
Well Analysis Corporation Inc (PA)	2411	E	661 283-9510	4021
West American Energy Corp	1381	F	661 747-7732	122
Western Nutrients Corporation	2873	E	661 327-9604	9077
Westrock Cp LLC	2631	E	661 327-3841	5365
Whitestone Industries Inc	3999	F	888 567-2234	24290
Zilift Inc	3561	F	661 369-8579	15103

BALDWIN PARK, CA - Los Angeles County

Company	SIC	EMP	PHONE	ENTRY #
Above All Co Forearm Forklift	3537	E	626 962-2990	14305
Alphena Technologies	3089	E	626 961-6098	9936
American Reliance Inc	3571	E	626 443-6818	15391
Ametek Ameron LLC	3812	E	626 337-4640	21255
Ametek Ameron LLC (HQ)	3823	D	626 337-4640	21546
Anura Plastic Engineerign	3089	D	626 814-9684	9950
B & B Red-I-Mix Concrete Inc	3273	E	626 359-8371	11049
Biosense Webster Inc	3845	A	909 839-7752	22955
Cal Bind	2789	E	626 338-3699	7595
Cera Inc	3821	E	626 814-2688	21460
Chaparral Concrete Company (DH)	3273	F	626 359-8371	11092
Checkworks Inc	2782	D	626 333-1444	7576
Color Sky Inc	3281	E	626 338-8565	11244
Condor Outdoor Products Inc	3949	E	626 358-3270	23542
Denovo Dental Inc	3843	E	626 480-0182	22868
Distinct Indulgence Inc	2051	E	818 546-1700	1231
Dreams Closets	2434	E	626 641-5070	4295
Exquisite Corporation	2844	E	626 856-0200	8747
EZ Inflatables Inc	3069	E	626 480-9100	9613
Fabtronic Inc	3444	E	626 962-3293	12586
Falcon Electric Inc	3612	E	626 962-7770	17092
Felly International Inc	2339	F	626 960-5111	3418
Freudenberg Medical LLC	3842	C	626 814-9684	22735
Front Edge Technology Inc	3479	E	626 856-8979	13591
G & I Islas Industries Inc (PA)	3556	E	626 960-5020	14851
Hanson Aggregates LLC	1442	E	626 856-6700	363
Hemosure Inc	2899	E	888 436-6787	9257
Inflatable Enterprises Inc	3069	F	818 482-6509	9627
Ipp Plastics Products Inc	2821	E	626 357-1178	7845
Johnson & Johnson	3842	E	909 839-8690	22760
Kal-Cameron Manufacturing (HQ)	3423	D	626 338-7308	11898
Lawrence Roll Up Doors Inc (PA)	3442	E	626 962-4163	12326
Lawrence Roll Up Doors Inc	3442	E	626 338-6041	12328
Little Digger Mining & Sup LLC	1041	E	626 856-3366	5
Los Angles Tmes Cmmnctions LLC	2711	E	909 980-3707	5929
Macdonald Carbide Co	3544	E	626 960-4034	14537
Mission Kleensweep Prod Inc	2841	D	323 223-1405	8597
Miyako Oriental Foods Inc	2075	E	626 962-9633	1510
Motek Industries	3599	F	626 960-6005	16773
My Machine Inc	3599	F	626 214-9223	16779
New York Frozen Foods Inc	2051	E	626 338-3000	1295
Nsd Industries Inc	3599	F	626 813-2001	16796
Pacific Award Metals Inc (HQ)	3444	D	626 814-4410	12701
Pacific Award Metals Inc	3444	D	626 814-4410	12703
Pacon Inc	3089	C	626 814-4654	10260
Performance Tube Bending Inc	3498	E	626 939-9000	13899
Philips Elec N Amer Corp	3827	C	626 480-0755	22122
PSC Circuits Inc	3679	E	626 373-1728	19692
R & R Metal Fabricators	3499	E	626 960-6400	13970
Reny & Co Inc	3089	E	626 962-3078	10331
Rigos Equipment Mfg LLC	3444	E	626 813-6621	12737
S & C Precision Inc	3679	F	626 338-7149	19714
Sanders Candy Factory Inc	2064	E	626 814-2038	1451
Scholastic Inc	2731	E	626 337-9996	6389
Standard Concrete Products (HQ)	3273	E	310 829-4537	11186
Superior Grounding Systems	3643	E	626 814-1981	17493
Survey Stake and Marker Inc	2499	F	626 960-4802	4658
Tim Guzzy Services Inc	3599	F	626 813-0626	17001
Touchdown Technologies Inc	3674	C	626 472-6732	19232
U S Bearings	3562	F	626 358-0181	15114
Ultimate Jumpers Inc	2599	F	626 337-3086	5260
Universal Steel Services Inc	3441	F	626 960-1455	12269
Upm Inc	3544	B	626 962-4001	14584
Yutaka Electric Intl Inc	3629	F	626 962-7770	17361

BALLICO, CA - Merced County

Company	SIC	EMP	PHONE	ENTRY #
Golden By-Products Inc	3559	D	209 668-4855	14962

BANNING, CA - Riverside County

Company	SIC	EMP	PHONE	ENTRY #
Allen Industrial Inc	3471	F	951 849-4966	13319
Belovac LLC	3559	F	951 427-4299	14920
Century Publishing	2759	F	951 849-4898	7269
DT Mattson Enterprises Inc	3944	E	951 849-9781	23419
KSD Inc	3599	F	951 849-7669	16667
Robertsons Distributors Inc	3273	F	951 849-4766	11164
Te Connectivity Corporation	3678	B	951 929-3323	19415
Zenner Performance Meters Inc	3824	E	951 849-8822	21697
Zoops Products Inc	3714	E	951 922-2396	20491

BARSTOW, CA - San Bernardino County

Company	SIC	EMP	PHONE	ENTRY #
Five Star Food Containers Inc	3086	D	626 437-6219	9842
Green Valley Foods Product	2022	F	760 964-1105	576
Kar Ice Service Inc (PA)	2097	F	760 256-2648	2416
Service Rock Products Corp	3273	E	760 252-1615	11171
Skechers USA Inc	3021	E	760 253-3707	9482
Valmont Industries Inc	3441	F	760 253-3070	12273

BAY POINT, CA - Contra Costa County

Company	SIC	EMP	PHONE	ENTRY #
Chemtrade Chemicals US LLC	2819	E	925 458-7300	7764
Criterion Catalysts & Tech LP	2819	D	925 458-9045	7767

BEAUMONT, CA - Riverside County

Company	SIC	EMP	PHONE	ENTRY #
Beaumont Juice Inc	2033	D	951 769-7171	785
Big Tex Trailer Mfg Inc	3523	F	951 845-5344	14046
Dura Plastic Products Inc (PA)	3089	D	951 845-3161	10080
Katchall Fltration Systems LLC	3589	F	866 528-2425	16063
Precision Stampings Inc (PA)	3643	E	951 845-1174	17487
Priority Pallet Inc	2448	C	951 769-9399	4502
Risco Inc	3452	E	951 769-2899	13081
Rudolph Foods Company Inc	2096	D	909 388-2202	2401

Mergent email: customerrelations@mergent.com
1350

2019 California
Manufacturers Register

(P-0000) Products & Services Section entry number
(PA)=Parent Co (HQ)=Headquarters (DH)=Div Headquarters

	SIC	EMP	PHONE	ENTRY #
Wholesale Shutter Company Inc	2431	F	951 845-8786	4256
Wolverine World Wide Inc	3143	F	800 253-2184	10493

BELL, CA - Los Angeles County

	SIC	EMP	PHONE	ENTRY #
A&R Lighting Co	3648	F	562 927-8617	17667
Alfred Picon	2542	F	562 928-2561	5126
Allied Blnding Ingredients Inc	2099	F	562 806-7560	2449
Bluprint Clothing Corp	2331	D	323 780-4347	3218
Carol Wior Inc	2339	D	562 927-0052	3391
Custom Building Products Inc	2891	D	323 582-0846	9139
Dcx-Chol Enterprises Inc	3679	F	562 927-5531	19509
Envision Led Lighting Inc	3641	F	213 741-1550	17426
Flores Brothers Inc	2099	E	562 806-9128	2522
J & F Design Inc	2339	D	323 526-4444	3432
J P Turgeon & Sons Inc	3471	F	323 773-3105	13435
Lynco Grinding Company Inc	3599	F	562 927-2631	16696
Marika LLC	2339	F	323 888-7755	3464
Power Brake Exchange Inc	3714	F	562 806-6661	20421
West Coast-Accudyne Inc	3542	E	562 927-2546	14462
Zoo Printing Inc (PA)	2752	D	310 253-7751	7196

BELL GARDENS, CA - Los Angeles County

	SIC	EMP	PHONE	ENTRY #
Barber Welding and Mfg Co	3599	E	562 928-2570	16306
Bus Services Corporation	3714	E	562 231-1770	20278
Cal Southern Braiding Inc	3679	D	562 927-5531	19476
Carnevale & Lohr Inc	3281	C	562 927-8311	11239
Construction TI & Threading Co	3599	F	562 927-1326	16402
Eurocraft Archtectural Met Inc	3446	E	323 771-1323	12853
Flexco Inc	3728	F	562 927-2525	20814
G R J Fashions	2284	F	323 537-5814	2952
Infinity Kitchen Products Inc	3444	F	562 806-5771	12620
Lingle Bros Coffee Inc	2095	E	562 927-3317	2359
Metal Surfaces Inc	3471	C	562 927-1331	13454
Rob Inc (PA)	2325	D	562 806-5589	3086
Wilcox Machine Co	3599	D	562 927-5353	17066

BELLFLOWER, CA - Los Angeles County

	SIC	EMP	PHONE	ENTRY #
Black & Decker (us) Inc	3546	F	562 925-7551	14698
Brooks Millwork Company	2431	F	562 920-3000	4112
Bryant Rubber Corp	3053	D	310 530-2530	9521
C Team Inc	3599	F	562 866-3887	16352
Express Sheet Metal Product	3444	F	562 925-9340	12581
Ice Man Inc	2097	F	562 633-4423	2415
Ivoprop Corporation	3728	F	562 602-1451	20853
Kamashian Engineering Inc	3544	F	562 920-9692	14530
Klj Mobile Notary Inc	3953	F	562 852-8253	23719
Timkev International Inc	2052	F	562 232-1691	1383

BELMONT, CA - San Mateo County

	SIC	EMP	PHONE	ENTRY #
Aco Pacific Inc	3829	F	650 595-8588	22156
Fineline Carpentry Inc	2434	E	650 592-2442	4300
Intex Forms Inc	3229	E	650 654-7855	10649
Js Trade Bindery Services Inc	2789	D	650 486-1475	7605
Megaprint Digital Prtg Corp	2752	F	650 517-0200	6966
Moquin Press Inc	2752	D	650 592-0575	6984
Nikon Research Corp America	3825	E	800 446-4566	21817
Oracle Systems Corporation	7372	B	650 654-7606	25028
Oracle Systems Corporation	7372	F	650 506-5062	25030
Pacific Screw Products Inc	3451	D	650 583-9682	13036
Solaicx	3674	D	408 988-5000	19176
Somerset Traveller Inc	2789	F	650 593-7350	7619
Village Collection Inc	2434	F	650 594-1635	4366

BELVEDERE TIBURON, CA - Marin County

	SIC	EMP	PHONE	ENTRY #
Ammi Publishing Inc	2711	F	415 435-2652	5758
Mila Usa Inc	3634	F	415 734-8540	17397

BENICIA, CA - Solano County

	SIC	EMP	PHONE	ENTRY #
American Pacific Mortgage Corp	2899	F	707 746-4920	9220
Applied Sewing Resources Inc	2211	E	707 748-1614	2721
Barrys Cultured Marble Inc	3281	F	707 745-3444	11234
Bay Area Coffee Inc	2095	E	707 745-1320	2328
Bay Valve Service & Engrg LLC	2599	F	707 748-7166	5221
Benicia Fabrication & Mch Inc	3443	C	707 745-8111	12364
Bio-RAD Laboratories Inc	3826	E	510 741-5790	21923
Bolttech Mannings Inc	3546	D	707 751-0157	14701
Bulls-Eye Marketing Inc	3714	F	707 745-5568	20275
California Motor Controls Inco	3625	F	707 746-6255	17259
Cameron International Corp	3533	F	707 752-8800	14214
Crane Co	3679	F	707 748-7166	19501
Custom Coils Inc	3677	F	707 752-8633	19330
Dga Inc	2834	E	925 299-9000	8140
Dunlop Manufacturing Inc (PA)	3931	D	707 745-2722	23364
Dunlop Manufacturing Inc	3931	F	707 745-2709	23365
Dusouth Industries	3823	E	707 745-5117	21575
Flowserve Corporation	3561	F	707 745-4710	15065
Frontline Environmental TEC	3823	F	707 745-1116	21588

	SIC	EMP	PHONE	ENTRY #
Frontline Instrs & Contrls	3829	F	707 747-9766	22204
Gibbs Plastic & Rubber Co	3069	F	707 746-7300	9616
Gibson Printing & Publishing	2711	F	707 745-0733	5862
Gold Rush Kettle Korn Llc	2064	E	707 747-6773	1425
Gunnebo Entrance Control Inc (HQ)	3829	F	707 748-0885	22208
Instrument & Valve Services Co	3823	E	707 745-4664	21605
Interhealth Nutraceuticals Inc	2833	E	800 783-4636	7949
J R Schneider Co Inc	3569	F	707 745-0404	15335
Johansing Iron Works Inc	3443	F	707 361-8190	12392
Larson-Juhl US LLC	2499	E	707 747-0555	4632
Metlsaw Systems Inc	3541	F	707 746-6200	14393
Nor Cal Truck Sales & Mfg	3537	F	925 787-9735	14338
Phillips 66 Spectrum Corp	2992	F	707 745-6100	9447
Praxair Inc	2813	E	707 745-5328	7721
Ralphs-Pugh Co Inc	3535	D	707 745-6222	14282
Rapid Accu-Form Inc	3089	F	707 745-1879	10325
Reyes Coca-Cola Bottling LLC	2086	C	707 747-2000	2205
S&S Investment Club (PA)	3799	F	707 747-5508	21240
Schoenstein & Co	3931	E	707 747-5858	23387
Sigmatex High Tech Fabrics Inc (HQ)	3624	D	707 751-0573	17242
Suba Mfg Inc	2541	E	707 745-0358	5105
Turnkey Technologies Inc	3599	E	707 745-9520	17019
Valero Energy Corporation	2869	B	707 745-7011	9048
Valero Ref Company-California	2911	B	707 745-7011	9372
Valley Fine Foods Company Inc (PA)	2041	B	707 746-6888	1050
Water One Industries Inc (PA)	3589	E	707 747-4300	16132
West Coast Fixtures Inc (PA)	2541	E	707 752-6373	5119

BERKELEY, CA - Alameda County

	SIC	EMP	PHONE	ENTRY #
3d Robotics Inc (PA)	3699	D	415 599-1404	19892
Acuity Brands Lighting Inc	3646	F	510 845-2760	17579
Aduro Biotech Inc (PA)	2834	D	510 848-4400	8002
Annies Inc (HQ)	2099	D	510 558-7500	2453
Annies Baking LLC (DH)	2051	E	510 558-7500	1175
Anto Offset Printing	2752	F	510 843-8454	6663
Apress L P	2721	C	510 549-5930	6104
Art of Muse	2511	E	510 644-1870	4669
Assoc Students University CA	2741	E	510 590-7874	6436
Autumn Press Inc (PA)	2752	E	510 654-4645	6672
Avid Technology Inc	3861	B	510 486-8302	23141
Barra LLC (HQ)	7372	B	510 548-5442	24409
Bayer Corporation	3841	B	510 705-5000	22359
Bayer Healthcare LLC	2834	C	510 705-7545	8065
Bayer Healthcare LLC	2834	B	510 705-7539	8066
Bayer Healthcare LLC	2834	C	510 705-4421	8067
Bayer Healthcare LLC	2834	C	510 705-4914	8068
Berkeley Forge & Tool Inc	3462	D	510 525-5117	13095
Berkeley Mllwk & Furn Co Inc	2511	E	510 549-2854	4678
Bonsai Ai Inc	7372	E	510 900-1112	24439
Bookpack Inc	2741	F	510 601-8301	6451
Buisness Leader Media	2721	E	510 665-9600	6119
Cadence Design Systems Inc	7372	F	510 647-2800	24466
California Gold Bars Inc (PA)	2066	F	510 848-9292	1467
Checkerspot Inc	2836	F	510 239-7921	8541
Cheese Cake City Inc	2051	F	510 524-9404	1220
Clp Apg LLC	2731	D	510 528-1444	6328
Comeback Brewing II Inc	2082	E	510 526-1160	1580
Consolidated Printers Inc	2732	C	510 843-8524	6417
Data Agent LLC	7372	F	800 772-8314	24549
Doughtronics Inc (PA)	2051	E	510 524-1327	1235
Doughtronics Inc	2051	E	510 843-2978	1236
Dynavax Technologies Corp (PA)	2836	C	510 848-5100	8547
Ed Jones Company	3999	F	510 704-0704	24087
Edition One Group	2752	F	510 705-1930	6805
Edward Koehn Co Inc	3451	F	510 843-0821	13022
Eko Devices Inc	3845	F	844 356-3384	22975
Fantasy Inc	3652	D	510 486-2038	17897
Four D Imaging	3829	F	510 290-3533	22203
Fra Mani LLC	2013	F	510 526-7000	485
George M Martin Co	3554	F	510 652-2200	14796
Gradescope Inc	7372	F	702 985-7442	24707
Graysix Company	3444	E	510 845-5936	12601
Gu	2834	F	510 527-4664	8199
Hesperian Health Guides (PA)	2731	E	510 845-1447	6347
Heyday	2731	E	510 549-3564	6348
Independent Berkeley Student	2711	D	510 848-8300	5885
Ironies LLC	2521	E	510 644-2100	4951
Janco Chemical Corporation	2851	E	510 527-9770	8909
John L Staton Inc	2431	D	510 527-3114	4175
Kirsen Technologies Inc	3663	F	510 540-5383	18145
Le Barbocce Inc	2043	E	510 526-7664	1067
Libby Laboratories Inc	2844	E	510 527-5400	8789
Living Tree Community Foods	2099	E	510 526-7106	2586
Luxfer-GTM Technologies LLC (PA)	3443	E	415 856-0570	12396
Machinables Inc	3577	F	415 216-9467	15796
Meyer Sound Laboratories Inc (PA)	3651	C	510 486-1166	17832

Employment Codes: A=Over 500 employees, B=251-500,
C=101-250, D=51-100, E=20-50, F=10-19

2019 California
Manufacturers Register

© Mergent Inc. 1-800-342-5647

1351

GEOGRAPHIC

	SIC	EMP	PHONE	ENTRY #
Mulholland Brothers (PA)	2512	E	415 824-5995	4801
NAPA Valley Kitchens Inc	2099	D	510 558-7500	2614
Nolo	2731	C	510 549-1976	6371
Parker Powis Inc	3579	D	510 848-2463	15910
Plexxikon Inc	2834	E	510 647-4000	8339
Poly-Seal Industries	3069	F	510 843-9722	9658
Precision Coatings Inc	2851	F	510 525-3600	8932
Primary Concepts Inc	3944	F	510 559-5545	23458
Rastergraf Inc (PA)	3672	F	510 849-4801	18579
Research & Dev GL Pdts & Eqp	3231	F	510 547-6464	10729
Scone Henge Inc	2051	F	510 845-5168	1320
Sensys Networks Inc (PA)	3669	D	510 548-4620	18362
Shelton Inc	2066	E	510 524-2430	1473
Siemens Hlthcare Dgnostics Inc	3661	F	510 982-4000	17991
Society For The Study O	2731	E	510 549-4270	6393
Spiritual Counterfeits Prj Inc	2721	F	510 540-0300	6261
Stat Clinical Systems Inc	7372	F	510 705-8700	25220
Sunsystem Technology LLC	3674	B	510 984-2027	19205
Suntech America Inc (PA)	3433	F	415 882-9922	12092
Sven Design Inc	3171	E	510 848-7836	10552
Takara Sake USA Inc (DH)	2085	E	510 540-8250	2079
Tarana Wireless Inc	3663	E	510 868-3359	18272
Tcho Ventures Inc (PA)	2066	E	844 877-8246	1476
Tech Air Northern Cal LLC	2813	F	510 524-9353	7735
Terminal Manufacturing Co LLC	3441	E	510 526-3071	12259
The Ligature Inc	2759	F	510 526-5181	7518
Three Stone Hearth	3411	F	510 981-1334	11872
Trans Bay Steel Corporation (PA)	3441	E	510 277-3756	12263
Two Star Dog Inc	2335	F	510 525-1100	3343
Two Star Dog Inc (PA)	2331	F	510 525-1100	3281
University Cal Press Fundation	2731	E	510 642-4247	6405
Vital Vittles Bakery Inc	2051	F	510 644-2022	1338
Walashek Industrial & Mar Inc	3731	F	206 624-2880	21016
Western Roto Engravers Inc	2759	F	510 525-2950	7539
Wheelskins Inc	3199	F	510 841-2128	10584
Xinet LLC (HQ)	7372	F	510 845-0555	25362

BEVERLY HILLS, CA - Los Angeles County

	SIC	EMP	PHONE	ENTRY #
Anthem Music & Media Fund LLC	2731	F	310 286-6600	6309
Baker Hghes Olfld Oprtions LLC	3533	D	310 843-9632	14209
Barfresh Food Group Inc	2087	E	310 598-7113	2242
Beverly Hills Courier Inc	2711	E	310 278-1322	5777
Building Components	3089	F	310 274-6516	9993
Capricor Therapeutics Inc (PA)	2834	F	310 358-3200	8098
Cerner Corporation	7372	F	310 247-7700	24482
Concord Music Group Inc	2731	C	310 385-4455	6330
Craig R Williams Cnstr Inc	1389	F	310 550-9250	201
Dermanew LLC (PA)	2844	F	626 442-2813	8739
Dermanew LLC	3841	F	310 276-0457	22420
Dogsport Inc	3999	F	323 362-6450	24081
Drywired Defense LLC	3479	E	310 684-3891	13576
ERA Products Inc	2531	E	310 324-4908	5013
Exploding Kittens LLC	3944	E	310 788-8699	23423
Fast Track Energy Drink LLC	2086	E	310 281-2045	2133
Gibson Brands Inc	3931	C	310 300-2369	23372
Goomby LLC	3949	F	323 556-0637	23574
H Silani & Associates Inc	3827	F	310 623-4848	22081
Ira Gold Group LLC	3339	F	800 984-6008	11546
Irene Kasmer Inc	2335	F	310 553-8986	3314
Jeffrey Rudes LLC	2329	F	310 281-0800	3166
Jivago Inc (PA)	2844	F	310 205-5535	8775
Kate Somerville Skincare LLC (DH)	2834	D	323 655-7546	8244
Klooma Holdings Inc	7372	E	305 747-3315	24834
L F P Inc (PA)	2721	D	323 651-3525	6201
Larry B LLC	2371	F	310 652-3877	3601
Leaner Creamer LLC	2023	F	818 621-5274	628
Levi Strauss & Co	2325	F	310 246-9044	3080
Lorber Industries California	2261	B	310 275-1568	2884
Mastini Designs	3911	F	800 979-4848	23296
Matchless LLC	3663	E	310 473-5100	18175
Melamed International Inc (PA)	2329	F	310 271-8585	3178
Nooshin Inc	2339	F	310 559-5766	3471
Oral Essentials Inc	2844	F	888 773-5273	8807
Playboy Japan Inc	2721	F	310 424-1800	6234
Ppl Entertainment Group Inc (PA)	2741	E	310 860-7499	6555
Rare Elements Hair Care	3999	F	310 277-6524	24220
Rockstar Inc	2086	C	323 785-2820	2213
Royal Blue Inc	2392	F	310 888-0156	3746
Southwest Wine & Spirits LLC (PA)	2084	F	213 765-3213	1983
Spyglass Entrmt Group LLC	3861	F	310 443-5800	23196
Status Collection & Co Inc	3911	F	310 432-7788	23320
Ubi Energy Corporation	2911	F	310 283-6978	9368
Vie Products Inc	2844	F	310 684-3566	8863
Vitacig Inc	2111	D	310 402-6937	2711
West World Productions Inc	2721	E	310 273-9874	6291
Workbook Inc	2731	E	323 856-0008	6412

	SIC	EMP	PHONE	ENTRY #
Xomv Media Corporation	2741	E	424 284-4024	6627
Yayyo Inc	7372	F	310 926-2643	25366
Zeons Inc	3229	B	323 302-8299	10672

BIEBER, CA - Lassen County

	SIC	EMP	PHONE	ENTRY #
Del Logging Inc	2411	E	530 294-5492	3986

BIGGS, CA - Butte County

	SIC	EMP	PHONE	ENTRY #
Bayliss Botanicals LLC	2834	F	530 868-5466	8071

BISHOP, CA - Inyo County

	SIC	EMP	PHONE	ENTRY #
Cal-Tron Corporation	3089	E	760 873-8491	10002
Horizon Publications Inc	2711	F	760 873-3535	5883
RW Wilson Inc	3089	F	760 873-5600	10352

BLOOMINGTON, CA - San Bernardino County

	SIC	EMP	PHONE	ENTRY #
Cooper Lighting LLC	3648	E	909 605-6615	17681
Cummins Pacific LLC	3519	E	909 877-0433	14020
Dayton Superior Corporation	3315	E	909 820-0112	11437
Dura Technologies Inc	2851	C	909 877-8477	8902
E-Z Mix Inc	2674	F	909 874-7686	5640
Frito-Lay North America Inc	2096	D	909 877-0902	2387
G & F Horse Trailer Repair	3799	F	909 820-4600	21229
Heater Designs Inc	3567	E	909 421-0971	15261
Hogan Co Inc	3315	E	909 421-0245	11445
Hydraulic Shop Inc	3537	E	909 875-9336	14327
Menasha Packaging Company LLC	2653	E	951 374-5281	5436
Mitco Industries Inc (PA)	3599	E	909 877-0800	16759
Muhlhauser Enterprises Inc (PA)	3441	E	909 877-2792	12216
Muhlhauser Steel Inc	3441	E	909 877-2792	12217
Preferred Pallets Inc	2448	F	909 875-7540	4500
Products/Techniques Inc	2851	F	909 877-3951	8934
Quality Tech Mfg Inc	3721	E	909 465-9565	20619
Remco Mch & Fabrication Inc	3599	F	909 877-3530	16895
Scor Industries	3999	F	909 820-5046	24232
Southern California Biodiesel	2911	F	951 377-4007	9361
Traditional Baking Inc	2052	D	909 877-8471	1384
Vsc Incorporated (PA)	3441	E	909 877-0975	12276
Wadco Industries Inc	3441	E	909 874-7800	12277
Westco Industries Inc	3449	E	909 874-8700	13004

BLUE LAKE, CA - Humboldt County

	SIC	EMP	PHONE	ENTRY #
Calgon Carbon Corporation	2819	F	707 668-5637	7757
Thomas Tellez	2431	E	707 668-1825	4246

BLYTHE, CA - Riverside County

	SIC	EMP	PHONE	ENTRY #
Blythe Energy Inc	1321	F	561 304-5126	89

BONITA, CA - San Diego County

	SIC	EMP	PHONE	ENTRY #
Pacific Integrated Mfg Inc	3841	C	619 921-3464	22578
Right Hand Manufacturing Inc	3625	C	619 819-5056	17299

BONSALL, CA - San Diego County

	SIC	EMP	PHONE	ENTRY #
Perrault Corporation	1442	F	760 466-1024	379

BOONVILLE, CA - Mendocino County

	SIC	EMP	PHONE	ENTRY #
Anderson Valley Brewing Inc	2082	E	707 895-2337	1558

BORON, CA - Kern County

	SIC	EMP	PHONE	ENTRY #
Rio Tinto Minerals Inc	1241	C	760 762-7121	20
US Borax Inc	2819	A	760 762-7000	7810

BRAWLEY, CA - Imperial County

	SIC	EMP	PHONE	ENTRY #
Alger Alternative Energy LLC	3295	F	317 493-5289	11316
Border Precast Inc	3272	F	760 351-1233	10890
Crown Citrus Company Inc	2037	F	760 344-1930	945
Fiesta Mexican Foods Inc	2051	E	760 344-3580	1248
Imperial Compost LLC	2879	F	760 351-1900	9104
Imperial Sugar Company	2063	C	760 344-3110	1403
Reddy Ice Corporation	2097	E	760 344-0535	2420
Spreadco Inc	2262	E	760 351-0747	2905
Spreckels Sugar Company Inc	2063	B	760 344-3110	1404
W Three Co	3523	E	760 344-5841	14117
Western Mesquite Mines Inc	3339	E	928 341-4653	11551

BREA, CA - Orange County

	SIC	EMP	PHONE	ENTRY #
Able Wire EDM Inc	3599	F	714 255-1967	16202
Absolute Screenprint Inc	2396	C	714 529-2120	3871
Aci Supplies LLC	3955	E	714 989-1821	23724
Advanced Mold Technology Inc	3544	F	714 990-0144	14473
Aerospace Engineering Corp	3728	E	714 996-8178	20722
Alatus Aerosystems	3728	D	714 732-0559	20730
Altinex Inc	3663	E	714 990-0877	18026
American Induction Tech Inc	3567	F	714 456-1102	15251
Ameron International Corp	3851	E	714 256-7755	23078
Applied Cmpsite Structures Inc (HQ)	3728	C	714 990-6300	20739
AST Sportswear Inc	2361	B	714 223-2030	3571
Avery Dennison Corporation	2672	B	714 674-8500	5549
Avery Products Corporation (DH)	2678	C	714 675-8500	5682

Mergent email: customerrelations@mergent.com
1352

2019 California
Manufacturers Register

(P-0000) Products & Services Section entry number
(PA)=Parent Co (HQ)=Headquarters (DH)=Div Headquarters

Company	SIC	EMP	PHONE	ENTRY #
B & W Precision Inc	3599	F	714 447-0971	16299
B O A Inc	2329	E	714 256-8960	3138
Baker Furnace Inc	3567	F	714 223-7262	15253
Bamberger Polymers Inc	2821	F	714 672-4740	7821
Beckman Coulter Inc	3841	C	818 970-2161	22360
Bedard Machine Inc	3599	F	714 990-4846	16313
Belt Drives Ltd	3751	E	714 693-1313	21091
Blower Drive Service Co	3714	E	562 693-4302	20270
California Cocktails Inc	2087	F	714 990-0982	2249
Caran Precision Engrg Mfg Corp	3469	D	714 447-5400	13179
Carolina Lquid Chmistries Corp	3841	F	336 722-8910	22397
Cks Solution Incorporated	3679	F	714 292-6307	19493
Clean America Inc	3699	F	562 694-5990	19927
Cnp Industries Inc	3639	F	714 482-2320	17413
Coyle Reproductions Inc (PA)	2752	C	866 269-5373	6762
Crossroads Software Inc	7372	F	714 990-6433	24532
Curtiss-Wright Controls	3842	F	714 982-1860	22715
Curtiss-Wright Flow Control	3491	D	714 528-2301	13715
Cybortronics Incorporated	3826	F	949 855-2814	21942
D G Industries	3541	F	714 990-3787	14367
Darbo Manufacturing Company	2339	E	714 529-7693	3401
Database Works Inc	7372	F	714 203-8800	24551
Ecmm Services Inc	3955	C	714 988-9388	23728
Educational Ideas Incorporated	2731	F	714 990-4332	6337
Electronic Precision Spc Inc	3471	E	714 256-8950	13406
Energy Cnvrsion Applctions Inc	3612	F	714 256-2166	17091
Fineline Circuits & Technology	3672	E	714 529-2942	18481
Fixtures By Design LLC	2541	F	714 572-5406	5062
Foxlink International Inc (HQ)	3643	F	714 256-1777	17467
Foxlink World Circuit Tech	3672	F	714 256-0877	18488
Goodrich Corporation	3728	C	714 984-1461	20831
Gryphon Mobile Electronics LLC	3663	F	626 810-7770	18118
Hand & Nail Harmony Inc	2844	D	714 773-9758	8763
Harbor Truck Bodies Inc	3713	D	714 996-0411	20209
Herrick Retail Corporation Th	2752	F	714 256-9543	6856
Iddea California Inc	3714	F	714 257-7389	20367
Imperial Cal Products Inc	3469	E	714 990-9100	13223
Instrument Design Eng Assoc I	3679	E	714 525-3302	19579
ITS Group Inc	3625	F	714 256-4100	17278
J Good In Inc	3911	F	714 257-9391	23277
Jade Range LLC	3631	C	714 961-2400	17370
Kanex	3699	F	888 975-1368	19995
Kingson Mold & Machine Inc	3544	F	714 871-0221	14532
Kirkhill Inc (HQ)	2822	E	714 529-4901	7906
Kirkhill Inc	3053	A	714 529-4901	9539
Kirkhill Inc	3053	A	714 529-4901	9540
Kworld (usa) Computer Inc	3663	F	626 581-0867	18149
La Paz Products Inc	2087	F	714 990-0982	2271
Ledconn Corp	3674	F	714 256-2111	18957
Life Science Outsourcing Inc	3841	D	714 672-1090	22508
Lifebloom Corporation	2834	E	562 944-6800	8259
Lite Line Frame Bags	3172	E	562 905-3150	10565
Lucky Devil LLC	2759	F	714 990-2237	7391
M3 Products Inc	2542	F	626 371-1900	5152
Media Blast & Abrasive Inc	3589	F	714 257-0484	16072
Metals USA Building Pdts LP (DH)	3355	A	713 946-9000	11620
Metals USA Building Pdts LP	3355	A	714 529-0407	11623
Mfg Packaging Products	3565	F	714 984-2300	15218
Mike Kenney Tool Inc	3599	F	714 577-9262	16745
Mildef Inc (PA)	3571	F	703 224-8835	15458
Mkt Innovations	3599	D	714 524-7668	16760
Mobility Specialist Inc	3999	E	714 674-0480	24177
Moravek Biochemicals Inc (PA)	2819	F	714 990-2018	7789
Moxa Americas Inc	3577	E	714 528-6777	15809
MPS Medical Inc	3841	E	714 672-1090	22549
MR Mold & Engineering Corp	3544	E	714 996-5511	14547
Muirsis Inc	3432	F	714 579-1555	12041
Mullen Technologies Inc (PA)	3711	F	714 613-1900	20160
North West Pharmanaturals, Inc	2833	E	714 529-0980	7959
Nycetek Inc	2541	F	714 671-3860	5086
Optasense Inc	1382	F	714 482-1922	143
Orangegrid LLC	7372	E	657 220-1519	25038
Pacific Archtectural Mllwk Inc (PA)	2431	D	562 905-3200	4207
Pacific Plastics Inc	3084	D	714 990-9050	9784
Pacific Quality Packaging Corp	2653	D	714 257-1234	5442
Paul Merrill Company Inc	3281	F	562 691-1871	11267
Perine Lowe Inc	3411	F	714 990-1590	11865
Pigs Tail USA LLC	3089	F	714 566-0011	10273
Precise Industries Inc	3444	C	714 482-2333	12719
President Enterprise Inc	2759	F	714 671-9577	7442
Production Systems Group Inc	2599	E	714 990-8997	5249
Q C M Inc	3629	E	714 414-1173	17352
Ramtec Associates Inc	3089	E	714 996-7477	10324
Rogers Holding Company Inc	3728	E	714 257-4850	20921
Rudolph International Inc	2844	E	714 529-5696	8831
S&B Industry Inc	3089	D	909 569-4155	10355
Scisorek & Son Flavors Inc	2087	E	714 524-0550	2281
Seismic Reservoir 2020 Inc	1382	E	562 697-9711	150
Sonic Air Systems Inc	3564	E	714 255-0124	15175
Span-O-Matic Inc	3444	E	714 256-4700	12767
SPX Cooling Technologies Inc	3443	C	714 529-6080	12423
Sr2020 Inc	1382	E	714 482-1922	154
Steelclad Inc	1389	F	714 529-0277	280
Stolo Cabinets Inc (PA)	2521	E	714 529-7303	4970
Sunon Inc (PA)	3564	E	714 255-0208	15178
Suppress Fire Atmtc Sprinklers	3569	F	714 671-5939	15366
Suzuki Motor of America Inc (HQ)	3751	C	714 996-7040	21140
Taylor Coml Foodservice Inc	3585	E	714 255-7200	15979
Taylor Communications Inc	2754	F	866 541-0937	7213
Tca Precision Products LLC	3728	F	714 257-4850	20945
TEC Lighting Inc	3648	F	714 529-5068	17735
Trane US Inc	3585	D	626 913-7123	15985
Trigon Components Inc	3675	E	714 990-1367	19303
Txc Technology Inc (HQ)	3679	F	714 990-5510	19775
Tyson Fresh Meats Inc	2011	F	714 528-5543	453
UNI-Caps LLC	2833	E	714 529-8400	7979
United Rock Products Corp	1422	E	626 358-4558	318
Uriman Inc (HQ)	3694	C	714 257-2080	19849
Ventura Foods LLC (PA)	2079	C	714 257-3700	1553
Virtual Composites Co Inc	2821	F	714 256-8850	7900
Viviglo Technologies Inc	3999	E	949 933-9738	24284
Water One Industries Inc	3589	F	707 747-4300	16131
Webedoctor Inc	7372	F	714 990-3999	25344
West Coast Gasket Co	3053	D	714 869-0123	9563
Western Pad	2752	E	714 671-1900	7181
Whittier Filtration Inc (DH)	3589	E	714 986-5300	16138
Wilsey Foods Inc	2079	A	714 257-3700	1555
Worldwide Envmtl Pdts Inc (PA)	3823	D	714 990-2700	21677

BRENTWOOD, CA - Contra Costa County

Company	SIC	EMP	PHONE	ENTRY #
Antioch Building Materials Co	3273	E	925 634-3541	11042
Bluewater Publishing LLC	2741	F	925 634-0880	6450
Brentwood Press & Pubg LLC	2711	E	925 516-4757	5780
Nyabenga Llc	2741	F	925 418-4221	6542
Ssg Alliance LLC (PA)	3699	F	925 526-6050	20079

BRISBANE, CA - San Mateo County

Company	SIC	EMP	PHONE	ENTRY #
Aimmune Therapeutics Inc	2834	C	650 614-5220	8006
Aircraft Technical Publishers (PA)	2741	D	415 330-9500	6426
Celerus Diagnostics Inc	3841	E	805 684-0854	22399
Cutera Inc (PA)	3845	C	415 657-5500	22968
Dolby Laboratories Inc	3663	D	415 715-2500	18090
Faster Faster Inc	3714	E	415 230-0755	20332
Florian Industries Inc	3441	F	415 330-9000	12163
Fong Brothers Printing Inc (PA)	2752	C	415 467-1050	6820
G Pucci & Sons Inc	3949	E	415 468-0452	23567
Goldensol Music LLC	3577	F	877 246-8958	15749
Innoviva Inc (PA)	2834	F	650 238-9600	8220
Leemah Corporation (PA)	3671	C	415 394-1288	18393
Macrogenics West Inc	2834	F	650 624-2600	8267
Pitney Bowes Inc	3579	E	415 330-9423	15912
Praxair Inc	2813	E	415 657-9880	7717
Sfo Apparel	2339	C	415 468-8816	3495
Sheng-Kee Bakery	2051	D	415 468-3800	1321
Statue Factory LLC	3299	E	415 468-4870	11372

BRODERICK, CA - Yolo County

Company	SIC	EMP	PHONE	ENTRY #
Gemini Bio Products	3568	F	916 471-3540	15283

BUELLTON, CA - Santa Barbara County

Company	SIC	EMP	PHONE	ENTRY #
Aero Industries LLC	3599	E	805 688-6734	16237
Alma Rosa Winery Vineyards LLC (PA)	2084	E	805 688-9090	1642
Cliff Bartlett	2434	F	805 693-1617	4287
Equestrian Designs LLC	2339	E	805 686-4455	3411
Gavial Holdings Inc	3679	E	805 688-6734	19550
Global Silicones Inc	2869	E	805 686-4500	9008
GP Machining Inc	3599	E	805 686-0852	16540
Infraredvision Technology Corp	3674	E	805 686-8848	18894
Korda & Geis Engineering LLC	3599	E	805 686-5468	16663
Lockheed Martin Corporation	3812	B	805 686-4069	21324
Terravant Wine Company LLC	2084	E	805 686-9400	2010
Terravant Wine Company LLC	2084	C	805 688-4245	2011
Tilton Engineering Inc	3714	E	805 688-2353	20466
True Precision Machining Inc	3599	E	805 964-4545	17016

BUENA PARK, CA - Orange County

Company	SIC	EMP	PHONE	ENTRY #
ABN Industrial Co Inc (PA)	3599	F	714 521-9211	16203
Advertising Services	2752	F	714 522-2781	6643
Alloy Die Casting Co	3363	B	714 521-9800	11685
Ameripec Inc	2086	C	714 690-9191	2094
Aqua Products Inc	3581	E	714 670-0691	15918
Awesome Products Inc (PA)	2842	E	714 562-8873	8623

	SIC	EMP	PHONE	ENTRY #
Big Time Digital	2752	F	310 329-1383	6698
Blasted Wood Products Inc	2421	F	714 237-1600	4032
Cleughs Frozen Foods Inc	2037	E	714 521-1002	944
Colorline Inc	2522	F	714 373-9500	4980
Creative Impressions Inc (PA)	3081	E	714 521-4441	9703
Cyu Lithographics Inc	2752	E	888 878-9898	6774
Dean Foods Company Cal Inc	2023	E	714 684-2160	611
Dream International Usa Inc	3942	F	714 521-6007	23396
Erika Records Inc	3652	E	714 228-5420	17895
Exemplis LLC	2522	E	714 995-4800	4986
Exemplis LLC	2522	B	714 898-5500	4987
G E M Water Systems Intl LLC	3589	E	714 736-9990	16044
General Container	2653	D	714 562-8700	5414
Guest Chex Inc	2752	F	714 522-1860	6844
Guiseppe Inc	3949	E	714 670-7700	23579
H Q Machine Tech Inc	3599	E	714 956-3388	16552
Haley Bros Inc (HQ)	2431	C	714 670-2112	4162
Hi-Tech Labels Incorporated (PA)	2759	E	714 670-2150	7343
Hq Machine Tech LLC	3728	E	714 956-3388	20837
International Paper Company	2621	C	714 736-0296	5292
International Paper Company	2621	D	562 868-2246	5305
Interntional Color Posters Inc	2759	E	949 768-1005	7360
Island Snacks Inc	2064	E	714 994-1228	1430
J & H Drilling Co Inc	1381	F	714 994-0402	107
Jaz Distribution Inc	3462	F	714 521-3888	13102
Knotts Berry Farm LLC (HQ)	2099	B	714 827-1776	2553
Leach International Corp (HQ)	3679	B	714 736-7537	19619
Leach International Corp	3625	E	714 739-0770	17283
Mar Cor Purification Inc	3589	E	800 633-3080	16068
Metals USA Building Pdts LP	3441	D	714 522-7852	12209
Mondelez Global LLC	2013	A	714 690-7428	509
Nectave Inc	2099	F	714 393-0144	2618
Netmarble Us Inc	2741	F	714 276-1196	6539
Norwich Aero Products Inc (HQ)	3812	D	607 336-7636	21375
Osmosis Technology Inc	3589	E	714 670-9303	16084
Park Engineering and Mfg Co	3599	E	714 521-4660	16831
Parker-Hannifin Corporation	3052	E	714 522-8840	9504
Pepsi-Cola Metro Btlg Co Inc	2086	B	714 522-9635	2166
Pharr-Palomar Inc	2281	A	714 522-4811	2946
Plh Products Inc	2452	E	714 739-6622	4578
Pop 82 Inc	2221	F	714 523-8500	2781
Pop Plastics Acrylic Disp Inc	3089	E	714 523-8500	10299
Precision Surfaces Inc	2541	E	951 680-9279	5095
President Global Corporation (HQ)	2052	F	714 994-2990	1376
Prima-Tex Industries Cal Inc	2261	D	714 521-6104	2890
Q Team Inc	2752	E	714 228-4465	7057
Quality Grinding Company Inc	3545	F	714 228-2100	14670
Rael Inc	2676	E	800 573-1516	5670
Secret Garden (tsg 1895) LLC	3999	F	562 716-5544	24236
Sinclair Companies	2911	C	714 826-5886	9358
Sovereign Packaging Inc	2653	E	714 670-6811	5464
Spn Investments Inc	3949	E	562 777-1140	23659
T M Cobb Company	2431	E	714 670-2112	4244
Trim-Lok Inc	3089	C	714 562-0500	10412
True Fresh Hpp LLC	3822	E	949 531-6519	21535
Tuff Kote Systems Inc	2851	F	714 522-7341	8951
Unique Garage Door Inc (PA)	3442	E	714 223-1493	12354
Wesco Mounting & Finishing Inc	2789	F	714 562-0122	7624
Wildflower Linen Inc (PA)	2299	E	714 522-2777	3021
Wire Cut Company Inc	3599	E	714 994-1170	17071
Yeager Enterprises Corp	3291	D	714 994-2040	11309
Zaolla	3651	E	714 736-9270	17884

BURBANK, CA - Los Angeles County

	SIC	EMP	PHONE	ENTRY #
24/7 Studio Equipment Inc	3663	D	818 840-8247	18011
3ality Digital LLC	3861	F	818 333-3000	23135
Accratronics Seals Corporation	3679	D	818 843-1500	19432
Acsco Products Inc	3714	E	818 953-2240	20238
Advanced Publishing Tech Inc	2741	E	818 557-3035	6422
Advanced Publishing Tech Inc (PA)	7372	E	818 557-3035	24328
American Fine Arts Foundry LLC	3366	E	818 848-7593	11753
Aphex Systems Ltd	3663	E	818 767-2929	18036
Aptiv Digital Inc	7372	D	818 295-6789	24380
Arte De Mexico Inc (PA)	2522	D	818 753-4559	4977
Astra Communications Inc	3663	E	818 859-7305	18044
Autocue Inc	3861	E	213 627-4570	23140
Avid Technology Inc	3861	E	818 557-2520	23142
Bandmerch LLC	2396	E	818 736-4800	3877
Bandy Manufacturing LLC	3728	D	818 846-9020	20759
Bargueiras Rene Inc	3911	F	818 500-8288	23243
Bico Inc	3821	F	818 842-7179	21459
BMC East LLC	2431	E	818 842-8139	4111
Brady Sheet Metal Inc	3444	F	818 846-4043	12510
Bravo Design Inc	2759	F	818 563-1385	7255
Bucy Die Casting	3544	F	818 843-5044	14487
Buildit Engineering Co Inc	3354	F	818 244-6666	11583

	SIC	EMP	PHONE	ENTRY #
Burbank Steel Treating Inc	3398	E	818 842-0975	11803
California Insulated Wire &	3357	D	818 569-4930	11649
Cardona Manufacturing Corp	3728	E	818 841-8358	20778
Carter Plating Inc	3471	F	818 842-1325	13366
Centerpoint Mfg Co Inc	3599	E	818 842-2147	16371
Chulada Inc	2833	E	818 841-6536	7927
Cinemills Corporation (PA)	3648	E	818 843-4560	17679
Color Service Inc	2796	E	323 283-4793	7641
Comco Inc	3589	E	818 333-8500	16030
Computer Prompting Service	3861	F	818 563-3465	23146
Connell Processing Inc	3471	E	818 845-7661	13380
Corona Pathology	2869	E	818 566-1891	9001
Crane Aerospace Inc	3812	D	818 526-2600	21278
Cydwoq Inc	3131	E	818 848-8307	10472
Delray Lighting Inc	3648	E	818 767-3793	17685
Disney Book Group LLC (HQ)	2731	E	818 560-1000	6336
Disney Publishing Worldwide (DH)	2721	E	212 633-4400	6146
Divine Pasta Company (PA)	2099	E	213 542-3300	2508
Dji Technology Inc	3861	E	818 235-0789	23150
Dolby Laboratories Inc	3651	E	818 562-1101	17791
Doremi Cinema LLC	3861	E	818 562-1101	23151
Doves Jewelry Corporation	3911	E	818 955-8886	23257
Eastwest Clothing Inc (PA)	2331	E	323 980-1177	3233
Eaton Aerospace LLC	3812	E	818 526-2600	21288
Eckert Zegler Isotope Pdts Inc	3829	E	661 309-1010	22190
Eckert Zegler Isotope Pdts Inc	3829	E	661 309-1010	22192
Edventures Co Inc	7692	F	818 848-1270	25402
Effective Graphics Inc	2796	D	310 323-2223	7642
ESM Aerospace Inc	3444	E	818 841-3653	12575
Excelline Food Products LLC	2038	C	818 701-7710	992
Excelline Foods Inc	2038	F	818 701-7710	993
Extreme Reach Inc	2741	F	818 588-3635	6482
Gary Schroeder Enterprises	3714	E	818 565-1133	20346
Gerhardt Gear Co Inc	3714	E	818 842-6700	20350
Gilderfluke & Company Inc (PA)	3651	F	818 840-9484	17803
Golden Fleece Designs Inc	2394	F	323 849-1901	3788
Granite Software Inc	7372	E	818 252-1950	24708
Hair By Couture Inc	3999	F	310 848-7676	24116
Haskel International LLC (HQ)	3561	C	818 843-4000	15073
Havana Graphic Center Inc	2752	E	818 841-3774	6850
Hollywood Records Inc	3652	E	818 560-5670	17903
Hutchinson Arospc & Indust Inc	3728	E	818 843-1000	20839
Hutchinson Arospc & Indust Inc	3069	E	818 843-1000	9626
Hydra-Electric Company (PA)	3613	C	818 843-6211	17146
Hydro-Aire Inc (DH)	3728	E	818 526-2600	20842
Ilona Draperies Inc	2391	E	818 840-8811	3694
Insomniac Games Inc (PA)	3944	D	818 729-2400	23431
J L Fisher Inc	3861	D	818 846-8366	23171
K & L Anodizing Corporation	3471	D	323 849-6815	13437
Kadi Enterprises Inc	2013	F	818 556-3400	498
Keystone Cabinetry Inc	2434	F	818 565-3330	4319
Klinky Manufacturing Co	3429	F	818 766-6256	11969
Kotonica Inc	3089	F	818 898-0978	10183
Linde Gas North America LLC	2813	F	626 855-8344	7693
Little Einsteins LLC	2731	F	818 560-1000	6359
Luminar Creations	3911	E	818 843-0010	23290
Makse Inc	3911	F	213 622-5030	23292
Matthews Studio Equipment Inc	3861	E	818 843-6715	23177
Matz Rubber Co Inc	3069	E	323 849-5170	9634
Mc Cormick G R Engrg & Mfg Co	3599	F	818 848-8511	16725
McMillin Mfg Corp	3444	D	323 981-8585	12662
Melrose Mac Inc	3571	F	818 840-8466	15453
Musclepharm Corporation (PA)	2023	D	303 396-6100	633
Mvp Rv Inc	3792	C	951 848-4288	21207
My Eye Media LLC (DH)	7372	E	818 559-7200	24940
Natural Balance Pet Foods Inc (DH)	2048	E	800 829-4493	1149
Nerdist Channel LLC	3663	E	818 333-2705	18197
New Gold Manufacturing Inc	3911	D	818 847-1020	23303
No Static Pro Audio Inc	3651	F	818 729-8554	17839
Omega Case Company Inc	2449	E	818 238-9263	4531
Origin LLC (HQ)	3999	E	818 848-1648	24196
Photronics Inc (DH)	3861	B	203 740-5653	23188
Printograph Inc	2752	E	818 252-3000	7050
Pro Power Products Inc	3629	F	818 558-6222	17351
Quality Heat Treating Inc	3398	D	818 840-8212	11828
Richline Group Inc	3911	C	818 848-5555	23308
Richline Group Inc	3911	E	818 848-5555	23309
Riedel Communications Inc	3669	F	818 559-6900	18359
S & H Machine Inc (PA)	3599	E	818 846-9847	16922
Sanctuary Clothing Inc	2331	E	818 505-0018	3270
Saturn Fasteners Inc	3429	C	818 973-1807	11990
Science of Skincare LLC	2844	D	818 254-7961	8837
Select Office Systems Inc	2893	F	818 861-8320	9208
Senior Operations LLC	3728	B	818 260-2900	20929
Sierra Automated Sys/Eng Corp	3663	E	818 840-6749	18251

Mergent email: customerrelations@mergent.com

1354

2019 California
Manufacturers Register

(P-0000) Products & Services Section entry number
(PA)=Parent Co (HQ)=Headquarters (DH)=Div Headquarters

	SIC	EMP	PHONE	ENTRY #
Slickote	3479	F	818 749-3066	13659
Staness Jonekos Entps Inc	2099	E	818 606-2710	2673
Steril-Aire Inc	3564	E	818 565-1128	15177
Steves Plating Corporation	2542	C	818 842-2184	5168
Superior Window Coverings Inc	2391	E	818 762-6685	3704
Swaner Hardwood Co Inc (PA)	2435	D	818 953-5350	4385
Take A Break Paper	2711	E	323 333-7773	6065
Teslaire	3589	F	310 590-5357	16122
Testronic Laboratories Inc	3825	F	818 845-3223	21876
Three-D Plastics Inc	3089	F	323 849-1316	10403
Three-D Plastics Inc (PA)	3089	E	323 849-1316	10404
U S Label Corporation	2679	F	818 558-3703	5745
United Bakery Inc	2051	F	818 843-1892	1335
US Gold Trading Inc	3911	F	818 558-7766	23327
US Steel Rule Dies Inc	3544	E	562 921-0690	14586
V J Provision Inc	2011	F	818 843-3945	454
Vesture Group Incorporated	2369	E	818 842-0200	3598
Warner Music Group Corp	3652	E	818 846-9090	17915
Warner Music Inc	3652	D	818 953-2600	17916
Westcott Press Inc	2752	F	626 794-7716	7179
Westrock CP LLC	2631	E	818 557-1500	5372
Westrock Rkt Company	2653	F	818 729-0610	5475
Y B S Enterprises Inc	3661	F	818 848-7790	18010
Zepco	3089	F	818 848-0880	10456

BURLINGAME, CA - San Mateo County

	SIC	EMP	PHONE	ENTRY #
A & C Trade Consultants Inc	3432	F	650 375-7000	12018
Advanced Chemblocks Inc	2834	F	650 692-2368	8003
Advanced Components Mfg	3599	E	650 344-6272	16226
Aldran Chemical Inc	2842	F	650 347-8242	8618
Asia America Enterprise Inc	2752	F	650 348-2333	6669
Asia Pacific California Inc (PA)	2711	E	650 513-6189	5763
Burlingame Htg Ventilation Inc	3444	F	650 697-9142	12513
Cal Signal Corp	3669	F	650 343-6100	18314
Collabrative DRG Discovery Inc	7372	F	650 204-3084	24509
Colorprint	2752	F	650 697-7611	6745
Corvus Pharmaceuticals Inc	2834	D	650 900-4520	8124
Devincenzi Metal Products Inc	3444	D	650 692-5800	12560
Devincnzi Archtctural Pdts Inc	3446	E	650 692-5800	12850
Garratt-Callahan Company (PA)	2899	E	650 697-5811	9253
Guittard Chocolate Co	2066	C	650 697-4427	1471
Hanergy Holding (america) LLC (HQ)	3674	F	650 288-3722	18869
Hysterical Software Inc	7372	F	415 793-5785	24742
Igenica Inc	2834	F	650 231-4320	8210
Imply Data Inc	7372	F	415 685-8187	24755
July Systems Inc (PA)	3695	F	650 685-2460	19867
Kindred Biosciences Inc (PA)	2834	E	650 701-7901	8248
Lahlouh Inc	2752	C	650 692-6600	6938
Lithiumstart Inc	3679	F	800 520-8864	19626
Loma Vista Medical Inc	3841	F	650 490-4747	22513
Mentzer Electronics	3845	E	650 697-2642	23019
Merrills Packaging Inc	3081	D	650 259-5959	9715
Middle East Baking Co	2051	E	650 348-7200	1290
Mixed Bag Designs Inc	2673	D	650 239-5358	5609
Motorola Mobility LLC	3663	D	206 383-7785	18190
Novasentis Inc	3699	E	814 238-7400	20033
Petits Pains & Co LP	2051	F	650 692-6000	1309
Phoenix Pharmaceuticals Inc	2834	E	650 558-8898	8337
Plasti-Print Inc	2759	F	650 652-4950	7438
Prestige Chinese Teas Co	2099	F	650 697-8989	2641
Proterra Inc (PA)	3711	C	864 438-0000	20164
Rapid Diagnostics Inc	3841	F	650 558-0395	22597
Renesas Electronics Amer Inc	3674	A	408 588-6750	19122
Sage Software Inc	7372	C	650 579-3628	25138
School Apparel Inc (PA)	2337	C	650 777-4500	3364
Sensbey Inc (PA)	3548	E	650 697-2032	14738
Sentient Energy Inc (PA)	3825	F	650 523-6680	21847
Sing Tao Newspapers (HQ)	2711	D	650 808-8800	6046
Sleeprite Industries Inc	2515	E	650 344-1980	4887
Smp Robotics Systems Corp	3535	D	415 572-2316	14288
Swedcom Corporation	3661	E	650 348-1190	17997
Sybron Dental Specialties Inc	3843	A	650 340-0393	22912
Tag-Connect LLC	3357	F	877 244-4156	11678
Tangent Computer Inc (PA)	3571	D	888 683-2881	15495
Vans Inc	3021	F	650 401-3542	9491
Vector Laboratories Inc (PA)	2836	D	650 697-3600	8585
Worldwide Energy & Mfg USA Inc (PA)	3674	D	650 692-7788	19275
Yb Media LLC	2741	E	310 467-5804	6629

BURNEY, CA - Shasta County

	SIC	EMP	PHONE	ENTRY #
Shasta Green Inc	2411	E	530 335-4924	4010
Sierra Pacific Industries	2421	F	530 378-8301	4058
Sierra Pacific Industries	2421	C	530 335-3681	4060
Tubit Enterprises Inc	2411	E	530 335-5085	4017

BUTTONWILLOW, CA - Kern County

	SIC	EMP	PHONE	ENTRY #
Albert Goyenetche Dairy	2026	F	661 764-6176	708
B W Implement Co	3523	E	661 764-5254	14044
JG Boswell Tomato - Kern LLC	2033	E	661 764-9000	810

BYRON, CA - Contra Costa County

	SIC	EMP	PHONE	ENTRY #
Covia Holdings Corporation	1446	E	925 634-3575	395
Marin Food Specialties Inc	2032	E	925 634-6126	767
Quick Deck Inc	3448	F	925 516-0603	12958

CALABASAS, CA - Los Angeles County

	SIC	EMP	PHONE	ENTRY #
Alcatel-Lucent USA Inc	3661	E	818 880-3500	17919
Ale USA Inc	3663	A	818 878-4816	18024
Apex Precision Tech Inc	3714	F	317 821-1000	20257
Art Impressions Inc	2741	F	818 591-0105	6435
Catapult Communications Corp (DH)	7372	E	818 871-1800	24478
Counterpoint Software Inc	7372	F	818 222-7777	24530
Dts LLC	3651	D	818 436-1000	17793
Fulcrum Microsystems Inc	3674	F	818 871-8100	18853
Global Edge LLC	7372	E	888 315-2692	24696
Global Edge LLC (PA)	7372	E	818 207-2694	24697
Immuncellular Therapeutics Ltd	2834	F	818 264-2300	8212
Ixia (HQ)	3825	B	818 871-1800	21779
Ixia	3825	F	818 871-1800	21780
Melco Engineering Corporation	3841	F	818 591-1000	22536
Netsol Technologies Inc (PA)	7372	E	818 222-9197	24953
Nia Energy LLC	3641	F	818 422-8000	17432
Nova-One Diagnostics LLC	2835	D	818 348-1543	8499
Optical Communication Pdts Inc	3661	A	818 876-8700	17974
PMS Systems Corporation	7372	F	310 450-2566	25068
Schroeder Tool & Die Corp	3599	E	818 786-9360	16931
Solid 21 Incorporated	3911	F	213 688-0900	23318
Spanish Castle Inc	2084	F	818 222-4496	1984
Spirent Communications Inc (HQ)	3663	B	818 676-2300	18260
Wixen Music Publishing Inc	2731	F	818 591-7355	6411
Yamaha Guitar Group Inc (HQ)	3931	C	818 575-3600	23393

CALEXICO, CA - Imperial County

	SIC	EMP	PHONE	ENTRY #
Bi Technologies Corporation	3679	F	714 447-2402	19467
Celestica LLC	3643	B	760 357-4880	17450
Creation Tech Calexico Inc (HQ)	3672	C	760 336-8543	18458
Cs Manfacturing Indus Svcs Inc (PA)	3678	F	760 890-7746	19385
Honeywell International Inc	3724	A	760 312-5300	20659
Imperial Valley Foods Inc	2037	B	760 203-1896	952
Lakim Industries Incorporated (PA)	3991	E	310 637-8900	23794
Lorenz Inc	3699	B	760 356-1019	20007
Orthodental International Inc	3843	D	760 357-8070	22898
Robert Bosch Tool Corporation	3546	C	760 357-5603	14709
Rockwell Collins Inc	3812	E	760 540-2232	21416
Sewing Experts Inc	2331	E	760 357-8525	3272
Skyworks Solutions	3629	F	301 874-6408	17355
Triumph Insulation Systems	3728	F	760 768-1700	20963
Vertiv Corporation	3613	F	760 768-7522	17170
Wabash Technologies Inc	3625	F	760 768-9343	17321

CALIF HOT SPG, CA - Tulare County

	SIC	EMP	PHONE	ENTRY #
California Hot Springs Water	2086	F	661 548-6582	2107

CALIFORNIA CITY, CA - Kern County

	SIC	EMP	PHONE	ENTRY #
Fabricor Products Inc	3446	E	760 373-8292	12855
Service Rock Products Corp	3273	E	760 373-9140	11172
Ward Enterprises	3599	F	661 251-4890	17050

CALIMESA, CA - Riverside County

	SIC	EMP	PHONE	ENTRY #
B & Y Machine Co	3592	F	909 795-8588	16145
Calimesa News Mirror	2711	E	909 795-8145	5794
Skat-Trak Inc	3011	C	909 795-2505	9467
William A Shubeck	3996	E	909 795-6970	24016

CALIPATRIA, CA - Imperial County

	SIC	EMP	PHONE	ENTRY #
Earthrise Nutritionals LLC	2099	F	760 348-5027	2510

CALISTOGA, CA - Napa County

	SIC	EMP	PHONE	ENTRY #
Bailey Essel William Jr	2084	F	707 341-3391	1651
Chateau Montelena Winery	2084	F	707 942-5105	1690
Coffee Guys Inc (PA)	2095	E	707 942-5747	2337
Diamond Creek Vineyard	2084	F	707 942-6926	1727
Envy Wines LLC	2084	F	707 942-4670	1750
Jack McMahon Landscape	2421	F	707 942-1122	4041
Lane Bennett Winery	2084	F	707 942-6684	1854
Madrigal Vineyard Management	2084	E	707 942-8691	1867
Reverie On Diamond Mtn LLC	2084	F	707 942-6800	1946
Silverado Brewing Co L L C	2082	F	707 341-3089	1624
Sterling Vineyards Inc (PA)	2084	F	707 942-3300	1991
Sterling Vineyards Inc	2084	F	707 942-9602	1993
Sugarloaf Farming Corporation	2084	F	707 942-4459	2001
Tonnellerie Francaise French C	2449	F	707 942-9301	4538
Villa Amorosa	2084	D	707 942-8200	2041

Employment Codes: A=Over 500 employees, B=251-500,
C=101-250, D=51-100, E=20-50, F=10-19

2019 California
Manufacturers Register

© Mergent Inc. 1-800-342-5647

1355

GEOGRAPHIC

	SIC	EMP	PHONE	ENTRY #
Vintage Wine Estates Inc	2084	F	707 942-4981	2047

CAMARILLO, CA - Ventura County

	SIC	EMP	PHONE	ENTRY #
3dcd	3695	F	805 383-3837	19854
Abel Automatics Inc	3451	E	805 484-8789	13006
Airborne Technologies Inc	3728	D	805 389-3700	20725
Americon	2521	F	805 987-0412	4927
Amh International Inc	3599	F	805 388-2082	16273
Askgene Pharma Inc	2834	E	805 807-9868	8047
Astrofoam Molding Company Inc	3089	E	805 482-7276	9960
August Hat Company Inc (PA)	2353	E	805 983-4651	3557
Barta-Schoenewald Inc (PA)	3621	C	805 389-1935	17181
Battery-Biz Inc	3694	D	805 437-7777	19829
Belport Company Inc (PA)	3843	F	805 484-1051	22859
Bimbo Bakeries Usa Inc	2051	F	805 384-1059	1205
Bnk Petroleum (us) Inc	1382	E	805 484-3613	126
Cal-Sensors Inc (PA)	3812	E	707 303-3837	21270
California Pharmaceuticals LLC	2834	F	805 482-3737	8092
California St UNI Channel Isla	3612	F	805 437-2670	17083
Calram LLC	3499	F	805 987-6205	13928
Camland Inc	7692	F	805 485-9242	25394
Chargetek Inc	3629	E	805 444-7792	17337
Chauhan Industries Inc	3089	F	805 484-1616	10022
Ciao Wireless Inc	3679	D	805 389-3224	19487
CK Technologies Inc (PA)	3823	E	805 987-4801	21562
Cooper Crouse-Hinds LLC	3678	C	805 484-0543	19381
Cooper Crouse-Hinds LLC	3069	C	805 484-0543	9602
Cooper Crouse-Hinds LLC	3069	C	805 484-0543	9603
Cooper Interconnect Inc (DH)	3643	D	805 484-0543	17456
Cooper Interconnect Inc	3678	D	805 553-9632	19382
Cooper Interconnect Inc	3644	E	805 553-9632	17509
Corprint Incorporated	2759	F	818 839-5316	7286
CPI Malibu Division	3663	D	805 383-1829	18078
Crockett Graphics Inc (PA)	2653	D	805 987-8577	5403
Deckers Outdoor Corporation	3021	F	805 437-2300	9470
Electronic Clearing House Inc (HQ)	7372	D	805 419-8700	24602
Enterprise Services LLC	7372	F	805 388-8000	24616
Evergreen Avionics Inc (PA)	3674	F	805 445-6492	18835
Galtech Computer Corporation	2521	E	805 376-1060	4945
Gc International Inc (PA)	3652	E	805 389-4631	17899
Gc International Inc	3652	E	805 389-4631	17900
GKN Aerospace Camarillo Inc	3444	F	805 383-6684	12599
Gms Landscapes Inc	3432	D	805 402-3925	12037
Golden State Medical Sup Inc	2834	C	805 477-9866	8196
Gtran Inc (PA)	3679	E	805 445-4500	19558
Hanson Lab Furniture Inc	3821	E	805 498-3121	21474
Hi-Temp Insulation Inc	3469	B	805 484-2774	13218
Hte Manufacturing Inc	3545	F	805 987-5449	14641
Hygiena LLC (PA)	2835	C	805 388-2383	8482
IL Helth Buty Natural Oils Inc	2899	E	805 384-0473	9260
Illinois Tool Works Inc	3674	E	805 499-0335	18882
Infab Corporation	3842	D	805 987-5255	22751
Innovative Integration Inc	3823	E	805 520-3300	21604
Insulfab Inc	3296	D	805 482-2751	11332
Integrity Bio Inc	2834	E	805 445-8422	8223
Interconnect Systems Inc (DH)	3674	D	805 482-2870	18920
Interglobal Waste Management	3826	F	805 388-1588	21977
International Paper Company	2621	F	805 933-4347	5294
J C Industries Inc	3999	F	805 389-4040	24135
Johanson Technology Inc	3675	C	805 389-1166	19299
Jolly Jumps Inc	3599	F	805 484-0026	16631
K9 Ballistics Inc	3999	F	805 233-8103	24143
Kinamed Inc	3842	E	805 384-2748	22763
Koltov Inc (PA)	3172	F	805 764-0280	10563
Linabond Inc	3479	F	805 484-7373	13612
Livewire Test Labs Inc	3825	F	801 293-8300	21793
Lucix Corporation (HQ)	3679	D	805 987-6645	19629
Lundberg Survey Inc	2721	F	805 383-2400	6210
Maddiebrit Products LLC	2851	F	818 483-0096	8916
Magicall Inc	3621	F	805 484-4300	17209
Mediapointe Inc	3651	F	805 480-3700	17830
Medical Packaging Corporation	3842	D	805 388-2383	22769
Mercury Systems Inc	3672	C	805 388-1345	18527
Merex Inc	3825	F	805 446-2700	21804
Meyers Publishing Inc	2721	F	805 445-8881	6216
Microsemi Communications Inc	3674	E	805 388-3700	19006
Microsemi Communications Inc (DH)	3674	C	805 388-3700	19007
Microvoice Corporation	3663	E	805 389-2922	18182
Mintronix Inc	3571	F	805 482-1298	15459
Mosaic Distributors LLC	2844	F	805 383-7711	8798
Mosaic Marketing Partners LLC	2844	F	805 383-7711	8799
Nanoprecision Products Inc	3469	E	310 597-4991	13252
Nevion Usa Inc	3663	D	805 247-8575	18198
Old New York Bagel & Deli Co (PA)	2051	E	805 484-3354	1301
Optim Microwave Inc	3663	E	805 482-7093	18207
Opto Diode Corporation	3674	E	805 465-8700	19063

	SIC	EMP	PHONE	ENTRY #
Organic Infusions Inc (PA)	2911	F	805 419-4118	9343
OSI Optoelectronics Inc	3674	E	805 987-0146	19068
Ossur Americas Inc	3842	E	805 484-2600	22788
Pacific Casual LLC	2514	E	805 445-8310	4838
Parker-Hannifin Corporation	3728	C	805 419-7000	20907
PDQ Engineering Inc	3721	E	805 482-1334	20617
Performance Materials Corp (PA)	2821	D	805 482-1722	7864
Performance Plus Laboratories	3821	C	805 383-7871	21486
Pico Crimping Tools Co	3545	F	805 388-5510	14663
Plt Enterprises Inc	3643	D	805 389-5335	17486
Polyfet Rf Devices Inc	3674	E	805 484-9582	19081
Price-Leho Co Inc	3469	F	805 482-8967	13263
Q Corporation	3826	E	805 383-8998	22008
Rache Corporation	3699	E	805 389-6868	20053
Recon 1 Inc	3021	F	805 388-3911	9479
Record Technology Inc	3652	E	805 484-2747	17912
Roboworm Inc	3949	F	805 389-1636	23637
Rocketstar Robotics Inc	3621	F	805 529-7769	17221
Ronlo Engineering Ltd	3599	E	805 388-3227	16915
Sani-Tech West Inc (PA)	3052	D	805 389-0400	9507
Scripps Media Inc	2711	C	805 437-0000	6041
Security Door Controls (PA)	3429	C	805 494-0622	11992
Semtech Corporation (PA)	3674	C	805 498-2111	19146
Shine & Pretty (usa) Corp	2844	E	805 388-8581	8841
Sierra Traffic Service Inc	3669	F	805 388-2474	18365
Signum Systems Corporation	3825	F	805 383-3682	21849
Skurka Aerospace Inc (DH)	3621	C	216 706-2939	17223
Snap Creative Manufacturing	3942	F	818 735-3830	23402
So-Cal Value Added LLC	3679	E	805 389-5335	19730
Structural Diagnostics Inc	3825	E	805 987-7755	21855
Superior Panoramic Hand Prnts	2261	D	805 445-7770	2897
Tactical Communications Corp	3669	E	805 987-4100	18369
Technical Film Systems Inc	3861	F	805 384-9470	23201
Technicolor Disc Services Corp (PA)	3695	C	805 445-1122	19885
Technicolor Thomson Group	3651	A	805 445-7652	17863
Thiessen Products Inc	3599	C	805 482-6913	16998
Thin-Lite Corporation	3648	E	805 987-5021	17738
Thingap LLC	3621	E	805 477-9741	17226
Thingap Holdings LLC	3621	F	805 477-9741	17227
Titan Medical Dme Inc	3841	F	818 889-9998	22651
Titan Metal Fabricators Inc (PA)	3441	D	805 487-5050	12260
Transonic Combustion Inc	3519	E	805 465-5145	14033
United Fabrication Inc	3444	F	805 482-2354	12799
United Western Enterprises Inc	3479	E	805 389-1077	13676
Ventura County Star	2711	F	805 437-0138	6079
Viade Products Inc	3843	E	805 484-2114	22922
Viavi Solutions Inc	3661	D	805 465-1875	18007
Vitesse Manufacturing & Dev	3674	C	805 388-3700	19264
VME Acquisition Corp (PA)	3842	F	805 384-2748	22844
Voiceboard Corporation	3571	F	805 389-3100	15504
Wave Circuits	3679	E	805 987-3008	19786
Western Gage Corporation	3545	F	805 445-1410	14694
Western Mfg & Distrg LLC	3751	E	805 988-1010	21149
Wilwood Engineering	3714	C	805 388-1188	20486
Xirgo Technologies LLC	3699	E	805 319-4079	20116
Zero Gravity Corporation	3751	E	805 388-8803	21153
Zpower LLC	3629	C	805 445-7789	17362

CAMBRIA, CA - San Luis Obispo County

	SIC	EMP	PHONE	ENTRY #
McClatchy Newspapers Inc	2711	D	805 927-8652	5951

CAMERON PARK, CA - El Dorado County

	SIC	EMP	PHONE	ENTRY #
Artisan Moss LLC	2077	F	833 667-7278	1518
First Gold Corp	1041	F	530 677-5974	3
JEI	3663	E	530 677-3210	18138
Preferred Mfg Svcs Inc (PA)	3599	D	530 677-2675	16856
Vultures Row Aviation LLC	3599	F	530 676-9245	17045
Wask Engineering Inc	3764	F	530 672-2795	21183
Works Connection	3751	F	530 642-9488	21151

CAMINO, CA - El Dorado County

	SIC	EMP	PHONE	ENTRY #
Crystal Basin Cellars	2084	F	530 303-3749	1713
Rainbow Orchards	2086	F	530 644-1594	2181
Sierra Pacific Industries	2421	B	530 644-2311	4063

CAMPBELL, CA - Santa Clara County

	SIC	EMP	PHONE	ENTRY #
20th Century Spring Mfg	3469	E	408 727-9100	13149
Activewire Inc	3577	F	650 465-4000	15656
Afn Services LLC	2599	E	408 364-1564	5218
Alternators Starters Etc	3694	F	408 559-3540	19826
Aoptix Technologies Inc	3699	D	408 558-3300	19910
Apama Medical Inc	3841	F	408 903-4094	22337
Arteris Inc	3674	F	408 470-7300	18721
Arteris Holdings Inc	3674	F	408 470-7300	18722
Barracuda Networks Inc (HQ)	7372	C	408 342-5400	24410
Bering Technology Inc	3577	F	408 364-6500	15680
Bluestack Systems Inc	7372	E	408 412-9439	24436

Mergent email: customerrelations@mergent.com
1356

2019 California
Manufacturers Register

(P-0000) Products & Services Section entry number
(PA)=Parent Co (HQ)=Headquarters (DH)=Div Headquarters

	SIC	EMP	PHONE	ENTRY #
Brilliant Instruments Inc	3823	F	408 866-0426	21554
Bruker Corporation	3577	E	408 376-4040	15693
Burman Cabinet Corporation	2434	E	408 377-6652	4277
C T V Inc	2752	F	408 378-1606	6712
Campbell Graphics Inc	2752	E	408 371-6411	6718
Carmel Instruments LLC	3823	F	408 866-0426	21558
Chargepoint Inc (PA)	3629	C	408 841-4500	17336
Christian Music Today Inc	2711	F	408 377-9232	5802
Collimated Holes Inc	3827	E	408 374-5080	22069
Condeco Software Inc (HQ)	7372	E	917 677-7600	24519
Consoldted Hnge Mnfctured Pdts	3599	F	408 379-6550	16401
Creganna Medical Devices Inc (DH)	3841	E	408 364-7100	22413
Dasher Technologies Inc (PA)	7372	E	408 409-2607	24546
Deluxe Corporation	2782	D	408 370-8801	7578
Dynalinear Technologies Inc	3559	F	408 376-5090	14941
Eos Software Inc	7372	F	855 900-4876	24620
Etched Media Corporation	3471	E	408 374-6895	13408
Exponential Technology Inc	3674	D	408 378-1850	18839
Firetide Inc (DH)	3577	D	408 399-7771	15742
Harris Precision	3444	F	408 866-4160	12610
Hotronic Inc	3661	F	408 378-3883	17955
Ic Manage Inc (PA)	7372	E	408 369-9227	24747
Imperative Care Inc	3842	E	650 274-3882	22748
Iwatt Inc (DH)	3674	E	408 280-1400	18933
JD Engineering & Assoc Inc	3599	F	408 866-0822	16618
Jessee Brothers Machine Sp Inc	3599	F	408 866-1755	16622
Kalila Medical Inc	3829	F	408 819-5175	22222
Keyssa Inc (PA)	3674	E	408 637-2300	18941
Keyssa Systems Inc	3559	F	408 637-2300	14979
List Biological Labs Inc	2836	F	408 866-6363	8566
Medleycom Incorporated	2711	F	408 745-5418	5966
Metric Design & Manufacturing	3544	F	408 374-4544	14541
Phoenix Technologies Ltd (HQ)	7372	F	408 570-1000	25057
Photon Inc	3823	F	408 226-1000	21632
Precision Identity Corporation	3599	F	408 374-2346	16854
Process Solutions Inc	3823	E	408 370-6540	21636
Prompter People Inc	3663	F	408 353-6000	18225
Reed Mariculture Inc	2048	F	408 377-1065	1158
Scientific Imaging Corporation (PA)	3827	F	408 374-7300	22130
Scientific Imaging Inc	3827	F	408 374-7300	22131
Semi Automation & Tech Inc	3674	F	408 374-9549	19139
Semprex Corporation	3825	F	408 379-3230	21846
Simmitri Inc	3674	F	408 779-3333	19163
Syntonic Microwave Inc	3663	F	408 866-5900	18269
Tactx Medical Inc (DH)	3841	C	408 364-7100	22642
Teammate Builders Inc	2542	F	408 377-9000	5170
Velo3d Inc	2752	C	408 666-5309	7168
Versatile Power Inc	3841	F	408 341-4600	22672
Vivus Inc (PA)	2834	F	650 934-5200	8439
Wg Security Products Inc	3699	E	408 241-8000	20113
Zipline Medical Inc	3841	F	408 412-7228	22685
Zircon Corporation (PA)	3546	E	408 866-8600	14714

CANOGA PARK, CA - Los Angeles County

	SIC	EMP	PHONE	ENTRY #
3M Company	3613	F	818 882-0606	17127
Abacus Printing & Graphics Inc	2752	F	818 929-6740	6633
Aben Machine Products Inc	3599	F	818 673-1627	16201
Advanced Safety Devices LLC	3825	F	818 701-9200	21702
Aerojet Rocketdyne De Inc (HQ)	2869	C	818 586-1000	8970
Aeromax Industries Inc	3724	F	818 701-9500	20643
Alexander Business Supplies	2752	F	818 346-1820	6646
Allman Products Inc	3086	E	818 715-0093	9814
American Activated Carbon Corp	3624	F	310 491-2842	17233
American Mfg Netwrk Inc	3599	F	818 786-1113	16271
B & R Accessories Inc	3961	E	213 688-8727	23743
B S K T Inc	3599	E	818 349-1566	16301
Best Data Products Inc	3577	D	818 534-1414	15681
Bimbo Bakeries USA Inc	2099	F	818 348-9716	2467
Boeing Company	3721	A	818 428-1154	20566
C P Films Inc	3081	F	818 678-1450	9701
California Natural Vitamins	2834	F	818 772-8441	8091
Casmari Inc	2253	F	818 727-1866	2829
Cg Manufacturing Inc	3444	F	818 886-1191	12530
Cicon Engineering Inc	3679	F	818 909-6060	19488
Cicon Engineering Inc	3679	F	818 882-6508	19489
Darrell Zbrowski	3537	D	818 324-5961	14322
Den-Mat Corporation	2844	E	800 445-0345	8736
Eca Medical Instruments	3841	E	818 998-7284	22432
Elite Generators Inc	3621	E	818 718-0200	17192
Emac Assembly Corp	3679	F	818 882-2999	19531
Glastar Corporation	3559	E	818 341-0301	14960
Holsum Bakery Inc	2051	F	818 884-6562	1272
Infinity Precision Inc	3599	F	818 447-3008	16582
Infinity Stamps Inc	3469	F	818 576-1188	13224
International Beauty Pdts LLC (PA)	2844	F	818 999-1222	8772
Interntnl Hmeopathic Mfg Dist	2834	F	818 884-8040	8229

	SIC	EMP	PHONE	ENTRY #
Interntnal Virtual PDT MGT Inc	3661	F	818 812-9500	17959
Jake Stehelin Etienne	3089	D	818 998-4250	10162
Jot Engineering Inc	3599	F	818 727-7572	16632
Kama Interconnect Inc	3679	F	818 713-9810	19605
Micro Steel Inc	3769	F	818 348-8701	21196
Mir Printing & Graphics	2752	F	818 313-9333	6977
Mixed Chicks LLC	2844	F	818 888-4008	8797
Mooney Industries	3599	F	818 998-0199	16769
Mww Inc	2499	F	800 575-3475	4638
National Ready Mixed Con Co	3273	F	818 884-0893	11148
Natural Wonders Ca Inc	2833	F	818 593-2001	7955
Odette Christiane LLC	2339	F	818 883-0410	3473
One Lambda Inc (HQ)	2833	C	818 702-0042	7961
Optron Scientific Company Inc	3829	F	818 883-6103	22243
Pacific Shore Holdings Inc	2834	F	818 998-0996	8325
Pastries By Edie Inc	2051	E	818 340-0203	1307
Penta Financial Inc	3671	F	818 882-3872	18394
Penta Laboratories LLC	3671	F	818 882-3872	18395
Pls Diabetic Shoe Company Inc	3021	E	818 734-7080	9477
PM Lithographers Inc	2752	F	818 704-2626	7030
Pratt	3724	E	818 586-1000	20674
Printfirm Inc	2759	F	818 992-1005	7445
Protemach Inc	2869	F	310 622-2693	9032
Rainbo Record Mfg Corp (PA)	3652	C	818 280-1100	17911
Small Wnders Hndcrfted Mntures	3999	F	818 703-7450	24245
Source Photonics Usa Inc (HQ)	3674	C	818 773-9044	19182
Spa La La Inc	3999	F	605 321-1276	24249
Steven Madden Ltd	3143	D	818 713-9681	10485
Temptron Engineering Inc	3829	F	818 346-4900	22287
US Nuclear Corp (PA)	3829	F	818 296-0746	22293
Video Reporter Inc	2741	E	800 266-9104	6617
Viking Ready Mix Co Inc	3273	E	818 884-0893	11210
Vision Imaging Supplies Inc	3955	F	818 710-7200	23741
Vitale Home Designs Inc	3873	F	818 888-2481	23226
Vomar Products Inc	2759	F	818 610-5115	7535
Weiser Litho Inc	2752	F	818 707-2708	7176
Works Performance Products Inc	3714	E	818 701-1010	20488

CANTIL, CA - Kern County

	SIC	EMP	PHONE	ENTRY #
US Rockets	3761	F	707 267-3393	21176

CANTUA CREEK, CA - Fresno County

	SIC	EMP	PHONE	ENTRY #
Pacific Ginning Company LLC	3559	E	559 829-9446	15004

CANYON COUNTRY, CA - Los Angeles County

	SIC	EMP	PHONE	ENTRY #
American Garment Finishing	2221	E	310 962-1929	2773
Box Master	3469	E	661 298-2666	13172
California Compactor Svc Inc	3499	E	661 298-5556	13927
Candlelight Press Inc	2752	E	323 299-3798	6719
Commercial Display Systems LLC	3585	E	818 361-8160	15945
Continental Security Inds	3669	F	661 251-8800	18316
Legacy Vulcan LLC	1442	F	661 252-1010	372
Next System Inc	2273	E	661 257-1600	2936
Rexhall Industries Inc	3716	E	661 726-5470	20525
Spragg Industries Inc	3999	F	661 424-9673	24252
Valley Publications	2741	E	661 298-5330	6614

CANYON LAKE, CA - Riverside County

	SIC	EMP	PHONE	ENTRY #
Golding Publications	2791	E	951 244-1966	7629

CAPISTRANO BEACH, CA - Orange County

	SIC	EMP	PHONE	ENTRY #
San Clemente Times LLC	2711	F	949 388-7700	6032
Schaeffler Group USA Inc	3562	B	949 234-9799	15110
Vs Vincenzo Ltd Inc	2844	F	949 388-8791	8864

CAPITOLA, CA - Santa Cruz County

	SIC	EMP	PHONE	ENTRY #
Alpha Machine Company Inc	3599	F	831 462-7400	16260
Timely Data Resources Inc	7372	F	831 462-2510	25278

CARDIFF, CA - San Diego County

	SIC	EMP	PHONE	ENTRY #
Alliance Multimedia LLC	2759	F	760 522-3455	7230

CARDIFF BY THE SEA, CA - San Diego County

	SIC	EMP	PHONE	ENTRY #
Aaron Chang Photo Active Wear	3552	F	760 635-0041	14773
Accurate Solutions Inc	3671	F	760 753-6524	18380
Biomet San Diego LLC	3842	F	760 942-2786	22707
Headline Graphics Inc	2796	E	760 436-0133	7647
Igrad Inc	7372	E	858 705-2917	24750
L&H Enterprises	3577	F	760 230-2275	15783
Nutrition Resource Connection	3652	F	760 803-8234	17908
Reinhart Oil & Gas Inc	1311	F	760 753-3330	71
Strategic Info Group Inc	7372	E	760 697-1050	25226

CARLSBAD, CA - San Diego County

	SIC	EMP	PHONE	ENTRY #
800total Gym Commercial LLC	3949	F	858 586-6080	23482
Acushnet Company	3949	B	760 804-6500	23486
Acutus Medical Inc	3842	F	858 673-1621	22687
Aea Technology Inc	3825	F	760 931-8979	21703

GEOGRAPHIC

Company	SIC	EMP	PHONE	ENTRY #
Aethercomm Inc	3663	C	760 208-6002	18017
Aih LLC (DH)	3679	E	760 930-4600	19438
Air Products and Chemicals Inc	2813	C	760 931-9555	7675
Aldila Inc	3949	D	858 513-1801	23493
Aldila Golf Corp (DH)	3949	D	858 513-1801	23496
Alphatec Holdings Inc (PA)	3841	E	760 431-9286	22328
Alphatec Spine Inc (HQ)	3842	C	760 494-6610	22695
Alphatec Spine Inc	3842	F	760 431-9286	22696
American Lithium Energy Corp	2819	F	760 599-7388	7752
American Rim Supply Inc	3714	E	760 431-3666	20255
Amigo Custom Screen Prints LLC	2759	E	760 452-7964	7236
Anchor Audio Inc	3651	D	760 827-7100	17760
Applied Biosystems LLC (DH)	7372	C	650 638-5000	24371
Arkeia Software Inc (DH)	7372	F	760 431-1319	24385
Astura Medical	3841	F	760 814-8047	22348
Avaak Inc	3699	E	858 453-9866	19915
Beckman Coulter Inc	3826	C	760 438-9151	21910
Biosource International Inc	2835	C	805 659-5759	8464
Bitchin Inc	2099	E	760 224-7447	2468
Borsos Engineering Inc	3571	E	760 930-0296	15396
Breg Inc (HQ)	3841	C	760 599-3000	22382
Brendan Technologies Inc	7372	E	760 929-7500	24450
Cable Builders Inc	2298	F	760 308-0042	2970
Cal-Comp USA (san Diego) Inc	3672	C	858 587-6900	18441
Calamp Corp	3663	C	760 438-9010	18059
California Sensor Corporation	3829	E	760 438-0525	22175
Callaway Golf Company	3949	A	760 804-4502	23531
Callaway Golf Company (PA)	3949	B	760 931-1771	23533
Carlsbad Technology Inc	2834	F	760 431-8284	8101
Carlsbad Technology Inc (DH)	2834	D	760 431-8284	8102
Carlsbad Technology Inc	2834	E	760 431-8284	8103
Chromacode Inc	3821	E	442 244-4369	21463
Chuao Chocolatier Inc (HQ)	2064	F	760 476-1668	1414
Continuous Cartridge	3861	E	760 929-4808	23147
Coola LLC	2844	E	760 940-2125	8722
Coplan & Coplan Inc	3545	E	760 268-0583	14619
Covidien Holding Inc	3841	F	760 603-5020	22410
CPS Printing	2752	D	760 494-9000	6764
Crown Circuits Inc	3672	D	949 922-0144	18461
Custopharm Inc (PA)	3559	F	760 683-0901	14938
Danville Materials LLC (HQ)	3843	E	760 743-7744	22866
Designer Drinks	2086	E	760 444-2355	2129
Designline Windows & Doors Inc	3442	E	760 931-9422	12308
Dexters Deli	2047	E	760 720-7507	1111
Diligent Solutions Inc	3599	E	760 814-8960	16440
Dimension One Spas Inc (HQ)	3999	C	800 345-7727	24079
Eagle Creek Inc (DH)	3161	D	760 431-6400	10520
Ecolink	3699	F	760 431-8804	19955
Ecolink Intelligent Tech Inc	3651	F	855 432-6546	17796
Edirect Publishing Inc	2741	F	760 602-8300	6473
Eevelle LLC	2399	F	760 434-2231	3944
Ef Composite Technologies LP	3949	F	800 433-6723	23555
Efgp Inc	3949	F	760 692-3900	23556
Eklin Medical Systems Inc	3841	D	760 918-9626	22435
Electro Surface Tech Inc	3672	D	760 431-8306	18470
Entropic Communications LLC (HQ)	3674	D	858 768-3600	18827
Ezoic Inc	7372	F	760 444-4995	24640
Fc Global Realty Incorporated	3841	E	760 602-3300	22448
Finishing Touch Moulding Inc	2434	D	760 444-1019	4301
First Circuit Inc	3672	F	760 560-0530	18482
Fish On Rice LLC	2082	F	619 696-6262	1593
Foundry Med Innovations Inc	3841	F	888 445-2333	22454
Funktion USA	3444	F	760 473-4171	12592
Gold Couture 22 K	3911	F	760 602-0690	23269
Graphics Ink Lithography LLC	2759	F	760 438-9052	7334
Great Lakes Data Systems Inc	7372	F	760 602-1900	24710
Greenwich Biosciences Inc (HQ)	2834	E	760 795-2200	8198
Gtr Enterprises Incorporated	3599	F	760 931-1192	16547
Heat Factory Inc	2673	E	760 734-5300	5602
Hudson Printing Inc	2759	F	760 602-1260	7344
Hygeia II Medical Group Inc	3845	E	714 515-7571	22986
Hygeia II Medical Group Inc	3845	E	714 515-7571	22987
Idex Health & Science LLC	3827	C	760 438-2131	22085
Impedimed Inc (HQ)	3841	E	760 585-2100	22477
Industrial Zinc Plating Corp	3471	E	760 918-6877	13431
International Mercantile	3714	E	760 438-2205	20373
International Stem Cell Corp (PA)	2834	E	760 940-6383	8226
Intevac Photonics Inc	3827	E	760 476-0339	22091
Ionis Pharmaceuticals Inc	2834	E	760 603-3567	8231
Ionis Pharmaceuticals Inc (PA)	2834	B	760 931-9200	8232
Ipitek Group Inc	3663	C	760 438-8362	18134
Iris Group Inc	2759	C	760 431-1103	7362
Jlab LLC	3679	E	405 445-7219	19601
Jones Glyn Productions Inc	2741	F	760 431-8955	6508
Kayo Corp (PA)	3949	F	760 918-0405	23601
KVA Inc	3312	F	760 489-1500	11403
L & L Printers Carlsbad LLC	2752	E	760 438-3456	6933
L & L Printers Inc	2752	F	858 278-4300	6934
L3 Technologies Inc	3669	C	760 431-6800	18339
Laird R & F Products Inc (DH)	3812	F	760 916-9410	21317
Laurelwood Industries Inc	3599	E	760 705-1649	16682
Lawinfocom Inc	7372	D	760 510-3000	24850
Leading Biosciences Inc	2834	F	858 395-6099	8254
LF Industries Inc	3599	F	951 471-0372	16686
Life Technologies Corporation (HQ)	2835	C	760 603-7200	8489
Life Technologies Corporation	2836	D	760 918-4259	8565
Lite Machines Corporation	3812	F	765 463-0959	21318
Lithographix Inc	2759	D	760 438-3456	7387
Living Wellness Partners LLC	2099	E	800 642-3754	2587
Lumistar Inc (DH)	3672	F	760 431-2181	18522
Luxtera Inc	3674	C	760 448-3520	18974
Machinetek LLC	3728	E	760 438-6644	20871
Maxlinear Inc (PA)	3674	E	760 692-0711	18986
Means Engineering Inc	3826	D	760 931-9452	21990
Mellace Family Brands Inc	2068	E	760 448-1940	1496
Mellace Family Brands Cal Inc	2068	E	760 448-1940	1497
Melles Griot Inc	3827	E	760 438-2131	22106
Meps Real-Time Inc	3829	E	760 448-9500	22234
Mercotac Inc	3643	F	760 431-7723	17483
Microvision Development Inc	7372	E	760 438-7781	24920
Mikroscan Technologies Inc	3841	F	760 893-8095	22542
Mizu Inc (PA)	3069	F	307 690-3219	9640
Myron L Company	3823	D	760 438-2021	21622
N M Floor Coverings Inc	2426	F	760 931-8274	4086
Nanostone Water Inc	2295	F	442 232-2595	2961
Naturemaker Inc	3999	E	760 438-4244	24186
Nordson Asymtek Inc (HQ)	3823	C	760 431-1919	21626
Nordson California Inc	3695	D	760 918-8490	19875
Nordson Dage Inc	3844	E	440 985-4496	22937
Nordson Yestech Inc	3827	E	949 361-2714	22111
Nova Mobile Systems Inc	3678	F	800 734-9885	19405
Obalon Therapeutics Inc	3841	C	760 795-6558	22564
Oceanside Glasstile Company (PA)	3253	B	760 929-4000	10787
Ogio International Inc	3161	D	801 619-4100	10528
OH Juice Inc	2033	F	619 318-0207	838
Opotek Inc	3845	F	760 929-0770	23029
Ortho Organizers Inc	3843	C	760 448-8600	22897
Outdoor Lfstyle Collective LLC	2331	F	858 336-5580	3267
Outsol Inc	3088	F	760 415-8060	9908
Pacific Cnc Machine Co	3599	F	760 431-7558	16820
Palomar Casework Inc	2542	F	760 941-9860	5161
Palomar Display Products Inc	3679	F	760 931-3200	19680
Palomar Technologies Inc (PA)	3559	D	760 931-3600	15005
Peag LLC	3679	F	520 349-9371	19683
Peak Servo Corporation	3625	F	760 438-4986	17292
Phoenix Footwear Group Inc (PA)	3143	F	760 602-9688	10482
Pro-Spot International Inc	3699	F	760 407-1414	20048
Providien Injction Molding Inc	3089	D	760 931-1844	10316
Qualcomm Incorporated	3674	B	858 651-8481	19099
Qualigen Inc (PA)	3841	E	760 918-9165	21487
Quorex Pharm Inc (PA)	2834	F	760 602-1910	8354
Ra Medical Systems Inc	3841	D	760 804-1648	22595
Reflex Corporation	2399	E	760 931-9009	3960
Rf Surgical Systems LLC	3841	D	855 522-7027	22605
Richard Paola	2024	E	442 500-8231	691
Rockwell Collins Optronics Inc	3812	F	319 295-1000	21417
Ronatec C2c Inc	2899	F	760 476-1890	9303
Sabre Sciences Inc	2833	F	760 448-2750	7970
SC Bluwood Inc	2491	E	909 519-5470	4597
Scape Goat Ind	3949	F	760 931-1802	23648
SCI Instruments Inc (PA)	3826	F	760 634-3822	22014
Seaspine Inc	3842	D	760 727-8399	22808
Seaspine Orthopedics Corp (HQ)	3842	E	866 942-8698	22809
Sendx Medical Inc (DH)	3823	C	760 930-6300	21652
Sigma-Aldrich Corporation	2899	E	760 710-6213	9304
Silk Screen Shirts Inc	2261	E	760 233-3900	2894
Simply Automated Inc	3643	F	760 431-1200	17489
Skiva Graphics Screen Prtg Inc	2759	E	760 602-9124	7486
Smiths Medical Asd Inc	3841	C	760 602-4400	22625
Soil Retention Products Inc (PA)	3271	F	951 928-8477	10863
Spectrum Assembly Inc	3672	E	760 930-9000	18615
Spinergy Inc	3751	D	760 496-2121	21137
Spy Inc (PA)	3851	D	760 804-8420	23125
Standard Filter Corporation (PA)	3564	E	323 663-2184	15176
Sunex Inc (PA)	3827	F	760 597-2966	22139
Sunrise Medical Inc	3842	E	619 930-1500	22825
Synergeyes Inc (PA)	3851	D	760 476-9410	23128
Syntron Bioresearch Inc	2835	B	760 930-2200	8519
Systems Machines Automatio (PA)	3625	C	760 929-7575	17314
Taylor Made Golf Company Inc	3949	C	760 918-6000	23671

Mergent email: customerrelations@mergent.com

1358

2019 California
Manufacturers Register

(P-0000) Products & Services Section entry number
(PA)=Parent Co (HQ)=Headquarters (DH)=Div Headquarters

	SIC	EMP	PHONE	ENTRY #
Taylormade Golf Company Inc (HQ)	3949	B	877 860-8624	23672
Ten Enthusiast Network LLC	2721	C	760 722-7777	6267
Torrey Pines Scientific Inc	3821	F	760 930-9400	21495
Trade Printing Services LLC	2752	E	760 496-0230	7140
Turbo International	3462	F	760 476-1444	13115
Typehaus Inc	3572	F	760 334-3555	15619
United Orthopedic Group LLC	3841	F	760 729-8585	22662
Upper Deck Company	2741	C	800 873-7332	6613
Upper Deck Company LLC	2752	B	800 873-7332	7158
USAopoly Inc	3944	E	760 431-5910	23475
Vanguard Industries East Inc	2399	D	800 433-1334	3971
Vanguard Industries West Inc (PA)	2399	C	760 438-4437	3972
Vertiflex Inc	3845	E	442 325-5900	23065
Viasat Inc (PA)	3663	B	760 476-2200	18296
Xenonics Inc	3699	F	760 477-8900	20115
Xenonics Holdings Inc	3648	F	760 477-8900	17746
Zonson Company Inc	3949	E	760 597-0338	23696
Zuza	2759	E	760 438-9411	7547

CARMEL, CA - Monterey County

	SIC	EMP	PHONE	ENTRY #
Caffe Cardinale Cof Roasting	2095	F	831 626-2095	2334
Fresco Plastics Inc	3089	E	831 625-9877	10107

CARMEL VALLEY, CA - Monterey County

	SIC	EMP	PHONE	ENTRY #
Bernardus LLC (PA)	2084	E	831 659-1900	1657
Durney Winery Corporation	2084	F	831 659-2690	1738
Georis Winery	2084	F	831 659-1050	1780

CARMICHAEL, CA - Sacramento County

	SIC	EMP	PHONE	ENTRY #
Maxit Designs Inc	2253	F	916 489-1023	2849
Solarroofscom Inc	3433	F	916 481-7200	12089
Tm Noodle	2098	F	916 486-2579	2443

CARPINTERIA, CA - Santa Barbara County

	SIC	EMP	PHONE	ENTRY #
32 Bar Blues LLC	2389	F	805 962-6665	3635
Agilent Technologies Inc	3825	F	805 566-6655	21708
Applied Silicone Corporation	2869	D	805 525-5657	8979
Astro Aerospace	3812	F	805 684-6641	21262
Bega/Us Inc	3648	D	805 684-0533	17674
Channel Islands Surfboards Inc	3949	F	805 745-2823	23538
Clipper Windpower PLC	3511	A	805 690-3275	13993
Dac International Inc (PA)	3545	E	805 684-8307	14622
Development Assoc Contrls	3541	E	805 684-8307	14370
Ditec Co	3841	F	805 566-7800	22427
Dsy Educational Corporation	2399	F	805 684-8111	3943
Essex Electronics Inc	3674	F	805 684-7601	18833
Freudenberg Medical LLC (DH)	3842	B	805 684-3304	22736
Gigavac LLC	3625	F	805 684-8401	17273
H S N Consultants Inc	2721	F	805 684-8800	6175
Inhealth Technologies	3842	F	800 477-5969	22752
Island Brewing Co	2082	F	805 745-8272	1602
Lufft Usa Inc	3829	F	805 335-8500	22229
Nusil Technology LLC	2821	D	805 684-8780	7861
Nusil Technology LLC	3069	D	805 684-8780	9649
Rincon Engineering Corporation	3599	F	805 684-0935	16902
Supersprings International	3493	F	805 745-5553	13756
Te Connectivity Corporation	3625	C	805 684-4560	17315
Zarif Companies	2084	F	805 318-1800	2065
Zbe Inc	3625	E	805 576-1600	17326

CARSON, CA - Los Angeles County

	SIC	EMP	PHONE	ENTRY #
A & R Engineering Co Inc	3599	E	310 603-9060	16187
Adaptive Modular Solutions Inc	3448	D	310 299-7680	12910
Air Products and Chemicals Inc	2813	F	310 847-7300	7672
Alpha Wire Corporation	3357	A	310 639-9473	11642
American Consumer Products LLC	2899	E	310 443-3330	9219
Andeavor	1311	F	310 847-5705	22
Arctic Glacier USA Inc	2097	C	310 638-0321	2408
Avalon Glass & Mirror Company	3231	F	323 321-8806	10677
Beach Patrol Inc (HQ)	2339	F	310 522-2700	3383
Beato Inc	3161	F	310 637-1180	10516
Big Heart Pet Brands	2033	F	310 519-3791	789
Bolttech Mannings Inc	3546	D	310 604-9500	14700
BP West Coast Products LLC	1311	B	310 816-8787	31
Brentwood Originals Inc (PA)	2392	A	310 637-6804	3711
Cal-Coast Pkg & Crating Inc	2441	E	310 518-7215	4438
Cali-Fame Los Angeles Inc	2353	D	310 747-5263	3559
Cardic Machine Products Inc	3599	F	310 884-3400	16362
CCL Tube Inc (HQ)	3089	C	310 635-4444	10016
Cedarlane Natural Foods Inc (PA)	2038	F	310 886-7720	985
Chagall Design Limited	2389	F	310 537-9530	3648
Cmp Display Systems Inc	3089	D	805 499-3642	10028
Consolidated Container Co LLC	3085	D	310 952-8736	9796
Cosway Company Inc (PA)	2844	D	310 900-4100	8731
Dan-Loc Group LLC	3053	D	310 538-2822	9525
Dermalogica LLC (HQ)	2844	D	310 900-4000	8738
DMC Power Inc (PA)	3643	D	310 323-1616	17462

	SIC	EMP	PHONE	ENTRY #
Ducommun Aerostructures Inc	3724	E	310 513-7200	20648
Ducommun Labarge Tech Inc (HQ)	3728	C	310 513-7200	20803
Duro-Sense Corp	3823	E	310 533-6877	21574
Dynamex Corporation	2298	E	310 329-0399	2974
Elite 4 Print Inc	2752	E	310 366-1344	6806
Elite Color Technologies Inc	2759	F	310 324-3040	7310
Empire Container Corporation	2653	D	310 537-8190	5407
First Lithium LLC	3691	E	310 489-6266	19808
General Mills Inc	2026	E	310 605-6108	726
Generation Alpha Inc	3645	F	888 998-8881	17536
Giuliano-Pagano Corporation	2051	D	310 537-7700	1263
Global Billiard Mfg Co Inc	3949	E	310 764-5000	23572
Gms Molds (PA)	3544	F	310 684-1168	14522
Gordon Laboratories Inc	2844	C	310 327-5240	8756
Huck International Inc	3452	C	310 830-8200	13072
Hydroform USA Incorporated	3728	C	310 632-6353	20843
I & I Sports Supply Company (PA)	3949	E	310 715-6800	23588
Idea Tooling & Engineering Inc	3544	D	310 608-7488	14526
International Paper Company	2621	E	310 549-5525	5304
Jarden Corporation	3089	D	800 755-9520	10163
Jnj Operations LLC	3999	E	855 525-6545	24137
Johnson Laminating Coating Inc	3083	D	310 635-4929	9751
Js Apparel Inc	2329	D	310 631-6333	3167
Jvic Catalyst Services LLC	2819	E	310 327-0991	7783
Kts Kitchens Inc	2099	C	310 764-0850	2557
Leiner Health Products Inc (DH)	2834	A	631 200-2000	8255
Letterhead Factory Inc	2752	E	310 538-3321	6945
Lpj Aerospace LLC	3728	F	310 834-5700	20869
Mag Aerospace Industries Inc	3431	B	310 631-3800	12016
Magtek Inc	3674	F	562 631-8602	18979
Mars Medical Ride Corp	3711	F	310 518-1024	20156
Mechanized Engineering Systems	3537	F	310 830-9763	14337
Mestek Inc	3585	C	310 835-7500	15971
Monogram Systems	3728	F	801 400-7944	20891
Moreau Wetzel Engineering Co	3544	F	310 830-5479	14546
Natures Bounty Co	2833	F	310 952-7107	7956
Northrop Grumman Corporation	3812	A	310 764-3000	21363
Nu-Health California LLC	2033	F	800 806-0519	834
O W I Inc	3651	F	310 515-1900	17840
Oak-It Inc	2541	E	310 719-3999	5087
Off Dock USA Inc	3537	F	310 522-4400	14339
Pacific Toll Processing Inc	3312	F	310 952-4992	11409
Parter Medical Products Inc	3821	C	310 327-4417	21484
Pepsi-Cola Metro Btlg Co Inc	2086	A	310 327-4222	2168
Phillips 66	2911	D	310 522-9300	9351
Polyone Corporation	2821	D	310 513-7100	7871
Proma Inc	3843	E	310 327-0035	22902
Puritan Bakery Inc	2051	C	310 830-5451	1312
Quality Magnetics Corporation	3499	F	310 632-1941	13968
Quartic West Technologies	3695	F	909 202-7038	19878
Richandre Inc	2038	F	310 762-1560	1011
Sac-TEC Labs Inc (PA)	3674	E	310 375-5295	19134
Saybolt LP	1389	F	310 518-4400	269
Sazerac Company Inc	2085	E	310 604-8717	2076
Simpson Industries Inc	2834	D	310 605-1224	8382
Solid-Scope Machining Co Inc	3429	F	310 523-2366	11993
Stanford Mu Corporation	3769	E	310 605-2888	21197
Street Glow Inc	3647	D	310 631-1881	17665
Strike Technology Inc	3679	E	562 437-3428	19738
Sumi Printing & Binding Inc	2752	E	310 769-1600	7122
Tnp Instruments Inc	3679	F	310 532-2222	19764
Trane US Inc	3585	D	310 971-4555	15989
Universal Plant Svcs Cal Inc (HQ)	3599	F	310 618-1600	17025
Wavenet Inc	3315	D	310 885-4200	11465
Weber Printing Company Inc	2752	E	310 639-5064	7175
Western Combustion Engrg Inc	3443	F	310 834-9389	12442
Yoplait U S A Inc	2026	A	310 632-9502	742
Yun Industrial Co Ltd	3672	E	310 715-1898	18656
Zodiac WATer&waste Aero System	3728	E	310 884-7000	20981

CARUTHERS, CA - Fresno County

	SIC	EMP	PHONE	ENTRY #
Batth Dehydrator LLC	2034	E	559 864-3501	876
Caruthers Raisin Pkg Co Inc (PA)	2034	D	559 864-9448	879
Mid Valley Mfg Inc	3599	F	559 864-9441	16744

CASTAIC, CA - Los Angeles County

	SIC	EMP	PHONE	ENTRY #
Castaic Clay Products LLC	3251	D	661 259-3066	10774
Castaic Lake R V Park Inc	2451	F	661 257-3340	4546
Castaic Truck Stop Inc	2911	F	661 295-1374	9324
Clay Castaic Manufacturing Co	3251	D	661 259-3066	10775
Nicole Fullerton	2389	F	661 257-0406	3673
So Cal Tractor Sales Co Inc	7692	F	818 252-1900	25435

CASTRO VALLEY, CA - Alameda County

	SIC	EMP	PHONE	ENTRY #
Jack Brain and Associates Inc	2741	F	510 889-1360	6505
Twin Design Co LLC	3569	F	510 329-4991	15369

GEOGRAPHIC

	SIC	EMP	PHONE	ENTRY #

CASTROVILLE, CA - Monterey County

	SIC	EMP	PHONE	ENTRY #
American Bottling Company	2086	D	831 632-0777	2092
Bimbo Bakeries Usa Inc	2051	E	831 633-7100	1201
California New Foods LLC	2099	E	831 444-1872	2480
Claudios Specialty Breads	2051	F	831 633-5051	1224
Corbin Pacific Inc	3751	E	408 633-2500	21098
Farmer Bros Co	2095	F	831 633-6521	2344
Fujifilm Ultra Pure Sltons Inc (DH)	2899	E	831 632-2120	9252
Ron Witherspoon Inc	3599	D	831 633-3568	16914
Seven Up Btlg Co San Francisco	2086	E	831 632-0777	2220

CATHEDRAL CITY, CA - Riverside County

	SIC	EMP	PHONE	ENTRY #
Cushion Works	2392	F	760 321-7808	3716

CAZADERO, CA - Sonoma County

	SIC	EMP	PHONE	ENTRY #
Dharma Mudranalaya (PA)	2731	E	707 847-3380	6335
Flowers Vineyard & Winery LLC	2084	F	707 847-3661	1766
Hagist Welding	7692	F	707 847-3362	25407

CERES, CA - Stanislaus County

	SIC	EMP	PHONE	ENTRY #
Aemetis Advnced Fels Keyes Inc	2869	E	209 632-4511	8968
B & H Manufacturing Co Inc (PA)	3565	C	209 537-5785	15196
Barrel Ten Qarter Cir Land Inc (HQ)	2084	E	707 258-0550	1653
Certified Stainless Svc Inc (PA)	3443	C	209 537-4747	12372
Classic Wine Vinegar Co Inc	2099	F	209 538-7600	2491
Enova Engineering LLC (PA)	3644	F	209 538-3313	17513
McMillan - Hendryx Inc	3053	F	209 538-2300	9543
Prompt Precision Metals Inc	3444	D	209 531-1210	12725
Robert R Wix Inc (PA)	2759	F	209 537-4561	7472
Seed Factory Northwest Inc (PA)	2048	E	209 634-8522	1164
Stiles Custom Metal Inc	3442	D	209 538-3667	12349
Stuart David Inc (PA)	2511	E	209 537-7449	4740
US Dies Inc (PA)	3544	E	209 664-1402	14585
Wildlife Fur Dressing Inc	3111	F	209 538-2901	10468

CERRITOS, CA - Los Angeles County

	SIC	EMP	PHONE	ENTRY #
A & H Engineering & Mfg Inc	3599	E	562 623-9717	16184
AB Mauri Food Inc	2099	F	562 483-4619	2446
Advanced Uv Inc	3589	E	562 407-0299	16007
Alpha Dental of Utah Inc	3843	E	562 467-7759	22855
Alumflam North America	3471	E	562 926-9520	13324
American Garment Company	2389	F	562 483-8300	3640
American Non Stop Label Corp	2759	F	562 921-9437	7234
Apperson Inc (PA)	2761	D	562 356-3333	7548
ARI Industries Inc	3585	D	714 993-3700	15938
Artistic Coverings Inc	3086	E	562 404-9343	9818
Award Packaging Spc Corp	2653	E	323 727-1200	5385
Bermingham Controls Inc A (PA)	3491	E	562 860-0463	13707
Best Label Company Inc (PA)	2759	C	562 926-1452	7248
Better Beverages Inc (PA)	2087	E	562 924-8321	2244
Big 5 Electronics Inc	3651	E	562 941-4669	17775
Blairs Metal Polsg Pltg Co Inc	3471	E	562 860-7106	13348
Calnetix Inc (PA)	3621	C	562 293-1660	17183
Calnetix Technologies LLC	3621	D	562 293-1660	17184
Captek Softgel Intl Inc (PA)	2077	C	562 921-9511	1523
Century Pattern Co Inc	3543	F	562 402-1707	14464
Clio Inc	3495	E	562 926-3724	13792
Compressed Air Concepts	3563	E	310 537-1350	15121
David L Long	2431	F	562 809-5740	4138
Dec Fabricators Inc	3499	F	562 403-3626	13933
Dji Service LLC	3728	F	818 235-0788	20795
Docupak Inc	2782	E	714 670-7944	7581
Dool Fna Inc	2221	C	562 483-4100	2776
Dr J Skinclinic Inc	2834	F	714 282-2290	8143
Eide Industries Inc	2394	D	562 402-8335	3786
Encore Seating Inc	2522	E	562 926-1969	4983
Foam Molders and Specialties (PA)	3086	D	562 924-7757	9847
Foam Molders and Specialties	3086	E	562 924-7757	9848
Ftg Inc (PA)	3714	E	562 865-9200	20342
Funtastic Factory Inc	3599	E	562 777-1140	16517
International Coatings Co Inc (PA)	2891	E	562 926-1010	9152
International Paper Company	2621	F	562 404-1856	5297
IPC Cal Flex Inc	3672	E	714 952-0373	18508
Ips Industries Inc	3089	D	562 623-2555	10156
J Summitt Inc	2431	E	562 236-5744	4171
Kaltec Electronics Inc (PA)	3861	F	813 888-9555	23172
LA Triumph Inc	2326	E	562 404-7657	3110
Lees Precision Tooling	3599	F	562 926-1302	16684
Madison Industries (HQ)	3448	E	323 583-4061	12942
Madison Industries Inc Arizona	3441	E	602 252-3083	12199
Molino Company	2752	D	323 726-1000	6979
Mpd Holdings Inc	3577	F	562 777-1051	15810
Ncla Inc	2679	E	562 926-6252	5718
North America Pwr & Infra	3241	E	562 403-4337	10767
Olea Kiosks Inc	3577	E	562 924-2644	15814
Pacific Die Cast Inc	3544	E	562 407-1390	14555

	SIC	EMP	PHONE	ENTRY #
Pankl Aerospace Systems	3369	D	562 207-6300	11780
Para Plate & Plastics Co Inc	3555	E	562 404-3434	14823
Parts Expediting and Dist Co	3714	E	562 944-3199	20418
Precision Metal Crafts	3441	E	562 468-7080	12230
Printing Management Associates (PA)	2752	E	562 407-9977	7047
Q Trade International Corp (PA)	2099	E	949 766-0070	2645
Quad/Graphics Inc	2752	E	310 751-3900	7062
Refrigerator Manufacters Inc (PA)	3632	E	562 926-2006	17382
Refrigerator Manufacturers LLC	3585	E	562 926-2006	15977
Repose Corp	3634	E	562 921-9299	17403
Sealed Air Corporation	2673	E	201 791-7600	5622
Sedenquist-Fraser Entps Inc	3714	E	562 924-5763	20445
T Hasegawa USA Inc (HQ)	2087	E	714 522-1900	2284
Thermal Engrg Intl USA Inc (HQ)	3443	C	323 726-0641	12433
True Vision Displays Inc	3679	F	562 407-0630	19773
Twin Eagles Inc	3631	D	562 802-3488	17378
UFO Designs	3714	E	562 924-5763	20473
US Dental Inc	3843	E	562 404-3500	22920
Villa Furniture Mfg Co	2531	C	714 535-7272	5031
Vycon Inc	3691	D	562 282-5500	19818
WCP Inc	3089	D	562 860-9040	10436
West Coast Switchgear (HQ)	3613	E	562 802-3441	17172
Winning Laboratories Inc	2833	F	562 921-6880	7983
XI Dynamics Inc	7372	E	562 916-1402	25363

CHATSWORTH, CA - Los Angeles County

	SIC	EMP	PHONE	ENTRY #
A & S Mold & Die Corp	3089	D	818 341-5393	9915
A B C Plastics Inc	3083	F	818 775-0065	9745
A F B Systems Inc	3724	F	818 775-0151	20638
A H Systems Inc	3825	F	818 998-0223	21699
Absolute Machining	3441	F	818 700-7367	12100
Academic Ch Choir Gwns Mfg Inc	2389	F	818 886-8697	3636
Acuity Brands Lighting Inc	3646	E	818 576-9774	17578
Advanced Cosmetic RES Labs Inc	3999	E	818 709-9945	24025
Aei Manufacturing Inc	3643	E	818 407-5400	17439
Aero Mechanism Precision Inc	3599	E	818 886-1855	16238
Aeroantenna Technology Inc	3812	C	818 993-3842	21252
Aerojet Rocketdyne De Inc	2869	C	818 586-1000	8971
Aitech Defense Systems Inc	3699	E	818 700-2000	19902
Aitech Rugged Group Inc (PA)	3699	E	818 700-2000	19903
Alan Hamilton Industries	2752	D	818 885-5121	6645
Alatus Aerosystems	3728	D	626 498-7376	20731
Align Aerospace Holding Inc (DH)	3324	F	818 727-7800	11506
Align Aerospace LLC (DH)	3728	E	818 727-7800	20732
Alliance Metal Products Inc	3444	C	818 709-1204	12473
Almack Liners Inc	2335	E	818 718-5878	3291
Andrews Powder Coating Inc	3479	E	818 700-1030	13551
Ansell Healthcare Products LLC	3841	E	205 423-8770	22336
Ansell Sndel Med Solutions LLC	3842	E	818 534-2500	22700
Apparel Prod Svcs Globl LLC	2339	E	818 700-3700	3375
Aquasyn LLC	3491	F	818 350-0423	13701
Aram Precision Tool Die Inc	3599	F	818 998-1000	16276
Astrodyne Group Inc (PA)	3599	E	818 709-5440	16287
Automoco LLC	3714	D	707 544-4761	20262
Avet Industries Inc	3949	F	818 576-9895	23509
Avn Media Network Inc	2731	E	818 718-5788	6310
Aware Products Inc	2844	E	818 206-6700	8698
Aware Products LLC	2844	C	818 206-6700	8699
Axess Products Corp	3651	F	818 785-4000	17770
Barrys Printing Inc	2752	E	818 998-8600	6685
BDR Industries Inc	3577	E	818 341-2112	15679
Bey-Berk International (PA)	3499	E	818 773-7534	13923
Bio-Nutraceuticals Inc	2834	E	818 727-0246	8075
Bizinkcom LLC	2759	E	818 676-0766	7249
Botanicalabs Inc	2844	E	818 466-5639	8708
Bragstr LLC	7372	E	818 917-0312	24446
Breakaway Press Inc	2759	E	818 727-7388	7256
Bvp Designs Inc	3581	F	818 280-2900	15919
Cac Fabrication	3441	E	818 882-2626	12125
California Deluxe Window Indus (PA)	2431	E	818 349-5566	4116
California Resources Corp (PA)	1382	D	888 848-4754	128
Canoga Perkins Corporation (HQ)	3669	D	818 718-6300	18315
Cdc Data LLC	3577	F	818 350-5070	15702
Celesco Transducer Products	3679	E	818 701-2701	19482
Celltron Inc	3679	F	620 783-1333	19484
Challenge Publications Inc	2721	E	818 700-6868	6127
Chatsworth Products Inc	3499	C	818 882-8595	13930
Chemsil Silicones Inc	2869	E	818 700-0302	8996
Cine Mechanics Inc	3861	E	818 701-7944	23145
Ciphertex LLC	3577	F	818 773-8989	15703
Classic Cosmetics Inc (PA)	2844	C	818 773-9042	8715
Cliffdale LLC	3761	F	818 885-0300	21158
Cliffdale Manufacturing LLC	3769	F	818 341-3344	21188
Colbrit Manufacturing Co Inc	3544	E	818 709-3608	14498
Commercial Clear Print Inc	2752	F	818 709-1220	6748
Cosmojet Inc	2754	F	818 773-6544	7199

2019 California
Manufacturers Register

(P-0000) Products & Services Section entry number
(PA)=Parent Co (HQ)=Headquarters (DH)=Div Headquarters

Company	SIC	EMP	PHONE	ENTRY #
Cott Manufacturing Company	3669	E	818 988-9500	18317
CRC Services LLC	1311	F	888 848-4754	53
Custom Control Sensors LLC (PA)	3613	C	818 341-4610	17138
Custom Design Iron Works Inc	3364	F	818 700-9182	11711
Cyron Inc	3648	F	818 772-1900	17682
Datadirect Networks Inc (PA)	3572	C	818 700-7600	15528
Dcx-Chol Enterprises Inc	3671	D	310 516-1692	18388
Dcx-Chol Enterprises Inc	3671	E	310 715-6946	18391
Delta Fabrication Inc	3444	D	818 407-4000	12557
Delta Hi-Tech	3599	C	818 407-4000	16428
Delta Tau Data Systems Inc Cal (HQ)	3569	C	818 998-2095	15314
Delta Tau International Inc	3569	F	818 998-2095	15315
DOT Copy Inc	2752	E	818 341-6666	6792
Double K Industries Inc	3523	E	818 772-2887	14063
Dream Products Incorporated	3171	E	818 773-4233	10546
Duclos Lenses	3089	F	818 773-0600	10079
Dwa Alminum Composites USA Inc	3365	E	818 998-1504	11739
Dynamic Cabinet Designs Inc	2434	E	818 700-1658	4296
Dynamic Sciences Intl Inc	3663	E	818 226-6262	18092
Dytran Instruments Inc	3679	E	818 700-7818	19520
Electro Adapter Inc	3643	C	818 998-1198	17463
Enormarel Inc	2844	F	818 882-4666	8746
Envy Medical Inc (PA)	2834	F	818 874-2700	8148
Epic Technologies LLC (HQ)	3661	C	818 734-6500	17945
Epic Technologies LLC	3577	B	423 461-2020	15738
Erbaviva Inc	2833	E	818 998-7112	7937
Euro Machine Inc	3599	F	818 998-5198	16479
Exact Cnc Industries Inc	3469	F	818 527-1908	13203
Excel Manufacturing Inc	3599	E	661 257-1900	16483
Excellence Opto Inc	3669	E	818 674-1921	18323
Execuprint Inc	2759	F	818 993-8184	7314
Executive Bus Solutions Inc	3555	F	805 499-3290	14807
Featherock Inc (PA)	1499	F	818 882-3888	411
Federal Manufacturing Corp	3452	F	818 341-9825	13069
Firan Tech Group USA Corp (HQ)	3812	F	818 407-4024	21294
Flowmetrics Inc	3823	E	818 407-3420	21583
Fluid Line Technology Corp	3841	E	818 998-8848	22451
Ftg Aerospace Inc (DH)	3364	F	818 407-4024	11715
Ftg Circuits Inc (DH)	3672	D	818 407-4024	18489
Gadia Polythylene Supplies Inc	3089	F	818 775-0096	10112
Ganesh Industries LLC	3549	F	818 349-9166	14751
General Ribbon Corp	3955	B	818 709-1234	23729
Globalvision Systems Inc	3572	F	888 227-7967	15542
Golden Bolt LLC	3452	F	818 626-8261	13070
Graphic Research Inc	3672	E	818 886-7340	18498
Graphics Factory Inc	2759	F	818 727-9040	7333
Gsp Acquisition Corporation	3471	E	310 532-9430	13420
Hallmark Lighting LLC	3646	D	818 885-5010	17613
Hart Electronic Assembly Inc	3679	D	818 709-2761	19562
Heritage Cabinet Co Inc	2541	F	818 786-4900	5069
Hitachi High-Technologies	3826	A	818 280-0745	21967
Huntco Industries LLC	3999	F	818 700-1600	24124
Hydraulics International Inc (PA)	3728	B	818 998-1231	20840
Hydraulics International Inc	3728	D	818 998-1236	20841
Hydromach Inc	3769	F	818 341-0915	21193
Imatte Inc	3651	F	818 993-8007	17816
Imperial Enterprises Inc	3229	E	818 886-5028	10648
Impress Communications Inc	2752	D	818 701-8800	6877
Innovative Cosmetic Labs Inc	2844	F	818 349-1121	8770
Intelligent Cmpt Solutions Inc (PA)	3825	E	818 998-5805	21775
International Precision Inc	3599	F	818 882-3933	16590
Invelop Inc	3523	E	818 772-2887	14071
J & J Products Inc	3499	F	818 998-4250	13950
Jackson Engineering Company	3612	F	818 886-9567	17102
Jim James Enterprises Inc	3444	F	818 772-8595	12631
Jmr Electronics Inc	3572	F	818 993-4801	15562
John List Corporation	3547	E	818 882-7848	14716
Just Cellular Inc	3663	E	818 701-3039	18139
Keene Engineering Inc (PA)	3561	F	818 485-2681	15081
Keith E Archambeau Sr Inc	3444	E	818 718-6110	12639
Kerning Data Systems Inc	3555	F	818 882-8712	14815
Key Item Sales Inc	3961	F	818 885-0928	23750
Key Items Sales Inc	3861	F	818 885-0586	23173
Labeling Hurst Systems LLC	2672	F	818 701-0710	5566
Lasalle Intl Hldings Group Inc	3533	E	818 233-8000	14232
Lca Promotions Inc	2759	E	818 773-9170	7383
Le Hung Tuan	3599	F	818 700-1008	16683
Lehrer Brllnprfktion Werks Inc (PA)	3089	E	818 407-1890	10189
Lf Illumination LLC	3646	D	818 885-1335	17626
Lightcraft Outdoor Environmnts	3645	F	818 349-2663	17542
Lighting Control & Design Inc (HQ)	3648	E	323 226-0000	17708
Line One Laboratories Inc USA	3069	F	818 886-2288	9633
Litepanels Inc	3641	F	818 752-7009	17431
Logicube Inc (PA)	3577	E	818 700-8488	15792
Logistical Support LLC	3724	C	818 341-3344	20668
Loungefly LLC	3961	E	818 718-5600	23753
Magic Gumball International	2064	E	818 716-1888	1440
Mat Mat	3411	F	818 678-9392	11861
Materials Development Corp (PA)	3825	F	818 700-8290	21801
Maxwell Alarm Screen Mfg Inc	3993	E	818 773-5533	23921
MBK Enterprises Inc	3842	E	818 998-1477	22767
Measurement Specialties Inc	3829	D	818 701-2750	22231
Mercury Magnetics Inc	3677	E	818 998-7791	19346
Metal Chem Inc	3471	E	818 727-9951	13452
Metal Improvement Company LLC	3398	D	818 407-6280	11821
Micro Plastics Inc	3643	E	818 882-0244	17484
Mist Incorporated	3545	E	818 678-5619	14653
Molnar Engineering Inc	3599	E	818 734-5685	16763
Mono Engineering Corp	3599	E	818 772-4998	16765
Moog Inc	3812	C	818 341-5156	21350
Mrv Communications Inc (PA)	3674	C	818 773-0900	19028
Narcotics Anonymous World Serv	2731	E	818 773-9999	6365
Natel Engineering Company Inc (PA)	3674	C	818 734-6523	19031
Natel Engineering Company Inc	3672	E	818 734-6552	18539
Natrol LLC (DH)	2834	C	818 739-6000	8291
Networks Electronic Co LLC	3489	E	818 341-0440	13695
Neutraderm Inc	2844	E	818 534-3190	8803
Newage Pavilions LLC	3699	F	818 701-9600	20028
Norsal Printing Inc	2752	F	818 886-4164	6998
Northrdge Tr-Mdlity Imging Inc	3821	F	818 709-2468	21483
Northrop Grumman Corporation	3812	A	818 715-3264	21358
Nydr Holdings Inc	2099	F	818 626-8174	2626
O & S Precision Inc	3599	F	818 718-8876	16800
Oncore Manufacturing Svcs Inc	3672	C	510 360-2222	18550
Owens Printing Co	2752	E	818 773-8900	7008
Pacific Air Industries Inc	3728	E	310 829-4345	20901
Pacific Coast Lighting Inc (PA)	3648	C	818 886-9751	17722
Pacific Precision Labs Inc	3829	E	818 700-8977	22248
Pacoima Clothing LLC	2341	E	818 897-8009	3542
Papco Screw Products Inc	3541	F	818 341-2266	14398
Paul Silver Enterprises Inc	2752	F	818 998-9900	7019
Pencil Grip Inc (PA)	2678	C	310 315-3545	5688
Perez Severino	3499	F	818 701-1522	13963
Pioneer Photo Albums Inc (PA)	2782	C	818 882-2161	7583
Planet Green Cartridges Inc	3955	D	818 725-2596	23736
Plateronics Processing Inc	3471	E	818 341-2191	13476
Pope Plastics Inc	3544	E	818 701-1850	14560
Printing Safari Co	2752	F	818 709-3752	7049
Prisha Cosmetics Inc	2844	F	818 773-8784	8825
Quality Fabrication	3444	D	818 407-5015	12727
Racaar Circuit Industries Inc	3672	E	818 998-7566	18578
Rapid Manufacturing (PA)	3999	F	818 899-4377	24219
Renau Corporation	3823	E	818 341-1994	21644
Resmed Motor Technologies Inc	3621	C	818 428-6400	17219
RJA Industries Inc	3679	E	818 998-5124	19708
Roberts Tool Company Inc (PA)	3593	C	818 341-3344	16159
Roy & Val Tool Grinding Inc	3599	F	818 341-2434	16918
RPS Inc	3496	E	818 350-8088	13852
Rs Machining Co Inc	3599	F	818 718-6400	16921
S2k Graphics Inc	3993	E	818 885-3900	23954
Samuel Raoof	2844	E	818 534-3180	8832
SARR Industries Inc	3599	F	818 998-7735	16929
Schea Holdings Inc	3993	E	818 888-3818	23959
Sega Holdings USA Inc (DH)	3999	C	415 701-6000	24237
Selane Products Inc (PA)	3843	D	818 998-7460	22909
Semco Aerospace	2394	F	818 678-9381	3810
Sensor Systems Inc	3812	B	818 341-5366	21429
Soundcraft Inc	3699	E	818 882-0020	20077
Strategic Distribution L P	2326	C	818 671-2100	3123
Strategic Partners Inc (PA)	3143	C	818 671-2100	10491
Teledyne Instruments Inc	3826	E	818 882-7266	22027
Teledyne Risi Inc	3724	E	818 718-6640	20681
Telemtry Cmmnctons Systems Inc	3663	E	818 718-6248	18279
Tetracam Inc	3861	F	818 718-2119	23202
Thibiant International Inc	2844	B	818 709-1345	8853
Tig/M LLC	3535	E	818 709-8500	14291
Torrance Precision Machining	3599	F	818 709-7838	17004
Toye Corporation	3577	E	818 882-4000	15873
Trident Diving Equipment	3949	E	818 998-7518	23676
Truly Green Solutions LLC	3648	E	818 206-4404	17741
Ultimatte Corporation	3663	E	818 993-8007	18294
Underwraps Costume Corporation	2389	F	818 349-5300	3685
United Precision Corp	3495	F	818 576-9540	13806
United States Pumice Company (PA)	1499	F	818 882-0300	419
Venstar Inc	3585	F	818 341-8760	15998
Veratex Inc (PA)	2211	C	818 994-6487	2767
Verdugo Tool & Engrg Co Inc	3469	F	818 998-1101	13293
Visible Graphics Inc	3993	F	818 787-0477	23998
Vmc Holdings Group Corp	3571	E	818 993-1466	15503
Wallace E Miller Inc	3599	F	818 998-0444	17049

G E O G R A P H I C

Company	SIC	EMP	PHONE	ENTRY #
Warrens Department Store Inc	2311	E	888 577-2735	3048
We Imagine Inc	3672	D	818 709-0064	18650
We The Pie People LLC	2024	E	818 349-1880	705
West Coast Business Prtrs Inc	2752	F	818 709-4980	7178
West Valley Plating Inc	3471	E	818 709-1684	13534
Woodpecker Cabinet Inc	2434	E	310 404-4805	4372
Worldwide Gaming Systems Corp	3944	E	818 678-9150	23480
Xceliron Corp	3545	F	818 700-8404	14696
Y Nissim Inc	3579	E	818 718-9024	15917

CHERRY VALLEY, CA - Riverside County

Company	SIC	EMP	PHONE	ENTRY #
Cherry Valley Sheet Metal	3523	F	951 845-1578	14053

CHESTER, CA - Plumas County

Company	SIC	EMP	PHONE	ENTRY #
Collins Pine Company	2421	B	530 258-2111	4034
Sierra Cascade Aggregate & Asp	1442	F	530 258-4555	381

CHICO, CA - Butte County

Company	SIC	EMP	PHONE	ENTRY #
2xwireless Inc	3663	D	877 581-8002	18012
A & A Ready Mixed Concrete Inc	3273	E	530 342-5989	11026
Agra Trading LLC	2873	F	530 894-1782	9056
Bertagna Orchards Inc	2084	E	530 343-8014	1658
Boards On Nord Inc	3949	F	530 513-3922	23525
Cal Traders	2068	F	530 566-1405	1484
California Olive Ranch Inc (PA)	2079	E	530 846-8000	1536
Chico Community Publishing (PA)	2711	D	530 894-2300	5797
Chico Custom Counter	2541	F	530 894-8123	5047
Chicoeco Inc	2393	E	530 342-4426	3761
Dan M Swofford	2721	F	530 343-9994	6142
Enviro-Commercial Sweeping	3991	F	408 920-0274	23790
Fafco Inc (PA)	3433	E	530 332-2100	12063
Fanno Saw Works	3425	F	530 895-1762	11918
Farmer Bros Co	2095	F	530 343-3165	2346
Gatehouse Media LLC	2711	D	530 891-1234	5859
Graphic Fox Inc	2752	F	530 895-1359	6838
Haemonetics Corporation	3841	B	530 774-2081	22464
Hcp Industries Inc	3261	F	530 899-5591	10805
Hupp Signs & Lighting Inc	3993	E	530 345-7078	23894
Industrial Power Products	3599	F	530 893-0584	16580
Infofax Inc	2721	F	530 895-0431	6191
Johnson Controls	3669	F	530 893-0110	18335
Joy Signal Technology LLC	3643	E	530 891-3551	17476
Keurig Dr Pepper Inc	2086	F	530 893-4501	2143
Klean Kanteen Inc	3411	E	530 592-4552	11860
Lares Research	3843	E	530 345-1767	22891
Lifetouch Nat Schl Studios Inc	2782	D	530 345-3993	7582
Linkus Corp	3663	F	530 342-0738	18166
Mabrey Products Inc	2431	F	530 895-3799	4186
Mathews Readymix Inc	3273	F	530 893-8856	11141
Matrix Logic Corporation	7372	F	415 893-9897	24886
Mobile Mini Inc	3448	E	530 345-7645	12946
Ms Aerospace Materials LLC	3728	F	323 813-4105	20892
Nature Zone Pet Products	3999	E	530 343-5199	24185
North Valley Rain Gutters	3444	F	530 894-3347	12694
Oogolow Enterprises	2099	F	530 899-9927	2629
Orient & Flume Art Glass Co	3229	E	530 893-0373	10663
Pacific West Forest Products	3449	E	530 899-7313	12989
Progressive Woodwork	2434	F	530 343-2211	4336
Quadco Printing Inc	2752	F	530 894-4061	7067
Quality Circle Institute Inc	2721	F	530 893-4095	6240
Rescue 42 Inc	3569	F	530 891-3473	15356
Selken Enterprises Inc	7692	F	530 891-4200	25433
Seven-Up RC of Chico	2086	E	530 893-4501	2222
Sierra Nevada Brewing Co (PA)	2082	B	530 590-5473	1623
Smucker Natural Foods Inc (HQ)	2086	C	530 899-5000	2225
Solo Steel Erectors Inc	3448	F	530 893-2293	12961
Square Deal Mattress Factory	2515	E	530 342-2510	4890
Srl Apparel Inc	2261	E	530 898-9525	2895
Synthesis	2721	E	530 899-7708	6265
Thomas Manufacturing Co LLC	7692	E	530 893-8940	25442
Thomas Welding & Mch Sp Inc	7692	E	530 893-8940	25443
Travidia Inc (PA)	7372	C	530 343-6400	25293
Truroots Inc	2099	F	925 218-2205	2694
Ultramar Inc	2911	E	530 345-7901	9369
United States Thermoelectric	3826	E	530 345-8000	22046
Videomaker Inc	2721	F	530 891-8410	6284
Weiss-Mcnair LLC (DH)	3523	D	530 891-6214	14123
Wizard Graphics Inc	2759	E	530 893-3636	7544
Wizard Manufacturing Inc	2068	F	530 342-1861	1506
Woof & Poof Inc	2392	E	530 895-0693	3757
Wrex Products Inc Chico	3089	D	530 895-3838	10452

CHILCOOT, CA - Plumas County

Company	SIC	EMP	PHONE	ENTRY #
Pau Hana Group LLC	3429	F	530 993-6800	11983

CHINO, CA - San Bernardino County

Company	SIC	EMP	PHONE	ENTRY #
AC Air Technology Inc	3465	F	855 884-7222	13135

Company	SIC	EMP	PHONE	ENTRY #
Acorn-Gencon Plastics LLC	3089	D	909 591-8461	9922
Acornvac Inc	3432	E	909 902-1141	12019
Action Graphic Arts Inc	2796	F	626 443-3113	7638
Air Craftors Engineering Inc	3599	F	909 900-0635	16246
Alaco Ladder Company	2499	E	909 591-7561	4604
Albers Mfg Co Inc (PA)	3523	E	909 597-5537	14039
All Stars Packaging Inc	2631	F	626 664-3797	5339
Alston Tascom Inc	3661	E	909 517-3660	17920
Alvarado Manufacturing Co Inc	3829	D	909 591-8431	22160
Amcor Rigid Plastics Usa LLC	3089	D	520 746-0737	9938
Amcor Rigid Plastics Usa LLC	3085	C	909 517-2700	9792
American Custom Golf Cars Inc	3711	F	909 597-2885	20125
American Pride Inc	3161	E	909 591-7688	10513
American SD Power Inc	3621	E	909 947-0673	17179
Anthony California Inc (PA)	3645	E	909 627-0351	17524
Apex Digital Inc	3645	F	909 923-8686	17525
Aranda Tooling Inc	3599	D	714 379-6565	16277
Arnold-Gonsalves Engrg Inc	3599	F	909 465-1579	16282
Artiva USA Inc (PA)	3645	E	909 628-1388	17528
Asrock America Inc	3672	E	909 590-8308	18427
B E & P Enterprises LLC (PA)	2499	E	909 591-7561	4607
Balaji Trading Inc	3661	D	909 444-7999	17925
Base Lite Corporation	3645	E	909 444-2776	17530
Beckman Coulter Inc	3826	D	909 597-3967	21908
Berry Global Inc	3089	C	909 465-9055	9978
Bill Wood Lathing	3496	E	909 628-1733	13812
Brad Barry Company Ltd	2095	E	909 591-9493	2330
Bright Shark Powder Coating	3479	F	909 591-1385	13561
Bti Aerospace & Electronics	3599	E	909 465-1569	16335
C & M Spring & Engineering Co	3495	E	909 597-2030	13791
C B Machine Products Inc	3599	F	909 517-1828	16345
Cal-India Foods International	2869	E	909 613-1660	8991
Capital Technology Inc	3634	F	909 293-8887	17388
CG Motor Sports Inc	3089	F	909 628-1440	10021
Champion Pblications Chino Inc	2711	E	909 628-5501	5796
Chemcor Chemical Corporation	2842	F	909 590-7234	8630
Chino Ice Service LLC	2097	E	909 628-2105	2409
Churchill Aerospace LLC	3546	C	909 266-3116	14702
Clariant Plas Coatings USA Inc	2869	F	909 606-1325	8999
Closetmaid Corporation	3496	F	909 590-4444	13819
Consolidated Container Co LP	3089	E	909 590-7334	10039
Consolidated Geoscience Inc	1382	F	909 393-9700	129
Corona Millworks Company (PA)	2434	D	909 606-3288	4288
CPI Advanced Inc	3612	C	909 597-5533	17085
Craneveyor Corp	3446	E	909 627-6801	12846
Custom Source Design Inc	3441	E	909 597-5221	12146
Dare Lithoworks Inc	2752	F	213 250-9062	6778
Delta Manufacturing Inc	3599	F	909 590-4563	16429
Diamond Wipes Intl Inc (PA)	2844	D	909 230-9888	8740
Dick Farrell Industries Inc	3567	F	909 613-9424	15257
Dupree Inc	3452	F	909 597-4889	13067
Dvtech Solution Corp	3613	F	909 308-0358	17142
E S M Plastics Inc	3599	F	909 591-7658	16460
E W Smith Chemical Co	2899	F	909 590-9717	9244
Eep Holdings LLC (PA)	3089	F	909 597-7861	10089
Enersys	3691	D	909 464-8251	19804
Exhaust Gas Technologies Inc	3714	F	909 548-8100	20329
Factory Reproductions	3714	F	909 590-5252	20331
Fenchem Inc (HQ)	2844	F	909 597-8880	8748
Ferco Color Inc	2821	E	909 548-2092	7837
Flexcon Company Inc	3081	E	909 465-0408	9708
Fsp Group USA Corp	3677	F	909 606-0960	19338
General Photonics Corp	3661	E	909 590-5473	17953
Gianno Co Ltd	2331	F	909 628-6928	3237
Globe Plastics Inc	3089	E	909 464-1520	10121
Golden Gate Hosiery Inc	2252	E	909 464-0805	2812
Gro-Power Inc	2873	E	909 393-5204	9061
H P Group	3999	F	909 364-1069	24115
H2 Environmental	3292	E	909 628-0369	11311
Hanson Truss Inc (PA)	2439	C	909 591-9256	4408
Hasbro Inc	3944	B	909 393-3248	23428
Hasco Fabrication Inc	3565	F	909 627-0326	15209
Health Plus Inc	2834	E	909 627-9393	8206
Hi-Lite Manufacturing Co Inc	3646	D	909 465-1999	17616
Hill Phoenix Inc	3585	E	909 592-8830	15960
HSG Manufacturing Inc	3469	F	909 902-5915	13221
Ht Multinational Inc	3714	F	626 964-2686	20366
Hua Rong International Corp	3799	F	909 591-8800	21232
Hussmann Corporation	3585	B	909 590-4910	15961
Hyponex Corporation	2873	E	909 597-2811	9062
Hyx Tech Corp	2759	F	951 907-3386	7345
Impact Printing & Graphics	2759	E	909 614-1678	7351
Imperial Rubber Products Inc	3555	E	909 393-0528	14813
Ingersoll Rand Indus Refrig	3131	F	909 477-2037	10473
Inter Packing Inc	3086	E	909 465-5555	9866

Mergent email: customerrelations@mergent.com
1362

2019 California
Manufacturers Register

(P-0000) Products & Services Section entry number
(PA)=Parent Co (HQ)=Headquarters (DH)=Div Headquarters

	SIC	EMP	PHONE	ENTRY #
ISC Engineering LLC	3629	D	909 596-3315	17344
Isiqalo LLC	2253	B	714 683-2820	2843
Jacuzzi Inc **(HQ)**	3589	C	909 606-7733	16059
Jacuzzi Whirlpool Bath Inc	3088	E	909 548-7732	9905
Kanetic Ltd LLC	3471	F	505 228-5692	13438
Kemper Enterprises Inc	3423	E	909 627-6191	11899
KVP International Inc	3842	E	888 411-7387	22765
Larin Corp	3423	E	909 464-0605	11900
Level Trek Corp	3089	F	626 689-4829	10190
Lifemed of California	3841	E	800 543-3633	22509
Liner Technologies Inc	3089	E	909 594-6610	10192
Liquid Technologies Inc	2844	E	909 393-9475	8790
Lollicup USA Inc **(PA)**	2656	E	626 965-8882	5499
M & M Printed Bag Inc	2673	E	909 393-5537	5606
M and M Sports	2395	F	909 548-3371	3851
M C O Inc	3714	F	909 627-3574	20391
Manley Laboratories Inc	3651	E	909 627-4256	17829
Maplegrove Gluten Free Foods	2099	E	909 334-7828	2595
Max Smt Corp	3563	F	877 589-9422	15131
Mikhail Darafeev Inc **(PA)**	2511	E	909 613-1818	4721
Morehouse-Cowles LLC	3559	E	909 627-7222	14993
Myers & Sons Hi-Way Safety Inc **(PA)**	3669	C	909 591-1781	18349
Myojo USA Inc	2098	F	909 464-1411	2430
National Sign & Marketing Corp	3993	D	909 591-4742	23932
Natura-Genics Inc	2834	F	909 597-6676	8292
Newport Thin Film Lab Inc	3089	F	909 591-0276	10240
Norco Injection Molding Inc	3089	D	909 393-4000	10242
Norco Plastics Inc	3089	D	909 393-4000	10243
North Pacific International	3497	F	909 628-2224	13871
Oak Design Corporation	2521	E	909 628-9597	4961
Omnia Leather Motion Inc	2392	C	909 393-4400	3735
Originals 22 Inc	3645	F	909 993-5050	17551
Pacific Boat Trailers Inc **(PA)**	3799	E	909 902-0094	21238
Pacific Coast Fabricators Inc	3441	F	909 627-3833	12222
Pacific Coast Mfg Inc	3631	D	909 627-7040	17374
Pacific Containerprint Inc	2759	E	909 465-0365	7428
Paclights LLC **(PA)**	3646	E	888 983-2165	17636
Paiho North America Corp	3965	E	661 257-6611	23771
Pdc LLC	3544	E	626 334-5000	14558
Pentair Water Pool and Spa Inc	3589	E	909 287-7800	16087
Precision Companies Inc	2431	F	909 548-2700	4214
Provena Foods Inc **(HQ)**	2013	D	909 627-1082	516
Quali-Tech Mold	3089	F	909 464-8124	10317
R Kern Engineering & Mfg Corp	3678	D	909 664-2440	19409
Reed LLC	3561	E	909 287-2100	15090
Repet Inc	3083	C	909 594-5333	9763
Roettele Industries	3053	F	909 606-8252	9551
Royal Custom Designs Inc	2512	C	909 591-8990	4810
RTS Powder Coating Inc **(PA)**	3479	E	909 393-5404	13650
Scott Engineering Inc	3629	E	909 594-9637	17353
Shamrock Marketing Co Inc **(HQ)**	3842	F	909 591-8855	22811
Sheffield Manufacturing Inc	3599	E	818 767-4948	16943
Shephard Casters	3562	F	909 393-0597	15111
Shield Realty California Inc **(PA)**	2813	E	909 628-4707	7732
Shine Company Inc	2499	E	909 590-5005	4656
Shirlee Industries Inc	3449	F	909 590-4120	12992
Shop4techcom	3572	E	909 248-2725	15607
Soaring America Corporation	3721	E	909 270-2628	20627
South Gate Engineering LLC	3443	D	909 628-2779	12422
Specilty Enzymes Btechnologies	2869	F	909 613-1660	9043
Spin Products Inc	3089	E	909 590-7000	10384
Steelcraft West	3914	F	909 548-2696	23337
Steven Madden Ltd	3143	D	909 393-7575	10490
Sundance Spas Inc **(HQ)**	3999	D	909 606-7733	24257
Superior Metal Shapes Inc	3354	E	909 947-3455	11606
Superior Tech Inc	3317	F	909 364-2300	11487
Syntech Development & Mfg Inc	3089	E	909 465-5554	10397
T McGee Electric Inc	3643	F	909 591-6461	17494
Tape Service Ltd	3069	F	909 627-8811	9684
Tarazi Specialty Foods LLC	2099	F	909 628-3601	2679
Tasco Molds Inc	3544	F	909 613-1926	14577
Tekram Usa Inc	3572	F	714 961-0800	15617
Texas Tst Inc	3341	E	951 685-2155	11568
Thermo Fisher Scientific Inc	3826	B	909 393-3205	22034
Top Quest Inc	3841	F	626 839-8618	22652
Top-Shelf Fixtures LLC **(PA)**	3496	D	909 216-6407	13857
Trend Technologies LLC **(DH)**	3444	C	909 597-7861	12792
Trinidad Benham Holding Co	2099	E	909 627-7535	2691
Tst Inc	3341	E	951 727-3169	11570
Tst Inc **(PA)**	3341	B	951 685-2155	11571
Ttl Holdings LLC **(HQ)**	3089	F	909 597-7861	10415
Tuffstuff Fitness Intl Inc	3949	C	909 629-1600	23678
U S Bowling Corporation	3949	F	909 548-0644	23680
United Castings Inc	3369	F	909 627-7645	11787
US Niutang Chemical Inc	2869	F	909 631-2895	8966

	SIC	EMP	PHONE	ENTRY #
Usglobalsat Inc	3663	F	909 597-8525	18295
Vacuum Tube Logic of America	3671	F	909 627-5944	18398
Val Plastic USA L L C	3523	F	909 390-9600	14114
Vitajoy USA Inc	2833	F	626 965-8830	7981
Vtl Amplifiers Inc	3651	F	909 627-5944	17879
Wacker Chemical Corporation	2869	E	909 590-8822	9052
West Coast Steel & Proc LLC **(PA)**	3325	D	909 393-8405	11530
Westrock Mwv LLC	2631	B	909 597-2197	5373
Wetmore Tool and Engrg Co	3545	F	909 364-1000	14695
Wright Business Forms Inc	2761	F	909 614-6700	7562
Yamamoto of Orient Inc	2393	F	909 591-7654	3775
Yankon Industries Inc	3646	E	909 591-2345	17658
Young Machine Inc	3599	F	909 464-0405	17075
Ziegenfelder Company	2024	E	909 590-0493	707

CHINO HILLS, CA - San Bernardino County

	SIC	EMP	PHONE	ENTRY #
Active Spt Lifestyle USA LLC	3949	E	909 203-4640	23485
Ad Industries LLC **(PA)**	2782	F	818 765-4200	7571
Cal Stitch Embroidery Inc	2395	F	909 465-5448	3833
Hoya Surgical Optics Inc	3841	E	909 680-3900	22471
Jacuzzi Brands LLC **(PA)**	3842	E	909 606-1416	22757
Jacuzzi Brands LLC	3999	F	909 606-1416	24136
Jacuzzi Inc	3088	E	909 606-1416	9903
Jacuzzi Products Co **(DH)**	3088	C	909 606-1416	9904
Ontario Binding Company Inc	2789	D	909 947-7866	7609
Plastic Color Technology	2816	F	909 597-9230	7743
Saunders Manufacturing Svcs	3999	F	714 961-8492	24228
Tri-Dim Filter Corporation	3564	E	626 826-5893	15182
TSS Embroidery Inc	2395	F	909 590-1383	3867
Vans Inc	3021	F	909 517-3141	9494

CHOLAME, CA - San Luis Obispo County

	SIC	EMP	PHONE	ENTRY #
Central Coast Water Authority	3589	F	805 463-2122	16021

CHOWCHILLA, CA - Madera County

	SIC	EMP	PHONE	ENTRY #
Allwire Inc	3084	E	559 665-4893	9774
Almond Company	2068	D	559 665-4405	1480
Blacks Irrigations Systems	3272	E	559 665-4891	10885
Central California Cont Mfg	3089	E	559 665-7611	10018
Certainteed Corporation	3296	B	559 665-4831	11330
Global Diversified Inds Inc **(PA)**	2452	E	559 665-5800	4574
Global Modular Inc **(HQ)**	2452	E	559 665-5800	4575
Piranha Pipe & Precast Inc	3272	E	559 665-7473	10975
Snyder Industries Inc	3089	D	559 665-7612	10381

CHULA VISTA, CA - San Diego County

	SIC	EMP	PHONE	ENTRY #
Ace Industries Inc	3599	E	619 482-2700	16210
Advanced McHning Solutions Inc	3599	E	619 671-3055	16230
Aker International Inc	3199	E	619 423-5182	10571
Allied Dvbe Inc	2321	E	619 690-4900	3050
American Design Inc	3089	E	619 429-1995	9940
American Metal Filter Company	3564	E	619 628-1917	15143
American Safety Technologies	3479	E	619 575-0590	13550
Bastan Corporation	2032	F	619 424-3416	746
Bellama Cstm Met Fbrcators Inc	3444	F	619 585-3351	12504
Boochery Inc	2085	F	619 738-1008	2067
Califrnia Furn Collections Inc	2519	C	619 621-2455	4908
Canvas Concepts Inc	2394	F	619 424-3428	3782
Career Cap Corporation	2353	F	619 575-2277	3561
Curbell Plastics Inc	3089	E	619 575-4633	10052
DStyle Inc	3499	F	619 662-0560	13937
El Super Leon Pnchin Sncks Inc	2064	F	619 271-0846	1420
Flagcrafters Inc	2399	F	619 585-1044	3947
Flexible Metal Inc **(HQ)**	3498	D	678 280-0127	13888
Ggtw LLC	2899	E	619 423-3388	9255
Glaxosmithkline LLC	2834	F	619 863-0399	8192
Gold Belt Line Inc	2326	F	619 424-5544	3103
Goodrich Corporation	3728	D	619 691-4111	20830
Hitachi Home Elec Amer Inc **(DH)**	3651	C	619 591-5200	17814
Husks Unlimited	2037	D	619 476-8301	951
Hyspan Precision Products Inc **(PA)**	3568	C	619 421-1355	15284
Hyspan Precision Products Inc	3499	D	619 421-1355	13947
Ichia Usa Inc	3674	C	619 482-2222	18879
Integrated Marine Services Inc	3731	C	619 429-0300	20997
Jack West Cnc Inc	3599	E	619 421-1695	16609
Kama-Tech Corporation	3827	E	619 421-7858	22096
Kinetic Electric Corporation	3699	C	619 654-1157	19998
Lamb Fuels Inc	2869	F	619 216-6940	9020
Laprensa San Diego	2711	F	619 425-7400	5908
Latina & Associates Inc **(PA)**	2711	F	619 426-1491	5909
Leemax International Inc	2329	F	619 208-2355	3173
Legacy Graphics LLC	2759	F	619 585-1044	7384
Leviton Manufacturing Co Inc	3643	B	619 205-8600	17479
Lyon Technologies Inc	3523	E	619 216-3400	14083
Marine Group Boat Works LLC	3731	C	619 427-6767	21000
Marshall Genuine Products LLC	3545	F	619 754-4099	14648
Mask U S Inc	2389	F	619 476-9041	3669

Employment Codes: A=Over 500 employees, B=251-500,
C=101-250, D=51-100, E=20-50, F=10-19

2019 California
Manufacturers Register

© Mergent Inc. 1-800-342-5647

1363

	SIC	EMP	PHONE	ENTRY #
McMahon Steel Company Inc	3429	C	619 671-9700	11975
Mgb Industries Inc	3728	F	619 247-9284	20886
Mk Digital Direct Inc	3826	F	619 661-0628	21995
Next Day Printed Tees	2396	F	619 420-8618	3909
Nypro Inc	3089	D	619 498-9250	10250
Nypro San Diego Inc	3089	D	619 482-7033	10251
Oak Land Furniture	2514	F	619 424-8758	4837
One Source Automation Inc	3549	F	619 422-4010	14761
P A S U Inc	3444	C	619 421-1151	12699
Pacmag Inc	3679	F	619 872-0343	19679
Professional Imaging Svcs Inc	3826	F	858 565-4217	22007
RCP Block & Brick Inc	3271	E	619 474-1516	10861
Rohr Inc (HQ)	3728	A	619 691-4111	20922
Sealed Air Corporation	2673	E	619 421-9003	5623
Shimmer Fashion	2331	F	619 426-7781	3273
Smartrunk Systems Inc	3663	E	619 426-3781	18254
SMK Manufacturing Inc	3575	E	619 216-6400	15646
Source of Health Inc	2023	E	619 409-9500	650
Southcoast Welding & Mfg LLC	7692	B	619 429-1337	25436
Stanford Sign & Awning Inc (PA)	3993	E	619 423-6200	23981
Star News Publishing Co Inc	2711	E	619 427-3000	6060
Stark Mfg Co	2394	E	619 425-5880	3812
Super Welding Southern Cal Inc	3548	E	619 239-8003	14741
Tap Manufacturing LLC	3714	F	619 216-1444	20459
Tecnico Corporation	3731	C	619 426-7385	21015
Tocabi America Corporation	2517	E	619 661-6136	4900
Toleeto Fastener International	3965	E	619 662-1355	23775
Tortilleria Santa Fe	2099	E	619 585-0350	2688
Trimek Inc (HQ)	2519	F	858 571-7475	4922
Va-Tran Systems Inc	3559	F	619 423-4555	15044
Vcp Mobility Holdings Inc	3842	B	619 213-6500	22839
Xylem Water Systems Cal Inc	3561	E	619 575-7466	15102

CITRUS HEIGHTS, CA - Sacramento County

	SIC	EMP	PHONE	ENTRY #
Hearst Communications Inc	2711	B	916 725-8694	5870
Lakeview Innovations Inc	2389	F	212 502-6702	3665
Mline Transportation Company	2075	E	916 729-1053	1511
Nvision Laser Eye Centers Inc	3851	F	916 723-7400	23111

CITY OF INDUSTRY, CA - Los Angeles County

	SIC	EMP	PHONE	ENTRY #
Abis Signs Inc	3993	F	626 818-4329	23805
Abrasive Wheels Inc	3291	F	626 935-8800	11287
Acorn Engineering Company (PA)	3448	A	800 488-8999	12909
Acromil LLC	3728	D	626 964-2522	20701
Acromil Corporation (PA)	3728	D	626 964-2522	20702
Adams-Campbell Company Ltd	3444	E	626 330-3425	12458
Adtech Photonics Inc	3827	E	626 956-1000	22057
Alatus Aerosystems (PA)	3728	C	610 251-1000	20729
All Label Inc	2679	F	626 964-6744	5694
Allfast Fastening Systems LLC	3452	D	626 968-9388	13057
Alta-Dena Certified Dairy LLC	2026	C	800 395-7004	710
Alta-Dena Certified Dairy (DH)	2026	B	626 964-6401	711
American Foam Fiber & Sups Inc	2299	D	626 969-7268	2987
American Steel Masters Inc	3441	E	626 333-3375	12112
Anima International Corp	3999	F	626 723-4960	24038
Anvil Cases Inc	3161	C	626 968-4100	10514
Aremac Heat Treating Inc	3398	E	626 333-3898	11793
Assa Abloy Rsdential Group Inc (HQ)	3429	C	626 961-0413	11930
Astrophysics Inc (PA)	3844	C	909 598-5488	22928
Bagcraftpapercon I LLC	2674	D	626 961-6766	5637
Battery Technology Inc (PA)	3691	D	626 336-6878	19798
Bentley Mills Inc	2273	F	800 423-4709	2925
Bentley Mills Inc (PA)	2273	C	626 333-4585	2926
Best Formulations Inc	2099	C	626 912-9998	2464
Beyond Ultimate LLC	2611	E	626 330-9777	5266
Blue PCF Flvors Fragrances Inc	2087	E	626 934-0099	2247
Boss Litho Inc	2752	E	626 912-7088	6701
Boxes R Us Inc	2657	D	626 820-5410	5504
Bryan Press Inc	2752	F	626 961-9257	6708
Burton James Inc	2512	F	626 961-7221	4761
C & F Foods Inc (PA)	2099	D	626 723-1000	2474
California Expanded Met Pdts (PA)	3444	D	626 369-3564	12519
California Hydroforming Co Inc	3444	F	626 912-0036	12520
California Steel and Tube LLC	3317	C	626 968-5511	11474
Cambro Manufacturing Company	3999	F	909 354-8962	24058
Cardinal Paint and Powder Inc	2851	E	626 937-6767	8892
Cast Parts Inc	3324	C	626 937-3444	11509
Central Blower Co	3564	E	626 330-3182	15148
Centric Parts Inc	3711	E	626 961-5775	20132
CH Image Inc	2752	F	626 336-6063	6726
Charades LLC (PA)	2389	C	626 435-0077	3649
China Master USA Entrmt Co	3299	F	626 810-9372	11354
Chronomite Laboratories Inc	3822	F	310 534-2300	21504
Circle Racing Wheels Inc (PA)	3714	F	800 959-2100	20290
Clay Laguna Co (HQ)	3295	C	626 330-0631	11318
Clayton Manufacturing Company (PA)	3569	C	626 443-9381	15308

	SIC	EMP	PHONE	ENTRY #
Clayton Manufacturing Inc (HQ)	3569	D	626 443-9381	15309
Clo Systems LLC	3621	F	626 939-4226	17185
Closets By Design Inc	2541	C	562 699-9945	5049
Coca-Cola Company	2086	E	626 855-4440	2117
Coi Rubber Products Inc	2822	B	626 965-9966	7903
Collection Development	3674	F	909 595-8588	18773
Colorwen International Corp	2816	F	626 363-8855	7740
Commercial Lbr & Pallet Co Inc (PA)	2448	C	626 968-0631	4461
Compucase Corporation	3572	A	626 336-6588	15525
Consolidated Cont Holdings LLC	3089	E	626 964-9657	10035
Consolidated Container Co LLC	3089	E	888 425-7343	10036
Consolidated Devices Inc (HQ)	3423	E	626 965-0668	11889
Cosmos Food Co Inc	2099	F	323 221-9142	2494
Cpp Ind	3812	F	909 595-2252	21277
Creftcon Industries Inc	3644	C	203 377-5944	17510
Custom Alloy Sales Inc (PA)	3341	C	626 369-3641	11554
D-Tech Optoelectronics Inc (DH)	3669	F	626 956-1100	18318
Dacor	3631	D	626 799-1000	17365
Dacor	3631	F	626 799-1000	17366
Dacor	3631	D	626 961-2256	17367
Darnell Corporation	3429	C	626 912-1688	11951
Define Toys Inc	3942	F	626 330-8800	23395
Delori Products Inc	2099	F	626 965-3006	2504
Dennison Inc	3446	E	626 965-8917	12849
Derek and Constance Lee Corp (PA)	2013	D	909 595-8831	480
Dispensing Dynamics Intl Inc (PA)	3089	D	626 961-3691	10071
Duro Corporation	3631	E	626 839-6541	17368
Dxg Technology USA Inc	3861	E	626 820-0687	23153
Easterncctv (usa) LLC	3699	F	626 961-8810	19954
Ecolab Inc	2841	F	626 935-1212	8591
El Burrito Mxican Fd Pdts Corp	2033	F	626 369-7828	799
Engineering Model Associates (PA)	3089	E	626 912-7011	10092
Environmental Ltg For Arch Inc	3646	E	626 965-0821	17603
Evans Industries Inc	3499	C	626 912-1688	13940
Express It Delivers	2741	E	626 855-1294	6481
Exxel Outdoors Inc	2399	E	626 369-7278	3945
Foot Imprint Inc	3555	E	626 991-4430	14809
Fremarc Industries Inc (PA)	2511	D	626 965-0802	4697
General Sealants Inc	2891	C	626 961-0211	9143
Geo A Diack Inc	2542	E	626 961-2491	5141
Gff Inc	2035	D	323 232-6255	913
Golden State Foods Corp	2038	C	626 968-6431	995
Goldencorr Sheets LLC	2653	C	626 369-6446	5419
Gordon Brush Mfg Co Inc (PA)	3991	D	323 724-7777	23792
Goulds Pumps	3561	E	562 949-2113	15068
Gruma Corporation	2051	C	562 692-9502	1269
H & H Specialties Inc	3999	E	626 575-0776	24114
Harvard Label LLC	2621	C	626 333-8881	5286
Henkel US Operations Corp	2891	E	626 968-6511	9147
Herbal Science International	2833	F	626 333-9998	7947
Heritage Distributing Company	2023	E	626 333-9526	622
Hexpol Compounding CA Inc	3069	D	626 961-0311	9620
Hill Brothers Chemical Company	2812	F	626 333-2251	7664
Hitex Dyeing & Finishing Inc	2399	E	626 363-0160	3951
Ht Window Fashions Corporation (PA)	2591	D	626 839-8866	5193
Hydro Extruder LLC	3354	B	626 964-3411	11590
Ideal Printing Co Inc	2752	E	626 964-2019	6871
Ilos Corp	3648	F	213 255-2060	17702
Integral Engrg Fabrication Inc	3441	E	626 369-0958	12180
Invenlux Corporation	3674	F	626 277-4163	18928
ITT LLC	3625	D	562 908-4144	17280
Jada Group Inc	3944	D	626 810-8382	23433
Jishan Usa Inc	3646	F	408 609-3286	17620
Jmu Dental Inc	3843	F	909 676-0000	22886
Johnson Wilshire Inc	3842	F	562 777-0088	22761
Jon Brooks Inc (PA)	3295	C	626 330-0631	11323
K-1 Packaging Group (PA)	2752	D	626 964-9384	6919
K-Tops Plastic Mfg Inc	3999	F	626 964-2002	24142
Kandi Usa Inc	3711	F	909 941-4588	20153
Kontech USA LLC	3646	F	626 622-1325	17622
Kopaskie Metallurgical Inc	3398	E	626 333-3898	11816
Krallcast Inc	3324	C	626 333-0678	11513
La Indiana Tamales Inc	2032	E	323 262-4682	766
Langer Juice Company Inc	2037	C	626 336-3100	958
Lanstreetcom	3575	E	626 964-2000	15638
Lee Kum Kee (usa) Foods Inc	2099	D	626 709-1888	2581
Lhoist North America Ariz Inc	3274	F	626 336-4578	11215
Likom Caseworks USA Inc (DH)	3575	E	210 587-7824	15639
Linde Gas North America LLC	2813	F	626 780-3104	7694
Linde LLC	2813	D	626 855-8366	7700
Lt Security Inc (PA)	3699	C	626 435-2838	20009
Magnell Associate Inc	3571	E	626 271-1320	15446
Marrs Printing Inc	2752	D	909 594-9459	6961
Maverick Aerospace Inc	3728	F	714 578-1700	20878
Maverick Aerospace LLC	3728	F	714 578-1700	20879

	SIC	EMP	PHONE	ENTRY #
Maverick Aerospace LLC	3728	E	714 578-1700	20880
Maxim Lighting	3645	C	626 956-4200	17546
Maxim Lighting Intl Inc (PA)	3645	C	626 956-4200	17547
Maxim Lighting Intl Inc	3645	D	626 956-4200	17548
Mercury Plastics Inc (PA)	2673	B	626 961-0165	5607
Metal Cutting Service Inc	3599	F	626 968-4764	16740
Microprint Inc	2752	E	626 369-1950	6973
Midern Computer Inc	3571	E	626 964-8682	15457
Miracle Bedding Corporation	2515	E	562 908-2370	4874
Monadnock Company	3429	C	626 964-6581	11977
Morehouse Foods Inc	2035	E	626 854-1655	922
Morris Group International (PA)	3448	C	626 336-4561	12952
Nefful USA Inc	2341	F	626 839-6657	3541
Newton Heat Treating Company	3398	D	626 964-6528	11826
Norman Fox & Co	2841	E	626 581-5600	8600
Nuset Inc	3429	E	626 246-1668	11980
Pape Material Handling Inc	3537	D	562 692-9311	14340
Par Engineering Inc	3632	E	626 964-8700	17381
Pgi Pacific Graphics Intl	2752	E	626 336-7707	7025
PHI	3542	E	626 968-9680	14451
Phillips Machine & Wldg Co Inc	7692	E	626 855-4600	25426
Physicians Formula Inc (DH)	2844	D	626 334-3395	8815
Physicians Formula Inc	2844	D	626 334-3395	8816
Physicians Formula Cosmt Inc	2844	C	626 334-3395	8818
Pilot Inc (PA)	3714	E	626 937-6988	20420
Plastruct Inc	3089	D	626 912-7017	10295
Playhut Inc	3944	E	909 869-8083	23455
Pocino Foods Company	2013	E	626 968-8000	515
PPG Industries Inc	2851	F	562 692-4010	8926
Premio Inc (PA)	3571	C	626 839-3100	15472
Prime Measurement Products LLC (PA)	3823	B	626 961-2547	21635
Prl Aluminum Inc	3334	D	626 968-7507	11541
Procter & Gamble Mfg Co	2841	A	513 627-4678	8605
Prolacta Bioscience Inc (PA)	2836	C	626 599-9260	8575
PS Intl Inc	3496	F	626 333-8168	13846
Puente Ready Mix Inc (PA)	3273	E	626 968-0711	11158
Qontrol Devices Inc	3559	F	626 968-4268	15014
Quemetco Inc	3341	C	626 937-3239	11565
Quemetco West LLC	3341	D	626 330-2294	11566
RC Furniture Inc	2512	D	626 964-4100	4805
Rectangular Tubing Inc	2655	E	626 333-7884	5493
Red Shell Foods Inc	2035	E	626 937-6501	930
Reuland Electric Co (PA)	3621	C	626 964-6411	17220
Rice Field Corporation	2013	C	626 968-6917	519
Roadster Wheels Inc	3714	E	626 333-3007	20442
Rosewill Inc	3571	E	626 271-1420	15478
S2e Inc	3651	E	626 965-1008	17852
Safe Plating Inc	3471	D	626 810-1872	13495
Sbm Dairies Inc (HQ)	2086	D	626 923-3000	2217
Sceptre Inc	3679	E	626 369-3698	19719
Scope Packaging Inc	2653	E	714 998-4411	5457
Sealed Air Corporation	3086	D	909 594-1791	9882
Shoes For Crews Intl Inc	3143	E	561 683-5090	10483
Shuttle Computer Group Inc	3571	E	626 820-9000	15484
Silao Tortilleria Inc	2099	E	626 961-0761	2667
Silveron Industries Inc	3625	F	909 598-4533	17309
Sincere Orient Commercial Corp	2099	D	626 333-8882	2669
Sing Tao Newspapers Ltd	2711	D	626 839-8200	6047
Smtcl Usa Inc	3545	F	626 667-1192	14676
Smurfit Kappa North Amer LLC	2653	B	626 333-6363	5458
Smurfit Kappa North Amer LLC (HQ)	2653	B	626 333-6363	5459
Smurfit Kappa North Amer LLC	2653	B	626 322-2123	5460
Solar Region Inc	3571	E	909 595-8500	15487
Solo Enterprise Corp	3599	E	626 961-3591	16950
Sonoco Products Company	2631	D	626 369-6611	5361
Spencer N Enterprises LLC (DH)	2392	D	909 895-8495	3750
Stoughton Printing Co	2752	E	626 961-3678	7117
Stud Welding Systems Inc	3452	E	626 330-7434	13085
Summer Rio Corp (PA)	3021	E	626 854-1498	9487
T S Microtech Inc	3577	F	626 839-8998	15865
Tekni-Plex Inc	2679	C	909 589-4366	5742
Teknor Apex Company	2821	C	626 968-4656	7896
Teledyne Instruments Inc	3823	C	626 934-1500	21663
Tje Company	3442	F	909 869-7777	12351
Tonusa LLC	2434	F	626 961-8700	4358
Topstar International Inc	3641	E	909 595-8807	17436
Touch Coffee & Beverages LLC	3634	F	626 968-0300	17404
TPC Advance Technology Inc	3843	F	626 810-4337	22917
Trend Manor Furn Mfg Co Inc	2511	E	626 964-6493	4745
Trio Metal Stamping Inc	3444	D	626 336-1228	12796
Triview Glass Industries LLC	3231	E	626 363-7980	10735
Tropicana Products Inc	2033	C	626 968-1299	865
Troy-Csl Lighting Inc	3645	D	626 336-4511	17564
Trulite GL Alum Solutions LLC	3354	F	800 877-8439	11607
Turnham Corporation (PA)	3545	F	626 330-0415	14689
Turnham Corporation	3545	F	626 968-6481	14690
Tyloon Media Corporation	2741	F	626 330-5838	6608
Union Flavors Inc	2087	F	626 333-1612	2285
Utility Trailer Mfg Co (PA)	3715	B	626 964-7319	20517
V & V Manufacturing Inc	3961	E	626 330-0641	23760
Valley Power Services Inc	3621	E	909 969-9345	17228
Valley Power Systems Inc (PA)	3519	D	626 333-1243	14035
Venus Foods Inc	2011	E	626 369-5188	455
Vida Corporation	3695	E	626 839-4912	19888
Visionmax Inc	2339	F	626 839-1602	3526
Viz Cattle Corporation	2011	E	310 884-5260	456
Vonnic Inc	3861	E	626 964-2345	23211
Waddington North America Inc	3089	C	626 913-4022	10434
Whitehall Manufacturing Inc	3842	A	626 336-4561	22849
Whittier Enterprise LLC	2038	E	844 767-5633	1021
Winstar Textile Inc	2361	E	626 357-1133	3590
Wjb Bearings Inc	3463	E	909 598-6238	13133
Wna Comet West Inc	3089	C	626 913-0724	10448
Wwf Operating Company	2026	C	626 810-1775	741
Ybcc Inc	2023	E	626 213-3945	654
Zacky & Sons Poultry LLC	2015	C	559 443-2700	557
Zenith Specialty Bag Co Inc (PA)	2673	C	626 912-2481	5635

CLAREMONT, CA - Los Angeles County

	SIC	EMP	PHONE	ENTRY #
Baumann Engineering Inc	3599	D	909 621-4181	16308
Bert & Rockys Cream Co Inc	2024	F	909 625-1852	658
Claremont Courier	2711	E	909 621-4761	5807
Conveyor Mfg & Svc Inc	3535	F	909 621-0406	14270
Feemster Co Inc	2051	F	909 621-9772	1247
Green Spot Packaging Inc	2086	E	909 625-8771	2136
HI Rel Connectors Inc	3643	B	909 626-1820	17470
National Scientific Sup Co Inc	3089	F	909 621-4585	10232
New Bedford Panoramex Corp	3648	E	909 982-9806	17719
Sunsation Inc	2037	E	909 542-0280	969
Therapak LLC	3821	C	626 357-5900	21493
Unisorb Inc	3499	F	626 793-1000	13980
Universal Defense	3443	E	909 626-4178	12437

CLARKSBURG, CA - Yolo County

	SIC	EMP	PHONE	ENTRY #
Carvalho Family Winery LLC	2084	F	916 744-1615	1680
Western Strata Exploration Inc	1381	F	916 744-1440	123

CLAYTON, CA - Contra Costa County

	SIC	EMP	PHONE	ENTRY #
Comco Sheet Metal Company	3444	F	510 832-6433	12534
Hanson Aggrgtes Md-Pacific Inc	3281	F	925 672-4955	11256
Underground Labs Inc	7372	F	925 297-5333	25308

CLEARLAKE, CA - Lake County

	SIC	EMP	PHONE	ENTRY #
Medianews Group Inc	2711	C	707 994-6656	5964
Zyrel Inc	3672	F	707 995-2551	18658

CLOVERDALE, CA - Sonoma County

	SIC	EMP	PHONE	ENTRY #
Bear Republic Brewing Co Inc (PA)	2082	F	707 894-2722	1568
Centersource Systems LLC	2731	F	707 838-1061	6324
Charlois Cooperage USA	2429	F	707 224-2377	4092
Classic Mill & Cabinet	2434	F	707 894-9800	4286
Dyna-King Inc	3949	F	707 894-5566	23551
Indian Head Industries Inc	3714	D	707 894-3333	20370
MGM Brakes	3714	D	707 894-3333	20401
New World Manufacturing Inc	3069	F	707 894-5257	9645
Peay Vineyards LLC	2084	F	707 894-8720	1919
Reuser Inc	2421	F	707 894-4224	4050
Treasury Wine Estates Americas	2084	E	707 894-2541	2025

CLOVIS, CA - Fresno County

	SIC	EMP	PHONE	ENTRY #
Anlin Industries	2431	C	800 287-7996	4099
Atmf Inc	3471	E	559 299-6836	13340
Crystal Lake Grinders	3599	D	559 297-0737	16411
Fresno Precision Plastics Inc (PA)	3089	E	559 323-9595	10108
Kw Automotive North Amer Inc	3714	E	800 445-3767	20384
Machine Exprnce & Design Inc	3599	E	559 291-7710	16705
MI Rancho Tortilla Inc	2099	D	559 299-3183	2604
Preferred Wire Products Inc	3496	F	559 324-0140	13844
Redcort Software Inc	7372	F	559 434-8544	25119
Snowflake Designs	2253	E	559 291-6234	2854
Valley Chrome Plating Inc	3471	E	559 298-8094	13531
Viking Ready Mix Co Inc	3273	E	559 225-3667	11204
Wawona Frozen Foods (PA)	2037	A	559 299-2901	973
Western Dning - Schneider Cafe	3699	E	559 292-1981	20110

COACHELLA, CA - Riverside County

	SIC	EMP	PHONE	ENTRY #
Armtec Countermeasures Co (DH)	3812	F	760 398-0143	21258
Armtec Defense Products Co (HQ)	3489	B	760 398-0143	13694
Ernie Ball Inc	3931	D	800 543-2255	23368
Paladar Mfg Inc	3931	D	760 775-4222	23381
Reyes Coca-Cola Bottling LLC	2086	E	760 396-4500	2195

Employment Codes: A=Over 500 employees, B=251-500,
C=101-250, D=51-100, E=20-50, F=10-19

2019 California
Manufacturers Register

© Mergent Inc. 1-800-342-5647

1365

GEOGRAPHIC

	SIC	EMP	PHONE	ENTRY #
COALINGA, CA - Fresno County				
Aera Energy LLC	3533	E	559 935-7418	14205
Valley Garlic Inc	2035	E	559 934-1763	939
COLFAX, CA - Placer County				
Crispin Cider Company (DH)	2099	E	530 346-9699	2496
Crispinian Inc	2082	E	530 346-8411	1582
Fox Barrel Cider Company Inc	2084	E	530 346-9699	1768
M B I Ready-Mix L L C	3273	E	530 346-2432	11139
Sourcing Group LLC	2752	F	530 346-1280	7109
COLMA, CA - San Mateo County				
Christy Vault Company (PA)	3272	E	650 994-1378	10901
COLTON, CA - San Bernardino County				
Alfonso Jaramillo	3495	F	951 276-2777	13784
Als Garden Art Inc (PA)	3299	B	909 424-0221	11344
Archer-Daniels-Midland Company	2041	F	909 783-7574	1025
Ardent Mills LLC	2041	E	951 201-1170	1030
Banner Mattress Inc (PA)	2515	E	909 835-4200	4852
Black Diamond Blade Company (PA)	3531	E	800 949-9014	14146
Boyd Specialties LLC	2013	D	909 219-5120	468
C & R Pier Mfg (PA)	3441	E	909 872-6444	12122
C and R Sales Inc	3441	E	951 686-6864	12124
Cal Portland Cement Co	3273	E	909 423-0436	11054
California Churros Corporation	2051	C	909 370-4777	1215
Calportland Company	3241	E	909 825-4260	10745
Cemex Materials LLC	3273	E	909 825-1500	11087
Clariant Corporation	2672	E	909 825-1793	5558
Computerized Embroidery Co	2395	F	909 825-3841	3839
Coronado Equipment Sales	3537	E	877 830-7447	14314
County of San Bernardino	3821	E	909 580-0015	21465
E-Z Up Directcom	2394	E	909 426-0060	3785
Elizabeth Shutters Inc	3442	E	909 825-1531	12314
Frank Kams & Associates Inc	2449	E	909 382-0047	4521
Hawa Corporation	2013	E	909 825-8882	490
HC Brill	2053	B	909 825-7343	1395
Hydro Conduit of Texas LP	3272	F	909 825-1500	10939
La Carreta Food Products	2099	F	909 825-0737	2559
Leemco Inc (PA)	3491	F	909 422-0088	13722
Lrb Millwork & Casework Inc	2541	F	951 328-0105	5081
Masterbrand Cabinets Inc	2434	E	951 686-3614	4327
McNeilus Truck and Mfg Inc	3713	E	909 370-2100	20218
Microdyne Plastics Inc	3089	D	909 503-4010	10210
Mrs Redds Pie Co Inc	2051	E	909 825-4800	1293
Ostoich Diesel Service	3594	F	909 885-0590	16168
Panadent Corporation	3843	E	909 783-1841	22899
Paul Hubbs Construction Inc (PA)	1429	F	951 360-3990	331
S & S Installations Inc	3589	E	909 370-1730	16104
Saab Enterprises Inc	2013	D	909 823-2228	521
Show Offs	2541	E	909 885-5223	5101
Sprizzi Drink Co	3585	F	909 528-7779	15978
Williams Furnace Co (HQ)	3585	C	562 450-3602	16002
Wirz & Co	2752	E	909 825-6970	7188
Wrenchware Inc	3263	F	951 784-2717	10814
COLUMBIA, CA - Tuolumne County				
Columbia Communications Inc	3663	F	203 533-0252	18070
Gerard H Tanzi Inc	3556	F	209 532-0855	14854
COLUSA, CA - Colusa County				
American Carports Inc (PA)	3448	F	866 730-9865	12916
Riverbend Rice Mill Inc	2044	F	530 458-8561	1090
COMMERCE, CA - Los Angeles County				
A-1 Metal Products Inc	3444	E	323 721-3334	12454
Aahs Enterprises Inc	3993	F	323 838-9130	23803
AB&r Inc	2339	E	323 727-0007	3367
Abisco Products Co	2782	E	562 906-9330	7570
Acclaim Lighting LLC	3646	E	323 213-4626	17577
Advance Screen Graphic	2759	F	323 724-9910	7222
Advanced Process Services Inc	3491	E	323 278-6530	13700
Ajg Inc	2386	E	323 346-0171	3606
Alarin Aircraft Hinge Inc	3429	E	323 725-1666	11925
Allegro Pacific Corporation	3172	E	323 724-0101	10557
Alliance Apparel Inc	2331	E	323 888-8900	3212
Alloy Machining and Honing Inc	3599	E	323 726-8248	16255
Alloy Machining Services Inc	3599	F	323 725-2545	16256
Amcor Flexibles LLC	2671	C	323 721-6777	5517
American & Efird LLC	2284	D	323 724-6884	2951
American Brass & Alum Fndry Co	3432	E	800 545-9988	12021
American Graphic Board Inc	2679	E	323 721-0585	5695
American International Inds	2844	A	323 728-2999	8693
American Vanguard Corporation	2879	C	323 526-2372	9090
American Vanguard Corporation	2879	C	323 264-3910	9092
American Vegetable Oils Inc	2076	F	800 728-8089	1514
Apex Drum Company Inc	2449	E	323 721-8994	4516
Arbo Box Inc	2441	E	562 404-2726	4433
Architectural Enterprises Inc	3446	E	323 268-4000	12833
Ardent Mills LLC	2041	F	323 725-0771	1031
Arevalo Tortilleria Inc	2099	E	323 888-1711	2456
Arthurmade Plastics Inc	3089	D	323 721-7325	9958
Asco Sintering Co	3429	E	323 725-3550	11929
Atk Space Systems Inc (DH)	3443	E	323 722-0222	12360
Atlas Carpet Mills Inc	2273	C	323 724-7930	2924
Avery Dennison Corporation	2672	E	323 728-8888	5554
B & B Battery (usa) Inc (PA)	3692	E	323 278-1900	19820
Ball of Cotton Inc	2253	E	323 888-9448	2824
Blisterpak Inc	3089	E	323 728-5555	9983
Bonded Fiberloft Inc	2211	B	323 726-7820	2725
Bottlemate Inc	3089	E	323 887-9009	9989
Bridge Publications Inc (PA)	2731	E	323 888-6200	6318
C-Quest Inc	2331	D	323 980-1400	3223
Canvas Specialty Inc	2394	E	323 722-1156	3783
Capitol Steel Fabricators Inc	3441	E	323 721-5460	12129
Cappac Plastic Products	3086	E	323 721-7542	9824
Carmi Flvr & Fragrance Co Inc (PA)	2087	E	323 888-9240	2251
Cee Sportswear	2339	E	323 726-8158	3392
Century Snacks LLC	2064	B	323 278-9578	1412
Century Wire & Cable Inc	3357	D	213 236-8879	11653
Chameleon Beverage Company Inc (PA)	2086	D	323 724-8223	2112
Colorcom Inc	2752	F	323 246-4640	6741
Commercial Intr Resources Inc	2512	D	562 926-5885	4764
Connected Apparel Company LLC (PA)	2339	E	323 890-8000	3397
Crystolon Inc	2542	E	323 725-3482	5135
Cure Apparel LLC	2331	F	562 927-7460	3227
Dart Warehouse Corporation (HQ)	3715	B	323 981-8205	20499
Datapage Inc	2759	F	323 725-7500	7294
Deamco Corporation	3535	D	323 890-1190	14273
Deco Enterprises Inc	3646	D	323 726-2575	17596
Deskmakers Inc	2521	E	323 264-2260	4942
Dynaflex Products (PA)	3713	D	323 724-1555	20203
E & J Gallo Winery	2084	B	323 720-6400	1746
E-Z Plastic Packaging Corp	2673	E	323 887-0123	5598
Echo Lighting Incorporated	3648	F	323 890-9008	17687
El Clasificado	2741	E	323 278-5310	6474
Elation Lighting Inc	3646	D	323 582-3322	17599
Elation Lighting Inc	3645	F	323 213-4552	17534
Elite Lighting	3648	C	323 888-1973	17690
Evy of California Inc (HQ)	2361	E	213 746-4647	3576
Fairway Trading Inc	2241	F	323 582-8111	2799
Fast Sportswear Inc	2339	D	323 720-1078	3417
Faustinos Chair Factory Inc	2521	F	323 724-8055	4943
Fleming Metal Fabricators	3713	F	323 723-8203	20205
Floride Products LLC (PA)	2819	E	323 201-4363	7778
Fungs Village Inc	2098	E	323 881-1600	2427
Furniture Technics Inc	2511	F	562 802-0261	4700
Galaxy Enterprises Inc	3999	E	323 728-3980	24103
Gehr Group Inc (PA)	3315	E	323 728-5558	11441
Gehr Industries Inc (HQ)	3357	C	323 728-5558	11663
General Industrial Repair	3599	E	323 278-0873	16530
Ginger Golden Products Inc	2035	E	323 838-1070	914
Global Syn-Turf Inc	3999	E	562 928-2800	24110
Globe Iron Foundry Inc (PA)	3321	D	323 723-8983	11494
Guardian Survival Gear Inc	3842	F	760 519-5643	22738
Hangers Randy West Coast Ctr	3315	F	323 728-2253	11444
Heeger Inc	3621	F	323 728-5108	17202
Heritage Distributing Company (PA)	2026	E	323 838-1225	728
HI Fashion Productions Inc	2396	E	323 722-8200	3898
Hollinger Metal Edge Inc	2653	E	323 721-7800	5424
Hollywood Bed Spring Mfg Inc	3429	D	323 887-9500	11962
Home Paradise LLC	3469	F	626 284-9999	13219
Hospitality Wood Products Inc	2431	F	562 806-5564	4165
Housewares International Inc (PA)	3089	E	323 581-3000	10141
Hse Usa Inc (PA)	3999	F	323 278-0888	24122
Huhtamaki Inc	3086	B	323 269-0151	9865
Hurley International LLC	2329	F	323 728-1821	3160
In Pro Car Wear Inc	3648	F	323 724-0568	17703
Indio Products Inc	2899	E	323 720-9117	9262
Ingenue Inc	2015	D	323 726-8084	544
Ink Makers Inc	2893	F	323 728-7500	9201
Interstate Meat Co Inc	3556	F	323 838-9400	14860
Java Printing Inc	2759	E	323 888-1601	7364
JC Window Fashions Inc	2591	F	909 364-8888	5197
JP Products LLC	2511	F	310 237-6237	4708
Jr Grease Services	2077	E	323 318-2096	1528
Jsl Foods Inc	2099	E	323 727-9999	2549
Just For Wraps Inc (PA)	2339	C	213 239-0503	3441
Kaiser Aluminum Corporation	3354	E	323 726-8011	11591
Kaiser Aluminum Fab Pdts LLC	3354	C	323 722-7151	11592
Kirk API Containers	3089	E	323 278-5400	10181
La Bath Vanity Inc	2434	EMP	909 303-3323	4323

	SIC	EMP	PHONE	ENTRY #
La Xpress Air & Heating Svcs	2741	D	310 856-9678	6514
LCI Laundry Inc	2335	C	323 767-1900	3324
Liberty Packg & Extruding Inc	2673	E	323 722-5124	5604
Lion Tank Line Inc	2911	E	323 726-1966	9337
Los Angeles Board Mills Inc	2631	C	323 685-8900	5354
Lucky Star Silkscreen LLC	2759	E	323 728-4071	7392
Maidenform LLC	2341	C	323 724-9558	3539
Mainetti USA Inc	2759	E	562 741-2920	7394
Martin Sprocket & Gear Inc	3566	F	323 728-8117	15243
Mascorro Leather Inc	3172	D	323 724-6759	10567
Mastertaste Inc	2087	D	323 727-2100	2272
Matthew Warren Inc	3493	D	800 237-5225	13752
Maxims Mattress Inc	2515	F	323 721-5616	4872
Mega Sign Inc	3993	E	888 315-7446	23924
MGM Transformer Co	3612	D	323 726-0888	17106
Milestones Products Inc	2844	F	323 728-3434	8796
Mojave Foods Corporation	2099	C	323 890-8900	2609
Monogram Aerospace Fas Inc (HQ)	3429	C	323 722-4760	11978
Motorshield LLC	2851	F	323 396-9200	8920
MSE Media Solutions	3695	E	323 721-1656	19873
Ni Industries Inc	3449	E	309 283-3355	12985
Nico Nat Mfg Corp	2541	E	323 721-1900	5084
Norstar Office Products Inc (PA)	2521	E	323 262-1919	4959
Nova Lifestyle Inc (PA)	2511	E	323 888-9999	4728
Oakhurst Industries Inc (PA)	2051	C	323 724-3000	1299
Oldcastle Buildingenvelope Inc	3231	D	323 722-2007	10724
Pacific Coast Home Furn Inc (PA)	2392	F	323 838-7808	3739
Pacific Die Casting Corp	3363	C	323 725-1308	11701
Pacific Spice Company Inc	2099	D	323 726-9190	2633
Pacific Testtronics Inc	3999	F	323 721-1077	24202
Pacific Vial Mfg Inc	3221	E	323 721-7004	10624
PCI Industries Inc	3444	D	323 728-0004	12710
Pearlman Enterprises Inc (DH)	3291	C	800 969-5561	11301
Pioneer Broach Company (PA)	3545	E	323 728-1263	14664
PM Corporate Group Inc	2752	C	619 498-9199	7029
Pommes Frites Candle Co	3999	E	213 488-2016	24212
Portos Food Product Inc	2051	D	323 480-8400	1310
Power Reps Inc	7694	E	323 724-6771	25464
Precision Wire Products Inc (PA)	3496	C	323 890-9100	13843
Progressive Label Inc	2679	E	323 415-9770	5728
Protrend Ltd (HQ)	2335	F	323 832-9323	3336
RDD Enterprises Inc	2311	F	213 746-0020	3039
Romac Supply Co Inc	3613	D	323 721-5810	17160
S Bravo Systems Inc	3443	C	323 888-4133	12418
Samson Pharmaceuticals Inc	2834	E	323 722-3066	8371
Samson Products Inc	2542	B	323 726-9070	5166
Sentiments Inc (PA)	3999	F	323 843-2080	24239
Shelter International Inc	2499	E	323 888-8856	4655
Sherwin-Williams Company	2295	E	323 726-7272	2962
Shugar Soapworks Inc	2841	F	323 234-2874	8608
Sid E Parker Boiler Mfg Co Inc	3443	D	323 727-9800	12420
Signature Flexible Packg Inc	2891	F	323 887-1997	9170
Siho Corporation	2339	F	323 721-4000	3496
Snak Club LLC	2068	E	323 278-9578	1503
Soft Gel Technologies Inc (HQ)	2834	E	323 726-0700	8385
Southern California Soap Co	2841	F	323 888-1332	8609
Specialty Enterprises Co	3086	D	323 726-9721	9884
Spirit Foodservice Inc	3089	D	323 724-0503	10385
Springs Industries Inc	2299	E	323 887-3920	3018
Steven Madden Ltd	3143	E	323 346-0205	10489
Stitch Industries Inc	2512	E	310 977-5556	4813
Sugar Foods Corporation	2051	D	323 727-8290	1324
Sun Plastics Inc	2673	E	323 888-6999	5626
Superb Chair Corporation	2512	F	562 776-1771	4815
Superior-Studio Spc Inc	3999	E	323 278-0100	24259
Tapestry Inc	3171	F	323 725-6792	10553
Tdg Operations LLC	2273	C	323 724-9000	2945
Teichman Enterprises Inc	2542	E	323 278-9000	5171
Torah-Aura Productions Inc	2731	F	323 585-1847	6402
Touch Litho Company	2752	F	562 927-8899	7138
Transdigm Inc	3728	E	323 269-9181	20954
Transdigm Inc	3728	E	323 269-9181	20955
Transdigm Inc	3728	C	323 269-9181	20956
Trixxi Clothing Company Inc (PA)	2331	E	323 585-4200	3280
Ultimate Metal Finishing Corp	3479	F	323 890-9100	13675
Ultra Pro Acquisition LLC	2782	C	323 725-1975	7587
Ultra Pro International LLC (PA)	2782	D	323 890-2100	7588
Urban Expressions Inc	3171	E	310 593-4574	10555
US Cover LLC	3448	F	323 838-2700	12968
US Polymers Inc	3354	F	323 727-6888	11610
Viatech Pubg Solutions Inc	2782	D	323 721-3629	7591
W R Grace & Co	2819	F	562 927-8513	7814
West Coast Catrg Trcks Mfg Inc	2511	F	323 278-1279	4748
Westcoast Inksolutions LLC	2893	F	323 726-8100	9215
Wiretech Inc (PA)	3315	D	323 722-4933	11466

	SIC	EMP	PHONE	ENTRY #
X-Igent Printing Inc	2752	F	323 837-9779	7192
Yavar Manufacturing Co Inc	2657	E	323 722-2040	5515
Zoo Piks International	2656	E	323 724-0503	5502

COMPTCHE, CA - Mendocino County

	SIC	EMP	PHONE	ENTRY #
Wells Dental Inc	3843	F	707 937-0521	22924

COMPTON, CA - Los Angeles County

	SIC	EMP	PHONE	ENTRY #
A & V Engineering Inc	3599	F	310 637-9906	16188
AAA Plating & Inspection Inc	3471	D	323 979-8930	13303
Accurate Anodizing Inc	3471	D	310 637-0349	13306
Ace Clearwater Enterprises Inc	3544	F	310 538-5380	14470
Advanced Materials Inc (HQ)	3086	E	310 537-5444	9812
Alameda Construction Svcs Inc	1442	E	310 635-3277	345
Allan Kidd	3643	E	310 762-1600	17442
Alpha Source Inc	2253	E	310 515-5560	2820
American Dawn Inc (PA)	2299	D	310 223-2000	2986
Andrew Alexander Inc	3111	D	323 752-0066	10457
Anoroc Precision Shtmtl Inc	3444	E	310 515-6015	12485
Audio Video Color Corporation (PA)	2671	D	424 213-7500	5519
Barkens Hardchrome Inc	3559	E	310 632-2000	14919
Bay Cities Italian Bakery Inc	2051	E	310 608-1881	1184
Bestway Hydraulics Co Inc	3561	D	310 639-2507	15054
BHC Industries Inc	3471	E	310 632-2000	13345
Bodycote Thermal Proc Inc	3398	E	310 604-8000	11797
Bowman Plating Co Inc	3471	C	310 639-4343	13352
Bruce Iversen	2448	E	310 537-4168	4456
Cal Pipe Manufacturing Inc (PA)	3498	C	562 803-4388	13880
California Decor	2431	E	310 603-9944	4115
California Metal Group Inc	3444	F	310 609-1400	12521
California Pak Intl Inc	3612	E	310 223-2000	17082
Cemex Cnstr Mtls PCF LLC	3273	C	310 603-9122	11079
Chem-Tainer Industries Inc	3089	E	310 635-5400	10024
Chemtex Print USA Inc	2759	E	310 900-1818	7270
Circle Industrial Mfg Corp (PA)	3567	E	310 638-5101	15255
Circle Industrial Mfg Corp	3542	E	310 638-5101	14435
Complete Cutng & Wldg Sups Inc	7692	F	310 638-1234	25396
Concrete Mold Corporation	3544	E	310 537-5171	14501
Continental Forge Company (PA)	3463	D	310 640-3104	13122
Cotton Knits Trading	2259	E	310 884-9600	2873
Cri Sub 1 (DH)	2521	E	310 537-1657	4941
Crossfield Products Corp (PA)	2821	D	310 886-9100	7827
De Menno-Kerdoon Trading Co (HQ)	2911	C	310 537-7100	9332
Demenno Kerdoon	1382	C	310 537-7100	133
E M E Inc	3471	C	310 639-1621	13393
Edmund Kim International Inc (PA)	2329	E	310 604-1100	3147
Electronic Stamping Corp	3613	E	310 639-2120	17145
Elite Leather LLC	2512	D	909 548-8600	4773
Elizabeths Food Co Inc (PA)	2051	E	310 638-2168	1245
Epsilon Plastics Inc	2673	D	310 609-1320	5600
ESP Corp	3679	E	310 639-2535	19536
Essilor Laboratories Amer Inc	3851	C	310 640-8468	23095
Excellon Acquisition LLC (HQ)	3559	F	310 668-7700	14951
Fastener Innovation Tech Inc	3451	D	310 538-1111	13023
First Choice International	3841	F	310 537-1500	22450
Fleetwood Continental Inc	3366	D	310 609-1477	11757
Flowserve Corporation	3561	D	310 667-4220	15064
Fmf Racing	3751	C	310 631-4363	21109
Foam Fabricators Inc	3089	F	310 537-5760	10103
Foam Factory Inc	3086	E	310 603-9808	9846
Forming Specialties Inc	3728	E	310 639-1122	20817
Foster Poultry Farms	2015	B	310 223-1499	543
Fs - Precision Tech Co LLC	3369	D	310 638-0595	11778
GP Design Inc	2396	E	310 638-8737	3895
Graphic Prints Inc	2396	E	310 768-0474	3896
Hammond Power Solutions Inc	3612	E	310 537-4690	17097
Harbor Green Grain LP	2048	E	310 609-1094	1136
Henkel Corporation	2843	C	310 764-4600	8686
Hf Group Inc (PA)	3861	E	310 605-0755	23162
Idemia America Corp	3089	C	310 884-7900	10147
Ilco Industries Inc	3498	E	310 631-8655	13890
Innovative Stamping Inc	3469	E	310 537-6996	13225
Insulated Products Corporation	2679	E	323 838-0900	5715
International Paper Company	2621	E	310 639-2310	5295
Ips Corporation (HQ)	2891	C	310 898-3300	9153
J L Furnishings LLC (PA)	2531	B	310 605-6600	5016
J L Furnishings LLC	2531	F	310 856-0412	5017
J&T Designs LLC	2599	E	310 868-5190	5238
James Kim Young	2339	E	310 605-5328	3433
Jaubin Sales & Mfg Corp	3444	F	310 631-8647	12628
Jbi LLC	2514	E	310 537-2910	4833
Jimway Inc	3648	D	310 886-3718	17705
Kens Spray Equipment Inc (DH)	3479	D	310 635-9995	13608
Kim & Roy Co Inc	2326	F	310 762-1896	3108
Kizure Product Co Inc	3634	E	310 604-0058	17395
Kmr Label LLC	2754	E	310 603-8910	7205

Name	SIC	EMP	PHONE	ENTRY #
Lamons Gasket Company	3053	F	310 886-1133	9541
Lekos Dye & Finishing Inc	2231	D	310 763-0900	2793
LMC Enterprises	2842	F	310 637-2124	8652
Los Angles Tmes Cmmnctions LLC	2711	F	310 638-9414	5931
Lynwood Pattern Service Inc	3365	F	310 631-2225	11745
M N M Manufacturing Inc	3442	D	310 898-1099	12329
Magnesium Alloy Pdts Co Inc	3363	E	310 605-1440	11699
Magnesium Alloy Products Co LP	3363	E	323 636-2276	11700
McCormick Fresh Herbs LLC	2099	D	323 278-9750	2603
Mercado Latino Inc	3999	E	310 537-1062	24173
Mikron Products Inc	3061	D	323 245-1251	9569
Morrells Electro Plating Inc	3471	E	310 639-1024	13459
Nabors Well Services Co	1389	C	310 639-7074	243
One Up Manufacturing LLC	2631	E	310 749-8347	5356
Optex Incorporated	3669	F	800 966-7839	18351
Orion Plastics Corporation	2821	D	310 223-0370	7862
Owens Corning Sales LLC	2952	C	310 631-1062	9416
Pacific Contntl Textiles Inc (HQ)	2269	E	310 604-1100	2916
Park Steel Co Inc	3441	F	310 638-6101	12227
Pedro Pallan	2051	F	310 638-1763	1308
Performance Composites Inc	3229	D	310 328-6661	10664
Permalite Plastics Corp	2865	F	310 669-9492	8965
Plaskolite West LLC	2821	F	310 637-2103	7866
Precision Babbitt Co Inc	3568	F	562 531-9173	15289
Prime Alliance LLC	2258	F	310 764-1000	2870
Prime Wheel Corporation	3714	E	310 516-9126	20425
Prison Ride Share Network	2741	E	314 703-5245	6557
Puratos Corporation	3556	F	310 632-1361	14879
Rsk Tool Incorporated	3089	F	310 537-3302	10350
S & K Plating Inc	3471	F	310 632-7141	13494
Sequoia Pure Water Inc	2086	F	310 637-8500	2218
Serra Manufacturing Corp (PA)	3469	E	310 537-4560	13273
Sew What Inc	2391	F	310 639-6000	3703
South Coast Screen and Casing	1389	F	310 632-3200	278
Ssb Manufacturing Company	2515	C	770 512-7700	4891
Tag Toys Inc	3999	D	310 639-4566	24264
Tajima USA Inc	3552	E	310 604-8200	14782
Techmer Pm Inc	2821	B	310 632-9211	7895
Technlgy Knwldgable Machining	3469	E	310 608-7756	13285
Thermal Equipment Corporation	3443	E	310 328-6600	12434
Trackstar Printing Inc	2752	F	310 216-1275	7139
Tridus International Inc	3499	E	310 884-3200	13979
Ufp Technologies Inc	3086	E	714 662-0277	9889
United Bakery Equipment Co Inc (PA)	3565	D	310 635-8121	15232
United Bakery Equipment Co Inc	3556	E	310 635-8121	14893
Utopia Lighting	3612	F	310 327-7711	17125
Viking Rubber Products Inc	3069	D	310 868-5200	9690
Visionaire Lighting LLC	3646	A	310 512-6480	17656
West Coast Aerospace Inc	3965	F	310 632-2064	23782
Young American Bindery	2789	E	310 898-1212	7625
Zoo Zoo Wham Whams Blip Blops	2299	F	213 248-9591	3022

CONCORD, CA - Contra Costa County

Name	SIC	EMP	PHONE	ENTRY #
Acme Press Inc	2752	D	925 682-1111	6639
Airgas Usa LLC	2813	F	925 969-0419	7682
Alvellan Inc	3599	E	925 689-2421	16264
Baker Petrolite LLC	1389	F	925 682-3313	180
Beko Radiator Cores Inc	3714	F	925 671-2975	20267
Benchmark Electronics Inc	3672	B	925 363-1151	18439
Biomicrolab Inc	3596	F	925 689-1200	16174
C&T Publishing Inc	2731	E	925 677-0377	6320
Cable Manufacturing Tech	2298	E	925 687-3700	2971
Cache Phlow Enterprise	2782	F	925 609-8649	7574
Caffe Classico Foods Inc	2095	F	925 602-5400	2336
Calex Mfg Co Inc	3679	E	925 687-4411	19477
Carols Roman Shades Inc (PA)	2591	E	925 674-9622	5184
Carols Roman Shades Inc	2591	F	925 674-9622	5185
Cemex Cnstr Mtls PCF LLC	3273	F	925 688-1025	11070
Cerus Corporation (PA)	3841	C	925 288-6000	22401
Clearwater Paper Corporation	2621	A	925 947-4700	5277
Cole Print & Marketing	2752	F	925 276-2344	6739
Contra Costa Newspapers Inc	2711	C	925 977-8520	5815
Coolsystems Inc (HQ)	3845	F	888 426-3732	22966
Cubic Trnsp Systems Inc	3829	F	925 348-9163	22183
Delta Rebar Services Inc	3441	F	925 798-4220	12152
Delta Turnstiles LLC	3699	F	925 969-1498	19943
Dresser-Rand LLC	3563	E	925 356-5700	15124
Eagle Iron Fabrication Inc	3446	F	925 686-9510	12851
Energy Steel Corporation	3599	F	925 685-5300	16474
Erg Transit Systems (usa) Inc	3589	C	925 686-8233	16039
Esmart Source Inc	7372	F	408 739-3500	24627
Force Flow	3545	E	925 686-6700	14633
Fresenius Usa Inc (DH)	2834	F	925 288-4218	8168
Frito-Lay North America Inc	2096	F	925 689-4260	2384
G Hartzell & Son Inc	3843	E	925 798-2206	22880
Gagne-Mulford Enterprises	3069	F	925 671-7434	9615

Name	SIC	EMP	PHONE	ENTRY #
Ggf Marble & Supply Inc	3281	F	925 676-8385	11252
GM Marble & Granite Inc	1429	F	925 676-8385	327
Golden State Granite Inc	2541	F	925 825-5888	5063
Hades Performance	2519	F	925 671-9197	4910
Hayward Pallet Company Inc	2448	F	510 538-3127	4476
Hnc Printing Services LLC	2752	F	925 689-1716	6860
Hyde Printing and Graphics	2752	F	925 686-4933	6865
Indepndent Flr Tstg Insptn Inc	3272	F	925 676-7682	10940
Laserbeam Software LLC	7372	F	925 459-2595	24845
Lehigh Southwest Cement Co (DH)	3241	F	972 653-5500	10762
Lids Corporation	2353	F	925 609-9516	3566
Marketing Bus Advantage Inc	3559	F	925 933-3637	14986
Marvac Scientific Mfg Co	3821	F	925 825-4636	21480
Meetville Inc	2741	C	415 755-0822	6526
Monterey Mechanical Co	3444	F	925 689-6670	12686
Nalco Company LLC	2899	F	800 798-2247	9286
New Logic Research Inc	3559	D	510 655-7305	15000
Pacific Instruments Inc	3829	F	925 827-9010	22247
Pacific Plaza Imports Inc (PA)	2091	E	925 349-4000	2300
Patriot Mritime Compliance LLC	3731	F	925 296-2000	21010
PPG Industries Inc	2851	F	925 798-0539	8925
Print-N-Stuff Inc	2752	F	925 798-3212	7041
Pulse Systems LLC	3842	F	925 798-4080	22799
Renaissance Precision Mfg Inc	3599	F	925 691-5997	16896
Sage (PA)	2836	F	925 288-4827	8578
Saxco International LLC (PA)	3221	F	844 766-7819	10627
Siemens Med Solutions USA Inc	3845	B	925 246-8200	23047
Smith & Nephew Inc	3842	E	925 681-3300	22815
Specialized Graphics Inc	3993	E	925 680-0265	23979
Sun Chemical Corporation	2893	C	925 695-2601	9210
Superheat Fgh Services Inc	3398	F	925 808-6711	11830
Systron Donner Inertial Inc	3679	C	925 979-4400	19741
Tech Air Northern Cal LLC	2813	F	925 568-9353	7736
Tuff Shed Inc	2452	F	925 681-3492	4582
West Coast Windows & Doors	3089	F	925 681-1776	10439

COOL, CA - El Dorado County

Name	SIC	EMP	PHONE	ENTRY #
A Teichert & Son Inc	1442	F	530 885-4244	339

COPPEROPOLIS, CA - Calaveras County

Name	SIC	EMP	PHONE	ENTRY #
Custom Equipment Coinc	3523	F	209 785-9891	14055
Meridian Gold Inc	1041	C	209 785-3222	7

CORCORAN, CA - Kings County

Name	SIC	EMP	PHONE	ENTRY #
Camfil USA Inc	3564	D	559 992-5118	15147
Clougherty Packing LLC	2013	F	559 992-8421	475
Corcoran Sawtelle Rosprim Inc	3441	F	559 992-2117	12144
Crookshanks Sales Co Inc	3273	F	559 992-5077	11100
Karl M Smith Inc	3444	E	559 992-4109	12637
Mar Vista Resources LLC	2873	F	559 992-4535	9065
Virtus Nutrition LLC	2048	F	559 992-5033	1169

CORNING, CA - Tehama County

Name	SIC	EMP	PHONE	ENTRY #
Barns By Harrahs	3448	F	530 824-4611	12920
Bell-Carter Foods Inc	2035	B	530 528-4820	910
Eco-Shell Inc	3999	F	530 824-8794	24085
Lucero Olive Oil Mnfacture LLC (PA)	2079	E	530 824-2190	1543
Sierra Pacific Industries	2431	B	530 824-2474	4228
Sunsweet Dryers	2034	F	530 824-5854	898
Thomes Creek Rock Co Inc	1442	F	530 824-0191	386

CORONA, CA - Riverside County

Name	SIC	EMP	PHONE	ENTRY #
2nd Gen Productions Inc	2842	F	800 877-6282	8614
2nd Gen Productions Inc	2842	F	951 280-9799	8615
3-V Fastener Co Inc	3452	D	951 734-4391	13055
3M Company	3295	C	951 737-3441	11314
A and M Ornamental Iron & Wldg	3446	F	951 734-6730	12821
Absolute Graphic Tech USA Inc	3625	E	909 597-1133	17246
Accent Plastics Inc	3089	D	951 273-7777	9918
Accurate Grinding and Mfg Corp	3724	C	951 479-0909	20640
Ace Heaters LLC	3585	E	951 738-2230	15932
Acker Stone Industries Inc (HQ)	3272	F	951 674-0047	10870
Acromil LLC	3599	D	951 808-9929	16218
Actavis LLC	2834	F	951 493-5582	7997
Actron Manufacturing Inc	3429	D	951 371-0885	11924
Adomani Inc	3714	F	951 407-9860	20239
Adura Led Solutions LLC	3672	F	714 660-2944	18408
Advanced Flow Engineering Inc (PA)	3714	D	951 493-7155	20243
Advanced Paper Forming LLC	3069	F	714 738-0300	9584
Aero-Craft Hydraulics Inc	3728	F	951 736-4690	20714
Aerospace Seals & Gaskets	3053	E	951 256-8380	9517
Aggregate Mining Products LLC	3561	F	951 277-1267	15051
Airspace Seal and Gasket Corp	3053	E	951 256-8380	9518
All Manufacturers Inc	3841	F	951 280-4200	22325
All Rise Records Inc	3634	F	951 279-2507	17385
Alpha Laser	3699	F	951 582-0285	19906
American National Mfg Inc	2515	C	951 273-7888	4850

	SIC	EMP	PHONE	ENTRY #
American Solar Advantage Inc	3674	E	951 496-1075	18692
Ameriflex Inc	3498	D	951 737-5557	13875
AMF Support Surfaces Inc (DH)	2515	C	951 549-6800	4851
Amrapur Overseas Incorporated (PA)	2299	D	714 893-8808	2988
Amron Manufacturing Inc	3728	F	714 278-9204	20736
Anaco Inc	3568	C	951 372-2732	15279
Anatomic Global Inc	2392	C	800 874-7237	3706
Anderson Bros Artistic Iron Co	3499	F	951 898-6880	13918
Approved Aeronautics LLC	3728	F	951 200-3730	20740
Aqua Mix Inc	2842	D	951 256-3040	8621
Aquatic Co (PA)	3088	D	714 993-1220	9896
Aqueous Technologies Corp	3589	E	909 944-7771	16012
Architectural Design Signs Inc (PA)	3993	E	951 278-0680	23818
Arms Precision Inc	3599	F	951 273-1800	16280
Artistic Plastics Inc	3089	F	951 808-9700	9959
Arvinyl Laminates LP	3081	E	951 371-7800	9697
Aseptic Sltons USA Vntures LLC	2086	C	951 736-9230	2096
Asturies Manufacturing Co Inc	3728	E	951 270-1766	20747
Avalon Mfg Co Incoirporated	3556	F	951 340-0280	14835
B & G Aerospace Metals	3369	E	951 738-8133	11770
B/E Aerospace Inc	3728	C	951 278-4563	20754
Band-It Rubber Company Inc	3069	F	951 735-5072	9593
Best- In- West	2395	E	909 947-6507	3830
Big Gun Inc	3714	F	714 970-0423	20269
Bills Pipes Inc	3751	E	951 371-1329	21092
Bimbo Bakeries Usa Inc	2051	F	951 280-9044	1189
Blue Desert International Inc	3589	D	951 273-7575	16020
Brasscraft Manufacturing Co	3494	D	951 735-4375	13762
Bu LLC	2082	F	951 277-7470	1575
C S America Inc (HQ)	2282	E	323 583-7627	2949
Cadence Gourmet LLC	2099	E	951 272-5949	2477
Cal Precision Inc	3599	E	951 273-9901	16354
California Wire Products Corp	3496	E	951 371-7730	13816
Carter Holt Harvey Holdings	3312	D	951 272-8180	11387
Case Automation Corporation	3535	F	951 493-6666	14268
Century Blinds Inc	2591	D	951 734-3762	5186
Certainteed Corona Inc	3089	E	951 272-1300	10019
Chandler Aggregates Inc (PA)	1411	E	951 277-1341	301
Circor Aerospace Inc	3728	B	951 270-6200	20781
Circor Aerospace Inc (HQ)	3491	C	951 270-6200	13711
Circor Aerospace Inc	3429	C	951 270-6200	11944
Circor Aerospace Pdts Group	3324	B	951 270-6200	11510
Clarcor Air Filtration Pdts	3564	C	951 272-1850	15149
Clear Path Technologies Inc	3699	F	951 278-3520	19928
Columbia Aluminum Products LLC	3354	D	323 728-7361	11585
Computrus Inc	3443	E	951 245-9103	12377
Corona Magnetics Inc	3677	C	951 735-7558	19329
Cramer Engineering Inc	3599	E	562 903-5556	16407
Creative Color Printing Inc	2752	F	951 737-4551	6766
Cremach Tech Inc (PA)	3541	D	951 735-3194	14364
Cremach Tech Inc	3541	F	951 735-3194	14365
Crescent Woodworking Co Ltd	2511	F	909 673-9955	4686
CTA Manufacturing Inc	2393	E	951 280-2400	3762
Currie Enterprises	3714	E	714 528-6957	20303
Custom Quality Door & Trim Inc	2431	F	951 278-0066	4133
Dacon Systems Inc	3357	F	951 735-2100	11657
Dairy Farmers America Inc	2026	F	951 493-4900	719
Dairy Farmers America Inc	2026	F	209 883-4461	720
Dart Container Corp California (PA)	3086	B	951 735-8115	9833
Data Physics Corporation	3559	E	408 216-8443	14939
Decra Roofing Systems Inc (DH)	3444	D	951 272-8180	12554
Della Robbia Inc	2515	E	951 372-9199	4859
Developlus Inc	3999	D	951 738-8595	24078
Dietzgen Corporation	2679	E	951 278-3259	5709
Do It American Mfg Company LLC	3499	F	951 254-9204	13935
Duonetics	3561	F	951 808-4903	15060
Duralum Products Inc	3355	F	951 764-4500	11617
Eclypse International Corp (PA)	3825	F	951 371-8008	21744
Eibach Springs Inc	3493	D	951 256-8300	13749
Eknowledge Group Inc	7372	E	951 256-4076	24599
Elastomer Technologies Inc	3053	F	951 272-5820	9527
Electrasem Corp	3822	F	951 371-6140	21511
Engineered Food Systems	3589	E	714 921-9913	16038
Ergononmic Comfort Design Inc	2522	F	951 277-1558	4985
Esl Power Systems Inc	3643	D	800 922-4188	17466
Excel Cabinets Inc	2434	E	951 279-4545	4299
Exide Technologies	3691	E	951 520-0677	19807
Extrumed Inc (DH)	3089	E	951 547-7400	10096
F & L Tools Corporation	3728	F	951 279-1555	20810
Fender Musical Instrs Corp	3931	A	480 596-9690	23370
Fiore Stone Inc	3272	F	909 424-0221	10926
Fireblast Global Inc	3569	F	951 277-8319	15320
Firstar International Group	3533	F	918 845-2402	14223
Fischer Mold Incorporated	3089	D	951 279-1140	10100
Fischler Investments Inc (DH)	2087	F	951 479-4682	2260
Fleetwood Enterprises Inc (DH)	3799	C	951 354-3000	21228
Fleetwood Enterprises Inc	2451	B	951 750-1971	4554
Fleetwood Homes of Kentucky (DH)	2451	F	800 688-1745	4560
Fletcher Bldg Holdings USA Inc (DH)	3444	D	951 272-8180	12587
Fmk Labs Inc	2844	E	951 736-1212	8749
Food For Life Baking Co Inc (PA)	2051	D	951 273-3031	1251
Four Seasons Restaurant Eqp	3444	E	951 278-9100	12591
Fovell Enterprises Inc	3993	E	951 734-6275	23882
Frutarom	2087	E	951 734-6620	2265
G & N Rubicon Gear Inc	3462	D	951 278-9860	13101
Gail Materials Inc	1442	E	951 667-6106	358
Galleys Plus Custom Cabinets	2434	E	951 278-4596	4305
Gibson Performance Corporation	3714	D	951 372-1220	20352
Glasman Shim & Stamping Inc	3569	F	951 278-8197	15326
Grand Metals Inc	3312	F	310 327-5554	11397
Grand Pacific Fire Protection	3524	F	951 226-8304	14127
Growest Inc (PA)	2084	E	951 638-1000	1799
H & N Tool & Die Co Inc	3542	F	951 372-9071	14437
Handbill Printers LP	2752	E	951 547-5910	6848
Hannan Products Corp (PA)	3565	F	951 735-1987	15208
Hanson Aggregates LLC	3241	F	951 371-7625	10755
Harrington Hoists Inc	3536	F	717 665-2000	14297
Herff Jones LLC	3911	F	951 541-3938	23273
His Company Inc	2672	E	951 493-0200	5562
Hoosier Plstic Fabrication Inc	3089	C	951 272-3070	10139
Icsn Inc	3363	F	951 687-2305	11696
Imperial Manufacturing Co	3589	C	951 281-1830	16054
Industrial Eqp Solutions Inc	3569	F	951 272-9540	15332
Inland Mailing Services Inc	2752	D	951 371-6245	6887
International Wind Inc (PA)	3724	E	562 240-3963	20664
Interstate Cabinet Inc	3999	E	951 736-0777	24132
J & L Metal Products	3444	F	951 278-0100	12627
Janda Company Inc	3548	E	951 734-1935	14727
Jayco Interface Technology Inc	3679	F	951 738-2000	19596
Jayco Mmi Inc	3679	F	951 738-2000	19597
Jhawar Industries Inc (PA)	3567	E	951 340-4646	15265
Jim Perry	2789	E	909 947-0747	7604
Johnson Caldraul Inc	3728	E	951 340-1067	20858
K & W Manufacturing Co Inc	3429	F	951 277-3300	11967
K S Printing Inc	2759	F	951 268-5180	7368
Kap Medical	3829	E	951 340-4360	22223
Kobelco Compressors Amer Inc	3563	D	951 739-3030	15129
Kobelco Compressors Amer Inc (HQ)	3563	D	951 739-3030	15130
Kurz Transfer Products LP	3999	E	951 738-9521	24153
Laticrete International Inc	3241	F	951 277-1776	10759
Lavey Craft Prfmce Boats Inc	3732	F	951 273-9690	21049
Le Elegant Bath Inc	3088	C	951 734-0238	9906
Leepers Wood Turning Co Inc (PA)	2431	D	562 422-6525	4183
Legacy Vulcan LLC	1422	E	714 737-2922	313
Lejon of California Inc	2387	E	951 736-1229	3630
Lock America Inc	3429	E	951 277-5180	11971
Lucas Oil Products Inc (PA)	2992	C	951 270-0154	9444
M & O Perry Industries Inc	3565	E	951 734-9838	15216
Machine Control Tech Inc	3825	E	951 808-0973	21796
Machine Control Tech Inc	3613	E	951 808-0973	17150
Maruhachi Ceramics America Inc	3259	E	800 736-6221	10802
Maskell Pipe & Supply Inc (PA)	3317	F	909 574-8662	11483
Master Fab Inc	3444	F	951 247-4772	12656
MBC Mattress Co Inc	2515	E	951 371-8044	4873
MCP Industries Inc (PA)	3069	E	951 736-1881	9635
MCP Industries Inc	3432	E	951 736-1313	12040
MD Engineering Inc	3599	E	951 736-5390	16729
Meggitt Airdynamics Inc (DH)	3564	E	951 734-0070	15168
Merit Aluminum Inc (PA)	3354	E	951 735-1770	11595
Merrick Engineering Inc (PA)	3089	C	951 737-6040	10209
Mighty Mover Trailers Inc	3799	E	951 736-0225	21235
Millworx Prcsion Machining Inc	3599	E	951 371-2683	16753
Mission Rubber Company LLC (HQ)	3494	D	951 736-1313	13771
Monson Machine Inc	3599	E	951 736-6615	16766
Monster Beverage 1990 Corp (HQ)	2086	D	951 739-6200	2150
Monster Beverage Company	2086	A	866 322-4466	2151
Monster Beverage Corporation	2086	D	951 739-6200	2152
Motor Technology Inc	3621	E	951 270-6200	17211
MS Industrial Shtmtl Inc	3444	F	951 272-6610	12689
Multimedia Led Inc (PA)	3679	F	951 280-7500	19656
Nafm LLC (PA)	3565	F	951 738-1114	15219
National Certified Fabricators	3677	F	951 278-8992	19348
Navcom Defense Electronics Inc (PA)	3812	D	951 268-9205	21355
Never Scrub	2841	F	951 272-9922	8599
Nibco Inc	3499	C	951 737-5599	13960
Northrop Grumman Innovation	3764	D	951 520-7300	21180
Northwestern Converting Co	3991	D	800 959-3402	23795
Nucast Industries Inc	3272	F	951 277-8888	10962
Oak-It Inc	2431	E	951 735-5973	4205
Omni Connection Intl Inc	3679	B	951 898-6232	19671

Employment Codes: A=Over 500 employees, B=251-500,
C=101-250, D=51-100, E=20-50, F=10-19

2019 California
Manufacturers Register

© Mergent Inc. 1-800-342-5647
1369

GEOGRAPHIC

	SIC	EMP	PHONE	ENTRY #
Optimum Bioenergy Intl Corp	2833	F	714 903-8872	7962
Organic Bottle Dctg Co LLC	2631	E	951 335-4600	5357
Pacific Packaging McHy LLC (HQ)	3556	E	949 369-2425	14875
Pacifica Foods LLC	2033	E	951 371-3123	847
Pacifica Foods LLC (PA)	2035	E	951 371-3123	928
Panel Shop Inc	3613	E	951 739-7000	17153
Panrosa Enterprises Inc	2841	D	951 339-5888	8603
Paragon Tactical Inc	3949	F	951 736-9440	23628
Parker-Hannifin Corporation	3594	E	951 280-3800	16170
Peabody Engineering & Sup Inc	3559	E	951 734-7711	15006
Pet Partners Inc (PA)	3999	C	951 279-9888	24208
Pheonica Inc	2759	F	951 268-5180	7435
Plas-Tech Sealing Tech LLC	2891	E	951 737-2228	9161
Polara Engineering Inc	3679	D	951 547-5500	19686
Polyair Inter Pack Inc	2394	D	951 737-7125	3805
Praxair Distribution Inc	2813	E	951 736-8113	7723
Precise Aerospace Mfg Inc	3089	E	951 898-0500	10302
Precision Injection Molding Co	3089	F	951 272-8028	10303
Premier Gear & Machining Inc	3462	E	951 278-5505	13112
Premier Steel Structures Inc	3441	E	951 356-6655	12232
Preproduction Plastics Inc	3089	E	951 340-9680	10308
Price Manufacturing Co Inc	3451	E	951 371-5660	13039
Pro Circuit Products Inc	3751	F	951 734-3320	21132
Proformance Manufacturing Inc	3469	E	951 279-1230	13265
Programmed Composites Inc	3728	C	951 520-7300	20916
Progressive Marketing Pdts Inc	3448	D	714 888-1700	12957
PSW Inc	2099	F	951 371-7100	2644
Purosil LLC	2869	F	951 271-3900	9035
Purosil LLC (HQ)	2869	E	951 271-3900	9036
PVA Tepla America Inc (HQ)	3599	E	951 371-2500	16866
Quikrete California LLC	3272	C	951 277-3155	10984
R & J Fabricators Inc	2599	E	951 817-0300	5250
R & R Stamping Four Slide Corp	3469	D	909 595-6444	13269
R W Lyall & Company Inc (DH)	1382	C	951 270-1500	147
R&M Deese Inc	3993	E	951 734-7342	23948
Red Star Fertilizer Co	2873	D	909 597-4801	9070
Rehau Incorporated	3084	F	951 549-9017	9789
Renu Chem Inc	2842	F	951 736-8072	8674
Republic Bag Inc (PA)	2673	C	951 734-9740	5618
Rey Nelson Printing Inc	2752	F	909 947-3505	7084
RGF Enterprises Inc	3479	E	951 734-6922	13648
Richards Neon Shop Inc	3993	E	951 279-6767	23952
Rivas Industries Inc	2752	E	951 880-8638	7085
Robertsons Ready Mix Ltd (HQ)	3273	D	951 493-6500	11167
Robertsons Ready Mix Ltd	3273	E	800 834-7557	11169
Roto Power Inc	3089	F	951 751-9850	10345
S C R Molding Inc	3089	E	951 736-5490	10354
Saleen Automotive Inc (PA)	3465	E	800 888-8945	13143
Saleen Incorporated (PA)	3711	B	714 400-2121	20170
Sammons Equipment Mfg Corp	2599	F	951 340-3419	5254
Sas Manufacturing Inc	3679	E	951 734-1808	19718
Service Rock Products Corp	3273	F	760 245-7997	11173
Shim-It Corporation	3728	F	562 467-8600	20930
Simsolve	3312	F	951 898-6880	11420
Sinkpad LLC	3679	F	714 660-2944	19725
Sora Power Inc (PA)	3679	E	951 479-9880	19731
Specialty Finance Inc	3469	E	951 735-5200	13279
Spectra Color Inc	2816	E	951 277-0200	7746
Spenuzza Inc (PA)	3589	C	951 281-1830	16112
Spring Delgau Inc	3495	E	951 371-1000	13802
Sprite Industries Incorporated	3826	E	951 735-1015	22021
Sream Inc	3231	E	951 245-6999	10732
Stang Industries Inc	3999	F	714 556-0222	24253
Stell Industries Inc	3448	E	951 369-8777	12962
Sterno Group LLC (DH)	3589	E	800 669-6699	16117
Sterno Products LLC (DH)	3589	E	951 682-9600	16118
Stj Orthotic Services Inc	3842	E	951 279-5650	22822
Summit Industries Inc	3441	E	951 739-5900	12252
Sun Precision Machining Inc	3599	F	951 817-0056	16970
Superior Ready Mix Concrete LP	3273	E	951 277-3553	11194
Suss McRtec Phtnic Systems Inc	3699	D	951 817-3700	20084
Suss Microtec Inc (HQ)	3559	C	408 940-0300	15034
T-Rex Truck Products Inc	3465	E	800 287-5900	13145
Tamshell Corp	3089	E	951 272-9395	10399
Taylor Communications Inc	2761	E	951 203-9011	7554
Technical America Inc	3999	D	951 272-9540	24267
Technicote Inc	2891	E	951 372-0627	9176
Temeka Advertising Inc	2541	E	951 277-2525	5112
Thermal Structures Inc (DH)	3724	B	951 736-9911	20682
Thoro-Packaging (DH)	2657	C	951 278-2100	5512
Tiffany Coachworks Inc	3711	E	951 657-2680	20178
TNT Plastic Molding Inc (PA)	3089	C	951 808-9700	10406
Tolar Manufacturing Co Inc	3441	E	951 808-0081	12262
Tree House Pad & Paper Inc	2678	D	800 213-4184	5689
Trendpoint Systems Inc	3825	F	925 855-0600	21880
Trical Inc	2879	F	951 737-6960	9118
TRM Manufacturing Inc	3081	C	951 256-8550	9733
Tube Technologies Inc	3714	E	951 371-4878	20470
UBS Printing Group Inc	2752	D	951 273-7900	7152
United Metal Products Inc	3399	C	951 739-9535	11851
Uniweb Inc (PA)	2542	D	951 279-7999	5174
US Continental Marketing Inc (PA)	2842	F	951 808-8888	8682
Vantage Vehicle Intl Inc	3694	E	951 735-1200	19850
Vinylvisions Company LLC	2851	E	800 321-8746	8953
Volvo Construction Eqp & Svcs	3531	E	951 277-7620	14198
W J Ellison Co Inc	3565	E	626 814-4766	15235
Webb-Stotler Engineering	3599	F	951 735-2040	17055
Wellington Foods Inc	2032	E	562 989-0111	781
Werner Corporation	3273	F	951 277-4586	11212
West Coast Porcelain Inc	3269	E	951 278-8680	10838
Western Equipment Mfg Inc	3531	F	951 284-2000	14199
Westrock Cp LLC	2653	C	951 734-1870	5470
Winbo Usa Inc	3444	E	951 738-9978	12820
Youcare Pharma (usa) Inc	2834	D	951 258-3114	8448
Zap Printing Incorporated	2752	F	951 734-8181	7194

CORONA DEL MAR, CA - Orange County

	SIC	EMP	PHONE	ENTRY #
Duron Incorporated	3559	E	949 721-0900	14940
Pfanner Communications Inc	2721	F	714 227-3579	6232

CORONADO, CA - San Diego County

	SIC	EMP	PHONE	ENTRY #
Eagle Newspapers LLC	2711	E	619 437-8800	5836
Earthologytech LLC	3523	E	619 435-5296	14066
Intercom Energy Inc	3612	F	619 863-9644	17100
Makerplace Inc	3944	F	619 435-1279	23438
University Blanket & Flag Corp (PA)	2399	F	619 435-4100	3969

CORTE MADERA, CA - Marin County

	SIC	EMP	PHONE	ENTRY #
Michaels Furniture Company Inc	2511	B	916 381-9086	4719
Micromega Systems Inc	7372	F	415 924-4700	24907
Pacific Catch Inc	2048	F	415 504-6905	1154
Quantum Solar Inc	3674	F	415 924-8140	19109

COSTA MESA, CA - Orange County

	SIC	EMP	PHONE	ENTRY #
Action Broaching Inc	3599	F	949 645-8212	16220
Advanced Conservation Technolo	3433	F	714 668-1200	12057
Advanced Micro Instruments Inc	3826	E	714 848-5533	21893
Advanced Prcsion Machining Inc	3599	F	949 650-6113	16232
Agility Fuel Systems LLC (DH)	3714	C	949 236-5520	20248
Agility Fuel Systems LLC	3519	F	256 831-6155	14013
Akzo Nobel Inc	2869	F	714 966-0934	8973
Allura Printing Inc	2752	F	714 433-0200	6651
Analog Devices Inc	3674	E	714 641-9391	18699
Armite Laboratories Inc	2992	F	949 646-9035	9424
Armstrong Petroleum Corp (PA)	1311	F	949 650-4000	23
Asml Inc	2752	F	714 754-1912	6670
Associated Microbreweries Inc	2082	D	714 546-2739	1563
Astro Haven Enterprises Inc	3829	F	949 215-3777	22165
Atomic Aquatics Inc (PA)	3949	F	714 375-1433	23508
Auto Club Enterprises	2721	B	714 885-2376	6106
Baier Marine Company Inc	3429	E	800 455-3917	11935
Batida Inc	2752	F	714 557-4597	6687
Bay Ornamental Iron Inc	3446	F	949 548-1015	12836
Bdfco Inc	3669	D	714 228-2900	18310
Beekee Corp	7372	F	949 275-5861	24413
Bio Creative Enterprises	2844	F	714 352-3600	8702
Blue Sphere Inc	2311	F	714 953-7555	3026
Burns Stainless LLC	3714	F	949 631-5120	20277
C-Fab	3429	E	949 646-2616	11940
California Blimps	3721	F	949 650-1183	20571
Caperon Designs Inc	3944	F	714 552-3201	23415
CCI Industries Inc (PA)	3089	F	714 662-3879	10015
Cevians LLC	3211	D	714 619-5135	10591
Chet Cooper	2721	F	949 854-8700	6128
Chup Corporation	2752	F	949 455-0676	6732
Cisco Systems Inc	3577	F	714 434-2100	15707
Coach Inc	3171	F	949 365-0771	10544
Coast Sheet Metal Inc	3444	E	949 645-2224	12533
Coiltech Incorporated	3677	F	714 708-8715	19327
Concept Studio Inc	3253	F	949 759-0606	10779
Contech Engnered Solutions Inc	3317	A	714 281-7883	11477
Cosmic Fog Vapors	2111	D	949 266-1730	2704
Criterion Machine Works	3545	E	949 631-5444	14621
CRP Sports LLC	3999	F	949 395-7759	24070
Crystaliner Corp	3732	E	949 548-0292	21027
Cytec Aerospace Mtls CA Inc	2295	C	714 899-0400	2958
Darcy AK Corporation	3599	F	949 645-5460	16421
Delphi Display Systems Inc	3577	D	714 825-3400	15728
Djh Enterprises	3663	F	714 424-6500	18088
Duffield Marine Inc (PA)	3732	E	760 246-1211	21033
Dynamic Cooking Systems Inc	3589	A	714 372-7000	16035
Dynglobal California Corp	3589	F	949 584-6198	16036

Mergent email: customerrelations@mergent.com

1370

2019 California
Manufacturers Register

(P-0000) Products & Services Section entry number
(PA)=Parent Co (HQ)=Headquarters (DH)=Div Headquarters

Company	SIC	EMP	PHONE	ENTRY #
E Virtual Corporation	3651	F	949 515-3670	17795
Eba Design Inc	2844	F	714 417-9222	8741
Ebanista Inc (PA)	2512	E	949 650-6397	4771
El Metate Foods Inc	2051	F	949 646-9362	1243
Emulex Design & Mfg Corp	3674	B	714 662-5600	18820
Endural LLC	3083	F	714 434-6533	9748
Eq Technologic Inc	7372	F	215 891-9010	24623
Eventure Interactive Inc	7372	F	855 986-5669	24630
Eyebrain Medical Inc	3851	F	949 339-5157	23097
Falkor Partners LLC	3674	D	714 721-8772	18841
Fineline Woodworking Inc	2431	F	714 540-5468	4155
Fire & Safety Electronics Inc	3625	E	714 850-1320	17270
Fisher & Paykel Appliances Inc (DH)	3639	C	949 790-8900	17414
Fisker Auto & Tech Group LLC	3711	C	714 723-3247	20141
Flare Group	3728	E	714 850-2080	20813
Fxc Corporation	2399	D	714 557-8032	3949
Fxc Corporation (PA)	3429	E	714 556-7400	11955
Gs Manufacturing	3563	F	949 642-1500	15127
Gsp Precision Inc	3599	E	818 845-2212	16546
Hamax America Inc (PA)	3826	F	714 641-7528	21963
Handcraft Mattress Company	2515	F	714 241-8316	4862
Hartley Company	3951	E	949 646-9643	23699
Haze Bert and Assosaties	1389	F	714 557-1567	221
Hurley International Inc (HQ)	2329	C	949 548-9375	3162
Husky Injection Molding	3089	F	714 545-8200	10144
Hw Holdco LLC	2721	F	714 540-8500	6185
Impac Technologies Inc	3663	D	714 427-2000	18130
Indian Ink Screen Print	2759	E	714 437-0882	7354
Irvine Sensors Corporation	3674	F	714 444-8700	18932
Jennis Group LLC	2741	F	714 227-7972	6506
Jenny Sammon	3728	F	951 926-4326	20855
JG Plastics Group LLC	3089	F	714 751-4266	10170
Kelly Pneumatics Inc	3699	F	949 278-5721	19996
Kingsley Mfg Co (PA)	3842	F	949 645-4401	22764
Kyocera Precision Tools Inc	3541	C	714 428-3600	14387
L & L Custom Shutters Inc	2431	C	714 996-9539	4180
L & S Machine Inc	3451	F	562 924-9007	13030
Labworks Inc	3679	F	714 549-1981	19615
Lambda Research Optics Inc	3826	D	714 327-0600	21982
Lava Products Inc	2752	E	949 951-7191	6939
Lexmark International Inc	3577	E	714 641-1000	15788
Livetime Software Inc	7372	F	415 905-4009	24862
Lynx Studio Technology Inc	3651	F	714 545-4700	17826
Macgregor Yacht Corporation	3732	D	310 621-2206	21052
Maurer Marine Inc	3732	F	949 645-7673	21055
Max-Q Systems Inc	2842	F	714 259-0181	8654
Membrane Switch and Panel Inc	3679	F	714 957-6905	19644
Metal X Direct Inc	3446	F	949 336-0055	12881
Mina Product Development Inc	3089	F	714 966-2150	10213
Minute Man Envmtl Systems Inc	2752	E	949 637-5446	6976
Mirth Corporation	7372	F	714 389-1200	24925
Moleculum	2911	F	714 619-5139	9340
Mpc Networkcom Inc	2741	F	949 873-1002	6533
Newport Custom Woodworking	2431	F	949 631-6397	4201
Newport Medical Instrs Inc	3841	D	949 642-3910	22557
Newport Mesa Usd Campus C	2752	F	714 424-8939	6991
Nils Inc (PA)	2339	F	714 755-1600	3470
Npi Services Inc	3672	F	714 850-0550	18548
Nwp Services Corporation (HQ)	7372	C	949 253-2500	24978
Old Bones Co	2512	F	714 641-2800	4802
Orange Coast Reprographics Inc	2752	E	949 548-5571	7006
Pacific Athletic Wear Inc	2339	D	714 751-8006	3475
Phillips-Medisize	3841	C	949 477-9495	22584
Pinecraft Custom Shutters Inc	2431	F	949 642-9317	4213
Pinpoint Media Group Inc	2721	F	714 545-5640	6233
Prb Logics Corp	3679	F	951 255-8963	19688
Preferred Milling Inc	2421	F	714 754-4230	4047
Pro-Lite Inc	3993	F	714 668-9988	23946
Qsc LLC (PA)	3651	B	714 754-6175	17848
Quilter Laboratories LLC	3931	F	714 519-6114	23382
Railmakers Inc	3429	F	949 642-6506	11986
Resinart Corporation	3089	F	949 642-3665	10333
Rip Curl Inc (DH)	3949	D	714 422-3600	23636
RPM Embroidery Inc	2395	F	949 650-0085	3860
Rss Manufacturing	3432	F	714 361-4800	12048
S E P E Inc	3571	E	714 241-7373	15480
Saddleback Educational Inc	2731	F	949 860-2500	6388
Safran Elec Def Avnics USA LLC	3812	C	949 642-2427	21421
Sakura Paper Inc	2679	F	714 886-3791	5732
Sanmina Corporation	3672	D	714 377-2800	18598
Sanmina Corporation	3672	C	714 913-2200	18600
Schneider Electric It Usa	3679	B	714 513-7313	19720
Schneider Electric Usa Inc	3699	E	714 662-4432	20063
Sellers Optical Inc	3827	D	949 631-6800	22134
Semicoa Corporation	3674	E	714 979-1900	19141

Company	SIC	EMP	PHONE	ENTRY #
Skyco Skylights Inc	3211	E	949 629-4090	10606
Smiths Intrcnnect Americas Inc	3679	B	714 371-1100	19728
Ss Metal Fabricators	3441	F	949 631-4272	12246
Starlineoem Inc	3612	F	949 342-8889	17122
Sunburst Products Inc	3873	E	949 722-0158	23224
Suns Out Inc	3944	F	714 556-2314	23469
Swiss Wire EDM	3599	F	714 540-2903	16979
Taylor Communications Inc	2761	E	714 708-2005	7558
Team China California LLC	3826	F	714 424-9999	22025
Team Color Inc	2396	E	949 646-6486	3925
Thomson Reuters Corporation	2741	B	949 400-7782	6602
Thoreen Designs Inc	2392	E	949 645-0981	3753
Tk Pax Inc	3052	E	714 850-1330	9510
Ttm Technologies Inc (PA)	3672	B	714 327-3000	18633
Unity Sales International Inc	3861	F	714 800-1700	23207
Vans Inc (DH)	3021	B	855 909-8267	9495
Vending Security Products	3443	F	949 646-1474	12438
West Newport Oil Company	1311	F	949 631-1100	87
Westar Nutrition Corp	2833	C	949 645-6100	7982
Wonder Grip USA Inc	3089	F	404 290-2015	10450
World Manufacturing Inc (PA)	3083	F	714 662-3539	9772
Ziething Cabinets Inc	2434	F	949 642-6344	4375

COTATI, CA - Sonoma County

Company	SIC	EMP	PHONE	ENTRY #
Barlow and Sons Printing Inc	2752	F	707 664-9773	6684
Biotherm Hydronic Inc	3433	F	707 794-9660	12058
H & H Enterprises Inc	2759	F	707 794-9988	7340
J&M Manufacturing Inc	3679	F	707 795-8223	19591
Lili Butler Studio Inc	2331	F	707 793-0222	3253
Making It Big Inc	2331	F	707 795-1995	3257
Rich Xiberta Usa Inc	2499	F	707 795-1800	4647
San Franstitchco Inc	2395	F	707 795-6891	3861
Shades Unlimited Inc	2591	F	707 285-2233	5209
Shamrock Materials Inc	3273	F	707 792-4695	11177
Stony Point Rock Quarry Inc (PA)	1442	F	707 795-1775	384
Studio 311 Inc	3911	F	707 795-6599	23321
Windsor Willits Company (PA)	2431	E	707 665-9663	4259

COTTONWOOD, CA - Shasta County

Company	SIC	EMP	PHONE	ENTRY #
Borden Manufacturing	3542	E	530 347-6642	14431
Plum Valley Inc	2421	E	530 262-6262	4046

COVELO, CA - Mendocino County

Company	SIC	EMP	PHONE	ENTRY #
Wylatti Resource MGT Inc	2411	E	707 983-8135	4027

COVINA, CA - Los Angeles County

Company	SIC	EMP	PHONE	ENTRY #
Amity Rubberized Pen Company	3951	E	626 969-0863	23697
Apricot Designs Inc	3841	E	626 966-3299	22343
Azusa Engineering Inc	3714	F	626 966-4071	20264
Caco-Pacific Corporation (PA)	3544	C	626 331-3361	14490
Chemeor Inc	2843	E	626 966-3808	8685
Cobel Technologies Inc	3613	E	626 332-2100	17136
Composites Horizons LLC (HQ)	3728	C	626 331-0861	20784
Covina Welding & Shtmtl Inc	3441	F	626 332-6293	12145
Cozzia USA LLC	3699	E	626 667-2272	19934
Data Label Products Inc	2679	F	626 915-6478	5708
Dauntless Industries Inc	3544	F	626 966-4494	14503
Dexin International Inc	3646	C	626 859-7475	17597
Don Pedros Meat	2011	F	626 339-3963	431
Edgewell Per Care Brands LLC	3421	B	949 466-0131	11879
Excelitas Technologies Corp	3829	C	626 967-6021	22195
G & D Industries Inc	3089	F	626 331-1250	10110
Haemonetics Manufacturing Inc (HQ)	3841	E	626 339-7388	22465
Hydro Fitting Mfg Corp	3491	E	626 967-5151	13719
Jeff J Polich Inc	3825	F	626 339-3070	21781
Matrix Document Imaging Inc	2759	D	626 966-9959	7397
Monterey Machine Products	3599	F	626 967-2242	16768
Moores Ideal Products LLC	3944	F	626 339-9007	23448
Pall Corporation	3569	B	626 339-7388	15347
Payne Magnetics Inc	3677	D	626 332-6207	19350
Physicians Formula Inc	2844	D	626 334-3395	8817
Processors Mailing Inc	2752	E	626 358-5075	7053
Qingmu International Inc	2759	F	626 965-7277	7454
R M Baker Machine & Tool Inc	3599	F	562 697-4007	16880
Raytheon Company	3812	C	626 675-2584	21389
RG Costumes & Accessories Inc	2389	F	626 858-9559	3677
RSR Metal Spinning Inc	3444	F	626 814-2339	12744
Shift Calendars Inc	2752	F	626 967-5862	7103
Short Run Swiss Inc	3599	F	626 974-9373	16945
Stabile Plating Company Inc	3471	F	626 339-9091	13509
Supermedia LLC	2741	B	626 331-9440	6597
Terra Furniture Inc	2512	E	626 912-8523	4816
Topper Plastics Inc	3086	F	626 331-0561	9888
Vans Instant Printers Inc	2752	F	626 966-1708	7164
Vipology Inc	2741	F	626 502-8661	6618
Vishay Intertechnology Inc	3676	F	626 331-0502	19310
Vita-Pakt Citrus Products Co (PA)	2033	E	626 332-1101	869

GEOGRAPHIC

Company	SIC	EMP	PHONE	ENTRY #
Westrock Rkt Company	2653	C	626 859-7633	5476
William J Hammett Inc	2752	F	626 966-1708	7187

CRESCENT CITY, CA - Del Norte County
Fashion Blacksmith Inc	3732	F	707 464-9219	21037
Rumiano Cheese Co	2022	E	707 465-1535	597
William McClung	3944	F	970 535-4601	23479

CRESCENT MILLS, CA - Plumas County
Pew Forest Products Inc	2421	E	530 284-7882	4044

CRESTLINE, CA - San Bernardino County
Alpenhorn Crestline Chronicle	2711	E	909 338-8484	5756

CRESTON, CA - San Luis Obispo County
Calf Canyon Winery LLC	2084	F	805 226-8600	1677

CROCKETT, CA - Contra Costa County
C&H Sugar Company Inc	2062	A	510 787-2121	1401
C&H Sugar Company Inc	2062	B	510 787-6763	1402

CROWS LANDING, CA - Stanislaus County
Darling International Inc	2077	E	209 667-9153	1527
San Joaquin Tomato Growers Inc	2033	F	209 837-4721	854

CUDAHY, CA - Los Angeles County
Alamillo Radolfo	3229	F	323 773-9614	10630
All American Frame & Bedg Corp	2514	E	323 773-7415	4822
Artsons Manufacturing Company	3312	E	323 773-3469	11379
Consoldted Precision Pdts Corp	3365	C	323 773-2363	11729
Day-Glo Color Corp	2816	E	323 560-2000	7741
Dur-Red Products	3444	E	323 771-9000	12564
G E Shell Core Co	3544	E	323 773-4242	14520
Grace Machine Co Inc	3599	E	323 771-6215	16541
Mfb Worldwide Inc (PA)	2299	F	323 562-2339	3009
Myers Mixers LLC	3569	E	323 560-4723	15342
Praxair Inc	2813	F	323 562-5200	7713
RAP Security	2542	D	323 560-3493	5163
Scot Gasket Company Inc	3053	F	323 560-6600	9555
Scott Craft Co (PA)	3599	F	323 560-3949	16932

CULVER CITY, CA - Los Angeles County
Apic Corporation	3674	D	310 642-7975	18702
Beats Electronics LLC (PA)	3679	F	424 268-3055	19461
Beats Electronics LLC (HQ)	3651	D	424 326-4679	17771
Big 10 Productions Inc	3993	D	310 280-1610	23827
Borin Manufacturing Inc	3561	E	310 822-1000	15055
Bull Hn Info Systems Inc	3571	E	310 337-3600	15397
Cal Southern Graphics Corp	2752	D	310 559-3600	6714
CMI Integrated Tech Inc	3621	E	760 431-7003	17186
Cosmetic Design Group LLC	2844	E	310 397-9300	8726
Dogeared Inc	3961	D	310 846-4444	23745
Ecoly International Inc	2844	E	818 718-6982	8742
Econ-O-Plate Inc	2752	F	310 342-5900	6801
Farchitecture Bb LLC	2024	E	917 701-2777	669
Fortune Casuals LLC (PA)	2331	C	310 733-2100	3236
Fulltone Musical Products Inc	3931	F	310 204-0155	23371
Given Imaging Los Angeles LLC	3845	C	310 641-8492	22981
Grand Casino On Main Inc	2051	F	310 253-9066	1268
Indi Molecular Inc	2835	F	310 417-4999	8484
Integrated Magnetics Inc	3621	E	310 391-7213	17205
J - Art Co Inc	2514	E	310 202-1126	4832
La Siciliana Inc	2335	E	323 870-4155	3321
Liveoffice LLC	7372	D	877 253-2793	24861
Loaded Boards Inc	3751	F	310 839-1800	21124
M Group Inc	3161	E	843 221-7830	10527
Magnet Sales & Mfg Co Inc (HQ)	3264	D	310 391-7213	10820
Metric Products Inc (PA)	2342	E	310 815-9000	3550
Minton-Spidell Inc (PA)	2511	F	310 836-0403	4723
Miracle Greens Inc	2023	C	800 521-5867	631
Moldex-Metric Inc	3842	B	310 837-6500	22774
Nutrition Without Borders LLC	3581	E	310 845-7745	15923
Oracle Corporation	7372	B	310 258-7500	25022
Ortho Engineering Inc (PA)	3842	E	310 559-5996	22784
Pacific Piston Ring Co Inc	3592	D	310 836-3322	16149
Paige LLC (PA)	2326	D	310 733-2100	3116
Photonic Corp	2752	F	310 642-7975	7026
Project Mustang Dev LLC	2834	C	323 275-4098	8346
Q Tech Corporation	3679	C	310 836-7900	19695
Robeks Corporation	2033	F	310 838-2332	853
Schwarzkopf Inc (DH)	3999	C	310 641-0990	24231
Scopely Inc (PA)	7372	C	323 400-6618	25155
Security Pro USA	3842	E	310 841-5845	22810
Smashbox Beauty Cosmetics Inc	2844	E	310 558-1490	8843
Sofie Biosciences Inc (PA)	2835	E	310 215-3159	8516
Sole Society Group Inc	3131	E	310 220-0808	10476
Sportsrobe Inc (PA)	2329	E	310 559-3999	3188
Spotlite America Corporation (PA)	3229	E	310 829-0200	10668

Company	SIC	EMP	PHONE	ENTRY #
Spotlite Power Corporation	3646	E	310 838-2367	17644
Stateside Merchants LLC	2322	E	424 251-5190	3066
Vans Inc	3021	F	310 390-7548	9489
Waiakea Inc	2086	F	855 924-2532	2233
Walmsley Design	2511	F	310 836-0772	4747
Water Studio Inc	3499	F	310 313-5553	13981

CUPERTINO, CA - Santa Clara County
Advin Systems Inc	3674	F	408 243-7000	18672
Aemetis Advnced Pdts Keyes Inc	2869	E	408 418-2415	8969
Altia Systems Inc	3861	F	408 996-9710	23138
America Techcode Semicdtr Inc	3674	F	408 910-2028	18691
Amino Technologies (us) LLC (HQ)	3663	D	408 861-1400	18028
Apple Inc (PA)	3663	A	408 996-1010	18037
Apple Inc	3663	F	408 606-5775	18038
Cellular Biomedicine Group Inc	2836	D	408 973-7884	8539
Cloudpic Inc	7372	D	408 786-1098	24504
Cmos Sensor Inc	3674	F	408 366-2898	18771
Codefast Inc	7372	F	408 687-4700	24508
Crystal Mining Corporation	1041	F	386 479-5823	2
Do-Nut Wheel Inc	2051	F	408 252-8193	1232
Durect Corporation (PA)	2834	D	408 777-1417	8144
Durect Corporation	2834	F	408 777-1417	8145
E-Transactions Software Tech	7372	F	408 873-9100	24586
Ecrio Inc	7372	E	408 973-7290	24588
Esq Business Services Inc (PA)	7372	D	925 734-9800	24628
Foresite Systems Limited (PA)	7372	E	408 855-8600	24661
Fortune Drink Inc	2086	F	408 805-9526	2135
Greenvolts Inc	3433	D	415 963-4030	12066
Gregory Associates Inc	3825	E	408 446-5725	21769
Hanson Aggregates LLC	1442	E	408 996-4000	362
Hantronix Inc	3559	E	408 252-1100	14964
Knova Software Inc (HQ)	7372	E	408 863-5800	24836
Lehigh Southwest Cement Co	3241	F	408 996-4271	10761
Lizal Inc	2673	E	408 252-5200	5605
Mockingbird Networks	3571	D	408 342-5300	15462
Paracor Medical Inc	3845	E	408 207-1050	23034
Read Corp	7372	E	408 705-2123	25104
Seagate Technology LLC (DH)	3572	A	408 658-1000	15603
Seagate Technology LLC	3572	F	405 324-4799	15604
Seagate US LLC	3572	F	408 658-1000	15605
Selfoptima Inc	2741	F	408 217-8667	6578
Sheng-Kee of California Inc	2052	E	408 865-6000	1379
Silicon Spread Corp	3674	D	855 446-7634	19156
Stack Labs Inc	3646	E	503 453-5172	17645
Supernova Spirits Inc	2085	E	415 819-3154	2078
Thales Alenia Space North Amer	3764	F	408 973-9845	21182
Trane US Inc	3585	F	408 257-5212	15983
Tropian Inc	3674	D	408 865-1300	19236
West Coast Venture Capital LLC (PA)	3661	A	408 725-0700	18009
Workspot Inc (PA)	7372	E	408 533-8669	25357

CYPRESS, CA - Orange County
Actodyne General Inc	3651	F	714 898-2776	17752
Advanex Americas Inc (HQ)	3495	D	714 995-4519	13783
Awake Inc	2335	D	818 365-9361	3294
Boeing Company	3721	A	714 952-1509	20546
Buena Park Anaheim Independent	2711	E	714 952-8505	5781
C&D Zodiac Inc	3728	C	562 344-4780	20767
Cavotec Dabico US Inc	3728	E	714 947-0005	20779
Cavotec Inet US Inc	3531	D	714 947-0005	14157
Cenic Ntwrk Operations Website	3761	E	714 220-3494	21157
Christie Digital Systems Inc (HQ)	3861	F	714 236-8610	23144
Community Media Corporation	2711	D	714 220-0292	5810
Creative Teaching Press Inc (PA)	2731	D	714 799-2100	6333
Dameron Alloy Foundries (PA)	3325	D	310 631-5165	11524
Dentium USA (HQ)	3843	F	714 226-0229	22869
Diasorin Molecular LLC	2835	C	562 240-6500	8474
Dmg Mori Usa Inc	3541	F	562 430-3800	14372
Drs Advanced Isr LLC	3674	F	714 220-3800	18805
Drs Ntwork Imaging Systems LLC	3674	D	714 220-3800	18806
Exemplis LLC (PA)	2522	E	714 995-4800	4988
Hitachi Automotive Systems	3621	D	310 212-0200	17204
International Paper Company	2621	F	714 889-4900	5298
J & F Machine Inc	3599	E	714 527-3499	16594
Johnson Controls Inc	2531	C	562 799-8882	5018
Lady Jayne LP	2678	F		5685
Luma Comfort LLC	3634	E	855 963-9247	17396
Magna Tool Inc	3599	E	714 826-2500	16709
Manhattan Beachwear Inc (PA)	2339	C	714 892-7354	3459
Manhattan Beachwear Inc	2339	D	714 892-7354	3460
Manhattan Components Inc	3089	C	714 761-7249	10199
Mitsubishi Electric Visual	3679	C	800 553-7278	19655
Ocean Protecta Incorporated	3732	E	714 891-2628	21059
Plastech Specialties Company (PA)	2396	F	626 357-6839	3913
Power - Trim Co	3524	F	714 523-8560	14130

Mergent email: customerrelations@mergent.com
1372

2019 California
Manufacturers Register

(P-0000) Products & Services Section entry number
(PA)=Parent Co (HQ)=Headquarters (DH)=Div Headquarters

	SIC	EMP	PHONE	ENTRY #
Primary Color Systems Corp (PA)	2752	B	949 660-7080	7037
Rockwell Automation Inc	3625	E	714 828-1800	17301
Shadow Industries Inc	3792	F	714 995-4353	21210
Shaw Industries Group Inc	2273	C	562 430-4445	2940
Siemens Industry Inc	3613	D	714 252-3100	17162
Simply Fresh Foods Inc	2092	F	714 562-5000	2323
Tayco Engineering Inc	3761	C	714 952-2240	21171
Toyo Ink International Corp	2893	E	714 899-2377	9213
Toyo Tire Hldings Americas Inc (HQ)	3011	E	562 431-6502	9468
Tr Theater Research Inc (PA)	3651	F	714 894-5888	17869
Venus Laboratories Inc	2819	D	714 891-3100	7813
Weldex Corporation (PA)	3674	E	714 761-2100	19272

DALY CITY, CA - San Mateo County

	SIC	EMP	PHONE	ENTRY #
Genesys Telecom Labs Inc (HQ)	7372	B	650 466-1100	24688
Irvine & Jachens Inc	3999	F	650 755-4715	24133
Oracle Systems Corporation	7372	D	650 506-8648	25027
Star Fish Inc	2396	F	650 468-6688	3923
View Rite Manufacturing	2541	F	415 468-3856	5116
Westlake Bakery Inc	2051	F	650 994-7741	1342

DANA POINT, CA - Orange County

	SIC	EMP	PHONE	ENTRY #
Captive Ocean Reef Enterprises	3569	F	949 581-8888	15306
Desert Shutters Inc	2426	E	949 388-8344	4078
Pw Brands LLC	3291	F	949 916-0600	11302
South Orange County Ww Auth	2899	F	949 234-5400	9308

DANVILLE, CA - Contra Costa County

	SIC	EMP	PHONE	ENTRY #
A Lot To Say Inc (PA)	2399	F	877 366-8448	3932
Advertiser Perceptions	2711	E	925 648-3902	5752
Aqueous Vets	3589	F	951 764-9384	16013
Choice Foodservices Inc	3365	D	925 837-0104	11728
Container Decorating Inc	2396	F	510 489-9212	3886
Eatyourmealscom LLC	3999	F	925 984-5452	24084
Morrison Mar & Intermodal Inc	3731	E	925 362-4599	21003
Peninsula Engrg Solutions Inc	3663	F	925 837-2243	18217
Redshark Group Inc	2752	F	925 837-3490	7082
Rocateq North America	3496	F	925 648-7794	13851
Stratcitycom LLC	7372	D	408 858-0006	25225
Trov Inc (PA)	7372	F	925 478-5500	25298
Whamcloud Inc	7372	F	925 452-7599	25349
Wireless Glue Networks Inc	7372	F	925 310-4561	25352

DAVENPORT, CA - Santa Cruz County

	SIC	EMP	PHONE	ENTRY #
Lundberg Studios Inc	3231	E	831 423-2532	10715
RMC Pacific Materials Inc	3241	C	831 429-7200	10770

DAVIS, CA - Yolo County

	SIC	EMP	PHONE	ENTRY #
Antibodies Incorporated	2835	F	530 758-4400	8460
Campbell Soup Company	2032	E	530 753-2116	752
Digital Technology Lab Corp	3545	D	530 746-7400	14625
Dmg Mori Manufacturing USA Inc (HQ)	3541	E	530 746-7400	14371
Electronic Resources Network	3577	E	530 758-0180	15737
Expression Systems LLC (PA)	2836	E	877 877-7421	8550
FMC Corporation	2812	D	530 753-6718	7662
Frontier AG Co Inc (PA)	2048	E	530 297-1020	1134
Marrone Bio Innovations Inc	2879	C	530 750-2800	9105
McNaughton Newspapers	2711	E	530 756-0800	5954
Phl Associates Inc	2836	F	530 753-5881	8573
Scarlet Saints Softball	3949	F	530 613-1443	23649
Signa Chemistry Inc	2819	E	212 933-4101	7803
Steps Mobile Inc	7372	F	408 806-5178	25223
Technipfmc US Holdings Inc	3533	E	530 753-6718	14241
Tyflong International Inc	3291	F	530 746-3001	11306

DEER PARK, CA - Napa County

	SIC	EMP	PHONE	ENTRY #
Viader Vineyards	2084	F	707 963-3816	2038

DEL MAR, CA - San Diego County

	SIC	EMP	PHONE	ENTRY #
Aztech Products International	3699	E	858 481-8412	19918
Fairmont Global LLC (PA)	2541	F	415 320-2929	5061
Interntional Thermal Instr Inc	3826	F	858 755-4436	21978
Knorr Beeswax Products Inc	3999	E	760 431-2007	24150
Societe Brewing Company LLC	2084	F	858 598-5415	1979

DEL REY, CA - Fresno County

	SIC	EMP	PHONE	ENTRY #
Chooljian & Sons Inc	3556	D	559 888-2031	14841
Cy Truss	2439	E	559 888-2160	4401
Del Rey Enterprises Inc	2034	F	559 233-4452	882
Del Rey Juice Co	2037	D	559 888-8533	946
Economy Stock Feed Company	2048	F	559 888-2187	1128

DELANO, CA - Kern County

	SIC	EMP	PHONE	ENTRY #
Agri Cel Inc	3086	D	661 792-2107	9813
Anthony Welded Products Inc (PA)	3537	E	661 721-7211	14309
Asv Wines Inc (PA)	2084	E	661 792-3159	1647
Cal Treehouse Almonds Inc	2068	C	661 725-6334	1485
Cemex Cnstr Mtls PCF LLC	3273	E	661 725-1819	11072
City of Delano	3589	E	661 721-3352	16024
Delano Growers Grape Products	2087	D	661 725-3255	2254
Ra-White Inc	3599	F	661 725-1840	16882
Randell Equiptment & Mfg	3523	E	661 725-6380	14098
San-Joaquin Helicopters Inc	3721	F	661 725-6603	20624
Styrotek Inc	3086	C	661 725-4957	9885

DELHI, CA - Merced County

	SIC	EMP	PHONE	ENTRY #
Glenn Engineering Inc	3715	F	209 667-4555	20502

DENAIR, CA - Stanislaus County

	SIC	EMP	PHONE	ENTRY #
Almond Valley Nut Co	2068	E	209 480-7300	1481

DESCANSO, CA - San Diego County

	SIC	EMP	PHONE	ENTRY #
Yaldo Enterprises Inc	2097	F	619 445-2578	2424

DESERT HOT SPRINGS, CA - Riverside County

	SIC	EMP	PHONE	ENTRY #
Back Support Systems Inc	3086	F	760 329-1472	9820
Western Golf Car Mfg Inc	3949	D	760 671-6691	23691

DI GIORGIO, CA - Kern County

	SIC	EMP	PHONE	ENTRY #
F Korbel & Bros	2084	E	661 854-6120	1756

DIAMOND BAR, CA - Los Angeles County

	SIC	EMP	PHONE	ENTRY #
Axm Pharma Inc	2834	C	909 843-6338	8057
Evensphere Incorporation	3678	E	909 247-3030	19389
Garden Pals Inc	3423	E	909 605-0200	11895
Impro Industries Usa Inc (DH)	3369	F	909 396-6525	11779
Quarton USA Inc	3699	F	888 532-2221	20051
Rafi Systems Inc	3851	D	909 861-6574	23118
Society For The Advancement of	2721	F	626 521-9460	6260
Ultimate Sound Inc	3651	B	909 861-6200	17871
US Gear & Pumps	3566	E	909 525-3026	15248

DIAMOND SPRINGS, CA - El Dorado County

	SIC	EMP	PHONE	ENTRY #
Adept Med International Inc (PA)	3841	F	530 621-1220	22314
Airpoint Precision Inc	3599	F	530 622-0510	16247
Demtech Services Inc	3089	F	530 621-3200	10066
Fastener Depot Inc	3452	F	530 621-3070	13068
McDaniel Manufacturing Inc	3429	F	530 626-6336	11974
Ruxco Engineering Inc	3841	F	530 622-4122	22610
S & H Enterprises Inc	3534	F	530 626-8043	14256
Western Sign Company Inc	3993	E	916 933-3765	24004

DINUBA, CA - Tulare County

	SIC	EMP	PHONE	ENTRY #
Amber Foods Inc	2099	D	559 591-4782	2450
Kobus Business Systems LLC	3578	F	559 595-1915	15897
Nutrient Technologies Inc (PA)	2873	F	559 595-8090	9069
Olive Bari Oil Company	2079	F	559 595-9260	1547
Packline Technologies Inc	3565	F	559 591-3150	15222
Ruiz Food Products Inc (PA)	2038	A	559 591-5510	1012
Sentinel Printing & Publishing	2711	F	559 591-4632	6042
Warren & Baerg Mfg Inc	3523	E	559 591-6790	14118

DISCOVERY BAY, CA - Contra Costa County

	SIC	EMP	PHONE	ENTRY #
Hydrohoist Marine Group Inc	3536	E	925 513-0507	14298

DIXON, CA - Solano County

	SIC	EMP	PHONE	ENTRY #
Alpha Alarm & Audio Inc	3651	F	707 452-8334	17757
Altec Industries Inc	3713	F	707 678-0800	20187
Altec Industries Inc	3531	D	707 678-0800	14140
Baxter Healthcare Corporation	3841	D	503 285-0212	22358
California Pipe Fabricators	3498	F	707 678-3069	13881
Campbell Soup Company	2032	C	707 678-4406	750
Castlelite Block LLC (PA)	3271	E	707 678-3465	10848
Cemex Cnstr Mtls PCF LLC	3271	F	707 580-3138	10850
Cemex Materials LLC	3273	E	707 678-4311	11082
Dixon Tribune	2711	F	707 678-5594	5831
Ellensburg Lamb Company Inc	2011	C	707 678-3091	432
Gibson Printing & Publishing	2711	F	707 678-5594	5865
Hemostat Laboratories Inc (PA)	2836	F	707 678-9594	8558
INX International Ink Co	2893	E	707 693-2990	9205
J & A Jeffery Inc	3999	F	707 678-0369	24134
Moller International Inc	3721	F	530 756-5086	20603
Transhumance Holding Co Inc	2011	C	707 693-2303	452
Tri Star Metals Inc	3449	F	707 678-1140	13001
Victorian Shutters Inc (PA)	2431	F	707 678-1776	4252

DOS PALOS, CA - Merced County

	SIC	EMP	PHONE	ENTRY #
C&S Global Foods Inc	2099	F	209 392-2223	2475

DOWNEY, CA - Los Angeles County

	SIC	EMP	PHONE	ENTRY #
A-1 Engraving Co Inc	3479	F	562 861-2216	13537
Ad-De-Pro Inc	3451	F	562 862-1915	13008
Advanced Building Systems Inc	3999	E	818 652-4252	24024
Advanced Lgs LLC	3441	F	818 652-4252	12104
Aerospace Lgacy Foundation Inc	3812	F	562 922-8068	21254
Alpha Grinding Inc	3599	F	562 803-1509	16259
American Pwdr Coating Pntg Inc	3479	F	562 861-6348	13549

Employment Codes: A=Over 500 employees, B=251-500,
C=101-250, D=51-100, E=20-50, F=10-19

2019 California
Manufacturers Register

© Mergent Inc. 1-800-342-5647
1373

GEOGRAPHIC

Company	SIC	EMP	PHONE	ENTRY #
American Security Educators	2741	F	562 928-1847	6431
Arrow Abrasive Company Inc	3291	F	562 869-2282	11288
Assoc Ready Mixed Concrete	3273	F	562 923-7281	11044
Bradley Manufacturing Co Inc	3089	E	562 923-5556	9990
Can Lines Engineering Inc (PA)	3565	D	562 861-2996	15201
Classic Graphix	2395	F	562 940-0806	3836
Commercial Truck Eqp Co LLC	3713	E	562 803-4466	20197
Cummins Pacific LLC	3519	E	866 934-4373	14019
Detroit Diesel Corporation	3519	E	562 929-7016	14026
Downey Grinding Co	3541	E	562 803-5556	14375
Downey Manufacturing Inc	3728	F	562 862-3311	20797
Downey Patriot	2711	F	562 904-3668	5834
Ebus Inc	3713	F	562 904-3474	20204
EJ Lauren LLC	2512	E	562 803-1113	4772
Engine Electronics Inc	3694	F	562 803-1700	19832
Gann Products Company Inc	3052	F	562 862-2337	9499
Hanger Prsthetcs & Ortho Inc	3842	F	562 803-3322	22743
Hartwick Combustion Tech Inc	3569	F	562 922-8300	15328
Hutchinson Seal Corporation (DH)	3053	B	248 375-4190	9535
Instant Web LLC	2752	C	562 658-2020	6889
J F Duncan Industries Inc (PA)	3589	D	562 862-4269	16057
Jeb-PHI Inc	2752	F	562 861-0863	6910
Jewels By Angelo Inc	3911	F	562 862-6293	23279
Kf Fiberglass Inc (PA)	3714	E	562 862-1536	20382
Kirkhill Inc	3069	D	562 803-1117	9631
Lugos of California Inc	2339	E	323 582-5164	3457
Lynx Grills Inc (HQ)	3631	F	323 722-4324	17371
Lynx Grills Inc	3631	F	323 838-1770	17372
MD Stainless Services	3498	E	562 904-7022	13897
On-Gard Metals Inc	3341	F	562 622-9057	11563
Pacific Southwest Molds	3544	F	562 803-9811	14557
Reyes Coca-Cola Bottling LLC	2086	D	562 803-8100	2189
Reyes Coca-Cola Bottling LLC	2086	C	562 803-8165	2200
Sees Candy Shops Incorporated	2064	F	562 928-2912	1455
Spyke Inc	3751	E	562 803-1700	21138
Sst Technologies	3823	E	562 803-3361	21659
Storopack Inc	2821	E	562 803-1584	7891
Sunrise Luxury Living Room Inc	2512	E	562 803-1301	4814
Thompson Tank Inc	3443	F	562 869-7711	12436
Umc Acquisition Corp (PA)	3356	E	562 940-0300	11638
United California Corporation	3544	C	562 803-1521	14583
United Drill Bushing Corp	3545	C	562 803-1521	14691
Universal Mlding Extrusion Inc (DH)	3354	E	562 401-1015	11609
Universal Molding Company (HQ)	3356	C	310 886-1750	11639
Van Grace Quality Injection	3089	F	323 931-5255	10428
Wesfac Inc	3589	D	562 861-2160	16137
Western Pacific Pulp and Paper (HQ)	2611	D	562 803-4401	5270

DUARTE, CA - Los Angeles County

Company	SIC	EMP	PHONE	ENTRY #
A & B Brush Mfg Corp	3991	F	626 303-8856	23784
Accu-Sembly Inc	3672	D	626 357-3447	18403
Assembly Automation Industries	3549	E	626 303-2777	14748
Cosmo Fiber Corporation (PA)	2759	E	626 256-6098	7287
Delafield Corporation (PA)	3599	C	626 303-0740	16426
Dynametric Inc	3661	E	626 358-2559	17941
Endodent Inc	3843	E	626 359-5715	22877
Flamous Brands Inc	2096	F	626 551-3201	2381
Jetco Torque Tools LLC	3566	E	626 359-2881	15240
Justice Bros Dist Co Inc	2843	E	626 359-9174	8687
Lee Machine Products	3544	F	626 301-4105	14534
Micro-OHM Corporation	3676	E	626 357-5377	19308
Modulex Inc	3442	E	626 256-9508	12336
Onex Enterprises Corporation	3569	E	626 358-6639	15344
Onex Rf Automation Inc	3548	E	626 358-6639	14734
Padywell Corp	2759	F	626 359-9149	7430
Prolacta Bioscience Inc	2023	E	626 599-9260	647
Quality Car Care Products Inc	2819	E	626 359-9174	7800
Ro Generation Inc	2679	F	323 771-5416	5729
Sew Forth Inc	2326	E	323 725-3500	3121
Soyfoods of America	2075	F	626 358-3836	1512
Spenuzza Inc	3589	E	626 358-8063	16113
Turbo Coil Manufacturing Inc	3677	E	626 599-7777	19369
Turbo Refrigeration Systems	3585	E	626 599-9777	15995
Viking Ready Mix Co Inc	3273	E	626 303-7755	11209
Woodward Hrt Inc	3728	B	626 359-9211	20974
Woodward Hrt Inc	3728	C	626 359-9211	20975

DUBLIN, CA - Alameda County

Company	SIC	EMP	PHONE	ENTRY #
A A Label Inc (PA)	2679	E	925 803-5709	5692
Advantec Mfs Inc	3564	F	925 479-0625	15138
Allyn James Inc	2752	F	925 828-5530	6652
Azure Biosystems Inc	2836	E	925 307-7127	8530
Carl Zeiss Inc	3827	E	925 557-4100	22061
Carl Zeiss Meditec Inc (DH)	3827	B	925 557-4100	22062
Carl Zeiss Meditec Inc	3827	E	858 716-0661	22063
Carl Zeiss Ophthalmic Systems	3841	C	925 557-4100	22396

Company	SIC	EMP	PHONE	ENTRY #
Eg Systems LLC (PA)	3674	E	510 324-0126	18813
Epicor Software Corporation	7372	C	925 361-9900	24621
Giga-Tronics Incorporated	3825	E	925 328-4650	21763
Glaxosmithkline LLC	2834	E	925 833-1551	8191
Hexcel Corporation	2295	D	925 551-4900	2960
ICEE Company	2087	F	925 828-5807	2268
Immunoscience Inc	2835	E	925 400-6055	8483
International Petroleum Produc	2992	F	925 556-5530	9438
Ipac Inc	2992	F	925 556-5530	9439
Kensington Laboratories LLC (PA)	3625	F	510 324-0126	17282
Lockheed Martin Corporation	3812	B	925 756-4594	21322
Matchpoint Solutions (PA)	7372	E	925 829-4455	24885
Microsource Inc	3825	D	925 328-4650	21806
Nexfon Corporation	3229	F	925 200-2233	10660
Oliver De Silva Inc (PA)	1429	E	925 829-9200	330
Onyx Optics Inc	3827	E	925 833-1969	22114
Oracle Taleo LLC	7372	A	925 452-3000	25037
Print Ink Inc	2329	E	925 829-3950	3185
Saba Software Inc (PA)	7372	D	877 722-2101	25136
San Francisco Elev Svcs Inc	3534	E	925 829-5400	14257
Sunar Rf Motion Inc	3663	E	925 833-9936	18266
Valent USA LLC	2879	E	925 256-2700	9120
Zeltiq Aesthetics Inc	3841	F	925 474-2519	22683

DURHAM, CA - Butte County

Company	SIC	EMP	PHONE	ENTRY #
Tink Inc	3531	E	530 895-0897	14193
Westgate Hardwoods Inc (PA)	2431	E	530 892-0300	4255

E RNCHO DMNGZ, CA - Los Angeles County

Company	SIC	EMP	PHONE	ENTRY #
Beu Industries Inc	2671	E	310 885-9626	5520
Coy Industries Inc	3444	D	310 603-2970	12541
Industrial Tctnics Brings Corp (DH)	3562	D	310 537-3750	15106
Modern Concepts Inc	3089	D	310 637-0013	10216
Pacific Contntl Textiles Inc	2261	F	310 639-1500	2887
Simso Tex Sublimation (PA)	2396	D	310 885-9717	3919
Sonora Mills Foods Inc (PA)	2052	F	310 639-5333	1380
Touchsport Footwear LLC	3021	F	310 763-0208	9488

EAST PALO ALTO, CA - Santa Clara County

Company	SIC	EMP	PHONE	ENTRY #
Calspray Inc	3479	F	650 325-0096	13565
La Estrellita Tizapan Mercado	2099	F	650 328-0799	2562

EASTVALE, CA - Riverside County

Company	SIC	EMP	PHONE	ENTRY #
Cal-Mold Incorporated	3089	C	951 361-6400	10001
Lennox	3585	F	800 953-6669	15966
Nortek Security & Control LLC	3699	E	760 438-7000	20032
Parker House Mfg Co Inc	2517	E	800 628-1319	4898
Rankin-Delux Inc (PA)	3589	F	951 685-0081	16098
Royal Range California Inc	3631	D	951 360-1600	17375
Snapware Corporation	3089	C	951 361-3100	10380

EDWARDS, CA - Kern County

Company	SIC	EMP	PHONE	ENTRY #
Boeing Company	3721	A	661 810-4686	20548
Jacobs Technology Inc	3761	C	661 275-6100	21159
Lockheed Martin Corporation	3812	A	661 277-0691	21330

EL CAJON, CA - San Diego County

Company	SIC	EMP	PHONE	ENTRY #
A-1 Plastics Incorporated	3553	F	619 444-9442	14784
Access Professional Inc	3446	F	858 571-4444	12825
Aerowind Corporation	3769	E	619 569-1960	21184
Agri-Tech Industries LLC	3269	E	619 205-9509	10826
Al & Krla Pipe Fabricators Inc	3498	F	619 448-0060	13874
Alturdyne Power Systems Inc	3511	E	619 343-3204	13987
American Metal Processing	3444	E	619 444-6171	12479
Asm Construction Inc	3444	E	619 449-1966	12491
Azusa Rock Inc	1422	E	619 440-2363	310
BJS&t Enterprises Inc	3479	F	619 448-7795	13560
Bowen Printing Inc	2679	F	619 440-8605	5700
Brantner and Associates Inc (DH)	3678	C	619 562-7070	19374
C L P Inc (PA)	7692	E	619 444-3105	25390
Calbiotech Inc	3841	E	619 660-6162	22384
California Panel Systems LLP	3444	E	619 562-7010	12522
Certified Metal Craft Inc	3398	E	619 593-3636	11806
Cummins Pacific LLC	3519	E	619 593-3093	14024
Custom Decals & Emblems Inc	2759	E	619 449-5611	7291
Dave Whipple Sheet Metal Inc	3444	E	619 562-6962	12552
Daymar Corporation	2095	E	619 444-1155	2339
Decco Castings Inc	3369	E	619 444-9437	11774
Deco Plastics Inc	3089	E	619 448-6843	10061
Delstar Technologies	3081	E	619 258-1503	9705
Derosa Enterprises Inc	3444	E	760 743-5500	12559
Dn Tanks Inc (PA)	3795	C	619 258-8181	21215
Doctors Signature Sales	2833	E	800 531-4877	7933
Dyk Incorporated (HQ)	3795	E	619 440-8181	21216
East County Gazette	2711	F	619 444-5774	5837
Ecp Powder Coating	3479	F	619 448-3932	13579
Eddy Pump Corporation (PA)	3594	E	619 258-7020	16165

Company	SIC	EMP	PHONE	ENTRY #
Emberton Machine & Tool Inc	3599	F	619 401-1870	16471
Entra Health Systems LLC	3841	E	877 458-2646	22440
Ethos Natural Medicine LLC	2833	F	858 267-7599	7939
First Class Packaging Inc	2631	E	619 579-7166	5349
Flexsystems Usa Inc	2399	E	619 401-1858	3948
Fox Factory Inc	3714	F	619 768-1800	20339
Fuzetron Inc	3559	F	619 244-5141	14957
Gear Vendors Inc	3714	F	619 562-0060	20347
Get Engineering Corp	3823	E	619 443-8295	21595
GKN Aerospace Chem-Tronics Inc	3724	F	619 258-5012	20650
GKN Aerospace Chem-Tronics Inc (HQ)	3724	A	619 448-2320	20651
Greenbroz Inc	3523	F	844 379-8746	14069
Hi-Tech Welding & Forming Inc	3599	E	619 562-5929	16562
High Precision Grinding	3599	E	619 440-0303	16564
Hollands Custom Cabinets Inc	2434	E	619 443-6081	4310
Inflatable Design Group Inc	3993	F	619 596-6100	23901
Integrated Sign Associates	3993	F	619 579-2229	23903
Jerames Industries Inc	3599	E	619 334-2204	16620
Jet Air Fbo LLC	3728	E	619 448-5991	20856
Johnson Outdoors Inc	3949	E	619 402-1023	23599
Kings Crating Inc (PA)	3724	F	619 590-1664	20667
Kings Crating Inc	3469	E	619 590-2631	13237
Life Line Packaging Inc	2671	F	619 444-2737	5525
Lorimar Group Inc	3663	F	619 954-9300	18170
M W Reid Welding Inc	3441	D	619 401-5880	12198
Micro-Mode Products Inc	3663	C	619 449-3844	18180
Mmix Technologies	3444	F	619 631-6644	12681
New Brunswick Industries Inc	3672	A	619 448-4900	18544
Norberg Crushing Inc	1429	F	619 390-4200	329
Omni Enclosures Inc	2541	E	619 579-6664	5089
Pacific Marine Shtmtl Corp	3444	C	858 869-8900	12705
Pacifitek Systems Inc	3663	F	619 401-1968	18214
Precision Metal Products Inc (HQ)	3462	C	619 448-2711	13110
Premier Metal Processing Inc	3471	F	760 415-9027	13479
Prime Heat Incorporated	3567	F	619 449-6623	15272
Pure Bioscience Inc (PA)	2842	F	619 596-8600	8669
Q Microwave Inc	3679	D	619 258-7322	19694
Raymert Press Incorporated	2752	F	858 576-0880	7076
Rks Inc (HQ)	3699	F	858 571-4444	20060
Robert Grove	3721	F	619 562-1268	20622
Rotron Incorporated	3564	F	619 593-7400	15174
Royale Energy Funds Inc	1311	F	619 383-6600	72
San Diego Electric Sign Inc	3993	F	619 258-1775	23957
Senior Operations LLC	3599	D	909 627-2723	16938
Spotless Water Systems LLC	3589	F	858 530-9993	16115
St Cyclewear/Gallop LLC	2329	F	619 449-9191	3189
Taylor-Listug Inc (PA)	3931	B	619 258-6957	23390
TBs Irrigation Products Inc	3432	E	619 579-0520	12052
Tiffany Structures	3448	E	619 905-9684	12964
Titan Steel Fabricators Inc	7692	F	619 449-1271	25445
Top Notch Manufacturing Inc	3469	F	619 588-2033	13287
Toro Company	3523	D	619 562-2950	14110
Transportation Equipment Inc (PA)	2394	F	619 449-8860	3816
Triumph Fabrications	3728	C	619 440-2504	20962
Tujayar Enterprises Inc	3646	F	619 442-0577	17652
Unique Drawer Boxes Inc	2441	F	619 873-4240	4447
US Print & Toner Inc	3955	E	619 562-6995	23740
Vcsd Inc	2434	F	619 579-6886	4365
Veridiam Inc (DH)	3548	C	619 448-1000	14743
Vertechs Enterprises Inc (PA)	3364	D	858 578-3900	11718
Viasat Inc	3812	D	619 438-6000	21454
Vulcan Materials Company	1422	F	619 440-2363	319
Waterdog Products Inc	3089	F	619 441-9688	10435
Weldmac Manufacturing Company	3599	C	619 440-2300	17056
Western Bay Sheet Metal Inc	3441	E	619 233-1753	12282

EL CENTRO, CA - Imperial County

Company	SIC	EMP	PHONE	ENTRY #
Associated Desert Newspaper (DH)	2711	E	760 337-3400	5766
Caliber Screenprinting Inc	2396	F	760 353-3499	3881
Complete Metal Fabrication Inc	3441	F	760 353-0260	12139
Ew Corprtion Indus Fabricators (PA)	3441	D	760 337-0020	12156
Imperial Printers Inc (PA)	2752	F	760 352-4374	6876
IV Welding & Mechanical Inc	7692	F	760 482-9353	25413
K C Welding Inc	7692	F	760 352-3832	25418
Mulherin Monumental Inc	3281	F	760 353-7717	11265
Reyes Coca-Cola Bottling LLC	2086	E	760 352-1561	2210
Rogar Manufacturing Inc	3679	C	760 335-3700	19710
Superior Ready Mix Concrete LP	3273	E	760 352-4341	11192
Western Electrical Advg Co	3993	E	760 352-0471	24003
Wymore Inc	7692	E	760 352-2045	25450

EL CERRITO, CA - Contra Costa County

Company	SIC	EMP	PHONE	ENTRY #
Renovare International Inc (PA)	3589	F	510 748-9993	16101

EL DORADO, CA - El Dorado County

Company	SIC	EMP	PHONE	ENTRY #
Cemex Cnstr Mtls PCF LLC	3273	E	530 626-3590	11063

Company	SIC	EMP	PHONE	ENTRY #
Hearthco Inc	3429	E	530 622-3877	11959

EL DORADO HILLS, CA - El Dorado County

Company	SIC	EMP	PHONE	ENTRY #
478826 Limited	3599	E	916 933-5280	16180
Access Systems Inc	3826	F	916 941-8099	21891
Aerometals Inc (PA)	3728	C	916 939-6888	20718
All Sales Manufacturing Inc	3714	F	916 933-0236	20250
Alpha Research & Tech Inc	3571	D	916 431-9340	15389
Ampac Fine Chemicals LLC	2834	F	916 245-6500	8027
Bar Manufacturing Inc	3674	D	916 939-0551	18742
Bruder Industry	3599	F	916 939-6888	16334
Bulletproof Brands Co Inc	2086	F	916 635-3718	2103
Cameo Crafts	2759	E	513 381-1480	7264
Cason Engineering Inc	3599	F	916 939-9311	16366
Cemex (PA)	3273	E	916 941-2800	11058
Clear Image Inc (PA)	2673	E	916 933-4700	5593
Filtration Development Co LLC	3677	F	415 884-0555	19335
Illinois Tool Works Inc	3674	D	916 939-4332	18883
Otto ARC Systems Inc	3548	F	916 939-3400	14735
Paragon Products LLC (PA)	3743	F	916 941-9717	21083
Planar Monolithics Inds Inc	3679	F	916 542-1401	19685
Precision Contacts Inc	3663	F	916 939-4147	18223
Ren Corporation	3523	F	916 739-2000	14099
School Innovations Achievement (PA)	7372	D	916 933-2290	25152
Sepasoft Inc	7372	F	916 939-1684	25163
Space Systems/Loral LLC	3663	F	916 605-5448	18259
Synvasive Technology Inc	3841	E	916 939-3913	22640
Terralink Communications Inc	3663	F	916 439-4367	18282
Weckworth Electric Group Inc	3699	F	916 933-3066	20107

EL GRANADA, CA - San Mateo County

Company	SIC	EMP	PHONE	ENTRY #
Acoustical Interiors Inc (PA)	3296	F	650 728-9441	11328

EL MONTE, CA - Los Angeles County

Company	SIC	EMP	PHONE	ENTRY #
Aero-k Inc	3599	E	626 350-5125	16239
Agra-Farm Foods Inc	2043	F	626 443-2335	1053
Air Dreams Mattresses	2515	F	626 573-5733	4849
All New Stamping Co	3469	C	626 443-8813	13162
American Apparel ACC Inc (PA)	3089	F	626 350-3828	9939
Andari Fashion Inc	2329	C	626 575-2759	3134
Applied Coatings & Linings	3479	E	626 280-6354	13552
Aviation Publishing Corp	2721	D	626 618-4000	6107
Azteca Soccer	3949	F	626 768-2704	23511
Cal Coil Magnetics Inc	3677	E	626 455-0011	19324
California Snack Foods Inc	2064	F	626 444-4508	1409
California Treats Inc	2033	D	626 444-4099	790
Craneveyor Corp (PA)	3536	F	626 442-1524	14295
Dianas Mexican Food Pdts Inc	2099	F	626 444-0555	2507
Dos Fashions	2211	E	626 454-4558	2734
Driftwood Dairy Inc	2026	C	626 444-9591	723
E E Systems Group Inc	3699	F	626 452-8988	19952
Eco World USA LLC	3646	F	626 433-1333	17598
El Gallito Market Inc	2099	E	626 442-1190	2511
El Monte Plating Company	3471	E	626 448-3607	13394
Fanboys Window Factory Inc (PA)	3442	F	626 280-8787	12316
Fay and Qrtrmine McHining Corp	3545	F	323 686-0224	14632
Flexfirm Holdings LLC	2295	F	323 283-1173	2959
GAI Manufacturing Co LLC	3534	F	626 443-8616	14249
Georg Fischer Signet LLC	3823	D	626 571-2770	21594
George Fischer Inc (HQ)	3599	F	626 571-2770	16534
Gill Corporation (PA)	3089	C	626 443-6094	10118
Gsl Tech Inc	2023	F	626 572-9617	620
Industrial Machine & Mfg Co	3441	F	626 444-0105	12178
Intelligent Fixture	3441	D	626 279-1300	12181
Jansen Ornamental Supply Co	3446	E	626 442-0271	12866
Jisoncase (usa) Limited	3111	F	888 233-8880	10460
Justin Inc	3612	E	626 444-4516	17103
Keck & Schmidt Tool & Die Inc	3544	F	626 579-3890	14531
L & N Fixtures Inc	2541	E	323 686-0041	5077
La Chapalita Inc (PA)	2099	F	626 443-8556	2560
Lanty Inc	2099	C	626 582-8001	2576
LAweb Offset Printing Inc	2759	C	626 454-2469	7381
Lawrence Equipment Inc (PA)	3556	C	626 442-2894	14867
Leyvas Mexican Food	2051	F	626 350-6328	1283
Liberty Industries	3599	F	626 575-3206	16687
Lith-O-Roll Corporation	3555	F	626 579-0340	14816
Lithotech International LLC	2759	F	626 443-4210	7388
Lithotechs Inc	2759	F	626 433-1333	7389
Los Angeles Ltg Mfg Co Inc	3646	D	626 454-8300	17629
Mercury Broach Company Inc	3545	F	626 443-5904	14850
Micro Gage Inc	3674	F	626 443-1741	18999
Newhouse Upholstery	2531	E	626 444-1370	5023
Optel-Matic Inc	3599	F	626 444-2671	16810
Peca Corporation	3069	E	626 452-8873	9654
Piston Hydraulic System Inc	3569	F	626 350-0100	15353
Precision Coil Spring Company	3495	D	626 448-9731	13800

Employment Codes: A=Over 500 employees, B=251-500, C=101-250, D=51-100, E=20-50, F=10-19

2019 California
Manufacturers Register

© Mergent Inc. 1-800-342-5647

1375

GEOGRAPHIC

	SIC	EMP	PHONE	ENTRY #
Pride Metal Polishing Inc	3471	F	626 350-1326	13480
Primus Lighting Inc	3648	F	626 442-4600	17726
R W Swarens Associates Inc	3646	E	626 579-0943	17640
Remington Roll Forming Inc	3316	F	626 350-5196	11471
Royal Apparel Inc	2339	D	626 579-5168	3492
Santoshi Corporation	3471	E	626 444-7118	13500
Seng Cheang Mong Co	2098	F	626 442-2899	2441
Smj Inc	2873	F	626 448-8042	9073
SOLE Designs Inc	2512	F	626 452-8642	4812
Sparling Instruments LLC	3823	E	626 444-0571	21658
Special Iron Security Systems	3446	F	626 443-7877	12893
Srco Inc	3599	F	626 350-8321	16963
Sunrise Pillow Co Inc	2392	F	626 401-9283	3751
Supreme Steel Treating Inc	3398	E	626 350-5865	11831
Sybman Inc	2499	F	626 579-9911	4659
Tacticombat Inc	3484	F	626 315-4433	13691
Tag Pax & Label Inc	2759	F	626 579-2000	7508
Taiga Embroidery Inc	2395	F	626 448-4812	3866
Tartan Fashion Inc	2329	E	626 575-2828	3195
Transgo	3714	E	626 443-7456	20467
Uncle Lees Tea Inc	2099	F	626 350-3309	2695
Unity Clothing Inc	3949	F	626 579-5588	23682
Vfly Corporation	2395	F	626 575-3115	3868
Videssence LLC (PA)	3645	E	626 579-0943	17567
Videssence LLC	3648	F	626 579-0943	17745
Wah Fung Noodles Inc	2098	F	626 442-0588	2444
Wells Mfg USA Inc	3694	F	626 575-2886	19853

EL PORTAL, CA - Mariposa County

	SIC	EMP	PHONE	ENTRY #
Yosemite Natural History Assn	2731	D	209 379-2646	6415

EL SEGUNDO, CA - Los Angeles County

	SIC	EMP	PHONE	ENTRY #
A Alpha Wave Guide Co (PA)	2211	F	310 322-3487	2716
Abl Space Systems Company	3812	F	650 996-8214	21249
Active Interest Media Inc (PA)	2721	D	310 356-4100	6096
Aerojet Rcketdyne Holdings Inc (PA)	3812	E	310 252-8100	21253
Alcatel-Lucent USA Inc	3577	E	310 297-2620	15660
Allegro Mfg	3172	F	323 724-0101	10556
Aptean Inc	7372	E	310 536-6080	24378
Artissimo Designs LLC (HQ)	2679	E	310 906-3700	5698
Atk Space Systems Inc	3812	A	310 343-3799	21263
Bandai America Incorporated (DH)	3944	D	714 816-9751	23409
Boeing Company	3663	E	310 662-9000	18053
Boeing Company	3721	A	310 426-4100	20555
Boeing Company	3721	A	310 416-9319	20565
Boeing Satellite Systems	3812	D	310 364-5088	21269
Boeing Satellite Systems Inc	3721	A	310 568-2735	20569
Boeing Satellite Systems Inc	3721	A	310 364-6444	20570
Boeing Satellite Systems Inc (HQ)	3663	A	310 791-7450	18055
Browntrout Publishers Inc (PA)	2741	E	424 290-6122	6454
Bundy Manufacturing Inc	3599	E	323 772-3273	16338
Chevron Corporation	2911	A	310 615-5000	9327
Continental Graphics Corp	2752	E	310 662-2307	6755
Coorstek Inc	2754	E	310 322-2545	7198
Craig Tools Inc	3545	E	310 322-0614	14620
Diane Markin Inc	3231	F	310 322-0200	10692
Dkp Designs Inc	3999	F	310 322-6000	24080
El Segundo Bread Bar LLC	2051	E	310 615-9898	1244
Federal Aviation ADM	3728	E	310 640-9640	20812
Federal Industries Inc	3494	F	310 297-4040	13765
Flight Microwave Corporation	3559	F	310 607-9819	14955
Glentek Inc	3621	D	310 322-3026	17198
Governmentjobscom Inc	7372	C	310 426-6304	24706
Haydenshapes Surfboards	3949	F	310 648-8268	23582
Hco Holding II Corporation	2952	D	310 955-9200	9407
Henry Company LLC (HQ)	2952	D	310 955-9200	9408
Hnc Parent Inc (PA)	2952	D	310 955-9200	9409
Infineon Tech Americas Corp (HQ)	3674	A	310 726-8000	18885
Infineon Tech Americas Corp	3674	A	951 375-2254	18886
Infineon Tech Americas Corp	3674	A	310 726-8000	18887
Integra Technologies Inc	3674	E	310 606-0855	18904
J L Cooper Electronics Inc	3679	E	310 322-9990	19589
James Hunkins	3724	F	310 640-8243	20665
Karl Storz Endscpy-America Inc	3841	E	508 248-9011	22501
Karl Storz Endscpy-America Inc (HQ)	3841	B	424 218-8100	22502
Keysight Technologies Inc	3825	E	310 524-4600	21785
Kinkisharyo International LLC (DH)	3743	F	424 218-4300	21078
Konami Digital Entrmt Inc (DH)	7372	D	310 220-8100	24838
Kore Infrastructure LLC	2869	E	310 367-1003	9018
Lambs & Ivy Inc	2392	D	310 322-3800	3730
Los Angles Tmes Cmmnctions LLC (PA)	2711	C	213 237-5000	5918
M Nexon Inc	7372	E	213 858-5930	24873
Mattel Inc (PA)	3944	A	310 252-2000	23440
Mattel Inc	3944	F	310 252-6434	23441
Mattel Inc	3944	A	310 252-3384	23442
Mattel Direct Import Inc (HQ)	3944	A	310 252-2000	23444

	SIC	EMP	PHONE	ENTRY #
Metalore Inc	3599	E	310 643-0360	16741
Millennium Space Systems Inc (HQ)	3812	E	310 683-5840	21348
Mod Electronics Inc	3873	E	310 322-2136	23221
MTI Laboratory Inc	3663	D	310 955-3700	18195
Murad LLC (HQ)	2834	C	310 726-0600	8286
N A Suez	3823	E	310 414-0183	21623
Northrop Grumman Corporation	3812	C	310 332-1000	21359
Northrop Grumman Systems Corp	3721	B	310 632-1846	20606
Northrop Grumman Systems Corp	3721	B	310 332-1000	20612
Oracle Corporation	7372	B	310 343-7405	25023
Oracle Systems Corporation	7372	D	818 817-2900	25026
Pace Americas Inc	3663	E	310 606-8300	18212
Phoenix Software Intl Inc (PA)	7372	E	310 338-0400	25056
Primary Color Systems Corp	2759	D	310 841-0250	7444
Primedia Enthsast Pblctons Inc (HQ)	2721	C	717 657-9555	6236
Quest Nutrition (PA)	2099	E	888 212-0601	2647
Quest Nutrition LLC	2099	E	562 446-3321	2648
Radlink Inc	3845	E	310 643-6900	23038
Raytheon Company	3812	E	310 647-1000	21388
Raytheon Company	3812	B	310 647-1000	21395
Raytheon Company	3812	E	310 647-8334	21396
Raytheon Company	3812	F	310 334-2050	21398
Raytheon Company	3812	A	310 647-9438	21400
Raytheon Company	3812	B	310 647-1000	21401
Raytheon Company	3812	E	310 647-1000	21402
Raytheon Company	3812	E	310 334-7675	21406
Raytheon Company	3812	A	310 647-9438	21408
Ross Racing Pistons	3592	D	310 536-0100	16151
Runners World Magazine	2721	E	310 615-4567	6250
Satco Inc (PA)	2448	C	310 322-4719	4505
Savage River Inc (PA)	2038	E	805 669-8673	1014
Savage River Inc	2038	E	310 567-3323	1015
Scenewise Inc	3695	D	310 466-7692	19881
Smart Action Company LLC	7372	E	310 776-9200	25181
Teledyne Controls LLC	3812	A	310 765-3600	21438
Teledyne Technologies Inc	3679	B	310 765-3600	19753
Trelleborg Sealing Solutions E	3053	D	310 322-8030	9562
Tri-Star Electronics Intl Inc (HQ)	3643	B	310 536-0444	17502
Tri-Star Technologies Inc	3845	F	310 536-0444	23061
Trio Manufacturing Inc	3728	E	310 640-6123	20959
Venice Baking Co	2051	E	310 322-7357	1337
Zico Beverages LLC (HQ)	2086	C	866 729-9426	2237
Zoasis Corporation	2721	E	800 745-4725	6299

EL TORO, CA - Orange County

	SIC	EMP	PHONE	ENTRY #
Amtec Human Capital Inc	3544	E	949 472-0396	14479
Assoc Ready Mixed Concrete	3273	F	949 580-1844	11045
Beverly Hillcrest Oil Corp	1311	F	949 598-7300	30
Dynamic Services Inc	2759	F	949 458-2553	7305
Freedom Communications Inc	2711	A	949 454-7300	5851
Kott Inc	2851	F	949 770-5055	8913
Mission Flavors Fragrances Inc	2087	F	949 461-3344	2273
Oakley Sales Corp	3851	F	949 951-0991	23113
The Black & Decker Inc	3546	B	949 672-4000	14712
Tri State Manufacturing Inc	3599	F	949 855-9121	17008

ELK GROVE, CA - Sacramento County

	SIC	EMP	PHONE	ENTRY #
Alldata LLC	7372	D	916 684-5200	24352
Assa Abloy Entrance Sys US Inc	3699	E	916 686-4116	19913
Boris Bs Frms Vtrnary Svcs Inc	2048	D	916 730-4225	1123
Cal-Asia Truss Inc	2439	E	916 685-5648	4394
Concrete Inc	3273	F	209 933-6999	11096
Decore-Ative Specialties	2431	C	916 686-4700	4142
Elk Grove Milling Inc	2048	E	916 684-2056	1129
Glacier Valley Ice Company LP (PA)	2097	E	916 394-2939	2413
GNB Corporation	3541	D	916 233-3543	14381
Hanford Ready-Mix Inc	3273	E	916 405-1918	11115
Hanford Sand & Gravel Inc	3273	F	916 782-9150	11116
Herburger Publications Inc	2711	E	916 685-3945	5877
International Paper Company	2621	D	916 685-9000	5291
Iparis LLC	3571	F	866 293-2872	15433
Jmgj Group Inc	3961	E	866 293-2872	23749
Pacific Modern Homes Inc	3444	E	916 685-9514	12707
Paramount Petroleum Corp	2951	E	916 685-9253	9392
Plantation Coffee Roasters	2095	E	916 714-2633	2365
Rapid Ramen Inc	3589	F	916 479-7003	16099
Universal Custom Display	3993	C	916 714-2505	23996

EMERALD HILLS, CA - San Mateo County

	SIC	EMP	PHONE	ENTRY #
Davtron	3812	F	650 369-1188	21283
Teamifier Inc	7372	F	408 591-9872	25260

EMERYVILLE, CA - Alameda County

	SIC	EMP	PHONE	ENTRY #
Adamas Pharmaceuticals Inc (PA)	2834	D	510 450-3500	7999
Alive & Radiant Foods Inc	2096	E	510 238-0128	2373
Amyris Inc (PA)	2869	B	510 450-0761	8978
Bacchus Press Inc (PA)	2752	E	510 420-5800	6681

	SIC	EMP	PHONE	ENTRY #
Bayer Healthcare LLC	2834	C	510 597-6150	8064
Biospacific Inc (DH)	2835	F	510 652-6155	8465
Cleaire Advanced Emission (PA)	2911	F	510 347-6103	9330
Coco Delice	2066	F	510 601-1394	1468
Coulter Forge Technology Inc	3462	F	510 420-3500	13096
Credence Id LLC	3663	E	888 243-5452	18079
Diassess Inc	3841	F	510 350-8071	22426
Elaine Gill Inc	2731	F	510 559-1600	6338
Elegance Embroidery Ltd	2329	F	510 654-0788	3148
Engine World LLC	3714	E	510 653-4444	20327
First American Building Svcs	3822	E	415 299-7597	21512
Folkmanis Inc	3999	E	510 658-7677	24098
FReal Foods LLC	2023	D	800 483-3218	618
Geo M Martin Company (PA)	3554	D	510 652-2200	14795
Gritstone Oncology Inc (PA)	2836	D	510 871-6100	8556
I3 Nanotec LLC	3559	F	510 594-2299	14967
Intelligrated Systems Inc	3535	B	510 263-2300	14277
Jayco Hawaii California	3355	F	510 601-9916	11619
Leapfrog Enterprises Inc (HQ)	3944	B	510 420-5000	23437
Lumigrow Inc	3646	E	800 514-0487	17631
Madesolid Inc	2821	F	510 858-5567	7853
Medtronic Inc	3845	C	510 985-9670	23010
Metalco	3471	F	510 652-7470	13455
Motorola Solutions Inc	3575	E	510 420-7400	15640
Novabay Pharmaceuticals Inc	2834	E	510 899-8800	8307
Novartis Corporation	2879	D	510 879-9500	9109
Novvi LLC	2911	E	281 488-0833	9341
Nugeneration Technologies LLC (PA)	2899	E	707 820-4080	9292
Nugentec Oilfield Chem LLC	2841	E	707 891-3012	8601
Peets Coffee & Tea LLC (HQ)	2095	B	510 594-2100	2364
Pirates Press Inc	3652	F	415 738-2268	17909
Pixscan	2759	F	510 595-2222	7437
Plum Inc	2043	F	510 225-4018	1072
Raco Manufacturing & Engrg Co	3699	F	510 658-6713	20054
Radiant Genomics Inc	2833	F	646 450-7332	7967
Sherbit Health Inc	7372	F	925 683-8116	25169
Suspender Factory Inc	2389	F	510 547-5400	3683
Tcho Ventures Inc	2066	F	415 981-0189	1475
Tien-Hu Knitting Co (us) Inc	2253	D	510 268-8833	2862
Tubemogul Inc	7372	D	510 653-0126	25300
Xoma Corporation (PA)	2834	D	510 204-7200	8447
Zogenix Inc (PA)	2834	D	510 550-8300	8451

ENCINITAS, CA - San Diego County

	SIC	EMP	PHONE	ENTRY #
Access Scientific Inc	3841	E	858 354-8761	22308
Bahne and Company Inc	3949	F	760 753-8847	23512
Black Box Distribution LLC	3949	D	760 268-1174	23523
Coast News	2711	F	760 436-9737	5808
Encinitas Oggis Inc	2082	F	760 579-3211	1589
Ideas In Motion	3861	F	760 635-1181	23166
Lees Fashions Inc	2335	E	760 753-2408	3325
Liquid Force Wakeboards	3949	F	760 943-8364	23607
Mako Labs LLC	7372	E	619 786-3618	24879
Neurohacker Collective LLC	2023	E	855 281-2328	640
Nphase Inc	7372	E	805 750-8580	24972
Ossic Corporation	7372	E	206 227-8585	25040
Penumbra Brands Inc	3679	F	385 336-6120	19684
Pong Research Corporation	3842	F	858 914-5299	22795
R B T Inc	2396	F	619 781-8802	3914
RCP Block & Brick Inc	3271	E	760 753-1164	10862
Rose Business Solutions Inc	7372	F	858 794-9401	25132
Software Partners LLC	7372	F	760 944-8436	25194
Surfy Surfy	3949	F	760 452-7687	23670
Three Sisters Design Inc	3911	F	760 230-2813	23325

ENCINO, CA - Los Angeles County

	SIC	EMP	PHONE	ENTRY #
Astraeus Aerospace LLC	3721	F	310 907-9205	20542
California Respiratory Care	2899	D	818 379-9999	9226
Caulipower LLC	2034	F	310 606-1648	880
Columbia Fabricating Co Inc	3446	E	818 247-4220	12844
Contempo Window Fashions	2211	F	818 768-1773	2731
D3publisher of America Inc	7372	D	310 268-0820	24545
Facefirst Inc	7372	E	805 482-8428	24641
Graypay LLC	7372	D	818 387-6735	24709
Ideal Brands Inc	2676	E	213 489-5557	5666
Ingrooves Fontana	2741	F	818 212-2550	6503
International Last Mfg Co	3089	E	818 767-2045	10154
Lord Leviason Enterprises LLC	2082	E	818 453-8245	1606
Mach Oil Corp	2992	F	818 783-3567	9445
Manning Holoff Co Inc	3823	E	818 407-2500	21615
Minestone	1411	F	818 775-5999	304
MSA West LLC	2342	E	213 536-9880	3551
Music Connection Inc	2721	F	818 995-0101	6222
National Cement Co Cal Inc (DH)	3273	E	818 728-5200	11146
National Cement Company Inc (HQ)	3241	E	818 728-5200	10766
National Ready Mixed Con Co (DH)	3273	E	818 728-5200	11149

	SIC	EMP	PHONE	ENTRY #
Nsi Group LLC (PA)	2034	E	818 639-8335	890
Oracle America Inc	7372	E	818 905-0200	25002
Pacific Controls Inc	3699	E	818 345-1970	20038
Pacific Paper Box Company (PA)	2652	E	323 771-7733	5379
Phorus LLC	3651	F	310 995-2521	17843
Superior Software Inc	7372	F	818 990-1135	25236
Vivometrics Inc	3845	E	805 667-2225	23068
Wondergrove LLC	7372	F	800 889-7249	25354
Zelzah Pharmacy Inc	2834	E	818 609-0692	8450
Zevia LLC	2086	E	310 202-7000	2236

ESCALON, CA - San Joaquin County

	SIC	EMP	PHONE	ENTRY #
Caron Compactor Co	3531	E	800 448-8236	14153
Hogan Mfg Inc (PA)	3999	C	209 838-7323	24118
Hogan Mfg Inc	3999	C	209 838-2400	24119
Kraft Heinz Foods Company	2033	B	209 552-6021	817
Lagier Ranches Inc	2824	F	209 982-5618	7914
Morrill Industries Inc	3494	D	209 838-2550	13772
P & L Concrete Products Inc	3273	E	209 838-1448	11154
Paddack Enterprises	2068	E	209 838-1536	1501

ESCONDIDO, CA - San Diego County

	SIC	EMP	PHONE	ENTRY #
A & D Plating Inc	3471	F	760 480-4580	13299
A C Manufacturing Inc	3599	F	760 745-3717	16190
Adti Media LLC	3993	E	951 795-4446	23810
Akzo Nobel Inc	2869	E	760 743-7374	8974
Arcmate Manufacturing Corp	3429	F	760 489-1140	11928
Aztec Perlite Company Inc	3295	F	760 741-1733	11317
Bimbo Bakeries Usa Inc	2051	E	760 737-7700	1194
Bliss Holdings LLC	3648	E	626 506-8696	17676
Brainstormproducts LLC	3944	E	760 871-1135	23412
Broken Token	3944	F	760 294-1923	23413
C & H Machine Inc	3593	D	760 746-6459	16154
Capstone Fire Management Inc (PA)	3569	E	760 839-2290	15305
Clorox Sales Company	2812	E	760 432-8362	7661
Continental Components LLC	2499	E	760 480-4420	4615
Davis Stone Inc	3281	E	760 745-7881	11247
Dcc General Engrg Contrs Inc	3272	D	760 480-7400	10913
Decratek Inc	3442	F	760 747-1706	12307
Escondido Sand & Gravel LLC	2951	F	760 432-4690	9384
Esperanzas Tortilleria Inc	2099	E	760 743-5908	2513
Estco Enterprises Inc	3069	E	760 489-8745	9611
Flux Power Inc	3825	F	760 741-3589	21759
Frans Manufacturing Inc	3841	F	760 741-9135	22455
Freeberg Indus Fbrication Corp	3441	D	760 737-7614	12165
Gem Enterprises LLC	3471	F	760 746-6616	13414
Generation Circuits LLC	3672	E	760 743-7459	18494
Gmj Woodworking	2431	F	760 294-7428	4160
Goddard Rotary Tool Co Inc	3541	F	760 743-6717	14382
Hometex Corporation	2392	E	619 661-0400	3724
Hydrabrush Inc	2844	F	760 743-5160	8767
Imerys Perlite Usa Inc	3569	F	760 745-5900	15331
Klein Electronics Inc	3663	E	760 781-3220	18146
Lisi Medical Jeropa Inc (DH)	3541	D	760 432-9785	14391
LL Baker Inc	2752	F	760 741-9899	6952
Lormac Plastics Inc (PA)	3089	E	760 745-9115	10195
Maas-Rowe Carillons Inc	3699	F	760 743-1311	20010
Manufacturing & Prod Svcs Corp	3714	F	760 796-4300	20395
Meziere Enterprises Inc	3599	E	800 208-1755	16742
Myers & Sons Hi-Way Safety Inc	3669	E	909 591-1781	18338
Natel Engineering Company Inc	3672	C	760 737-6777	18541
Nexsan Technologies Inc	3572	E	760 745-3550	15574
North County Polishing	3471	E	760 480-0847	13467
Olympic Coatings	3479	E	760 745-3322	13624
One Stop Systems Inc (PA)	3577	D	760 745-9883	15817
One Stop Systems Inc	3577	E	858 530-2511	15818
Orfila Vineyards Inc (PA)	2084	E	760 738-6500	1908
Planetary Machine and Engrg	3545	F	760 489-5571	14665
Pretium Packaging LLC	3085	C	760 737-7995	9806
Price Products Incorporated	3599	F	760 233-8704	16858
Pro Metal Products	3444	F	760 480-0212	12723
Pyramid Granite & Metals Inc	3281	E	760 745-6509	11273
Rancho Bernardo Printing Inc	2752	F	858 486-4540	7073
Rantec Microwave Systems Inc	3679	E	760 744-1544	19702
REAL Seal Co Inc	3053	E	760 743-7263	9550
Regina F Barajas	3531	F	760 500-0809	14187
Ritas Felicita	2024	F	760 975-3302	692
Rwnm Inc	3612	D	760 489-1245	17119
San Diego Cabinets Inc	2434	F	760 747-3100	4349
Sentinel Hydrosolutions LLC	3829	F	866 410-1134	22267
Separation Engineering Inc	3569	F	760 489-0101	15359
Southland Manufacturing Inc	3545	F	760 745-7913	14678
Summit Services Inc	3271	F	760 737-7630	10865
Superior Ready Mix Concrete LP	3273	F	760 728-1128	11193
Superior Ready Mix Concrete LP (PA)	3273	E	760 745-0556	11195
Tdg Aerospace Inc	3728	F	760 466-1040	20946

GEOGRAPHIC

	SIC	EMP	PHONE	ENTRY #
Tearlab Corporation **(PA)**	3841	F	858 455-6006	22644
Transportation Power Inc	3714	E	858 248-4255	20468
U S Circuit Inc	3679	D	760 489-1413	19776
URu By Kristine St Rrik Inc	2335	F	760 745-1800	3345
VIT Products Inc	3429	F	760 480-6702	12007
Vulcan Materials Co	3273	E	760 737-3486	11211
Western Metal Supply Co Inc	3448	F	760 233-7800	12969
Wickline Bedding Entp Corp	2515	E	760 747-7761	4893

ETIWANDA, CA - San Bernardino County

	SIC	EMP	PHONE	ENTRY #
Commercial Metals Company	3312	F	909 899-9993	11391

ETNA, CA - Siskiyou County

	SIC	EMP	PHONE	ENTRY #
Starr Design Fabrics Inc	2269	F	530 467-5121	2918

EUREKA, CA - Humboldt County

	SIC	EMP	PHONE	ENTRY #
Bien Padre Foods Inc	2032	E	707 442-4585	747
Carlson Wireless Tech Inc	3663	F	707 822-7000	18063
Cdh Painting Inc	2851	F	707 443-4429	8894
Coast Seafoods Company	2091	E	707 442-2947	2295
Coca Cola Btlg of Eureka Cal	2086	F	707 443-2796	2115
Eureka Record Works Inc **(PA)**	3651	F	707 442-8121	17800
Hanah Silk Inc	2241	F	707 442-0886	2800
Hilfiker Pipe Co	3272	E	707 443-5091	10937
Humboldt Newspaper Inc	2711	A	707 442-1711	5884
Ives Inc	2411	F	707 498-0311	3994
Jo Sonjas Folk Art Studio	2731	F	707 445-9306	6356
Marine Spill Response Corp	3826	E	707 442-6087	21988
Natural Decadence LLC	2053	F	707 444-2629	1399
North Coast Journal Inc	2711	E	707 442-1400	5998
Pasadena Newspapers Inc	2711	C	707 442-1711	6011
S-Matrix Corporation	7372	F	707 441-0404	25135
Schmidbauer Lumber Inc **(PA)**	2421	C	707 443-7024	4052
Table Bluff Brewing Inc **(PA)**	2082	E	707 445-4480	1628
Table Bluff Brewing Inc	2082	F	707 445-4484	1629

EXETER, CA - Tulare County

	SIC	EMP	PHONE	ENTRY #
Amarillo Wind Machine LLC	3523	F	559 592-4256	14040
Exeter Mercantile Company	3523	F	559 592-2121	14067
Foothills Sun-Gazette	2711	E	559 592-3171	5850
Fruit Growers Supply Company	2653	F	559 592-6550	5411
International Paper Company	2621	D	559 592-7279	5290
Peninsula Packaging LLC **(DH)**	3999	D	559 594-6813	24207
Valley Cutting System Inc	3541	E	559 684-1229	14422
Waterman Valve LLC **(HQ)**	3589	C	559 562-4000	16136

FAIR OAKS, CA - Sacramento County

	SIC	EMP	PHONE	ENTRY #
Modern Metal Installations	3446	F	916 316-0997	12882
Steve Rock & Ready Mix	3273	F	916 966-1600	11189
Wholesome Harvest Baking Inc	2011	F	916 967-1633	458

FAIRFAX, CA - Marin County

	SIC	EMP	PHONE	ENTRY #
Sonic Studio LLC	7372	F	415 944-7642	25199

FAIRFIELD, CA - Solano County

	SIC	EMP	PHONE	ENTRY #
Abbott Nutrition Mfg Inc **(HQ)**	2834	C	707 399-1100	7987
Abco Laboratories Inc **(PA)**	2834	D	707 427-1818	7989
Ball Metal Beverage Cont Corp	3411	C	707 437-7516	11857
Cemex Cnstr Mtls PCF LLC	3273	E	707 422-2520	11065
Cemex Cnstr Mtls PCF LLC	3271	E	707 422-2520	10849
Cemex Materials LLC	3273	F	707 448-7121	11084
Clorox Products Mfg Co	2842	D	707 437-1051	8635
Compu Tech Lumber Products	2439	D	707 437-6683	4400
Courage Production LLC	2013	E	707 422-6300	478
Crystal Geyser Water Company	2086	E	707 647-4410	2124
Dependable Plas & Pattern Inc	3086	E	707 863-4900	9835
Drake Enterprises Incorporated	2399	D	707 864-3077	3942
Duo Pane Industries	3231	E	707 426-9696	10693
Ethosenergy Field Services LLC	1389	F	707 399-0420	209
Fabricated Glass Spc Inc	3231	F	707 429-6160	10696
Frank-Lin Distillers Pdts Ltd	2085	D	408 259-8900	2071
Goodrich Corporation	3769	E	707 422-1880	21192
Halabi Inc **(PA)**	3281	C	707 402-1600	11254
IL Fiorello Olive Oil Co	2079	E	707 864-1529	1541
Innovative Combustion Tech **(PA)**	3433	F	510 652-6000	12071
Jelly Belly Candy Company **(PA)**	2064	B	707 428-2800	1431
Jelly Belly Candy Company	2064	E	707 428-2800	1432
Jsj Electrical Display Corp	3993	F	707 747-5595	23910
Lin Frank Distillers	2085	F	707 437-1092	2073
Macro Plastics Inc **(DH)**	3089	C	707 437-1200	10197
McNaughton Newspapers Inc **(PA)**	2711	D	707 425-4646	5955
Nippon Industries Inc	2038	E	707 427-3127	1003
OHara Metal Products	3493	E	707 863-9090	13753
Omega Industrial Supply Inc	2842	F	707 864-8164	8660
Pauli Systems Inc	3599	E	707 429-2434	16834
Primal Pet Foods Inc	2047	F	415 642-7400	1120
Saint Gobain Containers Inc	3221	F	707 437-8700	10625
Scott Lamp Company Inc	3646	D	707 864-2066	17643

FALLBROOK, CA - San Diego County

	SIC	EMP	PHONE	ENTRY #
Accurate Wire & Display Inc	3496	E	310 532-7821	13807
AVI	3679	F	760 451-9379	19453
Axelgaard Manufacturing Co Ltd **(PA)**	3845	D	760 723-7554	22950
Axelgaard Manufacturing Co Ltd	3845	E	760 723-7554	22951
Cord Industries Inc	3089	F	760 728-4590	10043
Cue Technologies Inc	3572	F	949 362-4002	15527
Don Conibear	3089	F	760 728-4590	10076
Fallbrook Industries Inc	3469	E	760 728-7229	13205
Fallbrook Printing Corp	2752	F	760 731-2020	6811
Med-Fit Systems Inc	3949	C	760 723-3618	23616
Pazzulla Plastics Inc	2541	F	714 847-2541	5092
Pole Danzer	3272	F	760 419-9514	10976
Rock Solid Stone LLC	3272	F	760 731-6191	10994
Scrape Certified Welding Inc	3441	D	760 728-1308	12241
Vmc International LLC	3843	E	760 723-1498	22923
Workman Holdings Inc	3841	F	760 723-5283	22682

FARMERSVILLE, CA - Tulare County

	SIC	EMP	PHONE	ENTRY #
Tortilleria La Mejor	2099	D	559 747-0739	2686

FARMINGTON, CA - San Joaquin County

	SIC	EMP	PHONE	ENTRY #
Ripon Milling LLC **(PA)**	2048	E	209 599-4269	1159

FELLOWS, CA - Kern County

	SIC	EMP	PHONE	ENTRY #
Freeport-Mcmoran Oil & Gas LLC	1311	E	661 768-4831	58
Pacific Perforating Inc	1389	E	661 768-9224	255
Pro Vac	1389	F	661 765-7298	260

FELTON, CA - Santa Cruz County

	SIC	EMP	PHONE	ENTRY #
Hudson Industries Inc	3999	F	831 335-4431	24123
Satellite Telework Centers Inc **(PA)**	3825	F	831 222-2100	21844

FERNDALE, CA - Humboldt County

	SIC	EMP	PHONE	ENTRY #
Pacific Timber Contracting	2411	F	707 498-1374	4005

FIELDS LANDING, CA - Humboldt County

	SIC	EMP	PHONE	ENTRY #
Environmental Technology Inc	2821	E	707 443-9323	7835

FILLMORE, CA - Ventura County

	SIC	EMP	PHONE	ENTRY #
Ameron International Corp	3272	C	425 258-2616	10872
Ameron International Corp	3272	D	805 524-0223	10874
Honey Bennetts Farm Inc	2099	E	805 521-1375	2536

FIREBAUGH, CA - Fresno County

	SIC	EMP	PHONE	ENTRY #
Eagle Valley Ginning LLC	3559	E	209 826-5002	14943
Hiller Aircraft Corporation	3721	E	559 659-5959	20591
Neil Jones Food Company	2033	E	559 659-5100	833

FOLSOM, CA - Sacramento County

	SIC	EMP	PHONE	ENTRY #
A Teichert & Son Inc	3273	E	916 985-0207	11032
Aerojet Rocketdyne Inc	3728	C	916 355-4000	20716
Agilent Technologies Inc	3825	C	916 985-7888	21707
Altergy Systems	3629	E	916 458-8590	17329
AMO Corporation	3545	E	916 791-2001	14599
Brehm Communications Inc	2711	E	916 985-2581	5779
Care Innovations LLC	3845	E	800 450-0970	22957
Gekkeikan Sake USAinC	2084	E	916 985-3111	1779
Hulls Norcal Window & Door	3089	F	916 983-5792	10142
Intel Corporation	3674	D	916 943-6809	18911
Intel Corporation	3674	E	916 356-8080	18915
Kikkoman Foods Inc	2035	E	916 355-8078	917
L3 Technologies Inc	3663	C	916 351-4556	18156
Micron Technology Inc	3674	A	916 458-3003	19004
Microsemi Corp- Rf Integrated **(DH)**	3674	C	916 850-8640	19010
Military Aircraft Parts **(PA)**	3599	E	916 635-8010	16749
Powerschool Group LLC **(HQ)**	7372	C	916 288-1636	25074
Sierra Nevada Corporation	3699	E	916 985-8799	20068
Style Media Group Inc	2721	E	916 988-9888	6262
Synapsense Corporation	3572	E	916 294-0110	15614
Trimble Inc	3812	E	916 294-2000	21447
United Reporting Pubg Corp	2741	E	916 542-7501	6609
Xolar Corporation	3999	E	916 983-6301	24292

FONTANA, CA - San Bernardino County

	SIC	EMP	PHONE	ENTRY #
101 Vertical Fabrication Inc	3441	E	909 428-6000	12095
A&R Tarpaulins Inc	2394	E	909 829-3828	3776
Aatech	3589	E	909 854-3200	16004
Advanti Racing Usa LLC **(DH)**	3714	E	951 272-5930	20245
Alabama Metal Industries Corp	3446	E	909 350-9280	12830
Allied West Paper Corp	2676	E	909 349-0710	5661

Mergent email: customerrelations@mergent.com
1378

2019 California
Manufacturers Register

(P-0000) Products & Services Section entry number
(PA)=Parent Co (HQ)=Headquarters (DH)=Div Headquarters

	SIC	EMP	PHONE	ENTRY #
American Die Casting Inc	3364	E	909 356-7768	11709
American Security Products Co	3499	C	951 685-9680	13916
American Truck Dismantling	1389	F	909 429-2166	166
Applied Systems LLC	3443	F	909 854-3200	12359
Arrow Steel Products Inc	3316	F	909 349-1032	11467
Arrow Truck Sales Incorporated	3713	F	909 829-2365	20193
ASC Profiles Inc	3441	C	909 823-0401	12114
Assisvis Inc	3084	E	909 628-2031	9775
Avery Dennison Corporation	2672	C	909 428-4238	5552
Avilas Garden Art (PA)	3272	D	909 350-4546	10880
Aztec Technology Corporation	2448	F	909 350-8830	4453
B & M Machine Inc	3599	F	909 355-0998	16298
Bab Steering Hydraulics (PA)	3714	E	208 573-4502	20266
Becker Specialty Corporation	3677	E	909 356-1095	19321
Betts Company	3495	F	909 427-9988	13790
Buildmat Plus Investments Inc	3272	F	909 823-0892	10892
Bway Corporation	3411	E	951 361-4100	11858
California Steel Inds Inc (HQ)	3312	B	909 350-6300	11383
California Steel Inds Inc	3312	E	909 350-6300	11384
California Turbo Inc	3564	F	909 854-2800	15145
Cameron West Coast (PA)	3533	F	909 355-8995	14217
Cannon Gasket Inc	3053	F	909 355-1547	9522
Castle Importing Inc	2022	F	909 428-9200	566
Cavallo & Cavallo Inc	3599	F	909 428-6994	16367
Cemex Cnstr Mtls PCF LLC	3273	C	909 355-8754	11077
Chemicals Incorporated	2899	F	951 681-9697	9228
Clark - Pacific Corporation	3272	C	909 823-1433	10904
Colonial Enterprises Inc	2844	E	909 822-8700	8717
Continental Coatings Inc	2851	F	909 355-1200	8897
Corbell Products Inc	3441	E	909 574-9139	12143
Creative Stone Mfg Inc (PA)	3272	E	909 357-8295	10911
Crown Technical Systems	3613	C	909 923-0900	17137
Custom Fabricated Metals LLC	3444	F	909 822-8828	12546
Cvc Technologies Inc	3565	E	909 355-0311	15204
Daniel Gerard Worldwide Inc	3496	F	800 635-8296	13824
Dayton Superior Corporation	3721	E	909 957-7271	20576
Dennie Manning Concrete Inc	3273	F	909 823-7521	11101
Door Components Inc	3442	C	909 770-5700	12310
Dorel Juvenile Group Inc	3089	C	909 428-0295	10077
DSM&t Co Inc	3694	C	909 357-7960	19830
Duro Dyne West Corp	3585	B	562 926-1774	15951
Ecoplast Corporation	3089	D	909 346-0450	10084
Edessa Inc	3272	E	909 823-1377	10919
Enjoy Foods International	2013	E	909 823-2228	482
Everett Charles Tech LLC (DH)	3825	D	909 625-5551	21752
Everett Charles Tech LLC	3825	F	909 625-5551	21753
Fabco Steel Fabrication Inc	3441	E	909 350-1535	12158
Fontana Foundry Corporation	3365	E	909 822-6128	11741
Fontana International Inc	3448	F	909 854-4532	12932
Fontana Paper Mills Inc	2952	D	909 823-4100	9404
Forged Metals Inc	3462	C	909 350-9260	13100
G O Pallets Inc	2448	E	909 823-4663	4473
Gator Machinery Company	3531	E	909 823-1688	14167
General Mills Inc	2043	D	951 685-7030	1061
Great Northern Corporation	2671	E	951 361-4770	5524
Greif Inc	3412	E	909 350-2112	11874
Harvest Asia Inc	3944	F	888 800-3133	23427
Ifco Systems North America Inc	2448	E	909 356-0697	4478
Indigo Designs	2434	F	909 997-0854	4313
Iparts Inc	3089	F	909 587-6059	10155
J-M Manufacturing Company Inc	2821	D	909 822-3009	7849
Jensen Enterprises Inc	3272	B	909 357-7264	10943
Jeti Inc (PA)	7692	F	909 357-2966	25416
Kemira Water Solutions Inc	2819	E	909 350-5678	7784
Kemira Water Solutions Inc	2899	F	909 429-4001	9267
Kemira Water Solutions Inc	2899	E	909 350-5678	9268
Kymera Industries Inc	3999	F	909 228-7194	24154
Lopez Pallets Inc	2448	F	909 823-0865	4485
Luster Cote Inc	3479	F	909 355-9995	13614
Lynam Industries Inc	3444	D	951 360-1919	12644
Material Supply Inc (PA)	3444	C	951 801-5004	12658
Metal Sales Manufacturing Corp	3444	F	909 829-8618	12669
Metal Tek Engineering Inc	2431	E	909 821-4158	4191
Meza Pallet Inc	2441	F	909 829-0223	4443
Michael Hagan	3949	E	909 213-5916	23618
Mission Custom Extrusion Inc	3089	E	909 822-1581	10214
Mohawk Industries Inc	2273	D	909 357-1064	2934
Morin Corp	3448	F	909 428-3747	12951
National Cnstr Rentals Inc	3677	E	909 574-1400	19349
New Greenscreen Incorporated	3444	F	951 685-9660	12691
Northrop Grumman Corporation	3812	A	626 812-2842	21357
Oldcastle Apg West Inc	3241	E	909 355-6422	10768
Oldcastle Precast Inc	3272	C	909 428-3700	10964
Pacific Award Metals Inc	3444	F	626 814-4410	12702
Pacific Forge Inc	3462	D	909 390-0701	13108
Patricks Cabinets	2434	F	909 823-2524	4334
Peri Formwork Systems Inc	3444	E	909 356-5797	12713
Pro Systems Fabricators Inc (PA)	3699	F	909 350-9147	20047
Rep-Kote Products Inc	2952	E	909 355-1288	9417
Ring Container Tech LLC	3085	E	909 350-8416	9808
River Valley Precast Inc	3272	E	928 764-3839	10992
Rnd Contractors Inc	3441	E	909 429-8500	12237
S & H Cabinets and Mfg Inc	2521	E	909 357-0551	4966
S&B Filters Inc	3714	D	909 947-0015	20443
Santa Fe Machine Works Inc	3599	E	909 350-6877	16928
Schroeder Iron Corporation	3441	E	909 428-6471	12240
Shawcor Pipe Protection LLC	3479	F	909 357-9002	13657
Simplex Strip Doors LLC (DH)	3081	E	800 854-7951	9727
Solar Atmospheres Inc	3398	E	909 217-7400	11829
Sole Technology Inc	3149	F	949 460-2020	10511
South Bay International Inc	2515	E	909 718-5000	4888
Southern Cal Bndery Mlng Inc	2789	D	909 829-1949	7620
Southwire Inc (HQ)	3353	F	310 884-8500	11580
Specfoam LLC	2515	F	951 685-3626	4889
Specialized Milling Corp	2851	F	909 357-7693	8942
Stl Fabrication Inc	3441	F	909 823-5033	12248
Suez Wts Services Usa Inc	3589	F	951 681-5555	16121
Sundown Foods USA Inc	2033	F	909 606-6797	860
Sunearth Inc	3433	E	909 434-3100	12091
Superior Sndblst & Coating	2851	F	909 428-9994	8945
Superior Trailer Works	3537	E	909 350-0185	14349
Tikos Tanks Inc	7692	E	951 757-8014	25444
Tpi Marketing LLC	3556	F	302 703-0283	14890
Tree Island Wire (usa) Inc	3315	D	909 594-7511	11461
Tri-Net Inc	3825	F	909 483-3555	21881
Tst/Impreso California Inc	2761	F	909 357-7190	7561
TTI Floor Care North Amer Inc	3052	B	440 996-2802	9511
Turret Punch Co Inc	3083	F	909 587-1820	9768
Ulmer Industries Inc	3441	E	909 823-7111	12266
Urethane Polymer International	2899	E	909 357-7200	9315
Utility Trailer Mfg Co	3715	F	909 428-8300	20519
Vanguard Fabrication Corp	3444	F	909 355-0832	12805
Verco Decking Inc	3444	F	909 822-8079	12806
Vista Metals Corp (PA)	3354	C	909 823-4278	11612
W E Hall Co	3444	F	909 829-4235	12814
Wagonmasters Corporation	3799	F	909 823-6188	21246

FOOTHILL RANCH, CA - Orange County

	SIC	EMP	PHONE	ENTRY #
A & J Manufacturing Company	3469	E	714 544-9570	13153
Allied Components Intl	3677	E	949 356-1780	19317
Avion Graphics Inc	2752	E	949 472-0438	6673
Bal Seal Engineering Inc (PA)	3495	B	949 334-8500	13787
Baldwin Hardware Corporation (DH)	3429	A	949 672-4000	11936
Carr Manufacturing Company Inc	3643	F	949 215-7952	17449
Chroma Systems Solutions Inc (HQ)	3825	D	949 297-4848	21734
Elite Global Solutions Inc	2821	F	949 709-4872	7834
Exhibit Works Inc	3993	F	949 470-0850	23871
Fredi & Sons Inc	3142	F	818 881-1170	10479
Gatekeeper Systems Inc (PA)	3699	E	949 268-1414	19972
Kaiser Aluminum Corporation (PA)	3334	D	949 614-1740	11539
Kaiser Aluminum Fab Pdts LLC (HQ)	3353	A	949 614-1740	11577
Kaiser Aluminum Investments Co (HQ)	3353	C	949 614-1740	11578
Lantic Inc	3089	F	949 830-9951	10188
Leoch Battery Corporation (PA)	3621	E	949 588-5853	17207
Nike Inc	2353	F	949 768-4000	3568
Oakley Inc	3851	D	949 672-6849	23112
Oakley Inc (DH)	2331	A	949 951-0991	3265
Oleumtech Corporation	3823	E	949 305-9009	21627
Ossur Americas Inc (DH)	3842	B	949 362-3883	22786
Ossur Americas Inc	3842	F	949 382-3883	22787
Price Pfister Inc	3432	C	949 672-4003	12045
Price Pfister Inc (DH)	3432	A	949 672-4000	12046
Protab Laboratories	2834	D	949 635-1930	8348
Renkus-Heinz Inc	3651	D	949 588-9997	17849
Ryadon Inc	3429	E	949 768-8333	11989
Tae Life Sciences LLC	3845	F	949 830-2117	23057
Trs International Mfg Inc	3643	F	949 855-0673	17503
Weiser Lock Corporation	3429	F	949 672-4000	12008

FORESTVILLE, CA - Sonoma County

	SIC	EMP	PHONE	ENTRY #
Canyon Rock Co Inc	1442	E	707 887-2207	351
Hartford Jackson LLC	2084	F	707 887-1756	1808
Kozlowski Farms A Corporation	2033	E	707 887-1587	814
Russian River Utility Inc	3713	F	707 887-7735	20225

FORT BRAGG, CA - Mendocino County

	SIC	EMP	PHONE	ENTRY #
Anderson Logging Inc	2411	D	707 964-2770	3978
Gatehouse Media LLC	2711	F	707 964-5642	5857
Goodall Guitars Inc	3931	F	707 962-1620	23373
H&M Logging	2411	F	707 964-2340	3990
Mendocino Lithographers	2752	F	707 964-0062	6968

Employment Codes: A=Over 500 employees, B=251-500,
C=101-250, D=51-100, E=20-50, F=10-19

2019 California
Manufacturers Register

© Mergent Inc. 1-800-342-5647
1379

GEOGRAPHIC

	SIC	EMP	PHONE	ENTRY #
North Coast Brewing Co Inc (PA)	2082	E	707 964-2739	1613
Ocean Fresh LLC (PA)	2091	E	707 964-1389	2299
Philbrick Inc	2411	E	707 964-2277	4006
Rent All Party Works Inc	7692	F	707 964-6661	25430
Roach Bros Inc (PA)	2411	E	707 964-9240	4007

FORT JONES, CA - Siskiyou County

	SIC	EMP	PHONE	ENTRY #
Eggtooth Originals Consulting	3944	F	530 468-5131	23420

FORTUNA, CA - Humboldt County

	SIC	EMP	PHONE	ENTRY #
Foster Dairy Farms	2023	C	707 725-6182	617
Huffman Logging Co Inc	2411	E	707 725-4335	3992

FOSTER CITY, CA - San Mateo County

	SIC	EMP	PHONE	ENTRY #
American Precision Gear Co	3566	E	650 627-8060	15238
Aoxing Pharmaceutical Co Inc	2834	B	646 367-1747	8035
Bright Horizons At Gilead	2834	E	650 312-1895	8086
Central Business Forms Inc	2752	F	650 548-0918	6724
Fortasa Memory Systems Inc	3572	F	888 367-8588	15537
Getgoing Inc	7372	F	415 608-7474	24691
Gilead Colorado Inc	2834	C	650 574-3000	8184
Gilead Palo Alto Inc (HQ)	2834	D	650 384-8500	8186
Gilead Sciences Inc (PA)	2834	B	650 574-3000	8187
Guidewire Software Inc (PA)	7372	C	650 357-9100	24717
Iar Systems Software Inc (HQ)	7372	F	650 287-4250	24746
Illumina Inc	3826	E	510 670-9300	21972
Inbenta Technologies Inc	7372	F	408 213-8771	24758
Life Technologies Corporation	3826	C	760 603-7200	21983
Louis Roesch Company	2752	F	650 212-2052	6955
Omics Group Inc	2721	B	650 268-9744	6224
Oracle Corporation	7372	B	650 678-3612	25010
Pioneer Materials Inc	3827	E	650 357-7130	22124
Powertronix Corporation	3612	E	650 345-6800	17115
Sciclone Pharmaceuticals Inc (HQ)	2834	E	650 358-3456	8374
Terarecon Inc (PA)	3577	D	650 372-1100	15869
Zoox Inc (PA)	3711	C	650 733-9669	20185

FOUNTAIN VALLEY, CA - Orange County

	SIC	EMP	PHONE	ENTRY #
Action Bag & Cover Inc	2393	D	714 965-7777	3759
Adrienne Designs LLC (PA)	3911	F	714 558-1209	23228
Adrienne Designs LLC	3911	F	800 621-5632	23229
Advanced Architectural Frames	3442	F	424 209-6018	12290
B-Lite Optical Inc	3851	F	714 964-8450	23079
California Clock Co (PA)	3873	F	714 545-4321	23218
Coast To Coast Label Inc (PA)	2679	F	657 203-2583	5704
Compuvac Industries Inc	3563	F	949 574-5085	15122
Custom Enamelers Inc	3479	F	714 540-7884	13573
D & D Gold Product Corp	2041	F	714 550-0372	1038
Duncan McIntosh Company Inc (PA)	2721	E	949 660-6150	6153
Epe Industries Usa Inc	3086	E	800 315-0336	9839
Epe Industries Usa Inc (HQ)	3086	E	800 315-0336	9841
Express Lens Lab Inc	3851	E	714 545-1024	23096
Fntech	3648	F	714 429-1686	17694
Freightgate Inc	7372	E	714 799-2833	24672
Gaffoglio Fmly Mtlcrafters Inc (PA)	3231	C	714 444-2000	10699
Genesis Group Sftwr Developers	7372	E	714 630-4297	24687
Gfmi Aerospace & Defense Inc	3728	E	714 361-4444	20824
Gigamem LLC	3572	F	949 461-9999	15540
Headed Reinforcement Corp	3469	F	714 557-1455	13215
Intercity Centerless Grinding	3599	F	714 546-5644	16589
Joy Products California Inc	3953	F	714 437-7250	23718
KB Sheetmetal Fabrication Inc	3444	F	714 979-1780	12638
Kingston Digital Inc (DH)	3577	F	714 435-2600	15780
Kingston Technology Corp (PA)	3577	B	714 445-3495	15781
Lakin Industries Inc (PA)	3471	F	714 968-6438	13443
Los Angles Tmes Cmmnctions LLC	2711	B	714 966-5600	5921
Makino Inc	3545	F	714 444-4334	14647
Meyco Machine and Tool Inc	3545	F	714 435-1546	14651
Microscale Industries Inc	2752	F	714 593-1422	6974
Microtech LLC	3843	E	714 966-1645	22893
Mobis Parts America LLC	3714	B	949 450-0014	20404
Moving Image Technologies LLC	3861	E	714 751-7998	23180
Neutronic Stamping & Plating	3471	E	714 964-8900	13464
Northrop Grumman Corporation	3812	A	310 332-6653	21362
Omni Metal Finishing Inc (PA)	3471	D	714 979-9414	13468
Openpro Inc	7372	F	714 378-4600	24988
Paderia LLC	2052	F	949 478-5273	1373
Panda Bowl	2599	F	714 418-0299	5248
Parker Printing	2752	F	714 444-4550	7015
Payton Technology Corporation	3674	C	714 885-8000	19073
Precision European Inc	3559	F	714 241-9657	15011
Printing Island Corporation	2752	F	714 668-1000	7046
Psitech Inc	3571	F	714 964-7818	15474
Quik Mfg Co	3531	F	714 754-0337	14185
Radflo Suspension Technology	3714	F	714 965-7828	20436
Richards Label Co Inc	2672	F	714 529-1791	5576
Ropak Corporation (DH)	3089	E	714 845-2845	10342

	SIC	EMP	PHONE	ENTRY #
Sams Tailoring	2311	F	714 963-6776	3043
Santa Fe Textiles Inc	2241	F	949 251-1960	2806
Sensonetics Inc	3829	F	714 799-1616	22266
Sherman Corporation	3599	E	310 671-2117	16944
Specialized Screen Printing	2759	E	714 964-1230	7493
SPX Corporation	3443	D	714 434-2576	12424
Surefire LLC	3648	C	714 545-9444	17734
Surefire LLC (PA)	3842	B	714 545-9444	22827
Sutura Inc	3842	E	714 427-0398	22828
Tape Factory Inc	2672	E	714 979-7742	5580
TN Sheet Metal Inc	3444	F	714 593-0100	12791
Touchpoint Solutions	7372	E	714 740-7242	25289
Watt Enterprise Inc	2329	F	714 963-0781	3205

FOWLER, CA - Fresno County

	SIC	EMP	PHONE	ENTRY #
Bobby Slzars Mxcan Fd Pdts Inc (PA)	2032	E	559 834-4787	748
Borga Stl Bldngs Cmponents Inc	3444	E	559 834-5375	12508
Dale Brisco Inc	3444	F	559 834-5926	12549
Jacobsen Trailer Inc	3715	E	559 834-5971	20505
Pps Packaging Company	2621	E	559 834-1641	5325
Sunshine Raisin Corporation (PA)	2064	C	559 834-5981	1460

FRAZIER PARK, CA - Kern County

	SIC	EMP	PHONE	ENTRY #
Trnlwb LLC	3999	A	661 245-3736	24278

FREEDOM, CA - Santa Cruz County

	SIC	EMP	PHONE	ENTRY #
Sage Instruments Inc	3825	D	831 761-1000	21842

FREMONT, CA - Alameda County

	SIC	EMP	PHONE	ENTRY #
3dconnexion Inc	3577	D	510 713-6000	15651
3par Inc (HQ)	3571	C	510 445-1046	15378
A & D Precision Machining Inc	3599	E	510 657-6781	16182
AB Supply	3711	E	510 651-1914	20119
ABC Assembly Inc	3679	F	408 293-3560	19431
Abd El & Larson Holdings LLC (PA)	3613	E	510 656-1600	17128
Acm Research Inc	3589	C	510 445-3700	16005
Acrometrix Corporation	2835	E	707 746-8888	8455
Adtec Technology Inc	3677	F	510 226-5766	19313
Advance Electronic Service	3672	E	510 490-1065	18409
Advanced Enterprises LLC	3663	F	408 923-5000	18016
Aehr Test Systems (PA)	3825	D	510 623-9400	21704
Air Liquide Electronics US LP	2819	E	510 624-4338	7750
Air Liquide USA LLC	2813	E	510 659-0162	7669
Airgas Usa LLC	2813	E	510 624-4000	7684
Alertenterprise Inc	3699	E	510 440-0840	19905
All Quality & Services Inc	3672	C	510 249-5800	18411
All West Fabricators Inc	3441	E	510 623-1200	12110
All-Tech Machine & Engrg Inc	3599	E	510 353-2000	16252
Alpha Ems Corporation	3672	C	510 498-8788	18414
Alta Manufacturing Inc	3672	E	510 668-1870	18415
Altair Technologies Inc	3559	E	650 508-8700	14905
Alterg Inc	3949	D	510 270-5900	23497
American Air Liquide Inc (DH)	2813	D	510 624-4000	7689
Ampro Systems Inc	3672	E	510 624-9000	18420
Antec Inc	3577	E	510 770-1200	15667
Applied Ceramics Inc (PA)	3674	F	510 249-9700	18704
Applied Materials Inc	3674	E	510 687-8018	18708
Applied Thin-Film Products (PA)	3679	C	510 661-4287	19446
Applied Thin-Film Products	3679	E	510 661-4287	19447
Ardelyx Inc	2834	D	510 745-1700	8039
Areesys Corporation	3699	E	510 979-9601	19911
Aries Research Inc	3577	F	925 818-1078	15671
Arkal Medical Inc	3841	E	510 933-1950	22345
Aruba Networks Inc	3663	E	408 227-4500	18042
Asante Technologies Inc	3577	E	408 435-8388	15675
Asteelflash USA Corp (HQ)	3672	C	510 440-2840	18429
Atlas Copco Compressors LLC	3563	F	510 413-5200	15118
Atlas Copco Compressors LLC	3563	F	510 413-5200	15119
Avalanche Technology Inc	3674	E	510 438-0148	18734
Avermedia Technologies Inc	3577	E	510 403-0006	15676
Avp Technology LLC	3565	E	510 683-0157	15195
Axp Technology Inc	3646	E	510 683-1180	17585
Axt Inc	3674	E	510 683-5900	18738
Axt Inc (PA)	3674	E	510 438-4700	18739
Ayantra Inc	3661	E	510 623-7526	17924
B & G Precision Inc	3599	F	510 438-9785	16297
Bace Manufacturing Inc	3089	D	510 657-5800	9968
Bart Manufacturing Inc	3999	E	408 320-4373	24048
BASF Catalysts LLC	2869	F	510 490-2150	8980
BASF Venture Capital Amer Inc	2869	F	510 445-6140	8984
Bay AR Yellow Pages	2741	F	650 558-8888	6445
Bay Area Circuits Inc	3672	E	510 933-9000	18434
Bay Associates Wire Tech Corp (DH)	2298	D	510 988-3800	2969
Bay Equipment Co Inc	3462	E	510 226-8800	13094
Bayview Plastic Solutions Inc	3089	E	510 360-0001	9972
Belden Inc	3357	F	510 438-9071	11645
Bema Electronic Mfg Inc	3679	E	510 490-7770	19463

Mergent email: customerrelations@mergent.com
1380

2019 California
Manufacturers Register

(P-0000) Products & Services Section entry number
(PA)=Parent Co (HQ)=Headquarters (DH)=Div Headquarters

Company	SIC	EMP	PHONE	ENTRY #
Benchmark Electronics Inc	3672	D	510 360-2800	18438
Berkeley Design Automation Inc	3674	E	408 496-6600	18745
Bestpro Machining	3599	F	510 490-6853	16321
Biogenex Laboratories (PA)	3841	E	510 824-1400	22371
Biokey Inc	2834	E	510 668-0881	8077
Biometric Solutions LLC	3577	F	408 625-7763	15683
Biotium Inc	2865	F	510 265-1027	8959
Bitmicro Networks Inc (PA)	3572	F	510 743-3124	15515
Bizlink Technology Inc (HQ)	3643	D	510 252-0786	17445
Blazer Exhibits & Graphics Inc	3993	F	408 263-7000	23832
Bo-Sherrel Corporation	3577	F	510 744-3525	15689
Bodycote Thermal Proc Inc	3398	E	510 492-4200	11800
Bold Data Technology Inc	3571	E	510 490-8296	15395
Bridgelux Inc (PA)	3674	D	925 583-8400	18750
Brooks Automation Inc	3585	D	510 498-8745	15942
C3-Ilex LLC (PA)	3822	E	510 659-8300	21501
Cable Connection Inc	3643	E	510 249-9000	17446
Cae Automation and Test LLC	3599	F	408 204-0006	16353
Cal-Weld Inc	3499	C	510 226-0100	13926
California Stone Coating	3531	F	510 284-2554	14151
Calogic LLC (PA)	3825	C	510 656-2900	21733
Cambridge Laser Laboratories	3231	F	510 651-0110	10682
Camtek Usa Inc	3674	E	510 624-9905	18759
Carl Herrmann Associates	3559	E	510 683-8554	14926
Celestica LLC	3679	C	510 770-5100	19483
Celestica Prcsion McHining Ltd	3599	F	510 252-2100	16369
Cellphone-Mate Inc	3663	D	510 770-0469	18066
Cenergy Solutions Inc	3714	F	510 474-7593	20287
Ceramic Tech Inc	3599	E	510 252-8500	16375
Certainteed Corporation	2952	D	510 490-0890	9403
Ceterix Orthopaedics Inc	3841	E	650 316-8660	22402
Chart Inc	3443	E	408 371-3303	12374
China Custom Manufacturing Ltd	3089	A	510 979-1920	10025
China Loco Szhou Precise Indus	3678	E	510 429-3700	19375
Chinese Overseas Mktg Svc Corp	2741	E	626 280-8588	6461
Cirrus Logic Inc	3674	D	510 226-1204	18767
Citragen Pharmaceuticals Inc	2834	F	510 249-9066	8113
Clean Sciences Inc	3471	E	510 440-8660	13373
Cleansmart Solutions Inc	2677	E	650 871-9123	5673
Cli Liquidating Corporation	3845	D	510 354-0300	22961
Colleen & Herb Enterprises Inc	3599	E	510 226-6083	16394
Comcore Technologies Inc	3827	E	510 498-8858	22070
Commercial Casework Inc (PA)	2431	D	510 657-7933	4125
Compass Components Inc (PA)	3679	C	510 656-4700	19498
Compugraphics USA Inc (HQ)	3674	D	510 249-2600	18776
Concentric Medical Inc	3841	E	650 938-2100	22408
Confluent Medical Tech Inc (PA)	3841	B	510 683-2000	22409
Content Management Corporation	2759	F	510 505-1100	7284
Contract Metal Products Inc	3444	E	510 979-4811	12538
Coorstek Inc	3599	D	510 492-6600	16403
Corsair Components Inc (PA)	3575	E	510 657-8747	15630
Corsair Memory Inc	3674	C	510 657-8747	18786
Creative Shower Door Corp	3088	F	510 623-9000	9898
Crossing Automation Inc (HQ)	3559	E	510 661-5000	14932
Custom Micro Machining Inc	3599	F	510 651-9434	16414
Custom Microwave Components	3679	F	510 651-3434	19506
Cyantek Corporation	2899	F	510 651-3341	9239
Cytek Biosciences Inc	3845	F	510 657-0110	22969
Cytek Development Inc	3826	F	510 657-0102	21943
D&H Manufacturing Company	3999	F	510 770-5100	24072
Dawn VME Products	3679	E	510 657-4444	19508
Dial Act Corporation	3081	F	510 659-8099	9706
Digital Power Corporation (HQ)	3679	E	510 657-2635	19513
Discopylabs (PA)	3652	E	510 651-5100	17892
Document Capture Tech Inc (PA)	3577	E	408 436-9888	15731
Du-All Safety LLC	3599	F	510 651-8289	16450
Duke Scientific Corporation	3821	E	650 424-1177	21468
Edc-Biosystems Inc	3823	E	510 257-1500	21577
Elma Electronic Inc (HQ)	3571	C	510 656-3400	15409
Enablence Systems Inc (HQ)	7372	E	510 226-8900	24608
Enablence USA Components Inc	3661	D	510 226-8900	17943
Envizio Inc	7372	E	650 814-4302	24619
Essai Inc (PA)	3825	C	510 580-1700	21750
Evolve Manufacturing Tech Inc	3841	D	650 968-9292	22446
Exar Corporation	3674	B	408 927-9975	18837
Excelitas Technologies Corp	3648	E	510 979-6500	17693
Fabri-Tech Components Inc	3679	F	510 249-2000	19538
Famsoft Corp	7372	E	510 683-3940	24645
Fancy Models Corp	3999	F	510 683-0819	24094
Fei Efa Inc (DH)	3678	D	510 897-6800	19390
Finisar Corporation	3674	F	408 548-1000	18842
FM Industries Inc	3599	C	510 673-0192	16504
FM Industries Inc (DH)	3599	C	510 668-1900	16505
Free-Flow Packaging Intl Inc	2671	E	302 737-2413	5522
Free-Flow Packaging Intl Inc (DH)	3086	E	650 261-5300	9853
Free-Flow Packaging Intl Inc	3086	E	323 722-5112	9854
Fremont Amgen Inc	2834	B	510 284-6500	8167
Fujikin of America Inc (HQ)	3492	E	408 980-8269	13742
Genoa Corporation	3674	E	510 979-3000	18856
Global Plating Inc	3471	E	510 659-8764	13417
Golden State Assembly Inc	3312	B	510 226-8155	11395
Gooch & Housego Palo Alto LLC (HQ)	3679	D	650 856-7911	19555
Hayward Quartz Technology	3674	C	510 657-9605	18870
Helitek Company Ltd	3674	F	510 933-7688	18871
Henry Plastic Molding Inc	3089	C	510 490-7993	10133
Hi/Fn Inc (DH)	3674	F	408 778-2944	18874
Highpoint Technologies Inc	3572	F	408 942-5800	15553
Hpe Government Llc	3575	D	916 435-9200	15633
I-Tech Company Ltd Lblty Co	3572	F	510 226-9226	15556
I2a Technologies Inc	3674	E	510 770-0322	18877
Ic Sensors Inc	3674	D	510 498-1570	18878
Ichor Systems Inc (HQ)	3674	E	510 897-5200	18880
Identiv Inc (PA)	3577	B	949 250-8888	15755
Igolping Inc	3949	F	866 507-4440	23589
Imtec Acculine LLC	3559	F	510 770-1800	14968
Incal Technology Inc	3577	E	510 657-8405	15758
Inforce Computing Inc (PA)	3679	F	510 683-9999	19577
Innodisk Usa Corporation	3674	E	510 770-9421	18896
Inspur Systems Inc (HQ)	3571	E	800 691-9893	15431
INTEL Corporation	3674	E	510 651-9841	18914
International Paper Company	2621	E	510 490-5887	5288
Intest Corporation	3674	E	408 678-9123	18925
Intest Silicon Valley Corp	3674	E	408 678-9123	18926
Intuity Medical Inc	3841	D	408 530-1700	22491
Iron Systems Inc	3577	F	408 943-8000	15771
Iscience Interventional Corp	3841	D	650 421-2700	22496
Isomedia LLC	3652	E	510 668-1656	17906
Ituner Networks Corporation	3577	F	510 226-6033	15773
Jaf International Inc	3571	F	510 656-1718	15434
Jaton Corporation	3672	E	510 933-8888	18514
Jeditron Technologies Corp	3577	F	510 226-1383	15774
Jem America Corp	3825	E	510 683-9234	21782
Johnson & Johnson	2676	D	650 237-4878	5667
Jusi Light Technology Inc	7372	E	510 585-5652	24820
Kaser Corporation	3571	E	510 657-9002	15437
Kashiyama USA Inc	3823	E	510 979-0070	21607
Kelly-Moore Paint Company Inc	2851	E	510 505-9834	8911
Key Solutions Inc	7372	E	510 456-4500	24828
KLA-Tencor Corporation	3825	D	510 456-2490	21790
Kln Precision Machining Corp	3599	D	510 770-5001	16659
Kmt International Inc	3533	E	510 713-1400	14231
Knightsbridge Plastics Inc	3089	D	510 249-9722	10182
Kore Print Solutions Inc	2752	F	510 445-1638	6928
Lab Vision Corporation (DH)	3826	F	510 979-5000	21981
Lam Research Corporation (PA)	3674	C	510 572-0200	18950
Lam Research Corporation	3559	C	510 572-3200	14981
Lam Research Corporation	3674	C	510 572-0200	18952
Lam Research Intl Holdg Co (HQ)	3559	C	510 572-0200	14982
Led One Distribution (PA)	3674	E	510 770-1189	18956
Lees Imperial Welding Inc	3441	C	510 657-4900	12193
Legacy Systems Incorporated	3559	F	510 651-2312	14983
Liantronics LLC	3646	F	510 438-0588	17627
Linear Integrated Systems Inc	3674	F	510 490-9160	18961
Luca International Group LLC (PA)	1382	F	510 498-8829	139
Lumens Integration Inc	3861	F	510 657-8367	23176
Lyncean Technologies Inc	3844	F	650 320-8300	22935
Magellan International Corp	3354	F	510 656-6661	11594
Mahindra Tractor Assembly Inc (DH)	3751	F	650 779-5180	21125
Manutronics Co	3571	E	510 438-0588	15447
Martinek Manufacturing	3599	E	510 438-0357	16717
Mass Precision Inc	3444	C	408 954-0200	12653
Materion Brush Inc	3497	E	510 623-1500	13870
Mattson Technology Inc (HQ)	3559	C	510 657-5900	14987
Mean Well Usa Inc	3679	F	510 683-8886	19643
Mecoptron Inc	3599	E	510 226-9966	16732
Medical Analysis Systems Inc (DH)	2835	C	510 979-5000	8494
Medika Therapeutics Inc	3841	F	510 377-0898	22529
Medplast Group Inc	3089	E	510 657-5800	10205
Melrose Metal Products Inc	3444	E	510 657-8771	12664
Mens Wearhouse	2326	E	510 657-9821	3112
Mercury Systms-Trstd Mssn Sltn (HQ)	3571	D	510 252-0870	15454
Micro Lambda Wireless Inc	3679	E	510 770-9221	19648
Microbar Inc	3559	B	510 659-9770	14990
Microgenics Corporation (HQ)	2834	C	510 979-9147	8283
Micron Consumer Pdts Group Inc (HQ)	3572	F	669 226-3000	15569
Microwave Technology Inc (DH)	3679	C	510 651-6700	19653
Millennium Automation	3569	F	510 683-5942	15341
Millennium Metalcraft Inc	3444	E	510 657-4700	12678
Minitouch Inc	3841	F	510 651-5000	22544
Mission Valley Regional Occu	2899	E	510 657-1865	9282

GEOGRAPHIC

	SIC	EMP	PHONE	ENTRY #
Mitac Usa Inc (DH)	3571	E	510 661-2800	15460
Mitxpc Inc	3571	F	510 226-6883	15461
Mobile Mini Inc	3448	F	510 252-9326	12945
Mohawk Industries Inc	2273	C	510 440-8790	2935
Mt Systems Inc	3559	F	510 651-5277	14995
Multi Power Products Inc	3699	F	415 883-6300	20020
Mvp Technology Intl Inc	3999	F	510 651-2425	24181
Myntahl Corporation	3661	E	510 413-0002	17966
Nationwide Boiler Incorporated (PA)	3443	D	510 490-7100	12402
Neophotonics Corporation	3674	F	510 933-4100	19035
Neptec Optical Solutions Inc	3229	E	510 687-1101	10659
Neptec Os Inc	3357	E	510 687-1101	11667
New Iem LLC	3613	E	510 656-1600	17152
New Wave Research Incorporated (HQ)	3699	C	510 249-1550	20027
Nitinol Development Corp	3851	A	510 683-2000	23110
Nitto Americas Inc (HQ)	2672	C	510 445-5400	5573
Norell Prsthtics Orthotics Inc (PA)	3842	F	510 770-9010	22779
Novanta Corporation	3679	F	510 770-1417	19663
NRC Manufacturing Inc	3679	F	510 438-9400	19665
Oldcastle Buildingenvelope Inc	3231	D	510 651-2292	10723
Omron Scientific Tech Inc (DH)	3823	C	510 608-3400	21628
Ooshirts Inc (PA)	2759	B	866 660-8667	7420
Optiworks Inc (PA)	3229	D	510 438-4560	10661
Optoma Technology Inc	3861	C	510 897-8600	23183
Optoplex Corporation (PA)	3661	D	510 490-9800	17976
Optovue Inc (PA)	3841	D	510 623-8868	22573
Orchard Printing	2752	F	510 490-1736	7007
Organic Spices (PA)	2099	E	510 440-1044	2630
Ortho-Clinical Diagnostics Inc	2835	E	908 704-5910	8501
Oryx Advanced Materials Inc (PA)	3572	F	510 249-1158	15579
Oudimentary LLC	2899	F	510 501-5057	9294
Owens Design Incorporated	3599	E	510 659-1800	16814
Pantronix Corporation	3674	E	510 656-5898	19071
Patriot Memory LLC (PA)	3674	C	510 979-1021	19072
Phonak LLC	3842	F	510 743-3939	22794
Pivotal Systems Corporation	3625	E	510 770-9125	17294
Plexus Corp	3672	C	510 668-9000	18561
Pol-Tech Precision Inc	3469	F	510 656-6832	13261
Prime Solutions Inc	3674	F	510 490-2255	19085
Printed Circuit Technology	3672	D	510 659-1866	18567
Ptec Solutions Inc	3599	D	510 358-3578	16864
Qcept Technologies Inc	3678	E	510 490-1120	19408
Quantum Global Tech LLC	2842	E	510 687-8000	8672
Quartet Mechanics Inc	3549	E	510 490-1886	14764
Quikrete Companies LLC	3272	D	510 490-4670	10988
Qxq Inc	3825	E	510 252-1522	21836
Raditek Inc	3663	F	408 266-7404	18235
Rapiscan Laboratories Inc (HQ)	3844	D	408 961-9700	22940
Raxium Inc	3648	E	408 712-1648	17727
Raymonds Little Print Shop Inc	2752	B	510 353-3608	7077
Rch Associates Inc	3559	F	510 657-7846	15017
Reliance Machine Products Inc	3599	E	510 438-6760	16894
Rfa Medical Solutions	3845	E	510 583-9500	23042
Rgblase LLC	3699	F	510 585-8449	20057
Rita Medical Systems Inc (HQ)	3845	D	510 771-0400	23043
Rj Media	2711	F	510 938-8667	6029
S3 Graphics Inc	3674	C	510 687-4900	19132
Sandys Drapery Inc	2391	E	510 445-0112	3702
Sangfor Technologies Inc	3825	A	408 520-7898	21843
Sangstat Medical Corp (DH)	3841	F	510 789-4300	22613
Sanmina Corporation	3672	B	510 897-2000	18596
Santur Corporation (HQ)	3559	E	510 933-4100	15028
Schmartboard Inc	3625	F	510 744-9900	17307
Sdo Communications Corp	3827	D	408 979-0289	22133
Seagate Systems (us) Inc (DH)	3572	C	510 687-5200	15601
Sensor Dynamics Inc	3845	F	510 623-1459	23046
Seradyn Inc	2835	D	317 610-3800	8512
Seven Up Btlg Co San Francisco (HQ)	2086	C	925 938-8777	2219
Sharp Dimension Inc	3599	F	510 656-8938	16942
Shockwave Medical Inc	3841	F	510 279-4262	22623
Sienna Medical Inc	3699	E	510 440-0200	20067
Sierra Nevada Corporation	3663	A	510 446-8400	18252
Silicon Valley Electro Plating	3471	E	408 945-1444	13504
Sipex Corporation (DH)	3674	C	510 668-7000	19164
Sipix Imaging Inc (DH)	3571	E	510 743-2928	15486
Smart Machines Inc	3535	E	510 661-5000	14287
Smart Modular Tech De Inc (HQ)	3674	E	510 623-1231	19173
Smtc Corporation	3699	E	510 737-0700	20071
Sna Electronics Inc	3672	E	510 656-3903	18609
Solaredge Technologies Inc (PA)	3629	E	510 498-3200	17356
Sonic Manufacturing Tech Inc	3672	B	510 580-8500	18612
Soraa Inc (PA)	3674	E	510 456-2200	19181
Soraa Laser Diode Inc	3699	E	805 696-6999	20076
South Bay Solutions Inc (PA)	3599	E	650 843-1800	16953
South Bay Solutions Texas LLC	3629	E	936 494-0180	17357

	SIC	EMP	PHONE	ENTRY #
Sparqtron Corporation	3629	D	510 657-7198	17358
Specialized Coating Services	3672	D	510 226-8700	18614
Spectranetics	3845	F	408 592-2111	23054
Spectranetics Corporation	3841	D	510 933-7964	22630
Spectrum Lithograph Inc	2752	E	510 438-9192	7113
Spine View Inc	3841	D	510 490-1753	22632
Spineex Inc	3841	E	510 573-1093	22633
Spire Manufacturing Inc	3643	E	510 226-1070	17491
Star Tool & Engineering Co Inc	3599	E	510 742-0500	16965
Stats Chippac Inc (DH)	3674	E	510 979-8000	19187
Stats Chippac Test Svcs Inc (DH)	3674	F	510 979-8000	19189
Stratamet Inc	3674	E	510 651-7176	19193
Stratamet Advanced Mtls Corp	3253	F	510 440-1697	10792
Streak Technology Inc	3944	F	408 206-2373	23467
Streamline Electronics Mfg Inc	3672	F	408 263-3600	18617
Stressteel Inc	3312	F	888 284-8752	11425
Stretch Inc	3674	D	408 543-2700	19195
Stryker Corporation	3841	E	510 413-2500	22637
Superior Automation Inc	3559	F	408 227-4898	15033
Surface Mount Tech Centre	3577	B	408 935-9548	15860
T C Media Inc	2721	F	510 656-5100	6266
T Ultra Equipment Company Inc	3559	F	510 440-3900	15036
Tangent Computer Inc	3571	D	650 342-9388	15494
TCI International Inc (HQ)	3663	C	510 687-6100	18274
Te Connectivity Corporation	3678	A	650 361-3615	19422
Techcomp (usa) Inc	3826	E	510 683-4300	22026
Telesynergy Research USA Inc	3577	F	408 200-9879	15867
Telirite Technical Svcs Inc	3672	E	510 440-3888	18625
Tenergy Corporation	3691	D	510 687-0388	19817
Terry B Lowe	3823	F	510 651-7350	21666
Tesla Inc	3711	E	707 373-4035	20175
Thermo Fisher Scientific Inc	3826	E	510 979-5000	22038
Thermo Fisher Scientific Inc	3826	E	317 490-5800	22042
Think Surgical Inc	3842	C	510 249-2300	22832
Transcontinental Nrthern CA 20	2759	C	510 580-7700	7525
Translarity Inc	3825	F	510 371-7900	21879
Tri Fab Associates Inc	3444	D	510 651-7628	12793
Tronson Manufacturing Inc	3599	E	408 533-0369	17013
Tru Machining	3599	F	510 573-3408	17014
United Pro Fab Mfg Inc	3674	F	510 651-5570	19248
United Sheetmetal Inc	3444	F	510 257-1858	12801
United Technologies Corp	3724	B	510 438-1300	20689
V-Silicon Inc	3674	F	510 897-0168	19250
Veex Inc	3823	F	510 651-0500	21674
Velos Inc	7372	E	510 739-4010	25322
Verseon Corporation (PA)	2834	E	510 668-1622	8431
Viant Medical LLC	3089	F	510 657-5800	10430
Vm Discovery Inc	2834	F	510 818-1018	8440
W2 Optronics Inc	3674	F	510 220-2796	19268
Walters & Wolf Glass Company	3272	D	510 226-9800	11017
Walters & Wolf Precast	3272	C	510 226-9800	11018
Wellex Corporation (PA)	3679	C	510 743-1818	19788
West Coast Quartz Corporation (HQ)	3229	D	510 249-2160	10670
Whats Happening Tri City	2759	E	510 494-1999	7541
William Ho	3577	F	510 226-9089	15886
Wintronics International Inc	3357	F	510 226-7588	11682
Wsglass Holdings Inc (HQ)	3211	E	510 623-5000	10613
Xilinx Inc	3674	F	510 770-9449	19277
Y-Change Inc	7372	F	510 573-2205	25365
Yadav Technology Inc	3674	F	510 438-0148	19280
Yaskawa America Inc	3699	E	510 651-5204	20117
Zerobase Energy LLC	3691	F	888 530-9376	19819
Zosano Pharma Corporation (PA)	2834	E	510 745-1200	8452

FRENCH CAMP, CA - San Joaquin County

	SIC	EMP	PHONE	ENTRY #
Parex Usa Inc	3299	E	209 983-8002	11368
Poly Processing Company LLC	2821	B	209 982-4904	7869

FRESNO, CA - Fresno County

	SIC	EMP	PHONE	ENTRY #
3 Ink Productions Inc	2221	F	559 275-4565	2771
A Plus Signs Inc	3993	E	559 275-0700	23802
A-1 Ornamental Ironworks Inc	3462	F	559 251-1447	13090
Ace Trailer Co	3715	E	559 442-1500	20492
Actagro LLC (PA)	2875	E	559 369-2222	9081
Advanced Metal Works Inc	3444	F	559 237-2332	12460
Advanced Prosthetics Llc	3842	F	559 298-0321	22694
Agi Publishing Inc (PA)	2741	E	559 251-8888	6423
Agi Publishing Inc	2741	C	559 251-8888	6424
Agricultural Manufacturing	3531	F	559 485-1662	14139
Agrifim Irrigation Pdts Inc	3523	F	559 443-6680	14037
Allied Electric Motor Svc Inc	7694	F	559 486-4222	25451
American Bottling Company	2086	F	559 442-1553	2085
American Carrier Systems	3711	D	559 442-1500	20124
Ampersand Ice Cream LLC	2024	F	559 264-8000	655
Ansons Transportation Inc	3537	E	559 892-1867	14308
Architectural Wood Design Inc	2431	E	559 292-9104	4105

Mergent email: customerrelations@mergent.com

1382

2019 California
Manufacturers Register

(P-0000) Products & Services Section entry number
(PA)=Parent Co (HQ)=Headquarters (DH)=Div Headquarters

Company	SIC	EMP	PHONE	ENTRY #
Arrow Electric Motor Service	7694	F	559 266-0104	25453
Atlas Pacific Engineering Co	3556	D	559 233-4500	14833
Auernheimer Labs Inc	3651	F	559 442-1048	17768
Automated Bldg Components Inc	2439	E	559 485-8232	4391
Automotive Electronics Svcs	3496	F	559 292-7851	13811
Aweta-Autoline Inc (PA)	3523	E	559 244-8340	14043
Axiom Industries Inc	3842	E	559 276-1310	22703
Bailey Valve Inc	3491	E	559 434-2838	13705
Barney & Co California LLC	2099	F	559 442-1752	2460
Bermad Inc (PA)	3494	E	877 577-4283	13761
Bestwall LLC	2656	C	559 485-4900	5498
Better World Manufacturing Inc (PA)	3089	F	559 291-4276	9981
Betts Company (PA)	3495	D	559 498-3304	13788
Betts Company	3495	E	559 498-3304	13789
Betts Company	3713	E	559 498-8624	20194
Beynon Sports Surfaces Inc	3949	E	559 237-2590	23519
Bimbo Bakeries Usa Inc	2051	F	559 498-3632	1196
Bimbo Bakeries Usa Inc	2051	E	650 291-3213	1209
Bimbo Bakeries Usa Inc	2051	C	559 489-0980	1210
Blue Eagle Stucco Products	3299	F	559 485-4100	11347
Bottling Group LLC	2086	E	559 485-5050	2101
Brandt Consolidated Inc	2875	F	559 499-2100	9082
Broadway Knitting Mills Corp	2253	E	559 456-0955	2825
Brownie Baker Inc	2052	D	559 277-7070	1358
Builders Concrete Inc (DH)	3273	E	559 225-3667	11052
Business Journal	2721	E	559 490-3400	6121
Busseto Foods Inc	2013	D	559 237-9591	470
Busseto Foods Inc (PA)	2013	C	559 485-9882	471
Cal West Construction Inc	3544	F	559 217-3306	14492
California Bedrooms Inc	2511	E	559 233-7050	4683
California Dairies Inc	2026	D	559 233-5154	714
California Dried Fruit Inc	2034	E	559 233-0970	877
Candies Tolteca	2064	E	559 266-9193	1410
Cargill Meat Solutions Corp	2011	C	559 268-5586	425
Caro Nut Company	2034	E	559 439-2365	878
Cemex Materials LLC	3273	E	559 275-2241	11086
Central Valley Machining Inc	3441	E	559 291-7749	12133
Central Valley Tank of Cal	3443	F	559 456-3500	12370
Central Vly Assembly Packg Inc	3432	E	559 486-4260	12029
Certified Meat Products Inc	2011	E	559 256-1433	427
Ch Industrial Technology Inc	3441	E	559 485-8011	12134
Charles Jj Inc	2491	E	559 264-6664	4590
Choice Food Products Inc	2013	F	559 266-1674	474
Clay Mix LLC	3273	F	559 485-0065	11093
CMr Marketing and RES Inc	2879	E	559 499-2100	9098
Cold Spring Granite Company	3281	E	559 438-2100	11243
Commercial Manufacturing	3556	E	559 237-1855	14842
Conagra Brands Inc	2068	D	559 291-0231	1486
Concept Vehicle Technologies	3715	F	559 233-1313	20497
Crown Equipment Corporation	3537	E	559 585-8000	14316
Cummins Pacific LLC	3519	D	559 277-6760	14021
Custom AG Formulators Inc (PA)	2879	D	559 435-1052	9099
D & M Manufacturing	3523	E	559 834-4668	14056
Dantel	3661	E	559 292-1111	17936
Darling Ingredients Inc	2077	E	559 268-5325	1525
Diamond Weld Industries Inc	3548	F	559 268-9999	14725
Digital Prototype Systems Inc	3663	F	559 454-1600	18087
Display Advertising Inc	2759	F	559 266-0231	7300
Dkp Inc	3523	E	559 266-2695	14060
Dreamteam Business Group LLC	2759	F	559 430-7676	7304
Dumont Printing Inc	2752	E	559 485-6311	6795
Duncan Enterprises (HQ)	2851	C	559 291-4444	8901
Duracite	2542	F	559 346-1181	5138
DV Kap Inc	2392	F	559 435-5575	3721
E & J Gallo Winery	2084	C	559 458-0807	1740
E & J Gallo Winery	2084	D	559 458-2500	1741
E-Z Haul Ready Mix Inc	3273	E	559 233-6603	11103
Eezer Products Inc	2821	E	559 255-4140	7832
Elite Fashion Accessories Inc	2387	F	559 435-0225	3629
Elliott Manufacturing Company	3599	F	559 233-6235	16469
Emerzian Woodworking	2541	E	559 292-2448	5058
Envelope Products Co (PA)	2621	E	925 939-5173	5281
Ernest Packaging Solutions (PA)	2819	E	800 757-4968	7776
Excelsior Metals Inc	3441	E	559 294-9284	12157
Fiore Di Pasta Inc	2099	E	559 457-0431	2519
Fresno Distributing Co	3651	E	559 442-8800	17801
Fresno French Bread Bakery Inc	2051	E	559 268-7088	1253
Fresno Gem & Mineral Society	3915	F	559 486-7280	23342
Fresno Neon Sign Co Inc	3993	F	559 292-2944	23883
Fruit Fillings Inc	2033	E	559 237-4715	800
Gallery Cabinet Connection	2434	F	559 294-7007	4304
Garabedian Bros Inc (PA)	3599	E	559 268-5014	16525
Gea Farm Technologies Inc	2842	E	559 497-5074	8642
Generitech Corporation	2844	F	559 346-0233	8753
Ghazarian Wldg Fabrication Inc	7692	F	559 233-1210	25405
Glaxosmithkline Consumer	2834	D	559 650-1550	8190
Glovefit International Corp	3089	F	559 243-1110	10122
GNA Industries Inc	3625	E	559 276-0953	17274
Golden Gate Freightliner Inc	3537	C	559 486-4310	14325
Gregor Inc	3732	F	559 441-7703	21040
Gruma Corporation	2096	D	559 498-7820	2391
Gusmer Enterprises Inc	3569	D	908 301-1811	15327
Helados Vallarta Inc	2024	F	559 709-1177	679
Henderson Services Inc	3732	E	559 435-8874	21042
Hershey Company	2098	C	559 485-8110	2428
Holcomb Products Inc	2395	E	559 822-2067	3849
HP Water Systems Inc	3561	E	559 268-4751	15075
Innovation Alley LLC	3441	F	559 453-6974	12179
Irritec Usa Inc	3523	F	559 275-8825	14072
ITT LLC	3561	F	559 265-4730	15080
J & L Irrigation Company Inc	3523	F	559 237-2181	14073
J P Lamborn Co (PA)	3585	C	559 650-2120	15962
Jain Irrigation Inc	3523	C	559 485-7171	14075
James Clark	2789	F	559 456-3893	7603
JR Simplot Company	2037	D	559 439-3900	954
Kasco Fab Inc	3441	D	559 442-1018	12190
Kearneys Aluminum Foundry Inc (PA)	3363	E	559 233-2591	11697
Keiser Corporation (PA)	3949	E	559 256-8000	23602
Klippenstein Corporation	3565	E	559 834-4258	15214
Kodiak Cartoners Inc	3565	E	559 266-4844	15215
Kraft Heinz Foods Company	2033	B	559 441-8515	815
Kraft Heinz Foods Company	2068	D	559 237-9206	1494
La Tapatia Tortilleria Inc	2099	C	559 441-1030	2571
Label Masters Inc	2759	E	559 445-1208	7375
Larson Brothers	2741	F	559 292-8161	6515
Legacy Vulcan LLC	3281	D	559 434-1202	11260
Lehmans Manufacturing Co Inc	3441	F	559 486-1700	12195
Lidestri Foods Inc	2033	D	559 251-1000	820
Lily Pond Products	3559	F	559 431-5203	14984
Los Gatos Tomato Products LLC (PA)	2033	E	559 945-2700	821
Louie Foods International	2099	F	559 264-2745	2589
Lyons Magnus Inc (PA)	2033	B	559 268-5966	823
Lyons Magnus Inc	2033	E	559 268-5966	824
M2 Antenna Systems Inc	3679	F	559 221-2271	19632
Manna Pro Products LLC	2048	E	559 486-1810	1146
Marquez Brothers Intl Inc	2022	E	559 276-7800	593
Mbtechnology	2952	E	559 233-2181	9413
McClatchy Newspapers Inc	2711	B	559 441-6111	5945
McGrayel Company Inc	2899	E	559 299-7660	9278
Meeder Equipment Company (PA)	3559	E	559 485-0979	14988
Michelsen Packaging Co Cal	2671	E	559 237-3819	5526
Mike Murach & Associates	2731	F	559 440-9071	6364
Miller Milling Company LLC	2041	E	559 441-8133	1046
Millerton Builders Inc	2591	E	559 252-0490	5204
Mineral King Minerals Inc (PA)	2873	F	559 582-9228	9066
Modern Custom Fabrication	3443	F	559 264-4741	12400
Moles Farm	2034	D	559 444-0324	889
Neclec	3471	E	559 797-0103	13462
Nestle Usa Inc	2023	E	559 834-2554	638
Nevocal Enterprises Inc	1442	D	559 277-0700	375
New Age Metal Finishing LLC	3471	E	559 498-8585	13465
New American Industries Inc	2393	E	559 251-1581	3767
Ohanyans Inc (PA)	2013	E	559 225-4290	510
Olam Tomato Processors Inc	2033	D	559 447-1390	839
Olson and Co Steel	3441	D	559 224-7811	12221
Outback Inc	3273	F	559 369-7261	11153
Pacific Choice Brands Inc (PA)	2035	B	559 892-5365	926
Pacific Tent and Awning	2394	E	559 486-8147	3801
Packaging Plus	2653	E	209 858-9200	5448
Pana-Pacific Corporation	3714	C	559 457-4700	20417
Paper Pulp & Film	2679	E	559 233-1151	5724
Pappys Meat Company Inc	2099	E	559 291-0218	2634
Pentair Flow Technologies LLC	3589	C	559 266-0516	16086
Performance Welding	7692	F	559 233-0042	25425
Pleasant Mattress Inc (PA)	2515	D	559 268-6446	4879
Pnm Inc	3599	E	559 291-1986	16849
Pollstar LLC (PA)	2721	D	559 271-7900	6235
Potential Design Inc	3556	F	559 834-5361	14878
Praxair Distribution Inc	2813	E	559 237-5521	7722
Premier Color Graphics Inc	2752	E	559 625-8606	7035
Prinsco Inc	3084	C	559 485-5542	9785
Professional Print & Mail Inc	2752	E	559 237-7468	7054
R & L Enterprises Inc	3599	E	559 233-1608	16877
Reyes Coca-Cola Bottling LLC	2086	D	559 264-4631	2192
Rich Products Corporation	2092	C	559 486-7580	2321
Rileys TANks/D&j Service	3443	F	559 237-1403	12415
Riviana Foods Inc	2099	D	559 485-8110	2655
Robert J Alandt & Sons	3599	E	559 275-1391	16907
Roger Enrico	2086	B	559 485-5050	2214
Rotary Corp	3524	F	559 445-1108	14132

Employment Codes: A=Over 500 employees, B=251-500,
C=101-250, D=51-100, E=20-50, F=10-19

2019 California
Manufacturers Register

© Mergent Inc. 1-800-342-5647

1383

GEOGRAPHIC

	SIC	EMP	PHONE	ENTRY #
S A Fields Inc	2394	F	559 292-1221	3807
Saf-T-Cab Inc **(PA)**	3713	D	559 268-5541	20227
Safety-Kleen Systems Inc	3559	F	559 486-1960	15026
Scafco Corporation	3399	E	559 256-9911	11847
Scrimco Inc	2221	F	559 237-7442	2782
Simply Smashing Inc	3993	E	559 658-2367	23976
Sinclair Companies	2911	D	559 997-3617	9359
Sinclair Companies	2911	D	559 351-1916	9360
Sinclair Systems Intl LLC	2759	E	559 233-4500	7483
Slam Specialties LLC **(PA)**	3714	F	559 348-9038	20450
Soex West Tex Recycl USA LLC	2273	D	559 233-1765	2941
South Valley Materials Inc **(DH)**	3273	C	559 277-7060	11182
Ssi G Debbas Chocolatier LLC	2066	E	559 294-2071	1474
Sturdy Gun Safe Manufacruing	3499	F	559 485-8361	13977
Subdirect LLC	2721	E	559 321-0449	6263
Suburban Steel Inc **(PA)**	3441	E	559 268-6281	12251
Sun Vlley Rsins Inc A Cal Corp	2034	F	559 233-8070	896
Sunrise Medical (us) LLC	3842	D	559 292-2171	22824
T G Schmeiser Co Inc	3429	E	559 486-4569	11999
Tanfield Engrg Systems US Inc	3531	F	559 443-6602	14192
Tech West Vacuum Inc	3843	E	559 291-1650	22916
Tempest Technology Corporation	3564	E	559 277-7577	15180
Tessenderlo Kerley Inc	2819	E	559 485-0114	7807
Tmr Executive Interiors Inc	2431	F	559 346-0631	4247
Total Concept Enterprises Inc	3965	E	559 485-8413	23777
TPC Industries LLC	3999	E	310 849-9574	24274
Trane US Inc	3585	E	559 271-4625	15991
Tranpak Inc	3089	E	800 827-2474	10409
Tri-State Stairway Corp	3446	E	559 268-0875	12900
Tru-Trailers Inc	3715	F	559 251-7591	20513
Tuff Shed Inc	2452	E	559 268-8833	4579
Turner Designs Hydrocarbon Ins	3699	E	559 253-1414	20092
United Western Industries Inc	3599	F	559 226-7236	17024
Upholstery By Wayne Stoec	2211	F	559 233-1960	2766
Valley Decorating Company	3089	E	559 495-1100	10427
Valley Lahvosh Baking Co Inc	2051	E	559 485-2700	1336
Valley Pipe & Supply Inc	3494	E	559 233-0321	13778
Valley Protein LLC	2013	D	559 498-7115	533
Valley Stairway Inc	3446	F	559 299-0151	12903
Vcp Mobility Inc	3842	B	559 292-2171	22838
Vcp Mobility Holdings Inc	3842	B	303 218-4500	22840
Vie-Del Company **(PA)**	2033	E	559 834-2525	868
Vitro Flat Glass LLC	3211	C	559 485-4660	10611
Vitro Flat Glass LLC	3211	C	559 485-4660	10612
Vm Custom Boat Trailers	3799	C	559 486-0410	21245
Wade Metal Products	3441	F	559 237-9233	12278
Walton Industries Inc	2851	F	559 233-6300	8954
Wasco Hardfacing Co	3523	E	559 485-5860	14119
Wasco Hardfacing Co	3523	D	559 485-5860	14120
Wasco Manufacturing Co	3523	E	559 485-5860	14121
Weather TEC Corp	3523	F	559 291-5555	14122
Weir Floway Inc **(HQ)**	3561	C	559 442-4000	15098
West Coast Growers Inc	2034	E	559 843-2294	907
Western Trade Printing Inc	2752	F	559 251-8595	7183
Westrock Cp LLC	2631	E	559 441-1166	5367
Westrock Cp LLC	2653	C	559 519-7240	5472
Westrock Rkt LLC	2652	F	559 441-1181	5380
Westrock Rkt Company	2653	C	559 497-1662	5474
Whipple Industries Inc	3564	F	559 442-1261	15187
Wilbur-Ellis Company LLC	3523	D	559 442-1220	14125
Wood-N-Wood Products Cal Inc **(PA)**	2449	E	559 896-3636	4542
Wood-N-Wood Products Inc	2449	E	559 896-3636	4544
Xylem Inc	3561	F	559 265-4731	15101
Zip Print Inc **(PA)**	2752	E	559 486-3112	7195

FULLERTON, CA - Orange County

	SIC	EMP	PHONE	ENTRY #
Accurate Laminated Pdts Inc	2542	E	714 632-2773	5124
Adams Rite Aerospace Inc **(DH)**	3728	C	714 278-6500	20704
ADB Industries	3398	D	310 679-9193	11790
Advanced Equipment Corporation **(PA)**	2542	E	714 635-5350	5125
Aero Engineering Inc	3599	F	714 879-6200	16236
Aerofit LLC	3498	C	714 521-5060	13873
Ampertech Inc	3545	E	714 523-4068	14601
Amtrend Corporation	2541	D	714 630-2070	5036
Anderco Inc	2431	E	714 446-9508	4098
Angelus Pacific Company Inc	2752	F	714 871-1610	6661
Arconic Global Fas & Rings Inc	3324	C	714 871-1550	11507
Arconic Inc	3334	B	714 871-1550	11535
Arconic Inc	3334	B	714 278-8981	11536
Aurident Inc	3843	E	714 870-1851	22858
Axceleon Inc	7372	F	714 960-5200	24404
Bbe Sound Inc **(PA)**	3931	E	714 897-6766	23356
Beckman Instruments Inc	2835	F	714 871-4848	8462
Bench-Craft Inc	2599	F	714 523-3322	5222
Betterline Products Inc	3599	E	760 535-5030	16323
BEX Engraving Company Inc	3479	F	714 879-6593	13559

	SIC	EMP	PHONE	ENTRY #
Bimbo Bakeries Usa Inc	2051	E	714 441-2555	1199
Biomed Instruments Inc	3845	F	714 459-5716	22952
Braiform Enterprises Inc	3089	D	714 526-0257	9991
Brentwood Home LLC **(PA)**	2515	C	562 949-3759	4854
Bushnell Ribbon Corporation	3955	F	562 948-1410	23725
Byrnes & Kiefer Co	2087	D	714 554-4000	2248
Cargill Incorporated	2833	D	714 449-6708	7925
Cargill Incorporated	2079	F	323 588-2274	1537
Centerline Manufacturing Inc	3679	F	714 525-9890	19485
Chefmaster	2099	E	714 554-4000	2486
CJ Foods Manufacturing Corp	2099	E	714 888-3500	2488
Coast Cutters Co Inc	3312	F	626 444-2965	11390
Comant Industries Incorporated **(DH)**	3663	E	714 870-2420	18071
Concreteaccessoriescom	3452	F	714 871-9434	13064
Consolidated Aerospace Mfg LLC **(PA)**	3812	F	714 989-2797	21276
Cook and Cook Incorporated	3443	F	714 680-6669	12383
Corru-Kraft IV	2652	F	714 773-0124	5374
Cove Four-Slide Stamping Corp **(PA)**	3496	D	516 379-4232	13820
Cove Four-Slide Stamping Corp	3496	F	714 525-2930	13821
Cura Medical Technologies LLC	3844	F	949 939-4406	22931
Cutting Edge Wood Tech Inc	2431	E	714 447-3667	4135
Dae Shin Usa Inc	2221	D	714 578-8900	2775
Delta Pacific Activewear Inc	2253	E	714 871-9281	2832
Delta Sportswear Inc	2331	F	714 568-1102	3230
Delta Stag Manufacturing	3713	D	562 904-6444	20199
Demes Gourmet Corporation	2013	E	714 870-6040	479
Direct Drive Systems Inc	3621	D	714 872-5500	17189
Dr Smoothie Brands Inc	2087	E	714 449-9787	2256
Dr Smoothie Enterprises	2087	E	714 449-9787	2257
Ecologic Engine Tstg Labs LLC	3519	E	714 774-3385	14027
Ejays Machine Co Inc	3599	E	714 879-0558	16465
Ellingson Inc	3599	F	714 773-1923	16468
Evo Manufacturing Inc	3999	F	714 879-8913	24093
Faac	3699	F	800 221-8278	19965
Fibco Composites Inc	3812	F	714 269-1118	21293
Fluid Power Ctrl Systems Inc	3823	E	714 525-3727	21585
FMC Technologies Inc	3533	F	714 872-5574	14224
Foam-Craft Inc	3086	C	714 459-9971	9850
Fuller Laboratories	2835	F	714 525-7660	8477
Fullerton Printing Inc	2752	F	714 870-7500	6830
Future Foam Inc	3086	F	714 871-2344	9855
Future Foam Inc	3086	F	714 459-9971	9857
Future Foam Inc	3086	F	714 459-9971	9858
Gard Inc	3444	E	714 738-5891	12594
Gaylords H R I Meats Inc	2011	F	714 526-2278	436
General Linear Systems	7694	F	714 994-4822	25461
GLC General Inc	2499	F	714 870-9825	4623
Global Infovision Inc	7372	F	714 738-4465	24698
Global Mfg Solutions LLC	3357	E	562 356-3222	11664
Gold Venture Inc	3086	C	909 623-1810	9862
Golden Pacific Seafoods Inc	3556	F	714 589-8888	14855
Golden West Technology	3672	D	714 738-3775	18496
Graphics 2000 LLC	2759	D	714 879-1188	7332
High Five Inc	2752	F	714 847-2200	6858
Interntnal Cnnctors Cable Corp	3661	C	888 275-4422	17958
Jonel Engineering	3596	E	714 879-2360	16175
Khyber Foods Incorporated	2099	E	714 879-0900	2552
Kimberly-Clark Corporation	2621	B	714 578-0705	5307
Kims Welding and Iron Works	3462	F	714 680-7700	13103
Kip Steel Inc	3316	F	714 461-1051	11470
KMW USA Inc **(HQ)**	3679	E	714 515-1100	19611
Kraft Heinz Foods Company	2099	B	714 870-8235	2555
Kryler Corp	3471	E	714 871-9611	13440
Lange Precision Inc	3599	F	714 870-5420	16674
Laser Industries Inc	3599	D	714 532-3271	16679
Magtech & Power Conversion Inc	3677	E	714 451-0106	19345
Marton Precision Mfg LLC	3724	E	714 808-6623	20670
McKenna Labs Inc **(PA)**	2834	F	714 687-6888	8269
Mica Lighting Company Inc	3648	F	714 738-8448	17714
Mozaik LLC	2652	F	562 207-1900	5378
Mytrex Inc	3523	F	949 800-9725	14085
National Signal Inc	3799	E	714 441-7707	21236
Nicholas Michael Designs Inc	2519	C	714 562-8101	4914
Nina Mia Inc	2099	D	714 773-5588	2622
OEM LLC	3599	E	714 449-7500	16803
Orora Visual LLC	2759	C	714 879-2400	7424
Pacmin Incorporated **(PA)**	3999	D	714 447-4478	24203
Pasco Industries Inc	3991	F	714 992-2051	23796
Penhall Diamond Products Inc	3545	D	714 776-0937	14661
Phenix Gourmet LLC	2052	C	562 404-5028	1375
Picture This Framing Inc	2499	F	714 447-8749	4641
Plexi Fab Inc	2821	F	714 447-8494	7868
Printec Ht Electronics LLC	3674	E	714 484-7597	19086
Ram Aerospace Inc	3728	F	714 853-1703	20920
Raytheon Company	3812	E	714 446-2584	21390

Company	SIC	EMP	PHONE	ENTRY #
Raytheon Company	3812	D	714 446-3513	21391
Raytheon Company	3829	D	714 446-2287	22259
Raytheon Company	3812	C	714 732-0119	21394
Raytheon Company	3812	B	714 446-3232	21404
Ross Publications Inc	2741	E	562 691-5013	6572
Rozak Engineering Inc	3599	F	714 446-8855	16919
S and H Rubber Company Inc	3069	E	714 526-2583	9673
Santa Ana Plating Corp (PA)	3471	D	310 923-8305	13498
Saputo Dairy Foods Usa LLC	2026	C	714 772-8861	736
Schreiber Foods Inc	2022	C	714 490-7360	601
Scientific Spray Finishes Inc	3479	E	714 871-5541	13655
Screen Printers Resource Inc (PA)	2759	F	714 441-1155	7479
Senor Snacks Inc	2096	F	714 739-1073	2403
Senor Snacks Manufacturing Ltd	2064	D	714 739-1073	1458
Soma Magnetics Corporation	3612	E	714 447-0782	17121
South Western Paving Company	2951	E	714 577-5750	9398
Stauber Prfmce Ingredients (HQ)	2833	C	714 441-3900	7973
Stein Industries Inc (PA)	3444	E	714 522-4560	12773
Sticker Hub Inc	2759	F	714 912-8457	7498
Stir Foods LLC	2038	E	714 871-9231	1017
Sun Trade Group Inc (PA)	2253	F	714 525-4888	2859
T and T Industries Inc (PA)	3496	F	714 284-6555	13856
Tct Advanced Machining Inc	3599	F	714 871-9371	16988
Terra Universal Inc	3564	C	714 526-0100	15181
Thunderbolt Manufacturing Inc	3599	F	714 632-0397	17000
UNI Filter Inc	3714	D	714 535-6933	20475
United Duralume Products Inc	3444	F	714 773-4011	12798
United Pharma Inc	2899	C	714 738-8999	9314
United Testing Systems Inc	3829	E	714 638-2322	22292
Universal Turbo Technology	3511	E	714 600-9585	14011
W/S Packaging Group Inc	2679	D	714 992-2574	5746
Western States Envelope Corp	2677	D	714 449-0909	5681
Western Yarn Dyeing Inc	2269	E	714 578-9500	2923
Wheel and Tire Club Inc	3312	E	714 422-3505	11429
Will-Mann Inc	3444	E	714 870-0350	12819
Wilsons Art Studio Inc	2759	D	714 870-7030	7542
Winonics Inc	3672	E	714 626-3755	18653
WMC Precision Machining	3599	F	714 773-0059	17072
Zmp Aquisition Corporation	3625	C	714 278-6500	17327

GALT, CA - Sacramento County

Company	SIC	EMP	PHONE	ENTRY #
Calstone Company	3271	E	209 745-2981	10847
Cardinal Glass Industries Inc	3211	C	209 744-8940	10589
Carsons Inc	3469	E	209 745-2387	13180
Consolidated Fabricators Corp	3469	D	209 745-4604	13187
Galt Pipe Company	3494	F	209 745-2936	13767
Herburger Publications Inc (PA)	2711	D	916 685-5533	5876
Lodi Iron Works Inc	3321	F	209 368-5395	11497
Southwest Products Corporation	3519	E	209 745-6000	14031
United Rotary Brush Corp	3991	E	913 888-8450	23798

GARDEN GROVE, CA - Orange County

Company	SIC	EMP	PHONE	ENTRY #
3M Company	2891	F	714 373-2837	9124
A Q Pharmaceuticals Inc	2834	E	714 903-1000	7985
Acco Brands USA LLC	3089	E	562 941-0505	9919
Adtek Media Inc	3993	E	949 680-4200	23809
Advanced Aerospace	3585	C	714 265-6200	15933
Advanced Chemistry & Tech Inc (HQ)	2891	E	714 373-8118	9127
Aero Dynamic Machining Inc	3728	D	714 379-1073	20708
Airflex5d LLC	2514	F	714 622-2600	4821
American Metal Bearing Company	3562	E	714 892-5527	15104
Assault Industries Inc	3799	F	714 799-6711	21222
B & E Manufacturing Co Inc	3728	E	714 898-2269	20753
Babys World	2032	F	714 539-2229	745
Banh MI & Che Cali	2051	F	714 534-6987	1183
Basic Electronics Inc	3679	E	714 530-2400	19460
Basic Energy Services Inc	1389	E	714 530-0855	184
Baton Lock & Hardware Co Inc	3429	E	714 265-3636	11937
Beauty & Health International (PA)	2834	E	714 903-9730	8072
Bentley Prtg & Graphics Inc	2752	F	714 636-1622	6693
Brandelli Arts Inc	3299	E	714 537-0969	11349
Broncs Inc	2211	C	310 637-9100	2726
C & A Transducers Inc	3679	E	714 554-9188	19471
C&D Zodiac Inc	3728	C	714 901-2672	20764
C&D Zodiac Inc	3728	B	714 891-1906	20768
Cali Chem Inc	2844	E	714 265-3740	8712
Carmen Abato Enterprises	3357	F	714 895-1887	11651
Catalina Cylinders Inc (PA)	3443	E	714 890-0999	12368
Chemical Methods Assoc LLC (DH)	3589	D	714 898-8781	16022
Coastline High Prfmce Coatings	3663	F	714 372-3263	18069
Coastline Metal Finishing Corp	3471	D	714 895-9099	13375
Commercial Cstm Sting Uphl Inc	2599	D	714 850-0520	5224
Criterion Composites Inc	3751	F	714 554-2717	21100
CTS Cement Manufacturing Corp (PA)	2891	E	714 379-8260	9136
Custom Pack Inc	3221	F	714 534-2201	10619
D & S Custom Plating Inc	3714	F	714 537-5411	20306

Company	SIC	EMP	PHONE	ENTRY #
Diversfied Mtllrgical Svcs Inc	3398	E	714 895-7777	11811
East West Printing	2752	F	714 899-7885	6799
Easyflex Inc	3312	E	888 577-8999	11393
Elasco Inc	2821	D	714 373-4767	7833
Electron Plating III Inc	3471	E	714 554-2210	13404
Essence Water Inc	2086	F	855 738-7426	2132
Esys Energy Control Company	3823	E	714 372-3322	21582
Evans Manufacturing Inc (PA)	3993	C	714 379-6100	23868
Expo-3 International Inc	3993	E	714 379-8383	23872
F T B & Son Inc	3444	E	714 891-8003	12582
Fei-Zyfer Inc (HQ)	3663	E	714 933-4000	18108
Fleet Management Solutions Inc	3663	E	800 500-6009	18109
Fourbro Inc	2329	F	714 277-3858	3155
Full Spectrum Omega Inc	2844	F	714 866-0039	8751
Gardena Furniture Mfg	2512	F	714 441-8436	4776
Gardena Sofa LLC	2512	F	714 441-8436	4777
GKN Aerospace Transparency Sys (DH)	3089	C	714 893-7531	10120
Goodwin Ammonia Company (PA)	2842	F	714 894-0531	8643
House Foods America Corp (HQ)	2075	C	714 901-4350	1509
Houston Bazz Co	3469	D	714 898-2666	13220
Hv Industries Inc	2426	F	651 233-5676	4082
Hyatt Die Cast Engrg Corp - S	3363	E	714 622-2131	11694
Hycor Biomedical LLC	3841	C	714 933-3000	22472
Inductor Supply Inc	3677	E	714 894-9050	19340
Infinite Engineering Inc	3599	F	714 534-4688	16581
Informer Computer Systems	3575	F	714 899-2049	15635
Innovative Casework Mfg Inc	3999	E	714 890-9100	24128
ITW Plymers Salants N Amer Inc	2821	E	714 898-0025	7846
J L Wingert Company (PA)	3589	D	714 379-5519	16058
Jason Tool & Engineering Inc	3089	E	714 895-5067	10164
Joong-Ang Daily News Cal Inc	2711	F	714 638-2341	5895
Jvr Sheetmetal Fabrication Inc	3721	E	714 841-2464	20594
Ken-Wor Corp	3312	E	714 554-6210	11402
Kimberly Machine Inc	3599	F	714 539-1360	16655
King Instrument Company Inc	3823	E	714 891-0008	21609
King Shock Technology Inc	3714	E	714 530-8701	20383
Korea Times Los Angeles Inc	2711	E	714 530-6001	5902
Kpi Services Inc	3398	E	714 895-5024	11817
L C Pringle Sales Inc (PA)	2591	E	714 892-1524	5200
Lear Baylor Inc	3732	E	714 799-9396	21050
Leiner Health Products Inc	2834	B	714 898-9936	8256
Little Saigon News Inc	2711	E	714 265-0800	5913
Luxe Laboratory	3851	F	714 221-2330	23107
Microsemi Corp-Analog (DH)	3674	D	714 898-8121	19011
Microsemi Corp-Power MGT Group	3625	C	714 994-6500	17287
Microsemi Corporation	3674	B	714 898-7112	19012
Mitchell Dean Collins	2434	E	714 894-6767	4331
Monco Products Inc	3089	E	714 891-2788	10224
Nails 2000 International Inc	3999	F	714 265-1983	24182
Natures Bounty Co	2833	F	714 898-9936	7957
Nelson Engineering Llc	3599	E	714 893-7999	16784
Nu Engineering	3599	E	714 894-1206	16798
Omana Group LLC	2023	F	714 891-9488	642
Pace Sportswear Inc	2339	F	714 891-7765	3474
Pacific Wave Systems Inc	3663	D	714 893-0152	18213
Paradigm Contract Mfg LLC	3999	F	714 889-7074	24204
Peerless Injection Molding LLC	3089	E	714 689-1920	10270
Probactive Biotech Inc	2824	E	714 903-1000	7915
R P M Electric Motors	7694	F	714 638-4174	25466
Rampone Industries LLC	3496	E	949 581-8701	13848
Riviera Beverages LLC	2086	E	714 895-5169	2212
Roger Industry	3672	E	714 896-0765	18583
Saint-Gobain Prfmce Plas Corp	2821	C	714 893-0970	7883
Saint-Gobain Prfmce Plas Corp	3221	F	714 688-2612	10626
Sales Office Accessories Inc	3993	E	714 896-9600	23956
Sanyo Foods Corp America (DH)	2098	E	714 891-3671	2440
Schlumberger Technology Corp	1389	D	714 379-7332	272
Select Graphics	2752	F	714 537-5250	7101
Southland Industries	3999	A	714 901-5800	24248
Spartan Manufacturing Co	3599	E	714 894-1955	16956
SPS Technologies LLC	3452	E	714 892-5571	13084
Sure Guard Socal	2431	E	714 556-5497	4241
Synertech PM Inc	3369	F	714 898-9151	11785
T L Machine Inc	3451	D	714 554-4154	13045
Tdk Machining	3728	F	714 554-4166	20947
Teacher Created Resources Inc	2731	D	714 230-7060	6398
Three Dots LLC	2331	D	714 799-6333	3277
Tj Aerospace Inc	3541	E	714 891-3564	14417
Transglobal Apparel Group Inc	2339	F	714 890-9200	3521
Tri A Machine Inc	3542	F	714 408-8907	14458
Tri Dental Innovators Corp	3843	F	714 554-1170	22918
TT Machine Corp	3545	E	714 534-5288	14688
Umpco Inc	3429	D	714 897-3531	12005
V & F Fabrication Company Inc	3441	E	714 265-0630	12271
Vertox Company	3825	F	714 530-4541	21884

GEOGRAPHIC

	SIC	EMP	PHONE	ENTRY #
Vianh Company Inc	3599	E	714 590-9808	17042
Walker Products **(PA)**	3714	E	714 554-5151	20484
Western Precision Aero LLC	3724	E	714 893-7999	20691
Zodiac Aerospace	3728	F	714 891-0683	20978

GARDEN VALLEY, CA - El Dorado County

	SIC	EMP	PHONE	ENTRY #
Toms Sierra Company Inc	1389	F	530 333-4620	283

GARDENA, CA - Los Angeles County

	SIC	EMP	PHONE	ENTRY #
3-D Polymers	3069	F	310 324-7694	9577
3deo Inc	3542	F	844 496-3825	14424
A & A Machine & Dev Co Inc	3451	F	310 532-7706	13005
A & A Ready Mixed Concrete Inc	3273	E	310 515-0933	11023
A & M Welding Inc	7692	E	310 329-2700	25381
A M Cabinets Inc **(PA)**	2521	D	310 532-1919	4925
A&W Precision Machining Inc	3599	F	310 527-7242	16197
AAA Air Support	3728	F	310 538-1377	20697
Abrasive Finishing Co	3398	F	310 323-7175	11788
Accucrome Plating Co Inc	3471	F	310 327-8268	13305
Ace Air Manufacturing	3728	F	310 323-7246	20698
Acrylicore Inc.	3083	F	310 515-4846	9746
Adtech Tool Engrg Corporations	3545	E	310 515-1717	14596
Advanced Foam Inc	3086	F	310 515-0728	9811
Aerodynamic Plating Co	3471	D	310 329-7959	13312
Agora Natural Surfaces Inc	3281	F	310 715-1088	11227
Ahf-Ducommun Incorporated **(HQ)**	3728	C	310 380-5390	20724
Alan Pre-Fab Building Corp **(PA)**	2452	F	310 538-0333	4566
Aldo Fragale	3599	F	310 324-0050	16248
All-Ways Metal Inc.	3444	E	310 217-1177	12472
American Aircraft Products Inc	3444	D	310 532-7434	12477
American Maple Inc	3949	F	310 515-8881	23498
Americhip Inc **(PA)**	2752	D	310 323-3697	6659
Angelus Plating Works	3714	F	310 516-1883	20256
Anvil Steel Corporation	3441	D	310 329-5811	12113
AR-Ce Inc.	3952	F	310 771-1960	23705
Arandas Woodcraft Inc.	2434	F	310 538-9945	4270
Arktura LLC **(PA)**	2519	E	310 532-1050	4906
Artemis Pet Food Company Inc	2048	F	818 771-0700	1122
Artistic Welding Inc.	3444	D	310 515-4922	12489
Arto Brick Veneer Mfgco	3251	F	310 768-8500	10772
Ashford Textiles LLC	2299	E	310 327-4670	2989
Autoflow Products Co.	3823	F	310 515-2866	21550
Avcorp Cmpsite Fabrication Inc	3728	B	310 970-5658	20749
Avcorp Cmpstes Fabrication Inc	3728	F	310 527-0700	20750
Bake R Us Inc	2051	F	310 630-5873	1179
Barco Uniforms Inc	2311	C	310 323-7315	3025
Barnes Plastics Inc.	3081	E	310 329-6301	9699
Bath Petals Inc	2844	F	310 532-4532	8700
Baxstra Inc	2426	D	323 770-4171	4074
Bay Cities Tin Shop Inc	3444	E	310 660-0351	12503
BDS Natural Products Inc **(PA)**	2099	D	310 518-2227	2462
Bega Supply Inc	3651	F	310 719-1252	17772
Better Nutritionals LLC	2023	E	310 502-2277	605
Binder Metal Products Inc	3469	D	323 321-4835	13170
Binders Express Inc	2782	F	310 329-4811	7572
Bixolon America Inc	3577	F	858 764-4580	15685
Bob Lewis Machine Company Inc	3599	F	310 538-9406	16329
Boinca Inc	2844	F	714 809-6313	8706
Bradley Tchnologies-California	2891	E	310 538-0714	9135
Briles Aerospace Inc	3452	F	310 701-2087	13061
Butler Inc	3452	F	310 323-3114	13062
C&J Fab Center Inc	3444	F	310 323-0970	12515
Cabletek Inc	3643	F	310 523-5000	17447
Caitac Garment Processing Inc	2261	C	310 217-9888	2879
Cal Pacific Dyeing & Finishing	2269	D	310 327-3792	2909
California Glass Bending Corp	3229	E	310 549-5255	10636
Capstan Permaflow	3599	F	310 366-5999	16361
Cast-Rite Corporation	3544	D	310 532-2080	14493
Cast-Rite International Inc **(PA)**	3369	F	310 532-2080	11771
Casual Lamps California Inc **(PA)**	3641	F	310 323-0105	17422
Centron Industries Inc	3663	E	310 324-6443	18067
Century Precision Engrg Inc	3599	F	310 538-0015	16373
CH Laboratories Inc	2834	F	310 516-8273	8110
Chief Neon Sign Co Inc	3993	F	310 327-1317	23844
Clegg Industries Inc	3993	C	310 225-3800	23845
Cliff Digital	2759	F	310 323-5600	7274
Coast Color Printing Inc	2752	F	310 352-3560	6738
Columbia Holding Corp	3442	B	310 327-4107	12304
Continental Bdr Specialty Corp **(PA)**	2782	C	310 324-8227	7577
Coral Head Inc **(PA)**	2329	F	310 366-7712	3141
Cosway Company Inc	2844	F	310 527-9135	8730
CR Laurence Co Inc.	3442	F	310 327-9300	12305
Crisol Metal Finishing	3471	F	310 516-1165	13382
CST Power and Construction Inc **(HQ)**	3355	D	310 523-2322	11615
Custom Displays Inc	2541	E	323 770-8074	5052
Custom Formulations Corp	2833	D	310 516-8273	7930

	SIC	EMP	PHONE	ENTRY #
Custom Metal Finishing Corp	3559	E	310 532-5075	14937
Cytydel Plastics Inc	3089	E	310 523-2884	10056
D & D Plastics Incorporated	3089	F	310 515-1934	10057
D and J Marketing Inc	2396	F	310 538-1583	3887
Dasol Inc	3641	C	310 327-6700	17424
Davis Gear & Machine Co	3599	F	310 337-9881	16425
Decore Plating Company Inc	3471	F	310 324-6755	13386
Del Mar Industries **(PA)**	3364	D	323 321-0600	11712
Del Mar Industries	3364	D	310 327-2634	11713
Designed Metal Connections Inc **(DH)**	3451	B	310 323-6200	13021
Doringer Manufacturing Co Inc	3541	F	310 366-7766	14374
Dr DBurr Inc	3541	F	310 323-6900	14376
Dr Teak Inc	2511	F	310 527-2675	4690
Ducommun Aerostructures Inc **(HQ)**	3724	B	310 380-5390	20646
Dunn Bros Commercial Prtrs Inc	2752	E	323 321-2211	6797
Dynamic Solutions	3829	F	253 273-7936	22188
El Camino Wood Products	2441	F	310 768-3447	4440
Electrical Rebuilders Sls Inc **(PA)**	3694	D	323 249-7545	19831
Elro Manufacturing Company **(PA)**	3993	E	310 380-7444	23864
Eptronics Inc	3646	F	310 536-0700	17604
Estar Limited	3641	E	310 989-6265	17427
Eternal Star Corporation	2678	E	310 768-1945	5684
Evergreen Oil Inc **(HQ)**	2992	E	949 757-7770	9433
Faber Enterprises Inc	3492	C	310 323-6200	13741
Finntech Inc.	3599	F	310 323-0790	16500
Flight Metals LLC	3812	F	800 838-9047	21295
Fluid Lubrication & Chem Co	2992	F	800 826-2415	9435
Foremost Enameling Co Inc	3479	F	323 321-3941	13590
French Tradition **(PA)**	2511	F	310 719-9977	4698
Gage Wafco Co Inc	3545	F	310 532-3106	14637
Ganar Industries Inc	2299	F	310 515-5683	2999
Gardena Valley News Inc **(PA)**	2711	E	310 329-6351	5855
Gardena Valley News Inc	2711	E	310 532-4882	5856
Gasket Manufacturing Co	3053	E	310 217-5600	9531
Geiger Plastics Inc	3089	F	310 327-9926	10114
German Machined Products Inc.	3599	F	310 532-4480	16535
Global Casuals Inc	2329	F	310 817-2828	3157
Gloria Lance Inc **(PA)**	2331	D	310 767-4400	3238
Gramercy Aerospace Mfg LLC	3812	F	310 515-0576	21302
Granath & Granath Inc	3471	F	310 327-5740	13418
Grow More Inc.	2879	F	310 515-1700	9102
GT Precision Inc.	3451	C	310 323-4374	13025
Hamilton Technology Corp	3646	F	310 217-1191	17614
Hammer Collection Inc.	2512	E	310 515-0276	4781
Hannahmax Baking Inc	2051	C	310 380-6778	1270
Hansens Welding Inc	7692	E	310 329-6888	25408
Hasala Engineering Inc	3599	F	310 538-4268	16556
Hawaiian Host Candies La Inc	2064	C	310 532-0543	1426
HI Tech Heat Treating Inc.	3398	E	310 532-3705	11814
Hi-Craft Metal Products	3471	E	310 323-6949	12612
His Life Woodworks.	2434	E	310 756-0170	4309
Hitco Carbon Composites Inc	2655	D	424 329-5250	5489
I M Ginsburg Furniture Inc.	2511	E	310 243-1260	4704
Imperial Prtg Ppr Box Mfg Inc	2657	F	310 323-7300	5507
Impresa Aerospace LLC **(PA)**	3728	N	310 354-1200	20846
Impresa Aerospace LLC.	3728	F	843 553-2021	20847
Inca One Corporation	3675	E	310 808-0001	19295
Independent Ink Inc	2899	E	310 523-4657	9261
Industrial Mdfication Repr Inc	2449	F	310 516-7992	4523
Integrated Communications Inc	2752	F	310 851-8066	6891
Investment Land Appraisers	2789	F	310 819-8831	7602
Ips Corporation	2891	F	310 516-7013	9154
J & S Inc.	3599	E	310 719-7144	16597
J&L Press Inc **(PA)**	2752	F	818 549-8344	6904
Jonathan Louis Intl Ltd **(PA)**	2512	C	323 770-3330	4788
Joy Active	2339	D	310 660-0022	3439
Juno Graphics	2752	F	310 329-0126	6917
Karrior Electric Vehicles Inc	3537	F	310 515-7600	14331
Keller Engineering	3599	F	310 532-0554	16649
Ken Mason Tile Inc.	3253	E	562 432-7574	10785
Keyline Lithography Inc	2752	F	310 538-8618	6921
Kingdom Mattress Inc	2515	F	562 630-5531	4867
Knk Apparel Inc	2326	C	310 768-3333	3109
Koam Knitech Inc	2253	E	310 515-1121	2845
Kumi Kookoon	2392	F	310 515-8811	3729
L J R Grinding Corp.	3599	F	310 532-7232	16671
L&F Wood LLC	2431	F	310 400-5569	4182
Learning Resources Inc	3999	E	800 995-4436	24160
Leo Molds	3544	F	562 714-4807	14535
Lets Do Lunch	2099	D	310 523-3664	2584
Lite Extrusions Manufacturing	3083	E	323 770-4298	9753
Little Brothers Bakery LLC	2051	D	310 225-3790	1285
Lobostar Inc	3499	D	310 516-9812	13955
Louis Sardo Upholstery Inc **(PA)**	2531	D	310 327-0532	5020
M M Book Bindery	2789	F	310 532-0780	7607

Mergent email: customerrelations@mergent.com

1386

2019 California
Manufacturers Register

(P-0000) Products & Services Section entry number
(PA)=Parent Co (HQ)=Headquarters (DH)=Div Headquarters

Company	SIC	EMP	PHONE	ENTRY #
Major Brass Foundry Inc (PA)	3366	F	310 324-0177	11761
Maneri Sign Co Inc	3993	E	310 327-6261	23918
Mark IV Metal Products Inc	3498	F	310 217-9700	13896
Mars Air Systems LLC	3564	D	310 532-1555	15167
Martin-Chandler Inc	3599	F	323 321-5119	16716
Martin/Brattrud Inc	2512	D	323 770-4171	4796
Matsuda House Printing Inc	2752	E	310 532-1533	6965
Matsui International Co Inc	2899	C	310 767-7812	9276
Matterhorn Filter Corporation	2819	F	310 329-8073	7786
Maya Steels Fabrication Inc	3441	D	310 532-8830	12203
Meadows Sheet Metal and AC Inc	3444	E	310 615-1125	12663
Megiddo Global LLC	3999	E	818 267-6686	24172
Melling Tool Rush Metals LLC	3399	D	580 725-3295	11842
Metco Manufacturing Inc	3469	E	310 516-6547	13248
Mills Iron Works	3494	D	323 321-6520	13770
Mod Shop	2511	E	310 523-1008	4724
Monte Allen Interiors Inc	2512	E	310 380-4640	4799
Moveel Fuel LLC	2869	F	213 748-1444	9023
MPS Industries Incorporated (PA)	3612	E	310 325-1043	17107
N Stitches Prints Inc	2395	E	310 323-7777	3853
Narayan Corporation	3085	E	310 719-7330	9802
Nasco Aircraft Brake Inc	3728	D	310 532-4430	20895
National Premium Merchandising (PA)	2395	D	310 217-2700	3855
Nationwide Plastic Products	3081	E	310 366-7585	9719
Natures Pwr Ntraceuticals Corp	2023	E	310 694-3031	636
NC Engineering Inc	3599	F	310 532-4810	16782
New Maverick Desk Inc	2521	C	310 217-1554	4957
Nike Inc	3021	E	310 670-6770	9476
Nissin Foods USA Company Inc (HQ)	2098	C	310 327-8478	2434
Noma Bearing Corporation	3562	E	310 329-1800	15109
Norberts Athletic Products	3949	F	310 830-6672	23625
Nugier Press Company Inc	3542	F	310 515-6025	14449
O Industries Corporation	2426	F	310 719-2289	4087
Ocean Direct LLC (PA)	2092	E	424 266-9300	2320
Onyx Industries Inc	3451	E	310 851-6161	13035
Pacific Artglass Corporation	3231	E	310 516-7828	10725
Parker-Hannifin Corporation	3599	D	310 308-0389	16832
Parquet By Dian Inc	2426	D	310 527-3779	4088
Pedavena Mould and Die Co Inc	3599	F	310 327-2814	16836
Perez Machine Inc	3599	F	310 217-9090	16838
Phantom Carriage Brewery	3556	F	310 538-5834	14877
Phillips Bros Plastics Inc	3083	E	310 532-8020	9757
Plasma Coating Corporation	3599	E	310 532-1951	16845
Plastic Processing Corp	3089	E	310 719-7330	10288
Power Paragon Inc	3612	F	310 523-4443	17114
Prime Wheel Corporation (PA)	3714	A	310 516-9126	20426
Principle Plastics	3021	E	310 532-3411	9478
Pro Design Group Inc	3089	E	310 767-1032	10311
Progressive Tool & Die Inc	3545	F	310 327-0569	14669
Quad R Tech	3911	C	310 851-6161	23307
Quadriga Americas LLC	2741	E	424 634-4900	6561
Quadrtech Corporation	3423	C	310 523-1697	11908
Qual-Pro Corporation (HQ)	3672	C	310 329-7535	18570
R B Welding Inc	7692	F	310 324-8680	25428
Radex Stereo Co Inc	3861	E	310 516-9015	23191
Ramda Metal Specialties Inc	3444	E	310 538-2136	12732
Ramonas Food Group LLC	2032	C	310 323-1950	771
Rayco Electronic Mfg Inc	3677	E	310 329-2660	19358
RB Racing	3714	E	310 515-5720	20438
Research Metal Industries Inc	3599	E	310 352-3200	16897
Rich Chicks LLC	2015	E	209 879-4104	550
Risvolds Inc	2099	D	323 770-2674	2653
Rnj Printing Corporation	2752	E	310 638-7768	7089
Rotational Molding Inc	3089	E	310 327-5401	10343
Ruggeri Marble and Granite Inc	3281	E	310 513-2155	11277
Russ International Inc	3444	E	310 329-7121	12745
Samsgazeboscom Inc	2421	E	310 523-3778	4051
Santee Cosmetics USA	2844	F	310 329-2305	8835
Sardo Bus & Coach Upholstery	2521	D	800 654-3824	4967
Scigen Inc	2869	F	310 324-6576	9039
Scotch Paint Corporation	2851	F	310 329-1259	8939
Screenworks Co Tim	2759	E	310 532-7239	7480
Sgps Inc	3999	D	310 538-4175	24240
Shelby Carroll Intl Inc (PA)	3711	E	310 538-2914	20171
Smart Inc	3089	E	310 674-8135	10378
Somar Corporation	3444	F	310 329-1446	12764
South Bay Corporation	3069	E	310 532-5353	9679
Southwest Offset Prtg Co Inc (PA)	2752	B	310 965-9154	7110
Space-Lok Inc	3728	C	310 527-6150	20935
SPS Technologies LLC	3452	B	310 323-6222	13083
SPS Technologies LLC	3494	D	562 426-9411	13775
Standard Homeopathic Co	2834	E	424 224-4127	8394
Standard Metal Products Inc	3471	E	310 532-9861	13511
Stanzino Inc	2211	C	213 746-8822	2764
Stepstone Inc (PA)	3272	E	310 327-7474	11006

Company	SIC	EMP	PHONE	ENTRY #
Sun Dyeing and Finishing Co	2253	F	310 329-0844	2858
Superior Metal Finishing Inc	3471	F	310 464-8010	13515
Sweet Ovations LLC	2869	D	310 719-2600	9045
Swift Fab	3444	F	310 366-7295	12781
Swift-Cor Precision Inc	3444	D	310 354-1207	12782
T & F Sheet Metals Fab	3728	E	310 516-8548	20943
T M W Engineering Inc	3728	F	310 768-8211	20944
T N T Auto Inc	3111	D	310 715-1117	10467
Talins Company	3444	E	310 378-3715	12783
Techflex Packaging LLC	2671	D	424 266-9400	5541
Thermally Engineered Manufactu	3443	E	310 523-9934	12435
Timbucktoo Manufacturing Inc	3589	F	310 323-1134	16124
Tomorrows Heirlooms Inc	3429	F	310 323-6720	12001
Tony Glazing Specialties Co	2541	F	323 770-8400	5113
Triune Enterprises Inc	2671	E	310 719-1600	5544
Tru-Cut Inc	3524	E	310 630-0422	14136
UNI Sport Inc	2752	E	310 217-4587	7154
US Blanks LLC (PA)	2821	E	310 225-6774	7899
US Hanger Company LLC	3315	E	310 323-8030	11464
US Industrial Tool & Sup Co	3542	E	310 464-8400	14460
US Packagers Inc	2782	E	310 327-7721	7589
Vege-Mist Inc	3585	E	310 353-2300	15997
Versafab Corp (PA)	3444	E	800 421-1822	12808
Victor Martin Inc	2514	C	323 587-3101	4847
Viver Co Inc	3444	E	310 327-4578	12810
Waltco Lift Corp	3537	D	323 321-4131	14351
Washington Orna Ir Works Inc	3446	F	310 327-8660	12904
Way Out West Inc	2326	E	310 769-6937	3126
Wcbm Company (PA)	3965	E	323 262-3274	23780
Welmark Textile Inc	2299	F	310 516-7289	3020
West Coast Laboratories Inc	2834	F	310 527-6163	8442
West Coast Laboratories Inc (PA)	2834	F	323 321-4774	8443
Westcoast Rotor Inc	3561	E	310 327-5050	15099
Windline Marine	3429	C	310 516-9812	12010
Windsor Textile Corporation	2281	F	310 323-3997	2948
Wyrefab Inc	3496	F	310 523-2147	13866

GEORGETOWN, CA - El Dorado County

Company	SIC	EMP	PHONE	ENTRY #
Georgetown Precast Inc	3272	F	530 333-4404	10933
Powerlift Dumbwaiters Inc	3534	E	800 409-5438	14255

GEYSERVILLE, CA - Sonoma County

Company	SIC	EMP	PHONE	ENTRY #
Clos Du Bois Wines Inc	2084	E	707 857-1651	1696
Francis Ford Cppola Prsnts LLC	2084	F	707 251-3200	1769
J Pedroncelli Winery	2084	F	707 857-3531	1819
Marietta Cellars Incorporated	2084	F	707 433-2747	1869
Mosaic Vineyards & Winery Inc	2084	F	707 857-2000	1888
Munselle Vineyards LLC	2084	F	707 857-9988	1889
Sbragia Family Vineyards LLC	2084	E	707 473-2992	1968

GILROY, CA - Santa Clara County

Company	SIC	EMP	PHONE	ENTRY #
Accent Manufacturing Inc	2599	E	408 846-9993	5217
American Steel & Stairways Inc	3446	E	408 848-2992	12831
Architctural Facades Unlimited	3272	D	408 846-5350	10878
B & R Vinyards Inc	2084	F	408 842-5649	1650
Blossom Valley Foods Inc	2087	F	408 848-5520	2246
Boulder Creek Guitars Inc	3931	F	408 842-0222	23358
Chalgren Enterprises	3845	F	408 847-3994	22959
Chameleon Like Inc	2782	E	408 847-3661	7575
Containment Consultants Inc	3443	F	408 848-6998	12379
Germains Seed Technology Inc	3999	D	408 848-8120	24107
Guess Inc	2329	E	408 847-3400	3158
Heart Wood Manufacturing Inc	2434	D	408 848-9750	4306
Instant Asphalt Inc	2891	F	408 280-7733	9149
International Paper Company	2621	D	408 846-2060	5293
International Paper Company	2621	F	408 847-6400	5301
Lloyd E Hennessey Jr	3599	F	408 842-8437	16688
Lucas/Signatone Corporation (PA)	3825	E	408 848-2851	21794
Mainstreet Media Group LLC	2711	C	408 842-6400	5933
Makplate LLC	3471	F	408 842-7572	13450
Metech Recycling Inc	3341	E	408 848-3050	11562
Morgan Hill Plastics Inc	3089	E	408 779-2118	10225
Northern California Stair	2431	F	408 847-0106	4204
Peninsula Spring Corporation	3495	F	408 848-3361	13798
Quinn Development Co	3271	F	408 842-9320	10858
Rancho De Solis Winery Inc	2084	F	408 847-6306	1939
Rap4	3949	F	408 434-0434	23632
Real Action Paintball Inc	3949	F	408 848-2846	23634
RMC Engineering Co Inc (PA)	3599	E	408 842-2525	16905
Trical Inc (PA)	2879	C	831 637-0195	9116
Versaco Manufacturing Inc	3556	F	408 848-2880	14895

GLEN ELLEN, CA - Sonoma County

Company	SIC	EMP	PHONE	ENTRY #
Bfw Associates LLC (HQ)	2084	F	707 935-3000	1659
Deerfield Ranch Winery LLC	2084	F	707 833-5215	1718
Lasseter Family Winery LLC	2084	F	707 933-2800	1857
Valley of Moon Winery	2084	E	707 939-4500	2037

GEOGRAPHIC

	SIC	EMP	PHONE	ENTRY #
Vintage Wine Estates Inc	2084	E	707 933-9675	2048

GLENDALE, CA - Los Angeles County

	SIC	EMP	PHONE	ENTRY #
4 Over LLC **(HQ)**	2759	B	818 246-1170	7216
4 Over LLC	2759	F	818 246-1170	7217
Accurate Dial & Nameplate Inc **(PA)**	3479	F	323 245-9181	13539
Aero Manufacturing & Pltg Co	3471	E	818 241-2844	13311
Alcotrevi Inc	3841	E	818 244-0400	22323
Ambrit Industries Inc	3542	E	818 243-1224	14427
Arecont Vision Costar LLC	3629	D	818 937-0700	17332
Art & Sign Production Inc	3993	F	818 245-6945	23822
Automation Plating Corporation	3471	E	323 245-4951	13341
Avery Dennison Corporation **(PA)**	2672	B	626 304-2000	5548
Bowtie Inc **(HQ)**	2721	E	213 385-2222	6114
Brickstone Group Inc	2052	F	818 242-8569	1357
Btrade LLC	7372	E	818 334-4433	24457
California Offset Printers Inc	2752	D	631 274-9530	6716
California Paper Bag Inc	2674	F	818 240-6717	5638
Calmat Co **(DH)**	2951	C	818 553-8821	9379
Challenger Ornamental Ir Works	3446	F	818 507-7030	12842
Chromatic Inc Lithographers	2752	E	818 242-5785	6731
Coda Energy Holdings LLC	3699	E	626 775-3900	19929
Color Inc	2752	E	818 240-1350	6740
Color Depot Inc	2759	F	818 500-9033	7280
Colour Concepts Inc	2752	C	951 787-9988	6746
Cryst Mark Inc A Swan Techno C	3559	E	818 240-7520	14936
Custom Characters Inc	2389	E	818 507-5940	3652
Cygnet Stampng & Fabrictng Inc	3469	F	818 240-7574	13190
Cygnet Stampng & Fabrictng Inc **(PA)**	3469	F	818 240-7574	13191
Daily Computing Solutions Inc	2711	F	818 240-5400	5820
De Novo Software	7372	F	213 814-1240	24555
Denttio Inc	3843	F	323 254-1000	22871
Dion Rostamian	3861	F	877 633-0293	23149
Dwa Nova LLC	7372	D	818 695-5000	24584
Farma Pharmaceuticals Inc **(PA)**	2834	E	818 638-3113	8157
Fortner Eng & Mfg Inc	3728	D	818 240-7740	20819
G Printing Inc	2759	F	818 246-1156	7323
Garlic Research Labs Inc	2879	F	800 424-7990	9101
Garlic Valley Farms Inc	2035	F	818 247-9600	912
Gcg Corporation	3471	F	818 247-8508	13413
General Mills Inc	2043	D	818 553-6777	1060
Glendale Rotary Offset Prtg Co **(PA)**	2752	E	818 548-1847	6834
Hi-Temp Forming Co Inc	3599	D	714 529-6556	16563
Hub Construction Spc Inc	3444	D	909 379-2100	12617
Huntmix Inc	2951	C	818 548-5200	9387
Information Integration Group	7372	E	818 956-3744	24770
Interntnal Desserts Delicacies	2052	F	818 549-0056	1365
Iog Products LLC	3674	F	818 350-5070	18930
Irl-Mex Manufacturing Company	3451	F	818 246-7211	13028
J P Weaver & Company Inc	3299	F	818 500-1740	11357
Jerry V Johnson & Assoc Inc	2754	F	818 543-6710	7204
Joar Labs Inc	2844	E	818 243-0700	8776
Jtea Inc	7372	F	847 878-2226	24818
K K Molds Inc	3442	F	818 548-8988	12324
Kadbanou LLC	2033	F	818 409-0118	812
Laufer Media Inc	2721	F	818 291-8408	6206
Le Chef Costumier Inc	2389	F	818 242-0868	3666
Learners Digest Intl LLC	3999	C	818 240-7500	24159
Lin MAI Inc	3999	E	818 890-1220	24162
Long Beach Woodworks LLC	2448	F	562 437-2293	4484
Los Angles Tmes Cmmnctions LLC	2711	D	818 637-3203	5922
Malakan Inc	2435	E	818 915-0014	4380
Manufacturing USA Enterprises	3911	E	818 409-3070	23294
Mar & Company Inc **(PA)**	2339	E	818 241-8882	3461
McCoppin Enterprises	3599	E	818 240-4840	16727
Mini Vac Inc	3635	E	818 244-6777	17407
Modern Engine Inc	3599	E	818 409-9494	16761
Mold Masters Inc	3544	F	323 999-2599	14543
N J P Sports Inc	2394	E	818 247-3914	3797
N2 Development Inc	3728	E	323 210-3251	20894
Nadin Company	2834	E	818 500-8908	8290
Nestle Holdings Inc **(HQ)**	2023	F	818 549-6000	637
Nestle Purina Petcare Company	2047	C	314 982-1000	1118
Nestle Refrigerated Food Co	2098	B	818 549-6000	2432
North American Textile Co LLC **(PA)**	2396	E	818 409-0019	3910
Notron Manufacturing Inc	3599	F	818 247-7739	16794
P E N Inc	2759	E	818 954-0775	7426
Pennoyer-Dodge Co	3545	E	818 547-2100	14662
Person & Covey Inc	2844	E	818 937-5000	8812
Pillsbury Company LLC	2041	D	818 522-3952	1047
Premac Inc	3599	F	818 241-8370	16857
Printefex Inc	2752	F	818 240-2400	7043
SAI Industries	3484	E	818 842-6144	13690
Saks Styling Incorporated	3911	F	818 244-0540	23314
Saxton Industrial Inc	3444	F	818 265-0702	12752
Snapmd Inc	7372	F	310 953-4800	25188

	SIC	EMP	PHONE	ENTRY #
Sonoco Corrflex LLC	2653	F	818 507-7477	5461
Susy Clothing Co	2339	E	818 500-7879	3511
Technicolor Usa Inc	3651	C	818 500-9090	17865
Technicolor Usa Inc	3651	C	818 260-3651	17866
Trattoria Amici/Americana LLC	2599	F	818 502-1220	5259
Triangle Rock Products LLC	1429	E	818 553-8820	334
Vege - Kurl Inc	2844	D	818 956-5582	8861
Victory Studio	3861	F	818 972-0737	23209
Vistanomics Inc	2721	F	818 249-1236	6285
Viva Holdings LLC **(PA)**	2678	F	818 243-1363	5690
Viva Print LLC **(HQ)**	2678	F	818 243-1363	5691
Vulcan Materials Company	1422	A	818 241-7356	320
Water Filter Exchange Inc	3569	F	818 808-2541	15374
World Industries International	3089	F	818 649-7858	10451
Yerma Jewelry Mfg Inc	3911	E	818 551-0690	23333
Zen Monkey LLC	2038	F	310 504-2899	1022

GLENDORA, CA - Los Angeles County

	SIC	EMP	PHONE	ENTRY #
Action Stamping Inc	3469	E	626 914-7466	13159
Americana Sports Inc	3949	F	626 914-0238	23501
Bashoura Inc	3911	F	626 963-7600	23245
Calportland	1442	F	760 343-3403	349
Calportland Company **(DH)**	3241	D	626 852-6200	10748
Cjd Construction Services Inc	1389	F	626 335-1116	197
Complete Metal Design	3599	F	626 335-3636	16395
Deccofelt Corporation	2299	E	626 963-8511	2995
Electro-Tech Products Inc	3679	F	909 592-1434	19527
Eshields LLC	2671	E	909 305-8848	5521
Ever-Glory Intl Group Inc	2339	F	626 859-6638	3414
Grico Precision Inc	3599	F	626 963-0368	16543
Grico Precision Inc	3599	F	626 963-0368	16544
Hallmark Metals Inc	3444	E	626 335-1263	12606
Mackenzie Laboratories Inc	3674	F	909 394-9007	18976
Mariba Corporation	2449	F	626 963-6775	4529
Metrex Valve Corp	3491	E	626 335-4027	13727
Millipart Inc **(PA)**	3599	F	626 963-4101	16752
National Hot Rod Association	2711	F	626 250-2300	5989
Oasis Medical Inc **(PA)**	3851	D	909 305-5400	23114
Southwest Machine & Plastic Co	3728	E	626 963-6919	20934
Sybron Dental Specialties Inc	3843	A	909 596-0276	22913
Tex Shoemaker & Son Inc	2386	F	909 592-2071	3624
Tom Clark Confections	2064	E	909 599-4700	1463

GLENHAVEN, CA - Lake County

	SIC	EMP	PHONE	ENTRY #
Cvps Inc	7372	E	707 998-9364	24538

GOLD RIVER, CA - Sacramento County

	SIC	EMP	PHONE	ENTRY #
Cleanworld	3949	F	916 635-7300	23541
Conquip Inc	3599	D	916 379-8200	16400
CTS Fabrication USA Inc	3351	F	916 852-6303	11573
Kirk A Schliger	3564	F	916 638-8433	15164
Levac Specialties Inc	3743	F	916 362-3795	21080
Markes International Inc	3826	D	513 745-0241	21989
Synergex International Corp	7372	D	916 635-7300	25243

GOLETA, CA - Santa Barbara County

	SIC	EMP	PHONE	ENTRY #
A&A Engineering Inc	3599	F	805 685-4882	16194
Acra Enterprises Inc	3599	F	805 964-4757	16215
Acroamatics Inc	3663	F	805 967-9909	18014
Advanced Vision Science Inc	3851	E	805 683-3851	23077
Alta-Dena Certified Dairy LLC	2026	C	805 685-8328	709
Arguello Inc	1382	E	805 567-1632	125
Atk Space Systems Inc	3769	D	805 685-2262	21186
Bardex Corporation	3569	D	805 964-7747	15299
Biopac Systems Inc	3826	E	805 685-0066	21927
Boone Printing & Graphics Inc	2759	D	805 683-2349	7252
Burnet Machining Inc	3599	F	805 964-6321	16339
C N C Machining Inc	3599	F	805 681-8855	16351
Calient Technologies Inc	3661	E	805 562-5500	17927
Calient Technologies Inc **(PA)**	3661	B	805 562-5500	17928
Caribbean Coffee Company Inc	2043	E	805 692-2200	1055
Carriercomm Inc	3663	E	805 968-9621	18064
Cbrite Inc	3823	F	805 722-1121	21559
Check Yourself Inc	3599	F	805 967-6190	16380
Cree Inc	3674	F	805 968-9460	18791
Deckers Outdoor Corporation **(PA)**	2389	B	805 967-7611	3653
DR Radon Boatbuilding Inc **(PA)**	3732	F	805 692-2170	21030
Electro Optical Industries	3827	E	805 964-7401	22075
Electromatic Inc **(PA)**	3471	E	805 964-9880	13402
Far West Technology Inc	3829	F	805 964-3615	22199
Flir Motion Ctrl Systems Inc	3559	E	650 692-3900	14956
Flir Systems Inc	3812	E	805 964-9797	21296
Freedom Photonics LLC	3699	E	805 967-4900	19969
Grind Food Company Inc	3599	F	805 964-8344	16545
Hollister Brewing Company LLC	2082	E	805 968-2810	1598
Icrco Inc	3845	F	310 921-9559	22989
Icrco Inc **(PA)**	3845	F	310 921-9559	22990

	SIC	EMP	PHONE	ENTRY #
Innovative Micro Tech Inc	3674	C	805 681-2807	18898
Inogen Inc (PA)	3841	C	805 562-0500	22480
Intouch Technologies Inc (PA)	7372	B	805 562-8686	24790
Intri-Plex Technologies Inc (HQ)	3469	D	805 683-3414	13227
JD Business Solutions Inc.	2752	E	805 962-8193	6909
Karl Storz Imaging Inc (HQ)	3829	B	805 968-5563	22224
Lastline Inc	7372	C	805 456-7075	24846
Launchpoint Technologies Inc	3568	F	805 683-9659	15288
Linvatec Corporation	3841	D	805 571-8100	22512
Lockheed Martin Corporation	3812	D	805 571-2346	21336
Madera Concepts	2499	F	805 692-0053	4634
Medtronic Inc	3845	C	805 571-3769	23011
Medtronic PS Medical Inc (DH)	3841	C	805 571-3769	22533
Megavision Inc	3699	F	805 964-1400	20014
Memory Glass LLC	3229	F	805 682-6469	10656
Microdyn-Nadir Us Inc (DH)	3589	D	805 964-8003	16073
Mission Research Corporation (DH)	3721	F	805 690-2447	20602
Moog Inc	3812	B	805 618-3900	21351
Moseley Associates Inc (HQ)	3663	C	805 968-9621	18189
Neal Feay Company	3354	D	805 967-4521	11598
Northrop Grumman Innovation	3764	D	805 961-8600	21181
Pacific Design Tech Inc	3812	E	805 961-9110	21377
Queenship Publishing Company	2731	F	805 692-0043	6385
R G Hansen Associates (PA)	3823	F	805 564-3388	21642
Raytheon Company	3699	C	805 967-5511	20055
Raytheon Company	3571	F	805 562-2730	15477
Raytheon Company	3812	D	805 562-4611	21403
Raytheon Company	3812	D	805 562-4611	21407
Raytheon Company	3812	C	805 967-5511	21410
Resonant Inc (PA)	3674	E	805 308-9803	19124
S B I F Inc	3479	F	805 683-1711	13651
Santa Barbara Coffee LLC	2095	F	805 683-2555	2366
Se-Ir Corporation	3826	F	805 571-6800	22016
Signature Woodworks	2431	F	805 685-4080	4230
Soilmoisture Equipment Corp	3829	E	805 964-3525	22274
Soraa Laser Diode Inc (PA)	3699	E	805 696-6999	20075
Superior Millwork of Sb Inc	2434	E	805 685-1744	4354
Surf To Summit	3949	F	805 964-1896	23669
Tan Set Corporation	3441	F	805 967-4567	12257
Tm Microscopes Vco Metrlgy Grp	3827	D	805 967-2700	22142
Truevision Systems Inc	3841	E	805 963-9700	22660
Veeco Process Equipment Inc	3826	C	805 967-1400	22047
Veeco Process Equipment Inc	3599	D	805 967-2700	17038
Venoco Inc	2911	E	805 961-2305	9374
Veoneer Us Inc	3694	E	805 571-1777	19851
Vista Steel Co Inc (PA)	3449	E	805 964-4732	13003
Wyatt Technology Corporation (PA)	3826	C	805 681-9009	22050

GONZALES, CA - Monterey County

	SIC	EMP	PHONE	ENTRY #
Ramsay Highlander Inc	3523	E	831 675-3453	14096

GRANADA HILLS, CA - Los Angeles County

	SIC	EMP	PHONE	ENTRY #
Almac Fixture & Supply Co	2299	E	818 360-1706	2985
Carpod Inc.	3089	F	818 395-8676	10014
Garys Leather Creations Inc	3172	D	818 831-9977	10561
How 2 Save Fuel LLC	2869	F	818 882-1145	9010
Kouzouians Fine Custom Furn	2599	F	818 772-1212	5242
Perrins Registration Office	3469	F	818 832-1332	13259
Rudex Broadcasting Ltd Corp	3663	F	213 494-3377	18242
Sweet Inspirations Inc	2335	E	310 886-9010	3340

GRAND TERRACE, CA - San Bernardino County

	SIC	EMP	PHONE	ENTRY #
Griswold Pump Company	3561	E	909 422-1700	15069
Wilden Pump and Engrg LLC (DH)	3561	B	909 422-1700	15100

GRANITE BAY, CA - Placer County

	SIC	EMP	PHONE	ENTRY #
Cal Nor Embroidery & Spc	2395	F	916 786-3131	3832
New Cal Metals Inc	3444	F	916 652-7424	12690
Recoating-West Inc (PA)	3444	E	916 652-8290	12735
Sweets 4jc LLC	2051	F	916 791-6453	1328

GRASS VALLEY, CA - Nevada County

	SIC	EMP	PHONE	ENTRY #
Aja Video Systems Inc (PA)	3663	E	530 274-2048	18022
Applied Science Inc.	3841	E	530 273-8299	22342
Autometrix Inc	3552	F	530 477-5065	14774
Benchmark Thermal Corporation	3567	D	530 477-5011	15254
Cabinet Company Inc.	2541	F	530 273-7533	5043
Countis Industries Inc	3264	E	530 272-8334	10817
CSS Global	3423	F	530 268-3324	11891
Datum Precision Inc	3728	F	530 272-8415	20793
Diamond Truss	2439	F	530 477-1477	4402
Eigen Inc	3651	E	530 274-1240	17797
Farlows Scntfic Glssblwing Inc	3229	E	530 477-5513	10642
Grass Valley Inc	3663	A	530 478-3000	18114
Grass Valley Inc (HQ)	3663	C	530 265-1000	18115
Grass Valley Usa LLC (HQ)	3663	B	800 547-8949	18116
Guy G Veralrud	3651	F	530 477-7323	17806

	SIC	EMP	PHONE	ENTRY #
Hansen Bros Enterprises (PA)	1442	D	530 273-3100	361
High Sierra Electronics Inc	3826	E	530 273-2080	21966
House of Print & Copy	2752	F	530 273-1000	6862
Huntington Mechanical Labs Inc	3563	E	530 273-9533	15128
Igraphics (PA)	2759	E	530 273-2200	7349
Lifekind Products Inc.	2841	E	530 477-5395	8596
Maier Manufacturing Inc.	3751	E	530 272-9036	21126
Manufacturers Coml Fin LLC	3433	E	530 477-5011	12075
Measurement Specialties Inc	3825	D	530 273-4608	21803
National Directory Services	2731	E	530 268-8636	6366
Nevada County Publishing Co.	2711	A	530 273-9561	5992
R G B Display Corporation	3575	F	530 268-2222	15644
Robert Snell Cast Specialist	3915	F	530 273-8958	23347
Seagate Technology LLC	3572	C	530 410-6594	15602
Thermo Products Inc.	3398	D	909 888-2882	11834
Vitalhue	3999	F	323 646-8775	24282
Vossloh Signaling Usa Inc.	3462	E	530 272-8194	13118
Zmk Medical Technologies Inc	3841	E	530 274-1240	22686

GRATON, CA - Sonoma County

	SIC	EMP	PHONE	ENTRY #
Empire West Inc	3089	E	707 823-1190	10090
Purple Wine Company LLC	2084	E	707 829-6100	1932
Sonoma Wine Company LLC	2084	C	707 829-6100	1980

GREENBRAE, CA - Marin County

	SIC	EMP	PHONE	ENTRY #
Petroleum Sales Inc	1311	D	415 256-1600	69

GREENFIELD, CA - Monterey County

	SIC	EMP	PHONE	ENTRY #
Wente Bros	2084	E	831 674-5642	2051

GREENVILLE, CA - Plumas County

	SIC	EMP	PHONE	ENTRY #
D L Stoy Logging Co	2411	F	530 283-3292	3983

GREENWOOD, CA - El Dorado County

	SIC	EMP	PHONE	ENTRY #
Red Line Engineering Inc	3599	F	530 333-2134	16890

GRIDLEY, CA - Butte County

	SIC	EMP	PHONE	ENTRY #
Bianchi Orchard Systems Inc	3523	C	530 846-5625	14045
California Industrial Mfg LLC (PA)	3999	F	530 846-9960	24057
Rio Pluma Company LLC (HQ)	2033	E	530 846-5200	852
Sundial Orchrds Hulling Drying	2068	E	530 846-6155	1505
Sunsweet Dryers	2034	D	530 846-5578	899
Wax Box Firelog Corporation	3433	E	530 846-2200	12094

GROVER BEACH, CA - San Luis Obispo County

	SIC	EMP	PHONE	ENTRY #
C F W Research & Dev Co	3351	F	805 489-8750	11572
David B Anderson	2752	F	805 489-0661	6779
H J Harkins Company Inc	2834	E	805 929-1333	8200
Hotlix (PA)	2064	E	805 473-0596	1428

GUADALUPE, CA - Santa Barbara County

	SIC	EMP	PHONE	ENTRY #
Apio Inc (HQ)	2099	D	800 454-1355	2454
Tri-Co Building Supply Inc	2439	D	805 343-2555	4429

GUALALA, CA - Mendocino County

	SIC	EMP	PHONE	ENTRY #
Independent Coast Observer	2711	F	707 884-3501	5886

GUERNEVILLE, CA - Sonoma County

	SIC	EMP	PHONE	ENTRY #
F Korbel & Bros (PA)	2084	B	707 824-7000	1755

GUSTINE, CA - Merced County

	SIC	EMP	PHONE	ENTRY #
John B Sanfilippo & Son Inc.	2068	B	209 854-2455	1491
Legacy Vulcan LLC	3272	F	209 854-3088	10952
Saputo Dairy Foods Usa LLC	2026	C	209 854-6461	735

HACIENDA HEIGHTS, CA - Los Angeles County

	SIC	EMP	PHONE	ENTRY #
Adamant Enterprise Inc	2673	E	626 934-3399	5584
Barhena Inc.	3589	E	888 383-8800	16018
Cotton Tale Designs Inc	2392	E	714 435-9558	3715
Gravity Boarding Company Inc	3949	F	760 591-4144	23576
Superior Equipment Solutions	3631	D	323 722-7900	17376

HALF MOON BAY, CA - San Mateo County

	SIC	EMP	PHONE	ENTRY #
Accurate Always Inc	3571	E	650 728-9428	15380
Fiber Network Engineering Co (PA)	3661	F	650 726-2639	17948
Romeo Packing Company	2674	E	650 728-3393	5647
Wick Communications Co	2711	E	650 726-4424	6088

HANFORD, CA - Kings County

	SIC	EMP	PHONE	ENTRY #
All Valley Printing Inc.	2752	E	559 584-5444	6648
Baker Commodities Inc	2077	E	559 686-4797	1521
Britz Fertilizers Inc.	3523	E	559 582-0942	14048
California Bio-Productex Inc.	2869	E	559 582-5308	8992
Central Valley Meat Co Inc	2011	C	559 583-9624	426
Del Monte Foods Inc	2033	C	559 639-6160	794
Hanford Sentinel Inc	2711	E	559 582-0471	5869
Helena Agri-Enterprises LLC	2879	E	559 582-0291	9103
Jack B Martin	3993	F	559 583-1175	23905
Kings Cabinet Systems	2521	F	559 584-9662	4953
Lacey Milling Company Inc	2041	F	559 584-6634	1045

Employment Codes: A=Over 500 employees, B=251-500,
C=101-250, D=51-100, E=20-50, F=10-19

2019 California
Manufacturers Register

© Mergent Inc. 1-800-342-5647
1389

Company	SIC	EMP	PHONE	ENTRY #
McLellan Equipment Inc	3713	D	559 582-8100	20216
McLellan Industries Inc	3713	D	650 873-8100	20217
Nichols Pistachio	2068	C	559 584-6811	1500
Norwesco Inc	3089	F	559 585-1668	10246
Pitman Family Farms	2048	C	559 585-3330	1155
Pyramid Systems Inc	2541	E	559 582-9345	5096
Rosa Brothers Milk Co Inc (PA)	2024	E	559 582-8825	693
South Valley Materials	3273	E	559 582-0532	11183
Superior Dairy Products Co	2024	E	559 582-0481	697
Tessenderio Kerly Inc	2875	E	559 582-9200	9086
Transcontinental US LLC	2673	C	559 585-2040	5629
Vandersteen Audio Inc	3651	E	559 582-0324	17874
Viking Ready Mix Co Inc	3273	F	559 344-7931	11205
Windtamer Tarps	2394	F	559 584-2080	3821

HAPPY CAMP, CA - Siskiyou County

Company	SIC	EMP	PHONE	ENTRY #
Northwest Skyline Logging Inc	2411	F	530 493-5150	4004

HARBOR CITY, CA - Los Angeles County

Company	SIC	EMP	PHONE	ENTRY #
A & J Industries Inc	2441	F	310 216-2170	4432
Adegbesan Adefemi	3571	E	310 663-0789	15382
Aerostar Engineering & Mfg Inc	3599	F	310 326-5098	16243
Basmat Inc (PA)	3444	D	310 325-2063	12502
Bjc	2121	F	310 977-6068	2712
Brea Canon Oil Co Inc	1311	F	310 326-4002	33
Bryant Rubber Corp (PA)	3053	E	310 530-2530	9520
Cal Partitions Inc	2542	F	310 539-1911	5130
City Industrial Tool & Die (PA)	3312	F	310 530-1234	11389
Corn Maiden Foods Inc	2032	D	310 784-0400	754
Decco Graphics Inc	3469	E	310 534-2861	13192
Integral Products Inc	2891	E	310 326-8889	9150
Joanka Inc	3442	F	310 326-8940	12323
La Espanola Meats Inc	2013	E	310 539-0455	503
Lumination Lighting & Tech Inc	3646	C	855 283-1100	17632
Monographx Inc	3993	F	310 325-6780	23928
Onyx Industries Inc (PA)	3451	F	310 539-8830	13034
Prime Surfaces Inc	3281	F	310 448-2292	11271
Prime Wheel Corporation	3714	B	310 326-5080	20424
Republic Machinery Co Inc (PA)	3541	F	310 518-1100	14403
Rocker Solenoid Company	3679	D	310 534-5660	19709
Ship Supply International Inc	3264	E	310 325-3188	10824
Simpson Performance Pdts Inc	3842	D	310 325-6035	22814
Slide Systems Inc	3469	F	310 539-3416	13277
Star Plastic Design	3089	D	310 530-7119	10389

HARMONY, CA - San Luis Obispo County

Company	SIC	EMP	PHONE	ENTRY #
Harmony Cellars	2084	F	805 927-1625	1807

HAWAIIAN GARDENS, CA - Los Angeles County

Company	SIC	EMP	PHONE	ENTRY #
Consolidated Color Corporation	2851	E	562 420-7714	8896
McLaren Industries Inc (PA)	3011	E	310 212-1333	9466

HAWTHORNE, CA - Los Angeles County

Company	SIC	EMP	PHONE	ENTRY #
Acuna Dionisio Able	3599	F	310 978-4741	16222
Adler Pool Tables Inc	3949	E	310 676-5331	23487
Advanced Engine Management Inc (PA)	3714	C	310 484-2322	20242
Astro Machine Co Inc	3599	F	310 679-8291	16286
Computerized Fashion Svcs Inc	2389	F	310 973-0106	3650
Cxc Simulations LLC	3699	F	888 918-2010	19937
D3 Inc (PA)	2522	D	310 223-2200	4981
Dolphin Medical Inc (HQ)	3845	D	800 448-6506	22972
Firstclass Foods - Trojan Inc	2011	C	310 676-2500	434
Fulham Co Inc (DH)	3612	E	323 779-2980	17095
Glen-Mac Swiss Co	3678	F	310 978-4555	19392
Greenform LLC	3531	F	310 331-1665	14171
Heinz Weber Incorporated	2796	E	310 477-3561	7648
Interplastic Corporation	2821	E	323 757-1801	7843
K & E Inc	3728	F	310 675-3309	20859
Katch Precision Machining Inc	3599	F	310 676-4989	16646
Lithographix Inc (PA)	2752	B	323 770-1000	6950
Lni Custom Manufacturing Inc	3446	E	310 978-2000	12875
Local Neon Co Inc	3993	E	310 978-2000	23916
Los Angeles Ale Works LLC	2082	F	213 422-6569	1607
Marco Fine Arts	2759	D	310 615-1818	7395
Marleon Inc	7692	E	310 679-1242	25421
Maxon Crs LLC	3731	E	424 236-4660	21001
OSI Electronics Inc (HQ)	3672	C	310 978-0516	18553
OSI Subsidiary Inc	3699	B	310 978-0516	20037
OSI Systems Inc (PA)	3674	B	310 978-0516	19069
Paulco Precision Inc	3599	F	310 679-4900	16833
Picnic At Ascot Inc	2449	E	310 674-3098	4532
Signquest	3993	E	310 355-0528	23970
Sonnet Tool	3545	E	310 219-7790	14677
Space Exploration Tech Corp (PA)	3761	A	310 363-6000	21169
Supreme Graphics Inc	2752	F	310 531-8300	7125
Symmetry Electronics LLC (DH)	3674	E	310 536-6190	19209
System Technical Support Corp	3625	F	310 845-9400	17313

Company	SIC	EMP	PHONE	ENTRY #
Technology Training Corp	2752	D	310 644-7777	7130
Teledyne Defense Elec LLC	3679	C	323 777-0077	19749
Tesla Inc	3714	F	310 219-4652	20463
Trio Tool & Die Co (PA)	3544	F	310 644-4431	14582
Triumph Aerostructures LLC	3721	A	310 322-1000	20632
Warmelin Precision Pdts LLC	3599	D	323 777-5003	17051
Wems Inc (PA)	3564	D	310 644-0251	15186
Wems Inc	3625	F	310 644-0255	17323
Wizard Enterprise	3253	F	323 756-8430	10797

HAYWARD, CA - Alameda County

Company	SIC	EMP	PHONE	ENTRY #
ABB Motors and Mechanical Inc	3621	F	510 785-9900	17174
Acologix Inc	2834	E	510 512-7200	7995
Action Laminates LLC	2521	E	510 259-6217	4926
Admail-Express Inc	2752	E	510 471-6200	6641
Advance Carbon Products Inc	3624	E	510 293-5930	17231
Advanced Transit Dynamics Inc	3799	D	510 619-8245	21221
Ajinomoto Foods North Amer Inc	2038	C	510 293-1838	974
Akas Manufacturing Corporation	3444	E	510 786-3200	12468
Alameda Newspapers Inc (DH)	2711	C	510 783-6111	5753
Alcatel-Lucent USA Inc	3661	E	510 475-5000	17918
All Bay Pallet Company Inc (PA)	2448	E	510 636-4131	4449
Allstate Plastics LLC	2673	E	510 783-9600	5586
Allure Labs Inc	2844	E	510 489-8896	8692
Alpha Magnetics Inc	3499	F	510 732-6698	13915
Amedica Biotech Inc	3841	E	510 785-5980	22332
American Blinds and Drap Inc	2391	E	510 487-3500	3689
American Poly-Foam Company Inc	3086	E	510 786-3626	9816
Ampex Data Systems Corporation (HQ)	3572	D	650 367-2011	15511
Annabelle Candy Inc	2064	D	510 783-2900	1408
Anthera Pharmaceuticals Inc	2834	E	510 856-5600	8034
Applied Photon Technology Inc	3641	E	510 780-9500	17420
Applied Silver Inc	2499	F	888 939-4747	4605
Aradigm Corporation (PA)	2834	E	510 265-9000	8038
Arch Foods Inc (PA)	3421	E	510 331-8352	11877
Archer-Daniels-Midland Company	2041	C	510 346-3309	1027
Armanino Foods Distinction Inc	2038	E	510 441-9300	981
Associated Screw Machine Pdts	3451	E	510 783-3831	13013
Autocam Acquisition Inc	3599	E	510 487-7600	16289
Automatic Control Engrg Corp	3829	E	510 293-6040	22167
Axl Musical Instruments Ltd	3931	C	415 508-1398	23355
Azuma Foods Intl Inc USA (HQ)	2092	D	510 782-1112	2308
B C Song International Inc	2911	D	510 785-8383	9322
Baxter Healthcare Corporation	2834	C	510 723-2000	8062
Bay Tech Manufacturing Inc	3599	F	510 783-0660	16310
Beeline Group LLC	3993	D	510 477-5400	23826
Best Express Foods Inc	2051	B	510 782-5338	1186
Bimbo Bakeries Usa Inc	2051	C	510 436-5350	1208
Biolog Inc	3826	E	510 785-2564	21925
Buffalo Distribution Inc	3613	E	510 324-3800	17132
C NC Noodle Co	2098	E	510 732-1318	2425
Carmel Food Group Inc	2099	E	510 471-4889	2482
CEC Print Solutions Inc	2752	E	510 670-0160	6723
Chawk Technology Intl Inc (PA)	3089	D	510 330-5299	10023
Chiquita Brands Intl Inc	2037	E	510 732-9500	943
Clarmil Manufacturing Corp (PA)	2099	D	510 476-0700	2489
Columbus Foods LLC	2011	B	510 921-3400	430
Columbus Manufacturing Inc (HQ)	2013	E	510 921-3423	476
Commercial Patterns Inc	3089	F	510 784-1014	10033
Commex Corporation	3081	C	510 887-6600	9702
Computer Plastics	3544	E	510 785-3600	14500
Conxtech Inc	3441	C	510 264-9111	12141
Corefact Corporation	2732	F	866 777-3986	6418
Corrugated Packaging Pdts Inc	2653	E	650 625-9180	5402
Crafton Carton	2657	E	510 441-5985	5505
Crown Equipment Corporation	3537	E	510 471-7272	14319
Custom Label and Decal LLC	2759	E	510 876-0000	7292
Cypress Furniture Inc	2511	F	510 723-4890	4687
Daily Review	2711	E	510 783-6111	5825
Danworth Manufacturing Co	3599	F	510 487-8290	16420
Davis Instruments Corporation	3812	D	510 732-9229	21282
Delphon Industries LLC (PA)	3089	C	510 576-2220	10064
Detention Device Systems	3599	F	510 783-0771	16433
Dielectric Coating Industries	3827	F	510 487-5980	22073
Do Dine Inc	7372	F	510 583-7546	24566
Dupont Electronic Technologies	2819	E	510 784-9105	7769
E-Z Mix Inc	2674	E	510 782-8010	5642
EDS Wrap and Roll Foods LLC	2032	E	510 266-0888	756
Ekc Technology Inc (DH)	2899	C	510 784-9105	9245
Electriq Power Inc	3825	F	408 393-7702	21747
Electro Plating Specialties	3471	E	510 786-1881	13395
EMD Millipore Corporation	3826	C	510 576-1367	21952
Fante Inc (PA)	2096	E	650 697-7525	2380
Farmer Bros Co	2095	F	510 638-1660	2343
First Impressions Printing	2752	E	510 784-0811	6816
Flo Stor Engineering Inc (PA)	3535	E	510 887-7179	14274

	SIC	EMP	PHONE	ENTRY #
Florence & New Itln Art Co Inc	3272	E	510 785-9674	10927
Flynn and Enslow Inc (PA)	3496	E	415 863-5340	13830
Folgergraphics Inc	2791	E	510 293-2294	7628
Forderer Cornice Works	3442	F	415 431-4100	12317
Four Dimensions Inc	3825	F	510 782-1843	21760
Glazier Steel Inc	3441	D	510 471-5300	12172
Goorin Brosinc	2353	F	-	3563
Grundfos CBS Inc	3561	F	510 512-1300	15071
H2j Corporation	3599	F	510 785-2100	16553
Haigs Delicacies LLC	2099	E	510 782-6285	2532
Hantel Technologies Inc	3841	E	510 400-1164	22467
Impax Laboratories Inc	2834	D	510 240-6000	8214
Impax Laboratories LLC (DH)	2834	A	510 240-6000	8215
Impax Laboratories Usa LLC	2834	E	510 240-6000	8216
IMT Precision Inc	3599	E	510 324-8926	16578
Induspac California Inc (HQ)	2821	E	510 324-3626	7842
Infrared Industries Inc	3826	F	510 782-8100	21975
Inland Marine Industries Inc	3499	C	510 785-8555	13948
Integrity Technology Corp	3679	E	270 812-8867	19581
Ironridge Inc (PA)	3433	F	800 227-9523	12073
Iwen Naturals	2844	D	510 589-8019	8773
J S Hackl Archi Signa Inc	3993	F	510 940-2608	23904
J W Floor Covering Inc	2099	D	858 444-1214	2541
Jupiter Systems LLC	3575	D	510 675-1000	15636
Justipher Inc	3993	F	510 918-6800	23911
Keen-Kut Products Inc	3545	F	510 785-5168	14643
Kinestral Technologies Inc (PA)	3231	C	650 416-5200	10711
King Abrasives Inc	2672	F	510 785-8100	5564
Kinwai USA Inc	2511	F	510 780-9388	4712
KLA Tencor	3568	E	510 887-2647	15287
Kosan Biosciences Incorporated	2834	D	650 995-7356	8249
Krisalis Inc (PA)	3599	F	510 786-0858	16666
La Tapatia - Norcal Inc	2099	C	510 783-2045	2570
Legend Silicon Corp	3663	E	408 735-9888	18163
Longevity Global Inc	3548	E	877 566-4462	14730
Ly Brothers Corporation (PA)	2051	E	510 782-2118	1287
Ly Brothers Corporation	2051	C	510 782-2118	1288
Lyrical Foods Inc	2022	E	510 784-0955	591
M&L Metals Inc	3444	F	510 732-1745	12648
Magico LLC	3651	E	510 649-9700	17828
Maier Racing Enterprises Inc	3714	E	510 581-7600	20394
Mdc Vacuum Products LLC (PA)	3674	D	510 265-3500	18987
Mdc Vacuum Products LLC	3491	E	510 265-3500	13725
Melrose Nameplate and Label Co (PA)	3479	E	510 732-3100	13616
Menches Tool & Die Inc	3728	E	650 592-2328	20885
Merchandising Systems Inc	2542	E	510 477-9100	5154
Micro Connectors Inc	3577	E	510 266-0299	15805
Mission Tocl and Mfg Co Inc	3599	E	510 782-8383	16757
Montague Company	3589	C	510 785-8822	16074
Morgan Technical Ceramics Inc	3299	F	510 491-1100	11362
National Metal Fabricators	3441	E	510 887-6231	12219
Norton Packaging Inc (PA)	3089	C	510 786-1922	10244
Nova Tool Co	3953	F	925 828-7172	23720
Octillion Power Systems Inc	3714	E	510 397-5952	20411
Oki Doki Signs	3993	F	510 940-7446	23936
Omnivore Technologies Inc	7372	E	800 293-4058	24983
Onq Solutions Inc (PA)	2542	E	650 262-4150	5158
Optiscan Biomedical Corp	3841	E	510 342-5800	22572
Oven Fresh Bakery Incorporated	2051	E	650 366-9201	1302
P & S Sales Inc	3714	F	510 732-2628	20416
P-Americas LLC	2086	E	510 732-9500	2160
Pacific Die Cut Industries	3053	D	510 732-8103	9545
Pacific States Felt Mfg Co Inc	3053	F	510 783-2357	9546
Pan Pacific Plastics Mfg Inc	3089	E	510 785-6888	10264
Pepsi-Cola Metro Btlg Co Inc	2086	B	510 781-3600	2176
Perry Tool & Research Inc	3399	E	510 782-9226	11845
Pinnacle Diversified Inc	2759	F	408 562-0111	7436
Pixley Construction Inc	1389	F	510 783-3020	259
Plastikon Industries Inc (PA)	3544	B	510 400-1010	14559
Platron Company West	3599	F	510 781-5588	16846
Primus Power Corporation	3692	E	510 342-7600	19822
Pro Colorflex Ink Corp	2893	F	510 293-3033	9207
Produce World Inc	2099	D	510 441-1449	2643
Protech Materials Inc	3364	F	510 887-5870	11717
Proteus Digital Health Inc	2836	C	650 632-4031	8576
Protoquick Inc	3599	F	510 264-0101	16863
Prozyme Inc	2835	F	510 638-6900	8505
Purolator Pdts A Filtration Co	3564	F	510 785-4800	15171
Qantel Technologies Inc	3571	E	510 731-2080	15475
Quad Express Printing Inc	2752	F	415 861-3433	7061
Rago Neon Inc	3993	F	510 537-1903	23949
Reflexion Medical Inc	3845	E	650 239-9070	23040
Resource Label Group LLC	2759	E	510 477-0707	7466
Ricman Mfg Inc	3599	F	510 670-1785	16900
Rinco International Inc	3086	F	510 785-1633	9880
Rmf Salt Holdings LLC	2844	F	510 477-9600	8829
Rodak Plastics Co Inc	3089	F	510 471-0898	10338
Royal Chemical Company Ltd	2841	E	510 782-8727	8607
San Francisco Pipe &	3498	E	510 785-9148	13904
Sapar Usa Inc (PA)	2013	E	510 441-9500	523
Seeo Inc	3691	F	510 782-7336	19814
Semano Inc	3471	E	510 489-2360	13502
Sepragen Corporation	3826	E	510 475-0650	22017
Sew-Eurodrive Inc	3566	E	510 487-3560	15246
Sharkrack Inc	3577	E	510 477-7900	15852
Shasta Beverages Inc (DH)	2086	D	954 581-0922	2223
Silicon Specialists Inc	3674	F	510 732-9796	19155
Solonics Inc (PA)	3661	F	650 589-9798	17992
Solta Medical Inc	3845	C	510 782-2286	23051
Sonoco Prtective Solutions Inc	2653	D	510 785-0220	5462
Sourcing Group LLC	2752	E	510 471-4749	7108
South Bay Diversfd Systems Inc	3444	F	510 784-3094	12765
Steinbeck Brewing Company	2082	D	510 888-0695	1626
Stiles Paint Manufacturing Inc	2851	F	510 887-8868	8944
Sun Deep Inc	2844	E	510 441-2525	8850
Superior Tube Pipe Bnding Fbco	3498	E	510 782-9311	13906
Surface Techniques Corporation (PA)	2541	E	510 887-6000	5107
Synectic Packaging Inc	2759	F	650 474-0132	7506
Tarps & Tie-Downs Inc (PA)	2394	F	510 782-8772	3814
Techtron Products Inc	3645	E	510 293-3500	17563
Tender Loving Things Inc	2844	F	510 300-1260	8852
Therm-X of California Inc (PA)	3829	C	510 441-7566	22288
Thorx Laboratories Inc	2834	F	510 240-6000	8416
Tli Enterprises Inc (PA)	3821	F	510 538-3304	21494
Tli Enterprises Inc	3471	D	510 786-0680	13521
Trade Only Screen Printing Inc	2759	F	510 887-2020	7524
Tresco Paint Co	2851	F	510 887-7254	8950
Tridecs Corporation	3599	E	510 785-2620	17012
Tung Fei Plastic Inc	2673	F	510 783-9688	5631
Turf Star Inc (PA)	3523	F	800 585-8001	14113
Turner Group Publications Inc	2759	F	408 297-3299	7528
U S Enterprise Corporation	2035	E	510 487-8877	938
UC Plastic Manufacture Inc	2673	F	510 785-6777	5632
Ultimate Rail Equipment Inc	3714	F	510 324-5000	20474
Ultra Clean Technology Systems (HQ)	3823	C	510 576-4400	21672
Ultrasil Corp	3674	E	510 266-3700	19244
United Foods Intl USA Inc (HQ)	2099	F	510 264-5850	2696
United Mech Met Fbricators Inc	3444	E	510 537-4744	12800
Universal Metal Spinning Inc	3646	E	510 782-0980	17653
Urban Trading Software Inc	7372	E	877 633-6171	25318
US Container and Housing Co	2452	F	844 762-8242	4584
Valdor Fiber Optics Inc (PA)	3825	F	510 293-1212	21883
Varni-Lite Coatings Associates	2891	F	510 887-8997	9179
Vicolo Wholesale (PA)	2041	E	510 475-6019	1051
Villa Pallet LLC	2448	F	510 794-6676	4511
Wohler Technologies Inc	3663	F	510 870-0810	18303
Wood Box Specialties Inc	2449	F	510 786-1600	4541
Woodford Wicks LLC	3999	F	614 554-8474	24291
Wpx Energy Inc	1382	F	510 727-9708	161
Xia LLC	3826	F	510 494-9020	22051
Yanfeng US Automotive	2531	E	616 886-3622	5033

HEALDSBURG, CA - Sonoma County

	SIC	EMP	PHONE	ENTRY #
Alexander Valley Gourmet LLC	2099	E	707 473-0116	2448
AVV Winery Co LLC	2084	F	707 433-7209	1648
Bear Republic Brewing Co Inc	2082	F	707 433-2337	1569
Cable Car Classics Inc	3743	F	707 433-6810	21074
Chateau Diana LLC (PA)	2084	F	707 433-6992	1688
Constellation Brands US Oprs	2084	A	707 433-8268	1706
Cooling Tower Resources Inc (PA)	2499	E	707 433-3900	4616
Copain Wine Cellars LLC	2084	F	707 836-8822	1707
Criveller California Corp	3556	F	707 431-2211	14843
DJ Grey Company Inc	3679	F	707 431-2779	19516
Dry Creek Vineyard Inc	2084	E	707 433-1000	1733
Duff Bevill Vineyard Managmnt	2084	E	707 433-6691	1737
E & J Gallo Winery	2084	F	707 431-1946	1742
Ferrar-Crano Vnyrds Winery LLC (PA)	2084	F	707 433-6700	1759
Field Stone Winery & Vineyard	2084	F	707 433-7266	1762
Franciscan Vinyards Inc	2084	D	707 433-6981	1773
General Dynmics Ots Ncvlle Inc	3593	D	707 473-9200	16156
Geyser Peak Winery	2084	F	707 857-9463	1781
Hanna Winery Inc (PA)	2084	F	707 431-4310	1805
HDD LLC	2084	F	707 433-9545	1809
Jackson Family Wines Inc	2084	E	707 433-9463	1826
Jordan Vineyard & Winery LP	2084	E	707 431-5250	1834
Jvw Corporation	2084	D	707 431-5250	1836
L Foppiano Wine Co	2084	E	707 433-2736	1846
Lambert Bridge Winery Inc	2084	F	707 431-9600	1852
Michel-Schlmberger Partners LP	2084	E	707 433-7427	1878
Mill Creek Vneyards Winery Inc	2084	F	707 433-4788	1880
Mix Garden Inc	3273	F	707 433-4327	11143

Employment Codes: A=Over 500 employees, B=251-500,
C=101-250, D=51-100, E=20-50, F=10-19

2019 California
Manufacturers Register

© Mergent Inc. 1-800-342-5647

1391

GEOGRAPHIC

Company	SIC	EMP	PHONE	ENTRY #
Overlook Vineyards LLC	2084	F	707 433-6491	1910
Pan Magna Group	2084	E	707 433-5508	1912
Pjk Winery LLC	2084	E	707 431-8333	1926
Preston Vineyards LLC	2084	F	707 433-3372	1930
RB Wine Associates LLC	2084	D	707 433-8400	1941
Redwood Milling Company LLC	2431	E	707 433-1343	4217
Rupert Gibbon & Spider Inc	2851	E	800 442-0455	8938
Santa Rosa Lead Products LLC **(PA)**	3531	F	800 916-5323	14188
Santa Rosa Lead Products Inc	3369	F	707 431-1477	11784
Seghesio Wineries Inc	2084	F	707 433-3579	1971
Selby Inc	2084	F	707 431-1703	1972
Serra Systems Inc **(HQ)**	7372	F	707 433-5104	25165
Sonoma Cider Mill	2099	F	707 433-8212	2670
Stonecushion Inc **(PA)**	2084	F	707 433-1911	1999
Tandem Wines LLC	2084	F	707 395-3902	2008
Toad Hollow Vineyards Inc	2084	F	707 431-1441	2018
Truett-Hurst Inc **(PA)**	2084	F	707 431-4423	2029
Williams & Selyem Winery	2084	F	707 433-6425	2057

HEBER, CA - Imperial County

Company	SIC	EMP	PHONE	ENTRY #
Gibson and Schaefer Inc **(PA)**	3273	E	619 352-3535	11112

HELENDALE, CA - San Bernardino County

Company	SIC	EMP	PHONE	ENTRY #
W A Murphy Inc	2892	F	760 245-8711	9186

HELM, CA - Fresno County

Company	SIC	EMP	PHONE	ENTRY #
JR Simplot Company	2874	E	559 866-5681	9080
True Organic Products Inc	2875	F	559 866-3001	9088

HEMET, CA - Riverside County

Company	SIC	EMP	PHONE	ENTRY #
Brazeau Thoroughbred Farms LP	3523	F	951 925-8957	14047
California Precast Stone Mfg	3272	F	951 657-7913	10896
Danaher Corporation	3824	C	951 652-6811	21684
Easy Ad Incorporated	2711	E	951 658-2244	5839
EZ Lube LLC	2992	A	951 766-1996	9434
J S M Productions Inc	2752	F	951 929-5771	6903
McCrometer Inc	3824	C	951 652-6811	21691
Medi Kid Company	3842	F	951 925-8800	22768
Omega 2000 Group Corp	3634	D	951 775-5815	17400
Ortega Manufacturing Inc	3999	F	951 766-9363	24197
Ramko Injection Inc	3089	D	951 652-3510	10323
Superior Ready Mix Concrete LP	3273	F	951 658-9225	11196
Te Connectivity	3678	F	951 765-2200	19412
Te Connectivity Corporation	3678	D	951 765-2250	19416
Te Connectivity Corporation	3678	B	760 757-7500	19421
Te Connectivity Corporation	3678	B	951 765-2200	19423
Washburn Grove Management Inc	2411	E	909 322-4690	4020

HERCULES, CA - Contra Costa County

Company	SIC	EMP	PHONE	ENTRY #
Benda Tool & Model Works Inc	3544	E	510 741-3170	14485
Bio RAD Laboratories	3826	D	510 741-1000	21913
Bio-RAD Laboratories Inc **(PA)**	3826	B	510 724-7000	21914
Bio-RAD Laboratories Inc	3826	A	510 741-6916	21915
Bio-RAD Laboratories Inc	3826	C	510 741-1000	21917
Bio-RAD Laboratories Inc	3826	C	510 741-6709	21918
Bio-RAD Laboratories Inc	3826	A	510 232-7000	21919
Bio-RAD Laboratories Inc	3826	B	510 741-6715	21920
Bio-RAD Laboratories Inc	3826	B	510 741-6999	21921
Bio-RAD Laboratories Inc	3826	B	510 232-7000	21922
Naia Inc	2024	E	510 724-2479	688

HERMOSA BEACH, CA - Los Angeles County

Company	SIC	EMP	PHONE	ENTRY #
Becker Surfboards Inc	3949	F	310 372-6554	23516
Bethebeast Inc	7372	E	424 206-1081	24416
Easy Reader Inc	2711	E	310 372-4611	5840
Hammitt Inc	3161	E	310 293-3787	10523
National Media Inc	2711	E	310 372-0388	5991
Rf Digital Corporation	3674	C	949 610-0008	19126

HESPERIA, CA - San Bernardino County

Company	SIC	EMP	PHONE	ENTRY #
A Terrycable California Corp	3714	E	760 244-9351	20235
Apex Specialty Cnstr Entps	2431	F	714 334-1118	4101
Brown & Honeycutt Truss Systms	2439	E	760 244-8887	4393
C & M Wood Industries	2591	C	760 949-3292	5183
CAr Enterprises Inc	3578	F	760 947-6411	15895
Daytec Center LLC	3751	E	760 995-3515	21105
Dial Precision Inc	3599	D	760 947-3557	16436
Dyell Machine	3599	F	760 244-3333	16453
E R Metals Inc	3366	F	760 948-2309	11756
Geeriraj Inc	3672	F	760 244-6149	18491
Hayes Welding Inc	7692	F	760 246-4878	25410
Hesperia Resorter	2711	E	760 244-0021	5878
High Tech Etch **(PA)**	3599	F	760 244-8916	16566
Jim Ellis	2439	F	760 244-8566	4416
Leadmasters	3949	E	760 949-6566	23606
Maurice & Maurice Engrg Inc	3334	F	760 949-5151	11540
Moore Tool Co	3429	E	760 949-4142	11979
P J Machining Co Inc	3599	F	760 948-2722	16816

Company	SIC	EMP	PHONE	ENTRY #
Plastech Moulding & Fabg	3089	E	760 244-8078	10282
Project Steel Company Inc	3441	F	760 947-0531	12233
R S R Steel Fabrication Inc	3312	E	760 244-2210	11413
Robar Enterprises Inc **(PA)**	3273	C	760 244-5456	11163
Southern California Components	2439	D	760 949-5144	4422
T L Timmerman Construction	2439	E	760 244-2532	4427
Trekell & Co Inc	3952	F	800 378-3867	23713
W R Grace & Co - Conn	3826	D	760 244-6107	22048
Western Fab Inc	3499	F	760 949-1441	13984

HICKMAN, CA - Stanislaus County

Company	SIC	EMP	PHONE	ENTRY #
Reed International **(HQ)**	3532	E	209 874-2357	14202

HIDDEN VALLEY LAKE, CA - Lake County

Company	SIC	EMP	PHONE	ENTRY #
Jensen Graphics & Printing	2752	F	707 987-8966	6911

HIGHLAND, CA - San Bernardino County

Company	SIC	EMP	PHONE	ENTRY #
Alpha I Publishing Inc	2741	F	909 862-9572	6428
Boudoir Spirits Inc	2085	F	909 714-6644	2068
Cemex Cnstr Mtls PCF LLC	3273	F	909 335-3105	11073
Master-Halco Inc	3315	E	909 350-4740	11448
Raemica Inc	2013	F	909 864-1990	518
Robertsons Ready Mix Ltd	3273	E	909 425-2930	11170

HILMAR, CA - Merced County

Company	SIC	EMP	PHONE	ENTRY #
Americore Inc	3448	E	209 632-5679	12917
Hilmar Cheese Company Inc **(PA)**	2022	B	209 667-6076	578
Hilmar Whey Protein Inc **(PA)**	2023	B	209 667-6076	623
Hilmar Whey Protein Inc	2023	D	209 667-6076	624
Perrys Custom Chopping	3523	F	209 667-8777	14092
Richard Veeck	3559	F	209 667-0872	15019

HOLLISTER, CA - San Benito County

Company	SIC	EMP	PHONE	ENTRY #
A & R Doors Inc	2431	F	831 637-8139	4094
Advantage Truss Company LLC	2439	E	831 635-0377	4388
C & C Built-In Inc	2434	F	831 635-5880	4278
Corbin Pacific Inc **(PA)**	3751	D	831 634-1100	21099
Debritos Chocolate Factory	2064	F	831 637-0164	1418
Diablo Precision Inc	3599	F	831 634-0136	16435
Food Equipment Mfg Co	3556	F	831 637-1624	14846
Gabilan Welding Inc	3599	F	831 637-3360	16523
Gimelli Vineyards	2084	F	831 637-5445	1783
Gregory Patterson	3446	E	831 636-1015	12859
Kmg Chemicals Inc	2899	E	800 956-7467	9270
Kmg Electronic Chemicals Inc	2813	F	831 636-5151	7692
Kopin Corporation	3674	F	831 636-5556	18944
Mandego Inc	2261	F	831 637-5241	2886
Marich Confectionery Co Inc	2064	C	831 634-4700	1441
Mc Electronics LLC	3679	E	831 637-1651	19642
Milgard Manufacturing Inc	3442	C	831 636-0114	12333
Mobil Pallets Exchange	2448	F	831 758-5203	4489
Nanotronics Imaging Inc	3699	F	831 630-0700	20022
Neil Jones Food Company	2033	D	831 637-0573	832
Ozeki Sake U S A Inc **(HQ)**	2084	F	831 637-9217	1911
Pacific Intrlock Pvngstone Inc **(PA)**	3272	F	831 637-9163	10972
Pacific Scientific Energetic **(HQ)**	2899	F	831 637-3731	9295
Peninsula Packaging LLC	3089	C	831 634-0940	10271
Pride Conveyance Systems Inc	3535	E	831 637-1787	14281
Reed Manufacturing Inc	3324	E	831 637-5641	11521
Royal Circuit Solutions Inc **(PA)**	3672	E	831 636-7789	18584
SBS America LLC **(PA)**	2431	E	831 637-8700	4225
Spices Unlimited Inc	2099	F	831 636-3596	2672
Trical Inc	2879	D	831 637-0195	9117

HOLLYWOOD, CA - Los Angeles County

Company	SIC	EMP	PHONE	ENTRY #
Aftermaster Inc **(PA)**	3861	F	310 657-4886	23137

HOOPA, CA - Humboldt County

Company	SIC	EMP	PHONE	ENTRY #
Hoopa Forest Industries	2411	E	530 625-4281	3991

HOPLAND, CA - Mendocino County

Company	SIC	EMP	PHONE	ENTRY #
Brutocao Cellars **(PA)**	2084	F	707 744-1066	1670
Duckhorn Wine Company	2084	E	707 744-2800	1734
Fetzer Vineyards **(HQ)**	2084	C	707 744-1250	1760
Mendocino Brewing Company Inc	2082	E	707 744-1015	1610
Steve Bruner	2431	E	707 744-1103	4236

HUGHSON, CA - Stanislaus County

Company	SIC	EMP	PHONE	ENTRY #
Assali Hulling & Shelling	2068	F	209 883-4263	1482
Calaveras Materials Inc **(DH)**	3273	E	209 883-0448	11055
Calaveras Materials Inc	3272	E	209 883-0448	10893
California Truss Company	2439	E	209 883-8000	4398
Grossi Fabrication Inc	3496	E	209 883-2817	13832
Hughson Nut Inc **(PA)**	2068	B	209 883-0403	1490
Nuwest Milling LLC	2048	F	209 883-1163	1153
Valley Tool & Mfg Co Inc	3599	E	209 883-4093	17032

HUNTINGTON BEACH, CA - Orange County

Company	SIC	EMP	PHONE	ENTRY #
A G Artwear Inc	3961	F	714 898-3636	23742

Mergent email: customerrelations@mergent.com
1392

2019 California
Manufacturers Register

(P-0000) Products & Services Section entry number
(PA)=Parent Co (HQ)=Headquarters (DH)=Div Headquarters

Company	SIC	EMP	PHONE	ENTRY #
ADS LLC	3823	E	714 379-9778	21541
Advanced Cmpsite Pdts Tech Inc	3089	E	714 895-5544	9926
Advanced Cutting Tools Inc	3423	E	714 842-9376	11885
Advanced Packaging & Crating	2449	F	714 892-1702	4515
Aero-Mechanical Engrg Inc	3599	F	714 891-2423	16240
Aerodynamic Engineering Inc	3599	E	714 891-2651	16241
Aerodyne Prcsion Machining Inc	3599	F	714 891-1311	16242
Airtech International (PA)	3728	C	714 899-8100	20728
All Forms Express	2759	F	714 596-8641	7227
All West Plastics Inc	3082	E	714 894-9922	9736
Allan Borushek & Assoc Inc	2731	F	949 642-8500	6305
Alphalogix	3695	D	714 901-1456	19855
American Automated Engrg Inc	3769	E	714 898-9951	21185
American Battery Charging Inc	3629	E	401 231-5227	17330
American Blast Systems Inc	3312	E	949 244-6859	11377
American Metal Enterprises Inc	3842	E	714 894-6810	22698
American Precision Hydraulics	3542	E	714 903-8610	14429
AMG Torrance LLC (DH)	3728	D	310 515-2584	20733
Asea Power Systems	3679	E	714 896-9695	19449
Astra Energy Holdings Inc	2911	C	714 969-6569	9321
Avalon Machine Products Inc	3728	E	323 979-8656	20748
B & B Enameling Inc	3479	F	714 848-0044	13555
Badge Co	3999	F	714 842-3037	24047
Baker Hghes Olfld Oprtions LLC	3533	D	714 893-8511	14208
Baker Hghes Olfld Oprtions LLC	1389	E	714 891-8544	172
Baker Hughes A GE Company LLC	3533	D	714 893-8511	14210
Bare Nothings Inc (PA)	2339	E	714 848-8532	3380
Bent Manufacturing Co Bdaa Inc	3089	F	714 842-0600	9974
Blue Iron Network Inc	7372	E	714 901-1456	24433
Blue-White Industries Ltd (PA)	3824	D	714 893-8529	21680
Boardriders Inc (DH)	2329	C	714 889-2200	3139
Boeing Company	3761	B	714 896-3311	21156
Boeing Company	3721	A	714 934-9801	20554
Boeing Company	3721	A	714 896-3311	20556
Boeing Company	3721	A	714 896-1301	20559
Boeing Company	3721	A	714 896-1670	20561
Boeing Company	3721	A	714 896-1839	20563
Boeing Company	3721	E	714 896-3311	20564
Boeing Intellectual	3721	E	562 797-2020	20568
Buena Park Tool & Engineering	3599	F	714 843-6215	16336
Byran Company Inc	3599	D	714 841-9808	16341
C&D Zodiac Inc (DH)	3728	B	714 934-0000	20765
Cable Harness Systems Inc	3679	E	714 841-9650	19474
Cal-Aurum Industries	3471	E	714 898-0996	13362
California Economizer	3625	E	714 898-9963	17258
California Faucets Inc	3432	F	657 400-1639	12027
California Faucets Inc (PA)	3432	D	714 890-0450	12028
Calmoseptine Inc	2834	F	714 848-2949	8095
Cambro Manufacturing Company (PA)	3089	B	714 848-1555	10007
Cambro Manufacturing Company	3089	B	714 848-1555	10008
Cambro Manufacturing Company	3089	B	714 848-1555	10009
Center Line Wheel Corporation	3714	D	562 921-9637	20288
Chase Corporation	3644	E	714 964-6268	17508
Circuit Automation Inc	3679	F	714 763-4180	19492
Coast To Coast Circuits Inc (PA)	3672	C	585 254-2980	18455
Coast To Coast Circuits Inc	3672	D	714 898-4901	18456
Conversion Devices Inc	3845	E	714 898-6551	22965
Creative Costuming Designs Inc	2389	F	714 895-0982	3651
Creative Sign Inc	3993	F	714 842-4343	23851
Crenshaw Die and Mfg Corp	3469	D	949 475-5505	13189
Crunch Metals Co Inc	3444	F	714 897-0552	12545
Curlin Healthcare Products Inc	3599	D	714 893-2200	16412
Custom Building Products Inc (DH)	2891	D	800 272-8786	9138
D & D Technologies USA Inc	3315	E	949 852-5140	11434
Dairy Conveyor Corp	3535	E	714 891-0883	14272
DC Shoes Inc (DH)	2329	D	714 889-4206	3143
Dime Research and Development	3711	E	714 969-7879	20135
Donoco Industries Inc	3229	E	714 893-7889	10641
Driessen Aircraft Interior	3728	E	714 861-7300	20800
Driessen Aircraft Interior (DH)	3728	C	714 861-7300	20801
Dynamet Incorporated	3356	E	714 375-3150	11627
Dynatrac Products Co Inc	3714	E	714 596-4461	20320
Electronic Waveform Lab Inc	3841	E	714 843-0463	22436
Encore Interiors Inc (PA)	3728	C	949 559-0930	20806
Encore International	3724	E	949 559-0930	20649
Encore Seats Inc (PA)	3728	E	949 559-0930	20807
Encore Seats Inc	3728	E	949 559-0930	20808
Enhanced Vision Systems Inc (HQ)	3851	E	714 374-1829	23093
European Services Group	3429	F	714 898-0595	11954
Fibreform Electronics Inc	3599	F	714 898-9641	16496
Fiolas Development LLC	3272	E	714 893-7559	10925
Foil Core Inc	3999	F	714 891-1695	24097
Fotis and Son Imports Inc	3556	E	714 894-9022	14849
Fox Hills Industries	3321	F	714 893-1940	11493
Fox Hills Machining Inc	3599	F	714 899-2211	16512
Frequency Management Intl (PA)	3679	F	714 373-8100	19546
Gachupin Enterprises LLC	2759	E	714 375-4111	7325
Glacier Design Systems Inc (PA)	2082	F	714 897-2337	1595
Global Tech Instruments Inc	3812	F	714 375-1811	21300
Harris Industries Inc (PA)	2672	F	714 898-8048	5561
HB Products LLC	2759	F	714 799-6967	7342
Hewitt Industries Los Angeles	3823	E	714 891-9300	21599
Home & Body Company (PA)	2842	E	714 842-8000	8647
Honeywell International Inc	3724	A	310 512-4237	20652
Hytron Mfg Co Inc	3599	E	714 903-6701	16576
Ideal Pallet System Inc	2448	F	714 847-9657	4477
Initium Eyewear Inc	3851	F	714 444-0866	23101
Inkwright LLC	2752	F	714 892-3300	6885
Innovative Plastics Inc	3083	F	714 891-8800	9750
Intertrade Aviation Corp	3728	E	714 895-3335	20849
Itech Medical Inc	3841	F	714 841-2670	22497
JCM Industries Inc (PA)	2542	E	714 902-9000	5149
Jet Performance Products Inc	3694	E	714 848-5500	19837
JGM Automotive Tooling Inc	3559	F	714 895-7001	14976
Johnson Manufacturing Inc	3599	E	714 903-0393	16629
Jolyn Clothing Company LLC	2339	E	714 794-2149	3438
Kadan Consultants Incorporated	3599	F	562 988-1165	16642
Kaged Muscle LLC	2023	E	208 850-0174	626
Karls Custom Sash and Doors	2431	E	714 842-7877	4176
Kastle Stair Inc (PA)	2431	E	714 596-2600	4177
Kennedy Hills Enterprises LLC	1221	F	714 596-7444	18
Kj Aero Holdings LLC	2752	F	714 891-6060	6924
Komax Systems Inc	3531	E	310 830-4320	14179
Laird Coatings Corporation	2851	E	714 894-5252	8914
Leda Corporation	3769	E	714 841-7821	21195
License Frame Inc	3479	E	714 903-7550	13611
Lightning Dversion Systems LLC	3643	F	714 841-1080	17480
Logi Graphics Incorporated	3672	F	714 841-3666	18521
M I T Inc	3544	F	714 899-6066	14536
Madsen Products Incorporated	3599	F	714 894-1816	16708
Marsha Vicki Originals Inc	2311	E	714 895-6371	3034
Mechanized Science Seals Inc	3829	E	714 898-5602	22232
Mesa Castings Inc (PA)	3321	C	714 962-1064	11499
Mgfso LLC	2834	E	949 500-7645	8282
Milco Wire Edm Inc	3599	F	714 373-0098	16747
Mill 42 Inc	2253	F	714 979-4200	2850
Miracle Cover (PA)	2851	E	714 842-8863	8918
Mission Crtical Composites LLC	3728	E	714 831-2100	20889
Mitsubishi Elc Auto Amer Inc	3694	F	714 902-1900	19839
Mjc Engineering and Tech Inc	3542	F	714 890-0618	14446
Momeni Engineering LLC	3599	E	714 897-9301	16764
NDT Systems Inc	3829	E	714 893-2438	22240
Newlight Technologies Inc	3089	E	714 556-4500	10236
Nordson Medical (ca) LLC	3841	D	657 215-4200	22559
Norm Harboldt	3479	E	714 596-4242	13622
Ocg Inc	3679	D	714 375-4024	19669
Oliphant Tool Company	3544	E	714 903-6336	14553
Opticolor Inc	3089	F	714 893-8839	10255
Organ-O-Sil Fiber Co Inc	3714	E	714 847-8310	20415
Orlando Spring Corp	3495	E	562 594-8411	13797
Pacific Link Corp	3827	E	714 897-3525	22119
Pakedge Device & Software Inc	7372	E	714 880-4511	25046
Paradise Road LLC	2842	E	714 894-1779	8662
Patten Systems Inc	3823	F	714 799-5656	21631
PCA Aerospace Inc (PA)	3728	D	714 841-1750	20908
Plasma Rggedized Solutions Inc	3471	E	714 893-6063	13475
PPG Industries Inc	2851	E	714 894-5252	8930
Precision Frrites Ceramics Inc	3264	D	714 901-7622	10822
Precision Resource Inc	3469	B	714 891-4439	13262
Premium Herbal USA LLC	2023	E	800 567-7878	646
Prestige Cosmetics Inc	2844	F	714 375-0395	8821
Primo Powder Coating & Sndblst	3479	F	714 596-4242	13641
Primus Inc (PA)	3993	D	714 527-2261	23944
Primus Inc	3993	F	714 527-2261	23945
Product Design Developments	3089	E	714 898-6895	10312
Pvd Coatings II LLC	3479	F	714 899-4892	13643
Ralph L Florimonte	3052	F	714 960-4470	9506
Ray Foster Dental Equipment	3843	F	714 897-7795	22905
Raycon Technology Inc (PA)	3678	F	714 799-4100	19410
Raytheon Company	3812	F	310 334-0430	21387
Reedex Inc	3511	F	714 894-0311	19704
Reloaded Technologies Inc	7372	F	949 870-3123	25125
Rima Enterprises Inc	3555	D	714 893-4534	14827
Rodon Products Inc	3677	E	714 898-3528	19360
Roger Cleveland Golf Co Inc (PA)	3949	C	714 889-1300	23638
Roto West Enterprises Inc	3089	F	714 899-2030	10346
Salco Dynamic Solutions Inc (PA)	2992	F	714 374-7500	9449
Sandia Plastics Inc	3089	E	714 901-8400	10358
Screen Art Inc	2759	F	714 891-4185	7478
Seven Wells LLC	2499	F	213 305-4775	4652

GEOGRAPHIC

	SIC	EMP	PHONE	ENTRY #
Sgt Boardriders Inc	3069	F	714 274-8000	9677
Shortcuts Software Inc	7372	E	714 622-6600	25170
Soberlink Healthcare LLC	3829	F	714 975-7200	22273
Soldermask Inc	3672	F	714 842-1987	18610
Solutions Safety Services Inc	2299	D	714 843-5653	3017
Space Spring and Stamping Co	3493	F	714 255-9800	13755
Specilized Crmic Powdr Coating	3479	F	714 901-2628	13662
STA-Rite Industries LLC	3561	B	714 371-1550	15092
Stablcor Technology Inc	2655	F	714 375-6644	5495
Steecon Inc	3728	F	714 895-5313	20937
Steripax Inc	2671	E	714 892-8811	5538
Submersible Systems Inc	3949	E	714 842-6566	23665
Sunbeam Trailer Products Inc	3647	E	714 373-5000	17666
Sunshine Makers Inc (PA)	2842	D	562 795-6000	8678
Surf City Garage	2842	E	714 894-1707	8679
Tarpin Corporation	3544	F	714 891-6944	14576
Teacher Created Materials Inc	2731	C	714 891-2273	6397
Therma-Tek Range Corp	3639	E	570 455-9491	17417
Thermal Bags By Ingrid Inc	2657	F	847 836-4400	5511
Third Degree Sportswear Inc	2339	F	714 890-9828	3518
Tiodize Co Inc (PA)	3479	D	714 898-4377	13673
Tiodize Co Inc	3479	F	248 348-6050	13674
Tolemar Inc	3751	E	714 362-8166	21142
Translogic Incorporated	3823	E	714 890-0058	21670
Travismathew LLC	2329	F	562 799-6900	3198
Tri Models Inc	3721	E	714 896-0823	20631
Tri Print LLC	2752	F	714 847-1400	7145
Trivec-Avant Corporation	3663	E	714 841-4976	18293
Truwest Inc	2329	F	714 895-2444	3199
U S Wheel Corporation	3714	E	714 892-0021	20472
UFO Designs (PA)	3089	F	714 892-4420	10417
Unilete Inc	2329	E	714 557-1271	3201
Urabe Incorporated	3599	F	714 377-9701	17026
Urethane Products Corporation	3089	F	800 913-0062	10421
V & S Engineering Company Ltd	3599	F	714 898-7869	17027
Vanguard Networing Products	3669	B	714 842-3330	18375
Victory Professional Products	2339	E	714 887-0621	3525
Vinatronic Inc	3672	E	714 845-3480	18647
Walton Company Inc	2499	F	714 847-8800	4663
Weatherman Products Inc (PA)	2851	F	949 515-8800	8955
West Coast Trends Inc	3949	E	714 843-9288	23689
Xr LLC	3842	F	714 847-9292	22850
Zadro Products Inc	3231	E	714 892-9200	10742
Zerouv	3851	F	714 584-0015	23134

HUNTINGTON PARK, CA - Los Angeles County

	SIC	EMP	PHONE	ENTRY #
Acme Castings Inc	3366	E	323 583-3129	11752
Acme Screw Products Inc	3449	E	323 581-8611	12970
Aircraft Foundry Co Inc	3365	F	323 587-3171	11721
B F Mc Gilla Inc	3498	E	323 581-8288	13877
Bodycote Thermal Proc Inc	3471	D	323 583-1231	13350
Cal-Pac Chemical Co Inc	2819	F	323 585-2178	7756
Citizens of Humanity LLC (PA)	2339	D	323 923-1240	3393
Coh-Fb LLC	2326	E	323 923-1240	3099
Cotton Generation Inc	2361	E	323 581-8555	3574
Covert Iron Works	3322	F	323 560-2792	11503
Crown Poly Inc	2673	C	323 268-1298	5596
Dynamic Machine Inc	3599	F	323 585-0710	16456
Eti Sound Systems Inc	3651	E	323 835-6660	17799
J Heyri Inc	2331	E	323 588-1234	3246
Los Angeles Galvanizing Co	3479	D	323 583-2263	13613
Los Angles Pump Valve Pdts Inc	3561	E	323 277-7788	15084
NL&a Collections Inc	3645	E	323 277-6266	17550
Oheck LLC	2386	C	323 923-2700	3621
Original Distributor Exchange	3694	F	323 583-8707	19842
Plycraft Industries Inc	2435	C	323 587-8101	4382
Reliance Upholstery Sup Co Inc	2392	D	323 321-2300	3745
Saydel Inc (PA)	2844	E	323 585-2800	8836
Small Paper Co Inc	2621	F	323 277-0525	5335
Traffic Works Inc	3081	E	323 582-0616	9731
UFO Inc	3089	E	323 588-5450	10418
Valco Planer Works Inc	3544	E	323 582-6355	14587
West Coast Foundry LLC (HQ)	3325	F	323 583-1421	11529
Wire Guard Systems Inc	3644	E	323 588-2166	17521

IDYLLWILD, CA - Riverside County

	SIC	EMP	PHONE	ENTRY #
South Bay Cable Corp (PA)	3357	D	951 659-2183	11674

IMPERIAL, CA - Imperial County

	SIC	EMP	PHONE	ENTRY #
Franklin Lee Enterprises LLC	2759	F	760 355-1500	7322
Honeywell International Inc	3714	E	760 355-3420	20363
United States Gypsum Company	3275	B	760 358-3200	11226

INDIAN WELLS, CA - Riverside County

	SIC	EMP	PHONE	ENTRY #
Callaway Golf Company	3949	A	760 345-4653	23532
Kenny Giannini Putters LLC	3949	F	760 851-9475	23603

INDIO, CA - Riverside County

	SIC	EMP	PHONE	ENTRY #
Coachelle Valley Ice Co	2097	E	760 347-3529	2410
Coronet Concrete Products	3273	E	760 398-2441	11099
Cortima Co	3281	E	760 347-5535	11245
Cv Ice Company Inc	2097	E	760 347-3529	2411
Dejagers Inc	3281	E	760 775-4755	11248
Latino Americanos Revista	2721	F	760 342-2312	6204
Lindsey Doors Inc	3083	E	760 775-1959	9752
M F G Eurotec Inc	2511	E	760 863-0033	4716
Master Washer Stamping Svc Co	3544	E	323 722-0969	14539
MTI De Baja Inc	3812	E	951 654-2333	21354
Panco Mens Products Inc	2844	E	760 342-4368	8810
Pepsi-Cola Metro Btlg Co Inc	2086	F	760 775-2660	2175
Stutz Packing Company	2034	F	760 342-1666	895
Swisstrax LLC	3253	F	760 347-3330	10794

INGLEWOOD, CA - Los Angeles County

	SIC	EMP	PHONE	ENTRY #
A H Machine Inc	3599	F	310 672-0016	16192
Acutek Adhesive Specialties	3069	E	310 419-0190	9583
AF Machine & Tool Co Inc	3599	F	310 674-1919	16244
All-Star Mktg & Promotions Inc	2395	F	323 582-4880	3826
Antique Designs Ltd Inc	2521	E	310 671-5400	4931
C C M D Inc	3471	E	310 673-5532	13359
Centinela Concrete Vault Co	3272	F	310 674-2115	10898
Creamer Printing Co	2752	F	310 671-9491	6765
Doorking Inc (PA)	3699	C	310 645-0023	19947
Empower Rf Systems Inc (PA)	3663	D	310 412-8100	18098
Engineered Magnetics Inc	3629	E	310 649-9000	17340
Farrar Grinding Company	3728	F	323 678-4879	20811
Glp Designs Inc	2599	F	310 652-6800	5234
Industrious Software Solution	7372	F	310 672-8700	24762
JGA Inc	2512	F	310 672-4000	4786
Kazmere Entertainment	3651	F	323 448-9009	17822
Larryron Enterprises Inc	2051	F	310 645-4707	1277
Leads360 LLC	7372	E	888 843-1777	24854
Line Publications Inc	2721	F	310 234-9501	6208
Marvin Engineering Co Inc (PA)	3728	A	310 674-5030	20874
Marvin Land Systems Inc	3711	E	310 674-5030	20157
Minus K Technology Inc	3674	C	310 348-9656	19020
Multichrome Company Inc (PA)	3471	E	310 216-1086	13460
N/S Corporation (PA)	3589	D	310 412-7074	16076
Odwalla Inc	2033	E	310 342-3920	836
Oopston Inc	7372	E	800 881-5901	24986
Overhill Farms Inc	2038	C	323 587-5985	1005
Relativity Space Inc	3365	F	972 978-8946	11749
Scapa Tapes North America LLC	2672	E	310 419-0567	5577
Shg Holdings Corp (PA)	3546	D	310 410-4907	14711
Signature Eyewear Inc (PA)	3851	C	310 330-2700	23122
Steel Toe Enterprises	3449	F	310 828-9677	12999
Water Planet Engineering LLC	3589	F	424 331-7700	16133
Weber Drilling Co Inc	3532	E	310 670-7708	14204
Wheels Magazine Inc	3732	F	310 402-9013	21070
Zephyr Manufacturing Co Inc	3546	D	310 410-4907	14713

INYOKERN, CA - Kern County

	SIC	EMP	PHONE	ENTRY #
Firequick Products Inc	3569	F	760 371-4279	15321
Indian Wells Companies	2082	E	760 377-4290	1601
Intelligence Support Group Ltd	3699	E	800 504-3341	19984

IONE, CA - Amador County

	SIC	EMP	PHONE	ENTRY #
Isp Granule Products Inc	3295	D	209 274-2930	11321
Mp Associates Inc	2892	C	209 274-4715	9183
Sanders Aircraft Inc	3812	E	209 274-2955	21425
Specialty Granules LLC	3295	E	209 274-5323	11327

IRVINE, CA - Orange County

	SIC	EMP	PHONE	ENTRY #
1891 Alton A California Co	3643	F	949 261-6402	17437
3 Point Distribution LLC	2329	E	949 266-2700	3128
3h Communication Systems Inc	3812	F	949 529-1583	21248
3M Company	3843	F	949 863-1360	22852
3y Power Technology Inc	3679	F	949 450-0152	19429
A S A Engineering Inc	3571	E	949 460-9911	15379
A-Info Inc	3728	E	949 346-7326	20696
Above & Beyond Balloons Inc	3999	E	949 586-8470	24021
Acclarent Inc	3841	B	650 687-5888	22310
Acti Corporation Inc	3651	E	949 753-0352	17750
Activision Blizzard Inc	7372	D	949 955-1380	24313
Adex Electronics Inc	3674	E	949 597-1772	18663
Advanced Biocatalytics Corp	2841	E	949 442-0880	8587
Advanced Sterlization (DH)	3841	E	800 595-0200	22317
Advanced Vsual Image Dsign LLC	2759	C	951 239-2138	7223
Advisys Inc	7372	E	949 752-4927	24332
Agents West Inc	3699	E	949 614-0293	19900
Alcon Laboratories Inc	3841	A	949 753-6488	22320
Alcon Lensx Inc (DH)	3841	D	949 753-1393	22321
Alcon Manufacturing Ltd	2834	E	949 753-1393	8008

Mergent email: customerrelations@mergent.com

1394

2019 California
Manufacturers Register

(P-0000) Products & Services Section entry number
(PA)=Parent Co (HQ)=Headquarters (DH)=Div Headquarters

	SIC	EMP	PHONE	ENTRY #
Alcon Research Ltd	3841	E	949 387-2142	22322
Aleks Corporation	7372	C	714 245-7191	24347
Allergan Spclty Thrpeutics Inc	2834	A	714 246-6400	8013
Allergan Usa Inc	2834	A	714 427-1900	8014
Allez Spine LLC (PA)	3841	F	949 752-7885	22326
Alliance Medical Products Inc	3841	C	949 768-4690	22327
Altaviz LLC (PA)	2834	F	949 656-4003	8017
Aluratek Inc	3651	E	949 468-2046	17758
American Audio Component Inc	3679	E	909 596-3788	19441
American Foil & Embosing Inc	2759	F	949 580-0080	7233
American Indus Systems Inc	3679	E	888 485-6688	19442
American PCF Prtrs College Inc	2752	E	949 250-3212	6656
American Scence Tech As T Corp	3721	D	310 773-1978	20539
Ametek Inc	3621	D	949 642-2400	17180
Amkor Technology Inc	3674	E	949 724-9370	18695
Anabolic Incorporated	2834	D	949 863-0340	8030
Anchen Pharmaceuticals Inc	2834	F	949 639-8100	8032
Anydata Corporation (PA)	3663	E	949 900-6040	18034
Apollo Instruments Inc	3827	E	949 756-3111	22059
Applied Cardiac Systems Inc	3841	D	949 855-9366	22338
Aptiv Services 3 (us) LLC (HQ)	3714	E	949 458-3100	20258
Aquatec International Inc	3561	D	949 225-2200	15053
Arbonne International LLC (HQ)	2844	E	949 770-2610	8695
Arrive-Ai Inc	3999	F	949 221-0166	24042
Aspect Software Inc	7372	E	408 595-5002	24388
Aspen Medical Products	3842	E	949 681-0200	22702
Astea International Inc	7372	E	949 784-5000	24390
Astron Corporation	3677	E	949 458-7277	19320
Astronics Test Systems Inc (HQ)	3825	C	800 722-2528	21725
Atlas Sheet Metal Inc	3444	E	949 600-8787	12493
Axcelis Technologies Inc	3829	B	949 477-5160	22168
Axent Corporation Limited (PA)	2676	F	949 900-4349	5662
B Braun Medical Inc	3841	A	610 691-5400	22353
B Gone Bird Inc	3082	F	949 387-5662	9737
Barrot Corporation	3544	E	949 852-1640	14484
Barton Perreira LLC (PA)	3851	E	949 305-5360	23080
Bauer International Corp	3589	F	714 259-9800	16019
Bausch & Lomb Incorporated	2834	D	949 788-6000	8059
Bausch & Lomb Incorporated	3851	C	949 788-6000	23081
Baxter Healthcare Corporation	3841	C	949 474-6301	22356
Baxter Healthcare Corporation	3841	D	949 250-2500	22357
Baywa RE Solar Projects LLC	3674	E	949 398-3915	18743
Bear Industrial Holdings Inc	3084	E	562 926-3000	9776
Bi-Search International Inc	3679	E	714 258-4500	19468
Bien Air Usa Inc	3843	F	949 477-6050	22860
Bio-Medical Devices Inc	3841	E	949 752-9642	22365
Bio-Medical Devices Intl Inc	3841	F	800 443-3842	22366
Bio-Nutritional RES Group Inc (PA)	2023	D	714 427-6990	607
Bio-RAD Laboratories Inc	3826	B	949 789-0685	21916
Bio-RAD Laboratories Inc	2833	C	949 598-1200	7924
Biodot Inc (PA)	3823	E	949 440-3685	21553
Biolase Inc (PA)	3843	C	949 361-1200	22861
Biomerica Inc (PA)	3841	E	949 645-2111	22374
Biorad Inc	3826	E	949 598-1200	21928
Biosense Webster Inc (HQ)	3845	C	909 839-8500	22954
Biosynthetic Technologies LLC (HQ)	3556	F	949 390-5910	14838
Bivar Inc	3679	E	949 951-8808	19469
Bk Sems Usa Inc	2499	F	949 390-7120	4608
Blazar Communications Corp	2782	F	949 336-7115	7573
Blitzz Technology Inc	3663	E	949 380-7709	18051
Blizzard Entertainment Inc (HQ)	7372	D	949 955-1380	24430
BMC Software Inc	7372	E	949 752-7281	24437
Bonnier Corporation	2721	D	760 707-0100	6113
Bowtie Inc	2721	D	949 855-8822	6115
Braille Signs Inc	3993	E	949 797-1570	23833
Breathe Technologies Inc	3842	E	949 988-7700	22711
Brent Engineering Inc	3531	F	949 679-5630	14148
Brewer Irvine Inc	3089	D	949 474-7000	9992
Broadley-James-Corporation	3823	D	949 829-5555	21555
Bsh Home Appliances Corp	3263	E	949 440-7100	10812
Bsh Home Appliances Corp (DH)	3639	C	949 440-7100	17412
Budget Enterprises Inc	3211	D	949 697-9544	10587
Burkert Contromatic Corp (PA)	3491	E	949 251-1224	13708
Burkert Contromatic Corp	3491	C	949 223-3100	13709
Buy Insta Slim Inc	2326	F	949 263-2301	3097
Cadence Design Systems Inc	7372	E	949 788-6080	24464
Calamp Corp (PA)	3663	B	949 600-5600	18058
Cardlogix	3577	F	949 380-1312	15700
Cartel Industries LLC	3444	E	949 474-3200	12529
Carttronics LLC (HQ)	3699	E	888 696-2278	19924
CBC Distribution Inc	3674	E	949 553-4240	18764
Cbj LP	2721	E	949 833-8373	6126
Central Admxture Phrm Svcs Inc (DH)	2834	F	949 660-2000	8107
Ceradyne Inc (HQ)	3299	B	949 862-9600	11352
Ceradyne Inc	3299	F	949 756-0642	11353

	SIC	EMP	PHONE	ENTRY #
Cercacor Laboratories Inc	3829	F	949 679-6100	22179
Certance LLC (HQ)	3572	B	949 856-7800	15521
Cheek Engineering & Stamping	3469	F	714 832-9480	13181
Chen-Tech Industries Inc (DH)	3841	E	949 855-6716	22403
Choose Manufacturing Co LLC	3672	E	714 327-1698	18448
Chromadex Corporation (PA)	2833	D	949 419-0288	7926
Circuit Assembly Corp (PA)	3678	E	949 855-7887	19376
Cisco Systems Inc	3577	A	408 526-4000	15708
Cisco Systems Inc	3661	B	949 823-1200	17932
Clariphy Communications Inc (HQ)	3674	D	949 861-3074	18769
Clr Analytics Inc	3799	F	949 864-6066	21223
CMS Products Inc	3572	E	714 424-5520	15524
Coast Composites LLC	3599	F	949 455-0665	16392
Coast Composites LLC (DH)	3599	C	949 455-0665	16393
Coastal Cocktails Inc (PA)	2086	F	949 250-3129	2114
Coca-Cola Company	2086	C	949 250-5961	2118
Coda Automotive Inc	3714	E	949 830-7000	20296
Colimatic Usa Inc	3565	F	949 600-6440	15202
Columbia Sanitary Products	3432	E	949 474-0777	12033
Combimatrix Corporation (HQ)	3826	E	949 753-0624	21936
Commerce Velocity LLC	7372	E	949 756-8950	24511
Compugroup Medical Inc	7372	E	949 789-0500	24514
Computer Asssted Mfg Tech Corp	3599	D	949 263-8911	16396
Concept Development Llc	3672	E	949 623-8000	18457
Conexant Systems LLC (HQ)	3674	E	949 483-4600	18780
Connectec Company Inc (PA)	3643	D	949 252-1077	17453
Connective Solutions LLC	3229	F	800 241-2792	10639
Control Systems Intl Inc	3533	E	949 238-4150	14219
Cooper Microelectronics Inc	3674	F	949 553-8352	18784
Core Industries Inc	3949	B	800 228-6635	23544
Corsair Elec Connectors Inc	3678	C	949 833-0273	19383
Cosemi Technologies Inc	3674	F	949 623-9816	18788
Covidien LP	3841	B	949 837-3700	22412
Cp-Carrillo Inc	3592	F	949 567-9000	16146
Cp-Carrillo Inc (DH)	3592	C	949 567-9000	16147
Creaform USA Inc	3577	F	855 939-4446	15723
Critical Io LLC	3577	F	949 553-2200	15724
Cryoport Systems Inc (HQ)	3559	F	949 540-7204	14934
Cs Systems Inc	3577	E	949 475-9100	15725
Ctc Global Corporation (PA)	3643	C	949 428-8500	17457
Cummins Pacific LLC (HQ)	3519	D	949 253-6000	14023
Cybernet Manufacturing Inc	3571	A	949 600-8000	15404
Cycle News Inc (PA)	2711	E	949 863-7082	5819
Cylance Inc (PA)	7372	C	949 375-3380	24542
Cyvex Nutrition Inc	2023	F	949 622-9030	610
Dannier Chemical Inc	2899	F	949 221-8660	9240
Danone Us LLC	2024	B	949 474-9670	665
Data Circle Inc	3674	F	949 260-6569	18798
Daz Inc	3613	F	949 724-8800	17139
Db Studios Inc	3999	E	949 833-0100	24076
De Vries International Inc (PA)	1389	F	949 252-1212	204
Delafoil Holdings Inc (PA)	3444	B	949 752-4580	12555
Dellarobbia Inc (PA)	2512	E	949 251-9532	4770
Diamon Fusion Intl Inc	2899	F	949 388-8000	9241
Digi Print Plus	2752	F	949 770-5000	6785
Dinsmore & Associates Inc	3081	F	714 641-7111	9707
Diversitycomm Inc	2721	F	949 825-5777	6148
DOT Printer Inc (PA)	2752	C	949 474-1100	6793
Double-Take Software Inc (HQ)	7372	E	949 253-6500	24573
Duraled Ltg Technolgies Corp	3641	E	949 753-0162	17425
Duramar Floor Inc	3253	F	949 724-8800	10780
Dyln Lifestyle LLC	3914	F	949 209-9401	23336
Dynalloy Inc	3679	E	714 436-1206	19519
Eaglemetric Corp	3829	F	949 288-3363	22189
Easydial Inc (PA)	3841	D	949 916-5851	22430
Eaton Aerospace LLC	3812	E	949 452-9500	21289
Eaton Industrial Corporation	3812	B	949 425-9700	20805
Eco-Gen Distributors Inc	3621	F	760 712-7460	17190
Edwards Lfsciences Cardiaq LLC	3841	F	949 387-2615	22433
Edwards Lifescience Fing LLC	3999	F	949 250-3480	24089
Edwards Lifesciences	3841	F	949 250-3783	22434
Edwards Lifesciences Corp	3842	E	949 250-3522	22722
Edwards Lifesciences Corp (PA)	3842	A	949 250-2500	22723
Edwards Lifesciences Corp	3842	E	949 553-0611	22724
Edwards Lifesciences US Inc	3845	E	949 250-2500	22974
Ei-Lo Inc	2321	F	949 200-6626	3054
Elafree Inc	3999	F	949 724-9390	24091
Electrolurgy Inc (PA)	3471	E	949 250-4494	13400
Elephant Filmz & Music Inc	3861	F	310 925-8712	23157
Elite Aviation Products Inc	3724	E	949 536-7195	21291
Ellsworth Corporation	2891	F	949 341-9329	9141
EMC Corporation	3571	D	949 794-9999	15410
Emcor Group Inc	3824	E	949 475-6020	21686
EMI Solutions Inc	3679	F	949 206-9960	19532
Endologix Inc (PA)	3841	E	949 595-7200	22439

Employment Codes: A=Over 500 employees, B=251-500,
C=101-250, D=51-100, E=20-50, F=10-19

2019 California
Manufacturers Register

© Mergent Inc. 1-800-342-5647
1395

GEOGRAPHIC

Company	SIC	EMP	PHONE	ENTRY #
Ener-Core Inc (PA)	3621	F	949 616-3300	17193
Ener-Core Power Inc (HQ)	3511	F	949 428-3300	13994
Energy Management Group Inc (PA)	3648	F	949 296-0764	17692
Enevate Corporation	3691	E	949 243-0399	19806
Entrepreneur Media Inc (PA)	2721	D	949 261-2325	6160
Epicor Software Corporation	3577	D	949 585-4000	15739
Equus Products Inc	3825	E	714 424-6779	21748
Eri Economic Research Inst Inc	7372	D	800 627-3697	24625
Ethicon Inc	3842	B	949 581-5799	22730
Evergreen Holdings Inc (PA)	2992	E	949 757-7770	9432
Evolus (DH)	2834	E	949 284-4555	8152
Evolve Dental Technologies Inc	3843	F	949 713-0909	22879
Excel Graphix International	2672	E	949 582-5970	5560
Eyeonics Inc	3851	F	949 788-6000	23099
Ezaki Glico USA Corp	2064	F	949 251-0144	1422
Farstone Technology Inc	3695	C	949 336-4321	19864
FCA US LLC	3714	E	949 450-5111	20334
Federal Custom Cable LLC	3679	E	949 851-3114	19541
Fema Electronics Corporation	3679	E	714 825-0140	19542
Fieldcentrix Inc	7372	E	949 784-5000	24646
Flame & Wax Inc	3999	E	949 752-4000	24095
Flow Control LLC	3561	F	949 608-3900	15062
Fmh Aerospace Corp	3728	D	714 751-1000	20816
Foampro Mfg Inc	3991	D	949 252-0112	23791
Focus Point of Sale	7372	F	949 336-7500	24657
Ford Motor Company	3711	C	949 453-9891	20143
Franklin Covey Co	2741	E	949 788-8102	6487
Freedom Innovations LLC (HQ)	3842	E	949 672-0032	22734
Fringe Studio LLC	3999	F	949 387-9680	24102
Futek Advanced Sensor Tech Inc	3823	C	949 465-0900	21591
Gary Bale Redi-Mix Con Inc	3273	D	949 786-9441	11110
Gas Recovery Systems LLC	1389	F	949 718-1430	215
Gateway Inc	3571	C	949 471-7000	15414
Gateway US Retail Inc	3571	F	949 471-7000	15415
GE Nutrients Inc	2833	F	949 502-5760	7943
Genovation Incorprated	3577	F	949 833-3355	15747
Gensia Sicor Inc (HQ)	2834	A	949 455-4700	8181
Gillette Company	3421	F	949 851-2222	11880
Git America Inc	2835	F	714 433-2180	8479
Global Future City Holding Inc	2834	F	949 769-3550	8194
Global Pcci (gpc) (PA)	3469	C	757 637-9000	13210
Golden State Foods Corp (PA)	2087	E	949 247-8000	2266
Grand Fusion Housewares Inc (PA)	3089	F	888 614-7263	10128
Graphic Packaging Intl Inc	2631	C	949 250-0900	5350
Graphtec America Inc (DH)	3823	E	949 770-6010	21596
Griswold Controls LLC (PA)	3494	C	949 559-6000	13768
H Co Computer Products	3572	F	949 833-3222	15546
Hanger Prsthetcs & Ortho Inc	3842	D	949 863-1951	22744
Harbor Medtech Inc	3841	F	949 679-4800	22468
Haymarket Worldwide Inc	2721	E	949 417-6700	6177
Health Naturals Inc	2834	F	714 259-1821	8205
Hearst Corporation	2721	D	760 707-0100	6179
Henkel Electronic Mtls LLC	2891	C	888 943-6535	9146
HIC Corporation (PA)	2721	F	949 261-1636	6182
Homefacts Management LLC	2741	F	949 502-8300	6500
Horiba Instruments Inc (DH)	3826	C	949 250-4811	21969
Horiba International Corp (HQ)	3829	D	949 250-4811	22215
Hormel Foods Corp Svcs LLC	2013	E	949 753-5350	494
I Amira Grand Foods Inc (PA)	2044	F	949 852-4468	1084
I Source Technical Svcs Inc	3679	F	949 453-1500	19572
I-5 Publishing LLC (PA)	2721	C	949 855-8822	6187
I-Flow LLC	3841	A	800 448-3569	22473
Iconn Inc	3678	F	949 297-8448	19396
Igo Inc (PA)	3663	F	888 205-0093	18128
Illuminate Education Inc	7372	F	951 739-0186	24751
Image Distribution Services (PA)	2752	F	949 754-9000	6873
Immport Therapeutics Inc	3844	F	949 679-4068	22934
Inari Medical Inc	3841	E	949 600-8433	22478
Incipio Technologies Inc (PA)	3577	D	949 250-4929	15759
Infinite Electronics Inc (HQ)	3679	E	949 261-1920	19576
Infinite Electronics Intl Inc (DH)	3678	C	949 261-1920	19397
Informa Business Media Inc	2741	E	949 252-1146	6502
Innova Electronics Corporation	3714	E	714 241-6800	20372
Innovative Tech & Engrg Inc	3577	F	949 955-2501	15761
Integrated Polymer Inds Inc	2891	E	949 788-1050	9151
Integrity Security Svcs Inc	3699	F	949 756-0690	19983
Intel Corporation	3674	E	408 765-8080	18912
Interctive Dsplay Slutions Inc	3679	E	949 727-9493	19582
Intermed Video Tech Inc	3651	F	203 270-9100	17818
International Rectifier Inc (PA)	3674	C	949 453-1008	18922
International Sensor Tech Inc	3829	F	949 452-9000	22218
International Vitamin Corp (PA)	2834	B	949 664-5500	8228
Interntnal Plymr Solutions Inc	3491	F	949 458-3731	13720
Interpore Cross Intl Inc (DH)	3842	D	949 453-3200	22754
Interventional Spine Inc	3841	F	949 472-0006	22486
INX Prints Inc	2262	D	949 660-9190	2903
Iomic Inc	3069	F	714 564-1600	9630
Irvine Electronics Inc	3672	D	949 250-0315	18509
Island Color Inc	2752	E	714 352-5888	6897
ITT Corporation	3625	B	714 557-4700	17279
J & J Electronics LLC	3646	E	949 455-4460	17619
J F Fong Inc	3841	E	949 553-8885	22499
Janteq Corp (PA)	3663	E	949 215-2603	18137
Jenavalve Technology Inc	3845	E	949 396-7555	22995
Jim Beam Brands Co	2085	F	949 200-7200	2072
Jonathan Engnred Slutions Corp (PA)	3429	E	714 665-4400	11966
Joseph Company International	3411	F	949 474-2200	11859
Jsn Industries Inc	3089	D	949 458-0050	10173
Jsn Packaging Products Inc	3082	D	949 458-0050	9739
Jump Start Juice Bar	2037	F	949 754-3120	955
Justenough Software Corp Inc (HQ)	7372	E	949 706-5400	24821
Karma Automotive LLC (DH)	3711	B	714 723-3247	20154
Kelley Blue Book Co Inc (DH)	2721	C	949 770-7704	6199
Kelmscott Communications LLC	2752	F	949 475-1900	6920
Knight LLC (HQ)	3569	C	949 595-4800	15337
Kofax Limited (DH)	7372	C	949 783-1000	24837
Kraft Heinz Foods Company	2032	C	949 250-4080	765
Kronos Incorporated	7372	D	800 580-7374	24842
Kuraray America Inc	2821	F	949 476-9600	7852
L A Supply Co	2759	E	949 470-9900	7371
L T Litho & Printing Co	2752	E	949 863-1340	6935
La Jolla Sport USA Inc (HQ)	2329	D	855 554-5930	3171
Lantronix Inc (PA)	3577	C	949 453-3990	15784
Lasergraphics Inc	3577	F	949 753-8282	15785
Lens Technology I LLC	3827	F	714 690-6470	22097
Lexmark International Inc	3577	F	714 368-0015	15789
Lg-Ericsson USA Inc	3661	E	877 828-2673	17961
Lifetime Memory Products Inc	3672	E	949 794-9000	18520
Links Medical Products Inc (PA)	3841	E	949 753-0001	22511
Linmarr Associates Inc	3562	F	949 215-5466	15108
Logitech Inc	3577	E	510 795-8500	15793
Lombard Medical Tech Inc (HQ)	3841	E	949 379-3750	22514
Lost International LLC	2329	F	949 600-6950	3176
Lps Agency Sales and Posting	2759	F	714 247-7500	7390
LSI Corporation	3674	E	800 372-2447	18970
Lspace America LLC	2331	E	949 596-8726	3255
Lubrication Scientifics Inc	3491	F	714 557-0664	13724
Lubrication Scientifics LLC	3569	F	714 557-0664	15339
Luna Sciences Corporation	3645	F	949 225-0000	17545
M K Products Inc	3548	D	949 798-1425	14731
M P C Industrial Products Inc	3471	E	949 863-0106	13448
Mahivr	2674	E	949 559-5470	5645
Mangia Inc	2033	F	949 581-1274	825
Marko Products Inc (PA)	3086	D	800 862-7561	9869
Maruchan Inc (HQ)	2099	B	949 789-2300	2597
Maruchan Inc	2098	C	949 789-2300	2429
Marukome USA Inc	2099	F	949 863-0110	2599
Marvin Test Solutions Inc	3825	D	949 263-2222	21800
Masimo Corporation	3845	E	949 297-7000	23003
Masimo Corporation	3845	E	949 297-7000	23004
Masimo Corporation (PA)	3845	E	949 297-7000	23005
Masimo Semiconductor Inc	3674	E	603 595-8900	18983
Meade Instruments Corp	3827	D	949 451-1450	22105
Medata Inc (PA)	7372	D	714 918-1310	24895
Medennium Inc (PA)	3851	E	949 789-9000	23109
Media Nation Enterprises LLC (PA)	3993	E	888 502-8222	23923
Mediatek USA Inc	3571	F	408 526-1899	15452
Medical Data Recovery Inc	7372	F	949 251-0073	24897
Medifarm So Cal Inc	3523	E	855 447-6967	14084
Medtronic Inc	3845	F	949 486-9973	23013
Medtronic Inc	3845	E	949 837-3700	23014
Mega Brands America Inc (HQ)	3944	D	949 727-9009	23446
Meggitt (orange County) Inc (HQ)	3829	B	949 493-8181	22233
Meggitt Defense Systems Inc	3728	C	949 465-7700	20883
Meguiars Inc (HQ)	2842	E	949 752-8000	8655
Menlo Microsystems Inc	3674	E	949 903-2369	18992
Mentor Graphics Corporation	7372	F	949 790-3200	24902
Mentor Worldwide LLC (DH)	3842	C	800 636-8678	22772
Micro Therapeutics Inc (HQ)	3841	F	949 837-3700	22539
Microsoft Corporation	7372	C	949 263-3000	24915
Microwave Dynamics	3663	F	949 679-7788	18183
Midas Technology Inc	3651	F	818 937-4774	17834
Min-E-Con LLC	3678	D	949 250-0087	19401
Mission Hockey Company (PA)	3949	F	949 585-9390	23620
Mitsubishi Chemical Crbn Fbr	2891	C	800 929-5671	9156
Motorsport Aftrmrket Group Inc (DH)	3751	F	949 440-5500	21130
Mri Interventions	3841	F	949 900-6833	22550
Multi-Fineline Electronix Inc (HQ)	3672	A	949 453-6800	18533
N H Research Incorporated	3825	D	949 474-3900	21810
Nanovea Inc (PA)	3826	E	949 461-9292	21999

	SIC	EMP	PHONE	ENTRY #
National Medical Products Inc	3089	F	949 768-1147	10231
Neomend Inc	3841	D	949 783-3300	22551
Netaphor Software Inc	7372	F	949 470-7955	24950
Netlist Inc (PA)	3674	D	949 435-0025	19038
Netwrix Corporation (PA)	7372	E	888 638-9749	24957
Neurostructures Inc	3842	F	800 352-6103	22777
Newmatic Engineering Inc (PA)	3822	E	415 824-2664	21518
Newport Corporation (HQ)	3821	B	949 863-3144	21482
Newport Energy LLC	1382	E	408 230-7545	142
Nexgen Pharma Inc (PA)	2834	C	949 863-0340	8300
Nexgen Pharma Inc	2834	E	949 260-3702	8301
Nexgen Pharma Inc	2834	F	949 863-0340	8302
Nexsun Electronics Inc	3679	E	949 680-4725	19660
Nextgen Healthcare Inc (PA)	7372	C	949 255-2600	24964
Ngd Systems Inc	3572	E	949 510-6327	15575
NGK Spark Plugs (usa) Inc	3694	E	949 580-2639	19840
Nihon Kohden Orangemed Inc	3845	F	949 502-6448	23027
Nimbus Data Inc	3572	E	650 276-4500	15577
Nitto Avecia Pharma Svcs Inc	2834	E	949 462-0814	8306
Nixsys Inc	3571	E	714 435-9610	15466
Novus Therapeutics Inc	2834	F	617 225-4305	8310
Ntrust Infotech Inc	7372	D	562 207-1600	24973
Numecent Inc	7372	E	949 833-2800	24975
Nutrawise Health & Beauty Corp (PA)	2834	E	949 900-2400	8311
Nxp Usa Inc	3674	E	949 399-4000	19050
Ocpc Inc	2752	D	949 475-1900	7000
Oct Medical Imaging Inc	3841	F	949 701-6656	22565
Oddbox Holdings Inc	2759	F	714 602-8864	7417
Old An Inc	3999	E	949 263-1400	24194
Omni Optical Products Inc (PA)	3829	F	714 634-5700	22241
Omnitron Systems Tech Inc	3577	D	949 250-6510	15816
Onset Medical Corporation	3841	E	949 716-1100	22570
Optima Technology Corporation	3577	B	949 253-5768	15820
Oracle Systems Corporation	7372	D	949 224-1000	25035
Oracle Systems Corporation	7372	B	949 623-9460	25036
Orange Circle Studio Corp	2759	E	949 727-0800	7422
Orange Coast Kommunications	2721	E	949 862-1133	6226
Orgain Inc	2086	F	949 930-0039	2159
Pace Punches Inc	3544	D	949 428-2750	14554
Pacific Handy Cutter Inc	3423	E	714 662-1033	11905
Paciolan LLC (HQ)	7372	D	949 476-2050	25045
Panoramic Software Corporation	7372	F	877 558-8526	25047
Paramount Dairy Inc (PA)	2026	E	949 265-8077	733
Parker-Hannifin Corporation	3724	B	949 833-3000	20673
Parker-Hannifin Corporation	3728	D	216 896-2663	20904
Parker-Hannifin Corporation	3728	E	949 833-3000	20905
Parker-Hannifin Corporation	3594	C	949 833-3000	16171
Parker-Hannifin Corporation	3728	A	949 833-3000	20906
Passy-Muir Inc	3842	F	949 833-8255	22790
Passy-Muir Inc (PA)	3842	F	949 833-8255	22791
Patron Solutions LLC	7372	C	949 823-1700	25050
Paydivvy Inc	7372	F	949 313-3451	25052
PCC Rollmet Inc	3339	D	949 221-5333	11549
Performance Sealing Inc	3053	F	714 662-5918	9548
Phiaro Incorporated	3999	F	949 727-1261	24210
Philip Morris USA Inc	2111	D	949 453-3500	2707
Plasto Tech International Inc	3089	E	949 458-1880	10293
Positex Inc	3721	F	307 201-0601	20618
Positive Energy Beverages LLC	2086	F	949 735-6080	2179
Ppst Inc (PA)	3679	E	800 421-1921	19687
Precise Technology Inc	3674	F	949 453-1997	19084
Presbibio LLC	3851	E	949 502-7010	23117
Princeton Technology Inc	3577	F	949 851-7776	15825
Printery Inc	2752	F	949 757-1930	7044
Printronix LLC (PA)	3577	C	714 368-2300	15827
Printronix Holding Corp	3577	C	714 368-2300	15828
Prism Software Corporation	7372	E	949 855-3100	25080
Pro-Dex Inc (PA)	3841	D	949 769-3200	22588
Pro-Mart Industries Inc (PA)	2392	E	949 428-7700	3743
Professnal Rprgraphic Svcs Inc	2759	E	949 748-5400	7450
Proshot Investors LLC	3663	F	949 586-9500	18226
Qlogic LLC (DH)	3674	C	949 389-6000	19093
Qpe Inc	2754	F	949 263-0381	7210
Qsi 2011 Inc (PA)	7372	F	949 855-6885	25093
Qualontime Corporation	3599	F	714 523-4751	16874
Quantum Corporation	3572	F	949 856-7800	15590
Quilting House	2392	E	949 476-7090	3744
Race Technologies LLC	3714	F	714 438-1118	20434
Racer Media & Marketing Inc	2721	F	949 417-6700	6242
Rainbow Magnetics Incorporated	2752	E	714 540-4777	7071
Rami Designs Inc	3446	E	949 588-8288	12885
Red Mountain Inc	3822	F	949 595-4475	21524
Redcom LLC (HQ)	3861	D	949 206-7900	23192
Research Way LI LLC	2834	F	608 830-6300	8361
Reverse Medical Corporation	3841	F	949 215-0660	22604
Reyes Coca-Cola Bottling LLC (PA)	2086	B	213 744-8616	2186
Rockwell Collins Inc	3812	D	714 929-3000	21415
Rogerson Aircraft Corporation (PA)	3812	C	949 660-0666	21418
Rose Chem Intl - USA Corp	2834	E	678 510-8864	8369
Royal Adhesives & Sealants LLC	2891	F	949 863-1499	9169
RR Donnelley & Sons Company	2759	E	949 852-1933	7474
RR Donnelley & Sons Company	2761	E	949 476-0505	7553
Rrds Inc (PA)	3827	F	949 284-6239	22128
S-Energy America Inc (HQ)	3674	F	949 281-7897	19131
Saeshin America Inc	3843	E	949 825-6925	22907
Sage Interior Inc	2434	F	949 654-0184	4348
Sage Software Holdings Inc (HQ)	7372	B	866 530-7243	25139
Sampling International LLC	2399	F	949 305-5333	3963
SDC Technologies Inc (DH)	3479	E	714 939-8300	13656
Sdi LLC	3599	E	949 351-1866	16935
Seagra Technology Inc (PA)	3577	F	949 419-6796	15847
Seal Science Inc (PA)	3053	D	949 253-3130	9556
Sega of America Inc (DH)	3999	E	415 806-0169	24238
Sekai Electronics Inc (PA)	3663	F	949 783-5740	18249
Sensoronix Inc	3674	F	949 528-0906	19148
Seyi - America Inc	3542	F	909 839-1151	14455
Sfc Communications Inc	3822	F	949 553-8566	21528
Shye West Inc (PA)	3993	F	949 486-4598	23960
Sierra Monolithics Inc	3812	F	949 269-4400	21430
Signature Control Systems Inc	3523	D	949 580-3640	14104
Silicon Energy LLC (PA)	3433	F	360 618-6500	12084
Skyworks Solutions Inc	3679	D	949 231-3000	19726
Smart Modular Technologies Inc	3674	E	949 753-0117	19174
Socialwise Inc	2741	F	949 861-3900	6581
Solar Turbines Incorporated	3511	F	949 450-0870	14006
Solarflare Communications Inc	3571	C	949 581-6830	15488
Sonnet Technologies Inc	3699	E	949 587-3500	20073
Soundcoat Company Inc	3625	E	631 242-2200	17311
Source Scientific LLC	3841	E	949 231-5096	22627
South Coast Baking LLC (HQ)	2052	D	949 851-9654	1382
South Coast Mold Inc	3544	F	949 253-2000	14571
Sparton Irvine LLC	3679	E	949 855-6625	19733
Specialty Rock Inc	1442	F	909 334-2265	382
Spectrum Scientific Inc	3827	F	949 260-9900	22137
Spellbound Development Group	3851	F	949 474-8577	23123
St John Knits Inc (DH)	2339	C	949 863-1171	3504
St John Knits Intl Inc (HQ)	2339	C	949 863-1171	3505
St John Knits Intl Inc	2253	B	949 399-8200	2855
St Jude Medical LLC	2834	E	949 769-5000	8391
Staco Systems Inc (HQ)	3613	D	949 297-8700	17166
Starix Technology Inc	3663	E	949 387-8120	18263
Stason Pharmaceuticals Inc (PA)	2834	E	949 380-0752	8395
Stec Inc (HQ)	3572	B	415 222-9996	15612
Steven Rhoades Ceramic Designs	3269	F	949 250-1076	10836
Stm Networks Inc	3663	E	949 273-6800	18264
Stracon Inc	3699	F	949 851-2288	20082
Strategy Companion Corp	7372	D	714 460-8398	25228
Streamline Avionics Inc	3612	E	949 861-8151	17124
STS Instruments Inc	3825	F	580 223-4773	21856
Suncore Inc	3674	E	949 450-0054	19199
Sunsports LP	3131	C	949 273-6202	10477
Super Color Digital LLC (PA)	2759	C	949 622-0010	7504
Support Technologies Inc (PA)	7372	F	949 442-2957	25237
Swift Health Systems Inc	3843	E	877 258-8677	22911
Syneron Inc (DH)	3845	D	866 259-6661	23056
Tagtrends Inc	2269	F	714 903-7792	2920
Talon Therapeutics Inc	2834	C	949 788-6700	8404
Target Technology Company LLC (PA)	3695	F	949 788-0909	19884
Taylor Graphics Inc	2759	F	949 752-5200	7510
Tb Kawashima Usa Inc	2399	F	714 389-5310	3968
Tc Communications Inc	3669	E	949 852-1972	18370
Techko Kobot Inc	3635	F	949 380-7300	17409
Tekia Inc	3851	E	949 699-1300	23129
Tempo Lighting Inc	3646	E	949 442-1601	17650
Teradyne Inc	3825	D	949 453-0900	21868
Teridian Semiconductor Corp (DH)	3674	D	714 508-8800	19223
Terra Tech Corp (PA)	3523	E	855 447-6967	14108
Terran Orbital Corporation (PA)	3761	E	212 496-2300	21172
Tetra Tech Ec Inc	3826	E	949 809-5000	22029
Teva Parenteral Medicines Inc	2834	A	949 455-4700	8411
Teva Pharmaceuticals Usa Inc	2834	E	949 457-2828	8412
Thales Avionics	3728	E	949 381-3033	20948
Thales Avionics Inc	3728	C	949 790-2500	20949
Thermaprint Corp	3861	E	949 583-0800	23203
Thompson Aerospace Inc (PA)	3724	F	949 264-1600	20683
Timevalue Software	7372	F	949 727-1800	25279
Tomorrows Look Inc	2261	D	949 596-8400	2898
Toshiba Amer Info Systems Inc	3571	D	949 587-6378	15497
Toshiba America Electronic (DH)	3651	B	949 462-7700	17868
Trantronics Inc	3672	E	949 553-1234	18627

Employment Codes: A=Over 500 employees, B=251-500,
C=101-250, D=51-100, E=20-50, F=10-19

2019 California
Manufacturers Register

© Mergent Inc. 1-800-342-5647
1397

GEOGRAPHIC

Company	SIC	EMP	PHONE	ENTRY #
Tricom Research Inc	3663	D	949 250-6024	18291
Trimedyne Inc (PA)	3845	E	949 951-3800	23063
Tropitone Furniture Co Inc (HQ)	2514	E	949 595-2000	4846
Truabutment Inc	3843	D	714 956-1488	22919
TSS Software Corporation	7372	E	443 321-5600	25299
Turn-Luckily International Inc	3577	F	949 465-0200	15876
Tylerco Inc	3645	E	949 769-3991	17565
Tyvak Nn-Satellite Systems Inc	3761	D	949 753-1020	21174
Ubm LLC	2721	D	415 947-6770	6277
Ultimate Ears Consumer LLC	3842	E	949 502-8340	22836
Upstanding LLC	7372	C	949 788-9900	25317
Urovant Sciences Inc (PA)	2834	E	949 226-6029	8427
US Direct LLC	2759	F	949 491-3342	7531
USA Fire Glass	3231	F	949 302-7728	10739
USA Vision Systems Inc (HQ)	3699	E	949 583-1519	20097
Ushio America Inc	3646	E	714 236-8600	17654
Valeant Pharmaceuticals Intl	2834	F	800 548-5100	8429
Vantari Medical LLC	3829	F	949 783-5300	22294
Variable Image Printing	2752	F	949 296-1444	7165
Veezee Inc	2331	E	949 265-0800	3286
Vertimass LLC	2869	F	949 417-1396	9049
Vertiv Corporation	3823	F	949 457-3600	21675
Vibes Audio LLC	3651	F	949 769-6806	17877
Viking Access Systems LLC	3699	F	949 753-1280	20102
Viking Products Inc	3545	E	949 379-5100	14693
Vinotemp International Corp (PA)	2519	D	310 886-3332	4923
Visage Software Inc	7372	F	949 614-0759	25334
Vision Quest Industries Inc (PA)	3842	D	949 261-6382	22842
Vizio Inc (PA)	3651	C	949 428-2525	17878
Vti Instruments Corporation (HQ)	3699	E	949 955-1894	20106
Wahlco Inc	3599	C	714 979-7300	17048
Wanada Investments LLC	7372	E	818 292-8627	25342
Waterhealth International Inc	3589	C	949 716-5790	16135
Waters Technologies Corp	3826	F	949 474-4320	22049
Webcloak LLC	7372	F	949 417-9940	25343
West Coast Consulting LLC (PA)	7372	C	949 250-4102	25346
West Coast Consulting LLC	7372	E	949 336-7700	25347
Western Prtg & Graphics LLC (PA)	2752	E	714 532-3946	7182
Western Telematic Inc	3577	E	949 586-9950	15885
Westside Resources Inc	3843	E	800 944-3939	22925
Window Solutions	3861	E	650 349-2499	23212
Xlsoft Corporation (PA)	7372	F	949 453-2781	25364
Yaskawa America Inc	3569	E	949 263-2640	15377
Zadara Storage Inc	3572	E	949 251-0360	15626
Zo Skin Health Inc (PA)	2844	D	949 988-7524	8871
Zygo Corporation	3827	E	714 918-7433	22152

IRWINDALE, CA - Los Angeles County

Company	SIC	EMP	PHONE	ENTRY #
A & M Engineering Inc	3599	D	626 813-2020	16186
Able Card LLC	2752	E	626 969-1888	6635
Able Card Corporation LLC	2759	D	626 969-1888	7219
Aero Seating Technologies LLC (HQ)	2531	E	626 286-1130	5004
Alpha Printing & Graphics Inc	2752	E	626 851-9800	6654
American Capacitor Corporation	3675	E	626 814-4444	19290
Arrow Engineering	3599	E	626 960-2806	16283
Bimeda Inc	2834	F	626 815-1680	8074
Bsst LLC	3714	E	626 593-4500	20274
Cal Springs LLC	2759	D	562 943-5599	7261
California Community News LLC (HQ)	2711	B	626 472-5297	5787
California Custom Fruits (PA)	2087	D	626 736-4130	2250
Calportland Company	3241	D	626 691-2596	10750
Chem Arrow Corp	2992	E	626 358-2255	9427
Clark - Pacific Corporation	3272	D	626 962-8751	10903
Cni Mfg Inc	3599	E	626 962-6646	16391
Connor J Inc	3714	E	626 358-3820	21739
Consolidated Container Co LLC	3089	E	626 856-2100	10037
Davis Wire Corporation (HQ)	3315	C	626 969-7651	11435
Decore-Ative Specialties	2431	C	626 960-7731	4141
Emdin International Corp	3843	F	626 813-3740	22876
Entreprise Arms Inc	3484	E	626 962-4692	13687
Fine Ptch Elctrnic Assmbly LLC	3672	E	626 337-2800	18480
Food Makers Bakery Eqp Inc	3556	E	626 358-1343	14847
Gentherm Incorporated	3714	F	626 593-4500	20349
Halcyon Microelectronics Inc	3674	F	626 814-4688	18868
Hanson Aggregates LLC	3273	E	626 358-1811	11117
Htk Automotive USA Corp	3694	F	888 998-9366	19834
Huy Fong Foods Inc	2033	E	626 286-8328	807
J & R Taylor Bros Assoc Inc	2047	D	626 334-9301	1115
J C S Volks Machine	3714	F	626 338-6003	20374
JE Thomson & Company LLC	3537	F	626 334-7190	14330
Johnson & Johnson	3842	B	909 839-8650	22759
Jonell Oil Corporation	2992	E	626 303-4691	9440
Kifuki USA Co Inc (HQ)	2015	D	626 334-8090	545
Km Printing Production Inc	2752	F	626 821-0008	6927
Kong Veterinary Products	3841	F	626 633-0077	22505
Legacy Vulcan LLC	1442	E	626 856-6150	366

Company	SIC	EMP	PHONE	ENTRY #
Legacy Vulcan LLC	1442	F	626 856-6153	368
Legacy Vulcan LLC	2951	E	626 633-4258	9388
Legacy Vulcan LLC	3272	F	626 856-6148	10950
Legacy Vulcan LLC	1442	F	626 856-6143	373
Martin Engineering Co Inc	3556	F	626 960-5153	14869
Matheson Tri-Gas Inc	2813	E	626 334-2905	7701
Mee Industries Inc (PA)	3585	F	626 359-4550	15970
Merestone Merchandise Corp	2844	F	626 337-6262	8794
Millercoors LLC	2082	D	626 969-6811	1612
Nellson Nutraceutical Inc (PA)	2064	B	626 812-6522	1445
Nkok Inc	3944	F	626 330-1988	23453
Pacific Panel Products Corp	2435	F	626 851-0444	4381
Pertronix Inc	3694	F	909 599-5955	19844
Q & B Foods Inc (DH)	2035	F	626 334-8090	929
Ready Pac Foods Inc (HQ)	2099	B	626 856-8686	2650
Roma Moulding Inc	2499	E	626 334-2539	4648
Schamas Mfg Coinc	3531	E	626 334-6870	14189
Seaboard Envelope Co Inc	2677	E	626 960-4559	5677
Sierra Alloys Company	3463	D	626 969-6711	13129
Spragues Rock and Sand Company (PA)	3273	E	626 445-2125	11184
Stratus Coml Cooking Eqp Inc	3469	F	626 969-7041	13282
Trio Engineered Products Inc (HQ)	3531	E	626 851-3966	14195
Universal Dynamics Inc	1382	F	626 480-0035	157
US Toyo Fan Corporation (HQ)	3564	E	626 338-1111	15183
V Himark (usa) Inc	2891	F	626 305-5766	9178
Vulcan Materials Company	1442	F	626 334-4913	389
Woojin Is America Inc	3743	F	626 386-0101	21085

ISLETON, CA - Sacramento County

Company	SIC	EMP	PHONE	ENTRY #
Ethanol Energy Systems LLC	2869	F	916 777-5654	9005

JACKSON, CA - Amador County

Company	SIC	EMP	PHONE	ENTRY #
Bradford Canning Stahl Inc	3599	F	209 257-1535	16331
Buy and Sell Press Inc	2741	F	209 223-3333	6455

JAMESTOWN, CA - Tuolumne County

Company	SIC	EMP	PHONE	ENTRY #
Fray Logging Inc	2411	E	209 984-5968	3989
M & M Sportswear Manufacturing	2253	F	209 984-5632	2848
Sierra Resource Management Inc	2411	E	209 984-1146	4012

JAMUL, CA - San Diego County

Company	SIC	EMP	PHONE	ENTRY #
Mikes Metal Works Inc	3312	F	619 440-8804	11407
P & E Rubber Processing Inc	3069	E	760 241-2643	9651

JUNCTION CITY, CA - Trinity County

Company	SIC	EMP	PHONE	ENTRY #
Eagle Rock Incorporated	3531	F	530 623-4444	14164

JURUPA VALLEY, CA - Riverside County

Company	SIC	EMP	PHONE	ENTRY #
Brothers Machine & Tool Inc	3542	E	951 361-9454	14432
Brothers Machine & Tool Inc (PA)	3542	E	951 361-2909	14433
Philips North America LLC	3645	E	909 574-1800	17554
Recon Services Inc	3443	F	951 682-1400	12413
Safeland Industrial Supply Inc (PA)	3315	F	909 786-1967	11455
Sports Hoop Inc	3949	F	626 387-6027	23661

KELSEYVILLE, CA - Lake County

Company	SIC	EMP	PHONE	ENTRY #
Lake County Walnut Inc	2068	F	707 279-1200	1495
Steele Wines Inc	2084	E	707 279-9475	1990
Stokes Ladders Inc	3499	F	707 279-4306	13975

KENSINGTON, CA - Alameda County

Company	SIC	EMP	PHONE	ENTRY #
Berkeley Scientific	3679	F	510 525-1945	19466
Sempervirens Group	2879	F	510 847-0801	9111
Union Publications Inc	2721	F	510 525-6300	6280

KENWOOD, CA - Sonoma County

Company	SIC	EMP	PHONE	ENTRY #
Kunde Enterprises Inc	2084	D	707 833-5501	1844
Muscardini Cellars LLC	2084	F	707 933-9305	1890
Overlook Vineyards LLC (DH)	2084	F	707 833-0053	1909
Pernod Ricard Usa LLC	2084	D	707 833-5891	1921
S L Cellars	2084	F	707 833-5070	1962
Treasury Wine Estates Americas	2084	E	707 833-4134	2024

KERMAN, CA - Fresno County

Company	SIC	EMP	PHONE	ENTRY #
Baker Commodities Inc	2077	E	559 237-4320	1520
California Mfg & Engrg Co LLC	3531	C	559 842-1500	14150
Jay Bellach Custom Harvesting	3599	F	559 846-9785	16616
Pinnacle Agriculture Dist Inc	3523	F	559 842-4601	14093
Purity Organics Inc	2033	E	559 842-5600	850
Salwasser Inc	2034	D	559 843-2882	891

KING CITY, CA - Monterey County

Company	SIC	EMP	PHONE	ENTRY #
Casey Printing Inc	2752	E	831 385-3221	6722
Delicato Vineyards	2084	F	831 385-7587	1723
King Rustler	2711	F	831 385-4880	5898
Montery Wine Company LLC	2084	F	831 386-1100	1885
South County Newspapers LLC	2711	F	831 385-4880	6052
Wm J Clark Trucking Svc Inc	1442	F	831 385-4000	393

Mergent email: customerrelations@mergent.com
1398

2019 California
Manufacturers Register

(P-0000) Products & Services Section entry number
(PA)=Parent Co (HQ)=Headquarters (DH)=Div Headquarters

	SIC	EMP	PHONE	ENTRY #

KINGSBURG, CA - Fresno County

	SIC	EMP	PHONE	ENTRY #
Cencal Cnc Inc	3599	E	559 897-8706	16370
Del Monte Foods Inc	2033	D	559 419-9214	793
Foster Commodities	2048	E	559 897-1081	1131
Foster Farms LLC	2048	E	559 897-1081	1132
Guardian Industries LLC	3211	B	559 891-8867	10595
Guardian Industries Corp	3211	D	559 891-8867	10596
Guardian Industries Corp	3211	F	559 638-3588	10597
Kingsburg Cabinet Inc	2434	F	559 897-7716	4320
Kingsburg Cultivator Inc	3523	F	559 897-3662	14078
Nutrius LLC	2048	E	559 897-5862	1152
Vie-Del Company	2084	E	559 896-3065	2039

KNEELAND, CA - Humboldt County

	SIC	EMP	PHONE	ENTRY #
J & S Stakes Inc	2499	F	707 668-5647	4625

KORBEL, CA - Humboldt County

	SIC	EMP	PHONE	ENTRY #
Simpson Timber Company	2421	F	707 668-4566	4066

LA CANADA, CA - Los Angeles County

	SIC	EMP	PHONE	ENTRY #
Foothill Instruments LLC	3829	F	818 952-5600	22202
Majestic Garlic Inc	2035	F	951 677-0555	921

LA CANADA FLINTRIDGE, CA - Los Angeles County

	SIC	EMP	PHONE	ENTRY #
Data Storm Inc	3699	F	818 352-4994	19942
Los Angles Tmes Cmmnctions LLC	2711	F	818 790-8774	5925

LA CRESCENTA, CA - Los Angeles County

	SIC	EMP	PHONE	ENTRY #
Accurate Screen Processing	2396	F	818 957-3965	3872
Air Transport Manufacturing	3444	F	818 504-3300	12465
Balita Media Inc	2711	E	818 552-4503	5773
Brains Out Media Inc	7372	F	818 296-1036	24448
Casa Mexico Enterprises Inc	2759	F	888 411-9530	7265
D X Communications Inc	3663	F	323 256-3000	18082
Faith Knight Inc	3911	F	213 488-1569	23263
Futureflite Inc	2531	F	818 957-0316	5014
RC Apparel Inc	2396	F	818 541-1994	3915
Wheeler & Reeder Inc	3535	F	323 268-4163	14292

LA HABRA, CA - Orange County

	SIC	EMP	PHONE	ENTRY #
American Acrylic Display Inc	3993	F	714 738-7990	23814
Auro Pharmaceuticals Inc	2834	F	562 352-9630	8051
Auro Pharmacies Inc	2834	E	562 352-9630	8052
B&W Custom Restaurant Eqp	3589	E	714 578-0332	16016
Candamar Designs Inc	3999	E	714 871-6190	24059
Castor Engineering Inc	3365	F	562 690-4036	11727
Ckd Industries Inc	3469	F	714 871-5600	13183
Cryopacific Incorporated	3999	F	562 697-7904	24071
Dp Print Services Inc	2269	F	310 600-5250	2910
Frost Bite Novelties Inc	2024	F	714 680-0030	673
J C Ford Company	3556	D	714 871-7361	14861
JB Industries Corp	3469	F	562 691-2105	13231
Jcr Aircraft Deburring LLC	3541	E	714 870-4427	14384
K&K World Inc	2599	F	714 234-6237	5241
Keyin Inc	3695	F	562 690-3888	19868
La Habra Cabinet Inc	2434	C	562 691-0681	4324
La Habra Plating Co Inc	3471	F	562 694-2704	13442
Marsal Packaging & Rfrgn	3585	F	714 812-6775	15969
Mmp Sheet Metal Inc	3444	F	562 691-1055	12682
Orbo Corporation	2531	E	562 806-6171	5024
Plastic Tops Inc (PA)	2542	F	714 738-8128	5162
Precision Forming Group LLC	3542	F	562 501-1985	14453
R & J Rule & Die Inc	2675	F	562 945-7535	5656
Ruhe Corporation (PA)	2096	C	714 777-8321	2402
Shepard Bros Inc (PA)	3589	C	562 697-1366	16107
Stop-Look Sign Co Intl Inc	3081	F	562 690-7576	9729
VIP Rubber Company Inc (PA)	3069	C	714 774-7635	9691

LA HABRA HEIGHTS, CA - Orange County

	SIC	EMP	PHONE	ENTRY #
Finn Industries Inc	2631	E	909 930-1500	5348
Flexo-Technologies Inc	2893	E	626 444-2595	9193
Viet Hung Paris Inc	2013	F	562 944-4919	534

LA HONDA, CA - San Mateo County

	SIC	EMP	PHONE	ENTRY #
Brodhead Steel Products Co (PA)	3446	E	650 871-8251	12840

LA JOLLA, CA - San Diego County

	SIC	EMP	PHONE	ENTRY #
Agilent Technologies Inc	3825	B	858 373-6300	21710
Agilent Technologies Inc	3825	B	858 373-6300	21716
Aira Tech Corp	7372	F	858 880-4454	24341
Altium LLC	7372	D	800 544-4186	24354
Ambrx Inc	2834	D	858 875-2400	8021
Aristamd Inc	7372	F	858 750-4777	24384
Auspex Pharmaceuticals Inc	2834	E	858 558-2400	8053
Berenice 2 AM Corp	2024	F	858 255-8693	657
Carbon Recycling Incorporated	2869	F	619 491-9200	8995
Commnexus San Diego	3674	F	888 926-3987	18774
Cv Sciences Inc	2834	E	619 546-8112	8130

	SIC	EMP	PHONE	ENTRY #
Dm Luxury LLC	2759	B	858 366-9721	7302
Dow Theory Letters Inc	2721	F	858 454-0481	6150
Edgewave	7372	D	800 782-3762	24590
Flexaust Company Inc (HQ)	3599	E	619 232-8429	16503
Froglanders La Jolla	2026	F	858 459-3764	725
Howardsoft	7372	F	858 454-0121	24739
International RES Dev Corp Nev (PA)	3694	F	858 488-9900	19835
Kyowa Hakko Kirin Cal Inc (DH)	2834	E	858 952-7000	8250
Madcap Software Inc (PA)	7372	F	858 320-0387	24875
Medicinova Inc (PA)	2834	F	858 373-1500	8272
Metabasis Therapeutics Inc	2834	E	858 550-7500	8281
Muller Company	3842	F	858 587-9955	22775
Orexigen Therapeutics Inc (HQ)	2834	D	858 875-8600	8320
Positive Publishing Inc	2741	F	858 551-0889	6554
Pred Technologies USA Inc	3679	D	858 999-2114	19691
Rusty Surfboards Inc	3949	F	858 551-0262	23645
Shire Rgenerative Medicine Inc	2834	E	858 202-0673	8380
Shire Rgenerative Medicine Inc	2836	D	858 754-3700	8582
Shire Rgenerative Medicine Inc	2834	D	858 754-5396	8381
Sova Pharmaceuticals Inc	2834	E	858 750-4700	8388
SPS Studios Inc	2771	E	858 456-2336	7568
Strauss Karl Brewery and Rest	2082	E	858 551-2739	1627
Texas Boom Company Inc	3533	E	281 441-2002	14242
U S Medical Instruments Inc (PA)	3841	E	619 661-5500	22661

LA MESA, CA - San Diego County

	SIC	EMP	PHONE	ENTRY #
California Countertop Inc (PA)	2542	E	619 460-0205	5131
Circlemaster Inc	3444	F	858 578-3900	12531
In To Ink	2752	F	858 271-6363	6878
Josef Mendelovitz	2752	E	619 231-3555	6914
Logic Beach Inc (PA)	3823	F	619 698-3300	21614
Ritas Fine Food	2099	F	619 698-3925	2654
Sierra National Corporation	3578	F	619 258-8200	15900
Steward Terra Inc	3612	E	619 713-0028	17123
Totalthermalimagingcom	3577	F	619 303-5884	15872
Velocity Imaging Products Inc	3861	F	619 433-8000	23208

LA MIRADA, CA - Los Angeles County

	SIC	EMP	PHONE	ENTRY #
365 Printing Inc	2752	F	714 752-6990	6631
Advanced Charging Tech Inc	3629	E	877 228-5922	17328
Airgas Inc	2873	F	714 521-4789	9057
App Winddown LLC	2389	F	213 272-1669	3642
Apparel Unified LLC	2759	F	562 639-7233	7237
Beemak Plastics LLC	3089	D	310 886-5880	9973
Bestwall LLC	2653	C	714 521-4270	5389
Bonsal American Inc	3272	E	714 523-1530	10887
Cook King Inc	3589	E	714 739-0502	16032
Dow Chemical Company	2819	C	714 228-4700	7768
Frito-Lay North America Inc	2096	C	714 562-7260	2382
G A Doors Inc	2431	D	714 739-1144	4156
Gallagher Rental Inc	3648	E	714 690-1559	17696
Garfield Commercial Entps	2521	E	714 690-5959	4946
Gemsa Enterprises LLC	2079	E	714 521-1736	1540
General Grinding & Mfg Co LLC	3593	E	562 921-7033	16157
Golden Kraft Inc	2679	D	562 926-8888	5714
Hager Mfg Inc	3728	E	714 522-8870	20835
Head First Productions Inc	3546	F	714 522-3311	14706
Headwaters Construction Inc	3241	E	714 523-1530	10757
Iqair North America Inc	3564	E	877 715-4247	15162
Jdh Pacific Inc (PA)	3321	E	562 926-8088	11495
Jmg Machine Inc	3599	E	562 926-2848	16625
Korea Aerospace Industries Ltd	3721	F	714 868-8560	20597
Lequios Japan Co Ltd	2099	F	410 629-8694	2583
Lindblade Metalworks Inc	3446	E	714 670-7172	12874
Meese Inc	3089	E	714 739-4005	10207
Monaero Engineering Inc	3728	E	714 994-5463	20890
Montebello Container Co LLC	2653	D	714 994-2351	5438
Nutri Granulations Inc	2023	D	714 994-7855	641
Oceania Inc	3081	E	562 926-8886	9722
Outlook Resources Inc	2395	D	714 522-2452	3856
Pittman Products International	3089	E	562 926-6660	10276
Respironics Inc	3842	F	562 483-6805	22803
Santa Ana Packaging Inc	2631	F	714 670-6397	5359
Shasta Beverages Inc	2086	D	714 523-2280	2224
Solid State Devices Inc	3674	C	562 404-4474	19179
Spartech LLC	3083	F	714 523-2260	9766
Superior Storage Tank Inc	3443	F	714 226-1914	12430
Tropical Asphalt LLC (PA)	2952	F	714 739-1408	9420
Twpm Inc	2657	F	714 522-8881	5513
United States Ball Corporation	3562	F	714 521-6500	15115
V Twest Inc	2541	F	714 521-2167	5115
V-T Industries Inc	3089	F	714 521-2008	10426
Wesanco Inc	3728	E	714 739-4989	20970
Wintflash Inc	2759	F	562 944-6548	7543

Employment Codes: A=Over 500 employees, B=251-500,
C=101-250, D=51-100, E=20-50, F=10-19

2019 California
Manufacturers Register

© Mergent Inc. 1-800-342-5647
1399

GEOGRAPHIC

	SIC	EMP	PHONE	ENTRY #

LA PALMA, CA - Orange County

Company	SIC	EMP	PHONE	ENTRY #
Filbur Manufacturing LLC	3569	E	714 228-6000	15319
Greif Inc	2655	D	714 523-9580	5488
Keebler Company	2052	D	714 228-1555	1368
Lapco West LLC	3714	E	714 773-1380	20385
Matthews International Corp	3555	E	562 921-0994	14818
Pamarco Global Graphics Inc	3555	E	714 739-0700	14822
Stoneware Design Co	3269	F	562 432-8145	10837

LA PUENTE, CA - Los Angeles County

Company	SIC	EMP	PHONE	ENTRY #
Blue Sky Remediation Svcs Inc	3669	F	626 961-5736	18312
Bomark Inc	2893	E	626 968-1666	9189
Cad Works Inc	3444	F	626 336-5491	12517
California Fashion Club Inc (PA)	2337	F	626 575-1838	3349
Cott Technologies Inc	3498	F	626 961-3399	13882
County of Los Angeles	3531	E	626 968-3312	14159
Craftsman Lighting	3645	F	626 330-8512	17532
Crown Pallet Company Inc	2448	E	626 937-6565	4463
Flint Group US LLC	2893	E	626 369-6900	9194
Genesis Tc Inc	2512	F	626 968-4455	4778
Goharddrive Inc	3572	F	626 593-9927	15543
Jona Global Trading Inc	2515	F	626 855-2588	4866
Ley Grand Foods Corporation	2051	E	626 336-2244	1282
Mymichelle Company LLC (HQ)	2331	B	626 934-4166	3261
One World Apparel Inc	2331	E	213 222-1010	3266
Oneworld Apparel LLC (HQ)	2335	E	213 222-1010	3330
Pacific Coast Pallets Inc	2448	E	626 937-6565	4492
Size Control Plating Co	3471	E	626 369-3014	13505
Soxnet Inc	2252	F	626 855-3200	2815
Total Media Enterprises Inc	2741	F	626 961-7887	6604
Tristar Global Inc	3714	F	626 363-6978	20469
Unger Fabrik LLC (PA)	2331	C	213 222-1010	3284

LA QUINTA, CA - Riverside County

Company	SIC	EMP	PHONE	ENTRY #
CT Oldenkamp LLC	3991	F	760 200-9510	23789
Donnashi Enterprises Inc	3823	E	760 200-3402	21573
Envirnmntal Pdts Applctons Inc	2842	F	760 779-1814	8640
LLC Marsh Perkins	2389	F	760 880-4558	3668
MDE Semiconductor Inc	3629	D	760 564-8656	17347
Optiscan Ltd	3827	F	760 777-9595	22116
Vermillions Environmental	3822	F	760 777-8035	21536

LA VERNE, CA - Los Angeles County

Company	SIC	EMP	PHONE	ENTRY #
Aero-Clas Heat Tran Prod Inc	3443	F	909 596-1630	12358
American Thermoform Corp (PA)	3555	F	909 593-6711	14799
Attends Healthcare Pdts Inc	2621	C	909 392-1200	5273
Beonca Machine Inc	3599	F	909 392-9991	16319
Biocalth International Inc	2834	F	909 267-3988	8076
Crown Equipment Corporation	3537	D	626 968-0556	14317
Dennis Reeves Inc	2541	F	909 392-9999	5053
Dhl Wire Products	3315	F	909 596-2905	11438
Dow Hydraulic Systems Inc (PA)	3599	D	909 596-6602	16448
DPI Labs Inc	3728	E	909 392-5777	20798
Durston Manufacturing Company	3423	F	909 593-1506	11892
Farbotech Color Inc	2893	F	909 596-9330	9192
Fortress Inc	2521	E	909 593-8600	4944
Gainey Ceramics Inc	3269	C	909 596-4464	10831
Heartbreaker Fashion	2331	F	909 599-0715	3245
Inseat Solutions LLC	3634	E	562 447-1780	17392
JL Mallard Inc	3441	E	909 593-3403	12187
Joann Lammens	3999	F	909 593-8478	24138
Juicy Whip Inc	3556	F	909 392-7500	14866
L & H Mold & Engineering Inc (PA)	3089	F	909 930-1547	10186
Layton Printing & Mailing	2759	F	909 592-4419	7382
Micro Analog Inc	3672	C	909 392-8277	18531
Mohawk Western Plastics Inc	2673	E	909 593-7547	5610
Novipax Inc (DH)	2679	D	909 392-1750	5719
Permeco Inc	3281	F	909 599-9600	11269
Pf Plastics Inc	2519	F	909 392-4488	4916
Plastifab Inc	3083	F	909 596-1927	9760
Postvision Inc	3572	F	818 840-0777	15585
S & S Bindery Inc	2789	F	909 596-2213	7615
Serco Mold Inc (PA)	3089	F	626 331-0517	10371
Synergetic Tech Group Inc	3429	E	909 305-4711	11998
Systems L C Womack	3829	F	909 593-7304	22281
TEC Color Craft (PA)	2759	F	909 392-9000	7511
Z Manufacturing Inc	3499	E	909 593-2191	13986
Zimmer Intermed Inc	3842	F	909 392-0882	22851

LADERA RANCH, CA - Orange County

Company	SIC	EMP	PHONE	ENTRY #
Emisense Technologies LLC (PA)	3674	F	949 502-8440	18819
Juicebot & Co LLC	3556	F	651 270-8860	14865
Ksu Corporation	3441	F	951 409-7055	12192

LAFAYETTE, CA - Contra Costa County

Company	SIC	EMP	PHONE	ENTRY #
Acp Ventures	2752	F	925 297-0100	6640
Clickscanshare Inc	3577	F	925 283-1400	15718
Econoday Inc	2741	F	925 299-5350	6472
Employerware LLC	2741	E	925 283-9735	6477
Frances Mary Accessories Inc	3171	A	925 962-2111	10547
Gildedtree Inc	7372	F	925 246-5624	24693
Legacy Vulcan LLC	3272	F	925 284-4686	10949
Optimum Solutions Group LLC	7372	C	415 954-7100	24996
Retrospect Inc	7372	E	888 376-1078	25127

LAGUNA BEACH, CA - Orange County

Company	SIC	EMP	PHONE	ENTRY #
American Historic Inns Inc	2741	F	949 499-8070	6430
Atlantis Computing Inc (PA)	7372	F	650 917-9471	24394
Awcc Corporation	2386	F	949 497-6313	3607
Blick Industries LLC	3565	F	949 499-5026	15199
Chantilly	2024	E	949 494-7702	661
Ear Charms Inc	3911	F	949 494-4147	23258
Firebrand Media LLC	2752	E	949 715-4100	6815
Lasertron Inc	3599	F	954 846-8600	16680
Ocean Avenue Brewing Co	2082	E	949 497-3381	1615
Ophthonix Inc	3851	D	760 842-5600	23115
Response Graphics In Print	2759	F	949 376-8701	7468
Symrise Inc	2087	F	949 276-4600	2283
Unimark International Inc	3556	F	949 497-1235	14892
Victoria Skimboards	3949	F	949 494-0059	23685

LAGUNA HILLS, CA - Orange County

Company	SIC	EMP	PHONE	ENTRY #
Adco Products Inc	3679	D	937 339-6267	19434
Anterra Group Inc	2843	F	949 215-0658	8684
Aot Electronics Inc	3577	F	949 600-6335	15669
Autotechbizcom Inc	3559	F	949 245-7033	14916
Benjamin Lewis Inc	2752	F	949 859-5119	6690
Bingo Publishers Incorporated	2741	F	949 581-5410	6446
Chavers Gasket Corporation	3053	F	949 472-8118	9523
Cmt Sheet Metal	3443	F	949 679-9868	12376
Epicuren Discovery	2835	D	949 588-5807	8475
Eurotech Showers Inc	3088	F	949 716-4099	9900
Garrett Precision Inc	3599	F	949 855-9710	16526
Gregory M Fink	3993	F	949 305-4242	23891
Hka Elevator Consulting Inc	3534	F	949 348-9711	14251
In Sync Computer Solutions Inc	7372	F	949 837-5000	24757
Intec Video Systems Inc (PA)	3651	F	949 859-3800	17817
Medelita LLC	2311	F	949 542-4100	3035
Metal Improvement Company LLC	3398	E	949 855-8010	11820
Metrolaser Inc	3826	F	949 553-0688	21993
Neuroptics Inc	3841	F	949 250-9792	22554
Pacific Pharmascience Inc	2834	F	949 916-6955	8324
Par Orthodontic Laboratory	3843	E	949 472-4788	22900
Planet Plexi Corp	3089	F	949 206-1183	10278
Plastic and Metal Center Inc	3089	E	949 770-0610	10284
R C Westburg Engineering Inc	3089	F	949 859-4648	10320
R Goodloe & Associates Inc	2752	F	714 380-3900	7069
Raintree Business Products	2752	F	949 859-0801	7072
Rls Enterprises	3089	F	714 493-1735	10336
Roadrunner Circuit Technology	3672	F	714 671-9517	18581
Saddleback Stair & Millwork	2431	F	949 460-0384	4223
Sonendo Inc (PA)	3843	E	949 766-3636	22910
Spatial Wave Inc	7372	F	949 540-6400	25204
Studio Two Printing Inc	2752	F	949 859-5119	7121
Yellow Pages Inc	2741	E	714 776-0534	6630

LAGUNA NIGUEL, CA - Orange County

Company	SIC	EMP	PHONE	ENTRY #
American Pacific Truss Inc	2439	E	949 363-1691	4390
Apnea Sciences Corporation	3069	F	949 226-4421	9587
Bau Furniture Manufacturing (PA)	2511	E	949 643-2729	4675
Burke Display Systems Inc	2542	E	949 248-0091	5129
Interface Associates Inc (HQ)	3841	C	949 448-7056	22483
Murrey International Inc	3949	E	310 532-6091	23621
N-Synch Technologies	3575	F	949 218-7761	15641
Neways Inc	3679	F	949 264-1542	19659
Pretika Corporation	2844	E	949 481-8818	8822
Qpc Fiber Optic LLC	3357	F	949 361-8855	11672
Redworks Industries LLC	2499	F	949 334-7081	4646
S & S Woodcarver Inc	2499	E	714 248-2222	4650
San Diego Daily Transcript	2621	D	619 232-4381	5333
Ultera Systems Inc	3577	F	949 367-8800	15877

LAKE ARROWHEAD, CA - San Bernardino County

Company	SIC	EMP	PHONE	ENTRY #
Hi-Desert Publishing Company	2711	E	909 336-3555	5880
Robertsons Rdy Mix Ltd A Cal	3273	F	909 337-7577	11165
Tapestry Inc	3171	F	909 337-5207	10554

LAKE ELSINORE, CA - Riverside County

Company	SIC	EMP	PHONE	ENTRY #
Acme Motor Corporation	3711	E	949 370-0441	20120
Aerofoam Industries Inc	2531	D	951 245-4429	5005
Afakori Inc	3441	E	949 859-4277	12107
American Compaction Eqp Inc	3531	E	949 661-2921	14141
Boozak Inc	3444	E	951 245-6045	12507
C N C Engineering Inc	3599	F	951 674-7486	16350

Mergent email: customerrelations@mergent.com
1400
2019 California
Manufacturers Register
(P-0000) Products & Services Section entry number
(PA)=Parent Co (HQ)=Headquarters (DH)=Div Headquarters

Company	SIC	EMP	PHONE	ENTRY #
California Cart Builder LLC	3715	F	951 245-1114	20494
Camsoft Corporation	3695	E	951 674-8100	19857
Castle & Cooke Inc	3531	D	951 245-2460	14154
CL Olson & Associates Inc	3548	F	951 245-6233	14722
Discount Blind Center	2591	F	951 678-3980	5187
Dura-Chem Inc	2899	F	951 245-7778	9243
Empire Pre Cast	3272	E	951 609-1590	10922
Faith Industries Inc	2499	E	951 351-1486	4619
Flour Fusion	2051	F	951 245-1166	1249
Golden Office Trailers Inc	3792	E	951 678-2177	21204
Hilz Cable Assemblies Inc	3829	E	951 245-0499	22213
Levi Strauss & Co	2325	F	951 674-2694	3081
Mercury Metal Die & Letter Co (PA)	3479	F	951 674-8717	13617
Mold Vision Inc	3544	F	951 245-8020	14545
Pacific Aggregates Inc	3273	D	951 245-2460	11155
Pelican Woodworks	2434	F	951 674-7821	4335
Precision Sports Inc	3949	D	951 674-1665	23629
Quality Foam Packaging Inc	3086	E	951 245-4429	9878
Rancho Ready Mix (PA)	3273	F	951 674-0488	11159
Rick Palenshus	3559	F	951 245-2100	15020
Roadracing World Publishing	2721	F	951 245-6411	6248
Thermal Electronics Inc	3679	F	951 674-3555	19761
Thrun Mfg Inc	3724	F	949 677-2461	20684
Van Heusen Factory Outlet	2321	F	951 674-1190	3064
Vertical Doors Inc	2591	F	951 273-1069	5214

LAKE FOREST, CA - Orange County

Company	SIC	EMP	PHONE	ENTRY #
ABC Custom Wood Shutters Inc	2431	E	949 595-0300	4097
AC&a Enterprises LLC (HQ)	3724	D	949 716-3511	20639
American Deburring Inc	3599	E	949 457-9790	16270
Aminco International USA Inc (PA)	3911	E	949 457-3261	23235
Approved Networks Inc (PA)	3299	D	800 590-9535	11345
Associated Electrics Inc	3944	E	949 544-7500	23407
Atmel Wireless McU Tech Corp	3674	D	949 525-4481	18727
BNP Enterprises LLC	3714	F	949 770-5438	20272
Boundary Devices LLC	3674	F	602 212-6744	18749
Cac Inc	3679	F	949 587-3328	19475
Camisasca Automotive Mfg Inc	3469	E	949 452-0195	13177
Camisasca Automotive Mfg Inc (PA)	3469	E	949 452-0195	13178
Campbell Engineering Inc	3545	E	949 859-3306	14613
Cod USA Inc	2531	E	949 381-7367	5008
Cyber Mdia Solutions Ltd Lblty	7372	E	877 480-8255	24539
Dss Networks Inc	3577	F	949 981-3473	15733
Dynacast Inc	3364	C	949 707-1211	11714
Ellison Educational Eqp Inc (PA)	3554	C	949 598-8822	14792
Equimine	7372	F	877 437-8464	24624
Fanuc America Corporation	3559	E	949 595-2700	14953
Focus Industries Inc	3646	D	949 830-1350	17610
Formtran Inc	7372	F	949 829-5822	24665
General Monitors Inc (DH)	3669	C	949 581-4464	18329
Global Power Tech Group Inc	3674	F	949 273-4373	18860
Greenshine New Energy LLC	3648	D	949 609-9636	17698
Herbalife Manufacturing LLC	2087	E	949 457-0951	2267
Hexagon Metrology Inc	3545	E	949 916-4490	14640
I Source Technical Svcs Inc (PA)	3679	F	949 453-1500	19573
I/Omagic Corporation (PA)	3572	E	949 707-4800	15557
IMC Networks Corp (PA)	3575	E	949 465-3000	15634
Infor (us) Inc	7372	C	678 319-8000	24765
Innovative Control Systems Inc	3589	E	610 881-8061	16055
Innovative R Advanced (PA)	2515	E	949 273-8100	4864
June Precision Mfg Inc	3451	F	949 855-9121	13029
Juniper Rock Corporation	1423	B	949 500-1797	321
L J Smith Inc	2431	F	949 609-0544	4181
Laminating Company of America	3672	E	949 587-3300	18518
Liquidmetal Technologies Inc (PA)	3325	E	949 635-2100	11525
Markap Inc	2387	F	949 240-1418	3631
Microtek Electronics Inc	3663	F	949 297-4930	18181
Monobind Inc (PA)	3841	E	949 951-2665	22547
Movement Products Inc	3751	F	949 206-0000	21131
Oceania International LLC	3356	F	949 407-8904	11635
Parylene USA Inc	3999	F	949 452-0770	24205
Pitney Bowes Inc	3579	D	949 885-0700	15911
Premier Magnetics Inc	3677	E	949 452-0511	19354
Pressed Right LLC	3421	F	866 257-5774	11882
Pssc Labs	3572	F	949 380-7288	15586
Pura Naturals Inc (HQ)	2844	F	949 273-8100	8827
Qf Liquidation Inc	3714	E	949 399-4500	20431
Qf Liquidation Inc (PA)	3714	C	949 930-3400	20432
Quantum Technologies Inc	1311	C	949 399-4500	70
Schneider Elc Systems USA Inc	3823	F	949 885-0700	21649
Se-GI Products Inc	3444	E	951 737-8320	12754
Semi-Kinetics Inc	3672	D	949 830-7364	18602
Shmaze Industries Inc	3479	E	949 583-1448	13658
Soaptronic LLC	2842	E	949 465-8955	8677
Sole Technology Inc (PA)	3149	C	949 460-2020	10510
SPX Flow Us LLC	3556	D	949 455-8150	14885

Company	SIC	EMP	PHONE	ENTRY #
Stanford Materials Corporation	2816	F	949 380-7362	7747
T/Q Systems Inc	3599	E	949 455-0478	16985
Tenex Health Inc	3841	D	949 454-7500	22647
To Industries Inc	3993	F	949 454-6078	23991
Torcano Industries Inc	3751	E	855 359-3339	21144
Tri-Star Laminates Inc	3672	E	949 587-3200	18629
Universal Printing Services	2752	F	951 788-1500	7157
US Critical LLC (PA)	3572	E	949 916-9326	15620
US Critical LLC	3572	F	800 884-8945	15621
Velco Tool & Die Inc	3544	F	949 855-6638	14589
Wide Open Industries LLC	3711	E	949 635-2292	20184
Young Engineers Inc	3429	D	949 581-9411	12011
Zentec Group	3679	F	949 586-3609	19795

LAKE ISABELLA, CA - Kern County

Company	SIC	EMP	PHONE	ENTRY #
Wick Communications Co	2711	E	760 379-3667	6087

LAKEPORT, CA - Lake County

Company	SIC	EMP	PHONE	ENTRY #
Lake County Publishing Co (DH)	2711	D	707 263-5636	5907
Mountain Lake Labs	3812	E	707 331-3297	21353
Nutrition Resource Inc (PA)	2834	F	707 263-0411	8312
Young & Family Inc	2431	E	707 263-8877	4263

LAKESIDE, CA - San Diego County

Company	SIC	EMP	PHONE	ENTRY #
Clark Steel Fabricators Inc	3446	E	619 390-1502	12843
Coating Services Group LLC	3479	F	619 596-7444	13569
Conductive Science Inc	2851	F	858 699-1837	8895
Dixietruss Inc	3272	E	619 873-0440	10916
Enniss Inc	1442	E	619 561-1101	356
Hanson Aggregates LLC	2951	E	858 715-5600	9386
Inland PCF Resource Recovery	2611	E	619 390-1418	5268
Lite Stone Concrete LLC	3272	E	619 596-9151	10955
M DAmico Inc	2599	E	619 390-5858	5244
Mardian Equipment Co Inc	3537	E	619 938-8071	14335
Masterpiece Leaded Windows	3231	E	858 391-3344	10720
McQuaide Brothers Corporation	3715	E	619 444-9932	20506
Oldcastle Precast Inc	3272	E	619 390-2251	10965
Rpc Inc	1389	F	619 647-9911	267
Southland Envelope Company Inc	2677	C	619 449-3553	5678
Superior Ready Mix Concrete LP	3273	E	619 443-7510	11197

LAKEWOOD, CA - Los Angeles County

Company	SIC	EMP	PHONE	ENTRY #
Bates Industries Inc	2386	F	562 426-8668	3609
Custom Aircraft Interiors Inc	3728	E	562 426-5098	20788
Long Beach Seafoods Co	2092	F	562 432-7300	2316
Magma Products Inc	3631	D	562 627-0500	17373
RDM Multi-Enterprises Inc	3295	F	562 924-1820	11325
TFC Manufacturing Inc	3444	D	562 426-9559	12788
Toyota Motor Engineering & Man	3711	D	562 428-3604	20179

LAMONT, CA - Kern County

Company	SIC	EMP	PHONE	ENTRY #
Franks Cabinet Shop Inc	2434	E	661 845-0781	4303

LANCASTER, CA - Los Angeles County

Company	SIC	EMP	PHONE	ENTRY #
A V Poles and Lighting Inc	3646	E	661 945-2731	17576
Advanced Clutch Technology Inc	3714	E	661 940-7555	20241
Aerotech News and Review Inc (PA)	2721	E	520 623-9321	6098
Antelope Valley Newspapers Inc	2711	E	661 940-1000	5761
Arrow Transit Mix	3273	E	661 945-7600	11043
Block Alternatives	3949	E	661 729-2800	23524
Bohns Printing	2752	F	661 948-8081	6700
Ccbcc Operations LLC	2086	C	661 723-0714	2109
Deluxe Corporation	2782	B	661 942-1144	7580
Do It Right Products LLC	3272	F	661 722-9664	10917
Geographic Data Mgt Solutions	7372	F	661 949-1025	24689
Griff Industries Inc	3089	F	661 728-0111	10130
Harvest Farms Inc	2038	D	661 945-3636	996
J & R Machine Works	3599	E	661 945-8826	16595
McWhirter Steel Inc	3441	F	661 951-8998	12206
Mobile Mini Inc	3448	C	909 356-1690	12949
Morton Grinding Inc	3965	C	661 298-0895	23770
National Band Saw Company	3556	E	661 294-9552	14873
National Metal Stampings Inc	3469	D	661 945-1157	13253
Pacific Seismic Products Inc	3491	E	661 942-4499	13729
Pavement Recycling Systems Inc	2951	F	661 948-5599	9393
Plastic Mart Inc	2821	E	310 268-1404	7867
PPG Industries Inc	2851	F	661 945-7871	8928
Precision Welding Inc	3441	E	661 729-3436	12231
Radford Cabinets Inc	2511	D	661 729-8931	4733
Robert F Chapman Inc	3444	D	661 940-9482	12738
Rta Sales Inc	2431	D	661 942-3553	4222

LARKSPUR, CA - Marin County

Company	SIC	EMP	PHONE	ENTRY #
Airpatrol Corporation	3699	F	410 794-1214	19901
Evolva Inc	2836	F	415 448-5451	8549
Kavi Skin Solutions Inc (PA)	2834	E	415 839-5156	8245
Marin Scope Incorporated	2711	E	415 892-1516	5940
Myway Learning Company Inc	7372	F	415 937-1722	24942

Employment Codes: A=Over 500 employees, B=251-500,
C=101-250, D=51-100, E=20-50, F=10-19

2019 California
Manufacturers Register

© Mergent Inc. 1-800-342-5647
1401

GEOGRAPHIC

	SIC	EMP	PHONE	ENTRY #
Phoenix Marine Corporation (PA)	3825	D	415 464-8116	21826

LATHROP, CA - San Joaquin County

	SIC	EMP	PHONE	ENTRY #
Accurate Heating & Cooling Inc	3444	E	209 858-4125	12457
Big Heart Pet Brands	2033	F	209 547-7200	788
Boise Cascade Company	2621	E	209 983-4114	5275
Brown Sand Inc	1442	F	209 234-1500	347
California Fleet Services Inc (PA)	3715	F	209 858-0283	20495
California Natural Products	2099	C	209 858-2525	2479
Captive Plastics Inc	3089	D	209 858-9188	10012
Cbc Steel Buildings LLC	3448	C	209 858-2425	12926
Clorox Company	2842	E	209 234-1094	8633
Con-Fab California Corporation (PA)	3272	E	209 249-4700	10906
Diamond Pet Food Processors O	2047	E	209 983-4900	1112
Heritage Paper Co	2752	F	925 449-1148	6855
Horizon Snack Foods Inc	2053	D	925 373-7700	1396
Mobile Mini Inc	3448	E	209 858-9300	12948
Pilkington North America Inc	3211	B	209 858-6249	10603
Pratt Industries Inc	2621	C	770 922-0117	5328
Provena Foods Inc	2013	E	209 858-5555	517
Rafael Sandoval	2421	E	209 858-4173	4048
Saramark Inc	3448	E	408 971-3881	12960
Schell & Kampeter Inc	2047	E	209 983-4900	1121
Simwon America Corp	3714	F	925 276-3412	20448
Soccer Learning Systems Inc	2721	F	209 858-4300	6259
Tesla Inc	3711	F	209 647-7037	20173

LAWNDALE, CA - Los Angeles County

	SIC	EMP	PHONE	ENTRY #
Anthonys Rdymx & Bldg Sups Inc (PA)	3273	F	310 542-9400	11041
Carbro Corporation	3545	E	310 643-8400	14615
Vellios Machine Shop Inc	3599	F	310 643-8540	17039

LE GRAND, CA - Merced County

	SIC	EMP	PHONE	ENTRY #
Oasis Foods Inc	2033	E	209 382-0263	835

LEBEC, CA - Kern County

	SIC	EMP	PHONE	ENTRY #
National Cement Co Cal Inc	3273	F	661 248-6733	11145
Technicolor Usa Inc	3651	C	661 496-1309	17864

LEMON GROVE, CA - San Diego County

	SIC	EMP	PHONE	ENTRY #
Custom Wire Products	3496	F	619 469-2328	13822
Imperial Custom Cabinet Inc	2511	F	619 461-4093	4705
Jci Metal Products (PA)	3441	D	619 229-8206	12186
Micro Tool & Manufacturing Inc	3545	F	619 582-2884	14652
RCP Block & Brick Inc (PA)	3271	F	619 460-9101	10859
West World Manufacturing Inc	2511	F	619 287-4403	4749

LEMOORE, CA - Kings County

	SIC	EMP	PHONE	ENTRY #
Agusa	2034	E	559 924-4785	872
Bennett & Bennett Inc	3272	F	559 896-0200	10883
Boeing Company	3721	E	559 998-8260	20543
Boeing Company	3812	E	559 998-8214	21267
Kay and Associates Inc	3721	E	559 410-0917	20595
L3 Communications Link	3699	F	559 998-5295	20002
Leprino Foods Company	2022	B	559 924-7722	587
Leprino Foods Company	2022	C	559 924-7939	588
Northland Process Piping Inc	3312	D	559 925-9724	11408
United States Dept of Navy	3519	A	559 998-2488	14034

LEWISTON, CA - Trinity County

	SIC	EMP	PHONE	ENTRY #
EH Suda Inc	3599	E	530 778-9830	16464

LINCOLN, CA - Placer County

	SIC	EMP	PHONE	ENTRY #
Cmd Products	3086	F	916 434-0228	9827
Earth & Vine Provisions Inc	2033	F	916 434-8399	798
Far West Equipment Rentals	3273	F	916 645-2929	11105
Gc Products Inc	3531	E	916 645-3870	14168
Gdas-Lincoln Inc	3721	D	916 645-8961	20578
Global Dolls Corp	3999	F	916 645-3000	24108
Jbr Inc (PA)	2099	C	916 258-8000	2543
Livingstons Concrete Svc Inc	3273	E	916 334-4313	11137
Marybelle Farms Inc	2048	E	916 645-8568	1147
Pabco Building Products LLC	3259	D	916 645-3341	10803
Pabco Clay Products LLC	3251	C	916 645-3341	10776
Palette Unlimited	2448	E	916 408-1914	4495
Robb-Jack Corporation (PA)	3541	D	916 645-6045	14405
Sierra Pacific Industries	2421	B	916 645-1631	4064
Stantec Consulting Svcs Inc	3589	F	916 434-5062	16116
Wise Villa Winery Inc	2084	F	916 543-0323	2064

LINDEN, CA - San Joaquin County

	SIC	EMP	PHONE	ENTRY #
Hyponex Corporation	2873	D	209 887-3845	9063
Pearl Crop Inc	2099	E	209 887-3731	2636
Stockton Rubber Mfgcoinc	3069	E	209 887-1172	9680

LINDSAY, CA - Tulare County

	SIC	EMP	PHONE	ENTRY #
Arts Custom Cabinets Inc	2511	F	559 562-2766	4670
Doug Deleo Welding Inc	7692	F	559 562-3700	25401
Harvest Container Company	2653	E	559 562-1394	5421

	SIC	EMP	PHONE	ENTRY #
Pallet Depot Inc (PA)	2448	E	916 645-0490	4496
Randy Nix Cstm Wldg & Mfg Inc	7692	F	559 562-1958	25429

LITTLE LAKE, CA - Inyo County

	SIC	EMP	PHONE	ENTRY #
Kiewit Corporation	1423	E	760 377-3117	322

LITTLEROCK, CA - Los Angeles County

	SIC	EMP	PHONE	ENTRY #
Hi-Grade Materials Co	3273	E	661 533-3100	11119
Legacy Vulcan LLC	1442	E	661 533-2127	370
Legacy Vulcan LLC	3273	E	661 533-2125	11132

LIVE OAK, CA - Sutter County

	SIC	EMP	PHONE	ENTRY #
Coe Orchard Equipment Inc	3523	D	530 695-5121	14054
Sunset Moulding Co (PA)	2421	E	530 790-2700	4068

LIVERMORE, CA - Alameda County

	SIC	EMP	PHONE	ENTRY #
3d Remodeling Inc	2434	E	925 449-5477	4265
Adams Label Company LLC (PA)	2759	F	925 371-5393	7220
Aero Precision Industries LLC (PA)	3728	C	925 455-9900	20712
Aerospace Composite Products (PA)	3728	E	925 443-5900	20720
Air Factors Inc	3564	F	925 579-0040	15141
Akira Seiki U S A Inc	3541	F	925 443-1200	14358
Alere Inc	2835	B	510 732-7200	8457
Altamont Manufacturing Inc	3541	F	925 371-5401	14360
Amerimade Technology Inc	3089	E	925 243-9090	9945
Aria Technologies Inc	3357	E	925 292-1616	11643
Bartolini Guitars	3679	F	386 517-6823	19459
Baycorr Packaging Inc (PA)	2653	E	925 449-1148	5387
Berkeley Nutritional Mfg Corp	2834	E	925 243-6300	8073
Bonner Metal Processing LLC	3449	E	925 455-3833	12973
Bonner Processing Inc	3471	E	925 455-3833	13351
Byer California	2331	D	925 245-0184	3222
C D International Tech Inc	3679	F	408 986-0725	19473
Cedar Mountain Winery Inc	2084	F	925 373-6636	1683
Chassis Unlimited	3842	F	925 339-6035	22713
Cooling Source Inc	3363	C	925 292-1293	11691
Country Floral Supply Inc	3999	D	925 960-9823	24069
Covan Systems Inc	3651	F	510 226-9886	17785
Curtis Instruments Inc	3824	D	925 961-1088	21683
Daa Draexlmaier Auto Amer LLC	3714	D	864 485-1000	20307
Darcie Kent Vineyards	2084	F	925 243-9040	1715
Eklavya LLC	3569	F	925 443-3296	15318
Elite Ready-Mix LLC	3273	E	916 366-4627	11104
Exacta-Technology Inc	3599	F	925 443-6200	16481
Fabco Holdings Inc	3714	A	925 454-9500	20330
Ferrotec (usa) Corporation	3053	C	925 371-4170	9528
Finis Inc (PA)	3949	E	925 454-0111	23561
Fitpro USA LLC	2833	F	877 645-5776	7940
Formfactor Inc	3674	F	925 290-4000	18846
Formfactor Inc (PA)	3674	C	925 290-4000	18847
Fred Matter Inc	3599	E	925 371-1234	16515
Fusion Coatings Inc	3479	F	925 443-8083	13592
G2 Metal Fab	3499	E	925 443-7603	13942
Gdca Inc	3577	E	925 456-9900	15746
Gillig LLC (HQ)	3713	B	510 785-1500	20208
Gillig LLC	3711	B	510 785-1500	20144
Goalsr Inc (PA)	7372	C	650 453-5844	24702
GS Cosmeceutical Usa Inc	2844	E	925 371-5000	8759
Hanger Prsthetcs & Ortho Inc	3842	F	925 371-5081	22746
IMG Companies LLC	3599	C	925 273-1100	16577
Individual Software Inc	7372	E	925 734-6767	24761
Inland Valley Publising Co	2711	F	925 243-8000	5890
Inphenix Inc	3674	E	925 606-8809	18899
Insidesalescom Inc	7372	D	385 207-7252	24776
Internationally Delicious Inc (PA)	2053	E	925 426-6155	1397
Jifco Inc (PA)	3498	C	925 449-4665	13891
Johnson Controls	3669	E	925 273-0100	18334
Johnson Controls Inc	3714	B	925 447-9200	20378
Konecranes Inc	3536	F	925 273-0140	14300
Lam Research Corporation	3674	E	510 572-8400	18951
Lazestar	7692	E	925 443-5293	25420
Legacy Vulcan LLC	1422	E	925 373-1802	314
Linde LLC	2813	E	925 371-4170	7699
Maranti Networks Inc	3572	D	408 834-4000	15565
Marpo Kinetics Inc	3949	F	925 606-6919	23611
Medical Device Resource Corp	3841	F	510 732-9950	22525
Meritor Specialty Products LLC (HQ)	3714	F	248 435-1000	20399
Metal Improvement Company LLC	3398	E	925 960-1090	11822
Modus Advanced Inc	3069	E	925 960-8700	9641
National Bedding Company LLC	2515	C	925 373-1350	4875
Nuprodx Inc	3842	F	925 292-0866	22781
Pacific Color Graphics Inc	2759	E	925 600-3006	7427
Pacon Mfg Inc	3599	F	925 961-0445	16823
Printegra Corp	2761	F	925 373-6368	7551
Pro-Tek Manufacturing Inc	3444	F	925 454-8100	12724
Process Materials Inc	3341	F	925 245-9626	11564
Progressive Housing Inc	3714	F	916 920-8255	20429

Mergent email: customerrelations@mergent.com
1402

2019 California
Manufacturers Register

(P-0000) Products & Services Section entry number
(PA)=Parent Co (HQ)=Headquarters (DH)=Div Headquarters

	SIC	EMP	PHONE	ENTRY #
Puronics Incorporated	3589	E	925 456-7000	16096
R K Larrabee Company Inc	3621	D	925 828-9420	17218
Ratermann Manufacturing Inc (PA)	3089	E	800 264-7793	10327
RC Readymix Co Inc	3273	E	925 449-7785	11160
Rh Usa Inc	3841	E	925 245-7900	22606
Rios-Lovell Estate Winery	2084	E	925 443-0434	1949
Rock Engineered McHy Co Inc	2911	E	925 447-0805	9355
Ron Nunes Enterprises LLC	3444	F	925 371-0220	12740
Screen Tech Inc	3444	D	408 885-9750	12753
Segundo Metal Products Inc	3444	D	925 667-2009	12755
Sensor Concepts Incorporated	3812	D	925 443-9001	21428
Sierra Design Mfg Inc (PA)	3647	E	925 443-3140	17663
Sierra Hygiene Products LLC	2621	F	925 371-7173	5334
Sierra Photonics Inc	3669	E	925 290-2930	18364
Skechers USA Inc	3021	E	925 447-2622	9483
Software Licensing Consultants	7372	E	925 371-1277	25193
Solarbos	3613	D	925 456-7744	17164
Steven Kent LLC	2084	F	925 243-6442	1994
Streivor Inc	3914	F	925 960-9090	23338
Stretch-Run Inc	3441	F	925 606-1599	12250
Sub-One Technology Inc	3479	F	925 924-1020	13668
Summit Window Products Inc	2431	D	408 526-1600	4237
Tapp Label Inc (HQ)	2679	F	707 252-8300	5741
Tech Air Northern Cal LLC	2813	F	925 449-9353	7734
Tesla Vineyards Lp	2084	F	925 456-2500	2012
Thomas E Davis Inc	3444	F	925 373-1373	12790
Topcon Med Laser Systems Inc	3845	E	888 760-8657	23060
Topcon Positioning Systems Inc (DH)	3829	C	925 245-8300	22289
Trans Western Polymers Inc	2673	B	925 449-7800	5628
Truroots Inc (HQ)	2099	E	925 218-2205	2693
Tyco Fire Products LP	3569	C	925 687-6957	15370
Universal Cell Site Svcs Inc	3441	E	925 447-4500	12268
Vi-TEC Manufacturing Inc	3599	F	925 447-4400	17041
Vintage 99 Label Mfg Inc	2672	E	925 294-5270	5582
Wang Nmr Inc	3841	E	925 443-0212	22680
Wente Bros (PA)	2084	D	925 456-2300	2050
Westco Iron Works Inc (PA)	3423	D	925 961-9152	11916
X Wiley Inc (PA)	3851	D	925 243-9810	23132
Yield Engineering Systems Inc	3674	E	925 373-8353	19281

LIVINGSTON, CA - Merced County

	SIC	EMP	PHONE	ENTRY #
E & J Gallo Winery	2084	C	209 394-6215	1744
Fortuna Tortilla Factory	2099	F	209 394-3028	2525
Foster Poultry Farms (PA)	2015	C	209 394-6914	539
Foster Poultry Farms	2015	C	209 394-7901	541
Foster Poultry Farms	2048	C	209 394-7950	1133
Menezes Hay Co	2048	F	209 394-3111	1148
Sensient Ntral Ingredients LLC	2034	F	209 394-7979	892
Sensient Technologies Corp	2099	F	209 394-7971	2666

LOCKEFORD, CA - San Joaquin County

	SIC	EMP	PHONE	ENTRY #
Elements By Grapevine Inc	2511	E	209 727-3711	4692
Kellogg Supply Inc	2873	E	209 727-3130	9064
Lomelis Statuary Inc (PA)	3299	E	209 367-1131	11358
Robertson-Ceco II Corporation	3448	C	209 727-5504	12959
Woodside Investment Inc	3499	D	209 787-8040	13985

LODI, CA - San Joaquin County

	SIC	EMP	PHONE	ENTRY #
Allied Disc Grinding	3599	F	209 339-0333	16253
American Mstr Tech Scntfic Inc	3841	E	209 368-4031	22334
Archer-Daniels-Midland Company	2041	C	209 339-1252	1029
Armorstruxx LLC (PA)	3728	D	209 365-9400	20744
Basalite Building Products LLC	3272	E	209 333-6161	10882
Baywood Cellars Inc	2084	F	415 606-4640	1654
Belco Cabinets Inc	3442	F	209 334-5437	12298
Bullzeye Mfg	3315	F	209 482-5626	11432
Campbell Grinding Inc	3599	F	209 339-8838	16358
D & M Fabrication Inc	3569	F	209 334-0407	15312
Dart Container Corp California	3086	C	209 333-8088	9834
Del Castillo Foods Inc	2099	F	209 369-2877	2502
Dependable Precision Mfg Inc	3444	F	209 369-1055	12558
Design Woodworking Inc (PA)	2431	E	209 334-6674	4143
Dimo Gear LLC	3172	E	916 684-1051	10560
Doors Plus Inc	2431	F	209 463-3667	4146
Duncan Press Inc	2752	F	209 462-5245	6796
Fairmont Sign Company	3993	F	209 365-6490	23874
Garys Signs and Screen Prtg	3993	F	209 369-8592	23887
General Mills Inc	2043	F	209 334-7061	1059
Goldstone Land Company LLC	2084	E	209 368-3113	1791
Holz Rubber Company Inc	3069	C	209 368-7171	9624
Honeywell International Inc	3724	A	209 323-8520	20657
Ipex USA LLC	3084	F	209 368-7131	9781
Jessies Grove Winery	2084	F	209 368-0880	1830
Kubota Tractor Corporation	3523	F	209 334-9910	14081
Larry Mthvin Installations Inc	3231	E	209 368-2105	10713
Liberty Foods Trading Co LLC	2033	F	209 367-8800	819

	SIC	EMP	PHONE	ENTRY #
Lodi Iron Works Inc (PA)	3321	E	209 368-5395	11496
Lodi News Sentinel	2711	D	209 369-2761	5916
Lustre-Cal Nameplate Corp	3449	D	209 370-1600	12984
Mepco Label Systems	2759	E	209 946-0201	7398
Miller Packing Company	2013	E	209 339-2310	508
North Amrcn Specialty Pdts LLC	2821	F	209 365-7500	7860
Oak Ridge Winery LLC	2084	E	209 369-4768	1903
Pacific Coast Producers	2033	D	209 334-3352	842
Pacific Coast Producers (PA)	2033	B	209 367-8800	843
Quashnick Tool Corporation	3089	E	209 334-5283	10318
Reed Group	1429	F	209 334-0790	332
Robert Mondavi Corporation	2084	E	209 365-2995	1951
Ron Grose Racing Inc	3599	F	209 368-2571	16913
Schaefer Systems Intl Inc	3089	E	209 365-6030	10362
Scholten Surgical Instrs Inc	3841	F	209 365-1393	22615
Scientific Specialties Inc	3081	D	209 333-2120	9726
Shellpro Inc	3999	F	209 334-2081	24241
Stama Winery LLC	2084	F	209 727-3314	1989
Superior Electrical Advg	3993	F	209 334-3337	23984
Takt Manufacturing Inc	3999	F	408 250-4975	24265
Tusco Casting Corporation	3325	F	209 368-5137	11528
USA Products Group Inc (PA)	2399	F	209 334-1460	3970
Vanderlans & Sons Inc (PA)	3589	E	209 334-4115	16129
Weibel Incorporated	2084	E	209 365-9463	2049
West Coast Canvas (PA)	2394	F	209 333-0243	3819

LOLETA, CA - Humboldt County

	SIC	EMP	PHONE	ENTRY #
Loleta Cheese Company Inc	2022	F	707 733-5470	590

LOMA LINDA, CA - San Bernardino County

	SIC	EMP	PHONE	ENTRY #
Dvele Inc	2451	E	909 796-2561	4552
Dvele Omega Corporation	2451	D	909 796-2561	4553
Loma Linda University	2752	E	909 558-4552	6953

LOMITA, CA - Los Angeles County

	SIC	EMP	PHONE	ENTRY #
Aab Garage Door Inc	2431	F	310 530-3637	4096
Anacrown Inc	3499	F	310 530-1165	13917
Coin Dealer Newsletter Inc	2721	F	310 515-7369	6131
Robinson Textiles Inc	2311	F	310 527-8110	3041
Underground Games Inc	3944	F	310 379-0100	23474

LOMPOC, CA - Santa Barbara County

	SIC	EMP	PHONE	ENTRY #
Alliance Technical Svcs Inc	3731	F	805 606-3020	20983
Celite Corporation	1499	F	805 736-1221	408
Chevron Corporation	1311	F	805 733-5174	47
Den-Mat Holdings LLC (HQ)	3843	F	805 346-3700	22867
Federal Prison Industries	3993	E	805 735-2771	23880
Federal Prison Industries	2511	C	805 736-4154	4696
Henry L Hudson (PA)	2752	F	805 736-2737	6852
Horizon Well Logging Inc	1389	F	805 733-0972	224
Imerys Clays Inc	1455	F	805 737-2445	399
Imerys Minerals California Inc	1481	B	805 736-1221	405
Imerys Minerals California Inc (DH)	1499	E	805 736-1221	416
Lockheed Martin Corporation	3663	B	805 606-4860	18168
Melville Winery LLC	2084	E	805 735-7030	1876
Orbital Sciences Corporation	3761	D	805 734-5400	21166
Pulitzer Inc	2711	E	805 735-1132	6021
Rodriguez Ismael	2096	F	805 736-7362	2400
Stolpman Vineyards LLC	2084	F	805 736-5000	1996

LONG BEACH, CA - Los Angeles County

	SIC	EMP	PHONE	ENTRY #
A & A Aerospace Inc	3728	F	562 901-6803	20694
A & A Aerospace Inc	3728	F	562 901-6803	20695
Aci Postal System	2752	D	562 987-2200	6638
Acme Headlining Co	3714	D	562 432-0281	20237
Air Marketing	2741	E	562 208-3990	6425
Air Products and Chemicals Inc	2813	E	562 437-0462	7673
Air Source Industries	2813	F	562 426-4017	7677
Altasens Inc (HQ)	3674	E	818 530-9400	18685
American Plant Services Inc (PA)	3312	D	562 630-1773	11378
Anivive Lifesciences Inc	2834	F	714 931-7810	8033
Antex Electronics Corporation	3577	F	310 532-3092	15668
APR Engineering Inc	3731	F	562 983-3800	20984
Arias Industries Inc	3714	F	310 532-9737	20259
Asphalt Products Oil Corp (HQ)	2952	F	562 423-6471	9401
Autumn Milling Co Inc	2421	E	310 635-0703	4030
B & B Pipe and Tool Co (PA)	3599	F	562 424-0704	16295
Backflow Apparatus & Valve	3494	E	310 639-5231	13760
Bandag Licensing Corporation	3069	D	562 531-3880	9594
Berg-Nelson Company Inc	3052	F	562 432-3491	9498
Berns Bros Inc	3599	F	562 437-0471	16320
Bestwall LLC	3275	E	562 435-7094	11216
Big Studio Inc	2261	F	562 989-2444	2878
Bill Williams Welding Co	3441	E	562 432-5421	12118
Boeing Company	3721	A	714 317-1070	20549
Boeing Company	3721	A	562 593-6668	20550
Boeing Company	3721	A	562 425-3613	20552

Employment Codes: A=Over 500 employees, B=251-500,
C=101-250, D=51-100, E=20-50, F=10-19

2019 California
Manufacturers Register

© Mergent Inc. 1-800-342-5647
1403

GEOGRAPHIC

Company	SIC	EMP	PHONE	ENTRY #
Boeing Company	3721	E	562 593-5511	20557
Boeing Company	3721	A	562 496-1000	20558
Boeing Company	3721	A	562 593-5511	20560
Cablestrand Corp	3496	F	562 595-4527	13815
California Jig Grinding Co	3599	F	323 723-4017	16356
California Plastic Cntrs Inc	3089	F	562 423-3900	10004
California Resources Corp	1311	C	562 624-3400	39
Califrnia Rsurces Long Bch Inc	1389	F	562 624-3204	192
Calwest Galvanizing Corp	3479	D	310 549-2200	13566
Canam Technology Inc	3663	F	562 856-0178	18061
Canzone and Company	3993	E	714 537-8175	23839
Cavanaugh Machine Works Inc	3599	E	562 437-1126	16368
Cemex Cnstr Mtls PCF LLC	1422	E	562 435-0195	312
Clariant Corporation	2869	E	661 763-5192	8998
Clay Designs Inc	3269	E	562 432-3991	10829
Coastal Marine Maint Co LLC **(PA)**	3731	F	562 432-8066	20990
Commercial Mini Freighters Inc	3713	E	562 437-2166	20196
Compulink Management Ctr Inc	7372	C	562 988-1688	24516
Continental Graphics Corp	2752	A	714 827-1752	6753
Control Switches Inc **(PA)**	3625	F	562 498-7331	17261
Control Switches Intl Inc	3625	E	562 498-7331	17262
Corazonas Foods Inc	2096	F	800 388-8998	2377
CRC Marketing Inc	1311	F	562 624-3400	52
Crestec Usa Inc	2752	E	310 327-9000	6769
Crown Equipment Corporation	3537	D	310 952-6600	14321
Csp Inc	3577	E	562 470-7236	15726
Custom Fibreglass Mfg Co	3792	C	562 432-5454	21200
Cw Industries	3441	F	562 432-5421	12148
CW Welding Service Inc **(PA)**	7692	E	562 432-5421	25397
D&A Unlimited Inc	2339	E	562 336-1528	3400
D&S Brewing Solutions Inc	2082	E	650 207-4524	1585
Diamond-U Products Inc	3492	F	562 436-8245	13739
Diecraft Corporation	3599	F	323 728-2601	16439
Dunstan Enterprises Inc	3541	F	562 630-6292	14378
Dynamite Sign Group Inc	3993	E	562 595-7725	23859
Eco Services Operations Corp	2819	D	310 885-6719	7771
Edgington Oil Company LLC	2951	D	562 423-1465	9383
Ej Usa Inc	3321	F	562 528-0258	11492
Ellegra Print & Imaging	2752	F	562 432-2931	6807
Engineering Materials Co Inc	3965	E	562 436-0063	23764
Epson America Inc **(DH)**	3577	A	800 463-7766	15740
Everson Spice Company Inc	2099	E	562 595-4785	2514
F-J-E Inc	2541	E	562 437-7466	5060
Fine Quality Metal Finshg Inc	3471	E	562 983-7425	13410
Flynn Signs and Graphics Inc	3993	F	562 498-6655	23881
Forty-Niners Publication	2721	F	562 985-5568	6165
Foss Maritime Company	3441	E	562 437-6098	12164
Frontier Engrg & Mfg Tech Inc	3599	F	562 606-2655	16516
FSI Field Specialties Inc	3563	F	562 685-8300	15126
Fundamental Tech Intl Inc	3823	F	562 595-0661	21589
G B Remanufacturing Inc	3089	F	562 272-7333	10111
Gambol Industries Inc	3732	E	562 901-2470	21039
Gazette Newspapers	2711	E	562 433-2000	5861
Get	3589	E	562 989-5400	16045
Ginza Collection Design Inc	2335	E	562 531-1116	3310
Glencore Ltd	2911	E	562 427-6611	9333
Gulf Streams	3721	E	562 420-1818	20589
H Roberts Construction	3448	D	562 590-4825	12934
Harbor Custom Canvas	2394	F	562 436-7708	3790
Harding Containers Intl Inc	2448	E	310 549-7272	4475
Harsco Corporation	3443	F	909 444-2527	12388
Hearts For Long Beach Inc	2711	E	562 433-2000	5875
Hi-Flo Corp	3561	F	562 468-0800	15074
Howell Dick Hole Drilling Svc	1381	F	562 633-9898	106
Hufcor California Inc **(HQ)**	2542	D	562 634-3116	5145
Indel Engineering Inc	3732	E	562 594-0995	21044
Industrial Mineral Company USA	3291	F	562 553-5203	11294
Ix Medical **(PA)**	3842	F	877 902-6446	22755
Ixys Long Beach Inc **(DH)**	3674	E	562 296-6584	18936
J & K Resources Inc	2752	E	503 252-4009	6899
J Howard Service Group Inc	3495	F	562 602-0224	13795
Jacobson Plastics Inc	3089	D	562 433-4911	10161
Jbi LLC **(PA)**	2599	C	310 886-8034	5240
Jeteffect Inc **(PA)**	3721	F	562 989-8800	20593
Joy Processed Foods Inc	2099	E	562 435-1106	2547
Katana Software Inc	7372	F	562 495-1366	24825
Kayline Enterprises Inc	3999	F	562 595-4515	24145
Kbr Inc	3624	E	562 436-9281	17238
Keystone Engineering Company **(HQ)**	3599	F	562 497-3200	16652
Kuster Co Oil Well Services	1381	F	562 595-0661	110
La Mar Industries Inc	3569	F	562 436-4228	15338
La Rutan	3999	F	310 940-7956	24156
Lester Box Inc	2449	F	562 437-5123	4528
Leviton Manufacturing Co Inc	3643	E	631 812-6041	17478
Long Beach Creamery LLC	2024	F	562 252-2730	681
Lubeco Inc	2992	E	562 602-1791	9441
M G Industries Inc	3053	F	562 436-9095	9542
M L Z Inc	3469	F	562 436-3540	13244
Macs Lift Gate Inc **(PA)**	3999	E	562 634-5962	24167
Macs Lift Gate Inc	3537	E	562 634-5962	14334
Maitlen & Benson Inc	3548	E	562 597-2200	14732
Malibu Ceramic Works	3253	E	310 455-2485	10786
Marisa Foods LLC	2013	E	562 437-7775	504
Maruhide Marine Products Inc	2092	D	562 435-6509	2317
Medianews Group Inc	2711	D	562 435-1161	5957
Medway Plastics Corporation	3089	C	562 630-1175	10206
Mercury Security Products LLC	3699	F	562 986-9105	20016
Metal Preparations	3471	E	213 628-5176	13453
Metra Electronics Corporation	3714	F	562 470-6601	20400
Midonna Inc	2759	F	562 983-5140	7407
Morton Salt Inc	1479	F	562 437-0071	402
National Emblem Inc **(PA)**	2395	C	310 515-5055	3854
NC Dynamics Incorporated	3728	C	562 634-7392	20896
NC Dynamics LLC	3599	C	562 634-7392	16781
Neill Aircraft Co	3728	E	562 432-7981	20897
Neurosmith LLC	3944	E	562 296-1100	23450
New Ngc Inc	3275	C	562 435-4465	11220
Obagi Cosmeceuticals LLC **(PA)**	2834	D	800 636-7546	8314
OK Mine Company Incorporated	1081	F	323 440-4333	14
Pacific Energy Resources Ltd **(PA)**	1311	F	562 628-1526	68
Panel Products Inc	3812	E	310 830-3331	21379
Paris Croissant LLC **(PA)**	2051	E	562 630-8711	1306
Pbf Energy Western Region LLC **(DH)**	2911	B	973 455-7500	9349
Pdf Print Communications Inc **(PA)**	2752	D	562 426-6978	7020
Pfanstiel Publishers & Prtrs	2752	E	562 438-5641	7024
Plasidyne Engineering & Mfg	3089	E	562 531-0510	10280
Plastic Fabrication Tech LLC	3089	D	773 509-1700	10286
Praxair Inc	2813	E	310 816-1066	7708
Private Label By G Inc **(PA)**	2335	E	562 531-1116	3334
Providence Industries LLC	2326	D	562 420-9091	3117
Queen Beach Printers Inc	2752	E	562 436-8201	7068
R E Michel Company LLC	3585	E	310 885-9820	15974
Radiology Support Devices	3841	E	310 518-0527	22596
RHS Gas Inc	2911	F	310 710-2331	9354
Rsg/Aames Security Inc	3669	E	562 529-5100	18360
Rubbercraft Corp Cal Ltd **(DH)**	3061	C	562 354-2800	9574
Sanders Industries **(HQ)**	2824	F	562 354-2920	7916
Sas Safety Corporation	3842	D	562 427-2775	22807
Schneiders Deisgn Studio Inc	3911	F	562 437-0448	23316
Seachrome Corporation	3431	C	310 447-8010	12017
Seaside Printing Co	2752	E	562 437-6437	7098
SJcontrols Inc	3823	F	562 494-1400	21656
Solvay USA Inc	2819	F	310 669-5300	7806
South Coast Publishing Inc	2711	F	562 988-1222	6051
South Street Inc	3949	E	562 984-6240	23656
Speed-O-Pin International	2591	F	562 433-4911	5212
SPEP Acquisition Corp **(PA)**	3429	D	310 608-0693	11994
Spike Chunsoft Inc	7372	F	562 786-5080	25207
Sportsmen Steel Safe Fabg Co **(PA)**	3499	E	562 984-0244	13974
Stearns Park	2531	E	562 570-1685	5029
Stem Consultants Inc	3824	F	612 987-8008	21694
Superior Electrical Advg **(PA)**	3993	D	562 495-3808	23983
T D I Signs	3993	E	562 436-5188	23986
Tabc Inc **(DH)**	3714	C	562 984-3305	20458
Talco Plastics Inc	3089	E	562 630-1224	10398
Tatung Company America Inc **(HQ)**	3663	D	310 637-2105	18273
TCI Texarkana Ltd	3353	F	562 808-8000	11581
Tenneco Automotive Oper Co Inc	3714	C	562 630-0700	20462
Termo Company	1311	E	562 595-7401	77
Tesoro Refining & Mktg Co LLC	2911	B	562 728-2215	9364
Texollini Inc	2297	C	310 537-3400	2967
Three Star Rfrgn Engrg Inc	3585	E	310 327-9090	15981
Tidelands Oil Production Inc **(DH)**	1311	E	562 436-9918	78
Tidelands Oil Production Inc	1311	E	562 436-2836	79
Tor C A M Industries Inc	3592	E	562 531-8463	16153
U S Chrome Corp California	3471	F	562 437-2825	13526
Ultracast LLC	3321	E	860 253-5015	11502
Union Pacific Railroad Company	3446	B	562 490-7000	12901
Vans Inc	3021	E	562 856-1695	9492
Virgin Orbit LLC	3489	B	562 384-4400	13697
Vision Publications Inc	2741	E	562 597-4000	6619
Visioneered Image Systems Inc	3993	F	818 613-7600	23999
Wallboard Tool Co Inc	3423	C	562 437-0701	11915
Weatherford International Inc	3533	F	562 595-0931	14244
Western Integrated Mtls Inc **(PA)**	2431	E	562 634-2823	4254
Western Tube & Conduit Corp **(HQ)**	3644	C	310 537-6300	17520
Wyatt Precision Machine Inc	3451	E	562 634-0524	13053

LOOMIS, CA - Placer County

Company	SIC	EMP	PHONE	ENTRY #
American Die & Rollforming	3544	F	916 652-7667	14476
Apex Brewing Supply	3556	F	916 250-7950	14832

Company	SIC	EMP	PHONE	ENTRY #
Bimbo Bakeries Usa Inc	2051	F	916 456-3863	1191
Gary Doupnik Manufacturing Inc	2452	D	916 652-9291	4573
Hillerich & Bradsby Co	3949	E	916 652-4267	23584
S&S Signature Mill Works Inc	2499	F	916 652-1046	4651
Valley Rock Lndscpe Material (PA)	3271	F	916 652-7209	10867
West Pacific Cabinet Mfg	2434	F	916 652-6840	4368

LOS ALAMITOS, CA - Orange County

Company	SIC	EMP	PHONE	ENTRY #
Absolute Sign Inc	3993	F	562 592-5838	23806
Aero Corporation	3721	E	562 598-2281	20530
Alliance Spacesystems LLC	3624	C	714 226-1400	17232
Arrowhead Products Corporation	3728	A	714 828-7770	20745
Bloomfield Bakers	2052	A	626 610-2253	1355
Brodhead Grating Products LLC	3446	F	562 598-4314	12839
Caravan Manufacturing Co Inc	3089	F	714 220-9722	10013
Cone Engineering Inc	3714	F	714 828-4861	20297
Dwi Enterprises	3651	E	714 842-2236	17794
Epoch International Entps Inc	3559	D	714 484-8015	14949
Flowline Inc	3829	E	562 598-3015	22201
Golf Design Inc	3949	D	714 899-4040	23573
Grating Pacific Inc (PA)	3441	E	562 598-4314	12174
Haus of Grey LLC	2326	F	562 270-4739	3104
Institute of Electrical and El	2754	D	714 821-8380	7203
James Jackson	3599	F	562 493-1402	16612
Katlan Industries Inc	3469	F	562 618-0940	13233
Kids Line LLC	2392	C	310 660-0110	3727
Lab-Clean Inc	2842	E	714 689-0063	8650
Merrill Corporation	2759	D	714 690-2200	7400
North American Petroleum	2899	E	562 598-6671	9291
Professional Bearing Svc Inc	3599	E	562 596-5023	16860
Spacesystems Holdings LLC	3624	C	714 226-1400	17243
Spinelli Graphic Inc	2759	F	562 431-3232	7495
Spintek Filtration Inc	3569	F	714 236-9190	15364
Spiracle Technology LLC	3829	F	714 418-1091	22279
Supermedia LLC	2741	B	562 594-5101	6598
Techpro Sales & Service Inc	2891	F	562 594-7878	9177
Timken Company	3562	B	714 484-2400	15113
Trend Offset Printing Svcs Inc	2752	C	859 449-2900	7141
Trend Offset Printing Svcs Inc (PA)	2752	A	562 598-2446	7142
Trend Offset Printing Svcs Inc	2752	B	562 598-2446	7143
Trend Offset Printing Svcs Inc	2752	D	714 826-2360	7144
Utbbb Inc	2052	C	562 594-4411	1387

LOS ALAMOS, CA - Santa Barbara County

Company	SIC	EMP	PHONE	ENTRY #
Bedford Winery	2084	F	805 344-2107	1655

LOS ALTOS, CA - Santa Clara County

Company	SIC	EMP	PHONE	ENTRY #
Anova Microsystems Inc	3577	F	408 941-1888	15666
Antypas & Associates Inc	3663	F	650 961-4311	18033
April Instrument	3825	F	650 964-8379	21722
Endosee Corporation	3842	F	650 383-5156	22727
Eurodesign Ltd (PA)	2511	F	650 948-5160	4695
Hambly Studios Inc	2396	E	408 496-1100	3897
Jemstep Inc	7372	E	650 966-6500	24815
Mediostream Inc	3695	E	650 625-8900	19869
Netcube Systems Inc	7372	D	650 862-7858	24951
Portworx Inc	7372	E	650 241-3222	25072
Select Communications Inc	2721	E	650 948-9000	6255
Simplefeed Inc	7372	F	650 947-7445	25176
True Circuits Inc	3679	F	650 949-3400	19772

LOS ALTOS HILLS, CA - Santa Clara County

Company	SIC	EMP	PHONE	ENTRY #
Apton Biosystems Inc	3826	F	650 284-6992	21905
Fabri-Corp	3599	E	650 941-2076	16490
Lw Consulting Services LLC	7372	F	650 919-3001	24869
Star Pacific Inc	2841	E	510 471-6555	8610

LOS ANGELES, CA - Los Angeles County

Company	SIC	EMP	PHONE	ENTRY #
10100 Holdings Inc (PA)	2451	F	310 552-0705	4545
2016 Montgomery Inc	2211	F	323 316-6886	2715
2bb Unlimited Inc	2311	E	213 253-9810	3023
3bd Holdings Inc (PA)	7372	E	323 524-0541	24298
515 W Seventh LLC	3646	F	323 278-8116	17575
5150 Fitness LLC	3949	E	323 461-1990	23481
55 Degree Wine	2084	F	323 662-5556	1635
5800 Sunset Productions Inc	2711	F	323 460-3987	5750
6f Resolution Inc	3714	D	209 467-0490	20234
A & A Jewelry Tools Findings	3999	F	213 627-8004	24019
A & M Sculptured Metals LLC	3444	E	323 263-2221	12451
A A Cater Truck Mfg Co Inc	2514	D	323 233-2343	4820
A P Smiley & Sons Inc	2512	E	323 937-2244	4757
A S G Corporation	3999	E	213 748-6361	24020
A-1 Estrn-Home-Made Pickle Inc	2035	E	323 223-1141	909
AAA Flag & Banner Mfg Co Inc	2399	C	310 836-3341	3933
Able Sheet Metal Inc (PA)	3444	E	323 269-2181	12456
Abraxis Bioscience LLC (DH)	2834	C	800 564-0216	7991
ABS By Allen Schwartz LLC (HQ)	2339	E	213 895-4400	3368
ABs Clothing Collection Inc	2339	F	213 895-4400	3369
Absolute Usa Inc	3651	E	213 744-0044	17749
Acapulco Mexican Deli Inc	2096	E	323 266-0267	2372
Accepted Co	2741	F	310 815-9553	6421
Accurate Plating Company	3471	E	323 268-8567	13307
Accurate Staging Mfg Inc (PA)	3999	E	310 324-1040	24023
Ace Holdings Inc	3911	C	213 972-2100	23227
Active Window Products	3442	D	323 245-5185	12288
Acuant Inc (HQ)	3577	E	213 867-2621	15657
Ad Hoc Labs Inc	7372	E	323 800-4927	24317
Adexa Inc (PA)	7372	E	310 642-2100	24322
Adfa Incorporated	3479	E	213 627-8004	13540
Adrienne Dresses Inc	2335	E	213 622-8557	3289
Advance Engineering & Tech Co	3821	F	213 250-8338	21457
Advance Finishing	3479	F	323 754-2889	13541
Advance Paper Box Company	2653	C	323 750-2550	5382
Advanced Skin & Hair Inc	2844	F	310 442-9700	8691
Adwear Inc (PA)	2326	E	213 629-2535	3091
Aercap US Global Aviation LLC (HQ)	3721	E	310 788-1999	20529
Aero Precision Engineering Inc	3444	F	310 642-9747	12463
Aerospace Welding Inc	7692	F	310 914-0324	25383
Agencycom LLC	7372	B	415 817-3800	24336
Agoura Music	3931	F	818 991-8316	23351
Agron Inc	2353	D	310 473-7223	3556
Ahr Signs Incorporated	3993	F	323 255-1102	23811
Al Foods Corporation	2013	E	323 222-0827	460
Aimez Closet Inc	2331	F	213 744-1222	3209
Aircoat Inc	3479	F	310 527-2258	13545
Airgas Usa LLC	2813	E	310 329-4390	7687
Ajinomoto Windsor Inc	2038	C	323 277-7000	977
Akn Holdings LLC (PA)	2721	E	310 432-7100	6100
Alan Lem & Co Inc	3231	E	310 538-4282	10674
Albatross USA Inc	2893	E	818 543-5850	9187
Albion Knitting Mills Inc	2339	E	213 624-7740	3370
Alco Plating Corp (PA)	3471	C	213 749-7561	13315
Alex Velvet Inc	3911	E	323 255-6900	23230
Alger-Triton Inc	3645	E	310 229-9500	17522
All American Label	2241	E	213 622-2222	2796
Allhealth Inc	3571	C	213 538-0762	15388
Allied Pressroom Products Inc	3952	F	323 266-6250	23704
Alna Envelope Company Inc	2754	E	323 235-3161	7197
Alona Apparel Inc	2329	F	323 232-1548	3132
Alpha Impressions Inc	2396	F	323 234-8221	3874
Alpha Polishing Corporation (PA)	3471	D	323 263-7593	13322
Alpha Productions Incorporated	3444	E	310 559-1364	12474
Alphacast Foundry Inc	3363	F	213 624-7156	11686
Altmans Products LLC	3431	E	310 559-4093	12013
Aluminum Pros Inc	3556	F	310 366-7696	14831
Alvarado Alta Calidad LLC	2519	F	323 222-0038	4904
Amays Bakery & Noodle Co Inc (PA)	2052	D	213 626-2713	1347
Ambassador Industries (PA)	2591	F	213 383-1171	5180
Ambiance USA Inc (PA)	2339	F	323 587-0007	3372
America Wood Finishes Inc	2851	F	323 232-8256	8876
American AP Dyg & Finshg Inc	2231	D	310 644-4001	2097
American Apparel (usa) LLC	2389	F	213 488-0226	3638
American Apparel Retail Inc (DH)	2211	F	213 488-0226	2719
American Fashion Group Inc (PA)	2329	F	213 748-2100	3133
American Fruits & Flavors LLC	2087	E	323 264-7791	2241
American Furniture Systems Inc	2522	F	626 457-9900	4975
American Israel Public Affairs	7372	E	323 937-1184	24356
American Marble & Granite Co (PA)	3281	F	323 268-7979	11229
American Marble & Onyx Coinc	3281	F	323 776-0900	11230
American Medical Sales Inc	3844	E	310 471-8900	22926
American Quilting Company Inc	2395	F	323 233-2500	3827
American Spring Inc	3493	F	310 324-2181	13747
American Straw Company LLC	3999	F	213 304-1095	24035
American System Publications	2741	E	323 259-1867	6432
American Zabin Intl Inc	2759	E	213 746-3770	7235
Americas Gold Inc	3911	E	213 688-4904	23234
Ames Rubber Mfg Co Inc	3069	E	818 240-9313	9586
AMG Employee Management Inc	3873	E	323 254-7448	23216
AMI/Coast Magnetics Inc	3677	E	323 936-6188	19318
Amko Restaurant Furniture Inc	2599	E	323 234-0388	5220
Amtex California Inc	2391	E	323 859-2200	3690
Amzart Inc	2099	E	323 404-9372	2452
Analytic and Computational Res	7372	F	310 471-3023	24357
Anchor Exportation USA LLC	2211	E	310 312-4575	2720
Andrea Bijoux	2389	E	213 236-0747	3641
Angell & Giroux Inc	2522	D	323 269-8596	4976
Angels Garments	2329	E	213 748-0581	3135
Angels Young Inc	2311	E	213 614-0742	3024
Angelus Aluminum Foundry Co	3365	E	323 268-0145	11725
Angelus Sheet Metal Mfg Co	3444	E	323 221-4191	12484
Anodizing Industries Inc	3471	E	323 227-4916	13331
Anschutz Film Group LLC (HQ)	3861	E	310 887-1000	23139

Employment Codes: A=Over 500 employees, B=251-500,
C=101-250, D=51-100, E=20-50, F=10-19

2019 California
Manufacturers Register

© Mergent Inc. 1-800-342-5647
1405

GEOGRAPHIC

Company	SIC	EMP	PHONE	ENTRY #
Antista Draperies Inc	2391	F	323 935-1912	3691
App Winddown LLC (HQ)	2389	E	213 488-0226	3643
Apparel Limited Inc	2339	D	323 859-2430	3374
Apparel News Group	2721	E	213 327-1002	6102
Appetize Technologies Inc	7372	C	877 559-4225	24367
Aptan Corp	2211	F	213 748-5271	2722
Aquahydrate Inc	2086	D	310 559-5058	2095
Aquarius Rags LLC (PA)	2335	E	213 895-4400	3293
Archer-Daniels-Midland Company	2041	E	323 266-2750	1026
Archer-Daniels-Midland Company	2041	F	323 269-8175	1028
Argonaut	2711	E	310 822-1629	5762
Aries 33 LLC	2329	E	310 355-8330	3137
Arnies Supply Service Ltd (PA)	2448	E	323 263-1696	4451
Arrow Diecasting Inc	3363	F	323 245-8439	11688
Arrowhead Brass & Plumbing LLC	3432	D	323 221-9137	12024
Arsenic Inc	2721	F	310 701-7559	6105
Arteffex Conceptioneering	3999	F	818 506-5358	24043
Arthur Dogswell LLC (PA)	2047	E	888 559-8833	1107
Artisan Crust	2051	E	323 759-7000	1177
Artistic Concepts	2521	F	323 257-8101	4932
Aryzta Holdings IV LLC (HQ)	2052	C	310 417-4700	1349
Aryzta LLC (DH)	2052	C	310 417-4700	1352
Arzy Company Inc	3911	F	213 627-7344	23239
Ashka Print LLC	2759	E	323 980-6008	7243
Ask Gold Company Inc	3911	E	213 622-4005	23240
Associated Students UCLA	2711	C	310 825-2787	5767
Assoluto Inc	2339	F	213 748-1116	3376
Astourian Jewelry Mfg Inc	3911	F	213 683-0436	23241
Astrochef Inc	2053	D	213 627-9860	1389
Ata Boy Inc	3999	E	323 644-0117	24045
Atlas Spring Mfgcorp	3495	C	310 532-6200	13786
Audience Inc	2741	E	323 413-2370	6441
Automation Printing Co (PA)	2791	E	213 488-1230	7626
Avalon Apparel LLC (PA)	2361	C	323 581-3511	3572
Avanzato Technology Corp	3559	E	312 509-0506	14917
Avis Roto Die Co	3544	E	323 255-7070	14482
Ax II Inc	2241	E	310 292-6523	2797
Azitex Trading Corp	2259	D	213 745-7072	2872
Azpire Print & Mediaworks LLC	2752	F	310 736-5952	6674
Azteca Jeans Inc	2339	E	323 758-7721	3378
B & C Plating Co	3471	E	323 263-6757	13342
B & Y Global Sourcing LLC	2335	F	213 891-1112	3296
B H Tank Works Inc	3443	F	323 221-1579	12361
B&F Fedelini Inc (PA)	2299	E	213 628-3901	2990
B&F Fedelini Inc	2299	E	213 628-3901	2991
B2 Apparel Inc	2389	F	323 233-0044	3644
Baatz Enterprises Inc	3711	F	323 660-4866	20129
Baby Box Company Inc (PA)	2676	F	844 422-2926	5663
Baby Guess Inc	2369	E	213 765-3100	3591
Backstage West	2721	E	323 525-2356	6108
Bae Systems Controls Inc	3511	C	323 642-5000	13990
Bandel Mfg Inc	3469	E	818 246-7493	13168
Barber-Webb Company Inc (PA)	3089	E	541 488-4821	9971
Barkevs Inc	3911	F	800 227-7321	23244
Barry Avenue Plating Co Inc	3471	D	310 478-0078	13344
Basic Industries Intl Inc	3443	C	951 226-1500	12363
Baxalta Incorporated	2834	A	818 240-5600	8060
Bb Co Inc	2339	E	213 747-4701	3381
Bd Impotex LLC	2335	F	323 521-1500	3297
Becker Woodworking	2426	F	323 564-2441	4075
Bee Darlin Inc (PA)	2335	D	213 749-2116	3298
Belagio Enterprises Inc	2211	E	323 731-6934	2724
Belair Gold Design Inc	3915	E	213 891-0152	23340
Bellas Pillow Inserts Inc	2392	F	323 235-3898	3708
Benigna	2321	F	323 262-2484	3051
Bentley Management Corporation	2721	F	323 653-8060	6112
Bereshith Inc (PA)	2331	F	213 935-8086	3216
Best Box Company Inc	2653	E	323 589-6088	5388
Best-Way Marble & Tile Co Inc	3281	E	323 266-6794	11237
Beta Box Inc	3651	E	323 383-9820	17774
Better Instant Copy	2752	F	323 782-6934	6695
Bez Ambar Inc	3911	E	213 629-9191	23246
Bhaktivedanta Book Tr Intl Inc	2731	F	310 837-5284	6315
Bidu Inc	2339	F	213 748-4433	3384
Bimbo Bakeries Usa Inc	2051	A	323 913-7214	1203
Bitmax LLC (PA)	3669	E	323 978-7878	18311
Blocks Wearables Inc	3873	F	650 307-9557	23217
Bombardier Transportation	3743	D	323 224-3461	21073
Boulevard Style Inc	2331	E	213 749-1551	3219
Boulevard Style Inc (PA)	2331	F	213 749-1551	3220
Breitburn GP LLC	1311	A	213 225-5900	34
Breitburn Operating LP (HQ)	1311	A	213 225-5900	35
Brent-Wood Products Inc	2499	E	800 400-7335	4609
Brentwood Home LLC	2515	F	213 457-7626	4855
Brighton Collectibles LLC	2387	E	626 961-9381	3627
Brite Lite Enterprises	3651	F	310 363-7120	17780
Brite Plating Co Inc	3471	D	323 263-7593	13353
Bromwell Company (PA)	3263	F	800 683-2626	10811
Bronze-Way Plating Corporation (PA)	3471	F	323 266-6933	13354
Bronze-Way Powder Coating Inc	3599	D	323 265-7024	16332
Bruce Eicher Inc (PA)	3645	F	310 657-4630	17531
Bruck Braid Company	2396	E	213 627-7611	3879
Brunettes Printing Service	2752	F	213 749-7441	6707
Brush Research Mfg Co	3991	C	323 261-2193	23787
Bulthaup Corp	2514	F	310 288-3875	4827
Bunkerhill Indus Group Inc	2326	F	323 227-4222	3096
Burning Torch Inc	2339	F	323 733-7700	3387
Byd Motors LLC (HQ)	3714	E	213 748-3980	20279
Byer California	2253	B	323 780-7615	2826
C & Y Investment Inc	2339	F	323 267-9000	3388
C Gonshor Fine Jewelry Inc	3911	E	213 629-1075	23247
C M H Records Inc	3652	E	323 663-8098	17887
C P Auto Products Inc	3471	E	323 266-3850	13360
Caer Inc	2032	E	415 879-9864	749
Cafecito Organico Oc LLC	2095	E	213 537-8367	2332
Cal Fiber Inc	2299	F	323 268-0191	2993
Cal Quake Construction Inc	1389	F	323 931-2969	191
Calhoun & Poxon Company Inc	3613	F	323 225-2328	17134
Califia Farms LLC (PA)	2086	E	213 694-4667	2104
California Broach Company	3599	F	323 260-4812	16355
California Dynamics Corp (PA)	3829	E	323 223-3882	22174
California Heavy Oil Inc	1311	E	888 848-4754	36
California Metal Processing Co	3471	E	323 753-2247	13364
California Potteries Inc	3253	E	323 235-4151	10778
California Stay Co Inc	3131	F	310 839-7236	10469
California Swatch Dyers Inc	2262	E	213 748-8425	2901
California Webbing Mills Inc	2299	F	323 753-0260	2994
Califrnia Cstume Cllctions Inc (PA)	2389	E	323 262-8383	3646
Calleen Cordero Designs Inc	3144	E	818 764-0715	10494
Camp Smidgemore Inc (DH)	2339	E	323 634-0333	3390
Cancer Genetics Inc	2835	C	323 224-3900	8466
Candella Lighting Co Inc	3646	E	323 798-1091	17592
Canterbury Designs Inc	3446	E	323 936-7111	12841
Capsa Solutions LLC	3572	E	800 437-6633	15518
Cardigan Road Productions	3679	E	310 289-1442	19478
Cardinal Glass Industries Inc	3231	E	323 319-0070	10683
Casa De Hermandad (PA)	3949	E	310 477-8272	23536
Caspian Research & Tech LLC	7372	E	310 474-3244	24475
Catalina Tempering Inc	3211	E	323 319-0070	10590
Catalina Tempering Inc (PA)	3423	E	323 789-7800	11888
Catame Inc (PA)	3965	E	213 749-2610	23763
Cbj LP	2721	E	323 549-5225	6124
Celerinos Pallets	2448	F	626 923-4182	4458
Cemcoat Inc	3471	E	323 733-0125	13367
Cemex Cnstr Mtls PCF LLC	3271	E	323 221-1280	11080
Center Thtre Group Los Angeles	2389	E	213 972-3751	3647
Cenveo Worldwide Limited	2677	D	323 261-7171	5672
Certified Enameling Inc	3479	D	323 264-4403	13567
Cha Bio & Diostech Co Ltd	2834	E	213 487-3211	8111
Chain & Charm Inc	3911	E	213 683-1039	23249
Champion-Arrowhead LLC	3432	E	323 221-9137	12030
Charles Gemeiner Cabinets	2431	E	323 299-8696	4124
Charles Ligeti Co	3911	E	213 612-0831	23251
Chevron Corporation	2911	C	310 538-7600	9328
Chol Enterprises Inc	3728	E	310 516-1328	20780
Choon Inc (PA)	2335	E	213 225-2500	3302
Christian Herald Inc	2711	E	213 353-0777	5801
Christian Today Inc	2711	F	323 931-0505	5804
Christine Alexander Inc	2395	E	213 488-1114	3835
Chromal Plating Company	3471	E	323 222-0119	13370
Chrome Hearts LLC (PA)	2386	E	323 957-7544	3610
Church Scientology Intl	2759	D	323 960-3500	7271
Cisco Bros Corp	2512	E	323 778-8612	4762
Cisco Bros Corp (PA)	2512	C	323 778-8612	4763
Citrix Online Division	7372	F	800 424-8749	24494
City Paper Box Co	2653	E	323 231-5900	5396
Civic Center News Inc	2711	E	213 481-1448	5806
Ckcc Inc	2396	E	213 629-0939	3884
Clean Water Technology Inc	3589	D	310 380-4648	16027
Cleanlogic LLC	2842	E	310 261-3001	8631
Clothing By Frenzii Inc	2331	E	213 670-0265	3225
Clothing Illustrated Inc (PA)	2339	F	213 403-9950	3395
Coalinga Corporation (PA)	1311	F	310 578-5900	49
Coast Heat Treating Co	3398	E	323 263-6944	11808
Coating Specialties Inc	3479	E	310 639-6900	20782
Coda Automotive Inc	3714	E	310 820-3611	20294
Colon Manufacturing Inc (PA)	2331	F	213 749-6149	3226
Color Image Apparel Inc	2253	E	855 793-3100	2830
Colormax Industries Inc (PA)	2211	E	213 748-6600	2730
Coltrin Inc	3317	F	323 266-6872	11476

Mergent email: customerrelations@mergent.com

2019 California
Manufacturers Register

(P-0000) Products & Services Section entry number
(PA)=Parent Co (HQ)=Headquarters (DH)=Div Headquarters

1406

Company	SIC	EMP	PHONE	ENTRY #
Commercial Sheet Metal Works	3441	E	213 748-7321	12138
Concepts By J Inc	2511	E	323 564-9988	4685
Connector Plating Corp	3471	E	310 323-1622	13379
Consolidated Graphics Inc	2759	D	323 460-4115	7283
Copenhagen Acquisition LLC (PA)	2053	D	310 899-9200	1392
Coral Reef Aquarium	3231	E	310 538-4282	10686
Cortez Furniture Mfg Inc	2512	F	323 581-5935	4765
Cougar Biotechnology Inc	2834	D	310 943-8040	8125
Cprint Holdings LLC	2752	F	213 488-0456	6763
CR & A Custom Apparel Inc	2759	E	213 749-4440	7289
Crave Foods Inc	2038	E	562 900-7272	987
Crellin Machine Company	3451	E	323 225-8101	13019
Crew Knitwear LLC (PA)	2339	D	323 526-3888	3398
Cristal Materials Inc	2515	F	323 855-1688	4857
Crucial Power Products	3679	F	323 721-5017	19502
CTS Cement Manufacturing Corp	2891	F	310 472-4004	9137
Cuadra Associates Inc (PA)	7372	E	310 591-2490	24535
Cuahutemoc Tortilleria	2099	E	323 262-0410	2497
Cubic Zee Jewelry Inc	3911	F	213 614-9800	23254
Cuddly Toys	3942	F	323 980-0572	23394
Cuevas Mattress Inc	2515	F	310 631-8382	4858
Custom Lithograph	2752	E	323 778-7751	6773
Custom Upholstered Furn Inc	2512	F	323 731-3033	4767
Cvr Nitrogen LP (DH)	2873	F	310 571-9800	9059
Cyber Medical Imaging Inc	3843	E	888 937-9729	22864
Cybrex Consulting Inc	7372	D	513 999-2109	24541
Cytrx Corporation (PA)	2836	E	310 826-5648	8544
D & R Brothers Inc	2331	E	213 747-4309	3229
D Hauptman Co Inc	3949	E	323 734-2507	23547
Dacon Systems Inc	3357	F	310 842-9933	11658
Daily Graphs Inc	2721	E	310 448-6843	6140
Daily Journal Corporation (PA)	2711	C	213 229-5300	5822
Daily Sports Seoul Usa Inc	2711	E	213 487-9331	5826
Dal-Tile Corporation	2824	F	323 257-7553	7912
Danbee Inc	2335	F	323 780-0077	3304
Darling Ingredients Inc	2077	D	323 583-6311	1526
Dash Sportswear	2339	E	323 846-2640	3402
David H Fell & Co Inc (PA)	3341	E	323 722-9992	11555
David Haid	2599	E	323 752-8096	5226
David Pirrotta Dist Inc	2844	F	323 645-7456	8733
Dbg Subsidiary Inc	2337	C	323 837-3700	3351
Dcx-Chol Enterprises Inc (PA)	3671	D	310 516-1692	18386
Dcx-Chol Enterprises Inc	3671	F	310 516-1692	18387
Dcx-Chol Enterprises Inc	3671	F	310 516-1692	18389
Dcx-Chol Enterprises Inc	3671	E	310 525-1205	18390
Dda Holdings Inc	2339	E	213 624-5200	3403
Decor Auto Inc	2396	F	323 733-9025	3888
Decor Fabrics Inc	2512	E	323 752-2200	4769
Deist Engineering Inc	2326	E	818 240-7866	3102
Delco Operating Co LP	1382	E	310 525-3535	132
Delgado Brothers LLC	2499	E	323 233-9793	4618
Delivery Zone LLC	2099	D	323 780-0888	2503
Demetrius Pohl	1481	F	323 735-1027	404
Desert Shades Inc	3999	F	323 731-5000	24077
Design Todays Inc (PA)	2339	D	213 745-3091	3406
Designed By Scorpio Inc	3911	F	213 612-4440	23255
Designs By Batya Inc	2311	F	213 746-7844	3028
Diaring Inc	3911	F	213 489-3894	23256
Didi of California Inc	2331	E	323 256-4514	3231
Digital Light LLC	3674	E	310 551-9999	18801
Discount Instant Printing	2752	F	213 622-4347	6789
DJ Safety Inc	2396	F	323 221-0000	3890
Dmbm LLC	2339	E	714 321-6032	3408
Dmh Media Network Corp	2721	E	818 732-4217	6149
Dosa Inc	2339	E	213 627-3672	3409
Doval Industries Inc	3429	D	323 226-0335	11952
Dpc Woodwork Inc	2431	E	323 935-4828	4148
Dry Aged Denim LLC (PA)	2325	F	323 780-6206	3069
Ds Services of America Inc	2086	D	323 551-5724	2131
Dubon & Sons Inc	2038	F	213 923-1182	991
Dynamation Research Inc	3728	F	909 864-2310	20804
Dynamics Orthotics & Prostheti	3842	F	213 383-9212	22719
E J Y Corporation	2395	E	213 748-1700	3843
E8 Denim House LLC	2329	F	310 386-4413	3146
Earth Lab Inc	2842	F	310 310-9009	8639
East La Lamination Inc	3089	F	323 881-9838	10083
East West Tea Company LLC	2043	F	310 275-9891	1057
Ebsco Productions Inc	3469	E	323 960-2599	13199
Eden Creamery LLC (PA)	2024	F	855 425-6867	667
Eden Equipment Company Inc	3569	F	909 629-2217	15317
Edey Manufacturing Co Inc	3442	E	323 566-6151	12312
Edmons Unque Furn Stone Gllery (PA)	2511	F	323 462-5787	4691
Edmund A Gray Co (PA)	3498	D	213 625-0376	13885
Eema Industries Inc	3648	F	323 904-0200	17688
Efaxcom (DH)	3577	D	323 817-3207	15735
EJ Diamonds Inc	3911	F	213 623-2329	23259
El Paraiso No 2	2024	E	323 587-2073	668
Electrolizing Inc	3471	E	213 749-7876	13399
Electronic Arts Inc	7372	F	310 754-7000	24601
Electronic Systems Innovation	3571	F	310 645-8400	15408
Electronic Theatre Contrls Inc	3648	F	323 461-0216	17689
Element Technica LLC	3861	F	323 993-5329	23156
Elevator Equipment Corporation (PA)	3534	D	323 245-0147	14246
Elevator Research & Mfg Co	3534	D	213 746-1914	14248
Embroidertex West Ltd (PA)	2395	F	213 749-4319	3844
Embroidery One Corp	2395	E	213 572-0280	3846
Emerald Expositions LLC	2721	C	323 525-2000	6158
Energy Lane Inc	2824	E	323 962-5020	7913
Environment Furniture Inc (HQ)	2511	E	323 782-0296	4694
Eps-Cineworks LLC	3861	F	818 766-5000	23158
Eqh Limited Inc	3423	E	310 736-4130	11893
Ergo Baby Carrier Inc (HQ)	3944	E	213 283-2090	23421
Eska Inc	2339	E	323 268-2134	3412
ET Balancing Inc	3599	F	310 538-9738	16478
Eunina Inc	2339	E	213 747-1672	3413
Euro Bello USA	2386	E	213 446-2818	3614
Everbrands Inc	3843	F	855 595-2999	22878
Everspring Chemical Inc	2899	D	310 707-1600	9248
Evy of California Inc	2361	F	213 746-4647	3577
Exactuals LLC	7372	E	310 689-7491	24633
Expert Worldwide LLC	2893	F	818 543-5850	9191
Express Sign and Neon	3993	F	323 291-3333	23873
EZ 2000 Inc	7372	F	800 273-5033	24638
F Conrad Furlong Inc	3911	F	213 623-4191	23262
Fabfad LLC	2389	F	213 488-0456	3656
Fabritex Inc	2221	F	213 747-1417	2777
Factory One Studio Inc	2211	D	323 752-1670	2737
Falcon Waterfree Tech LLC (HQ)	3069	E	310 209-7250	9614
Fansteel Inc	3462	D	323 221-1134	13098
Farsi Jewelry Mfg Co Inc	3911	F	213 624-0043	23264
Fashion Queen Mania Inc	2337	E	213 788-7310	3352
Fashion Today Inc	2339	E	213 744-1636	3415
Fashion Today Inc (PA)	2339	F	213 744-1636	3416
Fear of God LLC	2329	E	310 466-9751	3150
Felbro Inc	2542	C	323 263-8686	5139
Felbro Food Products Inc	2087	E	323 936-5266	2259
Fetish Group Inc (PA)	2329	E	323 587-7873	3152
Fierra Design Inc	2329	E	213 622-2426	3153
Fiesta Fashion Co Inc (PA)	2331	F	213 748-5775	3235
Filet Menu Inc	2754	E	310 202-8000	7201
Fisher Printing & Stamping Co	2759	F	323 933-9193	7317
Flame Gard Inc	3569	D	323 888-8707	15324
Flame Out Inc	3999	E	323 221-0000	24096
Flap Happy Inc	2369	F	310 453-3527	3592
Flash Code Solutions LLC	7372	F	800 633-7467	24653
Flaunt Magazine	2721	F	323 836-1044	6163
Flo-Mac Inc	3498	E	323 583-8751	13889
Flyer Defense LLC	3711	E	310 674-5030	20142
Foh Group Inc (PA)	2342	C	323 466-5151	3548
Food-O-Mex Corporation	2099	D	323 225-1737	2523
Foote Axle & Forge LLC	3714	E	323 268-4151	20337
Formsolver Inc	2499	F	323 664-7888	4620
Fortune Swimwear LLC (HQ)	2253	C	310 733-2130	2838
Foster Planing Mill Co	2499	F	323 759-9156	4621
Freedom Wood Finishing Inc	2269	D	213 534-6620	2912
Freeport-Mcmoran Oil & Gas LLC	1311	E	323 298-2200	60
Fresh Jive Manufacturing Inc	2321	E	213 748-0129	3055
Frisco Baking Company Inc	2051	C	323 225-6111	1254
Frm USA LLC	3497	E	323 469-9006	13869
Frontiers Media LLC	2741	E	323 930-3220	6488
Fun o Cake	2051	F	323 213-8684	1256
G & P Group Inc	2068	F	323 268-2686	1489
G&A Apparel Group	2396	F	323 234-1746	3894
Gabels Cosmetics Inc	2844	F	323 221-2430	8752
Galdaza Food Corporation	2051	E	213 747-4025	1259
Gali Corporation	3728	F	310 477-1224	20821
Gannett Co Inc	2711	E	310 444-2120	5852
Gans Ink and Supply Co Inc (PA)	2893	E	323 264-2200	9196
Gans Ink and Supply Co Inc	2893	F	770 529-7766	9197
Gardena Textile Inc	2253	E	310 327-5060	2840
Gault Millau Inc	2731	F	323 617-3982	6344
Gaze USA Inc	2339	E	213 622-0022	3420
Gaze USA Inc	2335	F	213 622-0022	3309
Gebe Electronic Services Inc	3479	E	323 731-2439	13595
Gem Box of West	2653	E	213 748-4875	5413
Gemini - G E L	2796	E	323 651-0513	7644
General Carbon Company	2816	F	323 588-9291	7742
Genesis Printing	2752	F	323 965-7935	6831
George Industries	3471	B	323 264-6660	13416
Gilli Inc	2389	F	213 744-9808	3657

Employment Codes: A=Over 500 employees, B=251-500, C=101-250, D=51-100, E=20-50, F=10-19

2019 California
Manufacturers Register

© Mergent Inc. 1-800-342-5647

1407

GEOGRAPHIC

Company	SIC	EMP	PHONE	ENTRY #
Gino Corporation	2321	F	323 234-7979	3056
Giving Keys Inc	3911	D	213 935-8791	23268
Gleason Corporation (PA)	2393	F	310 470-6001	3764
Glendale Iron	3446	F	818 247-1098	12857
Global Doors Corp	2431	F	213 622-2003	4159
Global Sales Inc	2844	E	310 474-7700	8755
Global Unlimited Export LLC	3171	F	213 365-7051	10549
GLS Apparel Usa Inc	2335	F	213 749-8484	3311
Gold Craft Jewelry Corp (PA)	3911	E	213 623-5460	23270
Gold Craft Jewelry Corp	3911	E	213 623-8673	23271
Gold Leaf & Metallic Powders	3999	E	323 769-4888	24112
Golden State Casket Co	3995	E	323 268-1783	24011
Golden Textile Inc	2211	E	323 620-2612	2740
Golf Apparel Brands Inc	2339	C	310 327-5188	3423
Good Worldwide LLC	2741	E	323 206-6495	6495
Gores Radio Holdings LLC	3699	A	310 209-3010	19976
Gory Electric Motors Inc	7694	F	323 221-3169	25462
Gourmet Coffee Warehouse Inc (PA)	2095	E	323 871-8930	2351
Grace Communications Inc (PA)	2711	E	213 628-4384	5866
Grain Craft Inc	2041	E	323 585-0131	1043
Grand West Inc (PA)	2253	F	323 235-2700	2841
Graphic Film Group LLC (PA)	2721	F	310 887-6330	6173
Grau Design Inc	2331	F	323 461-4462	3239
Greek Marble Inc	3281	F	323 221-6624	11253
Green Mattress Inc	2269	F	323 752-2026	2913
Green Mochi LLC	2335	F	213 225-2250	3312
Greneker Furniture	2541	E	323 263-9000	5065
Grenfield Consulting	1382	E	310 286-0200	138
Grey Studio Inc	2211	E	323 780-8111	2741
Grifols Biologicals LLC (DH)	2836	B	323 225-2221	8555
Group Martin LLC Johnathon	2331	E	323 235-1555	3240
Grover Products Co (PA)	3714	E	323 263-9981	20355
Grover Products Co	3714	D	323 263-9981	20356
Gtx Corp	3663	F	213 489-3019	18119
Guess Inc (PA)	2325	A	213 765-5100	3070
Guru Knits Inc	2331	D	323 235-9424	3241
GUSB Inc	2331	F	323 233-0044	3242
Gypsy 05 Inc	2339	E	323 265-2700	3424
H Starlet LLC	2339	F	323 235-8777	3425
H2 Wellness Incorporated	7372	D	310 362-1888	24718
Hanger Prosthetics & Ortho	3842	D	323 866-2555	22742
Harkham Industries Inc (PA)	2331	E	323 586-4600	3244
Hbc Solutions Holdings LLC	3663	A	321 727-9100	18124
Hd Window Fashions Inc (DH)	2591	B	213 749-6333	5192
Helicopter Tech Co Ltd Partnr	3728	E	310 523-2750	20836
Henrys Metal Polishing Works	3471	F	323 263-9701	13424
Hidden Jeans Inc (PA)	2211	F	213 746-4223	2742
High-End Knitwear Inc	2253	E	323 582-6061	2842
Hip & Hip Inc (PA)	2339	E	310 494-6742	3429
Hirsh Inc	1389	E	213 622-9441	223
Hits Magazine Inc	2721	D	323 946-7600	6184
Hive Lighting Inc	3645	E	310 773-4362	17539
Holloway House Publishing Co	2731	F	323 653-8060	6349
Hollywood Engineering Inc	3429	F	310 516-8600	11963
Home Portal LLC	3612	F	310 559-6100	17098
Honey Punch Inc (PA)	2339	F	323 800-3812	3430
Honeywell International Inc	3724	B	310 410-9605	20658
Hostrup Industries Inc	3999	F	310 477-6770	24121
HP Core Co Inc	3543	F	323 582-1688	14465
Hq Brands LLC	2389	F	213 627-7922	3658
Huge Usa Inc	2211	F	213 741-1707	2743
Hunter Digital Ltd	3577	F	310 471-5852	15754
Hunter/Gratzner Industries	3999	F	310 578-9929	24125
Huntsman Advanced Materials AM	2821	C	818 265-7221	7840
I Color Printing & Mailing Inc (PA)	2752	F	310 997-1452	6867
I Joah (PA)	2339	F	213 742-0500	3431
I T I Electro-Optic Corp (PA)	3823	E	310 445-8900	21601
I T I Electro-Optic Corp.	3823	E	310 312-4526	21602
IaMplus LLC	3699	F	323 210-3852	19979
Ibisworld Inc	2741	E	212 626-6794	6501
ICI Architectural Millwork Inc	2431	F	323 759-4993	4167
Impak Corporation	3081	F	323 277-4700	9710
Imperial Shade Venetian Blind	2542	F	323 233-4391	5147
Indie Source Inc	2326	E	424 200-2027	3107
Industrial Glass Products Inc	3231	F	323 526-7125	10704
Industry Inc (HQ)	7372	E	310 463-6157	24763
Infiniti Plastic Technologies	3089	F	310 618-8288	10150
Inflatable Advertising Co Inc	3993	F	213 387-6839	23900
Infokorea Inc	2721	E	213 487-1580	6192
Informa Media Inc	2721	D	301 755-0162	6194
Ink & Color Inc	2752	E	310 280-6601	6881
International Bus Mchs Corp	3571	A	310 412-8699	15432
Interntonal Metallurgical Svcs	3398	F	310 645-7300	11815
Interstate Steel Center Co	3355	E	323 583-0855	11618
Investors Business Daily Inc (HQ)	2711	C	310 448-6000	5892
IOu International Inc	2297	E	323 846-0056	2966
Iq Textile Ind Inc	2299	F	213 745-2290	3001
Izurieta Fence Company Inc	3315	F	323 661-4759	11447
J & C Apparel	2325	E	323 490-8260	3075
J Brand Inc	2211	D	213 749-3500	2745
J Hellman Frozen Foods Inc (PA)	2037	E	213 243-9105	953
J K Star Corp	2329	D	310 538-0185	3165
J P B Jewelry Box Co (PA)	2541	F	323 225-0500	5072
J&Company Jeans LLC	2211	E	323 260-7329	2746
J-M Manufacturing Company Inc (PA)	3084	C	800 621-4404	9782
James Stewart	2834	E	323 778-1687	8237
James West Inc (PA)	2325	F	310 380-1510	3076
Jamm Industries Corp	2339	F	213 622-0555	3434
Jan-Al Innerprizes Inc	3161	E	323 260-7212	10525
Janel Glass Company Inc	3231	E	323 661-8621	10708
Jason Markk Inc	2842	F	213 687-7060	8648
Jay-Cee Blouse Co Inc	2335	C	213 622-0116	3316
JC Trimming Company Inc	2335	D	323 235-4458	3317
Jerry Solomon Enterprises Inc	2499	E	323 556-2265	4626
Jet Plastics (PA)	3089	D	323 268-6706	10169
Jewelry Club House Inc	3911	F	213 362-7888	23278
Jimo Enterprises	2499	E	323 469-0805	4627
JM Kitchen Cabinets	2434	F	323 752-6520	4315
Jodi Kristopher LLC (PA)	2335	C	323 890-8000	3318
Joes Custom Furn & Frames	2511	F	323 721-1881	4707
Johnny Was Collection Inc (PA)	2335	E	323 231-8222	3319
Johnson & Johnson Consumer Inc	2844	E	310 642-1150	8777
Jonathan Louis Intl Ltd	2512	B	213 622-6114	4787
Jones Iron Works	3446	E	323 386-2648	12868
Joong-Ang Daily News Cal Inc (HQ)	2711	C	213 368-2500	5894
Jose Martinez	2064	E	323 263-6230	1434
Jouer Cosmetics LLC	2844	F	310 312-0500	8780
Journal of Bocommunication Inc	2711	E	310 475-4708	5896
Jsl Foods Inc (PA)	2099	C	323 223-2484	2548
JT Design Studio Inc (PA)	2339	E	213 891-1500	3440
Juan Brambila Sr	2511	E	323 939-8312	4709
Judson Studios Inc	3231	F	323 255-0131	10710
Judy O Productions Inc	2731	E	323 938-8513	6358
K Too	2331	E	213 747-7766	3247
K-Swiss Inc (HQ)	3021	C	323 675-2700	9474
Kalypsys Inc	2834	C	858 552-0674	8242
Kamiran Inc	2331	E	213 746-9161	3248
Kan Group Corp	2741	E	213 383-1236	6511
Kareem Corporation	3949	F	323 234-0724	23600
Karoun Dairies Inc	2022	F	323 666-6222	580
Kathryn M Ireland Inc (PA)	2211	E	323 965-9888	2750
Katz Millennium Sls & Mktg Inc	3663	D	323 966-5066	18143
Kayo of California (PA)	2337	E	323 233-6107	3353
Kc Exclusive Inc (PA)	2339	D	213 749-0088	3444
Keepcup Ltd	3089	E	310 957-2070	10175
Keller Entertainment Group Inc	3577	E	818 981-4950	15777
Kenneth Miller Clothing Inc	2339	E	213 746-8866	3445
Kesmor Associates	3911	E	213 629-2300	23281
Kim Seng Jewelry Inc	3915	F	213 628-8566	23344
King Wire Partitions Inc	3449	E	323 256-4846	12983
Kitsch LLC (PA)	3911	F	424 240-5551	23282
Kitty Textile Inc (PA)	2339	F	213 749-7278	3447
Klk Forte Industry Inc (PA)	2339	E	323 415-9181	3448
Knight Publishing Corp	2721	E	323 653-8060	6200
Knit Fit Inc	2396	F	213 673-4731	3901
Kobi Katz Inc	3911	D	213 689-0076	23283
Komarov Enterprises Inc	2337	D	213 244-7000	3355
Komex International Inc	2331	E	323 233-9005	3250
Krissy Op Shins USA Inc	2329	D	213 747-2591	3170
Kritech Corporation (PA)	3679	C	310 538-9940	19612
Kt Industries Inc	3613	F	323 255-7143	17149
Kwdz Manufacturing LLC (PA)	2361	D	323 526-3526	3580
Kymsta Corp	2339	E	213 380-8118	3450
Kyocharo USA LLC	2711	E	213 383-1236	5903
L Y A Group Inc	2339	F	213 683-1123	3451
La Aloe LLC	2037	E	888 968-2563	957
La Barca Tortilleria Inc	2099	E	323 268-1744	2558
LA Cabinet & Millwork Inc	2541	E	323 227-5000	5078
La Famosa Manufacture Inc	2512	F	323 241-3100	4790
La Fortaleza Inc	2099	D	323 261-1211	2564
LA Gem and Jwly Design Inc	3911	D	213 488-1290	23284
La Gloria Foods Corp (PA)	2099	D	323 262-0410	2565
La Gloria Foods Corp	2099	D	323 263-6755	2566
La La Land Production & Design	3111	E	323 267-8485	10461
La Mamba LLC	2331	E	323 526-3526	3251
La Mousse	2038	D	310 478-6051	999
La Opinion LP (HQ)	2711	C	213 896-2196	5904
La Princesita Tortilleria (PA)	2099	E	323 267-0673	2568
LA Printing & Graphics Inc	2752	E	310 527-4526	6937
La Swim LLC	2253	F	213 689-4575	2846

Company	SIC	EMP	PHONE	ENTRY #
La Times	2711	F	213 237-2279	5905
La Weekly	2711	C	310 574-7100	5906
La Zamorana Candy	2064	F	323 583-7100	1436
Labeltex Mills Inc (PA)	3965	C	323 582-0228	23769
Larry Spun Products Inc	3469	E	323 881-6300	13241
Lasani-Felt Co	2299	E	323 233-5278	3003
Lasercare Technologies Inc (PA)	3955	E	310 202-4200	23733
Lauras French Baking Co Inc	2051	E	323 585-5144	1280
Lavash Corporation	2051	F	323 663-5249	1281
Lavish Clothing Inc	2335	F	213 745-5400	3322
Lawrence O Lawrence Ltd	2299	F	323 935-1100	3005
Layered Luxe Inc	2335	F	323 513-8200	3323
Lee & Fields Publishing Inc	2741	F	213 380-5858	6516
Lee Thomas Inc (PA)	2339	E	310 532-7560	3454
Lefton Technologies Inc	3625	F	818 986-1728	17284
Legion Creative Group	2759	E	323 498-1100	7385
Lemor Trims Inc	2396	F	213 741-1646	3902
Leos Cabinets	2599	F	323 759-7649	5243
Lets Go Apparel Inc (PA)	2389	F	213 863-1767	3667
Lf Sportswear Inc (PA)	2331	E	310 437-4100	3252
Lialee Inc	2253	F	213 765-7788	2847
Line Euro-Americas Corp	7372	F	323 591-0380	24858
Lito	2341	E	323 260-4692	3538
Lito Childrens Wear Inc	2311	E	323 260-4692	3033
Livingstone Jewelry Co Inc	3911	F	213 683-1040	23288
Los Angeles Bus Jurnl Assoc	2721	E	323 549-5225	6209
Los Angeles Mills Inc	2211	E	424 307-0075	2751
Los Angeles Poultry Co Inc	2015	D	323 232-3475	546
Los Angeles Sentinel Inc	2711	E	323 299-3800	5917
Los Angles Tmes Cmmnctions LLC	2711	C	213 237-7203	5920
Los Angles Tmes Cmmnctions LLC	2711	E	213 237-7987	5927
Los Angles Tmes Cmmnctions LLC	2711	C	213 237-5691	5928
Lost Art Liquids LLC	3999	F	213 816-2988	24165
Louise Green Millinery Co Inc	2353	F	310 479-1881	3567
Low Voltage Architecture Inc	3699	E	310 573-7588	20008
Lucky Brand Dungarees LLC (HQ)	2325	D	213 443-5700	3083
Luis Wtkins Cstm Wrught Ir LLC	2514	E	310 836-5655	4836
Lumenton Inc	3648	E	323 904-0202	17709
Luna Imaging Inc	7372	F	323 908-1400	24868
Luna Mora LLC	2396	F	310 550-6979	3904
Lupitas Bakery Inc (PA)	2051	F	323 752-2391	1286
Lyric Culture LLC	2331	F	323 581-3511	3256
M & H Creative Design Inc	3911	F	213 627-8881	23291
M C Woodwork	2448	F	323 233-0954	4486
M Stevens Inc	2339	F	323 661-2147	3458
M-5 Steel Mfg Inc (PA)	3443	E	323 263-9383	12397
Machine Building Specialties	3556	E	323 666-8289	14868
Machnet Inc	3545	F	310 909-2020	14646
Major Fulfillment Inc	2752	F	310 323-2326	6958
Makerskit LLC	3944	E	213 973-7019	23439
March Vision Care Inc	3851	E	310 665-0975	23108
Margus Automotive Elc Exch	3714	D	323 232-5281	20396
Marina Sportswear Inc	2339	E	323 232-2012	3465
Marna Ro LLC	2361	F	310 801-5788	3583
Mars Food Us LLC	2044	B	562 616-7347	1088
Marshall & Swift/Boeckh LLC	2731	F	213 683-9000	6360
Martin Aerospace Corporation	3492	F	310 231-0055	13744
Martin Sports Inc (PA)	3949	E	509 529-2554	23612
Matchmaster Dyg & Finshg Inc (PA)	2269	C	323 232-2061	2914
Matchmaster Dyg & Finshg Inc	2257	D	323 232-2061	2866
Matteo LLC	2392	E	213 617-2813	3732
Matthews Manufacturing Inc	3444	E	323 980-4373	12659
Max Fischer & Sons Inc	2392	E	213 624-8756	3733
McKenna Boiler Works Inc	3443	F	323 221-1171	12398
Mdc Interior Solutions LLC	2389	D	800 621-4006	3671
Meadow Farms Sausage Co Inc	2013	F	323 752-2300	506
Meat Packers Butchers Sup Inc	3556	F	323 268-8514	14870
Mededge Inc	3841	F	310 745-2290	22523
Media Gobbler Inc	7372	F	323 203-3222	24896
Medical Tactile Inc	3841	F	310 641-8228	22527
Mercury Plastics Inc	3081	D	323 264-2400	9714
Merelex Corporation	2819	E	310 208-0551	7787
Merit Printing Ink Company	2893	F	323 268-1807	9206
Merle Norman Cosmetics Inc (PA)	2844	B	310 641-3000	8795
Merlos Precast Products	3272	F	310 323-0234	10956
Merrill Corporation	2759	D	213 253-5900	7399
Merrill Corporation	2759	E	949 252-9449	7404
Merrill Corporation Inc	2759	E	310 552-5288	7405
Metal Fabrication and Art LLC	3441	F	323 980-9595	12207
Metro Novelty & Pleating Co	2396	C	213 748-1201	3906
Mf Inc	2331	E	213 627-2498	3258
MGT Industries Inc (PA)	2339	C	310 516-5900	3467
Micro Surface Engr Inc (PA)	3399	E	323 582-7348	11843
Midthrust Imports Inc	2259	E	213 749-6651	2874
Mighty Soy Inc	3556	F	323 266-6969	14871
Mika Color	2796	F	323 254-1450	7652
Millennial Brands LLC	3144	F	925 230-0617	10500
Minachee Inc	2326	F	213 745-8100	3114
Mintie Corporation	3444	F	510 351-5868	12680
Miss Kim Inc	2335	F	213 747-4011	3327
Misyd Corp (PA)	2361	D	213 742-1800	3584
Mitratech Holdings Inc	7372	F	323 964-0000	24926
Mixmor Inc	3531	F	323 664-1941	14182
Mj Blanks Inc	2253	E	213 629-0006	2851
Mjw Inc	3561	D	323 778-8900	15085
Mk Tool and Abrasive Inc	3291	F	562 776-8818	11299
Mnm Corporation (PA)	2721	D	213 627-3737	6219
Mobile Tone Inc	3663	F	323 939-6928	18186
Mod2 Inc	7372	F	213 747-8424	24931
Modern Gold Design Inc	3911	F	213 614-1818	23298
Modern Metals Industries Inc	3841	E	800 437-6633	22546
Modular Communications Systems	3663	E	818 764-1333	18187
Monarchy Diamond Inc	1499	B	213 924-1161	417
Monopole Inc	2851	F	818 500-8585	8919
Monrow Inc	2331	E	213 741-6007	3259
Monterey Canyon LLC (PA)	2339	D	213 741-0209	3468
Morrissey Bros Printers Inc	2759	E	323 233-7197	7409
Mother Plucker Feather Co Inc	3999	F	213 637-0411	24179
Motorola Solutions Inc	3663	E	213 362-6706	18193
Motorola Solutions Inc	3663	C	954 723-4730	18194
MSP Group Inc	2211	E	310 660-0022	2752
Multi Packaging Solutions Inc	2752	E	818 638-0216	6985
Multimedia Operations Design (PA)	2542	E	818 848-1303	5156
MXF Designs Inc	2331	D	323 266-1451	3260
Naftex Westside Partners Limit	1311	E	310 277-9004	65
Naked Princess Worldwide LLC (PA)	2844	F	310 271-1199	8801
NAPA Industries Inc	3999	F	310 293-1209	24183
Napoleon Bakery Inc	2051	D	323 651-3822	1294
Nareg Jewelry Inc	3911	F	213 683-1660	23300
Nathan Kimmel Company LLC	2394	F	213 627-8556	3798
National Diamond Lab Cal	3545	F	818 240-5770	14657
National Ready Mixed Con Co	3273	F	323 245-5539	11147
Nationwide Jewelry Mfrs Inc	3911	F	213 489-1215	23301
Native American Media	2721	F	310 475-6845	6223
Nelson Jewellery (usa) Inc	3915	F	213 489-3323	23345
Nelson Name Plate Company (PA)	2759	C	323 663-3971	7412
Network Automation Inc	7372	E	213 738-1700	24955
Neural Analytics Inc	3841	F	818 317-4999	22553
New Fragrance Continental	2844	F	323 766-0060	8804
New Green Day LLC	2611	E	323 566-7603	5269
New Rise Brand Holdings LLC	2325	E	323 233-9005	3084
Nexsun Corp	2869	E	213 382-2220	9025
Nexxen Apparel Inc (PA)	2339	F	323 267-9900	3469
Night Fashion Inc	2335	E	213 747-8740	3328
Ninja Jump Inc	3944	D	323 255-5418	23452
Noahs Ark International Inc	2331	F	714 521-1235	3262
Nonstop Printing Inc	2752	F	323 464-1640	6996
Norchem Corporation (PA)	3559	D	323 221-0221	15001
Normandie Country Bakery Inc (PA)	2051	E	323 939-5528	1296
Not Only Jeans Inc	2211	E	213 765-9725	2754
Novela Designs Inc	3961	E	213 505-4092	23755
NRC USA Inc	3639	E	213 325-2780	17416
NRG Evgo	3694	F	310 268-8017	19841
Nuorder Inc	7372	E	310 954-1313	24976
Oak Apparel Inc	2339	F	213 489-9766	3472
Ocean Beauty Seafoods LLC	2091	C	213 624-2101	2298
Off Price Network LLC	2337	E	213 477-8205	3358
Offenhauser Sales Corp	3714	F	323 225-1307	20412
Offline Inc (PA)	2342	F	213 742-9001	3552
Ola Corporate Services Inc	3579	F	323 655-1005	15908
Old Country Millwork Inc	3547	E	323 234-2940	14717
Old Pueblo Ranch Inc (PA)	2099	C	323 268-2791	2628
Omega Graphics Printing Hollyw	2752	F	213 784-5200	7003
On-Line Power Incorporated (PA)	3612	E	323 721-5017	17109
On-Line Power Incorporated	3612	D	323 720-4125	17110
ONeil Capital Management	2754	C	310 448-6400	7209
ONeil Digital Solutions LLC	2752	C	310 448-6407	7005
Ophir Rf Inc	3663	E	310 306-5556	18206
Opti Lite Optical	3851	E	323 932-6828	23116
Orange Corporation	2342	F	323 266-0700	3553
Orbita Corp (PA)	2381	F	213 746-4783	3603
Ordway Metal Polishing	3471	E	323 225-3373	13471
Organicsorb LLC	1499	F	310 795-4011	418
Originclear Inc (PA)	3589	E	323 939-6645	16083
Orora Visual TX LLC	2759	D	323 258-4111	7425
Output Inc	7372	F	310 795-6099	25041
P & R Pallets Inc	2448	F	213 327-1104	4490
P Kay Metal Inc (PA)	3356	F	323 585-5058	11636
P&P Enterprises	3993	F	213 802-0890	23940
Pabst Brewing Company LLC (PA)	2082	B	310 470-0962	1619

Employment Codes: A=Over 500 employees, B=251-500,
C=101-250, D=51-100, E=20-50, F=10-19

2019 California
Manufacturers Register

© Mergent Inc. 1-800-342-5647

GEOGRAPHIC

1409

Company	SIC	EMP	PHONE	ENTRY #
Pac Fill Inc	2026	E	818 409-0117	732
Pacific Coast Bach Label Co	2269	E	213 612-0314	2915
Pacific Coast Ironworks Inc	3441	F	323 585-1320	12223
Pacific Manufacturing MGT Inc	2542	D	323 263-9000	5160
Pacific Play Tents Inc	2394	F	323 269-0431	3800
Padilla Jewelers Inc	3911	F	323 931-1678	23305
Padilla Remberto	2261	F	323 268-1111	2889
Pai Gp Inc	3231	D	323 549-5355	10726
Paint-Chem Inc	2851	F	213 747-7725	8922
Pallet Masters Inc	2448	D	323 758-1713	4497
Pallets 4 Less Inc	2448	F	213 377-7813	4499
Panavision Inc	3861	D	323 464-3800	23184
Panchos Bakery	2051	E	323 582-9109	1305
Papercutters Inc	2671	E	323 888-1330	5531
Paramount Mattress Inc	2515	F	323 264-3451	4877
Parts Out Inc (PA)	3694	F	626 560-1540	19843
Patriot Lighting Inc	3646	F	213 741-9757	17637
Peep Inc	2339	E	213 748-5500	3477
Peking Noodle Co Inc	2098	E	323 223-0897	2437
Penhouse Media Group Inc	2721	E	310 575-4835	6230
Pentrate Metal Processing	3471	E	323 269-2121	13473
Peoples Sausage Company	2013	F	213 627-8633	514
Perfection Machine and Tl Work	3599	E	213 749-5095	16839
Petrochem Marketing	2951	F	323 526-4084	9394
Petroil Americas Limited	2911	F	323 931-3720	9350
Pharmaco-Kinesis Corporation	3841	E	310 641-2700	22582
Phoenix Aerial Systems Inc	3829	E	323 577-3366	22250
Piccone Apparel Corp	2339	E	310 559-6702	3480
Pierre Mitri (PA)	2339	F	213 747-1838	3481
Piet Retief Inc	2339	E	323 732-8312	3482
Pinnacle Worldwide Inc	3629	F	909 628-2200	17349
Pioneer Diecasters Inc	3363	F	323 245-6561	11704
Pitney Bowes Inc	3579	E	310 312-4288	15913
Pixi Inc	2844	F	310 670-7767	8819
Planned Parenthood Los Angeles	2741	F	323 256-1717	6551
Plastique Unique Inc	3089	E	310 839-3968	10292
Plastpro 2000 Inc (PA)	3089	C	310 693-8600	10294
Playboy Enterprises Intl Inc	2741	D	310 424-1800	6552
Plush Home Inc	2511	E	323 852-1912	4731
Poetry Corporation (PA)	2337	E	213 765-8957	3359
Polyalloys	3532	D	310 715-9800	14201
Polymond Dk Inc	2339	E	213 327-0771	3484
Polytex Manufacturing Inc (PA)	2284	F	323 726-0140	2955
Popular TV Networks LLC	2711	F	323 822-3324	6016
Power Fasteners Inc	3452	E	323 232-4362	13080
PPG Industries Inc	2851	E	310 559-2335	8927
Practice Management Info Corp (PA)	2731	E	323 954-0224	6383
Precision Steel Products Inc	3444	E	310 523-2002	12721
Precision Wire Products Inc	3312	E	323 569-8165	11410
Press Brothers Juicery LLC	2033	E	213 389-3645	849
Pressure Profile Systems Inc	3823	F	310 641-8100	21634
Prints Charmn Inc (PA)	2752	F	310 312-0904	7051
Private Brand Mdsg Corp	2335	E	213 749-0191	3333
Pro Tag Corp	2253	E	213 272-9606	2853
Project Cloudkey Inc	7372	F	310 596-8160	25083
Project Social T LLC	2331	E	323 266-4500	3268
Promises Promises Inc	2335	E	213 749-7725	3335
Proto Homes LLC	3792	E	310 271-7544	21209
Prudential Lighting Corp (PA)	3646	C	213 477-1694	17639
PSM Industries Inc (PA)	3499	D	888 663-8256	13966
Puma Biotechnology Inc (PA)	2834	D	424 248-6500	8350
Pure Cotton Incorporated	2326	D	213 507-3270	3118
Pvh Neckwear Inc (HQ)	2323	A	213 688-7970	3067
Pw Eagle Inc	3084	B	800 621-4404	9786
Q&A7 LLC	2339	F	323 364-4250	3487
Q-Lite Usa LLC	3643	C	310 736-2977	17488
Qjm Corp	3911	F	213 622-0264	23306
Qre Operating LLC	1382	C	213 225-5900	145
Queens Bakery Inc (PA)	2051	F	323 222-6447	1314
R & R Industries Inc	2395	E	323 581-6000	3858
R R Donnelley & Sons Company	2759	E	310 789-4100	7460
R R Donnelley & Sons Company	2759	E	213 928-0967	7461
Rada Industry	3999	F	323 265-3727	24218
Rafu Shimpo	2711	E	213 629-2231	6022
Rainbow Manufacturing Co Inc	2521	F	323 778-2093	4964
Rainbow Novelty Creations Co	2261	E	323 855-9464	2891
Rainbow Sublymation Inc	2759	F	213 489-5001	7464
Ram Off Road Accessories Inc	3714	F	323 266-3850	20437
Randolph & Hein	2511	F	323 233-6010	4734
Rangefinder Publishing Co Inc	2721	F	310 846-4770	6243
Rapid Anodizing Inc	3559	F	323 753-5255	15016
Rapid Industries	3471	F	323 753-5255	13488
Rau Restoration	2431	F	310 445-1128	4216
Raytheon Company	3812	D	310 338-1324	21399
Ready Industries Inc	2752	F	213 749-2041	7079
Rebelkingsnugus LLc	2211	F	323 667-8565	2759
Recruitment Services Inc	2721	F	213 364-1960	6245
Red Brick Corporation	2752	F	323 549-9444	7080
Red Engine Inc	2325	F	213 742-8858	3085
Reeds Inc	2086	F	310 217-9400	2183
Regal Furniture Manufacturing	2512	F	323 971-9185	4806
Relational Center	7372	E	323 935-1807	25124
Remba Partners LLC	2741	F	310 858-8495	6568
Renee C	2337	F	213 741-0095	3361
Rentech Inc (PA)	2999	D	310 571-9800	9457
Rentech Ntrgn Pasadena Spa LLC	2873	E	310 571-9805	9071
Reyes Coca-Cola Bottling LLC	2086	F	213 744-8600	2206
Rezex Corporation	2269	E	213 622-2015	2917
Rfl Global Inc	7372	F	323 235-2580	25129
Rhapsody Clothing Inc	2339	D	213 614-8887	3489
Rheetech Sales & Services Inc	2759	F	213 749-9111	7470
Rhodes Publications Inc	2721	F	213 385-4781	6247
Richee Lighting Inc	3648	F	213 814-1638	17729
Richline Textile Inc	2211	E	323 792-1030	2760
Ricks America Inc	2254	F	323 232-6800	2864
Ricky Reader LLC	2731	F	323 231-4322	6386
Rider Circulation Services	2711	F	323 344-1200	6028
Ridgeline Power LLC	3674	E	800 504-5844	19127
Rising Beverage Company LLC	2086	D	310 556-4500	2211
RJ Jewelry Inc	3911	F	213 627-9936	23310
RJ Singer International Inc	3161	D	323 735-1717	10532
Rm 518 Management LLC	2389	E	213 624-6788	3678
Rnk Industries Co	2211	F	323 446-0777	2761
Rnovate Inc	3568	E	213 489-1617	15293
Robeks Corporation	2099	E	310 642-7800	2656
Rock Rag Inc	2741	F	818 919-9364	6570
Roman Empire Furn Parts Mfg	2512	E	323 264-8857	4808
Roman Upholstery Manufacturing	2512	E	310 479-3252	4809
Ron Teeguarden Enterprises Inc (PA)	2833	E	323 556-8188	7968
Ronald D Teson Inc	2426	E	310 532-5987	4090
Rondor Music International (PA)	2741	E	310 235-4800	6571
Roscoe Moss Manufacturing Co (PA)	3317	D	323 261-4185	11485
Roscoe Moss Manufacturing Co	3317	D	323 263-4111	11486
Rose Genuine Inc	2361	E	213 747-4120	3586
Rosenkranz Enterprises Inc	3471	F	323 583-9021	13493
Rosetti Gennaro Furniture	2511	E	323 750-7794	4736
Roy E Hanson Jr Mfg (PA)	3443	D	213 747-7514	12416
Rpsz Construction LLC	3949	E	314 677-5831	23642
Rtg Investment Group Inc	3949	F	310 444-5554	23643
Rucci Inc	3999	E	323 778-9000	24226
Ruth Training Center Sew Mchs	2399	F	213 748-8033	3962
S D M Furniture Co Inc	2511	F	323 936-0295	4737
S Sedghi Inc (PA)	2361	E	213 745-2019	3588
S Studio Inc	2337	D	213 388-7400	3363
S&H International Inc	3645	F	213 626-7112	17558
Sage Machado Inc	3911	F	323 931-0595	23313
Sakura Noodle Inc	2098	F	213 623-2396	2438
Salsbury Industries Inc (PA)	2542	C	323 846-6700	5165
Samis Sports	3949	F	323 965-8093	23647
Sams Trade Development Corp	3961	F	213 225-0188	23758
Samuel French Inc	2741	F	323 876-0570	6573
Samyang USA Inc	2098	F	562 946-9977	2439
San Antonio Winery Inc (PA)	2084	C	323 223-1401	1964
Sanitek Products Inc	2842	F	323 245-6781	8675
Santa Monica City of	3589	F	310 826-6712	16105
Sarahs Leather Mfg	3199	E	323 262-2594	10580
Scottex Inc	2399	F	310 516-1411	3964
Sea Snack Foods Inc (PA)	2092	E	213 622-2204	2322
Secret Road Music Pubg Inc	2731	F	323 464-1234	6390
Securedata Inc	7372	F	424 363-8529	25159
Security Textile Corporation	2396	D	213 747-2673	3918
Sedas Printing Inc	2752	F	323 469-1034	7099
Sees Candy Shops Incorporated	2064	C	310 559-4919	1456
Semore Inc	2325	E	213 746-4122	3087
Sencha Naturals Inc	2064	F	213 353-9908	1457
Sereechai Newspaper Inc	2711	F	323 465-7550	6043
Serv-Rite Meat Company Inc	2013	D	323 227-1911	525
Seven For All Mankind LLC- (DH)	2325	B	323 406-5300	3088
Sgk LLC	2796	C	323 258-4111	7657
Shane Hunter LLC	2389	E	213 749-9390	3680
Sieena Inc	7372	E	310 455-6188	25172
Siemens Hlthcare Dgnostics Inc	2835	D	310 645-8200	8513
Siemens Industry Inc	3569	E	724 772-1237	15361
Silver Textile Incorporated	2241	F	213 747-2221	2807
Silvestri Studio Inc (PA)	3999	D	323 277-4420	24242
Silvestri Studio Inc	3999	F	323 735-1481	24243
Silvias Costumes	2389	E	323 661-2142	3681
Silvus Technologies Inc (PA)	3663	E	310 479-3333	18253
Simcardz4u Inc	3728	F	213 359-0602	20932
Simon of California (PA)	3161	E	310 559-4871	10536

Mergent email: customerrelations@mergent.com
1410

2019 California
Manufacturers Register

(P-0000) Products & Services Section entry number
(PA)=Parent Co (HQ)=Headquarters (DH)=Div Headquarters

Name	SIC	EMP	PHONE	ENTRY #
Sissell Bros	3272	F	323 261-0106	11003
Skate Group Inc	2389	F	213 749-6651	3682
Skirt Inc	2326	E	213 553-1134	3122
Sky Jeans Inc	2211	E	323 778-2065	2762
Sky Luxury Corp	2339	E	323 940-0111	3498
Sledge Usa Inc	2339	E	213 747-4400	3499
Sleepow Ltd	2211	E	646 688-0808	2763
Smb Clothing Inc	2339	F	213 489-4949	3500
SMD Enterprises Inc	3253	E	323 235-4151	10790
Smiley Group Inc	2731	F	323 290-4690	6392
Snf Holding Company	2899	F	323 266-4435	9307
Sofa U Love (PA)	2512	E	323 464-3397	4811
Solow	2339	E	323 664-7772	3502
Songbird Ocarinas LLC	3931	F	323 269-2524	23389
Songs Music Publishing LLC	2741	F	323 939-3511	6583
Sonicsensory Inc (PA)	3021	F	818 256-7900	9486
Sonmez Emre	2399	F	323 589-6000	3967
Sony/Atv Music Publishing LLC	2741	E	310 441-1300	6584
Sooraksan Soojebi	3421	F	213 389-2818	11884
Soteleo Salvadar	3993	E	213 621-2040	23978
Southwest Plating Co Inc	3471	E	323 753-3781	13507
Specialists In Cstm Sftwr Inc	7372	E	310 315-9660	25205
Specialty Surface Grinding	3599	F	310 538-4352	16958
Spectrum Plating Company Inc	3471	E	310 533-0748	13508
Spinmedia Group Inc	2741	C	323 203-1333	6588
Spirit Sciences Usa Inc (PA)	2834	F	310 568-1030	8389
Spoety Cuts Corporation	2869	F	310 908-1512	9044
Spotlite Media Inc	7372	E	650 447-9135	25209
Stadco (PA)	3545	C	323 227-8888	14680
Stainless Industrial Companies	3544	D	310 575-9400	14572
Standard Homeopathic Co (PA)	2834	D	310 768-0700	8393
Standardvision LLC	3993	E	323 222-3630	23980
Staples Inc	2339	E	213 623-4395	3506
Star Ave	2339	E	213 623-5799	3507
Stardust Diamond Corp	3915	F	213 239-9999	23348
Starlion Inc	2321	E	323 233-8823	3060
Steeldeck Inc	3999	E	323 290-2100	24254
Stella Fashions Inc	2339	E	213 746-6889	3508
Steps Apparel Group Inc (PA)	2339	E	323 261-2233	3509
Stepstone Inc	3272	E	310 327-7474	11007
Stic-Adhesive Products Co Inc	2891	C	323 268-2956	9172
Stillhouse LLC	2085	E	323 498-1111	2077
Stion Corporation (PA)	3674	D	408 284-7200	19190
Stitch Factory	2395	F	310 523-3337	3863
Stone Merchants LLC	3281	D	310 471-1815	11282
Stony Apparel Corp (PA)	2339	C	323 981-9080	3510
Studio Systems Inc (PA)	2741	E	323 634-3400	6594
Style Plus Inc (PA)	2331	F	213 205-8408	3274
Style Up America Inc	3949	F	213 553-1134	23664
Sublitex Inc	2335	E	323 582-9596	3339
Sugarsync Inc	7372	E	650 571-5105	25233
Sun Valley Products Inc	3354	E	818 247-8350	11604
Sun Valley Products Inc (HQ)	3354	D	818 247-8350	11605
Sunflower Imports Inc	2329	F	213 748-3444	3193
Sunnyside Llc	2341	F	213 745-3070	3545
Sunrise Wood Products Inc	2431	E	323 971-6540	4239
Sunwood Doors Inc	2431	E	562 951-9401	4240
Super Vias & Trim	2396	F	323 233-2556	3924
Superior Emblem & Embroidery	2395	E	213 747-4103	3865
Superior Pipe Fabricators Inc	3498	F	323 569-6500	13905
Surco Products Inc	3446	F	310 323-2520	12895
Surgeon Worldwide Inc	3144	E	707 501-7962	10503
Suri Steel Inc	3441	F	323 224-3166	12253
Susan Zadi	2092	F	424 223-3526	2325
Sustain Technologies Inc (PA)	3695	F	213 229-5300	19883
Sweet Donaldson Met Spinning	3444	F	323 268-8730	12780
Swimwear	2339	F	323 584-7536	3512
Synchronized Technologies Inc	3577	F	213 368-3760	15864
Sysop Tools Inc	7372	F	310 598-3885	25249
Systems Wire & Cable Limited	3496	F	310 532-7870	13855
T Bags LLC	2339	F	323 225-9925	3513
Tae Gwang Inc	3993	F	323 233-2882	23987
Tallygo Inc (PA)	7372	F	510 858-1969	25254
Talyarps Corporation	2851	E	310 559-2335	8946
Tampico Spice Co Incorporated	2099	E	323 235-3154	2678
Target Media Partners Oper LLC	2711	E	323 930-3123	6067
Targeted Medical Pharma Inc (PA)	2834	E	310 474-9809	8407
Tarina Tarantino Designs LLC	3911	F	213 533-8070	23323
Taschen America LLC (PA)	2731	F	323 463-4441	6396
Taseon Inc	3825	D	408 240-7800	21862
Tasker Metal Products Inc	3714	F	213 765-5400	20460
Tcj Manufacturing LLC	2339	E	213 488-8400	3514
Tdg Operations LLC	2273	D	323 724-9000	2944
Teksun Inc	3089	F	310 479-0794	10400
Teledyne Technologies Inc	3812	F	310 893-1600	21440
Teledyne Technologies Inc	3679	B	310 820-4616	19754
Teledyne Technologies Inc	3679	B	310 822-8229	19756
Tenenblatt Corporation	2257	C	323 232-2061	2868
Tennis Media Co LLC	2721	E	310 966-8182	6268
Textured Coatings America Inc	2851	E	323 233-3111	8947
That Casting Place Inc	3915	F	323 258-5691	23350
Thats It Nutrition LLC	2064	F	818 782-1701	1461
The Microfilm Company of Cal	2731	F	310 354-2610	6400
Thebrain Technologies LP	7372	F	310 390-0100	25268
Thomson Reuters Corporation	3663	F	877 518-2761	18286
Tianello Inc	2331	C	323 231-0599	3279
Tidings	2711	E	213 637-7360	6070
Times Litho Inc	2752	E	503 359-0300	7136
Tk and Company Watches	3911	F	213 545-1971	23326
TLC Logistics Inc	2679	F	323 665-0474	5743
Tokyopop Inc	2731	D	323 920-5967	6401
Tomasini Inc	2221	F	323 231-2349	2785
Top Quality Sportswear	2329	F	323 262-0399	3197
Topline Game Labs LLC	7372	F	310 461-0350	25286
Topson Downs California Inc	2337	E	310 558-0300	3365
Tortilleria La California Inc	2099	E	323 221-8940	2685
Tortilleria San Marcos	2099	E	323 263-0208	2687
Tortolani Inc	3993	F	323 268-1488	23992
Tosco - Tool Specialty Company	3545	E	323 232-3561	14687
Toska Inc	2339	F	213 746-0088	3519
Touch ME Fashion Inc	2339	E	323 234-9200	3520
Tourism Development Corp (PA)	2721	E	310 280-2880	6273
Toykidz Inc	3999	F	213 688-2999	24273
Transformationnet Media LLC	2721	E	310 476-5259	6274
Travel Computer Systems Inc	7372	F	310 558-3130	25292
Tres Bien Inc (PA)	2339	F	213 747-3366	3522
Trialgraphix Inc	2752	E	213 621-4400	7146
Tribe Media Corp	2711	E	213 368-1661	6073
Tribune Los Angeles Inc	2711	E	213 237-5000	6074
Tripos Industries Inc	3432	E	323 669-0488	12053
Triyar Capital California LLC (PA)	3728	F	310 441-5654	20964
Tropical Preserving Co Inc	2033	E	213 748-5108	864
Trusted Energy LLC	1311	F	818 646-3137	82
Tua Fashion Inc (PA)	2211	F	213 422-2384	2765
Tubular Specialties Mfg Inc	3261	D	310 515-4801	10808
Tvs Distributors Inc (PA)	3965	F	323 268-1347	23778
Twelve Signs Inc	2721	D	310 553-8000	6275
Ubtech Robotics Corp	3549	C	213 261-7153	14771
Ultra Built Kitchens Inc	2434	E	323 232-3362	4361
Umeya Inc	2052	E	213 626-8341	1386
Umgee USA Inc	2331	E	323 526-9138	3283
Unique Apparel Inc	2339	D	213 321-8192	3523
Universal Dyeing & Printing	2262	D	213 746-0818	2906
Universal Surface Techlgy Inc	2841	E	310 352-6969	8612
University Southern California	2834	F	323 442-3858	8426
Upper Crust Enterprises Inc	2099	E	213 625-0038	2697
US Hosiery Inc	2252	F	213 742-0101	2818
US Premier Inc	2331	F	323 267-4463	3285
US Wholesale Drug Corp	2834	F	323 227-4258	8428
V & M Plating Co	3471	F	310 532-5633	13530
V I P Ironworks Inc	3446	F	310 216-2890	12902
Vagrant Records Inc	2782	E	323 302-0100	7590
Vahe Enterprises Inc	3713	D	323 235-6657	20233
Valerie Trading Inc	2269	F	323 231-4255	2921
Valmas Inc	2335	E	323 677-2211	3346
Valmont Industries Inc	3441	D	323 264-6660	12272
Vega Textile Inc	2241	F	323 923-0600	2809
Venator Americas LLC	2816	D	323 269-7311	7748
Venture Capital Entps LLC	2024	F	914 275-7305	702
Vf Contemporary Brands Inc	2325	F	213 747-7002	3090
Victor Wire and Cable LLC	3357	F	310 842-9933	11681
Vigilant Ballistics Inc	3271	F	213 212-3232	10868
Viking Ready Mix Co Inc	3273	F	818 243-4243	11202
Virgil M Stutzman Inc	3471	F	323 732-9146	13532
Vision Envelope & Prtg Co Inc (PA)	2677	F	310 324-7062	5680
Vision Smart Center Inc	2833	F	213 465-1807	7980
Visoy Food Products & Mfg Inc	2075	F	323 221-4079	1513
Vitality Furniture Group Inc	2599	F	323 937-4900	5262
Vitamin Friends Llc	2023	E	310 502-2277	652
Vm Provider Inc (PA)	2252	F	800 674-3233	2819
Voteblast Inc	2741	F	650 387-9147	6620
WAbenjamin Electric Co	3613	E	213 749-7731	17171
Walker Foods Inc	2099	D	323 268-5191	2699
Warnaco Swimwear Inc (DH)	2329	E	213 481-4300	3204
Warner/Chappell Music Inc (DH)	2741	C	310 441-8600	6623
Warren Printing & Mailing Inc	2752	F	323 258-2621	7173
Washington Garment Dyeing (PA)	2262	D	213 747-1111	2907
Washington Garment Dyeing	2261	E	213 747-1111	2899
Wave Community Newspapers Inc (PA)	2711	E	323 290-3000	6083
We Five-R Corporation	3471	F	323 263-6757	13533

Employment Codes: A=Over 500 employees, B=251-500, C=101-250, D=51-100, E=20-50, F=10-19

2019 California
Manufacturers Register

© Mergent Inc. 1-800-342-5647
1411

GEOGRAPHIC

	SIC	EMP	PHONE	ENTRY #
Wearable Integrity Inc	2339	E	213 748-6044	3528
Webalo Inc	3695	F	310 828-7335	19890
Weddingchannelcom Inc	2741	C	213 599-4100	6625
Weider Publications LLC (HQ)	2721	D	818 884-6800	6288
Wein Products Inc	3699	E	213 749-6250	20108
Wenner Media LLC	2721	E	323 930-3300	6290
Wesley Allen Inc (PA)	2514	C	323 231-4275	4848
Wessco International Ltd A C (PA)	2393	E	310 477-4272	3773
West E Cmnty Access Netwrk Inc	3721	D	323 967-0520	20634
West Publishing Corporation	2731	E	800 747-3161	6407
Western Bagel Baking Corp	2051	E	310 479-4823	1341
Western Die & Printing Corp	2759	F	323 665-0474	7538
Western Motor Works Inc	3553	F	310 382-6896	14789
Western Supreme Inc	2015	C	213 627-3861	555
Winter & Bain Manufacturing (PA)	3534	F	213 749-3568	14261
Winter & Bain Manufacturing	3534	F	213 749-3561	14262
Wire Technology Corporation	3357	E	310 635-6935	11683
Wise Living Inc	2519	E	323 541-0410	4924
Wls Coatings Inc	2851	F	310 538-2155	8956
Wolfson Knitting Mills Inc	2211	E	213 627-8746	2768
Wonder Marketing Inc	2851	F	310 235-1469	8957
Wonderful Pstchios Almonds LLC (HQ)	2068	E	310 966-4650	1507
Woodland Bedrooms Inc	2511	D	562 408-1558	4755
Worldflash Software Inc	7372	E	310 745-0632	25358
Worldwide Specialties Inc	2099	C	323 587-2200	2702
X Sublimation Inc	2389	F	213 700-1024	3687
Xcvi LLC (PA)	2211	C	213 749-2661	2769
Xhale Distributors	2023	F	888 942-5355	653
Y Y K Inc	3911	F	213 622-0741	23332
Yamasa Enterprises	2091	F	213 626-2211	2307
Yenor Inc	2759	F	310 410-1573	7546
YMI Jeanswear Inc (PA)	2335	F	323 581-7700	3347
YMi Jeanswear Inc	2339	D	213 746-6681	3530
Yocup Company	2656	F	310 884-9888	5501
York Engineering	3544	F	323 256-0439	14593
Young Knitting Mills	2253	E	323 980-8677	2863
Young Sung USA Inc	2399	F	213 427-2580	3974
Yucatan Foods LP	2032	F	310 342-5363	782
Z B P Inc	2679	F	323 266-3363	5748
Zada Graphics Inc	2752	F	323 321-8940	7193
Zl Chemicals	2819	F	818 827-1301	7816

LOS BANOS, CA - Merced County

	SIC	EMP	PHONE	ENTRY #
Azusa Rock Inc	3273	E	209 826-5066	11048
California Dairies Inc	2021	D	209 826-4901	559
Cheese Administrative Corp Inc	2022	E	209 826-3744	567
Ingomar Packing Company LLC (PA)	2033	D	209 826-9494	808
Kagome Inc (HQ)	2033	C	209 826-8850	813
Los Banos Abattoir Co Inc	2011	E	209 826-2212	442
McClatchy Newspapers Inc	2711	D	209 826-3831	5948
Morning Star Company	2033	D	209 827-2724	828

LOS GATOS, CA - Santa Clara County

	SIC	EMP	PHONE	ENTRY #
Accurite Technologies Inc	3577	F	408 395-7100	15653
Acquis Inc	7372	F	408 402-5367	24310
Adara Power Inc	3691	F	844 223-2969	19797
ARX Pax Labs Inc	3812	F	408 335-7630	21259
Atomera Incorporated	3674	F	408 442-5248	18728
Brightsign LLC	3993	D	408 852-9263	23834
C B Concrete Construction	3273	F	408 354-3484	11053
Chemical & Material Technology	3827	F	408 354-2656	22067
Cirtec Medical LLC	3841	D	408 395-0443	22405
Cryptic Studios Inc	3944	D	408 399-1969	23417
Depuy Synthes Products Inc	3841	F	408 246-4300	22219
E-Fuel Corporation	3699	F	408 267-2667	19953
Einstein Noah Rest Group Inc	2022	F	408 358-5895	571
Facilitron Inc	7372	E	800 272-2962	24642
Foodlink Online LLC	7372	E	408 395-7280	24659
Healthywealthyhack Inc	7372	E	669 225-3745	24724
Highwire Press Inc (PA)	2741	E	650 721-6388	6499
McCarthy Ranch	2452	F	408 356-2300	4577
Nanotech Entertainment Inc (PA)	7372	F	408 414-7355	24943
Pulsar Vascular Inc	3841	F	408 246-4300	22593
Pulver Laboratories Inc	3625	F	408 399-7000	17295
Ritchey Design Inc (PA)	3751	F	650 368-4018	21135
Sadra Medical Inc	3841	F	408 370-1550	22611
Semotus Inc	7372	F	408 667-2046	25161
Suvolta Inc	3559	F	408 866-4125	15035
Tascent Inc	3699	F	650 799-4611	20085
Tela Innovations Inc	3674	E	408 558-6300	19216
Testarossa Vineyards LLC	2084	F	408 354-6150	2013
Wacker Development Inc	3599	F	408 356-0208	17047
Automation & Entertainment Inc (PA)	3491	F	408 353-4223	13704
David Bruce Winery Inc	2084	F	408 354-4214	1717
Mja Vineyards LLC	2084	F	408 353-1600	1881
Ols Controls	3822	F	408 353-6564	21520

	SIC	EMP	PHONE	ENTRY #
Rhys Vineyards LLC	2084	F	650 419-2050	1947
Seton Scientific	3089	F	707 782-0900	10373
Vulcan Aggregates Company LLC	1442	F	408 354-7904	387

LOS OLIVOS, CA - Santa Barbara County

	SIC	EMP	PHONE	ENTRY #
Escalera-Boulet LLC	2084	F	805 691-1020	1752
Firestone Vineyard LP	2084	D	805 688-3940	1763
Stolpman Vineyards LLC (PA)	2084	F	805 736-5000	1995

LOS OSOS, CA - San Luis Obispo County

	SIC	EMP	PHONE	ENTRY #
California Resources Corp	1311	E	661 763-6107	37
Cygnet Aerospace Corp	3365	F	805 528-2376	11732
Rantec Power Systems Inc	3679	D	805 596-6000	19703

LOWER LAKE, CA - Lake County

	SIC	EMP	PHONE	ENTRY #
Aloha Bay	3999	E	707 994-3267	24032
Barrick Gold Corporation	1041	D	707 995-6070	1
Clearlake Lava Inc	3273	F	707 995-1515	11094
Naptech Test Equipment Inc	3825	F	707 995-7145	21811
Parker Plastics Inc	3089	E	707 994-6363	10268
Shannon Ridge Inc	2084	F	707 994-9656	1974

LUCERNE VALLEY, CA - San Bernardino County

	SIC	EMP	PHONE	ENTRY #
Mitsubishi Cement Corporation	3241	C	760 248-7373	10764
Omya California Inc	2819	D	760 248-7306	7793
Specialty Minerals Inc	1422	C	760 248-5300	316

LYNWOOD, CA - Los Angeles County

	SIC	EMP	PHONE	ENTRY #
Ace Machine Shop Inc	3599	D	310 608-2277	16211
Amerasia Furniture Components	2512	E	310 638-0570	4759
California Steel Products	3449	E	310 603-5645	12974
D & D Motorcycle Service Inc	3751	E	323 567-9480	21104
Ermm Corporation	3715	E	310 635-0524	20501
First Finish Inc	2211	E	310 631-6717	2739
Gomen Furniture Mfg Inc	2512	E	310 635-4894	4779
Hgc Holdings Inc	2064	C	323 567-2226	1427
Kayo of California	2339	F	310 605-2693	3443
La Candelaria Manufacturing	2511	F	310 763-0112	4714
Leos Metal Polishing	3471	F	310 635-5257	13444
Linens Exchange Inc	2299	F	310 638-5507	3008
Metal Improvement Company LLC	3398	E	323 585-2168	11818
Metal Improvement Company LLC	3398	F	323 563-1533	11824
Next Day Frame Inc	2519	D	310 886-0851	4913
Orthor Engineering Inc	3842	F	310 604-0000	22785
P & L Development LLC	2841	C	323 567-2482	8602
P & L Development LLC	2834	E	310 763-1377	8323
Pacific Ltg & Standards Co	3646	E	310 603-9344	17635
Polynt Composites USA Inc	2821	F	310 886-1070	7870
Roger R Caruso Enterprises Inc	2448	E	714 778-6006	4504
Therm-O-Namel Inc	3479	F	310 631-7866	13672
Tjs Metal Manufacturing Inc	3446	E	310 640-1445	12899
Triumph Processing Inc	3471	C	323 563-1338	13524
Wasatch Co	2392	C	310 637-6160	3756

MACDOEL, CA - Siskiyou County

	SIC	EMP	PHONE	ENTRY #
Ralphs Ranches	2011	F	530 398-4182	448

MADERA, CA - Madera County

	SIC	EMP	PHONE	ENTRY #
Advanced Drainage Systems Inc	3084	E	559 674-4989	9773
Ardagh Glass Inc	3221	E	559 675-4700	10615
B-K Lighting Inc	3645	D	559 438-5800	17529
Baltimore Aircoil Company Inc	3585	C	559 673-9231	15940
Better Cleaning Systems Inc	3635	E	559 673-5700	17406
Canandaigua Wine Company Inc	2084	A	559 673-7071	1679
Carris Reels California Inc (HQ)	2499	E	559 674-0804	4613
Church & Dwight Co Inc	2812	E	559 661-2790	7659
Color-Box LLC	2653	E	559 674-1049	5398
Constellation Brands US Oprs	2084	A	559 485-0141	1705
Design Industries Inc	3272	F	559 675-3535	10914
Domries Enterprises Inc	3523	E	559 485-4306	14062
Encore Fine Cabinetry Inc	2434	F	559 822-4333	4297
Evapco Inc	3585	C	559 673-2207	15956
Florestone Products Co (PA)	3088	E	559 661-4171	9902
Gardner Family Ltd Partnership	3429	E	559 675-8149	11956
Georgia-Pacific LLC	2653	C	559 674-4685	5417
Golden Vly Grape Jice Wine LLC (PA)	2084	F	559 661-4657	1790
Hastings Irrigation Pipe Co	3354	F	559 675-1200	11589
Horn Machine Tools Inc (PA)	3542	F	559 431-4131	14438
Innovtive Rttional Molding Inc	3089	F	559 673-4764	10153
John Bean Technologies Corp	3556	C	559 661-3200	14862
La Viena Ranch	2034	E	559 674-6725	884
Lees Concrete Materials Inc	3273	F	559 486-2440	11126
Madera Carports Inc	3448	F	559 662-1815	12941
Madera Glass	3211	E	559 673-3583	10601
Madera Printing & Pubg Co Inc	2711	F	559 674-2424	5932
Moore Quality Galvanizing Inc	3479	E	559 673-2822	13619
Moore Quality Galvanizing LP	3479	E	559 673-2822	13620
Muscle Road Inc	3714	F	559 499-6888	20407

	SIC	EMP	PHONE	ENTRY #
Nutra Blend LLC	2048	D	559 661-6161	1151
Oldcastle Precast Inc	3499	E	559 674-8093	13961
Oldcastle Precast Inc	3272	E	559 675-1813	10967
P T M Inc	2448	F	559 673-1552	4491
Pacific Sheet Metal Inc	3444	F	559 661-4044	12708
Performance Trailers Inc	3715	E	559 673-6300	20508
Praxair Inc	2813	E	559 674-7306	7710
Quady LLC (PA)	2084	E	559 673-8068	1934
Quady Winery Inc	2084	E	559 673-8068	1935
San Joaquin Wine Company Inc	2084	F	559 673-0066	1965
Sealed Air Corporation	3086	C	559 675-0152	9883
Shafer Metal Stake (PA)	3444	F	559 674-9487	12756
Sinbad Foods LLC	2099	D	559 674-4445	2668
Star Finishes Inc	3471	F	559 261-1076	13512
Steel Structures Inc	3443	E	559 673-8021	12427
Sunsweet Dryers Inc	2034	D	559 673-4140	900
Teka Illumination Inc	3648	F	559 438-5800	17736
Ultra Gro LLC	2873	E	559 661-0977	9076
US Rack Inc	3429	F	559 661-3050	12006
Victor Packing Inc	2034	E	559 673-5908	905
Warnock Food Products Inc	2096	D	559 661-4845	2406

MADISON, CA - Yolo County

	SIC	EMP	PHONE	ENTRY #
Cemex Cnstr Mtls PCF LLC	2951	E	530 666-2137	9380

MAGALIA, CA - Butte County

	SIC	EMP	PHONE	ENTRY #
Quality Craft Mold Inc	3312	F	530 873-7790	11412

MALIBU, CA - Los Angeles County

	SIC	EMP	PHONE	ENTRY #
Allen Reed Company Inc	2621	F	310 575-8704	5272
Cafecito Organico Oc LLC	2095	F	213 537-8367	2333
County of Los Angeles	3531	F	310 456-8014	14160
Curtco Media Group LLC	2721	E	310 589-7700	6138
Curtco Robb Media LLC (PA)	2721	E	310 589-7700	6139
Edgy Soul	3961	F	310 800-2861	23746
Games Production Company LLC	3944	F	310 456-0099	23425
Malibu Enterprises Inc	2711	E	310 457-2112	5934
Malibu Times Inc	2711	F	310 456-5507	5935
Marys Country Kitchen	2053	F	310 456-7845	1398
Road Champs Inc (HQ)	3944	F	310 456-7799	23460
Robb Curtco Media LLC	2721	E	310 589-7700	6249
Studio Krp LLC	2335	F	310 589-7797	3338
Sutherland Presses	3542	F	310 453-6981	14457
West Rapco Environmental Svcs	3544	E	310 450-3335	14591

MAMMOTH LAKES, CA - Mono County

	SIC	EMP	PHONE	ENTRY #
Fluidix Inc (PA)	3567	F	760 935-2016	15260
Horizon Cal Publications	2711	F	760 934-3929	5882
Nato LLC	3999	E	760 934-8677	24184

MANHATTAN BEACH, CA - Los Angeles County

	SIC	EMP	PHONE	ENTRY #
Applecore	2396	F	310 567-6768	3875
De Nora Water Technologies Inc	3589	D	310 618-9700	16033
Dhy Inc	2329	F	310 376-7512	3144
Joe Montana Footwear	3021	D	310 318-3100	9473
Sachs & Associates Inc	3572	F	310 356-7911	15594
Skechers Collection LLC (HQ)	3021	E	310 318-3100	9480
Skechers Direct	3021	F	310 318-3100	9481
Skechers USA Inc	3021	F	310 318-3100	9484
Skechers USA Inc (PA)	3149	D	310 318-3100	10509
Skechers USA Inc II (HQ)	3021	F	310 318-3100	9485
Stanton Carpet Corp	2273	F	562 945-8711	2942
Trlg Intermediate Holdings LLC (PA)	2369	F	323 266-3072	3596
True Religion Apparel Inc (HQ)	2369	B	323 266-3072	3597
Vista Coatings Inc	3479	E	310 635-7697	13679

MANTECA, CA - San Joaquin County

	SIC	EMP	PHONE	ENTRY #
American Modular Systems Inc	2452	D	209 825-1921	4567
Antoninas Artisan Bakery LLC	2051	E	209 665-4176	1176
AT&T Corp.	2741	C	209 275-3075	6439
California Stl Stair Rail Mfr	3312	E	209 824-1785	11385
Delicato Vineyards (PA)	2084	C	209 824-3600	1719
Delicato Vineyards	2084	F	209 824-3501	1720
Dkw Precision Machining Inc	3599	F	209 824-7899	16443
E-M Manufacturing Inc	3444	E	209 825-1800	12566
Frito-Lay North America Inc	2096	E	209 824-3700	2383
Gb Industrial Spray Inc	3479	F	209 825-7176	13594
Golnex Inc	3549	E	510 490-6003	14753
H Lima Company Inc	1499	E	209 239-6787	413
Lockheed Martin Corporation	3812	B	408 756-1400	21320
Morris Newspaper Corp Cal (HQ)	2711	D	209 249-3500	5980
Price Rubber Company Inc	3052	F	209 239-7478	9505
Rochas Cabinets	2434	F	209 239-2367	4343
Shawver Metal Tech Inc	3469	F	209 239-9896	13275
Sunnyvalley Smoked Meats Inc	2013	C	209 825-0288	529
Supermedia LLC	2741	B	209 472-6011	6595
Tuff Boy Holding Inc	3715	E	209 239-1361	20514

MARCH ARB, CA - Riverside County

	SIC	EMP	PHONE	ENTRY #
Boeing Company	3721	A	951 571-0122	20567

MARICOPA, CA - Kern County

	SIC	EMP	PHONE	ENTRY #
Aera Energy LLC	1381	D	661 665-3200	94
Calmat Co	1422	E	661 858-2673	311
Nestle Purina Petcare Company	3999	D	661 769-8261	24187

MARINA, CA - Monterey County

	SIC	EMP	PHONE	ENTRY #
Eldridge Products Inc	3823	E	831 648-7777	21578
English Ales Brewers Inc	2082	F	831 883-3000	1590
Fox Thermal Instruments Inc	3545	E	831 384-4300	14634
Hearst Corporation	2711	C	831 582-9605	5873
Indtec Corporation	3672	E	831 582-9388	18504
Lifeline Food Co Inc	2022	F	831 899-5040	589
Light & Motion Industries	3648	D	831 645-1525	17707
Wolf Canyon of America Inc	2046	F	831 626-1320	1104

MARINA DEL REY, CA - Los Angeles County

	SIC	EMP	PHONE	ENTRY #
Ace Iron Inc	3446	C	510 324-3300	12826
Arbor Snowboards Inc	3949	E	310 577-1120	23506
Barkstrong LLC	2047	E	855 381-5888	1108
Dollar Shave Club Inc (DH)	3541	E	310 975-8528	14373
Excavo LLC	2426	E	310 823-7670	4079
Ipressroom Inc	7372	E	310 499-0544	24802
Pipelinersales Inc (PA)	7372	F	323 317-7426	25064
Rockwell Collins Inc	3812	C	310 751-3298	21414
Sewer Rodding Equipment Co (PA)	3589	E	310 301-9009	16106
Sony Dadc US Inc	3695	E	310 760-8500	19882
Telesign Holdings Inc (DH)	7372	E	310 740-9700	25265
Twin Coast Metrology Inc (PA)	3827	E	310 709-2308	22143

MARIPOSA, CA - Mariposa County

	SIC	EMP	PHONE	ENTRY #
Haztech Systems Inc	2865	E	209 966-8088	8963
Mariposa Gazette & Miner	2711	F	209 966-2500	5941

MARTINEZ, CA - Contra Costa County

	SIC	EMP	PHONE	ENTRY #
Alhambra Valley Olive Oil Co (PA)	2079	F	925 370-8500	1534
Document Proc Solutions Inc	2621	E	925 839-1182	5279
Eco Services Operations Corp	2819	E	925 313-8224	7770
Euv Tech Inc	3826	F	925 229-4388	21958
Gibson Printing & Publishing	2711	F	925 228-6400	5864
Independent Printing Co Inc (PA)	2752	E	925 229-5050	6879
McCormacks Guides Inc	2741	F	925 229-1869	6525
Noel Burt	3592	E	925 439-7030	16148
PG Emminger Inc	2541	F	925 313-5830	5093
Shell Chemical LP	2819	D	925 313-8601	7802
Shell Martinez Refining Co	2911	A	925 313-3000	9357

MARYSVILLE, CA - Yuba County

	SIC	EMP	PHONE	ENTRY #
A Teichert & Son Inc	1442	E	530 749-1230	340
A Teichert & Son Inc	1442	E	530 743-6111	341
American Wood Fibers Inc	2421	E	530 741-3700	4028
Homewood Components Inc	2439	D	530 743-8855	4411
Mariani Packing Co Inc	2034	E	530 749-6565	886
Oldcastle Precast Inc	3272	E	530 742-8368	10968
Reyes Coca-Cola Bottling LLC	2086	E	530 743-6533	2203
Suttons Forest Products	3999	F	530 741-2747	24260
Team Casing	1389	F	530 743-5424	281
US Pipe Fabrication LLC	3084	E	530 742-5171	9790

MATHER, CA - Sacramento County

	SIC	EMP	PHONE	ENTRY #
Construction Innovations LLC	3699	C	855 725-9555	19931

MAXWELL, CA - Colusa County

	SIC	EMP	PHONE	ENTRY #
American Rice Inc	2044	D	530 438-2265	1073
California Heritage Mills Inc	2044	E	530 438-2100	1076
Polit Farms Inc	2044	F	530 438-2759	1089

MAYWOOD, CA - Los Angeles County

	SIC	EMP	PHONE	ENTRY #
Cook Induction Heating Co Inc	3398	E	323 560-1327	11810
Gemini Film & Bag Inc (PA)	3089	E	323 582-0901	10115
Heritage Leather Company Inc	3111	E	323 983-0420	10459
Kitchen Cuts Inc	2013	E	323 560-7415	499
Regal Machine & Engrg Inc	3599	E	323 773-7462	16891
Sonora Face Co	2435	E	323 560-8188	4383
W S Dodge Oil Co Inc	2992	F	323 583-3478	9454

MC FARLAND, CA - Kern County

	SIC	EMP	PHONE	ENTRY #
Amaretto Orchards LLC	3999	E	661 399-9697	24033
Aptco LLC	2821	D	661 792-2107	7820
S & L Contracting	3444	E	661 371-6379	12746

MC KITTRICK, CA - Kern County

	SIC	EMP	PHONE	ENTRY #
Aera Energy LLC	1381	E	661 665-4400	93
Dwaynes Engineering & Cnstr	1389	D	661 762-7261	206

MCCLELLAN, CA - Sacramento County

	SIC	EMP	PHONE	ENTRY #
ASC Profiles LLC	3448	E	916 376-2899	12918

Employment Codes: A=Over 500 employees, B=251-500,
C=101-250, D=51-100, E=20-50, F=10-19

2019 California
Manufacturers Register

© Mergent Inc. 1-800-342-5647

1413

GEOGRAPHIC

	SIC	EMP	PHONE	ENTRY #
Aviate Enterprises Inc	3585	E	916 993-4000	15939
Dmea MSC	3728	E	916 568-4087	20796
General Dynmics Mssion Systems	3669	F	916 565-5316	18327
Le Vu	3679	E	916 231-1594	19618
Meriliz Incorporated (PA)	2752	C	916 923-3663	6970
Northrop Grumman Systems Corp	3812	E	916 570-4454	21373
Northrop Grumman Systems Corp	3721	A	408 531-2524	20616
PCA Central Cal Corrugated LLC	2653	C	916 614-0580	5450

MCCLOUD, CA - Siskiyou County

	SIC	EMP	PHONE	ENTRY #
Hearst Corporation	2721	E	530 964-3131	6180

MCKINLEYVILLE, CA - Humboldt County

	SIC	EMP	PHONE	ENTRY #
Cabinets By Andy Inc	2434	F	707 839-0220	4282
Ford Logging Inc	2411	F	707 840-9442	3987
Oasis Structures & Water Works	3589	F	707 839-1683	16082
Steve Morris	2411	F	707 822-8537	4015

MECCA, CA - Riverside County

	SIC	EMP	PHONE	ENTRY #
Kerry Inc	2023	D	760 396-2116	627

MENDOCINO, CA - Mendocino County

	SIC	EMP	PHONE	ENTRY #
Iverson & Logging Inc	2411	F	707 937-0028	3993

MENIFEE, CA - Riverside County

	SIC	EMP	PHONE	ENTRY #
Blitzers Premium Frozen Yogurt	2024	F	951 679-7709	659
Datatronics Romoland Inc	3612	D	951 928-7700	17087
Quality Sheds Inc	2511	F	951 672-6750	4732
Southern California Mulch Inc	2499	F	951 352-5355	4657

MENLO PARK, CA - San Mateo County

	SIC	EMP	PHONE	ENTRY #
18 Media Inc (PA)	2721	F	650 324-1818	6094
Adverum Biotechnologies Inc	2836	D	650 272-6269	8523
Aha Labs Inc	7372	F	650 575-1425	24340
American Printing & Copy Inc	2752	F	650 325-2322	6657
Artifact Puzzles	3944	F	650 283-0589	23406
Biopharmx Corporation (PA)	2834	E	650 889-5020	8081
Bluerun Ventures LP	7372	F	650 462-7250	24434
C S Bio Co	2834	F	650 322-1111	8088
Calysta Inc (PA)	2869	F	650 492-6880	8993
Cfkba Inc (PA)	3357	D	650 847-3900	11654
Colby Pharmaceutical Company (PA)	2834	F	650 333-3150	8116
Corcept Therapeutics Inc	2834	C	650 327-3270	8121
Corium International Inc (PA)	2834	C	650 298-8255	8123
Countryman Associates Inc	3651	F	650 364-9988	17784
Coyne & Blanchard Inc	2721	E	650 326-6040	6136
Delmar Pharmaceutical Inc	2834	F	650 269-1984	8135
Dermira Inc	2834	C	650 421-7200	8138
Dssd Inc	3572	F	775 773-8665	15529
Earlens Corporation	3842	F	650 366-9000	22721
Evalve Inc	3841	D	650 330-8100	22444
Fmw Machine Shop	3599	F	650 363-1313	16506
GE Ventures Inc	3841	F	650 233-3900	22459
Geron Corporation (PA)	2834	E	650 473-7700	8183
Infoimage of California Inc (PA)	2759	D	650 473-6388	7355
Intersect Ent Inc (PA)	3841	B	650 641-2100	22485
Intuit Inc	7372	C	650 944-6000	24797
Iowa Approach Inc	3841	F	650 422-3633	22494
Jomar Machining Inc	3679	F	650 324-2143	19603
Katerra Inc (PA)	1389	D	650 422-3572	231
L3 Technologies Inc	3663	C	650 326-9500	18160
Ladera Foods Inc	2043	F	650 823-7186	1066
Lattice Data Inc	7372	E	650 800-7262	24848
Legacy Us LLC	3229	F	650 714-9750	10652
Marble Security Inc	7372	F	408 737-4300	24881
Matternet Inc	3728	F	650 260-2727	20877
Medianews Group Inc	2711	C	650 391-1000	5961
Medical Aesthetics Menlo Park	3841	F	650 336-3358	22524
Memry Corporation	3679	C	650 463-3400	19645
Monster Route Inc	3441	E	650 368-1628	12214
Motherly Inc	2741	E	917 860-9926	6532
Pacific Biosciences Cal Inc (PA)	3826	B	650 521-8000	22002
Polytec Products Corporation	3599	E	650 322-7555	16850
San Mateo Daily News	2711	E	650 327-9090	6037
Sanford Metal Processing Co	3471	E	650 327-5172	13497
Shelter Systems	2394	F	650 323-6202	3811
Sonoma Orthopedic Products Inc	3841	F	847 807-4378	22626
Stack Plastics Inc	3089	E	650 361-8600	10388
Step Mobile Inc	7372	F	203 913-9229	25222
Talis Biomedical Corporation	3826	E	650 433-3000	22024
Te Connectivity Corporation	3678	E	650 361-3333	19413
Te Connectivity Corporation	3678	B	650 361-3333	19414
Te Connectivity Corporation	3643	A	650 361-3333	17495
Te Connectivity Corporation	3613	B	650 361-3333	17167
Te Connectivity Corporation	3643	E	650 361-3306	17497
Te Connectivity Corporation	3678	C	650 361-3302	19418
Te Connectivity Corporation	3052	E	650 361-3333	9508

	SIC	EMP	PHONE	ENTRY #
Te Connectivity Ltd	3679	E	650 361-4923	19746
Transcend Medical Inc	3841	F	650 325-2050	22654
Tyco International MGT Co LLC	3357	B	650 361-3333	11680
Vello Systems Inc	3661	D	650 324-7688	18004
Wolfs Precision Works Inc	3599	F	650 364-1341	17073

MENTONE, CA - San Bernardino County

	SIC	EMP	PHONE	ENTRY #
Bausman and Company Inc (PA)	2521	C	909 947-0139	4933
Bps Tactical Inc	2321	F	909 794-2435	3052
Bristol Omega Inc	2541	E	909 794-6862	5042
Hovey Tile Art	3996	F	909 794-3815	24014
Marwell Corporation	3613	F	909 794-4192	17151

MERCED, CA - Merced County

	SIC	EMP	PHONE	ENTRY #
American Probe & Tech Inc	3825	F	408 263-3356	21719
Calif Frut and Tmto Ktchn LLC	2099	F	530 666-6600	2478
Fineline Industries Inc (PA)	3732	C	209 384-0255	21038
Greif Inc	2655	D	209 383-4396	5486
International Inboard Mar Inc	3732	E	209 384-2566	21046
Kirby Manufacturing Inc (PA)	3523	D	209 723-0778	14079
Label Technology Inc	2759	C	209 384-1000	7378
Laird Mfg LLC (PA)	3523	E	209 722-4145	14082
McClatchy Newspapers Inc	2711	C	209 722-1511	5949
Merced Screw Products Inc	3451	E	209 723-7706	13032
Mid Valley Publication	2711	E	209 383-0433	5970
Molding Acquisition Corp	2821	F	209 723-5000	7855
Olde World Corporation	2541	E	209 384-1337	5088
Qg LLC	2752	A	209 384-0444	7058
Quad/Graphics Inc	2752	B	209 384-0444	7066
Richwood Meat Company Inc	2011	D	209 722-8171	450
RTS Packaging LLC	2679	C	209 722-2787	5730
Scholle Ipn Corporation	3089	B	209 384-3100	10363
Scholle Ipn Packaging Inc	3089	B	209 384-3100	10364
Sun Power Security Gates Inc	3315	F	209 722-3990	11459
Tdl Aero Enterprises	3721	F	209 722-7300	20629
Werner Co	3499	F	209 383-3989	13983
Yosemite Vly Beef Pkg Co Inc	2011	E	626 435-0170	459

MI WUK VILLAGE, CA - Tuolumne County

	SIC	EMP	PHONE	ENTRY #
Olson Technology Inc	3663	E	209 586-1022	18204
T S Manufacturing Inc	3679	D	209 586-1025	19742

MIDDLETOWN, CA - Lake County

	SIC	EMP	PHONE	ENTRY #
Morris Welding Co Inc	7692	F	707 987-1114	25423
Reynolds Systems Inc	3483	F	707 928-5244	13684

MIDWAY CITY, CA - Orange County

	SIC	EMP	PHONE	ENTRY #
Lin Consulting LLC	3792	F	714 650-8595	21206

MILL VALLEY, CA - Marin County

	SIC	EMP	PHONE	ENTRY #
Endurance Ptc	3751	F	415 445-9155	21108
Latitude 38 Publishing Company	2721	F	415 383-8200	6205
Leslies Organics LLC	2869	F	415 383-9800	9021
Liz Palacios Designs Ltd	3961	E	415 626-4630	23752
Sunlink Corporation (PA)	3674	F	415 925-9650	19201
Wilderness Trail Bikes Inc (PA)	3751	F	415 389-5040	21150

MILLBRAE, CA - San Mateo County

	SIC	EMP	PHONE	ENTRY #
Aei Communications Corp	3661	E	650 552-9416	17917
American Ornamental Studio	3272	F	650 589-0561	10871
Brighton Collectibles LLC	3171	F	650 838-0086	10543
Cargo Chief Inc	7372	F	650 560-5001	24472
Cycle Shack Inc	3751	D	650 583-7014	21103
John N Hansen Co Inc (PA)	3944	F	650 652-9833	23436
Sinosource Intl Co Inc	3281	F	650 697-6668	11279
Stem Inc	3825	C	415 937-7836	21854
Unisoft Corporation	7372	F	650 259-1290	25312
World Journal Inc (PA)	2711	D	650 692-9936	6090

MILPITAS, CA - Santa Clara County

	SIC	EMP	PHONE	ENTRY #
ABC Printing Inc	2752	F	408 263-1118	6634
Adcotech Corporation	3559	D	408 943-9999	14901
Advanced Microtechnology Inc	3825	F	408 945-9191	21701
Advansor Corporation	3571	F	408 228-1008	15385
Alliance Analytical Inc	2836	E	800 916-5600	8524
Allied Telesis Inc	3577	D	408 519-6700	15662
Ambios Technology Inc (PA)	3826	E	831 427-1160	21901
Applied Materials Inc	3559	E	408 727-5555	14909
Appointy Software Inc	7372	E	408 634-4141	24375
Aras Power Technologies (PA)	3677	E	408 935-8877	19319
Asante Technologies Inc	3577	F	408 435-8388	15674
Avalent Technologies Inc (PA)	3672	E	408 727-6323	18432
Aviat Networks Inc (PA)	3663	D	408 941-7100	18045
Aviat US Inc (HQ)	3663	E	408 941-7100	18046
Bar-S Foods Co	2013	B	408 941-9958	466
Bestek Manufacturing Inc	3577	E	408 321-8834	15682
Blue Sky Research Incorporated (PA)	3827	E	408 941-6068	22060
Bmi Products Northern Cal Inc	3299	F	408 293-4008	11348

Mergent email: customerrelations@mergent.com
1414

2019 California
Manufacturers Register

(P-0000) Products & Services Section entry number
(PA)=Parent Co (HQ)=Headquarters (DH)=Div Headquarters

Company	SIC	EMP	PHONE	ENTRY #
Brandt Electronics Inc	3679	E	408 240-0014	19470
Builders Drapery Service Inc	2211	E	408 263-3300	2727
C-Cube Us Inc	3674	A	408 944-6300	18758
Circuit Check Inc	3825	D	408 263-7444	21735
Cisco Systems Inc	3577	A	408 570-9149	15705
Cisco Systems Inc	3577	A	408 526-4000	15710
Cisco Systems Inc	3577	A	408 525-5669	15711
Commercial Mtl & Door Sup Inc	2431	F	408 432-3383	4126
Composite Software LLC (HQ)	7372	D	800 553-6387	24513
Corasia Corp	3565	F	408 321-8508	15203
Crain Cutter Company Inc	3429	D	408 946-6100	11947
Creation Tech San Jose Inc	3672	C	408 954-8055	18459
Cummins Electrified Power NA	3714	F	408 624-1231	20302
Eico Inc (PA)	3825	D	408 945-9898	21745
Elantec Semiconductor Inc (DH)	3674	C	408 945-1323	18814
Elixir Medical Corporation (PA)	3841	F	408 636-2000	22437
Ess Technology Inc (HQ)	3674	C	408 643-8818	18832
Evoqua Water Technologies	3589	F	408 586-9745	16040
Extron Contract Mfg Inc	3944	C	510 353-0177	23424
Fireeye Inc	7372	C	408 321-6300	24650
Flex Interconnect Tech Inc	3679	E	408 956-8204	19544
Flextronics International Usa	3672	A	408 576-7000	18484
Flextronics Intl PA Inc	3444	F	408 577-2489	12588
Flextronics Intl USA Inc	3577	F	510 814-7000	15743
Flextronics Intl USA Inc	3672	F	408 678-3268	18485
Fluid Industrial Mfg Inc	3585	E	408 782-9900	15958
Frontier Semiconductor (PA)	3674	E	408 432-8338	18852
Frontrange Holding Inc	7372	B	408 601-2800	24675
Frontrange Solutions USA Inc	7372	F	925 398-1800	24676
Globe Motors Inc	3621	C	408 935-8989	17199
Golden Altos Corporation	3825	E	408 956-1010	21764
Grandis Inc	3572	E	408 945-2160	15544
Headway Technologies Inc (HQ)	3572	C	408 934-5300	15547
Headway Technologies Inc	3572	C	408 934-5300	15548
Headway Technology	3572	F	408 935-1020	15549
Heat Software USA Inc (DH)	7372	E	408 601-2800	24726
Hgst Inc	3572	F	408 801-2394	15551
HI Relblity McRelectronics Inc	3674	E	408 764-5500	18873
Hoya Corporation USA	3812	F	408 654-2200	21307
Hoya Corporation USA (DH)	3827	F	408 492-1069	22082
Hoya Holdings Inc (HQ)	3861	C	408 654-2300	23165
HP Inc	3571	A	650 857-1501	15422
Hunter Technology Corporation (HQ)	3679	C	408 957-1300	19569
Huntford Printing	2752	E	408 957-5000	6864
Hytek R&D Inc (PA)	3672	E	408 761-5271	18502
I-Bus Corporation (PA)	3572	F	408 942-1417	15555
Infineon Tech Americas Corp	3674	A	866 951-9519	18888
Infineon Tech N Amer Corp (DH)	3674	B	408 503-2642	18890
Infineon Tech US Holdco Inc (HQ)	3674	D	866 951-9519	18891
Innovative Machining	3599	E	408 262-2270	16585
Integra Tech Silicon Vly LLC (DH)	3674	C	408 618-8700	18903
Integrated Mfg Tech Inc (DH)	3471	F	408 934-5879	13433
Integrated Mfg Tech Inc	3599	F	510 366-8793	16587
Integrted Silicon Solution Inc	3559	E	408 969-6600	14971
Integrted Silicon Solution Inc (PA)	3674	D	408 969-6600	18909
Isolink Inc	3679	E	408 946-1968	19587
Ixys LLC (HQ)	3674	D	408 457-9000	18934
JIC Industrial Co Inc	3679	F	408 935-9880	19600
Johnson & Johnson	3841	E	408 273-4100	22500
Jt Manufacturing Inc	3999	F	408 674-4338	24140
K A Tool & Technology Inc	3599	E	408 957-9600	16638
Kelytech Corporation	3679	E	408 935-0888	19609
Khuus Inc	3599	D	408 522-8000	16653
KLA-Tencor Asia-Pac Dist Corp	3674	C	408 875-4144	18943
KLA-Tencor Corporation (PA)	3825	B	408 875-3000	21788
Larson Packaging Company LLC	2448	E	408 946-4971	4483
Lifescan Inc	2835	F	408 263-9789	8491
Lifescan Inc	2835	F	408 263-9789	8492
Lifescan Inc	2835	F	408 263-9789	8493
Lifescan Products LLC (HQ)	3841	D	408 719-8443	22510
Linear Technology Corporation	3674	F	408 428-2050	18962
Linear Technology Corporation	3674	D	408 434-6237	18963
Linear Technology LLC (HQ)	3674	A	408 432-1900	18964
Lite On Technology Intl Inc (HQ)	3577	E	408 945-0222	15791
Lumentum Holdings Inc (PA)	3669	C	408 546-5483	18343
Lumentum Operations LLC (HQ)	3669	C	408 546-5483	18344
Manutronics Inc	3679	F	408 262-6579	19637
Marburg Technology Inc	3577	C	408 262-8400	15799
Medtronic Inc	3845	E	408 548-6618	23016
Meridian Technical Sales Inc	2731	E	408 526-2000	6363
Meritronics Inc (PA)	3672	E	408 969-0888	18529
Micron Technology Inc	3674	E	408 855-4000	19003
Milpitas Post Newspapers Inc	2711	F	408 262-2454	5973
Mobiveil Inc	3674	F	408 791-2977	19022
Modulus Inc	3672	F	408 457-3712	18532
Nanometrics Incorporated (PA)	3559	B	408 545-6000	14998
Nanosys Inc	3674	C	408 240-6700	19030
Nichols Manufacturing Inc	3599	F	408 945-0911	16789
Nine West Holdings Inc	2337	F	408 946-2570	3356
Nortra Cables Inc	3679	D	408 942-1106	19662
Nova Drilling Services Inc	3672	E	408 732-6682	18547
Omnicell Inc	3571	F	408 907-8868	15467
Onanon Inc	3678	E	408 262-8990	19406
Optimedica Corporation	3841	C	408 850-8600	22571
Oracle America Inc	7372	B	408 635-3072	25003
Palpilot International Corp (PA)	3672	E	408 855-8686	18555
Pericom Semiconductor Corp (HQ)	3825	E	408 232-9100	21824
Philips & Lite-On Digital (DH)	3572	E	510 687-1800	15583
Ppm Products Inc	3599	F	408 946-4710	16852
Precision Fiber Products Inc	3357	F	408 946-4040	11670
Quality Transformer & Elec	3612	E	408 935-0231	17117
Quantum3d Inc (PA)	3812	E	408 600-2500	21384
Quellan Inc	3674	E	408 546-3487	19111
RDm Industrial Products Inc	2522	E	408 945-8400	4998
Renesas Electronics Amer Inc (DH)	3679	B	408 432-8888	19707
Rucker & Kolls Inc (HQ)	3559	E	408 934-9875	15024
Sandisk LLC	3572	F	408 801-2928	15596
Sandisk LLC (DH)	3572	C	408 801-1000	15597
Sandisk LLC	3572	D	408 321-0320	15598
Sierra Monitor Corporation (PA)	3829	D	408 262-6611	22269
Silicon 360 LLC	2674	F	408 432-1790	5648
Silicon Graphics Intl Corp (HQ)	3577	B	669 900-8000	15854
Silicon Microstructures Inc	3625	C	408 473-9700	17308
Silicon Motion Inc	3674	F	408 501-5300	19154
Silicon Turnkey Solutions Inc (HQ)	3674	E	408 904-0200	19158
Silicon Vly World Trade Corp	3613	F	408 945-6355	17163
Siliconcore Technology Inc	3674	E	408 946-8185	19160
Song Beoung	2782	F	510 670-8788	7585
Suba Technology Inc	3672	E	408 434-6500	18618
Symprotek Co	3672	F	408 956-0700	18621
Tek Labels and Printing Inc	2752	E	408 586-8107	7132
Teledesign Systems	3663	F	408 941-1808	18278
Teledyne Defense Elec LLC	3674	C	408 737-0992	19217
Teledyne Dgital Imaging US Inc	3829	F	408 736-6000	22285
Teledyne E2v, Inc.	3674	E	408 737-0992	19218
Teledyne Lecroy Inc	3825	E	408 727-6600	21865
Terabit Radios Inc	3663	F	408 431-6032	18281
Test-Um Inc	3825	F	818 464-5021	21874
Testmetrix Inc	3825	E	408 730-5511	21875
Tmarzetti Company	2035	C	408 263-7540	936
Tokyo Ohka Kogyo America Inc	2819	F	408 956-9901	7809
Tuff Shed Inc	2452	F	408 935-8833	4581
United Optronics Inc	3661	F	408 503-8900	18003
Varian Medical Systems Inc	3841	C	408 321-9400	22666
Vector Fabrication Inc (PA)	3672	E	408 942-9800	18644
Venta Medical Inc	3841	E	510 429-9300	22669
Viavi Solutions Inc	3674	C	408 546-5000	19258
View Inc (PA)	3231	D	408 263-9200	10740
Vlsi Standards Inc	3825	E	408 428-1800	21886
Westrock Cp LLC	2653	C	408 946-3600	5467
Westrock Cp LLC	2653	C	408 946-3600	5471
Winslow Automation Inc	3674	D	408 262-9004	19273
Yuhas Tooling & Machining	3599	F	408 934-9196	17076
Zilog Inc (DH)	3674	E	408 513-1500	19286
Zollner Electronics Inc	3672	E	408 434-5400	18657
Zuca Inc	3161	E	408 377-9822	10542
Zygo Corporation	3826	E	408 434-1000	22054
Zytek Corp	3672	E	408 520-4287	18659

MIRA LOMA, CA - Riverside County

Company	SIC	EMP	PHONE	ENTRY #
A and G Inc (HQ)	2329	A	714 765-0400	3129
Activeapparel Inc (PA)	2329	F	951 361-0060	3130
Aftermarket Parts Company LLC	3711	B	951 681-2751	20121
Allied Fitting LP	3462	C	909 390-0101	13093
Aluminum Die Casting Co Inc	3363	D	951 681-3900	11687
C & H Molding Incorporated	3544	E	951 361-5030	14488
Califrnia Indus Rfrgn Mchs Inc	3585	F	951 361-0040	15943
Calpaco Papers Inc (PA)	2679	C	323 767-2800	5702
Calstrip Industries Inc (PA)	3316	E	323 726-1345	11468
Calstrip Steel Corporation (HQ)	3398	D	323 838-2097	11805
Charles Komar & Sons Inc	2341	B	951 934-1377	3535
Cryoworks Inc	3498	C	951 360-0920	13883
Del Real LLC	2038	C	951 681-0395	989
Enhance America Inc	3993	E	951 361-3000	23867
General Electric Company	3646	E	951 360-2400	17612
Highland Plastics Inc	3089	C	951 360-9587	10136
Ideal Products Inc	2541	E	951 727-8600	5070
Innovative R Advanced	2515	E	949 273-8100	4865
International Vitamin Corp	2834	C	951 361-1120	8227
Koch Filter Corporation	3585	F	951 361-9017	15963
Langlois Company	2045	C	951 360-3900	1097

GEOGRAPHIC

	SIC	EMP	PHONE	ENTRY #
Levecke LLC	2084	D	951 681-8600	1861
Los Angles Tmes Cmmnctions LLC	2711	E	951 683-6066	5926
Luce Communications LLC	2752	E	951 361-7404	6956
McGrath Rentcorp	3448	C	951 360-6600	12944
Medtronic Inc	3845	E	951 332-3600	23017
Metal Container Corporation	3411	C	951 360-4500	11863
Middle Atlantic Products Inc	3444	F	800 266-7225	12676
Mitchell Rubber Products LLC (PA)	3069	C	951 681-5655	9638
Mitchell Rubber Products LLC	3069	D	951 681-5655	9639
Nestle Usa Inc	2038	E	951 360-7200	1002
Nfi Industries	3999	F	951 681-6455	24190
P R P Multisource Inc	3565	E	951 681-6100	15220
Paradigm Label Inc	2679	F	951 372-9212	5725
Plastic Innovations Inc	3083	E	951 361-0251	9758
Pura Naturals Inc	2515	E	949 273-8100	4881
Puri Tech Inc	3589	F	951 360-8380	16094
R & V Sheet Metal Inc	3444	F	951 361-9455	12730
Racing Plus Inc	3842	F	951 360-5906	22801
Robinson Engineering Corp	3547	E	951 361-8000	14718
Ronpak Inc	2621	E	951 685-3800	5332
Spartak Enterprises Inc	2517	E	951 360-0610	4899
Superior Filtration Pdts LLC	3564	E	951 681-1700	15179
Unitek Technology Inc	3571	F	909 930-5700	15502
Young Electric Sign Company	3993	D	909 923-7668	24009

MIRANDA, CA - Humboldt County

	SIC	EMP	PHONE	ENTRY #
Wheeler Lumber Co Inc	2411	F	707 943-3424	4023

MISSION HILLS, CA - Los Angeles County

	SIC	EMP	PHONE	ENTRY #
Electric Gate Store Inc	3699	C	818 361-6872	19957
Lawrence Roll Up Doors Inc	3442	F	818 837-1963	12327
Sky Signs & Graphics	2395	F	818 898-3802	3862
Valterra Products LLC (PA)	3494	E	818 898-1671	13779

MISSION VIEJO, CA - Orange County

	SIC	EMP	PHONE	ENTRY #
Axial Inc	3699	F	949 334-6008	19917
Bailey Industries Inc	3728	F	949 461-0807	20758
Boeing Company	3721	A	949 452-0259	20547
Community Merch Solutions LLC	3578	E	877 956-9258	15896
Elixir Industries	3469	F	949 860-5000	13200
Foundstone Inc	7372	D	949 297-5600	24668
Gregg Hammork Enterprizes Inc	1311	F	949 586-7902	61
Honeywell International Inc	3724	A	949 425-3992	20656
James Hardie Trading Co Inc	2952	C	949 582-2378	9411
Jorlind Enterprises Inc	2752	F	949 364-2309	6913
Nasco Petroleum LLC	1389	F	949 461-5212	245
Produce Apparel Inc	2339	F	949 472-9434	3485
Radio Frequency Simulation	3825	E	714 974-7377	21837
Socal Skateshop	3949	F	949 305-5321	23654
W G Holt Inc	3674	D	949 859-8800	19267

MODESTO, CA - Stanislaus County

	SIC	EMP	PHONE	ENTRY #
1le California Inc	3646	E	209 846-7541	17574
A B Boyd Co (PA)	3069	E	209 236-1111	9579
Accelrted Mtal Fabrication LLC	3441	E	209 846-7998	12101
Allied Concrete & Supply Co	3273	E	209 524-3177	11036
Amcor Manufacturing	2819	E	209 581-9687	7751
Arctic Glacier California Inc	2097	D	209 524-3128	2407
Atlas Pacific Engineering Co	3556	F	209 574-9884	14834
Bambacigno Steel Company	3312	E	209 524-9681	11380
Batchlder Bus Cmmnications Inc	2752	F	209 577-2222	6686
Bell-Carter Foods Inc	2033	F	209 549-5939	787
Billington Welding & Mfg Inc	3556	D	209 526-0846	14837
Bimbo Bakeries Usa Inc	2051	F	209 538-6170	1187
Boyd Corporation	2891	C	888 244-6931	9134
Bunge Oils Inc	2076	D	209 574-9981	1515
Cal-Sign Wholesale Inc	3993	E	209 523-7446	23836
Calchef Foods LLC	2035	D	888 638-7083	911
Cemex Cnstr Mtls PCF LLC	3273	E	209 524-6322	11078
Concentric Components Inc	3621	F	209 529-4840	17188
Consolidated Container Co LLC	3085	D	209 531-9180	9798
Container Graphics Corp	3555	D	209 577-0181	14805
Dawn Food Products Inc	2052	F	517 789-4400	1360
Dayton Superior Corporation	3537	E	209 869-1201	14323
Del Monte Foods Inc	2033	B	209 548-5509	795
Deltatrak Inc	3829	F	209 579-5343	22186
Dry Creek Nutrition Inc	2087	F	209 341-5696	2258
E & J Gallo Winery (PA)	2084	A	209 341-3111	1739
E & J Gallo Winery	2084	F	209 341-3111	1743
E & J Gallo Winery	2084	D	209 341-7862	1748
E & S Precision Machine Inc	3599	F	209 545-6161	16458
Fabricated Extrusion Co LLC (PA)	3089	E	209 529-9200	10097
Fabritec Precision Inc (PA)	3444	F	209 529-8504	12585
First Tactical LLC	2311	A	855 665-3410	3029
Fisher Graphic Inds A Cal Corp	3555	B	209 577-0181	14808
Fisher Nut Company	2099	F	209 527-0108	2520
Flowers Baking Co Modesto LLC	2051	D	209 857-4600	1250

	SIC	EMP	PHONE	ENTRY #
Foam Fabricators Inc	3086	F	209 523-7002	9845
Fowlers Machine Works Inc	3599	F	209 522-5146	16511
Frito-Lay North America Inc	2096	B	209 544-5400	2388
Gallo Glass Company (HQ)	3221	A	209 341-3710	10620
Georgia-Pacific LLC	2653	C	209 522-5201	5415
Gilwin Company	3442	E	209 522-9775	12318
Golden Valley Industries Inc	2011	E	209 939-3701	437
Graham Packaging Company LP	3089	D	209 578-1112	10127
Grand Packaging Pet Tech	3089	D	209 578-1112	10129
Hess Precision Laser Inc	3699	F	209 575-1634	19978
Honeywell International Inc	3724	A	951 500-6000	20655
Hoya Optical Inc (PA)	3851	D	209 579-7739	23100
Hsi Mechanical Inc	3444	F	209 408-0183	12616
International Paper Company	2631	C	209 526-4700	5351
Iron Works Enterprises Inc	3715	E	209 572-7450	20504
J S West Milling Co Inc	2048	E	209 529-4232	1140
Jims Optical	3827	F	209 549-2517	22094
Johnson United Inc (PA)	3993	E	209 543-1320	23909
JR Daniels Commercial Bldrs	3449	D	209 545-6040	12982
Kingspan Insulated Panels Inc	3448	D	209 531-9091	12938
Lamar Tool and Die Casting Inc	3312	C	209 545-5525	11404
LTI Boyd	3549	A	800 554-0200	14759
LTI Holdings Inc (HQ)	2822	F	209 236-1111	7907
Martinez Pallet Services LLC	2448	F	209 968-1393	4487
McClatchy Newspapers Inc	2711	F	209 578-2007	5946
McClatchy Newspapers Inc	2711	B	209 238-4636	5947
McClatchy Newspapers Inc	2711	B	209 587-2250	5950
Mercer Foods LLC	2034	E	209 529-0150	888
Modesto Pltg & Powdr Coating	3471	F	209 526-2696	13457
Modesto Tent and Awning Inc	2394	F	209 545-1607	3796
Nestle Usa Inc	2023	D	209 574-2000	639
Newly Weds Foods Inc	2099	E	209 491-7777	2621
Nick Sciabica & Sons A Corp	2079	E	209 577-5067	1546
Noahs Bottled Water	2086	E	209 526-2945	2155
Nutrien AG Solutions Inc	2875	E	209 551-1424	9085
Pacific Southwest Cont LLC (PA)	2671	B	209 526-0444	5529
Pacific Southwest Cont LLC	2653	E	209 373-2900	5444
Parker-Hannifin Corporation	3569	A	209 521-7860	15348
Peco Controls Corporation	3625	F	209 576-3345	17293
Phoenix Custom Promotions	3942	F	209 579-1557	23400
Reliable Rubber Products Inc	3069	E	209 525-9750	9668
Repsco Inc	3089	E	303 294-0364	10332
Ring Container Tech LLC	3085	E	209 238-3426	9807
Rizo-Lopez Foods Inc	2022	C	800 626-5587	595
Rj Boudreau Inc	3523	F	209 480-3712	14100
Royal Robbins LLC	3949	E	209 529-6913	23641
Sacramento Coca-Cola Btlg Inc	2086	E	209 541-3200	2216
San Joaquin Equipment LLC	3523	E	209 538-3831	14102
Seneca Foods Corporation	2033	C	209 572-5201	855
Seneca Foods Corporation	2033	B	209 572-5694	856
Sharcar Enterprises Inc	3281	E	209 531-2200	11278
Sign Designs Inc	3993	E	209 524-4484	23962
Silgan Containers Mfg Corp	3411	D	209 521-6469	11868
Stanislaus Food Products Co (PA)	2033	C	209 548-3537	859
Steven Varrati	3599	F	209 545-0107	16966
Triad Energy Resources Inc	2875	E	209 527-0607	9087
Truss Engineering Inc	2439	E	209 527-6387	4431
United Pallet Services Inc	2448	E	209 538-5844	4510
Varni Brothers Corporation (PA)	2086	E	209 521-1777	2231
Village Instant Printing Inc	2752	E	209 576-2568	7169
Vistech Mfg Solutions LLC (PA)	3565	E	209 544-9333	15233
Wardrobe Specialties Ltd	3231	F	209 523-2094	10741
Westland Technologies Inc	3061	D	800 877-7734	9576
Willey Printing Company Inc	2752	F	209 524-4811	7186
Wolfram Inc	3229	F	209 238-9610	10671
Wood Connection Inc	2431	F	209 577-1044	4261
Wright Pharma Inc	2834	E	209 549-9771	8445

MOFFETT FIELD, CA - Santa Clara County

	SIC	EMP	PHONE	ENTRY #
Aquila Space Inc	3663	F	650 224-8559	18040

MOJAVE, CA - Kern County

	SIC	EMP	PHONE	ENTRY #
Alpha Dyno Nobel	2892	F	661 824-1356	9181
Calportland Company	3241	C	661 824-2401	10744
Commodity Resource Envmtl Inc	3339	E	661 824-2416	11544
Golden Queen Mining Co LLC	1041	C	661 824-4300	4
Interorbital Systems	3365	F	661 824-1662	11743
Masten Space Systems Inc	3761	F	661 824-3423	21164
Mustang Hills LLC	2282	F	661 888-5810	2950
Pepsi-Cola Metro Btlg Co Inc	2086	D	661 824-2051	2174
PPG Industries Inc	2851	F	661 824-4532	8931
PRC - Desoto International Inc	2891	F	949 474-0400	9163
PRC - Desoto International Inc	2891	C	661 824-4532	9164
Scaled Composites LLC	3721	B	661 824-4541	20625
Trical Inc	2879	E	661 824-2494	9119
Tsc LLC	3761	A	661 824-6600	21173

Mergent email: customerrelations@mergent.com

1416

2019 California
Manufacturers Register

(P-0000) Products & Services Section entry number
(PA)=Parent Co (HQ)=Headquarters (DH)=Div Headquarters

MONROVIA, CA - Los Angeles County

	SIC	EMP	PHONE	ENTRY #
3M Company	3069	E	626 358-0136	9578
3M Unitek Corporation	3843	B	626 445-7960	22853
Aerovironment Inc	3721	D	626 357-9983	20532
Aerovironment Inc (PA)	3721	D	626 357-9983	20533
Aerovironment Inc	3721	D	626 357-9983	20534
Aerovironment Inc	3721	E	626 357-9983	20535
Aerovironment Inc	3721	E	626 357-9983	20537
Age Logistics Corporation	3536	F	626 243-5253	14293
Air Logistics Corporation (PA)	3089	F	626 633-0294	9931
Amada Miyachi America Inc (HQ)	3548	C	626 303-5676	14719
Amada Miyachi America Inc	3841	E	626 303-5676	22331
Aremac Associates Inc	3599	E	626 303-8795	16278
Arrowhead Press Inc	2752	E	626 358-1168	6667
Atlas Sponge Rubber Company	3069	F	626 359-5391	9589
B & H Signs Inc	3993	D	626 359-6643	23825
Beacon Media Inc	2711	E	626 301-1010	5776
Belco Packaging Systems Inc	3565	E	626 357-9566	15197
Bloss Inc	3089	E	626 599-9944	9984
Bond Furs Inc	2371	F	626 471-9912	3599
Burnett & Son Meat Co Inc	2011	D	626 357-2165	421
Cacique Inc (PA)	2022	C	626 961-3399	565
Califrnia Nwspapers Ltd Partnr (DH)	2711	B	626 962-8811	5790
Chromologic LLC	3841	E	626 381-9974	22404
Clary Corporation	3679	E	626 359-4486	19494
Consilio - A First Advantage	7372	E	626 921-1600	24522
CPS Gem Corporation	3911	F	213 627-4019	23253
Crescent Plastics Inc	3089	F	626 359-9248	10050
D & M Draperies Inc	2391	F	626 256-1993	3692
Decco US Post-Harvest Inc (HQ)	2879	E	800 221-0925	9100
Decore-Ative Specialties (PA)	2434	A	626 254-9191	4293
Ducommun Aerostructures Inc	3728	E	626 358-3211	20802
Duracold Refrigeration Mfg LLC	3448	E	626 358-1710	12928
Genzyme Corporation	2834	D	800 255-1616	8182
Global Compliance Inc	2741	E	626 303-6855	6492
Harbor Seal Incorporated	3053	F	626 305-5754	9534
Headwinds	3751	F	626 359-8044	21114
Hoya Holdings Inc	3827	D	626 739-5200	22083
Imagerlabs Inc	3674	F	949 310-9560	18884
Innovyze Inc (DH)	7372	F	626 568-6868	24775
ITT LLC	3594	E	626 305-6100	16166
K Short Inc	3441	F	626 358-8511	12189
Koncept Technologies Inc	3645	F	323 261-8999	17541
Kruse and Son Inc	2013	E	626 358-4536	502
Mask-Off Company Inc	2891	E	626 303-8015	9155
Mesa Industries Inc	3531	E	626 359-9361	14181
Micile Inc	3571	F	626 381-9974	15455
Mulgrew Arcft Components Inc	3728	D	626 256-1375	20893
Ondax Inc	3827	F	626 357-9600	22113
One World Enterprises LLC	2086	E	310 802-4220	2157
Peck Road Gravel Pit	1442	E	626 574-7570	378
Pednar Products Inc	3086	F	626 960-9883	9873
Production Lapping Company	3599	E	626 359-0611	16859
Quality Craft Cabinets Inc	2434	F	626 358-2021	4338
Radcal Partners IA California	3829	E	626 359-4575	22256
Rayco Burial Products Inc	3444	E	626 357-1996	12733
Roncelli Plastics Inc	2821	D	626 359-2551	7881
S W C Group Inc	2656	E	888 982-1628	5500
Shore Western Manufacturing	3826	E	626 357-3251	22018
Staar Surgical Company (PA)	3851	C	626 303-7902	23126
Torero Specialty Products LLC	3949	F	415 520-3481	23674
Vinyl Technology Inc	2671	C	626 443-5257	5546
Vioski Inc	2512	F	626 359-4571	4818
Wbt Group LLC	3999	E	323 735-1201	24286
Xencor Inc	2834	C	626 305-5900	8446

MONTAGUE, CA - Siskiyou County

	SIC	EMP	PHONE	ENTRY #
Chuck L Logging Inc	2411	E	530 459-3842	3982
Dave Richardson Trucking	2411	F	530 459-5088	3985

MONTCLAIR, CA - San Bernardino County

	SIC	EMP	PHONE	ENTRY #
Amazing Steel Company	3441	E	909 590-0393	12111
American Nail Plate Ltg Inc	3645	D	909 982-1807	17523
Ashley Furniture Inds Inc	2511	B	909 652-6840	4671
Brooks Street Companies	2051	C	909 983-6090	1214
Califoam Products Inc	3069	F	909 364-1600	9598
Carboline Company	2851	F	909 459-1090	8887
Cnc Industries Inc	3599	F	909 445-0300	16390
Cobra Performance Boats Inc	3732	F	909 482-0047	21026
Cpd Industries	3086	E	909 465-5596	9831
E & R Glass Contractors Inc	3231	E	909 624-1763	10694
Elements Food Group Inc	2052	D	909 983-2011	1363
Evk Inc	2891	E	617 335-3180	9142
Falcon Abrasive Manufacturing	3291	F	909 598-3078	11293
Fittings That Fit Inc	3496	F	909 248-2808	13829
Gang Yan Diamond Products Inc	3545	C	909 590-2255	14638

	SIC	EMP	PHONE	ENTRY #
Ingredients By Nature LLC	2099	E	909 230-6200	2540
John L Conley Inc	3448	D	909 627-0981	12936
Kois & Ponds Inc	2048	E	800 936-3638	1142
Lazy Daze Inc	3716	E	909 627-1103	20524
McDaniel Inc	3324	F	909 591-8353	11514
Mechanical and Mch Repr Svcs	3599	E	909 625-8705	16730
Micro Matrix Systems (PA)	3469	E	909 626-8544	13251
Mitchell Fabrication	3441	E	909 590-0393	12212
Montclair Bronze Inc (PA)	3366	E	909 986-2664	11764
Montclair Machine Shop Inc	3599	E	909 986-2664	16767
National Ewp Inc	1081	E	909 931-4014	13
Nef Tech Inc	3589	F	909 548-4900	16078
Pacific Duct Inc	3444	E	909 635-1335	12704
Purfect Packaging	2673	F	909 460-7363	5616
Thomas Burt	2752	F	626 301-9065	7134
US Lubricants	2992	E	909 469-1860	9452
Vertex Industrial Inc	3569	F	909 626-2100	15372
Westside Accessories Inc (PA)	2387	E	626 858-5452	3634

MONTEBELLO, CA - Los Angeles County

	SIC	EMP	PHONE	ENTRY #
Academy Awning Inc	2395	E	800 422-9646	3824
Advance Engineering RES Inc	3651	E	626 354-9282	17753
All Access Apparel Inc (PA)	2331	C	323 889-4300	3210
Allied Feather & Down Corp (PA)	3999	E	323 581-5677	24031
Amplifier Technologies Inc	3663	E	323 278-0001	18029
Arevalo Tortilleria Inc (PA)	2099	D	323 888-1711	2457
Atlas Survival Shelters LLC	2514	E	323 727-7084	4825
Beacon Concrete Inc	3273	E	323 889-7775	11050
Big Sleep Futon Inc	2515	E	800 647-2671	4853
Big Tree Furniture & Inds Inc (PA)	2511	E	310 894-7500	4679
Bimbo Bakeries Usa Inc	2051	A	323 720-6099	1190
Bltee LLC	2331	E	213 802-1736	3217
Bread Los Angeles	2052	E	323 201-3953	1356
Cavern Club LLC	2331	E	323 837-9800	3224
Cee Baileys Aircraft Plas Inc	3751	E	323 721-4900	21097
Conroy & Knowlton	3089	F	323 665-5288	10034
Craig Manufacturing Company (PA)	3714	D	323 726-7355	20300
Crawford Products Company Inc	2851	F	323 721-6429	8899
Delamo Manufacturing Inc	3089	F	323 936-3566	10062
Desert Brothers Craft	2082	F	323 530-0015	1587
Dony Corp	3161	E	323 725-7697	10519
Dow-Elco Inc	3612	E	323 723-1288	17090
Eagle Enterprises Inc	3714	E	323 721-4741	20321
General Truck Body Inc	3713	D	323 276-1933	20207
Graphicpak Corporation	2653	F	323 306-3054	5420
Grover Smith Mfg Corp	3561	E	323 724-3444	15070
H & L Tooth Company (PA)	3531	D	323 721-5146	14174
Icsh Parent Inc	2655	F	323 724-8507	5491
Ingalls Conveyors Inc	3535	E	323 837-9900	14276
Jade Apparel Inc	2335	E	323 867-9800	3315
Katzkin Leather Interiors Inc	3172	E	323 725-1243	10562
La Bottleworks Inc	2086	E	323 724-4076	2147
LA Envelope Incorporated	2677	E	323 838-9300	5676
Minson Corporation	2512	B	323 513-1041	4798
Monarch Litho Inc (PA)	2752	E	323 727-0300	6980
Montebello Plastics LLC	3081	E	323 728-6814	9718
National Cnstr Rentals Inc	1389	F	323 838-1800	246
Orb Media Broadcasting Inc	2741	F	323 246-4524	6545
Performance Forged Products	3462	E	323 722-3460	13109
Polerax USA	2389	E	323 477-1866	3675
Powers Bros Machine Inc	3599	F	323 728-2010	16851
Ppp LLC	3089	F	323 832-9627	10300
Reyes Coca-Cola Bottling LLC	2086	D	323 278-2600	2202
Robert Crowder & Co Inc	3069	F	323 248-7737	9670
Royal Paper Box Co California (PA)	2657	C	323 728-7041	5508
Saavy Inc	3541	F	323 728-2137	14409
Style Knits Inc	2253	D	323 890-9080	2857
Theta Digital Corporation	3651	E	818 572-4300	17867
Thistle Roller Co Inc	3555	E	323 685-5322	14828
Troy Sheet Metal Works Inc	3465	E	323 720-4100	13146
Truck Club Publishing Inc	2731	E	323 726-8620	6403
Turner Fiberfill Inc	2824	E	323 724-7957	7917
Universal Metal Plating	3471	F	626 969-7932	13529
Unix Packaging Inc	2086	C	213 627-5050	2230
Unlimited Trck Trlr Maint Inc	3715	E	323 727-2500	20516
US Polymers Inc (PA)	3089	D	323 728-3023	10423
Vft Inc	2392	E	323 728-2680	3755
Wilbur Curtis Co Inc	3589	B	323 837-2300	16139
Wilbur Curtis Co Inc	3589	B	323 837-2300	16140
Worldwide Aeros Corp	3721	D	818 344-3999	20635

MONTEREY, CA - Monterey County

	SIC	EMP	PHONE	ENTRY #
Acecad Inc	3577	F	831 655-1900	15654
China Circuit Tech Corp N Amer	3672	F	831 646-2194	18447
Cyberdata Corporation	3577	E	831 373-2601	15727
Dole Fresh Vegetables Inc (DH)	2099	C	831 422-8871	2509

Employment Codes: A=Over 500 employees, B=251-500,
C=101-250, D=51-100, E=20-50, F=10-19

2019 California
Manufacturers Register

© Mergent Inc. 1-800-342-5647

1417

GEOGRAPHIC

	SIC	EMP	PHONE	ENTRY #
Evan-Moor Corporation (HQ)	2731	E	831 649-5901	6339
Excelligence Learning Corp (PA)	3944	E	831 333-2000	23422
Great American Wineries Inc	2084	E	831 920-4736	1795
Hampton-Brown Company LLC	2732	F	831 620-6001	6419
Lockwood Vineyard (PA)	2084	F	831 642-9566	1863
Monterey County Herald Company (DH)	2711	E	831 372-3311	5976
Montero Printing Inc	2752	F	831 655-5511	6983
North Bay Rhblitation Svcs Inc	2331	F	831 372-4094	3263
Orbital Sciences Corporation	3679	D	703 406-5000	19676
Rapid Printers of Monterey	2752	F	831 373-1822	7075
Richard Macdonald Studios Inc (PA)	3299	F	831 655-0424	11369
Robert Talbott Inc (PA)	2311	E	831 649-6000	3040
Sage Metering Inc	3826	E	831 242-2030	22013
Summit Furniture Inc (PA)	2511	F	831 375-7811	4742
Vybion Inc	2824	F	607 227-2502	7919

MONTEREY PARK, CA - Los Angeles County

	SIC	EMP	PHONE	ENTRY #
Aero Powder Coating Inc	3479	E	323 264-6405	13544
Architectural Woodworking Co	2541	D	626 570-4125	5037
Asia Food Inc	2011	E	626 284-1328	420
CHI-AM Comics Daily Inc	2741	F	626 281-2989	6459
Derik Plastics Industries Inc	2631	A	626 371-7799	5346
Dermacare Neuroscience Inst	2844	F	323 780-2981	8737
DHm International Corp	2339	D	323 263-3888	3407
Elle Boutique	2335	E	626 307-9882	3308
Franco American Corporation	3292	F	323 268-2345	11310
Garfield Imaging Center Inc	3845	F	626 572-0912	22980
Graphic Color Systems Inc	2752	D	323 283-3000	6837
Inertech Supply Inc	3053	D	626 282-2000	9537
International Daily News Inc (PA)	2711	E	323 265-1317	5891
J E J Print Inc	2752	F	626 281-8989	6901
L C Miller Company	3567	E	323 268-3611	15266
L C Miller Company (PA)	3567	F	323 268-3611	15267
La Colonial Tortilla Pdts Inc	2099	C	626 289-3647	2561
Lightcross Inc	3679	E	626 236-4500	19624
Los Olivos Packaging Inc (PA)	2033	C	323 261-2218	822
Mako Inc	2241	E	323 262-2168	2802
Miholin Inc	2329	F	213 820-8225	3180
Optic Arts Inc	3641	E	213 250-6069	17433
Rigoli Enterprises Inc	3699	F	626 573-0242	20059
Ross Name Plate Company	3993	E	323 725-6812	23953
Shihs Printing	2759	F	626 281-2989	7481
Sweety Novelty Inc	2024	F	626 282-4482	698
Tck USA Corporation	2891	F	323 269-2969	9175
Union Technology Corp	3675	E	323 266-6603	19304
Wah Hung Group Inc (PA)	3714	E	626 571-8700	20482
Wah Hung Group Inc.	3714	E	626 571-8700	20483
West-Bag Inc	3089	E	323 264-0750	10440
Win Fat Food LLC	2015	E	323 261-1869	556
World Journal Inc	2711	E	323 261-6972	6091
World Journal La LLC (HQ)	2711	C	323 268-4982	6092

MONTROSE, CA - Los Angeles County

	SIC	EMP	PHONE	ENTRY #
Avalco Inc	3069	F	310 676-3057	9591
Flanagan-Gorham Inc (PA)	2011	F	818 279-2473	435
Flow N Control Inc	3491	F	818 330-7425	13717
Mercury Interactive LLC	7372	F	818 957-2887	24905
Micro/Sys Inc	3571	F	818 244-4600	15456
Vitachrome Graphics Inc (PA)	2759	E	818 957-0900	7534

MOORPARK, CA - Ventura County

	SIC	EMP	PHONE	ENTRY #
Ace Graphics Inc	2752	F	213 746-5100	6637
AG Machining Inc	3441	D	805 531-9555	12108
American Board Assembly Inc	3672	C	805 523-0274	18418
Amphenol Corporation	3678	F	805 378-6464	19373
Anc Technology	3672	D	805 530-3958	18422
AVC Specialists Inc	3822	E	513 458-2600	21500
Benchmark Elec Mfg Sol Moorpk	3679	A	805 532-2800	19464
Cemex Cement Inc	3273	A	805 529-1355	11060
Conversion Technology Co Inc (PA)	3952	F	805 378-0033	23706
Corporate Graphics & Printing	2752	F	805 529-5333	6760
Energy Recovery Products Inc (HQ)	3679	F	805 499-4090	19534
Ensign-Bickford Arospc Def Co	3812	E	805 292-4000	21292
Erp Power LLC (PA)	3825	E	805 517-1300	21749
G T Water Products Inc	3432	E	805 529-2900	12036
Garage Equipment Supply Inc	3559	F	805 530-0027	14958
Gooch and Housego Cal LLC	3827	D	805 529-3324	22079
H&F Technologies Inc	3651	F	805 523-2759	17807
Hudson Plating Works	3471	F	805 517-1222	13427
Jandy Industries Inc (DH)	3589	E	805 529-2000	16060
Koros USA Inc	3841	E	805 529-0825	22506
Laritech Inc	3672	E	805 529-5000	18519
Martronic Engineering Inc (PA)	3699	F	805 583-0808	20012
Mc Cully Mac M Corporation	3621	E	805 529-0661	17210
Mpo Videotronics Inc (PA)	3861	D	805 499-8513	23181
Nea Electronics Inc	3678	E	805 292-4010	19403

	SIC	EMP	PHONE	ENTRY #
Pentair Water Pool and Spa Inc	3589	E	805 553-5003	16088
SCI-Tech Glassblowing Inc	3231	F	805 523-9790	10730
Semiconductor Equipment Corp	3559	F	805 529-2293	15029
Sercomp LLC (PA)	3955	D	805 299-0020	23738
Spectrum Brands Inc	3999	C	805 222-3611	24251
Star Ring Inc	3911	D	818 773-4900	23319
Sterisyn Inc	2834	E	805 991-9694	8398
Topaz Systems Inc (PA)	3577	E	805 520-8282	15871
Turbonetics Holdings Inc	3714	E	805 581-0333	20471
Ultron Systems Inc	3559	F	805 529-1485	15043
Vision Aquatics Inc	3949	F	818 749-2178	23686
Wave Precision Inc	3827	D	805 529-3324	22146
Wayne J Sand & Gravel Inc	1442	F	805 529-1323	390
Wilmanco	3663	F	805 523-2390	18302

MORAGA, CA - Contra Costa County

	SIC	EMP	PHONE	ENTRY #
J F K & Associates Inc	7372	E	925 388-0255	24812

MORENO VALLEY, CA - Riverside County

	SIC	EMP	PHONE	ENTRY #
Accuturn Corporation	3812	E	951 656-6621	21250
Amro Fabricating Corporation	3728	E	951 842-6140	20734
BAS Recycling Inc	3011	E	951 214-6590	9460
California Supertrucks Inc	3713	E	951 656-2903	20195
Cardinal Glass Industries Inc	3211	D	951 485-9007	10588
Cimc Reefer Trailer Inc	3537	F	951 218-1414	14313
Envirnmntal Mlding Cncepts LLC	3069	F	951 214-6596	9610
Forest Laboratories LLC	2834	B	951 941-0024	8163
Harman Professional Inc	3651	B	951 242-2927	17808
Masonite Entry Door Corp	2431	F	951 243-2261	4188
Modular Metal Fabricators Inc	3444	C	951 242-3154	12684
Nursesbond Inc	7372	F	951 286-8537	24977
Pacific Kiln Insulations Inc	3567	F	951 697-4422	15271
Painted Rhino Inc	3088	E	951 656-5524	9909
Schurman Fine Papers	2771	C	951 653-1934	7567
Specks Industries LLC	3999	E	800 511-0497	24250
Supreme Corporation	3713	C	951 656-6101	20232
Westrock Converting Company	2653	F	951 601-4164	5466

MORGAN HILL, CA - Santa Clara County

	SIC	EMP	PHONE	ENTRY #
A & J Machining Inc	3599	F	903 566-0304	16185
A H K Electronic Shtmtl Inc	3444	E	408 778-3901	12452
Admi Inc	7372	E	408 776-0060	24323
Advanced McHning Tchniques Inc	3599	F	408 778-4500	16231
Airaya Corp	3663	F	408 776-2846	18020
Aircraft Covers Inc	2211	D	408 738-3959	2717
Airtronics Metal Products Inc (PA)	3444	C	408 977-7800	12467
All Sensors Corporation	3674	E	408 776-9434	18679
Almaden Valley Printing Co	2752	F	408 288-6886	6653
AMP III LLC	3545	D	408 779-2927	14600
Amtech Microelectronics Inc	3672	E	408 612-8888	18421
Anritsu Company (DH)	3663	B	408 201-1551	18031
Anritsu Instruments Company	3229	F	315 797-4449	10634
Anritsu US Holding Inc (HQ)	3825	D	408 778-2000	21720
Art Brand Studios LLC (PA)	2741	E	408 201-5000	6434
Barger & Associates	3069	E	408 779-5424	9595
California Kit Cab Door Corp (PA)	2434	D	408 782-5700	4283
Computrust Software Corp (PA)	7372	F	408 782-7470	24518
Coretest Systems Inc	3826	F	408 778-3771	21939
Creative Mfg Solutions	3444	E	408 327-0600	12543
Custom Chrome Manufacturing	3751	C	408 825-5000	21102
Custom Labeling & Btlg Corp	2086	E	408 371-6171	2127
Digital View Inc	3679	F	408 782-7773	19514
Don Vito Ozuna Foods Corp	2096	E	408 400-0495	2378
Elmech Inc	3444	E	408 782-2990	19530
Emtec Engineering	3444	E	408 779-5800	12572
Ericsson Inc	3663	F	408 776-0600	18102
Flextronics Intl USA Inc	3672	B	408 577-2262	18486
Fresco Solar Inc	3674	F	408 497-1579	18851
Global Motorsport Parts Inc	3751	C	408 778-0500	21112
Greif Inc	2655	D	408 779-2161	5487
Hanaps Enterprises (PA)	3577	E	669 235-3810	15753
Haug Manufacturing Corporation	3565	F	408 842-1285	15210
Italix Company Inc	3479	E	408 988-2487	13606
Kal Machining Inc	3599	F	408 782-8989	16643
Kalman Manufacturing Inc	3599	F	408 776-7664	16644
KDF Inc	3751	E	408 779-3731	21120
Koco Motion Us LLC	3823	E	408 612-4970	21611
Lin Engineering Inc	3621	C	408 919-0200	17208
Lynex Company Inc	2844	F	408 778-7884	8791
M & L Precision Machining Inc (PA)	3599	E	408 436-3955	16698
Marki Microwave Inc	3679	E	408 778-4200	19638
Metrophones Unlimited Inc	3661	F	650 630-5400	17963
Mitann Inc (HQ)	2899	F	408 782-2500	9283
Morgan Hill Precision Inc	3599	F	408 778-7895	16770
New Product Integration Solutn	3315	D	408 944-9178	11451
Newera Software Inc	7372	F	408 520-7100	24962

Company	SIC	EMP	PHONE	ENTRY #
Oml Inc	3825	F	408 779-2698	21822
Oncogenesis Inc	3841	F	408 636-7725	22569
Pacific Capacitor Co	3675	F	408 778-6670	19302
Paramit Corporation (PA)	3841	B	408 782-5600	22580
Pega Precision Inc	3444	E	408 776-3700	12711
Phoenix Deventures Inc	3069	E	408 782-6240	9655
Pinnacle Manufacturing Corp	3444	E	408 778-6100	12715
Quadrant Solutions Inc	3499	F	408 463-9451	13967
Quintel Corporation	3555	F	408 776-5190	14826
Rawson Custom Cabinets Inc (PA)	2434	E	408 779-9838	4341
Renesas Electronics Amer Inc	3674	A	408 546-3434	19121
Robson Technologies Inc	3599	F	408 779-8008	16910
Royal Riders	2399	F	408 779-1997	3961
Seagull Solutions Inc	3825	F	408 778-1127	21845
Seek Software Inc	7372	E	408 316-4169	25160
Sheathing Technologies Inc	3841	F	408 782-2720	22622
Shorai Inc	3692	F	408 720-8821	19824
Sierra Precast Inc	3272	D	408 779-1000	11002
Talamo Food Service Inc	2022	E	408 612-8751	603
Terrasat Communications Inc	3663	E	408 782-5911	18283
Tracet Manufacturing Inc	3599	F	408 779-8846	17006
Twin Glass Industries Inc	3231	F	408 779-8801	10737
U-C Components Inc (PA)	3452	E	408 782-1929	13088
Uhv Sputtering Inc	3674	F	408 779-2826	19243
US Concrete Inc	3272	F	408 779-1000	11014
US Eta Inc	3679	F	408 778-5875	19778
Valvex Enterprises Inc	3599	E	408 928-2510	17035
Velodyne Acoustics Inc	3651	D	408 465-2800	17876
Velodyne Lidar Inc	3812	B	408 465-2800	21453

MORRO BAY, CA - San Luis Obispo County

Company	SIC	EMP	PHONE	ENTRY #
Hanson Aggrtes Md-Pacific Inc	3273	F	805 928-3764	11118
Mills ASAP Reprographics (PA)	2678	F	805 772-2019	5686

MOSS LANDING, CA - Monterey County

Company	SIC	EMP	PHONE	ENTRY #
Calera Corporation	3272	E	831 731-6000	10894
Moss Landing Cement Co LLC	3241	F	831 731-6000	10765
Sweet Earth Inc	2099	D	831 375-8673	2677

MOUNT SHASTA, CA - Siskiyou County

Company	SIC	EMP	PHONE	ENTRY #
Alpine Industries	3469	F	530 926-2460	13163
Paul A Evans Inc	3531	F	530 859-2505	14183
Sousa Ready Mix LLC	3273	F	530 926-4485	11181

MOUNTAIN PASS, CA - San Bernardino County

Company	SIC	EMP	PHONE	ENTRY #
Chevron Mining Inc	1221	B	760 856-7625	16
Mp Mine Operations LLC	1481	C	702 277-0848	407

MOUNTAIN VIEW, CA - Santa Clara County

Company	SIC	EMP	PHONE	ENTRY #
Advanced Materials Analysis	3081	F	650 391-4190	9695
Agilepoint Inc (PA)	7372	E	650 968-6789	24338
Alcatel-Lucent USA Inc	3674	B	408 878-6500	18677
Alexza Pharmaceuticals Inc (HQ)	2834	E	650 944-7000	8009
Alivecor Inc	7372	E	650 396-8650	24351
Alza Corporation	3826	A	650 564-5000	21899
Anda Networks Inc	3661	C	408 519-4900	17922
Applied Physics Systems Inc (PA)	3829	E	650 965-0500	22162
Apteligent Inc	7372	D	415 371-1402	24379
Ardian Inc	3841	F	650 417-6500	22344
Asrc Aerospace Corp	3812	E	650 604-5946	21261
Audience Inc (HQ)	3674	D	650 254-2800	18730
Avid Systems Inc (HQ)	3663	C	650 526-1600	18047
Bdna Corporation (PA)	7372	D	650 625-9530	24411
Blue Coat LLC	7372	A	408 220-2200	24432
Boosted Inc (PA)	3949	E	650 549-4169	23527
C K Tool Company Inc	3599	F	650 968-0261	16347
Cal Moto	3751	F	650 966-1183	21096
Cathera Inc	3841	F	650 388-5088	22398
Celeros Corp	3572	E	650 325-6900	15519
Centrl Inc	7372	E	650 641-7092	24481
Chemocentryx Inc (PA)	2834	D	650 210-2900	8112
Cisc Semiconductor Corp	3674	F	847 553-4204	18768
Clearwell Systems Inc	7372	C	877 253-2793	24498
Codar Ocean Sensors Ltd (PA)	3812	E	408 773-8240	21273
Cpacket Networks Inc	3577	E	650 969-9500	15722
Cumulus Networks Inc (PA)	7372	C	650 383-6700	24537
Digital Video Systems Inc (PA)	3651	E	650 938-8815	17790
Driveai Inc	7372	C	650 729-0499	24578
Edcast Inc (PA)	7372	E	650 823-3511	24589
Enervault Corporation	3691	F	408 636-7519	19805
Ericsson Inc	3663	E	972 583-0000	18101
Euphonix Inc (HQ)	3663	D	650 526-1600	18106
Exotic Silks Inc	2211	F	650 948-8611	2736
Exploramed Nc7 Inc	3845	E	650 559-5805	22978
Eyefluence Inc	3851	E	408 586-8632	23098
Fernqvist Retail Systems Inc (HQ)	2754	F	650 428-0330	7200
FTC - Forward Threat Control	3669	F	650 906-7917	18324
Fujifilm Wako Diagnostics US	2835	E	650 210-9153	8476
Future Fibre Tech US Inc (HQ)	3699	F	650 903-2222	19971
Guidant Sales Inc	3841	E	650 965-2634	22463
Guy Chaddock & Company (PA)	2512	C	408 907-9200	4780
Guzik Technical Enterprises	3825	D	650 625-8000	21771
H45 Technology Corporation	3577	F	650 961-9114	15751
Hansen Medical Inc	3841	C	650 404-5800	22466
Hitachi Chem Diagnostics Inc	3821	C	650 961-5501	21475
Hytrust Inc (PA)	7372	E	650 681-8100	24743
Impeva Labs Inc (PA)	3699	F	650 559-0103	19981
Inmage Systems Inc (HQ)	7372	E	408 200-3840	24774
Intuit Inc	7372	D	650 944-6000	24792
Intuit Inc.	7372	C	650 944-6000	24793
Intuit Inc.	7372	E	650 944-6000	24794
Intuit Inc	7372	F	650 944-6000	24795
Iridex Corporation (PA)	3841	C	650 940-4700	22495
Iris Medical Instruments Inc	3845	C	650 940-4700	22994
Jumio Software & Dev LLC	7372	E	650 388-0264	24819
Kaye Sandy Enterprises Inc	3732	E	650 961-5334	21048
Kelly Computer Systems Inc	3577	E	650 960-1010	15778
Khan Academy Inc	7372	D	650 336-5426	24829
Kitty Hawk Corporation (PA)	3721	C	650 641-0076	20596
Knightscope Inc	3699	F	650 924-1025	19999
Lenz Precision Technology Inc	3599	F	650 966-1784	16685
Lifescience Plus Inc	3845	F	650 565-8172	22998
Medimmune LLC	2834	B	650 603-2000	8273
Medimmune LLC	2834	D	650 603-2000	8274
Microsemi Soc Corp	3674	E	650 318-4200	19017
Mint Software Inc	7372	F	650 944-6000	24924
Mobileiron Inc (PA)	7372	E	650 919-8100	24929
Mobius Photonics Inc	3699	F	408 496-1084	20018
Monterey Design Systems Inc	3695	C	408 747-7370	19871
Nextinput Inc (PA)	3625	F	408 770-9293	17290
Olio Devices Inc	3873	E	650 918-6546	23222
Omnicell Inc (PA)	3571	B	650 251-6100	15468
Pacific Western Systems Inc (PA)	3825	E	650 961-8855	21823
Pano Logic Inc	3577	E	650 743-1773	15822
Perceptimed Inc	3559	E	650 941-7000	15007
Phoenix Improving Life LLC	3842	E	650 248-0655	22793
Pickering Laboratories Inc	2819	E	650 694-6700	7798
Pinnacle Systems Inc	3663	E	650 237-1900	18220
Proteus Industries Inc	3823	E	650 964-4163	21637
PS Support Inc	7372	E	301 351-9366	25087
Pure Storage Inc (PA)	3572	B	800 379-7873	15587
Qualitau Incorporated (PA)	3825	D	650 282-6226	21834
Rakshak	7372	E	404 513-5867	25103
Realscout Inc	7372	F	650 397-6500	25110
Receivd Inc	7372	E	650 336-5817	25115
Red Hat Inc	7372	E	650 567-9039	25117
Red Robot Labs Inc	3944	E	650 762-8058	23459
Retail Solutions Incorporated (PA)	7372	E	650 390-6100	25126
Rod L Electronics Inc (PA)	3825	F	650 322-0711	21840
Samsung Sdi America Inc (HQ)	3577	E	408 544-4470	15845
Semnur Pharmaceuticals	2834	E	650 516-4310	8375
Simplelegal Inc	7372	F	415 763-5366	25177
Soliant Energy Inc	3699	E	626 396-9500	20072
Speculative Product Design LLC	3161	F	650 462-9086	10538
Spinalmotion Inc	3841	F	650 947-3472	22631
Squaglia Manufacturing (PA)	3599	E	650 965-9644	16961
Stackrox Inc	7372	E	650 489-6769	25216
Staffing Industry Analysts Inc	2741	E	650 390-6200	6590
Stewart Audio (HQ)	3679	F	209 588-8111	19737
Synopsys Inc (PA)	7372	B	650 584-5000	25245
Synplicity Inc (HQ)	7372	C	650 584-5000	25247
T-Ram Semiconductor Inc	3674	E	408 597-3670	19210
Tapinfluence Inc	7372	E	720 726-4071	25256
Tatung Telecom Corporation	3661	D	650 961-2288	18000
Teachers Curriculum Inst LLC (PA)	2731	E	800 497-6138	6399
Teledyne Defense Elec LLC (HQ)	3679	E	650 691-9800	19752
Teledyne Wireless LLC	3679	C	650 691-9800	19757
Tellme Networks Inc	2741	B	650 693-1009	6601
Thawte Inc	3663	E	650 426-7400	18284
Transfer Engineering & Mfg Inc	3565	E	510 651-3000	15231
Upguard Inc (PA)	7372	F	888 882-3223	25315
Ventus Medical Inc	3841	E	408 200-5299	22671
Veritas Software Global LLC	7372	E	650 335-8000	25327
Vibrynt Inc	3845	E	650 362-6100	23066
Virage Logic Corporation (HQ)	3674	B	650 584-5000	19260
Volcano Corporation	3845	B	650 938-5300	23071
Voyant International Corp	7372	F	800 710-6637	25339

MURPHYS, CA - Calaveras County

Company	SIC	EMP	PHONE	ENTRY #
Blastronix Inc	3577	F	209 795-0738	15687
Kaiser Enterprises Inc	3498	D	209 728-2091	13892
Northern California Power Agcy	3621	E	209 728-1387	17214

GEOGRAPHIC

	SIC	EMP	PHONE	ENTRY #

MURRIETA, CA - Riverside County

Company	SIC	EMP	PHONE	ENTRY #
Abbott Vascular Inc	3841	C	408 845-3186	22305
Apex Conveyor Corp	3535	E	951 304-7808	14265
Apex Conveyor Systems Inc	3535	F	951 304-7808	14266
Art Signworks Inc	3993	F	951 698-8484	23823
Aviator Systems Inc	3728	F	949 677-2461	20751
B P John Recycle Inc	2421	E	951 696-1144	4031
Cds Direct Inc	3823	F	760 747-2734	21560
Coldstone Creamery 256	2024	F	951 304-9777	663
Cryoquip LLC (HQ)	3559	C	951 677-2060	14935
Custom Wheels and ACC Inc	3714	F	714 827-5200	20304
Denso Pdts & Svcs Americas Inc	3714	C	951 698-3379	20315
Elite Cabinetry Inc	2599	F	951 698-5050	5229
Empower Software Tech LLC	7372	F	951 672-6257	24607
Express Systems & Engrg Inc	3089	F	951 461-1500	10095
Gamecloud Studios Inc	7372	E	951 677-2345	24681
Glassplax	3231	E	951 677-4800	10700
Global Link Sourcing Inc	2671	D	951 698-1977	5523
Guano Records LLC	2759	F	714 263-5398	7338
H & M Four-Slide Inc	3599	F	951 461-8244	16550
Hexco International (PA)	3559	F	951 677-2081	14965
Ikhana Group Inc	3728	C	951 600-0009	20845
International Immunology Corp	2835	E	951 677-5629	8487
J P Specialties Inc	3089	F	951 763-7077	10160
Jeluz Electric Ltd LLC	3699	E	800 216-8307	19994
Kingman Industries Inc	2841	E	951 698-1812	8595
Lobue Laser & Eye Medical Ctrs	3845	E	951 696-1135	23000
Martin Brass Foundry	3366	D	951 698-7041	11762
McCalls Country Canning Inc	3999	F	951 461-2277	24169
Medical Extrusion Tech Inc (PA)	3082	F	951 698-4346	9742
Nittobo America Inc	2836	D	951 677-5629	8568
Nuphoton Technologies Inc	3699	F	951 696-8366	20034
Real Goods Solar Inc	3433	C	951 304-3301	12081
Refresco Beverages US Inc	2086	D	951 461-3328	2185
Rk Sport Inc	3714	E	951 894-7883	20440
S C Coatings Corporation	3479	E	951 461-9777	13652
T & D Services Inc	1381	F	951 304-1190	120
TMC Ice Protection Systems LLC	3812	E	951 677-6934	21443
Touchpint Elctrnic Sltions LLC	3571	F	951 734-8083	15498
Trek Armor Incorporated	3999	F	951 319-4008	24277
Tuula Inc	2841	F	858 761-6045	8611
U S Air Filtration Inc (PA)	3823	F	951 491-7282	21671
USA Printer Company	2752	F	800 279-7768	7159
Vortex Whirlpool Systems Inc	3088	D	951 940-4556	9913
Vycom America Inc	3672	E	800 235-9195	18649
Waterstone LLC	3432	C	951 304-0520	12056
Yellow Magic Incorporated	7372	F	951 506-4005	25367

NAPA, CA - Napa County

Company	SIC	EMP	PHONE	ENTRY #
Advanced Pressure Technology	3823	D	707 259-0102	21543
Antinori California	2084	F	707 265-8866	1645
Archangel Investments LLC	2084	F	707 944-9261	1646
At Mobile Bottling Line LLC	2086	F	707 257-3757	2097
AUL Corp (PA)	7694	E	707 257-9700	25454
Awg Ltd Inc	2084	F	707 259-6777	1649
Babcock & Wilcox Company	3511	E	707 259-1122	13989
Barbour Vineyards LLC	2084	D	707 257-1829	1652
Bergin Glass Impressions Inc	3231	E	707 224-0111	10679
Biale Estate	2084	F	707 257-7555	1660
Birchwood Cabinets of Cal	2434	E	209 523-2323	4274
Black Stallion Winery LLC	2084	F	707 253-1400	1661
Blacktalon Industries Inc	3496	F	707 256-1812	13813
Bottlers Unlimited Inc	2086	E	707 255-0595	2100
Bouchaine Vineyards Inc	2084	F	707 252-9065	1666
California Etching Inc	3479	F	707 224-9966	13563
Cemex Materials LLC	3273	E	707 255-3035	11085
Chateau Potelle Inc	2084	E	707 255-9440	1691
Cliff Vine Winery Inc	2084	F	707 944-2388	1694
Clos Du Val Wine Company Ltd	2084	E	707 259-2200	1697
Codorniu Napa Inc	2084	D	707 254-2148	1700
Collotype Labels USA Inc (HQ)	2759	D	707 603-2500	7277
County of NAPA	3823	F	707 259-8620	21566
Crimson Wine Group Ltd (PA)	2084	C	800 486-0503	1712
Cultured Stone Corporation (DH)	3272	A	707 255-1727	10912
Darioush Khaledi Winery LLC	2084	E	707 257-2345	1716
Decor Shower Door and Glass Co	3231	F	707 253-0622	10691
Decrevel Incorporated	3544	F	707 258-8065	14504
Delicato Vineyards	2084	E	707 265-1700	1721
Delicato Vineyards	2084	E	707 253-1400	1722
Demptos NAPA Cooperage (HQ)	2449	E	707 257-2628	4520
Dexta Corporation	3843	D	707 255-2454	22872
Diageo North America Inc	2084	D	707 299-2600	1726
Distinctive Prpts NAPA Vly	2721	D	707 256-2251	6147
Don Sebastiani & Sons Internat	2084	E	707 224-0410	1732
Eco Global Solutions Inc	3822	F	707 254-9844	21510
Etude Wines Inc	2084	F	707 257-5300	1754
Eurostampa North America Inc	2759	F	707 927-4848	7312
Feather Farm Inc	3496	F	707 255-8833	13826
Golden State Vintners	2084	F	707 254-1985	1787
Hagafen Cellars Inc	2084	F	707 252-0781	1801
Hayward Enterprises Inc	2037	F	707 261-5100	950
Hedgeside Vintners	2084	E	707 963-2316	1810
Hess Collection Winery (DH)	2084	E	707 255-1144	1811
Huneeus Vintners LLC (PA)	2084	E	707 286-2724	1815
Hurleys LP	2599	D	707 944-2345	5237
Jarvis	2084	E	707 255-5280	1829
John Pina Jr & Sons	2084	F	707 944-2229	1833
Krupp Brothers LLC	2084	F	707 226-2215	1842
Laird Family Estate LLC (PA)	2084	E	707 257-0360	1851
Le Belge Chocolatier Inc	2064	E	707 258-9200	1438
Lixit Corporation (PA)	3999	D	800 358-8254	24164
Luna Vineyards Inc	2084	F	707 255-2474	1866
Mont St John Cellars Inc	2084	F	707 255-8864	1883
Monticello Cellars Inc	2084	F	707 253-2802	1886
Myers Wine Cntry Kitchens LLC	3221	E	707 252-9463	10622
NAPA Beaucanon Estate	2084	E	707 254-1460	1892
NAPA Printing & Graphics Ctr (PA)	2752	F	707 257-6555	6988
NAPA Valley Coffee Roasting Co (PA)	2095	F	707 224-2233	2360
NAPA Valley Publishing Co	2711	D	707 226-3711	5987
NAPA Valley Publishing Co (PA)	2711	E	707 226-3711	5988
North Bay Plywood Inc	2431	E	707 224-7849	4203
Pacific Steel Group	3449	E	707 669-3136	12988
Perfect Puree of NAPA Vly LLC	2037	F	707 261-5100	963
Pine Ridge Winery LLC	2084	D	707 253-7500	1925
Portocork America Inc	2499	F	707 258-3930	4642
Prolab Orthotics Inc	3069	F	707 257-4400	9663
Radiator Specialty Company	2899	F	707 252-0122	9300
Ramspur Winery LLC	2084	F	707 251-3948	1938
Rang Dong Joint Stock Company	2084	F	707 259-9446	1940
Regusci Vineyard MGT Inc	2084	E	707 254-0403	1944
River City	2599	E	707 253-1111	5252
Robert Mondavi Corporation (HQ)	2084	D	707 967-2100	1950
Robinson Family Winery	2084	F	707 287-8428	1952
Royal Drapery Manufacturing	2391	F	707 226-2022	3700
Saintsbury LLC	2084	F	707 252-0592	1963
Sciambi-Passini French Bky Inc	2051	E	707 252-3072	1319
Seguin Moreau Holdings Inc (PA)	2449	D	707 252-3408	4535
Shafer Vineyards	2084	F	707 944-2877	1973
Showertek Inc	3231	F	707 224-1480	10731
Silenus Vintners	2084	F	707 299-3930	1976
Stags Leap Wine Cellars	2084	C	707 944-2020	1988
Sterling Vineyards Inc	2084	E	707 252-7410	1992
Sutter Home Winery Inc	2084	E	707 963-3104	2003
Sweetie Pies LLC	2051	F	707 257-7280	1327
Tapp Label Inc	2752	F	707 253-8250	7129
Treasury Wine Estates Americas (HQ)	2084	B	707 259-4500	2021
Trefethen Vineyards Winery Inc	2084	E	707 255-7700	2027
Tschida Engineering	3599	F	707 224-4482	17017
Tulocay Winery	2084	F	707 255-4064	2030
Vignette Winery LLC	2084	F	707 637-8821	2040
Villa Encinal Partners LP	2084	F	707 945-1220	2042
Wild Horse Industrial Corp	3565	F	707 265-6801	15236
William Hill Winery	2084	F	707 224-5424	2056
Wine Country Cases Inc	2449	D	707 967-4805	4540
World Wine Bottles LLC	3221	E	707 339-2102	10628

NATIONAL CITY, CA - San Diego County

Company	SIC	EMP	PHONE	ENTRY #
Adelaide Marine Services LLC	2992	F	619 852-8722	9421
Adept Process Services Inc	3732	E	619 434-3194	21019
Apparel Enterprises Co Inc	2339	F	619 474-6916	3373
B and P Plastics Inc	3089	E	619 477-1893	9966
Bay City Marine Inc (PA)	3441	E	619 477-3991	12116
Bay City Marine Inc	3731	E	619 477-3991	20987
Carroll Metal Works Inc	3441	E	619 477-9125	12131
Coastal Decking Inc	3731	E	619 477-0567	20989
Craft Labor & Support Svcs LLC	3731	D	619 336-9977	20993
Dima-Tech Inc	3612	E	619 474-7006	17089
Fabrication Tech Inds Inc	3441	D	619 477-4141	12159
Family Loompya Corporation	2099	E	619 477-2125	2516
G V Industries Inc	3599	E	619 474-3013	16522
Gary Manufacturing Inc	3089	E	619 429-4479	10113
Hyperbaric Technologies Inc	3845	D	619 336-2022	22988
Indu Fashions	2325	E	619 336-4638	3074
Jaann Inc	3441	F	619 336-0584	12183
Motivational Systems Inc	3993	E	800 748-6584	23930
Navigational Services Inc	3731	F	619 409-6992	21005
Pacord Inc	3731	E	619 336-2200	21008
Paige Sitta & Associates Inc (PA)	3731	E	619 233-5912	21009
San Diego Arcft Interiors Inc	2511	E	619 474-1997	4738
Southern California Insulation	3731	E	619 477-1303	21014
Southland Clutch Inc	3714	E	619 477-2105	20451

Mergent email: customerrelations@mergent.com

1420

2019 California
Manufacturers Register

(P-0000) Products & Services Section entry number
(PA)=Parent Co (HQ)=Headquarters (DH)=Div Headquarters

	SIC	EMP	PHONE	ENTRY #
Special Forces Custom Gear Inc	2393	E	619 241-5453	3771
Tdk-Lambda Americas Inc	3679	C	619 575-4400	19745
Underground Autowerks Inc (PA)	3423	F	619 336-9000	11914
Vantage Associates Inc	3728	E	619 477-6940	20968
Vantage Associates Inc (PA)	3769	E	619 477-6940	21198
Walashek Industrial & Mar Inc	3731	E	619 498-1711	21017
Westflex Inc (PA)	3052	E	619 474-7400	9512

NEEDLES, CA - San Bernardino County

	SIC	EMP	PHONE	ENTRY #
Tri State Truss Corporation	2439	F	760 326-3868	4428

NELSON, CA - Butte County

	SIC	EMP	PHONE	ENTRY #
Far West Rice Inc	2044	E	530 891-1339	1078

NEVADA CITY, CA - Nevada County

	SIC	EMP	PHONE	ENTRY #
Barry Costello	2386	F	530 265-3300	3608
Best Sanitizers Inc	2842	D	530 265-1800	8625
Dylern Incorporated	3599	E	530 470-8785	16454
N C W G Inc	2084	F	530 265-9463	1891
Rcd Engineering Inc	3625	E	530 292-3133	17297
Savensealcom Ltd	2673	F	530 478-0238	5621
Sierra Metal Fabricators Inc	3441	E	530 265-4591	12242
Sonic Technology Products Inc	3674	E	530 272-4607	19180
Technicolor Usa Inc	3663	A	530 478-3000	18276
Witt Hillard	2842	E	530 510-0756	8683

NEW CUYAMA, CA - Santa Barbara County

	SIC	EMP	PHONE	ENTRY #
E & B Ntral Resources MGT Corp	1382	E	661 766-2501	134

NEWARK, CA - Alameda County

	SIC	EMP	PHONE	ENTRY #
Accurate Tube Bending Inc	3498	E	510 790-6500	13872
Agilent Technologies Inc	3825	B	510 794-1234	21706
Air Solutions LLC	3585	F	510 573-6474	15934
Atieva Usa Inc	3711	B	510 648-3553	20127
BASF Corporation	2869	F	510 796-9911	8982
Caliente Systems Inc	3443	E	510 790-0300	12367
Cellotape Inc (HQ)	3993	C	510 651-5551	23842
CMI Mfg Inc	3599	F	408 982-9580	16387
Crown Mfg Co Inc	3089	E	510 742-8800	10051
Cymabay Therapeutics Inc (PA)	2834	E	510 293-8800	8131
Dna Twopointo Inc	2836	D	650 853-8347	8546
Dwell Home Inc	2519	F	877 864-5752	4909
Emcore Corporation	3674	F	510 896-2139	18817
Envia Systems Inc	3699	E	510 509-1367	19961
Etm—Electromatic Inc (PA)	3663	D	510 797-1100	18105
Five Star Lumber Company LLC (PA)	2448	E	510 795-7204	4471
Foot Locker Retail Inc	3149	F	510 797-5750	10505
Fullbloom Baking Company Inc	2051	B	510 456-3638	1255
Futuris Automotive (ca) LLC	2396	B	510 771-2300	3893
Incarda Therapeutics Inc	2834	E	510 422-5522	8218
Jri Inc	3444	E	510 494-5300	12633
Kateeva Inc	3663	B	510 953-7600	18142
Knt Inc	3599	C	510 651-7163	16660
Knt Manufacturing Inc	3999	E	510 896-1699	24151
Kwj Engineering Inc (PA)	3829	E	510 794-4296	22226
Landmark Label Manufacturing	2759	E	510 651-5551	7380
Lifetrak Incorporated	3845	E	510 413-9030	22999
Logitech Inc (HQ)	3577	B	510 795-8500	15794
Logitech Streaming Media Inc	3679	E	510 795-8500	19627
Matheson Tri-Gas Inc	2813	F	510 714-3026	7702
Matheson Tri-Gas Inc	2813	D	510 793-2559	7704
Medina Medical Inc	3841	F	650 396-7756	22530
Mitac Information Systems	3577	E	510 668-3679	15807
Mitac Information Systems Corp (DH)	3572	C	510 284-3000	15570
Nakagawa Manufacturing USA Inc	2621	E	510 782-0197	5312
Neato Robotics Inc (HQ)	3549	D	510 795-1351	14760
Nefab Packaging Inc	2441	D	408 678-2500	4444
Nevada Heat Treating Inc (PA)	7692	E	510 790-2300	25424
Novaray Medical Inc	3844	F	510 619-9200	22939
Oatey Co	2891	E	800 321-9532	9158
Pabco Building Products LLC	3275	D	510 792-9555	11221
Pabco Building Products LLC	3275	E	510 792-1577	11222
Protagonist Therapeutics Inc	2834	E	510 474-0170	8349
Quality Quartz Engineering Inc (PA)	3679	E	510 791-1013	19699
Quark Pharmaceuticals Inc (DH)	2834	E	510 402-4020	8353
Revance Therapeutics Inc	2834	C	510 742-3400	8363
Rh Products Inc	2448	E	510 794-6676	4503
Salutron Incorporated (PA)	3845	E	510 795-2876	23045
San Francisco Bay Brand Inc (PA)	2048	E	510 792-7200	1162
Shotspotter Inc	7372	D	510 794-3100	25171
Silicon Valley Mfg Inc	3315	E	510 791-9450	11456
Smart Global Holdings Inc (PA)	3674	F	510 623-1231	19172
Smart Storage Systems Inc (DH)	3572	E	510 623-1231	15609
Socket Mobile Inc	3663	E	510 933-3000	18255
Specilized Packg Solutions Inc	2449	E	510 494-5670	4536
Svm Machining Inc	3441	E	510 791-9450	12254
Tesla Inc	3711	A	510 896-6400	20174

	SIC	EMP	PHONE	ENTRY #
Theranos Inc (PA)	3841	D	650 838-9292	22648
Tria Beauty Inc	3845	D	925 701-2500	23062
Venture Electronics Intl Inc	3672	F	510 744-3720	18646
Wintec Industries Inc	3577	E	510 953-7400	15887
Wintec Industries Inc (PA)	3577	C	510 953-7440	15888

NEWBERRY SPRINGS, CA - San Bernardino County

	SIC	EMP	PHONE	ENTRY #
Elementis Specialties Inc	1459	E	760 257-9112	401

NEWBURY PARK, CA - Ventura County

	SIC	EMP	PHONE	ENTRY #
360 Systems	3651	F	818 991-0360	17747
Alcoa Inc	3334	B	805 498-4594	11533
Amgen Inc	2834	E	805 499-0512	8023
Amgen Inc	2834	D	805 447-1000	8025
Amgen Manufacturing Limited	3999	F	787 656-2000	24037
Aqua Man Inc (PA)	3589	F	805 499-5707	16010
Arconic Inc	3334	B	805 262-4230	11534
Baxter Bioscience	2833	A	805 498-8988	7923
Boostpower USA Inc	3519	F	805 376-6077	14014
CHE Precision Inc	3599	F	805 499-8885	16379
Colorful Products Corporation	2844	F	805 498-2195	8719
Componetics Inc	3677	F	805 498-0939	19328
Compulink Business Systems Inc	7372	C	805 446-2050	24515
Condor Pacific Inds Cal Inc	3728	E	818 889-2150	20786
Corwin Press Inc	2731	F	805 499-9734	6331
Diamond Ground Products Inc	3548	E	805 498-3837	14724
Eca Medical Instruments (DH)	3841	E	805 376-2509	22431
Electronic Sensor Tech Inc	3826	F	805 480-1994	21951
Eli Lilly and Company	2834	C	805 499-5475	8146
Envel Design Corporation	3646	F	805 376-8111	17602
Excaliber Systems Inc	2759	E	805 376-1366	7313
Fc Management Services	3559	F	805 499-0050	14954
Filthy Grill Inc	3631	F	818 282-2017	17369
Follmer Development Inc	2813	E	805 498-4531	7691
Grateful Naturals Corp	2844	F	323 379-4553	8758
H and M Industries LLC	2541	F	805 499-5100	5067
H K Lighting Group Inc	3648	F	805 480-4881	17699
Isolutecom Inc (PA)	7372	E	805 498-6259	24804
JBW Precision Inc	3444	E	805 499-1973	12629
JW Molding Inc	3544	E	805 499-2682	14529
Ltd Tech Inc	3549	F	805 480-1886	14758
Millworks Etc Inc (PA)	3442	F	805 499-3400	12335
Multilayer Prototypes Inc	3672	F	805 498-9390	18534
Odcombe Press (nashville)	2752	E	615 793-5414	7001
Onyx Pharmaceuticals Inc	2834	A	650 266-0000	8318
Petunia Pickle Bottom Corp	2211	F	805 643-6697	2757
Point Nine Technologies Inc (PA)	3674	F	805 375-6600	19079
Qorvo California Inc	3679	E	805 480-5050	19697
Qorvo Us Inc	3679	E	805 480-5099	19698
R F Circuits and Assembly Inc	3672	F	805 499-7788	18576
Saco	3699	F	805 499-7788	20062
Scientific Surface Inds Inc	2541	F	805 499-5100	5099
Skyworks Solutions Inc	3674	D	805 480-4400	19170
Skyworks Solutions Inc	3674	D	805 480-4227	19171
Smith Precision Products Co	3561	F	805 498-6616	15091
Specialty Concepts Inc	3613	F	818 998-5238	17165
Transparent Devices Inc	3577	E	805 499-5000	15874
Victory Custom Athletics	2339	D	818 349-8476	3524
Weldlogic Inc	7692	D	805 375-1670	25448
Wirewright Inc	3089	F	805 499-9194	10447
WV Communications Inc	3663	F	805 376-1820	18304
Zed Audio Corporation	3651	F	805 499-5559	17885

NEWCASTLE, CA - Placer County

	SIC	EMP	PHONE	ENTRY #
Omega Diamond Inc	3545	F	916 652-8122	14659
Sierra Safety Company	3499	F	916 663-2026	13973

NEWHALL, CA - Los Angeles County

	SIC	EMP	PHONE	ENTRY #
Berry Petroleum Company LLC	1311	F	661 255-6066	25
Valley Stamping Inc	3469	F	661 259-4562	13291

NEWMAN, CA - Stanislaus County

	SIC	EMP	PHONE	ENTRY #
Cemex Cnstr Mtls PCF LLC	3273	E	209 862-0182	11075
Index Printing Inc	2759	F	209 862-2222	7353
Newman Flange & Fitting Co	3462	D	209 862-2977	13107
Stewart & Jasper Marketing Inc (PA)	2068	C	209 862-9600	1504
Vsp Products Inc	2034	D	209 862-1200	906
Westside Pallet Inc	2448	D	209 862-3941	4513

NEWPORT BEACH, CA - Orange County

	SIC	EMP	PHONE	ENTRY #
260 Resource Management LLC	1389	F	866 700-1031	162
A & A Ready Mixed Concrete Inc (PA)	3273	F	949 253-2800	11024
Adaptive Digital Systems Inc	3663	E	949 955-3116	18015
Air Products and Chemicals Inc	2813	F	949 474-1860	7674
American Vanguard Corporation (PA)	2879	D	949 260-1200	9091
AMS Drilling	1381	F	949 232-1149	96
Amvac Chemical Corporation (HQ)	2879	C	323 264-3910	9093

GEOGRAPHIC

	SIC	EMP	PHONE	ENTRY #
Amvac Chemical Corporation	2879	F	949 260-1212	9094
Anacapa Marine Services (PA)	3732	F	805 985-1818	21021
Applied Materials Inc	3559	E	949 244-1600	14908
Associated Ready Mix Con Inc (PA)	3273	E	949 253-2800	11046
Basin Marine Inc	3732	F	949 673-0360	21022
Builder & Developer Magazines	2721	F	949 631-0308	6118
C & H Hydraulics Inc	3728	F	949 646-6230	20762
C M Common Ground Inc	3613	E	949 646-9468	17133
Calor Apparel Group Intl Corp	2341	E	949 548-9095	3534
CDM Company Inc	3999	E	949 644-2820	24063
Churm Publishing Inc (PA)	2721	E	714 796-7000	6129
Clinical Formula LLC	2834	F	949 631-0149	8114
Comac America Corporation	3721	E	760 616-9614	20575
Conexant Holdings Inc	3674	A	415 983-2706	18779
Conexant Systems Worldwide Inc.	3674	D	949 483-4600	18781
Connected Holdings LLC	3812	F	714 907-6371	21275
Crm Co LLC (PA)	3061	E	949 263-9100	9565
Crossport Mocean	2311	E	949 646-1701	3027
Cure Medical LLC (PA)	3841	F	800 570-1778	22415
Duffield Marine Inc	3732	E	949 645-6812	21034
Electric Bike Company LLC	3751	F	949 264-4080	21107
Ericsson Inc.	3577	D	949 721-6604	15741
Fantasea Enterprises Inc	3732	F	949 673-8545	21036
Freeform Research & Dev	3545	F	949 646-3217	14635
Fusion Diet Systems Inc (PA)	2023	F	801 783-1194	619
Gst Inc	3572	D	949 510-1142	15545
Hacker Industries Inc (PA)	3275	F	949 729-3101	11219
Hixson Metal Finishing	3471	D	800 900-9798	13426
Hmr Building Systems LLC	2421	F	951 749-4700	4039
Image Magazine Inc	2721	E	949 608-5188	6190
Jazz Semiconductor Inc (DH)	3674	A	949 435-8000	18938
Lebata Inc	3272	E	949 253-2800	10948
Lewis Barricade Inc	2951	E	661 363-0912	9389
Lumens Audio Visual Inc	3669	F	970 988-6268	18342
M L Interiors Inc	2391	E	949 723-5001	3695
Macom Technology Solutions Inc	3663	E	310 320-6160	18173
Mercury Interactive LLC	7372	E	949 476-3780	24903
Mfi Inc	3999	F	949 313-6450	24174
Microtelematics Inc	7372	F	888 651-7133	24919
Mindspeed Technologies Inc (HQ)	3674	D	949 579-3000	19019
Morris Roberts LLC	3993	E	800 672-3974	23929
Mscsoftware Corporation (HQ)	7372	C	714 540-8900	24936
Nationals Elite Athletics Inc (PA)	2759	F	866 253-6614	7410
Newport Fab LLC	3674	D	949 435-8000	19040
Nima LLC	3651	E	949 404-1990	17838
Ohp Inc (DH)	2819	E	800 659-6745	7792
Optek Group Inc	3845	E	949 629-2558	23030
Peninsula Publishing Inc	2721	E	949 631-1307	6231
Platescan Inc	3469	E	949 851-1600	13260
Redart Corporation	2531	F	714 774-9444	5026
Rsdg International Inc	2361	E	626 256-4190	3587
RSI Home Products Inc	2514	A	949 720-1116	4841
SGB Holdings LLC	3911	E	949 722-1149	23317
Sky Global Services Inc	3999	F	949 291-5511	24244
Solar Enrgy World Ltd Lblty Co	3433	E	973 887-1082	12086
Strategic Medical Ventures LLC (PA)	3844	E	949 355-5212	22942
Synergy Oil LLC	3569	E	888 333-1933	15367
Theft Patrol LLC	3663	E	858 880-5841	18285
Towerjazz Texas Inc (PA)	3679	D	949 435-8000	19766
Tribeworx LLC	7372	D	800 949-3432	25294
Triton Chandelier Inc	3646	E	714 957-9600	17651
Tz Holdings LP	7372	A	949 719-2200	25304
Urban Decal LLC (HQ)	2844	E	949 574-9712	8857
Walden Structures Inc (PA)	2452	E	909 389-9100	4585
WE Hall Company Inc (PA)	3316	D	949 650-4555	11472

NEWPORT COAST, CA - Orange County

	SIC	EMP	PHONE	ENTRY #
AST Power LLC	3694	E	949 226-2275	19827

NICE, CA - Lake County

	SIC	EMP	PHONE	ENTRY #
Bent Fir Company	2511	F	707 274-6628	4677

NICOLAUS, CA - Sutter County

	SIC	EMP	PHONE	ENTRY #
Paulsen White Oak LP	2879	F	530 656-2201	9110

NIPOMO, CA - San Luis Obispo County

	SIC	EMP	PHONE	ENTRY #
LR Baggs Corporation	3931	E	805 929-3545	23379
Malcolm Demille Inc	3911	E	805 929-4353	23293
Statewide Safety and Signs I	3669	B	714 468-1919	18367
Triactive America Inc	3949	F	805 595-1005	23675
Troesh Readymix Inc	3273	D	805 928-3764	11200
Whites Hvac Services Inc	3585	F	805 801-0167	16001

NIPTON, CA - San Bernardino County

	SIC	EMP	PHONE	ENTRY #
NRG Energy Services LLC	3612	D	702 815-2023	17108

NORCO, CA - Riverside County

	SIC	EMP	PHONE	ENTRY #
Avid Idntification Systems Inc (PA)	3674	D	951 371-7505	18735
Canidae Corporation	2047	F	909 599-5190	1110
Gentle Giants Products Inc	2047	F	951 818-2512	1113
Halle-Hopper LLC	2431	F	951 284-7373	4163
Husk-ITT Distributors Corp	2992	F	951 340-4000	9436
Industrial Process Eqp Inc	3567	F	714 447-0171	15264
Inland Artfl Limb & Brace Inc (PA)	3842	F	951 734-1835	22753
Inland Color Graphics	2796	F	951 493-2999	7649
International E-Z Up Inc (PA)	2394	D	800 457-4233	3791
Jeffrey Court Inc	3253	D	951 340-3383	10784
Paragon Building Products Inc (PA)	3272	E	951 549-1155	10974
Positron Access Solutions Inc	3663	F	951 272-9100	18222
RPM Grinding Co Inc	3599	F	951 273-0602	16920
S R Machining-Properties LLC	3599	C	951 520-9486	16926
Sierra Woodworking Inc	2431	E	714 538-8440	4229
Sr Machining Inc	3599	F	951 520-9486	16962
Sr Plastics Company LLC (PA)	3089	F	951 520-9486	10386
Sr Plastics Company LLC	3089	E	951 479-5394	10387
Stadium Printing Inc	2752	F	951 371-3890	7115
W B Powell Inc	2431	F	951 270-0095	4253

NORTH FORK, CA - Madera County

	SIC	EMP	PHONE	ENTRY #
Crossroads Recycled Lumber LLC	2421	F	559 877-3645	4035

NORTH HIGHLANDS, CA - Sacramento County

	SIC	EMP	PHONE	ENTRY #
Determan Industries Inc	3469	F	916 974-1977	13193
Kacee Company	3599	F	916 348-3204	16641
Livingstons Concrete Svc Inc (PA)	3273	D	916 334-4313	11135
Livingstons Concrete Svc Inc.	3273	E	916 334-4313	11136
Mikes Sheet Metal Products	3444	E	916 348-3800	12677
New Wave Industries Ltd (PA)	3589	F	800 882-8854	16079
Pacific Coast Supply LLC	2439	F	916 339-8100	4419
Pisor Industries Inc.	3599	E	916 944-2851	16844
Scafco Corporation	3523	E	916 624-7700	14103
Security Contractor Svcs Inc	3446	E	916 338-4800	12890
Steeler Inc	3444	F	916 483-3600	12772

NORTH HILLS, CA - Los Angeles County

	SIC	EMP	PHONE	ENTRY #
Akupara Games LLC	7372	F	805 471-4933	24345
Alpha Aviation Components Inc (PA)	3599	E	818 894-8801	16257
Alpha Aviation Components Inc	3599	F	818 894-8468	16258
Challenge Graphics Inc	2752	E	818 892-0123	6727
Gits Manufacturing Company Inc	3714	C	641 782-2105	20353
Graphics Bindery	2789	F	818 886-2463	7600
Imperial Toy LLC (PA)	3944	C	818 536-6500	23430
Morris Enterprises Inc	3089	E	818 894-9103	10226
PCA Electronics Inc.	3677	E	818 892-0761	19351
S & J Prof Property Svcs	1321	F	818 892-0181	90
Schrillo Company LLC	3452	E	818 894-8241	13082
Valley Drapery Inc	2221	D	818 892-7744	2786

NORTH HOLLYWOOD, CA - Los Angeles County

	SIC	EMP	PHONE	ENTRY #
A T Parker Inc (PA)	3699	E	818 755-1700	19893
ABC Sun Control LLC	2394	F	818 982-6989	3778
Advanced Inst of Skin Care	2844	F	818 765-2606	8690
Advanced Semiconductor Inc (PA)	3674	D	818 982-1200	18669
Alco Tech Inc	3469	F	818 503-9209	13161
Allan Aircraft Supply Co LLC	3494	E	818 765-4992	13757
Almore Dye House Inc	2269	E	818 506-5444	2908
Alpena Sausage Inc	2013	F	818 505-9482	462
American Costume Corp	2389	F	818 432-4350	3639
Americh Corporation (PA)	3842	C	818 982-1711	22699
Anmar Precision Components	3728	E	818 764-0901	20737
Applica Inc.	3663	E	818 565-0011	18039
AR Casting Inc	3911	F	818 765-1202	23237
Architectural Plywood Inc	2435	E	818 255-1900	4376
Armenco Catrg Trck Mfg Co Inc	3713	F	818 768-0400	20191
Armored Group Inc.	2441	F	818 767-3030	4434
Artcrafters Cabinets Inc.	2434	F	818 752-8960	4271
Arte De Mexico Inc	3646	E	818 753-4510	17584
Artisan House Inc	3499	E	818 767-7476	13919
Asi Semiconductor Inc	3674	E	818 982-1200	18724
Astro Chrome and Polsg Corp	3471	E	818 781-1463	13339
Ave Jewelry Inc	3911	F	213 488-0097	23242
Avibank Mfg Inc (DH)	3728	C	818 392-2100	20752
Backstage Equipment Inc	3449	F	818 504-6026	12972
Basaw Manufacturing Inc (PA)	2441	F	818 765-6650	4435
Basaw Services Inc.	2441	F	818 765-6650	4436
Basaw Services Inc.	2441	F	818 765-6650	4437
Bauers & Collins	3842	F	818 983-1281	22704
Black Phoenix Inc.	2844	F	818 506-9404	8703
Bogner Amplification	3651	F	818 765-8929	17777
Brite-Lite Neon Corp	3993	F	818 763-4798	23835
Cal-June Inc (PA)	3429	E	323 877-4164	11941
Capco/Psa	3089	F	818 762-4276	10011

Mergent email: customerrelations@mergent.com
1422

2019 California
Manufacturers Register

(P-0000) Products & Services Section entry number
(PA)=Parent Co (HQ)=Headquarters (DH)=Div Headquarters

Company	SIC	EMP	PHONE	ENTRY #
Caretta Inc	3911	F	818 781-9486	23248
Carl Nersesian	2431	F	818 888-0111	4122
Cecilias Designs Inc	2395	E	323 584-6151	3834
Cheerpak	2043	F	818 922-5451	1056
City Wide Printing Inc	2711	F	818 752-9300	5805
Clarke Engineering Inc	3568	F	818 768-0690	15282
Corporate Impressions La Inc	2759	E	818 761-9295	7285
Cosmo - Pharm Inc	2833	E	818 764-0246	7928
Crabtree Glass Company Inc	3446	F	818 765-1840	12845
Crane Co	3492	E	310 403-2820	13738
Cryogenic Machinery Corp	3559	F	818 765-6688	14933
Dakotahouse Industries Inc	1499	E	310 596-1100	409
Datagenics Software Inc	7372	E	818 487-3900	24553
Davenport International Corp	3651	E	818 765-6400	17788
Dennis Bolton Enterprises Inc	2752	E	818 982-1800	6781
Deux Lux Inc (PA)	3172	E	213 746-7040	10559
Dowell Aluminum Foundry Inc	3365	F	323 877-9645	11738
Eiger Vision Corporation	3663	F	818 201-0471	18095
Electromatic Inc	3471	F	818 765-3236	13401
Empire Optical of California	3851	E	818 997-6474	23092
Enviro-Intercept Inc	3585	F	818 982-6063	15955
F & H Plating LLC	3471	F	818 765-1221	13409
Fastener Technology Corp	3965	D	818 764-6467	23765
Fayes Foods Inc	2099	E	818 508-8392	2517
G & H Precision Inc	3599	F	818 982-3873	16519
G2 Graphic Service Inc	2759	D	818 623-3100	7324
Gahh LLC (HQ)	3714	F	800 722-2292	20345
General Wax Co Inc (PA)	3999	D	818 765-5800	24106
Glima Inc	2339	E	818 980-9686	3421
Gourmet Coffee Warehouse Inc	2095	D	818 423-2626	2350
Graphic Visions Inc	2752	E	818 845-8393	6839
Harman Press	2752	E	818 432-0570	6849
Hope Plastic Co Inc	3089	E	818 769-5560	10140
Infinity Access Plus Inc	3446	F	818 270-8172	12861
Inter Color Plus Inter	2759	E	818 764-5034	7359
Jack C Drees Grinding Co Inc	3599	E	818 764-8301	16608
Jam Design Inc	3961	F	818 505-1680	23748
Jay Manufacturing Corp	3469	F	818 255-0500	13230
John A Thomson PHD	2833	E	323 877-5186	7953
Johnson Doc Enterprises	3089	E	818 764-1543	10172
Johnson Marble Machinery Inc	3559	F	818 764-6186	14977
Karapet Engineering Inc	3599	F	818 255-0838	16645
Kk Audio Inc	3861	F	818 765-2921	23174
Klune Industries Inc (DH)	3728	B	818 503-8100	20860
Kobis Windows & Doors Mfg Inc	2434	E	818 764-6400	4322
Lepera Enterprises Inc	3751	E	818 767-5110	21123
Lob-Ster Inc (PA)	3949	F	818 764-6000	23608
Lookout Enterprises Inc	2096	F	323 969-0178	2395
Mar Engineering Company	3599	E	818 765-4805	16712
Mave Enterprises Inc	2064	E	818 767-4533	1443
Meco-Nag Corporation	3144	D	818 764-2020	10499
Meggitt North Hollywood Inc (HQ)	3491	C	818 765-8160	13726
Metal Improvement Company LLC	3398	C	818 983-1952	11819
Mid Century Imports Inc	2511	F	818 509-3050	4720
Mid Michigan Trading Post Ltd	2741	D	517 323-9020	6528
Mid Valley Grinding Co Inc	3999	F	818 764-1086	24176
Modern Studio Equipment Inc	3861	F	818 764-8574	23179
Modern-Aire Ventilating Inc	3444	E	818 765-9870	12683
My Sign Design LLC	2752	F	818 384-0800	6986
Nelson Thread Grinding Inc	3599	F	818 768-2578	16785
North Hollywood Uniform Inc	2337	F	818 503-5931	3357
Norths Bakery California Inc	2051	F	818 761-2892	1297
Onnik Shoe Company Inc	3144	F	818 506-5353	10501
Orion Ornamental Iron Inc	3429	F	818 752-0688	11981
Pacific Wire Products Inc	3496	F	818 755-6400	13842
Perkins	3548	E	818 764-9293	14736
Perpetual Motion Group Inc	3441	D	818 982-4300	12228
Praxair Distribution Inc	2813	F	818 760-2011	7725
Precision Engineering Inds	3679	F	818 767-8590	19689
Prime Building Material Inc	3272	F	818 503-4242	10982
Quality Powder Coating LLC	3479	F	818 982-8322	13646
Raika Inc	3172	E	818 503-5911	10569
Reel Efx Inc	3999	F	818 762-1710	24221
S & K Theatrical Drap Inc	2391	F	818 503-0596	3701
Sealing Corporation	3053	F	818 765-7327	9557
Shafton Inc	2389	F	818 985-5025	3679
Spec Iron Inc	3441	F	818 765-4070	12245
Specialty Coatings & Chem Inc	2851	E	818 983-0055	8943
Sr3 Solutions LLC	2711	E	818 255-3131	6055
Steve Leshner Clear Systems	3089	F	818 764-9223	10392
Supreme Bean LLC	2095	C	818 506-6020	2367
Tech Air of California Inc	2813	F	818 787-6010	7739
United Audio Video Group Inc	3695	E	818 980-6700	19887
Utility Refrigerator	3585	F	818 764-6200	15996
Vaknin Juda	2434	F	818 503-8872	4363
Vector Electronics & Tech Inc	3672	E	818 985-8208	18643
Wes Go Inc	2759	E	818 504-1200	7537
Wilshire Precision Pdts Inc	3599	E	818 765-4571	17070

NORTH PALM SPRINGS, CA - Riverside County

Company	SIC	EMP	PHONE	ENTRY #
E & S Precision Sheetmetal Mfg	3444	F	760 329-1607	12565
Technique Designs Inc	2541	F	760 904-6223	5111

NORTHRIDGE, CA - Los Angeles County

Company	SIC	EMP	PHONE	ENTRY #
3M Company	2834	B	818 341-1300	7984
5 Star Redemption Inc	3999	F	818 709-0875	24018
A and C Electronics	3672	F	818 886-8900	18401
Afr Apparel International Inc	2341	D	818 773-5000	3533
Artistry In Motion Inc	2679	F	818 994-7388	5699
ATI Solutions Inc (PA)	3669	F	818 772-7900	18309
Cardiomart Inc	2678	F	818 516-6875	5683
Catalina Industries Inc	2851	F	818 772-8888	8893
Chemat Technology Inc	3821	E	818 727-9786	21462
Circuit Services Llc	3672	F	818 701-5391	18451
Color Design Laboratory	2844	E	818 341-5100	8718
DC Partners Inc	3365	F	818 285-0692	11735
DC Partners Inc (PA)	3365	D	714 558-9444	11736
DC Partners Inc	3365	F	818 718-1221	11737
Dealzer Com	2865	F	818 429-1155	8962
Dukes Research and Mfg Inc	3714	E	818 998-9811	20319
Dynamic Shutters Inc	2431	E	818 407-6310	4151
Emanuel Morez Inc	2511	E	818 780-2787	4693
First Responder Fire	3569	F	562 842-6602	15322
Germanex Imports Inc	3714	F	818 700-0441	2035i
Giannelli Cabinet Mfg Co	2542	F	818 882-9787	5142
Gst Industries Inc	3728	E	818 350-1900	20833
Harman Professional Inc (DH)	3651	B	818 893-8411	17809
Infinity Aerospace Inc (PA)	3724	D	818 998-9811	20663
Ink 2000 Corp	2893	F	818 882-0168	9200
Instrument Bearing Factory USA	3452	E	818 989-5052	13074
Instrumentation Tech Systems	3577	F	818 886-2034	15763
Laboratorios Camacho Inc	2834	F	818 764-2748	8253
Lloyd Design Corporation	2273	D	818 768-6001	2931
Mansoor Amarna Corp	3952	F	818 894-8937	23709
Maroney Company	3599	E	818 882-2722	16715
Medtronic Inc	3845	C	300 646-4633	23012
Medtronic Minimed Inc (DH)	3845	A	800 646-4633	23018
Micro Matic Usa Inc	3585	E	818 701-9765	15972
Micro Matic Usa Inc	3491	E	818 882-8012	13728
N M H Inc	2752	F	818 843-8522	6987
Numotech Inc	3841	D	818 772-1579	22560
Pacific Thermography	2759	E	323 938-3349	7429
Perez Brothers	2514	E	818 780-8482	4839
Pharmavite LLC (DH)	2833	C	818 221-6200	7964
Pro Food Inc	2099	F	818 341-4040	2642
Pure Water Centers Inc	3589	F	818 316-1250	16093
Radiant Detector Tech LLC	3829	F	818 709-2468	22257
Resonance Technology Inc	3845	E	818 882-1997	23041
Robert A Kerl	2789	E	818 341-9281	7613
Robert H Oliva Inc	3599	E	818 700-1035	16906
Rotating Prcsion McHanisms Inc	3663	E	818 349-9774	18241
Royal Systems Group	3549	E	818 717-5010	14765
S & S Numerical Control Inc	3599	E	818 341-4141	16923
Shb Instruments Inc	3825	E	818 773-2000	21848
Sheet Metal Prototype Inc	3444	F	818 772-2715	12757
Surfaces Tile Craft Inc	3253	E	818 609-0719	10793
Thermometrics Corporation (PA)	3823	E	818 886-3755	21668
Unique Image Inc	2752	E	818 727-7785	7155
Unitech Deco Inc	2759	E	818 700-1373	7529
Universal Ctrl Solutions Corp	3625	F	818 898-3380	17317
Verde Cosmetic Labs LLC	2844	E	818 284-4080	8862
What Kids Want Inc	3944	F	818 775-0375	23478
Zinsser Na Inc	3826	F	818 341-2906	22053

NORWALK, CA - Los Angeles County

Company	SIC	EMP	PHONE	ENTRY #
Ace Precision Mold Co Inc	3089	F	562 921-8999	9921
Advanced Sealing (DH)	3053	D	562 802-7782	9516
Aerospace Tool Grinding	3541	F	562 802-3339	14357
Aerotec Alloys Inc	3363	F	562 809-1378	11684
AG Global Products LLC	3634	E	323 334-2900	17384
American Relays Inc	3625	E	562 944-0447	17249
ARC Plastics Inc	3089	E	562 802-3299	9952
Architectural Cathode Lighting	3648	F	323 581-8800	17673
Argo Spring Mfg Co Inc	3493	D	800 252-2740	13748
Cabinets 2000 Inc	2434	C	562 868-0909	4281
Dianas Mexican Food Pdts Inc (PA)	2099	B	562 926-5802	2506
Dragon Valves Inc (PA)	3494	C	562 921-6605	13764
G & L Tooling Inc	3541	F	562 802-2857	14380
Golden Specialty Foods LLC	2099	E	562 802-2537	2531
I & I Deburring Inc	3541	F	562 802-0058	14383
International Paper Company	2621	F	562 483-6680	5299

Company	SIC	EMP	PHONE	ENTRY #
Jmt Inc	3599	F	562 404-2014	16626
Master Research & Mfg Inc	3728	D	562 483-8789	20876
McDowell & Craig Off Systems	2522	D	562 921-4441	4995
New Cntury Mtals Southeast Inc	3356	F	562 356-6804	11634
New Incorporation Now	2711	F	562 484-3020	5993
Paradise Printing Inc	2752	E	714 228-9628	7014
Polley Inc **(PA)**	3569	E	562 868-9861	15354
Riedon Inc	3825	F	562 926-2304	21839
Sonoco Products Company	2631	D	562 921-0881	5362
Tecno Industrial Engineering	3599	E	562 623-4517	16993

NOVATO, CA - Marin County

Company	SIC	EMP	PHONE	ENTRY #
Activision Blizzard Inc	7372	C	415 881-9100	24311
ADS Solutions	7372	F	415 897-3700	24327
Andalou Naturals	2844	F	415 446-9470	8694
Ang Newspaper Group Inc **(DH)**	2711	F	650 359-6666	5760
Bella Notte Linens Inc	2221	E	415 883-3434	2774
Biomarin Pharmaceutical Inc	2834	F	415 218-7386	8079
California Newspapers Inc	2711	A	415 883-8600	5788
Carousel Carpet Mills Inc	2273	D	415 892-8207	2927
Celamark Corp	3823	E	415 883-3386	21561
Cork Pops	3499	F	415 884-6000	13931
CRGsynergy	3822	E	415 497-0182	21508
Cricket Company LLC	3069	F	415 475-4150	9604
Crittenden Publishing Inc **(HQ)**	2741	F	415 475-1522	6464
Crittenden Research Inc **(PA)**	2741	E	415 475-1576	6465
Diamics Inc	3841	F	415 883-0414	22424
Dickinson Corporation	3821	F	415 883-7147	21467
Et Water Systems LLC	3829	F	415 945-9383	22194
Excellence Magazine Inc	2721	F	415 382-0582	6161
Forest Investment Group Inc	2752	F	415 459-2330	6823
Image Star LLC	2329	F	415 883-5815	3163
Integrity Support Services Inc	2899	F	415 898-0044	9264
Keys Cabinetry Inc	2541	F	415 382-1466	5075
Marin Scope Incorporated	2711	E	415 892-1516	5939
Marin USA	3429	F	415 382-6000	11973
Northbay Stone Wrks Cntertops	2541	F	415 898-0200	5085
Prima Fleur Botanicals Inc	2844	F	415 455-0957	8823
Ranch Systems LLC	3523	F	415 884-2770	14097
Raptor Pharmaceuticals Inc	2834	E	415 408-6200	8357
Safetychain Software Inc **(PA)**	7372	F	415 233-9474	25137
SCI Publishing Inc	2721	F	415 382-0580	6254
Shamrock Materials of Novato	3273	F	415 892-1571	11179
St Louis Post-Dispatch LLC	2711	F	415 892-1516	6056
Tukko Group LLC	7372	E	408 598-1251	25301
Ultragenyx Pharmaceutical Inc **(PA)**	2834	C	415 483-8800	8425
Whatever Publishing Inc	2731	F	415 884-2100	6408
Zacharon Pharmaceuticals Inc	2834	F	415 506-6700	8449

OAK HILLS, CA - San Bernardino County

Company	SIC	EMP	PHONE	ENTRY #
3M Company	3465	D	760 949-4204	13134

OAK PARK, CA - Ventura County

Company	SIC	EMP	PHONE	ENTRY #
Audio Impressions Inc	3931	F	818 532-7360	23354
Foldimate Inc	3634	E	805 876-4418	17389

OAK VIEW, CA - Ventura County

Company	SIC	EMP	PHONE	ENTRY #
Old Creek Ranch Winery Inc	2084	F	805 649-4132	1904

OAKDALE, CA - Stanislaus County

Company	SIC	EMP	PHONE	ENTRY #
Accu-Swiss Inc **(PA)**	3451	E	209 847-1016	13007
Ball Corporation	3411	B	209 848-6500	11856
Central Valley AG Grinding Inc **(PA)**	2041	E	209 869-1721	1035
Central Valley Professional SE	2673	F	209 847-7832	5591
Conagra Brands Inc	2033	A	209 847-0321	791
D & B Precision Shtmtl Inc	3444	F	209 848-3030	12547
Fisher Sand & Gravel Co	1442	F	602 619-0325	357
Formulation Technology Inc	2834	E	209 847-0331	8165
Haeger Incorporated **(DH)**	3549	E	209 848-4000	14755
Heighten America Inc	3599	F	209 845-0455	16557
Inter Mountain Truss & Girder	2439	F	209 847-9184	4415
Morris Publications **(PA)**	2711	E	209 847-3021	5981
Norsco Inc	3451	E	209 845-2327	13033
Oakdale Cheese & Specialties	2022	F	209 848-3139	594
Sconza Candy Company	2064	D	209 845-3700	1452
Valley Precision Inc	3599	F	209 847-1758	17031
Vierra Bros Farms LLC	3523	F	209 247-3468	14116
Weldway Inc	3441	F	209 847-8083	12279
Willie Bylsma	3556	F	209 847-3362	14898

OAKHURST, CA - Madera County

Company	SIC	EMP	PHONE	ENTRY #
Control Enterprises Inc	3492	F	559 683-2044	13737
Frost Magnetics Incorporated	3677	E	559 642-2536	19337
Webb Designs Inc	2591	F	559 641-5400	5215

OAKLAND, CA - Alameda County

Company	SIC	EMP	PHONE	ENTRY #
3 D Studios	3441	F	510 535-1809	12096
A Taste of Denmark	2051	E	510 420-8889	1171
A&M Products Manufacturing Co **(HQ)**	3295	E	510 271-7000	11315
Able Metal Plating Inc	3471	E	510 569-6539	13304
Advanced Metal Coatings Inc	3479	E	510 535-0185	13543
Agribag Inc	2299	E	510 533-2388	2984
Agriculture Bag Mfg USA Inc **(PA)**	2221	E	510 632-5637	2772
AJW Construction	2951	E	510 568-2300	9377
Alumatherm Incorporated	3442	E	510 832-2819	12291
American Cylinder Head Inc	3714	F	510 261-1590	20252
American Cylndr Hd RPR/Excg	3714	F	510 536-1764	20253
American Emperor Inc	3429	F	510 536-6868	11927
Anoto Incorporated	3951	E	510 777-0071	23698
Arbo Inc	2052	E	510 658-3700	1348
Arch Foods Inc	3421	E	510 868-6000	11876
Arrow Sign Co **(PA)**	3993	E	209 931-5522	23820
Art Craft Staturary Inc	3281	E	510 633-1411	11232
B C H Manufacturing Co Inc	3531	E	510 569-6586	14143
B-Flat Publishing LLC	2741	E	510 639-7170	6444
Babette **(PA)**	2339	E	510 625-8500	3379
Bay Area Indus Filtration Inc	3569	E	510 562-6373	15301
Bay Classifieds Inc	3555	E	510 636-1867	14803
Berrett-Koehler Publishers Inc **(PA)**	2731	E	510 817-2277	6311
Binti Inc	7372	E	844 424-6844	24425
Black Hills Nanosystems Corp	3674	F	605 341-3641	18747
Blank and Cables Inc	2511	F	415 648-3842	4680
Bobs Iron Inc	3441	E	510 567-8983	12119
Borden Lighting	3646	E	510 357-0171	17588
Brand X Hurarches	3143	E	510 658-9006	10480
Broadly Inc	7372	E	510 400-6039	24454
Building Robotics Inc	7372	E	510 761-6482	24458
Bulldog Reporter	2711	E	510 596-9300	5782
C H K Manufacturing Inc	2673	E	510 632-5637	5588
Cable Moore Inc **(PA)**	3496	E	510 436-8000	13814
Cellscope Inc	3661	F	510 282-0674	17930
Cemex Cnstr Mtls PCF LLC	3273	E	925 858-4344	11069
Channel Systems Inc	3272	E	510 568-7170	10900
CHI Fung Plastics Inc	3085	F	510 532-4835	9793
Chiodo Candy Co	2064	D	510 464-2097	1413
Chris French Metal Inc	3441	E	510 238-9339	12135
Clamp Swing Pricing Co Inc	3999	E	510 567-1600	24066
Clorox Company **(PA)**	2842	B	510 271-7000	8632
Clorox Company Voluntary	2812	E	510 271-7000	7660
Clorox International Company **(HQ)**	2879	D	510 271-7000	9097
Clorox Products Mfg Co **(HQ)**	2842	C	510 271-7000	8637
Cnc Noodle Corporation	2099	F	510 835-2269	2492
Commercial Energy Montana Inc	1311	E	510 567-2700	50
Conagra Brands Inc	2041	E	510 536-9555	1036
Conagra Flour Milling Company	2041	F	510 536-9555	1037
Concreteworks Studio Inc	3272	F	510 534-7141	10907
County of Alameda	3824	E	510 272-6964	21682
Creative Wood Products Inc	2521	E	510 635-5399	4940
Custom Mechanical Systems LLC	3585	E	510 347-5500	15948
Dasan Zhone Solutions Inc **(HQ)**	3661	C	510 777-7000	17938
Deluxe Corporation	2782	B	651 483-7100	7579
Design Workshops	2541	E	510 434-0727	5054
Diamond Tool and Die Inc	3599	E	510 534-7050	16437
Digicom Electronics Inc	3672	E	510 639-7003	18468
Dobake Bakeries Inc	2051	D	510 834-3134	1233
Dorado Network Systems Corp	7372	C	650 227-7300	24572
Eandi Metal Works Inc **(PA)**	3441	E	510 532-8311	12155
East Bay Fixture Company	2491	E	510 652-4421	4593
East Bay Glass Company Inc	3442	F	510 834-2535	12311
El Cerrito Woodworking	2541	F	510 647-3767	5056
ELF Beauty Inc **(PA)**	2844	E	510 778-7787	8745
Erg Aerospace Corporation	2819	D	510 658-9785	7775
Everett Graphics Inc	2657	D	510 577-6777	5506
Exo Systems Inc	3845	E	510 655-5033	22977
Fargo Choice Foods LLC	2051	F	510 774-0064	1246
Feeney Inc	3496	E	510 893-9473	13827
Five Flavors Herbs	2023	E	510 923-0178	616
Flipcause Inc	7372	F	800 523-1950	24655
Forem Manufacturing Inc	3339	E	510 577-9500	11545
Forward Printing & Design	2759	E	510 535-2222	7321
Foss Lampshade Studios Inc **(PA)**	3999	E	510 534-4133	24100
Franz Inc	7372	E	510 452-2000	24670
Gaming Fund Group	3845	E	510 532-8881	22979
Garner Heat Treat Inc	3398	E	510 568-0587	11812
General Graphic Chemicals Co	2899	F	510 832-4404	9254
General Grinding Inc	3471	E	510 261-5557	13415
Glad Products Company **(HQ)**	3081	C	510 271-7000	9709
Global Steel Products Corp	2542	E	510 652-2060	5143
GM Associates Inc	3679	D	510 430-0806	19554
Golden Gate Litho	2752	E	510 568-5335	6836
Golden Plastics Corporation	3089	F	510 569-6465	10123
H V Food Products Company	2035	C	510 271-7612	915
Hadal Inc	3531	E	510 864-0600	14175

	SIC	EMP	PHONE	ENTRY #
Hearst Communications Inc	2711	B	510 645-4250	5871
Higher One Payments Inc	7372	E	510 769-9888	24733
Idg Games Media Group Inc	2721	E	510 768-2700	6189
Industrial Wiper & Supply Inc	2241	E	408 286-4752	2801
Inter-City Printing Co Inc	2752	F	510 451-4775	6893
Interactive Solutions Inc (HQ)	7372	D	510 214-9002	24784
Kay Chesterfield Inc	2512	F	510 533-5565	4789
Kemeera Incorporated	3577	F	510 281-9000	15779
Key Source International (PA)	3575	F	510 562-5000	15637
Kingsford Products Company LLC (HQ)	2861	D	510 271-7000	8958
Kitanica Manufacturing	3999	F	707 272-7286	24149
Korea Daily News & Korea Times	2711	E	510 777-1111	5900
Korea Times Los Angeles Inc	2711	E	510 777-1111	5901
Kyoho Manufacturing California	3465	C	209 941-6200	13140
Label Art-Easy Stik Labels	2759	E	510 465-1559	7372
Learners Guild Ltd	7372	F	415 448-7054	24855
Leons Powder Coating	3479	F	510 437-9224	13610
Lewis John Glass Studio	3229	F	510 635-4607	10653
Lignum Vitae Cabinet	2521	F	510 444-2030	4954
Linoleum Sales Co Inc (PA)	3211	D	661 327-4053	10600
Lithograph Reproductions	2752	F	510 658-2367	6949
Mack & Reiss Inc	2369	D	510 434-9122	3593
McWane Inc (PA)	3321	C	510 632-3467	11498
Meditab Software Inc	7372	C	510 632-2021	24899
Meridian Jewelry & Design Inc	3911	F	510 428-2095	23297
Mettler-Toledo Rainin LLC (HQ)	3829	C	510 564-1600	22235
Mills Acquisition Corporation	3444	E	650 365-2801	12679
Miwa Inc	3496	E	510 261-5999	13841
Modern Bamboo Incorporated	2511	F	925 820-2804	4725
Moz Designs Inc	3446	F	510 632-0853	12883
National Recycling Corporation	2679	F	510 268-1022	5717
Nestle Pizza Company Inc	2038	F	510 261-8001	1001
Net Clearly	7372	F	510 465-0101	24948
New Harbinger Publications Inc (PA)	2731	E	510 652-0215	6369
Noodle Theory	2098	F	510 595-6988	2435
Nor-Cal Metal Fabricators	3444	D	510 350-0121	12693
Oakland Tribune Inc	2711	A	510 208-6300	6003
Onki Corp	3714	F	510 567-8875	20414
Outlaw Beverage Inc	2082	F	310 424-5077	1618
Owens-Brockway Glass Cont Inc	3221	D	510 436-2000	10623
Pacific Galvanizing Inc	3479	E	510 261-7331	13628
Pacific Steel Fabricators Inc	3441	E	209 464-9474	12225
Paylocity Holding Corporation	7372	B	847 956-4850	25053
Peerless Coffee Company Inc	2095	D	510 763-1763	2363
Pressure Cast Products Corp	3364	E	510 532-7310	11716
Productboard Inc	3537	F	844 472-6273	14343
Purity Organic LLC	2037	E	415 440-7777	964
Quaker Oats Company	2087	C	510 261-5800	2278
R J R Technologies Inc (PA)	3699	C	510 638-5901	20052
Rago & Son Inc	3469	E	510 536-5700	13271
Readytech Corporation	7372	D	510 834-3344	25106
Redacted-Studios LLC	7372	F	510 333-0030	25118
Rels Foods Inc (PA)	2099	E	510 652-2747	2651
Riffyn Inc (PA)	7372	F	510 542-9868	25130
Right Away Concrete Pmpg Inc	3273	E	510 536-1900	11161
Rolls-Royce Corporation	3724	B	510 635-1500	20676
Savnik & Company Inc	2273	F	510 568-4628	2938
Scientific Learning Corp	7372	E	510 444-3500	25153
Senetur LLC	7372	F	650 269-1023	25162
SF Global LLC	3089	F	888 536-5593	10374
Sighten Inc	7372	E	415 965-3000	25175
Sius Products-Distributor Inc (PA)	2673	E	510 382-1700	5624
Skasol Incorporated	2899	E	510 839-1000	9306
Social Brands LLC	3999	F	415 728-1761	24246
Sorrento Networks Corporation (DH)	3661	F	510 577-1400	17994
Squarebar Inc	2834	F	530 412-0209	8390
Sullivan Counter Tops Inc	2541	F	510 652-2337	5106
Sunrise Specialty Company	3432	F	510 729-7277	12051
Sunset Publishing Corporation (HQ)	2721	C	650 324-5558	6264
Supernutrition	2834	E	510 446-7980	8401
Svc Mfg Inc A Corp	2086	F	510 261-5800	2227
Tab Label Inc	2679	F	510 638-4411	5738
Tags & Labels	2679	E	510 465-1125	5739
Tech Air Northern Cal LLC	2813	F	510 533-9353	7738
TYT LLC (HQ)	2752	C	510 444-3933	7151
University Cal Press Fundation (PA)	2731	D	510 642-4247	6404
University California Berkeley	2731	E	510 642-4247	6406
Veronica Foods Company	2079	E	510 535-6833	1554
Vibrant Care Pharmacy Inc	2834	F	510 638-9851	8433
Vigilent Corporation (PA)	3822	E	888 305-4451	21537
Village Voice Media	2711	D	510 879-3700	6081
Vincent Electric Company (PA)	7694	E	510 639-4500	25471
Vulpine Inc	2899	F	510 534-1186	9317
Wcitiescom Inc	2741	F	415 495-8090	6624
Wilsted & Taylor Pubg Svcs	2791	F	510 428-9087	7637

	SIC	EMP	PHONE	ENTRY #
Window Hardware Supply	3089	F	510 463-0301	10445
Wood Tech Inc	2511	D	510 534-4930	4754
Xchanger Manufacturing Corp	3443	E	510 632-8828	12444
Zuo Modern Contemporary Inc (PA)	2521	E	510 777-1030	4974

OAKVILLE, CA - Napa County

	SIC	EMP	PHONE	ENTRY #
Far Niente Winery Inc	2084	D	707 944-2861	1758
Jackson Family Wines Inc	2084	E	707 948-2643	1822
NAPA Wine Company LLC	2084	E	707 944-8669	1893
Opus One Winery LLC (PA)	2084	D	707 944-9442	1907
Paradigm Winery	2084	F	707 944-1683	1913
Rudd Wines Inc (PA)	2084	F	707 944-8577	1960
Silver Oak Wine Cellars LP (PA)	2084	F	707 942-7022	1978
Turnbull Wine Cellars	2084	F	707 963-5839	2033

OCCIDENTAL, CA - Sonoma County

	SIC	EMP	PHONE	ENTRY #
Planet Inc	2842	F	250 478-8171	8666

OCEANSIDE, CA - San Diego County

	SIC	EMP	PHONE	ENTRY #
2 S 2 Inc	3679	F	760 599-9225	19428
Absolute Board Co Inc	3949	E	760 295-2201	23483
Ace Aviation Service Inc	3728	F	760 721-2804	20699
Advanced Fiberglass Inc	3229	F	760 433-8731	10629
Advanced Oxygen Therapy Inc (HQ)	3841	F	760 431-4700	22315
Advanced Thrmlforming Entp Inc	3089	F	760 722-4400	9930
Alpha Sensors Inc	3823	F	949 250-6578	21545
Alpha Technics Inc	3829	C	949 250-6578	22159
American Food Ingredients Inc	2034	F	760 967-6287	873
American Innotek Inc (PA)	3089	F	760 741-6600	9941
Amerillum LLC	3648	D	760 727-7675	17672
Amflex Plastics Incorporated	3089	F	760 643-1756	9946
Asigma Corporation	3599	F	760 966-3103	16285
Balda HK Plastics Inc	3451	D	760 757-1100	13016
Belching Beaver Brewery	2082	C	760 599-5832	1570
BMW Precision Machining Inc	3599	F	760 439-6813	16328
Brand Ink Inc	2759	F	760 721-4465	7254
Britcan Inc	2542	E	760 722-2300	5128
Cal-Mil Plastic Products Inc (PA)	3089	E	800 321-9069	10000
Car Sound Exhaust System Inc	3714	D	949 858-5900	20283
Car Sound Exhaust System Inc (PA)	3714	D	949 858-5900	20284
Car Sound Exhaust System Inc	2819	E	949 888-1625	7761
Carbon By Design LLC	3728	D	760 643-1300	20777
Coca-Cola Refreshments USA Inc	2086	D	760 435-7111	2122
Component Concepts LLC	3691	F	760 722-9559	19800
Core Supplement Technology	2834	F	760 452-7364	8122
Custom Converting Inc	3086	F	760 724-0664	9832
Custom Window Design Inc	2431	F	760 439-6213	4134
Dibella Baking Company Inc	2052	D	951 797-4144	1362
Dupaco Inc	3841	E	760 758-4550	22429
Envirnmental Catalyst Tech LLC	2819	E	949 459-3870	7774
Federal Heath Sign Company LLC (PA)	3993	D	760 941-0715	23879
Foxfury LLC	3648	E	760 945-4231	17695
Genentech Inc	2834	B	760 231-2440	8175
Genentech Inc	2836	B	760 231-2440	8554
Hexagon Metrology Inc	3829	D	760 994-1401	22211
Hobie Cat Company	3732	C	760 758-9100	21043
Hts-Engineering Inc	3451	F	760 631-2070	13027
Hydranautics (DH)	2899	B	760 901-2597	9259
International Sales Inc	3949	E	760 722-1455	23593
Isis Pharmaceuticals	2834	B	760 603-2631	8235
J B L Enterprises Inc	3949	F	760 754-2727	23597
Kapan - Kent Company Inc	2396	E	760 631-1716	3900
Kds Ingredients LLC	2099	F	760 310-5245	2551
Kellermyer Bergensons Svcs LLC (PA)	3589	F	760 631-5111	16064
Lab Surf Company	3949	F	760 757-1975	23605
Lamvin Inc	3296	F	760 806-6400	11337
Landmark Mfg Inc	3599	E	760 941-6626	16673
Lb Manufacturing LLC	3999	F	413 222-2857	24158
Legacy Vulcan LLC	3272	F	760 439-0624	10953
Lexstar Inc (PA)	3646	E	845 947-1415	17625
Mary Matava	2879	F	760 439-9920	9106
Metrotile Manufacturing LLC	2952	E	760 435-9842	9414
Miller Machine Inc	3599	E	814 723-5700	16750
Ms Cast Stone Inc	3273	E	760 754-9697	11144
Mtm Industrial Inc	3599	E	760 967-1346	16776
Nelgo Industries Inc	3599	F	760 433-6434	16783
Oceanside Marine Center Inc (PA)	3732	F	760 722-1833	21060
Oceanside Plastic Enterprises	3544	F	760 433-0779	14552
Olli Salumeria Americana LLC	2011	F	804 427-7866	446
Orco Block & Hardscape	3271	E	760 757-1780	10856
Oxbow Activated Carbon LLC	2819	E	760 630-5724	7794
Pacific Lasertec LLC	3999	F	760 450-4095	24200
Pacific Vista Foods Llc	2865	E	760 908-9840	8964
Performance Cnc Inc	3599	F	760 722-1129	16840
Pratt Industries Inc	2621	E	760 966-9170	5327
Pratt Industries Inc	2621	F	760 966-9170	5329

GEOGRAPHIC

Name	SIC	EMP	PHONE	ENTRY #
Precision Label Inc	2671	E	760 757-7533	5534
Precision One Medical Inc	3843	D	760 945-7966	22901
Proline Concrete Tools Inc	3559	E	760 758-7240	15012
Pryor Products	3841	E	760 724-8244	22591
Pure Allure Inc	2339	D	760 966-3650	3486
Rose Manufacturing Group Inc	3471	F	760 407-0232	13492
Salis International Inc	3952	E	303 384-3588	23710
San Juan Specialty Pdts Inc	2449	F	888 342-8262	4534
Schuman Enterprises Inc	3499	F	760 940-1322	13972
Secura Inc	2326	D	760 804-7313	3120
Solecta Inc (PA)	2295	E	760 630-9643	2963
Solution Box Inc	2754	F	949 387-3223	7212
Souther Cast Stone Inc	3272	E	760 754-9697	11005
Southwest Greene Intl Inc	3469	C	760 639-4960	13278
Speedskins Inc	3949	F	760 439-3119	23658
Steico Industries Inc	3469	C	760 438-8015	13281
Stone Truss LLC (PA)	2439	E	951 255-6958	4425
Superior Foam Products Inc	3949	F	760 722-1585	23666
Surf Ride	2329	F	760 433-4020	3194
Tarsal Pharmaceuticals Inc	2834	E	818 919-9723	8408
Te Connectivity Corporation	3678	A	760 757-7500	19417
Triangle Brass Mfg Co Inc (PA)	3429	D	323 262-4191	12003
Trinity Woodworks Inc	2431	E	760 639-5351	4249
USP Inc	2844	D	760 842-7700	8859

OJAI, CA - Ventura County

Name	SIC	EMP	PHONE	ENTRY #
Ellen Lark Farm	2043	F	805 272-8448	1058
Mastering Lab Inc	3652	F	805 640-2900	17907
Rotary Club of Ajai West	2084	F	805 646-3794	1956
Simpliphi Power Inc	3691	F	805 640-6700	19815

OLANCHA, CA - Inyo County

Name	SIC	EMP	PHONE	ENTRY #
Cg Roxane LLC (PA)	2086	D	760 764-2885	2111

OLIVEHURST, CA - Yuba County

Name	SIC	EMP	PHONE	ENTRY #
Ace Composites Inc	3089	D	530 743-1885	9920
D & D Cbnets - Svage Dsgns Inc	2434	E	530 634-9713	4291
Hanson Truss Components Inc	2439	D	530 740-7750	4409
Precast Con Tech Unlimited LLC	3272	E	530 749-6501	10978
Yuba River Moulding Mllwk Inc (PA)	2431	F	530 742-2168	4264

ONTARIO, CA - San Bernardino County

Name	SIC	EMP	PHONE	ENTRY #
A Lot To Say Inc	2399	F	925 964-5079	3931
AAA Stamping Inc	3469	E	909 947-4151	13156
Aamp of America	3699	D	805 338-6800	19895
Aaren Scientific Inc (DH)	3827	E	909 937-1033	22055
Abba Roller LLC (DH)	3069	D	909 947-1244	9580
Abba Rubber International Inc	3069	D	909 947-1244	9581
Able Industrial Products Inc (PA)	3053	F	909 930-1585	9515
Absolute Screen Graphics Inc	2396	F	909 923-1227	3870
Accufab Inc	3599	F	909 930-1751	16207
Ace Calendering Enterprises (PA)	3069	F	909 937-1901	9582
Action Embroidery Corp (PA)	2399	C	909 983-1359	3934
Acuity Brands Lighting Inc	3646	E	909 395-9009	17580
Adenna Inc	3842	F	909 510-6999	22688
Adesa International LLC	2032	E	909 321-8240	743
Advanced Color Graphics	2752	D	909 930-1500	6642
Advanced Pattern & Mold	3334	F	909 930-3444	11532
Advanced Refreshment LLC (HQ)	2086	F	425 746-8100	2080
Aerospace and Coml Tooling Inc	3541	F	909 930-5780	14356
Ajinomoto Foods North Amer Inc	2038	C	909 477-4700	975
Ajinomoto Foods North Amer Inc (DH)	2038	D	909 477-4700	976
Akra Plastic Products Inc	3089	F	909 930-1999	9933
Alger Precision Machining LLC	3451	C	909 986-4591	13009
Alhambra Reprographics Inc (PA)	2759	F	909 390-4839	7226
All Time Machine Inc	3599	F	909 673-1899	16251
Alpha Publishing Corporation	2731	E	909 464-0500	6306
Alta Advanced Technologies Inc	2836	E	909 983-2973	8525
Alum-Alloy Coinc	3463	E	909 986-0410	13119
Alumin-Art Plating Co Inc	3471	E	909 983-1866	13325
Am-Tek Engineering Inc	3599	F	909 673-1633	16268
AMD International Tech LLC	3444	E	909 985-8300	12475
American Fleet & Ret Graphics	3993	E	909 937-7570	23815
American Premier Corp	3949	E	909 923-7070	23499
American Publishing Corp	2731	E	909 390-7548	6308
AMF Pharma LLC	2834	E	909 930-9599	8022
Amish Country Gazebos Inc	2511	F	800 700-1777	4668
Amrep (PA)	3713	C	909 923-0430	20190
An Environmental Inks	2893	F	909 930-9656	9188
Andrew LLC	2041	F	909 270-9356	1024
Androp Packaging Inc	2653	E	909 605-8842	5384
Anvil International Inc	3498	F	909 418-3233	13876
Armcraft Products Company	3089	E	909 390-1365	9956
Arrow Truck Bodies & Equipment	3713	E	909 947-3991	20192
Artesia Sawdust Products Inc	2421	E	909 947-5983	4029
Aryzta LLC	2052	C	909 472-3500	1350
Ashtel Studios Inc	3844	E	909 434-0911	22927

Name	SIC	EMP	PHONE	ENTRY #
Astro Display Company Inc	3993	E	909 605-2875	23824
Athanor Group Inc	3451	C	909 467-1205	13014
Auburn Tile Inc	3272	F	909 984-2841	10879
Awning Matrix	3444	F	909 447-5100	12494
Axium Plastics LLC	3089	D	909 969-0766	9963
AZ Countertops Inc	3281	E	909 983-5386	11233
B & D Litho Group Inc	2752	E	909 390-0903	6675
B Braun Medical Inc	3841	A	909 906-7575	22352
B Stephen Cooperage Inc	3412	F	909 591-2929	11873
Bae Systems Info & Elec Sys	3679	D	603 885-4321	19457
Balda C Brewer Inc (DH)	3089	C	714 630-6810	9969
Balda C Brewer Inc	3089	F	714 630-6810	9970
Barzillai Manufacturing Co	3444	E	909 947-4200	12501
Baxter Healthcare Corporation	2834	C	303 222-6837	8061
Beals Castings Inc	3363	F	909 986-3849	11689
Bee Wire & Cable Inc	3357	E	909 923-5800	11644
Bericap LLC	3089	D	909 390-5518	9975
Bernman Mold and Engineering	3544	F	909 930-3844	14486
Bert-Co Industries Inc	2759	F	323 669-5700	7247
Bert-Co Industries Inc (PA)	2752	C	323 669-5700	6694
Bertolini Corporation	2522	C	909 613-1393	4979
Best Quality Furniture Mfg Inc	2512	D	909 230-6440	4760
Bhk Inc	3641	E	909 983-2973	17421
Bishamon Industries Corp	3537	E	909 390-0055	14312
Black & Decker Corporation	3546	F	909 390-5548	14699
Blackcoffee Fabricators Inc	3993	F	909 974-4499	23829
Blue Sky Home & ACC Inc	1459	E	909 930-6200	400
Bluefield Associates Inc	2844	E	909 476-6027	8705
Bmci Inc	3549	E	951 361-8000	14749
Bock Machine Company Inc	3599	F	909 947-7250	16330
Bomatic Inc	3089	F	909 947-3900	9988
Bradley Corp	3432	F	909 481-7255	12025
C & S Products CA Inc (PA)	2842	F	909 218-8971	8629
C&D Zodiac Inc	3728	B	909 947-2725	20770
Calidad Inc	3363	E	909 947-3937	11690
California Die Casting Inc	3364	E	909 947-9947	11710
California Exotic Novlt LLC	3999	D	909 606-1950	24056
California Mfg Cabinetry Inc	2541	F	909 930-3632	5044
California Quality Plas Inc	3089	F	909 930-5667	10006
Canvas Awning Co Inc	2394	F	909 447-5100	3781
Caraustar Industries Inc	2655	E	951 685-5544	5482
Carl Zeiss Meditec Prod LLC	3841	D	877 644-4657	22395
Carlstar Group LLC	3011	C	310 816-1015	9462
Carlyle Glasgow Wldg Svcs Inc	3441	F	909 902-1814	12130
Case Hardigg Center	2441	F	413 665-2163	4439
Case World Co	3172	F	626 330-1000	10558
Caterpillar Inc	3531	B	909 390-9035	14156
Celestica Aerospace Tech Corp	3672	C	512 310-7540	18445
Cemex Inc	3273	E	909 974-5500	11059
Cemex USA Inc	3273	F	909 974-5500	11089
Champion Discs Incorporated	3949	F	800 408-8449	23537
Chenbro Micom (usa) Inc	3572	E	909 937-0100	15522
Chladni & Jariwala Inc	3491	E	909 947-5227	13710
Clarke Pb & Associates Inc	3651	E	714 835-3022	17782
Classic Containers Inc	3085	B	909 930-3610	9794
Clearchem Diagnostics Inc	2819	E	714 734-8041	7766
Coca-Cola Company	2086	C	909 975-5200	2116
Coca-Cola Company	2087	D	909 975-5200	2252
Coco Products LLC	2842	F	909 218-8971	8638
Commander Packaging West Inc	2653	E	714 921-9350	5399
Compumeric Engineering Inc	3444	E	909 605-1697	12535
Consolidated Container Co LLC	3085	F	909 390-6637	9797
Creative Image Systems Inc	2844	F	909 947-8588	8732
Crown Equipment Corporation	3537	C	909 923-8357	14318
Crown Paper Converting Inc	2679	E	909 923-5226	5707
CTA Fixtures Inc	2541	D	909 390-6744	5051
Custom Plastics LLC (PA)	3089	F	909 984-0200	10054
Daaze Inc	3444	F	626 442-4961	12548
Danco Anodizing Inc	3471	E	909 923-0562	13385
DB Building Fasteners Inc (PA)	3449	E	909 581-6740	12977
Defoe Furniture For Kids Inc	2531	F	909 947-4459	5011
Delta Tech Industries LLC	3647	E	909 673-1900	17660
Diagnostic Solutions Intl LLC	3728	F	909 930-3600	20794
Diamond Injection Molds Inc	3544	F	909 390-2260	14505
Discopylabs	3652	E	909 390-3800	17893
Doble Engineering Company	3613	F	909 923-9196	17141
Donna Karan Company LLC	2335	C	909 484-1201	3307
Dorel Juvenile Group Inc	3089	C	909 390-5705	10078
Dspm Inc	3677	E	714 970-2304	19332
Dura Micro Inc	3572	E	909 947-4590	15531
Eagle Products - Plast Indust	3089	E	909 465-1548	10082
Eagle Signs Inc	3993	F	909 923-3034	23860
Ecko Products Group LLC	2653	E	909 628-5678	5406
Eclipse Prtg & Graphics LLC	2752	E	909 390-2452	6800
Edelmann Usa Inc (DH)	3993	E	323 669-5700	23861

Mergent email: customerrelations@mergent.com
1426

2019 California
Manufacturers Register

(P-0000) Products & Services Section entry number
(PA)=Parent Co (HQ)=Headquarters (DH)=Div Headquarters

Company	SIC	EMP	PHONE	ENTRY #
Edison Opto USA Corporation	3674	F	909 284-9710	18812
Egr Incorporated (DH)	3714	C	909 923-7075	20325
Elegance Upholstery Inc	2599	F	562 698-2584	5228
Emission Methods Inc	3829	E	909 605-6800	22193
Empire Sheet Metal Inc	3444	F	909 923-2927	12571
Encore Image Inc	3993	E	909 986-4632	23865
Envirokinetics Inc (PA)	3559	F	909 621-7599	14948
Eubanks Engineering Co (PA)	3549	E	909 483-2456	14750
Eugenios Sheet Metal Inc	3469	E	909 923-2002	13202
Evans Food West Inc (PA)	2096	F	909 947-3001	2379
Everest Group Usa Inc	2299	E	909 923-1818	2996
Excel Industries Inc	3469	F	909 947-4867	13204
F & D Flores Enterprises Inc	3829	F	909 975-4853	22198
Fan Fave Inc	3993	E	909 975-4999	23875
Fanlight Corporation Inc (DH)	3641	F	909 930-6868	17428
Ferrari Intrcnnect Sltions Inc	3679	F	951 684-8034	19543
Five Star Gourmet Foods Inc	2038	A	909 390-0032	994
Flor De California	2024	E	909 673-1968	671
Flow Dynamics Inc	3312	F	909 930-5522	11394
Forbes Industries Div	2599	C	909 923-4559	5233
Foundry Service & Supplies Inc	3299	E	909 284-5000	11356
Fruit Growers Supply Company	2653	D	909 390-0190	5410
Genius Tools Americas Corp (PA)	3545	F	909 230-9588	14639
Geo Labels Inc	2759	E	909 923-6832	7327
George Verhoeven Grain Inc (PA)	2048	F	909 605-1531	1135
Glenco Manufacturing Company	3451	F	909 984-3348	13024
Globalux Lighting LLC	3645	E	909 591-7506	17537
Gold Crest Industries Inc	2393	E	909 930-9069	3765
Graphic Sciences Inc	2893	E	909 947-3366	9198
Greenwood Products Inc	3211	E	909 548-4828	10594
Guess Inc	2325	E	909 987-7776	3073
Gund Company Inc	3644	F	909 890-9300	17515
H Fam Engineering Inc	3599	F	909 930-5678	16551
Haldex Brake Products Corp	3714	F	909 974-1200	20357
Halex Corporation (HQ)	3423	E	909 629-6219	11896
Hallmark Floors Inc (PA)	2426	F	909 947-7736	4081
Halsteel Inc (DH)	3315	F	909 947-1001	11442
Hannibal Lafayette	2448	F	909 322-0600	4474
Hchd	3711	F	909 923-8889	20149
Hco Holding I Corporation	2952	F	310 684-5320	9406
Heitman Brooks II LLC (PA)	3272	F	909 947-7470	10936
Herman Engineering & Mfg Inc	3089	F	909 483-1631	10134
HI Performance Electric Vehicl	3621	F	909 923-1973	17203
Hillerich & Bradsby Co	3949	D	800 282-2287	23585
Honor Plastics & Molding Inc	3089	F	909 923-9710	10137
Horizon Hobby LLC	3944	C	909 390-9595	23429
Hubbell Incorporated	3643	F	909 390-8002	17471
ICEE Company (HQ)	2038	D	800 426-4233	997
ICEE Company	2038	E	909 974-3518	998
IDB Holdings Inc (DH)	2022	F	909 390-5624	579
Idx Los Angeles LLC	2431	C	909 212-8333	4168
Imp International Inc (PA)	2833	E	909 321-1000	7948
Inca Plastics Molding Co Inc	3089	D	909 923-3235	10149
Induspac California Inc	2821	F	909 390-4422	7841
Industrial Furnace & Insul Inc	3567	F	909 947-2449	15263
Ink Fx Corporation	2759	E	909 673-1950	7356
Inland Empire Drive Line Svc (PA)	3714	F	909 390-3030	20371
Inland Powder Coating Corp	3479	C	909 947-1122	13603
Inline Plastics Inc	3089	E	909 923-1033	10151
International Paper Company	2631	D	909 605-2540	5352
International Paper Company	2653	D	323 724-5010	5428
Ivars Cabinet Shop Inc (PA)	2541	C	909 923-2761	5071
IVEX Protective Packaging Inc	2821	E	909 390-4422	7847
J R Rapid Print Inc	2752	F	909 947-4868	6902
Jamac Steel Inc	3441	E	909 983-7592	12184
James Jones Company	3491	C	909 418-2558	13721
Jasper Engine Exchange Inc	3714	F	800 827-7455	20375
Jcm Engineering Corp	3728	D	909 923-3730	20854
Jns Industries Inc	3599	F	909 923-8334	16628
K & Z Cabinet Co Inc	2434	D	909 947-3567	4317
Ketan Automated Equipment Inc	3565	F	909 930-0780	15213
Kik Pool Additives Inc	2899	C	909 390-9912	9269
Kingfa Global Inc	3452	F	909 212-5413	13076
Kitchen Equipment Mfg Co Inc	3469	E	909 923-3153	13238
Kls Doors LLC	2431	E	909 605-6468	4179
Korden Inc	2522	F	909 988-8979	4992
Kraft Heinz Foods Company	2099	F	909 605-7201	2556
Kushwood Chair Inc	2511	C	909 930-2100	4713
Lanpar Inc	2511	B	541 484-1962	4715
Larry Mthvin Installations Inc (HQ)	3231	C	909 563-1700	10712
Lassonde Pappas and Co Inc	2099	D	909 923-4041	2579
Leggett & Platt Incorporated	2515	D	909 937-1010	4868
Levco Fab Inc	3498	F	909 465-0840	13893
Lieder Development Inc	3679	F	909 947-7722	19623
Lightcap Industries, Inc.	3441	E	909 930-3772	12196
Lindahl Enterprises Ltd Inc	3823	E	909 391-7052	21613
Linpeng International Inc	3999	F	909 923-9881	24163
Liqui-Box Corporation	3085	E	909 390-4646	9800
Los Angles Tmes Cmmnctions LLC	2711	E	909 980-3707	5930
M and W Glass	3231	E	909 517-3585	10716
Mag Instrument Inc (PA)	3648	B	909 947-1006	17712
Magnussen Home Furnishings Inc	2511	F	336 841-4424	4717
Maney Aircraft Inc	3728	E	909 390-2500	20872
Marlee Manufacturing Inc	3841	E	909 390-3222	22519
Matsun America Corp	2326	F	909 930-0779	3111
Maury Microwave Inc	3679	C	909 987-4715	19640
Maximum Quality Metal Pdts Inc	3444	E	909 902-5018	12660
Meadow Decor Inc	2519	F	909 923-2558	4912
Medegen LLC (DH)	3089	E	909 390-9080	10203
Medrano Raymundo	2284	E	909 947-5507	2954
Melmarc Products Inc	2329	F	714 460-6691	3179
Melmarc Products Inc (PA)	2395	B	714 549-2170	3852
Metals USA Building Pdts LP	3355	E	800 325-1305	11621
Mid Ohio Field Services LLC	1389	F	614 755-5067	238
Minsley Inc	2099	E	909 458-1100	2606
Mission Plastics Inc	3089	C	909 947-7287	10215
Moldings Plus Inc	2431	E	909 947-3310	4195
Mpeg Industries Inc	3571	F	562 677-1268	15463
N S Ceramic Molding Co	3544	E	909 947-3231	14548
Nac Mfg Inc	2873	E	909 472-3033	9067
Naturestar Bio Tech Inc	2834	F	909 930-1878	8293
Neptune Trading Inc	3421	F	909 923-0236	11881
Net Shapes Inc	3324	C	909 947-3231	11518
New Greenscreen Incorporated	2542	E	800 767-9378	5157
New-Indy Containerboard LLC (DH)	2621	D	909 296-3400	5315
New-Indy Ontario LLC	2621	C	909 390-1055	5316
Newfield Technology Corp (PA)	3711	E	909 931-4405	20162
Nexus California Inc	3081	E	909 937-1000	9721
North American Composites Co	2821	E	909 605-8977	7859
Nyx Industries Inc	3523	F	909 937-3923	14087
Office Master Inc	2522	D	909 392-5678	4997
Omega Interconnect Inc	3599	F	909 986-1933	16805
One Stop Label Corporation	2679	F	909 230-9380	5720
Oracle America Inc	7372	F	909 605-0222	25005
Otto Instrument Service Inc (PA)	3728	C	909 930-5800	20899
Pacific Accent Incorporated	3634	F	909 563-1600	17401
Pacific Metals Group LLC	3444	E	909 218-8889	12706
Pacific Urethanes LLC	2392	C	909 390-8400	3740
Pacific Utility Products Inc	3824	F	909 923-1800	21693
Panob Corp	3089	E	909 947-8008	10265
Paramount Panels Inc (PA)	3089	E	909 947-8008	10266
Paramount Panels Inc	3728	E	909 947-5168	20903
Parco Inc (PA)	3053	C	909 947-2200	9547
Passport Food Group LLC (PA)	2099	C	909 627-7312	2635
Patch Place	2399	E	909 947-3023	3957
Pby Plastics Inc	3089	E	909 930-6700	10269
Pearson Education Inc	2731	F	800 653-1918	6378
Pennysaver	2711	E	909 467-8500	6012
Performance Aluminum Products	3363	E	909 391-4131	11703
Performance Truck and Trlr LLC	3715	E	909 605-0323	20509
Pharmapack North America Corp	2821	F	909 390-1888	7865
Phoenix Arms	3484	E	909 937-6900	13689
Phoenix Cars LLC	3711	F	909 987-0815	20163
Plasthec Molding Inc	3089	D	909 947-4267	10283
Plastics Research Corporation	3083	E	909 391-9050	9759
Pmr Precision Mfg & Rbr Co Inc	3069	E	909 605-7525	9657
PNC Proactive Nthrn Cont LLC	2653	E	909 390-5624	5452
Polytech Color & Compounding	3089	E	909 923-7008	10298
Popla International Inc	2045	E	909 923-6899	1098
Portable Spndle Repr Spcialist	3552	F	909 591-7220	14779
Pouches Incorporated	2671	F	909 923-1135	5533
Praxair Inc	2813	D	909 390-0283	7719
PRC Composites LLC	2519	E	909 391-2006	4917
Precast Repair	3272	E	909 627-5477	10980
Precise Media Services Inc	3652	E	909 481-3305	17910
Primebore Directional Boring	1381	E	909 821-4643	118
Pro Products Inc	3714	E	909 605-0545	20427
Proactive Packg & Display Inc (PA)	2653	D	909 390-5624	5453
Promarksvac Corporation	3565	F	909 923-3888	15225
Q1 Test Inc	3728	E	909 390-9718	20918
QEP Co Inc	2426	F	909 622-3537	4089
Quality Control Plating Inc	3471	E	909 605-0206	13486
Qycell Corporation	3086	E	909 390-6644	9879
R & I Industries Inc	3441	E	909 923-7747	12234
R & J Wldg Met Fabrication Inc	3613	F	909 930-2900	17158
R R Donnelley & Sons Company	2759	E	909 930-1605	7459
Rama Food Manufacture Corp	2099	E	909 923-5305	2649
RDS Group Inc	2752	F	909 923-8831	7078
Redline Prcision Machining Inc	3312	F	909 483-1273	11414
Regards Enterprises Inc	2493	E	909 983-0655	4601

Employment Codes: A=Over 500 employees, B=251-500,
C=101-250, D=51-100, E=20-50, F=10-19

2019 California
Manufacturers Register

© Mergent Inc. 1-800-342-5647

1427

GEOGRAPHIC

	SIC	EMP	PHONE	ENTRY #
Response Envelope Inc **(PA)**	2759	C	909 923-5855	7467
Rexnord Industries LLC	3568	F	602 682-1764	15292
Rexnord LLC	3566	C	909 467-8102	15245
Reyrich Plastics Inc	3089	F	909 484-8444	10334
Rfc Wire Forms Inc	3496	D	909 467-0559	13850
Roto Lite Inc	3089	E	909 923-4353	10344
Royal Angelus Macaroni Company	2099	C	909 627-7312	2660
Ryko Plastic Products Inc	3089	F	909 773-0050	10353
Safariland LLC	3199	B	909 923-7300	10579
Safariland LLC **(DH)**	3669	E	925 219-1097	18361
Sapa Extrusions Inc	3354	C	909 947-7682	11602
Scott Welsher	3161	F	949 544-4000	10534
Scripto-Tokai Corporation **(DH)**	3999	D	909 930-5000	24234
Security Metal Products Corp **(DH)**	3442	E	310 641-6690	12347
Sentran L L C **(PA)**	3829	F	888 545-8988	22268
Sentry Industries Inc	2821	F	909 986-3642	7884
Shred-Tech Usa LLC	3537	E	909 923-2783	14346
Sign Industries Inc	3993	F	909 930-0303	23964
Solartech Power Inc	3674	F	909 673-0178	19177
Soup Bases Loaded Inc	2034	E	909 230-6890	894
Southland Container Corp	2653	E	909 937-9781	5463
Specialized Dairy Service Inc	3523	E	909 923-3420	14106
Specialty Coating Systems Inc	3479	E	909 390-8818	13661
Sprayline Enterprises Inc	3479	E	909 627-8411	13663
Stanley Access Tech LLC	3423	C	909 628-9272	11911
Star Shield Solutions LLC	3089	D	866 662-4477	10391
Strada Wheels Inc	3312	F	626 336-1634	11424
Summit Machine LLC	3599	C	909 923-2744	16969
Sun Badge Co	3999	E	909 930-1444	24255
Sunny Products Inc	2782	E	909 947-5028	7586
Sunway Mechanical & Elec Tech	3715	F	909 673-7959	20512
Super Glue Corporation **(HQ)**	2891	C	909 987-0550	9173
Super Glue Corporation	2891	F	909 987-0550	9174
Superior Essex Inc	3357	F	909 481-4804	11677
Superior Mold Co Inc	3089	F	909 947-7028	10396
Supermedia LLC	2741	B	909 390-5000	6596
Supreme Machine Products Inc	3599	F	909 974-0349	16974
Table De France Inc	2051	F	909 923-5205	1329
Tc Cosmotronic Inc	3672	D	949 660-0740	18622
TCI Engineering Inc	3711	D	909 984-1773	20172
Tech Electronic Systems Inc	3679	F	909 986-4395	19747
Teefor 2 Inc	2752	F	909 613-0055	7131
Teklink Security Inc	3699	E	909 230-6668	20087
Thermodyne International Ltd	3089	C	909 923-9945	10402
Three Chiefs & No Indians LLC	2789	C	909 465-6314	7623
Torco International Corp	2911	F	909 980-1495	9365
Tower Industries Inc	3599	C	909 947-2723	17005
Tower Mechanical Products Inc	3812	C	714 947-2723	21444
Tracy Industries Inc	3519	C	562 692-9034	14032
Tradenet Enterprise Inc	3993	D	888 595-3956	23993
Transcontinental US LLC	2673	E	909 390-8866	5630
Triumph Equipment Inc	3728	E	909 947-5983	20961
Trmc Sale Corporation	3585	D	800 290-7073	15992
Tropicale Foods Inc	2024	E	909 635-0390	700
Txd International Usa Inc	2711	F	909 947-6568	6076
Ultimate Print Source Inc	2752	F	909 947-5292	7153
Ultra Chem Labs Corp	2842	F	909 605-1640	8681
Uncks Unique Plastics Inc	3089	F	909 983-5181	10419
United Partition Systems Inc	2452	F	909 947-1077	4583
Universal Wire Inc	3496	F	626 285-2288	13859
Upland Fab Inc	3089	F	909 933-9185	10420
Upm Raflatac Inc	2672	E	909 390-4657	5581
USA Sales Inc	2111	E	909 390-9606	2710
Uspar Enterprises Inc	3645	E	909 591-7506	17566
Ventura Foods LLC	2079	C	714 257-3700	1552
Ventura Foods LLC	2021	C	323 262-9157	563
Vigilant Marine Systems LLC	3714	F	909 597-9508	20480
Vishay Techno Components LLC	3625	D	909 923-3313	17320
Vishay Thin Film LLC	3674	E	909 923-3313	19261
Vishay Thin Film LLC	3676	D	909 923-3313	19311
Vishay Transducers Ltd	3674	E	626 363-7500	19262
Visionary Sleep LLC	2515	D	909 605-2010	4892
Voyager Learning Company	2741	E	909 923-3120	6622
Vsmpo Tirus US	3356	E	909 230-9020	11640
Vsmpo-Tirus US Inc	3356	E	909 230-9020	11641
Wagner Die Supply **(PA)**	3544	E	909 947-3044	14590
Walker Corporation	3496	F	909 390-4300	13862
Walker Spring & Stamping Corp	3469	C	909 390-4300	13294
Wallner Expac Inc **(PA)**	3549	D	909 481-8800	14772
Wangs Alliance Corporation	3645	E	909 230-9401	17569
Watercrest Inc	3443	F	909 390-3944	12440
Watsons Profiling Corp	3599	F	909 923-5500	17052
West Coast Chain Mfg Co	3699	E	909 923-7800	20109
Western States Wholesale Inc **(PA)**	3271	C	909 947-0028	10869
Will Pak Foods Inc	2034	F	800 874-0883	908

	SIC	EMP	PHONE	ENTRY #
Windshield Pros Incorporated	3714	E	951 272-2867	20487
Xerox Corporation	3861	F	909 605-7900	23213
Y & D Rubber Corporation	3069	F	909 517-1683	9694
Yawa Inc	3651	F	909 391-8888	17883
Yillik Precision Industries	3545	D	909 947-2785	14697
Yinlun Tdi LLC	3714	B	909 390-3944	20490
Yukon Trail Inc	3751	F	909 218-5286	21152
Z B Wire Works Inc	3496	F	909 391-0995	13867
Zodiac Cabin & Structures	3728	F	909 947-4115	20979

ORANGE, CA - Orange County

	SIC	EMP	PHONE	ENTRY #
5h Sheet Metal Fabrication Inc	3444	F	714 633-7544	12448
7 U P RC Bottling Company	3565	D	714 974-8560	15189
ADC Enterprises Inc	3599	F	714 538-3102	16223
Advanced Ceramic Technology	3599	F	714 538-2524	16225
Aerosysng Inc	3721	E	714 633-1901	20531
Air Tube Transfer Systems Inc	3535	E	714 363-0700	14263
All Diameter Grinding Inc	3599	F	714 744-1200	16250
Allen Mold Inc	3089	F	714 538-6517	9934
Allen Morgan	3567	E	714 538-7492	15249
Alliance Hose & Extrusions Inc	2869	E	714 202-8500	8975
Allied Mdular Bldg Systems Inc **(PA)**	3448	E	714 516-1188	12914
Amscan Inc	2656	D	714 972-2626	5497
Anaheim Precision Shtmtl Mfg **(HQ)**	3721	C	714 453-0100	20540
Angelus Block Co Inc	3271	E	714 637-8594	10843
Anillo Industries Inc **(PA)**	3452	E	714 637-7000	13058
Arden Engineering Inc	3728	E	714 998-6410	20742
Asco Automatic Switch	3491	E	714 937-0811	13702
Autobahn Construction Inc	3531	F	714 769-7025	14142
Avantec Manufacturing Inc	3672	E	714 532-6197	18433
B-J Machine Inc	3469	E	714 685-0712	13167
BASF Corporation	2869	E	714 921-1430	8981
Bayside Shutters	3442	F	714 628-9994	12297
Brothers Optical Laboratory	3851	D	714 639-9852	23082
Bryan Edwards Publishing Co	2731	F	714 634-0264	6319
Burlington Engineering Inc	3471	E	714 921-4045	13357
C W Moss Auto Parts Inc	3465	F	714 639-3083	13138
Cadillac Plating Inc	3471	F	714 639-0342	13361
Cal-West Machining Inc	3593	F	714 637-4161	16155
California Gasket and Rbr Corp **(PA)**	3069	E	310 323-4250	9599
Califrnia Anlytical Instrs Inc	3826	D	714 974-5560	21930
Cemex Cnstr Mtls PCF LLC	3273	F	714 637-9470	11067
Century Precision Machine Inc	3599	F	714 637-3691	16374
CF&b Manufacturing Inc	2673	E	714 744-8361	5592
City Steel Heat Treating Inc	3398	F	562 789-7373	11807
Cleatech LLC	3821	E	714 754-6668	21464
Coastal Component Inds Inc	3679	E	714 685-6677	19495
Coastal Enterprises	2821	E	714 771-4969	7824
Coatings By Sandberg Inc	3479	E	714 538-0888	13570
Coil Winding Specialist Inc	3677	F	714 279-9010	19326
Commercial Metal Forming Inc	3469	D	714 532-6321	13185
Commercial Metal Forming Inc **(PA)**	3469	E	714 532-6321	13186
Continuous Coating Corp **(PA)**	3471	E	714 637-4642	13381
Contract Illumination	3646	E	714 771-5223	17593
Convergint Technologies LLC	3699	E	714 546-2780	19933
Counterpart Automotive Inc	3714	F	714 771-1732	20298
Crd Mfg Inc	3429	F	714 871-3300	11948
Cytec Engineered Materials Inc	2821	C	714 630-9400	7829
Data Aire Inc **(HQ)**	3585	C	800 347-2473	15949
Daves Interiors Inc	2512	E	714 998-5554	4768
Dilco Industrial Inc	3552	F	714 998-5266	14775
Direct Edge Screenworks Inc	2759	F	714 579-3686	7299
Don Miguel Mexican Foods Inc **(HQ)**	2038	E	714 385-4500	990
Ducommun Aerostructures Inc	3724	F	714 637-4401	20647
Dunham Metal Processing Co	3471	F	714 532-5551	13391
E D D Investment Co	2051	E	714 637-3040	1239
Edgewood Press Inc	2752	F	714 516-2455	6804
El Metate Foods Inc	2051	F	714 542-3913	1242
Fabricated Components Corp	3672	C	714 974-8590	18478
Fabtex Inc	2221	C	714 538-0877	2778
Fat Performance Inc	3714	E	714 637-2889	20333
Fieldpiece Instruments Inc	3825	F	714 634-1844	21757
Fisher Printing Inc **(PA)**	2752	F	714 998-9200	6817
Fletcher Coating Co	3479	F	714 637-4763	13589
Fxi Inc	3086	C	714 637-0110	9860
G A Systems Inc	3589	F	714 848-7529	16043
G P Manufacturing Inc	3599	F	714 974-0288	16521
George L Kovacs	3547	E	714 538-8026	14715
Grand Meadows Inc	2834	F	714 628-1690	8197
Greenberg Teleprmpt	3661	F	714 633-1111	17954
H & R Aerospace Inc	3728	F	714 893-1737	20834
Haldor Topsoe Inc	2819	F	714 621-3800	7780
Hand Piece Parts and Products	3843	F	714 997-4331	22882
Heritage Carbide Inc	3599	F	714 974-6377	16560
Hexion Inc	2869	F	714 971-0180	9009
Hi-Line Industrial Saw and Sup	3425	F	714 921-1600	11919

Mergent email: customerrelations@mergent.com

1428

2019 California
Manufacturers Register

(P-0000) Products & Services Section entry number
(PA)=Parent Co (HQ)=Headquarters (DH)=Div Headquarters

	SIC	EMP	PHONE	ENTRY #
Hightower Metal Products	3599	D	714 637-7000	16567
Hightower Plating & Mfg Co	3471	E	714 637-9110	13425
His Industries Inc	3565	E	562 407-0512	15211
Howmedica Osteonics Corp	3841	E	714 557-5010	22470
Ice Link LLC	3556	F	714 771-6580	14859
ICM Packaging Inc	2441	E	714 744-4836	4442
Icon Screening Inc	2759	F	714 630-4266	7348
Independent Forge Company	3463	E	714 997-7337	13124
Innopack Usa Inc	2759	F	714 637-4091	7357
Integrated Marketing Group LLC	2211	F	714 771-2401	2744
Intellipower Inc	3677	D	714 921-1580	19341
ISI Detention Contg Group Inc	3599	E	714 288-1770	16593
J J Foil Company Inc	2675	E	714 998-9920	5653
Jeneric/Pentron Incorporated (HQ)	3843	C	203 265-7397	22885
John Bishop Design Inc	3993	F	714 744-2300	23908
Jtb Supply Company Inc	3669	F	714 639-9558	18337
K & D Graphics	2675	E	714 639-8900	5654
Kerr Corporation (DH)	3843	C	714 516-7400	22888
King Plastics Inc	3089	D	714 997-7540	10180
Label Impressions Inc	2759	E	714 634-3466	7374
Lcptracker Inc	7372	E	714 669-0052	24851
Liboon Group Inc	3541	F	714 639-3639	14390
Lido Industries Inc	3089	F	714 633-3731	10191
Lmm Enterprises	3599	F	714 543-8044	16689
Lochaber Cornwall Inc (PA)	3567	E	714 935-0302	15268
M & R Engineering Co	3599	F	714 991-8480	16699
Magcomp Inc	3612	F	714 532-3584	17105
Marbil Industries Inc	3826	E	714 974-4032	21987
Marcel Electronics Inc	3672	F	714 974-8590	18523
Marcel Electronics Inc	3672	F	714 974-8590	18524
Marimix Company Inc	2064	F	714 633-7300	1442
Merlex Stucco Inc	3299	E	877 547-8822	11360
Mesa Safe Company Inc	3499	E	714 202-8000	13958
Metal Art of California Inc	3993	D	714 532-7100	23925
Metal Art of California Inc (PA)	3993	F	714 532-7100	23926
Microflex Technologies LLC	3674	F	714 937-1507	19002
Mufich Engineering Inc	3599	F	714 283-0599	16777
National Oilwell Varco Inc	3533	F	714 978-1900	14233
National Oilwell Varco Inc	3533	F	714 978-1900	14234
National Oilwell Varco Inc	3533	F	714 978-1900	14235
National Oilwell Varco Inc	3533	F	714 978-1900	14236
National Oilwell Varco LP	1381	F	714 456-1244	114
Newport Flavors & Fragrances	2087	E	714 771-2200	2274
Next Level Elevator Inc	3534	F	888 959-6010	14253
Niedwick Corporation	3599	E	714 771-9999	16791
Nursery Supplies Inc	3089	E	714 538-0251	10249
Oc Baking Company	2051	D	714 998-2253	1300
Oc Waterjet	3441	F	714 685-0851	12220
Omega Products Corp	3299	E	714 935-0900	11365
Opal Service Inc (PA)	3299	E	714 935-0900	11366
Orange County Plating Coinc	3471	E	714 532-4610	13470
Ormco Corporation (DH)	3843	D	714 516-7400	22896
Ortho-Clinical Diagnostics Inc	2835	E	714 639-2323	8502
Pacific Aerodynamic Inc	3724	F	714 450-9140	20671
Pacifico Bindery Inc	2789	F	714 744-1510	7611
Patio & Door Outlet Inc (PA)	2519	F	714 974-9900	4915
Pgm Metal Finishing	3479	F	714 282-9193	13634
Positive Concepts Inc (PA)	2679	E	714 685-5800	5726
Praxair Inc	2813	E	515 963-3872	7716
Precast Innovations Inc	3272	F	714 921-4060	10979
Presentation Folder Inc	2675	E	714 289-7000	5655
Printing Division Inc	2752	F	714 685-0111	7045
Pro Detention Inc	3315	D	714 881-3680	11452
Prototype & Short-Run Svcs Inc	3469	F	714 449-9661	13267
Quality Aluminum Forge LLC (HQ)	3463	D	714 639-8191	13128
Quality Aluminum Forge LLC	3354	F	714 633-1195	11601
Quality Produced LLC	2037	F	310 592-8834	965
R & B Plastics Inc	3599	E	714 229-8419	16876
Radian Audio Engineering Inc	3663	E	714 288-8900	18232
Radiation Protection & Spc Inc	3444	F	714 771-7702	12731
Redline Detection LLC	3559	F	714 451-1411	15018
Remanfctured Converter MBL LLC	3568	F	714 744-8988	15291
Reyes Coca-Cola Bottling LLC	2086	C	714 974-1901	2204
Rlh Industries Inc (PA)	3661	E	714 532-1672	17989
SA Serving Lines Inc	3444	F	714 848-7529	12747
Sappi North America Inc	2679	D	714 456-0600	5734
Sas Institute Inc	7372	D	949 250-9999	25148
SE Industries Inc	2434	F	714 744-3200	4350
Seelect Inc	2099	F	714 744-3700	2665
Sign Source Inc	3993	F	714 979-9979	23966
SKB Corporation (PA)	3089	B	714 637-1252	10377
SKB Corporation	3161	B	714 637-1572	10537
Specialized Products & Design	2869	F	714 289-1428	9042
Sport Kites Inc	3721	E	714 998-6359	20628
Statek Corporation (HQ)	3679	D	714 639-7810	19736

	SIC	EMP	PHONE	ENTRY #
Stir Foods LLC (PA)	2038	C	714 637-6050	1018
Sunland Tool Inc	3599	F	714 974-6500	16971
Sybron Dental Specialties Inc (HQ)	3843	C	949 255-8700	22914
Systems Integrated LLC	3829	E	714 998-0900	22280
Tandem Design Inc	3999	E	714 978-7272	24266
Technical Screen Printing Inc	2759	E	714 541-8590	7512
Techserve Industries Inc	3672	E	714 505-2755	18624
Thermal-Vac Technology Inc	3398	E	714 997-2601	11833
Totty Printing	2759	F	714 633-7081	7523
Tri Precision Sheetmetal Inc	3444	E	714 632-8838	12794
Tri-Tech Precision Inc	3728	F	714 970-1363	20958
Trisar Inc	2759	E	714 972-2626	7527
Truer Medical Inc	3841	E	714 628-9785	22659
Ulti-Mate Connector Inc	3678	E	714 637-7099	19426
Ultra-Pure Metal Finishing	3471	F	714 637-3150	13527
United Snshine Amrcn Inds Corp	3496	E	801 972-5124	13858
US Sensor Corp	3674	D	714 639-1000	19249
Vintique Inc	3714	E	714 634-1932	20481
We Do Graphics Inc	2752	E	714 997-7390	7174
Webb Massey Co Inc	2517	E	714 639-6012	4901
West American Rubber Co LLC (PA)	3069	B	714 532-3355	9692
West American Rubber Co LLC	3069	C	714 406-5860	9693
Western Lighting Inds Inc	3645	E	626 969-6820	17571
Westrock Rkt Company	2653	C	714 978-2895	5473
William Getz Corp	3949	E	714 516-2050	23692
Zolt Information Sciences Inc	2869	F	714 921-7489	9054

ORANGEVALE, CA - Sacramento County

	SIC	EMP	PHONE	ENTRY #
BMC Technology	3599	F	510 429-7000	16327
Brand Identity Inc	2752	F	916 553-0000	6704
Natural Pest Controls & Firewd (PA)	2879	F	916 726-0855	9108

ORCUTT, CA - Santa Barbara County

	SIC	EMP	PHONE	ENTRY #
Den-Mat Corporation (DH)	2844	B	805 922-8491	8735

ORINDA, CA - Contra Costa County

	SIC	EMP	PHONE	ENTRY #
Bay Leaf Spice Company	2099	E	925 330-1918	2461

ORLAND, CA - Glenn County

	SIC	EMP	PHONE	ENTRY #
Barletta Dehydrator Inc	2034	F	530 865-9318	874
Decamilla Brothers LLC	2079	F	530 865-3379	1539
Honey Olivarez Bees Inc	2099	D	530 865-0298	2537
Jensen Enterprises Inc	3272	F	530 865-4277	10942
Kraemer & Co Mfg Inc	3448	F	530 865-7982	12939
Land OLakes Inc	2022	F	530 865-7626	584
Olive Musco Products Inc	2035	E	530 865-4111	924
Westside Research Inc	2396	F	530 330-0085	3929

ORO GRANDE, CA - San Bernardino County

	SIC	EMP	PHONE	ENTRY #
Calportland Company	3241	F	760 245-5321	10746

OROSI, CA - Tulare County

	SIC	EMP	PHONE	ENTRY #
Lochirco Fruit and Produce Inc	2064	E	559 528-4194	1439

OROVILLE, CA - Butte County

	SIC	EMP	PHONE	ENTRY #
Afc Finishing Systems	3448	E	530 533-8907	12911
Chico Metal Finishing Inc	3471	F	530 534-7308	13369
Conners Oro-Cal Mfg Co	3911	F	530 533-5065	23252
Direct Surplus Sales Inc	3444	F	530 533-9999	12562
Endeavor Homes Inc	3531	E	530 534-0300	14165
Feather River Concrete Product	3273	F	530 532-7915	11106
George Delallo Company Inc	2033	E	530 533-3303	802
Graphic Packaging Intl LLC	2759	C	530 533-1058	7329
J W Bamford Inc	2411	F	530 533-0732	3995
Jess Howard	3089	F	530 533-3888	10168
Martin Marietta Materials Inc	1422	F	530 534-4517	315
Night Optics Usa Inc	3669	F	714 899-4475	18350
North State Rendering Co Inc	2077	F	530 343-6076	1530
Pacific Coast Producers	2033	C	530 533-4311	844
Perfect Plank Co	2431	F	530 533-7606	4211
Roplast Industries Inc	2673	C	530 532-9500	5619
Setzer Forest Products Inc	2421	C	530 534-8100	4055
Sierra Pacific Industries	2421	C	530 532-6630	4059
Smb Industries Inc (PA)	3441	D	530 534-6266	12243
Tile Artisans Inc	3253	F	800 601-4199	10795
Vinyl Fabrications Inc	2394	F	530 532-1236	3818

OXNARD, CA - Ventura County

	SIC	EMP	PHONE	ENTRY #
ACC Precision Inc	3599	F	805 278-9801	16205
Advanced Structural Tech Inc	3714	C	805 204-9133	20244
Advantage Engineering Corp	3949	E	805 216-9920	23488
Alliance Chemical & Envmtl	3479	F	805 385-3330	13547
Alpha Products Inc	3678	E	805 981-8666	19372
Aluminum Precision Pdts Inc	3463	C	805 488-4401	13120
American Alupack Inds LLC	3353	F	805 485-1500	11574
American Tooth Industries	3843	D	805 487-9868	22856
Amiad USA Inc	3589	E	805 988-3323	16008
Angelus Block Co Inc	3271	E	805 485-1137	10842

Employment Codes: A=Over 500 employees, B=251-500, C=101-250, D=51-100, E=20-50, F=10-19

2019 California
Manufacturers Register

© Mergent Inc. 1-800-342-5647

1429

GEOGRAPHIC

Company	SIC	EMP	PHONE	ENTRY #
Applied Powdercoat Inc (PA)	3479	E	805 981-1991	13553
B & S Plastics Inc	3089	A	805 981-0262	9965
Basic Business Forms Inc	2759	E	805 278-4551	7246
Becker Automotive Designs Inc	3711	E	805 487-5227	20130
Beckman Industries	3965	F	805 375-3003	23761
Berry Petroleum Company LLC	1311	F	805 984-0053	28
Cal Simba Inc (PA)	3914	E	805 240-1177	23335
California Plastics Inc	3089	F	805 483-8188	10005
California Resources Prod Corp	1311	D	805 483-8017	43
California Woodworking Inc	2434	E	805 982-9090	4284
Casa Agria	2082	F	805 485-1454	1577
Casualway Usa LLC	2514	D	805 660-7408	4828
Catalytic Solutions Inc (HQ)	3822	E	805 486-4649	21502
Cdti Advanced Materials Inc (PA)	2819	E	805 639-9458	7763
Clamshell Structures Inc	3448	F	805 988-1340	12927
Cloudburst	3564	E	805 986-4125	15150
Complyright Distribution Svcs	2761	E	805 981-0992	7549
Component Equipment Coinc	3678	D	805 988-8004	19377
Cool-Pak LLC	3089	D	805 981-2434	10042
Cosmetic Specialties Intl LLC	3089	C	805 487-6698	10045
Cure Pharmaceutical Corp	2834	E	805 487-7163	8129
Dabmar Lighting Inc (PA)	3648	E	805 604-9090	17683
DBC Printing Incorporated	2752	F	805 988-8855	6780
Diversified Minerals Inc	3273	E	805 247-1069	11102
Diversified Panels Systems Inc	3585	E	805 487-9241	15950
Drum Workshop Inc (PA)	3931	D	805 485-6999	23362
E Vasquez Distributors Inc	2448	E	805 487-8458	4468
Eagle Dominion Energy Corp	1382	E	202 380-9649	136
Elite Metal Finishing LLC	3471	C	805 983-4320	13407
Ergonom Corporation	2599	D	805 981-9978	5231
Ets Express Inc (PA)	3479	E	805 278-7771	13585
Farmer Bros Co	2095	F	805 483-8406	2341
Force Fabrication Inc	3444	F	805 754-2235	12589
Frank Stubbs Co Inc	3842	F	805 278-4300	22732
Freeport-Mcmoran Oil & Gas LLC	1311	E	805 567-1601	57
Fresh Innovations LLC	2097	E	805 483-2265	2412
Gold Coast Ironworks	3446	E	805 485-6921	12858
Gramberg Machine Inc	3599	F	805 278-4500	16542
Granatelli Motor Sports Inc	3714	E	805 486-6644	20354
Hanson Aggregates LLC	3241	D	805 485-3101	10752
Harwil Precision Products	3679	E	805 988-6800	19563
Healthsport Inc	2834	F	818 593-4880	8207
Henry J Perez DDS	3843	F	805 983-6768	22883
Hypress Technologies Inc	3542	E	805 485-4060	14439
Illah Sports Inc A Corporation	3949	E	805 240-7790	23590
Image Casting Inc	3324	E	805 986-1106	11512
Industrial Tools Inc	3559	E	805 483-1111	14970
Infratab	2836	E	805 986-8880	8560
International Forming Tech Inc	3542	E	805 278-8060	14440
Interntnal Pwr DC Pwr Sups Inc	3679	E	805 981-1188	19586
J M Smucker Company	2033	E	805 487-5483	809
John L Perry Studio Inc	3089	E	805 981-9665	10171
Kerr Group LLC	3089	C	805 278-9155	10179
Kevita Inc (HQ)	2086	D	805 200-2250	2145
Kim Laube & Company Inc	2844	E	805 240-1300	8783
Kl-Megla America LLC	3429	E	818 334-5311	11968
Legacy Vulcan LLC	3273	E	805 647-1161	11128
Lennox Industries Inc	3585	C	805 288-8200	15967
Little Castle Furniture Co Inc	2512	E	805 278-4646	4791
Masters In Metal Inc	3263	E	805 988-1992	10813
Mgr Design International Inc	3999	C	805 981-6400	24175
Mirage Sprtfshng & Commrcl	3949	F	805 983-0975	23619
Mist & Cool LLC	3634	E	805 986-4125	17398
Mjolnir Industries LLC	3544	E	805 488-3550	14542
New-Indy Oxnard LLC	2621	E	805 986-3881	5317
Northrop Grumman Systems Corp	3812	A	805 278-2074	21369
Noushig Inc	2051	E	805 983-2903	1298
Nu Venture Diving Co	3563	E	805 815-4044	15132
Nutrien AG Solutions Inc	2873	F	805 488-3646	9068
Oxnard Lemon Company	2037	F	805 483-1173	960
Oxnard Prcsion Fabrication Inc	3444	F	805 985-0447	12698
Parker-Hannifin Corporation	3569	C	805 604-3400	15349
PC Vaughan Mfg Corp (PA)	3714	E	805 278-2555	20419
Periodico El Vida	2711	E	805 483-1008	6013
Pine Grove Industries Inc	2752	E	805 485-3700	7027
Plascene Inc	3089	F	562 695-0240	10279
Poole Ventura Inc	3563	E	805 981-1784	15134
Pratt Industries Inc	2621	E	805 483-5331	5331
Praxair Distribution Inc	2813	E	805 487-2742	7726
Primal Essence Inc	2087	E	805 981-2409	2277
Procter & Gamble Paper Pdts Co	2676	B	805 485-8871	5669
Produce Available Inc (PA)	3523	D	805 483-5292	14094
Pti Technologies Inc (DH)	3728	C	805 604-3700	20917
Rakar Incorporated	3089	E	805 487-2721	10322
Rapid Product Solutions Inc	3599	E	805 485-7234	16885
Raypak Inc (DH)	3433	B	805 278-5300	12079
Regal Kitchens LLC	2434	C	786 953-6578	4342
Robbins Auto Top LLC	3089	D	805 278-8249	10337
Rostar Auto Filter Mfg Corp	3569	C	805 278-2555	15357
Royal Wine Corporation	2084	E	805 983-1560	1959
Sandra Sparks & Associates	2844	F	805 985-2057	8833
Santa Barbara Design Studio (PA)	3269	D	805 966-3883	10835
Scosche Industries Inc	3651	C	805 486-4450	17854
Scully Sportswear Inc	2386	E	805 483-6339	3622
Sensortech Systems Inc	3823	F	805 981-3735	21653
Sound Storm Laboratory LLC	3651	E	805 983-8008	17861
South Amrcn Imging Sltions Inc	3621	E	805 824-4036	17225
Southern Cal Gold Pdts Inc	3312	E	805 988-0777	11422
Spatz Corporation	2844	C	805 487-2122	8847
Stainless Process Systems Inc	3441	F	805 483-7100	12247
State Ready Mix Inc	3273	E	805 647-2817	11187
Sun Coast Calamari Inc	2092	C	805 385-0056	2324
Survivor Industries Inc	2099	E	805 385-5560	2676
T & M Machining Inc	3599	E	805 983-6716	16980
Tbyci LLC	3732	F	805 985-6800	21065
TI Enterprises LLC (DH)	2721	E	805 981-8393	6272
Trans Fx Inc	3999	F	805 485-6110	24275
Travis Mike Inc	3469	F	805 201-3363	13288
Tree Top Inc	2033	C	509 697-7251	863
V3 Printing Corporation	2752	D	805 981-2600	7161
Vaca Energy LLC	1382	E	310 385-3684	158
Van R Dental Products Inc	3843	F	805 488-1122	22921
Ventura Printing Inc (PA)	2759	E	805 981-2600	7533
Vogue Sign Inc	3993	F	805 487-7222	24000
Vortech Engineering Inc	3564	E	805 247-0226	15185
West Coast Welding & Cnstr	7692	F	805 604-1222	25449
Western Saw Manufacturers Inc	3425	E	805 981-0999	11922
Wholesome Harvest Baking LLC	2051	C	805 487-5191	1344
Wiggins Lift Co Inc	3537	E	805 485-7821	14352
Willis Machine Inc	3599	E	805 604-4500	17068
Zev Technologies Inc (PA)	3484	F	805 486-5800	13693

PACHECO, CA - Contra Costa County

Company	SIC	EMP	PHONE	ENTRY #
Biocare Medical LLC	3841	C	925 603-8000	22367
Tesoro Refining & Mktg Co LLC	2911	A	925 372-3100	9363

PACIFIC GROVE, CA - Monterey County

Company	SIC	EMP	PHONE	ENTRY #
Carmel Communications Inc	2711	F	831 274-8593	5795
Happy Girl Kitchen Co	2033	F	831 373-4475	803
Manutech Mfg & Dist	3524	F	831 655-8794	14128

PACIFIC PALISADES, CA - Los Angeles County

Company	SIC	EMP	PHONE	ENTRY #
Intimate Grooming Escenusals	2833	F	310 230-4544	7951
Optimis Services Inc	7372	E	310 230-2780	24995
Pipeliner Crm	7372	E	424 280-6445	25063

PACIFICA, CA - San Mateo County

Company	SIC	EMP	PHONE	ENTRY #
Forever Young	2099	E	650 355-5481	2524
Jodel Enterprises	3651	F	650 343-4510	17821
Kibblwhite Precision Machining	3751	E	650 359-4704	21121
Maurice Landstrass	3825	E	650 355-5532	21802
Scalable Systems RES Labs Inc	3674	E	650 322-6507	19137
The French Patisserie Inc	2051	D	650 738-4990	1333

PACOIMA, CA - Los Angeles County

Company	SIC	EMP	PHONE	ENTRY #
A & A Custom Shutters	3442	F	818 383-1819	12286
American Cnc Inc	3599	F	818 890-3400	16269
American Etching & Mfg	3479	E	323 875-3910	13548
American Fruits & Flavors LLC (HQ)	2087	C	818 899-9574	2240
American Range Corporation	3444	C	818 897-0808	12480
Anwright Corporation	3451	E	818 896-2465	13012
APT Metal Fabricators Inc	3469	E	818 896-7478	13165
Brice Manufacturing Co Inc	3728	E	818 896-2938	20761
Burbank Plating Service Corp	3471	F	818 899-1157	13356
Cabrac Inc	3469	E	818 834-0177	13175
California Signs Inc	3993	E	818 899-1888	23838
California Trade Converters	2631	E	818 899-1455	5343
Color TEC Industrial Finishing	3479	E	818 897-2669	13571
Cosmetic Enterprises Ltd	2844	E	818 896-5355	8727
Excess Trading Inc	3829	E	310 212-0020	22196
Flamemaster Corporation	2899	E	818 890-1401	9251
Gscm Ventures Inc	2844	E	818 303-2600	8760
Hanmar LLC (PA)	3469	E	818 240-0170	13213
Hrk Pet Food Products Inc	2048	E	818 897-2521	1137
Imagemover Inc	2752	F	818 485-8840	6874
JKL Components Corporation	3647	E	818 896-0019	17662
Kdl Precision Molding Corp	3769	D	818 896-9899	21194
Kitch Engineering Inc	3599	E	818 897-7133	16657
Komfy Kings Inc	2519	D	818 899-8929	4911
LA Hardwood Flooring Inc (PA)	2426	F	818 361-0099	4083
Legacy Bands Inc	3911	F	818 890-2527	23285
Mayoni Enterprises	3444	D	818 896-0026	12661

Mergent email: customerrelations@mergent.com

1430

2019 California
Manufacturers Register

(P-0000) Products & Services Section entry number
(PA)=Parent Co (HQ)=Headquarters (DH)=Div Headquarters

	SIC	EMP	PHONE	ENTRY #
Merchants Metals LLC	3496	F	818 896-6111	13840
Metalite Manufacturing Company	3469	E	818 890-2802	13247
Moc Products Company Inc **(PA)**	2899	D	818 794-3500	9284
Molding Corporation America	3089	E	818 890-7877	10221
Nu-Hope Laboratories Inc	3842	E	818 899-7711	22780
Petra-1 LP	2844	F	866 334-3702	8813
Pyramid Powder Coating Inc	3479	E	818 768-5898	13644
RMR Products Inc **(PA)**	3272	F	818 890-0896	10993
S & R Cnc Machining	3724	F	818 767-5200	20677
Sdi Industries Inc **(PA)**	3535	C	818 890-6002	14286
Sun Valley Skylights Inc	3211	F	818 686-0032	10607
Sunland Aerospace Fasteners	3452	F	818 485-8929	13086
Topnotch Quality Works Inc	3728	F	818 897-7679	20953
Trico Sports Inc	3751	D	818 899-7705	21145
Twin Peak Industries Inc	3949	E	800 259-5906	23679
Ultramet	3471	D	818 899-0236	13528
Valley Motor Center Inc	3711	F	818 686-3350	20181
Westcoast Grinding Corporation	3599	F	818 890-1841	17060
Western States Packaging Inc	2673	E	818 686-6045	5634
Xentric Drapery Hardware Inc	2591	F	818 897-0444	5216
Zerran International Corp	2844	F	818 897-5494	8869

PALA, CA - San Diego County

	SIC	EMP	PHONE	ENTRY #
Tribal Print Source	2752	F	760 597-2650	7147

PALM DESERT, CA - Riverside County

	SIC	EMP	PHONE	ENTRY #
Associated Desert Shoppers **(DH)**	2741	D	760 346-1729	6437
Daniels Inc **(PA)**	2741	E	801 621-3355	6468
Equipment De Sport Usa Inc	2395	F	760 772-5544	3848
Farley Paving Stone Co Inc	3272	D	760 773-3960	10923
Karbz Inc	3714	F	760 567-9953	20380
Lf Visuals Inc	2299	F	760 345-5571	3007
Lucious Jewels	3911	F	760 779-1304	23289
Pd Group	3993	E	760 674-3028	23942
Pearpoint Inc	3663	F	760 343-7350	18216
Photobacks LLC	7372	F	760 582-2550	25058
Plumbing Products Inc	3432	F	760 343-3306	12044
PPG Industries Inc	2851	E	760 340-1762	8929
Trent Beverage Company LLC	2086	F	310 384-6776	2229
Wanda Matranga	2752	F	760 773-4701	7172

PALM SPRINGS, CA - Riverside County

	SIC	EMP	PHONE	ENTRY #
Adams Trade Press LP **(PA)**	2721	E	760 318-7000	6097
Agan Woodcrafters	2434	F	760 322-1310	4267
Bear Brothers Enterprises Ltd	2721	E	914 588-6885	6110
Carefusion 207 Inc	3841	B	760 778-7200	22390
Desert Publications Inc **(PA)**	2721	E	760 325-2333	6143
Desert Sun Publishing Co **(HQ)**	2711	C	760 322-8889	5828
Dimora Enterprises	3711	F	760 832-9070	20136
Door Service Company	3315	F	760 320-0788	11439
Galaxy Energy Systems Inc	3511	F	760 778-4254	13996
Gannett Co Inc	2711	D	760 322-8889	5854
Joe Blasco Enterprises Inc	3999	D	323 467-4949	24139
Just Off Melrose Inc	2052	E	714 533-4566	1367
Ken Hoffmann Inc	3471	F	760 325-6012	13439
Pleros LLC	2844	F	442 275-6764	8820
Quivera Marketing Inc	2299	F	213 746-8200	3014
Sierra Aviation	3161	E	760 778-2845	10535
Univocity Media Inc	2741	F	760 904-5200	6612
Xy Corp Inc	3542	F	760 323-0333	14463

PALMDALE, CA - Los Angeles County

	SIC	EMP	PHONE	ENTRY #
Aamstamp Machine Company LLC	3497	F	661 272-0500	13868
Aero Bending Company	3444	E	661 948-2363	12462
Azachorok Contract Svcs LLC	3444	F	661 951-6566	12497
Bimbo Bakeries Usa Inc	2099	F	661 274-8458	2465
Boeing Company	3812	B	661 212-0024	21268
D & J Printing Inc	2752	D	661 775-4586	6775
Ectec Inc	3812	F	661 451-1098	21290
Instathreads LLC	2284	F	661 470-7841	2953
Kennedy Engineered Products	3714	F	661 272-1147	20381
Lockheed Martin Corporation	3812	A	661 572-7428	21334
Lockheed Martin Skunk Works	3812	F	661 572-2974	21343
Lucky Luke Brewing Company	2082	F	661 270-5588	1608
Lusk Quality Machine Products	3599	F	661 272-0630	16695
Northrop Grumman Systems Corp	3721	B	661 272-7000	20607
Northrop Grumman Systems Corp	3721	B	661 540-0446	20609
Palmdale Heat Treating Inc	3443	F	661 274-8604	12406
Park-Rand Enterprises Inc	2842	F	818 362-2565	8663
Phase-A-Matic Inc	3699	F	661 947-8485	20040
RB Machining Inc	3599	F	661 274-4611	16886
Service Rock Products Corp	3273	E	661 533-3443	11175
Sharkey Technology Group Inc	3599	F	661 267-2118	16941
Sun Valley Ltg Standards Inc	3646	B	661 233-2000	17647
Ultramar Inc	2911	F	661 944-2496	9370
US Pole Company Inc **(PA)**	3648	C	800 877-6537	17742
Vision Engrg Met Stamping Inc	3646	D	661 575-0933	17655

	SIC	EMP	PHONE	ENTRY #
Western Edge Inc	3479	F	661 947-3900	13680

PALO ALTO, CA - Santa Clara County

	SIC	EMP	PHONE	ENTRY #
Abaqus Inc	7372	F	415 496-9436	24301
Adaptive Insights Inc **(HQ)**	7372	C	650 528-7500	24319
Alro Cstm Drapery Installation	2591	F	650 847-4343	5179
Anacor Pharmaceuticals Inc	2834	F	650 543-7500	8031
Appbackr Inc	7372	F	650 272-6129	24363
Applied Expert Systems Inc	7372	E	650 617-2400	24373
Ariba Inc **(DH)**	7372	C	650 849-4000	24383
Ascendis Pharma Inc	2834	E	650 352-8389	8045
Astro Technology Inc	7372	E	650 533-5087	24393
Billcom Inc	7372	C	650 353-3301	24423
Birdcage Press LLC	2741	F	650 462-6300	6447
Birdeye Inc	2741	E	800 561-3357	6448
Bloomboard Inc **(PA)**	7372	F	650 567-5656	24431
Bosch Enrgy Stor Solutions LLC	3621	F	650 320-2933	17182
Calmar Optcom Inc	3661	E	408 733-7800	17929
Carecognitics LLC	7372	F	702 355-8201	24470
Clariant Corporation	2869	C	650 494-1749	8997
Communications & Pwr Inds LLC	3671	C	650 846-3494	18382
Communications & Pwr Inds LLC	3663	A	650 846-3729	18073
Communications & Pwr Inds LLC **(DH)**	3671	A	650 846-2900	18383
Communications & Pwr Inds LLC	3671	A	650 846-2900	18384
Condor Electronics Inc	3823	E	408 745-7141	21564
Confluent Inc **(PA)**	7372	E	650 453-5860	24521
CPI International Inc **(HQ)**	3671	E	650 846-2801	18385
CPI International Holding Corp	3679	E	650 846-2900	19500
Cymmetria Inc	7372	E	415 568-6870	24543
Danisco US Inc **(DH)**	2835	C	650 846-7500	8472
Duda Mobile Inc	7372	E	855 790-0003	24583
Eiger Biopharmaceuticals Inc **(PA)**	2836	F	650 272-6138	8548
Embarcadero Publishing Company **(PA)**	2711	C	650 964-6300	5846
Eton Corporation	3699	E	650 903-3866	19964
Fiorano Software Inc	7372	D	650 326-1136	24649
Fono Unlimited Inc **(PA)**	2024	E	650 322-4664	672
Ghs Champion Inc	2051	F	650 326-8485	1262
Hammon Plating Corporation	3471	E	650 494-2691	13421
Hazelcast Inc	7372	E	650 521-5453	24720
Hewlett Packard Enterprise Co **(PA)**	7372	C	650 687-5817	24731
Hewlett-Packard Entps LLC **(HQ)**	3571	D	650 687-5817	15419
HP Inc **(PA)**	3571	A	650 857-1501	15420
HP Inc	3571	A	650 857-4946	15423
HP Inc	3571	D	650 857-1501	15424
HP Inc	3571	E	650 857-1501	15425
Hpe Enterprises LLC **(HQ)**	7372	E	650 857-5817	24740
Hpi Federal LLC **(HQ)**	3571	F	650 857-1501	15427
Inscopix Inc	3827	E	650 600-3886	22089
Intapp Inc **(PA)**	7372	C	650 852-0400	24780
Integral Development Corp **(PA)**	7372	C	650 424-4500	24781
Interntional Semicdtr Tech Inc	3674	F	650 941-7096	18924
Ivydoctors Inc	7372	F	415 890-3937	24810
Jazz Pharmaceuticals Inc **(HQ)**	2834	C	650 496-3777	8240
Kodiak Sciences Inc **(PA)**	2836	E	650 281-0850	8564
KUDos&co Inc	2741	E	650 799-9104	6513
Level Labs LP	7372	E	408 499-6839	24857
Light Labs Inc	3827	D	650 272-6942	22098
Liveaction Inc **(PA)**	7372	E	415 837-3303	24860
Lockheed Martin Corporation	3812	A	650 424-2000	21325
Lockheed Martin Corporation	3812	A	650 424-2000	21327
Magnet Systems Inc	7372	E	650 329-5904	24878
Maximus Holdings Inc	7372	A	650 935-9500	24887
Mda Cmmunications Holdings LLC	3663	A	650 852-4000	18177
Merck & Co Inc	2834	C	650 496-6400	8278
Mercury Interactive LLC **(HQ)**	7372	B	650 857-1501	24904
Merrill Corporation	2759	E	650 493-1400	7401
Metricstream Inc **(PA)**	7372	C	650 620-2900	24906
Mountain View Voice	2711	E	650 326-8210	5985
Network Chemistry Inc	3699	F	650 858-3120	20025
Nok Nok Labs Inc	7372	F	650 433-1300	24969
Nyansa Inc	7372	E	650 446-7818	24979
Palo Alto Cafe	2095	F	650 322-8644	2362
Pearson Electronics Inc	3677	F	650 494-6444	19352
Phantom Cyber Corporation	7372	E	650 208-5151	25055
Pilot Software Inc	7372	F	650 230-2830	25062
Predii Inc	7372	F	650 666-2524	25077
Quality Metal Spinning and	3469	E	650 858-2491	13268
Recomax Software Inc	3663	F	408 592-0851	18237
Recor Medical Inc **(PA)**	3841	F	631 676-2730	22598
Relateiq Inc	7372	E	650 409-2336	25123
RR Donnelley & Sons Company	2782	C	650 845-6600	7584
Sap AG	3572	C	650 849-4000	15599
Scene 53 Inc	7372	E	415 404-2461	25151
Sciton Inc	3841	D	650 493-9155	22617
Shalon Ventures	3821	F	650 324-9090	21491
Sinusys Corporation	2836	C	650 213-9988	8583

Employment Codes: A=Over 500 employees, B=251-500,
C=101-250, D=51-100, E=20-50, F=10-19

2019 California
Manufacturers Register

© Mergent Inc. 1-800-342-5647

1431

GEOGRAPHIC

	SIC	EMP	PHONE	ENTRY #
Sizto Tech Corporation	3491	F	650 856-8833	13733
Southwall Technologies Inc (DH)	3081	E	650 798-1285	9728
Stangenes Industries Inc (PA)	3677	C	650 855-9926	19365
Stemrad Inc	3842	F	650 933-3377	22819
Stoneside LLC	2591	F	650 422-2154	5213
Suitable Technologies Inc (PA)	3549	F	650 294-3170	14767
Sumopti	7372	F	650 331-1126	25234
Superfish Inc	3823	F	650 752-6564	21661
Suss McRtec Prcision Photomask	3861	E	415 494-3113	23199
Symphonyrm Inc	7372	F	650 336-8430	25242
Terrajoule Corporation	3511	F	650 269-0494	14010
Tesla Inc (PA)	3711	C	650 681-5000	20176
Third Mllennium Test Solutions	3825	F	650 949-1120	21877
Thoughtspot Inc	7372	F	800 508-7008	25274
Toky Inc	7372	F	844 332-6433	25283
Varian Associates Limited	3841	F	650 493-4000	22664
Varian Medical Systems Inc (PA)	3844	A	650 493-4000	22944
Varian Medical Systems Inc	3841	E	408 321-4468	22665
Varian Medical Systems Inc	3671	E	650 493-4000	18399
Varian Medical Systems Inc	3841	C	650 493-4000	22667
Vera Security Inc	7372	E	844 438-8372	25324
Verbio Inc	7372	F	650 862-8935	25325
Voelker Sensors Inc	2396	F	650 361-0570	3928
Xcelmobility Inc	7372	D	650 320-1728	25361
Xerox International Partners (HQ)	3555	F	408 953-2700	14830

PALOS VERDES ESTATES, CA - Los Angeles County

	SIC	EMP	PHONE	ENTRY #
QED Software LLC	7372	E	310 214-3118	25092

PANORAMA CITY, CA - Los Angeles County

	SIC	EMP	PHONE	ENTRY #
ARC Machines Inc (HQ)	3548	D	818 896-9556	14721
Mag High Tech	3444	F	818 786-8366	12651
Puretek Corporation	2834	C	818 361-3949	8351
Puretek Corporation (PA)	2834	E	818 361-3316	8352
Raspadoxpress	2741	E	818 892-6969	6563
Superior Awning Inc	2394	F	818 780-7200	3813
TMW Corporation	3471	E	818 374-1074	13522
Transit Care Inc (PA)	3211	F	818 267-3002	10609

PARADISE, CA - Butte County

	SIC	EMP	PHONE	ENTRY #
B C Yellow Pages	2741	F	530 876-8616	6443
Califrnia Nwspapers Ltd Partnr	2711	C	530 877-4413	5793
Compac Engineering Inc	3822	F	530 872-2042	21506

PARAMOUNT, CA - Los Angeles County

	SIC	EMP	PHONE	ENTRY #
Aerocraft Heat Treating Co Inc	3398	D	562 674-2400	11791
After Hours	3651	F	562 925-5737	17755
Air Frame Forming Inc	3542	F	562 663-1662	14426
Amrex-Zetron Inc	3699	E	310 527-6868	19909
Amsco US Inc	3679	C	562 630-0333	19444
Anaplex Corporation	3471	E	714 522-4481	13329
Apollo Metal Spinning Co Inc	3465	F	562 634-5141	13136
Ariza Cheese Co Inc	2022	E	562 630-4144	564
ARS Enterprises (PA)	3842	F	562 946-3505	22701
Bison Engineering Company	3599	F	562 408-1525	16324
Bkon Interior Soution	2521	F	562 408-1655	4934
Blue Circle Corp	3423	F	562 531-2711	13060
Bluegate Surface Works Inc	2434	F	562 630-9005	4276
C & J Metal Products Inc	3444	F	562 634-3101	12514
C S Dash Cover Inc	2396	F	562 790-8300	3880
Cad Manufacturing Inc	3728	F	562 408-1113	20771
California Screw Products Corp	3429	C	562 633-6626	11942
Danrich Welding Coinc	3444	F	562 634-4811	12550
Demaria Electric Inc	7694	E	310 549-4980	25456
Denmac Industries Inc	3479	E	562 634-2714	13574
Die Shop	3544	F	562 630-4400	14507
Dlc Laboratories Inc	2834	F	562 602-2184	8142
Drees Wood Products Inc	2431	E	562 633-7337	4149
Drees Wood Products Inc (PA)	2431	E	562 633-7337	4150
Exodust Collectors LLC	3564	F	562 808-0842	15156
Expert Computer Intl Inc (PA)	3571	F	562 630-3002	15411
Extrude Hone Deburring Service	3599	F	562 531-2976	16488
Fenico Precision Castings Inc	3369	D	562 634-5000	11777
Gammell Industries Inc	3441	F	562 634-6653	12168
George Jue Mfg Co Inc	3546	F	562 634-8181	14704
Golden State Engineering Inc	3549	C	562 634-3125	14752
Graphic Trends Incorporated	2759	E	562 531-2339	7331
Harbor Products Inc	3069	F	562 633-8184	9619
Hoffman Plastic Compounds Inc	2821	F	323 636-3346	7839
Instrument & Valve Services Co	3494	D	562 633-0179	13769
International Trend - 3 Corp	2329	F	562 360-5185	3164
Iron Works & Custom Racks	7692	F	323 581-2222	25412
Izorline International Inc	3949	F	562 531-6000	23596
Jade Spec LLC	2211	F	310 933-4338	2747
Jayone Foods Inc	2099	E	562 633-7400	2542
Jeffrey Fabrication LLC	3444	E	562 634-3101	12630
Jimenes Food Inc	2099	E	562 602-2505	2545

	SIC	EMP	PHONE	ENTRY #
Kum Kang Trading USAinC	2844	F	562 531-6111	8784
LMC Enterprises (PA)	2842	D	562 602-2116	8651
Logos Plus Inc	2396	F	562 634-3009	3903
Marukan Vinegar U S A Inc (HQ)	2099	C	562 630-6060	2598
Mattco Forge Inc (PA)	3462	D	562 634-8635	13106
Mc Lane Manufacturing Inc	3524	D	562 633-8158	14129
Mediland Corporation	3211	D	562 630-9696	10602
Merlin-Alltec Mold Making Inc	3089	F	562 529-5050	10208
Millbrook Kitchens Inc	2434	F	310 684-3366	4328
Mr T Transport	1389	F	562 602-5536	240
New Century Industries Inc	3714	E	562 634-9551	20409
Paramount Dairy Inc	2026	E	949 265-8000	734
Paramount Extrusions Company (PA)	3354	E	562 634-3291	11599
Paramount Extrusions Company	3354	E	562 634-3291	11600
Paramount Grinding Service	3599	F	562 630-6940	16829
Paramount Laminates Inc	3083	F	562 531-7580	9756
Paramount Petroleum Corp	2911	C	562 633-4332	9344
Paramount Petroleum Corp (DH)	2911	C	562 531-2060	9345
Paratech Inc	3295	C	562 633-2045	11324
Pecowood Inc	3429	F	562 633-2538	11984
Piedras Machine Corporation	3728	F	562 602-1500	20910
Pierce Textile Inc	2258	E	562 220-1177	2869
Popsalot LLC	2096	E	213 761-0156	2398
Premium Plastics Machine Inc	3089	F	323 979-3889	10307
Press Forge Company	3463	D	562 531-4962	13127
Quality Image Inc	2821	F	562 259-9872	7877
R & S Manufacturing & Sup Inc	2851	F	909 622-5881	8936
R & S Processing Co Inc	3069	D	562 531-0738	9667
Ramp Engineering Inc	3441	F	562 531-8030	12235
Robert W Wiesmantel	3599	F	562 634-0442	16908
Sandee Plastic Extrusions	3061	E	323 979-4020	9575
Schulz Leather Co Inc	2394	E	562 633-1081	3809
Scotts Food Products Inc	2035	F	562 630-8448	932
Sibyl Shepard Inc	2392	C	562 531-8612	3747
Supertec Machinery Inc	3541	F	562 220-1675	14415
Top Line Mfg Inc	3429	E	562 633-0605	12002
Total-Western Inc (HQ)	1389	E	562 220-1450	284
TP Solar Inc	3567	E	562 808-2171	15276
Trepanning Spcialty A Cal Corp	3599	E	562 408-0044	17007
Vast Enterprises	2992	E	562 633-3224	9453
Vi-Star Gear Co Inc	3462	E	323 774-3750	13117
Wagner Plate Works West Inc (PA)	3443	F	562 531-6050	12439
Weber Metals Inc	3463	B	562 602-0260	13132
Williams Metal Blanking Dies	3469	F	562 634-4592	13298
Z-Tronix Inc	3679	E	562 808-0800	19794

PARLIER, CA - Fresno County

	SIC	EMP	PHONE	ENTRY #
John Daniel Gonzalez	2449	E	559 646-6621	4526
W E Plemons McHy Svcs Inc	3565	E	559 646-6630	15234

PASADENA, CA - Los Angeles County

	SIC	EMP	PHONE	ENTRY #
A N Tool & Die Inc	3599	F	626 795-3238	16193
Accu-Gage & Thread Grinding Co	3823	F	626 568-2932	21540
ADS Water Inc	3589	F	415 448-6266	16006
Advanced Mtls Joining Corp (PA)	3728	E	626 449-2696	20706
Aea Ribbon Mics	3651	F	626 798-9128	17754
AGS Usa LLC	2335	C	323 588-2200	3290
Air Instrmnts Measurements LLC	3823	F	626 791-1912	21544
All Metal Fabrication	3444	F	626 449-6191	12470
Amera Machine Inc	3565	F	626 577-2819	15194
American Craftsmen Corporation	2511	F	626 793-3329	4667
Arrowhead Pharmaceuticals Inc (PA)	2834	F	626 304-3400	8044
Arts Elegance Inc	3911	E	626 793-4794	23238
At Systems Technologies Inc	3578	F	317 591-2616	15894
Avery Dennison Corporation	2672	C	626 304-2000	5553
Branch Messenger Inc	7372	E	323 300-4063	24449
C & D Precision Components	3599	F	626 799-7109	16343
Calimmune Inc	2834	F	310 806-6240	8093
Camtek LLC	2834	F	626 508-1700	8096
Chase Corporation	3644	F	626 395-7706	17507
Current Modular Inc	2452	E	909 792-9207	4572
Estephanian Engineering Inc	2261	E	626 358-7265	2880
Evolution Design Lab Inc	3144	E	626 960-8388	10496
Evolution Robotics Inc	7372	E	626 993-3300	24632
Fvo Solutions Inc	3479	D	626 449-0218	13593
George L Throop Co	3272	E	626 796-0285	10932
Get Ahead Learning LLC	7372	F	626 796-8500	24690
Gmto Corporation	3827	D	626 204-0500	22078
Guidance Software Inc (HQ)	7372	C	626 229-9191	24716
Hamilton Metalcraft Inc	3444	E	626 795-4811	12607
Hemodialysis Inc	3841	E	626 792-0548	22469
Honeybee Robotics Ltd	3569	F	510 207-4555	15329
House of Printing Inc	2752	E	626 793-7034	6863
Hybrid Kinetic Motors Corp	3711	F	626 683-7330	20151
Integrated Design Tools Inc (PA)	3861	F	850 222-5939	23168
K C Photo Engraving Co	3555	F	626 795-4127	14814

Mergent email: customerrelations@mergent.com

1432

2019 California
Manufacturers Register

(P-0000) Products & Services Section entry number
(PA)=Parent Co (HQ)=Headquarters (DH)=Div Headquarters

Company	SIC	EMP	PHONE	ENTRY #
L A Steel Craft Products (PA)	3949	E	626 798-7401	23604
L3 Cincinnati Electronics Corp	3585	E	626 395-7460	15965
Licher Direct Mail Inc	2752	E	626 795-3333	6947
Lida Childrens Wear Inc	2361	E	626 967-8868	3582
Lifesource Water Systems Inc (PA)	3589	E	626 792-9996	16066
Materia Inc (PA)	2819	C	626 584-8400	7785
Max Leon Inc (PA)	2339	D	626 797-6886	3466
Modetek Inc	3229	E	760 431-4190	10658
Myricom Inc	3571	E	626 821-5555	15465
Normandy Refinishers Inc	3471	E	626 792-9202	13466
Nutraceutical Brews For Lf Inc	2082	F	310 273-8339	1614
Openx Technologies Inc	7372	E	626 466-1141	24991
Orbits Lightwave Inc	3229	F	626 795-0667	10662
Pak Group LLC	2052	E	626 316-6555	1374
Pasadena Bio Cllbrtive Incbtor	3821	F	626 507-8487	21485
Pasadena Newspapers Inc (PA)	2711	C	626 578-6300	6010
Primed Productions Inc	2531	F	626 216-5822	5025
Red Gate Software Inc	7372	F	626 993-3949	25116
Replenish Inc	3841	F	626 219-7867	22599
Rogerson Kratos	3812	C	626 449-3090	21419
Sabrin Corporation	3444	E	626 792-3813	12748
Shamrock Die Cutting Company	2675	F	323 266-4556	5658
Southland Publishing	2741	E	626 584-1500	6585
Southland Publishing Inc	2711	E	626 584-1500	6053
Stir	3699	F	626 657-0918	20081
Stirworks Inc	3199	E	800 657-2427	10581
Surprisesilkcom	2221	F	626 568-9889	2783
Synopsys Inc	7372	D	626 795-9101	25246
Thermapak Technologies Inc	3429	F	909 612-9380	12000
Thomas T Bernstein	3451	F	626 351-0570	13046
Turbo Coil Inc	3585	F	626 644-6254	15994
Typecraft Inc	2752	F	626 795-8093	7150
Undercar Express Inc	3711	F	626 683-2787	20180
Urban Outfitters Inc	2335	E	626 449-1818	3344
Vitafoods America LLC	2026	F	800 695-4750	739
Wallaby Financial LLC	7372	E	626 600-2604	25341
Westcoast Companies Inc	2394	F	626 794-9330	3820
Wetzels Pretzels LLC (HQ)	2052	F	626 432-6900	1388
Yes To Inc	2844	E	626 365-1976	8867

PASO ROBLES, CA - San Luis Obispo County

Company	SIC	EMP	PHONE	ENTRY #
A B G Instruments & Engrg	3544	F	805 238-6262	14469
Acme Vial & Glass Co	3221	F	805 239-2666	10614
Advance Adapters Inc	3714	E	805 238-7000	20240
Advanced Keyboard Tech Inc	3571	F	805 237-2055	15383
Air Dry Co of America LLC	3822	E	805 227-0434	21497
AMC Machining Inc	3449	E	805 238-5452	12971
Applied Technologies Assoc Inc (HQ)	3829	C	805 239-9100	22163
Arbiter Systems Incorporated (PA)	3825	F	805 237-3831	21723
Broken Earth Winery	2084	E	805 239-2562	1668
Casa Grande Woodworks	2431	E	805 226-2040	4123
Central Coast Stainless	3443	E	805 238-0888	12369
Cornucopia Tool & Plastics Inc	3089	F	805 238-7660	10044
Cws Beverage	2082	E	805 286-2735	1583
Davis Boats	3732	F	805 227-1170	21028
Diversified Hangar Company	3441	F	805 239-8229	12153
Ennis Inc	2761	C	805 238-1144	7550
Eos Estate Winery	2084	E	805 239-2562	1751
Fetzer Vineyards	2084	F	805 467-0192	1761
Figueroa Machining	3599	E	805 238-7704	16499
Firestone Walker Inc (PA)	2082	C	805 225-5911	1591
Flight Environments Inc	3728	E	805 226-2912	20815
Foley Family Wines Inc (HQ)	2084	E	805 688-3940	1767
GP Industries Inc	3949	F	805 227-6565	23575
Halter Winery LLC	2084	E	805 226-9455	1803
Hope Family Wines (PA)	2084	E	805 238-4112	1813
James Tobin Cellars Inc	2084	E	805 239-2204	1828
Joslyn Sunbank Company LLC	3678	B	805 238-2840	19399
Justin Vineyards & Winery LLC (DH)	2084	E	805 238-6932	1835
Los Angles Tmes Cmmnctions LLC	2711	E	805 238-2720	5923
Lubrizol Advanced Mtls Inc	2899	D	805 239-1550	9274
Martin Weyrich Winery LLC	2084	F	805 226-9296	1872
Minatronic Inc	3679	F	805 239-8864	19654
Modern Dev Co A Ltd Partnr	2084	F	805 239-1167	1882
Nanometer Technologies Inc	3661	F	805 226-7332	17967
Navajo Concrete Inc	3273	F	805 238-0955	11151
News Media Inc	2711	F	805 237-6060	5996
Niner Wine Estates LLC	2084	E	805 239-2233	1902
Opolo Vineyards Inc (PA)	2084	F	805 238-9593	1906
Pacific Metal Finishing Inc	3479	F	805 237-8886	13629
Pear Valley Vineyard Inc	2084	F	805 237-2861	1918
Pic Manufacturing Inc	3555	F	805 238-5451	14825
Powder Coating Usa Inc	3479	F	805 237-8886	13638
Premier Bag Company LLC	2671	E	805 237-1910	5535
Pro Document Solutions (PA)	2752	D	805 238-6680	7052
Rbz Vineyards Inc	2084	E	805 542-0133	1942
Rogue River Rifleworks Inc	3949	F	805 227-4611	23639
Secondwind Products Inc	2842	E	805 239-2555	8676
Silver Horse Vineyards Inc	2084	F	805 467-9463	1977
Sligh Cabinets Inc	2434	F	805 239-2550	4351
Souriau Usa Inc (DH)	3643	E	805 238-2840	17490
Sport Rock International Inc	3949	F	805 434-5474	23660
Sylvester Winery Inc	2084	E	805 227-4000	2005
Tablas Creek Vineyard LLC	2084	E	805 237-1231	2006
Toomey Racing USA	3751	E	805 239-8870	21143
Treana Winery LLC	2084	E	805 237-2932	2019
Weatherby Inc	3484	E	307 675-7800	13692

PATTERSON, CA - Stanislaus County

Company	SIC	EMP	PHONE	ENTRY #
Bay Area Ems Solutions LLC	3672	F	408 753-3651	18435
Hpl Contract Inc	2521	F	209 892-1717	4949
Patterson Frozen Foods Inc	2037	F	209 892-5060	962
Sport Boat Trailers Inc	3799	F	209 892-5388	21241

PEARBLOSSOM, CA - Los Angeles County

Company	SIC	EMP	PHONE	ENTRY #
Doug Trim Sub Contractor	3479	F	661 944-2884	13575

PEBBLE BEACH, CA - Monterey County

Company	SIC	EMP	PHONE	ENTRY #
Aquest Inc	3432	E	831 622-9296	12023
Techmo Entertainment Inc	7372	F	408 309-3039	25262

PENN VALLEY, CA - Nevada County

Company	SIC	EMP	PHONE	ENTRY #
Firestone Walker LLC	2082	D	805 225-5911	1592
Ijot Development Inc	2531	A	925 258-9909	5015

PENRYN, CA - Placer County

Company	SIC	EMP	PHONE	ENTRY #
K S Telecom Inc	3661	F	916 652-4735	17960

PERRIS, CA - Riverside County

Company	SIC	EMP	PHONE	ENTRY #
AAA Pallet Recycling & Mfg Inc	2448	E	951 681-7748	4448
Alpha Corporation of Tennessee	2821	D	951 657-5161	7818
American Coffee Urn Mfg Co Inc	3444	E	951 943-1495	12478
Aoc LLC	2295	D	951 657-5161	2956
Avalon Shutters Inc	2431	C	909 937-4900	4107
Axxis Corporation	3599	E	951 436-9921	16292
California Composite Cont Corp	2655	C	951 940-9343	5481
California Trusframe LLC (PA)	2439	D	951 657-7491	4396
California Truss Company (PA)	2439	D	951 657-7491	4397
Clayton Homes Inc	2451	C	951 657-7491	4550
Coreslab Structures La Inc	3272	C	951 943-9119	10910
Craftech Metal Forming Inc	3365	E	951 940-6444	11731
Genesis Supreme Rv Inc	3799	E	951 337-0254	21230
Inland Empire Truss Inc (PA)	2439	E	951 300-1758	4412
Inland Truss Inc (PA)	2439	E	951 300-1758	4413
J & J Tape & Label Inc	2759	E	951 657-6631	7363
J & R Concrete Products Inc	3272	E	951 943-5855	10941
J F Christopher Inc	3949	F	951 943-1166	23598
J-M Manufacturing Company Inc	2821	D	951 657-7400	7848
Limos By Tiffany Inc	3713	C	951 657-2680	20213
Navigator Yachts and Pdts Inc	3732	C	951 657-2117	21058
Npg Inc (PA)	2951	D	951 940-0200	9390
Pacific Coachworks Inc	3792	C	951 657-7294	21208
Perris Skyventure	3443	E	951 940-4290	12408
Power Pt Inc	3537	E	951 490-4149	14341
Pw Eagle Inc	3084	B	951 657-7400	9787
R-Cold Inc	3585	D	951 436-5476	15975
Scale Services Inc	3596	F	909 266-0896	16176
Spaulding Equipment Company (PA)	3532	C	951 943-4531	14203
Star Milling Co	2048	C	951 657-3143	1167
Stearns Product Dev Corp (PA)	3569	D	951 657-0379	15365
Stretch Forming Corporation	3444	C	951 443-0911	12775
Timmons Wood Products Inc	2499	F	951 940-4700	4660
W D Schock Corp	3732	E	951 277-3377	21068
Warlock Industries	3711	E	951 657-2680	20182
Western Metal Spinning & Mfg	3469	F	951 657-0711	13297
World Traditions Inc	3269	F	951 990-6346	10839

PESCADERO, CA - San Mateo County

Company	SIC	EMP	PHONE	ENTRY #
Atmos Engineering Inc	3829	F	650 879-1674	22166

PETALUMA, CA - Sonoma County

Company	SIC	EMP	PHONE	ENTRY #
Accountmate Software Corp (PA)	7372	E	707 774-7500	24307
Ace Products Enterprises Inc	3161	E	707 765-1500	10512
American Bottling Company	2086	E	707 766-9750	2082
Amys Kitchen Inc	2038	E	707 568-4500	978
Architectural Plastics Inc	3089	F	707 765-9898	9953
Bechhold & Son Flasher & Lure	3949	F	530 367-6650	23515
Berkley Integrated Audio Softw	3695	E	707 782-1866	19856
Bibbero Systems Inc (HQ)	2752	E	800 242-2376	6696
Biosearch Technologies Inc (DH)	2836	C	415 883-8400	8537
Camelbak Acquisition Corp	3949	C	707 792-9700	23534
Camelbak Products LLC (HQ)	3949	D	707 792-9700	23535
Caracal Enterprises LLC	3581	E	707 773-3373	15920
Chad Empey	3211	F	707 762-1900	10592

GEOGRAPHIC

Company	SIC	EMP	PHONE	ENTRY #
Collidion Inc (PA)	2834	F	707 668-7600	8117
Colvin-Friedman LLC	3089	E	707 769-4488	10031
Coval Molecular Coatings Inc	2899	F	707 242-6900	9234
Dairymens Feed & Sup Coop Assn	2048	F	707 763-1585	1126
Deweyl Tool Co Inc	3545	E	707 765-5779	14623
Donal Machine Inc	3599	E	707 763-6625	16446
Dow Phrmaceutical Sciences Inc	3826	C	707 793-2600	21947
Eclipse Design Inc	3446	F	707 763-3104	12852
Empire Shower Doors Inc	3231	F	707 773-2898	10695
Enphase Energy Inc (PA)	3674	B	707 774-7000	18824
Field To Family Natural Foods	2015	F	707 765-6756	538
Fulton Acres Inc	2396	F	707 762-2280	3892
G M P C LLC	3993	F	707 766-9504	23885
Gefen LLC	3699	E	818 772-9100	19973
Gmpc LLC	3993	F	707 766-1702	23889
Hain Celestial Group Inc	2844	D	707 347-1200	8762
Hydrofarm LLC (PA)	3999	E	800 634-9990	24126
Hydropoint Data Systems Inc	3523	E	707 769-9696	14070
Illinois Tool Works Inc	3589	D	800 762-7600	16053
Katadyn Desalination LLC	3634	C	415 526-2780	17394
Kval Inc	3553	C	707 762-4363	14785
Labcon North America	3089	C	707 766-2100	10187
Lind Marine Inc (PA)	2048	E	707 762-7251	1144
Marin French Cheese Company	2022	F	707 762-6001	592
McEvoy of Marin LLC	2079	D	707 778-2307	1544
McGunagle William H & Sons Mfg (PA)	2511	E	707 762-7900	4718
Mesa/Boogie Limited (PA)	3651	D	707 765-1805	17831
Miyokos Kitchen	2021	E	415 448-5807	561
Morgan Manufacturing Inc	3423	E	707 763-6848	11902
MPS Lansing Inc	2672	E	707 778-1250	5572
Mrs Grossmans Paper Company	2678	D	707 763-1700	5687
Openclovis Solutions Inc	7372	E	707 981-7120	24987
Pangea Silkscreen	2396	F	707 778-0110	3912
Parmatech Corporation	3399	F	707 778-2266	11844
Petalumaidence Opco LLC	2084	D	707 763-4109	1924
Planet One Products Inc (PA)	2541	E	707 794-8000	5094
Pyramids Winery Inc	2084	F	707 765-2768	1933
Qor LLC	2329	F	707 658-2539	3186
Robert W Cameron & Co Inc	2731	F	707 769-1617	6387
Rotork Controls Inc	3625	F	707 769-4880	17304
RS Technical Services Inc (PA)	3826	D	707 778-1974	22011
Security People Inc	3679	E	707 766-6000	19722
Shamrock Materials Inc (PA)	3273	E	707 781-9000	11176
Sistema US Inc (PA)	3089	E	707 773-2200	10376
Small Precision Tools Inc	3299	D	707 765-4545	11370
Smart Caregiver Corporation	3845	E	707 781-7450	23049
Sonoma Cast Stone Corporation	3272	E	877 283-2400	11004
Sonoma Pharmaceuticals Inc (PA)	2834	D	707 283-0550	8387
Spectra Watermakers Inc (HQ)	3589	F	415 526-2780	16111
Spectrum Organic Products LLC	2079	D	888 343-6637	1551
St Louis Post-Dispatch LLC	2711	D	707 762-4541	6057
Stonecrop Technologies LLC	3663	E	781 659-0007	18265
Straus Family Creamery Inc	2021	D	707 776-2887	562
Streetwise Reports LLC	2741	E	707 981-8999	6592
TC Steel	7692	E	707 773-2150	25440
Textron Inc	3674	D	707 763-8855	19231
Three Twins Organic Inc (PA)	2024	E	707 763-8946	699
Torn Ranch Inc (PA)	2064	D	415 506-3000	1464
Ume Voice Inc	3651	F	707 939-8607	17872
Us1com Inc	2759	E	707 781-2560	7532
Womack International Inc	3569	E	707 763-1800	15376
World Centric	2679	E	707 241-9190	5747
Xandex Inc	3825	D	707 763-7799	21888
Zapworldcom (PA)	3621	E	707 525-8658	17230

PHILO, CA - Mendocino County

Company	SIC	EMP	PHONE	ENTRY #
Duckhorn Wine Company	2084	F	707 895-3202	1736
Handley Cellars Ltd	2084	F	707 895-3876	1804
Husch Vineyards Inc (PA)	2084	E	707 895-3216	1816
I & E Lath Mill Inc	2421	F	707 895-3380	4040
Navarro Winery	2084	D	707 895-3686	1894
TS Logging	2411	F	707 895-3751	4016

PICO RIVERA, CA - Los Angeles County

Company	SIC	EMP	PHONE	ENTRY #
Advanced Laser Dies Inc	3554	F	562 949-0081	14790
Allegheny Ludlum LLC	3312	F	562 654-3900	11376
Bakemark USA LLC (PA)	2045	B	562 949-1045	1095
Bay Cities Container Corp (PA)	2653	C	562 948-3751	5386
Bishop Electronics Corporation	3675	E	562 695-0446	19292
Brk Group LLC	2299	E	562 949-4394	2992
C&O Manufacturing Company Inc	3444	D	562 692-7525	12516
CD Container Inc	2653	E	562 948-1910	5395
Coastal Container Inc	2653	E	562 801-4595	5397
Coastwide Tag & Label Co	2759	E	323 721-1501	7276
Cordovan & Grey Ltd	2325	E	562 699-8300	3068
Custom Interiors Design Fixs	2599	E	562 942-7969	5225

Company	SIC	EMP	PHONE	ENTRY #
Dodge - Wasmund Mfg Inc	3089	F	562 692-8104	10074
Endpak Packaging Inc	2674	D	562 801-0281	5643
Feit Electric Company Inc (PA)	3645	C	562 463-2852	17535
Genesis Foods Corporation (DH)	2064	D	323 890-5890	1424
George Segovia	3499	F	562 699-8554	13943
Ibakeum Inc	2051	E	562 699-2296	1274
Jorge Segovia	3499	E	562 699-8554	13952
Kater-Crafts Incorporated	2789	E	562 692-0665	7606
Lombard Enterprises Inc	2752	E	562 692-7070	6954
Lubricating Specialties Co (PA)	2992	C	562 776-4000	9442
Madrid Inc	2435	F	562 404-9941	4379
Mannings Beef LLC	2011	D	562 908-1089	443
Metal Tite Products (PA)	3442	E	562 695-0645	12332
Noels Lighting Inc	3646	E	562 908-6181	17634
P W Wiring Systems LLC	3678	E	562 463-9055	19407
P-W Western Inc	3443	E	562 463-9055	12403
Pacific Coast Feather LLC	2392	C	562 222-5560	3737
Pacific Coast Feather Cushion (DH)	2392	C	562 801-9995	3738
Palace Textile Inc	3552	D	323 587-7756	14778
Pass & Seymour Inc	3643	A	562 505-4072	17485
Precision Deburring Services	3541	D	562 944-4497	14400
Qve Inc	3491	E	626 961-0114	13731
Reeve Store Equipment Company (PA)	2542	D	562 949-2535	5164
Rouchon Industries Inc	3577	F	310 763-0336	15843
Spiral Ppr Tube & Core Co Inc	2655	E	562 801-9705	5494
Suez Wts Services Usa Inc	3589	D	562 942-2200	16120
Tube Bending Llc	3498	F	562 692-5829	13909
W P Keith Co Inc	3567	E	562 948-3636	15277
Whittier Fertilizer Company	2873	D	562 699-3461	9079

PILOT HILL, CA - El Dorado County

Company	SIC	EMP	PHONE	ENTRY #
Ao Sky Corporation	3812	F	415 717-9901	21256

PINEDALE, CA - Fresno County

Company	SIC	EMP	PHONE	ENTRY #
Pacific Door & Cabinet Company	2431	E	559 439-3822	4208

PINOLE, CA - Contra Costa County

Company	SIC	EMP	PHONE	ENTRY #
Cameron International Corp	3533	D	510 928-1480	14216
Clemes & Clemes Inc	3429	F	510 724-2036	11946

PIONEER, CA - Amador County

Company	SIC	EMP	PHONE	ENTRY #
Pine Grove Group Inc	3699	E	209 295-7733	20042

PISMO BEACH, CA - San Luis Obispo County

Company	SIC	EMP	PHONE	ENTRY #
Alliance Ready Mix Inc	3273	F	805 556-3015	11034
Entropy Enterprises LLC	3841	F	805 305-1400	22441

PITTSBURG, CA - Contra Costa County

Company	SIC	EMP	PHONE	ENTRY #
Agra Tech Inc	3448	F	925 432-3342	12912
All Spec Sheet Metal Inc	3444	F	925 427-4900	12471
Atlas Pallet Corp	2448	E	925 432-6261	4452
Baker Filtration	3589	E	925 473-9659	16017
Bay Area Drilling Inc	1442	F	925 427-7574	346
Biozone Laboratories Inc (DH)	2834	F	925 473-1000	8083
Biozone Laboratories Inc	2834	E	925 431-1010	8084
Bishop-Wisecarver Corporation (PA)	3499	D	925 439-8272	13924
Black Diamond Manufacturing Co	3599	F	925 439-9160	16325
California Expanded Met Pdts	3448	E	925 473-9340	12924
Chrome Deposit Corp	3471	D	925 432-4507	13371
Creative Concepts Holdings LLC (HQ)	2087	F	949 705-6584	2253
Dow Chemical Company	2821	D	925 432-3165	7830
Frase Enterprises	3644	E	510 856-3600	17514
Generon Igs Inc	3569	E	925 431-1030	15325
Granberg Pump and Meter Ltd	3546	F	707 562-2099	14705
Hammond Enterprises Inc	3499	E	925 432-3537	13945
Hasa Inc	2812	E	661 259-5848	7663
Hospital Systems Inc	3845	D	925 427-7800	22985
K2 Pure Solutions LP	3589	D	925 203-1196	16062
K2 Pure Solutions Nocal LP	2899	E	647 776-0273	9265
Marble Shop Inc (PA)	3281	E	925 439-6910	11262
Merit Ends Inc	3444	E	925 427-2500	12665
Nustar Logistics LP	1311	F	925 427-6880	66
Petsport Usa Inc	3999	E	925 439-9243	24209
Praxair Inc	2813	D	925 427-1051	7707
Praxair Inc	3548	E	925 427-1950	14737
Qg Printing II Corp	2752	A	925 432-9740	7059
Ramar International Corp (PA)	2024	E	925 439-9009	690
Ramar International Corp	2011	E	925 432-4267	449
Tulkoff Food Products West Inc	2035	E	925 427-5157	937
USS-Psco Inds A Cal Jint Ventr (PA)	3312	A	800 877-7672	11426

PIXLEY, CA - Tulare County

Company	SIC	EMP	PHONE	ENTRY #
Cacciatore Fine Wns & Olv Oil (PA)	2084	F	559 757-9463	1674
Correa Pallet Inc (PA)	2448	E	559 757-1790	4462
Gfp Ethanol LLC	2869	E	559 757-3850	9007
J D Heiskell Holdings LLC	2048	EMP	559 757-3135	1139

PLACENTIA, CA - Orange County

Company	SIC	EMP	PHONE	ENTRY #
Aero Pacific Corporation (PA)	3728	D	714 961-9200	20710
Aero Pacific Corporation	3728	E	714 961-9200	20711
Alva Manufacturing Inc	3451	E	714 237-0925	13011
Anderson Bat Company LLC	3949	D	714 524-7500	23503
Arlon Graphics LLC	3081	C	714 985-6300	9696
Arnold Electronics Inc	3672	F	714 646-8343	18426
Atlas Match LLC	3999	D	714 993-3328	24046
Auger Industries Inc	3599	F	714 577-9350	16288
Bestest International	3823	E	714 974-8837	21552
Bioseal	3841	E	714 528-4695	22375
Btm-Beartech Manufacturing	3451	F	714 550-1700	13017
Caldigit Inc	3572	F	714 572-6668	15517
Cardinal Health 414 LLC	2834	E	714 572-9900	8100
Cinton	2672	E	714 961-8808	5557
CMi Precision Machining LLC	3599	E	714 528-3000	16388
CMi Precision Machining LLC	3599	E	714 528-3000	16389
Coast Aerospace Mfg Inc	3441	E	714 893-8066	12136
Cvc Audio & Video Supply Inc	3695	E	714 526-5725	19859
D & D Security Resources Inc (PA)	3699	E	714 985-9409	19941
Dee Engineering Inc (PA)	3714	E	714 979-4990	20311
Diversified Mfg Tech Inc	3544	F	714 577-7000	14508
Diversified Testing Service	3825	F	714 986-2250	21741
Eisel Enterprises Inc	3272	E	714 993-1706	10920
Excello Circuits Inc	3672	F	714 993-0560	18476
Farrs Custom Carbide Inc	3545	F	800 684-0411	14631
Foremost Precision Pdts Inc	3599	F	714 961-0165	16508
Gerard Roof Products LLC (DH)	3444	E	714 529-0407	12598
Hai Advnced Mtl Spcialists Inc	3399	F	714 414-0575	11840
Handy Service Corporation	2822	F	714 632-7832	7905
Hartwell Corporation (DH)	3429	C	714 993-4200	11958
HI Tech Solder	3356	F	714 572-1200	11630
Industrial Metal Finishing	3471	F	714 628-8808	13430
J B Tool Inc	3599	F	714 993-7173	16600
Jbb Inc	3699	E	888 538-9287	19991
Jet Abrasives Inc	3291	E	323 588-1245	11296
Keesee Tank Company	3443	F	714 528-1814	12393
Kipe Molds Inc	3544	F	714 572-9576	14533
L & M Machining Corporation	3678	D	714 414-0923	19400
Label Specialties Inc	2759	F	714 961-8074	7377
Las Colinas	3589	F	714 528-8100	16065
Marie Joann Designs Inc	2399	F	714 996-0550	3954
Microplex Inc	3674	F	714 630-8220	19005
Nalco Wtr Prtrtment Sltons LLC	3589	F	714 792-0708	16077
Nelson Case Corporation	2441	F	714 528-2215	4445
Packers Food Products Inc	2037	E	913 262-6200	961
Paul Dosier Associates Inc	3541	F	714 556-7075	14399
Power Pros Racg Exhust Systems	3714	F	714 777-3278	20422
Powertye Manufacturing	3613	F	714 993-7400	17157
Precision Waterjet Inc	3599	F	888 538-9287	16855
Progress Group	3714	F	714 630-9017	20428
Quikturn Prof Scrnprinting Inc	2759	F	800 784-5419	7458
R&Js Business Group Inc	2097	F	714 224-1455	2419
Richfield Engineering Inc	3443	E	714 524-3741	12414
Rotech Engineering Inc	3679	F	714 632-0532	19712
Sapphire Chandelier LLC	3646	E	714 630-3660	17641
Sapphire Manufacturing Inc	3446	E	714 401-3117	12889
Soft Touch Inc	2759	F	714 524-3382	7488
Southern Cal Tchnical Arts Inc	3599	E	714 524-2626	16954
Spacewall Inc	2435	F	714 941-1300	4384
Spyder Manufacturing Inc	3524	F	714 528-8010	14135
Superior Processing	3471	F	714 524-8525	13517
Totally Radical Associates Inc	3544	F	714 630-2740	14581
US Computers Inc	3577	F	714 528-0514	15879
Vanderveer Industrial Plas LLC (PA)	3083	E	714 579-7700	9769
Vertex Lcd Inc	3679	E	714 223-7111	19782
West Coast Metal Stamping Inc	3469	E	714 792-0322	13296
Western Mill Fabricators Inc	2599	E	714 993-3667	5263

PLACERVILLE, CA - El Dorado County

Company	SIC	EMP	PHONE	ENTRY #
Applied Control Electronics	3625	F	530 626-5181	17252
Boeger Winery Inc	2084	F	530 622-8094	1662
California Integration Coordin	3672	F	530 626-6168	18442
Chili Bar LLC	1429	F	530 622-3325	326
Dillon Precision Incorporated	3599	F	530 672-6794	16441
El Dorado Gold Panner Inc	2711	F	530 626-5057	5842
El Dorado Truss Coinc	2439	E	530 622-1264	4403
Gist Inc	3965	D	530 644-8000	23766
Lava Springs Inc	2084	E	530 621-0175	1859
Mother Lode Printing & Pubg Co	2711	D	530 344-5030	5982
Norden Millimeter Inc	3663	F	530 642-9123	18201
R-Quest Technologies LLC	3577	F	530 621-9916	15833
Rucker Mill & Cabinet Works	2434	F	530 621-0236	4346
Sierra Foothills Fudge Factory	2064	F	530 644-3492	1459
Sweet Septic Systems Inc (PA)	3272	F	530 622-8768	11010

Company	SIC	EMP	PHONE	ENTRY #
Vintage Transport Inc	3715	F	530 622-3046	20520

PLAYA DEL REY, CA - Los Angeles County

Company	SIC	EMP	PHONE	ENTRY #
Chipton-Ross Inc	3721	D	310 414-7800	20572
Keith Nichols	2084	E	310 305-0397	1838
L-Nutra Inc	2834	F	310 245-1724	8252
Mold USA	3544	E	310 823-6653	14544
Sheer Design Inc	2844	D	310 306-2121	8840

PLAYA VISTA, CA - Los Angeles County

Company	SIC	EMP	PHONE	ENTRY #
1on1 LLC	7372	E	310 448-5376	24296
Belkin Inc	3651	C	800 223-5546	17773
Chownow Inc	7372	D	888 707-2469	24488
Dimensional Plastics Corp	3089	E	305 691-5961	10070
Honest Company Inc (PA)	2341	C	310 917-9199	3537
Microsoft Corporation	7372	D	213 806-7300	24916

PLEASANT GROVE, CA - Sutter County

Company	SIC	EMP	PHONE	ENTRY #
A Teichert & Son Inc	3273	E	916 991-8170	11030

PLEASANT HILL, CA - Contra Costa County

Company	SIC	EMP	PHONE	ENTRY #
Castle Hill Holdings Inc	3842	F	925 943-1119	22712
Chemsw Inc	7372	F	707 864-0845	24487
Clark - Pacific Corporation	3272	D	925 746-7176	10905
Elson Electric	3699	F	925 464-7461	19960
Mosaic Brands Inc	3999	F	925 322-8700	24178
Phasespace Inc (PA)	3861	F	925 945-6533	23186
Samil Power US Ltd	3674	A	925 930-3924	19135
Storus Corporation	3429	F	925 322-8700	11997

PLEASANTON, CA - Alameda County

Company	SIC	EMP	PHONE	ENTRY #
10x Genomics Inc (PA)	2836	F	925 401-7300	8522
A&P Calibrations Inc	3699	F	925 417-6608	19894
Accsys Technology Inc	3699	E	925 462-6949	19898
Accusplit (PA)	3873	F	925 290-1900	23215
Alameda Newspapers Inc	2711	B	209 832-6144	5755
American Bottling Company	2086	D	925 251-3001	2093
Archeyy & Friends LLC	2047	E	703 579-7649	1105
Astex Pharmaceuticals Inc (DH)	2834	D	925 560-0100	8048
Avatier Corporation (PA)	7372	E	925 217-5170	24402
Axcelis Technologies Inc	3829	B	510 979-1970	22169
Biomer Technology LLC	2836	F	925 426-0787	8536
Blanco Basura Beverage Inc	2082	C	888 705-7225	1571
Boresha International Inc	2095	E	925 676-1400	2329
Boyd Corporation (DH)	2891	F	209 236-1111	9133
Cadence Design Systems Inc	7372	F	925 895-3202	24467
Carl Ziss X-Ray Microscopy Inc	3844	D	925 701-3600	22929
Cemex Cnstr Mtls PCF LLC	3273	E	925 846-2824	11062
Central Precast Concrete Inc	3272	F	925 417-6854	10899
Cerebrotech Medical Systems (PA)	3841	F	925 399-5392	22400
Cisco Systems Inc	3577	A	925 223-1006	15713
Clorox Company	2842	F	925 368-6000	8634
Compserv Inc	3679	F	415 331-4571	19499
Contra Costa Newspapers Inc	2711	D	925 847-2123	5813
Conxtech Inc (PA)	3441	C	510 264-9111	12142
Cooper Bussmann LLC	3629	F	925 924-8500	17338
Cooper Companies Inc (PA)	3851	C	925 460-3600	23086
Coopervision Inc	3851	D	925 251-6600	23087
Crazyondigital Inc	3651	E	925 294-9432	17786
Custom Blenders Corporation	2841	F	510 635-4352	8590
Deltatrak Inc (PA)	3829	E	925 249-2250	22187
Desert Sky Machining Inc	3599	E	925 426-0400	16432
Diablo Molding & Trim Company	3442	F	925 417-0663	12309
E2e Mfg LLC	3469	E	925 862-2057	13197
Eclipse Data Technologies Inc	3695	F	925 224-8880	19860
Ellie Mae Inc (PA)	7372	C	925 227-7000	24605
EMC Corporation	3572	F	925 425-1400	15532
EMC Corporation	3572	F	925 948-9000	15533
EMC Corporation	3572	F	925 600-6800	15535
Full Spectrum Analytics Inc (PA)	3826	F	925 485-9000	21961
Fusion Mphc Holding Corp	7372	C	925 201-2500	24678
Gitacloud Inc	7372	F	925 519-5965	24694
Handcraft Tile Inc	3255	F	408 262-1140	10799
Imagex Inc	2752	F	925 474-8100	6875
Inneos LLC	3827	F	925 226-0138	22088
Integenx Inc (HQ)	3821	D	925 701-3400	21477
Intermec Technologies Corp	3577	F	925 738-1100	15768
Interson Corp	3845	E	925 462-4948	22991
Inverse Solutions Inc	3599	E	925 931-9500	16591
It Concepts LLC	3827	F	925 401-0010	22093
Kapsch Trafficcom Usa Inc	3625	F	925 225-1600	17281
Leaf Healthcare Inc	3845	F	925 621-1800	22997
Leo Lam Inc	2752	F	925 484-3690	6943
Liqwiz LLC	3827	F	925 285-3100	22099
Lucerne Foods Inc	2099	E	925 951-4724	2590
Metamaterial Tech USA Inc	3827	F	650 993-9223	22107
Millennium Graphics Inc	2754	F	925 602-0635	7207

Employment Codes: A=Over 500 employees, B=251-500,
C=101-250, D=51-100, E=20-50, F=10-19

2019 California
Manufacturers Register

© Mergent Inc. 1-800-342-5647

1435

G E O G R A P H I C

	SIC	EMP	PHONE	ENTRY #
Natus Medical Incorporated **(PA)**	3845	B	925 223-6700	23024
Neocatena Networks Inc	3699	F	650 200-7340	20024
Neotract Inc **(DH)**	3841	F	925 401-0700	22552
New Source Technology LLC	3845	F	925 462-6888	23025
Oculeve Inc	3841	F	415 745-3784	22566
Optimum Design Associates Inc **(PA)**	3679	D	925 401-2004	19674
Oracle America Inc	7372	D	925 694-3314	25001
Oracle Corporation	7372	B	877 767-2253	25019
Oracle Systems Corporation	7372	B	925 694-3000	25034
Peridot Corporation	3495	E	925 461-8830	13799
Phoenix Technology Group Inc	3827	F	925 485-1100	22123
Pleasanton Main St Brewry Inc	2082	F	925 462-8218	1620
Pleasanton Ready Mix Concrete	3273	E	925 846-3226	11157
Pleasanton Tool & Mfg Inc	3599	E	925 426-0500	16848
Polycom Inc	3661	C	925 924-6151	17982
Positronics Incorporated	3549	F	925 931-0211	14762
Printpack Inc	2673	C	925 469-0601	5615
Purotecs Inc	3559	F	925 215-0380	15013
Rapidwerks Incorporated	3089	F	925 417-0124	10326
Real-Time Radiography Inc	3845	F	925 416-1903	23039
RMC Pacific Materials Inc **(DH)**	3241	C	925 426-8787	10771
RMC Pacific Materials Inc	3273	E	925 846-2824	11162
Roche Pharmaceuticals	2834	E	908 635-5692	8368
Sanarus Medical Incorporated	3841	F	925 460-6080	22612
Sanders Orthodontic Lab Inc	3843	F	925 251-0019	22908
Simpson Manufacturing Co Inc **(PA)**	3399	C	925 560-9000	11850
Simpson Strong-Tie Company Inc **(HQ)**	3449	C	925 560-9000	12993
Simpson Strong-Tie Intl Inc **(DH)**	3449	D	925 560-9000	12996
Software Development Inc	7372	E	925 847-8823	25192
Solta Medical Inc **(DH)**	3845	F	510 786-6946	23050
Thoratec Corporation **(DH)**	3845	F	925 847-8600	23059
Titan Photonics Inc	3661	F	510 687-0488	18001
Trireme Medical LLC	3841	D	925 931-1300	22656
Veeva Systems Inc **(PA)**	7372	C	925 452-6500	25321
Vertiv Corporation	3613	B	925 734-8660	17169
Visioneer Inc **(HQ)**	3577	E	925 251-6300	15883
Wefea Inc	3695	E	925 218-1839	19891
Zeltiq Aesthetics Inc **(DH)**	3841	E	925 474-2500	22684
Zoho Corporation **(HQ)**	7372	E	925 924-9500	25374

PLS VRDS PNSL, CA - Los Angeles County

	SIC	EMP	PHONE	ENTRY #
Converging Systems Inc	3577	F	310 544-2628	15721

PLUMAS LAKE, CA - Yuba County

	SIC	EMP	PHONE	ENTRY #
Packaging Specialists Inc	2448	F	530 742-8441	4494
Placer Waterworks Inc	3441	E	530 742-9675	12229

PLYMOUTH, CA - Amador County

	SIC	EMP	PHONE	ENTRY #
6630 Andis Wines C O Perf	2084	F	209 245-6177	1636
Acm Machining Inc	3599	E	916 804-9489	16213
Domaine De La Terre Rouge	2084	F	209 245-4277	1730
Ramador Inc **(PA)**	2084	F	209 245-6979	1936
Ren Acquisition Inc	2084	E	209 245-6979	1945
Sierra Sunrise Vineyard Inc	2084	E	209 245-6942	1975
Villa Toscano Winery	2084	E	209 245-3800	2043

POINT RICHMOND, CA - Contra Costa County

	SIC	EMP	PHONE	ENTRY #
Deepflight	3731	F	510 236-3422	20994

POLLOCK PINES, CA - El Dorado County

	SIC	EMP	PHONE	ENTRY #
Dan Arens and Son Inc	2411	F	530 644-6307	3984

POMONA, CA - Los Angeles County

	SIC	EMP	PHONE	ENTRY #
A E T C O Inc	2499	E	909 593-2521	4603
A/C Folding Gates	3446	E	909 629-3026	12822
Able Iron Works	3446	E	909 397-5300	12823
Acratech Inc	3599	E	909 392-5722	16216
American Rotary Broom Co Inc	3991	E	909 629-9117	23786
Analytical Industries Inc	3823	E	909 392-6900	21548
Atr Technologies Incorporated	3446	E	909 399-9724	12834
Avery Dennison Corporation	2672	C	626 304-2000	5555
Aw Industries Inc	2511	D	909 629-1500	4674
Baughn Engineering Inc	3825	F	909 392-0933	21729
Benjamin Moore & Co	2851	D	909 444-0390	8885
Bio Cybernetics International	3842	F	909 447-7050	22705
Boom Industrial Inc	3559	D	909 495-3555	14923
Bragel International Inc	2342	E	909 598-8808	3547
Bright Glow Candle Company Inc **(PA)**	3999	E	909 469-0119	24052
Ca-WA Corp	3069	E	909 868-0630	9597
Cabinets & Doors Direct Inc	2434	F	909 629-3388	4280
California Acrylic Inds Inc **(HQ)**	3999	E	909 623-8781	24055
California Plastix Inc	2673	E	909 629-8288	5589
Camlever Inc	3531	E	909 629-9669	14152
Casa Herrera Inc **(PA)**	3556	C	909 392-3930	14840
Consolidated Foundries Inc	3324	E	909 595-2252	11511
Consolidated Laundry LLC	3582	E	323 232-2417	15928
Cooltec Refrigeration Corp	3585	E	909 865-2229	15947

	SIC	EMP	PHONE	ENTRY #
Copp Industrial Mfg Inc	3444	E	909 593-7448	12539
CPS Wood Works Inc	2431	F	909 326-1102	4129
D G U Trading Corporation	3231	E	909 469-1288	10689
Da-Ly Glass Corp	3231	E	323 589-5461	10690
De Larshe Cabinetry LLC	2431	F	909 627-2757	4140
Deers Merchandise Inc	3269	F	909 869-8619	10830
Delphi Control Systems Inc	3823	F	909 593-8099	21569
Desiccare Inc	3295	E	909 444-8272	11319
Diagnostixx California Corp	3841	E	909 482-0840	22423
DOT Blue Safes Corporation	3499	E	909 445-8888	13936
Dow Hydraulic Systems Inc	3594	F	909 596-6602	16164
Ekko Material Hdlg Eqp Mfg Inc	3799	F	909 212-1962	21227
Electrocube Inc **(PA)**	3679	D	909 595-1821	19528
Epic Printing Ink Corp	3555	F	909 598-6771	14806
Equipment Design & Mfg Inc	3444	E	909 594-2229	12574
Essential Pharmaceutical Corp	2834	E	909 623-4565	8150
Everbrite West LLC	3993	F	909 468-0861	23869
FDS Manufacturing Company **(PA)**	2679	D	909 591-1733	5711
Floracraft Corporation	3086	F	909 620-4410	9843
G Powell Electric	7694	E	909 865-2291	25460
Gemini Aluminum Corporation	3354	E	909 595-7403	11587
General Nucleonics Inc	3829	F	909 593-4985	22206
Gonzalez Feliciano	2431	F	909 236-1372	4161
Gould & Bass Company Inc	3825	E	909 623-6793	21765
Gutierrez Grading	2759	F	909 397-8717	7339
Hamilton Sundstrand Corp	3826	F	909 593-3581	21964
Hamilton Sundstrand Spc Systms	3829	D	909 593-3581	22210
Headwaters Incorporated	3272	F	909 627-9066	10935
Holland & Herring Mfg Inc	3599	E	909 469-4700	16571
Image Distribution Services	2752	F	909 599-7680	6872
In House Custom Decals	2759	E	909 613-1403	7352
Inca Pallets Supply Inc	2448	E	909 622-1414	4480
Industrial Design Products	3537	F	909 468-0693	14328
Inland Envelope Company	2677	D	909 622-2016	5675
J & K Orthopedics Inc	3842	F	909 621-1180	22756
J E S Disc Grinding Inc	3599	F	909 596-3823	16603
Jacks Technologies & Inds Inc	3559	F	909 865-2595	14974
Juell Machine Coinc	3599	E	909 594-8164	16635
K-1 Packaging Group	2752	E	626 964-9384	6918
K-Max Health Products Internat	2023	F	909 455-0158	625
Kc Pharmaceuticals Inc	2834	E	909 598-9499	8246
Kelly & Thome	3599	E	909 623-2559	16651
Kensington Protective Products	2394	E	909 469-1240	3793
Kerber Industries Inc	3999	E	909 319-0877	24147
Kittrich Corporation **(PA)**	2591	C	714 736-1000	5199
Ld Smart Inc	3571	F	626 581-8887	15443
Lightwave Pdl Inc	3645	F	909 548-3677	17544
Lippert Components Mfg Inc	3231	E	909 628-5557	10714
Lock-Ridge Tool Company Inc	3469	D	909 865-8309	13242
Los Pericos Food Products LLC	2099	E	909 623-5625	2588
Lur Inc	3446	E	909 623-4999	12876
Luxor Industries International	2431	E	909 469-4757	4185
Marge Carson Inc **(PA)**	2512	D	626 571-1111	4794
Martin Purefoods Corporation	2013	F	909 865-4440	505
Med-Pharmex Inc	2834	F	909 593-7875	8270
Mil-Spec Magnetics Inc	3677	E	909 598-8116	19347
Mitchell Processing LLC	3069	E	909 519-5759	9637
Nancys Tortilleria & Mini Mkt	2099	E	909 629-5889	2613
Natural Envmtl Protection Co	2821	E	909 620-8028	7856
Noark Electric (usa) Inc	3699	E	626 330-7007	20031
Numatech West (kmp) LLC	2653	D	909 706-3627	5440
Pacific Bridge Packaging Inc	3411	F	909 598-1988	11864
Pacific Wtrprfing Rstrtion Inc	2899	E	909 444-2452	9296
Performnce Engineered Pdts Inc	3089	D	909 594-7487	10272
Phenix Enterprises Inc **(PA)**	3713	E	909 469-0411	20224
Pomona Quality Foam LLC	3086	D	909 628-7844	9876
Precision Pwdred Met Parts Inc	3399	E	909 595-5656	11846
Pregis	3086	E	909 469-8100	9877
Premium Pallet Inc	2448	F	909 868-9621	4501
Quality Container Corp	2671	F	909 482-1850	5536
R & S Automation Inc	3442	F	800 962-3111	12339
R & S Mfg Southern Cal Inc	3442	F	909 596-2090	12342
Rbf Group International	2521	F	626 333-5700	4965
Rbm Conveyor Systems Inc	3556	F	909 620-1333	14880
Rd Metal Polishing Inc	3471	E	909 594-8393	13489
Real Plating Inc	3471	E	909 623-2304	13490
Regal Cultured Marble Inc	3281	F	909 802-2388	11276
Robertsons Ready Mix Ltd	3273	E	909 623-9185	11168
ROC-Aire Corp	3599	E	909 784-3385	16911
Ronford Products Inc	3089	E	909 622-7446	10341
Royal Cabinets Inc	2434	A	909 629-8565	4344
Royal Industries Inc	2434	E	909 629-8565	4345
Siena Decor Inc	3952	F	909 895-8585	23711
Silpak Inc **(PA)**	2822	F	909 625-0056	7908
Sky One Inc	3262	F	909 622-3333	10810

Company	SIC	EMP	PHONE	ENTRY #
Specialty Car Wash System	3589	F	909 869-6300	16110
Stainless Fixtures Inc	2599	E	909 622-1615	5255
Structural Composites Inds LLC (DH)	3443	E	909 594-7777	12429
Superior Duct Fabrication Inc	3444	C	909 620-8565	12777
T & T Box Company Inc	2657	F	909 465-0848	5510
Technical Anodize	3353	F	909 865-9034	11582
Tesorx Pharma LLC (PA)	2834	F	909 595-0500	8410
Trademark Hoist Inc	3536	E	909 455-0801	14303
Traffic Sensor Corporation	3694	E	909 468-4625	19848
Travelers Choice Travelware	3161	D	909 529-7688	10540
Traxx Corporation	3999	D	909 623-8032	24276
Tree Island Wire (usa) Inc	3315	B	909 595-6617	11462
Tri-J Metal Heat Treating Co (PA)	3398	F	909 622-9999	11835
Tri-J Metal Heat Treating Co	3398	F	909 622-9999	11836
United Rotary Brush Corp	3991	E	909 629-9117	23797
Urocare Products Inc	3069	F	909 621-6013	9688
Valley Metal Treating Inc	3398	F	909 623-6316	11838
Valley Tool and Machine Co Inc	3599	F	909 595-2205	17033
Vefo Inc	3086	E	909 598-3856	9890
W R Meadows Inc	3272	E	909 469-2606	11016
Wan LI Industrial Dev Inc	3694	F	909 594-1818	19852
Westcoast Brush Mfg Inc	3991	E	909 627-7170	23799
Williams Sign Co	3993	F	909 622-5304	24005
Win-Holt Equipment Corp	3537	F	909 625-2624	14353
World Trend Inc (PA)	3991	F	909 620-9945	23800
Worthington Cylinder Corp	3443	C	909 594-7777	12443
Yawitz Inc	3645	E	909 865-5599	17573
Yf Manufacture Inc	3269	F	626 768-0029	10840
Yoshimasa Display Case Inc	2541	E	213 637-9999	5122

PORT HUENEME, CA - Ventura County

Company	SIC	EMP	PHONE	ENTRY #
Consoldted Precision Pdts Corp	3365	C	805 488-6451	11730
Cpp-Port Hueneme	3369	C	805 488-6451	11772
Dla Document Services	2752	E	805 982-4310	6790
Ironman Magazine	2721	E	805 385-3500	6198
Pac Foundries Inc	3365	C	805 986-1308	11748
Prime Alloy Steel Castings Inc	3369	C	805 488-6451	11782
Raytheon Company	3812	F	805 985-6851	21397
Stellar Biotechnologies Inc	2834	F	805 488-2147	8397
United States Dept of Navy	3728	E	805 989-5402	20965

PORTER RANCH, CA - Los Angeles County

Company	SIC	EMP	PHONE	ENTRY #
Jevin Enterprises Inc	3021	E	818 408-0488	9472

PORTERVILLE, CA - Tulare County

Company	SIC	EMP	PHONE	ENTRY #
Beckman Coulter Inc	3826	C	559 784-0800	21909
Chiapa Welding Inc (PA)	7692	F	559 784-3400	25395
Distributors Processing Inc	2087	F	559 781-0297	2255
Endurequest Corporation	3089	E	559 783-9220	10091
Foster Poultry Farms	2015	B	559 793-5501	542
Horizon International Ltd	3589	F	559 781-4640	16049
Hubbell Incorporated	3643	E	559 783-0470	17472
Noticiero Semanal Advertising	2711	D	559 784-5000	6002
Porterville Concrete Pipe Inc	3272	F	559 784-6187	10977
Quikrete Companies Inc	3272	F	559 781-1949	10985
Tdg Operations LLC	2281	D	559 781-4116	2947
Tri-K Truss Company	2439	F	559 784-8511	4430

PORTOLA, CA - Plumas County

Company	SIC	EMP	PHONE	ENTRY #
Coates Incorporated	3714	F	530 832-1533	20291
Wirta Logging Inc	2411	E	928 440-3446	4025

PORTOLA VALLEY, CA - San Mateo County

Company	SIC	EMP	PHONE	ENTRY #
Intuit Inc	7372	C	650 944-2840	24796
Westech Inv Advisors LLC (PA)	2038	E	650 234-4300	1020

POTTER VALLEY, CA - Mendocino County

Company	SIC	EMP	PHONE	ENTRY #
Matthews Skyline Logging Inc	2411	E	707 743-2890	4002

POWAY, CA - San Diego County

Company	SIC	EMP	PHONE	ENTRY #
Advanced Engineering & EDM Inc	3599	F	858 679-6800	16227
Advanced Enginering and EDM	3599	E	858 679-6800	16228
Advanced Machining Tooling Inc	3544	E	858 486-9050	14472
Aldila Inc	3949	C	858 513-1801	23494
Aldila Golf Corp	3949	C	858 513-1801	23495
Aldila Materials Technology (DH)	2895	E	858 513-1801	9218
Alfa Scientific Designs Inc	2835	D	858 513-3888	8459
Alta Solutions Inc	3825	F	858 668-5200	21718
American Ceramic Technology (PA)	3842	F	619 992-3104	22697
Apricorn	3577	E	858 513-2000	15670
Broadcast Microwave Services (PA)	3663	C	858 391-3050	18056
Brooks Automation Inc	3559	F	858 527-7000	14925
Cohu Inc (PA)	3825	C	858 848-8100	21736
Component Surfaces Inc	3471	E	858 513-3656	13378
Creative Foods LLC	2099	E	858 748-0070	2495
Darmark Corporation	3599	D	858 679-3970	16423
Data Device Corporation	3769	E	631 567-5600	21190
Data Device Corporation	3769	E	858 503-3300	21191

Company	SIC	EMP	PHONE	ENTRY #
Decision Sciences Med Co LLC	3845	E	858 602-1600	22971
Delta Design Inc (HQ)	3569	B	858 848-8000	15313
Delta Design Littleton Inc (HQ)	3825	F	858 848-8100	21740
Df Grafix Inc	2752	F	858 866-0858	6783
Digital One Printing Inc	2759	F	858 278-2228	7296
Digitalpro Inc	2759	D	858 874-7750	7298
Disguise Inc (HQ)	2389	E	858 391-3600	3654
Eagle Mold Technologies Inc	3089	E	858 530-0888	10081
Economy Printing	2752	E	858 679-8630	6803
Electron Imaging Incorporated	3826	F	858 679-1569	21950
EPC Power Corp	3629	E	858 748-5590	17341
Franklins Inds San Diego Inc	3599	E	858 486-9399	16514
Gaines Manufacturing Inc	3444	E	858 486-7100	12593
General Atomic Aeron	3721	F	858 455-4560	20579
General Atomic Aeron (DH)	3721	B	858 312-2810	20585
General Atomic Aeron	3721	B	858 312-2543	20586
Hanger Prsthetcs & Ortho Inc	3842	F	858 487-4516	22745
Harmonic Design Inc	3621	E	858 391-9085	17201
Hme Hospitality & Specialty Co	3669	E	858 535-6139	18331
Hoist Fitness Systems Inc	3949	D	858 578-7676	23586
Honeywell International Inc	3724	F	858 513-1223	20653
Honeywell International Inc	3724	A	858 848-3187	20660
Honeywell International Inc	3724	D	858 679-4140	20661
Honeywell International Inc	3724	E	858 513-6391	20662
Horizon Engineering Inc	3599	F	858 679-0785	16573
Imagine That Unlimited	3993	F	858 566-8868	23897
Integrity Municpl Systems LLC	3589	F	858 486-1620	16056
Jds Technologies	3679	F	858 486-8787	19599
K-Tube Corporation	3317	D	858 513-9229	11481
Kinder Scientific Company LLC	3629	F	858 679-1515	17345
L & T Precision Corporation	3444	C	858 513-7874	12640
Liberty Diversified Intl Inc	2653	C	858 391-7302	5435
Martellotto Inc	2084	F	619 567-9244	1871
Mesa Label Express Inc	2759	F	858 668-2820	7406
Micron Machine Company	3599	E	858 486-5500	16743
Mitchell Repair Info Co LLC (HQ)	2741	E	858 391-5000	6529
Mobile Mini Inc	3448	E	858 578-9222	12950
Mytee Products Inc	3589	E	858 679-1191	16075
Network Printing & Copy Center	2752	F	858 695-8221	6990
Oasis Materials Company LP	3679	E	858 486-8846	19667
Olaes Enterprises Inc	2329	E	858 679-4450	3183
Osram Sylvania Inc	3641	B	858 748-5077	17434
Oussoren Eppel Corporation	3993	E	858 483-6770	23938
Plastifab San Diego	3083	E	858 679-6600	9761
Production Assmbly Systems Inc	3549	E	858 748-6700	14763
Pure Forge	3714	F	760 201-0951	20430
Quality Steel Fabricators Inc	3449	E	858 748-8400	12991
Quatro Composites LLC	3624	C	712 707-9200	17241
Revolution Enterprises Inc	3949	F	858 679-5785	23635
Rugged Systems Inc	3571	C	858 391-1006	15479
San Diego Crating & Pkg Inc	2653	F	858 748-0100	5456
Seaspace Corporation	3663	E	858 746-1100	18246
Securus Inc	3446	E	858 391-0414	12891
Seirus Innovative ACC Inc	3949	E	858 513-1212	23650
Smoothreads Inc	2396	E	800 536-5959	3921
Softub Inc (PA)	3999	D	858 602-1920	24247
Somacis Inc	3672	C	858 513-2200	18611
Southern California Carbide	3541	E	858 513-7777	14413
Spooners Woodworks Inc	2541	D	858 679-9086	5104
Streeter Printing	2752	F	858 278-6611	7119
Sunstar Spa Covers Inc (HQ)	3999	E	858 602-1950	24258
Teck Advanced Materials Inc (DH)	3674	F	858 391-2935	19215
Teledyne Instruments Inc	3823	E	760 754-2400	21664
Teledyne Instruments Inc	3812	C	858 842-2600	21439
Teledyne Instruments Inc	3699	E	425 492-7400	20088
Tern Design Ltd	3823	E	760 754-2400	21665
Thyssenkrupp Bilstein Amer Inc	3714	E	858 386-5900	20465
Toray Membrane Usa Inc	3589	F	714 678-8832	16126
Toray Membrane Usa Inc (DH)	2899	D	858 218-2360	9312
Traffic Control & Safety Corp	3993	F	858 679-7292	23994
Traylor Management Inc (PA)	2741	F	858 486-7700	6606
United Security Products Inc	3699	E	800 227-1592	20095
Valley Metals LLC	3317	E	858 513-1300	11489
Vitrek LLC	3825	F	858 689-2755	21885
Wartsila Dynmc Positioning Inc (DH)	3625	E	858 679-5500	17322
Zmb Industries LLC	3999	F	858 842-1000	24293

PRINCETON, CA - Colusa County

Company	SIC	EMP	PHONE	ENTRY #
AA Production Services Inc	1381	E	530 982-0123	91

QUAIL VALLEY, CA - Riverside County

Company	SIC	EMP	PHONE	ENTRY #
Q I S Inc	3669	F	951 244-0500	18355

QUINCY, CA - Plumas County

Company	SIC	EMP	PHONE	ENTRY #
Feather Publishing Company Inc (PA)	2711	E	530 283-0800	5848

RAMONA, CA - San Diego County

Company	SIC	EMP	PHONE	ENTRY #
Blaha Oldrih	3545	F	760 789-9791	14609
EMD Millipore Corporation	3826	F	760 788-9692	21953
Gerald Gentellalli	3949	F	760 789-2094	23569
Hockin Diversfd Holdings Inc	3564	F	760 787-0510	15159
Millwork Co	2431	F	760 788-1533	4193
Ramona Home Journal	2711	F	760 788-8148	6023
Ramona Mining & Manufacturing	3915	F	760 789-1620	23346
S D Drilling	1389	F	760 789-5658	268

RANCHO CORDOVA, CA - Sacramento County

Company	SIC	EMP	PHONE	ENTRY #
A Teichert & Son Inc	1442	E	916 351-0123	342
Acm Machining Inc (PA)	3599	E	916 852-8600	16214
Aerojet Rocketdyne Inc (HQ)	3728	A	916 355-4000	20715
Ampac Fine Chemicals LLC (HQ)	2834	B	916 357-6880	8026
Arteez	2759	F	916 631-0473	7240
Atlas Granite & Stone	2541	F	916 638-7100	5039
Aztec Machine Co Inc	3599	F	916 638-4894	16293
Bmb Metal Products Corporation	3444	E	916 631-9120	12506
Cesca Therapeutics Inc (PA)	3821	D	916 858-5100	21461
Chemical Technologies Intl Inc	3589	F	916 638-1315	16023
Custom Furniture Design Inc	2434	F	916 631-6300	4289
D3 Led LLC (PA)	3993	E	916 669-7408	23854
E D M Sacramento Inc	3599	E	916 851-9285	16459
Elmco & Assoc (PA)	3088	C	916 383-0110	9899
Energy Operations Management	1311	F	916 859-4700	56
Fencer Enterprises LLC	3315	F	916 635-1700	11440
Folsom Ready Mix Inc (PA)	3272	E	916 851-8300	10929
Foremost Interiors Inc	3281	F	916 635-1423	11251
Form & Fusion Mfg Inc	3469	E	916 638-8576	13206
Form & Fusion Mfg Inc (PA)	3469	E	916 638-8576	13207
Group Manufacturing Services	3444	F	916 858-3270	12603
Guided Wave Inc	3827	E	916 638-4944	22080
Hadco Products Inc	2591	F	916 966-2409	5190
Infor (us) Inc	7372	C	916 921-0883	24766
Intercontinental N Mas	3999	E	916 631-1674	24130
J & C Custom Cabinets Inc	2521	E	916 638-3400	4952
J L Haley Enterprises	3599	C	916 631-6375	16604
Kargo Master Inc	3444	E	916 638-8703	12636
Loctronics Inc	3669	E	916 638-4900	18341
Metals USA Building Pdts LP	3355	E	916 635-2245	11622
Military Aircraft Parts	3599	E	916 635-8010	16748
Motivational Systems Inc	3993	E	916 635-0234	23931
Nca Laboratories Inc	3651	F	916 852-7029	17837
Nidec Motor Corporation	3534	B	916 638-4011	14254
Nightingale Vantagemed Corp (HQ)	7372	D	916 638-4744	24965
Pabco Building Products LLC (HQ)	3275	E	510 792-1577	11223
Pacful Inc (PA)	2752	D	916 233-1488	7009
Penfield Products Inc	3444	E	916 635-0231	12712
Perfect Image Printing Inc	2759	F	916 631-8350	7433
Precision Flight Controls	3699	F	916 414-1310	20045
Renaissance Food Group LLC (HQ)	2099	E	916 638-8825	2652
Residential Ctrl Systems Inc	3822	E	916 635-6784	21525
Resq Manufacturing	3999	E	916 638-6786	24222
River City Print and Mail Inc	2752	E	916 638-8400	7086
River City Printers LLC	2752	E	916 638-8400	7087
Rubicon Express (PA)	3559	F	916 858-8575	15023
Scribner Engineering Inc	3089	E	916 638-1515	10367
Scribner Plastics	3089	E	916 638-1515	10368
Solaron Pool Heating Inc (PA)	3569	F	916 858-8146	15362
Specialty Products Design Inc	3714	F	916 635-8108	20453
Stewart Tool Company	3545	D	916 635-8321	14682
Stroppini Enterprises	3537	F	916 635-8181	14348
Sunrise Mfg Inc (PA)	2679	E	916 635-6262	5736
Taylor Communications Inc	2761	E	916 368-1200	7560
Taylor Wings Inc	3444	E	916 851-9464	12784
Teledyne Defense Elec LLC	3679	C	916 638-3344	19751
Teledyne Wireless LLC	3679	C	916 638-3344	19758
Toffee Boutique Inc	2064	F	916 638-8462	1462
Volcano Corporation	3845	B	916 281-2932	23070
Volcano Corporation	3845	B	916 638-8008	23072
Vsp Labs Inc (PA)	3827	B	866 569-8800	22145
Ztech	3585	F	916 635-6784	16003

RANCHO CUCAMONGA, CA - San Bernardino County

Company	SIC	EMP	PHONE	ENTRY #
Accraply Inc	3565	E	909 605-8200	15190
Advanced Chemical Tech Inc	2819	E	800 527-9607	7749
Advantage Adhesives Inc	2891	E	909 204-4990	9128
Air Liquid Healthcare	2813	E	909 899-4633	7668
Airgas Usa LLC	2813	E	909 899-4670	7688
Akaranta Inc	2834	F	909 989-9800	8007
All Star Precision	3541	F	909 944-8373	14359
American Furniture Aliance Inc	2519	F	323 804-5242	4905
American HX Auto Trade Inc	3711	D	909 484-1010	20126
Ameron International Corp	3272	E	909 944-4100	10873
Ameron International Corp	3272	D	909 944-4100	10875

Company	SIC	EMP	PHONE	ENTRY #
Ameron International Corp	3317	C	909 944-4100	11473
Ameron International Corp	3272	E	909 944-4100	10876
Amphastar Pharmaceuticals Inc (PA)	2834	C	909 980-9484	8028
Aqua Measure Instrument Co	3829	F	909 941-7776	22164
Aquamar Inc	2091	C	909 481-4700	2288
AR Square	3161	C	909 985-5995	10515
Arga Controls Inc	3823	F	626 799-3314	21549
Avery Dennison Corporation	2672	C	909 987-4631	5551
B & G Electronic Assembly Inc	3679	E	909 608-2077	19455
B3digigrafx	2752	E	909 259-0153	6679
BASF Construction Chem LLC	2899	E	909 987-1758	9224
Bellasposa Wedding Center	2335	F	909 758-0176	3299
Bernell Hydraulics Inc (PA)	3594	F	909 899-1751	16162
Butler Home Products LLC	3991	F	909 476-3884	23788
C&D Zodiac Inc	3728	C	909 652-9700	20763
California Box II	2653	E	909 944-9202	5393
Califrnia Nwspapers Ltd Partnr	2711	B	909 987-6397	5791
Cargill Meat Solutions Corp	2011	E	909 476-3120	424
Carpenter Technology Corp	3312	E	909 476-4000	11386
Charlies Beer Company USA LLC	2082	F	909 980-0436	1578
Chick Publications Inc	2731	E	909 987-0771	6326
Ciuti International Inc	2079	F	909 484-1414	1538
Cold Jet LLC	3559	F	513 831-3211	14929
Comar LLC	3089	C	909 985-2750	10032
Comfort-Pedic Mattress USA	2515	F	909 810-2600	4856
Continental Graphics Corp	2752	E	909 758-9800	6754
Cooper Tire & Rubber Company	3011	F	909 481-6437	9464
Criticalpoint Capital LLC	2822	D	909 987-9533	7904
Cypress Magnetics Inc	3677	F	909 987-3570	19331
Davidson Optronics Inc	3829	F	626 962-5181	22185
Dicarlo Concrete Inc	3652	F	909 261-4294	17890
Digital Check Technologies Inc	3577	E	909 204-4638	15729
Diverse Optics Inc	3089	E	909 593-9330	10073
Doubleco Incorporated	3452	D	909 481-0799	13066
Dow Chemical International	2821	E	909 987-6261	7831
Ds Cypress Magnetics Inc	3678	F	909 987-3570	19387
Eagle Laboratories LLC	3851	D	909 481-0011	23090
Eddie Motorsports	3429	F	909 581-7398	11953
Electro Switch Corp	3613	C	909 581-0855	17143
Electro Switch Corp	3679	E	909 581-0855	19525
EMD Specialty Materials LLC	3672	F	909 987-9533	18474
ES Kluft & Company Inc (PA)	2515	C	909 373-4211	4860
Everidge Inc	3585	E	909 605-6419	15957
Executive Safe and SEC Corp (PA)	3499	E	909 947-7020	13941
Faust Printing Inc	2752	E	909 980-1577	6812
Firth Rixson Inc	3462	E	909 483-2200	13099
Fluorescent Supply Co Inc	3646	E	909 948-8878	17609
Formosa Meat Company Inc	2013	F	909 987-0470	484
Fresh Peaches Incorporated (PA)	2253	F	909 980-0172	2839
Frozen Bean Inc	2087	F	855 837-6936	2264
Future Molds Inc	3544	F	909 989-7398	14518
Gasket Specialties Inc	3053	F	909 987-4724	9532
General Micro Systems Inc (PA)	3571	D	909 980-4863	15417
Global Aerostructures	3728	F	909 987-4888	20827
GME Mfg Inc	3728	F	909 989-4478	20828
Golden Island Jerky Co Inc (DH)	2013	C	844 362-3222	488
Golden Island Jerky Co Inc	2013	C	844 362-3222	489
Golden Vantage LLC	2499	F	626 255-3362	4624
Good-West Rubber Corp (PA)	3069	D	909 987-1774	9617
Goodwest Rubber Linings Inc	3069	F	888 499-0085	9618
Graham Packaging Co Europe LLC	3085	C	909 989-5367	9799
Graham Packaging Company LP	3089	E	909 484-2900	10126
Gruma Corporation	2096	C	909 980-3566	2392
Gw Partners International	3229	F	909 980-1010	10644
Hartwell Corporation	3469	D	909 987-4616	13214
Heritage Bag Company	2673	F	909 899-5554	5603
Hillshire Brands Company	2013	B	909 481-0760	491
Hotech Corporation	3674	E	909 987-8828	18876
Icon Identity Solutions Inc	3993	D	909 942-5100	23895
Ifco Systems Us LLC	2448	E	909 484-4332	4479
Inland Signs Inc	3993	E	909 581-0699	23902
Inland Tek Inc	7372	F	909 900-8457	24773
Intermetro Industries Corp	3496	E	909 987-4731	13835
Ironwood Packaging LLC	3081	E	909 581-0077	9711
J T Walker Industries Inc	3442	E	909 481-1909	12321
JCPM	3599	E	909 484-9040	16617
Jet Cutting Solutions Inc	2452	E	909 948-2424	4576
Jsj Inc Corrugated	2653	E	909 987-4746	5432
Judith Von Hopf Inc	2541	E	909 481-1884	5073
Kindred Litho Incorporated	2752	E	909 944-4015	6922
Klatch Coffee Inc	2095	E	909 981-4031	2358
Lanic Engineering Inc (PA)	3728	E	877 763-0411	20864
Lee Augustyn Inc	2752	F	909 483-0688	6940
Lee Maxton Inc	2752	F	909 483-0688	6941
Lotusse LLC	3111	E	909 218-7757	10464

Company	SIC	EMP	PHONE	ENTRY #
Mape Engineering Inc	3724	F	626 338-7964	20669
Marino Enterprises Inc	3728	E	909 476-0343	20873
Material Handling Solutions	3537	F	909 908-9663	14336
Matheson Tri-Gas Inc	2813	E	909 758-5464	7703
Mercury United Electronics Inc	3679	E	909 466-0427	19646
Mes Enterprises	2591	F	909 484-6863	5202
Metal Coaters California Inc	3479	D	909 987-4681	13618
Milcomm Inc	3728	F	626 523-8305	20888
Mindrum Precision Inc	3824	E	909 989-1728	21692
Mizkan Americas Inc	2099	E	909 484-8743	2608
Modular Office Solutions Inc	2522	D	909 476-4200	4996
Molex LLC	3678	F	909 803-1362	19402
Nci Group Inc	3448	F	909 987-4681	12953
New World Medical Incorporated	3841	F	909 466-4304	22556
New York Toy Exchange Inc	3944	F	626 327-4547	23451
Newtex Industries Inc	3999	D	323 277-0900	24189
Norm Tessier Cabinets Inc	2434	F	909 987-8955	4332
Ohadi Management Corporation	3841	F	909 625-2000	22567
Omega Plastics Corp	2673	C	909 987-8716	5612
Pac-Rancho Inc (DH)	3324	C	909 987-4471	11519
Pacer Technology	2891	D	909 987-0550	9159
Pacific Plastic Technology Inc	3083	E	909 987-4200	9755
Pacific Pprbd Converting LLC (PA)	2679	F	909 476-6466	5722
Pamco Machine Works Inc	3599	F	909 941-7260	16824
Panolam Industries Intl Inc	2493	E	909 581-1970	4600
Paramount Machine Co Inc	3599	F	909 484-3600	16830
Paramunt Plstic Fbricators Inc	3089	F	909 987-4757	10267
Perimeter Solutions LP	2819	E	909 983-0772	7796
Pitbull Gym Incorporated	3089	F	909 980-7960	10275
Plaxicon Holding Corporation	3085	C	909 944-6868	9804
Pneudraulics Inc	3812	B	909 980-5366	21381
Pneumatic Scale Corporation	3565	F	909 527-7600	15223
Polyone Corporation	2821	E	909 987-0253	7872
Precision Aerospace Corp	3728	D	909 945-9604	20913
Prestige Mold Incorporated	3544	D	909 980-6600	14562
Prime Converting Corporation	2679	F	909 476-9500	5727
Proulx Manufacturing Inc	3089	E	909 980-0662	10315
Puricle Inc	2842	E	909 466-7125	8670
Pyramid Mold & Tool	3544	E	909 476-2555	14565
Qst Ingredients and Packg Inc	2099	F	909 989-4343	2646
Quality Aerostructures Company	3724	E	909 987-4888	20675
R H Pattern	3543	E	909 484-9141	14466
Rafco-Brickform LLC (PA)	3545	D	909 484-3399	14671
Rancho Cucamonga Maverick	2711	F	909 466-6445	6024
Rancho Technology Inc	3577	F	909 987-3966	15834
Raytheon Company	3812	D	909 483-4040	21405
Reyes Coca-Cola Bottling LLC	2086	C	909 980-3121	2197
Ritemp Refrigeration Inc	3632	F	909 941-0444	17383
Russell-Stanley	3089	D	909 980-7114	10351
Santa Fe Packaging Corp	2673	F	562 921-8991	5620
Satori Seal Corporation	3069	F	909 987-8234	9675
Schellinger Spring Inc	3493	F	909 373-0799	13754
Searing Industries Inc	3312	C	909 948-3030	11419
Siemens Rail Automation Corp	3669	C	909 532-5405	18363
Signworld America Inc (PA)	3993	F	844 900-7446	23975
Skyreach L S Extrsons USA Corp	3355	F	909 204-3550	11624
Smith International Inc	1389	C	909 906-7900	275
Socco Plastic Coating Company	3479	E	909 987-4753	13660
Spectrasensors Inc	3826	E	909 980-4238	22020
Steelscape Inc	3479	E	909 987-4711	13667
Superior Tank Co Inc (PA)	3443	E	909 912-0580	12431
Swabplus Inc	3053	E	909 987-7898	9560
T & R Lumber Company (PA)	2449	D	909 899-2383	4537
T E B Inc	3599	F	909 941-8100	16982
Tamco Inc (DH)	3449	D	909 899-0660	13000
Tervita (us Operations) LLC	1381	F	909 899-7504	121
Thermostatic Industries Inc	3292	F	323 277-0900	11313
Toner2print Inc	3577	F	909 972-9656	15870
Transcendia Inc	3081	F	909 944-9981	9732
Tree Island Wire (usa) Inc	3315	D	800 255-6974	11463
TSE Worldwide Press Inc	2741	F	909 989-8282	6607
United Advg Publications Inc	2721	F	909 466-1480	6282
Usl Parallel Products Cal	2869	E	909 980-1200	9046
Vacmet Inc	3479	E	909 948-9344	13677
Vanguard Tool & Mfg Co Inc	3469	E	909 980-9392	13292
Volant Cool Air Intakes Inc	3089	F	909 476-7225	10431
W R Grace & Co - Conn	2891	F	909 466-4610	9180
Walco Machines Co	3559	E	909 483-3333	15047
Weiser Iron Inc	3312	E	909 429-4600	11428
Wessex Industries Inc	3498	F	562 944-5760	13912
West Coast Lanyards Inc	3999	F	877 447-6030	24288
Western Metal Dctg Co Coil Div	2752	F	909 987-2506	7180
Western Wire Works Inc	3496	F	909 483-1186	13863
Wine Makers Inc	2084	F	909 481-5050	2063
Woodland Products Co Inc	2541	F	909 622-3456	5120

Company	SIC	EMP	PHONE	ENTRY #
Zodiac Aerospace	3721	F	909 652-9700	20636

RANCHO DOMINGUEZ, CA - Los Angeles County

Company	SIC	EMP	PHONE	ENTRY #
Adf Incorporated	3446	E	310 669-9700	12829
Aerol Co Inc (PA)	3365	E	310 762-2660	11720
Best Carbide Cutting Tools Inc	3541	D	310 464-8050	14363
Bi Nutraceuticals Inc (HQ)	2087	E	310 669-2100	2245
Buff and Shine Mfg Inc	3291	E	310 886-5111	11289
Carol Anderson Inc (PA)	2335	E	310 638-3333	3300
Dresser-Rand Company	3563	F	310 223-0600	15123
Enlink Geoenergy Services Inc	3585	E	424 242-1200	15954
Fairway Import-Export Inc	3949	E	310 637-6162	23559
Giovanni Cosmetics Inc	2844	D	310 952-9960	8754
Grand General Accessories Mfg	3612	E	310 631-2589	17096
KT Engineering Corporation	3599	F	310 537-3818	16668
Laclede Inc	3843	E	310 605-4280	22889
Mars Food Us LLC (HQ)	2044	B	310 933-0670	1087
Masco Corporation	3432	D	313 274-7400	12039
Optodyne Incorporation	3663	E	310 635-7481	18208
Protective Industries Inc	3069	D	310 537-2300	9665
S L Fusco Inc (PA)	3541	E	310 868-1010	14407
Shercon Inc	3069	E	800 228-3218	9678
Simple Container Solutions Inc	2631	E	310 638-0900	5360
Southwestern Industries Inc (PA)	3541	D	310 608-4422	14414
Standard Wire & Cable Co (PA)	3357	E	310 609-1811	11676
Starled Inc	3679	E	310 603-0403	19735
Tda Magnetics LLC	3499	E	424 213-1585	13978
Team Manufacturing Inc	3469	E	310 639-0251	13284
Western Sheld Acquisitions LLC	2754	E	310 527-6212	7215

RANCHO MIRAGE, CA - Riverside County

Company	SIC	EMP	PHONE	ENTRY #
Fujisawa Bristol Corporation	2833	D	760 324-1488	7941
Kathy Ireland Worldwide	2331	F	310 557-2700	3249
Natures Baby Products Inc	2844	F	818 521-5054	8802
Tfx International	2834	F	760 836-3232	8413
Toro Company	3523	D	760 321-8396	14112

RANCHO PALOS VERDES, CA - Los Angeles County

Company	SIC	EMP	PHONE	ENTRY #
Gardner Denver Inc	3561	C	310 544-5710	15067
Powerstorm Holdings Inc	3691	F	424 327-2991	19813
Scott Craft Co	3599	F	323 560-3949	16933
Summit International Packg Inc	2671	E	626 333-3333	5539
Western Summit Mfg Corp	3081	D	626 333-3333	9735

RANCHO SANTA FE, CA - San Diego County

Company	SIC	EMP	PHONE	ENTRY #
Black Silver Enterprises Inc (PA)	2339	F	858 623-9220	3386
Wep Transport Holdings LLC	1382	F	858 756-1010	159
Western Energy Production LLC	1382	F	858 756-1010	160

RANCHO SANTA MARGARI, CA - Orange County

Company	SIC	EMP	PHONE	ENTRY #
Allstar Microelectronics Inc	3572	F	949 546-0888	15509
Foundation 9 Entertainment Inc (PA)	7372	C	949 698-1500	24667
Jacksam Corporation	3565	E	800 605-3580	15212
Lubrizol Corporation	2899	F	949 212-1863	9275

RAYMOND, CA - Madera County

Company	SIC	EMP	PHONE	ENTRY #
Cold Spring Granite Company	3281	E	559 689-3257	11242

RCHO STA MARG, CA - Orange County

Company	SIC	EMP	PHONE	ENTRY #
Amest Corporation	3674	F	949 766-9692	18693
Applied Manufacturing LLC	3841	A	949 713-8000	22339
Applied Medical Corporation (PA)	3841	C	949 713-8000	22340
Applied Medical Resources Corp (HQ)	3841	B	949 713-8000	22341
Ats Tool Inc	3544	E	949 888-1744	14481
Ats Workholding Inc	3545	D	800 321-1833	14603
C3 Biosciences Inc	2834	F	949 635-9963	8089
Car Sound Exhaust System Inc	3714	E	949 858-5900	20285
Car Sound Exhaust System Inc	3714	E	949 858-5900	20286
Chapmn-Wlters Intrcoastal Corp	3949	E	949 448-9940	23539
Control Components Inc (DH)	3491	B	949 858-1877	13713
Delfin Design & Mfg Inc	3089	E	949 888-4644	10063
Desco Manufacturing Company (PA)	3599	F	949 858-7400	16431
Eastman Kodak Company	3861	D	949 306-9034	23155
Ep Holdings Inc	3572	F	949 713-4600	15536
Extreme Precision LLC	3599	F	949 459-1062	16487
Fluid Research Corporation	3823	E	714 258-2350	21586
Form Grind Corporation	3599	F	949 858-7000	16509
Fortron/Source Corporation (PA)	3612	E	949 766-9240	17094
Glas Werk Inc	3229	E	949 766-1296	10643
Golden Spoon Frozen Yogurt	2024	F	949 888-8810	675
Grandis Metals Intl Corp	3356	F	949 459-2621	11629
Impact LLC	3679	E	714 546-6000	19575
Inform Decisions	7372	F	949 709-5838	24767
Light Composite Corporation	3429	D	949 858-8820	11970
Mc Products Inc	2899	F	949 888-7100	9277
Multicoat Products Inc	2851	E	949 888-7100	8921
Opulence International	2221	E	949 360-7611	2780
Palomar Products Inc	3669	D	949 858-8836	18352

Employment Codes: A=Over 500 employees, B=251-500,
C=101-250, D=51-100, E=20-50, F=10-19

2019 California
Manufacturers Register

© Mergent Inc. 1-800-342-5647

1439

GEOGRAPHIC

	SIC	EMP	PHONE	ENTRY #
Phyto Tech Corp	2834	E	949 635-1990	8338
Point Conception Inc	2339	E	949 589-6890	3483
Q-Mark Manufacturing Inc	3823	F	949 457-1913	21638
R C Products Corp	3429	D	949 858-8820	11985
Racepak LLC	3714	E	949 709-5555	20435
Racepak LLC	3711	E	888 429-4709	20165
Renaissnce Frnch Dors Sash Inc (PA)	2431	C	714 578-0090	4219
RPM Products Inc (PA)	3053	E	949 888-8543	9553
South Coast Stairs Inc	2431	E	949 858-1685	4234
Swiss-Micron Inc	3451	D	949 589-0430	13043

RED BLUFF, CA - Tehama County

	SIC	EMP	PHONE	ENTRY #
Amundson Tom Tmber Flling Cntr	2411	F	530 529-0504	3977
Electro Star Indus Coating Inc	3479	F	530 527-5400	13582
Foothill Ready Mix Inc	3273	E	530 527-2565	11108
Hanger Inc	3842	F	530 528-1795	22741
John Wheeler Logging Inc	2411	C	530 527-2993	3997
Lassen Forest Products Inc	2439	E	530 527-7677	4418
Medianews Group Inc	2711	E	530 527-2151	5965
Sierra Pacific Industries	2421	B	530 527-9620	4065
Tetrad Services Inc	3599	F	530 527-5889	16997
Walker Lithograph	2752	F	530 527-2142	7171

REDDING, CA - Shasta County

	SIC	EMP	PHONE	ENTRY #
A&M Timber Inc	2411	F	530 515-1740	3975
AB Medical Technologies Inc	3841	F	530 605-2522	22301
Absolute Machine	3599	E	530 242-6840	16204
Best Value Textbooks LLC	2731	E	530 222-5980	6313
Bundy and Sons Inc	2411	E	530 246-3868	3981
Cameron International Corp	3533	D	530 242-6965	14215
Captive-Aire Systems Inc	3444	C	530 351-7150	12526
Cdg Technology LLC	3624	F	530 243-4451	17236
Contech Engnered Solutions LLC	3443	F	530 243-1207	12381
Cook Concrete Products Inc	3272	E	530 243-2562	10908
Cummins Pacific LLC	3519	F	530 244-6898	14017
Dataray Incorporated	3826	F	530 472-1717	21944
David Beard	2434	F	530 244-1248	4292
Donn & Doff Inc	3842	F	530 241-4040	22718
Estate Granite & Marble	1411	F	530 241-7866	303
Ferrosaur Inc	3441	E	530 246-7843	12161
Fife Metal Fabricating Inc	3441	F	530 243-4696	12162
Franklin Logging Inc	2411	E	530 549-4924	3988
Gerlinger Fndry Mch Works Inc (PA)	3441	E	530 243-1053	12171
Great Northern Wheels Deals	2711	E	530 533-2134	5867
Heritage Woodworking Co Inc	2434	F	530 243-7215	4307
Innespace Productions	3732	F	530 241-2800	21045
J F Shea Co Inc	3273	E	530 246-2200	11123
Jar Ventures Inc	3993	E	530 224-9655	23906
John Fitzpatrick & Sons	2086	F	530 241-3216	2141
Kings Way Sales and Mktg LLC	3569	F	530 722-0272	15336
Lehigh Southwest Cement Co	3273	C	530 275-1581	11134
Mc Clellan Bottling Group	2086	F	530 241-2600	2149
McHale Sign Company Inc	3993	F	530 223-2030	23922
Metals Direct Inc	3444	E	530 605-1931	12672
Miniature Precision Inc	3599	F	530 244-4131	16756
Mobile Designs Inc	3354	F	530 244-1050	11597
Morts Custom Sheetmetal	3444	F	530 241-7013	12688
Norcal Respiratory Inc	3845	E	530 246-1200	23028
North Valley Candle Molds	3999	F	530 247-0447	24192
Redding Metal Crafters Inc	3444	F	530 222-4400	12736
Redding Printing Co Inc (PA)	2752	E	530 243-0525	7081
Reyes Coca-Cola Bottling LLC	2086	E	530 241-4315	2199
Rounds Logging Company	2411	E	530 247-0517	4008
Seco Manufacturing Company Inc	3829	C	530 225-8155	22262
Sell Lumber Corporation	2421	F	530 241-2085	4054
Sierra Pacific Industries	2421	F	530 226-5181	4056
Snl Group Inc	3531	F	530 222-5048	14191
Sof-Tek Integrators Inc	3825	F	530 242-0527	21850
Southern Alum Finshg Co Inc	3355	D	530 244-7518	11625
Spectrum Prosthetics/Orthotics	3842	F	530 243-4500	22817
Swa Mountain Gate	1442	F	530 221-3406	385
Technisoil Global Inc	2879	E	530 605-4881	9113
Universal Precast Concrete Inc	3272	F	530 243-6477	11013
Vss Emultech Inc (HQ)	2951	F	530 243-0111	9399
Warner Enterprises Inc	2411	E	530 241-4000	4019
William R Schmitt	2411	E	530 243-3069	4024
Wit Group	2086	F	530 243-4447	2235
Wonder Metals Corporation	3442	F	530 241-3251	12356
Yates Gear Inc	3199	D	530 222-4606	10585

REDLANDS, CA - San Bernardino County

	SIC	EMP	PHONE	ENTRY #
American Custom Coach	3713	F	909 796-4747	20188
Ashley Furniture Inds Inc	2511	A	909 825-4900	4672
California Prtg Solutions Inc	2759	E	909 307-2032	7263
Califrnia Nwspapers Ltd Partnr	2711	A	909 793-3221	5792
Caseworx Inc	2521	F	909 799-8550	4936

	SIC	EMP	PHONE	ENTRY #
Cemex USA Inc	3273	C	909 798-1144	11088
Clorox Products Mfg Co	2842	D	909 307-2756	8636
Coast To Coast Mfg LLC	3089	F	909 798-5024	10029
Continental Datalabel Inc	2679	E	909 307-3600	5706
Daryls Pet Shop	3999	E	909 793-1788	24074
Duden Enterprises Inc	2395	F	909 795-0160	3842
Engineerd Pnt Applications LLC	2851	F	626 737-7400	8905
Express Container Inc	2653	E	909 798-3857	5408
Fast Access Inc	3272	E	909 748-1245	10924
Loran Inc	3612	E	405 340-0660	17104
Plastics Plus Technology Inc	3089	E	909 747-0555	10290
Precision Hermetic Tech Inc	3679	D	909 381-6011	19690
Reader Magazine	2721	E	909 335-8100	6244
Redlands CCI Inc	3751	E	909 307-6500	21133
Rettig Machine Inc	7692	E	909 793-7811	25431
Sensit Inc	3822	F	909 793-5816	21527
Superior Building Products	3442	E	909 930-1802	12350
Teledyne Technologies Inc	3691	D	909 793-3131	19816
Van Craeynest Inc	3911	F	415 362-1025	23328
Venturedyne Ltd	3564	D	909 793-2788	15184
Window Enterprises Inc	3442	E	951 943-4894	12355

REDONDO BEACH, CA - Los Angeles County

	SIC	EMP	PHONE	ENTRY #
Advanced Arm Dynamics (PA)	3842	E	310 372-3050	22690
Alcast Mfg Inc	3365	D	310 542-3581	11722
Athana International Inc	3572	F	310 539-7280	15514
B Dazzle Inc	3944	E	310 374-3000	23408
Body Glove International LLC	2329	E	310 374-3441	3140
Calpak Usa Inc	3672	E	310 937-7335	18443
Funktion Technologies Inc	3823	F	310 937-7335	21590
H3 High Security Solutions LLC	3482	E	310 373-2319	13683
Jariet Technologies Inc	3812	E	310 698-1001	21311
Mass Group	2752	E	310 214-2000	6963
Northrop Grumman Corporation	3812	F	310 812-4321	21366
Northrop Grumman Systems Corp	3663	C	310 812-5149	18202
Northrop Grumman Systems Corp	3721	B	310 812-4321	20610
Northrop Grumman Systems Corp	3721	B	310 812-1089	20614
Northrop Grumman Systems Corp	3721	B	310 812-4321	20615
Quantimetrix Corporation	2835	D	310 536-0006	8506
Raffaello Research Labs	2834	F	310 618-8754	8355
Spaceage Control Inc	3728	E	661 206-6666	20936
Sunset Islandwear	2261	F	310 372-7960	2896
Thorock Metals Inc	3341	E	310 537-1597	11569
Westend Software Inc (PA)	7372	F	310 370-0367	25348
Woodruff Corporation	3599	E	310 378-1611	17074

REDWOOD CITY, CA - San Mateo County

	SIC	EMP	PHONE	ENTRY #
AB Sciex LLC (HQ)	3826	D	877 740-2129	21890
Acelrx Pharmaceuticals Inc	2834	E	650 216-3500	7993
Actiance Inc	3446	E	650 631-6300	12827
Agiloft Inc	7372	E	650 587-8615	24339
Ai Industries LLC (PA)	3471	D	650 366-4099	13314
Alation Inc (PA)	7372	E	650 779-4440	24346
American Production Co Inc	3411	D	650 368-5334	11854
Apical Instruments Inc	3829	F	650 967-1030	22161
Applied Process Equipment	3599	F	650 365-6895	16275
Armo Biosciences Inc	2834	E	650 779-5075	8043
Astrazeneca Pharmaceuticals LP	2834	E	650 305-2600	8049
Auris Health Inc (PA)	3841	C	650 610-0750	22349
Avast Software Inc (PA)	7372	F	844 340-9251	24401
Avinger Inc	3841	D	650 241-7900	22351
Badgeville Inc	7372	E	650 323-6668	24407
Bay Precision Machining Inc	3599	E	650 365-3010	16309
Betterworks Systems Inc	7372	D	650 656-9013	24418
Biocentury Publications Inc (PA)	2711	E	650 595-5333	5778
Box Inc (PA)	7372	C	877 729-4269	24442
Brava Home Inc	3634	E	408 675-2569	17387
Bristol - Myers Sqibb Snnyvale	2834	F	609 897-2110	8087
Broadvision Inc (PA)	7372	D	650 331-1000	24455
Broadvision Rcao Broadvisi	2741	E	650 261-5100	6452
C3 Iot Inc	7372	C	650 503-2200	24459
Carbon Inc	3577	C	650 285-6307	15699
Ci Management LLC	3131	C	650 654-8900	10470
Coalign Innovations Inc	3841	E	888 714-4440	22406
Codexis Inc (PA)	2869	C	650 421-8100	9000
Coherus Biosciences Inc (PA)	2834	D	650 649-3530	8115
Coraid Inc (PA)	3572	D	650 517-9300	15526
Crystal Dynamics Inc	7372	E	650 421-7600	24534
D N G Cummings Inc	3993	E	650 593-8974	23853
Delphix Corp (PA)	7372	E	650 494-1645	24558
Douce De France	2051	F	650 369-9644	1234
Eclipse Metal Fabrication Inc	3444	E	650 298-8731	12568
Electronic Arts Inc (PA)	7372	B	650 628-1500	24600
Electronic Arts Redwood Inc (HQ)	3695	D	650 628-1500	19861
Ethical Naturals Inc	2833	F	650 336-1190	7938
Flywheel Software Inc	7372	E	650 260-1700	24656

Mergent email: customerrelations@mergent.com
1440

2019 California
Manufacturers Register

(P-0000) Products & Services Section entry number
(PA)=Parent Co (HQ)=Headquarters (DH)=Div Headquarters

Company	SIC	EMP	PHONE	ENTRY #
Friendslearn Inc	7372	F	734 678-8814	24673
Galen Robotics Inc	3841	F	408 502-5960	22458
Geneforge Inc	3825	F	650 219-9335	21762
Genelabs Technologies Inc (HQ)	2834	F	415 297-2901	8170
Genentech Inc	2834	B	650 216-2900	8176
Glasslab Inc	7372	E	415 244-5584	24695
Golden Octagon Inc	2051	D	650 369-8573	1265
Graffiti Entertainment LLC	3651	F	650 654-4800	17805
Granite Rock Co	2951	F	650 482-3800	9385
Grass Manufacturing Co Inc	3469	F	650 366-2556	13211
H N Lockwood Inc	3089	E	650 366-9557	10131
Holt Tool & Machine Inc	3312	F	650 364-2547	11399
Host Analytics Inc (HQ)	7372	F	650 249-7100	24738
Incline Therapeutics Inc	2834	F	650 241-6800	8219
Informatica LLC (DH)	7372	C	650 385-5000	24769
Instana Inc	7372	E	415 237-3245	24779
Internet Systems Cnsortium Inc	7372	F	650 423-1300	24786
Invoice2go Inc (PA)	7372	E	650 300-5180	24799
Ivalua Inc (HQ)	7372	E	650 930-9710	24808
Jobs & Careers Newspapers Inc	2711	F	650 367-6885	5893
Larson Electronic Glass Inc	3229	F	650 369-6734	10651
Lastline Inc (PA)	7372	E	805 456-7075	24847
Leland Stanford Junior Univ	2711	E	650 723-9434	5912
Mad Apparel Inc	2329	E	800 714-9697	3177
Menlo Therapeutics Inc	2834	E	650 486-1416	8277
Minerva Surgical Inc	3841	F	650 399-1770	22543
Mirapoint Software, Inc.	3663	D	650 286-7200	18184
Mongabay Org Corporation	2741	E	209 315-5573	6531
Monolith Materials Inc	2819	E	650 933-4957	7788
Mr Gears Inc	3599	F	650 364-7793	16775
Nanostellar Inc	3761	E	650 368-1010	21165
Neural Id LLC	3695	E	650 394-8800	19874
Nevro Corp	3841	B	650 251-0005	22555
Nextag Inc (PA)	2741	D	650 645-4700	6540
Nugen Technologies Inc	2819	E	650 590-3600	7791
Nvent Thermal LLC (DH)	3822	B	650 474-7414	21519
Oncomed Pharmaceuticals Inc	2834	D	650 995-8200	8317
Openwave Mobility Inc (PA)	7372	E	650 480-7200	24990
Oracle America Inc (HQ)	3571	A	650 506-7000	15469
Oracle America Inc	7372	F	408 702-5945	25000
Oracle Systems Corporation	7372	E	650 506-0300	25031
Oracle Systems Corporation	7372	E	650 506-5887	25033
Oratec Interventions Inc (DH)	3845	F	901 396-2121	23031
Oraya Therapeutics Inc	3841	E	510 456-3700	22575
Paw Prints Inc	2759	F	650 365-4077	7432
Paxata Inc	7372	D	650 542-7897	25051
Pdl Biopharma Inc	2836	E	650 454-1000	8572
Pebble Technology Corp	3873	E	888 224-5820	23223
Petersen Precision Engrg LLC	3599	C	650 365-4373	16843
Pierry Inc (PA)	7372	F	800 860-7953	25060
Precision Plastic LLC	3089	C	510 324-8676	10305
Prenav Inc	3812	F	650 264-7279	21382
Proteus Digital Health Inc (PA)	2836	C	650 632-4031	8577
Pulmonx Corporation (PA)	3841	E	650 364-0400	22592
Puredepth Inc (PA)	3577	F	408 394-9146	15831
Qwilt Inc (PA)	7372	F	866 824-8009	25102
Redwood Apps Inc	7372	F	408 348-3808	25121
Relypsa Inc	2834	B	650 421-9500	8359
Robertson Precision Inc	3674	F	650 363-2212	19129
Roxwood Medical Inc	3841	F	650 779-4555	22609
Rurisond Inc	3663	F	650 395-7136	18243
S F Enterprises Incorporated	3599	F	650 455-3223	16925
Sake Robotics Inc	3549	F	650 207-4021	14766
Salus North America Inc	3822	F	888 387-2587	21526
Singha North America Inc	2082	F	714 206-5097	1625
Skydio Inc	3812	F	408 203-8497	21432
Soccer 90	3949	F	650 599-9900	23655
Soleno Therapeutics Inc (PA)	2834	E	650 213-8444	8386
Sposato John	3663	F	408 215-8727	18262
Storm8 Inc	7372	F	650 596-8600	25224
Talos Corporation	3599	E	650 364-7364	16986
Te Connectivity Corporation	3643	F	650 361-2495	17496
Te Connectivity Corporation	3357	F	650 361-3333	11679
Te Connectivity Corporation	3643	B	650 361-2495	17498
Tilley Manufacturing Co Inc (PA)	3053	E	650 365-3598	9561
Trion World Network Inc	7372	F	650 394-1000	25296
Trion Worlds Inc	7372	B	650 631-9800	25297
Versant Corporation (HQ)	7372	F	650 232-2400	25329
Voyage Medical Inc	3841	E	650 503-7500	22678
Xtime Inc	3089	E	650 508-4300	10454

REDWOOD VALLEY, CA - Mendocino County

Company	SIC	EMP	PHONE	ENTRY #
Gregory Graziano	2084	F	707 485-9463	1796
Redwood Valley Gravel Products	3272	F	707 485-8585	10991

REEDLEY, CA - Fresno County

Company	SIC	EMP	PHONE	ENTRY #
Air-O Fan Products Corporation (PA)	3523	F	559 638-6546	14038
Durand-Wayland Machinery Inc (PA)	3523	E	559 591-6904	14065
Maxco Supply Inc	2631	D	559 638-8449	5355
Midvalley Publishing Inc	2711	E	559 638-2244	5971
Mission AG Resources LLC	2023	E	559 591-3333	632
Thiele Technologies Inc	3565	B	559 638-8484	15230
Valley Controls Inc	3823	F	559 638-5115	21673
Valley Packline Solutions	3556	E	559 638-7821	14894

RESEDA, CA - Los Angeles County

Company	SIC	EMP	PHONE	ENTRY #
Alumatec Inc	1381	D	818 609-7460	95
Audionics System Inc	3651	F	818 345-9599	17767
Hill Products Inc	3651	F	818 877-9256	17812
Rainbow Symphony Inc	2675	F	818 708-8400	5657
Test Laboratories Inc (PA)	2099	F	818 881-4251	2680

RIALTO, CA - San Bernardino County

Company	SIC	EMP	PHONE	ENTRY #
Advantage Business Forms Inc	2759	F	909 875-7163	7225
Biscomerica Corp	2052	C	909 877-5997	1354
Boral Roofing LLC	3272	D	909 822-4407	10889
Burlingame Industries Inc	3299	C	909 355-7000	11350
Calcraft Corporation	3441	F	909 879-2900	12127
Cemex Cnstr Mtls PCF LLC	3273	E	951 377-9657	11061
Columbia Steel Inc	3441	D	909 874-8840	12137
Dyell Machine (PA)	3599	E	909 350-4101	16452
Eagle Roofing Products Fla LLC (PA)	3259	E	909 822-6000	10801
Forest River Inc	3792	E	909 873-3777	21202
H Wayne Lewis Inc	3449	E	909 874-2213	12979
Kti Incorporated	3272	D	909 434-1888	10946
Legacy Vulcan LLC	1442	E	909 875-5180	371
Lippert Components Inc	3711	D	909 873-0061	20155
Martinez and Turek Inc	3599	C	909 820-6800	16718
Meerkat Inc	3599	F	909 877-0093	16735
Nelson Adams Inc	2531	E	909 256-8938	5022
Nelson Adams Naco Corporation	2511	E	909 256-8938	4726
Niagara Bottling LLC	2086	F	909 230-5000	2154
Solomon Colors Inc	2816	E	909 484-9156	7745
Spray Enclosure Technologies	3444	E	909 419-7011	12770
Techniform International Corp	3599	C	909 877-6886	16992
Uscps	3999	C	909 434-1888	24280
Villanueva Plastic Company Inc	3083	F	909 581-3870	9771

RICHMOND, CA - Contra Costa County

Company	SIC	EMP	PHONE	ENTRY #
A M T Metal Fabricators Inc	3441	E	510 236-1414	12098
AA Portable Power Corporation	3691	E	510 525-2328	19796
ACS Instrumentation Valves Inc	3491	D	510 262-1880	13699
Alion Energy Inc	3674	E	510 965-0868	18678
Amtecol Inc	2992	E	510 235-7979	9422
Andrus Sheet Metal Inc	3444	E	510 232-8687	12482
Ats Products Inc (PA)	3089	E	510 234-3173	9961
Bay Marine Boatworks Inc	3732	E	510 237-0140	21023
Bio-RAD Laboratories Inc	3826	B	510 724-7000	21924
Black Diamond Video Inc	3577	D	510 439-4500	15686
Black Point Products Inc	3661	E	510 232-7723	17926
BP Lubricants USA Inc	2992	E	510 236-6312	9425
BP West Coast Products LLC	1311	B	510 231-4724	32
Cemex Materials LLC	3273	E	510 234-3616	11083
Chemtrade Chemicals US LLC	2819	E	510 232-7193	7765
Chimes Printing Incorporated	2752	F	510 235-2388	6730
Coin Gllery of San Frncsco Inc	2542	F	510 236-8882	5134
Dicon Fiberoptics Inc (PA)	3679	C	510 620-5000	19512
Douglas & Sturgess Inc	3299	F	510 235-8411	11355
Eagle Systems Inc	3743	E	510 231-2686	21075
East Bay Brass Foundry Inc	3363	E	510 233-7171	11692
Ekso Bionics Inc (PA)	3559	D	510 984-1761	14945
Ekso Bionics Holdings Inc	3842	C	510 984-1761	22725
Galaxy Desserts	2053	E	510 439-3160	1394
Givens and Halpern Inc	2084	F	415 884-9999	1784
GK Welding Inc	7692	F	510 233-0133	25406
Hauser & Sons Inc	2591	F	510 234-8850	5191
Hero Arts Rubber Stamps Inc	3953	D	510 232-4200	23717
Hoefer Inc	3826	E	415 282-2307	21968
International Group Inc	2911	E	510 232-8704	9335
International Group Inc	2911	D	510 232-8704	9336
John Lompa	2759	F	510 965-6501	7365
Kodiak Precision Inc (PA)	3599	F	510 234-4165	16661
Linde LLC	2813	C	510 233-8911	7697
Metalset Inc	3441	E	510 233-9998	12210
Mom Enterprises Inc	2834	F	415 526-2710	8285
My True Image Mfg Inc	3842	D	510 970-7990	22776
Nady Systems Inc	3651	E	510 652-2411	17836
National Ewp Inc	1081	F	510 236-6282	12
Norman & Globus Inc	2731	F	510 222-2638	6372
Novacart	2621	F	510 215-8999	5318
Nutiva (PA)	2099	E	510 255-2700	2625

Employment Codes: A=Over 500 employees, B=251-500, C=101-250, D=51-100, E=20-50, F=10-19

	SIC	EMP	PHONE	ENTRY #
Oliso Inc	3634	F	415 864-7600	17399
Pacific Dry Goods Inc	2231	F	925 288-2929	2794
Paragon Machine Works Inc	3599	D	510 232-3223	16826
Parker-Hannifin Corporation	3823	D	510 235-9590	21630
Phoenix Day Co Inc	3645	F	415 822-4414	17555
Professional Finishing Inc	3471	D	510 233-7629	13484
R & K Industrial Products Co	3499	E	510 234-7212	13969
Richmond Metal Painting	3479	E	510 232-7541	13649
San Rafael Rock Quarry Inc	2951	E	510 970-7700	9397
Sealy Mattress Mfg Co Inc	2515	C	510 235-7171	4885
Siemens Industry Inc	3822	D	510 237-2325	21530
Stalker Software Inc	7372	E	415 569-2280	25217
String Letter Publishing Inc	2741	E	510 215-0010	6593
Sunwater Solar Inc	3433	F	650 739-5297	12093
Support Systems Intl Corp	3679	D	510 234-9090	19739
Tamalpais Coml Cabinetry Inc	2541	E	510 231-6800	5110
Thomas-Swan Sign Company Inc	3993	E	415 621-1511	23989
Tulip Pubg & Graphics Inc	2752	E	510 898-0000	7149
United Granite & Cabinets LLC	2434	F	510 558-8999	4362
Unovo LLC	3635	F	415 864-7600	17410
West Coast Fab Inc	3444	F	510 529-0177	12817
Wholesome Harvest Baking LLC	2051	C	510 231-7200	1343
Zygo Epo	3827	F	510 243-7592	22153

RICHVALE, CA - Butte County

	SIC	EMP	PHONE	ENTRY #
Wehah Farm Inc	2044	B	530 538-3500	1094

RIDGECREST, CA - Kern County

	SIC	EMP	PHONE	ENTRY #
American Ready Mix Inc	3273	F	760 446-4556	11040
Lockheed Martin Corporation	3812	C	760 446-1700	21342
Mpb Furniture Corporation	2512	F	760 375-4800	4800
Raytheon Company	3812	F	760 384-3295	21392
Service Rock Products Corp	3273	D	760 446-2606	11174
Sierra View Inc	2711	E	760 371-4301	6044
Structural Wood Systems	2439	F	760 375-2772	4426

RIO LINDA, CA - Sacramento County

	SIC	EMP	PHONE	ENTRY #
Cuora Corporation	2452	E	916 991-3028	4571

RIO VISTA, CA - Solano County

	SIC	EMP	PHONE	ENTRY #
Asta Construction Co Inc (PA)	1381	E	707 374-6472	97
California Resources Corp	1311	E	707 374-4109	40
Coughran Mechanical Services	3599	E	707 374-2100	16404
Dick Brown Technical Services	1381	F	707 374-2133	101
Dry Vac Environmental Inc (PA)	3826	E	707 374-7500	21948
I DES Inc	3823	E	707 374-7500	21600
Jim Graham Inc	1389	E	707 374-5114	229
Lindsay Trnsp Solutions Inc (HQ)	3272	D	707 374-6800	10954
Paul Graham Drilling & Svc Co	1381	C	707 374-5123	116
Resource Cementing LLC	1389	F	707 374-3350	264
Woodward Drilling Company	1381	E	707 374-4300	124

RIPON, CA - San Joaquin County

	SIC	EMP	PHONE	ENTRY #
Better Built Truss Inc	2439	E	209 869-4545	4392
California Nuggets Inc	2096	E	209 599-7131	2376
Franzia/Sanger Winery	2084	C	209 599-4111	1774
Gate-Or-Door Inc	7372	E	209 751-4881	24683
Guntert Zmmerman Const Div Inc	3531	E	209 599-0066	14173
Jackrabbit (PA)	3523	D	209 599-6118	14074
Kamper Fabrication Inc	3523	F	209 599-7137	14077
Ken Anderson	3273	E	209 604-8579	11124
Pearl Crop Inc	2076	E	209 982-9933	1516
Ripon Mfg Co	3556	E	209 599-2148	14882
Ripon Volunteer Firemans Assn	3711	F	209 599-4209	20168
Tetra Pak Processing Equip	2671	D	209 599-4634	5542
Wine Group Inc (HQ)	2084	C	209 599-4111	2062

RIVERBANK, CA - Stanislaus County

	SIC	EMP	PHONE	ENTRY #
Overholtzer Elvan	2499	E	209 869-2536	4640
Silgan Containers Mfg Corp	3411	E	209 869-3601	11870
Thunderbolt Sales Inc	2491	E	209 869-4561	4598
Thunderbolt WD Treating Co Inc (PA)	2491	E	209 869-4561	4599

RIVERDALE, CA - Fresno County

	SIC	EMP	PHONE	ENTRY #
C Case Company Inc	1389	E	559 867-3912	189

RIVERSIDE, CA - Riverside County

	SIC	EMP	PHONE	ENTRY #
220 Laboratories Inc	2844	C	951 683-2912	8688
220 Laboratories Inc (PA)	2844	C	951 683-2912	8689
Aarons Signs & Printing	3993	E	951 352-7303	23804
Accracutt Cabinets	2434	F	951 685-7322	4266
Accurate Metal Products Inc	3441	E	951 360-3594	12102
Acm Student Chapter At Ucr	7372	E	951 389-0713	24308
Acro-Spec Grinding Co Inc	3599	E	951 736-1199	16217
Adex Medical Inc	3842	E	951 653-9122	22689
Advanced Engrg Mlding Tech Inc	3089	E	951 656-6607	9928
Advanced Orthotic Designs	3842	E	951 710-1640	22693
Alectro Inc	3612	F	909 590-9521	17079

	SIC	EMP	PHONE	ENTRY #
Aleph Group Inc	3711	E	951 213-4815	20123
Aleph Group Inc	3841	F	951 213-4815	22324
Alpha Materials Inc	3273	E	951 788-5150	11038
Alstom Signaling Operation LLC	3669	C	951 343-9699	18307
AMA Plastics (PA)	3089	B	951 734-5600	9937
Amazon Environmental Inc (PA)	2851	E	951 588-0206	8875
American Quality Tools Inc	3545	E	951 280-4700	14598
AP Plastics	3089	F	951 782-0705	9951
Aqua Backflow and Chlorination	3671	F	909 598-7251	18381
Artech Industries Inc	3679	E	951 276-3331	19448
Arturo Campos	3471	F	951 300-2111	13337
Astro Seal Inc	3679	E	951 787-6670	19450
Auto Tech Engineering Inc	3714	E	909 428-9072	20260
BA Holdings (DH)	3443	E	951 684-5110	12362
Blacoh Fluid Controls Inc (PA)	3443	E	951 342-3100	12365
Blanchard Signs	3993	F	951 354-5050	23831
Blow Molded Products Inc	3089	E	951 360-6055	9985
Bottling Group LLC	2086	E	951 697-3200	2102
Bourns Inc (PA)	3677	C	951 781-5500	19323
Bourns Inc	3825	C	951 781-5690	21731
Brenner-Fiedler & Associates (PA)	3829	E	562 404-2721	22172
Brookhurst Mill	2048	F	951 688-3511	1124
C W Enterprises Inc	3648	F	951 786-9999	17678
California Interfill Inc	2844	F	951 351-2619	8713
Canine Caviar Pet Foods Inc	2048	E	714 223-1800	1125
Canyon Steel Fabricators Inc	3449	E	951 683-2352	12975
Captive-Aire Systems Inc	3444	E	951 231-5102	12525
Carbon Solutions Inc	3624	F	909 234-2738	17235
Cardinal Sheet Metal Inc	3444	F	951 788-8800	12527
Carlisle Interconnect Tech Inc	3315	E	951 788-0252	11433
Carpenter Co	3086	B	951 354-7550	9825
Cavco Industries Inc	2451	D	951 351-0378	4547
Cavco Industries Inc	2451	C	951 688-5353	4548
Celebrity Publishing LLC	2741	E	714 914-4635	6458
Champion Laboratories Inc	3714	F	951 275-0715	20289
City of Riverside	3589	D	951 351-6140	16025
Clarkwestern Dietrich Building	3444	F	951 360-3500	12532
Club Car LLC	3799	C	951 735-4675	21224
Cnc Machining Solutions Inc	3845	F	951 688-4267	22963
Coachworks Holdings Inc	3711	B	951 684-9585	20133
Connection Enterprises Inc	3643	F	951 688-8133	17455
Connector Kings Corporation	3678	F	951 710-1180	19380
Consolidated Cont Holdings LLC	3085	E	951 340-9390	9795
Criterion Automation Inc	3317	F	951 683-2400	11478
CT Coachworks LLC	3716	E	951 343-8787	20522
Cummings Resources LLC	3993	E	951 248-1130	23852
CV Wndows Dors Riverside Inc	3231	E	951 784-8766	10688
D L B Pallets (PA)	2448	F	951 360-9896	4465
D Mills Grnding Machining Inc	3599	F	951 697-6847	16417
D S McGee Enterprises Inc	2431	F	951 378-8473	4137
Dayton Superior Corporation	3315	D	951 782-9517	11436
Delta-Sigma Inc	3663	F	951 343-4005	18084
Desert Microsystems Inc	3823	E	951 682-3867	21570
DGA Machine Shop Inc	3599	F	951 354-2113	16434
Doan Inc	3523	F	951 275-2432	14061
Doka USA Ltd	3444	F	951 509-0023	12563
Dura Coat Products Inc (PA)	3479	D	951 341-6500	13577
E & R Pallets Inc	2448	F	951 790-1212	4467
Easy Networks Cabling	3679	F	951 742-8119	19522
Edge Plastics Inc (PA)	3089	E	951 786-4750	10086
Ejay Filtration Inc	3496	E	951 683-0805	13825
Eldorado National Cal Inc (HQ)	3711	B	951 727-9300	20137
Elisid Magazine	2721	E	619 990-9999	6156
Embroidery Outlet	2395	C	951 687-1750	3847
Esco Industries Inc	3462	F	951 782-2130	13097
Evans Walker Enterprises	3714	F	951 784-7223	20328
Everpac	3531	E	951 686-4560	14166
Everpac	3552	D	951 774-3274	14776
Fleetwood Homes Arizona Inc	2451	B	623 939-2600	4555
Fleetwood Homes Arizona Inc (DH)	2451	B	951 351-3000	4556
Fleetwood Homes California Inc (DH)	2451	E	951 351-2494	4557
Fleetwood Homes of Florida (DH)	2451	E	909 261-4274	4558
Fleetwood Homes of Idaho Inc	2451	C	951 354-3000	4559
Fleetwood Homes of Virginia	2451	C	951 351-3500	4561
Fleetwood Motor Homes-Califinc (DH)	3716	C	951 354-3000	20523
Fleetwood Travel Trlrs Ind Inc (DH)	3792	C	951 354-3000	21201
Fpc Graphics Inc	2752	E	951 686-0232	6826
Fusion Sign & Design Inc (PA)	3993	D	877 477-8777	23884
Future Tech Metals	3599	F	951 781-4801	16518
Gifts International Inc	3499	F	909 854-3977	13944
Glengarry Manufacturing Inc	3599	F	951 248-1111	16536
Global Circuit Solutions Inc	3672	F	951 353-2780	18495
Grech Motors LLC (PA)	7694	E	951 688-8347	25463
Greenscape Solutions Inc	3271	E	909 714-8333	10853
Harber All Natural Products	2844	F	347 921-1004	8764

Mergent email: customerrelations@mergent.com
1442

2019 California
Manufacturers Register

(P-0000) Products & Services Section entry number
(PA)=Parent Co (HQ)=Headquarters (DH)=Div Headquarters

Company	SIC	EMP	PHONE	ENTRY #
Harber Foods LLC (PA)	2844	F	347 921-1004	8765
Heritage Container Inc	2653	D	951 360-1900	5422
Hi-Rel Plastics & Molding Corp	3089	E	951 354-0258	10135
Hydraforce Incorporated	3561	F	951 689-3987	15076
Hydraforce Incorporated	3561	F	951 689-3987	15077
Hydraforce Incorporated	3561	F	951 689-3987	15078
Imperial Pipe Services LLC	3317	E	951 682-3307	11480
IMS Products Inc	3751	E	951 653-7720	21117
Inland Empire Foods Inc (PA)	2034	E	951 682-8222	883
Inland Empire Media Group Inc	2721	F	951 682-3026	6196
Innovative Design and Sheet ME	3444	E	951 222-2270	12621
Irrometer Company Inc	3829	E	951 689-1701	22219
It Retail Inc	7372	F	951 683-4950	24805
J & A Pallet Accessory Inc	2448	F	951 785-1594	4481
J D Tool & Machine Co Inc	3544	F	951 371-6652	14528
J&C Tapocik Inc	2389	F	951 351-4333	3661
Jacks Box & Crate LLC	2653	E	951 343-1790	5430
Jaffa Precision Engrg Inc	3599	F	951 278-8797	16611
Jimenez Mexican Foods Inc	2032	E	951 351-0102	761
Jlg Industries Inc	3531	C	951 509-1227	14177
Joa Corporation (PA)	3842	E	951 785-4411	22758
John Bean Technologies Corp	3556	E	951 222-2300	14863
K & N Engineering Inc (PA)	3751	A	951 826-4000	21119
Keurig Dr Pepper Inc	2086	D	951 341-7500	2142
L & L Louvers Inc	3442	F	951 735-9300	12325
L T Seroge Inc	3699	F	951 354-7141	20001
LSI Products Inc	3714	D	951 343-9270	20389
Luxfer Inc (DH)	3728	D	336 578-4515	20870
Luxfer Inc	3354	C	951 684-5110	11593
Luxfer Inc	3463	C	951 351-4100	13126
M G Deanza Acquisition Inc	3599	F	951 683-3080	16702
Mackie International Inc (PA)	2024	E	951 346-0530	682
Magnotek Manufacturing Inc	3677	D	951 653-8461	19344
Main Steel LLC	3471	D	951 789-3010	13449
Marlin Machine Products	3599	F	951 275-0050	16714
Martin Marietta Materials Inc	1423	E	951 682-0918	323
Mdi East Inc (HQ)	3089	D	951 509-6918	10202
Mega Machinery Inc	3559	F	951 300-9300	14989
Merchants Metals LLC	3315	F	951 686-1888	11449
Metal Container Corporation	3411	C	951 354-0444	11862
Metric Machining (PA)	3541	E	909 947-9222	14394
Metropolitan News Company	2711	E	951 369-5890	5969
Micromold Inc	3089	F	951 684-7130	10211
Millers Fab & Weld Corp	3441	E	951 359-3100	12211
Molded Devices Inc (PA)	3089	E	480 785-9100	10219
Morgan Truck Body LLC	3713	D	951 689-0800	20220
Mortan Industries Inc	3069	F	951 682-2215	9643
Neoplast Inc	3089	F	951 300-9300	10234
Nevada Window Supply Inc	2431	F	951 300-0100	4199
Newbasis West LLC	3272	C	951 787-0600	10960
Newman Bros California Inc (PA)	2431	E	951 782-0102	4200
ODonnell Manufacturing Inc	3599	F	562 944-9671	16802
Oldcast Precast (DH)	3272	E	951 788-9720	10963
Oldcastle Precast Inc	3272	E	951 683-8200	10969
Omf Performance Products	3799	F	951 354-8272	21237
OSI Industries LLC	3999	E	951 684-4500	24198
Owen Trailers Inc	3715	E	951 361-4557	20507
Pacific Consolidated Inds LLC	3569	D	951 479-0860	15345
pacific Molding Inc	3089	F	951 683-2100	10257
Paradise Ranch	2389	F	951 776-7736	3674
PCI Holding Company Inc (PA)	3569	C	951 479-0860	15350
Pepsi-Cola Metro Btlg Co Inc	2086	B	909 885-0741	2171
Pierco Incorporated	3999	F	909 251-7100	24211
Plascor Inc	3085	C	951 328-1010	9803
Poly-Fiber Inc (PA)	2851	F	951 684-4280	8924
Polymer Logistics Inc	3089	F	951 567-2900	10297
Poma GL Specialty Windows Inc	3211	D	951 321-0116	10605
Precise Aero Products Inc	3728	F	951 340-4554	20912
Precision Technology and Mfg	3451	E	951 788-0252	13038
Press-Enterprise Company (PA)	2711	A	951 684-1200	6019
Press-Enterprise Company	2711	F	951 684-1200	6020
Primetech Silicones Inc	2869	F	951 509-6655	9030
Prism Aerospace	3444	E	951 582-2850	12722
Prism Mfg	3728	E	310 538-3857	20915
Pro Mold Inc	3544	F	951 776-0555	14563
Progressive Products Inc	2299	F	951 784-9930	3013
Qg Printing Corp	2721	C	951 571-2500	6239
Qg Printing II Corp	2752	A	951 571-2500	7060
Quad/Graphics Inc	2752	C	951 689-1122	7063
R & D Nova Inc	3845	F	951 787-7332	23037
R & J Leathercraft	3199	F	951 688-1685	10578
Rain Mstr Irrgtion Systems Inc	3823	E	805 527-4498	21643
Rcs Custom Stoneworks	3281	F	714 309-0620	11275
Reisner Enterprises Inc	3599	F	951 786-9478	16893
Riverside Lamination Corp	2891	F	951 682-0100	9168
Riverside Machine Works Inc	3599	F	951 685-7416	16903
Riverside Tent & Awning Co	2393	F	951 683-1925	3770
Robert P Von Zabern	3841	F	951 734-7215	22608
Rochester Midland Corporation	2676	E	800 388-4762	5671
Rolenn Manufacturing Inc	3999	E	951 682-1185	24225
Rolenn Manufacturing Inc (PA)	3089	E	951 682-1185	10339
Roll-A-Shade Inc (PA)	2591	E	951 245-5077	5208
Royal Interpack Midwest Inc	3089	F	626 675-0637	10347
Royal Interpack North Amer Inc	3089	F	951 787-6925	10348
Ruiz Mexican Foods Inc (PA)	2099	C	909 947-7811	2661
S R S M Inc	2821	C	310 952-9000	7882
Sabert Corporation	3089	F	951 342-0240	10356
San Joaquin Window Inc (PA)	3442	D	909 946-3697	12345
Seymour Levinger & Co	3465	E	909 673-9800	13144
Sheet Metal Specialist Inc	3444	F	951 351-6828	12759
Sierra Aluminum Company (HQ)	3354	C	951 781-7800	11603
Simple Orthotic Solutions LLC	3131	F	951 353-8127	10475
Simpson Strong-Tie Company Inc	2439	C	714 871-8373	4421
Simpson Strong-Tie Company Inc	3449	C	714 871-8373	12995
SMS Fabrications Inc	3444	E	951 351-6828	12763
Sphere Alliance Inc	2821	E	951 352-2400	7889
SPX Corporation	3443	D	951 781-4484	12426
Steel Unlimited Inc (PA)	3443	F	909 873-1222	12428
Stone Valley Materials LLC	1442	F	951 681-7830	383
Stremicks Heritage Foods LLC	2024	F	951 352-1344	695
Structures Unlimited	3432	F	951 688-6300	12050
Summertree Interiors Inc	2511	F	951 549-0590	4741
Superform USA Incorporated	3463	F	951 341-4100	13130
Superior Metal Fabricators	3444	F	951 360-2474	12778
Swift Beef Company	2013	C	951 571-2237	530
T & V Printing Inc	2752	F	951 353-8470	7126
T C Quality Machining Inc	3599	F	951 509-4633	16981
T M Cobb Company (PA)	2431	E	951 248-2400	4242
T M P Services Inc (PA)	3448	E	951 213-3900	12963
T3m Inc	3751	E	909 464-1535	21141
Tait Cabinetry Woodworks	2431	F	951 776-1192	4245
Team Air Inc (PA)	3585	E	909 823-1957	15980
Techniglove International Inc	3842	F	951 582-0890	22830
Tim Hoover Enterprises	3663	D	951 237-9210	18287
Tolco Incorporated	3448	E	951 656-3111	12965
Tom Harris Inc	2099	D	951 352-5700	2683
Tom Leonard Investment Co Inc	3999	F	951 351-7778	24272
Toro Company	3523	D	951 688-9221	14111
Trademark Cosmetic Inc	2844	E	951 683-2631	8854
Trademark Plastics Inc	3559	C	909 941-8810	15038
Trane US Inc	3585	D	951 801-6020	15987
Triple H Food Processors LLC	2099	F	951 352-5700	2692
Tropical Functional Labs LLC	2023	F	951 688-2619	651
Trutouch Technologies Inc	3829	F	909 703-5963	22291
Tube One Industries Inc	3317	F	951 300-2998	11488
Unique Plex Inc	2824	F	951 653-2500	7918
United Carports LLC	3448	F	800 757-6742	12967
United Technologies Corp	3728	E	951 351-5400	20967
Universal Interior Industries	2511	F	951 743-5446	4746
Universal Specialty Vehicles	3716	F	951 943-7747	20526
Universal Trailers Inc	3799	F	951 784-0543	21244
US Door and Fence LLC	2411	F	951 300-0010	4018
US Environmental	2899	F	951 359-9002	9316
US Plastic Inc	3085	F	951 300-9360	9810
US Precision Sheet Metal Inc	3444	D	951 276-2611	12802
US Rubber Roller Company Inc	3555	F	951 682-2221	14829
Vast National Inc	3399	F	951 788-7030	11853
Virginia Park LLC	2099	F	816 592-0776	2698
Web CAM Inc	3714	F	951 341-0112	20485
West Coast Unlimited	3711	F	951 352-1234	20183
Western Case Incorporated	3089	F	714 838-8460	10441
Western Case Incorporated (PA)	3089	F	951 214-6380	10442
Western Hydrostatics Inc (PA)	3594	F	951 784-2133	16173
Yardney Water MGT Systems Inc (PA)	3589	F	951 656-6716	16141
Ziehm Instrumentarium	3844	E	407 615-8560	22946

RLLNG HLS EST, CA - Los Angeles County

Company	SIC	EMP	PHONE	ENTRY #
Chandlers Palos Verdes Sand A	1442		310 784-2900	352
Dincloud Inc	7372	D	310 929-1101	24562
Ecw Technology Inc	3564		310 373-0082	15152
Flipagram Inc	7372	F	415 827-8373	24654
National Media Inc (HQ)	2711	E	310 377-6877	5990
Sheervision Inc (PA)	3827	F	310 265-8918	22135

ROCKLIN, CA - Placer County

Company	SIC	EMP	PHONE	ENTRY #
Advantage Pharmaceuticals	2834	F	916 630-4960	8004
Amazing Facts Inc	2731	D	916 434-3880	6307
Asa Corporation	3826	F	530 305-3720	21906
Backyard Unlimited (PA)	2449	F	916 630-7433	4517
Cell Marque Corporation	2835	E	916 746-8900	8467
Cosmedica Skincare	2844	F	800 922-5280	8725

Employment Codes: A=Over 500 employees, B=251-500,
C=101-250, D=51-100, E=20-50, F=10-19

2019 California
Manufacturers Register

© Mergent Inc. 1-800-342-5647
1443

	SIC	EMP	PHONE	ENTRY #
Diamond Tech Incorporated	3546	F	916 624-1118	14703
Diverse McHning Fbrication LLC	3499	F	916 672-6591	13934
Energy Absorption Systems Inc	3499	C	916 645-8181	13939
Galil Motion Control Inc	3823	E	800 377-6329	21592
Greenheck Fan Corporation	3564	C	916 626-3400	15158
Hugin Components Inc	3469	F	916 652-1070	13222
Hydraulic Technology Inc	3561	F	916 645-3317	15079
J & M Printing Inc	2752	F	916 652-4600	6900
Jeld-Wen Inc	2431	C	916 782-4900	4173
Jlm Energy Inc	3511	E	916 304-1603	14000
Logan Smith Machine Co	3599	F	916 632-2692	16690
Oracle America Inc	7372	E	303 272-6473	24998
Oracle Corporation	7372	B	916 435-8342	25018
Oracle Corporation	7372	B	916 315-3500	25024
Pacific Mdf Products Inc (PA)	2431	D	916 660-1882	4209
Parallax Incorporated	3571	E	916 624-8333	15470
Progressive Technology Inc	3253	E	916 632-6715	10789
Sitek Process Solutions	3674	F	916 797-9000	19166
SMA America Production LLC	3433	C	720 347-6000	12085
Vanishing Vistas	2741	E	916 624-1237	6615
Vannelli Brands LLC	2033	F	916 824-1717	867

RODEO, CA - Contra Costa County

	SIC	EMP	PHONE	ENTRY #
Asbury Graphite Inc California	2911	F	510 799-3636	9320

ROHNERT PARK, CA - Sonoma County

	SIC	EMP	PHONE	ENTRY #
Arcturus Marine Systems	3511	D	707 586-3155	13988
Arcturus Uav Inc	3761	F	707 206-9372	21155
Asm Precision Inc	3444	F	707 584-7950	12492
Driven Raceway and Family Ente	3644	F	707 585-3748	17512
Green Sheet Inc	2759	F	707 284-1684	7337
Idex Health & Science LLC (HQ)	3821	D	707 588-2000	21476
Innovative Molding (HQ)	3089	D	707 584-9250	10152
KG Technologies	3679	F	888 513-1874	19610
Miller Manufacturing Inc	2591	F	707 584-9528	5203
Nelson Banner Inc	2673	F	707 585-9942	5611
Nonprofiteasy Inc (PA)	7372	F	707 929-3563	24970
North Bay Rhblitation Svcs Inc (PA)	2399	C	707 585-1991	3956
Parker-Hannifin Corporation	3625	C	707 584-7558	17291
Pasta Sonoma LLC	2098	F	707 584-0800	2436
Rieke Corporation	3466	C	707 238-9250	13148
Sodamail LLC	2741	F	707 794-1289	6582
Trinity Engineering	2542	E	707 585-2959	5172
Vaider Inc	3479	F	707 584-3655	13678

ROLLING HILLS, CA - Los Angeles County

	SIC	EMP	PHONE	ENTRY #
California Digital Inc (PA)	3577	D	310 217-0500	15696
Stitch and Hide LLC	3111	F	310 377-6912	10465

ROMOLAND, CA - Riverside County

	SIC	EMP	PHONE	ENTRY #
Datatronic Distribution Inc	3612	F	951 928-2058	17086
General Electric Company	3511	B	951 928-2829	13998
Orco Block & Hardscape	3271	E	951 928-3619	10857
Soil Retention Products Inc	3271	F	951 928-8477	10864

ROSAMOND, CA - Kern County

	SIC	EMP	PHONE	ENTRY #
American Performance Engi	3751	F	661 256-7309	21088

ROSEMEAD, CA - Los Angeles County

	SIC	EMP	PHONE	ENTRY #
Azteca Ornamental Metals	3446	F	626 280-2822	12835
C & R Extrusions Inc	3081	F	626 642-0244	9700
Chinese Overseas Mktg Svc Corp (PA)	2741	D	626 280-8588	6462
Fongs Graphics & Printing Inc	2754	E	626 307-1898	7202
HCC Industries Inc (HQ)	3678	F	626 443-8933	19393
Hermetic Seal Corporation (DH)	3679	C	626 443-8931	19566
Interior Corner Usa Inc	2542	F	626 452-8833	5148
J F McCaughin Co	3952	E	626 573-3000	23708
Ldvc Inc	2064	F	626 448-4611	1437
Lonix Pharmaceutical Inc	2023	E	626 287-4700	629
Lotus Beverages	2084	F	213 216-1434	1864
M Argeso & Co	2911	F	626 573-3000	9339
Phu Huong Foods Co Inc	2015	F	626 280-8607	549
Popular Printers Inc	2759	F	626 307-4281	7440
Prographics Inc	2752	E	626 287-0417	7055
Saigon Times Inc	2711	F	626 288-2696	6030
Tanbil Bakery Inc	2051	F	626 280-2638	1331
Tur-Bo Jet Products Co Inc	3677	D	626 285-1294	19368

ROSEVILLE, CA - Placer County

	SIC	EMP	PHONE	ENTRY #
A Teichert & Son Inc	3273	E	916 783-7132	11033
Agilent Technologies Inc	3825	F	916 785-1000	21711
Applied Materials Inc	3559	F	916 786-3900	14912
Arm Electronics Inc	3699	E	916 787-1100	19912
Arrive Technologies Inc	3674	F	888 864-6959	18719
Basalite Building Products LLC (HQ)	3272	E	707 678-1901	10881
Bead Shoppe	3999	F	916 782-8642	24049
Bioinitiatives Inc	3841	E	916 780-9100	22372
Brookshire Innovations LLC	3751	F	916 786-7601	21093

	SIC	EMP	PHONE	ENTRY #
Ca Inc	7372	E	800 405-5540	24462
California Bottling Company	2086	E	916 772-1000	2106
Contra Costa Newspapers Inc	2711	D	916 786-6500	5817
Cooks Truck Body Mfg Inc	3713	E	916 784-3220	20198
Cooltouch Corporation	3845	F	916 677-1975	22967
Coors Brewing Company	2082	E	916 786-2666	1581
David Corporation	7372	E	916 762-8688	24554
El Avisador Magazine	2711	E	916 903-7490	5841
Energy Exemplar LLC (DH)	7372	F	916 722-1484	24610
Garner Products Inc	3812	F	916 784-0200	21297
Gutterglove Inc	3444	D	916 624-5000	12604
Harris & Bruno Machine Co Inc (PA)	3555	D	916 781-7676	14810
HB Fuller Company	2891	E	916 787-6000	9145
Hewlett Packard Enterprise Co	7372	E	916 786-8000	24729
Hudson & Company LLC	2392	E	916 774-6465	3725
Intelligrated Systems Inc	3535	B	916 772-6800	14278
Iosafe Inc	3572	E	888 984-6723	15561
Jondo	2211	E	714 394-4344	2749
Kazan Networks Corporation	3571	E	916 259-0087	15438
Kellogg Sales Company	2043	E	916 787-0414	1065
Kenco Engineering Inc	3531	F	916 782-8494	14178
Kkp - Roseville Inc	2752	F	916 786-8573	6926
Kyles Rock & Redi-Mix Inc	3273	E	916 681-4848	11125
Merial Limited	2834	F	916 780-9292	8280
Nates Fine Foods LLC	2038	F	310 897-2690	1000
New Star Lasers Inc	3845	E	916 677-1900	23026
New Vision Display Inc (HQ)	3679	E	916 786-8111	19658
Pacific Coast Optics Inc	3827	E	916 789-0111	22118
Paul Baker Printing Inc	2752	E	916 969-8317	7018
Penguin Random House LLC	2731	E	916 787-7000	6380
Performance Polymer Tech LLC	3061	E	916 677-1414	9571
Phase 5 Weapon Systems Inc	3484	F	916 787-4273	13688
Praxair Inc	2813	E	916 786-3900	7720
Pride Industries One Inc	3999	A	916 788-2100	24214
Prima Games Inc	2731	C	916 787-7000	6384
Print & Mail Solutions Inc	2752	F	916 782-5489	7038
Providence Publications LLC	2741	F	916 774-4000	6560
S & J Carpet Cleaning	3635	F	916 630-9330	17408
Sigma Mfg & Logistics LLC	3571	E	916 781-3052	15485
Sims Recycling Solutions Inc	3341	E	916 772-5600	11567
Sinister Mfg Company Inc	3714	E	916 772-9253	20449
Smoothie Operator Inc	2037	E	916 773-9541	966
Star One Investments LLC	3429	F	916 858-1178	11996
Sunworks Inc (PA)	3674	D	916 409-6900	19206
Supermedia LLC	2741	B	916 782-6866	6599
Swiss-Tech Machining LLC	3451	F	916 797-6010	13044
Technical Sales Intl LLC (HQ)	7372	F	866 493-6337	25263
TRC Cocoa LLC	2066	F	916 847-2390	1477
Tsi Tech Devmnt & Commercializ	3674	F	916 786-3900	19237
United Advg Publications Inc	2721	E	916 746-2300	6281
W J Keenan	3825	E	916 783-5201	21887
Wright Technologies Inc	3679	F	916 773-4424	19789
Zoom Bookz LLC	2731	F	800 662-9982	6416

ROUGH AND READY, CA - Nevada County

	SIC	EMP	PHONE	ENTRY #
Gro-Tech Systems Inc	3448	F	530 432-7012	12933
Simply Country Inc	3523	F	530 615-0565	14105

ROWLAND HEIGHTS, CA - Los Angeles County

	SIC	EMP	PHONE	ENTRY #
Hubbell Lighting Inc	3646	D	714 386-5550	17617
Lip Hing Metal Inc	3542	F	714 871-9220	14441
Lip Hing Metal Mfg Amer Inc	3549	F	626 810-8204	14757
Quality Painting Co	3479	E	626 964-2529	13645
Suzhou South	3578	B	626 322-0101	15901
USA Topdon LLC	3699	E	833 233-5535	20096
Wholesome Yo Curd	2024	F	909 859-8758	706

ROYAL OAKS, CA - Santa Cruz County

	SIC	EMP	PHONE	ENTRY #
Classic Salads LLC	2099	E	928 726-6196	2490
Farmhouse Culture Inc (PA)	2834	E	831 466-0499	8158
Kristich-Monterey Pipe Co Inc	3272	F	831 724-4186	10945
Stainless Works Mfg Inc	3556	E	831 728-5097	14886

RUTHERFORD, CA - Napa County

	SIC	EMP	PHONE	ENTRY #
Alpha Omega Winery LLC	2084	F	707 963-9999	1643
Cakebread Cellars	2084	D	707 963-5221	1676
Diageo North America Inc	2085	D	707 967-5200	2070
Frogs Leap Winery	2084	F	707 963-4704	1777
Grgich Hills Cellar	2084	E	707 963-2784	1797
Inglenook	2084	F	707 968-1100	1817
Niebam-Cppola Estate Winery LP (PA)	2084	C	707 968-1100	1901
Pernod Ricard Usa LLC	2084	D	707 967-7770	1922
St Supery Inc (DH)	2084	E	707 963-4507	1987

SACRAMENTO, CA - Sacramento County

	SIC	EMP	PHONE	ENTRY #
A & A Ready Mixed Concrete Inc	3273	E	916 383-3756	11029
A Teichert & Son Inc	3273	E	916 386-6920	11031

Mergent email: customerrelations@mergent.com
1444

2019 California
Manufacturers Register

(P-0000) Products & Services Section entry number
(PA)=Parent Co (HQ)=Headquarters (DH)=Div Headquarters

Company	SIC	EMP	PHONE	ENTRY #
A Teichert & Son Inc	1442	E	916 386-6900	343
A&A Metal Finishing Entps LLC	3471	E	916 442-1063	13301
AAA Garments & Lettering Inc	2395	E	916 363-4590	3822
ABB Enterprises Inc	3699	F	916 649-3800	19896
Action Ironworks	3446	F	916 503-2270	12828
Admail West Inc	2655	D	916 554-5755	5479
Affordable Goods	3571	F	916 514-1049	15387
Ainor Signs Inc	3993	F	916 348-4370	23812
Aldetec Inc	3663	E	916 453-3382	18023
Alex Design Inc	2434	F	916 386-8020	4268
All Weather Inc	3829	D	916 928-1000	22158
Allied Printing Company	2752	F	916 442-1373	6650
Alpha Signs Inc	3993	F	916 379-0225	23813
Aluminum Coating Tech Inc	3471	E	916 442-1063	13326
American Bottling Company	2086	F	916 929-3575	2090
American Bottling Company	2086	D	916 929-7777	2091
American City Bus Journals Inc	2711	E	916 447-7661	5757
American Lithographers Inc	2752	D	916 441-5392	6655
Architectural Blomberg LLC	3442	F	916 428-8060	12293
Architectural S Weidner	3993	F	800 561-7446	23819
Arden & Howe Printing Inc	2752	F	916 444-7154	6666
Atlas Specialties Corporation (PA)	3231	E	503 636-8182	10676
Audio Fx LLC	3651	F	916 929-2100	17766
Baise Enterprises Inc	2752	E	916 446-0167	6683
Bauer Industries (PA)	3429	F	916 648-9200	11938
Beauty Craft Furniture Corp	2511	E	916 428-2238	4676
Bellaterra Home LLC	2434	F	916 896-3188	4273
Bennetts Baking Company	2053	F	916 481-3349	1390
Berkeley Farms LLC	2026	E	916 689-7613	712
Bimbo Bakeries Usa Inc	2051	E	916 681-8069	1192
Bimbo Bakeries Usa Inc	2051	A	916 732-4733	1193
Bimbo Bakeries Usa Inc	2051	E	916 922-1307	1207
Blomberg Building Materials (PA)	3442	D	916 428-8060	12300
Blomberg Windows Systems	3231	C	916 428-8060	10681
Blue Diamond Growers	2099	C	916 446-8464	2469
Business Printing and Copies	2752	F	916 920-1412	6710
C & Gtool Inc	3545	F	916 614-9114	14611
California Cab & Store Fix	2431	E	916 386-1340	4114
California Cascade Industries	2491	C	916 736-3353	4588
California Pro-Specs Inc	2426	E	916 455-9890	4076
California Surveying & Draftin (PA)	3577	E	916 344-0232	15698
Califrnia Mantel Fireplace Inc (PA)	2431	E	916 925-5775	4119
Camelia City Millwork Inc	2431	F	916 451-2454	4120
Campbell Soup Company	2032	D	916 922-2836	751
Capital Corrugated LLC	2653	D	916 388-7848	5394
Capitol Beverage Packers	2086	D	916 929-7777	2108
Capitol Iron Works Inc	3441	E	916 381-1554	12128
Capitol Neon	3993	F	916 349-1800	23840
Capitol Steel Products	3291	E	916 383-3368	11290
Capitol Store Fixtures	2521	E	916 646-9096	4935
Carbonyte Systems Incorporated	2851	F	916 387-0316	8888
Cemex Cnstr Mtls PCF LLC	3273	E	916 364-2470	11068
Cemex Cnstr Mtls PCF LLC	3273	E	916 383-0526	11071
Chico Community Publishing	2711	D	916 498-1234	5798
Clarus Lighting LLC	3648	F	916 363-2888	17680
Class A Powdercoat Inc	3479	E	916 681-7474	13568
Clayton Homes Inc	2451	F	916 363-2681	4549
Coffee Works Inc	2095	F	916 452-1086	2338
Colormarx Corporation (PA)	2752	F	916 334-0334	6744
Composite Technology Intl Inc	2431	E	916 551-1850	4127
Comstock Publishing Inc	2721	F	916 364-1000	6134
Conros Corp	2499	E	916 381-8511	4614
Counter Fit	3281	F	916 569-8570	11246
Creo Inc	2759	F	530 756-1477	7290
Crystal Bottling Company Inc	2086	D	916 568-3300	2123
Crystal Cream & Butter Co (HQ)	2026	D	916 444-7200	718
D & T Fiberglass Inc	2655	E	916 383-9012	5484
Daily Recorder	2711	F	916 444-2355	5824
Danoc Manufacturing Corp Inc	2337	F	916 455-2876	3350
Davison Iron Works Inc	3441	E	916 381-2121	12151
Delta Lath & Plaster Inc	3541	E	916 383-6756	14369
Dhm Enterprises Inc	3799	E	916 688-7767	21226
Dorris Lumber and Moulding Co (PA)	2431	C	916 452-7531	4147
Duralum Products Inc (PA)	3355	F	916 452-7021	11616
Ebara International Corp	3561	D	916 920-5451	15061
Ebara Technologies Inc (DH)	3563	E	916 920-5451	15125
Eg Wear Inc	3999	F	916 361-1508	24090
Eggleston Signs	3993	F	916 920-1750	23863
El Dorado Newspapers Inc (DH)	2711	C	916 321-1826	5843
Elevator Industries Inc	3534	F	916 921-1495	14247
Ellensburg Lamb Company Inc (HQ)	2011	F	530 758-3091	433
Ethosenergy Pwr Plant Svcs LLC	1389	E	916 391-2993	211
Evoqua Water Technologies LLC	3589	F	916 564-1222	16041
Farmers Rice Cooperative (PA)	2044	E	916 923-5100	1079
Farmers Rice Cooperative	2044	E	916 373-5549	1080
Fong Fong Prtrs Lthgrphers Inc	2752	E	916 739-1313	6821
Food To You Usa Inc	7372	F	559 549-0090	24658
Forterra Pipe & Precast LLC	3272	D	916 379-9695	10930
Freeport Bakery Inc	2051	F	916 442-4256	1252
Fremont Package Express	3537	F	916 541-1812	14324
Fresno Precision Plastics Inc	3089	F	916 689-5284	10109
Fruitridge Prtg Lithograph Inc (PA)	2752	E	916 452-9213	6828
Full Color Business	2752	F	916 218-7845	6829
Gazette Media Co LLC	2711	F	916 567-9654	5860
General Dynmics Mssion Systems	3571	C	916 339-3852	15416
General Truss Company Inc	2439	E	916 388-1000	4405
Geo Drilling Fluids Inc	3295	E	916 383-2811	11320
Gh Foods Ca LLC (DH)	2099	B	916 844-1140	2528
Gsl Fine Lithographers	2752	E	916 231-1410	6843
Gunthers Quality Ice Cream	2024	F	916 457-3339	676
Hand Biomechanics Lab Inc	3842	E	916 923-5073	22739
Hannibals Catrg & Events Inc (PA)	2099	E	916 638-4363	2533
Hansen Haulers Inc	3599	F	916 443-7755	16555
Helen Noble	2721	F	916 457-8990	6181
Hni Corporation	2522	B	916 927-0400	4990
HP Hood LLC	2026	B	916 379-9266	729
Hrh Door Corp	3442	E	916 928-0600	12320
Huhtamaki Inc	2655	E	916 688-4938	5490
Illuminated Creations Inc	3993	E	916 924-1936	23896
Immuno Concepts Inc	3841	E	916 363-2649	22476
Imperial Die Cutting Inc	2675	E	916 443-6142	5652
Intake Screens Inc	3496	F	916 665-2727	13834
Intelmail USA Inc	3579	F	916 361-9300	15906
Intermag Inc	3695	C	916 568-6744	19866
International Association of S	3444	F	916 922-1133	12624
Interpress Technologies Inc (HQ)	2631	E	916 929-9771	5353
Ips Printing Inc	2752	E	916 442-8961	6896
Ittavi Inc	7372	E	866 246-4408	24807
ITW Blding Cmponents Group Inc	3443	E	916 387-0116	12391
James Frasinetti & Sons	2084	E	916 383-2447	1827
Jampro Antennas Inc	3663	D	916 383-1177	18136
John Boyd Enterprises Inc	3714	C	916 504-3622	20376
John Boyd Enterprises Inc (PA)	3714	C	916 381-4790	20377
Johnson Controls	3669	D	916 283-0300	18336
Johnson Industrial Sheet Metal	3444	F	916 927-8244	12632
Katz & Klein	3851	E	916 444-2024	23104
Kds Nail Products	3999	E	916 381-9358	24146
Kitchens Now Inc	2434	F	916 229-8222	4321
Kratos Unmanned Aerial Systems	3089	B	916 431-7977	10184
L3 Technologies Inc	3571	D	916 363-6581	15442
Langills General Machine Inc	3599	E	916 452-0167	16675
Laser Recharge Inc (PA)	3955	F	916 737-6360	23731
Legacy Vulcan LLC	3273	F	916 682-0850	11131
Lifeline SEC & Automtn Inc	3699	E	916 285-9078	20005
Linde LLC	2813	E	916 381-1606	7698
Liqui-Box Corporation	3089	D	916 381-7052	10193
Lpa Insurance Agency Inc	7372	D	916 286-7850	24867
Mailrite Print & Mail Inc	2752	E	916 927-6245	6957
Martin Sprocket & Gear Inc	3566	E	916 441-7172	15242
Mary Anns Baking Co Inc	2051	C	916 681-7444	1289
Matterhorn Ice Cream Inc	2024	E	208 287-8916	685
McCarthys Draperies Inc	2391	E	916 422-0155	3698
McClatchy Company (PA)	2711	C	916 321-1844	5943
McClatchy Newspapers Inc (HQ)	2711	A	916 321-1855	5944
Mencarini & Jarwin Inc	3471	F	916 383-1660	13451
Merchants Metals LLC	3496	E	916 381-8243	13839
Mesotech International Inc	3826	E	916 568-2020	21991
Metal Manufacturing Co Inc	3442	E	916 922-3484	12331
Microform Precision LLC	3444	D	916 419-0580	12675
Microsoft Corporation	7372	E	916 369-3600	24913
Milgard Manufacturing Inc	3442	F	916 387-0700	12334
Mitsubishi Chemical Crbn Fbr (DH)	3624	C	916 386-1733	17239
MNC Bliss Enterprises Inc	3648	F	916 483-1167	17716
Mobile Mini Inc	3448	F	916 381-1351	12947
Montgomery Marble Co	3281	F	916 383-1563	11263
Mova Stone Inc	3281	F	916 922-2080	11264
Mpj Recycling LLC	3559	F	916 761-5740	14994
Mw McWong International Inc	3648	D	916 371-8080	17717
New Direction Silk Screen	2759	F	916 971-3939	7413
New Generation Software Inc	7372	E	916 920-2200	24960
New Image Foam Products LLC	3086	E	916 388-0741	9871
Newbold Cleaners	3582	F	916 481-1130	15930
Next Level Warehouse Solutions	3535	E	916 922-7225	14279
Norquist Salvage Corp Inc	2329	E	916 454-0455	3181
Norquist Salvage Corp Inc	2329	E	916 922-9942	3182
Northern Cal Pet Imaging Ctr	3844	E	916 737-3211	22938
Olympic Cascade Publishing (DH)	2711	E	916 321-1000	6005
Omega Products Corp (HQ)	3299	D	916 635-3335	11364
Ortech Inc	3253	E	916 549-9696	10788
Outreach Slutions As A Svc LLC	2741	F	800 824-8573	6546

GEOGRAPHIC

Company	SIC	EMP	PHONE	ENTRY #
Outword News Magazine	2711	E	916 329-9280	6006
Pabco Clay Products LLC	3251	D	916 859-6320	10777
Pacific Ethanol Central LLC (HQ)	2869	D	916 403-2123	9027
Pacific Ethanol West LLC	2869	C	916 403-2123	9028
Pacific Neon	3993	E	916 927-0527	23941
Pacific Northwest Pubg Co Inc	2711	B	916 321-1828	6008
Pacific Pallet Exchange Inc	2448	E	916 448-5589	4493
Pacific Powder Coating Inc	3479	E	916 381-1154	13630
Pacific Truck Tank Inc	3713	E	916 379-9280	20223
Pecofacet (us) Inc	3569	F	916 689-2328	15351
Pepsi-Cola Metro Btlg Co Inc	2086	B	916 423-1000	2169
Pettigrew & Sons Casket Co	3995	E	916 383-0777	24012
Philip A Stitt Agency	2394	F	916 451-2801	3804
Pittsburgh Glass Works LLC	3211	C	916 419-1853	10604
Pk1 Inc (HQ)	2653	D	916 858-1300	5451
Plastic Package LLC (PA)	3089	D	916 921-3399	10287
Poolmaster Inc	3944	C	916 567-9800	23457
Pos Portal Inc (HQ)	3578	E	530 695-3005	15899
Procter & Gamble Mfg Co	2841	C	916 383-3800	8604
Propel Biofuels Inc (PA)	2869	F	800 871-0773	9031
Quikrete Companies LLC	3272	E	510 490-4670	10986
Quikrete Companies LLC	3272	E	916 689-8840	10990
Raymar Information Tech Inc (PA)	3661	F	916 783-1951	17987
Raynguard Protective Mtls Inc	2891	F	916 454-2601	9166
Reed & Graham Inc	2951	E	888 381-0800	9396
Reed & Graham Inc	2911	E	916 381-9900	9353
Reflectech Inc	2842	F	916 388-7821	8673
River City Millwork Inc	2431	E	916 364-8981	4221
RR Donnelley & Sons Company	2761	F	916 929-8632	7552
S & H Welding Inc	3443	F	916 386-8921	12417
S M G Custom Cabinets Inc	2434	E	916 381-5999	4347
Sac Valley Ornamental Ir Outl	3315	F	916 383-6340	11454
Sacramental Color Coil	2789	E	916 383-9588	7617
Sacramento Baking Co Inc	2051	E	916 361-2000	1317
Sacramento Coca-Cola Btlg Inc (HQ)	2086	B	916 928-2300	2215
Sale 121 Corp (PA)	3572	D	888 233-7667	15595
Setzer Forest Products Inc (PA)	2431	C	916 442-2555	4226
Seven Up Btlg Co San Francisco	2086	F	916 929-7777	2221
Sheet Mtal Fabrication Sup Inc	3444	D	916 641-6884	12760
Shift Management Inc	3714	F	916 381-4700	20446
Siemens Industry Inc	3822	C	916 681-3000	21532
Sierra Office Systems Pdts Inc (PA)	2752	F	916 369-0491	7105
Silgan Can Company	2032	F	916 422-8030	774
Silver Eagle Corporation	2392	E	916 925-6843	3748
Solar Industries Inc	3433	E	916 567-9650	12087
SRC Milling Co LLC	2077	E	916 363-4821	1533
Stanford Furniture Mfg Inc	2599	E	916 387-5300	5256
State Hornet	2711	D	916 278-6583	6061
Sulzer Pump Solutions US Inc	3561	E	916 925-8508	15093
Tacoma News Inc (DH)	2711	B	916 321-1846	6064
Taylor Communications Inc	2761	F	916 927-1891	7555
Teeco Products Inc	3714	E	916 688-3535	20461
Teichert Inc (PA)	3273	C	916 484-3011	11199
Thermcraft Inc	2759	F	916 363-9411	7519
Time Prtg Solutions Provider	2752	F	916 446-6152	7135
Tmp LLC	3442	E	916 920-2555	12352
TNT Industrial Contractors Inc (PA)	3531	E	916 395-8400	14194
Toms Printing Inc	2752	F	916 444-7788	7137
Tri Quality Inc	3842	E	916 388-5939	22835
Ultra Glass	3231	F	916 338-3911	10738
Valley Community Newspaper	2711	F	916 429-9901	6077
Vampire Penguin LLC (PA)	2024	F	916 553-4197	701
Veterans Employment Agency Inc	3281	F	650 245-0599	11286
Vortran Laser Technology Inc	3699	F	916 283-8208	20105
Vortran Medical Technology 1 (PA)	3841	E	916 648-8400	22677
Vss Countertops Inc	2541	E	916 681-8677	5117
Washoe Equipment Inc	3645	E	916 395-4700	17570
Water Resources Cal Dept	3823	D	916 651-9203	21676
WE Hall Company Inc	3272	F	916 383-4891	11020
Westrock Cp LLC	2631	E	916 379-2200	5369
Wikoff Color Corporation	2893	F	916 928-6965	9216
World Textile and Bag Inc	2393	F	916 922-9222	3774
Worldradio Inc	2721	F	916 457-3655	6295
Wsglass Holdings Inc	3827	F	916 388-5885	22150
Young Electric Sign Company	3993	E	916 419-8101	24008

SAINT HELENA, CA - Napa County

Company	SIC	EMP	PHONE	ENTRY #
7 & 8 LLC	2084	F	707 963-9425	1637
Brown Estate Vineyard LLC	2084	F	707 963-2435	1669
Burgess Cellars Inc	2084	F	707 963-4766	1671
C Mondavi & Family (PA)	2084	D	707 967-2200	1673
Cain Cellars Inc	2084	F	707 963-1616	1675
Chappellet Winery Inc (PA)	2084	F	707 286-4268	1687
Chateau Potelle Holdings LLC	2084	F	707 255-9440	1692
Duckhorn Wine Company (HQ)	2084	E	707 963-7108	1735
E & J Gallo Winery	2084	F	707 963-2736	1747

Company	SIC	EMP	PHONE	ENTRY #
Flexcube Inc	2813	F	707 738-4001	7690
Flora Springs Wine Company	2084	F	707 963-5711	1765
Franciscan Vineyards Inc	2084	D	707 963-7111	1772
Freemark Abbey Wnery Ltd Prtnr	2084	E	707 963-9694	1775
Gandona Inc A California Corp	2084	F	707 967-5550	1778
Herdell Printing & Lithography	2752	E	707 963-3634	6854
Merryvale Vineyards LLC	2084	E	707 963-2225	1877
New Vavin Inc	2084	F	707 963-5972	1897
Newton Vineyard LLC (DH)	2084	F	707 963-9000	1898
Provenance Vineyards	2084	F	707 968-3633	1931
Red River Lumber Co	2449	E	707 963-1251	4533
Rombauer Vineyards Inc	2084	D	707 963-5170	1955
Ronald F Ogletree Inc	3444	F	707 963-3537	12741
Round Hill Cellars	2084	D	707 968-3200	1958
Seavey Vineyard Ltd Partnr	2084	F	707 963-8339	1969
Spring Mountain Vineyards Inc	2084	E	707 967-4188	1985
Stone Bridge Cellars (PA)	2084	F	707 963-2745	1997
Sutter Home Winery Inc (PA)	2084	C	707 963-3104	2002
Thomas Leonardini	2084	F	707 963-9454	2015
Treasury Wine Estates Americas	2084	D	707 963-7115	2022
Treasury Wine Estates Americas	2084	B	707 963-4812	2023
Treasury Wine Estates Americas	2084	F	707 963-7115	2026
Trinchero Family Estates Inc	2084	D	707 963-1160	2028
Turley Wine Cellars Inc	2084	F	707 968-2700	2032
Vineyard 29 LLC	2084	F	707 963-9292	2045
Wheeler Winery Inc	2084	E	415 979-0630	2053

SALIDA, CA - Stanislaus County

Company	SIC	EMP	PHONE	ENTRY #
Flory Industries	3523	D	209 545-1167	14068
Inventive Resources Inc	3444	F	209 545-1663	12626

SALINAS, CA - Monterey County

Company	SIC	EMP	PHONE	ENTRY #
A&G Machine Shop Inc	3599	F	831 759-2261	16195
Abrams Electronics Inc	3643	E	831 758-6400	17438
Aggrigator Inc	7372	F	650 245-5117	24337
All American Fabrication	3999	F	831 676-3490	24029
Alsop Pump	7694	F	831 424-3946	25452
Bindel Bros Grading &	3531	F	831 754-1490	14145
Bookette Software Co Inc	7372	F	831 484-9250	24440
Cal Pcific Specialty Foods LLC	2037	F	831 722-3615	940
California Kit Cab Door Corp	2431	C	831 784-5142	4117
Copymat Salinas LLC	2752	F	831 753-0471	6759
County of Monterey	2759	F	831 755-4790	7288
Cyberware Laboratory Inc	3823	F	831 484-1064	21568
Dales Welding Inc	3523	F	831 424-6583	14057
El Camino Machine & Wldg LLC (PA)	3599	F	831 758-8309	16466
Five Star Lumber Company LLC	2448	E	831 422-4493	4470
Fresh Express Incorporated	2099	A	831 424-2921	2527
Growers Ice Co	2097	E	831 424-5781	2414
Hollister Landscape Supply Inc (HQ)	3273	F	831 443-8644	11121
International Paper Company	2621	F	831 755-2100	5300
Lifeline Systems Company	3669	C	831 755-0788	18340
Magnetic Circuit Elements Inc	3679	E	831 757-8752	19633
McCormick & Company Inc	2099	D	831 775-3350	2601
McCormick & Company Inc	2099	C	831 758-2411	2602
Merrill Corporation	2759	F	831 759-9300	7403
Monterey Coast Brewing LLC	3556	F	831 758-2337	14872
Morgan Winery Inc (PA)	2084	F	831 751-7777	1887
Next Pharmaceuticals Inc	2834	E	831 621-8712	8303
Organicgirl LLC	2099	A	831 758-7800	2631
Pepsi-Cola Metro Btlg Co Inc	2086	F	831 796-2000	2173
Pro Pack Systems Inc	3565	F	831 771-1300	15224
Progressive Packg Group Inc (PA)	2653	E	831 424-2942	5454
Reyes Coca-Cola Bottling LLC	2086	D	831 755-8300	2196
Salinas Newspapers LLC	2711	C	831 424-2221	6031
Salinas Tallow Co Inc	2077	E	831 422-6436	1532
Salinas Valley Wax Paper Co	2679	E	831 424-2747	5733
Salomon Dominguez	3446	F	831 663-1190	12887
Sierra Natural Science Inc	2869	F	831 757-1702	9041
Smartwash Solutions LLC	2819	F	831 676-9750	7805
SMS Industrial Inc	3443	F	831 337-4271	12421
Star Sanitation Services	3089	F	831 754-6794	10390
Tailgater Inc	3792	F	831 424-7710	21212
Tom Bengard Ranch Inc	3585	F	831 758-5770	15982
Transfirst Corporation	3822	F	831 424-2911	21534
Uv Landscaping LLC	3271	F	831 275-5296	10866
Valley Fabrication Inc	3523	D	831 757-5151	14115
Westrock Cp LLC	2653	C	831 424-1831	5469

SAMOA, CA - Humboldt County

Company	SIC	EMP	PHONE	ENTRY #
Western Web Inc	2752	E	707 444-6236	7184

SAN ANDREAS, CA - Calaveras County

Company	SIC	EMP	PHONE	ENTRY #
Calaveras First Co Inc	2711	E	209 754-3861	5785
Krisalis Inc	3599	F	209 286-1637	16665

	SIC	EMP	PHONE	ENTRY #

SAN ANSELMO, CA - Marin County

Company	SIC	EMP	PHONE	ENTRY #
V-A Optical Company Inc	3827	F	415 459-1919	22144

SAN BERNARDINO, CA - San Bernardino County

Company	SIC	EMP	PHONE	ENTRY #
Adams and Brooks Inc	2064	D	213 392-8700	1406
Alexanders Textile Pdts Inc	2389	F	951 276-2500	3637
All Sports Services Inc	2759	F	909 885-4626	7228
Aluminum Seating Inc	2531	F	909 884-9449	5007
American Wire Inc	3496	F	909 884-9990	13809
Anco International Inc	3494	E	909 887-2521	13759
Anitas Mexican Foods Corp (PA)	2096	C	909 884-8706	2374
Ardent Mills LLC	2041	E	909 887-3407	1032
Blacklion Enterprises Inc (PA)	3446	F	951 328-0400	12837
Boral Roofing LLC	3272	E	909 796-8324	10888
C-Pak Industries Inc	3089	E	909 880-6017	9999
Cmtg	3999	F	310 908-6687	24067
Container Options Inc	3089	F	909 478-0045	10040
County of San Bernardino	3531	A	909 387-7942	14161
D&W Fine Pack LLC	3089	C	206 767-7777	10059
Dateline Products LLC	2511	F	909 888-9785	4688
Dean Distributors Inc	2099	E	323 587-8147	2500
Dean Distributors Inc	2099	F	323 923-5400	2501
Die-Namic Fabrication Inc	3469	F	909 350-2870	13195
Dynamic Bindery Inc	2789	F	909 884-1296	7598
Farmdale Creamery Inc	2026	D	909 888-4938	724
Fender Musical Instrs Corp	3931	D	909 773-1200	23369
Foamex LP	3086	F	909 824-8981	9852
Garner Holt Productions Inc	3571	E	909 799-3030	15413
Global Environmental Pdts Inc	3711	F	909 713-1600	20145
Ground Hog Inc	3531	E	909 478-5700	14172
Gunderson Rail Services LLC	3743	E	909 478-0541	21076
Hayden Products LLC	3443	D	951 736-2600	12389
Hospitality Sleep Systems Inc	2515	F	909 387-9779	4863
Inland Empire Cmnty Newspapers	2711	E	909 381-9898	5888
Innocor West LLC	3069	E	909 307-3737	9628
Innovative Metal Inds Inc	3449	D	909 796-6200	12980
Jon Steel Erectors Inc	7692	E	909 799-0005	25417
Juice Heads Inc	2033	F	909 386-7933	811
Kav America Ag Inc	2095	E	855 528-8721	2356
Kendra Group Inc	3669	F	909 473-7206	18338
Kmb Foods Inc (PA)	2013	E	626 447-0545	500
Kohler Co	3431	E	909 890-4291	12015
Las Cuatros Milpas	2051	F	909 885-3344	1279
Legacy Vulcan LLC	1442	E	909 875-1150	367
Legend Pump & Well Service Inc	1381	F	909 384-1000	111
Leitz Tooling Systems LP	3541	F	909 799-8494	14389
Lifetime Camper Shells Inc	3792	E	909 885-2814	21205
Live Fresh Corporation	2037	C	909 478-0895	959
M & L Pharmaceuticals Inc	2834	F	909 890-0078	8265
M D Software Inc	7372	E	909 881-7599	24872
Macroair Technologies Inc (PA)	3564	E	909 890-2270	15166
Magnum Abrasives Inc	3291	E	909 890-1100	11297
Mapei Corporation	2821	E	909 475-4100	7854
Mars Petcare Us Inc	2047	E	909 887-8131	1116
Mattel Inc	3944	F	909 382-3780	23443
McIntire Tool Die & Machine (PA)	3469	F	909 888-0440	13246
Millers American Honey Inc	2099	E	909 825-1722	2605
Mkkr Inc	3545	E	909 890-5994	14654
Nagles Veal Inc	2011	E	909 383-7075	445
Nitro 2 Go Inc	2833	F	909 864-4886	7958
Ocean Blue Inc	3086	E	909 478-9910	9872
On Press Printing Service Inc	2752	F	909 799-9599	7004
Optivus Proton Therapy Inc	3829	D	909 799-8300	22242
Park West Enterprises	2077	E	909 383-8341	1531
Patio Paradise Inc	3645	F	626 715-4869	17553
Precinct Reporter	2711	F	909 889-0597	6017
Quiel Bros Elc Sign Svc Co Inc	3993	E	909 885-4476	23947
R & R Machine Products Inc	3451	F	909 885-7500	13040
Rci Rack Cnvyor Instlltion Inc	3535	F	909 381-4818	14283
Reagent Chemical & RES Inc	2819	F	909 764-4059	7801
Refresco Beverages US Inc	2086	D	909 915-1400	2184
Rlt Seafood Supermarket Inc	2091	F	909 888-6520	2301
Romeros Food Products Inc	2099	F	909 884-5531	2659
San Brnrdino Cmnty College Dst	2759	C	909 888-6511	7477
Semco	3829	E	909 799-9666	22263
Shorett Printing Inc (PA)	2759	F	714 545-4689	7482
Shorett Printing Inc	2752	F	714 956-9001	7104
Soltech Solar Inc	3511	F	909 890-2282	14009
Stavatti Industries Ltd	1041	D	651 238-5369	8
Sun Company San Bernardino Cal (PA)	2711	B	909 889-9666	6062
Sun Company San Bernardino Cal	2911	E	909 889-9666	9362
Sunwest Printing Inc	2759	F	909 890-3898	7503
Systems Technology Inc	3565	D	909 799-9950	15229
T M Cobb Company	2541	C	909 796-6969	5109
Tgs Molding LLC	3089	F	909 890-1707	10401
Thermal Solutions Mfg Inc	3714	E	909 796-0754	20464
Tinker & Rasor Inc	3812	E	909 890-0700	21442
Trinity Office Furniture Inc	2521	D	909 888-5551	4972
United Cabinet Company Inc	2522	F	909 796-3015	5002
United States Mineral Pdts Co	3296	D	909 473-6993	11338
United Uniform Mfrs Inc	2321	F	909 381-2682	3063
WBwalton Enterprises Inc	3663	E	951 683-0930	18299

SAN BRUNO, CA - San Mateo County

Company	SIC	EMP	PHONE	ENTRY #
Davita Rx LLC (HQ)	2834	E	650 344-2319	8134
Green Creative LLC	3645	E	866 774-5433	17538
Infrastructureworld LLC	3826	E	650 871-3950	21976
Kuna Systems Corporation	3571	F	650 263-8257	15441
Locix Inc	3625	F	650 231-2180	17286
Qumu Inc	7372	D	650 396-8530	25101

SAN CARLOS, CA - San Mateo County

Company	SIC	EMP	PHONE	ENTRY #
Advanced Adbag Packaging Inc	2673	F	650 591-1625	5585
Allakos Inc	2834	F	650 597-5002	8011
Alliance Memory Inc	3674	F	650 610-6800	18680
Alphascript Inc	2834	F	650 654-2103	8016
Alpine Biomed Corp	3841	C	650 802-0400	22329
Apex Die Corporation	2675	D	650 592-6350	5650
Apexigen Inc	2834	F	650 931-6236	8036
Ardax Systems Inc	3663	F	650 591-2656	18041
Begovic Industries Inc	3599	F	650 594-2861	16314
Brew4u LLC	2082	F	415 516-8211	1573
Brown Wood Products Inc	2449	F	650 593-9875	4518
Carevault Corporation	7372	F	714 333-0556	24471
Check Point Software Tech Inc (HQ)	7372	C	650 628-2000	24486
Concepts & Methods Co Inc	3567	F	650 593-1064	15256
Delta Star Inc	3612	B	650 508-2850	17088
Education Elements Inc	7372	F	650 336-0660	24592
EH Suda Inc (PA)	3599	F	650 622-9700	16463
Ergodirect Inc	2522	F	650 654-4300	4984
Fable Inc	3446	F	650 598-9616	12854
Fabtron	3599	F	650 622-9700	16491
House of Bagels Inc (PA)	2051	F	650 595-4700	1273
Hy-Tech Plating Inc	3471	F	650 593-4566	13429
Incelldx Inc	3841	F	650 777-7630	22479
Iovance Biotherapeutics Inc (PA)	2834	E	650 260-7120	8233
J & L Digital Precision Inc	3679	F	650 592-0170	19588
Jerry Carroll Machinery Inc	3599	F	650 591-3302	16621
Kelly-Moore Paint Company Inc (PA)	2851	C	650 592-8337	8910
Kelly-Moore Paint Company Inc	2851	F	650 595-0333	8912
Kinetic Farm Inc	7372	F	650 503-3279	24831
L & M Electronics	3674	F	650 341-1608	18948
Lumascape USA Inc	3646	F	650 595-5862	17630
M S F Inc	2542	F	650 592-0239	5151
Magnitude Electronics LLC	3679	F	650 551-1850	19636
Marble City Company Inc	3281	F	650 802-8189	11261
Meskin Khosrow Kay	3172	F	650 595-3090	10568
Natus Medical Incorporated	3845	E	303 962-1800	23022
Nektar Therapeutics	2834	E	650 622-1790	8296
Novartis Corporation	2834	D	650 631-3100	8309
Pacful Inc	2752	D	650 200-4252	7010
Pacific Weaving Corporation	2211	F	650 592-9434	2756
Pencom Accuracy Inc	3451	D	510 785-5022	13037
Penta Biotech Inc	2869	F	650 598-9328	9029
Performex Machining Inc	3599	F	650 595-2228	16842
Pionetics Corporation	3089	F	650 551-0250	10274
Precision Design Inc	3672	F	650 508-8041	18565
Provence Stone	3281	F	650 631-5600	11272
Revjet	7372	C	650 508-2215	25128
Royalite Mfg Inc	3444	F	650 637-1440	12743
Service Press Inc	2752	F	650 592-3484	7102
Shores Press	2741	F	650 593-2802	6579
Svetwheel LLC	3827	E	650 245-6080	22140
Sweet Production Inc	2051	D	650 631-7777	1326
Tech Air Northern Cal LLC	2813	F	650 593-9353	7737
Telecommunications Engrg Assoc	3663	F	650 590-1801	18277
Valence Surface Tech LLC	3812	E	323 770-0240	21452
Whill Inc (PA)	3799	F	844 699-4455	21247

SAN CLEMENTE, CA - Orange County

Company	SIC	EMP	PHONE	ENTRY #
American Chain & Gear Company	3566	F	323 581-9131	15237
American Qualex Inc	3229	F	949 492-8298	10632
American Qualex International	2899	F	949 492-8298	9221
Aqua Prieta Tees LLC	2759	F	714 719-2000	7238
Armorstruxx LLC	3728	F	949 366-1300	20743
Atomic Monkey Industries Inc	2396	F	949 415-8846	3876
Azimuth Electronics Inc	3825	F	949 492-6481	21726
Bionorica LLC	2834	F	949 361-4900	8080
BT Sheet Metal Inc	3444	F	949 481-5715	12512
Buldoor LLC	3429	F	877 388-1366	11939
Bunker Corp (PA)	3714	D	949 361-3935	20276

Employment Codes: A=Over 500 employees, B=251-500,
C=101-250, D=51-100, E=20-50, F=10-19

2019 California
Manufacturers Register

© Mergent Inc. 1-800-342-5647
1447

GEOGRAPHIC

Company	SIC	EMP	PHONE	ENTRY #
Capistrano Labs Inc	3841	E	949 492-0390	22387
Clean Wave Management Inc	3721	F	949 488-2922	20573
Clean Wave Management Inc	3562	E	949 361-5356	15105
Code-In-Motion LLC	3569	F	949 361-2633	15311
Composite Manufacturing Inc	3841	E	949 361-7580	22407
Dana Innovations	3651	D	949 492-7777	17787
Dragon Alliance Inc	3851	E	760 931-4900	23089
Electric Visual Evolution LLC (PA)	3851	E	949 940-9125	23091
Elevate Inc	7372	E	949 276-5428	24604
Epica Medical Innovations LLC	3841	F	949 238-6323	22442
Flavorchem Corporation	2087	E	949 369-7900	2262
Flow Sports Inc (PA)	3949	E	949 361-5260	23563
Four Star Distribution	3021	D	949 369-4420	9471
Glaukos Corporation (PA)	3841	C	949 367-9600	22461
Gps Logic LLC	3663	F	949 812-6942	18113
H I S C Inc	3229	F	949 492-8968	10645
Hot Shoppe Designs Inc	2329	F	949 487-2828	3159
Icu Medical Inc (PA)	3841	B	949 366-2183	22474
Icu Medical Sales Inc (HQ)	3841	F	949 366-2183	22475
Innovative Earth Products	3949	E	888 588-5955	23591
Innovative Rv Technologies	1389	F	949 559-5372	227
International Rubber Pdts Inc (PA)	3069	D	909 947-1244	9629
Jordan Companys	3545	E	949 492-0804	14642
Kelcourt Plastics Inc (HQ)	3082	D	949 361-0774	9740
Kpi Agency Inc	2741	E	949 232-0220	6512
Kui Co Inc	2621	E	949 369-7949	5309
Left Coast Brewing Company	2082	F	949 218-3961	1604
Mvm Products LLC	3861	D	949 366-1470	23182
Nationwide Printing Svcs Inc	2759	F	714 258-7899	7411
Pacific Composites Inc	3324	F	949 498-8600	11520
Plastics Development Corp	3089	E	949 492-0217	10289
Quinn Medical Inc	3842	F	949 784-0310	22800
R & R Industries Inc	2389	F	949 361-9238	3676
R T C Group	2721	C	949 226-2000	6241
Reynard Corporation	3827	E	949 366-8866	22127
Roberto Martinez Inc	3911	F	800 257-6462	23311
Roman Global Resources Inc	3053	F	949 276-4100	9552
Rosen & Rosen Industries Inc	3949	D	949 361-9238	23640
Rox Medical Inc (PA)	3845	E	949 276-8968	23044
Sensory Neurostimulation Inc	2834	F	949 492-0550	8377
Shoreline Products Inc	3965	F	949 388-1919	23772
Snowpure LLC	3589	F	949 240-2188	16109
Space Jam Juice LLC	2111	D	714 660-7467	2709
Srsb Inc	7372	F	949 234-1881	25214
Streuter Technologies	3272	E	949 369-7630	11008
Surf More Products Inc	3949	F	949 492-0753	23668
Systems Upgrade Inc	3572	F	949 429-8900	15616
Toolander Engineering Inc	3469	F	949 498-8339	13286
Traffix Devices Inc (PA)	3669	F	949 361-5663	18372
Try All 3 Sports	3751	F	949 492-2255	21146
Ttb Products Inc (PA)	3669	F	949 369-1475	18373
Versicolor Inc	3552	F	949 361-9698	14783
Western Outdoors Publications (PA)	2711	E	949 366-0030	6085

SAN DIEGO, CA - San Diego County

Company	SIC	EMP	PHONE	ENTRY #
5 I Sciences Inc	3841	F	858 943-4566	22300
5th Axis Inc	3469	D	858 505-0432	13151
A Thanks Million Inc	2361	F	858 432-7744	3570
A&D Fire Sprinklers Inc (PA)	3569	E	858 277-3473	15295
Acadia Pharmaceuticals Inc (PA)	2834	B	858 558-2871	7992
Accel-Rf Corporation	3825	F	858 278-2074	21700
Accelrys Software Inc	7372	F	858 799-5000	24305
Acces I/O Products Inc	3577	E	858 550-9559	15652
Access Scientific LLC	3841	E	858 259-8333	22309
Accriva Dgnostics Holdings Inc (DH)	3841	B	858 404-8203	22311
Actavalon Inc	2834	E	949 244-5684	7996
Activeon Inc (PA)	3651	E	858 798-3300	17751
Aculon Inc	2869	E	858 350-9474	8967
Adamis Pharmaceuticals Corp (PA)	2834	E	858 997-2400	8000
Advanced Electromagnetics Inc	3823	E	619 449-9492	21542
Advanced Hpc Inc	3572	F	858 716-8262	15508
Advanced Intl Tech LLC	3559	F	858 566-2945	14903
Advanced Metal Forming Inc	3441	E	619 239-9437	12105
Advanced Refractive Tech	3841	F	949 940-1300	22316
Aem (holdings) Inc	3613	D	858 481-0210	17129
Aem Electronics (usa) Inc	3677	E	858 481-0210	19315
Agouron Pharmaceuticals Inc (HQ)	2834	E	858 622-3000	8005
Air & Gas Tech Inc	3732	F	619 557-8373	21020
Air-Trak	3663	F	858 677-9950	18019
Airgain Inc (PA)	3663	E	760 579-0200	18021
Al Shellco LLC (HQ)	3651	C	570 296-6444	17756
Alere Connect LLC	3845	E	888 876-3327	22948
Alere San Diego Inc	2835	A	858 455-4808	8458
All Energy Inc	3648	F	619 988-7030	17670
All Source Coatings Inc	3479	E	858 586-0903	13546
Allermed Laboratories Inc	2833	E	858 292-1060	7920

Company	SIC	EMP	PHONE	ENTRY #
Alliance Air Products Llc	3585	C	619 428-9688	15935
Alliance Tags	2759	E	858 549-7297	7231
Alor International Ltd	3911	E	858 454-0011	23232
Alphacoat Finishing LLC	3471	E	949 748-7796	13323
Althea Ajinomoto Inc	3841	C	858 882-0123	22330
Ambit Biosciences Corporation	2834	D	858 334-2100	8020
Amcan LLC	3572	F	858 587-1032	15510
Ameditech Inc	3841	E	858 535-1968	22333
Ametek Programmable Power Inc (HQ)	3679	C	858 450-0085	19443
Amex Manufacturing Inc	3999	F	619 391-7412	24036
Amkor Technology Inc	3674	D	858 320-6280	18694
Amobee Inc	3823	E	858 638-1515	21547
Ampliphi Biosciences Corp (PA)	2836	E	858 829-0829	8528
Amylin Pharmaceuticals LLC	2834	D	858 552-2200	8029
Ana Global LLC	2517	A	619 482-9990	4896
Anderson Desk Inc	2521	B	619 671-1040	4930
Anheuser-Busch LLC	2082	F	858 581-7000	1560
Anocote	3471	F	858 566-1015	13330
Anokiwave Inc (PA)	3674	E	858 792-9910	18701
Any Budget Printing & Mailing	2752	F	858 278-3151	6664
Aonix North America Inc (HQ)	7372	F	858 457-2700	24361
AP Parpro Inc	3571	C	760 931-7800	15394
AP Precision Metals Inc	3444	F	619 628-0003	12486
Apollo Manufacturing Services	3629	F	858 271-8009	17331
Appfolio Inc	7372	A	866 648-1536	24369
Apricus Biosciences Inc (PA)	2834	E	858 222-8041	8037
Apta Group Inc (PA)	3674	E	619 710-8170	18713
Aqua Logic Inc	3585	E	858 292-4773	15937
Aquadyne Computer Corporation	3625	F	858 495-1040	17253
Aquaneering Inc	3523	E	858 578-2028	14042
Arctic Zero Inc	2024	E	619 342-1423	656
Arena Pharmaceuticals Inc (PA)	2834	D	858 453-7200	8040
Argen Corporation	3843	C	858 455-7900	22857
Argen Corporation (PA)	3339	C	858 455-7900	11543
Arm Inc	3674	C	858 453-1900	18718
Arrk Product Dev Group USA Inc	3444	C	858 552-1587	12487
Asias Finest	3421	F	619 297-0800	11878
Asset Equity Holdings LLC	3825	F	925 339-5440	21724
Asset Science LLC	7372	E	858 255-7982	24389
Associated Microbreweries Inc	2082	D	858 587-2739	1562
Associated Microbreweries Inc (PA)	2082	E	858 273-2739	1564
Associated Microbreweries Inc	2082	E	619 234-2739	1565
Asteres Inc (PA)	3578	E	858 777-8600	15893
AT&T Corp	2741	C	619 521-6100	6438
Atlas Lithograph Company	2752	E	858 560-8273	6671
Atm Plus Inc	3069	F	619 575-3278	9590
Audatex North America Inc (DH)	7372	C	858 946-1900	24397
Aurum Assembly Plus Inc	3672	E	858 578-8710	18431
Autoanything Inc	3711	C	858 569-8111	20128
Autoliv Asp Inc	3714	C	619 661-9347	20261
Autoliv Safety Technology Inc	2399	A	619 662-8000	3938
Automotive Engineered Pdts Inc	3542	D	619 229-7797	14430
Automotive Exch & Sup of Cal (PA)	3714	C	619 282-3207	20263
Autosplice Inc (PA)	3643	C	858 535-0077	17444
Avery Plastics Inc	3089	D	619 696-1230	9962
Aviva Biosciences Corporation	3699	E	858 552-0888	19916
AVX Antenna Inc (DH)	3663	E	858 550-3820	18048
B & I Fender Trims Inc	3714	D	718 326-4323	20265
B D Pharmingen Inc (HQ)	2835	C	858 812-8800	8461
B T E Deltec Inc (DH)	3679	F	619 291-4211	19456
B&M Noble Co (PA)	2426	E	619 793-5899	4073
B-Efficient Inc	3646	F	209 663-9199	17586
Bae Systems Info & Elec Sys	3825	C	858 592-5000	21728
Bae Systems San Diego (DH)	3731	A	619 238-1000	20985
Bae Systems San Diego	3731	B	619 238-1000	20986
Bajasys LLC	3577	F	619 661-0748	15677
Balboa Manufacturing Co LLC (PA)	2253	C	858 715-0060	2823
Ballast Point Spirits LLC	2082	C	858 695-2739	1566
Barrett Engineering Inc	3694	F	858 256-9194	19828
BASF Enzymes LLC	2869	F	858 431-8520	8983
Becton Dickinson and Company	3841	B	858 812-8800	22361
Beejay LLC (PA)	3944	F	619 220-8697	23410
Beme International LLC	2392	E	858 751-0580	3709
Bernardo Winery Inc	2084	E	858 487-1866	1656
Bh-Tech Inc	3089	A	858 694-0900	9982
Bimbo Bakeries Usa Inc	2051	D	858 677-0573	1195
Biogeneral Inc	3841	E	858 453-4451	22370
Bioject Inc	3841	E	503 692-8001	22373
Biolegend Inc (PA)	2836	C	858 455-9588	8535
Biomatrica Inc	2655	E	858 550-0308	5480
Bionano Genomics Inc (PA)	3826	D	858 888-7600	21926
Bioserv Corporation	2835	E	917 817-1326	8463
Biospherical Instruments Inc	3812	F	619 686-1888	21266
Biota Technology Inc	7372	F	650 888-6512	24426
Biotix Inc (HQ)	2869	E	858 875-7696	8990

Mergent email: customerrelations@mergent.com
1448

2019 California
Manufacturers Register

(P-0000) Products & Services Section entry number
(PA)=Parent Co (HQ)=Headquarters (DH)=Div Headquarters

	SIC	EMP	PHONE	ENTRY #
Bit Group Usa Inc **(PA)**	3841	D	858 613-1200	22376
Blastrac NA	3531	F	800 256-3440	14147
Blue Book Publishers Inc **(PA)**	2741	D	858 454-7939	6449
Blue Planet Energy Solutions	3646	F	858 947-1000	17587
Blue Squirrel Inc	3669	D	858 268-0717	18313
Bonded Window Coverings Inc	2591	E	858 974-7700	5182
Bonelli Fine Food Inc	2021	F	650 906-9896	558
Bourns Inc	3825	F	951 781-5360	21732
Box Co Inc	2752	F	619 661-8090	6703
Branan Medical Corporation **(PA)**	3841	E	949 598-7166	22381
Bravo Sports	3949	E	858 408-0083	23528
Breezaire Products Co	3443	F	858 566-7465	12366
Brehm Communications Inc **(PA)**	2752	E	858 451-6200	6705
Brett Corp	2759	E	858 292-4919	7257
Bridgewave Communications Inc	3357	E	408 567-6900	11647
Broadcom Corporation	3674	A	858 385-8800	18755
Brothers Enterprises Inc	7692	E	619 229-8003	25389
Bumble Bee Capital Corp	2091	C	858 715-4000	2289
Bumble Bee Foods LLC **(DH)**	2091	B	858 715-4000	2290
Bumble Bee Holdings Inc **(HQ)**	2013	B	858 566-1105	469
Bumble Bee Seafoods LP	2091	E	858 715-4000	2291
Bumble Bee Seafoods Inc	2091	E	858 715-4000	2292
Bumble Bee Seafoods Inc	2091	A	858 715-4068	2293
Bumbleride Inc	3944	F	619 615-0475	23414
Bumjin America Inc **(PA)**	3089	F	619 671-0386	9995
C & L Tool and Die Inc	3544	F	619 270-8385	14489
C A Botana International Inc **(PA)**	2844	E	858 450-1717	8711
C&D Zodiac Inc	3728	C	619 671-0430	20769
Ca Inc	7372	D	631 342-6000	24461
CA Skyhook Inc	2431	E	619 229-2169	4113
Cabinets Galore Orange County	2511	E	858 586-0555	4682
Cafe Virtuoso LLC	2095	F	619 550-1830	2331
Caffe Clabria Cof Roasters LLC	2095	E	619 683-7787	2335
California Commercial Asp Corp **(PA)**	2951	F	858 513-0611	9378
California Industrial Fabrics	2231	E	619 661-7166	2790
California Neon Products	3993	D	619 283-2191	23837
California Precision Pdts Inc	3444	D	858 638-7300	12523
California Scene Publishing	2752	F	858 635-9400	6717
Camino Neurocare	3841	D	858 455-1115	22386
Cannalink Inc	3823	F	310 921-1955	21557
Canyon Graphics Inc	2431	D	858 646-0444	4121
Caps & Tabs Inc	2023	E	619 285-5400	608
Carbomer Inc	2819	D	858 552-0992	7762
Care Fusion	3841	A	858 617-2000	22389
Carefusion 213 LLC **(DH)**	3841	B	800 523-0502	22392
Carefusion Corporation	3841	F	888 876-4287	22393
Carefusion Corporation **(HQ)**	3845	B	858 617-2000	22958
Carl Zeiss Vision Inc **(DH)**	3851	C	858 790-7700	23084
Carlson & Beauloye Air Pwr Inc	3599	F	619 232-5719	16363
Carlson & Beauloye Mach Sp Inc	3599	F	619 232-5719	16364
Carreon Development Inc	3993	F	619 690-4973	23841
Casual Fridays Inc	2741	E	858 433-1442	6457
Caterpillar Pwr Gnrtn Sys	3511	E	858 694-6629	13992
Cbj LP	2721	E	858 277-6359	6125
CBS Scientific Co Inc **(PA)**	3829	E	858 755-4959	22178
CCM Assembly & Mfg Inc	3679	E	760 560-1310	19481
Celgene Corporation	2834	D	858 558-7500	8106
Cellesta Inc	2835	F	858 552-0888	8468
Center Health Services	3826	F	619 692-2077	22931
Central Admxture Phrm Svcs Inc	2834	E	858 578-1380	8109
Central Marble Supply Inc	3281	F	619 595-1800	11240
Centurum Information Tech Inc	3357	E	619 224-1100	11652
Cg Financial LLC	2032	E	619 656-2919	753
Chantilly Bakery Inc	2051	F	858 693-3300	1219
Chemdiv Inc	2899	E	858 794-4860	9227
Chemtreat Inc	2899	E	804 935-2000	9229
Chosen Foods LLC **(PA)**	2899	F	877 674-2244	9231
Chrontrol Corporation **(PA)**	3613	F	619 282-8686	17135
Cidara Therapeutics Inc **(PA)**	2836	E	858 752-6170	8542
Cimmaron Software Inc	7372	E	858 385-1291	24489
Cimrmaan Ivo	3469	F	858 693-1536	13182
City of San Diego	3826	E	619 758-2310	21934
Clarify Medical Inc	3845	E	877 738-6041	22960
Classy Inc	7372	E	619 961-1892	24496
Clear Blue Energy Corp	3823	F	858 451-1549	21563
Clickscanshare Inc **(PA)**	3577	F	619 461-5880	15719
Clint Precision Mfg Inc	3599	F	858 271-4041	16386
Coastal Die Cutting Inc	3542	F	619 677-3180	14436
Coastline International	3845	C	888 748-7177	22964
Cobham Adv Elec Sol Inc	3812	C	858 560-1301	21271
Coda Automotive Inc	3714	F	619 291-2040	20295
Cognella Inc	2731	D	858 552-1120	6329
Cohuhd Costar LLC	3651	D	858 391-1800	17783
Coi Ceramics Inc	3728	E	858 621-5700	20783
Cold Pack System Inc	3086	F	858 586-0800	9828

	SIC	EMP	PHONE	ENTRY #
Coldstone Mira Mesa 114	2024	F	858 695-9771	664
Colmol Inc	2759	E	858 693-7575	7279
Colonnas Shipyard West LLC	3731	E	619 557-8373	20991
Colorcards 960	3471	E	858 535-9311	13376
Commercial Truss Co	2439	E	858 693-1771	4399
Commsystems LLC	3663	F	858 824-0056	18072
Competitor Group Inc **(HQ)**	2721	C	858 450-6510	6132
Competitor Magazine	2721	E	858 768-6800	6133
Compliance Products Usa Inc	3825	F	619 878-9696	21737
Composite Optics Incorporated	3769	A	937 490-4145	21189
Concise Fabricators Inc	3444	E	520 746-3226	12537
Concisys Inc	3825	E	858 292-5888	21738
Confident Technologies Inc	7372	E	858 345-5640	24520
Continental Controls Corp	3823	E	858 638-1709	21565
Continental Feature/ News Svc	2721	E	858 492-8696	6135
Continental Graphics Corp	2752	B	858 552-6520	6752
Continental Maritime Inds Inc	3731	B	619 234-8851	20992
Continuous Computing Corp	3571	C	858 882-8800	15403
Contrctor Cmpliance Monitoring	3822	E	619 472-9065	21507
Cool Jams Inc	2326	F	858 566-6165	3100
Copley Press Inc	7372	D	619 718-5200	24524
Coronado Leather Co Inc	2386	F	619 238-0265	3612
Corrugados De Baja California	2653	A	619 662-8672	5401
Corrugated and Packaging LLC	3086	C	619 559-1564	9830
Corrugated Technologies Inc	7372	F	858 578-3550	24528
Covidien Holding Inc	3841	A	619 690-8500	22411
CP Kelco Us Inc	2899	E	858 467-6542	9235
CP Kelco US Inc	2899	E	858 292-4900	9236
CP Kelco US Inc	2899	F	858 292-4900	9237
CP Manufacturing Inc **(HQ)**	3559	C	619 477-3175	14931
Crazy Industries	3949	E	619 270-9090	23545
Creative Computer Products	3089	E	858 458-1965	10049
Creative Design Industries	2321	C	619 710-2525	3053
Crest Beverage LLC	2026	B	858 452-2300	717
Cri 2000 LP **(PA)**	2499	E	619 542-1975	4617
Crinetics Pharmaceuticals Inc	2834	E	858 450-6464	8127
Crisi Medical Systems Inc	2834	F	858 754-8640	8128
Crower Engrg & Sls Co Inc	3714	C	619 690-7810	20301
Crydom Inc **(DH)**	3625	B	619 210-1590	17263
Cubic Corporation **(PA)**	3812	A	858 277-6780	21280
Cubic Defense Applications Inc	3812	D	619 661-1010	21281
Cubic Defense Applications Inc	3699	C	858 505-2870	19935
Cubic Defense Applications Inc **(HQ)**	3699	A	858 277-6780	19936
Cubic Trnsp Systems Inc **(HQ)**	3829	A	858 268-3100	22182
Cue Health Inc	2835	F	256 661-1656	8471
Curtis Technology Inc	3679	F	858 453-5797	19505
Custom Engineering Plastics LP	3089	F	858 452-0961	10053
Cutwater Spirits LLC	2899	E	858 672-3848	9238
Cv Sciences Inc	2833	F	866 290-2157	7931
Cydea Inc	2082	E	800 710-9939	1584
Cymer LLC **(HQ)**	3699	A	858 385-7300	19940
Cynergy3 Components Corp **(PA)**	3625	F	858 715-7200	17265
Cytori Therapeutics Inc **(PA)**	3841	D	858 458-0900	22416
D A M Bindery Inc	2789	F	858 621-7000	7596
Dal-Tile Corporation	2824	F	858 565-7767	7910
Dangerous Coffee Co LLC	3999	F	619 405-8291	24073
Dare Bioscience Inc	2834	F	858 926-7655	8133
Dassault Systemes Biovia Corp **(DH)**	7372	C	858 799-5000	24547
Dawn Sign Press Inc	2731	E	858 625-0600	6334
Daylight Defense LLC	3845	C	858 432-7500	22970
Daylight Solutions Inc **(DH)**	3674	C	858 432-7500	18799
De Soto Clothing Inc	2339	F	858 578-6672	3404
Decatur Electronics Inc **(HQ)**	3812	D	888 428-4315	21285
Decisionlogic LLC	7372	E	858 586-0202	24556
Del Mar Datatrac Inc	7372	F	858 550-8810	24557
Delphi Connection Systems LLC	3714	F	949 458-3155	20313
Delta Group Electronics Inc	3679	D	858 569-1681	19511
Dexcom Inc **(PA)**	3841	B	858 200-0200	22421
Dgb LLC	3949	E	858 578-0414	23548
Diego & Son Printing Inc	2752	E	619 233-5373	6784
Diggimac Inc DBA Ltg Element	3643	F	858 322-6000	17461
Digivision Inc	3823	F	858 530-0100	21572
Dinner On A Dollar Inc	2741	E	858 693-3939	6469
Diversfied Nano Solutions Corp	2893	E	858 924-1017	9190
Diversified Nano Corporation **(PA)**	3577	F	858 673-0387	15730
Diving Unlimited International	3949	D	619 236-1203	23550
Dove Tree Canyon Software Inc	7372	F	619 236-8895	24575
Dream Communications Inc	2721	F	619 275-9100	6151
Driscoll Inc	3732	E	619 226-2500	21031
Driscoll Mission Bay LLC	3732	F	619 223-5191	21032
Dynamic E-Markets LLC	2111	E	619 327-4777	2705
E Phocus Inc	3861	F	858 646-5462	23154
E Seek Inc	3577	F	714 832-7980	15734
E-Band Communications LLC	3663	E	858 408-0660	18093
Eclipse Chocolate Bar & Bistro	2066	F	619 578-2984	1469

Employment Codes: A=Over 500 employees, B=251-500,
C=101-250, D=51-100, E=20-50, F=10-19

2019 California
Manufacturers Register

© Mergent Inc. 1-800-342-5647

1449

GEOGRAPHIC

Company	SIC	EMP	PHONE	ENTRY #
Economy Print & Image Inc	2752	F	619 295-4455	6802
Ecr4kids LP	2531	E	619 323-2005	5012
Ectron Corporation	3663	E	858 278-0600	18094
Edgate Correlation Svcs LLC	3999	E	858 712-9341	24088
Effector Therapeutics Inc	3844	E	858 546-3997	22932
El Chavito Inc	2064	F	844 424-2848	1419
El Super Leon Pnchin Sncks Inc	2064	F	619 426-2968	1421
Elco Rfrgn Solutions LLC	3585	A	619 255-5251	15952
Eldema Products	3647	F	619 661-5113	17661
Eleanor Rigby Leather Co	3199	F	619 356-5590	10574
Electronic Mfg Tech Inc	3672	E	858 613-1040	18472
Electronic Prtg Solutions LLC	2759	F	858 576-3000	7309
Electronic Surfc Mounted Inds	3672	E	858 455-1710	18473
Elm System Inc	3695	F	408 694-2750	19862
Elsevier Inc	2741	D	619 231-6616	6475
Embedded Designs Inc	3823	E	858 673-6050	21579
Emerson Process Management	3823	F	858 492-1069	21581
Endura Technologies LLC	3674	F	858 412-2135	18822
Energy Labs Inc (DH)	3585	B	619 671-0100	15953
Enfora Inc	3679	D	972 234-1689	19535
Entegris Inc	3089	D	858 452-0124	10093
Enterprise Informatics Inc	7372	E	858 625-3000	24615
Envision Solar Intl Inc	3433	F	858 799-4583	12062
Epicson Inc	2759	F	858 558-5757	7311
Equity Ford Research	2741	F	858 755-1327	6478
Escient Pharmaceuticals Inc	2834	F	858 617-8236	8149
Eurus Energy America Corp (DH)	3621	F	858 638-7115	17195
Evofem Inc	3841	F	858 550-1900	22445
Evofem Biosciences Inc (PA)	2834	F	858 550-1900	8151
Express Business Systems Inc	2759	F	858 549-9828	7315
Factory Direct Dist Corp	2842	F	619 435-3437	8641
Farmer Bros Co	2095	E	858 292-7578	2342
Fastec Imaging Corporation	3861	F	858 592-2342	23160
Fate Therapeutics Inc	2836	E	858 875-1800	8551
Filmetrics Inc (PA)	3826	E	858 573-9300	21959
Fine Electronic Assembly Inc	3672	F	858 573-0887	18479
Finest Food Inc	2099	F	858 699-4746	2518
Fitness Warehouse LLC (PA)	3949	E	858 578-7676	23562
Flame-Spray Inc	3479	E	619 283-2007	13588
Flo TV Incorporated	3663	F	858 651-1645	18110
Flydive Inc (PA)	3949	F	844 359-3483	23564
FM Plastics	3089	F	619 661-5929	10102
Fondo De Cultura Economica	2731	F	619 429-0455	6340
Foresight Sports LLC	3949	E	858 880-0179	23565
Formex LLC	2834	E	858 529-6600	8164
Forterra Pipe & Precast LLC	3272	F	858 715-5600	10931
Found Image Press Inc	2771	F	619 282-3452	7563
Four Seasons Design Inc (PA)	2396	C	619 761-5151	3891
Fourward Machine Inc	3599	F	858 272-0601	16510
Fragmob LLC	7372	F	858 587-6659	24669
Franklin Wireless Corp	3661	D	858 623-0000	17952
Freedom Meditech Inc	3841	E	858 638-1433	22456
Frito-Lay North America Inc	2096	F	858 576-3300	2386
Fusion Food Factory	2051	F	858 578-8001	1257
Fyfe Co LLC (HQ)	3449	F	858 444-2970	12978
G W Manufacturing Jewelers	3911	F	619 234-5850	23265
G7 Productivity Systems	7372	D	858 675-1095	24680
Gamma Scientific Inc	3829	E	858 635-9008	22205
Ganpac Distribution LLC	2051	E	858 586-1868	1260
Gantner Instruments Inc	3825	E	858 537-2060	21761
Gb006 Inc	2834	D	858 684-1300	8169
GE Healthcare Inc	2833	E	858 279-9382	7942
Gen-Probe Incorporated	2835	D	858 410-8000	8478
Genalyte Inc	3841	E	858 956-1200	22460
General Atomic Aeron	3721	B	858 964-6700	20580
General Atomic Aeron	3721	E	858 455-2810	20582
General Atomic Aeron	3721	E	858 455-4309	20583
General Atomics Intl Svcs Corp	3721	E	858 455-4141	20587
General Dynamics Corporation	3731	E	619 544-3400	20995
General Dynamics Glbl IMG Tech	3625	D	619 671-5400	17271
General Dynmcs Mtion Ctrl LLC	3625	F	619 671-5400	17272
Genetronics Inc	3821	E	858 597-6006	21473
Genopis Inc	2834	E	858 875-4700	8180
Geodetics Inc	3812	E	858 729-0872	21299
Gfbc Inc	2082	F	858 622-0085	1594
Gilbert Martin Wdwkg Co Inc (PA)	2517	E	800 268-5669	4897
Glimmer Gear	3949	F	619 399-9211	23571
Global Orthopedic Inc	3842	F	480 861-5122	22737
Global Packaging Solutions Inc	2653	B	619 710-2661	5418
Global Polishing Solutions LLC (HQ)	3531	E	619 295-5505	14169
Gnosis International Llc	2835	E	858 254-6369	8480
Gold Peak Inds N Amer Inc	3691	E	858 674-6099	19810
Goto California Inc (HQ)	3651	C	619 691-8722	17804
Gpr Stabilizer LLC	3751	F	619 661-0101	21113
Gps Metals Lab Inc	3341	E	858 433-6125	11558
Granite Gold Inc	2842	F	858 499-8933	8644
Greathouse Screen Printing	2759	F	858 279-4939	7336
Greenlee Textron Inc	3825	D	858 530-3100	21766
Groundmetrics Inc	1389	F	619 786-8023	218
Gruma Corporation	2096	F	858 673-5780	2390
Guardian Corporate Services	2394	E	619 295-2646	3789
Gulbransen Inc	3931	F	619 296-5760	23374
Halozyme Therapeutics Inc (PA)	2836	D	858 794-8889	8557
Hanson Aggregates LLC	3241	E	619 299-8640	10753
Hanson Aggregates LLC	3241	E	858 577-2727	10754
Harbor Biosciences Inc (PA)	2834	F	858 587-9333	8203
Hardy Process Solutions	3823	E	858 278-2900	21597
Haro Industries Inc	3444	C	619 407-0500	12609
Harris Corporation	3812	E	619 684-7511	21305
Harris Corporation	3823	C	619 296-6900	21598
Healthline Systems LLC (HQ)	7372	E	858 673-1700	24722
Healthstream Inc	7372	B	800 733-8737	24723
Healthy Times	2099	F	858 513-1550	2535
Hemosense Inc	3845	D	408 719-1393	22983
Herley Industries Inc	3679	D	858 812-7300	19565
Heron Therapeutics Inc (PA)	2834	F	858 251-4400	8208
HI Tech Honeycomb Inc	3469	C	858 974-1600	13217
Hi-Q Environmental Pdts Co Inc	3826	F	858 549-2818	21965
Hi-Tech Electronic Mfg Corp	3672	F	858 657-0908	18499
Hi-Z Technology Inc	3629	F	858 695-6660	17342
Hii San Diego Shipyard Inc	3731	B	619 234-8851	20996
Hire Elegance	2599	F	858 740-7862	5236
Hirok Inc	3531	F	619 713-5066	14176
HK Enterprise Group Inc	2899	F	858 652-4400	9258
Hodge Products Inc	3429	F	619 444-3147	11961
Holiday Foliage Inc	3999	F	619 661-9094	24120
Hologic Inc	3845	E	858 410-8000	22984
Home Brew Mart Inc	2082	E	858 695-2739	1599
Home Brew Mart Inc (HQ)	2082	C	858 790-6900	1600
Honeywell International Inc	3822	C	619 671-5612	21514
Honeywell Safety Pdts USA Inc	3842	C	619 661-8383	22747
Hot Can Inc	2095	E	707 601-6013	2353
Houghton Mifflin Harcourt Pubg	2731	F	617 351-5000	6351
Howco Inc	3714	F	619 275-1663	20365
Hubbell Lighting Inc	3648	B	619 946-1800	17701
Hughes Network Systems LLC	3663	F	858 455-9550	18127
Hwa In America Inc (PA)	3679	F	619 567-4539	19570
Hy Jo Mfg Imports Corp	3499	E	619 671-1018	13946
Hyundai Translead (HQ)	3443	D	619 574-1500	12390
I/O Select Inc	3823	F	858 537-2060	21603
Ignyta Inc (PA)	2834	D	858 255-5959	8211
Ikanos Communications Inc (DH)	3674	C	858 587-1121	18881
Ikegami Mold Corp America	3089	F	619 858-6855	10148
Illumina Inc (PA)	3826	B	858 202-4500	21971
Illumina Inc	3826	C	858 202-4500	21973
Illumina Inc	3826	B	800 809-4566	21974
Imageware Systems Inc (PA)	7372	E	858 673-8600	24752
Imaging Technologies	3577	F	858 487-8944	15756
Imprimis Pharmaceuticals Inc (PA)	2834	E	858 704-4040	8217
Impulse Enterprise	3643	F	858 565-7050	17473
Impulse Enterprise	3643	D	858 565-7050	17474
Incharacter Costumes LLC	2389	E	858 552-3600	3659
Industrial Fire Sprnklr Co Inc	3569	E	619 266-6030	15333
Industrial SEC Allianc Ptnrs	3861	F	619 232-7041	23167
Inetwork Inc	3571	F	619 401-7334	15429
Informa Media Inc	2721	E	619 295-7685	6193
Ingenu Inc (PA)	3663	E	858 201-6000	18131
Inno Tech Machining Inc	3599	F	858 565-4556	16584
Innominata	2835	F	858 592-9300	8485
Innophase Inc	3674	D	619 541-8280	18897
Innovacon Inc	2835	D	858 805-8900	8486
Innovive LLC (PA)	3496	E	858 309-6620	13833
Inovio Pharmaceuticals Inc	2836	E	267 440-4200	8561
Instant Imprints Franchising	2752	E	858 642-4848	6888
Integer Holdings Corporation	3675	F	619 498-9448	19296
Integra Lfscnces Holdings Corp	3841	E	609 529-9748	22481
Integrated Dna Tech Inc	2836	F	858 410-6677	8562
Integrated Energy Tech Inc	3562	C	619 421-1151	15107
Integrated Microwave Corp	3679	D	858 259-2600	19580
Intel Network Systems Inc	3577	F	858 877-4652	15766
Intelicare Direct Inc	2752	F	702 765-0867	6892
Intelligent Blends LP	2043	E	858 888-7937	1062
Intelligent Technologies LLC	3629	C	858 458-1500	17343
Intercept Pharmaceuticals Inc	2834	F	646 747-1005	8224
Intercontinental Cof Trdg LLC	2095	F	619 338-8335	2354
Interdigital Inc	3663	E	858 210-4800	18132
Interior Wood of San Diego	2521	F	619 295-6469	4950
Internacional De Elevadores SA	3534	F	619 955-6180	14252
International Mfg Tech Inc (DH)	3312	E	619 544-7741	11400
International Technidyne Corp (DH)	3841	C	858 263-2300	22484

Mergent email: customerrelations@mergent.com

1450

2019 California
Manufacturers Register

(P-0000) Products & Services Section entry number
(PA)=Parent Co (HQ)=Headquarters (DH)=Div Headquarters

Name	SIC	EMP	PHONE	ENTRY #
Internet Strategy Inc	7372	F	858 673-6022	24785
Interocean Industries Inc	3812	E	858 292-0808	21308
Interocean Systems LLC	3812	E	858 565-8400	21309
Intuit Inc	7372	E	858 215-8726	24791
Intuit Inc	7372	B	858 215-8000	24798
Iq-Analog Corporation	3674	E	858 200-0388	18931
Irisys LLC	2834	E	858 623-1520	8234
Isec Incorporated	3821	C	858 279-9085	21478
Ivera Medical LLC	3841	D	888 861-8228	22498
J M Mills Communications Inc (HQ)	3663	E	613 321-2100	18135
JA Ferrari Print Imaging LLC	2752	F	619 295-8307	6905
James Gang Company	2396	F	619 225-1283	3899
James Gang Custom Printing	2752	F	619 225-1283	6906
Jamis Software Corporation	7372	F	858 300-5542	24813
Janssen Research & Dev LLC	2834	C	858 450-2000	8238
Jay Brewer	2752	E	858 488-4871	6908
Jay Edward Group LLC	2599	E	858 799-1227	5239
Jeld-Wen Inc	2431	E	800 468-3667	4172
Jem-Hd Co Inc	3089	C	619 710-1443	10167
Jensen Meat Company Inc	2013	D	619 754-6400	496
JImachine Company Inc	3599	E	858 695-1787	16624
Jjs Truck Equipment LLC	3713	E	858 566-1155	20211
Joaos A Tin Fish Bar & Eatery	3356	E	619 794-2192	11632
John B Campbell MD A Prof Corp	2869	F	858 576-9960	9016
Johnson Controls	3669	C	858 633-9100	18333
K & B Foam Inc	3086	C	619 661-1870	9867
Kaar Drect Mail Flfillment LLC	2711	E	619 382-3670	5897
Kahoots Inc	3999	F	619 337-0825	24144
Kai Os Technologies Sftwr Inc	7372	F	858 547-3940	24823
Karl Strauss Brewing Company (PA)	2082	D	858 273-2739	1603
Katolec Development Inc	3679	E	619 710-0075	19606
Kavlico Corporation	3679	E	805 523-2000	19608
Keco Inc	3594	F	619 546-9533	16167
Kelco Bio Polymers	2899	E	619 595-5000	9266
Kelpac Medical	3082	D	619 710-2550	9741
Kia Incorporated (PA)	3149	E	858 824-2999	10506
Kieran Label Corp	2672	E	619 449-4457	5563
Kings Printing Corp	2752	E	619 297-6000	6923
Kintera Inc (HQ)	7372	D	858 795-3000	24833
Kjm Enterprises Inc	2759	E	858 537-2490	7369
Kontron America Inc	3571	D	800 822-7522	15439
Kontron America Incorporated (DH)	3571	C	858 677-0877	15440
Kovin Corporation Inc	2752	E	858 558-0100	6929
Krasnes Inc	2386	D	619 232-2066	3619
Kratos Def & SEC Solutions Inc (PA)	3663	B	858 812-7300	18148
Kratos Tech Trning Sltions Inc (HQ)	7372	C	858 812-7300	24841
KS Industries	3999	F	858 344-1146	24152
Ksc Industries Inc	3651	E	619 671-0110	17824
Kuantum Brands LLC	2086	C	760 412-2432	2146
Kyocera International Inc (HQ)	3674	E	858 492-1456	18946
Kyocera International Inc	3674	D	858 614-2581	18947
Kyriba Corp (HQ)	7372	E	858 210-3560	24844
Kyung In Printing Inc	2752	C	619 662-3920	6932
L-3 Communications Corporation	3663	F	858 694-7500	18150
L3 Applied Technologies Inc (HQ)	3663	E	858 404-7824	18151
L3 Applied Technologies Inc	3663	E	858 404-7824	18152
L3 Technologies Inc	3663	B	858 279-0411	18153
L3 Technologies Inc	3663	E	858 552-9716	18157
L3 Technologies Inc	3663	E	858 552-9500	18159
Label ID Technologies Inc	2759	F	619 661-5566	7373
Lansing Industries Inc	3999	F	858 523-0719	24157
Leadcrunch Inc (PA)	7372	F	888 708-6649	24853
Leatherock International Inc	3111	E	619 299-7625	10462
Ledpac LLC	3993	D	760 489-8067	23913
Legacy Vulcan LLC	3273	E	858 566-2730	11130
Legendary Holdings Inc	2353	E	619 872-6100	3565
Leidos Inc	3577	E	619 524-2581	15787
Lenus Handcrafted	2844	F	619 200-4266	8788
Leon Assembly Solutions Inc	3264	D	858 397-2826	10819
Lifeome Biolabs Inc	2835	F	619 302-0129	8490
Ligand Pharmaceuticals Inc	2834	E	858 550-7500	8260
Ligand Pharmaceuticals Inc (PA)	2834	E	858 550-7500	8261
Light Mobile Inc	3843	F	858 278-1750	22892
Lilly Biotechnology Center	2834	F	858 597-4990	8262
Lilly Tortilleria	2099	E	619 281-2890	2585
Limited Access Unlimited Inc	1481	F	619 294-3682	406
Linear Technology LLC	3674	D	408 432-1900	18966
Litel Instruments Inc	3825	E	858 546-3788	21792
Loanhero Inc	7372	F	888 912-4376	24863
Lockheed Martin Corporation	3812	C	858 740-5100	21332
Lockheed Martin Corporation	3812	E	858 740-5100	21338
Lockheed Martin Corporation	3721	B	619 298-8453	20601
Logisterra Inc	3161	E	619 280-9992	10526
Loud Mouth Inc	3949	E	619 743-0370	23609
Lrad Corporation (PA)	3651	E	858 676-1112	17825
Lytx Inc (PA)	3812	B	858 430-4000	21344
M B C Reprographics Inc	2759	E	858 541-1500	7393
M V Outer Limits	3732	F	858 689-1828	21051
Mabvax Thrpeutics Holdings Inc (PA)	2834	F	858 259-9405	8266
Machine Craft of San Diego	3599	E	858 642-0509	16704
Mad Engine LLC (PA)	2261	E	858 558-5270	2885
Maddox Defense Inc	2399	F	818 378-8246	3953
Magic-Flight General Mfg Inc	2499	C	619 288-4638	4635
Magnabiosciences LLC	3841	D	858 481-4400	22516
Magnebit Holding Corporation (PA)	3825	D	858 573-0727	21797
Mamma Linas Incorporated	2099	E	858 535-0620	2594
Mannis Communications Inc	2711	E	858 270-3103	5937
Mannis Communications Inc	2711	E	858 270-3103	5938
Manta Instruments	3826	F	858 449-5801	21986
Manzer Corporation	2391	E	619 295-6031	3696
Marathon Machine Inc	3599	F	858 578-8670	16713
Marcoa Media LLC (PA)	2741	E	858 635-9627	6523
Marcoa Quality Publishing LLC	2741	D	858 695-9600	6524
Marine & Rest Fabricators Inc	3444	E	619 232-7267	12652
Marine Tech	3732	F	619 225-0448	21053
Marinesync Corporation	3823	E	619 578-2953	21616
Maritime Solutions LLC	3732	E	619 234-2676	21054
Marketing Pro Consulting Inc	7372	E	619 233-8591	24882
Mast Biosurgery USA Inc	3842	E	858 550-8050	22766
Master Productions Inc	2752	F	858 677-0037	6964
Matthey Johnson Inc	3341	C	858 716-2400	11560
Matthey Johnson Inc	3341	C	858 716-2400	11561
Maxwell Technologies Inc (PA)	3694	B	858 503-3300	19838
Mbf Interiors Inc	2391	E	858 565-2944	3697
McAfee Inc	7372	E	858 967-2342	24890
McKinnon Enterprises	2721	E	858 571-1818	6215
McV Technologies Inc	3663	F	858 450-0468	18176
Med-Safe Systems Inc	3841	E	855 236-2772	22522
Medical Transcription Billing	7372	A	800 869-3700	24898
Medtronic Inc	3845	B	949 798-3934	23009
Medwaves Inc (PA)	3841	E	858 946-0015	22535
Meggitt (san Diego) Inc (DH)	3728	C	858 824-8976	20882
MEI Pharma Inc	2834	E	858 369-7100	8276
Memjet Labels Inc (DH)	3577	F	858 798-3300	15802
Memjet Labels Inc	3577	F	858 798-3061	15803
Merck Sharp & Dohme Corp	2834	D	619 292-4900	8279
Merrill Corporation	2759	D	858 623-0300	7402
Metal Master Inc	3444	E	858 292-8880	12668
Mgx Copy (PA)	2752	F	877 649-5463	6972
MI Technologies Inc	3672	C	619 710-2637	18530
Michael Martella	2732	C	858 695-9600	6420
Microbiotic Health Foods Inc	2052	E	858 273-5775	1371
Microsoft Corporation	7372	E	858 909-3800	24910
Microsoft Corporation	7372	D	619 849-5872	24912
Miller Machine Works LLC	3599	F	619 501-9866	16751
Miller Marine	3731	E	619 791-1500	21002
Mirati Therapeutics Inc	2834	D	858 332-3410	8284
Mlim LLC	2711	A	619 299-3131	5974
Modern Times Beer	2711	E	619 269-5222	5975
Moebius Design	2796	E	858 450-4486	7653
Mohammad Khan	3089	F	619 231-1664	10218
Monaco Sheet Metal	3444	F	858 272-0297	12685
Montbleau & Associates Inc (PA)	2521	D	619 263-5550	4955
Morgan Polymer Seals LLC (PA)	3053	E	858 679-4946	9544
Motorlamb International Acc	2399	F	858 569-8111	3955
Motorola Solutions Inc	3674	F	858 541-2163	19026
Motsenbocker Advanced Developm (PA)	2842	F	858 581-0222	8657
Mrv Systems LLC	3825	E	800 645-7114	21808
Musicmatch Inc	7372	C	858 485-4300	24939
Mv Excel	3949	F	619 223-7493	23623
Mya International Inc	2834	F	619 429-6012	8287
Mygrant Glass Company Inc	3714	E	858 455-8022	20408
Nadolife Inc	2024	D	619 522-6890	687
Nankai Enviro-Tech Corporation	3089	C	619 754-2250	10229
Nanoimaging Services Inc	3826	F	888 675-8261	21998
Nantkwest Inc (HQ)	2836	E	805 633-0300	8567
National Pen Co LLC (DH)	3951	C	866 388-9850	23700
National Stl & Shipbuilding Co (HQ)	3731	B	619 544-3400	21004
Natus Medical Incorporated	3845	D	858 260-2590	23023
Neil A Kjos Music Company (PA)	2741	E	858 270-9800	6536
Neil A Kjos Music Company	2741	E	619 225-6710	6537
Neil Patel Digital LLC	2741	E	619 356-8119	6538
Neo Tech Aqua Solutions Inc	2899	E	858 571-6590	9290
Neology Inc (HQ)	3825	E	858 391-0260	21814
Nerveda Inc	2834	D	858 705-2365	8298
Network Vigilance LLC	7372	E	858 695-8676	24956
Neurocrine Biosciences Inc (PA)	2834	C	858 617-7600	8299
Nevwest Inc	3812	E	619 420-8100	21356
New Bi US Gaming LLC	7372	D	858 592-2472	24958
Nextivity Inc (PA)	3663	E	858 485-9442	18200

Company	SIC	EMP	PHONE	ENTRY #
Nextpharma Tech USA Inc	2834	E	858 450-3123	8304
Nexus Dx Inc	3841	B	858 410-4600	22558
Neyenesch Printers Inc	2752	D	619 297-2281	6992
Nishiba Industries Corporation	3089	A	619 661-8866	10241
Niterider Technical Lighting &	3648	E	858 268-9316	17720
Nlp Furniture Industries Inc	2599	C	619 661-5170	5247
No Boundaries Inc	2752	E	619 266-2349	6995
No Second Thoughts Inc	2311	D	619 428-5992	3037
Non-Linear Systems	3823	F	619 521-2161	21624
North County Times (DH)	2711	C	800 533-8830	5999
North Sails Group LLC	2394	D	619 226-1415	3799
Northrop Grumman Corporation	3812	A	858 967-1221	21360
Northrop Grumman Corporation	3812	A	858 618-7617	21364
Northrop Grumman Corporation	3812	A	858 514-9259	21365
Northrop Grumman Innovation	3764	B	858 621-5700	21179
Northrop Grumman Systems Corp	3721	F	858 514-9020	20608
Northrop Grumman Systems Corp	3812	A	858 618-4349	21371
Northrop Grumman Systems Corp	3812	C	858 514-9000	21374
Northwest Circuits Corp	3672	D	619 661-1701	18546
Novartis Corporation	2834	E	858 812-1741	8308
Nu Visions De Mexico SA De Cv	3999	C	619 987-0518	24193
Nuvasive Inc (PA)	3841	D	858 909-1800	22561
Nypro Healthcare Baja Inc	3841	A	619 498-9250	22563
O & S California Inc	3699	B	619 661-1800	20035
Oberon Fuels Inc (PA)	2911	F	619 255-9361	9342
Ocean Aero Inc	3812	E	858 945-3768	21376
OCP Group Inc	3575	E	858 279-7400	15643
Ocunexus Therapeutics Inc	2834	F	858 480-2403	8315
Odonate Therapeutics Inc	2834	E	858 731-8180	8316
Offshore Promotion Inc (PA)	3089	F	619 690-2622	10254
Oggis Pizza & Brewing Co	2082	E	858 481-7883	1616
Omnitracs Midco LLC (PA)	7372	E	858 651-5812	24982
On-Line Stampco Inc	3953	E	800 373-5614	23721
One Resonance Sensors LLC	3674	F	407 637-0771	19059
Opera Patisserie Fines Inc (PA)	2053	E	858 536-5800	1400
Optec Laser Systems LLC	2759	E	858 220-1070	7421
Oracle America Inc	7372	D	858 625-5044	25004
Oracle Corporation	7372	C	858 202-0648	25014
Orca Arms LLC	3949	D	858 586-0503	23626
Orca Systems Inc	3672	E	858 679-9295	18551
Organovo Inc	2836	C	858 224-1000	8569
Ormet Circuits Inc	3679	E	858 831-0010	19677
Otonomy Inc	2834	D	619 323-2200	8322
Overland Storage Inc (HQ)	3572	C	858 571-5555	15580
P & R Paper Supply Co Inc	2679	F	619 671-2400	5721
Pacific Biotech Inc	2835	C	858 552-1100	8503
Pacific Diversified Capital Co	3829	A	619 696-2000	22246
Pacific Imaging	2752	F	858 536-2600	7011
Pacific Maritime Inds Corp	3441	C	619 575-8141	12224
Pacific Mfg Inc San Diego	3599	E	619 423-0316	16821
Pacific Millennium US Corp	2621	F	858 450-1505	5320
Pacific Pulp Molding Inc	2621	E	619 977-5617	5321
Pacific Ship Repr Fbrction Inc (PA)	3731	B	619 232-3200	21007
Pacific Steel Group (PA)	3449	D	858 251-1100	12987
Pacificgmp	2836	E	858 550-4094	8570
Pacira Pharmaceuticals Inc	2834	E	858 678-3950	8326
Pall Corporation	3569	D	858 455-7264	15346
Pan Probe Biotech Inc	3841	F	858 689-9936	22579
Panasonic Appliances Ref	3632	E	619 661-1134	17380
Pappalecco	3499	F	619 906-5566	13962
Parker-Hannifin Corporation	3594	C	619 661-7000	16169
Paxvax Inc	2836	F	858 450-9595	8571
PDM Solutions Inc	3672	E	858 348-1000	18558
Pearl Rove Inc	3961	F	858 869-1827	23756
PEC of America Corporation (HQ)	3613	F	619 710-8131	17154
Pepsi-Cola Metro Btlg Co Inc	2086	B	858 560-6735	2172
Performance Label Intl Inc	2759	F	619 429-6870	7434
Performance Plastics Inc	3728	C	619 482-5031	20909
Pfenex Inc	2834	D	858 352-4400	8330
Pfizer Inc	2834	C	858 622-7325	8332
Pfizer Inc	2834	A	858 622-3001	8333
Pgac Corp (PA)	2671	D	858 560-8213	5532
PH Labs Advanced Nutrition	2834	F	619 240-3263	8334
Phase II Products Inc (PA)	2591	E	619 236-9699	5205
Photostone LLC	3555	F	858 274-3400	14824
Phyto Animal Health LLC	2023	F	888 871-4505	645
Pico Digital Inc (DH)	3663	D	858 546-5050	18219
Pioneer Automotive Tech Inc	3663	F	937 746-6600	18221
Pixon Imaging Inc	3826	F	858 352-0100	22006
Pk Industries Inc	3161	D	619 428-6382	10530
Plantronics Inc	3661	F	831 458-7089	17978
Plural Publishing Inc	2731	F	858 492-1555	6382
Polaris Pharmaceuticals Inc	2834	E	858 452-6688	8340
Polymerex Medical Corp	3082	E	858 695-0765	9743
Port 80 Software Inc	7372	E	858 274-4497	25070
Potentia Labs Inc	7372	F	951 603-3531	25073
Power Efficiency Corporation	3621	F	858 750-3875	17217
PPG Architectural Finishes Inc	2821	F	619 284-2772	7874
Praxair Distribution Inc	2813	F	619 232-7341	7727
Pressnet Express Inc	2752	F	858 694-0070	7036
Prestige Flag & Banner Co	2399	D	619 497-2220	3958
Price Industries Inc	3312	D	858 673-4451	11411
Primapharma Inc	2834	E	858 259-0969	8344
Princess Brandy Corp (PA)	2051	F	619 563-9722	1311
Printer Cartridge USA	3861	F	858 538-7630	23190
Pro Line Paint Company	2851	E	619 232-8968	8933
Procede Software LP	7372	E	858 450-4800	25081
Prometheus Laboratories Inc	2834	B	858 824-0895	8347
Promex Industries Incorporated	3674	E	858 674-4676	19087
Pronto Products Co (PA)	3589	C	619 661-6095	16092
Provasis Therapeutics Inc	3841	E	858 712-2101	22590
Providien Thermoforming Inc (HQ)	3081	E	858 850-1591	9723
Psemi Corporation (DH)	3674	D	858 731-9400	19090
Psiber Data Systems Inc	3674	F	619 287-9970	19091
Publishers Development Corp	2721	E	858 605-0200	6238
Pulse Electronics Inc (DH)	3612	B	858 674-8100	17116
Pulse Electronics Corporation (HQ)	3679	D	858 674-8100	19693
Pyr Preservation Services	3731	E	619 338-8395	21011
Pyramid Precision Machine Inc	3599	D	858 642-0713	16867
Q-Vio LLC	3679	F	858 777-8299	19696
Q3-Cnc Inc	3599	F	858 790-0002	16868
QED Systems Inc	3699	F	619 424-3225	20050
Quake Global Inc (PA)	3661	D	858 277-7290	17984
Qualcomm Datacenter Tech Inc (HQ)	3674	F	858 567-1121	19098
Qualcomm Incorporated (PA)	3663	B	858 587-1121	18229
Qualcomm Incorporated	3674	B	858 909-0316	19102
Qualcomm Incorporated	3674	B	858 587-1121	19103
Qualcomm Incorporated	3663	B	858 587-1121	18230
Qualcomm Incorporated	3674	B	858 587-1121	19104
Qualcomm Innovation Center Inc (HQ)	7372	E	858 587-1121	25095
Qualcomm Limited Partner Inc	3674	E	858 587-1121	19105
Qualcomm Mems Technologies Inc	3669	E	858 587-1121	18356
Qualcomm Technologies Inc (HQ)	3674	C	858 587-1121	19106
Quality Cabinet and Fixture Co (HQ)	2434	E	619 266-1011	4337
Quality Systems Intgrated Corp (PA)	3672	B	858 587-9797	18574
Quantum Design Inc (PA)	3826	C	858 481-4400	22009
Quantum Dynasty	3572	F	347 469-1047	15591
Quantum Group Inc	3829	D	858 566-9959	22254
Quidel Corporation (PA)	2835	B	858 552-1100	8507
Quidel Corporation	2835	F	858 552-1100	8508
Quikrete Companies LLC	3272	E	858 549-2371	10987
Quorum Systems Inc	3674	F	858 546-0895	19112
R J Reynolds Tobacco Company	2111	C	858 625-8453	2708
R R Donnelley & Sons Company	2759	C	619 527-4600	7462
R R Donnelley & Sons Company	2759	C	619 527-4600	7463
Radx Technologies Inc	3825	F	619 677-1849	21838
Ranroy Company	2752	E	858 571-8800	7074
Rayotek Scientific Inc	3231	D	858 558-7651	10728
Raytheon Company	3812	C	619 628-3345	21393
Raytheon Company	3812	F	858 571-6598	21409
Raytheon Dgital Force Tech LLC	3812	E	858 546-1244	21411
Rdl Machine Inc	3599	E	858 693-3975	16888
Real Marketing	2741	E	858 847-0335	6565
Reel Picture Productions LLC	3695	E	858 587-0301	19880
Regent Publishing Services	2741	E	760 510-1936	6567
Reid & Clark Screen Arts Co	2262	F	619 233-7541	2904
Remcor Technical Industries	3812	E	619 424-8878	21412
Remec Broadband Wire	3663	C	858 312-6900	18238
Remec Broadband Wireless LLC (PA)	3663	C	858 312-6900	18239
Remote Ocean Systems Inc (PA)	3648	E	858 565-8500	17728
Rempex Pharmaceuticals Inc	2834	E	858 875-2840	8360
Renesas Electronics Amer Inc	3674	A	858 451-7240	19123
Repro Magic	2752	F	858 277-2488	7083
Res Med Inc	3841	E	858 746-2400	22600
Resmed Inc (PA)	3841	B	858 836-5000	22601
Respiratory Support Products	3841	E	619 710-1000	22602
Retrophin Inc (PA)	2834	E	760 260-8600	8362
Reva Medical Inc	3842	E	858 966-3000	22804
Reveal Imaging Tech Inc	3812	D	858 826-9909	21413
Reyes Coca-Cola Bottling LLC	2086	E	619 266-6300	2201
Rf Industries Ltd (PA)	3678	E	858 549-6340	19411
Rf-Lambda Usa LLC	3625	F	972 767-5998	17298
Rhino Linings Corporation (PA)	3563	D	858 450-0441	15136
Rhino Manufacturing Group Inc	3312	D	858 869-4010	11416
Richard Matz	2711	E	858 537-2280	6027
Richmond Engineering Co Inc	3999	D	800 589-7058	24223
Ridout Plastics Company	3081	E	858 560-1551	9724
Right Manufacturing LLC	3498	E	858 560-1551	13902
Rivera Yarn Products Inc	2241	E	619 661-6306	2804
Rj Machine Inc	3599	F	858 547-9482	16904

Company	SIC	EMP	PHONE	ENTRY #
Roa Pacific Inc	2821	F	619 565-2800	7880
Robanda International Inc	2844	E	619 276-7660	8830
Rock West Composites Inc (PA)	3083	E	801 566-3402	9764
Romla Co	3444	E	619 946-1224	12739
Rtmex Inc	2426	C	619 391-9913	4091
Rush Press Inc	2752	E	619 296-7874	7091
Rusty Surfboards Inc (PA)	3949	E	858 578-0414	23644
S K Digital Imaging Inc	2789	F	858 408-0732	7616
S R C Devices Inccustomer (PA)	3625	F	866 772-8668	17306
Sabia Incorporated (PA)	3823	E	858 217-2200	21647
Saehan Electronics America Inc (PA)	3672	F	858 496-1500	18587
Safran Pwr Units San Diego LLC	3724	D	858 223-2228	20678
Sago Systems Inc	3812	F	858 646-5300	21422
Saint-Gobain Solar Gard LLC (DH)	3081	D	866 300-2674	9725
San Dego Gographic Info Source	2741	F	858 874-7000	6574
San Dego Prcsion Machining Inc	3444	E	858 499-0379	12751
San Diego Ace Inc	3089	C	619 252-3148	10357
San Diego Afr Amrcn Gnlogy RSC	3999	E	619 231-5810	24227
San Diego County Truss Inc	2439	F	619 286-8787	4420
San Diego Family Magazine LLC	2721	F	619 685-6970	6252
San Diego Guide Inc	2741	E	858 877-3217	6575
San Diego Instruments Inc	3821	E	858 530-2600	21489
San Diego Magazine Pubg Co	2721	E	619 230-9292	6253
San Diego Pcb Design LLC	3672	F	858 271-5722	18588
San Diego Precast Concrete Inc (HQ)	3272	E	619 240-8000	10997
San Diego Union-Tribune LLC	2711	D	619 299-3131	6033
San Diego Union-Tribune LLC (PA)	2711	A	619 299-3131	6034
Sanders Composites Inc (DH)	3728	E	858 571-5220	20924
Santarus Inc	2834	E	858 314-5700	8373
Santier Inc	3674	D	858 271-1993	19136
Sapphire Energy Inc	2833	D	858 768-4700	7971
Sauvage Inc (PA)	2329	F	858 408-0100	3187
Sawhney Garcia Hernandez	2387	F	619 564-8400	3632
Schlage Lock Company LLC	3429	F	619 671-0276	11991
Schneider Electric Usa Inc	3613	C	858 385-5040	17161
Scholastic Sports Inc	2752	D	858 496-9221	7097
Schott Magnetics	3499	F	619 661-7510	13971
Scientific-Atlanta LLC	3812	B	619 679-6000	21427
Scripps Laboratories Inc	2836	E	858 546-5800	8581
SD Desserts LLC	2099	F	702 480-9083	2664
Seal For Life Industries LLC	3999	F	619 671-0932	24235
Seating Concepts LLC	2531	E	619 491-3159	5027
Seescan Inc (PA)	3546	C	858 244-3300	14710
Sekisui America Corporation	2835	E	858 452-3198	8510
Sempra Global (PA)	3612	D	619 696-2000	17120
Semtech San Diego Corporation	3674	E	858 695-1808	19147
Semtek Innvtive Solutions Corp	3577	E	858 436-2270	15850
Senior Aerospace Jet Pdts Corp (HQ)	3724	C	858 278-8400	20679
Senior Operations LLC	3599	B	858 278-8400	16937
Senior Operations LLC	3599	E	858 278-8400	16939
Shamir Insight Inc	3229	D	858 514-8330	10667
Sheffield Platers Inc	3471	E	858 546-8484	13503
Shelter Island Yachtways Ltd	3732	E	619 222-0481	21063
Shields Enterprises Inc	3541	E	619 276-9100	14412
Sidus Solutions LLC (PA)	3699	F	619 275-5533	20066
Sigma 6 Electronics Inc	3699	F	858 279-4300	20069
Sigma Circuit Technology LLC	3672	D	858 523-0146	18604
Signtech Electrical Advg Inc	3993	C	619 527-6100	23973
Silver Moon Lighting Inc	3645	F	858 613-3600	17561
Skagfield Corporation	2591	B	858 635-7777	5211
SKF Condition Monitoring Inc (DH)	3829	C	858 496-3400	22272
Skyepharma Inc	2834	E	858 678-3950	8384
Smart-Tek Automated Svcs Inc (HQ)	7372	F	858 798-1644	25182
Smartdraw Software LLC	7372	E	858 225-3300	25183
Smith Brothers Manufacturing	3599	F	619 296-3171	16949
Smithcorp Inc	2621	E	888 402-9979	5336
Smiths Medical Asd Inc	3842	E	619 710-1000	22816
Smooth Operator LLC	3949	E	619 233-8177	23653
Smooth Run Equine Inc	2048	F	760 751-8988	1165
Snaptracs Inc	3812	F	858 587-1121	21433
So Cal Soft-Pak Incorporated	7372	E	619 283-2338	25189
Solar Turbines Incorporated (HQ)	3511	A	619 544-5000	14004
Solar Turbines Incorporated	3566	E	619 544-5352	15247
Solar Turbines Incorporated	3511	C	858 715-2060	14005
Solar Turbines Intl Co (DH)	3511	E	619 544-5000	14007
Solar Turbines Intl Co	3511	E	858 694-1616	14008
Solectek Corporation	3663	E	858 450-1220	18256
Solv Inc	7372	E	858 622-4040	25196
Sonant Corporation	3661	F	858 623-8180	17993
Soncell North America Inc (HQ)	3812	E	619 795-4600	21434
Sonic Vr LLC	7372	F	206 227-8585	25200
Sony Corporation of America (PA)	3571	E	212 833-8000	15489
Sony Electronics Inc (DH)	3651	A	858 942-2400	17859
Sony Electronics Inc.	3651	E	858 942-2400	17860
Sony Electronics Inc.	3671	C	858 942-2400	18396
Sony Electronics Inc.	3652	E	858 824-6960	17913
Sony Interactive Entrmt LLC	7372	E	858 207-1500	25202
Sotera Wireless Inc	3845	C	858 427-4620	23052
Sound Imaging Inc	3845	F	858 622-0082	23053
South Bay Cstm Plstic Extrders	3089	E	619 544-0808	10382
South Pacific Tuna Corporation	2091	F	619 233-2060	2303
South Swell Screen Arts	2759	F	858 566-3095	7490
Southwest Products LLC	2099	C	619 263-8000	2671
Space Micro Inc	3663	D	858 332-0700	18258
Spec-Built Systems Inc	3444	D	619 661-8100	12768
Specialty Steel Products Inc	3496	F	664 637-6704	13853
Spectral Labs Incorporated	3829	E	858 451-0540	22278
Spectrum Accessory Distrs	3714	C	858 653-6470	20454
Speedplay Inc	3949	E	858 453-4707	23657
Speedy Bindery Inc	2789	E	619 275-0261	7622
Sportrx Inc	3851	E	858 571-1240	23124
Ssco Manufacturing Inc	3548	E	619 628-1022	14740
STA Pharmaceutical US LLC	2834	E	609 606-6499	8392
Stats Chippac Test Svcs Inc	3674	E	858 228-4084	19188
Steelcase Inc	2521	B	619 671-1040	4969
Steris Corporation	3699	D	858 586-1166	20080
Steven Madden Ltd	3143	D	619 690-9761	10487
Stingray Shields Corp	3842	F	619 325-9003	22821
Stone Yard Inc	2519	E	858 586-1580	4920
Stoneybrook Publishing Inc.	2731	E	858 674-4600	6395
Strafford Intl Group Inc	2542	F	619 446-6960	5169
Strategic Insights Inc	7372	D	858 452-7500	25227
Streeter Printing Inc	2752	E	858 566-0866	7120
Sumitronics USA Inc	3672	E	619 661-0450	18619
Suneva Medical Inc (PA)	2844	E	858 550-9999	8851
Sungear Inc.	3728	E	858 549-3166	20940
Sunline Energy Inc	3674	E	858 997-2408	19200
Sunrise Jewelry Mfg Corp	3911	B	619 270-5624	23322
Superior Labs Inc	2834	F	888 708-5227	8400
Superior Ready Mix Concrete LP	3273	E	619 265-0955	11190
Superior Ready Mix Concrete LP	3273	E	619 265-0296	11191
Superlamb Inc	2386	E	858 566-2031	3623
Surface Optics Corp	3825	E	858 675-7404	21857
Surface Technologies Corp	3625	E	619 564-8320	17312
Symcoat Metal Processing Inc	3471	E	858 451-3313	13519
Synbiotics LLC	2835	E	858 451-3771	8518
Systech Corporation	3669	E	858 674-6500	18368
T L Clark Co Inc	2434	E	619 230-1400	4355
T-Rex Products Incorporated	3999	F	619 482-4424	24262
Tabor Communications Inc.	2741	F	858 625-0070	6600
Tachyon Networks Incorporated	3663	D	858 882-8100	18270
Tandem Diabetes Care Inc (PA)	3841	C	858 366-6900	22643
Tangoe Inc.	7372	D	858 452-6800	25255
Tanvex Biologics Inc.	2834	E	858 210-4100	8406
Tapioca Express	2046	F	619 286-0484	1103
Tara Materials Inc.	3952	E	619 671-1018	23712
Taylor Communications Inc.	2761	F	866 541-0937	7556
Tdk Electronics Inc.	3679	F	858 485-4640	19744
Tdo Software Inc	7372	E	858 558-3696	25258
Te Connectivity Corporation	3678	C	619 454-5176	19420
Teal Electronics Corporation (PA)	3625	D	858 558-9000	17316
Tech4learning Inc (PA)	7372	F	619 283-6028	25261
Technology For Energy Corp	3825	F	858 278-4900	21863
Tecnova Advanced Systems Inc	3812	E	858 586-9660	21437
Tek84 Engineering Group LLC	3829	E	858 676-5382	22282
Teledyne Advanced Pollution	3823	E	858 657-9800	21662
Teledyne Instruments Inc	3829	D	619 239-5959	22286
Teledyne Instruments Inc	3674	E	858 842-3127	19219
Teledyne Instruments Inc	3549	D	619 239-5959	14768
Teledyne Instruments Inc	3643	D	858 565-7050	17500
Telegent Systems Usa Inc.	3674	E	408 523-2800	19221
Tensorcom Inc	3674	E	760 496-3264	19222
Tensys Medical Inc.	3845	E	858 552-1941	23058
Terry Town Corporation	2384	F	619 421-5354	3604
Textile 2000 Screen Printing	2759	E	858 735-8521	7516
Thai Union International Inc (HQ)	2091	F	858 558-9662	2305
Thermo Fisher Scientific Inc.	3826	B	858 453-7551	22040
Thermo Fisher Scientific Inc.	3826	E	858 882-1286	22043
Thermo Gamma-Metrics LLC (HQ)	3824	E	858 450-9811	21695
Thermx Temperature Tech	3823	F	858 573-0983	21669
Thompson Type Inc.	2791	E	619 224-3137	7635
Three Man Corporation	2759	E	858 684-5200	7520
Timlin Industries Inc	3993	E	541 947-6771	23990
Tocagen Inc.	2834	D	858 412-8400	8419
Tom Garcia Inc	7694	F	619 232-4861	25469
Tomahawk Power LLC	3629	F	619 255-7478	17360
Tomarco Contractor Spc Inc.	3965	F	858 547-0700	23776
Toolster Belts Inc.	3545	F	858 583-0681	14686
Top Art LLC	2741	F	858 554-0102	6603
Top Brands Distribution Inc	2022	F	858 578-0319	604

Employment Codes: A=Over 500 employees, B=251-500, C=101-250, D=51-100, E=20-50, F=10-19

2019 California
Manufacturers Register

© Mergent Inc. 1-800-342-5647

1453

GEOGRAPHIC

	SIC	EMP	PHONE	ENTRY #
Trademark Construction Co Inc **(PA)**	3694	D	760 489-5647	19847
Tragara Pharmaceuticals Inc	2834	F	760 208-6900	8420
Trane US Inc	3585	D	858 292-0833	15990
Trend Marketing Corporation	2499	E	800 468-7363	4661
Trex Enterprises Corporation **(PA)**	3571	C	858 646-5300	15500
Trexta Inc	3663	F	858 536-9100	18290
Tri Electronics Inc	3829	F	858 571-4881	22290
Tri-Union Seafoods LLC	2091	F	858 558-9662	2306
Triprism Inc	3861	F	858 675-7552	23204
Trius Therapeutics LLC	2834	D	858 452-0370	8422
Trovagene Inc	2835	D	858 952-7570	8521
True Temper Sports Inc	3949	E	858 404-0405	23677
Trumed Systems Incorporated	3585	E	844 878-6331	15993
Tsf Construction Services Inc	2298	F	619 202-7615	2983
Ttm Technologies Inc	3672	D	858 874-2701	18635
Tungsten Heavy Powder Inc **(PA)**	3313	D	858 693-6100	11431
Turbine Components Inc	3724	F	858 678-8568	20686
Turtle Beach Corporation **(PA)**	3679	C	914 345-2255	19774
U-Blox San Diego Inc	3661	F	858 847-9611	18002
Ultraneon Sign Corp	3993	E	858 569-6716	23995
Ultratype & Graphics	2791	F	858 541-1894	7636
Unico Incorporated	1081	F	619 209-6124	15
United Brands Company	2087	E	619 461-5220	2286
United Cerebral Palsy Assn San	3953	F	619 282-8790	23723
United Tote Company	3577	E	858 279-4250	15878
Utility Composite Solutions In **(PA)**	3272	F	858 442-3187	11015
V & P Scientific Inc	3089	F	858 455-0643	10425
Vanard Lithographers Inc	2752	E	619 291-5571	7163
Vangie L Cortes	2711	E	858 578-6807	6078
Variable Image Printing	2752	E	858 530-2443	7166
Vas Engineering Inc	3679	E	858 569-1601	19780
Vdp Direct LLC **(PA)**	2752	E	858 300-4510	7167
Veredatech LLC	2741	F	858 342-6468	6616
Verifone Inc	3577	E	858 436-2270	15881
Versacall Technologies Inc	3669	F	858 677-6766	18376
Verus Pharmaceuticals Inc	2834	F	858 436-1600	8432
Vesta Medical LLC	3841	F	949 660-8648	22674
Vetpowered LLC	7692	F	619 269-7116	25447
Via Telecom Inc	3674	C	858 350-5560	19255
Vical Incorporated **(PA)**	2836	D	858 646-1100	8586
Video Simplex Inc	3699	F	858 467-9762	20100
Vigitron Inc	3699	F	858 484-5209	20101
Vigor Systems Inc	3663	E	866 748-4467	18297
Viking Therapeutics Inc	2834	F	858 704-4660	8434
Vision Plastics Mfg Inc	3944	F	855 476-2767	23476
Vital Therapies Inc	2834	F	858 673-6840	8437
Vital Therapies Inc	2834	D	858 673-6840	8438
Volcano Corporation **(DH)**	3845	B	800 228-4728	23069
Von Hoppen Ice Cream	2024	F	858 695-9111	704
Walter N Coffman Inc	3086	D	619 266-2642	9892
WD-40 Company **(PA)**	2992	B	619 275-1400	9455
Wd-40 Company	2911	C	619 275-1400	9375
Wells Publishing Inc **(PA)**	2721	E	619 584-1100	6289
Westech Metal Fabrication Inc	3441	F	619 702-9353	12281
Western States Weeklies Inc	2711	F	619 280-2988	6086
WG Best Weinkellerei Inc	2084	F	858 627-1747	2052
Whalen Furniture Mfg Inc	2511	F	619 423-9948	4751
Whalen LLC **(DH)**	2511	C	619 423-9948	4752
Wind River Systems Inc	7372	A	858 824-3100	25351
Wintriss Engineering Corp	3827	E	858 550-7300	22149
Wissings Inc	2752	F	858 625-4111	7189
Wme Bi LLC	7372	D	877 592-2472	25353
Wordsmart Corporation	7372	F	858 565-8068	25356
Worldview Project	2731	F	858 964-0709	6414
X Controls Inc	3822	F	858 717-0004	21538
Yamagata America Inc	2741	F	858 751-1010	6628
Yellow Inc	3949	E	858 689-4851	23694
Ysi Incorporated	3826	E	858 546-8327	22052
Z-Communications Inc	3679	F	858 621-2700	19793
Zebra Technologies Corporation	3577	B	619 661-5465	15890

SAN DIMAS, CA - Los Angeles County

	SIC	EMP	PHONE	ENTRY #
Abeco Electric Service Inc	3699	E	909 599-7755	19897
AC Propulsion	3621	E	909 592-5399	17175
Act Now Instant Signs Inc	3993	F	909 394-7818	23807
Aircraft Stamping Company Inc	3444	E	323 283-1239	12466
Alfredo Hernandez	3599	F	909 971-9320	16249
Babe Hollywood Inc	2361	F	626 859-7700	3573
Bluelab Corporation USA Ltd	3569	E	909 599-1940	15303
Bolide Technology Group Inc	3699	D	909 305-8889	19920
Cabinet Concepts	2434	F	909 599-9191	4279
Co-Color	2752	F	909 394-7888	6737
Cosmobeauti Labs & Mfg Inc	2844	F	909 971-9832	8729
Craic Technologies Inc	3826	F	310 573-8180	21940
Elba Jewelry Inc	3911	F	909 394-5803	23260
Embroidery By P & J Inc	2395	F	909 592-2622	3845

	SIC	EMP	PHONE	ENTRY #
Gammalux Lighting Systems	3648	E	909 599-9669	17697
Gei Inc	3559	F	909 592-2234	14959
Gilead Palo Alto Inc	2834	B	909 394-4000	8185
Gilead Sciences Inc	2834	A	909 394-4090	8188
Gilead Sciences Inc	2834	C	909 394-4000	8189
Gms Elevator Services Inc	3534	E	909 599-5904	14250
Hagen-Renaker Inc **(PA)**	3269	C	909 599-2341	10832
J & D Business Forms Inc	2752	F	626 914-1777	6898
Kap Manufacturing Inc	3812	E	909 599-2525	21314
Louis Vuitton US Mfg Inc	3172	F	909 599-2411	10566
Magor Mold LLC	3544	D	909 592-5729	14538
Omega Fire Inc	3052	F	818 404-6212	9503
Organic Milling Inc	2043	D	800 638-8686	1069
Organic Milling Corporation **(PA)**	2043	C	909 599-0961	1070
Organic Milling Corporation	2043	F	909 305-0185	1071
Pertronix Inc **(PA)**	3822	E	909 599-5955	21522
Sharp Profiles LLC	3423	F	760 246-9446	11910
Sigtronics Corporation	3669	E	909 305-9399	18366
Spectrum Instruments Inc	3825	F	909 971-9710	21853
Superior Radiant Insul Inc	2679	F	909 305-1450	5737
Sypris Data Systems Inc **(HQ)**	3572	E	909 962-9400	15615
Thunderbird Industries Inc	3544	E	909 394-1633	14578
Tools & Production Inc	3544	F	626 286-0213	14580
Vertex Diamond Tool Company	3545	D	909 599-1129	14692
Wavestream Corporation **(HQ)**	3679	C	909 599-9080	19787
Western PCF Stor Solutions Inc **(PA)**	2542	D	909 451-0303	5177
Young Engineering & Mfg Inc **(PA)**	3823	E	909 394-3225	21679

SAN FERNANDO, CA - Los Angeles County

	SIC	EMP	PHONE	ENTRY #
Abex Display Systems Inc **(PA)**	2653	C	800 537-0231	5381
Airo Industries Company	2531	E	818 838-1008	5006
American Bottling Company	2086	C	818 898-1471	2087
American International Enginee	3365	E	818 365-8000	11724
Araca Merchandise LP	2759	E	818 743-5400	7239
Art Bronze Inc	3366	E	818 897-2222	11754
B & B Doors and Windows Inc	3442	F	818 837-8480	12295
Bellows Mfg & RES Inc	3599	F	818 838-1333	16316
Blue Cross Beauty Products Inc	2844	E	818 896-8681	8704
C A Schroeder Inc **(PA)**	3296	E	818 365-9561	11329
California Flex Corporation **(PA)**	3089	E	818 361-1169	10003
California Technical Pltg Corp	3471	E	818 365-8205	13365
Canady Manufacturing Co Inc	3599	F	818 365-9181	16359
Dg Displays LLC	3993	E	877 358-5976	23856
Diasol Inc **(PA)**	3841	E	818 838-7077	22425
DI Tool and Mfg Co Inc	3544	F	818 837-3451	14509
Electric Gate Store Inc **(PA)**	3699	C	818 504-2300	19956
Flannery Inc **(PA)**	3275	F	818 837-7585	11217
Foamation Inc	3086	F	818 837-6613	9851
Frazier Aviation Inc	3728	E	818 898-1998	20820
Fresh & Ready Foods LLC	2099	D	818 837-7600	2526
General Production Services	3599	F	818 365-4211	16531
Graphix Press Inc	2752	E	818 834-8520	6840
Haimetal Duct Inc	3444	F	818 768-2315	12605
International Tents & Supplies	2394	F	818 599-6258	3792
Iron Master	3446	F	818 361-4060	12862
J L Shepherd and Associates	3829	E	818 898-2361	22220
J Miller Co Inc	3053	F	818 837-0181	9538
Jay Gee Sales	3269	F	818 365-1311	10833
Karoun Dairies Inc **(PA)**	2022	D	818 767-7000	581
Kraft Tech Inc	3751	F	818 837-3520	21122
Krego Corporation	3613	F	818 837-1494	17148
Lehman Foods Inc	2099	E	818 837-7600	2582
Lumenyte International Corp	3648	F	949 279-8687	17710
New Haven Companies Inc	2299	D	213 749-8181	3010
Newco International Inc	2511	B	818 834-7100	4727
Omnical Inc	3842	F	818 837-7531	22783
Pharmavite LLC	2833	B	818 221-6200	7963
Prosound Communications Inc	3131	F	818 367-9593	10474
Ricon Corp **(HQ)**	3999	C	818 267-3000	24224
Santana Formal Accessories Inc	2311	E	818 898-3677	3044
Signature Tech Group Inc	3679	E	818 890-7611	19724
Simon Harrison	3829	E	818 898-1036	22270
Skaug Truck Body Works	3713	F	818 365-9123	20228
Slj Wholesale LLC	2051	E	323 662-8900	1322
Spira Manufacturing Corp	3053	E	818 764-8222	9559
Sto-Kar Enterprises	3441	E	818 886-5600	12249
TL Shield & Associates Inc **(PA)**	3534	E	818 509-8228	14260
Triumph Precision Products	3451	F	818 897-4700	13047
Vmg Engineering Inc	3599	F	818 837-6320	17044
W Machine Works Inc	3599	E	818 890-8049	17046
Westfield Hydraulics Inc	3492	F	818 896-6414	13746
Wyndham Collection LLC	2434	E	888 522-8476	4373

SAN FRANCISCO, CA - San Francisco County

	SIC	EMP	PHONE	ENTRY #
101 Roofing & Sheet Metal Co	3444	F	415 695-0101	12446
15five Inc	7372	E	208 816-4225	24295

	SIC	EMP	PHONE	ENTRY #
18 Rabbits Inc (PA)	2064	F	415 922-6006	1405
4505 Meats Inc	2096	E	415 255-3094	2371
500friends Inc (DH)	7372	E	800 818-8356	24300
A S Batle Company	3299	F	415 864-3300	11343
AA Products International Inc (PA)	3714	F	415 752-2075	20236
ABB Enterprise Software Inc	7372	C	415 527-2850	24302
Able Health Inc	7372	F	617 529-6264	24303
Ad Art Inc (PA)	3993	D	415 869-6460	23808
Addvocate Inc	7372	E	415 797-7620	24321
Adina For Life Inc	2087	E	415 285-9300	2239
Adobe Macromedia Software LLC (HQ)	7372	E	415 832-2000	24325
Adobe Systems Incorporated	7372	A	415 832-2000	24326
Aechelon Technology Inc (PA)	3571	E	415 255-0120	15386
Affectlayer Inc	7372	F	650 924-1082	24334
Afresh Technologies Inc	7372	F	805 551-9245	24335
Aktana Inc	7372	E	888 707-3125	24344
Alan Wofsy Fine Arts LLC	2731	F	415 292-6500	6303
All City Printing Inc	2752	F	415 861-8088	6647
Allegra	2752	F	415 824-9610	6649
Allen Sarah &	3577	E	415 242-0906	15661
Allied Concrete Rdymx Svcs LLC	3273	F	415 282-8117	11037
Alm Media Holdings Inc	2721	E	415 490-1054	6101
Amazon Prsrvation Partners Inc	2033	E	415 775-6355	784
American Giant Inc	2326	E	415 529-2429	3094
American Scence Tech As T Corp (PA)	3721	C	415 251-2800	20538
AMR Industries Enterprises Inc	3533	E	415 860-5566	14206
Anchor Distilling Company	2084	E	415 863-8350	1644
Angellist LLC	7372	E	415 857-0840	24359
Anin Co (PA)	2752	F	415 433-1341	6662
Anki Inc (PA)	3944	E	877 721-2654	23405
Appdirect Inc (PA)	7372	D	415 852-3924	24364
Appdynamics LLC (HQ)	7372	C	415 442-8400	24365
Ardica Technologies Inc	3674	E	415 568-9270	18715
Arete Therapeutics Inc	2834	F	650 737-4600	8041
Aria Systems Inc (PA)	7372	D	415 852-7250	24382
Arnold & Egan Manufacturing Co	2541	E	415 822-2700	5038
Asian Week	2711	F	415 397-0220	5765
Associated Arospc Activities	3724	E	510 483-9020	20645
Astoria Software	7372	E	415 956-3917	24392
AT&T Corp	2741	B	415 542-9000	6440
Atlas Screw Machine Pdts Co	3451	F	415 621-6737	13015
Atlassian Inc (DH)	7372	C	415 701-1110	24395
Attilas Byshore Art Studio LLC	3299	F	415 282-2815	11346
Audentes Tnerapeutics Inc	2836	D	415 818-1001	8529
Autodesk Inc	7372	D	415 356-0700	24398
Avolent Inc	7372	D	415 553-6400	24403
B & M Upholstery	2211	F	415 621-7447	2723
B & W Envmtl Solutions LLC	3559	F	415 931-3381	14918
Badger Maps Inc	7372	E	415 592-5909	24406
Baker Interiors Furniture Co	2519	E	415 626-1414	4907
Bar Media Inc	2711	F	415 861-5019	5774
Barebottle Brewing Company Inc	2082	F	415 926-8617	1567
Bay Guardian Company	2711	F	415 255-3100	5775
Bayer Healthcare LLC	2834	B	415 437-5800	8063
Bayer Hlthcare Phrmcticals Inc	2834	B	510 262-5000	8070
Beats Music LLC	7372	D	415 590-5104	24412
Bento Technologies Inc	7372	F	415 887-2028	24415
Bettercompany Inc	7372	F	415 501-9692	24417
Big Heart Pet Brands (DH)	2047	B	415 247-3000	1109
Blue Cedar Networks Inc	3577	E	415 329-0401	15688
Blue Rock Networks LLC	3825	F	415 577-8004	21730
Blurb Inc	2731	D	415 364-6300	6317
Borden Decal Company Inc	2759	E	415 431-1587	7253
Branded Spirits USA Ltd	2085	E	415 813-5045	2069
Brewmaster Inc	2082	F	415 642-3371	1574
Bright Lite Structures LLC	3272	F	636 575-7559	10891
Brightidea Incorporated	7372	E	415 814-1387	24452
Brilliant Worldwide Inc	7372	E	650 468-2966	24453
Business Jrnl Publications Inc	2711	E	415 989-2522	5784
Buzzworks Inc	2082	F	415 863-5964	1576
Byer California (PA)	2331	A	415 626-7844	3221
California Smart Foods	2051	E	415 826-0449	1216
Carpenter Group (PA)	3536	E	415 285-1954	14294
CB Mill Inc	2511	F	415 386-5309	4684
Cengage Learning Inc	2731	B	415 839-2300	6321
Cenveo Worldwide Limited	2752	D	415 821-7171	6725
Chevron USA Inc	3822	B	415 733-0063	21503
Chronicle Books LLC	2731	C	415 537-4200	6327
Circa 1605 Inc	7372	E	217 899-3512	24491
Cisco Systems Inc	3577	A	415 837-6261	15706
City & County of San Francisco	2759	E	415 557-5251	7272
Cjs Toffee & Toppings LLC	2064	F	415 929-7852	1415
Class Twist Inc	7372	F	650 646-8235	24495
Clearslide Inc (DH)	7372	D	877 360-3366	24497
Cleasby Manufacturing Co Inc (PA)	3531	F	415 822-6565	14158
Clic LLC	2752	F	415 421-2900	6735
Clinicloud Inc	3845	D	415 801-3283	22962
Clipcall Inc	7372	F	650 285-7597	24499
Clockware	7372	F	650 556-8880	24500
Cloud Engines Inc	3572	E	415 738-8076	15523
Cloudnco Inc	7372	F	408 605-8755	24503
Clover Garments Inc	2339	D	415 826-6909	3396
Club Donatello Owners Assn	3873	F	415 474-7333	23220
Cobalt Labs Inc	7372	E	415 651-7028	24507
Colloquy LLC	2386	E	415 863-6171	3611
Colour Drop	2759	F	415 353-5720	7282
Concentric Analgesics Inc	2834	F	415 771-5129	8119
Confections Michael Recchiuti (PA)	2064	F	415 826-2868	1416
Constellation Brands Inc	2084	E	415 912-3880	1702
Constellation Brands US Oprs	2084	E	415 912-3700	1704
Copper Crm Inc	7372	E	415 231-6360	24525
Copy 1 Inc	2752	E	415 986-0111	6758
Corporatecouch	3674	E	415 312-6078	18785
Creative Intl Pastries	2051	F	415 255-1128	1226
Ctg I LLC	2741	F	415 233-9700	6466
Cucina Holdings Inc	2051	F	415 986-8688	1227
Culture AMP Inc (HQ)	7372	E	415 326-8453	24536
Cushion Works Inc	2393	F	415 552-6220	3763
Cut Loose (PA)	2339	D	415 822-2031	3399
Da Global Energy Inc	3641	E	408 916-6303	17423
Daily Journal Corporation	2711	D	415 296-2400	5823
Darling Ingredients Inc	2077	D	415 647-4890	1524
Data Advantage Group Inc	7372	F	415 947-0400	24548
Datafox Intelligence Inc	7372	F	415 969-2144	24552
Davis Shoe Therapeutics	3144	F	415 661-8705	10495
Dcl Productions	2395	F	415 826-2200	3840
Dco Environmental & Recycl LLC	3089	F	573 204-3844	10060
Demandbase Inc (PA)	7372	D	415 683-2660	24559
Design Imagery	2542	F	650 589-6464	5137
Designer Printing Inc	2752	F	415 989-0008	6782
Diageo North America Inc	2084	E	415 835-7300	1725
Diamond Foods LLC	2068	E	209 467-6000	1488
Diamond Tree Investments LLC	2335	E	415 627-7730	3305
Die & Tool Products Co Inc	3599	F	415 822-2888	16438
Digisight Technologies Inc	7372	F	415 215-4440	24561
Digital Mania Inc	2752	E	415 896-0500	6786
Dispatcher Newspaper	2711	F	415 775-0533	5830
Divisadero 500 LLC	2599	F	415 572-6062	5227
Diy Co	3699	F	844 564-6349	19946
Docsend Inc	7372	F	888 258-5951	24567
Doctor On Demand Inc	7372	D	415 935-4447	24568
Docusign Inc (PA)	7372	B	415 489-4940	24569
Dogpatch Wineworks	2084	F	415 525-4440	1728
Dolby Laboratories Inc (PA)	3651	B	415 558-0200	17792
Domino Data Lab Inc	7372	F	415 570-2425	24571
Doubledutch Inc (PA)	7372	D	800 748-9024	24574
Doughtronics Inc	2051	E	415 288-2978	1237
Dow Jones & Company Inc	2711	B	415 765-6131	5832
Draftday Fantasy Sports Inc	7372	F	310 306-1828	24576
Dreams Duvets & Bed Linens	2392	F	415 543-1800	3720
Driver Inc	7372	F	415 999-4960	24579
Dropbox Inc (PA)	7372	C	415 857-6800	24581
Dualcor Technologies Inc	3572	F	831 684-2457	15530
Dwell Life Inc (PA)	2721	E	415 373-5100	6154
E2 Lighting Inc	3648	E	415 760-7793	17686
Egomotion Inc	7372	E	415 849-4662	24597
Eis Group Inc	7372	E	415 402-2622	24598
Ellipsis Health Inc	7372	F	650 906-6117	24606
EMC Corporation	3572	E	877 636-8589	15534
Emiliomiti LLC	3556	F	415 621-1171	14845
Epignosis LLC	7372	E	646 797-2799	24622
Eride Inc	7372	E	415 848-7800	24626
Ermico Enterprises Inc	3949	D	415 822-6776	23557
Evergood Sausage Co	2013	D	415 822-4660	483
Exin LLC	2711	C	415 359-2600	5847
Ezboard Inc	7372	F	415 773-0400	24639
Fabric Walls Inc	2392	F	415 863-2711	3722
Fastsigns	3993	F	415 537-6900	23877
Fat Wreck Chords Inc	3652	F	415 284-1790	17898
Fenix International Inc	3612	B	415 754-9222	17093
Fibrogen Inc (PA)	2834	C	415 978-1200	8159
First Advantage Talent Managem	7372	E	415 446-3930	24651
First Solar Inc	3674	F	415 935-2500	18843
Fitbit Inc (PA)	3829	B	415 513-1000	22200
Five Star Media Inc	2721	E	415 298-2510	6162
Flamestower Inc	3621	F	415 699-8650	17196
FML Inc	3961	F	415 864-5084	23747
Forager Project LLC	2037	D	855 729-5253	949
Forecross Corporation (PA)	7372	F	415 543-1515	24660
Forgerock Inc (PA)	7372	D	415 599-1100	24662

Employment Codes: A=Over 500 employees, B=251-500,
C=101-250, D=51-100, E=20-50, F=10-19

2019 California
Manufacturers Register

© Mergent Inc. 1-800-342-5647
1455

G
E
O
G
R
A
P
H
I
C

Company	SIC	EMP	PHONE	ENTRY #
Forgerock US Inc (HQ)	7372	D	415 599-1100	24663
Formation Inc	7372	D	650 257-2277	24664
Foundation For Nat Progress	2721	E	415 321-1700	6166
Four M Studios	2731	D	415 249-2362	6341
Fox Merchandising Intl Inc	2542	C	415 671-0635	5140
Franklin Electric Co Inc	3621	A	415 467-2693	17197
Freedom of Press Foundation	2721	F	415 321-1760	6168
Frontapp Inc	7372	D	415 680-3048	24674
Fundx Investment Group	2741	F	415 986-7979	6490
Future Us Inc (HQ)	2721	D	650 238-2400	6169
Fuzebox Software Corporation (HQ)	7372	F	415 692-4800	24679
Gatherapp Inc	7372	F	415 409-9476	24684
Gaze Inc	3674	F	415 374-9193	18854
Gergay and Associates	3469	E	415 431-4163	13209
Ggc Administration LLC (PA)	2591	E	415 983-2700	5189
Glaser Designs Inc	3171	F	415 552-3188	10548
Godiva Chocolatier Inc	2066	E	415 566-5058	1470
Golden Gate Tofu Incorporated	2075	F	415 822-5613	1508
Goodco Inc	7372	F	415 425-1012	24704
Goorin Bros Inc (PA)	2353	E	415 431-9196	3562
Greatdad LLC	2721	F	415 572-8181	6174
Green Acres Cannabis LLC	2833	F	415 657-3484	7944
Guadalupe Associates Inc (PA)	2741	F	415 387-2324	6497
Gum Sun Times Inc (PA)	2711	E	415 379-6788	5868
H&H Imaging Inc	2752	F	415 431-4731	6846
H2 Cards Inc	2759	F	415 788-7888	7341
H2o Plus LLC (PA)	2844	D	312 377-2132	8761
Habla Incorporated	7372	E	703 867-0135	24719
Halo Neuro Inc	3845	E	415 851-3338	22982
Halo Neuro Inc	3699	E	650 784-0881	19977
Harmless Harvest Inc (PA)	2099	E	347 688-6286	2534
Harpercollins Publishers LLC	2731	E	415 477-4400	6346
Hartle Media Ventures LLC	2721	E	415 362-7797	6176
Hearsay Social Inc (PA)	7372	D	888 990-3777	24725
Hearst Communications Inc	2711	C	415 537-4200	5872
Hearst Corporation	2711	F	415 777-0600	5874
Hello Network Inc	7372	F	408 891-4727	24727
Heroku Inc	7372	F	650 704-6107	24728
Highland Technology	3829	E	415 551-1700	22212
Hint Inc	2086	E	415 513-4051	2139
Hitachi Rail Usa Inc (PA)	3743	F	415 397-7010	21077
Ho Tai Printing Co Inc	2752	F	415 421-4218	6861
Homestead Publishing Inc	2731	E	307 733-6248	6350
HP Inc	3571	D	415 979-3700	15426
Humangear Inc	3089	F	415 580-7553	10143
Hydronovation Inc	3589	F	800 778-5092	16052
I E P Full Service Printing	2759	F	415 648-6002	7346
Icebreaker Health Inc	7372	F	415 926-5818	24748
Idg Consumer & Smb Inc (DH)	2721	C	415 243-0500	6188
IDO Cabinet Inc	2434	F	415 282-1683	4312
Ifwe Inc (HQ)	7372	D	415 946-1850	24749
Ijk & Co Inc	3699	E	415 826-8899	19980
Incandescent Inc	7372	E	415 464-7975	24759
Infoworld Media Group Inc (DH)	2721	D	415 243-4344	6195
Instagis Inc	7372	F	415 527-6636	24778
Intelligent Peripherals	3577	F	415 564-4366	15767
Internet Industry Publishing	2721	F	415 733-5400	6197
Internet Science Education Prj	3764	F	415 806-3156	21177
Interntnal Indian Traty Cuncil	3949	F	415 641-4482	23594
Intershop Communications Inc	7372	F	415 844-1500	24788
Invuity Inc	3841	C	415 665-2100	22493
Ionetix Corporation (PA)	3699	E	415 944-1440	19986
Irhythm Technologies Inc (PA)	3845	E	415 632-5700	22993
Isolation Network Inc (PA)	3651	E	415 489-7000	17819
J F Fitzgerald Company Inc	2512	F	415 648-6161	4784
Jaguar Health Inc (PA)	2834	E	415 371-8300	8236
James P McNair Co Inc	3429	F	415 681-2200	11965
Jasper Sinclaire Media MGT Inc	2731	C	559 380-7853	6355
JC Metal Specialists Inc (PA)	3441	F	415 822-3878	12185
Jeremiahs Pick Coffee Company	2095	F	415 206-9900	2355
Jessica McClintock Inc (PA)	2361	C	415 553-8200	3578
Jinkosolar (us) Inc	3674	F	415 402-0502	18939
John Wiley & Sons Inc	2731	F	415 433-1740	6357
Johnson Leather Corporation (PA)	2386	F	415 775-7393	3617
Johnson Leather Corporation	2386	F	415 863-8819	3618
JR Watkins LLC	2392	F	415 477-8500	3726
Just Inc	2035	C	844 423-6637	916
Juul Labs Inc (PA)	3999	C	415 829-2336	24141
K C A Engineered Plastics Inc (PA)	2821	D	415 433-4494	7851
Kaise Perma San Franc Medic Ce	3842	A	415 833-2000	22762
Kba2 Inc	7372	E	415 528-5500	24826
Khn Solutions Inc	3829	F	877 334-6876	22225
Kimball Office Inc	2522	F	415 397-1557	4991
Kings Asian Gourmet Inc	2032	E	415 222-6100	763
Klein Industries Inc	3599	F	415 695-9117	16658
Kpisoft Inc	7372	D	415 439-5228	24839
La Brothers Enterprise Inc	2752	E	415 626-8818	6936
Lcr-Dixon Corporation	7372	F	404 307-1695	24852
Leap Motion Inc (PA)	3571	E	954 234-6321	15444
Leewood Press Inc	2752	F	415 896-0513	6942
Levi Strauss & Co (PA)	2325	A	415 501-6000	3078
Levi Strauss & Co	2325	F	415 677-9927	3079
Levi Strauss International (HQ)	2329	F	415 501-6000	3174
Liberty Cafe	2051	E	415 695-8777	1284
Lifi Labs Inc (PA)	3229	F	650 739-5563	10654
Lion Semiconductor Inc	3674	F	415 462-4933	18967
Lithium Technologies LLC (PA)	7372	D	415 757-3100	24859
Live Journal Inc	2711	E	415 230-3600	5914
Log(n) LLC	2741	E	415 500-2558	6520
Lois A Valeskie	3829	F	415 641-2570	22228
Los Angles Tmes Cmmnctions LLC	2711	F	415 274-9000	5924
Lowpensky Moulding	2431	F	415 822-7422	4184
Loyyal Corporation	7372	F	415 419-9590	24866
Lyra Corporation	2741	F	415 668-2546	6521
M C Metal Inc	3446	F	415 822-2288	12877
Mac Publishing LLC (HQ)	2721	F	415 243-0505	6212
Magnamosis Inc	3841	F	707 484-8774	22517
Manta Solar Corporation	3433	F	928 853-6216	12074
Marco Fine Furniture Inc	2512	E	415 285-3235	4793
Margaret OLeary Inc (PA)	2339	D	415 354-6663	3463
Mark Resources LLC (PA)	2522	F	415 515-5540	4993
Marketron Mobile LLC	7372	F	415 981-0812	24883
Martinelli Envmtl Graphics	3993	F	415 468-4000	23920
McEvoy Properties LLC	2711	C	415 537-4200	6361
McLean Brewery Inc	2082	F	415 864-7468	1609
Medicines360	2834	F	415 951-8700	8271
Medium Entertainment Inc	3944	E	469 951-2688	23445
Medivation Inc (HQ)	2834	C	415 543-3470	8275
Medrio Inc (PA)	7372	F	415 963-3700	24900
Melian Labs Inc	7372	F	888 423-1944	24901
Menlo Energy LLC	2869	E	415 762-8200	9022
Method Home Products	2621	F	415 568-4600	5311
Metro World Plastics Inc	3081	F	415 255-8515	9716
Micro-Tracers Inc	2899	F	415 822-1100	9280
Microsoft Corporation	7372	C	415 972-6400	24917
Mindjolt	3944	F	415 543-7800	23447
Mindsnacks Inc	7372	F	415 875-9817	24923
Mixamo Inc	7372	F	415 255-7455	24927
Mixonic	2759	F	866 838-5067	7408
Mjus LLC (fka Mindjet Llc)	7372	D	415 229-4344	24928
Mode Analytics Inc	7372	F	415 271-7599	24932
Modern Luxury Media LLC (HQ)	2721	E	404 443-0004	6221
Molekule Inc (PA)	3822	E	352 871-3803	21517
Monitise Inc	7372	F	650 286-1059	24934
Motionloft Inc	3826	E	415 580-7671	21997
Mr S Leather	2386	E	415 863-7764	3620
Mulesoft Inc	7372	A	415 229-2009	24937
Munkyfun Inc	7372	E	415 281-3837	24938
Native Kjalii Foods Inc	2099	E	415 592-8670	2616
Naturener Usa LLC (DH)	3621	A	415 217-5500	17213
Naylor Corp	2066	E	415 421-1789	1472
Nebia Inc	3069	F	203 570-6222	9644
Nektar Therapeutics (PA)	2834	B	415 482-5300	8297
Neo Superwater Corp	2086	F	800 604-7051	2153
New Relic Inc (PA)	7372	C	650 777-7600	24961
Nexsys Electronics Inc (PA)	3577	F	415 541-9980	15813
Ng John	2752	F	415 929-7188	6993
Niebam-Cppola Estate Winery LP	2084	E	415 291-1700	1900
No Starch Press Inc	2731	F	415 863-9900	6370
Norcal Printing Inc (PA)	2752	E	415 282-8856	6997
Northern Quinoa Prod Corp	2043	E	806 535-8118	1068
Off Grid Labs Inc	3674	E	415 344-0953	19054
Ohio Inc	2521	F	415 647-6446	4963
Olive Bariani Oil LLC	2079	F	415 864-1917	1548
On24 Inc (PA)	7372	B	877 202-9599	24984
Onc Holdings Inc	7372	F	415 243-3343	24985
One Hat One Hand LLC	2353	E	415 822-2020	3569
Opentv Inc (DH)	7372	C	415 962-5000	24989
Oracle America Inc	7372	D	415 908-3609	24999
Oracle Corporation	7372	E	415 834-9731	25008
Oracle Corporation	7372	E	415 402-7200	25017
Oracle Corporation	7372	E	650 506-7000	25025
Otsuka America Inc (DH)	3829	E	415 986-5300	22244
Otsuka America Foods Inc (DH)	2099	F	424 219-9425	2632
Ouster Inc	3829	D	415 949-0108	22245
Outreach Corporation	7372	F	888 938-7356	25042
Owen Weldon Inc (HQ)	2731	E	415 291-0100	6374
Owen Weldon Publishing Inc (DH)	2731	F	415 291-0100	6375
P G Molinari & Sons Inc	2013	E	415 822-5555	511
Packageone Inc (PA)	2653	E	650 761-3339	5445

Mergent email: customerrelations@mergent.com
1456

2019 California
Manufacturers Register

(P-0000) Products & Services Section entry number
(PA)=Parent Co (HQ)=Headquarters (DH)=Div Headquarters

	SIC	EMP	PHONE	ENTRY #
Pan-O-Rama Baking Inc	2051	E	415 522-5500	1304
Panorama Intl CL Co Inc	2032	F	415 891-8478	770
Parasound Products Inc	3651	E	415 397-7100	17841
Pch International USA Inc **(PA)**	3679	E	415 643-5463	19682
Peachpit Press	2741	E	415 336-6831	6548
Pearson Education Inc	2731	E	415 402-2500	6379
Peek Arent You Curious Inc **(PA)**	2361	D	415 512-7335	3585
Penrose Studios Inc	2741	E	703 354-1801	6549
People Center Inc	7372	E	781 864-1232	25054
Pi-Coral Inc	3572	D	408 516-5150	15584
Plangrid Inc **(PA)**	7372	E	415 349-7440	25065
Pleasant Mattress Inc	2515	F	415 874-7540	4878
Pleasant Mattress Inc	2515	F	415 861-4532	4880
Pluot Communications Inc	3651	F	202 258-9223	17846
Pocket Gems Inc	3944	C	415 371-1333	23456
Poco Dolce Confections Inc	2064	F	415 817-1551	1447
Pointech	3366	E	415 822-8704	11765
Popsugar Inc **(PA)**	2741	C	415 391-7576	6553
Powwow Inc	7372	F	415 515-4947	25075
Presidio Pharmaceuticals Inc	2834	F	415 655-7560	8343
Prezi Inc **(PA)**	7372	E	415 398-8012	25079
Prism Skylabs Inc	3663	F	415 243-0834	18224
Project 1920 Inc	3171	E	415 990-9788	10551
Projectoris Inc	7372	F	917 972-5553	25084
Pubinno Inc	7372	F	669 251-6538	25088
Pull String Inc	7372	E	415 758-3339	25089
Punkpost Inc	2771	E	415 818-7677	7566
Quad/Graphics Inc	2752	A	267 267-3700	7064
Quad/Graphics Inc	2752	A	415 398-0624	7065
Quantal International Inc	7372	E	415 644-0754	25096
Quest Software Inc	7372	D	415 373-2222	25097
R A Jenson Manufacturing Co	2434	F	415 822-2732	4340
R E Dillard 1 LLC	3433	D	415 675-1500	12077
R J McGlennon Company Inc **(PA)**	2851	E	415 552-0311	8937
R R Donnelley & Sons Company	2754	E	415 362-2300	7211
Random Technologies LLC	3229	F	415 255-1267	10666
Rangeme Inc	2741	F	415 351-9268	6562
Rapid Lasergraphics **(HQ)**	2791	E	415 957-5840	7631
Rapid Typographers Company **(PA)**	2791	E	415 957-5840	7632
Rare Breed Distilling LLC **(DH)**	2085	E	415 315-8060	2075
RE Tranquillity 8 LLC	3433	D	415 675-1500	12080
Read It Later Inc	7372	E	415 692-6111	25105
Realpage Inc	7372	E	415 222-6996	25109
Reason8 Inc	7372	F	505 220-3683	25113
Rebecca Beeson Inc	2331	F	415 865-0471	3269
Recommind Inc **(HQ)**	3695	D	415 394-7899	19879
Reddit Inc	2741	E	415 666-2330	6566
Relx Inc	2721	E	415 908-3200	6246
Renee Rivera Hair Accessories	3069	F	415 776-6613	9669
Rickshaw Bagworks Inc	2393	F	415 904-8368	3769
Riverbed Technology Inc **(HQ)**	3577	D	415 247-8800	15842
Robert E Blake Inc	3731	F	415 391-2255	21012
Robert Yick Company Inc	3589	F	415 282-9707	16102
Rubel Marguerite Mfg Co	2337	F	415 362-2626	3362
Rypple	7372	F	888 479-7753	25134
Salesforcecom Inc	7372	F	415 323-8685	25140
Salesforcecom Inc	7372	F	703 463-3300	25141
Salesforcecom Inc **(PA)**	7372	A	415 901-7000	25142
San Francisco Print Media Co **(PA)**	2752	E	415 487-2594	7095
San Francisco Victoriana Inc	2431	F	415 648-0313	4224
Sanofi US Services Inc	2834	C	415 856-5000	8372
Sas Institute Inc	7372	E	415 421-2227	25146
Sawbird Inc **(PA)**	3425	F	415 861-0644	11921
Scafco Corporation	3999	E	415 852-7974	24229
Scality Inc	3572	E	650 356-8500	15600
SCM Accelerators LLC	7372	F	415 595-8091	25154
Seamaid Manufacturing Corp	2321	E	415 777-9978	3059
Segmentio Inc	3577	F	844 611-0621	15849
Sgk LLC	2796	D	415 438-6700	7656
Sight Machine Inc	7372	D	888 461-5739	25174
Siluria Technologies Inc	1311	E	415 978-2170	75
Simpa Networks Inc	3829	F	415 216-3204	22271
Sin MA Imports Company	2046	F	415 285-9369	1101
Singular Bio Inc	2835	F	415 553-8773	8515
Sirna Therapeutics Inc	2834	D	415 512-7200	8383
Sixteen Rivers Press Inc	2741	F	415 273-1303	6580
Slack Technologies Inc **(PA)**	7372	C	415 579-9153	25180
Social Imprints LLC	2759	E	415 956-0269	7487
Socialize Inc	7372	E	415 529-4019	25190
Solher Iron	3449	E	415 822-9900	12997
Source Surgical Inc	3841	F	415 861-7040	22628
Sparkcentral Inc **(PA)**	2741	E	866 559-6229	6586
Spectrum Grafix Inc	2752	F	415 648-2400	7112
Spigit Inc	7372	D	855 774-4480	25206
Splunk Inc **(PA)**	7372	E	415 848-8400	25208
Spoton Computing Inc	7372	E	650 293-7464	25210
Sprout Inc	2741	F	415 894-9629	6589
Sproutling Inc	3661	F	415 323-3270	17996
Squamtech Inc	7372	F	415 867-8300	25211
Square Inc **(PA)**	7372	E	415 375-3176	25212
Stackla Inc	7372	D	415 528-4910	25215
Stamats Communications Inc	2731	E	800 358-0388	6394
Standard Cognition Corp	7372	E	201 707-7782	25218
Stans Michegaas **(PA)**	2051	E	415 839-8442	1323
Steelcase Inc	2522	B	415 865-0261	5001
Strevus Inc	7372	F	415 704-8182	25230
Stryder Corp	7372	F	415 981-8400	25231
Stumbleupon Inc **(HQ)**	7372	F	415 979-0640	25232
Sun Basket Inc	2099	D	408 669-4418	2674
Sun Mountain Inc	2431	F	415 852-2320	4238
Sun Reporter Publishing Inc	2711	F	415 671-1000	6063
Super Binge Media Inc	7372	F	714 688-6231	25235
Supersonic ADS Inc	3993	E	650 825-6010	23985
Swift Navigation Inc	3663	D	415 484-9026	18268
Swiftstack Inc **(PA)**	7372	F	415 625-0293	25238
Syapse Inc	7372	F	650 924-1461	25240
Symphony Talent LLC	7372	F	415 968-3389	25241
Synergy Global Inc	7372	F	415 766-3540	25244
Takipi Inc	7372	F	408 203-9585	25250
Talisman Systems Group Inc	7372	F	415 357-1751	25251
Talix Inc	7372	D	628 220-3885	25252
Talkdesk Inc **(PA)**	7372	E	888 743-3044	25253
Tanko Streetlighting Inc	3646	E	415 254-7579	17649
Tartine LP	2051	E	415 487-2600	1332
Teaching Channel Inc	7372	E	415 800-4288	25259
Tempo Automation Inc	3679	E	415 320-1261	19759
Teselagen Biotechnology Inc	7372	F	650 387-5932	25267
Thai Thai Noodle	2098	F	415 441-5551	2442
Thinksmart LLC	7372	F	888 489-4284	25270
Thirdmotion Inc	7372	F	415 848-2724	25271
Thirsty Bear Brewing Co LLC	2082	D	415 974-0905	1631
Thomas Lundberg	2514	F	415 695-0110	4844
Thomson Reuters (markets) LLC	2721	B	415 344-6000	6270
Thought Inc	7372	F	415 836-9199	25273
Thousandeyes Inc **(PA)**	7372	D	415 513-4526	25275
Three Guys Holding Co LLC	2325	F	855 711-7686	3089
Tibco Software Inc	7372	F	415 344-0339	25277
Timbuk2 Designs Inc **(PA)**	2393	D	415 252-4300	3772
Time Inc	2721	E	415 434-5244	6271
Tivix Inc **(PA)**	7372	F	415 680-1299	25281
Tokbox Inc	7372	F	415 284-4688	25282
Toms Metal Specialists Inc	7692	E	415 822-7971	25446
Topquest Inc	7372	E	646 415-9402	25284
Toutapp Inc	7372	F	866 548-1927	25290
Tpg Partners III LP **(HQ)**	1311	E	415 743-1500	80
Trinet Construction Inc	3569	F	415 695-7814	15368
Trumaker Inc	2311	F	415 662-3836	3045
Tullys Coffee Co Inc **(HQ)**	2095	E	415 929-8808	2369
Tullys Coffee Co Inc	2095	F	415 213-8791	2370
Turbotools Corporation	7372	F	415 759-5599	25302
Twist Bioscience Corporation	2836	C	800 719-0671	8584
Uber Technologies Inc	7372	F	415 986-2715	25305
Ubiome Inc	2834	F	415 275-2461	8423
Ubm LLC	2721	C	415 947-6488	6278
Ubm Techweb **(DH)**	2721	F	415 947-6000	6279
Ucsf School of Pharmacy	2834	F	415 476-1444	8424
Unifyid Inc	7372	F	650 887-3760	25310
Universal McLoud USA Corp	7372	F	613 222-5904	25313
Universal Medical Press Inc	2721	F	415 436-9790	6283
Unmanned Innovation Inc **(PA)**	3721	D	877 714-4828	20633
Uphold Inc	7372	E	415 730-3988	25316
Uvify Inc	3812	F	628 200-4469	21451
Van Tisse Inc	2254	F	415 543-2404	2865
Vans Inc	3021	F	415 566-3762	9493
Velti Inc **(HQ)**	7372	E	415 362-2077	25323
Vf Outdoor LLC	3949	E	415 433-3223	23684
Vgw Us Inc	7372	F	415 240-0498	25330
Videoamp Inc **(PA)**	7372	F	949 294-0351	25331
Visionary Electronics Inc	3674	D	415 751-8811	19263
Viz Media LLC	2721	C	415 546-7073	6286
Walker/Dunham Corp	3161	F	415 821-3570	10541
Waterguru Inc	3589	F	415 692-3310	16134
Wave 80 Biosciences Inc	3841	F	415 487-7976	22681
West Coast Garment Mfg	2326	E	415 896-1772	3127
Whistle Labs Inc	3699	E	415 692-0200	20114
Willpower Labs Inc	2834	F	415 805-1518	8444
Window & Door Shop Inc **(PA)**	2431	E	415 282-6192	4257
Wired Ventures Inc	2721	C	415 276-8400	6293
Wizeline Inc	3571	F	650 389-7272	15505
Wonolo Inc	7372	E	415 766-7692	25355

Employment Codes: A=Over 500 employees, B=251-500,
C=101-250, D=51-100, E=20-50, F=10-19

2019 California
Manufacturers Register

© Mergent Inc. 1-800-342-5647

1457

GEOGRAPHIC

Company	SIC	EMP	PHONE	ENTRY #
World Harmony Organization	2731	F	415 246-6886	6413
World Tariff Limited	2721	E	415 391-7501	6294
Worldlink Media	7372	F	415 561-2141	25359
XYZ Graphics Inc (PA)	2759	F	415 227-9972	7545
Yong Kee Rice Noodle Co	2098	F	415 986-3759	2445
Youngs Custom Cabinet Inc	2434	F	415 822-8313	4374
Zendesk Inc (PA)	7372	C	415 418-7506	25369
Zenpayroll Inc (PA)	7372	B	800 936-0383	25370
Zinio Systems Inc	7372	D	415 494-2700	25373
Zip Notes LLC	2621	F	415 931-8020	5338
Zulip Inc	7372	F	617 945-7653	25376
Zynga Inc	7372	F	415 621-2391	25379

SAN GABRIEL, CA - Los Angeles County

Company	SIC	EMP	PHONE	ENTRY #
American Prcision Grinding Mch	3599	F	626 357-6610	16272
BF Suma Pharmaceuticals Inc	2023	F	626 285-8366	606
California Shellfish Co Inc (PA)	2092	F	415 923-7400	2309
Cambero Metal Works Inc	7692	F	626 309-5315	25392
Chain Smith Inc	3911	F	626 287-3666	23250
China Times Printing Inc	2711	D	626 576-7006	5800
Classic Tees Inc	2339	E	626 607-0255	3394
Desais Design Craft	3229	F	626 285-3189	10640
Hsiao & Montano Inc	3161	E	626 588-2528	10524
Jetstream Trading Co	3728	F	818 921-7158	20857
JW Wireless	3663	F	626 532-2511	18140
Lee Fasteners Inc	3399	F	626 287-6848	11841
Lotus Orient Corp (PA)	2335	F	626 285-5796	3326
Marples Gears Inc	3566	E	626 570-1744	15241
Media King Inc	3699	F	626 288-4558	20013
Mueller Gages Company	3545	F	626 287-2911	14656
R J Vincent Inc	2512	F	626 448-1509	4803
Sign Art Co	3993	F	626 287-2512	23961
Su Mano Inc	3111	F	562 529-8835	10466
Technipfmc US Holdings Inc	3533	F	310 328-1236	14240

SAN GREGORIO, CA - San Mateo County

Company	SIC	EMP	PHONE	ENTRY #
Cybernetic Micro Systems Inc	3575	F	650 726-3000	15631

SAN JACINTO, CA - Riverside County

Company	SIC	EMP	PHONE	ENTRY #
Amark Industries Inc (PA)	3567	C	951 654-7351	15250
Blind Man Inc	2591	F	951 654-5938	5181
C M Machine Inc	3599	F	951 654-6019	16349
Edelbrock Foundry Corp	3363	A	951 654-6677	11693
Edelbrock Holdings Inc	3714	C	951 654-6677	20323
Hilkers Custom Cabinets Inc	2434	F	951 487-7640	4308
Horizon Bottled Water	2086	F	951 654-0954	2140
Interstate Carports Corp	3448	F	951 654-1750	12935
J Talley Corporation (PA)	3446	F	951 654-2123	12864
Matthews International Corp	3366	E	951 537-6615	11763
Modern Wall Graphics LLC	3081	E	760 787-0346	9717
Rama Corporation	3567	F	951 654-7351	15273
Skyline Homes Inc	2451	C	951 654-9321	4563
Wallace Wood Products	2541	F	951 654-9311	5118

SAN JOSE, CA - Santa Clara County

Company	SIC	EMP	PHONE	ENTRY #
24x7saas Inc	7372	F	408 391-6205	24297
3b Machining Co Inc	3599	F	408 719-9237	16178
A & E Anodizing Inc	3471	C	408 297-5910	13300
A & J Precision Sheetmetal Inc	3444	D	408 885-9134	12450
A R S Mechanical	3444	F	408 288-8822	12453
A&T Precision Machining	3599	F	408 363-1198	16196
A-1 Jays Machining Inc (PA)	3599	D	408 262-1845	16198
AB Manufacturing Inc	3861	F	408 972-5085	23136
ABS Manufacturers Inc	3446	F	408 295-5984	12824
Accordent Technologies Inc	7372	F	310 374-7491	24306
Acer American Holdings Corp (DH)	3577	F	408 533-7700	15655
ACS Co Ltd	3541	C	408 981-7162	14355
Active ID LLC	3537	F	408 782-3900	14306
Adcon Lab Inc	3559	E	408 531-9187	14900
Addison Technology Inc	3672	F	408 749-1000	18407
Adobe Inc (PA)	7372	A	408 536-6000	24324
Advance Modular Technology Inc	3577	F	408 453-9880	15659
Advanced Analogic Tech Inc	3674	D	408 330-1400	18665
Advanced Industrial Ceramics	3559	E	408 955-9990	14902
Advanced Precision Spring	3495	F	408 436-6595	13782
Advanced Surface Finishing Inc	3471	F	408 275-9718	13309
Advancedcath Technologies LLC (HQ)	3841	E	408 433-9505	22318
Advantest America Inc (HQ)	3674	D	408 456-3600	18671
Aer-Dan Precision (PA)	3599	E	408 954-8704	16234
AF Gomes Inc	3444	E	408 453-7300	12464
AG Neovo Technology Corp	3575	F	408 321-8210	15629
Ahead Magnetics Inc	3679	D	408 226-9800	19437
Airgard Inc (PA)	3564	E	408 573-0701	15142
Airpanders Inc (PA)	3841	D	650 964-1437	22319
Ajile Systems Inc (PA)	3674	E	408 557-0829	18675
Akm Semiconductor Inc	3674	E	408 436-8580	18676
Akon Incorporated	3999	D	408 432-8039	24028

Company	SIC	EMP	PHONE	ENTRY #
Alien Technology LLC (PA)	3663	E	408 782-3900	18025
Align Technology Inc (PA)	3843	B	408 470-1000	22854
Alliant Tchsystems Oprtons LLC	3484	F	408 513-3271	13686
Allied Drapery Services Inc	2391	F	408 293-1600	3688
Allied Telesis Inc	3577	E	408 519-8700	15663
Allied Telesis Inc	3577	E	408 519-8700	15664
Alta Design and Manufacturing	3599	F	408 450-5394	16261
Altera Corporation (HQ)	3674	B	408 544-7000	18686
Altest Corporation	3599	F	408 436-9900	16262
Altierre Corporation	3674	E	408 435-7343	18687
Altigen Communications Inc	3661	C	408 597-9000	17921
Alumawall Inc	3448	D	408 275-7165	12915
Amberwood Products Inc	2434	F	408 938-1600	4269
American Gasket & Die Company	3053	F	408 441-6200	9519
Amphenol DC Electronics Inc	3643	B	408 947-4500	17443
Ampro Adlink Technology Inc	3571	D	408 360-0200	15392
Amtek Electronic Inc	3571	E	408 971-8787	15393
Anacom Inc	3663	E	408 519-2062	18030
Analog Devices Inc	3674	B	408 727-9222	18698
Andre-Boudin Bakeries Inc	2051	A	408 249-4101	1174
Angular Machining Inc	3599	E	408 954-8326	16274
Ansys Inc	7372	E	408 457-2000	24360
Aplus Flash Technology Inc	3674	F	408 382-1100	18703
Appformix Inc	7372	F	408 899-2240	24470
Applied Anodize Inc	3471	D	408 435-9191	13333
Applied Microstructures Inc	3825	E	408 907-2885	21721
Appro International Inc (HQ)	3572	E	408 941-8100	15513
Aquantia Corp (PA)	3674	D	408 228-8300	18714
Aquatic Av Inc	3651	E	408 559-1668	17762
Ardent Systems Inc	3672	E	408 526-0100	18425
Aridis Pharmaceuticals Inc	2834	E	408 385-1742	8042
Arm Inc	3674	F	408 576-1500	18716
Arm Inc (HQ)	3674	B	408 576-1500	18717
Arsh Incorporated	2752	F	408 971-2722	6668
Asante Technologies Inc (PA)	3577	E	408 435-8388	15673
Ascent Technology Inc	3444	E	408 213-1080	12490
Asic Advantage Inc	3674	E	408 541-8686	18725
Atlona Inc	3651	E	408 962-0515	17763
Atmel Corporation (HQ)	3674	B	408 735-9110	18726
Atp Electronics Inc	3674	E	408 732-5000	18729
Auxin Solar Inc	3674	E	408 225-4300	18731
Avago Technologies	3674	E	408 433-4068	18732
Avago Technologies US Inc (HQ)	3674	B	800 433-8778	18733
Avantis Medical Systems Inc	3845	E	408 733-1901	22949
Avogy Inc	3674	E	408 684-5200	18736
Axial Industries Inc	3444	C	408 977-7800	12495
Azazie Inc	2335	F	650 963-9420	3295
B R Printers Inc (PA)	2752	D	408 929-5403	6678
B W Padilla Inc	7692	E	408 275-9834	25387
B&Z Manufacturing Company Inc	3599	E	408 943-1117	16302
Babbitt Bearing Co Inc	3599	E	408 298-1101	16304
Babylon Printing Inc	2752	E	408 519-5000	6680
Bae Systems Imging Sltions Inc	3674	C	408 433-2500	18741
Bae Systems Land Armaments LP	3812	A	408 289-0111	21264
Bae Systems Land Armaments LP	3795	D	408 289-0111	21214
Ball Screws & Actuators Coinc (HQ)	3568	E	408 938-3031	15281
Banh An Binh	3679	E	408 935-8950	19458
Barracuda Networks Inc	3577	F	408 342-5400	15678
Bay Elctrnic Spport Trnics Inc	3672	C	408 432-3222	18436
Bayspec Inc	3229	F	408 512-5928	10635
Bd Biscnces Systems Rgents Inc	2819	C	408 518-5024	7753
Becton Dickinson and Company	3841	B	408 432-9475	22362
Benchmark Elec Mfg Sltions Inc (HQ)	3672	C	408 754-9800	18437
Benen Manufacturing LLC	3545	E	408 573-7252	14608
Benjamin Litho Inc	2752	F	408 232-3800	6691
Bentek Corporation	3674	F	408 954-9600	18744
Bentek Corporation	3679	D	408 954-9600	19465
Berkeley Magnetics Inc	3612	E	408 292-2023	17081
Bestronics Holdings Inc (PA)	3675	E	408 385-7777	19291
Beveled Edge Inc	3231	F	408 467-9900	10680
Bhogart LLC	3556	E	855 553-3887	14836
Big Ink Printing	2752	F	408 624-1204	6697
Billy Beez Usa LLC	3949	F	408 300-9547	23522
Binh-Nhan D Ngo	3672	F	408 641-1721	18440
Bionicsound Inc	3842	F	714 300-4809	22708
Bipolarics Inc	3674	E	408 372-7574	18746
Bizmatics Inc (PA)	7372	C	408 873-3030	24428
Blum Construction Co Inc	3442	F	408 629-3740	12301
Bode Concrete LLC	3273	D	415 920-7100	11051
Boston Scientific Corporation	3841	C	408 935-3400	22378
Boston Scientific Corporation	3841	B	408 935-3400	22380
Bravo Communications Inc	3577	E	408 297-8700	15690
Brion Technologies Inc	3674	F	408 653-1500	18751
Britelab	3824	D	650 961-0671	21681
Broadcom Corporation	3674	E	408 922-7000	18752

Company	SIC	EMP	PHONE	ENTRY #
Broadcom Corporation (HQ)	3674	B	408 433-8000	18753
Broadcom Corporation	3674	E	408 501-8200	18754
Brocade Cmmnctions Systems LLC	3577	F	408 333-8000	15691
Brocade Cmmnctions Systems LLC (DH)	3577	A	408 333-8000	15692
Bruker Biospin Corporation	3826	E	510 683-4300	21929
Burke Industries Inc (HQ)	3069	C	408 297-3500	9596
Burke Industries Inc	2952	C	408 297-3500	9402
Business Jrnl Publications Inc	2711	E	408 295-3800	5783
C & D Prescision Machining Inc	3599	E	408 383-1888	16344
C & D Semiconductor Svcs Inc (PA)	3674	E	408 383-1888	18757
C C Products	3751	F	408 295-0205	21095
C L Hann Industries Inc	3599	F	408 293-4800	16348
C8 Medisensors Inc	2834	E	408 623-7281	8090
Cade Corporation	2899	F	408 292-3435	9225
Cadence Design Systems Inc	7372	E	408 943-1234	24463
Cadence Design Systems Inc (PA)	7372	A	408 938-1234	24465
Cadence US Inc (PA)	7372	E	408 943-1234	24468
Cali Today Daily Newspaper	2711	F	408 297-8271	5786
California Newspapers Partnr (PA)	2711	C	408 920-5333	5789
Calix Inc (PA)	3663	B	408 514-3000	18060
Calypto Design Systems Inc	7372	F	408 850-2300	24469
Canary Communications Inc	3663	F	408 365-0609	18062
Cardinal Industrial Finishes	2851	E	408 452-8522	8890
Cavium Networks Intl Inc (DH)	3674	F	650 625-7000	18763
Ceenee Inc	3651	E	408 890-5018	17781
Celestica LLC	3674	C	408 574-6000	18765
Central Concrete Supply Coinc (HQ)	3273	D	408 293-6272	11090
Central Concrete Supply Coinc	3273	E	408 404-1000	11091
Central Tech Inc	3699	F	408 955-0919	19926
Cernex Inc	3679	E	408 541-9226	19486
Chavez Welding & Machining	3599	F	408 247-4658	16378
Chemical Safety Technology Inc	3559	F	408 263-0984	14927
Chipstart Inc	3643	F	650 204-7883	17451
Chrontel Inc (PA)	3674	C	408 383-9328	18766
Ciphercloud Inc (PA)	7372	D	408 519-6930	24490
Circuit Connections	3672	F	408 955-9505	18449
Circuit Spectrum Inc	3672	F	408 946-8484	18452
Cisco Ironport Systems LLC (HQ)	7372	B	650 989-6500	24493
Cisco Systems Inc	3577	A	408 526-7939	15704
Cisco Systems Inc	3577	A	408 225-5248	15709
Cisco Systems Inc	3577	A	408 526-6698	15712
Cisco Systems Inc (PA)	3577	A	408 526-4000	15714
Cisco Systems Inc	3577	A	408 434-1903	15715
Cisco Systems Inc	3577	A	408 424-4050	15716
Cisco Systems Inc	3577	A	408 526-5999	15717
City Canvas	2394	F	408 287-2688	3784
Clear View LLC	3442	F	408 271-2734	12303
CM Manufacturing Inc (HQ)	3674	C	408 284-7200	18770
Cnex Labs Inc	3674	E	408 695-1045	18772
Coast Engraving Companies	2796	E	408 297-2555	7640
Cobham Adv Elec Sol Inc	3812	B	408 624-3000	21272
Coda Automotive Inc	3714	E	408 763-4071	20293
Comet Technologies USA Inc	3829	E	408 325-8770	22180
Communications & Pwr Inds LLC	3663	C	650 846-2900	18074
Communications & Pwr Inds LLC	3679	C	650 846-2900	19497
Concept Part Solutions Inc	3545	E	408 748-1244	14616
Concept Systems Mfg Inc	3674	F	408 855-8595	18777
Concrete Ready Mix Inc	3273	E	408 224-2452	11098
Connectedyard Inc	3826	E	415 699-8844	21937
Construction On Time Inc	1442	F	408 209-1799	354
Continental Intelligent Transp	3011	E	408 391-9008	9463
Continuum Electro-Optics Inc	3826	D	408 727-3240	21938
Cortec Precision Shtmtl Inc (PA)	3444	C	408 278-8540	12540
Cpk Manufacturing Inc	3599	F	408 971-4019	16406
Creative Metal Products Corp	3599	F	408 281-0797	16408
Crunch LLC	7372	E	650 257-8000	24533
Csr Technology Inc (DH)	3679	C	408 523-6500	19504
CTS Corporation	3672	E	408 955-9001	18462
CTT Inc (PA)	3663	D	408 541-0596	18081
Cyber Switching Inc	3699	E	408 595-3670	19938
Cyberlinkcom Corp	7372	F	408 217-1850	24540
Cyberswitchingpatents LLC	3699	F	408 436-9830	19939
Cypress Semiconductor Corp	3674	F	408 943-2600	18795
Cypress Semiconductor Corp (PA)	3674	A	408 943-2600	18796
D & F Standler Inc	3599	F	408 226-8188	16415
Dale Grove Corporation	3556	E	408 251-7220	14844
DC Electronics Inc	3643	F	408 947-4531	17459
Deep Ocean Engineering Inc	3732	F	408 436-1102	21029
Delta Matrix Inc	3599	E	408 955-9140	16430
Demaiz Inc	2032	F	650 518-6268	755
Denali Software Inc (HQ)	7372	E	408 943-1234	24560
Dexerials America Corporation	3824	F	408 441-0846	21685
Dfine Inc (HQ)	3841	D	408 321-9999	22422
Diagnostics For Real World Ltd (PA)	2835	F	408 773-1511	8473
Dialogic Inc	3661	F	800 755-4444	17939
Diamanti Inc	3575	E	408 645-5111	15632
Diamond Multimedia Systems	3672	B	408 868-9613	18467
Dicar Inc	3357	E	408 295-1106	11069
Distinct Corporation	7372	E	408 445-3270	24564
Ditech Networks Inc (HQ)	3661	E	408 883-3636	17940
Dnp America LLC	3674	F	408 616-1200	18802
Du-All Anodizing Corporation	3471	F	408 275-6694	13389
Du-All Anodizing Inc	3471	F	408 275-6694	13390
Duel Systems Inc	3678	E	408 453-9500	19388
Dunan Sensing LLC	3699	F	408 613-1015	19949
Dynamic Intgrted Solutions LLC	3674	F	408 737-3400	18808
Dynamikos Inc (PA)	3086	F	408 432-1711	9837
Dynatec Mfg Inc	3599	F	408 265-8471	16457
Eargo Inc (PA)	3842	D	650 996-9508	22720
Eclipse Microwave Inc	3679	F	408 526-1100	19523
El Observador Publications Inc	2711	F	408 938-1700	5844
Elcon Inc	3679	F	408 292-7800	19524
Elcon Precision LLC	3545	E	408 292-7800	14630
Electromax Inc	3672	F	408 428-9474	18471
Electronic Interface Co Inc	3699	D	408 286-2134	19958
Elementcxi	3674	E	408 935-8090	18816
Elite Metal Fabrication Inc	3599	E	408 433-9926	16467
Emsolutions Inc	3672	F	510 668-1118	18475
Encore Industries	3444	E	408 416-0501	12573
Energous Corporation	3663	D	408 963-0200	18099
Energy Sales LLC (PA)	3691	E	503 690-9000	19802
Enpirion	3674	F	408 904-2800	18825
Ensphere Solutions Inc	3674	F	408 598-2441	18826
Enter Music Publishing Inc	2721	F	408 971-9794	6159
Environ-Clean Technology Inc	3674	F	408 487-1770	18828
Eoplex Inc	3699	F	408 638-5100	19962
Eoplex Technologies Inc	3699	F	408 638-5100	19963
Epson Electronics America Inc (DH)	3674	E	408 922-0200	18830
Ericsson Inc	3663	A	408 970-2000	18103
Esco Woodworks	2431	F	408 225-2777	4153
ESP Safety Inc	3842	F	408 886-9746	22729
Espace Enterprises Tech Inc	3559	F	408 844-8176	14950
Etd Precision Ceramics Corp	3674	F	408 577-0405	18834
Eugenus Inc (HQ)	3825	D	669 235-8244	21751
Evissap Inc	3663	E	408 432-7393	18107
Exar Corporation (HQ)	3674	C	669 265-6100	18836
Exatron Inc	3825	E	408 629-7600	21754
Expedite Precision Works Inc	3599	E	408 437-1893	16484
Extreme Networks Inc (PA)	3661	B	408 579-2800	17946
Extreme Precision Inc	3599	F	408 275-8365	16486
Famsoft Inc	7372	E	408 452-1550	24644
Fastrak Manufacturing Svcs Inc	3679	E	408 298-6414	19540
Fibersense & Signals Inc	3661	E	408 941-1900	17950
Filetrail Inc	7372	E	408 289-1300	24648
Flextronics America LLC (DH)	3672	C	408 576-7000	18483
Flextronics Intl USA Inc (HQ)	3672	A	408 576-7000	18487
Flextronics Semiconductor (DH)	3674	E	408 576-7000	18844
Foreal Spectrum Inc	3827	E	408 923-1675	22077
Fortrend Engineering Corp	3823	E	408 734-9311	21587
Four Colorcom	2752	F	408 436-7574	6825
Foveon Inc	3674	E	408 855-6800	18849
Foxsemicon Integrated Tech Inc	3674	E	408 383-9880	18850
Franchise Update Inc	2721	F	408 402-5681	6167
Frt of America LLC	3545	F	408 261-2632	14636
G B Mold & Tool Design	3544	F	408 254-3871	14519
G D M Electronic Assembly Inc	3643	D	408 945-4100	17468
Garage Doors Incorporated	2431	D	408 293-7443	4158
Gemfire Corporation	3699	D	408 519-6015	19974
General Dynmics Mssion Systems	3669	B	408 908-7300	18325
General Dynmics Mssion Systems	3669	B	408 955-1900	18328
General Elec Assembly Inc	3672	E	408 980-8819	18493
Genesis Engineering Inc	3812	E	408 249-5034	21298
Genetix Usa Inc	3826	E	408 719-6400	21962
Gentec Manufacturing Inc	3599	F	408 432-6220	16533
Geo Semiconductor Inc (PA)	3674	F	408 638-0400	18857
Geometrics Inc	3829	D	408 428-4244	22207
George Hood Inc	3444	F	408 295-6507	12597
Global Packing Solutions Inc	2449	F	408 279-4196	4522
GM Nameplate Inc	2679	C	408 435-1666	5713
Gold Technologies Inc	3643	E	408 321-9568	17469
Goose Manufacturing Inc	3599	F	408 747-0940	16539
Gordon Biersch Brewing Company	2082	E	408 792-1546	1596
Gorilla Circuits (PA)	3672	C	408 294-9897	18497
Grandesign Decor Inc	3442	E	408 436-9969	12319
Green Circuits Inc	3679	E	408 526-1700	19556
Greenvity Communications Inc (PA)	3559	F	408 935-9358	14963
Grinding & Dicing Services Inc	3674	E	408 451-2000	18863
Group Manufacturing Services (PA)	3444	D	408 436-1040	12602
Guavus Inc (HQ)	7372	D	650 243-3400	24714
H B R Industries Inc	3677	F	408 988-0800	19339

GEOGRAPHIC

Company	SIC	EMP	PHONE	ENTRY #
Haig Precision Mfg Corp	3599	D	408 378-4920	16554
Handa Pharmaceuticals LLC	2834	F	510 354-2888	8202
Hane & Hane Inc	3471	E	408 292-2140	13422
Hardcraft Industries Inc	3444	D	408 432-8340	12608
Harmonic Inc	3663	F	800 788-1330	18120
Harmonic Inc (PA)	3663	B	408 542-2500	18121
Henry Ll	3444	F	408 944-9100	12611
Herman Miller Inc	2521	E	408 432-5730	4948
Hermes-Microvision Inc	3674	E	408 597-8600	18872
Herotek Inc	3663	E	408 941-8399	18125
Hgst Inc	3572	C	408 418-4148	15550
Hgst Inc (DH)	3572	F	408 717-6000	15552
Hi-Tech Prcision Machining Inc	3599	F	408 251-1269	16561
Hillis Printing Co Inc	2752	F	408 450-7910	6859
Hilltron Corporation	3679	F	408 597-4424	19567
Hitech Global Distribution LLC	3674	E	408 781-8043	18875
Hoojook	7372	F	408 596-9427	24735
Hoopla Software Inc	7372	F	408 498-9600	24736
Hti Turnkey Manufacturing Svcs	3679	E	408 955-0807	19568
Hunter Douglas Fabrications	2591	B	408 435-8844	5194
I & A Inc	3444	E	408 432-8340	12618
Icu Medical Fleet Services LLC	2834	D	408 229-0560	8209
Idx Corporation	2542	C	408 270-8094	5146
IL Pastaio Foods Inc	2099	F	408 753-9220	2539
Illinois Tool Works Inc	2759	E	408 468-1230	7350
Imagine That Inc	7372	F	408 365-0305	24753
Imerys Filtration Minerals	1499	F	408 643-0092	414
Imerys Filtration Minerals Inc (DH)	1499	E	805 562-0200	415
Immersion Corporation (PA)	3577	D	408 467-1900	15757
Infinisim Inc	7372	E	408 934-9777	24764
Infiniti Solutions Usa Inc (PA)	3672	D	408 923-7300	18505
Infiniti Solutions Usa Inc	3672	D	408 923-7300	18506
Information Storage Dvcs Inc	3674	C	408 943-6666	18893
Ingrasys Technology USA Inc	3825	E	863 271-8266	21773
Initio Corporation	3674	E	408 943-3189	18895
Insieme Networks LLC	3661	F	408 424-1227	17957
Integrated Device Tech Inc (PA)	3674	B	408 284-8200	18906
Integrated Device Tech Inc	3674	B	408 284-1433	18907
Integrated Materials Inc	3674	E	408 964-7700	18908
Intel Corporation	3577	A	408 544-7000	15765
Intelligent Energy Inc	3429	E	562 997-3600	11964
Intelligent Storage Solution	3572	C	408 428-0105	15560
Interface Masters Tech Inc	3679	E	408 441-9341	19583
Intermolecular Inc (PA)	3674	C	408 582-5700	18921
International Rectifier Hirel	3674	C	408 944-0239	18923
Interniche Technologies Inc (PA)	7372	F	408 540-1160	24787
Invensas Corporation	3674	E	408 324-5100	18929
Invensense Inc (HQ)	3812	C	408 501-2200	21310
Iogyn Inc	3845	F	408 996-2517	22992
Isharya Inc	3911	E	415 462-6294	23276
Isign Solutions Inc (PA)	3577	F	650 802-7888	15772
ITW Semisystems Inc	3353	E	408 350-0244	11576
Ixsystems Inc (PA)	7372	D	408 943-4100	24811
J & R Machining Inc	3599	F	408 365-7314	16596
J Lohr Winery Corporation (PA)	2084	E	408 288-5057	1818
J&E Precision Machining Inc	3599	F	408 281-1195	16605
J3 Associates Inc	3599	F	408 281-4412	16607
Ja Solar USA Inc	3674	F	408 586-0000	18937
Jabil Circuit Inc	3672	D	408 361-3200	18511
Jabil Inc	3672	B	408 361-3200	18513
Jabil Silver Creek Inc (HQ)	7692	C	669 255-2900	25415
Jarvis Manufacturing Inc	3599	F	408 226-2600	16615
Javad Ems Inc	3679	D	408 770-1700	19594
Jazz Imaging LLC	3843	F	567 234-5299	22884
Jdi Display America Inc (PA)	3679	F	408 501-3720	19598
Jdsu Photonic Power (HQ)	3699	F	408 546-5000	19992
Jenards Window Coverings	2591	F	408 434-5937	5198
Jennings Technology Co LLC (DH)	3675	D	408 292-4025	19297
Jnc Machining	3599	F	408 920-2520	16627
Jrd Precision Machining Inc	3599	F	408 246-9327	16634
Jumping Cracker Beans LLC	2771	F	408 265-0658	7565
K C Sheetmetal Inc	3444	F	408 441-6620	12635
KC Metal Products Inc (PA)	3441	D	408 436-8754	12191
Kearney Pattern Works & Fndry	3365	E	408 293-7414	11744
Kellogg Company	2043	C	408 295-8656	1064
Kennerley-Spratling Inc	3089	C	408 944-9407	10177
Keri Systems Inc (PA)	3699	D	408 435-8400	19997
Ketera Technologies Inc (HQ)	7372	E	408 572-9500	24827
Keystone Coffee Company	2095	F	408 998-2221	2357
Kimball Electronics Indiana	3825	E	669 234-1110	21787
Kion Technology Inc	3479	E	408 435-3008	13609
Kisco Conformal Coating LLC (PA)	3674	E	408 224-6533	18942
Kmic Technology Inc	3663	E	408 240-3600	18147
Komag Incorporated	3264	F	408 576-2150	10818
Kramarz Enterprises	3599	F	408 293-1187	16664
Kranem Corporation	7372	C	650 319-6743	24840
Ksm Corp	3674	B	408 514-2400	18945
Ksm Vacuum Products Inc	3443	F	408 514-2400	12394
Kwan Software Engineering Inc	7372	F	408 496-1200	24843
L & B Laboratories Inc	3999	E	408 251-7888	24155
L & H Iron Inc	3446	F	408 287-8797	12872
L & T Precision Engrg Inc	3599	E	408 441-1890	16670
La Voies of San Jose	2591	E	408 297-1285	5201
Laird Technologies Inc	3823	E	408 544-9500	21612
Lam Research Corporation	3674	E	408 434-6109	18949
Landmark Technology Inc	3679	E	408 435-8890	19617
Lantin Enterprise Inc	3599	F	408 935-9327	16677
Lantiq North America Inc	3674	F	408 503-8700	18953
Laptalo Enterprises Inc	3444	D	408 727-6633	12641
Laser Reference Inc	3821	E	408 361-0220	21479
Lattice Semiconductor Corp	3674	B	408 826-6000	18955
Lavante Inc	7372	E	408 754-1410	24849
Ledengin Inc (PA)	3674	E	408 922-7200	18958
Lee Brothers Inc	2035	D	650 964-9650	920
Leeyo Software Inc (HQ)	7372	E	408 988-5800	24856
Leiters Enterprises Inc	2834	E	800 292-6772	8258
Lensvector Inc	3851	D	408 542-0300	23106
Leotek Electronics USA LLC	3993	E	408 380-1788	23914
Lg Innotek Usa Inc (HQ)	3679	E	408 955-0364	19620
Lgc Wireless Inc	3663	C	408 952-2400	18165
Lgphilips Lcd Amer Fin Corp	3699	D	408 350-7600	20004
Lights Fantastic	2752	E	408 266-2787	6948
Lobob Laboratories Inc	2834	E	408 324-0381	8264
Lockheed Martin Corporation	3663	A	408 473-3000	18167
Lockheed Martin Corporation	3812	A	408 473-7498	21328
Lockheed Martin Corporation	3761	B	408 747-2626	21162
Lockheed Martin Corporation	3721	B	408 742-5219	20600
Lohmann Prcision Die Cutng LLC	2672	F	408 453-9400	5569
LSI Corporation (DH)	3674	A	408 433-8000	18968
LSI Corporation	3674	F	408 436-8379	18971
Lucero Cables Inc	3679	C	408 536-0340	19628
Lumatronix Mfg Inc	3674	F	408 435-7820	17346
Lumenis Inc (DH)	3841	C	408 764-3000	22515
Lumentum Operations LLC	3827	C	408 546-5483	22100
Lumileds LLC (HQ)	3825	E	408 964-2900	21795
Lynx Software Technologies Inc (PA)	7372	D	408 979-3900	24870
Lyris Inc	7372	E	800 768-2929	24871
M C I Manufacturing Inc (PA)	3444	E	408 456-2700	12646
M R F Techniques Inc	3679	F	408 433-1941	19630
M-Pulse Microwave Inc	3674	E	408 432-1480	18875
Mac Cal Company	3444	D	408 441-1435	12650
Macquarie Electronics Inc	3674	E	408 965-3860	18977
Magellan West LLC	7372	E	408 324-0620	24876
Magnum Semiconductor Inc	3674	C	408 934-3700	18978
Mancias Steel Company Inc	3441	E	408 295-5096	12201
Maquet Medical Systems USA LLC	3845	A	408 635-3900	23002
Maskless Lithography Inc	2752	F	408 433-1864	6962
Mass Precision Inc (PA)	3444	C	408 954-0200	12654
Master Metal Products Company	3444	F	408 275-1210	12657
Matthey Johnson Inc	3841	E	408 727-2221	22520
Mavens Creamery LLC	2024	E	408 216-9270	686
Max Precision Machine Inc	3599	F	408 956-8986	16723
Maxim Integrated Products Inc (PA)	3674	A	408 601-1000	18984
McCash Manufacturing Inc	3841	E	408 748-8991	22521
McClatchy Newspapers Inc	2711	D	408 200-1000	5952
McNeal Enterprises Inc	3089	D	408 922-7290	10201
McUbe Inc (PA)	3571	E	408 637-5503	15450
Medianews Group Inc	2711	B	408 920-5713	5960
Mediatek USA Inc (PA)	3571	C	408 526-1899	15451
Mega Force Corporation	3577	C	408 956-9989	15801
Megachips Technology Amer Corp (HQ)	3674	E	408 570-0555	18988
Meivac Incorporated	3674	E	408 362-1000	18989
Mercury Systems Inc	3672	F	669 226-5800	18528
Merlin Solar Technologies Inc	3674	E	678 650-8892	18993
Michael T Mingione	2542	F	408 365-1544	5155
Micrel LLC	3674	A	408 944-0800	18996
Micrel LLC	3674	C	408 944-0800	18997
Micrel LLC	3674	C	408 944-0800	18998
Micro-Metric Inc	3829	F	408 452-8505	22236
Micro-Probe Incorporated (HQ)	3825	D	408 457-3900	21805
Microchip Technology Inc	3674	C	408 735-9110	19001
Microlux Inc	3699	F	408 435-1700	20017
Micronas USA Inc	3651	C	408 625-1200	17833
Microsemi Corporation	3674	F	408 643-6000	19015
Microsemi Frequency Time Corp	7372	F	408 433-0910	24908
Microsemi Soc Corp (DH)	3674	C	408 643-6000	19016
Micrus Endovascular LLC (HQ)	3841	C	408 433-1400	22541
Mission Bindery Inc	2789	E	510 623-8260	7608
MMR Technologies Inc (PA)	3559	F	650 962-9620	14991
Modern Ceramics Mfg Inc	3229	E	408 383-0554	10657

	SIC	EMP	PHONE	ENTRY #
Modutek Corp	3823	E	408 362-2000	21619
Mohawk Land & Cattle Co Inc	2011	D	408 436-1800	444
Mokume Software Inc	7372	F	408 839-7000	24933
Molecular Devices LLC (HQ)	3826	C	408 747-1700	21996
Monolithic Power Systems Inc (PA)	3674	C	408 826-0600	19023
Montage Technology Inc	3674	F	408 982-2788	19024
Montavista Software LLC (DH)	7372	C	408 572-8000	24935
Monterey Foam Company Inc	3299	F	408 279-6756	11361
Mortenson Precision	3444	E	408 441-7380	12687
MOSplastics Inc	3089	C	408 944-9407	10227
Mosys Inc	3674	E	408 418-7500	19025
Mota Group Inc (PA)	3695	E	408 370-1248	19872
Motiv Design Group Inc	3624	E	408 441-0611	17240
Mountz Inc (PA)	3823	E	408 292-2214	21621
MPS International Ltd	3674	A	408 826-0600	19027
Multis Inc	3999	E	510 441-2653	24180
Multivitamin Direct Inc	2833	E	408 573-7276	7954
Nanosilicon Inc	3674	E	408 263-7341	19029
Naprotek Inc	3672	D	408 830-5000	18537
Natel Engineering Company Inc	3672	C	408 228-5462	18540
Ndsp Delaware Inc	3674	E	408 626-1640	19033
Neoconix Inc	3674	E	408 530-9393	19034
Neodora LLC	3559	E	650 283-3319	14999
Neonode Inc (PA)	3826	D	408 496-6722	22000
Neophotonics Corporation (PA)	3674	B	408 232-9200	19036
Neosem Technology Inc (DH)	3825	E	408 643-7000	21815
Netgear Inc (PA)	3661	C	408 907-8000	17968
Network Pcb Inc	3672	E	408 943-8760	18543
Networked Energy Services Corp (HQ)	3699	E	408 622-9900	20026
New World Machining Inc	3599	E	408 227-3810	16786
Nexenta Systems Inc	7372	C	408 791-3341	24963
Nexlogic Technologies Inc	3672	E	408 436-8150	18545
Nextest Systems Corporation	3825	E	408 960-2400	21816
Nguyen Hiep Corp	3599	E	408 451-9042	16788
Nicholas R Hyland	2521	F	408 392-0600	4958
Nimble Storage Inc (HQ)	3572	C	408 432-9600	15576
Nippon Trends Food Service Inc	2099	D	408 214-0511	2624
NM Laser Products Inc	3699	F	408 227-8299	20030
NM Machining Inc	3599	E	408 972-8978	16792
Nokia of America Corporation	3661	F	408 363-5906	17969
Novanta Corporation	3679	E	408 754-4176	19664
NTL Precision Machining Inc	3599	F	408 298-6650	16797
NWT Infotech Services	3575	F	831 335-6500	15642
Nxp Usa Inc	3674	D	408 518-5500	19046
Nxp Usa Inc	3674	B	408 518-5500	19047
O and Y Precision Inc	3545	F	408 362-1333	14658
O-S Inc	3599	F	408 946-5890	16801
Oberon Co	3679	D	408 227-3730	19668
Oce Dsplay Grphics Systems Inc	3555	D	773 714-8500	14819
Oclaro Inc (PA)	3674	D	408 383-1400	19051
Oclaro (north America) Inc (HQ)	3661	B	408 383-1400	17971
Oclaro Fiber Optics Inc (HQ)	3674	E	408 383-1400	19052
Oclaro Photonics Inc (DH)	3827	D	408 383-1400	22112
Oclaro Subsystems Inc	3661	C	408 383-1400	17972
Oclaro Technology Inc (HQ)	3661	B	408 383-1400	17973
Odwalla Inc	2033	E	408 254-5800	837
Okamoto Corporation	3674	F	408 654-8400	19055
Oki Graphics Inc	2752	F	408 451-9294	7002
Olivera Egg Ranch LLC	2015	D	408 258-8074	548
Olympus America Inc	3841	B	408 935-5000	22568
Omneon Inc (HQ)	3663	C	408 585-5000	18205
Omnitec Precision Mfg Inc	3599	F	408 437-9056	16809
Onnet Usa Inc	2741	F	408 457-3992	6544
Opsveda Inc	7372	F	408 628-0461	24994
Optoelectronix Inc (PA)	3674	F	408 437-9488	19064
Oracle Corporation	7372	B	408 276-3822	25013
Oracle Corporation	7372	B	408 390-8623	25016
Oracle Corporation	7372	B	925 694-6258	25020
Orbotech Lt Solar LLC	3674	E	408 414-3777	19065
Orion Manufacturing Inc	3672	C	408 955-9001	18552
Ose Usa Inc (HQ)	3674	F	408 452-9080	19067
OT Precision Inc	3599	E	408 435-8818	16812
Ozmo Inc	3572	E	650 515-3524	15581
P H Machining Inc	3663	F	408 980-9895	18211
Pacific Press Corporation	2711	E	408 292-3422	6009
Palo Alto Awning Inc	2394	F	650 968-4270	3802
Papadatos Enterprises Inc	3599	F	408 299-0190	16825
Pavilion Integration Corp	3829	F	408 453-8801	22249
PEC Manufacturing Inc	3699	F	408 577-1839	20039
Perfectvips Inc	3674	F	408 912-2316	19074
Phil Wood & Company	3499	F	408 292-4137	13964
Photon Dynamics Inc (HQ)	3825	C	408 226-9900	21827
Phynexus Inc	3826	F	408 267-7214	22004
Pillar Data Systems Inc	7372	B	408 503-4000	25061
Piranha Ems Inc	3629	F	408 520-3963	17350
Pixelworks Inc (PA)	3674	D	408 200-9200	19076
Plasma Rggedized Solutions Inc (PA)	3479	D	408 954-8405	13635
Plx Technology Inc	7372	C	408 435-7400	25067
Pny Technologies Inc	3674	E	408 392-1400	19078
Polycom Inc (HQ)	3661	B	408 586-6000	17981
Pottery By Levine Acquisition	3269	E	408 773-0418	10834
Power Design Manufacturing LLC	3672	E	408 437-1931	18563
Power Integrations Inc (PA)	3674	B	408 414-9200	19083
Power Knot LLC	3589	F	408 480-2758	16090
Praxair Distribution Inc	2813	F	408 995-6089	7728
Precision Jewelry Tools & Sups	3423	E	408 251-7990	11906
Premiere Recycle Co	3443	E	408 297-7910	12410
Probe-Logic Inc	3571	D	408 416-0777	15473
Proformative Inc	2741	F	408 400-3993	6558
Prosurg Inc	3841	E	408 945-4040	22589
Proto Services Inc	3669	E	408 321-8688	18353
Providenet Communications Corp	7372	E	408 398-6335	25085
Proxim Wireless Corporation (PA)	3669	D	408 383-7600	18354
Proximex Corporation (DH)	7372	F	408 215-9000	25086
Prysm Inc	3999	D	408 586-1100	24217
Pushtotest Inc	7372	F	408 436-8203	25090
Qorvo Us Inc	3674	E	408 493-4304	19095
Qorvo Us Inc	3674	B	408 577-6200	19096
Qostronics Inc	3672	E	408 719-1286	18569
Qualcomm Atheros Inc (HQ)	3674	A	408 773-5200	19097
Qualectron Systems Corporation	3825	F	408 986-1686	21833
Quality Circuit Assembly Inc	3672	D	408 441-1001	18573
Quality Machining & Design Inc	3559	E	408 224-7976	15015
Quantenna Communications Inc (PA)	3674	F	669 209-5500	19107
Quantum 3d Headquarters	3674	F	408 361-9999	19108
Quantum Global Tech LLC	2842	E	408 487-1770	8671
Quantumscape Corporation	3674	C	408 452-2000	19110
Qulsar Inc (PA)	3625	F	408 715-1098	17296
Qulsar Usa Inc	3663	F	408 715-1098	18231
R Stephenson & D Cram Mfg Inc	3599	F	408 452-0882	16881
R&D Altanova Inc	3672	E	408 225-7011	18577
Radicom Research Inc (PA)	3661	F	408 383-9006	17986
Radio Frequency Systems Inc	3663	F	408 281-6100	18233
Raditek Inc (PA)	3663	D	408 266-7404	18234
Radius Product Development Inc	3089	A	408 361-6000	10321
Rapid Precision Mfg Inc	3599	E	408 617-0771	16884
Recortec Inc	3577	F	408 928-1488	15835
Redpine Signals Inc (PA)	3674	E	408 748-3385	19118
Reed & Graham Inc (PA)	2911	E	408 287-1400	9352
Regal Electronics Inc (PA)	3679	E	408 988-2288	19705
Relectric Inc	3613	E	408 467-2222	17159
Restoration Robotics Inc (PA)	3841	D	408 883-6888	22603
Reyes Coca-Cola Bottling LLC	2086	D	408 436-3700	2188
Rhubcommunications Inc	3699	E	408 899-2830	20058
Richard J Trevino MD	3842	F	408 926-5300	22805
Richards Machining Co Inc	3599	F	408 526-9219	16899
Richmond Optical Co	3851	F	510 783-1420	23119
Rite Track Equipment Svcs Inc	3559	F	408 432-0131	15021
Rivermeadow Software Inc	7372	F	408 217-6498	25131
Robecks Wldg & Fabrication Inc	3441	E	408 287-0202	12238
Robles Bros Inc (PA)	2099	E	408 436-5551	2657
Rockwell Automation Inc	3625	D	408 443-5425	17302
Roma Bakery Inc	2051	D	408 294-0123	1315
Ron Kehl Engineering	3471	F	408 629-6632	13491
Rose Metal Products Inc	3441	D	417 865-1676	12239
Roth Wood Products Ltd	2599	E	408 723-8888	5253
Rtec-Instruments Inc	3826	E	408 456-0801	22012
Rush Pcb Inc	3672	F	408 469-6013	18586
Rvision Inc (HQ)	3827	F	619 233-1403	22129
S J Sterilized Wiping Rags	2299	F	408 287-2512	3016
Saba Motors Inc	3711	F	408 219-8675	20169
Sal J Acsta Sheetmetal Mfg Inc	3444	D	408 275-6370	12750
Sal Rodriguez	3471	F	408 993-8091	13496
San Benito Supply (PA)	3272	C	831 637-5526	10996
San Jose Awning Company Inc	2394	F	408 350-7000	3808
San Jose Business Journal	2711	E	408 295-3800	6035
San Jose Die Casting Corp	3363	E	408 262-6500	11705
San Jose Mercury-News LLC (DH)	2711	A	408 920-5000	6036
Sandman Inc (PA)	3272	E	408 947-0669	10998
Sandman Inc	3272	E	408 947-0159	10999
Sanmina Corporation	3672	E	408 964-3500	18591
Sanmina Corporation	3672	E	408 964-3500	18592
Sanmina Corporation	3672	B	408 964-6400	18593
Sanmina Corporation	3672	E	408 964-3500	18594
Sanmina Corporation	3672	B	408 557-7210	18595
Sanmina Corporation	3672	E	408 964-3000	18597
Sanmina Corporation (PA)	3672	B	408 964-3500	18599
Sas Institute Inc	7372	F	919 677-8000	25147
Scintera Networks Inc	3674	E	408 636-2600	19138
Screen Shop Inc	3442	F	408 295-7384	12346

Employment Codes: A=Over 500 employees, B=251-500,
C=101-250, D=51-100, E=20-50, F=10-19

2019 California
Manufacturers Register

© Mergent Inc. 1-800-342-5647

1461

GEOGRAPHIC

Company	SIC	EMP	PHONE	ENTRY #
Semifab Inc	3823	D	408 414-5928	21651
Seminet Inc	3674	F	408 754-8537	19145
Semler Scientific Inc	3841	E	877 774-4211	22620
Senju Comtek Corp	3399	F	408 792-3830	11848
Seventh Heaven Inc	2399	E	408 287-8945	3966
Sharpe Energy Services Inc	1382	F	408 489-3581	151
Shasta Electronic Mfg Svcs Inc	3571	E	408 436-1267	15482
Sheldons Hobby Shop	3663	E	408 943-0220	18250
Shocking Technologies Inc	2821	E	831 331-4558	7885
Siemens Product Life Mgmt Sftw	7372	E	408 941-4600	25173
Sierra Pacific Machining Inc	3599	F	408 924-0281	16946
Silfine America Inc	2821	D	408 823-8663	7886
Silicon Genesis Corporation	3674	D	408 228-5858	19150
Silicon Image Inc (HQ)	3674	D	408 616-4000	19151
Silicon Valley Express	3721	E	408 292-0677	20626
Siliconix Incorporated (HQ)	3674	A	408 988-8000	19161
Silver Press Inc	2789	F	408 435-0449	7618
Simmons Stairways Inc	2431	E	408 920-0105	4231
Sine-Tific Solutions Inc	2759	F	408 432-3434	7484
Sirf Technology Holdings Inc (DH)	3674	D	408 523-6500	19165
Siui America Inc	3845	E	408 432-8881	23048
Sk Hynix Memory Solutions Inc (HQ)	3674	E	408 514-3500	19169
Skylight Software Inc	7372	E	408 858-3933	25179
Smartlogic Semaphore Inc	7372	F	408 213-9500	25184
Smithfield Packaged Meats Corp	2011	C	408 392-0442	451
Smtc Manufacturing Corp Cal	3672	A	408 934-7100	18608
Solarius Development Inc	3825	F	408 541-0151	21851
Sonasoft Corp (PA)	7372	E	408 708-4000	25197
Sony Biotechnology Inc	3699	D	800 275-5963	20074
Sony Electronics Inc	3577	E	408 352-4000	15857
Sony Optical Archive Inc	3572	F	844 725-0398	15611
Sotcher Measurement Inc	3825	F	408 574-0112	21852
South Bay Circuits Inc	3679	C	408 978-8992	19732
South Bay Marble Inc (PA)	3281	F	650 594-4251	11280
Southern Counties Oil Co	2992	E	408 251-0811	9451
Southwest Offset Prtg Co Inc	2759	D	408 232-5160	7491
Spansion Inc (HQ)	3674	E	408 962-2500	19183
Spansion LLC (HQ)	3674	D	512 691-8500	19184
Spartan	2759	E	800 743-6950	7492
Spectral Dynamics Inc (PA)	3829	E	760 761-0440	22277
Spin Tek Machining Inc	3599	F	408 298-8223	16960
Spirent Communications Inc	3663	E	408 894-7015	18261
Spt Microtechnologies USA Inc	3559	E	408 571-1400	15031
Spyrus Inc (PA)	3577	E	408 392-9131	15859
Starview Inc	7372	E	406 890-5910	25219
Stencil Master Inc	3953	F	408 428-9695	23722
Storopack Inc	3081	E	408 435-1095	9730
Stryker Enterprises Inc	3499	E	408 295-6300	13976
Suez Wts Services Usa Inc	3589	C	408 360-5900	16119
Sumco Phoenix Corporation	3674	D	408 352-3880	19196
Sumicom-Usa	3571	E	408 385-2046	15490
Summit Wireless Tech Inc	3674	E	408 627-4716	19198
Sun Sheetmetal Solutions Inc	3444	E	408 445-8047	12776
Sunnytech	3672	F	408 943-8100	18620
Sunpower Corporation (DH)	3674	A	408 240-5500	19202
Super Micro Computer Inc (PA)	3571	A	408 503-8000	15491
Superior Metals Inc	3444	F	408 938-3488	12779
Surface Art Engineering Inc	3674	E	408 433-4700	19208
Sv Probe Inc	3825	D	480 635-4700	21858
Sv Probe Inc	3825	F	408 653-2387	21859
Sv Probe Inc	3825	C	408 727-6341	21860
Swiftstack Inc	7372	E	408 642-1865	25239
Symmetricom Inc	3661	F	408 433-0910	17998
Symphonix Devices Inc	3842	F	408 323-8218	22829
Synaptics Incorporated	3577	F	408 904-1100	15862
Synaptics Incorporated (PA)	3577	B	408 904-1100	15863
Syntest Technologies Inc	7372	F	408 720-9956	25248
T T E Products Inc	3599	F	408 955-0100	16983
T&S Manufacturing Tech LLC	3441	E	408 441-0285	12256
Take It For Granite Inc	1411	E	408 790-2812	307
Tango Systems Inc	3679	D	408 526-2330	19743
Tapioca Express	2046	F	408 999-0128	1102
Taponix Inc	7372	F	408 725-2942	25257
Tcomt Inc	3663	D	408 351-3340	18275
Te Connectivity Corporation	3678	B	408 624-3000	19419
Team Econolite	3669	F	408 577-1733	18371
Tecan Systems Inc	3821	D	408 953-3100	21492
Tech Air Northern Cal LLC	2813	F	408 293-9353	7733
Tech-Semi Inc	3674	F	408 451-9588	19213
Technibuilders Iron Inc	3446	F	408 287-8797	12897
Technoprobe America Inc	3674	F	408 573-9911	19214
Techshop San Jose LLC	3543	F	408 916-4144	14468
Teikoku Pharma Usa Inc (HQ)	2834	D	408 501-1800	8409
Telemetria Telephony Tech Inc	3694	F	408 428-0101	19846
Telewave Inc	3663	F	408 929-4400	18280
Teradyne Inc	3825	C	408 960-2400	21869
Teseda Corporation	3825	F	650 320-8188	21870
Tesla Motors Store Santana Row	3711	F	408 249-2815	20177
Tessera Inc (DH)	3674	F	408 321-6000	19224
Tessera Intellectual Prpts Inc	3674	D	408 321-6000	19225
Tessera Intllctual Prprty Corp	3674	E	408 321-6000	19226
Tessera Technologies Inc (HQ)	3674	E	408 321-6000	19227
Therma LLC	3444	A	408 347-3400	12789
Thermo Finnigan LLC (HQ)	3826	B	408 965-6000	22030
Thermo Fisher Scientific	3826	B	408 894-9835	22033
Thermoquest Corporation	3826	A	408 965-6000	22044
Thin Film Electronics Inc	3679	C	408 503-7300	19762
Thirdrock Software	7372	F	408 777-2910	25272
Thunder Products Inc	3931	F	408 270-7800	23391
Tiger Construction Inc	2851	F	408 244-8124	8949
Tiger Jet Network Inc	3825	F	408 437-7727	21878
Times Media Inc	2711	F	408 494-7000	6071
TLC Machining Incorporated	3545	E	408 321-9002	14684
Tmk Manufacturing	3544	D	408 732-3200	14579
Tobar Industries	3643	F	408 494-3530	17501
Tolerance Technology Inc	3951	F	408 586-8811	23702
Toshiba America Electronic	3679	E	408 526-2400	19765
Tower Semiconductor Usa Inc	3674	F	408 770-1320	19233
Trane US Inc	3585	D	408 437-0390	15988
Tri-Phase Inc	3672	C	408 284-7700	18628
Triad Tool & Engineering Inc	3089	E	408 436-8411	10410
Trina Solar (us) Inc	3674	E	800 696-7114	19235
Triquint Wj Inc	3663	E	408 577-6200	18292
Tsmc Technology Inc	3674	D	408 382-8052	19238
Ttm Technologies Inc	3672	C	408 280-0422	18637
Ttm Technologies N Amer LLC	3672	C	408 719-4000	18638
Tung Tai Group	3469	F	408 573-8681	13290
Turner Designs Inc	3826	F	408 749-0994	22045
Twin Creeks Technologies Inc (PA)	3674	F	408 368-3733	19240
Ubicom Inc	3674	D	408 433-3330	19242
Ultratech Inc (HQ)	3559	C	408 321-8835	15042
Uniquify Inc	3679	E	408 235-8810	19777
United Craftsmen Priniting	2752	E	408 224-6464	7156
United Technologies Corp	3724	A	408 779-9121	20687
United Technologies Corp	3724	A	408 779-9121	20688
Untangle Holdings Inc	7372	E	408 598-4299	25314
US Concrete Inc	3273	F	408 947-8606	11201
V2 Lighting Group Inc	3648	F	707 383-4600	17743
Valiantica Inc (PA)	7372	F	408 694-3803	25319
Valley Images	2396	F	408 279-6777	3927
Valley View Packing Co Inc	2034	E	408 289-8300	904
Vander-Bend Manufacturing Inc	3679	A	408 245-5150	19779
Various Technologies Inc	3625	E	408 972-4460	17319
Vat Incorporated	3491	E	408 813-2700	13735
Verifone Inc (DH)	3578	C	408 232-7800	15902
Verifone Systems Inc (HQ)	3578	D	408 232-7800	15904
Verisilicon Inc (HQ)	3674	F	408 844-8560	19253
Vesta Technology Inc	3674	F	408 519-5800	19254
Via Mechanics (usa) Inc (DH)	3577	F	408 392-9650	15882
Viavi Solutions Inc	3674	C	408 577-1478	19256
Viavi Solutions Inc (PA)	3674	B	408 404-3600	19257
Viavi Solutions Inc	3699	C	408 546-5000	20099
Violin Systems LLC	3572	C	650 396-1501	15623
Virsec Systems Inc	7372	F	978 274-7260	25333
Vishay Siliconix LLC	2869	A	408 988-8000	9051
Visier Inc (PA)	7372	F	888 277-9331	25335
Visualon Inc	7372	C	408 645-6618	25336
Vital Connect Inc	3845	E	408 963-4600	23067
Vitron Electronic Services Inc	3672	D	408 251-1600	18648
Viv Labs Inc	7372	F	650 268-9837	25337
Vnus Medical Technologies Inc	3841	C	408 360-7200	22676
Vocera Communications Inc (PA)	3669	C	408 882-5100	18377
Volterra Semiconductor LLC (HQ)	3674	C	408 601-1000	19266
W A Call Manufacturing Co Inc	3444	F	408 436-1450	12813
Wafer Process Systems Inc	3559	F	408 445-3010	15046
Wafer Reclaim Services LLC (PA)	3674	C	408 945-8112	19269
Wafernet Inc	3674	F	408 437-9747	19270
Watt Stopper Inc (DH)	3643	E	408 988-5331	17505
Wb Machining & Mech Design	3599	E	408 453-5005	17054
WD Media LLC	3695	B	408 576-2000	19889
WEI Laboratories Inc	2032	F	408 970-8700	780
West Cast Architectural Shtmtl	3446	F	408 776-2700	12906
Westcoast Precision Inc	3599	E	408 943-9998	17061
Western Digital Corporation (PA)	3572	A	408 717-6000	15624
Western Digital Tech Inc (HQ)	3572	A	949 672-7000	15625
Western Widgets Cnc Inc	3599	F	408 436-1230	17063
Westrock Cp LLC	2631	E	770 448-2193	5366
Wi2wi Inc (PA)	3663	E	408 416-4200	18301
Wilkinson Mfg Inc	3599	F	408 809-7341	17067
Wine Cellar Impressions Inc	2084	F	408 277-0100	2060

	SIC	EMP	PHONE	ENTRY #
Wint Corporation	3827	C	408 532-8356	22148
Wooden Bridge Inc	2434	F	408 436-9663	4370
Xicato Inc (PA)	3645	E	408 829-4758	17572
Xilinx Inc (PA)	3672	A	408 559-7778	18654
Xilinx Inc	3674	F	408 879-6563	19278
Xilinx Development Corporation (HQ)	3674	F	408 559-7778	19279
Yageo America Corporation	3676	E	408 240-6200	19312
Yamamoto Manufacturing USA Inc (HQ)	3672	F	408 387-5250	18655
Yield Enhancement Services Inc	3674	F	408 410-5825	19282
Yuja Inc	7372	C	888 257-2278	25368
Zebra Technologies Intl LLC	3577	F	408 473-8500	15892
Zentera Systems Inc	7372	F	408 436-4811	25371
Zenverge Inc	3674	D	408 350-5052	19283
Zenyx Inc	7372	F	415 741-0170	25372
Zepp Labs Inc	3949	E	314 662-2145	23695
Zeptor Corporation	3624	F	408 432-6001	17244
Zest Labs Inc (HQ)	3674	E	408 200-6500	19285
Zoll Circulation Inc	3845	C	408 541-2140	23074
Zoll Medical Corporation	3845	F	408 419-2929	23075
Zoran Corporation (DH)	3674	E	972 673-1600	19287
Zscaler Inc (PA)	7372	C	408 533-0288	25375

SAN JUAN BAUTISTA, CA - San Benito County

	SIC	EMP	PHONE	ENTRY #
Monsanto Company	2879	C	831 623-7016	9107
True Leaf Farms LLC	2034	B	831 623-4667	902
Willis Construction Co Inc	3272	C	831 623-2900	11021

SAN JUAN CAPISTRANO, CA - Orange County

	SIC	EMP	PHONE	ENTRY #
3 Gen Inc	3841	F	949 481-6384	22299
Activa Global Spt & Entrmt LLC	3949	F	949 265-8260	23484
American Horse Products	2399	F	949 248-5300	3936
Carparts Technologies	7372	C	949 488-8860	24473
CI-One Corporation	2086	D	949 364-2895	2113
Emerald Expositions LLC	2721	D	949 226-5754	6157
Face First Screen Print Inc	2759	E	949 443-9895	7316
Fluidmaster Inc (PA)	3432	B	949 728-2000	12035
Heritage Design	3993	F	949 248-1300	23893
Hirsch Pipe & Supply Co Inc	3432	E	949 487-7009	12038
Iqinvision Inc	3861	D	949 369-8100	23169
Pioneer Sands LLC	1446	F	949 728-0171	397
Quest Diagnostics Nichols Inst (HQ)	3826	A	949 728-4000	22010
Richer Poorer Inc	2252	F	949 388-9994	2813
Seychelle Water Filtration	2834	E	949 234-1999	8379
Surrounding Elements LLC	2514	F	949 582-9000	4843
Sustainable Fibr Solutions LLC (PA)	2671	F	949 265-8287	5540
Techko Inc	3699	A	949 486-0678	20086
Vibration Impact & Pres	3559	F	949 429-3558	15045

SAN LEANDRO, CA - Alameda County

	SIC	EMP	PHONE	ENTRY #
1st Choice Fertilizer Inc	2873	F	800 504-5699	9055
Airspace Systems Inc	3625	F	310 704-7155	17247
Akido Printing Inc	2752	F	510 357-0238	6644
American Underwater Products (HQ)	3949	D	800 435-3483	23500
Amerisink Inc (PA)	3432	F	510 667-9998	12022
Artisan Brewers LLC	2082	E	510 567-4926	1561
Aryzta US Holdings I Corp	2052	A	800 938-1900	1353
Bargas Bindery	2789	F	510 357-7901	7594
Bayfab Metals Inc	3442	E	510 568-8950	12296
Bens Alternative Foods	2038	F	510 614-6745	983
Berber Food Manufacturing Inc	2099	C	510 553-0444	2463
Best Marble Co	3281	F	510 614-0155	11236
Bestwall LLC	2621	C	510 483-7580	5274
Bimbo Bakeries Usa Inc	2051	F	510 614-4500	1197
Bioclin Therapeutics Inc	2836	F	925 413-6140	8534
Botner Manufacturing Inc	3444	F	510 569-2943	12509
Braden Partners LP A Calif	3845	F	510 562-5501	22956
Brampton Mthesen Fabr Pdts Inc	2394	E	510 483-7771	3780
Cal Nor Design Inc (PA)	3544	F	925 829-7722	14491
California Coating Lab	3851	E	510 357-1800	23083
Carrier Corporation	3585	B	510 347-2000	15944
Cleophus Quealy Beer Company	2082	F	510 463-4534	1579
Coca-Cola Company	2086	C	510 476-7048	2120
Columbia Cosmetics Mfrs Inc (PA)	2844	C	510 562-5900	8720
Compatible Software Systems	7372	F	510 562-1172	24512
Contech Solutions Incorporated	3674	E	510 357-7900	18782
Coordnted Wire Rope Rgging Inc	2298	F	510 569-6911	2973
Copper Harbor Company Inc	2899	F	510 639-4670	9233
Crl Systems Inc	3663	D	510 351-3500	18080
Cummins Inc	3519	C	510 351-6101	14015
Custom Paper Products	2652	D	510 352-6880	5375
Dakota Press	2752	F	510 895-1300	6777
Dakota Press Inc	2711	F	510 895-1300	5827
Double V Industries	2395	E	510 347-3764	3841
Edge Electronics Corporation	3443	E	510 614-7988	12387
Energy Recovery Inc (PA)	3559	C	510 483-7370	14947
Environmental Sampling Sup Inc	3089	F	510 465-4988	10094

	SIC	EMP	PHONE	ENTRY #
Epac Technologies Inc (PA)	2752	C	510 317-7979	6808
Fxi Inc	3086	D	510 357-2600	9859
General Foundry Service Corp	3365	D	510 297-5040	11742
Georgia-Pacific LLC	2621	E	510 352-8269	5283
Hupalo Repasky Pipe Organs LLC	3931	F	510 483-6905	23377
India-West Publications Inc (PA)	2711	E	510 383-1140	5887
Innotech Energy Inc	3825	F	510 639-9197	21774
International Paper Company	2653	A	510 614-1600	5429
INX International Ink Co	2893	E	510 895-8001	9203
Japan Engine Inc	3694	E	510 532-7878	19836
Jessie Steele Inc	2399	F	510 204-0991	3952
Jetset California Inc	3241	F	510 632-7800	10758
Kennerley-Spratling Inc (PA)	3089	C	510 351-8230	10176
Kp LLC (PA)	2752	B	510 346-0729	6930
Kp LLC	2752	B	510 346-0729	6931
L3 Technologies Inc	3663	C	858 499-0284	18162
La Brea Bakery Holdings Inc	2051	B	818 742-4242	1276
Leeway Iron Works Inc	3441	F	510 357-8637	12194
Leitch & Co Inc	3423	F	510 483-2323	11901
Lightech Fiberoptic Inc	3679	E	510 567-8700	19625
Lindsay/Barnett Incorporated	3499	F	510 483-6300	13954
Loco Ventures Inc	2024	F	510 351-0405	680
Lyru Engineering Inc	3599	F	510 357-5951	16697
M-T Metal Fabrications Inc	3444	F	510 357-5262	12649
Marathon Products Incorporated	3829	F	510 562-6450	22230
MArs Engineering Company Inc	3451	E	510 483-0541	13031
Mas Metals Inc	3446	F	510 259-1426	12879
Medical Instr Dev Labs Inc	3841	E	510 357-3952	22526
Metro Poly Corporation	2673	E	510 357-9898	5608
My World Styles LLC	2844	F	800 355-4008	8800
Norcal Waste Equipment Co	3713	E	510 568-8336	20221
Norco Printing Inc	2791	F	510 569-2200	7630
Olson and Co Steel (PA)	3446	C	510 489-4680	12884
Optimization Corporation	3564	E	510 614-5890	15169
Oriental Odysseys Inc	3999	E	510 357-6100	24195
Osumo Inc	2396	F	510 346-6888	3911
Pacific Coast Laboratories	3842	F	510 351-2770	22789
Pacific Gaming	3944	E	510 562-8900	23454
PCC Structurals Inc	3369	C	510 568-6400	11781
Peggy S Lane Inc	3088	D	510 483-1202	9910
Pelagic Pressure Systems Corp	3545	D	510 569-3100	14660
Polymeric Technology Inc	3069	E	510 895-6001	9659
Porifera Inc	3589	F	510 695-2775	16089
Precision Die Cutting Inc	3714	E	510 636-9654	20423
R & S Erection Incorporated (PA)	3442	F	510 483-3710	12340
Realware Inc	7372	F	510 382-9045	25111
Reliable Powder Coatings LLC	3479	F	510 895-5551	13647
Reyes Coca-Cola Bottling LLC	2086	C	510 667-6300	2191
Ridge Foundry Inc	3321	E	510 352-0551	11500
Rip-Tie Inc	2298	F	510 577-0200	2978
Rotex Punch Company Inc (PA)	3544	F	510 357-3600	14566
Saags Products LLC	2013	D	510 678-3412	522
San Francisco Foods Inc	2038	D	510 357-7343	1013
Schindler Elevator Corporation	3534	E	510 382-2075	14258
Spar Sausage Co	2013	D	510 614-8100	527
Specialty Graphics Inc	2789	F	510 351-7705	7621
Steve and Cynthia Kizanis	2434	F	510 352-2832	4353
Sun Chemical Corporation	2893	E	510 618-1302	9212
Tap Plastics Inc A Cal Corp (PA)	2821	F	510 357-3755	7894
Trayer Engineering Corporation	3613	D	415 285-7770	17168
Triple C Foods Inc	2052	D	510 357-8880	1385
UNI-Poly Inc	2673	F	510 357-9898	5633
Union Solutions Inc	7372	F	510 483-1222	25311
Van Sark Inc (PA)	2512	F	510 635-1111	4817
Vistan Corporation	3556	F	510 351-0560	14896
Vitrico Corp	3229	F	510 652-6731	10669
Western Pacific Signal LLC	3669	F	510 276-6400	18379
Whitefish Enterprises Inc	3999	F	510 357-6100	24289
Woolery Enterprises Inc	2099	E	510 357-5700	2701
Wycen Foods Inc (PA)	2013	F	510 351-1987	535
Zinus Inc (HQ)	2515	D	925 417-2100	4895

SAN LORENZO, CA - Alameda County

	SIC	EMP	PHONE	ENTRY #
Aidells Sausage Company Inc	2013	A	510 614-5450	461
Foam Injection Plastics	3089	F	510 317-0218	10104
Golden W Ppr Converting Corp (PA)	3565	E	510 317-0646	15207
Hillshire Brands Company	2013	B	510 276-1300	492
Santini Foods Inc	2023	C	510 317-8888	648

SAN LUIS OBISPO, CA - San Luis Obispo County

	SIC	EMP	PHONE	ENTRY #
Abraham Steel Fabrication Inc	3441	F	805 544-8610	12099
Air-Vol Block Inc	3271	E	805 543-1314	10841
Alfred Domaine	2084	F	805 541-9463	1641
Amrich Energy Inc	2869	F	605 354-0830	8977
Baba Foods Slo LLC	2038	F	805 439-2250	982
Bimbo Bakeries Usa Inc	2051	D	805 544-7687	1188

	SIC	EMP	PHONE	ENTRY #
Calportland Company	3241	D	805 345-3400	10743
Calzyme Laboratories Inc (PA)	2869	F	805 541-5754	8994
Cattaneo Bros Inc	2013	E	805 543-7188	473
Chamisal Vineyards LLC	2084	F	866 808-9463	1686
Cloud Company (PA)	3569	F	805 549-8093	15310
Courtside Cellars LLC (PA)	2084	E	805 782-0500	1710
Crystal Engineering Corp	3823	E	805 595-5477	21567
Del Ozone Holding Company Inc	3589	F	805 541-1601	16034
E & J Gallo Winery	2084	C	805 544-5855	1745
Ednas Inc	2051	F	805 541-3563	1240
Ernie Ball Inc (PA)	3931	D	805 544-7726	23367
Flythissim Technologies Inc	3699	F	844 746-2846	19967
Fziomed Inc (PA)	3841	F	805 546-0610	22457
Gateworks Corporation	3823	F	805 781-2000	21593
H2o Engineering Inc	3589	F	805 542-9253	16047
Hanson Aggregates LLC	1442	F	805 543-8100	365
Humidtech Inc	3911	F	805 541-9500	23275
Hunter Spice Inc	2099	D	805 597-8900	2538
Imdex Technology Usa LLC	3829	E	805 540-2017	22216
ITW Global Tire Repair Inc	3011	D	805 489-0490	9465
J&J Products	3599	F	805 544-4288	16606
Jennings Aeronautics Inc	3812	F	805 544-0932	21312
Johanson Innovations Inc	3829	F	805 544-4697	22221
Kelsey See Canyon Vineyards	2084	F	805 595-9700	1839
M G A Investment Co Inc	2741	F	805 543-9050	6522
Mainland Machine	3599	F	805 543-7149	16710
McClatchy Newspapers Inc	2711	C	805 781-7800	5953
McKeague Patpatrick	2731	F	805 541-4593	6362
Next Intent Inc	3599	E	805 781-6755	16787
Noll Inc	3542	F	805 543-3602	14448
Oddworld Inhabitants Inc	7372	D	805 503-3000	24980
Ottano Inc	2082	F	805 547-2088	1617
Performance Apparel Corp	2339	F	805 541-0989	3478
Promega Biosciences LLC	2833	D	805 544-8524	7965
Prpco	2759	E	805 543-6844	7453
Rec Solar Commercial Corp	3822	C	844 732-7652	21523
RH Strasbaugh (PA)	3541	C	805 541-6424	14404
Saes Pure Gas Inc	3569	C	805 541-9299	15358
Slo New Times Inc	2711	E	805 546-8208	6048
Stellar Exploration Inc	3761	F	805 459-1425	21170
Straight Down Sportswear (PA)	2329	E	805 543-3086	3191
Taco Works Inc	2096	F	805 541-1556	2404
Triplett Harps	3931	F	805 544-2777	23392
Ultra-Stereo Labs Inc	3699	E	805 549-0161	20093
Weatherford International LLC	1389	D	805 781-3580	296
Wolfpack Gear Inc	2674	F	805 439-1911	5649
Ws Packaging-Blake Printery (HQ)	2752	E	805 543-6843	7190
Ws Packaging-Blake Printery	2752	E	805 543-6844	7191
Xcelaero Corporation	3564	F	805 547-2660	15188

SAN MARCOS, CA - San Diego County

	SIC	EMP	PHONE	ENTRY #
1254 Industries	3999	F	760 798-8531	24017
A & G Industries Inc	3444	F	760 891-0323	12449
Accu-Seal Sencorpwhite Inc	3565	F	760 591-9800	15191
Action Electronic Assembly Inc	3672	E	760 510-0003	18406
Advanced Honeycomb Tech	3469	E	760 744-3200	13160
Airgas Usa LLC	2813	F	760 744-1472	7679
Allied Coatings Inc	2851	F	800 630-2375	8874
American Rotary Broom Co Inc (PA)	3991	F	760 591-4025	23785
Arna Trading Inc (PA)	2611	F	760 940-2775	5265
Asi Tooling LLC	3545	E	760 744-2520	14602
Avista Technologies Inc	2899	F	760 744-0536	9223
Bbs Manufacturing Inc	3949	F	760 798-8011	23514
Bestop Baja LLC	3714	E	760 560-2252	20268
Black Oxide Service Inc	3471	F	760 744-8692	13347
Blisslights Inc	3699	E	888 868-4603	19919
Blisslights LLC	3648	E	888 868-4603	17677
Boinca Inc	2844	F	619 398-7252	8707
Bree Engineering Corp	3559	E	760 510-4950	14924
Byrum Technologies Inc	3699	E	760 744-6692	19921
Cliniqa Corporation (HQ)	2836	D	760 744-1900	8543
Columbia Stone Products	3291	F	760 737-3215	11292
Copley Press Inc	2711	F	760 752-6700	5818
Craneworks Southwest Inc	3537	F	760 735-9793	14315
Creative Electron Inc	3812	F	760 752-1192	21279
Crown Products Inc	3444	E	760 471-1188	12544
Culinary Specialties Inc	2099	D	760 744-8220	2499
David Duley	2652	D	619 449-8556	5376
Dexter Axle Company	3715	C	760 744-1610	20500
Doors Unlimited	2434	F	760 744-5590	4294
Duplan Industries	3599	E	760 744-4047	16451
Electro Tech Coatings Inc	3479	F	760 746-0292	13583
Enstrom Mold & Engineering	3544	F	760 744-1880	14513
Eriss	3695	F	858 722-2177	19863
Falmat Inc	3357	C	800 848-4257	11660
Fish House Foods Inc	2092	B	760 597-1270	2312

	SIC	EMP	PHONE	ENTRY #
Fluid Components Intl LLC (PA)	3823	C	760 744-6950	21584
Furniture Accessory Ret Group	2511	E	619 591-1150	4699
GK Foods Inc	2041	E	760 752-5230	1042
GKM International Llc	3089	D	310 791-7092	10119
Golden Rule Bindery Inc	2789	F	760 471-2013	7599
GSG LLC (PA)	2752	E	760 752-9500	6842
Gsi Capital Partners LLC	3949	F	760 745-1768	23578
H & M Cabinet Company	2541	F	760 744-0559	5066
Hadley Media Inc	2741	F	800 270-2084	6498
Health Breads Inc	2051	E	760 747-7390	1271
Hocking International Labs Inc (PA)	2842	E	760 432-5277	8646
Hollywood Chairs	2511	F	818 720-9946	4703
HP Precision Inc	3444	F	760 752-9377	12615
Hues Metal Finishing Inc	3479	F	760 744-5566	13602
Hughes Circuits Inc (PA)	3672	E	760 744-0300	18500
Hughes Circuits Inc	3672	C	760 744-0300	18501
Hunter Industries Incorporated (PA)	3084	B	760 744-5240	9780
Impact Project Management Inc	3672	E	760 747-6616	18503
Innovative Biosciences Corp	2844	E	760 603-0772	8769
Jensen Door Systems Inc	2431	F	760 736-4036	4174
Judd Wire Inc	3357	F	760 744-7720	11665
K-Tech Machine Inc	3599	C	800 274-9424	16640
L&S Stone LLC (DH)	3281	E	760 736-3232	11259
La Fe Tortilla Factory Inc (PA)	2099	E	760 752-8350	2563
Macdermid Prtg Solutions LLC	3555	D	760 510-6277	14817
Magic Touch Software Intl	7372	F	800 714-6490	24877
Manchester Feeds Inc (PA)	2048	F	714 637-7062	1145
Metal Etch Services Inc	3826	F	760 510-9476	21992
Microfab Manufacturing Inc	3444	F	760 744-7240	12674
Mitchell Instruments Co Inc	3825	F	760 744-2690	21807
Mitchell Test & Safety Inc	3829	F	760 744-2690	22239
Neighboring LLC	3843	F	818 271-0640	22894
Neville Industries Inc	3544	F	760 471-8949	14549
Oncore Manufacturing LLC	3672	C	760 737-6777	18549
Pac-West Rubber Products LLC	3061	F	760 891-0911	9570
Pacific Yacht Towers	3732	C	760 744-4831	21061
Parabilis Space Tech Inc	3761	F	855 727-2245	21168
Piercan Usa Inc	3069	F	760 599-4543	9656
Pipeline Products Inc	3569	F	760 744-8907	15352
Plasmetex Industries	3089	F	760 744-8300	10281
Port Brewing LLC	2082	F	800 918-6816	1621
Preserved Treescapes Intl Inc (PA)	3999	F	760 631-6789	24213
Prographics Screenprinting Inc	2759	F	760 744-4555	7451
Prowest Technologies Inc	2851	F	760 510-9003	8935
Quality Woodworks Inc	2434	E	760 744-4748	4339
R B III Associates	2337	C	760 471-5370	3360
Radtec Engineering Inc	3812	F	760 510-2715	21385
Roma Fabricating Corporation	3272	E	760 727-8040	10995
San Dieguito Publishers Inc	2752	D	760 593-5139	7094
Showdogs Inc	2591	E	760 603-3269	5210
Slivnik Machining Inc	3949	F	760 744-8692	23652
Stigtec Manufacturing LLC	3599	F	760 744-7239	16967
Sullins Electronics Corp (PA)	3643	E	760 744-0125	17492
Sumitomo Electric Interconn (DH)	3069	D	760 761-0600	9681
Superior On Site Service Inc	3799	F	760 744-4420	21243
Telecard LLC	2759	F	760 752-1700	7513
Trade Marker International	2298	F	760 602-4864	2982
Tri-M Co	3444	E	760 744-5115	12795
Trident Products Inc	3089	D	760 510-1160	10411
Trosak Cabinets Inc	2541	F	760 744-9042	5114
Tuscany Pavers Inc	3531	F	866 596-4092	14196
Wind & Shade Screens Inc	2221	F	760 761-4994	2787
Wrought Iron Fencing & Supply	3446	E	760 591-3110	12908
Zye Labs LLC	7372	F	904 800-9935	25378

SAN MARINO, CA - Los Angeles County

	SIC	EMP	PHONE	ENTRY #
A A A Engineering & Mfg Co	3599	E	626 447-5029	16189
America Mountain Wldg Inds Inc	3548	F	626 698-8066	14720
Cosmi Finance LLC	7372	F	310 603-5800	24529
Feihe International (PA)	2023	A	626 757-8885	615
Intelligent Barcode Systems	3829	F	626 576-8938	22217
L & P Button & Trimming Co	3965	F	626 796-0903	23768

SAN MARTIN, CA - Santa Clara County

	SIC	EMP	PHONE	ENTRY #
Calstone Company	3271	F	408 686-9627	10846
Clos La Chance Wines Inc	2084	E	408 686-1050	1698
Newline Rubber Company	3069	F	408 214-0359	9647

SAN MATEO, CA - San Mateo County

	SIC	EMP	PHONE	ENTRY #
Acco Brands USA LLC	3575	D	650 572-2700	15627
Actuate Corporation (HQ)	7372	F	650 645-3000	24315
Akamai Technologies Inc	7372	F	617 444-3000	24342
Akimbo Systems Inc	7372	E	650 292-3330	24343
Alameda Newspapers Inc	2711	D	650 348-4321	5754
Alfresco Software Inc (PA)	7372	D	888 317-3395	24348
Alienvault Inc (HQ)	7372	F	650 713-3333	24349

Mergent email: customerrelations@mergent.com

1464

2019 California
Manufacturers Register

(P-0000) Products & Services Section entry number
(PA)=Parent Co (HQ)=Headquarters (DH)=Div Headquarters

	SIC	EMP	PHONE	ENTRY #
Alienvault LLC (DH)	7372	D	650 713-3333	24350
Barkerblue Inc	2791	E	650 696-2100	7627
Bears For Humanity	2869	E	866 325-1668	8985
Borland Software Corporation	7372	D	650 286-1900	24441
Brilliant Home Technology Inc	3613	F	650 539-5320	17131
Celigo Inc (PA)	7372	E	650 579-0210	24479
Cirrent Inc	7372	F	650 569-1135	24492
Coen Company Inc (DH)	3433	F	650 522-2100	12061
Connor Manufacturing Svcs Inc (PA)	3599	D	650 591-2026	16399
Coupa Software Incorporated (PA)	7372	C	650 931-3200	24531
Daily Journal	2711	E	650 344-5200	5821
Dlive Inc	2741	E	650 397-1777	6471
Drapery Productions Inc	2211	F	650 340-8555	2735
Edmodo Inc	7372	E	310 614-6868	24591
Engagio Inc	7372	E	650 265-2264	24611
Eoplly Usa Inc	3674	F	650 225-9400	18829
Fastsigns	3993	F	650 345-0900	23878
Fujisoft America Inc	7372	F	650 235-9422	24677
Gopro Inc (PA)	3861	B	650 332-7600	23161
Itouchless Housewares Pdts Inc	3089	E	650 578-0578	10157
Jaunt Inc	7372	E	650 618-6579	24814
Jetlore LLC	7372	F	650 485-1822	24817
JH Baxter A Cal Ltd Partnr (PA)	2491	E	650 349-0201	4594
Jigsaw Data Corporation	2741	F	650 235-8400	6507
Medallia Inc (PA)	7372	C	650 321-3000	24894
NC Interactive LLC	7372	D	650 393-2200	24945
Netsuite Inc (DH)	7372	C	650 627-1000	24954
Nlyte Software Americas Ltd (DH)	7372	C	650 561-8200	24967
Okta Inc	7372	F	650 348-2620	24981
Opera Commerce LLC	7372	F	650 625-1262	24992
Opera Software Americas LLC	7372	F	650 625-1262	24993
Oracle Systems Corporation	7372	C	650 506-6780	25029
Oracle Systems Corporation	7372	F	650 378-1351	25032
Prezant Company	3554	F	650 342-7413	14798
Rapt Touch Inc	3571	F	415 994-1537	15476
Rumble Entertainment Inc	3944	E	650 316-8819	23461
Runa Inc	7372	F	508 253-5000	25133
San Francisco Circuits Inc	3672	F	650 655-7202	18589
Savory Creations International	2048	F	650 638-1024	1163
Sios Technology Corp (HQ)	7372	F	650 645-7000	25178
Smartqed Inc	7372	F	925 922-4618	25185
Snaplogic Inc (PA)	7372	C	888 494-1570	25187
Sony Mobile Communications USA	3663	C	866 766-9374	18257
Space Time Insight Inc	7372	E	650 513-8550	25203
Speculative Product Design LLC (DH)	3161	D	650 462-2040	10539
Swenson Group Inc	3861	F	650 655-4990	23200
Trilibis Inc (PA)	7372	F	650 646-2400	25295
Unifi Software Inc	7372	E	732 614-9522	25309
Vave Health Inc	3845	F	650 387-7059	23064
Vindicia Inc	7372	C	650 264-4700	25332
Vuze Inc	3577	F	650 963-4750	15884
Zs Pharma Inc	2834	F	650 753-1823	8453
Zuora Inc (PA)	7372	B	800 425-1281	25377

SAN MIGUEL, CA - San Luis Obispo County

	SIC	EMP	PHONE	ENTRY #
Castoro Cellars	2084	F	805 467-2002	1681
Courtside Cellars LLC	2084	E	805 467-2882	1709

SAN PABLO, CA - Contra Costa County

	SIC	EMP	PHONE	ENTRY #
Analytcal Scentific Instrs Inc	3826	E	510 669-2250	21902
Praxair Inc	2813	E	510 223-9593	7711
Rich Products	3714	F	510 234-7547	20439

SAN PEDRO, CA - Los Angeles County

	SIC	EMP	PHONE	ENTRY #
Advent Resources Inc	7372	D	310 241-1500	24330
Apartment Directory of L A	2741	F	310 832-0354	6433
Ardagh Metal Packaging USA Inc	3411	C	310 519-2400	11855
Composite Support and Sltns In	2655	F	310 514-3162	5483
Coppa Woodworking Inc	2431	F	310 548-4142	4128
Farlight LLC	3646	F	310 830-0181	17607
Florence Macaroni Company	2098	F	310 548-5942	2426
Highball Signal Inc	3669	F	909 341-5367	18330
J Deluca Fish Company Inc (PA)	2092	E	310 684-5180	2314
Kesclo Financial Inc	3446	E	800 322-8676	12871
Larson Al Boat Shop	3731	D	310 514-4100	20998
Party Time Ice Inc	2097	F	310 833-0187	2417
Paula Keller	2431	F	310 833-1894	4210
Seaborn Canvas	2399	F	310 519-1208	3965
STA-Slim Products Inc	3949	F	310 514-1155	23662
Two Bears Metal Products	3599	E	310 326-2533	17021
Victory Oil Company	1311	E	310 519-9500	86

SAN QUENTIN, CA - Marin County

	SIC	EMP	PHONE	ENTRY #
Distillery Inc	7372	D	415 505-5446	24563

SAN RAFAEL, CA - Marin County

	SIC	EMP	PHONE	ENTRY #
Ann Lilli Corp (PA)	2337	D	415 482-9444	3348

	SIC	EMP	PHONE	ENTRY #
Autodesk Inc (PA)	7372	B	415 507-5000	24399
Autodesk Inc	7372	C	415 507-5000	24400
Ben F Davis Company (PA)	2326	F	415 382-1000	3095
Bennett Industries Inc	2752	F	415 482-9000	6692
Bgl Development Inc	7372	F	415 256-2525	24419
Biomarin Pharmaceutical Inc (PA)	2834	B	415 506-6700	8078
Biotech Energy of America	2869	F	714 904-7844	8989
Bonjour Fleurette Inc	3142	F	415 382-1603	10478
Bordenaves Marin Baking	2051	D	415 453-2957	1213
Brush Dance Inc	2679	F	415 491-4950	5701
Christine Milne	2053	F	415 485-5658	1391
Continental Graphix	2752	E	415 864-2345	6756
County of Marin	2531	D	415 446-4414	5009
Dostal Studio	3952	F	415 721-7080	23707
Early Bird Alert Inc	3661	F	415 479-7902	17942
Fair Isaac International Corp (HQ)	7372	A	415 446-6000	24643
Fiorellos Italian Ice Cream	2024	F	415 459-8004	670
Goff Corporation	2731	E	415 526-1370	6345
Goff Investment Group LLC	2741	F	415 456-2934	6494
Hahnemann Labortories Inc	2834	F	415 451-6978	8201
Insight Editions LP (PA)	2731	E	415 526-1370	6352
Jeff Burgess & Associates Inc (PA)	3651	E	415 256-2800	17820
L P McNear Brick Co Inc	3271	D	415 453-7702	10854
Laurent Culinary Service	2099	F	415 485-1122	2580
Lpn Wireless Inc	3663	F	707 781-9210	18171
Marcaflex Inc	2672	F	415 472-4423	5570
Marin County Copy Shops Inc	2752	F	415 457-5600	6960
Marin Manufacturing Inc	3441	F	415 453-1825	12202
Megacycle Engineering Inc	3751	F	415 472-3195	21129
One Bella Casa Inc	2392	E	707 746-8300	3736
ONeil KG Bags	3161	F	415 460-0111	10529
Packaging Aids Corporation (PA)	3565	E	415 454-4868	15221
Palace Printing & Design LP	2731	E	415 526-1370	6376
Pantry Retail Inc	3581	F	415 234-3574	15925
Performance Printing Center	2752	E	415 485-5878	7023
Renos Floor Covering Inc	3996	F	415 459-1403	24015
San Francisco Network	2341	F	415 459-4700	3543
San Rafael Rock Quarry Inc (HQ)	1429	D	415 459-7740	333
Sanovas Inc	3841	E	415 729-9391	22614
Sars Software Products Inc	7372	F	415 226-0040	25145
Shamrock Materials Inc	3273	E	415 455-1575	11178
Shredding Paper	2731	F	415 454-2242	6391
Small World Trading Co	2844	C	415 945-1900	8842
Spectraprint Inc	2759	F	415 460-1228	7494
Spiral Water Technologies Inc	3589	F	415 259-4929	16114
Steve Zappetini & Son Inc	3446	E	415 454-2511	12894
Strahmcolor	2752	F	415 459-5409	7118
Streamline Development LLC (HQ)	7372	E	415 499-3355	25229
Tini Aerospace Inc	3663	E	415 524-2124	18288
Vans Inc	3021	F	415 479-1284	9496
Vionic Group LLC	3143	D	415 526-6932	10492
Wildthings Snap-Ons Inc	2361	F	415 457-0112	3589
Zep Solar Llc (DH)	3674	E	415 479-6900	19284

SAN RAMON, CA - Contra Costa County

	SIC	EMP	PHONE	ENTRY #
Accela Inc (PA)	7372	C	925 659-3200	24304
Acme Data Inc	7372	F	925 913-4591	24309
Allteq Industries Inc	3674	F	925 833-7666	18681
Anozira Incorporated	3272	F	925 771-8400	10877
Ascor Inc (HQ)	3625	E	925 328-4650	17254
Bass Angler	2721	F	925 362-3190	6109
Blossom Apple Moulding & Mllwk	2431	E	925 820-2345	4110
Chevron Captain Company LLC (HQ)	2911	C	925 842-1000	9325
Chevron Corporation (PA)	2911	A	925 842-1000	9326
Chevron Global Energy Inc (HQ)	2911	D	925 842-1000	9329
Chevron Oronite Company LLC (DH)	2899	E	713 432-2500	9230
Chevron Phillips Chem Co LP	3084	D	909 420-5500	9777
Chevron USA Inc	1311	D	925 842-0855	48
Cti-Controltech Inc	3625	F	925 208-4250	17264
D Laurence Gates Ltd	2421	E	925 736-8176	4036
Ecolab Inc	2841	D	925 215-8008	8592
Enact Systems Inc	7372	E	855 503-6228	24609
Evolphin Software Inc (PA)	7372	F	888 386-4114	24631
Fire & Earth Ceramics	3253	F	303 442-0245	10782
Five9 Inc (PA)	7372	C	925 201-2000	24652
Flyleaf Windows Inc	3231	E	925 344-1181	10698
GE Digital LLC (HQ)	7372	B	925 242-6200	24685
Gemini Consultants Inc	3672	F	925 866-8946	18492
General Electric Company	7372	D	925 242-6200	24686
Greyheller LLC	7372	F	925 415-5053	24712
Hanson Lehigh Inc	3241	E	925 244-6500	10756
Impulselogic Inc	7372	F	925 275-1028	24756
Japonesque LLC	2844	F	925 866-6670	8774
Keopsys Inc (HQ)	3663	F	610 758-8428	18144
Kraft Heinz Foods Company	2033	F	925 242-4504	816
Leica Geosystems Hds LLC	3577	D	925 790-2300	15786

GEOGRAPHIC

Employment Codes: A=Over 500 employees, B=251-500,
C=101-250, D=51-100, E=20-50, F=10-19

2019 California
Manufacturers Register

© Mergent Inc. 1-800-342-5647
1465

Company	SIC	EMP	PHONE	ENTRY #
Mic Labs	1389	F	925 822-2847	237
Mirion Technologies Inc (PA)	3829	C	925 543-0800	22237
Nobix Inc	7372	E	925 659-3500	24968
Omron Adept Technologies Inc (DH)	3535	C	925 245-3400	14280
Outsystems Inc	7372	F	925 804-6189	25043
Peterson Sheet Metal Inc	3444	F	925 830-1766	12714
Praxair Inc	2813	F	925 866-6800	7706
Reyes Coca-Cola Bottling LLC	2086	D	925 830-6500	2207
Rheosense Inc	3829	F	925 866-3801	22260
Rockwell Automation Inc	3625	E	925 242-5700	17303
Sieva Networks Inc (PA)	3812	F	408 475-1953	21431
Sorenson Publishing Inc	2752	F	925 866-1514	7106
Steadymed Therapeutics Inc	2834	F	925 361-7111	8396
Sun Tropics Inc	2037	F	925 202-2221	968
TAS Group Inc	2791	F	925 551-3700	7634
Trinity Marketing LLC	2752	F	925 866-1514	7148
Twin Industries Inc	3672	D	925 866-8946	18639
Unocal Corporation (HQ)	1311	B	310 726-7600	83
Z-Line Designs Inc (PA)	2522	D	925 743-4000	5003

SAN YSIDRO, CA - San Diego County

Company	SIC	EMP	PHONE	ENTRY #
Betty Stillwell	3281	D	619 428-2001	11238
Oceans Flavor Foods LLC	2899	F	619 793-5269	9293
Sentinel Plastics LLC	3089	E	619 734-0213	10370
Volex Inc	3089	E	619 205-4900	10433

SANGER, CA - Fresno County

Company	SIC	EMP	PHONE	ENTRY #
Adco Manufacturing	3565	C	559 875-5563	15193
Algonquin Power Sanger LLC	3612	E	559 875-0800	17080
Blue Diamond Growers	2068	C	559 251-4044	1483
California Trusframe LLC	2439	A	951 657-7491	4395
Cargill Meat Solutions Corp	2011	C	559 875-2232	423
Dole Packaged Foods LLC	2037	C	559 875-3354	948
Fresno Fab-Tech Inc	3441	E	559 875-9800	12166
Gibson Wine Company	2084	E	559 875-2505	1782
Hart & Cooley Inc	3446	E	559 875-1212	12860
If Copack LLC	2032	E	559 875-3354	759
Initiative Foods LLC	2032	C	559 875-3354	760
International Paper Company	2621	F	559 875-3311	5296
Kings River Casting Inc	2531	E	559 875-8250	5019
Melkonian Enterprises Inc	2034	E	559 485-6191	887
Midvalley Publishing Inc	2711	E	559 875-2511	5972
Perez Distributing Fresno Inc (PA)	2834	E	800 638-3512	8329
Pet Carousel Inc	2047	F	316 291-2500	1119
Royal Stall	3446	F	559 875-8100	12886
Soojians Inc	2052	E	559 875-5511	1381
Suspension Technologies Inc	3714	F	559 875-8883	20457
Triple A Pallets Inc	2448	F	559 313-7636	4509
Write Thought Inc	2721	F	559 876-2170	6296

SANTA ANA, CA - Orange County

Company	SIC	EMP	PHONE	ENTRY #
101 Apparel Inc (PA)	2321	F	714 454-8988	3049
2100 Freedom Inc (HQ)	2711	D	714 796-7000	5749
A F M Engineering Inc	3599	F	714 547-0194	16191
A Good Sign & Graphics Co	3993	F	714 444-4466	23801
A Plus Label Incorporated	2679	E	714 229-9811	5693
A World of Moulding	2431	E	714 361-9308	4095
A-Z Mfg Inc	3469	E	714 444-4446	13155
Aardvark Clay & Supplies Inc (PA)	3952	E	714 541-4157	23703
Abtech Incorporated	2542	E	714 550-9961	5123
Accelerated Memory Prod Inc	3674	E	714 460-9800	18660
Accent Industries Inc (PA)	3442	E	714 708-1389	12287
Accurate Circuit Engrg Inc	3672	D	714 546-2162	18404
Accurate Prfmce Machining Inc	3324	E	714 434-7811	11505
Acd LLC	3443	C	949 261-7533	12357
Ackley Metal Products Inc	3599	F	714 979-7431	16212
Acme United Corporation	2621	E	714 557-2001	5271
Acp Noxtat Inc	2821	E	714 547-5477	7817
Acrontos Manufacturing Inc	3469	E	714 850-9133	13158
Active Plating Inc	3471	E	714 547-0356	13308
Adapt Automation Inc	3549	E	714 662-4454	14747
ADM Works LLC	3365	E	714 245-0536	11719
Advanced Digital Research Inc	3575	F	949 252-1055	15628
Advanced Power & Controls LLC	3621	F	714 540-9010	17177
Advantage Manufacturing Inc	3621	E	714 505-1166	17178
AEC Group Inc	3714	F	714 444-1395	20246
Aftco Mfg Co Inc	3949	D	949 660-8757	23489
AGA Precision Systems Inc	3599	F	714 540-3163	16245
Airborne Systems N Amer CA Inc	2399	C	714 662-1400	3935
Airparts Express Inc	3728	D	714 308-2764	20727
Alco Engrg & Tooling Corp	3444	E	714 556-6060	12469
Alco Manufacturing Inc	3544	E	714 549-5007	14474
All American Racers Inc	3751	C	714 557-2116	21087
Allied Electronic Services	3672	F	714 245-2500	18412
Alloy Tech Electropolishing	3471	F	714 434-6604	13320
Alm Chrome	3471	E	714 545-3540	13321

Company	SIC	EMP	PHONE	ENTRY #
Almatron Electronics Inc	3672	E	714 557-6000	18413
Aluminum Precision Pdts Inc	3463	D	714 549-4075	13121
Ambrit Engineering Corporation	3544	D	714 557-1074	14475
American Aerospace Pdts Inc	3444	F	714 662-7620	12476
American Pneumatic Tools Inc	3542	F	562 204-1555	14428
American Sport Bags Inc	2393	E	714 547-8013	3760
AMO Usa Inc	3841	C	714 247-8200	22335
Anodyne Inc	3471	E	714 549-3321	13332
Arlon LLC	3089	C	714 540-2811	9955
Arsys Inc	3559	F	714 654-7681	14915
Art Manufacturers Inc	3645	E	714 540-9125	17526
Artisan Nameplate Awards Corp	2759	E	714 556-6222	7241
Aryzta LLC	2052	C	949 261-7400	1351
Ascent Tooling Group LLC	3812	A	949 455-0665	21260
Aspen Brands Corporation	2511	F	702 946-9430	4673
Assembly Technologies Co LLC	3672	F	714 979-4400	18428
Atr Sales Inc	3568	E	714 432-8411	15280
Audeze LLC (PA)	3651	F	714 581-8010	17764
Audio Dynamix Inc	3651	F	714 549-5100	17765
Autocal Inc	3545	F	714 550-7444	14604
Automation West Inc	3599	F	714 556-7381	16290
Avalon Chemical Inc	2899	E	714 540-3874	9222
Axiom Materials Inc	2891	E	949 623-4400	9129
Azteca News	2711	F	714 972-9912	5771
B and Z Printing Inc	2752	E	714 892-2000	6676
B J Bindery	2789	D	714 835-7342	7593
Bakerstone International LLC	3631	F	855 657-6836	17363
Balboa Acquisition LLC	2051	E	714 972-4972	1182
Bambeck Systems Inc (PA)	3823	F	949 250-3100	21551
Bdm Engineering Inc	3531	F	714 558-6129	14144
Behr Process Corporation	2851	C	714 545-7101	8877
Behr Process Corporation	2851	F	714 545-7101	8878
Behr Process Corporation (HQ)	2851	A	714 545-7101	8879
Behr Process Corporation	2851	D	714 545-7101	8880
Behr Process Corporation	2851	D	714 545-7101	8881
Behr Process Corporation	2851	F	714 545-7101	8882
Behr Process Corporation	2851	D	714 545-7101	8883
Behr Sales Inc (HQ)	2851	C	714 545-7101	8884
Bel-Air Machining Co	3599	F	714 953-6616	16315
Belmont Publications Inc	2721	F	714 825-1234	6111
Bend-Tek Inc	3444	E	714 210-8966	12505
Benmar Marine Electronics Inc	3812	F	714 540-5120	21265
Berry Global Inc	3089	F	714 751-2920	9976
Blackburn Alton Invstments LLC	2759	E	714 731-2000	7251
Blinking Owl Distillery	2082	F	949 370-4688	1572
Blower-Dempsay Corporation	2653	D	714 547-9266	5390
Boss Printing Inc	2752	F	714 545-2677	6702
Brasstech Inc	3432	B	949 417-5207	12026
Bristol Sounds Electronics	3651	F	714 549-5923	17779
Brixen & Sons Inc	2759	E	714 566-1444	7258
Brothers Intl Desserts	2024	C	949 655-0080	660
Brown Bag Sandwich Company LLC	2099	C	714 444-2126	2473
Bsnap LLC	7372	E	657 269-4410	24456
Bullfrog Printing and Graphics	2752	F	714 641-0220	6709
Bush Polishing & Chrome	3471	F	714 537-7440	13358
C & H Letterpress Inc	2759	E	714 438-1350	7259
Cable Devices Incorporated (HQ)	3577	C	714 554-4370	15695
Cal Pac Sheet Metal Inc	3444	E	714 979-2733	12518
Cal Trends Accessories LLC	2399	E	714 708-5115	3940
California Composites MGT Inc	3728	E	714 258-0405	20774
Calmont Engineering & Elec (PA)	3357	E	714 549-0336	11650
Candlebay Co	3999	F	949 307-1807	24060
Cascade Optical Coating Inc	3827	F	714 543-9777	22064
CD Alexander LLC	3577	E	949 250-3306	15701
CD Video Manufacturing Inc	3695	D	714 265-0770	19858
Cellco Partnership	3663	E	714 775-0600	18065
Centent Company	3571	E	714 979-6444	15399
Chang Food Company	2038	E	714 265-9990	986
Chapman Engineering Corp	3599	E	714 542-1942	16377
Ciasons Industrial Inc	3053	E	714 259-0838	9524
Clama Products Inc	3544	F	714 258-8606	14497
Classic Components Inc (PA)	3471	F	714 619-5690	13372
Classic Quilting	2395	F	714 558-8312	3837
Clear-Ad Inc	3089	E	877 899-1002	10027
Codan US Corporation	3089	C	714 430-1300	10030
Cole Instrument Corp	3621	D	714 556-3100	17187
Color Science Inc	2865	F	714 434-1033	8961
Colorstitch Inc	2395	F	714 754-4220	3838
Columbia Screw Products Inc	3451	F	714 549-1171	13018
Commerce Printers Inc	2752	E	714 549-5002	6747
Comstar Industries Inc	3625	E	714 556-1400	17260
Connectec Company Inc	3643	F	949 252-1077	17454
Connelly Machine Works	3599	E	714 558-6855	16398
Consolidated Container Co LP	3086	D	714 241-6640	9829
Continental Second Shift LLC	3443	F	619 985-6038	12382

2019 California
Manufacturers Register

(P-0000) Products & Services Section entry number
(PA)=Parent Co (HQ)=Headquarters (DH)=Div Headquarters

Name	SIC	EMP	PHONE	ENTRY #
Conveyant Systems Inc	3661	F	949 756-7100	17935
Corbin-Hill Inc	2051	D	714 966-6695	1225
Cowboy Direct Response	3993	E	714 824-3780	23850
CPC Fabrication Inc	3444	E	714 549-2426	12542
Creative Intgrated Systems Inc	3674	E	949 261-6577	18790
Crocs Inc	3021	F	714 568-0340	9469
Cult Cvlt	3751	F	714 435-2858	21101
Custom Hardware Mfg Inc	3429	F	714 547-7440	11950
Custom Metal Works	3446	F	714 953-5481	12848
Cypress Sponge Rubber Products	3069	F	714 546-6464	9605
D F Stauffer Biscuit Co Inc	2052	F	714 546-6855	1359
Da Vita Tustin Dialysis Ctr	3841	E	714 835-2450	22417
Dan R Hunt Inc	3599	F	714 850-9383	16418
Dana Creath Designs Ltd	3648	E	714 662-0111	17684
Danchuk Manufacturing Inc	3714	D	714 540-4363	20310
Danvo Machining	3599	F	714 751-1401	16419
Data Solder Inc	3643	F	714 429-9866	17458
Davco Enterprises Inc	2891	F	714 432-0600	9140
Dave Annala	3444	E	714 541-8383	12551
Deltronic Corporation	3827	D	714 545-5800	22071
Deschner Corporation	3569	E	714 557-1261	15316
Diamond Baseball Company Inc	3949	E	800 366-2999	23549
Digital First Media LLC	2711	A	714 796-7000	5829
Diversified Packaging Inc	3086	E	714 850-9316	9836
Dm Software Inc	7372	F	714 953-2653	24565
Documotion Research Inc	2752	E	714 662-3800	6791
Driven Concepts Inc	2329	F	714 549-2170	3145
Ducommun Incorporated (PA)	3679	C	657 335-3665	19518
Dynamic Fabrication Inc	3699	F	714 662-2440	19951
Dynasty Electronic Company LLC	3672	D	714 550-1197	18469
E F T Fast Quality Service	3471	F	714 751-1487	13392
Ecoolthing Corp	3499	E	714 368-4791	13938
El Indio Tortilleria	2099	F	714 542-3114	2512
Electrode Technologies Inc	3471	E	714 549-3771	13398
Electrolurgy Inc	3498	E	714 641-7488	13886
Energent Corporation	3511	F	949 885-0365	13995
Envita Labs LLC	2833	E	800 500-4376	7936
Evantec Corporation	3069	F	949 632-2811	9612
Express Chipping	2741	F	562 789-8058	6479
Express Manufacturing Inc (PA)	3679	C	714 979-2228	19537
Fabrica International Inc	2273	C	949 261-7181	2929
Falcon Automotive Inc	2399	F	714 569-1085	3946
Fast Ad Inc	3993	D	714 835-9353	23876
Finart Inc (PA)	3433	F	714 957-1757	12064
Fit-Line Inc	3089	E	714 549-9091	10101
Flathers Precision Inc	3599	E	714 966-8505	16502
Flexible Manufacturing LLC	3678	D	714 259-7996	19391
FM Systems Inc	3663	F	714 979-0537	18111
Foster Printing Company Inc	2752	D	714 731-2000	6824
Freudenberg-Nok General Partnr	3053	C	714 834-0602	9529
Frontera Solutions Inc	3624	D	714 368-1631	17237
Funny-Bunny Inc (PA)	2329	D	714 957-1114	3156
G G C Inc (PA)	3554	E	714 835-6530	14793
G G C Inc	3554	E	714 835-0551	14794
Gardner Systems Inc	3821	F	714 668-9018	21472
GBF Enterprises Inc	3599	E	714 979-7131	16528
Gemini Industries Inc	3341	D	949 250-4011	11557
Gemini Industries Inc	3999	E	949 553-4255	24105
Gemtech Inds Good Earth Mfg	3479	E	714 848-2517	13596
Gold Coast Baking Company Inc (PA)	2051	D	714 545-2253	1264
Graham Packaging Company LP	3089	D	714 979-1835	10125
Greenkraft Inc (PA)	3711	F	714 545-7777	20146
Greenkraft Inc	3711	F	714 545-7777	20147
Growthstock Inc	3679	C	949 660-9473	19557
Hannah Industries Inc	3589	F	714 939-7873	16048
Headmaster Inc (PA)	2353	E	714 556-5244	3564
Heart Rate Inc	3949	E	714 380-9716	23583
Helfer Enterprises	3599	E	714 557-2733	16558
Helica Biosystems Inc	2835	F	714 578-7830	8481
Heritage Paper Co (HQ)	2653	D	714 540-9737	5423
Hernandez Zeferino	2891	F	714 953-4010	9148
High End Seating Solutions LLC	3751	E	714 259-0177	21115
High-Tech Coatings Inc	3479	F	714 547-2122	13601
Hill Marine Products LLC	3599	E	714 855-2986	16568
Hitt Companies	3069	F	714 979-1405	9623
Hood Manufacturing Inc	3089	D	714 979-7681	10138
Hook It Up	2111	C	714 600-0100	2706
Hpv Technologies Inc	3651	E	949 476-7000	17815
Humberto Murillo Inc	3471	E	714 541-2628	13428
I J Research Inc	3679	E	714 546-8522	19571
I O Interconnect Ltd (PA)	3678	E	714 564-1111	19395
IHP Operations LLC	3433	B	714 549-7782	12068
Image Apparel For Business Inc	2326	E	714 541-5247	3105
Impco Technologies Inc (HQ)	3714	C	714 656-1200	20369
Industrial Cpu Systems Intl	3571	F	714 957-2815	15428
Industrial Tool and Die Inc	3544	F	714 549-1686	14527
Infinite Optics Inc	3827	E	714 557-2299	22087
Innovative Hearth Holdings LLC (PA)	3433	A	714 549-7782	12072
Innovative Hearth Products LLC (PA)	3634	E	615 925-3417	17390
Innovative Hearth Products LLC	3634	E	714 549-7782	17391
Inserts & Kits Inc	3599	F	714 708-2888	16586
Insultech LLC (PA)	2899	D	714 384-0506	9263
Intellitime Systems Corp	7372	F	714 444-3020	24783
Interactive Entertainment Inc	3944	F	714 460-2343	23432
International Disc Mfr Inc	3652	F	714 210-1780	17905
International Electronic Desig (PA)	3679	F	714 662-1018	19585
Iron Grip Barbell Company Inc	3949	D	714 850-6900	23595
Irvine Scientific Sales Co Inc (DH)	2836	E	949 261-7800	8563
Itc Sftware Slutions Group LLC (PA)	7372	F	877 248-2774	24806
Iteris Inc (PA)	3861	C	949 270-9400	23170
J & J Action Inc	3634	E	877 327-5268	17393
J D Industries	3599	F	714 542-5517	16602
J R V Products Inc	3679	F	714 259-9772	19590
JB Plastics Inc	3089	E	714 541-8500	10165
JD Processing Inc	3471	E	714 972-8161	13436
Jdr Engineering Cons Inc	3089	C	714 751-7084	10166
JI Design Enterprises Inc	2321	D	714 479-0240	3057
Johnson & Johnson (HQ)	3845	B	714 247-8200	22996
Johnson & Johnson	3827	E	714 247-8200	22095
Johnson Precision Products Inc	3599	F	714 824-6971	16630
Jolo Industries Inc	3679	E	714 554-6840	19602
Jwc Environmental LLC	3589	D	714 662-5829	16061
K-P Engineering Corp	3599	F	714 545-7045	16639
K-V Engineering Inc	3541	E	714 229-9977	14386
Kaga (usa) Inc	3469	E	714 540-2697	13232
Kalanico Inc	2541	E	714 532-5770	5074
Kenlor Industries Inc	3841	F	714 647-0770	22503
Kilgore Machine Company Inc	3599	F	714 540-3659	16654
KI Electronics Inc	3672	E	714 751-5611	18517
Kulicke Sffa Wedge Bonding Inc	3699	C	949 660-0440	20000
Laguna Cookie Company Inc	2052	F	714 546-6855	1369
Laperla Spice Co Inc	2099	F	714 543-0159	2577
Laszlo J Lak	3599	F	714 850-0141	16681
Laura Scudders Company LLC	2096	E	714 444-3700	2394
Lehman Millet Incorporated	2835	E	714 850-7900	8488
Leonard Craft Co LLC	3911	D	714 549-0678	23286
Limpus Prints Inc	2759	F	714 545-5078	7386
Liquid Graphics Inc	2329	C	949 486-3588	3175
Little Firefighter Corporation	3491	F	714 834-0410	13723
Lotus Hygiene Systems Inc	3261	E	714 259-8805	10806
Lynde-Ordway Company Inc	3579	F	714 957-1311	15907
M & W Machine Corporation	3599	F	714 541-2652	16701
M R S Foods Inc (PA)	2099	D	714 554-2791	2592
Machine Arts Incorporated	3599	F	805 965-5344	16703
Magnetic Design Labs Inc	3679	F	714 538-3355	19634
Maria Corporation	2759	F	714 751-2460	7396
Mark Optics Inc	3827	E	714 545-6684	22103
Markland Industries Inc (PA)	3751	D	714 245-2850	21127
Markzware	7372	F	949 756-5100	24884
Marlin Designs LLC	2512	C	949 637-7257	4795
Marteq Process Solutions Inc	3674	F	714 495-4275	18980
Marway Power Systems Inc (PA)	3577	E	714 917-6200	15800
Mask Technology Inc	3679	E	714 557-3383	19639
Master Inds Worldwide LLC	3999	F	949 660-0644	24168
Master Industries Inc	3949	F	949 660-0644	23613
Matrix USA Inc	3672	E	714 825-0404	18525
Maul Mfg Inc (PA)	3599	F	714 641-0727	16722
Maxtrol Corporation	3679	E	714 245-0506	19641
McGuff Pharmaceuticals Inc	2834	E	714 918-7277	8268
Mecadaq Aerospace LLC	3545	F	714 442-9703	14649
Medtronic Inc	3845	D	949 474-3943	23015
Medtronic Ats Medical Inc	3841	E	949 380-9333	22532
Mekong Printing Inc	2752	E	714 558-9595	6967
Memory Experts Intl USA Inc (HQ)	3572	E	714 258-3000	15567
Merit Cables Incorporated	3841	E	714 547-3054	22537
Metal Cast Inc	3325	E	714 285-9592	11526
Metal Improvement Company LLC	3398	F	714 546-4160	11823
Metro Digital Printing Inc	2752	E	714 545-8400	6971
Micro Trim Inc	3354	F	714 241-7046	11596
Miller & Pidskalny Cstm Wdwrk	2511	F	949 250-8508	4722
ML Kishigo Mfg Co LLC	2389	D	949 852-1963	3672
Modified Plastics Inc (PA)	3089	F	714 546-4667	10217
Monarch Precision Deburring	3541	E	714 258-0342	14395
Mustard Seed Technologies Inc	3679	C	714 556-7007	19657
Mx Electronics Mfg Inc	3357	D	714 258-0200	11666
National Casein of California	2891	F	714 979-8400	9157
Nazca Solutions Inc	7372	E	612 279-6100	24944
Nest Environments Inc	2431	F	714 979-5500	4198
Newport Laminates Inc	3089	E	714 545-8335	10237
Newport Metal Finishing Inc	3479	D	714 556-8411	13621

Employment Codes: A=Over 500 employees, B=251-500,
C=101-250, D=51-100, E=20-50, F=10-19

2019 California
Manufacturers Register

© Mergent Inc. 1-800-342-5647
1467

Company	SIC	EMP	PHONE	ENTRY #
Newport Plastic Inc	3089	E	714 549-1955	10238
Newport Plastics LLC (PA)	3089	E	800 854-8402	10239
Nis America Inc	7372	E	714 540-1199	24966
No Lift Nails Inc	2821	F	714 897-0070	7858
Norotos Inc	3599	C	714 662-3113	16793
Nova Print Inc	2335	F	951 525-4040	3329
Nutrade Inc	2211	E	949 477-2300	2755
Oc Metals Inc	3444	E	714 668-0783	12695
OEM Materials & Supplies Inc	2621	E	714 564-9600	5319
Ohno America Inc	2273	E	770 773-3820	2937
Omega Engineering Inc	3559	D	714 540-4914	15002
Omniprint Inc	3577	E	949 833-0080	15815
One Time Utility Sales Inc	3644	E	714 953-5700	17516
Optosigma Corporation	3827	E	949 851-5881	22117
Orange Cnty Mlt-Hsing Svc Corp	2721	E	714 245-9500	6225
Orange Container Inc	2653	D	714 547-9617	5441
Orange County Label Co Inc	2759	F	714 437-1010	7423
Orange Metal Spinning and Stam	3469	F	714 754-0770	13255
Orion Chandelier Inc	3645	F	714 668-9668	17552
P C I Manufacturing Division	3663	F	714 543-3496	18210
Pacific Aerospace Machine Inc	3599	E	714 534-1444	16818
Pacific Computer Products Inc	3955	E	714 549-7535	23735
Pacific Label Inc	2672	D	714 237-1276	5574
Pacific Quartz Inc	3827	E	714 546-8133	22120
Pacific Stone Design Inc	3272	E	714 836-5757	10973
Pan-A-Lite Products Inc	3648	F	714 258-7111	17723
Parpro Technologies Inc	3672	C	714 545-8886	18557
Pelican Rope Works	2298	F	714 545-1016	2977
Pioneer Circuits Inc	3672	B	714 641-3132	18560
Playa Tool & Marine Inc	3599	F	714 972-2722	16847
Polaris E-Commerce Inc	3561	E	714 907-0582	15088
Pollution Control Specialists	3564	E	949 474-0137	15170
Power Circuits Inc	3672	B	714 327-3000	18562
Power Distribution Inc	3677	E	714 513-1500	19353
Praxair Distribution Inc	2813	E	714 547-6684	7729
Precious Metals Plating Co Inc	3471	F	714 546-6271	13477
Precision Circuits West Inc	3672	F	714 435-9670	18564
Prime Forming & Cnstr Sups	3272	F	714 547-6710	10983
Printed Circuit Solutions Inc	3672	F	714 825-1090	18566
Promedia Companies	2721	F	714 444-2426	6237
Prototype Express LLC	3699	F	714 751-3533	20049
Pure One Environmental Inc	2869	F	714 641-1430	9034
Q-Flex Inc	3672	E	714 664-0101	18568
QED Inc	3823	E	714 546-6010	21639
Quantum Digital Technology Inc	3679	F	310 325-4949	19700
Qyk Brands LLC	3634	E	949 312-7119	17402
R & B Wire Products Inc	3496	E	714 549-3355	13847
R A Industries Llc	3599	E	714 557-2322	16878
Rbc Transport Dynamics Corp	3568	C	203 267-7001	15290
Reichert Enterprises Inc	3993	E	714 513-9199	23951
Remedy Blinds Inc	2591	D	714 245-0186	5207
Ricaurte Precision Inc	3599	E	714 667-0632	16898
Robinson Pharma Inc (PA)	2834	B	714 241-0235	8366
Robinson Pharma Inc	2834	C	714 241-0235	8367
Rooke Manufacturing Co	3599	F	714 540-6943	16916
Royal Manufacturing Inds Inc	3444	F	714 668-9199	12742
RTS Oil Holdings Inc	1382	E	714 665-8777	148
Rubberite Corp (PA)	3069	F	714 546-6464	9672
S & S Precision Mfg Inc	3599	E	714 754-6664	16924
Saf-T-Co Supply	3644	E	714 547-9975	17518
Sandberg Industries Inc (PA)	3679	D	949 660-9473	19717
Sanie Manufacturing Company	3446	F	714 751-7700	12888
Santos Precision Inc	3728	E	714 957-0299	20926
Scientific Components Systems	3646	E	714 554-3960	17642
Screen Works	2261	E	714 432-7900	2893
Secure Comm Systems Inc (HQ)	3663	C	714 547-1174	18247
Secure Comm Systems Inc	3663	F	714 547-1174	18248
Select Circuits	3672	F	714 825-1090	18601
Semiconductor Components Inc	3674	E	714 547-6059	19142
Senga Engineering Inc	3599	E	714 549-8011	16936
Sev-Cal Tool Inc	3545	E	714 549-3347	14674
Sigmatronix Inc	3651	E	714 436-1618	17857
Sign Specialists Corporation	3993	E	714 641-0064	23967
Silicon Tech Inc	3572	C	949 476-1130	15608
Skyco Shading Systems Inc	2431	E	714 708-3038	4233
Smithco Plastics Inc (PA)	3089	F	714 545-9107	10379
Smiths Action Plastic Inc (PA)	3088	F	714 836-4141	9911
Smiths Detection LLC	3826	A	714 258-4400	22019
Smt Electronics Mfg Inc	3674	E	714 751-8894	19175
Sound Waves Insullation Inc	3823	E	714 556-2110	21657
South Coast Circuits Inc	3672	D	714 966-2108	18613
South Coast Sewing Company Inc	2369	E	310 350-0535	3595
Southern California Plas Inc	2821	D	714 751-7084	7887
Spa Girl Corporation	2844	E	714 444-1040	8846
Spec Formliners Inc	3089	E	714 429-9500	10383
Specialty Equipment Co	3713	E	714 258-1622	20231
Spill Magic Inc	2621	E	714 557-2001	5337
SPS Technologies LLC	3965	B	714 545-9311	23773
SPS Technologies LLC	3965	F	714 371-1925	23774
Steady Clothing Inc	2329	F	714 444-2058	3190
Stec International Holding Inc	3572	D	949 476-1180	15613
Straightline Mechanical Inc	3494	F	714 204-0940	13776
Strata Forest Products Inc (PA)	2421	E	714 751-0800	4067
Stremicks Heritage Foods LLC (PA)	2026	B	714 775-5000	737
Sun & Sun Industries Inc	3646	D	714 210-5141	17646
Sundown Liquidating Corp (PA)	3211	C	714 540-8950	10608
Sunrise Imaging Inc	3861	F	949 252-3003	23198
Super Machining Inc	3599	E	714 662-2021	16973
Supreme Abrasives	3291	F	949 250-8644	11304
Swiss Pattern Corp	3543	F	714 545-8040	14467
Syagen Technology LLC	3826	E	714 258-4400	22023
Symbolic Displays Inc	3728	D	714 258-2811	20942
Synergistic Research Inc	3496	F	949 642-2800	13854
Tailgate Printing Inc	2759	C	714 966-3655	7509
Talimar Systems Inc	2531	E	714 557-4884	5030
Tammy Taylor Nails Inc	2821	E	949 250-9287	7893
Tardif Sheet Metal & AC	3441	F	714 547-7135	12258
Tay Ho Food Corporation	2032	E	714 973-2286	777
Taylor Communications	2761	E	714 664-8865	7559
Tdi2 Custom Packaging Inc	2673	F	714 751-6782	5627
Ted Rieck Enterprises Inc	3444	F	714 542-4763	12785
Tenacore Holdings Inc	3841	D	714 444-4643	22646
Tfn Architectural Signage Inc (PA)	3993	E	714 556-0990	23988
Tibbetts Newport Corporation	2851	E	714 546-6662	8948
Tivoli Industries Inc	3648	E	714 957-6101	17739
TMC Aerospace Inc	3728	E	949 250-4999	20951
Tmx Engineering and Mfg Corp	3599	D	714 641-5884	17002
Tobin Steel Company Inc	3441	E	714 541-2268	12261
Today Pvc Bending Inc	3644	E	714 953-5707	17519
Tomi Engineering Inc	3599	D	714 556-1474	17003
Top Greener Inc	3264	F	626 254-3367	10825
Triple DOT Corp	3085	E	714 241-0888	9809
Triumph Group Inc	3398	B	714 546-9842	11837
Ttm Printed Circuit Group Inc (HQ)	3672	D	714 327-3000	18631
Ttm Technologies Inc	3672	B	714 327-3000	18636
Twed-Dells Inc	3231	E	714 754-6900	10736
Two Brothers Racing Inc	3751	E	714 550-6070	21147
Ullman Sails Inc (PA)	2394	F	714 432-1860	3817
Ultimate Software Group Inc	7372	E	949 214-2710	25306
Ultra TEC Manufacturing Inc	3559	F	714 542-0608	15041
Undersea Systems Intl Inc	3699	D	714 754-7848	20094
Unit Industries Inc (PA)	3678	E	714 871-4161	19427
Universal Electronics Inc (PA)	3651	C	714 918-9500	17873
Universal Punch Corp	3542	D	714 556-4488	14459
Uremet Corporation	2821	E	714 641-8813	7898
US Rigging Supply Corp	3496	E	714 545-7444	13860
US Saws Inc (PA)	3531	F	860 668-2402	14197
Veros Software Inc	7372	E	714 415-6300	25328
Visibility Solutions Inc	2599	F	714 434-7040	5261
W R Grace & Co - Conn.	3086	E	714 979-4682	9891
Watermans Guild	3949	F	714 751-0603	23688
Weldtek Inc	3542	D	714 210-8966	14461
West Coast Form Grinding	3599	F	714 540-5621	17058
West Lake Food Corporation	2011	D	714 973-2286	457
Westerly Marine Inc	3732	E	714 966-8550	21069
Western Methods Machinery Corp	3728	E	949 252-6600	20971
Westminster Press Inc	2752	E	714 210-2881	7185
Westridge Laboratories Inc	2844	E	714 259-9400	8865
Westrock Cp LLC	2631	E	714 641-8891	5370
Wild Wood Designs Inc	2511	E	714 543-6549	4753
Wilkins Design and Mfg Inc	3441	E	714 564-3351	12283
Workstation Industries Inc	2599	E	714 258-7535	5264
Wright Capacitors Inc	3675	F	714 546-2490	19306
Wyvern Technologies Inc	3679	E	714 966-0710	19790
Xerox Corporation	3861	C	714 565-1200	23214
Xs Scuba Inc (PA)	3949	E	714 424-0434	23693
Ys Controls LLC	3829	E	714 641-0727	22298

SANTA BARBARA, CA - Santa Barbara County

Company	SIC	EMP	PHONE	ENTRY #
A B C-Clio Inc (PA)	2731	C	805 968-1911	6301
ABC - Clio LLC	2731	F	800 368-6868	6302
Adding Technology (PA)	7372	F	805 252-6971	24320
Alta Properties Inc	3699	B	805 683-1431	19907
Alta Properties Inc	3825	B	805 683-2575	21717
Alta Properties Inc	3699	B	805 690-5382	19908
Alta Properties Inc	3264	B	805 967-0171	10815
Alta Properties Inc (PA)	3264	C	805 967-0171	10816
Ampersand Publishing LLC (PA)	2711	E	805 564-5200	5759
Anthonys Christmas Trees	3999	E	805 966-6668	24040
Appfolio Inc (PA)	7372	C	805 364-6093	24368
Architctral Mllwk Snta Barbara	2431	E	805 965-7011	4104

Company	SIC	EMP	PHONE	ENTRY #
Arthrex Inc	3841	D	805 964-8104	22346
Axia Technologies LLC	7372	E	855 376-2942	24405
Axxcelera Brdband Wireless Inc (DH)	3663	F	805 968-9621	18049
B&B Hardware Inc	3452	E	805 683-6700	13059
Benefit Software Incorporated	7372	E	805 679-6200	24414
Biodico Westside LLC	2869	F	805 683-8103	8987
Bosch Auto Svc Solutions Inc (PA)	3714	F	805 964-2000	20273
Brandnew Industries Inc	3953	F	805 964-8251	23714
Christian Science Church	2711	E	805 966-6661	5803
Computational Sensors Corp	3812	E	805 962-1175	21274
Container Technology Inc (PA)	3089	E	805 683-5825	10041
Debbies Delights Inc	2053	E	805 966-3504	1393
Duncan Carter Corporation (PA)	3931	D	805 964-9749	23363
Ebix Inc	7372	E	805 568-0240	24587
Efaxcom	3577	E	805 692-0064	15736
Esperer Holdings Inc (PA)	3341	E	805 880-4220	11556
Esperer Webstores LLC	2023	F	805 880-1900	613
Federal Buyers Guide Inc (PA)	2741	F	805 963-7470	6483
Fei Efa Inc	3825	E	805 560-0404	21756
Foodtools Inc (PA)	3556	E	805 962-8383	14848
Forester Communications Inc	2721	E	805 682-1300	6164
Fuelbox Inc	3679	F	919 949-9179	19547
Future Fine Foods	2051	F	805 682-9421	1258
Gavial Itc LLC	3679	D	805 614-0060	19551
Graphiq LLC	2741	C	805 335-2433	6496
Green Hills Software Inc (PA)	7372	C	805 965-6044	24711
Guess Inc	2325	F	805 963-9490	3072
Hispanic Business Inc	2721	F	805 964-4554	6183
Idrive Inc	3714	F	805 308-6094	20368
Inform Solution Incorporated	7372	F	805 879-6000	24768
Innovative Technology Inc	3479	F	805 571-8384	13604
International Tranducer Corp	3825	C	805 683-2575	21777
Invenios LLC	3231	D	805 962-3333	10706
Ircamera LLC	3827	E	805 965-9650	22092
Jeannines Bkg Co Santa Barbara (PA)	2051	E	805 966-1717	1275
Kate Farms Inc	2099	C	805 845-2446	2550
Kollmorgen Corporation	3621	B	805 696-1236	17206
Kunin Wines LLC	2084	F	805 963-9633	1845
Linear Technology LLC	3674	D	805 965-6400	18965
Marketing Bulletin Board	2711	F	805 455-2255	5942
Maysoft Inc	7372	F	978 635-1700	24889
Motion Engineering Inc (HQ)	3577	D	805 696-1200	15808
Nobbe Orthopedics Inc	3842	F	805 687-7508	22778
Observables Inc	3699	F	805 272-9255	20036
Occam Networks Inc (HQ)	3661	E	805 692-2900	17970
Olaplex LLC (PA)	2844	F	805 258-7680	8806
Omtek Inc	3674	E	805 687-9629	19058
Oxford Instrs Asylum RES Inc (HQ)	3826	D	805 696-6466	22001
P J Milligan Company LLC (PA)	2511	F	805 963-4038	4730
Pacific Coast Bus Times Inc	2711	F	805 560-6950	6007
Pacific Operators Inc	1381	E	805 899-3144	115
Pacific Pickle Works Inc	2035	F	805 765-1779	927
Philips Medical Systems Clevel	3841	EM	805 681-0463	22583
Praxair Inc	2813	E	805 966-0829	7712
Praxair Distribution Inc	2813	E	805 966-0829	7724
Productplan LLC	7372	E	805 618-2975	25082
Qad Inc (PA)	7372	C	805 566-6000	25091
Raoul Textiles Inc	2759	F	805 965-1694	7465
Raouls Printworks	2261	F	805 965-1694	2892
Robert Bosch LLC	3841	E	805 966-2000	22607
Santa Barbara Control Systems	3823	F	805 683-8833	21648
Santa Barbara Independent Inc	2711	E	805 965-5205	6038
Santa Barbara Music Publishing	2741	F	805 962-5800	6576
Santa Barbara Winery	2084	F	805 963-3646	1966
Santa Brbara Essntial Fods LLC	2052	F	805 965-1948	1378
Scamsafe Inc	7372	F	800 960-5512	25150
Serbin Communications Inc	2721	F	805 564-7636	6256
Sientra Inc (PA)	3842	C	805 562-3500	22813
Sikama International Inc	3548	F	805 962-1000	14739
Skate One Corp	3949	D	805 964-1330	23651
Smith Publishing Inc	2721	F	805 965-5999	6258
Sonos Inc (PA)	3651	D	805 965-3001	17858
Steven Handelman Studios (PA)	3322	E	805 884-9070	11504
Strand Products Inc	2298	E	805 568-0304	2980
Strand Products Inc (PA)	3845	E	805 568-0304	23055
Telegraph Brewing Co Inc	2082	F	805 963-5018	1630
Templock Enterprises LLC	3086	F	805 962-3100	9886
Toad & Co International Inc (PA)	2329	E	805 957-1474	3196
Underground Energy Inc	1382	E	805 455-6042	156
Visionary Solutions Inc	3699	F	805 845-8900	20103
Von Hoppen Ice Cream (HQ)	2024	F	805 965-2009	703
Waiakea Investments LLC (PA)	2086	F	805 450-0981	2234
Xanadu French Bakery	2051	E	805 845-7232	1346

SANTA CLARA, CA - Santa Clara County

Company	SIC	EMP	PHONE	ENTRY #
5-Stars Engineering Associates	3549	E	408 380-4849	14746

Company	SIC	EMP	PHONE	ENTRY #
A-1 Machine Manufacturing Inc (PA)	3599	C	408 727-0880	16199
Abbott Laboratories	3841	B	408 330-0057	22302
Abbott Laboratories	3841	A	408 845-3000	22303
Abbott Vascular Inc (HQ)	3845	B	408 845-3000	22947
Abbott Vascular Inc	3841	A	408 845-3000	22306
Absolute Turnkey Services Inc	3672	E	408 850-7530	18402
AC Photonics Inc	3559	E	408 986-9838	14899
Accel Manufacturing Inc	3541	E	408 727-5883	14354
Access Closure Inc	3841	E	408 610-6500	22307
Accu Machine Inc	3599	F	408 855-8835	16206
Achronix Semiconductor Corp	3674	D	408 889-4100	18661
Acroscope LLC	3599	F	408 727-6896	16219
Actsolar Inc	3829	F	408 721-5000	22157
Acu Spec Inc	3599	F	408 748-8600	16221
Adem LLC	3599	E	408 727-8955	16224
Adesto Technologies Corp (PA)	3674	D	408 400-0578	18662
Advanced Assemblies Inc	3672	E	408 988-1016	18410
Advanced Component Labs Inc	3674	E	408 327-0200	18666
Advanced Laser Cutting Inc	3599	F	408 486-0700	16229
Advanced Micro Devices Inc (PA)	3674	B	408 749-4000	18668
Aella Data Inc	7372	F	408 391-4430	24333
Affymetrix Inc	3826	D	408 731-5000	21894
Affymetrix Inc	3826	D	408 731-5000	21895
Affymetrix Inc (HQ)	3826	B	408 731-5000	21896
Affymetrix Anatrace	3826	F	408 731-5756	21897
Agilent Tech World Trade Inc (HQ)	3825	A	408 345-8886	21705
Agilent Technologies Inc	3825	A	408 345-8886	21709
Agilent Technologies Inc (PA)	3825	A	408 345-8886	21712
Agilent Technologies Inc	3825	A	408 345-8886	21713
Agilent Technologies Inc	3825	A	408 553-7777	21714
Air Products and Chemicals Inc	2813	E	408 988-2142	7670
Aixtron Inc	3674	C	669 228-3759	18674
Akt America Inc (HQ)	3699	B	408 563-5455	19904
All Metals Inc (PA)	3341	E	408 200-7000	11552
Altaflex	3672	D	408 727-6614	18416
Alventive Inc (PA)	7372	D	408 969-8000	24355
AM&s Mfg Inc	3496	F	800 519-5709	13808
Ambarella Inc	3674	A	408 734-8888	18688
America Asia Trade Promotion	2392	F	408 970-8868	3705
American Precision Spring	3495	E	408 986-1020	13785
Amex Plating Incorporated	3471	E	408 986-2222	13327
Amimon Inc	2631	F	650 641-3191	5340
Amlogic Inc	3674	E	408 850-9688	18696
Amq Solutions LLC (HQ)	2521	F	877 801-0370	4929
Analogix Semiconductor Inc	3674	E	408 988-8686	18700
Apct Inc (PA)	3672	D	408 727-6442	18423
Applied Films Corporation	3674	E	408 727-5555	18705
Applied Materials Inc	3559	E	408 727-5555	14907
Applied Materials Inc	3674	E	406 752-2107	18706
Applied Materials Inc (PA)	3559	A	408 727-5555	14910
Applied Materials Inc	3674	E	408 727-5555	18707
Applied Materials Inc	3559	F	512 272-3692	14911
Applied Materials Inc	3559	E	408 727-5555	14913
Applied Materials Inc	3674	E	408 727-5555	18709
Applied Materials Inc	3674	D	408 727-5555	18710
Applied Materials Inc	2721	E	408 727-5555	6103
Applied Micro Circuits Corp (HQ)	3674	C	408 542-8600	18711
Applied Micro Circuits Corp	3674	E	408 542-8600	18712
Aruba Networks Inc (HQ)	3577	B	408 227-4500	15672
Atypon Systems LLC (PA)	7372	D	408 988-1240	24396
Avaya Holdings Corp (PA)	3661	E	908 953-6000	17923
B P I Corp	3599	F	408 988-7888	16300
B R & F Spray Inc (PA)	3479	F	408 988-7582	13557
B-Bridge International Inc	2836	E	408 252-6200	8531
Bachur & Associates	2752	E	408 988-5861	6682
Baffle Inc	7372	F	408 663-6737	24408
Bay Area Canvas Inc	2394	F	408 727-4314	3779
Beam Dynamics Inc	3545	F	408 764-4805	14607
Beam On Technology Corporation	3569	E	408 982-0161	15302
Bel Power Solutions Inc	3677	A	866 513-2839	19322
Bench-Tek Solutions Llc	2522	F	408 653-1100	4978
Berg Manufacturing Inc	3999	F	408 727-2374	24050
Bertolin Engineering Corp	3469	E	408 988-0166	13169
Big Switch Networks Inc (PA)	7372	D	650 322-6510	24421
Bimarian Inc	7372	E	408 520-2666	24424
Bitzer Mobile Inc	7372	E	866 603-8392	24427
Blue Danube Systems Inc (PA)	3663	E	650 316-5010	18052
Bluesnap Inc	7372	E	866 475-4687	24435
Brightlight Welding & Mfg Inc	7692	E	408 988-0418	25388
Broadlight Inc (DH)	3674	E	408 982-4210	18756
Byington Steel Treating Inc (PA)	3398	E	408 727-6630	11804
Ca Inc	7372	C	800 225-5224	24460
California Micro Devices Corp (HQ)	3676	F	408 542-1051	19307
Calmax Technology Inc (PA)	3599	D	408 748-8660	16357
Calperf Inc	2011	F	408 829-7779	422

GEOGRAPHIC

Company	SIC	EMP	PHONE	ENTRY #
Calstar Products Inc	3251	D	262 752-9131	10773
Capella Microsystems Inc	3672	E	408 988-8000	18444
Caraustar Industries Inc	2631	C	408 845-7600	5345
Cardiva Medical Inc	3841	C	408 470-7100	22388
Casemaker Inc	7372	F	408 261-8265	24474
Caspio Inc (PA)	7372	E	650 691-0900	24476
Catalyst Semiconductor Inc	3674	F	408 542-1000	18761
Cavium Inc (HQ)	3674	C	408 943-7100	18762
Centerline Precision Inc	2836	F	408 988-4380	8540
Cirexx Corporation	3672	C	408 988-3980	18453
Cirexx International Inc (PA)	3672	C	408 988-3980	18454
Cisco Mfg Inc	3599	E	510 584-9626	16384
Cleanpartset Inc	3559	E	408 886-3300	14928
Cloudcar Inc	7372	E	650 946-1236	24502
Cloudminds Technology Inc	3535	F	650 391-6817	14269
Cloudvelox Inc	7372	F	408 841-4800	24506
Coherent Inc	3699	A	408 764-4000	19930
Coherent Inc (PA)	3826	A	408 764-4000	21935
Coherent Asia Inc	3679	D	408 764-4000	19496
Colortokens Inc	7372	E	408 341-6030	24510
Communicart	2752	E	408 970-0922	6749
Component Re-Engineering Inc	3674	E	408 562-4000	18775
Computer Access Tech Corp	3571	D	408 727-6600	15402
Comtech Xicom Technology Inc (HQ)	3663	C	408 213-3000	18076
Condor Reliability Services	3674	C	408 486-9600	18778
Context Engineering Co	3469	F	408 748-9112	13188
Convergent Manufacturing Tech	3577	F	408 987-2770	15720
Corporate Sign Systems Inc	3993	E	408 292-1600	23849
Cortina Systems Inc (HQ)	3674	C	408 481-2300	18787
Coskata Inc	2869	F	630 657-5800	9002
Creation Tech Santa Clara Inc	3672	B	408 235-7500	18460
Crossbar Inc	3674	E	408 884-0281	18792
Crystal Solar Inc	3674	F	408 490-1340	18793
Csl Operating LLC	3471	D	408 727-0893	13383
Cupertronix Inc	3826	F	408 887-5455	21941
Custom Pad and Partition Inc	2653	D	408 970-9711	5405
Cytobank Inc	7372	F	650 918-7966	24544
D & T Machining Inc	3599	F	408 486-6035	16416
D-Tek Manufacturing	3674	E	408 588-1574	18797
Dahlhauser Manufacturing Co	3496	E	408 988-3717	13823
Darko Precision Inc	3599	D	408 988-6133	16422
Dell Inc	3571	F	408 206-5466	15405
Delong Manufacturing Co Inc	3599	F	408 727-3348	16427
Dialog Semiconductor Inc (DH)	3674	C	408 845-8500	18800
Digital Loggers Inc	3613	E	408 330-5599	17140
Dongbu Electronics Co	3674	F	408 330-0330	18803
Double Precision Mfg	3599	E	408 727-7726	16447
Dpss Lasers Inc	3699	E	408 988-4300	19948
Dynamic Intgrted Solutions LLC (PA)	3674	E	408 727-3400	18809
E P Z Inc	3559	F	408 735-1820	14942
E-Fab Inc	3479	E	408 727-5218	13578
Earthpro Inc	3271	E	408 294-1920	10851
Easic Corporation	3674	E	408 855-9200	18811
Echelon Corporation (HQ)	3825	D	408 938-5200	21743
Electronic Cooling Solutions	3571	F	408 738-8331	15407
Element Six Tech US Corp	2819	F	408 986-8184	7772
Elite E/M Inc	3444	E	408 988-3505	12570
Eme Technologies Inc	3599	E	408 720-8817	16472
Enki Technology Inc	2819	F	408 383-9034	7773
Enmo Technologies Inc	7372	F	408 475-6819	24613
Erb Investment Company LLC	3599	F	408 727-6908	16477
Excel Cnc Machining Inc	3599	E	408 970-9460	16482
Excel Precision Corp USA	3825	E	408 727-4260	21755
Exclara Inc	3674	E	408 329-9319	18838
Expandable Software Inc (PA)	7372	E	408 261-7880	24635
Expol Inc	3599	F	408 567-9020	16485
Fast Turn Machining Inc	3599	F	408 720-6888	16494
Feitian Technologies Us Inc	3699	E	408 352-5553	19966
Fiberlite Centrifuge LLC	3841	D	408 492-1109	22449
Filemaker Inc (HQ)	7372	C	408 987-7000	24647
Fizzy Color LLC	2752	F	408 623-6705	6819
Fja Industries Inc	3569	F	408 727-0100	15323
Fortemedia Inc (PA)	3674	E	408 716-8028	18848
Fortemedia Inc	3572	D	408 716-8011	15538
Fortemedia Inc	3572	D	408 716-8028	15539
Forward Integration Technology	3357	F	408 988-3330	11662
Four-D Metal Finishing Inc	3471	D	408 730-5722	13412
Fujifilm Dimatix Inc (DH)	3577	C	408 565-9150	15745
Galaxy Manufacturing Inc	3469	F	408 654-4583	13208
Gateway Precision Inc	3599	F	408 855-8849	16527
Gigamon Inc (HQ)	7372	C	408 831-4000	24692
Gilbert Spray Coat Inc	3479	E	408 988-0747	13597
Glimmerglass Networks Inc	3679	E	510 780-1800	19553
Globalfoundries US Inc (HQ)	3559	B	408 462-3900	14961
Greenliant Systems Inc	3674	C	408 217-7400	18862
Gsi Technology Inc	3674	D	408 980-8388	18864
Guidetech Inc	3825	E	408 733-6555	21770
H&M Precision Machining	3451	F	408 982-9184	13026
H-Square Corporation	3674	E	408 732-1240	18867
Halabi Inc	3281	F	800 660-4167	11255
Hana Microelectronics Inc	3679	F	408 452-7474	19559
Harbor Electronics Inc (PA)	3679	C	408 988-6544	19560
Haros Anodizing Specialist	3471	F	408 980-0892	13423
Harvatek International Corp	3646	F	408 844-9698	17615
Heliovolt Corporation	3679	D	512 767-6079	19564
High Speed Cnc	3599	F	408 492-0331	16565
Hill Manufacturing Company LLC	3444	E	408 988-4744	12613
Hitachi Vantara Corporation (DH)	3572	B	408 970-1000	15554
Honeywell International Inc	2819	D	408 962-2000	7781
Hortonworks Inc (PA)	7372	A	408 916-4121	24737
Hung Tung	3599	F	408 496-1816	16575
Imergy Power Systems Inc	3679	E	510 668-1485	19574
Impact Marketing Displays LLC	3993	F	408 217-6850	23898
Impakt Holdings LLC	3444	F	650 692-5800	12619
Information Scan Tech Inc	3825	F	408 988-1908	21772
Innowi Inc	3571	F	408 609-9404	15430
Inphi Corporation (PA)	3674	C	408 217-7300	18900
Inta Technologies Corporation	3471	E	408 748-9955	13432
Integra Technologies LLC	3674	E	408 923-7300	18905
Integrated Optical Svcs Corp	2851	E	408 982-9510	8908
Intel Americas Inc (HQ)	3674	E	408 765-8080	18910
Intel Corporation (PA)	3577	B	408 765-8080	15764
Intel Corporation	3674	E	408 425-8398	18913
Intel Federal LLC	3674	E	302 644-3756	18916
INTEL International Limited (HQ)	3674	F	408 765-8080	18917
Intel Network Systems Inc.	3674	E	408 765-8080	18918
INTEL Puerto Rico Inc.	3674	E	408 765-8080	18919
Intevac Inc (PA)	3559	D	408 986-9888	14972
Intevac Inc.	3559	E	408 986-9888	14973
Intevac Photonics Inc (HQ)	3827	F	408 986-9888	22090
Invecas Inc.	3674	E	408 758-5636	18927
Invenio Imaging Inc	3841	F	408 753-9147	22492
Irislogic Inc	7372	E	408 727-4940	24803
Ixia Inc	3612	E	408 988-8703	17101
J & B Refining Inc.	3339	F	408 988-7900	11547
James Stout	3599	E	408 988-8582	16614
Jasper Display Corp	3559	E	408 831-5788	14975
Jetnexus LLC	3571	E	800 568-9921	15435
JP Graphics Inc	2759	E	408 235-8821	7367
JP Graphics Inc.	2752	E	408 235-8821	6915
JWP Manufacturing LLC	3599	E	408 970-0641	16636
Kana Software Inc (HQ)	7372	D	650 614-8300	24824
Kelly Network Solutions Inc.	3825	E	650 364-7201	21783
Keysight Technologies Inc.	3825	E	408 553-3290	21786
KLA-Tencor Corporation	3825	D	408 496-2055	21789
Kno Inc	7372	E	408 844-8120	24835
L P Glassblowing Inc	3679	E	408 988-7561	19614
Landec Corporation (PA)	2033	C	650 306-1650	818
Lightstreams Inc	3229	F	408 492-1689	10655
Linde LLC	3561	D	408 496-1177	15082
Linkbit Inc	3577	E	408 969-9940	15790
Lockheed Martin Corporation	3812	A	408 734-4980	21321
Logicool Inc	7372	E	408 907-1344	24864
Lor-Van Manufacturing LLC	3444	E	408 980-1045	12642
Lumasense Tech Holdings Inc (HQ)	3845	D	408 727-1600	23001
Lunas Sheet Metal Inc	3444	F	408 492-1260	12643
Mac Engineering & Components	3429	F	408 286-3030	11972
Magnetic Rcrding Solutions Inc.	3825	E	408 970-8266	21798
Manufacturers/Hyland Ltd	3231	E	408 748-1806	10719
Marvell Semiconductor Inc	3825	F	408 855-8839	21799
Marvell Semiconductor Inc (HQ)	3674	A	408 222-2500	18981
Marvell Technology Group Ltd (HQ)	3674	E	408 222-2500	18982
Marx Digital Mfg Inc (PA)	3599	E	408 748-1783	16720
Master Precision Machining	3599	E	408 727-0185	16721
Matthias Rath Inc (HQ)	2023	F	408 567-5000	630
Maxford Technology LLC	3299	F	408 855-8288	11359
McAfee LLC (HQ)	7372	C	888 847-8766	24891
McAfee Finance 2 LLC	7372	E	888 847-8766	24892
McAfee Security LLC	7372	A	866 622-3911	24893
McKenzie Machining Inc	3599	F	408 748-8885	16728
Mecpro Inc	3599	E	408 727-9757	16733
Medconx Inc	3069	E	408 330-0003	9636
Memoryten Inc (PA)	3572	D	408 516-4141	15568
Mercury Networks LLC	3663	F	408 859-1345	18178
Metal Finishing Solutions Inc	3444	F	408 988-8662	12667
Metra Biosystems Inc (HQ)	2835	E	408 616-4300	8495
Metrotech Corporation (PA)	3812	D	408 734-3880	21347
Miasole	3674	B	408 919-5700	18994
Miasole Hi-Tech Corp (DH)	3674	C	408 919-5700	18995
Micro Semicdtr Researches LLC	3674	E	408 492-1369	19000

Mergent email: customerrelations@mergent.com

1470

2019 California
Manufacturers Register

(P-0000) Products & Services Section entry number
(PA)=Parent Co (HQ)=Headquarters (DH)=Div Headquarters

	SIC	EMP	PHONE	ENTRY #
Micropoint Bioscience Inc	2835	E	408 588-1682	8496
Microsemi Corp - Pwr Prdts Grp	3674	F	408 986-8031	19008
Microsemi Corp - Rf Power Pdts	3674	D	408 986-8031	19009
Microsoft Corporation	7372	D	408 987-9608	24918
Microunity Systems Engineering	3669	E	408 734-8100	18346
Mips Tech Inc (HQ)	3674	D	408 530-5000	19021
Miramar Labs Inc	3842	E	408 940-8700	22773
Modular Process Tech Corp	3567	F	408 325-8640	15270
Molding Company	2499	E	408 748-6968	4636
Montblanc North America LLC	3911	F	408 241-5188	23299
Monterey Bay Office Pdts Inc	2754	F	408 727-4627	7208
Montoya & Jaramillo Inc	3471	F	408 727-5776	13458
Multibeam Corporation	3559	F	408 980-1800	14996
Multimek Inc	3672	E	408 653-1300	18535
Multitest Elctrnic Systems Inc (DH)	3825	B	408 988-6544	21809
N D E Inc	3672	E	408 727-3955	18536
Nanoscale Combinatorial	2899	E	408 987-2000	9288
National Instruments Corp	3825	B	408 610-6800	21812
National Semiconductor Corp (HQ)	3674	A	408 721-5000	19032
Net Optics Inc	7372	D	408 737-7777	24949
Nethra Imaging Inc (PA)	3674	F	408 257-5880	19037
Netlogic Microsystems LLC	3674	A	408 454-3000	19039
Netsarang Inc	7372	F	669 204-3301	24952
Newnex Technology Corp	3577	F	408 986-9988	15811
Newpacket Wireless Corporation	3577	F	408 747-1003	15812
Newport Corporation	3699	A	408 980-4300	20029
Nexgen Power Systems Inc	3674	E	408 230-7698	19041
Nextec Microwave & Rf Inc	3663	F	408 727-1189	18199
Nova Measuring Instruments Inc (HQ)	3825	E	408 200-4344	21818
Nss Enterprises	2759	E	408 970-9200	7416
Nuvora Inc	2844	E	408 856-2200	8805
Nvidia Corporation (PA)	3674	B	408 486-2000	19043
Nvidia Corporation	3674	E	408 566-5364	19044
Nvidia Development Inc	3674	E	408 486-2000	19045
Nvidia US Investment Company	3663	A	408 615-2500	18203
Nwe Technology Inc	3572	C	408 919-6100	15578
Olympic Press Inc	2759	F	408 496-6222	7418
Omnivision Technologies Inc (HQ)	3674	C	408 567-3000	19057
Omniyig Inc	3679	E	408 988-0843	19672
Onspec Technology Partners Inc	3674	E	408 654-7627	19061
Optasense Inc	3674	F	408 970-3500	19062
Oracle America Inc	7372	C	408 276-4300	24997
Oracle America Inc	7372	C	408 276-7534	25006
Oracle Corporation	7372	B	408 421-2890	25011
Oracle Corporation	7372	B	408 276-5552	25012
Oracle Corporation	7372	B	650 506-9864	25015
P K Selective Metal Pltg Inc	3471	F	408 988-1910	13472
P M S D Inc	3599	D	408 988-5235	16817
P S C Manufacturing Inc	3089	E	408 988-5115	10256
Pac Tech USA Packg Tech Inc	3674	F	408 588-1925	19070
Pacific Impressions Inc	2261	F	408 727-4200	2888
Palex Metals Inc	3444	E	408 496-6111	12709
Palo Alto Networks Inc (PA)	3577	A	408 753-4000	15821
Par Global Resources Inc	2752	F	408 982-5515	7013
Paragon Swiss Inc	3599	F	408 748-1617	16827
Parametric Manufacturing Inc	3599	F	408 654-9845	16828
Patsons Press	2752	E	408 567-0911	7017
Pelican Sign Service Inc	3993	F	408 246-3833	23943
Pepsi-Cola Metro Btlg Co Inc	2086	C	408 617-2200	2167
Phase Matrix Inc	3825	E	408 610-6810	21825
Picarro Inc (PA)	3826	E	408 962-3900	22005
Picotrack	3559	F	408 988-7000	15010
Pneumrx Inc	3841	E	650 625-4440	22585
Polishing Corporation America	3674	E	888 892-3377	19080
Praxair Distribution Inc	2813	E	408 748-1722	7730
Probe-Rite Corp	3825	E	408 727-0100	21829
Process Stainless Lab Inc (PA)	3471	E	408 980-0535	13482
Prodigy Surface Tech Inc	3471	E	408 492-9390	13483
Products Usa LLC	2899	F	770 960-1120	9299
Promega Bsystems Sunnyvale Inc	3829	E	408 636-2400	22251
Promex Industries Incorporated (PA)	3674	D	408 496-0222	19088
Pss Communications Inc	3661	F	408 496-3330	17983
Purewave Networks Inc	3663	E	650 528-5200	18227
Pwp Manufacturing LLC	3444	F	408 748-0120	12726
Qmat Inc	3674	F	498 228-5858	19094
Quadbase Systems Inc	7372	F	408 982-0835	25094
Qualcomm Incorporated	3663	C	408 216-2500	18228
Qualcomm Incorporated	3674	B	408 216-6797	19100
Qualcomm Incorporated	3674	F	858 587-1121	19101
Qualtech Circuits Inc	3672	F	408 727-4125	18575
Quest Software Inc	7372	F	408 899-3823	25098
Questivity Inc	7372	F	408 615-1781	25100
Radian Thermal Products Inc	3369	D	408 988-6200	11783
Rdc Machine Inc	3599	E	408 970-0721	16887
Reaction Technology Inc (PA)	3674	E	408 970-9601	19117
Redfern Integrated Optics Inc	3827	E	408 970-3500	22126
Redline Solutions Inc	3577	F	408 562-1700	15836
Reliance Computer Corp	3674	C	408 492-1915	19120
Rennovia Inc	2869	F	650 804-7400	9037
Revera Incorporated	3577	E	408 510-7400	15837
Rimnetics Inc	3089	E	650 969-6590	10335
Rocket Ems Inc	3672	C	408 727-3700	18582
Roos Instruments Inc	3825	E	408 748-8589	21841
Ruckus Wireless Inc	3661	C	408 235-5500	17990
SAE Engineering Inc	3444	C	408 492-1784	12749
Sager Electrical Supply Co Inc	3679	F	408 588-1750	19716
San Jose Delta Associates Inc	3264	C	408 727-1448	10823
Sanmina Corporation	3672	A	408 244-0266	18590
Santa Clara Imaging	3829	E	408 296-5555	22261
Santa Clara Plating Co Inc	3471	D	408 727-9315	13499
Sbmc Solutions LLC	3545	D	408 732-3200	14672
Scientific Metal Finishing	3479	E	408 970-9011	13654
Secugen Corporation	3577	E	408 834-7712	15848
Secure Computing Corporation (DH)	7372	E	408 979-2020	25158
Semicndctor Cmponents Inds LLC	3674	C	408 542-1000	19140
Semiconix Corp (PA)	3674	E	408 986-8026	19144
Senju Comtek Corp (HQ)	3399	F	408 963-5300	11849
Sequent Software Inc	7372	F	650 419-2713	25164
Sesame Software Inc	7372	E	866 474-7575	25166
Shape Memory Medical Inc	3842	F	979 599-5201	22812
Sharedata Inc	7372	D	408 490-2500	25167
Silicon Standard Corp	3674	E	408 234-6964	19157
Silicon Vly McRelectronics Inc	3674	E	408 844-7100	19159
Silver Peak Systems Inc (PA)	3674	C	408 935-1800	19162
Sitime Corporation (HQ)	3674	D	408 328-4400	19167
Sj Valley Plating Inc	3471	F	408 988-5502	13506
Sjt Tech Industries Inc	3674	F	408 980-9547	19168
Software Ag Inc	7372	C	408 490-5300	25191
Solera Laboratories Inc	3674	F	408 200-3131	19178
Solflower Computer Inc	3577	F	408 733-8100	15856
Solid Data Systems Inc	3572	F	408 845-5700	15610
Solutionsoft Systems Inc	7372	E	408 346-1491	25195
Sonic Solutions Holdings Inc	7372	B	408 562-8400	25198
Sp3 Diamond Technologies Inc	3569	F	877 773-9940	15363
Spectra-Physics Inc	3699	A	650 961-2550	20078
Sra Oss Inc	7372	C	408 855-8200	25213
Star Products	3599	E	408 727-8421	16964
Step Tools Unlimited Inc	3545	F	408 988-8898	14681
Steris Corporation	3842	F	800 614-6789	22820
Stmicroelectronics Inc	3674	E	408 919-8400	19192
Stone Publishing Inc (PA)	2741	D	408 450-7910	6591
Streamline Circuits Corp	3672	C	408 727-1418	18616
Sun Marble Inc	3281	E	510 783-9900	11283
Superior Quartz Inc	3339	F	408 844-9663	11550
Sutter P Dahlglen Entps Inc	3599	F	408 727-4640	16977
Swiss Screw Products Inc	3599	E	408 748-8400	16978
Synthesys Research Inc (DH)	3825	D	408 753-1630	21861
T M Industries Incorporated	3441	E	408 736-5202	12255
Tekever Corporation	7372	D	408 730-2617	25264
Tektronix Inc	3825	E	408 496-0800	21864
Teledyne Wireless Inc	3631	C	408 986-5060	17377
Telenav Inc (PA)	3812	C	408 245-3800	21441
Tellus Solutions Inc	7372	E	408 850-2942	25266
Tembo Systems Inc	3577	E	408 300-9236	15868
Ter Inc	3599	E	408 986-9920	16995
Ter Precision Machining Inc	3599	E	408 986-9920	16996
Texas Instruments Incorporated	3674	C	669 721-5000	19229
Theater Publications Inc	2721	F	408 748-1600	6269
Thermo Fisher Scientific	3826	E	408 731-5056	22032
Thermo Fisher Scientific Inc	3826	F	408 988-1103	22035
Tmk Manufacturing Inc	3545	E	408 844-8289	14685
Tool Makers International Inc	3541	F	408 980-8888	14418
Total Phase Inc	3572	F	408 850-6500	15618
Translattice Inc (PA)	3571	E	408 749-8478	15499
Transmeta Corp	3674	F	408 327-9831	19234
Ttm Printed Circuit Group Inc	3672	C	408 486-3100	18630
Ttm Technologies Inc	3672	B	408 486-3100	18632
UNI-Pixel Displays Inc	3575	F	281 825-4500	15649
Uniq Vision Inc	3861	C	408 330-0818	23206
Unique Media Inc	3652	F	408 733-9999	17914
Unisem (sunnvale) Inc (PA)	3674	F	408 734-3222	19247
Unitech Tool & Machine Inc	3599	E	408 566-0333	17022
Uri Tech Inc	3672	F	408 456-0115	18641
Vacuum Engrg & Mtls Co Inc	2819	E	408 871-9900	7812
Vanderhulst Associates Inc	3599	E	408 727-1313	17036
Veeco Instruments Inc	3674	C	510 657-8523	19251
Verifone Inc	3578	C	408 232-7800	15903
Vertical Communication (HQ)	3661	D	408 969-9600	18005
Vicom Systems Inc	3572	F	408 588-1286	15622
Violin Mmory Fdral Systems Inc	3674	C	650 396-1500	19259

Employment Codes: A=Over 500 employees, B=251-500,
C=101-250, D=51-100, E=20-50, F=10-19

2019 California
Manufacturers Register

© Mergent Inc. 1-800-342-5647
1471

GEOGRAPHIC

Company	SIC	EMP	PHONE	ENTRY #
VIP Manufacturing & Engrg Corp	3724	F	408 727-6545	20690
Visger Precision Inc	3599	F	408 988-0184	17043
Vivid Inc	3444	D	408 982-9101	12811
Volex Inc (HQ)	3089	E	669 444-1740	10432
Vulcan Construction Mtls LLC	1442	F	408 213-4270	388
W L Gore & Associates Inc	3841	C	928 864-2705	22679
Watts Machining Inc	3599	E	408 654-9300	17053
Wavexing Inc	3674	F	408 896-1982	19271
Wes Manufacturing Inc	3599	F	408 727-0750	17057
Western Grinding Service Inc	3451	E	650 591-2635	13051
Westfab Manufacturing Inc	3444	E	408 727-0550	12818
Whizz Systems Inc	3672	E	408 207-0400	18652
Winnov Inc	3651	F	888 315-9460	17880
Winway Usa Inc	3674	E	203 775-9311	19274
Wti Jkb Inc (PA)	2431	F	408 297-8579	4262
Xceive Corporation	3679	E	408 486-5610	19791
Xingtera Inc	3577	E	408 916-4781	15889
Yaskawa America Inc	3621	C	408 748-4400	17229
Z K Celltest Inc	3825	F	408 541-2620	21889

SANTA CLARITA, CA - Los Angeles County

Company	SIC	EMP	PHONE	ENTRY #
3-D International LLC	2842	E	661 250-2020	8616
3d/International	2842	D	661 250-2020	8617
Applied Polytech Systems Inc	2452	E	818 504-9261	4568
B & B Manufacturing Co (PA)	3599	C	661 257-2161	16294
Billy Beez Usa LLC	3949	F	661 383-0050	23521
Blue Cross Laboratories Inc (PA)	2842	C	661 255-0955	8626
California Millworks Corp	2431	E	661 294-2345	4118
Certified Thermoplastics LLC	3089	F	661 222-3006	10020
Coast Air Supply Co Inc	3643	F	818 898-2288	17452
Curtiss-Wright Corporation	3491	E	661 257-4430	13714
Daisy Publishing Company Inc	2721	D	661 295-1910	6141
Door & Hardware Installers Inc	2431	F	661 298-9383	4145
Dulce Systems Inc	3669	F	818 435-6007	18321
Frametent Inc	2394	E	661 290-3375	3787
Grand-Way Fabri-Graphic Inc	3479	E	818 206-8560	13598
H2w Technologies Inc	3625	F	661 291-1620	17275
Iwerks Entertainment Inc	3699	D	661 678-1800	19988
K Tech Telecommunications Inc	3663	F	818 773-0333	18141
Lamsco West Inc	3728	C	661 295-8620	20863
Lansair Corporation	3599	F	661 294-9503	16676
Living Way Industries Inc	3993	F	661 298-3200	23915
Lockheed Martin Corporation	3812	B	661 572-7363	21339
Magic Plastics Inc	3089	D	800 369-0303	10198
Manzanita	3931	F	818 785-1111	23380
Metalpro Industries Inc	3444	E	661 294-0764	12671
Mikailian Meat Product Inc	2013	F	661 257-1055	507
Morgan Products Inc	3599	F	661 257-3022	16771
Morris Multimedia Inc	2711	D	661 259-1234	5979
Old English Mil & Woodworks (PA)	2431	F	661 294-9171	4206
Packaging Systems Inc	2891	E	661 253-5700	9160
Parrot Communications Intl Inc	2741	E	818 567-4700	6547
Processexchange Inc	3695	F	661 799-2548	19877
Projex International Inc	3999	F	661 268-0999	24216
Shadow Holdings LLC (PA)	2844	E	661 252-3807	8838
Shadow Holdings LLC	2844	B	661 252-3807	8839
Signal	2711	D	661 259-1234	6045
Source Print Media Solutions	2752	F	661 263-1880	7107
Steven Madden Ltd	3143	E	661 753-9510	10486
Stiers Rv Centers LLC	3799	F	661 254-6000	21242
Terryberry Company LLC	3911	D	661 257-9971	23324
Tesco Products	3541	F	661 257-0153	14416
True Warrior LLC	2389	F	661 237-6588	3684
Val Pak Products	3069	F	661 252-0115	9689
Valley Precision Metal Product	3444	F	661 607-0100	12804
Whitmor Plstic Wire Cable Corp (PA)	3496	D	661 257-2400	13864
Woodward Hrt Inc (HQ)	3625	A	661 294-6000	17324
Woodward Hrt Inc	3625	D	661 702-5552	17325

SANTA CRUZ, CA - Santa Cruz County

Company	SIC	EMP	PHONE	ENTRY #
Anatometal Inc	3911	E	831 454-9880	23236
AV Now Inc	3651	E	831 425-2500	17769
Bagelry Inc (PA)	2051	E	831 429-8049	1178
Beckmanns Old World Bakery Ltd	2051	C	831 423-9242	1185
Bimbo Bakeries Usa Inc	2051	E	831 465-1214	1206
Bonny Doon Vineyard (PA)	2084	F	831 425-3625	1664
Bonny Doon Winery Inc	2084	F	831 425-3625	1665
Community Printers Inc	2752	E	831 426-4682	6750
Cool Lumens Inc	3646	F	831 471-8084	17594
Crestor Inc	3369	F	831 475-4435	11773
Dallas Electronics Inc	3672	E	831 457-3610	18464
Doerksen Precision Products	3599	F	831 476-1843	16444
Drapery Enterprises	2391	F	831 458-2578	3693
Duke Empirical Inc	3841	D	831 420-1104	22428
Dynamic Engineering	3674	E	831 457-8891	18807
Elements Manufacturing Inc	2541	E	831 421-9440	5057

Company	SIC	EMP	PHONE	ENTRY #
Eschaton Foundation (PA)	2752	D	831 423-1626	6809
Eye Medical Group Santa Cruz	3841	F	831 426-2550	22447
Fiber Systems Inc	3661	E	831 430-0700	17949
Global Precision Manufacturing	3531	F	831 239-9469	14170
Harmony Foods Corporation (PA)	2834	C	831 457-3200	8204
Hydro-Logic Purification	3569	F	888 426-5644	15330
Jeff Frank	3993	F	831 469-8208	23907
Jim Beauregard	2084	D	831 423-9453	1832
Journeyworks Publishing	2741	E	831 423-1400	6510
Kevins Awnings Inc	2394	F	831 423-7918	3794
Keyfax Newmedia Inc	3651	F	831 477-1205	17823
King Precision Inc	3469	E	831 426-2704	13236
Lackey Woodworking Inc	2434	F	831 462-0528	4325
Larsens Inc	2394	F	831 476-3009	3795
Las Animas Con & Bldg Sup Inc	3531	E	831 425-4084	14180
Lifeaid Beverage Co	2086	D	800 855-1113	2148
Lockheed Martin Corporation	3812	A	831 425-6000	21319
Lockheed Martin Corporation	3761	D	831 425-6000	21160
Lockheed Martin Corporation	3812	D	831 425-6375	21335
Looker Data Sciences Inc (PA)	3572	E	831 244-0340	15564
Mariannes Ice Cream LLC (PA)	2024	F	831 457-1447	684
Mel & Associates Inc (PA)	3949	F	831 476-2950	23617
Metro Publishing Inc	2711	E	831 457-9000	5967
Mindsai Inc	7372	F	831 239-4644	24922
National Stock Sign Company	3993	F	831 476-2020	23933
Nhs Inc	3949	D	831 459-7800	23624
Obentec Inc (PA)	2449	F	831 457-0301	4530
ONeill Wetsuits LLC (PA)	3069	D	831 475-7500	9650
Overbeck Machine	3599	E	831 425-5912	16813
Persys Engineering Inc	3559	E	831 471-9300	15008
Plantronics Inc (PA)	3661	B	831 426-5858	17977
Plantronics Inc	3661	E	831 426-5858	17979
Predpol Inc	7372	F	831 331-4550	25078
Provac Sales Inc	3561	E	831 462-8900	15089
Reversica Design Inc	3429	F	831 459-9033	11987
Santa Cruz Bicycles LLC	3751	D	831 459-7560	21136
Santa Cruz Biotechnology Inc	2836	E	831 457-3800	8580
Santa Cruz Guitar Corporation	3931	E	831 425-0999	23386
Santa Cruz Industries Inc	2542	F	831 423-9211	5167
Socksmith Design Inc (PA)	2252	E	831 426-6416	2814
System Studies Incorporated (PA)	3661	E	831 475-5777	17999
Threshold Enterprises Ltd	2833	E	831 466-4014	7978
Toucaned Inc	2741	F	831 464-0508	6605
Two Pore Guys Inc	3674	F	831 515-8515	19241
Vapor Cleaners (PA)	3911	F	831 423-4646	23329

SANTA FE SPRINGS, CA - Los Angeles County

Company	SIC	EMP	PHONE	ENTRY #
2m Machine Corporation	3599	E	562 404-4225	16177
A-W Engineering Company Inc	3469	E	562 945-1041	13154
Aberdeen LLC	3572	E	562 903-1500	15507
Accuride International Inc (PA)	3429	E	562 903-0200	11923
Accutech Manufacturing Inc	3599	E	562 903-2365	16209
Ace Commercial Inc	2752	E	562 946-6664	6636
Advanced Ground Systems (HQ)	3724	E	562 906-9300	20641
Aero Chip Inc	3599	E	562 404-6300	16235
Aero Chip Intgrted Systems Inc	3812	F	310 329-8600	21251
Age Incorporated	3613	E	562 483-7300	17130
Air Products and Chemicals Inc	2813	E	562 944-3873	7671
Airgas Usa LLC	2813	E	562 946-8394	7680
Airgas Usa LLC	2813	E	562 945-1383	7683
Airgas Usa LLC	2813	E	562 906-8700	7685
Alegacy Foodservice Products	2599	D	562 320-3100	5219
All Power Manufacturing Co	3999	F	562 802-2640	24030
All-Star Lettering Inc	2759	E	562 404-5995	7229
Allblack Co Inc	3471	E	562 946-2955	13318
Altro Usa Inc	3996	F	562 944-8292	24013
Altura Pharmaceuticals Inc	2834	E	562 906-9000	8018
Alumafab	3646	F	562 630-6440	17582
Alumistar Inc	3365	E	562 633-6673	11723
Amity Washer & Stamping Co	3469	E	562 941-1259	13164
Angelus Shoe Polish Co Inc	2842	F	562 941-4242	8620
Apex Universal Inc (PA)	3993	F	562 944-8878	23817
Apffels Coffee Inc	2095	E	562 309-0400	2327
Artiva USA Inc	3645	E	562 298-8968	17527
Associated Plating Company	3471	E	562 946-5525	13338
Atlantic Representations Inc	2514	E	562 903-9550	4824
Auto Wash Concepts Inc	3589	E	562 948-2575	16014
Automated Packg Systems Inc	3532	E	562 941-1476	14200
B & B Refractories Inc	3255	F	562 946-4535	10798
B & G Millworks	2431	F	562 944-4599	4108
Baker Petrolite LLC	1389	F	562 406-7090	182
BD Classic Enterprizes Inc	2821	F	562 944-6177	7822
Berry Global Inc	3089	E	800 462-3843	9979
Best Living International Inc	2514	F	626 625-2911	4826
Best Roll-Up Door Inc	3442	E	562 802-2233	12299
Better-Way & Lovell Grinding	3599	F	562 693-8722	16322

Mergent email: customerrelations@mergent.com
1472

2019 California
Manufacturers Register

(P-0000) Products & Services Section entry number
(PA)=Parent Co (HQ)=Headquarters (DH)=Div Headquarters

Name	SIC	EMP	PHONE	ENTRY #
Blair Adhesive Products	2891	F	562 946-6004	9130
Blue Ribbon Cont & Display Inc	2653	F	562 944-1217	5391
Bodycote Thermal Proc Inc	3398	E	562 693-3135	11799
Bodycote Thermal Proc Inc	3398	E	562 946-1717	11801
Boise Hexacomb	2621	F	562 944-0052	5276
Bolero Inds Inc A Cal Corp	3089	E	562 693-3000	9986
Bot N Bot Inc	2096	E	562 906-4873	2375
Bravo Sports (HQ)	3949	D	562 484-5100	23529
Brown-Pacific	3312	F	562 921-3471	11381
Brunton Enterprises Inc	3441	C	562 945-0013	12121
Bumble Bee Plastics Inc	3089	F	562 903-0833	9994
Bumble Bee Seafoods LLC	2091	E	562 483-7474	2294
C & C Die Engraving	3599	F	562 944-3399	16342
C B Sheets Inc	2631	E	562 921-1223	5342
Cableco	2298	E	562 942-8076	2972
Cal-Tron Plating Inc	3471	E	562 945-1181	13363
California Reamer Company Inc	3545	F	562 946-6377	14612
California Specialty Painting	3479	E	562 622-7800	13564
Calmex Fireplace Equipment Mfg	3429	F	716 645-2901	11943
Capital Cooking Equipment	3433	E	562 903-1168	12060
Caps Corporate Office	2834	E	562 941-9515	8099
Carpenter Group	3496	F	562 942-8076	13818
Cascade Pump Company	3561	D	562 946-1414	15056
Catalina Carpet Mills Inc (PA)	2273	D	562 926-5811	2928
Central Admxture Phrm Svcs Inc	2834	E	562 941-9595	8108
Chapman Designs Inc	2421	F	562 698-4600	4033
Chubby Gorilla Inc	3089	E	844 365-5218	10026
City of Santa Fe Springs	3949	F	562 868-8761	23540
Cji Process Systems Inc	3443	D	562 777-0614	12375
Clw Plastic Bag Mfg Co Inc	2673	E	562 903-8878	5594
Collicutt Energy Services Inc	3432	E	562 944-4413	12032
Continental Heat Treating Inc	3398	D	562 944-8808	11809
Contract Transportation Sys Co	2851	D	562 696-3262	8898
Corrpro Companies Inc	3331	E	562 944-1636	11531
Crosstex International Inc	3843	F	562 921-3343	22863
Crt Color Printing Inc	2752	F	562 906-1517	6770
Crystal Lighting Corp	3646	F	562 944-0223	17595
Ctra Industrial Machine	3554	E	562 936-5188	14791
CTS Cement Manufacturing Corp	2674	E	562 802-2660	5639
CTS Printing	2752	F	562 941-8420	6771
Custom Mfg LLC	3599	F	562 944-0245	16413
Custom Steel Fabrication Inc	3441	F	562 907-2777	12147
Dab Inc	3645	D	562 623-4773	17533
David A Neal Inc	3599	F	562 941-5626	16424
Day Star Industries	2431	F	562 926-8800	4139
Deca International Corp	3812	E	714 367-5900	21284
Detoronics Corp	3678	E	626 579-7130	19386
Die Craft Engineering & Mfg Co	3544	E	562 777-8809	14506
Die Craft Stamping Inc	3494	E	562 944-2395	13763
Direct Label & Tag LLC	2752	E	562 948-4499	6788
Distinctive Inds Texas Inc	2386	E	512 491-3500	3613
Distinctive Industries	2396	B	800 421-9777	3889
Diversified Spring Tech	3495	F	562 944-4049	13793
DJ Bronson Inc (PA)	2335	F	562 945-9609	3306
Dorco Electronics Inc	2655	F	562 623-1133	5485
Dub Publishing Inc	2721	F	626 336-3821	6152
Dunweizer Machine Inc	3443	F	562 698-7787	12386
Duro Flex Rubber Products Inc	3069	F	562 946-5533	9608
Duro Roller Company Inc	3069	F	562 946-9609	9609
Dynamic Enterprises Inc	3599	E	562 944-0271	16455
E & L Electric Inc	7694	F	562 903-9272	25457
E Z Martin Stick Labels Inc	2759	F	562 906-1577	7306
E-Liq Cube Inc (PA)	3999	F	562 537-9454	24083
Eagleware Manufacturing Co Inc	3469	E	562 320-3100	13198
Electromatic Inc	3471	F	562 623-9993	13403
Electronic Chrome Grinding Co	3471	E	562 946-6671	13405
Elektron Technology Corp	3674	F	760 343-3650	18815
Elite Mfg Corp	2522	C	888 354-8356	4982
Employee Owned Pacific Cast PR	3365	E	562 633-6673	11740
Endotec Inc	3842	F	714 681-6306	22728
Ethosenergy Field Services LLC (DH)	1389	D	310 639-3523	210
Eurton Electric Company Inc	7694	E	562 946-4477	25459
Excel Sheet Metal Inc (PA)	3444	D	562 944-0701	12578
Field Foundation	1389	E	562 921-3567	212
Final Finish Inc	2262	E	562 777-7774	2902
Flexline Inc	2796	E	562 229-1141	7643
Flint Group US LLC	2893	F	562 903-7976	9195
Food Technology and Design LLC	2064	E	562 944-7821	1423
Foremost Spring Company Inc	3495	F	562 923-0791	13794
FPec Corporation A Cal Corp (PA)	3556	E	562 802-3727	14850
Fruiti Pops Inc	2024	F	562 404-2568	674
Fry Reglet Corporation (PA)	3354	C	562 903-9500	11586
Gabriel Container Co (PA)	2653	C	562 699-1051	5412
Galaxy Brazing Co Inc	7692	F	562 946-9039	25404
Gaylords Inc (PA)	3713	F	562 529-7543	20206
Gc Labels LLC	2759	F	951 270-1664	7326
Golden Supreme Inc	3999	E	562 903-1063	24113
Golden West Machine Inc	3599	E	562 903-1111	16538
Golden West Refining Company	2911	E	562 921-3581	9334
Goldilocks Corp California (PA)	2051	E	562 946-9995	1267
Goodrich Corporation	3728	F	562 906-7372	20829
Goodrich Corporation	3728	D	562 944-4441	20832
Gorlitz Sewer & Drain Inc	3589	E	562 944-3060	16046
GP Merger Sub Inc	3231	D	562 946-7722	10703
Grafico Inc	2796	F	562 404-4976	7645
Graphic Dies Inc	2796	F	562 946-1802	7646
Grayd-A Prcsion Met Fbricators	3444	E	562 944-8951	12600
Grimco Inc	3469	E	562 449-4964	13212
Gundrill Tech Inc	3599	F	562 946-9355	16548
Hamar Wood Parquet Company	2421	E	562 944-8885	4038
Hamrock Inc	3315	E	562 944-0255	11443
Heraeus Prcous Mtls N Amer LLC (DH)	3341	C	562 921-7464	11559
Hexpol Compounding LLC	3069	E	562 464-4480	9621
Hexpol Compounding LLC	3069	E	562 464-4482	9622
Hillshire Brands Company	2013	E	562 903-9900	493
Holzinger Indus Shtmtl Inc	3444	F	562 944-6337	12614
Honomatic Inc	3599	F	562 941-3295	16572
Howies Moulding Inc	2431	F	562 698-0261	4166
Hydraulic Pneumatic Inc	3593	F	562 926-1122	16158
I-Coat Company LLC	3827	E	800 832-2628	22084
Iclavis LLC	2752	F	310 503-6847	6868
Industrial Manufacturing Inc	3433	F	562 941-5888	12069
Industrial Sprockets Gears Inc	3568	E	323 233-7221	15286
Infinity Textile	2299	E	562 777-9770	3000
Ink Spot Inc	2752	E	626 338-4500	6882
Inkovation Inc (PA)	2752	E	800 465-4174	6883
Inkovation Inc	2752	E	800 465-4174	6884
International Paper Company	2653	C	323 946-6100	5426
International Paper Company	2621	E	562 692-9465	5303
INX International Ink Co	2893	F	562 404-5664	9204
J & J Processing Inc	2087	E	562 926-2333	2269
J & S Machine	3599	F	562 945-6419	16598
J C Grinding (PA)	3599	F	562 944-3025	16601
J R C Industries Inc	2621	D	562 698-0171	5306
J S Paluch Co Inc	2731	E	562 692-0484	6354
Jad Chemical Inc	2869	F	310 833-7457	9014
Jarrow Industries Inc	2834	C	562 906-1919	8239
JC Hanscom Inc	2435	F	562 789-9955	4378
Jj Lithographics Inc	2752	F	562 698-0280	6912
John Crane Inc	3295	E	562 802-2555	11322
JR Machine Company Inc	3599	F	562 903-9477	16633
K Metal Products Inc	3496	C	562 693-5425	13837
K S Designs Inc	3993	E	562 929-3973	23912
Kik-Socal Inc	2842	A	562 946-6427	8649
Kingsolver Inc	3991	F	562 945-7590	23793
KS Engineering Inc	3728	E	562 483-7788	20862
La Habra Welding Inc	7692	E	562 923-2229	25419
LA Supply Company LLC	2869	E	562 404-1502	9019
Lanshon Inc	2311	E	562 777-1688	3032
Larson-Juhl US LLC	2499	E	562 946-6453	4631
Liberty Vegetable Oil Company	2079	E	562 921-3567	1542
Life Paint Company (PA)	2851	E	562 944-6391	8915
Liquidspring Technologies Inc	3799	F	562 941-4344	21234
LM Scofield Company (DH)	2899	E	323 720-3000	9273
Lmw Enterprises LLC	3585	E	562 944-1969	15968
Lockhart Furniture Mfg Inc	2512	D	562 404-0561	4792
Long Bar Grinding Inc	3599	F	562 921-1983	16691
Long Beach Enterprise Inc (PA)	2092	E	562 944-8945	2315
Los Angeles Sleeve Co Inc	3714	E	562 945-7578	20388
Louis Levin & Son Inc	3542	F	562 802-8066	14442
Lowers Wldg & Fabrication Inc	3599	F	562 946-4521	16693
M C I Foods Inc	2099	C	562 977-4000	2591
M E D Inc	3714	D	562 921-0464	20392
Machine Precision Components	3599	F	562 404-0500	16706
Maruichi American Corporation	3317	D	562 903-8600	11482
Master Powder Coating Inc	2851	E	562 863-4135	8917
Maxon Industries Inc	3714	D	562 464-0099	20397
Mbf Transportation LLC	3743	E	562 282-0540	21081
Mc-Dowell-Craig Mfgco (PA)	2522	F	714 521-7170	4994
McAero LLC	3599	F	310 787-9911	16726
Medlin Material Handling Eqp	3542	F	562 229-1991	14445
Melfred Borzall Inc	3599	F	562 946-7524	16737
Menasha Packaging Company LLC	2653	D	562 698-3705	5437
Mid-West Fabricating Co	3714	E	562 698-9615	20402
Mission Microwave Tech LLC	3663	E	951 893-4925	18185
Moen Industries	3554	E	562 946-6381	14797
Montebello Container Co LLC	2653	E	562 948-3483	5439
Morgan Gallacher Inc	2842	E	562 695-1232	8656
Multi-Link International Corp	3086	E	562 941-5380	9870
Muscle Dynamics Corporation	3949	F	562 926-3232	23622

Employment Codes: A=Over 500 employees, B=251-500,
C=101-250, D=51-100, E=20-50, F=10-19

2019 California
Manufacturers Register

© Mergent Inc. 1-800-342-5647

1473

GEOGRAPHIC

	SIC	EMP	PHONE	ENTRY #
Nakamura-Beeman Inc	2521	E	562 696-1400	4956
Nashua Corporation	2621	D	323 583-8828	5313
Ncd Acquisition Inc (PA)	3081	E	203 565-8707	9720
ND Industries Inc	3452	E	562 926-3321	13078
Nelson Sports Inc	3149	E	562 944-8081	10507
New Century Machine Tools Inc	3541	F	562 906-8455	14396
New Global Food	2099	F	562 404-9953	2619
New Gordon Industries LLC	3469	E	562 483-7378	13254
New Technology Plastics Inc	2821	E	562 941-6034	7857
Nhk Laboratories (PA)	2834	D	562 903-5835	8305
Nikko Enterprise Corporation	2092	E	562 941-6080	2319
Northern California Labels Inc	2759	F	562 802-8528	7415
Oak Tree Furniture Inc	2511	D	562 944-0754	4729
Ocean Heat Inc	3842	F	951 208-1923	22782
Office Chairs Inc	2521	D	562 802-0464	4962
Oil Well Service Company (PA)	1389	C	562 612-0600	251
Olin Chlor Alkali Logistics	2812	C	562 692-0510	7666
Omega Precision	3599	E	562 946-2491	16806
Orange Cnty Name Plate Co Inc	3993	D	714 522-7693	23937
Our Powder Coating Inc	3479	F	562 946-0525	13626
P P Mfg Co Inc	3469	F	562 921-3640	13256
Pac-Com International	3291	F	562 903-3900	11300
Pacific Steam Equipment Inc	3443	E	562 906-9292	12404
Paco Plastics & Engrg Inc	3089	F	562 698-0916	10259
Pactiv Corporation	2679	E	562 944-0052	5723
Pactiv LLC	3089	D	562 693-1451	10262
Paramount Ready Mix Con Inc	3273	E	562 404-4125	11156
Paramount Roll Forming Co Inc	3441	E	562 944-6151	12226
Parker-Hannifin Corporation	3443	E	562 404-1938	12407
Paul Crist Studios Inc	3231	F	562 696-9992	10727
Pct-Gw Carbide Tools Usa Inc	2819	E	562 921-7898	7795
Pg Imtech of California LLC	3471	F	562 945-8943	13474
Phibro Animal Health Corp	2899	E	562 698-8036	9297
Phibro-Tech Inc	2819	E	562 698-8036	7797
Philatron International (PA)	3699	C	562 802-0452	20041
Pioneer Custom Elec Pdts Corp	3612	D	562 944-0626	17112
Plastiject LLC	3089	F	562 926-6705	10291
Plustek Technology Inc	3577	E	562 777-1888	15824
Polyvision Inc (PA)	2821	E	562 944-3924	7873
Post-Srgcal Rhab Spcalists LLC	3841	F	562 236-5600	22586
Precision Cutting Tools Inc	3545	E	562 921-7898	14667
Precision Mtal Fabrication Inc	3444	F	562 941-2169	12720
Precision Tube Bending	3728	D	562 921-6723	20914
Premier Media Inc	2711	F	562 802-9720	6018
Pressline Ink and Sup Co Inc	2796	E	562 907-1891	7655
Prima Lighting Corp	3645	F	562 407-3079	17556
Pronto Drilling Inc (PA)	3599	F	562 777-0900	16861
Proto Laminations Inc	3469	F	562 926-4777	13266
Pscmb Repairs Inc	3449	E	626 448-7778	12990
Ptm & W Industries Inc	3083	E	562 946-4511	9762
Qspac Industries Inc (PA)	2891	D	562 407-3868	9165
Quality Gears Inc	3566	F	562 921-9938	15244
Quality Lift and Equipment Inc	3537	F	562 903-2131	14344
Quality Vessel Engineering Inc	3443	F	562 696-2100	12412
R & D Racing Products USA Inc	3732	F	562 906-1190	21062
R & R Ductwork LLC	3444	F	562 944-9660	12729
R A Phillips Industries Inc	3715	B	562 781-2100	20510
R D Rubber Technology Corp	3061	E	562 941-4800	9573
Raytheon Company	3711	C	310 884-1825	20167
Rebas Inc	3537	C	562 941-4155	14345
Refunds Today LLC	7372	C	323 261-0240	25122
Reinhold Industries Inc (DH)	3089	C	562 944-3281	10330
Rev Co Spring Mfanufacturing	3495	F	562 949-1958	13801
Rogers Corporation	3069	D	562 404-8942	9671
Rohrback Cosasco Systems Inc (DH)	3823	D	562 949-0123	21645
Romeros Food Products Inc (PA)	2099	D	562 802-1858	2658
Rosemead Oil Products Inc	2992	F	562 941-3261	9448
Ross Bindery Inc	2789	C	562 623-4565	7614
Royal Flex Circuits Inc	3672	E	562 404-0626	18585
Rtm Products Inc	3312	E	562 926-2400	11417
S/R Industries Inc (HQ)	3949	F	562 968-5800	23646
Santa Fe Enterprises Inc	2752	E	562 692-7596	14569
Santa Fe Extruders Inc	3089	D	562 921-8991	10360
Santa Fe Footwear Corporation	3149	F	562 941-9689	10508
Seal Methods Inc (PA)	2672	D	562 944-0291	5578
Semiconductor Logistics Corp	3674	E	562 921-0399	19143
Serrano Industries Inc	3599	E	562 777-8180	16940
Shaw Industries Group Inc	2273	B	562 921-7209	2939
Shimada Enterprises Inc	3648	E	562 802-8811	17731
Sierra Foods Inc	3421	F	562 802-3500	11883
Sika Corporation	2899	E	562 941-0231	9305
Silenx Corporation	3823	F	562 941-4200	21655
Sisneros Inc	2522	E	562 777-9797	5000
Skyline Digital Images Inc	3993	E	562 944-1677	23977
SMI Ca Inc	3599	E	562 926-9407	16948
Southland Polymers Inc	2821	E	562 921-0444	7888
Spadia Inc	3645	F	562 206-2505	17562
Spec Tool Company	3812	C	323 723-9533	21436
Specialized Elevator Corp	3534	D	562 407-1200	14259
Spectratek Technologies Inc (PA)	2752	E	310 822-2400	7111
Sprayline Manufacturing	3563	F	562 941-5313	15137
Standridge Granite Corporation	3281	E	562 946-6334	11281
Star Die Casting Inc	3429	D	562 698-0627	11995
Steiner & Mateer Inc	2431	E	562 464-9082	4235
Steven Label Corporation	2759	F	562 906-2612	7496
Steven Label Corporation	2759	F	562 698-9971	7497
Stitch City Industries Inc (PA)	3552	F	562 408-6144	14780
Strand Energy Company	1311	C	562 944-9580	76
Strategic Prtg Solution Inc	2759	F	562 242-5880	7499
Sulzer Pump Services (us) Inc	7692	C	562 903-1000	25439
Sun Chemical Corporation	2893	E	562 946-2327	9211
Superior Food Machinery Inc	3556	E	562 949-0396	14888
Superior Printing Inc	2759	D	562 368-1700	7505
Superprint Lithographics Inc	2752	E	562 698-8001	7124
Surface Mdfication Systems Inc	3479	F	562 946-7472	13671
Sygma Inc	3545	F	562 906-8880	14683
T & S Die Cutting	3544	F	562 802-1731	14574
T-1 Lighting Inc	3646	F	626 234-2328	17648
Taokaenoi Usa Inc	2091	F	562 404-9888	2304
Tape & Label Converters Inc	2672	E	562 945-3486	5579
Teaze of California Inc	2339	C	562 944-8995	3516
Timken Gears & Services Inc	3462	E	310 605-2600	13114
Titan Medical Enterprises Inc	2834	F	562 903-7236	8417
Tj Giant Llc	2759	A	562 906-1060	7521
Tri-Star Dyeing & Finshg Inc	2231	D	562 483-0123	2795
Triangle Tool & Die Corp	3599	F	562 944-2117	17011
Trident Plating Inc	3471	E	562 906-2556	13523
Trojan Battery Company LLC (PA)	3692	B	800 423-6569	19825
Tru-Form Industries Inc (PA)	3469	D	562 802-2041	13289
True Design Inc	2434	F	562 699-2001	4359
Turbine Eng Cmpnents Tech Corp	3463	C	562 908-0200	13131
Twist Tite Mfg Inc	3452	E	562 229-0990	13087
United Drilling Co	3599	F	562 945-8833	17023
United Technologies Corp	3728	E	562 944-6244	20966
Universal Label Printers Inc	2759	E	562 944-0234	7530
US Armor Corporation	3842	E	562 207-4240	22837
US Motor Works LLC (PA)	3714	C	562 404-0488	20478
V&H Performance LLC	3751	D	562 921-7461	21148
Vantage Associates Inc	3089	D	562 968-1400	10429
Vantage Point Products Corp (PA)	3651	D	562 946-1718	17875
Vescio Threading Co	3599	D	562 802-1868	17040
Victor Wieteski	3679	F	562 946-9715	19783
Vomela Specialty Company	2752	E	562 944-3853	7170
Votaw Precision Tech Inc	3812	F	562 944-0661	21455
Wells Struthers Corporation	3443	F	814 726-1000	12441
Wesco Enterprises Inc	3089	F	562 944-3100	10437
West Coast Laminating LLC	2452	F	562 906-2489	4586
West Coast Machining Inc	3599	F	562 229-1087	17059
West Coast Plastics Inc	3089	F	562 777-8024	10438
Western Corrugated Design Inc	2653	E	562 695-5718	5465
Western Glove Manufacturing	3842	D	562 634-3720	22848
Western Screw Products Inc	3451	E	562 698-5793	13052
Westmont Industries (PA)	3536	D	562 944-6137	14304
Westrock Cp LLC	2653	C	714 523-3550	5468
Westrock Cp LLC	2631	D	714 523-3550	5371
Westrock Usc Inc	2653	F	562 282-4200	5477
Whiting Enterprises	3471	E	562 946-5100	13535
Whittier Mailing Products Inc (PA)	3579	F	562 464-3000	15916
Willick Engineering Co Inc	3844	F	562 946-4242	22945
Zenith Screw Products Inc	3451	E	562 941-0281	13054
Zumar Industries Inc	3993	D	562 941-4633	24010

SANTA MARIA, CA - Santa Barbara County

	SIC	EMP	PHONE	ENTRY #
A & F Metal Products	3469	F	805 346-2040	13152
Aegis Industries Inc	2851	F	805 922-2700	8873
Alan Johnson Prfmce Engrg Inc	3711	E	805 922-1202	20122
Alltec Integrated Mfg Inc	3089	E	805 595-3500	9935
American Bottling Company	2086	E	805 928-1001	2088
American Cleaner and Laundry	3582	E	805 925-1571	15927
Arrow Screw Products Inc	3599	E	805 928-2269	16284
Atlas Copco Mafi-Trench Co LLC (DH)	3564	C	805 352-0112	15144
B & B Label Inc	2759	F	805 922-0543	7244
Bottelsen Dart Co Inc	3944	F	805 922-4519	23411
C&D Zodiac Inc	3728	F	805 922-3013	20766
Cal Coast Acidizing Co	1389	F	805 934-2411	190
Central Coast Wine Warehouse (PA)	2084	F	805 928-9210	1685
Clendenen Lindquist Vintners	2084	F	805 937-9801	1693
Composite Plastic Systems Inc	3792	F	805 354-1391	21199
Engel & Gray Inc	1389	E	805 925-2771	207
Flood Ranch Company	2084	F	805 937-3616	1764
Gavial Engineering & Mfg Inc (HQ)	3672	E	805 614-0060	18490

Mergent email: customerrelations@mergent.com
1474

2019 California
Manufacturers Register

(P-0000) Products & Services Section entry number
(PA)=Parent Co (HQ)=Headquarters (DH)=Div Headquarters

	SIC	EMP	PHONE	ENTRY #
Gavial Holdings Inc (PA)	3679	F	805 614-0060	19549
Glb Investment Inc	3949	F	805 925-1971	23570
Greka Inc	1241	C	805 347-8700	19
Greka Integrated Inc (PA)	1382	E	805 347-8700	137
Hanson Aggregates LLC	1442	F	805 934-4931	364
Hvi Cat Canyon Inc	1389	C	805 621-5800	226
Impo International LLC	3144	E	805 922-7753	10497
Insight Management Corporation (PA)	3652	E	866 787-3588	17904
J & D Fabricating & Repair Inc	3469	E	805 928-9674	13228
Jackson Family Wines Inc	2084	E	805 938-7300	1825
Kenai Drilling Limited (HQ)	1381	E	805 937-7871	109
Krinos Foods LLC	2035	F	805 922-6970	918
Laguna County Sanatation Dist	2899	F	805 934-6282	9271
Lee Enterprises Incorporated	2711	C	805 925-2691	5911
Lindquist Robert N & Assoc (PA)	2084	F	805 937-9801	1862
Lockheed Martin Corporation	3812	A	805 614-3671	21329
Matthew Warren Inc	3493	E	805 928-3851	13751
Melfred Borzall Inc	3541	E	805 614-4344	14392
Mid-State Concrete Products	3272	E	805 928-2855	10957
Myogenix Incorporated	2834	F	800 950-0348	8288
Nicksons Machine Shop Inc	3599	E	805 925-2525	16790
North American Fire Hose Corp	3052	D	805 922-7076	9502
Okonite Company	3357	C	805 922-6682	11668
Osr Enterprises Inc	7372	E	805 925-1831	25039
PC Mechanical Inc	1389	E	805 925-2888	258
Pepsi-Cola Metro Btlg Co Inc	2086	D	805 739-2160	2165
Pictsweet Company	2038	B	805 928-4414	1010
Pratt Industries Inc	2621	E	805 348-1097	5326
Presquile Winery	2084	F	805 937-8110	1929
Prince Lionheart Inc (PA)	3089	E	805 922-2250	10309
Princeton Case West Inc	3089	E	805 928-8840	10310
Quintron Systems Inc (PA)	3661	D	805 928-4343	17985
Reyes Coca-Cola Bottling LLC	2086	A	805 614-3702	2198
Rlv Tuned Exhaust Products	3714	E	805 925-5461	20441
Santa Maria Enrgy Holdings LLC	1382	E	805 938-3320	149
Santa Maria Times Inc	2711	C	805 925-2691	6039
Scott Industries	3999	D	916 812-7217	24233
Signs of Success Inc	3993	F	805 925-7545	23972
Space Information Labs LLC	3812	F	805 925-9010	21435
Tognazzini Beverage Service	2086	F	805 928-1144	2228
Walker Creations	3842	F	805 349-0755	22845
Wasco Sales & Marketing Inc	3643	E	805 739-2747	17504
Zodiac Seat Shells US LLC	3728	A	805 922-5995	20980

SANTA MONICA, CA - Los Angeles County

	SIC	EMP	PHONE	ENTRY #
Abraxis Bioscience Inc	2834	D	310 883-1300	7990
Activision Blizzard Inc (PA)	7372	B	310 255-2000	24312
Activision Publishing Inc (HQ)	7372	A	310 255-2000	24314
Adolf Goldfarb	3944	E	310 451-1211	23404
Aft Corporation	2796	E	310 576-1007	7639
Americas Finest Products	2841	E	310 450-6555	8589
Apogee Electronics Corporation	3651	E	310 584-9394	17761
Auritec Pharmaceuticals Inc	2834	F	424 272-9501	8050
Automotive Lease Guide Alg Inc	2741	F	424 258-8026	6442
Berri Pro Inc	2087	F	909 964-1201	2243
Broadway AC Htg & Shtmtl	3444	E	310 829-3416	12511
C Publishing LLC	2741	E	310 393-3800	6456
C R W Distributors Inc	2013	F	310 463-4577	472
Carr Corporation (PA)	3844	E	310 587-1113	22930
Cequal Products Inc	2731	F	310 458-0441	6325
Clearlake Capital Group LP (PA)	2396	B	310 400-8800	3885
Coast Flagstone Co	3281	D	310 829-4010	11241
Cornerstone Ondemand Inc (PA)	7372	C	310 752-0200	24527
Design Journal Inc	2721	F	310 394-4394	6144
Dext Company of Maryland (DH)	2048	E	310 458-1574	1127
Draftday Fantasy Sports Inc	7372	F	310 306-1828	24577
Dsj Printing Inc	2752	F	310 828-8051	6794
Ecolight Inc	3999	F	310 450-7444	24086
Elkay Interior Systems Inc	2599	F	800 837-8373	5230
Elyptol Inc	2833	F	424 500-8099	7934
EMI Music Publishing Inc	2741	E	310 586-2700	6476
Engrade Inc	7372	F	800 305-1367	24612
Event Farm Inc (PA)	7372	E	888 444-8162	24629
Express Pipe & Supply Co LLC (DH)	3498	E	310 204-7238	13887
Extreme Group Holdings LLC	3652	F	310 899-3200	17896
Foot In Motion Inc	3842	F	312 752-0990	22731
Gayot Publications	2741	E	323 965-3529	6491
Go Green Mobile Power LLC	3621	F	877 800-4467	17200
Goodrx Inc (PA)	7372	F	310 500-6544	24705
Gosub 60	3577	F	310 394-4760	15750
Hallmark Labs LLC	2771	C	424 210-3600	7564
Hearst Corporation	2721	F	310 752-1040	6178
Hexacorp Ltd	7372	E	760 815-0904	24732
Hone & Strop Inc	2844	F	424 262-4474	8766
Hugo Boss Usa Inc	2311	C	310 260-0109	3030
Image Square Inc	2621	F	310 586-2333	5287

	SIC	EMP	PHONE	ENTRY #
International Processing Corp (DH)	2048	E	310 458-1574	1138
Jakks Pacific Inc (PA)	3944	B	424 268-9444	23435
Kingcom(us) LLC (HQ)	7372	C	424 744-5697	24832
Kona Bar LLC	2064	F	808 927-1934	1435
Lanza Research International	2844	D	310 393-5227	8786
Lincoln Iron Works	3312	E	310 684-2543	11405
Lorna Jane Usa Inc (HQ)	2339	E	310 828-0022	3456
Los Angles Tmes Cmmnctions LLC	2711	D	310 450-6666	5919
Lucky Brand Dungarees LLC	2325	F	310 587-3515	3082
Magna-Pole Products Inc (PA)	2542	F	310 453-3806	5153
Mammoth Media Inc	2711	D	310 393-3024	5936
Maui Toys	3949	E	330 747-4333	23615
My Dirty Jobs LLC	2841	F	310 393-5522	8598
Newlon Rouge LLC	2711	E	310 458-7737	5994
Observer Newspaper	2711	E	310 452-9900	6004
Omega Leads Inc	3679	E	310 394-6786	19670
Opiant Pharmaceuticals Inc	2834	F	301 598-5410	8319
Ovation R&G LLC (PA)	3663	E	310 430-7575	18209
Owl Territory Inc	7372	F	800 607-0677	25044
Patientpop Inc	7372	D	844 487-8399	25049
Pfizer Health Solutions Inc	2834	F	310 586-2550	8331
Phonesuit Inc	3663	E	310 774-0282	18218
Pranalytica Inc	3841	F	310 458-3345	22587
Preston Cinema Systems Inc	3861	F	310 453-1852	23189
Printing Palace Inc	2752	E	310 451-5151	7048
Proseries LLC	3949	F	213 533-6400	23630
Prototype Industries Inc (PA)	2741	F	310 255-0021	6559
Provivi Inc	2869	F	310 828-2307	9033
Purelife Dental	3843	F	310 587-0783	22903
Reconserve Inc (HQ)	2048	E	310 458-1574	1157
Red Bull North America Inc	2086	D	310 393-4647	2182
Ring LLC (HQ)	3612	B	800 656-1918	17118
Salesforcecom Inc	7372	E	310 752-7000	25143
Santa Monica Plastics Llc	3089	F	310 403-2849	10361
Santa Monica Propeller Svc Inc	3728	F	310 390-6233	20925
Scribble Press Inc	2741	F	212 288-2928	6577
SE Software Inc	7372	F	888 504-9876	25156
Solarreserve LLC (PA)	3433	E	310 315-2200	12088
Sonosim Inc	7372	F	323 473-3800	25201
Titan Gaming	3944	F	310 869-3326	23472
Tjeker LLC	3663	E	424 240-7696	18289
Transplant Connect Inc	7372	E	310 392-1400	25291
Ubm Canon LLC (DH)	2721	C	310 445-4200	6276
Universal Music Pubg Group	2741	E	310 235-4700	6611
Wholesome Valley Foods (PA)	2099	F	858 480-1543	2700

SANTA PAULA, CA - Ventura County

	SIC	EMP	PHONE	ENTRY #
Abrisa Industrial Glass Inc (HQ)	3211	D	805 525-4902	10586
Abrisa Technologies	3827	E	805 525-4902	22056
Aurora Casting & Engrg Inc	3369	D	805 933-2761	11769
Automotive Racing Products Inc	3429	D	805 525-1497	11932
Baker Petrolite LLC	1389	E	805 525-4404	183
Bendpak Inc	3559	C	805 933-9970	14921
California Resources Corp	1311	D	310 208-8800	42
Carbon California Company LLC	1311	D	805 933-1901	46
Comsat Inc	3663	E	805 933-4080	18075
Fowlie Enterprises Inc	2052	E	805 583-2800	1364
Granite Construction Inc	2952	D	805 879-0033	9405
Oil Well Service Company	1389	E	805 525-2103	253
Turtle Storage Ltd	2542	F	805 933-3688	5173
Weatherford International LLC	1389	E	805 933-0200	295
Weatherford International LLC	3498	D	805 933-0200	13911
Weber Orthopedic Inc (PA)	3842	E	805 525-8474	22846
Westlake Engrg Roto Form	3089	E	805 525-8800	10443
World Upholstery & Trim Inc	2396	F	805 921-0100	3930

SANTA ROSA, CA - Sonoma County

	SIC	EMP	PHONE	ENTRY #
23 Bottles of Beer LLC	2082	E	707 545-2337	1556
A W Direct LLC	2084	F	707 200-2859	1638
AEG Industries Inc	3728	E	707 575-0697	20707
Ahlborn Structural Steel Inc	3441	E	707 573-0742	12109
Air Monitor Corporation (PA)	3822	D	707 544-2706	21498
Alembic Inc	3931	F	707 523-2611	23352
Alluxa Inc	3827	E	707 284-1040	22058
Aluma USA Inc	3911	F	707 545-9344	23233
America Asian Trade Assn Prom	3646	D	408 588-0008	17583
Amys Kitchen Inc (PA)	2038	A	707 578-7188	979
Architectural Foam Products	3086	F	707 544-2779	9817
Barricade Co & Traffic Sup Inc (PA)	3499	F	707 523-2350	13922
Bcj Sand and Rock Inc	1446	F	707 544-0303	394
Bijans Protective Equipment	3949	D	707 528-4647	23520
Blentech Corporation	3556	D	707 523-5949	14839
Bo Dean Co Inc (PA)	1411	D	707 576-8205	300
Bohan & Canelis - Austin Crk	1429	F	707 632-5296	325
California Surveying & Draftin	3577	F	707 293-9449	15697
Conetech Custom Services LLC	2084	E	707 823-2404	1701

Employment Codes: A=Over 500 employees, B=251-500,
C=101-250, D=51-100, E=20-50, F=10-19

2019 California
Manufacturers Register

© Mergent Inc. 1-800-342-5647
1475

GEOGRAPHIC

Company	SIC	EMP	PHONE	ENTRY #
Creekside Managed Care	2834	F	707 578-0399	8126
Digital Music Corporation	3931	F	707 545-0600	23361
Dr Pepper/Seven Up Inc	2086	D	707 545-7797	2130
Duncan Design Inc	3993	F	707 636-2300	23858
Dynamic Pre-Cast Co Inc	3272	F	707 573-1110	10918
Dynatex International	3545	E	707 542-4227	14628
E M G Inc	3931	D	707 525-9941	23366
Endrun Technologies LLC	3821	F	707 573-8633	21470
Filtration Group LLC	3564	E	707 525-8633	15157
Flashco Manufacturing Inc (PA)	3356	E	707 824-4448	11628
Flex Products Inc	3827	C	707 525-6866	22076
Flowmaster Inc (HQ)	3714	F	707 544-4761	20336
Galvin Precision Machining Inc	3599	F	707 526-5359	16524
Gammon LLC	2721	F	707 575-8282	6170
Grape Links Inc	2084	F	707 524-8000	1794
Green Lake Investors LLC	3953	E	707 577-1301	23716
Guenoc Winery Inc	2084	F	707 987-2385	1800
Hybrinetics Inc	3612	D	707 585-0333	17099
Icore International Inc	3089	C	707 535-2750	10146
Iron Dog Fabrication Inc	3441	F	707 579-7831	12182
Itt LLC	3643	C	707 523-2300	17475
J RS Woodworks Inc	2431	F	707 588-8255	4170
Jackson Family Farms LLC (PA)	2084	F	707 837-1000	1820
Jackson Family Farms LLC	2084	F	707 836-2047	1821
Jackson Family Wines Inc (PA)	2084	D	707 544-4000	1824
James L Hall Co Incorporated (PA)	3679	F	707 547-0775	19592
James L Hall Co Incorporated	3677	F	707 544-2436	19342
Johns Formica Shop Inc	2542	F	707 544-8585	5150
Kendall-Jackson Wine Estates (HQ)	2084	B	707 544-4000	1840
Keysight Technologies Inc (PA)	3825	B	800 829-4444	21784
Kri Star Enterprises Inc (PA)	3272	E	800 579-8819	10944
Kuleto Villa LLC	2084	E	707 967-8577	1843
L-3 Cmmnications Sonoma Eo Inc	3861	C	707 568-3000	23175
L-3 Communications Wescam	3812	E	707 568-3000	21315
La Tortilla Factory Inc	2099	E	707 586-4000	2573
Laguna Oaks Vnyards Winery Inc	2084	F	707 568-2455	1850
Lancaster Vineyards Inc	2084	F	707 433-8178	1853
Light Guard Systems Inc	3625	F	707 542-4547	17285
Mac Thin Films Inc	3231	E	707 791-1650	10717
Macon Industries Inc	3699	F	707 566-2116	20011
Magazine Publishers Svc Inc	2721	D	707 571-7610	6213
Matanzas Creek Winery	2084	E	707 528-6464	1873
Medtronic Inc	3842	D	707 541-3281	22771
Medtronic Inc	3841	D	707 541-3144	22531
Metro Publishing Inc	2711	F	707 527-1200	5968
Microsemi Corporation	3674	C	707 568-5900	19014
Microsemi Frequency Time Corp	3661	D	707 528-1230	17964
Microsemi Semiconductor US Inc	3679	C	707 568-5900	19652
Mildara Blass Inc	2084	C	707 836-5000	1879
Milners Anodizing	3471	F	707 584-1188	13456
Molding Solutions Inc (PA)	3089	E	707 575-1218	10223
MS Intertrade Inc (PA)	2092	D	707 837-8057	2318
Neilmed Pharmaceuticals Inc	2834	B	707 525-3784	8295
Optical Coating Laboratory LLC (HQ)	3479	B	707 545-6440	13625
Osseon LLC	3841	F	707 636-5940	22576
P & L Specialties	3559	F	707 573-3141	15003
Pacific Hardwood Cabinetry	2434	F	707 528-8627	4333
Pacific Sun	2721	F	415 488-8100	6227
Pam Dee Publishing	2731	F	707 542-1528	6377
Paradise Ridge Winery	2084	F	707 528-9463	1914
Paragon Controls Incorporated	3822	F	707 579-1424	21521
Pellegrini Ranches	2084	F	707 545-8680	1920
Pellenc America Inc (HQ)	3523	E	707 568-7286	14091
Protonex LLC	3674	F	707 566-2260	19089
Quality Machine Engrg Inc	3599	E	707 528-1900	16872
Randal Optimal Nutrients LLC	2834	E	707 528-1800	8356
Ratebeer LLC	2741	D	302 476-2337	6564
Redwood Empire Awng & Furn Co	2394	F	707 633-8156	3806
Russian River Winery Inc	2084	F	707 824-2005	1961
Santa Rosa Press Democrat Inc (HQ)	2711	B	707 546-2020	6040
Santa Rosa Stain	3795	E	707 544-7777	21218
Scientific Molding Corp Ltd	3089	D	707 303-3041	10365
Selvage Concrete Products	3272	F	707 542-2762	11001
Sonoma Beverage Company LLC (PA)	2037	E	707 431-1099	967
Sonoma Photonics Inc	3677	E	707 568-1202	19364
Sonoma Valley Foods Inc	2032	E	707 585-2200	775
Spectraswitch Inc	3661	E	707 568-7000	17995
Srss LLC	3449	E	707 544-7777	12998
Stx Inc	3949	E	707 284-3549	23663
Supercloset	3423	E	831 588-7829	11912
Teh-Pari International	2899	F	707 829-9116	9311
Thermalsun Glass Products Inc	3231	F	707 579-9534	10733
Tonnellerie Radoux Usa Inc	2449	F	707 284-2888	4539
Trans-India Products Inc	2844	E	707 544-0298	8855
Trilogy Glass and Packg Inc	3231	E	707 521-1300	10734
Trivascular Inc (DH)	3841	E	707 543-8800	22657
Trivascular Technologies Inc (HQ)	3841	F	707 543-8800	22658
Tyco Simplexgrinnell	3569	F	707 578-3212	15371
Viavi Solutions Inc	3699	C	707 545-6440	20098
Wescam Usa Inc (HQ)	3812	F	707 236-1077	21456
Wildbrine LLC	2033	E	707 657-7607	871
Wright Engineered Plastics Inc	3544	D	707 575-1218	14592
Zelco Cabinet Mfg Inc	2517	F	707 584-1121	4902

SANTA YNEZ, CA - Santa Barbara County

Company	SIC	EMP	PHONE	ENTRY #
Bridlewood Winery	2084	E	805 688-9000	1667
Valley Oaks Industries	2521	F	805 688-2754	4973

SANTEE, CA - San Diego County

Company	SIC	EMP	PHONE	ENTRY #
A-I-M Plastics Inc	3089	F	619 562-1164	9917
ABC Mechanical Inc	3444	E	619 520-4643	12455
Aep-California LLC	3714	F	619 596-1925	20247
Alts Tool & Machine Inc	3599	D	619 562-6653	16263
Argee Mfg Co San Diego Inc	3089	D	619 449-5050	9954
Aymar Engineering	3444	E	619 562-1121	12496
Black Ruby Ventures LLC	3931	F	619 873-2000	23357
C & M Manufacturing Company	3082	E	619 449-7200	9738
CCM Enterprises	2541	E	619 562-2605	5045
CCM Enterprises (PA)	2541	D	619 562-2605	5046
Compucraft Industries Inc	3728	E	619 448-0787	20785
Computer Intgrted McHining Inc	3599	E	619 596-9246	16397
Cozza Inc	3599	F	619 749-5663	16405
Curapharm Inc	3841	E	619 449-7388	22414
Current Ways Inc	3629	F	619 596-3984	17339
D Benham Corporation	2752	F	619 448-8079	6776
Davis Gregg Enterprises Inc	3443	F	619 449-4250	12384
Decatur Electronics Inc	3812	F	619 596-1925	21286
Delstar Technologies Inc	3081	E	619 258-1503	9704
Discflo Corporation	3561	F	619 596-3181	15059
Ds Fibertech Corp	3567	E	619 562-7001	15258
Eastwood Machine LLC	3599	F	619 873-3660	16461
European Wholesale Counter	2541	C	619 562-0565	5059
Freds Fencing Inc	3496	F	619 562-5331	13831
Gondola Skate Mvg Systems Inc (PA)	3312	E	619 222-6487	11396
Hpf Corporation	3931	F	858 566-9710	23376
Impact Racing Inc (PA)	7692	E	619 449-9455	25411
Kevin Whaley	3496	E	619 596-4000	13838
Lhv Power Corporation (PA)	3679	E	619 258-7700	19621
LSI Corporation	3674	C	619 312-0903	18969
Mathy Machine Inc	3542	F	619 448-0404	14444
Novtek Inc	3825	F	408 441-9934	21820
Olson Irrigation Systems	3523	E	619 562-3100	14088
Pla-Cor Incorporated	3089	F	619 478-2139	10277
Praxair Inc	2813	E	619 596-4558	7709
Pure-Flo Water Co (PA)	2086	D	619 596-4130	2180
Quality Controlled Mfg Inc	3599	D	619 443-3997	16870
RCP Block & Brick Inc	3271	E	619 448-2240	10860
Rozendal Associates Inc	3812	E	619 562-5596	21420
S M L Industries Inc	3944	F	619 258-7941	23462
San Dego Prtective Coating Inc	3479	F	619 448-7795	13653
Scantibodies Laboratory Inc (PA)	2835	C	619 258-9300	8509
South West Lubricants Inc	2992	F	619 449-5000	9450
Specilty Mtals Fabrication Inc	2295	F	619 937-6100	2964
Stratedge Corporation	3674	E	866 424-4962	19194
T I B Inc	3544	F	619 562-3071	14575
Terra Nova Technologies Inc	3535	D	619 596-7400	14290
Vision Systems Inc	3354	D	619 258-7300	11611
Vortex Engineering LLC	3441	F	619 258-9660	12275

SARATOGA, CA - Santa Clara County

Company	SIC	EMP	PHONE	ENTRY #
Advanced Results Company Inc	3561	F	408 986-0123	15050
C-Scan Corp	3579	E	800 953-7888	15905
Chateau Masson LLC	2084	E	408 741-7002	1689
Electrofab Inc	3679	E	408 943-9380	19529
Inficold Inc	3564	F	408 464-8007	15160
Insight Solutions Inc	7372	E	408 725-0213	24777
Landmark Lcds Inc	3679	E	408 386-4257	19616
Lucidport Technology Inc	3643	E	408 720-8800	17481
Savannah Chanelle Vineyards	2084	E	408 741-2934	1967
Topi Systems Inc	7372	F	408 807-5124	25285
United Supertek Inc	3672	E	408 922-0730	18640

SAUSALITO, CA - Marin County

Company	SIC	EMP	PHONE	ENTRY #
Ascert LLC (PA)	7372	F	415 339-8500	24387
Bigtribe Corporation	7372	F	415 331-3687	24422
Boyd Lighting Fixture Co (PA)	3646	E	415 778-4300	17589
Bright Business Media LLC	2721	F	415 339-9355	6117
C P Shades Inc (PA)	2339	F	415 331-4581	3389
Eyvo Inc	7372	F	888 237-9801	24637
Humanconcepts LLC	7372	E	650 581-2500	24741
Lifefactory Inc	3221	E	415 729-9820	10621
Marin Magazine Inc	2721	F	415 332-4800	6214

	SIC	EMP	PHONE	ENTRY #
Onesun LLC	3674	F	415 230-4277	19060
Pasport Software Programs Inc	7372	F	415 331-2606	25048
Personal Awareness Systems	2741	F	415 331-3990	6550
Safe Catch Inc	2091	F	415 944-4442	2302
Sausalito Craftworks Inc	3911	F	415 331-4031	23315
Tazi Designs	2519	F	415 503-0013	4921
Tony Marterie & Associates (PA)	2335	E	415 331-7150	3342
Waggl Inc (PA)	7372	F	415 399-9949	25340

SCOTTS VALLEY, CA - Santa Cruz County

	SIC	EMP	PHONE	ENTRY #
Armored Mobility Inc	3083	E	831 430-9899	9747
Bell Sports Inc (HQ)	3949	D	469 417-6600	23518
Business With Pleasure	2752	F	831 430-9711	6711
Dakota Ultrasonics Corporation	3829	F	831 431-9722	22184
Digital Dynamics Inc	3823	F	831 438-4444	21571
Expert Semiconductor Tech Inc	3559	E	831 439-9300	14952
Fox Factory Holding Corp (PA)	3751	E	831 274-6500	21110
Fox Factory Inc (HQ)	3751	D	831 274-6500	21111
Innerstep BSE (PA)	3672	E	831 461-5600	18507
Interworking Labs Inc	7372	F	831 460-7010	24789
J A-Co Machine Works LLC	3599	F	831 429-8175	16599
Larkin Precision Machining	3599	F	831 438-2700	16678
Lintelle Engineering Inc	3699	F	831 439-8400	20006
Lumenetix Inc	3674	E	877 805-7284	18972
Maxtor Corporation (DH)	3572	D	831 438-6550	15566
Microtech Systems Inc	3695	E	650 596-1900	19870
Oxford Instruments X-Ray Tech	3679	D	831 439-9729	19678
Pacific Coast Products LLC (PA)	2087	E	831 316-7137	2275
Pacific Coast Products LLC	2087	E	831 316-7137	2276
Photoflex Inc	3861	F	831 786-1370	23187
Rkd Engineering Corp Inc	3674	F	831 430-9464	19128
Santa Cruz Mtn Pasta Fctry	2099	F	831 461-9900	2663
Scotts Valley Magnetics Inc	3677	E	831 438-3600	19361
Sessions	2339	E	831 461-5080	3493
Spraytronics Inc	3479	E	408 988-3636	13664
Sunopta Glbal Orgnic Ing Inc (DH)	2035	E	831 685-6506	934
Tapemation Machining Inc (PA)	3599	F	831 438-3069	16987
Thermo Kevex X-Ray Inc	3671	E	831 438-5940	18397
Threshold Enterprises Ltd (PA)	2833	B	831 438-6851	7975
Threshold Enterprises Ltd	2833	D	831 461-6413	7976
Threshold Enterprises Ltd	2833	E	831 461-6343	7977
Tr Engineering Inc	3561	F	831 430-9920	15096
Vista Outdoor Inc	3949	E	831 461-7500	23687

SEAL BEACH, CA - Orange County

	SIC	EMP	PHONE	ENTRY #
Boeing Company	3721	A	562 797-5831	20545
Boeing Company	3663	A	714 372-5361	18054
Cosmodyne LLC	3559	E	562 795-5990	14930
Dendreon Pharmaceuticals Inc	2834	F	562 253-3931	8136
Dendreon Pharmaceuticals LLC (HQ)	2834	E	562 252-7500	8137
Diversfied Tchncal Systems Inc (PA)	3679	E	562 493-0158	19515
Ftt Holdings Inc	3533	F	562 430-6262	14225
Hellman Properties LLC	1311	F	562 431-6022	63
Magtek Inc (PA)	3577	C	562 546-6400	15797
Modular Wind Energy Inc	3511	D	562 304-6782	14002
Samedan Oil Corporation	1311	B	661 319-5038	73

SEASIDE, CA - Monterey County

	SIC	EMP	PHONE	ENTRY #
Granite Rock Co	3273	E	831 392-3700	11114
Inter City Manufacturing Inc	3599	E	831 899-3636	16588
Lamorenita Tortillera & Mt Mkt	2099	F	831 394-3770	2575
Monterey County Weekly	2711	E	831 393-3348	5977
Monterey Signs Inc	2752	F	831 632-0490	6982

SEBASTOPOL, CA - Sonoma County

	SIC	EMP	PHONE	ENTRY #
Alasco Rubber & Plastics Corp	3069	F	707 823-5270	9585
Animal Lovers Pet Center	3999	F	360 683-0906	24039
KB Wines LLC	2084	E	707 823-7430	1837
Kosta Browne Wines LLC	2084	E	707 823-7430	1841
Kurtz Family Corporation	3089	F	707 823-1213	10185
Magito & Company LLC	2084	F	707 567-1521	1868
Manzana Products Co Inc	2033	E	707 823-5313	826
Marimar Torres Estate Corp	2084	F	707 823-4365	1870
Maxstraps Inc	2241	D	707 829-3000	2803
Occidental Manufacturing Inc	3199	F	707 824-2560	10576
OReilly Media Inc (PA)	2731	C	707 827-7000	6373
Paul Hobbs Winery LP	2084	F	707 824-9879	1917
Screamin Mimis Inc	2024	F	707 823-5902	694
Solmetric Corporation	3829	F	707 823-4600	22276
Sonoma West Publishers Inc (PA)	2711	F	707 823-7845	6050
Sprint Copy Center Inc	2752	F	707 823-3900	7114
Sumbody Union Street LLC	2844	F	707 823-4043	8849
Taft Street Inc	2084	F	707 823-2049	2007
Taylor Maid Farms LLC	2095	F	707 824-9110	2368
Thinkwave Inc	3695	F	707 824-6200	19886
Thomas Dehlinger	2084	F	707 823-2378	2014
Traditional Medicinals Inc (PA)	2099	C	707 823-8911	2690

SE!AD VALLEY, CA - Siskiyou County

	SIC	EMP	PHONE	ENTRY #
Mark Crawford Logging Inc	2411	F	530 496-3272	4000

SELMA, CA - Fresno County

	SIC	EMP	PHONE	ENTRY #
Fresno Valves & Castings Inc (PA)	3366	C	559 834-2511	11758
Harris Ranch Beef Company	2011	A	559 896-3081	439
Lee Central Cal Newspapers	2711	E	559 896-1976	5910
Lion Raisins Inc (PA)	2034	B	559 834-6677	885
Selma Pallet Inc	2448	E	559 896-7171	4506
Wood-N-Wood Products Cal Inc	2449	E	559 896-3636	4543
Xtreme Manufacturing LLC	3443	E	559 891-2978	12445

SHAFTER, CA - Kern County

	SIC	EMP	PHONE	ENTRY #
Baker Hghes Olfld Oprtions LLC	1389	F	661 834-9654	174
Baker Hughes A GE Company LLC	1389	F	661 834-9654	175
Baker Hughes A GE Company LLC	1389	D	661 831-7686	177
Blowout Tools Inc	1389	F	661 746-1700	186
California Farm Equipment Mag	3523	F	661 589-0435	14052
Cemex Cnstr Mtls PCF LLC	3273	E	661 746-3423	11074
Cummings Vacuum Service Inc	1389	D	661 746-1786	202
Elk Corporation of Texas	3272	C	661 391-3900	10921
Forterra Pipe & Precast LLC	3444	F	661 746-3527	12590
Frank Russell Inc	3599	F	661 324-5575	16513
Harbison-Fischer Inc	3533	F	661 399-0628	14227
Lufkin Industries LLC	3462	F	661 746-0792	13105
M-I LLC	1389	F	661 321-5400	235
McM Fabricators Inc	3441	C	661 589-2774	12205
Nikkel Iron Works Corporation	3523	F	661 746-4904	14086
Oil Well Service Company	1389	F	661 589-2333	252
Scientific Drilling Intl Inc	1381	F	661 831-0636	119
Scotts Cummings LLC	2873	F	661 387-9555	9072
Tryad Service Corporation	1389	D	661 391-1524	287
Tryınax	3498	F	661 391-1572	13908
U S Weatherford L P	1382	F	661 746-3415	155
Weatherford International LLC	3533	F	661 589-2146	14243

SHANDON, CA - San Luis Obispo County

	SIC	EMP	PHONE	ENTRY #
Svp Winery LLC	2084	F	805 237-8693	2004

SHASTA LAKE, CA - Shasta County

	SIC	EMP	PHONE	ENTRY #
Heritage Missional Community	2095	F	530 605-1990	2352
Knauf Insulation Inc	3296	C	530 275-9665	11335
Sierra Pacific Industries	2421	C	530 275-8851	4061

SHERIDAN, CA - Placer County

	SIC	EMP	PHONE	ENTRY #
Cemex Cnstr Mtls PCF LLC	3273	E	916 645-1949	11066
Entrussed LLC	2439	F	916 753-5406	4404

SHERMAN OAKS, CA - Los Angeles County

	SIC	EMP	PHONE	ENTRY #
American Printing & Design	2752	E	310 287-0460	6658
Bidchat Inc	7372	F	818 631-6212	24420
Caden Concepts LLC	2395	F	323 651-1190	3831
Designer Sound SEC Systems	3699	F	818 981-9249	19944
E Z Buy E Z Sell Recycler Corp (HQ)	2711	C	310 886-7808	5835
Eas Sensorsense Inc	2759	F	818 763-9186	7308
Envion LLC	3564	D	818 217-2500	15153
Hab Enterprises Inc	3053	F	310 628-9000	9533
Hd Garment Solutions Inc	2386	E	323 581-6000	3615
Inspired Properties LLC	2731	E	818 430-9634	6353
International Technologies	3577	F	818 382-2087	15769
Jesta Digital Entrmt Inc (HQ)	7372	F	323 648-4200	24816
Lisa and Lesley Co	2339	E	323 877-9878	3455
Lucky Strike Entertainment Inc (PA)	3949	E	818 933-3752	23610
Monterey Bay Beverage Co Inc	2033	E	818 784-4885	827
Navistar Inc	3711	D	818 907-0129	20161
Normal Centrix Inc	3999	E	310 715-9977	24191
Phil Blazer Enterprises Inc	2711	F	818 786-4000	6014
SA Hartman & Associates Inc	3861	E	818 907-9681	23195
Safcor Inc	3161	F	818 392-8437	10533
Sanguine Biosciences Inc	2836	D	818 926-5196	8579
Sidney Millers Black Radio Ex	2721	E	818 907-9959	6257
Spacetron Metal Billows Corp	3599	F	818 633-1075	16955
Steven Madden Ltd	3143	D	818 205-9563	10488
Vans Inc	3021	E	818 990-1098	9490
Vpro Inc	3993	F	818 905-5678	24002
Western Imperial Trading Inc	3911	F	818 907-0768	23331
Zalemark Holding Company Inc	3911	F	888 682-6885	23334

SHINGLE SPRINGS, CA - El Dorado County

	SIC	EMP	PHONE	ENTRY #
BBC Corp	2752	E	530 677-4009	6689
Foamtec LLC	3272	F	916 851-8621	10928
M & W Engineering Inc	3599	E	530 676-7185	16700
Pw Eagle Inc	3084	D	530 677-2286	9788
Sundance Uniform & Embroidery	2395	F	530 676-6900	3864
White Industrial Corporation	3548	F	530 676-6262	14744

SIERRA MADRE, CA - Los Angeles County

	SIC	EMP	PHONE	ENTRY #
Greg Ian Islands Inc	2541	E	626 355-0019	5064

	SIC	EMP	PHONE	ENTRY #
Hile Studio Inc	2512	E	626 359-7210	4783
Natus Inc	3845	F	626 355-3746	23021
Swissdigital USA Co Ltd	3999	F	626 351-1999	24261
Ward E Waldo & Son Inc	2033	F	626 355-1218	870

SIGNAL HILL, CA - Los Angeles County

	SIC	EMP	PHONE	ENTRY #
4x Development Inc	3469	F	562 424-2225	13150
AC Pumping Unit Repair Inc	1389	E	562 492-1300	164
Applied Business Software Inc	7372	F	562 426-2188	24372
Asphalt Fabric and Engrg Inc	3949	D	562 997-4129	23507
C J Precision Industries Inc	3599	F	562 426-3708	16346
Colt Services LP	1389	F	562 988-2658	199
Dawson Enterprises (PA)	3533	E	562 424-8564	14220
Flex-Mate Inc	3423	F	562 426-7169	11894
Floyd Dennee	2759	F	562 595-6024	7319
Gem Mobile Treatment Svcs Inc (HQ)	3822	E	562 595-7075	21513
Harper & Two Inc (PA)	3679	F	562 424-3030	19561
Hornedo Inc	3559	F	562 490-2120	14966
K & E Manufacturing Inc	3444	F	562 494-7570	12634
P T Industries Inc	3444	F	562 961-3431	12700
Pacific Valves	3491	D	562 426-2531	13730
Prosthetic and Orthotic Group (PA)	3842	F	562 595-6445	22798
R D Mathis Company	3313	E	562 426-7049	11430
Reldom Corporation	3699	F	562 498-3346	20056
Rode Microphones LLC	3651	C	310 328-7456	17851
Rossmoor Pastries MGT Inc	2051	D	562 498-2253	1316
Signal Hill Petroleum Inc	1382	E	562 595-6440	152
Southwest Products Corporation	3519	F	360 887-7400	14030
Tiger Cased Hole Services Inc	3523	F	562 426-4044	14109
United States Logistics Group	3715	F	562 989-9555	20515
Xcom Wireless Inc	3663	F	562 981-0077	18305

SILVERADO, CA - Orange County

	SIC	EMP	PHONE	ENTRY #
Program Data Incorporated	3825	F	714 649-2122	21830

SIMI VALLEY, CA - Ventura County

	SIC	EMP	PHONE	ENTRY #
Accell North America	3751	E	805 915-4900	21086
Advanced Metal Mfg Inc	3444	E	805 322-4161	12459
Aerovironment Inc	3721	E	626 357-9983	20536
Aquiesse	3999	F	805 583-4600	24041
Arxis Technology Inc	7372	E	805 306-7890	24386
Aveox Inc	3629	E	805 915-0200	17333
B & R Mold Inc	3544	F	805 526-8665	14483
Bemco Inc (PA)	3826	E	805 583-4970	21912
Boiron Inc	2834	F	805 527-9883	8085
CFS Tax Software	7372	D	805 522-1157	24484
Ci Systems Inc	3827	F	805 520-2233	22068
Cinemag Inc	3679	F	818 993-4644	19491
Circuit Express Inc	3672	F	805 581-2172	18450
Components For Automation Inc (PA)	3491	F	805 582-0065	13712
Computer Metal Products Corp	3444	D	805 520-6966	12536
Daicel Safety Systems (DH)	3714	F	805 387-1000	20308
Delt Industries Inc	3369	F	805 579-0213	11775
Dpa Labs Inc	3674	E	805 581-9200	18804
Embedded Systems Inc	3625	E	805 624-6030	17269
Emlinq LLC	3679	D	805 409-4807	19533
Enderle Fuel Injection	3714	E	805 526-3838	20326
Entech Instruments Inc	3826	D	805 527-5939	21957
Ericsson Inc	3663	F	805 584-6890	18100
Ferminics Opto-Technology Corp	3661	F	805 582-0155	17947
Fiberoptic Systems Inc	3357	E	805 579-6600	11661
Freedom Designs Inc	3842	C	805 582-0077	22733
Frontier Electronics Corp	3677	F	805 522-9998	19336
Globaluxe Inc	3999	F	805 583-4600	24111
Gold Coast Solar LLC	3674	E	310 351-7229	18861
Inkjetmadnesscom Inc	2893	F	805 583-7755	9202
Integrated MGT Concepts Inc	7372	E	805 778-1629	24782
Interscan Corporation	3824	E	805 823-8301	21689
Jaxx Manufacturing Inc	3679	E	805 526-4979	19595
JB Britches Inc	2325	D	818 898-4046	3077
Jessop Industries	3599	F	805 581-6976	16623
Jkf Construction Inc	2434	E	805 583-4228	4314
K & M Software Design LLC	7372	E	805 583-0403	24822
Key Material Handling Inc	3537	F	805 520-6007	14332
L3 Technologies Inc	3663	D	805 584-1717	18158
Laser Toner & Computer Supply	3955	F	805 529-3300	23732
Lee Aerospace Products Inc	3728	F	805 527-1811	20866
M Wave Design Corporation	3679	F	805 499-8825	19631
Mabel Baas Inc	3479	E	805 520-8075	13615
Maury Razon	2389	F	818 989-6246	3670
McBain Instruments Inc	3827	F	805 581-6800	22104
Meggitt	3728	C	877 666-0712	20881
Meggitt Safety Systems Inc (HQ)	3699	C	805 584-4100	20015
Meggitt Safety Systems Inc	3812	C	805 584-4100	21346
Meggitt-Usa Inc (HQ)	3728	B	805 526-5700	20884
Milgard Manufacturing Inc	3231	C	805 581-6325	10721

	SIC	EMP	PHONE	ENTRY #
Miller Electric Mfg Co	3548	C	805 520-7494	14733
Milodon Incorporated	3714	E	805 577-5950	20403
Nalco Company LLC	2899	F	805 584-9950	9287
Newman and Sons Inc (PA)	3272	E	805 522-1646	10961
Optical Physics Company	3827	F	818 880-2907	22115
Pacific Scientific Company (DH)	3812	E	805 526-5700	21378
Parks Optical Inc	3827	E	805 522-6722	22121
Pars Publishing Corp	2752	D	818 280-0540	7016
Pharmaceutic Litho Label Inc	2834	D	805 285-5162	8335
Piezo-Metrics Inc (PA)	3674	E	805 522-4676	19075
Plastic View Atc Inc	2591	F	805 520-9390	5206
Poly-Tainer Inc	3085	B	805 526-3424	9805
Puroflux Corporation	3677	E	805 579-0216	19355
PW Gillibrand Co Inc	1446	D	805 526-2195	398
Qualstar Corporation (PA)	3572	E	805 583-7744	15588
R F P & Welding	3714	F	805 526-3425	20433
Raindrip Inc	3523	E	818 710-4023	14095
Recycled Aggregate Mtls Co Inc (PA)	2951	E	805 522-1646	9395
Replacement Parts Inds Inc	3843	E	818 882-8611	22906
Revolution Lighting Tech Inc	3674	F	248 969-3800	19125
Rexnord Industries LLC	3556	C	805 583-5514	14881
Ricoh Prtg Systems Amer Inc (HQ)	3577	B	805 578-4000	15841
Rsa Engineered Products LLC	3728	E	805 584-4150	20923
Rugged Info Tech Eqp Corp (PA)	3577	F	805 577-9710	15844
S T E U Inc	3648	E	805 527-0987	17730
Saaz Micro Inc	3674	E	805 405-0700	19133
Scientific Cutting Tools Inc	3545	E	805 584-9495	14673
Scope City (PA)	3827	E	805 522-6646	22132
Seesmart Inc	3645	E	203 504-1111	17560
Senso-Metrics Inc	3829	F	805 527-3640	22265
Sensoscientific Inc	3823	E	800 279-3101	21654
Sheetmetal Engineering	3444	E	805 306-0390	12761
Sierra Aerospace LLC	3724	E	805 526-8669	20680
Special Devices Incorporated (HQ)	3714	B	805 387-1000	20452
Specialty Fabrications Inc	3444	E	805 579-9730	12769
Spragues Rock and Sand Company	3273	F	805 522-7010	11185
Stearns Scientific	2844	E	805 582-2710	8848
Thomas Craven Wood Finishers	2599	F	805 341-7713	5258
Timco/Cal Rf Inc	3678	E	805 582-1777	19425
Total Paper and Packaging Inc	2679	F	818 885-1072	5744
Vans Manufacturing Inc	3599	F	805 522-6267	17037
Ventura Technology Group	3674	E	805 581-0800	19252
Vibra Finish Co (PA)	3291	E	805 578-0033	11307
Weyerhaeuser Company	2653	C	800 238-3676	5478
Whittaker Corporation	3728	E	805 526-5700	20972
Xavient Info Systems Inc	7372	A	805 955-4111	25360
Xmultiple Technologies (PA)	3571	F	805 579-1100	15506
Xmultiple Technologies Inc	3643	A	805 579-1100	17506

SOLANA BEACH, CA - San Diego County

	SIC	EMP	PHONE	ENTRY #
Annona Company LLC	2043	F	858 299-4238	1054
Dare Technologies Inc (HQ)	3661	F	714 634-5900	17937
Expert Reputation LLC	7372	F	866 407-6020	24636
Future Wave Technologies Inc	2095	E	858 481-1112	2349
Kashi Company	2041	E	858 274-8870	1044
Mc Allister Industries Inc (PA)	2754	E	858 755-0683	7206
Sentynl Therapeutics Inc	2834	E	888 227-8725	8378
Thermo Fisher Scientific Inc	3826	B	858 481-6386	22036

SOLEDAD, CA - Monterey County

	SIC	EMP	PHONE	ENTRY #
Estancia Estates	2084	D	707 431-1975	1753
Golden State Vintners	2084	D	831 678-3991	1788
Hahn Estate	2084	D	831 678-2132	1802

SOLVANG, CA - Santa Barbara County

	SIC	EMP	PHONE	ENTRY #
Buttonwood Farm Winery Inc	2084	F	805 688-3032	1672
Graphic Systems	2759	F	805 686-0705	7330
Rideau Vineyard LLC	2084	F	805 688-0717	1948
Ynez Corporation	2711	F	805 688-5522	6093

SOMERSET, CA - El Dorado County

	SIC	EMP	PHONE	ENTRY #
Latcham Granite Inc	2084	F	530 620-6642	1858
Perry Creek Winery	2084	F	530 620-5175	1923

SOMIS, CA - Ventura County

	SIC	EMP	PHONE	ENTRY #
Dudes Brewing Company	2082	E	424 271-2915	1588
Hagle Lumber Company Inc	2421	E	805 987-3887	4037
Roman Kruchowhy	3679	F	805 386-7939	19711

SONOMA, CA - Sonoma County

	SIC	EMP	PHONE	ENTRY #
3 Badge Beverage Corporation	2084	F	707 343-1167	1634
All-Truss Inc	2439	E	707 938-5595	4389
Arbor Fence Inc	3446	F	707 938-3133	12832
Bonneau Wines LLC	2084	F	707 996-0420	1663
Briggs & Sons	2541	F	707 938-4325	5041
CCL Label Inc	3999	F	707 938-7800	24062
Collotype Labels USA Inc	2759	F	707 931-7400	7278

Mergent email: customerrelations@mergent.com

2019 California
Manufacturers Register

(P-0000) Products & Services Section entry number
(PA)=Parent Co (HQ)=Headquarters (DH)=Div Headquarters

1478

Company	SIC	EMP	PHONE	ENTRY #
Convergent Mobile Inc	3674	F	707 343-1200	18783
Diageo North America Inc	2084	D	707 939-6200	1724
Dnmc	3545	E	707 935-0353	14626
El Pelado LLC	2448	E	707 938-2877	4469
Estate Cheese Group LLC (PA)	2022	E	707 996-1000	572
Franciscan Vineyards Inc	2084	C	707 938-1960	1770
Freixenet Sonoma Caves Inc	2084	E	707 996-4981	1776
Golden West Glass	3231	F	707 939-9604	10702
Groskopf Warehouse & Logistics	2084	F	707 939-3100	1798
Hanzell Vineyards	2084	F	707 996-3860	1806
Hawaii Pacific Teleport LP	3663	F	707 938-7057	18123
Homewood Winery	2084	F	707 996-6353	1812
Innerstave LLC	2449	E	707 996-8781	4524
Krave Pure Foods Inc	2013	D	707 939-9176	501
La Villeta De Sonoma	3443	E	707 939-9392	12395
Larson Family Winery Inc	2084	F	707 938-3031	1856
Laura Chenels Chevre Inc	2022	D	707 996-4477	585
Marinpak	2099	F	707 996-3931	2596
Mike Fellows	2396	E	707 938-0278	3907
Monica Bruce Designs Inc	2396	E	707 938-0278	3908
Nicholson Ranch LLC	2084	E	707 938-8822	1899
Olive Press LLC (PA)	2079	E	707 939-8900	1550
Opal Moon Winery LLC	2084	F	707 996-0420	1905
Patz and Hall Wine Company (DH)	2084	F	707 265-7700	1916
Peregrine Mobile Bottling LLC	2086	F	707 637-7584	2178
Rams Gate Winery LLC	2084	E	707 721-8700	1937
Robledo Family Winery Inc (PA)	2084	F	707 939-6903	1953
Sebastiani Vineyards Inc	2084	D	707 938-5532	1970
Soft Flex Co	3315	E	707 938-3539	11457
Sonoma Access Ctrl Systems Inc	3446	E	707 935-3458	12892
Sonoma Gourmet Inc	2035	E	707 939-3700	933
Sonoma Index-Tribune	2711	D	707 938-2111	6049
Sonoma International	3944	D	707 935-0710	23466
Sonoma Pacific Company LLC	2448	D	707 938-2877	4507
Sonoma Pins Etc Corporation	2759	D	707 996-9956	7489
Stone Edge Winery LLC	2084	F	707 935-6520	1998
Three Sticks Wines LLC	2084	F	707 996-3328	2017
Toneleria Nacional Usa Inc	2429	F	707 501-8728	4093
Treasury Chateau & Estates	2084	F	707 996-5870	2020
Vineburg Wine Company Inc (PA)	2084	E	707 938-5277	2044
Vintage Point LLC	2084	F	707 939-6766	2046
Vode Lighting LLC	3645	F	707 996-9898	17568
Wine Communications Group	2721	F	707 939-0822	6292

SONORA, CA - Tuolumne County

Company	SIC	EMP	PHONE	ENTRY #
Alderman Timber Company Inc	2411	F	209 532-9636	3976
Bimbo Bakeries Usa Inc	2051	D	209 532-5185	1202
Birchwood Cabinets Sonora Inc	2434	F	209 532-1417	4275
J M Boone & Sons	3281	F	209 532-2506	11257
Kinematic Automation Inc	3841	D	209 532-3200	22504
L K Lehman Trucking	3272	E	209 532-5586	10947
O M Jones Inc	3679	E	209 532-1008	19666
Sandvik Thermal Process Inc	3559	D	209 533-1990	15027
Treat Enterprises	3541	F	209 532-2220	14419
Uv Skinz Inc	2329	F	209 536-9200	3202

SOQUEL, CA - Santa Cruz County

Company	SIC	EMP	PHONE	ENTRY #
Design Octaves	3089	E	831 464-8500	10067
Junopacific Inc	3089	C	831 462-1141	10174
Messana Inc	3567	F	855 729-6244	15269

SOUTH DOS PALOS, CA - Merced County

Company	SIC	EMP	PHONE	ENTRY #
Koda Farms Inc	2044	E	209 392-2191	1085
Koda Farms Milling Inc	2044	E	209 392-2191	1086

SOUTH EL MONTE, CA - Los Angeles County

Company	SIC	EMP	PHONE	ENTRY #
Abacus Powder Coating	3479	E	626 443-7556	13538
Al-Mag Heat Treat	3398	F	626 442-8570	11792
Amro Fabricating Corporation (PA)	3728	C	626 579-2200	20735
Antaeus Fashions Group Inc	2329	E	626 452-0797	3136
Asia Plastics	2673	F	626 448-8100	5587
BCI Inc	3599	F	626 579-4234	16312
Best Industrial Supply	3537	F	626 279-5090	14311
Bluetone Muffler Mfg Co	3714	E	626 442-1073	20271
Botanas Mexico Inc	2099	F	626 279-1512	2471
C W Cole & Company Inc	3646	E	626 443-2473	17590
Calfabco (PA)	3469	F	323 265-1205	13176
California Custom Caps	2353	E	626 454-1066	3560
California Ribbon Carbn Co Inc	3955	D	323 724-9100	23726
Calison Inc	2251	E	626 448-3328	2810
Cardinal Industrial Finishes (PA)	2851	D	626 444-9274	8889
Cardinal Paint and Powder Inc	2851	C	626 444-1201	8891
Clamp Manufacturing Co Inc	3429	F	626 579-5379	11945
CPC Group Inc	3089	F	626 350-8848	10047
Design Shapes In Steel Inc	3312	E	626 579-2032	11392
Dtbm Inc	2051	F	626 579-7033	1238
Eemus Manufacturing Corp	3479	F	626 443-8841	13580

Company	SIC	EMP	PHONE	ENTRY #
Electro-Mech Components Inc (PA)	3613	F	626 442-7180	17144
Electronic Auto Systems Inc	3651	F	626 280-3855	17798
Engineering Design Inds Inc	3599	F	626 442-1416	17476
Fabricast Inc (PA)	3679	E	626 443-3247	19539
Futon Express	2512	F	626 443-8684	4775
General Metal Engraving Inc	3953	E	626 443-8961	23715
Golden Color Printing Inc	2752	E	626 455-0850	6835
Halcore Group Inc	3711	D	626 575-0880	20148
Hoefner Corporation	3599	E	626 443-3258	16570
Hong Fat Dye Cutting Co	2789	E	626 452-0382	7601
Instyle Printing Inc	2342	E	626 575-2725	3549
Interntnal Mdction Systems Ltd	2833	F	626 459-5586	7950
Interntnal Mdction Systems Ltd	2834	A	626 442-6757	8230
Island Powder Coating	3479	E	626 279-2460	13605
J & L Cstm Plstic Extrsons Inc	3089	E	626 442-0711	10158
Kanamax International Inc (PA)	2834	F	213 399-3398	8243
Kinary Inc	2389	E	626 575-7873	3664
Kustom Lighting Products Inc	3648	E	626 443-0166	17706
La Mano Tortilleria	2099	F	626 350-4229	2567
Lee Pharmaceuticals	2844	D	626 442-3141	8787
Mama Sues Gourmet Pasta Inc	2099	E	626 241-2394	2593
Master Designs Sofa Inc	2512	F	626 444-1477	4797
Master Enterprises Inc	3444	F	626 442-1821	12655
Master Metal Works Inc	3446	E	626 444-8818	12880
Melkes Machine Inc	3599	F	626 448-5062	16738
Mikelson Machine Shop Inc	3728	F	626 448-3920	20887
Mikes Micro Parts Inc	3599	E	626 443-0675	16746
Mywi Fabricators Inc	3441	F	626 279-6994	12218
National Bright Lighting Inc	3648	E	909 818-9188	17718
Nicewell Inc	2326	F	626 455-0099	3115
Pacific Eagle USA Inc	3069	E	626 455-0033	9652
Pats Decorating Service Inc	2391	F	323 585-5073	3699
Pearson Engineering Corp	3479	F	626 442-7436	13632
Plastic Dress-Up Company	3089	D	626 442-7711	10285
Promotonal Design Concepts Inc	3069	D	626 579-4454	9664
Proto Space Engineering Inc	3599	F	626 442-8273	16862
R & R Rubber Molding Inc	3061	E	626 575-8105	9572
Ramon Lopez	2512	E	626 575-3891	4804
Robert P Martin Company	3315	F	323 686-2220	11453
Rocky Label Mills Inc	2241	E	323 278-0080	2805
Roselm Industries Inc	3663	E	626 442-6840	18240
S&H Melkes Inc	3492	E	626 448-5062	13745
Scodan Systems Inc	3462	F	626 444-1020	13113
Sense Fashion Corporation	2331	E	626 454-3381	3271
Smith Bros Strl Stl Pdts Inc	3312	E	626 350-1872	11421
South Alliance Industrial Mch	3599	F	626 442-3744	16952
Studio9d8 Inc	2253	E	626 350-0832	2856
Thienes Apparel Inc	2253	C	626 575-2818	2861
Tri Service Co Inc	2899	F	626 442-3270	9313
Tri-Fitting Mfg Company	3728	E	626 442-2000	20957
Unique Screen Printing Inc	2396	E	626 575-2725	3926
Vacco Industries (DH)	3494	C	626 443-7121	13777
Vclad Laminates Inc	3083	E	626 442-2100	9770
Vp Footwear Inc	3021	E	626 443-2186	9497
Wbp Associates Inc	2542	F	626 575-0747	5176
Westar Metal Fabrication Inc	3441	F	626 350-0718	12280

SOUTH GATE, CA - Los Angeles County

Company	SIC	EMP	PHONE	ENTRY #
2m Machining & Mfg Co	3825	F	323 564-9388	21698
Accurate Steel Treating Inc	3398	E	562 927-6528	11789
Anadite Cal Restoration Tr	3471	E	562 861-2205	13328
Arcadia Inc	3442	E	310 665-0490	12292
Astro Aluminum Treating Co Inc	3398	D	562 923-4344	11794
Bakercorp	3624	E	562 904-3680	17234
Bell Foundry Co (PA)	3949	D	323 564-5701	23517
Brookshire Tool & Mfg Co Inc	3599	F	562 861-2567	16333
Buddy Bar Casting Corporation	3365	D	562 861-9664	11726
C&C Metal Form & Tooling Inc	3469	E	562 861-9554	13174
Care Tex Industries Inc (PA)	2253	D	323 567-5074	2828
Caretex Inc	2865	D	323 567-5074	8960
Cimc Intermodal Equipment LLC (HQ)	3715	D	562 904-8600	20496
Conair Corporation	3631	D	323 724-0101	17364
Custom Leathercraft Mfg LLC (PA)	3199	C	323 722-2247	10573
Demenno/Kerdoon Holdings (DH)	2992	D	562 231-1550	9431
General Veneer Mfg Co	2435	E	323 564-2661	4377
Glasswerks La Inc (HQ)	3231	B	323 789-7800	10701
Golden Mattress Co Inc	2515	D	323 887-1888	4861
Graham Lee Associates Inc	2521	E	323 581-8203	4947
Granitize Products Inc	2842	E	562 923-5438	8645
Gwla Acquisition Corp (PA)	3211	E	323 789-7800	10598
Harbor Furniture Manufacturing (PA)	2512	E	323 636-1201	4782
Hughes Bros Aircrafters Inc	3544	E	323 773-4541	14525
In-O-Vate Inc	2952	F	562 806-7515	9410
Johns Manville Corporation	3296	D	323 568-2220	11334
K & L Precision Grinding Co	3599	F	323 564-5151	16637
Liberty Container Company	2653	C	323 564-4211	5434

	SIC	EMP	PHONE	ENTRY #
Lunday-Thagard Company (HQ)	2999	C	562 928-7000	9456
Lunday-Thagard Company	2952	E	562 928-6990	9412
M D H Burner & Boiler Co Inc	3564	F	562 630-2875	15165
Marquez Marquez Inc	2096	E	562 408-0960	2396
Master Body Works Inc	3713	E	323 564-6901	20214
Mercury Engineering Corp	3599	F	562 861-7816	16739
Metal Supply LLC	3441	D	562 634-9940	12208
Nextrade Inc (PA)	2299	E	562 944-9950	3011
Packaging Corporation America	2653	C	562 927-7741	5447
Poly Masters Industries Inc	3089	E	323 564-7824	10296
PQ Corporation	2819	F	323 326-1100	7799
Precision Forging Dies Inc	3544	E	562 861-1878	14561
Premco Forge Inc	3462	F	323 564-6666	13111
Productivity California Inc	3089	D	562 923-3100	10313
Saputo Cheese USA Inc	2022	C	562 862-7686	600
Sealy Mattress Mfg Co Inc	2515	C	323 567-7781	4884
Simons Brick Corporation	3297	E	951 279-1000	11342
Strategic Materials Corp	3325	E	323 567-2195	11527
Sunopta Fruit Group Inc (DH)	2087	F	323 774-6000	2282
Suregrip International Co	3949	D	562 923-0724	23667
T&T Precision Machining	3599	F	323 583-0064	16984
Techni-Cast Corp	3369	D	562 923-4585	11786
Three Brothers Cutting	2331	F	323 564-4774	3276
Tony Borges	3448	F	310 962-8700	12966
Tu-K Industries Inc	2844	E	562 927-3365	8856
Van Brunt Foundry Inc	3365	F	323 569-2832	11751
Viking Ready Mix Co Inc	3273	E	323 564-1866	11203
Win Soon Inc	2026	E	323 564-5070	740
World Oil Corp	1311	C	562 928-0100	88
World Oil Marketing Company (PA)	2911	C	562 928-0100	9376
YH Texpert Corporation	2339	F	323 562-8800	3529

SOUTH LAKE TAHOE, CA - El Dorado County

	SIC	EMP	PHONE	ENTRY #
Diamond Woodcraft	2431	F	530 541-0866	4144
Sierra-Tahoe Ready Mix Inc	3273	E	530 541-1877	11180
Terri Bell	7692	F	530 541-4180	25441

SOUTH PASADENA, CA - Los Angeles County

	SIC	EMP	PHONE	ENTRY #
Arroyo Seco Racquet Club	3069	F	323 258-4178	9588
Caesar Hardware Intl Ltd (HQ)	3999	E	800 306-3829	24054
Colormax Graphics Inc	2759	F	626 299-1289	7281
E M Emergency Power Supplies	3679	F	626 799-3549	19521
Finesse Apparel Inc (PA)	2339	E	213 747-7077	3419
Preco Aircraft Motors Inc	3694	F	626 799-3549	19845
Ximenez Icons	2392	F	310 344-6670	3758

SOUTH SAN FRANCISCO, CA - San Mateo County

	SIC	EMP	PHONE	ENTRY #
253 Inc	3444	F	650 737-5670	12447
Achaogen Inc (PA)	2834	C	650 800-3636	7994
Aclara Biosciences Inc	3829	D	800 297-2728	22155
Acme Bread Co	2051	D	650 938-2978	1172
Actelion Phrmaceuticals US Inc (DH)	2834	E	650 624-6900	7998
Airgas Usa LLC	2813	E	650 873-4212	7678
Alios Biopharma Inc	2834	E	650 635-5500	8010
Alvin D Troyer and Associates	3429	F	650 574-0167	11926
Amgen Inc	2834	E	650 244-2000	8024
B Metal Fabrication Inc	3444	E	650 615-7705	12500
Bai Inc	3728	F	650 872-1700	20757
Barrango (PA)	3599	F	650 737-9206	16307
Berlin Food & Lab Equipment Co	3821	E	650 589-4231	21458
Bimbo Bakeries Usa Inc	2051	A	650 583-5828	1198
Bimbo Bakeries Usa Inc	2051	E	650 583-3259	1204
Biocheck Inc	3841	E	650 573-1968	22368
Bonelli Enterprises	3442	E	650 873-3222	12302
Burton Ching Ltd	2392	E	415 522-5520	3712
Business Extension Bureau	2721	E	650 737-5700	6120
C&C Building Automation Co Inc	3829	E	650 292-7450	22173
Calithera Biosciences Inc	2834	E	650 870-1000	8094
Calpico Inc	3643	F	650 588-2241	17448
Catalyst Biosciences Inc (PA)	2834	F	650 266-8674	8105
Cav Distributing Corporation	3652	F	650 588-2228	17888
Cedarlane Natural Foods North	2099	E	650 742-0444	2483
Century Technology Inc	3672	F	650 583-8908	18446
City Baking Company	2051	D	650 589-8128	1223
Cytokinetics Incorporated (PA)	2834	C	650 624-3000	8132
Cytomx Therapeutics Inc	2833	D	650 515-3185	7932
D J Simpson Company (PA)	2851	E	650 225-9404	8900
Denali Therapeutics Inc	2836	F	650 866-8548	8545
Dolphin Press Inc	2759	F	650 873-9092	7303
Dvs Sciences Inc	3826	E	408 900-7205	21949
Essence Printing Inc (PA)	2752	D	650 952-5072	6810
Eureka Chemical Company (PA)	2899	F	650 873-5374	9247
Exelixis Inc	2834	C	650 837-8254	8153
First Databank Inc (DH)	2741	D	800 633-3453	6486
Five Prime Therapeutics Inc	2834	E	415 365-5600	8161
Five Prime Therapeutics Inc	2834	C	415 365-5600	8162

	SIC	EMP	PHONE	ENTRY #
Garnett Signs LLC	3993	F	650 871-9518	23886
Genentech Inc	2834	F	650 225-3639	8172
Genentech Inc (DH)	2834	A	650 225-1000	8173
Genentech Inc	2834	F	408 963-8759	8174
Genentech Inc	2834	F	650 225-3214	8177
Genentech Inc	2834	C	650 225-1000	8178
Genentech Usa Inc	2834	A	650 225-1000	8179
Georgia-Pacific LLC	2653	C	650 873-7800	5416
Giannini Garden Ornaments Inc	3272	E	650 873-4493	10934
Giant Horse Printing Inc	2752	F	650 875-7137	6833
Giustos Specialty Foods LLC (PA)	2041	E	650 873-6566	1040
Giustos Specialty Foods LLC	2041	E	650 873-6566	1041
Global Blood Therapeutics Inc	2834	C	650 741-7700	8193
Homestead Ravioli Company Inc	2032	E	650 615-0750	758
Hsin Tung Yang Foods Company	2013	F	650 589-7689	495
Immune Design Corp	2834	E	650 225-0214	8213
Intermune Inc (DH)	2834	C	415 466-4383	8225
Japanese Weekend Inc (PA)	2339	E	415 621-0555	3435
JC Metal	3499	F	650 827-1618	13951
Jesus Cabezas	2099	E	650 583-0469	2544
Kezar Life Sciences Inc	2834	E	650 822-5600	8247
Kk-Graphics Printing	2752	F	415 468-1057	6925
Lithotype Company Inc (PA)	2752	D	650 871-1750	6951
Magnolia Lane Soft HM Furn LLC	2392	E	650 624-0700	3731
Marjorie Baer Accessories	3911	E	650 872-2272	23295
Matsusada Precision Inc	3844	F	650 877-0151	22936
McLellan Equipment Inc (PA)	3713	D	650 873-8100	20215
Meyers Sheet Metal Box Inc	3444	F	650 873-8889	12673
Monogram Biosciences Inc	2835	B	650 635-1100	8498
Myokardia Inc	2834	D	650 741-0900	8289
New Hong Kong Noodle Co Inc	2098	E	650 588-6425	2433
New Method Fur Dressing Co	3999	F	650 583-9881	24188
Nexsteppe Inc	2048	E	650 887-5700	1150
Nexsteppe Seeds Inc	2869	E	650 887-5700	9024
Oneto Manufacturing Company	3444	F	650 875-1710	12696
Oric Pharmaceuticals Inc	2834	E	650 918-8818	8321
Petit Pot Inc	2099	E	650 488-7142	2637
Polywell Company Inc	3571	E	650 583-7222	15471
Portola Pharmaceuticals Inc (PA)	2834	C	650 246-7000	8341
Pre-Press International	2752	E	415 216-0031	7032
Principia Biopharma Inc	2834	D	650 416-7700	8345
Prothena Corp Pub Ltd Co	2833	F	650 837-8550	7966
Pyramid Graphics	2752	F	650 871-0290	7056
R Torre & Company Inc (PA)	2087	C	800 775-1925	2279
R Torre & Company Inc	2087	C	650 624-2830	2280
Rigel Pharmaceuticals Inc (PA)	2834	C	650 624-1100	8364
Rinat Neuroscience Corp	2834	E	650 615-7300	8365
Sees Candies Inc (DH)	2064	B	650 761-2490	1453
Sees Candy Shops Incorporated (HQ)	2064	F	650 761-2490	1454
Sequenta LLC	2835	D	650 243-3900	8511
Shannon Side Welding Inc	7692	E	415 408-3219	25434
Simpson Coatings Group Inc	2851	E	650 873-5990	8941
Sonoma Wine Hardware Inc	2084	E	650 866-3020	1981
Sp Controls Inc	3577	F	650 392-7880	15858
Sunesis Pharmaceuticals Inc (PA)	2834	C	650 266-3500	8399
Sutro Biopharma Inc (PA)	2834	C	650 392-8412	8403
T L Care Inc	2341	F	650 589-3659	3546
Tangle Inc	3944	E	650 616-7900	23470
Tanox Inc (DH)	2834	C	650 851-1607	8405
Tardio Enterprises Inc	2092	E	650 877-7200	2326
Theravance Biopharma Us Inc	2834	D	650 808-6000	8414
Theravnce Bphrma Antbotics Inc	2834	C	877 275-6930	8415
Thermo Fisher Scientific Inc	3826	F	650 876-1949	22037
Thermo Fisher Scientific Inc	3826	F	650 246-5265	22039
Thermo Fisher Scientific Inc	3826	C	650 638-6409	22041
Titan Pharmaceuticals Inc (PA)	2834	E	650 244-4990	8418
Tlm International Inc	3639	F	650 952-2257	17418
Tricida Inc	2834	D	415 429-7800	8421
Utap Printing Co Inc	2752	F	650 588-2818	7160
Vaxart Inc (PA)	2834	F	650 550-3500	8430
Vistagen Therapeutics Inc	2834	F	650 577-3600	8435
Vomela Specialty Company	3993	E	650 877-8000	24001
Windmill Corporation	2051	E	650 873-1000	1345
Wine Appreciation Guild Ltd	2731	F	650 866-3020	6410
Zion Health Inc	2844	E	650 520-4313	8870
Zymed Laboratories	3999	E	650 952-0110	24294

SPRING VALLEY, CA - San Diego County

	SIC	EMP	PHONE	ENTRY #
Arizona Paper Box Co Inc	2657	E	619 660-9566	5503
Crafted Metals Inc	3499	F	619 464-1090	13932
Deering Banjo Company Inc	3931	E	619 464-8252	23360
Euramco Safety Inc	3564	F	619 670-9590	15155
Everbrite West LLC	3993	F	619 444-9000	23870
Folex Co	2841	F	619 670-5588	8593
Gamboa Incorporated	3441	F	619 448-9995	12167
Hillholder Blocks By Modern	3272	F	619 463-6344	10938

Mergent email: customerrelations@mergent.com

2019 California
Manufacturers Register

(P-0000) Products & Services Section entry number
(PA)=Parent Co (HQ)=Headquarters (DH)=Div Headquarters

1480

	SIC	EMP	PHONE	ENTRY #
Homestead Sheet Metal	3441	E	619 469-4373	12177
Mailworks Inc	2621	E	619 670-2365	5310
Modern Stairways Inc	3272	E	619 466-1484	10958
Ram Centrifugal Products Inc	3564	F	619 670-9590	15173
Raphaels Inc	2499	F	619 670-7999	4645
Richardson Steel Inc	3441	E	619 697-5892	12236
S and S Carbide Tool Inc	3544	F	619 670-5214	14568
Safety America Inc	3851	F	619 660-6968	23120
San Diego Paper Box Co Inc	2657	F	619 660-9566	5509
Tru-Duct Inc	3444	E	619 660-3858	12797
Ttn Machining Inc	3599	F	619 303-4573	17018
Williams Aerospace & Mfg Inc	3728	E	619 660-6220	20973

SPRINGVILLE, CA - Tulare County

	SIC	EMP	PHONE	ENTRY #
CA-Te LP	3448	F	559 539-1530	12923

STANFORD, CA - Santa Clara County

	SIC	EMP	PHONE	ENTRY #
Leland Stanford Junior Univ	2741	C	650 723-5553	6517
Leland Stanford Junior Univ	2741	C	650 723-3052	6518
Leland Stanford Junior Univ	2741	D	650 723-4455	6519
Stanford Daily Publishing Corp	2711	E	650 723-2555	6059

STANTON, CA - Orange County

	SIC	EMP	PHONE	ENTRY #
Ace Bindery Inc	2789	F	714 220-0232	7592
Advanced Display Systems Inc	3799	F	714 995-2200	21220
All Metals Proc San Diego Inc	3471	C	714 828-8238	13317
Blaga Precision Inc	3599	F	714 891-9509	16326
Blake Sign Company Inc	3993	F	714 891-5682	23830
Cameron Welding Supply (PA)	7692	E	714 530-9353	25393
CJ Enterprises	3544	F	714 898-8558	14496
Continental Signs Inc	3993	F	714 894-2011	23847
Custom Pipe & Fabrication Inc (HQ)	3498	D	800 553-3058	13884
Cynthia Garcia	3728	F	714 897-4654	20789
Design Form Inc	3443	F	714 952-3700	12385
Electronic Connector Svc Inc	3643	E	714 750-9420	17464
Field Time Target Training LLC	3949	F	714 677-2841	23560
Inception Homes Inc	2451	F	714 890-1883	4562
M & G Custom Polishing	3471	E	714 995-0261	13446
Manti-Machine Co Inc	3599	F	714 902-1465	16711
Martinic Engineering Inc (DH)	3599	E	714 527-8988	16719
Muth Machine Works (HQ)	3599	F	714 527-2239	16778
Newcomb Spring Corp	3495	F	714 995-5341	13796
Newport Glass Works Ltd	3827	F	714 484-8100	22109
Newport Industrial Glass Inc	3231	E	714 484-7500	10722
Newport Optical Industries (PA)	3827	F	714 484-8100	22110
Oc Fleet Service Inc	3731	F	714 460-8069	21006
Orco Block & Hardscape (PA)	3271	D	714 527-2239	10855
Pac 21	3823	F	714 891-7000	21629
Precision Fastener Tooling	3542	F	714 898-8558	14452
Pure-Chem Products Company Inc	2841	F	714 995-4141	8606
RDfabricators Inc	3444	F	714 634-2078	12734
Sanitor Corporation	2844	F	714 799-2722	8834
Schaffer Laboratories Inc	3083	F	714 202-1594	9765
Sea & Sun Graphics Inc	2396	F	714 897-4020	3917
Signs and Services Company	3993	E	714 761-8200	23971
Stecher Enterprises Inc	3495	E	714 484-6900	13803
Two Thirty Two Productins Inc	3861	E	714 317-5317	23205
Urethane Science Inc	3089	F	714 828-3210	10422
Verlo Industries Inc	2542	F	714 236-2191	5175
Wce Products Inc	2822	F	714 895-4381	7909
West Coast Manufacturing Inc	3469	E	714 897-4221	13295
Wheeler Optical Lab	3851	F	714 891-2016	23131

STEVENSON RANCH, CA - Los Angeles County

	SIC	EMP	PHONE	ENTRY #
Phat N Jicy Burgers Brands LLC	2099	E	310 420-7983	2639

STOCKTON, CA - San Joaquin County

	SIC	EMP	PHONE	ENTRY #
A & A Ready Mixed Concrete Inc	3273	E	209 546-1950	11028
A & D Rubber Products Co Inc (PA)	3053	E	209 941-0100	9513
Advanced Indus Coatings Inc	3479	D	209 234-2700	13542
Advanced Polymer Tech LLC	3089	E	209 464-2701	9929
Aero Turbine Inc	3724	D	209 983-1112	20642
Aguda Wilson Ramos	3663	F	209 942-2446	18018
Aisin Electronics Inc	3625	C	209 983-4988	17248
Al Kramp Specialties	3648	E	209 464-7539	17668
All Good Pallets Inc	2448	E	209 467-7000	4450
Alpha Scientific Elec Inc	3679	F	510 782-4747	19439
Alpine Meats Inc	2013	E	209 477-2691	463
American Biodiesel Inc	2869	F	209 466-4823	8976
American Containers Inc	2653	E	209 460-1127	5383
Anderson Moulds Incorporated	3089	F	209 943-1145	9948
Anderson Signs	3993	E	209 367-0120	23816
Andrea Zee Corporation	3281	F	209 462-1700	11231
Applied Arospc Structures Corp (PA)	3728	C	209 982-0160	20738
Arandas Tortilla Company Inc	2099	E	209 464-8675	2455
Arrow Sign Co	3993	E	209 931-7852	23821
B & C Painting Solutions Inc	3479	E	209 982-0422	13556

	SIC	EMP	PHONE	ENTRY #
Bakakers Specialty Foods Inc	2041	F	209 234-5935	1033
Big GZ Pallets	2448	F	209 465-0351	4454
Bison Company	1381	F	209 474-8700	99
Buzz Converting Inc	2631	F	209 948-1341	5341
Cal Sheets LLC	2653	D	209 234-3300	5392
California Cedar Products Co (PA)	2499	E	209 932-5002	4611
California Cedar Products Co	2499	C	209 944-5800	4612
California Concrete Pipe Corp	3272	F	209 466-4212	10895
Calportland Company	3241	F	209 469-0109	10747
Carando Technologies Inc	3542	E	209 948-6500	14434
Caraustar Industries Inc	2631	C	209 464-6590	5344
Cencal Recycling LLC	2611	F	209 546-8000	5267
Central Pallets	2448	F	209 462-3019	4459
Concrete Inc	3273	E	209 830-1962	11095
Concrete Inc (DH)	3273	D	209 933-6999	11097
Conopco Inc	2844	C	209 466-9580	8721
Corn Products Development Inc (HQ)	2046	F	209 982-1920	1099
Cozad Trailer Sales LLC	3715	D	209 931-3000	20498
Custom Building Products Inc	3531	C	209 983-8322	14162
Cutter Lumber Products	2448	F	209 982-4477	4464
Cwi Trading	3644	F	209 981-7023	17511
Deck West Inc	3444	F	209 939-9700	12553
Del Rio West Pallets	2448	F	209 983-8215	4466
Dentonis Welding Works Inc (PA)	7692	E	209 464-4930	25399
Diamond Foods LLC (PA)	2068	A	209 467-6000	1487
Diamond Truck Body Mfg Inc	3713	F	209 943-1655	20201
Dietrich Industries Inc	3316	D	209 547-9066	11469
Dow Jones Lmg Stockton Inc	2711	C	209 943-6397	5833
DTE Stockton LLC	1389	F	209 467-3838	205
Electric Vehicles Intl LLC (PA)	3711	E	209 939-0405	20138
Enviroplex Inc	3448	D	209 466-8000	12930
Es West Coast LLC	3621	E	209 870-1900	17194
Exactacator Inc (PA)	3949	E	209 464-8979	23558
Farmer Bros Co	2095	E	209 466-0203	2348
Fleenor Company Inc	2621	E	209 932-0329	5282
Formurex Inc	2834	F	209 931-2040	8166
G & S Process Equipment Inc	3599	F	209 466-3630	16520
Gallien Technology Inc (PA)	3651	D	209 234-7300	17802
Gbm Manufacturing Inc	3253	F	888 862-8397	10783
Geiger Manufacturing Inc	3599	F	209 464-7746	16529
Gnekow Family Winery LLC	2084	F	209 463-0697	1785
Hackett Industries Inc	3556	E	209 955-8220	14856
Harbor Signs Inc	3993	F	209 463-8686	23892
Harley Murray Inc	3715	D	209 466-0266	20503
Herrick Corporation (PA)	3441	E	209 956-4751	12175
Herrick Corporation	3312	C	209 956-4751	11398
Highland Wholesale Foods Inc	2033	F	209 933-0580	805
IC Ink Image Co Inc	2759	E	209 931-3040	7347
Industrial Design Fabrication	3599	F	209 937-9128	16579
Inertia Engrg & Mch Works Inc	3613	F	800 791-9997	17147
Ingredion Incorporated	2046	D	209 982-1920	1100
Inland Valley Truss Inc	2439	F	209 943-4710	4414
International Paper Company	2653	F	209 931-9005	5427
Interplastic Corporation	2821	F	209 932-0396	7844
J & J Quality Door Inc	2431	E	209 948-5013	4169
J-M Manufacturing Company Inc	2821	C	209 982-1500	7850
Klein Bros Holdings Ltd	2068	E	209 465-5033	1492
Kp LLC	2759	F	209 466-6761	7370
Kraft Heinz Foods Company	2022	C	209 942-0102	582
Kraft Heinz Foods Company	2068	F	209 932-5700	1493
Kruger Foods Inc	2035	C	209 941-8518	919
Lam Enterprises Inc	2099	F	209 586-2217	2574
Lawleys Inc	2048	F	209 572-1700	1143
Lehigh Southwest Cement Co	3241	F	209 465-2624	10763
Lewis-Goetz and Company Inc	3052	F	209 944-0791	9500
Liberty Printing Inc	2752	E	209 467-8800	6946
Long Properties LLC (PA)	3462	E	209 948-4644	13104
Luus Family Corp	2015	E	209 466-1952	547
M & K Builders Inc	3448	F	209 478-7531	12940
Mark Ease Products Inc	3993	E	209 462-8632	23919
Martha Olsons Great Foods Inc	2052	F	209 234-5935	1370
Masonite International Corp	2431	F	209 948-0637	4189
Miller Products Inc	2672	D	209 467-2470	5571
Mina-Tree Signs Incorporated (PA)	3993	E	209 941-2921	23927
Murray Biscuit Company LLC	2052	E	209 472-3718	1372
National Pecan Shelling (HQ)	2068	F	800 952-7771	1499
Natural Std RES Collaboration	2731	E	617 591-3300	6368
Nmc Corporation	3678	E	209 986-0899	19404
Noll/Norwesco LLC	3444	C	209 234-1600	12692
Numeri Tech Inc	3599	F	209 463-1910	16799
O H I Company	3556	F	209 466-8921	14874
Off Lead Inc	3199	F	209 931-6909	10577
Oldcastle Apg West Inc	2951	F	209 983-1609	9391
Oldcastle Precast Inc	3272	E	209 235-1173	10966
Olive Corto L P	2079	F	209 888-8100	1549

Employment Codes: A=Over 500 employees, B=251-500,
C=101-250, D=51-100, E=20-50, F=10-19

2019 California
Manufacturers Register

© Mergent Inc. 1-800-342-5647
1481

	SIC	EMP	PHONE	ENTRY #
Pacific International Stl Corp	3449	E	209 931-0900	12986
Pacific Paper Tube Inc (PA)	2655	E	510 562-8823	5492
Pactiv LLC	2653	A	209 983-1930	5449
Pelton-Shepherd Industries Inc (PA)	2097	E	209 460-0893	2418
Pepsi-Cola Metro Btlg Co Inc	2086	E	209 367-7140	2170
Pre-Peeled Potato Co Inc	2099	F	209 469-6911	2640
Premier Coatings Inc	3479	D	209 982-5585	13640
Proco Products Inc (PA)	3069	E	209 943-6088	9662
Production Chemical Mfg Inc (PA)	2842	F	209 943-7337	8668
Quest Industries LLC	2759	E	209 234-0202	7457
Quiet Ride Solutions LLC	3089	F	209 942-4777	10319
Ramon Lopez	3711	F	209 478-9500	20166
Reyes Coca-Cola Bottling LLC	2086	F	209 466-9501	2194
Rgm Products Inc	2952	B	559 499-2222	9418
Robinson Farms Feed Company	2048	F	209 466-7915	1160
RR Donnelley & Sons Company	2752	B	209 983-6700	7090
S M S Briners Inc	2035	F	209 941-8515	931
San Joaquin Orthtics & Prsthtc	3842	F	209 932-0170	22806
Sardee Corporation California	3535	E	209 466-1526	14284
Sardee Industries Inc	3565	E	209 466-1526	15227
Scafco Corporation	3999	E	209 670-8053	24230
Sierra Lumber Manufacturers	2431	C	209 943-7777	4227
Simpson Manufacturing Co Inc	3291	B	209 234-7775	11303
Simpson Strong-Tie Company Inc	3449	D	209 234-7775	12994
Specialty Cellular Products Co	3299	F	925 454-3010	11371
Standard Industries Inc	2493	D	209 931-1277	4602
Stanley Electric Motor Co Inc	7694	E	209 464-7321	25467
Stockon Mailing & Printing	2752	F	209 466-6741	7116
Stockton Propeller Inc	3728	F	209 982-4000	20938
Stockton Tri-Industries Inc	3535	D	209 948-9701	14289
Street Graphics Inc	3993	F	209 948-1713	23982
Sumiden Wire Products Corp (HQ)	3315	E	209 466-8924	11458
Sunrise Fresh LP	2034	E	209 932-0192	897
Sust Manufacturing Company	3599	J	209 931-9571	16976
T M Cobb Company	2431	D	209 948-5358	4243
Taylor Company	2434	F	209 933-9747	4357
Teohc California Inc	3444	B	209 234-1600	12787
Tiger-Sul Products LLC	2819	F	209 451-2725	7808
Toufic Inc	2051	F	209 478-4780	1334
Transworld Printing Svcs Inc	2754	F	209 982-1511	7214
Tri Map International Inc	3571	F	209 234-0100	15501
Union Planing Mill (PA)	2431	E	209 466-9617	4250
Valimet Inc (PA)	3399	D	209 444-1600	11852
Valley Fresh Inc (HQ)	2015	E	209 943-5411	553
Value Products Inc	2841	E	209 345-3817	8613
Varni Brothers Corporation	2086	E	209 464-7778	2232
Vinotheque Wine Cellars	3585	F	209 466-9463	15999
Wardley Industrial Inc	3086	F	209 932-1088	9893
West Coast Orthotic/Prosthetic	3842	F	209 942-4166	22847
Western Organics Inc	2873	E	209 982-4936	9078
Western Square Industries Inc	3446	E	209 944-0921	12907
Westway Feed Products LLC	2048	F	209 466-4391	1170
Weyerhaeuser Company	2421	F	209 942-1825	4070
Whisperkool Corporation	2084	F	800 343-9463	2054
Wilmar Oils Fats Stockton LLC	2076	E	925 627-1600	1517
Wjlp Company Inc	3677	D	800 628-1123	19370
Wkf (friedman Enterprises Inc (PA)	3724	F	925 673-9100	20692

STRATHMORE, CA - Tulare County

	SIC	EMP	PHONE	ENTRY #
Cellu-Con Inc	2879	F	559 568-0190	9095
Michael D Wilson Inc	3499	F	559 568-1115	13959

STRAWBERRY VALLEY, CA - Yuba County

	SIC	EMP	PHONE	ENTRY #
Soper-Wheeler Company LLC (PA)	2411	E	530 675-2343	4014

STUDIO CITY, CA - Los Angeles County

	SIC	EMP	PHONE	ENTRY #
Chill Spot Inc	2024	F	818 762-0041	662
F R Industries Inc	2299	F	818 503-9143	2997
Fear of God LLC (PA)	2329	F	213 235-7985	3151
Hank Player Inc	2339	F	818 856-6079	3426
Harmony Infinite Inc	2599	F	818 780-4569	5235
Jbs Private Label Inc	2253	F	818 762-3736	2844
Mesgona Corporation	2741	E	310 926-3238	6527
Midrange Software Inc	7372	E	818 762-8539	24921
Players Press Inc	2731	E	818 789-4980	6381
Sugared + Bronzed LLC	2342	C	747 264-0477	3555

SUISUN CITY, CA - Solano County

	SIC	EMP	PHONE	ENTRY #
A & A Ready Mixed Concrete Inc	3273	E	707 399-0682	11027
Superior Sound Technology LLC	3842	F	707 863-7431	22826

SUN CITY, CA - Riverside County

	SIC	EMP	PHONE	ENTRY #
Dale C Sannipoli	3714	F	760 347-2033	20309
North County Sand and Grav Inc	1442	F	951 928-2881	376
Omnimax International Inc	3442	C	951 928-1000	12338
R & M Coils	3677	F	951 672-9855	19356

SUN VALLEY, CA - Los Angeles County

	SIC	EMP	PHONE	ENTRY #
Abbott Technologies Inc	3612	E	818 504-0644	17078
Accu-Grinding Inc	3545	F	818 768-4497	14595
Accurate Engineering Inc	3672	E	818 768-3919	18405
Acrylic Distribution Corp	2519	D	818 767-8448	4903
Alert Plating Company	3471	E	818 771-9304	13316
Alertlite Neon Co Inc	3641	F	818 767-2059	17419
American Grip Inc	3648	E	818 768-8922	17671
American Plastic Products Inc	3544	D	818 504-1073	14478
Architectural Foamstone Inc	2675	E	818 767-4500	5651
Aries Prepared Beef Company	2047	E	818 771-0181	1106
Art Mold Die Casting Inc	3544	E	818 767-6464	14480
ASC Group Inc	3674	C	818 896-1101	18723
Associated Ready Mix Concrete	3273	E	818 504-3100	11047
Avab America Inc	3625	E	707 778-8990	17255
AVX Filters Corporation	3569	D	818 767-6770	15298
B Cumming Company A Corp	3069	F	818 504-2571	9592
Ble Inc	1381	E	818 504-9577	100
Blue Can Water (PA)	2086	F	818 450-3290	2099
Brian Klaas Inc	2542	F	818 394-9881	5127
C A Buchen Corp	3441	E	818 767-5408	12123
C F Manufacturing	3714	E	818 504-9899	20280
Ca937 Afjrotc	3999	D	818 394-3600	24053
Cal Coast Stucco	3299	F	818 767-0115	11351
California Iron Design	7692	E	818 767-6690	25391
Calportland Company	3241	E	818 767-0508	10749
Cdeq	3229	E	818 767-5143	10638
Colorfx Inc	2752	E	818 767-7671	6743
Columbia Showcase & Cab Co Inc	2541	C	818 765-9710	5050
Coronado Manufacturing Inc	3728	E	818 768-5010	20787
Cosmetic Group Usa Inc	2844	C	818 767-2889	8728
De Leon Entps Elec Spclist Inc	3672	E	818 252-6690	18465
Desert Block Co Inc	2951	F	661 824-2624	9382
Dillon Aircraft Deburring	3471	E	818 768-0801	13387
Dip Braze Inc	7692	E	818 768-1555	25400
E-Z Mix Inc (PA)	2674	E	818 768-0568	5641
Earl Hays Press	2759	F	818 765-0700	7307
Emergent Group Inc (DH)	3842	D	818 394-2800	22726
Encore Cases Inc	3161	E	818 768-8803	10521
Excelity	3369	E	818 767-1000	11776
Florence International Company	3471	E	818 767-9650	13411
Forgiato Inc	3714	D	818 771-9779	20338
General Steel Fabricators Inc	3441	E	818 897-1300	12170
Gibbel Bros Inc	3273	E	323 875-1367	11111
Glenoaks Food Inc	2013	E	818 768-9091	487
Hanson Brass Inc	2511	E	818 767-3501	4702
Hey Baby of California	2339	E	818 504-2060	3428
Hollywood Film Company	3861	D	818 683-1130	23164
Industrial Battery Engrg Inc	3691	E	818 767-7067	19811
Insua Graphics Incorporated	2752	E	818 767-7007	6890
Jack J Engel Manufacturing Inc	3699	E	818 767-6220	19989
Jmi Steel Inc	3446	E	818 768-3955	12867
K V R Investment Group Inc	3559	D	818 896-1102	14978
Kenwalt Die Casting Corp	3363	E	818 768-5800	11698
Kimdurla Inc	3229	E	818 504-4041	10650
Kitcor Corporation	3469	E	323 875-2820	13239
Kleen Maid Inc	2392	E	323 581-3000	3728
Kuton Welding Inc	3548	E	818 771-0964	14728
L N L Anodizing Inc	3471	E	818 768-9224	13441
LA Gauge Co Inc	3599	D	818 767-7193	16672
La Propoint Inc	3499	E	818 767-6800	13953
Legacy Vulcan LLC	1442	E	818 983-1323	369
Legacy Vulcan LLC	3273	E	818 983-0146	11133
Leon Krous Drilling Inc	1381	E	818 833-4654	112
Lex Products LLC	3829	E	818 768-4474	22227
M & A Plastics Inc	3089	E	818 768-0479	10196
Monty Ventsam Inc	2431	F	818 768-6424	4196
Motion Industries Inc	3823	E	818 768-1200	21620
Normel Inc	2759	F	818 504-4041	7414
Nupla Corporation	3423	C	818 768-6800	11903
Ottos Pizza Stix Inc	2038	F	562 519-5304	1004
Over & Over Ready Mix Inc	3272	D	818 983-1588	10971
Pacesetter Fabrics LLC (HQ)	2299	E	213 741-9999	3012
Pacific Sky Supply Inc	3728	D	818 768-3700	20902
Pacobond Inc	2674	E	818 768-5002	5646
Paint Specialists Inc	2844	E	818 771-0552	13631
Pbh Marketing Inc	2844	E	818 374-9000	8811
Peen-Rite Inc	3398	F	818 767-3676	11827
Penguin Pumps Incorporated	3561	E	818 504-2391	15087
Pin Craft Inc	3961	E	818 248-0077	23757
Pipe Guard Inc	3432	E	818 765-2424	12042
Pipnsv Inc	2752	E	818 768-0550	7028
Pmc Inc (HQ)	3728	E	818 896-1101	20911
PMC Global Inc (PA)	3086	A	818 896-1101	9874
PMC Leaders In Chemicals Inc (HQ)	3086	C	818 896-1101	9875

Mergent email: customerrelations@mergent.com

1482

2019 California
Manufacturers Register

(P-0000) Products & Services Section entry number
(PA)=Parent Co (HQ)=Headquarters (DH)=Div Headquarters

Company	SIC	EMP	PHONE	ENTRY #
Polyplex Plastics of N Amer	3069	E	818 768-8866	9660
Precision Arcft Machining Inc	3599	E	818 768-5900	16853
Precision Tile Co	3272	F	818 767-7673	10981
Prime Plating Aerospace Inc	3471	E	818 768-9100	13481
Production Saw	3541	E	818 765-6100	14402
Pronk Technologies Inc (PA)	3825	F	818 768-5600	21831
Quikrete Companies LLC	3272	D	323 875-1367	10989
R L Anodizing	3471	E	818 252-3804	13487
Rico Corporation (HQ)	3931	E	818 394-2700	23384
Rico Holdings Inc	3931	C	818 394-2700	23385
Roan Mills LLC	2041	F	818 249-4686	1048
Rosco Laboratories Inc	3861	F	800 767-2652	23194
Schmidt Industries Inc	3471	D	818 768-9100	13501
Schneiders Manufacturing Inc.	3599	E	818 771-0082	16930
Sign Excellence LLC	3993	F	818 308-1044	23963
Soap & Water LLC	2844	E	310 639-3990	8845
Spartan Truck Company Inc	3713	E	818 899-1111	20230
Specialty International Inc	3469	D	818 768-8810	13280
Sscor Inc	3841	F	818 504-4054	22635
Sundial Industries Inc	3479	E	818 767-4477	13669
Sundial Powder Coatings Inc	3479	E	818 767-4477	13670
Superior Plating Inc	3471	E	818 252-1088	13516
Tatiossian Bros Inc	3144	D	818 768-3200	10504
Tecfar Manufacturing Inc	3599	F	818 767-0677	16989
Technical Heaters Inc	3052	F	818 361-7185	9509
Tee -N -Jay Manufacturing Inc	3444	E	818 504-2961	12786
Tempco Engineering Inc	3599	C	818 767-2326	16994
Travis American Group LLC	2431	C	714 258-1200	4248
Trimknit Inc	2241	F	818 768-7878	2808
Valley Mfg & Engrg Inc	3544	F	818 504-6085	14588
Viking Ready Mix Co Inc	3273	E	818 768-0050	11208
Walker Design Inc	3731	E	818 252-7788	21018
West Coast Custom Sheet Metal	3444	E	818 252-7500	12816
Zenith Manufacturing Inc	3728	E	818 767-2106	20977

SUNLAND, CA - Los Angeles County

Company	SIC	EMP	PHONE	ENTRY #
Engineered Products By Lee Ltd	3599	F	818 352-3322	16475
Richard Ray Custom Designs	3645	F	323 937-5685	17557
Sculptor Body Molding (PA)	3089	F	818 761-3767	10369

SUNNYVALE, CA - Santa Clara County

Company	SIC	EMP	PHONE	ENTRY #
Abekas Inc	3663	F	650 470-0900	18013
Accurate Technology Mfg Inc	3599	D	408 733-4344	16208
Accuray Incorporated (PA)	3841	C	408 716-4600	22312
Adeza Biomedical Corporation	2835	C	408 745-6491	8456
Adiana Inc	2834	E	650 421-2900	8001
Advanced Linear Devices Inc	3674	E	408 747-1155	18667
Advanced Microwave Inc	3679	E	408 739-4214	19435
Advenira Enterprises Inc	3559	F	408 732-3950	14904
Agilone Inc (PA)	3826	D	877 769-3047	21898
Ahn Enterprises LLC	3677	F	408 734-1878	19316
Alliance Fiber Optic Pdts Inc (HQ)	3229	D	408 736-6900	10631
Allvia Inc	3674	E	408 720-3333	18682
Alpha and Omega Semicdtr Inc (HQ)	3674	C	408 789-0008	18683
Alta Devices Inc	3674	C	408 988-8600	18684
AM and S Mfg Inc	3599	F	800 519-5709	16266
AMD International Sls Svc Ltd (HQ)	3674	E	408 749-4000	18689
AMD Ventures LLC	3674	C	408 749-4000	18690
American Liquid Packaging Syst (PA)	2821	E	408 524-7474	7819
Analog Bits	3674	E	650 279-9323	18697
Applied Materials Inc	3559	E	408 727-5555	14914
Applied Micro Circuits Corp	3572	E	408 523-1000	15512
Appvance Inc	7372	E	408 871-0122	24376
ARA Technology	3471	E	408 734-8131	13335
Arctic Wolf Networks Inc (PA)	7372	F	408 610-3263	24381
Aromyx Corporation	3822	F	650 430-8100	21499
Aruba Networks Inc	3663	F	408 227-4500	18043
Arvi Manufacturing Inc	3499	F	408 734-4776	13920
Asthmatx Inc	3841	D	408 419-0100	22347
Avantec Vascular Corporation	3841	E	408 329-5400	22350
Barrx Medical Inc	3841	D	408 328-7300	22354
Bayer Healthcare LLC	2834	D	408 499-0606	8069
Better Chinese Llc	2731	F	650 384-0902	6314
Bloom Energy Corporation (PA)	3674	B	408 543-1500	18748
Bondline Elctrnic Adhsive Corp	2891	E	408 830-9200	9131
Cal West Spcialty Coatings Inc	2851	F	408 720-7440	8886
Cantabio Pharmaceuticals Inc	2834	F	408 501-8893	8097
Cellfusion Inc	7372	F	650 347-4000	24480
Cepheid	3826	F	408 541-4191	21932
Cepheid (HQ)	3826	B	408 541-4191	21933
Changyoucom (us) LLC	7372	E	408 889-9866	24485
Clearlight Diagnostics LLC	2835	E	928 525-4290	8470
Cloudshield Technologies LLC	7372	F	408 331-6640	24505
Coadna Photonics Inc (DH)	3661	D	408 736-1100	17933
Colfax International	3571	E	408 730-2275	15401
Contactual Inc	7372	E	650 292-4408	24523
Covalent Metrology Svcs LLC	3821	F	408 498-4611	21466
Cutting Edge Machining Inc (PA)	3451	E	408 738-8677	13020
De Anza Manufacturing Svcs Inc	3679	D	408 734-2020	19510
Digilens Inc	3827	E	408 734-0219	22074
Dionex Corporation (HQ)	3826	B	408 737-0700	21945
Dionex Corporation	3826	D	408 737-0700	21946
Dolby Laboratories Inc	3663	F	408 730-5543	18089
Drivescale Inc	7372	E	408 849-4651	24580
Druva Inc (HQ)	7372	D	650 241-3501	24582
Ebr Systems Inc	3845	E	408 720-1906	22973
Egain Corporation (PA)	7372	C	408 636-4500	24595
Egain Corporation	7372	E	408 212-3400	24596
Elekta Inc	7372	E	408 830-8000	24603
Embolx Inc	3841	F	408 990-2949	22438
Engineered Outsource Solutions	3674	E	408 617-2800	18823
Enlighted Inc (PA)	3646	E	650 964-1094	17601
Entco LLC (DH)	7372	B	312 580-9100	24614
Enterprise Signal Inc	7372	D	877 256-8303	24617
Entit Software LLC (DH)	7372	F	801 861-7000	24618
ERC Concepts Co Inc	3469	E	408 734-5345	13201
Exp Computer	3829	E	408 530-8080	22197
Fairchild Semicdtr Intl Inc (HQ)	3674	E	408 822-2000	18840
Finisar Corporation (PA)	3661	E	408 548-1000	17951
Focus Enhancements Inc (DH)	3674	F	650 230-2400	18845
Fortinet Inc (PA)	7372	C	408 235-7700	24666
Fullfillment Systems Inc	2013	D	408 745-7675	486
Gannett Co Inc	2721	E	800 859-2091	6171
Gener8 LLC	3694	C	650 940-9898	19833
Glo-Usa Inc	3674	D	408 598-4400	18858
Gsi Technology Inc (PA)	3674	E	408 331-8800	18865
Guck Ariba	7372	C	650 390-1445	24715
Gulshan International Corp	3674	F	408 745-6090	18866
Harmonic Inc	3663	F	408 542-2500	18122
Hayes Manufacturing Svcs LLC	3544	E	408 730-5035	14524
Health Gorilla Inc	7372	E	844 446-7455	24721
Hewlett Packard Enterprise Co	7372	E	312 580-9100	24730
High Connection Density Inc	3678	E	408 743-9700	19394
Hologic Inc	3844	C	408 745-0975	22933
Horiba Instruments Inc	3829	D	408 730-4772	22214
Horvath Precision Machining	3599	F	510 683-0810	16574
HP Inc	3571	A	978 687-1501	15421
Hyatt Die Cast Engrg Corp - S	3363	E	408 523-7000	11695
I T M Software Corp	7372	E	650 864-2500	24744
Icad Inc	3061	D	408 419-2300	9567
Igs Inc	3211	F	408 733-4621	10599
Impac Medical Systems Inc (HQ)	7372	E	408 830-8000	24754
Impossible Aerospace Corp	3721	E	707 293-9367	20592
Indium Software Inc	7372	C	408 501-8844	24760
Infinera Corporation (PA)	3661	B	408 572-5200	17956
Infinera Corporation	3674	E	408 572-5200	18892
Inktomi Corporation (HQ)	7372	E	650 653-2800	24772
Innovalight Inc	3648	E	408 419-4400	17704
Insilixa Inc	3674	F	408 809-3000	18902
Intella Interventional Systems	3841	D	650 269-1375	22482
Intergen Inc	3699	F	408 245-2737	19985
Intuitive Srgcal Oprations Inc	3841	E	408 523-2100	22488
Intuitive Surgical Inc	3841	E	408 523-7314	22489
Intuitive Surgical Inc (PA)	3841	C	408 523-2100	22490
Ipolipo Inc	7372	D	408 916-5290	24801
Ismart Alarm Inc	3669	E	408 245-2551	18332
Ivanti Inc	7372	F	408 343-8181	24809
Jsl Partners Inc	2752	F	408 747-9000	6916
Jsr Micro Inc (HQ)	2869	C	408 543-8800	9017
Juniper Networks Inc (PA)	3577	B	408 745-2000	15775
Juniper Networks (us) Inc	3577	A	408 745-2000	15776
Kiana Analytics Inc	7372	F	650 575-3871	24830
Krytar Inc	3679	E	408 734-5999	19613
Kurdex Corporation	3577	F	408 734-8181	15782
Level 5 Networks Inc	3674	E	408 245-9300	18960
Liquid Robotics Inc (HQ)	3714	D	408 636-4200	20386
Liquid Robotics Federal Inc	3825	F	408 636-4200	21791
Lockheed Martin	3721	E	408 834-9741	20598
Lockheed Martin Corporation	3812	B	408 756-1868	21323
Lockheed Martin Corporation	3761	D	408 756-5751	21161
Lockheed Martin Corporation	3812	F	408 781-8570	21326
Lockheed Martin Corporation	3812	E	408 742-6688	21331
Lockheed Martin Corporation	3761	A	408 742-4321	21163
Lockheed Martin Corporation	3812	A	408 756-5836	21337
Lockheed Martin Corporation	3812	B	408 756-4386	21340
Lockheed Martin Corporation	3812	F	408 742-4321	21341
Locrian Networks Inc	3561	F	408 988-2288	15083
Logic Technology Inc (PA)	2672	F	408 530-1007	5568
Lotusflare Inc	7372	F	626 695-5634	24865
Luminus Inc (HQ)	3646	C	408 708-7000	17633
Luminus Devices Inc	3648	E	978 528-8000	17711

Company	SIC	EMP	PHONE	ENTRY #
Lyten Inc	3559	F	650 400-5635	14985
Material In Motion Inc (PA)	3571	C	650 967-3300	15448
Maui Imaging Inc	3845	F	408 744-1127	23006
Maxim-Dallas Direct Inc	3674	F	800 659-5909	18985
Mc Liquidation Inc	3845	E	408 636-1020	23007
Medtronic Spine LLC (DH)	3841	C	408 548-6500	22534
Meggitt (orange County) Inc	3812	F	408 739-3533	21345
Mellanox Technologies Inc	3674	C	408 970-3400	18990
Mellanox Technologies Inc (HQ)	3674	C	408 970-3400	18991
Meru Networks Inc (HQ)	3669	D	408 215-5300	18345
Micro Lithography Inc	3823	C	408 747-1769	21617
Microsemi Stor Solutions Inc (DH)	3674	D	408 239-8000	19018
Microsoft Corporation	7372	D	650 964-7200	24911
Microsoft Corporation	7372	C	650 693-1009	24914
Microsoft Corporation	3577	C	650 693-4000	15806
Mitel Networks Inc (DH)	3661	C	613 592-2122	17965
Mobile Crossing Inc	3812	F	916 485-2773	21349
Mobile Home Board	2721	E	408 744-1011	6220
Mobileops Corporation	7372	F	408 203-0243	24930
Motorola Mobility LLC	3663	D	847 576-5000	18191
MRr Moulding Industries Inc	2431	F	510 794-8116	4197
Myenersave Inc	7372	F	408 464-6385	24941
Myers-Briggs Company (PA)	2741	D	650 969-8901	6534
N-Tek Inc	3559	E	408 735-8442	14997
Nanostim Inc	3845	F	408 530-0700	23020
Netapp Inc (PA)	3572	A	408 822-6000	15572
Nexyn Corporation	3679	F	408 962-0895	19661
Ngcodec Inc	3674	E	408 766-4382	19042
Northrop Grumman Systems Corp	3721	B	408 735-2241	20604
Northrop Grumman Systems Corp	3721	A	408 735-3011	20613
Nova Measuring Instruments Inc	3825	F	408 746-9921	21819
Nuance Communications Inc	7372	C	781 565-5000	24974
Nxp Usa Inc	3674	E	408 991-2700	19048
Nxp Usa Inc	3674	E	408 991-2000	19049
Oakmead Prtg & Reproduction	2752	E	408 734-5505	6999
Oepic Semiconductors Inc	3674	E	408 747-0388	19053
Optibase Inc (HQ)	3577	E	800 451-5101	15819
Oracle Corporation	7372	B	650 607-5402	25009
Pacific Ceramics Inc	3264	E	408 747-4600	10821
Palm Inc (DH)	3663	B	408 617-7000	18215
Parallocity Inc	3695	E	408 524-1530	19876
Pcs Machining Service Inc	3599	F	408 735-9974	16835
Pharmacyclics LLC (HQ)	2834	C	408 215-3000	8336
Pictron Inc	7372	F	408 725-8888	25059
PMC-Sierra Us Inc	3674	F	408 239-8000	19077
Polargy Inc	3443	E	408 752-0186	12409
Polystak Inc	3674	E	408 441-1400	19082
Pport Com Inc	7372	F	516 393-6759	25076
Prodigy Press Inc	2759	F	408 962-0396	7449
Pyramid Semiconductor Corp	3674	F	408 542-9430	19092
Qualitek Inc (HQ)	3672	D	408 734-8686	18571
Qualitek Inc	3672	D	408 752-8422	18572
Quanergy Systems Inc (PA)	3812	D	408 245-9500	21383
Quicklogic Corporation	3823	D	408 990-4000	21641
R2 Semiconductor Inc	3674	E	408 745-7400	19113
Rae Systems Inc (DH)	3829	C	408 952-8200	22258
Rambus Inc	3674	E	440 397-2549	19114
Rambus Inc (PA)	3674	B	408 462-8000	19115
Rambus Inc	3674	E	408 462-8000	19116
Rank Technology Corp	3572	E	408 737-1488	15593
Raytheon Applied Signal (HQ)	3669	C	408 749-1888	18357
Realization Technologies Inc	7372	E	408 271-1720	25108
Redseal Inc	7372	D	408 641-2200	25120
Reflex Photonics Inc	3674	E	408 501-8886	19119
Samax Precision Inc	3599	E	408 245-9555	16927
Sass Labs Inc	7372	E	404 731-7284	25149
Savi Technology Holdings Inc (PA)	3663	E	650 316-4950	18245
Scigene Corporation	3841	F	408 733-7337	22616
Seagra Technology Inc	3577	E	408 230-8706	15846
Serious Energy Inc (PA)	2531	D	408 541-8000	5028
Sierra Circuits Inc	3672	C	408 735-7137	18603
Sign Solutions Inc	3993	F	408 245-7133	23965
Silicon Labs Integration Inc (HQ)	3674	F	408 702-1400	19152
Silicon Light Machines Corp (DH)	3674	F	408 240-4700	19153
Simplay Labs LLC	3841	E	408 616-4000	22624
Software Motor Company	3621	F	408 601-7781	17224
Spatial Photonics Inc	3674	E	408 940-8800	19185
Spiracur Inc (PA)	3841	D	650 364-1544	22634
St Jude Medical LLC	3841	B	408 738-4883	22636
Stanford Research Systems Inc	3826	C	408 744-9040	22022
Stealth Security Inc	7372	E	844 978-3258	25221
Summit Microelectronics Inc (HQ)	3674	E	408 523-1000	19197
Sunpreme Inc	3674	E	408 245-1112	19203
Supertex Inc (HQ)	3674	D	408 222-8888	19207
Surface Engineering Spc	3552	E	408 734-8810	14781
Takex America Inc	3674	E	877 371-2727	19212
Tangome Inc	3663	E	650 375-2620	18271
Tech-Star Industries Inc	3599	F	650 369-7214	16990
Telechem International Inc (HQ)	3944	E	408 744-1331	23471
Teledyne Technologies Inc	3674	B	408 773-8814	19220
Telepathy Inc	3577	E	408 306-8421	15866
Test Enterprises Inc (PA)	3823	E	408 542-5900	21667
Test Enterprises Inc	3825	E	408 778-0234	21873
Texas Instruments Incorporated	3674	E	408 541-9900	19228
Thomas West Inc (PA)	2392	E	408 481-3850	3752
Tipestry Inc	7372	F	650 421-1344	25280
Trane US Inc	3585	C	408 481-3600	15984
Trimble Inc	3812	F	408 481-8490	21445
Trimble Inc (PA)	3812	A	408 481-8000	21446
Trimble Inc	3812	F	408 481-8000	21448
Trimble Military & Advnced Sys	3812	D	408 481-8000	21449
Umc Group(usa)	3674	D	408 523-7800	19245
USI Manufacturing Services Inc	3577	D	408 636-9600	15880
Uvexs Incorporated	2893	F	408 734-4402	9214
V-Tech Manufacturing Inc	3599	F	408 730-9200	17028
Vention Med Design & Dev Inc	3841	F	603 707-8753	22670
Vnomic Inc	7372	F	408 890-2220	25338
Watergush Inc	3272	E	408 524-3074	11019
Way of The World Inc	2759	F	408 616-7700	7536
Westak Inc (PA)	3672	D	408 734-8686	18651
Xp Power LLC (DH)	3679	D	408 732-7777	19792
Zyrion Inc	7372	D	408 524-7424	25380

SUNOL, CA - Alameda County

Company	SIC	EMP	PHONE	ENTRY #
Cemex Cnstr Mtls PCF LLC	3241	F	925 862-2201	10751
Elliston Vineyards Inc	2084	D	925 862-2377	1749
Ge-Hitachi Nuclear Energy	2819	D	925 862-4382	7779

SUSANVILLE, CA - Lassen County

Company	SIC	EMP	PHONE	ENTRY #
Feather Publishing Company Inc	2711	F	530 257-5321	5849

SUTTER, CA - Sutter County

Company	SIC	EMP	PHONE	ENTRY #
Butte Sand and Gravel	1442	E	530 755-0225	348

SUTTER CREEK, CA - Amador County

Company	SIC	EMP	PHONE	ENTRY #
Amador Transit Mix Inc	3273	E	209 223-0406	11039
Ampine LLC	2521	C	209 223-1690	4928
Fuller Manufacturing Inc	3699	F	209 267-5071	19970
Sutter Gold Mining Inc	1041	F	209 736-2708	9
Usecb Joint Venture Inc	1041	F	209 267-5594	10

SYLMAR, CA - Los Angeles County

Company	SIC	EMP	PHONE	ENTRY #
Acufast Aircraft Products Inc	3728	E	818 365-7077	20703
Advanced Mnlythic Ceramics Inc	3675	C	818 364-9800	19289
Aged Timber Co Inc	2426	E	818 897-9663	4072
Anthony Doors Inc	3231	B	818 365-9451	10675
Anthony Doors Inc (DH)	3585	A	818 365-9451	15936
Arconic Inc	3334	E	818 367-2261	11538
Atlas Foam Products	3086	F	818 837-3626	9819
AWI Acquisition Company (PA)	3499	D	818 364-2333	13921
Bobbys Metal Finishing	3471	F	818 837-1928	13349
C & G Plastics	3089	E	818 837-3773	9996
C & S Plastics	3089	F	818 896-2489	9998
Clear Image Printing Inc	2752	E	818 547-4684	6734
Cosa Marble Co	1411	F	818 364-8800	302
Cotton Palm Inc	2329	E	818 890-3037	3142
Cylinder Head Exchange Inc	3714	F	818 364-2371	20305
Deiny Automotive Inc	3711	F	818 362-5865	20134
Dg Engineering Corp (PA)	3812	E	818 364-9024	21287
Drapes 4 Show Inc	2392	E	818 838-0852	3719
Eagle Access Control Systems	3625	E	818 837-7900	17267
Fat Cuts	3441	F	818 367-1540	12160
Fierrito Metal Stamping	3599	E	818 362-6136	16497
Fierritos Inc	3599	E	818 362-6136	16498
Fontal Controls Inc	3599	F	818 833-1127	16507
Gibraltar Plastic Pdts Corp	3089	E	818 365-9318	10117
Goldak Inc	3812	E	818 240-2666	21301
Houston Rubber Co Inc	3069	F	818 899-1108	9625
International Academy of Fin (PA)	2869	E	818 361-7724	9013
ISU Petasys Corp	3672	D	818 833-5800	18510
Johanson Dielectrics Inc (HQ)	3675	C	818 364-9800	19298
JW Manufacturing Inc	3452	D	805 498-4594	13075
Kay & James Inc	3599	F	818 998-0357	16647
L3 Technologies Inc	3812	C	818 833-2500	21316
L3 Technologies Inc	3663	C	818 367-0111	18161
Laser Operations LLC	3674	E	818 986-0000	18954
Llamas Plastics Inc	3728	C	818 362-0371	20867
Mason Electric Co	3728	B	818 361-3366	20875
MS Aerospace Inc	3452	B	818 833-9095	13077
Mulfat LLC	3571	E	818 367-0149	15464
Orange Bang Inc	2086	E	818 833-1000	2158

Mergent email: customerrelations@mergent.com
1484
2019 California
Manufacturers Register
(P-0000) Products & Services Section entry number
(PA)=Parent Co (HQ)=Headquarters (DH)=Div Headquarters

Company	SIC	EMP	PHONE	ENTRY #
Pacesetter Inc (DH)	3845	A	818 362-6822	23032
Pacific Fixture Company Inc	2542	F	818 362-2130	5159
Pacific Plastics Design Inc	3089	E	818 364-6677	10258
Professional Finishing Systems	3469	F	818 365-8888	13264
Promex International Plas Inc	3089	E	818 367-5352	10314
Qpc Lasers Inc	3845	F	818 986-0000	23036
Quallion LLC	3692	C	818 833-2000	19823
Ruiz Industries Inc	3172	F	818 582-6882	10570
Seaman Products of California	3728	F	818 361-2012	20927
Second Sight Medical Pdts Inc (PA)	3841	C	818 833-5000	22619
Sierracin Corporation (HQ)	2851	A	818 741-1656	8940
Sierracin/Sylmar Corporation	3089	F	818 362-6711	10375
Spectrolab Inc	3674	B	818 365-4611	19186
TMW Corporation (PA)	3728	C	818 362-5665	20952
Valley Business Printers Inc	2752	D	818 362-7771	7162
Valley-Todeco Inc (DH)	3452	E	800 992-4444	13089
Vallin Alida	3599	F	818 361-9020	17034
Ventura GL Inc	3281	F	818 890-1886	11285
Wayne Tool & Die Co	3312	E	818 364-1611	11427
Williams Foam Inc	2515	F	818 833-4343	4894
Williams Manufacturing Company	3494	F	818 898-2272	13780

TAFT, CA - Kern County

Company	SIC	EMP	PHONE	ENTRY #
Berry Petroleum Company LLC	1311	E	661 769-8820	26
Burke Je Construction	1389	F	661 745-4890	187
Dawson Enterprises	1389	F	661 765-2181	203
Gene Watson Construction A CA	1389	A	661 763-5254	216
Harbison-Fischer Inc	1389	F	661 765-7792	220
Jerry Melton & Sons Cnstr	1389	D	661 765-5546	228
Oil-Dri Corporation America	2842	F	661 765-7194	8659
St Louis Post-Dispatch LLC	2711	F	661 763-3171	6058
Taft Production Company	1241	D	661 765-7194	21
TRC Operating Company Inc	1311	F	661 763-0081	81
Watson ME Inc (PA)	1389	F	661 763-5254	293

TAHOE CITY, CA - Placer County

Company	SIC	EMP	PHONE	ENTRY #
James Betts Enterprises Inc	3732	E	530 581-1331	21047
Mount Rose Publishing Co Inc (PA)	2711	F	530 583-3487	5984
Tahoe House Inc	2051	F	530 583-1377	1330

TARZANA, CA - Los Angeles County

Company	SIC	EMP	PHONE	ENTRY #
Akm Fire Inc	3569	E	818 343-8208	15297
Avita Beverage Company Inc (PA)	2086	F	213 477-1979	2098
Cgm Inc	3915	E	818 609-7088	23341
Ggco Inc	3911	E	213 623-3636	23266
Hoffman Magnetics Inc	3695	E	818 717-5095	19865
Pavilion Products Inc	2392	F	818 345-4841	3742
Universal Merchandise Inc	2311	F	818 344-2044	3047
West Coast Clinical RES LLC	2834	F	818 776-0820	8441

TECATE, CA - San Diego County

Company	SIC	EMP	PHONE	ENTRY #
Benchpro Inc	2599	C	619 478-9400	5223
Broan-Nutone LLC	3433	C	262 673-8795	12059
Formula Plastics Inc	3089	B	866 307-1362	10105
Fusion Product Mfg Inc	3544	D	619 819-5521	14517

TEHACHAPI, CA - Kern County

Company	SIC	EMP	PHONE	ENTRY #
Adaptive Aerospace Corporation	3728	F	661 822-2850	20705
Chemtool Incorporated	2992	E	661 823-7190	9428
GE Wind Energy LLC	3511	C	661 823-6423	13997
Henway Inc	3965	F	661 822-6873	23767
Keller Classics Inc (PA)	2337	F	805 524-1322	3354
Legacy Vulcan LLC	3273	E	661 822-4158	11127
Lehigh Southwest Cement Co	3241	C	661 822-4445	10760
Pmrca Inc (PA)	2752	F	661 822-6760	7031
Sierra Technical Services Inc	3324	F	661 823-1092	11522
Stop Staring Designs	2335	E	213 627-1480	3337
Tehachapi News Inc (PA)	2711	F	661 822-6828	6068
Vintage Aero Engines	3732	F	661 822-4107	21067
Ward Automatic Machine Pdts	3451	F	661 822-7543	13050

TEMECULA, CA - Riverside County

Company	SIC	EMP	PHONE	ENTRY #
3-D Precision Machine Inc	3724	E	951 296-5449	20637
Aard Industries Inc	3495	E	951 296-0844	13781
Abbott Laboratories	2834	E	951 914-3000	7986
Abbott Vascular Inc	2834	B	951 941-2400	7988
Abbott Vascular Inc	3841	E	951 914-2400	22304
ABG Engineering Inc	3545	F	714 282-8204	14594
Advance Display Tech Inc	3674	E	951 757-0469	18664
Advanced Composites Engrg LLC	3089	E	951 694-3055	9927
Applied Statistics & MGT Inc	7372	E	951 699-4600	24374
Artificial Grass Liquidators	3999	F	951 677-3377	24044
ASPE Inc	3555	F	951 296-2595	14802
Axeon Water Technologies	3589	D	760 723-5417	16015
Basic Microcom Inc	3625	F	951 708-1268	17257
Bigfogg Inc (PA)	3585	F	951 587-2460	15941
Bomatic Inc (HQ)	3089	E	909 947-3900	9987

Company	SIC	EMP	PHONE	ENTRY #
Bostik Inc	2891	D	951 296-6425	9132
Brightwater Medical Inc	3841	F	951 290-3410	22383
Callaway Vineyard & Winery	2084	D	951 676-4001	1678
Canadas Finest Foods Inc	2037	D	951 296-1040	942
Carr Pattern Co Inc	3465	F	951 719-1068	13139
Celebration Cellars LLC	2084	F	951 506-5500	1684
Cengage Learning Inc	2731	F	951 719-1878	6322
Channell Commercial Corp (PA)	3661	D	951 719-2600	17931
Chh Lp	2099	E	951 506-5800	2487
Custom Art Services Corp	2752	F	951 302-9889	6772
Dale Chavez Company Inc	3111	F	951 303-0592	10458
Danza Del Sol Winery Inc	2084	F	951 302-6363	1714
Davids Natural Toothpaste	2844	F	949 933-1185	8734
Deans Certified Welding Inc	7692	F	951 676-0242	25398
Designer Sash and Door Sys Inc	3089	D	951 657-4179	10069
Egads LLC	3993	F	951 695-9050	23862
Electro-Support Systems Corp	3679	E	951 676-2751	19526
EMD Millipore Corporation	3826	C	951 676-8080	21954
EMD Millipore Corporation	3826	E	951 676-8080	21955
Falkner Winery Inc	2084	D	951 676-6741	1757
Flowserve Corporation	3561	C	951 296-2464	15066
Garmon Corporation	3999	D	951 296-6308	24104
Generic Manufacturing Corp	3556	F	951 296-2838	14853
Glasswerks La Inc	3211	E	800 729-1324	10593
Gold Prospectors Assn of Amer	2721	E	951 699-4749	6172
Gospel Recordings Inc	3652	E	951 719-1650	17901
Griffin Laboratories	3841	F	951 695-6727	22462
Hydro Flow Filtration Sys LLC	3955	F	951 296-0904	23770
Infineon Tech Americas Corp	3674	A	951 375-6008	18889
Intense Cycles Inc	3751	E	951 296-9596	21118
IPC Industries Inc (PA)	3799	F	951 695-2720	21233
Jwc Carbide Inc	3541	F	714 540-8870	14385
Kamm Industries Inc	3714	E	800 317-6253	20379
Label Productions of Cal	2759	F	951 296-1881	7376
Leonesse Cellars LLC	2084	F	951 302-7601	1860
Long Machine Inc	3599	E	951 296-0194	16692
Lost Dutchmans Minings Assn (DH)	1041	E	951 699-4749	6
Louidar LLC	2084	E	951 676-5047	1865
M & L Haight LLC	3199	E	951 587-2267	10575
MAC Products Inc	3312	D	951 296-3077	11406
Maurice Carrie Winery	2084	E	951 676-1711	1874
Medline Industries Inc	3842	F	951 296-2600	22770
Micro Grow Greenhouse Systems	3822	E	951 296-3340	21516
Mikes Precision Welding Inc	7692	F	951 676-4744	25422
Milgard Manufacturing Inc	3089	F	480 502-6000	10212
Molding Intl & Engrg Inc	3089	D	951 296-5010	10222
Monte De Oro Winery	2084	F	951 491-6551	1884
N C Industries	3599	F	951 296-9603	16780
National Sweetwater Inc	2899	E	951 303-0999	9289
Nimbus Water Systems	3589	F	951 984-2800	16081
North County Times	2711	E	951 676-4315	6000
Offerman Industries	3599	F	951 676-5016	16804
Opti-Forms Inc	3471	D	951 296-1300	13469
Opto 22	3679	C	951 695-3000	19675
Pachunga Gas Station	1389	F	951 506-4575	254
Pacific Barcode Inc	3555	F	951 587-8717	14821
Part Handling Engrg & Dev Corp	3845	F	951 308-4450	23035
Paulson Manufacturing Corp (PA)	3842	F	951 676-2451	22792
Polycraft Inc	2759	E	951 296-0860	7439
Premier Barricades	3499	F	877 345-9700	13965
Qc Manufacturing Inc	3564	D	951 325-6340	15172
Quality Control Solutions Inc	3829	F	951 676-1616	22253
Quicksilver Aeronautics LLC	3721	F	951 506-0061	20620
Ralc Inc	3721	F	951 693-0098	20621
Resina	3579	F	951 296-6585	15914
Robinson Printing Inc	2759	E	951 296-0300	7473
Scotts Temecula Operations LLC (DH)	3524	F	951 719-1700	14133
Source Bio Inc	2835	F	951 676-1000	8517
South Bay Cable Corp	3357	F	951 296-9900	11675
South Coast Winery Inc	2084	F	951 587-9463	1982
Spenco Machine & Manufacturing	3599	F	951 699-5566	16959
Stafford Soap Candle Co	3261	E	951 302-3476	10807
Stuart Cellars LLC	2084	F	951 676-6414	2000
Sunstone Components Group Inc (HQ)	3469	D	951 296-5010	13283
Surfacing Solutions Inc	3471	F	951 699-0035	13518
Tekvisions Inc (PA)	3829	F	951 506-9709	22283
Telsor Corporation	3825	F	951 296-3066	21866
Temecula Precison Fabrication	3549	F	951 699-4066	14769
Temecula Quality Plating Inc	3559	F	951 296-9875	15037
Temecula T-Shirt Printers Inc	2759	F	951 296-0184	7514
Temecula Valley Winery MGT LLC	2084	D	951 699-8896	2009
Tension Envelope Corporation	2677	C	951 296-0500	5679
The Valley Business Jurnl Inc	2711	F	951 461-0400	6069
Therapy Tubs	3088	F	951 553-7001	9912
Thompson Magnetics Inc	3679	F	951 676-0243	19763

Employment Codes: A=Over 500 employees, B=251-500,
C=101-250, D=51-100, E=20-50, F=10-19

2019 California
Manufacturers Register

© Mergent Inc. 1-800-342-5647
1485

GEOGRAPHIC

	SIC	EMP	PHONE	ENTRY #
Thornton Winery	2084	D	951 699-0099	2016
Top Heavy Clothing Company Inc **(PA)**	2321	D	951 442-8839	3062
Tortilleria Temecula	2099	F	951 676-5272	2689
Tradeincom Inc	2521	F	951 296-5566	4971
Transducer Techniques LLC	3679	E	951 719-3965	19768
TST Molding LLC	3089	E	951 296-6200	10414
TST Water LLC	3589	F	951 541-9517	16127
USA Solar Technology Inc	3999	F	714 356-8360	24279
Vesta Solutions Inc **(DH)**	3661	B	951 719-2100	18006
Villlage News Inc	2711	E	760 451-3488	6082
W Plastics Inc	3081	E	800 442-9727	9734
Waleeds Food Inc	2032	F	951 694-8800	779
Wiens Cellars LLC	2084	F	951 694-9892	2055
Wilsenergy LLC	3479	F	951 676-7700	13681
Wilson Creek Wnery Vnyards Inc	2084	C	951 699-9463	2058
Wsr Publishing Inc **(PA)**	2721	F	951 676-4914	6297
Zing Racing Products	3751	F	760 219-4700	21154

TEMPLE CITY, CA - Los Angeles County

	SIC	EMP	PHONE	ENTRY #
Ameba Technology Inc	3663	F	626 575-8811	18027
Art Microelectronics Corp	3674	F	626 447-7503	18720
B & G Metal Inc	3444	F	626 444-8566	12499
California Flexrake Corp	3423	E	626 443-4026	11887
D D Wire Co Inc **(PA)**	3441	E	626 442-0459	12149
D D Wire Co Inc	3441	E	626 285-0298	12150
Hillo America Inc	3651	F	626 570-8899	17813
Huang Qi	2335	F	626 442-6808	3313
Iron Shield Inc	3446	F	626 287-4568	12863
Jantek Electronics Inc	3699	F	626 350-4198	19990
Jon Davler Inc	2844	E	626 941-6558	8779
Prinko Image Co (usa) Inc **(HQ)**	3577	F	626 389-8988	15826
Zeeni Inc	2329	F	626 350-1024	3206

TEMPLETON, CA - San Luis Obispo County

	SIC	EMP	PHONE	ENTRY #
Castoro Cellars **(PA)**	2084	E	805 467-2002	1682
Flash Back USA	2836	F	805 434-0321	8552
JA Wouters Inc	1381	F	805 221-5333	108
Pegasus Med Services/Renalab	2834	F	805 226-8350	8327
Plasvacc USA Inc	2836	F	805 434-0321	8574
Pomar Junction Cellars LLC	2084	E	805 238-9940	1928
Rotta Winery Inc	2084	F	805 237-0510	1957
Sun Tees	2759	F	805 434-0074	7501
Turley Wine Cellars	2084	F	805 434-1030	2031

TERRA BELLA, CA - Tulare County

	SIC	EMP	PHONE	ENTRY #
Tuff Stuff Products	2821	B	559 535-5778	7897
Weldcraft Industries	3523	F	559 784-4322	14124

THERMAL, CA - Riverside County

	SIC	EMP	PHONE	ENTRY #
Aggregate Products Inc **(PA)**	1429	F	760 395-5312	324
Jewel Date Company Inc	2064	E	760 399-4474	1433
Oasis Date Garden Inc	2099	F	760 399-5665	2627
Spates Fabricators Inc	2439	D	760 397-4122	4423
West Coast Aggregate Supply	1442	E	760 342-7598	391

THOUSAND OAKS, CA - Ventura County

	SIC	EMP	PHONE	ENTRY #
Amgen Inc **(PA)**	2836	A	805 447-1000	8526
Amgen USA Inc	2836	D	805 447-1000	8527
Andromeda Software Inc	7372	F	805 379-4109	24358
Base Hockey LP **(PA)**	3949	F	805 405-3650	23513
Baxalta US Inc	3841	B	805 498-8664	22355
BEI North America LLC **(HQ)**	3679	F	805 716-0642	19462
Bonafide Management Systems	7372	F	805 777-7666	24438
Carros Sensors Systems Co LLC **(DH)**	3679	C	805 968-0782	19480
Coach Inc	3171	F	805 496-9933	10545
Custom Sensors & Tech Inc **(PA)**	3679	D	805 716-0322	19507
DC Shades & Shutters Awnings	3442	F	818 597-9705	12306
Easton Hockey Inc **(DH)**	3949	B	818 782-6445	23554
Instacure Healing Products	2834	E	818 222-9600	8222
Kamsut Incorporated	2844	F	805 495-7479	8781
Kavlico Corporation **(HQ)**	3679	A	805 523-2000	19607
Mallinckrodt Inc	3841	F	805 553-9303	22518
Meisei Corporation	3546	F	805 497-2626	14707
Natren Inc	2099	D	805 371-4737	2617
Nexsan Technologies Inc **(DH)**	3572	E	408 724-9809	15573
Rjw & Assoc	2741	F	818 706-0289	6569
Sensata Technologies Inc	3577	D	805 968-0782	15851
Sensata Technologies Inc	3679	C	805 968-0782	19723
Shrink Wrap Pros LLC	3565	F	805 207-9050	15228
Skymicro Inc	3577	F	805 491-8935	15855
Sunbritetv LLC	3663	E	805 214-7250	18267
Teledyne Inc **(PA)**	3679	C	805 373-4545	19755
Thousands Oaks Hand Wash	3589	F	805 379-2732	16123
Trak Microwave Corporation	3679	F	805 267-0100	19767
Xirrus Inc	3823	C	805 262-1600	21678

THOUSAND PALMS, CA - Riverside County

	SIC	EMP	PHONE	ENTRY #
A R Electronics Inc	3679	E	760 343-1200	19430
Apex Interior Source Inc	2431	E	760 343-1919	4100
Calportland	1442	F	760 343-3126	350
Demille Marble & Granite Inc	3281	E	760 341-7525	11249
Koolfog Inc **(PA)**	3585	F	760 321-9203	15964
LArtisan Valley Baking Co	2051	F	760 343-2888	1278
Microcool	3823	F	760 322-1111	21618
Plumberex Specialty Pdts Inc	3432	F	760 343-7363	12043
Pro-Tech Mats Industries Inc	3069	F	760 343-3667	9661
Superior Ready Mix Concrete LP	3273	E	760 343-3418	11198
Therapeutic Industries Inc	3841	F	760 343-2502	22649

THREE RIVERS, CA - Tulare County

	SIC	EMP	PHONE	ENTRY #
Innovative Structural GL Inc	3231	E	559 561-7000	10705

TIPTON, CA - Tulare County

	SIC	EMP	PHONE	ENTRY #
Agnaldos Welding Inc	7692	F	559 752-4254	25385
Mid Valley Milk Co	2026	F	661 721-8419	731

TOLUCA LAKE, CA - Los Angeles County

	SIC	EMP	PHONE	ENTRY #
Gmm Inc	2741	E	323 874-1600	6493
My Burbankcom Inc	2711	F	818 842-2140	5986
Toscanella Inc	2511	E	818 506-7283	4744

TOMALES, CA - Marin County

	SIC	EMP	PHONE	ENTRY #
Blue Mtn Ctr of Meditation Inc	2731	E	707 878-2369	6316

TOPANGA, CA - Los Angeles County

	SIC	EMP	PHONE	ENTRY #
Crashcam Industries Corp	3861	F	310 283-5379	23148

TORRANCE, CA - Los Angeles County

	SIC	EMP	PHONE	ENTRY #
A-Aztec Rents & Sells Inc **(PA)**	2394	C	310 347-3010	3777
Absolution Brewing Company **(PA)**	2082	E	310 787-9563	1557
Ace Clearwater Enterprises Inc **(PA)**	3728	D	310 323-2140	20700
Advanced Chip Magnetics Inc	3677	E	310 370-8188	19314
Advanced Enviromental	3544	F	310 782-9400	14471
Advanced Science & Novel Tech **(PA)**	3571	E	310 530-9400	15384
Advanced Tactics Inc	3721	E	310 701-3659	20528
Aero-Electric Connector Inc	3643	F	310 618-3737	17440
Aero-Electric Connector Inc **(PA)**	3643	B	310 618-3737	17441
Aeroliant Manufacturing Inc	3728	E	310 257-1903	20717
Alegio Fashions Inc	2339	E	310 539-0981	3371
All Access Stging Prdctns Inc **(PA)**	3648	E	310 784-2464	17669
Alliedsignal Arospc Svc Corp **(HQ)**	3369	E	310 323-9500	11768
Alpinestars USA	2326	E	310 891-0222	3092
Altus Positioning Systems Inc	3545	F	310 541-8139	14597
Amag Technology Inc **(DH)**	3577	E	310 518-2380	15665
American Ultraviolet West Inc	3535	E	310 784-2930	14264
Antcom Corporation	3663	E	310 782-1076	18032
Arconic Inc	3334	B	212 836-2674	11537
Arkema Inc	2812	C	310 214-5327	7658
Asclemed Usa Inc	2834	F	310 218-4146	8046
Asiana Cuisine Enterprises Inc	2099	A	310 327-2223	2458
Aviation and Indus Dev Corp	3081	F	310 373-6057	9698
Bachem Americas Inc **(DH)**	2836	C	310 784-4440	8532
Bachem Bioscience Inc	2836	E	310 784-7322	8533
Barranca Holdings Ltd	3545	F	310 523-5867	14606
Bel Aire Bridal Inc	2396	E	310 325-8160	3878
Beranek Inc	3728	E	310 328-9094	20760
Bnl Technologies Inc	3572	E	310 320-7272	15516
Body Care Resort Inc	3634	F	310 328-8888	17386
Boeing Company	3721	A	310 662-7286	20544
BQE Software Inc	7372	D	310 602-4020	24445
Bradshaw Kirchofer Home Furn	2511	E	310 325-0010	4681
Bridge USA Inc	2721	E	310 532-5921	6116
Broadata Communications Inc	3357	F	310 530-1416	11648
Cable Aml Inc **(PA)**	3663	F	310 222-5599	18057
Calcon Steel Construction	3441	E	310 768-8094	12126
Caleb Technology Corporation	3691	E	310 257-4780	19799
California Silkscreen	2396	F	310 320-5111	3883
Camfil USA Inc	3564	D	310 370-3673	15146
Carbide Products Co Inc	3291	F	310 320-7910	11291
Carley Inc **(PA)**	3229	B	310 325-8474	10637
Catalina Pacific Concrete	3273	E	310 532-4600	11057
Caterpillar Inc	3531	F	310 921-9811	14155
Celestron Acquisition LLC	3827	D	310 328-9560	22065
Celestron LLC	3827	E	310 328-9560	22066
Century Parts Inc	3599	F	310 328-0281	16372
Century Shower Door Co Inc **(PA)**	3231	E	310 327-8060	10685
Chemring Energetic Devices	3769	C	310 784-2100	21187
Classic Litho & Design Inc	2752	F	310 224-5200	6733
Coast/Dvnced Chip Mgnetics Inc	3677	F	310 370-8188	19325
Conesys Inc **(PA)**	3678	D	310 618-3737	19378
Conesys Inc	3678	E	310 212-0065	19379
Convaid Products Inc	3842	D	310 618-0111	22714
Counter	3131	E	310 406-3300	10471

Mergent email: customerrelations@mergent.com
1486

2019 California
Manufacturers Register

(P-0000) Products & Services Section entry number
(PA)=Parent Co (HQ)=Headquarters (DH)=Div Headquarters

Company	SIC	EMP	PHONE	ENTRY #
Creative Pathways Inc	3548	E	310 530-1965	14723
D Goldenwest Inc	2051	E	310 564-2641	1228
Dasco Engineering Corp	3728	C	310 326-2277	20792
Data Linkage Software Inc	7372	F	310 781-3056	24550
Diamond K2	3425	E	310 539-6116	11917
Diamotec Inc	3545	F	310 539-4994	14624
Dicaperl Corporation (DH)	1499	D	610 667-6640	410
Digi Group LLC	3663	E	800 521-8467	18086
Donovan Engineering Corp	3714	F	310 320-3772	20317
Doug Mockett & Company Inc	2511	E	310 318-2491	4689
Dreamgear LLC	3944	E	310 222-5522	23418
E H Publishing Inc	2721	E	310 533-2400	6155
Eai-Jr286 Inc	3949	F	310 297-6400	23553
Edelbrock LLC (HQ)	3751	B	310 781-2222	21106
Edelbrock Holdings Inc	3714	C	310 781-2290	20322
Efi Technology Inc	3714	E	310 793-2505	20324
Elements	3911	E	310 781-1384	23261
Ely Co Inc	3599	E	310 539-5831	16470
Emmaus Life Sciences Inc (PA)	2834	F	310 214-0065	8147
Emmaus Medical Inc (HQ)	2833	F	310 214-0065	7935
Emp Connectors Inc	3643	E	310 533-6799	17465
Encore Image Group Inc (PA)	3993	D	310 534-7500	23866
Escape Communications Inc	3663	F	310 997-1300	18104
Evelozcity Inc	3711	C	318 849-6327	20139
Excelpro Inc (PA)	2022	E	323 415-8544	573
Express Folding	2741	E	310 316-6762	6480
Family Medicine Center Torr	2834	F	310 326-8600	8156
Farad Industries Inc	2821	F	310 320-4260	7836
FCkingston Co	3491	D	310 326-8287	13716
Field Manufacturing Corp (PA)	3089	D	310 781-9292	10099
Fischer Cstm Cmmunications Inc (PA)	3825	E	310 303-3300	21758
Five-Star Graphics Inc	2752	F	310 325-6881	6818
Forrester Eastland Corporation	3999	E	310 784-2464	24099
G F Cole Corporation (PA)	3053	F	310 320-0601	9530
Gc Aero Inc (PA)	3433	F	310 539-7600	12065
General Dynmics Stcom Tech Inc	3663	D	310 539-6704	18112
General Forming Corporation	3444	E	310 326-0624	12596
General Motors LLC	3714	A	313 556-5000	20348
George P Johnson Company	3993	D	310 965-4300	23888
Gizmac Accessories LLC	3577	F	310 320-5563	15748
Global Comm Semiconductors LLC (HQ)	3674	E	310 530-7274	18859
Global Micro Solutions Inc	7372	F	310 218-5678	24699
Goeppner Industries Inc	3599	F	310 784-2800	16537
Hall Associates Racg Pdts Inc	3799	F	310 326-4111	21231
Heidelberg Instruments Inc	3555	F	310 530-7145	14811
Hi-Shear Corporation (DH)	3452	A	310 784-4025	13071
HI-Shear Corporation	3429	E	310 326-8110	11960
Honda Accessory America (DH)	3714	E	310 781-5300	20362
Honda North America Inc (HQ)	3711	B	310 781-4961	20150
Honeywell International Inc	3724	E	310 323-9500	20654
Honeywell International Inc	3812	B	734 392-5525	21306
Hugo Engineering Co Inc	3728	F	310 320-0288	20838
I Color Printing & Mailing Inc	2752	F	310 947-1452	6866
Image Solutions Apparel Inc	2326	E	310 464-8991	3106
Inaba Foods (usa) Inc	2047	F	310 818-2270	1114
Industrial Dynamics Co Ltd (PA)	3559	C	310 325-5633	14969
Industrial Gasket and Sup Co	3053	E	310 530-1771	9536
Irtronix Inc	3641	F	310 787-1100	17430
J & A Shoe Company Inc	3144	C	310 324-0139	10498
J-T E C H	3678	C	310 533-6700	19398
Japan Graphics Corp	2752	E	310 222-8639	6907
Jci Jones Chemicals Inc	2812	E	310 523-1629	7665
Just For Fun	2321	E	310 320-1327	3058
Kabushiki Kisha Higuchi Shokai	3645	F	310 212-7234	17540
Kakuichi America Inc	3084	D	310 539-1590	9783
KB Delta Inc	3469	E	310 530-1539	13234
Keller Engineering Inc	3599	E	310 326-6291	16650
Kepner Plas Fabricators Inc	3089	E	310 325-3162	10178
Keysource Foods LLC	2091	E	310 879-4888	2297
Kopykake Enterprises Inc (PA)	3469	F	310 373-8906	13240
Koto Inc	3942	F	310 327-7359	23397
L3 Electron Devices Inc (HQ)	3671	A	310 517-6000	18392
L3 Technologies Inc	3663	B	650 591-8411	18154
La Ejuice LLC	2131	E	310 531-3888	2714
Label Service Inc	2672	F	310 329-5605	5565
Laserod Technologies LLC	3699	E	310 328-5869	20003
Ledtronics Inc	3674	C	310 534-1505	18959
Lee Brothers Truck Body Inc	3713	F	310 532-7980	20212
Lenntek Corporation	3663	E	310 534-2738	18164
Lg Nanoh2o Inc	2899	E	424 218-4000	9272
Libra Cable Technologies Inc	3679	F	310 618-8182	19622
Linde LLC	2813	E	310 533-8394	7696
Loma Scientific International	3663	E	310 539-8655	18169
Luminit LLC	3827	E	310 320-1066	22101
Lyncole Grunding Solutions LLC	3643	E	310 214-4000	17482
Lynn Products Inc	3577	A	310 530-5966	15795
M2 Marketplace Inc	3571	F	310 354-3600	15445
Magnetic Component Engrg Inc (PA)	3499	D	310 784-3100	13956
Magnetron Power Inventions Inc	1382	E	310 462-6970	140
Mahmood Izadi Inc	3569	F	310 325-0463	15340
Mainline Equipment Inc	3663	D	800 444-2288	18174
Marcea Inc	2339	E	213 746-5191	3462
Medianews Group Inc	2711	C	310 540-5511	5959
Medical Chemical Corporation	2899	E	310 787-6800	9279
Medicool Inc	3841	F	310 782-2200	22528
Mega Precision O Rings Inc	3599	F	310 530-1166	16736
Metro Truck Body Incorporated	3713	E	310 532-5570	20219
Metromedia Technologies Inc	3577	E	818 552-6500	15804
Michael BS LLC	2032	E	310 320-0141	768
Microcosm Inc	3764	E	310 219-2700	21178
Micronova Manufacturing Inc	2392	E	310 784-6990	3734
Midmark Corporation	3648	F	310 516-5100	17715
Milo Machining Inc	3599	F	310 530-0925	16754
Minority Success Pubg Group	2721	E	310 373-2868	6218
Mistras Group Inc	3829	E	310 793-7173	22238
Mk Diamond Products Inc (PA)	3546	C	310 539-5221	14708
Momentum Management LLC	3069	F	310 329-2599	9642
Monterey Graphics Inc	2752	F	310 787-3370	6981
Moog Inc	3625	B	310 533-1178	17288
Moog Inc	3812	B	310 533-1178	21352
Morinaga Nutritional Foods Inc	2099	F	310 787-0200	2611
Motoart LLC	3299	F	310 375-4531	11363
Motorcar Parts of America Inc (PA)	3714	A	310 212-7910	20406
National Law Digest Inc	2731	E	310 791-9975	6367
Naturalife Eco Vite Labs	2023	D	310 370-1563	635
Navcom Technology Inc (HQ)	3663	E	310 381-2000	18196
Nearfield Systems Inc	3825	E	310 525-7000	21813
Neko World Inc	3944	E	301 649-1188	23449
Noatex Corporation	3544	F	310 783-0133	14551
Nothing To Wear Inc (PA)	2331	E	310 328-0408	3264
O K Color America Corporation	3089	F	310 320-9343	10252
Obatake Inc	3911	E	310 782-2730	23304
Omicron Engineering Inc	3599	F	310 328-4017	16808
One Touch Solutions Inc	3555	F	310 320-6868	14820
Onshore Technologies Inc	3679	E	310 533-4888	19673
Optima Industries Inc	3541	E	310 533-8448	14397
Paper Works Corporation	2759	F	310 781-9400	7431
Pasco Corporation of America	2038	E	503 289-6500	1009
Pbf Energy Inc	2911	F	310 212-2800	9348
Pel Manufacturing Leasng Corp	2789	F	310 530-7145	7612
Pelican Products Inc (PA)	3648	B	310 326-4700	17724
Phenomenex Inc (HQ)	3826	C	310 212-0555	22003
Photo Sciences Incorporated (PA)	3577	E	310 634-1500	15823
Phyn LLC	3823	F	310 400-4001	21633
Pioneer Electronics (usa) Inc (DH)	3651	B	310 952-2000	17844
Pioneer Speakers Inc (DH)	3651	E	310 952-2000	17845
Plasma Technology Incorporated (PA)	3479	D	310 320-3373	13636
Pmp Products Inc	3161	F	310 549-5122	10531
Praxair Distribution Inc	2813	E	310 371-1254	7731
Precision Fiberglass Products	3644	E	310 539-7470	17517
Prestone Products Corporation	2899	E	424 271-4836	9298
Probe Racing Components Inc	3592	E	310 784-2977	16150
Products Engineering Corp (PA)	3423	E	310 787-4500	11907
Proprietary Controls Systems	3829	E	310 303-3600	22252
Pulse Instruments	3825	E	310 515-5330	21832
Quality Forming LLC	3728	C	310 539-2855	20919
Quantum Chromodynamics Inc	2759	F	310 329-5000	7456
Ralph E Ames Machine Works	3599	E	310 328-8523	16883
Rapiscan Systems Inc (HQ)	3844	C	310 978-1457	22941
Retail Print Media Inc	2759	E	424 488-6950	7469
Reyes Coca-Cola Bottling LLC	2086	C	310 965-2653	2208
Roberts Research Laboratory	3489	F	310 320-7310	13696
Robinson Helicopter Co Inc	3721	A	310 539-0508	20623
Rock-Ola Manufacturing Corp	3651	D	310 328-1306	17850
RR Donnelley & Sons Company	2759	A	310 516-3100	7475
Rtg Inc	3674	F	310 534-3016	19130
Rtl Electronics	3951	F	310 320-0451	23701
Rytan Inc	3541	F	310 328-6553	14406
Sage Goddess Inc	3911	E	650 733-6639	23312
Sanko Electronics America Inc (HQ)	3714	E	310 618-1677	20444
Santan Software Systems Inc	7372	E	310 836-2802	25144
Santec Inc	3432	E	310 542-0063	12049
Scientific Repair Inc	3823	F	310 214-5092	21650
Sharp Industries Inc	3542	E	310 370-5990	14456
Shaver Specialty Coinc	3556	F	310 370-6941	14884
Shine Food Inc (PA)	2032	E	310 329-3829	773
Shine Food Inc	2038	E	310 533-6010	1016
Showerdoordirect LLC	3444	F	310 534-7500	12762
Signtronix Inc (PA)	3993	D	310 534-7500	23974
Sii Semiconductor USA Corp	3674	F	310 517-7771	19149

Company	SIC	EMP	PHONE	ENTRY #
Sirena Incorporated	2759	F	866 548-5353	7485
Southern California Ice Co	2097	F	310 325-1040	2421
Stewart Filmscreen Corp (PA)	3861	C	310 326-1422	23197
Storm Industries Inc (PA)	3523	D	310 534-5232	14107
Storm Manufacturing Group Inc	3491	D	310 326-8287	13734
Student Sports	2273	F	310 791-1142	2943
Sure Power Inc	3679	E	310 542-8561	19740
Swimwear Expert Inc	2253	F	310 941-4880	2860
Takane USA Inc (HQ)	3873	E	310 212-1411	23225
Takuyo Corporation	2711	F	310 782-6927	6066
Tcw Trends Inc	2339	F	310 533-5177	3515
Team Inc	3398	D	310 514-2312	11832
Technical Devices Company	3548	E	310 618-8437	14742
Teledyne Defense Elec LLC	3679	F	310 823-8551	19750
Textile Unlimited Corporation (PA)	2321	E	310 263-7400	3061
Topper Manufacturing Corp	3589	E	310 375-5000	16125
Torrance Refining Company LLC	2911	A	310 483-6900	9366
Torrance Steel Window Co Inc	3442	E	310 328-9181	12353
Torrence Trading Inc	3944	E	310 649-1188	23473
Totex Manufacturing Inc	3089	D	310 326-2028	10408
Ubst Inc	2331	F	424 222-9908	3282
Union Carbide Corporation	2631	D	310 214-5300	5363
Universal Cushion Company Inc (PA)	2392	E	323 887-8000	3754
Universal Imaging Tech Inc	3955	E	310 961-2098	23739
Universal Screw Products Inc	3451	E	310 371-1170	13048
US Hybrid Corporation (PA)	3714	E	310 212-1200	20477
Vaporbrothers Inc	3634	F	310 618-1188	17405
Varedan Technologies LLC	3625	E	310 542-2320	17318
Verilogix Inc	7372	F	310 527-5100	25326
Virco Mfg Corporation (PA)	2531	B	310 533-0474	5032
Watts Liquidation Corporation	2269	F	310 328-5999	2922
William Bounds Ltd	3556	F	310 375-0505	14897
Winther Technologies Inc (PA)	3548	E	310 618-8437	14745
Woodsource International	2435	F	310 328-9663	4387
Younger Mfg Co (PA)	3851	B	310 783-1533	23133
Z C & R Coating For Optics Inc	3827	E	310 381-3060	22151

TRABUCO CANYON, CA - Orange County

Company	SIC	EMP	PHONE	ENTRY #
CK Manufacturing and Trading	2541	E	949 529-3400	5048
R B S Inc	3577	F	949 766-2924	15832

TRACY, CA - San Joaquin County

Company	SIC	EMP	PHONE	ENTRY #
A & A Ready Mixed Concrete Inc	3273	F	209 830-5070	11022
A Teichert & Son Inc	1442	E	209 832-4150	336
A Teichert & Son Inc	1442	E	209 834-8300	338
American Custom Meats LLC	2013	D	209 839-8800	464
American Trck Trlr Bdy Co Inc (PA)	3713	E	209 836-8985	20189
Ameron International Corp	3494	C	209 836-5050	13758
Aubin Industries Inc	3087	F	800 324-0051	9894
Barbosa Cabinets Inc	2434	B	209 836-2501	4272
Basalite Building Products LLC	3271	C	209 833-3670	10845
Bescal Inc	3272	E	209 836-3492	10884
C C T Laser Services Inc	3699	F	209 833-1110	19922
Cemex Cnstr Mtls PCF LLC	3273	E	209 835-1454	11064
Clear Skies Solutions Inc	3822	F	925 570-4471	21505
Clonetab Inc	7372	F	209 292-5663	24501
Cmyk Enterprise Inc	2752	F	209 229-7230	6736
Consolidated Container Co LLC	3089	C	209 820-1700	10038
Dave Humphrey Enterprises Inc	3531	F	209 835-2222	14163
Drilling & Trenching Sup Inc (PA)	3545	E	510 895-1650	14627
Dynatect Ro-Lab Inc	3061	E	262 786-1500	9566
Encompass Dist Svcs LLC	3674	F	925 249-0988	18821
Feral Productions LLC	3599	F	510 791-5392	16495
Fuel Injection Corporation	3714	E	925 371-6551	20343
Future Foam Inc	3086	E	209 832-1886	9856
Gloriann Farms Inc	3086	C	209 221-7121	9861
Golden State Vintners (PA)	2084	F	707 254-4900	1786
Green Soap Inc (PA)	2841	F	925 240-5546	8594
Hand Crfted Dutchman Doors Inc	2431	F	209 833-7378	4164
Katerra Inc	2439	A	623 236-5322	4417
Kraft Heinz Foods Company	2032	E	209 832-4269	764
Leprino Foods Company	2022	B	209 835-8340	586
Lockheed Martin Corporation	3721	E	408 756-3008	20599
Lynx Enterprises Inc	3444	D	209 833-3400	12645
Madruga Iron Works Inc	3441	E	209 832-7003	12200
Medina Wood Products Inc	2448	F	209 832-4523	4488
Mission Bell Mfg Co Inc	2434	E	209 229-7280	4330
Moore Epitaxial Inc	3559	E	209 833-0100	14992
Mother Lode Plas Molding Inc	3089	E	209 532-5146	10228
Nq Engineering Inc	3599	F	209 836-3255	16795
Olin Chlor Alkali Logistics	2812	E	209 835-5424	7667
Olive Musco Products Inc (PA)	2033	B	209 836-4600	841
Omega Precision Machine	3599	F	209 833-6502	16807
Pallet Recovery Service Inc	2448	F	209 496-5074	4498
Polycom Inc	3661	E	209 830-5083	17980
Process Specialties Inc	3496	E	209 832-1344	13845

Company	SIC	EMP	PHONE	ENTRY #
Professional McHy Group Inc	3553	F	209 832-0100	14786
Ranks Big Data	2399	C	510 830-6926	3959
Rich Chicks LLC (PA)	2015	E	209 879-4104	551
RMC Pacific Materials Inc	3241	E	209 835-1454	10769
San-I-Pak Pacific Inc	3443	E	209 836-2310	12419
Surtec Inc	2842	E	209 820-3700	8680
Synnex Corporation	3571	F	510 656-3333	15493
Teledyne Risi Inc (HQ)	2892	E	925 456-9700	9185
Top Shelf Manufacturing LLC	3841	F	209 834-8185	22653
Tracy Press Inc	2711	E	209 835-3030	6072
W R Grace & Co	2819	C	209 839-2800	7815
West Coast Cryogenics Inc	3559	F	209 914-6989	15049

TRANQUILLITY, CA - Fresno County

Company	SIC	EMP	PHONE	ENTRY #
AG Spraying	3499	F	559 698-9507	13914

TRAVER, CA - Tulare County

Company	SIC	EMP	PHONE	ENTRY #
Maf Industries Inc (HQ)	3565	D	559 897-2905	15217

TRAVIS AFB, CA - Solano County

Company	SIC	EMP	PHONE	ENTRY #
Boeing Company	3721	A	707 437-8574	20562

TRONA, CA - San Bernardino County

Company	SIC	EMP	PHONE	ENTRY #
Searles Valley Minerals Inc	1479	A	760 372-2259	403
Searles Valley Minerals Inc	2869	E	760 372-2135	9040

TRUCKEE, CA - Nevada County

Company	SIC	EMP	PHONE	ENTRY #
A Teichert & Son Inc	1442	E	530 587-3811	335
Acureo Inc	7372	F	530 550-8801	24316
Moonshine Ink	2711	E	530 587-3607	5978
Mount Rose Publishing Co Inc	2711	F	530 587-6061	5983
Recycled Spaces Inc	2519	F	530 587-3394	4918
Sierra Asset Servicing LLC	1389	F	530 582-7300	274

TUJUNGA, CA - Los Angeles County

Company	SIC	EMP	PHONE	ENTRY #
David Kopf Instruments	3841	E	818 352-3274	22418
Kenneth Cronon Inc	2361	F	818 632-4972	3579
Nic Protection Inc	3645	F	818 249-2539	17549

TULARE, CA - Tulare County

Company	SIC	EMP	PHONE	ENTRY #
Carl & Irving Printers Inc	2752	F	559 686-8354	6721
Dean Foods Company	2026	F	559 687-1927	722
Dowdys Sales and Services	3523	F	559 688-6973	14064
Fisher Manufacturing Co Inc (PA)	3432	E	559 685-5200	12034
Gannett Co Inc	2711	C	559 688-0521	5853
Golden Valley Dairy Products	2022	C	559 687-1188	575
High Sierra Truss Company Inc	2439	E	559 688-6611	4410
Johnston Aircraft Service Inc	3812	F	559 686-1795	21313
Kirby Manufacturing Inc	3523	F	559 686-1571	14080
Kohler & Clark Screw Products	3599	E	559 688-1194	16662
Land OLakes Inc	2022	D	559 687-8287	583
Langston Companies Inc	2674	E	559 688-3839	5644
Russell Kc & Son	3523	E	559 686-3236	14101
Saputo Cheese USA Inc	2022	B	559 687-8411	598
Saputo Cheese USA Inc	2022	E	559 687-9999	599
Stainless Works Inc	7692	F	559 688-4310	25438
Tulare County Septic Tank Inc	3272	F	559 686-8531	11011
Westrock Cp LLC	2631	D	559 685-1102	5368
Whitten Machine Shop	3599	F	559 686-3428	17065

TULELAKE, CA - Siskiyou County

Company	SIC	EMP	PHONE	ENTRY #
Organic Horseradish Co	2035	E	530 664-3862	925

TURLOCK, CA - Stanislaus County

Company	SIC	EMP	PHONE	ENTRY #
Adtek Inc	3441	E	209 634-0300	12103
Arthur P Lamarre & Sons Inc	3444	F	209 667-6557	12488
Big Valley Pallet	2448	E	209 632-7687	4455
Blue Diamond Growers	2099	D	209 604-1501	2470
Bluescope Buildings N Amer Inc	3448	C	209 667-4951	12922
Cal-Coast Dairy Systems Inc	3523	E	209 634-9026	14051
California Dairies Inc	2021	D	209 656-1942	560
Clausen Meat Company Inc	2011	E	209 667-8690	428
Coast Wood Preserving Inc (PA)	2491	F	209 632-9931	4591
Dairy Farmers America Inc	2022	D	209 667-9627	569
Donald H Binkley	3441	E	209 664-9792	12154
Formax Technologies Inc	3699	E	209 668-1001	19968
Fusion 360 Inc	2836	F	209 632-0139	8553
Golden State Mixing Inc	2026	E	209 632-3656	727
Hilmar Cheese Company Inc	2022	D	209 667-6076	577
Jackson-Mitchell Inc (PA)	2026	E	209 667-0786	730
JDM Properties	2869	E	209 632-0616	9015
Kozy Shack Enterprises LLC	2099	D	209 634-2131	2554
Lock-N-Stitch Inc	3545	E	209 632-2345	14645
Nelson & Sons Electric Inc	3699	E	209 667-4343	20023
Neogen Corporation	2842	E	800 995-1607	8658
Nordic Saw & Tool Mfrs	3425	E	209 634-9015	11920
P & F Machine Inc	3599	F	209 667-2515	16815
Pernstner Sons Fabrication Inc	3498	F	209 345-2430	13900

Mergent email: customerrelations@mergent.com
1488
2019 California
Manufacturers Register
(P-0000) Products & Services Section entry number
(PA)=Parent Co (HQ)=Headquarters (DH)=Div Headquarters

	SIC	EMP	PHONE	ENTRY #
Purina Animal Nutrition LLC	2048	E	209 634-9101	1156
RJ Mfg	2298	F	209 632-9708	2979
Rootlieb Inc	3465	F	209 632-2203	13142
Seegers Industries Inc	2752	F	209 667-2750	7100
Sensient Ntral Ingredients LLC (HQ)	2034	D	209 667-2777	893
Sunrise Bakery	2051	F	209 632-9400	1325
Super Store Industries	2024	D	209 668-2100	696
Turlock Cabinet Shop Inc	2434	F	209 632-1311	4360
Turlock Journal	2711	D	209 634-9141	6075
Turlock Machine Works	3593	E	209 632-2275	16160
Turlock Sheet Metal & Wldg Inc	2041	E	209 667-4716	1049
Volk Enterprises Inc	3496	D	209 632-3826	13861
Vue-Temp Inc (PA)	2015	D	209 634-2914	554

TUSTIN, CA - Orange County

	SIC	EMP	PHONE	ENTRY #
Abcron Corporation	3651	F	714 730-9988	17748
Add-On Computer Peripheral Inc	3577	D	949 546-8200	15658
Aegis Principia LLC	3999	F	714 731-2283	24027
Alldigital Holdings Inc	7372	F	949 250-7340	24353
Alphabet Lighting	3646	F	714 259-0990	17581
Anajet LLC	3555	E	714 662-3200	14800
Avid Bioservices Inc (PA)	2834	C	714 508-6000	8055
Avid Bioservices Inc	2834	E	714 508-6000	8056
Baf Industries (PA)	2842	E	714 258-8055	8624
Balboa Water Group LLC (PA)	3625	C	714 384-0384	17256
Bar None Inc	2085	F	714 259-8450	2066
Belts By Simon Inc	2387	D	714 573-0303	3626
Bernhardt & Bernhardt Inc	3541	F	714 544-0708	14362
Bjb Enterprises Inc	2821	F	714 734-8450	7823
Braxton Caribbean Mfg Co Inc	3965	F	714 508-3570	23762
Brevity LLC	7372	F	949 250-0701	24451
Ces Electronics Mfg Inc	3999	F	714 505-3441	24065
CM Brewing Technologies	3589	F	888 391-9990	16029
Compass Water Solutions Inc (PA)	3589	D	949 222-5777	16031
Corcen Data International Inc	7372	F	714 251-6110	24526
Country House	2064	F	714 505-8988	1417
Custom Quilting Inc	2392	F	949 455-7337	3717
Custom Quilting Inc (PA)	2392	F	714 731-7271	3718
Design West Technologies Inc	3089	D	714 731-0201	10068
Distribution Electrnics Vlued	3699	F	714 368-1717	19945
Diversified Printers Inc	2741	D	714 994-3400	6470
Do Well Laboratories Inc	2023	F	949 252-0001	612
Doublesight Displays Inc	3577	F	949 253-1535	15732
Durabag Company Inc	2673	D	714 259-8811	5597
Edwin T Seki Inc	2631	F	714 838-1177	5347
Epinex Diagnostics Inc	3841	E	949 660-7770	22443
Expert Assembly Services Inc	3672	E	714 258-8880	18477
Fashion Camp	2299	E	714 259-0946	2998
Freeze Tag Inc (PA)	7372	F	714 210-3850	24671
GL Woodworking Inc	2499	D	949 515-2192	4622
Hall Research Technologies LLC (PA)	3577	F	714 641-6607	15752
Henrys Adio Vsual Slutions Inc	3651	E	714 258-7238	17811
Ifiber Optix Inc	3229	E	714 665-9796	10647
Ii-VI Optical Systems Inc	3827	E	714 247-7100	22086
Innovative Diversfd Tech Inc	3572	E	949 455-1701	15559
Intepro America LP (PA)	3825	E	714 953-2686	21776
Interplex Nascal Inc (DH)	3469	D	714 505-2900	13226
Jmp Electronics Inc	3672	F	714 730-2086	18515
Keithco Manufacturing Inc	3599	F	714 258-8933	16648
Kings Silk Embroidery Art	2395	F	714 505-0731	3850
Landscape Communications Inc	2721	E	714 979-5276	6203
LGarde Inc	3572	E	714 259-0771	15563
Lund Motion Products Inc	3714	E	949 221-0023	20390
Make Beverage Holdings LLC	2599	E	949 923-8238	5245
Meridian Graphics Inc	2752	D	949 833-3500	6969
Millenworks	3711	D	714 426-5500	20158
Mophie Inc (HQ)	3663	E	888 866-7443	18188
MTI Technology Corporation (PA)	3572	C	949 251-1101	15571
Myvoicecig LLC	2741	F	714 702-6006	6535
Oracle Corporation	7372	C	713 654-0919	25007
Palpilot International Corp	3672	E	714 460-0718	18554
Paper Group Company LLC	2621	E	714 566-0025	5322
Portellus Inc	7372	F	949 250-9600	25071
Precision Offset Inc	2752	D	949 752-1714	7034
Prestige Foil Inc	2759	F	714 556-1431	7443
Printyourcompany	2759	F	714 380-3900	7448
Priority Posting and Pubg Inc	2741	F	714 338-2568	6556
Pvp Advanced Eo Systems Inc	3827	E	714 508-2740	22125
Raj Manufacturing LLC	2339	F	714 838-3110	3488
Ricoh Electronics Inc (DH)	3861	B	714 566-2500	23193
Ricoh Electronics Inc	3579	B	714 259-1220	15915
Ronco Plastics Incorporated	3089	F	714 259-1385	10340
Saf-T-Kut LLC	3541	E	657 210-4426	14410
Staar Surgical Company	3851	F	626 303-7902	23127
Strata Technologies	3629	E	714 368-9785	17359
Stuart-Dean Co Inc	3471	F	714 544-4460	13513

	SIC	EMP	PHONE	ENTRY #
Sunny America & Global Autotec	3714	D	714 544-0400	20455
Systems Printing Inc	2791	F	714 832-4677	7633
Terumo Americas Holding Inc	3826	C	714 258-8001	22028
Texas Instruments Incorporated	3674	C	714 731-7110	19230
Thermeon Corporation (PA)	7372	F	714 731-9191	25269
Tivoli LLC	3641	F	714 957-6101	17435
Trelleborg Sealing Solutions (DH)	3841	C	714 415-0280	22655
TRT Bsness Ntwrk Solutions Inc	3825	F	714 380-3888	21882
Vitabest Nutrition Inc	2834	B	714 832-9700	8436
Wellprint Inc	2752	F	714 838-3962	7177
Werner Systems Inc	3355	F	714 838-4444	11626

UKIAH, CA - Mendocino County

	SIC	EMP	PHONE	ENTRY #
American Bottling Company	2086	F	707 462-8871	2083
B J Embroidery & Screenprint	2395	F	707 463-2767	3829
BJs Ukiah Embroidery	2759	F	707 463-2767	7250
Cal Nor Powder Coating Inc	3479	F	707 462-0217	13562
California Leisure Products	2452	F	707 462-2106	4570
Cold Creek Compost Inc	2875	F	707 485-5966	9083
Constellation Brands Inc	2084	E	707 467-4840	1703
Evden Enterprises Inc	3599	F	707 462-0375	16480
Liqua-Tech Corporation	3824	F	800 659-3556	21690
Maverick Enterprises Inc	3353	C	707 463-5591	11579
McNab Ridge Winery LLC	2084	F	707 462-2423	1875
Mendocino Brewing Company Inc (HQ)	2082	D	707 463-2627	1611
Nelson & Sons Inc	2084	F	707 462-3755	1896
North Cal Wood Products Inc	2421	E	707 462-0686	4043
Pamelas Products Incorporated	2051	D	707 462-6605	1303
Parducci Wine Estates LLC	2084	E	707 463-5350	1915
Performance Coatings Inc	2851	F	707 462-3023	8923
Peter Pugger Manufacturing	3531	F	707 463-1333	14184
Plc LLC	2084	F	707 462-2423	1927
Rebol Technologies Inc	7372	F	707 485-0599	25114
Reliable Mill Supply Co	3312	F	707 462-1458	11415
Retech Systems LLC	3433	C	707 462-6522	12082
Ukiah Brewing Co LLC	2082	E	707 468-5898	1633
Waneshear Technologies LLC	3553	E	707 462-4761	14788

UNION CITY, CA - Alameda County

	SIC	EMP	PHONE	ENTRY #
Abaxis Inc (HQ)	3829	C	510 675-6500	22154
Aei Electech Corp	3679	F	510 489-5088	19436
Airgas Usa LLC	2813	F	510 429-4200	7681
Ajax - Untd Pttrns & Molds Inc	3089	C	510 476-8000	9932
Alvarado Dye & Knitting Mill	2326	E	510 324-8892	3093
American Licorice Company	2064	B	510 487-5500	1407
Ariat International Inc (PA)	3199	C	510 477-7000	10572
Ate Micrographics Inc	3826	F	510 475-5882	21907
Axis Group Inc	3674	F	510 487-7393	18737
Axygen Inc (HQ)	3089	E	510 494-8900	9964
Azimuth Industrial Co Inc	3674	E	510 441-6000	18740
Bakemark USA LLC	2099	E	510 487-8188	2459
Bay Central Printing Inc	2752	F	510 429-9111	6688
Best Label Company Inc	3565	E	510 489-5400	15198
Blommer Chocolate Co Cal Inc	2066	C	510 471-4300	1466
California Performance Packg	3086	B	909 390-4422	9823
Caravan Bakery Inc	2051	E	510 487-2600	1217
Caravan Trading Company	2051	E	510 487-8090	1218
Chinese Overseas Mktg Svc Corp	2741	E	510 476-0880	6460
Compro Packaging LLC	2653	E	510 475-0118	5400
Conklin & Conklin Incorporated	3452	E	510 489-5500	13065
Dawn Food Products Inc	2051	E	510 487-9007	1229
Deep Foods Inc	2052	F	510 475-1900	1361
Delta Yimin Technologies Inc	3089	E	510 487-4411	10065
Electrochem Solutions Inc	3471	E	510 476-1840	13396
Electrochem Solutions LLC	3471	D	510 476-1840	13397
Emerald Packaging Inc	2673	C	510 429-5700	5599
Enersys	3691	F	510 887-8080	19803
Epe Industries Usa Inc	3086	F	800 315-0336	9840
Farallon Brands Inc (PA)	2392	F	510 550-4299	3723
Finelite Inc	3646	C	510 441-1100	17608
Fricke-Parks Press Inc	2752	D	510 489-6543	6827
Gcm Medical & OEM Division Inc	3444	D	510 475-0404	12595
Heco Pacific Manufacturing	3535	E	510 487-1155	14275
Ichor Systems Inc	3089	C	510 476-8000	10145
Jenson Mechanical Inc	3599	E	510 429-8078	16619
Kerrock Countertops Inc (PA)	2511	E	510 441-2300	4711
Knorr Brake Company LLC	3743	F	510 475-0770	21079
Korea Central Daily News	2711	F	213 368-2500	5899
La Terra Fina Usa Inc	2099	D	510 404-5888	2572
Lam Research Corporation	3559	D	510 572-2186	14980
Lamart California Inc	3296	E	973 772-6262	11336
Lamart Corporation	3292	C	510 489-8100	11312
Lane International Trading Inc (PA)	3143	D	510 489-7364	10481
M and M Cabinets Inc	2434	F	510 324-4034	4326
Mizuho Orthopedic Systems Inc (HQ)	3841	B	510 429-1500	22545
New Horizon Foods Inc	2099	F	510 489-8600	2620

Employment Codes: A=Over 500 employees, B=251-500,
C=101-250, D=51-100, E=20-50, F=10-19

2019 California
Manufacturers Register

© Mergent Inc. 1-800-342-5647
1489

GEOGRAPHIC

	SIC	EMP	PHONE	ENTRY #
Northwood Design Partners Inc	2521	E	510 731-6505	4960
Oracle Corporation	7372	B	510 471-6971	25021
Orcon Aerospace	3728	C	510 489-8100	20898
Printing and Marketing Inc	2759	F	510 931-7000	7446
Ptr Manufacturing Inc	3599	E	510 477-9654	16865
Quantum Performance Developmen	3572	F	510 870-6381	15592
R & S Manufacturing Inc (HQ)	3442	F	510 429-1788	12341
Rapid Displays Inc	3993	B	510 471-6955	23950
Reyes Coca-Cola Bottling LLC	2086	D	510 476-7000	2190
Ritescreen Inc	2431	F	800 949-4174	4220
Ryss Lab Inc	3821	F	510 477-9570	21488
Savory Creations International	2013	F	510 477-0395	524
Sheedy Drayage Co	3536	F	510 441-7300	14302
Sigmatron International Inc	3672	C	510 477-5000	18605
Sipi Company Inc	3944	F	650 201-1169	23464
Smart Wires Inc (PA)	3677	F	415 800-5555	19363
Spacesonics Incorporated	3444	D	650 610-0999	12766
Star Stainless Screw Co	3312	F	510 489-6569	11423
SW Safety Solutions Inc	2259	E	510 429-8692	2876
Thousandshores Inc	3571	F	510 477-0249	15496
Toppage Inc	7372	F	510 471-6366	25287
Tr Manufacturing LLC (HQ)	3699	C	510 657-3850	20089
Ultimo Software Solutions Inc	7372	C	408 943-1490	25307
Unistrut International Corp	3441	F	510 476-1200	12267
United Misc & Orna Stl Inc	3449	F	510 429-8755	13002
Usk Manufacturing Inc	3444	E	510 471-7555	12803
Zypcom Inc	3663	F	510 324-2501	18306

UPLAND, CA - San Bernardino County

	SIC	EMP	PHONE	ENTRY #
909 Media Group Inc	2721	F	909 608-7426	6095
Akzo Nobel Inc	2869	E	909 981-6540	8972
American Technical Molding Inc	3089	C	909 982-1025	9944
Analytik Jena US LLC (DH)	3826	D	909 946-3197	21903
Applied Instrument Tech Inc	3826	E	909 204-3700	21904
Build At Home LLC	3949	F	909 949-1601	23530
Cal Best Ceilings Inc	3646	E	909 946-1565	17591
California Ramp Works Inc	3448	E	909 949-1601	12925
CCL Label Inc	2759	C	909 608-2655	7266
CCL Label (delaware) Inc	2759	C	909 608-2260	7267
Charles Meisner Inc	3544	E	909 946-8216	14494
Claremont Institute Statesmans (PA)	2759	E	909 981-2200	7273
Dimic Steel Tech Inc	3444	E	909 946-6767	12561
Edco Die Inc	3599	F	909 985-4417	16462
Exhaust Center Inc	3444	F	951 685-8602	12580
Gar Enterprises	3679	E	909 985-4575	19548
Garhauer Marine Corporation	3429	E	909 985-9993	11957
Hair Syndicut	2899	F	909 946-3200	9256
Helens Place Inc	2752	F	909 981-5715	6851
Herbs Yeh Manufacturing Co	2023	F	909 946-0794	621
Holliday Rock Trucking Inc (PA)	3273	D	909 982-1553	11120
Inland Valley News Inc	2711	F	909 949-3099	5889
Innovativetek Inc	3699	E	909 981-3401	19982
Integrity Sheet Metal Inc	3444	F	909 608-0449	12622
Mectec Molds Inc	3544	F	909 981-3636	14540
Montclair Wood Corporation	2426	C	909 985-0302	4085
Motu Global LLC	2033	F	801 471-7800	830
Panic Plastics	2673	F	909 946-5529	5614
Plum Creek Timberlands LP	2421	C	909 949-2255	4045
Precision Molded Plastics Inc	3089	F	909 981-9662	10304
Redwood Scientific Tech Inc	2834	C	310 693-5401	8358
Sampav Inc	2311	F	909 984-8646	3042
Scheu Manufacturing Co (PA)	3433	F	909 982-8933	12083
Sport Pins International Inc	3961	F	909 985-4549	23759
Susan Biegel MD	2834	F	909 985-1908	8402
Test Connections Inc	3825	F	909 981-1810	21871
Wilson Imaging and Publishing	2741	F	909 931-1818	6626
Winner Industrial Chemicals	2869	E	909 887-6228	9053

VACAVILLE, CA - Solano County

	SIC	EMP	PHONE	ENTRY #
Ad Special TS EMB Screen Prtg	2396	F	707 452-7272	3873
Adidas North America Inc	2329	E	707 446-1070	3131
Alza Corporation (HQ)	2834	A	707 453-6400	8019
Alza Corporation	3826	A	707 453-6400	21900
Browntrout Publishers Inc	2741	F	707 451-8593	6453
Caborca Leather LLC	2387	E	707 463-7607	3628
Cherry Pit	2992	F	707 449-8378	9429
Designerx Pharmaceuticals Inc	2834	F	707 451-0441	8139
Dr Earth Inc	2873	F	707 448-4676	9060
Fortune Brands Windows Inc	3089	C	707 446-7600	10106
Genentech Inc	2834	E	707 454-1000	8171
Golden State Steel & Stair Inc (PA)	3441	E	707 455-0400	12173
Hurley International LLC	2329	C	707 446-6300	3161
Icon Aircraft Inc (PA)	3728	D	707 564-4000	20844
Joseph Charles Whitson	2741	F	707 694-8806	6509
M&G Duravent Inc (DH)	3444	B	707 446-1786	12647
Magellan Gold Corporation	1044	E	707 884-3766	11

	SIC	EMP	PHONE	ENTRY #
Master Plastics Incorporated	3089	E	707 451-3168	10200
McC Controls LLC	3589	E	218 847-1317	16070
Novartis Pharmaceuticals Corp	2835	E	707 452-8081	8500
Pre-Insulated Metal Tech Inc (HQ)	3448	C	707 359-2280	12956
R R Donnelley & Sons Company	2752	F	707 446-6195	7070
Reporter	2711	D	707 448-6401	6026
S & J Advertising Inc (PA)	2721	F	707 448-6446	6251
Siegwerk USA Inc	2893	E	707 469-7648	9209
SJ Electro Systems Inc	3589	E	707 449-0341	16108
Solano County Water Agency	2086	F	707 455-1105	2226
Synder Inc (PA)	3677	E	707 451-6060	19367
Under Armour Inc	2329	F	707 451-4736	3200
Vacaville Fruit Co Inc	2034	E	707 448-5292	903
Wunder-Mold Inc	3089	E	707 448-2349	10453

VALENCIA, CA - Los Angeles County

	SIC	EMP	PHONE	ENTRY #
A & M Electronics Inc	3672	E	661 257-3680	18400
A-H Plating Inc	3471	D	818 845-6243	13302
Abl Aero Inc	2891	E	661 257-2500	9125
Accu-Glass Products Inc	3679	F	818 365-4215	19433
Accurate Grinding Usa Inc	3999	E	818 768-4497	24022
Advanced Bionics LLC	3842	B	661 362-1400	22691
Advanced Bionics Corporation (HQ)	3842	C	661 362-1400	22692
Advanced Technology Machining	3599	F	661 257-2313	16233
Aero Engineering & Mfg Co Cal	3728	E	661 295-0875	20709
Aero Sense Inc	3728	F	661 257-1608	20713
Aerospace Dynamics Intl Inc	3728	B	661 257-3535	20721
Air Flow Research Heads Inc	3714	E	661 257-8124	20249
Airbolt Industries Inc	3369	E	818 767-5600	11767
Aircraft Hinge Inc	3728	E	661 257-3434	20726
Alinabal Inc	3399	E	661 877-9356	11839
Amzr Inc	2399	C	800 541-2326	3937
Aquafine Corporation (HQ)	3589	D	661 257-4770	16011
ASC Process Systems Inc	3567	C	818 833-0088	15252
Avibank Mfg Inc	3429	D	661 257-2329	11933
Avion TI Mfg Machining Ctr Inc	3599	F	661 257-2915	16291
Bayless Engineering Inc	3599	C	661 257-3373	16311
Bbk Specialties Inc	3261	F	661 255-2857	10804
Bertelsmann Inc	2731	B	661 702-2700	6312
Big Shine Los Angeles Inc	3663	F	818 346-0770	18050
Bioness Inc	3845	C	661 362-4850	22953
Bloomers Metal Stampings Inc	3469	E	661 257-2955	13171
Boston Scientific Corporation	3841	B	661 645-6668	22377
Boston Scientific Corporation	3841	E	800 678-2575	22379
Boston Scntfic Nrmdlation Corp	3842	F	661 949-4869	22709
Boston Scntfic Nrmdlation Corp (HQ)	3842	B	661 949-4310	22710
Canay Manufacturing Inc	3599	F	661 295-0205	16360
Canyon Engineering Pdts Inc	3728	D	661 294-0084	20776
Canyon Plastics Inc	3089	D	661 257-4293	10010
Capax Technologies Inc	3629	E	661 257-7666	17335
Cellestis Inc	2835	F	661 775-7480	8469
Cicoil LLC	3357	D	661 295-1295	11655
Classic Wire Cut Company Inc	3599	C	661 257-0558	16385
Cornerstone Display Group Inc (PA)	3993	E	661 705-1700	23848
Cosmic Plastics Inc	2821	C	661 257-3274	7825
Creations Grdn Natural Fd Mkts	2833	C	661 877-4280	7929
Crissair Inc	3594	C	661 367-3300	16163
Curran Engineering Company Inc	3446	E	800 643-6353	12847
Cypress Manufacturing LLC	3089	C	818 772-6592	10055
Da/Pro Rubber Inc	3069	D	661 775-6290	9606
Dansig (chapter S Corporation)	2086	F	661 295-0899	2128
Del West Engineering Inc (PA)	3714	C	661 295-5700	20312
Diversified Images Inc	2759	F	661 702-0003	7301
Donaldson Company Inc	3714	D	661 295-0800	20316
Eckert Zegler Isotope Pdts Inc (HQ)	3829	F	661 309-1010	22191
Electrofilm Mfg Co LLC	3492	D	661 257-2242	13740
Emco Fluid Systems Inc	3823	C	661 295-1015	21580
Exclusive Powder Coatings Inc	3479	F	661 294-9812	13586
Fire Mountain Beverage	2086	E	661 362-0716	2134
Foilflex Products Inc	2759	F	661 702-0775	7320
Forrest Machining Inc	3728	C	661 257-0231	20818
Fruit Growers Supply Company (PA)	2653	E	818 986-6480	5409
G-G Distribution & Dev Co Inc	3494	C	661 257-5700	13766
Galaxy Die & Engineering Inc	3366	E	661 775-9301	11759
Global Aerospace Tech Corp	3728	E	818 407-5600	20826
Gruber Systems Inc	3544	E	661 257-0464	14523
H2scan Corporation	3829	E	661 775-9575	22209
Hardcore Racing Components LLC	3944	F	661 294-5032	23426
Hemisphere Design & Mfg LLC	2541	F	661 294-9500	5068
Hydro Systems Inc (PA)	3431	D	661 775-0686	12014
Ibg Holdings Inc	2844	E	661 702-8680	8768
Indu-Electric North Amer Inc	3568	E	310 578-2144	15285
Industrial Tube Company LLC	3492	D	661 295-4000	13743
Input/Output Technology Inc	3577	C	661 257-1095	15762
ITT Aerospace Controls LLC (HQ)	3728	E	315 568-7258	20850
ITT Aerospace Controls LLC	3728	B	661 295-4000	20851

Mergent email: customerrelations@mergent.com

1490

2019 California
Manufacturers Register

(P-0000) Products & Services Section entry number
(PA)=Parent Co (HQ)=Headquarters (DH)=Div Headquarters

Company	SIC	EMP	PHONE	ENTRY #
ITT Aerospace Controls LLC	3728	E	661 295-4000	20852
J H P & Associates Inc	3511	E	661 799-5888	13999
Kcb Precision	3643	F	661 295-5695	17477
King Henrys Inc	2096	E	661 295-5566	2393
Koito Aviation LLC	3728	F	661 257-2878	20861
LA Turbine (PA)	3511	D	661 294-8290	14001
Lavi Industries (PA)	3446	D	877 275-5284	12873
Lean Manufacturing Group LLC	3541	E	661 702-9400	14388
Leggett & Platt Incorporated	2541	E	661 775-8500	5079
Leiner Health Products Inc	2834	D	661 775-1422	8257
Leonards Molded Products Inc	3069	E	661 253-2227	9632
Lightway Industries Inc.	3646	E	661 257-0286	17628
Lockwood Industries LLC	2672	C	661 702-6999	5567
Luran Inc	3599	F	661 257-6303	16694
Magnum Data Inc	3955	F	800 869-2589	23734
Mastey De Paris Inc	2844	E	661 257-4814	8793
Matrix Concepts LLC	3751	F	661 253-1592	21128
Mechanix Wear Inc (PA)	2381	D	800 222-4296	3602
Medianews Group Inc	2711	C	661 257-5200	5963
Medical Breakthrough Massage	3999	E	408 677-7702	24171
MP Tool Inc	3599	F	661 294-7711	16774
MWsausse & Co Inc (PA)	3625	D	661 257-3311	17289
Mye Technologies Inc	3699	E	661 964-0217	20021
Nasmyth Tmf Inc	3471	D	818 954-9504	13461
Nextclientcom Inc	2741	F	818 550-8989	6541
Northrop Grumman Corporation	3812	A	310 332-0412	21361
Novacap LLC	3675	B	661 295-5920	19301
Oupiin America Inc	3621	F	661 294-0228	17216
Pacific Aero Components Inc (PA)	3728	F	818 841-9258	20900
Pacific Lock Company (PA)	3429	E	661 294-3707	11982
Pacific Metal Stampings Inc	3469	E	661 257-7656	13257
Pacific Wstn Arostructures Inc	3599	F	661 607-0100	16822
Packaging Dist Assembly Group	2631	F	661 607-0600	5358
Palyon Medical Corporation	3845	E	661 705-5601	23033
Paragon Precision Inc	3724	E	661 257-1380	20672
Partsearch Technologies Inc (DH)	3679	E	800 289-0300	19681
Performance Machine Tech Inc	3599	E	661 294-8617	16841
PRC - Desoto International Inc (HQ)	2891	B	661 678-4209	9162
Precision Dynamics Corporation (HQ)	2672	C	818 897-1111	5575
Professional Skin Care Inc (PA)	2844	E	661 257-7771	8826
Prostat First Aid LLC	3842	F	661 705-1256	22797
Qmp Inc	3589	E	661 294-6860	16097
Quadriga USA Enterprises Inc	2759	F	888 669-9994	7455
Quantech Machining Inc	3599	E	661 775-3990	16875
Realwise Inc	7372	F	661 295-9399	25112
Remington Inc	3589	E	661 257-9400	16100
Remo (PA)	3931	B	661 294-5600	23383
Romi Industries Inc	3599	F	661 294-1142	16912
Ronan Engineering Company (PA)	3823	D	661 702-1344	21646
Safe Environment Engrg LP	3679	F	661 295-5500	19715
Santa Clarita Plastic Molding	3089	F	661 294-2257	10359
SCE Gaskets Inc	3053	F	661 728-9200	9554
Schrey & Sons Mold Co Inc	3544	E	661 294-2260	14570
Semco Instruments Inc (DH)	3829	C	661 257-2000	22264
Semiconductor Process Eqp Corp	3559	E	661 257-0193	15030
Servo Dynamics Corporation	3651	E	818 700-8600	17856
SGB Enterprises Inc.	3575	E	661 294-8306	15645
Sgl Technic Inc (DH)	3295	D	661 257-0500	11326
Shimtech Industries US Inc	3728	D	661 295-8620	20931
Skm Industries Inc	3469	F	661 294-8373	13276
Specialty Polymers & Svcs Inc	2891	F	661 294-1790	9171
Steinhausen Inc	3915	F	661 702-1400	23349
Stoll Metalcraft Inc.	3444	C	661 295-0401	12774
Stratasys Direct Inc (DH)	3089	E	661 295-4400	10394
Stratoflight (DH)	3728	D	949 622-0700	20939
Summit Electric & Data Inc	3699	E	661 775-9901	20083
Sunvair Inc (HQ)	3599	D	661 294-3777	16972
Sunvair Overhaul Inc	3728	E	661 257-6123	20941
Synergy Microsystems Inc (DH)	3571	D	858 452-0020	15492
Ta Aerospace Co (HQ)	3069	C	661 775-1100	9682
Ta Aerospace Co	2821	C	661 702-0448	7892
Talladium Inc (PA)	3843	E	661 295-0900	22915
Tara Enterprises Inc	2434	F	661 510-2206	4356
Technical Manufacturing W LLC	3999	E	661 295-7226	24268
Technical Trouble Shooting Inc	3599	E	661 257-1202	16991
Technifex Products LLC	3291	E	661 702-3800	11305
Timemed Labeling Systems Inc (DH)	3069	D	818 897-1111	9685
Transparent Products Inc	3575	E	661 294-9787	15648
Tri Tek Electronics Inc	3679	E	661 295-0020	19770
Triumph Actuation Systms-Valen	3728	C	661 295-1015	20960
True Position Technologies LLC	3599	E	661 294-0030	17015
Universal Hosiery Inc	2252	D	661 702-8444	2817
US Horizon Manufacturing Inc.	3211	E	661 775-1675	10610
Utak Laboratories Inc	2869	E	661 294-3935	9047
V M P Inc	3451	F	661 294-9934	13049
Val-Aero Industries Inc	3599	F	661 252-1047	17029
Valencia Pipe Company	3084	E	661 257-3923	9791
Valley Circuits	3672	F	661 294-0077	18642
Virgil Walker Inc	3441	F	661 797-4101	12274
Virgil Walker Inc	3675	F	661 294-9142	19305
Vitek Indus Video Pdts Inc	3861	F	661 294-8043	23210
Westwood Group	3827	F	661 702-8603	22147
Whitmor Plstic Wire Cable Corp	3496	F	661 257-2400	13865
Winning Team Inc.	2395	F	661 295-1428	3869

VALLECITO, CA - Calaveras County

Company	SIC	EMP	PHONE	ENTRY #
Twisted Oak Winery LLC (PA)	2084	E	209 728-3000	2035

VALLEJO, CA - Napa County

Company	SIC	EMP	PHONE	ENTRY #
Golden State Vintners	2084	E	707 553-6480	1789
Kolkka John	2514	E	707 554-3660	4834
N V Cast Stone LLC	3272	D	707 261-6615	10959
Arcmatic Welding Systems Inc (PA)	7692	F	707 643-5517	25386
Blu Homes Inc (PA)	2452	D	866 887-7997	4569
Carpenter Group	3496	F	707 562-3543	13817
Cordeiro Vault Co (PA)	3272	F	707 552-1045	10909
Dimensions Unlimited	2541	F	707 552-6800	5055
Dreamctchers Empwerment Netwrk	3679	F	707 558-1775	19517
Earthquake Protection Systems	3463	D	707 644-5993	13123
Ghiringhlli Spcialty Foods Inc	2099	C	707 561-7670	2529
Gibson Printing & Publishing (PA)	2711	F	707 643-2552	5863
Hestan Smart Cooking Inc	3469	F	773 710-1538	13216
Luther E Gibson Inc	2721	E	707 643-6104	6211
Mare Island Dry Dock LLC	3731	D	707 652-7356	20999
Meyer Cookware Industries Inc	3469	F	707 551-2800	13249
Meyer Corporation US (HQ)	3469	D	707 551-2800	13250
Moose Boats Inc	3732	F	707 778-9828	21057
NI Industries Inc	3339	E	707 552-4850	11548
Romeros Welding & Mar Svcs Inc.	7692	F	925 550-0518	25432
Syar Industries Inc	1422	E	707 643-3261	317
Titanium Metals Corporation	3356	D	707 552-4850	11637
Vallejo Electric Motor Inc	7694	F	707 552-7488	25470
Western Dovetail Incorporated	2511	E	707 556-3683	4750

VALLEY CENTER, CA - San Diego County

Company	SIC	EMP	PHONE	ENTRY #
Controlled Entrances Inc	3699	F	760 749-1212	19932
Electrowave Ultrasonics Corp	3699	E	858 695-2227	19959
Heatshield Products Inc	3297	E	760 751-0441	11341
Htr LLC	2084	F	760 297-4402	1814
International Decoratives Co	3999	E	760 749-2682	24131

VALLEY FORD, CA - Sonoma County

Company	SIC	EMP	PHONE	ENTRY #
Shubb Capos	3931	E	707 876-3001	23388

VALLEY SPRINGS, CA - Calaveras County

Company	SIC	EMP	PHONE	ENTRY #
Collette Fine Foods LLC (PA)	2099	D	209 430-7814	2493
Vti-Valtronics Inc.	3829	F	209 754-0707	22296

VALLEY VILLAGE, CA - Los Angeles County

Company	SIC	EMP	PHONE	ENTRY #
Cannalogic	3999	F	619 458-0775	24061
FBproductions Inc	2752	D	818 773-9337	6813

VAN NUYS, CA - Los Angeles County

Company	SIC	EMP	PHONE	ENTRY #
Advance Latex Products Inc	2341	E	310 559-8300	3532
Advance Overhead Door Inc	3442	E	818 781-5590	12289
Advanced Mobility Inc	3999	F	818 780-1788	24026
Aeroshear Aviation Svcs Inc (PA)	3728	F	818 779-1650	20719
Alfred Music Group Inc (PA)	2731	E	818 891-5999	6304
All American Cabinetry Inc	2541	D	818 376-0500	5035
Allison-Kaufman Co	3911	D	818 373-5100	23231
Alros Label Co Inc	2759	E	818 781-2403	7232
Alyn Industries Inc	3679	D	818 988-7696	19440
Ambay Circuits Inc	3672	F	818 786-8241	18417
Anheuser-Busch LLC	2082	C	818 989-5300	1559
Archwood Mfg Group Inc	1411	F	818 781-7673	299
Auto-Chlor System Wash Inc	2842	E	818 376-0940	8622
Automated Tape and Label Inc	2672	E	818 908-4400	5547
Avid Technology Inc	3861	C	818 779-7860	23143
Bespoke Coachworks Inc	3711	F	818 571-9900	20131
Bijan Rad Inc	3559	E	818 902-1606	14922
Blake Wire & Cable Corp	3357	F	818 781-8300	11646
Bluebarry Enterprises Inc	2752	F	818 956-0912	6699
Burtree Inc.	3599	E	818 786-4276	16340
Cal Star Systems Group Inc.	3699	E	818 922-2000	19923
Capstone Turbine Corporation (PA)	3511	C	818 734-5300	13991
Chef Merito Inc (PA)	2099	D	818 787-0100	2485
Cicon Engineering Inc (PA)	3679	C	818 909-6060	19490
Clear Water Corporation Inc	3589	F	818 765-8293	16028
Coloron Jewelry Inc	3961	F	818 565-1100	23744
Consolidated Fabricators Corp (PA)	3443	C	818 901-1005	12378
Contex Inc	3851	F	818 788-5836	23085
Cpp/Belwin Inc	2731	E	818 891-5999	6332
Creative Age Publications Inc	2721	E	818 782-7328	6137

Employment Codes: A=Over 500 employees, B=251-500,
C=101-250, D=51-100, E=20-50, F=10-19

2019 California
Manufacturers Register

© Mergent Inc. 1-800-342-5647
1491

GEOGRAPHIC

	SIC	EMP	PHONE	ENTRY #
Csdr International Inc	3674	F	844 330-0664	18794
Custom Muldings Sash Doors Inc	2431	F	818 787-7367	4132
Dal-Tile Corporation	2824	E	818 787-3224	7911
Dee Sign Co	3993	D	818 988-1000	23855
Delta D V H Circuits Inc	3672	F	818 786-8241	18466
Dgcc Inc	2789	F	818 787-5007	7597
Digital Room Holdings Inc **(PA)**	2759	C	310 575-4440	7297
Dolce Dolci LLC	2024	F	818 343-8400	666
Dress To Kill Inc	2331	F	818 994-3890	3232
E Alko Inc	3955	C	818 587-9700	23727
Eco-Gen Energy Inc	3621	F	818 756-4700	17191
Edwards Sheet Metal Supply Inc	3444	F	818 785-8600	12569
Espana Metal Craft Inc	3444	F	818 988-4988	12576
European Elegance Woodwork	2431	F	818 570-9401	4154
Exit Sign Warehouse Inc	3646	F	888 953-3948	17606
Experimental Aircraft Assn	3721	F	818 705-2744	20577
Felix Tool & Engineering	3544	F	818 994-9401	14515
Fitucci LLC	2434	F	818 785-3841	4302
Five Corner Conservation Inc	3599	F	818 792-1805	16501
Flannigans Merchandising Inc	2759	F	818 785-7428	7318
Full Void 2 Inc **(PA)**	2741	D	818 891-5999	6489
Great Western Packaging LLC	2759	F	818 464-3800	7335
H J S Graphics	2752	F	818 782-5490	6845
Harris Corporation	3812	B	818 901-2523	21303
Harris Corporation	3812	B	408 201-8000	21304
Harris Corporation	3625	F	408 201-8000	17276
Hollywood Software Inc	7372	F	818 205-2121	24734
I and E Cabinets Inc	2434	E	818 933-6480	4311
Industrial Electronic Engineer	3577	D	818 787-0311	15760
International Printing & Typsg	2752	F	818 787-6804	6895
Investment Enterprises Inc **(PA)**	2759	E	818 464-3800	7361
Ironhead Studios Inc	2389	F	818 901-7561	3660
Jet/Brella Inc	3724	E	818 786-5480	20666
Katzirs Floor & HM Design Inc	2431	F	818 988-9663	4178
Kimball Nelson Inc	3999	F	310 636-0081	24148
Kimberly-Clark Corporation	2621	F	818 986-2430	5308
Kutzin & Kutzin Inc	2499	F	818 994-0242	4630
Lavi Systems Inc	3728	E	818 373-5400	20865
Linea Pelle Inc **(PA)**	3111	F	310 231-9950	10463
M P M Building Services Inc	2842	D	818 708-9676	8653
Matrix Cab Parts Inc	2431	F	818 782-7022	4190
Microfabrica Inc	3679	E	888 964-2763	19649
Mike Printer Inc	2752	F	818 902-9922	6975
Monarch Art & Frame Inc	2499	E	818 373-6180	4637
Moticont	3699	E	818 785-1800	20019
Munchkin Inc **(PA)**	3085	C	818 893-5000	9801
Nat Aronson & Associates Inc	3052	F	818 787-5160	9501
Neiman/Hoeller Inc	3993	D	818 781-8600	23934
Neo Pacific Holdings Inc	3089	E	818 786-2900	10233
Niknejad Inc	2752	E	310 478-8363	6994
Omega Graphics Printing Inc	2759	F	818 374-9189	7419
Optical Zonu Corporation	3661	F	818 780-9701	17975
Orly International Inc	2844	D	818 994-1001	8808
Palermo Products LLC	2392	F	949 201-9066	3741
Paulsson Inc	1382	F	310 780-2219	144
Pegasus Interprint	2752	F	800 926-9873	7021
Pegasus Press 2010 LLC	2752	D	818 989-3600	7022
Photo Fabricators Inc	3672	F	818 781-1010	18559
Plasma Biolife Services L P	2835	D	818 947-5600	8504
Postcard Press Inc **(PA)**	2759	E	310 747-3800	7441
Precision Glass Bevelling Inc	3229	E	818 989-2727	10665
Printcom Inc	2752	F	818 891-8282	7042
Printrunner LLC	2759	F	888 296-5760	7447
Priority Tech Systems Inc	3699	F	818 756-5413	20046
Qortstone Inc	3281	F	877 899-7678	11274
Rbg Holdings Corp **(PA)**	3949	F	818 782-6445	23633
Renaissance Food Inc	2052	F	818 778-6230	1377
Renaissance Wdwrk & Design Inc	2431	F	818 787-7238	4218
Riggins Engineering Inc	3599	E	818 782-7010	16901
Rof LLC	2326	E	818 933-4000	3119
Rothlisberger Mfg A Cal Corp	3599	F	818 786-9462	16917
RPC Legacy Inc	3429	D	818 787-9000	11988
Sam Vaziri Vance Inc **(PA)**	3851	E	323 822-3955	23121
Sandstone Designs Inc	3272	E	818 787-5005	11000
Scotland Entry Systems Inc	3089	F	818 376-0777	10366
Shelcore Inc **(PA)**	3944	E	818 883-2400	23463
Sistone Inc	2541	E	818 988-9918	5102
Spec Engineering Co Inc	3599	E	818 780-3045	16957
Spinal and Orthopedic Devices	3842	F	818 908-9000	22818
Superior Inds Intl Hldings LLC **(HQ)**	3714	E	818 781-4973	20456
Tek Enterprises Inc	3679	E	818 785-5971	19748
Thermoplaque Company Inc	3999	F	818 988-1080	24269
Thompson Gundrilling Inc	3321	E	323 873-4045	11501
Tigers Plastics Inc	3089	F	818 901-9393	10405
Trio-Tech International **(PA)**	3559	F	818 787-7000	15040

	SIC	EMP	PHONE	ENTRY #
Tyler Technologies Inc	7372	F	818 989-4420	25303
Uruhu Highlands Ltd	3483	F	424 213-9725	13685
Viking Ready Mix Co Inc	3273	E	818 786-2210	11207
Western Bagel Baking Corp **(PA)**	2051	C	818 786-5847	1339
Wsw Corp **(PA)**	3714	F	818 989-5008	20489
Zodiak Services America	3728	D	310 884-7200	20982

VANDENBERG AFB, CA - Santa Barbara County

	SIC	EMP	PHONE	ENTRY #
Arctic Slope World Svcs Inc	3721	A	805 605-7560	20541
United Launch Alliance LLC	3761	D	303 269-5876	21175

VENICE, CA - Los Angeles County

	SIC	EMP	PHONE	ENTRY #
Gamemine LLC	7372	E	310 310-3105	24682
Globalex Corporation	7372	D	310 593-4833	24701
Hall Health and Longevity Cntr	2833	E	310 566-6690	7946
Jody Maronis Italian	2013	E	310 822-5639	497
MA Cher (usa) Inc **(HQ)**	3999	F	310 581-5222	24166
T3 Micro Inc **(PA)**	3999	E	310 452-2888	24263
Wemo Media Inc	7372	E	310 399-8058	25345
Windward Yacht & Repair Inc	3732	F	310 823-4581	21072

VENTURA, CA - Ventura County

	SIC	EMP	PHONE	ENTRY #
Abbs Vision Systems Inc	3851	F	805 642-0499	23076
Aquastar Pool Products Inc	3561	F	877 768-2717	15052
Aqueos Corporation	3533	E	805 676-4330	14207
Art Dreams Home Inc	2499	D	805 642-6444	4606
Art Glass Etc Inc	2431	F	805 644-4494	4106
Automotive Racing Products Inc **(PA)**	3429	D	805 339-2200	11931
Barnett Tool & Engineering	3751	E	805 642-9435	21090
Bell Powder Coating Inc	3479	E	805 658-2233	13558
Bentley-Simonson Inc	1311	D	805 650-2794	24
Biodico Inc	2869	F	805 689-9008	8986
C & R Molds Inc	3089	E	805 658-7098	9997
California Resources Corp	1311	A	805 641-5666	41
Cargo Data Corporation	3829	F	805 650-5922	22176
CCI Mail & Shipping Systems	2542	F	805 658-9123	5133
Channel Isl Opto Mech	3599	F	805 644-2153	16376
Chapala Iron & Manufacturing	3312	F	805 654-9803	11388
Chem-O-Lene Co	1389	F	805 648-6247	196
Coastal Connections	3661	E	805 644-5051	17934
Coca-Cola Refreshments USA Inc	2086	C	805 644-2211	2121
Connect Systems Inc	3663	E	805 642-7184	18077
Coorstek Inc	3545	D	805 644-5583	14617
Coorstek Inc	3545	E	805 644-5583	14618
Cord Intrnational/Hana Ola Rec	3652	F	805 648-7881	17889
Cummins Pacific LLC	3519	E	805 644-7281	14025
Dairy Farmers America Inc	2026	D	805 653-0042	721
Dcor LLC **(PA)**	1382	D	805 535-2000	130
Dcor LLC	1382	D	805 576-1200	131
Dna Health Institute Llc	2869	F	805 654-9363	9003
Dow-Key Microwave Corporation	3625	C	805 650-0260	17266
Dynatest Consulting Inc	3825	F	805 648-2230	21742
Edwards Assoc Cmmnications Inc **(PA)**	2672	B	805 658-2626	5559
Edwards Enterprises	3545	B	805 644-5583	14629
Exam Room Supply LLC	3845	F	805 298-3631	22976
Fabricmate Systems Inc	3089	F	805 642-7470	10098
Fca LLC	2441	F	805 477-9901	4441
Fed Ex Kinkos Ofc & Print Ctr	2752	F	805 604-6000	6814
Fence Factory	3446	F	805 644-5482	12856
Flir Eoc LLC	3826	E	805 642-4645	21960
Fnc Medical Corporation	2844	E	805 644-7576	8750
Frito-Lay North America Inc	2096	E	805 658-1668	2385
Glasspoole Masonry Inc	3271	F	805 368-0129	10852
Goldenwood Truss Corporation	2439	D	805 659-2520	4406
Guernsey Coating Laboratory	3479	F	805 642-1508	13599
Hammerhead Industries Inc	3089	F	805 658-9922	10132
Hampton Fitness Products Ltd	3949	F	805 339-9733	23580
Hearts Delight	2339	E	805 648-7123	3427
Hennis Enterprises Inc	2821	E	805 477-0257	7838
Herald Printing Ltd **(PA)**	2752	E	805 647-1870	6853
High Tech Pet Products Inc	3999	E	805 644-1797	24117
HK Canning Inc **(PA)**	2033	E	805 652-1392	806
HMcompany	3599	E	805 650-2651	16569
Implantech Associates Inc	3842	E	805 289-1665	22750
Interstate Rebar Inc	3312	E	805 643-6892	11401
Jetair Technologies LLC	3564	E	805 654-7000	15163
Jh Biotech Inc **(PA)**	2875	E	805 650-8933	9084
Juengermann Inc	3493	E	805 644-7165	13750
Key Energy Services Inc	1389	E	805 653-1300	234
Lamps Plus Inc	3646	F	805 642-9007	17624
Linktech Quick Couplings Inc	3498	E	805 339-0055	13894
Lockheed Martin Corporation	3812	E	805 650-4600	21333
Lynch Ready Mix Concrete Co	3273	F	805 647-2817	11138
Magna Charger Inc	2396	D	805 642-8833	3905
Magnum Fence and Security Inc	3446	F	805 641-3656	12878
Magnuson Products LLC	3714	E	805 642-8833	20393

Mergent email: customerrelations@mergent.com

1492

2019 California
Manufacturers Register

(P-0000) Products & Services Section entry number
(PA)=Parent Co (HQ)=Headquarters (DH)=Div Headquarters

Company	SIC	EMP	PHONE	ENTRY #
Mini-Flex Corporation	3599	F	805 644-1474	16755
Motran Industries Inc	3621	F	661 257-4995	17212
Naso Industries Corporation	3672	E	805 650-1231	18538
National Graphics LLC	2752	E	805 644-9212	6989
Neon Ideas	3993	F	805 648-7681	23935
Oil Country Manufacturing	3533	C	805 643-1200	14237
Omnisil	3674	E	805 644-2514	19056
P K Engineering & Mfg Co Inc	3841	E	805 628-9556	22577
P-Americas LLC	2086	C	805 641-4200	2161
Parker-Hannifin Corporation	3594	F	805 658-2984	16172
Point Blanks Inc	2085	F	805 643-8616	2074
Quality Machine Shop Inc	3599	F	805 653-7944	16873
Reyes Coca-Cola Bottling LLC	2086	D	805 644-2211	2193
Richard Yarbrough	1389	E	805 643-1021	265
Robert M Hadley Company Inc	3677	D	805 658-7286	19359
Ron Ungar	3565	F	805 642-3555	15226
Schlumberger Technology Corp	1389	E	805 642-8230	270
Schlumberger Technology Corp	1389	F	805 644-8325	273
Sessa Manufacturing & Welding	3469	E	805 644-2284	13274
Skjonberg Controls Inc	3625	F	805 650-0877	17310
SL Power Electronics Corp (PA)	3679	D	800 235-5929	19727
Solimar Energy LLC	1382	F	805 643-4100	153
Spin Shades Corporation	3648	E	805 650-4849	17732
State Ready Mix Inc (PA)	3273	E	805 647-2817	11188
Streamline Dsign Slkscreen Inc	2759	F	805 884-1025	7500
Streamline Dsign Slkscreen Inc (PA)	2329	D	805 884-1025	3192
Strenumed Inc	3842	F	805 477-1000	22823
Sun Power Source (PA)	3648	F	805 644-2520	17733
Swiss Productions Inc	3083	E	805 654-8379	9767
The Sloan Company Inc (PA)	3648	C	805 676-3200	17737
TMJ Solutions Inc	3842	F	805 650-3391	22833
Total Structures Inc	3648	E	805 676-3322	17740
Tricoss Inc	3495	F	805 644-4107	13805
Trinity Steel Corporation	3441	F	805 648-3486	12264
Trupart Manufacturing Inc	3541	F	805 644-4107	14420
Vacumetrics Inc	3841	F	805 644-7461	22663
Vasari Plaster and Stucco LLC	3299	F	805 845-2497	11374
Vastcircuits & Mfg LLC	3679	F	805 421-4299	19781
Venoco Inc	1311	E	805 644-1400	85
Ventura Coastal LLC (PA)	2037	D	805 653-7000	971
Ventura Harbor Boatyard Inc	3732	E	805 654-1433	21066
Ventura Hydrulic Mch Works Inc	3593	E	805 656-1760	16161
W L Rubottom Co	2434	D	805 648-6943	4367
Weatherford International LLC	1389	F	805 643-1279	298
Window Products Management Inc	2431	F	805 677-6800	4258
Wireless Technology Inc	3651	F	805 339-9696	17881
Wm J Matson Company	3479	F	805 684-9410	13682
Wombat Products Inc	3089	E	805 794-1767	10449

VERNON, CA - Los Angeles County

Company	SIC	EMP	PHONE	ENTRY #
4 You Apparel Inc	2335	F	323 583-4242	3288
A F C Hydraulic Seals	3053	F	323 585-9110	9514
A Rudin Inc (PA)	2512	D	323 589-5547	4758
A&A Global Imports Inc	3089	C	323 767-5990	9916
Aaron Corporation	2339	C	323 235-5959	3366
Ace Pleating & Stitching Inc	2395	E	323 582-8213	3825
Ajax Forge Company (PA)	3462	E	323 582-6307	13091
Ajax Forge Company	3462	E	323 582-6307	13092
All Star Clothing Inc	2331	F	323 233-7773	3211
All-American Mfg Co	3432	E	323 581-6293	12020
Amcor Industries Inc	3714	E	323 585-2852	20251
American Bottling Company	2086	B	323 268-7779	2089
AMP Plus Inc	3647	D	323 231-2600	17659
Anayas Cutting Inc	2335	D	323 582-5758	3292
Apparelway Inc	2297	F	323 581-5888	2965
Arcadia Inc (PA)	3355	C	323 269-7300	11614
Archipelago Inc	2844	C	213 743-9200	8696
Art Masterpiece Gallery	2392	F	323 277-9448	3707
AS Match Dyeing Co Inc	2261	C	323 277-0470	2877
Atlas Galvanizing LLC	3479	E	323 587-6247	13554
Atra International Traders Inc	2671	E	562 864-3885	5518
Atrevete Inc	2331	F	323 277-5551	3214
B D and G Sandblasting Co	3471	F	323 583-1741	13343
Bailey 44 LLC	2331	E	213 228-1930	3215
Baker Commodities Inc (PA)	2077	C	323 268-2801	1519
Baker Commodities Inc	2077	E	323 318-8260	1522
Baker Coupling Company Inc	3498	E	323 583-3444	13878
Bakery Depot Inc	2051	A	323 261-8388	1181
Bar-S Foods Co	2013	B	323 589-3600	467
Barksdale Inc (DH)	3829	C	323 583-6243	22170
Bcbg Maxazria Entrmt LLC	2339	F	323 277-4713	3382
Bender Ccp Inc	3599	D	707 745-9970	16317
Berney-Karp Inc	3269	E	323 260-7122	10828
Betterbilt Chemicals	2819	F	323 266-7111	7754
Big Bang Clothing Inc (PA)	2339	F	323 233-7773	3385
Bodycote Thermal Proc Inc	3398	F	323 264-0111	11796
Bodycote Usa Inc	3398	F	323 264-0111	11802
Bon Appetit Danish Inc	2051	D	323 584-9500	1212
Brentwood Appliances Inc	3639	F	323 266-4600	17411
California Coast Clothing LLC	2211	F	323 923-3870	2729
California Combining Corp	2295	E	323 589-5727	2957
California Feather Inds Inc	2392	F	323 585-5800	3713
Caltex Plastics Inc (PA)	2673	E	800 584-7303	5590
Camino Real Foods Inc	2038	B	323 585-6599	984
Camino Real Foods Inc (PA)	2099	B	323 585-6599	2481
Cardenas Enterprises Inc	2542	F	323 588-0137	5132
Cenveo Worldwide Limited	2679	C	323 262-6000	5703
Certified Steel Treating Corp	3471	E	323 583-8711	13368
Charman Manufacturing Inc	3317	E	213 489-7000	11475
Chasin Foods Inc	2092	E	323 544-0000	2310
Chua & Sons Inc	2241	E	323 588-8044	2798
Chunma Usa Inc	3161	F	323 846-0077	10518
Classic Slipcover Inc	2392	F	323 583-0804	3714
Clougherty Packing LLC (DH)	2011	B	323 583-4621	429
Colorfast Dye & Print Hse Inc	2752	C	323 581-1656	6742
Command Packaging LLC	2673	C	323 980-0918	5595
Commercial Sand Blast Company	3471	F	323 581-8672	13377
Complete Clothing Company (PA)	2335	D	323 277-1470	3303
Complete Garment Inc	2253	E	323 846-3731	2831
Continental Vitamin Co Inc	2834	C	323 581-0176	8120
Corporate Graphics Intl Inc	2752	D	323 826-3440	6761
Cortez Furniture Mfg Inc (PA)	2512	E	323 581-5935	4766
Cottyon Inc	2211	E	323 589-1563	2732
CR Laurence Co Inc (HQ)	3714	C	323 588-1281	20299
Crestone LLC	2361	E	323 588-8857	3575
Crown Carton Company Inc	2653	E	323 582-3053	5404
Ctd Machines Inc	3541	F	213 689-4455	14366
Culinary Brands Inc	2038	C	626 289-3000	988
Culinary International LLC	2099	C	626 289-3000	2498
D D Office Products Inc	2621	E	323 582-3400	5278
David Garment Cutng Fusing Svc	2326	F	323 583-9885	3101
Demenno/Kerdoon Holdings	2992	D	323 268-3387	9430
Denim-Tech LLC	3582	D	323 277-8998	15929
Design Concepts Inc	2339	F	323 277-4771	3405
Destiney Group Inc	2211	F	323 581-4477	2733
Dm Collective Inc	2253	E	323 923-2400	2833
E G Meat and Provision Inc (PA)	2013	F	323 588-5333	481
Edris Plastics Mfg Inc	3089	E	323 581-7000	10087
Elecoco Inc	2339	E	213 627-2377	3410
Ema Textiles Inc	2253	E	323 589-9800	2834
Engineered Application LLC	3479	F	323 585-2894	13584
Engineered Coating Tech Inc	2851	F	323 588-0260	8904
Erge Designs LLC	2331	F	310 614-9197	3234
Evergreen Industries Inc (DH)	3821	E	323 583-1331	21471
Evonik Corporation	2899	E	323 264-0311	9249
F Gavina & Sons Inc	2095	B	323 582-0671	2340
F I O Imports Inc	2099	B	323 263-5100	2515
Fantasy Activewear Inc (PA)	2253	E	213 705-4111	2835
Fantasy Activewear Inc	2253	E	323 983-9988	2836
Fantasy Dyeing & Finishing Inc	2253	D	323 983-9988	2837
Fishermans Pride Prcessors Inc	2092	F	323 232-1980	2313
Florentynas Fresh Pasta	2099	F	213 742-9374	2521
Flores Design Fine Furn Inc	2512	E	323 585-3200	4774
Flowserve Corporation	3561	B	323 584-1890	15063
Fresh Packing Corporation	2032	F	213 612-0136	757
G & G Quality Case Co Inc	3161	D	323 233-2482	10522
Galaxy Press Inc	2731	E	323 399-3433	6342
Gasser-Olds Inc	3366	E	323 583-9031	11760
General Mills Inc	2041	E	323 584-3433	1039
Geo Plastics	3089	E	323 277-8106	10116
Global Truss America LLC	3354	D	323 415-6225	11588
Golden West Food Group Inc (PA)	2011	E	888 807-3663	438
Goldman Global Greenfield Inc	3089	F	323 589-3444	10124
Great American Packaging	2673	E	323 582-2247	5601
Gts Living Foods LLC	2086	A	323 581-7787	2137
H & L Apparel Enterprise Inc	2331	F	323 589-1563	3243
H P Applications	3398	F	323 585-2894	11813
Haley Indus Cctings Linings Inc	3479	F	323 588-8086	13600
Hanger	3842	F	323 238-7738	22740
Hannibal Industries Inc (PA)	3317	C	323 513-1200	11479
Hannibal Material Handling	2542	C	323 587-4060	5144
Hollywood Lamp & Shade Co	3641	E	323 585-3999	17429
Isabelle Handbags Inc	3171	E	323 277-9888	10550
J & J Snack Foods Corp Cal (HQ)	2052	C	323 581-0171	1366
J H Textiles Inc	2299	E	323 585-4124	3002
Jaya Apparel Group LLC (PA)	2339	D	323 584-3500	3436
Jejomi Designs Inc	2386	E	323 584-4211	3616
Jml Textile Inc	2211	D	323 584-2323	2748
JNJ Apparel Inc	2339	F	323 584-9700	3437
Jobbers Meat Packing Co Inc	2011	F	323 585-6328	440
Js Glass Wholesale	3231	F	213 746-5577	10709

Employment Codes: A=Over 500 employees, B=251-500,
C=101-250, D=51-100, E=20-50, F=10-19

2019 California
Manufacturers Register

© Mergent Inc. 1-800-342-5647

1493

GEOGRAPHIC

	SIC	EMP	PHONE	ENTRY #
K & M Packing Co Inc	2011	C	323 585-5318	441
Karen Kane Inc (PA)	2339	C	323 588-0000	3442
Katie K Inc	2389	F	323 589-3030	3663
Kennedy Name Plate Co Inc	3479	E	323 585-0121	13607
Kim & Cami Productions Inc	2339	E	323 584-1300	3446
Koral LLC	2329	E	323 391-1060	3169
Koral Industries LLC (PA)	2339	D	323 585-5343	3449
L A Air Line Inc	2261	E	323 585-1088	2883
L A S A M Inc	2361	F	323 586-8717	3581
La Spec Industries Inc.	3646	F	323 588-8746	17623
Lac Bleu Inc	2339	F	213 973-5335	3452
LAT LLC	2339	E	323 233-3017	3453
Latourette Lift Services	3537	F	323 262-9111	14333
Lifoam Industries LLC	3081	F	323 587-1934	9713
Love Marks Inc (PA)	2331	F	323 859-8770	3254
Lubricating Specialties Co	2992	E	562 776-4000	9443
Luppen Holdings Inc (PA)	3469	F	323 581-8121	13243
Mahar Manufacturing Corp (PA)	3942	E	323 581-9988	23398
Makers Usa Inc	2322	F	323 582-1800	3065
Marspring Corporation (PA)	2273	E	323 589-5637	2932
Marspring Corporation	2515	E	800 522-5252	4870
Marspring Corporation	2515	E	310 484-6849	4871
Matheson Tri-Gas Inc	2813	F	323 773-2777	7705
Metal Products Engineering	3398	E	323 581-8121	11825
Mexapparel Inc (PA)	2326	F	323 364-8600	3113
Mikawaya (PA)	2051	E	323 587-5504	1291
Mixed Nuts Inc	2068	E	323 587-6887	1498
Mjck Corporation	2253	E	888 992-8437	2852
Modern Pattern & Fndry Co Inc	3324	E	323 583-4921	11517
Ms2 Technologies LLC	3356	F	310 277-4110	11633
Nanka Seimen Co	2098	F	323 585-9967	2431
National Corset Supply House (PA)	2341	D	323 261-0265	3540
New Chef Fashion Inc	2311	D	323 581-0300	3036
Niki-Viki Apparel Inc.	2211	F	323 587-5055	2753
Norman Paper and Foam Co Inc	2671	E	323 582-7132	5527
Norton Packaging Inc	3089	D	323 588-6167	10245
Nuconic Packaging LLC	3089	E	323 588-9033	10248
Oak Manufacturing Company Inc.	3581	F	323 581-8087	15924
Overhill Farms Inc (DH)	2038	E	323 582-9977	1006
Overhill Farms Inc.	2038	C	323 584-4375	1007
P&Y T-Shrts Silk Screening Inc.	3552	F	323 585-4604	14777
Pabco Building Products LLC	3275	D	323 581-6113	11224
Pacific Boulevard Inc.	2335	F	323 581-1656	3331
Packaging Corporation America.	2653	D	323 263-7581	5446
Pactiv Packaging Inc (DH)	2821	D	323 513-9000	7863
Pages Produce Company	2033	D	323 277-3660	848
Papa Cantellas Incorporated	2013	E	323 584-7272	513
Paper Surce Converting Mfg Inc	2621	E	323 583-3800	5324
Patterson Kincaid LLC	2339	F	323 584-3559	3476
Peerless Materials Company (PA)	2842	E	323 266-0313	8665
People Trend Inc	2329	F	213 995-5555	3184
Pershing Foods	2096	F	323 589-1658	2397
Peter K Inc (PA)	2339	E	323 585-5343	3479
Pjy Inc	2211	E	323 583-7737	2758
Popcornopolis LLC (PA)	2064	C	310 414-6700	1448
Ppp LLC	2821	E	323 581-6058	7875
Praxair Inc	2813	E	323 588-8181	7718
Princess Paper Inc	2676	E	323 588-4777	5668
Procases Inc	2441	F	323 585-4447	4446
Punch Press Products Inc.	3544	D	323 581-7151	14564
R A Reed Electric Company (PA)	7694	E	323 587-2284	25465
R B R Meat Company Inc.	2011	D	323 973-4868	447
Rcrv Inc	2673	E	323 235-7332	5617
RE Bilt Metalizing Co	3599	F	323 277-8200	16889
Rebecca International Inc	2395	E	323 973-2602	3859
Rehrig Pacific Company (HQ)	3089	C	800 421-6244	10328
Rehrig Pacific Holdings Inc (PA)	3089	F	323 262-5145	10329
Reliance Upholstery Supply Inc	2299	F	800 522-5252	3015
Republic Furniture Mfg Inc	2512	E	323 235-2144	4807
Reynaldos Mexican Food Co LLC (PA)	2032	C	562 803-3188	772
Riah Fashion Inc	2339	F	323 325-7308	3490
RJ Acquisition Corp (PA)	2759	C	323 318-1107	7471
Rmla Inc	2369	D	213 749-4333	3594
Romeo Systems Inc	3699	C	323 675-2180	20061
Rotax Incorporated	2339	E	323 589-5999	3491
Royal Trim	2396	E	323 583-2121	3916
S & C Foods Inc	2064	E	323 205-6887	1450
S S Schaffer Co Inc	3541	F	323 560-1430	14408
Sandberg Furniture Mfg Co Inc (PA)	2511	C	323 582-0711	4739
Sara Lee Fresh Inc	2051	A	215 347-5500	1318
Sas Textiles Inc	2259	E	323 277-5555	2875
Second Generation Inc	3651	E	213 743-8700	17855
Selectra Industries Corp.	2341	E	323 581-8500	3544
Sewing Collection Inc.	3053	D	323 264-2223	9558
Sffi Company Inc (PA)	2033	E	323 586-0000	857

	SIC	EMP	PHONE	ENTRY #
Shara-Tex Inc	2257	E	323 587-7200	2867
Siemens Industry Inc	3569	E	323 277-1500	15360
Sign of Times Inc.	2679	E	323 826-9766	5735
Simply Fresh Fruit Inc	2033	D	323 586-0000	858
SJ&I Bias Binding & Tex Co Inc	2396	E	213 747-5271	3920
Softmax Inc	2342	F	213 718-2100	3554
Southwest Processors Inc	2048	F	323 269-9876	1166
Spirit Clothing Company	2339	E	213 784-0251	3503
Square H Brands Inc.	2013	C	323 267-4600	528
Standard Bias Binding Co Inc	2396	E	323 277-9763	3922
Starco Enterprises Inc (PA)	3559	D	323 266-7111	15032
Stone Harbor Inc	2299	E	323 277-2777	3019
Streets Ahead Inc	2387	E	323 277-0860	3633
Superior Electric Mtr Svc Inc	7694	F	323 583-1040	25468
Superior Graphic Packaging Inc	2752	D	323 263-8400	7123
T & T Foods Inc	2032	E	323 588-2158	776
Tadashi Shoji & Associates Inc (PA)	2335	D	213 627-7145	3341
Tagtime U S A Inc	2679	B	323 587-1555	5740
Tajima USA Dissolving Corp	3446	F	323 588-1281	12896
Tapatio Foods LLC	2035	F	323 587-8933	935
Team Fashion	2331	F	323 589-3388	3275
Tempted Apparel Corp	2339	E	323 859-2480	3517
Teva Foods Inc	2099	E	323 267-8110	2681
The Ligature Inc	2759	F	800 421-8703	7517
The Ligature Inc (HQ)	2752	E	323 585-6000	7133
Three Plus One Inc	2331	E	213 623-3070	3278
Tile Guild Inc	3253	F	323 581-3770	10796
Tom York Enterprises Inc	3089	E	323 581-6194	10407
Topnotch Foods Inc.	2099	F	323 586-2007	2684
Transhumance Holding Co Inc	2013	E	323 583-5503	532
Tremco Incorporated	2952	E	323 587-3014	9419
Trend Chasers LLC	3199	E	213 749-2661	10583
Tube Rags	2258	E	323 264-7770	2871
Twenty-Niners Provisions Inc	2015	E	323 233-7864	552
Two Lads Inc (PA)	3965	E	323 584-0064	23779
Union Ice Company	2097	E	323 277-1000	2422
Unirex Corp	3674	E	323 589-4000	19246
UPD INC	3942	D	323 588-8811	23403
US Garment LLC	2326	E	323 415-6464	3125
US Radiator Corporation (PA)	3714	E	323 826-0965	20479
Vernon Machine and Foundry	3999	F	323 277-0550	24281
Vest Inc	3317	D	800 421-6370	11490
W & W Concept Inc	2339	E	323 233-9202	3527
W5 Concepts Inc	2331	E	323 231-2415	3287
Westaire Engineering Inc	3585	E	323 587-3347	16000
Western Abrasives Inc	3291	F	323 588-1245	11308
Westgate Mfg Inc	3699	F	877 805-2252	20111
YC Textile Inc	2211	F	323 233-9833	2770
Yen-Nhai Inc.	2512	E	323 584-1315	4819
Yonekyu USA Inc	2013	D	323 581-4194	536
Zk Enterprises Inc	2329	E	213 622-7012	3207
Zx Vecor	3229	F	323 587-7100	10673

VICTORVILLE, CA - San Bernardino County

	SIC	EMP	PHONE	ENTRY #
B Brays Card Inc	2752	F	760 265-4720	6677
Boeing Company	3721	A	760 246-0273	20553
California Bio-Mass Inc (PA)	2499	E	760 246-7946	4610
Customplanetcom Inc	2759	F	760 508-2648	7293
Demag Cranes & Components Corp	3536	E	909 880-8800	14296
Devoll Rubber Mfg Group Inc	3069	F	760 246-0142	9607
Exportech Worldwide LLC	3571	F	909 278-9477	15412
General Electric Company	3721	E	760 530-5200	20588
HI Desert Forklift Services	3537	F	760 241-4575	14326
Johns Incredible Pizza Co	2099	D	760 951-1111	2546
Lmg National Publishing Inc	2711	D	760 241-7744	5915
Mars Petcare Us Inc	2047	E	760 261-7900	1117
Mojave Copy & Printing Inc	2752	F	760 241-7898	6978
Newell Brands Inc	3089	F	760 246-2700	10235
Paradise Manufacturing Co Inc.	2394	C	909 477-3460	3803
Protech Minerals Inc	3255	F	760 245-3441	10800
Reyes Coca-Cola Bottling LLC	2086	E	760 241-2653	2209

VIEW PARK, CA - Los Angeles County

	SIC	EMP	PHONE	ENTRY #
Outdoor Recreation Group (PA)	2393	E	323 226-0830	3768

VILLA PARK, CA - Orange County

	SIC	EMP	PHONE	ENTRY #
Kett	3826	F	714 974-8837	21980
Quality Countertops Inc.	2541	F	909 597-6888	5097

VISALIA, CA - Tulare County

	SIC	EMP	PHONE	ENTRY #
AFP Advanced Food Products LLC	2032	C	559 627-2070	744
Approved Turbo Components	3724	F	559 627-3600	20644
Arctic Silver Incorporated	2992	F	559 740-0912	9423
Bluescope Buildings N Amer Inc	3448	C	559 651-5300	12921
Bushnell Industries Inc	2842	F	559 651-9039	8628
California Dairies Inc (PA)	2026	F	559 625-2200	713
Chef Brand Foods	2051	E	559 651-1696	1222

Mergent email: customerrelations@mergent.com

1494

2019 California
Manufacturers Register

(P-0000) Products & Services Section entry number
(PA)=Parent Co (HQ)=Headquarters (DH)=Div Headquarters

	SIC	EMP	PHONE	ENTRY #
Cnc Machining Service Inc	3469	F	559 732-5599	13184
Corrwood Containers	2449	E	559 651-0335	4519
Danair Inc (PA)	3541	E	559 734-1961	14368
Diamond Crystal Brands Inc	2099	E	559 651-7782	2505
Diamond Perforated Metals Inc	3469	D	559 651-1889	13194
Edeniq Inc	2869	D	559 302-1777	9004
Essilor Laboratories Amer Inc	3851	E	800 624-6672	23094
Food Machinery Sales Inc	3565	D	559 651-2339	15206
Graphic Packaging Intl LLC	2621	E	559 651-3535	5285
Hellwig Products Company Inc	3714	E	559 734-7451	20360
Hydrite Chemical Co	2819	E	559 651-3450	7782
Idea Printing & Graphics Inc	2752	F	559 733-4149	6869
Information Resources Inc	7372	F	559 732-0324	24771
International Paper Company	2621	C	559 651-1416	5289
John Bean Technologies Corp	3556	C	559 651-8300	14864
Jostens Inc	3911	C	559 622-5200	23280
Kaweah Container Inc (HQ)	2653	D	559 651-7850	5433
Kawneer Company Inc	3446	C	559 651-4000	12870
Kens Stakes & Supplies	2499	F	559 747-1313	4629
Oxbo International Corporation	3523	F	559 897-7012	14090
Pace International LLC	2842	E	559 651-4877	8661
Pacific Coast Supply LLC	3275	E	559 651-2185	11225
Pacific Southwest Cont LLC	2653	D	559 651-5500	5443
Packers Manufacturing Inc	3556	E	559 732-4886	14876
Pactiv LLC	3089	C	909 622-1151	10263
Precision Forklift	3537	F	559 805-5487	14342
Premier Trailer Manufacturing	3799	E	559 651-2212	21239
R Lang Company	3442	D	559 651-0701	12344
Screw Conveyor Pacific Corp	3535	E	559 651-2131	14285
Sorma USA LLC	2673	B	559 651-1269	5625
Spraying Devices Inc	3524	F	559 734-5555	14134
Stainless Technologies LLC	7692	F	559 651-0460	25437
Standard Lumber Company Inc (HQ)	2448	E	559 651-2037	4508
Tempo Plastic Co	3086	F	559 651-7711	9887
TI Inc	2873	F	559 972-1475	9075
Torian Group Inc	7372	F	559 733-1940	25288
Tri-Mag Inc	3679	E	559 651-2222	19771
Trical Inc	2879	F	559 651-0736	9115
US Cotton LLC	2844	B	559 651-3015	8858
Ventura Coastal LLC	2037	F	559 737-9836	972
Visalia Ctr 4 Ambltry Med & Sv	3842	E	559 740-4094	22841
Visalia Electric Motor Sp Inc	7694	F	559 651-0606	25472
Voltage Multipliers Inc (PA)	3674	C	559 651-1402	19265
West Coast Sand Gravel	1442	E	559 625-9426	392

VISTA, CA - San Diego County

	SIC	EMP	PHONE	ENTRY #
Accutech LLC	3841	E	760 599-6555	22313
Accutek Packaging Equipment Co (PA)	3565	E	760 734-4177	15192
Acells Corp	3826	E	760 727-6666	21892
Addition Mfg Tech CA Inc	3542	E	760 597-5220	14425
Advanced Web Offset Inc	2759	D	760 727-1700	7224
All One God Faith Inc	2841	C	844 937-2551	8588
Alvarado Micro Precision Inc	3541	F	760 598-0186	14361
Ameramatic Vtech LLC	2111	F	760 688-8561	2703
American General Tool Group	3011	E	760 745-7993	9459
Amron International Inc	3949	D	760 208-6500	23502
Apem Inc	3679	D	760 598-2518	19445
Apollo Sprayers Intl Inc	3563	F	760 727-8300	15117
Applied Membranes Inc (PA)	3589	D	760 727-3711	16009
Aqua-Lung America Inc (PA)	3949	C	760 597-5000	23505
Architctral Mlwk Slutions Inc	2431	F	760 510-6440	4103
Avid Lyfe Inc	2339	F	888 510-2517	3377
Aza Industries Inc (PA)	3949	E	760 560-0440	23510
Aztec Technology Corporation (PA)	3441	E	760 727-2300	12115
Bachem Americas Inc	2834	C	888 422-2436	8058
Baked In Sun	2051	C	760 591-9045	1180
Biofilm Inc	3841	D	760 727-9030	22369
Blue Sky Energy Inc	3629	F	760 597-1642	17334
Boom Movement LLC	3651	D	410 358-3600	17778
C Enterprises LP	3577	D	760 599-5111	15694
Cabo International	2211	F	760 597-9199	2728
California Cstm Furn & Uphl Co	2396	E	760 727-1444	3882
Carbide Company LLC	3545	E	760 477-1000	14614
Carturner Inc (PA)	3829	F	760 598-7448	22177
Chandler Signs LLC	3993	D	760 734-1708	23843
Clarity H2o LLC	3589	F	619 993-4780	16026
Conamco SA De CV	3843	D	760 586-4356	22862
Continental Litho LLC	2752	F	760 598-0291	6757
Coorstek Vista Inc	3297	C	760 542-7065	11340
Csi Technologies Inc	3675	F	760 682-2222	19293
Datron Wrld Communications Inc (PA)	3663	C	760 597-1500	18083
Ddh Enterprise Inc (PA)	3643	C	760 599-0171	17460
Dei Headquarters Inc	3669	B	760 598-6200	18319
Dei Holdings Inc (HQ)	3669	C	760 598-6200	18320
Denso International Amer Inc	3714	F	760 597-7400	20314
Denso Wreless Systems Amer Inc	3663	C	760 734-4600	18085
Dig Corporation	3523	D	760 727-0914	14059
Distinctive Plastics Inc	3089	D	760 599-9100	10072
Diversified Mfg Cal Inc	3599	F	760 599-9280	16442
Diversified Tool & Die	3469	E	760 598-9100	13196
Dj Orthopedics LLC	3842	F	760 727-1280	22716
Djo Global Inc (DH)	3842	A	760 727-1280	22717
Douglas Technologies Group Inc (PA)	3714	E	760 758-5560	20318
Dss-Cctv LLC	3663	F	609 850-9498	18091
Dutek Incorporated	3699	F	760 599-0171	19950
E/G Electro-Graph Inc	3674	D	760 438-9090	18810
Earthlite LLC (DH)	2514	D	760 599-1112	4830
Eden Beauty Concepts Inc	2844	E	760 330-9941	8744
Ellison Biner	3565	D	760 598-6500	15205
Enaqua	3589	E	760 599-2644	16037
Enertron Technologies Inc	3646	E	800 537-7649	17600
Epic Boats LLC (PA)	3732	F	760 542-6060	21035
Excellent Coatings Inc	2899	F	760 598-1234	9250
Exit Light Co Inc	3646	F	877 352-3948	17605
Fat Quarters Quilt Shop	2211	F	760 758-8308	2738
Ferro Corporation	2819	F	442 224-6100	7777
Flotron Inc	3544	E	760 727-2700	14516
Flux Power Holdings Inc (PA)	3691	E	877 505-3589	19809
Frontier Concrete Inc	3273	F	760 724-4483	11109
Fujikura Composite America Inc	3949	E	760 598-6060	23566
Greenlee Textron Inc	3825	D	760 598-8900	21767
Greenlee Tools Inc	3825	D	760 598-8900	21768
Gw Services LLC (DH)	3581	E	760 560-1111	15922
H P Solutions Inc	3549	F	760 727-2880	14754
Hatch Outdoors Inc	3949	F	760 734-4343	23581
Henry Machine Inc	3599	F	760 734-6792	16559
HI Rez Digital Solutions	2752	F	760 597-2650	6857
Horstman Manufacturing Co Inc	3714	E	760 598-2100	20364
Hruby Orbital Systems Inc	3589	F	760 936-8054	16050
Hydrocomponents & Tech Inc	3589	F	760 598-0189	16051
IDI Tools International LLC	3423	F	760 598-8888	11897
Imagine Communications Corp	3663	F	760 936-4000	18129
Innovative Metal Products Inc	3499	E	760 734-1010	13949
Integrated Mfg Solutions LLC	3999	E	760 599-4300	24129
Intubrite LLC	3841	F	760 727-1900	22487
J & B Manufacturing Corp	3231	C	760 846-6316	10707
J & D Laboratories Inc	2833	B	844 453-5227	7952
J A English II Inc	3089	E	760 598-5333	10159
J-Mark Manufacturing Inc	3469	E	760 727-6956	13229
Javo Beverage Company Inc	2087	D	760 560-5286	2270
K & K Laboratories Inc	2834	E	760 758-2352	8241
Kammerer Enterprises Inc	3281	C	760 560-0550	11258
Killion Industries Inc (PA)	2541	D	760 727-5102	5076
L & M Machining Center Inc	3599	F	760 437-3810	16669
Lancer Orthodontics Inc (PA)	3843	E	760 744-5585	22890
Leemarc Industries LLC	2329	E	760 598-0505	3172
Leica Biosystems Imaging Inc	3841	C	760 539-1100	22507
LMI Aerospace Inc	3728	C	760 597-7066	20868
LMI Aerospace Inc	3441	C	760 599-4477	12197
M Klemme Technology Corp	3651	F	760 727-0593	17827
Machine Vision Products Inc (PA)	3827	D	760 438-1138	22102
McCain Manufacturing Inc	3441	D	760 295-9290	12204
Metric Systems Corporation	3663	F	760 560-0348	18179
Micro-Tech Scientific Inc	3826	F	760 597-9088	21994
Moran Tools	3542	E	760 801-3570	14447
Myosci Technologies Inc	2023	F	760 433-5376	634
Nology Engineering Inc	3714	F	760 591-0888	20410
Nordson Asymtek Inc	3823	C	760 727-2880	21625
Nubs Plastics Inc	3089	F	760 598-2525	10247
Nutritional Engineering Inc	2834	E	760 599-5200	8313
Nuzee Inc	2095	C	858 549-6893	2361
Ocean Divers USA LLC	3089	F	760 599-6898	10253
Omnitek Engineering Corp (PA)	3714	F	760 591-0900	20413
Original Watermen Inc	2311	F	760 599-0990	3038
Polk Audio LLC	3651	E	888 267-5495	17847
Powerlux Corporation	3648	F	760 727-2360	17725
Precision Litho Inc	2752	F	760 727-9400	7033
Predator Motorsports Inc	3089	F	760 734-1749	10306
Primarch Manufacturing Inc	3999	F	760 730-8572	24215
Production Embroidery Inc	2395	F	760 727-7407	3857
Protec Arisawa America Inc	3443	E	760 599-4800	12411
Pulse Metric Inc	3841	F	760 842-8224	22594
Pyron Solar III LLC	3433	F	760 599-5100	12076
Quantum Focus Instruments Corp	3825	F	760 599-1122	21835
R Zamora Inc	3469	E	760 597-1130	13270
Raveon Technologies Corp	3663	E	760 444-5995	18236
Rayspan Corporation	3661	F	858 259-9596	17988
Rayzist Photomask Inc (PA)	3955	D	760 727-8561	23737
Rec Inc	3569	F	760 727-8006	15355
Regional Mtls Recovery Inc	1411	E	760 727-0878	305
Revlon Inc	2844	E	760 599-2900	8828

Employment Codes: A=Over 500 employees, B=251-500,
C=101-250, D=51-100, E=20-50, F=10-19

2019 California
Manufacturers Register

© Mergent Inc. 1-800-342-5647
1495

GEOGRAPHIC

Company	SIC	EMP	PHONE	ENTRY #
Riches International Inc	3751	F	760 598-3366	21134
Rmjv LP	3556	B	503 526-5752	14883
Rxsafe LLC	3559	F	760 593-7161	15025
Sandel Avionics Inc	3812	C	760 727-4900	21423
Sandel Avionics Inc (PA)	3812	C	760 727-4900	21424
Sea Breeze Technology Inc	3699	F	760 727-6366	20064
Select Supplements Inc	2833	E	760 431-7509	7972
Select Supplements Inc	2023	F	760 431-7509	649
Sensata Technologies Inc	3621	D	760 597-7042	17222
Sew Sporty	2339	E	760 599-0585	3494
Sherline Products Incorporated	3541	E	760 727-5181	14411
Solatube International Inc (PA)	3442	D	888 765-2882	12348
Starship Worldwide LLC	2521	F	760 727-1190	4968
Stines Machine Inc	3599	E	760 599-9955	16968
Suez Wts Services Usa Inc	3677	F	760 598-1800	19366
Surgistar Inc (PA)	3841	E	760 598-2480	22639
Tacupeto Chips & Salsa Inc	2096	F	760 597-9400	2405
Techniche Solutions	2326	E	619 818-0071	3124
Thirty Three Threads Inc	2252	E	877 486-3769	2816
TNT Assembly LLC	2298	E	760 410-1750	2981
Tony Hawk Inc	3949	F	760 477-2477	23673
Total Source Manufacturing	3821	A	760 598-2146	21496
Tube Form Solutions LLC	3549	F	760 599-5001	14770
U S Divers Co Inc	3949	C	760 597-5000	23681
United Research & Mfg	3714	D	760 727-4320	20476
Versaform Corporation	3444	D	760 599-0961	12809
Vision Quest Industries Inc	3842	D	760 734-1550	22843
Walz Caps Inc	2386	E	760 683-9259	3625
Waterless Co Inc	3432	D	760 727-7723	12055
Watkins Manufacturing Corp (HQ)	3999	B	760 598-6464	24285
Watkins Manufacturing Corp	3088	F	760 598-6464	9914
Wax Research Inc	2999	F	760 607-0850	9458
Westbridge Agricultural Pdts	2879	F	760 599-8855	9121
Westbridge Research Group (PA)	2879	F	760 599-8855	9122
Western Cactus Growers Inc	3524	E	760 726-1710	14138
Western Cnc Inc	3599	D	760 597-7000	17062
Wolfpack Inc	3993	F	760 736-4500	24006
Wyroc Inc (PA)	1411	F	760 727-0878	308
Youngdale Manufacturing Corp	3429	E	760 727-0644	12012
Zenon Environmental Corp	2899	E	760 598-1800	9318
Zodiac Pool Solutions LLC (DH)	3589	B	760 599-9600	16143
Zodiac Pool Systems LLC (DH)	3589	C	760 599-9600	16144

WALNUT, CA - Los Angeles County

Company	SIC	EMP	PHONE	ENTRY #
All Strong Industry (usa) Inc (PA)	2591	E	909 598-6494	5178
Amergence Technology Inc	3559	E	909 859-8400	14906
Biomechanical Analysis &	3842	E	714 990-5932	22706
Biostar Microtech USA Corp	3577	F	909 444-3785	15684
Body Flex Sports Inc (PA)	3949	E	909 598-9876	23526
C M Automotive Systems Inc (PA)	3563	E	909 869-7912	15120
Cast Parts Inc (DH)	3324	C	909 595-2252	11508
Cemex Cnstr Mtls PCF LLC	3273	E	909 594-0105	11076
Collana Clinics	2844	F	909 444-1515	8716
Color Marble Project Group Inc	1442	F	909 595-8858	353
Crush Master Grinding Corp	3599	E	909 595-2249	16410
Disc Replicator Inc	3652	F	909 385-0118	17891
Edro Engineering Inc (DH)	3544	D	909 594-5751	14510
Edro Specialty Steels Inc	3544	E	800 368-3376	14511
Essence Imaging Inc	3861	E	909 979-2116	23159
Fairway Injection Molds Inc	3544	D	909 595-2201	14514
Golden Applexx Co Inc	2759	E	909 594-9788	7328
Hardware Imports Inc	3713	F	909 595-6201	20210
Harrison Beverage Inc	2024	F	626 961-1959	678
Heritage Products LLC	3083	F	909 839-1866	9749
Hing WA Lee Inc	3915	E	909 595-3500	23343
Hiti Digital America Inc	3861	E	909 594-0099	23163
Hupa International Inc	3949	E	909 598-9876	23587
Ikong E-Commerce Inc	3555	F	888 556-1522	14812
In Win Development USA Inc	3572	E	909 348-0588	15558
Infinity Watch Corporation	3993	E	626 289-9878	23899
J F Shea Co Inc (PA)	3273	E	909 594-9500	11122
Jakks Pacific Inc	3944	E	909 594-7771	23434
Lights of America Inc	3645	B	909 594-7883	17543
Lucky Picture Frame Co Inc	2499	E	323 583-6710	4633
Manufacture Resource Pdts Inc	2298	E	909 839-2988	2975
Markwins International Corp (PA)	2844	C	909 595-8898	8792
Myc Direct Inc	3821	F	909 287-9919	21481
Myers Container LLC	3412	E	800 406-9377	11875
Naturas Foods California Inc	2032	F	909 594-7838	769
New Origins Accessories Inc (PA)	3961	F	909 869-7559	23754
Ninas Mexican Foods Inc	2099	E	909 468-5888	2623
Niron Inc	3544	E	909 598-1526	14550
Nu-Health Products Co	2833	E	909 869-0666	7960
Oppo Original Corp	3144	F	909 444-3000	10502
Papago Inc	3812	F	909 595-6896	21380
Physicans Formula Holdings Inc (HQ)	2844	E	626 334-3395	8814

Company	SIC	EMP	PHONE	ENTRY #
Prime Wire & Cable Inc (HQ)	3357	E	888 445-9955	11671
Prophecy Technology LLC	3577	E	909 598-7998	15830
Sea Shield Marine Products	3363	E	909 594-2507	11706
Servers Direct LLC	3571	C	800 576-7931	15481
Settlers Jerky Incorporated	2013	E	909 444-3999	526
Soderberg Manufacturing Co Inc	3647	D	909 595-1291	17664
Southcoast Cabinet Inc (PA)	2434	E	909 594-3089	4352
SW Fixtures Inc	2541	F	909 595-2506	5108
Total Resources Intl Inc (PA)	3842	E	909 594-1220	22834
Trane US Inc	3585	E	626 913-7913	15986
Tree Island Wire (usa) Inc (DH)	3315	C	909 594-7511	11460
Tri-Net Technology Inc	3577	D	909 598-8810	15875
Tul Inc	3429	D	909 444-0577	12004
Unicom Electric Inc	3669	E	626 964-7873	18374
Universal Mercantile Exchange (PA)	3993	F	909 839-0556	23997
Utility Trailer Mfg Co	3715	B	909 594-6026	20518
V Manufacturing Logistics Inc	2844	E	909 869-6200	8860
Wally International Inc (PA)	2631	C	805 444-7764	5364
Western Hardware Company	3429	F	909 595-6201	12009

WALNUT CREEK, CA - Contra Costa County

Company	SIC	EMP	PHONE	ENTRY #
Advisor Software Inc (PA)	7372	E	925 299-7778	24331
American Bottling Company	2086	D	925 938-8777	2086
American Tech Supply Inc (PA)	3669	E	925 944-0777	18308
Andre-Boudin Bakeries Inc	2051	F	925 935-4375	1173
Appery LLC	7372	D	925 602-5504	24366
Basic American Inc (PA)	2034	D	925 472-4438	875
Bell-Carter Foods Inc (PA)	2033	B	925 284-5933	786
Bpo Systems Inc (PA)	7372	E	925 478-4299	24444
Brighton Collectibles LLC	2389	E	925 932-1500	3645
C A N Enterprises	2253	D	925 939-9736	2827
Canadian Solar (usa) Inc	3674	C	925 807-7499	18760
Carros Sensors Systems Co LLC	3679	C	925 979-4400	19479
Computers and Structures Inc	7372	F	510 649-2200	24517
Contra Costa Newspapers Inc (DH)	2711	A	925 935-2525	5811
Contra Costa Newspapers Inc	2711	B	925 943-3925	5814
Cytosport Inc	2023	C	707 751-3942	609
Del Monte Foods Inc (HQ)	2033	C	925 949-2772	796
Del Monte Foods Inc	2033	C	925 944-7300	797
Diablo Clinical Research Inc	2834	E	925 930-7267	8141
Diablo Country Magazine Inc	2721	E	925 943-1111	6145
Direct Drilling	1381	E	925 472-6850	102
Domico Software	7372	F	510 841-4155	24570
Energetix Solutions Inc	2892	F	925 926-6412	9182
Exadel Inc (PA)	7372	D	925 363-9510	24634
Gmp Manufacturing Inc	2099	E	707 751-3942	2530
Insignia SC Holdings LLC (HQ)	2064	A	925 399-8900	1429
Institutional Real Estate (PA)	2741	E	925 933-4040	6504
Kainos Dental Technologies LLC (PA)	3843	E	800 331-4834	22887
Kellogg Company	2043	B	925 952-8423	1063
Keurig Dr Pepper Inc	2086	D	925 938-8777	2144
Main Street Kitchens	2679	E	925 944-0153	5716
Malikco LLC	7372	E	925 974-3555	24880
Nancys Specialty Foods	2099	B	510 494-1100	2612
Pyramid Breweries Inc	2082	D	925 946-1520	1622
Quint Measuring Systems Inc	3829	F	510 351-9405	22255
R & R Maintenance Group	3524	F	707 863-0328	14131
Seal Software Inc (PA)	7372	F	650 938-7325	25157
Sysmaster Corporation	3575	E	925 891-7813	15647
Vantiq Inc	7372	F	303 377-2882	25320
Wencon Development Inc	3444	D	925 687-6686	12815
Western Hellenic Journal Inc	2711	E	925 939-3900	6084
Westrock CP LLC	2672	D	925 946-0842	5583

WALNUT GROVE, CA - Sacramento County

Company	SIC	EMP	PHONE	ENTRY #
Wilcox Brothers Inc	3523	D	916 776-1784	14126

WASCO, CA - Kern County

Company	SIC	EMP	PHONE	ENTRY #
Ag-Weld Inc	7692	F	661 758-3061	25384
Carter Pump & Machine Inc	3599	F	661 393-8620	16365
Certis USA LLC	2879	E	661 758-8471	9096
Eggs West LLC	2015	E	661 758-9700	537
Primex Farms LLC (PA)	2068	E	661 758-7790	1502
Sunnygem LLC	2033	B	661 758-0491	862

WATERFORD, CA - Stanislaus County

Company	SIC	EMP	PHONE	ENTRY #
Foster Poultry Farms	2015	E	209 394-7901	540
Roberts Ferry Nut Company Inc	2064	F	209 874-3247	1449

WATSONVILLE, CA - Santa Cruz County

Company	SIC	EMP	PHONE	ENTRY #
Annieglass Inc (PA)	3229	E	831 761-2041	10633
Boyer Inc	2873	E	831 724-0123	9058
Carrera Construction Inc	1389	E	831 728-3299	194
Central Coast Cabinets	2521	F	831 724-2992	4937
Consolidated Training LLC	3999	E	831 768-8888	24068
Corralitos Market & Sausage Co	2013	F	831 722-2633	477
Craviotto Drum Co	3931	F	831 763-0855	23359

Mergent email: customerrelations@mergent.com
1496

2019 California
Manufacturers Register

(P-0000) Products & Services Section entry number
(PA)=Parent Co (HQ)=Headquarters (DH)=Div Headquarters

Company	SIC	EMP	PHONE	ENTRY #
Del Mar Food Products Corp	2033	B	831 722-3516	792
Del Mar Seafoods Inc (PA)	2092	C	831 763-3000	2311
Eagle Tech Manufacturing Inc	3823	E	831 768-7467	21576
Elecraft Incorporated	3825	E	831 763-4211	21746
Fox Factory Inc (HQ)	3714	C	831 274-6500	20340
Garroutte Inc (PA)	3556	D	831 722-2487	14852
Golden Sheaf Bread Co Inc	2051	E	831 722-0179	1266
Granite Rock Co (PA)	1442	D	831 768-2000	359
H A Rider & Sons	2086	E	831 722-3882	2138
Hephaestus Innovations	3556	F	831 254-8555	14858
Johnson Art Studio Inc	3646	F	831 763-2744	17621
K S Equipment Inc	3679	F	831 722-7173	19604
La Selva Beach Spice Company	2099	E	831 724-4500	2569
Larosa Tortilla Factory	2099	D	831 728-5332	2578
Mizkan Americas Inc	2099	F	831 728-2061	2607
Monterey Bay Rebar Inc (PA)	3441	F	831 724-3013	12215
News Media Corporation	2711	D	831 761-7300	5995
Nordic Naturals Inc (PA)	2077	C	800 662-2544	1529
Pratt Industries Inc	2621	E	831 763-0630	5330
Printworx Inc	3577	F	831 722-7147	15829
Rainbow Fin Company Inc	3949	E	831 728-2998	23631
S Martinelli & Company (PA)	2099	C	831 724-1126	2662
Samco Plastics Inc	2671	E	831 761-1392	5537
Schmid Thermal Systems Inc	3567	C	831 763-0113	15274
Seascape Lamps Inc	3645	E	831 728-5699	17559
Smith & Vandiver Corporation	2844	D	831 722-9526	8844
Stalfab	3556	F	831 786-1600	14887
Test Electronics	3825	E	831 763-2000	21872
Threshold Enterprises Ltd	2833	E	831 425-3955	7974
Titan Frozen Fruit LLC (PA)	2037	E	831 540-4110	970
Trufocus Corporation	3844	E	831 761-9981	22943
Vena Engineering Corp	3829	E	831 724-5738	22295
Walker Street Pallets LLC	2448	F	831 724-6088	4512
Walters Manufacturing Company	3589	F	831 724-1377	16130
Westek Electronics Inc	3669	F	831 740-6300	18378
Woodworks	2511	F	831 688-8420	4756

WEAVERVILLE, CA - Trinity County

Company	SIC	EMP	PHONE	ENTRY #
Emerald Kingdom Greenhouse LLC	3448	E	530 215-5670	12929
Trinity River Lumber Company (PA)	2421	C	530 623-5561	4069

WEED, CA - Siskiyou County

Company	SIC	EMP	PHONE	ENTRY #
Cg Roxane LLC	2086	D	530 225-1260	2110
M & M Logging	2411	F	530 938-0745	3999
Pacific States Treating Inc	2491	F	530 938-4408	4595
Sanders Prcsion Timber Falling	2411	E	530 938-4120	4009

WELDON, CA - Kern County

Company	SIC	EMP	PHONE	ENTRY #
Witten Logging	2411	F	760 378-3640	4026

WEST COVINA, CA - Los Angeles County

Company	SIC	EMP	PHONE	ENTRY #
Bellavuos	2844	F	626 653-0121	8701
Concorde Battery Corp (PA)	3692	E	626 813-1234	19821
Continental American Corp	3069	D	626 964-0164	9601
Filmagic Inc	2834	F	626 339-0120	8160
Graybills Metal Polishing Inc	3471	F	626 967-5742	13419
Guess Inc	2325	E	626 856-5555	3071
Inside Park	3949	F	626 964-1800	23592
Interspace Battery Inc (PA)	3356	F	626 813-1234	11631
Kulayful Silicone Bracelets	3961	E	626 610-3816	23751
Ocean Wayne Media Inc	2741	F	626 966-8808	6543
Yogi Investments Inc	3089	F	909 984-5703	10455

WEST HILLS, CA - Los Angeles County

Company	SIC	EMP	PHONE	ENTRY #
Inc Aerojet Rocketdyne of De	2869	C	818 586-9629	9011
Kelly Teegarden Organics LLC	2844	F	818 568-0707	8782
Mitrani USA Corp	3088	F	818 888-9994	9907
Thermo Fischer Scientific Inc	3826	F	747 494-1413	22031

WEST HOLLYWOOD, CA - Los Angeles County

Company	SIC	EMP	PHONE	ENTRY #
402 Shoes Inc	2341	E	323 655-5437	3531
A & J Enterprises Inc	2752	F	323 654-5902	6632
AAA Printing By Wizard	2395	E	310 285-0505	3823
Art Services Melrose	3089	F	310 247-1452	9957
Cemex Cnstr Mtls PCF LLC	3273	E	323 466-4928	11081
Chase-Durer Ltd (PA)	3873	F	310 550-7280	23219
Clique Brands Inc (PA)	2721	E	323 648-5619	6130
Cycle House LLC	3949	E	310 358-0888	23546
Fountainhead Industries	3999	E	310 248-2444	24101
Grade A Sign LLC	3993	E	310 652-9700	23890
Growdiaries LLC	7372	F	626 354-8935	24713
Halo Top International LLC	2024	E	434 409-2057	677
Haworth Inc	2522	F	310 854-7633	4989
Iac/Interactivecorp	7372	F	212 314-7300	24745
J R U D E S Holdings LLC	2311	F	310 281-0800	3031
Kathrine Baumann Beverly Hills	2335	E	310 274-7441	3320
Lavinder Inc	2299	F	310 278-2456	3004
ME & ME Costumes Inc	3861	F	323 876-4432	23178
Neatpocket LLC	7372	F	323 632-7440	24946
Neonroots LLC	7372	C	310 907-9210	24947
Palihuse Hllway Rsidences Assn	2335	F	323 656-4100	3332
Pro Tour Memorabilia LLC	2499	E	424 303-7200	4643
Sargam International Inc	3651	F	310 855-9694	17853
Sports Medicine Info Network	2711	F	310 659-6889	6054
Steven Madden Ltd	3143	D	323 656-0012	10484
Sunset Leather Group	3199	E	310 388-4898	10582
Zeco Systems Inc (HQ)	3699	E	888 751-8560	20118

WEST POINT, CA - Calaveras County

Company	SIC	EMP	PHONE	ENTRY #
Martin Fischer Logging Inc	2411	F	209 293-4847	4001

WEST SACRAMENTO, CA - Yolo County

Company	SIC	EMP	PHONE	ENTRY #
Aerospace Facilities Group Inc	3569	F	702 513-8336	15296
Agraquest Inc (DH)	2879	D	866 992-2937	9089
Arcadia Inc	3355	F	916 375-1478	11613
Beckman Coulter Inc	3826	D	916 374-3511	21911
Big Valley Metals	3441	F	916 372-2383	12117
Bullet Guard Corporation	3499	E	800 233-5632	13925
Bullseye Leak Detection Inc	3599	F	916 760-8944	16337
Carter Group (PA)	3441	E	916 333-5070	12132
Cintas Corporation	2326	F	916 375-8633	3098
Clark - Pacific Corporation (PA)	3272	B	916 371-0305	10902
Cosmo Import & Export LLC (PA)	2514	E	916 209-5500	4829
Crown Equipment Corporation	3537	E	916 373-8980	14320
Cummins Pacific LLC	3519	E	916 371-0630	14018
DCI Donor Services Inc	3523	E	916 567-1600	14058
Delta Web Printing Inc	2759	E	916 375-0044	7295
Douglas Hunter Inc	2591	C	916 288-4464	5188
East Penn Manufacturing Co	3691	F	916 374-9965	19801
ECB Corp	3444	E	916 492-8900	12567
Farmers Rice Cooperative	2044	C	916 373-5500	1081
Farmers Rice Cooperative	2044	E	916 373-5500	1082
Flowmaster Inc	3714	C	916 371-2345	20335
Heco Inc	3566	F	916 372-5411	15239
Hunter Douglas Inc	2591	E	425 430-6110	5196
Hydrolynx Systems Inc	3826	F	916 374-1800	21970
Icon Apparel Group LLC	2231	E	916 372-4266	2792
International Paper Company	2621	E	916 371-4634	5302
National Sales Inc	2621	E	916 912-2894	5314
Nor-Cal Beverage Co Inc	2086	E	916 372-1700	2156
Richard K Gould Inc	2899	E	916 371-5943	9302
Ryko Solutions Inc	3589	E	916 372-8815	16103
Sacramento Envelope Co Inc	2752	F	916 371-4747	7093
Siemens Hlthcare Dgnostics Inc	2835	E	916 372-1900	8514
Siemens Industry Inc	3822	F	916 553-4444	21531
Sign Technology Inc	3993	E	916 372-1200	23968
Tackett Volume Press Inc	2759	E	916 374-8991	7507
Talco Foam Inc (PA)	3069	F	916 492-8840	9683
Taylor Communications Inc	2761	D	916 340-0200	7557
Terminix Intl Co Ltd Partnr	2879	F	916 376-8770	9114
Tk Classics LLC	2514	E	916 209-5500	4845
Tomra Sorting Inc (DH)	3556	D	720 870-2240	14889
Tri-C Machine Corporation (PA)	3599	F	916 371-8090	17009
Tri-C Manufacturing Inc	3559	E	916 371-1700	15039
Tri-City Technologies Inc	2759	F	916 503-5300	7526
Vss Emultech Inc	2951	F	916 371-8480	9400
Woodsmiths Architectural Casew	2541	F	916 456-8871	5121
Yara North America Inc	2879	E	916 375-1109	9123

WESTLAKE VILLAGE, CA - Ventura County

Company	SIC	EMP	PHONE	ENTRY #
Agilent Technologies Inc	3825	A	408 345-8886	21715
American Clubs LLC	2741	F	805 496-1218	6429
Astera Software Corporation	7372	F	805 579-0004	24391
Beaudry International LLC	3915	F	213 623-5025	23339
Blue Microphones LLC	3651	F	818 879-5200	17776
Boatworks	3732	F	805 374-9455	21024
Borett Automation Technologies	3569	F	818 597-8664	15304
Cforia Software Inc	7372	E	818 871-9687	24483
Dole Packaged Foods LLC (HQ)	2037	A	805 601-5500	947
Earth Print Inc	2752	E	818 879-6050	6798
Edge Solutions Consulting Inc (PA)	3571	F	818 591-3500	15406
EKA Technologies Inc	3663	E	805 379-8668	18096
General Dynmics Mssion Systems	3669	C	805 497-5042	18326
Global Custom Security Inc	3699	F	818 889-6900	19975
Implant Direct Sybron Mfg LLC	3842	C	818 444-3300	22749
Innovista Sensors Americas Inc (PA)	3679	E	805 267-7176	19578
Inphi International Pte Ltd	3674	E	805 719-2300	18901
Interntional Photo Plates Corp	3471	E	805 496-5031	13434
Invia Robotics Inc (PA)	3569	F	818 597-1680	15334
K-Swiss Sales Corp	3021	C	818 706-5100	9475
Kythera Biopharmaceuticals Inc	2834	C	818 587-4500	8251
Logical Trading Co	3714	F	805 230-0099	20387
Millworks By Design Inc	2431	F	818 597-1326	4194

GEOGRAPHIC

	SIC	EMP	PHONE	ENTRY #
Omega Technologies Inc	3423	F	818 264-7970	11904
Packit LLC	2673	F	805 496-2999	5613
Paymentmax Processing Inc	3578	D	805 557-1692	15898
R & R Services Corporation	3069	E	818 889-2562	9666
Rantec Microwave Systems Inc (PA)	3812	D	818 223-5000	21386
Safe Publishing Company	2759	D	805 973-1300	7476
Satcom Solutions Corporation	3812	F	818 991-9794	21426
Satellite 2000 Systems	3663	F	818 991-9794	18244
Skyguard LLC	3699	E	703 262-0500	20070
Star Route LLC	2771	F	805 405-8510	7569
Terramar Graphics Inc	2759	F	805 529-8845	7515
Ventura Aerospace Inc	3728	F	818 540-3130	20969
Vitavet Labs Inc	3999	E	818 865-2600	24283
Wain Industries	3679	F	805 581-5900	19785
Xplain Corporation	2721	F	805 494-9797	6298

WESTMINSTER, CA - Orange County

	SIC	EMP	PHONE	ENTRY #
AA Laboratory Eggs Inc (PA)	2087	F	714 893-5675	2238
Adams Welding Inc	7692	F	714 412-7684	25382
Anthony Jones	3949	F	714 894-3483	23504
B/E Aerospace Inc	3599	D	714 896-9001	16303
B/E Aerospace Inc	3728	C	714 896-9001	20755
Biolargo Inc (PA)	2819	F	949 643-9540	7755
Bodycote Imt Inc	3398	F	714 893-6561	11795
Bodycote Thermal Proc Inc	3398	D	714 893-6561	11798
Cgr/Thompson Industries Inc	3612	D	714 678-4200	17084
Dang Tha	2531	F	714 898-0989	5010
Dolstra Automatic Products	3599	F	714 894-2062	16445
Ebs Products	3559	F	714 896-6700	14944
Einstein Noah Rest Group Inc	2022	F	714 847-4609	570
European Woodwork	2434	F	714 892-8831	4298
Finddoctr Inc	2741	F	657 888-2629	6485
Happy2ez Inc	3086	F	714 897-6100	9863
Lavang Tech Prcsion Sheet Mtls	3549	F	714 901-2782	14756
Lexor Inc	3999	D	714 444-4144	24161
Machining Specialist Corp	3599	F	714 847-1214	16707
New CAM Commerce Solutions LLC	7372	D	714 338-0200	24959
Nguoi Vietnamese People Inc (PA)	2711	E	714 892-9414	5997
Rnb Vending Inc	3581	F	714 548-6993	15926
STA-Brite-Ano	3479	F	323 581-1432	13666
Thompson Industries Ltd.	3728	E	310 679-9193	20950
Tru-Form Plastics Inc	3089	E	310 327-9444	10413
Vietnmese Amrcn Mdia Corp Vamc	2711	F	714 379-2851	6080
West Coast Timber Corp	2411	F	714 893-4374	4022
Western Illuminated Plas Inc	3646	F	714 895-3067	17657

WHITMORE, CA - Shasta County

	SIC	EMP	PHONE	ENTRY #
Purity Pool Inc	3589	F	530 472-3298	16095

WHITTIER, CA - Los Angeles County

	SIC	EMP	PHONE	ENTRY #
A & A Fabrication & Polsg Corp	3441	F	562 696-0441	12097
A F E Industries Inc (PA)	2759	D	562 944-6889	7218
AC Products Inc	2891	E	714 630-7311	9126
Aguilar Williams Inc	3471	F	562 693-2736	13313
Allergan Inc	2834	C	512 527-6688	8012
Boeing Company	3721	A	562 944-6583	20551
Calico Tag & Label Inc	2759	F	562 944-6889	7262
Cameron Technologies Us Inc	3823	D	562 222-8440	21556
Carson Valley Inc	3444	F	562 906-0062	12528
Chip-Makers Tooling Supply Inc	3544	F	562 698-5840	14495
Coastal Tag & Label Inc	2759	D	562 946-4318	7275
Comfort Industries Inc	2231	E	562 692-8288	2791
Compu Aire Inc	3585	C	562 945-8971	15946
Consteel Industrial Inc	3441	E	562 806-4575	12140
Cryostar USA LLC	3561	E	562 903-1290	15058
Cutting Edge Creative LLC	2542	D	562 907-7007	5136
Epmar Corporation	2851	E	562 946-8781	8907
General Transistor Corporation (PA)	3674	E	310 578-7344	18855
George Coriaty	2752	E	562 698-7513	6832
Georgia Pacific Holdings Inc	2676	A	626 926-1474	5665
Grand Motif Records	3652	F	562 698-8538	17902
Gulfstream Aerospace Corp GA	3721	A	562 907-9300	20590
Harris Organs Inc	3931	E	562 693-3442	23375
Harten Jewelry Co Inc	3911	E	562 652-5006	23272
Hedman Manufacturing (PA)	3714	E	562 204-1031	20359
Industry Color Printing Inc	2752	E	626 961-2403	6880
J G Hernandez Company	3851	E	562 698-2286	23103
Jason Incorporated	3291	E	562 921-9821	11295
Leggett & Platt Incorporated	2515	D	562 945-2641	4869
Linde LLC	2813	E	562 903-1290	7695
Loren Industries	3993	E	562 699-1122	23917
Mar Vista Wood Products Inc	2431	F	562 698-2024	4187
Medlin & Son Engrg Servinc	3599	D	562 464-5889	16734
Miller Castings Inc (PA)	3324	E	562 695-0461	11515
Miller Castings Inc	3324	E	562 695-0461	11516
Pacific Coast Bindery Inc	2789	E	562 908-5900	7610

	SIC	EMP	PHONE	ENTRY #
Pacific Die Services Inc	3544	F	562 907-4463	14556
Pacific Truck Equipment Inc	3713	D	562 464-9674	20222
Quaker City Plating	3471	C	562 945-3721	13485
Rahn Industries Incorporated (PA)	3585	D	562 908-0680	15976
Rasmussen Iron Works Inc	3433	E	562 696-8718	12078
Rgr Diversified Services Inc	2515	F	562 522-0028	4882
Russ Bassett Corp	2522	C	562 945-2445	4999
Santa Fe Rubber Products Inc	3069	E	562 693-2776	9674
Tops Slt Inc	2675	C	562 968-2000	5659
Tube-Tainer Inc	2655	E	562 945-3711	5496
United Memorial Products Inc	3272	C	562 699-3578	11012
West Coast Sheepskin Import	2399	F	562 945-5151	3973
Western Yankee Inc	2759	F	562 944-6889	7540
Windsor House Investments Inc	2675	E	323 261-0231	5660

WILDOMAR, CA - Riverside County

	SIC	EMP	PHONE	ENTRY #
Barns and Buildings Inc	3448	D	951 678-4571	12919
Fcp Inc	3448	D	951 678-4571	12931

WILLIAMS, CA - Colusa County

	SIC	EMP	PHONE	ENTRY #
Morning Star Packing Co LP	2033	E	530 473-3642	829
Tamaki Rice Corporation	2044	E	530 473-2862	1093

WILLITS, CA - Mendocino County

	SIC	EMP	PHONE	ENTRY #
Advanced Mfg & Dev Inc	3444	C	707 459-9451	12461
G and S Milling Co	2431	E	707 459-0294	4157
Magnetic Coils Inc	3677	E	707 459-5994	19343
Media News Group	2711	F	707 459-4643	5956
Norcal Recycled Rock Aggregate (PA)	3273	F	707 459-9636	11152
Northern Aggregates Inc	1442	E	707 459-3929	377
Shusters Logging Inc	2411	D	707 459-4131	4011
Westinghouse A Brake Tech Corp	3261	E	707 459-5563	10809
Willits Redwood Company Inc	2421	E	707 459-4549	4071
Windsor Willits Company	2431	E	707 459-8568	4260

WILLOWS, CA - Glenn County

	SIC	EMP	PHONE	ENTRY #
Johns Manville Corporation	3296	B	530 934-6243	11333
Rumiano Cheese Co (PA)	2022	C	530 934-5438	596
Sierra Nevada Cheese Co Inc	2022	D	530 934-8660	602
Western Ready Mix Concrete Co (PA)	3273	F	530 934-2185	11213

WILMINGTON, CA - Los Angeles County

	SIC	EMP	PHONE	ENTRY #
5 Ball Inc	2731	F	310 830-0630	6300
Air Products and Chemicals Inc	2813	E	310 952-9172	7676
Associated Wire Rope & Rigging	2298	E	310 448-5444	2968
Bgm Installation Inc	3011	F	310 830-3113	9461
California Carbon Company Inc	2819	F	562 436-1962	7758
California Sulphur Company	2819	E	562 437-0768	7760
Cooper & Brain Inc	1311	F	310 834-4411	51
D-1280-X Inc	2911	F	310 835-6909	9331
Japanese Truck Dismantling	3711	F	310 835-3100	20152
Juanitas Foods	2032	C	310 834-5339	762
Los Angeles Refining Co	2911	F	310 522-6000	9338
Marine Fenders Intl Inc	3465	F	310 834-7037	13141
Pacific Fibre & Rope Co Inc	2298	F	310 834-4567	2976
Pacific Green Trucking Inc	3743	F	310 830-4528	21082
Royal-Pedic Mattress Mfg LLC	2515	E	310 518-5420	4883
San Pedro Sign Company	3993	F	310 549-4661	23958
Sea Tek Spars & Rigging Inc	3731	F	310 549-1800	21013
Sepor Inc	3821	F	310 830-6601	21490
Ultramar Inc	1389	F	310 834-7254	290
US Borax Inc	2819	C	310 522-5300	7811
Valero Ref Company-California	2911	B	562 491-6754	9373
West Coast Aerospace Inc (PA)	3965	D	310 518-3167	23781
Wilmington Machine Inc	3599	F	310 518-3213	17069
Wilmington Woodworks Inc	2448	E	310 834-1015	4514

WILTON, CA - Sacramento County

	SIC	EMP	PHONE	ENTRY #
Gaines Well Service Inc (PA)	1389	F	916 687-6751	214

WINDSOR, CA - Sonoma County

	SIC	EMP	PHONE	ENTRY #
Advanced Viticulture Inc	2084	F	707 838-3805	1639
Denbeste Manufacturing Inc	3713	F	707 838-1407	20200
Digital Media Vending Intl LLC	3581	F	415 516-3243	15921
Fantasy Manufacturing Inc	3599	E	707 838-7686	16492
Hausenware Koyo LLC	3229	F	412 897-3064	10646
Jackson Family Wines Inc	2084	E	707 528-6278	1823
Micro-Vu Corp California (PA)	3827	D	707 838-6272	22108
Morgan Medesign Inc	3841	F	707 568-2929	22548
Nieco Corporation	3589	D	707 838-3288	16080
Regal III LLC	2084	D	707 836-2100	1943
Six Sigma Precision Inc	3599	F	707 836-0869	16947
Sonoma Tilemakers Inc (DH)	3253	D	707 837-8177	10791
Windsor Oaks Vineyards LLP	2084	E	707 433-4050	2059

WINNETKA, CA - Los Angeles County

	SIC	EMP	PHONE	ENTRY #
Green Cures Inc	2833	E	818 773-3929	7945
Life Media Inc	2721	E	800 201-9440	6207

Mergent email: customerrelations@mergent.com
1498

2019 California
Manufacturers Register

(P-0000) Products & Services Section entry number
(PA)=Parent Co (HQ)=Headquarters (DH)=Div Headquarters

	SIC	EMP	PHONE	ENTRY #

WINTERS, CA - Yolo County

	SIC	EMP	PHONE	ENTRY #
Access Mfg Inc	3713	F	530 795-0720	20186
Creative Concepts and Design	2431	F	707 812-9320	4130
J McDowell Wldg Frm Mchy Inc	7692	F	530 661-6006	25414
Pavestone LLC	3281	E	530 795-4400	11268

WINTON, CA - Merced County

	SIC	EMP	PHONE	ENTRY #
Koch Feeds Inc	2048	E	209 725-8253	1141
Santa Fe Aggregates Inc (HQ)	1442	F	209 358-3303	380
Winton Times	2711	E	209 358-5311	6089

WOODLAKE, CA - Tulare County

	SIC	EMP	PHONE	ENTRY #
Country Plastics Inc	3089	F	559 597-2556	10046
Dryvit Systems Inc	2899	E	559 564-3591	9242
Mosier Bros	3443	F	559 564-3304	12401
US Tower Corp	3441	D	559 564-6000	12270

WOODLAND, CA - Yolo County

	SIC	EMP	PHONE	ENTRY #
A Teichert & Son Inc	1442	E	530 661-4290	337
AA Production Services Inc (PA)	1389	E	530 668-7525	163
Acme Bag Co Inc (PA)	2674	F	530 662-6130	5636
Alemad Inc	2541	E	530 661-1697	5034
American International Mfg Co	3523	E	530 666-2446	14041
Ames Fire Waterworks	3625	D	530 666-2493	17250
Baron Usa LLC	3569	E	931 528-8476	15300
Bentec Medical Opco LLC	3841	E	530 406-3333	22363
Bentec Scientific LLC	3841	E	530 406-3333	22364
Bright People Foods Inc (PA)	2099	E	530 669-6870	2472
Bunge Milling Inc	2041	C	530 666-1691	1034
Bunge North America Inc	2044	D	530 666-1691	1074
Cache Creek Foods Inc	2099	F	530 662-1764	2476
California Cascade-Woodland	2491	F	530 666-1261	4589
Califrnia PCF Rice Mil A CA LP	2044	C	530 661-1923	1077
Cfarms Inc	2099	E	916 375-3000	2484
Coastal PVA Opco LLC	3571	F	530 406-3303	15400
Colombaras Cabinet & Mllwk Inc	2521	F	530 662-2665	4938
Culinary Farms Inc	2034	F	916 375-3000	881
Earthsavers Erosion Ctrl LLC	3822	F	530 662-7700	21509
Four Wheel Campers Inc	3792	E	530 666-1442	21203
Gayle Manufacturing Co Inc (PA)	3441	C	530 662-0284	12169
Gold River Mills LLC (PA)	2044	D	530 661-1923	1083
Hygieia Biological Labs (PA)	2836	E	530 661-1442	8559
Interlock Industries Inc	3444	D	530 668-5690	12623
Johnson Farm Machinery Co Inc	3523	F	530 662-1788	14076
Johnstons Trading Post Inc	2449	F	530 661-6152	4527
Jr3 Inc	3823	F	530 661-3677	21606
Kimzey Welding Works Inc	3599	F	530 662-9331	16656
Medianews Group Inc	2711	E	530 662-5421	5962
Noble Methane Inc	1389	F	530 668-7961	249
Olam West Coast Inc	2033	A	530 473-4290	840
Pacific Coast Producers	2033	B	530 662-8661	845
Pacific Coast Producers	2033	C	530 534-1344	846
Pgp International Inc (DH)	2099	F	530 662-5056	2638
Planit Solutions	7372	F	530 666-6647	25066
Prime Conduit Inc	2821	E	530 669-0160	7876
Pt Welding Inc	7692	F	530 406-0267	25427
Pure Nature Foods LLC	2096	E	530 723-5269	2399
Ricardo Ochoa	2653	F	530 668-1152	5455
Roudybush Inc (PA)	2048	F	530 668-6196	1161
Sachs Industries Inc	2679	F	631 242-9000	5731
Six Pac Campers Inc	3792	F	800 242-1442	21211
Skyline Homes Inc	2451	C	530 666-0974	4564
Sunfoods LLC	2044	F	530 661-1923	1092
Tacsense Inc	3841	F	530 797-0008	22641
Truck Accessories Group LLC	3792	C	530 666-0176	21213
Vogt Western Silver Ltd	3911	F	530 669-6840	23330
Weslan Systems Inc	3559	F	530 668-3304	15048
Western Foods LLC (PA)	2041	E	530 601-5991	1052
Woodland Welding Works	3441	F	530 666-5531	12284

WOODLAND HILLS, CA - Los Angeles County

	SIC	EMP	PHONE	ENTRY #
Allpakfoam & Packaging	3086	F	818 917-5660	9815
American Plastic Card Co	3089	C	818 784-4224	9943
Apex Communications Inc (DH)	7372	F	818 379-8400	24362
Asi/Silica Machinery LLC (PA)	3366	E	818 920-1962	11755
Baam Inc	2353	E	818 716-1818	3558
Blackline Systems Inc (HQ)	7372	C	818 746-4700	24429
Cabeau Inc	2399	E	877 962-2232	3939
Catalina Yachts Inc (PA)	3732	C	818 884-7700	21025
Cbj LP	2721	F	818 676-1750	6123
Cut & Trim Inc	2331	E	818 264-0101	3228
Eddies Perfume & Cosmtc Co Inc	2844	F	818 341-1717	8743
Final Data Inc	2741	E	818 835-9560	6484
Forsythe Tech Worldwide	3841	F	818 710-8694	22453
Goengineer Inc	7372	F	818 716-1650	24703
Graham Webb International Inc (DH)	2844	EMP	760 918-3600	8757

	SIC	EMP	PHONE	ENTRY #
Hillside Capital Inc	3663	C	650 367-2011	18126
ICON Line Inc	3999	F	818 709-4266	24127
Invotech Systems Inc	7372	F	818 461-9800	24800
King Nutronics Corporation	3823	E	818 887-5460	21610
La Parent Magazine (PA)	2721	E	818 264-2222	6202
Linx Bracelets Inc	3911	F	818 224-4050	23287
Lumio	3674	F	586 961-3400	18973
Lynx Phtnic Ntworks A Del Corp	3661	F	818 878-7500	17962
Medianews Group Inc	2711	A	818 713-3000	5958
Medic Ids	3999	F	818 705-0595	24170
Micro Devices of America Inc	3679	E	818 577-9543	19647
Moki International (usa) Inc	3651	E	205 208-0179	17835
National Diversified Sales Inc (HQ)	3089	C	559 562-9888	10230
Network Telephone Services Inc (PA)	2541	B	800 742-5687	5083
New Century Gold LLC	3911	F	818 936-2676	23302
Northrop Grumman Innovation	3812	B	818 887-8100	21367
Northrop Grumman Intl Trdg Inc	3812	A	818 715-3607	21368
Northrop Grumman Systems Corp	3721	A	818 715-4040	20605
Northrop Grumman Systems Corp	3812	E	818 715-2597	21370
Panavision International LP (HQ)	3861	B	818 316-1080	23185
Prince Development LLC	2844	F	866 774-6234	8824
Quantum Energy LLC	1382	E	800 950-3519	146
Quantum-Dynamics Co Inc	3823	F	818 719-0142	21640
Real Software Systems LLC (PA)	7372	D	818 313-8000	25107
Senju Usa Inc	2834	F	818 719-7190	8376
Silgan Containers Corporation (DH)	3411	D	818 348-3700	11866
Silgan Containers LLC (HQ)	3411	D	818 710-3700	11867
Silgan Containers Mfg Corp (DH)	3411	D	818 710-3700	11871
Sun-Mate Corp	3944	F	818 700-0572	23468
Tag-It Pacific Inc	2269	E	818 444-4100	2919
TI Limited LLC (PA)	7372	D	323 877-5991	25276
Tinyinklingcom LLC	3069	F	877 777-6287	9686
Weider Health and Fitness	2087	B	818 884-6800	2287
Weider Leasing Inc	2721	D	818 884-6800	6287
Western Bagel Baking Corp	2051	E	818 887-5451	1340
Wilshire Book Company Inc	2731	E	818 700-1522	6409

WOODSIDE, CA - San Mateo County

	SIC	EMP	PHONE	ENTRY #
Clos De La Tech LLC	2084	F	650 722-3038	1695
Langley Hill Quarry	1429	F	650 851-0179	328
Nemco Electronics Corp	3675	C	650 571-1234	19300
Wine Company of San Francisco	2084	F	650 851-0965	2061

YORBA LINDA, CA - Orange County

	SIC	EMP	PHONE	ENTRY #
Aaero Swiss	3599	F	714 692-0558	16200
Alpha Omega Swiss Inc	3451	E	714 692-8009	13010
Arbon Equipment Corporation	3537	F	414 355-2600	14310
Aseptic Technology LLC	3221	D	714 694-0168	10617
Astrodyne Corporation	3679	F	714 289-0055	19451
B&K Precision Corporation (PA)	3825	E	714 921-9095	21727
Beckers Fabrication Inc	2672	E	714 692-1600	5556
Boyd Corporation (PA)	3441	F	714 533-2375	12120
Bruce Parker	2752	F	714 970-2307	6706
C4 Litho	2752	F	714 259-1073	6713
Carefusion 211 Inc	3841	A	714 283-2228	22391
Carefusion Corporation	3841	E	800 231-2466	22394
Cobra Engineering Inc	3714	D	714 692-8180	20292
Dan Copp Crushing Corp	1442	E	714 777-6400	355
Digital Label Solutions Inc	2679	E	714 982-5000	5710
Engineering Jk Aerospace & Def	3728	E	714 414-6722	20809
Euroline Steel Windows	3442	E	877 590-2741	12315
Filter Concepts Incorporated	3677	E	714 545-7003	19334
Fixture Design & Mfg Co	2599	E	714 776-3104	5232
Fpg Oc Inc	2087	C	714 692-2950	2263
GE Aviation Systems LLC	3728	F	714 692-0200	20822
Gramic Enterprises Inc	2082	F	714 329-8627	1597
Infinity Systems Inc	3599	F	714 692-1722	16583
Inflight Warning Systems Inc	3728	F	714 993-9394	20848
Infrared Dynamics Inc	3433	E	714 572-4050	12070
Jondo Ltd	2759	E	714 279-2300	7366
Loritz & Associates Inc	3089	E	714 694-0200	10194
M B S Inc	3691	F	714 693-9952	19812
Maxxess Systems Inc (PA)	7372	E	714 772-1000	24888
Mc2 Sabtech Holdings Inc (PA)	3571	F	714 692-3800	15449
Multiquip Industries Corp	3442	F	888 996-7267	12337
Nasco Gourmet Foods Inc	2033	D	714 279-2100	831
Nobel Biocare Usa LLC	3843	B	714 282-4800	22895
Outdoor Sign System Inc (PA)	3993	F	714 692-2052	23939
Pacifictech Molded Pdts Inc	3069	F	714 279-9928	9653
Pdma Ventures Inc	3999	E	714 777-8770	24206
Precision Fluorescent West Inc (DH)	3646	D	352 692-5900	17638
Sabred International Packg Inc	3086	F	714 996-2800	9881
Specialteam Medical Svc Inc	3841	F	714 694-0348	22629
Specialty Motions Inc	3562	E	951 735-8722	15112
Studer Creative Packaging Inc	3089	F	818 344-1665	10395
Thomas Cnc Machining	3599	F	714 692-9373	16999

GEOGRAPHIC

	SIC	EMP	PHONE	ENTRY #
Tlk Industries Inc	3999	F	714 692-9373	24271
Trigon Electronics Inc	3699	F	714 633-7442	20091
Viasys Respiratory Care Inc	3841	C	714 283-2228	22675
Welland Industries LLC	3999	F	714 528-9900	24287
Zet-Tek Precision Machining (PA)	3599	F	714 777-8770	17077

YOUNTVILLE, CA - Napa County

	SIC	EMP	PHONE	ENTRY #
Cosentino Signature Wineries (PA)	2084	E	707 921-2809	1708
Domaine Chandon Inc (DH)	2084	D	707 944-8844	1729
Dominus Estate Corporation	2084	F	707 944-8954	1731
Goosecross Cellars A Cal Corp	2084	F	707 944-1986	1792
Goosecross Cellars Coorstek	2084	F	707 944-1986	1793
Jessup Cellars Inc	2084	E	707 944-8523	1831
Twin Peaks Winery Inc	2084	F	707 945-0855	2034

YREKA, CA - Siskiyou County

	SIC	EMP	PHONE	ENTRY #
Custom Crushing Industries	1221	F	530 842-5544	17
Fruit Growers Supply Company	2448	E	530 842-4530	4472
Gatehouse Media LLC	2711	E	530 842-5777	5858
Madrone Hospice Inc	3231	E	530 842-2547	10718
Nor-Cal Products Inc (DH)	3494	C	530 842-4457	13773
Ozotech Inc (PA)	3589	E	530 842-4189	16085
Shasta Forest Products Inc (PA)	2499	E	530 842-0527	4653
Shasta Forest Products Inc	2499	E	530 842-2787	4654
Timber Products Co Ltd Partnr	2435	C	530 842-2310	4386
Yreka Transit Mix Concrete	3273	F	530 842-4351	11214

YUBA CITY, CA - Sutter County

	SIC	EMP	PHONE	ENTRY #
A & A Ready Mixed Concrete Inc	3273	F	530 671-1220	11025
Am-Par Manufacturing Co Inc	3599	F	530 671-1800	16267
Big Hill Logging & Rd Building (PA)	2411	E	530 673-4155	3980
California Industrial Rbr Co	2822	E	530 674-2444	7902
California Olive and Vine LLC	2079	F	530 763-7921	1535

	SIC	EMP	PHONE	ENTRY #
California Resources Prod Corp	1311	E	530 671-8201	44
Chipco Manufacturing Co Inc	3599	F	530 751-8150	16382
Eagle Moulding Company 1 (PA)	2431	E	530 673-6517	4152
Mathews Ready Mix LLC	3273	E	530 671-2400	11140
Orchard Machinery Corporation (PA)	3523	D	530 673-2822	14089
Organic Mattresses Inc	2515	E	530 790-6723	4876
Pacific Sunshine Enterprises	3999	F	530 673-1888	24201
Paperboard Packaging Corp (HQ)	2671	D	530 671-9000	5530
Sharpe Software Inc	7372	F	530 671-6499	25168
Siller Brothers Inc (PA)	2411	D	530 673-0734	4013
Sunsweet Growers Inc (PA)	2034	A	800 417-2253	901
Unity Forest Products Inc	2431	E	530 671-7152	4251
Valley Fine Foods Company Inc	2038	F	530 671-7200	1019
Valley View Foods Inc	2033	D	530 673-7356	866
Vandorn Plastering	3299	F	530 671-2748	11373
Yuba City Steel Products Co	3441	E	530 673-4554	12285
Yuba Cy Wste Wtr Trtmnt Fcilty	3589	E	530 822-7698	16142

YUCAIPA, CA - San Bernardino County

	SIC	EMP	PHONE	ENTRY #
Aggtech Inc	1442	E	909 795-4774	344
Dentsply Sirona Inc	3843	D	909 795-2080	22870
Hi-Desert Publishing Company	2711	E	909 797-9101	5879
Morrison Engineering	3599	F	909 796-5319	16772
Sorenson Engineering Inc (PA)	3451	C	909 795-2434	13042
Technical Resource Industries (PA)	3643	E	909 446-1109	17499

YUCCA VALLEY, CA - San Bernardino County

	SIC	EMP	PHONE	ENTRY #
Catalyst Development Corp	7372	E	760 228-9653	24477
Hi-Desert Publishing Company (HQ)	2711	D	760 365-3315	5881

ZAMORA, CA - Yolo County

	SIC	EMP	PHONE	ENTRY #
Crew Wine Company LLC	2084	F	530 662-1032	1711

Mergent email: customerrelations@mergent.com
1500

2019 California
Manufacturers Register

(P-0000) Products & Services Section entry number
(PA)=Parent Co (HQ)=Headquarters (DH)=Div Headquarters